T0391322

2025

LexisNexis®
Corporate Affiliations™

LexisNexis®

Content Operations:
Director-News & Business Content Operations & Metadata: Tammy Bair
Manager-Corporate Affiliations & Entity Management: Elizabeth A. Powers
Lead Content Analysts: Eric Eelman, Kevin Gaven

Production:
Senior Production Specialist: Joseph C. Stewart

Reed Elsevier Philippines-Corporate Affiliations Iloilo Team:
Operations Manager: Timothy J. Vilches
Operations Supervisor: Kristel Faye B. De la Cruz
Product Lead: Raquel G. Gajardo

2025

LexisNexis®
Corporate Affiliations™
International Public & Private Companies

Volume VI
A-F

LexisNexis®

QUESTIONS ABOUT THIS PUBLICATION?

For CONTENT questions concerning this publication, please call:

Content Operations Department at 800-340-3244
FAX 908-790-5405

For CUSTOMER SERVICE ASSISTANCE concerning shipments, billing or other matters, please call:
Customer Service at 800-340-3244, press 3

For SALES ASSISTANCE, please call:
The Sales Department at 800-340-3244, press 2

No part of this publication may be reproduced or transmitted in any form or by any means sorted in any information storage and retrieval system without prior written permission of LexisNexis, Content Operations, 9443 Springboro Pike, Miamisburg, OH 45342.

Library of Congress Catalog Card Number: 67-22770

International Public & Private Companies Volume 6, ISBN: 979-8-3417-0464-0

Corporate Affiliations 8-Volume Library, ISBN: 979-8-3417-0458-9

©2025 LexisNexis Group.

All Rights Reserved

LexisNexis, the knowledge burst logo and Corporate Affiliations are trademarks of Reed Elsevier Properties Inc., used under license.

The LexisNexis Group has used its best efforts in collecting and preparing material for inclusion in Corporate Affiliations: International Public & Private Companies™ but does not assume, and hereby disclaims, any liability to any person for any loss or damage caused by errors or omissions in Corporate Affiliations: International Public & Private Companies whether such errors or omissions result from negligence, accident or any other cause.

Corporate Affiliations

Content Operations
9443 Springboro Pike
Miamisburg, OH 45342

www.lexisnexis.com

ISBN 979-8-3417-0464-0

9 798341 704640

CONTENTS

CONTENTS

CORPORATE AFFILIATIONS

Corporate Affiliations is a logically organized business reference tool that covers major public and private businesses in the United States and throughout the world. The set consists of eight volumes:

Volume I   Master Index I
Volume II   Master Index II
Volume III   U.S. Public Companies
Volume IV   U.S. Private Companies I
Volume V   U.S. Private Companies II
Volume VI   International Public & Private Companies I
Volume VII   International Public & Private Companies II
Volume VIII   International Public & Private Companies III

The principle of organization for the set is geographical (by parent company) and hierarchical (by company reportage). Subsidiaries of a parent company, no matter where they are located, will be found in the same volume as the ultimate parent.

Please note that guidelines on the organization of the entire set for this edition can be found in the *Master Index* Volume I.

Entry criteria for the set are flexible. Generally speaking, non-U.S. based companies must demonstrate revenue in excess of $10 million. U.S. based companies must demonstrate revenues in excess of $10 million, substantial assets, a work force in excess of 300 employees, or be traded on a major stock exchange.

THE *INTERNATIONAL PUBLIC AND PRIVATE COMPANIES* VOLUME

Corporate Affiliations: International Public and Private Companies contains listings for companies with non-U.S. located headquarters or holding companies. Subsidiaries for these parent companies are included, whether or not they are located in the United States. Also included are outside service firms attached to the parent companies. These are firms that perform specialized services such as accounting, legal, pension management, etc.

Content and Coverage in Corporate Affiliations-International Public and Private Companies

Listing statistics for this edition of International are as follows:

Ultimate parent companies 58,644
U.S. located sub companies 99,843
Non-U.S. located sub companies 144,707
Total entry units listed 303,194

Outside service firms: 58,637

Companies are arranged alphabetically by the name of the parent company. Subsidiary companies follow the parent in order of reporting hierarchy. The bold number in parentheses shows the level of corporate reportage. Each listing can contain an extensive number of informational items. Please refer to the helpful 'How to Use' section for a guide to referencing methods and comprehensive listing samples.

The *International Public and Private Companies* volume also contains several useful features in the frontmatter including 'New Listings' for this edition, 'Mergers and Acquisitions' and the 'Currency Exchange' table.

COMPILATION

Corporate Affiliations is compiled and updated from information supplied by the companies themselves, business publications, internet research and annual reports.

RELATED SERVICES

For information on the corporateaffiliations.com web site, please call (800) 340-3244.

Mailing lists compiled from information contained in *Corporate Affiliations* may be ordered from:
R. Michael Patterson, Inside Sales Representative
DM2 Decision Maker
2000 Clearwater Drive, Oak Brook, IL
Tel: (630) 288-8348
E-mail: robert.patterson@dm2decisionmaker.com

Electronic database tapes of the directory in raw data format are available for licensing. For electronic database tapes or alliance opportunities, please contact:
LexisNexis, Corporate Affiliations
9443 Springboro Pike, Miamisburg, OH 45342
Tel: (800) 285-3947
E-mail: information@lexisnexis.com

Companies who wish to add or correct their listings can send information to:
LexisNexis, Corporate Affiliations Content Operations
9443 Springboro Pike
Miamisburg, OH 45342
Tel: (937) 865-6800

In addition to keeping the information in our directories as up to date as possible, we are constantly trying to improve their design, and add useful new features. Any comments or suggestions in this regard can be directed to the Managers of Operations at the above address.

HOW TO USE
INTERNATIONAL PUBLIC AND
PRIVATE COMPANIES

Corporate Affiliations, International Public and Private Companies, contains a vast amount of useful information about firms whose ultimate parent companies are located outside the United States. Included in *International Public and Private Companies* are the parent companies and their subsidiaries, no matter where they are located.

This user guide is divided into three parts.

> **Part A**, 'How to Locate a Company' gives referencing instructions and samples of indexes. It demonstrates many useful methods for getting the information you need from this volume and from the *Corporate Affiliations* set at large.

> **Part B**, 'Sample Entries' shows the various data elements and listing style of companies in *Corporate Affiliations*.

> **Part C**, 'Understanding Levels of Reportage' demonstrates how company reportage structures are simply and clearly presented throughout *Corporate Affiliations*.

PART A: HOW TO LOCATE A COMPANY

1.   **If you know the name of the company, but do not know its nationality or ownership status:**

Look in the 'Master Index of Company Names' in volume I. This index will direct you to the correct volume of the set (i.e. Public, Private or International) and the correct page listing therein.

> **KOMAG, INCORPORATED**; *U.S. Public*, pg. 1023
> KOMAG MATERIAL TECHNOLOGY INC.—See
>   Komag, Incorporated; *U.S. Public*, pg. 1023
> KOMAGANE ELECTRONICS, INC.—See Kenwood
>   Corporation; *Int'l*, pg. 638

2.   **If you know the company is a non-U.S. held parent company:**

You can turn directly to the company listings in volumes VI, VII and VIII, all of which are alphabetized by the name of the parent company.

3. **If you cannot find the company's name in the master index:**

It may mean that the company has been acquired or changed its name. To confirm this, try looking in the 'Mergers and Acquisitions' section at the front of this volume.

Sample of Mergers Section

Distillers Corporation S.A.–acquired & absorbed by Rothmans UK Holdings Limited
Durr Beteiligungs-AG—name changed to Durr AG
Elosua S.A.—ceased operations (no longer in business)
Grand Metropolitan Plc–merged with Guinness Plc to form Diageo Plc

4. **To locate companies in a given line of business:**

Use the 'N.A.I.C.S. (North American Industrial Classification System) Master Index' in volume II. This index interfiles data from all six volumes of *Corporate Affiliations*, arranging companies by particular products and services according to their primary N.A.I.C.S. code. The index is preceded by two helpful compendia: one sorts the codes alphabetically by the name of the product or service, the other numerically by the code itself.

Sample of Alpha Compendium of N.A.I.C.S. Codes

Description	N.A.I.C.S.
Administration of Conservation Programs	924120
Administration of Education Programs	923110

Sample of Numeric Compendium of N.A.I.C.S. Codes

Code	Description
111150	Corn Farming
111160	Rice Farming
111191	Oilseed and Grain Combination Farming

Both parent and sub companies are covered in this index; parent companies are printed in bold type, sub companies in regular typeface, followed by the name of its ultimate parent. A sample of the N.A.I.C.S. Master Index is shown here:

337211 — WOOD OFFICE FURNITURE MANUFACTURING

ABCO—Jami, Inc.; *Int'l*, pg. 586
ANDERSON HICKEY, INC.—Haworth, Inc.; *U.S. Public*, pg. 516
BELVEDERE COMPANY—Smith Investment Company; *Int'l*, pg. 1019
BRAYTON INTERNATIONAL INC.—Steelcase Inc.; *U.S. Public*, pg. 1048
BRODART COMPANY; *U.S. Private*, pg. 172
COMMUNITY—Jasper Seating Co., Inc.; *U.S. Private*, pg. 589
CRAMER INC.; *U.S. Public*, pg. 288
EAC CORPORATION; *Int'l*, pg. 357

Following is an example of a typical parent company listing with tags to some of its basic components.

SULLIVAN GRAPHICS LTD. ——————— **Company Name**
52 Upper Fitzwilliam Road ——————— **Company Address**
Dublin 12, Ireland
Tel.: (353) 568 332 ——————— **Telecommunications Data**
Web Site: www.sulgrap.com
Year Founded: 1967
SULLI—(LSE) ——————— **Ticker Symbol & Stock Exchange**
Rev.: $9,325,224,000 ——————— **Financial Information**
Assets: $2,700,000,000
Liabilities: $2,038,000,000
Net Worth: $662,000,000
Emp.: 10,950 ——————— **No. of Employees, Including Sub-entries**
Fiscal Year End: 12/31/24
Designs, Manufactures & Markets
Electronic Design Automation (EDA)
Software & Systems for the PC &
Systems Design Markets
N.A.I.C.S.: 334119 ——————— **North American Industry Classification System Code**
Andrew Sullivan *(Pres)*

Following each parent company listing are the entries for each of that company's divisions, subsidiaries, affiliates, joint ventures, units, etc. Though companies vary widely in their usage of these terms, some of the more common company designations can be defined as follows:

Affiliate   A chartered business owned by the company at less than 50%.

Division   An internal unit of a company, not incorporated.

Joint Venture   A business in which two or more companies share responsibility and ownership.

Subsidiary   A chartered business owned by the company at 50% or more.

PART C: UNDERSTANDING LEVELS OF REPORTAGE

Each sub-unit of the company will have a number in parentheses to the right of the company name. This number represents the level of reportage for that particular company. Any company with a level (1) reports directly to the parent company. Level (2) companies report to the level (1) company immediately above them. Level (3) companies report to the level (2) company immediately above them, etc.

Subsidiaries:

Ericsson Systems, Inc. ———— **(1)** ———— **Reports to the Parent Company (Sullivan**
2 Wellington Road Killarney   **Graphics, Ltd. from previous example)**
County Kerry, Ireland
Tel.: (353) 718 348
Sales Range: $25-49.9 Million
Computer Peripheral Equipment Mfr
N.A.I.C.S.: 334119 ————————————— **North American Industry Classification System Code**
Thomas J. McSweeney (*Pres*)

Subsidiaries:

Kerrigan Co., Inc. ———— **(2)** ———— **Reports Direct to Level 1 Company Above**
8 Swords Road   **(Ericsson Systems, Inc.)**
Dublin 17, Ireland ———— **(100%)** ———— **Percentage of Ownership**
Tel.: (353) 611 457
KC—(ISE)
Emp.: 850
Computer Printer Mfr
N.A.I.C.S.: 334119

U.S. Branch:

Kerrigan Co., Inc. ———— **(3)** ———— **Reports Direct to Level 2 Company**
21 Reading Ave   **Above (Kerrigan Co., Inc.)**
Memphis, TN 38101
Tel.: (901) 324-8746   (100%)
Computer Printer Mfr
N.A.I.C.S.: 334119
Susan Havens (*CEO*)

Wellsley Technologies, Inc. ———— **(2)** ————— **Reports Direct to Level 1 Company**
Crown Hill Clonskeagh   **Above (Ericsson Systems, Inc.)**
Dublin 4, Ireland
Tel.: (353) 278 743   **(90%)**
Computer Peripheral Equipment Mfr
N.A.I.C.S.: 334119

Tennant & McDaniel, Inc. ———— **(1)** ————— **Reports Back to Parent Company (Sullivan**
Greenhills Road Tallaght   **Graphics, Ltd.)**
Dublin 24, Ireland
Tel.: (353) 268 324   **(100%)**
Emp: 1,200
Computer Peripheral Equipment Mfr
N.A.I.C.S.: 334119

Non-U.S. Subsidiary:

Padova Systems, Inc. ———— **(1)** ————— **Subsidiary Not in Ireland, and Not in the**
Via Laurentina, 449   **U.S. Reports to the Parent Company**
20097 Milan, Italy   **(Sullivan Graphics, Ltd.)**
Tel.: (39) 6 305291
Computer Printer Mfr
N.A.I.C.S.: 334119
Anthony Macaluso *(Pres)*

ABBREVIATIONS

Abbr.	Meaning		Abbr.	Meaning
Acct	Account		Matl	Material
Acctg	Accounting		Matls	Materials
Accts	Accounts		Mdse	Merchandise
Acq	Acquisition(s)		Mdsg	Merchandising
Admin	Administration		Mfg	Manufacturing
Admin	Administrative		Mfr	Manufacturer
Adv	Advertising		Mgmt	Management
Assoc	Associate		Mgr	Manager
Asst	Assistant		Mktg	Marketing
Brdcst	Broadcast		Mng	Managing
Bus	Business		Natl	National
CEO	Chief Executive Officer		Ops	Operations
CFO	Chief Financial Officer		Org	Organization
Chm	Chairman of the Board		Pkg	Packaging
CIO	Chief Information Officer		Plng	Planning
CMO	Chief Marketing Officer		Pres	President
Comm	Communication(s)		Prof	Professional
Comml	Commercial		Promo	Promotion
COO	Chief Operating Officer		Promos	Promotions
Coord	Coordinator		Pub	Public
Corp	Corporate/Corporation		Pub	Rel Public Relations
CTO	Chief Technology Officer		Publ	Publishing
Dept	Department		Publr	Publisher
Dev	Development		Pur	Purchasing
Dir	Director		R&D	Research & Development
Distr	Distribution		Reg	Regional
Div	Division		Rep	Representative
DP	Data Processing		Res	Research
Engr	Engineer		Sec	Secretary
Engrg	Engineering		Sls	Sales
Environ	Environmental		Sr	Senior
Exec	Executive		Supvr	Supervisor
Fin	Finance/Financial		Svc	Service
Gen	General		Svcs	Services
Govt	Government		Sys	Systems
Grp	Group		Tech	Technology
HR	Human Resources		Tech	Technical
Indus	Industry/Industrial		Telecom	Telecommunication(s)
Info	Information		Treas	Treasurer
Intl	International		Trng	Training
IR	Investor Relations		Vice Chm	Vice Chairman
IT	Information Technology		VP	Vice President
Jr	Junior			

COUNTRY ABBREVIATIONS

AF	Afghanistan	DK	Denmark	KG	Kyrgyzstan	KN	Saint Kitts & Nevis
Al	Albania	DJ	Djibouti	La	Laos	LC	Saint Lucia
DG	Algeria	DM	Dominica	LV	Latvia	VC	Saint Vincent &
AD	Andorra	DO	Dominican Republic	LB	Lebanon		Grenadines
AO	Angola	EC	Ecuador	LS	Lesotho	WS	Samoa
AI	Anguilla	EG	Egypt	LR	Liberia	SA	Saudi Arabia
AG	Antigua & Barbuda	SV	El Salvador	LY	Libya	SN	Senegal
Ar	Argentina	GQ	Equatorial Guinea	LI	Liechtenstein	YU	Serbia &
AM	Armenia	ER	Eritrea	LT	Lithuania		Montenegro
AW	Aruba	EE	Estonia	LU	Luxembourg	Sc	Seychelles
AU	Australia	ET	Ethiopia	Mo	Macau	SL	Sierra Leone
AT	Austria	FO	Faroe Islands	MK	Macedonia	SG	Singapore
Az	Azerbaijan	FJ	Fiji	MG	Madagascar	Sk	Slovakia
BS	Bahamas	FI	Finland	MW	Malawi	SI	Slovenia
BH	Bahrain	FR	France	MY	Malaysia	SB	Solomon Islands
BD	Bangladesh	GF	French Guiana	MV	Maldives	SO	Somalia
BB	Barbados	PF	French Polynesia	ML	Mali	ZA	South Africa
BY	Belarus	Ga	Gabon	Mt	Malta	ES	Spain
BE	Belgium	GM	Gambia	MQ	Martinique	LK	Sri Lanka
BZ	Belize	GE	Georgia	MR	Mauritania	Sd	Sudan
BJ	Benin	De	Germany	MU	Mauritius	SR	Suriname
BM	Bermuda	GH	Ghana	MX	Mexico	SZ	Swaziland
BT	Bhutan	GI	Gibraltar	Md	Moldova	SE	Sweden
BO	Bolivia	GR	Greece	MC	Monaco	CH	Switzerland
BA	Bosnia & Herzegovina	GL	Greenland	Mn	Mongolia	SY	Syria
BW	Botswana	GD	Grenada	Ms	Montserrat	TW	Taiwan
BR	Brazil	GP	Guadeloupe	Ma	Morocco	TJ	Tajikistan
BN	Brunei Darussalam	GT	Guatemala	MZ	Mozambique	TZ	Tanzania
BG	Bulgaria	Gu	Guiana	MM	Myanmar	TH	Thailand
BF	Burkina Faso	GN	Guinea	NA	Namibia	TG	Togo
BI	Burundi	GW	Guinea-Bissau	NP	Nepal	TO	Tonga
KH	Cambodia	GY	Guyana	NL	Netherlands	TT	Trinidad & Tobago
CM	Cameroon	HT	Haiti	AN	Netherlands Antilles	Tn	Tunisia
Ca	Canada	HN	Honduras	Nc	New Caledonia	TR	Turkey
CV	Cape Verde	HK	Hong Kong	NZ	New Zealand	TM	Turkmenistan
Ky	Cayman Islands	HU	Hungary	NI	Nicaragua	TC	Turks & Caicos
CF	Central African	IS	Iceland	Ne	Niger		Islands
	Republic	In	India	NG	Nigeria	TV	Tuvalu
TD	Chad	Id	Indonesia	NO	Norway	UG	Uganda
CL	Chile	IR	Iran	OM	Oman	UA	Ukraine
CN	China	IQ	Iraq	PK	Pakistan	AE	United Arab
Co	Colombia	IE	Ireland	Pa	Panama		Emirates
KM	Comoros	Il	Israel	PG	Papua New Guinea	UK	United Kingdom
CD	Congo, Democratic	IT	Italy	PY	Paraguay	UY	Uruguay
	Republic of	JM	Jamaica	PE	Peru	UZ	Uzbekistan
CG	Congo, Republic of	JP	Japan	PH	Philippines	VU	Vanuatu
CK	Cook Islands	JO	Jordan	PL	Poland	VE	Venezuela
CR	Costa Rica	KZ	Kazakhstan	PT	Portugal	VN	Vietnam
CI	Cote d'Ivoire	KE	Kenya	QA	Qatar	VG	Virgin Islands
HR	Croatia	KI	Kiribati	RE	Reunion		(British)
CU	Cuba	KN	Korea (North)	RO	Romania	YE	Yemen
CY	Cyprus	Ks	Korea (South)	RU	Russia	ZM	Zambia
CZ	Czech Republic	KW	Kuwait	RW	Rwanda	ZW	Zimbabwe

COMPANY DESIGNATIONS

The following designations indicate the forms of business enterprise in various countries; these forms usually represent the organizations for large enterprises.

AB	Aktiebolag	Finland, Sweden
AG	Aktiengesellschaft	Austria, Germany, Switzerland, Liechtenstein
A/S	Aksjeselskap	Norway
	Aktieselskab	Denmark
B.V.	Besloten Vennootschap	Holland
C.V.	Commanditaire Vennootschap	Holland
Cie.	Compagnie	France, Luxembourg
Co.	Company	United States, France, South Africa, Luxembourg
Ets.	Etablissement(s)	France, Luxembourg
GmbH	Gesellschaft mit beschrankter Haftung	Austria, Germany, Switzerland
I/S	Interessantelskab	Denmark, Norway
KG	Kommanditgesellschaft	Austria, Germany, Switzerland
KK	Kabushiki Kaisha	Japan
K/S	Kommanditselskab	Denmark
Lda.	Limitada	Portugal
Ltd.	Limited	United Kingdom, United States, South Africa
Ltda.	Limitada	Brazil, Portugal
Ltee.	Limitee	Canada
Mij.	Maatschappij	Holland
N.V.	Naamloze Vennootschap	Belgium, Holland
OHG	Offene Handelsgesellschaft	Austria
Oy	Osakeyhtiot	Finland
PLC	Public Limited Company	United Kingdom
P.T.	Perusahaan Terbatas	Indonesia
Pte.	Private	Singapore
Pty.	Proprietary	Australia, South Africa
Pvt.	Private	India, Rhodesia
S.A.	Societe Anonyme	Belgium, France, Luxembourg, Switzerland
Sociedad	Anonima	Spain, Latin America
S.A.C.I.	Sociedad Anonima Comercial e Industrial	Latin America
S.A. de C.V.	Sociedad Anonima de Capital Variable	Mexico
S.A.E.	Sociedad Anonima Espanola	Spain
S.A.I.C.	Sociedad Anonima Industrial y Comercial	Latin America
S.A.R.L.	Sociedad Anonima de Responsabilidade Limitada	Brazil
	Sociedade a Responsabilitie Limitee	France, Luxembourg
S.A.S.	Societa in Accomandita Semplice	Italy
S.C.	Societe en Commandite	France
S.p.A.	Societa per Azioni	Italy
S.P.R.L.	Societe de Personnes a Responsabilitie Limitee	Belgium
S.R.L.	Societa a Responsabilita Limitata	Italy
Sdn. Bhd.	Sendirian Berhad	Malaysia
Ste.	Societe	France, Switzerland
Ste. Cve.	Societe Cooperative	Belgium
V.o.F.	Vennootschap onder firma	Holland

STOCK MARKET ABBREVIATIONS

ABU	Abu Dhabi Securities Exchange
AIM	AIM Market of the London Stock Exchange
AMM	Amman Stock Exchange
ARM	Armenian NASDAQ OMX Armenia
ASX	Australian Stock Exchange
ATH	Athens Stock Exchange
BAH	Bahrain Bourse
BAK	Baku Stock Exchange
BAN	Bangalore Stock Exchange
BANJ	Banja Luka Stock Exchange
BAR	Barcelona Stock Exchange
BARB	Barbados Stock Exchange
BEL	Belgrade Stock Exchange
BER	Borse Berlin-Bremen Stock Exchange
BERM	Bermuda Stock Exchange
BERN	Bern Stock Exchange
BESA	Bond Exchange of South Africa
BEY	Beirut Stock Exchange
BHU	Royal Securities Exchange of Bhutan
BIL	Bilbao Stock Exchange
BOA	BOAG Borsen (Merger of Hannover & Hamburg Exchanges)
BOL	Bolsa de Valores de Bolivia
BOM	Bombay (Mumbai) Stock Exchange
BOT	Botswana Stock Exchange
BRA	Bratislava Stock Exchange
BRAZ	Brazil Stock Exchange (BM&F Bovespa)
BRVM	Bourse Regionale des Valeurs Mobilieres
BUC	Bucharest Stock Exchange
BUD	Budapest Stock Exchange
BUE	Buenos Aires Stock Exchange (Mercado de Valores Buenos Aires)
BUL	Bulgarian Stock Exchange
BVMAC	Securities Exchange of Central Africa
BVT	Bourse de Tunis
BX	Boston NASDAQ OMX BXSM
CAR	Caracas Stock Exchange
CAS	Casablanca Stock Exchange
CAT	Singapore Catalist
CAY	Cayman Islands Stock Exchange
CHA	Channel Islands Stock Exchange
CHI	Chicago Stock Exchange
CHIN	ChiNext (Chinese Exchange for Small & High-Tech Enterprises)
CHT	Chittagong Stock Exchange
CNSX	Canadian National Stock Exchange
COL	Colombo Stock Exchange
COLO	Colombia Bolsa de Valores
COR	Cordoba Stock Exchange
CSE	Copenhagen Stock Exchange
CYP	Cyprus Stock Exchange
DAR	Dar es Salaam Stock Exchange
DES	Delhi Stock Exchange
DEU	Deutsche Borse (Frankfurt Stock Exchange)
DFM	Dubai Financial Market
DHA	Dhaka Stock Exchange
DUS	Dusseldorf Stock Exchange
ECA	Eastern Caribbean Securities Exchange
EGX	Egyptian Exchange
EMI	Securities & Commodities Authority (d/b/a Emirates Securities Market)
EUR	Euronext
FKA	Fukuoka Stock Exchange
GEOR	Georgian Stock Exchange
GHA	Ghana Stock Exchange
GUA	Guayaquil Stock Exchange
HEL	Helsinki Stock Exchange
HKG	Hong Kong Stock Exchange
HNX	Hanoi Stock Exchange
HOSE	Ho Chi Minh Stock Exchange (Vietnam)
HYD	Hyderabad Stock Exchange
ICE	Iceland Stock Exchange
INDO	Indonesia Stock Exchange
IRAQ	Iraq Stock Exchange
ISDX	ICAP Securities & Derivatives Exchange Limited (formerly PLUS)
ISE	Irish Stock Exchange
ISL	Islamabad Stock Exchange
IST	Istanbul Stock Exchange
ISX	Inter-Connected Stock Exchange of India
ITA	Italian Stock Exchange
JAI	Jaipur Stock Exchange
JAM	Jamaica Stock Exchange
JAS	OSE JASDAQ
JSE	Johannesburg Stock Exchange
KAR	Karachi Stock Exchange
KAZ	Kazakhstan Stock Exchange
KHAR	Khartoum Stock Exchange
KLS	Bursa Malaysia (Formerly Kuala Lumpur Stock Exchange)
KOL	Kolkata Stock Exchange
KRS	Korea Exchange
KUW	Kuwait Stock Exchange
LAH	Lahore Stock Exchange
LIM	Lima Bolsa de Valores
LJU	Ljubljana Stock Exchange
LSE	London Stock Exchange
LUS	Lusaka Stock Exchange
LUX	Luxembourg Stock Exchange
MAC	Macedonian Stock Exchange
MAD	Madrid Stock Exchange
MAL	Malta Stock Exchange
MALA	Malawi Stock Exchange
MAU	Stock Exchange of Mauritius
MDS	Madras Stock Exchange
MEX	Bolsa Mexicana de Valores

MIC	MICEX Moscow Interbank Currency Exchange
MOLD	Moldova Stock Exchange
MON	Montreal Stock Exchange
MONG	Mongolian Stock Exchange
MUN	Munich Stock Exchange
MUS	Muscat Stock Exchange
NAI	Nairobi Stock Exchange
NAM	Namibian Stock Exchange
NASDAQ	National Association of Securities Dealers, Inc.
NASDAQDBAI	NASDAQ Dubai
NEP	Nepal Stock Exchange Ltd
NGO	Nagoya Stock Exchange
NIGE	Nigerian Stock Exchange
NSE	National Stock Exchange of India
NSXA	National Stock Exchange of Australia
NYSA	New York Stock Exchange Arca Options Trading System
NYSE	New York Stock Exchange
NYSE AMERICAN	NYSE American
NZE	New Zealand Exchange Limited
OMX	Stockholm/Nordic Stock Exchange
OSE	Osaka Stock Exchange
OSL	Oslo Stock Exchange
OTC	Over-the-Counter Pink Sheets
OTCB	Over-the-Counter Bulletin Board
OTCI	Over-the-Counter Exchange of India
PAL	Palestine Securities Exchange
PAN	Bolsa de Valores de Panama
PET	Saint Petersburg Stock Exchange
PHI	Philippine Stock Exchange
PHLX	Philadelphia - NASDAQ OMX PHLX
POM	Port Moresby Stock Exchange Limited (Papua New Guinea)
PRA	Prague Stock Exchange

PUN	Pune Stock Exchange (India)
QE	Qatar Stock Exchange
RIO	Rio de Janeiro, Bolsa de Valores
RSE	Riga Stock Exchange
RUS	Russian Trading System
SAP	Sapporo Stock Exchange
SARE	Sarejevo Stock Exchange
SAU	Saudi Stock Exchange
SES	Singapore Stock Exchange
SGO	Santiago Stock Exchange
SHG	Shanghai Stock Exchange
SPSE	South Pacific Stock Exchange
SSE	Shenzhen Stock Exchange
SSX	Swaziland Stock Exchange
STU	Stuttgart Stock Exchange (Baden)
SWX	Swiss Stock Exchange
TAE	Tel-Aviv Stock Exchange
TAI	Taiwan Stock Exchange
TAL	Tallinn Stock Exchange
TFE	Tokyo Financial Exchange (Futures)
THA	Stock Exchange of Thailand
THE	Tehran Stock Exchange
TKS	Tokyo Stock Exchange
TOSH	Tashkent Republican Stock Exchange
TRI	Trinidad & Tobago Stock Exchange
TSX	Toronto Stock Exchange
TSXV	Toronto Stock Venture Exchange
UGAN	Uganda Securities Exchange
UKR	Ukranian Stock Exchange
VAL	Bolsa de Valencia
VIE	Wiener Borse (Vienna Stock Exchange)
VLA	Vladivostok Stock Exchange
VSE	Vilnius Stock Exchange
WAR	Warsaw Stock Exchange
ZAG	Zagreb Stock Exchange
ZIM	Zimbabwe Stock Exchange

EXCHANGE RATES

Country	Currency	Rate	Country	Currency	Rate
Afghanistan	Afghani	0.01927	Egypt	Pound	0.14854
Albania	Lek	0.00948	El Salvador	Dollar	1
Algeria	Dinar	0.01273	Equatorial Guinea	Franc	0.00205
Andorra	Euro	1.34617	Eritrea	Nakfa	0.06623
Angola	Kwanza	0.01041	Estonia	Euro	1.34617
Antigua & Barbuda	Dollar	0.36807	Ethiopia	Birr	0.05412
Argentina	Peso	0.20132	Falkland Islands	Pound	1.58003
Armenia	Dram	0.00248	Faroe Islands	Krone	0.18036
Aruba	Guilder	0.55562	Fiji	Dollar	0.56329
Australia	Dollar	1.04210	Finland	Euro	1.34617
Austria	Euro	1.34617	France	Euro	1.34617
Azerbaijan	Manat	1.27307	French Guiana	Euro	1.34617
Bahamas	Dollar	0.99257	Gabon	Franc	0.00205
Bahrain	Dinar	2.59161	Gambia	Dalasi	0.02892
Bangladesh	Taka	0.01238	Georgia	Lari	0.60234
Barbados	Dollar	0.49196	Germany	Euro	1.34617
Belarus	Ruble	0.00012	Ghana	Cedi	0.52035
Belgium	Euro	1.34617	Gibraltar	Pound	1.58033
Belize	Dollar	0.49317	Greece	Euro	1.34617
Benin	Franc	0.00205	Greenland	Krone	0.18036
Bermuda	Dollar	1	Grenada	Dollar	0.36807
Bhutan	Ngultrum	0.01858	Guadeloupe	Euro	1.34617
Bolivia	Boliviano	0.01400	Guatemala	Quetzal	0.12538
Bosnia & Herzegovina	Marka	0.68820	Guernsey	Pound	1.57929
Botswana	Pula	0.12310	Guinea	Franc	0.00014
Brazil	Real	0.49189	Guinea-Bissau	Franc	0.00205
Brunei Darussalam	Dollar	0.80244	Guyana	Dollar	0.00500
Bulgaria	Lev	0.68350	Haiti	Gourde	0.02337
Burkina Faso	Franc	0.00205	Honduras	Lempira	0.04939
Burundi	Franc	0.00065	Hungary	Forint	0.00452
Cambodia	Riel	0.00025	Iceland	Krona	0.00782
Cameroon	CFA Franc BEAC	0.00205	India	Rupee	0.01854
Canada	Dollar	0.99402	Indonesia	Rupiah	0.00010
Cape Verde	Escudo	0.01194	Iran	Rial	0.00008
Caribbean Netherlands	Dollar	1	Iraq	Dinar	0.00084
Cayman Islands	Dollar	1.19325	Ireland	Euro	1.34617
Central African Republic	Franc	0.00205	Isle of Man	Pound	1.57929
Chad	Franc	0.00205	Israel	New Shekel	0.26868
Chile	Peso	0.00212	Italy	Euro	1.34617
China	Yuan Renminbi	0.15885	Jamaica	Dollar	0.01061
China (Hong Kong)	Dollar	0.12895	Japan	Yen	0.01100
China (Macau)	Pataca	0.12319	Jersey	Pound	1.57929
Colombia	Peso	0.00056	Jordan	Dinar	1.40489
Comoros	Franc	0.00273	Kazakhstan	Tenge	0.00655
Congo, Democratic Republic of	Franc	0.00105	Kenya	Shilling	0.01123
			Kiribati	Dollar	0.91406
Congo, Republic of	Franc	0.00205	Korea (North)	North Korean Won	0.00741
Cook Islands	Dollar	0.83700			
Costa Rica	Colon	0.00195	Korea (South)	South Korean Won	0.00093
Cote d'Ivoire	Franc	0.00205			
Croatia	Kuna	0.17771	Kuwait	Dinar	3.54359
Cuba	Peso	0.04320	Kyrgyzstan	Som	0.02096
Curacao	Guilder	0.54945	Laos	Kip	0.00012
Cyprus	Euro	1.34617	Latvia	Lat	1.89941
Czech Republic	Koruna	0.05257	Lebanon	Pound	0.00065
Denmark	Krone	0.18036	Lesotho	Loti	0.10957
Djibouti	Franc	0.00553	Liberia	Dollar	0.01342
Dominica	Dollar	0.36807	Libya	Dinar	0.78401
Dominican Republic	Peso	0.02446	Liechtenstein	Swiss Franc	1.07932
East Timor	Dollar	1	Lithuania	Litas	0.38428
Ecuador	Dollar	1	Luxembourg	Euro	1.34617

Country	Currency	Rate	Country	Currency	Rate
Macedonia	Denar	0.02108	Sakha	Ruble	0.03307
Madagascar	Ariary	0.00045	Samoa	Tala	0.42369
Malawi	Kwacha	0.00284	Saudi Arabia	Riyal	0.26630
Malaysia	Ringgit	0.32792	Senegal	Franc	0.00205
Maldives	Rufiyaa	0.06398	Serbia	Dinar	0.01199
Mali	Franc	0.00205	Seychelles	Rupee	0.07289
Malta	Euro	1.34617	Sierra Leone	Leone	0.00023
Marshall Islands	Dollar	1	Singapore	Dollar	0.80968
Martinique	Euro	1.34617	Slovakia	Euro	1.34617
Mauritania	Ouguiya	0.00327	Slovenia	Euro	1.34617
Mauritius	Rupee	0.03148	Solomon Islands	Dollar	0.13510
Mexico	Peso	0.07868	Somalia	Shilling	0.00062
Micronesia	Dollar	1	South Africa	Rand	0.11170
Moldolva	Leu	0.08084	Spain	Euro	1.34617
Monaco	Euro	1.34617	Sri Lanka	Rupee	0.00785
Mongolia	Tughrik	0.00072	Sudan	Pound	0.22511
Montenegro	Euro	1.34617	Sudan (South)	Pound	0.33070
Morocco	Dirham	0.11707	Suriname	Dollar	0.30303
Mozambique	Metical	0.03247	Swaziland	Lilangeni	0.10985
Myanmar	Kyat	0.00115	Sweden	Krona	0.15480
Namibia	Dollar	0.10957	Switzerland	Franc	1.07932
Nepal	Rupee	0.01150	Syria	Pound	0.01391
Netherlands	Euro	1.34617	Taiwan	New Dollar	0.03387
New Caledonia	Franc	0.01129	Tajikistan	Somoni	0.21000
New Zealand	Dollar	0.83700	Tanzania	Shilling	0.00061
Nicaragua	Cordoba	0.04078	Thailand	Baht	0.03313
Niger	Franc	0.00205	Togo	Franc	0.00205
Nigeria	Naira	0.00629	Tonga	Pa'anga	0.57887
Norway	Kroner	0.18099	Trinidad & Tobago	Dollar	0.15415
Oman	Rial	2.58772	Tunisia	Dinar	0.64350
Pakistan	Rupee	0.01013	Turkey	New Lira	0.56513
Panama	Balboa	0.97898	Turkmenistan	Manat	0.35088
Papua New Guinea	Kina	0.47154	Turks & Caico Islands	Dollar	1
Paraguay	Guarani	0.00023	Tuvalu	Dollar	1.04210
Peru	New Sol	0.38347	Uganda	Shilling	0.00037
Philippines	Peso	0.02449	Ukraine	Hryvnia	0.12179
Poland	Zloty	0.31713	United Arab Emirates	Dirham	0.27218
Portugal	Euro	1.34617	United Kingdom	Pound	1.57929
Qatar	Riyal	0.26710	Uruguay	Peso	0.05088
Reunion	Euro	1.34617	Uzbekistan	Som	0.00050
Romania	New Leu	0.30768	Vanuatu	Vatu	0.01105
Russia	Ruble	0.03307	Venezuela	Bolivar	0.23257
Rwanda	Franc	0.00159	Vietnam	Dong	0.00005
Saint Kitts & Nevis	Dollar	0.36807	Virgin Islands (British)	Dollar	1
Saint Lucia	Dollar	0.36807	Wallis & Futuna	Franc	0.01129
Saint Maarten	Guilder	0.54945	Yemen	Rial	0.00463
Saint Vincent & Grenadines	Dollar	0.36807	Zambia	Kwacha	0.00019

Nicaragua	Cordoba	0.0407
Niger	Franc	0.0020
Nigeria	Naira	0.0062
Norway	Kroner	0.1609
Oman	Rial	2.5817
Pakistan	Rupee	0.0101
Panama	Balboa	0.9789
Papua New Guinea	Kina	0.4715
Paraguay	Guarani	0.0002
Peru	New Sol	0.3553
Philippines	Peso	0.0224
Poland	Zloty	0.3171
Portugal	Euro	1.3447
Qatar	Riyal	0.2617
Reunion	Euro	1.3447
Romania	New Leu	0.3074
Russia	Ruble	0.0339
Rwanda	Franc	0.0015
Saint Kitts & Nevis	Dollar	0.3880
Saint Lucia	Dollar	0.3880
Saint Maarten	Guilder	0.5494
Saint Vincent & Grenadines	Dollar	0.3680

Country	Currency	Rate
Sabra	Ruble	0.03507
Samoa	Tala	0.42869
Saudi Arabia	Riyal	0.26630
Senegal	Franc	0.00205
Serbia	Dinar	0.01199
Seychelles	Rupee	0.07289
Sierra Leone	Leone	0.00023
Singapore	Dollar	0.80568
Slovakia	Euro	1.3447
Slovenia	Euro	1.3447
Solomon Islands	Dollar	0.13510
Somalia	Shilling	0.00092
South Africa	Rand	0.11170
Spain	Euro	1.3447
Sri Lanka	Rupee	0.00788
Sudan	Pound	0.2251
Sudan (South)	Pound	0.33070
Suriname	Dollar	0.30303
Swaziland	Lilangeni	0.0985
Sweden	Krona	0.15480
Switzerland	Franc	1.0792
Syria	Pound	0.01361
Taiwan	New Dollar	0.03387
Tajikistan	Somoni	0.21000
Tanzania	Shilling	0.00061
Thailand	Baht	0.03313
Togo	Franc	0.00205
Tonga	Pa'anga	0.5788
Trinidad & Tobago	Dollar	0.15415
Tunisia	Dinar	0.64350
Turkey	New Lira	0.5651
Turkmenistan	Manat	0.35088
Turks & Caicos Islands	Dollar	1
Tuvalu	Dollar	1.04210
Uganda	Shilling	0.00037
Ukraine	Hryvnia	0.12179
United Arab Emirates	Dirham	0.27218
United Kingdom	Pound	1.57829
Uruguay	Peso	0.05068
Uzbekistan	Som	0.00050
Vanuatu	Vatu	0.01105
Venezuela	Bolivar	0.23287
Vietnam	Dong	0.00005
Virgin Islands (British)	Dollar	1
Wallis & Futuna	Franc	0.01129
Yemen	Rial	0.00463
Zambia	Kwacha	0.00019

NEW LISTINGS 2025
Appearing for the first time in this publication

2

2KS CLOUD SERVICES GMBH; DARM-STADT, GERMANY

3

3AC CO., LTD.; SEOUL, KOREA (SOUTH)

A

A AGENCIA BRASILEIRA DE PROMO-CAO DE EXPORTACOES E INVESTIMEN-TOS; BRASILIA, BRAZIL

ABOVE FOOD INGREDIENTS INC.; RE-GINA, CANADA

ACCENT MICROCELL LTD.; AHMEDA-BAD, INDIA

ACCESS TECHNOLOGY GROUP LIM-ITED; LOUGHBOROUGH, UNITED KING-DOM

ACTIONSPORTGAMES A/S; ESPER-GAERDE, DENMARK

ACUREN CORPORATION; TORTOLA, VIRGIN ISLANDS (BRITISH)

ACWA POWER COMPANY; RIYADH, SAUDI ARABIA

ADENIA PARTNERS LTD; BEAU PLAN, MAURITIUS

AECC SHANGHAI COMMERCIAL AIR-CRAFT ENGINE MANUFACTURING CO.; SHANGHAI, CHINA

AEOON TECHNOLOGIES GMBH; KRAM-SACH, AUSTRIA

AFRICA RISK CONSULTING LTD.; LON-DON, UNITED KINGDOM

AGNORA LTD; COLLINGWOOD, CANADA

AI CO., LTD.; TOKYO, JAPAN

AICHI FINANCIAL GROUP CO., LTD.; NA-GOYA, JAPAN

AIP FOUNDATION; HANOI, VIETNAM

AKANKSHA POWER & INFRASTRUC-TURE LIMITED; NASHIK, INDIA

ALGOMA STEEL GROUP INC.; SAULT SAINTE MARIE, CANADA

ALICORN LIMITED; LONDON, UNITED KINGDOM

ALLIANZ GLOBAL INVESTORS LUXEM-BOURG S.A.; SENNINGERBERG, LUXEM-BOURG

ALLIED CRITICAL METALS CORP.; VAN-COUVER, CANADA

ALLU GROUP OY; PENNALA, FINLAND

ALMAVIVA S.P.A.; ROME, ITALY

ALPHA TECHNOLOGY GROUP LIMITED; KOWLOON, CHINA (HONG KONG)

AMAZONE H. DREYER GMBH & CO. KG; HASBERGEN, GERMANY

AMBIENTA SGR S.P.A; MILAN, ITALY

AMF-BRUNS GMBH & CO. KG; APEN, GERMANY

AMIA ENERGY GMBH; HAMBURG, GER-MANY

AMMANN SWITZERLAND LTD; LANGEN-THAL, SWITZERLAND

AMPYR GLOBAL ENERGY HOLDINGS PTE. LTD; SINGAPORE, SINGAPORE

ANCHOR LAS AB; ESKILSTUNA, SWE-DEN

ANDALUSI BEVERAGES S.L.; SEVILLE, SPAIN

ANDERCO INVESTMENT PTE LTD; SIN-GAPORE, SINGAPORE

ANGLO-EASTERN UNIVAN GROUP; KOWLOON, CHINA (HONG KONG)

ANYWIRE CORPORATION; NAGAOKA-KYO, JAPAN

APE ANGEWANDTE PHYSIK & ELEKTRONIK GMBH; BERLIN, GERMANY

APIARY CAPITAL LLP; LONDON, UNITED KINGDOM

ARA GROUP LIMITED; CROWS NEST, AUSTRALIA

ARAD-OPHIR LTD.; RAMAT HASHARON, ISRAEL

ARG MBH & CO. KG; OBERHAUSEN, GERMANY

ARRHYTHMIA NETWORK TECHNOLOGY SL; MADRID, SPAIN

ARVIND & COMPANY SHIPPING AGEN-CIES LIMITED; JAMNAGAR, INDIA

ASAS CAPITAL LTD; , UNITED ARAB EMIRATES

ASKO HOLDING A.S.; GAZIANTEP, TUR-KIYE

ASMPT GMBH & CO. KG; MUNICH, GER-MANY

ATMOKY GMBH; GRAZ, AUSTRIA

ATS-TANNER BANDING SYSTEMS AG; ZUG, SWITZERLAND

ATTIVO GROUP; CHRISTCHURCH, NEW ZEALAND

AUSTRALIAN MEAT INDUSTRY SUPER-ANNUATION TRUST PTY LTD.; PARRA-MATTA, AUSTRALIA

AUSTRALIAN OILSEEDS HOLDINGS LIM-ITED; COOTAMUNDRA, AUSTRALIA

AVERON PARK LIMITED; LONDON, UNITED KINGDOM

AZAD ENGINEERING LIMITED; HYDERA-BAD, INDIA

AZULIS CAPITAL; PARIS, FRANCE

B

B INVESTMENTS HOLDING SAE; CAIRO, EGYPT

BAC HOLDING INTERNATIONAL CORP.; BOGOTA, COLOMBIA

BANCA DI CIVIDALE S.P.A.; CIVIDALE DEL FRIULI, ITALY

BANCA POPOLARE PUGLIESE S.C.P.A.; MATINO, ITALY

BANCO MASTER S.A.; SAO PAULO, BRAZIL

BARRO GROUP PTY LTD; CARLTON, AUSTRALIA

BASILIC FLY STUDIO LIMITED; CHEN-NAI, INDIA

BASSETTI GROUP SAS; GRENOBLE, FRANCE

BAUER HOLZBAU GMBH; SATTELDORF, GERMANY

BAUMER HOLDING AG; FRAUENFELD, SWITZERLAND

BAUMGARTNER & LAMPERSTORFER INSTRUMENTS GMBH.; FELDKIRCHEN, GERMANY

BAYANAT AI PLC; ABU DHABI, UNITED ARAB EMIRATES

BAYLEYS CORPORATION LIMITED; AUCKLAND, NEW ZEALAND

BAYRIDGE RESOURCES CORP.; VAN-COUVER, CANADA

BBTV HOLDINGS INC.; VANCOUVER, CANADA

BD-CAPITAL PARTNERS LIMITED; LONDON, UNITED KINGDOM

BEEDIE CAPITAL PARTNERS; VANCOUVER, CANADA

BEIJING ZOHETEC CO., LTD; BEIJING, CHINA

BENDA SUNKWANG IND. CO., LTD.; INCHEON, KOREA (SOUTH)

BENNER HOLDING GMBH; WIESBADEN, GERMANY

BEST CHIPS CO., LTD.; SAITAMA, JAPAN

BETAMEK BERHAD; SELANGOR, MALAYSIA

BHARAT HIGHWAYS INVIT.; GURUGRAM, INDIA

BIG TREE CLOUD HOLDINGS LIMITED; SHENZHEN, CHINA

BIRN SERBIA; BELGRADE, SERBIA

BITFUFU INC.; SINGAPORE, SINGAPORE

BLUE INNOVATION CO., LTD.; TOKYO, JAPAN

BLUE JET HEALTHCARE LIMITED; MUMBAI, INDIA

BM CARPENTERIE OIL & GAS S.R.L.; MILAN, ITALY

BODY ACTION ENTERPRISE CO., LTD.; TAICHUNG, TAIWAN

BOHEMIA FAKTORING, A.S.; PRAGUE, CZECH REPUBLIC

BOLDYN NETWORKS GLOBAL LTD.; LONDON, UNITED KINGDOM

BOMSOWA CO. LTD.; SEONGNAM, KOREA (SOUTH)

BTSR INTERNATIONAL S.P.A.; OLGIATE OLONA, ITALY

BUSI GROUP S.R.L.; PAITONE, ITALY

C

C&H COMMUNICATIONS; DUBAI, UNITED ARAB EMIRATES

CADRE AS; KRISTIANSAND, NORWAY

CALASTONE LIMITED; LONDON, UNITED KINGDOM

CALLEJA S.A. DE C.V.; SAN SALVADOR, EL SALVADOR

CANDY TOY - INDUSTRIA E COMERCIO DE ALIMENTOS E PLASTICOS LTDA; SAO PAULO, BRAZIL

CANNAWORLD VENTURES INC.; BURNABY, CANADA

CAPMONT GMBH; MUNICH, GERMANY

CAPSTONE COPPER CORP.; VANCOUVER, CANADA

CAPTIVISION INC.; NAILSWORTH, UNITED KINGDOM

CARAVELLE INTERNATIONAL GROUP; SINGAPORE, SINGAPORE

CASI PHARMACEUTICALS, INC.; BEIJING, CHINA

CASSA RURALE ED ARTIGIANA DI BINASCO CREDITO COOPERATIVO; BINASCO, ITALY

CEDAROME CANADA INC.; CANDIAC, CANADA

CELLO WORLD LIMITED; MUMBAI, INDIA

CENTRAL GROUP; BUDAPEST, HUNGARY

CENTRO CARDIOLOGICO MONZINO S.P.A.; MILAN, ITALY

CETUS CAPITAL ACQUISITION CORP.; TAIPEI, TAIWAN

CEVOTEC GMBH; UNTERHACHING, GERMANY

CHAPS HOLDING SAS; SURESNES, FRANCE

CHAROENRUT KARNTAW CO., LTD.; BANGKOK, THAILAND

CHEUNG HO ELECTRIC CO., LIMITED; , CHINA (HONG KONG)

CHILDREN'S HOSPITAL TRUST; CAPE TOWN, SOUTH AFRICA

CHINA MOBILE IOT COMPANY LIMITED; CHONGQING, CHINA

CHUGIN FINANCIAL GROUP, INC.; OKAYAMA, JAPAN

CHUNGNAM NATIONAL UNIVERSITY; DAEJEON, KOREA (SOUTH)

CIGALAH TRADING ESTABLISHMENT; JEDDAH, SAUDI ARABIA

CIRCULAR WATERS SOLUTIONS S.R.L; , ROMANIA

CISALFA SPORT S.P.A.; LOMBARDIA, ITALY

CLARO PRODUCTS GMBH; ANIF, AUSTRIA

CLIFFSIDE LTD.; TORONTO, CANADA

CLINICAL DESIGN TECHNOLOGIES LTD.; EXETER, UNITED KINGDOM

COME TO AGREEMENT LTD.; RICHMOND HILL, CANADA

COMMITTED CARGO CARE LIMITED; NEW DELHI, INDIA

COMPAX SOFTWARE DEVELOPMENT GMBH; VIENNA, AUSTRIA

COMRIT INVESTMENTS 1 LP; TEL AVIV, ISRAEL

CONCORD BIOTECH LIMITED; AHMEDABAD, INDIA

CONNECTENS B.V.; HAAKSBERGEN, NETHERLANDS

CONVERGENCE PARTNERS (PTY) LIMITED; ROSEBANK, SOUTH AFRICA

CONVERGENT FINANCE LLP; MUMBAI, INDIA

COPILOT CAPITAL LIMITED; LONDON, UNITED KINGDOM

COPLUS INC.; TAINAN CITY, TAIWAN

COPPER STANDARD RESOURCES INC.; VANCOUVER, CANADA

CORE NICKEL CORP.; SASKATOON, CANADA

CREDITCHECK PARTNERS PRIVATE LIMITED; MUMBAI, INDIA

CREDO BRANDS MARKETING LIMITED; MUMBAI, INDIA

CRINSURANCE S.A.S.; LA PLATA, ARGENTINA

CRYSTAL GLOBE LIMITED; TIANJIN, CHINA

CUBE BIO-ENERGY PVT LTD.; HYDERABAD, TELANGANA, INDIA

CURIOX BIOSYSTEMS CO., LTD.; SEOUL, KOREA (SOUTH)

CXJ GROUP CO., LIMITED; HANGZHOU, CHINA

D

DADAM INVESTMENT CORP.; GANGNAM-GU, KOREA (SOUTH)

DAI-ICHI HIGH FREQUENCY CO., LTD.; TOKYO, JAPAN

DAIWA CYCLE CO., LTD.; OSAKA, JAPAN

DDC ENTERPRISE LIMITED; SHEUNG WAN, CHINA (HONG KONG)

DENNEMEYER SA; HOWALD, LUXEMBOURG

DFP HOLDINGS LIMITED; TAIPEI, TAIWAN

DR. SULAIMAN AL HABIB MEDICAL SERVICES GROUP COMPANY; RIYADH, SAUDI ARABIA

DT CLOUD ACQUISITION CORP.; LONDON, UNITED KINGDOM

DUNA ASZFALT ZTR; BUDAPEST, HUNGARY

E

E B TRANS SA; MUNSBACH, LUXEMBOURG

E2S CO., LTD.; HWASUNG-SI, KOREA (SOUTH)

ECARX HOLDINGS, INC.; SHANGHAI, CHINA

EKWB D.O.O.; KOMENDA, SLOVENIA

ELBI S.P.A.; LIMENA, ITALY

ELONG POWER HOLDING LIMITED; GANZHOU, CHINA

EMIL FREY HOLDING AG; ZURICH, SWITZERLAND

ENDOGENE LTD.; BRIGHTON, AUSTRALIA

ENGENE HOLDINGS INC.; MONTREAL, CANADA

EPIPROCARE GMBH; BERLIN, GERMANY

ES NETWORKS CO., LTD.; TOKYO, JAPAN

ESGL HOLDINGS LIMITED; SINGAPORE, SINGAPORE

ESSIX BIOSCIENCES LIMITED; DERABASSI, INDIA

EV8 TECHNOLOGIES LIMITED; LONDON, UNITED KINGDOM

EXECUS SPA; MILAN, ITALY

EXICOM TELE-SYSTEMS LIMITED; GURUGRAM, INDIA

EXPORT TRADING GROUP PTE LTD.; MAURITIUS, MAURITIUS

F

F&C INVESTMENT TRUST PLC; LONDON, UNITED KINGDOM

F.P. BOURGAULT INDUSTRIES LTD.; , CANADA

FARFALLI; MANIAGO, ITALY

FBS GLOBAL LIMITED; SINGAPORE, SINGAPORE

FENBO HOLDINGS LIMITED; KOWLOON, CHINA (HONG KONG)

FIN MILE LOGISTICS LIMITED; LONDON, UNITED KINGDOM

FIOR FAMILIE GMBH; MEERBUSCH, GERMANY

FIXIT AG; HOLDERBANK, SWITZERLAND

FLEXICARE (GROUP) LIMITED; CYNON VALLEY, UNITED KINGDOM

FLY SRL; VENETO, ITALY

FONUA LTD.; DUBLIN, IRELAND

FORMICA CAPITAL HOLDING AB; GOTHENBURG, SWEDEN

FORTENOVA GROUP D.D.; ZAGREB, CROATIA

FREE RUNNING BUILDINGS LTD.; ROTHERHAM, UNITED KINGDOM

FREMMAN CAPITAL LIMITED; LONDON, UNITED KINGDOM

G

GALAXY PAYROLL GROUP LIMITED; SHEUNG WAN, CHINA (HONG KONG)

GALEMED CORPORATION; TAIPEI, TAIWAN

GEBRUDER WEISS GESELLSCHAFT M.B.H.; LAUTERACH, AUSTRIA

GELTEQ LIMITED; SOUTH MELBOURNE, AUSTRALIA

GENROBOTIC INNOVATIONS PRIVATE LIMITED; THIRUVANANTHAPURAM, INDIA

GEUMSAN GINSENG HERB DEVELOPMENT AGENCY; GEUMSAN, KOREA (SOUTH)

GIA LAI ELECTRICITY JOINT STOCK COMPANY; PLEIKU, VIETNAM

GIACOM (CLOUD) HOLDINGS LIMITED; LONDON, UNITED KINGDOM

GL GMBH METALL- UND WERKSTATTTECHNIK; FRICKENHAUSEN, GERMANY

GLENTRA CAPITAL P/S; COPENHAGEN, DENMARK

GLOBAL LIGHTS ACQUISITION CORP.; BEIJING, CHINA

GLOBAL METCORP LTD; MIDDLESEX, UNITED KINGDOM

GLOBAL MOFY METAVERSE LIMITED; BEIJING, CHINA

GLOBAVEND HOLDINGS LIMITED; PERTH, AUSTRALIA

GOLD VALLEY PTY. LTD.; PERTH, AUSTRALIA

GOYAL SALT LIMITED; JAIPUR, INDIA

GRAFTON CAPITAL LIMITED; LONDON, UNITED KINGDOM

GRAPHISADS LIMITED; NEW DELHI, INDIA

GROUPE GARNIER; LOUDEAC, FRANCE

GRUPO DON MARIO; MARTINEZ, ARGENTINA

GRUPO LAR INVERSIONES INMOBILIARIAS, SA; MADRID, SPAIN

GUANGDONG LIANXUN PRECISION MANUFACTURING CO.,LTD.; ZHAOQING, CHINA

GURU APP FACTORY CORP.; LONDON, UNITED KINGDOM

H

HAMILTON & COMPANY LIMITED; MUMBAI, INDIA

HANSSAK CO., LTD.; SEOUL, KOREA (SOUTH)

HAO YONG AUTOMOTIVE CONTROLS LTD.; DONGGUAN, CHINA

HAPPY FORGING LIMITED; LUDHIANA, INDIA

HELMHOLTZ-ZENTRUM HEREON; GEESTHACHT, GERMANY

HEXONIA GMBH; NETTETAL, GERMANY

HFBG HOLDING B.V.; HOOFDDORP, NETHERLANDS

HIVEST CAPITAL PARTNERS SAS; PARIS, FRANCE

HOMEEASE INDUSTRIAL CO. LTD.; CHIAYI, TAIWAN

HONASA CONSUMER LIMITED; NEW DELHI, INDIA

HRH NEXT SERVICES LIMITED; HYDERABAD, INDIA

HUABO BIOPHARM (SHANGHAI) CO., LTD.; SHANGHAI, CHINA

HYGON INFORMATION TECHNOLOGY CO. LTD.; BEIJING, CHINA

HYPEX BIO EXPLOSIVES TECHNOLOGY AB; FARSTA, SWEDEN

I

IDEATION TRAINING PTY LTD.; GOODNA, AUSTRALIA

ILSHINWELLS CO., LTD.; SEOUL, KOREA (SOUTH)

IMT CO., LTD.; SUWON, KOREA (SOUTH)

INDEX INTERNATIONAL GROUP; STOCKHOLM, SWEDEN

INDIA SHELTER FINANCE CORPORATION LIMITED; GURGAON, INDIA

INDIFRA LIMITED; ANAND, INDIA

INDTACT GMBH; WURZBURG, GERMANY

INFIFRESH FOODS PVT. LTD.; KARNATAKA, INDIA

INFORMASCOPE; ANKARA, TURKIYE

INNOVA CAPTAB LIMITED; PANCHKULA, INDIA

INOX INDIA LIMITED; VADODARA, INDIA

INSTITUT NATIONAL DE RECHERCHE POUR L'AGRICULTURE L'ALIMENTATION ET L'ENVIRONNEMENT; PARIS, FRANCE

INSTITUTE OF NUCLEAR ENERGY RESEARCH; TAOYUAN, TAIWAN

INTEGRATED CYBER SOLUTIONS INC.; VANCOUVER, CANADA

INTERCAM BANCO, S.A.; MEXICO, MEXICO

INTERNATIONAL ASSET RECONSTRUCTION COMPANY PRIVATE LIMITED; MUMBAI, INDIA

INTERNATIONAL CONSOLIDATED BUSINESS GROUP PTY LTD.; MELBOURNE, AUSTRALIA

INTERNATIONAL HOLDING COMPANY PJSC; ABU DHABI, UNITED ARAB EMIRATES

INVESTCORP INDIA ACQUISITION CORP.; GEORGETOWN, CAYMAN ISLANDS

IRM ENERGY LIMITED; AHMEDABAD, INDIA

ISLAMIC CORPORATION FOR THE DEVELOPMENT OF THE PRIVATE SECTOR; JEDDAH, SAUDI ARABIA

IVECO GROUP N.V.; TURIN, ITALY

IYOGIN HOLDINGS CO.,LTD.; MATSUYAMA, JAPAN

J

JADESTONE ENERGY PLC; SINGAPORE, SINGAPORE

JAPAN M&A SOLUTION INCORPORATED; TOKYO, JAPAN

JAPANET HOLDINGS CO., LTD.; SASEBO, JAPAN

JIANGSU GUOJING HOLDING GROUP CO., LTD.; CHANGZHOU, CHINA

JIO FINANCIAL SERVICES LTD.; MUMBAI, INDIA

JNC CORPORATION; TOKYO, JAPAN

JSC SUEK; MOSCOW, RUSSIA

JUNEE LIMITED; SINGAPORE, SINGAPORE

JVSPAC ACQUISITION CORP.; WANCHAI, CHINA (HONG KONG)

K

KAIRIKIYA CO., LTD.; KYOTO, JAPAN

KARINGAL ST LAURENCE LIMITED; BELMONT, AUSTRALIA

KARNIKA INDUSTRIES LIMITED; HOWRAH, INDIA

KAUSHALYA LOGISTICS LIMITED; NEW DELHI, INDIA

KAY CEE ENERGY & INFRA LIMITED; KOTA, INDIA

KBI GROUP; SEOUL, KOREA (SOUTH)

KC CO.,LTD.; ANSEONG, KOREA (SOUTH)

KEEMO FASHION GROUP LIMITED; SHENZHEN, CHINA

KIBO CAPITAL PARTNERS LTD.; EBENE, MAURITIUS

KIRTI INVESTMENTS LIMITED; THANE, INDIA

KNIGHTEC AB; SOLNA, SWEDEN

KO GOLD INC.; TORONTO, CANADA

KONTOR SPACE LIMITED; THANE, INDIA

KOREA OCEAN BUSINESS CORPORATION; BUSAN, KOREA (SOUTH)

KUZCO LIGHTING, INC.; SURREY, CANADA

KYOTO FINANCIAL GROUP, INC.; KYOTO, JAPAN

L

L.E.K. CONSULTING GROUP LIMITED; LONDON, UNITED KINGDOM

LABFORWARD GMBH; BERLIN, GERMANY

LEASE OPERATORS LIMITED; SOUTH OROPOUCHE, TRINIDAD

LEDDARTECH HOLDINGS INC.; QUEBEC, CANADA

LEGEND SPICES, INC.; YEREVAN, ARMENIA

LEMON SISTEMI S.P.A.; BALESTRATE, ITALY

LENDLOCK GROUP LIMITED; CHESTER, UNITED KINGDOM

LIAN EE HYDRAULICS PTE LTD.; SINGAPORE, SINGAPORE

LINKAGE GLOBAL INC.; TOKYO, JAPAN

LINKERS INDUSTRIES LIMITED; SUNGAI PETANI, MALAYSIA

LUNIT, INC.; SEOUL, KOREA (SOUTH)

M

MACLAREN MINERALS LTD.; VANCOUVER, CANADA

MAINI CORPORATE PVT LTD.; BANGALORE, INDIA

MAITONG SUNSHINE CULTURAL DEVELOPMENT CO., LIMITED; BEIJING, CHINA

MARINETRANS INDIA LIMITED; NAVI MUMBAI, INDIA

MARLEY SPOON GROUP SE; LUXEMBOURG, LUXEMBOURG

MARUKOME CO., LTD.; NAGANO, JAPAN

MAXMIND PHARMACEUTICAL S.L.; MADRID, SPAIN

MAXO TELECOMMUNICATIONS PTY. LTD.; HARRISTOWN, AUSTRALIA

ME THERAPEUTICS HOLDINGS INC.; VANCOUVER, CANADA

MEDICINES DEVELOPMENT FOR GLOBAL HEALTH LIMITED; SOUTHBANK, AUSTRALIA

MEIDOH CO., LTD; TOYOTA, JAPAN

MERCANTIL SERVICIOS FINANCIEROS INTERNACIONAL, S.A.; PANAMA CITY, PANAMA

MERFORD HOLDING B.V.; GORINCHEM, NETHERLANDS

METRO SUPPLY CHAIN GROUP INC.; MONTREAL, CANADA

METROPOLITAN POLICE SERVICE; LONDON, UNITED KINGDOM

MF INTERNATIONAL LIMITED; WANCHAI, CHINA (HONG KONG)

MIJU CO., LTD.; SEOUL, KOREA (SOUTH)

MINGTENG INTERNATIONAL CORPORATION INC.; WUXI, CHINA

MINOX INTERNATIONAL GROUP BERHAD; PUCHONG, MALAYSIA

MISH DESIGNS LIMITED; MUMBAI, INDIA

MOBILE-HEALTH NETWORK SOLUTIONS; SINGAPORE, SINGAPORE

MOBILITAS SA; BEAUCHAMP, FRANCE

MONO PHARMACARE LIMITED; AHMEDABAD, INDIA

MOTISONS JEWELLERS LIMITED; JAIPUR, INDIA

MULTIPLICA INSIDE S.L.; BARCELONA, SPAIN

MURAL ONCOLOGY PLC; DUBLIN, IRELAND

MUTHOOT MICROFIN LIMITED; ERNAKULAM, INDIA

N

NADER HOLDING GMBH & CO. KG; DUDERSTADT, GERMANY

NANOHELIX CO. LTD.; DAEJEON, KOREA (SOUTH)

NAPLOY CORP.; ABUJA, NIGERIA

NATIONAL ASSET RECONSTRUCTION COMPANY LIMITED; MUMBAI, INDIA

NATIONAL LAGHUBITTA BITTIYA SANSTHA LIMITED; KAVREPALANCHOWK, NEPAL

NATIONALE-NEDERLANDEN OTWARTY FUNDUSZ EMERYTALNY; WARSAW, POLAND

NATIONWIDE FLEET INSTALLATIONS LTD.; MANCHESTER, UNITED KINGDOM

NBH CAPITAL CO., LTD.; SEOUL, KOREA (SOUTH)

NDC AUSTRALIA PTY LTD; MCMAHONS POINT, AUSTRALIA

NEO-CONCEPT INTERNATIONAL GROUP HOLDINGS LIMITED; KOWLOON, CHINA (HONG KONG)

NEOLARA CORP.; PUNTARENAS, COSTA RICA

NET AVENUE TECHNOLOGIES LIMITED; CHENNAI, INDIA

NEW HORIZON AIRCRAFT LTD.; LINDSAY, CANADA

NEWTON EUROPE LTD; OXFORDSHIRE, UNITED KINGDOM

NIKS PROFESSIONAL LTD.; SINGAPORE, SINGAPORE

NIMONIK, INC.; MONTREAL, CANADA

NIPPON EXPRESS HOLDINGS, INC.; TOKYO, JAPAN

NIPPON INSURE CO., LTD.; FUKUOKA, JAPAN

NIVIKA FASTIGHETER AB; JONKOPING, SWEDEN

NOBUL AI CORP.; TORONTO, CANADA

NOCO-NOCO INC.; SINGAPORE, SINGAPORE

NOH & PARTNERS CO., LTD.; SEOUL, KOREA (SOUTH)

NORDIC CORPORATE BANK ASA; OSLO, NORWAY

NOVAAGRO GROUP; KHARKIV, UKRAINE

NOVONESIS A/S; BAGSVAERD, DENMARK

NURTURE LANDSCAPES HOLDINGS LIMITED; WINDLESHAM, UNITED KINGDOM

O

O2 CAPITAL PARTNERS B.V.; OOSTERBEEK, NETHERLANDS

OAK WOODS ACQUISITION CORPORATION; NEPEAN, CANADA

OCI CO., LTD.; SEOUL, KOREA (SOUTH)

OFFICINE PICCOLI S.P.A; CASTEL D'AZZANO, ITALY

ON DOOR CONCEPTS LIMITED; BHOPAL, INDIA

ONET SA; MARSEILLE, FRANCE

ONODERA GROUP CO., LTD.; TOKYO, JAPAN

ONSITE ELECTRO SERVICES PVT. LTD.; MUMBAI, INDIA

OPEN AIRWAY DENTAL SOLUTIONS LTD; TARINGA, AUSTRALIA

ORAVEL STAYS LIMITED; AHMEDABAD, INDIA

OYOCAR GROUP, INC.; SOSUA, DOMINICAN REPUBLIC

P

PARAGON FINE & SPECIALITY CHEMICAL LIMITED; AHMEDABAD, INDIA

PARTNER ONE CAPITAL, INC.; LAVAL, CANADA

PATTYN BELGIUM NV; BRUGGE, BELGIUM

PELION GREEN FUTURE GMBH; MUNICH, GERMANY

PERFECT MOMENT LTD.; LONDON, UNITED KINGDOM

PHANTOM DIGITAL EFFECTS LIMITED; MUMBAI, INDIA

PHARMACOSMOS A/S; HOLBAEK, DENMARK

PHM GROUP HOLDING OYJ; HELSINKI, FINLAND

PINEAPPLE FINANCIAL INC.; NORTH YORK, CANADA

PLAYTIKA HOLDING CORP.; HERZLIYA PITUACH, ISRAEL

PREMIUM CATERING (HOLDINGS) LIMITED; SINGAPORE, SINGAPORE

PRESSTONIC ENGINEERING LIMITED; BENGALURU, INDIA

PROAX TECHNOLOGIES LTD.; MISSISSAUGA, CANADA

PROGRESSIVE STAR FINANCE PRIVATE LIMITED; KOLKATA, INDIA

PROTOPIA GLOBAL HOLDINGS INC.; KOWLOON, CHINA (HONG KONG)

PS INTERNATIONAL GROUP LTD.; HONG KONG, CHINA (HONG KONG)

PSYENCE BIOMEDICAL LTD.; TORONTO, CANADA

PT AGRO BAHARI NUSANTARA TBK; TANGERANG, INDONESIA

PT BARITO RENEWABLES ENERGY TBK; JAKARTA, INDONESIA

PT CHARLIE HOSPITAL SEMARANG TBK; KENDAL, INDONESIA

PT ITSEC ASIA TBK; JAKARTA, INDONESIA

PT JANU PUTRA SEJAHTERA TBK.; DEPOK, INDONESIA

PT KIAN SANTANG MULIATAMA TBK.; BEKASI, INDONESIA

PT KOKA INDONESIA TBK; JAKARTA SELATAN, INDONESIA

PT LOGISTICSPLUS INTERNATIONAL TBK; JAKARTA, INDONESIA

PT LOVINA BEACH BREWERY TBK; DENPASAR, INDONESIA

PT MAKNA PRAKARSA UTAMA; BOGOR, INDONESIA

PT MASTERSYSTEM INFOTAMA TBK.; JAKARTA PUSAT, INDONESIA

PT MULTI GARAM UTAMA TBK; SOUTH JAKARTA, INDONESIA

PT NUSANTARA SEJAHTERA RAYA TBK; JAKARTA, INDONESIA

PUIG BRANDS S.A.; BARCELONA, SPAIN

PURIT CO., LTD.; GYEONGJU, KOREA (SOUTH)

Q

QILU BANK CO., LTD.; JINAN, CHINA

QOO10 PTE. LTD; SINGAPORE, SINGAPORE

QUALITAS SEMICONDUCTOR CO., LTD.; SEONGNAM, KOREA (SOUTH)

R

RAIZEN S.A.; SAO PAULO, BRAZIL

RANMARINE TECHNOLOGY B.V.; ROTTERDAM, NETHERLANDS

RBZ JEWELLERS LIMITED; AHMEDABAD, INDIA

RED CANYON RESOURCES LTD.; VANCOUVER, CANADA

REDBRICK INVESTMENTS S.A R.L.; LUXEMBOURG, LUXEMBOURG

REGENT GAS HOLDINGS LIMITED; LONDON, UNITED KINGDOM

RENTA GROUP OY; VANTAA, FINLAND

RESOURCE CENTRIX HOLDINGS INC.; TORONTO, CANADA

RF ACQUISITION CORP II; SINGAPORE, SINGAPORE

RF PLAST GMBH; GUNZENHAUSEN, GERMANY

ROTALA GROUP LIMITED; TIPTON, UNITED KINGDOM

S

S J LOGISTICS (INDIA) LIMITED; THANE, INDIA

S&J CORPORATION; TOKYO, JAPAN

S&P SISTEMAS DE VENTILACIÓN, S.L.U.; BARCELONA, SPAIN

SAFE SUPPLY STREAMING CO., LTD.; VANCOUVER, CANADA

SAL SAUDI LOGISTICS SERVICES COMPANY; JEDDAH, SAUDI ARABIA

SALTUS PARTNERS LLP; WHITELEY, UNITED KINGDOM - ENGLAND

SAMEERA AGRO & INFRA LIMITED; TELANGANA, INDIA

SASATOKU PRINTING CO., LTD.; TOYOAKE, JAPAN

SATA GMBH & CO. KG; KORNWESTHEIM, GERMANY

SAUDI LIME INDUSTRIES COMPANY; RIYADH, SAUDI ARABIA

SBE-VARVIT S.P.A.; REGGIO EMILIA, ITALY

SEIBU GIKEN CO., LTD.; KOGA, JAPAN

SEKUR PRIVATE DATA LTD.; VANCOUVER, CANADA

SERVUS CREDIT UNION, LTD.; EDMONTON, CANADA

SG PRIVATE EQUITY CO., LTD.; SEOUL, KOREA (SOUTH)

SHANGHAI RURAL COMMERCIAL BANK CO., LTD.; SHANGHAI, CHINA

SHANTHALA FMCG PRODUCTS LIMITED; KARNATAKA, INDIA

SHEFFIELD GREEN LTD.; SINGAPORE, SINGAPORE

SHENGHONG HOLDING GROUP CO., LTD.; SUZHOU, CHINA

SHREE OSFM E-MOBILITY LIMITED; NAVI MUMBAI, INDIA

SIAT SOCIETA' INTERNAZIONALE APPLICAZIONI TECNICHE SPA; TURATE, ITALY

SIGHTRON JAPAN INC.; TOKYO, JAPAN

SIGNPOST INDIA LIMITED; MUMBAI, INDIA

SIGNPOST NV; LOKEREN, BELGIUM

SIMONE S.P.A.; NAPLES, ITALY

SIMPLY SOLVENTLESS CONCENTRATES LTD.; CALGARY, CANADA

SKYLAND GROUP S.R.L.; MILAN, ITALY

SNEF SA; MARSEILLE, FRANCE

SOILTECH AS; SANDNES, NORWAY

SOMAI PHARMACEUTICALS LTD; CARREGADO, PORTUGAL

SOPHORA UNTERNEHMERKAPITAL GMBH; MUNICH, GERMANY

SOUND CAVE TECHNOLOGY, INC.; TORONTO, CANADA

SRIVARU HOLDING LIMITED; GRAND CAYMAN, CAYMAN ISLANDS

SSF HOME GROUP BERHAD; PETALING JAYA, MALAYSIA

STAR FASHION CULTURE HOLDINGS LIMITED; XIAMEN, CHINA

STEMCELL TECHNOLOGIES CANADA INC.; VANCOUVER, CANADA

STEVE MARSHALL GROUP LTD.; CAMPBELL RIVER, CANADA

STEWART INVESTMENT & FINANCIAL PRIVATE LIMITED; KOLKATA, INDIA

STICKIT TECHNOLOGIES INC.; VANCOUVER, CANADA

STIF FRANCE SAS; SAINT-GEORGES-SUR-LOIRE, FRANCE

STONEWEG SA; GENEVA, SWITZERLAND

SU GROUP HOLDINGS LIMITED; KOWLOON, CHINA (HONG KONG)

SUPREME POWER EQUIPMENT LIMITED; CHENNAI, INDIA

SURAJ ESTATE DEVELOPERS LIMITED; MUMBAI, INDIA

SWVL HOLDINGS CORP.; DUBAI, UNITED ARAB EMIRATES

SYENSQO SA; BRUSSELS, BELGIUM

SYNERGY PARTNERS CO., LTD.; SEOUL, KOREA (SOUTH)

T

TAIYO KOKO CO LTD; KOBE, JAPAN

TALDE GESTION, S.G.E.I.C., S.A; BILBAO, SPAIN

TANKERSKA PLOVIDBA D.D; ZADAR, CROATIA

TEAM INDIA MANAGERS LTD.; MUMBAI, INDIA

TECT HOLDINGS LIMITED; TAURANGA, NEW ZEALAND

TELECEL GROUP LTD.; ROSE-HILL, MAURITIUS

TELESAT CORPORATION; OTTAWA, CANADA

TEYLOR AG; ZURICH, SWITZERLAND

THE CENTRE FOR GENOMIC REGULATION (CRG); BARCELONA, SPAIN

THE HELMHOLTZ ASSOCIATION; BONN, GERMANY

THE SALVATION ARMY INTERNATIONAL TRUST; LONDON, UNITED KINGDOM

TOHAN CORPORATION; TOKYO, JAPAN

TOP WEALTH GROUP HOLDING LIMITED; HONG KONG, CHINA (HONG KONG)

TPL CORP LIMITED; KARACHI, PAKISTAN

TRANSPORTS DESERT SA; ETRELLES, FRANCE

TRAXALL INTERNATIONAL LTD.; STAFFORDSHIRE, UNITED KINGDOM

TRIDENT TECHLABS LIMITED; NEW DELHI, INDIA

TUNGRAY TECHNOLOGIES INC.; SINGAPORE, SINGAPORE

U

UNIHEALTH CONSULTANCY LIMITED; MUMBAI, INDIA

UNITED AJOD INSURANCE LIMITED; KATHMANDU, NEPAL

ZKH GROUP LIMITED; SHANGHAI, CHINA

V

VALENS SEMICONDUCTOR LTD.; HOD HASHARON, ISRAEL

VAMA SUNDARI INVESTMENTS (DELHI) PRIVATE LIMITED; NOIDA, INDIA

VIETNAM PROSPERITY JOINT-STOCK COMMERCIAL BANK; HANOI, VIETNAM

VISHNUSURYA PROJECTS & INFRA LIMITED; CHENNAI, INDIA

VIVAA TRADECOM LIMITED; AHMEDABAD, INDIA

VNE S.P.A.; LUCCA, ITALY

VRUNDAVAN PLANTATION LIMITED; AHMEDABAD, INDIA

W

WEBUY GLOBAL LTD.; SINGAPORE, SINGAPORE

WEINERT INDUSTRIES AG; SONNEBERG, GERMANY

WILCOMPUTE SYSTEMS GROUP, INC.; TORONTO, CANADA

WILEE VEGETABLE OILS SDN. BHD.; SHAH ALAM, MALAYSIA

WIREX LIMITED; LONDON, UNITED KINGDOM

WOMANCART LIMITED; NEW DELHI, INDIA

WOODFIELD SYSTEMS INTERNATIONAL PVT LTD.; THANE, INDIA

WOT CO., LTD.; HWASEONG, KOREA (SOUTH)

X

XENIA HOTELLERIE SOLUTION S.P.A.; MILAN, ITALY

XIAOMI CORPORATION; BEIJING, CHINA

Y

YAKKYO S.P.A.; ROME, ITALY

YUWANG GROUP; SELANGOR, MALAYSIA

YY GROUP HOLDING LIMITED; SINGAPORE, SINGAPORE

Z

ZAGGLE PREPAID OCEAN SERVICES LIMITED; MUMBAI, INDIA

ZHEJIANG HAOTAI CHEMICAL CO., LTD.; SHAOXING, CHINA

Mergers and Acquisitions
January 2024—December 2024
(Parent Companies Only)

Impellam Group plc—acquired by HFBG Holding
   B.V.

INDIVA Limited—acquired by SNDL Inc.

Innofactor Plc—acquired by CapMan PLC and Osprey Capital LLC

IQGeo Group plc—acquired by KKR & Co. Inc.

IWATSU ELECTRIC Co Ltd—acquired by AI Holdings Corp.

J

Japan Foods Co., Ltd.—acquired by Marubeni Corporation

Japan Publications Trading Co., Ltd—acquired by
   TOHAN CORPORATION

JASTEC Co., Ltd.—acquired by Nippon Telegraph &
   Telephone Corporation

Joyspeed Global Cargo China Limited—acquired by
   Hon Hai Precision Industry Co., Ltd.

K

Karora Resources Inc.—acquired by Westgold Resources Limited

Kensington Capital Partners Limited—acquired by
   AGF Management Limited

Kerry Express (Thailand) Public Company
   Limited—acquired by S.F. Holding Co., Ltd.

Keywords Studios Plc—acquired by EQT AB,
   Canada Pension Plan Investment Board and Temasek Holdings (Private) Limited

Kin + Carta Plc—acquired by BC Partners LLP

KMC Properties ASA—acquired by Logistea AB

KRACHT GmbH—acquired by Atlas Copco AB

Kuchai Development Berhad—acquired by Sungei
   Bagan Rubber Company (MALAYA) Berhad

Kyoden Co., Ltd.—acquired by The Carlyle Group
   Inc.

L

Labrador Uranium Inc.—acquired by ATHA Energy
   Corp.

LHD Group Deutschland GmbH—acquired by Lakeland Industries, Inc.

Link Administration Holdings Limited—acquired by
   Mitsubishi UFJ Financial Group, Inc.

Lithium Power International Limited—acquired by
   Corporacion Nacional del Cobre de Chile

Logistec Corporation—acquired by Blue Wolf Capital
   Partners LLC

Luminex Resources Corp.—acquired by Adventus
   Mining Corporation

LXI REIT plc—acquired by LondonMetric Property
   Plc

M

Mac Chain Co. Ltd.—acquired by Renold plc

Marathon Gold Corporation—acquired by Calibre
   Mining Corp.

Masmovil Ibercom, S.A.—acquired by Orange S.A.

Masonite International Corporation—acquired by
   Owens Corning

Mattioli Woods plc—acquired by Pollen Street PLC

McGrath Limited—acquired by Knight Frank LLP and
   Bayleys Corporation Limited

mdf commerce, inc.—acquired by KKR & Co. Inc.

MEDIASEEK, Inc.—merged with Japan Living Warranty, Inc., to form Solvvy Inc.

MediaValet Inc.—acquired by Symphony Technology
   Group, LLC

Merricks Capital Pty Ltd.—acquired by Regal Partners Limited

Metallica Minerals Limited—acquired by Diatreme
   Resources Limited

MHM Automation Limited—acquired by KKR & Co.
   Inc.

Millennium Services Group Limited—acquired by
   SoftBank Group Corp.

Mimasu Semiconductor Industry Co., Ltd.—acquired
   by Shin-Etsu Chemical Co. Ltd.

MiX Telematics Limited—acquired by PowerFleet,
   Inc.

Modern Living Investments Holdings
   Limited—acquired by Asia Allied Infrastructure
   Holdings Limited

Modular Automation Ireland Ltd.—acquired by Ares
   Management Corporation

MorphoSys AG—acquired by Novartis AG

N

Nagatanien Holdings Co., Ltd.—acquired by Mitsubishi Corporation

Namoi Cotton Limited—acquired by Louis Dreyfus
   Company B.V.

Nanjing Iron & Steel Co., Ltd.—acquired by CITIC
   Group Corporation

Navkar Corporation Ltd.—acquired by JSW Steel
   Ltd.

Net One Systems Co Ltd—acquired by Sumitomo
   Corporation

Network International Holdings PLC—acquired by
   Brookfield Corporation

NewOrigin Gold Corp.—acquired by Harfang Exploration Inc.

Nighthawk Gold Corp.—acquired by Moneta Gold
   Inc., and name changed to STLLR Gold Inc.

Nordic Waterproofing Holding AB—acquired by King-
   span Group PLC

Novatech Group, Inc—acquired by Garaga Inc.

NSL limited—acquired by YTL Corporation Berhad

Sopheon Plc—acquired by Wellspring Worldwide, LLC

SpareBank 1 Sorost-Norge—acquired by SpareBank 1 SR-Bank ASA, to form SpareBank 1 Sør-Norge ASA

Stelco Holdings, Inc.—acquired by Cleveland-Cliffs, Inc.

Stillwell Motor Group—acquired by Autosports Group Limited

Symbio Holdings Limited—acquired by Aussie Broadband Ltd.

T

Tatsuta Electric Wire & Cable Co., Ltd.—acquired by ENEOS Holdings, Inc.

TClarke PLC—acquired by Regent Gas Holdings Limited

Technology Metals Australia Limited—acquired by Australian Vanadium Limited

Ten Entertainment Group plc—acquired by Trive Capital Inc.

Think Research Corporation—acquired by Beedie Capital Partners

TIM S.A.—acquired by Wurth Verwaltungsgesellschaft mbH

TIMES GUARANTY LTD.—acquired by Team India Managers Ltd.

TLI Co., Ltd.—acquired by Wonik Corporation

Toho Kinzoku Co., Ltd.—acquired by TAIYO KOKO Co Ltd

Tokai Carbon Korea Co., Ltd.—acquired by Tokai Carbon Co., Ltd.

Tosei Corporation—acquired by Electrolux Professional AB

Totens Sparebank—acquired by Sparebank 1 Oestlandet

Tricon Residential Inc.—acquired by Blackstone Inc.

Trident Royalties Plc—acquired by Deterra Royalties Limited

Trinity Exploration & Production plc—acquired by Lease Operators Limited

Tritium DCFC Limited—acquired by Exicom Tele-Systems Limited

Troy Income & Growth Trust plc—acquired by STS Global Income & Growth Trust plc

TrueContext Corporation—acquired by Battery Ventures, L.P.

Tyman plc—acquired by Quanex Building Products Corp.

U

UK Commercial Property REIT Limited—acquired by Tritax Big Box REIT plc

Universal Copper Ltd.—acquired by Vizsla Copper Corp.

Urb-it AB—acquired by Fin Mile Logistics Limited

V

Vanstar Mining Resources Inc.—acquired by IAM-GOLD Corporation

Vectron Systems AG—acquired by Shift4 Payments, Inc.

Virgin Money UK PLC—acquired by Nationwide Building Society

Visiodent S.A.—acquired by Cegedim S.A.

Vitesco Technologies Group AG—acquired by INA-Holding Schaeffler GmbH & Co. KG

Volatus Aerospace Corp.—acquired by Drone Delivery Canada Corp.

W

WalkMe Ltd.—acquired by SAP SE

Wincanton plc—acquired by GXO Logistics, Inc.

Woodfield Systems Limited—acquired by Woodfield Systems International Pvt Ltd.

Y

Yasue Corporation—acquired by Sala Corporation

Z

Zuken Elmic, Inc.—acquired by Zuken, Inc.

INTERNATIONAL PUBLIC & PRIVATE COMPANIES

&DO HOLDINGS CO., LTD.
670 Tearaimizu-cho, Nakagyo-ku,
Kyoto, 604-8152, Japan
Tel.: (81) 752293200
Web Site: https://www.housedo.co.jp
Year Founded: 2009
3457—(TKS)
Rev.: $420,341,380
Assets: $494,912,960
Liabilities: $387,617,960
Net Worth: $107,295,000
Earnings: $15,400,720
Emp.: 764
Fiscal Year-end: 06/30/24
Real Estate Services
N.A.I.C.S.: 531390
Masahiro Ando *(Pres & CEO)*

01 COMMUNIQUE LABORA-TORY INC.
Suite 700 789 Don Mills Road, To-ronto, M3C 1T5, ON, Canada
Tel.: (905) 795-2888
Web Site: https://www.01com.com
Year Founded: 1992
OONEF—(OTCQB)
Rev.: $358,298
Assets: $365,434
Liabilities: $158,482
Net Worth: $206,952
Earnings: ($545,281)
Fiscal Year-end: 10/31/23
Remote Access Software
N.A.I.C.S.: 513210

029 GROUP SE
Neue Schonhauserstrasse 3-5,
10178, Berlin, Germany
Tel.: (49) 3021782259
Web Site: https://www.029-group.com
Year Founded: 2018
Z29—(MUN)
Rev.: $50,062
Assets: $18,711,242
Liabilities: $1,814,931
Net Worth: $16,896,311
Earnings: ($6,070,182)
Fiscal Year-end: 12/31/23
Real Estate Investment Services
N.A.I.C.S.: 531190
Lorin Van Nuland *(Founder)*

Subsidiaries:

Emerald Stay S.A. (1)
Rue Fendt 1, 1201, Geneva, Switzerland
Tel.: (41) 225510111
Web Site: https://emeraldstay.com
Property Management Services
N.A.I.C.S.: 531311

Hotelbird GmbH (1)
Plinganserstrasse 150, 81369, Munich, Germany
Tel.: (49) 8921538010
Web Site: https://hotelbird.com
Hotel Services

N.A.I.C.S.: 721110

Limestone Capital AG (1)
Ober Altstadt 6, 6300, Zug, Switzerland
Tel.: (41) 417202126
Web Site: https://www.limestone-capital.com
Investment Services
N.A.I.C.S.: 523999

TRIP Drink Ltd. (1)
Unit 5 Drakes Courtyard 291 Kilburn High Rd, London, NW6 7JR, United Kingdom
Tel.: (44) 7862126624
Web Site: https://drink-trip.com
Soft Drinks Mfr
N.A.I.C.S.: 312111

09WOMEN CO., LTD.
1525 Pyeonghwa-ro, Yangju,
Gyeonggi-do, Korea (South)
Tel.: (82) 15880903
Web Site: https://www.09women.net
Year Founded: 2006
366030—(KRS)
Rev.: $45,012,837
Assets: $48,472,902
Liabilities: $2,991,863
Net Worth: $45,481,039
Earnings: $8,688,527
Emp.: 122
Fiscal Year-end: 12/31/22
Clothing Accessory Distr
N.A.I.C.S.: 458110
Chi Yeop Lee *(CFO)*

1000 ISLAND RV CENTRE
409 County Rd 2 E, Gananoque,
K7G 2V4, ON, Canada
Tel.: (613) 382-4400
Web Site: http://www.1000islandsrv.com
Sales Range: $10-24.9 Million
Emp.: 28
New & Used Car Dealers
N.A.I.C.S.: 441110

1000MERCIS S.A.
28 rue de Chateaudun, 75009, Paris,
France
Tel.: (33) 33149490660 FR
Web Site: https://www.numberly.com
Year Founded: 2000
ALMIL—(EUR)
Sales Range: $50-74.9 Million
Emp.: 130
Interactive Advertising & Marketing Services
N.A.I.C.S.: 541890
Thibaut Munier *(Co-Founder & Co-CEO)*

101013121 SASKATCHEWAN LTD
730 Brand Road, Saskatoon, S7J
5J3, SK, Canada
Tel.: (306) 955-5080

Web Site:
http://www.kiaofsaskatoon.com
Year Founded: 2000
Rev.: $17,475,935
Emp.: 45
New & Used Car Dealers
N.A.I.C.S.: 441110
Don Lepp *(Gen Mgr)*

101059035 SASKATCHEWAN LTD.
356 Industrial Dr, PO Box 26027, Re-gina, S4R 8R7, SK, Canada
Tel.: (306) 721-2270 SK
Web Site:
http://www.pinnacleindustrial.com
Year Founded: 1997
Industrial Machinery Distr
N.A.I.C.S.: 423830

1028918 ONTARIO INC
1249 Guelph Line, Burlington, L7P
2T1, ON, Canada
Tel.: (905) 335-0223
Web Site:
http://www.burlingtontoyota.ca
Year Founded: 1993
Rev.: $28,394,289
Emp.: 60
New & Used Car Dealers
N.A.I.C.S.: 441110
Ed Szela *(Mgr-New Car)*

1035312 ONTARIO LIMITED
190 Canam Crescent, Brampton, L7A
1A9, ON, Canada
Tel.: (905) 459-1810
Web Site:
http://www.bramptonchrysler dodge.com
Rev.: $33,495,059
Emp.: 70
New & Used Car Sales & Service
N.A.I.C.S.: 441110
Ed Lewis *(Pres)*

104 CORPORATION
10F No 119 1 Baozhong Rd, Xindian
Dist, New Taipei City, Taiwan
Tel.: (886) 229126104
Web Site: http://www.104.com.tw
Year Founded: 1996
3130—(TAI)
Rev.: $76,176,654
Assets: $115,359,654
Liabilities: $61,139,374
Net Worth: $54,220,280
Earnings: $14,767,127
Fiscal Year-end: 12/31/23
Online Recruitment Services
N.A.I.C.S.: 561320
Chi-Kuan Yang *(Chm & Pres)*

1042735 ONTARIO INC
15 Van Kirk Drive, Brampton, L7A
1W4, ON, Canada

Tel.: (905) 459-0290
Web Site:
https://www.mazdaofbrampton.ca
Year Founded: 1995
Rev.: $18,867,054
Emp.: 40
New & Used Car Dealers
N.A.I.C.S.: 441110

1053038 ONTARIO LIMITED
(Acquired by AutoCanada Inc.)

1060038 ONTARIO LTD
125 Bell Street, Ingersoll, N5C 2N9,
ON, Canada
Tel.: (519) 485-2921
Web Site:
http://www.midtown1938.com
Year Founded: 1938
Rev.: $16,432,596
Emp.: 29
Automobile Whlsr & Retailers
N.A.I.C.S.: 423110
Max Antony *(Founder)*

1092072 ONTARIO INC
4500 Thimens Boulevard, Ville Saint
Laurent, 4HR 2P2, QC, Canada
Tel.: (514) 344-3533
Web Site: http://www.elfe.net
Rev.: $43,472,475
Emp.: 70
Infant Products Distr
N.A.I.C.S.: 424350
Shell Bern *(Pres)*

11 BIT STUDIOS SA
Brzeska 2, 03-737, Warsaw, Poland
Tel.: (48) 222502910
Web Site: https://11bitstudios.com
Year Founded: 2009
11B—(WAR)
Rev.: $13,280,674
Assets: $65,632,151
Liabilities: $7,942,865
Net Worth: $57,689,287
Earnings: $133,539
Emp.: 299
Fiscal Year-end: 12/31/23
Custom Computer Programming Ser-vices
N.A.I.C.S.: 541511
Przemyslaw Marszal *(Chm-Mgmt Bd)*

11. MART A.D.
Potocari bb, Srebrenica, Bosnia &
Herzegovina
Tel.: (387) 56440861
Year Founded: 1975
MART-R-A—(BANJ)
Rev.: $492,304
Assets: $850,384
Liabilities: $745,946
Net Worth: $104,438

11. Mart A.D.—(Continued)

Earnings: ($179,446)
Emp.: 23
Fiscal Year-end: 12/31/12
Nonferrous Metal Casting Services
N.A.I.C.S.: 331523
Gostimir Jacimovic (Chm-Mgmt Bd)

1101489 ONTARIO LTD
65 Dufferin Street, Perth, K7H 3A5,
ON, Canada
Tel.: (613) 267-4021
Rev.: $17,342,619
Emp.: 38
New & Used Car Dealers
N.A.I.C.S.: 441110
Peter MacPhee (VP)

111, INC.
3-5/F No 295 ZuChongZhi Road, Pu-
dong New Area, Shanghai, 201203,
China
Tel.: (86) 2120536666   Ky
Web Site: https://ir.111.com.cn
Year Founded: 2012
YI—(NASDAQ)
Rev.: $2,069,689,992
Assets: $427,702,149
Liabilities: $389,473,305
Net Worth: $38,228,844
Earnings: ($48,935,672)
Emp.: 1,520
Fiscal Year-end: 12/31/23
Pharmaceutical Products Distr
N.A.I.C.S.: 424210
Gang Yu (Co-Founder & Co-Chm)

1133571 ALBERTA LTD
4120-56 Street, Wetaskiwin, T9A
1V3, AB, Canada
Tel.: (780) 352-2225
Web Site: http://www.toyotacity.ca
Rev.: $11,585,000
Emp.: 27
New & Used Car Dealers
N.A.I.C.S.: 441110
Wendy Ashwell (Mgr-Parts)

11336 NEWFOUNDLAND INC
73 Kenmount Road, Saint John's,
A1B 3N7, NL, Canada
Tel.: (709) 753-4051
Web Site: https://www.toyotaplaza.ca
Year Founded: 1977
Rev.: $20,231,200
Emp.: 100
New & Used Car Dealers
N.A.I.C.S.: 441110
Trevor Bradley (Mgr-Sls)

1166709 ONTARIO INC
2250 Queen Street East, Brampton,
L6S 5X9, ON, Canada
Tel.: (905) 458-7100
Web Site: http://www.acura2000.com
Year Founded: 1987
Rev.: $21,562,348
Emp.: 45
New & Used Car Dealers
N.A.I.C.S.: 441110
Mike Porco (Mgr-Sls)

1170880 ONTARIO LIMITED
7064 Yonge Street, Thornhill, L4J
1V7, ON, Canada
Tel.: (905) 882-4246
Web Site:
   http://www.acuraofnorthtoronto.com
Year Founded: 1996
Rev.: $39,070,709
Emp.: 86
New & Used Car Dealers
N.A.I.C.S.: 441110
David Yip (Mgr-Pre Owned Sls)

1211863 ONTARIO INC.

113-115 Cushman Road Unit 55 &
56, Saint Catharines, L2M 6S9, ON,
Canada
Tel.: (905) 988-9905
Web Site:
   http://www.autoexportcanada.com
Year Founded: 1996
Rev.: $48,271,867
Emp.: 11
New Vehicles & Parts Exporter
N.A.I.C.S.: 423120
Andrew Pilsworth (Gen Mgr)

123FAHRSCHULE SE
Klopstockstr 1, 50968, Cologne, Ger-
many
Tel.: (49) 22198259939
Web Site:
   https://www.123fahrschule.de
Year Founded: 2016
123F—(DUS)
Rev.: $22,753,797
Assets: $29,030,945
Liabilities: $10,914,013
Net Worth: $18,116,932
Earnings: ($4,312,474)
Emp.: 274
Fiscal Year-end: 12/31/23
Automobile Driving School Services
N.A.I.C.S.: 611692
Boris Polenske (CEO)

Subsidiaries:

123 Fahrschule Rhein-Sieg
GmbH   (1)
Wilhelmstrasse 26, 53721, Siegburg, Ger-
many
Tel.: (49) 22413243007
Web Site: https://www.123fahrschule.de
Driver Training Services
N.A.I.C.S.: 611692

1249270 ONTARIO INC
38 Taber Road, Toronto, M9W 3A8,
ON, Canada
Tel.: (416) 747-7244
Web Site: http://www.bramwood.com
Year Founded: 1990
Rev.: $11,136,682
Emp.: 30
Lumber Product Whslr
N.A.I.C.S.: 423310
Nir Meltzer (Gen Mgr)

1260261 ONTARIO INC
Corner of Hwy 101 & Hwy 129 Chap-
pise Township, PO Box 507, Chap-
leau, P0M 1K0, ON, Canada
Tel.: (705) 864-1974
Web Site:
   http://www.truenorthtimber.com
Year Founded: 1997
Rev.: $10,533,600
Emp.: 86
Timber Logging Services
N.A.I.C.S.: 113310
Raymond Duhaime (Mgr-Ops)

129157 CANADA INC
1831 boul Wilfrid-Hamel, Quebec,
G1N 3Z1, QC, Canada
Tel.: (418) 527-4489
Web Site: http://www.admsport.com
Year Founded: 1981
Rev.: $11,082,095
Emp.: 30
Motorcycle Clothing, Parts & Acces-
sories Retailer
N.A.I.C.S.: 423120
Chantale Matton (CEO)

1295908 B.C. LTD. (See Under Algoma Steel Group Inc.)

1300 SMILES LIMITED (Acquired by BGH Capital Pty

Ltd & Ontario Teachers' Pension Plan)

131448 CANADA INC
5400 Armand-Frappier, Saint-Hubert,
J3Z 1G5, QC, Canada
Tel.: (514) 382-0180
Web Site: http://www.adco.ca
Sales Range: $10-24.9 Million
Emp.: 80
Commercial Furnishings Retailer
N.A.I.C.S.: 449129
Salomon Diaz (Dir-Production & Sls)

**1369 CONSTRUCTION JOINT
STOCK COMPANY**
No 37 38 Da Tuong Street Le Thanh
Nghi, Hai Duong, Vietnam
Tel.: (84) 2203891898
Web Site:
   https://www.cpxd1369.com.vn
Year Founded: 2003
C69—(HNX)
Rev.: $13,522,818
Assets: $35,950,878
Liabilities: $7,673,433
Net Worth: $28,277,445
Earnings: $664,965
Fiscal Year-end: 12/31/21
Building Construction Services
N.A.I.C.S.: 236220
Le Minh Tan (Chm)

**138 STUDENT LIVING JA-
MAICA LIMITED**
Tel.: (876) 6651235
Web Site:
   http://www.138studentliving.com
138SL—(JAM)
Rev.: $9,116,684
Assets: $64,695,356
Liabilities: $32,793,970
Net Worth: $31,901,387
Earnings: $2,243,303
Emp.: 93
Fiscal Year-end: 09/30/23
Campus Accommodation Provider
N.A.I.C.S.: 721310
Ian Parsard (Chm)

1414 DEGREES LIMITED
136 Daws Road, Melrose Park, 5039,
SA, Australia
Tel.: (61) 883578273   AU
Web Site:
   https://www.1414degrees.com.au
Year Founded: 2009
14D—(ASX)
Rev.: $27,863
Assets: $6,271,381
Liabilities: $1,265,844
Net Worth: $5,005,537
Earnings: ($1,673,010)
Emp.: 18
Fiscal Year-end: 06/30/24
Electric Power Transmission Services
N.A.I.C.S.: 221121
Kevin Charles Moriarty (Chm)

142258 CANADA INC
3875 Isabelle Street, Brossard, J4Y
2R2, QC, Canada
Tel.: (450) 444-8151
Web Site: http://www.jcb.ca
Rev.: $24,320,107
Emp.: 60
Building Contractors
N.A.I.C.S.: 236220
Jean-Francois Gravel (VP & Gen
Mgr)

147766 CANADA INC
7180 Tecumseh Road East, Windsor,
N8T 1E6, ON, Canada
Tel.: (519) 945-8100

Web Site:
   http://www.windsorhonda.com
Year Founded: 1988
Rev.: $11,051,669
Emp.: 25
New & Used Car Dealers
N.A.I.C.S.: 441110
Gray Guignion (Mgr-Sls)

1507953 ONTARIO INC.
212 Bergey Court, New Hamburg,
N3A 2J5, ON, Canada
Tel.: (519) 662-3640
Web Site:
   http://www.granttransport.com
Year Founded: 1972
Rev.: $16,672,177
Emp.: 150
Truck Transportation Services
N.A.I.C.S.: 484121
Julie Jutzi (Pres)

151 PRODUCTS LTD.
The Old School House 39 Bengal
street, Manchester, M4 6AF, United
Kingdom
Tel.: (44) 161 228 3939
Web Site: http://www.151.co.uk
Year Founded: 1997
Sales Range: $25-49.9 Million
Emp.: 80
Sanitation Goods Mfr
N.A.I.C.S.: 325612
Ian George (Dir-Fin)

1512804 ONTARIO INC
47 Bovaird Dr W, Brampton, L6X
0G9, ON, Canada
Tel.: (905) 459-2600
Web Site:
   https://www.bramptonmitsubishi.ca
Rev.: $11,476,733
Emp.: 25
New & Used Car Dealers
N.A.I.C.S.: 441110

1520 GROUP OF COMPANIES
Prospect Mira 24 building 1, 129090,
Moscow, Russia
Tel.: (7) 4957211520
Web Site: http://1520.ru
Year Founded: 2014
Holding Company
N.A.I.C.S.: 551112
Alexey Krapivin (CEO)

Subsidiaries:

1520 Signal Ltd.   (1)
Letchika Babushkina str Estate 1 build 2,
129344, Moscow, Russia
Tel.: (7) 4959011520
Web Site: http://1520signal.ru
Transportation Services
N.A.I.C.S.: 488999

166606 CANADA INC
3303 Cote de Liesse, Saint Laurent,
H4N 3C2, QC, Canada
Tel.: (514) 747-7777
Web Site:
   http://www.lexusgabriel.com
Rev.: $49,650,000
Emp.: 105
New & Used Car Dealers
N.A.I.C.S.: 441110
Fadi Habre (Gen Mgr)

**17 EDUCATION & TECHNOL-
OGY GROUP INC.**
Floor 16 Block B Wangjing Greenland
Center, Chaoyang District, Beijing,
100102, China
Tel.: (86) 1059451082   CN
Web Site: https://ir.17zuoye.com
Year Founded: 2012
YQ—(NASDAQ)
Rev.: $81,364,315

Assets: $150,226,082
Liabilities: $33,960,682
Net Worth: $116,265,400
Earnings: ($27,251,769)
Emp.: 480
Fiscal Year-end: 12/31/22
Holding Company
N.A.I.C.S.: 551112
Andy Chang Liu (Co-Founder, Chm & CEO)

17LIVE GROUP LIMITED
250 North Bridge Road 11-01 Raffles City Tower, Singapore, 179101, Singapore
Tel.: (65) 68288088
Web Site: https://about.17.live
Year Founded: 2021
LVR—(SES)
Media Streaming Services
N.A.I.C.S.: 516210
Jiang Honghui (CEO & Exec Dir)

18 FEET & RISING LIMITED
Threeways House 40-44 Clipstone Street, London, W1W 5DW, United Kingdom
Tel.: (44) 2033716400   UK
Web Site: http://www.18feet.co.uk
Year Founded: 2009
Sales Range: $1-9.9 Million
Advetising Agency
N.A.I.C.S.: 541810
Jonathan Trimble (CEO)

180/AMSTERDAM
Herengracht 506, 1017 CB, Amsterdam, Netherlands
Tel.: (31) 20 4222 180
Web Site:
    http://www.180amsterdam.com
Year Founded: 1998
Emp.: 204
N.A.I.C.S.: 541810
Richard Bullock (Exec Dir-Creative)

Subsidiaries:

180 Los Angeles   (1)
1733 Ocean Ave 4th fl, Santa Monica, CA 90401
Tel.: (310) 382-1400
Web Site: http://www.180la.com
Emp.: 85
N.A.I.C.S.: 541810
William Gelner (Exec Dir-Creative)

1834 INVESTMENTS LIMITED
7 North Street, PO Box 40, Kingston, Jamaica
Tel.: (876) 9221834   JM
Web Site:
    https://1834investments.com
1834—(JAM)
Rev.: $902,380
Assets: $11,523,287
Liabilities: $1,042,263
Net Worth: $10,481,024
Earnings: $562,709
Fiscal Year-end: 03/31/20
Real Estate Investment Holding Company
N.A.I.C.S.: 551112
Joseph M. Matalon (Vice Chm)

1844 RESOURCES INC.
Suite 602 224-4th Avenue South, Saskatoon, S7K 5M5, SK, Canada
Tel.: (306) 653-2692
Web Site:
    https://www.1844resources.com
Year Founded: 2006
EFF—(TSXV)
Rev.: $32,656
Assets: $1,003,299
Liabilities: $653,406
Net Worth: $349,893
Earnings: ($575,952)

Fiscal Year-end: 04/30/24
Mineral Exploration Services
N.A.I.C.S.: 212290
Thomas M. MacNeill (Chm)

1911 GOLD CORPORATION
400 Burrard Street Suite 1050, Vancouver, V6C 3A6, BC, Canada
Tel.: (604) 900-5620   Ca
Web Site: https://www.1911gold.com
AUMBF—(OTCIQ)
Assets: $26,854,187
Liabilities: $3,805,029
Net Worth: $23,049,158
Earnings: ($1,514,763)
Fiscal Year-end: 12/31/23
Precious Metal Mining Services
N.A.I.C.S.: 212220
Ron Clayton (Pres & CEO)

1933 INDUSTRIES INC.
300 - 1055 West Hastings Street, Vancouver, V6E 2E9, BC, Canada
Tel.: (604) 728-4407
Web Site: https://1933industries.com
Year Founded: 2008
TGIFF—(OTCIQ)
Rev.: $13,631,867
Assets: $13,442,718
Liabilities: $17,369,029
Net Worth: ($3,926,311)
Earnings: ($10,413,231)
Fiscal Year-end: 07/31/23
Investment Services
N.A.I.C.S.: 523999
Terry Taouss (Chm)

1957 & CO. (HOSPITALITY) LIMITED
33/F Times Tower 391 - 407 Jaffe Road, Hong Kong, China (Hong Kong)
Tel.: (852) 28666191   Ky
Web Site: http://www.1957.com.hk
Year Founded: 2009
8495—(HKG)
Rev.: $50,841,981
Assets: $26,567,300
Liabilities: $17,168,915
Net Worth: $9,398,386
Earnings: $2,440,431
Emp.: 333
Fiscal Year-end: 12/31/21
Restaurant Management Services
N.A.I.C.S.: 722511
Wing Kuen Kwan (Vice Chm)

Subsidiaries:

Gonpachi Restaurant Limited   (1)
4/F Lee Garden One 33 Hysan Avenue, Causeway Bay, China (Hong Kong)
Tel.: (852) 27873688
Web Site: http://www.gonpachi.com.hk
Restaurant Operators
N.A.I.C.S.: 722511

Mango Tree (HK) Limited   (1)
Shop 2032 Elements 1 Austin Road West, Tsim Tsa Tsui, China (Hong Kong)
Tel.: (852) 26684884
Web Site: http://www.mangotree.com.hk
Restaurant Operators
N.A.I.C.S.: 722511

1CM INC.
625 Cochrane Dr Suite 802, Markham, L3R 9R9, ON, Canada
Tel.: (717) 888-8889   ON
Web Site: https://1cminc.com
Year Founded: 2011
EPIC—(CNSX)
Rev.: $5,676,086
Assets: $25,377,999
Liabilities: $7,030,068
Net Worth: $18,347,931
Earnings: ($681,737)
Fiscal Year-end: 08/31/23
Cannabis Company

N.A.I.C.S.: 325412

Subsidiaries:

Jekyll & Hyde Brand Builders
Inc.   (1)
Suite 116 250 The Esplanade, Toronto, M5H 4J6, ON, Canada
Tel.: (416) 806-0591
Web Site:
    https://www.wearejekyllandhyde.com
Marketing & Advertising Services
N.A.I.C.S.: 541810
Jayne Beckwith (COO)

1PM PLC (See Under Time Finance plc)

1ST GROUP LIMITED (Name Changed to Visionflex Group Limited)

1NKEMIA IUCT GROUP, S.A.
Calle Alvarez de Castro 63, Mollet de Vales, 08100, Barcelona, Spain
Tel.: (34) 935793432   ES
Web Site: https://www.inkemia.com
Year Founded: 1997
IKM—(MAD)
Biopharmaceutical Mfr
N.A.I.C.S.: 325412
David Cos Garcia (CEO & VP)

Subsidiaries:

Myogem Health Company S.L.   (1)
Alvarez de Castro 63, Mollet del Valles, 08100, Barcelona, Spain
Tel.: (34) 935793432
Web Site: https://myogemhealth.com
Nutrition Product Research & Development Services
N.A.I.C.S.: 621399

1SPATIAL PLC
Tennyson House Cambridge Business Park, Cambridge, CB4 0WZ, United Kingdom
Tel.: (44) 1223420414   UK
Web Site: https://www.1spatial.com
SPA—(AIM)
Rev.: $36,135,000
Assets: $46,421,430
Liabilities: $25,523,355
Net Worth: $20,898,075
Earnings: $1,276,770
Fiscal Year-end: 01/31/23
Software Developer
N.A.I.C.S.: 513210
Claire Milverton (CEO)

Subsidiaries:

1Spatial Australia Pty Limited   (1)
Level 1 29 Kiora Road, Miranda, 2228, NSW, Australia
Tel.: (61) 29 527 9592
Web Site: https://1spatial.com
Software Development Services
N.A.I.C.S.: 541511

1Spatial France SAS   (1)
Immeuble AXEO2 23-25 Avenue Aristide Briand, 94110, Arcueil, France
Tel.: (33) 17 133 0100
Web Site: https://1spatial.com
Data Processing Services
N.A.I.C.S.: 518210

1Spatial Group Limited   (1)
Tennyson House Cambridge Business Park, Cambridge, CB4 0WZ, United Kingdom
Tel.: (44) 122 342 0414
Web Site: https://1spatial.com
Data Processing Services
N.A.I.C.S.: 518210
Jonathan Shears (Mng Dir)

1Spatial Holdings Limited   (1)
Tennyson House Cambridge Business Park, Cambridge, CB4 0WZ, United Kingdom
Tel.: (44) 1223420414
Web Site: http://www.1spatial.com

Sales Range: $50-74.9 Million
Holding Company; Market Research Services
N.A.I.C.S.: 551112
Duncan Guthrie (Mng Dir)

Subsidiary (Non-US):

Avisen BV   (2)
Strawinskylaan 3051, Amsterdam, 1077ZX, North Holland, Netherlands
Tel.: (31) 20 3012105
Business Administration Software Development Services
N.A.I.C.S.: 541511

Subsidiary (Domestic):

Avisen UK Limited   (2)
Parkshot House 5 Kew Road, Richmond, TW9 2PR, United Kingdom
Tel.: (44) 2081006006
Web Site: http://www.avisen.com
Business Management Consulting Services
N.A.I.C.S.: 541611

IQ Research Limited   (2)
1st Fl 44 46 New Inn Yard, London, EC2A 3EY, United Kingdom
Tel.: (44) 2080990560
Business Management Consulting Services
N.A.I.C.S.: 541618

Solution Minds (UK) Limited   (2)
16 Devonshire Street, London, W1G 7AF, United Kingdom
Tel.: (44) 8708802978
Business Management Services
N.A.I.C.S.: 561110

Subsidiary (Non-US):

Star-Apic SA   (2)
Avenue du Prey Aily 24, Liege, 4031, Angleur, Belgium
Tel.: (32) 43675313
Sales Range: $10-24.9 Million
Geographic Information Systems Software Products & Related Services
N.A.I.C.S.: 513210
Issan Tannous (Mng Dir)

Subsidiary (Non-US):

Star-Apic SAS   (3)
191 Ave Aristide Briand, 94230, Cachan, France
Tel.: (33) 0171330100
Geographic Information Systems Software Products & Related Services
N.A.I.C.S.: 513210
Issam Tannous (Mng Dir)

1Spatial Inc.   (1)
8614 Westwood Center Dr, Vienna, VA 22182-2278
Tel.: (703) 444-9488
Web Site: https://1spatial.com
Software Solutions Services
N.A.I.C.S.: 541511
Sheila Steffenson (CEO)

1ST RED AG
Am Kaiserkai 62, 20457, Hamburg, Germany
Tel.: (49) 40356131070
Year Founded: 1911
Real Estate Manangement Services
N.A.I.C.S.: 531390

2-K PURCHASING CENTRE INC
61A Victoria Rd S, Guelph, N1E 5P7, ON, Canada
Tel.: (519) 763-4157
Year Founded: 1995
Rev.: $16,000,000
Emp.: 6
Safety Equipment & Clothing
N.A.I.C.S.: 423990
Karl Gortmaker (Pres)

20 MICRONS LIMITED
347 GIDC Industrial Estate Waghodia, Vadodara, 391 760, Gujarat, India
Tel.: (91) 2652321534

20 Microns Limited—(Continued)

Web Site:
　https://www.20microns.com
20MICRONS—(NSE)
Rev.: $83,998,073
Assets: $70,339,992
Liabilities: $35,886,806
Net Worth: $34,453,187
Earnings: $4,740,399
Fmp.: 320
Fiscal Year-end: 03/31/22
White Minerals Producer
N.A.I.C.S.: 327999
Rajesh C. Parikh (CEO & Mng Dir)

Subsidiaries:

20 MCC Private Limited　　　　(1)
Plot No 256 Waghodia GIDC, Waghodia
Dist, Vadodara, 391760, India
Tel.: (91) 7574008713
Web Site: https://www.20mcc.in
Waterproofing Contractor Services
N.A.I.C.S.: 238390

20 Microns Nano Minerals Ltd　　(1)
9 - 10 GIDC, Waghodia, Vadodara, 391
760, Gujarat, India
Tel.: (91) 2668262711
Web Site: https://www.20nano.com
Sales Range: $50-74.9 Million
Emp.: 60
Soft Mineral Mining Services
N.A.I.C.S.: 212323
Chandresh S. Parikh (Chm)

20 VIC MANAGEMENT INC.
One Queen St E Ste 300, PO Box
88, Toronto, M5C 2W5, ON, Canada
Tel.: (416) 955-0595
Web Site: http://www.20vic.com
Year Founded: 1995
Rev.: $52,584,400
Emp.: 750
Real Estate Manangement Services
N.A.I.C.S.: 531110
Chris Innes (VP-Bus Unit-GTA Indus-
trial Properties)

2020 BULKERS LTD.
S E Pearman Bldg 2nd Floor 9 Par-
la-Ville Road, Hamilton, HM 11, Ber-
muda
Tel.: (441) 5429329　　　　　BM
Web Site:
　https://www.2020bulkers.com
Year Founded: 2017
TTBKF—(OTCIQ)
Rev.: $77,300,000
Assets: $379,800,000
Liabilities: $223,900,000
Net Worth: $155,900,000
Earnings: $31,900,000
Emp.: 5
Fiscal Year-end: 12/31/22
Freight Transportation Services
N.A.I.C.S.: 483111
Magnus Halvorsen (CEO)

21 INVESTIMENTI SOCIETA' DI GESTIONE DEL RISPARMIO S.P.A.
Via G Felissent 90, 31100, Treviso,
Italy
Tel.: (39) 0422316611　　　　IT
Web Site: http://www.21invest.com
Year Founded: 1992
Investment Holding Company
N.A.I.C.S.: 551112
Alessandro Benetton (Founder & Mng
Partner)

Subsidiaries:

21 Centrale Partners SA　　　　(1)
9 Avenue Hoche, 75008, Paris, France
Tel.: (33) 156883300
Web Site:
　http://www.21centralepartners.com
Privater Equity Firm
N.A.I.C.S.: 523999

Francois Barbier (Mng Partner)

Holding (Domestic):

IMPACT Sales & Marketing SAS　(2)
85 rue Edouard Vaillant, 92300, Levallois-
Perret, France
Tel.: (33) 1 4127 9100
Web Site: http://www.agence-impact.com
Sales Range: $50-74.9 Million
Business Intelligence & Marketing Consult-
ing Services
N.A.I.C.S.: 541890
Francois Crepin (Partner)

Potel et Chabot SAS　　　　　(2)
3 rue de Chaillot, 75116, Paris, France
Tel.: (33) 153231582
Web Site: https://www.poteletchabot.com
Sales Range: $100-124.9 Million
Reception Event Organization & Manage-
ment Services
N.A.I.C.S.: 561920
Franck Jeantet (Chm & CEO)

21 Partners S.p.A.　　　　　　(1)
Viale G Felissent 90, 31100, Treviso,
Italy　　　　　　　　　　(100%)
Tel.: (39) 0422316611
Web Site: http://www.21investimenti.it
Sales Range: $50-74.9 Million
Emp.: 20
Privater Equity Firm
N.A.I.C.S.: 523999
Alessandro Benetton (Mng Partner)

Poligof SpA
Via S Antonio 4, Pieve Fissiraga, 26854,
Lodi, Italy
Tel.: (39) 0371 21351
Web Site: http://www.poligof.it
Sales Range: $100-124.9 Million
Hygienic Disposable Backsheet Film Prod-
uct Mfr
N.A.I.C.S.: 326113

21 LADY CO., LTD.
2-6-1 Nishishinjuku, Shinjuku, 163-
0242, Japan
Tel.: (81) 335562121
Web Site: http://www.21lady.com
Rev.: $23,099,230
Assets: $8,794,030
Liabilities: $6,593,230
Net Worth: $2,200,800
Earnings: ($1,164,590)
Fiscal Year-end: 03/31/19
Human Resource Consulting Ser-
vices
N.A.I.C.S.: 541612

235 HOLDINGS LTD.
6 N Mihaylov Str Fl 3, dist Sredets,
1142, Sofia, Bulgaria
Tel.: (359) 29630579
Web Site: https://www.235.world
Year Founded: 2017
235H—(BUL)
Sales Range: Less than $1 Million
Real Estate Services
N.A.I.C.S.: 531390
Yavor Boyadzhiev (Mgr-IR)

23RED LIMITED (Acquired by Capgemini SE)

24 IANUARIE S.A.
18 G-ral I Dragalina Street, 100157,
Ploiesti, Prahova, Romania
Tel.: (40) 244521956
Web Site: https://www.24january.ro
Year Founded: 1922
IANY—(BUC)
Rev.: $12,495,620
Assets: $13,945,288
Liabilities: $6,227,400
Net Worth: $7,717,888
Earnings: $334,576
Emp.: 266
Fiscal Year-end: 12/31/23
Ferrous & Metallurgic Equipment Mfr
N.A.I.C.S.: 331110

24 MOBILE ADVERTISING SO-LUTIONS AB
Hastholmsvagen 28 5th Floor, 131
30, Nacka, Sweden
Tel.: (46) 8 535 24 100　　　　SE
Web Site: http://www.24mas.com
Mobile Application Developer
N.A.I.C.S.: 513210
Tero Turunen (CEO)

Subsidiaries:

Liquid Air Lab GmbH　　　　　(1)
Vaihinger Markt 28, 70563, Stuttgart, Ger-
many
Tel.: (49) 711 8494 78 30
Web Site: http://www.liquidairlab.com
Sales Range: $25-49.9 Million
Emp.: 18
Mobile Advertising Application Services
N.A.I.C.S.: 513210

2639-1862 QUEBEC, INC.
1031 7th rang, Wickham, J0C 1S0,
QC, Canada
Tel.: (819) 398-6303
Web Site:
　http://www.plancherswickham.com
Year Founded: 1989
Rev.: $11,000,000
Emp.: 95
Hardwood Flooring Products Mfr &
Distr
N.A.I.C.S.: 238330
Jean-Pierre Nittolo (Pres)

29METALS LIMITED
Level 2 150 Collins Street, Mel-
bourne, 3000, VIC, Australia
Tel.: (61) 370375300　　　　　AU
Web Site: https://www.29metals.com
Year Founded: 2021
29M—(ASX)
Rev.: $306,346,979
Assets: $668,350,249
Liabilities: $380,669,573
Net Worth: $287,680,676
Earnings: ($300,022,478)
Emp.: 391
Fiscal Year-end: 12/31/23
Support Activities for Metal Mining
N.A.I.C.S.: 213114
Clifford Tuck (Chief Legal Officer)

2CONNECT BV
Gompenstraat 17, 5145 RM,
Waalwijk, Netherlands
Tel.: (31) 416671780
Web Site: https://www.2-connect.com
Emp.: 100
Special Cables & Connectors Mfr &
Distr
N.A.I.C.S.: 335921

2CRSI SA
11 rue Madeleine Rebrioux, FR-
67200, Strasbourg, France
Tel.: (33) 368411060
Web Site: https://www.2crsi.com
Year Founded: 2005
2CRSI—(EUR)
Rev.: $200,619,493
Assets: $197,767,520
Liabilities: $147,802,717
Net Worth: $49,964,803
Earnings: ($5,313,366)
Emp.: 373
Fiscal Year-end: 02/28/21
Software Development Services
N.A.I.C.S.: 541511
Alain Wilmouth (Founder, Chm &
CEO)

Subsidiaries:

2CRSI Corporation　　　　　　(1)
894 Faulstich Ct-Ste B, San Jose, CA
95112
Tel.: (408) 598-3176
High Performance Computing Product Mfr.

N.A.I.C.S.: 334111

2CRSI UK Ltd.　　　　　　　　(1)
2 Queensmead Pl, Stretford, M17 1PH,
Manchester, United Kingdom
Tel.: (44) 1614023036
High Performance Computing Product Mfr
N.A.I.C.S.: 334111

2CRSi ME FZE　　　　　　　　(1)
1708 SIT Tower Dubai Silicon Oasis, Dubai,
United Arab Emirates
Tel.: (971) 589038129
High Performance Computing Product Mfr
N.A.I.C.S.: 334111

Boston IT Solutions Pvt. Ltd.　　(1)
No 64 Ground Floor Railway Parallel Road,
Kumarapark, Bengaluru, Karnataka, India
Tel.: (91) 8043084000
Computer Hardware Product Mfr
N.A.I.C.S.: 334111

Boston Server & Storage Solutions
GmbH　　　　　　　　　　(1)
Kapellenstrasse 11/1 OG, Feldkirchen,
85622, Munich, Germany
Tel.: (49) 8990901993
Web Site: http://www.boston-it.de
Computer Hardware Product Mfr
N.A.I.C.S.: 334111

Escape Technology Gmbh　　　(1)
Kapellenstrasse 11, Feldkirchen, 85622,
Munich, Germany
Tel.: (49) 89124148420
Web Site: http://www.escape-technology.de
Computer & Network Security Services
N.A.I.C.S.: 541519

Escape Technology Ltd.　　　　(1)
Lower Ground Floor East Threeways House
40/44 Clipstone Street, London, W1W 5DW,
United Kingdom
Tel.: (44) 2077348809
Web Site: http://www.escape-
technology.com
Computer & Network Security Services
N.A.I.C.S.: 541519
Mark Cass (Mng Dir)

Tranquil PC Ltd.　　　　　　　(1)
2 Queensmead Place Trafford Park, Man-
chester, M17 PH, United Kingdom
Tel.: (44) 1614023036
Web Site: https://www.tranquil-it.co.uk
Computer Product Mfr
N.A.I.C.S.: 334111

2CUREX AB
Tel.: (45) 22115399
Web Site: https://www.2curex.com
2CUREX—(OMX)
Rev.: $902,293
Assets: $9,663,853
Liabilities: $587,937
Net Worth: $9,075,916
Earnings: ($2,311,829)
Emp.: 14
Fiscal Year-end: 12/31/21
Health Care Srvices
N.A.I.C.S.: 622310
Povl-Andre Bendz (Chm)

Subsidiaries:

2cureX GmbH　　　　　　　　(1)
Rontgenstrasse 24, 22335, Hamburg, Ger-
many
Tel.: (49) 1736000704
Web Site: https://www.2curex.com
Pharmaceuticals Product Mfr
N.A.I.C.S.: 325412

2G ENERGY AG
Benzstrabe 3, Heek, 48619, Borken,
Germany
Tel.: (49) 256893470
Web Site: https://2-g.com
2GB—(MUN)
Rev.: $402,978,782
Assets: $251,075,231
Liabilities: $114,206,390
Net Worth: $136,868,841
Earnings: $19,814,466
Emp.: 921

Fiscal Year-end: 12/31/23
Heat & Power Plant Construction Services
N.A.I.C.S.: 237990
Ludger Holtkamp *(COO & Member-Mgmt Bd)*

Subsidiaries:

2G CENERGY Power Systems Technologies Inc. **(1)**
205 Commercial Dr, Saint Augustine, FL 32092
Tel.: (904) 579-3217
Web Site: http://www.2g-energy.com
Sales Range: $125-149.9 Million
Emp.: 300
Power Plant Construction & Generation Services
N.A.I.C.S.: 237990

2G Drives GmbH **(1)**
Siemensstrasse 15, 48619, Heek, Germany
Tel.: (49) 2568 9347 140
Emp.: 28
Research & Development Services
N.A.I.C.S.: 541715

2G Energie SAS **(1)**
9 rue Jean Mermoz -ZAC Maison Neuve 2, Sainte-Luce-Sur-Loire, 44980, Nantes, France
Tel.: (33) 223278666
Biogas Power Generating Services
N.A.I.C.S.: 221117

2G Energy Corp. **(1)**
820 Gartshore St Unit 12, Fergus, N1M 2W8, ON, Canada
Tel.: (226) 383-4200
Renewable Power Generation Services
N.A.I.C.S.: 221118
Dan Culp *(Branch Mgr)*

2G Energy Inc. **(1)**
205 Commercial Dr, Saint Augustine, FL 32092
Tel.: (904) 579-3217
Heating Equipment Mfr
N.A.I.C.S.: 333414

2G Energy Ltd. **(1)**
Clifton House Ashville Pt Clifton Ln Sutton Weaver, Cheshire, WA7 3FW, United Kingdom
Tel.: (44) 1928 718533
Heat & Power Plant Construction Services
N.A.I.C.S.: 237990

2G Italia S.R.L. **(1)**
Via della Tecnica 7 Vago di Lavagno, 37030, Verona, Italy
Tel.: (39) 0458340861
Emp.: 10
Heat & Power Plant Construction Services
N.A.I.C.S.: 237990
Christian Manca *(CEO)*

2G Polska Sp. z o.o. **(1)**
ul Piekarska 86/18, 43-300, Bielsko-Biala, Poland
Tel.: (48) 338188050
Emp.: 2
Heat & Power Plant Construction Services
N.A.I.C.S.: 237990

2G Rental GmbH **(1)**
Oldenburger Allee 18, 30659, Hannover, Germany
Tel.: (49) 51153903912
Heat & Power Generation Services
N.A.I.C.S.: 221118
Thomas Gawlowski *(Gen Mgr)*

2G Solutions of Cogeneration S.L. **(1)**
Anselm Clave 2 4-3, 08500, Barcelona, Spain
Tel.: (34) 93 883 22 05
Heat & Power Plant Construction Services
N.A.I.C.S.: 237990

2G Station LLC **(1)**
st Usacheva 22, 119048, Moscow, Russia
Tel.: (7) 4954320401
Web Site: http://www.2g-station.ru
Biogas Power Generating Services
N.A.I.C.S.: 221117

2G Station Tunisie Sarl **(1)**

21 Mechanical Street, Zl Charguia 1, Tunis, Tunisia
Tel.: (216) 98107069
Power Generation Services
N.A.I.C.S.: 221118

2G Station for Africa GmbH **(1)**
Bertroisweg 11, Kevelaer, 47623, Kleve, Germany
Tel.: (49) 28329090121
Biogas Power Generating Services
N.A.I.C.S.: 221117

Aktive Energi Anlaeg A/S **(1)**
Industrivej Syd 11, 7400, Herning, Denmark
Tel.: (45) 70210150
Web Site: https://www.aea.dk
Turnkey Contractor Services
N.A.I.C.S.: 236220

B-Team Consult and Services SRL **(1)**
Str Vasile Voiculescu Nr 26 Sector 3, 31236, Bucharest, Romania
Tel.: (40) 212053020
Web Site: https://www.anticoroziv.eu
Coating Product Mfr & Distr
N.A.I.C.S.: 325510

CYSORE SA de CV **(1)**
Rio Mayo No 211 Col La Luz, 37458, Leon, Mexico
Tel.: (52) 4773327627
Web Site: https://cysore.com
Automotive Parts Mfr & Distr
N.A.I.C.S.: 336390

DUING d.o.o. **(1)**
Stupari 18b, Viskovo, 51216, Rijeka, Croatia
Tel.: (385) 51682492
Web Site: https://www.duing.hr
Marine Equipment Mfr & Distr
N.A.I.C.S.: 333618

Enerzea Power Solution Private Limited **(1)**
Plot No 90 Aerospace Sector, Devanahalli TQ, Bengaluru, 562129, Karnataka, India
Tel.: (91) 7349644903
Web Site: https://www.enerzea.com
Renewable Energy Services
N.A.I.C.S.: 221114

Filotipo, LDA **(1)**
Rua Candido dos Reis 1806, 4460-701, Matosinhos, Portugal
Tel.: (351) 229540082
Web Site: https://filotipo.com
Renewable Energy Services
N.A.I.C.S.: 221114

HJS Motoren GmbH **(1)**
Albert-Gluck-Strasse 4, 88279, Amtzell, Germany
Tel.: (49) 75209139790
Web Site: https://www.hjs-motoren.de
Engine Repair & Maintenance Services
N.A.I.C.S.: 811111

SenerTec-Center GmbH **(1)**
Carl-Zeiss-Strasse 18, 97424, Schweinfurt, Germany
Tel.: (49) 97216510
Web Site: https://www.senertec.de
Engine Parts Mfr & Distr
N.A.I.C.S.: 336310

Shmerling-Synchro Energy Engineering Ltd. **(1)**
Havoda 4, PO 762, New Industrial Zone, Ramla, 72100, Israel
Tel.: (972) 89210080
Web Site: https://www.shmerling.co.il
Generator Mfr & Distr
N.A.I.C.S.: 335312

2GEN NET
21 King Street West, Suite 1600, Hamilton, L8P 4W7, ON, Canada
Tel.: (905) 308-9155
Web Site: https://2gen.net
Digital Marketing Agency
N.A.I.C.S.: 541810
Mark Wu *(Mgr)*

Subsidiaries:

Pier 8 Group **(1)**

21 King St West Suite 1501, Hamilton, L8P 4W7, ON, Canada
Tel.: (289) 439-4611
Web Site: https://www.pier8group.com
Advertising Services
N.A.I.C.S.: 541810
Bob Mills *(Pres)*

Subsidiary (Domestic):

Wordsmith Design & Advertising **(2)**
605 James Street N 4th Floor, Hamilton, L8L 1J9, ON, Canada
Tel.: (905) 529-7312
Web Site: http://www.pier8group.com
Sales Range: Less than $1 Million
Advertising Agencies
N.A.I.C.S.: 541810
Bob Mills *(Pres & CEO)*

2INVEST AG
Ziegelhauser Landstr 3, 69120, Heidelberg, Germany
Tel.: (49) 6221649240
Web Site: https://www.2invest-ag.com
Year Founded: 1997
2INV—(DEU)
Assets: $66,878,912
Liabilities: $420,894
Net Worth: $66,458,019
Earnings: ($22,706,670)
Emp.: 2
Fiscal Year-end: 12/31/22
Holding Company; Biopharmaceutical Research, Development, Testing & Marketing
N.A.I.C.S.: 551112
Pilar de la Huerta *(Co-CEO)*

Subsidiaries:

4basebio S.L.U **(1)**
Faraday 7 Cantoblanco, 28049, Madrid, Spain
Tel.: (34) 911923650
Web Site: https://www.4basebioenzymes.com
Molecular Diagnostic Product Mfr
N.A.I.C.S.: 325413
Angel J. Picher *(Dir-R&D)*

SYGNIS Bioscience GmbH & Co. KG **(1)**
Im Neuenheimer Feld 515, D-69120, Heidelberg, Germany **(100%)**
Tel.: (49) 62214546
Web Site: http://www.sygnis.de
Sales Range: $25-49.9 Million
Biopharmaceutical Research, Development, Testing & Marketing
N.A.I.C.S.: 541715

TGR BioSciences Pty Ltd. **(1)**
31 Dalgleish Street, Thebarton, 5031, SA, Australia
Tel.: (61) 883546170
Web Site: http://www.tgrbio.com
Research Institute Operator
N.A.I.C.S.: 541713
Andrew Sneddon *(Chm)*

2KS CLOUD SERVICES GMBH
Bahnhofstrasse 54, Muhltal, 64367, Darmstadt, Germany
Tel.: (49) 61514934110
Software Development Services
N.A.I.C.S.: 541511

2S METAL PUBLIC COMPANY LIMITED
8/5 Village No 14, Tha Chang Subdistrict Bang Klam District, Songkhla, 90110, Thailand
Tel.: (66) 74800111
Web Site: https://www.ss.co.th
Year Founded: 1992
2S—(THA)
Rev.: $197,785,668
Assets: $63,646,814
Liabilities: $4,909,476
Net Worth: $58,737,338
Earnings: $4,665,198
Emp.: 411

Fiscal Year-end: 12/31/23
Steel Mfr & Distr
N.A.I.C.S.: 331110
Kunchit Singsuwan *(Co-Chm)*

2VALORISE N.V.
De Snep 3324, 3945, Ham, Belgium
Tel.: (32) 13 35 07 80
Web Site: http://www.2valorise.be
Year Founded: 2005
Renewable Energy Generation Services & Waste Management
N.A.I.C.S.: 221118
Filip Lesaffer *(CEO)*

Subsidiaries:

4BioFuels S.A. **(1)**
Chaussee d Ophain 181, 1420, Braine-l'Alleud, Belgium
Tel.: (32) 80540151
Firewood Biomass Production Services
N.A.I.C.S.: 321999

Renogen S.A. **(1)**
Holzstrasse 5, 1420, Liege, Amel, Belgium
Tel.: (32) 80540151
Web Site: http://www.4invest.net
Firewood Biomass Production Services
N.A.I.C.S.: 321999
Jean-Francois Meys *(Mng Dir)*

2X1 HOLDING CAPE MIDIA SHIPYARD
Incinta Port Nr 2, Constanta, Romania
Tel.: (40) 241 255633
Web Site:
http://www.2x1midiashipyard.ro
Ship Building & Repairing Services
N.A.I.C.S.: 336611
Dorin Stanescu *(Pres & Gen Mgr)*

3 SIXTY RISK SOLUTIONS LTD.
64 Signet Drive, North York, M9L 2Y4, ON, Canada
Web Site:
http://www.3sixtysecure.com
62P2—(BER)
Sales Range: $1-9.9 Million
Emp.: 600
Security Guards & Patrol Services
N.A.I.C.S.: 561612
Ernest Petrasovic *(CFO)*

3 SIXTY SECURE CORP.
12-83 Little Bridge Street, Almonte, K0A 1A0, ON, Canada
Tel.: (866) 360-3360
Web Site:
http://www.3sixtysecure.com
Year Founded: 2013
Oil & Natural Gas Exploration Services
N.A.I.C.S.: 211120
Ernest Petrasovic *(CFO)*

Subsidiaries:

Inkas Financial Corp. Ltd. **(1)**
3605 Weston Road, North York, ON M9L 1V7, ON, Canada
Tel.: (877) 464-6527
Web Site: http://www.inkas.ca
Security, Automated Teller Machines (ATMs), Point-of-Sale (POS), Cash Management, Armed Courier & Security Products Mfr
N.A.I.C.S.: 561621

3 STEP IT GROUP OY
Mechelininkatu 1A, 00180, Helsinki, Finland
Tel.: (358) 10 525 3200
Web Site: http://www.3stepit.com
Year Founded: 1997
Sales Range: $600-649.9 Million
Emp.: 350

3 Step It Group Oy—(Continued)

Holding Company; Commercial Information Technology Equipment Financing & Leasing Services
N.A.I.C.S.: 551112
Jarkko Veijalainen *(Founder & Chm)*

Subsidiaries:

3 Step IT (Hong Kong) Limited **(1)**
Unit 15C 15/F Neich Tower 128 Gloucester Road, Wanchai, China (Hong Kong)
Tel.: (852) 21370722
Electronic Device Distr
N.A.I.C.S.: 423690

3 Step IT (UK) Limited **(1)**
Building 329 Doncastle Road, Bracknell, RG12 8PE, Berkshire, United Kingdom
Tel.: (44) 1344209570
Electronic Device Distr
N.A.I.C.S.: 423690

3 Step IT AS **(1)**
Brynsalleen 4, PO Box 6344, Etterstad, 0604, Oslo, Norway
Tel.: (47) 24099900
Web Site: http://www.3stepit.no
Electronic Device Distr
N.A.I.C.S.: 423690
Pal Ostvold Myrland *(Acct Mgr)*

3 Step IT Malaysia Sdn. Bhd. **(1)**
B2-3-10 Solaris Dutamas No 1 Jalan Dutamas 1, 50480, Kuala Lumpur, Malaysia
Tel.: (60) 364110977
Electronic Device Distr
N.A.I.C.S.: 423690
Vikas Vig *(Country Mgr)*

3 Step IT OU **(1)**
Narva mnt 7d, 10117, Tallinn, Estonia
Tel.: (372) 6806900
Web Site: http://www.3stepit.ee
Electronic Device Distr
N.A.I.C.S.: 423690

3 Step IT Singapore Pte Ltd. **(1)**
101 Cecil Street 13-04 Tong Eng Building, Singapore, 069533, Singapore
Tel.: (65) 31252100
Electronic Device Distr
N.A.I.C.S.: 423690

3 Step IT Sweden AB **(1)**
Sveavagen 166, 11346, Stockholm, Sweden
Tel.: (46) 775703333
Web Site: http://www.3stepit.se
Electronic Device Distr
N.A.I.C.S.: 423690

3 Step IT UAB **(1)**
Lvovo 25, 09320, Vilnius, Lithuania
Tel.: (370) 68803004
Electronic Device Distr
N.A.I.C.S.: 423690

3 Step IT, Inc. **(1)**
402 Cheswold Ct, Chesterbrook, PA 19087
Tel.: (484) 988-2334
Electronic Device Distr
N.A.I.C.S.: 423690

3 Step It AS **(1)**
Brynsalleen 4, PO Box 6344, 0604, Oslo, Norway **(100%)**
Tel.: (47) 24099900
Web Site: http://www.3stepit.com
Emp.: 16
Commercial Information Technology Equipment Financing & Leasing Services
N.A.I.C.S.: 522220

3 Step It Oy **(1)**
Jaakonkatu 2, 01620, Vantaa, Finland
Tel.: (358) 10 525 3200
Web Site: http://www.3stepit.com
Commercial Information Technology Equipment Financing & Leasing Services
N.A.I.C.S.: 522220
Jarkko Veijalainen *(Chm & Founder)*

3-D MATRIX, LTD.
7th floor Kojimachi HF Building 3-2-4 Kojimachi Chiyoda-ku, Tokyo, 102-0083, Japan
Tel.: (81) 335113440
Web Site: http://www.3d-matrix.co.jp
Year Founded: 2004

7777—(TKS)
Rev.: $30,326,680
Assets: $38,906,460
Liabilities: $36,573,130
Net Worth: $2,333,330
Earnings: ($1,685,550)
Emp.: 108
Fiscal Year-end: 04/30/24
Medical Device Mfr
N.A.I.C.S.: 339112
Keiji Nagano *(Chm)*

Subsidiaries:

3-D Matrix (Beijing) Biotechnology Co., Ltd. **(1)**
A055 10th floor Jia 19 North Road of East 3rd Ring, Chaoyang District, Beijing, 100020, China
Tel.: (86) 1056835669
Medical Devices Supplier
N.A.I.C.S.: 423450

3-D Matrix Asia Pte. Ltd. **(1)**
435 Orchard Road 11/F Wisma Atria, Singapore, 238877, Singapore
Tel.: (65) 6408 3858
Medical Device Mfr
N.A.I.C.S.: 334510

3-D Matrix EMEA B.V. **(1)**
Polarisavenue 1, 2132 JH, Hoofddorp, Netherlands
Tel.: (31) 23 205 0292
Medical Device Mfr & Distr
N.A.I.C.S.: 339112

3-D Matrix Europe SAS **(1)**
11 Chemin des Petites Brosses, 69300, Caluire-et-Cuire, France
Tel.: (33) 427190340
Web Site: http://www.puramatrix.fr
Biopharmaceutical Product Mfr
N.A.I.C.S.: 325412

3-D Matrix Medical Technology Pty Ltd **(1)**
Caribbean Park 44 Lakeview Drive, Scoresby, 3179, VIC, Australia
Tel.: (61) 38 761 9104
Medical Device Mfr & Distr
N.A.I.C.S.: 339112

3-D Matrix Medical Technology, Ltd. **(1)**
Rooms 05-15 13A/F South Tower World Finance Centre Harbour City, 17 Canton Road Tsim Sha Tsui, Kowloon, China (Hong Kong)
Tel.: (852) 2 206 0092
Medical Device Mfr & Distr
N.A.I.C.S.: 339112

3-D Matrix UK Ltd. **(1)**
5 Merchant Square, Paddington, London, W2 1AY, United Kingdom
Tel.: (44) 203 950 5956
Medical Device Mfr & Distr
N.A.I.C.S.: 339112

3-D Matrix, Inc. **(1)**
250 1st Ave Ste 205, Needham, MA 02494
Tel.: (781) 373-9020
Web Site: http://www.puramatrix.com
Emp.: 12
Biopharmaceutical Product Mfr
N.A.I.C.S.: 325412
Marc G. Rioult *(Mng Dir)*

Beijing 3-D Matrix Investment Consulting, Ltd. **(1)**
A055 10th Floor Jia 19 North Road of East 3rd Ring, Chaoyang District, Beijing, 100020, China
Tel.: (86) 105 683 5669
Medical Device Mfr & Distr
N.A.I.C.S.: 339112

3. MAJ BRODOGRADILISTE D.D.
Liburnia 3, 51000, Rijeka, Croatia
Tel.: (385) 51611111
Web Site: http://www.uljanik.hr
Marine Construction Equipment Rental Services
N.A.I.C.S.: 488390

330542 BC LTD
259 McLean St, Quesnel, V2J 2N8, BC, Canada
Tel.: (250) 992-9293
Web Site: https://www.regencychrysler.com
Year Founded: 1985
New & Used Car Dealers
N.A.I.C.S.: 441110
Lisa Kozuchar *(Mgr-Sls)*

333D LTD.
Level 8 555 Bourke Street, Melbourne, 3000, VIC, Australia
Tel.: (61) 280110424
Web Site: https://www.333d.com.au
T3D—(ASX)
Rev.: $192,226
Assets: $16,477
Liabilities: $369,823
Net Worth: ($353,346)
Earnings: ($338,279)
Fiscal Year-end: 06/30/24
Commercial Printing Services
N.A.I.C.S.: 323111
John Conidi *(Chm)*

3463192 CANADA INC.
1261 St Joseph Blvd North, Gatineau, J8Z-3J6, QC, Canada
Tel.: (819) 770-2277
Web Site: http://www.megaautomobile.com
Year Founded: 1998
Rev.: $24,100,000
Emp.: 45
New Car Dealers
N.A.I.C.S.: 441110
Nader Dormani *(Pres)*

360 CAPITAL MORTGAGE REIT
Suite 3701 Level 37 1 Macquarie Place, Sydney, 2000, NSW, Australia
Tel.: (61) 284058860
Web Site: http://www.360capital.com.au
Year Founded: 2006
TCF—(ASX)
Rev.: $1,619,925
Assets: $17,451,255
Liabilities: $225,027
Net Worth: $17,226,229
Earnings: $1,372,196
Fiscal Year-end: 06/30/24
Investment Management Service
N.A.I.C.S.: 525990
Tony Pitt *(Grp Mng Dir)*

360 DIGITECH, INC. (Name Changed to Qifu Technology, Inc.)

360 FINANCE, INC. (Name Changed to Qifu Technology, Inc.)

360 LUDASHI HOLDINGS LIMITED
No 24 11th Floor Building 1 E District Tianfu Software Park, 1628 Middle Section of Tianfu Avenue, Chengdu, 610041, China
Tel.: (86) 2862037001 **Ky**
Web Site: http://www.ludashi.com
Year Founded: 2014
3601—(HKG)
Rev.: $111,343,615
Assets: $107,537,003
Liabilities: $16,902,563
Net Worth: $90,634,440
Earnings: $6,658,965
Emp.: 251
Fiscal Year-end: 12/31/23

Holding Company
N.A.I.C.S.: 551112
Fanchen Zhang *(CFO)*

360 ONE WAM LIMITED
Iifl Centre Kamala City, Senapati Bapat Marg Lower Parel, Mumbai, 400013, India
Tel.: (91) 2248765600
Web Site: https://www.360.one
Year Founded: 2008
542772—(BOM)
Rev.: $283,624,068
Assets: $1,465,943,252
Liabilities: $1,056,774,947
Net Worth: $409,168,305
Earnings: $78,861,237
Emp.: 907
Fiscal Year-end: 03/31/22
Wealth Management Services
N.A.I.C.S.: 523940
Karan Bhagat *(Co-Founder, Co-CEO & Mng Dir)*

Subsidiaries:

IIFL Asset Management (Mauritius) Ltd. **(1)**
Le Caudan 530 5th Floor Barkly Wharf, Port Louis, Mauritius
Tel.: (230) 2103486
Financial Services
N.A.I.C.S.: 523999

IIFL Asset Management Ltd. **(1)**
IIFL Center 7th Floor Kamala City, Senapati Bapat Marg Lower Parel, Mumbai, 400013, India
Tel.: (91) 2248765461
Financial Services
N.A.I.C.S.: 523150
Amar Merani *(Head-Real Estate)*

IIFL Capital (Canada) Limited **(1)**
121 King Street West Suite 1725, Toronto, M5H 3T9, ON, Canada
Tel.: (416) 792-5956
Financial Services
N.A.I.C.S.: 523999

IIFL Capital Pte. Ltd. **(1)**
137 Telok Ayer Street 04-08, Singapore, 068602, Singapore
Tel.: (65) 65377480
Financial Services
N.A.I.C.S.: 523999

IIFL Private Wealth Management (Dubai) Ltd. **(1)**
Office No 11 8th Floor Gate Village 10, PO Box 115064, Dubai International Financial Centre, 115064, Dubai, United Arab Emirates
Tel.: (971) 43863661
Financial Services
N.A.I.C.S.: 523999

360INSIGHTS.COM CANADA, INC.
300 King Street, Whitby, L1N 4Z4, ON, Canada
Tel.: (866) 684-2308
Web Site: http://www.360insights.com
Software Package & nformation Technology Services
N.A.I.C.S.: 513210
Jason Atkins *(Founder & CEO)*

Subsidiaries:

The Ohana Companies, LLC **(1)**
1405 Foulk Rd, Wilmington, DE 19803
Tel.: (302) 225-5505
Web Site: http://www.everybodywins.com
Sales Range: $1-9.9 Million
Emp.: 28
Rebate Processing & Fulfillment Services
N.A.I.C.S.: 561499
Alexander F. Giacco *(Chief Bus Dev Officer)*

361 DEGREES INTERNATIONAL LIMITED
Tel.: (852) 29077088 **Ky**

Web Site: https://ir.361sport.com
Year Founded: 2003
TSIOF—(OTCIQ)
Rev.: $887,505,315
Assets: $1,585,576,868
Liabilities: $384,822,795
Net Worth: $1,200,754,073
Earnings: $104,139,450
Emp.: 7,441
Fiscal Year-end: 12/31/22
Sporting Goods Mfr, Retailer & Distr
N.A.I.C.S.: 339920
Huihuang Ding (Chm & Exec Dir)

Subsidiaries:

361 Europe B.V. (1)
Fanny Blankers-Koenplein 50, 2031 VW,
Haarlem, Netherlands
Tel.: (31) 237370494
Web Site: https://www.361europe.com
Athletic Footwear Distr
N.A.I.C.S.: 424340
Jurian Elstgeest (CEO)

361 USA, Inc (1)
1200 Main St Ste G, Irvine, CA 92614
Tel.: (949) 600-7752
Web Site: https://www.361usa.com
Athletic Footwear Distr
N.A.I.C.S.: 424340

3617581 CANADA INC
346 Boul Greber, Gatineau, J8T 5R6,
QC, Canada
Tel.: (819) 561-6669
Web Site:
http://www.promenadekia.com
Rev.: $11,051,669
Emp.: 25
New & Used Car Dealers
N.A.I.C.S.: 441110
Marc Grenier (Owner)

365 HF
Sidumuli 28, 108, Reykjavik, Iceland
Tel.: (354) 5999000   IS
Web Site: http://www.365.is
Sales Range: $150-199.9 Million
Emp.: 1,500
Holding Company
N.A.I.C.S.: 551112
Ari Edwald (CEO)

36KR HOLDINGS INC.
Building B6 Hengtong International
Business Park No 10, Jiuxianqiao
Road Chaoyang District, Beijing,
100026, China
Tel.: (86) 1058254106   Ky
Web Site: https://www.36kr.com
Year Founded: 2018
KRKR—(NASDAQ)
Rev.: $49,409,765
Assets: $87,539,751
Liabilities: $34,623,468
Net Worth: $52,916,283
Earnings: $3,361,887
Emp.: 603
Fiscal Year-end: 12/31/22
Holding Company
N.A.I.C.S.: 551112
Chengcheng Liu (Founder & Co-
Chm)

37 CAPITAL INC.
Suite 575 510 Burrard Street, Van-
couver, V6C 3A8, BC, Canada
Tel.: (604) 681-1519   BC
Web Site:
https://www.37capitalinc.com
Year Founded: 1984
JJJ—(CNSX)
Assets: $89,661
Liabilities: $547,711
Net Worth: ($458,050)
Earnings: ($36,064)
Fiscal Year-end: 12/31/23

Mineral Mining & Exploration Ser-
vices
N.A.I.C.S.: 212210
Jacob H. Kalpakian (Pres & CEO)

3770818 CANADA INC
265 Rue John-F Kennedy, Saint-
Jerome, J7Y 4B5, QC, Canada
Tel.: (450) 438-1203
Web Site:
http://www.stjeromechevrolet.com
Rev.: $12,665,134
Emp.: 75
New & Used Car Sales
N.A.I.C.S.: 441110
Jean-Sebastien Martin (Pres)

3965546 CANADA INC
4480 Cote De Liesse Suite 355, Mon-
treal, H4N 2R1, QC, Canada
Tel.: (514) 668-2835
Web Site: http://www.ntint.com
Year Founded: 1996
Rev.: $30,900,000
Emp.: 400
Software Development & Services
N.A.I.C.S.: 513210
Parsa Famili (Pres & CEO)

3A-BESTGROUP JSC
152/1 Karasai batyr st 5th floor,
50000, Almaty, Kazakhstan
Tel.: (7) 7273750202
Web Site:
http://www.3abestgroup.com
BSGR—(KAZ)
Assets: $6,323,454
Liabilities: $5,383,600
Net Worth: $939,854
Earnings: ($380,705)
Fiscal Year-end: 12/31/20
Oil Exploration Services
N.A.I.C.S.: 213112

3AC CO., LTD.
1301-1306 181 Gasan digital 1-ro,
Geumcheon-gu, Seoul, 08503, Korea
(South)
Tel.: (82) 220262223
Web Site: https://www.3acltd.com
Year Founded: 2007
Investment Management Service
N.A.I.C.S.: 523999

3AM TECHNOLOGIES, INC.
129 The Queensway, Barrie, L4M
0B1, ON, Canada
Tel.: (702) 866-2500   NV
Year Founded: 2014
Assets: $14,813
Liabilities: $44,512
Net Worth: ($29,699)
Earnings: ($34,311)
Emp.: 3
Fiscal Year-end: 05/31/19
Information Technology Support Ser-
vices
N.A.I.C.S.: 541512
Simon Gee (Pres, CEO, CFO, Treas
& Sec)

3C-CARBON GROUP AG
3C-Ring 1, D-86899, Landsberg am
Lech, Germany
Tel.: (49) 819196963000
Web Site: http://www.3c-carbon-
group.com
High-tech Carbon Composite Struc-
tures Development & Production
N.A.I.C.S.: 326199
Karsten Jerschke (CEO)

Subsidiaries:

Medical Intelligence Medizintechnik
GmbH (1)
Robert Bosch Strasse 8, 86830, Schwab-
munchen, Germany

Tel.: (49) 823296920
Web Site: http://www.elekta.com
Medical Radiation Therapy Equipment Mfr
N.A.I.C.S.: 339112
Lutz Schaefer (CFO)

3CNERGY LIMITED
380 Jalan Besar 16-01 ARC 380, Sin-
gapore, 209000, Singapore
Tel.: (65) 69708117   SG
Web Site: http://www.3cnergy.com.sg
Year Founded: 1980
502—(CAT)
Rev.: $110,981
Assets: $61,090,662
Liabilities: $38,782,809
Net Worth: $22,307,854
Earnings: ($6,528,226)
Fiscal Year-end: 12/31/21
Real Estate Development Services
N.A.I.C.S.: 531390
Chee Khuen Chung (CEO)

Subsidiaries:

HSR Property Consultants Pte
Ltd (1)
HSR Building 3 Lorong 6 Toa Payoh 01-01,
Singapore, 319378, Singapore
Tel.: (65) 65598888
Real Estate Services
N.A.I.C.S.: 531210

3D ENERGI LIMITED
Level 18 41 Exhibition Street, Mel-
bourne, 3000, VIC, Australia
Tel.: (61) 396509866   AU
Web Site: https://3denergi.com.au
Year Founded: 2003
TDO—(ASX)
Rev.: $28,526
Assets: $7,700,104
Liabilities: $441,836
Net Worth: $7,258,269
Earnings: ($1,452,188)
Emp.: 11
Fiscal Year-end: 06/30/24
Crude Petroleum Extraction Services
N.A.I.C.S.: 211120
Noel Newell (Chm & Mng Dir)

3D MEDICINES INC.
No 3 & No 5 Laiyang Road, Qingdao,
Shandong, China   Ky
Web Site: https://en.3d-
medicines.com
Year Founded: 2014
1244—(HKG)
Rev.: $86,930,128
Assets: $204,085,372
Liabilities: $66,898,993
Net Worth: $137,186,379
Earnings: ($161,181,516)
Emp.: 245
Fiscal Year-end: 12/31/22
Biotechnology Research & Develop-
ment Services
N.A.I.C.S.: 541714
Fang Xia (Sec)

3D RESOURCES LIMITED
(See Under Adelong Gold
Limited)

**3DM DIGITAL MANUFACTUR-
ING LTD.**
13 Ha amal st Building B, Rosh
Ha'Ayin, Israel
Tel.: (972) 35754713
Web Site: https://3dm-tech.co.il
Year Founded: 2016
DM3—(TAE)
Assets: $3,979,555
Liabilities: $1,615,416
Net Worth: $2,364,139
Earnings: ($3,225,307)
Fiscal Year-end: 12/31/23

Printer Mfr
N.A.I.C.S.: 333310
Uri Feldman (CEO)

3F FILIPPI SPA
Via del Savena 28, 40065, Bologna,
Italy
Tel.: (39) 051 6529611   IT
Web Site: http://www.3f-filippi.com
Year Founded: 1952
Lighting Product Mfr
N.A.I.C.S.: 335139

Subsidiaries:

Targetti Sankey S.p.A. (1)
Via Pratese 164, 50145, Florence, Italy
Tel.: (39) 05537911
Web Site: http://www.targetti.com
Lighting Fixtures Design & Mfr
N.A.I.C.S.: 335139

Subsidiary (Domestic):

Duralamp S.p.A (2)
Via Pratese 164, 50145, Florence, Italy
Tel.: (39) 055894881
Web Site: http://www.duralamp.it
Lighting Equipment Mfr
N.A.I.C.S.: 335139

MLE S.r.l. (2)
Via Einstein 35 int 53, 50013, Campi Bisen-
zio, Italy
Tel.: (39) 055 88 04 701
Web Site: http://www.mlelighting.com
Residential Electric Lighting Fixture Mfr
N.A.I.C.S.: 335131

Subsidiary (Non-US):

Targetti Poulsen Poland Sp. z
o.o. (2)
al. Jerozolimskie 125/127, 02-017, Warsaw,
Poland
Tel.: (48) 22 699 71 52
Commercial Industrial & Institutional Electric
Lighting Fixture Mfr
N.A.I.C.S.: 335132

Targetti-MLE S.A. (2)
8 Rue Alfred de Vigny, 75008, Paris,
France
Tel.: (33) 1 4429 0909
Web Site: http://www.mlelighting.com
Residential Electric Lighting Fixture Mfr
N.A.I.C.S.: 335132

Subsidiary (US):

Tivoli, LLC (2)
15602 Mosher Ave, Tustin, CA 92780
Tel.: (714) 957-6101
Web Site: http://www.tivolilighting.com
Commercial Industrial & Institutional Electric
Lighting Fixtures Mfr
N.A.I.C.S.: 335132
Carrie Verkuil (Acct Mgr-Strategic)

3RD STREET GROUP LTD.
(Acquired by RELX plc)

3I GROUP PLC
16 Palace Street, London, SW1E
5JD, United Kingdom
Tel.: (44) 2079753131   UK
Web Site: https://www.3i.com
Year Founded: 1945
III—(LSE)
Rev.: $36,606,918
Assets: $27,317,596,608
Liabilities: $1,856,854,332
Net Worth: $25,460,742,275
Earnings: $4,842,211,570
Emp.: 600
Fiscal Year-end: 03/31/24
Investment Management Service
N.A.I.C.S.: 551112
Kevin Dunn (Gen Counsel & Sec)

Subsidiaries:

3i Benelux B.V. (1)
Cornelis Schuytstraat 74, 1071 JL, Amsterdam, Netherlands

3i Group plc—(Continued)

Tel.: (31) 203057444
Venture Capital Funding Services
N.A.I.C.S.: 523910

3i France SAS (1)
29 Rue de Berri, 75008, Paris, France
Tel.: (33) 173151100
N.A.I.C.S.: 523940
Pierre-Axel Botuha (Partner-Private Equity)

3i India Private Limited (1)
Level 7 B-Wing The Capital Bandra Kurla
Complex, Mumbai, 400051, India
Tel.: (91) 224 905 5850
Financial Services
N.A.I.C.S.: 523940

3i Infrastructure plc (1)
Aztec Group House IFC 6 The Esplanade,
Saint Helier, JE2 3BZ, Jersey
Tel.: (44) 3716640445
Web Site: https://www.3i-infrastructure.com
Rev.: $243,625,347
Assets: $4,963,393,083
Liabilities: $744,761,424
Net Worth: $4,218,631,659
Earnings: $438,020,702
Fiscal Year-end: 03/31/2024
Investment Management Service
N.A.I.C.S.: 523940
Bernardo Sottomayor (Head-Economic
Infrastructure-Europe)

Subsidiary (Non-US):

Infinis Limited (2)
First Floor 500 Pavilion Drive, Northampton
Business Park, Northampton, NN4 7YJ,
United Kingdom
Tel.: (44) 1604662400
Web Site: http://www.infinis.com
Renewable Power Generator Operators
N.A.I.C.S.: 221118
Tony Cocker (Chm)

Subsidiary (Domestic):

Alkane Energy Limited (3)
First Floor 500 Pavilion Drive, Northampton
Business Park, Northampton, NN4 7YJ,
United Kingdom
Tel.: (44) 1623827927
Power Generation & Oil & Gas Exploration
N.A.I.C.S.: 213112

3i Investments plc (1)
16 Palace Street, London, SW1E 5JD,
United Kingdom (100%)
Tel.: (44) 2079753456
Web Site: http://www.3iplc.com
Sales Range: $200-249.9 Million
Emp.: 350
Investment Management Service
N.A.I.C.S.: 523940

Subsidiary (US):

3i Corporation (2)
One Grand Central Pl 60 E 42nd St Ste
4100, New York, NY 10165
Tel.: (212) 848-1400
Web Site: http://www.3i.com
Sales Range: $50-74.9 Million
Emp.: 20
Investment Management Service
N.A.I.C.S.: 523940

Subsidiary (Non-US):

**3i Deutschland Gesellschaft fur In-
dustriebeteiligungen mbH** (2)
OpernTurm Bockenheimer Landstrasse 2-4,
60306, Frankfurt am Main,
Germany (100%)
Tel.: (49) 697100000
Web Site: http://www.3i.com
Sales Range: $50-74.9 Million
Emp.: 55
Investment Management Service
N.A.I.C.S.: 523940
Peter Wirtz (Head-Private Equity)

3i Gestion S.A. (2)
3 rue Paul Cezanne, 75008, Paris,
France (100%)
Tel.: (33) 173151100
Web Site: http://www.3i.com
Sales Range: $50-74.9 Million
Emp.: 30
Investment Management Service

N.A.I.C.S.: 523940
Remi Carnimolla (Partner)

3i Netherlands B.V. (1)
Cornelis Schuytstraat 72, 1071 JL, Amster-
dam, Netherlands
Tel.: (31) 20 305 7444
Financial Services
N.A.I.C.S.: 523940

3i plc (1)
16 Palace St, London, SW1 E5JD, United
Kingdom (100%)
Tel.: (44) 2079283131
Web Site: http://www.3i.com
Sales Range: $50-74.9 Million
Emp.: 200
Corporate Support & Administrative Ser-
vices
N.A.I.C.S.: 561499

Subsidiary (Domestic):

3i Asia Pacific plc (2)
16 Palace St, London, SW1E 5JD, United
Kingdom (100%)
Tel.: (44) 2079283131
Web Site: http://www.3i.com
Investment Advisory Services
N.A.I.C.S.: 523940

Branch (Non-US):

3i Asia Pacific Ltd (3)
6 Battery Road Level 42 Unit 07, Singa-
pore, 049909, Singapore (100%)
Tel.: (65) 62322937
Web Site: http://www.3i.com
Sales Range: $50-74.9 Million
Emp.: 8
Venture Capital
N.A.I.C.S.: 523910

3i Hong Kong (3)
26C Bank of China Tower 1 Garden Road,
Central, China (Hong Kong)
Tel.: (852) 29018188
Web Site: http://www.3i.com
Venture Capital
N.A.I.C.S.: 523160

Subsidiary (Domestic):

3i Europe plc (2)
16 Palace Street, London, SW1E 5JD,
United Kingdom (100%)
Tel.: (44) 2079753131
Web Site: http://www.3i.com
Investment Advisory Services
N.A.I.C.S.: 523940

Branch (Non-US):

3i Europe plc (3)
Avenida Diagonal 613 9th Floor, 8028, Bar-
celona, Spain (100%)
Tel.: (34) 934391991
Web Site: http://www.3i.com
Sales Range: $50-74.9 Million
Emp.: 4
Venture Capital
N.A.I.C.S.: 523910

3i Europe plc, Benelux (3)
Cornelis Schuytstraat 72, 1071 JL, Amster-
dam, Netherlands (100%)
Tel.: (31) 203057444
Web Site: http://www.3i.com
Sales Range: $50-74.9 Million
Emp.: 12
Venture Capital Services
N.A.I.C.S.: 523910
Pieter de Jong (Head-Private Equity)

3i SGR (3)
Via Orefici 2, 20123, Milan, Italy (100%)
Tel.: (39) 02880841
Web Site: http://www.3i.com
Sales Range: $50-74.9 Million
Emp.: 15
Venture Capital Business
N.A.I.C.S.: 523910

3i Switzerland Limited (3)
Othmarstrasse 8, 8008, Zurich,
Switzerland (100%)
Tel.: (41) 12504400
Web Site: http://www.3i.com
Sales Range: $50-74.9 Million
Emp.: 10
Venture Capital

N.A.I.C.S.: 523160

Subsidiary (Domestic):

3i Nordic plc (2)
16 Palace Street, London, SW1E 5JD,
United Kingdom (100%)
Tel.: (44) 2079283131
Web Site: http://www.3i.com
Sales Range: $50-74.9 Million
Emp.: 50
Investment Advisory Services
N.A.I.C.S.: 523940
Philip Yea (CEO)

Branch (Non-US):

3i Sweden (3)
Engelbrektsplan 1, PO Box 7847, 10399,
Stockholm, Sweden (100%)
Tel.: (46) 850610100
Web Site: http://www.3i.com
Sales Range: $75-99.9 Million
Emp.: 12
Venture Capital
N.A.I.C.S.: 523160
Mattias Eklund (Mng Dir)

Branch (Non-US):

3i plc (3)
Trinity Pk Bicken Hill, B37 7ES, Birming-
ham, United Kingdom - England (100%)
Tel.: (44) 1217823131
Web Site: http://www.3i.com
Sales Range: $50-74.9 Million
Emp.: 100
Venture Capital
N.A.I.C.S.: 523910

Arrivia (1)
15147 N Scottsdale Rd Ste 210, Scotts-
dale, AZ 85254
Tel.: (602) 749-2100
Web Site: https://www.arrivia.com
Sales Range: $10-24.9 Million
Emp.: 800
Private Resort & Cruise Club
N.A.I.C.S.: 721199

Subsidiary (Domestic):

WMPH Vacations, LLC (2)
220 Congress Park Dr Ste 330, Delray
Beach, FL 33445
Tel.: (561) 243-2100
Web Site: http://www.wmph.com
Travel Agencies
N.A.I.C.S.: 561510
Joanne Pereira (Supvr-Admin Ops)

Subsidiary (Domestic):

Cruise Now Inc. (3)
220 Congress Park Dr Ste 330, Delray
Beach, FL 33445
Tel.: (704) 670-0741
Web Site: http://www.cruisenow.com
Travel Arrangement & Reservation Services
N.A.I.C.S.: 561599
Megan Morra (Dir-Bus Dev)

Atle AB (1)
Birger Jarlsgatan 25, PO Box 7847, Stock-
holm, 111 99, Sweden
Tel.: (46) 8 50 61 01 00
Investment Management Service
N.A.I.C.S.: 523940

**Barclays Infrastructure Funds Man-
agement Limited** (1)
5 The North Colonnade Canary Wharf, Lon-
don, E14 4PB, United Kingdom
Tel.: (44) 2076232323
Web Site:
http://wwwbarclaysinfrastructurefunds.com
Fund Management Services
N.A.I.C.S.: 523940
Robert McClatchey (Mng Dir)

BoConcept Holding A/S (1)
Morupvej 16, 7400, Herning, Denmark
Tel.: (45) 7013 1366
Web Site: http://www.boconcept.com
Furniture Sales
N.A.I.C.S.: 449110

**Christ Juweliere und Uhrmacher seit
1863 GmbH** (1)
Kabeler Strasse 4, 58099, Hagen, Germany
Tel.: (49) 8001863300

Web Site: http://www.christ.de
Emp.: 2,400
Jewelry & Precious Stones Retailer
N.A.I.C.S.: 423940

Cirtec Medical, LLC (1)
9200 Xylon Ave N, Brooklyn Park, MN
55445
Tel.: (763) 493-8556
Web Site: http://www.cirtecmed.com
Medical Device Designer, Developer, Mfr &
Product Transfer Services
N.A.I.C.S.: 339112
Brian Highley (CEO)

Dynatect Manufacturing, Inc. (1)
2300 S Calhoun Rd, New Berlin, WI 53151-
2708
Tel.: (262) 786-1500
Web Site: http://www.dynatect.com
Sales Range: $75-99.9 Million
Emp.: 500
Bellows, Machinery Protectors & Cable Car-
riers Mfr
N.A.I.C.S.: 333515
Patrick Dupies (VP-SIs)

Division (Domestic):

Dynatect Polyclutch (2)
457 State St, North Haven, CT 06473-3019
Tel.: (203) 248-6398
Web Site: http://www.polyclutch.com
Sales Range: $25-49.9 Million
Emp.: 18
Mechanical & Pneumatic Slip Clutches Mfr
N.A.I.C.S.: 333613
Anthony Cavalco (Pres)

**Easysoft-Software e Sistemas
SA** (1)
sentri bussiness park edisicio 1, Amadora,
2714562, Portugal (100%)
Tel.: (351) 217229300
Web Site: http://www.easysoft.pt
Sales Range: $25-49.9 Million
Emp.: 40
Produces Software for the Leasing, Con-
sumer Credit & Car Rental Industries
N.A.I.C.S.: 334610
E. Miguel Rangel (Chm & CEO)

**Environmental Scientifics Group
Ltd.** (1)
ESG House Bretby Park Ashby Road,
Burton-on-Trent, DE15 0YZ, United King-
dom
Tel.: (44) 1283554400
Web Site: http://www.esg.co.uk
Testing, Inspection & Compliance Services
N.A.I.C.S.: 541380
Ian Sparks (CEO)

Subsidiary (Domestic):

**Environmental Services Group
Ltd.** (2)
Askern Rd, Carcroft, Doncaster, DN6 8DG,
United Kingdom
Tel.: (44) 1302723456
Web Site: http://www.esg.co.uk
Environmental Consulting Services
N.A.I.C.S.: 541620
David Clave (Mng Dir)

Esvagt A/S (1)
Dokvej 4, 6700, Esbjerg, Denmark
Tel.: (45) 78 730 730
Web Site: http://www.esvagt.com
Emp.: 1,000
Offshore Safety & Support Services
N.A.I.C.S.: 488390
Kristian Ole Jakobsen (Deputy CEO)

Formel D GmbH (1)
Brusseler Strasse 6, 53842, Troisdorf, Ger-
many
Tel.: (49) 22 41 996 0
Web Site: http://www.formeld.com
Vehicle Preparation & Engineering Svcs
N.A.I.C.S.: 541330
Martin Pekar (VP-Central & Eastern Eu-
rope)

**Gardens Pension Trustees
Limited** (1)
91 Finance House Waterloo Road, London,
SE1 8XP, United Kingdom (100%)
Tel.: (44) 2079283131
Pension Fund Trust Services

N.A.I.C.S.: 525110
John Davies *(Dir)*

Hans Anders Nederland B.V. (1)
Papland 21, 4206 CK, Gorinchem, Netherlands
Tel.: (31) 183697500
Web Site: http://www.hansanders.nl
Spectacles, Hearing & Contact Lenses Retailer
N.A.I.C.S.: 339115
Nikki Put *(Mgr-Digital Adv)*

JMJ Associates, LLC (1)
8310 1- N Capital of Texas Hwy Bldg 1 Ste 440, Austin, TX 78731-1048 **(55%)**
Tel.: (512) 795-0795
Web Site: http://www.jmj.com
Management Consulting Services
N.A.I.C.S.: 541611
Steve Knisely *(Partner-Global)*

Koninklijke Sanders BV (1)
Industriepark Vliedberg 12, 5251, Vlijmen, Netherlands
Tel.: (31) 73 5187 187
Web Site: http://www.royalsanders.com
Personal Care Product Mfr
N.A.I.C.S.: 325620
Bart Hullegie *(CEO)*

Plant (Non-US):

McBride plc - Ieper Personal Care Factory (2)
Paddevijverstraat 47, 8900, Ieper, West Flanders, Belgium
Tel.: (32) 57228922
Sales Range: $50-74.9 Million
Emp.: 200
Personal Care Product Mfr
N.A.I.C.S.: 325620
Marc DeWeerdt *(Plant Mgr)*

LNI Verkko Holding Oy (1)
Televisiokatu 4 A, FIN 00240, Helsingfors, Finland **(45%)**
Tel.: (358) 2058611
Holding Company; Energy Solutions Services
N.A.I.C.S.: 551112

MEMORA Servicios Funerarios S.L. (1)
Passeig de la Zona Franca 111 8th Floor, Barcelona, 08038, Spain **(75%)**
Tel.: (34) 916623554
Web Site: http://www.memora.es
Funeral Services
N.A.I.C.S.: 812210

Regional Rail, LLC (1)
505 S Broad St, Kennett Square, PA 19348
Tel.: (610) 925-0131
Web Site: http://www.regional-rail.com
Short Line Railroads Management Services
N.A.I.C.S.: 482112
Robert C. Parker *(Pres & CEO)*

Subsidiary (Domestic):

Conshohocken Recycling & Rail Transfer LLC (2)
1060 Conshohocken Rd, Conshohocken, PA 19428
Tel.: (610) 278-7454
Web Site: http://www.conshyrail.com
Construction & Demolition Waste Transfer Station Services
N.A.I.C.S.: 562219

East Penn Railroad, LLC (2)
505 S Broad St, Kennett Square, PA 19348
Tel.: (610) 925-0131
Web Site: http://www.eastpennrr.com
Short Line Railroad; Railroad Track Maintenance & Construction
N.A.I.C.S.: 482112
Ethel Nawrocki *(CFO)*

Sani-Tech West, Inc. (1)
321 Irving Dr, Oxnard, CA 93030
Tel.: (805) 389-0400
Web Site: http://www.sani-techwest.com
Sales Range: $1-9.9 Million
Emp.: 14
Plumbing & Heating Equipment & Supplies (Hydronics) Merchant Whslr
N.A.I.C.S.: 423720
Richard Shor *(Pres & CEO)*

3MV ENERGY CORP.
25 Adelaide Street East Suite 1900, Toronto, M5C 3A1, ON, Canada
Tel.: (306) 637-4440   Ca
Web Site: http://www.3mvenergy.com
Year Founded: 2009
Sales Range: Less than $1 Million
Investment Services
N.A.I.C.S.: 523999
William M. Abbey *(CFO & VP-Fin)*

3ONEDATA CO., LTD.
3/B Zone 1 Baiwangxin Industrial Park Songbai Road, Nanshan, Shenzhen, 518105, China
Tel.: (86) 75526702688
Web Site: https://www.3onedata.com
Year Founded: 2001
688618—(SHG)
Rev.: $47,130,665
Assets: $140,411,035
Liabilities: $29,303,095
Net Worth: $111,107,941
Earnings: $13,491,008
Fiscal Year-end: 12/31/22
Telecommunications Equipment Mfr
N.A.I.C.S.: 334290
Wei Xiong *(Chm & Gen Mgr)*

3P LAND HOLDINGS LIMITED
Jatia Chambers 60 Dr V B Gandhi Marg Fort, Mumbai, 400 023, India
Tel.: (91) 2230213333   In
Web Site: https://www.3pland.com
Year Founded: 1965
516092—(BOM)
Rev.: $293,147
Assets: $9,349,417
Liabilities: $239,448
Net Worth: $9,109,969
Earnings: $157,617
Emp.: 1
Fiscal Year-end: 03/31/22
Paper Seller & Mfr
N.A.I.C.S.: 322120
Jagadish Waman Patil *(CFO, Compliance Officer & Sec)*

Subsidiaries:

Pudumjee Paper Products Ltd. (1)
60 Dr V B Gandhi Marg Kalaghoda, Mumbai, 400 001, Maharashtra, India
Tel.: (91) 2230213333
Web Site: https://www.pudumjee.com
Rev.: $91,981,056
Assets: $75,042,707
Liabilities: $27,445,405
Net Worth: $47,597,302
Earnings: $7,121,312
Emp.: 588
Fiscal Year-end: 03/31/2023
Paper Product Mfr & Distr
N.A.I.C.S.: 322299
Vinay Jadhav *(Sec)*

3P LEARNING LIMITED
655 Parramatta Road, Leichhardt, Sydney, 2040, NSW, Australia
Tel.: (61) 1300850331   AU
Web Site:
      https://www.3plearning.com
Year Founded: 2003
3PL—(ASX)
Rev.: $73,480,235
Assets: $132,670,272
Liabilities: $39,608,039
Net Worth: $93,062,233
Earnings: $38,074,252
Emp.: 390
Fiscal Year-end: 06/30/24
Learning Software
N.A.I.C.S.: 513210
Tania Black *(Chief People Officer)*

Subsidiaries:

Blake eLearning Pty. Ltd. (1)
33 Colston Avenue, Bristol, BS1 4UA, United Kingdom

Tel.: (44) 1173600248
Educational Products Supplier
N.A.I.C.S.: 611691

3PEAK, INC.
4F Building 2 No 1761 Zhangdong Rd, Pudong, Shanghai, 201210, China
Tel.: (86) 2151090810
Web Site: https://www.3peak.cn
Year Founded: 2012
688536—(SHG)
Rev.: $250,382,888
Assets: $582,845,033
Liabilities: $51,336,684
Net Worth: $531,508,349
Earnings: $37,459,759
Fiscal Year-end: 12/31/22
Semiconductor Product Mfr & Distr
N.A.I.C.S.: 334413
Jiangang Wu *(CEO, Deputy Gen Mgr & Dir-Design)*

3Q HOLDINGS LIMITED
Ground Floor 35 Spring Street, Bondi Junction, 2022, NSW, Australia
Tel.: (61) 2 9369 8500
Web Site:
      http://www.islandpacific.com
Rev.: $21,284,534
Assets: $39,123,188
Liabilities: $17,948,228
Net Worth: $21,174,961
Earnings: $237,303
Emp.: 186
Fiscal Year-end: 06/30/19
Software Publisher
N.A.I.C.S.: 513210
Alan Treisman *(Sec)*

Subsidiaries:

AdvanceRetail Technology Asia Sdn Bhd (1)
No 2-3 2nd Floor Jalan USJ 9/5Q Subang Business Centre, 47620, Subang Jaya, Selangor Darul Ehsan, Malaysia
Tel.: (60) 3 8023 1896
Software Development Services
N.A.I.C.S.: 541511

AdvanceRetail Technology Limited (1)
Level 2 8 Rockridge Ave, Penrose, Auckland, 1061, New Zealand
Tel.: (64) 9 980 4580
Web Site: http://www.advanceretail.com
Software Development Services
N.A.I.C.S.: 541511
Mark McGeachen *(CEO)*

Intelligent Retail UK Limited (1)
Consort House 42 Bone Lane, Newbury, RG14 5RD, Berkshire, United Kingdom
Tel.: (44) 845 68 00 126
Web Site: http://www.intelligentretail.co.uk
Software Development Services
N.A.I.C.S.: 541511
David Mackley *(Mng Dir)*

Island Pacific (1)
17310 Redhill Ave Ste 320, Irvine, CA 92614
Tel.: (949) 476-2212
Web Site: http://www.islandpacific.com
Sales Range: $25-49.9 Million
Emp.: 185
Software & E-Commerce Business Solutions Mfr
N.A.I.C.S.: 513210
Richard Gaetano *(COO)*

3S KOREA CO., LTD.
1311 Gasan IS BIZ Tower 75-24 Gasan digital 1-ro, Geumcheon-gu, Seoul, 08589, Korea (South)
Tel.: (82) 28969474
Web Site: https://www.3sref.com
Year Founded: 1989
060310—(KRS)
Rev.: $21,599,676
Assets: $50,245,572
Liabilities: $16,622,954

Net Worth: $33,622,618
Earnings: $639,708
Emp.: 76
Fiscal Year-end: 03/31/21
Electronic Components Mfr
N.A.I.C.S.: 334419
H. W. You *(Mng Dir)*

3SBIO INC.
1st 3 10th Road Economic and Technological Development Zone, Shenyang, China
Tel.: (86) 2425386000   Ky
Web Site: http://www.3sbio.com
Year Founded: 1993
1530—(HKG)
Rev.: $963,064,393
Assets: $3,087,214,042
Liabilities: $924,990,862
Net Worth: $2,162,223,180
Earnings: $267,885,587
Emp.: 5,213
Fiscal Year-end: 12/31/22
Holding Company; Biopharmaceutical Product Mfr
N.A.I.C.S.: 551112
Jing Lou *(Founder, Chm & CEO)*

Subsidiaries:

Shenyang Sunshine Pharmaceutical Co., Limited (1)
1st 3 10th Road Economic and Technological Development Zone, Shenyang, 110027, Liaoning, China
Tel.: (86) 2425386000
Biopharmaceutical Product Mfr
N.A.I.C.S.: 325412

Shenzhen Sciprogen Bio-pharmaceutical Co., Ltd. (1)
No 14 Yayuan Road Bantian Street, Longgang District, Shenzhen, China
Tel.: (86) 57188270801
Biopharmaceutical Product Mfr
N.A.I.C.S.: 325412

Sirton Pharmaceuticals SpA (1)
Piazza XX Settembre 2, Villa Guardia, 22079, Como, Italy
Tel.: (39) 03 138 5111
Web Site: https://www.sirton.it
Pharmaceuticals Product Mfr
N.A.I.C.S.: 325411
Ivano Morlacchi *(Dir-Technical, Mgr-Production & New Project)*

Sunshine Guojian Pharmaceuticals (Shanghai) Co., Ltd. (1)
Tel.: (86) 2180297777
Web Site: http://www.3s-guojian.com
Rev.: $115,899,049
Assets: $715,815,879
Liabilities: $70,043,019
Net Worth: $645,772,861
Earnings: $6,921,355
Fiscal Year-end: 12/31/2022
Pharmaceutical Product Mfr & Distr
N.A.I.C.S.: 325412
Jing Lou *(Chm)*

Sunshine Guojian Pharmaceuticals (Shanghai) Co., Ltd. (1)
No 399 Libing Road Pilot Free Trade Zone, Shanghai, China
Tel.: (86) 2180297777
Biopharmaceutical Product Mfr
N.A.I.C.S.: 325412

Zhejiang Wansheng Co., Ltd. (1)
No 8 Jujing Rd Liangshui Development Zone, Linhai, 317000, Zhejiang, China
Tel.: (86) 57685322966
Web Site: https://www.ws-chem.com
Rev.: $500,415,252
Assets: $849,954,798
Liabilities: $284,971,045
Net Worth: $564,983,752
Earnings: $51,284,778
Fiscal Year-end: 12/31/2022
Fire Retardant Mfr & Distr
N.A.I.C.S.: 325998
Gao Xianguo *(Chm)*

Zhejiang Wansheng Pharmaceutical Co., Ltd. (1)

3SBio Inc.—(Continued)

10th Floor Block D West Yintai No 380
Fengtan Road, Gongshu District,
Hangzhou, China
Tel.: (86) 57188270801
Biopharmaceutical Product Mfr
N.A.I.C.S.: 325412

Zhengjiang Wansheng Pharmaceuti- (1)
cal Co., Ltd.
Room 502 building 11 Hangzhou Greenland
Central Plaza office building, No 96 Daguan
Road Gongshu District, Hangzhou, Zheji-
ang, China
Tel.: (86) 5718 827 0801
Web Site: http://www.wshpharm.com
Emp.: 690
Medicine Mfr
N.A.I.C.S.: 325412
Huijun Hu (VP)

Plant (Domestic):

Zhengjiang Wansheng Pharmaceuti- (2)
cal Co., Ltd. - Qingshan Plant
1 Wangjiashan Road Qingshanhu Street,
Lin'an, Hangzhou, China
Tel.: (86) 57188185573
Medicine Mfr
N.A.I.C.S.: 325412

3U HOLDING AG

Frauenbergstrasse 31-33, 35039,
Marburg, Germany
Tel.: (49) 64219991200   De
Web Site: https://www.3u.net
UUU—(MUN)
Rev.: $57,787,594
Assets: $131,702,730
Liabilities: $33,767,383
Net Worth: $97,935,346
Earnings: $2,814,868
Emp.: 159
Fiscal Year-end: 12/31/23
Holding Company
N.A.I.C.S.: 551112
Ralf Thoenes (Chm-Supervisory Bd)

Subsidiaries:

010017 Telecom GmbH (1)
Frauenbergstrasse 31-33, 35039, Marburg,
Germany
(49) 64213000502
Web Site: https://www.010017telecom.de
Mobile Network Services
N.A.I.C.S.: 516210

3U Energy AG (1)
Frauenbergstrasse 31-33, 35039, Marburg,
Germany
Tel.: (49) 64219991700
Web Site: http://www.3uenergy.de
Wind Farm Development Services
N.A.I.C.S.: 221115

3U Energy PE GmbH (1)
Poststrasse 4-5, 10178, Berlin, Germany
Tel.: (49) 30720213700
Web Site: https://www.3uenergy-pe.de
Wind Farm Development Services
N.A.I.C.S.: 221115

3U Telecom GmbH (1)
Frauenbergstrasse 31-33, 35039, Marburg,
Germany
Tel.: (49) 64219991666
Web Site: https://www.3utelecom.de
Telecommunication Servicesb
N.A.I.C.S.: 516210

Discount Telecom S&V GmbH (1)
Frauenbergstrasse 31-33, 35039, Marburg,
Germany
Tel.: (49) 64213000503
Web Site: https://www.discount-telecom.de
Mobile Network Services
N.A.I.C.S.: 516210

ITscope GmbH (1)
Durlacher Allee 73, 76131, Karlsruhe, Ger-
many
Tel.: (49) 7216273760
Web Site: https://www.itscope.com
Information Technology Services
N.A.I.C.S.: 541511

InnoHubs GmbH (1)
Magdalene-Schoch-Str 5, 97074, Wurzburg,
Germany
Tel.: (49) 93149738985
Web Site: https://innohubs.de
Building Rental Services
N.A.I.C.S.: 531110

LineCall Telecom GmbH (1)
Frauenbergstrasse 31-33, 35039, Marburg,
Germany
Tel.: (49) 64213000501
Web Site: https://www.linecall.de
Mobile Network Services
N.A.I.C.S.: 516210

OneTel Telecommunication (1)
GmbH
Frauenbergstrasse 31-33, 35039, Marburg,
Germany
Tel.: (49) 64213000506
Web Site: https://www.onetel.de
Mobile Network Services
N.A.I.C.S.: 516210

PELIA Gebaeudesysteme GmbH (1)
Horresser Berg 5, 56410, Montabaur, Ger-
many
Tel.: (49) 260295390
Web Site: http://www.pelia.de
Surface Heating & Cooling System Mfr
N.A.I.C.S.: 334512

RISIMA Consulting GmbH (1)
Frauenbergstrasse 31-33, 35039, Marburg,
Germany
Tel.: (49) 6421300030
Web Site: https://www.risima.de
Software Distribution Services
N.A.I.C.S.: 513210

Samoba GmbH (1)
Drieschweg 9, 53604, Bad Honnef, Ger-
many
Tel.: (49) 22249769480
Web Site: https://www.samoba.de
Drilling & Other Equipment Rental Services
N.A.I.C.S.: 532412

Selfio GmbH (1)
Drieschweg 9, 53604, Bad Honnef, Ger-
many
Tel.: (49) 222412376530
Web Site: http://www.selfio.de
Ventilation & Other Installation Services
N.A.I.C.S.: 238220

Weclapp SE (1)
Frauenbergstr 31-33, 35039, Marburg, Ger-
many
Tel.: (49) 69333901800
Web Site: http://www.weclapp.com
Cloud & ERP Software Services
N.A.I.C.S.: 541511

Windpark Langendorf GmbH & Co. (1)
KG
Frauenbergstr 31-33, 35039, Marburg, Ger-
many
Tel.: (49) 64219990
Web Site: https://www.windpark-
langendorf.de
Wind Farm Development Services
N.A.I.C.S.: 221115

fon4U Telecom GmbH (1)
Frauenbergstrasse 31-33, 35039, Marburg,
Germany
Tel.: (49) 64213000504
Web Site: https://www.fon4u.de
Mobile Network Services
N.A.I.C.S.: 516210

3W POWER S.A.

19 rue Eugene Ruppert, 2453, Lux-
ombourg, Luxembourg
Tel.: (352) 20 4077 800   LU
Web Site: http://www.aegps.com
Holding Company
N.A.I.C.S.: 551112
Franck Audrain (CEO-AEG Power
Solutions)

Subsidiaries:

AEG Power Solutions B.V. (1)
Weerenweg 29, 1161 AH, Zwanenburg,
Netherlands
Tel.: (31) 204077800

Web Site: http://www.aegps.com
Sales Range: $25-49.9 Million
Emp.: 50
Electrical Power Control System Mfr
N.A.I.C.S.: 335931
Hans Van Nikkelen Kuijper (VP-Sls)

Subsidiary (Non-US):

3W Power S p A (2)
Via Energy Park 14, 20871, Vimercate, MB,
Italy
Tel.: (39) 0396250421
Power Supplies Mfr & Distr
N.A.I.C.S.: 335999
Alberto Dall'Asta (Dir-Sls)

AEG Power Solutions (France) (2)
S.A.S
ZI 10 Rue Jean Perrin, 37173, Chambray
les Tours, France
Tel.: (33) 247808860
Web Site: http://www.aeg.com
Sales Range: $125-149.9 Million
Eletric Power Generation Services
N.A.I.C.S.: 221118

AEG Power Solutions (Russia) (2)
LLC
23 Novoslobodskaya Street Office 346,
127055, Moscow, Russia
Tel.: (7) 4957950744
Power Supplies Mfr & Distr
N.A.I.C.S.: 335999

AEG Power Solutions Aram. Kft (2)
Kondorfa utca 10, 1116, Budapest, Hungary
Tel.: (36) 12099550
Power Supplies Mfr & Distr
N.A.I.C.S.: 335999

AEG Power Solutions Co. (2)
N 10 Factory of KangSheng Industrial Park
11 Kangding Street, Beijing, 100176, China
Tel.: (86) 10 6780 3466
Web Site: http://www.aegps.com
Power Supplies Equipment Mfr & Distr
N.A.I.C.S.: 335999

AEG Power Solutions GmbH (2)
Emil Siepmann Strasse 32, D 59581, War-
stein, Germany
Tel.: (49) 29027630
Electrical Power Control System Mfr
N.A.I.C.S.: 335931

AEG Power Solutions Iberica SL (2)
Parque Tecnologico de Alava C/Albert Ein-
stein 31, 01510, Minano, Alava, Spain
Tel.: (34) 945214110
Web Site: http://www.aegps.es
Sales Range: $50-74.9 Million
Power Transmission Equipment Distr
N.A.I.C.S.: 423830

AEG Power Solutions Inc. (2)
2680 14th Avenue Units 1 2, Markham, L3R
5B2, ON, Canada
Tel.: (888) 727-7238
Sales Range: $10-24.9 Million
Electrical Power Control System Mfr
N.A.I.C.S.: 335931

AEG Power Solutions Ltd. (2)
Units 1 2 97 101 Peregrine Road, Hainault,
Ilford, IG6 3XJ, Essex, United Kingdom
Tel.: (44) 2084981177
Sales Range: $25-49.9 Million
Emp.: 50
Telecommunication Equipment Power Sup-
ply Products
N.A.I.C.S.: 335931

AEG Power Solutions Middle (2)
East
Office 5EA 225 Dubai Airport Free Zone,
PO Box 54887, Dubai, United Arab Emir-
ates
Tel.: (971) 4 6091 290
Web Site: http://www.aegps.com
Emp.: 50
Power Supplies Mfr & Distr
N.A.I.C.S.: 335999
John Lynch (Dir-Sls)

AEG Power Solutions S.A.S (2)
93/95 rue des Trois Fontanot, BP 404,
92004, Nanterre, France
Tel.: (33) 1 55 51 10 40
Power Generation Services
N.A.I.C.S.: 221118

AEG Power Solutions Sdn Bhd (2)
14th Floor Menara Safuan N 80, Jalan Am-
pang, Kuala Lumpur, 50450, Malaysia
Tel.: (60) 3 2078 8996
Web Site: http://www.aegps.com
Sales Range: $75-99.9 Million
Emp.: 7
Eletric Power Generation Services
N.A.I.C.S.: 221118
Mohan Chandran (Dir-Sls)

Subsidiary (US):

AEG Power Solutions USA, Inc. (2)
800 Klein Rd Ste 400, Plano, TX 75074
Tel.: (469) 299-9600
Sales Range: $25-49.9 Million
Emp.: 20
Electrical Power Control System Mfr
N.A.I.C.S.: 335931

Subsidiary (Non-US):

AEG Power Solutions spol. s.r.o. (2)
Na Vlastni Pude 6/1368, 102 00, Prague,
Czech Republic
Tel.: (420) 274773273
Web Site: http://www.aeg-ups.cz
Optical Fiber Cable Mfr
N.A.I.C.S.: 335921

AEG Power Solutions, S.L. (2)
Parque Tecnologico De Alava, C Albert Ein-
stein 31, Minano, 1510, Alava, Spain
Tel.: (34) 945214110
Web Site: http://www.spsi.es
Sales Range: $10-24.9 Million
Emp.: 50
Mfr of Batteries
N.A.I.C.S.: 335910
Jesus Maria Rodriguez (Gen Mgr)

Harmer & Simmons (2)
Via Trento 30, Vimercate, 20059, Milan,
Italy
Tel.: (39) 0396863837
Web Site: http://www.aegps.com
Sales Range: $25-49.9 Million
Emp.: 40
Telecommunication Equipment Power Sup-
ply Products
N.A.I.C.S.: 335931

4 GLOBAL PLC

Venture X 5th Floor Building 7 Chis-
wick Business Park, 566 Chiswick
High Road, London, W4 5YG, United
Kingdom
Tel.: (44) 208123469   UK
Web Site: https://www.4global.com
Year Founded: 2021
4GBL—(AIM)
Rev.: $4,942,006
Assets: $7,096,517
Liabilities: $2,339,353
Net Worth: $4,757,164
Earnings: ($2,249,973)
Emp.: 28
Fiscal Year-end: 03/31/22
Software Development Services
N.A.I.C.S.: 541511

4 OFFICE AUTOMATION LTD.

425 Superior Blvd Unit 1 & 2, Missis-
sauga, L5T 2W5, ON, Canada
Tel.: (905) 564-0522
Web Site: http://www.4office.com
Sales Range: $10-24.9 Million
Emp.: 75
Digital Office Equipment Sales
N.A.I.C.S.: 423420
Bill Norgate (Pres)

4. JULI A.D.

Mose Pijade 26, 25220, Crvenka,
Serbia
Tel.: (381) 25731140
Year Founded: 1999
CJUL—(BEL)
Sales Range: Less than $1 Million
Emp.: 21
Food Transportation Services
N.A.I.C.S.: 484121

4. SEPTEMBAR A.D.
Vojvode Misica Bb, 74270, Teslic, Bosnia & Herzegovina
Tel.: (387) 53 430 022
Web Site:
http://www.ad4septembar.com
SEPT—(BANJ)
Sales Range: $1-9.9 Million
Emp.: 28
Mechanical Engineering Services
N.A.I.C.S.: 541330

401 AUTO DEALERS EX-CHANGE
60 Rigney St, Kingston, K7K 6Z2, ON, Canada
Tel.: (613) 536-0401
Web Site: http://www.401ade.com
Year Founded: 2002
Sales Range: $25-49.9 Million
Emp.: 50
Auto Auction Whslr
N.A.I.C.S.: 423110
David Nelson (Pres)

401-DIXIE NISSAN
5500 Dixie Road Unit B, Mississauga, L4W 4N3, ON, Canada
Tel.: (289) 278-8760
Web Site:
http://www.401dixienissan.com
Rev.: $73,592,036
Emp.: 65
New & Used Car Sales & Service
N.A.I.C.S.: 441110
Keith de Podesta (Mgr-Sls)

4077491 CANADA INC
395 Stinson, Saint Laurent, H4N 2E1, QC, Canada
Tel.: (514) 748-2028
Web Site:
http://www.boislaurentien.com
Rev.: $10,742,517
Emp.: 100
Wooden Pallets Mfr & Distr
N.A.I.C.S.: 321920
Marcel Guertin (Pres & Gen Mgr)

413554 ONTARIO LIMITED
194 Earl Stewart Dr, Aurora, L4G 6V7, ON, Canada
Tel.: (905) 479-8300
Web Site:
http://www.chouinardbros.com
Year Founded: 1972
Rev.: $38,997,975
Emp.: 65
Residential Roofing Services
N.A.I.C.S.: 238160

4236009 MANITOBA LTD
(Acquired by AutoCanada Inc.)

429149 B.C. LTD
8168 Glenwood Dr, Burnaby, V3N 5E9, BC, Canada
Tel.: (604) 421-5520
Web Site: http://www.quiltsetc.com
Year Founded: 1992
Rev.: $27,213,769
Emp.: 350
Bed Linen Mfr & Retailer
N.A.I.C.S.: 812331
Howard Haugom (Pres)

450477 ONTARIO LTD
2401 Airport Road, Timmins, P4N 7C3, ON, Canada
Tel.: (705) 268-0510
Web Site:
http://www.chartrandequipment.com
Year Founded: 1980
Rev.: $19,562,614
Emp.: 120

Construction Engineering Services
N.A.I.C.S.: 541330
Maurice Chartrand (Co-Founder)

482 JOINT STOCK COMPANY
No 155 Truong Chinh Street, Vinh, Nghe An, Vietnam
Tel.: (84) 2383853200
Web Site:
http://www.congty482.com.vn
Year Founded: 1982
B82—(HNX)
Sales Range: $1-9.9 Million
Food Transportation Services
N.A.I.C.S.: 485999
Tran Van Long (Chm & Mgr)

49 NORTH RESOURCES INC.
Suite 602 - 224 4th Avenue S, Saskatoon, S7K 5M5, SK, Canada
Tel.: (306) 653-2692
Web Site: https://www.fnr.ca
FNR—(TSXV)
Rev.: $644,869
Assets: $12,707,846
Liabilities: $6,648,040
Net Worth: $6,059,805
Earnings: ($2,127,917)
Fiscal Year-end: 12/31/23
Oil & Gas Exploration Services
N.A.I.C.S.: 213112
Thomas M. MacNeill (Pres & CEO)

Subsidiaries:

Allstar Energy Limited **(1)**
409 Main Street, Kindersley, S0L 1S0, SK, Canada
Tel.: (306) 463-0181
Oil & Gas Exploration Services
N.A.I.C.S.: 213112

4AIM SICAF SPA
Corso Venezia 16, 20121, Milan, Italy
Tel.: (39) 0287399069
Web Site: https://www.4aim.it
Year Founded: 2016
AIM—(ITA)
Asset Management Services
N.A.I.C.S.: 523940
Giovanni Battista Natali (Chm, CEO & Chief Investment Officer)

4BASEBIO PLC
Tel.: (44) 1223967943 UK
Web Site: https://www.4basebio.com
Year Founded: 2019
4BB—(AIM)
Rev.: $332,802
Assets: $14,515,400
Liabilities: $5,673,784
Net Worth: $8,841,616
Earnings: ($6,395,270)
Emp.: 48
Fiscal Year-end: 12/31/22
Research & Development in Biotechnology (except Nanobiotechnology)
N.A.I.C.S.: 541714

4BY4 INC.
14th f 479 Gangnam-daero, Seocho-gu, Seoul, Korea (South)
Tel.: (82) 28384416
Web Site: https://www.4by4inc.com
Year Founded: 2017
389140—(KRS)
Motion Picture & Video Production Services
N.A.I.C.S.: 512110
Choi Chul-Ung (CFO)

4C GROUP AB
Vattugatan 17, 111 52, Stockholm, Sweden
Tel.: (46) 852227900
Web Site:
https://www.4cstrategies.com
Year Founded: 2000

4C—(OMX)
Rev.: $18,530,105
Assets: $24,887,255
Liabilities: $8,614,604
Net Worth: $16,272,652
Earnings: $1,039,635
Emp.: 189
Fiscal Year-end: 12/31/22
Software Development Services
N.A.I.C.S.: 541511
Anders Nordgren (CFO)

Subsidiaries:

4C Strategies AB **(1)**
Vattugatan 17, 111 52, Stockholm, Sweden
Tel.: (46) 852227900
Web Site: https://www.4cstrategies.com
Software & Advisory Services
N.A.I.C.S.: 541511

4CS HOLDINGS CO., LTD.
Yakuin Business Garden 8F Yakuin 1-1-1, Chuo Ward, Fukuoka, 810-0022, Japan
Tel.: (81) 927205460
Web Site: https://www.4cs-holdings.co.jp
Year Founded: 2003
3726—(TKS)
Rev.: $15,144,240
Assets: $11,648,870
Liabilities: $7,976,250
Net Worth: $3,672,620
Earnings: ($1,928,480)
Emp.: 176
Fiscal Year-end: 09/30/23
Holding Company
N.A.I.C.S.: 551112
Yoshimi Tendo (Chm & Pres)

Subsidiaries:

Cure Co., Ltd. **(1)**
I-Mark Annex 8F 3-11-13 Iidabashi, Chiyoda-ku, Tokyo, 102-0072, Japan
Tel.: (81) 362613685
Web Site: https://cure-skin.jp
Cosmetic Product Mfr & Distr
N.A.I.C.S.: 325620
Hiromasa Mizuno (CEO)

Favorina Co., Ltd. **(1)**
1-1-1 Yakuin Business Garden 8F, Chuo-ku, Fukuoka, Japan
Tel.: (81) 927205420
Web Site: http://www.favorina.com
Cosmetic Product Retailer
N.A.I.C.S.: 456120

Haccp Japan Co., Ltd. **(1)**
8th floor Yakuin Business Garden 1-1-1 Yakuin, Chuo-ku, Fukuoka, 810-0022, Japan
Tel.: (81) 927205470
Web Site: https://haccp-japan.jp
Management Consulting Services
N.A.I.C.S.: 541611

4D PHARMA PLC
9 Bond Court 5th Floor, Leeds, LS1 2JZ, United Kingdom
Tel.: (44) 1138950130 UK
Web Site:
http://www.4dpharmaplc.com
DDDD—(NASDAQ)
Rev.: $690,000
Assets: $49,099,000
Liabilities: $10,128,000
Net Worth: $38,971,000
Earnings: ($30,495,000)
Emp.: 92
Fiscal Year-end: 12/31/20
Pharmaceuticals Mfr
N.A.I.C.S.: 325412
Alexander Stevenson (Co-Founder & Chief Scientific Officer)

Subsidiaries:

Longevity Acquisition Corporation **(1)**
Yongda International Tower No 2277 Long-

yang Road, Pudong District, Shanghai, China
Tel.: (86) 21 60832028
Investment Services
N.A.I.C.S.: 523999

4DMED, LTD.
151 Gloucester Road 11/F Capital Centre, Wanchai, China (Hong Kong)
Tel.: (852) 93841733 NV
Web Site: http://www.4dmed.tech
Year Founded: 2016
Assets: $4,791,870
Liabilities: $43,097
Net Worth: $4,748,773
Earnings: ($2,336,135)
Emp.: 1
Fiscal Year-end: 12/31/19
N.A.I.C.S.:
Yuen May Cheung (Founder, Pres, CEO, CFO & Sec)

4DMEDICAL LIMITED
Level 7/700 Swanston Street, Carlton, 3053, VIC, Australia
Tel.: (61) 395455940 AU
Web Site:
https://www.4dmedical.com
Year Founded: 2012
4DX—(ASX)
Rev.: $468,528
Assets: $60,587,805
Liabilities: $13,994,354
Net Worth: $46,593,452
Earnings: ($20,512,354)
Emp.: 131
Fiscal Year-end: 06/30/23
Software Development Services
N.A.I.C.S.: 541511
Andreas Fouras (CEO)

Subsidiaries:

Australian Lung Health Initiative Pty Ltd. **(1)**
Level 7 Melbourne Connect 700 Swanston Street south, Carlton, 3053, VIC, Australia
Tel.: (61) 395455940
Web Site: https://alhi.com.au
Health & Medical Research Services
N.A.I.C.S.: 541715

4DS MEMORY LIMITED
Level 2 50 Kings Park Road, West Perth, 6005, WA, Australia
Tel.: (61) 863778043 AU
Web Site:
https://www.4dsmemory.com
4DS—(ASX)
Rev.: $18,117
Assets: $4,365,980
Liabilities: $222,213
Net Worth: $4,143,767
Earnings: ($5,158,052)
Fiscal Year-end: 06/30/22
Memory Storage Solutions
N.A.I.C.S.: 541519
Guido Arnout (CEO & Mng Dir)

4FINANCE HOLDING S.A.
Lielirbes iela 17a-8, Riga, 1046, Latvia
Tel.: (371) 660 550 99
Web Site: http://www.4finance.com
Year Founded: 2008
Financial Holding Company
N.A.I.C.S.: 551112
Mark Ruddock (Chm & CEO)

Subsidiaries:

TBI Bank EAD **(1)**
52-54 Dimitar Hadzhikotsev Str, Lozenets District, 1421, Sofia, Bulgaria **(100%)**
Tel.: (359) 700 17 571
Web Site: http://www.tbibank.bg
Bank Holding Company; Retail Banking, Consumer Finance, Leasing & Mortgage Services
N.A.I.C.S.: 551111

4finance Holding S.A.—(Continued)

Valentin Galabov *(Chm-Mgmt Bd)*

Subsidiary (Non-US):

TBI Leasing IFN S.A. (2)
Str Putul lui Zamfir nr 8-12 sector 1, Bucharest, Romania
Tel.: (40) 215 298 600
Web Site: http://www.tbileasing.ro
Financial Lending Services
N.A.I.C.S.: 522220

VAB Leasing (2)
17 Linejnaya str, 03038, Kiev, Ukraine
Tel.: (380) 44 481 2211
Web Site: http://www.vableasing.com.ua
Financial Lending Services
N.A.I.C.S.: 522220
Zolotareva Ljudmila Semenovna *(Dir Gen)*

4FUN MEDIA S.A.
Ul Fabryczna 5A, 00-446, Warsaw, Poland
Tel.: (48) 224884300
Web Site: http://www.4funmedia.pl
DIG—(WAR)
Rev.: $16,331,809
Assets: $25,778,963
Liabilities: $10,447,663
Net Worth: $15,331,301
Earnings: $6,282,012
Emp.: 60
Fiscal Year-end: 12/31/23
Television & Video Broadcasting, Production & Distribution Services
N.A.I.C.S.: 516120
Aneta Parafiniuk *(Member-Mgmt Bd & Dir-Fin)*

4IG NYRT.
Montevideo u 8, 1037, Budapest, Hungary
Tel.: (36) 12707600
Web Site: https://www.4ig.hu
Year Founded: 1990
4IG—(BUD)
Rev.: $835,769,484
Assets: $2,580,047,682
Liabilities: $1,764,652,527
Net Worth: $815,395,155
Earnings: ($51,605,831)
Emp.: 6,000
Fiscal Year-end: 12/31/22
Software Development Services
N.A.I.C.S.: 334610
Gellert Jaszai *(Chm & CEO)*

Subsidiaries:

ACE Network Zrt. Plc. (1)
Oktober huszonharmadika utca 8-10 5 em 30, 1117, Budapest, Hungary
Tel.: (36) 208014000
Web Site: https://www.acenet.tech
Information Technology Solutions Services
N.A.I.C.S.: 541512

AXIS Consulting 2000 Ltd (1)
Szekesfehervar Berenyi ut 7Videoton Ipari Park, 197 sz epulet az I-es Porta, Budapest, 1119, Hungary
Tel.: (36) 22 517 631
Web Site: http://www.axis.hu
Information Technology Consulting Services
N.A.I.C.S.: 541512

BankSoft Kft (1)
Montevideo Str 8, 1037, Budapest, Hungary
Tel.: (36) 1 363 7442
Web Site: http://www.banksoft.hu
Banking Software Development Services
N.A.I.C.S.: 541511

HUMANsoft Kft. (1)
Montevideo u 8, 1037, Budapest, Hungary
Tel.: (36) 1 270 7600
Web Site: http://www.humansoft.hu
Rev.: $36,557,990
Emp.: 180
Information Security Software Development Services
N.A.I.C.S.: 541511
Gabor Rado *(Deputy Chief Sls Officer)*

Humansoft Szerviz Kft. (1)
Makk utca 9-11 Corner of Makk and Ferto Streets, 1107, Budapest, Hungary
Tel.: (36) 61 270 7600
Web Site: https://szerviz.humansoft.hu
Electronic Computer Mfr
N.A.I.C.S.: 334111

INNObyte Zrt. (1)
Bartok Bela ut 105-113 6 emelet, 1115, Budapest, Hungary
Tel.: (36) 1 700 2563
Web Site: https://www.innobyte.hu
Software Publisher Services
N.A.I.C.S.: 513210
Lengyel Kalman *(CEO)*

Invitech ICT Services Kft. Ltd. (1)
Krisztina krt 39, 1013, Budapest, Hungary
Tel.: (36) 80820082
Web Site: https://www.invitech.hu
Telecommunication Servicesb
N.A.I.C.S.: 517810

One Crna Gora DOO (1)
4 Rimski Trg, 81000, Podgorica, Montenegro
Tel.: (382) 20235000
Web Site: https://1.me
Mobile Telecommunications Services
N.A.I.C.S.: 517112

Poli Computer PC Kft. Ltd. (1)
Ciprus u 2-6, 1087, Budapest, Hungary
Tel.: (36) 613540898
Web Site: https://www.policomputer.hu
Information Technology Solutions Services
N.A.I.C.S.: 541512

TR Consulting Kft. (1)
8 Montevideo St, 1037, Budapest, Hungary
Tel.: (36) 30 204 5155
Web Site: https://trconsult.hu
Security System Services
N.A.I.C.S.: 561621

Veritas Consulting Kft. (1)
Montevideo u 8, 1037, Budapest, Hungary
Tel.: (36) 1 270 7600
Web Site: https://veritasconsulting.hu
Consulting Services
N.A.I.C.S.: 541611

4IMPRINT GROUP PLC
Central Court 25 Southampton Buildings, London, WC2A 1AL, United Kingdom
Tel.: (44) 2037099680   UK
Web Site: https://www.4imprint.co.uk
Year Founded: 1921
FOUR—(LSE)
Rev.: $787,322,000
Assets: $167,782,000
Liabilities: $84,816,000
Net Worth: $82,966,000
Earnings: $22,586,000
Emp.: 1,207
Fiscal Year-end: 01/31/22
Promotional Products
N.A.I.C.S.: 561990
Kevin Lyons-Tarr *(CEO)*

Subsidiaries:

4imprint Inc. (1)
101 Commerce St, Oshkosh, WI 54901   (100%)
Tel.: (920) 236-7272
Web Site: http://www.4imprint.com
Sales Range: $75-99.9 Million.
Emp.: 400
Supplier of Promotional Goods
N.A.I.C.S.: 541890
Amanda Kelnhofer *(Mgr-HR)*

4IP MANAGEMENT AG
Feldeggstrasse 39, 8008, Zurich, Switzerland
Tel.: (41) 442131400   CH
Web Site: http://www.4ip.ch
Year Founded: 2007
Asset Management & Investment Banking Services
N.A.I.C.S.: 523150
Ulrich Kaluscha *(Mng Dir)*

4K INVEST INTERNATIONAL
Sendlinger Str 10, 80331, Munich, Germany
Tel.: (49) 89 189 426 0
Web Site: http://www.4k.ag
Privater Equity Firm
N.A.I.C.S.: 523999
Holger Kowarsch *(Mng Dir)*

Subsidiaries:

Adria Airways d.d. (1)
Zgornji Brnik 13h, SI 4210, Brnik, Slovenia
Tel.: (386) 42594506
Web Site: http://www.adria.si
Sales Range: $150-199.9 Million
Emp.: 552
Oil Transportation Services
N.A.I.C.S.: 481111

Anttila Oy (1)
Valimotie 15, Helsinki, 00380, Finland
Tel.: (358) 10 53 43
Web Site: http://www.anttila.com
Department Store, E-Commerce & Mail Order Services
N.A.I.C.S.: 455110

4SC AG
Fraunhoferstr 22, 82152, Martinsried, Germany
Tel.: (49) 897007630
Web Site: https://www.4sc.de
VSC—(DEU)
Rev.: $470,537
Assets: $17,700,194
Liabilities: $3,358,515
Net Worth: $14,341,679
Earnings: ($15,498,597)
Emp.: 17
Fiscal Year-end: 12/31/22
Drug Research & Development Services
N.A.I.C.S.: 541715
Clemens Doppler *(Chm-Supervisory Bd)*

4SIGHT HOLDINGS LTD.
Ground Floor Tower 1 NexTeracom Building, Cybercity, Ebene, Mauritius
Tel.: (230) 454 7367
Web Site:
   http://www.4sightholdings.com
Holding Company
N.A.I.C.S.: 551112
Wilhelm Swart *(Co-Chief IT Officer)*

5. OKTOBAR A.D.
Zrenjaninski put bb, Srpska Crnja, Serbia
Tel.: (381) 23 811 747
Year Founded: 1993
Sales Range: Less than $1 Million
Emp.: 1
Construction Product Mfr
N.A.I.C.S.: 327331

500.COM LIMITED (Name Changed to BIT Mining Ltd.)

500VOLT INC
31 Teheran-ro 30-gil Gangnam-gu, Seoul, 06223, Korea (South)
Tel.: (82) 25701903
Web Site: http://www.500v.co.kr
Bio Energy Services
N.A.I.C.S.: 513120

502386 ALBERTA LTD
888 Meridian Road NE, Calgary, T2A 2N8, AB, Canada
Tel.: (403) 291-1444
Web Site: https://www.tandthonda.ca
Year Founded: 1983
Rev.: $46,314,400
Emp.: 100
New & Used Car Dealers
N.A.I.C.S.: 441110

51 CREDIT CARD INC.
Building B3 CECEP Xixi Center No 588 Wenyi West Road, Xihu, Hangzhou, Zhejiang, China   Ky
Web Site: https://www.u51.com
Year Founded: 2012
2051—(HKG)
Rev.: $30,067,291
Assets: $161,299,014
Liabilities: $63,053,279
Net Worth: $98,245,735
Earnings: ($435,866)
Emp.: 309
Fiscal Year-end: 12/31/23
Investment Management Service
N.A.I.C.S.: 523999
Haitao Sun *(CEO)*

51JOB, INC.
Building 3 No 1387 Zhang Dong Road, Shanghai, 201203, China
Tel.: (86) 2161601888   Ky
Web Site: http://www.51job.com
Year Founded: 1997
JOBS—(NASDAQ)
Rev.: $565,184,183
Assets: $2,401,670,933
Liabilities: $473,028,674
Net Worth: $1,928,642,259
Earnings: $168,113,656
Emp.: 8,875
Fiscal Year-end: 12/31/20
Human Resource & Recruitment Related Services
N.A.I.C.S.: 541612
Rick Yan *(Co-Founder, Pres, CEO & Sec)*

51TALK ONLINE EDUCATION GROUP
6th Floor Deshi Building North Shangdi Street, Haidian District, Beijing, 100085, China
Tel.: (86) 1056928909
Web Site: http://www.51talk.com
Year Founded: 2011
COE—(NYSE)
Rev.: $15,048,000
Assets: $27,634,000
Liabilities: $21,057,000
Net Worth: $6,577,000
Earnings: ($42,556,000)
Emp.: 171
Fiscal Year-end: 12/31/22
Education Training Services
N.A.I.C.S.: 611630
Jack Jiajia Huang *(Co-Founder, Chm & CEO)*

52 WEEKS ENTERTAINMENT LIMITED
Tarabai Hall 97 Shivprasad Building, Marine Drive, Mumbai, 400 002, India
Tel.: (91) 22 22842127
Web Site: http://www.ssal.in
Year Founded: 1993
Sales Range: Less than $1 Million
Shrimp Hatchery & Shrimp Farming Services
N.A.I.C.S.: 112512
Surendra N. Morne *(Compliance Officer)*

524 PARTICIPACOES S.A.
Av Presidente Antonio Carlos n 51 10th floor pte, 20030021, Rio de Janeiro, 20020-010, Brazil
Tel.: (55) 2138043700
Web Site:
   http://www.524participacoes.com.br
Year Founded: 1997
QVQP3B—(BRAZ)
Sales Range: Less than $1 Million
Investment Management Service
N.A.I.C.S.: 523940

55 NORTH MINING INC.
646 Erin Street, Winnipeg, R3G 2V9, MB, Canada
Tel.: (204) 774-6771   Ca
Web Site:
  http://www.sgxresources.com
Year Founded: 2008
Sales Range: Less than $1 Million
Gold Mining Services
N.A.I.C.S.: 212220
Bruce Reid *(Pres & CEO)*

55 NORTH MINING, INC.
401 Bay Street Suite 2702, Toronto, M5H 2Y4, ON, Canada
Tel.: (416) 477-7771
Web Site: https://55northmining.com
Year Founded: 1937
FFF—(TSX)
Metal Mining Services
N.A.I.C.S.: 213114
Bruce D. Reid *(Pres & CEO)*

561870 ONTARIO LTD
460 McArthur Avenue, Ottawa, K1K 1G4, ON, Canada
Tel.: (613) 746-9646
Web Site:
  http://www.wallaceautomobiles.com
Year Founded: 1963
Rev.: $17,085,000
Emp.: 7
New & Used Car Dealers
N.A.I.C.S.: 441110
Bruce Wallace *(Owner)*

565 CONSTRUCTION JOINT STOCK COMPANY
Quiet Street Tan Thinh Ward, Hoa Binh, Vietnam
Tel.: (84) 2183854024
Web Site: http://www.tsc565.vn
Emp.: 320
Infrastructure Construction Services
N.A.I.C.S.: 237310
Toan Manh Nguyen *(Chm)*

577 INVESTMENT CORPORATION
Carina Plaza Building, 1648 Vo Van Kiet St Ward 16 District 8, Ho Chi Minh City, Vietnam
Tel.: (84) 862577577
Web Site: https://www.nbb.com.vn
Year Founded: 2005
NBB—(HOSE)
Rev.: $140,026,797
Assets: $163,628,498
Liabilities: $92,962,380
Net Worth: $70,666,117
Earnings: $13,091,647
Emp.: 134
Fiscal Year-end: 12/31/20
Real Estate Development Services
N.A.I.C.S.: 531390

Subsidiaries:

Quang Ngai Mineral Investment Joint Stock Company   **(1)**
Lot C1-3 Tinh Phong Industrial Zone, Tinh Phong Commune, Son Tinh, Quang Ngai, Vietnam
Tel.: (84) 553677777
Cane Sugar Mfr & Distr
N.A.I.C.S.: 311314

58.COM INC.
Building 105 10 Jiuxianqiao North Road Jia, Chaoyang District, Beijing, 100015, China
Tel.: (86) 10 5956 5858   Ky
Web Site: http://www.58.com
Year Founded: 2005
Rev.: $2,229,000,441
Assets: $6,205,132,394
Liabilities: $1,195,412,467
Net Worth: $5,009,719,928

Earnings: $1,184,612,423
Emp.: 21,743
Fiscal Year-end: 12/31/19
Online Retailer
N.A.I.C.S.: 531390
Hao Zhou *(Chief Strategic Officer, Pres-Bus-Intl & Head-IR)*

Subsidiaries:

Beijing 58 Daojia Information Technology Co., Ltd.   **(1)**
Tower E North America International Business Center, Yi 108 Beiyuan Road Chaoyang District, Beijing, China
Tel.: (86) 1064435588
Information Technology Consulting Services
N.A.I.C.S.: 541512

591182 ONTARIO LIMITED
2500 Airport Rd, Windsor, N8W 5E7, ON, Canada
Tel.: (519) 966-3333
Web Site:
  http://www.wolverinefreight.ca
Year Founded: 1984
Rev.: $40,625,562
Emp.: 300
Truckload & Milk Run Operation Services
N.A.I.C.S.: 484121
John LaMantia *(Principal)*

Subsidiaries:

Wolverine Warehousing & Distribution Limited   **(1)**
3950 Malden Road, Windsor, N9C 2G4, ON, Canada
Tel.: (519) 967-1097
General Warehousing & Distribution Services
N.A.I.C.S.: 493110

591226 SASKATCHEWAN LTD
110A Circle Drive East, Saskatoon, S7K 4K1, SK, Canada
Tel.: (306) 373-7477
Web Site: http://www.meidlhonda.ca
Year Founded: 1989
Rev.: $20,800,000
Emp.: 40
New & Used Vehicle Dealers
N.A.I.C.S.: 441110
John Rowan *(Gen Mgr)*

595242 BC LTD
3612 Island Highway North, Nanaimo, V9T 1W2, BC, Canada
Tel.: (250) 756-1515
Web Site:
  http://www.newcastlenissan.com
Year Founded: 1975
Rev.: $13,677,000
Emp.: 19
New & Used Car Dealers
N.A.I.C.S.: 441110
Jim Revenberg *(Pres)*

598755 B.C. LTD
19447 Langley Bypass, Surrey, V3S 6K1, BC, Canada
Tel.: (604) 539-2111
Web Site:
  http://www.acuraoflangley.com
Year Founded: 1995
Rev.: $13,292,400
Emp.: 30
New & Used Car Dealers
N.A.I.C.S.: 441110
Gary Daviduk *(Gen Mgr-Sls)*

5G NETWORKS LIMITED
Level 7 505 Little Collins St, Melbourne, 3000, VIC, Australia
Tel.: (61) 1300101112   AU
Web Site: https://5gnetworks.au
Year Founded: 2000
5GN—(ASX)
Rev.: $35,304,487

Assets: $67,930,021
Liabilities: $32,803,819
Net Worth: $35,126,202
Earnings: ($18,701,923)
Emp.: 180
Fiscal Year-end: 06/30/24
Offices of Other Holding Companies
N.A.I.C.S.: 551112
Brett Fenton *(CEO)*

Subsidiaries:

5G Network Operations Pty., Ltd.   **(1)**
Level 7 505 Little Collins St, Melbourne, 3000, VIC, Australia
Tel.: (61) 130010111
Web Site: https://5gnetworks.au
Telecommunication Servicesb
N.A.I.C.S.: 517810

5G Networks Holdings Pty. Ltd.   **(1)**
Level 8 99 William Street, Melbourne, 3000, VIC, Australia
Tel.: (61) 1300101112
Web Site: https://5gnetworks.au
Wireless Communication Carriers
N.A.I.C.S.: 517112
Albert Cheok *(Chm)*

Subsidiary (Domestic):

Anittel Group Limited   **(2)**
Level 10 9 Hunter Street, Sydney, 2000, NSW, Australia
Tel.: (61) 1300101112
Web Site: http://www.anittel.com.au
Holding Company; Information Technology Management & Consulting Services
N.A.I.C.S.: 551112
James Demirok *(Mgr-Bus Dev)*

Subsidiary (Domestic):

Anittel Pty. Ltd.   **(3)**
Level 10 9 Hunter Street, Sydney, 2000, NSW, Australia
Tel.: (61) 1300101112
Web Site: http://www.anittel.com.au
Sales Range: $25-49.9 Million
Emp.: 54
Information Technology Management & Consulting Services
N.A.I.C.S.: 541690
Vincent Pesquet *(CEO)*

Domainz Ltd   **(1)**
40 Mercer Street, Wellington, 6011, New Zealand
Tel.: (64) 98879824
Web Site: https://www.domainz.net.nz
Web Hosting Services
N.A.I.C.S.: 518210

Intergrid Group Pty. Ltd.   **(1)**
Level 7 505 Little Collins St, Melbourne, VIC, Australia
Tel.: (61) 1300351609
Web Site: https://intergrid.au
Cloud Infrastructure Services
N.A.I.C.S.: 518210

Melbourne IT GP Holdings Pty. Ltd.   **(1)**
505 Little Collins Street, Melbourne, VIC, Australia
Tel.: (61) 1300654677
Web Site: https://www.melbourneit.au
Digital Marketing Services
N.A.I.C.S.: 541613

WebCentral Group Pty Ltd   **(1)**
Level 5 100 Wickham Street, Fortitude Valley, 4006, QLD, Australia
Tel.: (61) 732307201
Web Site: http://www.webcentral.com.au
Web Hosting Services
N.A.I.C.S.: 518210

5I5J HOLDING GROUP CO., LTD.
Building No 7 Yard No 8 Beichen East Road, Chaoyang District, Beijing, 100101, China
Tel.: (86) 1053918088
Web Site: http://000560.5i5j.com
Year Founded: 1992
000560—(SSE)

Sales Range: $250-299.9 Million
Holding Company; Department Store Operator
N.A.I.C.S.: 551112
Yong Xie *(Chm & Pres)*

5N PLUS INC.
4385 Garand Street, Montreal, H4R 2B4, QC, Canada
Tel.: (514) 856-0644
Web Site: https://www.5nplus.com
Year Founded: 2000
FPLSF—(OTCIQ)
Rev.: $264,223,000
Assets: $347,985,000
Liabilities: $235,209,000
Net Worth: $112,776,000
Earnings: $22,999,000)
Emp.: 800
Fiscal Year-end: 12/31/22
Specialty Metal & Chemical Product Mfr
N.A.I.C.S.: 332999
Richard Perron *(CFO)*

Subsidiaries:

5N PV Gmbh   **(1)**
Oderlandstrasse 104, 15890, Eisenhuttenstadt, Germany
Tel.: (49) 3364 769 480
Chemical Products Distr
N.A.I.C.S.: 424690

5N Plus Asia Limited   **(1)**
8/F to 14/F New York House 60 Connaught Road, Central, China (Hong Kong)
Tel.: (852) 2 541 6122
Web Site: http://www.5nplus.com
Chemical Products Distr
N.A.I.C.S.: 424690

5N Plus Belgium SA   **(1)**
Rue de la Station 7, 1495, Tilly, Belgium
Tel.: (32) 71 87 88 21
Emp.: 19
Chemical Products Distr
N.A.I.C.S.: 424690
Desclee Xavier *(Dir-Administration)*

5N Plus Lubeck Gmbh   **(1)**
Kaninchenborn 24-28, 23560, Lubeck, Germany
Tel.: (49) 451 530040
Chemical Products Distr
N.A.I.C.S.: 424690

5N Plus UK Limited   **(1)**
1-4 Nielson Road Finedon Road Industrial Estate, Wellingborough, NN8 4PE, Northants, United Kingdom
Tel.: (44) 1933 225766
Web Site: http://www.5nplus.com
Emp.: 50
Chemical Products Distr
N.A.I.C.S.: 424690

5N Plus Wisconsin Inc   **(1)**
6474 Blanchar's Crossing, De Forest, WI 53598
Tel.: (608) 846-1357
Chemical Products Distr
N.A.I.C.S.: 424690

Azur Space Solar Power GmbH   **(1)**
Theresienstr 2, 74072, Heilbronn, Germany   **(100%)**
Tel.: (49) 713 167 2603
Web Site: https://www.azurspace.com
Emp.: 200
Solar Cell Mfr & Whlsr
N.A.I.C.S.: 334413
Jurgen Heizmann *(Mng Dir)*

5PAISA CAPITAL LTD.
Sun Infotech Park Road No 16V Plot No B-23, Thane Industrial Area Wagle Estate, Thane, 400604, India
Tel.: (91) 8976689766
Web Site: https://www.5paisa.com
Year Founded: 2016
540776—(BOM)
Rev.: $40,674,407
Assets: $219,568,986
Liabilities: $168,521,399

5paisa Capital Ltd.—(Continued)

Net Worth: $51,047,588
Earnings: $1,874,964
Emp.: 518
Fiscal Year-end: 03/31/22
Financial Advisory Services
N.A.I.C.S.: 523940
Prakarsh Gagdani *(CEO)*

5TH PLANET GAMES A/S

Gothersgade 11, 1123, Copenhagen, K, Denmark
Tel.: (45) 7833690674
Web Site:
https://www.5thplanetgames.com
Year Founded: 2011
5PG—(OSL)
Rev.: $1,445,769
Assets: $13,519,508
Liabilities: $871,104
Net Worth: $12,648,404
Earnings: $3,634,116
Emp.: 3
Fiscal Year-end: 12/31/23
Mobile Gaming & Licensing
N.A.I.C.S.: 513210
Peter Ekman *(Chief Acctg Officer)*

5V INC.

Floor 12 Bldg 5 Zhongchuang Plaza No 396 Tongjiang Zhong Road, Xinbei District, Changzhou, Jiangshu, China
Tel.: (86) 13510608355
Year Founded: 2010
Sales Range: Less than $1 Million
Investment Services
N.A.I.C.S.: 523999
Jun Jiang *(Chm & Pres)*

600956 ONTARIO LTD

469 Woodward Avenue, Hamilton, L8H 6N6, ON, Canada
Tel.: (905) 549-4572
Web Site: http://www.plasticsplus.ca
Year Founded: 1984
Rev.: $10,433,394
Emp.: 70
Plastic Injection Molding Mfr & Automotive Supplier
N.A.I.C.S.: 326199
Larry Mermuys *(Founder & Pres)*

602390 ONTARIO LIMITED

81 Scott Field Drive, Scarborough, M1S 5R4, ON, Canada
Tel.: (416) 740-9000
Web Site:
http://www.oceanseafood.ca
Year Founded: 1984
Rev.: $34,680,440
Emp.: 40
Seafood Whslr & Distr
N.A.I.C.S.: 311710
Patrick Lay *(Founder & Pres)*

615315 SASKATCHEWAN LTD

875 58th Street East, Saskatoon, S7K 6X5, SK, Canada
Tel.: (306) 653-5400
Web Site:
http://www.jbmlogistics.com
Rev.: $12,618,568
Emp.: 75
Truckload Transportation & Services
N.A.I.C.S.: 484121
Lindsay Keene *(Pres & Gen Mgr)*

63 MOONS TECHNOLOGIES LIMITED

FT Tower CTS No 256 and 257 Suren Road, Chakala Andheri East, Mumbai, 400093, Maharashtra, India
Tel.: (91) 912266861010
Web Site: https://www.63moons.com
Year Founded: 1988

526881—(BOM)
Rev.: $31,376,573
Assets: $459,777,605
Liabilities: $39,733,935
Net Worth: $420,043,670
Earnings: ($7,258,169)
Emp.: 694
Fiscal Year-end: 03/31/22
Next-generation Technology Ventures, Innovations & Platforms; IP & Domain Provider
N.A.I.C.S.: 541511
Jignesh P. Shah *(Co-Founder)*

Subsidiaries:

FT Knowledge Management Company Limited   (1)
FT Tower CTS No 256 & 257 Suren Road, Chakala Andheri E, Mumbai, 400093, Maharashtra, India
Tel.: (91) 2267318888
Sales Range: $50-74.9 Million
Emp.: 40
Financial Consulting Services
N.A.I.C.S.: 523999
Bandi Ram Prasad *(Pres)*

ICX Platform (Pty) Ltd.   (1)
3-5 Flemming Road, Bryanston, 2021, Gauteng, South Africa
Tel.: (27) 117062011
Web Site: https://www.icxafrica.com
Sales Range: $50-74.9 Million
Emp.: 2
Commodities Exchange Services
N.A.I.C.S.: 523210

National Bulk Handling Corporation   (1)
5th Floor Richa 9 Plot No 56 Road No 17 MIDC, Andheri East, Mumbai, 400 093, Maharashtra, India
Tel.: (91) 2245101000
Web Site: https://www.nbhcindia.com
Sales Range: $350-399.9 Million
Emp.: 1,000
Commodity & Collateral Management Services
N.A.I.C.S.: 523160
Anil K. Choudhary *(Vice Chm)*

National Spot Exchange Limited   (1)
Malkani Chambers 1st Floor Off Nehru Road Near Hotel Orchid, Ville Parle E, Mumbai, 400 099, Maharashtra, India
Tel.: (91) 2267619900
Web Site:
https://www.nationalspotexchange.com
Sales Range: $25-49.9 Million
Emp.: 100
Electronic Spot Trading Services
N.A.I.C.S.: 238990
Neeraj Sharma *(Sr VP)*

Subsidiary (Domestic):

Indian Bullion Market Association Limited   (2)
Malkani Chambers 3rd Floor Opp Air Link Hotel Off Nehru Road, Vile Parle E, Mumbai, 400 099, Maharashtra, India
Tel.: (91) 2267619900
Web Site: https://www.ibma.co.in
Sales Range: $50-74.9 Million
Emp.: 15
Bullion Market Services
N.A.I.C.S.: 523160

TickerPlant Limited   (1)
FT Tower 4th Floor CTS No 256 257 Suren Road Chakala, Andheri East, Mumbai, 400 093, Maharashtra, India
Tel.: (91) 2266866060
Web Site: https://www.tickerplantindia.com
Financial Information Software Publishing Services
N.A.I.C.S.: 513210
Arindam Saha *(Co-CEO)*

Westernghats Agro Growers Company Limited   (1)
28/715-B 1st Floor Thulasi K P Vallon Road, Kadavanthara, Cochin, 682020, Kerala, India
Tel.: (91) 944 655 1961
Web Site: https://www.wgagl.com
Agricultural Services

N.A.I.C.S.: 115116

66 RESOURCES CORP.
(See Under Nexus Uranium Corp.)

668824 ALBERTA LTD

46 Crowfoot Circle NW, Calgary, T3G 2T3, AB, Canada
Tel.: (403) 208-2487
Web Site: https://www.visions.ca
Year Founded: 1981
Emp.: 800
Electronics Stores
N.A.I.C.S.: 449210
Richard Stewart *(Founder)*

669069 ALBERTA LTD

901 11th Ave SE, High River, T1V 1P2, AB, Canada
Tel.: (403) 652-1365
Web Site:
http://www.highrivertoyota.ca
Year Founded: 1993
Rev.: $13,911,192
Emp.: 30
New & Used Car Dealers
N.A.I.C.S.: 441110
Saleem Budhwani *(Dir-Ops)*

7-ELEVEN MALAYSIA HOLDINGS BERHAD

Level 3A Podium Block Plaza Berjaya, No 12 Jalan Imbi, 55100, Kuala Lumpur, Malaysia
Tel.: (60) 321421136
Web Site:
https://www.7eleven.com.my
Year Founded: 1984
SEM—(KLS)
Rev.: $796,672,804
Assets: $566,608,889
Liabilities: $517,880,635
Net Worth: $48,728,254
Earnings: $17,847,196
Emp.: 10,511
Fiscal Year-end: 12/31/22
Convenience Store Owner & Operator
N.A.I.C.S.: 445131
U-Ming Tan *(Exec Dir)*

Subsidiaries:

Convenience Shopping (Sabah) Sdn. Bhd.   (1)
12th Floor Menara Symphony No 5 Jalan Prof Khoo Kay Kim Seksyen 13, 46200, Petaling Jaya, Selangor, Malaysia
Tel.: (60) 32142 1136
Convenience Store Operator
N.A.I.C.S.: 445131

Tonic Pharma Sdn. Bhd.   (1)
No 158 Ground Floor Jalan PSK 3 Pekan Simpang Kuala, 5400, Alor Setar, Kedah, Malaysia
Tel.: (60) 47716628
Web Site: https://my521208-realcare-pharmacy-k-sdn-bhd.contact.page
Cargo Logistics Services
N.A.I.C.S.: 488320

7-ELEVEN STORES PTY. LTD.

357 Ferntree Gully Road, Mount Waverley, 3149, VIC, Australia
Tel.: (61) 395410711
Web Site: http://www.7eleven.com.au
Sales Range: $550-599.9 Million
Emp.: 183
Convenience Store Operator
N.A.I.C.S.: 445131
Michael Smith *(Chm)*

7. JULI A.D.

Medunarodni put bb, 21214, Sirig, Serbia
Tel.: (381) 21 2949 632

Web Site: http://www.7juli-sirig.rs
Year Founded: 1990
Sales Range: Less than $1 Million
Emp.: 36
Wheat Farming Services
N.A.I.C.S.: 111140

7. JULI MAJKE JEVROSIME 47-49 A.D.

Majke Jevrosima 47-49, Belgrade, Serbia
Tel.: (381) 113043640
Web Site: http://www.7juli.rs
Year Founded: 1950
SJLB—(BEL)
Sales Range: Less than $1 Million
Emp.: 13
Automobile Whslr
N.A.I.C.S.: 423110
Biserka Pavlovic *(Exec Dir & Dir)*

714607 ONTARIO LTD.

4445 Harvester Rd, Burlington, L7L 4X1, ON, Canada
Tel.: (905) 681-8755
Year Founded: 1985
Rev.: $17,657,452
Emp.: 12
Food Mfr, Whslr & Distr
N.A.I.C.S.: 311999
John Katsiris *(Owner)*

723926 ONTARIO LIMITED

880 Farewell st, Oshawa, L1H 6N6, ON, Canada
Tel.: (905) 683-4463
Web Site: http://www.jjmcguire.com
Year Founded: 1987
Rev.: $14,519,807
Emp.: 50
Building Construction Services
N.A.I.C.S.: 236210
Mitch Newbold *(VP-Ops)*

733907 ONTARIO LTD

14 Westwyn Court, Brampton, L6T 4T5, ON, Canada
Tel.: (905) 453-6060
Web Site:
http://www.europeanmeats.com
Year Founded: 1959
Rev.: $40,000,000
Emp.: 225
Meat Products Mfr & Distr
N.A.I.C.S.: 424470
Morris Leider *(Founder & Pres)*

734758 ONTARIO LIMITED

3100 Ridgeway Dr Unit 16, Mississauga, L5L 5M5, ON, Canada
Tel.: (905) 820-2266
Web Site:
http://www.huntingtontravel.net
Year Founded: 1973
Rev.: $20,829,000
Emp.: 60
Tour & Travel Agency Services
N.A.I.C.S.: 561520
Kiran Budhdev *(Pres)*

786 INVESTMENTS LIMITED

G3 Ground Floor BRR tower Hassan Ali Street Off I I Chundrigarh Road, Karachi, Pakistan
Tel.: (92) 21111329663
Web Site:
https://www.786investments.com
Year Founded: 1990
786—(PSX)
Rev.: $90,457
Assets: $1,545,522
Liabilities: $116,414
Net Worth: $1,429,108
Earnings: $20,299
Emp.: 9
Fiscal Year-end: 06/30/21
Investment Management Service

N.A.I.C.S.: 525990
Tara Uzra Dawood *(CEO)*

79 RESOURCES LTD.
Suite 1240 789 W Pender Street,
Vancouver, V6C 1H2, BC, Canada
Tel.: (604) 683-3995
Web Site:
    https://www.79resources.com
SNR—(CNSX)
Assets: $494,144
Liabilities: $10,301
Net Worth: $483,843
Earnings: ($153,626)
Fiscal Year-end: 12/31/22
Mineral Exploration & Mining Services
N.A.I.C.S.: 213115
Steven Feldman *(CEO)*

79NORTH, INC. (Acquired by
Miata Metals Corp.)

7C SOLARPARKEN AG
An der Feuerwache 15, 95445, Bayreuth, Germany
Tel.: (49) 92123055777
Web Site:
    https://www.solarparken.com
HRPK—(MUN)
Rev.: $77,072,203
Assets: $622,980,073
Liabilities: $368,769,851
Net Worth: $254,210,222
Earnings: $11,127,010
Emp.: 23
Fiscal Year-end: 12/31/23
Large-Scale Photovoltaic System
Developer
N.A.I.C.S.: 334419
Steven De Proost *(CEO)*

Subsidiaries:

7C Solarparken Belgium B.V.   (1)
Houten Schoen 79, 9100, Saint-Niklaas,
Belgium
Tel.: (32) 92429230
Web Site: https://7csolarparken.eu
Solar Panels Installation Services
N.A.I.C.S.: 237130

7C Solarparken NV   (1)
Battelsesteenweg 455E, 2800, Mechelen,
Belgium
Tel.: (32) 15433155
Solar Component Distr
N.A.I.C.S.: 423690
Guy Noerens *(Mgr-IR)*

GSI Leasing GmbH   (1)
Dr-Wilke-Strasse 12, 63571, Gelnhausen,
Germany
Tel.: (49) 60519121370
Web Site: https://gs-leasing.de
Information Technology Services
N.A.I.C.S.: 541519

Renewagy A/S   (1)
Kongevejen 2100, 2100, Virum, Denmark
Tel.: (45) 43331343
Web Site: http://www.renewagy.com
Sales Range: $1-9.9 Million
Emp.: 4
Investment Services
N.A.I.C.S.: 523940

**7DAYS GROUP GMBH & CO.
KG**
Am Martinszehnten 13, 60437, Frankfurt am Main, Germany
Tel.: (49) 69 50004 222
Web Site: http://www.7days-
    group.com
Emp.: 275
Holding Company
N.A.I.C.S.: 551112
Thomas Kirschner *(Chm-Mgmt Bd &
CEO)*

Subsidiaries:

7Days Media Services GmbH   (1)
Riedstrasse 4, 4132, Egerkingen, Switzerland
Tel.: (41) 58 470 20 00
Web Site: http://www.7days-media.ch
Printed Media Distr & Logistics Services
N.A.I.C.S.: 541614
Thomas Kirschner *(Mng Dir)*

Gull GmbH   (1)
Heuriedweg 19, Lindau, 88131, Germany
Tel.: (49) 83 82 96 310
Web Site: http://www.guell-presseservice.de
Emp.: 150
Magazine Publishing Services
N.A.I.C.S.: 424920
Bernd Robke *(Mng Dir & Exec Dir)*

7FC LLP
71-75 Shelton Street, Covent Garden,
London, WC2H 9JQ, United Kingdom
Tel.: (44) 204 509 1149
Web Site: http://7fc.co.uk
Year Founded: 2020
Package Software Services
N.A.I.C.S.: 513210
Arfah Malik *(Partner)*

Subsidiaries:

Styles & Wood Limited   (1)
Aspect House Manchester Road, Altrincham, WA14 5PG, Cheshire, United
Kingdom   **(100%)**
Tel.: (44) 1619266000
Web Site: http://isite.co.uk
Sales Range: $75-99.9 Million
Emp.: 150
Commercial Property Development & Management Services
N.A.I.C.S.: 531312
Tony Lenehan *(CEO)*

7NR RETAIL LIMITED
Godown No-1 234/1234/2FP-69/3
Sadashiv Kanto B/h Bajaj Process,
Narol Chokdi Narol, Ahmedabad,
382405, India
Tel.: (91) 6351867039
Web Site: https://www.7nrretailltd.in
Year Founded: 2012
540615—(BOM)
Rev.: $3,316,063
Assets: $2,823,584
Liabilities: $1,346,941
Net Worth: $1,476,643
Earnings: $104,655
Emp.: 19
Fiscal Year-end: 03/31/22
Textile Products Distr
N.A.I.C.S.: 458110
Pinal Shah *(Chm & Mng Dir)*

7ROAD HOLDINGS LIMITED
No 2-18-1902 Long Shan Road, Xin
Wu, Wuxi, Jiangsu, China
Tel.: (86) 75589799777   Ky
0797—(HKG)
Rev.: $75,904,452
Assets: $371,517,775
Liabilities: $104,638,856
Net Worth: $266,878,919
Earnings: $39,256,682
Emp.: 424
Fiscal Year-end: 12/31/22
Holding Company
N.A.I.C.S.: 551112
Shuqi Meng *(Chm, CEO & Co-Chief
Production Officer)*

7SEAS ENTERTAINMENT LIMITED
5th Floor Plot No 92 93 94, Kavuri
Hills Madhapur, Hyderabad, 500 033,
Telangana, India
Tel.: (91) 4049533636
Web Site: https://www.7seasent.com

Year Founded: 2006
Rev.: $209,024
Assets: $1,915,333
Liabilities: $1,086,103
Net Worth: $829,229
Earnings: $14,232
Fiscal Year-end: 03/31/18
Mobile Games Publisher & Distr
N.A.I.C.S.: 459120
L. Maruti Sanker *(Mng Dir)*

7THSENSE DESIGN LIMITED
2 The Courtyard Shoreham Road Upper Beeding, Horsham, BN44 3TN,
West Sussex, United Kingdom
Tel.: (44) 1903812299
Web Site: http://7thsensedesign.com
Year Founded: 2004
Software Publisher
N.A.I.C.S.: 513210
Matt Barton *(CEO & Mng Dir)*

Subsidiaries:

Medialon Inc.   (1)
245 Catalonia Ave, Coral Gables, FL
33134-0000
Tel.: (305) 445-4045
Web Site: http://www.medialon.com
Software Publisher
N.A.I.C.S.: 513210
Medialon Showmaster *(Mgr-Medialon Show
& Media Control Software)*

8. NOVEMBAR A.D.
Stojana Ljubica 33, 16230, Lebane,
Serbia
Tel.: (381) 16 844 480
Year Founded: 2002
ONOL—(BEL)
Sales Range: Less than $1 Million
Emp.: 2
Food Store Operator
N.A.I.C.S.: 445110
Gordana Radoicic *(Exec Dir)*

845453 ONTARIO LTD
959 McGill Street, Hawkesbury, K6A
3K8, ON, Canada
Tel.: (613) 632-4125
Web Site:
    http://www.hawkesburymazda.com
Rev.: $19,320,131
Emp.: 28
New & Used Car Dealers
N.A.I.C.S.: 441110
Christian Joanisse *(Pres)*

866229 ONTARIO INC.
1401 Seymour St, North Bay, P1B
8G4, ON, Canada
Tel.: (705) 476-0206
Web Site:
    http://www.northernhonda.com
Rev.: $22,750,595
Emp.: 28
New & Used Car Dealers
N.A.I.C.S.: 441110
David Barber *(Partner & Gen Mgr)*

88 ENERGY LIMITED
Ground Floor 516 Hay Street, Subiaco, 6008, WA, Australia
Tel.: (61) 894850990
Web Site: http://88energy.com
EEENF—(OTCIQ)
Rev.: $14,527
Assets: $88,808,080
Liabilities: $901,172
Net Worth: $87,906,908
Earnings: ($47,213,952)
Emp.: 10
Fiscal Year-end: 12/31/22
Oil & Gas Exploration Services
N.A.I.C.S.: 211120
Sarah Smith *(Sec)*

Subsidiaries:

XCD Energy Pty Ltd   (1)
Level 1 35 Outram Street, Perth, 6005, WA,
Australia
Tel.: (61) 8 9381 4975
Oil & Gas Exploration
N.A.I.C.S.: 211120

89419 BC LTD
3401-48th Avenue, Vernon, V1T
9W1, BC, Canada
Tel.: (250) 545-0687
Web Site:
    https://www.vernontoyota.com
Year Founded: 1970
Rev.: $11,042,009
Emp.: 40
New & Used Car Dealers
N.A.I.C.S.: 441110

898984 ONTARIO INC
8051 Keele Street Unit 6-7, Vaughan,
L4K 1Y9, ON, Canada
Tel.: (905) 883-8638
Web Site:
    http://www.richmondhillfinecars.com
Rev.: $12,004,500
Emp.: 6
Used Car Dealers
N.A.I.C.S.: 441120
Patrick Ng *(Owner)*

8990 HOLDINGS, INC.
Unit 1104 Liberty Center 104 HV dela
Costa Street, Salcedo Village, Makati,
1227, Philippines
Tel.: (63) 284789659
Web Site:
    https://www.8990holdings.com
Year Founded: 2005
HOUSE—(PHI)
Rev.: $423,440,735
Assets: $1,862,802,898
Liabilities: $898,533,165
Net Worth: $964,269,733
Earnings: $150,070,590
Emp.: 370
Fiscal Year-end: 12/31/21
IT & Telecommunication Services
N.A.I.C.S.: 517810
Anthony Vincent S. Sotto *(Gen Mgr-
Post Takeout, Legal, Credit & Collection)*

Subsidiaries:

8990 Housing Development
Corp.   (1)
2nd Flr PGMC Bldg 76 Calbayog cor DM
Guevarra St, Mandaluyong, 1550, Philippines
Tel.: (63) 2 533 3915
Web Site: http://8990housing.com
Sales Range: $150-199.9 Million
Housing Development & Construction Services
N.A.I.C.S.: 236116
Anthony Vincent S. Sotto *(Gen Mgr-Ops)*

8I ACQUISITION 2 CORP.
(Name Changed to EUDA
Health Holdings Limited)

8IP EMERGING COMPANIES LIMITED (Name
Changed to Lanyon Investment Company Limited)

8K MILES SOFTWARE SERVICES LTD (Name Changed
to Securekloud Technologies
Ltd.)

8VIC HOLDINGS LIMITED

8990 Holdings, Inc.—(Continued)

(See Under 8VI Holdings Limited).

8COMMON LIMITED
Level 4 15 Moore Street, Canberra, 2601, NSW, Australia
Tel.: (61) 283280505　　　AU
Web Site: https://www.8common.com
Year Founded: 2014
8CO—(ASX)
Rev.: $5,495,533
Assets: $2,101,096
Liabilities: $1,822,441
Net Worth: $278,656
Earnings: ($1,701,615)
Fiscal Year-end: 06/30/24
Software Publisher
N.A.I.C.S.: 513210
Kah Wui Lim (Founder, Chm & Mng Dir)

Subsidiaries:

CardHero Pty. Ltd.　　　　　　(1)
PO Box 21022, World Square, Sydney, 2002, NSW, Australia
Tel.: (61) 283280505
Web Site: https://www.cardhero.co
Digital Payment Solution Services
N.A.I.C.S.: 522320

8I ENTERPRISES ACQUISITION CORP
6 Eu Tong Sen Street 08-13 The Central, Singapore, 059817, Singapore
Tel.: (65) 67880388　　　VG
Web Site: http://www.8icorp.com
Year Founded: 2017
JFKKU—(NASDAQ)
Rev.: $508,250
Assets: $59,324,673
Liabilities: $54,324,657
Net Worth: $5,000,016
Earnings: ($843,899)
Emp.: 2
Fiscal Year-end: 07/31/20
Investment Services
N.A.I.C.S.: 523999
James Meng Dong Tan (CEO)

8I HOLDINGS LIMITED
1557 Keppel Road 01-01, Singapore, 89066, Singapore
Tel.: (65) 68014500　　　SG
Web Site: https://www.8iholdings.com
Year Founded: 2008
8IH—(ASX)
Rev.: $12,078,307
Assets: $25,349,097
Liabilities: $12,410,200
Net Worth: $12,938,897
Earnings: ($10,955,180)
Emp.: 48
Fiscal Year-end: 03/31/23
Holding Company
N.A.I.C.S.: 551112
Ken Kuan Tat Chee (Co-Founder & Chm)

Subsidiaries:

Hidden Champions Capital Management Pte. Ltd.　　　　　　(1)
47 Scotts Road Goldbell Towers 03-03, Singapore, 228233, Singapore
Tel.: (65) 68014505
Web Site:
　http://www.hiddenchampionsfund.com
Investment Management Service
N.A.I.C.S.: 523940
Che Koon Tan (CEO)

8TELECOM INTERNATIONAL HOLDINGS CO. LTD.
6/F and Units A and B 18/F Tianyun Building 508 Wensan Road, Hangzhou, Zhejiang, China

Tel.: (86) 57188225288　　　BM
Web Site: http://www.8telecom.cn
Year Founded: 1997
Sales Range: Less than $1 Million
Investment Holding Services
N.A.I.C.S.: 523940
Tianyun Ye (Founder, Chm & CEO)

Subsidiaries:

Arete M Pte. Ltd.　　　　　　(1)
20 Sin Ming Lane Midview City 03-63, Singapore, 573968, Singapore
Tel.: (65) 63340314
Web Site: http://aretem.sg
Information Communication Services
N.A.I.C.S.: 541512

8VI HOLDINGS LIMITED
1557 Keppel Road 01-01, Singapore, 089066, Singapore
Tel.: (65) 62258480　　　SG
Web Site:
　https://www.8viholdings.com
Year Founded: 2008
8VI—(ASX)
Rev.: $7,817,996
Assets: $6,189,346
Liabilities: $3,358,770
Net Worth: $2,830,576
Earnings: ($355,786)
Fiscal Year-end: 03/31/24
Internet Advertising
N.A.I.C.S.: 541890
Ken Chee (Co-Founder, CEO & Exec Dir)

Subsidiaries:

8VIC Malaysia Sdn. Bhd.　　　(1)
17 19 Level 6 The Boulevard Offices, Mid Valley City, 59200, Kuala Lumpur, Malaysia
Tel.: (60) 322018089
Financial Education Services
N.A.I.C.S.: 523940

Subsidiary (Domestic):

8VIC JooY Media Sdn. Bhd.　　(2)
17 and 19 Level 6 The Boulevard Office Mid Valley City, 59200 Kuala Lumpur, Malaysia
Tel.: (60) 32 201 8089
Web Site: https://www.jooymedia.com
Motion Picture Services
N.A.I.C.S.: 512110

9 CAPITAL CORP. (Name Changed to Churchill Resources Inc.)

9039-7571 QUEBEC INC
9425 Boul Taschereau, Brossard, J4Y 2J3, QC, Canada
Tel.: (450) 659-6688
Web Site:
　http://www.volvobrossard.net
Rev.: $11,943,690
Emp.: 35
New & Used Car Dealers
N.A.I.C.S.: 441110

9083-7436 QUEBEC INC.
250 Henry-Bessemer, Terrebonne, J6Y 1T3, QC, Canada
Tel.: (450) 965-0200
Web Site: http://www.drytec.ca
Year Founded: 1997
Rev.: $11,136,682
Emp.: 60
Metal Surface Treatment & Corrosion Protection Services
N.A.I.C.S.: 332312
Francois Desmarais (Gen Mgr)

9101-9091 QUEBEC INC.
1610 Place de Lierre, Laval, H7G 4X7, QC, Canada
Tel.: (450) 669-1311
Web Site: http://www.mondoux.ca

Year Founded: 1967
Rev.: $20,000,000
Emp.: 100
Candy Importer, Mfr & Distr
N.A.I.C.S.: 311351
Normand Mondoux (Founder)

9116-4509 QUEBEC INC
271 Rue Saint-Jacques South, Coaticook, J1A 2P3, QC, Canada
Tel.: (819) 849-2786
Web Site: http://www.tpiplastics.com
Rev.: $23,186,357
Emp.: 219
Plastic Products Mfr & Retailer
N.A.I.C.S.: 325211
Angy Potvin (CEO)

9119-6832 QUEBEC INC
1 Chemin des Iles, Levis, G6W 8B6, QC, Canada
Tel.: (418) 835-6161
Web Site:
　http://www.paquetmitsubishi.com
Rev.: $12,751,926
Emp.: 14
New & Used Car Dealers
N.A.I.C.S.: 441110
Donald Marcotte (Mgr-New Vehicle Sls)

9164-4187 QUEBEC INC.
1111 Saint-Urbain - Suite 205, Montreal, H2Z 1Y6, QC, Canada
Tel.: (514) 299-8914
Web Site: https://www.amadis.ca
Year Founded: 2005
Software Development Services
N.A.I.C.S.: 541512
Olivier Chauvineau (Co-Founder)

92 ENERGY LIMITED (Acquired by ATHA Energy Corp.)

941-2401 HEATING LIMITED
400 Richardson Rd, Orangeville, L9W 4W8, ON, Canada
Tel.: (519) 941-2401
Web Site:
　http://www.bryansfuel.on.ca
Year Founded: 1956
Rev.: $13,563,412
Emp.: 45
Home Heating & Comfort Oil Products Distr
N.A.I.C.S.: 457210
Glen Bryan (Founder)

942599 ONTARIO LIMITED
316 Guelph Street, Georgetown, L7G 4B5, ON, Canada
Tel.: (905) 874-3021
Web Site:
　http://www.georgetownhonda.ca
Rev.: $12,000,000
Emp.: 21
New & Used Car Dealers
N.A.I.C.S.: 441110
Russ Millar (Mgr-Lease Renewal)

957447 ALBERTA LTD
5104 55th Avenue NW, Edmonton, T6B 3C6, AB, Canada
Tel.: (780) 463-9939
Web Site:
　http://www.nwsconstruction.com
Year Founded: 1978
Rev.: $20,633,928
Emp.: 90
Pre-Engineered Building & Cladding Construction Service
N.A.I.C.S.: 332311
Bill Richard (Project Mgr)

966850 ONTARIO INC

100 Carson St Unit A, Toronto, M8W 3R9, ON, Canada
Tel.: (416) 644-1010
Web Site: http://www.christielites.com
Rev.: $22,800,000
Emp.: 92
Stage Lighting Services
N.A.I.C.S.: 541890
Michael Hawson (Treas)

970207 ONTARIO LIMITED
851 Hwy 7, Otonabee, K9J 6X7, ON, Canada
Tel.: (705) 748-2777
Web Site:
　http://www.trentvalleyhonda.com
Sales Range: $10-24.9 Million
Emp.: 38
New & Used Car Dealers
N.A.I.C.S.: 441110
Monika Carmichael (Gen Mgr)

979094 ALBERTA LTD
9605-34 Ave, Edmonton, T6E 5W8, AB, Canada
Tel.: (780) 465-5252
Web Site:
　http://www.southsidemitsubishi.com
Year Founded: 2002
Rev.: $18,519,274
Emp.: 40
New & Used Car Dealers
N.A.I.C.S.: 441110
Mike Lowton (Gen Mgr)

982874 ONTARIO LTD
3045 Glen Erin Dr, Mississauga, L5L 1J3, ON, Canada
Tel.: (905) 607-4000
Web Site:
　http://www.mississaugahyundai.ca
Rev.: $18,447,786
Emp.: 40
New & Used Car Dealers
N.A.I.C.S.: 441110
Scott Pollock (Sr Mgr-Sls)

988883 ONTARIO INC
1515 Lansdowne St W, Peterborough, K9J 7M3, ON, Canada
Tel.: (705) 741-5766
Web Site:
　http://www.kawarthachrysler.com
Rev.: $18,532,799
Emp.: 40
New & Used Car Dealers
N.A.I.C.S.: 441110
Gary Hinks (Mgr-Fin Svcs)

99 LOYALTY LIMITED
Level 26 56 Pitt Street, Sydney, 2000, NSW, Australia
Tel.: (61) 92762000
Web Site: http://www.99tech.com
99L—(ASX)
Rev.: $31,887,896
Assets: $77,159,930
Liabilities: $34,493,054
Net Worth: $42,666,876
Earnings: ($11,373,021)
Emp.: 145
Fiscal Year-end: 12/31/21
Mobile Online Platform
N.A.I.C.S.: 541810
Amalisia Zhang (Exec Dir)

Subsidiaries:

Shanghai Handpal Trading Co., Ltd.　　　　　　(1)
4F I&F Plaza No 80 Xin Chang Road, Shanghai, 200003, China
Tel.: (86) 18101877680
Financial Management Services
N.A.I.C.S.: 523999

9F INC.

Room 1607 Building No 5 5 West Laiguangying Road, Chaoyang District, Beijing, 100012, China
Tel.: (86) 1085276996　Ky
Web Site: https://www.9fgroup.com
Year Founded: 2006
JFU—(NASDAQ)
Rev.: $19,748,006
Assets: $559,266,033
Liabilities: $64,622,286
Net Worth: $494,643,747
Earnings: ($19,432,460)
Emp.: 276
Fiscal Year-end: 12/31/23
Holding Company
N.A.I.C.S.: 551112
Lei Sun (Chm & CEO)

9R LIMITED
20 Collyer Quay 11-07, Singapore, 49319, Singapore
Tel.: (65) 89288467
Web Site: https://www.9rlimited.com
1Y1—(CAT)
Rev.: $4,980,866
Assets: $14,036,700
Liabilities: $5,508,030
Net Worth: $8,528,670
Earnings: ($3,981,445)
Emp.: 53
Fiscal Year-end: 12/31/23
Heating, Air Conditioning & Refrigeration Systems Mfr
N.A.I.C.S.: 333415
Andy Lim (Chm)

Subsidiaries:

9R Canary Sdn. Bhd.　(1)
E-5-Ground Floor Detached office at Empire Damansara, Damansara Perdana, 47820, Petaling Jaya, Selangor, Malaysia
Tel.: (60) 376603991
Investment Holding Services
N.A.I.C.S.: 551112

9R Leisure Sdn. Bhd.　(1)
E-5-Ground Floor Detached office at Empire Damansara, Damansara Perdana, 47820, Petaling Jaya, Selangor, Malaysia
Tel.: (60) 376603991
Investment Holding Services
N.A.I.C.S.: 551112

9R Management Sdn. Bhd.　(1)
E-5-Ground Floor Detached office at Empire Damansara, Damansara Perdana, 47820, Petaling Jaya, Selangor, Malaysia
Tel.: (60) 377337189
Chain Management Services
N.A.I.C.S.: 541614

Compact Sensation Sdn. Bhd.　(1)
E-5 Ground Floor Detached office at Empire Damansara Damansara Perdana, 47820, Petaling Jaya, Selangor, Malaysia
Tel.: (60) 376603991
Entertainment Services
N.A.I.C.S.: 722410

Diverse Supply Chain (SG) Pte. Ltd.　(1)
20 Collyer Quay 11-07, Singapore, 049319, Singapore
Tel.: (65) 81689211
Web Site: https://www.keenonsingapore.sg
Robotic Product Mfr & Distr
N.A.I.C.S.: 333248

Diverse Supply Chain Sdn. Bhd.　(1)
E-5 Ground Floor Detached office at Empire Damansara Damansara Perdana, 47820, Petaling Jaya, Selangor, Malaysia
Tel.: (60) 377337189
Web Site: https://www.dscmy.com
Supply Chain Management Services
N.A.I.C.S.: 541614

Marshal Offshore & Marine Engrg Co., Ltd.　(1)
Unit 108 Building 12, China Nantong Industrial Exposition City, Nantong, 226000, Jiangsu, China
Tel.: (86) 51383580817
Fire Protection System Services

N.A.I.C.S.: 922160

Marshal Systems Pte. Ltd.　(1)
21 Kian Teck Rd, Singapore, 628773, Singapore　(100%)
Tel.: (65) 66019500
Web Site: http://www.marshal-systems.com
Sales Range: $25-49.9 Million
Emp.: 60
Marine Engineering Services
N.A.I.C.S.: 541330
Andy Lim (Chm)

Subsidiary (Non-US):

Marshal Offshore & Marine Engineering Co. Ltd.　(2)
20 Zhongnan Century City Unit 2204/2205, Nantong, 226007, Jiangsu, China
Tel.: (86) 513 8358 0817
Heating, Air Conditioning & Refrigeration Systems Mfr
N.A.I.C.S.: 333415

PT Viking Offshore　(1)
Jl Dr Sahardjo No 206C, Tebet, Jakarta, 12870, Indonesia
Tel.: (62) 2183797364
Project Management Services
N.A.I.C.S.: 541618

Promoter Hydraulics Pte. Ltd.　(1)
　(100%)
Web Site: http://www.promoter.com.sg
Sales Range: $75-99.9 Million
Emp.: 150
Industrial Winch & Power Pack Distr
N.A.I.C.S.: 423830

Viking Airtech Pte. Ltd.　(1)
21 Kian Teck Road, Singapore, 628773, Singapore　(100%)
Tel.: (65) 66019500
Web Site: https://www.vikingairtech.com
Emp.: 200
Marine & Offshore Heating, Ventilation, Air Conditioning & Refrigeration Systems Designer, Mfr, Installation & Maintenance Services
N.A.I.C.S.: 333415
Yeau Chong Ng (Exec Dir)

Subsidiary (Non-US):

Viking Airtech (Shanghai) Co., Ltd.　(2)
Room 1607 Shengneng International Building, No 1 Fuxing (Middle) Road, Shanghai, 200021, China
Tel.: (86) 21 6390 0863
Heating, Air Conditioning & Refrigeration Systems Mfr
N.A.I.C.S.: 333415

Viking Airtech (Yantai) Co., Ltd.　(2)
No 89 Huan Hai Road, Zhi Fu District, Yantai, 264000, Shandong, China　(100%)
Tel.: (86) 5356871883
Web Site: http://www.vikingairtech.com.cn
Sales Range: $25-49.9 Million
Emp.: 30
Marine & Offshore Heating, Ventilation, Air Conditioning & Refrigeration Systems Designer, Mfr, Installation & Maintenance Services
N.A.I.C.S.: 333415

Viking Airtech Sdn. Bhd.　(2)
No 44 Jalan Permas 9/12, Bandar Baru Permas Jaya, 81750, Masai, Johor Bahru, Malaysia
Tel.: (60) 7 380 6680
Emp.: 4
Heating, Air Conditioning & Refrigeration Systems Mfr
N.A.I.C.S.: 333415
Issac Pang (Mgr-Sls)

A & A CONTRACT CUSTOMS BROKERS LTD.
Suite 101 120-176th Street, Surrey, V2S 9S2, BC, Canada
Tel.: (604) 538-1042
Web Site: http://www.aacb.com
Year Founded: 1979
Rev.: $44,376,702
Emp.: 100

Customs Brokerage, Freight Transportation, Warehousing & Shipping Services
N.A.I.C.S.: 488510
Graham Robins Jr. (Pres)

A & M FEBCON LIMITED
A-2 Hira Anand Tower Gordhanwadi Tekra Kankaria, Ahmedabad, 380 008, Gujarat, India
Tel.: (91) 9825363594
Web Site:
http://www.aandmfebcon.com
Rev.: $47,767
Assets: $2,874,785
Liabilities: $1,002,011
Net Worth: $1,872,774
Earnings: $1,816
Emp.: 9
Fiscal Year-end: 03/31/19
Metal Product Mfr & Distr
N.A.I.C.S.: 332420
Varun Jigneshkumar Shah (Mng Dir)

A & M JUMBO BAGS LTD.
Block 100 Old Bhagwati Rice Mill Opp Hp Petrol Pump, Jetalpur, Ahmedabad, 382426, Gujarat, India
Tel.: (91) 8980085084
Web Site:
https://www.aandmjumbobags.com
Year Founded: 2011
AMJUMBO—(NSE)
Emp.: 19
Jumbo Bag Mfr & Distr
N.A.I.C.S.: 326111
Zalak Purvesh Parikh (Mng Dir)

A & S GROUP (HOLDINGS) LIMITED
Room 11 14 th Floor Tower 2 Ever Gain Plaza 88 Container Port Road, Kwai Chung, China (Hong Kong)
Tel.: (852) 2 472 6275　Ky
Web Site: http://www.asl.hk
Year Founded: 2002
1737—(HKG)
Rev.: $52,688,330
Assets: $39,999,665
Liabilities: $11,573,762
Net Worth: $28,425,902
Earnings: $5,226,528
Emp.: 438
Fiscal Year-end: 03/31/21
Freight Forwarding & Transportation Services
N.A.I.C.S.: 488510
Alex Kwok Leung Law (Founder, Chm, Mng Dir & Compliance Officer)

A AGENCIA BRASILEIRA DE PROMOCAO DE EXPORTA-COES E INVESTIMENTOS
SAUN Quadra 05 Lote C Torre B 12 ao 18 andar Centro Empresarial CNC, Asa Norte, Brasilia, 70040-250, Brazil
Tel.: (55) 6120270202
Web Site:
https://www.apexbrasil.com.br
Year Founded: 1997
Investment Management Service
N.A.I.C.S.: 523999

A B COTSPIN INDIA LIMITED
Bathinda Road, Faridkot Jaito, Bathinda, 151202, Punjab, India
Tel.: (91) 1635232670
Web Site: https://www.abcotspin.com
Year Founded: 1997
ABCOTS—(NSE)
Rev.: $19,235,266
Assets: $11,302,664
Liabilities: $6,003,120
Net Worth: $5,299,544
Earnings: $932,732

Emp.: 51
Fiscal Year-end: 03/31/22
Textile Product Mfr & Distr
N.A.I.C.S.: 314999

A B INFRABUILD LIMITED
104 Shubhangan Chs Ltd Jawahar Nagar Near Railway Crossing, Goregaon West, Mumbai, 400104, India
Tel.: (91) 2228712114
Web Site:
https://www.abinfrabuild.com
Year Founded: 1999
ABINFRA—(NSE)
Rev.: $8,817,622
Assets: $14,073,096
Liabilities: $10,280,051
Net Worth: $3,793,045
Earnings: $117,994
Emp.: 22
Fiscal Year-end: 03/31/22
Civil Construction Services
N.A.I.C.S.: 236220
Amit Bholanath Mishra (Mng Dir)

A B N INTERCORP LIMITED
F-01 TDI Centre Jasola, New Delhi, 110025, India
Tel.: (91) 1141324180
ABNINT—(NSE)
Real Estate Investment Services
N.A.I.C.S.: 531190
Ajai Kumar Rastogi (Chm & Mng Dir)

A BENBOW HOLDING INC.
3F-B302D 185 Kewang Rd, Longtan Township, Taoyuan, 325, Taiwan
Tel.: (886) 34071938　NV
Year Founded: 2011
Management Consulting
N.A.I.C.S.: 541618
Chien Yang Yu (Pres, CEO, CFO, Treas & Sec)

A BROWN COMPANY, INC.
Xavier estates masterson Avenue Upper Balulang Cagayan de oro city, Exchange Road, Pasig, 9000, Philippines
Tel.: (63) 86318890
Web Site: https://www.abrown.ph
BRN—(PHI)
Rev.: $28,910,219
Assets: $208,350,443
Liabilities: $82,516,863
Net Worth: $125,833,580
Earnings: $9,723,612
Emp.: 65
Fiscal Year-end: 12/31/23
Real Estate & Property Development Services
N.A.I.C.S.: 531312
Jason C. Nalupta (Sec)

Subsidiaries:

Irradiation Solutions Inc.　(1)
Sitio Sibana Tanay-Sampaloc Road, Tanay, Rizal, 1980, Philippines
Tel.: (63) 286333315
Web Site: https://irradsolutions.com
Irradiation Equipment Mfr
N.A.I.C.S.: 334517

A GROUP OF RETAIL ASSETS SWEDEN AB
Strandvagen 5A, Box 16378, 103 27, Stockholm, Sweden
Tel.: (46) 706 088080
Web Site: http://www.agoraretail.se
Retail Property Owner & Manager
N.A.I.C.S.: 531312
Rutger Arnhult (CEO)

A INFRASTRUCTURE LIMITED (Name Changed to Ka-

A Group of Retail Assets Sweden AB—(Continued)

noria Energy & Infrastructure Limited)

A M FORD SALES LTD
2795 Highway Dr, Trail, V1R 2T1, BC, Canada
Tel.: (250) 364-0202
Web Site: http://www.amford.com
Year Founded: 1982
Rev.: $10,600,000
Emp.: 32
New & Used Car Dealers
N.A.I.C.S.: 441110
Dennis Bedin *(Mgr-Fin Svcs)*

A MENARINI INDUSTRIE FARMACEUTICHE RIUNITE SRL
Via Dei Vii Santi 3, 50131, Firenze, Italy
Tel.: (39) 05556801
Rev.: $809,300,000
Emp.: 1,189
N.A.I.C.S.: 325412
Alberto Aleotti *(Pres)*

Subsidiaries:

Berlin-Chemie AG   (1)
Glienicker Weg 125, 12489, Berlin, Germany
Tel.: (49) 030 6707 0
Web Site: http://www.berlin-chemie.com
Pharmaceutical Product Research & Production
N.A.I.C.S.: 325412
Reinhard Uppenkamp *(CEO)*

Subsidiary (US):

Stemline Therapeutics, Inc.   (2)
750 Lexington Ave 11th Fl, New York, NY 10022
Tel.: (646) 502-2310
Web Site: http://www.stemline.com
Rev.: $43,216,862
Assets: $186,979,004
Liabilities: $23,362,613
Net Worth: $163,616,391
Earnings: ($76,817,225)
Emp.: 100
Fiscal Year-end: 12/31/2019
Biopharmaceutical Mfr, Developer & Researcher
N.A.I.C.S.: 325412
David G. Gionco *(Chief Acctg Officer & Sr VP-Fin)*

A METAVERSE COMPANY
Building A10 50 Anjialou, Chaoyang District, Beijing, China
Tel.: (86) 1084793988   Ky
Web Site: http://www.starrise.cn
1616—(HKG)
Rev.: $13,493,704
Assets: $110,226,636
Liabilities: $48,552,988
Net Worth: $61,673,648
Earnings: ($74,990,167)
Emp.: 108
Fiscal Year-end: 12/31/21
Holding Company; Films & TV Series Production, Distribution & Authorization; Home Textile Fabric Mfr
N.A.I.C.S.: 551112
Dong Liu *(Chm)*

A ONE ALFORM CO., LTD.
Budang Techno Park B Bid 201-ho 723, Pangyo-ro Bundang-gu, Seongnam, Gyeonggi-do, Korea (South)
Tel.: (82) 3180175305
Web Site: https://www.aonealform.co.kr
Year Founded: 2005
234070—(KRS)
Aluminum Form Distr
N.A.I.C.S.: 423510
Ho-Jung Ahn *(CEO)*

A PANAYIDES CONTRACTING PUBLIC LTD
54 Griva Digeni Avenue, PO Box 23736, 1096, Nicosia, Cyprus
Tel.: (357) 22663333
Web Site: http://www.apco.com.cy
Year Founded: 1987
Construction Services
N.A.I.C.Q.: 237310
Stavros Theodosiou *(Chm)*

A PLUS ASSET ADVISOR CO., LTD.
14th Floor Mirim Tower 14 Teheran-ro 4-gil, Gangnam-gu, Seoul, 06232, Korea (South)
Tel.: (82) 15771713
Web Site: https://www.aplusga.com
Year Founded: 2007
244920—(KRS)
Rev.: $237,378,762
Assets: $262,742,161
Liabilities: $145,348,660
Net Worth: $117,393,500
Earnings: $14,179,967
Emp.: 403
Fiscal Year-end: 12/31/21
Insurance Services
N.A.I.C.S.: 524210
Cho Gyu Nam *(Co-CEO)*

A RAIZE-INSTITUICAO DE PAGAMENTOS S.A.
Rua Tierno Galvan Amoreiras Tower 3 17, 1070-274, Lisbon, Portugal
Tel.: (351) 308812518
Web Site: https://www.raize.pt
MLRZE—(EUR)
Sales Range: Less than $1 Million
Payment Processing Services
N.A.I.C.S.: 541214
Jose Maria Antunes dos Santos Rego *(Chm & CEO)*

A SELF-ADMINISTERED REAL ESTATE INVESTMENT TRUST INC.
9th floor 711 Eonju-ro, Gangnam-gu, Seoul, 06050, Korea (South)
Tel.: (82) 220775800
Web Site: https://www.areit.co.kr
Year Founded: 2010
140910—(KRS)
Rev.: $606,230
Assets: $68,492,271
Liabilities: $42,808,197
Net Worth: $25,684,074
Earnings: ($1,052,664)
Emp.: 14
Fiscal Year-end: 12/31/22
Real Estate Investment Trust
N.A.I.C.S.: 531390
Ho Su Oh *(Chm)*

A TOUTE VITESSE SA
28 avenue de la Republique, 93170, Bagnolet, France
Tel.: (33) 811655605
Web Site: http://www.coursier.com
Courier Service
N.A.I.C.S.: 492110
Julien Cohen *(Chm & CEO)*

A W HAINSWORTH & SONS LTD.
Spring Valley Mills Stanningley, Pudsey, LS28 6DW, W Yorks, United Kingdom
Tel.: (44) 1132570391
Web Site: http://www.hainsworth.co.uk
Year Founded: 1783
Specialist Textile Company; Fabric Mfr
N.A.I.C.S.: 313310
Thomas Hainsworth *(Mng Dir)*

A&A MATERIAL CORPORATION
2-5-5 Tsurumi-Chuo, Tsurumi-ku, Yokohama, 230-8511, Kanagawa, Japan
Tel.: (81) 455035760
Web Site: https://www.aa-material.co.jp
Year Founded: 1924
5391—(TKS)
Rev.: $272,874,020
Assets: $264,082,720
Liabilities: $138,942,200
Net Worth: $125,140,520
Earnings: $17,840,390
Emp.: 838
Fiscal Year-end: 03/31/24
Building Material Mfr & Distr
N.A.I.C.S.: 327120
Toru Makino *(Pres & CEO)*

Subsidiaries:

A&A Ibaraki Corporation   (1)
263-1 Uchiyodo, Chikusei, 300-4507, Japan
Tel.: (81) 296522281
Wood Product Mfr & Distr
N.A.I.C.S.: 321999

A&A Osaka Corporation   (1)
25-3 Imashiro-cho, Takatsuki, 569-1135, Japan
Tel.: (81) 726851928
Wood Product Mfr & Distr
N.A.I.C.S.: 321999

Ask Okinawa Corporation   (1)
5-1-1 Uebaru, Naha, 901-0153, Japan
Tel.: (81) 988919355
Web Site: https://www.askcorp.co.jp
Insulation Installation Services
N.A.I.C.S.: 238290

Ask Sanshin Engineering Corporation   (1)
2-5-5 Tsurumi Chuo, Tsurumi Ward, Yokohama, 230-0051, Kanagawa, Japan
Tel.: (81) 455037811
Web Site: https://www.askcorp.co.jp
Emp.: 170
Building Material Mfr & Distr
N.A.I.C.S.: 327120

Ask Technica Corporation   (1)
610 Takata Ichikawa-Misato Nishi-Yatsushiro, Yamanashi, 409-3606, Japan
Tel.: (81) 552721152
Web Site: https://www.asktechnica.co.jp
Brake Drum Mfr & Distr
N.A.I.C.S.: 336340

A&D COMPANY, LIMITED
(See Under A&D Co., Ltd.)

A&D CO., LTD.
3-23-14 Higashi-Ikebukuro, Toshima-ku, Tokyo, 170-0013, Japan
Tel.: (81) 353916123   JP
Web Site: https://www.aandd.jp
Year Founded: 1977
7745—(TKS)
Rev.: $500,804,480
Assets: $573,433,520
Liabilities: $311,676,640
Net Worth: $261,756,880
Earnings: $34,586,640
Emp.: 2,591
Fiscal Year-end: 03/31/22
Electronic DSP, Medical, Weighing, Testing & Measuring Equipment Mfr & Distr
N.A.I.C.S.: 334515
Sadao Ito *(Sr Mng Exec Officer-Bus Mgmt & Verification Office)*

Subsidiaries:

A&D Australasia Pty. Ltd.   (1)
32 Dew Street, Thebarton, 5031, SA, Australia
Tel.: (61) 883018100
Web Site: http://www.andaustralasia.com.au
Sales Range: $50-74.9 Million
Emp.: 17

Holding Company; Electronic Medical & Weighing Equipment Mfr & Distr
N.A.I.C.S.: 551112

Division (Domestic):

A&D Weighing Pty. Ltd.   (2)
32 Dew Street, Thebarton, 5031, SA, Australia
Tel.: (01) 000010100
Web Site: http://www.andweighing.com.au
Sales Range: $25-49.9 Million
Emp.: 20
Electronic Scale & Balance Mfr & Distr
N.A.I.C.S.: 333998

A&D Electronics (Shenzhen) Co., Ltd.   (1)
1-5/F Building 4 Hengchangrong High Tech Industry Park, Hongtian Shajing Bao'an District Shangnan East Road, Shenzhen, 518125, Guangdong, China
Tel.: (86) 75533002555
Web Site: http://www.andch.cn
Electromedical Equipment Mfr & Distr
N.A.I.C.S.: 334510

A&D Engineering, Inc.   (1)
1756 Automation Pkwy, San Jose, CA 95131
Tel.: (408) 263-5333
Web Site: http://www.andonline.com
Sales Range: $10-24.9 Million
Emp.: 60
Electronic DSP, Medical, Weighing, Testing & Measuring Equipment Distr
N.A.I.C.S.: 423440

A&D Europe GmbH   (1)
Berliner Allee 65, 64295, Darmstadt, Germany   (100%)
Tel.: (49) 61513975250
Web Site: http://www.aanddeurope.com
Sales Range: $50-74.9 Million
Emp.: 3
Electronic Weighing & Medical Equipment Distr
N.A.I.C.S.: 423440
Jurgen Bredenbeck *(Mng Dir)*

A&D Instruments (Thailand) Limited   (1)
168/16 Factory Yard Moo 1, Rangsit, Thanyaburi, 12110, Thailand
Tel.: (66) 20038911
Web Site: https://thai.andprecision.com
Emp.: 2,000
Weighing & Measurement Product Distr
N.A.I.C.S.: 423830

A&D Instruments India Pvt. Ltd.   (1)
D-48 Udyog Vihar Phase -V, Gurgaon, 122 016, Haryana, India   (99%)
Tel.: (91) 1244715555
Web Site: https://www.aanddindia.in
Sales Range: $50-74.9 Million
Emp.: 15
Electronic DSP, Medical, Weighing, Testing & Measuring Equipment Distr
N.A.I.C.S.: 423440
Chikara Arai *(Mng Dir)*

A&D Instruments Ltd.   (1)
24-26 Blacklands Way Abingdon Business Park, Abingdon, OX14 1DY, Oxfordshire, United Kingdom
Tel.: (44) 1235550420
Web Site: https://andprecision.com
Sales Range: $50-74.9 Million
Emp.: 20
Electronic DSP, Medical, Weighing, Testing & Measuring Equipment Distr
N.A.I.C.S.: 423440

A&D Korea Limited   (1)
Yeouido Department Store 33 Gukjegeumyung-ro 6-gil, Yeongdeungpo-gu, Seoul, 07331 8F, Korea (South)
Tel.: (82) 27804101
Web Site: https://www.andk.co.kr
Electronic Weighing Equipment Mfr & Distr
N.A.I.C.S.: 333998

A&D Rus Co., Ltd.   (1)
Vereyskaya Str 17, 121357, Russia
Tel.: (7) 4959373344
Web Site: http://www.and-rus.ru
Electronic Medical & Weighing Device Distr
N.A.I.C.S.: 423450

A&D Scales Co., Ltd.   **(1)**
101 CJ-ro, Jincheon-eup, Jincheon, 27845, Chungcheongbuk-do, Korea (South)
Tel.: (82) 435374101
Web Site: http://www.aandd.jp
Industrial Scale Mfr
N.A.I.C.S.: 333998

A&D Technology Inc.   **(1)**
4622 Runway Blvd, Ann Arbor, MI 48108
Tel.: (734) 973-1111
Web Site: http://www.aanddtech.com
Sales Range: $50-74.9 Million
Emp.: 100
Powertrain Testing & Measurement Equipment Distr & Engineering Services
N.A.I.C.S.: 423440

A&D Technology Trading (Shanghai) Co., Ltd.   **(1)**
32CD World Plaza No 855 South Pudong Road, Pilot Free Trade Zone, Shanghai, 200120, China
Tel.: (86) 2133932340
Web Site: http://www.aanddtech.cn
Wholesale Trade Agency
N.A.I.C.S.: 425120

A&D Vietnam Limited   **(1)**
No 28 Street 5 VSIP Bac Ninh Integrated Township & Industrial Park, Phu Chan Ward, Tu Son, Vietnam
Tel.: (84) 2413906666
Blood Pressure Monitor Mfr
N.A.I.C.S.: 339112

Best Instruments Co., Ltd.   **(1)**
111 Uetsuya Nakatsutsumi, Yawata, 614-8176, Kyoto, Japan
Tel.: (81) 759826007
Web Site: https://www.best-sokki.com
Measuring & Testing Equipments Mfr & Distr
N.A.I.C.S.: 333914

Holon Co., Ltd.   **(1)**
5-40-1 Kamisunacho, Tachikawa-shi, Tokyo, 190-0032, Japan   **(51%)**
Tel.: (81) 425377990
Web Site: http://www.holon-ltd.co.jp
Sales Range: Less than $1 Million
Emp.: 46
Semiconductor Inspection Tools Mfr
N.A.I.C.S.: 334413
Hao Zhang *(Pres)*

Kensei Industry Co., Ltd.   **(1)**
4210-15 Takasai, Shimotsuma, 304-0031, Ibaraki, Japan
Tel.: (81) 296437035
Electronic Balance Mfr & Sales
N.A.I.C.S.: 333998

Litra Co., Ltd.   **(1)**
Oaza Harajuku 7-5, Hidaka, 350-1205, Saitama, Japan
Tel.: (81) 429854668
Web Site: http://www.litra.co.jp
Emp.: 80
Weighing Scale Mfr
N.A.I.C.S.: 333998
Yo Furukawa *(Pres & CEO)*

Orientec Co., Ltd.   **(1)**
3-23-14 Higashi-Ikebukuro Toshima-ku Dist, Toshima-ku, Tokyo, 170-0013, Japan
Tel.: (81) 353916123
Web Site: http://www.aandd.co.jp
Testing Instruments Mfr
N.A.I.C.S.: 334515

A&D PHARMA HOLDINGS S.R.L.
133 Ciobanului St, Mogosoaia, 077135, Ilfov, Romania
Tel.: (40) 213017474   NL
Web Site: http://www.adpharma.ro
Year Founded: 1994
Sales Range: $650-699.9 Million
Emp.: 3,160
Holding Company; Pharmaceutical Wholesale, Retail Sales & Marketing Services
N.A.I.C.S.: 551112
Robert Popescu *(CEO)*

Subsidiaries:

Sensiblu S.R.L.   **(1)**
133 Ciobanului Street, Mogosoaia, 077135, Ilfov, Romania   **(100%)**
Tel.: (40) 213017474
Web Site: http://www.sensiblu.com
Retail Pharmacies Operator
N.A.I.C.S.: 456110
Lucian Neacsu *(Dir-Strategy & Dev)*

A&W (MALAYSIA) SDN BHD
(See Under Malayan United Industries Berhad)

A&W REVENUE ROYALTIES INCOME FUND (Acquired by TorQuest Partners Inc.)

A' SHARQIYA INVESTMENT HOLDING CO. SAOG
Al Harthy Complex, PO Box 47, 118, Muscat, PC, Oman
Tel.: (968) 24903900
Web Site: https://www.asharqiya.com
SIHC—(MUS)
Rev.: $1,746,287
Assets: $47,993,506
Liabilities: $10,034,203
Net Worth: $37,959,303
Earnings: $1,276,859
Fiscal Year-end: 12/31/23
Investment Services
N.A.I.C.S.: 523999
Saleh Ahmed Mohamed Al Harthy *(Vice Chm)*

A'AYAN LEASING AND INVESTMENT COMPANY KSCC
Alrai muhammed Bin Quasim Street Block 1223, PO Box 1426, Safat, Kuwait, 13015, Kuwait
Tel.: (965) 1804488
Web Site: http://www.aayan.com
Sales Range: $25-49.9 Million
Emp.: 200
Leasing & Investment Services
N.A.I.C.S.: 523999
Mansour Hamad Al-Mubarak *(CEO)*

Subsidiaries:

A'ayan Real Estate Company K.S.C.C.   **(1)**
Qibla - AL-Sour Street Al-Sour Tower 20th floor, PO Box 2973, Safat, Kuwait, 13030, Kuwait
Tel.: (965) 22212121
Web Site: https://www.aayanre.com
Rev.: $21,469,050
Assets: $302,661,331
Liabilities: $40,172,898
Net Worth: $262,488,433
Earnings: $11,897,387
Emp.: 37
Fiscal Year-end: 12/31/2022
Real Estate Services
N.A.I.C.S.: 531390
Mansour Hamad Al-Mubarak *(Chm)*

Mubarrad Holding Company (K.S.C)   **(1)**
No 3 Block C Building No 263 Street 33 Floor M1, PO Box 42132, Shuwaikh Industrial Area Shuwaikh, Kuwait, 70652, Kuwait   **(53.54%)**
Tel.: (965) 22269777
Web Site: https://www.mubarrad.com.kw
Rev.: $7,132,412
Assets: $75,591,014
Liabilities: $8,501,427
Net Worth: $67,089,587
Earnings: $4,942,439
Emp.: 15
Fiscal Year-end: 12/31/2022
Land Transportation Services
N.A.I.C.S.: 488490
Ramzi H. Al-Omani *(Dir-Support Svcs)*

A'SAFFA FOODS S.A.O.G
PO Box 3436, 112, Ruwi, Oman
Tel.: (968) 22360250
Web Site: https://www.asaffa.com

Year Founded: 2001
SPFI—(MUS)
Rev.: $98,060,566
Assets: $257,109,611
Liabilities: $154,765,010
Net Worth: $102,344,600
Earnings: ($4,707,280)
Emp.: 965
Fiscal Year-end: 12/31/21
Poultry Services
N.A.I.C.S.: 112390
Muhammad Rafique Chaudhry *(CFO)*

Subsidiaries:

ASaffa Logistics LLC   **(1)**
P O Box 402, 124, Rusayl, Oman
Tel.: (968) 22360290261
Web Site: https://www.asaffa-logistics.com
Goods & Material Distr
N.A.I.C.S.: 484110

A-1 ACID LIMITED
A1 Corporate House Shivalik Business Centre Opp Kens Ville, Golf Academy Bh Rajpath Club Off S G Highway Bodakdev, Ahmedabad, 380054, Gujarat, India
Tel.: (91) 7940091111
Web Site: https://www.a1acid.com
Year Founded: 1956
542012—(BOM)
Rev.: $42,911,300
Assets: $10,878,531
Liabilities: $4,529,370
Net Worth: $6,349,161
Earnings: $880,602
Emp.: 12
Fiscal Year-end: 03/31/22
Chemicals Mfr
N.A.I.C.S.: 325998
Himanshu Sunil Thakkar *(CFO)*

A-CAP ENERGY LIMITED
(Acquired by Lotus Resources Limited & Name Changed to Lotus Marula Pty. Ltd.)

A-DRIVE TECHNOLOGY GMBH
Ziegelhuttenweg 4, Taunusstein, 65232, Neuhof, Germany
Tel.: (49) 612897550   De
Web Site: http://www.a-drive.de
Motor Mfr
N.A.I.C.S.: 335312

A-GAS LIMITED
Banyard Road Portbury West, Bristol, BS20 7XH, United Kingdom
Tel.: (44) 127 537 6600   UK
Web Site: http://www.agas.com
Year Founded: 1993
Emp.: 60
Refrigeration & Air Conditioning Refrigerant Supplier
N.A.I.C.S.: 325998
John Ormerod *(Mng Dir)*

Subsidiaries:

A-Gas (Australia) Pty Ltd   **(1)**
9-11 Oxford Road, Laverton, 3026, VIC, Australia
Tel.: (61) 393689222
Air Conditioner Accessory Distr
N.A.I.C.S.: 423620

A-Gas (SEA) Pte Ltd   **(1)**
360 Orchard Road International Building 10-05, Singapore, 238869, Singapore
Tel.: (65) 68360065
Air Conditioner Accessory Distr
N.A.I.C.S.: 423620

A-Gas (Shanghai) Chemical Co. Ltd   **(1)**
Room1102 Yunding International Building 800 Chengshan Road, Pudong, Shanghai, China

Tel.: (86) 2150133199
Air Conditioner Accessory Distr
N.A.I.C.S.: 423620

A-Gas (South Africa) (Pty) Ltd   **(1)**
8 Railway Road Montague Gardens 7441, Cape Town, South Africa
Tel.: (27) 215518790
Air Conditioner Accessory Distr
N.A.I.C.S.: 423620
Gavin Bryce *(Mgr-Technical Ops)*

A-Gas (Thailand) Ltd   **(1)**
68-68/6 S&B Tower 7th Floor Room 702 Pan Road Silom, Bangrak, Bangkok, 10500, Thailand
Tel.: (66) 26378188
Air Conditioner Accessory Distr
N.A.I.C.S.: 423620

A-Gas Americas, Inc.   **(1)**
30045 FM 2978, Magnolia, TX 77354
Tel.: (800) 366-1356
Web Site: http://www.agasamericas.com
Air Conditioner Accessory Distr
N.A.I.C.S.: 423620
Ian Podmore *(Mng Dir-Intl)*

Subsidiary (Domestic):

Certified Refrigerant Services, Inc.   **(2)**
5481 Williamsburg Dr, Punta Gorda, FL 33982-1717
Tel.: (941) 637-6300
Web Site: http://www.certifiedrefrigerant.com
Nonhazardous Waste Treatment & Disposal
N.A.I.C.S.: 562219
Jeanne Roland *(Pres)*

A-Gas Electronic Materials Ltd   **(1)**
Unit 3 iO Centre Valley Drive, Rugby, CV21 1TW, Warwickshire, United Kingdom
Tel.: (44) 1788537535
Web Site: http://www.agasem.com
Electronic Components Distr
N.A.I.C.S.: 423690

Reclamation Technologies, Inc.   **(1)**
1100 Haskins Rd, Bowling Green, OH 43402
Tel.: (419) 867-8990
Web Site: http://www.remtec.net
Sales Range: $25-49.9 Million
Emp.: 50
Industrial Gas Mfr
N.A.I.C.S.: 325120
Jennifer Fonseca *(Dir-Quality)*

A-JIN INDUSTRY CO.,LTD
26-40 Gongdan 8-ro, Jillyang-eup, Gyeongsan, Gyeongsangbuk-do, Korea (South)
Tel.: (82) 538569100
Web Site: https://www.wamc.co.kr
Year Founded: 1978
013310—(KRS)
Rev.: $472,238,712
Assets: $536,139,238
Liabilities: $347,118,587
Net Worth: $189,020,651
Earnings: $23,447,497
Emp.: 652
Fiscal Year-end: 12/31/22
Automobile Parts Mfr
N.A.I.C.S.: 336110

A-LIVING SERVICES CO., LTD. (See Under A-Living Smart City Services Co., Ltd.)

A-LABS CAPITAL II CORP.
595 Howe St 10th Fl, Vancouver, V6C 2T5, BC, Canada
Tel.: (927) 545-2240
ALAB.P—(TSXV)
Assets: $10,148
Liabilities: $135,751
Net Worth: $125,603)
Earnings: ($21,084)
Fiscal Year-end: 12/31/23
Asset Management Services
N.A.I.C.S.: 523940
Doron Cohen *(CEO)*

A-Labs Capital II Corp.—(Continued)

A-LEHDET OY
Risto Rytin tie 33, 00570, Helsinki, Finland
Tel.: (358) 504144200
Web Site: http://www.a-lehdet.fi
Year Founded: 1933
Sales Range: $75-99.9 Million
Emp.: 268
Periodical Publishing Services
N.A.I.C.S.: 513120
Janne Pullinen (Chief Bus Officer)

Subsidiaries:

Faktum Oy   (1)
Hitsaajank. 7, SF-00810, Helsinki, Finland
Tel.: (358) 75961
Book Publishers
N.A.I.C.S.: 513120

A-LIVING SMART CITY SERVICES CO., LTD.
35/F Agile Center 26 Huaxia Road, Zhujiang New Town Tianhe District, Guangzhou, 510623, Guangdong, China
Tel.: (86) 4006983383   CN
Web Site:
  http://www.agileliving.com.cn
Year Founded: 1997
3319—(HKG)
Rev.: $2,159,152,070
Assets: $3,187,320,646
Liabilities: $1,204,227,648
Net Worth: $1,983,092,998
Earnings: $271,664,453
Emp.: 95,102
Fiscal Year-end: 12/31/22
Property Management Services
N.A.I.C.S.: 531210
Fengchao Huang (Co-Chm)

A-MAX TECHNOLOGY LIMITED
10th Floor A-Max Technology Tower, 12-16 Fui Yiu Kok Street, Tsuen Wan, NT, China (Hong Kong)
Tel.: (852) 27986699   HK
Year Founded: 1996
Sales Range: $300-349.9 Million
Emp.: 1,700
Portable Digital Audio Players Designer & Mfr
N.A.I.C.S.: 334310
Victor Chan (Chm & CEO)

Subsidiaries:

A- MAX Technology (China) Ltd.   (1)
No 8 Industrial Park Gonghe Village Shajing Town, Bao'an District, Shenzhen, 518104, China
Tel.: (86) 755 26980809
Audio & Video Equipment Mfr
N.A.I.C.S.: 334310

A-MAX Technology GmbH   (1)
Helmholtzstr 2-9, 10587, Berlin, Germany
Tel.: (49) 307900610
Web Site: http://www.amaxhk.com
Sales Range: $25-49.9 Million
Emp.: 4
Audio & Video Equipment Mfr
N.A.I.C.S.: 334310

A-Max Technology MCO Co., Ltd.   (1)
Avenida Da Praia Grande No 409 Edificio Dos Servicos, Juridicos Da China 5A, Macau, China (Macau)
Tel.: (853) 28717252
Audio & Video Equipment Mfr
N.A.I.C.S.: 334310

A-ONE SEIMITSU INC.
2-20-5 Bubai-cho, Fuchu, 183-0033, TKY, Japan
Tel.: (81) 423631039
Web Site: http://www.a-one-seimitsu.co.jp

Year Founded: 1990
6156—(JAS)
Sales Range: Less than $1 Million
Industrial Products Mfr; Machining Tools, Lathes & Precision Equipment & Time Piece Accessories
N.A.I.C.S.: 333248
Tetsuya Hayashi (Pres)

A-ONLINE CAPITAL LTD.
Yehuda Halevi 18, Tel Aviv, 65137, Israel
Tel.: (972) 35177123
Web Site: http://www.a-online.co.il
Year Founded: 1999
Rev.: $3,365,308
Assets: $1,339,561
Liabilities: $5,756,600
Net Worth: ($4,417,039)
Earnings: ($3,112,018)
Emp.: 30
Fiscal Year-end: 12/31/17
Software Development Services
N.A.I.C.S.: 541511
Yuval Golan (Co-Founder)

A-POWER ENERGY GENERATION SYSTEMS, LTD.
No 44 Jingxing North Street, Tiexi District, Shenyang, 110121, Liaoning, China
Tel.: (86) 102485617788
Web Site:
  http://www.apowerenergy.com
Sales Range: $300-349.9 Million
Emp.: 457
Designer & Mfr of Power Generation & Distribution Systems
N.A.I.C.S.: 541330
Jinxiang Lu (Chm & CEO)

Subsidiaries:

Liaoning GaoKe Energy Group Company Limited   (1)
NO 44 Jingxing N St, Tiexi District, Shenyang, 110021, China
Tel.: (86) 2485617888 8888
Web Site: http://www.ligkny.org
Energy Generation
N.A.I.C.S.: 221118

A-PRO CO., LTD.
41-14 Burim-ro 170beon-gil, Dongangu, Anyang, Gyeonggi-do, Korea (South)
Tel.: (82) 314414001
Web Site: https://aproele.com
Year Founded: 2000
262260—(KRS)
Rev.: $60,894,561
Assets: $107,574,907
Liabilities: $61,614,758
Net Worth: $45,960,149
Earnings: ($1,173,221)
Emp.: 147
Fiscal Year-end: 12/31/22
Battery Mfr
N.A.I.C.S.: 335910
Lim Jong Hyun (CEO)

A-RANK BERHAD
Lot 2-33 Jalan Perindustrian Mahkota 7, Taman Perindustrian Mahkota, 43700, Beranang, Selangor Darul Ehsan, Malaysia
Tel.: (60) 387244662
Web Site: https://www.arank.com.my
ARANK—(KLS)
Rev.: $137,011,509
Assets: $74,115,804
Liabilities: $39,184,785
Net Worth: $34,931,019
Earnings: $2,336,876
Emp.: 202
Fiscal Year-end: 07/31/23
Aluminum Billets Mfr
N.A.I.C.S.: 331314

Choon Sun Gan (Exec Dir)

A-SMART HOLDINGS LTD.
61 Tai Seng Avenue Print Media Hub Paya Lebar iPark No 03-03, Singapore, 534167, Singapore
Tel.: (65) 68802828
Web Site: https://www.a-smart.sg
Year Founded: 1999
BQC—(SES)
Rev.: $4,446,018
Assets: $15,938,172
Liabilities: $3,839,022
Net Worth: $12,099,149
Earnings: ($511,870)
Emp.: 451
Fiscal Year-end: 07/31/21
Investment Services
N.A.I.C.S.: 523999
Weidong Ma (Chm)

Subsidiaries:

A-Smart Commerce Pte Ltd   (1)
61 Tai Seng Avenue Print Media Hub Paya Lebar iPark 03-03, Singapore, 534167, Singapore
Tel.: (65) 68802828
Investment Services
N.A.I.C.S.: 523940

A-Smart Life Pte Ltd   (1)
61 Tai Seng Avenue Print Media Hub Paya Lebar iPark 03-03, Singapore, 534167, Singapore
Tel.: (65) 68802828
Food Service
N.A.I.C.S.: 562119

A-Smart Media Pte Ltd   (1)
61 Tai Seng Avenue Print Media Hub Paya Lebar iPark 03-03, Singapore, 534167, Singapore
Tel.: (65) 68802828
Media Broadcasting Services
N.A.I.C.S.: 516120

A-Smart Property Holdings Pte Ltd   (1)
61 Tai Seng Avenue Print Media Hub Paya Lebar iPark 03-03, Singapore, 534167, Singapore
Tel.: (65) 68802828
Real Estate Services
N.A.I.C.S.: 531210

A-Smart Technologies Pte Ltd   (1)
61 Tai Seng Avenue, Singapore, 534167, Singapore
Tel.: (65) 68802828
IT Services
N.A.I.C.S.: 519290

L.C. Hotels Pte Ltd   (1)
14 Kung Chong Road 06-01 Lum Chang Building, Singapore, 159150, Singapore
Tel.: (65) 62662222
Home Management Services
N.A.I.C.S.: 561110

Print Planner (Beijing) Co., Ltd.   (1)
No 2 H-3 District Guanglian Industrial Area, Beijing, China
Tel.: (86) 1057621828
Emp.: 35
Prepress Printing Services
N.A.I.C.S.: 323120

Xpress Print (Pte) Ltd.   (1)
Print Media Hub 61 Tai Seng Avenue 03-03, Singapore, 534167, Singapore   (100%)
Tel.: (65) 68802828
Web Site: https://www.xpress.sg
Emp.: 150
Commercial Printing Services
N.A.I.C.S.: 323111
Foong Siew Peng (Dir-Ops)

Subsidiary (Domestic):

Xpress Media Pte Ltd   (2)
No 1 Kallang Way 2A, Singapore, 347495, Singapore
Tel.: (65) 68802838
General Printing Services
N.A.I.C.S.: 323111

Subsidiary (Non-US):

Xpress Media Philippines Inc.   (3)
5th Floor The Linden Suites 37 San Miguel Avenue, Ortigas Center, Pasig, 1600, Philippines
Tel.: (63) 26876594
Web Site: http://www.xpressmediaphil.com
Graphic Design Services
N.A.I.C.S.: 541430
Agnes Sarmiento (Gen Mgr)

Subsidiary (Non-US):

Xpress Print (Australia) Pty Ltd   (2)
Level 6 369 Royal Parade, Parkville, 3052, VIC, Australia
Tel.: (61) 423318227
Web Site: http://www.xpress.com.sg
Emp.: 1
Commercial Printing Services
N.A.I.C.S.: 323111
Eleanor Fong (Exec Dir)

Xpress Print (Shanghai) Co., Ltd.   (1)
3/F West Block 2 Jinqiao 999 Ningqiao Road, Pudong New District, Shanghai, China
Tel.: (86) 2158883218
Photofinishing Services
N.A.I.C.S.: 812922

Xpress Print (Shenyang) Co., Ltd.   (1)
Room 103 21 Beijing Street, Shenhe District, Shenyang, Liaoning, China
Tel.: (86) 2422532128
Prepress Printing Services
N.A.I.C.S.: 323120

A-SONIC AEROSPACE LIMITED
10 Anson Road No 24-07 International Plaza, Singapore, 079903, Singapore
Tel.: (65) 62262072
Web Site: http://www.asonic-aerospace.com
Year Founded: 2003
BTJ—(SES)
Rev.: $218,524,000
Assets: $87,431,000
Liabilities: $41,658,000
Net Worth: $45,773,000
Earnings: $443,000
Emp.: 642
Fiscal Year-end: 12/31/23
Holding Company; Aerospace Components
N.A.I.C.S.: 551112
Janet L. C. Tan (Chm & CEO)

Subsidiaries:

A-Sonic Aviation Solutions Pte Ltd   (1)
10 Anson Road 24-07 International Plaza, Singapore, 079903, Singapore
Tel.: (65) 63243248
Web Site: https://www.asonic-aviation.com
Aircraft Products Sales & Leasing Services
N.A.I.C.S.: 423860

A-Sonic Express Logistics (India) Private Limited   (1)
Unit 308 2nd Floor Prestige Meridain II No 30 M G Road, Bengaluru, 560001, India
Tel.: (91) 80 4090 4734
Logistics Consulting Servies
N.A.I.C.S.: 541614

A-Sonic Logistics Pte. Ltd.   (1)
Unit 05-23 Cargo Agents Building D Changi Airfreight Centre, Box 591, Singapore, 918104, Singapore
Tel.: (65) 65429333
Logistics Consulting Servies
N.A.I.C.S.: 541614
Sherry Tong (Gen Mgr)

Subsidiary (Non-US):

A-Sonic Logistics (Australia) Pty Ltd   (2)
Level 1 Suite 4 72-74 Bathurst Street, Liverpool, 2170, NSW, Australia
Tel.: (61) 296951611

Logistics Consulting Servies
N.A.I.C.S.: 541614

A-Sonic Logistics (H.K.) Limited   (2)
Tel.: (852) 23642391
Logistics Consulting Servies
N.A.I.C.S.: 541614

**A-Sonic Logistics (Korea) Co.,
Ltd.**   (2)
A02L Acrofice 5FL Dream Plaza 80-1 8-Ga,
Po-Dong Po-gu, Seoul, Korea (South)
Tel.: (82) 226654715
Logistics Consulting Servies
N.A.I.C.S.: 541614

**A-Sonic Logistics (Netherlands)
B.V.**   (2)
Tel.: (31) 108080421
Logistics Consulting Servies
N.A.I.C.S.: 541614

A-Sonic Logistics (UK) Ltd.   (2)
Unit 204 Bedfont Industrial Park Challenge
Road, Ashford, TW15 1AX, Middlesex,
United Kingdom
Tel.: (44) 1784654034
Logistics & Transportation Services
N.A.I.C.S.: 488390
Luke Howell (Mgr-Bus Dev)

Subsidiary (US):

A-Sonic Logistics (USA), Inc.   (2)
71 S Central Ave Ste 300, Valley Stream,
NY 11580
Tel.: (718) 244-0977
Web Site: http://www.us.asonic-
logistics.com
Logistics Consulting Servies
N.A.I.C.S.: 541614
Matthew Wasserbach (Branch Mgr)

Subsidiary (Non-US):

**A-Sonic Logistics (Vietnam) Company
Limited**   (2)
Tel.: (84) 2854173317
Logistics Consulting Servies
N.A.I.C.S.: 541614
Kathy Nguyen (Mgr-Ops & Pricing)

Subsidiary (US):

**Express Customs Clearance (USA),
Inc.**   (2)
71 S Central Ave Ste 300, Valley Stream,
NY 11580
Tel.: (817) 488-7722
Web Site: http://www.e-
customsclearance.com
Ocean & Road Custom Clearance Services
N.A.I.C.S.: 488510
Matthew Wasserbach (Branch Mgr)

CALS Logistics, Inc.   (1)
211-6500 Silver Dart Drive Core B, PO Box
6033 AMF, Mississauga, L5P 1B2, ON,
Canada
Tel.: (905) 678-2257
Web Site: http://www.calslogistics.com
Logistics & Transportation Services
N.A.I.C.S.: 488390
Esther Song (Gen Mgr)

UBI Logistics (China) Limited   (1)
13/F Liyuan Mansion No16 Mingze Street,
Dalian, 116001, China
Tel.: (86) 41182825566
Logistics & Transportation Services
N.A.I.C.S.: 488390

UBI Logistics (HK) Limited   (1)
Unit 6 15/F Laford Centre 838 Lai Chi Kok
Road, Cheung Sha Wan, Kowloon, China
(Hong Kong)
Tel.: (852) 27437010
Logistics Consulting Servies
N.A.I.C.S.: 541614

Ultra Air Cargo, Inc.   (1)
17256 S Main St, Gardena, CA 90248
Tel.: (310) 961-9060
Logistics Consulting Servies
N.A.I.C.S.: 541614

A-TEC INDUSTRIES AG
Wachtergasse 1-3, 1010, Vienna,
Austria
Tel.: (43) 1227600

Web Site: http://www.a-
tecindustries.at
Year Founded: 2004
Sales Range: $1-4.9 Billion
Emp.: 11,883
Holding Company; Electric Motor &
Machine Tool Mfr
N.A.I.C.S.: 551112
Mirko Kovats (Chm-Mgmt Bd)

Subsidiaries:

**AE&E Energy & Environment Con-
sulting Shanghai Co. Ltd.**   (1)
Room 706-708 East Block China Merchants
Plaza No, 20004, Shanghai, China
Tel.: (86) 21 5298 1616
Power Generation Plant Construction & En-
gineering Services
N.A.I.C.S.: 237130

AE&E Nanjing Boiler Co. Ltd.   (1)
139 Tai Shan Road, Jianye District, 210019,
Nanjing, Jiangsu, China
Tel.: (86) 25 8680 5888
Web Site: http://www.aee-nanjing.cn
Boiler & Heat Exchanger Mfr
N.A.I.C.S.: 332410

**MEXPOL Werkzeugmaschinen
GmbH**   (1)
Kleinhulsen 31, 40721, Hilden,
Germany   (60%)
Tel.: (49) 2103 955 0
Web Site: http://www.mexpol.com
Industrial Machinery Mfr
N.A.I.C.S.: 333248
Adam Baranski (Mng Dir)

iDream Media Services GmbH   (1)
Karntner Strasse 17, 1010, Vienna, Austria
Tel.: (43) 1 6021775 0
Web Site: http://www.idream.at
Advertising Services
N.A.I.C.S.: 541810

A-TECH SOLUTION CO., LTD.
277 Gajang-ro Jeongnam-myeon,
Jeongnam-myeon, Hwaseong, 445-
962, Gyeonggi-do, Korea (South)
Tel.: (82) 313508168
Web Site:
https://www.atechsolution.co.kr
Year Founded: 2001
071670—(KRS)
Rev.: $191,384,167
Assets: $186,177,074
Liabilities: $122,123,723
Net Worth: $64,053,351
Earnings: $3,608,058
Emp.: 351
Fiscal Year-end: 12/31/22
Industrial Mold Mfr
N.A.I.C.S.: 333511
Young Mok Yoo (Pres & CEO)

Subsidiaries:

**A-TECH Solution Co., Ltd. - Cheonan
Factory**   (1)
51 Wangji 1-gil SeongHwan-eup, Seobuk-
gu, Cheonan, Chungcheongnam-do, Korea
(South)
Tel.: (82) 415908800
Industrial Mold Mfr
N.A.I.C.S.: 333511

**A-TECH Solution Co., Ltd. -
Gwang-ju Factory**   (1)
21 Hanamsandan 6beon-ro, Gwangsan-g,
Gwangju, 515-882, Jeollanam-do, Korea
(South)
Tel.: (82) 629596033
Web Site: http://www.atechsolution.co.kr
Industrial Mold Mfr
N.A.I.C.S.: 333511

Thaai Tech Solutions Pvt. Ltd.   (1)
219 m 5 t Bung A Sriracha, Chon Buri,
Thailand
Tel.: (66) 387608578
Injection Meld Mfr & Distr
N.A.I.C.S.: 333511

A-ZENITH HOME FURNISH-
INGS CO., LTD.

Yazhenqiao Caobu Town, Rudong
County, Nantong, 226400, China
Tel.: (86) 51384296002
Web Site: http://www.az.com.cn
603389—(SHG)
Rev.: $33,257,699
Assets: $111,134,406
Liabilities: $41,688,775
Net Worth: $69,445,631
Earnings: ($12,572,764)
Fiscal Year-end: 12/31/22
Furniture Product Mfr & Distr
N.A.I.C.S.: 337121
Wei Gao (Chm)

A. B. C. RECYCLING LTD
8081 Meadow Avenue, Burnaby, V3N
2V9, BC, Canada
Tel.: (604) 522-9727
Web Site:
https://www.abcrecycling.com
Year Founded: 1912
Sales Range: $75-99.9 Million
Emp.: 70
Metal Scrap Recycling & Recovery
N.A.I.C.S.: 331529

Subsidiaries:

Grande Prairie Salvage Ltd   (1)
9727 128 Avenue, Grande Prairie, T8V 4J2,
AB, Canada
Tel.: (780) 532-8028
Metal Recycling Services
N.A.I.C.S.: 562920
Tony Muratori (Gen Mgr)

A. BELANGER, LTEE.
8500 Pl Marien, Montreal, H1B 5W8,
QC, Canada
Tel.: (514) 648-5757
Web Site:
http://www.braultetmartineau.com
Year Founded: 1985
Sales Range: $300-349.9 Million
Emp.: 1,800
Furniture Retailer
N.A.I.C.S.: 449110
Yves Des Groseillers (Pres)

A. LIBENTAL HOLDINGS LTD.
74 Rothschild Ave, Tel Aviv, 6578517,
Israel
Tel.: (972) 36129988   II
LBTL—(TAE)
Rev.: $11,510,429
Assets: $81,515,954
Liabilities: $80,443,983
Net Worth: $1,071,971
Earnings: ($7,528,111)
Emp.: 3
Fiscal Year-end: 12/31/23
Offices of Other Holding Companies
N.A.I.C.S.: 551112
Rachel Malach (Dir-External)

A. METAXIOTIS S.A.
Neochorouda Warehouse, PO Box
1535, Ionia, 57008, Thessaloniki,
Greece
Tel.: (30) 2310785555
Web Site: http://www.metaxiotis.gr
Year Founded: 1986
Construction Material Whslr & Distr
N.A.I.C.S.: 423390
Konstantinos Papadopoulos (Mgr-
Transportation)

A. RACKE GMBH
Gaustrasse 20, 55411, Bingen, Ger-
many
Tel.: (49) 67211880
Web Site: http://www.racke.de
Year Founded: 1855
Sales Range: $100-124.9 Million
Emp.: 550
Wine & Spirits Mfr & Retailer
N.A.I.C.S.: 312130

Marcus Moller-Racke (Pres)

Subsidiaries:

Robert Stemmler Winery   (1)
PO Box 154 24520 Ramal Rd, Sonoma, CA
95476-9790
Tel.: (707) 939-2293
Web Site:
http://www.robertstemmlerwinery.com
Sales Range: $100-124.9 Million
Emp.: 350
Wines & Spirits Mfr
N.A.I.C.S.: 312130

The Donum Estate, Inc   (1)
PO Box 154, Sonoma, CA
95476-0154   (100%)
Tel.: (707) 939-2290
Web Site: http://www.thedonumestate.com
Sales Range: $25-49.9 Million
Emp.: 14
Premium Wines Producer
N.A.I.C.S.: 312130
Anne Moller-Racke (Pres)

A. RAPTIS & SONS PTY. LTD.
90 Colmslie Road, Colmslie, Bris-
bane, 4170, QLD, Australia
Tel.: (61) 732497888
Web Site: http://www.raptis.com.au
Year Founded: 1957
Fish & Seafood Distr
N.A.I.C.S.: 424460
Arty Raptis (CEO)

A. RAYMOND & CIE SCS
115 Cours Berriat, 38000, Grenoble,
France
Tel.: (33) 476334949
Web Site: http://www.araymond.com
Sales Range: $10-24.9 Million
Automotive Fastening & Fluid Han-
dling Connections Mfr
N.A.I.C.S.: 811114
Antoine Raymond (CEO)

Subsidiaries:

**A RAYMOND - PACIFIC SIGHT
Ltd**   (1)
Room 1226 - Century Tower 4014
Huaqiang Bei Rd, 518028, Shenzhen,
China
Tel.: (86) 75527603700
Automotive Spare Parts Mfr & Distr
N.A.I.C.S.: 336390

**A RAYMOND BAGLANTI ELEMAN-
LARI LTD. STI**   (1)
Taysad Organize Sanayi Bolgesi 1 Cadde
14 Sokak No 9, 41420, Gebze, Kocaeli,
Turkiye
Tel.: (90) 2626581058
Automotive Spare Parts Mfr & Distr
N.A.I.C.S.: 336390
Ergun Malli (Mgr-Supply Chain)

A RAYMOND ITALIANA S.r.l   (1)
Strada Complanare n 26, Carisio, 13040,
Vercelli, Italy
Tel.: (39) 0161 937311
Web Site: http://www.raymond.com
Automotive Spare Parts Distr
N.A.I.C.S.: 423120
Daniel Vizzi (Mgr-Pur)

A RAYMOND JAPAN Co., Ltd.   (1)
53-1 Suzukawa, Isehara, 259-1146, Kana-
gawa, Japan
Tel.: (81) 463 40 8600
Automotive Spare Parts Mfr & Distr
N.A.I.C.S.: 336390

**A RAYMOND TECNIACERO
SAU**   (1)
Carretera Manresa a Berga Km 0 5, Sant
Fruitos de Bages, Barcelona, 08272, Spain
Tel.: (34) 93 877 1314
Emp.: 100
Automotive Spare Parts Mfr & Distr
N.A.I.C.S.: 336390
Ivan Roca Brunet (Dir-Sls)

**A Raymond Automotive Fasteners
(Zhenjiang) Co., Ltd.**   (1)
19 Wei Si Road Ding Mao New Area,

A. Raymond & Cie SCS—(Continued)

212009, Zhenjiang, China
Tel.: (86) 511 85309000
Automotive Spare Parts Mfr & Distr
N.A.I.C.S.: 336390

**A Raymond Fasteners India Private
Limited**　　　　　　　　　　　　**(1)**
Gat No 259 276/8B Nighoje Chakan Taluka
Khed, 410501, Pune, Maharashtra, India
Tel.: (91) 2135 676 200
Automotive Spare Parts Mfr & Distr
N.A.I.C.S.: 336390
Aditya Vaze (Mgr-Supply Chain Mgmt)

**A Raymond Tinnerman Manufactur-
ing, Inc.**
1060 W 130th St, Brunswick, OH 44212-
2316
Tel.: (330) 220-5100
Web Site: http://www.tinnerman.com
Holding Company
N.A.I.C.S.: 551112
Dan Dolan (COO)

A. RAYMOND BRASIL LTDA　　　**(1)**
Av Comendador Joao Lucas 555, Distrito
Industrial Vinhedo, 13280-000, Sao Paulo,
Brazil
Tel.: (55) 19 3836 6900
Automotive Spare Parts Mfr & Distr
N.A.I.C.S.: 336390
Alessandro Andrade (Mgr-SAP Program &
Supvr-IT)

A. RAYMOND JABLONEC s.r.o.　　**(1)**
Cs Armady 27, 466 05, Jablonec nad Ni-
sou, Czech Republic
Tel.: (420) 483 358 111
Emp.: 230
Automotive Spare Parts Mfr & Distr
N.A.I.C.S.: 336390
Krivanek Martin (Acct Mgr-Sls)

A. RAYMOND KOREA Co. Ltd.　　**(1)**
29 Samsung 1-ro 4-gil, Hwaseong, 445-
170, Gyeonggi-do, Korea (South)
Tel.: (82) 70 5055 5000
Web Site: http://www.araymond.com
Emp.: 14
Automotive Spare Parts Distr
N.A.I.C.S.: 423120
Ray Park (Mgr-Sls)

A. RAYMOND Ltd.　　　　　　　　**(1)**
Mill Court Oast - Mill Street, East Malling,
ME19 6BU, Kent, United Kingdom
Tel.: (44) 1732 871934
Emp.: 10
Automotive Spare Parts Distr
N.A.I.C.S.: 423120

**A. RAYMOND SINGAPORE PTE.
LTD.**　　　　　　　　　　　　　　**(1)**
25 North Bridge Road, EFG Bank Building
08-01, 179104, Singapore, Singapore
Tel.: (65) 6221 3193
Automotive Spare Parts Mfr & Distr
N.A.I.C.S.: 336390

**A. RAYMOND TINNERMAN AUTO-
MOTIVE MEXICO S. de R.L. de
C.V.**　　　　　　　　　　　　　　**(1)**
Ave Roble 300 201 Valle del Campestre,
San Pedro Garza Garcia, 66265, Nuevo
Leon, Mexico
Tel.: (52) 248 226 5900
Automotive Spare Parts Mfr & Distr
N.A.I.C.S.: 336390

A. Raymond GmbH & Co. KG　　**(1)**
Teichstrasse 57, 79539, Lorrach, Germany
Tel.: (49) 7621 174 0
Automotive Spare Parts Mfr & Distr
N.A.I.C.S.: 336390
Yannick Munz (Mgr-Tooling)

A. Raymond RUS LLC　　　　　　**(1)**
Nizhegorodskaya oblast Igumnovskoe
shosse 5, 600000, Dzerzhinsk, Russia
Tel.: (7) 8313398111
Emp.: 9
Automotive Spare Parts Mfr & Distr
N.A.I.C.S.: 336390

**A. Raymond Tinnerman Automotive
Inc.**
3091 Research Dr, Rochester Hills, MI
48309

Tel.: (248) 260-2121
Web Site:
　http://www.araymondtinnerman.com
Automotive Spare Parts Mfr & Distr
N.A.I.C.S.: 336390

A.RAYMOND SLOVAKIA, s.r.o.　**(1)**
Halalovka 3371/69, 911 08, Trencin, Slova-
kia
Tel.: (421) 32 640 15 86
Automotive Spare Parts Mfr & Distr
N.A.I.C.S.: 336390

**A.RAYMOND TINNERMAN MANU-
FACTURING HAMILTON, Inc.**　**(1)**
686 Parkdale Avenue North, Hamilton, L8N
3K1, ON, Canada
Tel.: (905) 549-4661
Web Site: http://www.araymond-
　automotive.com
Automotive Spare Parts Mfr & Distr
N.A.I.C.S.: 336390

ARaymond Industrial　　　　　　**(1)**
123 rue Hilaire de Chardonnet, Technisud,
38000, Grenoble, France
Tel.: (33) 456525316
Web Site: http://www.araymond-
　industrial.com
Automotive Spare Parts Distr
N.A.I.C.S.: 423120

**ARaymond Tinnerman Industrial
Inc.**　　　　　　　　　　　　　　**(1)**
2600 Auburn Rd Ste 120, Auburn Hills, MI
48326
Tel.: (330) 220-5100
Automotive Spare Parts Mfr & Distr
N.A.I.C.S.: 336390

A. SORIANO CORPORATION

Tel.: (63) 288190251
Web Site: https://www.anscor.com.ph
ANS—(PHI)
Rev.: $212,536,144
Assets: $491,399,466
Liabilities: $53,411,652
Net Worth: $437,987,814
Earnings: $52,781,933
Emp.: 699
Fiscal Year-end: 12/31/21
Investment Management Service
N.A.I.C.S.: 523940
Eduardo J. Soriano (Vice Chm)

Subsidiaries:

A. Soriano Air Corporation　　　　**(1)**
A Soriano Hangar Andrews Avenue, Pasay,
1300, Manila, Philippines
Tel.: (63) 28520297
Web Site: http://www.asai.com.ph
Emp.: 10
Aircraft Support & Ground Handling Ser-
vices
N.A.I.C.S.: 488190
Genever G. Malvar (Gen Mgr)

Subsidiary (Domestic):

Pamalican Island Holdings, Inc.　**(2)**
7th Floor Pacific Star Building Sen Gil
Puyat Avenue, Corner Makati Avenue,
Makati, 1200, Philippines
Tel.: (63) 28190251
Business Management Services
N.A.I.C.S.: 551112

Subsidiary (Domestic):

Island Aviation, Inc.　　　　　　　**(3)**
A Soriano Hangar Andrews Ave, Pasay,
1300, Metro Manila, Philippines
Tel.: (63) 288333855
Web Site: https://islandaviation.com.ph
Aircraft Maintenance Services
N.A.I.C.S.: 488190
Leo Angelo S. Valeriano (Officer-
Procurement)

KSA Realty Corporation　　　　　**(1)**
The Enterprise Center Ayala Avenue cor
Paseo De Roxas, Makati, 1226, Philippines
Tel.: (63) 28865001
Real Estate Services
N.A.I.C.S.: 531390

Navegar LP　　　　　　　　　　　**(1)**
507 Zuellig Building Paseo de Roxas Cor-

ner Makati Avenue, Makati, 1226, Philip-
pines
Tel.: (63) 28 808 4566
Web Site: https://navegar.com.ph
Investment Services
N.A.I.C.S.: 523150
Honorio Poblador IV (Mng Partner)

A. TSOKKOS HOTELS PUBLIC LTD.

PO Box 30221, 5341, Ayia Napa,
Cyprus
Tel.: (357) 77 777 444
Web Site: http://www.tsokkos.com
Year Founded: 1981
Home Management Services
N.A.I.C.S.: 721110
Andreas Tsokkos (Chm)

Subsidiaries:

**Dome Investments Public Company
Ltd.**　　　　　　　　　　　　　　**(1)**
Dome Hotel Makronissos, 5341, Ayia Napa,
Cyprus　　　　　　　　　　**(99.17%)**
Tel.: (357) 23848000
Sales Range: Less than $1 Million
Home Management Services
N.A.I.C.S.: 721110
Maria Tsokkou (Exec Dir)

A. ZORBAS & SONS PUBLIC LTD.

Armenias 51, PO Box 20575, 2006,
Strovolos, Nicosia, Cyprus
Tel.: (357) 22 871700
Web Site: http://www.zorbas.com.cy
Year Founded: 1975
Bakery Products Mfr
N.A.I.C.S.: 311812
Constantinos Andreas Zorbas (Pres)

A.A.A. AG ALLGEMEINE AN-LAGEVERWALTUNG

Gutleutstrasse 175, Frankfurt am
Main, 60327, Germany
Tel.: (49) 692 400 0815
Web Site: http://www.aaa-ffm.de
AAA—(DEU)
Rev.: $7,123,792
Assets: $125,526,128
Liabilities: $68,412,968
Net Worth: $57,113,160
Earnings: ($3,439,072)
Emp.: 12
Fiscal Year-end: 12/31/20
Real Estate Management Services
N.A.I.C.S.: 531210

A.A.G. STUCCHI S.R.L.

Via IV Novembre 30/32, 23854,
Lecco, Olginate, Italy
Tel.: (39) 035996711
Web Site: http://www.aagstucchi.it
Lighting Product Mfr
N.A.I.C.S.: 335132
Aristide Stucchi (Owner)

Subsidiaries:

**A.A.G. STUCCHI ASIA PACIFIC
LTD.**　　　　　　　　　　　　　　**(1)**
Regional office Block D 2F Room5 Hop
Hing Industrial Building, 704 Castle Peak
Road, Hong Kong, Kowloon, China (Hong
Kong)
Tel.: (852) 25788988
Lighting Product Mfr
N.A.I.C.S.: 335132

**A.A.G. STUCCHI NORTH AMERICA,
INC.**　　　　　　　　　　　　　　**(1)**
3400 Peachtree Rd NE Ste 945, Atlanta,
GA 30326
Tel.: (404) 806-5399
Lighting Product Mfr
N.A.I.C.S.: 335132

**A.A.G. STUCCHI SHANGHAI
LTD.**　　　　　　　　　　　　　　**(1)**
Rm 3007 738 Chang Yang Road Yang Pu
area, Shanghai, 200082, China

Tel.: (86) 21 52389291
Lighting Product Mfr
N.A.I.C.S.: 335132

A.L.P. EUROPE LTD.　　　　　　**(1)**
Unit 3 Park Lane Industrial Estate Park
Lane, Oldbury, B69 4JX, United Kingdom
Tel.: (44) 121 5521519
Lighting Product Mfr
N.A.I.C.S.: 005102

ACHAT-VERRE AFLOX S.A.　　**(1)**
2/24 Av. de Stalingrad, 93240, Stains,
France
Tel.: (33) 1 42351001
Lighting Product Mfr
N.A.I.C.S.: 335132

**AMPLE TECHNOLOGY CO.
LTD.**　　　　　　　　　　　　　　**(1)**
16/F 29-3 Se 2, Chung-Cheng E Rd Tam-
shui Dist, Taipei, 416175, Taiwan
Tel.: (886) 2 262 42501
Lighting Product Mfr
N.A.I.C.S.: 335132

ANOMET INC.　　　　　　　　　　**(1)**
18 Regan Road Unit 25, Brampton, L7A
1C2, ON, Canada
Tel.: (905) 840-6868
Web Site: https://anomet.com
Lighting Product Mfr
N.A.I.C.S.: 335132

**ARCONA INTERNATIONAL (PTY)
LTD.**　　　　　　　　　　　　　　**(1)**
Randburg 2125, 14 Basil Street Ferndale
Ext 3, Randburg, 2194, South Africa
Tel.: (27) 11 792
Lighting Product Mfr
N.A.I.C.S.: 335132

**BRILLANTE ILUMINACION SA DE
CV**　　　　　　　　　　　　　　　**(1)**
Av Rio Consulado 121, Mexico, 02980,
Mexico
Tel.: (52) 55970219
Lighting Product Mfr
N.A.I.C.S.: 335132

C. RIBAS DE SOUSA LDA　　　　**(1)**
Avenida de Madrid 14, 1000 196, Lisbon,
Portugal
Tel.: (351) 21 8498485
Lighting Product Mfr
N.A.I.C.S.: 335132

CAIRO ELECRTRICAL GROUP　**(1)**
9 Rostom Street Garden City, Cairo, Egypt
Tel.: (20) 2 2796 1337
Emp.: 15
Lighting Product Mfr
N.A.I.C.S.: 335132
Sami Naggar (Mgr)

CALLEJA LTD.　　　　　　　　　　**(1)**
31 Bishop Labini Street, Birkirkara, Malta
Tel.: (356) 21 440341
Lighting Product Mfr
N.A.I.C.S.: 335132

**COMERCIAL TECNILUZ DE CHILE
LTDA.**　　　　　　　　　　　　　　**(1)**
El Cairo 811, Santiago, Chile
Tel.: (56) 98799298
Lighting Product Mfr
N.A.I.C.S.: 335132

COMPOLUX spol. s.r.o.　　　　　**(1)**
Osvetimany 332, 687 42, Zlin, Czech Re-
public
Tel.: (420) 572 594 208
Lighting Product Mfr
N.A.I.C.S.: 335132

DIAPA S.L.　　　　　　　　　　　　**(1)**
Sant Ramon 296-298, 08290, Barcelona,
Spain
Tel.: (34) 93 6918161
Lighting Product Mfr
N.A.I.C.S.: 335132

**ELINA TEJARAT KAVIR TRADING
COMPANY**　　　　　　　　　　　**(1)**
No 20 Block B Saman Housing Complex,
Sayyadshirazi BLVD, Isfahan, Iran
Tel.: (98) 3518228018
Lighting Product Mfr
N.A.I.C.S.: 335132

EROPED TRADING LTD.　　　　　**(1)**

Albert Qiosso St 15, Tel Aviv, 61220, Israel
Tel.: (972) 3 5183396
Lighting Product Mfr
N.A.I.C.S.: 335132

Ellis & Company Ltd. (1)
105 Morrin Road, Auckland, New Zealand
Tel.: (64) 95705267
Lighting Product Mfr
N.A.I.C.S.: 335132

GHIRARDELLI ALBERTO (1)
Via Canada 3, 35127, Padua, Italy
Tel.: (39) 049 8791464
Lighting Product Mfr
N.A.I.C.S.: 335132

HOLUX LIGHTING SYSTEM CO. LTD. (1)
Beke u 51-55, 1135, Budapest, Hungary
Tel.: (36) 1 4502700
Lighting Product Mfr
N.A.I.C.S.: 335132

I. & B. Agistriotis SA (1)
117 Kostantinoupoleos Str, 13671, Athens, Greece
Tel.: (30) 210 4523335
Lighting Product Mfr
N.A.I.C.S.: 335132

ITUS (1)
A-106 Seoul Business centre 647-26, Deungchon dong, Seoul, Korea (South)
Tel.: (82) 2 2689
Lighting Product Mfr
N.A.I.C.S.: 335132

KAPMAN ELEKTRIK VE ELEKTRONIK TIC. A.S. (1)
Maltepe Mah Davutpasa Cad Cebealibey Sok No 18, 34010, Istanbul, Türkiye
Tel.: (90) 212 2102705
Web Site: http://www.kapman.org
Emp.: 8
Lighting Product Mfr
N.A.I.C.S.: 335132

LIGHTING AUSTRALIA PTY. LTD. (1)
Unit 10/4-6 Junction Street, Auburn, 2144, NSW, Australia
Tel.: (61) 2 964 81999
Lighting Product Mfr
N.A.I.C.S.: 335132

LUCCHI LTDA. (1)
Rua Iguatemi 448 CJ 302, 01 451 010, Sao Paulo, Brazil
Tel.: (55) 11 3704 3737
Web Site: http://www.lucchi.com.br
Emp.: 300
Lighting Product Mfr
N.A.I.C.S.: 335132
Ricardo Lucchi (Mgr)

LUMEX LIGHTING LTD. (1)
83 James Baucher Blvd Office 4, 1407, Sofia, Bulgaria
Tel.: (359) 2 8624246
Lighting Product Mfr
N.A.I.C.S.: 335132

LUXTRON SISTEMS FZCO (1)
Block F Office 609, Dubay Silicon Oasis, Dubai, United Arab Emirates
Tel.: (971) 4 3712740
Lighting Product Mfr
N.A.I.C.S.: 335132

MABELEK SIGNLIGHT (1)
st Volokolamsk highway 89, Moscow, Russia
Tel.: (7) 4956385290
Web Site: http://www.signlight.ru
Lighting Product Mfr
N.A.I.C.S.: 335132

NARVA POLSKA Sp. z.o.o. (1)
Ul Szamocka 8, 01 748, Warsaw, Poland
Tel.: (48) 22 2576040
Lighting Product Mfr
N.A.I.C.S.: 335132

PAN-ISLAND INDUSTRIAL(S) PTE LTD. (1)
10 Kaki Bukit Road 1 # 03-10, Singapore, 416175, Singapore
Tel.: (65) 6 8426266
Lighting Product Mfr
N.A.I.C.S.: 335132

PPO-ELEKTRONIIKKA OY (1)
Kaarelantie 12, Helsinki, Finland
Tel.: (358) 9 566 0920
Lighting Product Mfr
N.A.I.C.S.: 335132

SHAMANJWALI METALS PVT. LTD. (1)
A Malani Group Company 12 Ho Chi Minh Sarani Unit 1 Floor 1, 700 071, Kolkata, India
Tel.: (91) 33 22825838
Lighting Product Mfr
N.A.I.C.S.: 335132

SOFIT-LUX LTD. (1)
Semya Hohlovyh Street 8A, Kiev, Ukraine
Tel.: (380) 44 5946706
Lighting Product Mfr
N.A.I.C.S.: 335132

SOYUZ-SVET LTD. (1)
Yakutskaya Street 8, 03134, Kiev, Ukraine
Tel.: (380) 44 4992250
Lighting Product Mfr
N.A.I.C.S.: 335132

TECHNOLAMP (1)
Cra 33 No 18A-70, Bogota, Colombia
Tel.: (57) 1 3608000
Lighting Product Mfr
N.A.I.C.S.: 335132

TECNILUZ S.A. (1)
Cerrito 3460 1752 Lomas Del Mirador, Buenos Aires, Argentina
Tel.: (54) 11 44417777
Lighting Product Mfr
N.A.I.C.S.: 335132

TERTIUM S.P.R.L. (1)
124 rue Beeckman, Brussels, Belgium
Tel.: (32) 2 3614 858
Lighting Product Mfr
N.A.I.C.S.: 335132

THORKILD LARSEN A/S (1)
Fabriksvangen 17, Slangerup, Denmark
Tel.: (45) 48 186666
Lighting Product Mfr
N.A.I.C.S.: 335132

VANPEE AB (1)
Karlsbodavagen 39, 168 67, Bromma, Sweden
Tel.: (46) 84452800
Web Site: http://www.vanpee.se
Emp.: 25
Lighting Product Mfr
N.A.I.C.S.: 335132
Hakam Donnelly (Gen Mgr)

VANPEE NORGE AS (1)
Vestvollveien 6E, 2019, Skedsmokorset, Norway
Tel.: (47) 64838280
Lighting Product Mfr
N.A.I.C.S.: 335132

W. GEUKEN B.V. (1)
Wattstraat 15 A, 2725, Zoetermeer, Netherlands
Tel.: (31) 79 3616070
Lighting Product Mfr
N.A.I.C.S.: 335132

ZENO ZANINI GmbH (1)
Tiergartenstrsse 130, 30559, Hannover, Germany
Tel.: (49) 511 5248720
Lighting Product Mfr
N.A.I.C.S.: 335132

A.AGRATI S.P.A.
Via Piave 28-30, 20837, Veduggio con Colzano, Monza and Brianza, Italy
Tel.: (39) 0362 980 1
Web Site: http://www.agrati.com
Year Founded: 1939
Sales Range: $400-449.9 Million
Fasteners & Fastening Systems Mfr & Distr
N.A.I.C.S.: 332722

Subsidiaries:

Agrati Gie (1)

41 rue Le Corbusier, 94046, Creteil, Cedex, France
Tel.: (33) 156717900
Web Site: http://www.agrati.com
Emp.: 27
Mechanical Fastener Sales
N.A.I.C.S.: 423510

Agrati Vieux Conde S.A.S. (1)
2 rue Dervaux, BP 29, 59690, Vieux Conde, France
Tel.: (33) 327191500
Web Site: http://www.acument.com
Sales Range: $50-74.9 Million
Emp.: 500
Bolts, Nuts, Rivets & Screws Mfr
N.A.I.C.S.: 332722

Continental/Midland, LLC (1)
24000 S Western Ave, Park Forest, IL 60466
Tel.: (708) 747-1200
Web Site: http://www.agrati.com
Fasteners, Fastener Assemblies & Installation Systems Fasteners Mfr
N.A.I.C.S.: 332722
Connie Hughes-Rice (Dir-HR)

A.C. DISPENSING EQUIPMENT INC.
100 Dispensing Way, Lower Sackville, B4C 4H2, NS, Canada
Tel.: (902) 865-9602
Web Site:
http://www.sureshotdispensing.com
Year Founded: 1985
Rev.: $21,341,410
Emp.: 140
Dispensing Systems Mfr
N.A.I.C.S.: 333914
Michael R. Duck (Founder)

A.C. SIMMONDS & SONS, INC.
3565 King Road, King City, L7B 1M3, ON, Canada
Tel.: (905) 833-3072
Web Site:
http://www.acsimmondsandsons.com
Sales Range: Less than $1 Million
Private Investment Firm
N.A.I.C.S.: 523999
Carrie J. Weiler (Sec)

A.D. USLUGA
Edvarda Kardelja 12, 24300, Backa Topola, Vojvodina, Serbia
Tel.: (381) 24715329
Web Site: https://www.usluga.co.rs
Year Founded: 1959
USBT—(BEL)
Rev.: $3,032,299
Assets: $3,563,716
Liabilities: $1,720,887
Net Worth: $1,842,829
Earnings: $34,085
Emp.: 94
Fiscal Year-end: 12/31/22
Funeral Outfit Mfr
N.A.I.C.S.: 339999

A.D. WORKS CORPORATION
13th Floor NBF Hibiya Building 1-1-7 Uchisaiwai-cho, Chiyoda-ku, Tokyo, 100-0011, Japan
Tel.: (81) 3 5251 7561
Web Site: http://www.re-adworks.com
Year Founded: 1936
Rev.: $225,240,660
Assets: $277,462,500
Liabilities: $169,222,680
Net Worth: $108,239,820
Earnings: $6,006,780
Emp.: 167
Fiscal Year-end: 03/31/19
Real Estate Services
N.A.I.C.S.: 531390
Hideo Tanaka (Chm, Pres & CEO)

A.D.WORKS GROUP CO., LTD.
5th Floor Hibiya Kokusai Bldg 2-2-3

Uchisaiwai-Cho, Chiyoda-ku, Tokyo, 100-0011, Japan
Tel.: (81) 352517642
Web Site: https://www.adwg.co.jp
Year Founded: 1886
2982—(TKS)
Rev.: $293,114,780
Assets: $417,274,860
Liabilities: $295,567,920
Net Worth: $121,706,940
Earnings: $10,060,710
Emp.: 232
Fiscal Year-end: 12/31/23
Real Estate Development Services
N.A.I.C.S.: 531311
Naoji Aoki (Founder)

Subsidiaries:

Sumikawa ADD Co., Ltd. (1)
1-2-3 Koyodai, Inagi-shi, Tokyo, 206-0803, Japan
Tel.: (81) 424015123
Interior Decoration Services
N.A.I.C.S.: 541410

A.F. ENTERPRISES LIMITED
Plot No 8 Main Mathura Road Sector-5, Faridabad, 121006, Haryana, India
Tel.: (91) 8744998855
Web Site: https://afenterprisesltd.in
Year Founded: 1983
538351—(BOM)
Rev.: $6,962,266
Assets: $19,620,978
Liabilities: $17,092,188
Net Worth: $2,528,790
Earnings: $152,424
Emp.: 23
Fiscal Year-end: 03/31/22
Investment Services
N.A.I.C.S.: 523999
Abhishek Singh (CFO)

A.F.W CO., LTD.
51 Gongdan-Ro 1-Gil, Waegwan-Eup, Chilgok, 39909, Gyeongsangbuk-do, Korea (South)
Tel.: (82) 548005500
Web Site: https://www.asanfw.com
Year Founded: 1998
312610—(KRS)
Rev.: $3,403,469
Assets: $51,709,819
Liabilities: $1,120,316
Net Worth: $50,589,503
Earnings: ($2,583,784)
Emp.: 60
Fiscal Year-end: 12/31/22
Electric Vehicle Mfr & Distr
N.A.I.C.S.: 336320
Junga Jin (CEO)

A.G. BARR PLC
Westfield House 4 Mollins Road, Cumbernauld, G68 9HD, United Kingdom
Tel.: (44) 3303903900   UK
Web Site: https://www.agbarr.co.uk
Year Founded: 1951
BAG—(LSE)
Rev.: $382,549,200
Assets: $454,698,750
Liabilities: $130,929,150
Net Worth: $323,769,600
Earnings: $40,832,550
Fiscal Year-end: 01/29/23
Holding Company; Soft Drink Mfr
N.A.I.C.S.: 551112
Roger A. White (CEO)

Subsidiaries:

Funkin Limited (1)
122 Arlington Road, Camden, London, NW1 7HP, United Kingdom
Tel.: (44) 2073284440
Web Site: http://www.funkincocktails.co.uk
Cocktail Product Retailer

A.G. Barr plc—(Continued)

N.A.I.C.S.: 424820

MOMA Foods Limited **(1)**
122 Arlington Road, London, NW1 7HP,
United Kingdom
Tel.: (44) 2073284440
Beverage Distr
N.A.I.C.S.: 424490

Tizer Limited **(1)**
Crossley Drive Magna Park, Milton Keynes,
MK17 8FL, United Kingdom
Tel.: (44) 3303904900
Beverage Distr
N.A.I.C.S.: 424490

A.G. UNIVERSAL LIMITED
Plot No 2 1st Floor Arihant Nagar
Near Shivaji Metro Station, West
Punjabi Bagh, New Delhi, 110026,
India
Tel.: (91) 8178801010
Web Site:
https://www.aguniversal.co.in
Year Founded: 2008
AGUL—(NSE)
Steel Product Mfr & Distr
N.A.I.C.S.: 331210
Amit Gupta (Mng Dir)

A.H. ALGOSAIBI & BROS.
PO Box 106, Al Khobar, 31952,
Saudi Arabia
Tel.: (966) 38822666
Web Site:
http://www.ahalgosaibi.com
Sales Range: $200-249.9 Million
Emp.: 1,000
Private Investment Company
N.A.I.C.S.: 523940
Yousef Ahmad Hamad Algosaibi
(Chm)

Subsidiaries:

Eastern Insulation Company **(1)**
PO Box 32245, Al Khobar, 31952, Saudi
Arabia
Tel.: (966) 3 847 3335
Web Site: http://www.eicofoam.com.sa
Polystyrene Foam Product Mfr
N.A.I.C.S.: 326140

Jeddah Beverage Can Making Co.
Ltd. **(1)**
Industrial city phase 3 Rd 153 Street 31,
PO Box 16626, Jeddah, B21474, Saudi
Arabia
Tel.: (966) 26361750
Web Site: http://www.jbcmc.com
Sales Range: $75-99.9 Million
Emp.: 256
Mfr of Packaging Products for Consumer
Goods; Joint Venture of Crown Cork & Seal
Co., Inc. & A.H. Algosaibi & Bros.
N.A.I.C.S.: 326199

Raymond Saudi Arabia Limited **(1)**
PO Box 6391, Al Khobar, 34423, Saudi
Arabia
Tel.: (966) 13 887 5296
Web Site: http://www.raymondsaudi.com
Pipeline Construction Services
N.A.I.C.S.: 237120
Saeed Haneefa (Engr-Matl)

Tecmo Arabia Ltd **(1)**
PO Box 31808, Al Khobar, 31952, Saudi
Arabia
Tel.: (966) 3 8822836
Web Site: http://www.tecmoarabia.com
Power Generation Services
N.A.I.C.S.: 221118

A.L.D. ADVANCED LOGIS-TICS DEVELOPMENTS LTD.
(Acquired by HUB Cyber Se-curity Ltd.)

A.I.S. AG
Friedrichstr 171, Hennigsdorf, 10117,
Berlin, Germany

Tel.: (49) 30303660502
Web Site: https://www.ais-ag.eu
LUM—(DEU)
Sales Range: $1-9.9 Million
Waste Management & Electric Power
Generation Services
N.A.I.C.S.: 924110
Johan Charles Bendien (Member-Mgmt Bd)

A.I.S. RESOURCES LIMITED
1120 - 789 West Pender Street, Van-couver, V6C 1H2, BC, Canada
Tel.: (604) 687-6820
Web Site:
https://www.aisresources.com
AISSF—(OTCIQ)
Rev.: $16,167
Assets: $1,867,629
Liabilities: $1,261,578
Net Worth: $606,051
Earnings: ($2,618,801)
Fiscal Year-end: 12/31/23
Gold Mining Services
N.A.I.C.S.: 212220
Martyn Element (Chm, Pres & CEO)

A.J. GREEN SHELL PLC
15 Ayion Omologiton Avenue, 1080,
Nicosia, Cyprus
Tel.: (357) 22452600
Web Site:
https://planetcleanrecycleplc.com
ROFOL—(CYP)
Rev.: $6,988
Assets: $2,245
Liabilities: $437
Net Worth: $1,809
Earnings: $1,878
Fiscal Year-end: 12/31/19
Real Estate Asset Management Ser-vices
N.A.I.C.S.: 531390

A.J. LUCAS GROUP LIMITED
Emirates House Lvl 22 167 Eagle
Street, Brisbane, 4000, QLD, Austra-lia
Tel.: (61) 33637333   AU
Web Site: https://www.lucas.com.au
AJL—(ASX)
Rev.: $106,239,984
Assets: $72,327,724
Liabilities: $110,947,516
Net Worth: ($38,619,792)
Earnings: ($476,763)
Emp.: 334
Fiscal Year-end: 06/30/24
Pipeline & Drilling Services
N.A.I.C.S.: 333132
Brett Tredinnick (CEO-Drilling Ops)

Subsidiaries:

AJ Lucas Coal Technologies Pty
Limited **(1)**
616 Danjrry RD, Brisbane, 4077, QLD, Aus-tralia
Tel.: (61) 733637333
Web Site: http://www.lucas.com
Sales Range: $50-74.9 Million
Emp.: 80
Drilling Services
N.A.I.C.S.: 213111
Brett Tredinnick (Gen Mgr)

AJ Lucas Drilling Pty Limited **(1)**
Level 2 394 Lane Cove Road, Locked Bag
2113, Macquarie Park, 2113, NSW, Austra-lia
Tel.: (61) 294904000
Sales Range: $400-449.9 Million
Drilling Services
N.A.I.C.S.: 237110

AJ Lucas Operations Pty Limited **(1)**
157 Church St, Ryde, 2113, NSW, Australia
Tel.: (61) 2 9809 6866
Sales Range: $25-49.9 Million
Emp.: 90
Building Construction & Drilling Services

N.A.I.C.S.: 236210

AJ Lucas Plant & Equipment Pty
Limited **(1)**
394 Lane Cove Rd, Macquarie Park, 2113,
NSW, Australia
Tel.: (61) 294904000
Web Site: http://www.lucas.com.au
Emp.: 15
Drilling Well & Pipeline Services
N.A.I.C.S.: 237110
John Stuart-Robertson (Gen Mgr)

AJ Lucas Testing Pty Limited **(1)**
Ste 6 Level 6 1 Elizabeth Plaza, Locked
Bag 2113, North Sydney, 2060, NSW, Aus-tralia
Tel.: (61) 294904000
Web Site: http://www.lucas.com.au
Sales Range: $25-49.9 Million
Emp.: 200
Inspecting & Testing Services
N.A.I.C.S.: 541350
Ian Ridsein (Gen Mgr)

Lucas SARL **(1)**
8 Rue Du Gen Barbot, Saint-Laurent-Blangy, 62223, Pas-de-Calais, France
Tel.: (33) 975524660
Machine Tools Mfr
N.A.I.C.S.: 333517

A.J. PLAST PUBLIC COMPANY LIMITED
95 Tha Kham Rd, Bang Khun Thian
District, Bangkok, 10150, Thailand
Tel.: (66) 24150035
Web Site: https://www.ajplast.co.th
Year Founded: 1987
AJ—(THA)
Rev.: $225,387,140
Assets: $417,394,294
Liabilities: $286,221,405
Net Worth: $131,172,889
Earnings: $11,743,842
Emp.: 1,591
Fiscal Year-end: 12/31/23
Biaxially Oriented Film Mfr
N.A.I.C.S.: 339999
Narong Suthisamphat (Pres)

A.K. AL-MUHAIDIB & SONS GROUP OF COMPANIES
PO Box 30, Dammam, 31411, Saudi
Arabia
Tel.: (966) 138455555
Web Site: http://www.muhaidib.com
Year Founded: 1946
Sales Range: $200-249.9 Million
Emp.: 200
Holding Company; Building Materials
& Food Stuffs Whslr
N.A.I.C.S.: 551112
Emad Abdul Kadi Al Muhaidib (Vice
Chm)

Subsidiaries:

Al Muhaidib Building Materials
Company **(1)**
PO Box 16197, Jeddah, 21464, Saudi Ara-bia
Tel.: (966) 12 617 2000
Building Materials Whslr
N.A.I.C.S.: 423320
Saleh Al Qadri (CIO & Head-Quality Mgmt)

Al Muhaidib Contracting Co. **(1)**
Hail Street, PO Box 9291, Jeddah, 21413,
Saudi Arabia
Tel.: (966) 9200 26220
Web Site: http://www.muhaidibco.com.sa
Residential Construction Services
N.A.I.C.S.: 237990
Abdulraheem Mahmoud Moumin (Mgr-Warehouse)

Al Muhaidib Foods Co. **(1)**
King Faisal Coastal Road - Salman Al
Faresi Street, PO Box 9149, Dammam,
31413, Saudi Arabia
Tel.: (966) 3 845 5555
Web Site: http://www.am-food.com
Food Product Mfr & Distr
N.A.I.C.S.: 311991

Khalid Al Mazrou (Mgr-HR)

Al Muhaidib Land Transport
Company **(1)**
PO Box 5356, Dammam, 31422, Saudi
Arabia
Tel.: (966) 3 814 1674
Web Site: http://www.mlt.com.sa
Freight Transportation Services
N.A.I.O.O.: 404110

Al Muhaidib Technical Supplies
Company **(1)**
Old Industrial City Al Senaya Prince Salman
Street, Riyadh, Saudi Arabia
Tel.: (966) 1 4489999
Industrial Supplies Distr
N.A.I.C.S.: 423840

Al-Muhaidib Hardware **(1)**
Amir Salman Street, PO Box 42300, Ri-yadh, 11541, Saudi Arabia
Tel.: (966) 14488404
Web Site: http://www.mhw.com.sa
Sales Range: $75-99.9 Million
Emp.: 250
Hardware Importer, Distr & Whslr
N.A.I.C.S.: 423710

Reem Rice Mills (Private)
Limited **(1)**
13/123 E-1 Hall Road Gulberg III, Lahore,
Pakistan
Tel.: (92) 425760101
Web Site: http://www.reemriz.com
Rice Producer
N.A.I.C.S.: 311212

Riyadh Cables Group of
Companies **(1)**
PO Box 26862, Riyadh, 11496, Saudi Ara-bia
Tel.: (966) 12651415
Web Site: http://www.riyadh-cables.com
Sales Range: $550-599.9 Million
Emp.: 1,800
Electrical Cables, Copper Rods, Telecom-munications & Fiber Optics Cables Mfr &
Distr
N.A.I.C.S.: 335921

Subsidiary (Domestic):

Saudi Modern Company for Cables
Industry Ltd. **(2)**
PO Box 26862, Riyadh, 11496, Saudi Ara-bia
Tel.: (966) 12651415
Web Site: http://www.riyadh-cables.com
Cable Mfr
N.A.I.C.S.: 335921

Saudi Modern Company for Metals,
Cables and Plastic Industry Ltd. **(2)**
PO Box 26862, Riyadh, 11496, Saudi Ara-bia
Tel.: (966) 012651415
Cable & Wire Mfr
N.A.I.C.S.: 335921

Saudi Modern Company for Special
Electric Wire & Cables Industry
Ltd. **(2)**
Al Kharj Road Street No 4, PO Box 26862,
2nd Industrial City Zone D, Riyadh, 11496,
Saudi Arabia
Tel.: (966) 12651415
Sales Range: $25-49.9 Million
Wire & Cable Mfr
N.A.I.C.S.: 335929

Saudi Modern Company for Tele-phone Cable Industry Ltd. **(2)**
PO Box 26862, Riyadh, 11496, Saudi Ara-bia
Tel.: (966) 12651415
Telephone Cable Mfr
N.A.I.C.S.: 335929

United Sugar Company **(1)**
PO Box 23023, Jeddah, Saudi Arabia
Tel.: (966) 26492222
Web Site: http://www.unitedsugar.com
Sugar Processor & Distr
N.A.I.C.S.: 111930

Veetee Rice Limited **(1)**
Veetee House Neptune Close, Medway City
Estate, Rochester, ME2 4LT, Kent, United
Kingdom

Tel.: (44) 1634290092
Web Site: http://www.veetee.com
Sales Range: $25-49.9 Million
Emp.: 60
Rice Distr
N.A.I.C.S.: 311212
Moni Varma *(CEO)*

Subsidiary (Non-US):

Kawther Grain (Private) Limited **(2)**
219-E Sarwar Road, Lahore, Pakistan
Tel.: (92) 42 6664 465
Web Site: http://www.kawthergrain.com
Rice Processor
N.A.I.C.S.: 311212

PICRIC Limited **(2)**
5th Fl 'B' Tower Aggarwal Cyber Plaza, Netaji Subash Place, Delhi, 110034, Pitampura, India
Tel.: (91) 1127352506
Rice Producer & Exporter
N.A.I.C.S.: 311212

A.K. CAPITAL SERVICES LTD.
601-603 6th Floor Windsor off CST
Road Kalina Santacruz - East, 215
Nariman Point, Mumbai, 400 098,
India
Tel.: (91) 2267546500
Web Site: https://www.akgroup.co.in
530499—(BOM)
Rev.: $44,074,635
Assets: $370,455,977
Liabilities: $262,970,785
Net Worth: $107,485,191
Earnings: $11,330,264
Emp.: 88
Fiscal Year-end: 03/31/22
Commercial Banking Services
N.A.I.C.S.: 522110
A. K. Mittal *(CEO & Mng Dir)*

A.K. SPINTEX LTD.
14th KM Stone Chittorgarh Road, Vil-
lage Biliya Kalan, Bhilwara, 311 001,
Rajasthan, India
Tel.: (91) 9887049006
Web Site: https://www.akspintex.com
539300—(BOM)
Rev.: $6,564,311
Assets: $6,424,073
Liabilities: $3,503,940
Net Worth: $2,920,133
Earnings: $62,399
Fiscal Year-end: 03/31/21
Textile Products Mfr
N.A.I.C.S.: 314999
Prakash Chand Chhabra *(Chm &
Mng Dir)*

A.L. PROCHOICE GROUP
PUBLIC LTD.
Spyrou Kyprianou 57, 6051, Larnaca,
Cyprus
Tel.: (357) 24 661192
Web Site: http://www.pro-
choice.com.cy
Sales Range: $1-9.9 Million
Financial Holding Company
N.A.I.C.S.: 551112
Andreas Leonidou *(Chm & Gen Dir)*

Subsidiaries:

Prochoice Chrimatistiriaki Ltd **(1)**
Spyrou Kyprianou 57, 6051, Larnaca, Cy-
prus
Tel.: (357) 24661192
Web Site: http://www.pro-choice.com.cy
Investment Services
N.A.I.C.S.: 523150
Andreas Leonidou *(Chm & Gen Dir)*

A.L.P.A. EQUIPMENT
55 Industrial Avenue, Truro, B2N
6V1, NS, Canada
Tel.: (902) 897-2717
Web Site:
   http://www.alpaequipment.com

Year Founded: 1976
Rev.: $13,665,920
Emp.: 60
Construction & Mining Machinery &
Equipment Merchant Whlsr
N.A.I.C.S.: 423830
Armand Landry *(Pres)*

A.P. MOLLER HOLDING A/S
Esplanaden 50, 1263, Copenhagen,
Denmark
Tel.: (45) 61 18 10 20   DK
Web Site: http://www.apmoller.com
Year Founded: 2013
Holding Company
N.A.I.C.S.: 551112
Jan Nielsen *(CIO)*

Subsidiaries:

Maersk Tankers A/S **(1)**
Nicolai Eigtveds Gade 28 4th, 1402, Copen-
hagen, Denmark
Tel.: (45) 8987 0040
Web Site: http://www.maersktankers.com
Oil & Natural Gas Transport Services
N.A.I.C.S.: 488510
Christian M. Ingerslev *(Chief Investment
Officer)*

A.P. MOLLER-MAERSK A/S
Esplanaden 50, 1263, Copenhagen,
Denmark
Tel.: (45) 33633363   DK
Web Site: https://www.maersk.com
Year Founded: 1904
MAERKS.A—(CSE)
Rev.: $51,065,000,000
Assets: $82,100,000,000
Liabilities: $27,010,000,000
Net Worth: $55,090,000,000
Earnings: $3,908,000,000
Emp.: 100,000
Fiscal Year-end: 12/31/23
Logistic Services
N.A.I.C.S.: 551112
Marc Engel *(Vice Chm)*

Subsidiaries:

A.P. Moller Singapore Pte. Ltd. **(1)**
3 Harbourfront Place 13-01 Harbourfront
Tower 2, Singapore, 099254, Singapore
Tel.: (65) 63238323
Web Site: http://www.apmsingapore.com
Sales Range: $1-4.9 Billion
Emp.: 3,300
Marine Vessel Service
N.A.I.C.S.: 488330

APM Terminals - Aarhus A/S **(1)**
Oesthavnsvej 43, 8000, Aarhus, Denmark
Tel.: (45) 89348800
Marine Transportation Services
N.A.I.C.S.: 488390

APM Terminals - Cargo Service
A/S **(1)**
Osthavnsvej 43, Box 165, 8100, Arhus,
Denmark
Tel.: (45) 8934 8800
Sales Range: $25-49.9 Million
Emp.: 30
Marine Cargo Handling Services
N.A.I.C.S.: 488320
Johan Uggla *(Mng Dir)*

APM Terminals Apapa Ltd. **(1)**
Container Terminal Apapa Port Wharf Road,
Apapa, Lagos, Nigeria
Tel.: (234) 8097627965
Web Site: https://www.apmterminals.com
Marine Transportation Services
N.A.I.C.S.: 488390

APM Terminals Bahrain B.S.C. **(1)**
Khalifa Bin Salman Port, PO Box 50490,
Hidd, Bahrain
Tel.: (973) 17365500
Marine Transportation Services
N.A.I.C.S.: 488390

APM Terminals Callao S.A. **(1)**
Av Atalaya, 07021, Callao, Peru
Tel.: (51) 12008800
Web Site: https://www.apmterminals.com

Marine Transportation Services
N.A.I.C.S.: 488390

APM Terminals Elizabeth, LLC **(1)**
5080 McLester St, Elizabeth, NJ 07207
Tel.: (908) 558-6000
N.A.I.C.S.: 541614
Henrik Kristensen *(Mng Dir-Port Ops)*

APM Terminals Gothenburg AB **(1)**
Port Entry Ytterhamnsvagen 1, Gothenburg,
Sweden
Tel.: (46) 101222000
Marine Transportation Services
N.A.I.C.S.: 488390

APM Terminals India Pvt. Ltd. **(1)**
URMI Estate 11th Floor Tower A Ganpatrao
Kadam Marg Lower Parel, Mumbai,
400013, India
Tel.: (91) 2233407622
Marine Transportation Services
N.A.I.C.S.: 488390

APM Terminals International B.V. **(1)**
Anna van Saksenlaan 71, Hague, 2593,
Netherlands
Tel.: (31) 703043100
Web Site: http://www.apmterminals.com
Sales Range: $50-74.9 Million
Emp.: 150
Container Terminal Operator
N.A.I.C.S.: 488510
Christian Moller Laursen *(CFO)*

Subsidiary (US):

APM Terminal Pacific Ltd. **(2)**
1002 Milwaukee Way, Tacoma, WA 98421
Tel.: (253) 680-4439
Sales Range: $25-49.9 Million
Emp.: 33
Freight Transportation Services
N.A.I.C.S.: 488510
Alan McCorkle *(Mng Dir)*

Subsidiary (Non-US):

APM Terminals **(2)**
5 Sati Road Killarney Gardens, 7420, Cape
Town, South Africa
Tel.: (27) 21 550 5562
Web Site: http://www.apmterminals.co.za
Sales Range: $25-49.9 Million
Emp.: 90
Container Handling & Storage Services
N.A.I.C.S.: 493190
Alan Ross *(Mgr-Ops)*

APM Terminals Algeciras S.A. **(2)**
Muelle Juan Carlos I, PO Box 160, Algeci-
ras, 11201, Cadiz, Spain
Tel.: (34) 95 667 1900
Web Site: http://www.apmterminals.com
Sales Range: $25-49.9 Million
Container Terminal Operation Services
N.A.I.C.S.: 493190

Subsidiary (Domestic):

APM Terminals B.V. **(2)**
Turfmarkt 107, Hague, 2511 DP, Nether-
lands
Tel.: (31) 703043100
Web Site: http://www.apmterminals.com
Container Terminal Operation Services
N.A.I.C.S.: 493110

Subsidiary (Non-US):

APM Terminals Liberia Ltd **(2)**
Freeport Monrovia Bushrod Island, PO Box
1929, 1000, Monrovia, Liberia
Tel.: (231) 880649068
Container Terminal Operation Services
N.A.I.C.S.: 493190
Clay Crain *(Mng Dir)*

Subsidiary (Domestic):

APM Terminals Management
B.V. **(2)**
Turfmarkt 107 5th Floor, 2511 DP, Hague,
Netherlands
Tel.: (31) 70 304 3100
Web Site: http://www.apmterminals.com
Rev.: $4,682,320,000
Container Terminal Operation Services
N.A.I.C.S.: 493190

APM Terminals North America
B.V. **(2)**
Turfmarkt 107, Hague, 2511 DP, Nether-
lands
Tel.: (31) 703043100
Emp.: 250
Container Terminal Operation Services
N.A.I.C.S.: 493190
Jim Pfeiffer *(Gen Mgr)*

Subsidiary (US):

APM Terminals North America,
Inc. **(2)**
9300 Arrowpoint Blvd, Charlotte, NC 28273
Tel.: (704) 571-2768
Web Site: http://www.apmterminals.com
Sales Range: $25-49.9 Million
Container Terminal Operator
N.A.I.C.S.: 488510
Jon Poelma *(Mng Dir-Elizabeth)*

Subsidiary (Domestic):

APM Terminals Rotterdam B.V. **(2)**
Coloradoweg 50 Port Number 8203, Maasv-
lakte, 3199 LA, Rotterdam, Netherlands
Tel.: (31) 181 372 222
Sales Range: $125-149.9 Million
Emp.: 600
Container Terminal Operation Services
N.A.I.C.S.: 493190
Hans van Kerkhof *(Mng Dir)*

Subsidiary (Non-US):

Gujarat Pipavav Port Limited **(2)**
Pipavav Port At Post Uchchaiya via Rajula,
District Amreli, Gandhinagar, 365 560, Gu-
jarat, India **(57.9%)**
Tel.: (91) 2794302400
Web Site: http://www.pipavav.com
Sales Range: $100-124.9 Million
Port Operations
N.A.I.C.S.: 488310
Manish Agnihotri *(Sec & Compliance Offi-
cer)*

APM Terminals Lazaro Cardenas
S.A. de C.V. **(1)**
Interior Recinto Portuario S/N, Lazaro
Cardenas, Mexico
Tel.: (52) 7535404300
Marine Transportation Services
N.A.I.C.S.: 488390

APM Terminals Maasvlakte II
B.V. **(1)**
Europaweg 910 Havenr 8410 Maasvlakte-
RT, 3199 LC, Rozenburg, Netherlands
Tel.: (31) 107549500
Marine Transportation Services
N.A.I.C.S.: 488390

APM Terminals Mobile, LLC **(1)**
901 Ezra Trice Blvd, Mobile, AL 36603
Tel.: (251) 410-6100
Web Site: https://www.apmterminals.com
Marine Transportation Services
N.A.I.C.S.: 488390

APM Terminals Moin S.A. **(1)**
Roble Corporate Center Contiguo a Hotel
Intercontinental Piso 3, Escazu, Costa Rica
Tel.: (506) 25206501
N.A.I.C.S.: 541614
Jose Rueda *(Mng Dir)*

APM Terminals Pacific LLC **(1)**
9300 Arrowpoint Blvd, Charlotte, NC 28273-
8136
Tel.: (704) 571-2000
N.A.I.C.S.: 541614

APM Terminals Tangier SA **(1)**
Zone Franche Ksar Al Majaz Oued R'Mel,
BP 216, Anjra Route de Fenideq, Ksar
Sghir, Morocco
Tel.: (212) 531061100
Web Site: http://www.apmterminals.com
Marine Transportation Services
N.A.I.C.S.: 488390

APM Terminals Valencia S.A. **(1)**
Lugar Muelle De Levante S/N, 46024, Va-
lencia, Spain
Tel.: (34) 963241680
Web Site: https://www.apmterminals.com
Yard Operation Machinery Maintenance
Services

A.P. Moller-Maersk A/S—(Continued)

N.A.I.C.S.: 811310

Addicks & Kreye Container Service GmbH & Co. KG **(1)**
Amerikaring 21, 27580, Bremerhaven, Germany **(51%)**
Tel.: (49) 47 198 3950
Container Trucking Services
N.A.I.C.S.: 484110

Alianca Navegacao e Logistica Ltda. **(1)**
Tel.: (55) 1151855600
Web Site: http://www.alianca.com.br
Marine Transportation Services
N.A.I.C.S.: 488390

Brostrom AB **(1)**
Molndalsvagen 24, 412 63, Gothenburg, Sweden
Tel.: (46) 31616100
Web Site: http://www.brostrom.se
Sales Range: $500-549.9 Million
Emp.: 1,526
Logistic Services
N.A.I.C.S.: 541614
Robert Maersk Uggla (Mng Dir)

Subsidiary (Domestic):

Brostrom Holding BV **(2)**
Molndalsvagen 24, 40523, Gothenburg, Sweden **(100%)**
Tel.: (46) 31616000
Web Site: http://www.brostrom.se
Sales Range: $25-49.9 Million
Emp.: 110
Process Physical Distribution & Logistics Consulting Services
N.A.I.C.S.: 541614
Robert Maersk Uggla (CEO)

Brostrom Tankers AB **(2)**
Molndalsvagen 24, 40330, Gothenburg, Sweden **(100%)**
Tel.: (46) 31616000
Web Site: http://www.brostrom.se
Sales Range: $25-49.9 Million
Emp.: 80
Other Support Activities for Water Transportation
N.A.I.C.S.: 488390

Subsidiary (Non-US):

Brostrom Tankers SAS **(2)**
52 avenue Champs Elysees, 75008, Paris, France **(100%)**
Tel.: (33) 142996666
Web Site: http://www.brostrom.no
Sales Range: $25-49.9 Million
Emp.: 54
Process Physical Distribution & Logistics Consulting Services
N.A.I.C.S.: 541614

Coman S.A. **(1)**
Maersk House Zone OCBN Lot 531 Parcelle B 01, BP 2826, Cotonou, Benin
Tel.: (229) 21 316092
Marine Cargo Handling Services
N.A.I.C.S.: 488320

Container Operators S.A. **(1)**
Av Las Factorias 8150 Malvilla, San Antonio, Chile
Tel.: (56) 352202700
Web Site: http://www.contopsa.cl
Sales Range: $25-49.9 Million
Emp.: 186
Container Terminal Operation Services
N.A.I.C.S.: 493190

Damco Australia Pty. Ltd. **(1)**
53 Harrick Road, Keilor Park, Melbourne, 3042, VIC, Australia
Tel.: (61) 399331300
Logistics & Supply Services
N.A.I.C.S.: 488510

Damco China Limited **(1)**
3&5/F Tian'An Center No 338 Nanjing West Road, Shanghai, 200003, China
Tel.: (86) 2123062000
Freight Forwarding Services
N.A.I.C.S.: 488510

Damco France S.A.S. **(1)**
40 rue de la Vague Heron Parc, Villeneuve

d'Ascq, 59650, France
Tel.: (33) 328765252
Web Site: http://www.damco.com
Emp.: 80
Freight Forwarding Services
N.A.I.C.S.: 488510

Damco India Private Limited **(1)**
3rd Floor Shobhan Building 6-3-927/ A & B Somajiguda Raj Bhavan Road, Hyderabad, Andhra Pradesh, India
Tel.: (91) 40 66567200
Sales Range: $50-74.9 Million
Emp.: 15
Freight Forwarding Services
N.A.I.C.S.: 488510
Lars Sorensen (CEO)

Damco International A/S **(1)**
Sommervej 31b, Aarhus V, 8210, Haslev, Denmark **(100%)**
Tel.: (45) 89316100
Web Site: http://www.damco.com
Sales Range: $1-9.9 Million
Emp.: 10,000
Freight Transportation & Storage Services
N.A.I.C.S.: 488510

Subsidiary (Domestic):

Damco A/S **(2)**
Sletvej 2e, 8310, Tranbjerg, Denmark
Tel.: (45) 89316600
Freight Forwarding Services
N.A.I.C.S.: 488510
Hanne Birgitte Breinbjerg Sorensen (CEO)

Subsidiary (US):

Damco Customs Services, Inc. **(1)**
445 Atlanta S Pkwy Ste 130, Atlanta, GA 30349
Tel.: (404) 419-7844
Web Site:
http://www.damcocustomsservices.com
Customs House Brokers
N.A.I.C.S.: 488510

Damco USA Inc. **(2)**
Giralda Farms Madison Ave Bldg 2, Madison, NJ 07940
Tel.: (973) 514-2076
Logistics Consulting Servies
N.A.I.C.S.: 541614

Damco Italy S.R.L. **(1)**
Street 7 Bldg T3 Rozzano, Milan, 20089, Italy
Tel.: (39) 01020921
Web Site: http://www.damco.com
Sales Range: $25-49.9 Million
Emp.: 14
Freight Forwarding Services
N.A.I.C.S.: 488510

Damco Sweden AB **(1)**
Terminalvagen 17, 418 79, Gothenburg, Sweden
Tel.: (46) 31 751 2400
Logistics Consulting Servies
N.A.I.C.S.: 541614

Damco UK Ltd. **(1)**
Suffolk Place Parker Avenue, Felixstowe, IP11 4BB, Suffolk, United Kingdom
Tel.: (44) 1394695745
Logistics & Supply Services
N.A.I.C.S.: 488510

Danbor Service AS **(1)**
Kanalen 1, 6700, Esbjerg, Denmark **(100%)**
Tel.: (45) 79111900
Web Site: http://www.danbor.dk
Rev.: $3,279,080
Emp.: 120
Logistics & Transportation Services
N.A.I.C.S.: 488510
Soeren Floe Knudsen (CEO)

Gateway Terminals India Pvt. Ltd. **(1)**
GTI House JNPT Sheva Taluka-Uran, District Raigad, Navi Mumbai, 400 707, Maharashtra, India
Logistics & Supply Services
N.A.I.C.S.: 488510
Amit Bhardwaj (Chief Comml Officer)

Hamburg Sudamerikanische Dampfschifffahrts-Gesellschaft A/S &

Co KG **(1)**
Tel.: (49) 4037050
Web Site: http://www.hamburgsud-line.com
Marine Transportation Services
N.A.I.C.S.: 488390

LF Logistics (Hong Kong) Limited **(1)**
14/F LiFung Centre 2 On Ping Street, Siu Lek Yuen, Shu Tin, New Territories, China (Hong Kong)
Tel.: (852) 2635 5813
Web Site: http://www.lflogistics.com
Logistic Services
N.A.I.C.S.: 488510
Joseph Chua Phi (CEO)

Lindo Industripark A/S **(1)**
Kystvejen 100, 5330, Munkebo, Denmark
Tel.: (45) 30 10 77 10
Web Site: http://www.lindo-industripark.dk
Storage & Transportation Services
N.A.I.C.S.: 493110
Lars-Erik Brenoe (Chm)

Maersk (China) Shipping Company Ltd. **(1)**
Room 6071 Guo Mao Yuan Guo Mao Hotel No 42 Renmin Road M, Zhangjiagang, 215600, China
Tel.: (86) 2123062222
Logistics & Supply Services
N.A.I.C.S.: 488510

Maersk (Hong Kong) Ltd. **(1)**
19th Floor One Kowloon 1 Wang Yuen Street, Kowloon Bay, China (Hong Kong)
Tel.: (852) 37653765
Web Site: http://www.maerskline.com
Sales Range: $125-149.9 Million
Emp.: 350
Freight Transportation Services
N.A.I.C.S.: 483111

Maersk A/S **(1)**
Esplanaden 50, 1098, Copenhagen, Denmark
Tel.: (45) 3363 3363
Web Site: http://www.maersk.com
Sales Range: $300-349.9 Million
Emp.: 1,500
Container Terminal Operation Services
N.A.I.C.S.: 493190
Soren Skou (CEO)

Subsidiary (US):

Performance Team, LLC **(2)**
12816 Shoemaker Ave, Santa Fe Springs, CA 90670
Tel.: (562) 345-2200
Web Site: http://www.ptgt.net
Supply Chain Logistic Services
N.A.I.C.S.: 484110
Cliff Katab (Pres)

Maersk Australia Pty. Ltd. **(1)**
Level 8 383 Kent Street, Sydney, 2000, NSW, Australia
Tel.: (61) 296969696
Web Site: http://www.maersk.com
Sales Range: $125-149.9 Million
Emp.: 450
Freight Transportation Services
N.A.I.C.S.: 483111

Maersk Bangladesh Ltd. **(1)**
Gulshan Center Point 20th Floor House 23-26 Road 90 Gulshan - 2, Dhaka, 1212, Bangladesh
Tel.: (880) 9612888187
N.A.I.C.S.: 541614

Maersk Benelux B.V. **(1)**
Boompjes 40, PO Box 240, 3011 XB, Rotterdam, Netherlands
Tel.: (31) 10 899 4530
Web Site: http://www.maersklines.com
Holding Company; Container Shipping Services
N.A.I.C.S.: 551112
Lodewijk Christiaan van Wachem (Chm)

Maersk Brasil Ltda. **(1)**
Av Ana Costa 433 5th 6th floor Gonzaga, 11060-003, Santos, SP, Brazil
Tel.: (55) 1330357777
Web Site: http://www.maersk.com
Sales Range: $25-49.9 Million
Emp.: 30
Freight Transportation Services

N.A.I.C.S.: 483111

Maersk Container Industri AS **(1)**
Bjerndrupvej 47, 6360, Tinglev, Denmark **(100%)**
Tel.: (45) 73643400
Web Site: http://www.mcicontainers.com
Sales Range: $25-49.9 Million
Emp.: 80
Mfr of Intermodal Dry Cargo & Reefer Containers
N.A.I.C.S.: 332439
Camilla Torno (CFO)

Maersk Container Industry Dongguan Ltd. **(1)**
Machong Town, Dasheng District, Dongguan, 523146, Guangdong, China
Tel.: (86) 769 888 26668
Emp.: 200
Container Mfr
N.A.I.C.S.: 332439
Rosa Cai (Dir-HR)

Maersk Container Industry Qingdao Ltd. **(1)**
No 2 Road, Weishan Village Liuting Town Chengyang District, Qingdao, China
Tel.: (86) 53287723960
N.A.I.C.S.: 333415

Maersk Denizcilik A.S. **(1)**
Buyukdere Cad No 121 Ercan Han A Blok Kat 3-6, Gayrettepe, Istanbul, 34350, Turkiye
Tel.: (90) 2124440675
Storage & Warehousing Services
N.A.I.C.S.: 493190

Maersk Deutschland A/S & Co.KG **(1)**
Ericusspitze 2-4, 20457, Hamburg, Germany
Tel.: (49) 40235210
Web Site: http://www.maerskline.com
Sales Range: $200-249.9 Million
Emp.: 800
Freight Transportation Services
N.A.I.C.S.: 488510

Maersk Drilling A/S **(1)**
Lyngby Hovedgade 85, 2800, Kongens Lyngby, Denmark
Tel.: (45) 6 336 0000
Web Site: https://www.maerskdrilling.com
Drilling Oil & Gas Services
N.A.I.C.S.: 213111
Jorn Madsen (CEO)

Maersk Drilling Holdings Singapore Pte. Ltd. **(1)**
200 Cantonment Road 06-02 Southpoint, Singapore, 089763, Singapore
Tel.: (65) 63183070
Drilling Oil & Gas Services
N.A.I.C.S.: 213111

Maersk Drilling Services A/S **(1)**
Lyngby Hovedgade 85, 2800, Lyngby, Denmark **(100%)**
Tel.: (45) 63360000
Web Site: http://www.maerskdrilling.com
Sales Range: $1-4.9 Billion
Emp.: 3,200
Drilling & Production of Oil & Gas
N.A.I.C.S.: 211120
Jorn Madsen (CEO)

Subsidiary (Non-US):

Maersk Drilling Norge AS **(2)**
Moseidveien 19 4033, Forus, 4033, Stavanger, Norway
Tel.: (47) 5201 7000
Oil & Gas Wells Drilling Services
N.A.I.C.S.: 213111
Jakob Korsgaard (Mng Dir)

Subsidiary (US):

Maersk Drilling USA Inc. **(2)**
2500 City W Blvd Ste 1850, Houston, TX 77042
Tel.: (713) 972-3300
Web Site: http://www.maerskdrilling.com
Emp.: 100
Oil & Gas Well Drilling Services
N.A.I.C.S.: 213111

Maersk France S.A. **(1)**
40 Boulevard de Dunkerque, 13002, Mar-

seilles, France
Tel.: (33) 491399696
Web Site: http://www.maerskline.com
Sales Range: $25-49.9 Million
Emp.: 42
Freight Transportation Services
N.A.I.C.S.: 488510

Maersk Gabon SA (1)
Getma Gabon Building Zone Portuaire d
Owendo, BP 3890, Libreville, Gabon
Tel.: (241) 11797700
N.A.I.C.S.: 541614

Maersk Global Service Centres (India) Private Limited (1)
4th Floor Prudential Bldg Hiranandani Business Park Powai, Central Avenue Road,
Mumbai, 400076, India
Tel.: (91) 2266799999
Sales Range: $300-349.9 Million
Emp.: 2,400
Container Terminal Operation Services
N.A.I.C.S.: 493190
Sreenivasan Geetha *(Mng Dir)*

Maersk Holding B.V. (1)
Tel.: (31) 107127000
Investment Management Service
N.A.I.C.S.: 523999

Maersk Inc. (1)
180 Park Ave Bldg 105, Florham Park, NJ
07932 **(100%)**
Tel.: (973) 514-5000
Web Site: http://www.maersk.com
Sales Range: $250-299.9 Million
Emp.: 750
Sea & Land Transporter Containerized
Cargo
N.A.I.C.S.: 488510
J. Russell Bruner *(Chm)*

Maersk Insurance A/S (1)
Esplanaden 50, DK-1098, Copenhagen,
Denmark
Tel.: (45) 33633363
Financial Insurance Services
N.A.I.C.S.: 524210

Maersk Italia spa (1)
Via Magazzini del Cotone 17 Modulo 3,
16128, Genoa, Italy
Tel.: (39) 01020961
Web Site: http://www.maerskline.com
Sales Range: $125-149.9 Million
Emp.: 380
Freight Transportation Services
N.A.I.C.S.: 483111

Maersk K.K. (1)
Akasaka Tameike Tower 10th Floor 2-17-7
Akasaka, Minato-Ku, Tokyo, 107-0052, Japan
Tel.: (81) 366304200
Web Site: http://www.maerskline.com
Sales Range: $50-74.9 Million
Emp.: 120
Freight Transportation Services
N.A.I.C.S.: 483111

Maersk Kenya Ltd. (1)
Maritime Centre Archbishop Makarios Close
Off Moi Avenue, PO Box 89911, 80100,
Mombasa, Kenya
Tel.: (254) 412150006
Web Site: http://www.maerskline.com
Sales Range: $25-49.9 Million
Emp.: 95
Freight Transportation Services
N.A.I.C.S.: 483111

Branch (Domestic):

Maersk Kenya Ltd. (2)
Dtb Center Block C 1st Floor Mombasa
Road, PO Box 43986, 00100, Nairobi, Kenya
Tel.: (254) 709928000
Web Site: http://www.maersklines.com
Freight Services
N.A.I.C.S.: 483111

Maersk Line Agency Holding A/S (1)
Esplanaden 50, 1098, Copenhagen, Denmark
Tel.: (45) 33633363
Web Site: http://www.maersk.com
Holding Company; Marine Freight Shipping
Services
N.A.I.C.S.: 551112

Subsidiary (Non-US):

Hamburg Sudamerikanische Dampfschifffahrts-Gesellschaft A/S & Co KG (2)
Willy-Brandt-Strasse 59-65, 20457, Hamburg, Germany
Tel.: (49) 4037050
Web Site: http://www.hamburgsud.com
Transportation Services & Travel Agency
N.A.I.C.S.: 483111
Arnt Vespermann *(CEO)*

Maersk Line Peru S.A.C. (1)
Av Ricardo Rivera Navarrete 475 4th Floor,
San Isidro, Lima, Peru
Tel.: (51) 1 616 0202
Web Site: http://www.maerskline.com
Sales Range: $25-49.9 Million
Emp.: 35
Shipping Container Operating Services
N.A.I.C.S.: 488330

Maersk Line, Limited (1)
2510 Walmer Ave Ste C, Norfolk, VA 23513-2601
Tel.: (757) 857-4800
Web Site: http://www.maersklinelimited.com
Emp.: 3,500
Marine Shipping Services
N.A.I.C.S.: 488330
Robbert van Trooijen *(CEO-Asia Pacific)*

Maersk Logistics & Services International A/S (1)
Bredskifte Alle 13, Aarhus, Denmark
Tel.: (45) 70716341
Logistics Management Services
N.A.I.C.S.: 541614

Maersk Logistics & Services Peru S.A. (1)
Highway Nestor Gambetta 14, 07046, Callao, Peru
Tel.: (51) 16140050
Web Site: https://www.inlandservices.com
Emp.: 80,000
Inland Transportation Services
N.A.I.C.S.: 926120

Maersk Malaysia Sdn Bhd (1)
Suites C-5-6-7-8 D-5-6-7-8 Level 6 Sky
Park One City Jalan USJ 25/1, 47650, Subang Jaya, Selangor, Malaysia
Tel.: (60) 80266688
Web Site: http://www.maerskline.com
Sales Range: $25-49.9 Million
Emp.: 100
Freight Transportation Services
N.A.I.C.S.: 483111

Maersk New Zealand Ltd. (1)
Level 3 Building B 2 Graham Street Victoria
Street West, PO Box 90616, 1142, Auckland, New Zealand
Tel.: (64) 93593499
Web Site: http://www.maerskline.com
Sales Range: $50-74.9 Million
Emp.: 110
Freight Transportation Services
N.A.I.C.S.: 483111

Maersk Singapore Pte. Ltd. (1)
200 Cantonment Road Southpoint 10-00,
Ste 10-00 Southpoint, Singapore, 089763,
Singapore
Tel.: (65) 63238323
Web Site: http://www.maerskline.com
Sales Range: $25-49.9 Million
Emp.: 100
Freight Transportation Services
N.A.I.C.S.: 483111

Maersk Spain, S.L.U. (1)
Aqua Calle del Pintor Maella, 46023, Valencia, Spain
Tel.: (34) 963 24 13 00
Container Terminal Operation Services
N.A.I.C.S.: 493190

Maersk Supply Service Apoio Maritimo Ltda. (1)
Av Republica do Chile 330 East Tower 5th
floor office 501-Downtown, RJ, Rio de Janeiro, 20031-170, Brazil
Tel.: (55) 2130322800
Integrated Marine Services
N.A.I.C.S.: 541990

Maersk Supply Service Canada Ltd. (1)

5 Springdale Street Suite 501, Saint John's,
A1E 0E4, NL, Canada
Tel.: (709) 753-4410
Web Site:
http://www.maersksupplyservice.com
Sales Range: $25-49.9 Million
Emp.: 13
Marine Vessel Operating Services
N.A.I.C.S.: 488330

Maersk Supply Service Holdings UK Limited (1)
Aldgate 2 Leman Street, London, E1 8FA,
United Kingdom
Tel.: (44) 2077125000
Investment Management Service
N.A.I.C.S.: 523999

Maersk Supply Service UK Limited (1)
Prime Four Business Park Kingswells
Causeway, Kingswells, Aberdeen, AB15
8PU, United Kingdom
Tel.: (44) 7 373 7000
Web Site:
https://www.maersksupplyservice.com
Sales Range: $25-49.9 Million
Emp.: 2
Ship Chartering Services
N.A.I.C.S.: 483111

Maersk Tankers Singapore Pte. Ltd (1)
3 Harbourfront Place 12-01 Harbourfront
Tower 2, Singapore, 99254, Singapore
Tel.: (65) 63238323
Web Site: http://www.maersktankers.com
Sales Range: $25-49.9 Million
Emp.: 10
Container Terminal Operation Services
N.A.I.C.S.: 493190

Maersk Vietnam Ltd. (1)
28 Phung Khac Khoan St Dakao Ward, Dist
1, Ho Chi Minh City, Vietnam
Tel.: (84) 88243252
Marine Vessel Service
N.A.I.C.S.: 488330

Mainstreet 1878 (Pty.) Ltd. (1)
Roggebaai Place 4 Jetty Street Foreshore,
Cape Town, 8001, South Africa
Tel.: (27) 215508850
N.A.I.C.S.: 541614

NTS International Transport Services Co. Ltd. (1)
8/F Shartex Plaza 88 Zunyi Road South,
Shanghai, China
Tel.: (86) 21 61206222
Freight Transportation Services
N.A.I.C.S.: 488510

Odense Steel Shipyard Ltd. (1)
Lintoealleen 150, PO Box 176, 5100,
Odense, Denmark **(100%)**
Tel.: (45) 63971234
Web Site: http://www.oss.dk
Sales Range: $400-449.9 Million
Emp.: 2,000
Shipyard
N.A.I.C.S.: 336611

Pilot Air Freight, LLC (1)
314 N Middletown Rd, Lima, PA 19037
Tel.: (610) 891-8100
Web Site: http://www.pilotdelivers.com
Emp.: 200
Air Freight Forwarder
N.A.I.C.S.: 488510
James Best *(CEO)*

Subsidiary (Domestic):

Air Charter of Ohio, Inc. (2)
6960 Engle Rd, Cleveland, OH 44130
Tel.: (440) 243-6300
Sales Range: $1-9.9 Million
Emp.: 13
Freight Transportation Arrangement
N.A.I.C.S.: 488510
Cathy Cunningham *(Mgr-Sls)*

Kerry Rockford Enterprises Inc. (2)
1835 Airport Exchange Blvd, Erlanger, KY
41018-1079
Tel.: (859) 371-7008
Web Site: http://www.pilotdeliver.com
Sales Range: $25-49.9 Million
Emp.: 100
Freight Transportation Arrangement

N.A.I.C.S.: 488510

Manna Freight Systems, Inc. (2)
2440 Enterprise Dr, Mendota Heights, MN
55120
Tel.: (651) 905-7560
Freight Transportation Arrangement Services
N.A.I.C.S.: 488510
Charles A. Martin *(COO)*

Pilot Truck Brokerage, LLC (1)
2280 Enrico Fermi Dr Ste 27, San Diego,
CA 92154
Tel.: (858) 863-5000
Web Site: https://pilotdelivers.taicloud.net
N.A.I.C.S.: 541614

Poti Sea Port Corporation (1)
38 D Aghmashenebeli Str, 4400, Poti, Georgia
Tel.: (995) 493277777
N.A.I.C.S.: 541614

Rederiet A.P. Moller A/S (1)
Esplanaden 50, 1098 k, Copenhagen, Denmark
Tel.: (45) 33 63 33 63
Web Site: http://www.maersk.com
Shipping Transportation Services
N.A.I.C.S.: 483111

SVITZER A/S (1)
Sundkrogsgade 17, 2100, Copenhagen,
Denmark **(100%)**
Tel.: (45) 39193919
Web Site: http://www.svitzer.com
Sales Range: $25-49.9 Million
Emp.: 50
Marine Towage, Salvage & Offshore Services
N.A.I.C.S.: 488310
Morten Henrik Engelstoft *(Chm)*

Subsidiary (Non-US):

SVITZER Australasia (2)
7 Cooper Street, Balmain, 2041, NSW, Australia
Tel.: (61) 98189400
Web Site: http://www.svitzer.com.au
Sales Range: $250-299.9 Million
Emp.: 1,000
Marine Towage, Salvage & Offshore Services
N.A.I.C.S.: 488310
Ivan Spanjic *(Chief Compliance Officer)*

Safmarine (Pty) Ltd. (1)
Safemarine Quay The Clocktower Precinct
Victoria & Alfred, Cape Town, 8001, South
Africa **(100%)**
Tel.: (27) 214086911
Web Site: http://www.safmarinemaersk.com
Sales Range: $125-149.9 Million
Emp.: 650
International Liner Shipping
N.A.I.C.S.: 483111
David Williams *(CEO)*

Safmarine Container Lines N.V. (1)
Schalienstraat 3, 2000, Antwerp,
Belgium **(100%)**
Tel.: (32) 442999
Web Site: http://www.safmarine.com
Sales Range: $50-74.9 Million
Emp.: 180
International Liner Shipping
N.A.I.C.S.: 483111

Sealand Europe A/S (1)
Bredskifte Alle 13, Aarhus, Denmark
Tel.: (45) 70716341
Transportation Logistics Services
N.A.I.C.S.: 488510

Sealand Maersk Asia Pte. Ltd. (1)
1 Paya Lebar Link Paya Lebar Quarter
13-0, Singapore, 408533, Singapore
Tel.: (65) 69832212
Logistics Management Services
N.A.I.C.S.: 541614

Sogester - Sociedade Gestora De Terminais S.A. (1)
Rua de Cercania do Porto de Luanda Estrada da Boavista S/N CP 2538, Luanda,
Angola
Tel.: (244) 226420800
Web Site: https://www.sogester.co.ao
N.A.I.C.S.: 541614

A.P. Moller-Maersk A/S—(Continued)

Suez Canal Container Terminal SAE (1)
East Portsaid Private Free Zone Shark El Tafreaa, Port-Said, Egypt
Tel.: (20) 663258970
N.A.I.C.S.: 541614
Steven Yoogalingam (Mng Dir)

Svitzer Australia Pty Ltd. (1)
7 Cooper Street, Balmain, 2041, NSW, Australia
Tel.: (61) 298189400
Web Site: https://svitzer.com.au
Marine Services
N.A.I.C.S.: 541990

Terminal 4 S.A. (1)
Avenida Tomas Edison Y Prefectura Naval Argentina, Ciudad De, Buenos Aires, Argentina
Tel.: (54) 1145900900
Container Terminal Operation Services
N.A.I.C.S.: 493190

The Maersk Company Limited (1)
Maersk House Braham Street, London, E1 8EP, United Kingdom **(100%)**
Tel.: (44) 2077125000
Web Site: http://www.maersklines.com
Sales Range: $1-4.9 Billion
Emp.: 150
Freight Transportation & Logistics Services
N.A.I.C.S.: 488510

U.S. Marine Management, Incorporated (1)
140 Corporate Blvd, Norfolk, VA 23502
Tel.: (757) 672-4059
Web Site: https://www.usmmi.com
N.A.I.C.S.: 541614

Vandegrift Forwarding Co, Inc. (1)
100 Walnut Ave Ste 600, Clark, NJ 07066
Tel.: (201) 915-9500
Web Site: http://www.vandegriftinc.com
Freight Transportation Arrangement
N.A.I.C.S.: 488510
Mark Zeitlin (Pres)

Visible Supply Chain Management, LLC (1)
5160 Wiley Post Way, Salt Lake City, UT 84116
Tel.: (385) 881-6287
Web Site: http://www.visiblescm.com
Shipping, Logistics, Packaging, Fulfillment, Transportation, Parcel, Kitting & Delivery Services
N.A.I.C.S.: 541614
Casey Adams (Pres)

Subsidiary (Domestic):

IntegraCore, LLC (2)
6077 Wells Park Rd, West Jordan, UT 84081-5684
Tel.: (801) 975-9411
Outsource Solutions
N.A.I.C.S.: 541519
Rob McCleary (Acct Mgr)

PC Synergy, Inc. (2)
804 N Twin Oaks Valley Rd, San Marcos, CA 92069
Tel.: (760) 931-0350
Web Site: http://www.pcsynergy.com
Sales Range: $1-9.9 Million
Emp.: 18
Custom Computer Programming Services
N.A.I.C.S.: 541511
Richard Crawford (Founder & Pres)

West Africa Container Terminal Nigeria Ltd. (1)
The Onne Port Complex Federal Ocean Terminal Onne, Port Harcourt, Rivers State, Nigeria
Tel.: (234) 8090335101
Web Site: http://www.wact.ng
Marine Transportation Services
N.A.I.C.S.: 488390

A.PLUS GROUP HOLDINGS LIMITED
2/F 35-45B Bonham Strand, Sheung Wan, China (Hong Kong)
Tel.: (852) 2 854 3199 **Ky**

Web Site: http://www.aplusgp.com
1841—(HKG)
Rev.: $16,475,776
Assets: $18,773,942
Liabilities: $4,239,057
Net Worth: $14,534,885
Earnings: $1,516,289
Emp.: 91
Fiscal Year-end: 03/31/22
Financial Printing Services
N.A.I.C.S.: 513120
Kim Wan Lam (Founder & Chm)

A.R. MEDICOM INC.
1200 55th Avenue, Montreal, H8T 3J8, QC, Canada
Tel.: (514) 636-6262 **QC**
Web Site: http://www.medicom-asia.com
Year Founded: 1988
Sales Range: $10-24.9 Million
Emp.: 100
Disposable Dental & Medical Supply Mfr
N.A.I.C.S.: 339114
Guillaume Laverdure (CEO)

Subsidiaries:

A.R. Medicom Inc. (Asia) Ltd. (1)
21/F Federal Centre 77 Sheung On Street, Chai Wan, China (Hong Kong)
Tel.: (852) 21797105
Web Site: http://www.medicom-asia.com
Disposable Medical Supplies Distr
N.A.I.C.S.: 423450
Carol Yip (Mgr-SAP)

A.R. Medicom Inc. (Japan) Ltd. (1)
Edomachi 96 Strong Bldg 8F, Chuo-Ku, Kobe, 650 0033, Hyogo, Japan
Tel.: (81) 78 327 2333
Web Site: http://www.medicom-japan.com
Disposable Medical Supplies Distr
N.A.I.C.S.: 423450

A.R. Medicom Inc. (Taiwan) Ltd. (1)
4F-3 No 163 Sec 1 Keelung Road, Xinyi District, Taipei, Taiwan
Tel.: (886) 2 2766 8655
Disposable Medical Supplies Distr
N.A.I.C.S.: 423450

A.R. Medicom Inc. Healthcare (Shanghai) Ltd. (1)
Rm 109-110 728 Xinhau Road, ChangNing District, Shanghai, 200050, China
Tel.: (86) 21 5273 9363
Disposable Medical Supplies Mfr & Distr
N.A.I.C.S.: 339113

Kolmi-Hopen SAS (1)
Rue de la chanterie, 49124, Saint-Barthelemy-d'Anjou, France
Tel.: (33) 2 41 96 34 34
Web Site: http://www.kolmi.fr
Disposable Medical Supplies Distr
N.A.I.C.S.: 423450

Medicom Healthcare B.V. (1)
Parallelweg 80a, 3931 MT, Woudenberg, Netherlands
Tel.: (31) 33 286 64 60
Web Site: http://www.medicom-eu.com
Emp.: 9
Disposable Medical Supplies Distr
N.A.I.C.S.: 423450

Medicom USA, Inc. (1)
4049 Allen Station Rd, Augusta, GA 30906
Tel.: (514) 636-6131
Disposable Medical Supplies Distr
N.A.I.C.S.: 423450

Medicom-Ukraine LLC (1)
Serpova Str 11, 03115, Kiev, Ukraine
Tel.: (380) 44 303 99 43
Disposable Medical Supplies Distr
N.A.I.C.S.: 423450

A.R. THOMSON GROUP
7930 130th Street, Surrey, V3Z1A7, BC, Canada
Tel.: (604) 507-6050
Web Site: http://www.arthomson.com

Year Founded: 1967
Rev.: $27,046,142
Emp.: 165
Gaskets & Other Fluid Containment Products Mfr
N.A.I.C.S.: 339991
James E. Thomson (Pres)

A.S. CREATION TAPETEN AG
South Street 47, D-51645, Gummersbach, Germany
Tel.: (49) 22615420
Web Site: https://www.as-creation.com
ACWN—(MUN)
Rev.: $133,811,121
Assets: $124,019,794
Liabilities: $44,044,413
Net Worth: $79,975,382
Earnings: ($1,567,495)
Emp.: 684
Fiscal Year-end: 12/31/23
Wallpaper & Paper Products Mfr
N.A.I.C.S.: 322220
Maik-Holger Kramer (Member-Mgmt Bd-Fin & Controlling & Fin Dir)

Subsidiaries:

A.S. Creation (France) SAS (1)
13-15 rue Jean Bart, 69003, Lyon, France
Tel.: (33) 478545417
Web Site: http://www.as-creation.fr
Sales Range: $25-49.9 Million
Emp.: 35
Wallpapers Mfr & Decorative Fabrics Sales
N.A.I.C.S.: 322220

Subsidiary (Domestic):

MCF Investissement SA (2)
17 rue Eugene Pereire, 91610, Ballancourt, Essonne, France
Tel.: (33) 169907200
Wallpaper Whslr
N.A.I.C.S.: 424950

A.S. Creation (NL) B.V. (1)
Calandstraat 20, Werkendam, 4251 NZ, North Brabant, Netherlands
Tel.: (31) 183504700
Web Site: http://www.as-creation.nl
Sales Range: $50-74.9 Million
Emp.: 12
Home Furnishings & Wallpapers Whslr
N.A.I.C.S.: 423220

A.S. Creation Textil GmbH (1)
Eichendorffstrasse 2, 51709, Marienheide, Germany
Tel.: (49) 22615420
Furnishing Fabrics Whslr
N.A.I.C.S.: 423220

Subsidiary (Domestic):

Indes Wontextil GmbH (2)
Eichendorffstr 2, Marienheide, 51709, Germany
Tel.: (49) 226420135700
Web Site: http://www.indes.de
Sales Range: $25-49.9 Million
Emp.: 80
Furnishing & Decoration Fabrics Whslr
N.A.I.C.S.: 423220

AS Creation (UK) Limited (1)
Burlington House Crosby Road North, Waterlooville, L22 0PJ, Merseyside, United Kingdom
Tel.: (44) 1519286136
Web Site: http://www.as-creation.com
Sales Range: $50-74.9 Million
Wallcoverings & Fabrics Distr
N.A.I.C.S.: 424950

Crealis S.A.S. (1)
Activillage 15 Allee des Ginkgos, 69500, Bron, France
Tel.: (33) 478545417
Wallpaper Product Mfr & Distr
N.A.I.C.S.: 325612

Indes Fuggerhaus Textil GmbH (1)
Eichendorffstrasse 2, 51709, Marienheide, Germany
Tel.: (49) 226420135700

Web Site: http://www.indesfuggerhaus.com
Textile Mfr
N.A.I.C.S.: 314999
Georg Hunnemeyer (Gen Mgr)

OOO A.S. Creation (RUS) (1)
Profsoyuznaya str 65 bld 1 floor 13, 117342, Moscow, Russia
Tel.: (7) 4052129049
Web Site: http://asc-wallpaper.ru
Wallpaper Mfr
N.A.I.C.S.: 322220

SCE-Societe de conception et d'edition SAS (1)
20 Boulevard Michel Strogoff, Boves, 80440, Picardie, France
Tel.: (33) 322468700
Decorative Fabric Product Mfr
N.A.I.C.S.: 332999

A.V.O.D. KURUTULMUS GIDA VE TARIM URUNLERI SAN. TIC. A.S.
Yildirim Mahallesi 35 Sokak No 62, Menemen, Izmir, Turkiye
Tel.: (90) 2328354524 **TR**
Web Site: https://www.avod.com.tr
AVOD—(IST)
Rev.: $37,213,459
Assets: $58,621,429
Liabilities: $22,861,297
Net Worth: $35,760,132
Earnings: $2,694,224
Fiscal Year-end: 12/31/23
Dried Vegetable Mfr & Distr
N.A.I.C.S.: 311423

Subsidiaries:

Sundown Foods U.S.A., Inc. (1)
10891 Business Dr, Fontana, CA 92337
Tel.: (909) 606-2800
Web Site: http://www.sundownfoods.com
Sales Range: $10-24.9 Million
Oven-Roasted Tomato Mfr & Distr
N.A.I.C.S.: 311423

A.W. FRASER LTD.
39 Lunns Road, PO Box 6055, Christchurch, 8024, New Zealand
Tel.: (64) 33410027
Web Site: http://www.awfraser.co.nz
Sales Range: $10-24.9 Million
Emp.: 155
Aluminum Extrusions Mfr
N.A.I.C.S.: 331314
Paul Isitt (Dir-Comml)

A/S SAF TEHNIKA
24a Ganibu Dambis, Riga, LV-1005, Latvia
Tel.: (371) 67046840
Web Site: https://www.saftehnika.com
Year Founded: 1999
VTZ—(MUN)
Rev.: $39,823,488
Assets: $30,471,488
Liabilities: $10,335,296
Net Worth: $20,136,192
Earnings: $3,623,232
Emp.: 265
Fiscal Year-end: 06/30/23
Data Transmission Equipment Mfr
N.A.I.C.S.: 334290
Normunds Bergs (Co-Founder, Chm & CEO)

Subsidiaries:

SAF North America LLC (1)
3250 Quentin St Unit 128, Aurora, CO 80011
Tel.: (720) 502-0728
Web Site: https://www.saftehnika.com
Emp.: 8
Data Transmission Equipment Distr
N.A.I.C.S.: 423690
Janis Berg (Mng Dir)

A1 CAPITAL YATIRIM MENKUL

DEGERLER A.S.
Buyukdere Cad Levent Plaza Block
No 173 Interior Door No 29,
Esentepe Mah Sisli, 34398, Istanbul,
Turkiye
Tel.: (90) 2123711800
Web Site:
https://www.a1capital.com.tr
Year Founded: 1990
A1CAP—(IST)
Investment Management Service
N.A.I.C.S.: 523940
Ayse Terzi *(Chm)*

A1 INVESTMENTS & RE-SOURCES LTD.
Suite 606 37 Bligh Street, Sydney,
2000, NSW, Australia
Tel.: (61) 291146888   AU
Web Site:
https://www.a1investments.com.au
Year Founded: 2004
AYI—(ASX)
Rev.: $320,314
Assets: $41,788
Liabilities: $177,026
Net Worth: ($135,238)
Earnings: ($498,616)
Fiscal Year-end: 06/30/23
Metal Mining Investment Services
N.A.I.C.S.: 523999
Peter Ashcroft *(Chm, Gen Counsel & Sec)*

A2A S.P.A.
Via Lamarmora 230, 25124, Brescia,
Italy
Tel.: (39) 03035531
Web Site: https://www.gruppoa2a.it
A2A—(ITA)
Rev.: $15,927,045,111
Assets: $20,287,071,012
Liabilities: $15,104,683,790
Net Worth: $5,182,387,222
Earnings: $711,202,245
Emp.: 13,958
Fiscal Year-end: 12/31/23
Electricity & Natural Gas Producer &
Distr; Fiber-Optic Network Operator
N.A.I.C.S.: 221122
Roberto Tasca *(Chm)*

Subsidiaries:

A2A Ambiente S.p.A.   (1)
Via Lamarmora 230, 25124, Brescia, Italy
Tel.: (39) 03035531
Web Site: http://www.a2aambiente.eu
Sales Range: $200-249.9 Million
Waste Systems
N.A.I.C.S.: 562111

A2A Calore & Servizi S.r.l.   (1)
Via Lamarmora, 230-25124, Brescia, Italy
Tel.: (39) 0277207602
Web Site: http://www.a2acaloreservizi.eu
Facility Management & District Heating
Supply Distribution Services
N.A.I.C.S.: 561210

A2A Ciclo Idrico S.p.A.   (1)
Via Lamarmora 230, 25124, Brescia, Italy
Tel.: (39) 030 35531
Web Site: http://www.a2aciclodrico.eu
Sales Range: $1-4.9 Billion
Water Supply & Treatment Services
N.A.I.C.S.: 221310

A2A Energia S.p.A.   (1)
Corso di Porta Vittoria 4, 20122, Milan, Italy
Tel.: (39) 0282841510
Web Site: http://www.a2aenergia.eu
Electric Power Generation & Distribution
Services
N.A.I.C.S.: 221118

A2A Energiefuture S.p.A.   (1)
Corso di Porta Vittoria 4, 20122, Milan, Italy
Tel.: (39) 0277201
Web Site: http://www.a2aenergiefuture.eu
Thermoelectric Power Plant Services
N.A.I.C.S.: 221116

A2A Gencogas S.p.A.   (1)
Corso di Porta Vittoria 4, 20122, Milan, Italy
Tel.: (39) 0277201
Web Site: http://www.a2agencogas.eu
Thermoelectric Power Plant Services
N.A.I.C.S.: 221116

A2A Logistica S.p.A.   (1)
Via Alessandro Lamarmora 230, Brescia,
25124, Italy
Tel.: (39) 03035531
Logistic Services
N.A.I.C.S.: 541614

A2A Montenegro d.o.o.   (1)
Bulevar Sv Petra Cetinjskog 1A, Podgorica,
81000, Montenegro
Tel.: (382) 20 201320
Web Site: http://www.a2amontenegro.eu
Emp.: 1
Electric Power Generation & Distribution
Services
N.A.I.C.S.: 221118

A2A Reti Gas S.p.A.   (1)
Via Lamarmora 230, 25124, Brescia, Italy
Tel.: (39) 030 35531
Web Site: http://www.a2aretigas.eu
Sales Range: $500-549.9 Million
Natural Gas Distribution Services
N.A.I.C.S.: 221210
Enzo Gerosa *(Gen Mgr)*

A2A Smart City S.p.A.   (1)
Via A Lamarmora 230, 25124, Brescia, Italy
Tel.: (39) 0800585100
Web Site: https://www.a2asmartcity.it
N.A.I.C.S.: 517810

A2A Trading S.r.l.   (1)
Corso di Porta Vittoria 4, Milan, 20122, Italy
Tel.: (39) 0277 20 31 61
Electric Power & Fuel Gas Distr
N.A.I.C.S.: 221122

AEM Service S.r.l.   (1)
Corso di Porta Vittoria 4, 20122, Milan, Italy
Tel.: (39) 0277201
Web Site: http://www.aemservice.it
Call Center Management, Meter Readings,
Back Office & Invoicing Services
N.A.I.C.S.: 561499

AEM Trading S.r.l.   (1)
Corso di Porta Vittoria 4, Milan, 20122, Italy
Tel.: (39) 0277201
Sales Range: $25-49.9 Million
Emp.: 20
Electrical, Gaseous & Non-Gaseous Fuels
Trading
N.A.I.C.S.: 425120

ASM Energia e Ambiente S.r.l.   (1)
Via Lamarmora 230, BS-25124, Brescia,
Italy
Tel.: (39) 030 228 7821
Web Site: http://www.asmea.it
Energy Sales & Services
N.A.I.C.S.: 221122

ASM Energy Srl   (1)
Via Lamarmora 230, 25124, Brescia,
25124, Italy
Tel.: (39) 03035531
Web Site: http://www.a2a.eu
Sales Range: $1-4.9 Billion
Emp.: 2,000
Energy Sales & Services
N.A.I.C.S.: 221122

ASMEA S.r.l.   (1)
Via Lamarmora 230, 25124, Brescia, Italy
Tel.: (39) 030 35531
Web Site: http://www.asmea.it
Electric Power Distribution Services
N.A.I.C.S.: 221122
Paolo Rossetti *(Gen Mgr)*

Abruzzoenergia S.p.A.   (1)
Localita Selva 1/A, Gissi, 66052, Chieti,
Italy
Tel.: (39) 0873943700
Eletric Power Generation Services
N.A.I.C.S.: 221118

Amsa SpA   (1)
Via Olgettina 25, 20132, Milan, Italy
Tel.: (39) 02272981
Web Site: http://www.amsa.it
Energy Services
N.A.I.C.S.: 221210

Aprica SpA   (1)
via Lamarmora 230, 25124, Brescia, Italy
Tel.: (39) 03035531
Web Site: http://www.apricaspa.it
Waste Services
N.A.I.C.S.: 562119

Aspem S.p.A.   (1)
Via San Giusto 6, 21100, Varese, Italy
Tel.: (39) 0332 290111
Sales Range: $250-299.9 Million
Emp.: 29
Electric Power Distribution Services
N.A.I.C.S.: 221122

Azienda Servizi Valtrompia
S.p.A.   (1)
Via Matteotti 325, 25063, Gardone Val
Trompia, Italy
Tel.: (39) 0308336163
Web Site: http://www.asvt-spa.it
Environmental Hygiene & Integrated Water
Services
N.A.I.C.S.: 562910

BAS Omniservizi Srl   (1)
via Suardi 26, 24124, Bergamo, Italy
Tel.: (39) 0302287822
Natural Gas Distribution
N.A.I.C.S.: 221210

Camuna Energia S.r.l.   (1)
Piazza Roma 1, 25051, Cedegolo, BS, Italy
Tel.: (39) 0364 770482
Web Site: http://www.camunaenergia.eu
Electric Power Distribution Services
N.A.I.C.S.: 221122

Consul System S.p.A.   (1)
Via Terenzio Mamiani 21/23, 63100, Ascoli
Piceno, Italy
Tel.: (39) 073626441
Web Site: http://www.consulsystem.net
Engineering Consultancy Services
N.A.I.C.S.: 541330

Fertilivita S.r.l.   (1)
Loc. Manzola Fornace, 27014, Pavia, Cor-
teolona, Italy
Tel.: (39) 0382 727 611
Web Site: http://www.fertilivita.it
Environmental Services
N.A.I.C.S.: 541620

Free Energy S.r.l.   (1)
Piazza Guido Monaco 10, 52100, Arezzo,
Italy
Tel.: (39) 0575370106
Web Site: http://www.free-energysrl.it
Energy Consulting Services
N.A.I.C.S.: 541690

La Bi.Co Due S.r.l.   (1)
Via Cavallera 27, Lograto, 25030, Brescia,
Italy
Tel.: (39) 030978226
Web Site: http://www.labicodue.com
Waste Disposal Services
N.A.I.C.S.: 562119

Linea Group Holding S.p.A.   (1)
Via Dell Innovazione Digitale Angolo Via
Del Macello, 26100, Cremona, Italy
Tel.: (39) 03728021
Web Site: http://www.lgh.it
Environmental & Disposal Facility Services
N.A.I.C.S.: 562998

Subsidiary (Domestic):

LD Reti S.r.l.   (2)
Strada Vecchia Cremonese snc, 26900,
Lodi, Italy
Tel.: (39) 03714502600
Web Site: http://www.ldreti.it
Natural Gas Distribution Services
N.A.I.C.S.: 221210

Linea Ambiente S.r.l.   (2)
Via Mezzana 81, Rovato, 25038, Brescia,
Italy
Tel.: (39) 0307714777
Web Site: http://www.linea-ambiente.it
Waste Treatment & Disposal Services
N.A.I.C.S.: 562119

Subsidiary (Domestic):

Lomellina Energia S.r.l.   (3)
Vecchia Vicinale Road for Vigevano, 27020,
Parona, Italy
Tel.: (39) 038425431
Web Site: http://www.lomellinaenergia.it
Waste Energy Treatment Services
N.A.I.C.S.: 562119

Subsidiary (Domestic):

Linea Gestioni S.r.l.   (2)
Via del Commercio 29, 26013, Crema, Italy
Tel.: (39) 03738971
Web Site: http://www.linea-gestioni.it
Waste Collection & Disposal Services
N.A.I.C.S.: 562119

Linea Green S.p.A.   (2)
Viale Trento e Trieste 38, 26100, Cremona,
Italy
Tel.: (39) 03724181
Web Site: http://www.linea-green.it
Photovoltaic Generation Energy Services
N.A.I.C.S.: 221114

Lumenergia S.p.A.   (1)
Via Francesco Glisenti 68/F, Villa Carcina,
25069, Brescia, Italy
Tel.: (39) 0308922150
Web Site: https://www.lumenergia.it
N.A.I.C.S.: 221122

Retragas srl   (1)
via Lamarmora 230, 25124, Brescia, Italy
Tel.: (39) 03035531
Web Site: http://www.retragas.it
Sales Range: $50-74.9 Million
Emp.: 6
Gas Services
N.A.I.C.S.: 213112

SED S.r.l.   (1)
Viale Kennedy 10, 10070, Robassomero,
Italy
Tel.: (39) 0119241182
Web Site: http://www.sed-srl.it
Special Electronic Design Services
N.A.I.C.S.: 541490

Selene Spa   (1)
via Lamarmora 230, 25124, Brescia, Italy
Tel.: (39) 0303554929
Web Site: http://www.selenebs.it
Telecommunications
N.A.I.C.S.: 517810

Sicura S.r.l.   (1)
Via Padania 24/38, Castel Mella, 25030,
Brescia, Italy
Tel.: (39) 0303583308
Web Site: http://www.sicurapersiane.com
Aluminium Shutter Mfr
N.A.I.C.S.: 332321

Solar Sicily S.r.l.   (1)
Via San Leonardo 6, San Pier Niceto,
98045, Messina, Italy
Tel.: (39) 03272403570
Web Site: https://www.solarsicily.com
N.A.I.C.S.: 333242

Suncity Energy S.r.l.   (1)
Via Tolemaide 28, 00192, Rome, Italy
Tel.: (39) 0687763199
Web Site: http://www.suncityenergy.it
Energy Renewable Services
N.A.I.C.S.: 221114

Tidonenergie Srl   (1)
Via Abbondanza n 34, 29100, Piacenza,
Italy
Tel.: (39) 0523336729
Web Site: http://www.tidonenergie.it
Energy Services
N.A.I.C.S.: 541614

Unareti S.p.A.   (1)
Via Lamarmora 230, 25124, Brescia, Italy
Tel.: (39) 0 30 3553 1
Web Site: http://www.unareti.it
Electric Power Distribution Services
N.A.I.C.S.: 221122

Unareti Servizi Metrici S.r.l.   (1)
Via Lamarmora 230, 25124, Brescia, Italy
Tel.: (39) 03035531
Web Site: http://www.unaretiservizimetrici.it
Electricity & Natural Gas Distribution Ser-
vices
N.A.I.C.S.: 221210

Varese Risorse S.p.A.   (1)
Via San Giusto 6, 21100, Varese, Italy
Tel.: (39) 0332 290111

A2A S.p.A.—(Continued)

Sales Range: $300-349.9 Million
Emp.: 298
Electric Power & Gas Distr
N.A.I.C.S.: 221122

A2E VENTURE CATALYSTS LIMITED

1 Marsden Street, Manchester, M2 1HW, United Kingdom
Tel.: (44) 161 923 6000
Web Site: http://www.a2evc.com
Emp.: 6
Privater Equity Firm
N.A.I.C.S.: 523999
Amin Amiri *(Founder & CEO)*

Subsidiaries:

BHW (Components) Limited (1)
Caxton Close, Wigan, WN3 6XU, Lancashire, United Kingdom
Tel.: (44) 1942 821205
Aerospace Component Mfr
N.A.I.C.S.: 336413

Muraspec Decorative Solutions Limited (1)
74-78 Wood Lane End, Hemel Hempstead, HP2 4RF, Herts, United Kingdom (100%)
Tel.: (44) 8705 117118
Web Site: http://www.muraspec.com
Sales Range: $25-49.9 Million
Emp.: 200
Commercial Wallcovering Mfr
N.A.I.C.S.: 337212
Tariq Rashid *(Mng Dir)*

A2MICILE EUROPE SA

48 rue du Faubourg de Saverne, 67000, Strasbourg, France
Tel.: (33) 3 88 60 66 30
Web Site: http://www.a2micile.com
Cleaning, Ironing, Gardening, Handyman & Child Care Services
N.A.I.C.S.: 812990
Joel Chaulet *(Chm & CEO)*

A2Z INFRA ENGINEERING LIMITED

0-116 First Floor Shopping Mall Arjun Marg DLF City, Phase - 1, Gurgaon, 122002, India
Tel.: (91) 4723383
Web Site: https://www.a2zgroup.co.in
533292—(BOM)
Rev.: $50,632,150
Assets: $194,814,807
Liabilities: $173,964,077
Net Worth: $20,850,730
Earnings: ($24,543,287)
Emp.: 24
Fiscal Year-end: 03/31/22
Engineeering Services
N.A.I.C.S.: 237990
Surendra Kumar Tuteja *(Chm)*

Subsidiaries:

A2Z Infraservices Lanka Private Limited (1)
8B1 Don Carolis Road, Colombo, Sri Lanka
Tel.: (94) 72 236 6266
Web Site: https://a2zlanka.lk
Corporate Services
N.A.I.C.S.: 561499

A2Z Infraservices Private Limited (1)
Cosmos Building B-38 Sector-32 Jharsa Chowk, Gurgaon, 122 001, Haryana, India
Tel.: (91) 1244517600
Web Site: http://www.a2zinfraservices.co.in
Emp.: 13,500
Facility Management Services
N.A.I.C.S.: 541611
Lovkesh Bajaj *(CEO)*

A2Z Infrastructure Limited (1)
Cosmos Building B-38 Sector 32 Jharsa Chowk, Gurgaon, 122 001, Haryana, India
Tel.: (91) 1244517600
Web Site: http://a2zinfra.com

Sales Range: $25-49.9 Million
Emp.: 5,300
Construction Engineering Services
N.A.I.C.S.: 541330

A2Z Powercom Limited (1)
Plot B 38 Sector 32 Institutional Area, Gurgaon, 122001, Haryana, India
Tel.: (91) 1244517600
Web Site: http://www.a2zpowercom.com
Eletric Power Generation Services
N.A.I.C.S.: 221118

A2Z Powertech Limited (1)
Enkay Tower Udyog Vihar Phase 5, Gurgaon, 122016, Haryana, India
Tel.: (91) 1244517600
Web Site: http://www.a2zpowertech.com
Power Transmission Line Construction & Maintenance Services
N.A.I.C.S.: 237130
Vikas Guliani *(Head-Bus Dev)*

CNCS Facility Solutions Private Limited. (1)
B 27 3rd Floor Shreeram Industrial Estate G D Ambedkar Road, Wadala Dadar East, Mumbai, 400031, India
Tel.: (91) 2224165962
Facility Management Services
N.A.I.C.S.: 561210

A2Z SMART TECHNOLOGIES CORP.

1600-609 Granville Street, Vancouver, V7Y 1C3, BC, Canada
Tel.: (647) 558-5564   Ca
Web Site: https://cust2mate.com
Year Founded: 2018
AZ—(NASDAQ)
Rev.: $11,375,000
Assets: $8,519,000
Liabilities: $10,828,000
Net Worth: ($2,309,000)
Earnings: ($18,057,000)
Emp.: 171
Fiscal Year-end: 12/31/23
Military Equipment Distr
N.A.I.C.S.: 423860
Bentsur Joseph *(CEO)*

Subsidiaries:

Cust2Mate Ltd. (1)
14 Haomanim St, Tel Aviv, 6789732, Israel
Tel.: (972) 33732288
Web Site: https://cust2mate.com
Emp.: 72
Smart Cart Mfr & Distr
N.A.I.C.S.: 333112

A3 ALLMANNA IT-OCH TELEKOMAKTI

Segelbatsvaegen 2, Stockholm, 112 64, Sweden
Tel.: (46) 851781000
Internet & Voice Communication Services
N.A.I.C.S.: 517810

A3 PRIVATE AB

Umestan Foretagsspark Hus 12, Vasterbotten, Umea, 903 47, Sweden
Tel.: (46) 0770910500
Web Site: http://www.a3.se
Year Founded: 2017
Telecommunication Servicesb
N.A.I.C.S.: 517810
Annika Westberg *(CFO)*

A4F-ALGAE FOR FUTURE SA

Estrada do Paco do Lumiar Campus do Lumiar Ed E R/C, 1649-038, Lisbon, Portugal
Tel.: (351) 218 072 499
Web Site: http://www.a4f.pt
Year Founded: 2008
Biotechnology Company
N.A.I.C.S.: 541714
Nuno Coelho *(CEO)*

Subsidiaries:

Solvay Portugal - Produtos Quimicos S.A. (1)
Rua Eng Clement Dumoulin, 2625-106, Povoa de Santa Iria, Portugal
Tel.: (351) 219534000
Web Site: http://www.solvay.com
Alkalis, Salt, Chlorine Products, Sodium Chlorate, Aquaculture Mfr
N.A.I.C.S.: 325180

A8 NEW MEDIA GROUP LTD.

22/F A8 Music Building No 99 Gaoxinnan 9th Avenue of Hi-tech Park, Nanshan District, Shenzhen, China
Tel.: (86) 75533326333
Web Site: http://ir.a8.com   Ky
0800—(HKG)
Rev.: $11,112,800
Assets: $233,643,290
Liabilities: $21,366,072
Net Worth: $212,277,218
Earnings: $1,959,563
Emp.: 18
Fiscal Year-end: 12/31/22
Digital Music Services
N.A.I.C.S.: 541519
Xiaosong Liu *(Chm & CEO)*

AA INDUSTRIAL BELTING (SHANGHAI) CO., LTD.

No 580 Xiangyin Road, Yangpu District, Shanghai, 200433, China
Tel.: (86) 2165305237   CN
Web Site: http://www.aabelt.com.cn
Year Founded: 1993
603580—(SHG)
Rev.: $24,783,113
Assets: $74,402,593
Liabilities: $10,527,417
Net Worth: $63,875,177
Earnings: ($393,429)
Fiscal Year-end: 12/31/22
Conveyor Belt Mfr & Distr
N.A.I.C.S.: 326220
Tu Mulin *(Chm)*

AA PLUS TRADELINK LIMITED

B-702 Divine Jalpa Gomati Bhuvan Near Jain Temple Jambli Gali, Borivali West, Mumbai, 400092, Maharashtra, India
Tel.: (91) 2228980308
Web Site:
http://www.aaplustradelink.com
Year Founded: 2016
543319—(BOM)
Metal Product Distr
N.A.I.C.S.: 423510
Ashok A. Shah *(Chm)*

AAA TECHNOLOGIES LIMITED

278-280 F Wing Solaris-1 Saki Vihar Road, Opp L And T Gate No 6 Powai Andheri East, Mumbai, 400072, India
Tel.: (91) 2228573815
Web Site:
https://www.aaatechnologies.co.in
Year Founded: 2000
543671—(BOM)
Rev.: $1,989,788
Assets: $3,798,918
Liabilities: $527,818
Net Worth: $3,271,100
Earnings: $273,232
Emp.: 64
Fiscal Year-end: 03/31/22
Information Technology Services
N.A.I.C.S.: 541511
Anjay Agarwal *(Chm & Mng Dir)*

AAB HOLDINGS PTY LIMITED

Building B 1A Bessemer Street, Blacktown, 2148, NSW, Australia
Tel.: (61) 288220600

Web Site: http://www.aabholdings.com
Year Founded: 2000
Sales Range: $50-74.9 Million
Emp.: 250
Holding Company Business Services
N.A.I.C.S.: 551112
Wayne Finkelde *(CFO)*

Subsidiaries:

Mailing and Print Services (1)
8 Aquatic Drive, French's Forest, 2086, NSW, Australia
Tel.: (61) 294516433
Web Site: http://www.mailandprint.com.au
Printing & Mailing Services
N.A.I.C.S.: 323111

Nature's Selection Foods (1)
Building 8 77-85 Roberts Road, Greenacre, 2190, NSW, Australia
Tel.: (61) 287557400
Web Site: http://www.naturesselection.com
Food Mfr, Packer & Distr
N.A.I.C.S.: 311999

Pegasus Printing (1)
Building B 1A Bessemer Street, Blacktown, 2148, NSW, Australia
Tel.: (61) 288220600
Web Site:
http://www.pegasusprintgroup.com.au
Sales Range: $25-49.9 Million
Emp.: 100
Printing Services & Supplies
N.A.I.C.S.: 323111
Wayne Finkelde *(CEO)*

AAC CAPITAL PARTNERS HOLDING B.V.

ITO Tower 22nd Floor Gustav Mahlerplein 106, 1082 MA, Amsterdam, Netherlands
Tel.: (31) 203331300   NI
Web Site:
http://www.aaccapitalpartners.com
Year Founded: 2007
Holding Company; Equity Investment Firm
N.A.I.C.S.: 551112
Marc Staal *(Chm & Mng Partner)*

Subsidiaries:

AAC Capital Benelux (1)
ITO Tower 22nd Floor Gustav Mahlerplein 106, 1082 MA, Amsterdam, Netherlands
Tel.: (31) 20 333 1300
Web Site: http://www.aaccapital.com
Equity Investment Firm
N.A.I.C.S.: 523999
Maurice Bronckers *(Mng Partner)*

Holding (Domestic):

Vetus N.V. (2)
Fokkerstraat 571, 3125 BD, Schiedam, Netherlands
Tel.: (31) 104377700
Web Site: http://www.vetus.nl
Sales Range: $75-99.9 Million
Emp.: 150
Marine Diesel Engine & Nautical Equipment Mfr
N.A.I.C.S.: 336310
Marcel Borsboom *(CEO)*

AAC Nordic Advisory AB (1)
Birger Jarlsgatan 12 1st Floor, PO Box 26124, 100 41, Stockholm, Sweden
Tel.: (46) 84074440
Web Site: http://www.aaccapitalnordic.com
Emp.: 8
Equity Investment Firm
N.A.I.C.S.: 523999

Joint Venture (Non-US):

BabySam AmbA (2)
Egelund.A27-29, DK-6200, Abenra, Denmark
Tel.: (45) 74632510
Web Site: http://www.babysam.dk
Sales Range: $75-99.9 Million
Baby Equipment Retailer
N.A.I.C.S.: 459999

Holding (Non-US):

Empower Oy (2)
Valimotie 9-11, 00380, Helsinki,
Finland (65%)
Tel.: (358) 29 020 011
Web Site: http://www.empower.fi
Sales Range: $200-249.9 Million
Energy Telecommunication & Industrial
Support Services
N.A.I.C.S.: 561990

Glud & Marstrand A/S (2)
Hedenstedvej 14, Losning, 8723,
Denmark (100%)
Tel.: (45) 63124200
Web Site: http://www.glud-marstrand.com
Sales Range: $350-399.9 Million
Metal Can & Packaging Products Mfr
N.A.I.C.S.: 332431
Jorgen Kjaergaard (Mng Dir)

AAC CLYDE SPACE AB
Uppsala Science Park Dag Hammar-
skjolds vag 48, 751 83, Uppsala,
Sweden
Tel.: (46) 18560130
Web Site: https://www.aac-
clyde.space
Year Founded: 2005
ACCMF—(OTCQX)
Rev.: $32,308,258
Assets: $93,153,257
Liabilities: $27,360,872
Net Worth: $65,792,385
Earnings: ($4,125,916)
Emp.: 180
Fiscal Year-end: 12/31/23
Information Technology Services
N.A.I.C.S.: 541512
Andrew Strain (CTO)

AAC TECHNOLOGIES HOLD-INGS INC.
Block A Nanjing University Research
Center Shenzhen Branch, No 6 Yuex-
ing 3rd Road, Shenzhen, 518057,
China
Tel.: (86) 75533972018   Ky
Web Site:
http://www.aactechnologies.com
2018—(OTCIQ)
Rev.: $2,626,052,953
Assets: $5,961,601,499
Liabilities: $2,618,431,368
Net Worth: $3,343,170,130
Earnings: $229,972,500
Emp.: 33,735
Fiscal Year-end: 12/31/20
Holding Company; Acoustic Products
Mfr
N.A.I.C.S.: 551112
Benjamin Zhengmin Pan (CEO)

Subsidiaries:

AAC Acoustic Technologies (1)
Lemminkaisenkatu 46a, 20520, Turku, Fin-
land
Tel.: (358) 22341005
Web Site: http://www.aactechnologies.com
Sales Range: $50-74.9 Million
Emp.: 5
Electronic Products Sales
N.A.I.C.S.: 423620

AAC Acoustic Technologies (Shen-
zhen) Co., Ltd. (1)
AAC Technologies Bldg No 18 Xinxi Rd N
Hi-Tech Indus Pk, Nanshan Dist, Shenzhen,
518057, Guangdong, China
Tel.: (86) 75533972018
Emp.: 3,000
Audio Components Distr
N.A.I.C.S.: 449210

AAC Acoustic Technologies Sweden
AB (1)
Kungsbron2 plan 12, 111 22, Stockholm,
Sweden
Tel.: (46) 87507130
Electrical Products Distr
N.A.I.C.S.: 423620

AAC Microtech (Changzhou) Co.,
Ltd. (1)
No 3 Changcao Rd Wujin High-New Tech
Indus Dev, Changzhou, 213167, Jiangsu,
China
Tel.: (86) 51983052018
Digital Cameras & Accessories Mfr & Sales
N.A.I.C.S.: 334118

AAC Wireless Technologies AB (1)
Rallarvagen 41, 184 40, Akersberga, Swe-
den
Tel.: (46) 8 540 20 000
Web Site: http://www.aacwireless.se
Antenna Mfr
N.A.I.C.S.: 334220

American Audio Component Inc. (1)
20957 Currier Rd Ste A, Walnut, CA 91789
Tel.: (909) 596-3788
Web Site: http://www.american-audio.com
Sales Range: $25-49.9 Million
Emp.: 5
Acoustic Product Mfr
N.A.I.C.S.: 334419
Zhong L Pan (Pres)

Camos Technologies Co.,Ltd. (1)
3F No 11 Beitou Rd Sec 2, Beitou Dist, Tai-
pei, Taiwan
Tel.: (886) 228959088
Camera Module Mfr
N.A.I.C.S.: 333310

WiSpry, Inc. (1)
20 Fairbanks Ste 198, Irvine, CA 92618
Tel.: (949) 458-9477
Web Site: http://www.wispry.com
Sales Range: $1-9.9 Million
Semiconductor Radio Frequency Integration
Services
N.A.I.C.S.: 541990
Arthur Morris (Co-Founder & CTO)

YEC Electronics Limited (1)
Rm G 6F Co Tack Indus Bldg 17 Kin Fat St,
Tuen Mun, New Territories, China (Hong
Kong)
Tel.: (852) 27640299
Audio Components Distr
N.A.I.C.S.: 449210

AADHAAR VENTURES INDIA LIMITED
4th Floor Office No 4019 World Trade
Center Ring Road, Surat, 390 002,
Gujarat, India
Tel.: (91) 2612346481
Web Site:
https://www.aadhaarltd.com
Year Founded: 1995
Rev.: $1,438,273
Assets: $98,762,276
Liabilities: $4,148,701
Net Worth: $54,385,710
Earnings: $18,983
Fiscal Year-end: 03/31/17
Textile Products Mfr
N.A.I.C.S.: 314999

AADI INDUSTRIES LTD.
421 4th Floor Kailash Plaza Vallabh
Baug Lane, Pantnagar Ghatkopar
East, Near R-Odeon Mall Ghatkopar
East, Mumbai, 400077, India
Tel.: (91) 2225012768
Web Site:
https://www.aadiindustries.in
Sales Range: $1-9.9 Million
Tarpaulin Mfr
N.A.I.C.S.: 314910

AAGAM CAPITAL LIMITED
Premises No 2 1st Floor Rahimtoola
House 7 Homji Street, Fort, Mumbai,
400001, India
Tel.: (91) 7400186121   In
Web Site:
https://www.aagamcap.com
Year Founded: 1991
Rev.: $26,219
Assets: $390,743
Liabilities: $17,707

Net Worth: $373,035
Earnings: $12,993
Fiscal Year-end: 03/31/18
Financial Investment Services
N.A.I.C.S.: 523150
Anil Manshukhlal Kothari (CFO)

AAGES S.A.
Str Agricultorilor Nr 16, Singeorgiu de
Mures, Tirgu Mures, Romania
Tel.: (40) 265213043
Web Site: https://www.aages.ro
Year Founded: 1990
AAG—(BUC)
Rev.: $10,072,001
Assets: $13,278,285
Liabilities: $6,531,159
Net Worth: $6,747,127
Earnings: $1,351,855
Emp.: 111
Fiscal Year-end: 12/31/22
Heating Machinery Mfr
N.A.I.C.S.: 333414
Gabor Jozsef Molnar (Chm & Gen
Mgr)

AAJ CAPITAL 2 CORP.
1055 West Georgia Street Suite
2050, Vancouver, V6E 3P3, BC,
Canada
Tel.: (604) 684-2181
AAJC.P—(TSXV)
Rev.: $165,145
Assets: $707,210
Liabilities: $416,973
Net Worth: $290,237
Earnings: ($1,649,086)
Fiscal Year-end: 09/30/23
Business Consulting Services
N.A.I.C.S.: 522299
Debbie Lew (Sec)

AAK AB
Pulpetgatan 20, 215 32, Malmo, Swe-
den
Tel.: (46) 406278300   SE
Web Site: https://www.aak.com
AAK—(OMX)
Rev.: $3,454,619,840
Assets: $2,719,698,240
Liabilities: $1,530,883,200
Net Worth: $1,188,815,040
Earnings: $193,008,480
Emp.: 3,969
Fiscal Year-end: 12/31/20
Specialty Vegetable Fats Mfr
N.A.I.C.S.: 311225
Anne Mette Olesen (Chief Strategy &
Sustainability Officer, VP & Head-
People)

Subsidiaries:

AAK (UK) Limited (1)
King George Dock, Hull, HU9 5PX, United
Kingdom
Tel.: (44) 1482701271
Web Site: http://www.aak-uk.com
Sales Range: $100-124.9 Million
Emp.: 300
Specialty Vegetable Fats Mfr
N.A.I.C.S.: 311225

Division (Domestic):

AarhusKarlshamn UK Ltd. - AAK
Foods (2)
Davy Road Astmoor Industrial Estate, Run-
corn, WA7 1PX, Cheshire, United Kingdom
Tel.: (44) 1482701271
Sales Range: $25-49.9 Million
Emp.: 60
Mustards & Condiments Mfr
N.A.I.C.S.: 311941

AAK (UK) Limited (1)
King George Dock, Hull, HU9 5PX, United
Kingdom
Tel.: (44) 148 270 1271
Web Site: https://www.aak-uk.com

Sales Range: $100-124.9 Million
Emp.: 350
Edible Vegetable Fats & Oils Mfr
N.A.I.C.S.: 311225
Helen Flower (Mgr-Mktg)

AAK Aust. Pty Ltd. (1)
Suite 4 10-12 Old Castle Hill Road, Castle
Hill, 2154, NSW, Australia
Tel.: (61) 288503522
Web Site: http://www.aak.com
Sales Range: $25-49.9 Million
Emp.: 3
Vegetable Oils Mfr & Distr
N.A.I.C.S.: 311999

AAK Aust. Pty. Ltd. (1)
Suite 4 10-12 Old Castle Hill Road, Castle
Hill, 2154, NSW, Australia
Tel.: (61) 288503522
Food Vegetable Oil & Fat Mfr
N.A.I.C.S.: 311225

AAK Australia Pty Ltd. (1)
Suite 4 10-12 Old Castle Hill Road, Castle
Hill, 2154, NSW, Australia
Tel.: (61) 288503522
Food & Beverage Mfr
N.A.I.C.S.: 311999

AAK BD Foods Ltd. (1)
68 Castleham Road, Hastings, Saint Leon-
ards, TN38 9NU, United Kingdom
Tel.: (44) 1424853000
Food & Beverage Mfr
N.A.I.C.S.: 311999

AAK BF SARL (1)
Route de Banfora - Samagan Arrond No 6,
BP 1020, cote Est de la Route Nationale
No 7, Bobo-Dioulasso, Burkina Faso
Tel.: (226) 20985150
Food Vegetable Oil & Fat Mfr
N.A.I.C.S.: 311225

AAK Belgium N.V. (1)
Noorderlaan 147, 2030, Antwerp, Belgium
Tel.: (32) 36414400
Food Vegetable Oil & Fat Mfr
N.A.I.C.S.: 311225

AAK Burkina Faso Sarl (1)
Route de Banfora -Samagan Arrond No 6,
B P 1020, Cote Est de la Route Nationale
No 7 01, Bobo-Dioulasso, Burkina Faso
Tel.: (226) 20985150
Plant Oil Mfr & Distr
N.A.I.C.S.: 311225

AAK Canada Ltd. (1)
2275 Upper Middle Road Ste 101, Oakville,
L6H 0C3, ON, Canada
Tel.: (973) 344-1300
Food Vegetable Oil & Fat Mfr
N.A.I.C.S.: 311225

AAK China Ltd. (1)
6F Building 6 3601 Dongfang Road, Shang-
hai, 200125, China
Tel.: (86) 2164667979
Food Vegetable Oil & Fat Mfr
N.A.I.C.S.: 311225
Weiyu Fan (Gen Mgr)

AAK Colombia S.A.S. (1)
Calle 90 11-13 Oficina 420, Bogota, Colom-
bia
Tel.: (57) 86818620
Food & Beverage Mfr
N.A.I.C.S.: 311999

AAK Cote d'Ivoire SASU (1)
S/C Proline Logistics Derriere Sonaco Zone
Industriel Yopougon, Abidjan, Cote d'Ivoire
Tel.: (225) 78314721
Food Vegetable Oil & Fat Mfr
N.A.I.C.S.: 311225

AAK Czech Republic Spol.s.r.o. (1)
Na Pankraci 1618/30, 140 00, Prague,
Czech Republic
Tel.: (420) 222210406
Web Site: http://www.aak.com
Sales Range: $25-49.9 Million
Emp.: 2
Vegetable Fats Mfr
N.A.I.C.S.: 311999

AAK Czech Republic s.r.o., (1)
Na Pankraci 1618/30, 140 00, Prague,
Czech Republic

AAK AB—(Continued)

Tel.: (420) 222210406
Food & Beverage Mfr
N.A.I.C.S.: 311999

AAK Dalby AB (1)
Albavagen 4, 247 50, Dalby, Sweden
Tel.: (46) 46205610
Food Vegetable Oil & Fat Mfr
N.A.I.C.S.: 311225

AAK Denmark A/S (1)
Slipvej 4, 8000, Aarhus, Denmark
Tel.: (45) 87306000
Web Site: https://www.aak.com
Emp.: 200
Vegetable Oils & Various Other Baking
Products Mfr
N.A.I.C.S.: 311225

AAK Germany GmbH (1)
Fuhrmannstrasse 6, 64289, Darmstadt,
Germany
Tel.: (49) 21517886682
Food Vegetable Oil & Fat Mfr
N.A.I.C.S.: 311225

AAK Havnen A/S (1)
Slipvej 4, 8000, Arhus, Denmark
Tel.: (45) 87306000
Web Site: http://www.aak.com
Sales Range: $100-124.9 Million
Emp.: 200
Vegetable Oil Mfr
N.A.I.C.S.: 311999

AAK Kamani Pvt. Ltd. (1)
14th Floor Quantum Central Avenue Hi-
ranandani Business Park, Hiranandani Es-
tate Ghodbunder Road, Mumbai, 400 607,
India (100%)
Tel.: (91) 18002666363
Web Site: https://www.aakindia.com
Emp.: 500
Food Vegetable Oil & Fat Mfr
N.A.I.C.S.: 311225
Ganesh Doifode (VP)

AAK Malaysia Sdn. Bhd. (1)
Suite 17 01 - 02 Level 17 Wisma Goldhill
No 67 Jalan Raja Chulan, 50200, Kuala
Lumpur, Malaysia
Tel.: (60) 327108493
Food Vegetable Oil & Fat Mfr
N.A.I.C.S.: 311225
Peter Brazel (Dir-Bus Dev)

AAK Mali SARL
s/c des Ensema Gare Marchandises Route
de Sotuba, Korofina Sud, Bamako, Mali
Tel.: (223) 76478559
Food Vegetable Oil & Fat Mfr
N.A.I.C.S.: 311225

AAK Mexico, S.A. de C.V (1)
Av Heroes de Nocupetaro 1022, Col Indus-
trial, 58130, Morelia, Michoacan, Mexico
Tel.: (52) 4431750402
Food & Beverage Mfr
N.A.I.C.S.: 311999

AAK Miyoshi Japan Co. Ltd. (1)
Mita Nitto Daibiru 201 3-11-36 Mita, Minato-
ku, Tokyo, 108-0073, Japan
Tel.: (81) 362312876
Food Vegetable Oil & Fat Mfr
N.A.I.C.S.: 311225

AAK Netherlands BV (1)
Kreeftstraat 1, PO Box 17, 1540 AA,
Zaandijk, Netherlands
Tel.: (31) 756278400
Sales Range: $25-49.9 Million
Emp.: 75
Fatty Acids Mfr
N.A.I.C.S.: 325199

AAK Netherlands BV (1)
Kreeftstraat 1, 1544 CK, Zaandijk, Nether-
lands
Tel.: (31) 756278400
Food & Beverage Mfr
N.A.I.C.S.: 311999

AAK Norway AS (1)
Solli, PO Box 2570, 0202, Oslo, Norway
Tel.: (47) 91846426
Food Vegetable Oil & Fat Mfr
N.A.I.C.S.: 311225

AAK OOO (1)

Podsosenskiy per 20 bld 1, Moscow,
105062, Russia
Tel.: (7) 4959376001
Food Vegetable Oil & Fat Mfr
N.A.I.C.S.: 311225

AAK Poland Sp. z o. o. (1)
ul Walecznych 44/3, 03-916, Warsaw, Po-
land
Tel.: (48) 226164182
Food Vegetable Oil & Fat Mfr
N.A.I.C.S.: 311225

AAK Rotterdam BV (1)
1e Welplaatdwarsweg 1-3 Harbour 4135,
3197 KT, Rotterdam, Netherlands
Tel.: (31) 103126100
Food Vegetable Oil & Fat Mfr
N.A.I.C.S.: 311225

AAK SG Pte. Ltd. (1)
21 Biopolis Road Nucleos South Tower 01-
25, Singapore, 138567, Singapore
Tel.: (65) 69160320
Food & Beverage Mfr
N.A.I.C.S.: 311999

AAK Singapore Pte. Ltd. (1)
21 Biopolis Road Nucleos South Tower 01-
25, Singapore, 138567, Singapore
Tel.: (65) 69160320
Food Vegetable Oil & Fat Mfr
N.A.I.C.S.: 311225

AAK Sweden AB (1)
Vastra Kajen, 374 82, Karlshamn, Sweden
Tel.: (46) 45482000
Food & Beverage Mfr
N.A.I.C.S.: 311999

**AAK Turkey Gida Sanay ve Ticaret
Limited** (1)
Meclis Mah Bogazici Cad Seheryeli Sok
Karsan Plaza No 1/2, Sancaktepe, 34785,
Istanbul, Turkey
Tel.: (90) 216 622 0424
Web Site: https://www.aak-tr.com
Food Vegetable Oil & Fat Mfr
N.A.I.C.S.: 311225
Ediz Kurt (Reg Sls Mgr)

**AAK Turkey Gida Sanayi ve Ticaret
Limited Sirketi** (1)
FSM Mahallesi Poligon Caddesi No 8A
Buyaka2 Sitesi Kule-1 18th floor, Umraniye,
34771, Istanbul, Turkiye
Tel.: (90) 2166220424
Web Site: https://www.aak-tr.com
Plant Base Oils & Fats Mfr
N.A.I.C.S.: 311225

AAK USA K1/K2 LLC (1)
2520 S 7th St Rd, Louisville, KY 40208
Tel.: (502) 636-3712
Food Vegetable Oil & Fat Mfr
N.A.I.C.S.: 311225

AAK USA Richmond Corp. (1)
1145 Harbour Way S, Richmond, CA 94804
Tel.: (510) 233-7660
Food Vegetable Oil & Fat Mfr
N.A.I.C.S.: 311225

**AAK do Brasil Industria e Comercia
de Oleos Vegetais Ltda.** (1)
Av Jose Alves de Oliveira 333 Distrito In-
dustrial, Jundiai, Sao Paulo, 13213-105,
Brazil
Tel.: (55) 1144310000
Food Vegetable Oil & Fat Mfr
N.A.I.C.S.: 311225

**AAK do Brasil Industria e Comercio
de Oleos Vegetais Ltda.** (1)
Av Jose Alves de Oliveira, 333 Distrito In-
dustrial Jundiai, Sao Paulo, 13213-105,
Brazil
Tel.: (55) 1144310000
Plant Base Oils & Fats Mfr
N.A.I.C.S.: 311225

Aarhus 3 A/S (1)
Slipvej 4, 8000, Arhus, Denmark
Tel.: (45) 87306000
Web Site: http://www.aak.com
Sales Range: $100-124.9 Million
Emp.: 280
Oils & Fats Rendering Services
N.A.I.C.S.: 311225

Aarhus Malaysia Sdn. Bhd. (1)

Jendarata Estate, 36009, Teluk Intan,
Perak, Malaysia
Tel.: (60) 56411411
Palm Oil Mfr
N.A.I.C.S.: 311225

**AarhusKarlshamn Baltic Holding
AB** (1)
Jungmansgatan 12, 211 19, Malmo, Swe-
den
Tel.: (46) 45482609
Investment Management Service
N.A.I.C.S.: 523999

AarhusKarlshamn Baltic Ltd. (1)
Kalvariju 125, LT-02648, Vilnius, Lithuania
Tel.: (370) 52700061
Web Site: http://www.aak.com
Vegetable Fats Mfr & Marketer
N.A.I.C.S.: 311999

AarhusKarlshamn Canada Ltd. (1)
2275 Upper Middle Rd Ste 101, Oakville,
L6H 0C3, ON, Canada
Tel.: (973) 344-1300
Sales Range: $50-74.9 Million
Emp.: 1
Vegetable Fats & Oils Distr
N.A.I.C.S.: 424490

AarhusKarlshamn Ghana Ltd. (1)
1st Floor SAGA GH Limited Building Plots
85-89 Tema Main Harbour, Tema, Ghana
Tel.: (233) 22 200647
Web Site: http://www.aak.com
Sales Range: $25-49.9 Million
Emp.: 7
Shea Oil Mfr
N.A.I.C.S.: 325620

**AarhusKarlshamn Latin America
S.A.** (1)
Camino al Paso de la Arena 2460, 12600,
Montevideo, Uruguay
Tel.: (598) 23135135
Sales Range: $25-49.9 Million
Emp.: 20
Vegetable Fats & Oils Distr
N.A.I.C.S.: 424490

**AarhusKarlshamn Mexico, S.A. de
C.V.** (1)
Av Heroes de Nocupetaro 1022 Col Indus-
trial, 58130, Morelia, Michoacan, Mexico
Tel.: (52) 443 175 0402
Web Site: http://www.aak.com
Vegetable Fats Distr
N.A.I.C.S.: 424490

AarhusKarlshamn Norway AS (1)
Fjordveien 3, 1363, Hovik, Norway
Tel.: (47) 9 184 6426
Web Site: http://www.aak.com
Vegetable Fats Mfr
N.A.I.C.S.: 311999

**AarhusKarlshamn Poland Sp.z
o.o.** (1)
Ul Walecznych 44/3, 03-916, Warsaw, Po-
land
Tel.: (48) 226164182
Web Site: https://www.aak.com
Sales Range: $25-49.9 Million
Emp.: 5
Vegetable Fats Mfr
N.A.I.C.S.: 311999

AarhusKarlshamn RU OOO (1)
Podsosenskiy per 20 Bldg 1, Moscow,
105062, Russia
Tel.: (7) 4959376001
Web Site: https://www.aak.com
Sales Range: $25-49.9 Million
Emp.: 17
Vegetable Fats Mfr
N.A.I.C.S.: 311999
Thomas Larsen (Dir-Keyclient)

AarhusKarlshamn Sweden AB (1)
Vastra Kajen, 374 82, Karlshamn, Sweden
Tel.: (46) 45482000
Web Site: http://www.aak.com
Sales Range: $150-199.9 Million
Emp.: 620
Specialty Vegetable Fats Mfr
N.A.I.C.S.: 311225

**AarhusKarlshamn do Brasil desenvol-
vimento de Negosios Ltda.** (1)
Av Das Nacoes Unidas 12 551 - 17 Andar

Sala 1783 WTC Tower, 06460-040, Sao
Paulo, Brazil
Tel.: (55) 1134437862
Sales Range: $50-74.9 Million
Emp.: 10
Confectionery Product Distr
N.A.I.C.S.: 424450
Edmond Borid (Gen Mgr)

BD Foods Ltd. (1)
68 Castleham Road Castleham Industrial
Est, Saint Leonards, TN38 9NU, East Sus-
sex, United Kingdom
Tel.: (44) 1424853000
Web Site: http://www.bdfoods.co.uk
Restaurant Operators
N.A.I.C.S.: 722511

Belico Holding AB (1)
Box 74, 247 24, Dalby, Sweden
Tel.: (46) 46205617
Investment Management Service
N.A.I.C.S.: 523940

Book & Claim Ltd. (1)
King George Dock, Hull, HU9 5PX, United
Kingdom
Tel.: (44) 1482334000
Web Site: http://www.bookandclaim.org
Sales Range: $50-74.9 Million
Oil Palm Trading Services
N.A.I.C.S.: 523160

Ceylon Trading Co. Ltd. (1)
36 Dr Wijewardena Mawatha, PO Box 161,
Colombo, 10, Sri Lanka
Tel.: (94) 112327336
Web Site: http://www.aak.com
Emp.: 11
Financial Management Consulting Services
N.A.I.C.S.: 541618

**Predstavnistvo AAK Poland Sp. z
o.o.** (1)
Partizanske avijacije 52, 11070, Belgrade,
Serbia
Tel.: (381) 63334757
Food Vegetable Oil & Fat Mfr
N.A.I.C.S.: 311225

Rapsona AB (1)
Albavagen 24, 247 50, Dalby, Sweden
Tel.: (46) 6205600
Web Site: https://www.rapsona.se
Vegetable Mfr & Distr
N.A.I.C.S.: 311411

**AAKASH EXPLORATION SER-
VICES LIMITED**
424 4th Floor Shukan Mall B/h Visat
Petrol Pump Sabarmati, Ahmedabad,
380005, Gujarat, India
Tel.: (91) 9825021894
Web Site:
   https://www.aakashexploration.com
AAKASH—(NSE)
Rev.: $10,563,483
Assets: $9,671,328
Liabilities: $3,154,355
Net Worth: $6,516,973
Earnings: $835,579
Emp.: 1,150
Fiscal Year-end: 03/31/22
Oil & Gas Distribution Services
N.A.I.C.S.: 213112
Vipul Haria (Mng Dir)

AALBERS TOOL & MOLD INC.
5390 Brendan Lane, Old Castle, N0R
1L0, ON, Canada
Tel.: (519) 737-1369
Web Site: http://www.aalberstool.com
Rev.: $19,430,925
Emp.: 100
Industrial Mold Mfr
N.A.I.C.S.: 333511
Gary Aalbers (Owner)

AALBERTS N.V.
WTC Utrecht Stadsplateau 18, NL-
3521, Utrecht, Netherlands
Tel.: (31) 303079300   NI
Web Site: http://www.aalberts.com
Year Founded: 1975

AAIB—(EUR)
Rev.: $3,485,862,292
Assets: $4,544,247,788
Liabilities: $1,994,496,007
Net Worth: $2,549,751,781
Earnings: $347,830,779
Emp.: 14,597
Fiscal Year-end: 12/31/22
Holding Company; Industrial Services & Flow Control System Activities
N.A.I.C.S.: 551112
Arno Monincx *(CFO)*

Subsidiaries:

AHC Oberflachentechnik GmbH **(1)**
Boelckestrasse 25 - 57, 50171, Kerpen, Germany
Tel.: (49) 22375020
Web Site: http://www.ahc-surface.com
Sales Range: $200-249.9 Million
Emp.: 130
Heat Treatment Services
N.A.I.C.S.: 332811
Hartmut Sauer *(CEO)*

Subsidiary (Non-US):

AHC B.V. **(2)**
Hurksestraat 32, NL 5652 AL, Eindhoven, Netherlands **(100%)**
Tel.: (31) 402507607
Web Site: http://www.ahcbenelux.nl
Sales Range: $25-49.9 Million
Emp.: 50
Metal Coating Products Mfr
N.A.I.C.S.: 325510

AHC Benelux B.V. **(2)**
Hurksestraat 32, Eindhoven, 5652 AL, Netherlands
Tel.: (31) 40 250 76 07
Web Site: http://www.ahcbenelux.nl
Sales Range: $25-49.9 Million
Emp.: 50
Electroplating Electroless Nickel & Synergetic Coating Services
N.A.I.C.S.: 332813
Peter Smits *(Mgr-Quality)*

AHC Italia S.R.L. **(2)**
Via Staffora 20/2, 20090, Opera, Milan, Italy
Tel.: (39) 02 57 60 65 09
Web Site: http://www.ahc-surface.com
Sales Range: $25-49.9 Million
Emp.: 25
Metal & Plastic Coating Services
N.A.I.C.S.: 332812
Hartmut Sauer *(CEO)*

AHC Oberflachentechnik Ges.m.b.H. **(2)**
Helpfau-Uttendorf Gewerbestrate 21, 5261, Sankt Pantaleon, Austria
Tel.: (43) 6277 74 00
Metal & Plastic Coating Solutions Mfr
N.A.I.C.S.: 332812
Marco Hof *(Gen Mgr)*

Subsidiary (Domestic):

AHC Special Coatings GmbH **(2)**
Dycker Feld 43, 42653, Solingen, Germany
Tel.: (49) 212 25 83 4 0
Sales Range: $25-49.9 Million
Emp.: 65
Metal & Plastic Coating Mfr
N.A.I.C.S.: 325510
Wilfrid Brake *(Gen Mgr)*

Subsidiary (Non-US):

AHC Surface Technology S.A.S. **(2)**
Avenue Bade Wurtemberg, 57380, Faulquemont, France
Tel.: (33) 3 87 00 43 80
Metal & Plastic Coating Solutions Mfr
N.A.I.C.S.: 332812

AIMT Traterh, S.A.U. **(1)**
Polig Ind Aproin Alcotanes 32 Nave, ES 28320, Madrid, Spain **(100%)**
Tel.: (34) 916923330
Sales Range: $25-49.9 Million
Emp.: 20
Thermal Product Mfr
N.A.I.C.S.: 333248

Aalberts Integrated Piping Systems APAC Inc. **(1)**

11F-2 No 175 Zhongzheng 2nd Rd, Lingya, Kaohsiung, 80274, Taiwan
Tel.: (886) 72253768
Metal & Plastic Pipe Mfr
N.A.I.C.S.: 332919
Holden Chen *(CEO)*

Aalberts Integrated Piping Systems B.V. **(1)**
Oude Amersfoortseweg 99, PO Box 498, 1212 AA, Hilversum, Netherlands
Tel.: (31) 356884211
Web Site: http://www.aalberts-ips.com
Metal & Plastic Pipe Mfr
N.A.I.C.S.: 332919

Aalberts Surface Technologies GmbH **(1)**
Boelckestrasse 25-57, 50171, Kerpen, Germany
Tel.: (49) 2237502520
Web Site: http://www.aalberts-st.com
Emp.: 150
Polymer Coating Services
N.A.I.C.S.: 238320
Oliver Jager *(Mng Dir)*

Aalberts Surface Treatment Tamworth Limited **(1)**
Kingsbury Link Trinity Road, Tamworth, B78 2EX, United Kingdom
Tel.: (44) 1827871400
Polymer Coating Services
N.A.I.C.S.: 238320

Accurate Brazing Corporation **(1)**
36 Cote Ave, Goffstown, NH 03045
Tel.: (603) 945-3761
Web Site: http://www.accuratebrazing.com
Sales Range: $25-49.9 Million
Emp.: 40
Vacuum Brazing & Heat Treating Services
N.A.I.C.S.: 332811
Brent Davis *(Mgr-Ops)*

Adex BV **(1)**
Tjalkkade 2, 5928 PZ, Venlo, Netherlands **(100%)**
Tel.: (31) 773898900
Web Site: http://adex-dies.com
Sales Range: $25-49.9 Million
Emp.: 85
Extrusion Die Mfr
N.A.I.C.S.: 333248

BROEN A/S **(1)**
Skovvej 30, 5610, Assens, Denmark **(100%)**
Tel.: (45) 64712095
Web Site: http://www.broen.com
Sales Range: $75-99.9 Million
Emp.: 230
Industrial Valve Mfr
N.A.I.C.S.: 332911
Motens Laursen *(Mng Dir)*

Subsidiary (Non-US):

BROEN Finland OY **(2)**
Robert Huberin tie 2 A, 01510, Vantaa, Finland
Tel.: (358) 207320100
Web Site: http://www.broen.fi
Heating Equipment Mfr
N.A.I.C.S.: 333414

BROEN Ltd. **(2)**
8-ja Tekstilshikov str 11/2, 109129, Moscow, Russia
Tel.: (7) 4952281150
Web Site: http://www.broen.ru
Emp.: 200
Heating Equipment Mfr
N.A.I.C.S.: 333414

BROEN Malaysia Sdn. Bhd. **(2)**
11 Jalan USJ 8/2B, UEP, Subang Jaya, 47610, Selangor, Malaysia **(100%)**
Tel.: (60) 3 5635 8799
Industrial Valve Mfr
N.A.I.C.S.: 332911

BROEN Raufoss AB **(2)**
Maskin Gatan 5, 411 21, Gothenburg, Sweden
Tel.: (46) 317610200
Sales Range: $25-49.9 Million
Emp.: 15
Heating Equipment Mfr
N.A.I.C.S.: 333414

BROEN S.A. **(2)**
ul Pieszycka 10, 58-200, Dzierzoniow, Poland **(60%)**
Tel.: (48) 748327000
Web Site: http://www.broen.pl
Sales Range: $25-49.9 Million
Emp.: 140
Industrial Valve Mfr
N.A.I.C.S.: 332911

BROEN SEI Srl. **(2)**
Str Fabricii Nr 47 Corp X Et 4 Sector 6, Bucharest, 060821, Romania
Tel.: (40) 21 316 96 19
Web Site: http://www.broen-sei.ro
Sales Range: $25-49.9 Million
Emp.: 4
Pipe Fitting & Valve Distr
N.A.I.C.S.: 423830
Ana Sebastian *(Dir)*

BROEN Singapore Pte Ltd **(2)**
10 Pukit Cresent Dr, Singapore, 658079, Singapore **(100%)**
Tel.: (65) 62980662
Web Site: http://www.broen.com
Sales Range: $25-49.9 Million
Emp.: 3
Industrial Valve Mfr
N.A.I.C.S.: 332911

BROEN Valves (Beijing) Co., Ltd. **(2)**
HuaTeng Plaza701 302 JinSong 3rd Zone, ChaoYang District, Beijing, 100021, China
Tel.: (86) 1067892995
Web Site: http://www.broen.com
Emp.: 20
Heating Equipment Mfr
N.A.I.C.S.: 333414

BROEN Valves Ltd. **(2)**
Unit 7 Cleton Street Business Park, Cleton Street, Tipton, DY4 7TR, West Midlands, United Kingdom **(100%)**
Tel.: (44) 1215224505
Web Site: http://www.broen.co.uk
Sales Range: $25-49.9 Million
Emp.: 5
Industrial Valve Mfr
N.A.I.C.S.: 332911

Subsidiary (US):

BROEN, Inc. **(2)**
6421 Lozano Dr, Houston, TX 77041 **(50%)**
Tel.: (713) 300-0480
Web Site: http://www.broen.us
Sales Range: $25-49.9 Million
Emp.: 10
Industrial Valve Mfr
N.A.I.C.S.: 332911
Misty Barnes *(Gen Mgr-Sls)*

Subsidiary (Non-US):

BROEN-Zawgaz Sp. z.o.o. **(2)**
ul Stara Droga 8, 62-002, Suchy Las, Poznania, Poland
Tel.: (48) 61 812 55 17
Web Site: http://www.broen-zawgaz.pl
Sales Range: $25-49.9 Million
Emp.: 110
Heating Equipment Mfr
N.A.I.C.S.: 333414

Clorius Controls A/S **(1)**
Skovvej 30, 5610, Assens, Denmark **(100%)**
Tel.: (45) 77323130
Web Site: http://cloriuscontrols.com
Sales Range: $1-9.9 Million
Emp.: 40
Heating, Cooling & Ventilation System Controls Mfr
N.A.I.C.S.: 334519

Comap S.A. **(1)**
16 avenue Paul Santy, 69008, Lyon, France
Tel.: (33) 478781600
Web Site: http://www.comap.fr
Sales Range: $200-249.9 Million
Emp.: 150
Industrial Fluid Control Components
N.A.I.C.S.: 334513

Subsidiary (Non-US):

Comap (UK) Limited **(2)**

Unit C6 William Way Moss Industrial Estate, Saint Helens Road, Leigh, WN7 3PT, Lancs, United Kingdom
Tel.: (44) 1942 603 351
Heating Equipment Distr
N.A.I.C.S.: 423720

Comap Hellas S.A. **(2)**
Terma Yakinthon, Lykovryssi, Athens, 14123, Greece
Tel.: (30) 2102842684
Sales Range: $25-49.9 Million
Emp.: 10
Plumbing & Heating Equipment Distr
N.A.I.C.S.: 423720
Spyros Tsakalos *(Gen Mgr)*

Comap Hungaria Kereskedelmi Kft. **(2)**
Gyar Utca 2, Budaors, 2040, Hungary
Tel.: (36) 23503871
Building Materials Distr
N.A.I.C.S.: 423390

Comap Italia S.r.l.u. **(2)**
Via G Di Vittorio 37, 25030, Roncadelle, BS, Italy
Tel.: (39) 0302586005
Web Site: http://www.comapitalia.com
Metal Products Mfr
N.A.I.C.S.: 332999

Comap N.V. **(2)**
Alsembergsesteenweg 454, 1653, Dworp, Belgium
Tel.: (32) 2 371 01 61
Metal Products Mfr
N.A.I.C.S.: 332999

Comap Nordic AB **(2)**
Carlsgatan 12A, Malmo, 211 20, Sweden
Tel.: (46) 40 42 96 60
Web Site: http://www.comap.se
Sales Range: $25-49.9 Million
Emp.: 14
Plumbing & Heating Equipment Distr
N.A.I.C.S.: 423830

Comap Polska Sp. z.o.o. **(2)**
ul Annopol 4a, 03-236, Warsaw, Poland
Tel.: (48) 22 679 00 25
Web Site: http://www.comap.pl
Emp.: 10,000
Steel Pole Mfr
N.A.I.C.S.: 331210

Comap Praha s.r.o. **(2)**
Krajni 801, 252 42, Jesenice, Czech Republic
Tel.: (420) 284 860 404
Web Site: http://www.comappraha.cz
Emp.: 1
Seal Products Distr
N.A.I.C.S.: 423510

Conbraco Industries, Inc. **(1)**
701 Matthews Mint Hill Rd, Matthews, NC 28105-1706
Tel.: (704) 841-6000
Web Site: http://www.apollovalves.com
Sales Range: $400-449.9 Million
Emp.: 1,500
Ball Valve Mfr
N.A.I.C.S.: 332912
Eric Miller *(CFO)*

Division (Domestic):

Conbraco Industries, Inc. - Pageland **(2)**
1418 S Pearl St, Pageland, SC 29728-0125
Tel.: (843) 672-6161
Web Site: http://www.apollovalves.com
Sales Range: $25-49.9 Million
Emp.: 500
Ball Valve Mfr
N.A.I.C.S.: 332912
Cal Mosack *(Exec VP)*

Conti Sanitararmaturen GmbH **(1)**
Hauptstrasse 98, Krofdorf/Gleiberg, 35435, Wettenberg, Germany
Tel.: (49) 6 41 9 82 21 0
Sanitary Fitting Services
N.A.I.C.S.: 238220

Cotterlaz Connectors Shenzhen Ltd. **(1)**
North Yongfa A-2 Building 4 Tongfuyu Industrial Zone, Shajing Town Bulian District Baoan District Guangdong industrial Park,

Aalberts N.V.—(Continued)

Shenzhen, 518000, China
Tel.: (86) 75581441255
Web Site: http://www.cotterlaz.com.cn
Sales Range: $50-74.9 Million
Emp.: 150
Metal Products Mfr
N.A.I.C.S.: 332999

Cotterlaz Jean S.A.S. (1)
250 rue de la Pointe d'orchex, Marnaz, 74460, France
Tel.: (33) 4 50 98 35 06
Sales Range: $25-49.9 Million
Emp.: 70
Connectors & Radio Frequency Component Mfr
N.A.I.C.S.: 334417
Cabot Patricia, (Gen Mgr)

DSI Getrankearmaturen GmbH & Co. KG (1)
Oberster Kamp 20, 59069, Hamm, Germany (100%)
Tel.: (49) 23857720
Web Site: http://www.dispensegroup.com
Sales Range: $25-49.9 Million
Emp.: 85
Beverage Dispensing Equipment Mfr
N.A.I.C.S.: 333914

Dispense Systems International (1)
Oberster Kamp 20, 59069, Hamm, Germany (100%)
Tel.: (49) 23857720
Web Site: http://www.dispensegroup.com
Sales Range: $25-49.9 Million
Emp.: 30
Beverage Dispensing Equipment Mfr
N.A.I.C.S.: 333914

Duralloy AG (1)
Industriepark Altgraben, 4624, Harkingen, Switzerland
Tel.: (41) 62 38 88 00 0
Metal & Plastic Coating Services
N.A.I.C.S.: 332812

Duralloy Sud GmbH (1)
Eckweg 6, 78048, Villingen-Schwenningen, Germany
Tel.: (49) 77214044410
Web Site: http://www.duralloy.info
Emp.: 5
Metal & Plastic Coating Mfr
N.A.I.C.S.: 332812
Helmut Grotenrath (Mgr)

Elkhart Products Limited (1)
178 Pennsylvania Ave Suite 2, Concord, L4K 4B1, ON, Canada
Tel.: (905) 336-6060
Emp.: 10
Plumbing & Heating Equipment Distr
N.A.I.C.S.: 423720

Fijnmechanische Industrie Venray B.V. (1)
Transportcentrum 2B, 5835 CT, Beugen, Netherlands
Tel.: (31) 485 31 17 11
Web Site: http://www.fivbv.nl
Emp.: 33
Small Series Turned & Milled Component Mfr
N.A.I.C.S.: 332721
J. Bakarbessy (Office Mgr)

Flamco B.V. (1)
Fort Blauwkapel 1, PO Box 502, 1358 DB, Almere, Netherlands
Tel.: (31) 365262300
Web Site: http://flamcogroup.com
Sales Range: $150-199.9 Million
Emp.: 700
HVAC Components Mfr & Whslr
N.A.I.C.S.: 333414
Maarten van de Veen (CEO-Climate Control)

Subsidiary (Non-US):

Flamco AG (2)
Fannring 1, 6403, Kussnacht, Switzerland
Tel.: (41) 41 854 30 50
Web Site: http://flamcogroup.com
HVAC Components Whslr
N.A.I.C.S.: 423720

Subsidiary (Domestic):

Flamco Flexcon B.V. (2)
Amersfoortseweg 9, 3751 LJ, Bunschoten, Netherlands
Tel.: (31) 332997500
Industrial Heating Equipment Mfr & Distr
N.A.I.C.S.: 333414

Subsidiary (Non-US):

Flamco Flexcon Ltd. (2)
Washway Lane, Saint Helens, WA10 6PB, Merseyside, United Kingdom
Tel.: (44) 1744 744 744
Web Site: http://flamcogroup.com
Emp.: 50
Plumbing & Heating Equipment Whslr
N.A.I.C.S.: 423720

Subsidiary (Domestic):

Flamco Limited (3)
Washway Lane, Saint Helens, WA10 6PB, Merseyside, United Kingdom
Tel.: (44) 1744 744 744
Web Site: http://www.flamcogroup.com
Sales Range: $25-49.9 Million
Emp.: 40
Heating Equipment Whslr
N.A.I.C.S.: 423720
Rob Clemson (Dir-Technical)

Subsidiary (Non-US):

Flamco GmbH (2)
Gold-Zack-Strasse 7 - 9, 40822, Mettmann, Germany
Tel.: (49) 21048000620
Web Site: http://flamcogroup.com
Heating Equipment Mfr
N.A.I.C.S.: 333414

Subsidiary (Domestic):

Flamco IMZ B.V. (2)
Hermesweg 2, 7202 BR, Zutphen, Netherlands
Tel.: (31) 575 59 55 55
Web Site: http://www.flamco-export.com
Steel Products Mfr
N.A.I.C.S.: 331110

Subsidiary (Non-US):

Flamco Kft. (2)
Gyar u 2, 2040, Budaors, Hungary
Tel.: (36) 23 880981
Web Site: http://www.flamcogroup.com
Heating Equipment Mfr & Distr
N.A.I.C.S.: 333415

Flamco STAG GmbH (2)
Berliner Chaussee 29, Genthin, 39307, Sachsen-Anhalt, Germany
Tel.: (49) 3933 8210
Emp.: 112
Heating Equipment Installation Services
N.A.I.C.S.: 238220
Michael Jungk (Mng Dir)

Flamco s.a.r.l. (2)
ZI du Vert Galant 1 rue de la Garenne 1, 95310, Saint-Ouen-l'Aumone, France
Tel.: (33) 1 34 21 91 91
Web Site: http://www.flamcogroup.com
Sales Range: $25-49.9 Million
Emp.: 18
Plumbing & Heating Equipment Mfr
N.A.I.C.S.: 333414
Olivier Mocquery (Dir)

Grupo Hidroaplicaciones y Gas, SL (1)
Calle Bronce Poligono Industriasl Aimayr 12a, 28330, San Martin de la Vega, Madrid, Spain
Tel.: (34) 916920553
Water Pipe Accessories Mfr
N.A.I.C.S.: 331511

H.S.F. Samenwerkende Fabrieken B.V. (1)
Marketing 23, 6921 RE, Duiven, Netherlands
Tel.: (31) 263195757
Metal Products Mfr
N.A.I.C.S.: 332999
Crown Tail (Gen Mgr)

Haerterei Hauck GmbH (1)

Walter Freitag Strasse 25, 42899, Remscheid, Luttringhausen, Germany (90%)
Tel.: (49) 219156200
Web Site: http://www.haerterei-hauck.de
Sales Range: $50-74.9 Million
Emp.: 160
Heat Treatment Services for High-Grade Components & Tools
N.A.I.C.S.: 332811

Subsidiary (Domestic):

Haerterei Hauck Gaidorf GmbH (2)
Wilhelm Bott Strasse 24, 74405, Gaildorf, Germany (100%)
Tel.: (49) 797196980
Web Site: http://www.haerterei-hauck.de
Sales Range: $25-49.9 Million
Emp.: 20
Heat Treatment Services for High-Grade Components & Tools
N.A.I.C.S.: 332811

Harterei Hauck Sud GmbH (2)
Wilhelm-Bott-Strasse 24, 74405, Gaildorf, Germany
Tel.: (49) 79 71 96 98 0
Web Site: http://www.hauk.de
Emp.: 50
Metal Heat Treating Services
N.A.I.C.S.: 332811

Hauck Heat Treatment Limited (1)
39-43 Bilton Way, Luton, LU1 1UU, Bedfordshire, United Kingdom
Tel.: (44) 1582488344
Web Site: http://www.hauckht.co.uk
Metal Heat Treatment Services
N.A.I.C.S.: 332811

Heat & Surface Treatment B.V. (1)
Achtsweg Noord 3, 5651 GG, Eindhoven, Netherlands
Tel.: (31) 40 2663000
Web Site: http://hauckht.nl
Sales Range: $25-49.9 Million
Emp.: 60
Heat & Surface Treatment Services
N.A.I.C.S.: 332811

Henco Floor N.V. (1)
Toekomstlaan 27, 2200, Herentals, Belgium
Tel.: (32) 14285660
Web Site: http://www.hencofloor.be
Sales Range: $25-49.9 Million
Emp.: 10
Plumbing Heating & Air Conditioning Equipment Mfr
N.A.I.C.S.: 333415

Henco Industries N.V. (1)
Toekomstlaan 27, 2200, Herentals, Belgium
Tel.: (32) 14 28 56 60
Web Site: http://www.henco.be
Sales Range: $50-74.9 Million
Emp.: 200
Metal Pipe Fitting Mfr
N.A.I.C.S.: 332919
Wim Verhoeven (Gen Mgr)

Holmgrens Metall Aktiebolaget (1)
Stenblocksvagen 1, Box 141, 335 32, Gnosjo, Sweden
Tel.: (46) 370307900
Web Site: http://www.holmgrensmetall.se
Sales Range: $25-49.9 Million
Emp.: 42
Metal Pipe Fitting Mfr
N.A.I.C.S.: 332919

Impreglon GmbH (1)
Hohenhorststrasse 1, D-21337, Luneburg, Germany (100%)
Tel.: (49) 413188210
Web Site: http://www.impreglon.de
Sales Range: $150-199.9 Million
Holding Company; Surface Coatings Developer & Mfr.
N.A.I.C.S.: 551112
Carsten Gralla (Member-Mgmt Bd & Dir-Polymer Coatings)

Subsidiary (US):

Impreglon, Inc. (2)
220 Fairburn Industrial Blvd, Fairburn, GA 30213
Tel.: (770) 969-9191
Web Site: http://www.impreglon.us
Emp.: 40
Surface Coating Services

N.A.I.C.S.: 332812
Marc Zirkle (Pres & CEO)

Plant (Domestic):

Impreglon Cellramic (3)
8399 N 87th St, Milwaukee, WI 53224
Tel.: (414) 357-0260
Web Site: http://www.impreglon-cellramic.us
Paint & Coating Mfr
N.A.I.C.S.: 325510

Impreglon, Inc. - Woonsocket (3)
222 Goldstein Dr, Woonsocket, RI 02895
Tel.: (401) 766-3353
Web Site: http://www.impreglon.us
Surface Coating Services
N.A.I.C.S.: 332812
Marc Zirkle (Pres & CEO)

Subsidiary (US):

Sun Belt Coating, LLC (2)
162 Corporate Dr SW, Cleveland, TN 37311
Tel.: (423) 559-9900
Web Site: http://www.sunbeltcoating.com
Metal Coating Application Systems
N.A.I.C.S.: 332812

Integrated Dynamics Engineering GmbH (1)
Hermannstrasse 9 - 13, 65479, Raunheim, Germany (80%)
Tel.: (49) 614294000
Web Site: https://www.ideworld.com
Sales Range: $100-124.9 Million
Emp.: 100
Measuring & Control Device Mfr
N.A.I.C.S.: 334519

Subsidiary (US):

Integrated Dynamics Engineering Inc. (2)
68 Mazzeo Dr, Randolph, MA 02368-3402
Tel.: (781) 326-5700
Web Site: http://www.ideworld.com
Sales Range: $25-49.9 Million
Emp.: 10
Semiconductor Manufacturing Machinery
N.A.I.C.S.: 333242

Subsidiary (Non-US):

Integrated Dynamics Engineering Ltd. (2)
1-2-4 Kamisuna-cho, Tachikawa, 190-0032, Tokyo, Japan
Tel.: (81) 42 535 7303
Material Handling Equipment Mfr
N.A.I.C.S.: 333248

Ionic Technologies, Inc. (1)
207 Fairforest Way, Greenville, SC 29607 (94%)
Tel.: (864) 288-9111
Web Site: http://ionic-tech.com
Sales Range: $25-49.9 Million
Emp.: 20
Metal Surface Coatings Mfr
N.A.I.C.S.: 325510
Neil Holmes (Mgr-Sls)

Isiflo SAS (1)
31 route Ecospace, 67120, Molsheim, France
Tel.: (33) 388045970
Web Site: https://isiflo.fr
Plumbing & Heating Equipment Distr
N.A.I.C.S.: 423720
Philippe Bliekast (Mng Dir)

KAN S.p. z o.o. (1)
Ul Wiaczynska 8A, 92-760, Lodz, Poland
Tel.: (48) 426777977
Web Site: http://www.kan.pl
Sales Range: $25-49.9 Million
Emp.: 100
Mfr of Plumbing Products
N.A.I.C.S.: 326191

KAN-therm GmbH (1)
Brusseler Strasse 2, 53842, Troisdorf, Germany
Tel.: (49) 2241 234 08 0
Web Site: http://de.kan-therm.com
Surface Heating & Cooling System Distr
N.A.I.C.S.: 423730

Kluin Wijhe BV (1)

Industrieweg 1, NL 8131 VZ, Wijhe, Netherlands **(100%)**
Tel.: (31) 570521413
Web Site: http://www.kluinwijhe.com
Sales Range: $25-49.9 Million
Emp.: 60
Cylinder & Screw Mfr
N.A.I.C.S.: 333248

Lamers High Tech Systems B.V. **(1)**
De Vlotkampweg 38, 6545 AG, Nijmegen, Netherlands
Tel.: (31) 243716777
Web Site: http://www.lamershts.nl
Semiconductor Equipment Distr
N.A.I.C.S.: 423690

Lasco Fittings Inc. **(1)**
414 Morgan St, Brownsville, TN 38012-0116
Tel.: (731) 772-3180
Web Site: http://www.lascofittings.com
Sales Range: $100-124.9 Million
Emp.: 500
Injection Molded Fittings for Irrigation, Plumbing, Industrial, Pool/Spa & Retail Markets
N.A.I.C.S.: 332919

Leco Products B.V. **(1)**
Radonstraat 18, 6718 WS, Ede, Netherlands **(100%)**
Tel.: (31) 318665060
Sales Range: $50-74.9 Million
Emp.: 200
Sliding Door Mfr
N.A.I.C.S.: 332321

METALIS Holding SAS **(1)**
Route de Pouligney, 25640, Chaudefontaine, France
Tel.: (33) 3 81 48 50 70
Web Site: http://www.metalis-group.com
Holding Company; Metal Stamping Services
N.A.I.C.S.: 551112

Subsidiary (US):

METALIS USA, Inc. **(2)**
88 Ford Rd, Denville, NJ 07834
Tel.: (973) 625-3500
Web Site: http://www.metalis-group.com
Metal Stamping Services
N.A.I.C.S.: 332119

Subsidiary (Domestic):

Metalis HPS S.A.S. **(2)**
37 Boulevard des Entreprises Z I de Vaure, 42600, Montbrison, France
Tel.: (33) 4 77 96 33 77
Metal Products Mfr
N.A.I.C.S.: 332999

Subsidiary (Non-US):

Metalis Polska Sp. z.o.o. **(2)**
Ul Strefowa 6, Dzierzoniow, 58200, Poland
Tel.: (48) 74 832 72 40
Metal Products Mfr
N.A.I.C.S.: 332999

Subsidiary (Domestic):

Metalis S.A.S. **(2)**
Route de Pouligney, 25640, Chaudefontaine, France
Tel.: (33) 3 81 48 50 70
Web Site: http://www.metalis.fr
Metal Stamping Services
N.A.I.C.S.: 332119

Mamesta B V **(1)**
Spikweien 27, NL 5943 AC, Lomm, Netherlands **(100%)**
Tel.: (31) 774731551
Web Site: http://www.mamesta.nl
Sales Range: $25-49.9 Million
Emp.: 50
Steel Hardening Services
N.A.I.C.S.: 332811

Meibes System-Technik GmbH **(1)**
Ringstrasse 18, Gerichshain, 04827, Machern, Germany
Tel.: (49) 342927130
Web Site: http://flamcogroup.com
Sales Range: $50-74.9 Million
Emp.: 200
Heating Equipment Mfr
N.A.I.C.S.: 333414

Subsidiary (Non-US):

Meibes Metall-Technik Sp. z.o.o. **(2)**
Miesza-I-Str 39, 66-400, Gorzow, Poland
Tel.: (48) 65 529 49 89
Heating Equipment Mfr
N.A.I.C.S.: 333414

Meibes RUS OOO **(2)**
st 8th Tekstilshchikov 11/2 entrance 7, 109129, Moscow, Russia
Tel.: (7) 4957272026
Web Site: http://flamcogroup.com
Sales Range: $25-49.9 Million
Emp.: 35
Heating Equipment Distr
N.A.I.C.S.: 423720
Khalepa Alexey *(Gen Dir)*

Meibes SK s.r.o. **(2)**
Svatoplukova 18, 979 01, Rimavska Sobota, Slovakia
Tel.: (421) 475 634 043
Heating Equipment Mfr
N.A.I.C.S.: 333414

Meibes s.r.o. **(2)**
K Bilemu vrchu 2978/5, 193 00, Prague, Czech Republic
Tel.: (420) 284 001 081
Web Site: http://www.meibes.cz
Heating Equipment Mfr
N.A.I.C.S.: 333414
Pavel Nonner *(Bus Mgr)*

Melcher & Frenzen Armaturen GmbH **(1)**
Industriestrasse 76, Velbert, 42551, Germany
Tel.: (49) 20 51 31 40 0
Web Site: http://www.melcher-frenzen.de
Sales Range: $25-49.9 Million
Emp.: 9
Metal Pipe Repair Clamps & Tapping Sleeves Mfr
N.A.I.C.S.: 332999
Vim Pelsam *(Pres)*

Metatherm 74 S.A.S. **(1)**
Zone Industrielle Les Iles D Arve 64 Allee Des Cerisiers, 74300, Thyez, France
Tel.: (33) 450346398
Web Site: http://www.metatherm.fr
Sales Range: $25-49.9 Million
Emp.: 3
Metal Plating Services
N.A.I.C.S.: 332812
Karen Carpino *(Gen Mgr)*

Metatherm S.A.S. **(1)**
15 Hay Rue de Acacias, 25150, Pont-de-Roide, France
Tel.: (33) 381964585
Web Site: http://www.metatherm.fr
Sales Range: $25-49.9 Million
Emp.: 33
Metal Heat Treatment Services
N.A.I.C.S.: 332811
Roger Gauthier *(Mgr)*

Mifa Aluminium B V **(1)**
Rijnaakkade 6, 5928 PT, Venlo, Netherlands **(100%)**
Tel.: (31) 773898888
Web Site: http://mifa.eu
Sales Range: $50-74.9 Million
Emp.: 220
Customized Extrusion Products Mfr
N.A.I.C.S.: 331523

Mogema 3.0 **(1)**
Industrieweg 9, 8084 GS, 't Harde, Netherlands
Tel.: (31) 525 65 15 33
Web Site: http://www.mogema.nl
Sales Range: $50-74.9 Million
Emp.: 120
Welding, Machining & Vacuum Technology
N.A.I.C.S.: 333992

Mogema B.V. **(1)**
Industrieweg 9, 8084 GS, 't Harde, Netherlands
Tel.: (31) 525 651 533
Web Site: http://www.mogema.nl
Sales Range: $50-74.9 Million
Emp.: 13
General Purpose Machinery Mfr
N.A.I.C.S.: 333998

Mogema Vessem BV **(1)**

De Hoefse Weg 2, 5512 CH, Vessem, Netherlands **(100%)**
Tel.: (31) 497592200
Web Site: http://www.mogema.com
Sales Range: $25-49.9 Million
Emp.: 100
Welding, Machining & Vacuum Technology
N.A.I.C.S.: 333992

Nexus Valve, Inc. **(1)**
9982 E 121st St, Fishers, IN 46037
Tel.: (317) 257-6050
Web Site: http://www.nexusvalve.com
Sales Range: $10-24.9 Million
Emp.: 60
Hydronic Components, Including Valves, Mfr & Whslr
N.A.I.C.S.: 332912
Kurt Fazekas *(Pres)*

Nova Comet S.r.l. **(1)**
Via Castel Mella 55/57, 25030, Torbole Casaglia, Brescia, Italy
Tel.: (39) 0302159111
Gas Regulator Mfr
N.A.I.C.S.: 334512

PUZ Meibes Sp. z.o.o. **(1)**
ul Gronowska 8, 64 100, Leszno, Poland
Tel.: (48) 65 529 49 89
Sales Range: $25-49.9 Million
Emp.: 38
Metal Products Mfr
N.A.I.C.S.: 332999

Pegler Yorkshire Group Ltd. **(1)**
St Catherines Avenue Balby, Doncaster, DN4 8DF, South Yorkshire, United Kingdom
Tel.: (44) 1302560560
Web Site: http://www.pegleryorkshire.co.uk
Sales Range: $200-249.9 Million
Emp.: 1,800
Industrial Valves, Building Products, Industrial Rubber Components, Metal Fabrications & Computer Stationery Mfr & Distributor; Desalination Plant Services
N.A.I.C.S.: 332911

Precision Plating Company, Inc. **(1)**
4123 W Peterson Ave, Chicago, IL 60646
Tel.: (773) 583-3333
Web Site: http://www.ppc1904.com
Electroplating, Plating, Polishing, Anodizing & Coloring
N.A.I.C.S.: 332813

Premier Thermal Solutions LLC **(1)**
209 W Mt Hope Ave, Lansing, MI 48910
Tel.: (517) 485-5090
Web Site: http://www.premierthermal.com
Cmmercial Metal Mfr
N.A.I.C.S.: 332999
Sara McMurray *(Dir-Sls & Mktg)*

Subsidiary (Domestic):

Alfe Heat Treating Inc. **(2)**
6290 Pointe Inverness Way Ste 140, Fort Wayne, IN 46804
Tel.: (260) 747-9422
Web Site: http://www.al-fe.com
Provider of Ferrous & Non-Ferrous Heat Treating
N.A.I.C.S.: 332811
Steve Carr *(Mgr-Sls-Reg)*

Prestorac SAS **(1)**
1 Rue Zack Dusoasne, Na Chatelle, 45380, Saint Mesmin, France **(100%)**
Tel.: (33) 233823333
Copper Tube Mfr
N.A.I.C.S.: 331420

RIAG Oberflachentechnik AG **(1)**
Murgstrasse 19 a, 9545, Wangi, Thurgau, Switzerland
Tel.: (41) 52 369 70 70
Sales Range: $25-49.9 Million
Emp.: 29
Metal & Plastic Coating Services
N.A.I.C.S.: 332812
Roland Ratschiller *(Gen Mgr)*

Raufoss Metall GmbH **(1)**
An Der Schleuse 8, 58675, Hemer, Germany
Tel.: (49) 2372 91975
Web Site: http://www.isiflo.com
Emp.: 13
Metal Products Mfr
N.A.I.C.S.: 332999

Isamu Osa *(Gen Mgr)*

Raufoss Water & Gas AS **(1)**
Raufoss Industrial Park Enggata 40 Building 1, PO Box 143, 2831, Raufoss, Norway
Tel.: (47) 61 15 27 00
Web Site: http://www.isiflo.com
Sales Range: $50-74.9 Million
Emp.: 12
Gas Industry Equipment Mfr & Distr
N.A.I.C.S.: 333132

Rossweiner Armaturen Und Messgerate Gmbh & Co OHG **(1)**
Wehrstrasse 8, 04741, Rosswein, Germany **(100%)**
Tel.: (49) 34322480
Web Site: http://www.rossweiner.de
Sales Range: $25-49.9 Million
Emp.: 55
Armature & Measuring Device Mfr
N.A.I.C.S.: 334519

Roy Metal Finishing Co, Inc. **(1)**
120 McDougall Ct, Greenville, SC 29607
Tel.: (864) 277-0420
Web Site: http://roymetalfinishing.com
Emp.: 200
Metal Finishing Services
N.A.I.C.S.: 332813
Ryan Spencer *(Mgr-Quality)*

SGI Societe de Galvanoplastie Industrielle S.A.S. **(1)**
Z I Les Gatines Rue Pierre Curie 51, 78370, Plaisir, France
Tel.: (33) 1 30 54 03 90
Surface Treatment Services
N.A.I.C.S.: 332813

Seppelfricke Armaturen GmbH & Co., OHG **(1)**
Haldenstrasse 27, 45881, Gelsenkirchen, Germany **(100%)**
Tel.: (49) 2094040
Web Site: http://www.seppelfricke.de
Sales Range: $50-74.9 Million
Emp.: 250
Industrial Valve Mfr
N.A.I.C.S.: 332911

Shurjoint Piping Products, Inc. **(1)**
1380 Beverage Dr Ste P, Stone Mountain, GA 30083
Tel.: (770) 817-0444
Web Site: http://www.shurjoint.com
Pipe Couplings & Fitting Mfr
N.A.I.C.S.: 326122

Simplex Armaturen & Systeme GmbH **(1)**
Isnyer Strasse 28, Eisenharz, 88260, Argenbuhl, Germany
Tel.: (49) 756694080
Web Site: http://www.simplex-armaturen.de
Emp.: 150
Heating Equipment Mfr & Distr
N.A.I.C.S.: 333414
Burkhard Haemer *(Chm)*

Simplex Wilfer GmbH & Co. **(1)**
Isnyer Strasse 28, 88260, Argenbuhl, Germany **(100%)**
Tel.: (49) 756694080
Web Site: http://www.simplex-set.de
Sales Range: $50-74.9 Million
Emp.: 140
Armature & Measuring Device Mfr
N.A.I.C.S.: 334519
Burkhardt Haemer *(Gen Mgr)*

Stalservice Produktion i Anderstorp AB **(1)**
Terassvagen 7, 334 91, Anderstorp, Sweden
Tel.: (46) 371 587170
Web Site: http://www.stalservice.se
Sales Range: $25-49.9 Million
Emp.: 6
Metal Heat Treating Services
N.A.I.C.S.: 332811

T. Termicos Metasa, S.A. **(1)**
CI Benjamin Franklin 30 P I Cogullada, 50014, Zaragoza, Spain
Tel.: (34) 976472741
Metal Heat Treating Services
N.A.I.C.S.: 332811

T. Termicos Sarasketa, S.L.U **(1)**

Aalberts N.V.—(Continued)

Cl Arriaga 5 P I Arriaga, 20870, Elgoibar, Gipuzkoa, Spain
Tel.: (34) 943741550
Sales Range: $25-49.9 Million
Emp.: 32
Metal Heat Treating Services
N.A.I.C.S.: 332811
Conde Gomez Jesus *(Gen Mgr)*

T. Termicos Sohetrasa, S.A.   **(1)**
Barrio Ibarra P I Condor II, 48340, Amorebieta-Etxano, Vizcaya, Spain
Tel.: (34) 946300000
Metal Heat Treating Services
N.A.I.C.S.: 332811

T. Termicos Tey, S.L.   **(1)**
Polig Ind Artia, 48291, Atxondo, Vizcaya, Spain
Tel.: (34) 94 621 55 90
Sales Range: $25-49.9 Million
Emp.: 3
Metal Heat Treating Services
N.A.I.C.S.: 332811
Roberto Granado *(Gen Mgr)*

T. Termicos Traterh, S.A.U   **(1)**
Cl Alcotanes 32 P I Aproin, 28320, Pinto, Madrid, Spain
Tel.: (34) 916923330
Metal Heat Treating Services
N.A.I.C.S.: 332811

TTI Group Limited   **(1)**
39-43 Bilton Way, Luton, LU1 1UU, Bedfordshire, United Kingdom   **(100%)**
Tel.: (44) 1582 488344
Web Site: http://www.ttigroup.co.uk
Sales Range: $25-49.9 Million
Emp.: 10
Surface Treatment & Heat Treatment Services
N.A.I.C.S.: 332811

Taprite-Fassco Mfg., Inc.   **(1)**
3248 Northwestern Dr, San Antonio, TX 78238   **(100%)**
Tel.: (210) 523-0800
Web Site: http://www.taprite.com
Sales Range: $50-74.9 Million
Emp.: 200
Mfr of Pressure Valves for the Beer & Soft Drink Industries
N.A.I.C.S.: 332999
Scott Cary *(Controller)*

VAF Instruments B.V.   **(1)**
Vierlinghstraat 24, 3316 EL, Dordrecht, Netherlands
Tel.: (31) 786183100
Web Site: http://www.vaf.nl
Measuring Instrument Mfr & Distr
N.A.I.C.S.: 334515

VSH Fabrieken B.V.   **(1)**
Oude Amersfoortseweg 99, PO Box 498, Hilversum, 1200 AL, Netherlands   **(100%)**
Tel.: (31) 356884211
Web Site: http://www.vsh.nl
Sales Range: $50-74.9 Million
Emp.: 200
Industrial Valve Mfr
N.A.I.C.S.: 332911

VSH Fittings B.V.   **(1)**
Oude Amersfoortseweg 99, 1212 AA, Hilversum, Netherlands
Tel.: (31) 356884330
Web Site: http://www.vsh.eu
Sales Range: $25-49.9 Million
Emp.: 100
Metal Pipe Fitting Mfr
N.A.I.C.S.: 332996

VTI Ventil Technik GmbH   **(1)**
Iserlohner Landstr 119, 58706, Menden, Germany   **(100%)**
Tel.: (49) 23739353
Web Site: http://www.vti.de
Sales Range: $50-74.9 Million
Emp.: 160
Industrial Valve Mfr
N.A.I.C.S.: 332911
Burkhard Haemer *(Mng Dir)*

Ventrex Automotive GmbH   **(1)**
Johann Sebastian Bach Gasse 1, 8010, Graz, Austria
Tel.: (43) 31646760

Web Site: http://www.ventrex.com
Automotive Products Mfr
N.A.I.C.S.: 336390
Burkhard Haemer *(Mng Dir)*

Vin Service S.r.l.   **(1)**
Via G Falcone 26/34, 24050, Zanica, BG, Italy
Tel.: (39) 035672361
Web Site: http://www.vinservice.it
Dispensing Equipment Distr
N.A.I.C.S.: 423830
Alberto Mangini *(Sls Mgr)*

Westco Flow Control Limited.   **(1)**
Unit C6 William Way Moss Industrial Estate, Saint Helens Road, Leigh, WN7 3PT, Lancs, United Kingdom
Tel.: (44) 1942 603 351
Web Site: http://www.westco.co.uk
Emp.: 50
Plumbing & Heating Equipment Distr
N.A.I.C.S.: 423720

Yorkshire Fittings Gyarto Kft   **(1)**
Maglodi ut 16/d, 1106, Budapest, Hungary
Tel.: (36) 1 4343 000
Web Site: http://www.yorkshirefittings.hu
Sales Range: $50-74.9 Million
Emp.: 200
Metal Pipe Fitting Mfr
N.A.I.C.S.: 332919

AALBORG BOLDSPILKLUB A/S
Hornevej 2, 9220, Aalborg, Denmark
Tel.: (45) 96355900
Web Site: https://www.aabsport.dk
AAB—(CSE)
Rev.: $12,322,206
Assets: $19,371,735
Liabilities: $10,435,387
Net Worth: $8,936,349
Earnings: ($2,281,836)
Emp.: 76
Fiscal Year-end: 12/31/22
Soccer Club Operator
N.A.I.C.S.: 711211

AALLON GROUP OY
Esterinportti 2, 240, Helsinki, Finland
Tel.: (358) 207701600
Web Site: https://aallon.fi
AALLON—(HEL)
Emp.: 386
Financial Support Services
N.A.I.C.S.: 541611
Mia Penttinen *(Mgr-HR)*

AAMAL COMPANY Q.S.C.
PO Box 22477, Doha, Qatar
Tel.: (974) 44223870
Web Site: https://www.aamal.com.qa
Year Founded: 2001
AHCS—(QE)
Rev.: $354,756,185
Assets: $2,472,826,358
Liabilities: $285,055,669
Net Worth: $2,187,770,689
Earnings: $88,305,764
Emp.: 1,071
Fiscal Year-end: 12/31/19
Real Estate Development Services
N.A.I.C.S.: 531390
Faisal Qassim Faisal Al Thani *(Founder & Chm)*

Subsidiaries:

Aamal Cement Industries W.L.L.   **(1)**
Gate 41 St 41 Industrial Area, PO Box 40632, Doha, 40632, Qatar
Tel.: (974) 44502010
Web Site: https://aamalcement.com
Cement Mfr
N.A.I.C.S.: 327310

Aamal Readymix   **(1)**
Building 47 St 546 Industrial Area, PO Box 40557, Doha, Qatar
Tel.: (974) 44603939
Web Site: https://aamalreadymix.com
Readymix Concrete Mfr & Distr
N.A.I.C.S.: 327320

Parveez Aslam *(Gen Mgr)*

Aamal Services W.L.L.   **(1)**
Aamal Tower West Bay, PO Box 7385, Doha, Qatar
Tel.: (974) 40337111
Web Site: https://aamal-services.com
Cleaning Service
N.A.I.C.S.: 561720

Aamal Travel & Tourism W.L.L.   **(1)**
Conference Center Street City Center Doha Mall, PO Box 726, Doha, Qatar
Tel.: (974) 40401000
Web Site: https://aamal-travel.com
Travel Agency Services
N.A.I.C.S.: 561510

Advanced Pipes and Casts Company W.L.L.   **(1)**
Plot 40 M 35, PO Box 9533, Abu Dhabi, United Arab Emirates
Tel.: (971) 2 5511400
Web Site: http://www.hedley-international.com
Pipe Fitting Mfr
N.A.I.C.S.: 326122

Al Farazdaq Company W.L.L.   **(1)**
City Center Mall Ground Parking area Near the pillar G1/F1, PO Box 22744, West Bay, Doha, Qatar
Tel.: (974) 44140193
Web Site: https://www.alfarazdaq-qa.com
Printing & Laminating Services
N.A.I.C.S.: 561439

Ebn Sina Medical W.L.L.   **(1)**
Aamal Tower Omar Al Mukhtar St Zone 63 West Bay, PO Box 337, Doha, Qatar
Tel.: (974) 44027400
Web Site: https://www.ebnsina.com
Pharmaceutical Products Distr
N.A.I.C.S.: 424210
Essam Faragalla *(Gen Mgr)*

Good Life Chemist   **(1)**
City Center Doha- Mezzanine Floor, Doha, 337, Qatar
Tel.: (974) 44839100
Emp.: 15
Pharmaceutical Product Whslr
N.A.I.C.S.: 424210
Zakaria Alwisi *(Reg Mgr)*

AAMRA TECHNOLOGIES LIMITED
Praasad Trade Center 14th Floor 6 Kemal Ataturk Avenue, Banani, Dhaka, 1213, Bangladesh
Tel.: (880) 29841100
Web Site:
https://www.aamratechnologies.com
Year Founded: 1990
AAMRATECH—(DHA)
Rev.: $26,781,832
Assets: $38,048,340
Liabilities: $20,992,663
Net Worth: $17,055,678
Earnings: $1,258,376
Emp.: 126
Fiscal Year-end: 06/30/22
Software Development Services
N.A.I.C.S.: 541511
Syed Faruque Ahmed *(Chm)*

AANANDA LAKSHMI SPINNING MILLS LIMITED
Surya Towers 6th Floor 105 Sardar Patel Road, Secunderabad, 500 003, Andhra Pradesh, India
Tel.: (91) 4030512700
Web Site:
https://www.aanandalakshmi.com
Rev.: $96,970
Assets: $5,036,103
Liabilities: $8,448,053
Net Worth: ($3,411,950)
Earnings: ($678,992)
Emp.: 373
Fiscal Year-end: 03/31/18
Spinning Mill Operator
N.A.I.C.S.: 313110

Devender Kumar Agarwal *(Mng Dir & CFO)*

AANCHAL ISPAT LTD.
Paridhan Park 19 Canal South Road, SDF-V Block-E Module-503, Kolkata, India
Tel.: (91) 3322510128
Web Site:
https://www.aanchalispat.com
538812—(BOM)
Rev.: $24,112,538
Assets: $18,060,261
Liabilities: $10,221,299
Net Worth: $7,838,962
Earnings: ($1,160,378)
Emp.: 97
Fiscal Year-end: 03/31/20
Steel Products Mfr
N.A.I.C.S.: 331110
Mukesh Goel *(Mng Dir)*

AAP IMPLANTATE AG
Lorenzweg 5, D-12099, Berlin, Germany
Tel.: (49) 30750190
Web Site: https://www.aap.de
AAQ—(DEU)
Rev.: $14,984,528
Assets: $28,249,520
Liabilities: $12,528,048
Net Worth: $15,721,472
Earnings: ($3,316,248)
Emp.: 109
Fiscal Year-end: 12/31/21
Biomaterial Implants Developer & Mfr
N.A.I.C.S.: 541714
Rubino Di Girolamo *(Chm-Mgmt Bd & CEO)*

Subsidiaries:

European Medical Contract Manufacturing B.V.   **(1)**
Middenkampweg 17, 6545 CH, Nijmegen, Netherlands
Tel.: (31) 24 3715252
Web Site: http://www.emcm.com
Sales Range: $25-49.9 Million
Emp.: 85
Develops & Manufactures Sterile Medical Products
N.A.I.C.S.: 325412
Gert Wentzel *(Mng Dir)*

AAP WINDOWS LTD
5690 268th Street, Langley, V4W 3X4, BC, Canada
Tel.: (604) 856-3311
Web Site:
http://www.alliedwindows.com
Year Founded: 1945
Rev.: $13,602,054
Emp.: 120
Windows & Doors Mfr
N.A.I.C.S.: 332321
Ian Hogg *(Gen Mgr)*

AAP, INC.
5th Floor 27SY Building 1-8-7, Shibuya, Tokyo, 150-0002, Japan
Tel.: (81) 354647015   CA
AAPJ—(OTCIQ)
Sales Range: Less than $1 Million
Agricultural Services
N.A.I.C.S.: 111998

AAPICO HITECH PLC
99 Moo 1 Hitech Industrial Estate Tambol Ban Lane Amphur Bang Pa-in, Ayutthaya, 13160, Thailand
Tel.: (66) 35350880
Web Site: https://www.aapico.com
AH—(THA)
Rev.: $887,129,069
Assets: $738,361,181
Liabilities: $408,008,632
Net Worth: $330,352,549

Earnings: $46,198,905
Emp.: 2,178
Fiscal Year-end: 12/31/23
Automotive Products Mfr
N.A.I.C.S.: 336390
Teo Ngo Lee *(Exec Dir)*

Subsidiaries:

A ERP Company Limited　　(1)
99 Moo 1 Hitech Industrial Estate Tambol
Banlane Amphur, Bangpa-in, Ayutthaya,
13160, Thailand
Tel.: (66) 35350880
Automotive Products Mfr
N.A.I.C.S.: 336390

AAPICO Agueda, S.A.　　(1)
Avenida das Duas Rodas 1091, Borralha,
3750-860, Agueda, Portugal
Tel.: (351) 234243400
Emp.: 134
Automotive Components Mfr
N.A.I.C.S.: 336330

AAPICO Amata Co., Ltd.　　(1)
700/483 M 2, T Ban-Kao A Panthong, Chon
Buri, 20160, Thailand
Tel.: (66) 3 871 7200
Web Site: https://www.aapico.com
Emp.: 230
Automobile Chassis Mfr
N.A.I.C.S.: 336390

AAPICO Electronics Company
Limited　　(1)
99 Moo 1 Hitech Industrial Estate Tambol
Banlane Amphur, Bangpa-in, Ayutthaya,
13160, Thailand
Tel.: (66) 35350880
Automotive Products Mfr
N.A.I.C.S.: 336390

AAPICO Engineering Company
Limited　　(1)
99 Moo 1 Hitech Industrial Estate Tambol
Banlane Amphur, Bangpa-in, Ayutthaya,
13160, Thailand
Tel.: (66) 35350880
Automotive Products Mfr
N.A.I.C.S.: 336390

AAPICO Engineering Sdn. Bhd.　　(1)
Lot 56 No 10 Jalan 51/127 Seksyen 51,
46050, Petaling Jaya, Selangor, Malaysia
Tel.: (60) 377848411
Web Site: http://www.aapico.com
Engineering Research & Development Services
N.A.I.C.S.: 541330

AAPICO Forging PLC　　(1)
700/20 Moo 6 T Nongmaidaeng, A Muang,
Chon Buri, 20000, Thailand
Tel.: (66) 3 821 3355
Web Site: http://www.aapico.com
Sales Range: $125-149.9 Million
Emp.: 245
Automotive Forging & Machining Parts Mfr
N.A.I.C.S.: 332112

AAPICO Forging Public Co., Ltd.　　(1)
700/20 Moo 6 Amatanakorn Industrial Estate Bangna-Trad Road Km 57, Muang,
Chon Buri, 20000, Thailand
Tel.: (66) 38213355
Sales Range: $200-249.9 Million
Emp.: 586
Automobile Forging Parts Mfr
N.A.I.C.S.: 335999

AAPICO Hitech Automation Company
Limited　　(1)
99 Moo 1 Hitech Industrial Estate Tambol
Ban lane, Amphur Bang Pa-in, Ayutthaya,
13160, Thailand
Tel.: (66) 35350880
Automotive Components Mfr
N.A.I.C.S.: 336330

AAPICO Hitech Parts Co., Ltd　　(1)
99 Moo 1 Hitech Industrial Estate Tambol
Ban Lane, Amphur Bangpa-in, 13160, Ayutthaya, Thailand　　(100%)
Tel.: (66) 35350880
Sales Range: $75-99.9 Million
Emp.: 300
Automotive Repair & Maintenance
N.A.I.C.S.: 811198
Sattha Phetin *(Gen Mgr)*

AAPICO Hitech Tooling Co., Ltd.　　(1)
99/2 Moo 1 Hitech Industrial Estate Tambol
Ban Lane, Amphur Bangpa-in, Ayutthaya,
13160, Thailand
Tel.: (66) 35350880
Sales Range: $200-249.9 Million
Emp.: 1,000
Car Assembly Jigs & Stamping Dies Mfr
N.A.I.C.S.: 333514

AAPICO Hitech plc - Pluakdaeng
Factory　　(1)
7/289 Moo 6 Amata City Rayong Industrial
Estate, Tambol Mabyangporn Ampur, Pluak
Daeng, 21140, Rayong, Thailand
Tel.: (66) 38650888
Automotive Products Mfr
N.A.I.C.S.: 336390

AAPICO ITS Company Limited　　(1)
141 Thailand Science Park Phaholyothin
Road Tambol Ampur, Khlong Nueng, Khlong
Luang, 12120, Pathumtani, Thailand
Tel.: (66) 35350880
Automotive Products Mfr
N.A.I.C.S.: 336390

AAPICO Investment Pte. Ltd.　　(1)
745 Lorong 5 Toa Paypoh The Actuary 03-
01, Singapore, 319455, Singapore
Tel.: (65) 68361919
Automotive Products Mfr
N.A.I.C.S.: 336390

AAPICO Lemtech (Thailand) Company Limited　　(1)
161 Moo 1 Hitech Industrial Estate Tambol
Banlane Amphur, Bangpa-in, Ayutthaya,
13160, Thailand
Tel.: (66) 35741808
Automotive Products Mfr
N.A.I.C.S.: 336390

AAPICO Maia, S.A.　　(1)
Rua Jorge Ferreirinha 679, 4470-314, Maia,
Portugal
Tel.: (351) 229430200
Automotive Components Mfr
N.A.I.C.S.: 336330

AAPICO Mitsuike (Thailand) Company Limited　　(1)
99 Moo 1 Hitech Industrial Estate Tambol
Banlane Ampur, Bangpa-in, Ayutthaya,
13160, Thailand
Tel.: (66) 35350880
Automotive Products Mfr
N.A.I.C.S.: 336390

AAPICO Plastics Public Co., Ltd.　　(1)
358-358/1 Moo 17 Bangplee Industrial Estate Tambol Bangsaothong, Bang Sao
Thong, 10540, Samut Prakan, Thailand
Tel.: (66) 23153456
Sales Range: $125-149.9 Million
Emp.: 500
Automotive Plastic Parts Mfr
N.A.I.C.S.: 326199

AAPICO Precision Company
Limited　　(1)
700/16 Moo 6 Amata City Chonburi Industrial Estate Tambol Nongmaidaeng, Amphur
Muang, 20000, Chonburi, Thailand
Tel.: (66) 38213355
Automotive Products Mfr
N.A.I.C.S.: 336390

AAPICO Shanghai Co., Ltd.　　(1)
3600 Wai Qing Song Road, Qingpu, Shanghai, 201709, China
Tel.: (86) 21 59744843
Web Site: http://www.aapico.com
Automotive Machining Parts Mfr
N.A.I.C.S.: 336390

AAPICO Structural Products Co.,
Ltd.　　(1)
700/16 Moo 6 Tambol Nongmaidaeng,
Chon Buri, Thailand
Tel.: (66) 38717200
Automobile Parts Mfr
N.A.I.C.S.: 336390

AAPICO Training Center Company
Limited　　(1)
99 Moo 1 Hitech Industrial Estate Tambol
Banlane Amphur, Bangpa-in, Ayutthaya,
13160, Thailand
Tel.: (66) 35350880

Automotive Products Mfr
N.A.I.C.S.: 336390

AAPICO Venture Company
Limited　　(1)
99 Moo 1 Hitech Industrial Estate Tambol
Banlane Amphur, Bangpa-in, Ayutthaya,
13160, Thailand
Tel.: (66) 35350880
Automotive Products Mfr
N.A.I.C.S.: 336390

Able Motors Co., Ltd.　　(1)
14/9 Moo 14 Phahonyothin Road, T Khlong
Nueng, Khlong Luang, 12120, Patumthani,
Thailand
Tel.: (66) 29 086 0017
Web Site: http://www.aapico.com
Emp.: 109
New Car Dealers
N.A.I.C.S.: 441110

Katsuya (Thailand) Co., Ltd.　　(1)
229/104-105 Moo 1 Teparak Rd Tambol
Bangsaothong, Bangsaothong, 10540,
Samut Prakan, Thailand
Tel.: (66) 27065915
Web Site: http://www.aapico.com
Sales Range: $200-249.9 Million
Emp.: 600
Water Transfer Printing Services
N.A.I.C.S.: 323111

Kunshan Chaitai-Xincheng Precision
Forging Co., Ltd.　　(1)
No 405 Yunque Road Development Zone,
Kunshan, 215331, Jiangsu, China
Tel.: (86) 5125 787 0880
Web Site: http://www.aapico.cn
Sales Range: $100-124.9 Million
Steel & Copper Forging Parts Mfr
N.A.I.C.S.: 331110

MG Able Motors Company
Limited　　(1)
88 Moo 5 Bang Bua Thong - Bang Phun
Road, Tambol Bang Phun Ampur Muang,
Pathumthani, 12000, Thailand
Tel.: (66) 290860017
Car Dealership Operator
N.A.I.C.S.: 423110

New Era Sales Co., Ltd.　　(1)
97 M 5 Ramintra Road Ramintra, Khannayao, Bangkok, 10230, Thailand
Tel.: (66) 25 195 8004
Web Site: http://www.aapico.com
Emp.: 71
New Car Dealers
N.A.I.C.S.: 441110

Sakthi Auto Component Limited　　(1)
180 Race Course Road, Coimbatore, 641
018, India　　(77.04%)
Tel.: (91) 4222221551
Web Site: https://www.sakthiauto.com
Sales Range: $200-249.9 Million
Emp.: 1,000
Automotive Component Mfr & Distr
N.A.I.C.S.: 336390

**AAR COMMERCIAL COMPANY
LTD.**
I-7 Jangpura Extension, New Delhi,
110014, India
Tel.: (91) 11 35112510
Web Site: http://www.aarccl.in
539632—(BOM)
Rev.: $3,750
Assets: $15,584,153
Liabilities: $879,436
Net Worth: $14,704,717
Earnings: ($32,648)
Emp.: 4
Fiscal Year-end: 03/31/20
Financial Investment Services
N.A.I.C.S.: 523999
Arvind Kumar Modi *(Compliance Officer & Sec)*

**AAR SHYAM INDIA INVEST-
MENT COMPANY LIMITED**
Office no 920 9th Floor Kirti Shikar
Building Dist Centre, Janakpuri, New
Delhi, 110017, India

Tel.: (91) 1145626909
Web Site: https://www.aarshyam.in
Year Founded: 1983
542377—(BOM)
Financial Services
N.A.I.C.S.: 523999
Princy Anand *(Sec)*

**AARAMBHA MICROFINANCE
BITTIYA SANSTHA LIMITED**
Banepa-10, Kavrepalanchowk, Dhulikhel, Nepal
Tel.: (977) 11664579
Web Site:
　http://www.aarambhamf.com.np
AMFI—(NEP)
Sales Range: Less than $1 Million
Financial Management Services
N.A.I.C.S.: 522299
Laxman Ghimire *(CEO)*

**AAREY DRUGS & PHARMA-
CEUTICALS LTD.**
1227 Hubtown Solaris 12th Floor N S
Phadke Marg Opp-Telli Galli, Andheri
Flyover Bridge Andheri East, Mumbai,
400 069, India
Tel.: (91) 2262872900
Web Site:
　https://www.aareydrugs.com
524412—(BOM)
Rev.: $67,625,860
Assets: $33,465,544
Liabilities: $17,954,058
Net Worth: $15,511,486
Earnings: $893,365
Fiscal Year-end: 03/31/22
Pharmaceutical Products Mfr & Distr
N.A.I.C.S.: 325412
Mihir Rajesh Ghatalia *(Chm & Mng Dir)*

AARNAV FASHIONS LIMITED
1 New Cloth Market O/S Raipur
Gate, Raipur, Ahmedabad, 380 002,
Gujarat, India
Tel.: (91) 7929702983
Web Site:
　https://www.aarnavgroup.com
539562—(BOM)
Rev.: $47,626,761
Assets: $50,197,770
Liabilities: $29,505,749
Net Worth: $20,692,021
Earnings: $45,729
Emp.: 127
Fiscal Year-end: 03/31/23
Financial Investment Services
N.A.I.C.S.: 523999
Rahulkumar Kantilal Kankaria *(Chm & Mng Dir)*

AARON INDUSTRIES LTD.
Plot B 65-66 Rd Number 4 Udhana
GIDC Udhna Udhyog Nagar, Udhna,
Surat, 394210, India
Tel.: (91) 2612278410
Web Site:
　https://www.aaronindustries.net
Year Founded: 2013
AARON—(NSE)
Rev.: $6,703,795
Assets: $4,647,419
Liabilities: $2,192,051
Net Worth: $2,455,368
Earnings: $647,971
Emp.: 139
Fiscal Year-end: 03/31/23
Elevator Product Mfr
N.A.I.C.S.: 333921

AARTECH SOLONICS LIMITED
Aashirwad E-2/57, Arera Colony,
Bhopal, 462016, Madhya Pradesh,
India
Tel.: (91) 7552463593

Aartech solonics Limited—(Continued)

Web Site:
https://www.aartechsolonics.com
Year Founded: 1985
542580—(BOM)
Rev.: $2,481,486
Assets: $4,763,653
Liabilities: $809,423
Net Worth: $3,954,229
Earnings: $193,455
Fiscal Year-end: 03/31/22
Chemical Products Mfr
N.A.I.C.S.: 325998
Anil Anant Raje *(Chm)*

Subsidiaries:

AIC-Aartech Solonics Private
Limited   **(1)**
35-A/36 Sector-B, Industrial Area Man-
dideep District, Raisen, Madhya Pradesh,
India
Tel.: (91) 9111105831
Web Site: https://www.aic-aartech.in
Management Consulting Services
N.A.I.C.S.: 541618
Ameya Waingankar *(CEO)*

AARTI DRUGS LTD.

Mahendra Industrial Estate Ground
Floor Road No 29 Plot No 109-D,
Sion East, Mumbai, 400 022, India
Tel.: (91) 2224019025   In
Web Site:
https://www.aartidrugs.co.in
Year Founded: 1984
AARTIDRUGS—(NSE)
Rev.: $341,244,772
Assets: $301,386,322
Liabilities: $159,931,181
Net Worth: $141,455,141
Earnings: $27,981,927
Emp.: 1,450
Fiscal Year-end: 03/31/22
Pharmaceutical Developer & Mfr
N.A.I.C.S.: 325412
Prakash M. Patil *(Chm & Co-Mng Dir)*

Subsidiaries:

Pinnacle Life Science Private
Limited   **(1)**
Mahendra Industrial Estate Ground Floor
Plot No 109D Road Num 29, Sion E, Mum-
bai, 400022, India
Tel.: (91) 2224019025
Web Site: https://pinnaclelifescience.com
Pharmaceutical Products Distr
N.A.I.C.S.: 424210
Vishwa Savla *(CEO & Founder)*

Suyash Laboratories Ltd.   **(1)**
Plot No 109 D Ground Fl, Mumbai, 400022,
Maharashtra, India
Tel.: (91) 2224019025
Web Site: http://www.aartidrugs.com
Sales Range: $25-49.9 Million
Emp.: 125
Pharmaceuticals Product Mfr
N.A.I.C.S.: 325412
Yogesh Padmashali *(Mgr)*

AARTI INDUSTRIES LTD.

Udyog Kshetra 2nd Floor Mulund
Goregaon Link Road Mulund West,
Mumbai, 400080, Maharashtra, India
Tel.: (91) 2267976666   In
Web Site: https://www.aarti-
industries.com
Year Founded: 1976
AARTIIND—(NSE)
Rev.: $765,049,527
Assets: $1,152,899,649
Liabilities: $518,571,097
Net Worth: $634,328,552
Earnings: $49,933,554
Emp.: 6,100
Fiscal Year-end: 03/31/24
Holding Company; Chemicals, Inter-
mediates, Allied Products, Pharma-
ceutical Ingredients, Pigments &
Dyes Mfr

N.A.I.C.S.: 551112
Rajendra V. Gogri *(Chm & Mng Dir)*

Subsidiaries:

Aarti Healthcare Ltd.   **(1)**
Udyog Kshetra 2nd Floor LBS Marg
Mulund-Goregaon Link Road, Mulund West,
Mumbai, 400 080, Maharashtra,
India   **(51%)**
Tel.: (91) 2267976666
Web Site: http://www.aartihealthcare.com
Sales Range: $75-99.9 Million
Emp.: 200
Active Pharmaceutical Ingredients Re-
searcher, Developer & Mfr
N.A.I.C.S.: 325411
Chandrakant V. Gogri *(Chm)*

Aarti Industries Ltd. - AARTI CRAMS
Division   **(1)**
Udyog Kshetra 2nd Floor Mulund Goregaon
Link Road, Mulund West, Mumbai, 400080,
Maharashtra, India
Tel.: (91) 22 6797 6666
Web Site: http://www.aarti-industries.com
Pharmaceutical Research & Development
Services
N.A.I.C.S.: 541715
Rajendra V. Gogri *(Chm & Mng Dir)*

Alchemie Europe Ltd.   **(1)**
7-9 St Marys Place, Bury, BL9 0DZ, Lan-
cashire, United Kingdom
Tel.: (44) 3031234500
Web Site:
http://www.beta.companieshouse.gov.uk
Dyes Mfr & Distr
N.A.I.C.S.: 325130

AARTI SURFACTANTS LIM-
ITED

Udyog Kshetra 2Nd Floor Mulund
Goregaon Link Road, Mulund West,
Mumbai, 400080, Maharashtra, India
Tel.: (91) 2280804350
Web Site: https://www.aarti-
surfactants.com
Year Founded: 2002
543210—(BOM)
Rev.: $78,597,724
Assets: $54,930,603
Liabilities: $36,377,837
Net Worth: $18,552,766
Earnings: $750,040
Emp.: 338
Fiscal Year-end: 03/31/22
Surface Active Agent Mfr
N.A.I.C.S.: 325613
Mulesh Manilal Savla *(Chm)*

AARTSENFRUIT HOLDING
B.V.

Heilaar-Noordweg 9, 4814 RR,
Breda, Netherlands
Tel.: (31) 765248100
Web Site: http://www.aartsenfruit.nl
Year Founded: 1907
Sales Range: $25-49.9 Million
Emp.: 100
Holding Company; Fruits & Veg-
etables Importer & Exporter
N.A.I.C.S.: 551112
Jack Aartsen *(Owner & CEO)*

Subsidiaries:

Aartsenfruit Asia Ltd.   **(1)**
Unit 1015 F/10 Rise Commercial Building,
5-11 Granville Circuit Tsim Sha Tsui, Hong
Kong, China (Hong Kong)
Tel.: (852) 3480 9165
Fruit & Vegetable Import & Export Services
N.A.I.C.S.: 424480

Aartsenfruit Breda B.V.   **(1)**
Heilaar Nordweg 9, Breda, 4814 RR,
Netherlands   **(100%)**
Tel.: (31) 765248100
Sales Range: $25-49.9 Million
Emp.: 55
Fruits & Vegetables Importer & Exporter
N.A.I.C.S.: 445230
Frank van Der Velden *(Dir-Ops)*

Aartsenfruit N.V.   **(1)**
Strijbroek 14, Saint-Katelijne-Waver, 2860,
Belgium
Tel.: (32) 15560860
Web Site: http://www.artsenfruit.com
Sales Range: $25-49.9 Million
Emp.: 15
Fruits & Vegetables Importer & Exporter
N.A.I.C.S.: 445230
Jack Aarthen *(Mng Dir)*

Aartsenfruit Venlo B.V.   **(1)**
Venrayseweg 136 A, Venlo, 5928 RH,
Netherlands   **(100%)**
Tel.: (31) 773241241
Web Site: http://www.aartsenfruit.com
Sales Range: $25-49.9 Million
Emp.: 25
Fruits & Vegetables Importer & Exporter
N.A.I.C.S.: 445230
Frans Jongereus *(Mgr)*

AARVEE DENIMS & EXPORTS
LTD.

191 Moje Shahwadi Narol - Sarkhej
Highway, Nr Old Octroi Naka,
Ahmedabad, 382 405, Gujarat, India
Tel.: (91) 7968147000
Web Site:
https://www.aarveedenims.com
AARVEEDEN—(NSE)
Rev.: $39,219,439
Assets: $97,001,377
Liabilities: $74,119,486
Net Worth: $22,881,891
Earnings: ($8,762,085)
Emp.: 753
Fiscal Year-end: 03/31/21
Fabrics & Garments Mfr
N.A.I.C.S.: 315250
Pankil K. Shah *(VP-Garment)*

AARVI ENCON LTD.

B1-603 G K Road Opp Peninsula
Corporate Park Lower Parel W, Mum-
bai, 400013, India
Tel.: (91) 2240499999
Web Site:
https://www.aarviencon.com
Year Founded: 1987
AARVI—(NSE)
Rev.: $39,547,572
Assets: $20,335,183
Liabilities: $7,410,121
Net Worth: $12,925,062
Earnings: $1,647,200
Emp.: 5,541
Fiscal Year-end: 03/31/22
Staff Recruitment Services
N.A.I.C.S.: 561320
Virendra D. Sanghavi *(Mng Dir)*

Subsidiaries:

Aarvi Encon FZE   **(1)**
Saif Zone, PO Box 122723, Sharjah, United
Arab Emirates
Tel.: (971) 556542629
Manpower Supply Services
N.A.I.C.S.: 561320

Aarvi Engineering & Consultants Pri-
vate Limited   **(1)**
B1-603 Innova Marathon NextGen G K
Road Opp Peninsula Park, Lower Parel W,
Mumbai, India
Tel.: (91) 2240499999
Web Site: http://www.aarviencon.com
Emp.: 3,500
Petrochemical Mfr
N.A.I.C.S.: 325110
V. D. Sanghavi *(Mng Dir)*

AASEN SPAREBANK

Stationsvegen 1, 7630, Asen, Norway
Tel.: (47) 74086300
Web Site: https://www.aasen-
sparebank.no
AASB-ME—(OSL)
Sales Range: Less than $1 Million
Commercial Banking Services
N.A.I.C.S.: 522110

Bjorn Asle Hynne *(CEO & Mgr-
Administration)*

AASHKA HOSPITALS LTD.

Between Sargasan and Reliance
Cross Road, Sargasan, Gandhinagar,
382421, Gujarat, India
Tel.: (91) 9879752777
Web Site:
https://www.aashkahospitals.in
Year Founded: 2012
543346—(BOM)
Rev.: $5,441,081
Assets: $17,624,552
Liabilities: $4,443,525
Net Worth: $13,181,027
Earnings: $322,850
Emp.: 324
Fiscal Year-end: 03/31/22
Hospital Services
N.A.I.C.S.: 622110
Bipin Shah *(Chm & Mng Dir)*

AASTAMANGALAM FINANCE
LIMITED

III Floor Auras Corporate Centre No
98 A Dr Radhakrishnan Salai, My-
lapore, Chennai, 600 004, Tamil
Nadu, India
Tel.: (91) 4428478605
Web Site:
https://www.upasanafinance.com
Year Founded: 1985
511764—(BOM)
Rev.: $401,655
Assets: $7,266,950
Liabilities: $4,439,782
Net Worth: $2,827,169
Earnings: $173,850
Emp.: 3
Fiscal Year-end: 03/31/23
Financial Management Services
N.A.I.C.S.: 523999
Monika Kedia *(Compliance Officer &
Sec)*

AATECH S.P.A.

Viale Carlo Espinasse 163, 20156,
Milan, Italy
Tel.: (39) 0280706631
Web Site: https://www.aatech.it
Year Founded: 2019
AAT—(ITA)
Software Development Services
N.A.I.C.S.: 541511
Alessandro Andreozzi *(CEO)*

AAVAS FINANCIERS LTD.

201-202 2nd Floor Southend Square,
Mansarover Industrial Area, Jaipur,
302020, India
Tel.: (91) 1416618888
Web Site: https://www.aavas.in
AAVAS—(NSE)
Rev.: $178,220,925
Assets: $1,503,886,116
Liabilities: $1,120,808,380
Net Worth: $383,077,736
Earnings: $48,482,152
Emp.: 5,222
Fiscal Year-end: 03/31/22
Financial Consulting Services
N.A.I.C.S.: 541611
Sandeep Tandon *(Chm)*

AAYUSH FOOD & HERBS LTD.

55 2nd Floor Lane 2 Westend Marg
Saidullajab Near Saket Metro Station,
New Delhi, 110030, India
Tel.: (91) 1146095455
Web Site:
https://www.aayushfoods.in
Year Founded: 1984
539528—(BOM)
Rev.: $1,006,201
Assets: $6,017,661

Liabilities: $123,617
Net Worth: $5,898,241
Earnings: $685,588
Emp.: 7
Fiscal Year-end: 03/31/24
Food & Herb Services
N.A.I.C.S.: 456191
Pallavi Mittal (Mng Dir)

AB AMBER GRID
Laisves ave 10, 04215, Vilnius, Lithuania
Tel.: (370) 69907301
Web Site: https://www.ambergrid.lt
Year Founded: 2013
Rev.: $61,319,054
Assets: $286,828,622
Liabilities: $132,451,442
Net Worth: $154,377,180
Earnings: $13,256,903
Emp.: 329
Fiscal Year-end: 12/31/19
Oil & Gas Distribution Services
N.A.I.C.S.: 221210
Algirdas Juozaponis (Chm)

AB BANK LIMITED
BCIC Bhaban 30-31 Dilkusha C/A,
PO Box 3522, Dhaka, 1000, Bangladesh
Tel.: (880) 29560312
Web Site: https://www.abbl.com
Year Founded: 1982
ABBANK—(CHT)
Rev.: $108,592,773
Assets: $3,763,085,679
Liabilities: $3,527,993,156
Net Worth: $235,092,523
Earnings: $6,516,044
Emp.: 2,262
Fiscal Year-end: 12/31/22
Retail & Corporate Banking Services
N.A.I.C.S.: 522110
Muhammad A. Ali (Chm)

Subsidiaries:

AB International Finance Ltd **(1)**
Unit 1608 16th Floor Tower1 Silvercord 30
Canton Road, Tsim Sha Tsui West, Kowloon, China (Hong Kong)
Tel.: (852) 28668094
Web Site: http://www.abbank.com.bd
Financial Investment Advisory Services
N.A.I.C.S.: 523940

AB Securities Limited **(1)**
WW Tower 68 Motijheel C/A, Dhaka, 1000,
Bangladesh
Tel.: (880) 2223390815
Security Broking Services
N.A.I.C.S.: 523150

AB BUILDERS GROUP LTD.
10th Floor Edf Comercial I Tak No
126, Rua De Pequim, Macau, China
(Macau)
Tel.: (853) 28838394 Ky
Web Site:
http://www.abbuildersgroup.com
1615—(HKG)
Rev.: $17,472,252
Assets: $38,938,713
Liabilities: $15,667,482
Net Worth: $23,271,231
Earnings: ($1,962,117)
Emp.: 49
Fiscal Year-end: 12/31/23
Construction Contractor Services
N.A.I.C.S.: 236116
Chio Seng Lao (Chm)

AB CERBO
Verkmastarevagen 1, PO Box 905,
461 29, Trollhattan, Sweden
Tel.: (46) 520409900
Web Site: http://www.Nolato.se
Sales Range: $25-49.9 Million
Emp.: 236

Plastic Packaging Mfr
N.A.I.C.S.: 326199
Klenn Svedberg (Pres)

AB DYNAMICS PLC
Middleton Drive, Bradford-on-Avon,
BA15 1GB, Wilshire, United Kingdom
Tel.: (44) 1225860200 UK
Web Site: https://www.abdplc.com
Year Founded: 1982
ABDP—(AIM)
Rev.: $125,136,186
Assets: $211,900,752
Liabilities: $56,477,064
Net Worth: $155,423,688
Earnings: $13,647,382
Emp.: 428
Fiscal Year-end: 08/31/23
Automotive Testing Systems Mfr
N.A.I.C.S.: 333248
James Mathew Routh (CEO)

Subsidiaries:

AB Dynamics Europe GmbH **(1)**
Vogelsang 11, 35398, Giessen, Germany
Tel.: (49) 640 377 4610
Automotive Testing Machine Mfr
N.A.I.C.S.: 334519

AB Dynamics GK **(1)**
Shinyokohama Takeo Building 606 2-2-3,
Shinyokohama Kohoku-ku, Yokohama, 222-
0033, Japan
Tel.: (81) 45 534 3938
Engineering Consulting Services
N.A.I.C.S.: 541330

AB Dynamics Inc. **(1)**
48325 Alpha Dr Ste 120, Wixom, MI 48393
Tel.: (248) 516-2500
Engineering Consulting Services
N.A.I.C.S.: 541330

Anthony Best Dynamics Limited **(1)**
Middleton Drive, Bradford-on-Avon, BA15
1GB, Wiltshire, United Kingdom
Tel.: (44) 122 586 0200
Web Site: https://www.abdynamics.com
Engineering Services
N.A.I.C.S.: 541330

DRI Advanced Test Systems Inc. **(1)**
355 Van Ness Ave Ste 200, Torrance, CA
90501
Tel.: (310) 212-5211
Web Site: https://www.dri-ats.com
Automotive Test System Mfr & Distr
N.A.I.C.S.: 334519

Dynamic Research, Inc. **(1)**
355 Van Ness Ave Ste 200, Torrance, CA
90501
Tel.: (310) 212-5211
Web Site: http://www.dynres.com
Engineering Services
N.A.I.C.S.: 541330

VadoTech Japan KK **(1)**
Level 8 Shinjuku Oak City Nittochi Nishi-
Shinjuku Building 6-10-1, Nishi Shinjuku
Shinjuku-ku, Tokyo, 160-0023, Japan
Tel.: (81) 353253020
Vehicle Testing Services
N.A.I.C.S.: 811198

Zynit China Co., Ltd. **(1)**
Jinma Yuan 2 Street No 13, Shunyi District,
Beijing, 101303, China
Tel.: (86) 1061417699
Vehicle Testing Services
N.A.I.C.S.: 811198

AB EFFECTENBETEILIGUN-GEN AG
Lehen 68 Innerschwand, 5311, Mond-
see, Austria
Tel.: (43) 623221051
Web Site: https://www.abe-ag.at
Year Founded: 1997
ABE—(VIE)
Sales Range: Less than $1 Million
Investment Management Service
N.A.I.C.S.: 523999
Michael Hoefer (Member-Mgmt Bd)

AB ELECTROLUX
St Goransgatan 143 Stadshagen, SE
105 45, Stockholm, Sweden
Tel.: (46) 87386000 SE
Web Site: https://www.electrolux.com
Year Founded: 1912
ELUX.B—(OTCIQ)
Rev.: $13,347,132,279
Assets: $11,917,823,382
Liabilities: $1,119,185,200
Net Worth: $10,798,638,182
Earnings: ($518,891,346)
Emp.: 45,452
Fiscal Year-end: 12/31/23
Household & Commercial Appliances,
Outdoor Products & Industrial Products Mfr
N.A.I.C.S.: 335220
Jonas Samuelson (Pres & CEO)

Subsidiaries:

AB Hoors Plat **(1)**
Ringsjovagen 9, S 243 22, Hoor,
Sweden **(100%)**
Tel.: (46) 41329600
Web Site: http://www.husqvarna.com
Sales Range: $10-24.9 Million
Emp.: 150
Sheet Metal Mfr
N.A.I.C.S.: 332322

ELECTROLUX ESTONIA LTD **(1)**
Parnu mnt 153, 11624, Tallinn, Estonia
Tel.: (372) 665 004
Sales Range: $25-49.9 Million
Emp.: 15
Household Appliance Distr
N.A.I.C.S.: 423620
Andres Kesker (Gen Mgr)

Electrolux (Far East) Ltd. **(1)**
Room 4312 Metroplaza Tower 1, 223 Hing
Fong Road, Kwai Chung, Kowloon, NT,
China (Hong Kong) **(100%)**
Tel.: (852) 24108386
Web Site: http://www.electrolux.com.cn
Sales Range: $200-249.9 Million
Emp.: 2,910
Household & Commercial Appliances, Out-
door Products & Industrial Products Mfr
N.A.I.C.S.: 335220
Ren Weiguang (Gen Mgr)

Electrolux (Hangzhou) Domestic Ap-
pliances Co. Ltd **(1)**
No 18 Ave Economic Development Zone,
Hangzhou, 310018, China
Tel.: (86) 57128085529
Sales Range: $50-74.9 Million
Emp.: 240
Home Appliance Mfr
N.A.I.C.S.: 449210

Electrolux (Malaysia) Holdings SDN.
BHD. **(1)**
Lot C6 No 28 Jalan 15/22 Taman Perindus-
trian Tiong Nam Seksyen 15, 40200, Shah
Alam, Selangor, Malaysia
Tel.: (60) 300881122
Web Site: http://www.electrolux.com.my
Investment Management Service
N.A.I.C.S.: 523999

Electrolux (NZ) Limited **(1)**
3 Niall Burgess Rd, Mount Wellington,
Auckland, 1060, New Zealand
Tel.: (64) 95732220
Web Site: http://www.electrolux.co.nz
Sales Range: $25-49.9 Million
Emp.: 30
Household & Commercial Appliances, Out-
door Products & Industrial Products Mfr
N.A.I.C.S.: 335220

Electrolux A.S. **(1)**
35 Tarlabasi Bulvari, Istanbul, 34435, Tur-
kiye
Tel.: (90) 212 293 1020
Household Appliance Distr
N.A.I.C.S.: 423620

Electrolux AG **(1)**
Badenerstrasse 587, 8048, Zurich, Switzer-
land
Tel.: (41) 44 405 81 11
Web Site: http://www.electrolux.ch

Emp.: 100
Household Appliance Distr
N.A.I.C.S.: 423620

Electrolux Appliances S.p.A. **(1)**
Corso Lino Zanussi 24, 33080, Porcia, PN,
Italy
Tel.: (39) 04343941
Home Appliance Distr
N.A.I.C.S.: 423620

Electrolux Argentina S.A. **(1)**
Av Battle Y Ordonez, 3436, Rosario, Argen-
tina
Tel.: (54) 8101220238
Web Site: http://www.electrolux.com.ar
Sales Range: $50-74.9 Million
Emp.: 140
Home Appliance Mfr
N.A.I.C.S.: 335220

Electrolux Associated Company
B.V. **(1)**
Vennootsweg 1, Alphen aan den Rijn, 2404
CG, Netherlands
Tel.: (31) 172468168
Emp.: 200
Home Appliance Distr
N.A.I.C.S.: 423620

Electrolux Austria GmbH **(1)**
Herziggasse 9, Vienna, 1230,
Austria **(100%)**
Tel.: (43) 1866400
Web Site: http://www.electrolux.co.at
Sales Range: $150-199.9 Million
Emp.: 80
Household & Commercial Appliances, Out-
door Products & Industrial Products Mfr
N.A.I.C.S.: 335220

Electrolux Belgium N.V. **(1)**
Raketstraat 40, 1130, Brussels, Belgium
Tel.: (32) 27162600
Emp.: 300
Home Appliance Mfr
N.A.I.C.S.: 335220
Barb Crols (Gen Mgr)

Electrolux CEE G.m.b.H. **(1)**
Herziggasse 9, 1230, Vienna, Austria
Tel.: (43) 186640284
Home Appliance Mfr
N.A.I.C.S.: 335210

Electrolux Central and Eastern Eu-
rope Ges. m.b.H. Nfg. KG. **(1)**
Herziggasse 9, Vienna, 2345, Austria
Tel.: (43) 1 866400
Household Appliance Distr
N.A.I.C.S.: 423740

Electrolux Comercial Venezuela
C.A **(1)**
Av Ppal de Las Mercedes Entre Calle Mu-
cuchies y Monterrey, Las Mercedes, Cara-
cas, 1060, Venezuela
Tel.: (58) 212 993 1511
Sales Range: $25-49.9 Million
Emp.: 45
Home Appliance Distr
N.A.I.C.S.: 423620

Electrolux Deutschland GmbH **(1)**
Tel.: (49) 9113230
Emp.: 2,000
Household Vacuum Cleaner Mfr
N.A.I.C.S.: 335210

Electrolux Do Brasil SA **(1)**
360 Rua Ministro Gabriel Passos Guabiro-
tuba, Curitiba, CEP 81520 900, PR, Brazil
Tel.: (55) 41 3371 7000
Web Site: http://www.electrolux.com.br
Sales Range: $800-899.9 Million
Emp.: 5,000
Household & Commercial Appliances, Out-
door Products & Industrial Products Mfr
N.A.I.C.S.: 335220

Electrolux Espana S.A. **(1)**
Avenida de Europa 16, La Moraleja, 28108,
Alcobendas, Madrid, Spain **(100%)**
Tel.: (34) 902144145
Web Site: http://www.electrolux.es
Sales Range: $400-449.9 Million
Emp.: 2,553
Household & Commercial Appliances, Out-
door Products & Industrial Products Mfr
N.A.I.C.S.: 335220

AB Electrolux—(Continued)

Electrolux Filter AB (1)
Mossevagen 6, Nygard, Vastra Gotaland,
460 11, Sweden **(100%)**
Tel.: (46) 520470400
Web Site: http://www.electrolux.se
Sales Range: $50-74.9 Million
Emp.: 120
Household & Commercial Appliances, Outdoor Products & Industrial Products Mfr
N.A.I.C.S.: 335220

Electrolux Floor Care and Small Appliances AB (1)
Sankt Goransgatan 143, Stockholm, 112
17, Sweden
Tel.: (46) 87386000
Web Site: http://www.electrolux.se
Home Appliance Mfr
N.A.I.C.S.: 335210
Chris Craam *(Mgr-Appliances)*

Electrolux France S.A. (1)
43 Avenue Felix Louat, 60307, Senlis,
France
Tel.: (33) 809100100
Sales Range: $800-899.9 Million
Emp.: 400
Household & Commercial Appliances, Outdoor Products & Industrial Products Mfr
N.A.I.C.S.: 335220

Electrolux Hausgerate G.m.b.H. (1)
Herziggasse 9, 1230, Vienna, Austria
Tel.: (43) 1 86640 0
Home Appliance Mfr
N.A.I.C.S.: 335210

Electrolux Hausgerate GmbH (1)
Further Str 246, 90429, Nuremberg,
Germany **(100%)**
Tel.: (49) 911 3230
Web Site: https://shop.electrolux.de
Sales Range: $1-4.9 Billion
Emp.: 8,200
Household & Commercial Appliances, Outdoor Products & Industrial Products Mfr
N.A.I.C.S.: 335220
Ralf Hansel *(Mng Dir)*

Electrolux HemProdukter AB (1)
St Goransgatan 143, 105 45, Stockholm,
Sweden
Tel.: (46) 770770103
Web Site: https://www.electroluxhome.se
Electronic Home Appliances Distr
N.A.I.C.S.: 423620

Electrolux Holding AG (1)
Badenerstrasse 587, 8048, Zurich,
Switzerland **(100%)**
Tel.: (41) 444058111
Web Site: http://www.electrolux.ch
Sales Range: $50-74.9 Million
Emp.: 170
Household & Commercial Appliances, Outdoor Products & Industrial Products Mfr
N.A.I.C.S.: 335220

Subsidiary (Domestic):

A&T Hausgerate AG (2)
Badenerstrasse 587, 8048, Zurich,
Switzerland **(100%)**
Tel.: (41) 444058111
Web Site: http://www.electrolux.ch
Sales Range: $25-49.9 Million
Emp.: 40
Household & Commercial Appliances, Outdoor Products & Industrial Products Mfr
N.A.I.C.S.: 335220

**Electrolux Home Appliances Sdn
Bhd** (1)
7th Floor Tower 2 Jaya 33 No 3 Jalan Semangat Seksyen 13, 46100, Petaling Jaya,
Selangor, Malaysia
Tel.: (60) 3 7843 5999
Home Appliance Distr
N.A.I.C.S.: 423620

Electrolux Home Products (Nederland) B.V. (1)
Vennootsweg 1 2400AC, Postbus 120,
2400, Alphen aan den Rijn, Netherlands
Tel.: (31) 0172468468
Sales Range: $200-249.9 Million
Emp.: 1,000

Household & Commercial Appliances, Outdoor Products & Industrial Products Mfr
N.A.I.C.S.: 335220

Electrolux Home Products AS (1)
Okern Rislokkveien 2, Box 77, Okern, 508,
Oslo, Norway
Tel.: (47) 815 30 222
Household Appliance Distr
N.A.I.C.S.: 423620

Electrolux Home Products Corporation N.V. (1)
Raket Straat 40, Brussels, 1130,
Belgium **(100%)**
Tel.: (32) 27162600
Web Site: http://www.electrolux.com
Sales Range: $150-199.9 Million
Emp.: 300
Household & Commercial Appliances, Outdoor Products & Industrial Products Mfr
N.A.I.C.S.: 335220

**Electrolux Home Products Denmark
A/S** (1)
Strevelinsvej 38 - 40, 7000, Fredericia,
Denmark
Tel.: (45) 79221100
Web Site: https://www.electrolux.dk
Sales Range: $75-99.9 Million
Emp.: 150
Home Appliance Distr
N.A.I.C.S.: 423620

**Electrolux Home Products Espana
S.A.** (1)
Calle Albacete 3, 28027, Madrid, Spain
Tel.: (34) 90 214 41 45
Web Site: http://www.electrolux.es
Sales Range: $125-149.9 Million
Emp.: 500
Home Appliance Mfr & Distr
N.A.I.C.S.: 335220

**Electrolux Home Products Norway
AS** (1)
Lilleaker Drammensveien 260, PO Box 91,
0277, Oslo, Norway
Tel.: (47) 22722400
Web Site: http://www.electrolux.no
Electrical Household Appliance Whslr
N.A.I.C.S.: 423620

**Electrolux Home Products Pty.
Ltd.** (1)
L1 - 163 O'Riordan Street, Mascot, 2020,
NSW, Australia
Tel.: (61) 29 317 9504
Web Site: https://www.electrolux.com.au
Sales Range: $600-649.9 Million
Emp.: 4,018
Household & Commercial Appliances, Outdoor Products & Industrial Products Mfr
N.A.I.C.S.: 335220
Chris Coen *(Gen Mgr-Retail Sls)*

Electrolux Ireland Ltd (1)
Long Mile Road, Dublin, Ireland
Tel.: (353) 8185430
Household Appliance Distr
N.A.I.C.S.: 423620

Electrolux Italia S.p.A. (1)
Tel.: (39) 04343951
Web Site: http://www.electrolux.it
Emp.: 2,000
Home Appliance Mfr
N.A.I.C.S.: 335220

Electrolux Japan Ltd. (1)
Yasuda Shibaura Bldg 2 3-2-12 Kaigan,
Minato-ku, Tokyo, 108-0022, Japan
Tel.: (81) 3 5445 3360
Sales Range: $50-74.9 Million
Emp.: 100
Household Electronic Appliance Distr
N.A.I.C.S.: 423620

**Electrolux Laundry Systems Denmark
A/S** (1)
Hammerholmen 24-28, DK-2650, Hvidovre,
Denmark **(100%)**
Tel.: (45) 63762000
Web Site:
http://www.laundrysystems.electrolux.dk
Sales Range: $25-49.9 Million
Emp.: 20
Commercial Laundry Equipment Mfr
N.A.I.C.S.: 333310

**Electrolux Laundry Systems Sweden
AB** (1)
Ringvagen 14, PO Box 325, Ljungby, 341
32, Sweden **(100%)**
Tel.: (46) 37266500
Web Site: http://www.electrolux.se
Sales Range: $200-249.9 Million
Emp.: 540
Semi-Industrial Laundry Equipment Mfr
N.A.I.C.S.: 333310
Bo-Lennart Jonasson *(Dir-Mktg-Global)*

Electrolux Lda. (1)
Edificio Goncalves Zarco Q35 Quinto da
Fonte, Paco d'Arcos, 2774518, Portugal
Tel.: (351) 214403900
Web Site: http://www.electrolux.pt
Sales Range: $75-99.9 Million
Emp.: 45
Household & Commercial Appliances, Outdoor Products & Industrial Products Mfr
N.A.I.C.S.: 335220

Electrolux Lehel Hutogepgyar Kft (1)
Erzsebet Kiralyne Utja 87, 1142, Budapest,
Hungary
Tel.: (36) 1 467 3200
Electrical Household Appliances Mfr
N.A.I.C.S.: 335220
Zsolt Belenyesi *(Gen Mgr)*

Electrolux Ljubljana d.o.o. (1)
110 Gerbiceva Ulica, 1000, Ljubljana, Slovenia
Tel.: (386) 1 24 25 733
Sales Range: $25-49.9 Million
Emp.: 14
Household Appliance Distr
N.A.I.C.S.: 423620

Electrolux North America, Inc. (1)
10200 David Taylor Dr, Charlotte, NC
28262-8060
Tel.: (980) 236-2000
Web Site: http://www.electroluxusa.com
Holding Company; Regional Managing Office
N.A.I.C.S.: 551112

Subsidiary (Domestic):

Electrolux Professional, Inc. (2)
4003 Collins Ln, Louisville, KY 40245
Tel.: (980) 236-2000
Web Site:
https://www.electroluxprofessional.com
Commercial Cooking, Refrigeration, Dishwashing & Laundry Equipment Mfr & Distr
N.A.I.C.S.: 333310
Angelo Grillas *(Dir-Project Bus-East)*

Subsidiary (Domestic):

Grindmaster Corporation (3)
4003 Collins Ln, Louisville, KY 40245
Tel.: (502) 425-4776
Web Site: http://www.grindmaster.com
Hot, Cold & Frozen Beverage Dispensing
Equipment Mfr
N.A.I.C.S.: 333241
Greg Immell *(VP-Sls)*

Subsidiary (Domestic):

White Westinghouse Puerto Rico (2)
F St Lot 34, Guaynabo, PR 00968
Tel.: (787) 753-5100
Web Site: http://www.electroluxusa.com
Sales Range: $25-49.9 Million
Emp.: 85
Electrical Household Appliance Whslr
N.A.I.C.S.: 449210

Electrolux Outdoor Products A/S (1)
Lundtoftegardsvej 93 A, 2800, Lyngby,
Denmark **(100%)**
Tel.: (45) 45877577
Web Site: http://www.husqvarna.dk
Sales Range: $25-49.9 Million
Emp.: 36
Household & Commercial Appliances, Outdoor Products & Industrial Products Mfr
N.A.I.C.S.: 335999

Electrolux Phillippines, Inc. (1)
25th Fl Equitable Bank Tower, 8751 Paseo
de Roxas, Makati, 1226, Philippines
Tel.: (63) 28452273
Web Site: http://www.electrolux.com.ph

Sales Range: $1-9.9 Million
Emp.: 35
Household & Commercial Appliances, Outdoor Products & Industrial Products Mfr
N.A.I.C.S.: 335220

Electrolux Poland Spolka Z.o.o. (1)
Home Appliance Mfr
N.A.I.C.S.: 335220

Electrolux Professional AS (1)
Tel.: (47) 22503333
Web Site:
https://www.electroluxprofessional.com
Sales Range: $25-49.9 Million
Emp.: 4
Laundry Equipment Distr
N.A.I.C.S.: 423620

Electrolux Professional BV (1)
Van Nelleweg 1, PO Box 188, Expedition
Building, 3044 BC, Rotterdam, Netherlands
Tel.: (31) 207219610
Web Site:
https://www.electroluxprofessional.com
Sales Range: $25-49.9 Million
Emp.: 30
Cooking Appliances Distr
N.A.I.C.S.: 423720

Electrolux Professional GmbH (1)
Europaring F16-201, AT-2845, Brunn am
Gebirge, Austria
Tel.: (43) 186348200
Web Site:
https://www.electroluxprofessional.com
Sales Range: $25-49.9 Million
Emp.: 3
Kitchen Appliances Mfr
N.A.I.C.S.: 335220

Electrolux Professional Ltd (1)
Addington Way, Luton, LU4 9QQ, Bedfordshire, United Kingdom
Tel.: (44) 3444631260
Web Site:
https://www.electroluxprofessional.com
Emp.: 72
Household Cooking Appliance Mfr
N.A.I.C.S.: 335220

Electrolux Professional S.p.A. (1)
Viale Treviso 15, 33170, Pordenone, Italy
Tel.: (39) 04343801
Web Site:
https://www.electroluxprofessional.com
Household Cooking Appliance Mfr
N.A.I.C.S.: 335220

Electrolux Professionnel SAS (1)
10 Avenue du Stade De France, 93200,
Saint Denis, France
Tel.: (33) 806800900
Web Site:
https://www.electroluxprofessional.com
Sales Range: $25-49.9 Million
Emp.: 40
Home Appliance Mfr.
N.A.I.C.S.: 335220
Andrea Rossi *(Gen Mgr)*

Electrolux Pty. Ltd. (1)
13 Gilbert Park Drive, Knoxfield, 3180, VIC,
Australia **(100%)**
Tel.: (61) 387567300
Web Site: http://www.electrolux.com.au
Sales Range: $25-49.9 Million
Emp.: 50
Household & Commercial Appliances, Outdoor Products & Industrial Products Mfr
N.A.I.C.S.: 335220

Electrolux Romania SA (1)
Bdul Aviatorilor nr 41 et 1 sect 1, Bucharest, Romania
Tel.: (40) 219913
Web Site: http://www.electrolux.ro
Household Appliances Mfr
N.A.I.C.S.: 335220

Electrolux S.E.A. Private Ltd. (1)
11 Lorong 3 Toa Payoh Blk B #01-13/14/15
Jackson Square, Singapore, 319579,
Singapore **(100%)**
Tel.: (65) 6507 8900
Web Site: http://www.electrolux.com.sg
Sales Range: $10-24.9 Million
Emp.: 74
Household & Commercial Appliances, Outdoor Products & Industrial Products Mfr
N.A.I.C.S.: 335220

Electrolux Slovakia s.r.o. o.z. **(1)**
Galvaniho 17/B, 821 04, Bratislava, Slovakia
Tel.: (421) 232141336
Web Site: http://www.electrolux.sk
Household Appliances Mfr
N.A.I.C.S.: 335220

Electrolux Thailand Co. Ltd. **(1)**
1910 New Petchburi Rd, Bangkok, 10310, Thailand
Tel.: (66) 27259000
Web Site: http://www.electrolux.co.th
Sales Range: $25-49.9 Million
Emp.: 337
Household & Commercial Appliances, Outdoor Products & Industrial Products Mfr
N.A.I.C.S.: 335220

Electrolux Ukraine LLC **(1)**
2a Avtozavodskaya Str, 04074, Kiev, Ukraine
Tel.: (380) 44 586 20 60
Household Appliances Mfr
N.A.I.C.S.: 335220

Electrolux Zanussi Italia SpA **(1)**
Corso Lino Zanussi 24, Porcia, 33080, Pordenone, Italy
Tel.: (39) 04341580088
Web Site: http://www.electrolux.it
Sales Range: $75-99.9 Million
Emp.: 225
Holding Company; Household & Commercial Appliances, Outdoor Products & Industrial Products Mfr
N.A.I.C.S.: 551112

Subsidiary (Domestic):

Vecta Vending Solutions S.p.A. **(2)**
Via Roma 24, 24030, Valbrembo, Bergamo, Italy **(100%)**
Tel.: (39) 035606111
Web Site: http://www.electrolux.com
Vending Machine Mfr
N.A.I.C.S.: 333310

Electrolux d.o.o. **(1)**
Slavonska Avenija 6a, 10000, Zagreb, Croatia
Tel.: (385) 16323338
Web Site: https://www.electrolux.hr
Sales Range: $25-49.9 Million
Household Appliance Distr
N.A.I.C.S.: 423620

Electrolux de Chile S.A. **(1)**
Alberto Llona No 777, Maipu Commune, Santiago, Chile
Tel.: (56) 6006005353
Web Site: https://www.electrolux.cl
Electronic Product Mfr & Distr
N.A.I.C.S.: 334419

Electrolux de Colombia S.A. **(1)**
Cl 97a 9a-34 Piso 2 Chico, Bogota, Colombia
Tel.: (57) 16189000
Household Appliances Mfr
N.A.I.C.S.: 335220

Electrolux del Paraguay S.A. **(1)**
Estrella 764 Ayolas, Casilla Postal 1550 - 1993, Asuncion, Paraguay
Tel.: (595) 21 491 907
Home Appliance Distr
N.A.I.C.S.: 423620

Electrolux del Peru S.A. **(1)**
Av El Polo 214 Monterrico Surco, Lima, 33, Peru
Tel.: (51) 16172121
Web Site: http://www.electrolux.com.pe
Sales Range: $50-74.9 Million
Emp.: 200
Household & Commercial Appliances, Outdoor Products & Industrial Products Mfr
N.A.I.C.S.: 335220

Electrolux plc **(1)**
Addington Way, Luton, LU4 9QQ, Bedfordshire, United Kingdom **(100%)**
Tel.: (44) 3445613613
Web Site: https://www.electrolux.co.uk
Sales Range: $800-899.9 Million
Emp.: 2,134
Household & Commercial Appliances, Outdoor Products & Industrial Products Mfr
N.A.I.C.S.: 335220

Subsidiary (Domestic):

Electrolux Home Products UK **(2)**
Cornwall House, 55 77 High Street, Slough, SL1 1DZ, Berkshire, United Kingdom
Tel.: (44) 8705 950 950
Web Site: http://www.electrolux.co.uk
Sales Range: $150-199.9 Million
Emp.: 660
Household & Commercial Appliances, Outdoor Products & Industrial Products Mfr
N.A.I.C.S.: 335220

Electrolux-Juno Kuchentechnik GmbH **(1)**
Further Strasse 246, 90429, Nuremberg, Germany
Tel.: (49) 9113230
Web Site: http://www.aeg.de
Sales Range: $200-249.9 Million
Emp.: 630
Household & Commercial Appliances, Outdoor Products & Industrial Products Mfr
N.A.I.C.S.: 335220

Electroservice AB **(1)**
Saint Goransgatan 143, Stockholm, 10545, Sweden **(100%)**
Tel.: (46) 87386000
Web Site: http://www.electrolux.se
Sales Range: $300-349.9 Million
Emp.: 2,600
Service Division
N.A.I.C.S.: 811210

Kwikot (Pty) Ltd. **(1)**
3 Aberdeen Rd, Benoni, 1500, South Africa
Tel.: (27) 118974600
Web Site: https://www.kwikot.com
N.A.I.C.S.: 331110

OY Electrolux Kotitalouskoneet AB **(1)**
Lautatarhankatu 8B, Helsinki, 00580, Finland
Tel.: (358) 30 600 5120
Sales Range: $50-74.9 Million
Emp.: 100
Household Appliance Distr
N.A.I.C.S.: 423620
Kari Haeyri (Mng Dir)

Oy Electrolux AB **(1)**
Lautatarhankatu 8 B, PO Box 1002, 00581, Helsinki, Finland **(100%)**
Tel.: (358) 306005120
Web Site: http://www.electrolux.fi
Sales Range: $25-49.9 Million
Emp.: 75
Household & Commercial Appliances, Outdoor Products & Industrial Products Mfr
N.A.I.C.S.: 335220

Division (Non-US):

Electrolux Professional Oy **(2)**
Tel.: (358) 939612403
Web Site:
    https://www.electroluxprofessional.com
Emp.: 376
Household & Commercial Appliances, Outdoor Products & Industrial Products Mfr
N.A.I.C.S.: 335220
Mats Lundblad (CEO)

SC Electrolux Romania SA **(1)**
Calea Traian No 23-29, Satu-Mare, Romania
Tel.: (40) 219913
Web Site: https://www.electrolux.ro
Electronic Product Mfr & Distr
N.A.I.C.S.: 334419

AB INDUSTRIVARDEN
Storgatan 10, 114 51, Stockholm, Sweden
Tel.: (46) 86666400   SE
Web Site:
    https://www.industrivarden.se-gb
Year Founded: 1944
INDU.A—(OMX)
Rev.: $2,542,264,932
Assets: $14,847,846,245
Liabilities: $809,800,781
Net Worth: $14,038,045,463
Earnings: $2,514,260,024
Emp.: 15

Fiscal Year-end: 12/31/23
Holding Company
N.A.I.C.S.: 551112
Helena Stjernholm (CEO & Mng Dir)

Subsidiaries:

Industrivarden Service AB **(1)**
Storgatan 10, 114 51, Stockholm, Sweden
Tel.: (46) 86666400
Web Site: http://www.industrivarden.se
Investment Management Service
N.A.I.C.S.: 523999

AB LKI KALDMAN OY
Ojesvagen 74, 68910, Bennas, Finland
Tel.: (358) 6 781 5424
Sales Range: $50-74.9 Million
Emp.: 100
Industrial Machinery Distr
N.A.I.C.S.: 423830
Tom Nordstrom (Gen Mgr)

AB MONSTERAS METALL
Gjuterivagen 4, 383 92, Monsteras, Sweden
Tel.: (46) 499 495 00
Metal Fabrication
N.A.I.C.S.: 332999

Subsidiaries:

Ankarsrum Die Casting AB **(1)**
Bruksvagen 1, S-590 90, Ankarsrum, Sweden
Tel.: (46) 49053300
Web Site: http://www.ankarsrum.com
Die Casting Services
N.A.I.C.S.: 333514
Marcus Grimero (CEO)

AB S.A.
ul Europejska 4, 55-040, Warsaw, Poland
Tel.: (48) 713937600
Web Site: https://www.ab.pl
Year Founded: 1990
ABE—(WAR)
Rev.: $4,829,829,423
Assets: $1,066,813,043
Liabilities: $739,812,591
Net Worth: $327,000,452
Earnings: $48,068,130
Emp.: 1,300
Fiscal Year-end: 09/30/23
Consumer Electronics Distr
N.A.I.C.S.: 423430
Zbigniew Madry (Dir-Sls)

Subsidiaries:

AT Computers Holding a.s. **(1)**
Tesinska 1970/56, Ostrava-Slezska, 710 00, Ostrava, Czech Republic
Tel.: (420) 552300111
Web Site: http://www.atcomputers.cz
Sales Range: $50-74.9 Million
Emp.: 330
Computer Peripheral Mfr & Distr
N.A.I.C.S.: 334118
Martin Wanke (Dir-Mktg)

Subsidiary (Domestic):

AT Compus s.r.o. **(2)**
Tesinska 1970/56, Slezska, 710 00, Ostrava, Czech Republic
Tel.: (420) 596253111
Web Site: https://www.atcomp.cz
Sales Range: $25-49.9 Million
Emp.: 20
Computer Peripherals Mfr
N.A.I.C.S.: 334118

Comfor Stores a.s. **(2)**
Brno Bela Pazoutove 742 / 1, 624 00, Brno, Czech Republic
Tel.: (420) 515266300
Web Site: https://www.comfor.cz
Sales Range: $25-49.9 Million
Emp.: 60
Computer Peripherals Mfr
N.A.I.C.S.: 334112

Alsen Marketing Sp. z o.o. **(1)**
Ul Katowicka 146, 41-500, Chorzow, Poland
Tel.: (48) 327752700
Web Site: https://www.alsen.pl
Computer Peripheral Retailer
N.A.I.C.S.: 423430

AB SAGAX
Engelbrektsplan 1, 114 34, Stockholm, Sweden
Tel.: (46) 854583540
Web Site: https://www.sagax.se
Year Founded: 2004
SAGA.A—(OMX)
Rev.: $346,174,380
Assets: $6,727,827,887
Liabilities: $3,593,619,751
Net Worth: $3,134,208,135
Earnings: $254,573,042
Emp.: 94
Fiscal Year-end: 12/31/22
Real Estate Manangement Services
N.A.I.C.S.: 531390
Bjorn Garat (Deputy Mng Dir & Head-Fin)

Subsidiaries:

Sagax Finland Asset Management OY **(1)**
Keskuskatu 5B 3 krs, 00101, Helsinki, Finland
Tel.: (358) 103200320
Commercial Property Services
N.A.I.C.S.: 531312

Sagax Germany Holding GmbH **(1)**
Oper46 Bockenheimer Anlage 46, 60322, Frankfurt, Germany
Tel.: (49) 69247432500
Commercial Property Management Services
N.A.I.C.S.: 531312

Sagax Nederland B.V. **(1)**
Weena 738, 3014 DA, Rotterdam, Netherlands
Tel.: (31) 103035445
Commercial Property Services
N.A.I.C.S.: 531312

Turun Konekeskus Oy **(1)**
Ruopankatu 8, 20360, Turku, Finland
Tel.: (358) 207459700
Web Site: https://www.turunkonekeskus.fi
Agricultural Machinery Mfr & Distr
N.A.I.C.S.: 333111

AB SCIENCE SA
3 Avenue George V, 75008, Paris, France
Tel.: (33) 147200014
Web Site: https://www.ab-science.com
Year Founded: 2001
ABSCF—(OTCEM)
Rev.: $1,021,420
Assets: $25,419,274
Liabilities: $63,450,628
Net Worth: ($38,031,354)
Earnings: ($14,516,313)
Emp.: 103
Fiscal Year-end: 12/31/22
Pharmaceuticals Mfr
N.A.I.C.S.: 325412
Laurent Guy (CFO)

AB SVENSK EXPORTKREDIT
Klarabergsviadukten 61-63, PO Box 194, Stockholm, SE-101 23, Sweden
Tel.: (46) 8 613 8300
Web Site: http://www.sek.se
Year Founded: 1962
EEH—(NYSA)
Rev.: $1,934,000,000
Assets: $333,647,000,000
Liabilities: $312,839,000,000
Net Worth: $20,808,000,000
Earnings: $1,034,000,000
Emp.: 253
Fiscal Year-end: 12/31/21
Supplier of Long Term Financial Solutions

AB Svensk Exportkredit—(Continued)

N.A.I.C.S.: 522299
Per Akerlind *(Deputy CEO, Exec VP & Head-Strategic Partnerships & Rels)*

AB VILNIAUS VINGIS
Savanoriu Av 176, 03154, Vilnius, Lithuania
Tel.: (370) 52392500
Web Site: http://www.vingis.lt
Year Founded: 1959
Sales Range: $25-49.9 Million
Emp.: 4
Electronic Components Mfr
N.A.I.C.S.: 334220
Neringa MenAiuniene *(Mng Dir)*

AB VOLVO
Gropegardsgatan 2, 417 15, Gothenburg, Sweden
Tel.: (46) 31660000   **SE**
Web Site:
   https://www.volvogroup.com
Year Founded: 1927
VOLV.B—(OMX)
Rev.: $30,403,800
Assets: $15,447,302,100
Liabilities: $7,307,999,100
Net Worth: $8,139,303,000
Earnings: $6,438,633,300
Emp.: 84,953
Fiscal Year-end: 12/31/21
Holding Company; Trucks, Aircraft, Space Engines & Buses Mfr
N.A.I.C.S.: 551112
Nils Jaeger *(Pres-Volvo Autonomous Solutions)*

Subsidiaries:

AB Volvo - Volvo de Mexico Autobuses Division   **(1)**
Lago de Guadalupe 289 Fracc Ind, Cartagena, 54900, Tultitlan, Mexico
Tel.: (52) 55 50 90 37 00
Web Site: http://www.volvobuses.com
Trucks Mfr
N.A.I.C.S.: 336120

AB Volvo Penta   **(1)**
Gropegatan, 40508, Gothenburg, Sweden   **(100%)**
Tel.: (46) 31668129
Web Site: http://www.volvopenta.com
Sales Range: $150-199.9 Million
Emp.: 400
Supplier of Automobiles
N.A.I.C.S.: 423110
Prabhakaran S. *(VP-Product Mgmt Indus)*

Subsidiary (Non-US):

AB Volvo Penta Italia S.p.A   **(2)**
Via Gallarate 182, Buccinasco, 20151, Milano, Italy   **(100%)**
Tel.: (39) 02484301
Web Site: http://www.volvopenta.com
Sales Range: $25-49.9 Million
Emp.: 25
Marine & Automotive Engines Mfr
N.A.I.C.S.: 336412
Matteo Gasperetto *(Mng Dir)*

VOLVO PENTA SINGAPORE   **(2)**
33 Joo Koon Circle, Singapore, 629111, Singapore
Tel.: (65) 6221 3111
Automotive Engine Distr
N.A.I.C.S.: 423120

VOLVO PENTA TURKEY   **(2)**
Tekneyan Sanayisektoru 54 Sahsuvarolu Yan, Umraniye, 34768, Istanbul, Türkiye
Tel.: (90) 216 655 75 00
Web Site: http://www.volvopenta.com
Sales Range: $25-49.9 Million
Emp.: 10
Marine Engine Mfr
N.A.I.C.S.: 333618
Mehdi Kilic *(Gen Mgr)*

Volvo Cars S.L   **(2)**
Paseo De La Castellana 130, 28046, Ma-

drid, Spain
Tel.: (34) 915666100
Web Site: http://www.volvocars.com
Sales Range: $25-49.9 Million
Emp.: 70
Automobile Mfr
N.A.I.C.S.: 336110
German Lopez Madrid *(Pres)*

Volvo Penta Benelux B.V.   **(2)**
Stationsweg 2, PO Box 48, Beesd, 4153 ZG, Netherlands   **(100%)**
Tel.: (31) 345688700
Web Site: http://www.volvopenta.com
Sales Range: $25-49.9 Million
Emp.: 25
Automobile Mfr
N.A.I.C.S.: 423110
Mariska van Selm *(Mgr)*

Volvo Penta Canada Ltd.   **(2)**
7972 Enterprise St, Burnaby, V5A 1V7, BC, Canada   **(100%)**
Tel.: (604) 872-7511
Web Site: http://www.volvopenta.com
Sales Range: $25-49.9 Million
Emp.: 20
Marine Engine Distr
N.A.I.C.S.: 423860
Martin Laprate *(Mgr-Warranty)*

Volvo Penta Central Europe GmbH   **(2)**
Amq Kanal 1, PO Box 9013, Kiel, 24106, Germany   **(100%)**
Tel.: (49) 43139940
Web Site: http://www.volvopenta.com
Sales Range: $50-74.9 Million
Emp.: 25
Automotive Assemblies
N.A.I.C.S.: 336412
Susanne Hermann *(Mng Dir)*

Volvo Penta France S.A.   **(2)**
99 Route de Lyon, 69802, Saint Priest, Cedex, France
Tel.: (33) 134290101
Web Site: http://www.volvopenta.fr
Sales Range: $50-74.9 Million
Emp.: 150
Truck & Automobile Sales
N.A.I.C.S.: 336110

Subsidiary (Domestic):

Volvo Penta Norden AB   **(2)**
Gropegardsgatan, SE 405 08, Gothenburg, Sweden   **(100%)**
Tel.: (46) 31686400
Automotive & Bus Mfr
N.A.I.C.S.: 336110

Subsidiary (Non-US):

Volvo Penta UK Limited   **(2)**
Imperial Park, Imperial Way, Watford, WD24 4AW, Herts, United Kingdom   **(100%)**
Tel.: (44) 1923228544
Web Site: http://www.volvopenta.com
Sales Range: $25-49.9 Million
Emp.: 35
Ship Building & Repairing
N.A.I.C.S.: 336611

Volvo Penta do Brasil Ltda.   **(2)**
Av das Americas 13443 Recreio dos Bandeirantes, 22790-700, Rio de Janeiro, RJ, Brazil
Tel.: (55) 2124379544
Web Site: http://www.volvo.com
Aircraft Engine Parts
N.A.I.C.S.: 336412

Subsidiary (US):

Volvo Penta of the Americas, Inc.   **(2)**
1300 Volvo Penta Dr, Chesapeake, VA 23320   **(100%)**
Tel.: (757) 436-2800
Web Site: http://www.volvopenta.com
Sales Range: $75-99.9 Million
Emp.: 200
Distr of Marine, Diesel & Industrial Engines
N.A.I.C.S.: 423860
Ed Monacchio *(Head-Mktg)*

Subsidiary (Non-US):

Volvo Peru S.A.   **(2)**

Panamericana Sur km 23.88, Ate Vitarte, Lima, 3, Peru   **(100%)**
Tel.: (51) 13171200
Web Site: http://www.volvo.com.pe
Sales Range: $50-74.9 Million
Emp.: 150
Trucks & Buses Distr
N.A.I.C.S.: 423110

Subsidiary (US):

Volvo-Penta North America, Inc.   **(2)**
7900 National Service Rd, Greensboro, NC 27409
Tel.: (336) 393-2000
Automobile Parts Distr
N.A.I.C.S.: 336390
Jonas Nilsson *(Head-India)*

Al-Futtaim Auto & Machinery Company LLC   **(1)**
Plot B -131 Al Ramool - Rashidiya, PO Box 5502, Dubai, United Arab Emirates
Tel.: (971) 8 003 2626
Web Site: http://www.famcouae.com
Emp.: 500
Bus & Construction Equipment Distr
N.A.I.C.S.: 423110
Paul Floyd *(Mng Dir)*

Alviva AB   **(1)**
Maskingatan 5 Van 4, Gothenburg, 417 64, Sweden
Tel.: (46) 3 17 44 98 00
Web Site: http://www.alviva.se
Health Care Srvices
N.A.I.C.S.: 621999

BRS Ltd   **(1)**
Houghton Hall Business Park Porz Avenue, Dunstable, LU5 5FT, United Kingdom
Tel.: (44) 1582 479 666
Web Site: http://www.brs.co.uk
Automotive Truck Rental Services
N.A.I.C.S.: 532120

EBP AB   **(1)**
Agrasjovagen 3 5, PO Box 34, Olofstrom, 29340, Sweden   **(100%)**
Tel.: (46) 454301700
Web Site: http://www.ebp.se
Sales Range: $50-74.9 Million
Emp.: 190
N.A.I.C.S.: 336412
Mattias Ivansson *(CEO)*

First Rent A Car AB   **(1)**
Primusgatan 18, Stockholm, 11262, Sweden   **(70%)**
Tel.: (46) 86573000
Web Site: http://www.hertz.se
Sales Range: $25-49.9 Million
Emp.: 50
N.A.I.C.S.: 336412

Merkavim Transportation Technologies Ltd.   **(1)**
22 Granit Street The Industrial Park, 38900, Caesarea, Israel
Tel.: (972) 46176000
Web Site: http://www.merkavim.co.il
Sales Range: $100-124.9 Million
Emp.: 700
Bus Bodies Mfr
N.A.I.C.S.: 336211

Rossareds Fastighets AB   **(1)**
Kalenderv 22, 415 11, Gothenburg, Sweden
Tel.: (46) 31 46 99 11
Commercial Vehicle Mfr
N.A.I.C.S.: 336110

Transport Financial Services   **(1)**
105 Bauer Place, Waterloo, N2L 6B5, ON, Canada
Tel.: (519) 886-8070
Web Site: https://www.tfsgroup.com
Sales Range: $25-49.9 Million
Emp.: 25
Accounting, Bookkeeping, Tax Return Preparation & Consulting Services for Transportation Industry
N.A.I.C.S.: 541219
Steve Mulligan *(VP-Bus Dev)*

VFS Renting Sociedade Unipessoal Lda.   **(1)**
Avenida D Joao II N 50 - 4 Piso Edificio Mar Vermelho, 1990-095, Lisbon, Portugal
Tel.: (351) 915523826

N.A.I.C.S.: 525990

VNA Holding Inc.   **(1)**
7825 National Service Rd, Greensboro, NC 27409
Tel.: (336) 393-4890
Investment Management Service
N.A.I.C.S.: 523940
Shumaker Donald *(Chief Tax Officer, Treas & VP)*

VOLVO ESPANA, S.A.U.   **(1)**
Calle Procion Edf Oficor 1-3 Ctra Coruna Km 11 5, Madrid, 28023, Spain
Tel.: (34) 913727800
Web Site: http://www.volvocars.es
Commercial Vehicle Mfr
N.A.I.C.S.: 336110

VOLVO PENTA SVERIGE   **(1)**
Bjornhammarvagen 25, 184 94, Akersberga, Sweden
Tel.: (46) 8 540 271 10
Web Site: http://www.volvopenta.com
Sales Range: $25-49.9 Million
Emp.: 10
Automobile Parts Mfr
N.A.I.C.S.: 336390

Volvalb Sh.p.k   **(1)**
Autostrada Durres - Tirane Km 4, Durres, Albania
Tel.: (355) 692044404
Sales Range: $25-49.9 Million
Emp.: 7
Industrial Truck Mfr
N.A.I.C.S.: 336120

Volvo (China) Investment Co. Ltd   **(1)**
22F Tower C Office Park No 5 Jinghua Street South Chaoyang District, Beijing, 100020, China
Tel.: (86) 10 6582 9199
Web Site: http://www.volvoit.com
Commercial Vehicle Mfr
N.A.I.C.S.: 336110

Subsidiary (Domestic):

Shandong Lingong Construction Machinery   **(2)**
Shuntai Square Office Building No 9, Room 902 Shunhua Road No 2000, Jinan High-Tech Industrial Pk, Jinan, 250100, China
Tel.: (86) 531 66590966
Web Site: http://www.sdlg.cn
Construction Equipment Mfr
N.A.I.C.S.: 333120

Volvo (Southern Africa) Pty Ltd   **(2)**
Cnr Jet Park Road & Saligna Avenue, Witfield, Gauteng, South Africa
Tel.: (27) 11 842 5000
Sales Range: $25-49.9 Million
Emp.: 80
Trucks Mfr
N.A.I.C.S.: 336120
Tersia Koen *(Mgr-HR)*

Volvo Automotive Finance (China) Ltd   **(1)**
11F Tower C Office Park No 5 Jinghua Street South Chaoyang District, Beijing, 100020, China
Tel.: (86) 10 6598 2199
Web Site: http://www.vfsco.com
Financial Management Services
N.A.I.C.S.: 523999

Volvo Bulgaria Ltd.   **(1)**
630 Slivnitsa Blvd, 1331, Sofia, Bulgaria
Tel.: (359) 28106700
Web Site: http://www.volvocars.com
Commercial Truck Mfr
N.A.I.C.S.: 336120

Volvo Bus Corporation   **(1)**
Gropegardsgatan 11, 405 08, Gothenburg, Sweden   **(100%)**
Tel.: (46) 31668308
Web Site: http://www.volvobuses.com
Development, Design, Production & Marketing of Buses & Bus Chassis
N.A.I.C.S.: 327910
Akash Passey *(Sr VP-Intl)*

Subsidiary (Non-US):

Nova Bus Corporation   **(2)**
1000 Industriel Blvd, Saint-Eustache, J7R 5A5, QC, Canada

Tel.: (450) 472-6410
Web Site: https://www.novabus.com
Sales Range: $100-124.9 Million
Emp.: 650
Bus Mfr
N.A.I.C.S.: 336390
Ralph Acs *(Pres)*

Prevost Car, Inc. (2)
35 Gagnon Blvd, Sainte-Claire, G0R 2V0,
QC, Canada (100%)
Tel.: (418) 883-3391
Web Site: https://www.prevostcar.com
Sales Range: $25-49.9 Million
Emp.: 1,000
Buses Mfr
N.A.I.C.S.: 336340
Tommy Nolet *(Mgr-Customer Support-Eastern North America)*

Subsidiary (US):

Nova Bus Incorporated (3)
201 South Ave, South Plainfield, NJ 07080
Tel.: (505) 347-2011
Web Site: http://www.novabus.com
Mfr of Buses
N.A.I.C.S.: 336110

Subsidiary (Non-US):

Volvo Bus Australia (2)
120 Hume Highway, Chullora, 2190, NSW,
Australia
Tel.: (61) 287138200
Web Site: http://www.volvobuses.com.au
Emp.: 16
Commercial Vehicle Mfr
N.A.I.C.S.: 336110
Ray Andrich *(Reg Mgr-Sls)*

Volvo Bus Hong Kong Limited (2)
Units 1601-03 Kwun Tong View 410 Kwun
Tong Road, Kowloon, China (Hong Kong)
Tel.: (852) 2 827 1688
Web Site: https://www.volvobuses.com
Sales Range: $25-49.9 Million
Emp.: 13
Commercial Vehicle Mfr
N.A.I.C.S.: 336110
Jeremy Knight *(Gen Mgr)*

Volvo Bus Nederland B.V. (2)
Stationsweg 2, 4153 RD, Beesd, Netherlands
Tel.: (31) 88 882 3390
Web Site: https://www.volvobuses.com
Sales Range: $50-74.9 Million
Emp.: 10
Commercial Vehicle Whslr
N.A.I.C.S.: 423110
Piet Tijsen *(Mgr-Sls)*

Volvo Bus Poland Co. (2)
Medlana St 2, 51 502, Wroclaw,
Poland (100%)
Tel.: (48) 713021700
Web Site: http://www.volvo.com
Sales Range: $400-449.9 Million
Emp.: 2,500
Bus Manufacturer
N.A.I.C.S.: 336412
Bengt Lindstrom *(Gen Mgr)*

Volvo Busse Deutschland GmbH (2)
Lichtenbergerstrassen 26, 74076, Heilbronn, Germany (100%)
Tel.: (49) 713115740
Web Site: http://www.volvobusse.com
Sales Range: $25-49.9 Million
Emp.: 40
N.A.I.C.S.: 336412

Volvo Cars Austria GmbH (2)
Am Concorde Park 1 A1, 2320, Schwechat,
Austria (100%)
Tel.: (43) 1701280
Web Site: http://www.volvocars.at
Sales Range: $25-49.9 Million
Emp.: 50
Engine Parts
N.A.I.C.S.: 336412

Volvo East Asia (Pte.) Ltd. (2)
33 Joon Koon Cir, Singapore, 629111,
Singapore (100%)
Tel.: (65) 62213111
Web Site: http://www.volvo.com
Sales Range: $50-74.9 Million
Emp.: 200

Manufacturers of heavy duty vehicles & diesel engines
N.A.I.C.S.: 327910

Subsidiary (Domestic):

Volvo-Saffle AB (2)
PO Box 59, 661 22, Saffle,
Sweden (100%)
Tel.: (46) 53346600
Web Site: http://www.volvo.se
Sales Range: $100-124.9 Million
Emp.: 350
N.A.I.C.S.: 336412

Volvo Business Services AB (1)
Faestningsvaegen 1, Gothenburg, 405 08,
Sweden
Tel.: (46) 31660700
Financial & Accounting Services
N.A.I.C.S.: 523999

Volvo Bussar AB (1)
Fastningsvagen 1, Gothenburg, 40508,
Sweden
Tel.: (46) 31668000
Web Site: http://www.vovlogroup.com
Emp.: 1,000
Commercial Vehicle Mfr
N.A.I.C.S.: 336110
Hakan Agnevall *(CEO)*

Volvo Busser Danmark A/S (1)
Taastrupgardsvej 32, 2630, Taastrup, Denmark
Tel.: (45) 44546600
Web Site: http://www.volvobuses.com
Sales Range: $25-49.9 Million
Emp.: 100
Commercial Vehicle Mfr
N.A.I.C.S.: 336110
Soeren Wettreen *(CEO)*

**Volvo Construction Equipment
Corporation** (1)
Moorfield Road, Cambridge, CB22 4QX,
United Kingdom (100%)
Tel.: (44) 1223836636
Sales Range: $25-49.9 Million
Emp.: 95
Front End Loaders Mfr
N.A.I.C.S.: 333120
Dimitrov Krishnan *(VP-Sls & Mktg-India)*

Subsidiary (Non-US):

**ABG Allgemeine Baumaschinen-
Gesellschaft mbH** (2)
Kuhbruckenstrasse 18, 31785, Hameln,
Germany
Tel.: (49) 51512090
Web Site: http://www.volvoce.com
Sales Range: $75-99.9 Million
Emp.: 500
Pneumatic, Hydraulic & General Machinery
& Tools, Pumps, Compressors, Drilling
Equipment, Locks, Bearings, Hoists,
Winches & Off-Road Forklifts Mfr
N.A.I.C.S.: 333998
David Bittenseld *(Dir-Adv)*

Subsidiary (Domestic):

Terex Equipment Limited (2)
Newhouse Industrial Estate, Newhouse,
Motherwell, ML1 5RY, Scotland, United
Kingdom
Tel.: (44) 1698732121
Web Site: http://www.terextrucks.com
Emp.: 280
Articulated & Rigid Off-Highway Trucks Mfr
N.A.I.C.S.: 333924
Paul Douglas *(Gen Mgr)*

Subsidiary (Non-US):

Volvo Articulated Haulers AB (2)
Carlslimellsveg, 360 42, Braås, Sweden
Tel.: (46) 470779500
Web Site: http://www.volvogroup.com
N.A.I.C.S.: 336412

Volvo Construction Equipment Australia Pty. Ltd. (2)
65 Epping Road, North Ryde, 2113, NSW,
Australia
Tel.: (61) 2 9903 9200
Web Site: http://www.volvocars.com.au
N.A.I.C.S.: 336412

**Volvo Construction Equipment Cabs
AB** (2)
Hyttjatam 2, 694 82, Hallsberg,
Sweden (100%)
Tel.: (46) 58283100
Web Site: http://www.volvo.com.cn
N.A.I.C.S.: 336412

Volvo Construction Equipment Components AB (2)
Bolingervagen, 631 85, Eskilstuna,
Sweden (100%)
Tel.: (46) 6151000
Web Site: http://www.volvo.com.cn
N.A.I.C.S.: 336412

Volvo Construction Equipment Customer Support AB (2)
Bolingervagen, SE 631 85, Eskilstuna,
Sweden (100%)
Tel.: (46) 016151000
Web Site: http://www.volvoce.com
N.A.I.C.S.: 336412

**Volvo Construction Equipment East
Asia (Pte.) Ltd.** (2)
33 Joon Koon Cir, Singapore, 629111,
Singapore (100%)
Tel.: (65) 62213111
Sales Range: $50-74.9 Million
Emp.: 120
Engine Manufacturing
N.A.I.C.S.: 336412
Vincent Tan *(Pres-Sls-Asia Reg)*

Volvo Construction Equipment Europe AB (2)
Akermansv 5, PO Box 115, SE 241 22, Eslov, Sweden (100%)
Tel.: (46) 41367300
Web Site: http://www.volvoconstruction.com
Sales Range: $25-49.9 Million
Emp.: 30
Mfr of Excavators
N.A.I.C.S.: 333120
Judith Lantz *(Sec)*

Volvo Construction Equipment Europe GmbH (2)
Max Planck Strasse 1, 54329, Konz,
Germany (100%)
Tel.: (49) 65018402
Web Site: http://www.volvo.com
Heavy Construction Machinery
N.A.I.C.S.: 333120
Carl Goeransson *(Pres)*

Volvo Construction Equipment Europe Holding GmbH (2)
Max Planck Str 1, 54329, Konz,
Germany (100%)
Tel.: (49) 65018401
Web Site: http://www.volvo.com
Sales Range: $100-124.9 Million
Emp.: 500
Aircraft Engine Parts Manufacturing
N.A.I.C.S.: 336412
Matthias Keller *(Gen Mgr)*

Volvo Construction Equipment Europe SAS (2)
47 Ave George Poltzier, PO Box 117,
78192, Trappes, Cedex, France (100%)
Tel.: (33) 130692828
Web Site: http://www.volvoce.com
Sales Range: $25-49.9 Million
Emp.: 100
Engine Part Mfr
N.A.I.C.S.: 336412

Volvo Construction Equipment International (2)
Bolingervagen, SE 631 85, Eskilstuna,
Sweden (100%)
Tel.: (46) 16151000
Web Site: http://www.volvo.com
Sales Range: $25-49.9 Million
Emp.: 70
Construction Equipment Mfr & Sales
N.A.I.C.S.: 336120

**Volvo Construction Equipment Korea
Ltd.** (2)
Fl 5 Volvo Bldg 726 173 Hannam Dong,
Yong San Ku, Seoul, 140-210, Korea
(South) (100%)
Tel.: (82) 237809050
Web Site: http://www.volvoce.com

Sales Range: $25-49.9 Million
Emp.: 80
Construction, Mining & Forestry Machinery
& Equipment Rental & Leasing
N.A.I.C.S.: 327910

Subsidiary (Domestic):

**Volvo Construction Equipment
Ltd.** (2)
Moorfield Road, Cambridge, CB22 4QX,
United Kingdom (100%)
Tel.: (44) 1223836636
Web Site: http://www.volvoce.co.uk
Sales Range: $50-74.9 Million
Emp.: 120
N.A.I.C.S.: 336412
Nick Allen *(Mng Dir)*

Subsidiary (US):

**Volvo Construction Equipment North
America, Inc.** (2)
1 Volvo Dr, Asheville, NC 28803-3447
Tel.: (828) 650-2000
Web Site: http://www.volvo.com
Sales Range: $1-4.9 Billion
N.A.I.C.S.: 336412

Subsidiary (Domestic):

**ASC Construction Equipment USA,
Inc.** (3)
9115 Harris Corners Pkwy Ste 450, Charlotte, NC 28269
Tel.: (704) 494-8100
Web Site: http://www.volvo.com
Sales Range: $250-299.9 Million
Emp.: 35
Construction Equipment Dealer
N.A.I.C.S.: 441227
Brad Stimel *(Pres)*

Subsidiary (Non-US):

**Volvo Equipamentos de Construcao
Ltda.** (2)
Av Juscelino Kubitscheck de Oliveira 2600 -
CIC, Curitiba, 81260-900, Parana,
Brazil (100%)
Tel.: (55) 413 317 8111
Web Site: http://www.volvo.com.br
Mfr of Automotive Chassis
N.A.I.C.S.: 336412
Klaus Nilsson *(Pres)*

Volvo Wheel Loaders AB (2)
Hallsberg Verken, 694 82, Hallsberg,
Sweden (100%)
Tel.: (46) 16151000
Web Site: http://www.volvo.com
Sales Range: $100-124.9 Million
N.A.I.C.S.: 336412

Volvo Danmark A/S (1)
Taastrupgardsvej 32, 2630, Taastrup, Denmark
Tel.: (45) 44546600
Web Site: https://www.volvotrucks.dk
N.A.I.C.S.: 336120

Volvo Deutschland GmbH (1)
Siegburger Str 229, Cologne, 50679,
Germany (100%)
Tel.: (49) 22193930
Web Site: http://www.volvocars.com
Sales Range: $125-149.9 Million
Emp.: 150
N.A.I.C.S.: 336412
Frank Denzen *(Dir-Cust Svc)*

Volvo Finance Australia Pty Ltd. (1)
20 Westgate Street, Wacol, 4076, QLD,
Australia
Tel.: (61) 737183500
Web Site: http://www.volvofinance.com.au
Sales Range: $50-74.9 Million
Emp.: 20
Credit Information Services
N.A.I.C.S.: 522299
Nicholas Harty *(Controller-Fin)*

Volvo Finance Peru S.A. (1)
Av Republica de Panama 3535 Piso 9 Ofic
901-902, Centro Empresarial San Isidro,
Lima, 27, Peru
Tel.: (51) 1 222 1122
Web Site: http://www.vfsco.com
Automotive Financial Leasing Services
N.A.I.C.S.: 522220

AB Volvo—(Continued)

Volvo Financial Services LLC **(1)**
7025 Albert Pick Rd Ste 105, Greensboro,
NC 27409
Tel.: (336) 931-4000
Web Site: https://www.vfsco.com
Holding Company; Sales Financing
N.A.I.C.S.: 551112
Stephen Yonce *(VP-Truck Fin Svcs)*

Subsidiary (Non-US):

VFS Canada Inc **(2)**
205 Industrial Parkway North Unit 5, Aurora,
L4G 4C4, ON, Canada
Tel.: (905) 726-5500
Financial Management Services
N.A.I.C.S.: 523999

VFS Denmark AS **(2)**
Taastrupgardsvej 32, 2630, Taastrup, Denmark
Tel.: (45) 44 54 66 26
Web Site: http://www.vfsco.com
Sales Range: $50-74.9 Million
Financial Management Services
N.A.I.C.S.: 523999
Jacques Rossel *(Sales Dir)*

VFS Deutschland GmbH **(2)**
Hugenottenallee 175, 63263, Neu-
Isenburg, Germany
Tel.: (49) 610236693814
Sales Range: $50-74.9 Million
Emp.: 70
Financial Management Services
N.A.I.C.S.: 523999
Markus Wickenhoefer *(Mng Dir)*

VFS Financial Services (Austria)
GmbH **(2)**
Volvostrasse 1, Tribuswinkel, 2512, Austria
Tel.: (43) 5 7500
Web Site: http://www.vfsco.com
Financial Management Services
N.A.I.C.S.: 523999

VFS Financial Services (UK) Ltd **(2)**
Wedgnock Lane, Warwick, CV34 5YA,
United Kingdom
Tel.: (44) 1926 401 203
Sales Range: $25-49.9 Million
Emp.: 50
Automotive Financial Leasing Services
N.A.I.C.S.: 522220

VFS Financial Services BV **(2)**
Stationsweg 2, Gelderland, Beesd, 4153
RD, Netherlands
Tel.: (31) 345688688
Web Site: http://www.vfsco.com
Financial Management Services
N.A.I.C.S.: 523999

VFS Financial Services Belgium
NV **(2)**
Hunderenveldlaan 10, 1082, Brussels, Belgium
Tel.: (32) 24825521
Web Site: https://www.vfsco.com
Sales Range: $50-74.9 Million
Emp.: 8
Financial Management Services
N.A.I.C.S.: 523999
Gavin Armitt *(Bus Dir-Svc)*

VFS Financial Services Czech Republic, s.r.o. **(2)**
se sidlem Obchodni 109, Cestlice, 251 01,
Ricany, Czech Republic
Tel.: (420) 27 102 1704
Web Site: https://www.vfsco.com
Sales Range: $50-74.9 Million
Emp.: 10
Financial Management Services
N.A.I.C.S.: 523999
Michal Hlavaty *(Country Mgr)*

VFS Financial Services Slovakia,
s.r.o. **(2)**
Dialnicna Cesta 9, 903 01, Senec, Slovakia
Tel.: (421) 232 66 24 33
Web Site: http://www.vfsco.com
Sales Range: $50-74.9 Million
Emp.: 10
Financial Management Services
N.A.I.C.S.: 523999
Martin Pisko *(Gen Mgr)*

VFS Financial Services Spain EFC,
SA **(2)**
Calle Procion Cr Coruna Km 11.500 1-3,
Madrid, 28023, Spain
Tel.: (34) 913727800
Financial Management Services
N.A.I.C.S.: 523999

VFS Finansal Kiralama A.S. **(2)**
Icerenkoy Mahallesi Engin Sokak No 9
Kadikoy, 34752, Istanbul, Turkiye
Tel.: (90) 216 655 75 00
Web Site: http://www.vfsco.com
Financial Management Services
N.A.I.C.S.: 523999

VFS Finland AB **(2)**
Vetokuja 1 E, 01610, Vantaa, Finland
Tel.: (358) 10 655 7500
Web Site: http://www.vfsco.com
Financial Management Services
N.A.I.C.S.: 523999

VFS France **(2)**
99 route de Lyon, 69800, Saint Priest,
France
Tel.: (33) 481937942
Web Site: http://www.vfsco.com
Emp.: 35
Financial Management Services
N.A.I.C.S.: 523999

VFS Japan Co., Ltd. **(2)**
NBF Shibakoen Daimondori Bldg 3F-1-8-12
Shibakoen, Tokyo, 105-0011, Japan
Tel.: (81) 3 4330 0000
Web Site: http://www.vfsco.com
Financial Management Services
N.A.I.C.S.: 523999
Takashi Kurokawa *(Mng Dir)*

VFS LT, UAB **(2)**
Minsko Pl 9, Vilnius, 2121, Lithuania
Tel.: (370) 5 210 5094
Emp.: 2
Commercial Truck Mfr
N.A.I.C.S.: 336120

VFS Latvia SIA **(2)**
Granita Iela 28a, Stopini, 1057, Latvia
Tel.: (371) 67813245
Emp.: 3
Financial Management Services
N.A.I.C.S.: 523999
Dzintars Spengelis *(Mgr-Sls)*

VFS Penzugyi Szolgaltato Kft. **(2)**
Cinkotai Ut 34, 1172, Budapest, Hungary
Tel.: (36) 1 254 0627
Web Site: http://www.vfsco.com
Sales Range: $50-74.9 Million
Emp.: 8
Financial Management Services
N.A.I.C.S.: 523999

Subsidiary (Domestic):

VFS US LLC **(2)**
7025 Albert Pick Rd Ste 105, Greensboro,
NC 27402-6131
Tel.: (336) 931-4000
Web Site: http://www.us.vfsco.com
Financial Management Services
N.A.I.C.S.: 523999

Subsidiary (Non-US):

VFS Uslugi Finansowe Polska Sp. z
o.o. **(2)**
Al Katowicka 215, 05-831, Mlochow, Poland
Tel.: (48) 22 383 48 15
Web Site: http://www.vfsco.com
Sales Range: $50-74.9 Million
Emp.: 50
Financial Management Services
N.A.I.C.S.: 523999

VFS Vostok **(2)**
19 Panfilova St Business Center Country
Park, 141407, Khimki, Russia
Tel.: (7) 4959161030
Web Site: http://www.vfs.volvorussia.ru
Financial Management Services
N.A.I.C.S.: 523999

VGFS Financial Services Estonia
OU **(2)**
Kurekivi tee 10, Lehmja kula Rae vald,
75306, Peetri, Harjumaa, Estonia
Tel.: (372) 5 342 9258
Web Site: https://www.vfsco.com

Sales Range: $50-74.9 Million
Emp.: 2
Financial Management Services
N.A.I.C.S.: 523999
Margus Saik *(Territory Mgr)*

Volvo Finance (Suisse) SA Vaud **(2)**
Route De Divonne 50 A, Nyon, 1260, Switzerland
Tel.: (41) 227356830
Sales Range: $50-74.9 Million
Emp.: 12
Financial Management Services
N.A.I.C.S.: 523999
Serge Hunziker *(Mgr-Ops)*

Volvo Financial Services AB **(2)**
ARCE5 Fastningsvagen 16, 405 08, Gothenburg, Sweden
Tel.: (46) 31666500
Web Site: http://www.vfsco.com
Holding Company; Sales Financing
N.A.I.C.S.: 551112
Hakan Agnevall *(Gen Mgr)*

Subsidiary (Domestic):

VFS International AB **(3)**
Fastningsv 1, 405 08, Gothenburg, Sweden
Tel.: (46) 31 66 43 69
Web Site: http://www.vfsco.com
Financial Management Services
N.A.I.C.S.: 523999

VFS Nordic AB **(3)**
ARCE 5 Fastningsvagen 16, 405 08, Gothenburg, Sweden
Tel.: (46) 3 166 0000
Web Site: https://www.vfsco.com
Sales Financing
N.A.I.C.S.: 522220
Per-Olof Olsson *(Sls Mgr)*

Subsidiary (Non-US):

Volvo Financial Services GmbH **(2)**
Hugenottenallee 175, 63263, Neu-Isenburg,
Germany
Tel.: (49) 6102 36693 0
Web Site: http://www.vfsco.com
Sales Range: $50-74.9 Million
Emp.: 50
Financial Management Services
N.A.I.C.S.: 523999

Volvo Finans Norge AS **(2)**
Stromsveien 314, Oslo, 1081, Norway
Tel.: (47) 23176600
Sales Range: $50-74.9 Million
Emp.: 11
Financial Management Services
N.A.I.C.S.: 523999
Attila Sparre *(Territory Mgr)*

Volvo Group Australia Pty Ltd **(1)**
41 Bivouac Place, Wacol, 4076, QLD, Australia
Tel.: (61) 737183500
Web Site: http://www.volvotrucks.com.au
Automotive Distr
N.A.I.C.S.: 423110

Volvo Group Automotive Ticaret,
Ltd **(1)**
Icerenkoy Mah Engin Sok No 9 Volvo Is
Merkezi, Istanbul, Turkiye
Tel.: (90) 2166557500
Automobile Mfr
N.A.I.C.S.: 336110

Volvo Group Canada Inc. **(1)**
2100 Derry Road West Suite 410, Mississauga, L5N 0B3, ON, Canada
Tel.: (289) 998-0020
Trucks Mfr
N.A.I.C.S.: 336120

Volvo Group Insurance Forsakrings
AB **(1)**
Grutejardgatan, Gothenburg, 40508, Sweden
Tel.: (46) 3 166 0000
Web Site: http://www.volvo.com
Insurance Management Services
N.A.I.C.S.: 524210

Volvo Group Mexico **(1)**
Prolongacion Paseo De La Reforma 600,
2nd Floor, Santa Fe, 01210, Mexico, DF,
Mexico **(100%)**
Tel.: (52) 5552593011

Web Site:
http://www.volvotrucksmexico.com
Sales Range: $25-49.9 Million
Emp.: 37
N.A.I.C.S.: 336412

Volvo Group North America, LLC **(1)**
570 Lexington Ave 20th Fl, New York, NY
10022-6885 **(100%)**
Tel.: (212) 418-7400
Web Site: http://www.volvo.com
Sales Range: $25-49.9 Million
Emp.: 4
Mfr of Trucks
N.A.I.C.S.: 541611

Volvo Group Real Estate AB **(1)**
Faestningsvaegen 16, 405 08, Gothenburg,
Sweden
Tel.: (46) 31660400
Real Estate Development Services
N.A.I.C.S.: 531390

Volvo Group Representation **(1)**
Nordic House Rue du Luxembourg 3, 1000,
Brussels, Belgium **(100%)**
Tel.: (32) 24825875
Web Site: http://www.volvo.com
Sales Range: $25-49.9 Million
Emp.: 5
N.A.I.C.S.: 336412
Fedrique Biston *(Sr VP)*

Volvo Group Venture Capital AB **(1)**
Lindholmspiren 5, 402 78, Gothenburg,
Sweden
Tel.: (46) 3 166 0000
Industrial Equipment Mfr & Distr
N.A.I.C.S.: 333248
Martin Witt *(Pres)*

Volvo Holding Danmark A/S **(1)**
Lyskar 3B, 2730, Herlev, Denmark **(100%)**
Tel.: (45) 44546770
Web Site: http://www.volvopenta.dk
Sales Range: $25-49.9 Million
Emp.: 80
N.A.I.C.S.: 336412

Volvo Holding France SA **(1)**
37 Avenue Georges Politzer, Trappes,
78190, France
Tel.: (33) 1 30 69 28 28
Investment Management Service
N.A.I.C.S.: 523999
Jean-Marie Osdoit *(Gen Mgr)*

Subsidiary (Domestic):

VFS Finance France s.a.s. **(2)**
Immeuble Kupka C Hauts De Seine 14, Puteaux, 92800, France
Tel.: (33) 176661800
Financial Management Services
N.A.I.C.S.: 523999

VFS Location France s.a.s. **(2)**
Immeuble Kupka C Hauts De Seine, Puteaux, 92800, France
Tel.: (33) 176661800
Industrial Truck Rental Services
N.A.I.C.S.: 532120

Volvo CE Europe s.a.s. **(2)**
37 Avenue Georges Politzer, Trappes,
78190, France
Tel.: (33) 1 30 69 28 28
Emp.: 100
Engineering Services
N.A.I.C.S.: 541330

Volvo Compact Equipment s.a.s. **(2)**
Rue Pierre Pingon, Belley, 01300, France
Tel.: (33) 4 79 81 15 09
Construction Equipment Mfr
N.A.I.C.S.: 333120

Volvo Holding Mexico, S.A. De
C.V. **(1)**
Calle Lago De Guadalupe No 289, Naucalpan, 54900, Mexico
Tel.: (52) 5550811700
Sales Range: $50-74.9 Million
Emp.: 4
Investment Management Service
N.A.I.C.S.: 523999
Luis Elena Hurato *(Gen Mgr)*

Volvo Holding Sverige AB **(1)**
Arhk 5, Gothenburg, 405 08, Sweden
Tel.: (46) 31 660000

Web Site: http://www.volvogroup.com
Investment Management Service
N.A.I.C.S.: 523940

Subsidiary (Non-US):

Banco Volvo (Brasil) SA   **(2)**
Avenida Juscelino Kubitschek, Oliveira,
81170-300, Brazil
Tel.: (55) 41 3317 7711
Financial Management Services
N.A.I.C.S.: 523999

Volvo Hrvatska d.o.o.   **(1)**
Karlovacka Cesta 94, Lucko, Zagreb,
10094, Croatia
Tel.: (385) 13867660
Web Site: http://www.volvo.hr
Sales Range: $25-49.9 Million
Emp.: 30
Automobile Parts Mfr
N.A.I.C.S.: 336390
Johannes Kjellgren (Gen Mgr)

Volvo IT Belgium   **(1)**
Smalleheerweg 29, 9041, Gent, Belgium
Tel.: (32) 9 255 60 00
Web Site: http://www.volvoit.com
Information Technology Consulting Services
N.A.I.C.S.: 541512

Volvo IT Canada   **(1)**
35 Boulevard Gagnon, Sainte-Claire, G0R
2V0, QC, Canada
Tel.: (418) 883-2888
Web Site: http://www.volvoit.com
Information Technology Consulting Services
N.A.I.C.S.: 541512

Volvo IT Eskilstuna   **(1)**
Brunnsta Industriomrade, 631 85, Eskil-
stuna, Sweden
Tel.: (46) 16 15 10 00
Information Technology Consulting Services
N.A.I.C.S.: 541512

Volvo IT Koping   **(1)**
Eksaardserrjweg 188, 9041, Gent, Belgium
Tel.: (32) 9 255 60 00
Information Technology Consulting Services
N.A.I.C.S.: 541512

Volvo IT Korea   **(1)**
726-173 Hannam-dong, Yongsan-ku, 140-
210, Seoul, Korea (South)
Tel.: (82) 2 37809235
Information Technology Consulting Services
N.A.I.C.S.: 541512

Volvo IT South Africa   **(1)**
Cnr Jetpark Road & Saligna Street, Witfield,
1459, Gauteng, South Africa
Tel.: (27) 11 842 5052
Web Site: http://www.volvoit.com
Emp.: 100
Information Technology Consulting Services
N.A.I.C.S.: 541512

Volvo IT Thailand   **(1)**
42/5 Moo 7 Bang-na Trad Highway Km 26
T Bangsaothong Khing, Bangsaothong,
Samut Prakan, 10540, Thailand
Tel.: (66) 2 707 1747
Web Site: http://www.volvoit.com
Sales Range: $75-99.9 Million
Emp.: 300
Information Technology Consulting Services
N.A.I.C.S.: 541512

**Volvo Information Technology (Tian-
jin) Co., Ltd**   **(1)**
22F Tower C Office Park No 5 Jinghua
Street South, Chaoyang District, Beijing,
100020, China
Tel.: (86) 10 6582 9199
Web Site: http://www.volvo.com
Information Technology Consulting Services
N.A.I.C.S.: 541512

Volvo Information Technology AB   **(1)**
9000 VBA, 405 08, Gothenburg,
Sweden   **(100%)**
Tel.: (46) 31660000
Web Site: http://www.volvoit.com
Sales Range: $450-499.9 Million
Emp.: 2,000
Magnus Carlander (Head-Corp Process &
IT)

**Volvo Information Technology
France**   **(1)**

402 Avenue Charles de Gaulle, 69635,
Venissieux, France
Tel.: (33) 472968111
Information Technology Consulting Services
N.A.I.C.S.: 541512

**Volvo Information Technology
Malaysia**   **(1)**
Jalan Bicu 15/6, Shah Alam, 40200, Malay-
sia
Tel.: (60) 3 5517 9000
Web Site: http://www.volvoit.com
Emp.: 20
Information Technology Consulting Services
N.A.I.C.S.: 541512
Matte Maison (CEO)

**Volvo Information Technology
Mexico**   **(1)**
Lago de Guadalupe 289 Fracc Industrial
Cartagena, 54900, Tultitlan, Mexico
Tel.: (52) 55 50 90 37 00
Web Site: http://www.volvoit.com
Information Technology Consulting Services
N.A.I.C.S.: 541512

**Volvo Information Technology North
America Inc.**   **(1)**
7821 National Service Rd, Greensboro, NC
27409
Tel.: (336) 393-2000
Web Site: http://www.volvo.com
Information Technology Consulting Services
N.A.I.C.S.: 541512

Branch (Domestic):

**Volvo Information Technology
Rockleigh**   **(2)**
6 Volvo Dr, Rockleigh, NJ 07647
Tel.: (201) 768-7300
Information Technology Consulting Services
N.A.I.C.S.: 541512

**Volvo Information Technology
Poland**   **(1)**
Ul Mydlana 2, 51 502, Wroclaw, Poland
Tel.: (48) 71 302 1700
Information Technology Consulting Services
N.A.I.C.S.: 541512

Volvo International Holding BV   **(1)**
Stationsweg 2, PO Box 95, 4153 RD,
Beesd, Netherlands   **(100%)**
Tel.: (31) 345688500
Web Site: http://www.volvotruck.nl
Sales Range: $25-49.9 Million
Emp.: 100
N.A.I.C.S.: 336412

Volvo Italia Spa   **(1)**
Corso Europa 2 Boltiere, Bergamo, 24040,
Italy
Tel.: (39) 035889111
Web Site: http://www.volvocars.com
Sales Range: $25-49.9 Million
Emp.: 100
Automobile Mfr
N.A.I.C.S.: 336110
Manuele Bartolini (Product Mgr)

Volvo Lastvagnar AB   **(1)**
Media Relations, 405 08, Gothenburg, Swe-
den
Tel.: (46) 31666000
Web Site: https://www.volvotrucks.se
N.A.I.C.S.: 336120

Volvo Logistics AB   **(1)**
Amazonvaegen, Gothenburg, 418 78, Vaes-
tra Goetaland, Sweden
Tel.: (46) 31669300
Logistics Consulting Servies
N.A.I.C.S.: 541614

Volvo Logistics Corporation   **(1)**
Smalleheerweg 31, Gent, 9041, Belgium
Tel.: (32) 9 250 42 11
Web Site: http://www.volvogroup.com
Sales Range: $25-49.9 Million
Emp.: 200
Logistics Consulting Servies
N.A.I.C.S.: 541614
Wini Vanderheyden (Mgr-Svc Center)

Volvo Makedonija Ltd.   **(1)**
Terry 1550 #5, Skopje, 1000, North Mace-
donia
Tel.: (389) 2 2652112
Web Site: http://www.volvobuses.com

Automobile Repair & Maintenance Services
N.A.I.C.S.: 811198

Volvo Maskin AS   **(1)**
Mellomasveien 1, 1414, Trollasen, Norway
Tel.: (47) 66818686
Web Site: http://www.volvoce.com
Construction Equipment Mfr
N.A.I.C.S.: 333120
Ton Yeslea (Gen Mgr)

Volvo Parts Gent NV   **(1)**
Smalleheerweg 29, 9041, Gent, Belgium
Tel.: (32) 9 341 39 11
Web Site: http://www.volvogroup.com
Automobile Parts Distr
N.A.I.C.S.: 423140

Volvo Powertrain AB   **(1)**
Herkulesgatan 72, Gothenburg, 40508,
Vaestra Goetaland, Sweden
Tel.: (46) 31660000
Web Site: http://www.volvogroup.com
Automotive Engine & Gear Box Mfr
N.A.I.C.S.: 336390

Volvo Technology Transfer AB   **(1)**
Gotaverksgatan 2, Dept 3300 M2.7, SE 405
08, Gothenburg, Sweden   **(100%)**
Tel.: (46) 31669165
Web Site: http://www.volvogroup.com
Sales Range: $450-499.9 Million
Emp.: 2,000
Automotive Research & Development Tech-
nologies
N.A.I.C.S.: 336110

Volvo Treasury AB   **(1)**
O4000 VGF, Gothenburg, 40508,
Sweden   **(100%)**
Tel.: (46) 31669500
Web Site: http://www.volvogroup.com
Sales Range: $50-74.9 Million
Emp.: 45
Provider of Financial Services
N.A.I.C.S.: 523940
Ulf Niklasson (Gen Mgr)

Volvo Treasury Asia Ltd.   **(1)**
33 Joo Koon Circle, 629111, Singapore,
Singapore
Tel.: (65) 68614582
Web Site: http://www.volvogroup.com
Management Consulting Services
N.A.I.C.S.: 541618

Volvo Truck Corporation   **(1)**
, Gropegardsgatan, 405 08, Gothenburg,
Sweden   **(100%)**
Tel.: (46) 31666000
Web Site: http://www.volvo.com
Development, Design, Production & Market-
ing of Trucks
N.A.I.C.S.: 336211
Martin Jerrasand (Mng Dir-Volvo Trucks)

Subsidiary (US):

Mack Trucks, Inc.   **(2)**
7900 National Service Rd, Greensboro, NC
27409-9416   **(100%)**
Tel.: (610) 709-3011
Web Site: http://www.macktrucks.com
Sales Range: $200-249.9 Million
Emp.: 800
Heavy-Duty Truck Mfr
N.A.I.C.S.: 336120
Martin Weissburg (Pres-Global)

Subsidiary (Non-US):

Mack Canada, Inc.   **(3)**
2100 Derry Road W Ste 410, Mississauga,
L5N 0B3, ON, Canada   **(100%)**
Tel.: (289) 998-0070
Sales Range: $350-399.9 Million
Emp.: 50
Heavy Duty Diesel Trucks
N.A.I.C.S.: 336120

Subsidiary (Domestic):

Mack Leasing System   **(3)**
2100 Mack Blvd, Allentown, PA
18103-5622   **(100%)**
Tel.: (610) 709-3011
Web Site: http://www.macktrucks.com
Sales Range: $300-349.9 Million
Mfr of Trucks & Truck Leasing Services
N.A.I.C.S.: 532102

Mack Remanufacturing Center   **(3)**
2800 Commerce Dr, Middletown, PA 17057-
3204
Tel.: (717) 939-1338
Web Site: http://www.volvo.com
Sales Range: $50-74.9 Million
Emp.: 160
N.A.I.C.S.: 336110
Imran Malik (Mgr-Site)

Subsidiary (Non-US):

Mack Trucks Australia Pty. Ltd.   **(3)**
20 W Gate Street, PO Box 1047, 4074,
Wacol, QLD, Australia   **(100%)**
Tel.: (61) 737183333
Web Site: http://www.macktrucks.com.au
Rev.: $117,988,000
Emp.: 300
Mfr of Trucks & Bus Bodies
N.A.I.C.S.: 336120
Gary Bone (Gen Mgr-Volvo)

Subsidiary (Domestic):

**Mack Trucks-Macungie
Assembly**   **(3)**
7000 Alburtis Rd, Macungie, PA 18062-
9632
Tel.: (610) 351-8800
Web Site: http://www.macktrucks.com
Sales Range: $200-249.9 Million
Assembly of Heavy Duty Diesel Truck Mfr
N.A.I.C.S.: 336120

Subsidiary (Non-US):

Renault Trucks S.A.S.   **(2)**
99 Route de Lyon, 69806, Saint Priest, Ce-
dex, France
Tel.: (33) 472965111
Web Site: http://www.renault-trucks.com
Sales Range: $1-4.9 Billion
Emp.: 14,000
Trucks Mfr
N.A.I.C.S.: 336120
Stefano Chmielewski (CEO)

Subsidiary (Non-US):

Renault Trucks Italia Spa   **(3)**
Via Sempione Sud 197, Pero, Milan, 20016,
Italy
Tel.: (39) 02339771
Web Site: http://www.renault-trucks.it
Emp.: 60
Trucks Mfr
N.A.I.C.S.: 336120

Renault Trucks UK Ltd.   **(3)**
Houghton Hall Business Park Porz Avenue,
Dunstable, LU5 5FT, Beds, United Kingdom
Tel.: (44) 1582471122
Web Site: http://www.renault-trucks.co.uk
Sales Range: $25-49.9 Million
Emp.: 10
Truck Dealer & Customer Support Services
N.A.I.C.S.: 561499
James Charnock (Dir-Comml Trucks &
Svcs-UK & Ireland)

Subsidiary (Non-US):

UD Trucks Corporation   **(2)**
1-1, Ageo, 362-8523, Saitama, Japan
Tel.: (81) 120672301
Web Site: https://www.udtrucks.com
Sales Range: $1-4.9 Billion
Emp.: 2,858
Holding Company; Diesel Engines, Light-,
Medium- & Heavy-Duty Diesel Trucks,
Buses & Special-Purpose Vehicles Mfr
N.A.I.C.S.: 336211
Mourad Hedna (Grp Pres-Middle East, East
& North Africa)

Subsidiary (Domestic):

UD Trucks Japan Co., Ltd.   **(3)**
1-1 Ageo, Ageo, 362-8523, Saitama, Japan
Tel.: (81) 48 781 2301
Web Site: http://www.udtrucks.com
Diesel Engines, Light-, Medium- & Heavy-
Duty Diesel Trucks, Buses & Special-
Purpose Vehicles Mfr
N.A.I.C.S.: 336120

Plant (Domestic):

**UD Trucks Japan Co., Ltd. - Hanyu
Plant**   **(4)**

AB Volvo—(Continued)

24-705-2 Komatsudai, Hanyu, 348-0038,
Saitama, Japan
Tel.: (81) 48 563 2360
Web Site: http://www.udtrucks.com
Financial Management Services
N.A.I.C.S.: 523999

UD Trucks Japan Co., Ltd. - Konosu **(4)**
Plant
3121-1 Mida, Konosu, 365-0062, Saitama,
Japan
Tel.: (81) 48 596 5051
Web Site: http://www.udtrucks.com
Sales Range: $100-124.9 Million
Emp.: 150
Financial Management Services
N.A.I.C.S.: 523999

Affiliate (US):

UD Trucks North America, Inc. **(3)**
5930 W Campus Cir, Irving, TX
75063 **(50%)**
Tel.: (972) 756-5500
Web Site: http://www.udtrucksna.com
Sales Range: $50-74.9 Million
Emp.: 52
Diesel Truck Sales
N.A.I.C.S.: 423110

Subsidiary (Non-US):

UD Trucks South Africa (Pty)
Ltd. **(3)**
5 Piet Rautenbach Street, Rosslyn, 200,
Pretoria, South Africa
Tel.: (27) 12 564 9500
Web Site: http://www.udtrucks.co.za
Sales Range: $100-124.9 Million
Emp.: 300
Trucks Mfr
N.A.I.C.S.: 336120
Frans Jacobs (Gen Mgr)

Subsidiary (Non-US):

VOLVO TRUCKS BULGARIA
EOOD **(2)**
Boulevard Slivnitsa, 1331, Sofia, Bulgaria
Tel.: (359) 2 8106 700
Commercial Vehicle Mfr
N.A.I.C.S.: 336120

VOLVO TRUCKS ESTONIA **(2)**
Kurekivi Tee 10 Lehmja Kuela, 75306,
Harjumaa, Harjumaa, Estonia
Tel.: (372) 671 8360
Web Site: http://www.volvotrucks.com
Commercial Vehicle Mfr
N.A.I.C.S.: 336120

VOLVO TRUCKS FINLAND **(2)**
Vetotie 13, PL 13, 01611, Vantaa, Finland
Tel.: (358) 10 655 00
Web Site: http://www.volvotrucks.com
Commercial Vehicle Mfr
N.A.I.C.S.: 336110

VOLVO TRUCKS IRAN **(2)**
14th Karaj Special Road, PO Box 13895-
141, 13861-81198, Tehran, Iran
Tel.: (98) 21 44196513 15
Web Site: http://www.volvotrucks.com
Automotive Distr
N.A.I.C.S.: 423110

VOLVO TRUCKS LITHUANIA **(2)**
Minsko Pl 9, 02121, Vilnius, Lithuania
Tel.: (370) 52159500
Web Site: https://www.volvotrucks.lt
Emp.: 100
Commercial Vehicle Mfr
N.A.I.C.S.: 336110
Jarkko Aine (Mng Dir)

VOLVO TRUCKS MACEDONIA **(2)**
Kacanicki Pat Bb, 1000, Skopje, North
Macedonia
Tel.: (389) 2 2652 112
Web Site: http://www.volvotrucks.com
Sales Range: $25-49.9 Million
Emp.: 13
Commercial Vehicle Distr
N.A.I.C.S.: 423110

VOLVO TRUCKS
NETHERLANDS **(2)**
Stationsweg 2, 4153 RD, Beesd, Nether-
lands

Tel.: (31) 345 688500
Web Site: http://www.volvotrucks.com
Sales Range: $25-49.9 Million
Emp.: 150
Commercial Vehicle Mfr
N.A.I.C.S.: 336120
Cynthia Vant Hoff (Coord-Mktg Comm &
PR)

VOLVO TRUCKS NIGERIA **(2)**
322A Ikorodu Road Ikeja Mr Ade Ojuoko,
Lagos, Nigeria
Tel.: (234) 70 56427174
Commercial Vehicle Mfr
N.A.I.C.S.: 336120

VOLVO TRUCKS POLAND **(2)**
Aleja Katowicka 215, 05-831, Mlochow,
Warsaw, Poland
Tel.: (48) 22 383 45 00
Web Site: http://www.volvotrucks.pl
Emp.: 200
Commercial Vehicle Mfr
N.A.I.C.S.: 336110
Malgorzata Kulis (Mng Dir)

VOLVO TRUCKS RUSSIA **(2)**
St Panfilov 19 Business Center Country
Park, 141407, Khimki, Russia
Tel.: (7) 495 961 1030
Commercial Vehicle Mfr
N.A.I.C.S.: 336120

VOLVO TRUCKS SAUDI
ARABIA **(2)**
Kllo 14 Makkah Rd, PO Box 1588, Jeddah,
21441, Saudi Arabia
Tel.: (966) 2 620 9173
Web Site: http://www.volvotrucks.com
Commercial Vehicle Mfr
N.A.I.C.S.: 336110

VOLVO TRUCKS SYRIA **(2)**
Damascus Free Zone, PO Box 3050, Da-
mascus, Syria
Tel.: (963) 11 212 97 36
Web Site: http://www.volvotrucks.com
Commercial Vehicle Distr
N.A.I.C.S.: 423110
Emad Hamdan (Mgr-After Sls)

VPL Limited **(2)**
49C Jail Road, PO Box 1990, Lahore,
54000, Pakistan **(100%)**
Tel.: (92) 42111875875
Web Site: http://www.vpl.com.pk
Construction Equipment Marketing & After-
Sales
N.A.I.C.S.: 336120
Konoz Mohiuddin (Chm)

Volvo Europa Truck N.V. **(2)**
PO Box 10, BE 9041, Gent,
Belgium **(100%)**
Tel.: (32) 092504211
Web Site: http://www.volvo.be
Sales Range: $400-449.9 Million
Emp.: 2,500
Truck Mfr & Distr
N.A.I.C.S.: 336120
Kamel Sid (Mng Dir)

Volvo India Private Ltd. **(2)**
Yelachahalli Tavarekere Post, Hosakote,
Bengaluru, 562 122, India
Tel.: (91) 8066914000
Web Site: http://www.volvotrucks.com
Sales Range: $200-249.9 Million
Emp.: 600
Heavy Duty Truck & Automobile Mfr &
Sales
N.A.I.C.S.: 336120
Kamal Bali (Mng Dir)

Division (Domestic):

Volvo India Ltd - Volvo Financial Ser-
vices India Division **(3)**
65/2 Block A 5th Floor Parin Building Bag-
mane Tech Park, CV Raman Nagar,
560093, Bengaluru, Karnataka, India
Tel.: (91) 80 66912106
Web Site: http://www.vfsco.com
Financial Management Services
N.A.I.C.S.: 523999

Subsidiary (Non-US):

Volvo Kuorma-ja Linja-autot Oy
AB **(2)**

Dragganden 1E, 01610, Vantaa,
Finland **(100%)**
Tel.: (358) 950791
Sales Range: $50-74.9 Million
Emp.: 150
Automobile Mfr
N.A.I.C.S.: 336412

Subsidiary (Domestic):

Volvo Lastvagnar Sverige AB **(2)**
Ravebergsvagen, Dept 20100 Bldg VLH8,
Gothenburg, 40508, Sweden **(100%)**
Tel.: (46) 31 66 60 00
Web Site: http://www.volvotrucks.com
Heavy Duty Truck Assemblies
N.A.I.C.S.: 336120
Olof Persson (Pres)

Subsidiary (Non-US):

Volvo Group UK Ltd **(3)**
Wedgnock Lane, Warwick, CV34 5YA,
United Kingdom
Tel.: (44) 1926401777
Web Site: http://www.volvotrucks.co.uk
Sales Range: $25-49.9 Million
Emp.: 15
Trucks Mfr
N.A.I.C.S.: 336120
Nigel Hanwell (Officer-Press)

Subsidiary (Domestic):

Volvo Truck Center Sweden AB **(3)**
Knistavagen 3, 191 62, Sollentuna, Sweden
Tel.: (46) 86255500
Web Site: https://www.volvotruckcenter.se
Trucks Mfr
N.A.I.C.S.: 336120
Hans Olsson (Gen Mgr)

Subsidiary (Non-US):

Volvo Lastvogne Danmark A/S **(2)**
Taastrupgardsvej 32, PO Box 535, 2630,
Taastrup, Denmark **(100%)**
Tel.: (45) 43555800
Web Site: http://www.volvotruckcenter.dk
Sales Range: $25-49.9 Million
Emp.: 100
N.A.I.C.S.: 336412
Lars Bo Larsen (Mgr)

Volvo Norge A/S **(2)**
Stroms Vien 314 Alnabru, PO Box 103,
Oslo, 1081, Norway
Tel.: (47) 23176600
Web Site: http://www.volvo.com
Sales Range: $50-74.9 Million
Emp.: 150
Automobile Mfr
N.A.I.C.S.: 336110
Odd Tolleffrod (Mgr-Acctg)

Subsidiary (Domestic):

Volvo Parts Corporation **(2)**
Bldg ARH 12, 405 08, Gothenburg,
Sweden **(100%)**
Tel.: (46) 31660300
Web Site: http://www.volvo.com
Sales Range: $75-99.9 Million
Emp.: 350
Mfr of Automotive Parts
N.A.I.C.S.: 336340
Mikael Kromli (Mgr-Fin)

Subsidiary (Non-US):

Volvo Poland Sp. Z.o.o. **(2)**
Aleja Katowicka 215, 05-831, Mlochow,
Warsaw, Poland **(100%)**
Tel.: (48) 223834500
Sales Range: $25-49.9 Million
Emp.: 100
Retailer of Trucks
N.A.I.C.S.: 423830
Boguzki Andrzej (Project Mgr)

Volvo Truck **(2)**
55 Ave Des Champs Pierreux, 92757, Nan-
terre, France
Tel.: (33) 55175517
Web Site: http://www.volvotrucks.fr
Sales Range: $25-49.9 Million
Emp.: 100
N.A.I.C.S.: 336412

Volvo Truck & Bus (Thailand) Co.
Ltd. **(2)**

42 5 Moo 7 Bangna Trad Rd Km 26 Bant-
sao Tong, Samut Prakan, 10540, Thailand
Tel.: (66) 27011747
Web Site: http://www.volvotrucks.volvo.co.th
Sales Range: $50-74.9 Million
Emp.: 225
N.A.I.C.S.: 336412

Volvo Truck & Bus Botswana Pty
Ltd. **(2)**
Lot 14400 Gaboronoe West, PO Box
41259, Gaborone, Botswana
Tel.: (267) 323 117
Truck & Bus Mfr
N.A.I.C.S.: 336120

Volvo Truck Australia Pty. Ltd. **(2)**
120 Hume Hwy, Chullora, 2190, NSW, Aus-
tralia
Tel.: (61) 290368200
Sales Range: $100-124.9 Million
Emp.: 300
N.A.I.C.S.: 336412

Subsidiary (Domestic):

Volvo Truck Corporation Powertrain
Division Engine **(2)**
Volvov 5, 541 87, Skovde,
Sweden **(100%)**
Tel.: (46) 500474000
Web Site: http://www.volvo.com
Sales Range: $700-749.9 Million
Emp.: 3,000
Mfr of Transmissions
N.A.I.C.S.: 336350
Magnus Holm (Gen Mgr)

Subsidiary (Non-US):

Volvo Truck Czech s.r.o. **(2)**
Obchodni 109, 251 01, Cestlice, Czech
Republic **(100%)**
Tel.: (420) 271021111
Web Site: http://www.volvotrucks.cz
Sales Range: $25-49.9 Million
Emp.: 100
Trucks Mfr
N.A.I.C.S.: 336120

Volvo Truck Latvia Sia **(2)**
28A Granita St, 1057, Riga, Latvia **(100%)**
Tel.: (371) 20293001
Web Site: http://www.volvotrucks.lv
Sales Range: $25-49.9 Million
Emp.: 100
Commercial Vehicle Sales & Repair Ser-
vices
N.A.I.C.S.: 336412

Volvo Truck Slovak s.r.o. **(2)**
Devialnappna No 9, 903 01, Senec,
Slovakia **(100%)**
Tel.: (421) 232662424
Truck Engine & Engine Parts Manufacturing
N.A.I.C.S.: 336310
Tomas Kovac (Gen Mgr)

Volvo Truck en Bus Nederland
B.V. **(2)**
Stationsweg 2, 4153 RD, Beesd, Nether-
lands
Tel.: (31) 345688500
Web Site: http://www.volvotrucks.nl
Sales Range: $25-49.9 Million
Emp.: 70
Automobile Mfr
N.A.I.C.S.: 336412
Wabe Van Solkema (Controller)

Volvo Trucks (Deutschland)
GmbH **(2)**
Oskar Messter Str 20, Ismaning, 85737,
Germany **(100%)**
Tel.: (49) 89800740
Web Site: http://www.volvo.de
Sales Range: $25-49.9 Million
Emp.: 100
Mfr of Diesel Trucks
N.A.I.C.S.: 336110
Thomas Mrurer (Office Mgr)

Volvo Trucks (Schweiz) AG **(2)**
Lindenstrasse 6, 8108, Dallikon,
Switzerland **(100%)**
Tel.: (41) 448476100
Web Site: http://www.volvogrouptrucks.ch
Sales Range: $25-49.9 Million
Emp.: 50
Trucks Mfr

N.A.I.C.S.: 336120

Volvo Trucks (Suisse) SA   (2)
Lindenstrasse 6, Dallikon, 8108, Switzerland
Tel.: (41) 44 847 61 00
Web Site: http://www.volvotrucks.com
Sales Range: $25-49.9 Million
Emp.: 50
Commercial Vehicle Distr
N.A.I.C.S.: 423110

Volvo Trucks Austria GmbH   (2)
Volvostrasse 1, 2512, Tribuswinkel, Austria
Tel.: (43) 5 7500 0
Web Site: http://www.volvotrucks.com
Sales Range: $75-99.9 Million
Emp.: 130
Commercial Vehicle Sales & Repair Services
N.A.I.C.S.: 423110

Volvo Trucks Belgium N.V.   (2)
Hunderenveldlaan 10, 1082, Brussels, Belgium   **(100%)**
Tel.: (32) 24825111
Web Site: http://www.volvotrucks.be
Sales Range: $25-49.9 Million
Emp.: 60
N.A.I.C.S.: 336412

Volvo Trucks Canada   (2)
2100 Derry Road West Suite 410, Mississauga, L5N 0B3, ON, Canada
Tel.: (289) 998-0020
Web Site: https://www.volvotrucks.ca
Marketing, Sales & Distribution of Volvo Trucks
N.A.I.C.S.: 441227
Carol Girard *(Mgr-Truck Mktg)*

Volvo Trucks Espana, S.A.   (2)
Protion 113, 28013, Madrid, Spain   **(100%)**
Tel.: (34) 913727800
Web Site: http://www.volvospain.com
Sales Range: $25-49.9 Million
Emp.: 100
Heavy Duty Truck Mfr
N.A.I.C.S.: 336120
Johan Carlsson *(Mgr-Fin)*

Volvo Trucks India Pvt Ltd   (2)
Yelachahalli Tavarekere Post Hosakote, Bengaluru, 562 122, India
Tel.: (91) 80 6691 4000
Web Site: http://www.volvotrucks.com
Sales Range: $200-249.9 Million
Emp.: 600
Commercial Vehicle Mfr
N.A.I.C.S.: 336110
Siddharth Kirtane *(Head-Mktg)*

Volvo Trucks Indonesia   (2)
Sentral Senayan III 12th Floor Jl Asia Afrika No 8 Gelora Bung, Karno Senayan Jakarta Pusat, Jakarta, 10270, Indonesia
Tel.: (62) 21 2903 9216
Web Site: http://www.volvotrucks.com
Emp.: 100
Commercial Vehicle Mfr
N.A.I.C.S.: 336110
Imelda Sitorus *(Mgr-Sls Strategy-Asia)*

Subsidiary (US):

Volvo Trucks North America, Inc.   (2)
7900 National Service Rd, Greensboro, NC 27409   **(100%)**
Tel.: (336) 393-2000
Sales Range: $400-449.9 Million
Emp.: 2,000
Mfr & Distr of Trucks
N.A.I.C.S.: 336120
Scott Kress *(VP-Sls)*

Subsidiary (Non-US):

Volvo Trucks Philippines   (2)
77 Mindanao Avenue Pag-Asa, Metro Manila, Quezon City, 1100, Philippines
Tel.: (63) 2 924 2261
Web Site: http://www.volvotrucks.com
Emp.: 100
Commercial Vehicle Distr
N.A.I.C.S.: 423110
Anthony L. Ngo *(Pres)*

Volvo Trucks Region Central Europe GmbH   (2)
Oskar-Messter-Str 20, Ismaning, 85737, Germany

Tel.: (49) 89 800740
Web Site: http://www.volvotrucks.com
Sales Range: $50-74.9 Million
Emp.: 120
Commercial Vehicle Mfr
N.A.I.C.S.: 336110

Subsidiary (Domestic):

Volvo Trucks Sweden AB   (2)
Affaersregion Norden ARH 4, 405 08, Gothenburg, Sweden
Tel.: (46) 31 66 60 00
Web Site: http://www.volvotrucks.com
Heavy Duty Truck Mfr
N.A.I.C.S.: 336120

Subsidiary (Non-US):

Volvo Trucks Thailand   (2)
42/5 Moo 7 Bang-na Trad Highway Km 26 Khing Amphur, Bangsaothong, Samut Prakan, 10540, Thailand
Tel.: (66) 2 707 1747
Commercial Vehicle Mfr
N.A.I.C.S.: 336120

Volvo Trucks de Mexico S.A. de C.V.   (2)
Prolongacion Paseo De La Reforma 600 Fl 2 341, 01210, Mexico, DF, Mexico **(100%)**
Tel.: (52) 5550816850
Web Site: http://www.volvotrucksmexico.com
Sales Range: $25-49.9 Million
Emp.: 70
N.A.I.C.S.: 336412

Volvo do Brasil Veiculos Ltda.   (2)
Av Juscelino Kubitcheck de Oliveira 2600, Curitiba, 81260-900, PR, Brazil   **(58%)**
Tel.: (55) 800411050
Web Site: http://www.volvo.com
Volvo Trucks & Buses Exporter & Mfr
N.A.I.C.S.: 336412

Volvo do Brasil Veiculos Ltda.   (1)
Caixa Postal 7981, CEP 81290-000, Curitiba, PR, Brazil   **(100%)**
Tel.: (55) 41 3317 4255
Web Site: http://www.volvogroup.com
Sales Range: $200-249.9 Million
Emp.: 1,000
Automotive Mfr & Distr
N.A.I.C.S.: 336110

Xi'an Silver Bus Corporation   (1)
Yanling Economic Development Zone, Xi'an, 710089, Shaanxi, China   **(50%)**
Tel.: (86) 29 6801 8888
Web Site: http://www.silverbus.com
Bus Mfr
N.A.I.C.S.: 485113

ZAO Volvo Vostok   (1)
Business Centre Country Park Panfilova Str 19, Khimki, 141407, Moscow, Russia
Tel.: (7) 495 961 1030
Web Site: http://www.volvotrucks.com
Emp.: 300
Construction Equipment Distr
N.A.I.C.S.: 423810
Andrey Komov *(Gen Mgr-Construction Equipment)*

AB&COMPANY CO., LTD.

Shinjuku East Square Bldg 6F
2-16-6, Shinjuku-ku, Tokyo, 160-0022, Japan
Tel.: (81) 345001383
Web Site: https://ab-company.co.jp
Year Founded: 2009
9251—(TKS)
Rev.: $119,041,100
Assets: $173,485,210
Liabilities: $111,866,020
Net Worth: $61,619,190
Earnings: $7,855,720
Fiscal Year-end: 10/31/23
Beauty Product Distr
N.A.I.C.S.: 456120

Subsidiaries:

ALIVE Co., Ltd.   (1)
Nishi-Shinbashi Naka Building 6th Floor 1-12-8, Nishi-Shinbashi Minato-ku, Tokyo, 105-0003, Japan

Tel.: (81) 355103838
Web Site: https://alive-oem.com
Goods Mfr & Distr
N.A.I.C.S.: 339920

B-light Co., Ltd.   (1)
3-10-19 Shiratori, Atsuta-ku, Nagoya, 456-0035, Japan
Tel.: (81) 522125736
Web Site: https://www.b-lightgroup.co.jp
Construction Equipment Design & Materials Distr
N.A.I.C.S.: 423810

HAGU Co., Ltd.   (1)
8F Shinjuku Kasen Building 3-1-5, Nishi-Shinjuku Shinjuku-ku, Tokyo, 160-0023, Japan
Tel.: (81) 5031551897
Web Site: https://hagu.co.jp
Information Technology Services
N.A.I.C.S.: 561499

AB-BIOTICS S.A.

S 1 - Avinguda Can Fatjo dels Aurons, 308174 Sant Cugat del Valles, 8172, Barcelona, Spain
Tel.: (34) 935803876
Web Site: https://www.ab-biotics.com
Rev.: $13,602,435
Assets: $17,333,318
Liabilities: $9,488,170
Net Worth: $7,845,148
Earnings: $1,393,402
Emp.: 30
Fiscal Year-end: 12/31/18
Pharmaceutical & Nutraceutica Mfr
N.A.I.C.S.: 325412
Miquel Angel Bonachera *(Co-Founder)*

ABA CHEMICALS CORPORATION

No 18 Dongfang East Road, petrochemical District, Taicang, 215433, Jiangsu, China
Tel.: (86) 51253641234
Web Site: https://www.abachem.com
300261—(CHIN)
Rev.: $280,937,592
Assets: $562,782,168
Liabilities: $210,414,672
Net Worth: $352,367,496
Earnings: $28,494,180
Fiscal Year-end: 12/31/22
Chemicals, Agricultural Chemicals, Advanced Intermediates & Active Pharmaceutical Ingredients Mfr
N.A.I.C.S.: 325998

Subsidiaries:

ABA Chemicals (Shanghai) Limited   (1)
Block F floor 24 No 201 Ningxia road, Putuo District, Shanghai, 200063, China
Tel.: (86) 2151159199
Fine Chemicals & Pharmaceutical Ingredients Mfr
N.A.I.C.S.: 325180

Amino Chemicals Limited   (1)
MRA 050X Marsa Industrial Estate, MRS 3000, Marsa, Malta
Tel.: (356) 2 124 9223
Web Site: https://aminochemicals.com
Pharmaceutical Products Distr
N.A.I.C.S.: 424210

Shanghai Puyi Chemical Co., Ltd.   (1)
3th Floor Building 11 No 201 Min Yi Road, Songjiang District, Shanghai, 201612, China
Tel.: (86) 215768.750 5238
Chemicals Mfr
N.A.I.C.S.: 325998

ABA RESOURCES PTY. LTD.

1st Floor 9/30 Prohasky Street, Port Melbourne, 3207, VIC, Australia
Tel.: (61) 3 8369 0122   AU
Web Site:
http://www.abaresources.com.au

Gold & Other Resource Mining Trust
N.A.I.C.S.: 525990
Nigel Harrison *(Sec)*

ABACORE CAPITAL HOLD-INGS, INC.

No 28 N Domingo St Near Corner Gilmore St, Quezon City, New Manila, Philippines
Tel.: (63) 7243759   PH
Web Site:
https://www.abacorecapital.com
Year Founded: 1981
ABA—(PHI)
Rev.: $107,133,746
Assets: $365,406,391
Liabilities: $49,024,068
Net Worth: $316,382,323
Earnings: $97,382,307
Fiscal Year-end: 12/31/21
Equipment Rental Services
N.A.I.C.S.: 532490
Leonardo S. Gayao *(Pres)*

ABACUS GROUP, LLC

Level 13 77 Castlereagh Street, Sydney, 2000, NSW, Australia
Tel.: (61) 292538600
Web Site:
https://abacusgroup.com.au
Year Founded: 1996
ABP—(ASX)
Rev.: $567,603,512
Assets: $4,142,834,535
Liabilities: $1,460,319,831
Net Worth: $2,682,514,705
Earnings: $396,246,651
Emp.: 76
Fiscal Year-end: 06/30/22
Real Estate Management & Investment Services
N.A.I.C.S.: 531390
Gavin Lechem *(Exec Gen Mgr-Corp Dev & Legal)*

Subsidiaries:

Abacus Funds Management Limited   (1)
Level 34 Australia Square 264-278 George Street, Sydney, 2000, NSW, Australia
Tel.: (61) 292538600
Web Site:
http://www.abacusproperty.com.au
Sales Range: $50-74.9 Million
Emp.: 50
Fund Management Services
N.A.I.C.S.: 523940
Rod De Aboitiz *(CFO)*

ABACUS MINING & EXPLORA-TION CORPORATION

701 West Georgia Street Suite 1500, Vancouver, V7Y 1G5, BC, Canada
Tel.: (604) 682-0301
Web Site:
https://www.amemining.com
DGV2—(DEU)
Assets: $5,960,264
Liabilities: $20,965,466
Net Worth: ($15,005,201)
Earnings: ($1,259,348)
Fiscal Year-end: 12/31/23
Mineral Exploration Services
N.A.I.C.S.: 213114
Michael McInnis *(Chm)*

Subsidiaries:

Almadex Minerals Limited   (1)
Suite 210-1333 Johnston Street, Vancouver, V6H 3R9, BC, Canada
Tel.: (604) 689-7644
Web Site: https://almadexminerals.com
Gold Ore Mining Services
N.A.I.C.S.: 212220
Duane Poliquin *(Founder & Chm)*

ABADGARAN IRAN TOURISM AND WELFARE COMPLEXES

ABADGARAN IRAN TOURISM AND WELFARE COMPLEXES —(CONTINUED)

(PUBLIC LIMITED COMPANY)
Shahid Qassem Soleimani Highway
Shahid Soleimani, PO Box
91775/1546, 9176983151, Mashhad,
Iran
Tel.: (98) 5138718080
Web Site:
https://www.abadgaraniran.com
Year Founded: 1994
ABAD1—(THE)
Sales Range: Less than $1 Million
Tourism Bureaus
N.A.I.C.S.: 561591
Mehdi Manoochehri *(Mng Dir)*

ABALANCE CORPORATION LTD.
Tennozu First Tower F16 2-2-4 Hi-
gashishinagawa, Shinagawa-Ku, To-
kyo, 140-0002, Japan
Tel.: (81) 368644001   JP
Web Site: https://www.abalance.co.jp
Year Founded: 2000
3856—(TKS)
Rev.: $1,299,805,840
Assets: $934,076,060
Liabilities: $670,149,020
Net Worth: $263,927,040
Earnings: $59,276,600
Emp.: 1,684
Fiscal Year-end: 06/30/24
Knowledge Management Software &
Consulting Services
N.A.I.C.S.: 513210
Nishimoto Shigeo *(Auditor)*

Subsidiaries:

AskMe Corporation   **(1)**
2300 130th Ave Ne Ste 101, Bellevue, WA
98005-1755
Tel.: (425) 564-9000
Web Site: http://www.askmecorp.com
Sales Range: $25-49.9 Million
Enterprise Software Solutions
N.A.I.C.S.: 541511

Birdy Fuel Cells LLC   **(1)**
Tennozu First Tower 5F 2-2-4 Higashi shi-
nagawa, Shinagawa-ku, Tokyo, 1400002,
Japan
Tel.: (81) 364332788
Web Site: https://www.birdyfuelcells.com
Automotive Fuel Cell Technology Mfr
N.A.I.C.S.: 335312

FORTHINK Co., Ltd.   **(1)**
Sun Keisei Building 3F 1-4-1 Kita 1-jo Hi-
gashi, Chuo-ku Hokkaido, Sapporo, 060-
0031, Japan
Tel.: (81) 112114701
Data Security Services
N.A.I.C.S.: 561621

Japan Photocatalyst Center Co.,   **(1)**
Ltd.
22646 Matsunokihara, Yamauchi-cho,
Takeo, 849-2305, Saga, Japan
Tel.: (81) 95 420 7115
Web Site: https://www.jphoc.jp
Photocatalyst Technology Services
N.A.I.C.S.: 541519
Yuichiro Masuda *(Pres)*

PV Repower inc.   **(1)**
5F Tennozu First Tower 2-2-4 Higashi-
Shinagawa, Shinagawa-ku, Tokyo, 140-
0002, Japan
Tel.: (81) 5036123439
Web Site: https://www.pvr.inc
Solar Panel Mfr & Distr
N.A.I.C.S.: 333414

Realcom Technology India PVT
Ltd.   **(1)**
3rd Floor Pride-Purple Accord Baner Road,
Pune, 411045, Maharashtra, India
Tel.: (91) 2066454900
Web Site: https://www.realcom-inc.com
Software Development Services
N.A.I.C.S.: 541511

VSUN Japan Co., Ltd.   **(1)**
2-2-4 Higashi-Shinagawa Tennozu First
Tower 5F, Shinagawa-ku, Tokyo, 140-0002,
Japan
Tel.: (81) 36 810 3006
Web Site: https://www.vsunjapan.jp
Solar Panel Mfr
N.A.I.C.S.: 334413

Vietnam Sunergy Joint Stock
Company   **(1)**
Lot !!! - Dong Vang Dinh Tram industrial
Park, Nenh Town, Viet Yen, Bac Giang,
Vietnam
Tel.: (84) 204 356 6688
Solar Energy Services
N.A.I.C.S.: 221114

ABAN OFFSHORE LIMITED
Janpriya Crest 113 Pantheon Road,
Egmore, Chennai, 600008, India
Tel.: (91) 04449060606
Web Site:
https://www.abanoffshore.com
Year Founded: 1986
523204—(BOM)
Rev.: $83,714,358
Assets: $405,186,327
Liabilities: $3,068,639,847
Net Worth: ($2,663,453,520)
Earnings: ($297,171,147)
Emp.: 39
Fiscal Year-end: 03/31/22
Oil Drilling Services
N.A.I.C.S.: 213111
Reji Abraham *(Mng Dir)*

Subsidiaries:

Aban Energies Limited   **(1)**
Janpriya Crest 113 Pantheon Road,
Egmore, Chennai, 600 008, India
Tel.: (91) 4449060606
Web Site: https://www.aban.com
Wind Energy Services
N.A.I.C.S.: 221115
V. Vasanthakumar *(Gen Mgr)*

Aban Singapore Pte. Ltd.   **(1)**
No 10 Jalan Basar Unit No 11-06 Sim Lim
Tower, Singapore, 038986, Singapore
Tel.: (65) 62946364
Oil Drilling Services
N.A.I.C.S.: 213111

Subsidiary (Non-US):

Sinvest AS   **(2)**
Kreenslyst Alle 8B, 0278, Oslo, Norway
Tel.: (47) 90847718
Web Site: http://www.sinvest.no
Sales Range: $400-449.9 Million
Oil & Natural Gas Exploration Services
N.A.I.C.S.: 211120
Geir Worum *(Chm)*

Subsidiary (Domestic):

DDI Holding AS   **(3)**
Gyldenloves gate 2 B, 4611, Kristiansand,
Norway   **(100%)**
Tel.: (47) 38041940
Web Site: https://www.sinvest.no
Holding Company
N.A.I.C.S.: 551112

ABANCA CORPORACION BANCARIA, SA
Cl Canton Claudino Pita 2, 15300, La
Coruna, Baetanzos, Spain
Tel.: (34) 981910522
Web Site: http://www.abanca.com
Holding Company
N.A.I.C.S.: 522390
Juan Carlos Escotet Rodriguez *(Pres)*

Subsidiaries:

Banco Caixa Geral Brasil, S.A.   **(1)**
Avenue Branca Biodo 5A, Itaim, 4285,
Brazil   **(99.8%)**
Tel.: (55) 11 35099300
Web Site: http://www.bcgbrasil.com.br
Commercial Banking Services
N.A.I.C.S.: 522110

Deutsche Bank (Portugal) SA   **(1)**
Rua Castilho No 20, 1250 069, Lisbon,
Portugal   **(100%)**
Tel.: (351) 213111200
Web Site: http://www.deutschebank.com
Sales Range: $100-124.9 Million
Emp.: 200
Investment Bank
N.A.I.C.S.: 523910

ABANS ELECTRICALS PLC
506B Galle Road, Wellawatta, 6, Co-
lombo, Sri Lanka
Tel.: (94) 115776430
Web Site: https://abanservice.lk
ABAN—(COL)
Rev.: $17,465,682
Assets: $16,301,847
Liabilities: $10,118,911
Net Worth: $6,182,936
Earnings: $444,458
Emp.: 905
Fiscal Year-end: 03/31/23
Home Appliance Repair & Mainte-
nance Services
N.A.I.C.S.: 811412
Nilanka Kumudini *(Mgr-HR)*

ABANS ENTERPRISES LIM-ITED
36/37/38A 3rd Floor 227 Nariman
Bhavan, Backbay Reclamation Nari-
man Point, Mumbai, 400 021, India
Tel.: (91) 2261790000
Web Site:
https://www.abansenterprises.com
Year Founded: 1985
512165—(BOM)
Rev.: $2,988,846,670
Assets: $44,211,463
Liabilities: $14,597,801
Net Worth: $29,613,661
Earnings: $3,960,152
Emp.: 6
Fiscal Year-end: 03/31/22
Security Brokerage Services
N.A.I.C.S.: 523150
Abhishek Bansal *(Chm & Mng Dir)*

Subsidiaries:

Zicuro Technologies Private
Limited   **(1)**
36 37 38A 3rd Floor 227 Nariman Bhavan
Backbay Reclamation, Nariman Point,
Mumbai, 400 021, MH, India
Tel.: (91) 2261790000
Web Site: https://www.zicuro.com
Financial Services
N.A.I.C.S.: 523999
Shiv Shankar Singh *(VP-IT)*

ABANS FINANCE PLC
456 R A De Mel Mawatha, Colombo,
Sri Lanka
Tel.: (94) 112208888
Web Site:
https://www.abansfinance.lk
Year Founded: 2006
AFSL.N0000—(COL)
Rev.: $10,485,493
Assets: $49,095,160
Liabilities: $38,492,400
Net Worth: $10,602,761
Earnings: $1,527,856
Emp.: 274
Fiscal Year-end: 03/31/21
Financial Lending Services
N.A.I.C.S.: 523999
Dharshan Silva *(CEO)*

ABANS HOLDINGS LIMITED
36 37 38A 3rd Floor 227 Nariman
Bhavan Backbay Reclamation, Nariman Point, Mumbai, 400021, Maharashtra, India
Tel.: (91) 2261790000
Web Site:
https://www.abansholdings.com

Year Founded: 2009
543712—(BOM)
Rev.: $139,563,216
Assets: $223,366,369
Liabilities: $114,932,906
Net Worth: $108,433,463
Earnings: $8,427,996
Emp.: 112
Fiscal Year-end: 03/31/23
Holding Company
N.A.I.C.S.: 551112

ABATE AS INDUSTRIES LTD.
Abate AS Alsalama Eye Hospital
Palakkad Road, Perinthalmanna
Malappuram DT, Kerala, 679322,
India
Tel.: (91) 9072558877
Web Site: https://www.abateas.com
Year Founded: 1991
531658—(BOM)
Rev.: $215
Assets: $76,277
Liabilities: $75,185
Net Worth: $1,092
Earnings: ($42,435)
Fiscal Year-end: 03/31/23
Software Development Services
N.A.I.C.S.: 541511
Ashok Bhanushali Trikamji *(CFO)*

ABATTIS BIOCEUTICALS CORPORATION
1200-625 Howe St, Vancouver, V6C
2T6, BC, Canada
Tel.: (604) 647-1868   BC
Web Site: http://www.abattis.com
Year Founded: 1997
ATTBF—(OTCEM)
Rev.: $588,000
Assets: $2,552,000
Liabilities: $112,000
Net Worth: $2,440,000
Earnings: ($930,000)
Fiscal Year-end: 12/31/20
Botanical-Based Antiviral Products
Mfr
N.A.I.C.S.: 325411

Subsidiaries:

Pro Natura B.V.   **(1)**
Parklaan 3, 5061 JV, Oisterwijk, Nether-
lands
Tel.: (31) 134556600
Web Site: http://www.pronatura.nl
Natural Supplement Retailer
N.A.I.C.S.: 456191

ABATTOIR SA/NV
Rue Ropsy-Chaudron 24, 241070,
Brussels, Belgium
Tel.: (32) 25215419
Consumer Products Distr
N.A.I.C.S.: 423620
Luc Blancke *(Chm)*

ABAXX TECHNOLOGIES INC.
334 Adelaide Street West Suite 307,
Toronto, M5V 1R4, ON, Canada
Tel.: (647) 494-0296   AB
Web Site: https://www.abaxx.tech
Year Founded: 2003
ABXXF—(OTCIQ)
Rev.: $588,899
Assets: $22,915,771
Liabilities: $1,058,238
Net Worth: $21,857,533
Earnings: ($10,095,348)
Emp.: 42
Fiscal Year-end: 12/31/21
Software Publisher
N.A.I.C.S.: 513210
Joshua Crumb *(CEO)*

Subsidiaries:

LabMag Services Inc.   **(1)**

450 Avalon Dr, Labrador City, A2V1K7, NL, Canada
Tel.: (709) 944-5592
Web Site: http://www.nml.com
Iron Ore Mining Services
N.A.I.C.S.: 212290

ABB LTD.

Affolternstrasse 44, CH-8050, Zurich, Switzerland
Tel.: (41) 433177111   CH
Web Site: https://www.abb.com
Year Founded: 1988
ABBNY—(OTCIQ)
Rev.: $32,235,000,000
Assets: $40,940,000,000
Liabilities: $26,883,000,000
Net Worth: $14,057,000,000
Earnings: $3,745,000,000
Emp.: 105,000
Fiscal Year-end: 12/31/23
Engineeering Services
N.A.I.C.S.: 541330
Sami Atiya *(Pres-Robotics & Discrete Automation)*

Subsidiaries:

ABB (China) Investment Limited   (1)
10 Jiuxianqiao Avenue ABB Tower Universal Plaza, Beijing, 100015, China
Tel.: (86) 1084566688
Electrical & Electronic Product Mfr
N.A.I.C.S.: 335999

ABB (China) Ltd.   (1)
8F Tower C One East 768 South Zhongshan No 1 Road, Huangpu District, Shanghai, 200023, China   (100%)
Tel.: (86) 2123288888
Web Site: http://www.abb.com.cn
Power & Automation Products
N.A.I.C.S.: 335311
Chunyuan Gu *(Chm)*

Subsidiary (Domestic):

ABB Bailey Beijing Engineering Co. Ltd.   (2)
Universal Plaza 10 Jiuxianqiao Avenue ABB Tower, Beijing, 100015, China
Tel.: (86) 1084566688
Electrical Equipment Sales & Maintenance Services
N.A.I.C.S.: 811310

ABB Beijing Drive Systems Co. Ltd.   (2)
No 1 Block D A-10 Jiuxianqiao Beilu, Chaoyang District, Beijing, 100015, China
Tel.: (86) 1058217788
Sales Range: $200-249.9 Million
Emp.: 1,000
Speed Control Drive Mfr & Distr
N.A.I.C.S.: 335999

ABB Electrical Machines Ltd.   (2)
380 TianXing Rd, Minhang District, Shanghai, 200245, China
Tel.: (86) 2161137688
Web Site: http://www.abb.co.in
Electric Motor Mfr
N.A.I.C.S.: 335312

ABB Engineering (Shanghai) Ltd.   (2)
No 4528 Kangxin Highway, Pudong New District, Shanghai, 201319, China
Tel.: (86) 2161056666
Web Site: http://www.abb.com.cn
Sales Range: $350-399.9 Million
Emp.: 2,000
Flow Measurement Equipment Mfr
N.A.I.C.S.: 334513

ABB Generators Ltd.   (2)
Development Zone, 330096, Nanchang, Jiangxi, China
Tel.: (86) 791 8835 0800
Web Site: http://www.abb.com
Emp.: 170
Diesel Generator Mfr
N.A.I.C.S.: 335312
Jason Huang *(Pres)*

ABB Hefei Transformer Co. Ltd.   (2)
3318 Lianhua Road Hefei ETDZ, Hefei, 230601, Anhui, China
Tel.: (86) 551 6227 3790

Web Site: http://www.abb.com
Sales Range: $150-199.9 Million
Emp.: 800
Power & Distribution Transformer Mfr
N.A.I.C.S.: 335311
Qing Zheng *(Pres & Gen Mgr-Distr Transformer)*

ABB High Voltage Switchgear (Xiamen) Company Ltd.   (2)
6 Chuang Xin 3rd Road Guang Hui Bldg Torch Hi-Tech Zone, Xiamen, 361006, Fujian, China
Tel.: (86) 592 571 0330
Web Site: http://www.abb.com
Sales Range: $75-99.9 Million
Emp.: 300
Electric Switchgear Mfr
N.A.I.C.S.: 335313

ABB LV Installation Materials Co. Ltd.   (2)
No 17 Kangding Street Beijing Economic-Technological Development Area, Beijing, 100176, China
Tel.: (86) 1058085000
Web Site: http://www.abb.com.cn
Emp.: 517
Low Voltage Product Mfr
N.A.I.C.S.: 335999

ABB Shanghai Motors Co. Ltd.   (2)
88 Tianning Road Minhang Economic Development Zone, Shanghai, 200245, China
Tel.: (86) 2154723133
Sales Range: $150-199.9 Million
Emp.: 800
Induction Motor Mfr
N.A.I.C.S.: 335312

ABB Shanghai Transformer Co. Ltd.   (2)
2300 Shen Jiang Road, Pudong District, Shanghai, 201206, China
Tel.: (86) 21 2069 0300
Electrical Transformer Distr
N.A.I.C.S.: 423610
JianHua Zhang *(Pres)*

ABB Tianjin Switchgear Co., Ltd.   (2)
No 76 Gaoxin Road Tianjin Beichen Hi-tech Industrial Park, Tianjin, 300409, China
Tel.: (86) 2286880188
Web Site: http://www.abb.com.cn
Switchgear Mfr & Distr
N.A.I.C.S.: 335313

ABB Xi'an Power Capacitor Company Limited   (2)
3 Floor No 158 Wenjing Road, Xian Economic &Technological Development Zone, Xi'an, 710021, Shaanxi, China
Tel.: (86) 29 8575 8288
Electrical Component Mfr
N.A.I.C.S.: 334416

ABB Xiamen Electrical Controlgear Co. Ltd.   (2)
No 559 Weili Road Information And Photoelectricity Park, Torch Hi-Tech Industrial Development Zone, Xiamen, 361009, Fujian, China
Tel.: (86) 592 6303 000
Switchgear Product Distr
N.A.I.C.S.: 423610

ABB Xiamen Low Voltage Equipment Co. Ltd.   (2)
No 881 FangShanXiEr Road, Xiang'an District, Xiamen, 361101, Fujian, China
Tel.: (86) 5925719201
Low Voltage Switchgear Mfr
N.A.I.C.S.: 335313
Ian Lui *(Pres)*

ABB Zhongshan Transformer Company Ltd.   (2)
No 1 Haicheng North Rd Hengmen, Nanlang Town, Zhongshan, 528449, Guangdong, China
Tel.: (86) 760 2339 2288
Web Site: http://new.abb.com
Transformer Mfr
N.A.I.C.S.: 335311
Jim Huang *(Pres)*

Hangzhou Winmation Automation Company Limited   (2)
No 111 Hongxing Road, Xiaoshan District,

Hangzhou, 311215, China
Tel.: (86) 57183876000
Web Site: http://www.winmation.com.cn
Industrial Control System Mfr & Distr
N.A.I.C.S.: 334513

Maska Power Transmission (Changzhou) Co. Ltd.   (2)
No 8 Bldg Zhisi Industrial Park No 18 Fengming Road, Wujin District, Changzhou, 213161, Jiangsu, China
Tel.: (86) 519 86220880
Web Site: http://www.maskachina.com
Sales Range: $25-49.9 Million
Emp.: 150
Power Transmission Equipment Mfr
N.A.I.C.S.: 333613

Yangzhou SAC Switchgear Co., Ltd.   (2)
No 88 Hanjianghe Lu, Yangzhou, 225101, Jiangsu, China
Tel.: (86) 514 8971 1956
Web Site: http://www.sac-switchgear.com
Emp.: 50
Switchgear Mfr
N.A.I.C.S.: 335313

ABB (Hong Kong) Ltd.   (1)
No 3 Dai Hei St, HK-Tai Po, Hong Kong, China (Hong Kong)   (100%)
Tel.: (852) 29293718
Web Site: http://www.abb.com
Sales Range: $25-49.9 Million
Emp.: 10
Electronic Assemblies & Systems Mfr & Sales
N.A.I.C.S.: 334419

Subsidiary (Domestic):

ABB Turbo Systems (Hong Kong) Limited   (2)
No 3 Dai Hei St Tai Po Industrial Estate, Tai Po, New Territories, China (Hong Kong)
Tel.: (852) 2929 3630
Web Site: http://www.abb.com
Turbocharger Mfr
N.A.I.C.S.: 335999

ABB (Private) Ltd.   (1)
Norfolk Road Building No 6 Arundel Office Park, Mount Pleasant, Harare, Zimbabwe   (100%)
Tel.: (263) 4369072
Web Site: http://www.abb.com
Power & Automation Products Sales & Distr
N.A.I.C.S.: 423830

ABB (Pty) Ltd.   (1)
Plot 64517 Unit 35 The Office Fairgrounds, Gaborone, Botswana
Tel.: (267) 3180848
Web Site: http://www.new.abb.com
Sales Range: $25-49.9 Million
Emp.: 2
Electrical Engineering Services
N.A.I.C.S.: 541330

ABB A/S   (1)
Bergerveien 12, 1396, Billingstad, Norway   (100%)
Tel.: (47) 81520915
Web Site: http://www.abb.no
Sales Range: $400-449.9 Million
Emp.: 2,000
Electrical Products Mfr
N.A.I.C.S.: 444180

Subsidiary (Domestic):

ABB Robotics   (2)
Nordlysvegen 7, Bryne, 4340, Rogaland, Norway
Tel.: (47) 22 87 2000
Web Site: http://www.no.abb.com
Sales Range: $25-49.9 Million
Emp.: 92
Robotics Mfr
N.A.I.C.S.: 333248

ABB A/S   (1)
Meterbuen 33, 2740, Skovlunde, Denmark   (100%)
Tel.: (45) 44504450
Web Site: https://new.abb.com
Sales Range: $200-249.9 Million
Emp.: 700
Electrical Products Mfr & Sales
N.A.I.C.S.: 335999

ABB AB   (1)
Kopparbergsvagen 2, ABB AB Business Center, 721 71, Vasteras, Vastmanlands Lan, Sweden
Tel.: (46) 21325000
Web Site: https://new.abb.com
Sales Range: $1-4.9 Billion
Emp.: 4,500
Power & Automation Technology Products Mfr
N.A.I.C.S.: 335311

Subsidiary (Domestic):

ABB Automation Technologies AB   (2)
PO Box 1005, S 61129, Nykoping, Sweden   (100%)
Tel.: (46) 155295000
Web Site: http://www.abb.se
Sales Range: $1-4.9 Billion
Low-Voltage Apparatus Mfr; Boards, Heat Exchangers, Heat Pumps Distr
N.A.I.C.S.: 333415

ABB Power Technologies AB   (2)
PO Box 273, 94126, Pitea, Sweden   (100%)
Tel.: (46) 91177700
Web Site: http://www.abb.se
Sales Range: $25-49.9 Million
Emp.: 250
Electrical Insulating Materials & Industrial Plastics Mfr
N.A.I.C.S.: 333511

ABB Power Technologies AB   (2)
Valhalawagen 2, PO Box 702, Ludvika, 77180, Sweden   (100%)
Tel.: (46) 240782000
Web Site: http://www.abb.se
Sales Range: $350-399.9 Million
Emp.: 2,500
Transformers & Reactors Mfr
N.A.I.C.S.: 335311
Johan Soderstrom *(CEO)*

ABB Robotics AB   (2)
ABB Ab Robotics, Vastmanland, 721 68, Vasteras, Sweden   (100%)
Tel.: (46) 21344000
Web Site: http://www.abb.se
Sales Range: $150-199.9 Million
Emp.: 1,000
Industrial Robots, Robot Systems & Vision Systems Mfr
N.A.I.C.S.: 333248

ABB Robotics AB   (2)
Lunnagardsdagan 4, 43187, Molndal, Sweden   (100%)
Tel.: (46) 317738500
Web Site: http://www.abb.se
Sales Range: $10-24.9 Million
Emp.: 200
Robot Systems Mfr
N.A.I.C.S.: 541512

Lorentzen & Wettre AB   (2)
Viderogatan 2, PO Box 4, Kista, 164 40, Sweden   (100%)
Tel.: (46) 84779000
Web Site: http://www.lorentzen-wettre.com
Sales Range: $25-49.9 Million
Emp.: 150
Mfr & Supplier of Quality Control, Measurement & Process Automation Equipment for Paper Mill Industries
N.A.I.C.S.: 333243

Subsidiary (Non-US):

Kajaani Process Measurements Ltd.   (3)
Kettukalliontie 9E, Kajaani, 87100, Finland
Tel.: (358) 10 548 76 00
Web Site: http://www.prokajaani.com
Sales Range: $25-49.9 Million
Emp.: 10
Consistency Transmitter & Break Detection Equipment Mfr
N.A.I.C.S.: 334419

Subsidiary (Domestic):

Lorentzen & Waettre Skandinavien AB   (3)
Viderogatan 2, Box 1196, 164 40, Kista, Sweden
Tel.: (46) 7325000

ABB Ltd.—(Continued)

Web Site: http://www.lorentzen-wettre.com
Sales Range: $25-49.9 Million
Emp.: 100
Testing & Quality Control Instrument Mfr
N.A.I.C.S.: 334513

Lorentzen & Wettre International AB (3)
Box 4, Kista, 16493, Sweden
Tel.: (46) 8 477 90 00
Web Site: http://www.lorentzen-wettre.com
Emp.: 90
Paper Product Testing Services
N.A.I.C.S.: 541380

Subsidiary (Non-US):

Lorentzen & Wettre Ltda (3)
Rua Machado Bittencourt 406 Vila Mariana,
Sao Paulo, 04044-001, Brazil
Tel.: (55) 11 50844505
Testing & Quality Control Instrument Mfr
N.A.I.C.S.: 327910

Lorentzen & Wettre s.a.r.l. (3)
91 Rue Pereire, F 78100, Saint Germain-
en-Laye, France (100%)
Tel.: (33) 130870220
Web Site: http://www.lorentzen-wettre.com
Sales Range: $50-74.9 Million
Emp.: 10
Sales & Service of Equipment for Pulp &
Paper Industry
N.A.I.C.S.: 423830

ABB AG (1)
Kallstadter Strasse 1, 68309, Mannheim,
Germany (100%)
Tel.: (49) 62143810
Web Site: http://www.abb.com
Rev.: $3,634,800,128
Emp.: 2,000
Energy & Automation Products Mfr
N.A.I.C.S.: 335313

Subsidiary (Domestic):

ABB Automation GmbH (2)
Kallstadter Str 1, 68309, Mannheim, Ger-
many
Tel.: (49) 621 381 0
Web Site: http://www.abb.com
Emp.: 6,000
Industrial Automation System Mfr
N.A.I.C.S.: 333248

ABB Automation Products GmbH (2)
Haenchener Strasse 14, 03050, Cottbus,
Brandenburg, Germany
Tel.: (49) 355 596 0
Web Site: http://new.abb.com
Electric Equipment Mfr
N.A.I.C.S.: 335999

**ABB Beteiligungs- und Verwal-
tungsges. mbH** (2)
Kallstadter Str 1, 68319, Mannheim, Ger-
many
Tel.: (49) 6213810
Web Site: http://www.abb.com
Financial Services
N.A.I.C.S.: 523999

ABB Business Services GmbH (2)
Lessingstrasse 79, Berlin, 13158, Germany
Tel.: (49) 6221 70100
Electrical Engineering Services
N.A.I.C.S.: 541330

**ABB Calor Emag Mittelspannung
GmbH** (2)
Oberhausener Str 33, 40472, Ratingen,
Germany
Tel.: (49) 2102120
Web Site: http://www.abb.de
Sales Range: $350-399.9 Million
Emp.: 1,296
Switchgears & Control Systems Mfr
N.A.I.C.S.: 335313

**ABB Logistics Center Europe
GmbH** (2)
Braeukerweg 132, Menden, 58708,
Nordrhein-Westfalen, Germany
Tel.: (49) 237 39 69 50
Logistics Consulting Servies
N.A.I.C.S.: 541614

ABB Service GmbH (2)

Max-Fischer-Strasse 11, 86399, Bobingen,
Germany
Tel.: (49) 8234822322
Web Site: https://www.mlb-is.de
Industrial Machinery Maintenance Services
N.A.I.C.S.: 811310

ABB Stotz-Kontakt GmbH (2)
Eppelheimer Str 82, 69123, Heidelberg,
Germany
Tel.: (49) 6221701434
Web Site: http://new.abb.com
Electrical Equipment Mfr & Distr
N.A.I.C.S.: 335999

**ABB Stotz-Kontakt/Striebel & John
Vertriebs-GmbH** (2)
Eppelheimer Strasse 82, 69123, Heidel-
berg, Germany
Tel.: (49) 180 569 2002
Sales Range: $50-74.9 Million
Emp.: 114
Electronic Product Distr
N.A.I.C.S.: 423690

**ABB Training Center GmbH & Co.
KG** (2)
Lessingstrasse 85/89, 13158, Berlin, Ger-
many
Tel.: (49) 30 9177 0
Web Site: http://new.abb.com
Emp.: 2,000
Commercial & Technical Training Services
N.A.I.C.S.: 611519

ABB Wirtschaftsbetriebe GmbH (2)
Kallstadter Strasse 1, 68309, Mannheim,
Germany
Tel.: (49) 6213812874
Catering Services
N.A.I.C.S.: 722310

Busch-Jaeger Elektro GmbH (2)
Freisenbergstr 2, 58513, Ludenscheid, Ger-
many
Tel.: (49) 23519561600
Web Site: http://www.busch-jaeger.de
Sales Range: $200-249.9 Million
Emp.: 800
Electrical Equipment Mfr & Distr
N.A.I.C.S.: 335999

**Pucaro Elektro-Isolierstoffe
GmbH** (2)
Pucarostrasse 1, 74255, Roigheim, Ger-
many
Tel.: (49) 6298270
Web Site: https://www.pucaro.com
Sales Range: $75-99.9 Million
Emp.: 300
Electrical Insulation System Mfr
N.A.I.C.S.: 335999

Striebel & John GmbH & Co. KG (2)
Am Fuchsgraben 2-3, Sasbach, 77880,
Germany (100%)
Tel.: (49) 7841 609 0
Web Site: http://www.striebelundjohn.com
Sales Range: $75-99.9 Million
Emp.: 400
Electric Power Distribution System Mfr
N.A.I.C.S.: 335311

Subsidiary (Domestic):

ABB Striebel & John GmbH (3)
Am Fuchsgraben 2 - 3, 77880, Sasbach,
Germany
Tel.: (49) 78416090
Web Site: https://www.striebelundjohn.com
Sales Range: $100-124.9 Million
Emp.: 400
Power Transmission Equipment Mfr
N.A.I.C.S.: 333613

Subsidiary (Non-US):

Striebel & John France S.A.R.L. (3)
Zi Zone Industrielle, 68470, Fellering,
France
Tel.: (33) 389382728
Plastics Product Mfr
N.A.I.C.S.: 326199

ABB AG (1)
Clemens-Holzmeister-Strasse 4, AT-1109,
Vienna, Austria (100%)
Tel.: (43) 1601096530
Web Site: http://www.abb.at

Sales Range: $250-299.9 Million
Emp.: 450
Power Generation, Power Transmission,
Industrial & Building Systems Mfr
N.A.I.C.S.: 221118

ABB AS (1)
Arukula tee 83, Rae vald, EE-75301, Juri,
Harju maakond, Estonia
Tel.: (372) 6801800
Web Site: https://new.abb.com
Electric Power Distribution Services
N.A.I.C.S.: 221122

ABB Algeria SpA (1)
Chemin de la Madeleine Lot D/E - Zone
Djenane El Haroual, Haut Site d'Hydra, Hy-
dra, 16040, Algeria
Tel.: (213) 21794080
Power & Electrical Engineering Services
N.A.I.C.S.: 541330

Subsidiary (Domestic):

ABB International Marketing Ltd. (2)
2 Impasse Ahmed Kara, PO Box 156, Cite
Malki Ben Aknoun, DZ-16035, Hydra, Alge-
ria
Tel.: (213) 21546099
Web Site: http://www.mena.abb.com
Power & Automation Products Marketer &
Distr
N.A.I.C.S.: 423830

ABB Asea Brown Boveri Ltd. (1)
Affolternstrasse 44, 8050, Zurich, Switzer-
land
Tel.: (41) 433177111
Web Site: https://new.abb.com
Software Development Services
N.A.I.C.S.: 423610
Morten Wierod (CEO)

ABB Australia Pty Limited (1)
Bapaume Road, Moorebank, 2170, NSW,
Australia (100%)
Tel.: (61) 297382277
Web Site: http://www.abbaustralia.com.au
Sales Range: $50-74.9 Million
Emp.: 20
Electric Motors, Switchgear & Circuit-
Breaker Assembly
N.A.I.C.S.: 423610
Julian Bechini (Head-Legal & Integrity-New
Zealand)

Subsidiary (Domestic):

**ABB Group Investment Management
Pty. Ltd.** (2)
L 20 Goldfields House 1 Alfred St, Sydney,
2000, NSW, Australia
Tel.: (61) 2 9255 3999
Investment Management Service
N.A.I.C.S.: 523999

ABB Automation E.C. (1)
Road 4304 Building 175 Block 343 Mina
Sulman, Manama, Bahrain
Tel.: (973) 1 781 0666
Web Site: http://www.mena.abb.com
Sales Range: $50-74.9 Million
Emp.: 100
Power & Automation Products Sales & Distr
N.A.I.C.S.: 423830

ABB B.V. (1)
Frankeneng 15, 6716 AA, Ede,
Netherlands (100%)
Tel.: (31) 318669225
Sales Range: $100-124.9 Million
Emp.: 500
Switchgear & Converters Mfr
N.A.I.C.S.: 335313

Subsidiary (Domestic):

ABB Holdings BV (2)
Burgemeester Haspelslaan 65, 1181 NB,
Amstelveen, Netherlands
Tel.: (31) 20 543 44 44
Web Site: http://www.abb.be
Sales Range: $50-74.9 Million
Emp.: 5
Investment Management Service
N.A.I.C.S.: 523999

ABB Beijing Switchgear Limited (1)
No 12 Jingyuan Street Beijing Economic-
Technological Development Area, Beijing,
100176, China

Tel.: (86) 1087099199
Switch Cabinet Mfr
N.A.I.C.S.: 335313

ABB Bulgaria EOOD (1)
89 B Vitosha Blvd Building A floor 17, 1463,
Sofia, Bulgaria (100%)
Tel.: (359) 28075500
Web Site: http://www.abb.com
Sales Range: €200 £49.9 Million
Emp.: 1,000
Power & Automation Products Mfr
N.A.I.C.S.: 335311
Maurizio Riva (Officer-Holding)

Subsidiary (Domestic):

ABB Automation EOOD (2)
14 Industrialen Put 1, Stryama, 4142, Plov-
div, Bulgaria
Tel.: (359) 32 998800
Web Site: http://new.abb.com
Sales Range: $150-199.9 Million
Emp.: 800
Mfr of Components for Low & Medium Volt-
age Equipment
N.A.I.C.S.: 335311

ABB Avangard AD (2)
32 Nikola Petkov Str, 5400, Sevlievo, Bul-
garia
Tel.: (359) 675 39222
Sales Range: $25-49.9 Million
Emp.: 100
Electric Equipment Mfr
N.A.I.C.S.: 335999

**ABB Business Services Sp. z
o.o.** (1)
ul Dr Stefana Kopcinskiego 62, 90-032,
Lodz, Lodzkie, Poland
Tel.: (48) 222237777
Electrical & Electronic Product Mfr
N.A.I.C.S.: 335999

ABB E-mobility B.V. (1)
Achtseweg Zuid 151a, 5651 GW, Eind-
hoven, Netherlands
Tel.: (31) 884404600
N.A.I.C.S.: 423610

ABB Ecuador S.A. (1)
Av Atahualpa Oe1-198 y Av 10 de Agosto,
Casilla 17-08-8431 Edificio Atahualpa Busi-
ness Center pisos 10 y 11, EC170150,
Quito, Ecuador
Tel.: (593) 23994100
Web Site: http://www.abb.com.ec
Sales Range: $50-74.9 Million
Emp.: 100
Industrial Machinery Distr
N.A.I.C.S.: 423830

ABB Eletrificacao Ltda. (1)
Rod Sen Jose Ermirio de Moraes km11,
Sorocaba, 18087-125, Sao Paulo, Brazil
Tel.: (55) 1533306150
Electrical & Electronic Product Mfr
N.A.I.C.S.: 335999

**ABB Engineering Technologies Co.
(KSCC)** (1)
Alghunaim Commercial Tower 5th Floor Al
Qibla Area, PO Box 4275, Abu Baker Al-
Sadique Street Safat, 13043, Kuwait, Ku-
wait
Tel.: (965) 2428626
Web Site: http://www.mena.abb.com
Power & Automation Products Engineering,
Sales & Distr
N.A.I.C.S.: 541330

**ABB Engineering Trading and Service
Ltd.** (1)
Kassak Lajos Utca 19-25, 1134, Budapest,
Hungary (100%)
Tel.: (36) 14432100
Web Site: http://www.abb.hu
Sales Range: $150-199.9 Million
Emp.: 320
Power & Automation Products Sales & Distr
N.A.I.C.S.: 423830

ABB FZ-LLC (1)
Concord Tower Media City 9th 10th 15th
Floor Office No 01-14 1514, 11070, Dubai,
United Arab Emirates
Tel.: (971) 4 4241900
Web Site: http://www.abb.com
Project Management Consulting Services

N.A.I.C.S.: 541618

Subsidiary (Domestic):

ABB Energy Automation S.p.A. (2)
Al Ghaith Office Tower 15th Floor Hamdan
Street, PO Box 45710, Abu Dhabi, United
Arab Emirates
Tel.: (971) 26264062
Web Site: http://www.mena.abb.com
Sales Range: $25-49.9 Million
Emp.: 100
Engineeering Services
N.A.I.C.S.: 541330

ABB Global Marketing FZ LLC (2)
Media City Building No 08 Office No 221,
Dubai, United Arab Emirates
Tel.: (971) 4 4464959
Automation Equipment Distr
N.A.I.C.S.: 423830

ABB Industries (L.L.C.) (2)
Al Quoz Industrial Area 3 Behind Traffic De-
partment 4th Street, PO Box 11070, Near
Mall of Emirates, Dubai, United Arab Emir-
ates
Tel.: (971) 43147500
Web Site: http://www.abb.com
Power & Automation Products Marketer &
Distr
N.A.I.C.S.: 423830

ABB Industries LLC (2)
Concord Tower Media City 9th 10th 15th
Floor Office No 01-14 1514, 11070, Dubai,
United Arab Emirates
Tel.: (971) 43147500
Web Site: http://www.mena.abb.com
Sales Range: $25-49.9 Million
Protection, Control & Power Communication
Equipment Mfr & Engineering Services; LV
Products, Speed Drives, Motors & Ma-
chines Sales
N.A.I.C.S.: 334290

ABB Transmission & Distribution
Ltd. (2)
Mussafah Industrial area M2 Plot 16, PO
Box 45710, Ste 1501, Abu Dhabi, United
Arab Emirates
Tel.: (971) 24938000
Web Site: http://www.mena.abb.com
Engineering & Project Management Ser-
vices
N.A.I.C.S.: 541330

ABB France SAS (1)
7 Boulevard D'Osny val-d'oise, CS 88570,
Cergy, 95892, Cergy-Pontoise, France
Tel.: (33) 134402525
Electrical & Electronic Product Mfr
N.A.I.C.S.: 335999

ABB Group Holdings Pty. Ltd. (1)
Bapaume Road, Moorebank, 2170, NSW,
Australia
Tel.: (61) 297382277
N.A.I.C.S.: 423610

ABB Holding A.S. (1)
Organize Sanayi Bolgesi 2 Cadde 16, Istan-
bul, 34776, Turkiye   **(99.95%)**
Tel.: (90) 2165282200
Sales Range: $200-249.9 Million
Emp.: 800
Power & Automation Products Mfr
N.A.I.C.S.: 335311

Subsidiary (Domestic):

ABB Elektrik Sanayi A.S. (2)
Aydinevler Mah Siteler Yolu No1A K 5-6 Ic
Kapi No7-9-10, HiltownOfis Kucukyali
Maltepe, 34854, Istanbul, Turkiye
Tel.: (90) 2165282200
Web Site: http://www.abb.com.tr
Sales Range: $150-199.9 Million
Power Transformer & Circuit Breaker Mfr
N.A.I.C.S.: 335999

Elmek Elektromekanik Sanayi ve Ti-
caret Anonim Sirketi AS (2)
Istasyon Mahallesi Ibisaga Caddesi No 2,
Tuzla, 34940, Istanbul, Turkiye
Tel.: (90) 216 395 40 00
Web Site: http://www.elmek.com.tr
Sales Range: $25-49.9 Million
Emp.: 150
Electrical Products Mfr
N.A.I.C.S.: 335999

ABB Holdings Pte. Ltd. (1)
2 Ayer Rajah Crescent, Singapore, 139935,
Singapore
Tel.: (65) 67765711
Web Site: http://www.abb.com.sg
Sales Range: $150-199.9 Million
Emp.: 1,200
Power & Automation Technology Products
Mfr
N.A.I.C.S.: 335311
Maria Cheong (Fin Mgr)

ABB Inc. (1)
305 Gregson Dr, Cary, NC 7511   **(100%)**
Tel.: (919) 856-2360
Web Site: https://new.abb.com
Power & Automation Products, Systems,
Solutions & Services
N.A.I.C.S.: 335311

Unit (Domestic):

ABB Inc. (2)
579 Executive Campus Dr, Westerville, OH
43082-8870
Tel.: (614) 818-6300
Web Site: http://www.abb.us
Sales Range: $25-49.9 Million
Emp.: 150
Measuring & Controlling Instruments Mfr
N.A.I.C.S.: 334519

ABB Inc. (2)
16250 W Glendale Dr, New Berlin, WI
53151
Tel.: (940) 397-7000
Web Site: http://www.abb-control.com
Sales Range: $50-74.9 Million
Emp.: 150
Industrial Motor Control Products, Discon-
nect Switches, Programmable Logic Con-
trollers, Circuit Breakers, Capacitors Mfr
N.A.I.C.S.: 335314

ABB Inc. (2)
1250 Brown Rd, Auburn Hills, MI
48326   **(100%)**
Tel.: (248) 391-9000
Web Site: http://www.abb.com
Sales Range: $75-99.9 Million
Emp.: 450
Automation Technologies
N.A.I.C.S.: 335999

ABB Inc. (2)
12808 W Airport Blvd, Sugar Land, TX
77478-2579
Tel.: (281) 274-5000
Web Site: http://www.abb.us.com
Sales Range: $25-49.9 Million
Emp.: 77
Electric Power Transmission, Distribution &
Generation Control Systems
N.A.I.C.S.: 335311

ABB Inc. (2)
1021 Main Campus Dr, Raleigh, NC
27606   **(100%)**
Tel.: (919) 856-2360
Web Site: http://www.abb.us
Rev.: $303,900,000
Emp.: 150
Business Services
N.A.I.C.S.: 561499

ABB Inc. - Analytical & Advanced
Solutions (2)
843 N Jefferson St, Lewisburg, WV 24901-
9509
Tel.: (304) 647-4358
Web Site: http://www.abb.us
Sales Range: $50-74.9 Million
Emp.: 220
Process Analytical Instruments Mfr
N.A.I.C.S.: 335311

ABB Inc. - Automation
Technologies (2)
29801 Euclid Ave, Wickliffe, OH 44092
Tel.: (440) 585-8500
Web Site: http://www.abb.us
Sales Range: $100-124.9 Million
Emp.: 500
Computerized Industrial Control System Mfr
& Distr
N.A.I.C.S.: 334513

ABB Inc. - Automation Technologies
Drives & Motors (2)

16250 W Glendale Dr, New Berlin, WI
53151-2840
Tel.: (262) 785-3200
Web Site: http://www.abb-drives.com
Sales Range: $100-124.9 Million
Emp.: 307
AC/DC Drives, Large Electric Motors, Gen-
erators, Power Electronics, Rectifier Sys-
tems, Sheet Metal Forming Presses Mfr
N.A.I.C.S.: 335311

ABB Inc. - Automation Technologies
Instrumentation Products (2)
125 E County Line Rd, Warminster, PA
18974-4995
Tel.: (215) 674-6000
Web Site: http://www.abb.us
Sales Range: $75-99.9 Million
Emp.: 100
Process Control Instruments & Systems Mfr
N.A.I.C.S.: 334513

ABB Inc. - Power Systems (2)
2000 Day Hill Rd, Windsor, CT 06095-1580
Tel.: (860) 285-6870
Web Site: http://www.abb.us
Sales Range: $25-49.9 Million
Emp.: 50
Power Control Equipment Mfr
N.A.I.C.S.: 335311

ABB Inc. - Power Technologies Com-
ponents Factory (2)
1133 S Cavalier Dr, Alamo, TN 38001-3813
Tel.: (731) 696-5561
Web Site: http://www.abb.us
Sales Range: $50-74.9 Million
Emp.: 165
Transformer Components Mfr
N.A.I.C.S.: 335312

ABB Inc. - Power Technologies Me-
dium Voltage (2)
680 Century Pt Ste B, Lake Mary, FL
32746-2137
Tel.: (407) 732-2000
Web Site: http://www.abb.com
Sales Range: $50-74.9 Million
Emp.: 230
Switch Gears Mfr
N.A.I.C.S.: 335311

ABB Inc. - SSAC (2)
8242 Loop Rd, Baldwinsville, NY 13027
Tel.: (315) 638-1300
Web Site: http://www.ssac.com
Sales Range: $50-74.9 Million
Emp.: 132
Electronic Controls Mfr
N.A.I.C.S.: 335314

ABB Inc. - Turbocharging (2)
1460 Livingston Ave, North Brunswick, NJ
08902-6005
Tel.: (732) 932-6103
Web Site: http://www.new.abb.com
Sales Range: $25-49.9 Million
Emp.: 12
Turbocharger Mfr
N.A.I.C.S.: 423610

Subsidiary (Domestic):

ABB Motors and Mechanical Inc. (2)
5711 RS Boreham St, Fort Smith, AR
72901-8394
Tel.: (479) 646-4711
Web Site: http://www.baldor.com
Energy-Efficient Electric Motors & Electronic
Drives Designer, Mfr & Marketer
N.A.I.C.S.: 335312
Kyle Sobke (Dir-Sls)

Subsidiary (Non-US):

ABB Limited (3)
Motion Control Centre Hawkley Drive, 6
Bristol Distribution Park, Bristol, BS32 0BF,
United Kingdom
Tel.: (44) 1454850000
Electric Motors & Electronic Drives Distr
N.A.I.C.S.: 335312

Australia Baldor Pty Ltd (3)
Unit 3 6 Stanton Road, Seven Hills, 2147,
NSW, Australia
Tel.: (61) 296745455
Web Site: http://www.baldor.com.au
Electric Motors & Electronic Drives Marketer
N.A.I.C.S.: 335312

Baldor Electric Canada Inc. (3)
2901 Brighton Rd, Oakville, L6H 5S3, ON,
Canada
Tel.: (905) 829-3301
Sales Range: $25-49.9 Million
Emp.: 100
Electric Motor Mfr
N.A.I.C.S.: 335312

Plant (Domestic):

Baldor Electric Company (3)
3560 Scarlet Oak Blvd, Saint Louis, MO
63122-6604
Tel.: (636) 225-5022
Sales Range: $75-99.9 Million
Emp.: 275
Mfr of Electric Motors & Generators
N.A.I.C.S.: 335312

Subsidiary (Non-US):

Baldor Electric Company de Mexico
S.A. de C.V. (3)
Km 2.0 Blvd Aeropuerto, Leon, 37545, Gua-
najuato, Mexico
Tel.: (52) 477 761 2030
Web Site: http://www.baldor.com
Electric Motors & Electronic Drives Marketer
N.A.I.C.S.: 335312

Plant (Domestic):

Baldor Electric Company, Manufactur-
ing Facility (3)
305 Ballman Rd, Westville, OK 74965-0305
Tel.: (918) 723-5451
Web Site: http://www.baldor.com
Sales Range: $125-149.9 Million
Emp.: 450
Electric Motor Mfr
N.A.I.C.S.: 335312

Subsidiary (Non-US):

Baldor Electric Switzerland AG (3)
Schutzenstrasse 59, 8245, Feuerthalen,
Switzerland
Tel.: (41) 52 647 47 00
Electric Motor Mfr
N.A.I.C.S.: 335312

Subsidiary (Domestic):

Baldor Holdings Inc (3)
5711 R S Boreham Jr St, Fort Smith, AR
72901
Tel.: (479) 646-4711
Investment Management Service
N.A.I.C.S.: 523999

Subsidiary (Non-US):

Baldor Panama S.A. (3)
Ave Ricardo J Alfaro Edificio Sun Towers
Mall - Local 55 2 Piso, A Lado del Autocen-
tro, Panama, Panama
Tel.: (507) 236 5155
Electric Motor Mfr
N.A.I.C.S.: 335312

Subsidiary (Domestic):

Dodge Manufacturing Company (3)
6040 Ponders Ct, Greenville, SC
29615-4601   **(100%)**
Tel.: (864) 297-4800
Web Site: http://www.dodge-pt.com
Sales Range: $125-149.9 Million
Emp.: 400
Mechanical Power Transmission Equipment
Designer & Mfr
N.A.I.C.S.: 333613

Nupar Manufacturing (3)
13902 E 550th Rd, Claremore, OK 74019
Tel.: (918) 341-8000
Web Site: http://www.nupar.com
Sales Range: $50-74.9 Million
Emp.: 100
Metal Stamping
N.A.I.C.S.: 332119

Subsidiary (Non-US):

Shanghai ABB Power Transmission
Co., Ltd (3)
160 Song Sheng Road Songjiang Industrial
Zone, Shanghai, 20016, China
Tel.: (86) 21 57605335
Web Site: http://www.new.abb.com

ABB Ltd.—(Continued)

Electrical Product Mfr & Distr
N.A.I.C.S.: 335999

Subsidiary (Domestic):

Southwestern Die Casting, Inc. (3)
600 Raleigh St, Fort Smith, AR 72901-8358
Tel.: (479) 441-6400
Web Site: http://www.baldor.com
Sales Range: $50-74.9 Million
Emp.: 130
Mfr of Aluminum Base Alloy Castings
N.A.I.C.S.: 331523

Subsidiary (Domestic):

ABB Susa Inc. (2)
1460 Livingston Ave Bldg B, North Brunswick, NJ 08902-1873
Tel.: (732) 932-6100
Construction Engineering Services
N.A.I.C.S.: 541330

APS Technology Group, Inc. (2)
3949 Ruffin Rd Ste A, San Diego, CA 92123
Tel.: (858) 836-7990
Web Site: http://www.aps-technology.com
Sales Range: $10-24.9 Million
Emp.: 50
Port & Terminal Automation Equipment Mfr
N.A.I.C.S.: 333248

Hitachi Energy USA Inc. (2)
400 Perimeter Ctr Ter Ste 500, Atlanta, GA 30346
Tel.: (678) 830-1000
Web Site: http://www.hitachiabb-powergrids.com
Asset Management Software & Services
N.A.I.C.S.: 513210

Subsidiary (Non-US):

Hitachi Energy UK Limited (3)
Dukes Court - Block D Duke Street, Woking, GU21 5BH, Surrey, United Kingdom
Tel.: (44) 1483722777
Web Site: https://www.hitachienergy.com
Asset Management Software & Services
N.A.I.C.S.: 513210
Claudio Facchin (CEO)

Subsidiary (Domestic):

Obvient Strategies, Inc. (3)
2550 Northwinds Pkwy, Alpharetta, GA 30004
Tel.: (678) 336-1472
Web Site: http://www.obvient.com
Sales Range: $10-24.9 Million
Emp.: 26
Computer System Design Services
N.A.I.C.S.: 541512

Ventyx Asia Inc. (3)
400 Perimeter Center Ter Ste 500, Atlanta, GA 30346
Tel.: (678) 830-1000
Sales Range: $25-49.9 Million
Emp.: 200
Software Development Services
N.A.I.C.S.: 541511

Subsidiary (Non-US):

Ventyx Barranquilla (3)
Cra 54 No 68-196 302 Ed Prado Office Ctr, Barranquilla, Colombia
Tel.: (57) 53686645
Asset Management Software & Services
N.A.I.C.S.: 513210

Ventyx France (3)
Immeuble Central Gare, 1 Place Charles de Gaulle, Montigny-le-Bretonneux, 78180, France
Tel.: (33) 139301717
Web Site: http://www.ventyx.com
Sales Range: $25-49.9 Million
Emp.: 16
Asset Management Software & Services
N.A.I.C.S.: 513210

Ventyx Johannesburg (3)
11 Autumn Rd, 2128, Rivonia, South Africa
Tel.: (27) 112604600
Web Site: http://www.mincom.com

Sales Range: $25-49.9 Million
Emp.: 20
Asset Management Software & Services
N.A.I.C.S.: 513210

Ventyx Lima (3)
Av Argentina 3120, Lima, Peru
Tel.: (51) 14155100
Sales Range: $25-49.9 Million
Emp.: 3
Asset Management Software & Services
N.A.I.C.S.: 513210

Ventyx Poland (3)
OddziaA w Polsce, Korfantego 79, 40160, Katowice, Poland
Tel.: (48) 322592839
Web Site: http://www.ventyx.com
Sales Range: $25-49.9 Million
Emp.: 5
Asset Management Software & Services
N.A.I.C.S.: 513210

Subsidiary (Domestic):

Ventyx USA, Inc. (3)
6455 S Yosemite St Ste 800, Greenwood Village, CO 80111-4918
Tel.: (303) 446-9000
Web Site: http://www.ventyx.com
Asset Management Software & Services
N.A.I.C.S.: 513210

Subsidiary (Domestic):

Ventyx Managed Services, Inc. (4)
6455 S Yosemite St Ste 800, Greenwood Village, CO 80111
Tel.: (303) 446-9000
Web Site: http://www.ventyx.com
Software Development Services
N.A.I.C.S.: 541511

Subsidiary (Domestic):

Kuhlman Electric Corporation (2)
3101 Beaumont Centre Cir Ste 225, Lexington, KY 40513-1886
Tel.: (859) 879-2999
Web Site: http://www.kuhlman.com
Sales Range: $25-49.9 Million
Emp.: 100
Designs, Manufactures & Markets Electrical Transformers for Electric Utility Use
N.A.I.C.S.: 335311

LMI Connectors (2)
1181 S Rogers Cir Ste 25, Boca Raton, FL 33487-2727
Tel.: (561) 994-5896
Web Site: https://www.lmicorp.com
Sales Range: $25-49.9 Million
Emp.: 4
Electronic Circuits Mfr
N.A.I.C.S.: 334419

Power-One Inc. (2)
740 Calle Plano, Camarillo, CA 93012-8555
Tel.: (805) 987-8741
Electronic Supplies Mfr
N.A.I.C.S.: 334418

Subsidiary (Non-US):

Power-One Italy S.p.A. (2)
Via S Giorgio 642, Terranuova Bracciolini, 52028, Arezzo, Italy
Tel.: (39) 05591951
Electronic Components Mfr
N.A.I.C.S.: 334419

Group (Domestic):

Thomas & Betts Corporation (2)
860 Ridge Lk Blvd 8155 T&B Blvd, Memphis, TN 38120
Tel.: (901) 252-5000
Web Site: http://www.tnb.com
Sales Range: $1-4.9 Billion
Emp.: 9,400
Electrical Connectors & Related Components Mfr
N.A.I.C.S.: 334417

Subsidiary (Non-US):

Adaptaflex Limited (3)
Station Road, Coleshill, B46 1HT, Birmingham, United Kingdom
Tel.: (44) 2476 368500
Web Site: http://www.adaptaflex.com

Flexible Electric Conduit Systems Mfr
N.A.I.C.S.: 335929

Cable Management Products Ltd. (3)
Station Road, Coleshill, B46 1HT, Birmingham, United Kingdom
Tel.: (44) 1675468200
Web Site: http://www.cm-products.co.uk
Sales Range: $25-49.9 Million
Emp.: 300
Holding Company; Electrical Conduit & Energy Management Device Mfr
N.A.I.C.S.: 551112

Division (Domestic):

Elkay Electrical (4)
Station Rd, Coleshill, B46 1HT, Birmingham, United Kingdom
Tel.: (44) 1675468232
Web Site: http://www.elkay.co.uk
Sales Range: $25-49.9 Million
Emp.: 150
Electrical Wiring & Energy Management Accessories Mfr
N.A.I.C.S.: 335931

Subsidiary (Domestic):

JT Packard & Associates, Inc. (3)
275 Investment Ct, Verona, WI 53593
Tel.: (608) 845-9900
Web Site: http://www.tnbpowersolutions.com
Sales Range: $50-74.9 Million
Emp.: 217
Network Power Equipment Services
N.A.I.C.S.: 423850

Jennings Technology (3)
970 McLaughlin Ave, San Jose, CA 95122-2611
Tel.: (408) 292-4025
Web Site: http://www.jenningstech.com
Sales Range: $100-124.9 Million
Electrical Component Mfr
N.A.I.C.S.: 334416

Joslyn Hi-Voltage Company, LLC (3)
8155 T&B Boulevard, Memphis, TN 38125
Tel.: (901) 252-5000
Sales Range: $100-124.9 Million
Electric Power Switching Equipment Mfr
N.A.I.C.S.: 335313

Subsidiary (Non-US):

Kaufel GmbH & Co. KG (3)
Colditzstrasse 34-36, 12099, Berlin, Germany (100%)
Tel.: (49) 30 70173300
Web Site: http://www.kaufel.de
Sales Range: $25-49.9 Million
Emp.: 75
Emergency Lighting Systems Mfr
N.A.I.C.S.: 335139

Division (Domestic):

T&B Retail Consumer Products (3)
32425 Aurora Rd Ste A, Solon, OH 44139
Web Site: https://www.lamson-home.com
Sales Range: $50-74.9 Million
Emp.: 150
Conduit Products Mfr for the Electrical, Telecommunications, Utility & Sewer Industries
N.A.I.C.S.: 423610

Subsidiary (Domestic):

Thomas & Betts Caribe, Inc. (3)
Rd 686 Lot 32-34 Cabo Caribe Industrial Park, Vega Baja, PR 00693
Tel.: (787) 855-3046
Web Site: http://www.tnb.com
Sales Range: $150-199.9 Million
Emp.: 500
Electrical Component Mfr
N.A.I.C.S.: 335931

Thomas & Betts Power Solutions, LLC (3)
5900 E Port Blvd, Richmond, VA 23231 (100%)
Tel.: (804) 236-3300
Web Site: http://www.tnbpowersolutions.com
Sales Range: $50-74.9 Million
Emp.: 150

Aircraft & Other Specialized Lightning Arresters, Microwave Station, Railroad Communications Systems & Telephone Station Protectors Mfr
N.A.I.C.S.: 335999

Subsidiary (Domestic):

Validus DC Systems Inc. (2)
50 Pocono Rd, Brookfield, CT 00004
Tel.: (203) 448-3600
Web Site: http://www.validusdc.com
Sales Range: $25-49.9 Million
Emp.: 20
Direct Current Powered Equipment Distr
N.A.I.C.S.: 423610

ABB India Ltd. (1)
Disha - 3rd Floor Plot No5 & 6 2nd Stage Peenya Industrial Area IV, Peenya, Bengaluru, 560058, Karnataka, India (75%)
Tel.: (91) 8022949150
Web Site: https://new.abb.com
Rev.: $1,302,683,052
Assets: $1,333,344,228
Liabilities: $612,858,708
Net Worth: $720,485,520
Earnings: $151,279,416
Emp.: 3,384
Fiscal Year-end: 12/31/2023
High Voltage Apparatus, Relays, Switchgear, Industrial Plants & Electronics Mfr.
N.A.I.C.S.: 335313
Peter R. Voser (Member-Exec Bd & Chm)

ABB Industrial Solutions (Bielsko-Biala) Sp. z o.o. (1)
ul Rudawka 96, 43-382, Bielsko-Biala, Slaskie, Poland
Tel.: (48) 338286102
Electrical & Electronic Product Mfr
N.A.I.C.S.: 335999

ABB Industrial Solutions (Klodzko) Sp.z o.o. (1)
ul Pilsudskiego 5, 57-300, Klodzko, dolnoslaskie, Poland
Tel.: (48) 748654100
Electrical & Electronic Product Mfr
N.A.I.C.S.: 335999

ABB Information Systems Ltd. (1)
Affolternstrasse 44 CityPort, 8050, Zurich, Switzerland
Tel.: (41) 433177111
Web Site: http://www.abb.com
Information Technology Consulting Services
N.A.I.C.S.: 541512

ABB Installation Products Inc. (1)
8001 W Buckeye Rd, Phoenix, AZ 85043
Tel.: (602) 643-3990
N.A.I.C.S.: 423610

ABB Insurance Limited (1)
Suite 3 Weighbridge House Le Pollet, Saint Peter Port, GY1 1WL, Guernsey
Tel.: (44) 1481 716686
General Insurance Services
N.A.I.C.S.: 524210

ABB International Finance Limited (1)
Weighbridge House Le Pollet Suite 3, Saint Peter Port, GY1 1WL, Guernsey
Tel.: (44) 1481 729 016
Financial Management Services
N.A.I.C.S.: 523999

ABB Investments (Pty.) Ltd. (1)
2 Lake Road Longmeadow Business Estate, Modderfontein, 1609, South Africa
Tel.: (27) 102025000
N.A.I.C.S.: 423610

ABB K.K. (1)
ThinkPark Tower 22F 2-1-1 Osaki, Shinagawa-ku, Tokyo, 141-6022, Japan (100%)
Tel.: (81) 345236170
Web Site: http://www.abb.co.jp
Power & Automation Products
N.A.I.C.S.: 335311

Subsidiary (Domestic):

ABB Bailey Japan Limited (2)
511 Baraki, Izunokuni, 410-2193, Shizuoka, Japan
Tel.: (81) 559493311
Web Site: http://www.bailey.co.jp

Sales Range: $25-49.9 Million
Emp.: 250
Electrical Component Mfr
N.A.I.C.S.: 335999

ABB LLC (1)
218 Hatat House, PO Box 778, Al Hamriya,
131, Muscat, Oman
Tel.: (968) 24567410
Web Site: http://www.abb.com
Sales Range: $25-49.9 Million
Emp.: 82
Electrical Engineering Services
N.A.I.C.S.: 541330

ABB Limited (1)
570 Mt Wellington Highway, Mt Wellington,
Auckland, 1052, New Zealand (100%)
Tel.: (64) 92595481
Web Site: http://www.nzabb.co.nz
Sales Range: $25-49.9 Million
Emp.: 80
Power & Automation Technology Products
N.A.I.C.S.: 335311

ABB Limited (1)
Vision Plaza 3rd Floor Mombasa Road,
00623, Nairobi, Kenya
Tel.: (254) 20828811
Industrial Machinery Distr
N.A.I.C.S.: 423830

ABB Ltd. (1)
161/1 SG Tower 1st-4th Floor Soi Maha-
dlekluang 3 Rajdamri Road, Lumpini Pa-
thumwan, 10330, Bangkok,
Thailand (100%)
Tel.: (66) 26651000
Web Site: http://www.abb.co.th
Sales Range: $250-299.9 Million
Emp.: 600
Power & Automation Sales & Services
N.A.I.C.S.: 423830
Nirundorn Chaovanapricha (Country Mgr-
HR)

ABB Ltd. (1)
Belgard Road, Tallaght, Dublin, D24 KD78,
Ireland (100%)
Tel.: (353) 14057300
Web Site: http://www.ie.abb.com
Sales Range: $50-74.9 Million
Emp.: 100
Power & Automation Product Sales
N.A.I.C.S.: 423840

ABB Ltd. (1)
Daresbury Park Daresbury, Warrington,
WA4 4BT, Cheshire, United
Kingdom (100%)
Tel.: (44) 1925741111
Web Site: http://www.abb.com
Sales Range: $75-99.9 Million
Emp.: 300
Engineering Consulting & Services
N.A.I.C.S.: 541330

Subsidiary (Non-US):

ABB Holdings Limited (2)
3100 Daresbury Park, WA4 4BT, Warrington, Cheshire, United Kingdom - England
Tel.: (44) 1925 741 111
Investment Management Service
N.A.I.C.S.: 523999

Branch (Domestic):

ABB Ltd. (2)
3100 Daresbury Park Gr floor 1st floor East,
Warrington, WA4 4BT, Cheshire, United
Kingdom (100%)
Tel.: (44) 1925741111
Web Site: http://www.abb.co.uk
Rev.: $29,446,000,000
Assets: $39,148,000,000
Liabilities: $25,876,000,000
Net Worth: $13,272,000,000
Earnings: $2,594,000,000
Fiscal Year-end: 12/31/2022
Power Systems
N.A.I.C.S.: 335312

ABB Ltd. (2)
Howard Rd Eaton Socon, Saint Neots,
PE19 8EU, Cambridgeshire, United King-
dom
Tel.: (44) 1480475321
Web Site: http://www.abb.co.uk

Sales Range: $75-99.9 Million
Process Controls
N.A.I.C.S.: 334513

ABB Ltd. (2)
Tower Court Courtaulds Way Foleshill En-
terprise Park, Coventry, CV6 5NX, West
Midlands, United Kingdom (100%)
Tel.: (44) 2476368500
Web Site: http://www.abb.co.uk
Sales Range: $50-74.9 Million
Emp.: 100
Industrial Motor Control Products, Disconn-
ect Switches, Programmable Logic Con-
trollers, Circuit Breakers, Capacitors Mfr &
Distr
N.A.I.C.S.: 335313

ABB Ltd. - Stonehouse (2)
Oldends Lane, Stonehouse, GL10 3TA,
Gloucestershire, United Kingdom (100%)
Tel.: (44) 1453826661
Web Site: http://www.abb.com
Sales Range: $25-49.9 Million
Emp.: 200
Water & Gas Analysis Equipment & Flow
Products Mfr
N.A.I.C.S.: 334513

Subsidiary (Domestic):

Lutech Resources Ltd (2)
2 New Square Bedfont Lakes Business
Park, Feltham, TW14 8HA, Surrey, United
Kingdom
Tel.: (44) 2077639090
Sales Range: $25-49.9 Million
Emp.: 15
Recruitment Services
N.A.I.C.S.: 541612

ABB Ltd. (1)
2/1 Mykoly Grinchenka Street, 03680, Kiev,
Ukraine (100%)
Tel.: (380) 444952211
Web Site: http://www.abb.com
Sales Range: $50-74.9 Million
Emp.: 185
Power & Automation Products Mfr
N.A.I.C.S.: 335311

ABB Ltd. (1)
157-33 Samsung-dong, Kangnam-Ku, KR-
135090, Seoul, Korea (South) (100%)
Tel.: (82) 25282783
Web Site: http://www.abb.co.kr.com
Sales Range: $200-249.9 Million
Emp.: 560
Power & Automation Products
N.A.I.C.S.: 335311

ABB Ltd. (1)
5F/10F No 18 Jihu Rd, Neihu Dist, Taipei,
11492, Taiwan
Tel.: (886) 287516090
Web Site: https://new.abb.com
Emp.: 300
Power & Automation Products
N.A.I.C.S.: 335311

ABB Ltd. (1)
Bulevar Peka Dapcevica 13, 11000, Bel-
grade, Serbia
Tel.: (381) 113094300
Web Site: https://global.abb
Power & Automation Products Sales & Distr
N.A.I.C.S.: 423830

ABB Ltd. (1)
Koprska Ulica 92, 1000, Ljubljana, Slovenia
Tel.: (386) 12445455
Web Site: http://www.abb.com
Sales Range: $25-49.9 Million
Emp.: 28
Power & Automation Products Sales & Distr
N.A.I.C.S.: 423830

ABB Ltd. (1)
162 Al Khayatt Center Mecca St 3rd Floor,
11190, Amman, Jordan
Tel.: (962) 65620181
Emp.: 55
Industrial Automation Equipments Mfr
N.A.I.C.S.: 333248

Subsidiary (Non-US):

ABB International Marketing Ltd. (2)
Kafr Souseh Iranian School Str Building No
146, SY-16080, Damascus, Syria
Tel.: (963) 112129551

Web Site: http://www.abb.com
Sales Range: $25-49.9 Million
Emp.: 50
Power & Automation Products Marketer &
Distr
N.A.I.C.S.: 423830

Subsidiary (Domestic):

ABB Near East Trading Ltd. (2)
3rd Floor Al Khaiat Centre Street No 162
Mecca Street, Amman, 11190, Jordan
Tel.: (962) 6 5507733
Industrial Automation Equipment Distr
N.A.I.C.S.: 423830

ABB Ltda. (1)
Nicolas Boer Avenue 399, Sao Paulo,
01140-060, SP, Brazil (100%)
Tel.: (55) 1136889111
Web Site: http://www.abb.com
Sales Range: $250-299.9 Million
Emp.: 1,000
Power & Automation Products Sales & Distr
N.A.I.C.S.: 423830

Subsidiary (Domestic):

ABB SACE Limitada (2)
Avenida Monteiro Lobato 3411 Sao Roque,
Guarulhos, 07190-904, SP, Brazil
Tel.: (55) 1124648188
Web Site: http://www.abb.com
Sales Range: $700-749.9 Million
Emp.: 5,000
Circuit Breakers, Load Break Switches, Iso-
lators, Fusegear, MV/LV Switchboards &
Control Centers, HV/MV Bushings & Insu-
lating Material Mfr
N.A.I.C.S.: 335313

ABB Maghreb Services S.A. (1)
Jardin du Lac-Lot 6-2-3 Les Berges du Lac
II, TN-1053, Tunis, Tunisia
Tel.: (216) 71194440
Web Site: http://www.mena.abb.com
Power & Automation Products Sales & Distr
N.A.I.C.S.: 423830

ABB Malaysia Sdn. Bhd. (1)
Subang Jaya, Selangor, 47500, Petaling
Jaya, Darul Ehsan, Malaysia
Tel.: (60) 356284488
Web Site: http://www.abb.com.my
Electric Power Generation & Distribution
Services
N.A.I.C.S.: 221118

Subsidiary (Domestic):

ABB Holdings Sdn. Bhd. (2)
Lot 608 Jalan Lagoon Selatan Bandar Sun-
way, 47500, Subang Jaya, Selangor,
Malaysia (100%)
Tel.: (60) 356284888
Web Site: http://www.abb.com.my
Sales Range: $50-74.9 Million
Emp.: 175
Power & Automation Products Mfr
N.A.I.C.S.: 335313

ABB Manufacturing Sdn. Bhd. (2)
Lot 608 Jalan SS13/1K, Subang Jaya,
47500, Malaysia
Tel.: (60) 3 5628 4888
Industrial Automation System Mfr
N.A.I.C.S.: 333248

ABB Management Services Ltd. (1)
Affolternstrasse 44 CityPort, 8050, Zurich,
Switzerland
Tel.: (41) 433177111
N.A.I.C.S.: 423610

ABB Mexico S.A. de C.V (1)
Avenida Ejercito Nacional 843-B Piso 12
Colonia Granada, Miguel Hidalgo, 11520,
Mexico, Estado de Mexico, Mexico (100%)
Tel.: (52) 5536019500
Web Site: http://www.abb.com.mx
Sales Range: $100-124.9 Million
Emp.: 300
Electric Equipment Mfr
N.A.I.C.S.: 335999

Subsidiary (Domestic):

Asea Brown Boveri S.A. de C.V. (2)
Calle 5 de Mayo 706 Col Frutos de la
Revolucion, 96470, Coatzacoalcos, Vera-
cruz, Mexico

Tel.: (52) 921 211 2700
Web Site: http://www.abb.com.mx
Power Transmission Equipment Distr
N.A.I.C.S.: 423610

ABB NG Ltd (1)
Plot 8c MetalBox Road Off Acme Road
Ogba Industrial Area Ikeja, Lagos, Nigeria
Tel.: (234) 17005669
Web Site: http://www.ng.abb.com
Sales Range: $50-74.9 Million
Emp.: 150
Mfr of Industrial Machinery
N.A.I.C.S.: 333248

Branch (Domestic):

ABBNG Limited (2)
Plot 8c MetalBox road off Acme road Ogba
Industrial Area, Ikeja, Nigeria
Tel.: (234) 17005669
Web Site: http://www.ng.abb.com
Electric Power Generation & Distribution
Services
N.A.I.C.S.: 221118

ABB Norden Holding AB (1)
Kopparbergsvagen 2 Bnr 235 Visit, Vast-
manlands Lan, 721 71, Vasteras, Sweden
Tel.: (46) 107325000
Web Site: http://www.abb.com
Emp.: 4,300
Investment Management Service
N.A.I.C.S.: 523999

ABB Oy (1)
Porvoon Sisakeha 2, 06100, Porvoo,
Finland (100%)
Tel.: (358) 102211
Web Site: http://www.abb.fi
Rev.: $1,696,240,000
Emp.: 5,500
Power & Automation Products Mfr
N.A.I.C.S.: 335311

ABB Pte. Ltd. (1)
2 Ayer Rajah Crescent, Singapore, 139935,
Singapore
Tel.: (65) 67765711
Web Site: http://www.abb.com.sg
Sales Range: $550-599.9 Million
Emp.: 1,200
Electrical & Automation Product Distr
N.A.I.C.S.: 423610
Johan De Villiers (Mng Dir)

ABB Romania (1)
Green Court Str Herastrau railway station
no 4D Building C Floor 8, 020334, Bucha-
rest, Romania
Tel.: (40) 372158200
Web Site: http://www.abb.com
Sales Range: $25-49.9 Million
Emp.: 75
Power & Automation Products
N.A.I.C.S.: 335311

ABB S.A. (1)
Quinta da Fonte, Edificio Plaza I, PT-2774-
002, Paco d'Arcos, Portugal (100%)
Tel.: (351) 214256000
Web Site: http://www.abb.pt
Sales Range: $200-249.9 Million
Emp.: 700
Sales, Service & Assembly of Switchgear &
Surge Arresters
N.A.I.C.S.: 335313

ABB S.A. (1)
Jose Ignacio Rucci 1051 Valentin Alsina,
B1822CJU, Buenos Aires,
Argentina (100%)
Tel.: (54) 1142295500
Web Site: http://www.abb.com
Sales Range: $250-299.9 Million
Emp.: 600
Sales Company; Assembly of Switchgear &
High-Voltage Apparatus
N.A.I.C.S.: 423840

ABB S.A. (1)
Edificio Trilogia 2 Oficina No 221 Autopista
Prospero Fernandez, Frente Al PriceSmart
De Escazu, San Jose, Costa Rica
Tel.: (506) 22885484
Web Site: https://new.abb.com
Sales Range: $50-74.9 Million
Emp.: 7
Power & Automation Products Sales & Distr
N.A.I.C.S.: 423830

ABB Ltd.—(Continued)

ABB S.A. (1)
Avenida Balboa Torre Banco BVBA Piso 14,
PO Box 5039, Panama, 5, Panama
Tel.: (507) 2255458
Web Site: http://www.abb.com
Sales Range: $25-49.9 Million
Emp.: 11
Power & Automation Products Sales & Distr
N.A.I.C.S.: 423800

ABB S.A. (1)
9 Ave Edouard Belin, 92566, Rueil-
Malmaison, Cedex, France (100%)
Tel.: (33) 00141964500
Web Site: http://www.abb.fr
Sales Range: $25-49.9 Million
Emp.: 40
Power & Automation Products
N.A.I.C.S.: 335311

Subsidiary (Domestic):

L'Ebenoid S.A. (2)
8 rue des fleurs, 69100, Villeurbanne,
France
Tel.: (33) 4 72113990
Electrical Component Mfr
N.A.I.C.S.: 335999

ABB S.A. (1)
Vicuna Mackenna 1602 Nunoa, 7780006,
Santiago, Chile
Tel.: (56) 224714000
Web Site: http://www.abb.com
Sales Range: $50-74.9 Million
Emp.: 119
Power & Automation Products Mfr
N.A.I.C.S.: 335313

ABB S.A. (1)
13th KM National Road, Lamia, 14452, Ath-
ens, Attica, Greece
Tel.: (30) 2102891900
Web Site: http://www.abb.gr
Sales Range: $50-74.9 Million
Emp.: 83
Electrical Products Sales
N.A.I.C.S.: 423610

Branch (Domestic):

Asea Brown Boveri S.A. (2)
13th Km Athens - Lamia National Road,
Metamorfosis, 14452, Athens, Greece
Tel.: (30) 210 28 91 900
Web Site: http://www.abb.gr
Sales Range: $25-49.9 Million
Emp.: 200
Electric Equipment Mfr
N.A.I.C.S.: 335999

ABB S.A. de CV (1)
Calle El Mirador y 87 Av Norte Edif Quattro
ofic 09-08 Colonia Escalon, 01101, San
Salvador, El Salvador
Tel.: (503) 22076400
Electrical Engineering Services
N.A.I.C.S.: 541330

ABB S.A./N.V. (1)
Hoge Wei 27, 1930, Zaventem, Belgium
Tel.: (32) 27186311
Web Site: http://www.abb.be
Sales Range: $150-199.9 Million
Emp.: 300
Plumbing & Heating Equipment
N.A.I.C.S.: 423720

ABB S.p.A. (1)
Via Luciano Lama 33, Sesto S Giovanni,
20099, Milan, Italy (100%)
Tel.: (39) 0800551166
Web Site: http://www.abb.it
Sales Range: $25-49.9 Million
Emp.: 67
Sales & Service of Switchgear & Converters
N.A.I.C.S.: 335313

Subsidiary (Domestic):

ABB SACE S.p.A. (2)
Via Statale 113, 22016, Lenno, CO,
Italy (100%)
Tel.: (39) 034458111
Web Site: http://www.abb.it
Sales Range: $50-74.9 Million
Electronic & Pneumatic Process Control &
Instrumentation, Control Valves & Actuators
Mfr

N.A.I.C.S.: 334513

ABB SACE S.p.A. (2)
Via Baioni 35, 24123, Bergamo, BG,
Italy (100%)
Tel.: (39) 035395111
Web Site: http://www.abb.it
Sales Range: $25-49.9 Million
Circuit Breaker Mfr
N.A.I.C.S.: 335313

Intermagnetics Srl (2)
Via dei Mestieri 5/7 - Fraz Macchie, 6061,
Castiglione del Lago, Italy
Tel.: (39) 0759525314
Web Site: http://www.intermagneticsrl.com
Sales Range: $25-49.9 Million
Emp.: 60
Transformer & Reactor Mfr
N.A.I.C.S.: 335311

Italtrasfo Srl (2)
Piazza Fusina 2, 20133, Milan, Italy
Tel.: (39) 0332 51 02 37
Web Site: http://www.italtrasfo.com
Emp.: 35
Power Transmission Equipment Mfr
N.A.I.C.S.: 333613

ABB SIA (1)
Tiraines iela 3a, Riga, LV-1058, Latvia
Tel.: (371) 67063600
Web Site: http://www.abb.lv
Sales Range: $75-99.9 Million
Emp.: 150
Power & Automation Products Sales & Distr
N.A.I.C.S.: 423830

ABB Saudi Arabia (1)
Al Ahsa Street Malaz, PO Box 325841, Ri-
yadh, 11371, Central Region, Saudi
Arabia (100%)
Tel.: (966) 114845600
Web Site: http://www.abb.com.sa
Sales Range: $25-49.9 Million
Emp.: 15
Mfr of Industrial Machinery
N.A.I.C.S.: 333248

Subsidiary (Domestic):

ABB Automation Co. Ltd. (2)
PO Box 251, Riyadh, 11383, Saudi Arabia
Tel.: (966) 1 265 3030
Industrial Automation System Mfr
N.A.I.C.S.: 333248

ABB Contracting Company Ltd. (2)
Industrial Support Area Building No 2696
Road 118 Intersection 175, 31961, Jubail,
Saudi Arabia
Tel.: (966) 13 340 7036
Electrical Engineering Services
N.A.I.C.S.: 541330

ABB Electrical Industries Ltd. (2)
Al Ahsa Street Malaz, PO Box 251, Malaz
Riad, Riyadh, 11371, Saudi Arabia
Tel.: (966) 12653030
Electrical Engineering Services
N.A.I.C.S.: 541330

ABB Service Co. Ltd. (2)
Dammam - Al-Khobar Highway 1st Floor
SADAT Engineering Tower, PO Box 2873,
Al Khobar, 31952, Saudi Arabia
Tel.: (966) 13 806 3777
Web Site: http://www.abb.com.sa
Business Support Services
N.A.I.C.S.: 561499

ABB Schweiz Holding AG (1)
Brown Boveri Strasse 6, 5540, Baden, Swit-
zerland
Tel.: (41) 585850000
Web Site: http://www.abb.com
Sales Range: $1-4.9 Billion
Emp.: 7,000
Holding Company
N.A.I.C.S.: 551112

Subsidiary (Domestic):

ABB Immobilien AG (2)
Brown Boveri Strasse 6, 5401, Baden,
5401, Switzerland
Tel.: (41) 585857799
Web Site: http://www.abb.ch
Sales Range: $25-49.9 Million
Emp.: 15

Real Estate Investment & Asset Management Services
N.A.I.C.S.: 531390

ABB Insurance Brokers Ltd (2)
Brown Boveri Str 6, CH-5400, Baden, Swit-
zerland
Tel.: (41) 0585857800
Web Site: http://www.abb.ch
Sales Range: $150-199.9 Million
Emp.: 400
General Insurance Contractor
N.A.I.C.S.: 524210

ABB Secheron Ltd. (2)
Rue des Sabli res 4-6, CH-1217, Meyrin,
Switzerland (100%)
Tel.: (41) 585862211
Web Site: http://www.abb.ch
Sales Range: $75-99.9 Million
Emp.: 350
Energy & Power Distr & Supplier; Trans-
formers Mfr
N.A.I.C.S.: 335311

Unit (Domestic):

**ABB Switzerland Ltd - CMC Low Volt-
age Products** (2)
Fulachstrasse 150, Schaffhausen, 8201,
Switzerland
Tel.: (41) 585864111
Web Site: http://www.abb.ch
Sales Range: $75-99.9 Million
Emp.: 300
Low Voltage Electrical Switching & Protec-
tive Equipment
N.A.I.C.S.: 335313

**ABB Switzerland Ltd - Corporate
Research** (2)
Segelhof 1K, 5405, Baden, Switzerland
Tel.: (41) 585868411
Web Site: http://www.abb.ch
Sales Range: $25-49.9 Million
Emp.: 150
Research Services
N.A.I.C.S.: 541715

ABB Switzerland Ltd - Drives (2)
Austrasse, CH-5300, Turgi, Switzerland
Tel.: (41) 585892795
Web Site: http://www.abb.ch
Sales Range: $25-49.9 Million
Emp.: 200
Drive Mfr
N.A.I.C.S.: 333612

**ABB Switzerland Ltd - High Voltage
Products** (2)
Affolgernstrasse 44, PO Box 8131, Zurich,
8050, Switzerland
Tel.: (41) 585883300
Web Site: http://www.abb.ch
Sales Range: $25-49.9 Million
Emp.: 100
High Voltage Products Mfr
N.A.I.C.S.: 335999

**ABB Switzerland Ltd - Manufacturing
& Robotics** (2)
Fabrikstrasse 13, Birr, 5242, Switzerland
Tel.: (41) 585867766
Web Site: http://www.abb.ch
Sales Range: $75-99.9 Million
Emp.: 290
Engineering, Manufacturing & Production
Plant Servicing
N.A.I.C.S.: 541330

**ABB Switzerland Ltd - Minerals &
Printing** (2)
Segelhofstrasse, 5405, Baden, Switzerland
Tel.: (41) 585867319
Web Site: http://www.abb.ch
Electrical Equipment & Control Technology
N.A.I.C.S.: 335999

ABB Switzerland Ltd - Normelec (2)
Brown Boveri Strasse 6, Baden, 5400, Swit-
zerland
Tel.: (41) 585860000
Web Site: http://www.abb.ch
Sales Range: $75-99.9 Million
Emp.: 100
Electric Motors, Drives & Low Voltage Prod-
ucts Sales & Distr
N.A.I.C.S.: 221122

**ABB Switzerland Ltd - Power
Electronics** (2)

Austrasse, Turgi, 5300, Switzerland
Tel.: (41) 585893809
Web Site: http://www.abb.ch
Sales Range: $75-99.9 Million
Emp.: 350
Power Electronics Mfr
N.A.I.C.S.: 335311

**ABB Switzerland Ltd - Power
Systems** (2)
Brown Boveri Strasse 5, CH-8057, Zurich,
Switzerland
Tel.: (41) 585883886
Web Site: http://www.abb.ch
Substation Electrical Power Supply
N.A.I.C.S.: 335311

**ABB Switzerland Ltd -
Semiconductors** (2)
Fabrikstrasse 3, Lenzburg, 5600, Aargau,
Switzerland
Tel.: (41) 58 586 10 00
Web Site: http://www.abb.ch
Sales Range: $75-99.9 Million
Emp.: 300
Semiconductor Mfr
N.A.I.C.S.: 334413

ABB Switzerland Ltd., Micafil (2)
Badenerstrasse 780, CH-8048, Zurich, Swit-
zerland
Tel.: (41) 4158586033
Web Site: http://www.micafil.ch
Sales Range: $25-49.9 Million
Emp.: 170
Transformer Mfr
N.A.I.C.S.: 335311

Subsidiary (Domestic):

ABB Turbo Systems Holding Ltd. (2)
Brown Boveri Strasse 6, Baden, 5401, Swit-
zerland
Tel.: (41) 58 585 77 77
Investment Management Service
N.A.I.C.S.: 523999

Subsidiary (Domestic):

ABB Turbo Systems Ltd (3)
Bruggerstrasse 71A, Baden, 5400, Aargau,
Switzerland
Tel.: (41) 58 585 77 77
Web Site: http://www.abb.ch
Sales Range: $350-399.9 Million
Emp.: 1,600
Turbocharging Diesel & Gas Engines Mfr
N.A.I.C.S.: 336310

Subsidiary (Domestic):

Consenec Ltd (2)
Segelhof, Daettwil, 5405, Baden, Switzer-
land
Tel.: (41) 585868360
Web Site: https://www.consenec.ch
Rev.: $7,340,036
Emp.: 50
Management Consulting Services
N.A.I.C.S.: 541611
Peter Bill (Mgr-Bus Unit Operational Excel-
lence)

Subsidiary (Non-US):

Newave Energy Holding SA (2)
Tel.: (41) 918502929
Web Site: http://www.newavenergy.com
Sales Range: $75-99.9 Million
Emp.: 120
Holding Company; Uninterruptible Power
Supply Systems Designer, Mfr & Distr
N.A.I.C.S.: 551112

Subsidiary (Non-US):

ABB Schweiz AG (3)
(100%)
Tel.: (41) 585858161
Web Site: https://www.new.abb.com
UPS Mfr & Sales
N.A.I.C.S.: 335999

Newave Energy (Jiangmen) Ltd. (3)
Tel.: (86) 750 368 0239
Web Site: http://www.newavenergy.cn
Inverter Distr
N.A.I.C.S.: 423610

Newave Energy AG (3)
Tel.: (41) 56 416 01 01

Web Site: http://www.newavenergy.ch
Inverter Mfr
N.A.I.C.S.: 335312

Newave Espana S.A. (3)
Tel.: (34) 917682222
Web Site: http://www.newaveups.com
UPS Mfr
N.A.I.C.S.: 335999

Newave Finland OY (3)
Tel.: (358) 104219400
Web Site: http://www.newaveups.fi
Sales Range: $25-49.9 Million
Emp.: 10
UPS Mfr
N.A.I.C.S.: 335999

Newave Italia SRL (3)
Tel.: (39) 066531316
Web Site: https://www.newaveitalia.it
Sales Range: $25-49.9 Million
Emp.: 6
Inverter Mfr
N.A.I.C.S.: 335312

Newave Osterreich GmbH (3)
Tel.: (43) 1710967016
Web Site: http://www.newwaveups.at
Sales Range: $25-49.9 Million
Emp.: 9
Uninterruptible Power Supply Sales
N.A.I.C.S.: 335999

Newave S.A. (3)
Tel.: (41) 918502929
Web Site: http://www.newaveups.com
Sales Range: $25-49.9 Million
Emp.: 100
UPS Mfr
N.A.I.C.S.: 335999

**Newave South America Elettro-
elettronica LTDA** (3)
Tel.: (55) 1130450809
Web Site: http://www.newaveups.com
Sales Range: $25-49.9 Million
Emp.: 3
UPS Mfr
N.A.I.C.S.: 335999

Newave UPS Systems BV (3)
Tel.: (31) 183646474
Web Site: http://www.newaveenergy.nl
Sales Range: $25-49.9 Million
Emp.: 7
UPS Mfr
N.A.I.C.S.: 335999

Newave USV Systeme GmbH (3)
Tel.: (49) 722918660
Web Site: http://www.newave-usv.de
Sales Range: $25-49.9 Million
Emp.: 20
UPS Mfr
N.A.I.C.S.: 335999

ABB South Africa (Pty) Ltd. (1)
2 Lake Road Longmeadow Business Estate
North, Port Elizabeth, 1069, South Africa
Tel.: (27) 102025000
Web Site: https://new.abb.com
Sales Range: $450-499.9 Million
Emp.: 1,800
Industrial Machinery Mfr & Distr
N.A.I.C.S.: 333248
Sumaya Abdool *(Partner-Cluster Comm)*

Subsidiary (Domestic):

ABB Holdings (Pty) Ltd. (2)
2 Lake Road, Longmeadow Business Estate, Modderfontein, 1609, Gauteng, South
Africa **(80%)**
Tel.: (27) 10 202 5000
Web Site: http://www.abb.co.za
Sales Range: $75-99.9 Million
Emp.: 300
Engineering Services
N.A.I.C.S.: 541330

K-TEK Instruments (PTY) Ltd. (2)
2 Lake Road Longmeadow Business Estate
North, Edenvale, 1609, South Africa
Tel.: (27) 10 202 6458 9
Web Site: http://www.ktekcorp.co.za
Induatrial Measurement Instrument Mfr
N.A.I.C.S.: 334513

**Primkop Airport Management (Pty)
Ltd.** (2)

R538 Karino Rd White River-Plaston, Nelspruit, 1200, South Africa
Tel.: (27) 137537500
Airport Management Services
N.A.I.C.S.: 488119

ABB Sp. z o.o. (1)
Ul Zaganska 1, 04-713, Warsaw,
Poland **(96.01%)**
Tel.: (48) 222237777
Web Site: https://new.abb.com
Sales Range: $400-449.9 Million
Emp.: 2,000
Power & Automation Products
N.A.I.C.S.: 335311

Subsidiary (Domestic):

ABB Entrelec Sp. z.o.o. (2)
Ul Grunwaldzka 38, 84-351, Nowa Wies
Leborska, Pomorskie, Poland
Tel.: (48) 59 86 15 800
Web Site: http://www.abb.pl
Sales Range: $100-124.9 Million
Emp.: 140
Eletric Power Generation Services
N.A.I.C.S.: 221118

ABB Striebel & John GmbH (1)
Am Fuchsgraben 2 -3, 77880, Sasbach,
Germany
Tel.: (49) 78416090
Web Site: https://www.striebelundjohn.com
Emp.: 10,700
Energy Distribution System Mfr & Distr
N.A.I.C.S.: 335311

ABB Technologies Ltd. (1)
Nahum Hat 5, 35085, Haifa,
Israel **(99.99%)**
Tel.: (972) 48519211
Web Site: http://www.abb.co.il
Sales Range: $25-49.9 Million
Emp.: 50
Power & Automation Products
N.A.I.C.S.: 335311

ABB Technologies S.A. (1)
Km 3 Boulevard du Centénaire, de la commune de Dakar Route des Brasseries, Dakar, Senegal
Tel.: (221) 338327751
Web Site: http://www.abb.com
Power & Automation Products Sales & Distr
N.A.I.C.S.: 423830

ABB Technologies W.L.L. (1)
Bldg 175 Road 4304 Block 343 Mina Sulman, Manama, Bahrain
Tel.: (973) 17810663
Web Site: http://www.abb.com.sa
Industrial Automation Equipments Mfr
N.A.I.C.S.: 333248

ABB UAB (1)
Parko G 37, Avizieniu K, 14198, Vilnius,
Lithuania
Tel.: (370) 52738300
Web Site: http://www.abb.lt
Sales Range: $50-74.9 Million
Emp.: 70
Power & Automation Products Sales & Distr
N.A.I.C.S.: 423830

ABB Verwaltungs AG (1)
Affolternstrasse 44, 8050, Zurich, Switzerland
Tel.: (41) 433177111
Web Site: http://www.abb.com
Financial Management Services
N.A.I.C.S.: 523999

ABB Vietnam (1)
Milestone 9 National Highway 1A, Thanh Tri
District, Hanoi, Vietnam
Tel.: (84) 48611010
Web Site: http://www.abb.com
Power & Automation Products Sales & Distr
N.A.I.C.S.: 423830
Pham Thu Thuy *(Country Mgr-Comm)*

ABB Xiamen Switchgear Co. Ltd. (1)
No 319 Torch Road, Xiamen, 361006, Fujian, China
Tel.: (86) 5926026033
N.A.I.C.S.: 423610

**ABB Xinhui Low Voltage Switchgear
Co. Ltd.** (1)
Jinguzhou Industrial development zone,
Xinhui District, Jiangmen, 529100, Guang-

dong, China
Tel.: (86) 4008209696
Switchgear Mfr
N.A.I.C.S.: 335313
Luo Hui *(Pres)*

ABB d.o.o. (1)
Bulevar Peka Dapcevica 13, 11000, Belgrade, Serbia
Tel.: (381) 113094300
Web Site: http://www.abb.com
Sales Range: $25-49.9 Million
Emp.: 42
Electronic & Electrical Component Mfr
N.A.I.C.S.: 334419

ABB d.o.o., Zagreb (1)
Ulica grada Vukovara 284, 10000, Zagreb,
Croatia
Tel.: (385) 16008500
Web Site: https://new.abb.com
Power & Automation Products Distr
N.A.I.C.S.: 423830

ABB s.r.o. (1)
Vyskocilova 1561/4a, 140 00, Prague,
Czech Republic **(100%)**
Tel.: (420) 234322110
Web Site: https://new.abb.com
Emp.: 120
Power & Automation Products
N.A.I.C.S.: 335311

ABB s.r.o. (1)
Tuhovska 29, 831 06, Bratislava, Slovakia
Tel.: (421) 908676490
Web Site: https://new.abb.com
Sales Range: $25-49.9 Million
Emp.: 100
Power & Automation Products
N.A.I.C.S.: 335311

Asea Brown Boveri (Pty) Ltd (1)
58 Industria Street Erf 204 Lafrenz Industrial Windhoek, Windhoek, 9000, Khomas,
Namibia
Tel.: (264) 61240341
Web Site: http://www.abb.com
Emp.: 10
Power & Automation Products Sales & Distr
N.A.I.C.S.: 423830

Asea Brown Boveri Inc. (1)
Km 20 West Service Road Barangay Marcelo Green South Superhighway,
Paranaque, 1700, Sucat,
Philippines **(100%)**
Tel.: (63) 28244581
Web Site: https://new.abb.com
Emp.: 150
Automation & Power Technology Products
Mfr
N.A.I.C.S.: 335313

Asea Brown Boveri Ltd. (1)
Obrucheva 30/1, 117861, Moscow,
Russia **(100%)**
Tel.: (7) 4959602200
Web Site: http://www.abb.ru
Sales Range: $150-199.9 Million
Emp.: 500
Power & Automation Products Sales & Distr
N.A.I.C.S.: 423830

Branch (Domestic):

ABB Ltd. (2)
Nakhimovskiy Prospekt 58, RU-117335,
Moscow, Russia
Tel.: (7) 495 960 2200
Web Site: http://www.abb.ru
Eletric Power Generation Services
N.A.I.C.S.: 221118

Subsidiary (Domestic):

**ABB Power and Automation Systems
Ltd.** (2)
Yakovleva Pr 1, Cheboksary, 428020, Russia
Tel.: (7) 8352 2561 62
Sales Range: $25-49.9 Million
Emp.: 150
Industrial Automation Equipments Mfr
N.A.I.C.S.: 333248

Asea Brown Boveri Ltd. (1)

A1 Royal Road G R N W, Port Louis, Mauritius
Tel.: (230) 4333036
Web Site: http://www.abb.mu
Sales Range: $25-49.9 Million
Emp.: 10
Industrial Automation & Process Control
System Mfr
N.A.I.C.S.: 334513

Asea Brown Boveri Ltda. (1)
Carrera 100 No 25D-61, Bogota,
Colombia **(99.99%)**
Tel.: (57) 14178000
Web Site: http://www.abb.com.co
Sales Range: $50-74.9 Million
Emp.: 80
Automation & Power Technology Products
Sales
N.A.I.C.S.: 423840

Asea Brown Boveri S.A.E. (1)
Building 208 North 90 St 5th Settlement,
PO Box 51, 1st Settlement New Cairo,
Cairo, Egypt **(100%)**
Tel.: (20) 226251300
Web Site: http://www.abb.com
Heavy Construction Services
N.A.I.C.S.: 237990

Subsidiary (Domestic):

ABB Transformers S.A.E. (2)
7 Dr Mohamed Kamel Hussein St El Nozha
El Gedieda, Heliopolis, Cairo, Egypt
Tel.: (20) 226222665
Web Site: http://www.abb.com.eg
Transformer Mfr
N.A.I.C.S.: 335311

Asea Brown Boveri, S.A. (1)
Av Atahualpa Oe1-198 y 10 de Agosto,
Quito, Ecuador **(96.87%)**
Tel.: (593) 23994100
Web Site: http://www.abb.com.ec
Sales Range: $25-49.9 Million
Emp.: 45
Power & Automation Products Sales & Distr
N.A.I.C.S.: 423830

Asea Brown Boveri, S.A. (1)
Avenida Sanchez Bustamante 275 Between
8-9 St Calacopo, La Paz, Bolivia
Tel.: (591) 22788181
Web Site: http://www.abb.com
Sales Range: $25-49.9 Million
Emp.: 30
Power & Automation Products Sales & Distr
N.A.I.C.S.: 423830

Asea Brown Boveri, S.A. (1)
7 Boulevard Capitaine Vuillanier, BP 2648,
Ain Sebaa, 20250, Casablanca, Morocco
Tel.: (212) 522349000
Web Site: http://www.mena.abb.com
Power & Automation Products Sales & Distr
N.A.I.C.S.: 423830

Asea Brown Boveri, S.A. (1)
Avenida Don Diego Cisneros, PO Box
6640, Los Ruices, 1071, Caracas,
Venezuela **(100%)**
Tel.: (58) 2122031740
Web Site: http://www.abb.com
Power & Automation Products Mfr
N.A.I.C.S.: 335311

Asea Brown Boveri, S.A. (1)
Avenida Argentina 3120, PO Box 3846,
Lima, 15081, Peru **(99.99%)**
Tel.: (51) 14155100
Web Site: http://www.abb.com.pe
Sales Range: $50-74.9 Million
Emp.: 150
Power & Automation Products
N.A.I.C.S.: 335311

Asea Brown Boveri, S.A. (1)
Calle San Romualdo 13, 28037, Madrid,
Spain **(100%)**
Tel.: (34) 915819393
Web Site: https://new.abb.com
Sales Range: $100-124.9 Million
Emp.: 500
Automation Technology Products Mfr
N.A.I.C.S.: 335311

Subsidiary (Domestic):

ABB Sistemas Industriales AB (2)
Calle Torrent De l'Olla 220, 08012, Barce-

ABB Ltd.—(Continued)

Iona, Spain (100%)
Tel.: (34) 934842121
Web Site: http://www.abb.es
Industrial Robots & Converters Mfr
N.A.I.C.S.: 333248

ABB Stotz-Kontakt S.A. (2)
C/ Carabanchel 35, 28902, Getafe, Madrid, Spain
Tel.: (34) 916950200
Web Site: http://www.abb.es
Sales Range: $25-49.9 Million
Emp.: 100
Circuit Breaker Mfr
N.A.I.C.S.: 335313

Bernecker + Rainer Industrie Elektronik GmbH (1)
B R Strasse 1, 5142, Eggelsberg, Austria
Tel.: (43) 774865860
Web Site: http://www.br-automation.com
Automated Electronic Machines Mfr
N.A.I.C.S.: 334419

Subsidiary (Non-US):

B&R Automacao Industrial Ltda. (2)
AV Alexander Grahan Bell 200 D2, Campinas, 13069-310, Brazil
Tel.: (55) 1925138400
Industrial Equipment Distr
N.A.I.C.S.: 423830

B&R Automatyka Przemyslowa Sp. z.o.o.
ul Malachowskiego 10, 61-129, Poznan, Poland
Tel.: (48) 618460500
Industrial Equipment Distr
N.A.I.C.S.: 423830

B&R Automazione Industriale S.r.l. (2)
Via Ruggero Leoncavallo 1, Cesate, 20031, Milan, Italy
Tel.: (39) 029320581
Web Site: https://www.br-automation.com
Industrial Equipment Distr
N.A.I.C.S.: 423830

B&R Industrial Automation (2)
Vallsolana Garden Business Park Cami de Can Camps 17-19 Edif Kibo, 08174, Sant Cugat del Valles, Spain
Tel.: (34) 935689965
Web Site: https://www.br-automation.com
Industrial Equipment Distr
N.A.I.C.S.: 423830

B&R Industrial Automation A/S (2)
Rolundvej 17-19, 5260, Odense, Denmark
Tel.: (45) 63153080
Web Site: https://www.br-automation.com
Industrial Equipment Distr
N.A.I.C.S.: 423830

B&R Industrial Automation Co. Ltd. (2)
No 21 Building Gems Park No 487 Tianlin Road, Xuhui District, Shanghai, 200233, China
Tel.: (86) 2154644800
Web Site: https://www.br-automation.com
Industrial Equipment Distr
N.A.I.C.S.: 423830

B&R Industrial Automation Co., Ltd. (2)
11 F Daego Building 55 Pyeongchon-daero 212 beon-gil, Dongan-gu, Anyang, 14067, Gyeonggi-do, Korea (South)
Tel.: (82) 314764766
Industrial Equipment Distr
N.A.I.C.S.: 423830

Subsidiary (US):

B&R Industrial Automation Corp. (2)
1250 Northmeadow Pkwy 100, Roswell, GA 30076 (100%)
Tel.: (770) 772-0400
Sale of Programmable Controllers, Industrial Computers, Interface Products & Industrial Video Terminals
N.A.I.C.S.: 423830
Buck Tanner (Reg Mgr)

Subsidiary (Non-US):

B&R Industrial Automation Inc. (2)

5895 Kennedy Road, Mississauga, L4Z 2G3, ON, Canada
Tel.: (905) 417-9500
Industrial Equipment Distr
N.A.I.C.S.: 423830

B&R Industrial Automation Ltd. (2)
Bakewell Road Orton Southgate, Broadoak Southgate Park, PE2 6YS, Peterborough, United Kingdom
Tel.: (44) 1733371320
Industrial Equipment Distr
N.A.I.C.S.: 423830

B&R Industrial Automation Pte Ltd (2)
2 Ayer Rajah Crescent, Singapore, 139935, Singapore
Tel.: (65) 67105618
Industrial Equipment Distr
N.A.I.C.S.: 423830

B&R Industrial Automation Pvt. Ltd. (2)
8 Tara Heights Mumbai Pune Road, Wakdewadi, Pune, 411003, India
Tel.: (91) 2041478999
Web Site: https://www.br-automation.com
Industrial Equipment Distr
N.A.I.C.S.: 423830

B&R Industrial Automation, ooo (2)
Leninskiy prospekt 119A 5th floor, 119571, Moscow, Russia
Tel.: (7) 4956579501
Emp.: 25
Industrial Equipment Distr
N.A.I.C.S.: 423830

B&R Industriautomation AB (2)
Hyllie Alie 31, 215 33, Malmo, Sweden
Tel.: (46) 40 315980
Industrial Equipment Distr
N.A.I.C.S.: 423830

B&R Industrie-Automation AG (2)
Langfeldstrasse 90, 8500, Frauenfeld, Switzerland
Tel.: (41) 527285600
Industrial Equipment Distr
N.A.I.C.S.: 423830

B&R Industrie-Elektronik GmbH (2)
Am Weidenring 56, 61352, Bad Homburg, Germany
Tel.: (49) 617240190
Web Site: https://www.br-automation.com
Industrial Equipment Distr
N.A.I.C.S.: 423830

B&R Industriele Automatisierung B.V. (2)
Hoge Schouw 1, 4817 BZ, Breda, Netherlands
Tel.: (31) 765715303
Web Site: https://www.br-automation.com
Industrial Equipment Distr
N.A.I.C.S.: 423830

B&R Industrielle Automatisering BV (2)
Guldensporenpark 28, 9820, Merelbeke, Belgium
Tel.: (32) 92325001
Industrial Equipment Distr
N.A.I.C.S.: 423830

B&R K.K. (2)
1-2 Yokohama Mitsui Bldg 23F, Takashima Nishi-ku, Yokohama, 220-0011, Japan
Tel.: (81) 452638460
Industrial Equipment Distr
N.A.I.C.S.: 423830

B+R automatizace, spol. s r.o. (2)
Stranskeho 39, 616 00, Brno, Czech Republic
Tel.: (420) 541420311
Web Site: https://www.br-automation.com
Industrial Equipment Distr
N.A.I.C.S.: 423830

BR Endustriyel Otomasyon Sanayi ve Ticaret Limited (2)
Niyazibey is Merkezi Altaycesme Mahallesi Zuhal Sokak No 22/9, Maltepe, 34843, Istanbul, Turkiye
Tel.: (90) 2164424100
Web Site: https://www.br-automation.com.tr
Emp.: 7

Industrial Equipment Distr
N.A.I.C.S.: 423830

Cylon Controls Ltd. (1)
Clonshaugh Business & Technology Park, Clonshaugh, Dublin, 17, Ireland
Tel.: (353) 1 245 0500
Web Site: http://www.cylon.com
Emp.: 60
Building Energy Management System Mfr
N.A.I.C.S.: 334512

Subsidiary (Non-US):

Cylon Controls (Beijing) Ltd (2)
Building-A Rm-509 HeQiao Mansion No 8 GuangHua Road, ChaoYang District, Beijing, 100026, China
Tel.: (86) 1065812498
Electronic Components Distr
N.A.I.C.S.: 423690

Cylon Controls (UK) Limited (2)
Endeavour House Coopers End Road, Stansted, CM24 1SJ, Essex, United Kingdom
Tel.: (44) 870 178 1800
Building Energy Management System Mfr
N.A.I.C.S.: 334512

Cylon Controls Limited (2)
Riyadh Exit 11 Khalid Bin Walid Street Arabian Kinn Office Floor 1, PO Box 28051, Riyadh, 11437, Saudi Arabia
Tel.: (966) 112401707
Electronic Components Distr
N.A.I.C.S.: 423690

Subsidiary (US):

Cylon Energy Inc. (2)
8025 S Willow St Ste 107/108, Manchester, NH 03103
Tel.: (603) 782-8870
Building Energy Management System Mfr
N.A.I.C.S.: 334512
Marina Greene (Mgr-Sls Support & Bus Ops)

Subsidiary (Domestic):

American Auto-Matrix Inc. (3)
1 Technology Ln, Export, PA 15632
Tel.: (724) 733-2000
Web Site: http://www.aamatrix.com
Environmental Control Mfr
N.A.I.C.S.: 334512
Rocky Moore (Reg Mgr-Sls)

Subsidiary (Non-US):

Cylon GmbH (2)
Greschbachstrasse 6 A, 76229, Karlsruhe, Germany
Tel.: (49) 800 2001287
Building Energy Management System Mfr
N.A.I.C.S.: 334512

PT ABB Sakti Industri (1)
Jl Jend Sudirman Kav 29-31, 12920, Jakarta, Indonesia
Tel.: (62) 2125515555
Web Site: http://www.abb.com
Sales Range: $25-49.9 Million
Emp.: 31
Switchgear Sales
N.A.I.C.S.: 423830

SEAM Group LLC (1)
6210 Technology Center Dr Ste 200, Indianapolis, IN 46278
Web Site: http://www.seamgroup.com
Sales Range: $25-49.9 Million
Emp.: 230
Safety & Asset Management Services
N.A.I.C.S.: 523940

Subsidiary (Domestic):

Electrical Engineering & Service Co., Inc. (2)
289 Centre St, Holbrook, MA 02343-1075
Tel.: (781) 767-9922
Web Site: http://www.eescousa.com
Appliance Repair & Maintenance
N.A.I.C.S.: 811412
Joseph Cipolla (Owner)

Trasfor SA (1)
Via Cantonale 11, Molinazzo di, 6995, Monteggio, Ticino, Switzerland
Tel.: (41) 585886888

Web Site: https://www.trasfor.ch
Rev.: $109,675,370
Emp.: 300
Transformer & Inductor Mfr
N.A.I.C.S.: 335311
Sebastiano Zumbino (CEO)

ABBEY CAPITAL LIMITED
1-2 Cavendish Row, Dublin, 1, Ireland
Tel.: (353) 1 828 0400
Web Site:
http://www.abbeycapital.com
Year Founded: 2000
Emp.: 58
Investment Management Service
N.A.I.C.S.: 523940
Anthony Gannon (Founder & Chief Investment Officer)

Subsidiaries:

Abbey Capital (US) LLC (1)
330 Madison Ave Ste 602, New York, NY 10017
Tel.: (646) 495-5546
Investment Management Service
N.A.I.C.S.: 523940
Helen Doody (CEO & Mng Dir)

ABBEY FORGED PRODUCTS LIMITED
Beeley Wood Works Beeley Wood Lane, Sheffield, S6 1ND, United Kingdom
Tel.: (44) 114 231 2271
Web Site:
http://www.abbeyforgedproducts.co.uk
Year Founded: 1982
Sales Range: $50-74.9 Million
Emp.: 175
Steel Forging Product Mfr
N.A.I.C.S.: 332111
Jackie Neal (Mng Dir)

ABBEY MORTGAGE BANK PLC.
23 Karimu Kotun Street, Victoria Island, Lagos, Nigeria
Tel.: (234) 2012271695
Web Site:
https://www.abbeymortgagebank.com
Year Founded: 1991
ABBEYBDS—(NIGE)
Rev.: $3,579,232
Assets: $29,502,982
Liabilities: $23,804,631
Net Worth: $5,698,350
Earnings: $567,109
Fiscal Year-end: 12/31/22
Commercial Banking Services
N.A.I.C.S.: 522110
Emmanuel Kanu Okoroafor Ivi (Chm)

ABBISKO CAYMAN LIMITED
Building 3 No 898 Halei Road, Zhangjiang Hi-Tech Park Pudong New Area, Shanghai, China Ky
Web Site: https://www.abbisko.com
Year Founded: 2016
2256—(HKG)
Rev.: $2,639,012
Assets: $292,891,837
Liabilities: $18,592,158
Net Worth: $274,299,679
Earnings: ($59,756,175)
Emp.: 258
Fiscal Year-end: 12/31/23
Biotechnology Research & Development Services
N.A.I.C.S.: 541714
Yao-Chang Xu (Chm)

Subsidiaries:

Abbisko Therapeutics Co., Ltd. (1)
12Bth Floor Building 1 Lane 515 Huanke Road, Pudong New Area, Shanghai, China
Tel.: (86) 2168911058
Technical Consulting Services

N.A.I.C.S.: 541690

ABBOTSFORD CHRYSLER DODGE JEEP RAM LTD.
30285 Automall Drive, Abbotsford, V2T 5M1, BC, Canada
Tel.: (604) 857-8888
Web Site:
https://www.abbotsfordchrysler.com
Year Founded: 1971
New & Used Car Dealers
N.A.I.C.S.: 441110
Mitch Trotman (Principal)

ABBVIE A/S
Emdrupvej 28C, 2100, Copenhagen, Denmark
Tel.: (45) 72302028   DK
Web Site: http://www.abbvie.dk
Emp.: 35
Pharmaceutical Preparation Mfr
N.A.I.C.S.: 325412

ABC ARBITRAGE S.A.
18 Rue du Quatre Septembre, 75002, Paris, France
Tel.: (33) 153005500
Web Site: https://www.abc-arbitrage.com
Year Founded: 1995
ABCA—(EUR)
Rev.: $18,181,919
Assets: $189,987,857
Liabilities: $18,435,810
Net Worth: $171,552,048
Earnings: $18,192,957
Emp.: 101
Fiscal Year-end: 12/31/23
Financial Trading Services
N.A.I.C.S.: 525990
Dominique Ceolin (Chm & CEO)

Subsidiaries:

ABC Arbitrage Asset
Management   (1)
18 rue du 4 Septembre, 75 002, Paris, France
Tel.: (33) 153005500
Web Site: http://www.abc-arbitrage.com
Sales Range: $25-49.9 Million
Asset Management Services
N.A.I.C.S.: 541618

ABC GAS (INTERNATIONAL) LTD.
1 Mahesh Villa Worli, Mumbai, 400 018, Maharashtra, India
Tel.: (91) 2224935508
Web Site: https://www.abcgas.co.in
Rev.: $174,549
Assets: $734,673
Liabilities: $436,844
Net Worth: $297,829
Earnings: $18,323
Fiscal Year-end: 03/31/19
Copper Product Mfr
N.A.I.C.S.: 331420
Satish Shymalprasad Shorewala (Mng Dir)

ABC INDIA LTD.
P-10 New C I T Road, Kolkata, 700073, India
Tel.: (91) 3322371745
Web Site: https://www.abcindia.com
520123—(BOM)
Rev.: $18,491,855
Assets: $11,928,275
Liabilities: $6,823,092
Net Worth: $5,105,183
Earnings: $373,215
Emp.: 97
Fiscal Year-end: 03/31/22
Logistics & Freight Transportation Services
N.A.I.C.S.: 541614
Ashish Agarwal (Mng Dir)

ABC MOTORS COMPANY LIMITED
ABC Centre Military Road, Port Louis, Mauritius
Tel.: (230) 2069900
Web Site: https://www.abcmotors.mu
Year Founded: 1985
ABC—(MAU)
Rev.: $58,915,191
Assets: $71,009,738
Liabilities: $39,211,401
Net Worth: $31,798,337
Earnings: $2,734,254
Emp.: 400
Fiscal Year-end: 06/30/23
Automobile Parts Distr
N.A.I.C.S.: 423140
Vincent Ah-Chuen (Chm)

ABC MULTIACTIVE LIMITED
23/F On Hing Building No 1 On Hing Terrace, Central, China (Hong Kong)
Tel.: (852) 25982027   BM
Web Site:
http://www.abcmultiactive.com
Year Founded: 2000
8131—(HKG)
Rev.: $2,229,326
Assets: $995,563
Liabilities: $3,848,448
Net Worth: ($2,852,885)
Earnings: ($637,556)
Emp.: 24
Fiscal Year-end: 11/30/19
Software Development Services
N.A.I.C.S.: 541511
Joseph Chi Ho Hui (Chm)

ABC ORTHODONTICS SA
Rue dAirmont 7, Porrentruy, 2900, Switzerland
Tel.: (41) 324668651
Orthodontic Material Mfr & Distr
N.A.I.C.S.: 339114
Orlando Coccorullo (Chm)

ABC TRANSPORT PLC
Km 5 MCC Uratta Road, Owerri, 1111, Imo, Nigeria
Tel.: (234) 8139862090
Web Site:
https://www.abctransport.com
Year Founded: 1993
Rev.: $4,449,453
Assets: $12,294,238
Liabilities: $6,954,874
Net Worth: $5,339,364
Earnings: $1,411,460
Emp.: 1,435
Fiscal Year-end: 12/31/17
Food Transportation Services
N.A.I.C.S.: 488490
Frank Nneji (Founder, CEO & Mng Dir)

ABC-MART, INC.
19F Shibuya Mark City West 1-12-1 Dogenzaka Shibuya-ku, Tokyo, 150-0043, Japan
Tel.: (81) 334765452   JP
Web Site: http://www.abc-mart.co.jp
Year Founded: 1985
2670—(TKS)
Rev.: $2,440,356,730
Assets: $2,746,212,240
Liabilities: $323,885,380
Net Worth: $2,422,326,860
Earnings: $283,663,810
Emp.: 9,822
Fiscal Year-end: 02/29/24
Shoes, Apparel & General Merchandise Retailer
N.A.I.C.S.: 458210
Minoru Noguchi (Pres & Exec Officer)

Subsidiaries:

ABC-MART KOREA, INC.   (1)
4th Floor S-dong Gangnam Dongyang Paragon 241-1 Nonhyeon 2-dong, Gangnam-gu, Seoul, 135-830, Korea (South)
Tel.: (82) 2 587 7880
Footwear Retailer
N.A.I.C.S.: 459999

LaCrosse Footwear, Inc.   (1)
17634 NE Airport Way, Portland, OR 97230-4999
Tel.: (503) 262-0110
Web Site: http://www.lacrossefootwear.com
Sales Range: $125-149.9 Million
Protective Footwear & Apparel Designer, Developer, Marketer & Mfr for the Sporting, Occupational & Recreational Markets
N.A.I.C.S.: 316210

Subsidiary (Domestic):

Danner, Inc.   (2)
17634 NE Airport Way, Portland, OR 97230-1027   (100%)
Tel.: (503) 251-1100
Web Site: http://www.danner.com
Sales Range: $50-74.9 Million
Leather Footwear Mfr
N.A.I.C.S.: 316210

ABCELLERA BIOLOGICS INC.
2215 Yukon Street, Vancouver, V5Y 0A1, BC, Canada
Tel.: (604) 559-9005   BC
Web Site: https://www.abcellera.com
Year Founded: 2012
ABCL—(NASDAQ)
Rev.: $375,203,000
Assets: $1,488,094,000
Liabilities: $335,776,000
Net Worth: $1,152,318,000
Earnings: $153,744,000
Emp.: 586
Fiscal Year-end: 12/31/23
Biotechnology Research & Development Services
N.A.I.C.S.: 541714
Carl L.G. Hansen (Co-Founder, Chm, Pres & CEO)

Subsidiaries:

Tetragenetics, Inc.   (1)
85 Bolton St, Cambridge, MA 02140
Tel.: (617) 500-7471
Web Site: http://www.tetragenetics.com
Chemicals Mfr
N.A.I.C.S.: 325414
John P. Reilly (VP-Bus Dev)

ABCHECK S.R.O
Vedeckotechnicky park Plzen Teslova 3, 301 00, Plzen, Czech Republic
Tel.: (420) 378051500   CZ
Web Site:
https://www.abcheckantibodies.com
Year Founded: 2009
Emp.: 100
Drug Mfr & Distr
N.A.I.C.S.: 325412
Volker Lang (Mng Dir)

ABCLON, INC.
1401 285 Digital-ro, Guro-gu, Seoul, 08381, Korea (South)
Tel.: (82) 221091294   KR
Web Site: https://www.abclon.com
Year Founded: 2010
174900—(KRS)
Rev.: $2,612,744
Assets: $41,464,610
Liabilities: $13,389,707
Net Worth: $28,074,903
Earnings: ($7,097,660)
Emp.: 64
Fiscal Year-end: 12/31/22
Biotechnology Research & Development Services
N.A.I.C.S.: 541714

Jong-Seo Lee (CEO)

ABCO ELECTRONICS CO., LTD.
31 Dunchon-daero 388beon-gil, Jungwon-Gu, Seongnam, Gyeonggi-do, Korea (South)
Tel.: (82) 317305000
Web Site: https://www.abco.co.kr
Year Founded: 1973
036010—(KRS)
Rev.: $126,322,413
Assets: $113,094,613
Liabilities: $23,363,637
Net Worth: $89,730,976
Earnings: $7,178,022
Emp.: 130
Fiscal Year-end: 12/31/22
Electronic Components Mfr
N.A.I.C.S.: 334416
Chang-Soo Kim (CEO)

Subsidiaries:

ABCO Electronics Co., Ltd. - ABCO SHENYANG Plant   (1)
No 1 10-1 Zuxing Road Hunhe Natior Development Zone, Dongling District, Shenyang, China
Tel.: (86) 24 23702150
Electronic Components Mfr
N.A.I.C.S.: 334419

ABCO Electronics Co., Ltd. - ABCO WEIHAI Plant   (1)
Downtown Gangxi-Zhen, Rongcheng, Shandong, China
Tel.: (86) 6317861477
Web Site: http://www.abco.co.kr
Electronic Components Mfr
N.A.I.C.S.: 334419

ABCO Electronics Co., Ltd. - ABCO YANTAI Plant   (1)
17 XiuLin Road Laishan Economic Development Zone, Laishan, Yantai, Shandong, China
Tel.: (86) 535 691 9671
Electronic Components Mfr
N.A.I.C.S.: 334419

ABCO Electronics Vina Co., Ltd.   (1)
Lot CN2-4 Que Vo III Industrial Park, Viet Hung Commune Que Vo District, Bac Ninh, Vietnam
Tel.: (84) 222 390 3234
Electronic Products Mfr
N.A.I.C.S.: 334111

ABCO Hungary Kft   (1)
Ganz Abraham utca 2, H-2001, Godollo, Hungary
Tel.: (36) 28 420 055
Electronic Components Mfr
N.A.I.C.S.: 334416

ABCO Slovakia sro   (1)
Priemyselna 8, 924 01, Galanta, Slovakia
Tel.: (421) 317807087
Electronic Components Mfr
N.A.I.C.S.: 334416

ABCO Tech Co., Ltd.   (1)
36 Naeyong-gil, Jeungpyeong-eup, Jeungpyeong, Chungcheong, Korea (South)
Tel.: (82) 43 820 1121
Electronic Products Mfr
N.A.I.C.S.: 334111

Tianjin Hana International Trading Co., Ltd.   (1)
No 4 Jianfu Road Xiqing District, Tianjin, China
Tel.: (86) 22 2397 7103
Electronic Components Mfr
N.A.I.C.S.: 334416

ABCOURT MINES INC.
475 Avenue de l'eglise, Rouyn-Noranda, J0Z 1Y1, QC, Canada
Tel.: (819) 768-2857
Web Site: https://abcourt.ca
ABI—(TSXV)
Rev.: $5,296,756
Assets: $13,139,684

Abcourt Mines Inc.—(Continued)

Liabilities: $14,550,192
Net Worth: ($1,410,508)
Earnings: ($4,030,087)
Fiscal Year-end: 12/31/23
Mining Exploration Services
N.A.I.C.S.: 213114
Julie Godard (Sec)

Subsidiaries:

Pershimex Resources
Corporation **(1)**
11 Rue Perreault E, Rouyn-Noranda, Montreal, J9X 3CI, QC, Canada
Tel.: (819) 797-2180
Rev.: $139,128
Assets: $6,935,345
Liabilities: $78,660
Net Worth: $6,856,685
Earnings: ($24,510)
Fiscal Year-end: 02/28/2021
Metal Mining Services
N.A.I.C.S.: 212290
Robert Gagnon (CEO)

ABDA INSURANCE
Plaza Asia Lt 27 Jl Jend Sudirman
Kav 59 Jakarta Selatan, Jakarta,
12190, Indonesia
Tel.: (62) 2151401688   Id
Web Site:
     https://www.abdainsurance.co.id
Year Founded: 1982
ABDA—(INDO)
Rev.: $63,239,292
Assets: $173,444,715
Liabilities: $76,338,195
Net Worth: $97,106,520
Earnings: $9,673,320
Emp.: 503
Fiscal Year-end: 12/31/20
Insurance Management Services
N.A.I.C.S.: 524298
Herliniawaty Sutanto (Chm)

ABDI COMPANY JSC
465/191 Seifullin Ave, 050050, Almaty, Kazakhstan
Tel.: (7) 7272333523
Web Site: http://www.abdi.kz
Sales Range: $500-549.9 Million
Emp.: 950
Office Supplies Stores
N.A.I.C.S.: 459410
Abdibek Bimendiev (Pres & CEO)

**ABDUL AALI AL AJMI CO.
LTD.**
Imam Saud Street, PO Box 86059,
Riyadh, 11622, Saudi Arabia
Tel.: (966) 124 02450   SA
Web Site:
     http://www.alajmicompany.com
Year Founded: 1981
Sales Range: $10-24.9 Million
Emp.: 7,000
Engineering & Construction Management Services
N.A.I.C.S.: 541330
Ali Abdulali Al-Ajmi (Chm)

**ABDUL LATIF JAMEEL
GROUP OF COMPANIES**
PO Box 248, Jeddah, 21411, Saudi
Arabia
Tel.: (966) 26930000
Web Site: http://www.alj.com
Year Founded: 1955
Sales Range: $1-4.9 Billion
Emp.: 6,300
Holding Company; Automobile Sales
& Services; Real Estate Services;
Financing; Advertising Services; Consumer Electronics; Durables; Hotels;
Shipping
N.A.I.C.S.: 551112
Saad Alghamdi (Gen Mgr)

Subsidiaries:

Toyota Turkiye Motorlu Araclar
A.S. **(1)**
Gulsuyu Mevkii Ankara Asfalti, 34846, Istanbul, Turkiye **(65%)**
Tel.: (90) 2164585858
Web Site: http://www.toyotasa.com.tr
Sales Range: $50-74.9 Million
Emp.: 150
Automobiles Mfr; Joint Venture of Haci
Omer Sabanci Holding A.S., Toyota Motor
Corp. & Mitsui & Co., Ltd.
N.A.I.C.S.: 336110

**ABDUL MOHSEN AL-HOKAIR
GROUP FOR TOURISM AND
DEVELOPMENT COMPANY**
North Ring Road between exit 4 and
5 after Double Tree Hilton, PO Box
57750, Al Murooj District, Riyadh,
11584, Saudi Arabia
Tel.: (966) 114134444
Web Site: https://www.alhokair.com
Year Founded: 1975
1820—(SAU)
Rev.: $192,212,505
Assets: $551,109,985
Liabilities: $473,742,701
Net Worth: $77,367,284
Earnings: ($21,727,236)
Emp.: 4,100
Fiscal Year-end: 12/31/22
Hotels & Tourism
N.A.I.C.S.: 721110
Mosaad Abdulmohsen Al-Hokair
(Chm)

Subsidiaries:

Sparky's Oceanica Amusement Toys
LLC **(1)**
PO Box 57750, Riyadh, 11584, Saudi Arabia
Tel.: (966) 920006699
Amusement Park Services
N.A.I.C.S.: 713110

**ABDULAZIZ & MANSOUR
IBRAHIM ALBABTIN COM-
PANY**
Khures Road, King Abdullah, Riyadh,
Saudi Arabia
Tel.: (966) 112440849
Web Site:
     https://www.albabtainfood.com
Year Founded: 1998
9549—(SAU)
Rev.: $34,017,961
Assets: $23,831,453
Liabilities: $11,018,695
Net Worth: $12,812,758
Earnings: $4,227,246
Fiscal Year-end: 12/31/21
Foods & Beverage Mfr
N.A.I.C.S.: 333241

**ABDULLA AHMED NASS
GROUP WLL**
Bldg 453 Rd 4308 Block 343, PO
Box 669, Mina Salman Industrial
Area, Manama, 669, Bahrain
Tel.: (973) 17725522
Web Site: http://www.nassgroup.com
Year Founded: 1963
Sales Range: $800-899.9 Million
Emp.: 3,300
Holding Company; Construction,
Manufacturing, Industrial & Trading
Services
N.A.I.C.S.: 551112
Sameer Abdulla Nass (Chm)

Subsidiaries:

Abdulla Nass & Partners Co.
Ltd. **(1)**
AlSalah Tower Prince Faisal Bin Fahd St
28th St, Post Box 31401, Al Khobar, 31952,
Saudi Arabia

Tel.: (966) 3 867 1909
Web Site: http://www.nass-sa.net
Industrial Machinery & Equipment Whslr
N.A.I.C.S.: 423830
Abdulla Ahmed Nass (Chm)

Gulf City Cleaning Company **(1)**
Compound 526 Road 4311 Block 343 Mina
Salman Industrial Area, Post Box 669, Manama, Bahrain
Tel.: (973) 17 729 151
Web Site: http://www.gulfcitycleaning.com
Emp.: 1,200
Cleaning & Waste Disposal Services
N.A.I.C.S.: 221320
James Robert MacDonald (Mgr-Transport &
Maintenance)

Gulf Development Corporation **(1)**
Building 453 Rd 4308 Block 343, PO Box
669, Mina Salman Industrial Area, Manama,
Bahrain
Tel.: (973) 17725522
Web Site: http://www.nassgroup.com
Sales Range: $25-49.9 Million
Emp.: 20
International Marine Services
N.A.I.C.S.: 336611

Nass Corporation B.S.C. **(1)**
PO Box 669, Manama, Bahrain **(51%)**
Tel.: (973) 17725522
Web Site: https://www.nassgroup.com
Rev.: $329,848,015
Assets: $362,605,766
Liabilities: $261,125,700
Net Worth: $101,480,067
Earnings: $1,517,201
Emp.: 1,000
Fiscal Year-end: 12/31/2022
Civil Engineering, Mechanical & Electrical
Contracting Services
N.A.I.C.S.: 237990
Adel Abdulla Nass (Exec Dir)

Subsidiary (Domestic):

Abdulla Ahmed Nass Contracting
Company WLL **(2)**
Bldg 1 007 Rd 31Block 635, PO Box 669,
Ma'ameer, Manama, Bahrain
Tel.: (973) 17725522
Web Site: http://www.nassgroup.com
Rev.: $5,305,000
Emp.: 2,500
Civil Engineering & Building Projects
N.A.I.C.S.: 237990

Delmon Precast Company WLL **(2)**
PO Box No-936, PO Box 669, Manama,
Bahrain
Tel.: (973) 17783838
Web Site: http://www.delmonprecast.com
Sales Range: $25-49.9 Million
Emp.: 100
Precast Concrete Products Mfr
N.A.I.C.S.: 327390

Delmon Ready Mixed Concrete &
Products Co. WLL **(2)**
Rd 239 Block 702 Bldg 1295, PO Box 936,
936, Salmabad, Bahrain
Tel.: (973) 17783838
Web Site: http://www.delmonprecast.com
Sales Range: $200-249.9 Million
Emp.: 550
Readymix Concrete Mfr
N.A.I.C.S.: 327320
Mike Vine (Mgr-Sls)

Division (Domestic):

Nass Commerical **(2)**
Building 989 Road 31 Block 634 Ma'ameer,
PO Box 669, Manama, Bahrain
Tel.: (973) 17 703 123
Sales Range: $25-49.9 Million
Emp.: 40
Agent for Equipment & Manufacturers
N.A.I.C.S.: 423440
Bashar Nass (Dir-Comml)

Nass Corporation BSC (c) - Nass
Foods Division **(2)**
Building 118 Road 3502 Block 635
Ma'ameer, Post Box 669, Manama, Bahrain
Tel.: (973) 17 703 101
Frozen Food Whslr
N.A.I.C.S.: 424420
Abdul Razak (Mgr-Sls & Mktg)

Nass Electrical **(2)**
Building 453 Road 4308 Block 343, PO Box
669, Mina Salman Industrial Area, Manama,
669, Bahrain
Tel.: (973) 17 725 522
Web Site: http://www.nassgroup.com
Electrical & Instrumentation Contracting
N.A.I.C.S.: 238210
Gill JS (Mng Dir)

Nass Mechanical **(2)**
Building 630 Road 102 Block 117, PO Box
669, Hidd, Hidd, Bahrain
Tel.: (973) 17465477
Sales Range: $150-199.9 Million
Emp.: 600
Mechanical Engineering-Design & Fabrication
N.A.I.C.S.: 541330
Gynandra Kumar Roy (Gen Mgr)

Nass Scafform **(2)**
PO Box 669, Manama, Bahrain
Tel.: (973) 17 701 584
Web Site: http://www.nassscafform.com.bh
Scaffolding & Form Work Services
N.A.I.C.S.: 238190

Nop-Nass WLL **(1)**
Shop 704 Al Mazhira Highway Al Jasrah,
Post Box 669, 1004, Manama, Bahrain
Tel.: (973) 17 611 167
Water Supply Services
N.A.I.C.S.: 221310

Shaw Nass Middle East WLL **(1)**
Road 5136 Building 1242 Askar Village, PO
Box 15545, South Alba Industrial Area, Manama, Bahrain
Tel.: (973) 17830988
Web Site: http://www.cbi.com
Sales Range: $100-124.9 Million
Emp.: 350
Fabricated Piping Systems
N.A.I.C.S.: 332996
Mazen Aviziah (VP-Internal Ops)

**ABDULLA FOUAD HOLDING
CO.**
Prince Muhd St, PO Box 257, Dammam, 31411, Saudi Arabia
Tel.: (966) 138141414
Web Site: http://www.abdulla-
fouad.com
Year Founded: 1947
Sales Range: $150-199.9 Million
Emp.: 3,500
Trading Agency Contracting Import
Hospital Computer & Educational Aid
Travel Telecommunication & Electronic Services
N.A.I.C.S.: 523160
Faisal Abdulla (Pres)

Subsidiaries:

Abdulla Fouad Corporation Ltd. **(1)**
PO Box 257, Dammam, 31411, Saudi
Arabia **(100%)**
Tel.: (966) 38141414
Web Site: http://www.abdulla-fouad.com
General Constructors; Civil, Electrical &
Mechanical
N.A.I.C.S.: 237120

Abdulla Fouad Impalloy Ltd. Co. **(1)**
First Industrial Area, Dammam, 31411,
Saudi Arabia **(100%)**
Tel.: (966) 38473300
Web Site: http://www.abdulla-fouad.com
Sales Range: $25-49.9 Million
Emp.: 100
Mfr of Cathodic Protection Systems &
Equipment
N.A.I.C.S.: 335999
Abdullah Fouad (Chm)

Abdulla Fouad Information Technology Co. Ltd. **(1)**
PO Box 257, Dammam, 31411, Saudi
Arabia **(100%)**
Tel.: (966) 38324400
Web Site: http://www.abdulla.fouad.com
Sales Range: $550-599.9 Million
Emp.: 2,000
Sale & Service of Office Machines & Computer Systems

N.A.I.C.S.: 423420

Abdulla Fouad Medical Supplies Division (1)
PO Box 13539, Jeddah, 21414, Saudi Arabia (100%)
Tel.: (966) 126394455
Web Site: http://www.abdulla-fouad.com
Sales Range: $25-49.9 Million
Emp.: 50
Provider of Medical Supplies
N.A.I.C.S.: 423450
Anas Afash (Mgr-Natl Sls)

Abdulla Fouad-Supply & Services Division (1)
PO Box 257, Dammam, 31411, Saudi Arabia (100%)
Tel.: (966) 38101878
Web Site: http://www.abdulla-fouad.com
Sales Range: $25-49.9 Million
Emp.: 18
Petroleum Product Distr
N.A.I.C.S.: 324199
Anes Afash (Gen Mgr)

Abdulla Fouad-Testrade Division (1)
PO Box 257, Dammam, 31411, Saudi Arabia (100%)
Tel.: (966) 38172900
Web Site: http://www.abdullafouad.com
Sales Range: $1-9.9 Million
Emp.: 3
Marketer of Testing Equipment; Paint Inspection Equipment, Radiation Safety Signs & Monitors, Industrial X-Ray Films & Chemicals, Inspection Gauges, Mirrors & Thermometers
N.A.I.C.S.: 423830

Fouad Travel & Cargo Agency (1)
King Saud Street near Hyper Panda, PO Box 257, Dammam, 31411, Eastern Province, Saudi Arabia (100%)
Tel.: (966) 38352020
Web Site: http://www.abdulla-fouad.com
Sales Range: $25-49.9 Million
Emp.: 50
Air Transportation Support Services
N.A.I.C.S.: 488119

Mantech Co., Ltd. (1)
PO Box 257, Dammam, 31411, Saudi Arabia (100%)
Tel.: (966) 38572646
Web Site: http://www.abdullafouad.com
Sales Range: $125-149.9 Million
Emp.: 350
Sales of Toys, Educational Aids & Amusement Facilities
N.A.I.C.S.: 459120

Mantech Computer & Telecommunications Co., Ltd. (1)
Prince Mohammed St, PO Box 257, Dammam, 31411, Saudi Arabia (100%)
Tel.: (966) 38324400
Sales Range: $50-74.9 Million
Emp.: 164
Mfr of Computers, Electronic Games & Software Agencies
N.A.I.C.S.: 449210

ABDULLAH A M AL-KHODARI SONS CO JSC
NSH Tower 10th Floor Dammam AlKhobar Highway, PO Box 3589, Al Khobar, 31952, Saudi Arabia
Tel.: (966) 138147200
Web Site: http://www.alkhodari.com
Year Founded: 1966
1330—(SAU)
Sales Range: $25-49.9 Million
Engineering & Construction Services
N.A.I.C.S.: 541330
Ali Hussain Al Bu Saleh (CEO)

ABDULLAH ABDUL MOHSIN AL-KHODARI SONS COMPANY
NSH Tower 10th Floor Dammam AlKhobar Highway, PO Box 3589, Al Khobar, 31952, Saudi Arabia
Tel.: (966) 13 814 7200
Web Site: http://www.alkhodari.com

Year Founded: 1966
Rev.: $274,531,491
Assets: $742,173,043
Liabilities: $536,948,943
Net Worth: $205,224,100
Earnings: ($31,435,847)
Fiscal Year-end: 12/31/16
General Contracting Services
N.A.I.C.S.: 236220
Ahmed Kanawati (Dir-Tendering)

Subsidiaries:

Al-Khodari Industrial Trading & Services (1)
PO Box 3589, 31952, Al Khobar, Saudi Arabia
Tel.: (966) 38952840
Web Site: http://www.kitsgulf.com
Sales Range: $50-74.9 Million
Emp.: 200
Industrial Equipment Design, Maintenance & Sales
N.A.I.C.S.: 333248

MACE Saudi Arabia Co. Ltd. (1)
PO Box 4164, Al Khobar, Saudi Arabia
Tel.: (966) 3 898 2584
Sales Range: $200-249.9 Million
Emp.: 560
Oil, Gas & Water Pipelines, Petrochemical & Refinery Construction, Industrial Plants & Building Construction & Fire Fighting Systems
N.A.I.C.S.: 237120

ABDULLAH AL-OTHAIM MARKETS COMPANY
Riyadh Kingdom of Saudi Arabia Rabwah East Ring Road Exit 14, PO Box 41700, Riyadh, 11531, Saudi Arabia
Tel.: (966) 118299905　　　　SA
Web Site:
　https://www.othaimmarkets.com
Year Founded: 1956
4001—(SAU)
Rev.: $2,546,205,987
Assets: $1,523,343,563
Liabilities: $1,138,288,479
Net Worth: $385,055,083
Earnings: $288,631,549
Emp.: 18,000
Fiscal Year-end: 12/31/22
Consumer Wholesale Supermarkets, Retail Supermarkets & Convenience Stores Owner & Operator
N.A.I.C.S.: 445110
Fahad Abdullah Al Othaim (Vice Chm)

Subsidiaries:

Abdullah Al Othaim Market Co. (1)
287 Street Apartment 37 off Palestine Street, Maadi, Egypt
Tel.: (20) 19279
Grocery Whslr
N.A.I.C.S.: 424490

Marafeq Al Tashgheel Company (1)
Road 100, Support Industrial Zone, Jubail, 35717, Saudi Arabia
Tel.: (966) 920020084
Web Site: https://www.marafiq.com.sa
Real Estate Development Services
N.A.I.C.S.: 531390

Marafiq Company (1)
Road 100 Support Industrial Zone, Jubail Industrial City, Jubail, 35717, Saudi Arabia
Tel.: (966) 920020084
Web Site: https://www.marafiq.com.sa
Power & Water Utility Services
N.A.I.C.S.: 926130
Abdullah K. Al-Buainain (Pres & CEO)

ABDULLAH HASHIM INDUSTRIAL GASES & EQUIPMENT CO. LTD.
7413 Al-Madinah Al-Munawarah Rd, Al Bawadi, 23443, Jeddah, Saudi Arabia

Tel.: (966) 122 638 222
Web Site: https://www.ahg.com.sa
Emp.: 100
Industrial Gas Mfr
N.A.I.C.S.: 325120
Khalid Hashim (Mng Dir)

Subsidiaries:

Air Liquide Al-Khafrah Industrial Gases LLC (1)
PO Box 43239, 2nd Industrial City, 11561, Riyadh, Saudi Arabia
Tel.: (966) 114981286
Industrial Gas Mfr
N.A.I.C.S.: 325120
Omar Germouni (Gen Mgr)

ABDULLAH SHAH GHAZI SUGAR MILLS LIMITED
65Infantry Road, Lahore, Pakistan
Tel.: (92) 4236834016
Web Site: https://www.asgsml.com
AGSML—(PSX)
Rev.: $1,386,054
Assets: $12,744,456
Liabilities: $14,386,258
Net Worth: ($1,641,802)
Earnings: ($1,020,302)
Emp.: 54
Fiscal Year-end: 09/30/23
Sugar Mfr
N.A.I.C.S.: 311314
Muhammad Irshad Butt (CEO)

ABEN MINERALS LTD
Suite 1610 - 777 Dunsmuir Street, Vancouver, V7Y 1K4, BC, Canada
Tel.: (604) 687-3376
Web Site:
　http://www.abenresources.com
ABN—(OTCIQ)
Rev.: $1,482
Assets: $11,514,310
Liabilities: $82,800
Net Worth: $11,431,511
Earnings: ($470,365)
Fiscal Year-end: 09/30/21
Mineral Exploration Services
N.A.I.C.S.: 213114
Ronald Kort Netolitzky (Chm)

ABENEX CAPITAL S.A.
9 Avenue Matignon, 75008, Paris, France
Tel.: (33) 153936900　　　　FR
Web Site:
　http://www.abenexcapital.com
Rev.: $730,056,000
Emp.: 15
Equity Investment Firm
N.A.I.C.S.: 523999
Herve Claquin (Pres)

Subsidiaries:

Buffalo Grill S.A. (1)
Route Nationale 20, 91630, Avrainville, France
Tel.: (33) 160825400
Web Site: http://www.buffalo-grill.fr
Sales Range: $350-399.9 Million
Restaurant Operators
N.A.I.C.S.: 722511

ABENGOA S.A.
C/ Energia Solar n 1 Palmas Altas, 41014, Seville, Spain
Tel.: (34) 954937000　　　　ES
Web Site: http://www.abengoa.com
Year Founded: 1941
ABGOF—(OTCIQ)
Rev.: $1,671,950,980
Assets: $3,762,729,600
Liabilities: $9,057,427,680
Net Worth: ($5,294,698,080)
Earnings: ($578,967,620)
Emp.: 14,025
Fiscal Year-end: 12/31/19

Industrial Engineering & Construction Services
N.A.I.C.S.: 541330
Gonzalo Urquijo Fernandez De Araoz (Chm)

Subsidiaries:

AAGES Devco Services S.A. (1)
Campus Palmas Altas Calle Energia Solar 1, 41014, Seville, Spain
Tel.: (34) 95 493 7000
Web Site: http://www.aa-ges.com
Energy & Water Infrastructure Services
N.A.I.C.S.: 221116
Armando Zuluaga Zilbermann (CEO)

Joint Venture (Non-US):

Liberty Group Limited (2)
27 Serpentine Road, Pembroke, HM DX, Bermuda
Tel.: (441) 2986100
Web Site: http://www.liberty.bm
Sales Range: $200-249.9 Million
Holding Company; Electric Power Generation & Energy Distribution Services
N.A.I.C.S.: 551112
Wayne M. Caines (Pres)

Subsidiary (Non-US):

BTS Limited (3)
Grevgatan 34, 114 53, Stockholm, Sweden
Tel.: (46) 858707000
Web Site: https://bts.com
Investment Management Service
N.A.I.C.S.: 541611
Henrik Ekelund (Founder)

Subsidiary (Domestic):

Bermuda Electric Light Company Limited (3)
27 Serpentine Road, Pembroke, HM 07, Bermuda
Tel.: (441) 2955111
Web Site: https://www.belco.bm
Electric Power Distribution
N.A.I.C.S.: 221122

Subsidiary (Domestic):

BELCO Properties Limited (4)
PO Box HM 1026, Hamilton, Bermuda
Tel.: (441) 2955111
Residential Property Managers
N.A.I.C.S.: 531311

Subsidiary (Domestic):

PureNERGY Renewables, Ltd (3)
25 Serpentine Road, Pembroke, HM 07, Bermuda
Tel.: (441) 2992808
Web Site: http://www.purenergy.bm
Sales Range: $25-49.9 Million
Emp.: 4
Wind Turbine Mfr
N.A.I.C.S.: 333611

Abengoa Bioenergy Corp. (1)
16150 Main Cricle Dr Ste 300, Chesterfield, MO 63017 (100%)
Tel.: (636) 728-0508
Web Site:
　http://www.abengoabioenergy.com
Sales Range: $50-74.9 Million
Emp.: 200
Producer of Ethanol
N.A.I.C.S.: 325193
Christopher G. Standlee (Exec VP-Institutional Relationships & Global Affairs)

Subsidiary (Domestic):

Abengoa Bioenergy Inc. (2)
523 E Union Ave, Colwich, KS 67030-9723
Tel.: (316) 796-1234
Web Site:
　http://www.abengoabioenergy.com
Sales Range: $25-49.9 Million
Emp.: 55
Ethanol Production
N.A.I.C.S.: 115112

ABEO SAS
6 rue Benjamin Franklin, BP10, 70190, Rioz, France

Abeo SAS—(Continued)

Tel.: (33) 384912450
Web Site: https://www.groupe-abeo.fr
Year Founded: 1955
ABEO—(EUR)
Sales Range: $250-299.9 Million
Emp.: 1,677
Gymnastic Equipment Mfr
N.A.I.C.S.: 339920
Olivier Esteves (CEO)

ABERA BIOSCIENCE AB
Virdings alle 32, PO Box 26029, 750
26, Uppsala, Sweden
Tel.: (46) 704330449
Web Site: https://www.aberabio.com
Year Founded: 2012
8WK—(DEU)
Biotechnology Research & Development Services
N.A.I.C.S.: 541714
Anders Ericson (Chm)

ABERCROSS HOLDINGS LTD.
2 Eaton Gate, SW1W 9BL, London,
United Kingdom - England
Tel.: (44) 7917993394
Web Site: http://www.abercross.com
Privater Equity Firm
N.A.I.C.S.: 523999
Alex Loudon (Partner)

ABERDEEN EMERGING MARKETS EQUITY INCOME, INC.
Bow Bells House 1 Bread Street,
London, EC4M 9HH, United Kingdom
Tel.: (44) 2074636000
C1E—(BER)
Rev.: $11,675,957
Assets: $355,067,818
Liabilities: $61,900,590
Net Worth: $293,167,228
Earnings: $6,144,846
Fiscal Year-end: 12/31/22
Investment Management Service
N.A.I.C.S.: 525990
Devan Kaloo (Mgr-Fund)

ABERDEEN EMERGING MARKETS INVESTMENT CO., LTD.
40 Princes Street, Edinburgh, EH2
2BY, United Kingdom
Tel.: (44) 1315284000
Web Site:
   http://www.aberdeenmarkets.co.uk
Year Founded: 2009
Rev.: $55,349,520
Assets: $433,247,712
Liabilities: $33,380,220
Net Worth: $399,867,492
Earnings: $50,431,020
Fiscal Year-end: 10/31/19
Investment Management Service
N.A.I.C.S.: 523940
Andrew Lister (Mgr-Fund)

ABERDEEN INTERNATIONAL INC.
198 Davenport Road, PO Box 75,
Toronto, M5R 1J2, ON, Canada
Tel.: (416) 861-5882   **ON**
Web Site:
   https://www.aberdeeninternational.ca
Year Founded: 1987
AAB—(TSX)
Sales Range: Less than $1 Million
Emp.: 10
Metal Mining Services
N.A.I.C.S.: 212290
Stan Bharti (Chm)

ABERDEEN STANDARD EUROPEAN LOGISTICS INCOME PLC
Financial Ombudsman Service Ex-

change Tower, London, E14 9SR,
United Kingdom
Tel.: (44) 2079640500
Web Site:
   https://www.eurologistics.co.uk
ASLI—(LSE)
Rev.: $39,022,920
Assets: $871,917,036
Liabilities: $349,500,360
Net Worth: $522,416,676
Earnings: ($19,660,728)
Fiscal Year-end: 12/31/22
Financial Support Services
N.A.I.C.S.: 541611
Tony Roper (Chm)

ABERFORTH PARTNERS LLP
14 Melville St, Edinburgh, EH3 7NS,
United Kingdom
Tel.: (44) 1312200733   **UK**
Web Site: http://www.aberforth.co.uk
Year Founded: 1990
Sales Range: $1-4.9 Billion
Emp.: 11
Equity Investment Firm
N.A.I.C.S.: 523999
Richard Newbery (Partner)

ABERFORTH SMALLER COMPANIES TRUST PLC
14 Melville Street, Edinburgh, EH3
7NS, United Kingdom
Tel.: (44) 1312200733   **UK**
Web Site: http://www.aberforth.co.uk
ASL—(LSE)
Rev.: $71,946,531
Assets: $1,743,316,366
Liabilities: $91,849,778
Net Worth: $1,651,466,588
Earnings: $126,090,389
Fiscal Year-end: 12/31/23
Investment Management Service
N.A.I.C.S.: 525990
Alistair Whyte (Partner)

ABERFORTH SPLIT LEVEL INCOME TRUST PLC
14 Melville Street, Edinburgh, EH3
7NS, United Kingdom
Tel.: (44) 1312200733
Web Site: http://www.aberforth.co.uk
Year Founded: 1990
ASIT—(LSE)
Rev.: $9,813,391
Assets: $200,019,000
Liabilities: $68,921,957
Net Worth: $131,097,043
Earnings: ($74,235,248)
Fiscal Year-end: 06/30/20
Investment Trust Management Services
N.A.I.C.S.: 523940
Angus C. Gordon Lennox (Chm)

ABETRANS LOGISTICS LTD.
58 Hamacabim Street, Rishon le
Zion, Israel
Tel.: (972) 3 7958888
Web Site: http://www.abetrans.net
Year Founded: 1983
Sales Range: $50-74.9 Million
Freight Forwarding Services
N.A.I.C.S.: 488510
Abe Biryan (Founder & CEO)

ABFAR COMPANY (PUBLIC JOINT STOCK)
Lashkari Express Way Karaj Special
Road Km 18, Tehran, Iran
Tel.: (98) 21 44984035
Web Site: http://www.abfar.com
Year Founded: 1968
Water Meter Mfr
N.A.I.C.S.: 339999
Ali Mojtahedi khansari (Mng Dir)

ABG SUNDAL COLLIER HOLDING ASA
Tel.: (47) 22016000
Web Site: http://www.abgsc.com
0IZM—(DEU)
Rev.: $157,428,690
Assets: $361,824,589
Liabilities: $266,987,530
Net Worth: $94,837,059
Earnings: $26,049,233
Emp.: 342
Fiscal Year-end: 12/31/22
Investment Banking Services
N.A.I.C.S.: 523150
Knut Brundtland (Chm)

Subsidiaries:

ABG Sundal Collier AB   **(1)**
Regeringsgatan 65 5th Floor, PO Box 7269,
103 89, Stockholm, Sweden
Tel.: (46) 856628600
Sales Range: $50-74.9 Million
Emp.: 91
Investment Banking Services
N.A.I.C.S.: 523150
Jessica Blink (Head-Compliance)

ABG Sundal Collier Asset Management AS   **(1)**
Munkedamsveien 45 E 7th Floor, Oslo,
0250, Norway
Tel.: (47) 22016000
Web Site: http://www.abgsc.com
Fund Management Services
N.A.I.C.S.: 525910

ABG Sundal Collier Forvaltning
AS   **(1)**
Munkedamsveien 45 D, PO Box 1444,
0115, Oslo, Norway
Tel.: (47) 22016055
Sales Range: $100-124.9 Million
Emp.: 150
Stock Broking Services
N.A.I.C.S.: 523150
Pertha Raldsem (Mgr-IT)

ABG Sundal Collier Inc.   **(1)**
850 Third Ave Ste 9-C, New York, NY,
10022
Tel.: (212) 605-3800
Web Site: http://www.abgsc.com
Securities Brokerage Services
N.A.I.C.S.: 523150

ABG Sundal Collier Ltd.   **(1)**
St Martin's Court 25 Newgate St 5th Floor,
London, EC4M 7EJ, United Kingdom
Tel.: (44) 2079055600
Web Site: http://www.abgsc.com
Sales Range: $50-74.9 Million
Investment Banking Services
N.A.I.C.S.: 523150

ABG Sundal Collier Norge ASA   **(1)**
Munkedamsveien 45 7th Floor, 0250, Oslo,
Norway
Tel.: (47) 22016000
Investment Banking Services
N.A.I.C.S.: 523150
Jan Petter Collier (Mng Dir)

Vika Project Finance AS   **(1)**
Munkedamsveien 45 E, 0250, Oslo, Norway
Tel.: (47) 22016000
Web Site: https://www.vikapf.no
Real Estate Investment Services
N.A.I.C.S.: 531210

ABH HOLDINGS S.A.
27 Kalanchevskaya str, 107078, Moscow, Russia
Tel.: (7) 495 795 3711   **LU**
Sales Range: $5-14.9 Billion
Investment Holding Company
N.A.I.C.S.: 551112
Petr Aven (Chm)

Subsidiaries:

ABH Financial Limited   **(1)**
27 Kalanchevskaya str, 107078, Moscow,
Russia   **(100%)**
Tel.: (7) 495 795 3711
Web Site: http://www.alfabank.com
Rev.: $5,537,000,000

Assets: $59,466,000,000
Liabilities: $51,324,000,000
Net Worth: $8,142,000,000
Earnings: $975,000,000
Fiscal Year-end: 12/31/2019
Bank Holding Company
N.A.I.C.S.: 551111

Subsidiary (Domestic):

Alfa-Bank JSC   **(2)**
27 Kalanchevskaya Street, 107078, Moscow, Russia   **(100%)**
Tel.: (7) 4956209191
Web Site: http://alfabank.ru
Emp.: 23,755
Commercial & Investment Banking Services
N.A.I.C.S.: 522110
Mikhail Grachev (Head-Capital Markets)

Subsidiary (Non-US):

Amsterdam Trade Bank N.V.   **(3)**
World Trade Center Tower I Level 6
Strawinskylaan 1939, 1077 XX, Amsterdam,
Netherlands
Tel.: (31) 205 209 209
Web Site:
   http://www.amsterdamtradebank.com
Rev.: $61,295,537
Assets: $1,560,546,187
Liabilities: $1,368,359,174
Net Worth: $192,187,014
Earnings: ($22,879,860)
Emp.: 116
Fiscal Year-end: 12/31/2019
Commodity Financing Services
N.A.I.C.S.: 522299
Oren Bass (CEO & Member-Mgmt Bd)

ABHIJIT TRADING COMPANY LTD.
16/121-122 Jain Bhawan Faiz Road,
W E A Karol Bagh, New Delhi, 110
005, India
Tel.: (91) 9891095232
Web Site:
   https://www.abhijittrading.in
Year Founded: 1982
539560—(BOM)
Rev.: $46,219
Assets: $1,223,927
Liabilities: $8,640
Net Worth: $1,215,287
Earnings: $20,530
Emp.: 3
Fiscal Year-end: 03/31/21
Financial Support Services
N.A.I.C.S.: 523999
Dharmesh Jha (CFO)

ABHINAV CAPITAL SERVICES LIMITED
B709 Experss Zone Western Express
Highway, Gokuldham Goregaon East,
Mumbai, 400063, Maharashtra, India
Tel.: (91) 2228425907
Web Site:
   https://www.abhinavcapital.com
Year Founded: 1994
532057—(BOM)
Rev.: $443,790
Assets: $4,367,014
Liabilities: $23,379
Net Worth: $4,343,635
Earnings: $109,343
Emp.: 5
Fiscal Year-end: 03/31/21
Financial Management Services
N.A.I.C.S.: 523999
Chetan Rasik Karia (Chm & Mng Dir)

ABHINAV LEASING & FINANCE LIMITED
S-524 Ist Floor Vikas Marg Shakarpur, New Delhi, 110092, India
Tel.: (91) 1140108941
Web Site:
   https://www.abhinavleasefinltd.in
Year Founded: 1984

538952—(BOM)
Rev.: $5,162,512
Assets: $7,553,289
Liabilities: $6,881,438
Net Worth: $671,851
Earnings: $11,597
Fiscal Year-end: 03/31/23
Financial Support Services
N.A.I.C.S.: 523999
Himanshu Agarwal *(CFO)*

ABHISHEK FINLEASE LIMITED
402 Wall Street 1 Opp Orient Club
Near Gujarat College Ellisbridge,
Ahmedabad, 380 009, Gujarat, India
Tel.: (91) 7926464089
Web Site:
https://www.finservices.co.in
Year Founded: 1995
538935—(BOM)
Rev.: $10,186,231,965
Assets: $61,907,852,370
Liabilities: $5,856,613,035
Net Worth: $56,051,239,335
Earnings: $1,278,046,770
Fiscal Year-end: 03/31/22
Investment Management Service
N.A.I.C.S.: 523940
Mahendrabhai Manchndlal Shah
(Chm & Mng Dir)

ABHISHEK INFRAVENTURES LIMITED
Block No 6C/2 6th Floor Melange
Towers, Madhapur, Hyderabad,
500081, Telangana, India
Tel.: (91) 7013808380
Web Site:
https://www.abhishekinfra.co.in
539544—(BOM)
Rev.: $15,185,303
Assets: $856,835
Liabilities: $510,752
Net Worth: $346,083
Earnings: ($35,423)
Emp.: 2
Fiscal Year-end: 03/31/22
Construction Engineering Services
N.A.I.C.S.: 541330
Ramachandra Murthy Adiraju *(CFO)*

ABHISHEK INTEGRATIONS LIMITED
801 Venus Benecia Pakvan Dining
Lane Opp Rajpath Club S G High-
way, Bodakdev, Ahmedabad, 380053,
India
Tel.: (91) 7946048231
Web Site:
https://www.abhishekintegration.com
Year Founded: 2017
AILIMITED—(NSE)
Rev.: $2,712,116
Assets: $1,701,493
Liabilities: $686,458
Net Worth: $1,015,035
Earnings: $80,631
Emp.: 568
Fiscal Year-end: 03/31/23
Business Development Services
N.A.I.C.S.: 541611

ABHOTEL CO., LTD.
6F 2nd Tosho Building 1-9-2 Mikawa,
Aichi, Anjo, 446-0056, Japan
Tel.: (81) 566793013
Web Site: https://www.ab-hotel.jp
Year Founded: 2014
6565—(TKS)
Sales Range: Less than $1 Million
Hotel & Resort Operator
N.A.I.C.S.: 721110
Kazuki Kutsuna *(Pres & CEO)*

ABICO GROUP
4F No 8 Lane 7 Wu-Chuan Road,

Wugu District, Taipei, 248, Taiwan
Tel.: 2 2299 9898
Web Site: http://www.abico.com.tw
Holding Company
N.A.I.C.S.: 551112
Ching-Hsiung Tong *(Co-Founder & Chm)*

Subsidiaries:

Ability Enterprise Co., Ltd **(1)**
No 200 Sec 3 Zhonghuan Rd, Xinzhuang
Dist, New Taipei City, 24242, Taiwan
Tel.: (886) 285229788
Web Site: http://www.abilitycorp.com.tw
Rev.: $161,314,168
Assets: $296,345,254
Liabilities: $75,478,271
Net Worth: $220,866,983
Earnings: $7,932,660
Emp.: 555
Fiscal Year-end: 12/31/2023
Optical Imaging Products Mfr
N.A.I.C.S.: 333310
Ching-Hsi Tong *(Founder)*

Ability International Co., Ltd. **(1)**
37 Dongxing Road 2nd Floor, Xinyi District,
Taipei, Taiwan
Tel.: (886) 2 8768 3658
Web Site: http://ai.abico.com.tw
Office Machine Distr
N.A.I.C.S.: 423430

Daiichi Kasei Co., Ltd. **(1)**
154 Shimokoyama, Shimotsuke, 329-0502,
Tochigi, Japan **(100%)**
Tel.: (81) 285537211
Web Site: http://www.ikka.co.jp
Precision Injection Moldings & Assemblies
Mfr
N.A.I.C.S.: 339999
Masami Ohara *(Pres & Dir)*

Subsidiary (Non-US):

IKKA (HONG KONG) CO.,
LIMITED **(2)**
Room 802 Empire Centre 68 Mody Road
Tsimshatsui East, Kowloon, China (Hong
Kong)
Tel.: (852) 26340633
Sales Range: $25-49.9 Million
Emp.: 3
Precision Tools Distr
N.A.I.C.S.: 423830
Taka Yuki Saito *(Mng Dir)*

Subsidiary (Non-US):

IKKA Technology DongGuan Co.,
Ltd. **(3)**
15 Building The Shilong Hi Tech Infomation
Industrial Park, Shilong Town, Dongguan,
523000, Guangdong, China
Tel.: (86) 76986186060
Precision Moldings & Assemblies Mfr
N.A.I.C.S.: 333511

Subsidiary (Non-US):

IKKA TECHNOLOGY (VIETNAM)
CO., LTD. **(2)**
Lot 6 Tan Truong Industrial Zone, Cam Gi-
ang, Hai Duong, Vietnam
Tel.: (84) 3203570188
Web Site: http://www.ikka.co.jp
Precision Injection Molded Products & As-
semblies Mfr
N.A.I.C.S.: 332321

M.A.C. Technology (M) Sdn.
Bhd. **(2)**
Lot 16 Jalan Bunga Tanjung 2, Senawang
Industrial Park, Seremban, 70400, Negeri
Sembilan, Malaysia
Tel.: (60) 66781311
Web Site: http://www.mactech-my.com
Sales Range: $25-49.9 Million
Automotive Moldings Mfr
N.A.I.C.S.: 339999
Hooi Chee Whitlock *(COO)*

ABICO HOLDINGS PUBLIC COMPANY LIMITED
401/1 Moo 8 5th floor ABICO Building
Phaholyothin Road, Khookhot Sub-

District Lamlukka District, Pa-
thumthani, 12130, Thani, Thailand
Tel.: (66) 20807899
Web Site: http://www.abicogroup.com
Year Founded: 1984
ABICO—(THA)
Rev.: $77,036,010
Assets: $65,564,298
Liabilities: $32,532,814
Net Worth: $33,031,484
Earnings: $1,536,480
Emp.: 396
Fiscal Year-end: 12/31/21
Holding Company
N.A.I.C.S.: 551112
Kitti Vilaivarangkul *(Mng Dir)*

ABICO NETCOM CO., LTD.
13F-1 No 27 Lane 169 Kang-Ning St,
Hsi-Chih Dist, New Taipei City, Tai-
wan
Tel.: (886) 226923636
Web Site: https://www.fstdisc.com.tw
Year Founded: 1993
8071—(TPE)
Rev.: $79,822,156
Assets: $79,752,400
Liabilities: $45,309,414
Net Worth: $34,442,985
Earnings: $1,992,496
Fiscal Year-end: 12/31/22
Computer Product Mfr
N.A.I.C.S.: 334111

ABILENE OIL & GAS LIMITED
Level 4 100 Albert Road, South Mel-
bourne, 3205, VIC, Australia
Tel.: (61) 3 9692 7222
Web Site: http://www.abilene.com.au
Rev.: $248,875
Assets: $4,424,708
Liabilities: $4,556,666
Net Worth: ($131,958)
Earnings: ($1,038,282)
Emp.: 6
Fiscal Year-end: 06/30/18
Oil Production Services
N.A.I.C.S.: 211120
Melanie Leydin *(Sec)*

ABILITY INC.
Yad Harutzim 14, Tel Aviv, 6770007,
Israel
Tel.: (972) 36879777 DE
Web Site:
http://www.interceptors.com
Year Founded: 2013
ABIL—(TAE)
Rev.: $535,958
Assets: $4,290,765
Liabilities: $7,163,696
Net Worth: ($2,872,931)
Earnings: ($2,083,279)
Emp.: 14
Fiscal Year-end: 12/31/21
Satellite Telecommunication Services
Provider
N.A.I.C.S.: 517410
Anatoly Hurgin *(Co-Founder, Chm & CEO)*

ABILITY OPTO-ELECTRONICS TECHNOLOGY CO., LTD.
2F No 33 Keya Rd, Daya, Taichung,
428, Taiwan
Tel.: (886) 425659888
Web Site: http://www.aoet.com.tw
Year Founded: 1986
3362—(TPE)
Rev.: $114,507,051
Assets: $225,281,712
Liabilities: $129,625,395
Net Worth: $95,656,317
Earnings: $12,932,620
Emp.: 2,500
Fiscal Year-end: 12/31/22
Optical Equipment Distr

N.A.I.C.S.: 423460
Lin Chung-Ho *(Chm)*

Subsidiaries:

Top Opto Tec Co., Ltd. **(1)**
Road 22 Tan Thuan Export Processing
Zone, District 7, Ho Chi Minh City, Vietnam
Tel.: (84) 837700305
Optical Glass Mfr & Distr
N.A.I.C.S.: 334610

**ABINGDON FURNITURE GAL-
LERY LIMITED**
Unit 3 Eyston Way, Abingdon, OX14
1TR, Oxfordshire, United Kingdom
Tel.: (44) 1235558000
Web Site: http://www.afgltd.eu
Year Founded: 2007
Emp.: 5
Kitchen Designing & Installation Ser-
vices
N.A.I.C.S.: 541490
Sue Watson *(Mgr-Design)*

ABINGDON HEALTH PLC
York Biotech Campus Sand Hutton,
York, YO41 1LZ, United Kingdom
Tel.: (44) 1904406050 UK
Web Site:
https://www.abingdonhealth.com
Year Founded: 2008
ABDX—(AIM)
Rev.: $5,106,034
Assets: $7,650,846
Liabilities: $3,852,562
Net Worth: $3,798,283
Earnings: ($4,356,223)
Emp.: 82
Fiscal Year-end: 06/30/23
Diagnostic Equipment Mfr
N.A.I.C.S.: 325412
Chris Hand *(Chm)*

ABINGTON RESOURCES LTD.
125A - 1030 Denman Street, Vancou-
ver, V6G 2M6, BC, Canada
Tel.: (604) 683-6657 BC
Web Site:
http://www.abingtonresources.com
Year Founded: 1999
Sales Range: Less than $1 Million
Emp.: 1
Oil & Gas Exploration Services
N.A.I.C.S.: 211120

ABINGWORTH LLP
38 Jermyn Street, London, SW1Y
6DN, United Kingdom
Tel.: (44) 20 7534 1500
Web Site: http://www.abingworth.com
Investment Services
N.A.I.C.S.: 523999
Bali Muralidhar *(Partner)*

ABION, INC.
9th Fl HanWha Biz Metro Building
242, Digital-ro Guro-gu, Seoul,
08394, Korea (South)
Tel.: (82) 260067657
Web Site: https://www.abionbio.com
Year Founded: 2007
Pharmaceuticals Product Mfr
N.A.I.C.S.: 325412
Shin Young Key *(CEO & CTO)*

ABIONYX PHARMA SA
33 43 av Georges Pompidou Bat D2,
31130, Balma, France
Tel.: (33) 562249706
Web Site: https://www.abionyx.com
ABNX—(EUR)
Sales Range: Less than $1 Million
Pharmaceuticals Mfr
N.A.I.C.S.: 325412
Cyrille Tupin *(CEO)*

Abionyx Pharma SA—(Continued)

Subsidiaries:

Cerenis Therapeutics Inc. **(1)**
900 Victors Way Ste 280, Ann Arbor, MI
48108-5211
Tel.: (734) 769-1110
Web Site: http://www.cerenis.com
Pharmaceuticals Mfr
N A I C S : 325412
Shawn Siddall-Benoit *(Controller-Fin)*

Lypro Biosciences, Inc. **(1)**
1236 Hawthorne St, Alameda, CA 94502
Tel.: (510) 748-9100
Web Site: http://www.lyprobio.com
Research & Development in the Physical,
Engineering & Life Sciences
N.A.I.C.S.: 541715

**ABIRAMI FINANCIAL SER-
VICES INDIA LTD.**
New No 16 Old No 50 South Boag
Road T Nagar, Chennai, 600 017,
Tamil Nadu, India
Tel.: (91) 4424356224
Web Site: https://www.afslindia.in
511756—(BOM)
Rev.: $63,293
Assets: $1,066,940
Liabilities: $10,064
Net Worth: $1,056,876
Earnings: ($25,510)
Fiscal Year-end: 03/31/22
Financial Services
N.A.I.C.S.: 522220
P. Sankaran *(Exec Dir)*

ABIRD HOLDING BV
Wolgaweg 21, 3198 LR, Rotterdam,
Netherlands
Tel.: (31) 104165511
Web Site: http://www.abird.nl
Sales Range: $10-24.9 Million
Emp.: 120
Industrial Equipment Rental Services
N.A.I.C.S.: 532412
Michel Hogervorst *(Mng Dir)*

Subsidiaries:

De Wit Las- en Snijtechniek BV **(1)**
Kampstraat 80, 6163 HG, Geleen, Limburg,
Netherlands
Tel.: (31) 464740404
Web Site: http://www.dewitlastechniek.nl
Industrial Equipment Rental Services
N.A.I.C.S.: 532490

Hef & Hijs Nederland B.V. **(1)**
Valkenierstraat 34, 2984 AZ, Ridderkerk,
South Holland, Netherlands
Tel.: (31) 180440044
Web Site: http://www.hefhijs.nl
Industrial Equipment Rental Services
N.A.I.C.S.: 532490

Kamphuis Lastechniek BV **(1)**
Phileas Foggstraat 56, 7825 AL, Emmen,
Netherlands
Tel.: (31) 591631313
Web Site:
http://www.kamphuislastechniek.nl
Industrial Equipment Rental Services
N.A.I.C.S.: 532490

ABIST CO., LTD.
5th floor Tricona 3-36-1 Shimorenjaku
Mitaka, Nakano-ku, Tokyo, 181-0013,
Japan
Tel.: (81) 422265960
Web Site: https://www.abist.co.jp
Year Founded: 2006
6087—(TKS)
Rev.: $64,785,040
Assets: $57,989,600
Liabilities: $15,417,760
Net Worth: $42,571,840
Earnings: $2,518,880
Emp.: 1,271
Fiscal Year-end: 09/30/22
Machine & Machine Parts Mfr

N.A.I.C.S.: 332710
Norikazu Maruyama *(Mng Dir)*

ABITARE IN S.P.A.
Via degli Olivetani 10/12, Milan, Italy
Tel.: (39) 026702550
Web Site:
https://www.abitareinspa.com
ART—(ITA)
Rev.: $128,384,560
Assets: $308,115,019
Liabilities: $187,070,302
Net Worth: $121,044,717
Earnings: $26,671,265
Emp.: 54
Fiscal Year-end: 09/30/23
Building Construction Services
N.A.I.C.S.: 562910
Luigi Francesco Gozzini *(Chm)*

ABITIBI MINING CORP.
711-675 West Hastings Street, Van-
couver, V6B 1N2, BC, Canada
Tel.: (604) 685-2222
Web Site: http://www.abitibi-
mining.com
Mineral Exploration Services
N.A.I.C.S.: 213114
Richard W. Hughes *(Pres, CEO &
Sec)*

ABITS GROUP INC.
Room 1202 Block B Jiahui Center 6
Jiqing Li Chaoyangmenwai Street,
Chaoyang District, Beijing, 100020,
China
Tel.: (86) 1053320602
Web Site:
https://www.moxianglobal.com
ABTS—(NASDAQ)
Rev.: $219,330
Assets: $7,737,112
Liabilities: $1,170,096
Net Worth: $6,567,016
Earnings: ($2,739,850)
Emp.: 8
Fiscal Year-end: 12/31/21
Investment Services
N.A.I.C.S.: 523999

Subsidiaries:

Moxian (Hong Kong) Limited **(1)**
Unit 911 Tower 2 Silvercord 30 Canton
Road, Tsimshatsui, Hong Kong, China
(Hong Kong)
Tel.: (852) 29614888
Holding Company; Mobile Payment Applica-
tions & Digital Advertising Services
N.A.I.C.S.: 551112

ABIVAX SA
7-11 Boulevard Haussmann, 75009,
Paris, France
Tel.: (33) 153830841
Web Site: https://www.abivax.com
Year Founded: 2013
ABVX—(EUR)
Rev.: $4,987,049
Assets: $352,969,998
Liabilities: $141,433,197
Net Worth: $211,536,801
Earnings: ($159,443,125)
Emp.: 61
Fiscal Year-end: 12/31/23
Pharmaceuticals Mfr
N.A.I.C.S.: 325412
Hartmut J. Ehrlich *(CEO & Member-
Exec Bd)*

ABKO CO., LTD.
M Signature 7th Floor 20 Magokjun-
gang 1-Ro, Gangsero-Gu, Seoul, Ko-
rea (South)
Tel.: (82) 27491311
Web Site:
https://www.abkoglobal.com
Year Founded: 2001

129890—(KRS)
Rev.: $63,402,799
Assets: $76,490,613
Liabilities: $33,432,056
Net Worth: $43,058,557
Earnings: ($13,521,143)
Emp.: 81
Fiscal Year-end: 12/31/22
Computer Equipment Mfr
N.A.I.C.S.: 334118
Kwang Geun Oh *(CEO)*

ABL BIO, INC.
2nd Floor16 Daewangpangyo-Ro 712
Beon-Gil, Bundang-Gu, Seongnam,
13488, Gyeonggi-do, Korea (South)
Tel.: (82) 3180189800
Web Site: https://www.ablbio.com
Year Founded: 2016
298380—(KRS)
Rev.: $4,905,503
Assets: $60,216,535
Liabilities: $8,739,831
Net Worth: $51,476,704
Earnings: ($40,073,308)
Emp.: 92
Fiscal Year-end: 12/31/21
Medicinal Chemical Mfr
N.A.I.C.S.: 325411
Weon Kyoo You *(Head-R&D)*

ABL GROUP ASA
Karenslyst alle 4, 1387, Asker, Nor-
way
Tel.: (47) 2072643250
Web Site: https://www.abl-group.com
26Q—(DEU)
Rev.: $167,897,000
Assets: $126,928,000
Liabilities: $58,501,000
Net Worth: $68,427,000
Earnings: $6,253,000
Emp.: 1,027
Fiscal Year-end: 12/31/22
Marine & Engineering Services to Oil
& Gas Industry
N.A.I.C.S.: 237990
David Wells *(CEO)*

Subsidiaries:

AqualisBraemar Technical Services
Ltd. **(1)**
5th Floor 6 Bevis Marks, London, EC3A
7BA, United Kingdom
Tel.: (44) 203 142 4300
Web Site: http://www.aqualisbraemar.com
Marine Consulting Services
N.A.I.C.S.: 541330

Subsidiary (Domestic):

AqualisBraemar Technical Services
(Adjusting) Limited **(2)**
5th Floor 6 Bevis, London, EC3N 2JY,
United Kingdom **(100%)**
Tel.: (44) 203 142 4300
Web Site: http://braemaradjusting.com
Sales Range: $25-49.9 Million
Emp.: 12
Marine Engineering Services
N.A.I.C.S.: 541330
George Mowatt *(Dir-Technical)*

Subsidiary (Non-US):

Braemar Steege Canada Limited **(3)**
840-7th Ave SW Ste 820, Calgary, T2P
3G2, AB, Canada
Tel.: (403) 538-5450
Marine Engineering Services
N.A.I.C.S.: 541330

Subsidiary (US):

Braemar Steege Inc **(3)**
2800 N Loop W, Houston, TX 77092
Tel.: (713) 688-5353
Marine Shipping Services
N.A.I.C.S.: 483111
Deborah Eakin *(Gen Mgr)*

Subsidiary (Non-US):

Braemar Steege Rio de Janeiro **(3)**
Rua Dalcidio Jurandire 255 Conj 311/312,
Barra da Tijuca, Rio de Janeiro, 22631-250,
Brazil
Tel.: (55) 2135932008
Sales Range: $25-49.9 Million
Emp.: 7
Marine Engineering Services
N.A.I.C.S.: 541330
Jaime Talbot *(COO)*

Braemar Steege Shanghai **(3)**
440-442 The Bund 12 Zhong Shan Dong Yi
Road, Shanghai, 200002, China
Tel.: (86) 21 6321 2233
Sales Range: $25-49.9 Million
Emp.: 10
Marine Engineering Services
N.A.I.C.S.: 541330

Subsidiary (US):

Braemar Steege, LLC **(3)**
1000 Memorial Dr, Houston, TX 77024
Tel.: (832) 203-5238
Sales Range: $25-49.9 Million
Emp.: 10
Marine Engineering Services
N.A.I.C.S.: 541330

ABLE & PARTNERS CO., LTD.
10th Floor 107-0051 Minato-ku, To-
kyo, Japan
Tel.: (81) 357702600
Web Site: http://www.able-
partners.co.jp
Year Founded: 2010
Emp.: 3,266
Real Estate Brokerage & Other Real
Estate Services
N.A.I.C.S.: 531210
Ryu-shi Hirata *(Pres & COO)*

ABLE C&C CO., LTD.
7F TIMEWALK Myeongdong,
Namdaemun-ro, Seoul, 04534, Korea
(South)
Tel.: (82) 221990123
Web Site: https://www.able-cnc.com
078520—(KRS)
Rev.: $190,118,736
Assets: $149,896,158
Liabilities: $60,866,356
Net Worth: $89,029,801
Earnings: $717,502
Emp.: 274
Fiscal Year-end: 12/31/22
Cosmetics Mfr
N.A.I.C.S.: 325620

**ABLE ENGINEERING HOLD-
INGS LIMITED**
155 Waterloo Road Kowloon Tong,
Kowloon, China (Hong Kong)
Tel.: (852) 27960960
Web Site: http://www.ableeng.com.hk
Year Founded: 1976
1627—(HKG)
Rev.: $719,387,756
Assets: $506,428,104
Liabilities: $322,963,985
Net Worth: $183,464,119
Earnings: $15,849,062
Emp.: 352
Fiscal Year-end: 03/31/22
Engineering & Construction Services
N.A.I.C.S.: 541330
Kwok Fai Yau *(Chm & Exec Dir)*

ABLE GLOBAL BERHAD
PTD 124298 Jalan Kempas Lama
Kampung Seelong Jaya, Johor Darul
Takzim, 81300, Johor Bahru, 81300,
Johor, Malaysia
Tel.: (60) 75998990
Web Site:
https://www.ableglobalbhd.com.my

ABLEGLOB—(KLS)
Rev.: $116,364,489
Assets: $152,510,664
Liabilities: $67,260,100
Net Worth: $85,250,564
Earnings: $7,108,666
Emp.: 199
Fiscal Year-end: 12/31/22
Tins, Cans & Containers Mfr
N.A.I.C.S.: 332431
May Li Yong *(Co-Sec)*

Subsidiaries:

Kluang Tin And Can Factory Sdn.
Bhd.   **(1)**
PTD 124298 Jalan Kempas Lama Kampung Seelong Jaya, 81300, Skudai, Johor
Darul Takzim, Malaysia
Tel.: (60) 75998990
Web Site: http://www.johoretin.com.my
Sales Range: $25-49.9 Million
Emp.: 60
Tin & Can Mfr
N.A.I.C.S.: 332431

ABLEGROUP BERHAD

Block D4 U2 10 Level 2 Solaris Dutamas No 1 Jalan Dutamas 1, 50480,
Kuala Lumpur, Malaysia
Tel.: (60) 362078186
Web Site:
  https://www.ablegroup.com.my
ABLEGRP—(KLS)
Rev.: $941,821
Assets: $9,659,525
Liabilities: $570,554
Net Worth: $9,088,971
Earnings: $14,206
Fiscal Year-end: 12/31/22
Processing, Trading, Exporting &
Contract Workmanship of Marble &
Granite Slabs
N.A.I.C.S.: 327991
Kim Huat Lim *(Mng Dir)*

Subsidiaries:

Atlas Rhythm Sdn. Bhd.   **(1)**
Block D4-U2-10 Level 2 Solaris Dutamas
No 1 Jalan Dutamas 1, 50480, Kuala Lumpur, Malaysia
Tel.: (60) 362078186
Granite & Marble Mfr
N.A.I.C.S.: 327991

Syarikat Bukit Granite Sdn. Bhd. **(1)**
10th Floor Plaza Montkiara Blok E Jln
1/70c, 50480, Kuala Lumpur, Malaysia
Tel.: (60) 362013978
Sales Range: $25-49.9 Million
Emp.: 30
Marble & Granite Mfr
N.A.I.C.S.: 339999

ABLEREX ELECTRONICS CO., LTD.

1F No 3 Lane 7 Baogao Rd, Xindian
Dist, 23144, New Taipei City, 23144,
Taiwan
Tel.: (886) 229176857
Web Site:
  https://www.ablerex.com.tw
Year Founded: 1994
3628—(TPE)
Rev.: $95,606,009
Assets: $116,140,325
Liabilities: $61,473,877
Net Worth: $54,666,448
Earnings: $3,558,891
Emp.: 527
Fiscal Year-end: 12/31/22
Electric Equipment Mfr
N.A.I.C.S.: 335999

Subsidiaries:

Ablerex Corporation   **(1)**
1175 S Grove Ave Ste 103, Ontario, CA
91761
Tel.: (909) 930-0201
Web Site: http://www.ablerexusa.com
UPS Mfr

N.A.I.C.S.: 339940
Ablerex Electronics (Beijing) Co.,
Ltd.   **(1)**
A-9C1 Golden Resources Business Center
No 2 East Road, LanDianChang HaiDian
District, Beijing, China
Tel.: (86) 1088865103
UPS Distr
N.A.I.C.S.: 423610

Ablerex Electronics (S) Pte. Ltd. **(1)**
23 New Industrial Road 05-03 Solstice
Business Center, 23 New Industrial Road,
Singapore, 536209, Singapore
Tel.: (65) 62826535
Web Site: https://www.ablerex.com.sg
UPS Whslr
N.A.I.C.S.: 423610
Dex Lim *(Mgr-Engrg)*

Ablerex Electronics (Suzhou) Co.,
Ltd.   **(1)**
No 36 Wang Wu Road, Wu Zhong District,
Suzhou, 215128, China
Tel.: (86) 51265250225
UPS Distr
N.A.I.C.S.: 423610

Ablerex Electronics (Thailand) Co.,
Ltd.   **(1)**
18 Srichaloernchai Building Room 9C 9th
Floor Tiwanon Road, Taladkwan Muang,
Nonthaburi, 11000, Thailand
Tel.: (66) 20498262
Web Site: http://www.ablerexthailand.com
UPS Mfr & Whslr
N.A.I.C.S.: 339940

Ablerex Electronics Italy S.R.L. **(1)**
Viale Milanofiori-Strada 6 Palazzo N1,
20089, Rozzano, MI, Italy
Tel.: (39) 0236696420
Web Site: https://www.ablerex.eu
UPS Distr
N.A.I.C.S.: 423610
Roberto Sabbadin *(Mng Dir)*

Ablerex Latam Corporation   **(1)**
1500 NW 89th Ct Ste 122, Doral, FL 33172
Tel.: (786) 340-3769
UPS Mfr & Whslr
N.A.I.C.S.: 339940
Tito M. Chamorro *(Dir-Svc Support)*

Wada Denki Co., Ltd.   **(1)**
1-7-10 Ningyocho, Nihonbashi Chuo-ku,
Tokyo, Japan
Tel.: (81) 366616447
UPS Distr
N.A.I.C.S.: 423610

ABLETON AG

Schonhauser Allee 6/7, 10119, Berlin,
Germany
Tel.: (49) 30 2887630
Web Site: http://www.ableton.com
Year Founded: 1999
Emp.: 270
Music Production Software Mfr
N.A.I.C.S.: 513210
Robert Henke *(Co-Founder)*

Subsidiaries:

Cycling 74   **(1)**
340 S Lemon Ave #4074, Walnut, CA
91789
Tel.: (415) 974-1818
Web Site: http://www.cycling74.com
Electronics Stores
N.A.I.C.S.: 449210
Andrea R. Isom *(Mgr-Acctg)*

ABLIVA AB

Medicon Village, SE-223 81, Lund,
Sweden
Tel.: (46) 462756220
Web Site: https://abliva.com
Year Founded: 2000
NEVPF—(OTCIQ)
Rev.: $13,600
Assets: $8,686,144
Liabilities: $1,665,873
Net Worth: $7,020,271
Earnings: ($9,481,307)

Emp.: 8
Fiscal Year-end: 12/31/23
Pharmaceuticals Mfr
N.A.I.C.S.: 325412
Eskil Elmer *(Chief Scientific Officer &
VP-Discovery)*

ABLON GROUP LIMITED

Frances House Sir William Place,
Saint Peter Port, GY1 4HQ, Guernsey
Tel.: (44) 2074483244
Web Site: http://www.ablongroup.com
Sales Range: $25-49.9 Million
Real Estate Services
N.A.I.C.S.: 531210
Uri Heller *(CEO)*

Subsidiaries:

ABLON Kft.   **(1)**
Vaci ut 30, 1132, Budapest, Hungary
Tel.: (36) 12256600
Web Site: http://www.ablon.hu
Sales Range: $25-49.9 Million
Emp.: 50
Real Estate Property Development Services
N.A.I.C.S.: 531390
Matyas Gereben *(Mng Dir)*

ABLON Sp. z o.o.   **(1)**
ul Nowy Swiat 60 Apt 2C, 00-357, Warsaw,
Poland
Tel.: (48) 228920610
Web Site: http://www.ablon.pl
Sales Range: $25-49.9 Million
Emp.: 8
Real Estate Property Development Services
N.A.I.C.S.: 531210

ABLON s.r.l.   **(1)**
Delea Veche 24 Building A 1 Fl, Bucharest,
024102, Romania
Tel.: (40) 318059346
Web Site: http://www.ablon.ro
Sales Range: $50-74.9 Million
Emp.: 2
Real Estate Development Services
N.A.I.C.S.: 531311

ABLON s.r.o.   **(1)**
Sokolovska 100 94, Karlin, 186 00, Prague,
Czech Republic
Tel.: (420) 227133111
Web Site: http://www.ablon.cz
Sales Range: $50-74.9 Million
Emp.: 11
Real Estate Property Development Services
N.A.I.C.S.: 531390

Global Center Kft.   **(1)**
Vaci 30, 1132, Budapest, Hungary
Tel.: (36) 12256600
Web Site: http://www.cpigroup.hu
Emp.: 35
Real Estate Property Development Services
N.A.I.C.S.: 531390
Matyas Gereben *(Gen Mgr)*

Global Development Kft.   **(1)**
Pille U 7 Fszt 1, 6723, Szeged, Hungary
Tel.: (36) 308555288
Web Site: http://www.globaldev.hu
Sales Range: $25-49.9 Million
Emp.: 30
Real Estate Property Development Services
N.A.I.C.S.: 531311
Matyas Gereben *(Country Mgr)*

RSL Real Estate Development
S.R.L.   **(1)**
Str Delea Veche 24, Bucharest, 024102,
Romania
Tel.: (40) 318059346
Sales Range: $50-74.9 Million
Emp.: 8
Real Estate Property Development Services
N.A.I.C.S.: 531390
Acher Chmulavitz *(Mng Dir)*

ABM FUJIYA BERHAD

Lot 2224 Section 66 Lorong Pangkalan Off Jalan Pangkalan, Pending
Industrial Estate, 93450, Kuching,
Sarawak, Malaysia

Tel.: (60) 82333344
Web Site:
  http://www.abmfujiya.com.my
Year Founded: 2003
AFUJIYA—(KLS)
Rev.: $21,324,731
Assets: $77,953,762
Liabilities: $43,742,886
Net Worth: $34,210,875
Earnings: ($446,800)
Fiscal Year-end: 12/31/22
Automotive & Other Batteries Mfr
N.A.I.C.S.: 335910
Ah Ching Tay *(Chm)*

ABM INTERNATIONAL LIMITED

10/60 Industrial Area, Kirti Nagar,
New Delhi, 110015, Delhi, India
Tel.: (91) 1141426044
Web Site: http://www.abmintl.in
Year Founded: 1983
Rev.: $11,155,115
Assets: $3,717,573
Liabilities: $1,181,774
Net Worth: $2,535,800
Earnings: ($256,112)
Emp.: 8
Fiscal Year-end: 03/31/19
Plastic Raw Material Distr
N.A.I.C.S.: 423720
Virender Kumar Gandhi *(Chm & Mng
Dir)*

ABM KNOWLEDGEWARE LTD

ABM House Plot No 268 Linking
Road Bandra West, Mumbai, 400
050, India
Tel.: (91) 2242909700
Web Site: https://www.abmindia.com
Year Founded: 1993
531161—(BOM)
Rev.: $10,167,004
Assets: $29,645,585
Liabilities: $4,060,632
Net Worth: $25,584,953
Earnings: $1,744,236
Emp.: 422
Fiscal Year-end: 03/31/23
E-Governance & System Integration
Solutions
N.A.I.C.S.: 541519
Prakash B. Rane *(Founder & Mng
Dir)*

Subsidiaries:

InstaSafe Inc.   **(1)**
340 S Lemon Ave 1364, Walnut, CA 91789
Tel.: (408) 400-3673
Software Development Services
N.A.I.C.S.: 541511

ABN AMRO GROUP N.V.

Gustav Mahlerlaan 10, 1082 PP, Amsterdam, Netherlands
Tel.: (31) 102411720   NI
Year Founded: 2010
0RDM—(LSE)
Sales Range: $1-4.9 Billion
Bank Holding Company
N.A.I.C.S.: 551111
A. C. Dorland *(Vice Chm-Supervisory
Bd)*

Subsidiaries:

ABN AMRO Bank N.V.   **(1)**
Gustav Mahlerlaan 10, 1082 PP, Amsterdam, Netherlands
Sales Range: $15-24.9 Billion
Retail & Commercial Banking
N.A.I.C.S.: 522110
Robert Swaak *(Chm & CEO)*

Subsidiary (Domestic):

ABM AMRO Commercial Finance
N.V.   **(2)**
Hambakenwetering 2, 5321 DC, 's-

ABN AMRO Group N.V.—(Continued)

Hertogenbosch, Netherlands
Tel.: (31) 736467777
Web Site: http://www.abnamrocomfin.com
Sales Range: $100-124.9 Million
Emp.: 500
Commercial Finance, Factoring, Credit
Management, Debt Administration & Other
Financial Services
N.A.I.C.S.: 522299

Subsidiary (Non-US):

ABN AMRO Bank Brussels (2)
Kanselarijstraat 17A, B 1000, Brussels,
Belgium (100%)
Tel.: (32) 25460460
Web Site: http://www.abnamrobelgium.be
Sales Range: $200-249.9 Million
Emp.: 400
Private Banking Services
N.A.I.C.S.: 522110

Subsidiary (US):

ABN AMRO Clearing Chicago
LLC (2)
175 W Jackson Blvd Ste 400, Chicago, IL
60604 (100%)
Tel.: (312) 604-8000
Web Site:
    http://www.us.abnamroclearing.com
Sales Range: $75-99.9 Million
Emp.: 170
Security & Trade Clearing Services
N.A.I.C.S.: 522320
Tom Chlada (VP & Bus Mgr)

Subsidiary (Non-US):

ABN AMRO Clearing Hong Kong
Ltd. (2)
Level 70 International Commerce Centre, 1
Austin Road West, Kowloon, China (Hong
Kong)
Tel.: (852) 03653 0790
Financial Services
N.A.I.C.S.: 523150

ABN AMRO Clearing Singapore Pte
Ltd (2)
10 Collyer Quay 07-01 Ocean Financial
Centre, Singapore, 049315, Singapore
Tel.: (65) 68089001
Financial Services
N.A.I.C.S.: 523150

ABN AMRO Clearing Sydney Pty (2)
50 Bridge Street 8th floor, Sydney, '2000,
NSW, Australia
Tel.: (61) 2 8221 3070
Financial Services
N.A.I.C.S.: 523150

ABN AMRO Clearing Tokyo Ltd (2)
39F Atago Green Hills Mori Tower, Minato-
ku, Tokyo, Japan
Tel.: (81) 3 5425 9900
Financial Services
N.A.I.C.S.: 523150

ABN AMRO Commercial Finance
(UK) Ltd (2)
Sheencroft House 10-12 Church Road,
Haywards Heath, RH16 3SN, West Sussex,
United Kingdom
Tel.: (44) 01444441717
Web Site: https://www.abnamrocomfin.com
Financial Investment Services
N.A.I.C.S.: 523150
Andrew Johnston (Head-Sls SME)

ABN AMRO Commercial Finance
GmbH (2)
Gereonstrabe 15 23, 50670, Cologne, Ger-
many
Tel.: (49) 0 221 88887 0
Financial Investment Services
N.A.I.C.S.: 523150

ABN AMRO Commercial Finance
S.A. (2)
39 rue Anatole France, 92535, Levallois-
Perret, France
Tel.: (33) 0 1 41 49 93 96
Financial Investment Services
N.A.I.C.S.: 523150

Subsidiary (Domestic):

ABN AMRO Groenbank B.V. (2)

Foppingadreef 22, Amsterdam, 1102 BS,
Netherlands
Tel.: (31) 10 40 24 275
Commercial Banking Services
N.A.I.C.S.: 522110

ABN AMRO Hypotheken Groep
B.V. (2)
Ruimtevaart 24, 3824 MX, Amersfoort,
Netherlands
Tel.: (31) 33 750 40 00
Mortgage Services
N.A.I.C.S.: 522310

ABN AMRO Lease N.V. (2)
Franz Lisztplantsoen 100, 3533 JG,
Utrecht, Netherlands (100%)
Tel.: (31) 302906406
Web Site: http://www.abnamrolease.nl
Sales Range: $75-99.9 Million
Emp.: 160
Equipment Leasing
N.A.I.C.S.: 532490

ABN AMRO MeesPierson (2)
Prins Bernhardplein 200, NL-1097 JB, Am-
sterdam, Netherlands
Tel.: (31) 205272516
Web Site: http://www.meespierson.nl
Sales Range: $500-549.9 Million
Emp.: 300
Private Banking & Wealth Management
Services
N.A.I.C.S.: 523150

Subsidiary (Non-US):

ABN AMRO (Guernsey) Limited (3)
Martello Court Admiral Park, Saint Peter
Port, GY1 2HR, Guernsey
Tel.: (44) 1481751000
Web Site:
    http://www.abnamroprivatebanking.gg
Sales Range: $50-74.9 Million
Emp.: 75
Private Banking & Wealth Management
Services
N.A.I.C.S.: 523150
Graham Thoume (CEO)

MeesPierson (Curacao) N.V. (3)
1 Berg Ararat, PO Box 3860, Willemstad,
Curacao
Tel.: (599) 94639627
Sales Range: $50-74.9 Million
Emp.: 50
Private Banking & Wealth Management
Services
N.A.I.C.S.: 523150

Subsidiary (Domestic):

ABN AMRO Participates (2)
Gustav Mahlerlaan 10, 1082 PP, Amster-
dam, Netherlands
Tel.: (31) 20 628 1276
Web Site: http://www.abnamro.com
Investment Fund Management Services
N.A.I.C.S.: 523940
Friso Janmaat (Mng Dir)

Joint Venture (Domestic):

Koninklijke Ten Cate, B.V. (3)
Stationsstraat 11, 7607 GX, Almelo, Nether-
lands
Tel.: (31) 546544911
Web Site: http://www.tencate.com
Emp.: 3,796
Holding Company; Technical Textiles &
Technical Components Mfr & Whslr
N.A.I.C.S.: 551112
Don M. Olsen (CEO-Protective Fabrics)

Subsidiary (Domestic):

GreenFields Holding BV (4)
G van der Muelenweg 2, 7443 RE, Nijver-
dal, Netherlands
Tel.: (31) 548633333
Web Site: http://www.greenfields.eu
Holding Company; Artificial Turf Installation
Services
N.A.I.C.S.: 551112

Subsidiary (Domestic):

GreenFields BV (5)
G van der Muelenweg 2, 7443 RE, Nijver-
dal, Netherlands
Tel.: (31) 548633333

Web Site: http://www.greenfields.eu
Artificial Turf Installation Services
N.A.I.C.S.: 339999

Subsidiary (Non-US):

GreenFields Sports & Leisure Pty
Ltd. (6)
20 Chesterfield Road, Pietermaritzburg,
3201, South Africa
Tel.: (27) 338977500
Sport Goods Distr
N.A.I.C.S.: 532284

GreenFields Swiss AG (6)
Talstrasse 26, CH-8200, Schaffhausen,
Switzerland
Tel.: (41) 526320101
Web Site: http://www.greenfields.eu
Artificial Turf Installation Services
N.A.I.C.S.: 339999

Subsidiary (US):

Polyloom Corporation of America (4)
1131 Broadway St, Dayton, TN 37321-1802
Tel.: (423) 775-0792
Web Site: http://www.tencategrass.com
Artificial Turf Fibers & Backing Mfr
N.A.I.C.S.: 325220

Subsidiary (Non-US):

SOLMAX (4)
Av Puente Cultural 10, San Sebastian de
los Reyes, 28702, Madrid, Spain
Tel.: (34) 607499962
Web Site: http://www.tencatego.eu
Geosynthetics & Industrial Fabrics Mfr
N.A.I.C.S.: 313220

Solmax (4)
Bd Mircea Voda 43 Bucuresti-Sector 3, Bu-
charest, Romania
Tel.: (40) 740955194
Web Site: http://www.tencatego.eu
Geosynthetics & Industrial Fabrics Mfr
N.A.I.C.S.: 313220

Ten Cate Advanced Armour UK
Limited (4)
Regus 2430/2440 The Quadrant Aztec
West, Bristol, BS32 4AQ, United Kingdom
Tel.: (44) 1454877600
Web Site:
    http://www.tencateadvancedarmor.com
Customized Lightweight Ballistic Protection
Solutions Mfr
N.A.I.C.S.: 336992

Subsidiary (Domestic):

Ten Cate Advanced Textiles BV (4)
G van der Muelenweg 2, PO Box 186, 7440
AD, Nijverdal, Netherlands
Tel.: (31) 548 633922
Web Site: http://eu.tencatefabrics.com
Holding Company
N.A.I.C.S.: 551112

Subsidiary (US):

Southern Mills, Inc. (5)
6501 Mall Blvd, Union City, GA 30291
Tel.: (770) 969-1000
Web Site: http://us.tencatefabrics.com
Industrial Textiles & Protective Fabrics Mfr
N.A.I.C.S.: 313210
Jean Harris (VP-HR)

Subsidiary (Non-US):

Ten Cate Danmark a/s (4)
Damsbovej 10, 5492, Vissenbjerg, Denmark
Tel.: (45) 65481600
Web Site:
    http://www.tencateadvancedarmour.com
Protective Fabrics Mfr
N.A.I.C.S.: 313220

Subsidiary (Domestic):

Ten Cate Advanced Armour Danmark
a/s (5)
Damsbovej 10, 5492, Vissenbjerg, Denmark
Tel.: (45) 65481600
Web Site:
    http://www.tencateadvancedarmour.com
Customized Lightweight Ballistic Protection
Solutions Mfr
N.A.I.C.S.: 336992

Helle Specht (Mng Dir)

Subsidiary (Non-US):

Ten Cate Geosynthetics (UK)
Limited (4)
39 High Street, Wednesfield, Wolverhamp-
ton, WV11 1ST, W Midlands, United King-
dom
Tel.: (44) 1052500000
Web Site: http://www.tencatego.eu
Geosynthetics & Industrial Fabrics Mfr
N.A.I.C.S.: 313220

Subsidiary (Domestic):

Ten Cate Thiobac bv (4)
Hoge Dijkje 2, 7442 AE, Nijverdal, Nether-
lands
Tel.: (31) 548633944
Web Site: http://www.tencate.com
Synthetic Turf Components Mfr
N.A.I.C.S.: 325220

Subsidiary (Non-US):

TenCate Advanced Armour
SASU (4)
50 Route de Louvier, 38270, Primarette,
France
Tel.: (33) 474795050
Web Site:
    http://www.tencateadvancedarmor.com
Customized Lightweight Ballistic Protection
Solutions Mfr
N.A.I.C.S.: 336992

TenCate France SASU (4)
9 Rue Marcel Paul, BP 40080, F-95873,
Bezons, Cedex, France
Tel.: (33) 134235363
Web Site: http://www.tencatego.eu
Geosynthetics & Industrial Fabrics Mfr
N.A.I.C.S.: 325998

TenCate Geosynthetics (Thailand)
Ltd (4)
555 Rasa Tower 26th Floor Phaholyothin
Road Soi 19, Chatuchak, Bangkok, 10900,
Thailand
Tel.: (66) 26926680
Web Site: http://www.tencatego.asia
Geosynthetics & Industrial Fabrics Mfr
N.A.I.C.S.: 313220

TenCate Geosynthetics Asia Sdn.
Bhd. (4)
14 Jalan Sementa 27/91 Seksyen 27, Shah
Alam, 40400, Selangor Darul Ehsan, Malay-
sia
Tel.: (60) 351928568
Web Site: http://www.tencatego.asia
Geosynthetics & Industrial Fabrics Mfr
N.A.I.C.S.: 314999

TenCate Geosynthetics Austria
GES.M.B.H (4)
Schachermayerstrasse 18, A-4021, Linz,
Austria
Tel.: (43) 73269830
Web Site: https://www.tencatego.eu
Geosynthetics & Industrial Fabrics Mfr
N.A.I.C.S.: 314999

TenCate Geosynthetics France
S.A.S. (4)
9 rue Marcel Paul, BP 40080, F-95873, Be-
zons, Cedex, France
Tel.: (33) 134235363
Web Site: https://www.tencatego.eu
Geosynthetics Products Mfr
N.A.I.C.S.: 325998

TenCate Geosynthetics Malaysia Sdn
Bhd (4)
14 Jalan Sementa 27/91 Seksyen 27, Shah
Alam, 40400, Selangor, Malaysia
Tel.: (60) 351928568
Web Site: http://www.tencatego.asia
Geosynthetics & Industrial Fabrics Mfr
N.A.I.C.S.: 313220

Subsidiary (Domestic):

TenCate Geosynthetics Netherlands
B.V. (4)
Europalaan 206, 7559 SC, Hengelo, Neth-
erlands
Tel.: (31) 546544811
Web Site: http://www.tencatego.eu

Geosynthetics & Industrial Fabrics Mfr
N.A.I.C.S.: 313220

Subsidiary (Non-US):

TenCate Industrial Zhuhai Co. Ltd. **(4)**
South of Nangang West Road Gaolan Port Economic Zone, Zhuhai, 519050, Guangdong, China
Tel.: (86) 7568861616
Web Site: http://www.tencategeo.asia
Geosynthetics & Industrial Fabrics Mfr
N.A.I.C.S.: 313220
Nell Nong *(Mgr-Production)*

Subsidiary (Domestic):

TenCate Protective Fabrics Holding BV **(4)**
G van der Muelenweg 2, PO Box 186, 7440 AD, Nijverdal, Netherlands
Tel.: (31) 548 633922
Web Site: http://eu.tencatefabrics.com
Protective Workwear Mfr
N.A.I.C.S.: 339999

Subsidiary (US):

TenCate Protective Fabrics USA Inc. **(4)**
6501 Mall Blvd, Union City, GA 30291
Tel.: (770) 969-1000
Web Site: http://us.tencatefabrics.com
Protective Workwear Mfr
N.A.I.C.S.: 339999
Daniel Hauert *(VP-Sls & Bus Dev-Americas)*

Subsidiary (Non-US):

TigerTurf (UK) Limited **(4)**
229 Ikon Droitwich Road, Hartlebury, DY10 4EU, Worcs, United Kingdom
Tel.: (44) 1299 253 966
Web Site: http://www.tigerturf.com
Synthetic Turf Mfr
N.A.I.C.S.: 339999
Paul Langford *(Mng Dir-EMEA)*

TigerTurf Australia Pty Ltd **(4)**
2/12 Latitude Boulevard, Thomastown, Melbourne, 3074, VIC, Australia
Tel.: (61) 3 9464 5052
Web Site: http://tigerturf.com
Synthetic Turf Mfr
N.A.I.C.S.: 325130

TigerTurf NZ Limited **(4)**
384 Neilson Street, Onehunga, Auckland, 1061, New Zealand
Tel.: (64) 96344134
Web Site: http://www.tigerturf.co.nz
Synthetic Grass & Turf Mfr
N.A.I.C.S.: 339999
Peter Leeves *(Gen Mgr)*

Subsidiary (Domestic):

Xtra Grass **(4)**
G van der Muelenweg 2, 7443 RE, Nijverdal, Netherlands
Tel.: (31) 548633333
Web Site: http://www.xtragrass-hybrid-turf.com
Artificial Turf Installation Services
N.A.I.C.S.: 238990

Affiliate (Domestic):

ABN Assurantie Holding B.V. **(2)**
Prins Bernhardstraat 1, PO Box 10085, 8000 GB, Zwolle, Netherlands
Tel.: (31) 384992299
Sales Range: $300-349.9 Million
Emp.: 800
Insurance
N.A.I.C.S.: 524298

Subsidiary (Non-US):

ABN International Diamond Division **(2)**
Pelikaan St 70 76, 2018, Antwerp, Belgium **(100%)**
Tel.: (32) 32220401
Web Site: http://www.abnamro.be
Sales Range: $25-49.9 Million
Emp.: 80
Diamond Sales
N.A.I.C.S.: 458310

Vijay Goel *(Mgr-Rels)*

Subsidiary (Domestic):

ALFAM Holding N.V. **(2)**
Kosterijland 10, 3981 AJ, Bunnik, Netherlands
Tel.: (31) 30 659 65 00
Web Site: http://www.alfam.nl
Mortgage Services
N.A.I.C.S.: 522310

Attema B.V. **(2)**
Schelluinsestraat 1, 4203 NJ, Gorinchem, Netherlands
Tel.: (31) 0183650650
Plastics Product Mfr
N.A.I.C.S.: 326199

Subsidiary (Non-US):

Banque de Neuflize OBC S.A. **(2)**
3 avenue Hoche, 75008, Paris, France **(99.84%)**
Tel.: (33) 156217000
Web Site: http://www.banquedeneuflize.com
Sales Range: $200-249.9 Million
Emp.: 950
Bank Holding Company
N.A.I.C.S.: 551111

Subsidiary (Domestic):

Banque de Neuflize **(3)**
3 Ave Hoche, 75410, Paris, Cedex, France **(99%)**
Tel.: (33) 156217000
Web Site: http://www.banquedeneuflize.fr
Sales Range: $350-399.9 Million
Emp.: 950
Commericial Banking
N.A.I.C.S.: 522110
Philippe Vayssettes *(CEO)*

Subsidiary (Non-US):

Bethmann Bank AG **(2)**
Bethmannstrsse 7 9, D-60311, Frankfurt am Main, Germany **(100%)**
Tel.: (49) 8001010760
Web Site: http://www.bethmannbank.de
Sales Range: $75-99.9 Million
Emp.: 150
Private Banking Services
N.A.I.C.S.: 523150
Horst Schmiet *(CEO)*

Subsidiary (Domestic):

Credit Suisse (Deutschland) AG **(3)**
Junghofstrasse 16, 60311, Frankfurt am Main, Germany
Tel.: (49) 69 26911 0
Web Site: http://www.credit-suisse.de
Investment Banking & Asset Management Services
N.A.I.C.S.: 523150
Helene von Roeder *(CEO-Germany & Member-Exec Bd)*

Subsidiary (Domestic):

DEFAM B.V. **(2)**
Schoudermantel 2, 3981AH, Bunnik, Netherlands
Tel.: (31) 306596600
Web Site: http://www.defam.nl
Sales Range: $100-124.9 Million
Emp.: 130
Consumer Lending & Credit Services
N.A.I.C.S.: 522291

Direktbank N.V. **(2)**
Prof JH Bavincklaan 3, NL-1183 AT, Amstelveen, Netherlands
Tel.: (31) 205970707
Web Site: http://www.direktbank.nl
Sales Range: $75-99.9 Million
Emp.: 150
Mortgage Brokerage Services
N.A.I.C.S.: 522310

GroeiVermogen N.V. **(2)**
Burgerweeshuispad 201, NL-1076 GR, Amsterdam, Netherlands
Tel.: (31) 205275255
Sales Range: $50-74.9 Million
Emp.: 30
Investment Products & Services
N.A.I.C.S.: 523940

Interbank **(2)**
Entrada 600 400, PO Box 12565, 11 14AN, Amsterdam, Netherlands **(100%)**
Tel.: (31) 203125125
Web Site: http://www.interbank.nl
Sales Range: $200-249.9 Million
Emp.: 350
Trade Financing
N.A.I.C.S.: 522299
Susan Dellosso *(CEO)*

International Card Services B.V. **(2)**
Wisselwerking 58, 1112 XS, Diemen, Netherlands **(100%)**
Tel.: (31) 206600678
Web Site: http://www.icscards.nl
Sales Range: $150-199.9 Million
Emp.: 300
Issuer of Credit Cards
N.A.I.C.S.: 522210
Gigs Wildeboer *(Gen Mgr)*

MoneYou B.V. **(2)**
Science Park 404, 1098 XH, Amsterdam, Netherlands
Tel.: (31) 800 666 399
Web Site: http://www.moneyou.nl
Mortgage Services
N.A.I.C.S.: 522310

Subsidiary (Non-US):

Neuflize Vie S.A. **(2)**
3 avenue Hoche, 75008, Paris, France
Tel.: (33) 156218000
Web Site: http://www.neuflizevie.fr
Fire Insurance Services
N.A.I.C.S.: 524113

ABN AMRO Clearing London Ltd. **(1)**
4th & 5th floor 5 Aldermanbury Square, London, EC2V 7HR, United Kingdom
Tel.: (44) 2031929000
Financial Clearing Services
N.A.I.C.S.: 523999

ABN AMRO Clearing Sydney Nominees Pty. Ltd. **(1)**
Level 11 580 George Street, Sydney, 2000, NSW, Australia
Tel.: (61) 282213000
Banking Services
N.A.I.C.S.: 522110

ABN AMRO Investment Solutions S.A. **(1)**
3 Avenue Hoche, 75008, Paris, France
Tel.: (33) 156216060
Web Site: https://www.abnamroinvestments.com
Asset Management Services
N.A.I.C.S.: 531390

ABN AMRO Verzekeringen B.V. **(1)**
Prins Bernhardstraat 1, PO Box 100085, 8000 PM, Zwolle, Netherlands
Tel.: (31) 384992299
Web Site: http://www.abnamro.nl
Sales Range: $350-399.9 Million
Emp.: 800
Insurance
N.A.I.C.S.: 524298

Alpha Credit Nederland B.V. **(1)**
Shoulder Cape 2/A, 3981 AH, Bunnik, Netherlands
Tel.: (31) 306596700
Web Site: https://www.alphacredit.nl
Car Loan Financial & Investment Services
N.A.I.C.S.: 523999

Credivance N.V. **(1)**
Beneluxlaan 1010, 3526KK, Utrecht, Netherlands
Tel.: (31) 306596600
Web Site: https://www.credivance.nl
Personal Loan Financial Services
N.A.I.C.S.: 522310

Franx B.V. **(1)**
Hessenbergweg 73, 1101 CX, Amsterdam, Netherlands
Tel.: (31) 884405500
Web Site: https://www.franx.com
Digital Banking Services
N.A.I.C.S.: 522320

New10 B.V. **(1)**

Mr Treublaan 7, 1097 DP, Amsterdam, Netherlands
Tel.: (31) 202621800
Web Site: https://new10.com
Emp.: 126
Business Financial Services
N.A.I.C.S.: 541611

ABNOVA (TAIWAN) CORPORATION

9th Fl No 108 Jhouzih St, Neihu District, Taipei, 114, Taiwan
Tel.: (886) 287511888
Web Site: https://www.abnova.com
4133—(TAI)
Rev.: $12,493,933
Assets: $44,335,752
Liabilities: $2,270,316
Net Worth: $42,065,435
Earnings: $1,428,366
Emp.: 220
Fiscal Year-end: 12/31/23
Antibodies & Proteins Mfr
N.A.I.C.S.: 325414

Subsidiaries:

Abnova GmbH **(1)**
Boxbergring 107, 69126, Heidelberg, Baden-Wurttemberg, Germany
Tel.: (49) 62213632226
Antibody & Protein Mfr
N.A.I.C.S.: 325411

ABO FARM S.A.

Str Jokai Mor Nr 32, Covasna, Sfantu Gheorghe, Romania
Tel.: (40) 731 791 761
Sales Range: $1-9.9 Million
Emp.: 12
Poultry Operator
N.A.I.C.S.: 112340

ABO MIX S.A.

Str Depozitelor Nr 31, Satu-Mare, Romania
Tel.: (40) 261769266
NUIA—(BUC)
Rev.: $11,518,194
Assets: $6,166,466
Liabilities: $1,293,418
Net Worth: $4,873,048
Earnings: $521,696
Emp.: 77
Fiscal Year-end: 12/31/23
Animal Feed Mfr
N.A.I.C.S.: 311119

ABO WIND AG

Unter den Eichen 7, 65195, Wiesbaden, Germany
Tel.: (49) 611 26 765 0
Web Site: http://www.abo-wind.com
Sales Range: $25-49.9 Million
Emp.: 600
Wind Power Generation
N.A.I.C.S.: 221118
Alexander Koffka *(Mng Dir-PR & IR)*

Subsidiaries:

ABO Wind Belgium SPRL **(1)**
Avenue Adolphe Lacomble 69-71, 1030, Brussels, Belgium
Tel.: (32) 27396293
Wind Power Generation Services
N.A.I.C.S.: 221115

ABO Wind Betriebs GmbH **(1)**
Oberdorfstrasse 10, 55262, Heidesheim am Rhein, Germany
Tel.: (49) 61328988123
Wind Power Generation Services
N.A.I.C.S.: 221115
Sybille Marx-Pfaffe *(Mgr-HR)*

ABO Wind Bulgaria EOOD **(1)**
36 Solunska Street Office no 6, 1000, Sofia, Bulgaria
Tel.: (359) 28116274
Wind Power Generation Services
N.A.I.C.S.: 221115

ABO Wind AG—(Continued)

ABO Wind Energias Renovables S.A. (1)
Av Alicia M de Justo 1050 Piso 4 Of 196 Dock 7, Puerto Madero, C1107AAP, Buenos Aires, Argentina
Tel.: (54) 1159171235
Wind Power Generation Services
N.A.I.C.S.: 221115

ABO Wind Espana S.A.U. (1)
Embajador Vich 3 3 Q, 46002, Valencia, Spain
Tel.: (34) 902198937
Web Site: http://www.abo-wind.es
Wind Power Generation Services
N.A.I.C.S.: 221115
Manuel Crespo Marcos (Dir Gen)

ABO Wind Ireland Ltd. (1)
Unit 4 Aspen Court, Cornelscourt, Dublin, Ireland
Tel.: (353) 12070452
Wind Power Generation Services
N.A.I.C.S.: 221115
Joe Jellie (Project Mgr)

ABO Wind Mezzanine GmbH & Co. KG (1)
Hirtenstrasse 26, 65193, Wiesbaden, Germany
Tel.: (49) 6111885461
Wind Power Generation Services
N.A.I.C.S.: 221115

ABO Wind Oy (1)
Jaakonkatu 3b 7 krs, 00100, Helsinki, Finland
Tel.: (358) 61126765636
Web Site: http://www.abo-wind.fi
Wind Power Generation Services
N.A.I.C.S.: 221115
Karl Schultheis (Project Mgr)

ABO Wind SARL (1)
19 boulevard Alexandre Martin, 45000, Orleans, France
Tel.: (33) 238522165
Web Site: http://www.abo-wind.fr
Emp.: 30
Wind Power Generation Services
N.A.I.C.S.: 221115

ABO Wind UK Ltd. (1)
The Greenhouse Beechwood Park North, Inverness, IV2 3BL, United Kingdom
Tel.: (44) 1463713555
Web Site: http://www.abo-wind.co.uk
Emp.: 5
Wind Power Generation Services
N.A.I.C.S.: 221115
Christian Wild (Head-UK Dev)

ABO-GROUP NV/SA
Derbystraat 255, 9051, Gent, Belgium
Tel.: (32) 92428866
Web Site: https://www.abo-group.eu
Year Founded: 1995
ABO—(EUR)
Sales Range: $50-74.9 Million
Emp.: 400
Holding Company; Environmental & Geotechnical Services
N.A.I.C.S.: 551112
Jan Gesquiere (Chm)

Subsidiaries:

ABO ERG (1)
ZI Jean Monnet 243 Avenue de Bruxelles, 83500, La Seyne-sur-Mer, France
Tel.: (33) 4 9411 0490
Web Site: http://www.erg-sa.fr
Engineeering Services
N.A.I.C.S.: 541330

ABO Geomet BV (1)
Curieweg 19, 2408 BZ, Alphen aan den Rijn, Netherlands
Tel.: (31) 17 244 9822
Web Site: https://www.geomet.nl
Soil Remediation Services
N.A.I.C.S.: 562910
Peter Schoppen (Gen Mgr)

ABO NV (1)
Derbystraat 55, Sint-Denijs-Westrem, 9051, Gent, Belgium

Tel.: (32) 9 242 8866
Web Site: https://www.abo.be
Soil Remediation Services
N.A.I.C.S.: 562910
Patrick Hambach (Gen Dir)

ABO mllieuconsult bv (1)
Amundsenweg 29, Postbus 207, 4462 GP, Goes, Netherlands
Tel.: (31) 113 362280
Web Site: http://www.abo-milieuconsult.nl
Environmental Consulting Services
N.A.I.C.S.: 541620

ABO-Milieuconsult BV (1)
Amundsenweg 29, 4462 GP, Goes, Netherlands
Tel.: (31) 11 336 2280
Web Site: https://www.abo-milieuconsult.nl
Soil Remediation Services
N.A.I.C.S.: 562910

Asper BV (1)
Watermolendreef 176, 9100, Saint-Niklaas, Belgium
Tel.: (32) 3 334 4500
Web Site: https://www.asperbvba.be
Soil Remediation Services
N.A.I.C.S.: 562910

Ecorem (1)
Kontichsesteenweg 38, 2630, Aartselaar, Belgium
Tel.: (32) 3 871 0900
Web Site: http://www.ecorem.be
Emp.: 12
Engineering Consulting Services
N.A.I.C.S.: 541330
Walter Mondt (Founder & CEO)

GEO+ Environnement SAS (1)
Le Chateau, Gardouch, 31290, Toulouse, France
Tel.: (33) 53 466 4342
Web Site: https://www.geoplusenvironnement.com
Soil Remediation Services
N.A.I.C.S.: 562910

Geosonda Environment nv (1)
Derbystraat 57, Sint-Denijs-Westrem, 9051, Gent, Belgium
Tel.: (32) 9 242 9900
Web Site: http://www.geosonda.be
Environmental Consulting Services
N.A.I.C.S.: 541620

Geosonda Netherlands BV (1)
Franse Akker 13, 4824 AL, Breda, Netherlands
Tel.: (31) 76 522 0566
Web Site: https://www.geosonda.nl
Soil Remediation Services
N.A.I.C.S.: 562910

Geosonda bvba (1)
Keizer Karellaan 292, 1083, Ganshoren, Belgium
Tel.: (32) 2 479 3241
Web Site: http://www.geosonda.be
Geotechnical Services
N.A.I.C.S.: 541620

Geosonic France SAS (1)
243 Avenue de Bruxelles, 83500, La Seyne-sur-Mer, France
Tel.: (33) 62 163 0464
Soil Remediation Services
N.A.I.C.S.: 562910
Mathieu Lacroute (Gen Mgr)

Innogeo SAS (1)
27 allee du lac d Aiguebelette, BP 90306, 73370, Le Bourget du Lac, Cedex, France
Tel.: (33) 47 925 0140
Web Site: https://www.innogeo.fr
Soil Remediation Services
N.A.I.C.S.: 562910

Sialtech B.V. (1)
Vleugelboot 61, 3991 CM, Houten, Netherlands
Tel.: (31) 30 659 4060
Web Site: https://www.sialtech.nl
Soil Remediation Services
N.A.I.C.S.: 562910
Harold Uittenbosch (Gen Mgr)

Translab NV (1)
Oeverstraat 21, 9160, Lokeren, Belgium
(32) 9 369 3837

Web Site: https://www.translab.be
Environmental Laboratory Services
N.A.I.C.S.: 541380

ABOCOM SYSTEMS, INC.
No 77 Yu-Yih Rd Chu-Nan Miao-lih County, Hsin-chu, 35059, Taiwan
Tel.: (886) 37580777
Web Site: http://www.abocom.com.tw
2444—(TAI)
Rev.: $59,588,735
Assets: $67,356,811
Liabilities: $35,292,978
Net Worth: $32,063,833
Earnings: ($519,016)
Emp.: 595
Fiscal Year-end: 12/31/23
Communication Equipment Mfr
N.A.I.C.S.: 334220

Subsidiaries:

AboCom Systems, Inc. - Miao-Lih Hsuan Factory (1)
77 Yu-Yih Road, Chu-Nan Chen, Miao-li, 35059, Taiwan
Tel.: (886) 37580777
Networking Components Mfr
N.A.I.C.S.: 334111

ABOITIZ EQUITY VENTURES, INC.
Gov Manuel A Cuenco Avenue, 6000, Cebu, 6000, Kasambagan, Philippines
Tel.: (63) 324111800
Web Site: https://www.aboitiz.com
ABTZY—(OTCIQ)
Rev.: $5,608,361,218
Assets: $15,055,965,534
Liabilities: $8,278,924,089
Net Worth: $6,777,041,445
Earnings: $774,960,849
Emp.: 14,079
Fiscal Year-end: 12/31/23
Investment Services
N.A.I.C.S.: 523999
Julie Ann T. Diongzon (VP-Treasury Svcs Grp)

Subsidiaries:

AEV CRH Holdings, Inc. (1)
NAC Tower 32nd Street, Bonifacio Global City, Taguig, 1634, Philippines   **(60%)**
Tel.: (63) 2 886 2800
Holding Company
N.A.I.C.S.: 551112

Subsidiary (Domestic):

Republic Cement & Building Materials Inc. (2)
20F The Salcedo Tower 169 HV Dela Costa Street, Salcedo Village, Makati, 1227, Metro Manila, Philippines
Tel.: (63) 2 885 4599
Web Site: http://www.republiccement.com
Cement Mfr
N.A.I.C.S.: 327310
Mary Margaret L. San Pedro (Treas)

Subsidiary (Domestic):

Republic Cement Services, Inc. (3)
15/F Menarco Tower 32nd Street, Bonifacio Global City, Taguig, 1632, Philippines
Tel.: (63) 288854599
Cement & Building Materials Mfr
N.A.I.C.S.: 327310

Plant (Domestic):

Republic Cement Services, Inc. - Batangas Plant (4)
Barrio Mapulo, Taysan, Batangas, Philippines
Tel.: (63) 288854598
Web Site: http://republiccement.com
Cement Mfr
N.A.I.C.S.: 327310

Republic Cement Services, Inc. - Bulacan Cement Plant (4)

Barrio Minuyan, Norzagaray, Bulacan, Philippines
Tel.: (63) 2 885 4598
Web Site: http://republiccement.com
Cement Mfr
N.A.I.C.S.: 327310

Republic Cement Services, Inc. - Norzagaray Plant (4)
Barrio Biyte, Norzagaray, Bulacan, Philippines
Tel.: (63) 288854598
Web Site: http://republiccement.com
Cement Mfr
N.A.I.C.S.: 327310

Republic Cement Services, Inc. - Teresa Plant (4)
Barangay Dulumbayan, Teresa, Rizal, Philippines
Tel.: (63) 288854598
Web Site: http://republiccement.com
Cement Mfr
N.A.I.C.S.: 327310

Aboitiz Power Corporation (1)
  (51.9%)
Tel.: (63) 288862800
Web Site: https://www.aboitizpower.com
Rev.: $3,739,277,693
Assets: $8,793,415,210
Liabilities: $5,291,124,641
Net Worth: $3,502,290,569
Earnings: $658,399,091
Emp.: 4,262
Fiscal Year-end: 12/31/2023
Electricity Generation & Distribution Services
N.A.I.C.S.: 221111
Mikel A. Aboitiz (Vice Chm)

AboitizLand, Inc. (1)
Aboitiz Corporate Center Gov Manuel A Cuenco Avenue, Kasambagan, Cebu, 6000, Banilad, Philippines
Tel.: (63) 324111600
Web Site: http://www.aboitizland.com
Sales Range: $50-74.9 Million
Emp.: 100
Real Estate Services
N.A.I.C.S.: 531390
Robin Sarmiento (CFO)

Subsidiary (Domestic):

Lima Land, Inc. (2)
2nd Floor Twin Cities Condominium, 110 Legaspi St. Legaspi Villag, Makati, 1229, Philippines   **(100%)**
Tel.: (63) 2 886 2800
Web Site: http://www.lima.com.ph
Emp.: 20
Real Estate Manangement Services
N.A.I.C.S.: 531210
Juliet Avenido (Asst VP-Ops)

GNPower Mariveles Energy Center Ltd. Co. (1)
Barangay Alasasin, Mariveles, Bataan, 2105, Philippines
Tel.: (63) 476122246
Web Site: https://gmec.ph
Electric Energy Distribution Services
N.A.I.C.S.: 221112

Gold Coin Services Singapore Pte. Ltd. (1)
47 Scotts Road Goldbell Towers 16-01/02, Singapore, 228233, Singapore
Tel.: (65) 67509600
Web Site: http://www.goldcoin-group.com
Feed Mfr & Distri
N.A.I.C.S.: 311119

Subsidiary (Non-US):

Gold Coin (Zhangzhou) Co., Ltd. (2)
Zhangzhou Economic Development Zone, Gangwei, Zhangzhou, 363105, Fujian, China
Tel.: (86) 59668 51500
Web Site: http://www.goldcoin-group.com
Livestock Feed Whslr
N.A.I.C.S.: 424910

Gold Coin (Zhuhai) Co., Ltd. (2)
Tel.: (86) 758729909
Web Site: http://www.goldcoin-group.com
Feed Mfr
N.A.I.C.S.: 311119

Gold Coin Feedmills (M) Sdn Bhd (2)
Port Kelang Mill Jalan Parang Loh Pelabuhan Utara, Pelabuhan Kelang, 42000, Port Klang, Selangor Darul Ehsan, Malaysia
Tel.: (60) 331767311
Emp.: 70
Feed Mfr
N.A.I.C.S.: 311119
James Kueh (Gen Mgr)

Gold Coin Feedmills Malaysia (2)
Jalan Parang Pelabuhan Utara Pelabuhan, Kelang, 42000, Selangor Darul Ehsan, Malaysia
Tel.: (60) 3 3176 7311
Web Site: http://www.goldcoin-group.com
Feed Mfr
N.A.I.C.S.: 311119
Kok Kuang Tan (Country Dir-Livestock)

Gold Coin Feedmills Malaysia Sdn Bhd (2)
No 432 Jalan Air Bemban Ayer Bemban, 81000, Kulai, Johor, Malaysia
Tel.: (60) 76561152
Feed Mfr
N.A.I.C.S.: 311119

Gold Coin Feedmills Sdn Bhd (2)
4824 Mak Mandin Industrial Estate, 13400, Butterworth, Malaysia
Tel.: (60) 43237977
Feed Mfr
N.A.I.C.S.: 311119
Teoseng Leong (Gen Mgr)

Mactan EnerZone Corporation (1)
Zone 2 Mactan Ecpnomic Dinagyang, Cebu, Lapu-Lapu, 6015, Philippines
Tel.: (63) 323404692
Web Site: https://mactanenerzonecorporation.business.site
Power Generation Services
N.A.I.C.S.: 221118

Pilmico Foods Corporation (1)
Kiwalan Cove Dalipuga, Iligan, 9200, Philippines
Tel.: (63) 63 2251317
Web Site: http://www.pilmico.com
Food Products Mfr
N.A.I.C.S.: 311999

San Fernando Electric Light & Power Co., Inc. (1)
Teopaco Street Brgy Lourdes, San Fernando, Philippines
Tel.: (63) 459612727
Web Site: https://www.sfelapco.com
Power Generation Services
N.A.I.C.S.: 221118

Therma Mobile, Inc. (1)
Navotas Fish Port Complex, Metro Manila, Navotas, Philippines
Tel.: (63) 282829810
Electric Energy Distribution Services
N.A.I.C.S.: 221122

Therma South, Inc. (1)
Binugao, Toril, Davao, Philippines
Tel.: (63) 822446500
Electric Energy Distribution Services
N.A.I.C.S.: 221122

ABONMAX CO., LTD
3F-8 No 268 Sec 1 Gaotiezhanqian W Rd, Zhongli Dist, Taoyuan, Taiwan
Tel.: (886) 34336666
Web Site: https://www.abonmax.com.tw
Year Founded: 1978
2429—(TAI)
Rev.: $16,761,306
Assets: $15,104,189
Liabilities: $6,996,501
Net Worth: $8,107,688
Earnings: ($1,613,526)
Fiscal Year-end: 12/31/23
Printed Circuit Board Mfr
N.A.I.C.S.: 334412
Wei-Kun Zhou (Chm)

ABOUT YOU HOLDING SE
Domstrasse 10, 20095, Hamburg, Germany
Tel.: (49) 40638569359
Web Site: https://ir.aboutyou.de
Year Founded: 2014
YOU—(DEU)
Rev.: $2,136,209,224
Assets: $1,263,599,989
Liabilities: $968,535,538
Net Worth: $295,064,451
Earnings: ($123,854,214)
Emp.: 1,359
Fiscal Year-end: 02/28/24
Holding Company
N.A.I.C.S.: 551112

Subsidiaries:

Adference GmbH (1)
Auf der Hude 74, 21339, Luneburg, Germany
Tel.: (49) 41312173014
Web Site: https://www.adference.com
Google Bid Management Services
N.A.I.C.S.: 518210

ABOV SEMICONDUCTOR CO., LTD.
93 Gangni 1-gil, Cheongwon-gu, Ochang, 28126, Chungcheongbuk-do, Korea (South)
Tel.: (82) 432195200 KR
Web Site: https://www.abov.co.kr
Year Founded: 2006
102120—(KRS)
Rev.: $154,098,855
Assets: $123,390,970
Liabilities: $20,408,511
Net Worth: $102,882,459
Earnings: $12,610,847
Emp.: 225
Fiscal Year-end: 12/31/21
Semiconductor Mfr
N.A.I.C.S.: 334413
Won Choi (CEO)

ABOVE FOOD INGREDIENTS INC.
2305 Victoria Avenue #001, Regina, S4P 0S7, SK, Canada
Tel.: (306) 779-2268 AB
Web Site: https://abovefood.com
ABVE—(NYSEAMEX)
Disruptive Agriculture & Rudimentary Ingredients & Consumer Packaged Goods
N.A.I.C.S.: 311999
Lionel Kambeitz (Founder, Chm & CEO)

Subsidiaries:

Above Food Corp. (1)
2305 Victoria Ave Suite 001,, Regina, S4P 0S7, SK, Canada
Tel.: (306) 779-2268
Web Site: https://abovefood.com
Food Service
N.A.I.C.S.: 311999

Subsidiary (US):

Bite Acquisition Corp. (2)
720 N State St, Chicago, IL 60654
Tel.: (347) 685-5236
Rev.: $2,428,142
Assets: $30,419,211
Liabilities: $31,180,007
Net Worth: ($760,796)
Earnings: $991,838
Emp.: 2
Fiscal Year-end: 12/31/2022
Investment Services
N.A.I.C.S.: 523999
Axel Molet (CFO)

ABPRO BIO CO., LTD.
139 TechnoJungang-daero Yuga-eup, Dalseong-gun, Daegu, 43020, Korea (South)
Tel.: (82) 535828036
Web Site: https://www.ugint.co.kr
Year Founded: 1991
195990—(KRS)
Rev.: $16,959,958
Assets: $120,147,554
Liabilities: $12,617,490
Net Worth: $107,530,065
Earnings: ($6,246,947)
Emp.: 60
Fiscal Year-end: 12/31/22
Machine Tools Mfr
N.A.I.C.S.: 333517
Lee Jae Yong (CEO)

Subsidiaries:

DASA CNC (Weihai) Co., Ltd. (1)
Kaiyuan Road, Industrial Newly District, Weihai, Shandong, China
Tel.: (86) 63159670368
Automobile Machinery Mfr
N.A.I.C.S.: 336110

ABR HOLDINGS, LTD.
41 Tampines Street 92 ABR Building, Singapore, 528881, Singapore
Tel.: (65) 67862866
Web Site: http://www.abr.com.sg
Year Founded: 1996
Sales Range: $100-124.9 Million
Emp.: 1,000
Holding Company
N.A.I.C.S.: 311520
Keith Tiang Choon Chua (Chm)

Subsidiaries:

Oishi Japanese Pizza Pte Ltd (1)
3 South Buona Vista Road Suite 02-15, The Village Centre, Singapore, 118136, Singapore
Tel.: (65) 6555 5656
Web Site: http://www.oishipizza.com
Pizza Delivery Services
N.A.I.C.S.: 722513

Season Confectionary & Bakery Sdn. Bhd. (1)
1 Jalan Dewani Satu Kawasan Perindustrian Temenggong, Off Jalan Tampoi, 81100, Johor Bahru, Johor Darul Takzim, Malaysia
Tel.: (60) 7 333 1626
Confectionary & Candy Mfr.
N.A.I.C.S.: 311351

Swensen's of Singapore Pte. Ltd. (1)
41 Tampines St 92 ABR, Building, 528881, Singapore, Singapore
Tel.: (65) 67862866
Web Site: http://www.swensens.com.sg
Sales Range: $75-99.9 Million
Emp.: 230
Distr of Ice Cream & Frozen Yogurt
N.A.I.C.S.: 424430
Ana Lei (Head-Mktg)

Yogen Fruz Canada, Inc. (1)
210 Shields Court, Markham, L3R 8V2, ON, Canada
Tel.: (905) 479-8762
Web Site: http://www.yogenfruz.com
Food Products Distr
N.A.I.C.S.: 424490
Aaron Serruya (Pres & CEO)

ABRA MINING & INDUSTRIAL CORPORATION
Suite 3 3/F Jafer Building 118 West Avenue, Quezon City, 1104, Philippines
Tel.: (63) 925 1605
Year Founded: 1964
Metal Mining Services
N.A.I.C.S.: 212290
Jeremias B. Beloy (Chm & Pres)

ABRAAJ CAPITAL LIMITED
Dubai International Financial Centre Gate Village 8 3rd Floor, Dubai, 504904, United Arab Emirates
Tel.: (971) 45064400
Web Site: http://www.abraaj.com
Sales Range: $100-124.9 Million
Emp.: 300
Investment Holding Company
N.A.I.C.S.: 551112
Arif Naqvi (Founder)

Subsidiaries:

ART MARINE LLC (1)
Sh Zayed Road 3rd Interchange, PO Box 118063, Al Quoz Industrial Area, Dubai, United Arab Emirates
Tel.: (971) 4 338 8955
Web Site: http://www.artmarine.ae
Yacht Building Services
N.A.I.C.S.: 336611
Gregor Stinner (CEO)

K-Electric Limited (1)
KE House 39-B Sunset Boulevard Phase-II Defence Housing Authority, Karachi, Pakistan
Tel.: (92) 2132637133
Web Site: https://www.ke.com.pk
Rev.: $1,869,739,145
Assets: $3,685,876,829
Liabilities: $2,768,528,322
Net Worth: $917,348,506
Earnings: ($111,461,166)
Emp.: 9,619
Fiscal Year-end: 06/30/2023
Electric Power Distr
N.A.I.C.S.: 221122
Shan A. Ashary (Chm)

Mouka Limited (1)
Plot M Awosika Avenue Ikeja Industrial Estate, Lagos, Nigeria
Tel.: (234) 8104000100
Web Site: http://www.mouka.com
Polyurethane Foam Mfr
N.A.I.C.S.: 326150
Emmanuel Eze (Head-Ops)

Stanford Marine Group (1)
16TH Floor Single Business Tower Business Bay, PO Box 32456, Sheik Zayed Road, Dubai, 32456, United Arab Emirates
Tel.: (971) 4 380 8001
Web Site: http://www.stanfordmarinegroup.com
Ship Building & Repair Services
N.A.I.C.S.: 336611
Elias Nassif (CEO)

ABRASILVER RESOURCE CORP.
220 Bay St Suite 550, Toronto, M5J 2W4, ON, Canada
Tel.: (416) 306-8334 AB
Web Site: https://www.abrasilver.com
Year Founded: 1993
ABRA—(TSXV)
Rev.: $177,046
Assets: $27,114,773
Liabilities: $455,917
Net Worth: $26,658,856
Earnings: ($14,217,836)
Fiscal Year-end: 12/31/21
Oil & Gas Exploration Services
N.A.I.C.S.: 213112
Hernan Zaballa (Chm)

Subsidiaries:

Aethon Minerals Corp. (1)
550-220 Bay Street, Toronto, M5J 2W4, ON, Canada
Tel.: (416) 306-8334
Web Site: http://www.aethonminerals.com
Sales Range: Less than $1 Million
Investment Services
N.A.I.C.S.: 523999
John Miniotis (CEO-Interim)

ABRAU-DURSO AO
Bldg 2 43a Sevastopolsky Avenue, 117186, Moscow, Russia
Tel.: (7) 4959333333 RU
Web Site: https://www.abraudurso.ru
Year Founded: 1870
ABRD—(MOEX)
Winery & Wine Distr
N.A.I.C.S.: 312130
Boris Titov (Owner)

Abrau-Durso AO—(Continued)

ABRDN ASIA FOCUS PLC
Financial Ombudsman Service Exchange Tower, London, E14 9SR, United Kingdom
Tel.: (44) 2079640500   UK
Web Site: https://www.asia-focus.co.uk
Year Founded: 1995
AAS—(LSE)
Rev.: $49,634,732
Assets: $734,716,884
Liabilities: $99,908,999
Net Worth: $634,807,886
Earnings: $47,175,177
Fiscal Year-end: 07/31/24
Investment Management Service
N.A.I.C.S.: 523999

ABRDN NEW INDIA INVESTMENT TRUST PLC
Financial Ombudsman Service Exchange Tower, London, E14 9SR, United Kingdom
Tel.: (44) 2079640500
Web Site: https://www.aberdeen-newindia.co.uk
NIQ—(BER)
Rev.: $7,484,329
Assets: $499,530,193
Liabilities: $55,066,379
Net Worth: $444,463,814
Earnings: ($42,551,519)
Fiscal Year-end: 03/31/23
Investment Management Service
N.A.I.C.S.: 525990
Kristy Fong (Dir)

ABRDN PLC
1 George Street, Edinburgh, EH2 2LL, United Kingdom
Tel.: (44) 3456462383   UK
Web Site: https://www.abrdn.com
Year Founded: 1825
ABDN—(LSE)
Rev.: $2,287,758,200
Assets: $15,502,446,960
Liabilities: $4,836,198,640
Net Worth: $10,666,248,320
Earnings: $1,350,931,400
Emp.: 5,463
Fiscal Year-end: 12/31/21
Holding Company; Life Insurance, Pensions, Unit Trusts & Savings Products
N.A.I.C.S.: 551112
Douglas Flint (Chm)

Subsidiaries:

Aberdeen Asset Management PLC   (1)
10 Queen's Terrace, Aberdeen, AB10 1XL, United Kingdom
Tel.: (44) 1224631999
Institutional & Private Client Asset Management Services
N.A.I.C.S.: 523940
Kevin Lyons (Sr Mgr-Investment)

Subsidiary (Non-US):

Aberdeen Asset Management Company Limited   (2)
No 179 Bangkok City Tower 28th Floor South Sathorn Road, Thungmahamek, Sathorn, Bangkok, 10120, Thailand
Tel.: (66) 2352 3333
Asset Management Services
N.A.I.C.S.: 523940

Aberdeen Asset Management Finland Oy   (2)
Kaivokatu 6 7th Floor, FI-00100, Helsinki, Finland
Tel.: (358) 103040100
Real Estate Investments & Asset Management Services
N.A.I.C.S.: 525990

Subsidiary (Domestic):

Aberdeen Asset Managers Ltd.   (2)
10 Queen's Terrace, Aberdeen, AB10 1XL, United Kingdom
Tel.: (44) 1224 631 999
Fund Management Services
N.A.I.C.S.: 525910

Branch (Domestic):

Aberdeen Asset Managers Ltd.   (3)
Bow Bells House 1 Bread St, London, EC4M 9HH, United Kingdom
Tel.: (44) 2074636000
Fund Management Services
N.A.I.C.S.: 523940

Subsidiary (Non-US):

Aberdeen Global Services S.A.   (2)
35a Av John F Kennedy, 1855, Luxembourg, Luxembourg
Tel.: (352) 26 43 30 00
Investment Management Service
N.A.I.C.S.: 523999

Aberdeen Global State Street Bank Luxembourg S.A
49 Avenue John F Kennedy, 1855, Luxembourg, Luxembourg
Tel.: (352) 46 40 10-820
Commercial Banking Services
N.A.I.C.S.: 522110

Aberdeen Investment Management K.K.   (2)
1-9-2 Otemachi Financial City Grand Cube 9th Floor, Chiyoda-ku, Tokyo, 100-0004, Japan
Tel.: (81) 3 4578 2211
Investment Management Service
N.A.I.C.S.: 523999

Aberdeen Property Investors France SAS   (2)
29 Rue de Berri, 75008, Paris, France
Tel.: (33) 1 73 09 03 00
Real Estate Invesment Trust Services
N.A.I.C.S.: 525990

Aberdeen Property Investors The Netherlands B.V.   (2)
WTC H-Tower 20th Floor Zuidplein 166, 1077, Amsterdam, Netherlands
Tel.: (31) 206870500
Real Estate Investment Trust Services
N.A.I.C.S.: 525990

Subsidiary (Domestic):

Aberdeen Standard Fund Managers Limited   (2)
PO Box 12233, Chelmsford, CM99 2EE, United Kingdom
Tel.: (44) 1268445488
Investment Fund Services
N.A.I.C.S.: 525910
Megan Hughes (Mgr-Client)

Subsidiary (US):

Aberdeen Standard Investments Inc.   (2)
1900 Market St Ste 200, Philadelphia, PA 19103
Tel.: (215) 405-5700
Investment Management Service
N.A.I.C.S.: 523150
Andrew Smith (Pres)

Subsidiary (Domestic):

Aberdeen Capital Management LLC   (3)
201 Broad St Ste 501, Stamford, CT 06901
Tel.: (203) 352-0440
Investment Advisory & Asset Management Services
N.A.I.C.S.: 523940

Artio Global Investors Inc.   (3)
330 Madison Ave, New York, NY 10017
Tel.: (212) 297-3600
Web Site: http://www.artioglobal.com
Rev.: $124,293,000
Assets: $216,600,000
Liabilities: $62,512,000
Net Worth: $154,088,000
Earnings: ($45,594,000)

Emp.: 131
Fiscal Year-end: 12/31/2012
Holding Company; Investment & Asset Management Services
N.A.I.C.S.: 551112

Subsidiary (Non-US):

Aberdeen Standard Investments Sweden AB   (2)
Kungsgatan 8, 111 43, Stockholm, Sweden
Tel.: (46) 84128000
Asset Management Services
N.A.I.C.S.: 523940

Subsidiary (Domestic):

Aberdeen Property Investors Sweden AB   (3)
Sveavagen 24, 111 34, Stockholm, Sweden
Tel.: (46) 84128000
Fund Management Services
N.A.I.C.S.: 525990

Subsidiary (Domestic):

Aberdeen Unit Trust Managers Ltd.   (2)
10 Queen's Terrace, Aberdeen, AB10 1XL, United Kingdom
Tel.: (44) 1224 631 999
Property Investment Services
N.A.I.C.S.: 525990

Subsidiary (Non-US):

Aberdeen do Brasil Gestao de Recursos Ltd.   (2)
Joaquim Floriano Street 913-7th Floor-Cj 71, Sao Paulo, 04534-013, Brazil
Tel.: (55) 1139561100
Investment Fund Services
N.A.I.C.S.: 525910

abrdn Asia Limited   (2)
21 Church Street Ste 01-01 Capital Square Two, Singapore, 049480, Singapore
Tel.: (65) 6395 2700
Fund Management Services
N.A.I.C.S.: 525910
Annie Tong (Head-Ops-Asia Pacific)

abrdn Australia Ltd.   (2)
Level 10 255 George Street, Sydney, 2000, NSW, Australia
Tel.: (61) 299502888
Fund Management Services
N.A.I.C.S.: 525910
Brett Jollie (Mng Dir)

Aberdeen Standard Asset Management (Shanghai) Co., Ltd.   (1)
Unit 1901-1903 Platinum Tower 233 Tai Cang Road, Huang Pu District, Shanghai, 200020, China
Tel.: (86) 2151525600
Investment Fund Services
N.A.I.C.S.: 525910
Arthur Qian (Head-Compliance)

Aberdeen Standard Asset Management (Thailand) Limited   (1)
No 179 Bangkok City Tower 28th Floor South Sathorn Road Thungmahamek, Sathorn, Bangkok, 10120, Thailand
Tel.: (66) 23523333
Investment Fund Services
N.A.I.C.S.: 525910
Saranya Pienluprasith (Head-Client Svcs)

Aberdeen Standard Investments (Canada) Limited   (1)
161 Bay Street 44th Floor TD Canada Trust Tower, Toronto, M5J 2S1, ON, Canada
Tel.: (416) 777-5570
Web Site: https://www.abrdn.com
Investment Fund Services
N.A.I.C.S.: 525910
Steven Goth (Sr Mgr-Client Relationship)

Aberdeen Standard Investments (Hong Kong) Limited   (1)
30th Floor Luhaitong Building 31 Queen's Road Central, Central, China (Hong Kong)
Tel.: (852) 21034700
Investment Fund Services
N.A.I.C.S.: 525910
Kennise Pang (Asst Mgr-Mktg)

Aberdeen Standard Investments (Switzerland) AG   (1)
Schweizergasse 14, 8001, Zurich, Switzerland
Tel.: (41) 442082626
Investment Fund Services
N.A.I.C.S.: 525910
Paola Bissoli (Dir-Bus Dev)

Aberdeen Standard Investments Co. Ltd.   (1)
Otemachi Financial City Grand Cube 9th Floor, Otemachi Chiyoda-ku, Tokyo, 100-0004, Japan
Tel.: (81) 345782211
Investment Fund Services
N.A.I.C.S.: 525910

Aberdeen Standard Investments Deutschland AG   (1)
Bockenheimer Landstrasse 25, 60325, Frankfurt am Main, Germany
Tel.: (49) 697680720
Investment Fund Services
N.A.I.C.S.: 525910
Peter Dombeck (Head-Institutional Bus Dev)

Aberdeen Standard Investments Luxembourg S.A.   (1)
35a Avenue John F Kennedy, 1855, Luxembourg, Luxembourg
Tel.: (352) 26433000
Investment Fund Services
N.A.I.C.S.: 525910
Christopher Palumbo (Head-Bus Dev)

Aberdeen Standard Investments Taiwan Limited   (1)
8F No 101 Songren Rd, New Taipei City, Taiwan
Tel.: (886) 287224500
Investment Fund Services
N.A.I.C.S.: 525910
Peter Lu (Mgr-Mktg)

Aberdeen Standard Islamic Investments (Malaysia) Sdn. Bhd.   (1)
Suite 26 3 Level 26 Menara IMC, PO Box 66, No 8 Jalan Sultan Ismail, 50250, Kuala Lumpur, Malaysia
Tel.: (60) 320533800
Investment Fund Services
N.A.I.C.S.: 525910
Zafir Shukor (Mgr-Investment)

Cumberland Place Financial Management Limited   (1)
7th Floor 4 Chiswell Street, London, EC1Y 4UP, United Kingdom
Tel.: (44) 2079360300
Web Site: http://www.cumberlandplace.co.uk
Investment & Advisory Management Services
N.A.I.C.S.: 523940

Focus Solutions Group Ltd.   (1)
Cranford House Kenilworth Road, Leamington Spa, CV32 6RQ, Warwickshire, United Kingdom
Tel.: (44) 1926468300
Web Site: http://www.focus-solutions.co.uk
Sales Range: $10-24.9 Million
Software & Computer Services for Financial Services Industry
N.A.I.C.S.: 513210
Dave Upton (Mng Dir)

HDFC Standard Life Insurance Company Ltd.   (1)
Trade Star 2nd floor A-Wing Junction of Kondivita & MV Road, Andheri-Kurla Road, Andheri East, Mumbai, 400 059, Maharashtra, India   (35%)
Tel.: (91) 2228220055
Insurance Services
N.A.I.C.S.: 524298
Vibha Padalkar (CEO & Mng Dir)

Interactive Investor Limited   (1)
8 Devonshire Square, London, United Kingdom
Tel.: (44) 1204 443 901
Web Site: http://www.iii.co.uk
Investment Products & Services
N.A.I.C.S.: 523940
Barry Bicknell (Fin Dir)

Subsidiary (Domestic):

Alliance Trust Savings Limited   (2)

8 West Marketgait, PO Box 164, Dundee, DD1 9YP, United Kingdom
Tel.: (44) 1382 573 737
Web Site:
http://www.alliancetrustsavings.co.uk
Investment Management Service
N.A.I.C.S.: 523940
Ramsay Urquhart *(Exec Dir)*

Interactive Investor Services Limited (2)
Exchange Court Duncombe Street, Leeds, LS14AX, W Yorks, United Kingdom
Tel.: (44) 1133462309
Web Site: http://www.ii.co.uk
Investment Banking Services
N.A.I.C.S.: 523150

Share plc (2)
Oxford House Oxford Road, Aylesbury, HP21 8SZ, Buckinghamshire, United Kingdom
Tel.: (44) 1296414141
Web Site: http://www.share.com
Sales Range: $25-49.9 Million
Stockbroking & Investment Services
N.A.I.C.S.: 523150
Richard William Stone *(CEO)*

PT Aberdeen Standard Investment (1)
Menara DEA Tower II Lantai 16 Kawasan Mega Kuningan Jl Mega Kuningan, Barat Kav E4 3 No 1-2, Jakarta Selatan, 12950, Indonesia
Tel.: (62) 2129812800
Investment Fund Services
N.A.I.C.S.: 525910

Pearson Jones plc (1)
Clayton Wood Close West Park Ring Road, Leeds, LS16 6QE, United Kingdom
Tel.: (44) 113 228 0900
Web Site: http://www.1825.com
Financial Planning & Investment Advice Services
N.A.I.C.S.: 523940
Tim Johnson *(Mng Dir)*

Standard Life Asia Limited (1)
40th Floor Tower 1 Times Square, 1 Matheson Street, Causeway Bay, China (Hong Kong)
Tel.: (852) 21690300
Web Site: http://www.standardlife.hk
Life Issurance & Investment Products
N.A.I.C.S.: 524113

Standard Life Wealth Limited (1)
1 George Street, Edinburgh, EH2 2LL, United Kingdom
Tel.: (44) 8452798880
Web Site: http://www.standardlifewealth.com
Financial Investment Management Services
N.A.I.C.S.: 523999
Richard Charnock *(CEO)*

ABRDN UK SMALLER COMPANIES GROWTH TRUST PLC
1 George Street, Edinburgh, EH2 2LL, United Kingdom
Tel.: (44) 1268448222   UK
Web Site:
https://www.abrdnuksmaller.co.uk
Year Founded: 1993
AUSC—(LSE)
Rev.: $15,101,920
Assets: $735,267,835
Liabilities: $58,293,708
Net Worth: $676,974,127
Earnings: ($261,237,547)
Fiscal Year-end: 06/30/22
Other Financial Vehicles
N.A.I.C.S.: 525990
Harry Nimmo *(Dir-Investment)*

ABRIL ABOGADOS SLU
Calle Amador de los Rios 1 1, 28010, Madrid, Spain
Tel.: (34) 91 702 03 31
Web Site:
http://www.abrilabogados.com
Year Founded: 2001
Emp.: 16
Law firm

N.A.I.C.S.: 541110
Cristina Gomez Bernal *(Atty)*
Subsidiaries:

Jacobacci & Partners S.P.A. (1)
Corso Emilia 8, 10152, Turin, Italy
Tel.: (39) 011 2440311
Web Site: http://www.jacobacci.com
Emp.: 52
Law firm
N.A.I.C.S.: 541110
Fabrizio Jacobacci *(Atty)*

ABRIS CAPITAL PARTNERS SP. Z O.O.
Grzybowska Park 6th Floor ul Grzybowska 5A, 00-132, Warsaw, Poland
Tel.: (48) 22 564 5858   PL
Web Site: http://www.abris-capital.com
Year Founded: 2006
Emp.: 33
Private Equity Fund Management Services
N.A.I.C.S.: 523999
Pawel Gierynski *(Mng Partner)*
Subsidiaries:

AAA Auto International a.s. (1)
Dopravaku 874/15, 184 00, Prague, 8, Czech Republic
Tel.: (420) 284 022 081
Web Site: http://www.aaaauto.eu
Holding Company; Motor Vehicle Sales & Support Services
N.A.I.C.S.: 551112
Karolina Topolova *(CEO)*

Cargus International S.R.L. (1)
Calea Bucuresti Nr 169A Cladirea A Etaj 8 Sector 1, Bucharest, 014459, Romania
Tel.: (40) 21 933 00 00
Courier Service
N.A.I.C.S.: 492210

Scanmed S.A. (1)
Tel.: (48) 126298800
Web Site: http://scanmed.pl
Genaral Health Care Services
N.A.I.C.S.: 622110

Subsidiary (Domestic):

Lux MED Sp. z.o.o (2)
ul Postepu 21C, Warsaw, 02-676, Poland
Tel.: (48) 223322888
Web Site: http://www.luxmed.pl
Emp.: 4,100
Health Care Srvices
N.A.I.C.S.: 621999
Anna Rulkiewicz *(Pres & Member-Mgmt Bd)*

ABS MANUFACTURING & DISTRIBUTING LIMITED
185 Magill St, Lively, P3Y 1K6, ON, Canada
Tel.: (705) 692-5445
Web Site:
http://www.absmanufacturing.com
Year Founded: 1973
Rev.: $16,400,000
Emp.: 52
Rubber Product Distr
N.A.I.C.S.: 326291
John Bradley *(Pres & CEO)*

ABSA FINANCIAL CORP.
Central 7th Avenue Sector The Blade Calidonia, PO Box 0816-05098, Titan Building Ground Floor, Panama, Panama
Tel.: (507) 225 2222
Year Founded: 2012
ABSA—(PAN)
Sales Range: Less than $1 Million
Real Estate Prorperty Leasing Services
N.A.I.C.S.: 531190

ABSA GROUP LIMITED
7th Floor Absa Towers West 15 Troye

Street, Johannesburg, 2001, South Africa
Tel.: (27) 113504000   ZA
Web Site: https://www.absa.africa
55AM—(LSE)
Rev.: $5,526,146,242
Assets: $99,012,241,363
Liabilities: $90,330,432,303
Net Worth: $8,681,809,060
Earnings: $1,191,552,509
Emp.: 37,107
Fiscal Year-end: 12/31/23
Financial Investment Services
N.A.I.C.S.: 551111
Charles S. Wheeler *(Grp Gen Counsel)*

Subsidiaries:

Absa Bank Limited (1)
Absa Towers West 15 Troye Street, Johannesburg, South Africa
Tel.: (27) 102113117
Web Site: http://www.absa.co.za
Banking, Mortgage & Credit Card Services
N.A.I.C.S.: 522110
Charles S. Wheeler *(Grp Gen Counsel)*

Subsidiary (Domestic):

Absa Vehicle Management Solutions Proprietary Limited (2)
Block A 151 Katherine Street, Johannesburg, South Africa
Tel.: (27) 116859500
Fleet Management Services
N.A.I.C.S.: 532112

Absa Bank Mozambique, SA (1)
Sommershield Neighborhood, Marginal Avenue, Office Building, o 141, 16th Floor, Rani Torres, Mozambique
Tel.: (258) 21344400
Web Site: https://www.absa.co.mz
Commercial Banking Services
N.A.I.C.S.: 522110

Absa Capital Representative Office Nigeria Limited (1)
38A Glover Rd, Ikoyi, Lagos, 106104, Nigeria
Tel.: (234) 12210000
Business Management Consulting Services
N.A.I.C.S.: 541618

Absa Financial Services Limited (1)
7th Floor Absa Towers West 15 Troye Street, Johannesburg, 2001, South Africa
Tel.: (27) 113504000
Web Site: http://www.absa.co.za
Finance & Insurance Services
N.A.I.C.S.: 523999

Subsidiary (Domestic):

Absa Financial Services Africa Holdings Proprietary Limited (2)
7th Floor Absa Towers West 15 Troye Street, Johannesburg, 2001, South Africa
Tel.: (27) 113504000
Financial Management Services
N.A.I.C.S.: 523999

Absa Insurance Company Limited (2)
7th Floor Absa Towers West 15 Troye Street, Johannesburg, 2001, South Africa
Tel.: (27) 113504000
Web Site: https://www.absa.co.za
General Insurance Services
N.A.I.C.S.: 524210

Absa Life Limited (2)
7th Floor Absa Towers West 15 Troye Street, Johannesburg, 2001, South Africa
Tel.: (27) 113504000
Web Site: https://www.absa.africa
General Insurance Services
N.A.I.C.S.: 524298

Absa Trust Limited (2)
56 Eloff Street, Johannesburg, 11 244 9000, South Africa
Tel.: (27) 112449000
Financial Management Services
N.A.I.C.S.: 523999

Subsidiary (Non-US):

Absa Wealth & Investment Management (2)

4th Floor Absa Towers North 180 Commissioner Street, Johannesburg, 2001, Sudan (South)
Tel.: (27) 860111456
Web Site: https://www.absa.co.za
Wealth & Investment Management Services
N.A.I.C.S.: 523999

Absa Insurance and Financial Advisers Proprietary Limited (1)
7th Floor Absa Towers West 15 Troye Street, Johannesburg, 2001, South Africa
Tel.: (27) 113504000
Web Site: http://www.absa.com
General Insurance & Financial Advice Services
N.A.I.C.S.: 524210

Absa Manx Insurance Company Limited (1)
3rd Floor Saint Georges Court Upper Church Street, Douglas, IMI 1EE, Isle of Man
Tel.: (44) 1624692411
Insurance Underwriting Services
N.A.I.C.S.: 524113

Absa Portfolio Managers Proprietary Limited (1)
7th Floor Absa Towers West 15 Troye Street, Johannesburg, 2001, South Africa
Tel.: (27) 113504000
Asset Management Services
N.A.I.C.S.: 523940

Absa Vehicle Management Proprietary Limited (1)
7th Floor Absa Towers West 15 Troye Street, Johannesburg, 2001, South Africa
Tel.: (27) 113504000
Fleet Management Services
N.A.I.C.S.: 532112

Absa idirect Limited (1)
7th Floor Absa Towers West 15 Troye Street, Johannesburg, 2001, Korea (South)
Tel.: (27) 113504000
General Insurance Services
N.A.I.C.S.: 524210

National Bank of Commerce Limited (1)
Sokoine Drive and Azikiwe Street, Dar es Salaam, Tanzania (55%)
Tel.: (255) 768984000
Web Site: http://www.nbctz.com
Rev.: $110,633,292
Assets: $1,221,882,648
Liabilities: $1,073,495,904
Net Worth: $148,386,744
Earnings: $24,514,984
Emp.: 984
Fiscal Year-end: 12/31/2022
Banking Services
N.A.I.C.S.: 522110
Waziri Barnabas *(CFO)*

ABSAL COMPANY
Narmak Street Beside Iran University Of Science And Technology No 54, Tehran, Iran
Tel.: (98) 2177451089
Year Founded: 1957
ASAL—(THE)
Sales Range: Less than $1 Million
Refrigerator Equipment Mfr
N.A.I.C.S.: 333415

ABSOLENT AIR CARE GROUP AB
Staplaregatan 1, SE-531 40, Lidkoping, Sweden
Tel.: (46) 510484000
Web Site:
https://www.absolentgroup.com
ABSO—(OMX)
Rev.: $125,443,349
Assets: $156,034,262
Liabilities: $91,005,929
Net Worth: $65,028,333
Earnings: $14,213,662
Emp.: 457
Fiscal Year-end: 12/31/22
Filter Mfr
N.A.I.C.S.: 333413

Absolent Air Care Group AB—(Continued)

Axel Berntsson *(Pres & CEO)*

Subsidiaries:

Absolent (Beijing) Co., Ltd. (1)
Rm 2101 East Ocean Centre No 24A Jianwai Avenue, Chaoyang District, Beijing, 100004, China
Tel.: (86) 1065156051
Industrial Air Cleaning Equipment Mfr
N.A.I.C.S.: 333413

Absolent Filtermist India Private Ltd. (1)
Level 15 Eros Corporate Tower Nehru Place, New Delhi, 110019, India
Tel.: (91) 9910057521
Web Site: https://www.filtermist.in
Vacuum Cleaner Product Mfr & Distr
N.A.I.C.S.: 333310

Absolent GmbH (1)
Am Leveloh 15B, 45549, Sprockhovel, Germany
Tel.: (49) 23249778760
Web Site: https://absolent.de
Industrial Air Cleaning Equipment Mfr
N.A.I.C.S.: 333413

Absolent Inc. (1)
6541-125 Meridien Dr, Raleigh, NC 27616
Tel.: (919) 570-2862
Filter Mfr
N.A.I.C.S.: 333413

Absolent Japan Ltd. (1)
1-10-3 Roppongi, Minato-ku, Tokyo, 106-0032, Japan
Tel.: (81) 8069798134
Industrial Air Cleaning Equipment Mfr
N.A.I.C.S.: 333413

Absolent S.R.L. (1)
Via Quarto 43, 20861, Brugherio, Italy
Tel.: (39) 0399636354
Air Cleaning Equipment Mfr & Distr
N.A.I.C.S.: 333413

Absolent SAS (1)
29 Rue François Arago, Tossiat, 01000, Bourg-en-Bresse, France
Tel.: (33) 474550868
Web Site: https://www.absolent.fr
Industrial Air Cleaning Equipment Mfr
N.A.I.C.S.: 333413

Aerofil Inc. (1)
30 Boul Hymus, Pointe-Claire, H9R 1C9, QC, Canada
Tel.: (514) 630-6656
Web Site: https://www.aerofil.ca
Air Cleaning Equipment Distr
N.A.I.C.S.: 423120

Bristol Tool & Gauge International GmbH (1)
Am Sagewerk 1, Dombuhl, 91601, Ansbach, Germany
Tel.: (49) 98 689 8260
Web Site: https://www.bristolfilter.de
Vacuum Cleaner Product Mfr & Distr
N.A.I.C.S.: 333310
Dominique Ullmann *(Natl Sls Mgr)*

C&C Mechanical Ltd. (1)
984 Farewell St S Unit 3, Oshawa, L1H 6N6, ON, Canada
Tel.: (416) 276-9211
Web Site: https://www.ccmechanical.ca
Air Filtration Equipment Maintenance Services
N.A.I.C.S.: 811310

Diversitech Equipment & Sales (1984) Ltd. (1)
3200 rue Guenette, Saint-Laurent, Montreal, H4S 2G5, QC, Canada
Tel.: (514) 631-7300
Web Site: https://www.diversitech.ca
Industrial Air Cleaning Equipment Mfr
N.A.I.C.S.: 333413
David Kings *(Sls Mgr)*

Filtermist Asia Pte. Ltd. (1)
300 Tampines Avenue 5 Tampines Junction 09-02, Singapore, 529653, Singapore
Tel.: (65) 67898519
Vacuum Cleaner Product Mfr & Distr
N.A.I.C.S.: 333310

Filtermist GmbH (1)
Am Leveloh 15B, 45549, Sprockhovel, Germany
Tel.: (49) 1702233931
Web Site: https://www.filtermist.de
Industrial Machinery Mfr & Distr
N.A.I.C.S.: 333248

Filtermist Shanghai Ltd. (1)
Room 2006 Zhongchuang Building No 819 Nanjing West Road, Jing'an District, Shanghai, China
Tel.: (86) 13901397068
Web Site: https://www.filtermist.cn
Vacuum Cleaner Product Mfr & Distr
N.A.I.C.S.: 333310

Filtermist Systems Ltd. (1)
Telford 54 Business Park Nedge Hill, Telford, TF3 3AL, United Kingdom
Tel.: (44) 1952290500
Web Site: https://www.filtermist.co.uk
Industrial Air Cleaning Equipment Mfr
N.A.I.C.S.: 333413

Gallito Ltd. (1)
Unit 407 Birch Park Thorpe Arch Estate, Wetherby, LS23 7FG, West Yorkshire, United Kingdom
Tel.: (44) 193 784 4698
Web Site: https://www.gallito.co.uk
Painting & Wall Coverage Services
N.A.I.C.S.: 238320

Interzon AB (1)
Propellervagen 4A, Taby, 183 62, Stockholm, Sweden
Tel.: (46) 85 444 4430
Web Site: https://www.interzon.com
AirMaid Ozone Generator Mfr
N.A.I.C.S.: 335312
Johnny Groth *(Sys Engr)*

Kerstar Ltd. (1)
1A Weddell Way, Brackmills Industrial Estate, Northampton, NN4 7HS, United Kingdom
Tel.: (44) 195 229 0500
Web Site: https://www.kerstar.co.uk
Vacuum Cleaner Product Mfr & Distr
N.A.I.C.S.: 333310

Quatro Air Technologies Inc. (1)
30 Hymus Blvd, Pointe-Claire, H9R 1C9, QC, Canada
Web Site: https://quatroair.com
Cartridge Filter Mfr
N.A.I.C.S.: 333413

Tessu Systems B.V. (1)
Bolderweg 57, 1332 BA, Almere, Netherlands
Tel.: (31) 365320710
Web Site: https://www.tessu.nl
Industrial Machinery Mfr & Distr
N.A.I.C.S.: 333248

ABSOLICON SOLAR COLLECTOR AB
Fiskaregatan 11, 871 33, Harnosand, Sweden
Tel.: (46) 611557000
Web Site: https://www.absolicon.com
Year Founded: 2007
Renewable Energy Equipment Mfr
N.A.I.C.S.: 334413
Joakim Bystrom *(Founder & CEO)*

ABSOLUT BANK OAO
18 Tsvetnoy Boulevard, 127051, Moscow, Russia
Tel.: (7) 495 777 71 71   RU
Web Site:
  http://www.absolutbank.com
Year Founded: 1993
Commericial Banking
N.A.I.C.S.: 522110
Andrey V. Degtyarev *(Chm-Mgmt Bd)*

ABSOLUT CAPITAL MANAGEMENT HOLDING LTD
Tsvetnoy Blvd 18, 127051, Moscow, Russia
Tel.: (7) 4957777171

Web Site:
  http://www.absolutbank.com
Sales Range: $50-74.9 Million
Finance Investment Services
N.A.I.C.S.: 523150
Nikolay Sidorov *(Chm)*

ABSOLUTE CLEAN ENERGY PUBLIC COMPANY LIMITED
140/6 ITF Tower 7th Floor Silom Rd, Suriyawong Bangrak, Bangkok, 10500, Thailand
Tel.: (66) 800530072   TH
Web Site: https://www.ace-energy.co.th
Year Founded: 2015
ACE—(THA)
Rev.: $179,997,066
Assets: $634,551,873
Liabilities: $187,838,944
Net Worth: $446,712,928
Earnings: $31,299,980
Emp.: 871
Fiscal Year-end: 12/31/23
Electric Power Distribution Services
N.A.I.C.S.: 221122
Tanachai Bunditvorapoom *(CEO)*

Subsidiaries:

ACE Solar Co., Ltd. (1)
140/6 ITF Tower 7th Floor Silom Road, Suriyawong Bangrak, Bangkok, 10500, Thailand
Tel.: (66) 854880080
Web Site: http://www.acesolar.co.th
Biomass & Solar Power Generation Services
N.A.I.C.S.: 221118

ABSON INDUSTRIES LIMITED
Anum Estate 8th Floor Accross Duty Free Shop 49, Darul-Aman Cooperative Society Sharea Faisal, Karachi, Pakistan
Tel.: (92) 21 4313012
Import & Export Trading Services
N.A.I.C.S.: 522299

ABT SPORTSLINE GMBH
Daimlerstrasse 2, 87437, Kempten, Germany
Tel.: (49) 831571400
Web Site: http://www.abt-sportsline.de
Year Founded: 1896
Rev.: $40,282,138
Emp.: 173
Automotive Products Mfr
N.A.I.C.S.: 811198
Hans-Jurgen Abt *(Mng Dir)*

ABTERRA LTD.
7 Temasek Boulevard 11-01 Suntec Tower 1, Singapore, 038987, Singapore
Tel.: (65) 6885 9800
Web Site: http://www.abterra.com.sg
L5I—(SES)
Sales Range: Less than $1 Million
Iron Ore & Coal Distr
N.A.I.C.S.: 423510
Bee Leng Chew *(Sec)*

Subsidiaries:

Abterra Macao Commercial Offshore Limited (1)
Avenida Infante D Henrique No 43-53A Edif The Macau Square 8 Andar K, Macau, China (Macau)
Tel.: (853) 28718685
Iron Ore Mining Services
N.A.I.C.S.: 212210

ABTEY PRODUCTIONS
BP 14 RN 466A, Heimsbrunn, 68990, France
Tel.: (33) 389819210

Web Site: http://www.abtey.fr
Rev.: $14,500,000
Emp.: 143
N.A.I.C.S.: 311351
Thierry Crenner *(Dir-Fin)*

ABU DHABI AVIATION
PO Box 2723, Abu Dhabi, United Arab Emirates
Tel.: (971) 25758000
Web Site: https://ada.ae
Year Founded: 1976
ADAVIATION—(ABU)
Rev.: $712,015,366
Assets: $1,646,137,575
Liabilities: $430,644,473
Net Worth: $1,215,493,101
Earnings: $134,291,278
Emp.: 9,500
Fiscal Year-end: 12/31/23
Air Freight Services
N.A.I.C.S.: 488510
Nader Ahmed Mohammed Al Hammadi *(Chm)*

Subsidiaries:

ADA International Real Estate Owned by Abu Dhabi Aviation-Sole Proprietorship Co. L.L.C. (1)
Abu Dhabi International Airport, PO Box 2723, Abu Dhabi, United Arab Emirates
Tel.: (971) 25051140
Web Site: https://www.adaire.ae
Real Estate Services
N.A.I.C.S.: 531210
H. E. Nadir Ahmed Al Hammadi *(Chm)*

ADA Millennium Consulting-Owned by Abu Dhabi Aviation Sole Proprietorship L.L.C. (1)
Abu Dhabi International Airport, PO Box 2723, Abu Dhabi, United Arab Emirates
Tel.: (971) 569971383
Web Site: https://www.adame.ae
Aviation Consulting Services
N.A.I.C.S.: 488190
H. E. Mohamed Ibrahim Al Mazrouei *(Chm)*

Maximus Air L.L.C. (1)
Maximus Air Cargo Villa Street No 25, PO Box 35367, Abu Dhabi, United Arab Emirates
Tel.: (971) 24198666
Web Site: http://www.maximus-air.com
Oil Transportation Services
N.A.I.C.S.: 481111

ABU DHABI COMMERCIAL BANK PJSC
Abu Dhabi Commercial Bank Building Shk Zayed street, PO Box 939, Abu Dhabi, United Arab Emirates
Tel.: (971) 26962222   AE
Web Site: https://www.adcb.com
Year Founded: 1985
ADCB—(ABU)
Rev.: $6,863,677,804
Assets: $154,452,110,394
Liabilities: $135,049,156,659
Net Worth: $19,402,953,735
Earnings: $2,234,584,593
Emp.: 2,096
Fiscal Year-end: 12/31/23
Commercial Banking Services
N.A.I.C.S.: 522110
Eissa Mohamed Ghanem Al Suwaidi *(Chm)*

Subsidiaries:

ADCB Asset Management Limited (1)
Level 10 Al Sila TowerADGM SquareAl Maryah Island, PO Box 939, Abu Dhabi, United Arab Emirates
Tel.: (971) 600502322
Web Site: https://www.adcbam.com
Financial Services
N.A.I.C.S.: 541611
Ilias Kakos *(Head-Institutional Sls)*

ADCB Finance (Cayman) Limited   **(1)**
Al Salam St, Abu Dhabi, United Arab Emirates
Tel.: (971) 26962222
Investment Management & Share Trading Services
N.A.I.C.S.: 541618

ADCB Securities LLC   **(1)**
Abu Dhabi Commercial Bank Building
Sheikh Zayed Bin Sultan Street, Abu Dhabi, United Arab Emirates
Tel.: (971) 600503325
Web Site: https://www.adcbsecurities.com
N.A.I.C.S.: 522110

Abu Dhabi Commercial Bank   **(1)**
Building Shk Zayed street, PO Box 939, Abu Dhabi, United Arab Emirates
Tel.: (971) 26962222
Web Site: http://www.adcb.com
Commercial Banking Services
N.A.I.C.S.: 522110
Ala'a Eraiqat (CEO)

Abu Dhabi Commercial Engineering Services LLC   **(1)**
6th Floor Sheikh Zayed Bin Sultan St, PO Box 939, Abu Dhabi, United Arab Emirates
Tel.: (971) 26973579
Web Site: https://www.adce.ae
Engineeering Services
N.A.I.C.S.: 541330

Orient Takaful PJSC   **(1)**
Al Futtaim Building Deira, PO Box 183368, Dubai, United Arab Emirates
Tel.: (971) 46017500
Web Site: https://www.orienttakaful.ae
Rev.: $174,205,058
Assets: $292,461,134
Liabilities: $215,134,723
Net Worth: $77,326,410
Earnings: $13,646,588
Emp.: 130
Fiscal Year-end: 12/31/2023
Insurance Services
N.A.I.C.S.: 524128
Yousuf Ali Ahmed Obaid Zayed Alfalasi (Chm)

Union National Bank PJSC   **(1)**
UNB Head Office Sheikh Zayed Street, PO Box 3865, Abu Dhabi, United Arab Emirates
Tel.: (971) 26930120
Web Site: http://www.unb.com
Rev.: $1,263,178,423
Assets: $29,129,951,934
Liabilities: $23,968,725,034
Net Worth: $5,161,226,900
Earnings: $322,797,594
Fiscal Year-end: 12/31/2018
Banking Services
N.A.I.C.S.: 522110
Nahayan Mabarak Al Nahayan (Chm)

ABU DHABI DEVELOPMENTAL HOLDING COMPANY PJSC

Capital Gate - Al Khaleeh Al Arabi Street Building 10th Floor, Abu Dhabi, United Arab Emirates
Web Site: https://adq.ae
Holding Company
N.A.I.C.S.: 551112

Subsidiaries:

Abu Dhabi Ports Company PJSC   **(1)**
Mina Zayed, 54477, Abu Dhabi, United Arab Emirates
Tel.: (971) 8000651204
Web Site: https://www.adportsgroup.com
Emp.: 100
Port Operations; Transportation, Logistics, Supply Chain & Storage
N.A.I.C.S.: 541614

Subsidiary (Non-US):

International Associated Cargo Carrier S.A.E.   **(2)**
PO Box 4636, 31412, Dammam, Saudi Arabia   **(70%)**
Tel.: (966) 138140460
Web Site: https://iaccsaudi.com
Shipping Company
N.A.I.C.S.: 488330

ABU DHABI GROUP

Al Naeem Tower Khalifa Street, PO Box 44222, Abu Dhabi, United Arab Emirates
Tel.: (971) 26266406
Year Founded: 1997
Sales Range: $5-14.9 Billion
Emp.: 25,000
Investment Holding Company
N.A.I.C.S.: 551112
Nahayan Mabarak Al Nahayan (Chm)

Subsidiaries:

Bank Alfalah Limited   **(1)**
B A Building I I Chundrigar Road, PO Box 6773, Karachi, 74000, Pakistan   **(74%)**
Tel.: (92) 32414030
Web Site: https://www.bankalfalah.com
Rev.: $360,153,181
Assets: $6,872,190,841
Liabilities: $6,297,207,116
Net Worth: $574,983,724
Earnings: $83,924,837
Emp.: 10,118
Fiscal Year-end: 12/31/2019
Commercial & Investment Banking Services
N.A.I.C.S.: 522110
Mohib Hasan Khan (CIO)

Subsidiary (Domestic):

Alfalah GHP Investment Management Limited   **(2)**
Office 8-B 8th Floor Executive Tower Dolmen City Block 4 Clifton, I I Chundrigar Road, Karachi, Pakistan   **(56%)**
Tel.: (92) 213530674144
Web Site: http://www.alfalahghp.com
Sales Range: $1-9.9 Million
Emp.: 50
Asset Management & Investment Advisory Services
N.A.I.C.S.: 523940
Maheen Rahman (CEO)

Alfalah Insurance Company Limited   **(2)**
5-Saint Mary Park, Gulberg- III, Lahore, Pakistan
Tel.: (92) 111786234
Web Site: http://www.alfalahinsurance.com
Property & Other Insurance Services
N.A.I.C.S.: 524126

Alfalah Securities (Pvt.) Ltd.   **(2)**
Saima Trade Towers 12th Floor Tower A, I I Chundrigar Road, Karachi, Pakistan
Tel.: (92) 2199217810
Web Site: http://www.alfalahsec.com
Sales Range: $75-99.9 Million
Emp.: 16
Equity Investment, Money Market Brokerage & Investment Banking Services
N.A.I.C.S.: 523999
Sohail Ahmed Faruqi (Head-Treasury)

Standard Bank JSC   **(1)**
3 K Tsamebuli Ave, Tbilisi, 0103, Georgia   **(100%)**
Tel.: (995) 322550000
Web Site: http://www.ksb.ge
Sales Range: $1-9.9 Million
Commercial Banking Services
N.A.I.C.S.: 522110
Ana Nicoladze (Head-Central Outlet)

Wateen Telecom Limited   **(1)**
PO Box 3527, Lahore, Pakistan
Tel.: (92) 111365111
Web Site: http://www.wateen.com
Sales Range: $100-124.9 Million
Emp.: 320
Fixed, Mobile & Internet Telecommunications Services
N.A.I.C.S.: 517111
Zafar Iqbal (Gen Mgr-HR & Admin)

ABU DHABI INVESTMENT AUTHORITY

211 Corniche, PO Box 3600, Abu Dhabi, 3600, United Arab Emirates
Tel.: (971) 24150000
Web Site: http://www.adia.ae
Year Founded: 1976
Investment Holding Company
N.A.I.C.S.: 551112

Mohammed Khalifa Zayed Al Nahyan (Chm)

Subsidiaries:

Autobahn Tank & Rast GmbH   **(1)**
Andreas Hermes Strasse 729, 53175, Bonn, Germany
Tel.: (49) 2289220
Web Site: http://www.tank.rast.de
Gas Station Operator
N.A.I.C.S.: 457110
Karl-H. Rolfes (CEO)

Subsidiary (Domestic):

AXXE Reisegastronomie GmbH   **(2)**
Clevischer Ring 127, 51063, Cologne, Germany
Tel.: (49) 2219647670
Web Site: http://www.axxe.de
Motorway Restaurant & Hotel Services
N.A.I.C.S.: 722511
Wolfgang Fritze (Mng Dir)

Galderma Holding S.A.   **(1)**
Avenue de Gratta Paille 2, 1018, Lausanne, Switzerland
Tel.: (41) 21 642 7800
Web Site: http://www.galderma.com
Holding Company; Skin Health Products Mfr & Whslr
N.A.I.C.S.: 551112
Janusz Czernielewski (VP-Medical Affairs)

Subsidiary (US):

ALASTIN Skincare, Inc   **(2)**
3129 Tiger Run Ct Ste 109, Carlsbad, CA 92010
Web Site: http://www.alastin.com
Skin Care Product Mfr
N.A.I.C.S.: 325620
Cam L. Garner (Co-Founder)

Subsidiary (Domestic):

Galderma Pharma S.A.   **(2)**
Avenue de Gratta Paille 2, 1018, Lausanne, Switzerland
Tel.: (41) 21 642 78 00
Web Site: http://www.galderma.com
Holding Company; Dermatology Products Developer, Mfr & Marketer
N.A.I.C.S.: 551112

Subsidiary (Non-US):

Galderma Brasil Ltda.   **(3)**
Edifico E Tower Ruafunchal 418 6 Andar, 04551-060, Sao Paulo, SP, Brazil
Tel.: (55) 1135246300
Web Site: http://www.galderma.com.br
Sales Range: $25-49.9 Million
Emp.: 50
Dermatology Products Sales & Marketing
N.A.I.C.S.: 424210

Galderma Canada, Inc.   **(3)**
55 Commerce Valley Dr W 400, Thornhill, L3T 7V9, ON, Canada
Tel.: (905) 762-2500
Web Site: http://www.galderma.com
Sales Range: $25-49.9 Million
Emp.: 25
Dermatology Product Mfr
N.A.I.C.S.: 325412

Galderma International SAS   **(3)**
Tour Europlaza La Defense 4 20 Avenue Andre Prothin, La Defense, 92927, Paris, Cedex, France
Tel.: (33) 158864545
Web Site: http://www.galderma.com
Sales Range: $125-149.9 Million
Emp.: 300
Dermatology Products Sales & Marketing
N.A.I.C.S.: 424210

Subsidiary (US):

Galderma Laboratories, L.P.   **(3)**
14501 N Fwy, Fort Worth, TX 76177-3304
Tel.: (817) 961-5000
Web Site: http://www.galdermausa.com
Sales Range: $50-74.9 Million
Emp.: 250
Dermatology Product Mfr.
N.A.I.C.S.: 325412
Kelly Huang (VP & Gen Mgr-Aesthetic & Corrective Bus)

Subsidiary (Non-US):

Galderma Laboratorium GmbH   **(3)**
Toulouser Allee 23a, 40211, Dusseldorf, Germany
Tel.: (49) 2115860100
Web Site: http://www.galderma.de
Sales Range: $50-74.9 Million
Emp.: 200
Dermatology Product Mfr
N.A.I.C.S.: 325412
Marion Bock (Mng Dir, Head-DACH & Gen Mgr)

Galderma Production Canada Inc.   **(3)**
19400 Transcanada Highway, Baie-d'Urfe, H9X 3S4, QC, Canada
Tel.: (514) 457-3366
Web Site: http://www.galderma.com
Sales Range: $50-74.9 Million
Emp.: 220
Dermatology Product Mfr
N.A.I.C.S.: 325412

Laboratoires Galderma SAS   **(3)**
Zone Industrielle Touviere, 74540, Alby-sur-Cheran, France
Tel.: (33) 158864545
Sales Range: $50-74.9 Million
Emp.: 200
Dermatology Product Mfr
N.A.I.C.S.: 325412

Q-Med AB   **(3)**
Seminariegatan 21, 752 28, Uppsala, 75228, Sweden
Tel.: (46) 184749000
Web Site: http://www.q-med.com
Sales Range: $200-249.9 Million
Emp.: 636
Biotechnology & Medical Devices
N.A.I.C.S.: 339112

Subsidiary (Non-US):

Q-Med (Sweden) Australia Pty Ltd.   **(4)**
37 Belmore Street, Surry Hills, 2010, Sydney, NSW, Australia
Tel.: (61) 292817727
Web Site: http://www.revitaliseyourskin.com.au
Sales Range: $25-49.9 Million
Emp.: 20
Pharmaceutical Preparation Mfr
N.A.I.C.S.: 325412

Q-Med Brasil Comercio e Importacao de Produtos Medicos Ltda   **(4)**
Rua Alexandre Dumas 2100 conjunto 22, Chacara Santo Antonio, 04717-004, Sao Paulo, SP, Brazil
Tel.: (55) 1151855589
Web Site: http://www.q-med.com
Sales Range: $50-74.9 Million
Emp.: 8
Medical Dental & Hospital Equipment & Supplies Whslr
N.A.I.C.S.: 423450

Q-Med ICT S.r.l.   **(4)**
Via M Borsa 11, Codogno, 26845, Lodi, Italy
Tel.: (39) 0377436091
Web Site: http://www.q-med.com
Sales Range: $25-49.9 Million
Emp.: 50
Toilet Preparation Mfr
N.A.I.C.S.: 325620

Q-Med International Ltd   **(4)**
39 Healthy Street East, Kodak House II Rm 2207-08 22nd, North Point, China (Hong Kong)
Tel.: (852) 25165002
Surgical & Medical Instrument Mfr
N.A.I.C.S.: 339112

Q-Med International Trading (Shanghai) Ltd   **(4)**
Room 2017 No 1 Ji Long Road, Waigaoqiao Free Trade Zone, Shanghai, 200131, China
Tel.: (86) 1085321642
Web Site: http://www.q-med.com
Drugs & Druggists Sundries Whslr
N.A.I.C.S.: 424210

Q-Med Mexico S.A de C.V.   **(4)**

Abu Dhabi Investment Authority—(Continued)

Lglesia 2 Torre E Despacho 503, Colonia
Tizapan San Angel, 1090, Mexico, Mexico
Tel.: (52) 5556168292
Web Site: http://www.q-med.com
Sales Range: $25-49.9 Million
Emp.: 18
Surgical Appliance & Supplies Mfr
N.A.I.C.S.: 339113

Q-Med Polska SP. Z.o.o **(4)**
Nowy Swiat 47, 00-042, Warsaw, Poland
Tel.: (48) 228929120
Web Site: http://www.q-med.com
Sales Range: $25-49.9 Million
Emp.: 15
Surgical & Medical Instrument Mfr
N.A.I.C.S.: 339112

Q-Med S.a.r.l. **(4)**
49 Rue de Lisbonne, 75008, Paris, France
Tel.: (33) 156434300
Web Site: http://www.q-med.com
Drugs & Druggists Sundries Whslr
N.A.I.C.S.: 424210

Q-Med Spain S.L. **(4)**
Agustin Foxa 29 Planta Baja, Modulo 1 C-
Jose Echegaray 8, 28036, Madrid, Spain
Tel.: (34) 916369205
Web Site: http://www.q-med.com
Sales Range: $25-49.9 Million
Emp.: 30
Drugs & Druggists Sundries Whslr
N.A.I.C.S.: 424210

Merchants Automotive Group,
LLC **(1)**
14 Central Park Dr 1st Floor, Hooksett, NH
03106
Tel.: (603) 669-4100
Web Site: https://www.merchantsfleet.com
Used Car Dealer; Car & Truck Rental &
Leasing Services
N.A.I.C.S.: 441120
Gary J. Singer *(VP)*

ABU DHABI INVESTMENT COMPANY

Capital Tower ADNEC Area between
ADCB and Finance House buildings,
PO Box 46309, Abu Dhabi, United
Arab Emirates
Tel.: (971) 2 692 6101
Web Site: http://www.investad.com
Emp.: 80
Investment Services
N.A.I.C.S.: 523999
Faras Al Ramahi *(CEO)*

Subsidiaries:

Ekol Lojistik AS **(1)**
Ekol Caddesi No 2, Sultanbeyli, Istanbul,
34935, Turkiye
Tel.: (90) 2165643000
Web Site: http://www.ekol.com
Integrated Logistics Services
N.A.I.C.S.: 541614
Gulcin Poyraz *(Gen Mgr-HR)*

Subsidiary (Non-US):

Europa Multipurpose Terminals
S.p.A. **(2)**
Punto Franco Nuovo - Molo VI, Trieste,
Italy **(65%)**
Tel.: (39) 040 3220333
Web Site: http://www.emterminals.com
Logistics Consulting Servies
N.A.I.C.S.: 541614

ABU DHABI ISLAMIC BANK PJSC

PO Box 313, PO Box 313, Abu
Dhabi, United Arab Emirates
Tel.: (971) 26100600 AE
Web Site: https://www.adib.ae
Year Founded: 1998
ADIB—(ABU)
Rev.: $3,374,709,038
Assets: $52,508,561,937
Liabilities: $45,362,531,384
Net Worth: $7,146,030,553
Earnings: $1,429,989,108

Emp.: 5,000
Fiscal Year-end: 12/31/23
Commercial Banking Services
N.A.I.C.S.: 522110
Jawaan Awaidha Suhail Al Khaili
(Chm)

Subsidiaries:

ADIR (UK) Limited **(1)**
One Hyde Park 100 Knightsbridge, London,
SW1X 7LJ, United Kingdom
Tel.: (44) 203 813 4125
Web Site: https://www.adib.co.uk
Real Estate Services
N.A.I.C.S.: 531390
Stephanie Heath *(Mgr-HR)*

Kawader Services **(1)**
Room No 1502 15th Floor Arabian Com-
pany Building Airport Road, Abu Dhabi,
United Arab Emirates
Tel.: (971) 2 691 9000
Web Site: https://www.kawader.biz
Sales Range: $150-199.9 Million
Emp.: 1,000
Staffing Services
N.A.I.C.S.: 541612

MPM Properties LLC **(1)**
ADIB Building on Ground Floor, King Abdul-
lah bin Abdulaziz Al Saud Street Al Bateen,
Abu Dhabi, United Arab Emirates
Tel.: (971) 26100252
Real Estate Manangement Services
N.A.I.C.S.: 531390

ABU DHABI ISLAMIC BANK-EGYPT

9A Rostom Street, Garden City,
11511, Cairo, Egypt
Tel.: 238289300
Web Site: https://www.adib.eg
Commercial Banking Services
N.A.I.C.S.: 522210
Hesham Mabrouk *(CIO)*

ABU DHABI MEDIA

PO Box 63, Abu Dhabi, United Arab
Emirates
Tel.: (971) 2 414 4000
Web Site: http://www.admedia.ae
Year Founded: 2007
Media Holding Company
N.A.I.C.S.: 516120
Noura Al Kaabi *(Chm)*

Subsidiaries:

United Printing and Publishing **(1)**
PO Box 39955, Abu Dhabi, United Arab
Emirates
Tel.: (971) 2 503 9999
Web Site: http://www.upp.ae
Printing Services
N.A.I.C.S.: 323111

VEVO LLC **(1)**
825 8th Ave 23rd Fl, New York, NY 10019
Tel.: (212) 331-1357
Web Site: http://www.vevo.com
Music Video Website Operator
N.A.I.C.S.: 516210
Alan Price *(CEO)*

ABU DHABI NATIONAL COMPANY FOR BUILDING MATERIAL

Al Zahiyah -E16-01, PO Box 2443,
Abu Dhabi, United Arab Emirates
Tel.: (971) 26455500
Web Site: https://www.bildco.ae
Year Founded: 1974
BILDCO—(ABU)
Rev.: $11,203,370
Assets: $96,568,970
Liabilities: $88,692,249
Net Worth: $7,876,721
Earnings: ($8,566,769)
Fiscal Year-end: 12/31/23
Building Material Mfr & Whslr
N.A.I.C.S.: 332311

Ali Rasheed Naser Al Omaira *(Mng Dir)*

Subsidiaries:

Bildco Cement Products LLC **(1)**
PO Box 2443, Abu Dhabi, United Arab
Emirates
Tel.: (971) 25511990
Web Site: https://bildco.ae
Cement Mfr
N.A.I.C.S.: 327310
H. E. Saif Darwish Ahmed Alketbi *(Chm)*

Bildco Reinforcing Steel Services **(1)**
PO Box 2443, Abu Dhabi, United Arab
Emirates
Tel.: (971) 2 5559183
Sales Range: $25-49.9 Million
Emp.: 75
Steel Reinforcement Services
N.A.I.C.S.: 238120
Pramond Chawdhry *(Gen Mgr)*

ABU DHABI NATIONAL HO-TELS PJSC

PO Box 46806, Abu Dhabi, United
Arab Emirates
Tel.: (971) 24447228 AE
Web Site: https://www.adnh.com
Year Founded: 1975
ADNH—(ABU)
Rev.: $444,093,655
Assets: $2,985,979,302
Liabilities: $581,830,927
Net Worth: $2,404,148,375
Earnings: $115,033,760
Emp.: 25,000
Fiscal Year-end: 12/31/23
Transportation, Tourism, Catering &
Hotel Management Services
N.A.I.C.S.: 721110
Ahmed Mohammed Sultan Suroor Al
Dhaheri *(Vice Chm)*

Subsidiaries:

Al Ghazal Transport Co. **(1)**
MusaffahMusaffah Industrial, PO Box 8200,
Abu Dhabi, United Arab Emirates **(100%)**
Tel.: (971) 124088400
Web Site: https://www.agt.ae
Sales Range: $150-199.9 Million
Ground Transportation Services
N.A.I.C.S.: 485999

Sunshine Tours **(1)**
Abu Dhabi National Hotels, PO Box 8200,
Abu Dhabi, United Arab Emirates
Tel.: (971) 4446856
Sales Range: $150-199.9 Million
Tour Operator
N.A.I.C.S.: 561520

ABU DHABI NATIONAL INSUR-ANCE COMPANY

Building No 403, PO Box 839, Abu
Dhabi, United Arab Emirates
Tel.: (971) 24080100 AE
Web Site: https://www.adnic.ae
Year Founded: 1972
ADNIC—(EMI)
Rev.: $1,022,333,653
Assets: $2,156,177,588
Liabilities: $1,531,091,693
Net Worth: $625,085,895
Earnings: $77,375,693
Fiscal Year-end: 12/31/19
Insurance Management Services
N.A.I.C.S.: 524298
Mohamed Saif Al-Nahyan *(Chm)*

Subsidiaries:

ADNIC International Ltd. **(1)**
Level 30 The Leadenhall Building 122
Leadenhall Street, London, EC3V 4AB,
United Kingdom
Tel.: (44) 2037534686
Web Site: https://adnic-international.com
Reinsurance Services
N.A.I.C.S.: 524130

ABU DHABI NATIONAL OIL COMPANY

PO Box 898, Abu Dhabi, United Arab
Emirates
Tel.: (971) 26020000 AE
Web Site: https://www.adnoc.com
Year Founded: 1971
Sales Range: $1-4.9 Rillion
Emp.: 14,000
Petroleum Exploration, Production,
Transport & Refined-Product Distribu-
tion
N.A.I.C.S.: 211120
Ahmed Al Jaber *(CEO & Mng Dir)*

Subsidiaries:

ADNOC Distribution **(1)**
Sh Zayed Street next to National Drilling
Company and UNB building, PO Box 4188,
Abu Dhabi, United Arab Emirates
Tel.: (971) 2 677 1300
Web Site: http://www.adnocdistribution.ae
Fuel Oil Distr
N.A.I.C.S.: 424710
Sultan Al Jaber *(Chm)*

ADNOC Drilling Company PJSC **(1)**
SKEC 2 Zone 1 E-17, PO Box 4017, Abu
Dhabi, United Arab Emirates **(84%)**
Tel.: (971) 26776100
Web Site: https://www.adnocdrilling.ae
Rev.: $3,056,865,000
Assets: $6,740,125,000
Liabilities: $3,475,904,000
Net Worth: $3,264,221,000
Earnings: $1,032,799,000
Emp.: 10,249
Fiscal Year-end: 12/31/2023
Oil & Gas Onshore & Offshore Drilling Ser-
vices
N.A.I.C.S.: 213111
Ahmed Al Jaber *(Chm)*

Abu Dhabi Company Onshore Oil
Operations **(1)**
PO Box 270, Abu Dhabi, United Arab
Emirates **(60%)**
Tel.: (971) 26040000
Web Site: http://www.adco.ae
Sales Range: $750-799.9 Million
Emp.: 1,450
Onshore Exploration, Development & Pro-
duction of Crude Oil
N.A.I.C.S.: 211120

Abu Dhabi Gas Development Co.
Ltd. **(1)**
PO Box 44115, Abu Dhabi, United Arab
Emirates
Tel.: (971) 2 654 2222
Web Site: http://www.alhosngas.com
Natural Gas Extraction Services
N.A.I.C.S.: 211130
Saif Ahmed Al Ghafli *(CEO)*

Abu Dhabi Gas Industries
Limited **(1)**
PO Box 665, Abu Dhabi, United Arab
Emirates **(68%)**
Tel.: (971) 26030000
Web Site: http://www.gasco.ae
Sales Range: $1-4.9 Billion
Emp.: 3,500
Processing of Associate & Non-Associate
Gas from Onshore Oil Production
N.A.I.C.S.: 325120
Adel Salem Al Khaff *(VP-Comml)*

Abu Dhabi Gas Liquefaction
Limited **(1)**
PO Box 3500, Abu Dhabi, United Arab
Emirates **(70%)**
Tel.: (971) 26061111
Web Site: http://www.adgas.com
Sales Range: $400-449.9 Million
Emp.: 200
Production & Export of Liquefied Natural
Gas & Liquefied Petroleum Gas
N.A.I.C.S.: 211130
Hasan Al-Marzooqi *(Deputy Gen Mgr)*

Abu Dhabi Marine Operating
Company **(1)**
PO Box 303, Abu Dhabi, United Arab
Emirates **(60%)**
Tel.: (971) 26060000

Web Site:
http://www.abudhabimargroup.com
Sales Range: $400-449.9 Million
Emp.: 1,504
Ship Building & Repairing Services
N.A.I.C.S.: 336611

Abu Dhabi National Oil Company for Distribution (1)
Sheikh Zayed Street next to ADCB Building, PO Box 4188, Abu Dhabi, United Arab Emirates
Tel.: (971) 26771300
Web Site: https://www.adnocdistribution.ae
Petroleum Products Marketing & Distribution
N.A.I.C.S.: 424720
Khaled Salmeen (Exec Dir)

Abu Dhabi National Tanker Company (1)
Sheikh Khalifa Energy Complex Takreer Tower 11th & 12th Floors, PO Box 2977, Khalifa Street, Abu Dhabi, United Arab Emirates (100%)
Tel.: (971) 26028400
Web Site: http://www.adnatco.com
Sales Range: $50-74.9 Million
Emp.: 68
Transport of Crude Oil & Petroleum Products
N.A.I.C.S.: 486910

Abu Dhabi Oil Refining Company (1)
PO Box 3593, Abu Dhabi, United Arab Emirates (65%)
Tel.: (971) 26027001
Web Site: http://www.takreer.com
Refining of Crude Oil, Salt, Chlorine & Petroleum Condensates, Sulphur Treatment & Mixing of Petroleum Products
N.A.I.C.S.: 324110

Abu Dhabi Petroleum Ports Operating Company (1)
PO Box 61, Abu Dhabi, United Arab Emirates (60%)
Tel.: (971) 26028000
Web Site: http://www.irshad.ae
Sales Range: $150-199.9 Million
Emp.: 338
Petroleum Terminals & Ports Maintenance Operations
N.A.I.C.S.: 424710

Borouge PLC (1)
Sheikh Khalifa Energy Complex Corniche Road, PO Box 692 5, Abu Dhabi, United Arab Emirates (54%)
Tel.: (971) 27080000
Web Site: https://www.borouge.com
Rev.: $5,791,345,000
Assets: $8,943,896,000
Liabilities: $4,398,060,000
Net Worth: $4,545,836,000
Earnings: $1,000,670,000
Emp.: 3,000
Fiscal Year-end: 12/31/2023
Holding Company; Polymer Products Mfr & Distr
N.A.I.C.S.: 551110
Hazeem Sultan Al Suwaidi (CEO)

Subsidiary (Domestic):

Abu Dhabi Polymers Co. Ltd (2)
Borouge Tower Shaikh Khalifa Energy Complex Corniche Road, PO Box 6925, Abu Dhabi, United Arab Emirates (100%)
Tel.: (971) 27080000
Web Site: https://www.borouge.com
Emp.: 1,700
Polymers Mfr
N.A.I.C.S.: 325211
Hazeem Sultan Al Suwaidi (CEO)

Subsidiary (Non-US):

Borouge Pte. Ltd. (2)
1 George Street 18-01, 049145, Singapore, Singapore (84.74%)
Tel.: (65) 62754100
Petrochemical Product Distr
N.A.I.C.S.: 424690
Rainer Hoefling (CEO)

Subsidiary (Non-US):

Borouge Australia Pty Ltd (3)
Suite 1013 10th Floor St Kilda Road Towers

1 Queens Road, Melbourne, 3004, VIC, Australia
Tel.: (61) 3 9938 5800
Petrochemical Product Distr
N.A.I.C.S.: 424690
Tom Baines (Mgr-Sls)

Borouge Hong Kong Ltd (3)
14/F The Toy House 100 Canton Road Tsimshatsui, Kowloon, Hong Kong, China (Hong Kong)
Tel.: (852) 2 377 2688
Petrochemical Product Distr
N.A.I.C.S.: 424690

Borouge Ltd. (3)
Yurakucho ITOCiA 12F 2-7-1 Yurakucho, Chiyoda-ku, Tokyo, 100-0006, Japan
Tel.: (81) 3 6860 4785
Petrochemical Product Distr
N.A.I.C.S.: 424690
Wim Roels (CEO)

Borouge Pvt Ltd. (3)
1501/02 B Wing Lotus Corporate Park Near Jay coach signal W E Highway, Goregoan East, Mumbai, India
Tel.: (91) 22 6656 9800
Petrochemical Product Distr
N.A.I.C.S.: 424690

Borouge Sales and Marketing Co. Ltd (3)
Room 4003-4013 Tower II Plaza 66 1366 Nan Jing Xi Road, Shanghai, 200040, China
Tel.: (86) 21 6137 6888
Petrochemical Product Distr
N.A.I.C.S.: 424690

ESNAAD (1)
PO Box 46121, Abu Dhabi, United Arab Emirates (100%)
Tel.: (971) 26029000
Web Site: http://www.esnaad.com
Sales Range: $200-249.9 Million
Emp.: 1,000
Production & Marketing of Mud Chemicals, Material Handling Services, Waste Management, Specialty Chemicals Blending, Operating, Chartering or Leasing Vessels
N.A.I.C.S.: 325998

Fertiglobe plc (1)
Unit 1 20th Floor Al Sila Tower Abu Dhabi Global Market Square, Al Maryah Island, Abu Dhabi, United Arab Emirates (86.2%)
Tel.: (971) 23338888
Web Site: https://fertiglobe.com
Rev.: $2,416,200,000
Assets: $4,625,800,000
Liabilities: $2,756,100,000
Net Worth: $1,869,700,000
Earnings: $505,000,000
Emp.: 2,718
Fiscal Year-end: 12/31/2023
Chemicals Mfr
N.A.I.C.S.: 325311
Ahmed El-Hoshy (CEO)

NMDC Energy (1)
Zone No 6 7 71 Mustafa, PO Box 2058, Street No 7, 2058, Abu Dhabi, 2058, United Arab Emirates (100%)
Tel.: (971) 25549000
Web Site: https://www.nmdc-energy.com
Sales Range: $1-4.9 Billion
Emp.: 10,000
Engineering, Procurement & Construction Contracting Services for Onshore & Offshore Oil, Gas & Petrochemical Industries
N.A.I.C.S.: 237120
Aqeel A. Madhi (CEO)

National Gas Shipping Company Ltd. (NGSCO) (1)
Sheikh Khalifa Energy Complex, PO Box 2600, Takreer Tower, Abu Dhabi, United Arab Emirates
Tel.: (971) 26028600
Web Site: http://www.adnatcongsco.com
Sales Range: $50-74.9 Million
Emp.: 250
Shipping of Liquefied Gas Products
N.A.I.C.S.: 483111
Ali Al-Yabhouni (CEO)

Zakum Development Company (1)
Khalifa Energy Complex Khalifa St, PO Box 46808, Abu Dhabi, United Arab Emirates (51%)

Tel.: (971) 26050000
Web Site: http://www.zadco.ae
Sales Range: $800-899.9 Million
Emp.: 1,200
Production & Development of Oil & Gas
N.A.I.C.S.: 211120
Seif El Sewedy (Gen Mgr)

ABU DHABI NATIONAL TAKAFUL CO. P.S.C
Tamouh Tower 25th Floor Marina Square Al Reem Island, PO Box 35335, Abu Dhabi, United Arab Emirates
Tel.: (971) 24107700
Web Site: https://www.takaful.ae
Year Founded: 2003
Rev.: $49,747,430
Assets: $276,413,020
Liabilities: $178,234,780
Net Worth: $98,178,240
Earnings: $18,608,439
Fiscal Year-end: 12/31/18
Insurance Services
N.A.I.C.S.: 524298
Osama Abdeen (CEO)

ABU DHABI SECURITIES EXCHANGE
Al Ghaith Tower Ground Fl Hamdan Street, PO Box 54500, Abu Dhabi, United Arab Emirates
Tel.: (971) 26277777
Web Site: http://www.adx.ae
Year Founded: 2000
Securities Exchange Services
N.A.I.C.S.: 523210
Mohammad Al Muhairi (Head-Clearing, Settlement & Depository Dept)

ABU DHABI SHIP BUILDING PJSC
Musafah Industrial Area, PO Box 8922, Abu Dhabi, United Arab Emirates
Tel.: (971) 25028000
Web Site: https://www.adsb.ae
Year Founded: 1996
ADSB—(ABU)
Rev.: $342,394,636
Assets: $726,718,045
Liabilities: $652,099,769
Net Worth: $74,618,276
Earnings: $10,994,065
Emp.: 914
Fiscal Year-end: 12/31/23
Ship Building Services
N.A.I.C.S.: 336611
Ali Mohammed Ali Al Shehhi (COO)

ABU DHABI WATER & ELECTRICITY AUTHORITY
PO Box 6120, Abu Dhabi, United Arab Emirates
Tel.: (971) 26943333
Web Site: http://www.adwea.ae
Year Founded: 1998
Sales Range: $1-4.9 Billion
Emp.: 15,000
Water & Electric Utility Administration Services
N.A.I.C.S.: 926130
Diab Bin Zayed Al Nahyan (Chm)

Subsidiaries:

Abu Dhabi National Energy Company PJSC (1)
Al Maqam Tower Abu Dhabi Global Market Square, PO Box 55224, Abu Dhabi, United Arab Emirates
Tel.: (971) 26914900
Web Site: https://www.taqa.com
Rev.: $12,436,818,000
Assets: $49,049,623,400
Liabilities: $29,124,039,000
Net Worth: $19,925,584,400
Earnings: $1,631,839,000

Emp.: 6,906
Fiscal Year-end: 12/31/2021
Refined Petroleum Product Distr
N.A.I.C.S.: 486910
Saeed Mubarak Al-Hajeri (Vice Chm)

Subsidiary (Domestic):

Emirates CMS Power Company (2)
Taweelah Power & Water Complex, PO Box 47688, Abu Dhabi, United Arab Emirates (60%)
Tel.: (971) 25067100
Electric Power Generation & Water Desalination Plant Owner & Operator
N.A.I.C.S.: 221112

Subsidiary (Non-US):

TAQA Energy B.V. (2)
Prinsenhof, Prinses Margrietplantsoen 40, 2502 AN, Hague, Netherlands
Tel.: (31) 703337500
Web Site: http://www.taqaglobal.ae
Sales Range: $50-74.9 Million
Emp.: 100
Oil & Natural Gas Drilling & Exploration
N.A.I.C.S.: 213111

TAQA North Ltd. (2)
PO Box 2350, STN M, Calgary, T2P 2M6, AB, Canada
Tel.: (403) 724-5000
Web Site: https://www.taqa.com
Sales Range: $125-149.9 Million
Emp.: 500
Oil & Natural Gas Exploration & Production
N.A.I.C.S.: 486210

Subsidiary (Domestic):

Taweelah Asia Power Company (2)
Taweelah Power & Water Complex, PO Box 32255, Abu Dhabi, United Arab Emirates (70%)
Tel.: (971) 25627000
Web Site: http://www.tapco.ae
Sales Range: $125-149.9 Million
Emp.: 100
Electric Power Generation & Water Desalination Plant Owner & Operator
N.A.I.C.S.: 221112
Saif Al Seiari (Chm)

Abu Dhabi Transmission & Despatch Company (1)
PO Box 173, Abu Dhabi, United Arab Emirates
Tel.: (971) 2 4164000
Electric Power Transmission Services
N.A.I.C.S.: 221121
Abdulla Saif Al Nuaimi (Chm)

Al Mirfa Power Company (1)
PO Box 32277, Abu Dhabi, United Arab Emirates
Tel.: (971) 2 8952200
Web Site: http://www.ampc.ae
Power Generation Services
N.A.I.C.S.: 221118
Nidal Dajani (Engr-Plng)

Bainounah Power Company (1)
PO Box 33477, Abu Dhabi, United Arab Emirates
Tel.: (971) 26731100
Web Site: http://www.bpc.ae
Sales Range: $550-599.9 Million
Emp.: 750
Electric Power Generation & Water Desalination Plant Owner & Operator
N.A.I.C.S.: 221112

Subsidiary (Domestic):

Abu Dhabi Distribution Company (2)
PO Box 219, Abu Dhabi, United Arab Emirates (100%)
Tel.: (971) 26423000
Web Site: http://www.addc.ae
Electric Power & Water Distr
N.A.I.C.S.: 221122
Ahmed Saeed Al Muraikhi (Mng Dir)

Al Ain Distribution Company (2)
PO Box 1065, Al Ain, United Arab Emirates (100%)
Tel.: (971) 37636000
Web Site: http://www.aadc.ae
Electric Power & Water Distr
N.A.I.C.S.: 221122

Abu Qir Fertilizers and Chemical Industries
Co.—(Continued)

ABU QIR FERTILIZERS AND CHEMICAL INDUSTRIES CO.
El Tabya Rasheed Road, Alexandria,
21 911, Egypt
Tel.: (20) 35603053
Web Site: http://www.abuqir.com
Year Founded: 1976
Sales Range: $50-74.9 Million
Emp.: 2,950
Ammonium Nitrate, Urea & Anhy-
drous Liquid Ammonia Producer
N.A.I.C.S.: 325311
Saad Ibrahim Hassan El-Maati *(Chm
& Mng Dir)*

ABUNDANCE INTERNATIONAL LTD.
9 Joo Koon Circle, Singapore,
629041, Singapore
Tel.: (65) 68614040
Web Site:
   https://www.abundance.com.sg
541—(CAT)
Rev.: $623,360,000
Assets: $69,064,000
Liabilities: $32,928,000
Net Worth: $36,136,000
Earnings: ($299,000)
Emp.: 59
Fiscal Year-end: 12/31/23
Chemicals Mfr & Trader
N.A.I.C.S.: 325998
Jiangang Shi *(Chm)*

Subsidiaries:

Orient-Salt Chemicals (Shanghai)
Co., Ltd.   (1)
Room 507 Cimic Tower 1090 Century Av-
enue, Pudong New District, Shanghai,
200120, China
Tel.: (86) 2158360688
Web Site: http://www.orisalt.com
Chemicals Mfr
N.A.I.C.S.: 325998

Orient-Salt Chemicals Pte. Ltd.   (1)
9 Joo Koon Circle, Singapore, 629041, Sin-
gapore
Tel.: (65) 68639371
Chemicals Mfr
N.A.I.C.S.: 325998

Touen Japan Co., Ltd.   (1)
4-1-10 Toranomon, Minato-ku, Tokyo, 105-
0001, Japan
Tel.: (81) 364358348
Chemicals Mfr
N.A.I.C.S.: 325998

ABUNDANT PRODUCE LIMITED
Unit 23 376-380 Eastern Valley Way,
Chatswood, 2067, NSW, Australia
Tel.: (61) 475 148 018   AU
Web Site:
   http://www.abundantproduce.com
Year Founded: 2015
Rev.: $958,980
Assets: $1,769,778
Liabilities: $188,386
Net Worth: $1,581,393
Earnings: ($2,124,238)
Fiscal Year-end: 06/30/19
Vegetable Production & Distribution
Services
N.A.I.C.S.: 111219
Anthony Crimmins *(CEO-Acting)*

ABUNDANTE LIMITED
150 Changi Road 03-05 Guthrie
Building, Singapore, 41997, Singa-
pore
Tel.: (65) 63443922
Web Site: https://www.tmcltd.com.sg
Year Founded: 1979

570—(SES)
Rev.: $5,808,147
Assets: $13,981,497
Liabilities: $915,185
Net Worth: $13,066,312
Earnings: $617,999
Fiscal Year-end: 02/28/23
Readymix Concrete Mfr
N.A.I.C.S.: 327320

ABURAIHAN PHARMACEUTICAL COMPANY
No 1-Opposite Shahr Hotel-Tirandaz
Ave Damavand Road, Tehran Pars
Cross Road, Tehran, 16546 13111,
Iran
Tel.: (98) 21 77707173
Year Founded: 1965
DABO—(THE)
Sales Range: Less than $1 Million
Emp.: 426
Pharmaceuticals Product Mfr
N.A.I.C.S.: 325412
Mohsen Hashem *(Chm)*

ABUS LEVAGE FRANCE S.A.S.
Zone Industrielle de Fleville 25 Rue
Edouard Michelin, 54710, Ludres,
France
Tel.: (33) 3 83 59 22 22
Web Site: http://www.abus-levage.fr
Rev.: $17,900,000
Emp.: 60
Industrial Equipment Mfr
N.A.I.C.S.: 423830
Jean-Martin Durst *(Pres & Dir Gen)*

ABV CONSULTING, INC.
Room 10C 10/F ACME Building 28
Nanking Street, Jordan, Kowloon,
China (Hong Kong)
Tel.: (852) 35848263   NV
Web Site: http://www.abvnus.com
Year Founded: 2013
ABVN—(OTCBB)
Assets: $3,428
Liabilities: $345,132
Net Worth: ($341,704)
Earnings: ($36,756)
Emp.: 4
Fiscal Year-end: 12/31/20
Merchandising & Consulting Services
to Craft Beer Brewers & Distributors
N.A.I.C.S.: 541611
Andrew Gavrin *(Founder)*

ABVI AYMOND BRUNEL VEHICULES INDUSTRIEL
78 rue Emile Clapeyron, 60010, Per-
pignan, France
Tel.: (33) 468857785
Web Site: http://www.abvi.fr
Sales Range: $25-49.9 Million
Emp.: 71
Automobile Dealers
N.A.I.C.S.: 423110
Andre Brunel *(Chm)*

ABX GROUP LIMITED
Level 4 100 Albert Road, South Mel-
bourne, 3205, VIC, Australia
Tel.: (61) 396927222
Web Site:
   https://www.australianbauxite.com
Year Founded: 2009
ABX—(ASX)
Rev.: $884,817
Assets: $14,737,416
Liabilities: $6,067,707
Net Worth: $8,669,709
Earnings: ($1,225,393)
Fiscal Year-end: 12/31/23
Bauxite Mining Services
N.A.I.C.S.: 212290
Ian Levy *(CEO & Mng Dir)*

ABYAAR REAL ESTATE DEVELOPMENT COMPANY K.S.C.C.
Qebla Area Sahara Tower Delta Real
Estate Complex Block 13 - Bldg 9,
Floor 5 - Office No 1, Kuwait, Kuwait
Tel.: (965) 22415197
Web Site: http://www.abyaar.com
ABYAAR—(KUW)
Assets: $418,037,945
Liabilities: $291,205,000
Net Worth: $126,832,944
Earnings: ($51,921,887)
Emp.: 14
Fiscal Year-end: 12/31/19
Real Estate Services
N.A.I.C.S.: 531390
Hani Arikat *(Mgr-Fin)*

ABZU GOLD LTD.
2300-1177 West Hastings Street,
Vancouver, V6E 2K3, BC, Canada
Tel.: (604) 408-7488   BC
Web Site: http://www.abzugold.com
Gold Mining Services
N.A.I.C.S.: 212220
Robert William Baxter *(Pres & CEO)*

AC IMMUNE SA
EPFL Innovation Park Building B,
1015, Lausanne, Switzerland
Tel.: (41) 213459121
Web Site:
   https://www.acimmune.com
Year Founded: 2003
ACIU—(NASDAQ)
Rev.: $17,590,988
Assets: $217,274,439
Liabilities: $26,350,233
Net Worth: $190,924,205
Earnings: ($64,455,920)
Emp.: 161
Fiscal Year-end: 12/31/23
Pharmaceuticals Product Mfr
N.A.I.C.S.: 325412
Andrea Pfeifer *(Founder & CEO)*

AC MARCA, S.A
Avda Carrilet 293-297, L'Hospitalet
de Llobregat, 08907, Barcelona,
Spain
Tel.: (34) 932606800   ES
Web Site: http://www.acmarca.com
Year Founded: 1922
Home & Personal Care Mfr
N.A.I.C.S.: 456199

Subsidiaries:

Pacer Technology   (1)
3281 E Guasti Rd Ste 260, Ontario, CA
91761
Tel.: (909) 987-0550
Web Site: http://pacerprivatelabel.com
Adhesive & Sealant Mfr
N.A.I.C.S.: 325520
Larry K Reynolds *(Sec)*

Subsidiary (Domestic):

Super Glue Corporation   (2)
9420 Santa Anita Ave, Rancho Cucamonga,
CA 91730-6117
Tel.: (909) 987-0550
Web Site: http://www.supergluecorp.com
Sales Range: $50-74.9 Million
Emp.: 113
Mfr & Supplier of Glues, Epoxies & Other
Adhesives for Household, Office & Con-
sumer Applications
N.A.I.C.S.: 325520
Ronald T. Gravette *(Pres)*

AC S.A.
ul 42 Pulku Piechoty 50, 15-181, Bia-
lystok, Poland
Tel.: (48) 857438100
Web Site: https://www.ac.com.pl
ACG—(WAR)
Rev.: $66,060,975

Assets: $56,700,711
Liabilities: $20,092,988
Net Worth: $36,607,723
Earnings: $7,235,772
Emp.: 700
Fiscal Year-end: 12/31/23
Motor Vehicle Parts Mfr
N.A.I.C.S.: 336310
Anatol Timoszuk *(CEO)*

AC&C INTERNATIONAL CO., LTD.
3F No 27 Sec 3 Xinyi Rd, Da an Dist,
Taipei, Taiwan
Tel.: (886) 227071199
Web Site: http://www.accintl.com.tw
6131—(TAI)
Rev.: $2,643,064
Assets: $6,141,587
Liabilities: $586,585
Net Worth: $5,555,002
Earnings: $466,536
Fiscal Year-end: 12/31/20
Television Closed Circuit Equipment
Mfr
N.A.I.C.S.: 334220

Subsidiaries:

ArcVision Technology Corp.   (1)
10415 Slusher Dr 2, Santa Fe Springs, CA
90670
Tel.: (562) 777-7712
Web Site: http://www.arcvisioncctv.com
Emp.: 10
Surveillance Systems Mfr & Distr
N.A.I.C.S.: 334419
Jerry Garcia *(Gen Mgr)*

IVIGIL Corporation   (1)
8403 Cross Park Dr St Cd1, Austin, TX
78754
Tel.: (512) 835-2300
Web Site:
   http://www.ivigilcctv.comwww.ivigilcctv.com
Surveillance System Mfr & Distr
N.A.I.C.S.: 334511

IVIGIL UK LIMITED   (1)
11a Vermont Place, Tongwel, Milton
Keynes, MK15 8JA, Buckinghamshire,
United Kingdom
Tel.: (44) 1908214420
Web Site: http://www.ivigil.co.uk
Emp.: 5
Surveillance Systems Import & Distr
N.A.I.C.S.: 423610

ACA PARTNERS PTE LTD.
8 Temasek Boulevard #34-02 Suntec
Tower 3, Singapore, 038988, Singa-
pore
Tel.: (65) 6890 0730
Web Site: http://www.acaisg.com
Investments & Fund Management
Services
N.A.I.C.S.: 523999
Akihiro Azuma *(Chm)*

Subsidiaries:

Cytori Cell Research Institute
Inc.   (1)
3-5-1 Kasumigaseki Building 4th floor,
Chiyoda-ku, Tokyo, 107-0062,
Japan   (65.01%)
Tel.: (81) 355014100
Web Site: https://cytori.co.jp
Rev.: $10,311,600
Assets: $38,443,760
Liabilities: $19,968,810
Net Worth: $18,474,950
Earnings: $912,180
Fiscal Year-end: 03/31/2024
Financial, Real Estate & Asset Management
Businesses
N.A.I.C.S.: 522320

ACACIA CAPITAL PARTNERS LIMITED
CPC1 Capital Park, Cambridge,
CB21 5XE, United Kingdom
Tel.: (44) 2072997399
Web Site: http://www.acaciacp.com

Year Founded: 2000
Rev.: $2,000,000,000
Emp.: 3
Venture Capital Fund Management Services
N.A.I.C.S.: 523150
Hitesh Mehta *(Gen Partner)*

ACACIA INVERSION S.G.I.I.C., S.A.U.
Gran Via 40 Bis Planta 3a, 48009, Bilbao, Vizcaya, Spain
Tel.: (34) 944356740
Web Site: http://www.acacia-inversion.com
Sales Range: $10-24.9 Million
Emp.: 6
Investment Management Service
N.A.I.C.S.: 523999
Fernandez Arantza *(Mgr-Customer Svc)*

ACADEMEDIA AB
Adolf Fredriks Kyrkogata 2, PO Box 213, 101 24, Stockholm, Sweden
Tel.: (46) 87944200
Web Site:
   https://www.academedia.se
ACAD—(OMX)
Rev.: $1,455,412,253
Assets: $1,865,557,710
Liabilities: $1,291,035,620
Net Worth: $574,522,090
Earnings: $54,136,578
Emp.: 14,459
Fiscal Year-end: 06/30/23
Holding Company
N.A.I.C.S.: 551112
Marcus Stromberg *(CEO)*

Subsidiaries:

AcadeMedia Education GmbH   (1)
Leibnizstrasse 32, 10625, Berlin, Germany
Tel.: (49) 30219158200
Web Site: https://academedia.education
Personal Development Education Services
N.A.I.C.S.: 611710

AcadeMedia GmbH   (1)
Haidelweg 46, 81241, Munich, Germany
Tel.: (49) 89201843310
Web Site: https://academedia.de
Kindergarten School Operator
N.A.I.C.S.: 611110

Akanova GmbH   (1)
Am Friedrichshain 22, 10407, Berlin, Germany
Tel.: (49) 15159990128
Web Site: https://www.akanova.de
Personal Development Education Services
N.A.I.C.S.: 611710

Banerporten AB   (1)
Karlavagen 121, 115 26, Stockholm, Sweden
Tel.: (46) 850531100
Web Site: https://www.innovitaskolan.se
Kindergarten Educational Services
N.A.I.C.S.: 518210

Changemaker Educations AB   (1)
Hammarby Fabriksvag 61, 120 30, Stockholm, Sweden
Tel.: (46) 8336015
Web Site: https://cmeducations.se
Education Training & Support Services
N.A.I.C.S.: 611710

Cybergymnasiet Malmo AB   (1)
Ostra Kanalgatan 3, 211 41, Malmo, Sweden
Tel.: (46) 406314400
Cyber Security Education Training Services
N.A.I.C.S.: 611710

EC Utbildning AB   (1)
Tomtebodavagen 3B, 17165, Solna, Sweden
Tel.: (46) 406416300
Web Site: https://ecutbildning.se
Educational Support Services
N.A.I.C.S.: 611710

Espira Abol AS   (1)
Lingelemveien 84, 3225, Sandefjord, Norway
Tel.: (47) 40004797
Kindergarten Educational Services
N.A.I.C.S.: 518210

Espira Arhaug AS   (1)
Eikjeveien 255, Kolnes, 5541, Rogaland, Norway
Tel.: (47) 52822214
Kindergarten Educational Services
N.A.I.C.S.: 518210

Espira Arkjaer AS   (1)
Daleveien 274, Lindesnes Kommune, 4517, Mandal, Norway
Tel.: (47) 38261425
Kindergarten School Operator
N.A.I.C.S.: 611110

Espira Arolia AS   (1)
Arolivegen 47, Molde Kommune, 6421, Molde, Norway
Tel.: (47) 92219090
Kindergarten School Operator
N.A.I.C.S.: 611110

Espira Arosfjellet AS   (1)
Kjoyafaret 54, Aros, 3474, Asker, Norway
Tel.: (47) 98036848
Kindergarten School Operator
N.A.I.C.S.: 611110

Espira Baggerodbanen AS   (1)
Framveien 6A, 3188, Horten, Norway
Tel.: (47) 92422359
Kindergarten School Operator
N.A.I.C.S.: 611110

Espira Bjorgene AS   (1)
Peer Gyntsveg 6E, 5538, Haugesund, Norway
Tel.: (47) 92815098
Children Educational Services
N.A.I.C.S.: 611110

Espira Blakstad AS   (1)
Strandveien 57, 1392, Asker, Norway
Tel.: (47) 23898903
Children Educational Services
N.A.I.C.S.: 611110

Espira Bradalsfjellet AS   (1)
Bradalsfjellet 1, 2022, Gjerdrum, Norway
Tel.: (47) 40035206
Children Educational Services
N.A.I.C.S.: 611110

Espira Brasteintunet AS   (1)
Wergelands Gate 19, 5522, Haugesund, Norway
Tel.: (47) 92414276
Kindergarten School Operator
N.A.I.C.S.: 611110

Espira Dragerskogen AS   (1)
Bakkerudvegen 70, 2830, Raufoss, Norway
Tel.: (47) 92862174
Children Educational Services
N.A.I.C.S.: 611110

Espira Dvergsnes AS   (1)
Valsvigveien 11, 4639, Kristiansand, Norway
Tel.: (47) 38120810
Children Educational Services
N.A.I.C.S.: 611110

Espira Eikenga AS   (1)
Vestre Eikenga 17, Lierbyen, 3404, Lier, Norway
Tel.: (47) 32240280
Emp.: 20
Children Educational Services
N.A.I.C.S.: 611110

Espira Eikenotta Naturbarnehage AS   (1)
Kyrkjevollveien 19, Hommersak, 4310, Sandnes, Norway
Tel.: (47) 51688870
Children Educational Services
N.A.I.C.S.: 611110

Espira Evangtunet AS   (1)
Evangjordet 2, Arnes, 2150, Nes, Norway
Tel.: (47) 40432391
Kindergarten School Operator
N.A.I.C.S.: 611110

Espira Eventyrskogen AS   (1)

Bjorgeveien 316, Bjorndalstrae Laksevag, 5170, Bergen, Norway
Tel.: (47) 55500610
Kindergarten School Operator
N.A.I.C.S.: 611110

Espira Evje AS   (1)
Stanga 14-18, 1346, Gjettum, Norway
Tel.: (47) 45287807
Children Educational Services
N.A.I.C.S.: 611110

Espira Fasanveien AS   (1)
Fasanveien 16, 1580, Rygge, Norway
Tel.: (47) 69260140
Children Educational Services
N.A.I.C.S.: 611110

Espira Fenstad AS   (1)
Grinderstubben 1, Nes, 2170, Fenstad, Norway
Tel.: (47) 45500645
Children Educational Services
N.A.I.C.S.: 611110

Espira Finnas AS   (1)
Motorsportvegen 7, Finnas, 5437, Bomlo, Norway
Tel.: (47) 92204943
Kindergarten School Operator
N.A.I.C.S.: 611110

Espira Garhaug AS   (1)
Hestaberg 15, Tysvaer, 5570, Aksdal, Norway
Tel.: (47) 52770212
Children Educational Services
N.A.I.C.S.: 611110

Espira Gartnerlokka AS   (1)
Lorenvangen 24 Hus 4C, Grunerlokka, 0585, Oslo, Norway
Tel.: (47) 21525205
Emp.: 28
Kindergarten School Operator
N.A.I.C.S.: 611110

Espira Gaserud AS   (1)
Pettersvolent 31, 3032, Drammen, Norway
Tel.: (47) 32889302
Kindergarten School Operator
N.A.I.C.S.: 518210

Espira Gjemble AS   (1)
Friggs veg 2B, 7602, Levanger, Norway
Tel.: (47) 95781964
Children Educational Services
N.A.I.C.S.: 611110

Espira Grefsen AS   (1)
Borger Withs Gate 39, Sagene, 0482, Oslo, Norway
Tel.: (47) 21525275
Emp.: 40
Kindergarten School Operator
N.A.I.C.S.: 611110

Espira Gronnestolen AS   (1)
Fredlundsveien 45, Minde Arstad, 5073, Bergen, Norway
Tel.: (47) 55612030
Kindergarten School Operator
N.A.I.C.S.: 611110

Espira Gruppen AS   (1)
Helganesvegen 41, Karmoy, 4262, Avaldsnes, Norway
Tel.: (47) 21088088
Web Site: https://www.espira.no
Emp.: 2,700
Educational Support Services
N.A.I.C.S.: 611110

Espira Gullhella AS   (1)
Korpefaret 3, 1386, Asker, Norway
Tel.: (47) 66758484
Children Educational Services
N.A.I.C.S.: 611110

Espira Halsnoy Kloster AS   (1)
Eidsnesvegen 73, Kvinnherad, 5455, Halsnoy Kloster, Norway
Tel.: (47) 94007991
Children Educational Services
N.A.I.C.S.: 611110

Espira Helldalsasen AS   (1)
Sanddalsringen 260, Fana district, 5225, Bergen, Norway
Tel.: (47) 92456825
Children Educational Services
N.A.I.C.S.: 611110

Espira Holbekk Idrettsbarnehage AS   (1)
Bergemoveien 64, 4886, Grimstad, Norway
Tel.: (47) 93449919
Children Educational Services
N.A.I.C.S.: 611110

Espira Hollund AS   (1)
Hollundsvegen 43, Urangsvag Bremnes, 5427, Bomlo, Norway
Tel.: (47) 53424942
Kindergarten School Operator
N.A.I.C.S.: 611110

Espira Holum AS   (1)
Laustoheia 22, Holum Lindesnes, 4519, Mandal, Norway
Tel.: (47) 38266370
Kindergarten School Operator
N.A.I.C.S.: 611110

Espira Hovsmarka AS   (1)
Hovsmarkveien 20, Ringerike, 3515, Honefoss, Norway
Tel.: (47) 31004660
Kindergarten School Operator
N.A.I.C.S.: 611110

Espira Hoytorp Fort AS   (1)
Vardeveien 72, 1850, Mysen, Norway
Tel.: (47) 92072043
Kindergarten Educational Services
N.A.I.C.S.: 518210

Espira Husebyparken AS   (1)
Loshavnveien 45, 4550, Farsund, Norway
Tel.: (47) 38795755
Kindergarten School Operator
N.A.I.C.S.: 611110

Espira Jeloy AS   (1)
Orkerodgata 43, 1511, Moss, Norway
Tel.: (47) 69270540
Children Educational Services
N.A.I.C.S.: 611110

Espira Juberg AS   (1)
Juberg Midtre, Gardsbarnehage, 7633, Frosta, Norway
Tel.: (47) 40401409
Kindergarten School Operator
N.A.I.C.S.: 611110

Espira Karmsund AS   (1)
Spannavegen 320, Norheim Karmoy, 5542, Haugesund, Norway
Tel.: (47) 40645308
Kindergarten School Operator
N.A.I.C.S.: 611110

Espira Kloverenga AS   (1)
Ovre Drognesveg 2, Nes, 2150, Arnes, Norway
Tel.: (47) 92238367
Children Educational Services
N.A.I.C.S.: 611110

Espira Knerten AS   (1)
Drammensveien 180, 3300, Hokksund, Norway
Tel.: (47) 94851004
Children Educational Services
N.A.I.C.S.: 611110

Espira Kniveasen AS   (1)
Kniveveien 55, 3036, Drammen, Norway
Tel.: (47) 45211131
Children Educational Services
N.A.I.C.S.: 611110

Espira Krystallveien AS   (1)
Krystallveien 2, 4321, Sandnes, Norway
Tel.: (47) 92413389
Children Educational Services
N.A.I.C.S.: 611110

Espira Kulturstien AS   (1)
Forvaldsveg 20, 3720, Skien, Norway
Tel.: (47) 95789452
Children Educational Services
N.A.I.C.S.: 611110

Espira Kunnskapsbyen AS   (1)
Elvengveien 14, Lillestrom, 2007, Kjeller, Norway
Tel.: (47) 64840350
Kindergarten School Operator
N.A.I.C.S.: 611110

Espira Kuventrae AS   (1)
Industrivn 99, Bjornafjorden, 5210, Osoyro, Norway

AcadeMedia AB—(Continued)

Tel.: (47) 56574666
Children Educational Services
N.A.I.C.S.: 611110

Espira Kystad Gard AS　　　　　　(1)
Kystad Alle 25 A, Byasen, 7024, Trondheim, Norway
Tel.: (47) 97401090
Children Educational Services
N.A.I.C.S.: 611110

Espira Lindesnes AS　　　　　　(1)
Rodbergsveien 33, Lindesnes, 4520, Vigeland, Norway
Tel.: (47) 790599
Children Educational Services
N.A.I.C.S.: 611110

Espira Litlasund AS　　　　　　(1)
Fagervollvegen 4, Karmoy, 4260, Torvastad, Norway
Tel.: (47) 52856320
Children Educational Services
N.A.I.C.S.: 611110

Espira Lovestad AS　　　　　　(1)
Nordmyrstubben 25, 1820, Spydeberg, Norway
Tel.: (47) 69833320
Kindergarten Educational Services
N.A.I.C.S.: 518210

Espira Lura AS　　　　　　(1)
Midtbergmyra 6, 4313, Sandnes, Norway
Tel.: (47) 93002598
Kindergarten School Operator
N.A.I.C.S.: 611110

Espira Marienfryd AS　　　　　　(1)
Hovinveien 37e/43c, Grunerlokka, 0576, Oslo, Norway
Tel.: (47) 21059190
Kindergarten School Operator
N.A.I.C.S.: 611110

Espira Marthahaugen AS　　　　　　(1)
Adlandsvegen 325, Alver, 5919, Frekhaug, Norway
Tel.: (47) 46412030
Children Educational Services
N.A.I.C.S.: 611110

Espira Moster AS　　　　　　(1)
Faeravagen 2, Mosterhamn, 5440, Bomlo, Norway
Tel.: (47) 45419489
Kindergarten School Operator
N.A.I.C.S.: 611110

Espira Muruvik AS　　　　　　(1)
Flatholmveien 30, Malvik, 7550, Hommelvik, Norway
Tel.: (47) 48863167
Children Educational Services
N.A.I.C.S.: 611110

Espira Myraskogen AS　　　　　　(1)
Ostensbuveien 137, Myra, 4848, Arendal, Norway
Tel.: (47) 37059130
Children Educational Services
N.A.I.C.S.: 611110

Espira Nordmo AS　　　　　　(1)
Gaupevegen 12, 2406, Elverum, Norway
Tel.: (47) 62409290
Children Educational Services
N.A.I.C.S.: 611110

Espira Nykirke AS　　　　　　(1)
Sletterodasen 7, Nykirke, 3180, Horten, Norway
Tel.: (47) 21525203
Kindergarten School Operator
N.A.I.C.S.: 611110

Espira Opaker AS　　　　　　(1)
Skolealleen 4, Nes, 2166, Oppaker, Norway
Tel.: (47) 92437658
Children Educational Services
N.A.I.C.S.: 611110

Espira Opsahl AS　　　　　　(1)
Opsahlveien 41, Indre Ostfold, 1850, Mysen, Norway
Tel.: (47) 45275115
Children Educational Services
N.A.I.C.S.: 611110

Espira Oreid AS　　　　　　(1)

Orodgrenda 15, Tistedal, 1793, Halden, Norway
Tel.: (47) 51207177
Kindergarten School Operator
N.A.I.C.S.: 611110

Espira Ormdalen AS　　　　　　(1)
Erleveien 3, 4353, Klepp, Norway
Tel.: (47) 51786280
Children Educational Services
N.A.I.C.S.: 611110

Espira Ostrem AS　　　　　　(1)
Austreiveien 9, 4250, Kopervik, Norway
Tel.: (47) 92278479
Kindergarten Educational Services
N.A.I.C.S.: 518210

Espira Ra AS　　　　　　(1)
Steinsvikveien 397 A og B, Radal, 5239, Bergen, Norway
Tel.: (47) 40557425
Children Educational Services
N.A.I.C.S.: 611110

Espira Rambjora AS　　　　　　(1)
Kattuglebrotet 3, Nattland Arstad District, 5099, Bergen, Norway
Tel.: (47) 92058759
Children Educational Services
N.A.I.C.S.: 611110

Espira Ree AS　　　　　　(1)
Lineveien 19, Time, 4340, Bryne, Norway
Tel.: (47) 92660672
Children Educational Services
N.A.I.C.S.: 611110

Espira Romholt AS　　　　　　(1)
Moldengutua 4, Sore Alsbygd, 2750, Gran, Norway
Tel.: (47) 61330422
Children Educational Services
N.A.I.C.S.: 611110

Espira Rubbestadneset AS　　　　　　(1)
Sollia 30, Bomlo, 5420, Rubbestadneset, Norway
Tel.: (47) 91592644
Children Educational Services
N.A.I.C.S.: 611110

Espira Salamonskogen AS　　　　　　(1)
Leirdalen 50, Bomlo, 5430, Bremnes, Norway
Tel.: (47) 41352078
Children Educational Services
N.A.I.C.S.: 611110

Espira Sandtoppen Naturbarnehage AS　　　　　　(1)
Sandvikbakken 21, 4329, Sandnes, Norway
Tel.: (47) 40007263
Children Educational Services
N.A.I.C.S.: 611110

Espira Sangereidasen AS　　　　　　(1)
Sangereidlia 2, 4790, Lillesand, Norway
Tel.: (47) 37400911
Kindergarten School Operator
N.A.I.C.S.: 611110

Espira Sanum AS　　　　　　(1)
Rennesveien 40, Lindesnes Kommune, 4513, Mandal, Norway
Tel.: (47) 94022860
Kindergarten School Operator
N.A.I.C.S.: 611110

Espira Scala Hundvag AS　　　　　　(1)
Hundvag Ring 100, Stavanger, 4085, Hundvag, Norway
Tel.: (47) 47478300
Children Educational Services
N.A.I.C.S.: 611110

Espira Scala Tasta AS　　　　　　(1)
Eskelandssvingene 18, 4028, Stavanger, Norway
Tel.: (47) 47478350
Children Educational Services
N.A.I.C.S.: 611110

Espira Skaredalen AS　　　　　　(1)
Tommerdalen 24, 5533, Haugesund, Norway
Tel.: (47) 92821104
Children Educational Services
N.A.I.C.S.: 611110

Espira Skjeraberget AS　　　　　　(1)
Skjeraberget 20, Ha, 4365, Naerbo, Norway

Tel.: (47) 94022922
Children Educational Services
N.A.I.C.S.: 611110

Espira Skolegata AS　　　　　　(1)
Skolegata 15, Indre Ostfold, 1830, Askim, Norway
Tel.: (47) 45519417
Children Educational Services
N.A.I.C.S.: 611110

Espira Sletten AS　　　　　　(1)
Slettatunet 10, Karmoy Kommune, 4276, Vedavagen, Norway
Tel.: (47) 90533555
Kindergarten School Operator
N.A.I.C.S.: 611110

Espira Snurrefjellet AS　　　　　　(1)
Skysetveien 8, Nittedal, 1481, Hagan, Norway
Tel.: (47) 93206447
Children Educational Services
N.A.I.C.S.: 611110

Espira Solknatten AS　　　　　　(1)
Solasen 2, Fana Bergen, 5223, Nesttun, Norway
Tel.: (47) 45519507
Children Educational Services
N.A.I.C.S.: 611110

Espira Solkroken AS　　　　　　(1)
Svehaugen 10, Ekrene, 5550, Sveio, Norway
Tel.: (47) 45208840
Kindergarten School Operator
N.A.I.C.S.: 611110

Espira Spirea AS　　　　　　(1)
Spireaveien 14D, Bydel Bjerke, 0580, Oslo, Norway
Tel.: (47) 21043240
Kindergarten School Operator
N.A.I.C.S.: 611110

Espira Steinsviken AS　　　　　　(1)
Steinsvikveien 89, Soreidgrend Ytrebygda, 5251, Bergen, Norway
Tel.: (47) 55102222
Kindergarten School Operator
N.A.I.C.S.: 611110

Espira Stjordal AS　　　　　　(1)
Husbykleiva 2, 7506, Stjordal, Norway
Tel.: (47) 98603095
Children Educational Services
N.A.I.C.S.: 611110

Espira Stongafjellet AS　　　　　　(1)
Stongafjellsvegen 40, Kleppesto, 5300, Askoy, Norway
Tel.: (47) 56156300
Kindergarten Educational Services
N.A.I.C.S.: 518210

Espira Sundbyfoss AS　　　　　　(1)
Lindeveien 1, Sundbyfoss, 3092, Holmestrand, Norway
Tel.: (47) 46505479
Children Educational Services
N.A.I.C.S.: 611110

Espira Taremareby AS　　　　　　(1)
Sandvikbakken 23, 4329, Sandnes, Norway
Tel.: (47) 92655662
Children Educational Services
N.A.I.C.S.: 611110

Espira Tastarusta AS　　　　　　(1)
Tastatunet 7, 4027, Stavanger, Norway
Tel.: (47) 93020069
Children Educational Services
N.A.I.C.S.: 611110

Espira Tau AS　　　　　　(1)
Kvednanesveien 74, Kvednaneset, 4120, Tau, Norway
Tel.: (47) 90625825
Kindergarten School Operator
N.A.I.C.S.: 611110

Espira Tjosvoll AS　　　　　　(1)
Tostemvegen 35, Karmoy, 4270, Akrehamn, Norway
Tel.: (47) 92820294
Children Educational Services
N.A.I.C.S.: 611110

Espira Torsbergskogen AS　　　　　　(1)
Djupdalsveien 227, Konnerud, 3033, Drammen, Norway

Tel.: (47) 32888840
Children Educational Services
N.A.I.C.S.: 611110

Espira Torshovdalen AS　　　　　　(1)
Hans Nielsen Hauges Gate 39 F, Bydel Sagene, 0481, Oslo, Norway
Tel.: (47) 94002214
Kindergarten School Operator
N.A.I.C.S.: 611110

Espira Tristilbakken AS　　　　　　(1)
Nautasvegen 15, Hektnerasen Fjerdingby, 2008, Raelingen, Norway
Tel.: (47) 48867820
Kindergarten School Operator
N.A.I.C.S.: 611110

Espira Trygstad AS　　　　　　(1)
Trygstadveien 16, Ringerike, 3511, Honefoss, Norway
Tel.: (47) 40004868
Kindergarten School Operator
N.A.I.C.S.: 611110

Espira Ulsetskogen AS　　　　　　(1)
Midtkleiva 56, Ulset Asane, 5119, Bergen, Norway
Tel.: (47) 55253110
Children Educational Services
N.A.I.C.S.: 611110

Espira Ulvenvatnet AS　　　　　　(1)
Industrivegen 111, Bjornafjorden Kommune, 5200, Os, Norway
Tel.: (47) 46746536
Kindergarten School Operator
N.A.I.C.S.: 611110

Espira Vannverksdammen AS　　　　　　(1)
Stollen 5, Konnerud, 3030, Drammen, Norway
Tel.: (47) 32887055
Children Educational Services
N.A.I.C.S.: 611110

Espira Varbak Arcen AS　　　　　　(1)
Abraham Berges vei 7A, Vanse, 4560, Farsund, Norway
Tel.: (47) 95368130
Kindergarten Educational Services
N.A.I.C.S.: 518210

Espira Vedderheia AS　　　　　　(1)
Skytterveien 50, Vedderheia Kristiansand Kommune, 4642, Sogne, Norway
Tel.: (47) 91186125
Kindergarten School Operator
N.A.I.C.S.: 611110

Espira Veldetun AS　　　　　　(1)
Veldetunveien 20, Karmoy, 4262, Avaldsnes, Norway
Tel.: (47) 92826791
Children Educational Services
N.A.I.C.S.: 611110

Espira und Joki Kinderbetreuung GmbH　　　　　　(1)
Haidelweg 46, 81241, Munich, Germany
Tel.: (49) 89201843310
Web Site: https://www.espira-kinderbetreuung.de
Kindergarten Educational Services
N.A.I.C.S.: 518210

Framtidsutveckling i Sverige AB　　　(1)
Ostra Larmgatan 13, 411 07, Gothenburg, Sweden
Tel.: (46) 313015200
Web Site: https://www.framtidsutveckling.se
Digital Advertising Services
N.A.I.C.S.: 541850

Furstenwalder Aus- und Weiterbildungszentrum GmbH　　　　　　(1)
Julius-Pintsch-Ring 25, 15517, Furstenwalde, Germany
Tel.: (49) 3361358400
Web Site: https://fawz.de
Training Education Services
N.A.I.C.S.: 611513

Hermods AB　　　　　　(1)
Box 36, 101 20, Stockholm, Sweden
Tel.: (46) 841025100
Web Site: https://www.hermods.se
Educational Support Services
N.A.I.C.S.: 611710

Internationella hotell- och restaurangskolan IHR AB　　　　　　(1)

Tullgardsgatan 12, 116 68, Stockholm,
Sweden
Tel.: (46) 84292440
Web Site: https://restaurangskolan.se
International Hotel & Restaurant School
Services
N.A.I.C.S.: 928120

KTS Verwaltungs GmbH (1)
Haidelweg 46, 81241, Munich, Germany
Tel.: (49) 89416162710
Web Site: https://www.kita-luna.de
Children Educational Services
N.A.I.C.S.: 611110

KYH AB (1)
Arstaangsvagen 33, 117 43, Stockholm,
Sweden
Tel.: (46) 19100080
Web Site: https://kyh.se
Educational Support Services
N.A.I.C.S.: 611710

**Kompetensutvecklingsinstitutet Sver-
ige AB** (1)
Drottningholmsvagen 37 2Tr, 112 42, Stock-
holm, Sweden
Tel.: (46) 852250650
Web Site: https://kui.se
Educational & Training Services
N.A.I.C.S.: 611710

Lilleba & Herreman AS (1)
Strandsvingen 14B, 4032, Stavanger, Nor-
way
Tel.: (47) 605266
Web Site: https://www.lilleba.no
Apparel Accessories Mfr & Distr
N.A.I.C.S.: 315990

Limhamns Forskola AB (1)
Limhamnsgardens Alle 2, 21616, Limhamn,
Sweden
Tel.: (46) 761003219
Preschool Education Services
N.A.I.C.S.: 624410

Movant AB (1)
Norra Deltavagen 3, 417 05, Gothenburg,
Sweden
Tel.: (46) 761082952
Web Site: https://www.movant.se
Vocational Training Services
N.A.I.C.S.: 611519

NTI-skolan AB (1)
Drottningholmsvagen 37, 112 42, Stock-
holm, Sweden
Tel.: (46) 850637500
Web Site: https://www.nti.se
Vocational Training Services
N.A.I.C.S.: 611519

Plek voor kinderen B.V. (1)
Ravelstraat 10, 4614 XD, Bergen-op-Zoom,
Netherlands
Tel.: (31) 4901608723214
Web Site: https://www.plekvoorkinderen.nl
Kindergarten Services
N.A.I.C.S.: 611110

Pops Academy AB (1)
Adolf Fredriks kyrkogata 2, 11137, Stock-
holm, Sweden
Tel.: (46) 852522260
Web Site: https://popsacademy.se
Primary Music School Services
N.A.I.C.S.: 611310

**ProCivitas Privata Gymnasium
AB** (1)
Tullgardsgatan 12, 116 68, Stockholm,
Sweden
Tel.: (46) 722331618
Web Site: https://www.procivitas.se
Educational Support Services
N.A.I.C.S.: 611710

**Pysslingen Forskolor och Skolor
AB** (1)
Adolf Fredriks Kyrkogata 2, 11137, Stock-
holm, Sweden
Tel.: (46) 84515400
Web Site: https://www.pysslingen.se
Preschool Education Services
N.A.I.C.S.: 611110

Rytmus AB (1)
Lilla Bommen 4A, 411 04, Gothenburg,
Sweden
Tel.: (46) 855586260

Web Site: https://www.rytmus.se
Educational Support Services
N.A.I.C.S.: 611610

Skogen Barnehage AS (1)
Folleseveien 97, 5302, Strusshamn, Norway
Tel.: (47) 45617490
Web Site: https://www.skogenbarnehage.no
Kindergarten Services
N.A.I.C.S.: 611110

Step Kids Education GmbH (1)
Am Friedrichshain 22, 10407, Berlin, Ger-
many
Tel.: (49) 3042025929
Children Educational Services
N.A.I.C.S.: 611110

Step Kids KiTas GmbH (1)
Am Friedrichshain 22, 10407, Berlin, Ger-
many
Tel.: (49) 3042025929
Web Site: https://www.stepke-kitas.de
Children Educational Services
N.A.I.C.S.: 611110

TGA Utbildning AB (1)
Jungmansgatan 3, Skeppsgatan 19, 211 11,
Malmo, Sweden
Tel.: (46) 761035244
Web Site: https://thegameassembly.com
Game Developing Services
N.A.I.C.S.: 513210

**Tomm Murstad Friluftsbarnehage
AS** (1)
Ovreseterveien 30, Frognerseteren, 0791,
Oslo, Norway
Tel.: (47) 794830
Children Educational Services
N.A.I.C.S.: 611110

ACADEMIES AUSTRALASIA
GROUP LIMITED

Level 6 505 George Street, Sydney,
2000, NSW, Australia
Tel.: (61) 292245555 AU
Web Site:
https://www.academies.edu.au
AKG—(ASX)
Rev.: $30,963,542
Assets: $55,996,928
Liabilities: $44,203,392
Net Worth: $11,793,536
Earnings: ($6,445,646)
Fiscal Year-end: 06/30/24
Training & Education Services
N.A.I.C.S.: 923110
Christopher Elmore Campbell (CEO
& Mng Dir)

Subsidiaries:

**Academies Australasia College Pte.
Limited** (1)
Level 1-5 45 Middle Rd, Singapore,
188954, Singapore
Tel.: (65) 63379949
Web Site: https://www.aac.edu.sg
Educational Institution Services
N.A.I.C.S.: 611710

**Academies Australasia Hair & Beauty
Pty Limited** (1)
Queen Adelaide Building 90-112 Queen St,
Brisbane, 4000, QLD, Australia
Tel.: (61) 732292999
Web Site: https://www.brishair.com.au
Hairdressing Schools
N.A.I.C.S.: 611699
Lina Wood (Founder)

**Academies Australasia Institute Pty.
Limited** (1)
Level 6 505 George Street, Sydney, 2000,
NSW, Australia
Tel.: (61) 292245500
Vocational Institution Services
N.A.I.C.S.: 611210

**Academies Australasia Polytechnic
Pty Limited** (1)
Level 7 628 Bourke Street, Melbourne,
3000, VIC, Australia
Tel.: (61) 38 610 4100
Web Site: https://aapoly.edu.au
Education Services

N.A.I.C.S.: 611710
Christopher Campbell (Chm)

**Academies Australasia Pty
Limited** (1)
L 6 505 George St, Sydney, NSW, Australia
Tel.: (61) 292231116
Web Site: http://www.aca.nsw.edu.au
Educational Training & Support Services
N.A.I.C.S.: 611710

Subsidiary (Domestic):

**Academies Australasia (Management)
Pty Limited** (2)
L 6 505 George St, Sydney, 2000, NSW,
Australia
Tel.: (61) 292245500
Web Site: http://www.aca.nsw.edu.au
Education Training & Support Services
N.A.I.C.S.: 611710

Academy of English Pty. Limited (1)
Level 6 505 George Street, Sydney, 2000,
NSW, Australia
Tel.: (61) 292245500
Tertiary Education Services
N.A.I.C.S.: 611310

**Developing Excellence Pty.
Limited** (1)
Level 14-15 459 Little Collins Street, Mel-
bourne, 3000, VIC, Australia
Tel.: (61) 1300656669
Web Site: https://skillstraining.edu.au
Nursing & Ageing Support Services
N.A.I.C.S.: 623110

Discover English Pty Ltd (1)
247 Collins Street, Melbourne, 3000, VIC,
Australia
Tel.: (61) 39 602 4800
Web Site: https://discoverenglish.vic.edu.au
Education Services
N.A.I.C.S.: 611710

Humanagement Pty. Limited (1)
Unit 17 169 Unley Road, Unley, 5061, SA,
Australia
Tel.: (61) 392928000
Web Site: https://www.printtrain.edu.au
Printing & Graphic Arts Training Services
N.A.I.C.S.: 611519

**International College of Capoeira Pty.
Limited** (1)
Level 6 505 George St, Sydney, 2000,
NSW, Australia
Tel.: (61) 292674768
Web Site: https://csf.edu.au
Cloud Data Migration Services
N.A.I.C.S.: 518210

Kreate Pty. Limited (1)
Gadigal Country Level 3 55 Pyrmont Bridge
Road, Pyrmont, 2009, NSW, Australia
Tel.: (61) 292812777
Web Site: https://www.kreate.com.au
Marketing & Advertising Services
N.A.I.C.S.: 541810

**Language Links International Pty.
Limited** (1)
Level 1 120 Roe Street, Northbridge, Perth,
6003, WA, Australia
Tel.: (61) 894604200
Web Site:
https://www.languagelinks.wa.edu.au
English Language Teaching Services
N.A.I.C.S.: 611630

**Vostro Institute of Training Australia
Pty. Limited** (1)
Level 14 459 Little Collins Street, Mel-
bourne, 3000, VIC, Australia
Tel.: (61) 390201433
Web Site: https://www.vostro.vic.edu.au
Vocational Institution Services
N.A.I.C.S.: 611210

ACADEMY OF ENVIRONMEN-
TAL PLANNING & DESIGN,
CO., LTD.

9F Science Building No 16 Jinyin
Street, Gulou District, Nanjing,
210003, Jiangsu, China
Tel.: (86) 2583685680
Web Site: http://www.njuae.cn

Year Founded: 2012
300864—(CHIN)
Rev.: $105,448,493
Assets: $248,913,444
Liabilities: $68,775,154
Net Worth: $180,138,291
Earnings: $21,753,254
Fiscal Year-end: 12/31/23
Engineeering Services
N.A.I.C.S.: 541330
Wu Junfeng (Chm)

ACADEMY PRESS PLC.

28/32 Industrial Avenue Ilupeju Indus-
trial Estate, PO Box 3445, Lagos,
Nigeria
Tel.: (234) 7014900034
Web Site:
https://www.academypress-plc.com
Year Founded: 1965
ACADEMY—(NIGE)
Rev.: $3,337,064
Assets: $2,299,274
Liabilities: $2,194,693
Net Worth: $104,581
Earnings: $54,487
Emp.: 30
Fiscal Year-end: 03/31/24
Commercial Printing Services
N.A.I.C.S.: 323117
Olugbenga Ladipo (Mng Dir)

ACADIAN TIMBER CORP.

Suite 2408-1055 West Georgia Street
Royal Centre, PO Box 11179, Van-
couver, V6E 3R5, BC, Canada
Tel.: (604) 661-9622
Web Site:
http://www.acadiantimber.com
779—(DEU)
Rev.: $85,361,030
Assets: $428,872,669
Liabilities: $188,002,982
Net Worth: $240,869,688
Earnings: $22,226,202
Emp.: 38
Fiscal Year-end: 12/31/23
Forest Products Supplier
N.A.I.C.S.: 113110
Adam Sheparski (CFO)

ACANDO AB

Vasagatan 16, Box 16061, SE-111
20, Stockholm, Sweden
Tel.: (46) 771501000
Web Site:
http://www.acandogroup.com
Rev.: $297,369,493
Assets: $239,243,201
Liabilities: $91,541,446
Net Worth: $147,701,755
Earnings: $21,846,062
Emp.: 1,817
Fiscal Year-end: 12/31/17
Management & IT Consultant Ser-
vices
N.A.I.C.S.: 541611
Carl-Magnus Mansson (Pres & CEO)

Subsidiaries:

Acando AS (1)
Klarabergsveidukten 63, 101 23, Stock-
holm, Sweden
Tel.: (46) 93001000
Web Site: http://www.acando.no
Sales Range: $25-49.9 Million
Emp.: 90
Business Consultancy Services
N.A.I.C.S.: 541611
Aasmund Froseth (CEO)

Acando Business Intelligence AB (1)
PO Box 5528, 11485, Stockholm, Sweden
Tel.: (46) 87530730
IT Consultancy Services
N.A.I.C.S.: 541611

Acando Consulting AB (1)
Klarabergsviadukten 63, 101 23, Stock-

Acando AB—(Continued)

holm, Sweden
Tel.: (46) 86997000
Web Site: http://www.acando.com
Sales Range: $75-99.9 Million
Emp.: 300
Business Management Services
N.A.I.C.S.: 541611

Acando Denmark A/S   **(1)**
Stationsparken 37, 2600, Glostrup, Denmark
Tel.: (45) 70229015
Sales Range: $25-49.9 Million
Emp.: 30
Business Consultancy Services
N.A.I.C.S.: 541611

Acando Incentive AB   **(1)**
PO Box 5528, 11485, Stockholm, Sweden
Tel.: (46) 8 4702261
Business Consultancy Services
N.A.I.C.S.: 541611

Acando Ltd   **(1)**
7750 Daresbury Bus Park, Daresbury, Warrington, WA4 4BS, Cheshire, United Kingdom
Tel.: (44) 8700119118
Sales Range: $25-49.9 Million
Emp.: 40
Business Consultancy Services
N.A.I.C.S.: 541611

Acando Management Consulting AB   **(1)**
Jakobsgatan 6, 111 52, Stockholm, Sweden
Tel.: (46) 87530730
Business Management & Consulting Services
N.A.I.C.S.: 541611

Acando Sverige AB   **(1)**
Klarabergsviadukten 63, Stockholm, 10123, Sweden
Tel.: (46) 86997000
Web Site: http://www.acando.com
Sales Range: $75-99.9 Million
Emp.: 300
Business Management & Consulting Services
N.A.I.C.S.: 541611

Frontec AB   **(1)**
St Eriksgatan 5, Box 6090, 400 60, Gothenburg, Sweden
Tel.: (46) 31 345 30 00
Web Site: http://www.acando.com
Business Management & Consulting Services
N.A.I.C.S.: 541611

Frontec Affarssystem AB   **(1)**
PO Box 5528, 114 85, Stockholm, Sweden
Tel.: (46) 46317071000
Business Management & Consulting Services
N.A.I.C.S.: 541611

Frontec Business Integration AB   **(1)**
PO Box 5528, 114 85, Stockholm, Sweden
Tel.: (46) 8 7337400
Business Consulting Services
N.A.I.C.S.: 541611

Frontec Business Solutions AB   **(1)**
PO Box 6090, 400 60, Gothenburg, Sweden
Tel.: (46) 313453000
Sales Range: $75-99.9 Million
Emp.: 300
Business Management & Consulting Services
N.A.I.C.S.: 541611
John Karnblad *(Mgr)*

Frontec Multidesign AB   **(1)**
PO Box 5528, 114 85, Stockholm, Sweden
Tel.: (46) 92075200
IT Consultancy Services
N.A.I.C.S.: 541611

ACANTHE DEVELOPPEMENT SA

2 Rue de Bassano, 75116, Paris, France
Tel.: (33) 156524500

Web Site:
https://www.acanthedevelopment.fr
ACAN—(EUR)
Sales Range: $1-9.9 Million
Real Estate Investment Services Provider
N.A.I.C.S.: 531390
Alain Dumenil *(Chm & Mng Dir)*

ACARIX AB

Ryvangs Alle 81-83, 2900, Hellerup, Denmark
Tel.: (45) 709237105
Web Site: https://www.acarix.com
Year Founded: 2009
ACARIX—(NASDAQ)
Rev.: $619,544
Assets: $6,242,495
Liabilities: $1,091,871
Net Worth: $5,150,624
Earnings: ($7,727,078)
Emp.: 14
Fiscal Year-end: 12/31/23
Medical Equipment Mfr
N.A.I.C.S.: 339112
Philip Siberg *(Chm)*

Subsidiaries:

Acarix USA Inc.   **(1)**
287 Park Ave S Ste 700, New York, NY 10010
Medical Device Mfr
N.A.I.C.S.: 339112

ACASA GROUP BVBA

Kortrijksesteenweg 62, 9830, Sint-Martens-Latem, Belgium
Tel.: (32) 09 321 03 00
Web Site: http://www.acasa.be
Real Estate Investment
N.A.I.C.S.: 531390
Yves Boxoen *(Sls Mgr)*

Subsidiaries:

Microfibres Europe N.V.   **(1)**
Lange Meire 56, 9270, Laarne, Belgium
Tel.: (32) 93689711
Web Site: http://www.microfibres.be
Synthetic Fabrication Product Distr
N.A.I.C.S.: 424310
Luc Steyaert *(Asst Gen Mgr)*

ACAST AB

Kungsgatan 28, 111 35, Stockholm, Sweden
Web Site: https://www.acast.com
Year Founded: 2014
ACAST—(OMX)
Advertising Agency Services
N.A.I.C.S.: 541810
Daniel Adrian *(Gen Counsel)*

ACASTA ENTERPRISES, INC.

1 Apollo Place, Toronto, M3J 0H2, ON, Canada
Tel.: (416) 531-9497
Web Site:
http://www.acastaenterprises.com
Investment Management Service
N.A.I.C.S.: 525910
Richard Wachsberg *(CEO)*

ACBEL POLYTECH INC.

No 159 Section 3 Danjin Road, Tamsui District, New Taipei City, 251, Taiwan
Tel.: (886) 226217672
Web Site: https://www.acbel.com.tw
Year Founded: 1981
6282—(TAI)
Rev.: $910,595,734
Assets: $1,575,724,326
Liabilities: $806,654,667
Net Worth: $769,069,659
Earnings: $1,276,857
Emp.: 7,424
Fiscal Year-end: 12/31/23

Adapters & Converters Mfr
N.A.I.C.S.: 332993
Hsu Chieh-Li *(Chm)*

Subsidiaries:

AcBel Electronic (Dong Guan) Co., Ltd.   **(1)**
NO 17-28 HongYe Rd HongYe Industrial Park, TangXia Town, Dongguan, 523710, Guangdong, China
Tel.: (86) 76987726756
Power Supplies Mfr
N.A.I.C.S.: 335999

AcBel Electronic (Wuhan) Co., Ltd.   **(1)**
No 1 DuTai North Road, Economic Development Zone, Xiantao, 433000, Hubei, China
Tel.: (86) 7283900888
Electronic Product Mfr & Distr
N.A.I.C.S.: 334111

AcBel Polytech (Philippines) Inc.   **(1)**
No 2 Tagaytay Ridge Drive Carmelray Industrial Park II, Km 54 National Highway, Calamba, 4027, Laguna, Philippines
Tel.: (63) 495027253
Electronic Product Mfr & Distr
N.A.I.C.S.: 334111

AcBel Polytech (UK) Co. Ltd.   **(1)**
32 Hepburn Road Hillington Business Park, Glasgow, G52 4RT, United Kingdom
Tel.: (44) 1418838631
Sales Range: $25-49.9 Million
Emp.: 7
Power Supplies Mfr & Distr
N.A.I.C.S.: 335999
Vincent Kong *(Mgr)*

AcBel Polytech Japan Inc.   **(1)**
Yamashita-Shibadaimon Bldg 4F 1-5-3, shiba daimon, Tokyo, 108-0014, Japan
Tel.: (81) 357772683
Power Supplies Mfr
N.A.I.C.S.: 335999

AcTel Electronic (Dong Guan) Co., Ltd.   **(1)**
No 17-28 Hong Yeh Rd, Hong Yehindustrial District Tang Xia Town, Dongguan, 523710, Guangdong, China
Tel.: (86) 76987726756
Web Site: http://www.acbel.com
Electric Products Mfr & Distr
N.A.I.C.S.: 335999

AcTel Power Co., Ltd.   **(1)**
112 6th Floor No 32 Section 2 Zhongyang South Road, Beitou District, Taipei, Taiwan
Tel.: (886) 226217672
Web Site: https://www.actelpower.com
Energy Transfer Services
N.A.I.C.S.: 541350

Acbel (USA) Polytech Inc.   **(1)**
251 Dominion Dr Ste 103, Morrisville, NC 27560-7334
Tel.: (919) 388-4316
Computer System Storage Devices Mfr
N.A.I.C.S.: 334112

Acbel Polytech (Malaysia) SDN. BHD.   **(1)**
1-5-27 Krystal Point II Corporate Park Jalan Tun Dr Awang, 11900, Sungai Nibong, Penang, Malaysia
Tel.: (60) 46437678
Web Site: http://www.acbel.com
Sales Range: $25-49.9 Million
Emp.: 15
Electric Component Whslr
N.A.I.C.S.: 423610

Itasca Technology Inc.   **(1)**
320 E Main St B11, Anoka, MN 55303
Tel.: (919) 388-4316
Web Site: https://www.itascatechnology.com
Engineering Design Services
N.A.I.C.S.: 541330

ACC AVIATION LTD.

40-44 Church Street, Reigate, RH2 0AJ, Surrey, United Kingdom
Tel.: (44) 1737 232 230
Web Site: http://www.flyacc.com
Year Founded: 2002

Sales Range: $75-99.9 Million
Emp.: 25
Aircraft Leasing & Charter Services
N.A.I.C.S.: 532411
Phil Aird-Mash *(CEO)*

ACC LIMITED

Cement House 121 Maharshi Karve Road, Mumbai, 400 020, India
Tel.: (91) 2241593321
Web Site: https://www.acclimited.com
Year Founded: 1936
ACC—(NSE)
Rev.: $1,911,371,280
Assets: $2,484,331,395
Liabilities: $750,457,890
Net Worth: $1,733,873,505
Earnings: $195,230,490
Emp.: 6,401
Fiscal Year-end: 12/31/20
Cement Mfr
N.A.I.C.S.: 327310
Procyon Mukherjee *(Co-Chief Procurement Officer)*

Subsidiaries:

ACC Concrete Limited   **(1)**
Survey No 334 IDA, Qutubullapur Mandal Rangareddy, 500055, Bachupally, Andhra Pradesh, India
Tel.: (91) 9160016168
Cement Mfr
N.A.I.C.S.: 327310

ACC Limited - Bachupally Plant   **(1)**
Survey No 334 IDA Bachupally Quthbullapur Mandal, Behind SRR Weighbridge Ranga Reddy Dist, Hyderabad, 500 049, Andhra Pradesh, India
Tel.: (91) 9160016155
Web Site: http://www.acclimited.com
Sales Range: $25-49.9 Million
Emp.: 80
Concrete Products Mfr
N.A.I.C.S.: 327320

ACC Limited - Bargarh Cement Works   **(1)**
Cement Nagar, Bardol, Bargarh, 768 038, Orissa, India
Tel.: (91) 6646247161
Web Site: http://www.acclimited.com
Cement Mfr
N.A.I.C.S.: 327310

ACC Limited - Chanda Cement Works   **(1)**
P O Cementnagar, Ghugus, Chandrapur, 442 502, Maharashtra, India
Tel.: (91) 7172285026
Web Site: http://www.acclimited.com
Cement Mfr
N.A.I.C.S.: 327310

ACC Limited - Changodar Plant   **(1)**
Block No 259 Near Chehar Mata Mandir Opp Laxmi Narayan petrol pump, Sarkhej Bavda Highway Changodar, Ahmedabad, 382 213, Gujarat, India
Tel.: (91) 9687634211
Web Site: http://www.accconcrete.com
Sales Range: $25-49.9 Million
Emp.: 12
Readymix Concrete Mfr
N.A.I.C.S.: 327320

ACC Limited - Damodhar Cement Works   **(1)**
Madhukunda, Sunuri, Puruliya, 723 121, West Bengal, India
Tel.: (91) 8170021926
Cement Mfr
N.A.I.C.S.: 327310

ACC Limited - Ghaziabad Concrete Plant   **(1)**
Plot No C 181 Industrial Area Site I Bulundshahar Road, Ghaziabad, 2010009, Uttar Pradesh, India
Tel.: (91) 9582217106
Sales Range: $25-49.9 Million
Emp.: 30
Concrete Mfr
N.A.I.C.S.: 327320

ACC Limited - Greater Noida Concrete Plant (1)
13a/1 Udyog Kendra Near Grazino Behind New Holland Tractors, Noida, 201304, Uttar Pradesh, India
Tel.: (91) 7829687777
Web Site: http://www.acclimited.com
Sales Range: $25-49.9 Million
Concrete Mfr
N.A.I.C.S.: 327320

ACC Limited - Jaipur Plant (1)
Plot No 148 C Road No 9 J Vishwakarma Industrial Area, Jaipur, 302013, Rajasthan, India
Tel.: (91) 9587017100
Web Site: http://www.acclimited.com
Emp.: 25
Concrete Mfr
N.A.I.C.S.: 327320

ACC Limited - Jamul Cement Works (1)
Jamul Cement Works, 490 024, Durg, 490 024, Chhattisgarh, India
Tel.: (91) 7882285081
Cement Mfr
N.A.I.C.S.: 327310

ACC Limited - Kundali Plant (1)
Ready Mixed Concrete Plant Nathupur, 131 029, Sonipat, Haryana, India
Tel.: (91) 9671400940
Cement Mfr
N.A.I.C.S.: 327310

ACC Limited - Kymore Cement Works (1)
Kymore, 483 880, Katni, 483 880, Madhya Pradesh, India
Tel.: (91) 7626272301
Cement Mfr
N.A.I.C.S.: 327310

ACC Limited - Lakheri Cement Works (1)
Lakheri, Bundi, 323 603, Rajasthan, India
Tel.: (91) 7438261642
Web Site: http://www.acclimited.com
Sales Range: $200-249.9 Million
Cement Mfr
N.A.I.C.S.: 327310

ACC Limited - Ludhiana Plant (1)
Survey No HB 261 Giaspur GT Road, Industrial Estate C Mauza Village, Ludhiana, 141010, Punjab, India
Tel.: (91) 9780928421
Web Site: https://www.acclimited.com
Sales Range: $125-149.9 Million
Emp.: 400
Concrete Mfr
N.A.I.C.S.: 327320

ACC Limited - Mandoli Plant (1)
Mandoli Prison Complex, Mandoli, 110093, New Delhi, India
Tel.: (91) 95822 17124
Sales Range: $50-74.9 Million
Emp.: 150
Concrete Mfr
N.A.I.C.S.: 327320

ACC Limited - Mohali Plant (1)
Plot No C 103 Phase 7 Industrial Area Focal Point, Mohali, 160 055, Punjab, India
Tel.: (91) 9780928405
Web Site: http://www.acclimited.com
Sales Range: $25-49.9 Million
Emp.: 12
Concrete Mfr
N.A.I.C.S.: 327320

ACC Limited - Patancheru Plant (1)
Survey no 405/1 Opp Srujana Steel Fabricators Patancheru IDA Lane, Beside Reliance Petrol Pump Opp ICRISAT Medak District, Hyderabad, 502 319, Andhra Pradesh, India
Tel.: (91) 9160016169
Web Site: http://www.acclimited.com
Sales Range: $25-49.9 Million
Emp.: 7
Concrete Products Mfr
N.A.I.C.S.: 327320

ACC Limited - Rajarhat Plant (1)
J L 44 Langal Pota station 24 Paragnas North Near 211 Bus stand, Rajarhat Bishnupur, Kolkata, 700135, West Bengal, India

Tel.: (91) 9674168711
Web Site: http://www.acclimited.com
Sales Range: $25-49.9 Million
Emp.: 9
Concrete Products Mfr
N.A.I.C.S.: 327320

ACC Limited - Ravirala Plant (1)
Ravirala village Maheswaram Mandal, Rangareddy District, Hyderabad, 500049, Andhra Pradesh, India
Tel.: (91) 916 001 6131
Web Site: http://www.acclimited.com
Concrete Products Mfr
N.A.I.C.S.: 327390

ACC Limited - Tikaria Cement Grinding and Packing Plant (1)
Tikaria Industrial Area Tehsil Gauriganj, Sultanpur, 227409, Uttar Pradesh, India
Tel.: (91) 5368244096
Emp.: 500
Cement Mfr
N.A.I.C.S.: 236210
Pankaj Sharma (Gen Mgr)

ACC Limited - Vadodara Franchisee Plant (1)
Behind Umiya Weigh Bridge Sama-Savli Road, 391740, Vadodara, Gujarat, India
Tel.: (91) 96876 24225
Web Site: http://www.acclimited.com
Sales Range: $25-49.9 Million
Emp.: 50
Concrete Products Mfr
N.A.I.C.S.: 327310

ACC Mineral Resources Limited (1)
Cement House 121 Maharshi Karve Road, Mumbai, 400 020, India
Tel.: (91) 2266654321
Web Site: http://www.acclimited.com
Coal Exploration Services
N.A.I.C.S.: 213113

Bulk Cement Corporation (India) Limited (1)
W-7 KWC, Dist Raigad, Kalamboli, 410 218, India
Tel.: (91) 222 742 4285
Web Site: http://www.acc.com
Sales Range: $50-74.9 Million
Emp.: 55
Cement Storage, Packaging & Shipping
N.A.I.C.S.: 327320

ACCEDERE LIMITED
Andheri Industrial Estate115B Andheri Industrial Estate, Veera Desai Road, Mumbai, 400053, Maharashtra, India
Tel.: (91) 2232944663   In
Web Site: https://accedere.io
Year Founded: 1983
531533—(BOM)
Rev.: $81,081
Assets: $637,046
Liabilities: $61,179
Net Worth: $575,866
Earnings: $2,703
Fiscal Year-end: 03/31/21
Information Technology Consulting Services
N.A.I.C.S.: 541512
Ashwin K. Chaudhary (Mng Dir)

ACCEDO GROUP LTD.
1 Brindley Road South West Industrial Estate Peterlee, Durham, SR8 2LT, United Kingdom
Tel.: (44) 1915181555   UK
Web Site: https://accedogroup.co.uk
Engineering Design & Consulting Services
N.A.I.C.S.: 541330

Subsidiaries:

Alpha Process Controls (International) Ltd. (1)
1 Brindley Road South West Industrial Estate, Peterlee, SR8 2LT, Durham, United Kingdom
Tel.: (44) 1915181555
Web Site: http://www.alphaprocess.co.uk
Engineering Safety Coupling Mfr

N.A.I.C.S.: 333613

ACCEL GROUP HOLDINGS LIMITED
Room 09 7/F The Octagon 6 Sha Tsui Rd, Tsuen Wan, China (Hong Kong)
Tel.: (852) 2 529 8888   Ky
Web Site: http://www.chittathk.com
Year Founded: 2000
1283—(HKG)
Rev.: $65,638,438
Assets: $60,182,971
Liabilities: $14,689,016
Net Worth: $45,493,955
Earnings: $9,454,621
Emp.: 162
Fiscal Year-end: 03/31/21
Holding Company
N.A.I.C.S.: 551112
Lai Hung Ko (Chm & CEO)

Subsidiaries:

Accel Innovations Limited (1)
Unit A 19/F TML Plaza 3 Hoi Shing Road, Tsuen Wan, New Territories, China (Hong Kong)
Tel.: (852) 26110032
Electric Equipment Mfr
N.A.I.C.S.: 334419

ACCEL LIMITED
3rd Floor SFI Complex No 178 Valluvar Kottam High Road, Nungambakkam, Chennai, 600034, Tamil Nadu, India
Tel.: (91) 4428222262
Web Site: https://www.accel-india.com
Year Founded: 1991
517494—(BOM)
Rev.: $16,010,645
Assets: $27,222,386
Liabilities: $14,942,873
Net Worth: $12,279,513
Earnings: $803,985
Emp.: 1,093
Fiscal Year-end: 03/31/22
Information Technology Consulting Services
N.A.I.C.S.: 541512
N. R. Panicker (Founder & Mng Dir)

Subsidiaries:

Accel Media Ventures Ltd. (1)
1063 Munusamy Salai First Floor K K Nagar West, Vadapalani, Chennai, 600 078, India
Tel.: (91) 4424741800
Web Site: https://www.accelmedia.in
IT & Media Services
N.A.I.C.S.: 541840
S. V. Deepak (Creative Dir)

Computer Factory (India) Private Limited (1)
2H Continental Plaza 705 Mount Road, Chennai, 600 006, Tamil Nadu, India
Tel.: (91) 4428297703
Web Site: http://www.cfindia.net
IT Infrastructure Software Services
N.A.I.C.S.: 541511
N. R. Panicker (CEO & Mng Dir)

ACCEL SOLUTIONS LTD.
25 Bazel Street, Petah Tikva, 4951038, Israel
Tel.: (972) 33733433
Web Site: https://www.accel.co.il
Year Founded: 2004
ACCL—(TAE)
Rev.: $75,827,323
Assets: $60,333,747
Liabilities: $24,490,399
Net Worth: $35,843,348
Earnings: $2,627,987
Fiscal Year-end: 09/30/23
All Other Telecommunications
N.A.I.C.S.: 517810

Zohar Shpitz (CFO)

ACCEL, S.A.B. DE C.V.
Circuito No 5 Parque Industrial Las Americas, 31220, Chihuahua, Mexico
Tel.: (52) 6144260024
Web Site: https://www.accel.com.mx
Year Founded: 1992
ACCELSA—(MEX)
Rev.: $731,787,712
Assets: $702,804,678
Liabilities: $365,437,221
Net Worth: $337,367,457
Earnings: $18,795,665
Emp.: 5,354
Fiscal Year-end: 12/31/23
Contract Manufacturing Services
N.A.I.C.S.: 561499

Subsidiaries:

Accel Distribucion, S. A. de C. V. (1)
Virginia Fabregas No 80, Col San Rafael, 06470, Mexico, Mexico
Tel.: (52) 5557052788
Warehousing & Storage
N.A.I.C.S.: 493190
Ricardo Alonso (Mng Dir)

Accel Logistica S.A. de C.V. (1)
Virginia Fabregas 80, Col San Rafael, 06470, Mexico, Mexico
Tel.: (52) 5557052788
Web Site: http://www.accellogistica.com.mx
Refrigerated Warehousing & Storage
N.A.I.C.S.: 493120
Ricardo Alonso (Mgr-Comml)

Accel Servicios, S. A. de C. V. (1)
Virginia Fabregas No 80, Col San Rafael, 06470, Mexico, Mexico   (99.99%)
Tel.: (52) 5557052788
Management Consulting Services
N.A.I.C.S.: 541618

Almacenadora Accel, S. A. (1)
Virginia Fabregas No 80, Col San Rafael, 06470, Mexico, Mexico   (100%)
Tel.: (52) 5557052788
Web Site: http://www.accelonline.com
Warehousing & Storage
N.A.I.C.S.: 493190

Corporativo de Negocios de Comercio Exterior, S.A. de C.V. (1)
Manuel J Clouthier No 1251, Ciudad Juarez, 32550, Mexico   (65%)
Tel.: (52) 6563970354
Web Site: http://recintofiscalizado.com
Emp.: 18
Freight Transportation Arrangement
N.A.I.C.S.: 488510

Elamex, S.A. de C.V. (1)
4171 N Mesa Bldg D, El Paso, TX 79902   (56%)
Tel.: (915) 351-2382
Web Site: http://www.elamex.com
Sales Range: $75-99.9 Million
Emp.: 937
Contract Manufacturing Services
N.A.I.C.S.: 336320
Richard A. Harshman (CEO)

Servicios Administrativos Accel, S.A. de C.V. (1)
Virginia Fabregas No 80, Col San Rafael, 6470, Mexico, Mexico   (98%)
Tel.: (52) 5557052788
Web Site: http://www.accel.com
Management Consulting Services
N.A.I.C.S.: 541618

Servilogistics de Mexico, S.A. de C.V. (1)
Virginia Fabregas No 80, Col San Rafael, 6470, Mexico, Mexico   (98%)
Tel.: (52) 5557052788
Sales Range: $200-249.9 Million
Emp.: 700
Freight Transportation Arrangement
N.A.I.C.S.: 488510
Ricardo Alonso (Dir-Comml)

ACCELER8 VENTURES PLC
28 Esplanade, Saint Helier, JE2 3QA, Jersey

ACCELER8 VENTURES PLC

Acceler8 Ventures Plc—(Continued)

Tel.: (44) 1534700000   JE
Web Site:
  https://www.acceler8.ventures
Year Founded: 2021
AC8—(LSE)
Rev.: $127,282
Assets: $213,235
Liabilities: $68,356
Net Worth: $144,878
Earnings: ($70,320)
Emp.: 2
Fiscal Year-end: 12/31/23
Investment Management Service
N.A.I.C.S.: 523999
David Williams (Chm)

ACCELERATE PROPERTY FUND LTD.

1st Floor Cnr Willow Ave & Cedar
Rd, Fourways, Johannesburg, 2055,
South Africa
Tel.: (27) 114656925
Web Site:
  https://www.acceleratepf.co.za
APF—(JSE)
Rev.: $43,276,016
Assets: $514,679,959
Liabilities: $264,793,771
Net Worth: $249,886,189
Earnings: ($32,992,426)
Emp.: 61
Fiscal Year-end: 03/31/24
Investment Management Service
N.A.I.C.S.: 525990
Michael Georgiou (CEO)

ACCELERATE RESOURCES LIMITED

Ground Floor Suite 1/16 Ord Street,
West Perth, 6005, WA, Australia
Tel.: (61) 62489663   AU
Web Site: https://www.ax8.com.au
AX8—(ASX)
Rev.: $36,249
Assets: $8,474,410
Liabilities: $619,498
Net Worth: $7,854,912
Earnings: ($1,755,095)
Fiscal Year-end: 06/30/24
Mineral Exploration Services
N.A.I.C.S.: 213114
Yaxi Zhan (Mng Dir)

ACCELERATEBS INDIA LIMITED

604 Quantum Tower Rambaug Lane
Off S V Road Malad West, Mumbai,
400064, Maharashtra, India
Tel.: (91) 9653642716
Web Site:
  https://www.acceleratebs.com
Year Founded: 2012
543938—(BOM)
Software Development Services
N.A.I.C.S.: 541511

ACCELERATED SYSTEMS, INC.

60 Northland Road Unit 6, Waterloo,
N2V 2B8, ON, Canada
Tel.: (519) 342-2507
Web Site: http://www.accelerated-
  systems.com
Year Founded: 1990
Sales Range: $50-74.9 Million
Emp.: 20
Programmable Electronic Motor
Speed Control Product Mfr
N.A.I.C.S.: 336320
Rob Lankin (Owner)

ACCELERO CAPITAL HOLDINGS SARL

29 rue de Berri, 75008, Paris, France

Tel.: (33) 1 83 81 94 61
Web Site:
  http://www.accelerocapital.com
Year Founded: 2011
Telecommunication, Digital Media &
Technology Investment & Management Services
N.A.I.C.S.: 523999
Khaled Bichara (Co-Founder & Mng
Partner)

ACCELEWARE LTD.

435 10th Avenue SE, Calgary, T2G
0W3, AB, Canada
Tel.: (403) 249-9099
Web Site:
  https://www.acceleware.com
Year Founded: 2004
AXE—(TSXV)
Rev.: $210,686
Assets: $1,140,170
Liabilities: $7,166,580
Net Worth: ($6,026,410)
Earnings: ($1,544,494)
Emp.: 18
Fiscal Year-end: 12/31/23
Software Development Services
N.A.I.C.S.: 541511
Jens Horstmann (Mgr-Investment
Fund)

ACCELINK TECHNOLOGIES CO., LTD.

1 Tanhu Road Canglongdao Development Zone, Jiangxia, Wuhan,
430205, Hubei, China
Tel.: (86) 2787692735
Web Site: http://www.accelink.com
Year Founded: 2001
Sales Range: $50-74.9 Million
Emp.: 1,900
Fiber Optic Product Mfr
N.A.I.C.S.: 335921
Guo Hua Tong (Chm)

Subsidiaries:

Accelink Denmark A/S   (1)
Blokken 84, Birkerod, 3460, Frederiksborg,
Denmark
Tel.: (45) 45903000
Web Site: http://www.accelink.tk
Emp.: 45
Fiber Optic Product Distr
N.A.I.C.S.: 423610
Yueqiang Shen (CEO)

Accelink Technologies Europe
GmbH   (1)
Emanuel Leutze-Strasse 21, North Rhine-
Westphalia, 40547, Dusseldorf, Germany
Tel.: (49) 211 5291599
Electronic Components Distr
N.A.I.C.S.: 423690

Wuhan Accelink Polytron Technologies Inc   (1)
Lake Road Jiangxia District No 1, Hidden
Dragon Island Development Zone, Wuhan,
430205, Hubei, China
Tel.: (86) 27 87692735
Fiber Optic Product Mfr
N.A.I.C.S.: 335921

ACCELL GROUP N.V.

Industrieweg 4, 8444 AR, Heerenveen, Netherlands
Tel.: (31) 513638703
Web Site: http://www.accell-
  group.com
ACCEL—(OTCIQ)
Rev.: $1,592,511,419
Assets: $1,080,329,198
Liabilities: $618,568,685
Net Worth: $461,760,513
Earnings: $79,625,571
Emp.: 2,624
Fiscal Year-end: 12/31/20
Design, Production, Marketing &
Sales of Bicycles

N.A.I.C.S.: 336991
Jeroen J. Both (Chief Supply Chain
Officer)

Subsidiaries:

Accell Asia Ltd.   (1)
Elevator 12F 11F No 287 Sec 3 Nanjing E
Rd, Songshan Dist, Taipei, 105, Taiwan
Tel.: (886) 227402214
Bicycle Accessory Mfr
N.A.I.C.S.: 336991
Janet Hsu (Mng Dir)

Accell Bisiklet Sanayi ve Ticaret
A.S.   (1)
Organize Sanayi Bolgesi 3 Kisim Ahmet
Tutuncuoglu Caddesi No 1, Manisa, Turkiye
Tel.: (90) 2362130045
Web Site: https://accellbisiklet.com.tr
Bicycle Accessory Mfr
N.A.I.C.S.: 336991
Gurol Caydas (Mgr-Product Dev)

Accell Duitsland B.V.   (1)
Industrieweg 4, Heerenveen, 8444 AR,
Netherlands   (100%)
Tel.: (31) 513638254
Web Site: http://www.accell-group.com
Sales Range: $350-399.9 Million
Emp.: 2,000
Religious Organizations
N.A.I.C.S.: 813110

Accell Germany GmbH   (1)
Max-Planck-Strasse 4, 97526, Sennfeld,
Germany
Tel.: (49) 9721 675160
Sales Range: $25-49.9 Million
Emp.: 2
Bicycle Mfr
N.A.I.C.S.: 336991
Susanne Puello (Gen Mgr)

Subsidiary (Domestic):

E. Wiener Bike Parts GmbH   (2)
Max-Planck-Strasse 8, 97526, Sennfeld,
Germany   (100%)
Tel.: (49) 97 216 5010
Web Site: https://www.bike-parts.de
Emp.: 400
Motorcycle Bicycle & Parts Mfr
N.A.I.C.S.: 336991

Winora Staiger GmbH   (2)
Max-Planck-Strasse 6, 97526, Sennfeld,
Germany   (100%)
Tel.: (49) 177 353 2691
Web Site: https://www.winora.com
Sales Range: $50-74.9 Million
Sporting & Recreational Goods & Supplies
Whslr
N.A.I.C.S.: 423910

Accell Hunland Kft   (1)
Parkolo ter 1, 5091, Toszeg,
Hungary   (100%)
Tel.: (36) 5 658 6481
Web Site: https://accell-hunland.hu
Sales Range: $200-249.9 Million
Emp.: 600
Motorcycle Bicycle & Parts Mfr
N.A.I.C.S.: 336991
Attila Vass (Gen Mgr)

Accell IT B.V.   (1)
Industrieweg 4, 8444 AR, Heerenveen,
Netherlands
Tel.: (31) 513647027
Web Site: http://www.accell-it.com
Bicycle Accessory Mfr
N.A.I.C.S.: 336991

Accell IT Services B.V.   (1)
Jagtlustweg 5, 8444 AV, Heerenveen, Netherlands
Tel.: (31) 513638777
Sales Range: $25-49.9 Million
Emp.: 45
Software Consulting Services
N.A.I.C.S.: 541512
Menno Bokslag (Mgr-IT)

Accell Nederland B.V.   (1)
Industrieweg 4, 8444 AR, Heerenveen,
Netherlands
Tel.: (31) 513638500
Web Site: http://www.accellnederland.nl
Bicycle Accessory Mfr

N.A.I.C.S.: 336991
Martin Veter (Mgr-Quality)

Accell Suisse AG   (1)
Industriestrasse 21, 6055, Alpnach, 6055,
Switzerland
Tel.: (41) 416702190
Web Site: https://www.accell-suisse.ch
Sales Range: $50-74.9 Million
Emp.: 0
Bicycle Parts Distr
N.A.I.C.S.: 423120

Babboe B.V.   (1)
Koedijkerweg 12 A, 3816 BV, Amersfoort,
Netherlands
Tel.: (31) 337410740
Web Site: https://www.babboe.nl
Bike Accessory Part Retailer
N.A.I.C.S.: 459110
Eelco Lobach (Dir-Ops)

Batavus B.V.   (1)
Industrieweg 4, 8444AR, Heerenveen,
Netherlands   (100%)
Tel.: (31) 513638999
Web Site: http://www.batavus.com
Sales Range: $100-124.9 Million
Emp.: 350
Motorcycle Bicycle & Parts Mfr
N.A.I.C.S.: 336991

Brasseur S.A.   (1)
13 rue de Steppes, 4000, Liege, Belgium
Tel.: (32) 4 228 72 60
Web Site: http://www.brasseur-bicycles.com
Sales Range: $25-49.9 Million
Emp.: 20
Bicycle Parts Mfr & Distr
N.A.I.C.S.: 336991

Comet Distribuciones Commerciales
S.L.   (1)
Poligono Industrial Erratzu 440, 20130,
Urnieta, Spain
Tel.: (34) 94 333 1393
Web Site: http://www.comet.es
Sport Bicycle Accessory Mfr
N.A.I.C.S.: 336991
Aner Sarasa (Sls Mgr)

Cycle Services Nordic ApS   (1)
Emil Neckelmanns Vej 6, 5220, Odense,
Denmark
Tel.: (45) 65992411
Web Site:
  https://www.cycleservicenordic.com
Bicycle Accessory Mfr
N.A.I.C.S.: 336991
Bo Baekkelund (Gen Mgr)

Cycles France-Loire S.A.S.   (1)
Rue Branly, PO Box 61, 42162, Andrezieux-
Boutheon, France
Tel.: (33) 477 55 54 00
Bicycle Parts Mfr & Distr
N.A.I.C.S.: 336991

Cycles Lapierre S.A.   (1)
Rue Edmond Voisenet, 21005, Dijon, Cedex, France   (100%)
Tel.: (33) 8001 946 2121
Web Site: https://www.lapierrebikes.com
Sales Range: $25-49.9 Million
Emp.: 65
Motorcycle Bicycle & Parts Mfr
N.A.I.C.S.: 336991

Cycles Mercier France-Loire S.A.   (1)
Ave Industrie, Saint-Cyprien, Dordogne,
42160, France   (100%)
Tel.: (33) 477555400
Web Site: http://www.cyclesfranceloire.com
Sales Range: $25-49.9 Million
Emp.: 38
Motorcycle Bicycle & Parts Mfr
N.A.I.C.S.: 336991
Jeane Lapierre (Mgr)

Juncker Bike Parts B.V.   (1)
Wilmersdorf 37, 7327 AD, Apeldoorn,
Netherlands   (100%)
Tel.: (31) 513788118
Web Site: https://www.juncker.nl
Sales Range: $25-49.9 Million
Emp.: 40
Sporting & Recreational Goods & Supplies
Whslr
N.A.I.C.S.: 423910

Koga B.V.   (1)

Tinweg 9, Heerenveen, 8445 PD, Netherlands **(100%)**
Tel.: (31) 513630111
Web Site: http://www.koga.com
Sales Range: $25-49.9 Million
Emp.: 85
Motorcycle Bicycle & Parts Mfr
N.A.I.C.S.: 336991
Wouter Jager *(Mng Dir)*

Koga Trading A.G. **(1)**
Postfach 161, 6018, Buttisholz, Switzerland **(100%)**
Tel.: (41) 9281841
Sporting & Recreational Goods & Supplies Whslr
N.A.I.C.S.: 423910

Loekie B.V. **(1)**
Wilmersdorf 37, 7327 AD, Apeldoorn, Netherlands **(100%)**
Tel.: (31) 553578700
Web Site: http://www.loekie.nl
Sales Range: $25-49.9 Million
Emp.: 50
Bicycle Whslr
N.A.I.C.S.: 423910
Hyoup Snellen *(Gen Mgr)*

Raleigh Cycle Co. Ltd **(1)**
Church Street Eastwood, Nottingham, NG16 3HT, United Kingdom
Tel.: (44) 1773532600
Web Site: http://www.raleigh-group.co.uk
Sales Range: $250-299.9 Million
Emp.: 200
Bicycle Designer, Mfr & Marketer
N.A.I.C.S.: 336991
Mark Gouldthorp *(Mng Dir)*

Subsidiary (Domestic):

Raleigh UK Ltd **(2)**
Church Street Eastwood, Nottingham, NG16 3HT, United Kingdom
Tel.: (44) 1773532600
Web Site: https://www.raleigh.co.uk
Bicycle Designer, Mfr & Marketer
N.A.I.C.S.: 336991

Sparta B.V. **(1)**
Wilmersdorf 37, Apeldoorn, 7327, Netherlands **(100%)**
Tel.: (31) 553578700
Web Site: http://www.sparta.nl
Sales Range: $50-74.9 Million
Emp.: 200
Motorcycle Bicycle & Parts Mfr
N.A.I.C.S.: 336991

Tunturi New Fitness B.V. **(1)**
Purmerweg 1, 1311 XE, Almere, Netherlands **(100%)**
Tel.: (31) 36 546 0050
Web Site: https://www.tunturi.com
Sales Range: $25-49.9 Million
Emp.: 50
Sporting & Recreational Goods & Supplies Whslr
N.A.I.C.S.: 423910
Steef Ploeger *(CEO)*

Tunturi-Hellberg Oy Ltd. **(1)**
Varusmestarintie 26, PO Box 750, 20361, Turku, Finland **(100%)**
Tel.: (358) 102733200
Web Site: http://www.tunturi.fi
Sales Range: $25-49.9 Million
Emp.: 25
Fitness Equipment & Products
N.A.I.C.S.: 339920
Rene Takens *(CEO)*

Vartex AB **(1)**
Batterivagen 14, 432 32, Varberg, Sweden
Tel.: (46) 340549690
Web Site: https://www.vartex.se
Bicycle Accessory Whslr
N.A.I.C.S.: 423910

ACCELONIX LIMITED

Unit 2 McClintock Building Granta Park, Great Abington, Cambridge, CB21 6GP, Hants, United Kingdom
Tel.: (44) 1223659965
Web Site: http://www.accelonix.co.uk
Sales Range: $10-24.9 Million
Emp.: 12

Microelectronics Packaging & PCB Assembly Mfr
N.A.I.C.S.: 334515

Subsidiaries:

Accelonix B.V. **(1)**
Troy C 7F, 5653 LC, Eindhoven, Noord Brabant, Netherlands
Tel.: (31) 407501650
Web Site: http://www.accelonix.nl
Sales Range: $1-9.9 Million
Emp.: 10
Microelectronics Packaging, PCB Assembly & Test & Device Programming Services
N.A.I.C.S.: 334515

Accelonix Iberica S.L. **(1)**
C/Emporda N 8 Nave 15, Cubelles, 08880, Barcelona, Spain
Tel.: (34) 902 733 898
Web Site: http://www.accelonix.es
Electronic Components Distr
N.A.I.C.S.: 423690

Accelonix SARL **(1)**
260 Rue Clement Ader, Evreux, 27000, France
Tel.: (33) 232356480
Web Site: http://www.accelonix.com
Emp.: 25
Microelectronics Packaging, PCB Assembly & Test & Device Programming Services
N.A.I.C.S.: 334515

ACCENT EQUITY PARTNERS AB

Engelbrektsgatan 7, PO Box 5784, 114 87, Stockholm, Sweden
Tel.: (46) 8 545 073 00 **SE**
Web Site: http://www.accentequity.se
Year Founded: 1994
Sales Range: $25-49.9 Million
Emp.: 10
Privater Equity Firm
N.A.I.C.S.: 523999
Jan Ohlsson *(Founder & Chm)*

Subsidiaries:

Eurowrap A/S **(1)**
Odinsvej 30, 4100, Ringsted, Denmark
Tel.: (45) 5768 0321
Web Site: http://www.winnie.dk
Gift Shop Operator
N.A.I.C.S.: 459420

Subsidiary (Non-US):

Eurowrap Ltd **(2)**
Unit 2 Pikelaw Place West Pimbo Industrial Estate, Skelmersdale, WN8 9PP, United Kingdom
Tel.: (44) 1695 558 511
Web Site: http://www.eurowrap.co.uk
Gift Shop Operator
N.A.I.C.S.: 459420

Mont Blanc Industri AB **(1)**
Toarpsdal, Dalsjofors, 516 90, Sweden
Tel.: (46) 33 22 27 00
Web Site: http://www.montblancgroup.se
Sales Range: $50-74.9 Million
Mfr of Car Load Carrying Equipment, Including Roof Racks, Bicycle Holders, Roof Boxes & Other Accessories
N.A.I.C.S.: 336390
Claes Umoffon *(CEO)*

Subsidiary (Non-US):

Automaxi International **(2)**
24 Rue Claude Bernard, 35400, Saint-Malo, Ille Et Vilaine, France
Tel.: (33) 299211270
Web Site: http://www.automaxi.fr
Sales Range: $10-24.9 Million
Designer & Mfr of Automobile Carrying Accessories, Including Roof Racks & Bike Carriers
N.A.I.C.S.: 336390
Christophe Guillois *(Mgr-Sys)*

MB Automaxi UK Ltd **(2)**
1 Chapel Street, Warwick, CV34 4HL, United Kingdom
Tel.: (44) 1926 405596
Industrial Supplies Whslr

N.A.I.C.S.: 423840

Mont Blanc France SAS **(2)**
24 Rue Claude Bernard, 35400, Saint-Malo, France
Tel.: (33) 299211270
Industrial Supplies Whslr
N.A.I.C.S.: 423840

Mont Blanc Industri UK Ltd **(2)**
Eden Way, Leighton Buzzard, LU7 4TZ, Bedfordshire, United Kingdom
Tel.: (44) 1525 850800
Web Site: http://www.montblancgroup.com
Aftermarket Sales of Car Load Carrying Equipment
N.A.I.C.S.: 423120

San Sac Group AB **(1)**
Molijns vag 6, PO Box 423, 581 04, Linkoping, Sweden
Tel.: (46) 13 13 04 20
Web Site: http://www.sansacgroup.com
Waste Disposal Equipment Mfr
N.A.I.C.S.: 562998

Subsidiary (Domestic):

Orwak Group AB **(2)**
Svetsaregatan, 576 33, Savsjo, Sweden
Tel.: (46) 38215700
Web Site: http://www.orwak.com
Holding Company; Waste Compactor & Baling System Mfr
N.A.I.C.S.: 551112
Conny Sundqvist *(VP-Fin)*

Subsidiary (Domestic):

Orwak AB **(3)**
Svetsaregatan, 576 33, Savsjo, Sweden
Tel.: (46) 382 157 00
Web Site: http://www.orwak.com
Waste Compactor & Baling System Mfr
N.A.I.C.S.: 333998
Conny Sundqvist *(VP-Fin)*

Subsidiary (Non-US):

Orwak Polska Sp. z o.o. **(3)**
ul Felsztynskiego 50, 93-582, Lodz, Poland
Tel.: (48) 426487917
Web Site: http://www.orwakpolska.pl
Waste Compactor & Baling System Mfr
N.A.I.C.S.: 333998
Magda Nowak *(Mng Dir)*

Steni AS **(1)**
Lagendalsveien 2633, 3277, Steinsholt, Norway
Tel.: (47) 33 15 56 00
Web Site: http://www.steni.no
Wall Panels Mfr
N.A.I.C.S.: 332323

Textilia Tvatt & Textilservice AB **(1)**
Idrottsvagen 35, 702 32, Orebro, Sweden **(82.54%)**
Tel.: (46) 1919 4500
Web Site: http://www.textiliaab.se
Sales Range: $75-99.9 Million
Emp.: 450
Laundry & Other Textile Support Services
N.A.I.C.S.: 812332
Fredrik Lagerkvist *(Pres & CEO)*

ACCENT GROUP LIMITED

2/64 Balmain Street, Richmond, 3121, VIC, Australia
Tel.: (61) 394279422 **AU**
Web Site:
https://www.accentgr.com.au
AX1—(ASX)
Rev.: $971,121,791
Assets: $766,524,436
Liabilities: $486,873,663
Net Worth: $279,650,773
Earnings: $39,750,267
Emp.: 6,500
Fiscal Year-end: 06/30/24
Athletic Footwear Mfr
N.A.I.C.S.: 339920
Daniel Agostinelli *(CEO)*

Subsidiaries:

Shoe Superstore Pty Ltd. **(1)**
Unit 9A The Junction 2 Windsor Rd, N Parramatta, Sydney, 2151, NSW, Australia

Tel.: (61) 296301555
Web Site:
http://www.shoesuperstore.com.au
Sales Range: $50-74.9 Million
Emp.: 3
Men & Women Footwear Retailer
N.A.I.C.S.: 424340

Subtype Pty. Ltd. **(1)**
2/350 George Street, Sydney, 2000, NSW, Australia
Tel.: (61) 291599146
Web Site: https://www.subtypestore.com
Footwear Product Distr
N.A.I.C.S.: 424340

The Athlete's Foot Australia Pty Limited **(1)**
719 Elizabeth St, Waterloo, 2017, NSW, Australia
Tel.: (61) 285949222
Web Site: http://www.theathletesfoot.com.au
Sales Range: $25-49.9 Million
Emp.: 50
Shoe Store Operation Services
N.A.I.C.S.: 459110
Michael Cooper *(Mng Dir)*

ACCENT MICROCELL LTD.

314 Shangrilla Arcade Shyamal Cross Roads Anand Nagar Road Satellite, Ahmedabad, 380015, Gujarat, India
Tel.: (91) 7940042367 **In**
Web Site:
https://www.accentmicrocell.com
Year Founded: 2001
ACCENTMIC—(NSE)
Rev.: $24,941,166
Assets: $13,749,558
Liabilities: $7,637,721
Net Worth: $6,111,837
Earnings: $1,482,531
Emp.: 334
Fiscal Year-end: 03/31/23
Pharmaceutical Product Mfr & Distr
N.A.I.C.S.: 325412

ACCENT RESOURCES N.L.

Level 9 250 Queen Street, Melbourne, 3000, VIC, Australia
Tel.: (61) 396700888 **AU**
Web Site:
https://www.accentresources.com.au
ACS—(ASX)
Rev.: $228,365
Assets: $14,839,744
Liabilities: $13,635,817
Net Worth: $1,203,926
Earnings: ($2,648,905)
Emp.: 5
Fiscal Year-end: 06/30/24
Minerals Exploration
N.A.I.C.S.: 212220
Dian Zhou He *(Deputy Chm)*

ACCENTIA TECHNOLOGIES LIMITED

D-207 2nd Floor International Infotech Centre, Belapur Railway Station Complex CBD Belapur, Navi Mumbai, 400 614, India
Tel.: (91) 22 2757 5922
Web Site:
http://www.accentiatech.com
Sales Range: $10-24.9 Million
IT Products & Services
N.A.I.C.S.: 541519

Subsidiaries:

Accentia Technologies - Cochin Unit **(1)**
39 1463-c Near S over Bridge Valanjambalam, Cochin, 682016, Kerala, India
Tel.: (91) 4842375215
Sales Range: $10-24.9 Million
Emp.: 50
Business Management Services
N.A.I.C.S.: 561110

Accentia Technologies Limited—(Continued)

Accentia Technologies Ltd. - Trivandrum Unit (1)
233 241 Nila, Techno Park Campus, Trivandrum, 695 581, Kerala, India
Tel.: (91) 4712700964
Web Site: http://www.accentiatech.com
Sales Range: $75-99.9 Million
Emp.: 400
Business Process Management Services
N.A.I.C.S.: 561110
Viswambharan S. Pradeep (CEO & Mng Dir)

Asscent Infoserve Pvt. Ltd. (1)
MKB Towers No 3802/B, 7th Main HAL 2nd Stage, 56038, Bengaluru, Karnataka, India
Tel.: (91) 25275603
Information Services & Solutions
N.A.I.C.S.: 519290

ACCENTIS SA/NV
Noorderlaan 139/3V, 2030, Antwerp, Belgium
Tel.: (32) 32349413
Web Site: https://www.accentis.com
ACCB—(EUR)
Sales Range: $10-24.9 Million
Property Management & Project Development Services
N.A.I.C.S.: 531312
Jacques De Bliek (Chm)

Subsidiaries:

BBS Verwaltungs GmbH (1)
Hafenweg 24a, Munster, 48155, Germany
Tel.: (49) 7643933980
Real Estate Manangement Services
N.A.I.C.S.: 531390

ACCENTUATE LIMITED
32 Steele Street, Steeledale, Johannesburg, 2197, South Africa
Tel.: (27) 114064100   ZA
Web Site:
http://www.accentuateltd.co.za
Year Founded: 1953
Rev.: $19,748,688
Assets: $11,148,522
Liabilities: $4,810,100
Net Worth: $6,338,422
Earnings: ($1,615,136)
Emp.: 234
Fiscal Year-end: 06/30/19
Chemical & Floor Covering Product Distr
N.A.I.C.S.: 424690
Sirkien Van Schalkwyk (Sec)

Subsidiaries:

FloorworX Africa (Pty) Limited (1)
404 Southern Kliprviersberg Road, Steeledale, Johannesburg, 2197, South Africa
Tel.: (27) 11 406 4100
Web Site: http://www.floorworx.co.za
Emp.: 25
Floor Covering Product Distr
N.A.I.C.S.: 423220
Theresa Venter (Dir-Mktg)

ACCENTURE PLC
1 Grand Canal Square, Grand Canal Harbour, Dublin, D02 P820, Ireland
Tel.: (353) 16462000   IE
Web Site: https://www.accenture.com
Year Founded: 2009
ACN—(NYSE)
Rev.: $64,111,745,000
Assets: $51,245,305,000
Liabilities: $24,786,712,000
Net Worth: $26,458,593,000
Earnings: $6,871,557,000
Emp.: 733,000
Fiscal Year-end: 08/31/23
Information Technology Services
N.A.I.C.S.: 551112
Julie T. Sweet (Chm & Co-CEO)

Subsidiaries:

?What If! Holdings Limited (1)
The Glassworks 3-4 Ashland Place, London, W1U 4AH, United Kingdom
Tel.: (44) 20 7535 7500
Web Site: http://www.whatifinnovation.com
Sales Range: $50-74.9 Million
Emp.: 212
Business Management Services
N.A.I.C.S.: 561110
Sal Pajwani (CEO-Grp)

AD Dialeto Agencia de Publicidade SA (1)
R Gomes de Carvalho 1510 - 4 andar - Vila Olimpia, Sao Paulo, 04547-005, Brazil
Tel.: (55) 1139385007
Web Site: http://www.addialeto.net
Digital Marketing Services
N.A.I.C.S.: 541613
Leo Cid Ferreira (Pres & CEO)

Accenture (Ireland) (1)
1 Grand Canal Square, Dublin, D02 P820, Ireland   (100%)
Sales Range: $125-149.9 Million
Emp.: 1,000
Business Services
N.A.I.C.S.: 561499
Mark Ryan (Mng Dir)

Accenture A/S (1)
Arne Jacobsens Alle 15, Copenhagen, 2300, Denmark
Tel.: (45) 72288000
Software Development Services
N.A.I.C.S.: 513210
Lars Wodschow (Head-External Comm & Stakeholder Rels)

Accenture Australia Ltd. (1)
Level 30 10 Eagle Street, Brisbane, 4000, QLD, Australia
Tel.: (61) 731174001
N.A.I.C.S.: 541512

Accenture Bulgaria EOOD (1)
65A Svoboda Blvd, 4002, Plovdiv, Bulgaria
Tel.: (359) 879595008
N.A.I.C.S.: 541512

Accenture Global Services Ltd. (1)
3 Grand Canal Plaza Upper Grand Canal Street, Dublin, 4, Ireland
Tel.: (353) 14076000
Business Process Outsourcing Services
N.A.I.C.S.: 561499
Mark Ryan (Country Mng Dir)

Subsidiary (Domestic):

Accenture European Service Centre Ltd. (2)
3 Grand Canal Plz, Grand Canal upper, Dublin, 4, Ireland   (100%)
Tel.: (353) 14076000
Web Site: http://www.accenture.com
Sales Range: $250-299.9 Million
Emp.: 1,700
Business Services
N.A.I.C.S.: 561499

Accenture Holdings plc (1)
1 Grand Canal Square Grand Canal Harbour, Dublin, 2, Ireland
Tel.: (353) 1 646 2000
Rev.: $36,765,477,000
Assets: $22,689,889,000
Liabilities: $12,979,689,000
Net Worth: $9,710,200,000
Earnings: $3,588,629,000
Emp.: 424,999
Fiscal Year-end: 08/31/2017
Holding Company
N.A.I.C.S.: 551112
Richard P. Clark (Chief Acctg Officer & Controller)

Subsidiary (Non-US):

Accenture (Botswana) (PTY) Ltd. (2)
Plot 113 Unit 28 Kgale Mews, PO BOX 2691, Gaborone, Botswana
Tel.: (267) 3659900
Sales Range: $10-24.9 Million
Emp.: 30
Business Process Outsourcing Services
N.A.I.C.S.: 561499

Accenture (China) Co., Ltd. (2)
21F West Tower World Financial Center No 1 East 3rd Ring Middle Road, Chaoyang District, Beijing, 100020, China
Tel.: (86) 1085958700
Emp.: 1,000
Management Consulting & Technology Services
N.A.I.C.S.: 541611

Accenture (China) Co., Ltd. - Shanghai (2)
Shanghai Central Plaza Floor 30 No 381 Huaihai Zhong Road, 381 Huai Hai Zhong Road, Shanghai, 200020, China
Tel.: (86) 2123053333
Management Consulting Services
N.A.I.C.S.: 541618

Accenture (Korea) Ltd. (2)
10th Fl Posco P&S Tower Yoido Dong, Youngdeungpo Ku, Seoul, 150 737, Korea (South)   (100%)
Tel.: (82) 237778888
Web Site: http://www.accenture.com
Sales Range: $25-49.9 Million
Emp.: 500
Various Business Services
N.A.I.C.S.: 561499

Accenture (South Africa) Pty. Ltd. (2)
Bldg 19 Harrowdene Ofc Park, Kelvin Dr Sandton, Woodmead, 2054, South Africa   (100%)
Tel.: (27) 112083000
Sales Range: $250-299.9 Million
Emp.: 1,200
Business Services
N.A.I.C.S.: 561499
William Nzinda (Country Mng Partner)

Accenture (UK) Ltd. (2)
30 Fenchurch St, 30 Fenchurch St, London, EC3M 3BD, United Kingdom
Tel.: (44) 2078444000
Web Site: https://www.accenture.com
Sales Range: $75-99.9 Million
Emp.: 500
Management Consulting, Technological & Outsourcing Services
N.A.I.C.S.: 541611

Accenture A.B. (2)
Alstromergatan 12, PO Box 1331, 112 47, Stockholm, Sweden   (100%)
Tel.: (46) 84513000
Sales Range: $75-99.9 Million
Emp.: 350
Various Business Services
N.A.I.C.S.: 561499
Mattias Lewren (Mng Dir)

Accenture A.S (2)
Rolfsbuktveien 2, 1364, Fornebu, Norway
Tel.: (47) 67126700
Web Site: http://www.accenture.com
Business Process Outsourcing Services
N.A.I.C.S.: 561499

Accenture AG (2)
Fraumunsterstrasse 16, 8001, Zurich, Switzerland   (100%)
Tel.: (41) 442199889
Sales Range: $125-149.9 Million
Emp.: 1,000
Various Business Services
N.A.I.C.S.: 561499

Accenture Argentina (2)
Roque Saenz Pena 777, Buenos Aires, 1035, Argentina   (100%)
Tel.: (54) 1143188500
Sales Range: $550-599.9 Million
Emp.: 5,000
Business Services
N.A.I.C.S.: 561499

Accenture Australia (2)
Level 5/161 Collins Street, Melbourne, 3000, VIC, Australia   (100%)
Tel.: (61) 398387000
Sales Range: $250-299.9 Million
Emp.: 2,000
Business Services
N.A.I.C.S.: 561499

Accenture Austria (2)
Borsegebaude Schottenring 16, 1010, Vienna, Austria   (100%)

Tel.: (43) 1205020
Sales Range: $75-99.9 Million
Emp.: 500
Business Services
N.A.I.C.S.: 561499

Accenture Automacao e TI Industrial Ltda (2)
Afonso Pena 4 001 9 Andar Funcionarios, 30130-008, Belo Horizonte, Minas Gerais, Brazil
Tel.: (55) 3132897700
Web Site: http://www.accenture.com
Software Development Services
N.A.I.C.S.: 541511

Accenture BPM S.A. (2)
1 Arkadias, Kifissia, 14564, Greece
Tel.: (30) 2106781400
Web Site: http://www.accenture.com
Emp.: 380
Business Process Outsourcing Services
N.A.I.C.S.: 561499

Accenture BPM is Yonetimi Limited Sirketi (2)
Rbs Binasi 13 Tamburi Ali Efendi Sokak, Istanbul, 34337, Turkiye
Tel.: (90) 2123493200
Web Site: http://www.acccenture.com
Sales Range: $75-99.9 Million
Emp.: 350
Business Process Outsourcing Services
N.A.I.C.S.: 561499

Accenture BV (2)
Gustav Mahlerplein 90, 1082 MA, Amsterdam, Netherlands
Tel.: (31) 204938383
Information Technology Consulting Services
N.A.I.C.S.: 541512
Anja Montijn-Groenewoud (Grp CEO-Resources & Country Mng Dir)

Accenture Belgium (2)
Picardstraat 11 Rue Picard bus/boite 100, 1000, Brussels, Belgium   (100%)
Tel.: (32) 22267211
Sales Range: $250-299.9 Million
Emp.: 1,400
Business Services
N.A.I.C.S.: 561499

Subsidiary (Domestic):

Accenture Technology Solutions (ATS) NV (3)
Medialaan 38, 1800, Vilvoorde, Belgium
Tel.: (32) 2 226 72 11
Web Site: http://www.accenture.com
Information Technology Consulting Services
N.A.I.C.S.: 541512

Subsidiary (Non-US):

Accenture Branch Holdings B.V. (2)
Tel.: (31) 204938383
Web Site: http://www.accenture.com
Investment Management Service
N.A.I.C.S.: 523999

Accenture Brazil (2)
Rio Metropolitan Building Avenida Republica Do Chile 500 18, Andar - Centro, Rio de Janeiro, 20031-170, Brazil
Tel.: (55) 2145019000
Sales Range: $25-49.9 Million
Emp.: 80
Business Services
N.A.I.C.S.: 561499

Accenture Business Services for Utilities Inc. (2)
401 West Georgia Street Suite 1400, Vancouver, V6B 5A1, BC, Canada
Tel.: (604) 663-3800
Business Process Outsourcing Services
N.A.I.C.S.: 561499

Accenture Business Services of British Columbia Limited Partnership (2)
401 Georgia St W 14th Floor, Vancouver, V6B 5A1, BC, Canada
Tel.: (604) 663-3800
Web Site: http://www.accenture.com
Business Process Outsourcing Services
N.A.I.C.S.: 561499

Accenture C.A. (2)

Centro SegurosLa Paz Piso 7 Ala Noreste Avenida Francisco de Miranda, La California Norte, Caracas, 1070, Venezuela
Tel.: (58) 2122735000
Web Site: http://www.accenture.com
Sales Range: $25-49.9 Million
Emp.: 80
Management Consulting & Technology Services
N.A.I.C.S.: 541611

Accenture Canada (2)
145 King St West Ste 1401, Toronto, M5H 1J8, ON, Canada (100%)
Tel.: (416) 641-5220
Web Site: http://www.accenture.com
Sales Range: $25-49.9 Million
Emp.: 130
Business Services
N.A.I.C.S.: 561499
Piyush Bhatnagar (Mng Dir)

Accenture Canada Holdings Inc. (2)
5450 Explorer Dr Ste 400, Mississauga, L4W 5M1, ON, Canada
Tel.: (416) 641-5000
Sales Range: $550-599.9 Million
Emp.: 1,800
Investment Management Service
N.A.I.C.S.: 551112
Dave Seibel (Mng Dir)

Accenture Central Europe B. V. (2)
V Parku 2316/12, Chodov, 148 00, Prague, 4, Czech Republic (100%)
Tel.: (420) 221984545
Sales Range: $25-49.9 Million
Emp.: 200
Business Services
N.A.I.C.S.: 561499
Nauirzio Barini (Mng Dir)

Accenture Central Europe B.V. (2)
Versterkerstraat 6, 1322 AP, Almere, Netherlands
Tel.: (31) 36 546 14 70
Web Site: http://www.accenture.com
Business Management Consulting Services
N.A.I.C.S.: 541611

Accenture Chile Asesorias y Servicios Ltda. (2)
Rosario Norte 530 Piso 6, Las Condes, 7561186, Santiago, Chile (100%)
Tel.: (56) 23377100
Web Site: http://www.accenture.com
Sales Range: $125-149.9 Million
Emp.: 600
Business Services
N.A.I.C.S.: 561499
Rodrigo Gonzalez (Pres)

Accenture Co Ltd. (2)
88 The ParQ Building 9th Floor Ratchadaphisek Rd, Khlong Toei, Bangkok, 10110, Thailand
Tel.: (66) 26361616
Sales Range: $75-99.9 Million
Emp.: 40
Business Process Outsourcing Services
N.A.I.C.S.: 561499

Accenture Co. Ltd. (Taiwan) (2)
218 Tun Hwa S Rd Sec 2 21st Fl Cathay Taipei Intl Bldg B, Taipei, 106, Taiwan (100%)
Tel.: (886) 221926030
Sales Range: $10-24.9 Million
Emp.: 50
Various Business Services
N.A.I.C.S.: 561499
Kevin Liu (Gen Mgr)

Accenture Colombia (2)
Carrera 7 Numero 71-52, Torre A Oficina 706, Bogota, Colombia (100%)
Tel.: (57) 3131000
Web Site: http://www.accenture.com
Business Services
N.A.I.C.S.: 561499

Accenture Company Ltd. (2)
85 Floor International Commerce Center 1 Austin Road West, Kowloon, China (Hong Kong)
Tel.: (852) 22492388
Web Site: http://www.accenture.com
Sales Range: $10-24.9 Million
Emp.: 20
Business Services

N.A.I.C.S.: 561499

Accenture Consultores de Gestao S.A. (2)
Santos Building Rua Boqueirao do Duro n 37, 1200-163, Lisbon, Portugal
Tel.: (351) 213803500
Emp.: 50
Business Management Consulting Services
N.A.I.C.S.: 541611

Accenture Danismanlik Limited Sirketi (2)
Esentepe Mahallesi Yuzbasi Kaya Aldogan Sk No 4/4 Sisli, Istanbul, Turkiye
Tel.: (90) 2123493200
Sales Range: $100-124.9 Million
Emp.: 500
Management Consulting & Technology Services
N.A.I.C.S.: 541611

Accenture Denmark (2)
Bohrsgade 35, PO Box 2677, 1799, Copenhagen, Denmark (100%)
Tel.: (45) 72288000
Sales Range: $125-149.9 Million
Emp.: 550
Business Services
N.A.I.C.S.: 561499
Philip Wiig (Mng Dir)

Accenture Denmark Holdings A/S (2)
Tel.: (45) 72288000
Emp.: 50
Investment Management Service
N.A.I.C.S.: 523999

Accenture Dienstleistungen GmbH (2)
Campus Kronberg 1, 61476, Kronberg, Germany (100%)
Tel.: (49) 61739499
Web Site: https://www.accenture.com
Sales Range: $25-49.9 Million
Emp.: 200
Business Services
N.A.I.C.S.: 561499
Frank Riemensperger (Gen Mgr)

Accenture Finance and Accounting BPO Services SpA (2)
Via Strada 4 Palazzo Q, Rozzano, 20089, Italy
Tel.: (39) 0257581
Financial Business Process Outsourcing Services
N.A.I.C.S.: 561499

Accenture GmbH (2)
Campus Kronberg 1, Hessen, 61476, Kronberg, Germany (100%)
Tel.: (49) 61739499
Sales Range: $25-49.9 Million
Emp.: 5,000
Business Services
N.A.I.C.S.: 561499

Accenture GmbH (2)
Borsegebaude Schottenring 16, 1010, Vienna, Austria
Tel.: (43) 1205020
Management Consulting & Technology Services
N.A.I.C.S.: 541611
Frank Riemensperger (Chm)

Accenture Healthcare Processing Inc. (2)
27F GT Tower International Ayala Ave Cor HV dela Costa St, H V Dela Costa Street, Makati, 1226, Philippines
Tel.: (63) 28410111
Business Process Outsourcing Services
N.A.I.C.S.: 561499

Accenture Holding GmbH & Co. KG (2)
Campus Kronberg 1, Taunus, 61476, Kronberg, Germany
Tel.: (49) 61739499
Investment Management Service
N.A.I.C.S.: 523999

Accenture Holdings (Iberia) S.L. (2)
Edificio Torre Picasso Plaza Pablo Ruiz Picasso s/n, Madrid, 28020, Spain
Tel.: (34) 915967000
Web Site: http://www.accenture.com

Investment Management Service
N.A.I.C.S.: 523999

Accenture Holdings B.V. (2)
Tel.: (31) 204938383
Web Site: http://www.accenture.com
Investment Management Service
N.A.I.C.S.: 523999

Accenture Human Capital Mgmt. Sol. S.L. (2)
Avinguda Diagonal 615, 8028, Barcelona, Spain
Tel.: (34) 93 227 10 00
Financial Investment Services
N.A.I.C.S.: 523999

Accenture Inc. (2)
Sun Life Plaza Suite 300 140 4th Avenue SW, Calgary, T2P 3N3, AB, Canada
Tel.: (403) 476-1510
Web Site: http://www.accenture.com
Sales Range: $50-74.9 Million
Emp.: 200
Management Consulting & Technology Services
N.A.I.C.S.: 541611

Accenture Inc. (2)
Makati Stock Exchange Bldg Ayala Avenue, Makati, Philippines
Tel.: (63) 29082100
Web Site: http://www.accenture.com
Management Consulting & Technology Services
N.A.I.C.S.: 541611

Accenture India Private Ltd. (2)
Worldmark 3 5th floor Asset Area No 7 Delhi Aerocity, Hospitality District Near Indira Gandhi International Airport, New Delhi, 110 037, India (100%)
Tel.: (91) 1140341300
Sales Range: $10-24.9 Million
Emp.: 50
Business Services
N.A.I.C.S.: 561499

Accenture International Capital SCA (2)
Avenue J F Kennedy 46a, Luxembourg, 1855, Luxembourg
Tel.: (352) 26 423 1
Investment Management Service
N.A.I.C.S.: 523999

Accenture International Sarl (2)
Avenue J F Kennedy 46a, Luxembourg, 1855, Luxembourg
Tel.: (352) 264231
Sales Range: $25-49.9 Million
Emp.: 6
Information Technology Consulting Services
N.A.I.C.S.: 541512
Pascal Denis (Gen Mgr)

Accenture Japan Ltd. (2)
1-11-44 Akasaka Akasaka Intercity, Minato-ku, Tokyo, 107-8672, Japan
Tel.: (81) 335883000
Business Services
N.A.I.C.S.: 561499
Chikatomo Hodo (Chm)

Subsidiary (Domestic):

ALBERT Inc. (3)
Shinjuku Front Tower 15F 2-21-1, Kita-Shinjuku Shinjuku-ku, Tokyo, 169-0074, Japan (100%)
Tel.: (81) 359097525
Web Site: http://www.albert2005.co.jp
Sales Range: $1-9.9 Million
Emp.: 40
Data Management & Analytics Consulting Services
N.A.I.C.S.: 518210
Yoshisuke Yamakawa (Chm & CEO)

Subsidiary (Non-US):

Accenture Ltd. (2)
11 Galgalei Haplada Street, Herzliyya, 46733, Israel
Tel.: (972) 9961 9600
Sales Range: $25-49.9 Million
Emp.: 2
Management Consulting Services
N.A.I.C.S.: 541618

Accenture Ltd. Nigeria (2)

2nd Floor Citi Bank Building, 27 Kofo Abayomi Street, Victoria Island, 1712, Lagos, Nigeria (100%)
Tel.: (234) 12707100
Business Services
N.A.I.C.S.: 561499

Accenture Ltda (2)
Carrera 7 Numero 71-52 Torre A Piso 10, Bogota, Colombia
Tel.: (57) 13266400
Sales Range: $25-49.9 Million
Emp.: 250
Business Process Outsourcing Services
N.A.I.C.S.: 561499
Beatriz Carmona (Gen Mgr)

Accenture Management GmbH (2)
Campus Kronberg 1, 61476, Kronberg, Germany (100%)
Tel.: (49) 61739499
Sales Range: $250-299.9 Million
Emp.: 5,000
Business Management Services
N.A.I.C.S.: 561110
Frank Riemensperger (Sr Mng Dir)

Accenture Mauritius Ltd. (2)
Royal Road Cassis, Port Louis, Mauritius
Tel.: (230) 2032600
Sales Range: $150-199.9 Million
Emp.: 800
Business Process Outsourcing Services
N.A.I.C.S.: 561499

Subsidiary (Domestic):

Accenture (Mauritius) Onshore Ltd. (3)
NexTeracom Tower 2 9th Floor, Ebene, Mauritius
Tel.: (230) 4021700
Business Process Outsourcing Services
N.A.I.C.S.: 561499

Subsidiary (Non-US):

Accenture Middle East B.V. (2)
Gustav Mahlerplein 90, 1082 MA, Amsterdam, Netherlands
Tel.: (31) 204938383
Business Process Outsourcing Services
N.A.I.C.S.: 561499

Accenture NV SA (2)
Waterloolaan 16 boulevard de Waterloo, 1000, Brussels, Belgium
Tel.: (32) 22267211
Web Site: http://www.accenture.com
Sales Range: $25-49.9 Million
Emp.: 120
Business Process Outsourcing Services
N.A.I.C.S.: 561499
Olivier Gillerod (Mng Dir)

Accenture OOO (2)
2 Str 2 Paveletskaya Pl, Moscow, 115054, Russia
Tel.: (7) 4957559770
Web Site: http://www.accenture.com
Emp.: 700
Business Process Outsourcing Services
N.A.I.C.S.: 561499

Accenture Outsourcing Services S.A. (2)
Paseo De La Finca Bl 2d 1, Pozuelo de Alarcon, 28223, Spain
Tel.: (34) 915966000
Web Site: http://www.accenture.com
Business Process Outsourcing Services
N.A.I.C.S.: 561499

Accenture Oy (2)
Porkkalankatu 5, 00180, Helsinki, Finland (100%)
Tel.: (358) 205725000
Web Site: https://www.accenture.com
Sales Range: $250-299.9 Million
Emp.: 1,100
Business Services
N.A.I.C.S.: 561499
Tuomas Lattu (Mng Dir-Tech)

Accenture Participations BV (2)
Gustav Mahlerplein 90, 1082 MA, Amsterdam, Netherlands
Tel.: (31) 204938383
Business Process Outsourcing Services
N.A.I.C.S.: 561499

Accenture plc—(Continued)

Accenture Pte. Ltd. (2)
35-00 Raffles City Tower 250 North Bridge
Road, Singapore, 179101,
Singapore (100%)
Tel.: (65) 64108000
Web Site: https://www.accenture.com
Sales Range: $150-199.9 Million
Emp.: 4,010
Business Services
N.A.I.C.S.: 541511
Caspar Schlickum (Mng Dir-Interactive-
South East Asia & Growth Markets)

Accenture S.A. (2)
1 Arcadias Str, Kifissia, 14564, Athens,
Greece
Tel.: (30) 2106781400
Web Site: https://www.accenture.com
Emp.: 35
Business Process Outsourcing Services
N.A.I.C.S.: 561611
Evangelia Pateraki (Country Mgr)

Accenture S.C. (2)
Torre Arcos Bosques II Paseo de los Tama-
rindos No 90 Torre 2 Piso 26, Col Bosques
de las Lomas Deleg Cuajimalpa de More-
los, 05120, Mexico, Mexico
Tel.: (52) 5552847300
Web Site: https://www.accenture.com
Management & Technical Consulting Ser-
vices
N.A.I.C.S.: 541618

Accenture SAS (2)
118 Avenue de France, 75013, Paris,
France (100%)
Tel.: (33) 153235555
Web Site: http://www.accenture.fr
Sales Range: $550-599.9 Million
Emp.: 4,000
Business Services
N.A.I.C.S.: 561499

Subsidiary (Domestic):

Accenture Holdings France SAS (3)
118 Avenue De France, 75013, Paris,
France
Tel.: (33) 153235555
Sales Range: $1-4.9 Billion
Emp.: 3,000
Investment Management Service
N.A.I.C.S.: 551112

**Accenture Technology Solutions
SAS** (3)
125 Avenue de Paris, 92320, Chatillon,
France
Tel.: (33) 472831620
Web Site: http://www.accenture.com
Management Consulting & Technology Ser-
vices
N.A.I.C.S.: 541611
Roxanne Taylor (CMO & Chief Comm Offi-
cer)

Octo Technology SA (3)
34 avenue de l'Opera, 75002, Paris,
France (94.88%)
Tel.: (33) 158561000
Information Systems Design & IT Consult-
ing Services
N.A.I.C.S.: 541512
Francois Hisquin (CEO)

Subsidiary (Non-US):

Accenture Sarl (2)
7 Rue Lou Hemmer, Niederanven, 1748,
Luxembourg, Luxembourg
Tel.: (352) 264231
Web Site: https://www.accenture.com
Sales Range: $25-49.9 Million
Emp.: 129
Business Process Outsourcing Services
N.A.I.C.S.: 561499
Olivier Gillerot (Mng Dir-Belgium)

Accenture Sdn. Bhd. (2)
Level 66 Twr 2 Petronas Twin, KLCC
50088, Kuala Lumpur, Malaysia (100%)
Tel.: (60) 327314000
Business Services
N.A.I.C.S.: 561499

Accenture Service Center SRL (2)
RSP Building Roque Saenz Pena 777,

Capital Federal, Buenos Aires, C1035AAC,
Argentina
Tel.: (54) 1143188500
Web Site: http://www.accenture.com
Emp.: 8,000
Management Consulting & Technology Ser-
vices
N.A.I.C.S.: 541611

**Accenture Service Centre Morocco
SA** (2)
Park Casanearshore Shore 1100 Bd Ei
Qods, Casablanca, 20270, Morocco
Tel.: (212) 522461950
Web Site: http://www.accenture.com
Sales Range: $25-49.9 Million
Emp.: 17
Business Process Outsourcing Services
N.A.I.C.S.: 561499

**Accenture Services (Mauritius)
Ltd.** (2)
Royal Road Cassis, Port Louis, Mauritius
Tel.: (230) 2032600
Web Site: http://www.accenture.com
Management Consulting & Technology Ser-
vices
N.A.I.C.S.: 541611

**Accenture Services (South Africa) Pty
Ltd.** (2)
Bld 19 Harrowdene Office Park Kelvin
Drive, Johannesburg, 2191, Gauteng, South
Africa
Tel.: (27) 112083000
Web Site: http://www.accenture.com
Sales Range: $350-399.9 Million
Emp.: 200
Management Consulting Services
N.A.I.C.S.: 541618
Vukani Mngxati (Mng Dir)

Accenture Services AG (2)
Fraumunsterstrasse 16, 8001, Zurich, Swit-
zerland
Tel.: (41) 442199889
Sales Range: $150-199.9 Million
Emp.: 700
Business Process Outsourcing Services
N.A.I.C.S.: 561499
Thomas Meyer (Mng Dir)

Accenture Services GmbH (2)
Campus Kronberg 1, 61476, Kronberg, Ger-
many
Tel.: (49) 61739499
Sales Range: $150-199.9 Million
Emp.: 100
Business Process Outsourcing Services
N.A.I.C.S.: 561499

Accenture Services Oy (2)
Itamerenkatu 1, 180, Helsinki, Finland
Tel.: (358) 205725000
Web Site: http://www.accenture.com
Emp.: 130
Business Process Outsourcing Services
N.A.I.C.S.: 561499
Stefan Damlin (CEO)

Accenture Services Private Ltd. (2)
6th Fl DLF Ctr Sansad Marg, New Delhi,
110 001, India (100%)
Tel.: (91) 1142980100
Web Site: http://www.accenture.com
Sales Range: $25-49.9 Million
Emp.: 100
Business Services
N.A.I.C.S.: 561499

Accenture Services S.r.l. (2)
24 Preciziei Bd Westgate Office Park H1
Building 1st Floor, 6th district, Bucharest,
62204, Romania
Tel.: (40) 372286000
Web Site: http://www.accenture.com
Management Consulting & Technology Ser-
vices
N.A.I.C.S.: 541611

Accenture Services Sp. z.o.o. (2)
ul Chocimska 17, 00-791, Warsaw, Poland
Tel.: (48) 223497000
Sales Range: $150-199.9 Million
Emp.: 60
Business Process Outsourcing Services
N.A.I.C.S.: 561499
Wojciech Poplawski (Dir)

Accenture Services s.r.o (2)

Bucharova 8, 158 00, Prague, Czech Re-
public
Tel.: (420) 225045000
Sales Range: $150-199.9 Million
Emp.: 800
Business Process Outsourcing Services
N.A.I.C.S.: 561499

Accenture Services s.r.o. (2)
Plynarenska 7/C Street, Bratislava, 02109,
Slovakia
Tel.: (421) 259290290
Web Site: http://www.accenture.com
Business Process Outsourcing Services
N.A.I.C.S.: 561499

Accenture Solutions Co. Ltd. (2)
30th Fl Abdulrahim Pl, 990 Rama IV Rd,
10500, Bangkok, Thailand (100%)
Tel.: (66) 26361616
Sales Range: $25-49.9 Million
Emp.: 400
Various Business Services
N.A.I.C.S.: 561499

Accenture Solutions Sdn Bhd (2)
Level 35 The Gardens North Tower Mid Val-
ley City, Lingkaran Syed Putra, Kuala Lum-
pur, 59200, Malaysia
Tel.: (60) 320884000
Web Site: http://www.accenture.com
Management Consulting & Technology Ser-
vices
N.A.I.C.S.: 541611

Accenture Sp. z.o.o. (2)
Ul Sienna 39, Warsaw, 121,
Poland (100%)
Tel.: (48) 225288000
Web Site: http://www.accenture.pl
Sales Range: $250-299.9 Million
Emp.: 1,100
Business Services
N.A.I.C.S.: 561499

Accenture SpA (2)
Via Maurizio Quadrio 17, 20154, Milan,
Italy (100%)
Tel.: (39) 0277751111
Sales Range: $25-49.9 Million
Emp.: 100
Management Consulting, Technology & Out-
sourcing Services
N.A.I.C.S.: 561499

**Accenture Tanacsado Korlatolt Felel-
ossegu Tarsasag KFT** (2)
Rakoczi u 1-3, Budapest, 1088, Hungary
Tel.: (36) 13273700
Web Site: http://www.accenture.hu
Software Development Services
N.A.I.C.S.: 541511

**Accenture Technolgy Solutions (Thai-
land) Ltd.** (2)
30th Floor Abdulrahim Place 990 Rama IV
Road, Silom Bangrak, Bangkok, 10500,
Thailand
Tel.: (66) 2 636 1616
Web Site: http://www.accenture.com
Information Technology Consulting Services
N.A.I.C.S.: 541512

**Accenture Technology Services
Ltda.** (2)
Rua Alexandre Dumas 2051 Chacara,
Santo Antonio, Sao Paulo, 04717-004,
Brazil (100%)
Tel.: (55) 1151883000
Technology Services
N.A.I.C.S.: 561499

**Accenture Technology Solutions (Da-
lian) Co Ltd.** (2)
No 1 North Section Digital Road, Dalian,
116023, China
Tel.: (86) 41182147800
Business Process Outsourcing Services
N.A.I.C.S.: 561499

**Accenture Technology Solutions (HK)
Co. Ltd.** (2)
85 Fl International Commerce Center, 1
Austin Rd W, Kowloon, China (Hong Kong)
Tel.: (852) 22492388
Sales Range: $25-49.9 Million
Emp.: 150
Technology Services
N.A.I.C.S.: 561499

**Accenture Technology Solutions
A/S** (2)
Arne Jacobsens Alle, Orestad, Copenha-
gen, 2300, Denmark
Tel.: (45) 72288188
Business Process Outsourcing Services
N.A.I.C.S.: 561499

**Accenture Technology Solutions
BV** (2)
Gustav Mahlerplein 90, 1082 MA, Amster-
dam, Netherlands
Tel.: (31) 204938383
Web Site: http://www.accenture.com
Sales Range: $150-199.9 Million
Emp.: 800
Information Technology Consulting Services
N.A.I.C.S.: 541511

**Accenture Technology Solutions
GmbH** (2)
Kronberg 1 Campus, Kronberg, 61476,
Germany (100%)
Tel.: (49) 61739499
Sales Range: $550-599.9 Million
Emp.: 5,000
Technology Services
N.A.I.C.S.: 561499

**Accenture Technology Solutions
GmbH** (2)
Boersengebaeude Schottenring 16, 1010,
Vienna, Austria
Tel.: (43) 1 205020
Business Process Outsourcing Services
N.A.I.C.S.: 561499

**Accenture Technology Solutions
Ltd.** (2)
10th Fl Posco P&S Tower 735-3 Yeoksam-
Dong, Gangnam-Gu, Seoul, 135-923, Korea
(South)
Tel.: (82) 237778888
Web Site: http://www.accenture.com
Emp.: 300
Management Consulting & Technology Ser-
vices
N.A.I.C.S.: 541611

**Accenture Technology Solutions
Oy** (2)
Porkkalankatu 5, 00180, Helsinki,
Finland (100%)
Tel.: (358) 205725000
Sales Range: $125-149.9 Million
Emp.: 950
Technology Services
N.A.I.C.S.: 561499
Pasi Koivunen (Mng Dir)

**Accenture Technology Solutions Pte
Ltd.** (2)
250 North Bridge Road 33-00 Raffles City
Tower, Singapore, 179101, Singapore
Tel.: (65) 6410 8000
Information Technology Consulting Services
N.A.I.C.S.: 541512

**Accenture Technology Solutions Pty
Ltd.** (2)
Level 30 10 Eagle Street, Brisbane, 4000,
QLD, Australia
Tel.: (61) 731174001
Management Consulting & Technology Ser-
vices
N.A.I.C.S.: 541611

**Accenture Technology Solutions
S.A.** (2)
Avenida da Boavista n 1837 Edificio Torre
Burgo 13 Andar Sala 3, 4100-133, Porto,
Portugal
Tel.: (351) 229471430
Information Technology Consulting Services
N.A.I.C.S.: 541512

**Accenture Technology Solutions
S.C.** (2)
Blvd Manuel Avila Camacho No 138 Piso 7
Lomas de Chapultepec, Mexico, 11000,
Mexico
Tel.: (52) 5552847300
Web Site: http://www.accenture.com
Management Consulting & Technology Ser-
vices
N.A.I.C.S.: 541611

**Accenture Technology Solutions
SRL** (2)

Via Maurizio Quadrio 17, Milan, 20154, Italy
Tel.: (39) 0277751111
Web Site:
http://www.accenturetechnologysolutions.it
Information Technology Consulting Services
N.A.I.C.S.: 541512

Accenture Technology Solutions Sdn Bhd (2)
Level 35 The Gardens North Tower Mid Valley City Lingkaran Syed Putra, 59200, Kuala Lumpur, Malaysia
Tel.: (60) 320884000
Web Site:
http://www.accenturetechnologysolutions.it
Sales Range: $150-199.9 Million
Emp.: 1,000
Information Technology Consulting Services
N.A.I.C.S.: 541512

Accenture Technology Solutions s.r.o. (2)
V Parku 12, 120 00, Prague, Czech Republic
Tel.: (420) 221984545
Web Site: http://www.accenture.com
Management Consulting & Technology Services
N.A.I.C.S.: 541611

Accenture Technology Solutions-Canada, Inc. (2)
630 Blvd Rene-Levesque Ouest, Montreal, H3B 1S6, QC, Canada
Tel.: (514) 848-1648
Web Site: http://www.accenture.com
Sales Range: $75-99.9 Million
Emp.: 30
Business Process Outsourcing Services
N.A.I.C.S.: 561499

Accenture Technology Solutions-Slovakia s.r.o. (2)
Plynarenska 7/C, Bratislava, 821 09, Slovakia
Tel.: (421) 259290290
Information Technology Consulting Services
N.A.I.C.S.: 541512

Accenture Technology Solutions-Solucoes Informaticas Integrados, S.A. (2)
Avenida Eng Duarte Pacheco Amoreiras Torre 1-16 Piso, 1070-101, Lisbon, Portugal
Tel.: (351) 213803500
Business Process Outsourcing Services
N.A.I.C.S.: 561499
Jose Galamba de Oliveira (Mng Dir)

Accenture Technology Ventures BV (2)
Gustav Mahlerplein 90, 1082 MA, Amsterdam, Netherlands
Tel.: (31) 204938383
Web Site: https://www.accenture.com
Management Consulting & Technology Services
N.A.I.C.S.: 541611

Accenture Technology Ventures S.P.R.L. (2)
Rue Royale 145 Koningsstraat, Brussels, 1000, Belgium
Tel.: (32) 22267211
Information Technology Consulting Services
N.A.I.C.S.: 541512

Accenture Turkey (2)
Teknopark Istanbul Sanayi Mah, Teknopark Bulvari D Blok No 1/5A Ic Kapi No 201 TR Pendik, 34906, Istanbul, Turkiye **(100%)**
Tel.: (90) 2166252002
Web Site: https://www.accenture.com
Sales Range: $25-49.9 Million
Emp.: 200
Business Consulting Services
N.A.I.C.S.: 561499

Accenture do Brasil Ltda (2)
Rua Alexandre Dumas 2051, Chacara Santo Antonio, Sao Paulo, 04717-004, Brazil
Tel.: (55) 1151883000
Emp.: 500
Business Process Outsourcing Services
N.A.I.C.S.: 561499

Accenture s.r.o. (2)
Plynarenska 7/C, 821 09, Bratislava, Slovakia **(100%)**

Tel.: (421) 259290290
Web Site: https://www.accenture.com
Sales Range: $125-149.9 Million
Emp.: 1,000
Various Business Services
N.A.I.C.S.: 561499

Subsidiary (US):

Accenture, Inc. (2)
500 W Madison St, Chicago, IL 60661-4544
Tel.: (312) 693-5009
Sales Range: $600-649.9 Million
Emp.: 5,000
Business Management, Outsourcing & Technology Consulting Services
N.A.I.C.S.: 541611

Subsidiary (Domestic):

Accenture 2, Inc. (3)
1345 Ave, New York, NY 10105-0103
Tel.: (917) 452-4400
Business Process Outsourcing Services
N.A.I.C.S.: 561499

Accenture Capital Inc. (3)
1501 S MoPac Ste 300, Austin, TX 78746
Tel.: (512) 732-5300
Web Site: http://www.accenture.com
Financial Investment Services
N.A.I.C.S.: 523999

Accenture Federal Services LLC (3)
800 N Glebe Rd Ste 300, Arlington, VA 22203
Tel.: (703) 947-2000
Web Site: http://www.accenture.com
Consulting Services to US Government
N.A.I.C.S.: 541618
John Goodman (CEO)

Subsidiary (Domestic):

ASM Research LLC (4)
4050 Legato Rd Ste 1100, Fairfax, VA 22033
Tel.: (703) 645-0420
Web Site: https://www.asmr.com
Sales Range: $50-74.9 Million
Emp.: 400
IT Services to Government Organizations
N.A.I.C.S.: 519290
John Fraser (Pres)

Cognosante LLC (4)
3110 Fairview Park Dr Ste 800, Falls Church, VA 22042
Tel.: (703) 206-6000
Web Site: http://www.cognosante.com
Healthcare Consulting Technology Solutions & Business Process Outsourcing Services
N.A.I.C.S.: 541690
Michele Kang (Founder & CEO)

Subsidiary (Domestic):

Business Information Technology Solutions, Inc. (5)
3190 Fairview Park Dr Ste 350, Falls Church, VA 22042
Tel.: (703) 822-0970
Web Site: https://www.thebitsgroup.com
Sales Range: $10-24.9 Million
Emp.: 80
Information Technology Services
N.A.I.C.S.: 541519
Zach McQuay (Dir-Ops)

Enterprise Information Services, Inc. (5)
1945 Old Gallows Rd Fl 5 Ste 500, Vienna, VA 22182-3931
Tel.: (703) 749-0007
Web Site: https://www.goeis.com
Sales Range: $10-24.9 Million
Emp.: 215
Systems Engineering & Software Development Services for the Federal Government
N.A.I.C.S.: 541512
Vinod Goyal (Founder, Co-Pres & CEO)

Subsidiary (Domestic):

Accenture Financial Corporation (3)
300 Campus Dr, Florham Park, NJ 07932
Tel.: (973) 301-1000
Financial Management Services
N.A.I.C.S.: 523999

Accenture LLC (3)

1120 S Tryon St, Charlotte, NC 28203
Tel.: (704) 332-6411
Business Process Outsourcing Services
N.A.I.C.S.: 561499

Subsidiary (Non-US):

Avanade Inc. (3)
Guldensporenpark 76 BLOK H, 9820, Merelbeke, Belgium
Tel.: (206) 239-5600
Web Site: https://www.avanade.com
Sales Range: $50-74.9 Million
Managed IT Services
N.A.I.C.S.: 541511
Stella Goulet (CMO)

Subsidiary (Non-US):

Avanade Asia Pte Ltd. (4)
250 North Bridge Road 30-03 Raffles City Tower, No 30-03 Raffles City Tower, Singapore, 179101, Singapore
Tel.: (65) 65922133
Application Program Development & Outsourcing Services
N.A.I.C.S.: 541511

Avanade Australia Pty Ltd. (4)
Level 30 10 Eagle Street, Brisbane, 4000, QLD, Australia
Tel.: (61) 731174540
Application Program Development & Outsourcing Services
N.A.I.C.S.: 541511

Subsidiary (Domestic):

Avanade Belgium SPRL (4)
Porien Park no 76, 1800, Merelbeke, Belgium
Tel.: (32) 22267774
Web Site: http://www.avanade.com
Application Program Development & Outsourcing Services
N.A.I.C.S.: 541511

Subsidiary (Non-US):

Avanade Canada Inc. (4)
140 4th Avenue West Suite 300, Calgary, T2P 3N3Â , AB, Canada
Tel.: (403) 774-9555
Web Site: http://www.avanade.com
Application Program Development & Outsourcing Services
N.A.I.C.S.: 541511
Andre Nadeau (Mng Dir)

Avanade Denmark ApS (4)
Bohrsgade 35, 1799, Copenhagen, Denmark
Tel.: (45) 70107172
Sales Range: $25-49.9 Million
Emp.: 60
Management Consulting & Technology Services
N.A.I.C.S.: 541611

Avanade Deutschland GmbH (4)
Campus Kronberg 1, 61476, Kronberg, Germany
Tel.: (49) 61739463800
Web Site: https://www.avanade.com
Sales Range: $25-49.9 Million
Emp.: 50
Application Program Development & Outsourcing Services
N.A.I.C.S.: 541511
Robert Gogele (Gen Mgr-Austria & Switzerland)

Avanade Finland Oy (4)
Porkkalankatu 5, 00180, Helsinki, Finland
Tel.: (358) 207433380
Application Program Development & Outsourcing Services
N.A.I.C.S.: 541511

Avanade France (4)
125 avenue de Paris, 92320, Chatillon, France
Tel.: (33) 147466600
Rev.: $15,500,000
Emp.: 79
N.A.I.C.S.: 541611

Avanade Guangzhou (4)
Unit 7 10th Floor The Hna Tower No 8 Linhe Zhong Lu, Tianhe District, Guangzhou, 510610, Guangdong, China

Tel.: (86) 2028317367
Web Site: http://www.avanade.com
Application Program Development & Outsourcing Services
N.A.I.C.S.: 541511

Avanade Italy SRL (4)
Via del Mulino 11 A, 20057, Assago, Italy
Tel.: (39) 02760491
N.A.I.C.S.: 541511

Avanade Japan KK (4)
Izumi Garden Tower 1-6-1 Roppongi, Minato-ku, Tokyo, 106-6009, Japan
Tel.: (81) 362340150
Application Program Development & Outsourcing Services
N.A.I.C.S.: 541511

Avanade Malaysia Sdn Bhd (4)
Suite 29 07 Level 29 Menara Exchange 106 Lingkaran TRX, Tun Razak Exchange, 55188, Kuala Lumpur, Malaysia
Tel.: (60) 320887111
Web Site: https://www.avanade.com
Sales Range: $25-49.9 Million
Emp.: 70
Application Program Development & Outsourcing Services
N.A.I.C.S.: 541511

Avanade Netherlands BV (4)
Amplifier Street 6, Almere, 1322 AP, Netherlands
Tel.: (31) 365475100
Web Site: http://www.avanade.com
Sales Range: $75-99.9 Million
Emp.: 370
Application Program Development & Outsourcing Services
N.A.I.C.S.: 541511
Johann Corlemeijer (Country Dir-Belux)

Avanade Norway AS (4)
Rolfsbuktveien 2, 1364, Fornebu, Norway
Tel.: (47) 67128570
Application Program Development & Outsourcing Services
N.A.I.C.S.: 541511
Goran Karlsson (Sr Dir-Bus Dev)

Avanade Schweiz GmbH (4)
Peter Merian-Strasse 90, 4052, Basel, Switzerland
Tel.: (41) 43 430 43 43
Application Program Development & Outsourcing Services
N.A.I.C.S.: 541511
Andrew Smith (Gen Mgr)

Avanade South Africa (4)
Building 19 Harrowdene Office Park Kelvin Drive, Woodmead, Sandton, South Africa
Tel.: (27) 112083000
N.A.I.C.S.: 541512

Avanade Spain SL (4)
Passeig Sant Gervasi no 51 floor 4 module B, 08022, Barcelona, Spain
Tel.: (34) 934459300
Web Site: https://www.avanade.com
Application Program Development & Outsourcing Services
N.A.I.C.S.: 541511

Avanade Sweden AB (4)
Alstromergatan 12, Box 12502, 102 29, Stockholm, Sweden
Tel.: (46) 84021270
Application Program Development & Outsourcing Services
N.A.I.C.S.: 541511

Avanade UK Ltd. (4)
30 Fenchurch Street, London, EC3M 3BD, United Kingdom
Tel.: (44) 2070251000
Sales Range: $25-49.9 Million
Emp.: 300
Information Technology Consultants
N.A.I.C.S.: 611420

Avanade do Brasil Ltda (4)
Rua Alexandre Dumas 2 051 Ch Santo Antonio, Sao Paulo, 04717-004, Brazil
Tel.: (55) 1151883000
Sales Range: $75-99.9 Million
Emp.: 350
Application Program Development & Outsourcing Services
N.A.I.C.S.: 541511

Accenture plc—(Continued)

Concert Srl (4)
Via Adamello 5, 20099, Sesto San Giovanni, Italy
Tel.: (39) 02 23202460
Eletric Power Generation Services
N.A.I.C.S.: 221118
Sencer Aydin *(Pres)*

Subsidiary (Domestic):

Avventa Worldwide, LLC (3)
1150 Hungryneck Blvd, Mount Pleasant, SC 29464
Tel.: (843) 881-3515
Web Site: http://www.avventa.com
Sales Range: $10-24.9 Million
Emp.: 600
Motion Picture & Video Production Services
N.A.I.C.S.: 512110
David Matt *(Chief Creative Officer)*

BABCN LLC (3)
333 S 7th St Ste 500, Minneapolis, MN 55402-2443
Tel.: (612) 317-7777
Web Design Services
N.A.I.C.S.: 541511

Beacon Consulting Group, LLC (3)
407R Mystic Ave Ste 32C, Medford, MA 02155
Tel.: (781) 395-1650
Web Site: https://www.beacon.ws
N.A.I.C.S.: 541618
Dennis P. O'Neill *(Pres)*

Cloud Sherpas, Inc. (3)
3525 Piedmont Rd, Atlanta, GA 30305
Tel.: (888) 260-7660
Web Site: http://www.cloudsherpas.com
Sales Range: $100-124.9 Million
Emp.: 350
Cloud Infrastructure Design Solutions
N.A.I.C.S.: 541512
Gary DiOrio *(Pres-Salesforce Bus Unit)*

Corliant, Inc. (3)
1210 Northbrook Dr Ste100, Trevose, PA 19053
Tel.: (215) 244-5000
Web Site: http://www.corliant.com
Sales Range: $10-24.9 Million
Emp.: 150
Information Technology Consulting & Network Solution Services
N.A.I.C.S.: 541512

Davies Consulting Inc. (3)
6935 Wisconsin Ave, Chevy Chase, MD 20815
Tel.: (301) 652-4535
Administrative Management & General Management Consulting Service
N.A.I.C.S.: 541611
Grant Davies *(CEO)*

DayNine Consulting Inc. (3)
6200 Stoneridge Mall Rd Ste 250, Pleasanton, CA 94588
Tel.: (925) 475-5700
Web Site: http://www.daynine.com
Financial Management Services
N.A.I.C.S.: 523999

First Annapolis Consulting, Inc. (3)
3 Park Pl Ste 200, Annapolis, MD 21401
Tel.: (410) 855-8500
Web Site: http://www.firstannapolis.com
Emp.: 80
Management Consulting Services
N.A.I.C.S.: 541618

Gestalt, LLC (3)
1040 1st Ave, King of Prussia, PA 19406
Tel.: (610) 768-0800
Management Consulting Services
N.A.I.C.S.: 541618

Kurt Salmon Associates, Inc. (3)
1355 Peachtree St NE, Atlanta, GA 30309
Tel.: (404) 892-3436
Web Site: http://www.kurtsalmon.com
Management Consulting Services
N.A.I.C.S.: 541611

Mortgage Cadence LLC (3)
1999 Broadway Ste 1200, Denver, CO 80202-5738
Tel.: (303) 991-8200

Web Site: http://www.mortgagecadence.com
Real Estate Credit
N.A.I.C.S.: 522292
Brian K. Davis *(Chief Info & Platform Officer)*

NaviSys, Inc. (3)
499 Thornall St, Edison, NJ 08837
Tel.: (732) 549-3663
Sales Range: $125-149.9 Million
Emp.: 350
Developer of Insurance Software
N.A.I.C.S.: 513210

Octagon Research Solutions, Inc. (3)
585 E Swedesford Rd Ste 200, Wayne, PA 19087
Tel.: (610) 535-6500
Web Site: http://www.octagonresearch.com
Sales Range: $10-24.9 Million
Emp.: 150
Software Mfr
N.A.I.C.S.: 423430
Neal S. Walker *(Co-Founder)*

Origin Digital, Inc. (3)
1200 Harbor Blvd 8th Fl, Weehawken, NJ 07086
Tel.: (201) 537-8600
Web Site: http://www.origindigital.com
Sales Range: $25-49.9 Million
Emp.: 50
Video Capture, Transformation & Delivery Services
N.A.I.C.S.: 513210

SolutionsIQ, LLC (3)
6801 185th Ave NE Ste 200, Redmond, WA 98052-2727
Tel.: (425) 451-2727
Web Site: http://www.solutionsiq.com
Agile Transformation Services
N.A.I.C.S.: 541990
Charlie Rudd *(Mng Dir)*

Subsidiary (Non-US):

Accenture, S.L. (2)
Castellana 85 P de la Castellana 85, 28046, Madrid, Spain (100%)
Tel.: (34) 915966000
Web Site: https://www.accenture.com
Sales Range: $25-49.9 Million
Emp.: 100
Various Business Services
N.A.I.C.S.: 561499

Alnova Technologies Corporation S.L. (2)
Ramirez de Arellano 35, Madrid, 28043, Spain
Tel.: (34) 91 596 60 76
Web Site: http://www.alnovatech.com
Information Technology Consulting Services
N.A.I.C.S.: 541512

Beaumont Development Centre Holding Ltd. (2)
Royal Road Cassis, Port Louis, Mauritius
Tel.: (230) 4021700
Investment Management Service
N.A.I.C.S.: 523999

Coritel S.A. (2)
Paseo de la Finca 1 Bloque 2, Pozuelo de Alarcon, 28223, Madrid, Spain
Tel.: (34) 915967000
Web Site: http://www.coritel.es
Sales Range: $700-749.9 Million
Emp.: 5,000
Application Program Development & Outsourcing Services
N.A.I.C.S.: 541511
Antonio Moncada *(Partner)*

CustomerWorks Europe SL (2)
Parque Tecnologico Edificio 207A Planta 1, Zamudio, 48170, Spain
Tel.: (34) 944062200
Web Site: http://www.accenture.com
Business Management Consulting Services
N.A.I.C.S.: 541611

IMJ Corporation (2)
Sumitomo Fudosan Azabujuban Building 9F 1-4-1 Mita, Minato-ku, Tokyo, 108-0073, Japan
Tel.: (81) 364154250
Web Site: https://www.imjp.co.jp

Emp.: 572
Digital Marketing Services
N.A.I.C.S.: 541613
Junichiro Kurokawa *(Chm)*

Operaciones Accenture S.A. de C.V. (2)
Boulevard Manuel Avila Camacho No 138 Piso 7 Lomas de Chapultepec, Miguel Hidalgo, Mexico, 11000, Mexico
Tel.: (52) 5552847300
Business Process Outsourcing Services
N.A.I.C.S.: 561499

P.T. Accenture (2)
Wisma 46 Kota BNI-18th Floor Jl Jendral Sudirman Kav 1 RT 10/RW 11, Karet Tengsin, Jakarta, 10220, Indonesia (100%)
Tel.: (62) 215746575
Sales Range: $75-99.9 Million
Emp.: 800
Business Services
N.A.I.C.S.: 561499
Kher Tean Chen *(Mng Dir)*

Accenture NZ Limited (1)
Level 12 125 Queen Street, Auckland, 1010, New Zealand
Tel.: (64) 93511600
N.A.I.C.S.: 541512

Accenture SRL (1)
Avenida Presidente Roque Saenz Pena 777 Ciudad De, Buenos Aires, Argentina
Tel.: (54) 1143188500
Information Technology Consulting Services
N.A.I.C.S.: 541512

Accenture Saudi Arabia Ltd (1)
Al Khobar Gate Tower King Abdulaziz Road, Bandriah District Khobar Andriah District, Al Khobar, 31952, Saudi Arabia
Tel.: (966) 112838000
N.A.I.C.S.: 541512

Accenture Solutions Private Limited (1)
Plant-3 Godrej Boyce Complex LBS Marg Vikhroli W, Mumbai, 400 079, Maharashtra, India
Tel.: (91) 226600300
Software Development Services
N.A.I.C.S.: 513210
Sunil Jangle *(Mng Dir)*

Adaptly, Inc. (1)
22 W 19th St 3rd Fl, New York, NY 10011
Tel.: (212) 300-8599
Web Site: http://www.adaptly.com
Sales Range: $1-9.9 Million
Marketing Coordination Services
N.A.I.C.S.: 541613
Nikhil Sethi *(Founder)*

Advocate Networks, Inc. (1)
6200 The Corners Pkwy Ste 310, Norcross, GA 30092
Tel.: (678) 987-5900
Web Site: https://advocateinsiders.com
Rev.: $5,200,000
Emp.: 25
Business Consulting Services
N.A.I.C.S.: 541690
Scott Fogle *(Co-Founder & Co-Pres)*

Agave Consultants Limited (1)
Canarias 1178, Col Chapultepec Country, 44620, Guadalajara, Jalisco, Mexico
Tel.: (52) 17520700
Web Site: https://agaveconsultant.com
N.A.I.C.S.: 541618

Altitude, Inc. (1)
363 Highland Ave, Somerville, MA 02144
Tel.: (617) 623-7600
Web Site: http://www.altitudeinc.com
Sales Range: $1-9.9 Million
Emp.: 19
Engineeering Services
N.A.I.C.S.: 541330
Brian J. Matt *(Founder & Chm)*

Anser Advisory LLC (1)
529 E Crown Point Rd Ste 170, Ocoee, FL 34761
Tel.: (407) 897-5354
Web Site: http://anseradvisory.com
Emp.: 800
Management Consulting Services
N.A.I.C.S.: 541611
Matthew Dean *(COO)*

Subsidiary (Domestic):

Cambridge Construction Management, Inc. (2)
97 Grayrock Rd, Clinton, NJ 08809
Tel.: (908) 638-9700
Web Site: http://www.cambridgecm.com
Construction Management Professional Services
N.A.I.C.S.: 541611
Dan Connelly *(Mng Dir)*

DHS Consulting, LLC (2)
2677 N Main St Ste 400, Santa Ana, CA 92705
Tel.: (714) 276-1135
Process & Results-driven Program, Project & Construction Management Consulting Firm
N.A.I.C.S.: 541611

Inline Management, LLC (2)
1703 Sand Lily Dr, Golden, CO 80401
Tel.: (303) 526-7928
Web Site: http://www.inlinemanagement.com
Heavy & Civil Engineering Construction Services
N.A.I.C.S.: 237990
Michael Hall *(Founder)*

R L H Engineering, Inc. (2)
541 E Garden Dr Unit S, Windsor, CO 80550
Tel.: (970) 686-5695
Web Site: http://www.rlhengineering.com
Sales Range: $1-9.9 Million
Emp.: 10
Engineering Services Business Consulting Services
N.A.I.C.S.: 541330
Jeffrey M. Chamberlin *(Partner & Principal)*

RW Block Consulting, Inc. (2)
871 Outer Rd Ste B, Orlando, FL 32814
Tel.: (407) 897-5354
Web Site: http://www.rwblockconsulting.com
General Management Consulting Services
N.A.I.C.S.: 541611
Roy Block *(Pres)*

Avanade Ireland Limited (1)
3 Grand Canal Plaza Grand Canal Street Upper, Dublin, D04 EE70, Ireland
Tel.: (353) 14076000
Web Site: https://www.avanade.com
Software Development Services
N.A.I.C.S.: 513210
Andy Gillett *(Gen Mgr)*

Avanade Osterreich GmbH (1)
Schottenring 16, 1010, Vienna, Austria
Tel.: (43) 6768441110
Software Development Services
N.A.I.C.S.: 513210

Avanade Poland Sp. z o.o. (1)
Ul Pawia 21, 31-154, Krakow, Poland
Tel.: (48) 123419600
Software Development Services
N.A.I.C.S.: 513210

Award Solutions, Inc. (1)
2100 Lakeside Blvd, Richardson, TX 75082
Tel.: (972) 664-0727
Web Site: http://www.awardsolutions.com
Sales Range: $1-9.9 Million
Emp.: 41
Business Consulting Services
N.A.I.C.S.: 541690
Ramki Rajagopalan *(Co-Founder & VP)*

BRIDGE Energy Group, Inc. (1)
c/o Accenture 888 Boylston St Fl #12, Boston, MA 02199
Tel.: (508) 281-7133
Web Site: http://www.bridgeenergygroup.com
Sales Range: $10-24.9 Million
Emp.: 85
Smart Grid Integration & Utility Solutions
N.A.I.C.S.: 541690
Thomas J. Leone *(CFO)*

Bionic Solution LLC (1)
4 Columbus Cir, New York, NY 10019
Tel.: (646) 723-9929
Web Site: http://www.bionicsolution.com
Sales Range: $10-24.9 Million
Emp.: 32
Business Consulting Services

N.A.I.C.S.: 541611
David Kidder *(Founder)*

Brand Learning LLC **(1)**
80 Broad St Ste 2101, New York, NY 10004
Tel.: (212) 392-4898
Marketing Consulting Services
N.A.I.C.S.: 541613

Clarity Solution Group, LLC **(1)**
150 S Wacker Dr Ste 2750, Chicago, IL
60606
Tel.: (312) 288-8428
Web Site: http://www.clarityinsights.com
Data Management Services
N.A.I.C.S.: 541513

ClearEdge Partners, Inc. **(1)**
254 2nd Ave Ste 140, Needham, MA 02494
Tel.: (858) 558-1500
Web Site: http://www.clearedgepartners.com
General Management Consulting Services
N.A.I.C.S.: 541611
Ann Shuman *(Mgr-Mktg & Summit Programs)*

Concentric Partners LLC **(1)**
1 World Trade Center 285 Fulton St Fl 68,
New York, NY 10007
Tel.: (212) 633-9700
Web Site: http://concentrichx.com
Emp.: 150
Advertising Agencies
N.A.I.C.S.: 541890
Michael Sanzen *(Co-Founder & Chief Creative Officer)*

Cutting Edge Solutions Ltd. **(1)**
Station Point Old Station Way Eynsham,
Witney, Oxford, OX29 4TL, United Kingdom
Tel.: (44) 1865954300
Web Site: https://oneplm.com
Software Development Services
N.A.I.C.S.: 513210

Daz Systems, Inc. **(1)**
880 Apollo St Ste, El Segundo, CA 90245
Tel.: (310) 640-1300
Web Site: http://www.dazsi.com
Sales Range: Less than $1 Million
Custom Computer Programming Services
N.A.I.C.S.: 541511
Walt Zipperman *(CEO)*

**Designaffairs Business Consulting
(Shanghai) Co. Ltd.** **(1)**
Room A126 Building 7 No 2188 Guanghua
Road, Minhang District, Shanghai, 200060,
China
Tel.: (86) 2162984733
Industrial Interface Design Services
N.A.I.C.S.: 541420
Lidan Liu *(Mng Dir)*

Designaffairs GmbH **(1)**
Balanstr 73 / Haus 32, 81541, Munich, Germany
Tel.: (49) 894423290
Industrial Interface Design Services
N.A.I.C.S.: 541420
Viktoria Nolte *(Sr Mgr-Bus Dev)*

Digital Unlimited Group Ltd. **(1)**
Unlimited House 10 Great Pulteney Street,
London, W1F 9NB, United Kingdom
Tel.: (44) 20 7349 4000
Web Site: http://www.unlimitedgroup.com
Advetising Agency
N.A.I.C.S.: 541810
Tim Bonnet *(Pres)*

Subsidiary (US):

Health Unlimited LLC **(2)**
111 5th Avenue, New York, NY 10003
Tel.: (212) 886-2200
Web Site: http://www.healthunlimited.com
Advertising Services
N.A.I.C.S.: 541810
Susan Duffy *(Chief Strategy Officer)*

Subsidiary (Domestic):

Corkery Group Unlimited **(3)**
111 5th Ave 2nd Fl, New York, NY 10003
Tel.: (212) 584-5030
Web Site: http://www.corkeryunlimited.com
Public Relations Services
N.A.I.C.S.: 541820
Karen O'Malley *(Pres)*

Subsidiary (Domestic):

Nelson Bostock Group Limited **(2)**
Unlimited House 10 Great Pulteney Street,
London, W1F 9NB, United Kingdom
Tel.: (44) 20 7229 4400
Web Site:
http://www.nelsonbostockunlimited.com
Public Relations Services
N.A.I.C.S.: 541820
Tim Lines *(Dir)*

Tullo Marshall Warren Ltd. **(2)**
Unlimited House 10 Great Pulteney Street,
London, W1F 9NB, United Kingdom
Tel.: (44) 2073494000
Web Site: http://www.tmwunlimited.com
Advertising Services
N.A.I.C.S.: 541810
Phil Rhodes *(Creative Dir)*

Fairway Technologies, Inc. **(1)**
4370 La Jolla Vlg Dr 5th Fl, San Diego, CA
92121
Tel.: (858) 454-4471
Custom Computer Programming Services
N.A.I.C.S.: 541511
Mike Mannion *(COO)*

Fjord Oy **(1)**
Keskuskatu 6, 00100, Helsinki, Finland
Tel.: (358) 9677873
Software Development Services
N.A.I.C.S.: 541511

Future State **(1)**
3100 Oak Rd Ste 205, Walnut Creek, CA
94597
Tel.: (925) 299-3900
Web Site: http://www.futurestate.com
Sales Range: $10-24.9 Million
Emp.: 18
It Consulting
N.A.I.C.S.: 541690
Kathy Krumpe *(COO)*

Gekko SAS **(1)**
12 rue d Alsace, 92300, Levallois-Perret,
France
Tel.: (33) 158744600
Web Site: http://www.gekko.fr
Software Management Services
N.A.I.C.S.: 541511
Roland Esnis *(Co-Founder)*

Incapsulate, LLC **(1)**
1620 L St NW 3rd Fl Ste D, Washington,
DC 20036
Web Site: http://www.incapsulate.com
Sales Range: $10-24.9 Million
Emp.: 158
Information Technology Services
N.A.I.C.S.: 541512

Informatica de Euskadi S.L **(1)**
Bizkaiko Teknologia Parkea 803, 48160,
Derio, Bizkaia, Spain
Tel.: (34) 944145500
Web Site: https://www.ide-website.net
Software Development Services
N.A.I.C.S.: 513210

Inspirage, LLC **(1)**
800 Bellevue Way NE Ste 500, Bellevue,
WA 98004
Web Site: https://www.inspirage.com
Custom Computer Programming Services
N.A.I.C.S.: 541511
Srini Subramanian *(CEO)*

**Interactive Broadband Consulting
Group LLC** **(1)**
1628 JFK Blvd Ste 1701, Philadelphia, PA
19103
Tel.: (215) 687-4460
Web Site: http://www.accenture.com
Computer Related Services
N.A.I.C.S.: 541519
John Dreboty *(VP-Fin)*

Intrigo Systems, Inc. **(1)**
42808 Christy St 221, Fremont, CA 94538
Custom Computer Programming Services
N.A.I.C.S.: 541511

Kolle Rebbe GmbH **(1)**
Dienerreihe 2, 20457, Hamburg, Germany
Tel.: (49) 403254230
Web Site: http://www.kolle-rebbe.de
Sales Range: $25-49.9 Million
Emp.: 294

Advertising, Production (Ad, Film, Broadcast), Production (Print)
N.A.I.C.S.: 541810
Lennart Wittgen *(Mng Dir-Acct Mgmt)*

Logic Information Systems, Inc. **(1)**
5814 Blackshire Path, Inver Grove Heights,
MN 55076
Tel.: (651) 203-3300
Web Site: http://www.logicinfo.com
Sales Range: $1-9.9 Million
Emp.: 18
Custom Computer Programming Services
N.A.I.C.S.: 541511
Prabhu Kumar *(Co-Founder & CFO)*

MacGregor Partners, LLC **(1)**
207 E Buffalo St Ste 301, Milwaukee, WI
53202
Tel.: (414) 930-4783
Web Site:
http://www.macgregorpartners.com
Sales Range: $1-9.9 Million
Emp.: 31
Logistic Services
N.A.I.C.S.: 541614
Jason R. Ziegler *(Pres)*

Mackevision CG Technology & Service (Shanghai) Co. Ltd. **(1)**
331 North Caoxi Rd, Shanghai, 200030,
China
Tel.: (86) 2124261902
Visualization & Animation Services
N.A.I.C.S.: 512191

Mackevision Corporation **(1)**
1965 Research Dr, Troy, MI 48083
Tel.: (248) 656-6566
Visualization & Animation Services
N.A.I.C.S.: 512191
Heiko Wenczel *(Pres)*

Mackevision Japan Co., Ltd. **(1)**
1-4-1 Mita, Minato-Ku, Tokyo, 108-0073,
Japan
Tel.: (81) 342148339
Visualization & Animation Services
N.A.I.C.S.: 512191

**Mackevision Medien Design GmbH -
Stuttgart** **(1)**
Forststrasse 7, 70174, Stuttgart, Germany
Tel.: (49) 7119330480
Visualization & Animation Services
N.A.I.C.S.: 512191

Myrtle Consulting Group LLC **(1)**
16225 Park Ten Pl Ste 620, Houston, TX
77084
Tel.: (281) 600-7275
Web Site: http://www.myrtlegroup.com
Sales Range: $1-9.9 Million
Business Consulting Services
N.A.I.C.S.: 541611
Edwin Bosso *(Founder & CEO)*

NaviSite LLC **(1)**
400 Minuteman Rd, Andover, MA 01810
Tel.: (978) 682-8300
Web Site: http://www.navisite.com
Cloud Management & Application Hosting
Services
N.A.I.C.S.: 518210
Sumeet Sabharwal *(Grp VP & Gen Mgr)*

Subsidiary (Non-US):

NaviSite Europe Limited **(2)**
5th Floor DST House St Marks Hill, Surbiton, KT6 4QD, Surrey, United Kingdom
Tel.: (44) 8006122933
Web Site: http://www.navisite.com
Cloud Management & Application Hosting
Services
N.A.I.C.S.: 518210

NaviSite India Private Limited **(2)**
Vipul Orchid Plaza Golf Course Road Sector 54, Suncity, Gurgaon, 122 002, Haryana, India
Tel.: (91) 1244913300
Web Site: http://www.navisite.com
Cloud Management & Application Hosting
Services
N.A.I.C.S.: 518210

Subsidiary (Domestic):

**Velocity Technology Solutions,
Inc.** **(2)**

1901 Roxborough Rd, Charlotte, NC 28211
Tel.: (704) 357-7705
Web Site: http://www.velocitycloud.com
Enterprise Software Application Management, Hosting & Consulting Services
N.A.I.C.S.: 513210
Christopher Heller *(Gen Counsel & Sr VP-Legal)*

Subsidiary (Domestic):

Mercury Technology Group, Inc. **(3)**
111 Pacifica Ste 320, Irvine, CA 92618
Tel.: (949) 417-0260
Software Publisher
N.A.I.C.S.: 513210

TITAN Technology Partners, Ltd. **(3)**
2105 Water Ridge Pkwy Ste 500, Charlotte,
NC 28217
Tel.: (704) 556-0150
Web Site: http://www.ttpartners.com
Sales Range: $10-24.9 Million
Outsourcing Services
N.A.I.C.S.: 561499
Michael Vadini *(Pres)*

**Velocity Technology Solutions III,
Inc.** **(3)**
1100 Olive Way Ste 1100, Seattle, WA
98101
Tel.: (206) 436-3300
Web Site: http://www.velocity.cc
Data Processing, Hosting & Related Services
N.A.I.C.S.: 518210
Keith Angell *(Pres & CEO)*

Nytec Inc. **(1)**
416 6th St S, Kirkland, WA 98033
Tel.: (206) 634-2760
Web Site: http://www.nytec.com
Software Engineering Services
N.A.I.C.S.: 541330
Rich Lerz *(CEO)*

Octo Technology Pty. Ltd. **(1)**
402/55 Lime Street, Sydney, 2000, NSW,
Australia
Tel.: (61) 280726262
Software Development Services
N.A.I.C.S.: 513210
David Alia *(CEO)*

Octo Technology SA **(1)**
28 rue Jbel Oukaimden Agdal, 10000, Rabat, Morocco
Tel.: (212) 537778843
Software Development Services
N.A.I.C.S.: 513210

Pillar Technology Group, LLC **(1)**
5180 Washakie Trail, Brighton, MI 48116
Tel.: (313) 887-2000
Custom Computer Programming Services
N.A.I.C.S.: 541511

Procurian India Private Limited **(1)**
Unit No 05-02 5th Floor, Hyderabad,
500081, Andhra Pradesh, India
Tel.: (91) 4046475800
Information Technology Consulting Services
N.A.I.C.S.: 541512

Procurian LLC **(1)**
211 S Gulph Rd Ste 500, King of Prussia,
PA 19406
Tel.: (484) 690-5000
Information Technology Consulting Services
N.A.I.C.S.: 541512

PureApps Limited **(1)**
101 Finsbury Pavement, London, EC2A
1RS, United Kingdom
Tel.: (44) 2071837840
Web Site:
https://pureapps.dev.russellnewman.co.uk
N.A.I.C.S.: 541513

Redcore (India) Private Limited **(1)**
65 35th Main BTM 2nd Stage 100 Feet
Ring Road, Bengaluru, 560 068, Karnataka,
India
Tel.: (91) 8066995871
Software Development Services
N.A.I.C.S.: 513210

Root LLC **(1)**
5470 Mian St, Sylvania, OH 43560
Tel.: (419) 874-0077
Web Site: https://www.rootinc.com

Accenture plc—(Continued)

Sales Range: $25-49.9 Million
Emp.: 156
Business Management Consulting Services
N.A.I.C.S.: 541618
James A. Haudan (Co-Founder & Chm)

Search Technologies Limited (1)
Venture House Arlington Square, Bracknell,
RG12 1WA, United Kingdom
Tel.: (44) 2078444000
Search Analytic Services
N.A.I.C.S.: 541910

Search Technologies, LLC (1)
1110 Herndon Pkwy Ste 306, Herndon, VA
20170
Tel.: (703) 953-2791
Web Site:
　http://www.searchtechnologies.com
Search Engine Expertise Services
N.A.I.C.S.: 518210
John Back (VP-Sls-North America)

SinnerSchrader
Aktiengesellschaft (1)
Volckersstrasse 38, 22765, Hamburg, Germany
Tel.: (49) 403988550
Web Site: http://sinnerschrader.ag
Digital Agencies; E-Business Solutions Marketer
N.A.I.C.S.: 541613
Thomas Dyckhoff (CFO & Member-Mgmt
Bd)

Subsidiary (Domestic):

SinnerSchrader Content GmbH (2)
Volckersstrasse 38, 22765, Hamburg, Germany
Tel.: (49) 403988550
Content Marketing
N.A.I.C.S.: 541890

SinnerSchrader Deutschland
GmbH (2)
Volckersstrasse 38, Hamburg, 22765, Germany
Tel.: (49) 403988550
Web Site: http://www.sinnerschrader.com
E Commerce Solutions
N.A.I.C.S.: 425120

SinnerSchrader Commerce
GmbH (1)
Volckersstrasse 38, 22765, Hamburg, Germany
Tel.: (49) 403988550
Web Site:
　http://www.sinnerschradercommerce.com
Digital Media Services
N.A.I.C.S.: 541613
Patrick Sindt (Dir-Consulting & Client Mgmt)

SinnerSchrader Praha s.r.o. (1)
Drahobejlova 2400/15, Liben, 190 00,
Prague, Czech Republic
Tel.: (420) 776163258
Software Development Services
N.A.I.C.S.: 513210

The Monkeys Pty. Ltd. (1)
531 Sth Dowling St, Surry Hills, 2010,
NSW, Australia
Tel.: (61) 286654200
Web Site: https://www.themonkeys.com.au
Advertisement Development Services
N.A.I.C.S.: 541810
Mark Green (Founder)

Work & Co (1)
231 Front St 5th Fl, Brooklyn, NY 11201
Tel.: (347) 470-4803
Web Site: http://www.work.co
Sales Range: $25-49.9 Million
Emp.: 400
Application Development Services
N.A.I.C.S.: 541511
Gene Liebel (Partner-Product Mgmt)

Workforce Insight LLC (1)
355 S Teller St Ste 200, Lakewood, CO
80226
Tel.: (303) 309-4006
Web Site: http://www.workforceinsight.com
Workforce Management Solutions
N.A.I.C.S.: 541612
Tony Santora (CEO)

droga5, LLC (1)
120 Wall St Fl 11, New York, NY, 10005
Tel.: (917) 237-8888
Web Site: https://www.droga5.com
Advertising Agencies
N.A.I.C.S.: 541810
David Droga (Founder & Chm-Creative)

Branch (Non-US):

Droga5 (2)
L2 4 - 16 Yurong St, E Sydney, Sydney,
2010, NSW, Australia
Tel.: (61) 2 8063 4500
Web Site: http://www.droga5.com.au
Advertising Agencies
N.A.I.C.S.: 541810

ACCESS CAPITAL PARTNERS
SA
121 Avenue des Champs-Elysees,
75008, Paris, France
Tel.: (33) 1 56 43 61 00　　　　　**FR**
Web Site: http://www.access-capital-
partners.com
Year Founded: 1998
Privater Equity Firm
N.A.I.C.S.: 523999
Dominique Peninon (Co-Founder &
Chm)

Subsidiaries:

GSV Materieludlejning AS (1)
Baldersbuen 5, 2640, Hedehusene, Denmark
Tel.: (45) 70 12 13 15
Web Site: http://www.gsv.dk
Machinery & Equipment Rental Services
N.A.I.C.S.: 532412

Subsidiary (Domestic):

Ramirent A/S (2)
Hundigevej 85, Greve, 2670, Denmark
Tel.: (45) 43958888
Web Site: http://www.ramirent.dk
Machinery & Equipment Rental Services
N.A.I.C.S.: 532412
Carsten Boris (Mgr-Sourcing)

ACCESS CO., LTD.
Daito Bldg 3 Kandaneribei-cho,
Chiyoda ku, Tokyo, 101 0022, Japan
Tel.: (81) 368539088　　　　　　**JP**
Web Site: https://www.access-
company.com
Year Founded: 1979
4813—(TKS)
Rev.: $117,502,570
Assets: $193,422,290
Liabilities: $33,081,940
Net Worth: $160,340,350
Earnings: ($1,985,200)
Emp.: 809
Fiscal Year-end: 01/31/24
Mobile Content Delivery & Internet
Access Technologies
N.A.I.C.S.: 517112
Eiji Suzuki (Exec Officer & VP-Sls
Unit)

Subsidiaries:

ACCESS (Beijing) Co., Ltd. (1)
C206 Yeqing Plaza No 9 Wangjingbeilu,
Chaoyang District, Beijing, 100102, China
Tel.: (86) 1084782120
Web Site: http://www.access-company.com
Sales Range: $25-49.9 Million
Emp.: 100
Software Technologies to the Mobile &
Beyond-PC Markets
N.A.I.C.S.: 517810

ACCESS Europe GmbH (1)
Essener Strasse 2-24, 46047, Oberhausen,
Germany
Tel.: (49) 2088271010
Web Site: https://eu.access-company.com
Sales Range: $25-49.9 Million
Emp.: 20
Custom Computer Programming Services
N.A.I.C.S.: 541511
Neale Foster (Mng Dir)

ACCESS Publishing Co., Ltd. (1)
Sarugaku-cho 2-8-16, Chiyoda-ku, 101-
0064, Tokyo, Japan
Tel.: (81) 352593511
Web Site: http://www.tokyo-calendar.tv
Periodical Publishers
N.A.I.C.S.: 513120

ACCESS Seoul Co. Ltd (1)
16F Hansol Education Building 361 World
Cup buk-ro, Mapo-gu, Seoul, 03908, Korea
(South)
Tel.: (82) 231535200
Web Site: http://wwwaccess-company.com
Sales Range: $25-49.9 Million
Emp.: 100
Software Reproducing
N.A.I.C.S.: 334610

ACCESS Systems France SARL (1)
Port Inland 701 Avenue Gaston de Fontmi-
chel, Rue Henri Becquerel BP 59, 06210,
Mandelieu-la-Napoule, France
Tel.: (33) 499524300
Web Site: http://www.access-company.com
Sales Range: $25-49.9 Million
Emp.: 70
Custom Computer Programming Services
N.A.I.C.S.: 541511

ACCESS Systems USA, Inc. (1)
1188 E Arques Ave, Sunnyvale, CA 94085
Tel.: (408) 400-1900
Web Site: http://www.access-company.com
Operating Systems for Handheld Comput-
ers
N.A.I.C.S.: 541511

ACCESS Taiwan Lab Co., Ltd. (1)
No 11 No 36 Nanjing West Road, Datong
District, Taipei, 103614, Taiwan
Tel.: (886) 225631717
Web Site: https://access-taiwanlab.com
Integrated Technology Services
N.A.I.C.S.: 541512

Access AP Taiwan Co., Ltd. (1)
10F No 2 Sec 4 Renai Rd, Daan Dist, Tai-
pei, 10684, Taiwan
Tel.: (886) 22 708 1969
Software Solutions Services
N.A.I.C.S.: 541511

Acess Taiwan Lab. Co., Ltd. (1)
No 2 Section 2 Nanjing E Rd, Zhongshan
District, Taipei, 10491, Taiwan
Tel.: (886) 22 563 1717
Web Site: https://access-taiwanlab.com
Software Solutions Services
N.A.I.C.S.: 541511

IP Fusion, Inc. (1)
3965 Freedom Cir Ste 200, Santa Clara,
CA 95054
Tel.: (408) 400-1900
Web Site: https://www.ipinfusion.com
Software Developer
N.A.I.C.S.: 513210
Atsushi Ogata (Pres & CEO)

IP Infusion Software India Pvt.
Ltd. (1)
RMZ Centennial Block D - 401 4th Floor
Kundanahalli Main Road, Mahadevapura
Post Doddanakundi Industrial Area, Benga-
luru, 560 048, Karnataka, India
Tel.: (91) 806 728 7000
Software Solutions Services
N.A.I.C.S.: 541511

NetRange MMH GmbH (1)
Monckebergstr 22, 20095, Hamburg, Ger-
many
Tel.: (49) 40 280 9530
Web Site: https://netrange.com
Television Broadcasting Services
N.A.I.C.S.: 516120
Tao Pan (Mng Dir)

Northforge Innovations Inc. (1)
72 Laval Street 3rd Level, Gatineau, J8X
3H3, QC, Canada
Tel.: (819) 776-6066
Web Site: https://www.gonorthforge.com
Computer Networking Services
N.A.I.C.S.: 541512
Brenda Pastorek (Pres & COO)

ACCESS COMMERCIAL IN-
VESTORS 4 PLC

4 Brewery Place, Leeds, LS10 1NE,
United Kingdom
Tel.: (44) 3330069141　　　　　**UK**
Web Site:
　http://www.accessbond.co.uk
Investment Services
N.A.I.C.S.: 523940

ACCESS CORPORATION
Plot 14/15 Prince Alaba Oniru Street
Oniru Estate, Victoria Island, Lagos,
Nigeria
Tel.: (234) 14619264
Web Site:
　https://www.accessbankplc.com
Year Founded: 1989
ACCESS—(NIGE)
Rev.: $1,224,544,963
Assets: $19,755,017,432
Liabilities: $18,137,215,671
Net Worth: $1,617,801,760
Earnings: $458,422,342
Emp.: 7,334
Fiscal Year-end: 12/31/23
Banking Services
N.A.I.C.S.: 522110
Hebert Onyewumbu Wigwe (CEO &
Mng Dir-Grp)

Subsidiaries:

Access Bank (D.R. Congo) Sarl (1)
158 Av de la Democratie ex oil mill, Gombe,
Kinshasa, Congo, Democratic Republic of
Tel.: (243) 812222160
Web Site:
　https://www.congo.accessbankplc.com
Banking Services
N.A.I.C.S.: 522110

Access Bank (Gambia) Limited (1)
47 Kairaba Avenue, Ksmd, Fajara, Gambia
Tel.: (220) 4396679
Web Site:
　https://www.gambia.accessbankplc.com
Banking Services
N.A.I.C.S.: 522110
Papa Yusupha Njie (Chm)

Access Bank (Ghana) Limited (1)
Starlets 91 Road Opposite Accra Sports
Stadium, PO Box GP 353, Osu, Accra,
Ghana
Tel.: (233) 302684860
Web Site: http://www.accessbankplc.com
Banking Services
N.A.I.C.S.: 522110
Frank Beecham (Chm)

Access Bank (Rwanda) Limited (1)
KN4 Ave 3rd Floor- KIC Building, PO Box
2059, Kigali, Rwanda
Tel.: (250) 788145300
Web Site:
　https://www.rwanda.accessbankplc.com
Banking Services
N.A.I.C.S.: 522110

Access Bank (Sierra Leone)
Limited (1)
30 Siaka Stevens Street, Freetown, Sierra
Leone
Tel.: (232) 30969943
Web Site:
　https://sierraleone.accessbankplc.com
Banking Services
N.A.I.C.S.: 522110

Access Bank (UK) Limited (1)
4 Royal Court Gadbrook Way, Gadbrook
Park, Northwich, CW9 7UT, Cheshire,
United Kingdom
Tel.: (44) 1606813020
Web Site:
　http://www.theaccessbankukltd.co.uk
Sales Range: $50-74.9 Million
Emp.: 50
Banking Services
N.A.I.C.S.: 522110
Jamie Simmonds (CEO & Mng Dir)

Access Bank (Zambia) Limited (1)
Plot 682 Cairo Road North end, PO Box
35273, Lusaka, Zambia
Tel.: (260) 211227941

Web Site:
https://zambia.accessbankplc.com
Banking Services
N.A.I.C.S.: 522110

Finbank SA (1)
16 Boulevard de La Liberte, BP 2998, Place
de l'Independence, Bujumbura, Burundi
Tel.: (257) 2 224 3313
Web Site: https://www.finbank.co.bi
Banking Services
N.A.I.C.S.: 522110

Finibanco Angola, S.A. (1)
Travessa Engracia Fragoso No 24 R / C,
Municipality of Ingombota, Luanda,
Angola (51%)
Tel.: (244) 222636000
Web Site: http://www.finibancoangola.co.ao
Marketing Services
N.A.I.C.S.: 541613

Intercontinental Homes Savings &
Loans Limited (1)
26 Adeola Hopewell Street, Victoria Island,
Lagos, Nigeria
Tel.: (234) 1 2771127
Mortgage Banking
N.A.I.C.S.: 522310

Intercontinental Life Assurance Com-
pany Limited (1)
6 Hughes Avenue, Alagomeji, Yaba, Lagos,
Nigeria
Tel.: (234) 1 4611637
Web Site:
http://www.intercontinentallifeng.com
Life Insurance
N.A.I.C.S.: 524113

Intercontinental Properties
Limited (1)
IPL Plaza 274 Murtala Mohammed Way
Herbert Macaulay Street, Alagomeji, Yaba,
Lagos, Nigeria
Tel.: (234) 1 2771459
Web Site:
http://www.intercontinentalproperties.com
Property Development & Support Services
N.A.I.C.S.: 531390

Wapic Insurance Plc (1)
119 Awolowo Road, Ikoyi, Lagos, Nigeria
Tel.: (234) 1 4615153
Web Site:
http://www.intercontinentalwapicinsplc.com
Insurance Services
N.A.I.C.S.: 524126
Adeyinka Adekoya (Mng Dir)

ACCESS GROUP HOLDINGS CO., LTD.
15F Shin-Aoyama Building East Wing
1-1-1 Minami-Aoyama, Minato-Ku,
Tokyo, 107-0062, Japan
Tel.: (81) 354133001
Web Site: https://www.access-t.co.jp
Year Founded: 1982
7042—(TKS)
Rev.: $22,817,720
Assets: $15,718,580
Liabilities: $10,080,250
Net Worth: $5,638,330
Earnings: $839,470
Emp.: 145
Fiscal Year-end: 03/31/24
Holding Company
N.A.I.C.S.: 551112
Haruki Kimura (Chm)

ACCESS INTERNATIONAL EDUCATION LTD.
100 B1 2451 Dieppe Avenue SW,
Calgary, T3E 7K1, AB, Canada
Tel.: (403) 217-3830
Web Site:
http://www.accessinternational
education.com
Year Founded: 1967
Sales Range: Less than $1 Million
Education Services
N.A.I.C.S.: 611110
Chris Gee (Pres & CEO)

ACCESS TECHNOLOGY GROUP LIMITED
The Armstrong Building 10 Oakwood
Drive, Loughborough, LE11 3QF,
United Kingdom
Tel.: (44) 8453453300
Web Site:
https://www.theaccessgroup.com
Software Development Services
N.A.I.C.S.: 513210

Subsidiaries:

Paytronix Systems, Inc. (1)
74 Bridge St Ste 400, Newton, MA 02458
Tel.: (617) 649-3300
Web Site: http://www.paytronix.com
Software Publishing Services
N.A.I.C.S.: 513210
Lee Barnes (Dir-Data Insights)

Sceptre Hospitality Resources,
LLC (1)
1334 Brittmoore Ste 2410, Houston, TX
77043
Tel.: (713) 333-9944
Web Site: http://www.shr.global
Application Software Development Services
N.A.I.C.S.: 541511
Sarah Jones (Sr Dir-Product Mktg & Comm)

ACCESS WORLD AG
Baarerstrasse 53/55, 6300, Zug,
Switzerland
Tel.: (41) 417298620
Web Site:
https://www.accessworld.com
Year Founded: 1933
Emp.: 180
Marine Cargo Stevedoring Services
N.A.I.C.S.: 488320
Boris Sviderskii (Mgr-Bus Dev)

ACCESSO TECHNOLOGY GROUP PLC
Unit 5 The Pavilions Ruscombe Park,
Reading, Twyford, RG10 9NN, Berk-
shire, United Kingdom
Tel.: (44) 1189347400
Web Site: https://accesso.com
Year Founded: 2000
ACSO—(AIM)
Rev.: $139,730,000
Assets: $228,101,000
Liabilities: $42,714,000
Net Worth: $185,387,000
Earnings: $10,056,000
Emp.: 965
Fiscal Year-end: 12/31/22
Theme Park Ride Reservation & Vir-
tual Queuing Product Mfr
N.A.I.C.S.: 334419
Steve Brown (CEO)

Subsidiaries:

Lo-Q Virtual Queuing Inc. (1)
420 Thornton Rd Ste 109, Lithia Springs,
GA 30122
Tel.: (678) 838-6930
Web Site: http://www.lo-qusa.com
Sales Range: $50-74.9 Million
Emp.: 18
Virtual Queuing Product Sales & Support
N.A.I.C.S.: 423690
John Alder (CFO)

Siriusware, Inc. (1)
302 Camino de la Placita, Taos, NM 87571
Tel.: (505) 751-4166
Web Site: http://www.siriusware.com
Sales Range: $1-9.9 Million
Emp.: 58
Point of Sale Software
N.A.I.C.S.: 513210

VisionOne, Inc. (1)
6781 N Palm Ave Ste 120, Fresno, CA
93704
Tel.: (559) 432-8000
Web Site: http://www.showare.com

Sales Range: $1-9.9 Million
Emp.: 44
Ticketing Software
N.A.I.C.S.: 513210

ACCIAIERIE VALBRUNA S.P.A.
Viale della Scienza 25, 36100, Vice-
nza, Italy
Tel.: (39) 0444968211
Web Site: http://www.acciaierie-
valbruna.com
Sales Range: $250-299.9 Million
Emp.: 2,500
Stainless Steel Products & Metal Al-
loys Supplier & Mfr
N.A.I.C.S.: 331110
Roberto Bertelli (Mgr-Quality)

Subsidiaries:

Acciaierie Valbruna S.p.A. - Bolzano
Plant (1)
Via A Volta 4, 39100, Bolzano, Italy
Tel.: (39) 0471 924111
Stainless Steel Products Mfr
N.A.I.C.S.: 331110

Amenduni Nicola S.p.A. (1)
Via delle Mimose 3 ZI, 70026, Modugno,
BA, Italy
Tel.: (39) 080 531 4910
Web Site: https://www.amenduni.it
Olive Oil Machinery Mfr
N.A.I.C.S.: 333248

BHH Mikromed Sp. z o.o. (1)
ul Katowicka 11, 42-530, Dabrowa Gor-
nicza, Poland
Tel.: (48) 32 261 0220
Web Site: https://www.mikromed.eu
Polish Mfr
N.A.I.C.S.: 325612

Ferlat Acciai S.p.A. (1)
Via Massimo d'Azeglio 43/45, 36077, Al-
tavilla Vicentina, VI, Italy
Tel.: (39) 044 433 4711
Web Site: https://www.ferlatacciai.com
Steel Mfrs
N.A.I.C.S.: 332312

Steelcom Fittings S.r.l. (1)
Str S Romano Casetto 3/5, 46035, Ostiglia,
MN, Italy
Tel.: (39) 03 863 2300
Web Site: https://steelcomfittings.it
Steel Mfrs
N.A.I.C.S.: 332312

Ugivis S.A.S. (1)
ZI de l'Ousson Est, 01300, Belley, France
Tel.: (33) 47 981 3690
Web Site: https://www.ugivis.com
Steel Mfrs
N.A.I.C.S.: 332312

Valbruna AG (1)
Neuenburgstrasse 54, 3282, Bargen, Swit-
zerland
Tel.: (41) 32 391 71 81
Web Site: http://www.valbruna.ch
Stainless Steel, Nickel Alloys & Titanium
Products Distr
N.A.I.C.S.: 423510
Maurizio Carlotto (Gen Mgr)

Valbruna Asia Limited (1)
Room 1701 17F Golden Centre 188 Des
Voeux Road, Sheung Wan, Central, China
(Hong Kong)
Tel.: (852) 2854 1199
Web Site: http://www.valbruna.org
Stainless Steel Product Mfr & Distr
N.A.I.C.S.: 331110

Valbruna Australia Pty Ltd (1)
11-13 Southfork Drive, Kilsyth, 3137, VIC,
Australia
Tel.: (61) 3 9761 7955
Web Site: http://www.valbruna.com.au
Emp.: 10
Stainless Steel Product Mfr & Distr
N.A.I.C.S.: 331110
Ian Moffat (Gen Mgr)

Valbruna Canada Ltd. (1)
8724 Holgate Crescent, Milton, L9T 5Z1,
ON, Canada
Tel.: (905) 878-3288

Stainless Steel Products Distr
N.A.I.C.S.: 423510
Kevin MacNeil (VP & Gen Mgr)

Subsidiary (Domestic):

ASW Steel Inc. (2)
42 Centre Street, PO Box 56, Welland, L3B
5N9, ON, Canada
Tel.: (905) 735-5500
Web Site: http://www.asw-steel.com
Steel Mfrs
N.A.I.C.S.: 332111

Valbruna Edel Inox GmbH (1)
Siemensstrasse 14, 41542, Dormagen,
Germany
Tel.: (49) 2133 2706 0
Web Site: http://www.valbruna.de
Stainless Steel Mill & Service Center
N.A.I.C.S.: 331110
Christian Pottbecker (Exec Dir)

Valbruna Gulf FZE (1)
Jebel Ali Free Zone, PO Box No 17285,
Dubai, United Arab Emirates
Tel.: (971) 4 8860200
Web Site: http://www.valbrunagulf.com
Stainless Steel Products Distr
N.A.I.C.S.: 423510
Sachin Karkhanis (Project Mgr-Sls)

Valbruna Mexico, S.A. DE C.V. (1)
Av de Las Misiones No 24 Parque industrial
Bernardo Quintana, El Marques, 76246,
Queretaro, Mexico
Tel.: (52) 442 221 5910
Web Site: http://www.valbruna.com.mx
Stainless Steel Products Distr
N.A.I.C.S.: 423510

Valbruna Nederland B.V. (1)
Utrechthaven 15 Straat 55, 3433 PN,
Nieuwegein, Netherlands
Tel.: (31) 30 60 80 100
Web Site: http://www.valbruna.nl
Stainless Steel, Nickel Alloys & Titanium
Products Distr
N.A.I.C.S.: 423510

Valbruna Nordic AB (1)
Lovartsgatan 7, Karlstad, 652 21,
Sweden (100%)
Tel.: (46) 54 14 45 00
Web Site: http://www.valbrunanordic.se
Sales Range: $25-49.9 Million
Emp.: 28
Stainless Steel Products Distr
N.A.I.C.S.: 423510
Torbjorn Nilsson (Mng Dir)

Valbruna Nordic Oy (1)
Lappersintie 675, 02590, Lappers, Finland
Tel.: (358) 207 414 250
Web Site: http://www.valbruna.fi
Stainless Steel, Nickel Alloys & Titanium
Products Importer & Whslr
N.A.I.C.S.: 423510
Seppo Jarvinen (Mng Dir)

Valbruna Polska Sp. Z.o.o (1)
ul Katowicka 11, 42 530, Dabrowa Gor-
nicza, Poland
Tel.: (48) 322625843
Web Site: http://www.valbruna.pl
Stainless Steel Nickel Alloys & Titanium
Products Mfr & Distr
N.A.I.C.S.: 423510
Luciano Danti (Chm)

Valbruna Slater Stainless, Inc. (1)
2400 Taylor St, Fort Wayne, IN 46801
Tel.: (260) 434-2800
Web Site: http://www.valbrunastainless.com
Emp.: 75
Stainless Steel & Nickel Alloy Long Round
Bars Mfr
N.A.I.C.S.: 331110
Steve Fuller (Controller)

Valbruna Stainless Sdn. Bhd (1)
14-8 Wisma uoa II 21 Jalan Pinang, 50450,
Kuala Lumpur, Malaysia
Tel.: (60) 3 21668158
Emp.: 8
Stainless Steel Products Distr
N.A.I.C.S.: 423510

Valbruna Stainless, Inc. (1)
4400 Taylor St W, Fort Wayne, IN 46801
Tel.: (260) 434-2894

Acciaierie Valbruna S.p.A.—(Continued)

Web Site: http://www.valbrunastainless.com
Steel Bars & Tubing Whslr
N.A.I.C.S.: 423510
Matt Brown *(Mgr-IT)*

Branch (Domestic):

Valbruna Stainless (2)
4747 Oates Rd. Houston, TX 77013
Tel.: (713) 676-1700
Web Site: http://www.valbrunastainless.com
Sales Range: $25-49.9 Million
Emp.: 50
Stainless Steel Products Supplier
N.A.I.C.S.: 423510
David Nelson *(Mgr-US Inventory)*

Valbruna Stainless (2)
13950 Benson Ave, Chino, CA 91710
Tel.: (562) 921-9724
Web Site: http://www.valbruna-stainless-steel.com
Emp.: 10
Stainless Steel Products Distr
N.A.I.C.S.: 423510

Valbruna UK Ltd (1)
Oldbury Road, Oldbury, West Bromwich, B70 9BT, United Kingdom
Tel.: (44) 121 553 5384
Web Site: http://www.valbruna.co.uk
Stainless Steel, Nickel Alloys & Titanium Products Distr
N.A.I.C.S.: 423510
Keith Underhill *(Deputy Mng Dir)*

ACCIDENT EXCHANGE GROUP PLC

Alpha 1 Canton Lane, Hams Hall, Birmingham, B46 1GA, United Kingdom
Tel.: (44) 8700116720
Web Site:
http://www.accidentexchange.com
Year Founded: 2001
Sales Range: $150-199.9 Million
Emp.: 775
Vehicle Replacement Services
N.A.I.C.S.: 811198
Stephen Evans *(CEO)*

Subsidiaries:

Accident Exchange Limited (1)
Alpha One Canton Ln, Hams Hall, Coleshill, B46 1GA, Warwickshire, United Kingdom
Tel.: (44) 8700116720
Web Site: http://www.accidentexchange.com
Sales Range: $200-249.9 Million
Emp.: 500
Automobile Insurance Services
N.A.I.C.S.: 524298
Steve Evans *(CEO)*

DCML Limited (1)
Trinity House Bredbury Pkwy, Bredbury, Stockport, SK6 2SN, Cheshire, United Kingdom
Tel.: (44) 8444152400
Web Site: http://www.dcml.co.uk
Sales Range: $25-49.9 Million
Emp.: 25
Software Development Services
N.A.I.C.S.: 541511

ACCIONA, S.A.

Avenida de la Gran Via de Hortaleza 3, 28033, Madrid, Spain
Tel.: (34) 916632850   ES
Web Site: https://www.acciona.com
Year Founded: 1997
ANA—(BIL)
Rev.: $18,789,049,567
Assets: $34,937,631,090
Liabilities: $27,374,986,205
Net Worth: $7,562,644,885
Earnings: $685,506,127
Emp.: 57,843
Fiscal Year-end: 12/31/23
Holding Company; Infrastructure, Energy & Water Facility Construction, Real Estate Development, Environmental & Transportation Services

N.A.I.C.S.: 551112
Rafael Mateo *(CEO-Acciona Energy)*

Subsidiaries:

Acciona Agua, S.A. (1)
Avda de Europa 22 Parque Empresarial, La Moraleja, 28108, Alcobendas, Madrid, Spain (100%)
Tel.: (34) 917907700
Web Site: http://www.acciona-agua.es
Sales Range: $550-599.9 Million
Emp.: 1,900
Water Treatment Facilities Design, Construction, Operation & Maintenance Services
N.A.I.C.S.: 236210

Acciona Airport Services, S.A. (1)
C/ Anabel Segura 11 Albatros Business Centre, 28108, Alcobendas, Madrid, Spain (100%)
Tel.: (34) 911420300
Web Site: http://www.acciona-service.com
Sales Range: $250-299.9 Million
Emp.: 1,000
Cargo Handling & Air Transportation Support Services
N.A.I.C.S.: 488119

Acciona Aparcamientos, S.L. (1)
Anabel Segura 11 1a Planta, Parque Empresarial La Moraleja, 28108, Alcobendas, Madrid, Spain (100%)
Tel.: (34) 916632950
Web Site: http://www.acciona-inmobiliaria.es
Car Park Facility Leasing Services
N.A.I.C.S.: 531120

Acciona Concesiones, S.L. (1)
Avda de Europa 18 Parque Empresarial, La Moraleja, 28108, Alcobendas, Madrid, Spain (100%)
Tel.: (34) 916632850
Web Site: http://www.acciona-concesiones.com
Sales Range: $50-74.9 Million
Emp.: 35
Infrastructure Construction Projects Financing Services
N.A.I.C.S.: 522220

Acciona Do Brasil, Ltda (1)
Infrastructures Rua Das Olimpicos 134 7th Floor, Vila Olimpia, Sao Paulo, 04551-000, SP, Brazil
Tel.: (55) 1130472900
Web Site: https://www.acciona.com
N.A.I.C.S.: 221118

Acciona Energia, S.A. (1)
Avda Ciudad de la Innovacion 5, 31621, Sarriguren, Navarra, Spain (66.6%)
Tel.: (34) 948006000
Web Site: http://www.acciona-energia.com
Sales Range: $1-4.9 Billion
Emp.: 400
Renewable Energy Facility Development, Construction, Operation & Maintenance Services
N.A.I.C.S.: 221118
Rafael Mateo *(CEO)*

Subsidiary (Domestic):

Acciona Solar, S.A. (2)
Avd Ciudad De La Innovacion 3, 31621, Sarriguren, Navarra, Spain (75%)
Tel.: (34) 948166800
Web Site: http://www.accionasolar.es
Emp.: 400
Solar Energy Panel Installation, Operation & Maintenance Services
N.A.I.C.S.: 221118

Acciona Energy Global Poland Sp. Z.O.O. (1)
Lwowska 19 Str, 00-660, Warsaw, Poland
Tel.: (48) 224038195
Web Site: https://www.acciona-energia.pl
N.A.I.C.S.: 221118

Acciona Energy USA Global LLC (1)
55 E Monroe Ste 1925, Chicago, IL 60603
Tel.: (312) 673-3000
Web Site: https://www.acciona.us
N.A.I.C.S.: 221118

Acciona Facility Services Sur, S.A. (1)

Avenida de Tenerife 4 - Prisma Building 2 Floor, 28702, San Sebastian de los Reyes, Madrid, Spain
Tel.: (34) 915879631
N.A.I.C.S.: 221118

Acciona Facility Services, S.A. (1)
Paseo de la Zona Franca 69-73, 08038, Barcelona, Abrera, Spain (100%)
Tel.: (34) 902092600
Web Site: http://www.acciona-service.com
Sales Range: $25-49.9 Million
Emp.: 100
Environmental Conservation & Sustainable Development Services
N.A.I.C.S.: 561210

Acciona Infraestructuras, S.A. (1)
Avda Europa 18 Parque Empresarial, La Moraleja, 28108, Alcobendas, Madrid, Spain (100%)
Tel.: (34) 916632850
Web Site: http://www.acciona.com
Sales Range: $5-14.9 Billion
Emp.: 15,409
Infrastructure Construction Services
N.A.I.C.S.: 237310

Acciona Inmobiliaria, S.L. (1)
Anabel Segura 11, Parque Empresarial La Moraleja, 28108, Alcobendas, Madrid, Spain (100%)
Tel.: (34) 911420300
Web Site: http://www.acciona-inmobiliaria.es
Sales Range: $650-699.9 Million
Emp.: 401
Real Estate Developer & Property Leasing Services
N.A.I.C.S.: 531390

Subsidiary (Non-US):

Acciona Nieruchomosci Sp. z o.o. (2)
ul Lwowska 19, 00-660, Warsaw, Poland (100%)
Tel.: (48) 225140880
Web Site: http://www.acciona-nieruchomosci.pl
Sales Range: $50-74.9 Million
Emp.: 100
Real Estate Developers
N.A.I.C.S.: 531390

Affiliate (Domestic):

Compania Urbanizadora del Coto, S.L. (2)
C/o Machupichu 89, Madrid, 28043, Spain (50%)
Tel.: (34) 914043337
Web Site: http://www.cucsa.es
Emp.: 12
Residential Housing Developer & Rental Services
N.A.I.C.S.: 531390
Monica Rodriguez Ramon *(Mng Dir)*

Acciona Logistica, S.A. (1)
Avenida de Europa 10, Parque Empresarial La Moraleja, 28108, Alcobendas, Madrid, Spain (100%)
Tel.: (34) 917907700
Web Site: http://www.acciona.com
Sales Range: $100-124.9 Million
Emp.: 150
Holding Company; Maritime Passenger & Cargo Transportation Services
N.A.I.C.S.: 551112

Acciona Medio Ambiente (1)
C/ Universidad 4-4, CP 46003, Valencia, Spain (100%)
Tel.: (34) 963524500
Web Site: http://www.acciona-medioambiente.es
Sales Range: $50-74.9 Million
Emp.: 180
Garden, Reforestation & Irrigation Project Planning, Construction & Maintenance Services
N.A.I.C.S.: 115310

Bestinver, S.A. (1)
Juan De Mena 8, 28014, Madrid, Spain (100%)
Tel.: (34) 915959101
Web Site: http://www.bestinver.es
Pension & Mutual Funds Asset Management Services

N.A.I.C.S.: 523940
Beltran De La Lastra *(CEO & Chief Investment Officer)*

General de Producciones y Diseno, S.A. (1)
Avenida de la Borbolla 57, CP 41013, Seville, Spain (100%)
Tel.: (34) 954238595
Web Site: http://www.gpdsa.es
Sales Range: $25-49.9 Million
Emp.: 200
Exhibitions, Events Planning & Support Services
N.A.I.C.S.: 561499

Geotech Pty Ltd. (1)
174 Turner Street, Port Melbourne, 3207, VIC, Australia
Tel.: (61) 396244200
Web Site: https://geotech.net.au
N.A.I.C.S.: 541330
Adam McMahon *(Ops Mgr)*

Hijos de Antonio Barcelo, S.A. (1)
Calle de Anabel Segura 11, Alcobendas, 28108, Spain (100%)
Tel.: (34) 915006000
Web Site: http://www.habarcelo.es
Sales Range: $25-49.9 Million
Emp.: 40
Wineries
N.A.I.C.S.: 312130
Richer Grand *(Mng Dir)*

Pitagora Srl (1)
Via Basilicata 1/A, 53045, Montepulciano, SI, Italy
Tel.: (39) 0578707050
Web Site: https://www.studiopitagora.net
N.A.I.C.S.: 236210

Red Hills Finance, LLC (1)
22 Bridge St Ste 17, Concord, NH 03301
Tel.: (603) 219-0852
Web Site: https://redhillfinancial.com
N.A.I.C.S.: 541219

Terminal de Contenedores de Algeciras, S.A. (1)
Gaitan de Ayala s/n, Muelle de Isla Verde, Cadiz, 11207, Algeciras, Spain (100%)
Tel.: (34) 956604958
Web Site: http://www.acciona.com
Marine Cargo Terminal Operations
N.A.I.C.S.: 488320

ACCLIME

United Centre 95 Queensway Admiralty, Unit B, 17/F, China (Hong Kong)
Tel.: (852) 8522151226
Web Site: https://www.acclime.com
Year Founded: 2019
Emp.: 950
Financial Services
N.A.I.C.S.: 523999
Martin Crawford *(Founder & CEO)*

ACCONEER AB

Vastra Varvsgatan 19 211 77 Malmo, 223 63, Lund, Sweden
Tel.: (46) 102189200
Web Site: https://www.acconeer.com
ACCON—(OMX)
Rev.: $3,526,269
Assets: $19,776,569
Liabilities: $6,644,538
Net Worth: $13,132,031
Earnings: ($4,616,452)
Emp.: 52
Fiscal Year-end: 12/31/23
Sensor Product Mfr
N.A.I.C.S.: 334511
Lars Lindell *(CEO)*

ACCOR ACQUISITION COMPANY S.A.

82 rue Henri Farman, 92130, Issy-les-Moulineaux, France
Tel.: (33) 145388668   FR
Web Site:
https://www.accoracquisitions.com
Year Founded: 2021
AAC—(EUR)

Investment Management Service
N.A.I.C.S.: 523999
Amir Nah *(Mng Dir)*

ACCOR S.A.
82 rue Henri Farman, 92130, Issy-
les-Moulineaux, France
Tel.: (33) 145388600   FR
Web Site: https://group.accor.com
Year Founded: 1967
ACCYY—(OTCIQ)
Rev.: $5,581,189,978
Assets: $12,437,355,118
Liabilities: $6,574,677,118
Net Worth: $5,862,678,001
Earnings: $717,518,490
Emp.: 336,641
Fiscal Year-end: 12/31/23
Holding Company; Hotel Franchisor &
Operator
N.A.I.C.S.: 551112
Iris Knobloch *(Vice Chm)*

Subsidiaries:

21C Museum Hotels LLC   (1)
700 W Main St, Louisville, KY 40202
Tel.: (502) 217-6300
Web Site:
     https://www.21cmuseumhotels.com
Hotel & Resort Management Services
N.A.I.C.S.: 721110
Chett Abramson *(COO)*

Academie Accor SA   (1)
1 rue de la Mare-Neuve, 91021, Evry, Ce-
dex, France
Tel.: (33) 169368600
Web Site: http://www.accor.com
Home Management Services
N.A.I.C.S.: 721110

Accor (U.K.) Limited   (1)
255 Hammersmith Rd, London, W6 8SJ,
United Kingdom   **(100%)**
Tel.: (44) 02082377474
Web Site: http://www.accorhotel.com
Sales Range: $50-74.9 Million
Emp.: 100
Holding Co. for UK Operations
N.A.I.C.S.: 551112
Michael Flexmen *(CEO)*

Subsidiary (Domestic):

Accor UK Economy Hotels
Limited   (2)
Mile Lane, Coventry, CV1 2LN, United
Kingdom
Tel.: (44) 24 7625 0500
Web Site: http://www.accorhotels.com
Sales Range: $10-24.9 Million
Emp.: 14
Home Management Services
N.A.I.C.S.: 721110
Steven Daines *(CEO-Hotel Svcs-United
Kingdom, Ireland, Benelux & Switzerland)*

Accor Austria AG   (1)
Am Euro Platz 1, 1120, Vienna, Austria
Tel.: (43) 1 81 43 46 00
Home Management Services
N.A.I.C.S.: 721110

Accor Brasil SA   (1)
Avenida das Nacoes Unidas 7815, Pin-
heiros, Sao Paulo, 05425-905, SP,
Brazil   **(99.99%)**
Tel.: (55) 1138186200
Web Site: http://www.accor.com.br
Sales Range: $25-49.9 Million
Emp.: 200
Hotel & Catering Services
N.A.I.C.S.: 721199

Accor Casinos   (1)
35 Blvd de Capocinas Distt 2, Paris, 75002,
France   **(50%)**
Tel.: (33) 142865400
Web Site: http://www.lucemoeneaffeofo.com
Sales Range: $25-49.9 Million
Emp.: 150
Casino Hotels
N.A.I.C.S.: 721120
Christine Hussel *(Gen Mgr)*

Accor Gestion Maroc SA   (1)

La Colline ii N 33 Route de Nouaceur-Sidi
Maarouf, Casablanca, 20190, Morocco
Tel.: (212) 522977800
Web Site: http://www.accor.com
Sales Range: $10-24.9 Million
Emp.: 40
Home Management Services
N.A.I.C.S.: 721110
Onton Zugo *(CEO)*

Accor GmbH   (1)
Palmgasse 3, 1150, Vienna,
Austria   **(100%)**
Tel.: (43) 1892052500
Web Site: http://www.accor.com
Sales Range: $10-24.9 Million
Emp.: 20
Hotel Operator
N.A.I.C.S.: 721199

Accor Hospitality Argentina SA   (1)
Arroyo 841, Buenos Aires, 1007, Argentina
Tel.: (54) 1141310000
Web Site: http://www.sofitel.com
Emp.: 18
Home Management Services
N.A.I.C.S.: 721110
Fernando Mendez *(Office Mgr)*

Accor Hospitality Germany
GmbH   (1)
Tel.: (49) 8963002447
Web Site: http://www.accor.com
Emp.: 25
Home Management Services
N.A.I.C.S.: 721110

Accor Hospitality Nederland B.V   (1)
Joan Muyskenweg 10, Amsterdam, 1096
CJ, Netherlands
Tel.: (31) 206658181
Web Site: http://www.mercure.com
Sales Range: $25-49.9 Million
Emp.: 125
Home Management Services
N.A.I.C.S.: 721110
Robert Gangliet *(Gen Mgr)*

Accor Hoteles Espana S.A.   (1)
Calle Ribera del Loira 56-58, 28042, Ma-
drid, Spain
Tel.: (34) 902100463
Web Site: http://www.accorhotels.com
Home Management Services
N.A.I.C.S.: 561110

Accor Hotels Belgium NV   (1)
Avenue des Arts 56, Brussels, 1000, Bel-
gium
Tel.: (32) 24816965
Web Site: http://www.accorhotels.com
Home Management Services
N.A.I.C.S.: 721110
Yves Fonck *(CEO)*

Accor Hotels Romania S.R.L.   (1)
37b Calea Victoriei, Bucharest, 010061,
Romania
Tel.: (40) 213088500
Web Site: http://www.accorhotels.com
Home Management Services
N.A.I.C.S.: 721110
Christph Chambocel *(Gen Mgr)*

Accor North America, Inc.   (1)
4001 International Pkwy, Carrollton, TX
75007   **(100%)**
Tel.: (972) 360-9000
Sales Range: $50-74.9 Million
Emp.: 300
Holding Company; Hotel & Restaurant Op-
erator
N.A.I.C.S.: 721110
Sue MacGregor *(VP-Risk Mgmt)*

Subsidiary (Domestic):

Accor Business & Leisure North
America Inc.   (2)
223 Twin Dolphin Dr, Redwood City, CA,
94065
Tel.: (650) 598-9000
Home Management Services
N.A.I.C.S.: 721110

Subsidiary (Non-US):

Accor Canada Inc.   (2)
3670 Hurontario St, Mississauga, L5B 1P3,
ON, Canada
Tel.: (905) 896-1000

Web Site: http://www.novotel.com
Emp.: 150
Home Management Services
N.A.I.C.S.: 721110
Didier Dolivet *(Gen Mgr)*

Fairmont Raffles Hotels International
Inc.   (2)
RBC Building 155 Wellington Street West
Suite 3300, Toronto, M5V 0C3, On, Canada
Tel.: (866) 662-6060
Web Site: http://www.frhi.com
Holding Company; Luxury Hotels & Resorts
Owner & Operator
N.A.I.C.S.: 551112
Michael Glennie *(Pres & COO)*

Subsidiary (Domestic):

Fairmont Hotels & Resorts Inc.   (3)
100 Wellington Street West Suite 1600, To-
ronto, M5K 1B7, ON, Canada
Tel.: (800) 257-7544
Web Site: http://www.fairmontcareers.com
Luxury Hotels & Resorts Owner & Operator
N.A.I.C.S.: 721110
Kiaran MacDonald *(VP-Bermuda & Carib-
bean & Gen Mgr-Fairmont Southampton)*

Unit (US):

The Fairmont Sonoma Mission Inn &
Spa   (4)
100 Boyes Blvd, Sonoma, CA 95476
Tel.: (707) 938-9000
Web Site: http://www.m.fairmont.com
Emp.: 500
Resort Hotel & Spa
N.A.I.C.S.: 721110

Subsidiary (Non-US):

Raffles International Ltd   (3)
1 Beach Road, Singapore, 189673, Singa-
pore
Tel.: (65) 63371886
Web Site: http://www.raffles.com
Luxury Hotels & Resorts Operator
N.A.I.C.S.: 721110

Unit (Domestic):

Workplace Options, LLC   (2)
3020 HighWoods Blvd, Raleigh, NC
27604   **(100%)**
Web Site:
     https://www.workplaceoptions.com
Benefit Administrator for Companies Providing Pre-Tax Dependent Care Benefit to Employees
N.A.I.C.S.: 541612
Alan King *(Pres & COO)*

Subsidiary (Domestic):

Essi Systems, Inc.   (3)
132 Beaver St, San Francisco, CA 94103-
1236
Tel.: (415) 252-8224
Web Site: http://www.essisystems.com
Professional & Management Development
Training
N.A.I.C.S.: 611430
Esther M. Orioli *(Pres & CEO)*

Accor Reservation   (1)
28 Rue Blaise Pascal, 91025, Evry,
France   **(99.88%)**
Tel.: (33) 60879400
Web Site: http://www.accorhotels.com
Sales Range: $25-49.9 Million
Emp.: 50
Floor Covering Retailer
N.A.I.C.S.: 449121

Accor centre de contacts clients   (1)
31 Rue du Colonel-Pierre-Avia, 75904,
Paris, France
Tel.: (33) 825 88 00 00
Web Site: http://www.accor.com
Home Management Services
N.A.I.C.S.: 721110

All Seasons Hotels   (1)
Immeuble Odyssey 110 Av de France,
75210, Paris, France
Tel.: (33) 1 45 38 86 00
Web Site: http://www.all-seasons-hotels.com
Home Management Services
N.A.I.C.S.: 721110
Pierre Lagrange *(Dir-Publ)*

Availpro SAS   (1)
14-16 Bd Poissonniere, 75009, Paris,
France
Tel.: (33) 158625815
Web Site: http://www.site.availpro.com
Software Management Services
N.A.I.C.S.: 541511

Compagnie Internationale des Wag-
ons Lits et du Tourisme S.A.   (1)
51-53 bd Clovis, 1040, Brussels,
Belgium   **(99.44%)**
Home Management Services
N.A.I.C.S.: 721110

Developpements Immobiliers Et Com-
merciaux S.A.   (1)
4 Rue De La Mare Neuve, 91080,
Courcouronnes, France   **(100%)**
Tel.: (33) 169136361
Home Management Services
N.A.I.C.S.: 721110

El Gezirah Hotels Tourism   (1)
El Gezirah Sofitel Hotel Bldg, Cairo, Egypt
Tel.: (20) 227363770
Emp.: 5
Home Management Services
N.A.I.C.S.: 721110
Marie Claire *(Chm)*

Etap Hotels Ltd   (1)
ZI Rue Rene Dingeon, 80100, Abbeville,
France
Tel.: (33) 892680772
Web Site: http://www.etaphotel.com
Home Management Services
N.A.I.C.S.: 721110
Pierre Lagrange *(Dir-Publ)*

Fastbooking S.A.   (1)
64-66 Rue des Archives, 75003, Paris,
France
Tel.: (33) 187213940
Web Site: https://www.d-edge.com
Software Management Services
N.A.I.C.S.: 541511

Formula1 Pty   (1)
Block B 2nd Floor Edenburg Terraces 348
Rivonia Boulevard, Rivonia, Johannesburg,
2128, South Africa
Tel.: (27) 11 807 0750
Home Management Services
N.A.I.C.S.: 721110

Frantour Group   (1)
3 3 Bis, Villa Thoreton, 75015, Paris,
France   **(100%)**
Tel.: (33) 156826000
Web Site: http://www.govoyages.com
Sales Range: $10-24.9 Million
Emp.: 100
Hotel Chain & Travel Business
N.A.I.C.S.: 721110

Go Voyages   (1)
14 Rue De Clery, 75002, Paris,
France   **(100%)**
Tel.: (33) 153404400
Web Site: http://www.govoyages.com
Sales Range: $75-99.9 Million
Emp.: 400
Travel Services
N.A.I.C.S.: 561510
Carlos da Silva *(CEO)*

Hospitality Int. Thailande   (1)
33/JJ6 Wall Street Tower Surawongse
Road, Bangkok, Thailand   **(99.95%)**
Business Services
N.A.I.C.S.: 561499

Katerinska Hotels S.R.O   (1)
Katerinska 38/1476, Prague, 120 00, Czech
Republic
Tel.: (420) 111222333
Web Site: http://www.katerinskahotel.cz
Home Management Services
N.A.I.C.S.: 721110

Mantra Group Limited   (1)
Level 15 50 Cavill Avenue, Surfers Para-
dise, 4217, QLD, Australia
Tel.: (61) 756312500
Web Site: http://www.mantragroup.com.au
Emp.: 5,500
Holding Company; Hotel & Resort Owner,
Operator & Marketer
N.A.I.C.S.: 551112

Accor S.A.—(Continued)

John Lord *(Gen Counsel)*

Subsidiary (Domestic):

Mantra Group Operations Pty. Ltd. (2)
Level 15 50 Cavill Avenue, Surfers Para-
dise, 4217, QLD, Australia
Tel.: (61) 766312600
Web Site: http://www.mantragroup.com.au
Hotel & Resort Operator & Marketer
N.A.I.C.S.: 721110

Subsidiary (Domestic):

Peppers Leisure Pty. Ltd. (3)
Level 15 50 Cavill Avenue, Surfers Para-
dise, 4217, QLD, Australia
Tel.: (61) 7 5631 2500
Web Site: http://www.peppers.com.au
Hotel & Resort Operator
N.A.I.C.S.: 721110

Marara SA (1)
PO Box 6, 98730, Vaitape, French Polyne-
sia
Tel.: (689) 605500
Sales Range: $10-24.9 Million
Emp.: 80
Home Management Services
N.A.I.C.S.: 721110

Mercure (1)
2 Rue De La Mare Neuve, 91021, Evry,
France (100%)
Tel.: (33) 0169368080
Sales Range: $200-249.9 Million
Emp.: 1,200
Business & Leisure Hotels
N.A.I.C.S.: 721110

Movenpick Hotels & Resorts AG (1)
Flughofstrasse 61, CH-8152, Glattbrugg,
Switzerland
Tel.: (41) 447122222
Web Site: http://www.movenpickhotels.com
Sales Range: $1-4.9 Billion
Emp.: 15,000
Hotel & Motel Operator
N.A.I.C.S.: 721110
Paul Mulcahy *(Sr VP-Comml)*

**Movenpick Hotels & Resorts Manage-
ment AG** (1)
Oberneuhofstrasse 12, 6340, Baar, Switzer-
land
Tel.: (41) 417591919
Web Site: http://www.movenpick.com
Hotel & Resort Management Services
N.A.I.C.S.: 721110

Muranowska Sp. z o.o. (1)
Bracka 16, Warsaw, 00-028, Poland
Tel.: (48) 223101000
Home Management Services
N.A.I.C.S.: 721110
Sébastien Deneasr *(Gen Mgr)*

Newrest Wagons-Lits S.A.S. (1)
87 rue du Charolais, 75012, Paris,
France (40%)
Tel.: (33) 153441801
Web Site: http://www.newrest.eu
Sales Range: $300-349.9 Million
Emp.: 1,500
Train Catering & Support Services Contrac-
tor; Owned 60% by Newrest Group Interna-
tional S.A.S. & 40% by Accor S.A.
N.A.I.C.S.: 722320

Novotel (1)
3670 Hurontario St, Mississauga, L5B 1P3,
ON, Canada (100%)
Tel.: (905) 896-1000
Web Site: http://www.novotel.com
Sales Range: $10-24.9 Million
Emp.: 100
Business Travel Accomodations
N.A.I.C.S.: 721110
Alain D'Addio *(Gen Mgr-New York Times
Square)*

Novotel Amsterdam City (1)
Europaboulevard 10, 1083 AD, Amsterdam,
Netherlands (100%)
Tel.: (31) 207219179
Web Site:
https://www.novotelamsterdamcity.com

Sales Range: $25-49.9 Million
Emp.: 60
Hotel
N.A.I.C.S.: 721199

Novotel Athens S.A. (1)
4 Michail Voda Str, 10439, Athens,
Greece (98.53%)
Tel.: (30) 15068707179
Web Site: http://www.novotel.gr
Sales Range: $10-24.9 Million
Emp.: 70
Hotel Line
N.A.I.C.S.: 721110

Novotel Goteborg AB (1)
Klippan 1, S 414 51, Gothenburg,
Sweden (100%)
Tel.: (46) 317202200
Web Site: http://www.novotel.se
Sales Range: $10-24.9 Million
Emp.: 40
Hotel Operator
N.A.I.C.S.: 721110
Jerker Dellblad *(Gen Mgr)*

Orbis S.A. (1)
(52.69%)
Tel.: (48) 228293969
Rev.: $382,370,635
Assets: $854,602,994
Liabilities: $220,839,708
Net Worth: $633,763,287
Earnings: $96,482,450
Emp.: 4,300
Fiscal Year-end: 12/31/2018
Hotel Owner & Operator; Hotel Construction
Services; Car Rental Services
N.A.I.C.S.: 721110
Ireneusz Andrzej Weglowski *(Chm-
Supervisory Bd)*

Subsidiary (Domestic):

Orbis Transport Sp. z o.o. (2)
Ul Lopuszanska 47, Warsaw, 02 232, Po-
land
Tel.: (48) 225001680
Web Site: http://www.orbis-transport.pl
Sales Range: $25-49.9 Million
Emp.: 35
Business Services
N.A.I.C.S.: 926120

Subsidiary (Domestic):

PKS Tarnobrzeg Sp. z o.o. (3)
Ul Zwierzyniecka 30, Tarnobrzeg, 39-400,
Sandomierz, Eoj Podkarpackie, Poland
Tel.: (48) 15 822 17 45
Web Site: http://www.pks.tarnobrzeg.pl
Bus Transportation Services
N.A.I.C.S.: 485113

Subsidiary (Domestic):

PBP Orbis Sp. z o.o. (2)
Ul Kremerowska 5, PL 31130, Krakow, Po-
land
Tel.: (48) 124221805
Travel & Tour Services
N.A.I.C.S.: 561520

Pannonia Hotels RT (1)
Kethly Anna Ter 1, Budapest, 1075, Hun-
gary
Tel.: (36) 14855550
Web Site: http://www.accor.com
Emp.: 5
Home Management Services
N.A.I.C.S.: 721110
Antoine Guego *(COO)*

Pradotel SAS (1)
6 Rue Du Bois Briard, 91080,
Courcouronnes, France
Tel.: (33) 169367500
Home Management Services
N.A.I.C.S.: 721110

Premier Lodge South Africa (1)
33 Bradford Rd Bedford Gardens, Bedford-
view, 2047, South Africa
Tel.: (27) 11 622 1556
Web Site: http://www.accor.com
Sales Range: $10-24.9 Million
Emp.: 25
Home Management Services
N.A.I.C.S.: 721110
Michael Delaney *(Gen Mgr)*

Pullman International Hotels (1)
2, rue de la Mare Neuve, 91021, Evry,
France (100%)
Hotel
N.A.I.C.S.: 721110
Aldina Duarte Ramos *(Dir-Well Being)*

SNC NMP France (1)
Avenue de Verdun, Saint Jean de Braye,
45800, France
Tel.: (33) 238846565
Web Site: http://www.accorhotel.com
Sales Range: $10-24.9 Million
Emp.: 20
Home Management Services
N.A.I.C.S.: 721110
Varriale Mirko *(Mgr)*

Service Concierge SAS (1)
64-66 rue des Archives, 75003, Paris,
France
Tel.: (33) 1 42 89 85 00
Web Site: http://www.johnpaul.com
Emp.: 1,000
Customer Support Services
N.A.I.C.S.: 561499
David Amsellem *(Founder)*

Subsidiary (US):

John Paul San Francisco (2)
575 Market St 4th Fl, San Francisco, CA
94105
Tel.: (415) 905-0922
Concierge Services
N.A.I.C.S.: 812990
Amber Treshnell *(CEO-Americas)*

Subsidiary (Domestic):

2 Places at 1 Time, Inc. (3)
1000 NW 57th Ct Ste 590, Miami, FL
33126 (100%)
Web Site: http://www.2placesat1time.com
All Other Personal Services
N.A.I.C.S.: 812990

So Luxury HMC Sarl (1)
2 rue de la Mare Neuve, 91000, Evry,
France
Tel.: (33) 1 61 61 80 80
Web Site: http://www.sofitel.com
Home Management Services
N.A.I.C.S.: 721110

Societe Abidjanaise (1)
1 Rue Des Gallions Zone Portuaire, San
Pedro, 0101, Cote d'Ivoire
Tel.: (225) 21240361
Home Management Services
N.A.I.C.S.: 721110

**Societe Francaise de Promotion Tour-
istique et Hoteliere SA** (1)
31, rue du Colonel Pierre Avia, Paris,
75015, France (69.54%)
Budget Branded Hotel Operations
N.A.I.C.S.: 721110

**Societe Hoteliere 61 Quai de
Grenelle** (1)
61 Quai Grenelle, 75015, Paris, France
Tel.: (33) 140582000
Home Management Services
N.A.I.C.S.: 721110

Societe Hoteliere Paris Vanves (1)
110 rue Jean Bleuzen, 92170, Vanves,
France (100%)
Tel.: (33) 155950215
Hotel Operations
N.A.I.C.S.: 721110

**Societe Internationale des Hotels
Novotel** (1)
2 Rue De La Mare Neuve, 91021, Evry,
Cedex, France (100%)
Tel.: (33) 169368080
Web Site: http://www.novotel.com
Sales Range: $200-249.9 Million
Emp.: 1,200
Operator of Hotels
N.A.I.C.S.: 721110
Fredrice Gosenhans *(Sr VP-Mktg)*

**Societe Parisienne des Hotels
Economiques** (1)
2 Rue de la Mare Neuve, 91080,
Courcouronnes, France
Tel.: (33) 1 69 36 75 00

Home Management Services
N.A.I.C.S.: 721110

**Societe d'Exploitation d'Agences de
Voyages et de Tourisme SA** (1)
31 rue du Colonel Pierre Avia, 75015, Paris,
France (49.72%)
Tel.: (33) 1 41 33 6000
Web Site: http://www.carlsonwagonlit.fr
Sales Range: $25-49.9 Million
Emp.: 200
Travel Agencies
N.A.I.C.S.: 561510

**Sofitel Luxury Hotels France
SAS** (1)
2 rue de la Mare Neuve, 91000, Evry,
France (100%)
Tel.: (33) 161618080
Web Site: http://www.sofitel.com
Business & Leisure Hotels
N.A.I.C.S.: 721110
Alexandra Byrne *(Gen Mgr-Washington)*

W.L. Tourisme (1)
51-53, bd Clovis, 1040, Brussels,
Belgium (42.26%)
Travel Agency
N.A.I.C.S.: 561510

World Tourist Rejsebureau A/S (1)
Orestads Boulevard 35, 2300, Copenhagen,
Denmark (100%)
Tel.: (45) 33637878
Web Site: http://www.carlsonwagonlit.dk
Sales Range: $25-49.9 Million
Emp.: 100
Travel Agency
N.A.I.C.S.: 561510

ACCORD FINANCIAL CORP.
40 Eglinton Avenue East Suite 602,
Toronto, M4P 3A2, ON, Canada
Tel.: (416) 961-0007   ON
Web Site:
https://www.accordfinancial.com
Year Founded: 1978
ACCFF—(OTCIQ)
Rev.: $60,186,840
Assets: $387,739,018
Liabilities: $320,787,813
Net Worth: $66,951,205
Earnings: ($11,623,562)
Fiscal Year-end: 12/31/23
Finance Company
N.A.I.C.S.: 525990
Ken Hitzig *(Founder & Chm)*

Subsidiaries:

Accord CapX LLC (1)
155 N Wacker Dr 1760, Chicago, IL 60606
Tel.: (312) 893-7400
Web Site: https://www.capxpartners.com
Loan Financing Services
N.A.I.C.S.: 522220
Jeffry S. Pfeffer *(Mng Partner)*

Accord Financial Inc. (1)
40 Eglinton Avenue East Suite 602, To-
ronto, M4P 3A2, ON, Canada (100%)
Tel.: (416) 961-0007
Sales Range: $50-74.9 Million
Emp.: 35
Financial Services
N.A.I.C.S.: 522220

Accord Financial, Inc. (1)
75 Beattie Pl Ste 910, Greenville, SC 29601
Tel.: (864) 271-4384
Web Site: http://www.accordfinancialus.com
Sales Range: $50-74.9 Million
Emp.: 20
Provider of Financial Services
N.A.I.C.S.: 522299

**Accord Small Business Finance
Corp** (1)
889 Harbourside Dr 300, North Vancouver,
V7P 3S1, BC, Canada
Web Site:
https://www.accordsmallbusinessfinance.ca
Loan Financing Services
N.A.I.C.S.: 522220

CapX Partners (1)
155 N Wacker Ste 1760, Chicago, IL
60606

Tel.: (312) 893-7400
Web Site: http://www.capxpartners.com
Specialty Finance Company
N.A.I.C.S.: 522299
Stephen Healey (Mng Dir)

ACCORD GROUP LIMITED

1250 High Road, London, N20 0PB,
United Kingdom
Tel.: (44) 2089209020   **UK**
Web Site:
   http://www.accordgroup.co.uk
Year Founded: 1999
Sales Range: $150-199.9 Million
Emp.: 70
Holding Company; Advertising & Direct Marketing Services
N.A.I.C.S.: 551112
Robert J. Walton (Chm)

Subsidiaries:

MKH   **(1)**
Castlewood House 77-91 New Oxford St,
London, WC1 A 1DG, United Kingdom
Tel.: (44) 2089209173
Web Site: http://www.mkh.co.uk
Sales Range: $25-49.9 Million
Emp.: 30
N.A.I.C.S.: 541810

Branch (Domestic):

MKH   **(2)**
Vega House Opal Drive Fox Milne, Milton
Keynes, MK15 0DF, Buckinghamshire,
United Kingdom
Tel.: (44) 1908 572457
Web Site: http://www.mkh.co.uk
Recruitment Advertising Services
N.A.I.C.S.: 541810
Patricia Keane (Acct Dir)

MKH   **(2)**
235 High Holborn, London, WC1V 7DN,
United Kingdom
Tel.: (44) 20 7395 9600
Web Site: http://www.mkh.co.uk
N.A.I.C.S.: 541810
Danny Cannon (Exec Dir)

ACCORD SYNERGY LTD.

302 Shine Plaza Race Course, Vadodara, 390007, India
Tel.: (91) 2652356800
Web Site:
   https://www.accordsynergy.com
ACCORD—(NSE)
Rev.: $5,387,371
Assets: $3,765,867
Liabilities: $1,029,170
Net Worth: $2,736,698
Earnings: $149,142
Emp.: 251
Fiscal Year-end: 03/31/21
Telecommunication Servicesb
N.A.I.C.S.: 517810
Betulla Asdulla Khan (Mng Dir)

ACCORDIA GOLF TRUST

80 Robinson Road 22-03A, Singapore, 068898, Singapore
Tel.: (65) 65921050
Web Site: http://www.agtrust.com.sg
Year Founded: 2014
ADQU—(CAT)
Rev.: $463,500,540
Assets: $1,435,303,320
Liabilities: $853,017,120
Net Worth: $582,286,200
Earnings: ($113,186,580)
Fiscal Year-end: 03/31/19
Investment Trust Services
N.A.I.C.S.: 525990
Kee Cheok Khoo (Chm)

ACCREDITED DISTRIBUTORS PTY. LTD.

2 Nathan Road, Dandenong, 3175,
VIC, Australia
Tel.: (61) 397038500

Web Site:
   http://www.accredited.com.au
Confectionery Product Distr
N.A.I.C.S.: 445292
Craig Bain (Mng Dir)

ACCRELIST LTD.

10 Ubi Crescent Ubi Techpark Lobby
E 03-95, Singapore, 408564, Singapore
Tel.: (65) 63112900   **SG**
Web Site: http://www.weh.sg
Year Founded: 1986
QZG—(SES)
Rev.: $27,095,152
Assets: $44,643,491
Liabilities: $25,468,301
Net Worth: $19,175,190
Earnings: ($7,451,334)
Emp.: 1,897
Fiscal Year-end: 03/31/23
Holding Company; Electronic Components, Systems & Power Products
Distr & Services
N.A.I.C.S.: 551112
Tc Teh (Dir)

Subsidiaries:

Accrelist A.I. Tech Pte. Ltd.   **(1)**
10 Ubi Crescent 03 94/95/096 Ubi Techpark
Lobby E, Singapore, 408564, Singapore
Tel.: (65) 63112942
Electronic Component Product Mfr
N.A.I.C.S.: 334419
Han Xiao Fang (VP)

Accrelist Crowdfunding Pte. Ltd.   **(1)**
10 UBI Crescent 03-94 UBI Techpark, Singapore, 408564, Singapore
Tel.: (65) 63112900
Financial Services
N.A.I.C.S.: 523999

Accrelist Medical Aesthetics (BM)
Pte. Ltd.   **(1)**
311 New Upper Changi Road B1-12 Bedok
Mall, Singapore, 467360, Singapore
Tel.: (65) 68449768
Electronic Component & Equipment Distr
N.A.I.C.S.: 423690

Subsidiary (Non-US):

Accrelist Medical Aesthetics (Penang)
Sdn. Bhd.   **(2)**
88-N Jalan Masjid Negeri Greenlane,
11600, Penang, Malaysia
Tel.: (60) 46588555
Electronic Component & Equipment Distr
N.A.I.C.S.: 423690

Accrelist Medical Aesthetics (CM)
Pte. Ltd.   **(1)**
Clementi Mall No 04-50, Singapore,
129588, Singapore
Tel.: (65) 69081917
Aesthetic Clinic Operator
N.A.I.C.S.: 621111

Accrelist Medical Aesthetics (CentralaClarke Quay) Pte. Ltd.   **(1)**
Clarke Quay Central No 04-77-82, Singapore, 059817, Singapore
Tel.: (65) 65920762
Aesthetic Clinic Operator
N.A.I.C.S.: 621111

Accrelist Medical Aesthetics (LOT1)
Pte. Ltd.   **(1)**
21 Choa Chu Kang Avenue 4 02-26 Lot
One Shoppers' Mall, Singapore, 689812,
Singapore
Tel.: (65) 62199819
Electronic Component & Equipment Distr
N.A.I.C.S.: 423690

Accrelist Medical Aesthetics (Orchard
Central) Pte. Ltd.   **(1)**
Orchard Central No 05-33/36, Singapore,
238896, Singapore
Tel.: (65) 65091200
Aesthetic Clinic Operator
N.A.I.C.S.: 621111

Accrelist Medical Aesthetics (Raffles
City) Pte. Ltd.   **(1)**

Raffles City Shopping Centre No B2-06/07,
Singapore, 179103, Singapore
Tel.: (65) 62556109
Aesthetic Clinic Operator
N.A.I.C.S.: 621111

Accrelist Medical Aesthetics (SPC)
Pte. Ltd.   **(1)**
10 Eunos Road 8 02-140/141 Singapore
Post Centre, Singapore, 408600, Singapore
Tel.: (65) 67411038
Electronic Component & Equipment Distr
N.A.I.C.S.: 423690

Jubilee Industries Holdings Ltd.   **(1)**
10 Ubi Crescent 03-94 Lobby E, Ubi Techpark, Singapore, 408564,
Singapore   **(65.8%)**
Tel.: (65) 63112900
Web Site: https://www.jihldgs.com
Rev.: $2,469,804
Assets: $16,979,622
Liabilities: $2,957,392
Net Worth: $14,022,230
Earnings: ($2,265,283)
Emp.: 617
Fiscal Year-end: 03/31/2024
Precision Plastic Injection Mold Designer &
Mfr
N.A.I.C.S.: 333511
Terence Yeok Kian Tea (Chm)

Subsidiary (Non-US):

E'Mold Manufacturing (Kunshan) Co.,
Ltd.   **(2)**
No 8 Jiefang Road Technical Development
Zone, Kunshan, 215300, China
Tel.: (86) 512 5730 0011
Precision Mold Design & Fabrication Services
N.A.I.C.S.: 333511

Subsidiary (Domestic):

E'mold Holding Pte. Ltd.   **(2)**
10 Ubi Crescent 03 94/95/96 Ubi Techpark
Lobby E, Singapore, 408564, Singapore
Tel.: (65) 63112968
Plastic Moulding Product Mfr
N.A.I.C.S.: 326199

Jubilee Industries (S) Pte Ltd.   **(2)**
10 Ubi Crescent 03 94/95/96 Ubi Techpark
Lobby E, #01-35 Woodlands Spectrum 1,
Singapore, 738068, Singapore
Tel.: (65) 63112968
Precision Mold Design & Fabrication Services
N.A.I.C.S.: 333511

Subsidiary (Non-US):

Jubilee Manufacturing Sdn Bhd   **(2)**
No 11 Jalan Gemilang 3 Taman Perindustrian Cemerlang, Ulu Tiram, 81800, Johor,
Malaysia
Tel.: (60) 7 867 3681
Precision Mold Design & Fabrication Services
N.A.I.C.S.: 333511

PT Honfoong plastic Industries   **(2)**
Jalan Gaharu Lot 232 233 and 247 Mukakuning, Batamindo Industrial Park,
Batam, Indonesia
Tel.: (62) 611448
Plastic Moulding Product Mfr
N.A.I.C.S.: 326199

ACCRETE, INC.

Kanda Ogawamachi 3-28-5 Axle
Ochanomizu 3rd floor 301, Chiyodaku, Tokyo, 1010052, Japan
Tel.: (81) 5053693778
Web Site: https://www.accreteinc.com
Year Founded: 2014
4395—(TKS)
Rev.: $38,519,970
Assets: $29,855,990
Liabilities: $14,640,850
Net Worth: $15,215,140
Earnings: $233,970
Emp.: 50
Fiscal Year-end: 12/31/23
Information Technology Services
N.A.I.C.S.: 541512

Yusei Tanaka (CEO)

ACCSYS TECHNOLOGIES PLC

4th Floor 3 Moorgate Place, London,
EC2R 6EA, United Kingdom
Tel.: (44) 2074214300   **UK**
Web Site: https://www.accsysplc.com
Year Founded: 2005
AXS—(AIM)
Rev.: $173,164,838
Assets: $242,102,438
Liabilities: $111,172,301
Net Worth: $130,930,138
Earnings: ($74,668,506)
Emp.: 250
Fiscal Year-end: 03/31/23
Intellectual Property & Chemical
Technology Company (Focused on
the Sustainable Transformation of
Wood Through Acetylation)
N.A.I.C.S.: 321999
Hal Stebbins (Dir-Supply Chain &
Customer Svc)

Subsidiaries:

Titan Wood Limited   **(1)**
Brettenham House 2-19 Lancaster Place,
66 Hammersmith Road, London, WC2E
7EN, United Kingdom
Tel.: (44) 2074214300
Web Site: http://www.accsysplc.com
Sales Range: $25-49.9 Million
Biotechnology Research & Development
Services
N.A.I.C.S.: 541714

Subsidiary (US):

Titan Wood Inc.   **(2)**
5000 Quorum Dr 620, Dallas, TX 75254
Tel.: (972) 233-6565
Web Site: http://www.accoya.com
Sales Range: $10-24.9 Million
Biotechnology Research & Development
Services
N.A.I.C.S.: 541714

Titan Wood Technology B.V.   **(1)**
Westervoortsedijk 73, Postbus 2147, 6827
AV, Arnhem, Netherlands
Tel.: (31) 263201400
Web Site: http://www.accoya.com
Sales Range: $25-49.9 Million
Emp.: 50
Wood Products Mfr
N.A.I.C.S.: 321999
Victor Vos (Mgr-Sls)

Tricoya Technologies Limited   **(1)**
Brettenham House 19 Lancaster Place,
London, WC2E 7EN, United Kingdom
Tel.: (44) 2074214300
Timber Wood Mfr
N.A.I.C.S.: 321113

ACCTON TECHNOLOGY CORPORATION

No 1 Creation 3rd Rd Hsinchu Science Park, East Dist, Hsinchu,
30077, Taiwan
Tel.: (886) 35770270
Web Site: http://www.accton.com
Year Founded: 1997
Rev.: $428,000,000
Emp.: 900
Computer Networking & Communication Equipment Mfr
N.A.I.C.S.: 334118
Samuel Chang (VP-Sls & Mktg)

Subsidiaries:

ALFA Network Inc   **(1)**
4F-1 No 106 Rueiguang Rd, Neihu District,
Taipei, Taiwan
Tel.: (886) 227968477
Web Site: http://www.alfa.com.tw
Communication Equipment Mfr
N.A.I.C.S.: 335929

Accton Technology Corp   **(1)**
1200 Crossman Ave Ste 130, Sunnyvale,
CA 94089
Tel.: (408) 747-0994

Accton Technology Corporation—(Continued)

Communication Equipment Distr
N.A.I.C.S.: 423690

E-Direct Corp (1)
3773 E Cherry Creek N Dr Ste 575, Denver, CO 80209
Tel.: (303) 648-4046
Communication Equipment Distr
N.A.I.C.S.: 423690

SMC Networks Inc (1)
20 Mason, Irvine, CA 92618
Tel.: (949) 679-8000
Communication Equipment Distr
N.A.I.C.S.: 423690

SMC Networks Spain SL (1)
Calle Fructuos Gelabert 6-8 2 Edificio Conata II, Sant Joan Despi, 8970, Spain
Tel.: 934774920
Communication Equipment Distr
N.A.I.C.S.: 423690

ACCU HOLDING AG
Gerliswilstrasse 17, 6021, Emmenbrucke, Switzerland
Tel.: (41) 44 318 88 00
Web Site: http://www.accuholding.ch
Year Founded: 1896
Sales Range: $25-49.9 Million
Emp.: 113
Real Estate Development Services
N.A.I.C.S.: 531390
Andreas Kratzer *(Interim Chm & Interim CEO)*

Subsidiaries:

RCT Hydraulic-Tooling AG (1)
Von Roll-Areal 2, CH-4712, Klus, Switzerland
Tel.: (41) 62 386 9020
Industrial Machinery
N.A.I.C.S.: 333248

RCT Sachsen GmbH (1)
Tuchschererstrasse 15, D-09116, Chemnitz, Germany
Tel.: (49) 371 236 2059
Industrial Services
N.A.I.C.S.: 333248

ACCURA MACHINERY & MANUFACTURING (TAICANG) CO., LTD.
78 Ningbo Eastroad, Taicang, Jiangsu, China
Tel.: (86) 51281604263
Web Site:
http://www.greatwallmachinery.com.cn
Year Founded: 2004
Industrial Machinery Mfr & Distr
N.A.I.C.S.: 333248

ACCURACY SHIPPING LIMITED
ASL House Plot no 11 Survey No 42 Near Genus Factory, Indian Oil Pump Road Meghpar Borichi, Anjar, 370110, Gujarat, India
Tel.: (91) 2836258251
Web Site: https://www.aslindia.net
Year Founded: 2001
ACCURACY—(NSE)
Rev.: $106,333,608
Assets: $34,686,713
Liabilities: $20,671,145
Net Worth: $14,015,568
Earnings: $996,143
Emp.: 430
Fiscal Year-end: 03/31/23
Logistic Services
N.A.I.C.S.: 488510
Vinay D. Tripathi *(Mng Dir)*

Subsidiaries:

ARS International Private Limited (1)
ASPL House Plot No 11 Survey No 42 B/H Genus Factory Meghpar Borichi, IOC Petrol Pump Road, Anjar, 370201, Gujarat, India

Tel.: (91) 2836228254
Web Site: https://www.arsint.org
Truck Trailer Mfr
N.A.I.C.S.: 336212

ACCURSIA CAPITAL GMBH
Maximilianstrasse 52, D-80538, Munich, Germany
Tel.: (49) 89 2421 8877 00
Web Site: http://www.accursia-capital.de
Private Equity
N.A.I.C.S.: 523999
Martin Scheiblegger *(Mng Dir)*

Subsidiaries:

Cenpa S.A.S. (1)
5 rue de la Gare, 67590, Schweighouse, France
Tel.: (33) 38872090
Web Site: http://www.cenpa.fr
Converted Paper Products Mfr & Sales
N.A.I.C.S.: 322299

Plati Elettroforniture S.p.A. (1)
Via Napione 22, 10124, Turin, BG, Italy.
Tel.: (39) 0354993511
Web Site: http://www.plati.it
Automotive Cable Harnesses Distr
N.A.I.C.S.: 423610

ACCUSTEM SCIENCES, INC.
14-15 Conduit Street, London, W1S 2XJ, United Kingdom
Tel.: (44) 2074952379
Web Site: https://www.accustem.com
Year Founded: 2020
ACUT—(OTCQB)
Assets: $939,689
Liabilities: $1,079,239
Net Worth: ($139,550)
Earnings: ($3,746,419)
Emp.: 4
Fiscal Year-end: 12/31/22
Biotechnology Research & Development Services
N.A.I.C.S.: 541714
Wendy Blosser *(CEO)*

ACD SYSTEMS INTERNATIONAL INC.
129-1335 Bear Mountain Pkwy, Victoria, V9B 6T9, BC, Canada
Tel.: (778) 817-1168
Web Site:
http://www.acdsystems.com
Year Founded: 1993
Sales Range: $10-24.9 Million
Emp.: 141
Digital Imaging & Communications Software Products
N.A.I.C.S.: 541511

ACDC METALS LTD.
Level 6 111 Collins Street, Melbourne, 3000, VIC, Australia
Tel.: (61) 385487880
Web Site:
https://www.acdcmetals.com.au
Year Founded: 2021
ADC—(ASX)
Rev.: $128,494
Assets: $7,283,257
Liabilities: $216,933
Net Worth: $7,066,324
Earnings: ($335,123)
Fiscal Year-end: 06/30/24
Support Activities for Metal Mining
N.A.I.C.S.: 213114
Tamara Barr *(Sec)*

ACE ACHIEVE INFOCOM LIMITED
Clarendon House 2 Church Street, Hamilton, HM 11, Bermuda
Tel.: (441) 441 295 1422
Year Founded: 2004
A75—(SES)

Sales Range: $25-49.9 Million
Investment Holding Services
N.A.I.C.S.: 551112
Zelin Deng *(Founder, Chm & CEO)*

ACE EDUTREND LTD.
812 Aggarwal Cyber Plaza-1 Netaji Subhash Place, Shahdara, New Delhi, 110034, India
Tel.: (91) 1125702148
Web Site:
https://www.aceedutrend.co.in
Year Founded: 1993
530093—(BOM)
Rev.: $46,096
Assets: $1,975,101
Liabilities: $625,639
Net Worth: $1,349,462
Earnings: ($73,098)
Fiscal Year-end: 03/31/20
Educational Support Services
N.A.I.C.S.: 611710
Monendra Srivastava *(Mng Dir)*

ACE GLOBAL BUSINESS ACQUISITION LIMITED
6/F Unit B Central 88 88-98 Des Voeux Road, Central, K3 00000, China (Hong Kong)
Tel.: (852) 90867042
Year Founded: 2020
ACBA—(NASDAQ)
Rev.: $1,923,070
Assets: $49,073,620
Liabilities: $53,148,551
Net Worth: ($4,074,931)
Earnings: $1,084,218
Emp.: 2
Fiscal Year-end: 12/31/22
Investment Services
N.A.I.C.S.: 523999
Eugene Wong *(Chm & CEO)*

ACE HIGHTECH CO., LTD.
15 Gwahaksaneop 4-Ro Oksan-Myeon, Heungdeok-gu, Cheongju, 363911, Korea (South)
Tel.: (82) 31 7636240
Sales Range: $1-9.9 Million
Emp.: 22
Electronic Component Mfr & Distr
N.A.I.C.S.: 334413
Seok Su Jang *(CEO)*

ACE INTEGRATED SOLUTIONS LTD.
B-13 DSIDC Complex Patparganj Industrial Area, Noida, 201301, Uttar Pradesh, India
Tel.: (91) 9650339995
Web Site:
https://www.aceintegrated.com
Year Founded: 1995
ACEINTEG—(NSE)
Rev.: $852,467
Assets: $2,463,881
Liabilities: $251,783
Net Worth: $2,212,098
Earnings: $56,352
Emp.: 11
Fiscal Year-end: 03/31/23
Information Technology Management Services
N.A.I.C.S.: 541512
Chandra Shekhar Verma *(Mng Dir)*

ACE LIBERTY & STONE PLC
3A Pont Street, London, SW1X 9EJ, United Kingdom
Tel.: (44) 2072018340
Web Site:
https://www.acelibertyandstone.com
Year Founded: 2007
ALSP—(AQSE)
Rev.: $7,075,590
Assets: $105,408,374

Liabilities: $63,201,473
Net Worth: $42,206,901
Earnings: $1,610,372
Emp.: 2
Fiscal Year-end: 04/30/22
Real Estate Investment Services
N.A.I.C.S.: 531190
Ismail Ghandour *(CEO)*

ACE MEN ENGG WORKS LIMITED
Office No 16 Gulab Tower Thaltej, Ahmedabad, 380054, Gujarat, India
Tel.: (91) 9681662494
Web Site:
https://www.acumenengg.co.in
539661—(BOM)
Rev.: $95,842
Assets: $479,683
Liabilities: $39,553
Net Worth: $440,129
Earnings: $33,135
Fiscal Year-end: 03/31/21
Financial Support Services
N.A.I.C.S.: 523999
Priti Sharma *(CFO)*

ACE PILLAR CO., LTD.
12F No 558 Zhongyuan Road, Sanchong Dist, New Taipei City, 241, R.O.C, Taiwan
Tel.: (886) 229958400
Web Site: https://www.acepillar.com
Year Founded: 1984
8374—(TAI)
Rev.: $99,800,611
Assets: $96,668,691
Liabilities: $29,162,954
Net Worth: $67,505,737
Earnings: ($558,553)
Emp.: 365
Fiscal Year-end: 12/31/23
Automatic Mechatronics Components
N.A.I.C.S.: 333612

Subsidiaries:

Ace Pillar (S) Pte Ltd (1)
1 Kaki Bukit Ave 3 KB-1 06-02, Singapore, 416087, Singapore
Tel.: (65) 6 748 6586
Web Site: http://www.acepillar.com
Sales Range: $50-74.9 Million
Emp.: 4
Automation Components Supplier
N.A.I.C.S.: 423610

Hong Kong Ace Pillar Enterprise Co., Ltd. (1)
Room 10 12/F Shatin Galleria 18-24 Shan Mei Street, Fo Tan, Sha Tin, China (Hong Kong)
Tel.: (852) 2 690 1859
Automation Product Mfr & Distr
N.A.I.C.S.: 333998

HongKong Ace Pillar Co., Ltd (1)
Rm 10 12 F Shatin Galleria 18-24 Shan Mei St, Fotan, China (Hong Kong)
Tel.: (852) 26901859
Web Site: http://www.acepillar.com.hk
Sales Range: $25-49.9 Million
Emp.: 4
Automatic Mechatronics Distr
N.A.I.C.S.: 423610

Suzhou Super Pillar Automation Equipment Co., Ltd. (1)
Block F 2nd Boji Technology Pioneer Park Room 301 Taishan Road, Suzhou High-tech Zone, Suzhou, 215000, China
Tel.: (86) 5126 958 1355
Automation Product Mfr & Distr
N.A.I.C.S.: 333998

Tianjin Ace Pillar Co., Ltd. (1)
Tel.: (86) 2223556000
Automation Product Mfr & Distr
N.A.I.C.S.: 333998

Tianjin Ace Pillar Enterprise Co., Ltd. (1)
No 3 West 10 Avenue, Tianjin Airport Eco-I

nomic Area, Tianjin, 300308, China
Tel.: (86) 2223556000
Web Site: http://www.acepillar.com.cn
Sales Range: $10-24.9 Million
Emp.: 60
Automatic Mechanic Components Distr
N.A.I.C.S.: 423830

ACE SOFTWARE EXPORTS LTD.
801 Everest Commercial Complex
Limda Chowk, Rajkot, 360 001, Gujarat, India
Tel.: (91) 6464800614
Web Site: https://www.acesoftex.com
531525—(BOM)
Rev.: $1,445,972
Assets: $3,181,747
Liabilities: $441,837
Net Worth: $2,739,910
Earnings: ($110,333)
Emp.: 42
Fiscal Year-end: 03/31/22
Electronic Publishing Services
N.A.I.C.S.: 513130
Vikram Bhupat Sanghani (Co-Founder & Co-Mng Dir)

Subsidiaries:

Speedwell Engineers Pvt. Ltd. (1)
R C Electronics Compound Opp Rajkamal
Petrol Pump Outside, Octroi Naka Gondal
Road Samrat Industrial Area, Rajkot, 360
004, Gujarat, India
Tel.: (91) 8047642557
Web Site: https://www.frpproductindia.com
Engineering Consulting Services
N.A.I.C.S.: 541330

ACE TECHNOLOGIES CORP.
16 Harmony-ro 187 beon-gil, Yeonsu-gu, Incheon, 22013, Korea (South)
Tel.: (82) 328185500
Web Site: https://www.acetech.co.kr
Year Founded: 1980
088800—(KRS)
Rev.: $189,920,318
Assets: $299,822,031
Liabilities: $246,252,804
Net Worth: $53,569,227
Earnings: ($23,856,407)
Emp.: 90
Fiscal Year-end: 12/31/22
Radio Frequency Products Mfr
N.A.I.C.S.: 334220
Koo Gwan Young (CEO)

Subsidiaries:

Ace Antenna Co., Ltd. (1)
Dong Van II Industrial park, Bach Thuong
commune Duy Tien district, Ha Nam, Vietnam
Tel.: (84) 3516259800
Wireless Communication Equipment Mfr
N.A.I.C.S.: 334220

Ace Antenna Company Inc. (1)
47 Post, Irvine, CA 92618
Tel.: (949) 215-2888
Wireless Communication Equipment Mfr
N.A.I.C.S.: 334220

Ace Antenna India Private
Limited (1)
272 Mettupalayam Road, Panrutti A Village
Sri Perumbudur Taluk, Kanchipuram, 631
604, Tamil Nadu, India
Tel.: (91) 4437175603
Wireless Communication Equipment Mfr
N.A.I.C.S.: 334220

AceAxis Ltd (1)
602 Delta Business Park Welton Road,
Swindon, SN5 7XF, United Kingdom
Tel.: (44) 1793540884
Web Site: https://www.aceaxis.co.uk
Wireless Communication Equipment Development Services
N.A.I.C.S.: 517112

Antenna & Technology Corp. (1)
Dalvagen 14, 169 56, Solna, Sweden
Tel.: (46) 87127374

Wireless Communication Equipment Mfr
N.A.I.C.S.: 334220

Dongguan Ace Technology Co.,
Ltd. (1)
Gaolong West Road, Gaobu Town, Dong-
guan, Guangdong, China
Tel.: (86) 76988783009
Wireless Communication Equipment Mfr
N.A.I.C.S.: 334220

Gaoyao Ace Mechatronix Co.,
Ltd. (1)
Century Road Jindu Foreign Investment
Zone, Gaoyao, Guangdong, China
Tel.: (86) 7588507591
Wireless Communication Equipment Mfr
N.A.I.C.S.: 334220

Gaoyao Acedie Casting Technology
Co., Ltd. (1)
Century Road Jindu Foreign Investment
Zone, Gaoyao, Guangdong, China
Tel.: (86) 7588512118
Wireless Communication Equipment Mfr
N.A.I.C.S.: 334220

Gaoyao G-Ace Industry Co., Ltd. (1)
Century Road Jindu Foreign Investment
Zone, Gaoyao, Guangdong, China
Tel.: (86) 7588512190
Wireless Communication Equipment Mfr
N.A.I.C.S.: 334220

Jiangmen Ace Surface Treatment
Co., Ltd. (1)
B Building No102, Plating Industry Zone
Yamne Town Xinhui Distirct, Jiangmen,
Guangdong, China
Tel.: (86) 7506238060
Wireless Communication Equipment Mfr
N.A.I.C.S.: 334220

Shin Ah Limited (1)
Unit 703A 7/F Mirror Tower 61 Mody Road
TST East, Kowloon, China (Hong Kong)
Tel.: (852) 23696300
Wireless Communication Equipment Mfr
N.A.I.C.S.: 334220

ACEA S.P.A.
Piazzale Ostiense 2, 00154, Rome,
Italy
Tel.: (39) 0657991   IT
Web Site: https://www.acea.it
Year Founded: 1909
ACE—(ITA)
Rev.: $226,336,819,769
Assets: $13,011,440,558
Liabilities: $9,895,109,837
Net Worth: $3,116,330,721
Earnings: $224,043,535,742
Emp.: 733
Fiscal Year-end: 12/31/23
Water & Electric Power Distribution &
Production Services
N.A.I.C.S.: 221310
Stefano Antonio Donnarumma (CEO)

Subsidiaries:

Acea Ato 2 S.p.A. (1)
Piazzale Ostiense 2, 00154, Rome, Italy
Tel.: (39) 0657991
Web Site: http://www.aceaato2.it
Drinking Water Supplier
N.A.I.C.S.: 221310

Acea Dominicana S.A. (1)
Autopista las Americas Esq Calle Mason-
eria Ensanche Ozama, Santo Domingo,
Distrito Nacional, Dominican Republic
Tel.: (809) 5981722
Web Site: https://www.aceadominicana.com
Sales Range: $125-149.9 Million
Emp.: 120
Waste Treatment Services
N.A.I.C.S.: 221310

Acea Energia S.p.A. (1)
Ple Ostiense 2, 00154, Rome, Italy
Tel.: (39) 0657991
Web Site: https://www.acea.it
Natural Gas Services
N.A.I.C.S.: 561790

Acea Molise srl (1)
Piazzale Ostiense 2, 00154, Rome, Italy

Tel.: (39) 0657991
Web Site: https://www.gruppo.acea.it
Drinking Water Supplier
N.A.I.C.S.: 221310

Acearieti S.R.L. (1)
Piazzale Ostiense 2, 00154, Rome, Italy
Tel.: (39) 0657991
Drinking Water Supplier
N.A.I.C.S.: 221310

Acque Industriali S.R.L. (1)
Via Bellatalla 1, Ospedaletto, Pisa, Italy
Tel.: (39) 050843553
Web Site: https://www.acqueindustriali.net
Environmental Consulting Services
N.A.I.C.S.: 541620

Acque Servizi S.R.L. (1)
Via ABellatalla 1, Ospedaletto, 56121, Pisa,
Italy
Tel.: (39) 050843111
Web Site: https://www.acqueservizi.net
Emp.: 120
Water Structure Construction Services
N.A.I.C.S.: 237110

Adistribuzionegas S.R.L. (1)
Via L Galvani 17/A, 47122, Forli, FC, Italy
Tel.: (39) 0543722046
Web Site: https://www.adistribuzionegas.it
Natural Gas Distr
N.A.I.C.S.: 486210

Areti SPA (1)
Piazzale Ostiense 2, 00154, Rome, Italy
Tel.: (39) 0657991
Sales Range: $75-99.9 Million
Emp.: 100
Electric Power Distribution Services
N.A.I.C.S.: 221122

Cesap Vendita Gas S.R.L. (1)
P zza Umberto I n 2-3 p t, 06083, Bastia
Umbra, Italy
Tel.: (39) 0758010703
Web Site: https://www.cesap.it
Natural Gas Supplier
N.A.I.C.S.: 221210

Consorcio Agua Azul S.A. (1)
Calle Amador Merino Reyna n 307 Oficina
803, San Isidro, Lima, Peru
Tel.: (51) 12049860
Web Site: http://www.caa.com.pe
Water Supply Projects Operation & Mainte-
nance Services
N.A.I.C.S.: 221310

Ferrocart S.R.L. (1)
Via A Vanzetti 34/E, 05100, Terni, Italy
Tel.: (39) 0744300515
Web Site: https://www.ferrocart.it
Recycling & Waste Materials Services
N.A.I.C.S.: 562920

Italmacero S.R.L. (1)
Sede Amm Via Raimondo dalla Costa
48/50, 41122, Modena, Italy
Tel.: (39) 059254041
Web Site: https://www.italmacero.it
Recycling & Waste Paper Services
N.A.I.C.S.: 562119

Le Soluzioni Scarl (1)
Via Garigliano 1, Empoli, 50053, Florence,
Italy
Tel.: (39) 05711963716
Web Site: https://www.lesoluzioni.net
Business Consulting Services
N.A.I.C.S.: 541611

S.E.R. Plast S.R.L. (1)
Contrada Stampalone, Cellino Attanasio,
64036, Teramo, Italy
Tel.: (39) 086157276
Web Site: https://www.serplast-srl.it
Plastic Materials Mfr
N.A.I.C.S.: 325211

SIMAM S.p.A. (1)
Via Cimabue 11/2, 60019, Senigallia, AN,
Italy
Tel.: (39) 0716610040
Web Site: https://www.simamspa.it
Environmental Consulting Services
N.A.I.C.S.: 541620

Technologies for Water Services
S.p.A. (1)
Via Ticino 9, 25015, Desenzano del Garda,

BS, Italy
Tel.: (39) 0309990553
Web Site: https://www.twsacea.com
Environmental Consulting Services
N.A.I.C.S.: 541620

Umbra Acque S.p.A. (1)
Via G Benucci N 162, 06135, Perugia, Italy
Tel.: (39) 0755978011
Web Site: http://www.umbraacque.it
Drinking Water Supplier
N.A.I.C.S.: 221310

ACEBED CO. LTD.
55-35 Sanggok-ro, Samseong-
myeong, Eumseong, 27658,
Chungcheongbuk-do, Korea (South)
Tel.: (82) 438771881
Web Site: https://www.acebed.com
Year Founded: 1963
003800—(KRS)
Rev.: $266,338,633
Assets: $529,870,384
Liabilities: $63,488,968
Net Worth: $466,381,416
Earnings: $45,380,901
Emp.: 619
Fiscal Year-end: 12/31/20
Bed Mfr
N.A.I.C.S.: 337122
Sungho Ahn (CEO)

Subsidiaries:

ACE BED International Pte Ltd. (1)
11 Woodlands Close 08-39, Singapore,
737853, Singapore
Tel.: (65) 62629077
Web Site: http://eng-acebed.com
Mattresses Distr
N.A.I.C.S.: 423210

Acebed Co. Ltd. - Guangzhou
Factory (1)
Industrial Bldg Da Shi Shan Rd Zhu Jiang
Cun, Huang Pu District, Guangzhou, China
Tel.: (86) 20 8228 7293
Mattress Mfr
N.A.I.C.S.: 337910

Acebed Co. Ltd. - Yeoju Factory (1)
23-13 Heonbadi-gil, Ganam-eup, Yeoju,
12655, Gyeonggi-do, Korea (South)
Tel.: (82) 318838781
Mattress Mfr
N.A.I.C.S.: 337910

ACEGAS-APS SPA
Via Del Teatro 5, 34121, Trieste, Italy
Tel.: (39) 0407793459
Web Site: http://www.acegas-aps.it
Rev.: $647,267,650
Emp.: 1,000
Water, Electricity, Gas Distribution &
Waste Collection
N.A.I.C.S.: 221122
Carlo Emanuele Pepe (Mgr)

Subsidiaries:

APS Sinergia S.p.A. (1)
Via Monta 29, 35138, Padua, Italy
Tel.: (39) 0498908111
Web Site: http://www.sinergiespa.com
Facility Management & Energy Services
N.A.I.C.S.: 561210

ACEITES BORGES PONT, S.A.
Avenida Jose Trepat s/n, Tarrega,
25300, Lerida, Spain
Tel.: (34) 973501212   ES
Web Site:
http://www.borgesinternational.com
Year Founded: 1896
Sales Range: $100-124.9 Million
Emp.: 800
Mfr of Edible Oils & Dried Foods
N.A.I.C.S.: 311423
Jose Pont (Founder)

Subsidiaries:

STAR Fine Foods-Borges USA (1)
4652 E Date Ave, Fresno, CA 93725

Aceites Borges Pont, S.A.—(Continued)

Tel.: (559) 498-2900
Web Site: http://www.starfinefoods.com
Sales Range: $25-49.9 Million
Emp.: 24
Olive Oil, Wine Vinegar, Maraschino Cherries, Onions, Olives, Sundried Tomatoes, Pickle Specialties, Capers, Anchovies, Peppers, Jalapeno Peppers, Chili Peppers Importer
N.A.I.C.S.: 424490

ACEK DESARROLLO Y GESTION INDUSTRIAL SL

Alfonso XII 16, Madrid, 28014, Spain
Tel.: (34) 91 379 19 99
Holding Company
N.A.I.C.S.: 551112

Subsidiaries:

Gestamp Automacion S.A.   **(1)**
Pol Ind de Lebario s/n, 48220, Abadino, Biscay, Spain   **(100%)**
Tel.: (34) 944507010
Web Site: http://www.gestamp.com
Sales Range: $1-4.9 Billion
Emp.: 8,000
Automotive Component & Structural System Mfr
N.A.I.C.S.: 336370
Francisco Jose Riberas Mera *(Chm)*

Subsidiary (Domestic):

Adral, matriceria y puesta a punto, S.L.   **(2)**
Poligono Industrial De Santelices S/N Pabellon A7, Muskiz, 48550, Spain
Tel.: (34) 946323030
Automobile Parts Mfr
N.A.I.C.S.: 336390

Subsidiary (Non-US):

Autotech Engineering Deutschland, GmbH   **(2)**
Westfalenstrasse 36, 33647, Bielefeld, Germany
Tel.: (49) 521 922790 01
Automotive Spare Parts Distr
N.A.I.C.S.: 423120

Edscha Holding GmbH   **(2)**
Hohenhagener Strasse 26-28, 42855, Remscheid, Germany
Tel.: (49) 21913630
Web Site: http://www.edscha.com
Emp.: 3,000
Holding Company; Motor Vehicle Hinge Systems & Driver Controls Developer & Mfr
N.A.I.C.S.: 551112
Francisco Jose Riberas Mera *(Chm-Mgmt Bd)*

Subsidiary (Non-US):

Edscha AAPICO Automotive Co., Ltd.   **(3)**
99 Moo1 Hitec Industrial Estate Tambol Ban Lane, Amphur Bang Pa-In, Ayutthaya, 13160, Thailand
Tel.: (66) 35 350 880
Automobile Spare Parts Mfr
N.A.I.C.S.: 336390

Subsidiary (Domestic):

Edscha Automotive Hauzenberg GmbH   **(3)**
Wastlmuhlstr 16, 94051, Hauzenberg, Germany
Tel.: (49) 8586 608 0
Automotive Spare Parts Distr
N.A.I.C.S.: 423120

Edscha Automotive Hengersberg GmbH   **(3)**
Scharwachterstr 5, 94491, Hengersberg, Germany
Tel.: (49) 9901 17 0
Automotive Spare Parts Distr
N.A.I.C.S.: 423120

Subsidiary (US):

Edscha Automotive Michigan Inc.   **(3)**

100 Fair St, Lapeer, MI 48446
Tel.: (810) 245-3100
Automotive Spare Parts Distr
N.A.I.C.S.: 423120

Subsidiary (Non-US):

Edscha Briey, S.A.S.   **(3)**
Pole d'Activites Industrielles Technologiques de Briey, BP 101, 54154, Briey, France
Tel.: (33) 3824 71150
Automotive Spare Parts Distr
N.A.I.C.S.: 423120

Edscha Burgos, S.A.   **(3)**
C/Gregorio Lopez Bravo 89, Poligono Industrial, 09001, Burgos, Spain
Tel.: (34) 947 473 400
Automotive Spare Parts Distr
N.A.I.C.S.: 423120

Edscha Do Brasil, Ltda.   **(3)**
Alameda Edscha 81, 18103-006, Sorocaba, Brazil
Tel.: (55) 15 2101 8800
Web Site: http://www.edscha.com
Emp.: 409
Automotive Spare Parts Distr
N.A.I.C.S.: 423120
Henrique Deutsch *(Mgr-Pur)*

Edscha Engineering France S.A.S   **(3)**
Pole Technique et Commercial 4 Avenue du Quebec, 91978, Les Ulis, France
Tel.: (33) 1 6092 1490
Automotive Spare Parts Distr
N.A.I.C.S.: 423120

Subsidiary (Domestic):

Edscha Engineering, GmbH.   **(3)**
Hohenhagener Str 26-28, 42855, Remscheid, Germany
Tel.: (49) 2191 36 30
Automotive Spare Parts Distr
N.A.I.C.S.: 423120

Subsidiary (Non-US):

Edscha Hradec S.R.O.   **(3)**
Dolni Skrychov 118, 37701, Jindrichuv Hradec, Czech Republic
Tel.: (420) 384 341 511
Automotive Spare Parts Distr
N.A.I.C.S.: 423120

Edscha PHA Ltd.   **(3)**
21-12 Asan-ro 1233, Chungcheongnam-do, Asan, Korea (South)
Tel.: (82) 41 542 2620
Automobile Spare Parts Mfr
N.A.I.C.S.: 336390

Edscha Santander, S.L.   **(3)**
Poligono Industrial de Guarnizo 44 a 47, 39611, Guarnizo, Spain
Tel.: (34) 942 296 200
Automotive Spare Parts Distr
N.A.I.C.S.: 423120
Christiaan Blokpoel *(Dir-Tech)*

Edscha Velky Meder S.R.O.   **(3)**
Mostova 41, 93201, Velky Meder, Slovakia
Tel.: (421) 31 5904 211
Web Site: http://www.hr.com
Emp.: 130
Automotive Spare Parts Distr
N.A.I.C.S.: 423120
Fulop Tebor *(Mng Dir)*

Jui Li Edscha Body Systems, Co., Ltd.   **(3)**
TaiwanNo 10 1 Alley, 960 Lane Min-Tsu 1st Road, Kaohsiung, Taiwan
Tel.: (886) 7346 4685
Automotive Spare Parts Distr
N.A.I.C.S.: 423120

Shanghai Edscha Machinery Co., Ltd.   **(3)**
No 2 Jiang Yang South Rd, Shanghai, 200434, China
Tel.: (86) 21 5681 5681
Automotive Spare Parts Distr
N.A.I.C.S.: 423120
Chong Long *(Gen Mgr)*

Subsidiary (Non-US):

GGM Puebla, S.A. de C.V.   **(2)**

Parque Ind FINSA Lateral Arco Norte Km 25 No 4 San Francisco, Ocotlan Parque Industrial Ocotlan, 72680, Puebla, Mexico
Tel.: (52) 2226364160
Automotive Spare Parts Distr
N.A.I.C.S.: 423120

Subsidiary (Domestic):

Gestamp Abrera, S.A.   **(?)**
Doctor Fleming 9-13 Pol Ind Can Estella s/n 08635, Barcelona, Spain
Tel.: (34) 93 775 85 00
Automotive Spare Parts Distr
N.A.I.C.S.: 423120

Subsidiary (Non-US):

Gestamp Aguas Calientes, S.A. de C.V.   **(2)**
Avda Japon n 124, San Francisco de los Romos, 20300, Aguascalientes, Mexico
Tel.: (52) 449 910 91 40
Automotive Spare Parts Distr
N.A.I.C.S.: 423120

Subsidiary (Domestic):

Gestamp Aragon, S.A.   **(2)**
Pol Ind El Pradillo 6, Pedrola, Spain
Tel.: (34) 976 61 61 44
Automotive Spare Parts Distr
N.A.I.C.S.: 423120

Subsidiary (Non-US):

Gestamp Autocomponents (Dongguan),Co. Ltd.   **(2)**
Fuxing Road, ECO-Indrustrial Park, 523000, Dongguan, China
Tel.: (86) 769 8938 1300
Automotive Spare Parts Distr
N.A.I.C.S.: 423120

Gestamp Autocomponents (Shenyang), Co. Ltd.   **(2)**
No 188 of No 22 Kaifa Road, 110141, Shenyang, China
Tel.: (86) 24 2550 3847
Automotive Spare Parts Distr
N.A.I.C.S.: 423120

Plant (Non-US):

Gestamp Automocion S.A. - GMF Otomotiv Plant   **(2)**
TOSB 1 Cad 14, Yol Cayirova Kocaeli, Gebze, Turkiye
Tel.: (90) 2626 582612
Automobile Spare Parts Mfr
N.A.I.C.S.: 336390

Gestamp Automocion S.A. - Gestamp Baires-Escobar (I, II) Plant   **(2)**
Colectora Este Km 48, y c/ Victoria Escobar, 1625, Buenos Aires, Argentina
Tel.: (54) 11 4014 0300
Automobile Spare Parts Mfr
N.A.I.C.S.: 336390

Gestamp Automocion S.A. - Gestamp Beycelik (I, II) Plant   **(2)**
Dermitas Organize San Bol, Kardelen Sk n 10, 16013, Bursa, Turkiye
Tel.: (90) 224 294 83 00
Web Site: http://www.beycelik.com
Automobile Spare Parts Mfr
N.A.I.C.S.: 336390

Gestamp Automocion S.A. - Gestamp Gravatai Plant   **(2)**
Rodovia BR 290 Km 67 Complexo Ind, Automotivo de Gravatai, 94060-520, Gravatai, Brazil
Tel.: (55) 51 3208 6600
Automobile Spare Parts Mfr
N.A.I.C.S.: 336390

Gestamp Automocion S.A. - Gestamp Griwe Haynrode Plant   **(2)**
Unterdorf 35, 37339, Haynrode, Germany
Tel.: (49) 360772560
Web Site: http://www.griwe.de
Automobile Spare Parts Mfr
N.A.I.C.S.: 336390

Gestamp Automocion S.A. - Gestamp Llanelli Plant   **(2)**
Llethri Road, Felinfoel, Llanelli, SA14 8EU, United Kingdom

Tel.: (44) 1554 772233
Automobile Spare Parts Mfr
N.A.I.C.S.: 336390

Gestamp Automocion S.A. - Gestamp Nilufer Turkey Plant   **(2)**
Organice San Bol Kahverengi, Cd n13 16159 Nilufer, Bursa, Turkiye
Tel.: (90) 224 270 06 00
Automobile Spare Parts Mfr
N.A.I.C.S.: 336390

Gestamp Automocion S.A. - Gestamp Parana Plant   **(2)**
Rod BR Contorno Leste 4 000, 83015-000, Sao Jose dos Pinhais, Brazil
Tel.: (55) 41 2169 5100
Automobile Spare Parts Mfr
N.A.I.C.S.: 336390

Plant (Domestic):

Gestamp Automocion S.A. - Gestamp SantPedor Plant   **(2)**
Pol Ind Santa Anna, Santpedor, 08251, Barcelona, Spain
Tel.: (34) 93 827 39 44
Automobile Spare Parts Mfr
N.A.I.C.S.: 336390

Plant (Non-US):

Gestamp Automocion S.A. - Gestamp Santa Isabel Plant   **(2)**
Rodovia Presidente Dutra km 184, 07500-000, Sao Paulo, Brazil
Tel.: (55) 11 4656 8500
Automobile Spare Parts Mfr
N.A.I.C.S.: 336390

Gestamp Automocion S.A. - Gestamp Taubate Plant   **(2)**
Av Eurico Ambrogi Santos 1800, 12042-010, Taubate, Brazil
Tel.: (55) 12 3627 6400
Automobile Spare Parts Mfr
N.A.I.C.S.: 336390

Gestamp Automocion S.A. - Gestamp Wroclaw Plant   **(2)**
Stargardzka 2A, 54-156, Wroclaw, Poland
Tel.: (48) 713 523 790
Automobile Spare Parts Mfr
N.A.I.C.S.: 336390

Plant (Domestic):

Gestamp Automocion S.A. - Loire Safe Plant   **(2)**
Zikunaga 22, 20120, Hernani, Spain
Tel.: (34) 943 33 12 14
Web Site: http://www.loiresafe.com
Automobile Spare Parts Mfr
N.A.I.C.S.: 336390

Plant (Non-US):

Gestamp Automocion S.A. - Sofedit Sermaises Plant   **(2)**
7 Tte de Pithiviers, BP 14, 45300, Paris, France
Tel.: (33) 2 38 32 37 00
Automobile Spare Parts Mfr
N.A.I.C.S.: 336390

Gestamp Automocion S.A. - Sofedit St. Romain Plant   **(2)**
Parc d'Activiie de L'aerodrome 170, B P 23, Voie St Exupery, 76430, Saint-Romain-de-Colbosc, France
Tel.: (33) 2 35 13 63 85
Automobile Spare Parts Mfr
N.A.I.C.S.: 336390

Gestamp Automocion S.A. -Sofedit Le Theil Plant   **(2)**
Rue de la Pecherie, 61260, Le Theil, France
Tel.: (33) 2 37 53 73 00
Automobile Spare Parts Mfr
N.A.I.C.S.: 336390

Subsidiary (Non-US):

Gestamp Automotive Chennai Private Limited   **(2)**
Plot No B-12 SIPCOT Industrial Park, Kerala, 602105, India
Tel.: (91) 44 67188708
Automotive Spare Parts Distr

N.A.I.C.S.: 423120

Gestamp Automotive India Private Ltd. (2)
E-1 Part Chakan MIDC Phase-III, Nighoje Mhalung, Pune, 410501, India
Tel.: (91) 2135 396300
Automotive Spare Parts Distr
N.A.I.C.S.: 423120
Vijaykumar Gontumukkula (Sr Engr-Robotics)

Gestamp Aveiro, S.A. (2)
Zona Industrial, 3701-905, Nogueira do Cravo, Portugal
Tel.: (351) 256 861 100
Web Site: http://www.gestampaverio.com
Emp.: 400
Automotive Spare Parts Distr
N.A.I.C.S.: 423120
Adriana Elvis (Gen Dir)

Gestamp Baires, S.A (2)
Panamericana Km 48, Escobar, Buenos Aires, Argentina
Tel.: (54) 11 4014 0300
Automobile Parts Distr
N.A.I.C.S.: 423120

Subsidiary (Domestic):

Gestamp Bizkaia, S.A. (2)
Pol Ind de Lebario, 48220, Abadino, Spain
Tel.: (34) 94 450 70 00
Automotive Spare Parts Distr
N.A.I.C.S.: 423120

Subsidiary (Non-US):

Gestamp Cerveira, Lda. (2)
Zona Industrial Campos 2 Polo Parcela 24 Campos, Viana do Castelo, Portugal
Tel.: (351) 251 700 400
Automobile Parts Distr
N.A.I.C.S.: 423120

Subsidiary (US):

Gestamp Chattanooga, Llc. (2)
3063 Hickory Valley Rd, Chattanooga, TN 37421
Tel.: (423) 305-6300
Automotive Spare Parts Distr
N.A.I.C.S.: 423120
Mark Vallee (Controller)

Subsidiary (Non-US):

Gestamp Cordoba, S.A. (2)
Camino Interfabrica esq, Camino El Carmelo, 5020, Cordoba, Argentina
Tel.: (54) 351 414 7000
Automotive Spare Parts Distr
N.A.I.C.S.: 423120

Gestamp Edscha Japan Co., Ltd. (2)
PMO Hatchobori 3F, 3-22-13 Hatchobori Chuo-ku, Tokyo, 104-0032, Japan
Tel.: (81) 3 6280 3213
Automotive Spare Parts Distr
N.A.I.C.S.: 423120

Subsidiary (Domestic):

Gestamp Esmar, S.A. (2)
Pol Ind Zona Franca Sector B Calle B 19-23, 08040, Barcelona, Spain
Tel.: (34) 93 336 89 50
Automotive Spare Parts Distr
N.A.I.C.S.: 423120

Gestamp Galvanizados, S.A. (2)
Camino De Los Barcos Sn Finca 26, Duenas, Palencia, 34210, Spain
Tel.: (34) 979787100
Web Site: http://www.gestamp.com
Emp.: 300
Automobile Parts Mfr
N.A.I.C.S.: 336390
Francisco J. Riberas (Chm)

Subsidiary (Non-US):

Gestamp Griwe Westerburg, GmbH (2)
Boschstrasse 16, 56457, Westerburg, Germany
Tel.: (49) 26 63 2 98 0
Automotive Spare Parts Distr
N.A.I.C.S.: 423120

Gestamp HardTech, A.B. (2)
Ektjarnsvagen 5, 97125, Lulea, Sweden
Tel.: (46) 920 47 40 00
Automotive Spare Parts Distr
N.A.I.C.S.: 423120
Ulf Brorsson (Dir-Pur)

Gestamp Hungaria, Kft (2)
Akai u 3, 8060, Mor, Hungary
Tel.: (36) 225 60 600
Automotive Spare Parts Distr
N.A.I.C.S.: 423120

Subsidiary (Domestic):

Gestamp Ingenieria Europa Sur, S.L. (2)
Camino Les Arenes 1, Santpedor, Barcelona, 08251, Spain
Tel.: (34) 938273800
Automobile Parts Mfr
N.A.I.C.S.: 336390

Subsidiary (Non-US):

Gestamp Kartek Co, Ltd. (2)
70 Komori, Jinre-myun, Gimhae, Korea (South)
Tel.: (82) 55 340 4220
Automotive Spare Parts Distr
N.A.I.C.S.: 423120

Subsidiary (Domestic):

Gestamp Levante, S.A. (2)
Pol Ind Juan Carlos I Avda de la Foia n 34-36, 46440, Valencia, Spain
Tel.: (34) 96 179 70 70
Web Site: http://www.gestamp.com
Providing Health Care
N.A.I.C.S.: 423120
Francisco Lafarga (Mgr-Engrg)

Gestamp Linares, S.A. (2)
Pol Ind Los Rubiales, 23700, Linares, Spain
Tel.: (34) 953 64 99 00
Automotive Spare Parts Distr
N.A.I.C.S.: 423120

Subsidiary (Non-US):

Gestamp Louny, S.R.O. (2)
Industrial Zone Triangle, Minice 61, 43801, Zatec, Czech Republic
Tel.: (420) 415 236 200
Automotive Spare Parts Distr
N.A.I.C.S.: 423120
Vladimir Manica (Mgr-Fin)

Subsidiary (Domestic):

Gestamp Manufacturing Autochasis, S.L. (2)
Pol Ind El Pradillo, Aneto 5 Pedrola, 50690, Zaragoza, Spain
Tel.: (34) 976 65 46 00
Automotive Spare Parts Distr
N.A.I.C.S.: 423120

Subsidiary (US):

Gestamp Mason, Llc. (2)
200 Kipp Rd, Mason, MI 48854
Tel.: (517) 244-8800
Automotive Spare Parts Distr
N.A.I.C.S.: 423120
Stacy Brown (Mgr-Acctg)

Subsidiary (Non-US):

Gestamp Metal Forming (Chongqing) Co., Ltd (2)
Jia Yun Road No 121, Caijia Town, Beibei District, 400707, Chongqing, China
Tel.: (86) 23 6646 4517
Automotive Spare Parts Distr
N.A.I.C.S.: 423120

Gestamp Metal Forming (Wuhan), Ltd. (2)
Guannan Road Section 4 No33, East Lake High, Wuhan, China
Tel.: (86) 27 87514413
Automotive Spare Parts Distr
N.A.I.C.S.: 423120
Zhang Lei (Mgr-HR)

Subsidiary (Domestic):

Gestamp Navarra, S.A. (2)

Pol Ind Meseta de Salinas, 31110, Noain, Spain
Tel.: (34) 948 97 83 00
Automotive Spare Parts Distr
N.A.I.C.S.: 423120
Francisco Javier Oderiz Minguez (Area Mgr-Pur)

Subsidiary (US):

Gestamp North America, Inc. (2)
2701 Troy Centre Dr Ste 150, Troy, MI 48084
Tel.: (248) 743-3400
Automotive Component & Structural System Mfr
N.A.I.C.S.: 336370

Subsidiary (Domestic):

Gestamp Alabama, Inc. (3)
7000 Jefferson Metro Pkwy, Bessemer, AL 35111
Tel.: (205) 497-6400
Web Site: http://www.gestamp.com
Rev.: $27,100,000
Emp.: 250
Automotive Component & Structural System Mfr
N.A.I.C.S.: 336370
Jeffrey Wilson (Pres)

Subsidiary (Domestic):

Gestamp North Europe Services, S.L (2)
Barrio Lebario S, Abadino, 48220, Spain
Tel.: (34) 944507000
Automotive Spare Parts Distr
N.A.I.C.S.: 423120

Subsidiary (Non-US):

Gestamp Noury S.A.S. (2)
Zone Industrielle 33, Rue Ampere, 77220, Gretz-Armainvilliers, France
Tel.: (33) 64 42 29 00
Automotive Spare Parts Distr
N.A.I.C.S.: 423120
Laurent Bancharel (Mgr-IT)

Subsidiary (Domestic):

Gestamp Palencia, S.A. (2)
Camino de los Barcos, Finca 26, 34210, Palencia, Spain
Tel.: (34) 979 78 71 00
Automotive Spare Parts Distr
N.A.I.C.S.: 423120

Subsidiary (Non-US):

Gestamp Polska SP. Z.O.O. (2)
Ul Dzialkowcow 12, Wrzesnia Wielkopolska, Poznan, Poland
Tel.: (48) 61 436 96 00
Automotive Spare Parts Distr
N.A.I.C.S.: 423120
Mario Eikelmann (Gen Mgr)

Gestamp Prisma S.A.S (2)
Route de Messempre, BP 6, 08110, Pure, France
Tel.: (33) 3 242785 85
Automotive Spare Parts Distr
N.A.I.C.S.: 423120

Gestamp Puebla, S.A. de C.V. (2)
Calle Automocion 8, Col San Lorenzo Almecatla, 72710, Cuautlancingo, Mexico
Tel.: (52) 222 303 13 00
Automotive Spare Parts Distr
N.A.I.C.S.: 423120

Gestamp Ronchamp, S.A.S. (2)
5 rue des Croix, ZA des Champs May, Champagney, France
Tel.: (33) 3 844 55 00
Automobile Spare Parts Distr
N.A.I.C.S.: 423120

Gestamp Severstal Kaluga, Llc. (2)
Avtomobilnaya str 1, 248926, Kaluga, Russia
Tel.: (7) 4842211030
Automotive Spare Parts Distr
N.A.I.C.S.: 423120
Inigo Mandaluniz (Mgr-Production)

Gestamp Severstal Vsevolozhsk Llc. (2)
Industrial Zone Kirpichny Zavod District 11

Site 2, Vsevolozhsk, 188640, Saint Petersburg, Russia
Tel.: (7) 8123136810
Automotive Spare Parts Distr
N.A.I.C.S.: 423120
Andrey Khomchuk (Engr-Project Process)

Subsidiary (Domestic):

Gestamp Solblank Navarra, S.L.U (2)
Pol Ind Arazuri-Orkoien Calle C, 31160, Orkoien, Spain
Tel.: (34) 948 32 43 85
Automotive Spare Parts Distr
N.A.I.C.S.: 423120

Gestamp Solblank, S.A. (2)
Pol Ind San Vicente 17, Castellbisbal, 08755, Barcelona, Spain
Tel.: (34) 93 773 45 00
Automotive Spare Parts Distr
N.A.I.C.S.: 423120
Adolfo Costa (Gen Mgr)

Subsidiary (US):

Gestamp South Carolina, Llc. (2)
1 LSP Rd, Union, SC 29379
Tel.: (864) 466-3960
Automotive Spare Parts Distr
N.A.I.C.S.: 423120

Subsidiary (Non-US):

Gestamp Tallent, Ltd. (2)
Aycliffe Business Park, Newton Aycliffe, DL5 6EP, United Kingdom
Tel.: (44) 1325 313 232
Web Site:
  http://www.tallent.thyssenkrupp.com
Automobile Spare Parts Mfr
N.A.I.C.S.: 336390
Keith Jackson (Key Acct Mgr)

Gestamp Togliatti, Llc. (2)
Cevernaya str 20, Samara region, 445043, Togliatti, Russia
Tel.: (7) 8482691700
Automotive Spare Parts Distr
N.A.I.C.S.: 423120

Subsidiary (Domestic):

Gestamp Toledo, S.A. (2)
Camino de los Pontones, Pol Ind de las Monjas, 45224, Toledo, Spain
Tel.: (34) 91 875 18 99
Automotive Spare Parts Distr
N.A.I.C.S.: 423120

Subsidiary (Non-US):

Gestamp Toluca, S.A. de C. V. (2)
Avda Independencia Manzana 2, Lote I Col Zona Industrial, 50070, Toluca, Mexico
Tel.: (52) 722 275 8900
Automotive Spare Parts Distr
N.A.I.C.S.: 423120

Subsidiary (Domestic):

Gestamp Tool Hardening, S.L. (2)
Pol El Campiilo II Pabellon 11 2, Abanto y Ciervana, 48500, Gallarta, Spain
Tel.: (34) 944 50 79 00
Automotive Spare Parts Distr
N.A.I.C.S.: 423120

Subsidiary (Non-US):

Gestamp Umformtechnik GmbH (2)
Gotenstrasse 91, Bielefeld, Germany
Tel.: (49) 521 4472 0
Web Site: http://www.gestamp-umformtechnik.com
Automobile Spare Parts Mfr
N.A.I.C.S.: 336390
Reinhold Sommer (Head-Tool Center Engr)

Gestamp Vendas Novas, Lda. (2)
Estrada Nacional N 4, 7080-111, Vendas Novas, Portugal
Tel.: (351) 265 807 400
Automotive Spare Parts Distr
N.A.I.C.S.: 423120

Subsidiary (Domestic):

Gestamp Vigo, S.A. (2)
Pol Ind As Gandaras Parcela 105-106b, Porrino, 36400, Pontevedra, Spain

Acek Desarrollo y Gestion Industrial
SL—(Continued)

Tel.: (34) 986 21 66 00
Automotive Spare Parts Distr
N.A.I.C.S.: 423120

Subsidiary (Non-US):

Gestamp Washington, UK Ltd. **(2)**
Rutherford Road, Stephenson Industrial Estate, Washington, NE37 3HX, United Kingdom
Tel.: (44) 191 418 05 80
Web Site: http://www.uk.gestamp.com
Automotive Spare Parts Distr
N.A.I.C.S.: 423120
Peter Handy (Controller-Matl)

Subsidiary (US):

Gestamp West Virginia Llc. **(2)**
3100 MacCorkle Ave Bldg 307, Charleston, WV 25303
Tel.: (304) 941-1800
Automotive Spare Parts Distr
N.A.I.C.S.: 423120
Paul Meisel (Controller)

Subsidiary (Domestic):

Ingenieria y Construccion de Matrices, S.A. **(2)**
Poligono El Campillo Fase II Parcela 8-1, 48500, Gallarta, Spain
Tel.: (34) 946 668 050
Web Site: http://www.icticm.com
Automobile Spare Parts Mfr
N.A.I.C.S.: 336390

Matriceria Deusto, S.L. **(2)**
Torrelarragoiti s/n, 48170, Zamudio, Spain
Tel.: (34) 944 52 00 12
Automotive Spare Parts Distr
N.A.I.C.S.: 423120

ACELON CHEMICALS & FIBER CORPORATION
No 94 Fan Chin Road, Puyan, Chang
Hua, Taiwan
Tel.: (886) 47638869
Web Site: https://www.acelon.com.tw
Year Founded: 1988
1466—(TAI)
Rev.: $80,240,391
Assets: $112,514,368
Liabilities: $65,306,482
Net Worth: $47,207,886
Earnings: ($4,949,442)
Emp.: 449
Fiscal Year-end: 12/31/23
Polyester Filament Mfr
N.A.I.C.S.: 325220

Subsidiaries:

Acegreen Eco-Material Technology
Co., Ltd. **(1)**
No 50 Ln 20 Sec 1 Nantong Rd, Ershui
Township Changhua County, Chang-Hua,
530, Taiwan
Tel.: (886) 48796000
Web Site: https://www.acegreen.com.tw
Fibber Product Mfr & Distr
N.A.I.C.S.: 325220

Acenature Biotechnology Co.,
Ltd. **(1)**
No 94 Fanjin Rd, Changhua County 516,
Puyan, Taiwan
Tel.: (886) 48652321
Web Site: https://www.acenaturelife.com
Fabric Mfr & Distr
N.A.I.C.S.: 313310

ACENTA STEEL LIMITED
Planetary Road, Willenhall, WV13
3SW, West Midlands, United Kingdom
Tel.: (44) 1902 308 600   **UK**
Web Site:
http://www.acentasteel.com
Sales Range: $125-149.9 Million
Emp.: 345
Steel Products Mfr & Distr
N.A.I.C.S.: 423510

Colin Mills (CEO)

Subsidiaries:

Acenta Steel Limited - Hot Rolled
Division **(1)**
Peartree Lane Woodside, Dudley, DY2
0QS, United Kingdom
Tel.: (44) 1384471200
Steel Bar Mfr
N.A.I.C.S.: 331221

ACEP FRANCE
15 rue de Vezelay, 75008, Paris,
France
Tel.: (33) 146451518   **FR**
Web Site: http://www.opticvideo.com
Year Founded: 1994
Virtual & Augmented Reality Software
Developer & Marketer
N.A.I.C.S.: 513210

Subsidiaries:

American Bright Signs, Inc. **(1)**
80 SW 8th St Ste 2000, Miami, FL 31130
Virtual & Augmented Reality Software Marketer
N.A.I.C.S.: 423430
Fabian Bruneau (VP)

ACER GADGET INC.
No 163 Songxin Road, Xinyi District,
Taipei, Taiwan
Tel.: (886) 227677299
Web Site:
https://www.acergadget.com
Year Founded: 1986
2432—(TAI)
Rev.: $68,212,365
Assets: $60,849,535
Liabilities: $19,200,169
Net Worth: $41,649,366
Earnings: $3,965,564
Fiscal Year-end: 12/31/23
Electronic Product Mfr & Distr
N.A.I.C.S.: 334111
Jerry Kao (Chm)

ACER INCORPORATED
1F 88 Sec 1Xintai 5th Rd, Xizhi, New
Taipei City, 221, Taiwan
Tel.: (886) 226961234   **TW**
Web Site: https://www.acer.com
Year Founded: 1976
2353—(TAI)
Rev.: $7,891,302,295
Assets: $6,826,051,804
Liabilities: $4,198,691,133
Net Worth: $2,627,360,671
Earnings: $184,151,339
Emp.: 7,724
Fiscal Year-end: 12/31/23
Computers & Computer Peripherals
Mfr
N.A.I.C.S.: 334111
R. C. Chang (CTO)

Subsidiaries:

AOpen Inc. **(1)**
No 92 Section 1 Xintaiwu Road, Xizhi District, Taipei, 115, Taiwan
Tel.: (886) 277101195
Web Site: http://www.aopen.com.tw
Mfr & Designer of Motherboards, Housings,
CD-ROMs, Optical Devices & Multimedia
Products
N.A.I.C.S.: 334118

Acer AI Cloud Inc. **(1)**
8th Floor No 88 Section 1 Xintai 5th Road,
Xizhi District, New Taipei City, Taiwan
Tel.: (886) 226963131
Web Site: https://www.aceraicloud.com
Cloud Computing Services
N.A.I.C.S.: 518210

Acer Africa Pty. Ltd. **(1)**
2nd Floor The District 8 Kikuyu St, Sunninghill, Sandton, 2128, South Africa **(100%)**
Tel.: (27) 871513400
Web Site: http://www.acer.com

Sales Range: $25-49.9 Million
Emp.: 45
N.A.I.C.S.: 334111

Acer America Corporation **(1)**
1730 N 1st St Ste 400, San Jose, CA
95112 **(100%)**
Tel.: (408) 533-7700
Web Site: http://www.acer.com
Sales Range: $50-74.0 Million
Emp.: 180
Computer Sales & Service
N.A.I.C.S.: 334111

Branch (Non-US):

Acer America Corporation **(2)**
5600 Explorer Drive Suite 201, Mississauga, L4W 4Y2, ON, Canada **(100%)**
Tel.: (905) 755-7570
Web Site: http://www.acer.com
Sales Range: $25-49.9 Million
Emp.: 50
Computers & Computer Accessories
N.A.I.C.S.: 334111

Acer American Holding Corp. **(1)**
1730 N First St Ste 400, San Jose, CA
95112
Tel.: (408) 533-7700
Web Site: http://www.acer.com
Investment Management Service
N.A.I.C.S.: 523999

Acer Asia Pacific Sdn Bhd **(1)**
Level 24 Menara Ambank No 8 Jalan Yap
Kwan Seng, Kuala Lumpur, 50450, Malaysia
Tel.: (60) 3 2162 1388
Web Site: http://www.acer-group.com
Sales Range: $50-74.9 Million
Emp.: 60
Computer Peripheral Equipment Distr
N.A.I.C.S.: 423430

Acer Austria GmbH **(1)**
Europaring F14 202, 2345, Brunn am Gebirge, Austria
Tel.: (43) 22363075200
Web Site: https://www.acer.com
Sales Range: $25-49.9 Million
Emp.: 11
Computer & Computer Equipment Whslr
N.A.I.C.S.: 541519

Acer CIS, Inc. **(1)**
Hi-Tec House 5/4 Bolshaya Academicheskaya Str, 127299, Moscow, Russia
Tel.: (7) 495 212 2888
Web Site: http://www.acer.ru
Sales Range: $25-49.9 Million
Emp.: 50
Mfr & Distr of Computers & Accessories
N.A.I.C.S.: 334111

Acer Capital Corporation **(1)**
8F 88 Hsin Tai Wu Road Sec 1 Hsichih,
Taipei, 221, Taiwan
Tel.: (886) 2 2696 1234
Web Site: http://www.acer.com
Financial Investment Services
N.A.I.C.S.: 523999

Acer Cloud Technology Co. **(1)**
800 W California Ave Ste 200, Sunnyvale,
CA 94086
Tel.: (650) 810-2000
Cloud Computing Software Developer
N.A.I.C.S.: 513210
Andy Chan (Mgr-Software Dev)

Acer Computec Mexico, S.A. de
C.V. **(1)**
Blvd Adolfo Ruiz Cortinez 3720 Tower 2
floor 9 suite B111, Pedregal Gardens Alvaro
Obregon, 01900, Mexico, Mexico
Tel.: (52) 5559999400
Web Site: https://www.acer.com.mx
Sales Range: $300-349.9 Million
Emp.: 420
Product Assembly, Marketing & Sales
N.A.I.C.S.: 334111

Acer Computer (Far East)
Limited **(1)**
Unit 2301-02 08 Level 23 Tower 1 Millennium City 1 388 Kwun Tong Rd, Kowloon,
China (Hong Kong) **(100%)**
Tel.: (852) 28210200
Web Site: http://www.acer.com.hk

Sales Range: $50-74.9 Million
Emp.: 150
Mfr of Computers
N.A.I.C.S.: 334111

Acer Computer (M.E.) Ltd. **(1)**
Jebel Ali Free Zone, PO Box 16951, Dubai,
United Arab Emirates **(100%)**
Tel.: (971) 48056400
Web Site: http://www.acer.com
Sales Range: $200-249.9 Million
Emp.: 90
N.A.I.C.S.: 334111

Acer Computer (Shanghai) Ltd. **(1)**
801-806 Building MT2 Vientiane Enterprise
Center No 225 Haowen Road, Minhang
District, Shanghai, 201102, China
Tel.: (86) 400 700 1000
Web Site: https://www.acer.com.cn
Sales Range: $75-99.9 Million
Emp.: 150
Consumer Peripherals Distr
N.A.I.C.S.: 423430

Acer Computer (Singapore) Pte.
Ltd. **(1)**
29 International Business Park, 08-01 Acer
Building Tower A, Singapore, 609923, Singapore
Tel.: (65) 65636563
Web Site: http://www.acer.com
Emp.: 150
Marketer, Retailer & Assembler of Computer
Products
N.A.I.C.S.: 334111

Acer Computer (Switzerland) AG **(1)**
Moosmattstrasse 30, 8953, Dietikon, Switzerland
Tel.: (41) 447455858
Web Site: https://www.acer.com
Sales Range: $25-49.9 Million
Emp.: 40
Computers & Computer Equipment Whslr
N.A.I.C.S.: 423430

Acer Computer Australia Pty.
Ltd. **(1)**
Building G Level 2 350 Parramatta Road,
Homebush West, Sydney, 2140, NSW,
Australia **(100%)**
Tel.: (61) 287623000
Web Site: http://www.acer.com
Sales Range: $200-249.9 Million
Emp.: 100
N.A.I.C.S.: 334111

Acer Computer B.V. Benelux **(1)**
Europalaan 89, 5232 BC, 's-
Hertogenbosch, Netherlands **(100%)**
Tel.: (31) 736459645
Web Site: http://www.acer.com
Sales Range: $25-49.9 Million
Emp.: 150
Electronic Computers
N.A.I.C.S.: 334111

Acer Computer Co., Ltd. **(1)**
493 / 7-8 Nang Linchi Road, Chong Nonsi
Yannawa, Bangkok, 10120,
Thailand **(100%)**
Tel.: (66) 21539888
Web Site: http://www.acer.com
Sales Range: $50-74.9 Million
Emp.: 150
N.A.I.C.S.: 334111

Acer Computer Czech and Slovak
Republics **(1)**
Novodvorska 1010 14B, 142 00, Prague, 4,
Czech Republic **(100%)**
Tel.: (420) 244112555
Web Site: http://www.acer.cz
Sales Range: $25-49.9 Million
Emp.: 10
N.A.I.C.S.: 334111

Acer Computer Finland Oy **(1)**
Konalantie 47F, 00390, Helsinki,
Finland **(100%)**
Tel.: (358) 969379230
Web Site: http://www.acer.fi
Sales Range: $25-49.9 Million
Emp.: 11
N.A.I.C.S.: 334111

Acer Computer France S.A.R.L. **(1)**
2 - 8 Rue Sarah Bernhardt, CS 90045,
92601, Asnieres-sur-Seine, Cedex,
France **(100%)**

Tel.: (33) 148635295
Web Site: http://www.acer.com
Sales Range: $150-199.9 Million
Emp.: 30
N.A.I.C.S.: 334111

Acer Computer GmbH (1)
Kornkamp 4, 22926, Ahrensburg,
Germany (100%)
Tel.: (49) 41024880
Web Site: https://www.acer.com
Sales Range: $100-124.9 Million
Emp.: 300
N.A.I.C.S.: 334111
Wilfried Thom (Mng Dir)

Acer Computer Iberica, S.A.U. (1)
Design 3-5, 08850, Barcelona,
Spain (100%)
Tel.: (34) 934922400
Web Site: https://www.acer.com
Sales Range: $25-49.9 Million
Emp.: 40
Computers & Computer Equipment Whslr
N.A.I.C.S.: 423430

Acer Computer International Ltd. (1)
29 International Business Park Acer Build-
ing Tower A, Singapore, 609923, Singapore
Tel.: (65) 65636563
Web Site: http://www.acer.com.sg
Sales Range: $50-74.9 Million
Emp.: 100
Computer Peripheral Equipment Distr
N.A.I.C.S.: 423430

**Acer Computer New Zealand
Ltd.** (1)
Suite 2 Ground Floor Building A Millenium
Phase II, 600 Great South Road Ellerslie,
Auckland, 1051, New Zealand (100%)
Tel.: (64) 99695600
Web Site: http://www.acer.com
Sales Range: $25-49.9 Million
Emp.: 11
N.A.I.C.S.: 334111

Acer Computer Norway A/S (1)
Lysaker Torg 8, 1366, Lysaker,
Norway (100%)
Tel.: (47) 32843000
Web Site: http://www.acer.com
Sales Range: $10-24.9 Million
Emp.: 40
N.A.I.C.S.: 334111

Acer Computer Poland (1)
Ul Domaniewska 41 Fl 9, Budynek Saturn
IX p, 02-672, Warsaw, Poland (100%)
Tel.: (48) 226062590
Web Site: http://www.acer.pl
Sales Range: $25-49.9 Million
Emp.: 5
Computers & Computer Equipment Distr
N.A.I.C.S.: 541519

Acer Computer Sweden AB (1)
Mariehallsvagen 37B, SE 16865, Bromma,
Sweden (100%)
Tel.: (46) 84447910
Web Site: http://www.acercomputer.se
Sales Range: $25-49.9 Million
Emp.: 15
N.A.I.C.S.: 334111

Acer Cyber Center Services Ltd (1)
No 69 Lane 368 shin-ho Rd Sanhe Village,
Lungtan Shiang, Taoyuan, 325, Taiwan
Tel.: (886) 3 407 2000
Web Site: http://www.accsi.net
Web Hosting Services
N.A.I.C.S.: 518210
Ben Wan (Gen Mgr)

Acer Czech Republic s.r.o. (1)
On Hrebeny II 1718/10, 140 00, Prague,
Czech Republic
Tel.: (420) 531027777
Web Site: https://www.acer.com
Computer & Computer Peripheral Equip-
ment Whslr
N.A.I.C.S.: 541519

Acer Denmark A/S (1)
Strandvejen 70 3 Tv, 2900, Hellerup,
Denmark (100%)
Tel.: (45) 39168800
Web Site: http://www.acer.com
N.A.I.C.S.: 334111

Acer Europe SA (1)

Via della Posta 28, 6934, Bioggio, Switzer-
land
Tel.: (41) 912610111
Web Site: http://www.acer-euro.com
Computer Peripheral Equipment Distr
N.A.I.C.S.: 423430

Acer Europe Services S.R.L. (1)
Viale Delle Industrie 1/a, 20024, Arese,
Milano, Italy
Tel.: (39) 0236000130
Web Site: http://www.acer-group.com
Computer Software Development Services
N.A.I.C.S.: 541511

Acer Hellas LTD (1)
Grigoriou Lambraki 54, 11674, Glyfada, Ath-
ens, Greece
Tel.: (30) 210 96 06 430
Web Site: http://www.acer.gr
Computer Peripheral Equipment Mfr & Distr
N.A.I.C.S.: 423430

Acer India (Pvt) Ltd. (1)
Embassy Heights 6th Floor No 13 Magrath
Road, Bengaluru, 560025, India (100%)
Tel.: (91) 8039408700
Web Site: http://www.acer.com
Emp.: 70
Computer Mfr
N.A.I.C.S.: 334111
Chandrahas Panigrahi (CMO & Head-
Consumer Bus)

Acer Information Products Group (1)
8 Fl 88 Hsin Tai Wu Rd, Sec 1 Hsichih,
Hsien, 221, Taiwan (100%)
Tel.: (886) 226961234
Web Site: http://www.acer.com.tw
Sales Range: $350-399.9 Million
Emp.: 2,000
Mfr & Designer of Computer Systems,
Components & Consumer Electronics Prod-
ucts
N.A.I.C.S.: 541512
Sscottl Lin (Pres)

**Acer Information Services
International** (1)
, Barreal, Heredia, Costa Rica
Tel.: (506) 2930942
Web Site: http://www.aisinternational.com
N.A.I.C.S.: 334111

Acer Internet Services Inc. (1)
5F 88 Hsin Tai Wu Rd, Hsien, 221, Taiwan
Tel.: (886) 226963131
Web Site: http://www.acer.net
Sales Range: $200-249.9 Million
Emp.: 1,000
Internet Communication Services
N.A.I.C.S.: 517810

Acer Italy S.r.l. (1)
Viale Delle Industrie 1/A, 20044, Arese, Mi-
lan, Italy
Tel.: (39) 02939921
Web Site: https://www.acer.com
N.A.I.C.S.: 334111

Acer Japan Corporation (1)
18F Nishi Shinjuku Mitsui Building 6-24-1
Nishi Shinjuku, Shinjuku ku, Tokyo, 160
0023, Japan
Tel.: (81) 3 5324 2788
Web Site: http://www.acer.co.jp
Computer Manufacturer
N.A.I.C.S.: 334111
Bob Sam (Pres)

Acer Latin America, Inc. (1)
3750 NW 87th Ave Ste 640, Miami, FL
33178
Tel.: (305) 392-7000
Web Site: http://www.acla.acer.com
Sales Range: $10-24.9 Million
Emp.: 9
Sales of Computers & Computer Hardware
N.A.I.C.S.: 334111

Acer Magyarorszag (1)
Arpad Fejedelem utja 26-28, 1023, Buda-
pest, Hungary (100%)
Tel.: (36) 13363307
Web Site: http://www.acer.hu
Sales Range: $25-49.9 Million
Emp.: 6
Computers & Computer Equipment Distr
N.A.I.C.S.: 541519
Tamas Borhi (Country Mgr)

Acer Philippines, Inc. (1)
1172 - 1180 Pres Quirino Ave Ext Brgy 827
Zone 89, Paco, Manila, Philippines (100%)
Tel.: (63) 27200090
Web Site: http://www.acer.com
Sales Range: $1-9.9 Million
Emp.: 39
Mfr & Marketer of Computers & Related
Products
N.A.I.C.S.: 334111

Acer Property Development, Inc. (1)
Aspire Pk Kur Wong Rd, Kao Yuan Village,
Taoyuan, 325, Hsien, Taiwan (100%)
Tel.: (886) 3 407 1888
Web Site: http://www.aspirepark.com.tw
Sales Range: $50-74.9 Million
Emp.: 22
Real Estate Services
N.A.I.C.S.: 525990

Acer Sales & Services Sdn. Bhd. (1)
No 6 Jalan TP6 Sime UEP Industrial Park,
47600, Subang Jaya, Selangor,
Malaysia (100%)
Tel.: (60) 380222188
Web Site: http://www.acer.com
Sales Range: $25-49.9 Million
Emp.: 50
N.A.I.C.S.: 334111

Subsidiary (Domestic):

**Highpoint Service Network Sdn
Bhd** (2)
1 Jalan TP6 Sime UEP Industrial Park,
47600, Subang Jaya, Selangor, Malaysia
Tel.: (60) 80 088 1918
Web Site: http://www.highpoint.com.my
Sales Range: $25-49.9 Million
Emp.: 100
Information Technology Consulting Services
N.A.I.C.S.: 541512

Servex (Malaysia) Sdn Bhd (2)
No 8 Jalan TP 6 Taman Perindustrian Uep,
47600, Subang Jaya, Selangor, Malaysia
Tel.: (60) 38 024 6688
Web Site: https://web.servex.com.my
Computer Peripheral Equipment Distr
N.A.I.C.S.: 423430

Acer Sweden AB (1)
Greta Garbos vag 13, 169 40, Solna, Swe-
den
Tel.: (46) 850557300
Web Site: http://www.acer.com
Sales Range: $25-49.9 Million
Emp.: 15
Computers & Computer Equipment Distr
N.A.I.C.S.: 541519

Acer Technologies Corp. (1)
16F 84 Hsin Tai Wu Rd, Sec 1, Hsien, 221,
Taiwan
Tel.: (886) 226964055
Web Site: http://www.acer.com.tw
Sales Range: $100-124.9 Million
Emp.: 300
Multimedia Peripherals, Information Storage
Media, Computer Communications Prod-
ucts, Memory, Upgrade Kits, Image Process
Products
N.A.I.C.S.: 334118

Acer Technology, Inc. (1)
8F 88 Sec 1 Xintai 5th Rd Xizhi, Taipei,
221, Taiwan
Tel.: (886) 2 2696 1234 3131
Web Site: http://www.acer.com.tw
Sales Range: $25-49.9 Million
Emp.: 11
Mfr, Designer, Marketer & Retailer of
Memory Modules
N.A.I.C.S.: 334118

Acer UK Limited (1)
Heathrow Boulevard III 282 Bath Road,
West Drayton, UB7 0DQ, Middlesex, United
Kingdom
Tel.: (44) 371 760 1005
Web Site: https://www.acer.com
Sales Range: $25-49.9 Million
Emp.: 33
Computers & Computer Equipment Whslr
N.A.I.C.S.: 423430
Craig Booth (Country Mgr)

Acer Vietnam Co., Ltd. (1)
Floor 704-705 37 Ton Duc Thang, Ben

Nghe Ward District 1, Ho Chi Minh City,
Vietnam (100%)
Tel.: (84) 39106888
Web Site: https://www.acer.com
Sales Range: $1-9.9 Million
Emp.: 22
N.A.I.C.S.: 334111

Acer do Brasil Limitada (1)
Rua Campos Sales 303 Pavimento Inferior
Ed Centro Empresarial, Barueri, 60411 150,
SP, Brazil
Tel.: (55) 11 2764 6410
Web Site: http://www.acer.com
Computer Mfr & Distr
N.A.I.C.S.: 334111

Asplex Sp. z.o.o. (1)
Graniczna 8d/4, 54-610, Wroclaw, Poland
Electronic Components Mfr
N.A.I.C.S.: 334419

Enfinitec B.V. (1)
Europalaan 89, 5232, 's-Hertogenbosch,
Netherlands
Tel.: (31) 737440464
Web Site: https://www.enfinitec.com
E-Mobility & Smart Home Device Services
N.A.I.C.S.: 561990

**Eten Information System Co.,
Ltd.** (1)
6th Floor No 68 Ruiguang Road, Neihu Dis-
trict, Taipei, 114, Taiwan
Tel.: (886) 2 7721 0000
Web Site: http://www.eten.com.tw
Sales Range: $50-74.9 Million
Communication Equipment Mfr
N.A.I.C.S.: 334290

Gateway Europe B.V. (1)
Prins Bernhardplein, 200 1097, Amsterdam,
Netherlands
Tel.: (31) 20 5214777
Computer Peripheral Equipment Retailer
N.A.I.C.S.: 449210

Gateway, Inc. (1)
7565 Irvine Center Dr, Irvine, CA 92618
Tel.: (949) 471-7000
Web Site: http://www.gateway.com
Sales Range: $1-4.9 Billion
Emp.: 1,645
Personal Computer Products Mfr
N.A.I.C.S.: 334111

Subsidiary (Domestic):

Acer Service Corporation (2)
1394 Eberhardt Rd, Temple, TX 76504-
8832
Tel.: (254) 298-4000
Electronic Computer Mfr
N.A.I.C.S.: 334111
Keith Hogwood (Dir-Svc Plng & Logistics)

Subsidiary (Non-US):

Gateway Hong Kong Ltd (2)
13 Canton Road, Harbour City, Kowloon,
China (Hong Kong)
Tel.: (852) 2113 0888
Electronic Computer Mfr
N.A.I.C.S.: 334111

Subsidiary (Domestic):

Gateway Manufacturing LLC (2)
7565 Irvine Ctr Dr, Irvine, CA 92618-2930
Tel.: (949) 471-7000
Computer Peripheral Equipment Mfr
N.A.I.C.S.: 334118

Gateway US Retail, Inc. (2)
7565 Irvine Ctr Dr, Irvine, CA 92618
Tel.: (949) 471-7000
Electronic Computer Mfr
N.A.I.C.S.: 334111

**HigHPoint Service Network
Corporation** (1)
6th Floor No 86 Section 1 Xintai 5th Road,
Xizhi District, Taipei, Taiwan
Tel.: (886) 226960660
Web Site: http://www.hsnservice.com
Information Technology Services
N.A.I.C.S.: 541511

PT Acer Indonesia (1)
The Plaza Office Tower Floor 42 Jalan MH
Thamrin No 28 - 30 Gondangdia, Menteng,

Acer Incorporated—(Continued)

Jakarta, 10350, Indonesia　**(100%)**
Tel.: (62) 211500155
Web Site: https://www.acer.com
Sales Range: $25-49.9 Million
Emp.: 70
N.A.I.C.S.: 334111

Packard Bell (UK) Ltd.　**(1)**
Heathrow Boulevard III 282 Bath Road,
West Drayton, UB7 0DQ, Middlesex, United
Kingdom
Tel.: (44) 3714670008
Web Site: http://www.packardbell.com
Computer Peripheral Equipment Mainte-
nance Services
N.A.I.C.S.: 811210

Packard Bell Belgium BVBA　**(1)**
Senneberg Jean Monnetlaan 1, 1804, Vil-
voorde, Belgium
Tel.: (32) 736459645
Web Site: http://www.packardbell.be
Computer Peripheral Equipment Distr
N.A.I.C.S.: 423430

Packard Bell Deutschland GmbH　**(1)**
Kornkamp 4, 22926, Ahrensburg, Germany
Tel.: (49) 4102 488 0
Web Site: http://www.packardbell.de
Sales Range: $75-99.9 Million
Emp.: 20
Computer Peripheral Equipment Distr
N.A.I.C.S.: 423430
Wilfried Thom (Mng Dir)

**Vision Tech Information Technology,
Inc.**　**(1)**
7F 135 Section 2 Chien Kuo North Rd, Tai-
pei, 104, Taiwan　**(100%)**
Tel.: (886) 225178500
Software Distr
N.A.I.C.S.: 423430

Weblink International, Inc.　**(1)**
2-4F 39 sec Chung Hsiao W Rd, Taipei,
100, Taiwan
Tel.: (886) 22 371 6000
Web Site: https://www.weblink.com.tw
Sales Range: $25-49.9 Million
Emp.: 267
Computer Services
N.A.I.C.S.: 541512

Wistron Nexus Inc.　**(1)**
2nd Fl 5 Hsin An Rd, Science Based Indus-
trial Park, Hsin-chu, 300, Taiwan　**(100%)**
Tel.: (886) 35631000
Web Site: http://www.wnexus.com.tw
Sales Range: $25-49.9 Million
Emp.: 80
Mfr of ISDN, Computer Networking/Data
Communications Equipment, Intergrating
INternet Protocol (IP) & PSTN (Public
Switched Telephone Networks) Technolo-
gies
N.A.I.C.S.: 334210

ACERINOX, S.A.
Santiago de Compostela n 100,
28035, Madrid, Spain
Tel.: (34) 913985100　　**ES**
Web Site: https://www.acerinox.com
Year Founded: 1970
ACX—(BAR)
Rev.: $5,350,878,097
Assets: $4,923,797,088
Liabilities: $2,763,599,467
Net Worth: $2,160,197,622
Earnings: ($66,682,064)
Emp.: 6,605
Fiscal Year-end: 12/31/19
Steel Plates, Sheets, Strips, Rods,
Bars & Tubing Mfr & Distr
N.A.I.C.S.: 331210
Bernardo Velazquez Herreros (CEO)

Subsidiaries:

ACERINOX EUROPA, S.A.U.　**(1)**
Stainless Steel Products Mfr
N.A.I.C.S.: 331110

Acerinox (Schweiz) A.G.　**(1)**
Weihermattstr 2, 5507, Mellingen, Switzer-
land
Tel.: (41) 56 481 82 42

Web Site: http://www.acerinox.ch
Emp.: 7
Stainless Flat Rolled Products Mfr
N.A.I.C.S.: 331221

Acerinox Argentina, S.A.　**(1)**
Av Velez Sarsfield 1535, 1285, Buenos Ai-
res, Argentina
Tel.: (54) 1143030349
Stainless Steel Products Distr
N.A.I.C.S.: 423510

Acerinox Australasia Pty Ltd　**(1)**
Suite 502 Level 5 781 Pacific Highway,
Chatswood, 2067, NSW, Australia
Tel.: (61) 417219349
Sales Range: $25-49.9 Million
Emp.: 3
Stainless Steel Distr
N.A.I.C.S.: 332111
Claudio Leon (Mng Dir)

Acerinox Benelux, S.A./NV　**(1)**
Avenue Tervueren 100, 1040, Brussels,
Belgium　**(100%)**
Tel.: (32) 27432200
Web Site: http://www.acerinox.com
Sales Range: $25-49.9 Million
Emp.: 4
Steel Product Distr
N.A.I.C.S.: 331221

Acerinox Chile, S.A.　**(1)**
Parque Industrial Valle Grande Calle Don
Luis 590, Lampa, Santiago, Chile
Tel.: (56) 27385030
Web Site: http://www.acerinox.com
Sales Range: $25-49.9 Million
Emp.: 22
Warehouse & Distr for Steel Products
N.A.I.C.S.: 423510

Acerinox Colombia, S.A.S.　**(1)**
Calle 93 A n 14-17 Centro 93 Oficina 509,
Santafe de Bogota, Bogota, DC,
Colombia　**(100%)**
Tel.: (57) 16220666
Sales Range: $25-49.9 Million
Emp.: 5
Steel Product Distr
N.A.I.C.S.: 423510
Gonzalo del Campo (Gen Mgr)

Acerinox Deutschland GmbH　**(1)**
Poensgenstrasse No 10, Langenfeld,
40764, Dusseldorf, Germany　**(100%)**
Tel.: (49) 217327070
Sales Range: $25-49.9 Million
Emp.: 65
Steel Products Distr & Servicing
N.A.I.C.S.: 331221

Acerinox Deutschland GmbH　**(1)**
Berner Feld 15, 78628, Rottweil,
Germany　**(100%)**
Tel.: (49) 217327070
Web Site: http://www.acerinox.com
Steel Mfr Service Center
N.A.I.C.S.: 331221

Acerinox France SAS　**(1)**
5 Rue Gay Lussac, PO Box 89, Paris,
95503, Gonesse, France　**(100%)**
Tel.: (33) 139876656
Web Site: http://www.acerinox.com
Sales Range: $25-49.9 Million
Emp.: 45
Steel Product Distr
N.A.I.C.S.: 423510

Acerinox Italia Srl　**(1)**
Via Chiesaccia SNC, Crespellano, 40056,
Bologna, Italy
Tel.: (39) 051736567
Web Site: http://www.acerinox.es
Sales Range: $25-49.9 Million
Emp.: 45
Steel Products Servicing & Distr
N.A.I.C.S.: 331221

Acerinox Malaysia Sdn. Bhd.　**(1)**
Ptd 175189 Batu 11 1/2 Jalan Bahru Kota
Tinggi, Ulu Tiram, 81800, Johor, Malaysia
Tel.: (60) 78625252
Web Site: http://www.acerinox.es
Steel Products Whslr
N.A.I.C.S.: 331221

**Acerinox Metal Sanayii Ve Tikaret
L.S.**　**(1)**

Omer Avni Mah Inonu CAD N 32 KAT 5
A/9, Opera Residence Taksim Gumussuyu,
34437, Istanbul, Turkiye
Tel.: (90) 2122445833
Stainless Steel Products Marketing
N.A.I.C.S.: 423510

Acerinox Norway A.S.　**(1)**
Tollbugata 17, PO Box 819, 152, Oslo, Nor-
way
Tel.: (47) 22479660
Web Site: http://www.acerinox.com
Sales Range: $25-49.9 Million
Emp.: 8
Steel Product Distr
N.A.I.C.S.: 331221

Acerinox Pacific Ltd.　**(1)**
Unit 1021 12/F Austin Plaza 83 Austin
Road, Kowloon, China (Hong Kong)
Tel.: (852) 28023666
Web Site: http://www.acerinox.com
Sales Range: $25-49.9 Million
Emp.: 3
Stainless Steel Products Distr
N.A.I.C.S.: 423510

Acerinox Polska Sp.Zo.O.　**(1)**
Ul Daniszewska 23, 03-230, Warsaw, Po-
land
Web Site: https://www.acerinox.com
Sales Range: $25-49.9 Million
Emp.: 24
Steel Product Distr
N.A.I.C.S.: 331221

Acerinox Russia, L.L.C.　**(1)**
Professora Popova street Building 23 lit B,
B/c Gayot - office 305, 197376, Saint Pe-
tersburg, Russia　**(100%)**
Tel.: (7) 8126128178
Web Site: https://www.acerinox.com
Stainless Steel Products Sales
N.A.I.C.S.: 423510
Butyrin Roman Stanislavovich (Mng Dir)

Acerinox Scandinavia A.B.　**(1)**
Sandtagsgatan 2, PO Box 21057, 211 24,
Malmo, Sweden
Tel.: (46) 406919400
Sales Range: $25-49.9 Million
Emp.: 40
Steel Products Servicing
N.A.I.C.S.: 331221

Acerinox Sea Pte Ltd　**(1)**
Tel.: (65) 62265405
Web Site: http://www.acerinox.com
Sales Range: $25-49.9 Million
Emp.: 5
Steel Product Distr
N.A.I.C.S.: 331221

**Acerinox South East Asia, Pte.
Ltd.**　**(1)**
16 Raffles Quay 20-02 Hong Leong Build-
ing, Shentonway, Singapore, 048581, Sin-
gapore
Tel.: (65) 62265405
Web Site: http://www.acerinox.com
Emp.: 1
Stainless Steel Products Mfr
N.A.I.C.S.: 331110

Acerinox UK Ltd　**(1)**
Heath Rd, Darlaston, WS10 8XL, West Mid-
lands, United Kingdom
Tel.: (44) 1215268000
Web Site: http://www.acerinox.co.uk
Sales Range: $25-49.9 Million
Emp.: 60
Steel Product Distr
N.A.I.C.S.: 331221

Acerinox, S.A. - Venezuela　**(1)**
Avenida Principal de la Castellana Edificio
Banco Lara Piso 3 Ofic D-1, La Castellana,
Caracas, Venezuela
Tel.: (58) 212 263 44 97
Web Site: http://www.acerinox.com
Sales Range: $25-49.9 Million
Emp.: 100
Stainless Steel Products Distr
N.A.I.C.S.: 423510

**Acerol Comercio E Industria De Acos
Inoxidaveis Unipessoal, Ltda.**　**(1)**
Estrada das Ligeiras 22 Armazen 1,
Cacem-Sintra, 2735-337, Lisbon, Portugal
Tel.: (351) 214267370

Web Site: http://www.acerinox.com
Metals Service Center
N.A.I.C.S.: 423510

**Acx Do Brasil Representacoes,
Ltda.**　**(1)**
Alameda Campinas no 728 8 andar Con-
junto 802, Sao Paulo, 01404-200, Brazil
Tel.: (55) 1131812204
Web Site: http://www.acerinox.es
Sales Range: $50-74.9 Million
Emp.: 3
Steel Product Distr
N.A.I.C.S.: 423510

Betinoks Turkey　**(1)**
Omer Avni Mah Inonu Cad N 32 Kat 5 A/9
Opera Residence Taksim, Kucukcekmece,
34437, Istanbul, Turkiye
Tel.: (90) 2122445833
Web Site: http://www.betainternational.be
Sales Range: $25-49.9 Million
Emp.: 30
Metals Service Center & Distr
N.A.I.C.S.: 423510

Columbus Stainless (Pty) Ltd　**(1)**
Hendrina Road, PO Box 133, Middelburg,
1050, South Africa　**(76%)**
Tel.: (27) 132479111
Web Site:
　http://www.columbusstainless.co.za
Sales Range: $450-499.9 Million
Emp.: 1,000
Stainless Steel Products
N.A.I.C.S.: 332111

**Corporacion Acerinox Peru,
S.A.C.**　**(1)**
Calle Alfonso Ugarte n 349 int oficina 402,
Miraflores, Lima, Peru
Tel.: (51) 14453391
Web Site: https://www.acerinox.com
Sales Range: $50-74.9 Million
Emp.: 3
Stainless Steel Products Distr
N.A.I.C.S.: 423510

Haynes International, Inc.　**(1)**
Tel.: (765) 456-6012
Web Site: https://www.haynesintl.com
Rev.: $589,956,000
Assets: $706,281,000
Liabilities: $271,957,000
Net Worth: $434,324,000
Earnings: $41,975,000
Emp.: 1,248
Fiscal Year-end: 09/30/2023
Nickel & Cobalt-Based Alloys Mfr
N.A.I.C.S.: 331314
Daniel W. Maudlin (CFO, Treas & VP-Fin)

Division (Non-US):

Haynes International S.r.l.　**(2)**
Tel.: (39) 0331469975
Web Site: http://www.haynesintl.it
Nickel & Cobalt-Based Alloys Mfr
N.A.I.C.S.: 331314

Haynes International sarl　**(2)**
16 ave de la Patellu, PO Box 70303, Cergy-
Pontoise, 95617, France
Tel.: (33) 134483100
Web Site: http://www.haynesintl.fr
Sales Range: $10-24.9 Million
Emp.: 12
Nickel & Cobalt-Based Alloys Mfr
N.A.I.C.S.: 331314

Subsidiary (Non-US):

Haynes International, AG　**(2)**
Hohlstrasse 534, CH-8048, Zurich, Switzer-
land
Tel.: (41) 444347080
Web Site: http://www.haynes.ch
Industrial Cutting Tool Distr
N.A.I.C.S.: 423120

Haynes International, Inc.　**(2)**
No 5A 5th Floor Century Plaza 560-561
Anna Salai, Teynampet, Chennai, 600018,
India
Tel.: (91) 4443546101
Web Site: http://www.haynesintl.com
Metal Alloy Product Distr
N.A.I.C.S.: 423510

Division (Non-US):

Haynes International, Ltd.　**(2)**

Parkhouse Street, Openshaw, Manchester, M11 2ER, United Kingdom   **(100%)**
Tel.: (44) 161230777
Web Site: http://www.haynesintl.com
Nickel & Cobalt-Based Alloys Mfr
N.A.I.C.S.: 331314

Haynes Pacific Pte Ltd   **(2)**
18 Boon Lay Way 09-132 TradeHub 21, Singapore, 609966, Singapore
Tel.: (65) 64688768
Sales Range: $150-199.9 Million
Emp.: 4
Nickel & Cobalt-Based Alloys Mfr
N.A.I.C.S.: 331314
Greg Chirieleison (Mng Dir)

Subsidiary (Non-US):

Haynes International (China) Ltd.   **(3)**
Part C First Floor 320 Hedan Road, Waigaoqiao Free Trade Zone, Shanghai, 200131, China
Tel.: (86) 2158683928
Web Site: http://www.haynesintl.com.cn
Sales Range: $10-24.9 Million
Nickel & Cobalt Based Alloys Mfr
N.A.I.C.S.: 331314

Haynes International K. K.   **(3)**
Kabushiki Kaisha Kamiyacho MT Building 14/F 4-3-20 Toranomon, Minato-ku, Tokyo, 105-0001, Japan
Tel.: (81) 354043518
Web Site: http://www.haynesintl.co.jp
Metal Alloy Product Mfr
N.A.I.C.S.: 331110

Subsidiary (Domestic):

Haynes Wire Company   **(2)**
158 N Egerton Rd, Mountain Home, NC 28758-0677
Tel.: (828) 692-5791
Web Site: http://www.hayneswire.com
Sales Range: $25-49.9 Million
Emp.: 60
Stainless & Nickel Alloy Wires Mfr
N.A.I.C.S.: 331222

LaPorte Custom Metal Processing, LLC   **(2)**
3236 N Hwy 39, La Porte, IN 46350
Tel.: (219) 326-8530
Web Site: https://www.laportemetal.com
Steel Mills & Ferroalloy Mfr
N.A.I.C.S.: 331110
Julius Kretlow (Gen Mgr)

INOXCENTER CANARIAS, S.A.   **(1)**
Pol Ind Salinetas C/ Tornero s/n, Gran Canaria, 35214, Telde, Las Palmas, Spain
Tel.: (34) 928 13 60 15
Stainless Steel Products Distr
N.A.I.C.S.: 423510

INOXIDABLES DE EUSKADI S.A.   **(1)**
Pol Ind de Jundiz C/ Lermandabide 17, 01015, Vitoria, Alava, Spain
Tel.: (34) 945 18 48 00
Web Site: http://www.acerinox.es
Flat Steel Processing Services
N.A.I.C.S.: 423510

INOXPLATE, LTDA.   **(1)**
Zona Industrial Maia I Sector Vii-Rua E Lt 2-A, Maia, 4470-000, Portugal
Tel.: (351) 229479280
Metal Products Mfr
N.A.I.C.S.: 332999

METALINOX BILBAO, S.A.   **(1)**
Aranaztegi Etorbidea 13, 20140, Andoain, Guipuzcoa, Spain
Tel.: (34) 943 59 17 99
Sales Range: $10-24.9 Million
Emp.: 35
General Warehousing Services
N.A.I.C.S.: 493110
Joaquin Beorlegui (Gen Mgr)

North American Stainless, Inc.   **(1)**
6870 US Hwy 42 E, Ghent, KY 41045-9615   **(100%)**
Tel.: (502) 347-6000
Web Site:
    http://www.northamericanstainless.com
Sales Range: $600-649.9 Million
Flat & Long Stainless Steel Products Mfr & Sales

N.A.I.C.S.: 331221
Chris Lyons (VP-Comml)

Subsidiary (Non-US):

North American Stainless Mexico S.A. de C.V.   **(2)**
Priv Andres Guajardo No 360 Parque Ind Apodaca I, Parque Industrial Apodaca I, 66600, Apodaca, NL, Mexico
Tel.: (52) 8112537700
Emp.: 10
Steel Product Distr
N.A.I.C.S.: 423510
Edgar Garza (Gen Mgr)

North American Steel Canada, Inc.   **(2)**
740 Imperial Road North, Guelph, N1K 1Z3, ON, Canada
Tel.: (519) 767-6830
Web Site:
    https://www.northamericanstainless.com
Sales Range: $25-49.9 Million
Emp.: 18
Steel Product Distr
N.A.I.C.S.: 423510
Roger Mansfield (Sls Mgr)

ROLDAN S.A.   **(1)**
Calle Santiago De Compostela 100, Madrid, 28035, Spain
Tel.: (34) 913 98 52 33
Iron & Steel Products Mfr
N.A.I.C.S.: 331110

Subsidiary (Domestic):

INOXFIL S.A.   **(2)**
C/ Paises Bajos N 11-15, 08700, Igualada, Barcelona, Spain
Tel.: (34) 938018200
Emp.: 99
Stainless Steel Products Mfr
N.A.I.C.S.: 331210
Angel Brunen (Gen Mgr)

VDM Metals GmbH   **(1)**
Plettenberger Str 2, 58791, Werdohl, Germany   **(100%)**
Tel.: (49) 2392550
Web Site: https://www.vdm-metals.com
Non-Ferrous Metals & Nickel Alloys Mfr & Distr
N.A.I.C.S.: 423510
Klaus Basse (Sr VP-Metal Trading)

Subsidiary (Non-US):

VDM (Shanghai) High Performance Metals Trading Co., Ltd.   **(2)**
Room 3306B 33F Chong Hing Finance Center No 288 West Nanjing Road, Huangpu District, Shanghai, 200003, China
Tel.: (86) 2163750966
Metal & Non-Ferrous Alloy Whslr & Service Center Operator
N.A.I.C.S.: 423510
Tom Xu (Mng Dir)

VDM Metals (Guangzhou) Trading Co., Ltd.   **(2)**
Stock & Service Center Guangzhou Free Trade Zone Guangbao Ave 213, 518730, Guangzhou, Guangdong, China
Tel.: (86) 20 82214097
Web Site: http://www.vdm-metals.com
Steel Product Distr
N.A.I.C.S.: 423510
Wang Dan (Head-Svc Center & Stock Sls)

VDM Metals Australia Pty. Ltd.   **(2)**
724 Springvale Road, Mulgrave, 3170, VIC, Australia
Tel.: (61) 385420900
Web Site: https://www.vdm-metals.com
Steel & Alloy Mfr
N.A.I.C.S.: 331110
Lutz Toriedt (Mng Dir)

VDM Metals Austria GmbH   **(2)**
Liebermannstr A02 505, 2345, Brunn am Gebirge, Austria   **(100%)**
Tel.: (43) 72098091910
Web Site: https://www.vdm-metals.com
Steel Mfrs
N.A.I.C.S.: 331110
Sascha Kremmer (Mng Dir)

VDM Metals Benelux B.V.   **(2)**

Hoedemakersstraat 9, 3334 KK, Zwijndrecht, Netherlands
Tel.: (31) 653240831
Steel & Nickel Alloy Whslr
N.A.I.C.S.: 423510

VDM Metals Canada Limited   **(2)**
3700 Steeles Ave W Suite 304, Vaughan, L4L 8K8, ON, Canada
Tel.: (905) 477-2064
Web Site: http://www.vdm-metals.com
Emp.: 4
Steel & Nickel Alloy Mfr
N.A.I.C.S.: 331110

VDM Metals France S.A.S.   **(2)**
Douglas 2 / Batiment A 97 allee Alexandre Borodine, 69800, Saint Priest, France
Tel.: (33) 426078714
Steel & Alloy Mfr
N.A.I.C.S.: 331110
Eric Vidal (Mng Dir)

VDM Metals Italia S.r.l.   **(2)**
Via Milanese 20, 20099, Sesto San Giovanni, Italy
Tel.: (39) 022410461
Web Site: https://www.vdm-metals.com
Steel & Metal Mfr
N.A.I.C.S.: 331110
Roberto Briano (Mng Dir)

VDM Metals Japan K.K.   **(2)**
Daido Seimei Kasumigaseki Bldg 7th Floor 1-4-2 Kasumigaseki, Chiyoda-ku, Tokyo, 100-0013, Japan
Tel.: (81) 362054341
Web Site: https://www.vdm-metals.com
Steel & Metal Alloy Mfr
N.A.I.C.S.: 331110
Eduard Gabric (Mng Dir)

VDM Metals Korea Co., Ltd.   **(2)**
1213 3 Hwanngsaeul 240 Beon, Bundang-Gu, Songnam, 463-783, Gyeonggi, Korea (South)
Tel.: (82) 317126313
Web Site: http://www.vdm-metals.com
Steel & Metal Service Center Operator & Whslr
N.A.I.C.S.: 423510
Seung Chun Chang (Mng Dir)

VDM Metals Schweiz AG   **(2)**
Lange Gasse 90, 4002, Basel, Switzerland
Tel.: (41) 612058450
Web Site: http://www.vdm-metals.com
Emp.: 6
Steel & Alloy Mfr
N.A.I.C.S.: 331110
Bernhard Ammon (Head-Sls)

VDM Metals U.K. Ltd.   **(2)**
St Andrews House Upper Ham Road, Richmond, TW10 5LA, Surrey, United Kingdom
Tel.: (44) 1372467137
Steel & Alloy Mfr
N.A.I.C.S.: 331110
David Munasinghe (Mng Dir)

Subsidiary (US):

VDM Metals USA, LLC   **(2)**
14255 Mt Bismark St, Reno, NV 89506
Tel.: (775) 386-1200
Web Site: http://www.vdm-metals.com
Steel Mfrs
N.A.I.C.S.: 331110

Subsidiary (Non-US):

VDM Metals de Mexico S.A. de C.V.   **(2)**
Blvd Manuel Avila Camacho No 80 Ph A, Edo De Mexico Juarez, 53390, Mexico, Mexico
Tel.: (52) 5555571471
Web Site: http://www.vdm-metals.com
Steel & Nickel Alloy Mfr
N.A.I.C.S.: 331110

VDM Metals Holding GmbH   **(1)**
Plettenberger Str 2, 58791, Werdohl, Germany
Tel.: (49) 2392550
Stainless Steel Material Mfr & Distr
N.A.I.C.S.: 331210

VDM Metals International GmbH   **(1)**
Kleffstrasse 23, 58762, Altena, Germany
Tel.: (49) 2392550

Stainless Steel Material Mfr & Distr
N.A.I.C.S.: 331210

ACEROLUX SL

Carrer Joan Guell 111, 08028, Barcelona, Spain
Tel.: (34) 934911225   ES
Metal Product Mfr & Whslr
N.A.I.C.S.: 332999
Jose Luis Carrillo Rodriguez (Mgr)

Subsidiaries:

Mecalux, S.A.   **(1)**
Silici 1-5, Cornella, 8940, Spain
Tel.: (34) 932616901
Web Site: http://www.mecalux.com
Sales Range: $650-699.9 Million
Emp.: 3,709
Holding Company; Steel Shelving & Storage Systems Mfr & Distr
N.A.I.C.S.: 551112
Jose Luis Carrillo Rodriguez (Pres)

Subsidiary (US):

Interlake Mecalux, Inc.   **(2)**
1600 N 25th Ave, Melrose Park, IL 60160-1868   **(100%)**
Tel.: (708) 344-9999
Web Site: http://www.interlakemecalux.com
Sales Range: $25-49.9 Million
Emp.: 200
Steel Shelving & Storage Systems Mfr & Distr
N.A.I.C.S.: 332312
Javier Carrillo (Pres)

Subsidiary (Non-US):

Mecalux (UK) Ltd.   **(2)**
Unit 9 Network Park Duddeston Mill Road, Saltley, Birmingham, B8 1AU, United Kingdom   **(100%)**
Tel.: (44) 121 3336 602
Web Site: http://www.mecalux.co.uk
Sales Range: $25-49.9 Million
Emp.: 15
Steel Shelving & Storage Systems Whslr
N.A.I.C.S.: 423830

Mecalux Argentina, S.A.   **(2)**
Boulogne Sur Mer 2538, Villa Maipu, Buenos Aires, 1650, Argentina   **(100%)**
Tel.: (54) 11 4006 4444
Web Site: http://www.mecalux.com.ar
Steel Shelving & Storage Systems Mfr & Distr
N.A.I.C.S.: 332312
Angel Jimenez Pastor (Mng Dir)

Mecalux Belgium S.A.   **(2)**
Boulevard Paepsem 11 A, 1070, Anderlecht, Belgium   **(100%)**
Tel.: (32) 2 346 90 71
Web Site: http://www.mecalux.be
Steel Shelving & Storage Systems Whslr
N.A.I.C.S.: 423830

Subsidiary (Domestic):

Mecalux Esmena   **(2)**
Pol Ind Los Campones Ataulfo Friera Tarfe 12, 33211, Gijon, Asturias, Spain   **(100%)**
Tel.: (34) 985178000
Web Site: http://www.esmena.com
Sales Range: $125-149.9 Million
Emp.: 500
Steel Shelving & Storage Systems Designer, Mfr, Distr & Installer
N.A.I.C.S.: 332312
Jose Luis Carrillo (Pres)

Subsidiary (Non-US):

Mecalux France S.a.r.l.   **(2)**
1 rue Colbert, ZAC de Montavas, 91320, Wissous, France   **(100%)**
Tel.: (33) 1 60 11 92 92
Web Site: http://www.mecalux.fr
Sales Range: $25-49.9 Million
Emp.: 50
Steel Shelving & Storage Systems Whslr
N.A.I.C.S.: 423830

Mecalux GmbH   **(2)**
Moselstrasse 19, 41464, Neuss, Germany   **(100%)**
Tel.: (49) 2131 40 760
Web Site: http://www.mecalux.de

Acerolux SL—(Continued)

Sales Range: $25-49.9 Million
Emp.: 10
Steel Shelving & Storage Systems Whslr
N.A.I.C.S.: 423830
Juan Maria Santos Veira *(Mng Dir)*

Mecalux Milano, S.r.l. (2)
Via Benaco 14, San Giuliano Milanese,
20098, MI, Italy **(100%)**
Tel.: (39) 02 98836601
Web Site: http://www.mecalux.it
Sales Range: $25-49.9 Million
Emp.: 14
Steel Shelving & Storage Systems Whslr
N.A.I.C.S.: 423830
Emmanuel Beghin *(Gen Mgr)*

Unit (Domestic):

Mecalux SA (2)
Avda Maresme nro 64, Cornella de Llobregat, 08940, Cornella, Spain
Tel.: (34) 902121312
Web Site: http://www.logismarket.es
Logistics, Storage, Packaging & Industrial
Equipment Business-to-Business Corporate
Directory Publisher
N.A.I.C.S.: 513140
Miguel Davila *(Dir-Mktg)*

Subsidiary (Domestic):

Mecalux Servis, S.A. (2)
Calle Julio Palacios 14, Pol Ind Ntra Sra
Butarque, 28914, Leganes, Spain
Tel.: (34) 916 888 333
Web Site: http://www.mecalux.es
Emp.: 80
Steel Shelving & Storage Systems Whslr
N.A.I.C.S.: 423830
Julian Moreno Diaz *(CEO)*

Subsidiary (Non-US):

Mecalux Sp. z o.o. (2)
ul Wyczolkowskiego 125, Gliwice, 05-082,
Poland **(100%)**
Tel.: (48) 32 331 69 66
Web Site: http://www.mecalux.pl
Sales Range: $200-249.9 Million
Emp.: 600
Steel Shelving & Storage Systems Whslr
N.A.I.C.S.: 423830
Juan Maria Santos Veira *(Mng Dir)*

Mecalux do Brasil Sistemas de Armazenagem Ltda. (2)
Rua Eonio Moreira Diniz s/n, Jardim Nova
Europa, Hortolandia, 13184-861, SP,
Brazil **(100%)**
Tel.: (55) 19 3809 6800
Web Site: http://www.mecalux.com.br
Steel Shelving & Storage Systems Designer, Mfr & Distr
N.A.I.C.S.: 332312
Ivan Poblet Menendez *(Mng Dir)*

ACERTEC PLC
15 Shottery Brook Timothys Bridge
Road, Stratford-upon-Avon, CV37
9NR, Warks, United Kingdom
Tel.: (44) 1789 403070
Sales Range: $600-649.9 Million
Emp.: 48
Engineered Steel Products Mfr
N.A.I.C.S.: 331221
Mick Hayhurst *(Sec)*

ACERUS PHARMACEUTICALS CORPORATION
7025 Langer Drive Suite 205, Mississauga, L5N 0E8, ON, Canada
Tel.: (416) 679-0771 ON
Web Site:
https://www.aceruspharma.com
Year Founded: 2009
ASP—(OTCIQ)
Rev.: $2,121,000
Assets: $9,652,000
Liabilities: $35,666,000
Net Worth: ($26,014,000)
Earnings: ($33,817,000)
Emp.: 14
Fiscal Year-end: 12/31/21

Pharmaceuticals Mfr
N.A.I.C.S.: 325412
Ian O. Ihnatowycz *(Chm)*

ACES ELECTRONIC CO., LTD.
No 13 Dongyuan Road, Zhongli District, Taoyuan, 32063, Taiwan
Tel.: (886) 34632808
Wob Site: https://www.acescorin.com
Year Founded: 1996
3605—(TAI)
Rev.: $277,518,156
Assets: $400,630,777
Liabilities: $228,731,637
Net Worth: $171,899,140
Earnings: ($8,770,332)
Emp.: 7,000
Fiscal Year-end: 12/31/23
Electronic Connector Mfr
N.A.I.C.S.: 334417
Wan-Ting Yuan *(Chm)*

Subsidiaries:

Aces Dong Guan (1)
Hong San Industrial Park Xin An Community, Chang An Town, Dongguan, Guangdong, China
Tel.: (86) 76985393066
Electronic Goods Mfr
N.A.I.C.S.: 334419

ACESA-DRIVES S.A. DE C.V.
Nebraska No 46 Col Napoles, 03810,
Mexico, Distrito Federal, Mexico
Tel.: (52) 5526363540
Web Site: http://www.lenze.com
Sales Range: $50-74.9 Million
Emp.: 15
Holding Company Automotive Controls Mfr
N.A.I.C.S.: 551112

ACESIAN PARTNERS LIMITED
33 Mactaggart Road 04-00, Singapore, 368082, Singapore
Tel.: (65) 67575310
Web Site: http://acesian.com
Sales Range: $10-24.9 Million
Stainless Steel Ducts Mfr & Sales
N.A.I.C.S.: 331513
Kok Chye Wong *(CEO)*

Subsidiaries:

Air System Technology (S) Pte Ltd (1)
33 Mactaggart Rd, Singapore, Singapore, 368082, Singapore
Tel.: (65) 67465188
Web Site: http://www.linair.com.sg
Emp.: 52
Air Conditioning & Mechanical Ventilation
Systems Installation Services
N.A.I.C.S.: 238220

Linair Bio-Science Pte. Ltd. (1)
33 Metaga Road Level, Singapore, 368082, Singapore
Tel.: (65) 67575310
Web Site: http://www.linair.com.sg
Emp.: 38
Life Science Equipments Mfr
N.A.I.C.S.: 333310

Linair Engineering Pte. Ltd. (1)
110 Paya Lebar Road 04-01 Singapore
Warehouse, Singapore, Singapore
Tel.: (65) 67575310
Web Site: http://www.linair.com.sg
Sales Range: $25-49.9 Million
Emp.: 200
Construction Engineering Services
N.A.I.C.S.: 541330
William Tan *(CEO)*

Linair Technologies (Taiwan) Co., Ltd (1)
No 1-20 Dashe Road, Dashe Township, Kaohsiung, 81566, Taiwan
Tel.: (886) 73533277
Web Site: http://www.linair.com.sg
Air Control Equipments Distr
N.A.I.C.S.: 423610

ACESO LIFE SCIENCE GROUP LIMITED
Rm 2501-2509 25/F Shui On Centre
6-8 Harbour Road, Wanchai, China
(Hong Kong)
Tel.: (852) 31608466 Ky
Web Site:
https://www.acesogrouphk.com
04/4—(HKG)
Rev.: $40,628,700
Assets: $807,801,740
Liabilities: $443,175,280
Net Worth: $364,626,460
Earnings: ($76,872,080)
Emp.: 166
Fiscal Year-end: 03/31/22
Investment Holding Company
N.A.I.C.S.: 551112
Chi Tak Fok *(Exec Dir)*

Subsidiaries:

Fujian Nuoqi Co., Ltd. (1)
Nuoqi Creative Enterprises Zone 55 Chongwen Road, Economic & Technical Development Zone, Quanzhou, Fujian,
China **(59.93%)**
Tel.: (86) 595 2826 5777
Web Site: http://www.nuoqi.com.hk
Sales Range: $75-99.9 Million
Men's Clothing Mfr
N.A.I.C.S.: 315250
Hui Ding *(Chm & CEO)*

King International Financial Holdings Limited (1)
1702B-03A International Commerce Centre
1 Austin Road West, Kowloon, China (Hong Kong)
Tel.: (852) 2652 3474
Web Site: http://www.kinggold.com.hk
Holding Company; Commodities Trading &
Brokerage Services; Asset Management
Services
N.A.I.C.S.: 551112
Cho Yan Lo *(CEO)*

Subsidiary (Domestic):

King International Bullion Limited (2)
1702B-03A International Commerce Centre
1 Austin Road West, Kowloon, China (Hong Kong)
Tel.: (852) 2652 3474
Web Site: http://www.kinggold.com.hk
Precious Metals Trading Services
N.A.I.C.S.: 523160
Cho Yan Lo *(CEO)*

ACEWIN AGRITECK LIMITED
Unit 1 4th Floor Pinnacle Ascendas
International Tech Park, CSIR Road
Taramani, Chennai, 600113, Tamil
Nadu, India
Tel.: (91) 4443313364
Web Site:
http://www.acewinagriteck.com
539570—(BOM)
Rev.: $4,812,653
Assets: $5,066,089
Liabilities: $1,150,661
Net Worth: $3,915,428
Earnings: $1,736,852
Emp.: 22
Fiscal Year-end: 03/31/20
Technology Services
N.A.I.C.S.: 561499
Jesudas Premkumar *(Mng Dir)*

ACEZ INSTRUMENTS PTE. LTD.
2 Joo Koon Circle, Singapore,
629031, Singapore
Tel.: (65) 62680100
Web Site: http://www.acez.com.sg
Year Founded: 1985
Sales Range: $1-9.9 Million
Emp.: 75
Measuring & Controlling Devices; Engineering & Construction Products
Mfr
N.A.I.C.S.: 334513

Ricky Yeo *(Co-Founder)*

Subsidiaries:

ACEZ Instruments Philippines Corporation (1)
Unit 301-303 DMG Center Libertad cor Calbayog Street, Mandaluyong, 1553, Philippines
Tul.: (63) 2 4708088
Web Site: http://www.acezphil.com
Emp.: 10
Thermal Sensing Equipment Mfr
N.A.I.C.S.: 333248
Sockalingam Jayabalan *(Pres & Gen Mgr)*

Acez Instruments (Shenzhen) Co., Ltd (1)
2105B Seg Plaza Huaqiang Road, Futian,
Shenzhen, China
Tel.: (86) 755 6136 2528
Web Site: http://www.acez.com.cn
Thermal Sensing Equipment Mfr
N.A.I.C.S.: 333248

Acez Sensing Pte Ltd. (1)
Blk 28E Penjuru Close 01-04, Singapore,
629031, Singapore
Tel.: (65) 6265 1588
Web Site: http://www.acezsensing.com
Emp.: 26
Thermal Sensing Equipment Mfr
N.A.I.C.S.: 333248
Khin Maung Myint *(Gen Mgr)*

PT Acez Instruments Indonesia (1)
Jl Mangga Besar Raya No 33B Mangga
Besar Taman Sari Jakarta Barat, Jakarta,
11180, Indonesia
Tel.: (62) 21 6232 0237
Thermal Sensing Equipment Mfr
N.A.I.C.S.: 333248

ACG ADVISORS (UK) LLP
80 Coleman Street, London, EC2R
5BJ, United Kingdom
Tel.: (44) 2035405150 UK
Web Site:
http://www.acgadvisors.com
Year Founded: 2013
Emp.: 20
Investment Advisory & Asset Management Services
N.A.I.C.S.: 523940
Alberto Ferro-Villani *(Principal)*

Subsidiaries:

Quaker Securities (1)
Place Bel-Air 8, 1260, Nyon, Switzerland
Tel.: (41) 22 365 8111
Web Site: http://www.quakersec.com
Investment Advisory & Securities Brokerage
Services
N.A.I.C.S.: 523150
Benjamin Zumstein *(Co-Founder & Mng Dir)*

ACH, D.D.
Baragova 5, Ljubljana, 1000, Slovenia
Tel.: (386) 15883100 SI
Web Site: http://www.ach.si
Year Founded: 1952
Sales Range: $650-699.9 Million
Emp.: 2,394
Holding Company
N.A.I.C.S.: 551112
Herman Rigelnik *(Gen Dir)*

ACHAL INVESTMENTS LIMITED
407 Prabhat Kiran Building Rajendra
Place, Delhi, 110008, India
Tel.: (91) 1132317170 In
Web Site: http://www.achalinvest.com
Year Founded: 1980
Rev.: $141,013
Assets: $2,498,466
Liabilities: $914,968
Net Worth: $1,583,498
Earnings: $5,288
Emp.: 2
Fiscal Year-end: 03/31/18

Financial Services
N.A.I.C.S.: 523999
Pradeep Ram *(CFO)*

ACHEM TECHNOLOGY COR-PORATION
7F No 397 Xingshan Rd, Neihu Dist, Taipei, 114, Taiwan
Tel.: (886) 2 81706199   TW
Web Site: http://www.achem.com.tw
Year Founded: 1960
1715—(TAI)
Sales Range: $300-349.9 Million
Holding Company; Sealing Plastic Tape Mfr & Distr
N.A.I.C.S.: 551112
Jian Yu Lin *(CFO)*

Subsidiaries:

Achem Industry America, Inc.   (1)
13226 Alondra Blvd, Cerritos, CA 90703
Tel.: (562) 802-0998
Web Site: http://www.achem-usa.com
Industrial Supplies Merchant Whslr
N.A.I.C.S.: 423840

ACHERON PORTFOLIO CORP (LUXEMBOURG) SA
37 rue d Anvers, 1130, Luxembourg, Luxembourg
Tel.: (352) 26334242
Web Site:
http://www.acheronportfolio.lu
144723—(LUX)
Sales Range: Less than $1 Million
Financial Investment Services
N.A.I.C.S.: 523999
Yves Mertz *(Chm)*

ACHESON & GLOVER LTD.
127 Creevehill Rd, Fivemiletown, Dungannon, BT75 0SY, Tyrone, United Kingdom
Tel.: (44) 2889521275   IE
Web Site: http://www.acheson-glover.com
Year Founded: 1960
Sales Range: $200-249.9 Million
Emp.: 600
Stone & Concrete Products Mfr
N.A.I.C.S.: 327320
Brian Mulgrew *(Mgr-Bus Dev)*

ACHIEVE LIFE SCIENCES, INC.
1040 West Georgia Street Suite 1030, Vancouver, V6E 4H1, BC, Canada
Tel.: (604) 210-2217   DE
Web Site:
https://www.achievelifesciences.com
Year Founded: 1991
ACHV—(NASDAQ)
Rev.: $199,000
Assets: $29,971,000
Liabilities: $21,668,000
Net Worth: $8,303,000
Earnings: ($42,350,000)
Emp.: 20
Fiscal Year-end: 12/31/22
Pharmaceutical Developer & Mfr
N.A.I.C.S.: 325412
Cindy Jacobs *(Pres & Chief Medical Officer)*

ACHIKO AG
Tessinerplatz 7, 8002, Zurich, Switzerland
Tel.: (41) 442666767   Ky
Web Site: https://www.achiko.com
Year Founded: 2018
ACHI—(SWX)
Rev.: $62,507
Assets: $1,914,416
Liabilities: $6,499,342
Net Worth: ($4,584,926)

Earnings: ($9,321,779)
Fiscal Year-end: 12/31/21
Information Technology Services
N.A.I.C.S.: 541512

ACHILLES CORPORATION
Shinjuku Front Tower 2-21-1 Kita-Shinjuku, Shinjuku-Ku, Tokyo, 169-8885, Japan
Tel.: (81) 353389200   JP
Web Site: https://www.achilles.jp
Year Founded: 1947
5142—(TKS)
Rev.: $519,592,270
Assets: $546,395,820
Liabilities: $284,976,930
Net Worth: $261,418,890
Earnings: ($54,268,100)
Emp.: 1,256
Fiscal Year-end: 03/31/24
Footwear, Supported & Unsupported PVC Sheeting, Polyurethane, Industrial & Insulation Products Mfr
N.A.I.C.S.: 316210

Subsidiaries:

Achilles (Shanghai) International Trading Co., Ltd.   (1)
Room 1507 International Trade Center 2201 YanAn West Road, Shanghai, 200336, China
Tel.: (86) 216 364 8024
Plastic Product Mfr & Distr
N.A.I.C.S.: 326199

Achilles Advanced Technology Co., Ltd.   (1)
6th Floor No 415 Section 2 Gongdao 5th Road, East District, Hsinchu, Taiwan
Tel.: (886) 3 573 7300
Web Site: https://www.achilles-at.com.tw
Plastic Product Mfr & Distr
N.A.I.C.S.: 326199

Achilles Hong Kong Co., Ltd.   (1)
Unit A 5/F Winner Building 36 Man Yue Street, Hung Hom, Kowloon, China (Hong Kong)
Tel.: (852) 2 362 8324
Web Site: http://www.achilles.jp
Sales Range: $50-74.9 Million
Emp.: 5
Footwear Merchant Whslr
N.A.I.C.S.: 424340

Achilles USA, Inc.   (1)
1407 80th St SW, Everett, WA 98203-6220   (100%)
Tel.: (425) 353-7000
Web Site: http://www.achillesusa.com
Sales Range: $75-99.9 Million
Emp.: 175
Plastics Product Mfr
N.A.I.C.S.: 326113
Mike Burrows *(Mgr-HR & Safety)*

Kunshan Achilles Artificial Leather Co., Ltd.   (1)
No 288 Yun Que Road Kunshan Economics Developing Zone, Kunshan, 215300, Jiangsu, China
Tel.: (86) 512 577 22858
Web Site: http://www.achilles.jp
Leather Goods Mfr
N.A.I.C.S.: 316990

Kunshan Achilles New Material Technology Co., Ltd.   (1)
No 288 Yun Que Road, Kunshan Economics Developing Zone, Kunshan, 215300, Jiangsu, China
Tel.: (86) 5125 772 2858
Plastic Product Mfr & Distr
N.A.I.C.S.: 326199

Winfast Technology Ltd.   (1)
Unit A 5/F Winner Building 36 Man Yue Street, Hung Hom, Kowloon, China (Hong Kong)
Tel.: (852) 2 314 0366
Plastic Product Mfr & Distr
N.A.I.C.S.: 326199

ACHILLES THERAPEUTICS PLC

245 Hammersmith Road, London, W6 8PW, United Kingdom
Tel.: (44) 2081544600   UK
Web Site: https://www.achillestx.com
ACHL—(NASDAQ)
Rev.: $7,318,000
Assets: $220,358,000
Liabilities: $23,314,000
Net Worth: $197,044,000
Earnings: ($71,176,000)
Emp.: 234
Fiscal Year-end: 12/31/22
Offices of Physical, Occupational & Speech Therapists & Audiologists
N.A.I.C.S.: 621340
Iraj Ali *(CEO)*

ACHIT ALKABY JOINT STOCK COMPANY
Khoskharagai Bag, Nogoonnuur Soum, Ulaanbaatar, Bayan-Olgii, Mongolia
Tel.: (976) 99428844
NOG—(MONG)
Sales Range: Less than $1 Million
Crop Farming Services
N.A.I.C.S.: 111998

ACHMEA B.V.
Handelsweg 2, 3707 NH, Zeist, Netherlands
Tel.: (31) 30693700   NI
Year Founded: 1811
Rev.: $24,403,903,440
Assets: $93,580,322,640
Liabilities: $82,479,840,690
Net Worth: $11,100,481,950
Earnings: $360,293,850
Emp.: 13,714
Fiscal Year-end: 12/31/18
Holding Company; Insurance Services
N.A.I.C.S.: 551112
Bianca E.M. Tetteroo *(Member-Exec Bd)*

Subsidiaries:

Achmea Bank N.V.   (1)
Spoorlaan 298, 5017 JZ, Tilburg, Netherlands
Tel.: (31) 134612010
Web Site: http://www.achmeabank.nl
Commercial Banking Services
N.A.I.C.S.: 522110
Pierre Huurman *(CEO & Member-Exec Bd)*

Achmea Interne Diensten N.V.   (1)
Laan van Malkenschoten 20, 7333 NP, Apeldoorn, Netherlands
Tel.: (31) 555799111
Web Site: http://www.ripe.net
Internet Service Provider
N.A.I.C.S.: 517112

Achmea Pensioen - en Levensverzekeringen N.V.   (1)
Prins Willem-Alexanderln 651, 7311 RC, Apeldoorn, Netherlands
Tel.: (31) 555799111
Commercial Banking Services
N.A.I.C.S.: 522110

DFZ Tussenholding N.V.   (1)
Harlingertrekweg 55, Leeuwarden, 8913 HR, Netherlands
Tel.: (31) 582913131
Commercial Banking Services
N.A.I.C.S.: 522110

Eureko RE N.V.   (1)
Spoorlaan 298, 5017 JZ, Tilburg, Netherlands   (100%)
Tel.: (31) 13 462 3822
Sales Range: $50-74.9 Million
Emp.: 3
Reinsurance Services
N.A.I.C.S.: 524130

Eureko Sigorta A.S.   (1)
Altunizade Mahallesi Ord Prof Fahrettin Kerim Gokay Cad No20, Uskudar, Istanbul, 34662, Turkiye   (100%)
Tel.: (90) 216 400 10 00

Web Site: http://www.eurekosigorta.com.tr
Sales Range: $10-24.9 Million
Emp.: 529
Insurance Services
N.A.I.C.S.: 524298
Uco Vegter *(Gen Mgr-Intl-BV Div & Member-Exec Bd)*

Eurocross Assistance Netherlands B.V.   (1)
Dellaertweg 1, 2316 WZ, Leiden, Netherlands
Tel.: (31) 713641333
Web Site: http://www.eurocross.nl
General Insurance Services
N.A.I.C.S.: 524210
Roberto ter Hark *(Acct Mgr)*

Eurocross international Central Europe S.R.O.   (1)
Narodni 984, Stredocesky, 11000, Prague, Czech Republic
Tel.: (420) 296339633
General Insurance Services
N.A.I.C.S.: 524210

Friends First Holdings Ltd.   (1)
Friends First House Cherrywood Business Park, Loughlinstown, Dublin, 18, Ireland   (100%)
Tel.: (353) 16610600
Web Site: http://www.friendsfirst.ie
Assets: $5,477,770,000
Emp.: 390
Financial Services
N.A.I.C.S.: 523940

Subsidiary (Domestic):

First Life Assurance Company Ltd.   (2)
Friends First House Cherrywood Business Park, Loughlinstown, Dublin, 18, Ireland
Tel.: (353) 16610600
Web Site: http://www.friendsfirst.ie
Sales Range: $150-199.9 Million
Emp.: 300
Pension Administrator
N.A.I.C.S.: 524292

Friends First Ireland   (2)
Cherrywood Business Park Loughlinstown, Dublin, 18, Ireland
Tel.: (353) 16610600
Web Site: http://www.friendsfirst.ie
Sales Range: $250-299.9 Million
Emp.: 300
N.A.I.C.S.: 524298

Interamerican hellenic life insurance company S.A.   (1)
Leof Andrea Siggrou 124, 11782, Athens, Greece
Tel.: (30) 2109461111
Web Site: http://www.interamerican.gr
General Insurance Services
N.A.I.C.S.: 524210

Klant Contact Services B.V   (1)
Nicolaas Beetsstraat 222, 3511 HG, Utrecht, Netherlands
Tel.: (31) 302348888
Web Site: http://www.klantcontactservices.nl
General Insurance Services
N.A.I.C.S.: 524210
Lorenzo Khoe Lie *(Mgr-Team)*

Pim Mulier B.V.   (1)
Papendallaan 52, Postbus 50010, 6816 VD, Arnhem, Netherlands
Tel.: (31) 264822315
Web Site: http://www.pimmulier.nl
General Insurance Services
N.A.I.C.S.: 524210

Risk & Insurance S.A.   (1)
1 A Ruedunord, PO Box 237, 2163, Luxembourg, Luxembourg   (100%)
Tel.: (352) 222474
Sales Range: $75-99.9 Million
Emp.: 2
N.A.I.C.S.: 524298
Christin Christiansen *(Dir-Risk Insurance)*

Staalbankiers N.V.   (1)
Lange Houtstraat 8, 2511 CW, Hague, Netherlands
Tel.: (31) 703101510
Web Site: http://www.staalbankiers.nl
Commercial Banking Services

Achmea B.V.—(Continued)

N.A.I.C.S.: 522110
R. O. Dielbandhoesing *(Mgr-Fin Risk)*

Syntrus Achmea Pensioenbeheer N.V. **(1)**
Rijnzathe 10, 3454 PV, De Meern, Netherlands
Tel.: (31) 2453999
Pension Fund Management Services
N.A.I.C.S.: 523940
Peter Jaspers *(Dir-Fin)*

Syntrus Achmea Real Estate & Finance B.V. **(1)**
Gatwickstraat 1, 1043 GK, Amsterdam, Netherlands
Tel.: (31) 206065600
Web Site: http://www.achmeavastgoed.nl
Pension Fund Management Services
N.A.I.C.S.: 523940
Niels Nieboer *(Mgr-Bus Dev & Mktg)*

Union Poist'ovna A.S. **(1)**
Karadzicova 10, 813 60, Bratislava, Slovakia
Tel.: (421) 850111211
Web Site: http://www.union.sk
General Insurance Services
N.A.I.C.S.: 524210

Winnock Zorg B.V. **(1)**
Spaklerweg 14, 1096 BA, Amsterdam, Netherlands
Tel.: (31) 889466200
General Insurance Services
N.A.I.C.S.: 524210

ACHYUT HEALTHCARE LTD.
610 Colonade Iscon-Ambali Road
Behind Vikas Stove Veraval Shapar, Ahmedabad, 380058, Gujarat, India
Tel.: (91) 7948982691
Web Site:
  https://www.achyuthealthcare.com
Year Founded: 1996
543499—(BOM)
Health Care Srvices
N.A.I.C.S.: 621610
Jigen Jagdishbhai Modi *(CEO & Mng Dir)*

ACI BRANDS INC.
2616 Sheridan Garden Drive, Oakville, L6J 7Z2, ON, Canada
Tel.: (905) 829-1566
Web Site: http://www.acibrands.com
Year Founded: 1981
Sales Range: $25-49.9 Million
Emp.: 167
Accessories & Personal Care Product Mfr
N.A.I.C.S.: 315990
Jeff Goraieb *(Pres)*

ACI D.D.
Rudolfa Strohala 2, 51000, Rijeka, Croatia
Tel.: (385) 51271288
Web Site: https://www.aci-marinas.com
Year Founded: 1983
ACI—(ZAG)
Rev.: $263,580,633
Assets: $741,165,731
Liabilities: $181,018,370
Net Worth: $560,147,362
Earnings: $27,340,567
Emp.: 331
Fiscal Year-end: 12/31/22
Marina Tourism Services
N.A.I.C.S.: 713930
Kristijan Pavic *(Chm & Pres)*

ACI ELEVATION S.A.
49 Rue De Boult, Isles-sur-Suippes, 51110, France
Tel.: (33) 326032959
Web Site: http://www.aci-elevation.com
Sales Range: $25-49.9 Million

Emp.: 65
Newspaper Publishers
N.A.I.C.S.: 321215
Sylvie Owen *(Pres & CEO)*

ACI INFOCOM LIMITED
121 V Mall Thakur Complex Near Sai Dham Temple Kandivali East, Mumbai, 401101, India
Tel.: (91) 2240166323
Web Site: https://www.acirealty.co.in
Year Founded: 1982
517356—(BOM)
Rev.: $84,057
Assets: $2,328,403
Liabilities: $47,461
Net Worth: $2,280,942
Earnings: $5,542
Emp.: 4
Fiscal Year-end: 03/31/22
Information Technology Support Services
N.A.I.C.S.: 541512
Anand Kumar Jain *(Mng Dir)*

ACICO INDUSTRIES CO. K.S.C.C.
Sharq Al-Hamra Business Tower 34th Floor, PO Box 24079, Safat, 13101, Kuwait, 13101, Kuwait
Tel.: (965) 1888811   **KW**
Web Site:
  https://www.acicogroup.com
Year Founded: 1990
ACICO—(KUW)
Rev.: $264,258,416
Assets: $1,156,125,269
Liabilities: $1,015,490,864
Net Worth: $140,634,405
Earnings: ($150,791,972)
Emp.: 2,759
Fiscal Year-end: 12/31/22
Concrete Products Mfr; Real Estate Developer
N.A.I.C.S.: 327331
Abdul Aziz Ahmed Abdullah Al-Ayyoub *(Co-Chm)*

ACKERMANS & VAN HAAREN NV
Begijnenvest 113, 2000, Antwerp, Belgium
Tel.: (32) 32318770   **NL**
Web Site: https://www.avh.be
AVHNF—(OTCIQ)
Rev.: $4,802,725,460
Assets: $19,932,792,531
Liabilities: $14,059,141,278
Net Worth: $5,873,651,253
Earnings: $340,976,619
Emp.: 11,317
Fiscal Year-end: 12/31/20
Investment Company
N.A.I.C.S.: 525910
Hilde Delabie *(Controller-Grp)*

Subsidiaries:

Agidens AG **(1)**
Hohenrainstrasse 10, 4133, Pratteln, Switzerland
Tel.: (41) 617130080
Engineering Consulting Services
N.A.I.C.S.: 541330

Agidens Inc. **(1)**
N Post Oak Rd 1000, Houston, TX 77055
Tel.: (616) 256-0916
Engineering Consulting Services
N.A.I.C.S.: 541330

Agidens International NV **(1)**
Baarbeek 1, 2070, Zwijndrecht, Belgium
Tel.: (32) 36411770
Web Site: https://www.agidens.com
Emp.: 500
Automation Event & Training Course Services
N.A.I.C.S.: 561920
Hedwig Maes *(CEO)*

Algemene Aannemingen Van Laere NV **(1)**
Kattestraat 77, 9150, Kruibeke, Belgium   **(100%)**
Tel.: (32) 32522020
Web Site: http://www.vanlaere.be
Sales Range: $125-149.9 Million
Emp.: 300
Construction & Civil Engineering
N.A.I.C.S.: 236210

Anfima NV **(1)**
Tel.: (32) 318770
Emp.: 35
Investment Management Service
N.A.I.C.S.: 523999
Luc Bertrand *(Gen Mgr)*

Anima NV **(1)**
Zandvoortstraat 27, 2800, Mechelen, Belgium
Tel.: (32) 1 528 7740
Web Site: https://www.animagroup.be
Assisted Living Care Services
N.A.I.C.S.: 623312

Anmeco N.V. **(1)**
Antwerpsesteenweg 320, Burcht, Zwijndrecht, 2070, Belgium
Tel.: (32) 541117
Web Site: http://www.anmeco.be
Heavy Engineering Construction Services
N.A.I.C.S.: 237990
Geert Van De Velde *(Gen Mgr)*

Bank Delen N.V. **(1)**
Jan Van Rijswijcklaan 184, 2020, Antwerp, Belgium   **(75%)**
Tel.: (32) 445566
Web Site: http://www.delen.be
Sales Range: $100-124.9 Million
Emp.: 250
Banking Services
N.A.I.C.S.: 522110

Bank J. Van Breda & Co. N.V. **(1)**
Ledeganckkaai 7, 2000, Antwerp, Belgium
Tel.: (32) 32450020
Web Site: http://www.bankvanbreda.be
Sales Range: $100-124.9 Million
Emp.: 200
Commercial Banking Services
N.A.I.C.S.: 522110

Biolectric NV **(1)**
Jan De Malschelaan 2, 9140, Temse, Belgium
Tel.: (32) 36892928
Web Site: https://biolectric.com
Biogas Generation Services
N.A.I.C.S.: 221117

Brinvest NV **(1)**
Begijnenvest 113, 2000, Antwerp, Belgium
Tel.: (32) 32318770
Web Site: http://www.avh.be
Sales Range: $50-74.9 Million
Emp.: 35
Financial Management Services
N.A.I.C.S.: 523999
Luc Bertrand *(Pres-Bd)*

Compagnie d'Enterprises CFE SA **(1)**
Av Edmond Van Nieuwenhuyse 30, 1160, Brussels, Belgium   **(60.39%)**
Tel.: (32) 26611211
Web Site: https://www.cfe.be
Rev.: $1,259,681,632
Assets: $1,141,894,021
Liabilities: $899,582,344
Net Worth: $242,311,677
Earnings: $250,019,426
Emp.: 3,074
Fiscal Year-end: 12/31/2022
Construction Services
N.A.I.C.S.: 236220
Luc Bertrand *(Chm)*

Subsidiary (Domestic):

AMART S.A. **(2)**
Rue du Pavillon 4, 1000, Brussels, Belgium
Tel.: (32) 2 241 89 70
Web Site: http://www.amart.be
Construction Engineering Services
N.A.I.C.S.: 541330
Ivan De Wilde *(Mng Dir)*

Aannemingen Van Wellen **(2)**

Klinkaardstraat 198, 2950, Kapellen, Belgium
Tel.: (32) 3 660 21 21
Web Site: http://www.vanwellen.be
Sales Range: $75-99.9 Million
Emp.: 250
Construction Engineering Services
N.A.I.C.S.: 541330
Kurt Kesteloot *(Gen Mgr)*

BPC sa/nv **(2)**
Chaussee de la Hulpe 166, 1170, Watermael-Boitsfort, Belgium
Tel.: (32) 2 663 60 00
Web Site: http://www.bpc.be
Sales Range: $25-49.9 Million
Emp.: 200
Construction Engineering Services
N.A.I.C.S.: 541330
Frederic Claes *(Mng Dir)*

BPI sa/nv **(2)**
Avenue Herrmann-Debroux 42, 1160, Brussels, Belgium
Tel.: (32) 2 663 60 10
Web Site: http://www.bpisa.be
Construction Engineering Services
N.A.I.C.S.: 541330

Benelmat sa **(2)**
Avenue Albert 1er 83a, Limelette, 1342, Belgium
Tel.: (32) 10438911
Construction Engineering Services
N.A.I.C.S.: 541330

CFE Brabant **(2)**
Avenue Herrmann-Debroux 42, 1160, Brussels, Belgium
Tel.: (32) 2 661 12 11
Web Site: http://www.vinci.com
Construction Engineering Services
N.A.I.C.S.: 541330

Subsidiary (Domestic):

Leloup Entreprise Generale SPRL **(3)**
Avenue Herrmann-Debroux 42, 1160, Brussels, Belgium
Tel.: (32) 2 661 12 11
Sales Range: $25-49.9 Million
Emp.: 200
Construction Engineering Services
N.A.I.C.S.: 541330
Christophe van Ophem *(Gen Mgr)*

Subsidiary (Non-US):

CFE Hungary Epitoipari Kft. **(2)**
Hercegprimas Utca 21, Budapest, 1051, Hungary
Tel.: (36) 1 332 73 12
Web Site: http://www.cfehungary.hu
Emp.: 5
Construction Engineering Services
N.A.I.C.S.: 541330

Subsidiary (Domestic):

CFE Immo **(2)**
Avenue Herrmann-Debroux 42, Brussels, 1160, Belgium
Tel.: (32) 26611211
Web Site: http://www.cfe.be
Sales Range: $25-49.9 Million
Emp.: 250
Real Estate Manangement Services
N.A.I.C.S.: 531390

CFE International **(2)**
Avenue Herrmann-Debroux 42, Auderghem, 1160, Brussels, Belgium
Tel.: (32) 26611211
Web Site: http://www.cfe.be
Sales Range: $25-49.9 Million
Emp.: 25
Construction Engineering Services
N.A.I.C.S.: 541330

Subsidiary (Non-US):

CFE Polska Sp. z o.o. **(2)**
ul Komitetu Obrony Robotnikow 48, 02-146, Warsaw, Poland
Tel.: (48) 224561600
Web Site: http://cfe.com.pl
Sales Range: $10-24.9 Million
Emp.: 30
Construction Engineering Services
N.A.I.C.S.: 541330

CFE Tunisia (2)
Rue du Lac de Come Res La Rose Blanche
- Building B 1 G, 1053, Tunis, Tunisia
Tel.: (216) 71 961 236
Construction Engineering Services
N.A.I.C.S.: 541330

CLE S.A. (2)
Westside Village Building B 89 rue
Pafebruch, 8308, Capellen, Luxembourg
Tel.: (352) 44 65 491
Web Site: http://www.cle.lu
Construction Engineering Services
N.A.I.C.S.: 541330
Olivier Vanderdeelen (Dir Gen)

Subsidiary (Domestic):

Construction management sa/nv (2)
Avenue Herrmann-Debroux 42, 1160, Brussels, Belgium
Tel.: (32) 2 661 16 61
Web Site: http://www.comanag.com
Construction Engineering Services
N.A.I.C.S.: 541330

Dredging International NV (2)
Haven 1025 Scheldedijk 30, 2070, Zwijndrecht, Antwerp, Belgium (48%)
Tel.: (32) 32505211
Web Site: http://www.deme.be
Sales Range: $200-249.9 Million
Emp.: 800
Dredging Services
N.A.I.C.S.: 237110

Subsidiary (Domestic):

Baggerwerken Decloedt en Zoon N.V. (3)
Slijkensesteenweg 2, 8400, Oostende, Belgium
Tel.: (32) 59 242 140
Web Site: http://www.decloedt.be
Port Dredging & Sea Lane Maintenance
N.A.I.C.S.: 488390
Bart Verboomen (Gen Mgr)

C-Power N.V. (3)
Buskruitstraat 1, 8400, Oostende, Belgium
Tel.: (32) 59797980
Web Site: http://www.c-power.be
Emp.: 15
Environmental Services
N.A.I.C.S.: 541620

DEME Blue Energy N.V. (3)
Haven 1025, Scheldedijk 30, B-2070, Zwijndrecht, Belgium (69.99%)
Tel.: (32) 360 52 11
Environmental Services
N.A.I.C.S.: 541620

DEME Building Materials N.V. (3)
Haven 1025 Scheldedijk 30, 2070, Zwijndrecht, Belgium
Tel.: (32) 3 250 5423
Web Site: http://www.dbmnv.be
Dredging, Environmental & Marine Services
N.A.I.C.S.: 237110

DEME Environmental NV (3)
Haven 1025, Scheldedijk 30, 2070, Zwijndrecht, Belgium
Tel.: (32) 32505411
Web Site: http://www.deme-group.com
Emp.: 200
Dredging, Environmental & Marine Engineering
N.A.I.C.S.: 541330

Subsidiary (Non-US):

DEME Infra Marine Contractors B.V. (3)
Kilkade 2, 3316 BC, Dordrecht, Netherlands
Tel.: (31) 786321020
Web Site: http://www.deme-group.com
Sales Range: $25-49.9 Million
Emp.: 25
Construction Engineering Services
N.A.I.C.S.: 541330

Subsidiary (Domestic):

DEME Offshore BE NV (3)
Haven 1025, Scheldedijk 30, 2070, Zwijndrecht, Belgium
Tel.: (32) 32505312
Web Site: http://www.geosea.be
Emp.: 400

Environmental Services
N.A.I.C.S.: 541620

Subsidiary (Non-US):

Dredging International Asia Pacific (PTE) Ltd (3)
Ste 04-03 Bosch Build 11 Bishan Street 21, Singapore, 573943, Singapore (100%)
Tel.: (65) 68632108
Web Site: http://www.deme-group.com
Sales Range: $25-49.9 Million
Emp.: 45
Dredging Services
N.A.I.C.S.: 237990

Subsidiary (Domestic):

Ecoterres S.A. (3)
Avenue Jean Mermoz 3C, Gosselies, 6041, Belgium
Tel.: (32) 71 256 041
Web Site: http://www.deme-group.com
Emp.: 50
Environmental Services
N.A.I.C.S.: 541620

Grondrecyclage Centrum Kallo N.V. (3)
Haven 1562 Sint-Jansweg 10, 9130, Kallo, Belgium
Tel.: (32) 35709030
Web Site: http://grckallo.be
Emp.: 25
Soil & Waste Management Services
N.A.I.C.S.: 115112
Dirk Ponnet (Mng Dir)

Power@Sea N.V. (3)
Haven 1025 Scheldedijk 30, 2070, Zwijndrecht, Belgium
Tel.: (32) 3 250 5633
Web Site: http://www.poweratc.com
Environmental Services
N.A.I.C.S.: 541620

Scaldis Salvage and Marine Contractors N.V. (3)
North Trade Building, Box 31, Noorderlaan 133, 2030, Antwerp, Belgium
Tel.: (32) 35416955
Web Site: http://www.scaldis-smc.com
Emp.: 25
Dredging, Marine & Environmental Services
N.A.I.C.S.: 541620

Subsidiary (Domestic):

Druart S.A. (2)
Avenue Leopold III 31 7134, 7134, Binche, Belgium
Tel.: (32) 64 310920
Web Site: http://www.druart-hvac.be
Sales Range: $25-49.9 Million
Heating & Air Conditioning Equipment Installation Services
N.A.I.C.S.: 238220
Jean Marie Chabart (Gen Mgr)

Subsidiary (Domestic):

Prodfroid SA (3)
Rue des Pieds d Alouette 12, 5100, Namur, Belgium
Tel.: (32) 81 51 39 91
Web Site: http://www.prodfroid.be
Industrial Cooling System Sales & Installation Services
N.A.I.C.S.: 423730
Jean Marie Chabart (Mng Dir)

Subsidiary (Domestic):

ETEC SA (2)
Zoning Industriel de Manage Zone D Rue Jean Perrin 2, 7170, Manage, Belgium
Tel.: (32) 64 54 85 35
Lighting Equipment Installation Services
N.A.I.C.S.: 238210
Luc Dutrieux (Mgr)

Electronizet SA (2)
Rue Laid Burniat 2, 1342, Louvain-la-Neuve, Belgium
Tel.: (32) 10 45 18 63
Web Site: http://www.voltis.be
Sales Range: $25-49.9 Million
Emp.: 20
Consumer Electronics Distr
N.A.I.C.S.: 423620
Senzot Philippe (Gen Mgr)

Engema Lignes (2)
Route de Sainte-Ode 34, 6681, Sainte-Ode, Belgium
Tel.: (32) 61 68 88 52
Web Site: http://www.en.engema.be
Electrical Line Support Installation Services
N.A.I.C.S.: 335999
Bruno Lambert (Mgr)

Engema Montage (2)
Avenue Albert 1er 83a Limelette, Ottignies, 1342, Louvain-la-Neuve, Belgium
Tel.: (32) 10 43 89 42
Sales Range: $25-49.9 Million
Emp.: 40
Railway Signalling System Installation Services
N.A.I.C.S.: 238210

Engema Rail (2)
Horizonpark 3 bus 14 Leuvensesteenweg 510, Zaventem, 1930, Belgium
Tel.: (32) 2 717 89 80
Web Site: http://www.engema.be
Sales Range: $25-49.9 Million
Emp.: 25
Railroad Construction & Maintenance Services
N.A.I.C.S.: 237990

Engema sa/nv (2)
Horizonpark 3 bus 14 Leuvensesteenweg 510, Zaventem, 1930, Belgium
Tel.: (32) 2 717 89 80
Web Site: http://www.engema.be
Emp.: 15
Railway Signaling Installation Services
N.A.I.C.S.: 238210

MBG Brugge (2)
Hertogenstraat 69, Sint-Andries, 8200, Brugge, Belgium
Tel.: (32) 50 39 57 64
Web Site: http://www.mbg.be
Emp.: 5
Construction Engineering Services
N.A.I.C.S.: 541330
Luc Stuyck (Gen Mgr)

MBG Wilrijk (2)
Garden Square Blok D Laarstraat 16 Bus 12, Wilrijk, 2610, Antwerp, Belgium
Tel.: (32) 3 820 40 11
Web Site: http://www.mbg.be
Sales Range: $25-49.9 Million
Emp.: 150
Construction Engineering Services
N.A.I.C.S.: 541330
Yves Weyts (Gen Dir)

MOBIX Stevens (2)
Stadsbeemd 13-14, 3545, Halen, Belgium
Tel.: (32) 13441571
Web Site: https://www.mobix.be
Sales Range: $50-74.9 Million
Emp.: 150
Rail Signaling Equipment Installation Services
N.A.I.C.S.: 238210

Nizet Entreprise SA (2)
Parc Scientifique Fleming Rue Laid Burniat 2, Louvain-la-Neuve, 1348, Belgium
Tel.: (32) 10 45 18 67
Web Site: http://www.nizet.be
Sales Range: $50-74.9 Million
Emp.: 150
Electrical Equipment Installation Services
N.A.I.C.S.: 238210

Remacom NV (2)
Hoogstraat 2, Beervelde, Lochristi, 9080, Belgium
Tel.: (32) 93 56 98 24
Emp.: 90
Railroad Construction & Maintenance Services
N.A.I.C.S.: 237990

VMA nv (2)
Kortrijksesteenweg 14B, 9830, Sint-Martens-Latem, Belgium
Tel.: (32) 92809525
Web Site: http://www.vma.be
Sales Range: $25-49.9 Million
Emp.: 150
Electrical Engineering Services
N.A.I.C.S.: 541330
Thomas Ducamp (CEO, Mng Dir, Mng Dir & CFO)

Vanderhoydoncks Elektrotechnieken nv (2)
Kolmen 1108, Alken, 3570, Belgium
Tel.: (32) 11 59 02 00
Web Site: http://www.vdhs.be
Sales Range: $25-49.9 Million
Emp.: 60
Security System Installation Services
N.A.I.C.S.: 238210

be.Maintenance (2)
Humaniteitslaan 114, Brussels, 1070, Belgium
Tel.: (32) 2 526 60 40
Web Site: http://www.bemaintenance.be
Sales Range: $25-49.9 Million
Emp.: 40
Air Conditioning Equipment Installation Services
N.A.I.C.S.: 238210
Andre Vandenbauw (Gen Mgr)

DEME NV (1)
Haven 1025 Scheldedijk 30, 2070, Zwijndrecht, Belgium
Tel.: (32) 32505211
Web Site: https://www.deme-group.com
Emp.: 5,600
Marine Engineering Services
N.A.I.C.S.: 541330

De Toekomst vzw (1)
Sint Kamielstraat 85, 9300, Aalst, Belgium
Tel.: (32) 53607500
Web Site: http://www.vzwdetoekomst.be
Sales Range: $25-49.9 Million
Emp.: 65
Residential Services
N.A.I.C.S.: 236118
Geert Vaes (Mgr)

Delen Private Bank NV (1)
Jan Van Rijswijcklaan 184, 2020, Antwerp, Belgium
Tel.: (32) 32445566
Web Site: https://www.delen.bank
Asset Management Services
N.A.I.C.S.: 523940
Rene Havaux (Exec Dir, Co-Pres & CEO)

EXTENSA ROMANIA S.R.L (1)
Ady Endre Street 7, 01373, Bucharest, Romania
Tel.: (40) 31 425 40 62
Web Site: http://www.extensa.be
Sales Range: $50-74.9 Million
Emp.: 4
Real Estate Manangement Services
N.A.I.C.S.: 531390

Extensa Development SA (1)
Avenue Du Port 86c Internal, PO Box 316, Brussels, 1000, Belgium
Tel.: (32) 22370820
Web Site: http://www.extensa.be
Emp.: 10
Real Estate Manangement Services
N.A.I.C.S.: 531390

Extensa Group SA (1)
Avenue du Port 86C Boite 316, 1000, Brussels, Belgium
Tel.: (32) 22370820
Web Site: http://extensa.eu
Sales Range: $25-49.9 Million
Emp.: 15
Apartment Construction Services
N.A.I.C.S.: 236220

Subsidiary (Non-US):

Extensa Istanbul (2)
Maya Akar Center Kat 18 Buyukdere Cad No 100-102, Esentepe, Turkiye
Tel.: (90) 2122742484
Web Site: http://www.extensa.com.tr
Sales Range: $50-74.9 Million
Emp.: 8
Real Estate Development Services
N.A.I.C.S.: 531390

Subsidiary (Domestic):

Extensa NV (2)
Avenue Du Port 86c Bus 316, Brussels, 1000, Belgium
Tel.: (32) 22370820
Web Site: http://www.extensa.eu
Sales Range: $25-49.9 Million
Emp.: 15
Real Estate Manangement Services

Ackermans & van Haaren NV—(Continued)

N.A.I.C.S.: 531390

Subsidiary (Non-US):

Extensa Slovakia s.r.o.   **(2)**
C/o ES Partners Zahradnicka 51, 821 08,
Bratislava, Slovakia
Tel.: (421) 918 625 395
Web Site: http://www.extensa.be
Sales Range: $50-74.9 Million
Emp.: 1
Real Estate Manangement Services
N.A.I.C.S.: 531390

Extensa Land II SA   **(1)**
Havenlaan 86c 316, Brussels, 1000, Belgium
Tel.: (32) 22370820
Web Site: http://www.extensa.eu
Emp.: 30
Real Estate Manangement Services
N.A.I.C.S.: 531390

Finaxis Nv   **(1)**
Begijnenvest 113, 2000, Antwerp, Belgium
Tel.: (32) 32318770
Web Site: http://www.finaxis.be
Financial Management Services
N.A.I.C.S.: 523999

GROUPE THIRAN SA.   **(1)**
Rue du Parc Industriel D Achene 2,
Achene, 5590, Belgium
Tel.: (32) 83230790
Web Site: http://www.thiran.be
Sales Range: $25-49.9 Million
Emp.: 120
Construction Engineering Services
N.A.I.C.S.: 541330
Luc Huybrechts (Gen Mgr)

Huize Philemon & Baucis WZC   **(1)**
Zoutleeuwsesteenweg 11, Dormaal, 3440,
Zoutleeuw, Belgium
Tel.: (32) 11782266
Web Site:
    http://www.huizephilemonbaucis.be
Nursing Home Operator
N.A.I.C.S.: 621610

Mabeco NV   **(1)**
Begijnenvest 113, 2000, Antwerp, Belgium
Tel.: (32) 32318770
Web Site: http://www.avh.be
Sales Range: $50-74.9 Million
Emp.: 35
Financial Management Services
N.A.I.C.S.: 523999

Nextensa NV   **(1)**
Gare Maritime Picardstraat 11, B505, 1000,
Brussels, Belgium   **(61.55%)**
Tel.: (32) 28821000
Web Site: https://www.nextensa.eu
Rev.: $75,625,193
Assets: $1,523,690,676
Liabilities: $925,278,637
Net Worth: $598,412,039
Earnings: $9,436,568
Emp.: 3
Fiscal Year-end: 12/31/2020
Real Estate Investment Services
N.A.I.C.S.: 531390
Tim Rens (CFO)

Subsidiary (Non-US):

Leasinvest Immo Lux SA   **(2)**
6D route de Treves, 2633, Senningerberg,
Luxembourg
Tel.: (352) 26954722
Real Estate Manangement Services
N.A.I.C.S.: 531210
Michel Van Geyte (Mng Dir)

Subsidiary (Domestic):

Leasinvest Services NV   **(2)**
Schermersstraat 42, 2000, Antwerp, Belgium
Tel.: (32) 32422510
Real Estate Manangement Services
N.A.I.C.S.: 531210

Rent-A-Port Green Energy N.V.   **(1)**
Av Hermann-Debroux 42, 1160, Brussels,
Belgium
Tel.: (32) 3 203 4790
Web Site: https://www.rentaportgreen.be

Renewable Energy Services
N.A.I.C.S.: 221114

Rusthuis Kruyenberg Nv   **(1)**
Turfputstraat 100, 9290, Berlare, Belgium
Tel.: (32) 52423057
Web Site: http://www.rusthuiskruyenberg.be
Sales Range: $50-74.9 Million
Emp.: 66
Senior Citizen Homes Management Services
N.A.I.C.S.: 531390
Kathleen de Cock (Gen Mgr)

Sofinim N.V.   **(1)**
Begijnvest 113, B-2000, Antwerp,
Belgium
Tel.: (32) 38979230
Web Site: http://www.sofinim.be
Sales Range: $50-74.9 Million
Emp.: 7
Private Equity Investment Firm
N.A.I.C.S.: 523999

Holding (Domestic):

Dynea N.V.   **(2)**
Moervaartkaai 7, 9042, Gent,
Belgium   **(100%)**
Tel.: (32) 93423434
Sales Range: $25-49.9 Million
Resin Mfr
N.A.I.C.S.: 325211
Guido Duytschaeve (Mgr-Sharepoint)

TRASYS S.A   **(1)**
Tarhulpsestaanveg No C 1660, B 1200,
Hoeilaart, Belgium
Tel.: (32) 27737111
Web Site: http://www.trasys.be
Sales Range: $200-249.9 Million
Emp.: 600
IT & Software Business Support Services
N.A.I.C.S.: 541511

Subsidiary (Domestic):

TRASYS Charleroi   **(2)**
Terhulp Sesteenweg 6C, 1560, Hoeilaart,
Belgium
Tel.: (32) 71378211
Web Site: http://www.trasys.be
Sales Range: $50-74.9 Million
Emp.: 130
IT & Software Business Support Services
N.A.I.C.S.: 541511

Subsidiary (Non-US):

TRASYS Greece   **(2)**
3 Arkadias St, Athens, 11526, Attica,
Greece
Tel.: (30) 2107769800
Web Site: http://www.trasys.gr
Sales Range: $25-49.9 Million
Emp.: 30
IT & Software Business Support Services
N.A.I.C.S.: 541511

TRASYS Luxembourg   **(2)**
Route d'Arlon 283, 8011, Strassen, Luxembourg
Tel.: (352) 2611101
Web Site:
    http://www.trasysinternational.com
Sales Range: $25-49.9 Million
Emp.: 43
IT & Software Business Support Services
N.A.I.C.S.: 541511

Van Breda Car Finance Nv   **(1)**
Ledeganckkaai 7, 2000, Antwerp, Belgium
Tel.: (32) 32176047
Web Site: http://www.vanbredacarfinance.be
Financial Management Services
N.A.I.C.S.: 523999

Van Breda Immo Consult NV   **(1)**
Ledeganckkaai 7, 2000, Antwerp, Belgium
Tel.: (32) 32942331
Web Site:
    https://www.vanbredaimmoconsult.be
Real Estate Investment Services
N.A.I.C.S.: 531390

Vandendorpe NV   **(1)**
Rue Aurimont 10, 1457, Walhain-Saint-Paul,
Belgium
Tel.: (32) 10237960
Web Site: http://www.vandendorpe.be
Emp.: 2

Building Materials Mfr
N.A.I.C.S.: 332311

Vouvray Acquisition Limited   **(1)**
1st Floor 63 Queen Victoria Street, London,
EC4N 4UA, United Kingdom
Tel.: (44) 2380 258 381
Web Site: http://www.vgrouplimited.com
Holding Company; Ship Management &
Shipping Industry Support Services
N.A.I.C.S.: 551112
Graham Westgarth (CEO)

Subsidiary (US):

Global Marine Travel LLC   **(2)**
1800 SE 10th Ave Ste 320, Fort Lauderdale, FL 33316-2907
Tel.: (954) 761-9595
Web Site: http://www.flygmt.com
Ship Crew & Seafarers Travel Arrangement
Agency
N.A.I.C.S.: 561510
Timothy D. Davey (Mng Dir)

Subsidiary (Domestic):

V.Scope Risk Management Ltd.   **(2)**
1st Floor 63 Queen Victoria Street, London,
EC4N 4UA, United Kingdom
Tel.: (44) 20 7332 8540
Web Site: http://www.vgrouplimited.com
Marine Insurance Brokerage Services
N.A.I.C.S.: 524210
John Sullivan (Mng Dir)

Subsidiary (Non-US):

V.Ships Group Ltd.   **(2)**
2 Rue du Gabian, Les Industries Cedex,
Monaco, 98013, Monaco
Tel.: (377) 92051010
Web Site: http://www.vgrouplimited.com
Ship Management & Support Services
N.A.I.C.S.: 488390
Franck Kayser (CEO)

Subsidiary (Domestic):

V.Ships Leisure Ltd.   **(3)**
2 Rue du Gabaian, PO Box 639, 24 Ave de
Fontvieille, Monaco, 98013, Monaco
Tel.: (377) 92051010
Web Site: http://www.vgrouplimited.com
Passenger Ship Management Support Services
N.A.I.C.S.: 488390
Lucy Hodgson (Mgr-Recruitment-Global)

Subsidiary (US):

V.Ships Leisure (USA) LLC   **(4)**
1800 SE 10th Ave Ste 320, Fort Lauderdale, FL 33316
Tel.: (305) 455-0101
Passenger Vessel Management Support
Services
N.A.I.C.S.: 488390

Subsidiary (Non-US):

V.Ships Offshore (Asia) Pte. Ltd.   **(3)**
Prudential Tower 24/01-02 30 Cecil Street,
Singapore, 049721, Singapore
Tel.: (65) 6603 9270
Ship Management Services
N.A.I.C.S.: 541618

V.Ships UK Ltd.   **(3)**
Skypark 8 Elliot Place, Glasgow, G3 8EP,
United Kingdom
Tel.: (44) 1412432435
Web Site: http://www.vgrouplimited.com
Technical & Personnel Ship Support Services
N.A.I.C.S.: 488390
John Adams (Mng Dir)

Subsidiary (Domestic):

Seatec UK Ltd.   **(4)**
1st Floor Skypark 8 Elliot Place, Glasgow,
G3 8EP, United Kingdom
Tel.: (44) 1413051300
Web Site: http://www.seatec-services.com
Ship Repair, Maintenance, Inspection &
Ship Building Support Project Services
N.A.I.C.S.: 488390
Johannes Paulus Henricus Engels (Gen
Mgr-UK)

Subsidiary (Domestic):

U.M.C. International Plc   **(5)**
Warrior Close Chandlers Ford, Eastleigh,
SO53 4TE, Southants, United Kingdom
Tel.: (44) 2380269866
Web Site: http://www.seatec-services.com
Commercial & Naval Ship Underwater
Maintenance, Repair & Support Services.
N.A.I.C.S.: 000011
Alan Trevarthen (Mng Dir)

Wefima N.V   **(1)**
Antwerpsesteenweg 320, 2070, Zwijndrecht, Belgium
Tel.: (32) 32522020
Construction Engineering Services
N.A.I.C.S.: 541330

ACKNIT INDUSTRIES LTD.
ECO Station BP-7 Sector-V 5th Floor
Suit No 504, Salt Lake City, Kolkata,
700091, India
Tel.: (91) 8420047801
Web Site:
    https://www.acknitindia.com
011078—(KOL)
Rev.: $29,831,433
Assets: $20,075,178
Liabilities: $11,649,442
Net Worth: $8,425,736
Earnings: $1,083,551
Emp.: 185
Fiscal Year-end: 03/31/22
Hand Glove & Safety Products Mfr
N.A.I.C.S.: 315990
Shri Krishan Saraf (Mng Dir)

ACKROO INC.
1250 South Service Road Unit A3-1
3rd Floor, Hamilton, L8E 5R9, ON,
Canada
Tel.: (613) 599-2396
Web Site: https://hs.ackroo.com
AKR—(OTCIQ)
Rev.: $4,730,898
Assets: $8,744,352
Liabilities: $5,757,805
Net Worth: $2,986,547
Earnings: ($1,019,018)
Fiscal Year-end: 12/31/20
Customer Loyalty Programs
N.A.I.C.S.: 561499
Steve Levely (Chm-Acting & CEO)

ACL CABLES PLC
Tel.: (94) 117608300
Web Site: https://www.acl.lk
ACL—(COL)
Rev.: $120,334
Assets: $144,812
Liabilities: $63,522
Net Worth: $81,290
Earnings: $9,330
Emp.: 1,641
Fiscal Year-end: 03/31/21
Power Cables & Conductors Mfr
N.A.I.C.S.: 335929
Suren Madanayake (Mng Dir)

Subsidiaries:

ACL Cables PLC - Factory   **(1)**
Madapatha Road, Batakettara, Piliyandala,
Sri Lanka
Tel.: (94) 11 270 7361
Web Site: http://www.acl.lk
Sales Range: $200-249.9 Million
Emp.: 600
Cable Mfr
N.A.I.C.S.: 335921

ACL INTERNATIONAL LTD.
Suite 1600 144 - 4th Ave SW, Calgary, T2P 3N4, AB, Canada
Tel.: (587) 952-5085
Web Site: http://acinternational.ca
Year Founded: 1989
Sales Range: $1-9.9 Million
Insurance Brokerage Services
N.A.I.C.S.: 524210

ACL PLASTIC PLC
No 60 Rodney Street, 08, Colombo, 08, Sri Lanka
Tel.: (94) 2697652
Year Founded: 1991
APLA.N0000—(COL)
Rev.: $10,113,196
Assets: $10,943,692
Liabilities: $2,548,756
Net Worth: $8,394,936
Earnings: $953,817
Emp.: 55
Fiscal Year-end: 03/31/21
Cable Mfr & Distr
N.A.I.C.S.: 335929
Upali G. Madanayake *(Chm)*

ACLARA RESOURCES INC.
Av Cerro el Plomo 5630 piso 15, Las Condes, 5630, Santiago, Chile
Tel.: (56) 225651033
Web Site: https://www.aclara-re.com
Year Founded: 2021
ARAAF—(OTCIQ)
Rev.: $2,338,000
Assets: $147,009,000
Liabilities: $8,648,000
Net Worth: $138,361,000
Earnings: ($11,383,000)
Emp.: 71
Fiscal Year-end: 12/31/23
Support Activities for Nonmetallic Minerals (except Fuels) Mining
N.A.I.C.S.: 213115
Barry Murphy *(COO)*

ACMA LTD.
19 Jurong Port Road, Singapore, 619093, Singapore
Tel.: (65) 62687733
Web Site: https://www.acmaltd.com
Year Founded: 1965
AYV—(SES)
Rev.: $8,351,890
Assets: $24,996,592
Liabilities: $22,969,022
Net Worth: $2,027,569
Earnings: ($1,554,950)
Emp.: 391
Fiscal Year-end: 12/31/23
Plastic Interior Parts Mfr
N.A.I.C.S.: 326199
Keloth Raj Kumar *(Sec)*

Subsidiaries:

Acma Engineers Private Limited (1)
No 17 Jurong Port Road, Singapore, 619092, Singapore
Tel.: (65) 62687228
Web Site: https://www.acmaeng.com.sg
Air Conditioner Equipment Mfr
N.A.I.C.S.: 333415

Acot Plastics (Xiamen) Co., Ltd. (1)
Web Site: http://www.acotgroup.cn
Sales Range: $125-149.9 Million
Emp.: 400
Molded Goods Mfr
N.A.I.C.S.: 326291

Acot Tooling Xiamen Ltd. (1)
No 3 Factory Building Malong Development District, Huli, Xiamen, 361006, Fujian, China
Tel.: (86) 592 5705753
Emp.: 200
Machine Tools Mfr
N.A.I.C.S.: 333517

Ray Tech Acot Singapore Pte. Ltd. (1)
17 Jurong Port Road, Singapore, 619092, Singapore
Tel.: (65) 62619168
Sales Range: $50-74.9 Million
Emp.: 4
Steel Molds Distr
N.A.I.C.S.: 423510

ACME ELECTRONICS CORPORATION
8th Floor No 39 Ji-Hu Rd, Nei-Hu Dist, Taipei, 114, Taiwan
Tel.: (886) 227980337
Web Site: https://www.acme-ferrite.com.tw
Year Founded: 1991
8121—(TPE)
Rev.: $95,588,813
Assets: $149,419,754
Liabilities: $87,259,263
Net Worth: $62,160,492
Earnings: $460,151
Emp.: 1,224
Fiscal Year-end: 12/31/22
Ferrite Powder & Core Mfr & Distr
N.A.I.C.S.: 332117
Quintin Wu *(Co-Chm)*

Subsidiaries:

Acme Electronics (Guangzhou) Co. Ltd. (1)
No 1 Fuqian Road Zengjiang Street, Zengcheng District, Guangzhou, 511300, Guangdong, China
Tel.: (86) 2032851888
Ferrite Cores Mfr
N.A.I.C.S.: 327110

Acme Electronics (Kunshan) Co. Ltd. (1)
No 533 Huangpujiang North Rd, Kunshan, 215337, Jiang-Su, China
Tel.: (86) 51257932888
Ferrite Cores Mfr
N.A.I.C.S.: 327110

Acme Ferrite Products Sdn. Bhd. (1)
Plot 15 Jalan Industri 6 Kawasan Perindustrian Jelapang II Zon, Perindustrian Bebas Jelapang, 30020, Ipoh, Perak Darul Ridzuan, Malaysia
Tel.: (60) 55269149
Web Site: https://www.acme.com.my
Emp.: 300
Ferrite Product Mfr
N.A.I.C.S.: 327110

ACME HOLDINGS BERHAD
488A-16-01 Office Tower, Kompleks Midlands Park Jalan Burma, 10350, Penang, Kedah, Malaysia
Tel.: (60) 42109911
Web Site: https://acmeholdings.com.my
ACME—(KLS)
Rev.: $12,928,204
Assets: $31,951,688
Liabilities: $7,932,163
Net Worth: $24,019,525
Earnings: $1,448,026
Emp.: 100
Fiscal Year-end: 03/31/24
Audio Speakers Mfr
N.A.I.C.S.: 334310
Hong Soon Ooi *(Exec Dir)*

ACME INTERNATIONAL HOLDINGS LIMITED
Units A & B 12/F Yin Da Commercial Building No 181 Wai Yip Street, Kwun Tong, Kowloon, China (Hong Kong)
Tel.: (852) 28032102
Web Site: http://www.acmehld.com
Year Founded: 1989
1870—(HKG)
Rev.: $19,407,413
Assets: $20,495,498
Liabilities: $9,636,705
Net Worth: $10,858,793
Earnings: ($10,172,333)
Emp.: 56
Fiscal Year-end: 12/31/22
Holding Company
N.A.I.C.S.: 551112
Kam Tim Kwan *(Chm)*

ACME PRINTING & PACKAGING PLC
No 318 Gonamaditta Road, Piliyandala, Sri Lanka
Tel.: (94) 114368468
Web Site: https://www.acmelk.com
Year Founded: 1949
ACME.N0000—(COL)
Rev.: $3,300,020
Assets: $5,788,772
Liabilities: $4,456,782
Net Worth: $1,331,990
Earnings: $397,567
Emp.: 156
Fiscal Year-end: 03/31/23
Flexible Packaging Mfr
N.A.I.C.S.: 326112
Hemaka Amarasuriya *(Chm)*

ACME RESOURCES LIMITED
984 9th Floor Aggarwal Cyber Plaza II Netaji Subhash Place, Pitampura, New Delhi, 110034, India
Tel.: (91) 1127026766
Web Site: https://www.acmeresources.in
Year Founded: 1985
539391—(BOM)
Rev.: $1,116,311
Assets: $16,620,390
Liabilities: $1,166,911
Net Worth: $15,453,479
Earnings: $362,517
Emp.: 6
Fiscal Year-end: 03/31/22
Financial Services
N.A.I.C.S.: 541611
Vivek Chaturvedi *(Mng Dir)*

ACMOS INC.
Tokyu Toranomon Bldg 1-21-19 Toranomon, Minato-Ku, Tokyo, 105-0001, Japan
Tel.: (81) 355398800
Web Site: https://www.acmos.co.jp
Year Founded: 1991
6888—(TKS)
Rev.: $38,750,600
Assets: $32,723,420
Liabilities: $11,202,220
Net Worth: $21,521,200
Earnings: $2,624,840
Emp.: 456
Fiscal Year-end: 06/30/24
Information Technology Services
N.A.I.C.S.: 519290
Hideyuki Iijima *(CEO)*

Subsidiaries:

ACMOS Sourcing Service Inc. (1)
3-8-8 Kandaogawamachi UNIZO Kandaogawamachi 3-chome Building 4th floor, Chiyoda-Ku, Tokyo, 101-0052, Japan
Tel.: (81) 352173332
Web Site: http://www.acmos-ss.jp
Information Technology Consulting Services
N.A.I.C.S.: 541512

Fieldone Corporation (1)
3-87-4 Haramachi NT Building 1F, Shinjuku-ku, Tokyo, 162-0053, Japan
Tel.: (81) 353682111
Web Site: https://field-one.com
Computer Hardware Maintenance Services
N.A.I.C.S.: 423430

ACNE STUDIO AB
Lilla Nygatan 23, 111 28, Stockholm, Sweden
Tel.: (46) 855 119400
Web Site: http://www.acnestudios.com
Year Founded: 1996
Unisex Jeans Mfr & Clothing Retailer
N.A.I.C.S.: 315250
Jonny Johansson *(Founder & Creative Dir)*

Subsidiaries:

Acne Corp. (1)

33 Greene St Ste 1, New York, NY 10013
Tel.: (212) 334-8345
Emp.: 20
Men & Women Clothing Retailer
N.A.I.C.S.: 458110

ACNOVER, S.L.
Avenida Diagonal 123 planta 9, 08005, Barcelona, Spain
Tel.: (34) 93 545 9000 ES
Web Site: http://www.anv.eu.com
Sales Range: $75-99.9 Million
Emp.: 1,000
Insurance Underwriting & Agency Development Services
N.A.I.C.S.: 524298

Subsidiaries:

ANV Services US Inc. (1)
101 Hudson St Ste 3606, Jersey City, NJ 07302
Tel.: (201) 830-2260
General Insurance Services
N.A.I.C.S.: 524210

ANV Syndicate Management Limited (1)
1 Minister Court Mincing Lane 4th Floor, London, EC3R 7AA, United Kingdom
Tel.: (44) 20 7456 1800
Emp.: 7
Reinsurance Underwriting Services
N.A.I.C.S.: 524298
Vincent Dupuis *(Mng Dir)*

ACO GROUP BERHAD
PLO 264 No 14 Jalan Firma 3 Kawasan Perindustrian Tebrau 4, Taman Johor Jaya, 81100, Johor Bahru, Malaysia
Tel.: (60) 73619399 MY
Web Site: https://www.acogroup.com.my
Year Founded: 1991
ACO—(KLS)
Rev.: $29,910,584
Assets: $34,381,694
Liabilities: $14,334,126
Net Worth: $20,047,567
Earnings: $658,157
Emp.: 150
Fiscal Year-end: 02/28/24
Electrical Equipment Distr
N.A.I.C.S.: 423610
Chong Su Yee *(Head-HR)*

Subsidiaries:

Maydenki Sdn. Bhd. (1)
No 108 and 110 Jalan Seroja 39, Taman Johor Jaya, 81100, Johor Bahru, Johor Darul Takzim, Malaysia
Tel.: (60) 73511671
Web Site: https://www.maydenki.com.my
Electrical Products Distr
N.A.I.C.S.: 423610

ACOEM GROUP
200 Chemin des Ormeaux, 69578, Limonest, France
Tel.: (33) 472 524 800
Web Site: http://www.acoemgroup.com
Sales Range: $50-74.9 Million
Emp.: 670
Industrial Machinery Mfr
N.A.I.C.S.: 333248
Fabien Condemine *(CEO)*

Subsidiaries:

ACOEM AB (1)
Ostergardsgatan 9, Box 7, SE-431 21, Molndal, Sweden
Tel.: (46) 317062800
Web Site: http://www.fixturlaser.se
Sales Range: $25-49.9 Million
Emp.: 35
Measuring & Controlling Device Mfr
N.A.I.C.S.: 334519
Hans Svensson *(CEO)*

VibrAlign Inc. (1)

ACOEM Group—(Continued)

530-G Southlake Blvd, Richmond, VA 23236
Web Site: http://www.vibralign.com
Industrial Machinery Distr
N.A.I.C.S.: 423610
John Walden (Pres)

ACOMMERCE GROUP PUBLIC COMPANY LIMITED

33rd Floor 689 Bhiraj Tower
Sukhumvit Road, Klongton-Nua Wattana, Bangkok, 10110, Thailand
Tel.: (66) 2 261 3540
Web Site:
   https://www.acommerce.asia
Year Founded: 2013
ACOM—(THA)
Online Shopping Services
N.A.I.C.S.: 493120
Paul Srivorakul (CEO)

ACOMO N.V.

WTC Beursplein 37 21st Floor, 3011 AA, Rotterdam, Netherlands
Tel.: (31) 104051195
Web Site: https://www.acomo.nl
Year Founded: 1908
ACOMO—(EUR)
Rev.: $1,535,480,250
Assets: $928,939,132
Liabilities: $482,447,658
Net Worth: $446,491,474
Earnings: $59,012,519
Emp.: 1,191
Fiscal Year-end: 12/31/22
Agricultural Products Trader & Distr
N.A.I.C.S.: 425120
Bernard H. Stuivinga (Chm)

Subsidiaries:

Acomo Investments B.V.,   **(1)**
Beursplein 378E Etage, 3001 DD, Rotterdam, Netherlands
Tel.: (31) 104051195
Web Site: http://www.acomo.com
Emp.: 8
Investment Management Service
N.A.I.C.S.: 523999

Catz International B.V.   **(1)**
Blakeburg Building Blaak 22, 3011, Rotterdam, Netherlands
Tel.: (31) 104113440
Web Site: http://www.catz.nl
Sales Range: $25-49.9 Million
Emp.: 42
Food Trading & Distributing Services
N.A.I.C.S.: 425120

King Nuts & Raaphorst B.V.   **(1)**
Spanjeweg 4, PO Box 1044, 2410 CA, Bodegraven, Netherlands
Tel.: (31) 172632222
Web Site: http://www.kingnuts-raaphorst.com
Emp.: 27
Nuts & Dried Fruits Distr
N.A.I.C.S.: 424490

King Nuts Holding B.V.,   **(1)**
Spanjeweg 4, PO Box 1044, 2410 CA, Bodegraven, South Holland, Netherlands
Tel.: (31) 172632222
Investment Management Service
N.A.I.C.S.: 523999

P.T. Van Rees Indonesia   **(1)**
Wisma Kemang 4th Floor Jl Kemang Selatan Raya No 1, Jakarta, 12560, Indonesia
Tel.: (62) 217817044
Tea Products Distr
N.A.I.C.S.: 424490

Red River Commodities Inc   **(1)**
PO Box 3022, Fargo, ND 58102
Tel.: (800) 437-5539
Web Site: http://www.redriv.com
Sales Range: $25-49.9 Million
Emp.: 50
Ingredient Products Mfr
N.A.I.C.S.: 311999
Mike Williams (Gen Mgr-Southern Procurement)

Subsidiary (Domestic):

Sungold Food Inc.   **(2)**
501 42nd St NW, Fargo, ND 58102
Tel.: (701) 282-5325
Web Site: http://www.sunbutter.com
Sales Range: $25-49.9 Million
Sunflower Kernel Butter Mfr
N.A.I.C.S.: 311911

Red River van Eck B.V.   **(1)**
Huizersdijk 11, PO Box 14, Zevenbergen, 4761 PT, Noord-Brabant, Netherlands
Tel.: (31) 168323555
Emp.: 10
Agricultural Supplements Distr
N.A.I.C.S.: 424910
Anton Van Eck (Gen Mgr)

Snick EuroIngredients N.V.,   **(1)**
De Leiteweg 13, Ruddervoorde, 8020, Oostkamp, West Flanders, Belgium
Tel.: (32) 50361685
Web Site: http://www.snick.be
Sales Range: $25-49.9 Million
Emp.: 10
Food Ingredients Mfr & Distr
N.A.I.C.S.: 311999

Tovano B.V.   **(1)**
Transportweg 47, Maasdijk, 2676 LM, Hague, Netherlands   **(100%)**
Tel.: (31) 174528333
Web Site: http://www.tovano.nl
Sales Range: $50-74.9 Million
Emp.: 6
Grocery & Related Products Whslr
N.A.I.C.S.: 424490

Van Rees B.V   **(1)**
Tel.: (31) 104021750
Sales Range: $25-49.9 Million
Emp.: 40
Tea Products Mfr & Distr
N.A.I.C.S.: 311920
Flip Van Rijen (Mng Dir)

Van Rees Ceylon Ltd.   **(1)**
51/27 New Nuge Road, Peliyagoda, Colombo, Sri Lanka
Tel.: (94) 11 2931698
Web Site: http://www.vanrees.com
Sales Range: $25-49.9 Million
Emp.: 26
Tea Mfr
N.A.I.C.S.: 311920

Van Rees LLC   **(1)**
2nd Tverskaya-Yamskaya str 16 8th floor room 1 office 15, 125047, Moscow, Russia
Tel.: (7) 4952254504
Sales Range: $50-74.9 Million
Emp.: 7
Tea Whslr
N.A.I.C.S.: 424490
Andrey Machavariani (Gen Dir)

Van Rees North America Inc   **(1)**
2200 Yonge Street Suite 1006, Toronto, M4S 2C6, ON, Canada
Tel.: (416) 482-7878
Sales Range: $50-74.9 Million
Emp.: 6
Tea Product Whslr
N.A.I.C.S.: 424490

Van Rees UK Ltd,   **(1)**
First Floor Access House 25-29 Church Street, Basingstoke, RG21 7QQ, Hampshire, United Kingdom
Tel.: (44) 1256810020
Web Site: http://vanrees.com
Tea Products Distr
N.A.I.C.S.: 424490

ACORDY INVEST S.A.

C Cordoba 6, E-29001, Malaga, Spain
Tel.: (34) 951490254
Web Site: http://acordyinvest.com
Year Founded: 2013
Emp.: 25
Private Investment Firm
N.A.I.C.S.: 523999
Frances G. Baez (CEO)

Subsidiaries:

Megola Inc.   **(1)**

---

214 La Salle Line, Sarnia, N7T 7H5, ON, Canada
Web Site: http://www.megola.com
Sales Range: Less than $1 Million
Water Treatment Products Mfr
N.A.I.C.S.: 221310

ACORN CAPITAL LIMITED

Level 12 90 Collins Street, Melbourne, 3000, VIC, Australia
Tel.: (61) 3 9639 0522
Web Site:
   http://www.acorncapital.com.au
Year Founded: 1998
Emp.: 25
Investment Management Service
N.A.I.C.S.: 523999
Robert Officer (Chm)

Subsidiaries:

Acorn Capital Investment Fund Limited   **(1)**
Level 4 2 Russell Street, Melbourne, 3000, VIC, Australia
Tel.: (61) 396390522
Web Site: http://www.acorncapital.com.au
Rev.: $2,477,965
Assets: $63,522,302
Liabilities: $506,143
Net Worth: $63,016,159
Earnings: $1,179,220
Fiscal Year-end: 06/30/2024
Investment Fund
N.A.I.C.S.: 525910
John Steven (Chm)

ACORN INCOME CORP.

Unit 9 606 Meredith Road NE, Calgary, T2E 5A8, AB, Canada
Tel.: (403) 265-6540   **AB**
Year Founded: 1997
Sales Range: Less than $1 Million
Investment Services
N.A.I.C.S.: 523999
Elias A. Foscolos (Pres, CEO & CFO)

ACORN INTERNATIONAL, INC.

5/F YueShang Plaza 1 South Wuning Road, Shanghai, 200042, China
Tel.: (86) 21 5151 8888   **Ky**
Web Site:
   http://www.acorninternational.com
Year Founded: 1998
Rev.: $37,484,493
Assets: $80,164,064
Liabilities: $13,723,948
Net Worth: $66,440,116
Earnings: $9,836,231
Emp.: 113
Fiscal Year-end: 12/31/19
Direct Sales Services
N.A.I.C.S.: 541613
Jacob A. Fisch (Pres & CEO)

ACOT GROUP OF COMPANIES

17 Jurong Port Road, Singapore, 619092, Singapore
Tel.: (65) 62687740
Web Site: http://www.acotgroup.com
Sales Range: $1-4.9 Billion
Emp.: 10,000
Holding Company; Moulded Plastic Products Mfr
N.A.I.C.S.: 551112
Graham Wright (Mng Dir-Europe)

ACOTEC SCIENTIFIC HOLDINGS LIMITED

4-5/F Building 1 No 16 North Hongda Road, Beijing Economic technological Development Area, Beijing, China
Tel.: (86) 1067872107   **Ky**
Web Site: https://www.acotec.cn
Year Founded: 2011
6669—(HKG)
Rev.: $60,601,449
Assets: $216,109,599
Liabilities: $20,600,004

Net Worth: $195,509,596
Earnings: $10,746,456
Emp.: 607
Fiscal Year-end: 12/31/22
Holding Company
N.A.I.C.S.: 551112
Hui Zhang (VP)

ACOUSOFT INFORMATISER-ING BV

Leerlooierstraat 4, 4871 EN, Etten-Leur, Netherlands
Tel.: (31) 76 5012336
Web Site: http://www.acousoft.nl
Sales Range: $25-49.9 Million
Emp.: 3
Software Reproducing
N.A.I.C.S.: 334610
Hans Schneider (CEO)

ACOUSORT AB

Medicon Village, 223 81, Lund, Sweden
Tel.: (46) 4520450854
Web Site: https://www.acousort.com
Year Founded: 2010
Diagnostic Care Services
N.A.I.C.S.: 621511
Martin Linde (Chm)

ACP ENERGY PLC

13 Hanover Square, Mayfair, London, W1S 1HN, United Kingdom
Tel.: (44) 2071932376   **UK**
Web Site:
   https://www.acpenergyplc.com
Year Founded: 2021
ACPE—(LSE)
Assets: $868,802
Liabilities: $49,356
Net Worth: $819,446
Earnings: ($378,839)
Emp.: 4
Fiscal Year-end: 06/30/22
Miscellaneous Financial Investment Activities
N.A.I.C.S.: 523999
Paul Welch (Chm)

ACP MARKETING, INC.

8375 Rue Bougainville Suite 100, Montreal, H4P 2G5, QC, Canada
Tel.: (514) 733-5247   **Ca**
Web Site:
   http://www.acpmarketing.net
Year Founded: 1994
Sales Range: $10-24.9 Million
Emp.: 35
Rail Ticket & Rail Pass Marketer Retailer & Distr
N.A.I.C.S.: 488999
Alex Popescu (Founder & Pres)

Subsidiaries:

ACP Marketing UK Ltd.   **(1)**
Sutton House, 158 Victoria St 2nd Fl, London, SW1E 5LB, United Kingdom
Tel.: (44) 2078344712
Web Site: http://www.acp.com
Rail Ticket & Rail Pass Marketer, Retailer & Distr
N.A.I.C.S.: 488999

ACP Marketing US Inc.   **(1)**
2 Hudson Pl Ste 100, Hoboken, NJ 07030
Tel.: (201) 798-4553
Web Site: http://www.britrail.com
Rail Ticket & Rail Pass Marketer, Retailer & Distr
N.A.I.C.S.: 561599

ACRINOVA AB

Krusegrand 42B, 212 25, Malmo, Sweden
Tel.: (46) 102069010
Web Site: http://www.acrinova.se
ACRI—(NASDAQ)
Rev.: $10,081,482

Assets: $87,162,433
Liabilities: $44,259,067
Net Worth: $42,903,366
Earnings: $4,392,898
Emp.: 40
Fiscal Year-end: 12/31/19
Real Estate Manangement Services
N.A.I.C.S.: 531390
Ulf Wallen (CEO)

ACROBIOSYSTEMS CO., LTD.
Floor 4 Building 5 No 8 Hongda
North Road, Beijing Economic and
Technological Development Zone,
Beijing, 100176, China
Tel.: (86) 1053395173
Web Site:
   https://www.acrobiosystems.cn
Year Founded: 2010
301080—(CHIN)
Rev.: $76,570,887
Assets: $396,267,309
Liabilities: $31,721,803
Net Worth: $364,545,506
Earnings: $21,632,831
Emp.: 500
Fiscal Year-end: 12/31/23
Biotechnology Research & Develop-
ment Services
N.A.I.C.S.: 541714
Yiding Chen (Chm & Gen Mgr)

ACROMEC ENGINEERS PTE LTD.
11 Woodlands Terrace, Singapore,
738436, Singapore
Tel.: (65) 67431300
Web Site: https://acromec.com
Year Founded: 1996
Engineeering Services
N.A.I.C.S.: 541330

ACROMETA GROUP LIMITED
4 Kaki Bukit Avenue 1 04-04 Kaki
Bukit Industrial Estate, Singapore,
417939, Singapore
Tel.: (65) 67431300   SG
Web Site: http://www.acromec.com
Year Founded: 1996
43F—(CAT)
Rev.: $51,499,956
Assets: $25,384,917
Liabilities: $26,771,180
Net Worth: ($1,386,262)
Earnings: $2,039,917
Emp.: 241
Fiscal Year-end: 09/30/23
Engineeering Services
N.A.I.C.S.: 541330
Say Chin Lim (Co-Founder, Chm &
Mng Dir)

ACRON AG
Splugenstrasse 14, 8002, Zurich,
Switzerland
Tel.: (41) 442043400
Web Site: http://www.acron.ch
Real Estate Firm
N.A.I.C.S.: 531390
Klaus Bender (Chm)

Subsidiaries:

CapStar San Francisco Company,
LLC   (1)
2500 Mason St, San Francisco, CA 94133-
1450
Tel.: (415) 362-5500
Hotel Operator
N.A.I.C.S.: 721110
Marc Babin (Mktg Mgr)

ACROPOLIS TELECOM S.A.
163 avenue Gallienili Porte de Bag-
nolet, 93170, Paris, France
Tel.: (33) 170725000
Sales Range: $1-9.9 Million
Emp.: 30

IP, VoIP Telephony, Voice, Video &
Data Convergence Services
N.A.I.C.S.: 334210
Samir Kolietat (Chm)

ACROUD AB
Stureplan 6 4 tr, 11435, Stockholm,
Sweden
Tel.: (46) 841038044
Year Founded: 2003
ACROUD—(OMX)
Rev.: $33,353,119
Assets: $86,204,403
Liabilities: $59,958,990
Net Worth: $26,245,413
Earnings: ($19,880,207)
Emp.: 66
Fiscal Year-end: 12/31/22
Asset Management Services
N.A.I.C.S.: 523940

Subsidiaries:

FTT LLC   (1)
6020 NW 99th Ave Ste 212, Doral, FL
33178
Tel.: (305) 629-9540
Web Site: https://www.fttgroups.com
Mobile Distr
N.A.I.C.S.: 423610

ACROW INDIA LTD.
Plot NO T-27 STPI MIDC, Chika-
Ithana, Chhatrapti Sambhaj Nagar,
431006, Maharashtra, India
Tel.: (91) 9552872991
Web Site:
   https://www.acrowindia.com
Year Founded: 1960
513149—(BOM)
Rev.: $132,522
Assets: $2,674,024
Liabilities: $6,019
Net Worth: $2,668,006
Earnings: $2,206
Emp.: 2
Fiscal Year-end: 03/31/23
Sugar Elevator Mfr & Distr
N.A.I.C.S.: 333921
Harshavardhan B. Doshi (Chm)

ACROW LIMITED
2a Mavis Street, Revesby, Sydney,
2212, NSW, Australia
Tel.: (61) 297806500   AU
Web Site: https://www.acrow.com.au
Year Founded: 1950
ACF—(ASX)
Rev.: $128,949,598
Assets: $208,630,902
Liabilities: $114,506,762
Net Worth: $94,124,140
Earnings: $16,930,117
Fiscal Year-end: 06/30/24
Gold Exploration & Mining Services
N.A.I.C.S.: 212220
Andrew Crowther (CFO)

Subsidiaries:

Natform (QLD) Pty Ltd   (1)
2 Morrison Lane, PO Box 1480, Beenleigh,
4207, QLD, Australia
Tel.: (61) 738079800
Construction Services
N.A.I.C.S.: 236220

Natform Pty Ltd   (1)
Suite 52 The Hub 89-97 Jones Street, Ul-
timo, 2007, NSW, Australia
Tel.: (61) 292121566
Web Site: http://www.natform.com.au
Construction Services
N.A.I.C.S.: 236220

Unispan Australia Pty Ltd   (1)
2 Morrison Lane, Beenleigh, 4207, QLD,
Australia
Tel.: (61) 734424000
Web Site: http://www.uni-span.com.au
Construction Materials Distr
N.A.I.C.S.: 423390

Gareth Caple (Mgr-Comml & Fin)

ACROW MISR FOR SCAF-FOLDING & FORMWORK
Wady Houf, Helwan, Egypt
Tel.: (20) 22369061636
Web Site: https://www.acrow.co
Year Founded: 1977
ACRO.CA—(EGX)
Sales Range: Less than $1 Million
Metal Products Mfr
N.A.I.C.S.: 332312
Ousama Kamal Mohammed Kamal Al
Jarf (Chm & Mng Dir)

ACRUX LIMITED
103-113 Stanley Street, Melbourne,
3003, VIC, Australia
Tel.: (61) 383790100
Web Site: https://www.acrux.com.au
ARUXF—(OTCIQ)
Rev.: $3,909,868
Assets: $10,958,049
Liabilities: $3,993,382
Net Worth: $6,964,667
Earnings: ($7,534,712)
Emp.: 444,000
Fiscal Year-end: 06/30/22
Health Care Products Development
N.A.I.C.S.: 621610
Michael Kotsanis (CEO & Mng Dir)

Subsidiaries:

Acrux DDS Pty Ltd   (1)
103 113 Stanley St, Melbourne, 3003, VIC,
Australia
Tel.: (61) 393268300
Web Site: http://www.acrux.com.au
Medicine Mfr
N.A.I.C.S.: 325412

Acrux Pharma Pty Ltd   (1)
103 113 Stanley St, Melbourne, 3003, VIC,
Australia
Tel.: (61) 383790100
Web Site: http://www.acrux.com.au
Emp.: 20
Pharmaceuticals Product Mfr
N.A.I.C.S.: 325412

Fempharm Pty Ltd   (1)
103 113 Stanley St, West Melbourne, 3003,
VIC, Australia
Tel.: (61) 383790100
Web Site: http://www.acrux.com.au
Pharmaceuticals Product Mfr
N.A.I.C.S.: 325412

ACRYLON PLASTICS INC.
122 Paquin Road, Winnipeg, R2J
3V4, MB, Canada
Tel.: (204) 669-2224
Web Site: http://www.acrylon.com
Year Founded: 1978
Rev.: $13,654,933
Emp.: 100
Plastics Product Mfr
N.A.I.C.S.: 326199
Craig McIntosh (Pres & CEO)

ACS BUSINESS SUPPLIES LIMITED
5-6 Aire Valley Business Park Wagon
Lane, Bingley, BD16 1WA, United
Kingdom
Tel.: (44) 8444 123 170
Web Site: http://www.acsacs.co.uk
Year Founded: 2008
Sales Range: $10-24.9 Million
Emp.: 85
Office Product Whslr
N.A.I.C.S.: 424120
Mike Hussain (Mng Dir)

ACS DOBFAR SPA
Palazzo Pegaso Ingresso 3, Viale
Colleoni 25, 20864, Agrate Brianza,
Italy
Tel.: (39) 02 90 69 31   IT

Web Site: http://www.acsdobfar.it
Year Founded: 1973
Pharmaceutical Preparation Mfr
N.A.I.C.S.: 325412

ACS TECHNOLOGIES LIMITED
Pardha's Picasa Level 7 Durgam
Cheruvu Road, Madhapur, Hydera-
bad, 500081, Telangana, India
Tel.: (91) 4049034464
Web Site:
   https://www.acstechnologies.co.in
Year Founded: 1993
Rev.: $1,129,921
Assets: $29,064,415
Liabilities: $5,068,157
Net Worth: $23,996,259
Earnings: $810,800
Emp.: 12
Fiscal Year-end: 03/31/18
Yarn Mfr & Distr
N.A.I.C.S.: 313110
Prabhakara Rao Alokam (CFO)

ACS, ACTIVIDADES DE CON-STRUCCION Y SERVICIOS, S.A.
Avda Pio XII n 102, 28036, Madrid,
Spain
Tel.: (34) 913439200   ES
Web Site: https://www.grupoacs.com
Year Founded: 1997
ACS—(MAD)
Rev.: $36,278,042,305
Assets: $40,557,198,360
Liabilities: $33,676,260,522
Net Worth: $6,880,937,837
Earnings: $721,160,155
Emp.: 128,721
Fiscal Year-end: 12/31/22
Construction & Engineering Services
N.A.I.C.S.: 541330
Florentino Perez Rodriguez (Chm)

Subsidiaries:

ACS Infrastructure Canada, Inc.   (1)
155 University Avenue Suite 900, Toronto,
M5H 3B7, ON, Canada
Tel.: (416) 642-2161
Web Site: http://www.grupoacs.com
Sales Range: $25-49.9 Million
Emp.: 12
Building Construction Services
N.A.I.C.S.: 236220
Lissette Alizaga (Office Mgr)

ACS Infrastructure Development,
Inc.   (1)
1 Alhambra Plz Ste 710, Coral Gables, FL
33134-5216
Tel.: (305) 423-7606
Construction Engineering Services
N.A.I.C.S.: 237990
Chad Kishick (Coord-Proposal)

ACS Servicios y Concesiones,
S.L.   (1)
Avenida Camino De Santiago 50-Edif 1
Planta 4a, Madrid, 28050, Spain
Tel.: (34) 917036000
Sales Range: $25-49.9 Million
Emp.: 2
Environmental Consulting Services
N.A.I.C.S.: 541620
Reinoso Torres Francisco (Gen Mgr)

ACS Telefonia Movil, S.L.   (1)
Avda Pio XII 102, Madrid, 28036, Spain
Tel.: (34) 91 343 92 00
Web Site: http://www.grupoacs.com
Telecommunication Servicesb
N.A.I.C.S.: 517810

ACS, Servicios Comunicaciones y
Energa, S.L.   (1)
Cardenal Marcelo Spinola 10, 28016, Ma-
drid, Spain
Tel.: (34) 91 456 9500
Web Site: https://www.acsindustria.com
Construction Services
N.A.I.C.S.: 236220

ACS, Actividades de Construccion y Servicios, S.A.—(Continued)

ACS, Servicios Comunicaciones y Energia, S.L. (1)
Cardenal Marcelo Spinola 10, 28016, Madrid, Spain (100%)
Tel.: (34) 91 456 95 00
Web Site: http://www.grupoacs.com
Industrial Cleaning Services
N.A.I.C.S.: 562998

API Fabricacion, S.A. (1)
Calle Del Raso De La Estrella S/N, Aranjuez, 28300, Madrid, Spain
Tel.: (34) 918090990
Sales Range: $25-49.9 Million
Emp.: 80
Industrial Machinery Mfr
N.A.I.C.S.: 333248
Juan Cruz Martinez Madrid (Gen Mgr)

API Movilidad, S.A. (1)
Avenida Manoteras 26, Madrid, 28050, Spain
Tel.: (34) 917443900
Highway Construction Services
N.A.I.C.S.: 237310

Actividades de Servicios e Instalaciones Cobra, S.A. (1)
29 Av 13-35 Zona 17 Complejo De Ofibodegas Las Almendras Bodega 3, Guatemala, Guatemala
Tel.: (502) 23896600
Industrial Building Construction Services
N.A.I.C.S.: 236210

Albatros Logistic, Maroc, S.A. (1)
Hangars 10 11 Et 12 Lotissement At-tawfik Rue Ibnou El Koutia, Quartier Industriel OU-KACHA Ain Sebaa, Casablanca, Morocco
Tel.: (212) 522 66 62 33
Web Site: http://www.albatroslogistic.ma
Logistics Consulting Servies
N.A.I.C.S.: 541614

Albatros Logistic, S.A. (1)
C / Franklin 15, 28096, Getafe, Madrid, Spain
Tel.: (34) 91 665 46 40
Web Site: http://www.albatroslogistic.es
Logistics Consulting Servies
N.A.I.C.S.: 541614

Argencobra, S.A. (1)
Nicaragua 5935 Piso 2, Buenos Aires, 1414, Argentina
Tel.: (54) 1147746200
Sales Range: $50-74.9 Million
Emp.: 5
Auxiliary Electric Power Distribution Services
N.A.I.C.S.: 221122
Dracut Xavier (Gen Mgr)

Artemis Transmissora de Energia, Ltda. (1)
Rua Deputado Antonio Edu Vieira 999 Terreo, Bairro Pantanal, Florianopolis, 88040-901, Brazil
Tel.: (55) 48 3231 7282
Web Site: http://www.artemisenergia.com.br
Electricity Transmission Line Construction Services
N.A.I.C.S.: 237130

Asistencia Offshore, S.A. (1)
Benitez Perez Galdos, Cadiz, 11003, Spain
Tel.: (34) 956290940
Sales Range: $25-49.9 Million
Emp.: 3
Oil & Gas Offshore Engineering Services
N.A.I.C.S.: 541330
Juan Carlos Vichera (Gen Mgr)

Atil-Cobra, S.A. (1)
Calle Orense 4, Madrid, 28020, Spain
Tel.: (34) 915551315
Web Site: http://www.grupocobra.com
Emp.: 70
Construction Engineering Services
N.A.I.C.S.: 541330
Felix Pereira Lopez (Gen Mgr)

Audeli, S.A. (1)
Calle De Ana Isabel Segura 11 A Second Floor C, Alcobendas, 28108, Madrid, Spain
Tel.: (34) 916259900
Logistics Consulting Servies

N.A.I.C.S.: 541614

Autovia Medinaceli-Calatayud Soc.Conces.Estado, S.A. (1)
Avenida Camino De Santiago 50, Madrid, 28050, Spain
Tel.: (34) 976897000
Business Support Services
N.A.I.C.S.: 561499

Autovia de La Mancha, S.A. (1)
21 500 de la CM-42 en el, 54430, Mascaraque, Toledo, Spain
Tel.: (34) 925 30 15 40
Web Site: http://www.aumancha.com
Highway Construction Services
N.A.I.C.S.: 237310

Autovia del Camp del Turia, S.A. (1)
Calle Alvaro De Bazan 10-Ent, Valencia, 46010, Spain
Tel.: (34) 960454500
Sales Range: $25-49.9 Million
Emp.: 7
Highway Construction Services
N.A.I.C.S.: 237310
Miguel Escriva (Gen Mgr)

Autovia del Pirineo, S.A. (1)
Calle Emilio Arrieta 8-Plt 6, Pamplona, 31002, Navarra, Spain
Tel.: (34) 948223754
Highway Construction Services
N.A.I.C.S.: 237310

Barra do Peixe Montagens e Servicos, Ltda. (1)
Mal Camara 160, Rio de Janeiro, 20020-080, Brazil
Tel.: (55) 2122157317
Construction Engineering Services
N.A.I.C.S.: 541330

Benisaf Water Company, Spa (1)
12 Rue Slimane Allili Djnane Malik El, Hydra, Algiers, Algeria
Tel.: (213) 23482197
Web Site: http://www.benisafwater.com
Water Treatment & Recycling Services
N.A.I.C.S.: 221310

Broad Construction Services Pty Ltd (1)
202 Pier Street, Perth, 6000, WA, Australia
Tel.: (61) 89 238 0300
Web Site: https://www.broad.com.au
Construction Services
N.A.I.C.S.: 236220
Cyril Cahill (Gen Mgr)

CAT Desenvolupament de Concessions Catalanes, S.L (1)
Avenida Josep Tarradellas 8-10 Second Floor, Barcelona, 08029, Spain
Tel.: (34) 934443236
Web Site: http://www.acs.com
Investment Management Service
N.A.I.C.S.: 523999

CCR Platforming Cangrejera S.A. de C.V. (1)
Carretera Coatzacoalcos-Villahermosa Km 11 Complejo Petroquimico, Cangrejera, Coatzacoalcos, 96400, Veracruz, Mexico
Tel.: (52) 9212112170
Construction Engineering Services
N.A.I.C.S.: 237990

CME Chile, SPA (1)
Puerto Madero 970 35 Y 36-A Pudahuel, Santiago, Chile
Tel.: (56) 25858161
Sales Range: $25-49.9 Million
Emp.: 150
Logistics Consulting Servies
N.A.I.C.S.: 541614

COGESA S.p.A. (1)
Calle Orense 34 1st Floor, 28020, Madrid, Spain
Tel.: (34) 91 417 9650
Web Site: https://www.grupocogesa.es
Real Estate Manangement Services
N.A.I.C.S.: 531312

COSERSA CONTRATAS Y SERVICIOS, S.A. (1)
Calle Bronce 23, 28500, Arganda del Rey, Madrid, Spain
Tel.: (34) 918720978

Web Site: http://www.coser-sa.com
Industrial Cleaning Services
N.A.I.C.S.: 562998

CPB Contractors Pty Limited (1)
Level 18 177 Pacific Highway, North Sydney, 2060, NSW, Australia
Tel.: (61) 28 668 6000
Web Site: https://www.cpbcon.com.au
Construction Services
N.A.I.C.S.: 236220
Jason Spears (Mng Dir)

Can Brians 2, S.A. (1)
Avenida Josep Tarradellas 34-36 9 E D, Barcelona, 8029, Spain
Tel.: (34) 934443236
Real Estate Agency Services
N.A.I.C.S.: 531210

Cariatide, S.A. (1)
Avenida Pio XII 102, Madrid, Spain
Tel.: (34) 913439337
Construction Engineering Services
N.A.I.C.S.: 541330

Catalana de Treballs Publics, S.A. (1)
Carretera Mig 37, Cornella de Llobregat, 08940, Barcelona, Spain
Tel.: (34) 938499736
Civil Construction Engineering Services
N.A.I.C.S.: 237990

Catxere Transmissora de Energia, S.A. (1)
Av Marechal Camara 160 - sala 1036, Rio de Janeiro, 20020-080, Brazil
Tel.: (55) 21 2101 9970
Sales Range: $75-99.9 Million
Emp.: 9
Electric Power Transmission Services
N.A.I.C.S.: 221121

Central Termica de Mejillones, S.A. (1)
Av Chacaya S/N, Mejillones, Chile
Tel.: (56) 55566900
Construction Engineering Services
N.A.I.C.S.: 237990

Centro de Transferencias, S.A (1)
Poligono Los Barriales S/N, Santovenia de Pisuerga, 47155, Valladolid, Spain
Tel.: (34) 983310520
Industrial Waste Treatment & Disposal Services
N.A.I.C.S.: 562219

Cesionaria Valles Occidental, S.A. (1)
Avenida Josep Tarradellas 8-10 Plt Novena D, Barcelona, 08029, Spain
Tel.: (34) 934443236
Construction Engineering Services
N.A.I.C.S.: 237990

Claerh, S.A. (1)
Poligono Industrial Oeste Avda Del Descubrimiento Parc 5 5, Alcantarilla, 30820, Murcia, Spain
Tel.: (34) 968897005
Sanitary Waste Collection & Treatment Services
N.A.I.C.S.: 562219

Clece, S.A. (1)
Parque Via Nortec C/ Quintanavides 19 - Bloque 4, 28050, Madrid, Spain (100%)
Tel.: (34) 91 745 91 00
Web Site: http://www.clece.es
Sales Range: $1-4.9 Billion
Emp.: 79,007
Public Organizations Cleaning Services
N.A.I.C.S.: 561720

Cobra Concesiones, S.L. (1)
Calle Cardenal Marcelo Spinola 10, Madrid, 28016, Spain
Tel.: (34) 914569500
Civil Engineering Construction Services
N.A.I.C.S.: 237990

Subsidiary (Non-US):

Cobra Chile, S.A. (1)
Av Jose Pedro Alessandri 2323 Macul, Santiago, Chile
Tel.: (56) 22379700
Electrical Equipment Installation Services
N.A.I.C.S.: 238210

Subsidiary (Domestic):

Cobra Concesiones Brasil, S.L. (2)
Calle Cardenal Marcelo Spinola 10, Madrid, 28016, Spain
Tel.: (34) 914569500
Financial Management Services
N.A.I.C.S.: 523999

Cobra Gestion de Infraestructuras, S.L.U (2)
Calle Cardenal Marcelo Spinola 10, Madrid, 28016, Spain
Tel.: (34) 914569500
Civil Engineering Construction Services
N.A.I.C.S.: 237990

Cobra Infraestructuras Hidraulicas, S.A. (2)
Calle Cardenal Marcelo Spinola 10, Madrid, 28016, Spain
Tel.: (34) 914569500
Construction Engineering Services
N.A.I.C.S.: 237990
Eugenio Llorente Gomez (Gen Mgr)

Cobra Instalaciones y Servicios Internacional, S.L. (2)
Calle Cardenal Marcelo Spinola 10, Madrid, 28016, Spain
Tel.: (34) 914569500
Web Site: http://www.grupocobra.com
Emp.: 10,960
Civil Engineering Construction Services
N.A.I.C.S.: 237990

Subsidiary (Non-US):

Cobra La Rioja Sur SA (2)
Concepcion Arenal 2630, Buenos Aires, C1426 DGB, Argentina
Tel.: (54) 11 4774 6200
Web Site: http://www.cobralariojasur.com.ar
Electric Power Generation & Distribution Services
N.A.I.C.S.: 221118

Cobra Peru, S.A. (2)
Av Victor A Belaunde Na 887 Urb Carmen De La Legua Reynoso, Carmen De La Legua, Callao, Peru
Tel.: (51) 15623003
Construction Engineering Services
N.A.I.C.S.: 541330

Subsidiary (Domestic):

Cobra Servicios Auxiliares, S.A. (2)
Calle Cardenal Marcelo Spinola 10, Madrid, 28016, Spain
Tel.: (34) 914569500
Electrical Installation Services
N.A.I.C.S.: 238210

Cobra Sistemas de Seguridad, S.A. (2)
Calle Cardenal Marcelo Spinola 10 Y 6, 28016, Madrid, Spain
Tel.: (34) 914569500
Web Site: http://www.grupocobra.com
Security System Installation Services
N.A.I.C.S.: 238210

Cobra Sistemas y Redes, S.A. (2)
Calle Cardenal Marcelo Spinola 10, Madrid, 28016, Spain
Tel.: (34) 914569500
Sales Range: $50-74.9 Million
Emp.: 600
Electrical Contracting Services
N.A.I.C.S.: 238210
Antonio Gomez Zamora (Gen Mgr)

Cobra Termosolar USA, S.L. (2)
Calle Cardenal Marcelo Spinola 10, Madrid, 28016, Spain
Tel.: (34) 914569500
Web Site: http://www.grupocobra.com
Emp.: 9,000
Eletric Power Generation Services
N.A.I.C.S.: 221118

Affiliate (Domestic):

Cobra-Udisport Conde de Guadalhorce, S.L (2)
Paseo Cerrado De Calderon 18-Ed Mercurio, Malaga, 29018, Spain
Tel.: (34) 952041098

Sports Facilities Operation & Maintenance Services
N.A.I.C.S.: 713940

Concesionaria San Rafael, S.A.   **(1)**
Calle Del Diputat Josep Ribas S/N, San Antonio Abad, 07820, Baleares, Spain
Tel.: (34) 915969715
Web Site:
   http://www.concesionariasanrafael.com
Highway Construction Services
N.A.I.C.S.: 237310

Consenur, S.A.   **(1)**
C/Rio Ebro s/n Poligono Industrial Finanzauto, Arganda del Rey, 28500, Spain
Tel.: (34) 918 76 06 70
Web Site: http://www.consenur.es
Clinical Waste Management Services
N.A.I.C.S.: 562998

Consorcio Tecdra, S.A.   **(1)**
Almirante Pastene 244 Oficina 702 Providencia, Santiago, Chile
Tel.: (56) 2 6162500
Web Site: http://www.tecdracentro.cl
Railway Construction Engineering Services
N.A.I.C.S.: 237990

Constructora Dycven, S.A.   **(1)**
Urbanizacion Las Mercedes Calle Veracruz, Edificio Torreon 3er Piso Oficina 3B, Caracas, 1060, Venezuela
Tel.: (58) 212 992 31 11
Web Site: http://www.dycvensa.com.ve
Sales Range: $25-49.9 Million
Emp.: 40
Civil Engineering Construction Services
N.A.I.C.S.: 237990

Construrail, S.A.   **(1)**
Orense 11 - 2, 28020, Madrid, Spain
Tel.: (34) 915 980 770
Web Site: http://www.constru-rail.es
Rail Cargo Operating Services & Coal Distr
N.A.I.C.S.: 488210

Continental Rail, S.A.   **(1)**
Orense 11 - 2, 28020, Madrid, Spain
Tel.: (34) 915 980 773
Web Site: http://www.continentalrail.es
Rail Freight Transportation Services
N.A.I.C.S.: 488510

Control y Montajes Industriales CYMI, S.A.   **(1)**
Calle Via de los Poblados 9-11, 28033, Madrid, Spain
Tel.: (34) 91 659 33 60
Web Site: http://www.en.cymisa.com
Electrical Installation & Assembly Services
N.A.I.C.S.: 238210

Subsidiary (US):

ACT Industrial Process Services LLC   **(2)**
5315 Greenwood Rd, Shreveport, LA 71109
Tel.: (318) 675-1772
Web Site: http://www.appcontech.com
Electrical Engineering Services
N.A.I.C.S.: 541330
Ritchie Thompson *(Pres)*

Applied Control Technology, LLC.   **(2)**
5005 Stateline Ave 12400 Coit Rd Ste 700, Dallas, TX 75251
Tel.: (903) 791-3000
Web Site: http://www.appcontech.com
Electrical Engineering Services
N.A.I.C.S.: 541330
Brian Steed *(VP-Engrg)*

Cymi Holding, S.A.   **(1)**
Presidente Wilson Avenue 231, Downtown, Rio de Janeiro, 20030-021, Brazil
Tel.: (55) 2121019900
Web Site: http://www.cymimasa.com.br
Emp.: 40
Financial Investment Services
N.A.I.C.S.: 523999
Marcelo Vargas *(Gen Mgr)*

Subsidiary (Domestic):

CymiMasa Brasil, Ltda.   **(2)**
Av Presidente Wilson 231-s1701, Centro, Rio de Janeiro, 20030/021, Brazil
Tel.: (55) 21 2101 9900
Web Site: http://www.cymimasa.com.br

Power Plant Construction Services
N.A.I.C.S.: 237130
Tatiana Madeira Vaccani Herzog *(Mgr-Pur)*

Cymi Seguridad, S.A.   **(1)**
Calle Teide 5, San Sebastian de los Reyes, 28703, Madrid, Spain
Tel.: (34) 916593360
Civil Engineering Construction Services
N.A.I.C.S.: 237990

DRAMAR ANDALUCIA TRATA-MIENTO DE MARPOLES, S.L.U.   **(1)**
Muelle Isla Verde s/n, 11207, Algeciras, Cadiz, Spain
Tel.: (34) 956 57 37 33
Web Site: http://www.dramarmarpol.com
Sales Range: $10-24.9 Million
Waste Treatment Services
N.A.I.C.S.: 562211

Desarrollo Informatico, S.A.   **(1)**
Pradillo 46, 28002, Madrid, Spain
Tel.: (34) 918066300
Web Site: http://www.dinsa.es
Emp.: 25
Information Technology Consulting Services
N.A.I.C.S.: 541512

Desarrollo de Concesionarias Viarias Dos, S.L.   **(1)**
Avenida Camino De Santiago 50, Madrid, 28050, Spain
Tel.: (34) 917038482
Construction Engineering Services
N.A.I.C.S.: 541330

Desarrollo de Concesionarias Viarias Uno, S.L.   **(1)**
Avenida De Tenerife 4, San Sebastian de los Reyes, 28700, Madrid, Spain
Tel.: (34) 917038482
Civil Engineering Construction Services
N.A.I.C.S.: 237990

Desarrollo de Concesiones Ferroviarias, S.L.   **(1)**
Avenida Camino De Santiago 50, Madrid, 28050, Spain
Tel.: (34) 917038708
Railway Construction Services
N.A.I.C.S.: 237990

Drace Geocisa, S.A.   **(1)**
Avenida del Camino de Santiago n0 50, 28050, Madrid, Spain
Tel.: (34) 917035600
Web Site: https://www.drace.com
Environmental Engineering Services
N.A.I.C.S.: 541330

Drace Infraestructuras, S.A.   **(1)**
Avenida Del Camino De Santiago No 50, 28050, Madrid, Spain
Tel.: (34) 91 703 5600
Web Site: https://www.drace.com
Waste Water Treatment Services
N.A.I.C.S.: 221320

Drace Medio Ambiente, S.A.   **(1)**
Avenida Camino de Santiago 50 Edif 4, 28050, Madrid, Spain
Tel.: (34) 91 703 56 00
Web Site:
   http://www.dracemedioambiente.com
Environmental Consulting Services
N.A.I.C.S.: 541620

Dragados Canada, Inc.   **(1)**
150 King Street West Suite 2103, Toronto, M5H 1J9, ON, Canada
Tel.: (647) 260-5001
Web Site: https://www.dragados-canada.com
Emp.: 230
Construction Services
N.A.I.C.S.: 236220

Dragados Gulf Construction, Ltda.   **(1)**
Al-Saeed Business Tower Office 903 Dammam-Khobar Highway 605 Khobar, PO Box 39477, Al Khobar, 34227, Saudi Arabia
Tel.: (966) 3 814 7525
Web Site: http://www.dragadosgulf.com
Construction Engineering Services
N.A.I.C.S.: 237990

Dragados Inversiones USA, S.L.   **(1)**
Avenida Camino De Santiago 50 Edif 3 Pl

6, Madrid, 28050, Spain
Construction Engineering Services
N.A.I.C.S.: 237990

Dragados Offshore de Mejico KU-A2, S.A de C.V.   **(1)**
Juan Racine n 112 Piso 8, Col Los Morales, Mexico, 11510, Mexico
Tel.: (52) 938 131 0697
Metal Mining Services
N.A.I.C.S.: 212290

Dragados Offshore, S.A.   **(1)**
Bajo de la Cabezuela s/n, 11510, Puerto Real, Cadiz, Spain
Tel.: (34) 956470700
Web Site:
   https://www.dragadosoffshore.com
Sales Range: $1-4.9 Billion
Oil & Gas Offshore Services
N.A.I.C.S.: 213112
Pedro Ascorbe *(Chm & CEO)*

Dragados S.A.   **(1)**
Avda Camino de Santiago 50, Madrid, 28050, Spain
Tel.: (34) 913439300
Sales Range: $1-4.9 Billion
Emp.: 17,000
Building Construction, Maintenance, Civil Works & Infrastructure Maintenance Services
N.A.I.C.S.: 236210
Pedro Lopez Jimenez *(Vice Chm)*

Subsidiary (US):

Dragados USA Inc.   **(2)**
810 7th Ave 9th Fl, New York, NY 10019
Tel.: (212) 779-0900
Web Site: https://www.dragados-usa.com
Sales Range: $25-49.9 Million
Emp.: 100
Construction Services
N.A.I.C.S.: 237990
Ricardo Bustamante *(CEO)*

Subsidiary (Domestic):

J.F. White Contracting Co.   **(3)**
10 Burr St, Framingham, MA 01701
Tel.: (508) 879-4700
Web Site: https://www.jfwhite.com
Highway, Street & Bridge Construction Services
N.A.I.C.S.: 237310
Peter White *(Pres)*

John P. Picone Inc.   **(3)**
31 Garden Ln, Lawrence, NY 11559
Tel.: (516) 239-1600
Web Site: http://www.johnpicone.com
Sales Range: $50-74.9 Million
Sewer Line Construction Services
N.A.I.C.S.: 237110

Prince Contracting, LLC   **(3)**
10210 Highland Manor Dr Ste 110, Tampa, FL 33610
Tel.: (813) 699-5900
Web Site: http://princecontracting.com
Sales Range: $150-199.9 Million
Construction Services
N.A.I.C.S.: 237990
Jack Calandros *(Exec Dir)*

Schiavone Construction Co. LLC   **(3)**
150 Meadowlands Pkwy - 3rd Fl, Secaucus, NJ 07094-1589
Tel.: (201) 867-5070
Web Site: https://schiavoneconstruction.com
Heavy Construction Services
N.A.I.C.S.: 236210

Subsidiary (Domestic):

Flota Proyectos Singulares, S.A   **(2)**
Avenida del Camino de Santiago no 50, 28050, Madrid, Spain
Tel.: (34) 91 545 4777
Web Site: http://www.flotaps.com
Sales Range: $25-49.9 Million
Emp.: 7
Construction Engineering Services
N.A.I.C.S.: 541330
Juan Mata *(Gen Mgr)*

Subsidiary (Non-US):

Przedsiebiorstwo Robot In-zynieryjnych POL-AQUA S.A.   **(2)**

ul Dworska 1, 05-500, Warsaw, Poland   **(66%)**
Tel.: (48) 222017300
Web Site: http://www.pol-aqua.com.pl
Sales Range: $250-299.9 Million
Engineering & Construction Services
N.A.I.C.S.: 541330
Marek Sobiecki *(Dir-Fin & Org)*

Dragados UK Limited   **(1)**
Regina House 2nd Floor 1-5 Queen Street, London, EC4N 1SW, United Kingdom
Tel.: (44) 207 651 0900
Web Site: https://www.dragados.co.uk
Construction Services
N.A.I.C.S.: 236220

Dycasa S.A.   **(1)**
Av Leandro N Alem 986 4th Floor, C1001AAR, Buenos Aires, Argentina
Tel.: (54) 114 318 0200
Web Site: https://www.dycasa.com
Construction Services
N.A.I.C.S.: 236220

EIC Activities Pty Ltd   **(1)**
Level 19 177 Pacific Highway, North Sydney, 2060, NSW, Australia
Tel.: (61) 28 668 6333
Web Site: https://www.eicactiv.com
Engineeering Services
N.A.I.C.S.: 541330
Geoff Sewell *(Mng Dir)*

ENYSE Enclavamientos y Senalizacion Ferroviaria, S.A.   **(1)**
C/Valportillo II 8-Bis, Pol Ind Alcobendas, 28108, Alcobendas, Madrid, Spain
Tel.: (34) 91 490 1383
Web Site: https://www.enyse.com
Railroad Services
N.A.I.C.S.: 488210

Ecocivil Electromur G.E., S.L.   **(1)**
Poligono Industrial Oeste Pg Industrial Oeste 13-3, Murcia, 30169, Spain
Tel.: (34) 968826153
Civil Engineering Construction Services
N.A.I.C.S.: 237990

Ecologia y Tecnicas Sanitarias, S.L.   **(1)**
Calle Josefina Mayor Ur Ind El Goro 9-Nv 3, Telde, 35219, Palmas Las, Spain   **(100%)**
Tel.: (34) 928700980
Sanitary Waste Collection Services
N.A.I.C.S.: 562119

Ecoparc de Barcelona S.A.   **(1)**
Calle Lletra A De La Zona Franca 26, Barcelona, 8040, Spain
Tel.: (34) 932623010
Waste Treatment Services
N.A.I.C.S.: 562211

Edafologia y Restauracion del Entorno Gallego, S.L.   **(1)**
Rua Enrique Marinas 36-4, 15009, La Coruna, Spain
Tel.: (34) 981175100
Waste Treatment Services
N.A.I.C.S.: 562211
Fernando Rodriguez *(Gen Mgr)*

Eix Diagonal Concessionaria de la Generalitat de Catalunya, S.A.   **(1)**
Avenida Josep Tarradellas 34-Piso 9 Dr, Barcelona, 08029, Spain
Tel.: (34) 938992079
Emp.: 50
Road Construction Services
N.A.I.C.S.: 237310
Victor Minguellon *(Mgr)*

Electren, S.A.   **(1)**
Avenida Del Brasil 6 2a Pl, 28020, Madrid, Spain
Tel.: (34) 915548207
Web Site: http://electren.es
Electrical Engineering Services
N.A.I.C.S.: 541330

Electromur, S.A.   **(1)**
Ctra Del Palmar 530 El Palmar, 30120, Murcia, Spain
Tel.: (34) 968 88 08 62
Web Site: http://www.electromur.net
Electrical Lightning Installation Services
N.A.I.C.S.: 238120

ACS, Actividades de Construccion y Servicios, S.A.—(Continued)

Electronic Traffic, S.A. (1)
Avda Tres Forques 147, 46014, Valencia, Spain
Tel.: (34) 96 313 4082
Web Site: https://www.grupoetra.com
Construction Services
N.A.I.C.S.: 236220

Emurtel, S.A. (1)
Ctra Del Palmar 530 El Palmar, 30120, Murcia, Spain
Tel.: (34) 968 90 11 00
Web Site: http://www.emurtel.com
Telecommunications Installation Services
N.A.I.C.S.: 517111

Energias Ambientales de Novo, S.A. (1)
Calle Jose Luis Bugallal Marchesi 20, La Coruna, 15008, Spain
Tel.: (34) 981169470
Electrical Installation Services
N.A.I.C.S.: 238210

Energias Ambientales, S.A. (1)
Calle Jose Luis Bugallal Marchesi 20, La Coruna, 15008, Spain
Tel.: (34) 981169470
Eletric Power Generation Services
N.A.I.C.S.: 221118

Equipos de Senalizacion y Control, S.A. (1)
Severino Cobas 100 - Poligono La Bagunda, 36214, Vigo, Pontevedra, Spain
Tel.: (34) 98 625 24 33
Web Site: http://www.grupoetra.com
Electrical Installation Services
N.A.I.C.S.: 238210

Etra Interandina, S.A. (1)
100 N 8- 51 Ofic 503-504 Torre B World Trade Center, Bogota, Colombia
Tel.: (57) 1 611 29 25
Electrical Equipment Installation Services
N.A.I.C.S.: 238210

Etra Investigacion y Desarrollo, S.A. (1)
Tres Forques 147, 46014, Valencia, Spain
Tel.: (34) 963134082
Electrical Equipment Research & Development Services
N.A.I.C.S.: 541715
Ortis Lotez (Gen Mgr)

Etralux, S.A. (1)
Avda Manoteras 28, 28050, Madrid, Spain
Tel.: (34) 913 834 120
Electrical Equipment Installation Services
N.A.I.C.S.: 238210

Etranorte, S.A. (1)
Pl Zabalondo-C/ Erreruena Pabellon G, 48100, Munguia, Bizkaia, Spain
Tel.: (34) 946 742 060
Web Site: http://www.grupoetra.com
Electrical Equipment Installation Services
N.A.I.C.S.: 238210

Explotacion Comercial de Intercambiadores, S.A. (1)
Avenida America Intercambiador De Transportes 9-A, Madrid, 28002, Spain
Tel.: (34) 917130626
Business Support Services
N.A.I.C.S.: 561499

France Semi, S.A. (1)
20-22 Rue Louis Armand, 75015, Paris, France
Tel.: (33) 140604040
Sales Range: $25-49.9 Million
Emp.: 24
Electrical Installation Services
N.A.I.C.S.: 238210
Illy Laurent (Gen Dir)

GPL Limpiezas, S.L. (1)
Calle Diputacio 180-10, Barcelona, 08011, Spain
Tel.: (34) 932094300
Interior Cleaning Services
N.A.I.C.S.: 238990

Gasoductos y Redes Gisca, S.A. (1)
Orense 11, Madrid, 28020, Spain
Tel.: (34) 915554593

Petroleum Pipeline Construction Services
N.A.I.C.S.: 237120

Geotecnia y Cimientos, S.A. (1)
Los Llanos de Jerez 10 y 12, 28823, Coslada, Madrid, Spain
Tel.: (34) 91 660 30 00
Web Site: http://www.geocisa.com
Highway Construction Services
N.A.I.C.S.: 237310

Gestion y Proteccion Ambiental, S.L. (1)
Calle Condado De Trevino 19, Burgos, 09001, Spain
Tel.: (34) 947298687
Industrial Waste Collection & Treatment Services
N.A.I.C.S.: 562219

Golden State Environmental Tedagua Corporation, S.A. (1)
Calle Cardenal Marcelo Spinola 6, Madrid, 28016, Spain
Tel.: (34) 914569500
Emp.: 50
Electronic Components Mfr
N.A.I.C.S.: 334419
Megualanger Fernande (Mgr)

HOCHTIEF AG (1)
Alfredstrasse 236, 45133, Essen, Germany (66.54%)
Tel.: (49) 2018240
Web Site: https://www.hochtief.com
Rev.: $30,639,070,913
Assets: $20,980,351,917
Liabilities: $19,616,542,609
Net Worth: $1,363,809,308
Earnings: $577,048,042
Emp.: 41,575
Fiscal Year-end: 12/31/2023
Planning, Design, Financing & Construction of Building & Civil Engineering Work; Airport Management; Project Development; Facility Management
N.A.I.C.S.: 237990
Marcelino Fernandez Verdes (Chm-Exec Bd)

Holding (Non-US):

Abertis Infraestructuras, S.A. (2)
Avinguda de Pedralbes 17, 08034, Barcelona, Spain (78.79%)
Tel.: (34) 915951000
Web Site: https://www.abertis.com
Rev.: $6,375,845,828
Assets: $35,733,094,537
Liabilities: $30,011,307,820
Net Worth: $5,721,786,718
Earnings: $1,196,632,194
Emp.: 15,046
Fiscal Year-end: 12/31/2017
Transport & Communications Infrastructure Management & Tollway Development & Maintenance Services
N.A.I.C.S.: 488210
Marcelino Fernandez Verdes (Chm)

Subsidiary (Domestic):

Abertis Airports S.A. (3)
Avinguda de Pedralbes 17, 08034, Barcelona, Spain
Tel.: (34) 932305000
Web Site: http://www.abertis.com
Sales Range: $350-399.9 Million
Emp.: 2,000
Airport Operator
N.A.I.C.S.: 488119

Subsidiary (Non-US):

TBI plc (4)
72-104 TBI House Frank Lester Way, London Luton Airport, Luton, LU2 9NQ, Beds, United Kingdom
Tel.: (44) 1582817400
Web Site: http://www.tbiairports.aero
Airport Operator
N.A.I.C.S.: 488119
Carlos Delrio (CEO)

Subsidiary (Domestic):

Belfast International Airport Ltd. (5)
Belfast International Airport, Belfast, BT29 4AB, United Kingdom (100%)
Tel.: (44) 2894484848
Web Site: http://www.belfastairport.com

Sales Range: $50-74.9 Million
Emp.: 4,500
Airport Operator
N.A.I.C.S.: 488119
Graham Keddie (Mng Dir)

Subsidiary (Non-US):

Stockholm Skavsta Flygplats AB (5)
General Schybergs plan 22, Box 44, 611 92, Nykoping, Sweden (100%)
Tel.: (46) 155280400
Web Site: http://www.skavsta.se
Sales Range: $125-149.9 Million
Emp.: 400
Airport Operator
N.A.I.C.S.: 488119

Subsidiary (US):

TBI Airport Management Inc. (5)
3212 Red Cleveland Blvd, Sanford, FL 32773 (100%)
Tel.: (407) 585-4500
Web Site: http://www.orlandosanfordairport.com
Sales Range: $25-49.9 Million
Emp.: 65
Airport Management
N.A.I.C.S.: 488119
Larry Gouldthorpe (Pres)

Subsidiary (Domestic):

Orlando Sanford International Inc. (6)
1200 Red Cleveland Blvd, Sanford, FL 32773 (100%)
Tel.: (407) 585-4500
Web Site: http://flysfb.com
Sales Range: $25-49.9 Million
Airport Operator
N.A.I.C.S.: 488119

TBI Cargo Inc. (6)
2971 Carrier Ave, Sanford, FL 32773 (100%)
Tel.: (407) 585-4620
Sales Range: $25-49.9 Million
Emp.: 6
Air Cargo Transportation Services
N.A.I.C.S.: 481112
David Logan (Dir-Ops)

Subsidiary (Domestic):

Abertis Logistica, S.A. (3)
Avinguda Parc Logistic 22-26, 08040, Barcelona, Spain
Tel.: (34) 93 230 52 00
Web Site: http://www.abertislogistica.com
Logistic Services
N.A.I.C.S.: 541614

Subsidiary (Non-US):

Abertis Logistica Chile (4)
El Golf 150 Piso 6, Las Condes, Santiago, Chile
Tel.: (56) 2 680 90 00
Web Site: http://www.abertislogistica.cl
Sales Range: $25-49.9 Million
Emp.: 3
Logistics Consulting Servies
N.A.I.C.S.: 541614

Subsidiary (Domestic):

Autopistas de Leon, S.A.C.E. (3)
Carretera Leon Astorga Area De Mantenimiento S/N, Villadangos Del Paramo, Leon, 24392, Spain
Tel.: (34) 987390919
Highway Construction Services
N.A.I.C.S.: 237310

Subsidiary (Non-US):

Grupo Concesionario del Oeste, S.A. (3)
Avenida Gaona Km 25 920, Ituzaingo, Buenos Aires, 1714, Argentina
Tel.: (54) 1144898200
Highway Construction Services
N.A.I.C.S.: 237310

Holding d'Infrastructures de Transport SAS (3)
Le Crossing 30 boulevard Gallieni, F-92130, Issy-les-Moulineaux, France (72.63%)
Tel.: (33) 1 4190 5900

Web Site: http://www.sanefgroupe.com
Holding Company; Roadway Infrastructure Development & Toll Collection Services
N.A.I.C.S.: 551112

Subsidiary (Domestic):

Sanef (4)
30 Boulevard Gallieni, 92130, Issy-les-Moulineaux, France
Tel.: (33) 970808709
Web Site: http://www.sanef.com
Roadway Infrastructure Development & Toll Collection Services
N.A.I.C.S.: 488490

Subsidiary (Non-US):

Emovis Operations Ireland Limited (5)
Cape House, Westend Office Park, Dublin, 15, Ireland
Tel.: (353) 1 4610 122
Web Site: http://www.eflow.ie
Tolling Systems Operator
N.A.I.C.S.: 541512

Subsidiary (Domestic):

Eurotoll SAS (5)
35 rue Camille Desmoulins, 40199-92442, Issy les Moulineaux, France
Tel.: (33) 180879243
Web Site: http://www.eurotoll.fr
Emp.: 200
Electronic Toll Collection Services
N.A.I.C.S.: 561990

Subsidiary (Domestic):

Infrastructures Viaries de Catalunya, S.A. (3)
Avenida Parc Logistic 12-20, Barcelona, 08040, Spain
Tel.: (34) 932305000
Construction Engineering Services
N.A.I.C.S.: 237990

Subsidiary (US):

Orlando Sanford Domestic Inc (3)
3217 Red Cleveland Ave, Sanford, FL 32773
Tel.: (407) 585-4500
Telecommunication Servicesb
N.A.I.C.S.: 517810

Subsidiary (Non-US):

Rutas del Pacifico S.A. (3)
Route 68 km 17 9, Pudahuel, Santiago, Chile
Tel.: (56) 226800001
Web Site: http://www.rutasdelpacifico.cl
Expressway Construction & Management Services
N.A.I.C.S.: 237310

Subsidiary (Domestic):

Serviabertis, S.L. (3)
Av Parc Logistic 12-20, Barcelona, 08040, Spain
Tel.: (34) 932305000
Telecommunication Infrastructure Management Services
N.A.I.C.S.: 517810

Subsidiary (Non-US):

Sociedad Concesionaria Autopista Central S.A. (3)
San Jose N 1145, San Bernardo, Chile (100%)
Tel.: (56) 224707500
Web Site: https://www.autopistacentral.cl
Rev.: $250,948,141
Assets: $1,122,713,395
Liabilities: $901,010,674
Net Worth: $221,702,721
Earnings: $63,166,682
Fiscal Year-end: 12/31/2016
Motorway Operator
N.A.I.C.S.: 488490
Christian Barrientos (Gen Mgr)

Holding (Non-US):

CIMIC Group Limited (2)
Level 25 177 Pacific Highway, North Sydney, 2060, NSW, Australia (76.68%)

Tel.: (61) 29 925 6666
Web Site: http://www.cimic.com.au
Rev.: $7,421,776,054
Assets: $6,748,907,996
Liabilities: $5,922,035,748
Net Worth: $826,872,248
Earnings: $308,084,999
Emp.: 28,717
Fiscal Year-end: 12/31/2021
Holding Company
N.A.I.C.S.: 551112
Marcelino Fernandez Verdes *(Chm)*

Subsidiary (Domestic):

Devine Limited　　　　**(3)**
Level 2 KSD1 485 Kingsford Smith Drive,
PO Box 780, Hamilton, 4007, QLD,
Australia　　　　**(81.54%)**
Tel.: (61) 736086300
Web Site: http://www.devine.com.au
Rev.: $12,658,260
Assets: $87,349,615
Liabilities: $36,246,586
Net Worth: $51,103,029
Earnings: ($14,319,311)
Emp.: 20
Fiscal Year-end: 12/31/2019
Land Development
N.A.I.C.S.: 236117
David P. Robinson *(Chm)*

Subsidiary (Domestic):

Devine Civil Contracting Pty Ltd.　**(4)**
Level 18 175 Eagle St, Brisbane, 4001,
Queensland, Australia
Tel.: (61) 733802500
Web Site: http://www.divine.com.au
Sales Range: $75-99.9 Million
Emp.: 150
Construction Management Services
N.A.I.C.S.: 423390
Andrew Cooper *(CEO)*

Pioneer Homes Australia Pty Ltd　**(4)**
KSD1 485 Kingsford Smith Drive Hamilton
B, Springwood, Brisbane, 4007, QLD, Aus-
tralia
Tel.: (61) 733802500
Sales Range: $25-49.9 Million
Emp.: 50
Construction Management Services
N.A.I.C.S.: 237990
David Keir *(CEO)*

Joint Venture (Domestic):

Leighton Contractors Pty. Limited　**(3)**
Level 8 Tower 1, 495 Victoria Avenue,
Chatswood, 2067, NSW, Australia　**(50%)**
Tel.: (61) 286686000
Web Site: http://www.broad.com.au
Sales Range: $100-124.9 Million
Emp.: 500
Contractor Services
N.A.I.C.S.: 236220
Roman Garrido *(Acting Mng Dir)*

Subsidiary (Domestic):

Sedgman Pty Limited　　　**(3)**
Level 5 179 Grey St South Bank, Brisbane,
4101, QLD, Australia
Tel.: (61) 735141000
Web Site: http://www.sedgman.com
Sales Range: $250-299.9 Million
Emp.: 1,000
Engineering & Mining Services
N.A.I.C.S.: 541330
Samantha Douglas *(Gen Mgr-People &
Corp Svcs)*

Joint Venture (Domestic):

Thiess Pty. Limited　　　**(3)**
Level 5 179 Grey Street, Southbank, 4101,
QLD, Australia
Tel.: (61) 730029000
Web Site: http://www.thiess.com.au
Emp.: 350
Construction Engineering & Mining
N.A.I.C.S.: 237310
Abdul Jarrah *(Exec Gen Mgr-Strategy, Gov-
ernance & Transformation)*

Subsidiary (Domestic):

PYBAR Holdings Pty. Ltd.　　**(4)**
1668 to 1670 Forest Road, Orange, 2800,
NSW, Australia

Tel.: (61) 263616400
Holding Company; Hard Rock Mining Ser-
vices Contractor
N.A.I.C.S.: 551112

Subsidiary (Domestic):

PYBAR Mining Services Pty. Ltd.　**(5)**
1668-1670 Forest Road, PO Box 2154, Or-
ange, 2800, NSW, Australia
Tel.: (61) 263616400
Hard Rock Mining Services Contractor
N.A.I.C.S.: 213115
Paul Rouse *(Co-Founder & Chm)*

Subsidiary (Domestic):

Quantum Explosives　　　**(4)**
Level 7 371 Queen St, Brisbane, 4001,
QLD, Australia
Tel.: (61) 7 3221 4066
Mining Contractor
N.A.I.C.S.: 213114

Tarong Coal Ltd　　　　**(4)**
280 Nibby Smith Way, PO Box 1165, Kinga-
roy, 4610, QLD, Australia
Tel.: (61) 741607211
Web Site: http://www.thiess.com
Sales Range: $75-99.9 Million
Emp.: 400
Coal Mining
N.A.I.C.S.: 212114
David Waddell *(Project Mgr)*

Subsidiary (Domestic):

UGL Pty Limited　　　　**(3)**
Level 8 40 Miller Street, Locked Bag 903,
North Sydney, 2060, NSW, Australia
Tel.: (61) 2 8925 8925
Web Site: http://www.ugllimited.com
Diversified Services Company; Asset Man-
agement, Engineering, Construction, Fabri-
cation & Manufacturing
N.A.I.C.S.: 541611
Stephen Barrett-White *(Gen Counsel)*

Subsidiary (US):

C&W Secure Services Inc.　　**(4)**
901 N Pitt St Ste 220, Alexandria, VA 22314
Tel.: (703) 631-1090
Construction Engineering Services
N.A.I.C.S.: 541330

Subsidiary (Non-US):

UGL (NZ) Limited　　　　**(4)**
Level 1 7 McColl Street Newmarket, Auck-
land, 1023, New Zealand
Tel.: (64) 95254620
Web Site: http://www.ugllimited.com
Engineeering Services
N.A.I.C.S.: 541330

UGL (Singapore) Pte Ltd　　**(4)**
Block 750 Chai Chee Road 03-01, Viva
Business Park, Singapore, 469000, Singa-
pore
Tel.: (65) 64499225
Web Site: http://www.ugllimited.com
Waste Treatment Services
N.A.I.C.S.: 221310

UGL Canada Inc.　　　　**(4)**
14830 119 Ave Nw, Edmonton, T5L 2P2,
AB, Canada
Tel.: (780) 453-2255
Marine Engineering Services
N.A.I.C.S.: 541330

Subsidiary (Domestic):

UGL Engineering Pty Ltd　　**(4)**
Level 8 40 Miller Street, Locked Bag 903,
North Sydney, 2060, NSW, Australia
Tel.: (61) 2 8925 8925
Web Site: http://www.ugllimited.com
Construction Engineering Services
N.A.I.C.S.: 237990

UGL Operations and Maintenance
Pty Ltd　　　　　　**(4)**
Brookfield Place 125 St Georges Terrace
Level 18 & 19, Perth, 6000, WA, Australia
Tel.: (61) 892195000
Web Site: http://www.ugllimited.com
Mineral Exploration Services
N.A.I.C.S.: 213115

UGL Rail Pty Ltd　　　　**(4)**

Level 8 40 Miller Street, North Sydney,
2060, NSW, Australia
Tel.: (61) 289258925
Web Site: http://www.ugllimited.com
Soil Engineering Services
N.A.I.C.S.: 541330

UGL Rail Services Pty Limited　**(4)**
Level 8 40 Miller Street, North Sydney,
2060, NSW, Australia
Tel.: (61) 289258925
Railway Transportation Services
N.A.I.C.S.: 488210

Subsidiary (Non-US):

DURST-BAU GmbH　　　**(2)**
Montressorigasse 7, 1230, Vienna, Austria
Tel.: (43) 1877944110
Web Site: http://www.durstbau.at
Construction Services
N.A.I.C.S.: 237990
Christian Huber *(Mng Dir)*

Subsidiary (Domestic):

Dieter Hafemeister Erdbau GmbH &
Co.　　　　　　　　**(2)**
Baureutherstrasse 36, 18789, Berlin,
Germany　　　　　**(100%)**
Tel.: (49) 3033206332
Web Site: http://www.hafemeister.de
Civil Works Construction & Engineering
N.A.I.C.S.: 237990

Eurafrica Baugesellschaft mbH　**(2)**
Steinstrasse 1, 45128, Essen, Germany
Tel.: (49) 201 8240
Construction Engineering Services
N.A.I.C.S.: 541330

Subsidiary (Non-US):

HOCHTIEF Aktiengesellschaft Vorm.
Gebr. Helfman Ges. M.b.H.　　**(2)**
Rossaugasse 3, 6020, Innsbruck,
Austria　　　　　　**(100%)**
Tel.: (43) 5123342310
Web Site: http://www.hochtief.de
Heavy Construction
N.A.I.C.S.: 237990

Group (Domestic):

HOCHTIEF Americas GmbH　　**(2)**
Opernplatz 2, Essen, 45128, Germany
Tel.: (49) 2018240
Web Site: http://www.hochtief.com
Holding Company
N.A.I.C.S.: 551112

Subsidiary (US):

EE Cruz & Company Inc.　　**(3)**
The Cruz Building 165 Ryan St, South
Plainfield, NJ 07080　　**(100%)**
Tel.: (908) 462-9600
Web Site: http://www.eecruz.com
Heavy Civil Construction Services
N.A.I.C.S.: 237310

Flatiron Construction Corp.　　**(3)**
385 Interlocken Crescent Ste 900, Broom-
field, CO 80021　　　**(100%)**
Tel.: (303) 485-4050
Web Site: http://www.flatironcorp.com
Heavy Civil Construction Services
N.A.I.C.S.: 237990
John A. DiCiurcio *(CEO)*

Division (Domestic):

Ellsworth Paulsen Construction
Co.　　　　　　　　**(4)**
195 E 600 S, American Fork, UT 84003
Tel.: (801) 756-0404
Sales Range: $25-49.9 Million
Emp.: 17
Industrial Building Construction
N.A.I.C.S.: 236210

Flatiron Construction Corp. - Heavy
Civil Division　　　　**(4)**
385 Interlocken Cres Ste 900, Broomfield,
CO 80021
Tel.: (303) 485-4050
Web Site: http://www.flatironcorp.com
Heavy Civil Engineering & Construction
N.A.I.C.S.: 237310

Subsidiary (Non-US):

HOCHTIEF Construcciones S.A.　**(3)**
Av Corrientes 222 Piso 11, C 1043 AAP,
Buenos Aires, Argentina
Tel.: (54) 11 4510 0410
Construction of Buildings & Civil Engineer-
ing Projects
N.A.I.C.S.: 237310

Subsidiary (US):

Turner Construction Company　**(3)**
375 Hudson St, New York, NY
10014-3658　　　　**(100%)**
Tel.: (212) 229-6000
Web Site: http://www.turnerconstruction.com
Non-Residential & Industrial Construction
N.A.I.C.S.: 236220
Donald G. Sleeman *(Sr VP)*

Subsidiary (Non-US):

Clark Builders Limited　　　**(4)**
800-5555 Calgary Trail NW, Edmonton,
T6H 5P9, AB, Canada
Tel.: (780) 395-3300
Web Site: https://www.clarkbuilders.com
Sales Range: $450-499.9 Million
Construction Services
N.A.I.C.S.: 236220
Paul Verhesen *(Co-Pres & CEO)*

Subsidiary (Domestic):

The Lathrop Company, Inc.　　**(4)**
28 N St Clair St Ste 200, Toledo, OH
43604　　　　　　**(100%)**
Tel.: (419) 893-7000
Web Site: http://www.turnerconstruction.com
Sales Range: $50-74.9 Million
Emp.: 150
Contracting & Construction Services
N.A.I.C.S.: 236220
Thomas J. Manahan *(Chm & CEO)*

Tomkins Builders, Inc.　　　**(4)**
2220 25th Pl NE, Washington, DC 20018-
3563
Tel.: (202) 635-0255
Web Site: http://www.tompkinsbuilders.com
Sales Range: $50-74.9 Million
Emp.: 200
Construction Services
N.A.I.C.S.: 236220
Jim Lears *(Pres)*

Turner Construction International
LLC　　　　　　　　**(4)**
375 Hudson St 6th Fl, New York, NY
10014-3658　　　　**(100%)**
Tel.: (212) 229-6000
Web Site: http://www.turnerconstruction.com
Sales Range: $125-149.9 Million
Emp.: 1,000
Provider of Program & Project Management
Services; Construction Consulting
N.A.I.C.S.: 236220
Abrar Sheriff *(Exec VP)*

Group (Domestic):

HOCHTIEF Asia Pacific GmbH　**(2)**
Opernplatz 2, 45128, Essen, Germany
Tel.: (49) 2018240
Web Site: http://www.hochtief.com
Sales Range: $1-4.9 Billion
Emp.: 5,000
Holding Company
N.A.I.C.S.: 551112

Subsidiary (Non-US):

HOCHTIEF CZ a.s.　　　**(2)**
Plzenska 16/3217, 150 00, Prague, Czech
Republic
Tel.: (420) 257406000
Web Site: https://www.hochtief.cz
Sales Range: $350-399.9 Million
Emp.: 1,100
Construction Engineering Services
N.A.I.C.S.: 541330
Tomas Koranda *(Chm)*

Group (Domestic):

HOCHTIEF Concessions AG　　**(2)**
Opernplatz 2, 45128, Essen, Germany
Tel.: (49) 2018240
Web Site: http://www.hochtief

ACS, Actividades de Construccion y Servicios,
S.A.—(Continued)

Industrial Infrastructure Service, Including
Airports, Roads & Social Infrastructure Segments
N.A.I.C.S.: 541330

Subsidiary (Domestic):

HOCHTIEF Insurance Broking & Risk
Management Solutions GmbH **(2)**
Opernplatz 2, 45128, Essen, Germany
Tel.: (49) 2018242271
Web Site: http://www.hochtief.com
Sales Range: $50-74.9 Million
Emp.: 12
Insurance & Risk Management Services
N.A.I.C.S.: 524298
Lutz Kalkofen (Mng Dir)

Subsidiary (Non-US):

HOCHTIEF Polska Sp. z.o.o. **(2)**
ul Zwirki i Wigury 14, 02-092, Warsaw,
Poland **(100%)**
Tel.: (48) 223645100
Web Site: https://www.hochtief.pl
Sales Range: $50-74.9 Million
Emp.: 240
Construction of Building & Civil Engineering
Work
N.A.I.C.S.: 237310
Klaus Boede (CFO, Member-Mgmt Bd &
VP)

Group (Domestic):

HOCHTIEF Solutions AG **(2)**
Alfredstrasse 236, 45133, Essen,
Germany **(100%)**
Tel.: (49) 2018244261
Web Site: http://www.hochtief-solutions.com
Sales Range: $1-4.9 Billion
Emp.: 8,500
Building Construction & Civil & Structural
Engineering
N.A.I.C.S.: 541330

Subsidiary (Non-US):

HOCHTIEF (UK) Construction
Ltd. **(3)**
Whitehill House Windmill Hill Business
Park, Whitehill Way, Swindon, SN5 6PE,
Wilts, United Kingdom **(100%)**
Tel.: (44) 1793755555
Web Site: http://hochtief.co.uk
Sales Range: $50-74.9 Million
Emp.: 150
Construction of Building & Civil Engineering
Work
N.A.I.C.S.: 237310

HOCHTIEF Construction Austria
GmbH & Co KG **(3)**
Amalienstrasse 65, 1130, Vienna,
Austria **(100%)**
Tel.: (43) 190769070
Web Site: http://www.hochtief-construction.at
Civil Engineering & Construction Services
N.A.I.C.S.: 237990
Marcus Hermes (Mgr-Comml)

Subsidiary (Domestic):

HOCHTIEF PPP Solutions
GmbH **(3)**
Alfredstrasse 236, 45133, Essen, Germany
Tel.: (49) 2018241273
Web Site: http://www.hochtief-pppsolutions.de
Sales Range: $50-74.9 Million
Emp.: 150
Infrastructure Construction Services
N.A.I.C.S.: 237990

Subsidiary (Non-US):

HOCHTIEF PPP Solutions (UK)
Ltd. **(4)**
Kingsley Hall 20 Bailey Lane, Great Britain,
Manchester, M90 4AN, Wilts, United Kingdom
Tel.: (44) 1614981210
Web Site: http://www.ppp.hochtief.com
Infrastructure Construction Services
N.A.I.C.S.: 237990

Subsidiary (Domestic):

HOCHTIEF Projektentwicklung
GmbH **(3)**
Alfredstrasse 236, 45133, Essen, Germany
Tel.: (49) 2018240
Web Site: http://www.hochtief-solutions.com
Sales Range: $150-199.9 Million
Emp.: 260
Project Development of Office, Hotel,
Mixed-Use & Special-Purpose Properties
N.A.I.C.S.: 531390

Subsidiary (Domestic):

HOCHTIEF Projektentwicklung Helfmann Park GmbH & Co. KG **(4)**
Opernplatz 2, Essen, 45128, North Rhine,
Germany
Tel.: (49) 201824
Real Estate Manangement Services
N.A.I.C.S.: 531390

Subsidiary (Domestic):

Streif Baulogistik GmbH **(3)**
Alfredstrasse 236, 45133, Essen,
Germany **(100%)**
Tel.: (49) 2011064700
Web Site: http://www.streif-baulogistik.de
Sales Range: $1-4.9 Billion
Emp.: 3,000
Construction, Mining & Forestry Equipment
Rental & Leasing Services
N.A.I.C.S.: 532412
Thorsten Wiesendorfer (Mng Dir)

Subsidiary (Domestic):

Prum-Turenwerk GmbH **(4)**
Andreas Stihl Strasse 1 Eifel, 54595, Weinheim, Germany **(100%)**
Tel.: (49) 6551147001
Web Site: https://www.tuer.de
Sales Range: $50-74.9 Million
Emp.: 450
Production & Marketing of Prefabricated
Homes
N.A.I.C.S.: 321992

Subsidiary (Domestic):

Turner HOCHTIEF Construction Management GmbH **(3)**
Opernplatz 2, Essen, 45128, Germany
Tel.: (49) 2018244261
Construction Engineering Services
N.A.I.C.S.: 541330

Subsidiary (Non-US):

HOCHTIEF VSB A/S **(2)**
Primatorska 361323, 18000, Prague, 8,
Czech Republic **(100%)**
Tel.: (420) 283843272
Web Site: http://www.hochtief-vsb.cz
Sales Range: $125-149.9 Million
Emp.: 1,800
Construction of Building & Civil Engineering
Work
N.A.I.C.S.: 541310

Subsidiary (Domestic):

HOCHTIEF Verkehrswegebau
GmbH **(2)**
Opernplatz 2, D-45128, Essen,
Germany **(100%)**
Tel.: (49) 2018240
Web Site: http://www.hochtief.com
Sales Range: $25-49.9 Million
Emp.: 50
Road Construction
N.A.I.C.S.: 237310

Subsidiary (Non-US):

HOCHTIEF-Luxembourg S.A. **(2)**
249 Rue de Beggen, 1221, Luxembourg,
Luxembourg **(100%)**
Tel.: (352) 426630212
Web Site: http://www.hochtief.lu
Sales Range: $50-74.9 Million
Emp.: 130
Construction of Building & Civil Engineering
Work
N.A.I.C.S.: 237310

Affiliate (Domestic):

Rheinische Baustoffwerke GmbH &
Co. KG **(2)**
Auenheimer Strasse 25, Niederassem,
50129, Bergheim, Germany **(33%)**
Tel.: (49) 227175125468
Web Site:
https://www.rheinischebaustoffwerke.de
Sales Range: $100-124.9 Million
Emp.: 200
Sale of Sand & Gravel
N.A.I.C.S.: 212321
Wolfgang Miller (Pres)

Subsidiary (Domestic):

Suddeutsche Wohnungsbau
GmbH **(2)**
Klosestrasse 42, 76137, Karlsruhe,
Germany **(100%)**
Tel.: (49) 721 31140
Manages Flats & Industrial Units
N.A.I.C.S.: 333413

Affiliate (Domestic):

Sudwestdeutsche Rohrleitungsbau
GmbH **(2)**
Intzestrasse 14-16, 60314, Frankfurt am
Main, Germany **(45%)**
Tel.: (49) 699443250
Web Site: http://www.swr-gmbh.de
Sales Range: $50-74.9 Million
Emp.: 150
Construction & Operation of Pipe Networks
N.A.I.C.S.: 237120

Subsidiary (Domestic):

ZOB an der Hackerbrucke GmbH &
Co. KG **(2)**
Alfredstr 236, 45133, Essen, Germany
Tel.: (49) 201 8241223
Real Estate Management Services
N.A.I.C.S.: 531390

Hidraulica del Chiriqui, S.A. **(1)**
Dr Ernesto Perez Balladares, Panama,
Panama
Tel.: (507) 7759944
Construction Engineering Services
N.A.I.C.S.: 541330

Hidrogestion, S.A. **(1)**
Calle Luxemburg 2 Fl 1, Madrid, 28232, Las
Rozas, Spain **(100%)**
Tel.: (34) 91 633 24 54
Web Site: http://www.hidrogestion.es
Water Treatment Facilities & Maintenance
Services
N.A.I.C.S.: 221320

Hochtief Engineering GmbH **(1)**
Alfredstrasse 236, 45133, Essen, Germany
Tel.: (49) 201 8240
Web Site: https://www.hochtief-engineering.com
Engineering Services
N.A.I.C.S.: 541330
Hansgeorg Balthaus (Gen Mgr)

Hochtief Infrastructure GmbH **(1)**
Alfredstrasse 236, 45133, Essen, Germany
Tel.: (49) 201 8240
Web Site: https://www.hochtief-infrastructure.com
Construction Services
N.A.I.C.S.: 236220
Jose Ignacio Legorburo (Gen Mgr)

Humiclima Centro, S.A. **(1)**
Calle Orense 4-Primero, Madrid, 28020,
Spain
Tel.: (34) 915551315
Air Conditioning System Installation Services
N.A.I.C.S.: 238220
Felix Pereira (Gen Mgr)

Humiclima Est Catalunya, S.L. **(1)**
Carretera Mig 37, 08041, Cornella de Llobregat, Barcelona, Spain
Tel.: (34) 934464200
Climate Control System Installation Services
N.A.I.C.S.: 238220

Humiclima Est, S.A. **(1)**
Gran Via Asima 29 bajoPol Ind Son Castello, 07009, Palma de Mallorca, Spain
Tel.: (34) 971431216
Web Site: https://www.humiclima.com
Air Conditioning System Installation Services & Mfr

N.A.I.C.S.: 333415
Antonio Bonet Gambins (Mng Dir)

Humiclima Sac, S.A. **(1)**
Camino Vell De Bunyola 37, Pol Son Castello, 07009, Palma de Mallorca, Baleares,
Spain
Tel.: (34) 971431216
Web Site: http://www.humiclima.com
Air Conditioning System Installation Services
N.A.I.C.S.: 238220
Antonio Bonet Gambins (Mng Dir)

Humiclima Sur, S.L. **(1)**
Calle Marruecos Pol Ind El Portal 12, Jerez
de la Frontera, 11408, Cadiz, Spain
Tel.: (34) 952105401
Oil & Gas Exploration Services
N.A.I.C.S.: 213112

Humiclima Valladolid, S.L. **(1)**
Calle Puente Colgante 46, Valladolid,
47006, Spain
Tel.: (34) 915551315
Construction Engineering Services
N.A.I.C.S.: 541330

I 595 Express, LLC **(1)**
10368 State Rd 84 Ste 202, Davie, FL
33324
Tel.: (954) 671-5500
Web Site: http://www.i595express.com
Highway Road Construction Services
N.A.I.C.S.: 237310

Iberoamericana de Hidrocarburos,
S.A. de C.V. **(1)**
Batallon De San Patricio No 111 Int 109
Valle Oriente, Garza Garcia, 66260, Nuevo
Leon, Mexico
Tel.: (52) 8183638290
Industrial Plant Construction Services
N.A.I.C.S.: 236210

ImesAPI, S.A. **(1)**
C/ Via De Los Poblados 9-11 Parque Empresarial Trianon - Edificio C, 28033, Madrid, Spain
Tel.: (34) 91 744 39 00
Web Site: http://imesapi.es
Electrical System Installation Services
N.A.I.C.S.: 238210

Subsidiary (Domestic):

Viabal Mateniment i Conservacio,
S.A. **(2)**
C/ Gerrers nave 26, 07141, Marratxi,
Baleares, Spain
Tel.: (34) 971431163
Web Site: http://www.imesapi.es
Painting & Signalling Equipment Installation
Services
N.A.I.C.S.: 238320

Infraestructuras Energeticas Castellanas, S.L **(1)**
Calle Aluminio 17, Valladolid, 47012, Spain
Tel.: (34) 983390443
Eletric Power Generation Services
N.A.I.C.S.: 221118

Initec Energia, S.A. **(1)**
C/ Via De Los Poblados 11 Edificio Trianon
C, 28033, Madrid, Spain
Tel.: (34) 911 330 100
Web Site: http://www.initec-energia.es
Sales Range: $250-299.9 Million
Electric Power Plant Construction Services
N.A.I.C.S.: 237130

Injar, S.A. **(1)**
Cl Leon y Castillo N 421 Pi 4 Pta A, Las
Palmas, 35007, Spain
Tel.: (34) 928 268 650
Air Conditioning Sales & Installation Services
N.A.I.C.S.: 423730

Instalaciones y Montajes de Aire Climatizado, S.L. **(1)**
Camino Bunyola 37, Palma de Mallorca,
07009, Baleares, Spain
Tel.: (34) 971431216
Web Site: http://www.humiclima.com
Emp.: 70
Climate Control System Installation Services
N.A.I.C.S.: 238210

Instalaciones y Servicios Codeven, C.A. **(1)**
Avda Sfco Miranda Torre Parque Cristal Torre Este Planta 8 Oficiana, Chacao, Caracas, Venezuela
Tel.: (58) 212 793 1415
Construction Engineering Services
N.A.I.C.S.: 237990

Intecsa Ingenieria Industrial, S.A. **(1)**
Via de los Poblados 11, 28033, Madrid, Spain
Tel.: (34) 91 749 7000
Web Site: http://www.intecsaindustrial.com
Construction Engineering Services
N.A.I.C.S.: 541330

Integra Mantenimiento, Gestion y Servicios Integrados Centro Especial de Empleo, S.L. **(1)**
Avenida Manoteras 46-Bj Modulo C, Madrid, 28050, Spain
Tel.: (34) 913588033
Interior Cleaning Services
N.A.I.C.S.: 238990

Subsidiary (Domestic):

Integra Manteniment, Gestio i Serveis Integrats, Centre Especial de Treball, Catalunya, S.L **(2)**
Calle Pamplona 54, Barcelona, 08005, Spain
Tel.: (34) 933568578
Interior Cleaning Services
N.A.I.C.S.: 238990

Integra Mantenimiento, Gestion y Servicios Integrados Centro Especial de Empleo Galicia S.L. **(2)**
Avda Hispanidad 75, 36203, Vigo, Pontevedra, Spain
Tel.: (34) 913588033
Interior Cleaning Services
N.A.I.C.S.: 238990

Intercambiador de Transportes de Principe Pio, S.A. **(1)**
Avenida America 2-Plt 17 B, 28028, Madrid, Spain
Tel.: (34) 917130626
Ground Passenger Transportation Services
N.A.I.C.S.: 485999

Interenvases, S.A. **(1)**
Calle Bariceta Pg Industrial Asparrena-San Millan 8, Araya, 01250, Alava, Spain
Tel.: (34) 945314760
Container Storage Services
N.A.I.C.S.: 493190

Iridium Aparcamientos, S.L. **(1)**
Avenida Camino De Santiago 50, Madrid, 28050, Spain
Tel.: (34) 917038768
Web Site: http://www.iridiumconcesiones.com
Sales Range: $25-49.9 Million
Emp.: 3
Parking Management Consulting Services
N.A.I.C.S.: 812930

Iridium Concesiones de Infraestructuras, S.A. **(1)**
Avenida del Camino de Santiago 50 Edificio I P1, 28050, Madrid, Spain **(100%)**
Tel.: (34) 913439300
Web Site: https://www.iridiumconcesiones.com
Infrastructure Engineering & Construction Services
N.A.I.C.S.: 237990
Salvador Myro Cuenco *(Exec VP-Bus Dev)*

Jingtang International Container Terminal Co. Ltd. **(1)**
Jingtang Port, Tangshan, Hebei, China
Tel.: (86) 315 2915963
Commercial Storage Services
N.A.I.C.S.: 493190

Leighton Properties Pty Limited **(1)**
Level 18 100 Pacific Highway, North Sydney, 2060, NSW, Australia
Tel.: (61) 29 925 6111
Construction Services
N.A.I.C.S.: 236220

Limpiezas Deyse, S.L. **(1)**

Calle Lleida 1, Manresa, 8242, Barcelona, Spain
Tel.: (34) 938722777
Interior Cleaning Services
N.A.I.C.S.: 238990

Limpiezas Lafuente, S.L. **(1)**
Calle Puerto de Santa Maria 8, 46026, Valencia, Spain
Tel.: (34) 96 334 08 05
Web Site: http://www.limpiezaslafuente.es
Sales Range: $300-349.9 Million
Emp.: 1,500
Industrial Cleaning Services
N.A.I.C.S.: 562998

Lireba Serveis Integrats, S.L. **(1)**
Camino De Jesus S/N-Edf Son Valenti 8 Plt 1, Palma de Mallorca, 7011, Baleares, Spain
Tel.: (34) 971758410
Interior Cleaning Services
N.A.I.C.S.: 238990

Lumican, S.A. **(1)**
Agaete st, Las Palmas, 35010, Spain
Tel.: (34) 928482120
Web Site: http://www.groupoetra.com
Emp.: 40
Electrical Installation Services
N.A.I.C.S.: 238210

Maessa Telecomunicaciones, Ingenieria, Instalaciones Y Servicios, S.A. **(1)**
Parque Empresarial Plaza C Bari 33 Edificio 3, 50197, Zaragoza, Spain
Tel.: (34) 97 606 6666
Web Site: https://www.maetel.com
Eletric Power Generation Services
N.A.I.C.S.: 221118

Maessa Telecomunicaciones, S.A. **(1)**
Plaza Business Park C/ Bari 33 Building 3, 50197, Zaragoza, Spain
Tel.: (34) 976066666
Web Site: https://www.maetel.com
Sales Range: $300-349.9 Million
Emp.: 300
Electric Power Generation & Distribution Services
N.A.I.C.S.: 221118
Jose Luis Celorrio Garcia *(Gen Mgr)*

Makiber, S.A. **(1)**
Paseo de la Castellana 182, 28046, Madrid, Spain
Tel.: (34) 91 4843000
Web Site: http://www.makiber.com
Logistics Consulting Servies
N.A.I.C.S.: 541614

Manchasol 1 Central Termosolar Uno, S.L. **(1)**
Calle Cardenal Marcelo Spinola 10, Madrid, 28016, Spain
Tel.: (34) 914569500
Web Site: http://www.gruppocobra.com
Emp.: 2,000
Eletric Power Generation Services
N.A.I.C.S.: 221118

Manchasol 2 Central Termosolar Dos, S.L. **(1)**
Calle Cardenal Marcelo Spinola 10, Madrid, 28016, Spain
Tel.: (34) 914569486
Renewable Energy Generation Services
N.A.I.C.S.: 926130

Mant. Ayuda a la Explot. y Servicios, S.A **(1)**
Mendez Alvaro S 9 Fl 2 Right Edificio Atocha Centro, 28045, Madrid, Spain
Tel.: (34) 914 360 480
Web Site: http://www.maessa.com
Industrial Assembly & Maintenance Services
N.A.I.C.S.: 811310

Manteniment i Conservacio del Valles, S.A. **(1)**
Avenida Josep Tarradellas 8 10 D, Barcelona, 8029, Spain
Tel.: (34) 934443236
Real Estate Development Services
N.A.I.C.S.: 531390

Mantenimiento y Montajes Industriales, S.A **(1)**

Calle Teide 5-Plt 1 Ed Milenium, San Sebastian de los Reyes, 28703, Madrid, Spain
Tel.: (34) 914843030
Industrial Machinery Maintenance Services
N.A.I.C.S.: 811310

Mantenimientos, Ayuda a la Explotacion y Servicios, S.A. **(1)**
Cardenal Marcelo Spinola 10, 28016, Madrid, Spain
Tel.: (34) 91 456 9500
Construction Services
N.A.I.C.S.: 236220

Mapide, S.A. **(1)**
C/ Sta Juliana 16, 28039, Madrid, Spain
Tel.: (34) 91 311 60 02
Web Site: http://www.mapide.es
Interior Cleaning Services
N.A.I.C.S.: 238990

Masa Algeciras, S.A. **(1)**
Avenida Blas Infante Ed Centro Blas Infante Loc 8, Algeciras, 11201, Cadiz, Spain
Tel.: (34) 956635636
Industrial Machinery Maintenance Services
N.A.I.C.S.: 811310

Masa Galicia, S.A. **(1)**
Poligono Industrial De La Grela Bens Cl Guttenberg 2, La Coruna, 15008, Galicia, Spain
Tel.: (34) 981262011
Industrial Machinery Maintenance Services
N.A.I.C.S.: 811310

Masa Huelva, S.A. **(1)**
Calle Alonso De Ojeda 1, Huelva, 21002, Spain
Tel.: (34) 959253308
Industrial Machinery Maintenance Services
N.A.I.C.S.: 811310

Masa Norte, S.A. **(1)**
Calle Ribera De Axpe Etorbidea 50-30 Plt, Erandio, 48950, Vizcaya, Spain
Tel.: (34) 944316277
Industrial Machinery Maintenance Services
N.A.I.C.S.: 811310

Masa Puertollano, S.A. **(1)**
Carretera Cr-503 Calzada De Calatrava Km 3 400, Puertollano, 13500, Ciudad Real, Spain
Tel.: (34) 926425654
Industrial Equipment Maintenance Services
N.A.I.C.S.: 811310

Masa Servicios, S.A. **(1)**
Calle Lletra B De La Zona Franca Sector B 4 Numero, Barcelona, 08040, Spain
Tel.: (34) 932630120
Web Site: http://www.masagroup.com
Emp.: 420
Industrial Machinery Maintenance Services
N.A.I.C.S.: 811310
Jose Maria Bello *(Mng Dir)*

Masa Tenerife, S.A. **(1)**
Calle La Marina 7-50 Oficina 66, Santa Cruz de Tenerife, 38002, Tenerife, Spain
Tel.: (34) 922278593
Industrial Machinery Maintenance Services
N.A.I.C.S.: 811310

Moncobra, S.A. **(1)**
Calle Cardenal Marcelo Spinola 10 and 6, 28016, Madrid, Spain
Tel.: (34) 914569500
Web Site: http://www.grupocobra.com
Emp.: 3,500
Industrial Machinery Maintenance Services
N.A.I.C.S.: 811310
Manuel Manresa *(Gen Mgr)*

Monegros Depura, S.A. **(1)**
Cm De Albalatillo-Estacion Depuradora S/N, Sarinena, 22200, Huesca, Spain
Tel.: (34) 876242600
Waste Treatment Services
N.A.I.C.S.: 221310

Monelec, S.L. **(1)**
Ceramista 14, Malaga, 29006, Spain
Tel.: (34) 952311649
Web Site: http://www.monelec.com
Electrical Installation Services
N.A.I.C.S.: 238210

Murciana de Trafico, S.A. **(1)**

Carril Molino Nerva 21, 30007, Murcia, Spain
Tel.: (34) 968 242 347
Electrical Installation Services
N.A.I.C.S.: 238210

Net Brill, S.L. **(1)**
Lugar Caminet De Les Vinyes 15, Mataro, 8302, Barcelona, Spain
Tel.: (34) 937 996 514
Web Site: http://www.netbrill.cat
Interior Cleaning Services
N.A.I.C.S.: 238990

Octeva, S.A.S. **(1)**
Za Marcel Doret 293 Rue Jacques Monod, BP 100, 62100, Calais, Pas De Calais, France
Tel.: (33) 321977420
Waste Treatment Services
N.A.I.C.S.: 562998

Oficina Tecnica de Estudios y Control de Obras, S.A **(1)**
C/ La Granja 29, 28108, Alcobendas, Spain
Tel.: (34) 91 535 22 10
Web Site: http://www.ofiteco.com
Sales Range: $25-49.9 Million
Engineering Consulting Services
N.A.I.C.S.: 541330

Opade Organizac. y Promoc de Actividades Deportivas, S.A. **(1)**
C/ Arte 21 3 A, 28033, Madrid, Spain
Tel.: (34) 917251020
Web Site: http://www.opade.net
Emp.: 100
Sports Activities Promoting Services
N.A.I.C.S.: 711310

Orto Parques y Jardines, S.L. **(1)**
San Roman No 18-Orto, 15318, Abegondo, A Coruna, Spain
Tel.: (34) 981 676 812
Web Site: http://www.orto.es
Sales Range: $25-49.9 Million
Emp.: 75
Garden Maintenance Services
N.A.I.C.S.: 561730

Pacific Partnerships Pty Ltd **(1)**
Level 19 177 Pacific Hwy, North Sydney, 2060, NSW, Australia
Tel.: (61) 28 668 6444
Web Site: https://www.pacificpartnerships.com.au
Heavy Construction Services
N.A.I.C.S.: 237990
Jeremy Chung *(CFO)*

Puerto Seco Santander-Ebro, S.A. **(1)**
C/ Ramon y Cajal 17, 50640, Luceni, Zaragoza, Spain
Tel.: (34) 976 65 12 20
Web Site: http://www.puertoseco-se.com
Automobile Maintenance Services
N.A.I.C.S.: 811198

Pulice Construction, Inc. **(1)**
8660 E Hartford Dr Ste 305, Scottsdale, AZ 85255
Tel.: (602) 944-2241
Web Site: http://www.pulice.com
Highway Construction Engineering Services
N.A.I.C.S.: 237310
Steven W. Campbell *(Sr VP & Mgr-Arizona Reg)*

Recuperacion de Rodas e Madeira, S.L. **(1)**
Calle F Parc 5 Pol Industrial Lalin 2000, Lalin, 36500, Pontevedra, Spain
Tel.: (34) 986787517
Waste Treatment Services
N.A.I.C.S.: 221310

Red Top Wind Power, LLC. **(1)**
2800 Post Oak Blvd Ste 5858, Houston, TX 77056-5399
Tel.: (713) 599-1188
Eletric Power Generation Services
N.A.I.C.S.: 221118

Residencial Monte Carmelo, S.A **(1)**
c/ Bolonia 4 2 Izquierda, 50008, Zaragoza, Spain
Tel.: (34) 976 237 338
Web Site: http://www.residencialmontecarmelo.com

ACS, Actividades de Construccion y Servicios, S.A.—(Continued)

Residential Property Management Services
N.A.I.C.S.: 531311

Residuos Industriales de Zaragoza, S.A (1)
Carretera Castellon Cartuja Baja Km 8 3, Zaragoza, 50720, Spain
Tel.: (34) 976469725
Industrial Wastes Treatment Services
N.A.I.C.S.: 562211

RetraOil, S.L. (1)
Poligono Industrial Tambarria Par 20, Alfaro, 26540, La Rioja, Spain
Tel.: (34) 941184203
Web Site: http://www.retraoil.es
Sales Range: $10-24.9 Million
Emp.: 30
Oil Waste Treatment & Recycling Services
N.A.I.C.S.: 562219

Ribagrande Energia, S.L. (1)
Calle Cardenal Marcelo Spinola 10, Madrid, 28016, Spain
Tel.: (34) 914569500
Sales Range: $50-74.9 Million
Emp.: 60
Renewable Energy Generation Services
N.A.I.C.S.: 926130

Roura Cevasa, S.A (1)
C/ Caracas 5, 08030, Barcelona, Spain
Tel.: (34) 93 3600080
Web Site: http://www.roura-cevasa.com
Sales Range: $100-124.9 Million
Emp.: 342
Signage Mfr
N.A.I.C.S.: 339950

SICE PTY, Ltd. (1)
200 Carlisle Street, Saint Kilda, 3182, VIC, Australia
Tel.: (61) 382566900
Web Site: http://www.sice.com
Civil Engineering Construction Services
N.A.I.C.S.: 237990

SICE, Inc. (1)
14350 NW 56TH Ct Unit 105, Miami, FL 33054
Tel.: (305) 222-7040
Web Site: http://www.sice.com
Construction Engineering Services
N.A.I.C.S.: 541330

Salins Residuos Automocion, S.L. (1)
Calle Numero 31 Chaflan Cl 27 Pg Ind Catarroja, Catarroja, 46470, Valencia, Spain
Tel.: (34) 961220445
Petroleum Refinery Services
N.A.I.C.S.: 211120

Salmantina de Seguridad Vial, S.A. (1)
Calle Cascajales Pg Ind Los Villares 65-69, Villares de la Reina, 37184, Salamanca, Spain
Tel.: (34) 923220107
Civil Engineering Construction Services
N.A.I.C.S.: 237990

Sanypick Plastic, S.A. (1)
C/ Carlos Jimenez Diaz 23, 28806, Alcala de Henares, Madrid, Spain
Tel.: (34) 91 884 11 86
Web Site: http://sanypick.com
Sales Range: $25-49.9 Million
Hospital Waste Container Mfr
N.A.I.C.S.: 326199

Seguridad Integral Metropolitana, S.A. (1)
Calle De La Granja Pg Ind 29, Alcobendas, 28108, Madrid, Spain
Tel.: (34) 916232200
Security System Maintenance Services
N.A.I.C.S.: 561621

Semi Maroc, S.A. (1)
5 Rue Fakir Mohamed, Casablanca, Morocco
Tel.: (212) 522 47 68 74
Electrical Assembly Services
N.A.I.C.S.: 238210

Sermicro, S.A. (1)
Calle Pradillo 48-50, 28002, Madrid, Spain

Tel.: (34) 91 744 86 00
Web Site: http://www.sermicro.com
Software Consulting Services
N.A.I.C.S.: 541512

Serveis Catalans, Serveica, S.A. (1)
Calle Dels Enamorats 117, Barcelona, 08026, Spain
Tel.: (34) 933070708
Electrical System Installation Services
N.A.I.C.S.: 238210

Servicios Corporativos TWC, S.A. de C.V. (1)
Lazaro Cardenas Km 6 Las Minitas, Hermosillo, 83310, Sonora, Mexico
Tel.: (52) 6622178330
Business Support Services
N.A.I.C.S.: 561499

Sice Energia, S.L. (1)
C/ Sepulveda 6, 28108, Alcobendas, Madrid, Spain
Tel.: (34) 91 623 22 00
Web Site: http://www.sice.es
Photovoltaic Generating System Installation Services
N.A.I.C.S.: 238210

Sice Hellas Sistemas Tecnologicos Sociedad Unipersonal de Responsabilidad Limitada (1)
Omirou 2 2nd Floor, Kifissia, Athens, 14562, Greece
Tel.: (30) 210 62 34 032
Construction Engineering Services
N.A.I.C.S.: 541330
Jose Luis (Mgr-Project)

Sice Tecnologia y Sistemas, S.A. (1)
Calle Sepulveda 6, 28108, Alcobendas, Madrid, Spain
Tel.: (34) 916232200
Web Site: http://www.sice.com
Electrical System Installation Services
N.A.I.C.S.: 238210

Sidetel, S.A (1)
Avenida Manoteras 28, Madrid, 28050, Spain
Tel.: (34) 913834120
Electrical Installation Services
N.A.I.C.S.: 238210

Sintax Logistica Transportes, S.A. (1)
Estrada Algeruz Setubal, Setubal, 2910-279, Portugal
Tel.: (351) 265739600
Web Site: http://www.sintax.com
Emp.: 79
Logistics Consulting Servies
N.A.I.C.S.: 541614
Fernando Velasco (Mng Dir)

Sintax Navigomes, Ltda. (1)
Av Luisa Todi Nr 73, Setubal, 2904-505, Portugal
Tel.: (351) 265546300
Logistic Services
N.A.I.C.S.: 541614

Sistemas Integrales de Mantenimiento, S.A. (1)
C/ Teide 5-1, 28709, San Sebastian de los Reyes, Madrid, Spain
Tel.: (34) 926421658
Industrial System Maintenance Services
N.A.I.C.S.: 811310

Sistemas Radiantes F. Moyano, S.A. (1)
C/ Canada 53Pol Ind La Yegua, 28850, Torrejon de Ardoz, Madrid, Spain
Tel.: (34) 916610750
Web Site: https://www.moyano.com
Sales Range: $25-49.9 Million
Emp.: 37
Radiant System Installation Services & Mfr
N.A.I.C.S.: 335999
Jose Iglesias (Mgr-Antennas)

Sistemas Sec, S.A. (1)
Miraflores 383 Oficina 1004, Santiago, Chile
Tel.: (56) 2 345 46 00
Web Site: http://www.sistemas-sec.cl
Communication Line Construction Services
N.A.I.C.S.: 237130

Soc Iberica de Construcciones Electricas de Seguridad, S.L. (1)

Calle De La Granja P I Alcobendas 29, Alcobendas, 28108, Spain
Tel.: (34) 916616927
Security System Installation Services
N.A.I.C.S.: 238210

Soc. Espanola de Montajes Industriales, S.A. (1)
Avda Manoteras 6 - 2, 28050, Madrid, Spain (00.73%)
Tel.: (34) 91 308 93 35
Web Site: http://www.gruposemi.com
Transmission Line Construction & Installation Services
N.A.I.C.S.: 237130

Socamex, S.A. (1)
Calle Cobalto Pol Ind San Cristobal 12-Parc 213 Nave A, Valladolid, 47012, Spain
Tel.: (34) 983208011
Water Treatment Plant Construction Services
N.A.I.C.S.: 237110

Sociedad Espanola De Montajes Industriales S.A. (1)
Avda Manoteras 6-20, 28050, Madrid, Spain
Tel.: (34) 91 308 9335
Web Site: https://www.gruposemi.com
Electricity Distribution Services
N.A.I.C.S.: 221122

Sociedad de Generacion Eolica Manchega, S.L. (1)
Calle Cardenal Marcelo Spinola 10, Madrid, 28016, Spain
Tel.: (34) 914569500
Sales Range: $125-149.9 Million
Emp.: 200
Eletric Power Generation Services
N.A.I.C.S.: 221118

Suministros, Importaciones Y Mantenimientos Electronicos, S.A. (1)
Calle Pradillo 48-50, 28002, Madrid, Spain
Tel.: (34) 91 744 8600
Web Site: https://www.gruposermico.com
Information Technology Services
N.A.I.C.S.: 541511

Sumipar, S.L. (1)
Ctra De Santa Creu De Calafell 47 B, 08830, Sant Boi de Llobregat, Spain
Tel.: (34) 931983072
Web Site: http://www.sumipar.com
Parking Equipment Installation Services
N.A.I.C.S.: 238990

Synexs Gmbh (1)
Alfredstrasse 236, 45133, Essen, Germany
Tel.: (49) 201 824 7365
Web Site: https://www.synexs.de
Real Estate Services
N.A.I.C.S.: 531390

Talher, S.A. (1)
Avenida Manoteras 46 bis Modulo D planta 1, 28050, Madrid, Spain
Tel.: (34) 917459100
Web Site: http://www.talher.com
Gardening Services
N.A.I.C.S.: 444240

Tecmed Maroc, S.A.R.L. (1)
Quartier Souissi 292 Rue Mohamed Belyazid Cite OLM, Rabat, 10000, Morocco
Tel.: (212) 537650011
Solid Waste Treatment Services
N.A.I.C.S.: 562219

Tecneira, S.A. (1)
Rua Rui Teles Palhinha 4 Leiao, 2740 278, Porto Salvo, Portugal
Tel.: (351) 214233770
Web Site: http://en.tecneira.com
Eletric Power Generation Services
N.A.I.C.S.: 221118

Tecnicas de Desalinizacion de Aguas, S.A. (1)
Cardenal Marcelo Spinola 10, 28016, Madrid, Spain
Tel.: (34) 91 456 95 00
Web Site: http://www.tedagua.com
Water Treatment Plant Construction Services
N.A.I.C.S.: 237110

Tecnicas e Imagen Corporativa, S.L. (1)

Avda Paris N 1 Esq Avd De La Industria, 19200, Azuqueca de Henares, Guadalajara, Spain
Tel.: (34) 949277859
Web Site: http://www.teicorporativa.com
Signage Mfr
N.A.I.C.S.: 339950

Tecnotel Clima, S.L. (1)
Poligono Industrial Vallo Do Guimar Cl Manzana 6 12, Arafo, 38550, Tenerife, Spain
Tel.: (34) 922583166
Climate Control System Installation Services
N.A.I.C.S.: 238220

Tecsa Empresa Constructora, S.A. (1)
Avda Madariaga 1-4a Planta, 48014, Bilbao, Spain
Tel.: (34) 94 448 86 00
Web Site: http://www.tecsa-constructora.com
Railway Construction Engineering Services
N.A.I.C.S.: 237990

Tedagua Internacional, S.L. (1)
Calle Cardenal Marcelo Spinola 10, Madrid, 28016, Spain
Tel.: (34) 914569500
Web Site: http://www.tedagua.com
Sales Range: $25-49.9 Million
Emp.: 30
Civil Engineering Construction Services
N.A.I.C.S.: 237990
Miguel Fernandez (Gen Mgr)

Telsa Instalaciones de Telecomunicaciones y Electricidad, S.A. (1)
C/ La Granja 29 P I Alcobendas, 28108, Alcobendas, Madrid, Spain
Tel.: (34) 91 657 40 04
Web Site: http://www.telsa.es
Telecommunication & Electrical Installation Services
N.A.I.C.S.: 238210

Tesca Ingenieria del Ecuador, S.A. (1)
Av 6 De Diciembre 3445 Y Checoslovaquia, Quito, Pichincha, Ecuador
Tel.: (593) 22454960
Civil Engineering Construction Services
N.A.I.C.S.: 237990

Tirmadrid, S.A. (1)
Calle Canada Real De Merinas-Valdemingomez S/N, Madrid, 28052, Spain
Tel.: (34) 913324131
Web Site: http://www.tirmadrid.es
Emp.: 118
Solid Waste Treatment Services
N.A.I.C.S.: 562211

Trafiurbe, S.A. (1)
Estrada Octavio Pato 177-a, Talalde, 2785-723, Sao Domingos de Rana, Portugal
Tel.: (351) 214 239 410
Web Site: http://trafiurbe.pt
Sales Range: $25-49.9 Million
Construction Engineering Services
N.A.I.C.S.: 541330

Trans Inter Europe, S.A.S (1)
Rue De Phaffans, 90380, Roppe, France
Tel.: (33) 384299125
Logistic Services
N.A.I.C.S.: 541614

Tratamiento Integral de Residuos de Cantabria S.L.U. (1)
Barrio Vierna San Bartolome S/N, San Miguel de Meruelo, 39192, Cantabria, Spain
Tel.: (34) 942674898
Waste Treatment Services
N.A.I.C.S.: 562998

Trenmedia, S.A. (1)
Avenida Manoteras 46-Bis Planta 2, Madrid, 28050, Spain
Tel.: (34) 914842290
Emp.: 8
Advertising Agency Services
N.A.I.C.S.: 541810
Francico Lazaro (Gen Mgr)

Urbacet, S.L. (1)
Calle Fra Juniper Serra 59-75, Barcelona, 08030, Spain

Tel.: (34) 933984646
Garden Maintenance Services
N.A.I.C.S.: 561730

Urbaenergia, S.L. (1)
Calle Cardenal Marcelo Spinola 10, Madrid,
28016, Spain
Tel.: (34) 914569500
Eletric Power Generation Services
N.A.I.C.S.: 221118

**Urbamar Levante Residuos Industri-
ales, S.L.** (1)
Olg Ind Catarroja N 31 Chaflan, Catarroja,
46470, Valencia, Spain
Tel.: (34) 961 220 445
Industrial Wastes Treatment Services
N.A.I.C.S.: 562211

Urbaoil, S.A. (1)
Avenida De Tenerife 4-6, San Sebastian de
los Reyes, 28703, Spain
Tel.: (34) 911218000
Oil Refinery Services
N.A.I.C.S.: 213112

Urbasys, S.A.S. (1)
Route Du Tremblay, 91480, Varennes-
Jarcy, Essonne, France
Tel.: (33) 169005741
Waste Treatment Services
N.A.I.C.S.: 562998
Teixeira Gregory (Mng Dir)

Valorga International, S.A.S. (1)
1140 Avenue Albert Einstein, BP 51, 34935,
Montpellier, Cedex, France
Tel.: (33) 467994100
Web Site: https://www.valorgainternational.fr
Water Treatment Plant Construction Ser-
vices
N.A.I.C.S.: 237110
Jose Daniel Fernandez Moreno (Pres)

**Venezolana de Limpiezas Industri-
ales, C.A.** (1)
Piso 6 Plaza Venezuela, Caracas, 1050,
Venezuela
Tel.: (58) 212 782 9075
Web Site: http://www.venelin.com.ve
Industrial Cleaning & Maintenance Services
N.A.I.C.S.: 562998

Vias Y Construcciones S.A. (1)
Avda del Camino de Santiago 50, 28050,
Madrid, Spain
Tel.: (34) 91 417 9800
Web Site: https://www.vias.es
Construction Services
N.A.I.C.S.: 236220

Viass y Construcciones S.A. (1)
Calle Orense 11, 28020, Madrid, Spain
Tel.: (34) 914 179 800
Web Site: http://www.vias.es
Construction Engineering Services
N.A.I.C.S.: 237990
Gonzalo Gomez (CEO)

Villa Aurea, S.L. (1)
Avenida Pio Xii 102, Madrid, 28036, Spain
Tel.: (34) 913439200
Construction Engineering Services
N.A.I.C.S.: 541330

Villanova, S.A. (1)
Avenida Pio Xii 102, Madrid, 28036, Spain
Tel.: (34) 913439200
Construction Engineering Services
N.A.I.C.S.: 541330

Zenit Servicios Integrales, S.A. (1)
Calle Cardenal Marcelo Spinola 42, Madrid,
28016, Spain
Tel.: (34) 913836800
Airport Integral Services
N.A.I.C.S.: 488119

ACSION LIMITED
Tel.: (27) 126568957　　　　　　　ZA
Web Site: https://www.acsionsa.co.za
Year Founded: 1997
ACS—(JSE)
Rev.: $62,601,210
Assets: $705,918,894
Liabilities: $210,105,250
Net Worth: $495,813,644
Earnings: $47,887,546
Emp.: 412

Fiscal Year-end: 02/28/23
Portfolio Management Services
N.A.I.C.S.: 523940
Kiriakos Anastasiadis (Founder &
CEO)

Subsidiaries:

Omelia Limited (1)
Gladstonos 55 Roussos Center Point Office
3C-3D, 3040, Limassol, Cyprus
Tel.: (357) 25250314
Web Site: http://www.omilia.com
Information Technology Services
N.A.I.C.S.: 541511
Dimitris Vassos (CEO & Partner)

ACSIP TECHNOLOGY CORP.
3F No 246 Boai St, Shulin Dist, New
Taipei City, 23805, Taiwan
Tel.: (886) 286859877
Web Site: https://www.acsip.com.tw
Year Founded: 2009
6403—(TAI)
Telecommunication Servicesb
N.A.I.C.S.: 517112
Chuang Hsing-Yu (Pres & CEO)

ACSL LTD
Hulic Kasai Rinkai Building 2F 3-6-4
Rinkaicho, Edogawa-ku, Tokyo, 134-
0086, Japan
Tel.: (81) 433055871
Web Site: http://www.acsl.co.jp
6232—(TKS)
Rev.: $6,352,640
Assets: $36,116,460
Liabilities: $20,064,700
Net Worth: $16,051,760
Earnings: ($18,029,870)
Emp.: 86
Fiscal Year-end: 12/31/23
Autonomous Control System Mfr
N.A.I.C.S.: 334512
Kensuke Hayakawa (CFO)

ACSM-AGAM S.P.A.
Via Canova 3, Monza, 20900, Italy
Tel.: (39) 03923851
Web Site: http://www.acsm-agam.it
ACS—(ITA)
Sales Range: Less than $1 Million
Gas & Water Distr
N.A.I.C.S.: 221140
Paolo Giuseppe Busnelli (VP)

ACSUD
ZI Courtine Chaternay BP 1016,
84096, Avignon, Vaucluse, France
Tel.: (33) 432743000
Web Site: http://www.acsud.com
Sales Range: $25-49.9 Million
Emp.: 48
Automobile Parts Mfr
N.A.I.C.S.: 336110

ACTA S.P.A.
Via di Lavoria 56/g - Loc Lavoria,
56040, Crespina, Pisa, Italy
Tel.: (39) 050 644281　　　　　　IT
Web Site: http://www.actagroup.it
Year Founded: 2004
Sales Range: $1-9.9 Million
Clean Technology Product Mfr
N.A.I.C.S.: 335999

ACTBLUE CO., LTD.
No 12 Yujing Road, High-tech Indus-
trial Development Zone, Chizhou,
247100, Anhui, China
Tel.: (86) 5665255708
Web Site: https://www.act-blue.com
Year Founded: 2009
300816—(SSE)
Rev.: $114,621,156
Assets: $251,723,160
Liabilities: $139,181,328
Net Worth: $112,541,832

Earnings: ($1,479,816)
Fiscal Year-end: 12/31/22
Natural Gas Extraction Services
N.A.I.C.S.: 211130

ACTCALL INC.
2-12-5 Yotsuya, Shinjuku-ku, Tokyo,
160-0004, Japan
Tel.: (81) 3 5312 2303
Web Site: http://www.actcall.jp
Year Founded: 2005
Rev.: $41,650,140
Assets: $54,213,040
Liabilities: $42,686,350
Net Worth: $11,526,690
Earnings: $4,960,970
Emp.: 393
Fiscal Year-end: 11/30/19
Computer Related Services
N.A.I.C.S.: 541519
Akira Kikui (Sr Mng Dir)

Subsidiaries:

Insite Co., Ltd. (1)
6-8-11 Minami-Nagareyama, Nagareyama,
270-0163, Chiba, Japan
Tel.: (81) 471508880
Web Site: http://www.insite.vc
Rent Settlement Services
N.A.I.C.S.: 541191

**ACTCELERATE INTERNA-
TIONAL GROUP LIMITED**
Level 8 99 St Georges Terrace,
Perth, 6000, WA, Australia
Tel.: (61) 282160842　　　　　　Ky
Web Site:
https://www.actcelerategroup.com
Year Founded: 2015
ACT—(NSXA)
Rev.: $30,312
Assets: $419,871
Liabilities: $236,125
Net Worth: $183,745
Earnings: ($215,571)
Fiscal Year-end: 12/31/20
Diversified Investment Company
N.A.I.C.S.: 523940
Chen Khan Cheong (CEO)

ACTEOS S.A.
2-4 rue Duflot, F-59100, Roubaix,
France
Tel.: (33) 33320114464
Web Site: https://www.acteos.com
Year Founded: 1986
EOS—(EUR)
Sales Range: $10-24.9 Million
Emp.: 120
Supply Chain Management Services
N.A.I.C.S.: 561499
Joseph Felfeli (Chm & CEO)

Subsidiaries:

Acteos GmbH & Co. KG (1)
Talhofstr 30a, 82205, Gilching, Germany
Tel.: (49) 810538510
Computer Software Services
N.A.I.C.S.: 541511

ACTER CO., LTD.
19th Floor No 201 Section 2 Wenxin
Road, Xitun Dist, Taichung, 407, Tai-
wan
Tel.: (886) 422615288
Web Site: https://www.acter.com.tw
Year Founded: 1979
5536—(TPE)
Rev.: $883,668,980
Assets: $847,841,760
Liabilities: $510,203,796
Net Worth: $337,637,964
Earnings: $78,145,765
Emp.: 1,509
Fiscal Year-end: 12/31/22
Civil Engineering Services
N.A.I.C.S.: 541330

Jin-Li Liang (Chm & CEO)

Subsidiaries:

Acter Technology Co., Ltd. (1)
MD Tower 5F Room C 1 soi Bangna-Trad
25, Bangna, Bangkok, 10260, Thailand
Tel.: (66) 20066530
Engineeering Services
N.A.I.C.S.: 541330

Enrich Tech Co., Ltd. (1)
No 109-3 Bo'ai St, Nantun Dist, Taichung,
Taiwan
Tel.: (886) 422546798
Engineeering Services
N.A.I.C.S.: 541330

Nova Technology Corp. (1)
10F No 76 Sec 2 Jiafeng S Rd, Zhubei,
30272, Hsinchu, Taiwan
Tel.: (886) 36676868
Web Site: https://www.novatech.com.tw
Chemical Products Mfr
N.A.I.C.S.: 325998
Liang Chin Li (Chm)

Subsidiary (Non-US):

Novatech Engineering & Construction
Pte., Ltd. (2)
1 Pemimpin Drive 08-09 One Pemimpin,
Singapore, 576151, Singapore
Tel.: (65) 65474183
Engineeering Services
N.A.I.C.S.: 541330

Suzhou Winmax Technology
Corp. (2)
1F 189 Shilin Rd, Gaoxin, Suzhou, 215151,
Jiangsu, China
Tel.: (86) 51285186368
Engineeering Services
N.A.I.C.S.: 541330

Winmax Technology Corp. (2)
10F No 34 Lane 2777 Jinxiu Rd E, Shang-
hai, China
Tel.: (86) 2150320886
Engineeering Services
N.A.I.C.S.: 541330

Subsidiary (Domestic):

Winmega Technology Corp. (2)
10F No 257 Wenxing Rd, Zhubei, 30264,
Hsinchu, Taiwan
Tel.: (886) 36582727
Web Site: https://www.winmega.com.tw
Industrial Equipment & Material Distr
N.A.I.C.S.: 423840

PT. Novamex Indonesia (1)
Ruko Galeri Niaga Mediterania Blok C8-I J1
Pantai Indah Utara 2, Kapuk Muara, Ja-
karta Utara, 14460, Indonesia
Tel.: (62) 3199031159
Engineeering Services
N.A.I.C.S.: 541330

Sheng Huei (Shenzhen) Engineering
Co., Ltd. (1)
602RM Building A Nanxian Commercial
Plaza Meilong Rd Minzhi St, Longhua,
Shenzhen, China
Tel.: (86) 75529829905
Engineeering Services
N.A.I.C.S.: 541330

**ACTERA GROUP STRATEJIK
YONETIM HIZMETLERI A.S.**
Kuleli Caddesi No 43 A Cengelkoy,
34810 Anadolu Hisari, 34684, Istan-
bul, Turkiye
Tel.: (90) 216 516 0100　　　　　TR
Web Site:
http://www.acteragroup.com
Year Founded: 2006
Privater Equity Firm
N.A.I.C.S.: 523999
Isak Antika (Co-Founder & Mng
Partner)

ACTIA GROUP SA
5 rue Jorge Semprun, 31432, Toulouse, France
Tel.: (33) 561176198

Actia Group Sa—(Continued)

Web Site:
https://www.actiagroup.com
Year Founded: 1986
ALATI—(EUR)
Rev.: $639,498,841
Assets: $678,196,269
Liabilities: $521,645,877
Net Worth: $156,550,392
Earnings: $9,582,735
Emp.: 4,092
Fiscal Year-end: 12/31/23
Electronic & Automotive Equipment
Mfr
N.A.I.C.S.: 334419
Louis Pech *(Chm-Supervisory Bd)*

Subsidiaries:

ACTIA Corporation **(1)**
2809 Bridger Ct, Elkhart, IN 46514
Tel.: (574) 264-2373
Web Site: http://www.actiaus.com
Emp.: 150
Automotive Electrical Component Distr
N.A.I.C.S.: 423120
Adam Ramouni *(Pres)*

ACTIA IME GmbH **(1)**
Dresdenstr 17/18, 38124, Braunschweig,
Germany
Tel.: (49) 531387010
Web Site: https://www.ime-actia.de
Sales Range: $25-49.9 Million
Emp.: 150
Automotive Diagnostic Equipment Mfr
N.A.I.C.S.: 336390
Jens Uphoff *(Mng Dir)*

ACTIA INDIA Pvt Ltd **(1)**
C-15 Sector-58, Noida, 201 301, Uttar
Pradesh, India
Tel.: (91) 1202582290
Web Site: http://www.actia.com
Sales Range: $25-49.9 Million
Emp.: 50
Automotive Diagnostic Equipment Mfr
N.A.I.C.S.: 336390
Pascal Perhirin *(CEO)*

ACTIA Italia Srl **(1)**
Corso Unione Sovietica 612 / 15 B, 10135,
Turin, Italy
Tel.: (39) 0113402711
Web Site: http://www.actiaitalia.com
Sales Range: $25-49.9 Million
Emp.: 50
Automotive Diagnostic Equipment Mfr
N.A.I.C.S.: 336390
Pierre Calmels *(Co-Pres)*

ACTIA Nederland BV **(1)**
Automotive Campus 30, 5708 HN, Hel-
mond, Netherlands
Tel.: (31) 492562111
Web Site: http://www.actia.nl
Automotive Diagnostic Equipment Whslr
N.A.I.C.S.: 423120
P. F. Calmels *(Principal)*

ACTIA Nordic AB **(1)**
Science Park Mjardevi Datalinjen 3b, 583
30, Linkoping, Sweden
Tel.: (46) 13121800
Web Site: https://www.actia.se
Sales Range: $25-49.9 Million
Emp.: 75
Automotive Electronic Equipment Mfr
N.A.I.C.S.: 336390
Hilding Keussen *(CEO)*

ACTIA VIDEO BUS, S.A. **(1)**
Pol Ind Los Olivos C Calidad 66, 28906,
Getafe, Madrid, Spain
Tel.: (34) 91 665 2626
Web Site: http://www.vbactia.com
Sales Range: $25-49.9 Million
Emp.: 50
Automotive Audio & Video Equipments Mfr
N.A.I.C.S.: 334310

ACTIA de Mexico S.A. de C.V. **(1)**
Av Central No 176 Nueva Industrial Vallejo,
7700, Mexico, Mexico
Tel.: (52) 5551192350
Web Site: https://www.actia.com.mx
Sales Range: $25-49.9 Million
Emp.: 100
Automotive Diagnostic Equipment Mfr

N.A.I.C.S.: 336320
Jose Oriol Admirable *(Gen Mgr)*

ACTIA-POLSKA Sp. z o.o. **(1)**
Ul Pulawska 38, 05-500, Piaseczno, Poland
Tel.: (48) 227263590
Web Site: http://www.actiapolska.pl
Sales Range: $25-49.9 Million
Emp.: 12
Automotive Diagnostic Equipment Whslr
N.A.I.C.S.: 423120

ATAL spol s.r.o. **(1)**
Lesni 47, Horky, 390 01, Tabor, Czech Re-
public
Tel.: (420) 381410100
Web Site: https://www.atal.cz
Sales Range: $25-49.9 Million
Emp.: 45
Electronic Equipment Distr
N.A.I.C.S.: 423690
Horejsi Joses *(Mgr)*

Actia (UK) Limited **(1)**
Unit 81 Mochdre Enterprise Park, Newtown,
SY16 4LE, Powys, United Kingdom
Tel.: (44) 1686611150
Web Site: https://www.actia.co.uk
Sales Range: $25-49.9 Million
Emp.: 25
Automotive Diagnostic Equipment Mfr
N.A.I.C.S.: 336390
Matthew Beedle *(Mgr-IT)*

Subsidiary (Domestic):

Actia Muller (UK) Ltd. **(2)**
Unit 81 Mochdre Industrial Estate, New-
town, SY16 4LE, Powys, United Kingdom
Tel.: (44) 16 8661 1177
Web Site: http://www.actiamuller.co.uk
Garage Equipments & Diagnostic Tools
Distr
N.A.I.C.S.: 423120
Simon Stone *(Mgr)*

Actia 3E S.A. **(1)**
Savoie Technolac, BP 282, 73375, Le Bour-
get du Lac, cedex, France
Tel.: (33) 479252390
Web Site: http://www.actia-3e.com
Electronic Products Mfr
N.A.I.C.S.: 334419

**Actia Automotive Joint Stock
Company** **(1)**
8 Rue Reaumur Jardin entreprises, 28000,
Chartres, France
Tel.: (33) 237333400
Engineeering Services
N.A.I.C.S.: 541330

**Actia China Automotive Electronics
Co., Ltd** **(1)**
4/F 5 Building 128 Jiu Jing Road Songjiang
High-Tech Park, Jiuting Songjiang, Shang-
hai, 201615, China
Tel.: (86) 2137639808
Web Site: http://www.actia.com.cn
Sales Range: $50-74.9 Million
Emp.: 130
Automotive Electronic Mfr
N.A.I.C.S.: 336320
Xiaoping Zhang *(Gen Mgr)*

Actia China Co., Ltd. **(1)**
5th-7th Floor Building 17B 470 Jiujing
Road, Jiuting Songjiang, Shanghai, 201615,
China
Tel.: (86) 2137639808
Engineeering Services
N.A.I.C.S.: 541330
Louise Shu *(Mktg Mgr)*

Actia Colomiers SA **(1)**
10 avenue E Serres, BP 60112, 31772, Co-
lomiers, Cedex, France
Tel.: (33) 562743400
Engineeering Services
N.A.I.C.S.: 541330

Actia Do Brasil Ltda. **(1)**
Av Sao Paulo 555, Sao Geraldo, Porto
Alegre, 90230-161, Brazil
Tel.: (55) 5133580200
Engineeering Services
N.A.I.C.S.: 541330
Vanda Machado *(Gen Mgr)*

Actia Electronics, Inc. **(1)**
15385 Pine, Romulus, MI 48174

Tel.: (734) 304-0007
Web Site: https://www.actiaelectronics.com
Electronic Products Mfr
N.A.I.C.S.: 334419

Actia Engineering Services SA **(1)**
Technopole El-Ghazela 2 rue Newton,
BP99, 2088, Ariana, Tunisia
Tel.: (216) 70687917
Engineeering Services
N.A.I.C.S.: 541330

**Actia Group SA - ACTIA MULLER
(France) Division** **(1)**
5 Rue De La Taye, Luce, 28110, Eure-et-
Loir, France
Tel.: (33) 2 3733 3400
Web Site: http://www.actiamuller.com
Emp.: 150
Automotive Repair & Maintenance Services
N.A.I.C.S.: 811111
Marin Prevost *(Mgr-Comm)*

**Actia Group SA - ACTIA Tunisie
Division** **(1)**
Impasse des Entrepreneurs ZI La Charguia
2, Ariana Aeroport, Tunis, 2080, Tunisia
Tel.: (216) 71 941 922
Sales Range: $50-74.9 Million
Emp.: 200
Automotive Diagnostic Equipment Mfr
N.A.I.C.S.: 336390

**Actia Group SA - CIPI ACTIA
Division** **(1)**
Rue des Entrepreneurs ZI Charguia 2 Tunis
Ariana Aeroport, 2080, Tunis, Tunisia
Tel.: (216) 70838115
Sales Range: $200-249.9 Million
Emp.: 680
Automotive Electrical Diagnostic Equipment
Mfr
N.A.I.C.S.: 336390
Philippe Alberto *(Gen Mgr)*

**Actia Group SA - Colomiers
Division** **(1)**
10 Avenue Edouard Serres, 31772, Colom-
iers, France
Tel.: (33) 5 6274 3400
Sales Range: $50-74.9 Million
Emp.: 250
Automotive Electrical Components Mfr
N.A.I.C.S.: 336320

Actia Japan K.K. **(1)**
Cerulean Tower 15F 26-1 Sakuragaoka-
cho, Shibuya-ku, Tokyo, 150-8512, Japan
Tel.: (81) 354565695
Engineeering Services
N.A.I.C.S.: 541330

Actia S.A. **(1)**
25 Chemin de Pouvourville, BP 4215,
31432, Toulouse, Cedex 04, France
Tel.: (33) 561176161
Web Site: http://www.actia.com
Sales Range: $125-149.9 Million
Emp.: 500
Automotive Electronics
N.A.I.C.S.: 335999
Louis Pech *(Chm)*

Actia Systems S.A.U. **(1)**
Poligono Industrial Los Olivos C/Calidad 66,
28906, Getafe, Madrid, Spain
Tel.: (34) 916652626
Engineeering Services
N.A.I.C.S.: 541330

Actia Telematics Services SA **(1)**
Chee de Marche 774, Naninne, 5100,
Namur, Belgium
Tel.: (32) 81331111
Web Site: https://www.actia.be
Electronic Products Mfr
N.A.I.C.S.: 334419

Actia Tunisie SA **(1)**
Rue des Entrepreneurs ZI La Charguia 2
Tunis Ariana Aeroport, 2080, Ariana, Tunisia
Tel.: (216) 70838115
Engineeering Services
N.A.I.C.S.: 541330

Actia do Brasil Ind. e Com. Ltda. **(1)**
555 Sao Paulo Street, Porto Alegre, 90230-
161, Rio Grande do Sul, Brazil
Tel.: (55) 51 3358 0200
Web Site: http://www.actia.com.br

Automotive Electronic Devices Mfr
N.A.I.C.S.: 334310

Actia-Aixia **(1)**
Savoie Technolac, PO Box 282, 73375, Le
Bourget du Lac, Cedex, France
Tel.: (33) 479252390
Web Site: http://www.actia-e3.com
Sales Range: $25-49.9 Million
Emp.: 10
Industrial & On-Board Electronic Devices
Mfr
N.A.I.C.S.: 334515
Davide Loy *(Gen Mgr)*

Aton Systemes S.A. **(1)**
14 rue Charles Martigny, 94700, Maisons-
Alfort, France
Tel.: (33) 142071800
Web Site: http://www.aton-sys.fr
Sales Range: $25-49.9 Million
Emp.: 15
Develops, Manufactures & Sells PC Com-
patible Boards for Industrial Applications
N.A.I.C.S.: 334111

ACTIC GROUP AB

Drottning Kristinas Esplanad 12, PO
Box 1805, 17121, Solna, Sweden
Tel.: (46) 851921100
Web Site: https://www.acticgroup.se
Year Founded: 1981
ATIC—(OMX)
Rev.: $70,225,819
Assets: $137,173,471
Liabilities: $117,942,810
Net Worth: $19,230,661
Earnings: ($3,383,068)
Emp.: 524
Fiscal Year-end: 12/31/22
Fitness Training Services
N.A.I.C.S.: 812990
Linda Nilsson *(Head-HR)*

ACTICOR BIOTECH SA

Wojo Building 82 avenue du Maine,
75014, Paris, France
Tel.: (33) 676233813   **FR**
Web Site: https://www.acticor-
biotech.com
Year Founded: 2013
ALACT—(EUR)
Rev.: $8,550
Assets: $13,833,478
Liabilities: $16,230,797
Net Worth: ($2,397,318)
Earnings: ($16,970,406)
Emp.: 21
Fiscal Year-end: 12/31/22
Biotechnology Research & Develop-
ment Services
N.A.I.C.S.: 541714
Gilles Avenard *(CEO)*

ACTINOGEN MEDICAL LIM-
ITED

Suite 901 Level 9 109 Pitt Street,
Sydney, 2000, NSW, Australia
Tel.: (61) 289647401
Web Site:
https://www.actinogen.com.au
ACW—(ASX)
Rev.: $6,825,938
Assets: $14,230,680
Liabilities: $1,078,638
Net Worth: $13,152,043
Earnings: ($8,710,124)
Emp.: 1
Fiscal Year-end: 06/30/24
Biotechnology Research
N.A.I.C.S.: 541714
Peter Webse *(Sec)*

ACTINVER S.A. DE C.V.

Guillermo Gonzalez Camarena 1200
Centro de Cd, Santa Fe, 01210,
Mexico, DF, Mexico
Tel.: (52) 5511036699
Web Site: http://www.actinver.com

ACTINVR—(MEX)
Rev.: $1,054,996,376
Assets: $14,082,019
Liabilities: $14,082,019
Earnings: $67,683,425
Emp.: 2,076
Fiscal Year-end: 12/31/23
Brokerage & Investment Services
N.A.I.C.S.: 523150
Hector Madero Rivero *(Chm, Pres & CEO)*

ACTION ASIA LIMITED

3 Anson Road 27-01 Springleaf
Tower, Singapore, 079909, Singapore
Tel.: (65) 65323488   SG
Web Site:
  http://www.actionind.com.my
Year Founded: 1987
Sales Range: $75-99.9 Million
Holding Company; Mobile Audio &
Video Entertainment Products Mfr
N.A.I.C.S.: 551112
Chiun-Ping Peng *(Exec Dir)*

ACTION CHEVROLET BUICK GMC INC.

7955 Chambly Road, Saint-Hubert,
J3Y 5K2, QC, Canada
Tel.: (450) 445-7333
Web Site:
  http://www.actionchevroleteng.ca
Year Founded: 1989
Sales Range: $10-24.9 Million
New & Used Car Dealers
N.A.I.C.S.: 441110
Stephane Guilbault *(Pres)*

ACTION CONSTRUCTION EQUIPMENT LTD.

Dudhola Link Road, Dudhola Distt,
Palwal, 121102, Haryana, India
Tel.: (91) 1275280111
Web Site: https://www.ace-cranes.com
Year Founded: 1995
ACE—(NSE)
Rev.: $224,486,753
Assets: $175,042,932
Liabilities: $72,073,324
Net Worth: $102,969,608
Earnings: $14,332,227
Emp.: 1,184
Fiscal Year-end: 03/31/22
Construction Equipment Mfr
N.A.I.C.S.: 333120
Sorab Agarwal *(Exec Dir)*

ACTION ELECTRONICS CO., LTD.

4F No 423-7 Zhengguang Rd,
Zhongli, 330, Taoyuan, Taiwan
Tel.: (886) 34515494
Web Site: https://www.action.com.tw
Year Founded: 1976
3024—(TAI)
Rev.: $49,925,699
Assets: $168,583,302
Liabilities: $76,634,714
Net Worth: $91,948,589
Earnings: $3,564,309
Fiscal Year-end: 12/31/23
Electronic Product Mfr & Distr
N.A.I.C.S.: 334419
Ting-Yu Peng *(Chm)*

Subsidiaries:

Action Asia (Shenzhen) Co., Ltd. **(1)**
DeDe Industrial Park Jian an Road High-
Tech Industrial Park Fuyong own, Bao an
Dist, Shenzhen, 201821, China
Tel.: (86) 75529179999
Audio Video Equipment Distr
N.A.I.C.S.: 423690

Action Industries (M) Sdn. Bhd. **(1)**
2480 Tingkat Perusahaan Enam Prai Free
Trade Zone, 13600, Perai, Penang, Malaysia
Tel.: (60) 43997600
Web Site: https://www.actionind.com.my
Audio & Video Entertainment Product Mfr
N.A.I.C.S.: 334310

Action Technology (Jian) Co.,
Ltd. **(1)**
Industrial Park, Jian, 343100, China
Tel.: (86) 7968404118
Audio Video Equipment Distr
N.A.I.C.S.: 423690

America Action Inc. **(1)**
13620 5th St, Chino, CA 91710
Tel.: (909) 548-6600
Audio Video Equipment Distr
N.A.I.C.S.: 423690

Best Taiwan Inc. **(1)**
No 198 Zhongyuan Rd, Zhongli, 320,
Taoyuan, Taiwan
Tel.: (886) 34515494
Audio Video Equipment Distr
N.A.I.C.S.: 423690

Realise Tech-Service Co., Ltd. **(1)**
8F-9 No 4 Lane 609 Section 5 Zhongcheng
Road, Sanchong District, New Taipei City,
24159, Taiwan
Tel.: (886) 229995286
Web Site: https://www.realise.com.tw
Audio Video Equipment Distr
N.A.I.C.S.: 423690

ACTION FINANCIAL SERVICES (INDIA) LTD.

46/47 6th Floor Rajgir Chambers
12/14 S B Road, Fort, Mumbai, 400
001, India
Tel.: (91) 2243654444
Web Site: http://www.actionfin.com
Rev.: $660,583
Assets: $5,307,702
Liabilities: $1,653,129
Net Worth: $3,654,573
Earnings: $34,703
Emp.: 22
Fiscal Year-end: 03/31/19
Financial Services
N.A.I.C.S.: 523999
Bakul R. Parekh *(Co-Mng Dir & CFO)*

ACTION FLOORING

810 Development Drive, Kingston,
K7M 5V7, ON, Canada
Tel.: (613) 634-3657
Web Site:
  http://www.actionflooring.com
Year Founded: 1992
Rev.: $18,532,799
Emp.: 40
Flooring Contractors
N.A.I.C.S.: 238330

ACTION GROUP HOLDINGS COMPANY K.S.C.C.

Rakan Tower 27th Floor Al-Shohada
St Al-Qibla, PO Box 3866, Safat, Kuwait, 1309, Kuwait
Tel.: (965) 22247500   KW
Web Site:
  http://www.actionkuwait.com
Year Founded: 1998
Holding Company
N.A.I.C.S.: 551112
Souad M. Al-Sabah *(Chm)*

Subsidiaries:

Action Hotels Plc **(1)**
The Gate Village 2 Level 4, PO Box 23506,
Dubai, United Arab Emirates **(72.49%)**
Tel.: (971) 4 317 9500
Web Site: http://www.actionhotels.com
Hotel Developer & Owner
N.A.I.C.S.: 721110
Mubarak A. M. Al-Sabah *(Founder & Chm)*

ACTION S.A.

Zamienie ul Dawidowska 10, 05-500,
Piaseczno, Poland
Tel.: (48) 223321600
Web Site: https://www.action.pl
Year Founded: 1991
ACT—(WAR)
Rev,: $594,622,921
Assets: $162,793,800
Liabilities: $51,584,686
Net Worth: $111,209,114
Earnings: $12,295,383
Emp.: 521
Fiscal Year-end: 12/31/22
Computer, Consumer Electronics &
Household Appliances Distr
N.A.I.C.S.: 423620
Piotr Bielinski *(Pres, CEO & Member-Mgmt Bd)*

Subsidiaries:

ACTION EUROPE GmbH **(1)**
Kocherstrasse 2, D 38120, Braunschweig,
Germany
Tel.: (49) 531 12900 0
Web Site: http://www.actioneu.de
Sales Range: $350-399.9 Million
Emp.: 240
Computer & Consumer Electronics Distr
N.A.I.C.S.: 423430
Dina Homann *(Mgr)*

ACTIONS SEMICONDUCTOR CO., LTD.

No 1 Ke Ji Si Road Hi-Tech Zone,
Zhuhai, 519085, Guangdong, China
Tel.: (86) 756 339 2353   Ky
Web Site: http://www.actions-semi.com
Year Founded: 2001
Sales Range: $25-49.9 Million
Emp.: 589
Integrated Circuit Designer & Mfr
N.A.I.C.S.: 334413
David Hsiang-Wei Lee *(Chm)*

Subsidiaries:

Actions Technology (HK) Company
Limited **(1)**
Room F 6th Floor West Gate Tower, Lai Chi
Kok, Kowloon, China (Hong Kong) **(100%)**
Tel.: (852) 27436925
Other Electronic Parts & Equipment Whslr
N.A.I.C.S.: 423690

ACTIONSPORTGAMES A/S

Bjergvangen 1, 3060, Espergaerde,
Denmark
Tel.: (45) 89281888
Year Founded: 1992
Sports Product Mfr & Distr
N.A.I.C.S.: 339920

ACTIONWEAR SASKATOON INC.

114 Melville Street, Saskatoon, S7J
0R1, SK, Canada
Tel.: (306) 933-3088
Web Site: http://www.actionwear.ca
Year Founded: 1974
Emp.: 110
Apparels Mfr
N.A.I.C.S.: 315990
Kathy Reaser *(Founder)*

ACTIV C.S.A.

56-60, bd Amiral Mouchez, BP 643,
76059, Le Havre, France
Tel.: (33) 35247474
Web Site: http://www.activfrance.com
Sales Range: $10-24.9 Million
Emp.: 112
Office Equipment
N.A.I.C.S.: 423420
Henri Roth *(Pres)*

ACTIV8 DISTRIBUTION LTD.

Greenhill House 26 Greenhill Crescent, Watford, WD18 8JA, United
Kingdom
Tel.: (44) 845 45 85 008
Web Site: http://www.a8uk.com
Year Founded: 2000
Sales Range: $10-24.9 Million
Emp.: 30
Mobile Accessory Whslr
N.A.I.C.S.: 423690
Stuart Conroy *(Mng Dir)*

ACTIVA CAPITAL S.A.S.

203 Rue du Faubourg Saint-Honore,
75008, Paris, France
Tel.: (33) 143125012
Web Site:
  http://www.activacapital.com
Sales Range: $25-49.9 Million
Emp.: 500
Investment Services
N.A.I.C.S.: 523999
Charles Diehl *(Mng Partner)*

Subsidiaries:

Armatis Sa **(1)**
79 Avenue Edouard Vaillant, Billancourt,
92100, Paris, France
Tel.: (33) 146 20 04 04
Web Site: http://www.armatis.com
Telemarketing Services
N.A.I.C.S.: 561422
Denis Akriche *(CEO)*

La Maison Bleue sa **(1)**
31 rue d aguesseau, 92100, Boulogne,
France
Tel.: (33) 1 46 54 05 74
Web Site: http://www.la-maison-bleue.fr
Child Day Care Services
N.A.I.C.S.: 624410
Sylvain Forestier *(CEO)*

Primavista Group **(1)**
307 rue Estienne d Orves, 92707, Colombes, Cedex, France
Tel.: (33) 811 56 04 51
Web Site: http://www.primavista.fr
Direct Marketing Services
N.A.I.C.S.: 541613
Laurent Lecoeuvre *(Mng Dlr)*

Subsidiary (Non-US):

Primaphot SPRL **(2)**
Rue Charles Parentestraat 11, 1070, Brussels, Belgium
Tel.: (32) 800 57 202
Direct Marketing Services
N.A.I.C.S.: 541613

Selpro S.A. **(1)**
Le Chateau Rouge 276 Ave De La Marne,
59700, Marcq-en-Baroeul, France
Tel.: (33) 320661766
Web Site: http://www.selpro.fr
Sales Range: $75-99.9 Million
Employment Agency Services
N.A.I.C.S.: 561311

ACTIVA RESOURCES AG

Hessenring 107, D-61348, Bad Homburg, Germany
Tel.: (49) 6172 4 83 23 52   De
Web Site:
  http://www.activaresources.com
Year Founded: 2005
NXIC—(DEU)
Sales Range: Less than $1 Million
Holding Company; Oil & Gas Exploration Services
N.A.I.C.S.: 551112
Walter Bluementhal *(Chm-Supervisory Bd)*

Subsidiaries:

Activa Resources, LLC **(1)**
403 E Commerce Str, San Antonio, TX
78205 **(30%)**
Tel.: (210) 271-9875
Oil & Gas Exploration Services
N.A.I.C.S.: 213112
John W. Hayes *(Pres & Member-Mgmt Bd)*

ACTIVATION GROUP HOLDINGS LIMITED

Activation Group Holdings Limited—(Continued)

8/F No 399A Liu Zhou Rd, Xu Hui,
Shanghai, 200235, China
Tel.: (86) 2162488023
Web Site: http://www.activation-gp.com
Year Founded: 2019
9919—(HKG)
Rev.: $97,550,903
Assets: $99,858,938
Liabilities: $50,214,902
Net Worth: $49,644,036
Earnings: $3,965,458
Emp.: 270
Fiscal Year-end: 12/31/22
Holding Company
N.A.I.C.S.: 551112
Kam Yiu Lau *(Co-Chm & CEO)*

ACTIVE BIOTECH AB

Scheelevagen 22, 223 63, Lund,
Sweden
Tel.: (46) 46192000
Web Site:
http://www.activebiotech.com
Year Founded: 1983
ACTI—(OMX)
Rev.: $4,589
Assets: $4,777,225
Liabilities: $1,544,859
Net Worth: $3,232,366
Earnings: ($5,467,232)
Emp.: 9
Fiscal Year-end: 12/31/22
Biotechnology Product Research &
Development Services
N.A.I.C.S.: 541714
Hans Kolam *(CFO)*

ACTIVE CAPITAL COMPANY HOLDING BV

Vossiusstraat 13A, 1071, AC, Amsterdam, Netherlands
Tel.: (31) 20 262 0275
Web Site:
http://www.activecapital.com
Private Investment Firm
N.A.I.C.S.: 523999
Albert Hartog *(Founder)*

Subsidiaries:

Codi Group BV   (1)
Turbinestraat 19, 3903 LV, Veenendaal,
Netherlands
Tel.: (31) 318 564 811
Web Site: http://www.codigroup.com
Holding Company
N.A.I.C.S.: 551112

Subsidiary (Domestic):

Codi International B.V.   (2)
Turbinestraat 19, 3903 LV, Veenendaal,
Netherlands
Tel.: (31) 318 564 811
Web Site: http://www.codi.nl
Wet Wiping Cloths Mfr
N.A.I.C.S.: 322291

ACTIVE CLOTHING CO., LTD.

Plot no E-225 Phase 8B Ind Area,
Mohali, 160059, Punjab, India
Tel.: (91) 1724313300
Web Site:
https://www.activesourcing.org
Year Founded: 1997
541144—(BOM)
Rev.: $15,757,320
Assets: $19,871,851
Liabilities: $11,395,026
Net Worth: $8,476,825
Earnings: $70,975
Emp.: 876
Fiscal Year-end: 03/31/22
Apparels Mfr
N.A.I.C.S.: 315250
Rajesh Mehra *(Mng Dir)*

ACTIVE CONTROL TECHNOLOGY INC.

3200 Ridgeway Drive Unit 17, Mississauga, L5L 5Y6, ON, Canada
Tel.: (905) 670-5500   ON
Web Site:
http://www.activecontrol.com
Year Founded: 1997
Sales Range: $1-9.9 Million
Wireless Communication Equipment
Mfr
N.A.I.C.S.: 334220
Jonathan Emanuel *(CEO)*

Subsidiaries:

PowerCart Systems Inc.   (1)
40 Great Gulf Drive Unit 30, Concord, L4K
0K7, ON, Canada
Tel.: (905) 364-0050
Web Site: http://www.powercart.com
Industrial Printing Cart Mfr
N.A.I.C.S.: 339999

ACTIVE ENERGY GROUP PLC

27-28 Eastcastle Street, London,
W1W 8DH, United Kingdom
Tel.: (44) 2045665090
Web Site: https://www.aegplc.com
AEG—(AIM)
Rev.: $1,810,206
Assets: $18,141,869
Liabilities: $24,858,427
Net Worth: ($6,716,558)
Earnings: ($8,757,919)
Emp.: 37
Fiscal Year-end: 12/31/20
Engineeering Services
N.A.I.C.S.: 541330
Michael Rowan *(CEO)*

Subsidiaries:

Active Energy Limited   (1)
75 Brook Street, Mayfair, London, W1K
4AD, United Kingdom   (100%)
Tel.: (44) 20 7491 9533
Web Site: http://www.active-energy.com
Sales Range: $25-49.9 Million
Voltage Optimising Transformers Mfr & Distr
N.A.I.C.S.: 335311

Derlite Co Ltd.   (1)
470/13 Moo 5 Soi Klong Arsia Puttaraksa
Road Tambon Praksa-Mai, Amphur Muang,
Samut Prakan, 10280, Thailand
Tel.: (66) 2 136 8900
Web Site: https://www.derlite.com
Sales Range: $50-74.9 Million
Emp.: 150
Gas Ignition Components Mfr & Distr
N.A.I.C.S.: 334512
Kevin Baker *(Mng Dir)*

Redline Engineering Services
Ltd   (1)
75 Brook Street, London, W1K 4AD, United
Kingdom   (100%)
Tel.: (44) 2074919533
Web Site:
http://www.redlineengservices.com
Engineeering Services
N.A.I.C.S.: 541330

ACTIVE EXHAUST CORP.

1865 Birchmount Road, Toronto, M1P
2J5, ON, Canada
Tel.: (416) 445-9610
Web Site:
http://www.activexhaust.com
Year Founded: 1973
Sales Range: $25-49.9 Million
Emp.: 200
Exhaust System & Tubular Metal Mfr
N.A.I.C.S.: 336390
Peter Hampton *(Pres)*

ACTIVE FINE CHEMICALS LIMITED

214/D Gulshan-Tejgaon Link Road,
Dhaka, 1208, Bangladesh
Tel.: (880) 28836830

Web Site: https://www.afchem.com
Year Founded: 2004
ACTIVEFINE—(CHT)
Rev.: $19,391,116
Assets: $105,315,719
Liabilities: $43,880,551
Net Worth: $61,435,168
Earnings: $300,561
Fiscal Year-end: 06/30/22
Pharmaceuticals Product Mfr
N.A.I.C.S.: 325412
Mohammed Zia Uddin *(Chm)*

Subsidiaries:

AFC Capital Ltd.   (1)
Saiham Sky View Tower 11 th Floor Old
Bijoy Nagar New 195 Shahid Syed, Nazrul
Islam Sharani, Dhaka, 1000, Bangladesh
Tel.: (880) 28392371
Web Site: http://www.afccl.asia
Asset Management Services
N.A.I.C.S.: 523940
Mahbub H. Mazumdar *(CEO)*

AFC Health Ltd.   (1)
Navana Osman Link 214/D 1st Floor
Tejgaon-Gulshan Link Road, Tejgaon C/A,
Dhaka, 1208, Bangladesh
Tel.: (880) 258811422
Web Site: http://www.afchealthbd.com
Health Care Srvices
N.A.I.C.S.: 621999
A. B. M. Ghulam Mostafa *(Chm)*

ACTIVE PRIVATE EQUITY ADVISORY LLP

5th Floor 6 Chesterfield Gardens,
London, W1J 5BQ, United Kingdom
Tel.: (44) 207 016 6480
Web Site: http://www.apeq.co.uk
Privater Equity Firm
N.A.I.C.S.: 523999
Gavyn Davies *(Partner)*

Subsidiaries:

Evans Holdings Ltd.   (1)
Camino Park James Watt Way, Crawley,
RH10 9TZ, West Sussex, United Kingdom
Tel.: (44) 1293 574900
Web Site: http://www.evanscycles.com
Sales Range: $125-149.9 Million
Emp.: 1,500
Bicycle Retailer
N.A.I.C.S.: 459110
Mike Rice *(Mng Dir)*

ACTIVEOPS LTD.

1 Valpy 20 Valpy Street, Reading,
RG1 1AR, United Kingdom
Tel.: (44) 118 907 5000
Web Site: http://activeops.com
Year Founded: 2005
Digital Operations Management Solutions
N.A.I.C.S.: 541511
Richard Jeffery *(Co-Founder & CEO)*

ACTIVEPORT GROUP LIMITED

Level 1 1 Altona Street, West Perth,
6005, WA, Australia
Tel.: (61) 861497550   AU
Web Site:
https://www.activeport.com.au
Year Founded: 2017
ATV—(ASX)
Rev.: $12,652,131
Assets: $25,075,508
Liabilities: $6,761,432
Net Worth: $18,314,076
Earnings: ($2,220,182)
Fiscal Year-end: 06/30/23
Software Development Services
N.A.I.C.S.: 541511
Mark Middleton *(CTO)*

Subsidiaries:

Starboard IT Pty. Ltd.   (1)
Level 19 323 Castlereagh Street, Sydney,
2000, NSW, Australia
Tel.: (61) 1300674966

Web Site: https://www.starboardit.com.au
Information Technology Services
N.A.I.C.S.: 541519

Vizstone Pty. Ltd.   (1)
Ground Floor 12 Newcastle St, Perth, 6000,
WA, Australia
Tel.: (61) 1300849466
Web Site: https://www.vizstone.com.au
Computer Software Consulting Services
N.A.I.C.S.: 541512

ACTIVEX LIMITED

2/3B Macquarie Street, Sydney,
2000, NSW, Australia
Tel.: (61) 292519088
Web Site: https://www.activex.com.au
AIV—(ASX)
Rev.: $5,821
Assets: $3,939,342
Liabilities: $1,785,130
Net Worth: $2,154,213
Earnings: ($1,803,428)
Emp.: 1
Fiscal Year-end: 06/30/24
Mineral Exploration Services
N.A.I.C.S.: 213115
Min Yang *(Chm)*

ACTIVIA PROPERTIES INC.

16-3 Dogenzaka 1-chome, Shibuya-ku, Tokyo, Japan
Tel.: (81) 364153120
Web Site: https://www.activia-reit.co.jp
Year Founded: 2011
3279—(TKS)
Sales Range: $50-74.9 Million
Investment Management Service
N.A.I.C.S.: 523940
Kazuyuki Murayama *(Exec Dir)*

ACTIVINSTINCT LTD.

60 The Broadway Mill Hill, London,
NW7 3TE, United Kingdom
Tel.: (44) 208 959 5539
Web Site:
http://www.activinstirict.com
Year Founded: 1987
Sales Range: $10-24.9 Million
Emp.: 75
Electronic Shopping Services
N.A.I.C.S.: 459110
Mike Thornhill *(CEO)*

ACTOM (PTY) LTD.

2 Magnet Road Knights, Germiston,
1413, South Africa
Tel.: (27) 118205111
Web Site: http://www.actom.co.za
Electro-mechanical Equipment Mfr &
Distr
N.A.I.C.S.: 335999

Subsidiaries:

LH Marthinusen (Pty.) Ltd.   (1)
338 Main Reef Road, Denver, Johannesburg, 2094, South Africa
Tel.: (27) 116156722
Web Site: http://www.lhm.co.za
Sales Range: $75-99.9 Million
Electro-Mechanical Repair & Manufacturing
Services
N.A.I.C.S.: 811210
Julie Cowell *(Dir-Fin)*

Marthinusen & Coutts (Pty.) Ltd. (1)
53 Hospital St, PO Box 40018, Cleveland,
2022, South Africa
Tel.: (27) 116071700
Web Site: http://www.mandc.co.za
Sales Range: $75-99.9 Million
Electric Motor Repair Services
N.A.I.C.S.: 811210
Mike Chamberlain *(Dir-Mktg)*

Reid & Mitchell (Pty.) Ltd.   (1)
24 Van Dyk Road, Benoni, 1502, South
Africa
Tel.: (27) 119149600
Web Site: http://www.reidmitchell.co.za

Sales Range: $25-49.9 Million
Emp.: 132
Repair of Electrical Motors
N.A.I.C.S.: 811210
Mike Shaw *(Mng Dir)*

Transwire (Pty.) Ltd. **(1)**
28 Main Rd, PO Box 92, Olifantsfontein,
1665, South Africa
Tel.: (27) 113162480
Web Site: http://www.transwire.co.za
Sales Range: $50-74.9 Million
Magnet Wire Mfr
N.A.I.C.S.: 332618
Howard Eldridge *(Exec Dir)*

WILEC **(1)**
Unit 6 City Deep Mini Park Cnr Outspan &
Heidelberg Rds, City Deep Ext 7, Johan-
nesburg, 2197, South Africa
Tel.: (27) 116299300
Web Site: http://www.wilec.co.za
Electrical & Industrial Product Mfr & Distr
N.A.I.C.S.: 423610
Steve Jordaan *(CEO)*

ACTON LEATHER CO. INC.
49 Eastern Avenue, Acton, L7J 2E6,
ON, Canada
Tel.: (519) 853-1031
Web Site: http://www.hidehouse.ca
Year Founded: 1980
Rev.: $10,715,710
Emp.: 16
Leather Goods Mfr
N.A.I.C.S.: 316990
Stephanie Miller *(Mgr-Store)*

ACTRO CO., LTD.
Heungdeok IT Valley 3504 Tower 13
Heungdeok 1-ro, Yeongdeok-dong
Giheung-gu, Yongin, Gyeonggi-do,
Korea (South)
Tel.: (82) 316894567
Web Site: https://www.actro.co.kr
Year Founded: 2016
290740—(KRS)
Rev.: $105,054,544
Assets: $72,691,211
Liabilities: $22,423,607
Net Worth: $50,267,604
Earnings: ($7,370,918)
Emp.: 55
Fiscal Year-end: 12/31/22
Optical Instrument Mfr
N.A.I.C.S.: 333310
Moon-Yong Jang *(Pres)*

ACTUAL EXPERIENCE PLC
Quay House The Ambury, Bath, BA1
1UA, United Kingdom
Tel.: (44) 122 558 5868
Web Site: http://www.actual-
experience.com
ACT—(AIM)
Rev.: $2,364,072
Assets: $14,204,483
Liabilities: $2,207,756
Net Worth: $11,996,727
Earnings: ($7,938,854)
Emp.: 72
Fiscal Year-end: 09/30/21
IT Application Solutions
N.A.I.C.S.: 513210
Steve Bennetts *(CFO)*

ACTUAL FENSTER GMBH
Actualstrasse 31, 4053, Ansfelden,
Austria
Tel.: (43) 72298660
Web Site: http://www.actual.at
Wood-aluminum & Plastic-aluminum
Windows Marketer & Mfr
N.A.I.C.S.: 321911

ACTURIS LTD.
100 Hatton Garden, London, EC1N
8NX, United Kingdom
Tel.: (44) 2070794000
Web Site: http://www.acturis.com

Year Founded: 2000
Sales Range: $10-24.9 Million
Emp.: 400
Insurance Software Development
Services
N.A.I.C.S.: 513210
David McDonald *(Co-CEO)*

Subsidiaries:

Nordic Insurance Software A/S **(1)**
Aarhusgade 88 6th Fl, 2100, Copenhagen,
Denmark
Tel.: (45) 70222723
Web Site: http://www.nisportal.com
Software Development Services
N.A.I.C.S.: 541511
Erik Skaarup *(Exec VP & Head-Bus Dev)*

ACUCORT AB
Scheeletorget 1, Medicon Village,
223 81, Lund, Sweden
Tel.: (46) 5900990
Web Site: https://www.acucort.se
Year Founded: 2006
Healtcare Services
N.A.I.C.S.: 622110
Ann Gidner *(CEO)*

ACUITYADS INC.
181 Bay Street Suite 320 Brookfield
Place, Bay Wellington Tower, Toronto,
M5J 2T3, ON, Canada
Tel.: (416) 218-9888   **ON**
Web Site: http://www.acuityads.com
Year Founded: 2009
Marketing Platform Developer & Ser-
vices
N.A.I.C.S.: 541511
Tal Hayek *(Co-Founder & CEO)*

Subsidiaries:

Visible Measures Corporation **(1)**
143 S St 5th Fl, Boston, MA 02111
Tel.: (617) 482-0222
Web Site: http://www.visiblemeasures.com
Software Application Development Services
N.A.I.C.S.: 541511
Nana C. Shin *(Gen Counsel)*

ACULA TECHNOLOGY CORP.
11 Alley 21 Lane 20 Dashing Rd, Lu-
zhu District, Taoyuan, 338024, Tai-
wan
Tel.: (886) 33135577
Web Site: https://acula.com
Year Founded: 1993
3434—(TPE)
Rev.: $23,912,610
Assets: $17,208,079
Liabilities: $7,930,557
Net Worth: $9,277,522
Earnings: $1,260,169
Emp.: 120
Fiscal Year-end: 12/31/22
Security Monitor Mfr & Distr
N.A.I.C.S.: 334419
Chien Li-Lien *(Chm)*

ACUMENTIS GROUP LIMITED
Level 7 283 Clarence Street, Sydney,
2000, NSW, Australia
Tel.: (61) 1300882401   **AU**
Web Site:
  https://www.acumentis.com.au
Year Founded: 1905
ACU—(ASX)
Rev.: $38,182,425
Assets: $25,689,102
Liabilities: $8,452,190
Net Worth: $17,236,912
Earnings: $951,522
Emp.: 300
Fiscal Year-end: 06/30/24
Real Estate Valuation & Property
Consulting Services
N.A.I.C.S.: 531390
Bradley J. Piltz *(Founder & Founder)*

Subsidiaries:

Acumentis Brisbane Pty Ltd **(1)**
GPO Box 1776, Brisbane, 4001, QLD, Aus-
tralia
Tel.: (61) 73 840 3000
Web Site: https://www.acumentis.com.au
Real Estate Services
N.A.I.C.S.: 531210
Timothy Rabbit *(CEO & Mng Dir)*

Acumentis Gold Coast Pty Ltd **(1)**
Suite 14D Level 4 Town Centre, Carrara,
Gold Coast, 4211, QLD, Australia
Tel.: (61) 75 634 7100
Real Estate Services
N.A.I.C.S.: 531210

Acumentis Melbourne Pty Ltd **(1)**
Shop 3 Podium Level 766 Toorak Road,
Glen Iris, 3146, VIC, Australia
Tel.: (61) 39 599 3000
Real Estate Services
N.A.I.C.S.: 531210
Dave Jessup *(Natl Dir-Risk-Compliance)*

LMW Residential Pty Ltd **(1)**
15 McDougall St, Milton, 4064, Australia
Tel.: (61) 733672333
Web Site: http://www.lmwres.com.au
Sales Range: $25-49.9 Million
Emp.: 30
Residential Real Estate Management Ser-
vices
N.A.I.C.S.: 531311

**LandMark White (Brisbane) Pty
Ltd** **(1)**
Level 12 241 Adelaide St, Brisbane, 4000,
QLD, Australia
Tel.: (61) 732260000
Sales Range: $25-49.9 Million
Emp.: 20
Real Estate Agency Services
N.A.I.C.S.: 531210

**LandMark White (Gold Coast) Pty
Ltd** **(1)**
26 Marine Parade, Southport, 4215, Austra-
lia
Tel.: (61) 755103100
Web Site: http://www.landmarkwhite.com.au
Sales Range: $50-74.9 Million
Emp.: 8
Property Solutions Provider
N.A.I.C.S.: 531190
Dax Roep *(Mng Dir)*

**LandMark White (Sydney) Pty
Ltd** **(1)**
Level 6 Clarence Street, Sydney, 2000,
NSW, Australia
Tel.: (61) 288236300
Web Site: http://www.lmw.com.au
Sales Range: $25-49.9 Million
Emp.: 50
Real Estate Services
N.A.I.C.S.: 531390
Robert Wilson *(Mng Dir)*

LandMark White (VIC) Pty Ltd **(1)**
Level 11 45 William St, Melbourne, 3000,
VIC, Australia
Tel.: (61) 396146611
Web Site: http://www.landmarkwhite.com.au
Sales Range: $50-74.9 Million
Emp.: 6
Property Solutions Provider
N.A.I.C.S.: 531190
Terry Dwyer *(Assoc Dir)*

ACUREN CORPORATION
Ritter House Wickhams Cay II Road
Town, Tortola, VG1 110, Virgin Is-
lands (British)
Tel.: (786) 482-6320   **VG**
Web Site:
  https://www.admiralacquisition.com
Year Founded: 2022
ADMRI—(LSE)
Investment Services
N.A.I.C.S.: 523999

Subsidiaries:

Acuren Group Inc. **(1)**
7450 - 18th Street, Edmonton, T6P 1N8,
AB, Canada

Tel.: (780) 440-2131
Web Site: http://www.acuren.com
Sales Range: $750-799.9 Million
Emp.: 300
Holding Company; Non-Destructive Testing,
Inspection & Materials Engineering Services
N.A.I.C.S.: 551112
Peter O. Scannell *(Chm)*

Subsidiary (US):

Acuren Inspection, Inc. **(2)**
705 Albany St, Dayton, OH 45417
Tel.: (937) 228-9729
Web Site: http://www.acuren.com
Sales Range: $200-249.9 Million
Emp.: 300
Non-Destructive Testing, Inspection & Mate-
rials Engineering Services
N.A.I.C.S.: 541990
John Lockwood *(VP)*

Branch (US):

**Acuren Inspection, Inc. - North
Region** **(2)**
4250 N 126th St, Brookfield, WI 53005
Tel.: (262) 781-0105
Sales Range: $1-9.9 Million
Non-Destructive Testing, Inspection & Mate-
rials Engineering Services
N.A.I.C.S.: 541990

**Acuren Inspection, Inc. - South
Region** **(2)**
405 N Eastman Rd, Longview, TX 75601
Tel.: (903) 753-2375
Web Site: http://www.acuren.com
Sales Range: $25-49.9 Million
Emp.: 100
Non-Destructive Testing, Inspection & Mate-
rials Engineering Services
N.A.I.C.S.: 541990

ACUSENSUS LIMITED
Level 6 31 Queen Street, Melbourne,
3000, VIC, Australia
Tel.: (61) 1300214697
Web Site:
  https://www.acusensus.com
Year Founded: 2018
ACE—(ASX)
Rev.: $34,141,960
Assets: $32,512,687
Liabilities: $8,524,973
Net Worth: $23,987,714
Earnings: ($1,016,960)
Emp.: 164
Fiscal Year-end: 06/30/24
Custom Computer Programming Ser-
vices
N.A.I.C.S.: 541511
Olivia Byron *(Sec)*

ACUVI AB
Stationsgatan 23, 753 40, Uppsala,
Sweden
Tel.: (46) 184895000
Web Site: https://acuvi.com
ACUVI—(OMX)
Rev.: $17,334,476
Assets: $46,380,623
Liabilities: $14,561,241
Net Worth: $31,819,382
Earnings: ($9,030,693)
Emp.: 56
Fiscal Year-end: 12/31/22
Micro Motor Mfr
N.A.I.C.S.: 335312
Anders Kottenauer *(CEO)*

ACWA HOLDING CO.
PO Box 321, Riyadh, 11411, Saudi
Arabia
Tel.: (966) 114779590
Web Site:
  http://www.acwaholding.com
Year Founded: 2002
Private Investment Firm
N.A.I.C.S.: 523999
Abdulrahman Al Khamis *(Mng Dir)*

ACWA Holding Co.—(Continued)

ACWA POWER COMPANY
Building 1 Ground Floor Business
Gate Office Complex Airport Road,
Riyadh, 11416, Saudi Arabia
Tel.: (966) 112835555   **SA**
Web Site:
  https://www.acwapower.com
Year Founded: 2004
2082—(SAU)
Rev.: $1,624,929,666
Assets: $14,667,882,512
Liabilities: $9,146,892,172
Net Worth: $5,520,990,341
Earnings: $472,236,311
Emp.: 3,701
Fiscal Year-end: 12/31/23
Power Generation & Desalinated Water Production Plants Developer &
Operator
N.A.I.C.S.: 221122
Marco Arcelli *(CEO)*

AD 2-ONE
246 Westminster Bridge Rd, London,
SE1 7PD, United Kingdom
Tel.: (44) 207 401 0333
Year Founded: 2001
Sales Range: $10-24.9 Million
Emp.: 30
N.A.I.C.S.: 541810
Grant Allaway *(Owner)*

AD DRAGAN MARKOVIC
Kralja Petra I broj 27, 11500, Obrenovac, Serbia
Tel.: (381) 11 872 11 61
Web Site: http://www.dramar.co.rs
Year Founded: 1998
Sales Range: $10-24.9 Million
Pig Farming Services
N.A.I.C.S.: 112210

AD DULAYL INDUSTRIAL PARK & REAL ESTATE CO.
11 AlSharif AlHussein Bin Ali Street
Fourth Floor, PO BOX 5656, Amman,
11118, Jordan
Tel.: (962) 64645416
Web Site: https://www.dleil.com
IDMC—(AMM)
Rev.: $2,831,743
Assets: $59,892,202
Liabilities: $7,697,103
Net Worth: $52,195,099
Earnings: $1,620,900
Emp.: 29
Fiscal Year-end: 12/31/20
Real Estate Development Services
N.A.I.C.S.: 531390
Ahmad Al-Rqaibat *(Chm)*

AD INSURANCE POLICY
Blvd St Kliment Ohridski no 26, 1000,
Skopje, North Macedonia
Tel.: (389) 23244600
Web Site:
  https://www.insurancepolicy.com.mk
Insurance Services
N.A.I.C.S.: 524298
Anela Darkovska *(Head-Legal Svcs Dept)*

AD JAVNA SKLADISTA SUBOTICA
Tuk Ugarnice BB, 24000, Subotica,
Serbia
Tel.: (381) 24 546 281
Web Site:
  http://www.javnaskladista.rs
Goods Storage Services
N.A.I.C.S.: 493190
Bruic Aleksandar *(Mgr-Sls)*

AD ME TECH CO., LTD.

5F Ezaki Honsha Bldg 1-8-16 Kukodori, Matsuyama, 790-0054, Ehime,
Japan
Tel.: (81) 89 9895917
Web Site: http://www.admetech.co.jp
Year Founded: 2003
Sales Range: Less than $1 Million
Medical Device Mfr
N.A.I.C.G.: 000112
Toshio Furukawa *(Pres)*

AD MISSIONS
120 Avenue Charles De Gaulle,
92200, Neuilly-sur-Seine, Hauts De
Seine, France
Tel.: (33) 141929860
Web Site: http://www.admissions.fr
Rev.: $20,900,000
Emp.: 23
Management Consulting Services
N.A.I.C.S.: 541618
Richard Puybasset *(Dir)*

AD PEPPER MEDIA INTERNATIONAL NV
Frankenstrasse 150 C, 90461,
Nuremberg, Germany
Tel.: (49) 9119290570
Web Site: https://www.adpepper.com
Year Founded: 1999
APM—(DEU)
Rev.: $24,009,172
Assets: $47,400,178
Liabilities: $27,905,834
Net Worth: $19,494,344
Earnings: ($1,037,638)
Emp.: 217
Fiscal Year-end: 12/31/23
Advertising, Affiliate Marketing, Public
Relations
N.A.I.C.S.: 541810
Jens Korner *(CEO)*

Subsidiaries:

Ad Agents AG   **(1)**
Europaallee 41, 8004, Zurich, Switzerland
Tel.: (41) 442146980
Web Site: https://www.ad-agents.ch
Digital Marketing Services
N.A.I.C.S.: 541810

EMSEAS TEKNIK AB   **(1)**
Drottninggatan 67, 111 36, Stockholm, Sweden
Tel.: (46) 8 562 604 50
Advetising Agency
N.A.I.C.S.: 541810

Webgains GmbH   **(1)**
Frankenstrasse 150C, 90461, Nuremberg,
Germany
Tel.: (49) 89248830039
Marketing Service Provider
N.A.I.C.S.: 541810

Webgains Ltd.   **(1)**
Third Floor 21 Farringdon Road, London,
EC1M 3HA, United Kingdom
Tel.: (44) 2075096393
Web Site: https://www.webgains.com
Affiliate Advertising
N.A.I.C.S.: 541810
Richard Dennys *(CEO)*

Webgains S.L.   **(1)**
Avenida Alberto Alcocer 46A 4A, 28016,
Madrid, Spain
Tel.: (34) 914177455
Marketing & Advertiser Services
N.A.I.C.S.: 541810

ad agents GmbH   **(1)**
Am Joachimsberg 10-12, 71083, Herrenberg, Germany
Tel.: (49) 70329969800
Web Site: https://www.ad-agents.com
Advetising Agency
N.A.I.C.S.: 541810
Dirk Lajosbanyai *(Mng Dir)*

ad pepper media France
S.A.R.L.   **(1)**

92 Rue De Richelieu Drouot, 75002, Paris,
France
Tel.: (33) 158562929
Emp.: 230
Advetising Agency
N.A.I.C.S.: 541810

ad pepper media GmbH   **(1)**
Frankenstrasse 150 D, FrankenCampus,
D-90461, Nuremberg, Germany
Tel.: (49) 9111313460
Web Site: https://adpepper.com
Advetising Agency
N.A.I.C.S.: 541810

ad pepper media Spain S.A.   **(1)**
Avda Alberto Alcocer 46 1A, 28016, Madrid,
Spain
Tel.: (34) 914177450
Web Site: https://adpepper.com
Advetising Agency
N.A.I.C.S.: 541810

ad pepper media UK Ltd   **(1)**
3rd Floor Buchanan House 30 Holborn,
London, EC1N 2HS, United Kingdom
Tel.: (44) 207 269 1200
Web Site: http://www.adpepper.co.uk
Advetising Services
N.A.I.C.S.: 541810

ad pepper media USA LLC   **(1)**
225 W 39th St 6th Fl Ste 600, New York,
NY 10018
Tel.: (212) 391-7317
Advetising Agency
N.A.I.C.S.: 541810

AD PK SOMBOR HOLDING CO.
Preradoviceva 71, Petrovaradin, Serbia
Tel.: (381) 25 437 495
Web Site: http://www.pksombor.co.rs
Year Founded: 1989
PKSO—(BEL)
Sales Range: Less than $1 Million
Emp.: 3
Holding Company
N.A.I.C.S.: 551112
Jovan Dikic *(CEO)*

AD PLASTIK D.D.
Matoseva 8, 21210, Solin, Croatia
Tel.: (385) 21206444
Web Site: https://www.adplastik.hr
Year Founded: 1992
ADPL—(ZAG)
Rev.: $117,805,238
Assets: $193,486,468
Liabilities: $82,511,728
Net Worth: $110,974,740
Earnings: ($10,403,824)
Emp.: 1,983
Fiscal Year-end: 12/31/22
Plastics Product Mfr
N.A.I.C.S.: 326199
Mladen Peros *(Member-Mgmt Bd-Sls & Project)*

Subsidiaries:

AD PLASTIK d.o.o.   **(1)**
Belokranjska Cesta 4, 8000, Novo Mesto,
Slovenia
Tel.: (386) 73379820
Plastics Product Mfr
N.A.I.C.S.: 326199

AD Plastik Tisza Kft.   **(1)**
TVK Ipartelep 2117/12 hrsz, 3580, Tiszajvaros, Hungary
Tel.: (36) 49887610
Automotive Component Mfr & Distr
N.A.I.C.S.: 336390

AD Plastik d.d. - Zagreb Plant 1   **(1)**
Jankomir 5, 10000, Zagreb, Croatia
Tel.: (385) 14803999
Plastics Product Mfr
N.A.I.C.S.: 326199

AD Plastik d.d. - Zagreb Plant 2   **(1)**
Jankomir 25, 10000, Zagreb, Croatia
Tel.: (385) 13473501
Plastics Product Mfr

N.A.I.C.S.: 326199

ADP d.o.o.   **(1)**
Ulica Kralja Petra I 334, 11400, Mladenovac, Serbia
Tel.: (381) 117152999
Plastics Product Mfr
N.A.I.C.S.: 326199

AO AD Plastik Togliatti   **(1)**
Sadovaya 13 Vintay, krasnoglinsky, 443902,
Samara, Russia
Tel.: (7) 8482692830
Plastics Product Mfr
N.A.I.C.S.: 326199

Tisza Automotive Kft   **(1)**
TKV Ipartelep 2117/12 Hrsz, 3580, Tiszajvaros, Hungary
Tel.: (36) 49887610
Web Site: http://www.t-a.hu
Emp.: 400
Automotive Vehicle Parts Mfr & Distr
N.A.I.C.S.: 336390
Sandor Kelemen *(Dir-Comml)*

ZAO AD Plastik Kaluga   **(1)**
Skladskaja 6, 248016, Kaluga, Kaluska
oblast, Russia
Tel.: (7) 4842714870
Plastics Product Mfr
N.A.I.C.S.: 326199

AD PUTEVI UZICE
38 Nikole Pasica St, 31000, Uzice,
Serbia
Tel.: (381) 31512822
Web Site:
  https://www.puteviuzice.com
Year Founded: 1962
PUUE—(BEL)
Rev.: $83,441,961
Assets: $71,092,650
Liabilities: $51,520,095
Net Worth: $19,572,555
Earnings: $3,050,669
Emp.: 9,000
Fiscal Year-end: 12/31/23
Road Construction Services
N.A.I.C.S.: 237310
Vasilije Micic *(Chm-Mgmt Bd)*

AD SERVO MIHALJ INZENJERING
Petra Drapsina 15, 23 000, Zrenjanin,
Serbia
Tel.: (381) 23 544 725
Web Site: http://www.sming.co.rs
Year Founded: 1947
Emp.: 25
Engineering & Consulting Services
N.A.I.C.S.: 541330

AD VETPRODUKT
Vojvode Stepe BB, 78430, Prnjavor,
Bosnia & Herzegovina
Tel.: (387) 51863222
Web Site: http://www.vetprodukt-prnjavor.com
Year Founded: 1989
VTPR—(BANJ)
Sales Range: Less than $1 Million
Emp.: 24
Chicken Egg Production Services
N.A.I.C.S.: 112310

AD-COMM CO., LTD.
Tech Hiroo Building Hiroo 9F 1-10-5,
Shibuya-ku, Tokyo, 150-0012, Japan
Tel.: (81) 354235335   **JP**
Web Site: http://www.ad-comm.com
Year Founded: 1987
Sales Range: $10-24.9 Million
Emp.: 100
Advetising Agency
N.A.I.C.S.: 541810
Andreas Dannenberg *(Pres & CEO)*

Subsidiaries:

Ad-comm Group Inc.   **(1)**
500 S Raymond Ave, Pasadena, CA 91105

Tel.: (626) 792-9600
Web Site: http://www.ad-comm.com
Advetising Agency
N.A.I.C.S.: 541810

Ad-event K.K. **(1)**
Tech Hiroo Bldg 3F Hiroo 1-10-5, Shibuya-
ku, Tokyo, 150-0012, Japan
Tel.: (81) 354235341
Web Site: http://www.ad-comm.com
N.A.I.C.S.: 541810

Ad-media K.K **(1)**
Tech Hiroo Building 9F Hiroo 1-10-5,
Shibuya-ku, Tokyo, 150-0012, Japan
Tel.: (81) 354235421
Web Site: http://www.ad-comm.com
N.A.I.C.S.: 541810
Andreas Dannenberg *(Pres & CEO)*

BrandVision K.K. **(1)**
Tech Hiroo Bldg 9F Hiroo 1-10-5, Shibuya-
ku, Tokyo, 150-0012, Japan
Tel.: (81) 354235336
Web Site: http://www.ad-comm.com
Emp.: 80
N.A.I.C.S.: 541810
Andreas Dannenberg *(Mng Dir)*

Capital IR K.K. **(1)**
Tech Hiroo Bldg 9F Hiroo 1-10-5, Shibuya-
ku, Tokyo, 150-0012, Japan
Tel.: (81) 354236651
Web Site: http://www.ad-comm.com
N.A.I.C.S.: 541810
Siobhan Keaton *(Dir-Client Svcs)*

CyberMedia K.K. **(1)**
Tech Hiroo Bldg 1F Hiroo 1-10-5, Shibuya-
ku, Tokyo, 150-0012, Japan
Tel.: (81) 354235333
Web Site: http://www.ad-comm.com
N.A.I.C.S.: 541810
Marco Koeder *(Pres)*

Trimedia K.K. **(1)**
Tech Hiroo Bldg 2F Hiroo 1-10-5, Shibuya-
ku, Tokyo, 150-0012, Japan
Tel.: (81) 354235330
Web Site: http://www.ad-comm.com
N.A.I.C.S.: 541810
Andreas Dannenberg *(Pres & CEO)*

AD-MANUM FINANCE LTD.
Agarwal House 5 Yeshwant Colony,
Indore, 452003, MP, India
Tel.: (91) 7314714000
Web Site:
    https://www.admanumfinance.com
511359—(BOM)
Rev.: $1,217,084
Assets: $8,965,847
Liabilities: $1,231,362
Net Worth: $7,734,485
Earnings: $331,813
Emp.: 6
Fiscal Year-end: 03/31/22
Vehicle Finance Services
N.A.I.C.S.: 525990
Mohammad Raees *(Officer-
Compliance & Nodal)*

AD-SOL NISSIN CORPORA-
TION
Rivarge Shinagawa 4-1-8 Konan Mi-
nato Ward, Tokyo, 108-0075, Japan
Tel.: (81) 357963131
Web Site: http://www.adniss.jp
Year Founded: 1976
3837—(TKS)
Rev.: $93,055,580
Assets: $67,428,610
Liabilities: $19,241,710
Net Worth: $48,186,900
Earnings: $6,471,190
Emp.: 645
Fiscal Year-end: 03/31/24
Information Systems Solutions
N.A.I.C.S.: 519290
Tomizo Ueda *(Chm, Pres & CEO)*

AD1 HOLDINGS LIMITED
Level 4 90 William Street, Melbourne,
3000, VIC, Australia

Tel.: (61) 381990455   AU
Web Site:
    https://www.ad1holdings.com.au
Year Founded: 2008
AD1—(ASX)
Rev.: $3,890,771
Assets: $5,449,669
Liabilities: $5,331,484
Net Worth: $118,186
Earnings: ($876,418)
Fiscal Year-end: 06/30/24
Holding Company; Online Recruit-
ment Portal Provider
N.A.I.C.S.: 551112
Todd Perkinson *(CEO)*

Subsidiaries:

Utility Software Services Pty. Ltd. **(1)**
Suite 102/697 Burke Rd, Hawthorn East,
3123, VIC, Australia
Tel.: (61) 1300255877
Web Site:
    http://www.utilitysoftwareservices.com
Software Development Services
N.A.I.C.S.: 541511
Danny Milsom *(Sls Dir)*

ADACEL TECHNOLOGIES LIM-
ITED
Suite 31 Level 4 150 Albert Road,
South Melbourne, 3205, VIC, Austra-
lia
Tel.: (61) 370246060   AU
Web Site: https://www.adacel.com
Year Founded: 1987
ADA—(ASX)
Rev.: $30,971,000
Assets: $26,101,000
Liabilities: $20,793,000
Net Worth: $5,308,000
Earnings: ($4,405,000)
Emp.: 75
Fiscal Year-end: 06/30/24
Software Design Services for Aviation
N.A.I.C.S.: 541512
Brian Hennessey *(VP-Business
Development-Strategic Planning)*

Subsidiaries:

Adacel Inc. **(1)**
895 Rue De La Gauchetiere West Suite
300, PO Box 48, Montreal, H3B 4G1, QC,
Canada
Tel.: (514) 636-6365
Sales Range: $25-49.9 Million
Emp.: 120
Software Solutions
N.A.I.C.S.: 541511

Adacel Systems, Inc. **(1)**
9677 Tradeport Dr, Orlando, FL 32827-5318
Tel.: (407) 581-1560
Web Site: http://www.adacel.com
Sales Range: $1-9.9 Million
Emp.: 43
Search & Navigation Equipments Mfr
N.A.I.C.S.: 334511

ADAGENE INC.
4F Building C14 No 218 Xinghu
Street Suzhou Industrial Park, Su-
zhou, 25125, Jiangsu, China
Tel.: (86) 51287773632   Ky
Web Site: https://www.adagene.com
Year Founded: 2011
ADAG—(NASDAQ)
Rev.: $18,111,491
Assets: $115,728,838
Liabilities: $45,169,341
Net Worth: $70,559,497
Earnings: ($18,946,370)
Emp.: 174
Fiscal Year-end: 12/31/23
Biotechnology Research & Develop-
ment Services
N.A.I.C.S.: 541714
Peter Luo *(Founder, Chm & CEO)*

ADAIRS LIMITED
2 International Court, Caribbean Busi-
ness Park, Scoresby, 3179, VIC, Aus-
tralia
Tel.: (61) 388884500   AU
Web Site: https://www.adairs.com.au
Year Founded: 1918
ADH—(ASX)
Rev.: $421,575,798
Assets: $404,348,682
Liabilities: $267,141,734
Net Worth: $137,206,948
Earnings: $25,676,476
Fiscal Year-end: 06/25/23
Bed Linen, Bedding Products, Tow-
els, Cushions, Throws, Homewares,
Wall Art & Furniture Retailer
N.A.I.C.S.: 449129

ADALTA LIMITED
Room 204 LIMS2 La Trobe Institute
of Molecular Science Science Drive,
La Trobe University, Melbourne,
3086, VIC, Australia
Tel.: (61) 394795159   AU
Web Site: https://www.adalta.com.au
Year Founded: 2006
1AD—(ASX)
Rev.: $1,191,589
Assets: $3,721,288
Liabilities: $2,365,488
Net Worth: $1,355,800
Earnings: ($3,593,262)
Emp.: 9
Fiscal Year-end: 06/30/24
Drug Mfr
N.A.I.C.S.: 325412
Paul MacLeman *(Chm)*

ADAM SUGAR MILLS LIMITED
Haji Adam Chambers Altaf Hussain
Road New Challi, Karachi, 2, Paki-
stan
Tel.: (92) 32401139
Web Site: https://www.adam.com.pk
Year Founded: 1965
ADAMS—(PSX)
Rev.: $19,521,476
Assets: $31,698,839
Liabilities: $11,971,560
Net Worth: $19,727,279
Earnings: $364,512
Emp.: 479
Fiscal Year-end: 09/30/23
Sugar Mfr
N.A.I.C.S.: 311314
Qamar Rafi Khan *(Sec & Dir-Fin)*

ADAMANT DRI PROCESSING
& MINERALS GROUP
4D Block D Nanhai Building, Nan-
shan District, Shenzhen, 075600,
China
Tel.: (86) 18126523457   NV
Web Site: http://www.adamant-
dri.com
ADMG—(OTCIQ)
Rev.: $48,749
Assets: $536,815
Liabilities: $91,115
Net Worth: $445,700
Earnings: $21,255,066
Emp.: 7
Fiscal Year-end: 12/31/18
Iron Ore Processing Services
N.A.I.C.S.: 212210
Jing Xie *(CEO & CFO)*

ADAMANT HOLDING INC.
1200-750 West Pender Street, Van-
couver, V6C 2T8, BC, Canada
Tel.: (646) 766-1275   BC
Web Site: https://adamantglobal.com
Year Founded: 2012
UCCPF—(OTCEM)
Rev.: $496,221
Assets: $1,465,455
Liabilities: $522,866

Net Worth: $942,589
Earnings: ($684,380)
Fiscal Year-end: 12/31/21
Metal Mining
N.A.I.C.S.: 212290
Andrea Pagani *(CEO)*

Subsidiaries:

Upco Systems Inc. **(1)**
747 3rd Ave 2nd Fl 116, New York, NY
10017
Tel.: (212) 461-3676
Telecom Services
N.A.I.C.S.: 517810

ADAMANTEM CAPITAL MAN-
AGEMENT PTY LIMITED
Level 27 Chifley Tower, 2 Chifley
Square, Sydney, 2000, NSW, Austra-
lia
Tel.: (61) 290046060
Web Site: http://adamantem.com.au
Privater Equity Firm
N.A.I.C.S.: 523999
Andrew Bullock *(Mng Dir)*

Subsidiaries:

Legend Corporation Limited **(1)**
1 Butler Drive, Hendon, 5014, SA, Australia
Tel.: (61) 884019888
Web Site: http://www.legendcorporate.com
Rev.: $89,679,081
Assets: $109,146,063
Liabilities: $52,406,782
Net Worth: $56,739,282
Earnings: $4,665,769
Emp.: 100
Fiscal Year-end: 06/30/2018
Electric, Information Technology & Semicon-
ductor Services
N.A.I.C.S.: 335999
Bradley R. Dowe *(CEO & Mng Dir)*

Subsidiary (Domestic):

Cable Accessories (Australia) Pty
Ltd **(2)**
8 Distribution Pl, PO Box 72, Seven Hills,
Sydney, 2147, NSW, Australia
Tel.: (61) 133122
Web Site: http://www.cabac.com.au
Sales Range: $25-49.9 Million
Computer Terminal Mfr
N.A.I.C.S.: 334118
Bradley Dowe *(CEO)*

Legend Corporate Services Pty
Ltd **(2)**
1 Butler Dr, Hendon, 5014, SA, Australia
Tel.: (61) 884019888
Web Site: http://www.legend.com.au
Sales Range: $50-74.9 Million
Emp.: 220
Computer Peripherals Mfr
N.A.I.C.S.: 334118
Bradley Dowe *(CEO)*

QANTM Intellectual Property
Limited **(1)**
1 Nicholson Street, Melbourne, 3002, VIC,
Australia
Tel.: (61) 392542666
Web Site: http://www.qantmip.com
Rev.: $97,519,131
Assets: $109,378,986
Liabilities: $54,255,446
Net Worth: $55,123,540
Earnings: $5,472,129
Emp.: 380
Fiscal Year-end: 06/30/2022
Intellectual Property Services
N.A.I.C.S.: 541199
Craig Dower *(CEO & Mng Dir)*

Subsidiary (Non-US):

Advanz Fidelis IP Sdn Bhd **(2)**
Suite 609 Block D Phileo Damansara 1 No
9 Jalan 16/11, 46350, Petaling Jaya, Selan-
gor, Malaysia
Tel.: (60) 379571472
Web Site: https://www.dccadvanz.com
Legal Aid Services
N.A.I.C.S.: 541110

DCC Hong Kong Ltd. **(2)**

Adamantem Capital Management Pty
Limited—(Continued)

General Post Office, PO Box 6523, Central,
China (Hong Kong)
Tel.: (852) 64282667
Web Site: https://www.dcc.hk
Civic & Social Organization Services
N.A.I.C.S.: 813410

Davies Collison Cave Asia Pte
Ltd   (2)
10 Collyer Quay 07-01 Ocean Financial
Centre, Singapore, 049315, Singapore
Tel.: (65) 67273777
Web Site: http://www.davies.com.sg
Intellectual Property Services
N.A.I.C.S.: 541199
Thomas Griffiths *(Mng Principal & Atty-Patent)*

FPA Patent Attorneys Asia Pte
Ltd.   (2)
10 Collyer Quay 40-39 Ocean Financial
Centre, Singapore, 049315, Singapore
Tel.: (65) 69569944
Legal Aid Services
N.A.I.C.S.: 541110

Subsidiary (Domestic):

FPA Patent Attorneys Pty Ltd   (2)
Level 42 Level 43 101 Collins Street, Melbourne, 3000, VIC, Australia
Tel.: (61) 386627300
Web Site: http://www.fpapatents.com
Intellectual Property Services
N.A.I.C.S.: 541199
Anna Rosemeyer *(Head-People & Culture)*

Zenitas Healthcare Limited   (1)
Level 9 417 St Kilda Road, Melbourne,
3004, VIC, Australia
Tel.: (61) 398213701
Web Site: http://www.zenitas.com.au
Healtcare Services
N.A.I.C.S.: 621491
Justin Walter *(CEO & Mng Dir)*

Subsidiary (Domestic):

Modern Medical Group Pty Ltd   (2)
Office 1 379-381 Whitehorse Road, Balwyn,
3103, VIC, Australia
Tel.: (61) 388091200
Web Site:
   http://www.modernmedical.com.au
Health Care Srvices
N.A.I.C.S.: 621498
Todd Cameron *(Founder)*

NexttCare Pty Ltd   (2)
Unit 2 Railway Parade Camberwell, Melbourne, 3124, VIC, Australia
Tel.: (61) 398299120
Web Site: http://www.nextt.com.au
Women Healthcare Services
N.A.I.C.S.: 621610

Zenitas Caring Choice Pty Ltd   (2)
2/315 Unley Road, Malvern, 5061, SA, Australia
Tel.: (61) 881221433
Web Site: http://www.zenitascare.com.au
Women Healthcare Services
N.A.I.C.S.: 621610

Zenitas Ontrac Pty Ltd   (2)
Whiteman s Arcade Ste 4 100 Argyle
Street, Camden Park, 2570, NSW, Australia
Tel.: (61) 246552266
Web Site: http://ontrachealth.com.au
Exercise Physiology Services
N.A.I.C.S.: 621340

ADAMAS INCORPORATION PUBLIC COMPANY LIMITED
344/1 Soi Soonvijai 4 Rama 9 Road,
Bangkapi Huai Khwang, Bangkok,
10310, Thailand
Tel.: (66) 2719 6720
Web Site: http://www.adamas.co.th
Year Founded: 2002
Sales Range: $1-9.9 Million
Holding Company
N.A.I.C.S.: 551112

ADAMAS VENTURES, INC.

Room 1403 No 408 Jie Fang Zhong
Road, Guangzhou, 510030, Guangdong, China
Tel.: (86) 20288808   NV
Year Founded: 2014
ADMV—(OTCBB)
Baby Products Distr
N.A.I.C.S.: 423920
Jinshan Dai *(Pres, Sec & Treas)*

ADAMERA MINERALS CORP.
11th Floor - 1111 Melville St, Vancouver, V6E 3V6, BC, Canada
Tel.: (604) 689-2010   Ca
Web Site: https://www.adamera.com
Year Founded: 2006
AQMO—(DEU)
Rev.: $75,307
Assets: $6,587,535
Liabilities: $771,978
Net Worth: $5,815,556
Earnings: ($1,047,982)
Fiscal Year-end: 12/31/23
Gold & Silver Exploration Services
N.A.I.C.S.: 213114
Mark Kolebaba *(Pres & CEO)*

ADAMJEE INSURANCE COMPANY LIMITED
Adamjee House 80/A Block E-1 Main
Boulevard Gulberg-III, Lahore, 54000,
Pakistan
Tel.: (92) 4235772960   PK
Web Site:
   https://www.adamjeeinsurance.com
Year Founded: 1960
AICL—(KAR)
Rev.: $179,035,272
Assets: $573,192,651
Liabilities: $431,481,172
Net Worth: $141,711,479
Earnings: $13,073,722
Emp.: 1,900
Fiscal Year-end: 12/31/19
Marine, Fire, Motor & Medical Insurance Services
N.A.I.C.S.: 524128
Muhammad Ali Zeb *(CEO & Mng Dir)*

Subsidiaries:

Adamjee Insurance Company
Limited   (1)
The City Business Centre Suite 18, 2 London Wall Building, London Wall, London,
EC2M 5UU, United Kingdom
Tel.: (44) 20 75885506
Insurance Services
N.A.I.C.S.: 524298

Adamjee Life Assurance Company
Limited   (1)
3rd and 4th Floor Adamjee House I I Chundrigar Road, Karachi, 74000, Sindh, Pakistan
Tel.: (92) 21111115433
Web Site: https://www.adamjeelife.com
Fire Insurance Services
N.A.I.C.S.: 524113
Manzar Mushtaq *(CEO)*

ADAMS ENTERPRISES (1993) LTD
PO Box 973, Whitecourt, T7S 1N9,
AB, Canada
Tel.: (780) 778-8440
Year Founded: 1991
Rev.: $14,503,435
Emp.: 40
General Freight Trucking Services
N.A.I.C.S.: 484110
Sharon Adams *(Owner)*

ADAMS PLC
55 Athol Street, Douglas, IM1 1LA,
Isle of Man
Tel.: (44) 1624681250   IM
Web Site:
   https://www.adamsplc.co.uk

Year Founded: 2005
ADA—(AIM)
Assets: $6,504,671
Liabilities: $54,279
Net Worth: $6,450,391
Earnings: ($2,991,669)
Emp.: 3
Fiscal Year-end: 03/31/23
Heal Estate Investment Services
N.A.I.C.S.: 531390
Philip Peter Scales *(Sec)*

ADAMSON ASSOCIATES ARCHITECTS
401 Wellington St W 3rd Floor, Toronto, M5V 1E7, ON, Canada
Tel.: (416) 967-1500
Web Site: http://www.adamson-associates.com
Year Founded: 1934
Rev.: $10,000,000
Emp.: 200
Architectural Services
N.A.I.C.S.: 541310
Alan Tearle *(Principal)*

Subsidiaries:

AAI Architects, P.C.   (1)
14 Wall St 2nd Fl, New York, NY 10005
Tel.: (212) 964-4040
Architectural Services
N.A.I.C.S.: 541310
Nick Zigomanis *(Principal)*

Adamson Associates (International)
Limited   (1)
6th floor One Canada Square Canary
Wharf, London, E14 5AB, United Kingdom
Tel.: (44) 2074182068
Architectural Services
N.A.I.C.S.: 541310
Megan Beth Royston *(Principal)*

Adamson Associates, Inc.   (1)
17383 W Sunset Blvd B-200, Pacific Palisades, CA 90272
Tel.: (310) 230-0088
Architectural Services
N.A.I.C.S.: 541310
George Metzger *(Principal)*

ADANI ENERGY SOLUTIONS LIMITED
Shantigram Near Vaishnodevi Circle
S G Highway, Navarangpura,
Ahmedabad, 382421, Gujarat, India
Tel.: (91) 7925555555
Web Site:
   https://www.adanienergysolutions.com
ADANIENSOL—(NSE)
Rev.: $1,659,428,092
Assets: $6,466,249,026
Liabilities: $4,936,365,925
Net Worth: $1,529,883,101
Earnings: $153,539,956
Emp.: 5,002
Fiscal Year-end: 03/31/23
Electric Power Distr
N.A.I.C.S.: 221122
Gautam Adani *(Founder & Chm)*

Subsidiaries:

Adani Electricity Mumbai Limited (1)
Devidas Lane Off SVP Road, Near Devidas
Telephone Exchange Borivali W, Mumbai,
400 103, Maharashtra, India
Tel.: (91) 2250745004
Web Site: https://www.adanielectricity.com
Electric Power Distribution Services
N.A.I.C.S.: 221122

ADANI ENTERPRISES LIMITED
Shantigram Near Vaishnodevi Circle
S G Highway, Ahmedabad, 382421,
Gujarat, India
Tel.: (91) 7926565555   In
Web Site:
   https://www.adanienterprises.com

Year Founded: 1988
512599—(BOM)
Rev.: $5,499,711,945
Assets: $7,049,250,390
Liabilities: $4,468,034,025
Net Worth: $2,581,216,365
Earnings: $142,746,240
Emp.: 790
Fiscal Year-end: 03/31/21
Other Airport Operations Services
N.A.I.C.S.: 488119
Gautam S. Adani *(Founder & Chm)*

Subsidiaries:

AMG Media Networks Limited   (1)
Shantigram Near Vaishnodevi Circle S G
Highway, Ahmedabad, 382421, Gujarat,
India
Tel.: (91) 7926565555
Agro Products, Fertilizers, Petrochemicals,
Petroleum & Lubricants Trading Services
N.A.I.C.S.: 425120

Adani Aerospace & Defence
Limited   (1)
Shantigram Near Vaishnodevi Circle S G
Highway, Ahmedabad, 382 421, Gujarat,
India
Tel.: (91) 7926565555
Web Site: https://www.adanidefence.com
Aircraft Mfr
N.A.I.C.S.: 336411
Hardik Shah *(Head-IT)*

Adani Agri Fresh Ltd   (1)
Plot No 83 Institutional Area Sector 32, Gurgaon, 122001, Haryana, India
Tel.: (91) 9873588521
Web Site: http://www.farmpik.com
Emp.: 100
Fruit Whslr
N.A.I.C.S.: 424480
Srinivasan Ramanujam *(Head-Bus)*

Adani Agri Logistics Ltd   (1)
Adani House Plot No 83, Institutional Area
Sector 32, Gurgaon, 122001, Haryana, India
Tel.: (91) 1242555555
Sales Range: $25-49.9 Million
Emp.: 250
Logistics Consulting Servies
N.A.I.C.S.: 541614

Subsidiary (Domestic):

Snowman Logistics Ltd.   (2)
No 54 Old Madras Road, Virgonagar, Bengaluru, 560 049, Karnataka, India (70.5%)
Tel.: (91) 8067693700
Web Site: https://www.snowman.in
Rev.: $32,838,324
Assets: $91,013,928
Liabilities: $33,706,245
Net Worth: $57,307,682
Earnings: $81,900
Emp.: 424
Fiscal Year-end: 03/31/2021
Integrated Temperature Controlled Logistics
Services
N.A.I.C.S.: 493120
A. M. Sundar *(CFO, Compliance Officer & Sec)*

Adani Airport Holdings Limited   (1)
Shantigram Near Vaishnodevi Circle S G
Highway, Ahmedabad, 382421, Gujarat,
India
Tel.: (91) 7926565555
Web Site: https://www.adaniairports.com
N.A.I.C.S.: 713910
Gautam Adani *(Chm)*

Adani Bunkering Private Limited   (1)
Adani Corporate House - 2 Aravalli Building
12th Floor, Adani Shantigram Near
Vaishnodevi Circle S G Highway, Ahmedabad, 382 421, Gujarat, India
Tel.: (91) 7926565555
Web Site: https://www.adanibunkering.com
Petroleum Product Distr
N.A.I.C.S.: 424720
Vinay Prakash *(CEO)*

Adani Gas Ltd   (1)
8th Floor Heritage Building Nr Gujarat Vidhyapith Bh Visnaga, Nagrik Bank Usmanpura, Ahmedabad, Gujarat, India

Tel.: (91) 7927623264
Web Site: http://www.adanigas.com
Natural Gas Distribution Services
N.A.I.C.S.: 221210

Adani Global FZE **(1)**
Jebel Ali Free Zone, PO Box 17186,
Dubai, United Arab Emirates
Tel.: (971) 48818048
Ferrous & Non Ferrous Metals Import &
Distr
N.A.I.C.S.: 237120

Adani Global Ltd. **(1)**
Suite 501 Saint James Court Saint Denis
Street, Port Louis, Mauritius
Tel.: (230) 2109961
Oil & Gas Exploration Services
N.A.I.C.S.: 213112
Rajiv Reemul *(Dir)*

Adani Green Energy Ltd. **(1)**
Adani Corporate House, Shantigram Near
Vaishnodevi Circle S G Highway, Ahmeda-
bad, 382 421, India
Tel.: (91) 7926565555
Web Site:
　https://www.adanigreenenergy.com
Rev.: $1,257,078,616
Assets: $10,640,461,425
Liabilities: $8,543,567,764
Net Worth: $2,096,893,661
Earnings: $151,426,296
Emp.: 1,597
Fiscal Year-end: 03/31/2024
Semiconductor Devices Mfr
N.A.I.C.S.: 334413
Kaushal Shah *(CFO)*

Adani Infrastructure Private
Limited **(1)**
Nr Mithakhali Circle, Navrangpura, Ahmeda-
bad, 380 009, Gujarat, India
Tel.: (91) 7926565555
Web Site: http://www.adaniinfra.com
Electric Power Transmission Services
N.A.I.C.S.: 221121

Adani Ports and Special Economic
Zone Limited **(1)**
Adani Corporate House Shantigram Near
Vaishnodevi Circle S G Highway, Ahmeda-
bad, 382421, Gujarat, India
Tel.: (91) 7926565555
Web Site: https://www.adaniports.com
Rev.: $2,686,336,551
Assets: $13,776,767,580
Liabilities: $8,150,954,979
Net Worth: $5,625,812,601
Earnings: $646,573,946
Emp.: 1,426
Fiscal Year-end: 03/31/2023
Port Operations
N.A.I.C.S.: 488310
Karan Adani *(Mng Dir)*

Subsidiary (Domestic):

Adani Logistics Ltd **(2)**
Infrastructure House Nr Mithakhali Circle,
Navrangpura Ahmedabad, Ahmedabad,
India
Tel.: (91) 7925555801
Logistic Services
N.A.I.C.S.: 541614
Manoj Yadav *(Asst Mgr-HR & Admin)*

Adani Power Limited **(1)**
Shantigram Near Vaishnodevi Circle S G
Highway, Ahmedabad, 382421, Gujarat,
India **(81.53%)**
Tel.: (91) 7926565555
Web Site: http://www.adanipower.com
Rev.: $5,160,424,435
Assets: $10,289,703,255
Liabilities: $6,707,704,574
Net Worth: $3,581,998,681
Earnings: $1,286,090,762
Emp.: 2,805
Fiscal Year-end: 03/31/2023
Power Generator & Distr
N.A.I.C.S.: 221122
Gautam S. Adani *(Chm)*

Subsidiary (Domestic):

Udupi Power Corporation Limited **(2)**
Lotus Towers 1st Floor 34 Devaraja Urs
Road Race Course, Race Course, Benga-
luru, 560 001, Karnataka, India

Tel.: (91) 804 025 4025
Web Site: https://www.adanipower.com
Power Plant Construction Services
N.A.I.C.S.: 237130

Adani Welspun Exploration
Limited **(1)**
Welspun House 3rd Floor Kamala City
Lower Parel West, Mumbai, 400 013, India
Tel.: (91) 2266136000
Web Site: http://www.adaniwelspun.com
Oil & Gas Exploration Services
N.A.I.C.S.: 213112
Sandeep Garg *(Mng Dir)*

Ambuja Cements Ltd **(1)**
Elegant Business Park MIDC Cross Road B
Off Andheri-Kurla Road, Andheri E, Mum-
bai, 400059, India **(63.15%)**
Tel.: (91) 2240667000
Web Site: https://www.ambujacement.com
Rev.: $4,756,877,885
Assets: $6,201,242,132
Liabilities: $1,554,452,371
Net Worth: $4,646,789,761
Earnings: $309,741,622
Emp.: 2,819
Fiscal Year-end: 03/31/2023
Cement Mfr
N.A.I.C.S.: 327120
Gautam S. Adani *(Chm)*

Subsidiary (Domestic):

Ambuja Cement Rajasthan Ltd. **(2)**
Rabriyawas Tehsil-Jaitaran, Rajasthan State
Highway 59, Jaipur, 306709, Rajasthan,
India
Tel.: (91) 2939 288 011
Cement Mfr
N.A.I.C.S.: 327310

Dirk India Private Limited **(2)**
Plot No 10 India House Gitanjali Colony
Indira Nagar Mumbai-Agra Road, Nashik,
422 009, Maharashtra, India
Tel.: (91) 2532322815
Web Site: http://www.pozzocrete.co.in
Emp.: 76
Cement Mfr
N.A.I.C.S.: 327310
Ranjit Varma *(Head-Unit)*

Lucky Minmat Limited **(2)**
Lakheri Cement Works, PO 323 603, Bundi
District, Bundi, 323 603, Rajasthan, India
Tel.: (91) 7438261642
Cement Mfr
N.A.I.C.S.: 327310

OneIndia BSC Private Limited **(2)**
Crescent-1 12th Floor Prestige Shanthinike-
than Whitefield Main Road, Bengaluru, 560
048, India
Tel.: (91) 8046529500
Web Site: http://www.oneindiabsc.com
Cement Mfr
N.A.I.C.S.: 327310
Narendra Jawahrani *(CEO)*

Sanghi Industries Ltd **(2)**
10th Floor Kataria Arcade Off S G Highway,
Makarba District, Ahmedabad, 380 051,
India **(54.51%)**
Tel.: (91) 7926838000
Web Site: https://www.sanghicement.com
Rev.: $129,425,205
Assets: $491,959,650
Liabilities: $247,114,140
Net Worth: $244,845,510
Earnings: $10,672,935
Emp.: 798
Fiscal Year-end: 03/31/2021
Cement
N.A.I.C.S.: 423320
Ravi Sanghi *(Chm & Mng Dir)*

Mundra Solar Technopark Private
Limited **(1)**
Adani House Nr Mithakali Crossing,
Navrangpura, Ahmedabad, 380 009, Guja-
rat, India
Tel.: (91) 7926565555
Web Site: https://www.mundraemc.com
Solar Product Mfr
N.A.I.C.S.: 334413

PT Adani Global **(1)**
Trinity Tower 47th Floor Jl H R Rasuna Said
Kav C22 Block IIB, Jakarta Selatan, 12940,
Indonesia

Tel.: (62) 2150916720
Oil & Gas Exploration Services
N.A.I.C.S.: 213112

Rahi Shipping Pte. Ltd **(1)**
10 Anson Road 34 16 International Plaza,
Singapore, 079903, Singapore
Tel.: (65) 65764621
Web Site: http://www.adanipower.com
Sales Range: $25-49.9 Million
Emp.: 4
Ship Management Services
N.A.I.C.S.: 483111

Vanshi Shipping Pte. Ltd **(1)**
80 Raffels Place UOB Plaza 2 Level 33,
Singapore, 48624, Singapore
Tel.: (65) 65764621
Sales Range: $75-99.9 Million
Emp.: 25
Shipping Services
N.A.I.C.S.: 483111

ADANI WILMAR LTD.
Fortune House Nr Navrangpura Rail-
way Crossing, Ahmedabad, 380 009,
Gujarat, India
Tel.: (91) 7926455650
Web Site:
　https://www.adaniwilmar.com
Year Founded: 1999
543458—(BOM)
Rev.: $7,007,512,739
Assets: $2,515,410,347
Liabilities: $1,536,362,328
Net Worth: $979,048,019
Earnings: $69,794,377
Emp.: 2,600
Fiscal Year-end: 03/31/23
Food Products Distr
N.A.I.C.S.: 424490
Angshu Mallick *(CEO)*

ADAPTEO OYJ
Ayritie 12 B, FI-01510, Vantaa, Fin-
land
Tel.: (358) 10 661 550
Web Site: http://www.adapteo.com
Rev.: $242,124,931
Assets: $836,546,619
Liabilities: $623,560,445
Net Worth: $212,986,173
Earnings: $9,395,625
Emp.: 407
Fiscal Year-end: 12/31/19
Office Space Rental Services
N.A.I.C.S.: 531120

ADAPTIMMUNE THERAPEU-
TICS PLC
60 Jubilee Avenue Milton Park,
Abingdon, OX14 4RX, Oxfordshire,
United Kingdom
Tel.: (44) 1235430000　　　　UK
Web Site:
　https://www.adaptimmune.com
Year Founded: 2007
ADAP—(NASDAQ)
Rev.: $27,148,000
Assets: $328,916,000
Liabilities: $247,038,000
Net Worth: $81,878,000
Earnings: ($165,456,000)
Emp.: 534
Fiscal Year-end: 12/31/22
Pharmaceutical Preparation Manufac-
turing
N.A.I.C.S.: 325412
John Lunger *(Chief Patient Supply*
Officer)

ADAPTIVE PLASMA TECH-
NOLOGY CORPORATION
58-47 Seoicheon-ro, Majang-myeon,
Icheon, Gyeonggi, Korea (South)
Tel.: (82) 2316451000
Web Site: https://www.iaptc.com
Year Founded: 2002

089970—(KRS)
Rev.: $108,442,493
Assets: $120,138,351
Liabilities: $29,700,106
Net Worth: $90,438,245
Earnings: $21,382,563
Emp.: 69
Fiscal Year-end: 12/31/22
Semiconductor Equipment Mfr
N.A.I.C.S.: 334413
Woo-Hyung Choi *(Pres & CEO)*

ADAPTOGENICS HEALTH
CORP.
1100-1111 Melville Street, Vancouver,
V6E 3V6, BC, Canada
Tel.: (604) 782-4264
Web Site:
　https://www.adaptogenicshealth.com
Year Founded: 2021
ADPT—(CNSX)
Health Care Srvices
N.A.I.C.S.: 621610
Daryl Ware-Lane *(CEO)*

ADARSH MERCANTILE LIM-
ITED
8A & 8B Satyam Towers 3 Alipore
Road, Kolkata, 700 027, India
Tel.: (91) 3324791951
Web Site:
　https://www.adarshmercantile.in
Year Founded: 1984
538563—(BOM)
Rev.: $164,112
Assets: $1,498,041
Liabilities: $565,067
Net Worth: $932,974
Earnings: ($29,514)
Emp.: 5
Fiscal Year-end: 03/31/21
Investment Management Service
N.A.I.C.S.: 523999
Suchita Chhawchharia *(Exec Dir)*

ADARSH PLANT PROTECT
LTD.
Plot No 604 GIDC Vitthal Udyogna-
gar, Anand, 388121, Gujarat, India
Tel.: (91) 2692236705
Web Site:
　https://www.adarshplant.com
Year Founded: 1992
526711—(BOM)
Rev.: $2,339,717
Assets: $1,147,845
Liabilities: $1,034,707
Net Worth: $113,138
Earnings: $14,176
Emp.: 13
Fiscal Year-end: 03/31/22
Plant Protection Equipment Mfr
N.A.I.C.S.: 333111
Naishadbhai N. Patel *(Chm)*

ADASTRA CORPORATION
Le Parc Office Tower 8500 Leslie
Street Suite 600, Markham, L3T 7M8,
ON, Canada
Tel.: (905) 881-7946
Web Site:
　http://www.adastracorp.com
Year Founded: 2000
Rev.: $28,564,314
Emp.: 240
IT Services
N.A.I.C.S.: 541513
Shauna Walker *(Dir-Fin)*

ADASTRA HOLDINGS LTD.
5451 275th Street, Langley, V4W
3X8, BC, Canada
Tel.: (778) 715-5011
Web Site: https://adastraholdings.ca
Year Founded: 1987
D2E—(DEU)

Adastra Holdings Ltd.—(Continued)

Biotechnology Research
N.A.I.C.S.: 541714
Michael Forbes *(CEO)*

ADASTRIA CO., LTD.
Shibuya Hikarie 19F 2-21-1 Shibuya,
Shibuya-ku, Tokyo, 1508510, Japan
Tel.: (81) 354662010
Web Site: https://www.adastria.co.jp
Year Founded: 1953
2685—(TKS)
Rev.: $1,953,975,640
Assets: $906,917,350
Liabilities: $399,408,060
Net Worth: $507,509,290
Earnings: $95,807,170
Emp.: 6,603
Fiscal Year-end: 02/29/24
Holding Company; Casual Wear
Whslr
N.A.I.C.S.: 551112
Michio Fukuda *(Chm)*

Subsidiaries:

Adastria Asia Co., Ltd.   **(1)**
Unit 2205-07 22/F Laws Commercial Plaza
788 Cheung Sha Wan Road, Kowloon,
China (Hong Kong)
Tel.: (852) 29593297
Clothing Whslr
N.A.I.C.S.: 424350
Masahiro Sato *(Pres)*

Adastria Eat Creations Co., Ltd.   **(1)**
9th floor VORT Shibuya briller 1-20-5 Jin-
nan, Shibuya-ku, Tokyo, 150-0041, Japan
Tel.: (81) 354661720
Web Site: https://www.adastria-ec.co.jp
Restaurant Services
N.A.I.C.S.: 722511

Adastria General Support Co.,
Ltd.   **(1)**
19F Shibuya Hikarie 2-21-1 Shibuya,
Shibuya-ku, Tokyo, 150-8510, Japan
Tel.: (81) 354662018
Web Site: https://www.adastria-gs.co.jp
Emp.: 290
Logistic Services
N.A.I.C.S.: 424350

Adastria Korea Co., Ltd.   **(1)**
12th Floor Samsung Building 7 Samsung ro
86 gil, Gangnam-gu, Seoul, Korea (South)
Tel.: (82) 25631030
Clothing Whslr
N.A.I.C.S.: 424350

Adastria Logistics Co., Ltd.   **(1)**
Chuokogyodanchi 1-15 Ibaraki-cho,
Higashiibaraki-gun, Ibaraki, Japan
Tel.: (81) 292190171
Emp.: 31
Logistic Services
N.A.I.C.S.: 541330

Adastria Taiwan Co., Ltd.   **(1)**
2F-3 No 142 Sec 4 Zhongxiao E Rd, Da'an
Dist, New Taipei City, 10688, Taiwan
Tel.: (886) 227314102
Clothing Whslr
N.A.I.C.S.: 424350

Buzzwit Co., Ltd.   **(1)**
Daiba Frontier Building 7F 2-3-2 Daiba,
Minato-ku, Tokyo, Japan
Tel.: (81) 354661728
Web Site: https://www.buzzwit.co.jp
Emp.: 119
Clothing Mfr & Whslr
N.A.I.C.S.: 315250

Element Rule Co., Ltd.   **(1)**
1-1-1 Minami-Aoyama Shin-Aoyama Build-
ing West Building 19F, Minato-ku, Tokyo,
107-0062, Japan
Tel.: (81) 354662077
Web Site: https://www.elementrule.co.jp
Clothing Mfr & Whslr
N.A.I.C.S.: 315250

POINT (Shanghai) Co., Ltd.   **(1)**
Collec3a-La Jiuguang Department Store 3,
Cenghong Zone No 268, Suzhou, 215021,
Jiangsu, China

Tel.: (86) 2161372438
Women Apparel Distr
N.A.I.C.S.: 458110

Velvet, LLC   **(1)**
3961 Landmark St, Culver City, CA 90232
Web Site: http://velvet-tees.com
Velvet Product Mfr
N.A.I.C.S.: 315250
Claudia Gonzalez *(Dir-HR)*

Zetton, Inc.   **(1)**
4-1-23 Siba, Minato-Ku, Tokyo, 106-0014,
Japan   **(51%)**
Tel.: (81) 36 865 1450
Web Site: http://www.zetton.co.jp
Rev.: $45,650,880
Assets: $34,276,880
Liabilities: $32,834,560
Net Worth: $1,442,320
Earnings: ($12,109,680)
Fiscal Year-end: 02/28/2021
Restaurant Management Services
N.A.I.C.S.: 722511
Shinsuke Suzuki *(Pres)*

ADATA TECHNOLOGY CO., LTD.
18F No 258 Lian Cheng Rd, Chung
Ho Dist, New Taipei City, 235, Taiwan
Tel.: (886) 282280886
Web Site: https://www.adata.com
Year Founded: 2001
3260—(TPE)
Rev.: $1,092,047,056
Assets: $1,123,356,502
Liabilities: $728,526,530
Net Worth: $394,829,972
Earnings: $27,689,304
Emp.: 2,092
Fiscal Year-end: 12/31/22
Semiconductor Product Mfr
N.A.I.C.S.: 334413
Simon Chen *(Chm & CEO)*

Subsidiaries:

ADATA Technology (Suzhou) Co.,
Ltd.   **(1)**
No 28 Xinfa Road, Suzhou Industrial Park,
Suzhou, 215123, China
Tel.: (86) 51265930886
Computer Peripheral Equipment Mfr & Distr
N.A.I.C.S.: 334112

ADATA Technology Mexico Sdrl de
CV   **(1)**
Calle de Berna No 6 Piso 3 Col Juarez,
Delegacion Cuauhtemoc, 6600, Mexico,
Mexico
Tel.: (52) 55437427
Electronic Components Distr
N.A.I.C.S.: 423690

Adata Electronics (Shanghai) Co.
Ltd.   **(1)**
No 7 Lane 268 Taihong Road, Minhang Dis-
trict, Shanghai, 201107, China
Tel.: (86) 2162331010
Computer Hardware Mfr
N.A.I.C.S.: 334112

Adata Technology (Hk) Co. Ltd.   **(1)**
Unit No 11&12 6/F Block A Focal Industrial
Centre No 21 Man Lok Street, Hung Hom,
Kowloon, China (Hong Kong)
Tel.: (852) 21277072
Computer Hardware Mfr
N.A.I.C.S.: 334112

ADAVALE RESOURCES LIM-ITED
Level 2 49 Oxford Close, West Leed-
erville, 6007, WA, Australia
Tel.: (61) 280036733
Web Site:
    https://www.adavaleresources.com
ADD—(ASX)
Assets: $387,491
Liabilities: $225,846
Net Worth: $161,645
Earnings: ($3,578,212)
Fiscal Year-end: 06/30/22
Mining Exploration

N.A.I.C.S.: 213113
Allan Ritchie *(CEO)*

ADBIOTECH CO., LTD.
39 Geodudanji 1-gil, Dongnae-
Myeon, Chuncheon, Gyeonggi-do,
Korea (South)
Tel.: (82) 332614907
Web Site: https://www.adbiotech.com
Year Founded: 2000
179530—(KRS)
Rev.: $8,154,418
Assets: $23,790,908
Liabilities: $11,376,800
Net Worth: $12,414,109
Earnings: $2,068,047
Emp.: 65
Fiscal Year-end: 12/31/22
Biological Product Mfr
N.A.I.C.S.: 325414
Hong-Gul Cheong *(CEO)*

ADC ACQUISITION CORP. PJSC
Office 410, Royal Group Headquar-
ters Building, Khalifa Park,, Abu
Dhabi, United Arab Emirates
Tel.: (971) 28856666
Web Site: https://adcspac.com
ADC—(ABU)
Financial Services
N.A.I.C.S.: 523999

ADC THERAPEUTICS SA
Tel.: (41) 216530200   CH
Web Site:
    https://www.adctherapeutics.com
Year Founded: 2011
ADCT—(NYSE)
Rev.: $209,908,000
Assets: $529,168,000
Liabilities: $440,441,000
Net Worth: $88,727,000
Earnings: ($155,800,000)
Emp.: 317
Fiscal Year-end: 12/31/22
Biotechnology Research & Develop-
ment Services
N.A.I.C.S.: 541714
Ron Squarer *(Chm)*

ADCAPITAL AG
Im Ermlisgrund 11, Waldbronn,
76337, Karlsruhe, Germany
Tel.: (49) 72435054150
Web Site: https://www.adcapital.de
Year Founded: 2003
ADC—(DEU)
Rev.: $182,271,014
Assets: $123,666,556
Liabilities: $70,813,260
Net Worth: $52,853,296
Earnings: ($2,726,559)
Emp.: 1,349
Fiscal Year-end: 12/31/23
Electrotechnical Product Mfr
N.A.I.C.S.: 335999
Hans-Juergen Doeringer *(Member-Mgmt Bd)*

Subsidiaries:

BDT Bavaria Digital Technik
GmbH   **(1)**
Rehbichler Weg 26, 87459, Pfronten, Ger-
many
Tel.: (49) 836391080
Web Site: http://www.bdt-online.de
Electronic Components Mfr
N.A.I.C.S.: 334419

EJR Erich Jaeger Roznov s.r.o.   **(1)**
1 Maje 2635, PO Box 1, 75661, Roznov
pod Radhostem, Czech Republic
Tel.: (420) 571843610
Web Site: http://www.ejr.cz
Screw Mfr
N.A.I.C.S.: 332722

EP Connectors GmbH   **(1)**

Im Ermlisgrund 11, Waldbronn, 76337,
Karlsruhe, Germany
Tel.: (49) 7243354770
Web Site: http://www.epconnectors.de
Metal Products Mfr
N.A.I.C.S.: 332999

ESPO s.r.o.   **(1)**
Videnska 55, 639 00, Brno, Czech Republic
Tel.: (420) 5101100420
Web Site: http://www.espo.cz
Computer Peripheral Distr
N.A.I.C.S.: 423430

EW Hof Antr. u. Systeme GmbH   **(1)**
Oberkotzauer Str 3, Hof/Saale, 95032,
Wunsiedel, Germany
Tel.: (49) 92815850
Web Site: http://www.ewhof.de
Electric Motor & Generator Mfr
N.A.I.C.S.: 335312

Erich Jaeger GmbH + Co. KG   **(1)**
Strassheimer Strasse 10, 61169, Friedberg,
Germany
Tel.: (49) 60317940
Web Site: http://www.erich-jaeger.com
Automotive Components Mfr
N.A.I.C.S.: 336390
Oliver Neil *(Mng Dir)*

Erich Jaeger Mexico, S. de R.L.   **(1)**
Las Americas 601 Lomas del Norte, 26089,
Piedras Negras, Mexico
Tel.: (52) 8781410230
Automotive Components Mfr
N.A.I.C.S.: 336390

Erich Jaeger U.S.A. Inc.   **(1)**
470 Forest Ave Ste 22, Plymouth, MI 48170
Tel.: (734) 404-5940
Automotive Components Mfr
N.A.I.C.S.: 336390
Terri L. Miller *(Pres)*

FRAKO Capacitors & Plant Construc-
tion GmbH   **(1)**
Tscheulinstrasse 21a, 79331, Teningen,
Germany
Tel.: (49) 76414530
Web Site: http://www.frako.com
Electronic Components Mfr
N.A.I.C.S.: 334419
Dietmar Wiesler *(Project Mgr)*

Jaeger France SARL   **(1)**
Parc d' Activites de Limonest 540 Allee des
Hetres, 69760, Limonest, France
Tel.: (33) 472520354
Automotive Components Mfr
N.A.I.C.S.: 336390

Jaeger Poway Automotive Systems
(Shenzhen) Ltd.   **(1)**
Block B High Technology, Industrial Area
Shashi Village Shajing Baoan, Shenzhen,
518104, China
Tel.: (86) 75581768399
Electrical Connector & Cable Distr
N.A.I.C.S.: 423610

KTS Kunststoff Technik Schmolln
GmbH   **(1)**
Altenburger Str 72, 04626, Schmolln, Ger-
many
Tel.: (49) 3449174122
Web Site: http://www.kts-schmoelln.de
Plastics Product Mfr
N.A.I.C.S.: 326199
Matthias Keller *(Exec Dir)*

OPUS Formenbau GmbH & Co.
KG   **(1)**
In den Kreuzwiesen 2, 69250, Schonau,
Germany
Tel.: (49) 6228912900
Web Site: http://www.opus-mold.de
Emp.: 50
Measuring Machine Mfr
N.A.I.C.S.: 334515
Markus Menchen *(Mng Dir)*

ADCITYMEDIA AB
Magasin 3 Frihamnsgatan 22, Stock-
holm, 115 56, Sweden
Tel.: (46) 853528050
Web Site:
    http://www.adcitymedia.com
Advertising & Marketing Services

N.A.I.C.S.: 541810
Jonas Glad (COO)

ADCON CAPITAL SERVICES LTD.
9 Shivshakti Industrial Estate J R Boricha Marg, Lower Parel, Mumbai, 400 011, Maharashtra, India
Tel.: (91) 2223016761
Web Site: https://www.adconcap.com
Year Founded: 1994
539506—(BOM)
Rev.: $67,274
Assets: $3,613,452
Liabilities: $10,659
Net Worth: $3,602,794
Earnings: ($81,926)
Emp.: 7
Fiscal Year-end: 03/31/23
Financial Support Services
N.A.I.C.S.: 523999
Sanjay R. Vishwakarma (CFO, Compliance Officer & Sec)

ADCONION MEDIA GROUP LTD.
180 Great Portland Street, London, W1W 5QZ, United Kingdom
Tel.: (44) 20 3 073 2900   UK
Web Site: http://www.adconion.com
Sales Range: $200-249.9 Million
Emp.: 700
Holding Company; Advertising Content Distribution Software Publisher
N.A.I.C.S.: 551112
T. Tyler Moebius (Founder & CEO)

Subsidiaries:

Adconion GmbH   (1)
Lindwurmstrasse 114, 80337, Munich, Germany
Tel.: (49) 89780178
Media Buying
N.A.I.C.S.: 541830

Branch (Domestic):

Adconion GmbH   (2)
Heuberg 1, 20354, Hamburg, Germany
Tel.: (49) 403099780
Media Buying
N.A.I.C.S.: 541830

Adconion GmbH   (2)
Neusser Strasse 72, 40219, Dusseldorf, Germany
Tel.: (49) 2119943070
Media Buying
N.A.I.C.S.: 541830

Adconion Media Inc.   (1)
20 Maud St Suite 305, Toronto, MV5 2M5, ON, Canada
Tel.: (416) 637-4658
Media Buying
N.A.I.C.S.: 541830

Adconion Media, Inc.   (1)
3301 Exposition Blvd, Santa Monica, CA 90404
Tel.: (310) 382-5500
Web Site: http://www.adconion.com
Media Buying Services
N.A.I.C.S.: 541830
T. Tyler Moebius (Founder & CEO)

Subsidiary (Domestic):

RedLever, Inc.   (2)
1322 3rd St Promenade 2nd Fl, Santa Monica, CA 90401
Tel.: (310) 382-5500
Sales Range: Less than $1 Million
Emp.: 50
Advetising Agency
N.A.I.C.S.: 541810

Adconion S.L.   (1)
Avnida Europa 19 1st Fl Parque de las Naciones, Edificio Germania Principal C, Madrid, 28224, Spain
Tel.: (34) 915987836
Web Site: http://www.adconion.com
Emp.: 60

Media Buying
N.A.I.C.S.: 541830
Angel Fernandez Nebot (Country Mgr)

ADCORE, INC.
100 King Street West Suite 1600, Toronto, M5X 1G5, ON, Canada
Tel.: (647) 497-5337
Web Site: https://www.adcore.com
Year Founded: 2006
ADCOF—(OTCQX)
Rev.: $23,134,000
Assets: $14,428,000
Liabilities: $5,555,000
Net Worth: $8,873,000
Earnings: ($944,000)
Emp.: 57
Fiscal Year-end: 12/31/23
Digital Advertising Services
N.A.I.C.S.: 541810
Roy Nevo (COO)

ADCORP AUSTRALIA LIMITED
Level 2 309 Geroge Street, Sydney, 2000, NSW, Australia
Tel.: (61) 2 8524 8500   AU
Web Site: http://www.adcorp.com.au
Year Founded: 1981
Rev.: $9,979,503
Assets: $8,776,564
Liabilities: $9,851,720
Net Worth: ($1,075,156)
Earnings: ($1,627,121)
Emp.: 235
Fiscal Year-end: 06/30/18
Advertising Services
N.A.I.C.S.: 541810
David Morrison (CEO & Mng Dir)

Subsidiaries:

Adcorp Australia (QLD) Pty Ltd   (1)
Level No 484 Adelaide Street, Brisbane, 4000, QLD, Australia
Tel.: (61) 7 3302 8500
Web Site: http://www.adcorp.com.au
Emp.: 20
Advetising Agency
N.A.I.C.S.: 541810
Michelle Muirhead (Gen Mgr)

Adcorp Australia (VIC) Pty Ltd   (1)
Mitchell House Level 2 Annex 358 Lonsdale St, Melbourne, 3000, VIC, Australia
Tel.: (61) 3 9223 0999
Advetising Agency
N.A.I.C.S.: 541810

Adcorp New Zealand Limited   (1)
Level 2 20 Beaumont Street, Auckland, 1010, New Zealand
Tel.: (64) 9 968 4800
Web Site: http://www.adcorp.co.nz
Advetising Agency
N.A.I.C.S.: 541810
Emma Oloi (Mgr-Client Svcs)

Quadrant Creative Pty Ltd   (1)
66 Township Drive, PO Box 388, Burleigh Heads, 4219, QLD, Australia
Tel.: (61) 7 5508 2900
Web Site: http://www.quadrant.com.au
Advetising Agency
N.A.I.C.S.: 541810
Byron Scott (Gen Mgr & Acct Dir)

ADCORP HOLDINGS LIMITED
Adcorp Place 102 Western Service Road, Gallo Manor Ext 6, Johannesburg, 2191, South Africa
Tel.: (27) 108000000
Web Site:
     http://www.adcorpgroup.com
Year Founded: 1972
ADR—(JSE)
Rev.: $636,305,358
Assets: $166,967,596
Liabilities: $85,921,271
Net Worth: $81,046,325
Earnings: $6,377,021
Emp.: 1,799
Fiscal Year-end: 02/28/23

Staffing & Recruitment Consulting Services
N.A.I.C.S.: 541612
Phil Roux (CEO)

Subsidiaries:

Adcorp Management Services (Pty) Limited   (1)
3 Angus Crescent Long Medor Business Park Estate, Edenvale, 1609, Gauteng, South Africa
Tel.: (27) 114578007
Sales Range: $100-124.9 Million
Emp.: 120
Investment Management Service
N.A.I.C.S.: 523940

Capital Outsourcing Group (Pty) Limited   (1)
21a Hampden Court Hampden Road, Morningside, Durban, 4001, KwaZulu-Natal, South Africa
Tel.: (27) 313628000
Web Site: http://www.cog.co.za
Rev.: $135,270,000
Recruitment & Training Services
N.A.I.C.S.: 561320
David Francis (Reg Mgr)

DAV Professional Placement Group (Pty) Limited   (1)
Adcorp Office Park Near William Nichole Drive, Johannesburg, 2021, South Africa
Tel.: (27) 112170000
Web Site: http://www.dav.co.za
Sales Range: $25-49.9 Million
Emp.: 150
Employment Placement Agencies
N.A.I.C.S.: 561311
Anita Hoole (Mng Dir)

Gold Fields External Training Services (Pty) Limited   (1)
Pamodzi FS 1 Shaft, Welkom, 9459, Free State, South Africa
Tel.: (27) 573919300
Web Site: http://www.adcorp.co.za
Emp.: 100
Artisan & Mining Commercial Training Services
N.A.I.C.S.: 624310
Hannes Fourie (Mgr)

Kelly Group Limited   (1)
6 Protea Place cnr Fredman Drive, Sandton, South Africa   (29.37%)
Tel.: (27) 117228000
Web Site: http://www.kellygroup.co.za
Sales Range: $125-149.9 Million
Emp.: 855
Temporary Staffing & Consulting Services
N.A.I.C.S.: 541613
Kevin Fihrer (Sec)

Subsidiary (Domestic):

Frontline Recruitment (Pty), Ltd.   (2)
6 Protea Place Cnr Fredman & Protea Street, Sandton, 2196, South Africa
Tel.: (27) 11 706 9222
Web Site: http://www.frontlinesolutions.co.za
Sales Range: $10-24.9 Million
Emp.: 33
Financial Recruitment Services
N.A.I.C.S.: 561311

InnStaff (Pty) Ltd   (2)
6 Protea Place, cnr Fredman Drive, Sandton, South Africa
Tel.: (27) 21 421 4233
Web Site: http://www.innstaff.co.za
Hospitality Recruitment Services
N.A.I.C.S.: 561311
Peter Czakan (Mng Dir)

Division (Domestic):

Kelly Group Limited - Renwick Talent   (2)
Fredman Dr First Floor, 2196, Johannesburg, Gauteng, South Africa
Tel.: (27) 11 269 8898
Sales Range: $25-49.9 Million
Emp.: 9
Executive Search Service
N.A.I.C.S.: 541612

Subsidiary (Domestic):

Paxsal Business Process Outsourcing (Pty) Ltd   (2)

6 Protea Pl Corner Fredman Dr Protea Rd, Sandton, 2196, Gauteng, South Africa
Tel.: (27) 117228000
Web Site: http://www.paxsal.co.za
Payroll Processing Services
N.A.I.C.S.: 541214
Alicia Timothy (Mgr)

Subsidiary (Domestic):

Paxsal Payroll Outsourcing (Pty) Ltd   (3)
6 Protea Pl Corner Fredman Dr, Sandton, 2132, Gauteng, South Africa
Tel.: (27) 117228345
Sales Range: $10-24.9 Million
Emp.: 45
Payroll Processing Services
N.A.I.C.S.: 541214

Subsidiary (Domestic):

Payaccsys Services (Pty) Ltd   (2)
Unit 59 The Sanctuary 10 Niblick Way, Somerset West, Cape Town, 7130, South Africa
Tel.: (27) 105934800
Web Site: https://www.payaccsys.com
Electronic Funds Transfer & Payroll Processing Services
N.A.I.C.S.: 522320

Labour Solutions Australia Proprietary Limited   (1)
Level 3 2 Gardner Close, Milton, 4064, QLD, Australia
Tel.: (61) 1300268986
Web Site:
     https://www.laboursolutions.com.au
Recruitment Services
N.A.I.C.S.: 561311

Paracon Holdings Limited   (1)
Adcorp Office Park Nicolway, Bryanston, South Africa
Tel.: (27) 114606000
Web Site: http://www.paracon.co.za
Sales Range: $125-149.9 Million
Emp.: 260
ICT Resource & Talent Management Services
N.A.I.C.S.: 238210
Mark Jurgens (CEO)

Subsidiary (Domestic):

Paracon SA (Pty) Limited   (2)
Adcorp Office Park Nicolway, Bryanston, 2021, South Africa
Tel.: (27) 114606000
Sales Range: $25-49.9 Million
Emp.: 70
Information & Communication Technology Services
N.A.I.C.S.: 541512
Chantel Bertram (Sr Acct Mgr)

allaboutXpert (Pty) Limited   (2)
Adcorp Office Park Nicolway, Bryanston, 2021, South Africa   (70%)
Tel.: (27) 115498600
Web Site: http://www.allaboutxpert.com
Sales Range: $25-49.9 Million
Emp.: 165
Project Management Services
N.A.I.C.S.: 561110
Nadine Damoense (Acct Mgr)

Paxus Australia Pty. Limited   (1)
Level 9 333 Collins Street, Melbourne, 3000, VIC, Australia
Tel.: (61) 386804200
Web Site: https://www.paxus.com.au
Information Technology Staffing Services
N.A.I.C.S.: 541612

Production Management Institute of South Africa (Pty) Limited   (1)
1st Floor Quest House 3 Margaret Avenue, Kempton Park, 1619, Gauteng, South Africa
Tel.: (27) 219496652
Web Site: http://www.pmi-sa.co.za
Sales Range: $10-24.9 Million
Emp.: 30
Educational Support Services
N.A.I.C.S.: 611710

Quest Flexible Staffing Solutions (Pty) Limited   (1)
No 33 Hoofd Street Forum 5 Braampark,

Adcorp Holdings Limited—(Continued)

2017, Johannesburg, South Africa
Tel.: (27) 116280300
Web Site: http://www.quest.co.za
Sales Range: $25-49.9 Million
Emp.: 200
Employment Placement Agencies
N.A.I.C.S.: 561311

ADCURAM GROUP AG

Theatinerstrasse 7 Arco Palais Ein-
gang Maffeistrasse, Munich, 80333,
Germany
Tel.: (49) 8920209590   De
Web Site: http://www.adcuram.de
Year Founded: 2003
Sales Range: $550-599.9 Million
Emp.: 4,000
Investment Holding Company
N.A.I.C.S.: 551112
Florian Meise (Co-Founder)

Subsidiaries:

IMA Asia Pacific Pte. Ltd.   (1)
No 21 Bukit Batok Cresent 09-75 WCEGA
Tower, Singapore, 658065, Singapore
Tel.: (65) 567 496 58 8
Web Site: http://www.ima-sg.com
Industrial Machinery Distr
N.A.I.C.S.: 423830
Burkhard Sydow (Pres & Mng Dir)

Nuvisan Pharma Services GmbH &
Co KG   (1)
Wegenerstrasse 13, 89231, Neu-Ulm, Ger-
many
Tel.: (49) 7319840000
Web Site: http://www.nuvisan.de
Sales Range: $75-99.9 Million
Emp.: 300
Pharmaceutical Testing Services
N.A.I.C.S.: 541380
Dietrich Bruchmann (Gen Mgr)

S.A. Citrique Belge N.V.   (1)
Pastorijstraat 249, 3300, Tienen, Belgium
Tel.: (32) 16 806 211
Web Site: http://www.citriquebelge.com
Emp.: 250
Chemical Products Mfr
N.A.I.C.S.: 325199
Peter Desauw (Mng Dir)

STEINEL Vertrieb GmbH   (1)
Dieselstrasse 80-84, 33442, Herzbrock-
Clarholz, Germany   (75%)
Tel.: (49) 52454480
Web Site: http://www.steinel.de
Sales Range: $150-199.9 Million
Emp.: 1,520
Sensor Mfr
N.A.I.C.S.: 334516
Ingo Steinel (Co-Mng Dir)

Subsidiary (Non-US):

STEINEL (UK) Ltd.   (2)
25 Manasty Road Axis Park, Peterborough,
PE2 6UP, Cambs, United Kingdom
Tel.: (44) 1733366700
Electronic Product Distr
N.A.I.C.S.: 423690
Kevin Pugh (Dir-Sls)

Vitrulan Holding GmbH   (1)
Berhecker Strasse 8, Marktschorgast,
95509, Kulmbach, Germany
Tel.: (49) 9227 77 210
Web Site: http://www.vitrulan.com
Emp.: 400
Glassfibre Products Mfr
N.A.I.C.S.: 327211
Ralf Barthmann (CEO)

Subsidiary (Non-US):

Vitrulan Composites Oy   (2)
Insinoorinkatu 2, 50100, Mikkeli, Finland
Tel.: (358) 10 888 12
Web Site: http://www.vitrulan.com
Glass & Carbon-Based Reinforcement Fab-
rics Mfr
N.A.I.C.S.: 313310

Plant (Domestic):

Ahlstrom Glassfibre Oy - Mikkeli
Plant   (3)

Insinoorinkatu 2, Mikkeli, 50100, Finland
Tel.: (358) 1088812
Sales Range: $1-4.9 Billion
Emp.: 100
Glassfiber Products Mfr
N.A.I.C.S.: 327213
Matti Valkonen (Plant Mgr)

ADD INDUSTRY (ZHEJIANG) CORPORATION LIMITED

No 55 Changshun Road, Yuhuan,
Taizhou, 317607, Zhejiang, China
Tel.: (86) 57687278888
Web Site: https://www.addchina.com
Year Founded: 1994
603089—(SHG)
Rev.: $246,769,219
Assets: $339,752,368
Liabilities: $154,567,441
Net Worth: $185,184,927
Earnings: $9,598,607
Fiscal Year-end: 12/31/21
Suspension System Mfr & Distr
N.A.I.C.S.: 336330
Nianhui Zheng (Chm & Gen Mgr)

ADD NEW ENERGY INVEST-MENT HOLDINGS GROUP LIM-ITED

Suite 3105 31/F Tower 6 The Gate-
way, Harbour City, Kowloon, China
(Hong Kong)
Tel.: (852) 21753126
Web Site:
   http://www.addnewenergy.com.hk
2623—(HKG)
Rev.: $261,971,237
Assets: $104,744,718
Liabilities: $55,045,364
Net Worth: $49,699,354
Earnings: $8,091,954
Emp.: 190
Fiscal Year-end: 12/31/22
Holding Company; Investment Ser-
vices
N.A.I.C.S.: 551112
Yunde Li (Chm)

ADD-SHOP ERETAIL LTD.

Rachna Industrial Zone 3 Plot No 34,
Village Padvala Lothda Road, Kotda
Sangani, Rajkot, 360025, Gujarat,
India
Tel.: (91) 2363023
Web Site: https://www.addshop.co
Year Founded: 2013
541865—(BOM)
Rev.: $21,792,648
Assets: $6,920,536
Liabilities: $1,543,952
Net Worth: $5,376,585
Earnings: $2,605,348
Emp.: 24
Fiscal Year-end: 03/31/22
Ayurveda Product Mfr & Distr
N.A.I.C.S.: 325320
Dineshbhai Pandya (Mng Dir)

ADDCN TECHNOLOGY CO., LTD.

10F No 12 Ln 609 Sec 5 Chongxin
Rd, Sanchung, New Taipei City, 241,
Taiwan
Tel.: (886) 229995691
Web Site: https://www.addcn.com.tw
Year Founded: 2007
5287—(TPE)
Rev.: $61,231,904
Assets: $101,697,183
Liabilities: $42,831,723
Net Worth: $58,865,460
Earnings: $20,364,037
Emp.: 473
Fiscal Year-end: 12/31/22
Online Apparel Retailer
N.A.I.C.S.: 458110
Shih Fang Liao (Chm)

ADDENTAX GROUP CORP.

Kingkey 100 Block A Room 4805,
Luohu District, Shenzhen, 518000,
China
Tel.: (86) 75586961405   NV
Year Founded: 2014
ATXG—(NASDAQ)
Rev.: $5,153,753
Assets: $52,338,748
Liabilities: $26,291,648
Net Worth: $26,047,100
Earnings: ($3,109,418)
Emp.: 112
Fiscal Year-end: 03/31/24
Garment Mfr & Distr
N.A.I.C.S.: 315250
Zhida Hong (Chm, Pres, CEO, CFO,
COO & Sec)

ADDERACARE AB

Hans Michelsensgatan 9, 211 20,
Malmo, Sweden
Tel.: (46) 406600408
Web Site:
   http://www.adderacare.com
ADDERA—(OMX)
Rev.: $25,053,258
Assets: $32,214,470
Liabilities: $13,295,733
Net Worth: $18,918,738
Earnings: $1,215,917
Emp.: 78
Fiscal Year-end: 12/31/20
Lift & Escalator Mfr
N.A.I.C.S.: 333921
Per Nilsson (Chm)

Subsidiaries:

Erimed International KB   (1)
Ellipsvagen 11, 141 75, Kungens Kurva,
Sweden
Tel.: (46) 8 449 5650
Web Site: https://www.erimed.se
Orthopedic Product Distr
N.A.I.C.S.: 423450

Huka B.V.   (1)
Munsterstraat 13, 7575 ED, Oldenzaal,
Netherlands
Tel.: (31) 54 157 2472
Web Site: https://www.huka.nl
Motor Vehicle Parts Mfr
N.A.I.C.S.: 336390

Trident Industri AB   (1)
Metallgatan 25, 262 72, Angelholm, Swe-
den
Tel.: (46) 43 144 9500
Web Site: https://www.trident.se
Lamp Mfr
N.A.I.C.S.: 335139

ADDEV MATERIAL SAS

30 quai Perrache, 69002, Lyon,
France
Tel.: (33) 4 72 11 35 00
Web Site: http://www.addev.fr
Specialized Adhesives Manufacturing
N.A.I.C.S.: 325520
Julien Duvanel (CFO-Aerospace &
Defense)

Subsidiaries:

Andpak, Inc.   (1)
400 Jarvis Dr, Morgan Hill, CA 95037
Tel.: (408) 782-2500
Web Site: http://www.andpak.com
Repackaging Service
N.A.I.C.S.: 561910
Steve Henthorne (Office Mgr)

Materials Converting, Inc.   (1)
2121 S 116th St, West Allis, WI 53227
Tel.: (414) 546-9550
Web Site:
   http://www.materialsconverting.com
Paper Products Mfr
N.A.I.C.S.: 322299
Mark J. Hahn (VP-Sls)

VMS Aircraft Company, Inc.   (1)

9755 Birch Canyon Pl, San Diego, CA
92126-1077
Tel.: (858) 277-9500
Web Site: http://www.vmsaircraft.com
Sales Range: $1-9.9 Million
Emp.: 13
Aviation Equipment Supplier
N.A.I.C.S.: 336999
Mehul Sheth (Founder)

ADDEX THERAPEUTICS LTD.

Chemin des Mines 9, 1202, Geneva,
Switzerland
Tel.: (41) 228841555
Web Site:
   https://www.addextherapeutics.com
ADXN—(NASDAQ)
Rev.: $1,610,868
Assets: $9,379,173
Liabilities: $3,815,449
Net Worth: $5,563,724
Earnings: ($23,560,147)
Emp.: 24
Fiscal Year-end: 12/31/22
Pharmaceutical Research & Develop-
ment Services
N.A.I.C.S.: 541715
Tim Dyer (Founder & CEO)

Subsidiaries:

Addex Pharma S.A.   (1)
Chemin des Mines 9, 1202, Geneva, Swit-
zerland
Tel.: (41) 228841555
Web Site:
   http://www.addextherapeutics.com
Sales Range: $25-49.9 Million
Emp.: 20
Physical Science Research & Development
Services
N.A.I.C.S.: 541715

ADDI INDUSTRIES LIMITED

A-104 Third floor Okhla Industrial
Area Phase - II, New Delhi, 110020,
Delhi, India
Tel.: (91) 1145025459
Web Site:
   https://www.addiindustries.com
Year Founded: 1980
507852—(BOM)
Sales Range: Less than $1 Million
Emp.: 7
Garment Product Mfr
N.A.I.C.S.: 315120
Chaman Lal Jain (Mng Dir)

ADDICKS & KREYE HOLDING GMBH

Konsul-Smidt-Strasse 8c, 28217,
Bremen, Germany
Tel.: (49) 421 69 435 13
Web Site: http://www.addicks.de
Year Founded: 1908
Emp.: 3,000
Container Trucking Services
N.A.I.C.S.: 484110
Rudiger Rempe (Mng Dir)

Subsidiaries:

Addicks & Kreye Container Logistik
GmbH & Co   (1)
Amerikaring 21, Bremerhaven, 27570, Ger-
many
Tel.: (49) 471 98395 0
Web Site: http://www.addicks.de
Logistics Consulting Servies
N.A.I.C.S.: 541614
Ruediger Rempe (Mgr)

Addicks & Tally Union GmbH &
Co   (1)
Container-Terminal Gatehouse II, 27568,
Bremerhaven, Germany
Tel.: (49) 471 413065
Cargo Handling Services
N.A.I.C.S.: 488320
Ruediger Rempe (Mgr)

Tally-Union GmbH & Co. KG   (1)
Container Terminal Gatehouse III Senator-

Bortscheller-Str 1, 27568, Bremerhaven, Germany
Tel.: (49) 471413065
Marine Cargo Handling Services
N.A.I.C.S.: 488320

ADDIKO BANK AG

Canetti Tower Canettistrase 512 OG, 1100, Vienna, Austria
Tel.: (43) 502320   AU
Web Site: https://www.addiko.com
Year Founded: 1984
ADKO—(VIE)
Rev.: $305,773,264
Assets: $6,790,484,602
Liabilities: $5,906,170,660
Net Worth: $884,313,942
Earnings: $45,369,246
Emp.: 2,562
Fiscal Year-end: 12/31/23
Banking Services
N.A.I.C.S.: 522110
Hans-Hermann Lotter *(Chm-Supervisory Bd)*

Subsidiaries:

Addiko Bank a.d.   (1)
Aleja Svetog Save 13, 78 000, Banja Luka, Bosnia & Herzegovina
Tel.: (387) 51951000
Web Site: https://www.addiko-rs.ba
Banking Services
N.A.I.C.S.: 522210
Srdjan Lamesic *(Dir-Internal Audit)*

Addiko Bank a.d.   (1)
Milutina Milankovica 7v, 11 070, Belgrade, Serbia
Tel.: (381) 11 222 6000
Web Site: https://www.addiko.rs
Banking Services
N.A.I.C.S.: 522210
Zdravko Cvetkovic *(Mgr-Application Support & Dev)*

Addiko Bank a.d.   (1)
Bulevar Dzordza Vasingtona 98, 81000, Podgorica, Montenegro
Tel.: (382) 20408600
Web Site: https://www.addiko.me
Banking Services
N.A.I.C.S.: 522210
Bojan Tomcic *(Mgr-Relationship)*

Addiko Bank d.d.   (1)
Trg solidarnosti 12, 71 000, Sarajevo, Bosnia & Herzegovina
Tel.: (387) 33866666
Web Site: https://www.addiko-fbih.ba
Banking Services
N.A.I.C.S.: 522210
Suzana Tihi-Babic *(Dir-HR Mgmt Dept)*

Addiko Bank d.d.   (1)
Slavonska avenija 6, 10000, Zagreb, Croatia
Tel.: (385) 1 603 0000
Web Site: https://www.addiko.hr
Banking Services
N.A.I.C.S.: 522210
Ivan Gjurovic *(Exec Dir-Retail Risk Mgmt)*

Addiko Bank d.d.   (1)
Dunajska cesta 117, 1000, Ljubljana, Slovenia
Tel.: (386) 1 580 4000
Web Site: https://www.addiko.si
Banking Services
N.A.I.C.S.: 522210

ADDISON SAWS LIMITED

Attwood Street Lye, Stourbridge, DY9 8RU, West Midlands, United Kingdom
Tel.: (44) 1384264950   UK
Web Site:
    http://www.addisonsaws.co.uk
Year Founded: 1956
Sales Range: $10-24.9 Million
Emp.: 50
Metal Sawing Machine Mfr
N.A.I.C.S.: 333517
Gary Knight *(Pres)*

Subsidiaries:

SAW MART LTD   (1)
Attwood Street Lye, Stourbridge, DY9 8RU, West Midlands, United Kingdom
Tel.: (44) 1384 264950
Web Site: http://www.sawmart.co.uk
Workshop Sawing Machine Mfr
N.A.I.C.S.: 333517
Gary Walter Knight *(Mng Dir)*

Tube Fabrication Machinery
Limited   (1)
Attwood Street Lye, Stourbridge, DY9 8RU, West Midlands, United Kingdom
Tel.: (44) 1384 264950
Web Site: http://www.tubefab.co.uk
Tube Bending Machine Mfr
N.A.I.C.S.: 333248
Alan Price *(Mng Dir)*

ADDLIFE AB

Birger Jarlsgatan 43, Box 3145, 103 62, Stockholm, Sweden
Tel.: (46) 842003830
Web Site: http://www.add.life
Year Founded: 2015
ALIF.B—(OMX)
Rev.: $643,764,464
Assets: $506,583,168
Liabilities: $275,815,344
Net Worth: $230,767,824
Earnings: $63,444,976
Emp.: 1,112
Fiscal Year-end: 12/31/20
Biomedical Research Services
N.A.I.C.S.: 541715
Peter Simonsbacka *(Mgr-Bus Area Labtech)*

Subsidiaries:

BioCat GmbH   (1)
Im Neuenheimer Feld 584, 69120, Heidelberg, Germany
Tel.: (49) 62217141516
Web Site: https://www.biocat.com
Cancer Treatment Services
N.A.I.C.S.: 541715

BioNordika (Denmark) A/S   (1)
Marielundvej 46E 2 tv, 2730, Herlev, Denmark
Tel.: (45) 39562000
Web Site: https://bionordika.dk
Biological Product Mfr & Distr
N.A.I.C.S.: 325414
Heinrich Biehl *(Mng Dir)*

BioNordika (Sweden) AB   (1)
Berzelius Vag 13 Floor 5, 171 65, Solna, Sweden
Tel.: (46) 8306010
Web Site: https://www.bionordika.se
Life Science Product Mfr & Distr
N.A.I.C.S.: 325414
Hedvig Vrethammar *(Fin Mgr)*

BioNordika Bergman AS   (1)
Gladengveien 3 B, 0661, Oslo, Norway
Tel.: (47) 23035800
Web Site: https://bionordika.no
Aspiration System Mfr
N.A.I.C.S.: 339112
Joachim Nedreklepp *(Sls Mgr)*

Biolin Scientific AB   (1)
Hangpilsgatan 7, 426 77, Vastra Frolunda, Sweden   (100%)
Tel.: (46) 317697690
Emp.: 60
Analytical Laboratory Instrument Mfr
N.A.I.C.S.: 334516
Maria Andersson *(CFO)*

Subsidiary (Non-US):

Biolin Scientific Limited   (2)
The Copper Room Deva Centre Trinity Way, Manchester, M3 7BG, United Kingdom
Tel.: (44) 1614369700
Analytical Instrument Mfr
N.A.I.C.S.: 334516

Biolin Scientific Oy   (2)
Tietajantie 2, 02130, Espoo, Finland
Tel.: (358) 954973300

Analytical Instrument Mfr
N.A.I.C.S.: 334516

Sophion Bioscience A/S   (2)
Baltorpvej 154, 2750, Ballerup, Denmark
Tel.: (45) 44 60 88 00
Web Site: http://www.sophion.com
Automated Patch Clamping Product Mfr
N.A.I.C.S.: 339112
Thais T. Johansen *(CEO)*

Biomedica Bulgaria OOD   (1)
2E Akad Ivan E Geshov blvd Business center Serdika build 2 floor 2, 1330, Sofia, Bulgaria
Tel.: (359) 24472833
Web Site: https://www.bmgrp.eu
Emp.: 280
Medical Equipment Distr
N.A.I.C.S.: 423450

Biomedica CS s.r.o.   (1)
Radlicka 740/113d, Jinonice, 158 00, Prague, Czech Republic
Tel.: (420) 283933605
Web Site: https://www.bmgrp.eu
Medical Equipment Distr
N.A.I.C.S.: 423450

Biomedica Dijagnostika doo   (1)
Zagrebacka cesta 130a, 10000, Zagreb, Croatia
Tel.: (385) 18885727
Web Site: https://www.bmgrp.eu
Medical Equipment Distr
N.A.I.C.S.: 423450
Michaele Weblacher *(Sls Dir)*

Biomedica Hungaria Kft.   (1)
Hungaria krt 128-132, 1146, Budapest, Hungary
Tel.: (36) 12253850
Web Site: https://www.bmgrp.eu
Medical Equipment Distr
N.A.I.C.S.: 423450

Biomedica Italia s.r.l.   (1)
Via T A Edison 6, 20057, Assago, MI, Italy
Tel.: (39) 0249540340
Web Site: https://biomedica-italia.it
Medical Equipment Distr
N.A.I.C.S.: 423450

Biomedica MP d.o.o.   (1)
Lazara Mamuzica 26a, 11186, Zemun, Serbia
Tel.: (381) 11 630 1882
Web Site: https://www.bmgrp.rs
Medical Equipment Distr
N.A.I.C.S.: 423450
Luca Marenzl *(Mng Dir-Operations-Finance)*

Biomedica Medizinprodukte
GmbH   (1)
Divischgasse 4, 1210, Vienna, Austria
Tel.: (43) 129107
Web Site: https://www.bmgrp.eu
Medical Equipment Distr
N.A.I.C.S.: 423450

Biomedica Medizinprodukte Romania
SRL   (1)
B-dul Dimitrie Pompeiu nr 5-7, Sector 2 Cladirea Hermes Business Campus HBC1 parter, 020335, Bucharest, Romania
Tel.: (40) 372766844
Web Site: https://www.bmgrp.eu
Medical Equipment Distr
N.A.I.C.S.: 423450

Biomedica Poland Sp. z o.o.   (1)
Raszynska 13, 05-500, Piaseczno, Poland
Tel.: (48) 227375996
Web Site: https://www.bmgrp.eu
Medical Equipment Distr
N.A.I.C.S.: 423450

Biomedica Slovakita s.r.o.   (1)
Drobneho 27, 841 01, Bratislava, Slovakia
Tel.: (421) 269309901
Web Site: https://www.bmgrp.eu
Medical Equipment Distr
N.A.I.C.S.: 423450

Biomedica d.o.o.   (1)
Tvornicka 3, 71210, Ilidza, Bosnia & Herzegovina
Tel.: (387) 33262725
Web Site: https://www.bmgrp.com
Health Care Srvices
N.A.I.C.S.: 622110

D-A-CH Germany Medical Group
GmbH   (1)
Munchener Strasse 67, 83395, Freilassing, Germany
Tel.: (49) 8654608734
Medical Device Distr
N.A.I.C.S.: 423450

Dach Austria Medical Group
GmbH   (1)
Steinbach 9, Ostermiething, 5121, Braunau, Austria
Tel.: (43) 627871200
Web Site: https://www.dach-medical-group.com
Medical Device Distr
N.A.I.C.S.: 423450

Dach Switzerland Medical Group
GmbH   (1)
Chaltenbodenstrasse 6F, 8834, Schindellegi, Switzerland
Tel.: (41) 438880907
Medical Device Distr
N.A.I.C.S.: 423450

EuroClone S.p.A.   (1)
Via Figino 20/22, 20016, Pero, MI, Italy
Tel.: (39) 02381951
Web Site: https://www.euroclonegroup.it
Medical Equipment Distr
N.A.I.C.S.: 423450

Euromed Swiss AG   (1)
Langfeldstrasse 53A, 8500, Frauenfeld, Switzerland
Tel.: (41) 447828080
Web Site: https://www.euromed.ch
Commercial Equipment Distr
N.A.I.C.S.: 423440

Funksjonsutstyr AS   (1)
Martin Linges vei 25, 0692, Oslo, Norway
Tel.: (47) 23380000
Web Site: https://www.funksjonsutstyr.no
Marble Mfr
N.A.I.C.S.: 327991

Hospidana A/S   (1)
Kleinsvej 6, 4930, Maribo, Denmark
Tel.: (45) 54784588
Web Site: https://hospidana.com
Elastic Bandage Mfr
N.A.I.C.S.: 339113

Immuno Diagnostics Oy   (1)
Kaivokatu 16, 13100, Hameenlinna, Finland
Tel.: (358) 3615370
Web Site: https://www.immunodiagnostic.fi
Medical Equipment Distr
N.A.I.C.S.: 423450

Koldt & Ryo El A/S   (1)
Lerhoj 15, 2880, Bagsvaerd, Denmark
Tel.: (45) 8 988 1843
Web Site: https://www.koldt-ryo.dk
Lab Technician Services
N.A.I.C.S.: 541380

Lab-Vent Controls A/S   (1)
Adolf Meyers Vej 7, 8000, Aarhus, Denmark
Tel.: (45) 8 628 9700
Web Site: https://www.lab-vent.dk
Control Systems Mfr
N.A.I.C.S.: 335314
Henning Rasmussen *(CEO)*

Mediplast A/S   (1)
Marielundvej 46E, 2730, Herlev, Denmark
Tel.: (45) 43444000
Web Site: https://www.mediplast.com
Medical Device Distr
N.A.I.C.S.: 423450

Mediplast AB   (1)
Bronsaldersgatan 2, 213 76, Malmo, Sweden
Tel.: (46) 406712300
Web Site: https://www.mediplast.com
Medical Equipment Distr
N.A.I.C.S.: 423450

Mediplast AS   (1)
Tollbugata 115, Drammen, 3041, Norway
Tel.: (47) 32881100
Web Site: https://www.mediplast.no
Medical Equipment Distr
N.A.I.C.S.: 423450

Mediplast Benelux B.V.   (1)

AddLife AB—(Continued)

Eeckersteghe 14, 6181 KZ, Elsloo, Netherlands
Tel.: (31) 468200264
Web Site: https://www.mediplast.info
Medical Device Distr
N.A.I.C.S.: 423450

Mediplast GmbH (1)
Buldernweg 57, 48163, Munster, Germany
Tel.: (49) 25197569
Medical Device Distr
N.A.I.C.S.: 423450

Mediplast S.r.l. (1)
Via Martiri della Liberta 1/B, Roncanova di Gazzo, Verona, VR, Italy
Tel.: (39) 0442510536
Web Site: https://www.mediplast.com
Medical Equipment Distr
N.A.I.C.S.: 423450

O'Flynn Medical Limited (1)
Macroom Environmental Industrial Park Bowl Road, Macroom, Cork, P12 YD92, Ireland
Tel.: (353) 2921799
Web Site: https://www.oflynnmedical.com
Medical Equipment Distr
N.A.I.C.S.: 423450

Ropox A/S (1)
Ringstedgade 221, 4700, Naestved, Denmark
Tel.: (45) 55750500
Web Site: https://www.ropox.com
Medical Equipment Distr
N.A.I.C.S.: 423450

Spectrum Ophthalmology Ltd. (1)
Fernbank House Springwood Way, Tytherington, Macclesfield, SK10 2XA, United Kingdom
Tel.: (44) 1625618816
Web Site:
　https://www.spectrumophthalmics.uk
Emp.: 200
Ophthalmic Product Mfr
N.A.I.C.S.: 339115

Svan Care AB (1)
Alvagen 1, 771 41, Ludvika, Sweden
Tel.: (46) 24010102
Web Site: https://svancare.se
Women Healthcare Services
N.A.I.C.S.: 621610

Triolab AB (1)
Bifrostgatan 30, 431 44, Molndal, Sweden
Tel.: (46) 31817200
Web Site: https://www.triolab.se
Medical Equipment Mfr
N.A.I.C.S.: 339112

V-Tech AB (1)
Bronsaldersgatan 2, 213 76, Malmo, Sweden
Tel.: (46) 406712300
Web Site: https://www.v-tech.se
Medical Equipment Distr
N.A.I.C.S.: 423450
Magnus Ekstrom *(Product Mgr)*

Vaino Korpinen Oy (1)
Kalkkipellontie 6, 02650, Espoo, Finland
Tel.: (358) 954914400
Web Site: https://www.korpinen.com
Accessible Bathroom Mfr
N.A.I.C.S.: 326191
Eeti Hirsimaki *(Product Mgr)*

Zafe Care Systems AB (1)
Industrigatan 2, 291 36, Kristianstad, Sweden
Tel.: (46) 102096210
Web Site: https://www.zafe.se
Security System Services
N.A.I.C.S.: 561621

ADDNODE GROUP AB
Hudiksvallsgatan 4B, SE-113 30, Stockholm, Sweden
Tel.: (46) 86307070
Web Site:
　http://www.addnodegroup.com
ANOD.B—(OMX)
Rev.: $497,720,160
Assets: $527,629,760

Liabilities: $320,948,320
Net Worth: $206,681,440
Earnings: $27,223,840
Emp.: 1,776
Fiscal Year-end: 12/31/21
Information Technology Services
N.A.I.C.S.: 541519
Staffan Hanstorp *(Chm)*

Subsidiaries:

Addnode Balkan d.o.o. (1)
Ruzveltova 48, 11000, Belgrade, Serbia
Tel.: (381) 112452544
Web Site: https://addnodebalkan.com
Information Technology System Construction Services
N.A.I.C.S.: 236220
Kristin Wigren *(CEO)*

Adtollo AB (1)
Norra Stationsgatan 93A, 113 64, Stockholm, Sweden
Tel.: (46) 841041500
Web Site: https://adtollo.se
Software Publisher
N.A.I.C.S.: 513210

Arkiva AB (1)
Brandthovdagatan 9, 721 35, Vasteras, Sweden
Tel.: (46) 21187010
Web Site: https://www.arkiva.nu
Software Development Services
N.A.I.C.S.: 541511

Budsoft Sp. z o.o. (1)
St June 28 1956 No 406, Poznan Technology and Industry Park, 61-441, Poznan, Poland
Tel.: (48) 616735472
Web Site: https://budsoft.com.pl
Software Development Services
N.A.I.C.S.: 541511

Cad Quality A/S (1)
Mars Alle 38, 8700, Horsens, Denmark
Tel.: (45) 76281415
Web Site: http://www.cad-q.dk
Emp.: 4
Computer Aided Design Services
N.A.I.C.S.: 541512
Jorn Robdrup *(Gen Mgr)*

Cad-Quality Finland Oy (1)
Ayritie 8 B, 1510, Vantaa, Finland
Tel.: (358) 9 5422 6500
Web Site: http://www.cad-q.fi
Sales Range: $25-49.9 Million
Emp.: 20
Data Management Services
N.A.I.C.S.: 541519

Cad-Quality Sverige AB (1)
Forskargatan 3, 781 27, Borlange, Sweden
Tel.: (46) 24373660
Web Site: http://www.cad-q.com
Computer Aided Design Services
N.A.I.C.S.: 541512
Rolf Kjaernsli *(CEO)*

Cartesia GIS AB (1)
Storgatan 28, Lycksele, 92131, Sweden (100%)
Tel.: (46) 95012005
Web Site: http://www.cartesia.se
Sales Range: $25-49.9 Million
Emp.: 100
Computer Related Services
N.A.I.C.S.: 541519
Lennrat Nielsen *(Chm)*

Claytex Services Ltd. (1)
Edmund House Rugby Road, Leamington Spa, CV32 6EL, United Kingdom
Tel.: (44) 1926885900
Web Site: https://www.claytex.com
Software Development Services
N.A.I.C.S.: 541511

Claytex USA inc. (1)
18605 Northline Dr Ste E20, Cornelius, NC 28031
Tel.: (704) 951-7461
Software Development Services
N.A.I.C.S.: 541511

Decerno AB (1)
Electrum 234, 164 40, Kista, Sweden
Tel.: (46) 8 630 7500

Web Site: https://www.decerno.se
Computer Peripheral Equipment Whslr
N.A.I.C.S.: 423430

Decerno Vast AB (1)
Vasagatan 45, 411 37, Gothenburg, Sweden
Tel.: (46) 317777790
Web Site: https://www.decerno.se
Computer Related Services
N.A.I.C.S.: 541519

Elpool i Umea AB (1)
Matrosgrand 2, 652 16, Karlstad, Sweden
Tel.: (46) 90184540
Web Site: https://www.elpool.se
Project Management Consulting Services
N.A.I.C.S.: 541611

Evitbe AB (1)
Hudiksvallsgatan 4, 113 30, Stockholm, Sweden
Tel.: (46) 771213213
Web Site: https://www.evitbe.com
Custom Computer Programming Services
N.A.I.C.S.: 541511
Veronica Carlson *(Project Mgr)*

Ida Infront AB (1)
St Larsgatan 18, Box 576, 581 07, Linkoping, Sweden (100%)
Tel.: (46) 13373700
Web Site: https://idainfront.se
Sales Range: $25-49.9 Million
Emp.: 60
Computer Related Services
N.A.I.C.S.: 541519

IntraPhone Solutions AB (1)
Sodra Forstadsgatan 26, 211 43, Malmo, Sweden
Tel.: (46) 406405100
Web Site: https://www.intraphone.com
Software & Tech Services
N.A.I.C.S.: 541511

Kartena AB (1)
Otterhallegatan 1, 411 18, Gothenburg, Sweden
Tel.: (46) 31 777 77 90
Web Site: http://www.kartena.se
Geographic Information Technology Consulting Services
N.A.I.C.S.: 541512

Linewise Services AB (1)
Hudiksvallsgatan 4, 113 30, Stockholm, Sweden
Tel.: (46) 8 562 400 00
Web Site: http://www.linewise.se
Sales Range: $10-24.9 Million
Emp.: 30
Business Process Outsourcing Services
N.A.I.C.S.: 561499

Microdesk LLC (1)
10 Tara Blvd Ste 420, Nashua, NH 03062-2800
Tel.: (603) 657-3800
Software Development Services
N.A.I.C.S.: 541511

Mittbygge AB (1)
Norrgatan 16, 432 41, Varberg, Sweden
Tel.: (46) 736791062
Web Site: http://www.mittbygge.com
Residential Construction Management Services
N.A.I.C.S.: 531311

Mogul AB (1)
Hudiksvallsgatan 4, Stockholm, 113 30, Sweden (100%)
Tel.: (46) 850666100
Web Site: http://www.mogul.com
Sales Range: $25-49.9 Million
Emp.: 120
Computer Related Services
N.A.I.C.S.: 541519
Joakim Dahlgren *(CEO)*

Netpublicator Apps AB (1)
Hamngatan 2, 553 16, Jonkoping, Sweden
Tel.: (46) 363320900
Web Site: https://www.netpublicator.com
Computer Related Services
N.A.I.C.S.: 541511
Andreas Karlsson *(CEO)*

Prosilia Software AB (1)
Sveavagen 39, 11330, Stockholm, Sweden

Tel.: (46) 8202950
Web Site: http://www.prosilia.se
Computer Related Services
N.A.I.C.S.: 541519

S-GROUP Solutions AB (1)
Blekingegatan 1, 371 57, Karlskrona, Sweden
Tel.: (46) 45575600
Web Site: https://sgroupsolutions.se
Information Technology Services
N.A.I.C.S.: 541511

Scanscot Technology AB (1)
Edison Park Emdalavagen 10, 223 69, Lund, Sweden
Tel.: (46) 85 992 0400
Web Site: https://scanscot.com
Engineeering Services
N.A.I.C.S.: 541330

Service Works Global Nordic AB (1)
Bruksgatan 17, 632 17, Eskilstuna, Sweden
Tel.: (46) 16135500
Web Site: https://www.swg.com
Software & Tech Services
N.A.I.C.S.: 541511

Service Works Global Pty. Ltd. (1)
Level 19 15 William Street, Melbourne, 3000, VIC, Australia
Tel.: (61) 370190975
Software & Tech Services
N.A.I.C.S.: 541511

Simuleon B.V. (1)
Pettelaarpark 84, 5216 PP, 's-Hertogenbosch, Netherlands
Tel.: (31) 85 049 8165
Web Site: https://www.simuleon.com
Software Services
N.A.I.C.S.: 541611

Sokigo AB (1)
Box 315, 731 27, Koping, Sweden
Tel.: (46) 8235600
Web Site: https://sokigo.com
Computer Related Services
N.A.I.C.S.: 541519

Stamford Stockholm AB (1)
Hudiksvallsgatan 4B, 113 30, Stockholm, Sweden
Tel.: (46) 820 2950
Web Site: https://www.hem.stamford.se
Software Services
N.A.I.C.S.: 541511

Strategic Simulation & Analysis Ltd. (1)
Southill Barn Southill Business Park Cornbury Park, Charlbury, OX7 3EW, Oxfordshire, United Kingdom
Tel.: (44) 1608811777
Web Site: https://www.ssanalysis.co.uk
Software Training Services
N.A.I.C.S.: 611420

Symetri A/S (1)
Robert Jacobsens Vej 70 1 floor, 2300, Copenhagen, Denmark
Tel.: (45) 70107110
Web Site: https://www.symetri.dk
Software Services
N.A.I.C.S.: 541511

Symetri AB (1)
Korta Gatan 7 6 tr, Solna, 171 54, Stockholm, Sweden
Tel.: (46) 87042200
Web Site: https://www.symetri.se
Software Services
N.A.I.C.S.: 541511

Subsidiary (US):

Cad Technology Center (2)
1000 Boone Ave N Ste 200, Minneapolis, MN 55427
Tel.: (952) 941-1181
Sales Range: $1-9.9 Million
Emp.: 12
Computer System Design Services
N.A.I.C.S.: 541512
Kyle Davis *(Engr-Application)*

D3 Technical Services, LLC (2)
4600 W Kearney St Ste 100, Springfield, MO 65803
Tel.: (417) 831-7171
Web Site: https://www.teamd3.com

Emp.: 200
Engineeering Services
N.A.I.C.S.: 541330
Dennis Schlack *(Admin)*

Subsidiary (Domestic):

CADMIN Services, Inc. **(3)**
2875 Patterson Rd, Florissant, MO 63031-
1709
Tel.: (636) 281-8000
Web Site: http://www.cadminservices.com
Computer & Computer Peripheral Equip-
ment & Software Merchant Whslr
N.A.I.C.S.: 423430
Paul Kessler *(Pres)*

Symetri AS **(1)**
Gaustadalleen 21, 0349, Oslo, Norway
Tel.: (47) 22020700
Web Site: https://www.symetri.no
Software Services
N.A.I.C.S.: 541511

Symetri Ltd. **(1)**
Portal House Raheen Business Park, Ra-
heen, Limerick, V94 FHX7, Ireland
Tel.: (353) 61919000
Web Site: https://www.symetri.ie
Software Development Services
N.A.I.C.S.: 541511

Symetri Oy **(1)**
Lentajantie 3, 01530, Vantaa, Finland
Tel.: (358) 954226500
Web Site: https://www.symetri.fi
Software Development Services
N.A.I.C.S.: 541511

Technia AB **(1)**
Tradgardsgatan 41, 553 16, Jonkoping,
Sweden
Tel.: (46) 859920400
Web Site: http://www.technia.com
Computer Related Services
N.A.I.C.S.: 541519

Subsidiary (Non-US):

Technia AS **(2)**
Hoffsveien 1C, 0275, Oslo, Norway
Tel.: (47) 22020707
Web Site: http://www.technia.com
Sales Range: $25-49.9 Million
Emp.: 10
Computer Related Services
N.A.I.C.S.: 541519

Technia PLM Oy **(2)**
Stella Business Park Solaris Lars Sonchin
Kaari 12, FI-02600, Espoo, Finland
Tel.: (358) 424 7221
Web Site: http://www.technia.com
Sales Range: $25-49.9 Million
Emp.: 100
Product Lifecycle Management (PLM) Cus-
tomizable Business Solutions
N.A.I.C.S.: 541519

Technia B.V. **(1)**
Ringwade 31, 3439 LM, Nieuwegein, Neth-
erlands
Tel.: (31) 850498161
Software & Tech Services
N.A.I.C.S.: 541511

Technia Inc. **(1)**
200 E 5th Ave Ste 124, Naperville, IL
60563-3173
Tel.: (978) 973-9349
Software Development Services
N.A.I.C.S.: 541511

Technia K.K. **(1)**
Nihonbashi Honcho Ys Building 2F 2
Chome-2-2, Nihonbashihoncho Chuo City,
Tokyo, 103-0023, Japan
Tel.: (81) 8099775502
Software & Tech Services
N.A.I.C.S.: 541511

Technia Ltd. **(1)**
Brunleys Kiln Farm, Milton Keynes, MK11
3EW, Buckinghamshire, United Kingdom
Tel.: (44) 1908776776
Software & Tech Services
N.A.I.C.S.: 541511

Technia S.a.s. **(1)**
36 Boulevard de la Bastille, 75012, Paris,
France

Tel.: (33) 143142772
Software Development Services
N.A.I.C.S.: 541511

Technia Slovakia s.r.o. **(1)**
Pribinova 4, 811 09, Bratislava, Slovakia
Tel.: (421) 415139301
Software & Tech Services
N.A.I.C.S.: 541511

Tekis AB **(1)**
Box 315, 731 27, Koping, Sweden
Tel.: (46) 221 168 70
Web Site: http://www.tekis.se
Sales Range: $25-49.9 Million
Emp.: 45
Information Technology Consulting Services
N.A.I.C.S.: 541512
Lars Osterberg *(Mng Dir)*

Teknik I Media Datacenter Stockholm
AB **(1)**
Gjorwellsgatan 30, 112 60, Stockholm,
Sweden
Tel.: (46) 771247247
Web Site: http://www.datacenter.se
Sales Range: $25-49.9 Million
Emp.: 20
Computer Related Services
N.A.I.C.S.: 541519

Tribia AB **(1)**
Korta Gatan 7, Solna, 171 54, Stockholm,
Sweden
Tel.: (46) 84555330
Web Site: https://www.tribia.com
Software & Tech Services
N.A.I.C.S.: 541511

Tribia AS **(1)**
Hoffsveien 1C, 0275, Oslo, Norway
Tel.: (47) 22504550
Web Site: https://www.tribia.com
Construction Projects Services
N.A.I.C.S.: 236220
Steinar Svino *(CEO)*

UAB S-Group Lietuva **(1)**
Lukiskiu g 5, 01108, Vilnius, Lithuania
Tel.: (370) 852127891
Web Site: https://www.sgroup.lt
Software Development Services
N.A.I.C.S.: 541511

Voice Provider Sweden AB **(1)**
Norra Stationsgatan 93 A, 113 64, Stock-
holm, Sweden **(100%)**
Tel.: (46) 852508000
Web Site: https://voiceprovider.com
Sales Range: $25-49.9 Million
Emp.: 15
Computer Related Services
N.A.I.C.S.: 541519
Mikael Janemon *(Mgr-Sls)*

d2m3 Ltd. **(1)**
52 Bramhall Lane South, Bramhall, Man-
chester, SK7 1AH, United Kingdom
Tel.: (44) 1614408122
Web Site: https://www.d2m3.com
Software Services
N.A.I.C.S.: 541511

ADDSINO CO., LTD.
No 67 Wuyi South Road, Taijiang
District, Fuzhou, 350009, Fujian,
China
Tel.: (86) 59183283128
Web Site: http://www.szxrjt.com
Year Founded: 1993
000547—(SSE)
Rev.: $485,250,480
Assets: $2,057,748,732
Liabilities: $626,893,020
Net Worth: $1,430,855,712
Earnings: $4,869,072
Emp.: 1,506
Fiscal Year-end: 12/31/22
Communication Product Mfr
N.A.I.C.S.: 334290
Qingrong Hu *(Chm)*

ADDTECH AB
Birger Jarlsgatan 43, PO Box 5112,
SE-102 43, Stockholm, Sweden
Tel.: (46) 8 470 4900

Web Site: http://www.addtech.com
ADDTB—(OMX)
Rev.: $1,713,759,040
Assets: $1,517,088,160
Liabilities: $997,149,440
Net Worth: $519,938,720
Earnings: $136,363,360
Emp.: 3,556
Fiscal Year-end: 03/31/22
Industrial Products & Components
Developer & Seller
N.A.I.C.S.: 335999
Niklas Stenberg *(Pres & CEO)*

Subsidiaries:

ABH Stromschienen GmbH **(1)**
Borsigstrasse 23, 47169, Duisburg, Ger-
many
Tel.: (49) 203393560
Web Site: https://www.abh-
stromschienen.de
Electricity Distribution Services
N.A.I.C.S.: 221122

ASI Automatikk AS **(1)**
Sankt Hallvards vei 3, 3414, Lierstranda,
Norway
Tel.: (47) 90061100
Web Site: http://www.asiflex.no
Electromechanical Parts & Component Mfr
N.A.I.C.S.: 334419

AVT Industriteknik AB **(1)**
Industrigatan 1, 441 38, Alingsas, Sweden
Tel.: (46) 322642500
Web Site: http://www.avt.se
Industrial Equipment Mfr
N.A.I.C.S.: 333248

Abatel AB **(1)**
Domherrev 11 B, Sollentuna, Stockholm,
Sweden
Tel.: (46) 8 444 59 60
Web Site: http://www.abatel.com
Battery Mfr
N.A.I.C.S.: 335910
Jesper Bjoerken *(Mng Dir)*

Addtech Business Support AB **(1)**
Jarlsgatan 43, PO Box 6068, 14106, Stock-
holm, Sweden **(100%)**
Tel.: (46) 84704900
Sales Range: $25-49.9 Million
Emp.: 15
Data Processing Services
N.A.I.C.S.: 518210
John Sjo *(Mng Dir)*

Addtech Components AB **(1)**
Birger Jarlsgatan 43, Box 5112, Stockholm,
10435, Sweden **(100%)**
Tel.: (46) 854541400
Sales Range: $25-49.9 Million
Emp.: 15
Electrical Apparatus & Equipment Wiring
Supplies & Related Equipment Merchant
Whslr
N.A.I.C.S.: 423610

Subsidiary (Non-US):

Triple-S AS **(2)**
Kristoffer Robins vei 13, 0978, Oslo, Nor-
way
Tel.: (47) 22790520
Web Site: http://www.triple-s.no
Sales Range: $10-24.9 Million
Emp.: 23
Industrial Automation & Communication
Products Distr
N.A.I.C.S.: 423830
Knut-Erik Tovslid *(Head-Network & Cyber
Security)*

Addtech Energy & Equipment AB **(1)**
Fakturavagen 6, 17562, Jarfalla,
Sweden **(100%)**
Tel.: (46) 84458440
Web Site: http://www.kmc.se
Sales Range: $25-49.9 Million
Emp.: 15
Power Distribution; Industrial Machinery &
Equipment Merchant Whslr
N.A.I.C.S.: 423830
Ake Darfeldt *(Mgr-Bus)*

Subsidiary (Non-US):

Hansabattery Oy **(2)**

Hoylaamontie 11A, 00380, Helsinki, Finland
Tel.: (358) 2079996
Web Site: http://www.hansabattery.fi
Sales Range: $25-49.9 Million
Emp.: 5
Battery Mfr
N.A.I.C.S.: 335910
Jon Sandstrom *(Mng Dir)*

Subsidiary (Domestic):

KMC AB **(2)**
Fakturavagen 6, 17562, Jarfalla,
Sweden **(100%)**
Tel.: (46) 84458440
Web Site: http://www.kmc.se
Sales Range: $25-49.9 Million
Emp.: 16
Industrial Machinery & Equipment Merchant
Whslr
N.A.I.C.S.: 423830
Mikael Keranen *(Mng Dir)*

Addtech Life Science AB **(1)**
St Eriksgatan 117, PO Box 23045, 10435,
Stockholm, Sweden **(100%)**
Tel.: (46) 859411350
Web Site: http://www.addtech.com
Sales Range: $50-74.9 Million
Emp.: 3
Professional Equipment & Supplies Whslr
N.A.I.C.S.: 423490
Vohan Seo *(Mng Dir)*

Addtech Transmission AB **(1)**
Eriksgatan 117, 23087, 10435, Stockholm,
Sweden **(100%)**
Tel.: (46) 854546925
Web Site: http://www.addtech.com
Sales Range: $50-74.9 Million
Emp.: 4
Electrical Apparatus & Equipment Wiring
Supplies & Related Equipment Merchant
Whslr
N.A.I.C.S.: 423610

Adiator AB **(1)**
Halsingeg 40 14 Floor, 113 43, Stockholm,
Sweden
Tel.: (46) 8 729 17 00
Web Site: http://www.adiator.se
Electrical Switch Products Distr
N.A.I.C.S.: 423610

Adigo Drives AB **(1)**
Neongatan 10, 431 53, Molndal, Sweden
Tel.: (46) 31 672 340
Web Site: http://adigoab.com
Sales Range: $25-49.9 Million
Emp.: 20
Electric Equipment Mfr
N.A.I.C.S.: 335999
Peter Mayer *(Mng Dir)*

Advanced Valve Solutions B.V. **(1)**
Keplerstraat 8, 1704 SJ, Heerhugowaard,
Netherlands
Tel.: (31) 725762890
Web Site:
https://www.advancedvalvesolutions.nl
Oil & Gas Distr
N.A.I.C.S.: 486990

Allan Rehnstrom AB **(1)**
Marbackagatan 27, Box 644, 123 43,
Farsta, Sweden
Tel.: (46) 2 618 8100
Web Site: https://rehnstrom.se
Vacuum Pump Distr
N.A.I.C.S.: 423620

Amitronic Oy **(1)**
Tarmontie 2, 15860, Hollola, Finland
Tel.: (358) 102318800
Web Site: https://amitronic.fi
Emp.: 8
Electronic Components Mfr
N.A.I.C.S.: 334419

Analyser Services Trinidad Ltd. **(1)**
9 Eylul Mah 333 Sok Metro Park Sitesi No
13 B Blok D 1, Gaziemir, 35410, Izmir, Turkiye
Tel.: (90) 2322522606
Gas Detection Equipment Distr
N.A.I.C.S.: 423690

Aratron AB **(1)**
Strandvag 78 4 tr, 171 54, Solna, Sweden
Tel.: (46) 84041600
Mechanical Component Distr

Addtech AB—(Continued)
N.A.I.C.S.: 423840

Aratron Hydraulikk AS (1)
Skvadronveien 25, 4050, Sola, Norway
Tel.: (47) 51719900
Web Site: http://www.aratronhydraulikk.com
Fluid Pump Equipment Mfr
N.A.I.C.S.: 333996

Aratron Kurt Wiig AS (1)
Skvadronveien 25, 4050, Sola, Norway
Tel.: (47) 51 71 99 00
Web Site: http://www.aratronkurtwiig.no
Hydraulic Component Distr
N.A.I.C.S.: 423840

BEVI Finland Oy (1)
Hannuksenpelto 6, 02270, Espoo, Finland
Tel.: (358) 9 27091210
Web Site: http://www.bevi.fi
Electric Motor & Generator Mfr
N.A.I.C.S.: 335312

BEVI Teknik & Service AB (1)
Bevivagen 1, Blomstermala, 38430, Sweden
Tel.: (46) 499 271 00
Web Site: http://www.bevi.se
Emp.: 50
Electric Motor Mfr
N.A.I.C.S.: 335312
Jan Folkhammar (Gen Mgr)

BTC Industribatterier AB (1)
Tel.: (46) 4 918 4455
Web Site: https://www.btc.nu
Sales Range: $1-9.9 Million
Emp.: 5
Battery Distr
N.A.I.C.S.: 423690
Carl Johan Sabelsjo (Gen Mgr)

BV Teknik A/S (1)
Nybo Bakke 6, 7500, Holstebro, Denmark
Tel.: (45) 97413212
Web Site: https://bv-teknik.dk
Electric Equipment Mfr
N.A.I.C.S.: 334413

Batteriunion AB (1)
Aggelundavägen 2, 175 62, Jarfalla, Sweden
Tel.: (46) 8 795 28 50
Web Site: http://www.batteriunion.se
Battery Mfr
N.A.I.C.S.: 335911

Bergman AS (1)
Gladengveien 3B, 2001, Oslo, Norway
Tel.: (47) 63 83 56 00
Web Site: http://www.bionordika.no
Emp.: 17
Laboratory Instrumentation Mfr
N.A.I.C.S.: 334516

Bergman Diagnostika AS (1)
Jogstadveien 21, 2007, Kjeller, Norway
Tel.: (47) 63835750
Sales Range: $25-49.9 Million
Emp.: 23
Diagnostic Equipment Mfr
N.A.I.C.S.: 334510
Tove Nyhus (Mng Dir)

BergmanLabora AB (1)
Karlsrovagen 2D, 182 53, Danderyd, Sweden
Tel.: (46) 8 625 18 50
Web Site: http://www.bergmanlabora.se
Sales Range: $25-49.9 Million
Emp.: 30
Laboratory Instruments Distr
N.A.I.C.S.: 423450

Best Seating Systems GmbH (1)
Kremstalstrasse 1A, 4053, Haid, Austria
Tel.: (43) 722981776
Web Site: https://www.bestseating.at
Seat System Mfr
N.A.I.C.S.: 336360
Walter Tausch (Mng Dir)

Betech A/S (1)
Vesterlundvej 4, 2730, Herlev, Denmark
Tel.: (45) 44858100
Web Site: https://www.betech.dk
Emp.: 70
Polymer Product Mfr & Sales
N.A.I.C.S.: 339991

Bevi China (1)
Room 801 Modern Communication Building
201 Xinjinqiao Road, Pudong New Area,
Shanghai, 201206, China
Tel.: (86) 21 50325200
Web Site: http://www.bevi.cn
Emp.: 5
Electric Motor & Generator Mfr
N.A.I.C.S.: 335312
Diane Chen (Mgr)

Bevi Danmark A/S (1)
Baldersbuen 14, 2640, Hedehusene, Denmark
Tel.: (45) 39 673605
Web Site: http://www.bevi.dk
Sales Range: $50-74.9 Million
Emp.: 6
Electric Motor Distr
N.A.I.C.S.: 423610
Michael Hallengren (Gen Mgr)

Bevi Electric Shanghai Co., Ltd. (1)
Room 801 Modern Communications Building
No 201 Xinjinqiao Road, Pudong New
Area, Shanghai, 201206, China
Tel.: (86) 2150325200
Web Site: https://www.bevi.cn
Power Station Equipment Distr
N.A.I.C.S.: 423610

Bevi Est Ou (1)
Parnu mnt 238, 116 24, Tallinn, Estonia
Tel.: (372) 5 155 8353
Web Site: http://www.bevi.ee
Electric Motor & Generator Mfr
N.A.I.C.S.: 335312

Bevi Nord AB (1)
Kontaktvagen 8, 901 33, Umea, Sweden
Tel.: (46) 90 70 44 30
Electric Motor & Generator Mfr
N.A.I.C.S.: 335312

Bevi Norge AS (1)
Electric Motor & Generator Mfr
N.A.I.C.S.: 335312

Bevi UAB (1)
Savanoriu 219, 02300, Vilnius, Lithuania
Tel.: (370) 5 2611112
Web Site: http://www.bevi.lt
Electric Motor & Generator Mfr
N.A.I.C.S.: 335312

Beving Elektronik AB (1)
Storsatragrand 10, 127 39, Skarholmen, Sweden
Tel.: (46) 8 680 1199
Web Site: https://beving.se
Electric Meters Mfr
N.A.I.C.S.: 335999

Birepo A/S (1)
Handvaerkerbyen 17, 2670, Greve, Denmark
Tel.: (45) 43903733
Web Site: https://www.birepo.dk
Electronic Locking System Mfr
N.A.I.C.S.: 332510

Blasterprodukter i Koping AB (1)
Glasgatan 21, 731 30, Koping, Sweden
Tel.: (46) 221 760 880
Web Site: http://www.blasterprodukter.se
Abrasive & Diamond Tools Whslr
N.A.I.C.S.: 423840

Bondy LMT A/S (1)
Hassellunden 14, 2765, Smorum, Denmark
Tel.: (45) 70151414
Web Site: https://bondy.dk
Sales Range: $25-49.9 Million
Emp.: 11
Motors & Gear Mfr
N.A.I.C.S.: 333612
Leif Johansson (CEO)

Breve Tufvassons Sp. z o.o. (1)
Postepowa 25/27, 93-347, Lodz, Poland
Transformer Mfr
N.A.I.C.S.: 334416
Adam Szaniewski (Comml Dir)

C.K. Environment A/S (1)
Walgerholm 3, 3500, Vaerlose, Denmark
Tel.: (45) 44989906
Web Site: https://www.cke.dk
Measurement Product Mfr & Distr
N.A.I.C.S.: 334513

CALDARO AB (1)
Warfvinges vag 39, 112 51, Stockholm, Sweden
Tel.: (46) 8 736 1270
Web Site: https://caldaro.com
Sales Range: $25-49.9 Million
Emp.: 15
Electronic Components Distr
N.A.I.C.S.: 423690

COLUMBIA ELEKTRONIK AB (1)
Sjoviksvagen 53, 618 30, Kolmarden, Sweden
Tel.: (46) 11 398005
Web Site: http://www.columbia.se
Emp.: 30
Electronic Components Mfr
N.A.I.C.S.: 334419
Mats Klarholm (Mng Dir)

CTM Lyng AS (1)
Verkstedveien 19, 7125, Vanvikan, Norway
Tel.: (47) 74855510
Web Site: http://www.ctmlyng.no
Home Security Product Mfr & Distr
N.A.I.C.S.: 334290

Caldaro Inc. (1)
2733 Harvey St, Hudson, WI 54016
Tel.: (715) 808-8684
Industrial Joystick Mfr & Distr
N.A.I.C.S.: 335314

Carbex AB (1)
Kvarnbacksvagen 12, 592 41, Vadstena, Sweden
Tel.: (46) 1 432 9440
Web Site: https://carbonbrushsolution.com
Sales Range: $25-49.9 Million
Emp.: 28
Carbon Brush Mfr
N.A.I.C.S.: 335991
Kenneth Johanson (CFO)

CellTech-Harring A/S (1)
Lejrvej 25, 3500, Vaerlose, Denmark
Tel.: (45) 7025 2201
Web Site: http://celltech.dk
Sales Range: $25-49.9 Million
Emp.: 8
Battery Mfr
N.A.I.C.S.: 335910
Michael Ankjaer (Mng Dir)

Cellite AB (1)
Lerbacksgatan 2, 571 38, Nassjo, Sweden
Tel.: (46) 38 055 5050
Web Site: https://www.rutab.se
Sales Range: $50-74.9 Million
Emp.: 3
Battery Distr
N.A.I.C.S.: 423690

Celltech AS (1)
Bjornerudveien 12C, 1266, Oslo, Norway
Tel.: (47) 22753500
Web Site: https://celltech.no
Battery Mfr & Distr
N.A.I.C.S.: 335999

Celltech Abatel AB (1)
Allmanningsvagen 81, 176 78, Jarfalla, Sweden
Tel.: (46) 84457870
Web Site: https://celltech.se
Battery Mfr & Distr
N.A.I.C.S.: 335999

Celltech Energy Systems AB (1)
Tredenborgsvagen 16, 294 35, Solvesborg, Sweden
Tel.: (46) 45623456
Web Site: http://www.celltech.se
Emp.: 26
Battery Mfr
N.A.I.C.S.: 335910
Peter Hakansson (Mng Dir)

Celltech Oy (1)
Sinimaentie 6 A 3rd floor, 02630, Espoo, Finland
Tel.: (358) 207999640
Web Site: https://celltech.fi
Sales Range: $25-49.9 Million
Emp.: 16
Battery Mfr & Sales
N.A.I.C.S.: 335910

Chemo Electric A/S (1)
Hassellunden 14, 2765, Smorum, Denmark
Tel.: (45) 3677 3044

Web Site: http://www.chemoelectric.dk
Sales Range: $50-74.9 Million
Emp.: 1
Electronic Equipment Distr
N.A.I.C.S.: 423690
Claus Hedin Vind (Mgr-FAE & Product)

Codan Tech Qingdao Rubber & Plastic Parts Co., Ltd. (1)
Jinling no 3, Jihongtan Chenqyang, Qingdao, 266000, Shandong, China
Tel.: (86) 5328 790 9363
Web Site: https://www.codantech.com
Rubber & Molded Plastic Parts Mfr
N.A.I.C.S.: 326299

Compotech AB (1)
Halsingegatan 43, Box 21029, 100 31, Stockholm, Sweden
Tel.: (46) 84415800
Web Site: http://www.compotech.se
Sales Range: $25-49.9 Million
Emp.: 20
Electronic Components Mfr
N.A.I.C.S.: 334419
Michael Ullskog (CEO)

Compotech Provider AB (1)
Gustavslundsvagen 145, 167 51, Bromma, Sweden
Tel.: (46) 84415800
Web Site: https://en.compotech.se
Emp.: 30
Industrial Design Services
N.A.I.C.S.: 541611

Control Cutter AS (1)
Energiveien 20, 4056, Tananger, Norway
Tel.: (47) 47475030
Web Site: https://controlcutter.com
Oil & Gas Distr
N.A.I.C.S.: 486990

Craig & Derricott Ltd. (1)
46 Hall Lane, Walsall Wood, Walsall, WS9 9DP, West Midlands, United Kingdom
Tel.: (44) 1543375541
Web Site: http://www.craigandderricott.co.uk
Automatic Transfer Switch Mfr & Distr
N.A.I.C.S.: 335313
Kevin Miller (Mng Dir)

Cumatix AB (1)
Gustavslundsvagen 145 4tr, 167 51, Bromma, Sweden
Tel.: (46) 87686591
Electromechanical Component Distr
N.A.I.C.S.: 423690

DMC Digital Motor Control GmbH (1)
Auf dem Hochstuck 11, 45701, Herten, Germany
Tel.: (49) 236610070
Web Site: http://www.dmcde.de
Motor Speed Controller Mfr & Distr
N.A.I.C.S.: 336320

Dafine Engineering OU (1)
Parnu mnt 142, 11317, Tallinn, Estonia
Tel.: (372) 5167754
Web Site: http://www.dafine.ee
Emp.: 5
Automobile Parts Mfr
N.A.I.C.S.: 336390

Dovitech A/S (1)
Blokken 59, 3460, Birkerod, Denmark
Tel.: (45) 70252650
Web Site: https://www.dovitech.dk
Electromechanical Component & Automation Equipment Distr
N.A.I.C.S.: 423690

Drivhuset AB (1)
Kungsvagen 41, 595 51, Mjolby, Sweden
Tel.: (46) 142290660
Web Site: https://www.drivh.se
Electronic Equipment Distr
N.A.I.C.S.: 423610

Duelco A/S (1)
Systemvej 8, 9200, Aalborg, Denmark
Tel.: (45) 70101007
Web Site: http://www.duelco.dk
Electrical & Automation Equipment Distr
N.A.I.C.S.: 423690
Lone Hald (CFO)

EB Elektro AS (1)
Storgata 18, 2000, Lillestrom, Norway

Tel.: (47) 22832900
Web Site: http://www.eb-elektro.no
High-Voltage Equipment Distr
N.A.I.C.S.: 423610

EK Power Solutions AB (1)
Rinkebyvagen 19B, 182 36, Danderyd,
Sweden
Tel.: (46) 84465600
Web Site: https://ekpower.se
Power Generation Services
N.A.I.C.S.: 221114

ESD-Center AB. (1)
Ringugnsgatan 8, 216 16, Malmo, Sweden
Tel.: (46) 40363240
Web Site: https://www.esd-center.se
Sales Range: $1-9.9 Million
Emp.: 12
Electronic Products Packaging Materials
Distr
N.A.I.C.S.: 423840
Stefan Sjoekvist *(CEO)*

ESi Controls Ltd. (1)
Unit 21 Angelvale, Top Angel Buckingham
Industrial Park, Buckingham, MK18 1TH,
United Kingdom
Tel.: (44) 1280816868
Web Site: http://www.esicontrols.co.uk
Heating Control Product Mfr
N.A.I.C.S.: 333415

ETS (Portsmouth) Limited (1)
Unit 43 Barwell Business Park Leatherhead
Road, Chessington, KT9 2NY, Surrey,
United Kingdom
Tel.: (44) 2084056789
Web Site:
    http://www.etscablecomponents.com
Power Cable Accessory Distr
N.A.I.C.S.: 423610

Egil Eng & Co. AS (1)
Jernkroken 7, 0976, Oslo, Norway
Tel.: (47) 22900560
Web Site: https://egileng.no
Construction Equipment Distr
N.A.I.C.S.: 423810

Electra-Box Diagnostica A/S (1)
Strandveien 6, 3050, Mjondalen, Norway
Tel.: (47) 32237950
Laboratory Product Distr
N.A.I.C.S.: 423490

Electra-Box Diagnostica AB (1)
Solkraftsvagen 18B, 135 70, Stockholm,
Sweden
Tel.: (46) 8 448 73 70
Laboratory Product Distr
N.A.I.C.S.: 423450

Electra-Box Diagnostica APS (1)
Hvidsvaermervej 147, 2610, Rodovre, Den-
mark
Tel.: (45) 44 53 62 11
Emp.: 5
Diagnostics Products Distr
N.A.I.C.S.: 424210
Stefan Korpe *(Gen Mgr)*

Electra-Box Diagnostica Oy (1)
Lyhtytie 8, 00700, Helsinki, Finland
Tel.: (358) 9 72 44 330
Sales Range: $50-74.9 Million
Emp.: 2
Medical Equipment Distr
N.A.I.C.S.: 423450
Annika Karlen *(Gen Mgr)*

**Electric Control Systems Automation
AS** (1)
Industrivegen 2, 4344, Bryne, Norway
Tel.: (47) 51770970
Web Site: https://www.ecs.as
Emp.: 80
System Integration Services
N.A.I.C.S.: 541512

Electrum Automation AB (1)
Industrivagen 8, 901 30, Umea, Sweden
Tel.: (46) 90184550
Web Site: https://electrumab.se
Electronic Equipment Mfr & Distr
N.A.I.C.S.: 334416

Elgood Oy (1)
Juurakkotie 5B, 01510, Vantaa, Finland
Tel.: (358) 207 981 140
Web Site: http://www.elgood.fi

Sales Range: $25-49.9 Million
Emp.: 10
Electronic Component Retailer
N.A.I.C.S.: 449210

Elkome Group Oy (1)
Helletorpankatu 37, 5840, Hyvinkaa, Fin-
land
Tel.: (358) 290074410
Web Site: https://elkome.com
Security System Product Distr
N.A.I.C.S.: 423610

Elkome Oy (1)
Helletorpankatu 37, 05840, Hyvinkaa, Fin-
land
Tel.: (358) 290074410
Web Site: http://www.elkome.com
Industrial Equipment Mfr & Distr
N.A.I.C.S.: 333248

Elsystem i Perstorp AB (1)
Tjaderstigen 33, 284 36, Perstorp, Sweden
Tel.: (46) 435443470
Web Site: http://www.elsystem.se
Electrical Distribution Product Mfr
N.A.I.C.S.: 335999

Eltech A/S (1)
Hassellunden 14, 2765, Smorum, Denmark
Tel.: (45) 7010 1410
Web Site: http://www.eltech.dk
Sales Range: $25-49.9 Million
Emp.: 6
Electronic Components Mfr
N.A.I.C.S.: 334419
Kenth Kohler *(Dir-Admin)*

Eltech Automation A/S (1)
Hassellunden 14, 2765, Smorum, Denmark
Tel.: (45) 7010 1410
Web Site: http://www.eltech.dk
Sales Range: $50-74.9 Million
Emp.: 1
Electronic Product Distr
N.A.I.C.S.: 423690
Kent Koehler *(Gen Mgr)*

Eltech Solutions A/S (1)
Hassellunden 14, 2765, Smorum, Denmark
Tel.: (45) 70101410
Web Site: https://www.eltechsolutions.dk
Electrical & Electronic Product Mfr
N.A.I.C.S.: 335999
Jan Larsen *(Sls Mgr)*

Elteco AS (1)
Floodmyrvegen 24, 3946, Porsgrunn, Nor-
way
Tel.: (47) 35562070
Web Site: https://www.elteco.no
Sales Range: $25-49.9 Million
Emp.: 19
Industrial Automation Component Distr
N.A.I.C.S.: 423840

Emcomp International AB (1)
Tomtagatan 17, Box 7, 702 32, Orebro,
Sweden
Tel.: (46) 581621550
Electric Component Whslr
N.A.I.C.S.: 423690

Emcomp Scandinavia AB (1)
Smidesvagen 4-8, 171 41, Solna, Sweden
Tel.: (46) 8 564 899 00
Web Site: http://www.emcomp.se
Sales Range: $50-74.9 Million
Emp.: 4
Electric Component Whslr
N.A.I.C.S.: 423690

Eurolaite Oy (1)
Sinimaentie 6 A 3rd floor, 02630, Espoo,
Finland
Tel.: (358) 20 155 7444
Web Site: http://www.eurolaite.fi
Sales Range: $50-74.9 Million
Emp.: 5
Electrical Product Whslr
N.A.I.C.S.: 423610
Tuomo Luukkainen *(Pres & CEO)*

FB Chain Limited (1)
Works Road, Letchworth, SG6 1LP, Hert-
fordshire, United Kingdom
Tel.: (44) 1462670844
Web Site: http://www.fbchain.com
Sales Range: $25-49.9 Million
Emp.: 15
Conveyor Chain Mfr

N.A.I.C.S.: 333613
Nigel Eames *(Mgr-Ops)*

FB Kedjor AB (1)
Sattargatan 4, Box 304, 631 04, Eskilstuna,
Sodermanland, Sweden
Tel.: (46) 16153300
Sales Range: $25-49.9 Million
Emp.: 16
Roller Chain Mfr
N.A.I.C.S.: 333613
John Karlsson *(CEO)*

FB Ketjutekniikka Oy (1)
Kokemaentie 451, Koylio, 27500, Finland
Tel.: (358) 2 540 111
Web Site: http://www.fbketjutekniikka.fi
Emp.: 70
Conveyor Chain Mfr
N.A.I.C.S.: 333922

FB Ketten GmbH (1)
Stakelbrauk 11, 59889, Eslohe, Germany
Tel.: (49) 297 397 9140
Web Site: https://www.fb-ketten.de
Conveyor Chain Mfr
N.A.I.C.S.: 333922
Matthias Berls *(Mng Dir)*

FB Ketten Handels Gmbh (1)
Gewerbepark Sud 5, 6330, Kufstein, Austria
Tel.: (43) 537261466
Wood Products Mfr
N.A.I.C.S.: 321999

FB Kjeder AS (1)
Jernkroken 7, 0976, Oslo, Norway
Tel.: (47) 47459004
Web Site: http://www.fb-kedjor.se
Precision Machine Tools Mfr
N.A.I.C.S.: 332721

Fairfield Solutions Limited (1)
Unit 4 Ashgrove Farm, Piltdown, Uckfield,
TN22 3XN, East Sussex, United Kingdom
Tel.: (44) 1825722116
Web Site: http://www.fairfield-solutions.com
Battery Mfr & Distr
N.A.I.C.S.: 335910

Fairfield Trading Company Ltd. (1)
Unit 4 Ashgrove Farm, Piltdown, Uckfield,
TN22 3XN, East Sussex, United Kingdom
Tel.: (44) 1825722116
Web Site: https://fairfield-solutions.com
Battery Distr
N.A.I.C.S.: 423610

Fibersystem AB (1)
Gardsfogdevagen 18 A, 168 67, Bromma,
Sweden
Tel.: (46) 856482880
Web Site: http://www.fibersystem.com
Fiber Optical Product Distr
N.A.I.C.S.: 423690

Finnchain Oy (1)
Koillisvayla 7, 26510, Rauma, Finland
Tel.: (358) 283873800
Web Site: https://finnchain.fi
Waste Water Treatment Services
N.A.I.C.S.: 221320

Flow-Teknikk AS (1)
Olav Brunborgsvei 27, 1396, Billingstad,
Norway
Tel.: (47) 66775400
Web Site: https://www.flow.no
Measuring Instrument Equipment Distr
N.A.I.C.S.: 423610

Fox Electronics AS (1)
PO Box 67, Kjelsas, 0411, Oslo, Norway
Tel.: (47) 23896900
Web Site: http://www.foxelectronics.no
Sales Range: $25-49.9 Million
Emp.: 7
Fibre Optic Component Mfr
N.A.I.C.S.: 334419

Frameco AS (1)
Installatorvegen 19, 461 37, Trollhattan,
Sweden
Tel.: (46) 520488230
Web Site: http://www.frameco.se
Arm Vehicle Mfr
N.A.I.C.S.: 336992

Gevea AB (1)
Vagngatan 9, 603 63, Norrkoping, Sweden
Tel.: (46) 11184800

Web Site: https://gevea.se
Electrical Power Products Mfr & Distr
N.A.I.C.S.: 334515

Gigacom AB (1)
Vastberga Alle 5, 126 30, Hagersten, Swe-
den
Tel.: (46) 86266990
Web Site: http://www.gigacom.se
Fiber Optic Component Distr
N.A.I.C.S.: 423690

Gotapack International AB (1)
August Barks Gata 30 B, 421 32, Vastra
Frolunda, Sweden
Tel.: (46) 317010990
Web Site: https://www.gotapack.se
Packaging Product Distr
N.A.I.C.S.: 424130

HF Danyko AS (1)
Bark Silas Vei 8, 4876, Grimstad, Norway
Tel.: (47) 37090940
Web Site: http://www.danyko.no
Automation Cable Product Distr
N.A.I.C.S.: 423690

Hans Folsgaard A/S (1)
Theilgaards Torv 1, 4600, Koge, Denmark
Tel.: (45) 43208600
Web Site: https://www.folsgaard.com
Telecom Related Product Mfr & Distr
N.A.I.C.S.: 334290
Bent Madsen *(CEO)*

Hjulex AB (1)
Makadamgatan 1, 254 64, Helsingborg,
Sweden
Tel.: (46) 425 6700
Web Site: https://www.hjulex.se
Roller Conveyor Products Distr
N.A.I.C.S.: 423840

Holm & Halby A/S (1)
Vallensbaekvej 35, 2605, Brondby, Den-
mark
Tel.: (45) 43269400
Web Site: https://www.holm-halby.dk
Emp.: 42
Laboratory Equipment Distr
N.A.I.C.S.: 423490
Morten Dyrner *(CEO)*

Hydro Material Oy (1)
Ruohosuontie 3, 02580, Helsinki, Finland
Tel.: (358) 105742500
Web Site: http://www.hydro-material.fi
Hydraulic Product Mfr & Whslr
N.A.I.C.S.: 332912

Hydro Service A/S (1)
Glarmerstervej 18, 6710, Esbjerg, Denmark
Tel.: (45) 7515 5855
Web Site: http://www.hydroservice.dk
Sales Range: $25-49.9 Million
Emp.: 7
Hydraulic Components & Pump Mfr
N.A.I.C.S.: 333914

IETV Elektroteknik AB (1)
Trikagatan 1, 523 60, Gallstad, Sweden
Tel.: (46) 321531900
Web Site: http://www.ietv.se
Power Supply Services
N.A.I.C.S.: 221122

IPAS AS (1)
Ostre Rosten 2A, 7075, Tiller, Norway
Tel.: (47) 40001559
Web Site: http://www.ipas.no
Lighting Product Distr
N.A.I.C.S.: 423610

ITEK AS (1)
Havnegata 1, PO Box 78, 4791, Lillesand,
Norway
Tel.: (47) 37267000
Web Site: http://www.itek.no
Industrial Air Equipment Distr
N.A.I.C.S.: 423830
Rich Ivar Hakonsen *(Gen Mgr)*

ITEK PL (1)
Ul Charzykowska 17A, 80-178, Gdansk,
Poland
Tel.: (48) 587463542
Web Site: http://www.itek.com.pl
Construction & Engineering Services
N.A.I.C.S.: 541330

Immunkemi F&D AB (1)

Addtech AB—(Continued)

Veddestra Centrum, 175 72, Jarfalla, Sweden
Tel.: (46) 8 583 615 00
Web Site: http://www.immunkemi.se
Diagnostics & Biochemical Research Services
N.A.I.C.S.: 541715

Immuno Diagnostic Oy　　　　　　(1)
Kaivokatu 16, 13100, Hameenlinna, Finland
Tel.: (358) 3 615 370
Web Site: http://www.immunodiagnostic.fi
Sales Range: $25-49.9 Million
Emp.: 10
Diagnostic & Research Services
N.A.I.C.S.: 541715
Jarmo Laakkonen (Mng Dir)

Impact Air Systems Ltd.　　　　　　(1)
3 Kingsley Street, Leicester, LE2 6DY, United Kingdom
Tel.: (44) 1162448855
Web Site: http://www.impactairsystems.com
Air Conveying Equipment Distr
N.A.I.C.S.: 423830
Nick Ball (Mng Dir)

Impact Technical Services Ltd.　　　(1)
3 Kingsley Street, Leicester, LE2 6DY, United Kingdom
Tel.: (44) 1162448855
Web Site:
　http://www.impacttechnicalservices.co.uk
Ventilation Equipment Maintenance Services
N.A.I.C.S.: 238220
Tony Bosworth (Dir-Ops)

Impulseradar Sweden AB　　　　　　(1)
Skolgatan 22, 939 31, Mala, Sweden
Tel.: (46) 95310008
Web Site: https://impulseradargpr.com
Emp.: 27
Electric Appliances Mfr
N.A.I.C.S.: 334416

Insatech A/S　　　　　　　　　　　(1)
Naestvedvej 73C, Praesto, 4720, Vordingborg, Denmark
Tel.: (45) 70848569
Web Site: https://www.insatech.com
Sales Range: $25-49.9 Million
Emp.: 55
Industrial Component Distr
N.A.I.C.S.: 423830
Mariann Jensen During (Mgr-Admin)

Intertrafo Oy　　　　　　　　　　　(1)
Unkarinkatu 16, 20750, Turku, Finland
Tel.: (358) 22442111
Web Site: https://www.intertrafo.fi
Shopping Centre Services
N.A.I.C.S.: 812990

Isotron Systems B.V.　　　　　　　(1)
Afrikalaan 19-23, 5232 BD, 's-Hertogenbosch, Netherlands
Tel.: (31) 736391639
Web Site: https://isotron.eu
Industrial Automation Equipment Mfr & Distr
N.A.I.C.S.: 334513

KMC Ytbehandling AB　　　　　　　(1)
Bruttovagen 9, 175 43, Jarfalla, Sweden
Tel.: (46) 84458440
Web Site: https://www.kmc.se
Mechanical Equipment Mfr & Distr
N.A.I.C.S.: 333613

KRV AS　　　　　　　　　　　　　(1)
Barstolveien 3, 4636, Kristiansand, Norway
Tel.: (47) 94157000
Web Site: https://www.krv.as
Ventilation Equipment Installation Services
N.A.I.C.S.: 238290

KZ Handels AB　　　　　　　　　　(1)
Hanhals Kyrkvag 123, 439 73, Fjaras, Sweden
Tel.: (46) 300541610
Web Site: https://kzhandels.se
Pipe Equipment Mfr & Distr
N.A.I.C.S.: 326122

Kaptas Oy　　　　　　　　　　　　(1)
Rannankuja 1, Ylamylly, 80400, Joensuu, Finland
Tel.: (358) 104208100
Web Site: http://www.kaptas.fi

Emp.: 50
Industrial Automation Machinery Mfr
N.A.I.C.S.: 333998
Markku Noroaho (CEO)

Ko Hartog Verkeerstechniek B.V.　　(1)
Marconistraat 35, 1704 RH, Heerhugowaard, Netherlands
Tel.: (31) 725350540
Web Site: https://www.kohartog.nl
Signal System Mfr & Distr
N.A.I.C.S.: 334290

Kouvo Automation Oy　　　　　　　(1)
Puhjontie 17, 45720, Kuusankoski, Finland
Tel.: (358) 207406160
Web Site: https://www.kouvo.fi
Sales Range: $50-74.9 Million
Emp.: 7
Measuring Equipment Distr
N.A.I.C.S.: 423830

LabRobot Products AB　　　　　　　(1)
Munkerodsvagen 4, 444 32, Stenungsund, Sweden
Tel.: (46) 3 038 4673
Web Site: https://labrobot.com
Laboratory Instruments Mfr & Distr
N.A.I.C.S.: 334516
Herve Laisis (CEO)

MCS Europe Group B.V.　　　　　　(1)
Kyoto Road 719-721, 3047 BG, Rotterdam, Netherlands
Tel.: (31) 884375555
Web Site: https://www.mcs-nl.com
Wireless Engineering Services
N.A.I.C.S.: 541511

Martin Bruusgaard AS　　　　　　　(1)
Eyvind Lyches vei 19 A, 1338, Sandvika, Norway
Tel.: (47) 67549330
Web Site: http://www.bruusgaard.no
Gas Detection Equipment Distr
N.A.I.C.S.: 423690

Maxeta AS　　　　　　　　　　　　(1)
Amtmand Aallsgate 89, PO Box 177, 3716, Skien, Norway
Tel.: (47) 35914000
Web Site: https://maxeta.no
Sales Range: $50-74.9 Million
Emp.: 50
Electrical Equipment Distr
N.A.I.C.S.: 423610

Mechatronics Controls Systems Yangzhou Co., Ltd.　　　　　　　　(1)
20 Hongfa Rd Development zone A-7 Wenhui, Industrial Park, Yangzhou, China
Tel.: (86) 51485881846
Web Site: http://www.mcsy.cn
Electronic Throttle Control Mfr
N.A.I.C.S.: 336320

Metric Industrial A/S　　　　　　　(1)
Hassellunden 14, 2765, Smorum, Denmark
Tel.: (45) 70 300 810
Web Site: http://www.metric.dk
Sales Range: $25-49.9 Million
Emp.: 5
Testing & Measurement Services
N.A.I.C.S.: 541380

Metric Industrial AB　　　　　　　(1)
Sjoangsvagen 5, SE 192 72, Sollentuna, Sweden
Tel.: (46) 86264840
Web Site: http://www.metric.se
Sales Range: $10-24.9 Million
Emp.: 10
Automation & Test & Measurement Equipment
N.A.I.C.S.: 334515
Patrik Klerck (Mng Dir-Grp)

Metric Industrial AS　　　　　　　(1)
Bjornerudveien 17, 1266, Oslo, Norway
Tel.: (47) 23896900
Web Site: http://www.metricindustrial.no
Industrial Automation Equipments Mfr
N.A.I.C.S.: 333248

Metric Industrial Oy　　　　　　　(1)
Piispantilankuja 4, PL 14, 02241, Espoo, Finland
Tel.: (358) 9 4761 600
Web Site: http://www.metric.fi
Sales Range: $25-49.9 Million
Emp.: 16
Testing & Measuring Equipment Distr

N.A.I.C.S.: 423830
Tero Haaskola (Mng Dir)

Mobile Control Systems SA　　　　　(1)
Rue de Lusambo 34 A, 1190, Brussels, Belgium
Tel.: (32) 23451810
Web Site: http://www.mcs-electronic-throttle-control.com
Electronic Throttle Control Mfr
N.A.I.C.S.: 336320

Movetec Oy　　　　　　　　　　　(1)
Suokalliontie 9, 01740, Vantaa, Finland
Tel.: (358) 95259230
Web Site: https://www.movetec.fi
Sales Range: $25-49.9 Million
Emp.: 40
Industrial Equipment Whsr
N.A.I.C.S.: 423830
Joakim Boijer (Mgr-Sls)

Necks Electric AB　　　　　　　　　(1)
Tegelbruksvagen 22, 821 43, Bollnas, Sweden
Tel.: (46) 278621660
Power Transmission Lines Products & Services
N.A.I.C.S.: 221122
Bengt Pettersson (Pres & Mng Dir)

Nordautomation AB　　　　　　　　(1)
Strandvagen 64, 873 71, Nyland, Sweden
Tel.: (46) 703308936
Web Site: https://nordautomation.fi
Industrial Machinery Mfr
N.A.I.C.S.: 334419

Nordautomation Oy　　　　　　　　(1)
Hevoshaantie 5, 64100, Kristiinankaupunki, Finland
Tel.: (358) 207616200
Web Site: https://www.nordautomation.fi
Wood Products Mfr
N.A.I.C.S.: 321999
Keijo Lamminen (Sls Dir)

Nordic Battery AB　　　　　　　　　(1)
Battery Mfr & Whslr
N.A.I.C.S.: 335910

Nordic Battery AS　　　　　　　　　(1)
Bjornerud Veien 17, 1266, Oslo, Norway
Tel.: (47) 22 76 38 80
Web Site: http://www.nordicbattery.no
Battery Mfr
N.A.I.C.S.: 335910

Norsk Analyse A/S　　　　　　　　(1)
Strandvejen 99, 4600, Koge, Denmark
Tel.: (45) 70224550
Oil & Gas Distribution Services
N.A.I.C.S.: 221210
Leif Abildgaard (Sls Mgr)

Norsk Analyse AS　　　　　　　　　(1)
Wirgenesvei 10, Barkaker, 3157, Tonsberg, Norway
Tel.: (47) 33375100
Web Site: http://www.norskanalyse.com
Emp.: 91
Oil & Gas Distribution Services
N.A.I.C.S.: 221210

Norsk Analyse Oy　　　　　　　　　(1)
Ruukintie 3, 02330, Espoo, Finland
Tel.: (358) 207981040
Oil & Gas Operation Services
N.A.I.C.S.: 213112

Ofira Italiana S.R.L.　　　　　　　(1)
Via N Tartaglia 5/7, 25064, Gussago, BS, Italy
Tel.: (39) 030241941
Web Site: https://www.ofira.it
Auto Parts Retailer
N.A.I.C.S.: 441330

Omni Ray AG　　　　　　　　　　(1)
Im Schorli 5, 8600, Dubendorf, Switzerland
Tel.: (41) 448022880
Web Site: http://www.omniray.ch
Industrial Equipment Mfr
N.A.I.C.S.: 333248

OmniProcess AB　　　　　　　　　(1)
Solna Strandvag 3, 171 54, Solna, Sweden
Tel.: (46) 856480840
Web Site: https://www.omniprocess.se
Sales Range: $25-49.9 Million
Emp.: 30
Analytical Laboratory Equipment Distr

N.A.I.C.S.: 423490

Oscar Fah AG　　　　　　　　　　(1)
Sandackerstrasse 28, 9245, Oberburen-Uzwil, Switzerland
Tel.: (41) 588100810
Web Site: https://www.oscarfaeh.ch
Automobile Component Distr
N.A.I.C.S.: 423120

PLD Finland Oy　　　　　　　　　(1)
Kutomotie 18 B, 380, Helsinki, Finland
Tel.: (358) 207 410 270
Web Site: http://www.pld.fi
Sales Range: $25-49.9 Million
Emp.: 7
Analytical Laboratory Instrument Mfr
N.A.I.C.S.: 334516
Tommi Virtanen (Gen Mgr)

Penlink AB　　　　　　　　　　　　(1)
Vretensborgsvagen 28 Floor 6, 126 30, Hagersten, Sweden
Tel.: (46) 84011010
Web Site: http://www.penlink.se
Electro Mechanical Component Distr
N.A.I.C.S.: 423610

Peter Andersson AB　　　　　　　(1)
Vastra Rydsvagen 134, 196 31, Kungsangen, Sweden
Tel.: (46) 858175300
Web Site: http://www.p-andersson.se
Furnishing Equipment Retailer
N.A.I.C.S.: 449110

Power Technic ApS　　　　　　　　(1)
Elsenbakken 7, 3600, Frederikssund, Denmark
Tel.: (45) 70208210
Web Site: https://www.powertechnic.dk
Electronic Parts Distr
N.A.I.C.S.: 423690

PowerNor AS　　　　　　　　　　(1)
Hvamsvingen 4, 2013, Skjetten, Norway
Tel.: (47) 90707000
Web Site: http://www.powernor.no
Battery Distr
N.A.I.C.S.: 423610

Powermec AB　　　　　　　　　　(1)
Bergkallavagen 27D, 192 79, Sollentuna, Sweden
Tel.: (46) 84443650
Web Site: https://www.powermec.se
Electric Motor Component Distr
N.A.I.C.S.: 423610

Powermec AS　　　　　　　　　　(1)
Soliveien 264, 1667, Rolvsoy, Norway
Tel.: (47) 69398000
Web Site: https://www.powermec.no
Electrical Motor Equipment Distr
N.A.I.C.S.: 423610
Thomas Markussen (Mng Dir)

Powermec ApS　　　　　　　　　　(1)
Mollevej 9 L21, 2990, Nivaa, Denmark
Tel.: (45) 49146660
Web Site: https://www.powermec.dk
Electrical Motor & Electro Mechanical Component Distr
N.A.I.C.S.: 423610

PrismaTibro AB　　　　　　　　　(1)
Jarnvagsgatan 19, 543 50, Tibro, Sweden
Tel.: (46) 50440040
Web Site: http://www.prismatibro.se
Electric Device Mfr
N.A.I.C.S.: 334419
Malin Buss (CEO, Sls Mgr & Product Mgr-Prisma Daps, Button & Lights)

Pulsteknik AB　　　　　　　　　　(1)
Von Utfallsgatan 16A, 415 05, Gothenburg, Sweden
Tel.: (46) 31840300
Web Site: http://www.pulsteknik.se
Electrical Component Mfr
N.A.I.C.S.: 335999

Q-tronic B.V.　　　　　　　　　　(1)
Oosterdorpsstraat 107b, 3871 AC, Hoevelaken, Netherlands
Tel.: (31) 332535063
Web Site: http://www.en.q-tronic.nl
Automobile Parts Distr
N.A.I.C.S.: 423110

R&K TECH AB　　　　　　　　　　(1)

Smidesvagen 4-8, 171 41, Solna, Sweden
Tel.: (46) 8 544 40 560
Web Site: http://www.rk.se
Electronic Equipment Whslr
N.A.I.C.S.: 423690
Patrick Hahne *(Gen Mgr)*

Ramstrom Transmission AB   **(1)**
Makadamgatan 1, 254 64, Helsingborg,
Sweden
Tel.: (46) 4256700
Web Site:
http://www.ramstromtransmission.se
Mechanical Transmission Component Distr
N.A.I.C.S.: 423840

Recab AB   **(1)**
Vastberga Alle 5, 126 30, Hagersten, Sweden
Tel.: (46) 86830300
Web Site: http://www.recab.com
Emp.: 60
Data Communication Product Mfr
N.A.I.C.S.: 334111
Adam Ringh *(CFO)*

Recab UK Ltd.   **(1)**
Suite 13 Ashford House Beaufort Court,
Rochester, ME2 4FA, United Kingdom
Tel.: (44) 1634300900
Web Site: http://www.recabuk.com
Embedded Computing Equipment Distr
N.A.I.C.S.: 423430

Rollco A/S   **(1)**
Skomagervej 13 E, 7100, Vejle, Denmark
Tel.: (45) 75522666
Web Site: http://www.rollco.dk
Automation Product Mfr
N.A.I.C.S.: 333613

Rollco AB   **(1)**
Box 22234, 250 24, Helsingborg, Sweden
Tel.: (46) 42150040
Web Site: http://www.rollco.eu
Automation Product Mfr
N.A.I.C.S.: 333613

Rollco Norge AS   **(1)**
Industrigata 6, 3414, Lierstranda, Norway
Tel.: (47) 32840034
Web Site: http://www.rollco.no
Automation Product Mfr
N.A.I.C.S.: 333613
Mads Dyhrfjeld *(Mng Dir)*

Rollco Oy   **(1)**
Sarankulmankatu 12, 33900, Tampere, Finland
Tel.: (358) 207579790
Web Site: https://www.rollco.fi
Linear Motion Product Mfr
N.A.I.C.S.: 332991

Rollco Taiwan Co., Ltd.   **(1)**
No 28 Lane 125 Daan Road, Shulin District,
New Taipei City, 23847, Taiwan
Tel.: (886) 286872726
Web Site: http://www.rollco-tw.com
Automation Product Mfr
N.A.I.C.S.: 333613

Rutab AB   **(1)**
Lerbacksgatan 2, 571 38, Nassjo, Sweden
Tel.: (46) 380555050
Sales Range: $1-9.9 Million
Marine Cable Mfr
N.A.I.C.S.: 335921
Frank Robertsson *(CEO)*

Rutab AS   **(1)**
Amtmand Aallsgate 89, 3716, Skien, Norway
Tel.: (47) 380555055
Web Site: https://www.rutab.no
Electronic Equipment Distr
N.A.I.C.S.: 423610

S. Tygesen Energi A/S   **(1)**
Strandvangen 33, 5300, Kerteminde, Denmark
Tel.: (45) 65324380
Web Site: https://tygesen-energi.dk
Telecommunication Engineering Services
N.A.I.C.S.: 541330

SABP Elteknik AB   **(1)**
Honungsgatan 10, 432 95, Varberg, Sweden
Web Site: http://www.sabp.se

Sales Range: $25-49.9 Million
Emp.: 9
Power Industrial Machinery Mfr
N.A.I.C.S.: 333248

SCN UK Group Ltd.   **(1)**
46 Hall Lane Walsall Wood, Walsall, WS9
9DP, West Midlands, United Kingdom
Tel.: (44) 1634300900
Web Site: https://scn.uk
Electronic Components Distr
N.A.I.C.S.: 423690

SW Automatik AB   **(1)**
Marbackagatan 27, Box 64, 123 22, Farsta,
Sweden
Tel.: (46) 86203320
Web Site: https://www.swautomatik.se
Automation Equipment Wiring Mfr & Distr
N.A.I.C.S.: 334519

Sammet Dampers Oy   **(1)**
Ylistonmaentie 33c, 40500, Jyvaskyla, Finland
Tel.: (358) 143391650
Web Site: http://www.sammet.fi
Industrial Damper Mfr
N.A.I.C.S.: 332322

Sensor Control Nordic AB   **(1)**
Truckvagen 16B, 194 52, Upplands Vasby,
Sweden
Tel.: (46) 86682100
Web Site: http://www.scnnordic.com
Industrial Sensor Component Distr
N.A.I.C.S.: 423690

Sensor ECS A/S   **(1)**
Priorparken 355 3rd floor, 2605, Brondby,
Denmark
Tel.: (45) 43754480
Web Site: https://www.sensorecs.dk
Computer Hardware Distr
N.A.I.C.S.: 423430

Sittab AB   **(1)**
Industrivagen 10, 781 60, Gustafs, Sweden
Tel.: (46) 243244250
Web Site: https://sittab.se
Construction Equipment Mfr
N.A.I.C.S.: 333120

Sittab Inc.   **(1)**
2733 Harvey St, Hudson, WI 54016
Tel.: (715) 690-2992
Seat Accessory Mfr & Distr
N.A.I.C.S.: 336360

Sittab Stol AB   **(1)**
Industrivagen 10, 781 60, Gustafs, Sweden
Tel.: (46) 24 324 4250
Web Site: https://www.sittab.se
Seat Accessories Mfr & Distr
N.A.I.C.S.: 336360
Anders Claesson *(Mng Dir)*

Skyltar & Marken Gruppen AB   **(1)**
Finlandsgatan 10, 164 74, Kista, Sweden
Tel.: (46) 84498200
Web Site: https://www.skyltar.se
Innovative & Customized Sign Product Distr
N.A.I.C.S.: 423440

Staubo Elektro Maskin AS   **(1)**
Bjornerudveien 12C, 1266, Oslo, Norway
Tel.: (47) 22753500
Web Site: http://www.staubo.no
Battery Distr
N.A.I.C.S.: 423610

Stig Wahlstrom Automatik AB   **(1)**
Ralsgatan 6A, 802 91, Gavle, Sweden
Tel.: (46) 8 620 3320
Web Site: https://www.swautomatik.se
Sales Range: $50-74.9 Million
Emp.: 60
Electronic Equipment Whslr
N.A.I.C.S.: 423690
Robert Svantesson *(CEO)*

Stig Wahlstrom Hydraulik AB   **(1)**
Marbackagatan 27, 123 43, Farsta, Sweden
Tel.: (46) 8 683 33 00
Web Site: http://www.wahlstromhydraulik.se
Emp.: 20
Pumps Mfr
N.A.I.C.S.: 333914
Anders Berkevall *(Mng Dir)*

Stig Wahlstrom Oy   **(1)**
Suokalliontie 9, 01740, Vantaa, Finland

Tel.: (358) 95024400
Web Site: https://www.swoy.fi
Communication Equipment Mfr
N.A.I.C.S.: 334290

Stigab AB   **(1)**
Fagelviksvagen 18, 145 53, Norsborg, Sweden
Tel.: (46) 8970990
Web Site: http://www.stigab.se
Industrial Equipment Mfr & Distr
N.A.I.C.S.: 333248
Claes Eriksson *(Sls Mgr)*

Stigab OY   **(1)**
Kankurinkatu 4-6, 05810, Hyvinkaa, Finland
Tel.: (358) 409614476
Automotive Component Mfr & Distr
N.A.I.C.S.: 336390

Swelex AB   **(1)**
Marbackagatan 27, 123 43, Farsta, Sweden
Tel.: (46) 86833300
Web Site: https://swelex.se
Electronic Equipment Mfr & Distr
N.A.I.C.S.: 335314

Switchgear AB   **(1)**
Utmarksvagen 6, 802 91, Gavle, Sweden
Tel.: (46) 26541550
Sales Range: $25-49.9 Million
Emp.: 20
Switchgear Mfr & Distr
N.A.I.C.S.: 335313

Synective Labs AB   **(1)**
Andra Langgatan 48, 413 27, Gothenburg,
Sweden
Tel.: (46) 317607240
Web Site: http://www.synective.se
Computer System Design Services
N.A.I.C.S.: 541512
Mikael Pettersson *(Reg Mgr)*

Systerra Computer GmbH   **(1)**
Kreuzberger Ring 22, 65205, Wiesbaden,
Germany
Tel.: (49) 61144889400
Web Site: http://www.systerra.de
Computer Peripheral Equipment Mfr & Distr
N.A.I.C.S.: 334112

TLS Energimatning AB   **(1)**
Skeppsbron 32, 111 30, Stockholm, Sweden
Tel.: (46) 840020845
Web Site: https://www.tls.se
Heating & Cooling Measuring Equipment
Distr
N.A.I.C.S.: 423830

Tampereen Sahkopalvelu Oy   **(1)**
Autokeskuksentie 16, 33960, Pirkkala, Finland
Tel.: (358) 32515111
Web Site: https://www.tsp.fi
Emp.: 50
Electrical Products Distr
N.A.I.C.S.: 423690
Lasse Tukiainen *(Sls Dir)*

Teknikprodukter Nordic AB   **(1)**
Grannavagen 24, 561 34, Huskvarna, Sweden
Tel.: (46) 36376200
Emp.: 25
Industrial Component Distr
N.A.I.C.S.: 423830
Per Alfredsson *(CEO)*

Thiim A/S   **(1)**
Transformervej 31, 2860, Soborg, Denmark
Tel.: (45) 44858000
Web Site: https://www.thiim.com
Emp.: 20
Industrial Component Mfr
N.A.I.C.S.: 334419

Thurne Teknik AB   **(1)**
Lugnets Alle 1, 120 65, Stockholm, Sweden
Tel.: (46) 855769300
Web Site: http://www.thurne.se
Bulk Material Handling Equipment Mfr &
Distr
N.A.I.C.S.: 333998
Martin Evers *(CEO)*

Thurne Teknik AB   **(1)**
Malminkartanonkuja 4, 00390, Helsinki,
Finland
Tel.: (358) 942451070

Bulk Material Handling Equipment Mfr &
Distr
N.A.I.C.S.: 333998
Jenny Jensen *(Head-Sls-Finland & Baltics)*

Trinergi AB   **(1)**
Halltorpsvagen 1, 702 29, Orebro, Sweden
Tel.: (46) 19 18 86 60
Web Site: http://www.trinergi.se
Electrical Power Measurement Products
Distr
N.A.I.C.S.: 423610

Triolab A/S   **(1)**
Vallensbaekvej 35, 2605, Brondby, Denmark
Tel.: (45) 43 96 00 12
Web Site: http://www.triolab.dk
Sales Range: $25-49.9 Million
Emp.: 21
Diagnostic Equipment Mfr
N.A.I.C.S.: 334510

Tube Control AB   **(1)**
Storsatragrand 10, 127 39, Skarholmen,
Sweden
Tel.: (46) 8 555 92100
Web Site: http://www.tubehydraulik.se
Sales Range: $10-24.9 Million
Emp.: 20
Hydraulic Components Whslr
N.A.I.C.S.: 423840

Tufvasson Tesch AB   **(1)**
Marstavagen 20, 193 40, Sigtuna, Sweden
Tel.: (46) 859480900
Web Site: https://www.tufvassons.se
Electrical Engineering & Power Distribution
Services
N.A.I.C.S.: 423610

Tufvassons Transformator AB   **(1)**
Marstavagen 20, 193 40, Sigtuna, Sweden
Tel.: (46) 8 594 809 00
Web Site: http://www.tufvassons.se
Transformer Mfr
N.A.I.C.S.: 334416

Vactek A/S   **(1)**
Tinvej 20A, 3060, Espergaerde, Denmark
Tel.: (45) 4824 4433
Web Site: http://www.vactek.dk
Sales Range: $50-74.9 Million
Emp.: 4
Electronic Components Distr
N.A.I.C.S.: 423690
Rainer Joachim Wagner *(Gen Mgr)*

Vallin Baltic AS   **(1)**
Maepealse 2, 12618, Tallinn, Estonia
Tel.: (372) 6593200
Web Site: https://www.vallin.ee
Electric Equipment Mfr
N.A.I.C.S.: 335999

Valnor AS   **(1)**
Torneroseveien 8, 4315, Sandnes, Norway
Tel.: (47) 51827420
Web Site: http://www.valnor.no
Emp.: 10
Oil & Gas Distribution Services
N.A.I.C.S.: 221210
Rolf Selnes *(Mng Dir)*

Valutec AB   **(1)**
Klockarbergsvagen 50, 931 70, Skelleftea,
Sweden
Tel.: (46) 91087950
Web Site: https://www.valutec.se
Wood Dryer Equipment Distr
N.A.I.C.S.: 423850

Valutec Group AB   **(1)**
Klockarbergsvagen 50, 931 70, Skelleftea,
Sweden
Tel.: (46) 91087950
Web Site: https://www.valutec.se
Wood Product Distr
N.A.I.C.S.: 423310

Valutec Oy   **(1)**
Tehdaskylankatu 11A, 11710, Riihimaki,
Finland
Tel.: (358) 757561401
Web Site: https://www.valutec.fi
Wood Dryer Equipment Distr
N.A.I.C.S.: 423850

Valutec Wood Dryers Inc.   **(1)**
3924 Oxford Street, Port Coquitlam, V3B
4E8, BC, Canada

Addtech AB—(Continued)

Tel.: (416) 640-7478
Web Site: http://www.valutec.ca
Wood Dryer Distr
N.A.I.C.S.: 423390
Ingo Wallocha (Mng Dir)

Wendler AB (1)
Stockstigen 11, 132 46, Stockholm, Sweden
Tel.: (46) 8 19 08 68
Web Site: http://www.wendler.se
Fuses & Exterior Lightning Distr
N.A.I.C.S.: 423610

ADDVALUE TECHNOLOGIES LTD.

202 Bedok South Ave 1 01-11, Singapore, 469332, Singapore
Tel.: (65) 65095700
Web Site:
    https://www.addvaluetech.com
Year Founded: 1994
A31—(SES)
Rev.: $7,548,912
Assets: $16,350,688
Liabilities: $10,519,548
Net Worth: $5,831,140
Earnings: ($2,992,497)
Emp.: 72
Fiscal Year-end: 03/31/23
Wireless & Broadband Communication Solutions
N.A.I.C.S.: 517112
Colin Kum Lok Chan (Co-Founder, Chm & CEO)

Subsidiaries:

Addvalue Innovation Pte Ltd (1)
28 Tai Seng Street 06-02, Singapore, 534106, Singapore
Tel.: (65) 95700
Sales Range: $25-49.9 Million
Telecommunication Servicesb
N.A.I.C.S.: 517810

Zhongxin Chuangzhi (Beijing) Technology Ltd., Co. (1)
Room 913/913B No 52 Zhongguancun South Street, Haidian District, Beijing, 100081, China
Tel.: (86) 1062160867
Wireless Telecommunication Services
N.A.I.C.S.: 517112

ADDVISE GROUP AB

Grev Turegatan 30, 114 38, Stockholm, Sweden
Tel.: (46) 812876600
Web Site:
    https://www.addvisegroup.com
Year Founded: 1989
ADDV.A—(OMX)
Rev.: $44,799,453
Assets: $42,208,305
Liabilities: $31,093,044
Net Worth: $11,115,262
Earnings: $1,786,885
Emp.: 108
Fiscal Year-end: 12/31/20
Medical Facility Equipment Distr
N.A.I.C.S.: 423450
Erland Pontusson (COO)

Subsidiaries:

AB Germa (1)
Industrig 54-56, 291 36, Kristianstad, Sweden
Tel.: (46) 44123030
Web Site: https://www.germa.se
Vaccum Pump Mfr
N.A.I.C.S.: 333914
Patrik Thornstrom (Ops Mgr)

ADDvise Tillquist AB (1)
Renvagen 1, 352 45, Vaxjo, Sweden
Tel.: (46) 84793900
Web Site: https://www.tillquist.se
Hospital Equipments Mfr
N.A.I.C.S.: 339112

CliniChain Holding B.V. (1)

Televisieweg 62, 1322 AM, Almere, Netherlands
Tel.: (31) 367676049
Web Site: https://www.clinichain.com
Medical Equipment Logistics Services
N.A.I.C.S.: 532490

Clinichain BV (1)
Televisieweg 62, 1322 AM, Almere, Netherlands
Tel.: (31) 367676040
Web Site: https://www.clinichain.com
Medical Equipment Distr
N.A.I.C.S.: 423450

GraMedica Ltd. (1)
16137 Leone Dr, Macomb, MI 48042
Web Site: https://www.gramedica.com
Laboratory Equipment Mfr
N.A.I.C.S.: 334516

Graham Medical Technologies, L.L.C. (1)
16137 Leone Dr, Macomb, MI 48042
Tel.: (586) 677-9600
Web Site: https://www.gramedica.com
Medical Device Distr
N.A.I.C.S.: 423450

Hettich Labinstrument AB (1)
Wenngarn's business center, 193 91, Sigtuna, Sweden
Tel.: (46) 87520030
Web Site:
    https://www.hettichlabinstrument.se
Lab Instrument Mfr
N.A.I.C.S.: 334516

IM-Medico Svenska AB (1)
Industrivaagen 7, 171 48, Stockholm, Sweden
Tel.: (46) 87155510
Web Site: http://www.im-medico.se
Hospital Equipments Mfr
N.A.I.C.S.: 339112

Jtech Medical Industries, Inc. (1)
7633 S Main Bldg D, Midvale, UT 84047
Tel.: (385) 695-5000
Web Site: https://www.jtechmedical.com
Medical Equipment Mfr
N.A.I.C.S.: 339112

LabRum AB (1)
Industrivaagen 7, 171 48, Solna, Sweden
Tel.: (46) 850557800
Web Site: http://www.labrum.se
Chair Mfr
N.A.I.C.S.: 337121
Jonas Dahlgren (Sls Mgr)

MRC Systems FZE (1)
Jafza, PO Box 17264, Dubai, United Arab Emirates
Tel.: (971) 48835908
Web Site: https://www.mrc-cleanrooms.com
HVAC Installation Services
N.A.I.C.S.: 238220

Medisuite, LLC (1)
160 MacGregor Pines Dr Ste 110, Cary, NC 27511
Tel.: (919) 200-6952
Web Site: https://medisuite.com
Pharmaceutical Products Distr
N.A.I.C.S.: 424210
Tim Furman (Pres)

Sonar Oy (1)
Taivalmaki 11, 02200, Espoo, Finland
Tel.: (358) 207411990
Web Site: https://sonar.fi
Laboratory Equipment Mfr
N.A.I.C.S.: 334516

Southern Life Systems, Inc. (1)
7320 Central Ave, Savannah, GA 31406
Tel.: (912) 355-9494
Web Site: https://nurserosie.com
Medical Equipment Distr
N.A.I.C.S.: 423450

Surgical Tables Inc. (1)
2 DeBush Ave Unit Ste C3, Middleton, MA 01949
Tel.: (978) 767-4211
Web Site: https://www.surgicaltables.com
Arm Table Mfr
N.A.I.C.S.: 332994

Surplus Diabetic, Inc. (1)

265 S Federal Hwy Ste 280, Deerfield Beach, FL 33441
Tel.: (954) 204-0817
Web Site: https://surplusdiabetic.com
Diabetic Testing Tool Distr
N.A.I.C.S.: 424210

ADECCO GROUP AG

Bellerivestrasse 30, 8008, Zurich, Switzerland
Tel.: (41) 448788888   CH
Web Site:
    https://www.adeccogroup.com
Year Founded: 1957
ADEN—(SWX)
Rev.: $25,854,737,751
Assets: $13,414,634,146
Liabilities: $9,528,383,337
Net Worth: $3,886,250,809
Earnings: $352,903,087
Emp.: 37,000
Fiscal Year-end: 12/31/23
Human Resource Management Services
N.A.I.C.S.: 551112
Jean-Christophe Deslarzes (Chm)

Subsidiaries:

ADO Professional Solutions, Inc. (1)
8655 Baypine Rd 100 Business Ctr I, Jacksonville, FL 32256
N.A.I.C.S.: 541611
Marcus Maschmedt (Mgr-Global Sales Enablement)

Accounting Principals Inc. (1)
10151 Deerwood Park Blvd Bldg 400 1st Fl, Jacksonville, FL 32256 (100%)
Tel.: (904) 360-2400
Web Site:
    http://www.accountingprincipals.com
Financial Staffing Service
N.A.I.C.S.: 561311
John Marshall (Pres)

Branch (Domestic):

LHH Recruitment Solutions (2)
1000 Abernathy Rd Northpark 400 Ste 100, Atlanta, GA 30328
Tel.: (770) 671-0006
Web Site:
    http://www.accountingprincipals.com
Sales Range: $1-9.9 Million
Emp.: 17
Labor Resource Services Supplier
N.A.I.C.S.: 561320
John P. Marshall III (Pres)

Unit (Domestic):

Parker & Lynch (2)
15301 N Dallas Pkwy Ste 300, Addison, TX 75001-4669
Tel.: (972) 813-0470
Web Site: http://www.parkerlynch.com
Sales Range: $10-24.9 Million
Emp.: 15
Accounting & Financial Executive Recruitment & Staffing
N.A.I.C.S.: 561311
Bob Crouch (Pres)

Adecco Argentina S.A. (1)
Carlos Pellegrini 855 1er piso, C1009ABQ, Buenos Aires, Argentina
Tel.: (54) 9112 155 1681
Web Site: https://www.adecco.com.ar
Human Resource Consulting Services
N.A.I.C.S.: 541612

Adecco Australia Pty Ltd. (1)
Level 3 530 Collins Street, CBD, Melbourne, 3000, VIC, Australia (100%)
Tel.: (61) 39 954 2100
Web Site: https://www.adecco.com.au
Sales Range: $50-74.9 Million
Emp.: 150
Employee Recruiting Services
N.A.I.C.S.: 561330

Subsidiary (Non-US):

Adecco Personnel Limited (2)
Level 10 1/191 Queen Street, 191 Queen St, Auckland, 1010, New Zealand (100%)
Tel.: (64) 309 7572

Web Site: https://www.adecco.co.nz
Sales Range: $25-49.9 Million
Emp.: 25
Temporary & Permanent Personnel, Accountancy Services, Employment Agencies, Executive Search, Personnel Management & Outplacement Services
N.A.I.C.S.: 561330

Subsidiary (Domestic):

Modis (2)
Level 12 / 108 St Georges, Terrace, Perth, 6000, WA, Australia
Tel.: (61) 893248400
Web Site: https://www.modis.com
Temporary Employee Recruitment Services
N.A.I.C.S.: 561330
Rod Crozier (Gen Mgr-Staffing)

Subsidiary (Non-US):

Icon Recruitment Limited (3)
Qantas House Level 8 191 Queen St, Auckland, New Zealand (100%)
Tel.: (64) 93773848
Temporary Employment Services
N.A.I.C.S.: 561330

Icon Recruitment Ltd. (3)
Mezzanine 330 Lambton Quay, 6011, Wellington, New Zealand (100%)
Tel.: (64) 44721566
Employee Recruiter Services
N.A.I.C.S.: 561330

Adecco Beteiligungs GmbH (1)
Niederkasseler Lohweg 18, 40547, Dusseldorf, Germany
Tel.: (49) 211301400
Employment Consulting Services
N.A.I.C.S.: 541612

Adecco Bulgaria EOOD (1)
Business Park Sofia Building 4 floors 0-3, Mladost, Sofia, 1766, Bulgaria
Tel.: (359) 882272574
Web Site: http://www.adeccobulgaria.com
Staffing Services
N.A.I.C.S.: 561320

Adecco Caledonie SARL (1)
24 Avenue Marechal Foch, 98800, Noumea, New Caledonia (100%)
Tel.: (687) 242018
Web Site: http://www.adecco.nc
Sales Range: $25-49.9 Million
Emp.: 30
Temporary Employment Recruitment Services
N.A.I.C.S.: 561330

Adecco Coordination Center NV (1)
Brusselstraat 338, Vlaams-Brabant, 1702, Groot-Bijgaarden, Belgium
Tel.: (32) 2 453 2049
Web Site: https://www.adecco.be
Business Management Consulting Services
N.A.I.C.S.: 541611

Adecco Denmark A/S (1)
Falkoner Alle 1, 2000, Frederiksberg, Denmark (100%)
Tel.: (45) 3 888 9400
Web Site: https://www.adecco.dk
Sales Range: $25-49.9 Million
Emp.: 70
Temporary & Permanent Personnel, Accountancy Services, Employment Agencies, Executive Search, Personnel Management & Outplacement Services
N.A.I.C.S.: 561330

Adecco Detachering BV (1)
Hogeweg 123, 5301 LL, Zaltbommel, Netherlands
Tel.: (31) 883746304
Web Site: http://www.adecco.nl
Sales Range: $25-49.9 Million
Human Resource Consulting Services
N.A.I.C.S.: 541612

Adecco Finland Oy (1)
Vernissakatu 1, 01300, Vantaa, Finland (100%)
Tel.: (358) 46 710 2500
Web Site: https://www.adecco.fi
Sales Range: $50-74.9 Million
Emp.: 125
Temporary Staffing, Recruitment Services, Outsourcing, Data Entry Services

N.A.I.C.S.: 561330
Ketil Kjeltsbert *(CEO & Country Mgr)*

Adecco France SASU (1)
4 rue Louis Guerin, Villeurbanne, 69626,
France
Tel.: (33) 4 72 82 58 58
Web Site: http://www.adecco.fr
Recruitment Services
N.A.I.C.S.: 561311
Alain Dehaze *(Pres)*

Adecco GmbH (1)
Mariahilferstrasse 123/6 Stock, 1060, Vi-
enna, Austria **(100%)**
Tel.: (43) 5991120000
Web Site: http://www.adecco.at
Sales Range: $25-49.9 Million
Emp.: 40
Temporary Staffing, Recruitment Services,
Outsourcing, Data Entry Services
N.A.I.C.S.: 561330
Mario Trusgnach *(Mng Dir)*

Adecco Group Norway AS (1)
Sjolyst Plass 2, 0278, Oslo, Norway
Tel.: (47) 23290000
Web Site: https://www.adecco.no
Emp.: 5,000
Staffing & Recruitment Services
N.A.I.C.S.: 541612

Adecco Groupe France (1)
2 Rue Henri Legay, 69100, Villeurbanne,
Cedex, France **(100%)**
Tel.: (33) 47 282 5858
Web Site: https://www.adecco.fr
Sales Range: $750-799.9 Million
Emp.: 4,000
Temporary Staffing, Recruitment Services,
Outsourcing, Data Entry Services
N.A.I.C.S.: 561330

Subsidiary (Domestic):

Adia France (2)
7 Rue Louis Guerin, PO Box 2133, 69626,
Villeurbanne, France **(100%)**
Tel.: (33) 472822828
Web Site: http://www.adia.fr
Sales Range: $25-49.9 Million
Emp.: 140
Temporary & Permanent Personnel, Ac-
countancy Services, Employment Agencies,
Executive Search, Personnel Management
& Outplacement Services
N.A.I.C.S.: 561330
Alain Dehaze *(Pres)*

Subsidiary (Domestic):

Movadis SA (3)
57-59 Boulevard Malesherbes, BP 40213,
75364, Paris, France
Tel.: (33) 177691310
Web Site: http://www.movadis.fr
Temporary & Permanent Personnel, Ac-
countancy Services, Employment Agencies,
Executive Search, Personnel Management
& Outplacement Services
N.A.I.C.S.: 561330

Adecco H.R. d.o.o (1)
Ameriska ulica 8, 1000, Ljubljana, Slovenia
Tel.: (386) 15609250
Web Site: http://www.adecco.si
Staffing Services
N.A.I.C.S.: 561320

**Adecco Hizmet Ve Danisnanlik
A/S** (1)
Hacimimi Mah Luleciler Sok No4, 80620,
Istanbul, Turkiye **(100%)**
Tel.: (90) 2122492987
Web Site: http://www.adecco.com.tr
Temporary Staffing, Recruitment Services,
Outsourcing, Data Entry Services
N.A.I.C.S.: 561330

Adecco Holding France SASU (1)
69 Boulevard Bataille De, Stalingrad, Vil-
leurbane, 69100, France
Tel.: (33) 1 77 69 13 25
Investment Management Service
N.A.I.C.S.: 523999

Adecco Iberia SA (1)
C Orense 4 3 Izda, 28020, Madrid,
Spain **(100%)**
Tel.: (34) 91 391 7646
Web Site: https://www.adecco.es

Sales Range: $50-74.9 Million
Emp.: 200
Temporary Staffing, Recruitment Services,
Outsourcing, Data Entry Services
N.A.I.C.S.: 561330

Adecco India Private Limited (1)
No 73/1 13th Floor Summit B Brigade Me-
tropolis, Garudachar Palya Mahadevapura
Post Whitefield Main Road, Bengaluru,
560048, Karnataka, India
Tel.: (91) 806 840 7000
Web Site: https://www.adecco.co.in
Sales Range: $75-99.9 Million
Emp.: 500
Human Resource Consulting Services
N.A.I.C.S.: 541612
Marco Valsecchi *(Mng Dir & Country Mgr)*

Adecco Industrial Pty Ltd (1)
Level 16 28 Freshwater Place, Southbank,
3006, VIC, Australia
Tel.: (61) 399542100
Web Site: http://www.adecco.com.au
Sales Range: $25-49.9 Million
Human Resource Consulting Services
N.A.I.C.S.: 541612
Gerard Doyle *(CEO)*

**Adecco International Financial Ser-
vices BV.** (1)
Hogeweg 123, 5301 LL, Zaltbommel, Neth-
erlands
Tel.: (31) 418784000
N.A.I.C.S.: 523999

**Adecco Israel Staffing Services
Ltd.** (1)
Nitsba Building 17 Yitzhak Sade, Tel Aviv,
6775, Israel **(100%)**
Tel.: (972) 35652007
Web Site: http://www.adecco.co.il
Emp.: 80
Temporary & Permanent Personnel, Ac-
countancy Services, Employment Agencies,
Executive Search, Personnel Management
& Outplacement Services
N.A.I.C.S.: 561330

Adecco Italia S.p.A. (1)
Via Tolmezzo 15, 20132, Milan, Italy
Tel.: (39) 0288141
Web Site: https://www.adecco.it
Human Resouce Services
N.A.I.C.S.: 541612

Adecco Italy Spa (1)
Via Tolmezzo 15, 20132, Milan,
Italy **(100%)**
Tel.: (39) 0288141
Web Site: https://www.adecco.it
Emp.: 1,000
Temporary & Permanent Personnel, Ac-
countancy Services, Employment Agencies,
Executive Search, Personnel Management
& Outplacement Services
N.A.I.C.S.: 561330
Federico Vione *(Gen Mgr)*

Adecco Kft (1)
Fiastyuk utca 4-8 Vaci Greens iroda F epu-
let 7 emelet, 1139, Budapest,
Hungary **(100%)**
Tel.: (36) 13233500
Web Site: https://www.adecco.hu
Sales Range: $25-49.9 Million
Emp.: 90
Temporary Staffing, Recruitment Services,
Outsourcing, Data Entry Services
N.A.I.C.S.: 561330

Adecco Ltd. (1)
Kowa Bldg No 45 1-15-9 Minami Aoyama,
Tokyo, 107 0062, Japan **(100%)**
Tel.: (81) 334709300
Web Site: http://www.adecco.co.jp
Sales Range: $750-799.9 Million
Emp.: 2,600
Temporary & Permanent Personnel, Ac-
countancy Services, Employment Agencies,
Executive Search, Personnel Management
& Outplacement Services
N.A.I.C.S.: 561330

Adecco Luxembourg S.A. (1)
5 rue des Merovingiens - z a Bourmicht,
ZAI Bourmicht, 8070, Bertrange,
Luxembourg **(100%)**
Tel.: (352) 4825511
Web Site: https://www.adecco.lu

Sales Range: $25-49.9 Million
Emp.: 10
Temporary & Permanent Personnel, Ac-
countancy Services, Employment Agencies,
Executive Search, Personnel Management
& Outplacement Services
N.A.I.C.S.: 561330
Sabrice Ponce *(Mng Dir)*

**Adecco Management & Consulting
S.A.** (1)
Sagereistrasse 10, CH-8152, Glattbrugg,
Switzerland
Tel.: (41) 448788888
Web Site: http://www.adecco.ch
Workforce Management & Human Re-
source Consulting Services
N.A.I.C.S.: 541612
Stephan Howeg *(Head-Grp Comm)*

Adecco Medical SASU (1)
2 rue Henri Legay, 69100, Villeurbanne,
France
Tel.: (33) 47 282 5858
Web Site: https://www.adecco.fr
Sales Range: $75-99.9 Million
Emp.: 300
Medical Staffing Services
N.A.I.C.S.: 561320
Jerick Develle *(Gen Mgr)*

Adecco Monaco SAM (1)
4 Rue Baron De Sainte Suzanne, 98000,
Monaco, Monaco **(100%)**
Tel.: (377) 97975300
Web Site: https://www.adecco.fr
Sales Range: $25-49.9 Million
Emp.: 10
Temporary & Permanent Personnel, Ac-
countancy Services, Employment Agencies,
Executive Search, Personnel Management
& Outplacement Services
N.A.I.C.S.: 561330

Adecco Morocco (1)
10 Rue EL Bassatines 2eme etage, Casa-
blanca, 20120, Morocco **(100%)**
Tel.: (212) 522925500
Web Site: https://www.adecco.ma
Sales Range: $1-9.9 Million
Emp.: 50
Temporary & Permanent Personnel, Ac-
countancy Services, Employment Agencies,
Executive Search, Personnel Management
& Outplacement Services
N.A.I.C.S.: 561311

Adecco Netherlands Beheer B.V. (1)
Hogeweg 123, 5301 LL, Zaltbommel,
Netherlands **(100%)**
Tel.: (31) 418784000
Web Site: http://www.adecco.nl
Sales Range: $50-74.9 Million
Emp.: 150
Temporary & Permanent Personnel, Ac-
countancy Services, Employment Agencies,
Executive Search, Personnel Management
& Outplacement Services
N.A.I.C.S.: 561330

Adecco Norge AS (1)
Sjolyst plass 2, 0278, Oslo,
Norway **(100%)**
Tel.: (47) 23290000
Web Site: https://www.adecco.no
Sales Range: $50-74.9 Million
Emp.: 200
Temporary & Permanent Personnel, Ac-
countancy Services, Employment Agencies,
Executive Search, Personnel Management
& Outplacement Services
N.A.I.C.S.: 561330
Anders Owre-Johnsen *(CEO)*

Adecco Outsourcing d.o.o. (1)
Ul fra Grge Tuskana 37, 10000, Zagreb,
Croatia
Tel.: (385) 14002170
Web Site: http://www.adecco.hr
Staffing Services
N.A.I.C.S.: 561320

**Adecco Personaldienstleistungen
GmbH** (1)
Fritz-Vomfelde-Strasse 26, 40547, Dussel-
dorf, Germany
Tel.: (49) 2116 688 6688
Web Site: https://www.adecco.de
Professional Employment Services
N.A.I.C.S.: 561311

Adecco Personeelsdiensten BV (1)
Venne 129, 9671 ER, Winschoten, Nether-
lands
Tel.: (31) 597 421522
Sales Range: $25-49.9 Million
Emp.: 4
Recruitment Services
N.A.I.C.S.: 561311

**Adecco Personnel Consultants Co.,
Ltd. Taiwan** (1)
Song Xinyi District, High Road 18th Floor
No 11, Taipei, 110, Taiwan **(100%)**
Tel.: (886) 255526168
Web Site: http://www.adecco.com.tw
Sales Range: $25-49.9 Million
Emp.: 10
Temporary & Permanent Personnel, Ac-
countancy Services, Employment Agencies,
Executive Search, Personnel Management
& Outplacement Services
N.A.I.C.S.: 561330

Adecco Personnel Pte. Ltd. (1)
1 Scotts Road, 18-08 Shaw Centre, Singa-
pore, 228208, Singapore **(100%)**
Tel.: (65) 6 835 3400
Web Site: https://www.adecco.com.sg
Emp.: 500
Temporary & Permanent Personnel, Ac-
countancy Services, Employment Agencies,
Executive Search, Personnel Management
& Outplacement Services
N.A.I.C.S.: 561330

Adecco Personnel Services S.A. (1)
Brusselstraat 338, 1702, Groot-Bijgaarden,
Belgium **(100%)**
Tel.: (32) 24532049
Web Site: http://www.adecco.be
Sales Range: $50-74.9 Million
Emp.: 120
Temporary & Permanent Personnel, Ac-
countancy Services, Employment Agencies,
Executive Search, Personnel Management
& Outplacement Services
N.A.I.C.S.: 561330

Adecco Peru S.A. (1)
Av Camino Real 159, San Isidro, Lima,
Peru **(100%)**
Tel.: (51) 6114444
Web Site: http://www.adecco.com.pe
Sales Range: $25-49.9 Million
Emp.: 50
Temporary & Permanent Personnel, Ac-
countancy Services, Employment Agencies,
Executive Search, Personnel Management
& Outplacement Services
N.A.I.C.S.: 561330

Adecco Phaholyothin (1)
No 388 S P Building 11th Floor Zone A
Phaholyothin Road, Samsennai Phayathai,
Bangkok, 10400, Thailand **(100%)**
Tel.: (66) 2 121 3555
Web Site: https://www.adecco.co.th
Temporary & Permanent Personnel, Ac-
countancy Services, Employment Agencies,
Executive Search, Personnel Management
& Outplacement Services
N.A.I.C.S.: 561330

Adecco Poland Sp. z o.o. (1)
Plac Europejski 2, Mazowieckie, 00-844,
Warsaw, Mazowieckie, Poland **(100%)**
Tel.: (48) 22 376 0900
Web Site: https://www.adecco.pl
Sales Range: $25-49.9 Million
Emp.: 55
N.A.I.C.S.: 561330

**Adecco Rama IV Recruitment
Ltd.** (1)
No 388 Sp Building 11th Floor, Zone A,
Bangkok, 10400, Bangrak,
Thailand **(100%)**
Tel.: (66) 21213555
Web Site: http://www.adecco.co.th
Sales Range: $25-49.9 Million
Emp.: 19
Temporary & Recruitment Services
N.A.I.C.S.: 541612

Adecco Recruitment Services (1)
Derby Downs Office Park Building 5 Level 3
Unit 5 & 6, Westville, 3629, South
Africa **(100%)**
Tel.: (27) 312671433
Web Site: https://www.adecco.co.za

Adecco Group AG—(Continued)

Sales Range: $25-49.9 Million
Emp.: 50
Temporary & Permanent Personnel, Accountancy Services, Employment Agencies, Executive Search, Personnel Management & Outplacement Services
N.A.I.C.S.: 561330
Mark Smith (Gen Mgr)

Adecco Recursos Humanos   **(1)**
Avddjoao Lote 1 06 2 5 th Fl, 1150-045, Lisbon, Portugal   **(100%)**
Tel.: (351) 213168300
Web Site: http://www.adecco.pt
Sales Range: $25-49.9 Million
Emp.: 100
Temporary & Permanent Personnel, Accountancy Services, Employment Agencies, Executive Search, Personnel Management & Outplacement Services
N.A.I.C.S.: 561330

Adecco Recursos Humanos S.A.   **(1)**
Rosario Norte 100 Piso 10, Las Condes, Santiago, 7561258, Chile   **(100%)**
Tel.: (56) 22 560 7200
Web Site: https://www.adecco.cl
Sales Range: $750-799.9 Million
Emp.: 250
Temporary & Permanent Personnel, Accountancy Services, Employment Agencies, Executive Search, Personnel Management & Outplacement Services
N.A.I.C.S.: 561330

Adecco Ressources Humaines S.A.   **(1)**
Rue des Fontenailles 16, 1007, Lausanne, Switzerland   **(100%)**
Tel.: (41) 582339292
Web Site: http://www.adecco.ch
Sales Range: $50-74.9 Million
Emp.: 140
Staffing & Recruiting Services
N.A.I.C.S.: 561330

Adecco Resurse Umane SRL   **(1)**
Pipera Road No 42 2nd Floor, 2nd District, 020112, Bucharest, Romania
Tel.: (40) 213003546
Web Site: https://adecco.ro
N.A.I.C.S.: 561311

Adecco Romania SRL   **(1)**
Pipera Road No 42 2nd Floor, 2nd District, 020112, Bucharest, Romania
Tel.: (40) 213003546
Web Site: http://www.adecco.ro
Staffing Services
N.A.I.C.S.: 561320

Adecco Slovakia, s.r.o   **(1)**
Digital Park III blok F 4th floor Einsteinova 19, 851 01, Bratislava, Slovakia
Tel.: (421) 253630223
Web Site: http://www.adecco.sk
Staffing Services
N.A.I.C.S.: 561320

Adecco Sweden AB   **(1)**
Svetsarvagen 6, Solna, 171 41, Stockholm, Sweden
Tel.: (46) 10 173 7300
Web Site: https://www.adecco.se
Sales Range: $25-49.9 Million
Emp.: 150
Professional Employment Services
N.A.I.C.S.: 561311

Adecco Szemelyzeti Kozvetito Kft.   **(1)**
Fiastyuk Utca 4-8 Vaci Greens Iroda F epulet 7 Emelet, 1139, Budapest, Hungary
Tel.: (36) 613233500
Web Site: https://www.adecco.hu
N.A.I.C.S.: 561311

Adecco TT SA   **(1)**
Calle Acanto 22 1 Planta Local 1 2, 28045, Madrid, Spain
Tel.: (34) 913106090
Web Site: https://www.adecco.es
Employment Consulting Services
N.A.I.C.S.: 541612

Adecco UK Ltd.   **(1)**
Hazlitt House 4 Bouverie Street, London, EC4Y 8AX, United Kingdom   **(100%)**
Tel.: (44) 2073009000

Web Site: http://www.adecco.co.uk
Sales Range: $50-74.9 Million
Emp.: 250
Job Recruitment & Training
N.A.I.C.S.: 561330
Peter Searle (CEO)

Subsidiary (Domestic):

Roevin Limited   **(2)**
4th Floor Clydesdale Bank House, 33 Lower Regent Street, London, SW1Y 4NB, United Kingdom
Tel.: (44) 8456430486
Web Site: http://www.adecco.co.uk
Sales Range: $75-99.9 Million
Temporary & Permanent Personnel, Accountancy Services, Employment Agencies, Executive Search, Personnel Management & Outplacement Services
N.A.I.C.S.: 561330

Subsidiary (Domestic):

Roevin Management Services Ltd.   **(3)**
57 Spring Gardens, Manchester, M2 2BY, United Kingdom   **(100%)**
Tel.: (44) 8456430518
Web Site: http://www.roevin.co.uk
Sales Range: $25-49.9 Million
Emp.: 60
Temporary & Permanent Personnel, Accountancy Services, Employment Agencies, Executive Search, Personnel Management & Outplacement Services
N.A.I.C.S.: 561330

Subsidiary (Non-US):

Roevin Technical People Limited   **(3)**
5770 Hurontario Street Unit 300, Mississauga, L5R 3G5, ON, Canada   **(100%)**
Tel.: (905) 366-3898
Web Site: https://www.roevin.ca
Sales Range: $25-49.9 Million
Emp.: 7
Temporary & Permanent Personnel, Accountancy Services, Employment Agencies, Executive Search, Personnel Management & Outplacement Services
N.A.I.C.S.: 561311

Subsidiary (Domestic):

Spring Group Limited   **(2)**
2 Lambeth hill, London, EC4V 4BG, United Kingdom   **(100%)**
Tel.: (44) 2073009000
Web Site: http://www.spring.com
Emp.: 150
Employment Placement Agency
N.A.I.C.S.: 561311

Subsidiary (Non-US):

Adecco Ireland Ltd.   **(3)**
29/31 South William Street 1st Floor, Dublin, D02 EY96, Ireland   **(100%)**
Tel.: (353) 1 852 6930
Web Site: https://www.adecco.ie
Emp.: 25
Temporary & Permanent Personnel, Accountancy Services, Employment Agencies, Executive Search, Personnel Management & Outplacement Services
N.A.I.C.S.: 561330

Subsidiary (Domestic):

Hy-Phen.com Limited   **(3)**
Hazlitt House, 4 Bouverie Street, London, EC4Y 8AX, United Kingdom   **(100%)**
Tel.: (44) 2073009000
Web Site: http://www.hyphen.com
Sales Range: $25-49.9 Million
Emp.: 100
Employment Placement Agencies
N.A.I.C.S.: 561311

Office Angels Limited   **(3)**
2nd Floor 30-38 Hammersmith Broadway, London, W6 7AB, United Kingdom
Tel.: (44) 2087418080
Web Site: http://www.office-angels.com
Sales Range: $25-49.9 Million
Emp.: 6
Help Supply Services
N.A.I.C.S.: 561320
Sarah Day (Branch Mgr)

Subsidiary (Non-US):

Spring Group Australia Pty Limited   **(3)**
Level 11 95 Pitt St, Sydney, 2000, NSW, Australia
Tel.: (61) 292480422
Web Site: http://www.springfg.com
Temporary & Permanent Personnel, Accountancy Services, Employment Agencies, Executive Search, Personnel Management & Outplacement Services
N.A.I.C.S.: 561330

Subsidiary (Domestic):

Spring Personnel Limited   **(3)**
Hazlitt House 4 Bouverie Street, London, EC4Y 8AX, United Kingdom   **(100%)**
Tel.: (44) 2073009000
Web Site: http://www.springpersonnel.com
Sales Range: $75-99.9 Million
Employment Placement Agencies
N.A.I.C.S.: 561311
Steven Kirkpatrick (CEO)

Subsidiary (Non-US):

Spring Professional Singapore Pte Ltd   **(3)**
1 Scotts Road 26-06 Shaw Centre, Singapore, 228208, Singapore
Tel.: (65) 6 593 7950
Web Site: https://www.springasia.com
Emp.: 20
Temporary & Permanent Personnel, Accountancy Services, Employment Agencies, Executive Search, Personnel Management & Outplacement Services
N.A.I.C.S.: 561311

Subsidiary (Domestic):

Spring Technology Staffing Services Limited   **(3)**
Hazlitt House 4 Bouverie Street, London, EC4Y 8AX, United Kingdom   **(100%)**
Tel.: (44) 2073009000
Web Site: http://www.spring-technology.co.uk
Sales Range: $75-99.9 Million
Employment Placement Agencies
N.A.I.C.S.: 561311

Adecco USA, Inc.   **(1)**
175 Broadhollow Rd, Melville, NY 11747-4902
Tel.: (631) 844-7800
Web Site: http://www.adeccousa.com
Sales Range: $150-199.9 Million
Emp.: 600
Temporary Personnel & Healthcare Services
N.A.I.C.S.: 561330
Joyce Russell (Pres & Exec VP)

Holding (Non-US):

Adecco Employment Services Limited   **(2)**
20 Bay Street Suite 800, Toronto, M5J 2N8, ON, Canada   **(100%)**
Tel.: (416) 646-3322
Web Site: https://www.adecco.ca
Sales Range: $10-24.9 Million
Emp.: 35
Employment Agency
N.A.I.C.S.: 561311

Subsidiary (Domestic):

Adecco Irvine   **(2)**
36 Discovery Ste 250, Irvine, CA 92618
Tel.: (949) 255-0488
Web Site: http://www.adecco.com
Sales Range: $10-24.9 Million
Emp.: 5
Temporary Staffing Services
N.A.I.C.S.: 561320

Branch (Domestic):

Adecco Puerto Rico   **(2)**
Marginal A-6 Urb San Salvador, Manati, PR 00674
Tel.: (787) 854-4263
Web Site: http://www.adeccopr.com
Sales Range: $25-49.9 Million
Emp.: 120
Employment Services

N.A.I.C.S.: 561311

Subsidiary (Domestic):

Ajilon North America, LLC   **(2)**
175 Broad Hollow Rd, Melville, NY 11747   **(100%)**
Tel.: (631) 844-7800
Web Site: http://www.ajilonconsulting.com
Sales Range: $400-449.9 Million
Business Information Technology Services
N.A.I.C.S.: 541512

Subsidiary (Domestic):

Ajilon Professional Staffing LLC   **(3)**
Pk 80 W Plz 2 Fl 9, Saddle Brook, NJ 07663   **(100%)**
Tel.: (201) 843-0006
Web Site: http://www.ajilon.com
Sales Range: $75-99.9 Million
Emp.: 300
Accounting Firm
N.A.I.C.S.: 561311
Jodi Chavez (Sr VP)

Subsidiary (Domestic):

Lee Hecht Harrison, Inc.   **(2)**
115 W Century Rd Ste 110 1st Fl, Paramus, NJ 07652   **(100%)**
Tel.: (201) 930-9333
Web Site: https://www.lhh.com
Sales Range: $25-49.9 Million
Emp.: 85
Management Consulting & Outplacement Services
N.A.I.C.S.: 541611

Subsidiary (Domestic):

Career Resources, Inc.   **(3)**
350 Fairfield Ave, Bridgeport, CT 06604
Tel.: (203) 368-1899
Web Site: http://www.careerresources.org
Sales Range: $1-9.9 Million
Emp.: 152
Job Training & Placement Services
N.A.I.C.S.: 561311
Anne Carr (Dir-One-Stop)

Branch (Domestic):

Lee Hecht Harrison   **(3)**
7676 Woodway Dr Ste 325, Houston, TX 77063
Tel.: (713) 952-2000
Sales Range: $75-99.9 Million
Human Resource Consulting Services
N.A.I.C.S.: 541618
Sherry Blakelock (VP-Bus Dev)

Lee Hecht Harrison   **(3)**
500 W Monroe St Ste 3200, Chicago, IL 60661
Tel.: (312) 377-2300
Sales Range: $25-49.9 Million
Emp.: 40
Employment Agencies
N.A.I.C.S.: 459420
Linda Guza (Office Mgr)

Lee Hecht Harrison   **(3)**
1122 Kenilworth Dr Ste 212 B, Baltimore, MD 21204
Tel.: (410) 494-0960
Web Site: http://www.lhh.com
Sales Range: $10-24.9 Million
Emp.: 3
Human Resource Consulting Services
N.A.I.C.S.: 541612

Branch (Non-US):

Lee Hecht Harrison   **(3)**
#401 77 City Centre Drive East Tower, Mississauga, L5B 1M5, ON, Canada   **(100%)**
Tel.: (905) 277-4700
Web Site: http://www.lhh-canada.ca
Sales Range: $10-24.9 Million
Emp.: 15
Management Consulting Services
N.A.I.C.S.: 541611
Angela Payne (Country Mgr)

Lee Hecht Harrison   **(3)**
888 3rd St SW, Calgary, T2P 5C5, AB, Canada
Tel.: (403) 269-7828
Web Site: http://www.lhh-canada.ca

Sales Range: $25-49.9 Million
Emp.: 8
Management Consulting Services & Out-placement Agency
N.A.I.C.S.: 541611
Terry Lende *(Office Mgr)*

Subsidiary (Non-US):

Lee Hecht Harrison AG **(3)**
Stampfenbachstrasse 138, Zurich, 8006, Switzerland **(100%)**
Tel.: (41) 443859955
Web Site: http://www.lhh.ch
Sales Range: $25-49.9 Million
Emp.: 20
Management Consulting & Outplacement Services
N.A.I.C.S.: 561330
Ranjit de Sousa *(Mgr-Sls)*

Lee Hecht Harrison Limited **(3)**
The Royal Exchange 2 Royal Exchange Steps 2nd Floor East, London, EC3V 3DG, United Kingdom **(100%)**
Tel.: (44) 20 7036 8317
Web Site: http://www.lhhuk.com
Emp.: 50
Talent Development, Transition & Consult-ing Services
N.A.I.C.S.: 541612
Nick Goldberg *(Mng Dir & Head-UK & Ire-land)*

Subsidiary (Domestic):

Penna Consulting Limited **(4)**
10 Bishops Sq, London, E1 6EG, United Kingdom
Tel.: (44) 2038492777
Web Site: http://www.penna.com
Emp.: 500
Recruiting, Executive Coaching, Outplace-ment & Other Career Management Consult-ing Services
N.A.I.C.S.: 541612

Subsidiary (Domestic):

Lee Hecht Harrison, LLC **(3)**
230 Park Ave rm 600, New York, NY 10169
Tel.: (212) 557-0009
Web Site: http://www.lhh.com
Sales Range: $100-124.9 Million
Human Resouce Services
N.A.I.C.S.: 541612

Affiliate (Domestic):

Messenger Associates, Inc. **(4)**
4719 Limberlost Ln, Manlius, NY 13104
Tel.: (607) 772-8607
Web Site: http://www.amgr.com
Sales Range: $10-24.9 Million
Emp.: 15
Management Consulting Services
N.A.I.C.S.: 541611

Unit (Domestic):

The Center for Executive Options **(4)**
200 Park Ave, New York, NY 10166
Tel.: (212) 299-3333
Sales Range: $10-24.9 Million
Emp.: 10
Executive Placement Services
N.A.I.C.S.: 541612

Subsidiary (Domestic):

MasteryWorks, Inc. **(3)**
The Renaissance 2230 George C Marshall Dr Ste 122, Falls Church, VA 22043
Tel.: (703) 256-5712
Web Site: http://www.masteryworks.com
Emp.: 10
Staffing & Career Management Services
N.A.I.C.S.: 561311
Caela Farren *(CEO)*

Adecco Uruguay S.A. **(1)**
Reconquista 517 Floor 7 And 8, Montevi-deo, 11200, Uruguay **(100%)**
Tel.: (598) 2 402 11 18
Web Site: http://www.adecco.com.uy
Sales Range: $1-9.9 Million
Temporary & Permanent Personnel, Ac-countancy Services, Employment Agencies, Executive Search, Personnel Management & Outplacement Services

N.A.I.C.S.: 561330

Adecco Vietnam Joint Stock Company **(1)**
14 Floor E town Central Building 11 Doan Van Bo, Ward 13 District 4, Ho Chi Minh City, Vietnam
Tel.: (84) 2836365811
Web Site: http://www.adecco.com.vn
Staffing Services
N.A.I.C.S.: 561320

Adecco do Brasil Ltda. **(1)**
Alameda Joaquim Eugenio de Lima 696 12 andar, 01403-000, Sao Paulo, SP, Brazil
Tel.: (55) 31780400
Web Site: http://www.adecco.com.br
Temporary & Permanent Personnel, Ac-countancy Services, Employment Agencies, Executive Search, Personnel Management & Outplacement Services
N.A.I.C.S.: 561330

Adecco spol. s r.o. **(1)**
Qubix 4 Stetkova 1638/18, Radlicka 113a 714, 140 00, Prague, Czech Republic **(100%)**
Tel.: (420) 25 100 1411
Web Site: https://www.adecco.cz
Sales Range: $25-49.9 Million
Emp.: 24
Temporary & Permanent Personnel, Ac-countancy Services, Employment Agencies, Executive Search, Personnel Management & Outplacement Services
N.A.I.C.S.: 561330

Adecco-Colombia **(1)**
Calle 70A No 9-46, Bogota, Colombia **(70%)**
Tel.: (57) 1 347 5766
Web Site: http://www.adecco.com.co
Temporary & Permanent Personnel, Ac-countancy Services, Employment Agencies, Executive Search, Personnel Management & Outplacement Services
N.A.I.C.S.: 561320

Adecco-Kuala Lumpur **(1)**
Suite 32 03 Level 32 Menara Citibank 165 Jalan Ampang, 50450, Kuala Lumpur, Malaysia **(100%)**
Tel.: (60) 321625724
Sales Range: $25-49.9 Million
Emp.: 100
Temporary & Permanent Personnel, Ac-countancy Services, Employment Agencies, Executive Search, Personnel Management & Outplacement Services
N.A.I.C.S.: 561330
Alma Othman *(Gen Mgr)*

Adecco-Shanghai **(1)**
Room 1801 Hong Kong New World Tower, No 300 Middle Huai Hai Road, Shanghai, 200021, China **(100%)**
Tel.: (86) 2133119518
Web Site: http://china.adecco.com
Temporary & Permanent Personnel, Ac-countancy Services, Employment Agencies, Executive Search, Personnel Management & Outplacement Services
N.A.I.C.S.: 561330

Adecco-Stockholm **(1)**
Welding road 6, PO Box 1240, Solna, 171 41, Stockholm, Sweden **(100%)**
Tel.: (46) 10 173 7300
Web Site: http://www.adecco.se
Sales Range: $25-49.9 Million
Emp.: 12
Temporary & Permanent Personnel, Ac-countancy Services, Employment Agencies, Executive Search, Personnel Management & Outplacement Services
N.A.I.C.S.: 561330

Adecco-Venezuela **(1)**
Avenida Francisco de Miranda Edif Caven-des, Floor 3 ofics 301-302, Los Palos Grandes, Caracas, Venezuela
Tel.: (58) 2122867016
Web Site: http://www.adecco.com.ve
Emp.: 45
Temporary & Permanent Personnel, Ac-countancy Services, Employment Agencies, Executive Search, Personnel Management & Outplacement Services
N.A.I.C.S.: 561330
Aquilef Tonelli *(Pres)*

Adecco-Wanchai **(1)**
10/F Lee Man Commercial Center 169 Electric Road, North Point, China (Hong Kong) **(100%)**
Tel.: (852) 2 895 2616
Web Site: https://www.adecco.com.hk
Sales Range: $25-49.9 Million
Emp.: 30
Temporary & Permanent Personnel, Ac-countancy Services, Employment Agencies, Executive Search, Personnel Management & Outplacement Services
N.A.I.C.S.: 561330

Subsidiary (Domestic):

Templar International Consultants Limited **(2)**
12 Floor Fortis Tower, 77-79 Gloucester Road, Wanchai, China (Hong Kong)
Tel.: (852) 29702722
Web Site: http://www.templarsearch.com
Sales Range: $25-49.9 Million
Temporary & Permanent Personnel, Ac-countancy Services, Employment Agencies, Executive Search, Personnel Management & Outplacement Services
N.A.I.C.S.: 561330

Subsidiary (Non-US):

Templar Human Search Inc **(3)**
6th Floor Dong Sung Building 158-24, Samsung-dong, 135-880, Seoul, Korea (South)
Tel.: (82) 260003800
Temporary & Permanent Personnel, Ac-countancy Services, Employment Agencies, Executive Search, Personnel Management & Outplacement Services
N.A.I.C.S.: 561330

Templar International Consultants Limited-Guangzhou **(3)**
Room 605, 6th Floor Yi An Plaza, 33 Jin She Liu Ma Road, 510060, Guangzhou, China
Tel.: (86) 2083633227
Temporary & Permanent Personnel, Ac-countancy Services, Employment Agencies, Executive Search, Personnel Management & Outplacement Services
N.A.I.C.S.: 561311

Akkodis Group AG **(1)**
Gotthardstrasse 20, Zug, 6300, Switzerland
Web Site: https://www.akkodis.com
IT Services & Consulting & Engineering Services
N.A.I.C.S.: 541330
Jan Gupta *(Pres)*

Subsidiary (Non-US):

AKKA Technologies SE **(2)**
Avenue Louise 235, 1050, Brussels, Bel-gium
Tel.: (32) 6 22 67 4141
Web Site: http://www.akka-technologies.com
Technology Consulting & Engineering Ser-vices
N.A.I.C.S.: 541690
Jan Gupta *(Pres)*

Subsidiary (Domestic):

AKKA Benelux NV/SA **(3)**
Av Louise 149 bte 24, B 1050, Brussels, Belgium
Tel.: (32) 2 712 60 00
Web Site: http://www.akka-benelux.eu
Technology Consulting & Engineering Ser-vices
N.A.I.C.S.: 541690

Akka Belgium SA **(3)**
Avenue Jules Bordet 168, Evere, 1140, Brussels, Belgium
Tel.: (32) 27126000
Emp.: 800
Engineering & Consulting Services
N.A.I.C.S.: 541330
Serge Vandenhoudt *(CEO)*

Subsidiary (Non-US):

Akka Consulting GmbH **(3)**
Flugfeld-Allee 12, 71063, Sindelfingen, Ger-many
Tel.: (49) 70316863000

Consulting Services
N.A.I.C.S.: 541618

Akka Czech Republic s.r.o. **(3)**
Daimlerova 1161/6, 301 00, Plzen, Czech Republic
Tel.: (420) 251050300
Emp.: 500
Automotive Engine Mfr & Distr
N.A.I.C.S.: 336390
Petra Sucha *(Dir-HR)*

Akka Middle East DMCC **(3)**
Tiffany Tower 1801-04-Jumeirah Lakes Tow-ers, PO Box 112413, Dubai, United Arab Emirates
Tel.: (971) 43661739
Emp.: 166
Engineering & Consulting Services
N.A.I.C.S.: 541330
Antoine Vuillemenot *(CFO-Asia & Middle East)*

Akka Technologies Beijing Ltd. **(3)**
No 1603 Office Building A Phoenix Place Tower 21 No A5 Shuguangxili, Chaoyang District, Beijing, 100028, China
Tel.: (86) 1084554661
Engineering & Consulting Services
N.A.I.C.S.: 541330
Faouzi Abbes *(CEO)*

CTP System SRL **(3)**
Localita Salceto 91/93, Poggibonsi, 53036, Siena, Italy
Tel.: (39) 057798481
Web Site: http://www.ctpsystem.com
Emp.: 200
Computer System Validation Consulting Services
N.A.I.C.S.: 541512
Luca Conti *(Sls Mgr-Center Italy)*

Data Respons ASA **(3)**
Sandviksveien 26 Hovik, 1363, Oslo, Norway **(100%)**
Tel.: (47) 67112000
Web Site: http://dataresponse.com
Sales Range: $150-199.9 Million
Emp.: 125
Embedded Solutions, Real-Time Wireless Applications & Machine-to-Machine Com-munication for Technology-Based Compa-nies
N.A.I.C.S.: 423430
Kenneth Ragnvaldsen *(CEO)*

Subsidiary (Non-US):

Data Respons A/S **(4)**
Smedeholm 10, 2730, Herlev, Denmark
Tel.: (45) 67112000
Web Site: http://www.dataresponse.com
Sales Range: $25-49.9 Million
Emp.: 50
Embedded Solutions Supplier
N.A.I.C.S.: 423430

Data Respons AB **(4)**
Jan Stenbecks Torg 17 3, 164 40, Kista, Sweden
Tel.: (46) 850168800
Web Site: http://www.dataresponse.com
Sales Range: $50-74.9 Million
Emp.: 100
Embedded Solutions Supplier
N.A.I.C.S.: 423430

Data Respons GmbH **(4)**
Amalienbadstr 41 bau 53, 76227, Karlsruhe, Germany
Tel.: (49) 72148088710
Web Site:
    http://www.solutions.dataresponse.com
Sales Range: $25-49.9 Million
Emp.: 50
Embedded Solutions Supplier
N.A.I.C.S.: 541519

Unit (Domestic):

Data Respons Norge AS **(4)**
Kirkegardsveien 45, PO Box 44, Kokstad, 5863, Kongsberg, Norway
Tel.: (47) 55114780
Web Site: http://www.dataresponse.com
Sales Range: $75-99.9 Million
Emp.: 20
Embedded Solutions Supplier
N.A.I.C.S.: 423430

Adecco Group AG—(Continued)

Data Respons Norge AS (4)
Technolog Park Kongsberg, PO Box 1022,
Kongsberg, NO-3601, Norway
Tel.: (47) 32299400
Sales Range: $25-49.9 Million
Emp.: 22
Embedded Solutions Supplier
N.A.I.C.S.: 423430

Data Respons Norge AS (4)
Sandviksveien 26, 1363, Hovik, Norway
Tel.: (47) 67112000
Web Site: http://www.datarespons.com
Sales Range: $50-74.9 Million
Emp.: 100
Embedded Solutions Supplier
N.A.I.C.S.: 423430

Subsidiary (Non-US):

Data Respons Syren AB (4)
Theres Svenssons Gata 10, Gothenburg,
417 55, Sweden
Tel.: (46) 317071480
Computer Software Consulting Services
N.A.I.C.S.: 541512

Ipcas GmbH (4)
Gundstrasse 15, 91056, Erlangen, Ger-
many
Tel.: (49) 913176770
Web Site: http://www.ipcas.com
Emp.: 50
Information Technology Consulting Services
N.A.I.C.S.: 541512
Jochen Staeudinger (Gen Mgr)

Sylog Sverige AB (4)
Jan Stenbecks Torg 17 3 tr, PO Box 1186,
Kista, Sweden
Tel.: (46) 8750490000
Web Site: http://www.sylog.se
Sales Range: $25-49.9 Million
Emp.: 10
Information Technology Consulting Services
N.A.I.C.S.: 541512
Camilla Hjelm (Partner & Mgr-Sls)

Subsidiary (Non-US):

Donat It GmbH (3)
Eriagstrasse 28a, 85053, Ingolstadt, Ger-
many
Tel.: (49) 841370810
Web Site: http://www.donat-it.de
Information Technology Services
N.A.I.C.S.: 541511

**Elektronische Fahrwerksysteme
GmbH** (3)
Dr-Ludwig-Kraus-Strasse 6, 85080, Gaim-
ersheim, Germany
Tel.: (49) 84583973000
Web Site: http://www.efs-auto.com
Automotive Products Mfr
N.A.I.C.S.: 336110

Epos Cat GmbH (3)
Friedrichshofener Strasse 1s, 85049, Ingol-
stadt, Germany
Tel.: (49) 84188197070
Web Site: http://www.epos-cat.de
Software Development Services
N.A.I.C.S.: 541511

**It Sonix Custom Development
GmbH** (3)
Georgiring 3, 04103, Leipzig, Germany
Tel.: (49) 341355760
Web Site: http://www.itsonix.eu
Software Development Services
N.A.I.C.S.: 541511
Artur Schiefer (CTO)

Iwise AB (3)
Jan Stenbecks torg 17 3 tr, Box 1186, 164
26, Kista, Sweden
Tel.: (46) 704239923
Web Site: http://www.iwise.se
Computer Software Consulting Services
N.A.I.C.S.: 541512

**MBtech Group GmbH & Co.
KGaA** (3)
Kolumbusstrasse 19+21, 71063, Sindelfin-
gen, Germany (65%)
Tel.: (49) 7031 686 3000
Web Site: http://www.mbtech-group.com

Sales Range: $450-499.9 Million
Emp.: 3,000
Motor Vehicle Components & Systems De-
velopment, Engineering & Testing Services
N.A.I.C.S.: 541330
Harald Keller (CEO)

Subsidiary (Domestic):

**ATP Automotive Testing Papenburg
GmbH** (4)
Johann-Bunte-Strasse 176, 26871, Papen-
burg, Germany
Tel.: (49) 49619750
Web Site: http://atp-papenburg.de
Sales Range: $25-49.9 Million
Emp.: 70
Motor Vehicle Testing Services
N.A.I.C.S.: 541380

Subsidiary (US):

MB-technology NA LLC (4)
400 E Big Beaver Rd, Troy, MI
48083 (100%)
Tel.: (248) 312-0277
Sales Range: $10-24.9 Million
Motor Vehicle Components & Systems De-
velopment, Engineering & Testing Services
N.A.I.C.S.: 541330
Jurgen Kiehne (Pres)

Subsidiary (Domestic):

**MBtech Auto Testing Properties
LLC** (5)
1220 Uniroyal Dr, Laredo, TX 78045
Tel.: (956) 728-8500
Web Site: http://www.mbtech-group.com
Motor Vehicle Testing Services
N.A.I.C.S.: 541380

Subsidiary (Non-US):

MBtech Bohemia s.r.o. (4)
Daimlerova 1161/6, CZ-301 00, Plzen,
Czech Republic (100%)
Tel.: (420) 377487300
Motor Vehicle Components & Systems De-
velopment, Engineering & Testing Services
N.A.I.C.S.: 541330

Subsidiary (Domestic):

MBtech Consulting GmbH (4)
Posener Strasse 1, 71065, Sindelfingen,
Germany
Tel.: (49) 7031 686 4780
Web Site: http://www.mbtech-group.com
Motor Vehicle Design Technical Consulting
Services
N.A.I.C.S.: 541690
Ralf Bechmann (Mng Dir)

Subsidiary (Non-US):

MBtech Polska Sp. z o.o. (3)
ul Kamienskiego 51/05, PL-30 644, Krakow,
Poland (100%)
Tel.: (48) 123505525
Web Site: http://www.mbtech-group.com
Motor Vehicle Components & Systems De-
velopment, Engineering & Testing Services
N.A.I.C.S.: 541330

**Microdoc Computersysteme
GmbH** (3)
Elektrastrasse 6a, 81925, Munich, Germany
Tel.: (49) 895519690
Web Site: http://www.microdoc.com
Emp.: 68
Software Development Services
N.A.I.C.S.: 541511
Christian Kuka (Co-Mng Dir)

Subsidiary (US):

PDS Tech, Inc. (3)
300 E John Carpenter Fwy Ste 700, Irving,
TX 75062-3216
Tel.: (214) 647-9600
Web Site: http://www.pdstech.com
Staffing Services
N.A.I.C.S.: 561320
Arthur R. Janes (Pres & CEO)

Subsidiary (Domestic):

PDS Technical Services (4)
108 Packerland Dr Ste A, Green Bay, WI
54303-4861

Tel.: (920) 499-9943
Web Site: http://www.pdstech.com
Sales Range: $10-24.9 Million
Emp.: 300
Staffing Services
N.A.I.C.S.: 561320
Cash Nickerson (Chm & CEO)

PDS Technical Services (4)
1839 S Alma School Rd Ste 250, Mesa, AZ
85210
Tel.: (480) 929-9922
Web Site: http://www.pdstech.com
Sales Range: $10-24.9 Million
Emp.: 12
Staffing Services
N.A.I.C.S.: 561320
Art James (Pres)

**PDS Technical Services, Seattle
Branch** (4)
12781 Gateway Dr, Tukwila, WA 98168-
2569
Tel.: (206) 763-2840
Web Site: http://www.pdstech.com
Sales Range: $25-49.9 Million
Emp.: 500
Contract Employment
N.A.I.C.S.: 541330

**PDS Technical Services, Wichita
Branch** (4)
11828 W Central Ste 100, Wichita, KS
67212 (100%)
Tel.: (316) 729-1800
Web Site: http://www.pdstech.com
Sales Range: $10-24.9 Million
Emp.: 5
Staffing Services
N.A.I.C.S.: 561320

Subsidiary (Non-US):

Sylog Ost AB (3)
Agatan 55 A, 582 22, Linkoping, Sweden
Tel.: (46) 133400390
Computer Software Consulting Services
N.A.I.C.S.: 541512

Sylog Systems AB (3)
Jan Stenbecks Torg 17 3 trp, 164 40, Kista,
Sweden
Tel.: (46) 87504900
Web Site: http://www.sylogsystems.se
Information Technology Services
N.A.I.C.S.: 541511

Tech People AS (3)
Smedeholm 10, 2730, Herlev, Denmark
Tel.: (45) 24762891
Web Site: http://www.techpeople.dk
Computer Software Consulting Services
N.A.I.C.S.: 541512
Nina Jensen (Acct Mgr)

Xpure GmbH (3)
Georgiring 3, 04103, Leipzig, Germany
Tel.: (49) 34135576400
Web Site: http://www.xpure.de
Software Development Services
N.A.I.C.S.: 541511
Burkhard Urban (Head-Sls)

Subsidiary (US):

Modis, Inc. (2)
10151 Deerwood Park Blvd Bldg 200 Ste
400, Jacksonville, FL 32256
Tel.: (904) 360-2000
Web Site: http://www.modis.com
Information Technology Staffing Services &
Project Managment
N.A.I.C.S.: 561311

Subsidiary (Non-US):

Modis Canada Inc. (3)
20 Bay Street 15th Floor Suite 1500, To-
ronto, M5J 2N8, ON, Canada
Tel.: (416) 367-2020
Web Site: http://www.modis.com
Sales Range: $25-49.9 Million
Emp.: 150
Information Technology Staffing Services
N.A.I.C.S.: 561311

Modis International Co. (3)
20 Bay Street 15th Floor Suite 1500, Toronto, M5J 2N8, ON, Canada
Tel.: (416) 367-2020
Web Site: https://www.modis.com

Sales Range: $10-24.9 Million
Emp.: 20
Management Consulting Services
N.A.I.C.S.: 541611

Modis International Limited (3)
33 Queen Street, London, EC4R 1BR,
United Kingdom
Tel.: (44) 2070386400
Web Site: http://www.modisintl.com
Sales Range: $75-99.9 Million
Payroll Contracting Solutions
N.A.I.C.S.: 541214
Roy Dungworth (Gen Mgr)

Subsidiary (Non-US):

**Ajilon Technology Professionals
B.V.** (4)
Beukenlaan 125, 5616 VD, Eindhoven,
Netherlands
Tel.: (31) 407999010
Web Site: http://www.ajilon.nl
Sales Range: $10-24.9 Million
Emp.: 20
Technology Staffing Services & Project
Management
N.A.I.C.S.: 561311
Chris Wright (Mgr-Client)

Branch (Domestic):

Modis Amsterdam (5)
Kabelweg 37, Amsterdam, 1014 BA, Neth-
erlands
Tel.: (31) 205914175
Web Site: http://www.modisnederland.nl
Information Technology Staffing Solutions
N.A.I.C.S.: 561311
Steven Beekhuis (Gen Mgr)

Subsidiary (Non-US):

Modis International-Brussels (4)
9-13 Rue D'Idalie, Brussels, B 1050, Bel-
gium
Tel.: (32) 27916550
Web Site: http://www.modisintl.com
Sales Range: $100-124.9 Million
Information Technology Staffing
N.A.I.C.S.: 561311

Subsidiary (Domestic):

Modis London (4)
33 Queen St, London, EC4R 1BR, United
Kingdom
Tel.: (44) 2070386400
Web Site: http://www.modisintl.com
Sales Range: $10-24.9 Million
Emp.: 25
Information Technology Staffing Solutions
N.A.I.C.S.: 561311

Subsidiary (Non-US):

Modis Polska Sp.z.o.o (4)
Buma Business Center ul Wadowicka 6,
Krakow, 30-415, Poland
Tel.: (48) 122923905
Web Site: http://www.modisintl.com
Sales Range: $100-124.9 Million
Emp.: 15
Staffing Solutions
N.A.I.C.S.: 561311

**Personality IT People Power
GmbH** (4)
Theodor-Heuss Strasse 14, Stuttgart,
70174, Germany
Tel.: (49) 7113516630
Web Site: http://www.personality-it.de
Sales Range: $100-124.9 Million
Emp.: 35
Information Technology Staffing Solutions
N.A.I.C.S.: 561311
Christos Seiler (Office Mgr)

Branch (Domestic):

**Modis, Inc.-National Enterprise
Practice** (3)
400 Southpointe Blvd, Canonsburg, PA
15317-8549
Tel.: (724) 745-4900
Web Site: http://www.modisit.com
Sales Range: $10-24.9 Million
Emp.: 17
Computer Related Consulting Services
N.A.I.C.S.: 541512

Brittany Ferrin *(Mgr-Resource Dev)*

Altedia SAS **(1)**
7-11 Quai Andre Citroen, 75015, Paris, France
Tel.: (33) 1 44 91 50 00
Web Site: http://www.altedia.fr
Human Resource Consulting Services
N.A.I.C.S.: 541612

Beeline **(1)**
14911 Quorum Dr Ste 120, Dallas, TX 75254
Tel.: (972) 813-0465
Web Site: http://www.beeline.com
Sales Range: $10-24.9 Million
Emp.: 6
Training Tech Writing Courseware Development
N.A.I.C.S.: 541511

BioBridges LLC **(1)**
230 3rd Ave Ste 3206, Waltham, MA 02451
Tel.: (781) 416-0909
Web Site: https://www.biobridges.com
Clinical Development & Testing Services
N.A.I.C.S.: 541380

DIS AG **(1)**
Fritz-Vomfelde-Strasse 26, 40547, Dusseldorf, Germany
Tel.: (49) 2115306530
Web Site: https://www.dis-ag.com
Staffing Services
N.A.I.C.S.: 561330
Peter Blersch *(CEO)*

Ecco Servicios de Personal SA de CV **(1)**
Montecito No 38 Piso 10 Int 28, Mexico, 03810, Mexico
Tel.: (52) 55 5062 5000
Employment Consulting Services
N.A.I.C.S.: 541612

Entegee Inc. **(1)**
70 Blanchard Rd, Burlington, MA 01803
Tel.: (781) 221-5800
Web Site: http://www.entegee.com
Sales Range: $10-24.9 Million
Emp.: 40
Engineering & Technical Employee Recruitment
N.A.I.C.S.: 561311

Lee Hecht Harrison HK Limited **(1)**
Unit 1004 Li Po Chun Chambers 189 Des Voeux Road, Central, China (Hong Kong)
Tel.: (852) 28400838
Management Consulting Services
N.A.I.C.S.: 541618

Lee Hecht Harrison Polska Sp. z o.o. **(1)**
ul Chocimska 4, 00-791, Warsaw, Poland
Tel.: (48) 798745017
Web Site: http://www.lhhpolska.pl
Staffing Services
N.A.I.C.S.: 561320

Modis Bulgaria EOOD **(1)**
9 Vitoshki Kambani str, Sofia, 1766, Bulgaria
Tel.: (359) 24513400
Web Site: http://www.modis.com
Technical Consulting Services
N.A.I.C.S.: 541690

Modis GmbH **(1)**
Dannenkamp 4, 22869, Schenefeld, Germany
Tel.: (49) 4083099282
Web Site: https://modis-gmbh.net
N.A.I.C.S.: 531390

OnForce, Inc. **(1)**
10 Maguire Rd Bldg 2 Ste 232, Lexington, MA 02421
Tel.: (781) 761-9100
Web Site: http://www.onforce.com
IT-Related Employment Placement Services
N.A.I.C.S.: 561311
Gabe Miano *(VP-Products Mgmt)*

Paladin Companies Inc. **(1)**
200 S Michigan Ave Ste 700, Chicago, IL 60604-2416 **(100%)**
Tel.: (312) 654-2600
Web Site: https://www.paladinstaff.com
Sales Range: $25-49.9 Million
Emp.: 15

Marketing, Creative & Communications Staff Recruitment
N.A.I.C.S.: 561311

Special Counsel Inc. **(1)**
10151 Deerwood Park Blvd Bldg 400 Ste 150, Jacksonville, FL 32256 **(100%)**
Tel.: (904) 513-5225
Web Site: http://www.specialcounsel.com
Sales Range: $75-99.9 Million
Emp.: 100
Legal Staffing Placement & Recruiting Service
N.A.I.C.S.: 561311

Division (Domestic):

Doculegal, LLC **(2)**
222 Andrews St Ste 200, Rochester, NY 14604
Tel.: (585) 232-4010
Web Site: http://www.specialcounsel.com
Data Collection
N.A.I.C.S.: 541519

Subsidiary (Domestic):

D4 LLC **(3)**
222 Andrews St, Rochester, NY 14604
Tel.: (585) 385-4040
Emp.: 100
Electronic Discovery & Litigation Support Services
N.A.I.C.S.: 541199
Joseph Reges *(VP-Discovery Svcs)*

Branch (Domestic):

Special Counsel Inc. **(2)**
250 W Pratt St Ste 1300, Baltimore, MD 21201-2459
Tel.: (410) 385-5350
Web Site: http://www.specialcounsel.com
Sales Range: $1-9.9 Million
Emp.: 5
Temporary Help Service
N.A.I.C.S.: 561330

Spring Professional Luxembourg SA. **(1)**
2A rue d'Anvers, 1130, Luxembourg, Luxembourg
Tel.: (352) 4642461
Web Site: http://www.springprofessional.lu
Staffing Services
N.A.I.C.S.: 561320
Julie Noirhomme *(Mng Dir)*

TUJA Zeitarbeit GmbH **(1)**
Friedrich-Ebert-Strasse 110, 48153, Munster, Germany
Tel.: (49) 251 7184 0
Web Site: http://www.tuja.de
Sales Range: $25-49.9 Million
Emp.: 40
Employment Consulting Services
N.A.I.C.S.: 541612
Thomas Baumer *(CEO)*

euro engineering AG **(1)**
Lise-meitner-strasse 15, 89081, Ulm, Germany
Tel.: (49) 731935650
Web Site: http://www.ee-ag.com
Engineeering Services
N.A.I.C.S.: 541330
Peter Blesch *(CEO)*

ADECOAGRO S.A.
28 Boulevard F W Raiffeisen, L-2411, Luxembourg, Luxembourg
Tel.: (352) 26449372 LU
Web Site: https://www.adecoagro.com
Year Founded: 2002
AGRO—(NYSE)
Rev.: $1,347,724,000
Assets: $3,108,855,000
Liabilities: $1,945,212,000
Net Worth: $1,163,643,000
Earnings: $108,606,000
Emp.: 9,776
Fiscal Year-end: 12/31/22
Farming Crops, Agricultural Products, Cattle & Dairy Operations, Sugar, Ethanol & Energy Production, Land Transformation

N.A.I.C.S.: 111998
Alan Leland Boyce *(Co-Founder)*

Subsidiaries:

Girasoles del Plata S.A. **(1)**
Parque Industrial Pehuajo, 6450, Buenos Aires, Argentina **(100%)**
Tel.: (54) 2396555200
Web Site: https://www.girasolesdelplata.com
Farm Supply Whslr
N.A.I.C.S.: 424910

ADEKA CORPORATION
7-2-35 Higashi-ogu, Arakawa-ku, Tokyo, 1168554, Japan
Tel.: (81) 344552811
Web Site: https://www.adeka.co.jp
Year Founded: 1917
4401—(TKS)
Rev.: $2,642,479,700
Assets: $3,589,606,770
Liabilities: $1,344,308,750
Net Worth: $2,245,298,020
Earnings: $151,877,970
Emp.: 5,512
Fiscal Year-end: 03/31/24
Resins, Surfactants, Organic Chemicals, Inorganic Chemicals & Edible Oils
N.A.I.C.S.: 325199
Haruhiko Tomiyasu *(Sr Mng Exec Officer & Sr Mng Exec Officer)*

Subsidiaries:

ADEKA Europe GmbH **(1)**
Berliner Allee 22, 40212, Dusseldorf, Germany
Tel.: (49) 2111792450
Web Site: https://www.adeka.eu
Chemical Product Mfr & Distr
N.A.I.C.S.: 325998

Adeka (Asia) Pte. Ltd. **(1)**
8 Jurong Town Hall Road 23-02 The JTC Summit, Singapore, 609434, Singapore
Tel.: (65) 67768809
Chemical Product Whslr
N.A.I.C.S.: 424690

Adeka (China) Co., Ltd. **(1)**
RM 1001-1010 10F Metro Plaza No 555 Loushanguan Road, Shanghai, 200051, China
Tel.: (86) 2162296622
Chemical Product Whslr
N.A.I.C.S.: 424690

Adeka (Singapore) Pte. Ltd. **(1)**
213 Pandan Loop, Singapore, 128404, Singapore
Tel.: (65) 67759355
Web Site: http://www.adeka.com.sg
Processed Vegetable Oil & Fat Product Mfr
N.A.I.C.S.: 311225

Adeka Al Otaiba Middle East LLC **(1)**
Plot No 37B4, Abu Dhabi, United Arab Emirates
Tel.: (971) 25508361
Web Site: https://www.adekaalotaiba.com
Chemical Product Mfr & Distr
N.A.I.C.S.: 325998

Adeka Brasil Ltda. **(1)**
Alameda Araguaia 750-751 Araguaia Plaza CJ 103 Alphaville Industrial, Barueri, Sao Paulo, 06455-000, SP, Brazil
Tel.: (55) 1143953527
Sales & Marketing Support Services
N.A.I.C.S.: 541613

Adeka Chemical Supply Corporation **(1)**
2-5-12 NMF Surugadai Building 5F Kanda Surugadai, Chiyoda-ku, Tokyo, 101-0062, Japan
Tel.: (81) 338117191
Web Site: https://www.adeka-acs.co.jp
Chemical & Allied Products Merchant Whslr
N.A.I.C.S.: 424690

Adeka Clean Aid Corporation **(1)**
2-5-12 Kanda Surugadai, Chiyoda-ku, Tokyo, 101-0062, Japan

Tel.: (81) 338161249
Web Site: https://www.acajp.com
Emp.: 136
Detergent & Disinfectant Whslr
N.A.I.C.S.: 424690

Adeka Engineering & Construction Corp. **(1)**
2th 5th Floor Kouyosha Bldg 5-48-5 Higashi-Nippori, Arakawa-ku, Tokyo, Japan
Tel.: (81) 338057451
Electrical & Pipe Work Construction Services
N.A.I.C.S.: 238220

Adeka Fine Chemical (Changshu) Co., Ltd. **(1)**
No 101 Changchun Road Changshu Economic Development Zone, Riverside Industrial Park, Jiangsu, 215537, China
Tel.: (86) 51252648000
Polymer Additive Mfr & Whslr
N.A.I.C.S.: 325998

Adeka Fine Chemical (Shanghai) Co., Ltd. **(1)**
228 Bnanqiao East Road, Shanyang Town Jinshan District, Shanghai, 201508, China
Tel.: (86) 2157245988
Chemical Product Mfr & Whslr
N.A.I.C.S.: 325199

Adeka Fine Chemical (Thailand) Co., Ltd. **(1)**
300/12MOO 1 Tambon Tasit Amphur, Eastern Seaboard Industrial Estate, Pluak Daeng, 21140, Rayong, Thailand
Tel.: (66) 38959032
Polymer Additive Mfr & Whslr
N.A.I.C.S.: 325998

Adeka Fine Chemical Taiwan Corp. **(1)**
No 32 Gongye 6th Rd, Annan District, Tainan City, 709, Taiwan
Tel.: (886) 63841388
Chemical Product Mfr & Whslr
N.A.I.C.S.: 325199

Adeka Fine Foods Corporation **(1)**
207 Takeuchi Danchi, Sakaiminato, Sakaiminato, 684-0046, Tottori, Japan
Tel.: (81) 859454771
Web Site: https://www.adeka.co.jp
Mayonnaise Dressing & Sauce Mfr
N.A.I.C.S.: 311941

Adeka Foods (Asia) Sdn. Bhd. **(1)**
PLO 167 Jalan Nibong 3, Tanjung Langsat Industrial Complex, 81700, Pasir Gudang, Johor, Malaysia
Tel.: (60) 72516005
Web Site: http://www.adeka.com.my
Bread & Confectionary Product Mfr
N.A.I.C.S.: 311812

Adeka Foods (Changshu) Co., Ltd. **(1)**
No 10 Xinhua Gangqu Road Changshu Economic Technology Development Zone, Jiangsu, 215513, China
Tel.: (86) 51252296828
Processed Oil & Fat Product Mfr
N.A.I.C.S.: 311225

Adeka Foods Sales Corporation **(1)**
3rd floor Urban Center Kanda Tsukasa-cho 2-6 Kanda Tsukasa-cho, Chiyoda-ku, Tokyo, 101-0048, Japan
Tel.: (81) 344552397
Web Site: https://www.adeka-fs.co.jp
Sales Range: $25-49.9 Million
Emp.: 76
Confectionery Whslr
N.A.I.C.S.: 424450

Adeka India Pvt. Ltd. **(1)**
A-206 Dynasty Business Park J B Nagar, Andheri Kurla Road Andheri East, Mumbai, 400059, Maharashtra, India
Tel.: (91) 2240263301
Web Site: http://www.adekaindia.com
Chemical Products Mfr
N.A.I.C.S.: 325998

Adeka Korea Corporation **(1)**
839 yongam-ri Bongdong-eup, Wanju-gun, Yeongam, 55323, Jeollabuk-do, Korea (South)
Tel.: (82) 632600400

Adeka Corporation—(Continued)

Web Site: https://www.adekakorea.co.kr
Sales Range: $25-49.9 Million
Emp.: 98
Plastic Additive Mfr
N.A.I.C.S.: 326199
Takahisa Uenoyama (CEO)

Adeka Life-Create Corp. (1)
6th floor Koyosha Building 5-48-5 Higashi
Nippori, Arakawa-ku, Tokyo, 116-0014, Ja-
pan
Tel.: (81) 367431000
Web Site: https://www.adeka-lifecreate.co.jp
Real Estate Services
N.A.I.C.S.: 531390

Adeka Logistics Corp. (1)
5-48-5 Higashinippori Building 4th Floor
Koyosha, Arakawa-ku, Tokyo, Japan
Tel.: (81) 338078161
Logistic Services
N.A.I.C.S.: 541614

**Adeka Polymer Additives Europe
Sas** (1)
13 rue du 17 Novembre, 68100, Mulhouse,
France
Tel.: (33) 368750530
Web Site: http://www.adeka-pa.eu
Polymer Additive Mfr & Distr
N.A.I.C.S.: 325998

Adeka Usa Corp. (1)
777 Terrace Ave Ste 602A, Hasbrouck
Heights, NJ 07604
Tel.: (201) 525-1150
Chemical Products Distr
N.A.I.C.S.: 424690

**Agricultural Chemicals (Malaysia)
Sdn. Bhd.** (1)
962 Lrg Perusahaan 8, Taman Perindus-
trian, 13600, Perai, Pulau Pinang, Malaysia
Tel.: (60) 43907988
Web Site: https://www.agrichem.com.my
Agrochemical Product Mfr
N.A.I.C.S.: 325320

Agrimart Corp. (1)
12-2 Kyobashi 3-Chome, Chuo-ku, Tokyo,
104-0031, Japan
Tel.: (81) 351591711
Pest Control Device Whslr
N.A.I.C.S.: 423620

Am Stabilizers Corp. (1)
705 Silhavy Rd, Valparaiso, IN 46383
Tel.: (219) 844-3980
Web Site: https://www.amstabilizers.com
Polymer Additive Mfr & Distr
N.A.I.C.S.: 325998

Asahi Architects Office Co., Ltd. (1)
5-48-2 Higashi Nippori, Arakawa-ku, Tokyo,
Japan
Tel.: (81) 338062731
Architectural Design Services
N.A.I.C.S.: 541310

**Chang Chiang Chemical Co.,
Ltd.** (1)
No 237 16 th Fl Songkiang Rd, Taipei, 104,
Taiwan
Tel.: (886) 225097431
Sales Range: $25-49.9 Million
Emp.: 10
Antioxidants & PVC Products
N.A.I.C.S.: 325211

Co-Op Clean Co., Ltd. (1)
1-17-18 Nishikicho, Warabi, Saitama, Japan
Tel.: (81) 484462907
Soap & Detergent Mfr & Whslr
N.A.I.C.S.: 325611

Crown Co., Ltd. (1)
3-6-35 Nishitenma, Kita-ku, Osaka, 530-
0047, Japan
Tel.: (81) 663656321
Web Site: https://www.crown-net.co.jp
Food Material Whslr
N.A.I.C.S.: 424490

**Kanto Sodium Silicate Glass Co.,
Ltd.** (1)
29 Toh-Wada, Kamisu, Ibaraki, Japan
Tel.: (81) 299962131
Chemical Products Mfr
N.A.I.C.S.: 325180

Mizushima Plasticizer Co., Ltd. (1)
2-5-2 Marunouchi, Chiyoda-ku, Tokyo, Ja-
pan
Tel.: (81) 332834733
Chemical Products Mfr
N.A.I.C.S.: 325199

NIHON NOHYAKU Co., Ltd. (1)
19-8 Kyobashi 1-Chome, Chuo-ku, Tokyo,
104-8386, Japan (51%)
Tel.: (81) 570091177
Web Site: http://www.nichino.co.jp
Rev.: $681,048,130
Assets: $1,044,267,630
Liabilities: $512,850,070
Net Worth: $531,417,560
Earnings: $31,575,970
Emp.: 1,472
Fiscal Year-end: 03/31/2024
Agricultural Chemicals Mfr & Sales
N.A.I.C.S.: 325320
Yosuke Tomoi (Pres)

Subsidiary (US):

Nichino America Inc. (2)
4550 Linden Hill Rd Ste 501, Wilmington,
DE 19808
Tel.: (302) 636-9001
Web Site: https://www.nichino.net
Crop Protection Product Mfr
N.A.I.C.S.: 325320

Subsidiary (Non-US):

Nichino Europe Co., Ltd. (2)
5 Pioneer Court Vision Park, Histon, Cam-
bridge, CB24 9PT, United Kingdom
Tel.: (44) 1223855720
Web Site: https://www.nichino-europe.com
Crop Protection Products Mfr & Suppliers
N.A.I.C.S.: 424910

Subsidiary (Domestic):

Nichino Ryokka Co., Ltd. (2)
14-4 Nihonbashi Kodemmacho Okaya
Building 6F, Chuo-Ku, Tokyo, 103-0001,
Japan
Tel.: (81) 338082281
Web Site: https://www.nichino-ryokka.co.jp
Chemical Pesticides Whslr
N.A.I.C.S.: 325320
Shiro Takahashi (Pres)

Subsidiary (Non-US):

Nichino Service Co., Ltd. (2)
Tel.: (81) 243237715
Web Site: http://www.nichino.co.jp
Logistic Services
N.A.I.C.S.: 541614

Subsidiary (Domestic):

Nihon EcoTech Co., Ltd. (1)
Kyobashi No 2 Yuraku Building 7F 3-12-2
Kyobashi, Chuo-ku, Tokyo, 104-0031, Ja-
pan
Tel.: (81) 363611429
Web Site: https://www.ecotech.co.jp
Emp.: 76
Pesticide Mfr
N.A.I.C.S.: 325320
Toyokazu Iijima (Pres)

Subsidiary (Non-US):

Taiwan Nihon Nohyaku Co., Ltd. (2)
9F-2 No 22 Nanjing W Rd, Datong, Taipei,
103, Taiwan
Tel.: (886) 225558709
Web Site: https://nika-nohyaku.com.tw
Crop Protection Products Mfr & Suppliers
N.A.I.C.S.: 325320

Nichino Chemical India Pvt. Ltd. (1)
Plot No 60 61 IDA, Pashamylaram, Medak,
502307, Telangana, India
Tel.: (91) 8455224340
Agrochemical Product Mfr
N.A.I.C.S.: 325320

Nichino India Pvt. Ltd. (1)
A-24/25 Apie, Balanagar, Hyderabad,
500037, Telangana, India
Tel.: (91) 4023772502
Web Site: http://www.nichinoindia.com
Industrial Chemical Products Mfr
N.A.I.C.S.: 325998

Oxirane Chemical Corporation (1)
10th floor 4-1-13 Nihonbashi Honcho,
Chuo-ku, Tokyo, 103-0023, Japan
Tel.: (81) 332311761
Organic Chemical Mfr
N.A.I.C.S.: 325199

Showa Kosan Co., Ltd. (1)
6-13-18 Akasaka, Minato-ku, Tokyo, 107-
8452, Japan
Tel.: (81) 335849111
Web Site: https://www.showakosan.co.jp
Emp.: 159
Synthetic Rising & Chemical Product Mfr
N.A.I.C.S.: 325998
Takashi Ito (Pres & CEO)

Sipcam Europe S.P.A (1)
Via Del Carroccio 8, 20123, Milan, MI, Italy
Tel.: (39) 0235378400
Agrochemical Mfr & Whslr
N.A.I.C.S.: 325320

Sipcam Nichino Brasil S.A. (1)
R Lgarapava 599, Distrito Industrail III,
Uberaba, 38044-755, MG, Brazil
Tel.: (55) 3433195500
Web Site: https://www.sipcamnichino.com.br
Agrochemical Product Mfr & Whslr
N.A.I.C.S.: 325320

**Tokyo Environmental Measurement
Center Co., Ltd** (1)
8-5-2 Higashiokyu, Arakawa-ku, Tokyo, 116-
0012, Japan
Tel.: (81) 338951141
Web Site: http://www.toukansoku.co.jp
Sales Range: $25-49.9 Million
Emp.: 50
Environmental Consulting Services
N.A.I.C.S.: 541620

Uehara Foods Industry Co., Ltd (1)
6-52-14 Higashi-Ogu, Arakawa-ku, Tokyo,
Japan
Tel.: (81) 344552961
Web Site: http://www.adk.co.jp
Mfr & Sales of Flour Paste for Bread &
Pouch-Packed Foods
N.A.I.C.S.: 311999

Yongo Co., Ltd (1)
2-1102 Kamisuga, Meito-ku, Nagoya, 465-
0014, Aichi, Japan
Tel.: (81) 527744511
Web Site: https://www.yongo.co.jp
Confectionery Whslr
N.A.I.C.S.: 424450

ADEL KALEMCILIK TICARET VE SANAYI A.S.
Sekerpinar Mah Yanyol Street No 7,
Kartal, TR-41480, Kocaeli, Turkiye
Tel.: (90) 8502242335
Web Site: https://www.adel.com.tr
Year Founded: 1967
ADEL—(IST)
Emp.: 390
Stationery Product Mfr
N.A.I.C.S.: 322230
Ibrahim Yazici (Vice Chm)

ADELIS EQUITY PARTNERS AB
Regeringsgatan 20, 111 46, Stock-
holm, Sweden
Tel.: (46) 852520000
Web Site:
http://www.adelisequity.com
Year Founded: 2012
Privater Equity Firm
N.A.I.C.S.: 523999
Johan Seger (CFO)

Subsidiaries:

AddPro AB (1)
Arenagatan 8B, 212 31, Malmo, Sweden
Tel.: (46) 40 59 24 00
Web Site: http://www.addpro.se
Emp.: 140
Cyber Security Services
N.A.I.C.S.: 541519
Johan Andersson (Project Mgr)

Avidly Oy (1)

Konepajankuja 1, 00510, Helsinki, Finland
Tel.: (358) 102319000
Web Site: http://www.avidlyagency.com
Rev.: $36,812,809
Assets: $27,150,245
Liabilities: $14,080,543
Net Worth: $13,069,702
Earnings: ($267,756)
Emp.: 242
Fiscal Year-end: 12/31/2021
Advetising Agency
N.A.I.C.S.: 541810
Sami Savolainen (Mgr-IT)

Subsidiary (Non-US):

NetPress GmbH (2)
Alte Landstrasse 21, 85521, Ottobrunn,
Germany
Tel.: (49) 8912503080
Web Site: http://www.netpress.de
Digital Marketing Services
N.A.I.C.S.: 541613
Achim B. C. Karpf (Mng Dir)

Subsidiary (Domestic):

Sugar Helsinki Oy (2)
Uudenmaankatu 7 B 1, 00120, Helsinki,
Finland
Tel.: (358) 102319006
Web Site: http://www.sugarhelsinki.com
PR Agency Services
N.A.I.C.S.: 541820
Saana Sillanpaa (Head-Lifestyle PR)

SSI Diagnostica A/S (1)
2 Herredsvejen, 3400, Hillerod, Denmark
Tel.: (45) 4829 9100
Web Site: http://www.ssidiagnostica.com
In Vitro Diagnostic Products Manufacturer
And Distributor
N.A.I.C.S.: 325413
Soren Skjold Mogensen (CEO)

Subsidiary (US):

TechLab, Inc. (2)
2001 Kraft Dr, Blacksburg, VA 24060-6358
Tel.: (540) 953-1664
Web Site: http://www.techlab.com
Rev.: $5,000,000
Emp.: 100
Develops, Manufactures & Distributes Rapid
Non-Invasive Intestinal Diagnostics
N.A.I.C.S.: 325411
David Lyerly (Chief Scientific Officer)

ADELONG GOLD LIMITED
Level 4 91 William Street, Melbourne,
3000, VIC, Australia
Tel.: (61) 86115320   AU
Web Site: https://adelonggold.com
Year Founded: 2006
ADG—(ASX)
Rev.: $19,384
Assets: $4,336,709
Liabilities: $280,901
Net Worth: $4,055,808
Earnings: ($1,511,002)
Fiscal Year-end: 06/30/24
Mineral Exploration Services
N.A.I.C.S.: 212220
Ian Hastings (Chm)

Subsidiaries:

Cosmo Gold Pty Ltd (1)
Level 4 91 William Street, Melbourne, 3000,
VIC, Australia
Tel.: (61) 38 611 5333
Web Site: https://www.cosmogold.com.au
Gold Exploration Services
N.A.I.C.S.: 212220
Ian Hastings (Chm)

ADENIA PARTNERS LTD
1st Floor Office 12, The Strand 1,
Beau Plan Business Park,, 21001,
Beau Plan, Mauritius
Tel.: (230) 2459400
Web Site: https://www.adenia.com
Year Founded: 2002
Private Equity
N.A.I.C.S.: 523940

Subsidiaries:

AIR LIQUIDE GABOA (1)
Z I D Owendo, PO Box 545, Libreville, Gabon
Tel.: (241) 540 6700
Web Site: http://www.airliquide.com
Sales Range: $25-49.9 Million
Emp.: 57
Industrial Gas Storage Equipment Mfr
N.A.I.C.S.: 333132

Air Liquide Benin S.A. (1)
Route de Porto Novo PK 3, BP 06674, Cotonou, Benin
Tel.: (229) 21331075
Emp.: 22
Industrial Gas Mfr
N.A.I.C.S.: 325120

Air Liquide Burkina Faso S.A. (1)
Rue 9 107 Porte 466-01, BP 623, Ouagadougou, Burkina Faso
Tel.: (226) 25344243
Emp.: 40
Industrial Gas Mfr
N.A.I.C.S.: 325120

Air Liquide Cameroun S.A. (1)
Zone industrielle de Bassa Tunnel Ndokotti, BP 4031, Bassa, Douala, Cameroon
Tel.: (237) 677092033
Emp.: 60
Industrial Gas Mfr
N.A.I.C.S.: 325120

Air Liquide Congo S.A. (1)
Quartier Industriel du Km 4, BP 734, Pointe Noire, Congo, Republic of
Tel.: (242) 44440202
Emp.: 80
Industrial Gas Mfr
N.A.I.C.S.: 325120

Air Liquide Cote d'Ivoire S.A. (1)
131 Boulevard de Marseille, BP 1753, Abidjan, Cote d'Ivoire
Tel.: (225) 21210440
Emp.: 70
Industrial Gas Mfr
N.A.I.C.S.: 325120

Subsidiary (Non-US):

Comcare Medical B.V. (2)
Langendijk 27 A, 5652 AX, Eindhoven, Netherlands
Tel.: (31) 40 250 35 02
Web Site: http://www.comcaremedical.com
Health Care Srvices
N.A.I.C.S.: 621999
Patrick Hondsmerk *(Gen Mgr)*

Air Liquide Ghana Ltd. (1)
Heavy Industrial Area, PO Box 24, Tema, Ghana
Tel.: (233) 303308273
Emp.: 60
Industrial Gas Mfr
N.A.I.C.S.: 325120

Air Liquide Madagascar S.A. (1)
Anosivavaka Ambohimanarina, BP 53, 101, Antananarivo, Madagascar
Tel.: (261) 202322506
Emp.: 88
Industrial Gas Mfr
N.A.I.C.S.: 325120

Air Liquide Mali S.A. (1)
Route de Sotuba, BP 5, Bamako, Mali
Tel.: (223) 20212394
Emp.: 60
Industrial Gas Mfr
N.A.I.C.S.: 325120

Air Liquide Senegal S.A. (1)
Km 3 5 Bd Du Centenaire De La Commune, BP 45, Dakar, Senegal
Tel.: (221) 8493030
Emp.: 50
Industrial Gas Mfr
N.A.I.C.S.: 325120

Air Liquide Togo S.A. (1)
933 Avenue Des Hydrocarbures, BP 1082, Lome, Togo
Tel.: (228) 22214626
Emp.: 25
Industrial Gas Mfr
N.A.I.C.S.: 325120

Subsidiary (Non-US):

Societe d'Installations et de Diffusion de Materiel Technique S.P.A. (2)
2 Boulevard Aissat Idir Alger Premier Mai, Algiers, Algeria
Tel.: (213) 21 65 06 96
Industrial Gas Mfr
N.A.I.C.S.: 325120

ADEPTIO LLC
Office E 519 Level 5, Old Town Island, Dubai, United Arab Emirates
Tel.: (971) 4 4533904
Private Investment Firm
N.A.I.C.S.: 523999
Mohamed Alabbar *(Chm)*

Subsidiaries:

Kuwait Food Company (Americana) S.A.K. (1)
Dajeej Area-Qasima no 81 beside Dalal Hypermarket, PO Box 941051, Opposite Immigration Office Americana Building Farwaniyah, Kuwait, Kuwait (95.97%)
Tel.: (965) 22230830
Web Site: http://www.americana-group.com
Sales Range: $1-4.9 Billion
Restaurant Franchise Owner & Operator; Food Products Mfr
N.A.I.C.S.: 722513
Faisal Bari *(CFO)*

Subsidiary (Non-US):

Al Ahlia Restaurants Co. (2)
PO Box 8030, Jeddah, 21482, Saudi Arabia (99.96%)
Tel.: (966) 265200733
Web Site: http://www.americana-group.com
Restaurant Operators
N.A.I.C.S.: 722511
Hany Dawoud *(Ops Mgr-Jeddah & Central Reg)*

Gulf Food Industries Company (2)
PO Box 17100, Dubai, United Arab Emirates (100%)
Tel.: (971) 48815633
Web Site: http://www.gficg.com
Food Packaging Services
N.A.I.C.S.: 424420
Adel Fahmy *(Gen Mgr)*

Gulf and Arab World Restaurants Co. (2)
PO Box 15750, Manama, Bahrain (94%)
Tel.: (973) 17262998
Restaurant Operators
N.A.I.C.S.: 722511

International Touristic Projects Lebanese Company (2)
Zouhour Building 2nd Floor, Beirut, Lebanon (98%)
Tel.: (961) 1825921
Web Site: http://www.americana-group.com
Restaurant Services
N.A.I.C.S.: 722513

Kuwait Food Company (UAE) (2)
PO Box 3901, Dubai, United Arab Emirates (100%)
Tel.: (971) 65554545
Web Site: http://www.americana-group.com
Restaurant Services
N.A.I.C.S.: 722513

Subsidiary (Non-US):

Cairo Poultry Company (3)
32H Mourad st, PO Box 42, Giza, Egypt
Tel.: (20) 235714124
Web Site: https://www.cpg.com.eg
Sales Range: $125-149.9 Million
Poultry Processing Services
N.A.I.C.S.: 311615
Tarek Tawfik *(Chm & Mng Dir)*

Subsidiary (Non-US):

National Food Industries Company Limited (2)
Industrial Area Phase 5, Jeddah, Saudi Arabia
Tel.: (966) 26081515
Web Site: http://www.luna.com.sa
Dairy Products Mfr

N.A.I.C.S.: 311514

Qatar Food Company (2)
PO Box 4548, Doha, Qatar (100%)
Tel.: (974) 4281111
Web Site: http://www.americana-group.com
Restaurant Services
N.A.I.C.S.: 722513

The Caspian International Restaurants Company, LLP (2)
151/115 Abay Avenue corner of Radostovetz St, Business Center Alatau Office 1009, 050009, Almaty, Kazakhstan (100%)
Tel.: (7) 7273341156
Web Site: http://www.americana-group.com
Restaurant Services
N.A.I.C.S.: 722513

ADERANS CO., LTD.
1-6-3 Shinjuku, Shinkjuku-ku, Tokyo, 160-0007, Japan
Tel.: (81) 333503111 JP
Web Site: http://www.aderans.co.jp
Year Founded: 1969
Emp.: 6,382
Wigs & Accessories Mfr & Whslr
N.A.I.C.S.: 315990
Nobuo Nemoto *(Chm & Founder)*

Subsidiaries:

Aderans (Shanghai) Co., Ltd (1)
15th Floor 1 Grand Gateway No 1 Hongqiao Rd, Shanghai, 200030, China
Tel.: (86) 2164486300
Web Site: http://www.universal-hair.com
Wigs Whslr
N.A.I.C.S.: 424990

Aderans (Shanghai) Trading Co., Ltd (1)
15th Floor 1 Grand Gateway No 1 Hongqiao Road, Shanghai, 200030, China
Tel.: (86) 21 6448 6300
Web Site: http://www.universal-hair.com
Hair Care Services
N.A.I.C.S.: 812199

Aderans France SAS (1)
6 Allee des Saules, Europarc, 94042, Creteil, France
Tel.: (33) 1 48 90 30 60
Web Site: http://www.universal-hair.com
Investment Management Service
N.A.I.C.S.: 523999

Aderans Hairgoods, Inc. (1)
15551 Cabrito Rd, Van Nuys, CA 91406-1410
Tel.: (818) 908-3103
Wig Retailer
N.A.I.C.S.: 458110

Aderans Inc (1)
3 F 39 Chung Hsiao West Road Section 1, Taipei, 10041, Taiwan
Tel.: (886) 223888905
Cosmetic Products Mfr & Whslr
N.A.I.C.S.: 325620

Aderans Philippines, Inc. (1)
Lot A 5 Clark Premiere Industrial Park M A Roxas Highway, Clark Freeport Zone 2009, Pampanga, 2009, Philippines
Tel.: (63) 455996477
Web Site: http://www.aderans.com
Sales Range: $400-449.9 Million
Emp.: 1,500
Wigs Mfr
N.A.I.C.S.: 339999
Masao Kaneko *(Gen Mgr)*

Aderans Thai. Ltd. (1)
109 Moo1 Export Processing Zone Banwah Hi-tech Industrial Estate, Amphur Bangpain, 13160, Ayutthaya, Thailand
Tel.: (66) 35 350 540 1
Web Site: http://www.universal-hair.com
Wigs Whslr
N.A.I.C.S.: 424990

Aderans Thai., Ltd. (Buriram Factory) (1)
122 Moo 9 Sai Buriram-Prakonchai Road Tambol I-San Amphur Muang, Bangkok, 31000, Buriram, Thailand
Tel.: (66) 44 613 000
Web Site: http://www.aderans.com

Hair Products Mfr
N.A.I.C.S.: 424990

Bosley Medical (1)
9100 Wilshire Blvd E Tower, Beverly Hills, CA 90212
Tel.: (310) 288-9999
Web Site: http://www.bosley.com
Hair Restoration
N.A.I.C.S.: 423450
Robert D. B. Spurrell *(VP-Sls & Mktg)*

Carl M Lundh AB (1)
Kalendegatan 12, PO Box 30136, 200 61, Malmo, Sweden
Tel.: (46) 40 36 87 20
Web Site: http://www.carlmlundh.se
Hair Care Product Mfr & Sales
N.A.I.C.S.: 339999

Creations de Paris Camaflex Vertriebs GmbH (1)
Ettore Bugatti St 7, 51149, Cologne, Germany (100%)
Tel.: (49) 2203977020
Web Site: http://www.camaflex.de
Sales Range: $25-49.9 Million
Emp.: 30
Sale of Wigs
N.A.I.C.S.: 424990

D. van Nooijen B.V. (1)
Rue Van Hammee 17, 1030, Brussels, Belgium (100%)
Tel.: (32) 2 215 5800
Web Site: http://www.camaflex.be
Sales Range: $1-9.9 Million
Emp.: 25
Retail & Wholesale of Wigs & Hair Extensions
N.A.I.C.S.: 424990

D. van Nooijen B.V. (1)
Eglantierbaan 49, Capelle aan den IJssel, 2908 LV, Netherlands (100%)
Tel.: (31) 22155800
Web Site: http://www.vannooijen.nl
Sales Range: $50-74.9 Million
Emp.: 5
Sale of Women's & Men's Wigs
N.A.I.C.S.: 424990

Hair Club for Men, Ltd., Inc. (1)
1515 S Federal Hwy Ste 401, Boca Raton, FL 33432
Tel.: (561) 361-7600
Web Site: http://www.hairclub.com
Sales Range: $125-149.9 Million,
Emp.: 60
Hair Restoration Services
N.A.I.C.S.: 812199

Subsidiary (Domestic):

Hair Club for Men, LLC (2)
9201 Sunset Blvd Ste 510, Los Angeles, CA 90069
Tel.: (310) 601-4660
Emp.: 20
Beauty Salon Operator
N.A.I.C.S.: 812112
Alexander Gonzales *(Mgr)*

Hair Club for Men, Ltd., Inc. (1)
551 Madison Ave 5th Fl, New York, NY 10022-2049
Tel.: (212) 758-9232
Web Site: http://www.hairclub.com
Sales Range: $50-74.9 Million
Emp.: 50
Hair Restoration Centers Operator
N.A.I.C.S.: 812199
Carlos Sariol *(CEO)*

International Hairgoods Inc. (1)
18684 Lake Dr E, Chanhassen, MN 55317 (100%)
Tel.: (952) 906-9900
Web Site: http://www.internationalhairgoods.com
Sales Range: $25-49.9 Million
Emp.: 23
Mfr & Sales of Wigs
N.A.I.C.S.: 339999
Peter Gensler *(Pres)*

Monfair Moden Vertriebs GmbH (1)
Ettore Bugatti Strasse 7, 51149, Cologne, Germany (100%)
Tel.: (49) 22033697413
Web Site: http://www.camaflex.de

Aderans Co., Ltd.—(Continued)

Sales Range: $10-24.9 Million
Emp.: 100
Sales of Wigs, Hairpieces & Wig-Related
Products
N.A.I.C.S.: 424990

Rene' of Paris (1)
9100 Wilshire Blvd E Tower 9th Fl, Beverly
Hills, CA 90212
Tel.: (818) 908-3100
Web Site: http://www.reneofparis.com
Sales Range: $1-9.9 Million
Emp.: 25
Wig Importing & Designing
N.A.I.C.S.: 424990

Trendco Hair Supplies Co., Ltd (1)
Sheridan House 114/116 Western Road,
Hove, BN3 JDD, United Kingdom
Tel.: (44) 1273 774977
Web Site: http://www.trendco.co.uk
Emp.: 15
Hair Care Products Distr
N.A.I.C.S.: 621999
Lynne Harris (Mng Dir-Brighton)

TressAllure/General Wig (1)
1480 Sw 3rd St Ste 3, Pompano Beach, FL
33069-3225
Tel.: (305) 823-0600
Web Site: http://www.tressallure.com
Sales Range: $50-74.9 Million
Emp.: 100
Mfr of Wigs & Hairpieces
N.A.I.C.S.: 424990

ADES INTERNATIONAL HOLDING PLC

Unit 517 Level 5 Index Tower Dubai
International Financial Centre, Dubai,
507, 118, United Arab Emirates
Tel.: (971) 43550255　　　**AE**
Web Site:
　　http://www.investors.adihgroup.com
Year Founded: 2002
ADES—(LSE)
Rev.: $477,757,547
Assets: $1,431,566,982
Liabilities: $978,842,502
Net Worth: $452,724,480
Earnings: $31,533,562
Emp.: 10
Fiscal Year-end: 12/31/19
Oil & Gas Drilling Services
N.A.I.C.S.: 213111
Ayman Mamdouh Abbas (Chm)

Subsidiaries:

Prime innovations for Trade
S.A.E. (1)
6 Yaquob Attallah St-Haram Rd, 12111,
Cairo, Egypt
Tel.: (20) 1222185820
Web Site: http://www.egyprime.com
Information Technology Services
N.A.I.C.S.: 541511

ADESHWAR MEDITEX LIMITED

Unit No 111 1st Floor Lok Centre Marol Maroshi Road Marol Andheri East,
Mumbai, 400059, Maharashtra, India
Tel.: (91) 2247835180
Web Site:
　　https://www.adeshwarmeditex.com
Year Founded: 1951
543309—(BOM)
Rev.: $8,870,371
Assets: $9,906,051
Liabilities: $5,680,857
Net Worth: $4,225,194
Earnings: $108,231
Emp.: 29
Fiscal Year-end: 03/31/22
Medical Product Mfr & Distr
N.A.I.C.S.: 339113
Siddharth Talati (Chm & Mng Dir)

ADESSO SE

Adessoplatz 1, 44269, Dortmund,
Germany
Tel.: (49) 23170007000
Web Site: https://www.adesso.de
ADN1—(MUN)
Rev.: $1,253,885,933
Assets: $867,619,743
Liabilities: $643,534,133
Not Worth: $224,085,610
Earnings: $3,532,384
Emp.: 9,512
Fiscal Year-end: 12/31/23
Information Technology Services
N.A.I.C.S.: 519290
Volker Gruhn (Co-Founder)

Subsidiaries:

A3a Strategy Consulting GmbH (1)
Agrippinawerft 26, 50678, Cologne, Germany
Tel.: (49) 23170007000
Web Site: http://www.a3a-consulting.com
Business Management Services
N.A.I.C.S.: 541611

ARITHNEA GmbH (1)
Prof-Messerschmitt-Strabe 1, 85579, Neubiberg, Germany
Tel.: (49) 89 244 105 400
Web Site: http://www.arithnea.de
Content Management Services
N.A.I.C.S.: 541513

Adesso Health Solutions GmbH (1)
Tungendorfer Strasse 10, 24536, Neumunster, Germany
Tel.: (49) 432199950
Web Site: http://www.adesso-health.de
Emp.: 70
Computer Software Development Services
N.A.I.C.S.: 541511

**Adesso Insurance Solutions
GmbH** (1)
Adessoplatz 1, 44269, Dortmund, Germany
Tel.: (49) 23170008000
Web Site: https://www.adesso-insure.de
Computer Software Development Services
N.A.I.C.S.: 541511
Werner Breitfuss (Mng Dir)

Adesso Lakes GmbH (1)
Adessoplatz 1, 44269, Dortmund, Germany
Tel.: (49) 1607638929
Web Site: www.adesso-lakes.com
Data Processing & Consulting Services
N.A.I.C.S.: 541511

Adesso Spain Consultoria Y Soluciones Tecnologicas S. L. (1)
Avda Via Augusta 15 25 Arroba Sant Cugat
Business Park, Sant Cugat del Valles,
08173, Barcelona, Spain
Tel.: (34) 931514585
Computer Software Development Services
N.A.I.C.S.: 541511
Alejandro Andres Saez (Mgr-Salesforce Delivery)

**Adesso Turkey Bilgi Teknolojileri Ltd.
Sti.** (1)
Maslak Mahallesi Ahi Evran Cad Olive
Plaza No 11 Kat 9, Sariyer, 34398, Istanbul,
Turkiye
Tel.: (90) 2123462002
Web Site: https://www.adesso.com.tr
Computer Software Development Services
N.A.I.C.S.: 541511
Mutlu Onder (Mgr-Bus Dev)

Adesso U.K. Limited (1)
City Point 1 Ropemaker St Moorgate, London, EC2Y, United Kingdom
Tel.: (44) 7783025546
Information Technology Consulting Services
N.A.I.C.S.: 541512

Adesso as a service GmbH (1)
Adessoplatz 1, 44269, Dortmund, Germany
Tel.: (49) 23170007000
Web Site: http://adesso-service.com
Information Technology Services
N.A.I.C.S.: 541512

Adesso benefit solutions GmbH (1)
Adessoplatz 1, 44269, Dortmund, Germany
Tel.: (49) 23170003344
Web Site: https://adesso-benefit.com

Information Technology Services
N.A.I.C.S.: 541512

Adesso orange Austria GmbH (1)
Wipplingerstrasse 24-26 1 UG/Top IX,
A-1010, Vienna, Austria
Tel.: (43) 6643437881
Digital Transformation Services
N.A.I.C.S.: 518210

Alleato Assekuranzmakler GmbH (1)
Adessoplatz 1, 44269, Dortmund, Germany
Tel.: (49) 23170008300
Web Site: http://www.alleato.eu
Insurance Services
N.A.I.C.S.: 524210

Blue4IT Professionals B.V. (1)
Zoomstede 21a, 3431 HK, Nieuwegein,
Netherlands
Tel.: (31) 885500350
Web Site: https://www.blue4it.nl
Software Development Services
N.A.I.C.S.: 541511

Bluefront B.V. (1)
Zoomstede 21a, 3431 HK, Nieuwegein,
Netherlands
Tel.: (31) 885500360
Web Site: https://www.bluefront.nl
Premium Fronted Development Services
N.A.I.C.S.: 541511

Codesquad B.V. (1)
Zoomstede 21A, 3431 HK, Nieuwegein,
Netherlands
Tel.: (31) 885500370
Web Site: https://www.codesquad.nl
Software Development Services
N.A.I.C.S.: 541511

Com2m GmbH (1)
Adessoplatz 1, 44269, Dortmund, Germany
Tel.: (49) 23170007020
Web Site: https://www.com2m.de
Information Technology Services
N.A.I.C.S.: 541511
Martin Schluter (Head-Sls)

E-spirit Inc. (1)
1 Cranberry Hill Ste 300, Lexington, MA
02421
Tel.: (781) 862-5511
Web Site: http://www.e-spirit.com
Emp.: 150
Digital Technology Services
N.A.I.C.S.: 541511
Michael Gerard (CMO)

E-spirit Schweiz AG (1)
Vulkanstrasse 106, 8048, Zurich, Switzerland
Tel.: (41) 585209800
Digital Technology Services
N.A.I.C.S.: 541519

E-spirit Uk Ltd. (1)
3 Sceptre House Hornbeam Square North,
Harrogate, HG2 8PB, North Yorkshire,
United Kingdom
Tel.: (44) 1622808519
Digital Technology Services
N.A.I.C.S.: 541519

Inqventures GmbH (1)
Rotherstrasse 19, 10245, Berlin, Germany
Tel.: (49) 3072620330
Web Site: http://www.inqventures.com
Information Technology Services
N.A.I.C.S.: 541511
Gregor Schwald (Gen Mgr)

IoT Deutschland GmbH (1)
Koboldstrasse 4, 24118, Kiel, Germany
Tel.: (49) 4312202288
Information Technology Consulting Services
N.A.I.C.S.: 541512

**KIWI Consulting EDV-Beratung
GmbH** (1)
Odenwaldstr 14, 69190, Walldorf, Germany
Tel.: (49) 7134510395
Web Site: https://kiwi-consulting.de
Information Technology Consulting & Software Development Services
N.A.I.C.S.: 541512

LeanNetworking Kft. (1)
Infopark Setany 1i 6 Emelet, 1117, Budapest, Hungary
Tel.: (36) 12312260

Web Site: https://leannet.eu
Cloud Native Computing Services
N.A.I.C.S.: 518210

Material.one AG (1)
Provinostrasse 52, 86153, Augsburg, Germany
Tel.: (49) 8218994960
Supply Chain Management Services
N.A.I.C.S.: 621491

Medgineering GmbH (1)
Stockholmer Allee 24, 44269, Dortmund,
Germany
Tel.: (49) 23170007000
Web Site: http://www.medgineering.de
Information Technology Services
N.A.I.C.S.: 541511
Maximilian Krinninger (Mng Dir)

Percision Services GmbH (1)
Agrippinawerft 26, 50678, Cologne, Germany
Tel.: (49) 22127850555
Web Site: http://www.percision.de
Information Technology Services
N.A.I.C.S.: 541511
Svijetlana Jekic (Acct Mgr-IT)

Reachbird Solutions GmbH (1)
Streitfeldstrasse 25, 81673, Munich, Germany
Tel.: (49) 89411117206
Web Site: https://www.reachbird.io
Internet Marketing Services
N.A.I.C.S.: 541613

adesso Austria GmbH (1)
Modecenterstrasse 17 Object 2 3rd floor A,
1110, Vienna, Austria
Tel.: (43) 1 2198790 0
Web Site: http://www.adesso.at
Sales Range: $25-49.9 Million
Software Development Services
N.A.I.C.S.: 541511

adesso Schweiz AG (1)
Vulkanstrasse 106, 8048, Zurich, Switzerland
Tel.: (41) 585209800
Web Site: http://www.adesso.ch
Software Development Services
N.A.I.C.S.: 541511
Hansjorg Suess (CEO)

adesso mobile solutions GmbH (1)
Adessoplatz 1, 44269, Dortmund, Germany
Tel.: (49) 23199953850
Web Site: http://www.adesso-mobile.de
Mobile Solution Development & Consulting
Services
N.A.I.C.S.: 541618

adesso orange AG (1)
Robert-Henseling-Str. 11, 31789, Hameln,
Germany
Tel.: (49) 5151406669
Web Site: https://www.adesso-orange.com
Emp.: 100
Business Consulting & Services
N.A.I.C.S.: 541611
Olaf Reiter (Mng Partner)

Subsidiary (Non-US):

VITEC Vienna Information Technology Consulting GmbH (2)
Schottengrund 30, 1010, Vienna, Austria
Tel.: (43) 5039020259
Web Site: https://www.viennaitec.com
Management Consulting Services
N.A.I.C.S.: 541618
Johann Grafl (Mng Dir)

e-Spirit AG (1)
Stockholmer Allee 24, 44269, Dortmund,
Germany
Tel.: (49) 231 477 77 0
Web Site: http://www.e-spirit.com
Content Management Services
N.A.I.C.S.: 541513

evu.it GmbH (1)
Freie-Vogel-Str 391, 44269, Dortmund,
Germany
Tel.: (49) 231 930 1155
Web Site: http://www.evu-it.de
Environmental Consulting Services
N.A.I.C.S.: 541620

gadiv GmbH (1)

Bovingen 148, 53804, Much, Germany
Tel.: (49) 2245 9160 0
Web Site: http://www.gadiv.de
Software Development Services
N.A.I.C.S.: 541511

percision GmbH   (1)
Agrippinawerft 28, 50678, Cologne, Germany
Tel.: (49) 22127850555
Web Site: http://www.percision.de
Recruitment Services
N.A.I.C.S.: 561311

ADEUNIS RF
283 Rue Louis Neel, 38920, Crolles, France
Tel.: (33) 476920162
Web Site: https://www.adeunis.com
ALARF—(EUR)
Sales Range: $10-24.9 Million
Wireless Product Mfr
N.A.I.C.S.: 334220
Herve Vincent (CEO)

ADEVINTA ASA
Akersgata 55, Oslo, 0180, Norway
Tel.: (47) 7809 214 347
Web Site: http://www.adevinta.com
Marketing & Advertising Service Provider
N.A.I.C.S.: 541613
Cassandra Lord (Dir-Comm)

ADEX MINING INC.
36 Toronto Street Suite 850, Toronto, M5C 2C5, ON, Canada
Tel.: (647) 243-8452   ON
Web Site:
   https://www.adexmining.com
ADE—(TSXV)
Assets: $1,394,171
Liabilities: $5,284,757
Net Worth: ($3,890,587)
Earnings: $579,692
Fiscal Year-end: 12/31/23
Metal Ore Mining Services
N.A.I.C.S.: 212290
Linda Lam Kwan (CEO)

Subsidiaries:

Adex Minerals Corp.   (1)
Mount Pleasant, PO Box 1106, Saint George, E5C 3S9, NB, Canada
Tel.: (506) 755-3393
Web Site: http://www.adexmining.com
Emp.: 3
Mining Services
N.A.I.C.S.: 212390

ADEX SECURITIES, INC.
1095 W Pender St Ste 900, Vancouver, V6E 2M6, BC, Canada
Tel.: (604) 681-8882
Sales Range: $25-49.9 Million
Emp.: 2
Securities Brokering
N.A.I.C.S.: 523150
Terence Hui (Pres & CEO)

Subsidiaries:

Concord Pacific Group   (1)
9th Floor 1095 W Pender Street, Vancouver, V6E 2M6, BC, Canada
Tel.: (604) 681-8882
Web Site: http://www.concordpacific.com
Sales Range: $25-49.9 Million
Emp.: 35
Urban Residential Real Estate Developer
N.A.I.C.S.: 531210

ADF FOODS LTD.
Marathon Innova B2 G01 on the Ground Floor, Opp Peninsula Corporate Park G K Road Lower Parel, Mumbai, 400 013, India
Tel.: (91) 2261415555
Web Site: https://www.adf-foods.com
Year Founded: 1932

ADFFOODS—(NSE)
Rev.: $58,789,403
Assets: $64,239,466
Liabilities: $17,066,772
Net Worth: $47,172,694
Earnings: $6,623,335
Emp.: 332
Fiscal Year-end: 03/31/22
Indian Foods Production & Marketing Services
N.A.I.C.S.: 311999
Shalaka Ovalekar (Sec & Asst VP-Legal)

Subsidiaries:

Elena's Food Specialties, Inc.   (1)
405 Allerton Ave, South San Francisco, CA 94080-4818
Tel.: (650) 871-8700
Sales Range: $1-9.9 Million
Emp.: 60
Food Mfr
N.A.I.C.S.: 311412

ADF GROUP INC.
300 Henry-Bessemer Street, Terrebonne, J6Y 1T3, QC, Canada
Tel.: (450) 965-1911   Ca
Web Site: https://www.adfgroup.com
Year Founded: 1956
4QM—(DEU)
Rev.: $249,962,088
Assets: $248,136,208
Liabilities: $125,708,602
Net Worth: $122,427,606
Earnings: $28,409,125
Emp.: 550
Fiscal Year-end: 01/31/24
Steel Superstructures & Architectural & Various Other Metals Designer, Engineering, Mfr & Installer
N.A.I.C.S.: 238120
Pierre Paschini (Pres & COO)

Subsidiaries:

ADF International Inc.   (1)
1900 Great Bear Ave, Great Falls, MT 59404
Tel.: (406) 315-3781
Structural Steel Mfr
N.A.I.C.S.: 331221
Christopher Vuckovich (Mgr-Bus Dev)

ADFACTORS PR PVT. LTD.
1st floor Shalaka Maharashi Karve Marg, Cooperage, Mumbai, 400 021, India
Tel.: (91) 22 22813565
Web Site: http://www.adfactorspr.com
Emp.: 250
N.A.I.C.S.: 541810
Arwa Husain (VP)

ADFAST CORP.
2670 rue Paulus, Saint Laurent, H4S 1G1, QC, Canada
Tel.: (514) 337-7307
Web Site: http://www.adfastcorp.com
Year Founded: 1989
Rev.: $20,033,742
Emp.: 150
Construction, Packaging & Engineering Industries
N.A.I.C.S.: 541330
Claude Dandurand (Co-Owner)

ADFONIC LTD.
Level 10 Orion House 5 Upper St Martins Lane, London, WC2H 9EA, United Kingdom
Tel.: (44) 203 021 1250
Web Site: http://www.adfonic.com
Sales Range: $10-24.9 Million
Emp.: 1,000
Mobile Advertising Services
N.A.I.C.S.: 541890
Wesley Biggs (CTO)

Subsidiaries:

Adfonic GmbH   (1)
Ludwigstrasse 8, 80539, Munich, Germany
Tel.: (49) 89 20 60 21 170
Mobile Advertising Services
N.A.I.C.S.: 541890
Albert Pescheck (Gen Mgr)

Adfonic Inc.   (1)
37 W 26th St Ste 317, New York, NY 10010
Tel.: (212) 686-5925
Mobile Advertising Services
N.A.I.C.S.: 541890

ADFORMATIX, INC.
4/F Republic Glass Building 196 Salcedo Street, Legaspi Village, Makati, 1229, Philippines
Tel.: (63) 2 892 2991
Year Founded: 1969
Emp.: 100
N.A.I.C.S.: 541810
Liane E. Vergara (Pres)

ADGAR INVESTMENTS AND DEVELOPMENT LIMITED
35 Efal Street, 49511, Petah Tiqwa, 49511, Israel
Tel.: (972) 39166691
Web Site: https://www.adgar.com
ADGR—(TAE)
Rev.: $96,857,852
Assets: $1,562,273,494
Liabilities: $1,153,414,542
Net Worth: $408,858,952
Earnings: $26,386,241
Fiscal Year-end: 12/31/23
Lessors of Other Real Estate Property
N.A.I.C.S.: 531190
Liat Manor (CFO)

Subsidiaries:

Adgar Canada Inc.   (1)
1 Richmond Street West Suite 900, Toronto, M5H 3W4, ON, Canada
Tel.: (416) 941-9553
Web Site: https://www.adgarcanada.com
Commercial Real Estate Services
N.A.I.C.S.: 531210
Chris G. Tambakis (CEO)

Adgar Poland Sp. z o.o   (1)
Adgar Park West Building B 5th Floor Aleje Jerozolimskie 181B, 02-222, Warsaw, Poland
Tel.: (48) 22 323 8100
Web Site: https://www.adgar.pl
Commercial Real Estate Services
N.A.I.C.S.: 531210
Eyal Litwin (CEO)

Immo Wauters BVBA   (1)
Italielei 124 bus 78, 2000, Antwerp, Belgium
Tel.: (32) 32341263
Commercial Real Estate Services
N.A.I.C.S.: 531210

ADHARSHILA CAPITAL SERVICES LTD.
C/o Uttam Toyota A-11 Meerut Road Industrial Area, Ghaziabad, 201 003, Uttar Pradesh, India
Tel.: (91) 1204193799
Web Site:
   http://www.adharshilacapital.in
539493—(BOM)
Rev.: $22,215
Assets: $5,158,365
Liabilities: $897,749
Net Worth: $4,260,616
Earnings: ($95)
Fiscal Year-end: 03/31/22
Financial Investment Services
N.A.I.C.S.: 523999
Amita Adlakha (Mng Dir)

ADHBHUT INFRASTRUCTURE LIMITED

910 Ansal Bhawan, 16 KG Marg, Delhi, 110 001, India
Tel.: (91) 1123752586
Web Site: https://adhbhutinfra.in
Year Founded: 1985
539189—(BOM)
Sales Range: Less than $1 Million
Real Estate Support Services
N.A.I.C.S.: 531390

ADHERIUM LIMITED
Tel.: (64) 93072771   AU
Web Site: http://www.adherium.com
Year Founded: 2001
ADR—(ASX)
Rev.: $2,083,197
Assets: $8,268,240
Liabilities: $2,260,546
Net Worth: $6,007,694
Earnings: ($6,427,593)
Fiscal Year-end: 06/30/23
Inhaler Mfr & Distr
N.A.I.C.S.: 339112
Rob Turnbull (Co-Sec & Gen Mgr)

Subsidiaries:

Adherium North America, Inc.   (1)
1800 Gateway Dr Ste 150, San Mateo, CA 94404
Tel.: (650) 446-8589
Inhaler Distr
N.A.I.C.S.: 423450

ADHIRAJ DISTRIBUTORS LTD.
76B Mahanirban Road, Kolkata, 700029, India
Tel.: (91) 3322110040   In
Web Site:
   http://www.adhirajdistributors.com
Sales Range: Less than $1 Million
Emp.: 9
Textile Product Trading Services
N.A.I.C.S.: 523160
Srikrishan Churiwala (Mng Dir)

ADI CORPORATION
4F No 2 Lane 235 Bauchiau Road, Shindian City, Taipei, 231, Taiwan
Tel.: (886) 289115123
Web Site: http://www.adi.com.tw
Year Founded: 1979
Sales Range: $50-74.9 Million
Emp.: 32
Mfr, Designer & Marketer of Computer Monitors & Telecommunications Products
N.A.I.C.S.: 334419
James C. Liao (Chm & Pres)

ADI GROUP INC.
385 Wilsey Road Unit 10, Fredericton, E3B 5N6, NB, Canada
Tel.: (506) 451-7433
Year Founded: 1945
Construction & Water Treatment Services
N.A.I.C.S.: 924110

Subsidiaries:

ADI Systems USA Inc.   (1)
5150 Race Ct, Denver, CO 80216
Tel.: (506) 452-7307
Waste Treatment Services
N.A.I.C.S.: 924110

Adi Systems Asia Pacific Limited   (1)
Level 4 229 Moray Place, PO Box 5892, Dunedin, New Zealand
Tel.: (64) 39510240
Waste Treatment Services
N.A.I.C.S.: 924110
Grenville Delfs (Pres)

ADIDAS AG
Adi-Dassler-Strasse 1, 91074, Herzogenaurach, Germany
Tel.: (49) 9132840   De

adidas AG—(Continued)

Web Site: https://www.adidas-group.com
Year Founded: 1949
ADS—(MUN)
Rev.: $23,652,622,490
Assets: $19,891,737,400
Liabilities: $14,836,012,800
Net Worth: $5,055,724,600
Earnings: ($82,790,250)
Emp.: 59,030
Fiscal Year-end: 12/31/23
Sporting & Athletic Goods Mfr
N.A.I.C.S.: 339920
Jan Runau (Chief Corp Comm Officer)

Subsidiaries:

GEV Grundstucksgesellschaft Herzogenaurach mbH & Co. KG **(1)**
Adi-Dassler-Str 1, 91074, Herzogenaurach, Bavaria, Germany
Tel.: (49) 9132 84 4766
Financial Investment Services
N.A.I.C.S.: 523999

Immobilieninvest und Betriebsgesellschaft Herzo-Base GmbH & Co. KG **(1)**
Adi-Dassler-Str 1, 91074, Herzogenaurach, Bavaria, Germany
Tel.: (49) 9132 844089
Real Estate Manangement Services
N.A.I.C.S.: 531390

Immobilieninvest und Betriebsgesellschaft Herzo-Base Verwaltungs GmbH **(1)**
Adi-Dassler-Str 1, Herzogenaurach, 91074, Bayern, Germany
Tel.: (49) 9132844089
Real Estate Investment Services
N.A.I.C.S.: 531390

Life Sport Ltd. **(1)**
6 Hamachtesh, Holon, 58810, Israel
Tel.: (972) 36505300
Sportswear Distr
N.A.I.C.S.: 424350

P.T. adidas Indonesia Ltd. **(1)**
Plaza DM 11th Floor Jl Jenderal Sudirman Kav 25, Jakarta, 12920, Indonesia
Tel.: (62) 2 1520 5566
Sporting & Athletic Goods Distr
N.A.I.C.S.: 423910

SC adidas Ukraine **(1)**
Bud 15/15 Vul Vikentiya Khvoiky, Kiev, 01021, Ukraine
Tel.: (380) 444902830
Web Site: http://www.adidas.ro
Sporting Goods Distr
N.A.I.C.S.: 423910

Taylor Made Korea Ltd. **(1)**
Seocho 2-dong 1321-15 Samsung Life Seocho Tower 8th Floor, Seoul, Korea (South)
Tel.: (82) 2 2186 0800
Web Site: http://korea.taylormadegolf.com
Sporting Goods Distr
N.A.I.C.S.: 423910

Textronics, Inc. **(1)**
4 Hillman Dr Ste 130, Chadds Ford, PA 19317
Tel.: (302) 351-5152
Web Site: http://www.textronicsinc.com
Wearable Sports Electronics Mfr
N.A.I.C.S.: 339920

adidas (China) Ltd. **(1)**
Xujiahui Two Itc No 160 Gongcheng Road, Shanghai, 200030, China
Tel.: (86) 2125255000
Web Site: http://www.adidas.com
Sporting & Athletic Products Mfr & Distr
N.A.I.C.S.: 339920

adidas (Cyprus) Limited **(1)**
140 Athalassis Ave, Nicosia, 2024, Strovolos, Cyprus
Tel.: (357) 22519701
Web Site: http://www.adidas.com
Sales Range: $50-74.9 Million
Emp.: 7
Sporting & Athletic Goods Distr

adidas (Ireland) Ltd. **(1)**
Unit C1 Nangor Road Business Park Nangor Road, Clondalkin, Dublin, 662860, Ireland **(100%)**
Tel.: (353) 818294003
Web Site: https://www.adidas.ie
Sales Range: $25-49.9 Million
Emp.: 9
Sporting Goods Distributor
N.A.I.C.S.: 459110

Subsidiary (Domestic):

Reebok Ireland Limited **(2)**
Unit 10 Leopardstown Office Park, Foxrock, Dublin, 18, Ireland
Tel.: (353) 1294 35 50
Web Site: http://www.reebok.com
Sales Range: $25-49.9 Million
Emp.: 4
Sporting Goods Distr
N.A.I.C.S.: 423910

adidas (Malaysia) Sdn. Bhd. **(1)**
19-1 The Bousteador No 10 Jalan PJU 7/6, Mutiara Damansara, 47800, Petaling Jaya, Selangor, Malaysia
Tel.: (60) 340656996
Web Site: https://www.adidas.com.my
Sporting & Athletic Goods Distr
N.A.I.C.S.: 423910

adidas (South Africa) (Pty) Ltd. **(1)**
3rd Floor-Unit 2C Black River Park Fir Road Observatory, Cape Town, 7925, South Africa
Tel.: (27) 214426200
Web Site: https://www.adidas.com
Sales Range: $75-99.9 Million
Emp.: 15
Sporting & Athletic Goods Distr
N.A.I.C.S.: 423910

adidas (Suzhou) Co. Ltd. **(1)**
3/f C No 5 Xinghan Street Industrial Park, Suzhou, 215021, Jiangsu, China
Tel.: (86) 51267611502
Sporting & Athletic Goods Distr
N.A.I.C.S.: 423910

adidas (Thailand) Co., Ltd. **(1)**
22nd Floor CRC Tower All Seasons Place 87/2 Wireless Road Lumpini, Patumwan, Bangkok, 10330, Thailand
Tel.: (66) 20268196
Web Site: https://www.adidas.co.th
Sporting & Athletic Goods Distr
N.A.I.C.S.: 423910

adidas (UK) Ltd. **(1)**
The Adidas Ctr Pepper Rd, Hazel Grove, Stockport, SK7 5SD, United Kingdom
Tel.: (44) 8702404204
Web Site: http://www.adidas.co.uk
Sales Range: $150-199.9 Million
Emp.: 450
Sporting & Athletic Goods Distr
N.A.I.C.S.: 423910

adidas America, Inc. **(1)**
adidas Vlg 5055 N Greeley Ave, Portland, OR 97217 **(100%)**
Tel.: (971) 234-2300
Web Site: http://www.adidas.com
Sales Range: $1-4.9 Billion
Emp.: 1,200
Holding Company; Regional Managing Office
N.A.I.C.S.: 551112
Chris Murphy (Dir-Comm)

Subsidiary (Domestic):

Sports Licensed Division of the adidas Group, LLC **(2)**
1895 J W Foster Blvd, Canton, MA 02021-1099
Tel.: (781) 401-5000
Web Site: http://www.reeebok.com
Sales Range: $450-499.9 Million
Emp.: 1,200
Sporting & Athletic Goods Distr
N.A.I.C.S.: 423910
John Warren (Gen Mgr)

Stone Age Equipment, Inc. **(2)**
1419 W State St, Redlands, CA 92373-8164
Tel.: (909) 798-4222

Web Site: http://www.fiveten.com
Sales Range: $25-49.9 Million
Emp.: 37
Footwear Retailer
N.A.I.C.S.: 424340
Valley Parker (CEO)

Subsidiary (Non-US):

Five Ten Europe NV/SA **(3)**
Avenue Lavoisier 13, 1300, Wavre, Belgium
Tel.: (32) 10 23 23 50
Web Site: http://www.fiveteneurope.be
Sporting Goods Distr
N.A.I.C.S.: 423910

Subsidiary (Domestic):

Tee Off, LLC **(2)**
16 Downing Dr, Phenix City, AL 36869-3341
Tel.: (334) 291-5151
Sporting Goods Distr
N.A.I.C.S.: 423910

adidas Team, Inc. **(2)**
951 32nd Ave SW, Cedar Rapids, IA 52404-3905
Tel.: (319) 368-0338
Web Site: http://www.adidas-group.com
Emp.: 170
Sporting Goods Distr
N.A.I.C.S.: 423910

adidas Argentina S.A. **(1)**
Cuyo 3532/3512-Edificio III-Martinez, San Isidro, Buenos Aires, Argentina
Tel.: (54) 1168420923
Web Site: https://www.adidas.com.ar
Emp.: 120
Sporting Equipment & Accessories Distr
N.A.I.C.S.: 423910

adidas Australia Pty. Limited **(1)**
Level 1 37 Dunlop Road, Mulgrave, 3170, VIC, Australia
Tel.: (61) 61272569046
Web Site: https://www.adidas.com.au
Sales Range: $75-99.9 Million
Emp.: 200
Sporting & Athletic Goods Distr
N.A.I.C.S.: 423910

adidas Austria GmbH **(1)**
Adi-Dassler-Gasse 6, 9073, Viktring, Klagenfurt, Austria **(100%)**
Tel.: (43) 206092926
Web Site: https://www.adidas.at
Sales Range: $25-49.9 Million
Emp.: 50
Marketer & Retailer of Sporting & Athletic Goods
N.A.I.C.S.: 423910

Subsidiary (Non-US):

LLC adidas, Ltd. **(2)**
Krylatskaya St 15, Moscow, 121614, Russia
Tel.: (7) 4956516555
Web Site: https://www.adidas.ru
Emp.: 600
Sporting Goods Distr
N.A.I.C.S.: 423910

adidas Baltics SIA **(1)**
Toma St 4 Ste 100, Riga, 1003, Latvia
Tel.: (371) 67359400
Sales Range: $50-74.9 Million
Emp.: 8
Sporting & Athletic Goods Distr
N.A.I.C.S.: 423910

adidas Belgium N.V. **(1)**
Atomiumsquare 1, BP 320, 1020, Brussels, Belgium
Tel.: (32) 24 77 19 89
Web Site: http://www.adidas.com
Sports Goods Mfr & Distr
N.A.I.C.S.: 339920

adidas Benelux B.V. **(1)**
Plesmanstraat 1, Leusden, 3833 LA, Netherlands
Tel.: (31) 334963301
Web Site: http://www.adidas.com
Sales Range: $50-74.9 Million
Emp.: 70
Sporting Goods Distr
N.A.I.C.S.: 423910

adidas Beteiligungsgesellschaft mbH **(1)**

Adi-Dassler-Str 1, 91074, Herzogenaurach, Germany
Tel.: (49) 9132 840
Web Site: http://www.adidas-group.com
Financial Management Services
N.A.I.C.S.: 523999

Subsidiary (Non-US):

adidas Sports (China) Co. Ltd. **(2)**
Xujiahui TWO ITC No 160 Gongcheng Road, Xuhui District, Shanghai, 200030, China
Tel.: (86) 2125255000
Web Site: https://www.adidas.com.cn
Athletic & Sports Product Mfr & Distr
N.A.I.C.S.: 339920

adidas Budapest Kft. **(1)**
Ratrium 45 G Bldg, PO Box 79, 1334, Budapest, Hungary **(100%)**
Tel.: (36) 14511400
Web Site: http://www.adidas.com
Sales Range: $50-74.9 Million
Emp.: 95
Marketer & Retailer of Sporting & Athletic Goods
N.A.I.C.S.: 423910

adidas Bulgaria EAD **(1)**
Sredets Distr 5 Vitosha, Sofia, 1000, Bulgaria
Tel.: (359) 28114200
Sales Range: $25-49.9 Million
Emp.: 23
Sporting & Athletic Goods Distr
N.A.I.C.S.: 423910

adidas CDC Immobilieninvest GmbH **(1)**
Tel.: (49) 9132840
Web Site: http://www.adidas.com
Financial Investment Services
N.A.I.C.S.: 523999

adidas CR s.r.o. **(1)**
Pekarsa 16, Jinonice, 155 00, Prague, Czech Republic **(100%)**
Tel.: (420) 228883158
Web Site: https://www.adidas.cz
Sales Range: $25-49.9 Million
Emp.: 35
Marketer & Retailer of Sporting & Athletic Goods
N.A.I.C.S.: 423910

adidas Chile Ltda. **(1)**
Av Las Condes 13033, Las Condes, Santiago, Chile
Tel.: (56) 2 431 3800
Web Site: http://www.adidas.com
Sales Range: $250-299.9 Million
Emp.: 650
Sporting Goods Distr
N.A.I.C.S.: 423910

adidas Colombia Ltda. **(1)**
Av-Cll 100 19-54 piso 8, Edificio Prime Tower, Bogota, DC, Colombia
Tel.: (57) 6013557233
Web Site: https://www.adidas.co
Sporting Equipment & Accessories Distr
N.A.I.C.S.: 423910

adidas Croatia d.o.o. **(1)**
Oreskoviceva 6H, Zagreb, 10000, Croatia
Tel.: (385) 15630700
Web Site: http://www.adidas.com
Sporting & Athletic Goods Distr
N.A.I.C.S.: 423910

adidas Danmark A/S **(1)**
Oster Alle 56 2 sal, 2100, Copenhagen, Denmark
Tel.: (45) 47372561
Web Site: http://www.adidas.dk
Sporting And Recreation Goods
N.A.I.C.S.: 423910

adidas Emerging Market L.L.C. **(1)**
9th Floor Easa Saleh Al Gurg Tower Baniyas Road, PO Box 32512, Dubai, United Arab Emirates
Tel.: (971) 4 2273033
Sales Range: $75-99.9 Million
Emp.: 115
Sporting & Athletic Goods Distr
N.A.I.C.S.: 423910
Osman Ayaz (Gen Mgr)

adidas Emerging Markets FZE **(1)**

Building 2 Level 4, Box 32512, Dubai Design District, Dubai, United Arab Emirates
Tel.: (971) 600575226
Web Site: http://www.adidas.com
Sales Range: $150-199.9 Million
Emp.: 100
Sport Equipment Distr
N.A.I.C.S.: 423910

Subsidiary (Non-US):

adidas Levant Limited (2)
Arar Mustafa Wahbi Al Tal St, Amman, Jordan
Tel.: (962) 6 5602383
Emp.: 16
Sporting Goods Distr
N.A.I.C.S.: 423910

adidas Espana S.A. (1)
Avenida Maria Zambrano 31 Edificio WTC - Torre Este 6a Planta, Zaragoza, 50018, Spain
Tel.: (34) 976 710 100
Web Site: http://www.adidas.com
Emp.: 100
Sporting Athletic Goods Mfr & Distr
N.A.I.C.S.: 339920

adidas Espana S.A.U. (1)
Avenida Maria Zambrano 31 WTC Torre Este Building 4th floor, 50018, Zaragoza, Spain
Tel.: (34) 919030052
Web Site: https://www.adidas.es
Sales Range: $25-49.9 Million
Emp.: 1,100
Sporting & Athletic Goods Marketer & Retailer
N.A.I.C.S.: 423910

adidas Finance Spain S.A. (1)
Calle Maria Zambrano Ed Wtc Torre Este 31, Zaragoza, 50018, Spain
Tel.: (34) 902311000
Financial Management Services
N.A.I.C.S.: 523999

adidas France S.a.r.l. (1)
1 Allee des Orcades, PO Box 80067, 67000, Strasbourg, France
Tel.: (33) 388878800
Web Site: http://www.adidas.fr
Emp.: 200
Sporting Goods Distr
N.A.I.C.S.: 423910
Guillaume De Monplanet *(Gen Mgr)*

adidas Hellas A.E. (1)
38-40 26th Oktovriou, Thessaloniki, 54627, Greece
Tel.: (30) 2310505399
Web Site: http://www.adidas.com
Sporting & Athletic Goods Distr
N.A.I.C.S.: 423910

adidas Hong Kong Ltd. (1)
18Fl Aia Kowloon Tower Landmark East Ste100, Howming St Kundong, Kowloon, China (Hong Kong) **(100%)**
Tel.: (852) 21493888
Web Site: http://www.adidas.com.hk
Sales Range: $50-74.9 Million
Emp.: 100
Sales & Marketing of Sporting & Athletic Goods
N.A.I.C.S.: 423910
Adrian Siu *(Gen Mgr-Hong Kong)*

adidas India Private Ltd. (1)
Unitech Commercial Tower-II 5th Floor Sector-45 Block-B, Greenwood City, Gurgaon, 122001, India
Tel.: (91) 124 4569100
Web Site: http://www.adidas.co.in
Emp.: 250
Sportswear & Equipment Distr
N.A.I.C.S.: 423910

adidas Industrial, S.A. de C.V. (1)
Blvd Adolfo Ruiz Cortinez No 3642 Piso 11 Jardines Del Pedregal, Colonia Jaedines del Pedregal, 1900, Mexico, Mexico
Tel.: (52) 50914712
Web Site: http://www.adidas.mx
Sporting Goods Mfr & Distr
N.A.I.C.S.: 339920

adidas Insurance & Risk Consultants GmbH (1)
Adi-Dassler-Str 1, 91074, Herzogenaurach, Germany
Tel.: (49) 9132840
General Insurance Services
N.A.I.C.S.: 524210

adidas International B.V. (1)
Atlas Arena Offices Africa Building Hoogoorddreef 9-A, Zuidoost, 1101 BA, Amsterdam, Netherlands
Tel.: (31) 205734573
Sports Equipment Mfr
N.A.I.C.S.: 339920

adidas International Finance B.V. (1)
Hoogoorddreef 9a, Zuidoost, 1101 BA, Amsterdam, Netherlands
Tel.: (31) 205734573
Web Site: http://www.adidas.com
Emp.: 450
Financial Management Services
N.A.I.C.S.: 523999

adidas International Marketing B.V. (1)
Atlas Arena Offices Africa Building Hoogoorddreef 9-A, Zuidoost, 1101 BA, Amsterdam, Netherlands
Tel.: (31) 205734573
Web Site: http://www.adidasgroup.com
Sporting & Athletic Goods Whslr
N.A.I.C.S.: 423910

adidas International Trading B.V. (1)
Hoogoorddreef 9a, Zuidoost, 1102 BA, Amsterdam, Netherlands
Tel.: (31) 205734573
Web Site: http://www.adidas.com
Sales Range: $25-49.9 Million
Emp.: 50
Sports Goods Whslr
N.A.I.C.S.: 423910

adidas Israel Ltd. (1)
8 HaMlakha Street, Holon, 58810, Israel
Tel.: (972) 36505300
Sporting & Athletic Goods Distr
N.A.I.C.S.: 423910

adidas Italy S.p.A (1)
Via Monte San Primo 1, 20900, Monza, Italy
Tel.: (39) 0399300580
Web Site: https://www.adidas.it
Sporting Athletic Goods Mfr & Distr
N.A.I.C.S.: 339920

adidas Japan K.K. (1)
1-9-10 Roppongi, Minato-ku, Tokyo, 106-0032, Japan
Tel.: (81) 570033033
Web Site: https://shop.adidas.jp
Sporting & Athletic Goods Distr
N.A.I.C.S.: 423910

adidas Korea Ltd. (1)
23rd Floor Seocho Tower Samsunglife 4 Seocho Daero 74-Gil Seocho, Seocho-gu, Seoul, 6620, Korea (South)
Tel.: (82) 15888241
Web Site: http://www.adidas.com
Sporting & Athletic Goods Mfr & Distr
N.A.I.C.S.: 339920

adidas Latin America, S.A. (1)
Business Park Ave Principal y Ave La Rotonda Torre Sur-4th floor, Costa del Este, Panama, Panama
Tel.: (507) 3035700
Sporting Goods & Accessories Distr
N.A.I.C.S.: 423910

adidas New Zealand Limited (1)
adidas House Building C Level 1 600 Great South Rd, Greenlane, Auckland, New Zealand
Tel.: (64) 32889425
Web Site: https://www.adidas.co.nz
Sales Range: $50-74.9 Million
Emp.: 150
Sporting & Athletic Goods Mfr
N.A.I.C.S.: 339920

adidas Norge A/S (1)
Sommerrovn 5, 2816, Gjovik, Norway **(100%)**
Tel.: (47) 61136500
Web Site: http://www.adidas.com
Sales Range: $25-49.9 Million
Emp.: 40

Marketer & Retailer of Sporting & Athletic Goods
N.A.I.C.S.: 423910

Subsidiary (Domestic):

Reebok-CCM Hockey AS (2)
Pancoveien 26, Gressvik, 1624, Norway
Tel.: (47) 69364555
Emp.: 2
Sporting Equipment Whslr
N.A.I.C.S.: 423910
Janne Hemo *(Gen Mgr)*

adidas North America, Inc. (1)
5055 N Greeley Ave, Portland, OR 97217
Tel.: (971) 234-2300
Web Site: http://www.adidas.com
Sporting Goods Distr
N.A.I.C.S.: 423910

adidas Poland Sp. z. o. o. (1)
Olbrachta 94, 01 102, Warsaw, Poland **(100%)**
Tel.: (48) 225331800
Web Site: http://www.adidas.com
Sales Range: $50-74.9 Million
Emp.: 60
Marketer & Retailer of Sporting & Athletic Goods
N.A.I.C.S.: 423910

adidas Romania S.R.L. (1)
42-44 Sos 2nd Floor Building A, Bucharest, Romania
Tel.: (40) 213067900
Web Site: http://www.adidas.com
Sales Range: $25-49.9 Million
Emp.: 20
Sporting & Athletic Goods Distr
N.A.I.C.S.: 423910

adidas Sarragan France S.A.R.L. (1)
Rte De Saessolsheim, PO Box 67, 67702, Landersheim, Saverne Cedex, France **(100%)**
Tel.: (33) 388878800
Web Site: http://www.adidas.com
Sales Range: $250-299.9 Million
Emp.: 1,000
Sales & Marketing of Sporting & Athletic Goods
N.A.I.C.S.: 423910

adidas Serbia d.o.o. (1)
Milutina Milankovica 11a, Belgrade, 11070, Serbia
Tel.: (381) 11 285 49 00
Sales Range: $25-49.9 Million
Emp.: 25
Sporting & Athletic Goods Distr
N.A.I.C.S.: 423910
Steven Baker *(Gen Mgr)*

adidas Services Limited (1)
10/F City Plaza Ph 4 12 Taikoo Wan Rd, Taikoo Shing, China (Hong Kong)
Tel.: (852) 23028888
Business Support Services
N.A.I.C.S.: 561499

adidas Singapore Pte. Ltd. (1)
109 North Bridge Road 09-21, Singapore, 179097, Singapore
Tel.: (65) 64075478
Web Site: https://www.adidas.com.sg
Emp.: 100
Sporting & Athletic Goods Distr
N.A.I.C.S.: 423910

adidas Slovakia s.r.o. (1)
Galvaniho 15/A, 821 04, Bratislava, Slovakia
Tel.: (421) 268623057
Web Site: https://www.adidas.sk
Sales Range: $50-74.9 Million
Emp.: 90
Sporting & Athletic Goods Distr
N.A.I.C.S.: 423910

adidas Sourcing Limited (1)
10/F Cityplaza Four 10th floor 12 Taikoo Wan Road, Island East, Taikoo Shing, China (Hong Kong)
Tel.: (852) 23028888
Web Site: http://www.adidasgroup.com
Sporting & Athletic Goods Distr
N.A.I.C.S.: 423910

Subsidiary (Non-US):

adidas Korea Technical Services Ltd. (2)

609-809 83 - 8 Geumsa-dong, Geumjeong-gu, Pusan, 609-809, Korea (South)
Tel.: (82) 515201100
Footwear Mfr
N.A.I.C.S.: 316210

adidas Spor Malzemeleri Satis ve Pazarlama A.S. (1)
Ronesans Biz Plaza Mecidiyekoy Mah Oguz St No 4, Sisli, 34387, Istanbul, Turkiye
Tel.: (90) 2123553600
Web Site: https://www.adidas.com.tr
Sporting & Athletic Goods Distr
N.A.I.C.S.: 423810

adidas Sport GmbH (1)
Brunnmatt 20, 6330, Cham, Switzerland
Tel.: (41) 715880237
Web Site: https://www.adidas.ch
Sales Range: $25-49.9 Million
Emp.: 50
Marketer & Retailer of Sporting & Athletic Goods
N.A.I.C.S.: 423910

adidas Suomi Oy (1)
Porkkalankatu 13 J, 00180, Helsinki, Finland
Tel.: (358) 753252139
Web Site: https://www.adidas.fi
Sales Range: $25-49.9 Million
Emp.: 16
Sporting Goods Distr
N.A.I.C.S.: 423910

adidas Sverige AB (1)
Gardsvagen 13, 169 07, Solna, Sweden **(100%)**
Tel.: (46) 859929100
Web Site: http://www.adidas.se
Sales Range: $75-99.9 Million
Emp.: 150
Marketer & Retailer of Sporting & Athletic Goods
N.A.I.C.S.: 423910
Ian Brown *(Dir-Sales)*

Subsidiary (Domestic):

Reebok-CCM Hockey AB (2)
Vastra Industrigatan 10, Malung, 782 33, Dalarna, Sweden
Tel.: (46) 28044400
Sports Goods Mfr
N.A.I.C.S.: 339920

adidas Taiwan Limited (1)
13f 2 Min Chuan E Rd Sec 3, Taipei, 10477, Taiwan
Tel.: (886) 225095900
Web Site: http://www.adidas.com
Sporting & Athletic Goods Mfr & Distr
N.A.I.C.S.: 339920

adidas Trefoil Trading (U.K.) Limited (1)
The Adidas Centre Pepper Road, Stockport, SK7 5SA, United Kingdom
Tel.: (44) 1614 192500
Web Site: http://www.adidas.com
Sales Range: $150-199.9 Million
Emp.: 500
Clothing & Footwear Whslr
N.A.I.C.S.: 424340

adidas Trgovina d.o.o. (1)
Letaliska 29 C, 1000, Ljubljana, Slovenia
Tel.: (386) 51368891
Sales Range: $50-74.9 Million
Emp.: 7
Sporting & Athletic Goods Distr
N.A.I.C.S.: 423910

adidas de Mexico S.A. de C.V. (1)
Insurgentes Sur 2475 Floor 11 Loreto Neighborhood Colony, Alvaro Obregon, 1090, Mexico, Mexico
Tel.: (52) 44401442
Web Site: https://www.adidas.mx
Sales Range: $75-99.9 Million
Emp.: 200
Sales & Marketing of Sporting & Athletic Goods
N.A.I.C.S.: 423910

adidas do Brasil Ltda. (1)
Rua Pataxos n 241 Galpao 1 Bairro Jardim Magali, Embu, 06833-073, Sao Paulo, Brazil **(100%)**

adidas AG—(Continued)

Tel.: (55) 1155463700
Web Site: https://www.adidas.com.br
Sales Range: $75-99.9 Million
Emp.: 140
Sales & Marketing of Sporting & Athletic Goods
N.A.I.C.S.: 423910

ADIENT PLC

3 Dublin Landings North Wall Quay
IFSC, Dublin, D01 H104, Ireland
Tel.: (353) 7342545000   IE
Web Site: https://www.adient.com
Year Founded: 2016
ADNT—(NYSE)
Rev.: $15,395,000,000
Assets: $9,424,000,000
Liabilities: $6,878,000,000
Net Worth: $2,546,000,000
Earnings: $205,000,000
Emp.: 70,000
Fiscal Year-end: 09/30/23
Automotive Seat Mfr
N.A.I.C.S.: 336360
Mark A. Oswald *(CFO & Exec VP)*

Subsidiaries:

Adient (Thailand) Co., Ltd.   (1)
64/65 Moo 5 Eatern, Seaboard Industrial Estate T Pluakdaeng, Rayong, Thailand
Tel.: (66) 38656000
Automotive Seating Product Mfr
N.A.I.C.S.: 336360

Adient Automotive Argentina
S.R.L.   (1)
Pueblo Esther, Santa Fe, S2129BYA, Argentina
Tel.: (54) 34149891900
Automotive Seating Product Mfr
N.A.I.C.S.: 336360

Adient Automotive Romania
S.R.L.   (1)
Conului Street no 3, Prahova, 100213, Ploiesti, Romania
Tel.: (40) 372447914
Emp.: 1,800
Automotive Seating Product Mfr
N.A.I.C.S.: 336360

Adient Belgium BVBA   (1)
Paul Christiaenstraat 1, 9960, Assenede, Belgium
Tel.: (32) 93418700
Automotive Seating Product Mfr
N.A.I.C.S.: 336360

Adient Bor s.r.o.   (1)
Nova Hospoda 29 Hall F, Prumyslova zona Bór, 348 02, Plzen, Czech Republic
Tel.: (420) 800888900
Automotive Seating Product Mfr
N.A.I.C.S.: 336360

Adient Clanton Inc.   (1)
2541 7th St S, Clanton, AL 35045
Tel.: (205) 280-7903
Automotive Seating Product Mfr
N.A.I.C.S.: 336360

Adient Eldon Inc.   (1)
1101 E 8th St, Eldon, MO 65026
Tel.: (573) 392-2702
Automotive Seating Product Mfr
N.A.I.C.S.: 336360

Adient India Private Limited   (1)
India Tech Center ICC - Devi Gaurav Tech Park 501 - 5th Floor and 601, 6th Floor South Wing S No 191 & 192 Part Sub Plot B Mumbai-Pune Road, Pune, 411 018, Maharashtra, India
Tel.: (91) 2066757777
Automotive Seating Product Mfr
N.A.I.C.S.: 336360

Adient Ltd. & Co. KG.   (1)
Industriestrasse 20-30, 51399, Burscheid, Germany
Tel.: (49) 2174650
Emp.: 1,400
Automotive Seating Product Mfr
N.A.I.C.S.: 336360

Adient Novo mesto, proizvodnja avto-
mobilskih sedezev, d.o.o.   (1)
Kandijska cesta 60, 8000, Novo Mesto, Slovenia
Tel.: (386) 76200333
Automotive Seating Product Mfr
N.A.I.C.S.: 336360

Adient Poland Sp. z o.o.   (1)
ul Zachodnia 78, 66-200, Swiebodzin, Poland
Tel.: (48) 683820433
Automotive Seating Product Mfr
N.A.I.C.S.: 336360

Adient Saarlouis Ltd. & Co. KG.   (1)
Halle Mitte, Ford Industrial Supplier Park, 66740, Saarlouis, Germany
Tel.: (49) 6831950110
Automotive Seating Product Mfr
N.A.I.C.S.: 336360

Adient Seating Canada LP.   (1)
100 Townline Road, Tillsonburg, N4G 2R7, ON, Canada
Tel.: (519) 842-5971
Emp.: 200
Automotive Seating Product Mfr
N.A.I.C.S.: 336360

Adient Seating d.o.o.   (1)
JIT plant Oktobarskih zrtava bb, 34202, Kragujevac, Serbia
Tel.: (381) 34503202
Automotive Seating Product Mfr
N.A.I.C.S.: 336360

Adient South Africa (Pty) Ltd.   (1)
20 Bennett Street, Neave Industrial, Port Elizabeth, 6001, Eastern Cape, South Africa
Tel.: (27) 419954400
Automotive Seating Product Mfr
N.A.I.C.S.: 336360

Adient Sweden AB   (1)
Hamneviksvagen 101, 41879, Gothenburg, Sweden
Tel.: (46) 317996400
Automotive Seating Product Mfr
N.A.I.C.S.: 336360

Beijing Adient Automotive Compo-
nents Co., Ltd.   (1)
No 1 Linhe South Road, Linhe Industry Development Zone Shunyi, Beijing, 101300, China
Tel.: (86) 1089407755
Automotive Seating Product Mfr
N.A.I.C.S.: 336360

Hoover Universal, Inc.   (1)
49200 Halyard Dr, Plymouth, MI 48170
Tel.: (734) 254-5000
Web Site: http://www.adient.com
Automotive Seating & Interior Components Designer & Mfr
N.A.I.C.S.: 336360

Subsidiary (Domestic):

Adient US LLC   (2)
49200 Halyard Dr, Plymouth, MI 48170
Tel.: (734) 254-5000
Web Site: http://www.adient.com
Automotive Interior Product Mfr
N.A.I.C.S.: 336360

Joint Venture (Domestic):

Intertec Systems, LLC   (2)
45000 Helm St, Plymouth, MI 48170
Tel.: (248) 254-3300
Automotive Instrument Panels & Systems Mfr
N.A.I.C.S.: 336390

Subsidiary (Non-US):

Johnson Controls Automotive Sys-
tems KK   (2)
771 Kozono, Ayase, 252 1121, Kanagawa, Japan
Tel.: (81) 467700511
Web Site: http://www.johnsoncontrols.com
Sales Range: $125-149.9 Million
Emp.: 400
Motor Vehicle Seat & Interior Parts Mfr
N.A.I.C.S.: 336360

Plant (Domestic):

Johnson Controls, Inc. - Murfreesboro
Plant   (2)

1501 Molloy Ln, Murfreesboro, TN 37130
Tel.: (615) 890-5559
Web Site: http://www.adient.com
Automobile Seating Mfr
N.A.I.C.S.: 336360

RECARO Automotive Seating
GmbH   (1)
Stuttgarter Strasse 73, 73230, Kirchheim unter Teck, Germany
Tel.: (49) 7021 9350 00
Web Site: http://www.recaro-automotive.com
Emp.: 1,000
Automotive Seating Component Mfr
N.A.I.C.S.: 336360
Cathleen Ann Ebacher *(Mng Dir)*

Subsidiary (US):

RECARO North America, Inc.   (2)
4120 Luella Ln, Auburn Hills, MI 48326
Tel.: (248) 364-3818
Web Site: http://www.recaro-automotive.com
Automotive Commercial Components & Seats Mfr
N.A.I.C.S.: 336360

TechnoTrim de Mexico, S. de R.L. de
C.V.   (1)
Blvd Fco I Madero 2973 Colonia Fco I Madero, 25120, Saltillo, Coahuila, Mexico
Tel.: (52) 8444383100
Automotive Seating Product Mfr
N.A.I.C.S.: 336360

ADIKA STYLE LTD.

3 Yona Kremnitzky Street, Tel Aviv, Israel
Tel.: (972) 38001000
ADKA—(TAE)
Rev.: $67,572,878
Assets: $59,207,469
Liabilities: $43,166,317
Net Worth: $16,041,153
Earnings: $1,355,420
Fiscal Year-end: 12/31/20
Clothing Apparel & Accessory Retailer
N.A.I.C.S.: 458110

ADIL BEY HOLDING A.S.

Burhaniye mah Kisikli No 65, Uskudar, 34676, Istanbul, Turkiye
Tel.: (90) 2165569000
Web Site: http://www.adilbeyholding.com.tr
Holding Services
N.A.I.C.S.: 551112

Subsidiaries:

Dogan Sirketler Grubu Holding
A.S.   (1)
Burhaniye Mahallesi Kisikli Caddesi No 65, Uskudar, 34676, Istanbul, Türkiye   (52%)
Tel.: (90) 2165569000
Web Site: https://www.doganholding.com.tr
Rev.: $1,416,873,871
Assets: $1,304,429,986
Liabilities: $578,440,642
Net Worth: $725,989,344
Earnings: $185,770,413
Emp.: 8,335
Fiscal Year-end: 12/31/2022
Energy Distribution, Insurance, Media, Industry, Trade & Tourism
N.A.I.C.S.: 221122
Hanzade V. Dogan Boyner *(Vice Chm)*

Subsidiary (Non-US):

Celik Halat ve Tel Sanayii AS   (2)
Tel.: (90) 2623711280
Web Site: https://www.celikhalat.com.tr
Rev.: $43,923,516
Assets: $21,868,764
Liabilities: $21,018,222
Net Worth: $850,542
Earnings: $281,850
Fiscal Year-end: 12/31/2022
Mineral Exploration Services
N.A.I.C.S.: 213114
Selim Baybas *(Chm)*

Subsidiary (Domestic):

Dogan Gazetecilik A.S.   (2)

Kustepe Mah Mecidiyekoy Yolu Trump Towers Kule 2 Kat 9 No 12, Mecidiyekoy, Istanbul, 34387, Turkiye
Tel.: (91) 212 505 61 11
Newspaper Publishing Services
N.A.I.C.S.: 513110

Doruk Finansman A.S.   (2)
Kule 12 Kat Kustepe Mahallesi Mecidiyekoy Yolu Cad No 12, Trump Towers 2 Sisli, 34387 Istanbul, Turkiye   (97%)
Tel.: (90) 2123568900
Web Site: http://www.dorukfinansman.com.tr
Financial Consulting Services
N.A.I.C.S.: 541611

Hurriyet Gazetecilik ve Matbaacilik
A.S.   (2)
Demiroren Medya Center 100 Yl Mah 2264 . Sokak No1, 34218, Istanbul, Turkiye
Tel.: (90) 2126770000
Web Site: https://www.hurriyetkurumsal.com
Rev.: $14,990,340
Assets: $85,826,301
Liabilities: $29,124,454
Net Worth: $56,701,846
Earnings: $3,637,659
Emp.: 1,233
Fiscal Year-end: 12/31/2022
Newspaper Publishing Services
N.A.I.C.S.: 513110
Meltem Oktay *(Vice Chm)*

Milpa Ticari Ve Sinai Urunler Pazar-
lama Sanayi Ve Ticaret A.S.   (2)
Ali Dede Cad Acibadem Mah No 4/1, Kadikoy, Istanbul, Turkiye
Tel.: (90) 216 3399739
Web Site: http://www.milpa.com.tr
Transportation Equipment Whslr
N.A.I.C.S.: 423860
Yener Senok *(Chm)*

ADIL TEXTILE MILLS LIMITED

156-N Block Model Town Ext Lahore, Lahore, Pakistan
Tel.: (92) 42 35161952
Textile Spinning Mill Operator
N.A.I.C.S.: 313110

ADIMMUNE CORPORATION

No 3 Sec 1 Tanxing Rd, Tanzih Dist, Taichung, 427003, Taiwan
Tel.: (886) 425381220
Web Site:
https://www.adimmune.com.tw
Year Founded: 1965
4142—(TAI)
Rev.: $58,376,465
Assets: $310,161,799
Liabilities: $121,222,795
Net Worth: $188,939,003
Earnings: ($25,179,992)
Emp.: 553
Fiscal Year-end: 12/31/23
Human Vaccine Mfr & Distr
N.A.I.C.S.: 325412
Chi-Hsien Chan *(Chm & CEO)*

ADINATH BIO-LABS LTD.

4 N S Road 1st Floor, Kolkata, 700 001, India
Tel.: (91) 33 22315718
Web Site: http://www.adinathbio.com
Rev.: $3,753
Assets: $997,934
Liabilities: $123,162
Net Worth: $874,772
Earnings: ($359,332)
Fiscal Year-end: 03/31/19
Pharmaceutical Research & Development Services
N.A.I.C.S.: 325412
Kishan Singh *(Exec Dir)*

ADINATH EXIM RESOURCES LTD.

601 Astron Tower Opp Iskon Mandir Nr Casalla Tower Satellite, Ahmedabad, 380015, Gujarat, India
Tel.: (91) 6351738619

Web Site:
https://www.adinathexim.com
Year Founded: 1995
532056—(BOM)
Rev.: $119,573
Assets: $2,097,045
Liabilities: $36,221
Net Worth: $2,060,824
Earnings: $81,662
Emp.: 2
Fiscal Year-end: 03/31/23
Financial Management Services
N.A.I.C.S.: 523999

ADING AD
Novoselski Pat ul 1409 br 11, 1060,
Skopje, North Macedonia
Tel.: (389) 22034820
Web Site: https://www.ading.com.mk
Year Founded: 1969
ADIN—(MAC)
Rev.: $7,680,954
Assets: $9,623,524
Liabilities: $3,158,441
Net Worth: $6,465,083
Earnings: $685,377
Emp.: 150
Fiscal Year-end: 12/31/19
Construction Materials Distr
N.A.I.C.S.: 423390
Doncev Blagoja (Chm & Gen Mgr)

Subsidiaries:

ADING Bulgaria EOOD　　　　(1)
Blvd Vitosha Entrance B 3rd floor, Sofia,
Bulgaria
Tel.: (359) 29556106
Sports Equipment Mfr
N.A.I.C.S.: 339920

ADING d.o.o.　　　　　　　(1)
82 Nehruova, 11070, Belgrade, Serbia
Tel.: (381) 116160576
Sports Equipment Mfr
N.A.I.C.S.: 339920

Nord Comat Shpk.　　　　　(1)
Rruga Muhamet Deliu Pallati i firmes Dodaj
Kati I, Afer Restorant Fresku Dajt, Tirana,
Albania
Tel.: (355) 692134888
Web Site: http://www.nordcomat.al
Laboratory Construction Services
N.A.I.C.S.: 236220
Defrim Shkupi (Dir-Technical)

TOO Alfar　　　　　　　　(1)
Str Bekmahanova 96/12, Almaty, Kazakh-
stan
Tel.: (7) 7273386929
Sports Equipment Mfr
N.A.I.C.S.: 339920

ADISH CO., LTD.
6F Hulic Gotanda Yamate-dori Build-
ing 1-21-8 Nishi-Gotanda,
Shinagawa-ku, Tokyo, 141-0031, Ja-
pan
Tel.: (81) 357590334
Web Site: https://www.adish.biz
Year Founded: 2014
7093—(TKS)
Rev.: $24,956,800
Assets: $8,337,840
Liabilities: $5,225,330
Net Worth: $3,112,510
Earnings: ($1,368,370)
Emp.: 612
Fiscal Year-end: 12/31/23
Application Development Services
N.A.I.C.S.: 541511
Mitsuki Matsuda (Mgr-Corp Strategy
& Plng)

Subsidiaries:

Adish International Corporation　(1)
12F 6780 Ayala Avenue, Makati, 1226, Phil-
ippines
Tel.: (63) 28 804 1210
Web Site: https://adish-intl.com
Global-Outsourcing Services

N.A.I.C.S.: 423990
Joseph Pangilinan (Pres & CEO)

Adish Plus Co., Ltd.　　　　(1)
9th floor Ryukyu Lease General Building
1-7-1 Kumoji, Naha, 900-0015, Okinawa,
Japan
Tel.: (81) 988698555
Web Site: https://adishplus.co.jp
Emp.: 112
Marketing Consulting Services
N.A.I.C.S.: 541613

**ADISHAKTI LOHA & ISPAT
LIMITED**
325 Aggarwal Plaza Sector-14, Ro-
hini, New Delhi, 110085, India
Tel.: (91) 1127860681
Web Site:
https://www.adishaktiloha.com
Year Founded: 2015
543377—(BOM)
Metal Mining Services
N.A.I.C.S.: 213114
Pragati Taneja (CEO)

ADISYN LTD
27 Aspiration Circuit, Bibra Lake,
6163, WA, Australia
Tel.: (61) 861411011
Web Site: https://adisyn.com.au
Year Founded: 2012
AI1—(ASX)
Rev.: $1,861,413
Assets: $6,460,881
Liabilities: $4,841,359
Net Worth: $1,619,522
Earnings: ($1,134,878)
Fiscal Year-end: 06/30/23
Computer System Design Services
N.A.I.C.S.: 541512
Bradley Goodsell (CFO)

Subsidiaries:

Attained Pty. Ltd.　　　　　(1)
27 Aspiration Circuit, Bibra Lake, 6163, WA,
Australia
Tel.: (61) 63113200
Web Site: https://www.attained.com.au
Digital Transformation & Technology Ser-
vices
N.A.I.C.S.: 541512

ADITRI INDUSTRIES LIMITED
GF 012 - Satyam Mall Opp Saman
Complex Near Vishweshwar Ma-
hadev, Mandir Satellite, Ahmedabad,
380015, Gujarat, India
Tel.: (91) 9331852424
Web Site:
http://www.aditriindustries.co.in
Year Founded: 2005
534707—(BOM)
Rev.: $270
Assets: $11,745
Liabilities: $232,423
Net Worth: ($220,678)
Earnings: ($60,141)
Fiscal Year-end: 03/31/20
Sarees & Other Women's Clothing
Mfr
N.A.I.C.S.: 315250
Ravi Bhandari (Mng Dir & Compli-
ance Officer)

ADITYA BIRLA CAPITAL LTD.
Indian Rayon Compound, Veraval,
362266, Gujarat, India
Tel.: (91) 2876243257
Web Site:
https://www.adityabirlacapital.com
Year Founded: 2007
540691—(BOM)
Rev.: $3,035,944,275
Assets: $19,265,541,750
Liabilities: $16,932,659,835
Net Worth: $2,332,881,915
Earnings: $226,599,555
Emp.: 27

Fiscal Year-end: 03/31/22
Financial Services
N.A.I.C.S.: 523999
Vishakha Mulye (CEO)

**ADITYA BIRLA SUN LIFE AMC
LTD.**
Tower 1 17th Floor One World Center
Jupiter Mills, Senapati Bapat Marg
Elphinstone Road Null, Mumbai,
400013, Maharashtra, India
Tel.: (91) 8002707000
Year Founded: 1994
543374—(BOM)
Investment Management Service
N.A.I.C.S.: 523940

**ADITYA CONSUMER MARKET-
ING LIMITED**
Lower Ground and Ground Floor Adi-
tya House M-20 Road No 26 SK Na-
gar, Patna, 800 001, Bihar, India
Tel.: (91) 6122520854
Web Site:
https://www.adityaconsumer.com
540146—(BOM)
Rev.: $11,959,590
Assets: $5,858,801
Liabilities: $2,254,552
Net Worth: $3,604,249
Earnings: $19,978
Fiscal Year-end: 03/31/22
Consumer Goods Retailer
N.A.I.C.S.: 445110
Yashovardhan Sinha (Chm & Mng
Dir)

ADITYA FORGE LIMITED
415 G I D C Raman Gamdi, 391 243,
Vadodara, 391 243, Gujarat, India
Tel.: (91) 2652830325
Web Site:
https://www.adityaforge.com
Year Founded: 1981
Rev.: $2,241,252
Assets: $1,347,766
Liabilities: $2,804,463
Net Worth: ($1,456,697)
Earnings: ($148,029)
Emp.: 130
Fiscal Year-end: 03/31/18
Steel Products Mfr
N.A.I.C.S.: 331110
Nitin Rasiklal Parekh (Mng Dir)

ADITYA ISPAT LTD.
Plot No 20 Phase V IDA Jeedimetla,
Hyderabad, 500 055, AP, India
Tel.: (91) 4023773675
Web Site:
https://www.adityaispat.com
Year Founded: 1992
513513—(BOM)
Rev.: $5,760,764
Assets: $7,040,179
Liabilities: $5,612,320
Net Worth: $1,427,858
Earnings: $51,256
Emp.: 30
Fiscal Year-end: 03/31/22
Steel Bar Mfr
N.A.I.C.S.: 331110
Satya Bhagwan Chachan (Chm &
Mng Dir)

ADITYA SPINNERS LTD.
6-3-668/10/66 Durganagar Colony
Punjagutta, Hyderabad, 500 082,
Andhra Pradesh, India
Tel.: (91) 4023404708
Web Site:
https://www.adityaspinners.net
Year Founded: 1991
521141—(BOM)
Rev.: $4,636,223
Assets: $6,924,481

Liabilities: $3,367,073
Net Worth: $3,557,408
Earnings: $57,903
Emp.: 220
Fiscal Year-end: 03/31/21
Yarn Mfr & Distr
N.A.I.C.S.: 313110
R. Shiv Kumar (Vice Chm)

ADITYA VISION LIMITED
First Floor Second Floor Third Floor
Aditya House M20 Road No 26, S K
Nagar, Patna, 800 001, Bihar, India
Tel.: (91) 9955555544
Web Site: https://www.adityavision.in
540205—(BOM)
Rev.: $122,928,195
Assets: $58,294,255
Liabilities: $47,552,679
Net Worth: $10,741,576
Earnings: $4,816,011
Emp.: 1,084
Fiscal Year-end: 03/31/22
Consumer Electronic Product Retailer
N.A.I.C.S.: 423620
Yashovardhan Sinha (Chm & Mng
Dir)

ADIUVA CAPITAL GMBH
Messberg 1, 20095, Hamburg, Ger-
many
Tel.: (49) 40 3019 1670
Web Site:
http://www.adiuvacapital.de
Year Founded: 2011
Privater Equity Firm
N.A.I.C.S.: 523999
Tobias Osing (Partner)

Subsidiaries:

transtec AG　　　　　　　(1)
Gerhard Kindler Strasse 8, 72770, Reutlin-
gen, Germany
Tel.: (49) 7121 2678 0
Web Site: http://www.transtec.de
Sales Range: $25-49.9 Million
Emp.: 90
Computers & Storage Solutions; Network
Components & Peripherals Supplier
N.A.I.C.S.: 423430
Daniel Speidel (VP-Products, Pur & HR)

Subsidiary (Non-US):

transtec Computer AG　　　(2)
Ruchstuckstrasse 25, 8306, Bruttisellen,
Switzerland
Tel.: (41) 44 818 47 00
Web Site: http://www.transtec.ch
Computer Hardware, Software & Network-
ing Products Sales
N.A.I.C.S.: 423430
Christof Koller (Country Mgr)

transtec Computers Ltd.　　(2)
Unit 5 29-30 Horse Fair, Banbury, OX16
OBW, Oxon, United Kingdom
Tel.: (44) 1295 814 500
Web Site: http://www.transtec.co.uk
Emp.: 5
Computer Hardware, Software & Network-
ing Products Sales
N.A.I.C.S.: 423430
Matthew Prew (Mng Dir)

transtec S.A.R.L.　　　　　(2)
Parc d'Innovation Immeuble le Pythagore,
11 rue Jean Sapidus, 67400, Strasbourg,
France
Tel.: (33) 3 88 55 16 00
Web Site: http://www.transtec.fr
Computer Hardware, Software & Network-
ing Products Sales
N.A.I.C.S.: 423430
Vincent Pfleger (Country Mgr)

ttec Computer B.V.　　　　(2)
Kerkenbos 1097 D, Postbus 38040, 6503
AA, Nijmegen, Netherlands
Tel.: (31) 24 34 34 210
Web Site: http://www.ttec.nl
Emp.: 7
Computer Hardware, Software & Network-
ing Products Sales

Adiuva Capital GmbH—(Continued)

N.A.I.C.S.: 423430
Marc van Schijndel *(Country Mgr)*

ADIUVO INVESTMENTS SA

ul Szara 10, 00-420, Warsaw, Poland
Tel.: (48) 2224347990
Web Site:
  https://www.adiuvoinvestments.com
Year Founded: 2013
ADV—(WAR)
Rev.: $251,524
Assets: $560,467
Liabilities: $11,923,780
Net Worth: ($11,363,313)
Earnings: ($3,069,360)
Fiscal Year-end: 12/31/23
Business Services
N.A.I.C.S.: 541611
Marek Orlowski *(Founder, Chm & Pres)*

ADJIA TECHNOLOGIES LIMITED

102 Fairdeal House Opp Xaviers Ladies Hostel Swastik Char Rasta, Navrangpura, Ahmedabad, 380009, Gujarat, India
Tel.: (91) 8780038297
Web Site:
  https://www.adjiatechnologies.com
Year Founded: 2015
543269—(BOM)
Rev.: $12,640
Assets: $313,636
Liabilities: $9,487
Net Worth: $304,149
Earnings: ($22,714)
Emp.: 2
Fiscal Year-end: 03/31/22
Information Technology Services
N.A.I.C.S.: 541512
Roshan Kumar Rawal *(Chm & Mng Dir)*

ADJUVANT HOLDINGS CO., LTD.

5-5 Shimoyamatedori, Chuo-ku, Kobe, 650-0011, Hyogo, Japan
Tel.: (81) 783513100
Web Site: https://www.adjuvant-hd.co.jp
Year Founded: 1990
4929—(TKS)
Rev.: $29,335,180
Assets: $34,880,970
Liabilities: $7,013,210
Net Worth: $27,867,760
Earnings: ($654,390)
Fiscal Year-end: 03/31/24
Cosmetics Mfr & Sales
N.A.I.C.S.: 325620
Yutaka Nakamura *(Founder, Chm & CEO)*

ADL BIONATUR SOLUTIONS

Av del Desarrollo Tecnologico 11
Cadiz, 11591, Jerez de la Frontera, Spain
Pharmaceuticals Product Mfr
N.A.I.C.S.: 325412
Jaime Feced *(CEO)*

ADL PLC

Corbie Steps 89 Harehills Ln, LS7 4HA, Leeds, United Kingdom - England
Tel.: (44) 1132392957   **UK**
Web Site: http://www.adlcare.com
Sales Range: $1-9.9 Million
Emp.: 30
Nursing Facilities
N.A.I.C.S.: 623110
Jeremy Davies *(Mng Dir & Sec)*

ADLER GROUP SA

55 Allee Scheffer, L-2520, Luxembourg, Luxembourg
Tel.: (352) 20334210   **CY**
Web Site: https://adler-group.com
Year Founded: 2007
ADJ—(MUN)
Rev.: $491,310,460
Assets: $8,518,332,977
Liabilities: $8,770,964,666
Net Worth: ($252,631,688)
Earnings: ($1,828,560,655)
Emp.: 721
Fiscal Year-end: 12/31/23
Real Estate Services
N.A.I.C.S.: 531390
Thierry Beaudemoulin *(Co-CEO)*

Subsidiaries:

Adler Real Estate AG   **(1)**
Am Karlsbad 11, 10789, Berlin, Germany   **(96.72%)**
Web Site: http://www.adler-ag.com
Rev.: $491,309,195
Assets: $8,518,365,163
Liabilities: $8,471,556,464
Net Worth: $46,808,699
Earnings: ($1,997,829,783)
Emp.: 721
Fiscal Year-end: 12/31/2023
Real Estate Services
N.A.I.C.S.: 531390
Carsten Wolff *(Head-Acctg & Fin)*

Subsidiary (Non-US):

A.D.O. Group Ltd.   **(2)**
Hayarden 1A Eyirport Siti, Lod, 70100, Israel
Tel.: (972) 3 5416302
Real Estate Investment Services
N.A.I.C.S.: 523999

Subsidiary (Domestic):

Adler Real Estate Hotel GmbH   **(2)**
Neuer Wall 77, 20354, Hamburg, Germany
Tel.: (49) 402981300
Real Estate Manangement Services
N.A.I.C.S.: 531312

Adler Real Estate Properties GmbH & Co. KG   **(2)**
Neuer Wall 77, 20354, Hamburg, Germany
Tel.: (49) 4029813030
Web Site: http://www.alder-ag.de
Real Estate Manangement Services
N.A.I.C.S.: 531312

Adler Wohnen Service GmbH   **(2)**
Gansemarkt 50, 20354, Hamburg, Germany
Tel.: (49) 402981300
Web Site: http://www.adler-wohnen.com
Real Estate Services
N.A.I.C.S.: 531390

Subsidiary (Non-US):

Brack Capital Properties NV   **(2)**
Herengracht 456, 1017CA, Amsterdam, Netherlands   **(62.78%)**
Tel.: (31) 202404330
Web Site: https://www.bcp-nv.com
Rev.: $54,946,462
Assets: $1,355,583,398
Liabilities: $717,277,845
Net Worth: $638,305,553
Earnings: ($161,165,692)
Emp.: 88
Fiscal Year-end: 12/31/2023
Real Estate Investment Services
N.A.I.C.S.: 531300

Subsidiary (Non-US):

Glasmacherviertel GmbH & Co. KG   **(3)**
Neumannstrasse 6, 40235, Dusseldorf, Germany
Tel.: (49) 21154226450
Web Site: https://www.glasmacherviertel.de
Property Development Services
N.A.I.C.S.: 531390

RT Facility Management GmbH & Co. KG   **(3)**
Neumannstr 6, 40235, Dusseldorf, Germany

Tel.: (49) 2115422640
Web Site: https://www.rt-facility.com
Facility Management Services
N.A.I.C.S.: 561210

Subsidiary (Domestic):

Dritte ADLER Real Estate GmbH & Co. KG   **(2)**
Neuer Wall 77, 20354, Hamburg, Germany
Tel.: (49) 402981300
Web Site: http://www.adler-ag.com
Emp.: 40
Real Estate Manangement Services
N.A.I.C.S.: 531312

Jade Immobilien Management GmbH   **(2)**
Lessingstrasse 2, 26382, Wilhelmshaven, Germany
Tel.: (49) 44211850
Web Site: http://www.jade-immobilien.de
Real Estate Services
N.A.I.C.S.: 531390

MBG Dallgow GmbH & Co. KG   **(2)**
Neuer Wall 77, 20354, Hamburg, Germany
Tel.: (49) 699720800
Real Estate Manangement Services
N.A.I.C.S.: 531312

MBG Sachsen GmbH   **(2)**
Anton-Graff-Strasse 20, 01309, Dresden, Germany
Tel.: (49) 35144090
Web Site: https://www.mbg-sachsen.de
Real Estate Services
N.A.I.C.S.: 531390

Munchener Baugesellschaft mbH   **(2)**
Alstertor 17, 20095, Hamburg, Germany
Tel.: (49) 40 29 81 30 0
Web Site: http://www.adler-ag.com
Sales Range: $50-74.9 Million
Emp.: 3
Real Estate Manangement Services
N.A.I.C.S.: 531312
Peter Stommel *(Mng Dir & CTO)*

Westgrund AG   **(2)**
Am Karlsbad 11, 10785, Berlin, Germany
Tel.: (49) 3039801810
Web Site: http://www.westgrund.de
Sales Range: $75-99.9 Million
Residential Property Investment & Management
N.A.I.C.S.: 531390
Carsten Wolff *(Deputy Chm/Deputy Chm-Supervisory Bd)*

Grafental GmbH & Co. KG   **(1)**
Neumannstrasse 6, 40235, Dusseldorf, Germany
Tel.: (49) 21154 226 4100
Web Site: https://www.grafental.de
Real Estate Services
N.A.I.C.S.: 531210

ADLER PLASTIC SPA

Via Mozzoni, 80044, Naples, Italy
Tel.: (39) 0818278172
Web Site: http://www.adlergroup.it
Emp.: 9,000
Vehicle Parts Designer, Distr & Mfr
N.A.I.C.S.: 423120

Subsidiaries:

Adler Pelzer Holding GmbH   **(1)**
Kabeler Str 4, 58099, Hagen, Germany
Tel.: (49) 2331 69780
Web Site: http://www.adlerpelzer.com
Emp.: 10,000
Acoustical & Thermal Automotive Components Design, Engineering & Mfr
N.A.I.C.S.: 336330
Pietro Lardini *(CEO & Mng Dir)*

Subsidiary (Non-US):

STS Acoustics S.p.A.   **(2)**
Strada del Fornacino 119, 10040, Leini, Turin, Italy   **(100%)**
Tel.: (39) 0119965122
Web Site: http://www.sts-acoustics.com
Sales Range: $125-149.9 Million
Emp.: 730

Mfr & Distr of Noise Reduction & Heat Management Solutions & Products for Motor Vehicles
N.A.I.C.S.: 336390
Andreas Becker *(CEO)*

Subsidiary (Domestic):

STS Group AG   **(2)**
Kabeler Str 4, 58099, Hagen, Germany   **(73.25%)**
Tel.: (49) 475694545
Web Site: https://www.sts.group
Rev.: $306,765,473
Assets: $294,181,355
Liabilities: $242,741,013
Net Worth: $51,440,342
Earnings: ($1,324,644)
Emp.: 1,392
Fiscal Year-end: 12/31/2023
Automotive Parts Mfr & Distr
N.A.I.C.S.: 336320
Stefan Hummel *(Head-IR)*

ADLINE CHEM LAB LIMITED

904 Shapath-I Opp Rajpath Club S G Highway, Ahmedabad, 380 015, Gujarat, India
Tel.: (91) 9228003900   **In**
Web Site:
  https://www.kamronlabs.com
Year Founded: 1990
524604—(BOM)
Rev.: $768,676
Assets: $769,003
Liabilities: $505,483
Net Worth: $263,520
Earnings: ($175,178)
Emp.: 27
Fiscal Year-end: 03/31/21
Pharmaceutical Preparation Mfr & Distr
N.A.I.C.S.: 325412
Kamlesh Jagdish Laskari *(Mng Dir)*

ADLINK TECHNOLOGY, INC.

No 66 Huaya 1st Rd, Guishan Dist, Taoyuan, 333411, Taiwan
Tel.: (886) 32165088
Web Site: https://www.adlinktech.com
Year Founded: 1995
6166—(TAI)
Rev.: $373,279,655
Assets: $427,258,004
Liabilities: $248,775,588
Net Worth: $178,482,416
Earnings: $9,610,549
Emp.: 361
Fiscal Year-end: 12/31/23
Measurement & Automation Products Mfr
N.A.I.C.S.: 334413
Jim Liu *(Founder, Chm & CEO)*

Subsidiaries:

ADLINK Technology (China) Co., Ltd.   **(1)**
300 Fang Chun Road Zhangjiang Hi-Tech Park, Pudong New Area, Shanghai, 201203, China
Tel.: (86) 21 5132 8988
Industrial Measuring Equipment Distr
N.A.I.C.S.: 423830

ADLINK Technology B.V.   **(1)**
Amarilstraat 30, 7554 TV, Hengelo, Netherlands
Tel.: (31) 74 247 2570
Electronic Products Mfr
N.A.I.C.S.: 334419

ADLINK Technology Japan Corporation   **(1)**
Kdx Kanda Ekimae Bldg 4f 3-7-4 Kanda Kajicho, Chiyoda-ku, Tokyo, 101-0045, Japan
Tel.: (81) 3 4455 3722
Web Site: http://www.adlinktech.com
Industrial Measuring Equipment Distr
N.A.I.C.S.: 423830

ADLINK Technology Korea Ltd.   **(1)**
A-1503 U-Tower 767 Sinsu-ro, Suji-gu,

Yongin, 16827, Gyeonggi, Korea (South)
Tel.: (82) 31 786 0585
Electronic Products Mfr
N.A.I.C.S.: 334419

ADLINK Technology Ltd. (1)
The Edge 5th Avenue Team Valley, Gateshead, NE11 0XA, Tyne and Wear, United Kingdom
Tel.: (44) 191 497 9900
Electronic Products Mfr
N.A.I.C.S.: 334419

ADLINK Technology SARL (1)
Thales building - Parc des Algorithmes
Route de Orme des Merisiers, 91190, Saint Aubin, France
Electronic Products Mfr
N.A.I.C.S.: 334419

ADLINK Technology Singapore Pte. Ltd. (1)
84 Genting Lane 07-02A, Axxel Innovation Centre, Singapore, 349584, Singapore
Tel.: (65) 6844 2261
Web Site: http://www.adlinktech.com
Electronic Testing Instrument Mfr
N.A.I.C.S.: 334515

Ampro ADLINK Technology, Inc. (1)
5215 Hellyer Ave Ste 110, San Jose, CA 95138
Tel.: (408) 360-0200
Web Site: http://www.adlinktech.com
Electronic Automation Software Development Services
N.A.I.C.S.: 541511

LIPPERT ADLINK Technology GmbH (1)
Hans-Thoma-Strasse 11, Mannheim, 68163, Germany
Tel.: (49) 621432140
Emp.: 40
Measurement & Automation Products Mfr
N.A.I.C.S.: 334513
Edcao Shen (Gen Mgr)

Zettascale Technology B.V. (1)
Amarilstraat 30, 7554TV, Hengelo, Netherlands
Tel.: (31) 742472570
Software Development Services
N.A.I.C.S.: 541511

ADLON INTELLIGENT SOLUTIONS GMBH

Albersfelder Str 30, 88213, Ravensburg, Germany
Tel.: (49) 75176070
Web Site: http://www.adlon.com
Year Founded: 1988
Sales Range: $25-49.9 Million
Emp.: 80
IT Consulting Services
N.A.I.C.S.: 541511
Andreas Richstatter (CEO)

ADLPARTNER SA

3 rue Henri Rol Tanguy, 93100, Montreuil, France
Tel.: (33) 141587000
Web Site:
   http://www.adlperformance.com
Year Founded: 1993
ALP—(EUR)
Sales Range: $150-199.9 Million
Emp.: 500
Periodical Loyalty Marketing & Management Services
N.A.I.C.S.: 541613

Subsidiaries:

ADLP Assurances SAS (1)
3 Avenue de Chartres, 60507, Chantilly, Cedex, France
Tel.: (33) 974750175
Web Site: http://www.avocotes.com
Property Liability Insurance Services
N.A.I.C.S.: 524126

Activis SAS (1)
1 Place Guillaume Tell, CS 12495, 68057, Mulhouse, Cedex, France
Tel.: (33) 389607160

Web Site: http://www.activis.net
Marketing & Advertising Services
N.A.I.C.S.: 541810

Converteo SAS (1)
117 - 119 Quai de Valmy, 75010, Paris, France
Tel.: (33) 184160660
Web Site: http://converteo.com
Marketing Consulting Services
N.A.I.C.S.: 541613
Flora Herbet (Mgr-HR & Recruitment)

Leoo SAS (1)
16/18 quai de la Loire, 75019, Paris, France
Tel.: (33) 153206767
Web Site: http://www.leoo.fr
Marketing & Advertising Services
N.A.I.C.S.: 541810
Etienne Oddon (Founder & Chm)

OFUP (1)
3 avenue de Chartres, BP 90132, 60500, Chantilly, France
Tel.: (33) 173600884
Web Site: http://www.ofup.com
Magazine Publishing Services
N.A.I.C.S.: 513130

SIDD Sarl (1)
88 Rue Saint Denis, 93130, Noisy-le-Sec, Seine-Saint-Denis, France
Tel.: (33) 148304286
Financial Management Services
N.A.I.C.S.: 541611

Suscripciones Espana (1)
Calle Velazquez No 126 Seventh Floor AB, 28006, Madrid, Spain
Tel.: (34) 915611400
Magazine Marketing Services
N.A.I.C.S.: 541613
Michel Gauthier (Mgr)

ADM ENERGY PLC

60 Gracechurch Street, London, EC3V 0HR, United Kingdom
Tel.: (44) 2074594718   UK
Web Site:
   https://www.admenergyplc.com
P4JC—(DEU)
Rev.: $835,648
Assets: $22,734,158
Liabilities: $8,586,216
Net Worth: $14,147,942
Earnings: ($2,678,617)
Emp.: 6
Fiscal Year-end: 12/31/22
Miscellaneous Financial Investment Activities
N.A.I.C.S.: 523999
Richard James Carter (COO)

ADMARK ADVERTISING LIMITED

Toronto House 128-132 Crossbrook St, Cheshunt, EN8 8JH, Hertfordshire, United Kingdom
Tel.: (44) 1992636999
Web Site: http://www.admark.co.uk
Year Founded: 1985
Sales Range: $25-49.9 Million
Emp.: 40
N.A.I.C.S.: 541810
Nigel V. Beckwith (Chm & New Bus Contact)

ADMEA SA

12 rue Jules Ferry, 93110, Rosny-sous-Bois, France
Tel.: (33) 148121414   FR
Web Site:
   http://www.schneiderconsumers.com
Year Founded: 1994
Sales Range: $25-49.9 Million
Emp.: 30
Home Appliance Whslr
N.A.I.C.S.: 423620
Stephane Bibas (Gen Mgr)

ADMET SA

Str al moruzzi 130, Galati, Romania

Tel.: (40) 236415522
ADMY—(BUC)
Rev.: $74,008
Assets: $1,202,394
Liabilities: $229,834
Net Worth: $972,560
Earnings: ($118,702)
Emp.: 3
Fiscal Year-end: 12/31/20
Metal Product Whslr
N.A.I.C.S.: 423510
Ajay Kumar Aggarwal (Pres)

ADMICOM OYJ

Vainonkatu 26 A 29, 40100, Jyvaskyla, 40100, Finland
Tel.: (358) 405759709   FI
Year Founded: 2004
ADMCM—(HEL)
Rev.: $37,885,921
Assets: $44,799,320
Liabilities: $12,432,597
Net Worth: $32,366,722
Earnings: $6,973,072
Emp.: 271
Fiscal Year-end: 12/31/23
Software Development Services
N.A.I.C.S.: 541511

ADMIN NUCOAL

Unit 8 24 Garnett Road, PO Box 307, Greenhills, Newcastle, 2283, NSW, Australia
Tel.: (61) 240136181   AU
Web Site: https://www.nucoal.com.au
NCR—(ASX)
Rev.: $72,991
Assets: $1,723,737
Liabilities: $22,544
Net Worth: $1,701,193
Earnings: ($224,436)
Fiscal Year-end: 06/30/24
Coal Production & Exploration Services
N.A.I.C.S.: 324199
Megan Etcell (CEO, CFO & Sec)

ADMINISTER OY

Itamerenkatu 5, 00180, Helsinki, Finland
Tel.: (358) 207032000
Web Site: http://www.administer.fi
Year Founded: 1985
Sales Range: Less than $1 Million
Emp.: 700
Electronic Financial Services
N.A.I.C.S.: 522320
Peter Aho (CEO)

Subsidiaries:

Silta Oy (1)
Makelankatu 87, 00610, Helsinki, Finland
Tel.: (358) 207595500
Web Site: http://www.silta.fi
Emp.: 300
Human Resource Management Services
N.A.I.C.S.: 541612

ADMINISTRADORA DE FONDOS DE PENSIONES Y CESANTIA PROTECCION SA

Cll 49 No 63-100, Medellin, Colombia
Tel.: (57) 42307500
Web Site: http://www.proteccion.com
PROTECCION—(COLO)
Sales Range: Less than $1 Million
Financial Services
N.A.I.C.S.: 523999

ADMIRAL GROUP PLC

David Street, Cardiff, CF10 2EH, United Kingdom
Tel.: (44) 3332202062   UK
Web Site:
   https://www.admiralgroup.co.uk
Year Founded: 1993

ADM—(LSE)
Rev.: $4,400,530,169
Assets: $8,957,586,468
Liabilities: $7,704,367,584
Net Worth: $1,253,218,884
Earnings: $425,650,088
Emp.: 12,641
Fiscal Year-end: 12/31/23
Financial Investment Services
N.A.I.C.S.: 523999
Mark Waters (Sec)

Subsidiaries:

Able Insurance Services Limited (1)
No 1 Langdon Rd Admiral Grp House, Swansea Waterfront, Swansea, SA1 8AG, United Kingdom
Tel.: (44) 8718828283
Insurance Services
N.A.I.C.S.: 524210

Admiral Insurance (Gibraltar) Limited (1)
Montagu Pavilion No 8-10 Queens Way, 1 Corral Rd, Gibraltar, Gibraltar
Tel.: (350) 20042575
Web Site: http://www.admiralgroupplc.com
Emp.: 2
Insurance Services
N.A.I.C.S.: 524210

Admiral Law Limited (1)
9th Floor Brunel House 2 Fitzalan Road, Cardiff, CF24 0EB, United Kingdom
Tel.: (44) 3442510075
Web Site: http://www.admirallaw.co.uk
Injury Claim Insurance Services
N.A.I.C.S.: 524291
Adam Gavin (Head-Admiral Law)

BDE Law Limited (1)
Floor 6 Admiral House Queensway, Newport, NP20 4AG, Gwent, United Kingdom
Tel.: (44) 3442510075
Web Site: http://www.bdelaw.co.uk
Injury Claim Insurance Services
N.A.I.C.S.: 524291
Natasha Clatworthy (Mgr-Case Handling Ops)

Elephant Insurance Company (1)
9950 Mayland Dr 4th Fl, Henrico, VA 23233
N.A.I.C.S.: 525990

Elephant Insurance Services LLC (1)
Deep Run I 9950 Mayland Dr, Henrico, VA 23233
Web Site: http://www.elephant.com
Insurance Services
N.A.I.C.S.: 524126

Rastreator.com Limited (1)
Calle Sanchez Pacheco 85, 28002, Madrid, Spain
Tel.: (34) 913457896
Web Site: https://www.rastreator.com
Insurance Services
N.A.I.C.S.: 524126
Victor Lopez (CEO)

compare.com Insurance Agency LLC (1)
140 Eastshore Dr Ste 300, Glen Allen, VA 23059
Tel.: (804) 887-3737
Web Site: http://www.compare.com
Insurance Services
N.A.I.C.S.: 524126
Andrew Rose (Pres & CEO)

ADMIRAL MARINE SUPPLIES LIMITED

Unit C Nova Distribution Centre Nova Way, Bristol, S11 9DJ, United Kingdom
Tel.: (44) 117 982 1229
Web Site: http://www.admiral-marine.com
Sales Range: $10-24.9 Million
Emp.: 44
Marine Products Distr
N.A.I.C.S.: 423860
R. T. Blake (Mng Dir)

Admiral Marine Supplies Limited—(Continued)

Subsidiaries:

Admiral Marine Continental Supplies
BV   (1)
Klompenmakerstraat 26, Hoogvliet, 3194
DE, Rotterdam, Netherlands
Tel.: (31) 104165133
Web Site: http://www.admiral-marine.nl
Marine Equipment Distr
N.A.I.C.S.: 423860

Admiral Marine Services Pvt Ltd   (1)
23 Moore Street, Chennai, 600 001, Tamil
Nadu, India
Tel.: (91) 4443475050
Web Site: http://www.admiralmarine.com
Marine Equipment Distr
N.A.I.C.S.: 423860
Ramkumar Shanmugam (CEO)

Admiral Marine Supplies Ltd   (1)
PO Box 52056, Port Saeed, Dubai, United
Arab Emirates
Tel.: (971) 42858201
Marine Equipment Distr
N.A.I.C.S.: 423860

Admiral Marine Supplies Ltd   (1)
PO Box 915, 211, Salalah, Oman
Tel.: (968) 211691
Marine Equipment Distr
N.A.I.C.S.: 423860

Admiral Marine Supplies Pte Ltd   (1)
9 Temasek Boulevard 31-02 Suntec Tower
Two, Singapore, 38929, Singapore
Tel.: (65) 63356244
Marine Equipment Distr
N.A.I.C.S.: 423860

ADMIRALTY RESOURCES NL

Suite 305 Level 3 35 Lime Street,
Sydney, 2000, NSW, Australia
Tel.: (61) 292836502   AU
Web Site: https://www.ady.com.au
ADY—(ASX)
Rev.: $399,798
Assets: $17,122,538
Liabilities: $12,010,770
Net Worth: $5,111,768
Earnings: ($1,384,094)
Fiscal Year-end: 06/30/23
Mineral Mining
N.A.I.C.S.: 212390
Qing Zhong (CEO & Mng Dir)

ADNAMS PLC

East Green, Southwold Suffolk, Nor-
folk, IP18 6JW, Suffolk, United King-
dom
Tel.: (44) 1502727200
Web Site: https://www.adnams.co.uk
Rev.: $98,040,788
Assets: $82,245,190
Liabilities: $45,799,760
Net Worth: $36,445,429
Earnings: $38,036
Emp.: 556
Fiscal Year-end: 12/31/19
Food Products Mfr
N.A.I.C.S.: 311999
Jonathan Adnams (Chm)

ADO OPTRONIC CORP.

NO 858 Guangfu Rd, Taoyuan
County, Bade, 334-55, Taiwan
Tel.: (886) 33768380
Web Site: https://www.adotek.com.tw
Year Founded: 1991
3516—(TPE)
Rev.: $30,059,969
Assets: $75,116,281
Liabilities: $30,386,674
Net Worth: $44,729,606
Earnings: $1,876,466
Fiscal Year-end: 12/31/22
Optic Cable & Connector Part Mfr
N.A.I.C.S.: 334417
Shu-Wei Liao (Chm & Pres)

ADOCIA SAS

115 avenue Lacassagne, 69003,
Lyon, France
Tel.: (33) 472610610
Web Site: https://www.adocia.com
Year Founded: 2005
ADOC—(OTCIQ)
Rev.: $6,676,234
Assets: $27,548,295
Liabilities: $35,180,484
Net Worth: ($7,632,189)
Earnings: ($23,360,194)
Emp.: 109
Fiscal Year-end: 12/31/23
Biotechnology Products Mfr
N.A.I.C.S.: 541714
Gerard Soula (Co-Founder, Chm,
Pres & CEO)

ADOLF SCHUCH GMBH

Mainzer Str 172, Worms, 67547, Ger-
many
Tel.: (49) 624140910
Web Site: http://www.schuch.de
Rev.: $50,419,134
Emp.: 327
Light Fitting Mfr
N.A.I.C.S.: 335132

ADOLFO DOMINGUEZ, S.A.

Poligono Industrial Calle 4 Parcela 8,
San Ciprian de Vinas, 32901,
Orense, Spain
Tel.: (34) 988398705   ES
Web Site:
   https://www.adolfodominguez.com
Year Founded: 1973
ADZ—(MAD)
Sales Range: $125-149.9 Million
Emp.: 1,195
Clothing & Accessories Mfr, Designer
& Retailer
N.A.I.C.S.: 315990
Adolfo Dominguez Fernandez (Chm)

ADOMOS SA

75 Avenue Des Champs Elysees,
75008, Paris, France
Tel.: (33) 158364500
Web Site: https://www.adomos.com
Year Founded: 1999
ALADO—(EUR)
Sales Range: $10-24.9 Million
Emp.: 40
Real Estate Brokerage Services
N.A.I.C.S.: 531210
Fabrice Rosset (Chm & CEO)

Subsidiaries:

Acheter Louer fr SA   (1)
2 Rue de Tocqueville, 75017, Paris, France
Tel.: (33) 160929600
Web Site: https://www.acheter-louer.fr
Sales Range: $1-9.9 Million
Real Estate Support Services
N.A.I.C.S.: 531390
Laurent Campagnolo (Chm, Deputy CEO &
Dir-IR)

ADON PRODUCTION AG

Industriestrasse 15, 5432, Neuenhof,
Switzerland
Tel.: (41) 56 416 46 46
Web Site: http://www.adon.ch
Emp.: 25
Smart Cards & Identity Cards Mfr
N.A.I.C.S.: 326199
Rover Schudel (Chm & CEO)

Subsidiaries:

Multicard AG   (1)
Widenholzstrasse 1, Wallisellen, 8304, Swit-
zerland
Tel.: (41) 448779000
Web Site: http://www.multicard.ch
Sales Range: $25-49.9 Million
Emp.: 6
Identity Management Solutions & Services

N.A.I.C.S.: 423690
Thierry Gattlen (Chm)

Subsidiary (Domestic):

Polyright SA   (2)
10 Rue de l Industrie, PO Box 1146, 1950,
Sion, Switzerland   (100%)
Tel.: (41) 273230910
Web Site: http://www.polyright.com
Sales Range: $25-49.9 Million
Emp.: 50
Identity Management Solutions
N.A.I.C.S.: 513210

ADONIS CONSTRUCTION LTD

Ham Lane, Kingswinford, DY6 7JU,
West Midlands, United Kingdom
Tel.: (44) 1384298989
Web Site: http://www.adonis-
   group.co.uk
Year Founded: 1978
Rev.: $74,612,938
Emp.: 20
Construction Services
N.A.I.C.S.: 236220
Neville Clements (Chm)

ADOR WELDING LTD

Ador House 6 K Dubash Marg Fort,
Mumbai, 400 001, India
Tel.: (91) 2222842525
Web Site:
   https://www.adorwelding.com
ADORWELD—(NSE)
Rev.: $91,040,040
Assets: $53,619,930
Liabilities: $15,114,645
Net Worth: $38,505,285
Earnings: $6,164,340
Emp.: 537
Fiscal Year-end: 03/31/22
Welding Equipments & Accessories
N.A.I.C.S.: 333992
N. Malkani Nagpal (Chm)

Subsidiaries:

Ador Fontech Ltd.   (1)
Belview 7 Haudin Road, Bengaluru, 560
042, India
Tel.: (91) 8025596045
Web Site: https://www.adorfon.com
Rev.: $29,217,825
Assets: $21,528,780
Liabilities: $4,765,215
Net Worth: $16,763,565
Earnings: $2,919,735
Emp.: 184
Fiscal Year-end: 03/31/2022
Mineral Resources Distr
N.A.I.C.S.: 423510
Melville Ferns (Exec VP-Technical, Life En-
hancement Products & Svcs)

Ador Multiproducts Ltd.   (1)
Ador House 6 K Dubash Marg Fort, Mum-
bai, 400 001, Maharashtra, India
Tel.: (91) 2266239300
Web Site:
   https://www.adormultiproducts.com
Rev.: $3,222,856
Assets: $2,602,605
Liabilities: $1,108,870
Net Worth: $1,493,735
Earnings: $204,084
Emp.: 24
Fiscal Year-end: 03/31/2021
Personal Care Products Mfr & Distr
N.A.I.C.S.: 325620
Deep Ashda Lalvani (Chm)

Ador Powertron Ltd.   (1)
Plot 51 Ramnagar Complex D II Block
MIDC Chinchwad, Pune, 411 019, Maha-
rashtra, India
Tel.: (91) 2027472532
Web Site: http://www.adorpowertronltd.com
Battery Testing Equipment Mfr
N.A.I.C.S.: 334515

ADORABLE LINGERIE INC.

710 rue Deslauriers, Montreal, H4N
1W5, QC, Canada
Tel.: (514) 593-1717

Web Site:
   http://www.adorableintimates.com
Rev.: $20,871,772
Emp.: 47
Apparel Stores
N.A.I.C.S.: 458110
Mikael Abergel (Pres)

ADORE BEAUTY GROUP LIM-
ITED

Level 1 421 High Street, Northcote,
3070, VIC, Australia
Tel.: (61) 393941671   AU
Web Site:
   https://www.adorebeautygroup.com
Year Founded: 2000
ABY—(ASX)
Rev.: $117,746,626
Assets: $40,693,095
Liabilities: $17,078,959
Net Worth: $23,614,136
Earnings: ($364,478)
Fiscal Year-end: 06/30/23
Beauty Product Distr
N.A.I.C.S.: 456120
Marina Go (Chm)

ADOS PAKISTAN LIMITED

2nd Floor FJ Plaza Block 2 College
Road Markaz F-7, PO Box 1416, Is-
lamabad, Pakistan
Tel.: (92) 512651365
Web Site: http://www.ados.com.pk
ADOS—(PSX)
Rev.: $273,335
Assets: $2,010,607
Liabilities: $1,675,399
Net Worth: $335,208
Earnings: ($492,282)
Fiscal Year-end: 06/30/19
Oil Field Equipment Mfr
N.A.I.C.S.: 339999

ADPR LTD.

The Old Apple Store New Cross Ct,
West Lambrook South Petherton,
Somerset, TA13 5HZ, United King-
dom
Tel.: (44) 1460241641
Web Site: http://www.adpr.co.uk
Year Founded: 1991
Sales Range: $10-24.9 Million
Emp.: 10
Public Relations
N.A.I.C.S.: 541820
Alice Driscoll (Founder)

ADRENNA PROPERTY GROUP
LIMITED

2969 William Nicol Drive Wedgewood
Link, Bryanston, Johannesburg, 2021,
South Africa
Tel.: (27) 11 340 3333   ZA
Web Site:
   http://www.adrennapropertygroup.co.za
Rev.: $2,224,857
Assets: $22,109,100
Liabilities: $9,010,716
Net Worth: $13,098,384
Earnings: $1,265,348
Fiscal Year-end: 02/28/18
Real Estate Development Services
N.A.I.C.S.: 531390
Reccared P. Fertig (CEO & Exec Dir)

ADREXO SAS

D5 Building 1330 Avenue Guillibert
de la Lauziere, ZI des Milles Eu-
roparc Pichaury, 13592, Aix-en-
Provence, Cedex 3, France
Tel.: (33) 4 42 33 65 00   FR
Web Site: http://www.adrexo.fr
Year Founded: 1972
Printed Advertising Distribution Ser-
vices
N.A.I.C.S.: 541870

Vincent Ouvrard *(Deputy Dir Gen)*

ADRIACHEM D.D.
Ulica dr F Tudmana 344, 21212, Kastel Sucurac, Croatia
Tel.: (385) 21224944
Web Site: http://www.adriachem.com
Sales Range: $125-149.9 Million
Emp.: 400
Plastic & Chemical Products
N.A.I.C.S.: 325998

ADRIANO CARE SOCIMI S.A.
C/ Villanueva 2 bis planta jardin, 28001, Madrid, Spain
Tel.: (34) 913106370
Web Site: https://www.adrianocare.es
Year Founded: 2003
YADR—(MAD)
Real Estate Investment Services
N.A.I.C.S.: 531190
Monica Garay Irizar *(Mng Partner)*

ADRIATIC METALS PLC
Ground Floor Regent House 65 Rodney Road, Cheltenham, GL50 1HX, United Kingdom
Tel.: (44) 2079930066　　　　　UK
Web Site:
　　https://www.adriaticmetals.com
Year Founded: 2017
ADMLF—(OTCQX)
Rev.: $334,497
Assets: $174,729,990
Liabilities: $66,826,964
Net Worth: $107,903,026
Earnings: ($47,142,818)
Emp.: 192
Fiscal Year-end: 12/31/22
Mineral Exploration Services
N.A.I.C.S.: 213114
Gabriel Chiappini *(Co-Sec)*

Subsidiaries:

Eastern Mining d.o.o　　　　　　(1)
Kalmija Baruha No 1, Sarajevo, Bosnia & Herzegovina
Tel.: (387) 33201782
Web Site: http://www.easternmining.co.uk
Mineral Exploration Services
N.A.I.C.S.: 213115
Graham Hill *(COO)*

ADRIATIC OSIGURANJE D.D.
Trg International Prijateljstva 20, 71000, Sarajevo, Bosnia & Herzegovina
Tel.: (387) 80020050
Web Site: https://www.adriatic.ba
BSOSRK1—(SARE)
Sales Range: Less than $1 Million
Insurance Management Services
N.A.I.C.S.: 524298
Marina Miocic-Hamidovic *(Pres)*

ADRIS GRUPA D.D.
Obala Vladimira Nazora 1, 52210, Rovinj, Croatia
Tel.: (385) 52801122　　　　　HR
Web Site: https://www.adris.hr
Year Founded: 2003
ADRS2—(ZAG)
Rev.: $6,021,683,674
Assets: $21,841,320,976
Liabilities: $11,452,455,712
Net Worth: $10,388,865,264
Earnings: $540,464,413
Emp.: 7,175
Fiscal Year-end: 12/31/22
Tourism Services & Tobacco Products Mfr
N.A.I.C.S.: 312230
Tomislav Budin *(Deputy Chm-Supervisory Bd)*

Subsidiaries:

Abilia d.o.o.　　　　　　　　　(1)

Obala Vladimira Nazora 1, 52210, Rovinj, Croatia
Tel.: (385) 52801341
Web Site: https://www.abilia.hr
Sales Range: $25-49.9 Million
Emp.: 14
Commercial Building Construction Services
N.A.I.C.S.: 236220

Adria Resorts d.o.o.　　　　　　(1)
Obala Vladimira Nazora 6, 52210, Rovinj, Croatia
Tel.: (385) 52800300
Web Site: http://www.adris.hr
Tourism Management Services
N.A.I.C.S.: 561591

Astoria d.o.o.　　　　　　　　　(1)
Zanonova 1, 51000, Rijeka, Croatia
Tel.: (385) 51301182
Web Site: http://www.astoria.hr
Magazine Publisher
N.A.I.C.S.: 513120

Croatia Poliklinika　　　　　　　(1)
Ulica grada Vukovara 62, 10000, Zagreb, Croatia
Tel.: (385) 16332891
Web Site: http://www.poliklinikacroatia.hr
Health Care Srvices
N.A.I.C.S.: 621999

Croatia osiguranje d.d.　　　　　(1)
Vatroslava Jagica 33, 10000, Zagreb, Croatia
Tel.: (385) 72001884
Web Site: https://kompanija.crosig.hr
Health Insurance Services
N.A.I.C.S.: 524114
Mario Puljiz *(Dir-Bus Transaction & Fin Institutions)*

Subsidiary (Domestic):

Croatia-Tehnicki Pregledi d.o.o.　(2)
Savska cesta 41, 10000, Zagreb, Croatia
Tel.: (385) 16138380
Web Site: http://www.tehnicki-pregledi.hr
Automobile Parts Mfr
N.A.I.C.S.: 336211

Subsidiary (Non-US):

Hotel Hum d.o.o.　　　　　　　(2)
Nikole Kordica bb, 88320, Ljubuski, Bosnia & Herzegovina
Tel.: (387) 39839400
Web Site: http://www.hotelhum.com
Hotel Operator
N.A.I.C.S.: 721110
Marija Barac *(Mgr)*

Cromaris Italy s.r.l.　　　　　　(1)
Via delle Industrie n 2/1, 31032, Treviso, Casale sul Sile, Italy
Tel.: (39) 0422786948
Web Site: http://cromaris.com
Fish Distr
N.A.I.C.S.: 424460

Cromaris d.d.　　　　　　　　　(1)
Gazenicka cesta 4b, HR-23000, Zadar, Croatia
Tel.: (385) 23254960
Web Site: https://cromaris.com
Sales Range: $25-49.9 Million
Emp.: 300
Finfish Production Services
N.A.I.C.S.: 114111

Hoteli Dubrovacka Rivijera d.d.　(1)
Setaliste Marka Marojice 40 Hrvatska, Mlini, 20207, Zagreb, Croatia
Tel.: (385) 52800250
Web Site: http://www.dubrovnik-rivijera-hotels.hr
Hotel Operator
N.A.I.C.S.: 721110

Maistra d.d.　　　　　　　　　(1)
V Nazora 6, 52210, Rovinj, 52210, Croatia　　　　　　　　　(84.05%)
Tel.: (385) 52800250
Web Site: https://www.maistra.com
Rev.: $257,767,966
Assets: $586,172,867
Liabilities: $209,087,096
Net Worth: $377,085,771
Earnings: $32,820,400
Emp.: 2,048
Fiscal Year-end: 12/31/2023

Home Management Services
N.A.I.C.S.: 721110
Ante Vlahovic *(Chm-Supervisory Bd & Pres)*

Milenijum Osiguranje a.d.　　　(1)
Bulevar Milutina Milankovica 3B, Belgrade, 11070, Serbia
Tel.: (381) 117152300
Web Site: http://www.mios.rs
Insurance Services
N.A.I.C.S.: 524210
Milica Todorovic *(Mgr-Sls)*

Rovinjturist d.d.　　　　　　　(1)
Monsena Bb, 52210, Rovinj, Croatia
Tel.: (385) 52805504
Tourist Accommodation Services
N.A.I.C.S.: 713990

ADRITEC GROUP INTERNATIONAL, E.C.
87 Abdul Hameed Sharaf St, PO Box 5474, Amman, 11183, Jordan
Tel.: (962) 65603779
Web Site: http://www.adritec.com
Year Founded: 1999
Holding Company: Offshore Investments
N.A.I.C.S.: 551112
Hatim Sharif Zu'bi *(Chm)*

Subsidiaries:

Adritec De Las Americas S. de R.L. de C.V.　　　　　　　　　(1)
Kanalto 481 Col Loma Bonita Ejidal, Zapopan, Guadalajara, 45080, CP, Mexico
Tel.: (52) 3335638842
Web Site: http://www.adritec.com
Sales Range: $75-99.9 Million
Emp.: 10
Irrigation, Drip & Sprinkler Products Distr
N.A.I.C.S.: 221310
Ali Wasfi *(Mgr)*

Adritec Egypt　　　　　　　　(1)
103 Haram Street El Riyadh Tower 1st Floor Suite No 2, Giza, Egypt
Tel.: (20) 2 33 879 311
Agricultural Equipment Distr
N.A.I.C.S.: 423820

Adritec Europe　　　　　　　　(1)
16th Km Larissa AGIA, Platykampos, Larissa, Greece
Tel.: (30) 2410975170
Web Site: http://www.adritec.com
Sales Range: $50-74.9 Million
Emp.: 50
Drip Irrigation Products Mfr
N.A.I.C.S.: 221310
Yannis G. Bozikis *(Co-Founder & Mng Partner)*

Adritec Jordan　　　　　　　　(1)
87 Abdul Hameed Sharaf St, PO Box 5474, Amman, 11183, Jordan　　(100%)
Tel.: (962) 65603779
Sales Range: $125-149.9 Million
Emp.: 150
Micro-Irrigation & Filtration Systems Mfr
N.A.I.C.S.: 221310

Adritec Lebanon　　　　　　　(1)
PO Box 7911, Beirut, Lebanon
Tel.: (961) 5 804685
Agricultural Equipment Distr
N.A.I.C.S.: 423820

Adritec Maroc　　　　　　　　(1)
Zone Industrielle, El Jadida, Morocco　　　　　　　　　　(100%)
Tel.: (212) 523372043
Irrigation Components & Accessories Distr
N.A.I.C.S.: 221310

Adritec Romania S.L.R　　　　　(1)
Advanced Drip Irrigation Technology Calea Lui Traian 210 St, Bucharest, 245100, Valcea, Romania
Tel.: (40) 250 765301
Agricultural Equipment Distr
N.A.I.C.S.: 423820

Adritec South Africa　　　　　　(1)
Ditlou Street Factory 34, Seshego, 0742, Polokwane, South Africa
Tel.: (27) 15 223 5703
Agricultural Equipment Distr

N.A.I.C.S.: 423820

Adritec Trading & Services Company　　　　　　　　　　(1)
Abdul Hameed Sharaf Street, PO Box 5474, Amman, 11183, Jordan
Tel.: (962) 65603779
Sales Range: $125-149.9 Million
Emp.: 125
Irrigation Services
N.A.I.C.S.: 221310

Adritec Tunis　　　　　　　　(1)
ZI Ksar Said 2086, Douar Hicher, Tunis, Tunisia
Tel.: (216) 71546404
Web Site: http://www.adritec.com
Irrigation Components & Accessories Mfr & Distr; 50% Owned by Adritec Group International, E.C. & 50% Owned by Societe Commerciale et Industrielle des Produits en Plastique
N.A.I.C.S.: 221310

Adritec Turkey　　　　　　　　(1)
Cilek Mahallesi 133 Cadde No 76, Ankara, 33020, Turkiye　　　　　(100%)
Tel.: (90) 324 221 2042
Web Site: http://www.adritec.com
Emp.: 5
Irrigation Distribution Systems
N.A.I.C.S.: 221310
Mohamad Darawwad *(Gen Mgr)*

Arab Drip Irrigation Technology Company Ltd.　　　　　　　　(1)
PO Box 270, Lattakia, Syria
Tel.: (963) 41461861
Web Site: http://www.sleiman-agri.com
Sales Range: $75-99.9 Million
Emp.: 70
Irrigation Systems; 50% Owned by Adritec Group International, E.C. & 50% Owned by Sleiman Agricultural Establishment
N.A.I.C.S.: 221310

Premier Irrigation Adritec India　(1)
17 1c Alipore Road, Kolkata, 700027, India
Tel.: (91) 33 2479 5155
Agricultural Equipment Distr
N.A.I.C.S.: 423820

ADS DIAGNOSTICS LIMITED
114 Sant Nagar East of Kailash, New Delhi, 110065, Delhi, India
Tel.: (91) 1141622193
Web Site:
　　https://adsdiagnosticlimited.com
Year Founded: 1984
523031—(BOM)
Rev.: $1,427,435
Assets: $1,639,529
Liabilities: $1,079,974
Net Worth: $559,554
Earnings: $60,005
Emp.: 20
Fiscal Year-end: 03/31/22
Medical Equipment Whslr
N.A.I.C.S.: 423450
Gautam Sehgal *(Mng Dir)*

ADS INC.
485 rue des Erables, Quebec, G0S 2J0, QC, Canada
Tel.: (418) 387-5910　　　　　Ca
Web Site: http://www.adsinc.ca
Sales Range: $75-99.9 Million
Emp.: 350
Nonwoven Materials Designer, Developer & Mfr
N.A.I.C.S.: 313230
Richard Faucher *(Dir-Mktg & Sls)*

ADS MARITIME HOLDING PLC
OSM House 22 Amathountos, Agios Tychonas, 4532, Limassol, Cyprus
Tel.: (357) 25335501
Web Site: https://www.adsmh.com
Year Founded: 2018
ADS—(OSL)
Rev.: $150,000
Assets: $27,968,000
Liabilities: $11,454,000

ADS Maritime Holding Plc—(Continued)

Net Worth: $16,514,000
Earnings: $1,957,000
Emp.: 4
Fiscal Year-end: 12/31/22
Marine Shipping Services
N.A.I.C.S.: 488320
Bjorn Tore Larsen *(Chm)*

ADS-TEC ENERGY PUBLIC LIMITED COMPANY

10 Earlsfort Terrace, Dublin, D02
T380, Ireland
Tel.: (353) 19201000   IE
Web Site: https://ads-tec-energy.com
Year Founded: 2021
ADSE—(NASDAQ)
Emp.: 109
Holding Company
N.A.I.C.S.: 551112
Hakan Konyar *(Chief Production Officer)*

ADSLOT LTD.

Level 2 419 Collins St, Melbourne,
3000, VIC, Australia
Tel.: (61) 386959100   AU
Web Site: https://www.adslot.com
ADS—(ASX)
Rev.: $5,840,487
Assets: $4,735,983
Liabilities: $5,779,764
Net Worth: ($1,043,781)
Earnings: ($7,147,356)
Emp.: 60
Fiscal Year-end: 06/30/24
Advertising Services
N.A.I.C.S.: 541890
Andrew Barlow *(Co-Founder)*

Subsidiaries:

Adslot Inc.   **(1)**
79 Madison Ave, New York, NY 10016
Marketing & Advertising Services
N.A.I.C.S.: 541810

Adslot UK Limited   **(1)**
Three Tuns House 109 Borough High
Street, London, SE1 1NL, United Kingdom
Tel.: (44) 743 263 9166
Marketing & Advertising Services
N.A.I.C.S.: 541810

Ansearch.com.au Pty Ltd   **(1)**
85 Coventry Street, South Melbourne,
3205, VIC, Australia
Tel.: (61) 3 8695 9199
Web Site: http://www.ansearch.com.au
Sales Range: $25-49.9 Million
Emp.: 30
Internet Search Portal Operation Services
N.A.I.C.S.: 519290

Facilitate Digital Holdings Limited **(1)**
Level 6 241 Commonwealth St, Surry Hills,
2010, NSW, Australia
Tel.: (61) 296903900
Web Site: http://www.facilitatedigital.com
Sales Range: $1-9.9 Million
Emp.: 50
Integrated Digital Marketing Solutions for
Media Agencies, Advertisers & Publishers
N.A.I.C.S.: 541613

Webfirm Pty Ltd   **(1)**
2/419 Collins St, Melbourne, 3000, VIC,
Australia
Tel.: (61) 1300932347
Web Site: https://www.webfirm.com
Sales Range: $25-49.9 Million
Emp.: 30
Website Design Development & Online
Marketing Services
N.A.I.C.S.: 541490
L. Taryn *(Sr Mgr-Acct)*

Webfirm Search Pty Ltd   **(1)**
Ste 4 Boston Gardens 16 Broadie Hall Dr
Tech Park, Bentley, 6102, WA, Australia
Tel.: (61) 862525252
Web Site: http://www.searchworld.com.au
Search Engine Portals Development & Opti-
mization Services

N.A.I.C.S.: 519290

ADTEC PLASMA TECHNOLOGY CO., LTD.

5-6-10 Hikino, Fukuyama, 721-0942,
Hiroshima, Japan
Tel.: (81) 849451359
Web Site: https://www.adtec-rf.co.jp
Year Founded: 1985
6668—(TKS)
Rev.: $70,273,560
Assets: $165,738,120
Liabilities: $90,501,000
Net Worth: $75,237,120
Earnings: $7,544,860
Fiscal Year-end: 08/31/24
Electrical Component Mfr
N.A.I.C.S.: 335999
Hidenori Morishita *(Pres)*

Subsidiaries:

AD Technology Ltd.   **(1)**
1F No 208 Aikou 1st St, Jhubei, 302, Hsin-
chu, Taiwan
Tel.: (886) 3 6681 852
Electrical Component Distr
N.A.I.C.S.: 423610

ADTEC Plasma Technology China
Ltd.   **(1)**
Room 11/14 5F Block B No 5 Xinghan
Street Suzhou Industrial Park, Jiangsu,
China
Tel.: (86) 51266832252
RF Plasma Generator Mfr & Distr
N.A.I.C.S.: 334419

ADTEC Plasma Technology Korea
Co., Ltd.   **(1)**
Ojeong-dong 5F 1333 511beon-gil
Sinheung-ro, Bucheon, Gyeonggi-do, Korea
(South)
Tel.: (82) 326849566
Radio Frequency Plasma Generator Mfr &
Distr
N.A.I.C.S.: 335312

ADTEC Plasma Technology Taiwan
Ltd.   **(1)**
1F No 208 Aikou 1st St, Hsinchu County,
Zhubei, 302, Taiwan
Tel.: (886) 36681852
Radio Frequency Plasma Generator Mfr &
Distr
N.A.I.C.S.: 335312

ADTEC Plasma Technology Vietnam
Co., Ltd.   **(1)**
Lot J2 Que Vo IP Expanded area, Nam Son
Ward, Bac Ninh, Vietnam
Tel.: (84) 2222222089
Medical Device Mfr
N.A.I.C.S.: 334510

ADTEC Technology, Inc.   **(1)**
48625 Warm Springs Bvld, Fremont, CA
94539
Tel.: (510) 226-5766
Web Site: http://www.adtecusa.com
Emp.: 7
Electrical Component Distr
N.A.I.C.S.: 423610
Taras Bodrouk *(VP)*

Adtec Europe Limited   **(1)**
Unit 1 Alice Way Hounslow Business Park,
Hounslow, TW3 3UD, Middlesex, United
Kingdom
Tel.: (44) 2087375500
Web Site: http://www.adtec-rf.eu
Electrical Component Distr
N.A.I.C.S.: 423610

Hana Technology Co., Ltd.   **(1)**
227-1 Nae-Dong, Ojeong-GU, Bucheon,
Gyeonggi-do, Korea (South)
Tel.: (82) 326849566
Electrical Products Distr
N.A.I.C.S.: 423610

IDX Inc.   **(1)**
568-113 Ishizuka-Cho, Sano, 327-0103,
Tochigi, Japan
Tel.: (81) 283251576
Web Site: https://english.idx-net.co.jp
Emp.: 80

Electrical Component Mfr & Distr
N.A.I.C.S.: 335999

Phuc Son Technology Co., Ltd.   **(1)**
Thuong village, Khac Niem, Bac Ninh, Viet-
nam
Tel.: (84) 2413737178
Electrical Component Distr
N.A.I.C.S.: 423610

Suzhou Cuizhuo Dianzi Ltd.   **(1)**
Block B 4F 03/04 No 5 Xinghan Street, Su-
zhou Industrial Park, Suzhou, Jiangsu,
China
Tel.: (86) 5126 683 2252
Electronic Product Mfr & Distr
N.A.I.C.S.: 334419

ADTECHNOLOGY CO., LTD.

7-8 Gwanggyojungang-ro 248beon-
gil, Yeongtong-gu, Suwon, 13493,
Gyeonggi-do, Korea (South)
Tel.: (82) 312199700
Web Site: https://www.adtek.co.kr
Year Founded: 2002
200710—(KRS)
Rev.: $129,756,528
Assets: $184,903,516
Liabilities: $52,480,620
Net Worth: $132,422,896
Earnings: $4,440,710
Emp.: 264
Fiscal Year-end: 12/31/22
Semiconductor Devices Mfr
N.A.I.C.S.: 334413
Junsuk Kim *(Co-CEO)*

Subsidiaries:

SNS Technology Co., Ltd.   **(1)**
PO Box 281, Gosford, 2250, NSW, Austra-
lia
Tel.: (61) 67581106236
Information Technology Development Ser-
vices
N.A.I.C.S.: 541512

ADTHENA LTD.

9th Floor Fountain House 130
Fenchurch Street, London, EC3M
5DJ, United Kingdom
Tel.: (44) 203603 8003
Web Site: http://www.adthena.com
Year Founded: 2012
Online Advertising Services
N.A.I.C.S.: 541810
Will Richards *(CFO)*

Subsidiaries:

AdGooroo, LLC   **(1)**
730 W Randolph St, Chicago, IL 60661
Tel.: (312) 205-4260
Web Site: http://www.adgooroo.com
Sales Range: $1-9.9 Million
Emp.: 25
Digital Marketing Software & Services
N.A.I.C.S.: 513210
Richard Stokes *(Founder & CEO)*

ADTHINK MEDIA SA

79 rue Francois Mermet, BP 30, Tas-
sin, 69160, Lyon, France
Tel.: (33) 478429099
Web Site: http://www.adthink-
media.com
ALADM—(EUR)
Sales Range: $10-24.9 Million
Emp.: 91
Internet Services
N.A.I.C.S.: 541810
Sylvain Morel *(Co-Founder & Chm)*

ADTRACTION GROUP AB

Biblioteksgatan 29, 114 35, Stock-
holm, Sweden
Tel.: (46) 8359200
Web Site: https://www.adtraction.com
Year Founded: 2007
Q59—(DEU)
Digital Marketing Services
N.A.I.C.S.: 541810

Andreas Hagstrom *(CFO)*

ADUNO HOLDING AG

Hagenholzstrasse 56, PO Box 7007,
Oerlikon, 8050, Zurich, Switzerland
Tel.: (41) 589586000
Web Site: http://www.aduno-
gruppe.ch
Year Founded: 2006
Sales Range: $000 340.0 Million
Emp.: 800
Credit Card Issuing; Credit & Leasing
Services; Payment Services
N.A.I.C.S.: 522210
Roland Zwyssig *(CEO-Mktg)*

Subsidiaries:

Aduno Finance AG   **(1)**
Hansmatt 32, 6370, Stans, Switzerland
Tel.: (41) 41 7117876
Electronic Payment Services
N.A.I.C.S.: 522320

AdunoKaution PLC   **(1)**
Gattikonerstrasse 127, 8136, Gattikon,
Switzerland
Tel.: (41) 800 100 201
Web Site: http://www.adunokaution.ch
Electronic Payment Services
N.A.I.C.S.: 522320
Cornelia Hannig *(CEO)*

Vibbek AG   **(1)**
In der Luberzen 25, 8902, Urdorf, Switzer-
land
Tel.: (41) 44 500 35 40
Web Site: http://www.vibbek.com
Electronic Payment Services
N.A.I.C.S.: 522320
Stefan Kohler *(Founder & CTO)*

Subsidiary (Non-US):

Vibbek GmbH   **(2)**
Muhlenkamp 63b, 22303, Hamburg, Ger-
many
Tel.: (49) 40 60945800
Web Site: http://www.vibbek.de
Electronic Payment Services
N.A.I.C.S.: 522320

Viseca Card Services SA   **(1)**
Europa-Strasse 18, 8152, Glattbrugg, Swit-
zerland
Tel.: (41) 589588200
Web Site: http://www.viseca.ch
Credit Intermediation
N.A.I.C.S.: 522299

ADURO CLEAN TECHNOLO-GIES INC.

542 Newbold St, London, N6E 5S5,
ON, Canada
Tel.: (604) 681-1568
Web Site:
https://www.adurocleantech.com
Year Founded: 2018
ACTHF—(OTCQB)
Rev.: $29,672
Assets: $2,369,500
Liabilities: $946,711
Net Worth: $1,422,789
Earnings: ($2,510,130)
Fiscal Year-end: 05/31/21
Software Development Services
N.A.I.C.S.: 541511
W. Marcus Trygstad *(Co-Founder & CTO)*

ADUX SA

27 rue de Mogador, 75009, Paris,
France
Tel.: (33) 173038900
Web Site: https://www.adux.com
Year Founded: 1996
ADUX—(EUR)
Rev.: $27,734,453
Assets: $38,688,923
Liabilities: $43,360,979
Net Worth: ($4,672,056)
Earnings: ($416,588)
Fiscal Year-end: 12/31/19

Online Advertising, Internet Publishing & Broadcasting Services
N.A.I.C.S.: 541890
Cyril Zimmermann *(Founder)*

Subsidiaries:

Admoove Sweden AB　　　(1)
Norra Jarnvagsgatan 49, 827 32, Ljusdal, Sweden
Tel.: (46) 651768200
Web Site: http://www.admoove.se
Media Advertising Services
N.A.I.C.S.: 541810

Adux Benelux Sprl　　　(1)
Avenue Arnaud Fraiteur 15-23, 1050, Brussels, Belgium
Tel.: (32) 28965858
Marketing & Advertising Services
N.A.I.C.S.: 541810
Vincent Delmotte *(Mng Dir)*

Fotolog, Inc.　　　(1)
101 5th Ave & E 17th, New York, NY 10001
Tel.: (212) 620-6001
Web Site: http://www.fotolog.com
Online Social Networking Website
N.A.I.C.S.: 516210
Adam Seifer *(Co-Founder & Chief Product Officer)*

Hi-Media Belgium Sprl　　　(1)
19 Avenue des Volontaires, 1160, Brussels, Belgium
Tel.: (32) 2 894 84 00
Web Site: http://www.himediagroup.com
Emp.: 3
Internet Publishing Services
N.A.I.C.S.: 513199
Marko Blazevic *(Gen Mgr)*

Hi-Media Deutschland AG　　　(1)
Emanuel-Leutze-Strasse 8, 40574, Dusseldorf, Germany
Tel.: (49) 211 302 77 0
Web Site: http://www.hi-media.de
Online Advertising Services
N.A.I.C.S.: 541890

Subsidiary (Domestic):

Hi-media Perfomance Gmbh　　　(2)
ABC-Strasse 21, 20354, Hamburg, Germany
Tel.: (49) 40 22 69 290 0
Web Site: http://www.hi-media.de
Marketing Consulting Services
N.A.I.C.S.: 541613

Hi-Media Italy Srl　　　(1)
Via Stendhal 36, 20144, Milan, Italy
Tel.: (39) 028550111
Marketing & Advertising Services
N.A.I.C.S.: 541810

Hi-Media Portugal Lda　　　(1)
Rua Alexandre Herculano 9, 4 Floor, 1150-005, Lisbon, Portugal
Tel.: (351) 213 947 340
Web Site: http://www.hi-media.pt
Sales Range: $25-49.9 Million
Emp.: 3
Internet Publishing Services
N.A.I.C.S.: 513199
Benedita Simas *(Gen Mgr)*

Hi-media Ltd　　　(1)
New Penderel House 283-288 High Holborn, London, WC1V 7HP, United Kingdom
Tel.: (44) 2074009250
Sales Range: $25-49.9 Million
Emp.: 13
Internet Publishing Services
N.A.I.C.S.: 513199

Hi-media Nederland BV　　　(1)
Zijlstraat 76, Postbus 5543, 2000 GM, Haarlem, Netherlands
Tel.: (31) 235165544
Web Site: http://www.himedia-advertising.nl
Online Advertising Services
N.A.I.C.S.: 541890

Hi-media Network Internet Espana SL　　　(1)
Calle Velazquez 12 Pit 7, Madrid, 28001, Spain
Tel.: (34) 915913268
Internet Publishing Services
N.A.I.C.S.: 513199

Hi-media Sales AB　　　(1)
Box 71 Ljusdal 82722 , 302 43, Halmstad, Sweden
Tel.: (46) 35 260 70 00
Web Site: http://www.hi-media.se
Internet Publishing Services
N.A.I.C.S.: 513199

Premium Audience Network, Sl.　　　(1)
Calle Arlaban 7 8 Floor, 28014, Madrid, Spain
Tel.: (34) 912866840
Web Site: http://www.lagora-evolution.com
Marketing & Advertising Services
N.A.I.C.S.: 541810

ADVADIS S.A.
ul Henryka Pachonskiego 5, 31-223, Krakow, Poland
Tel.: (48) 12 415 8773
Web Site: http://www.advadis.com
Alcoholic Beverages Mfr
N.A.I.C.S.: 312120
Adam Tadeusz Brodowski *(Chm-Mgmt Bd)*

ADVAIT INFRATECH LIMITED
First Floor KIFS Corporate Office Besides Hotel Planet Landmark, S G highway, Ahmedabad, 380054, Gujarat, India
Tel.: (91) 7948956677
Web Site:
　　https://www.advaitinfra.com
Year Founded: 2009
543230—(BOM)
Rev.: $10,912,561
Assets: $11,008,099
Liabilities: $5,941,623
Net Worth: $5,066,476
Earnings: $726,065
Emp.: 57
Fiscal Year-end: 03/31/22
Eletric Power Generation Services
N.A.I.C.S.: 221114
Shalin Sheth *(Chm & Mng Dir)*

ADVAL TECH HOLDING AG
Freiburgstrasse 556, CH-3172, Niederwangen, Switzerland
Tel.: (41) 319808444
Web Site: https://www.advaltech.com
Year Founded: 1924
ADVN—(SWX)
Rev.: $207,793,792
Assets: $183,629,712
Liabilities: $49,065,410
Net Worth: $134,564,302
Earnings: ($2,603,104)
Emp.: 1,185
Fiscal Year-end: 12/31/22
Tools, Subassemblies Systems & Volume Components Supplier & Mfr
N.A.I.C.S.: 333515
Willy Michel *(Chm)*

Subsidiaries:

Adval Tech (Grenchen) AG　　　(1)
Niklaus-Wengi-Strasse 38, 2540, Grenchen, Switzerland
Tel.: (41) 326531935
Emp.: 42
Injection Molding Plastic Component Mfr
N.A.I.C.S.: 333511

Adval Tech (Hungary) Kft.　　　(1)
Bern u 40, 7100, Szekzard, Hungary
Tel.: (36) 74555160
Emp.: 139
Injection Molding Plastic Component Mfr
N.A.I.C.S.: 333511

Adval Tech (Hungary) Plant 2 Kft.　　　(1)
Bern u 40, 7100, Szekzard, Hungary
Tel.: (36) 74555160
Emp.: 110
Automobile Parts Mfr
N.A.I.C.S.: 336390

Adval Tech (Mexico) S.A. de C. V.　　　(1)
Prolongacion Circuito El Marques Norte No 4, Parque Industrial El Marques, 76246, El Marques, Queretaro, Mexico
Tel.: (52) 4422904500
Emp.: 100
Injection Molding Plastic Component Mfr
N.A.I.C.S.: 333511

Adval Tech (Suzhou) Co. Ltd.　　　(1)
Building B No 46 Chunxing Road Caohu Street, XiangCheng Economic Development Zone, Suzhou, 215144, China
Tel.: (86) 51266616556
Emp.: 95
Injection Molding Plastic Component Mfr
N.A.I.C.S.: 333511

Adval Tech (Switzerland) AG　　　(1)
Freiburgstrasse 556, 3172, Niederwangen, Switzerland
Tel.: (41) 319808111
Emp.: 191
Automobile Parts Mfr
N.A.I.C.S.: 336390

Adval Tech Management Ltd　　　(1)
Freiburgstrasse 556, CH-3172, Niederwangen, Switzerland
Tel.: (41) 319808444
Emp.: 250
Metal Stamping Mfr
N.A.I.C.S.: 332119
Juerg Spieler *(Gen Mgr)*

Adval Tech US Inc.　　　(1)
12200 Brookpark Rd, Cleveland, OH 44130-1146
Tel.: (216) 362-1850
Automobile Parts Mfr
N.A.I.C.S.: 336390

Adval Tech do Brasil Industria de Autopecas Ltda.　　　(1)
Av Rocha Pombo 2561 Aguas Belas-Aeroporto, Sao Jose dos Pinhais, 83010-620, PR, Brazil
Tel.: (55) 4132991700
Emp.: 67
Automobile Parts Mfr
N.A.I.C.S.: 336390

Awm Mold Service Us Inc.　　　(1)
900 Cummings Ctr Ste 219u, Beverly, MA 01915-6182
Tel.: (978) 720-4080
Sales Range: $25-49.9 Million
Emp.: 1
Injection Molding Machine Mfr
N.A.I.C.S.: 333248

Awm Mold Tech International Trading (Shanghai) Co. Ltd.　　　(1)
Room 1807 He Yi Bldg, 420 Jiang Ning Road, Shanghai, China
Tel.: (86) 2162678603
Sales Range: $25-49.9 Million
Emp.: 2
Injection Molding Machine Mfr
N.A.I.C.S.: 333248

Awm Plastpack Ltd.　　　(1)
Pilatusstr 19, CH 5630, Muri, Switzerland
Tel.: (41) 566754455
Web Site: http://teuscher-ag.ch
Sales Range: $25-49.9 Million
Emp.: 80
Injection Molding Machine Mfr
N.A.I.C.S.: 333248

FOBOHA (Switzerland) AG　　　(1)
Pilatusrint 2, CH 5630, Muri, Switzerland
Tel.: (41) 566754440
Web Site: http://www.advaltech.com
Sales Range: $25-49.9 Million
Emp.: 70
Plastic Molding Mfr
N.A.I.C.S.: 333248

FOBOHA (US) Inc.　　　(1)
900 Cummings Ctr Ste 219-U, Beverly, MA 01915-6182
Tel.: (514) 616-1018
Web Site: http://www.foboha.clever-kunden.de
Injection Molding Machine Mfr
N.A.I.C.S.: 333511

Omni Engineering Shanghai Co. Ltd　　　(1)

Part No 49 Plant No 199, Shanghai, 200131, China
Tel.: (86) 2150460808
Industrial Mold Mfr
N.A.I.C.S.: 333511

Omni Investors Pte. Ltd　　　(1)
331 North Bridge Road 13-04/06 Odeon Towers, Singapore, 188720, Singapore
Tel.: (65) 65577900
Investment Management Service
N.A.I.C.S.: 523999

Omni Plastics (Thailand) Co. Ltd　　　(1)
64/65 Eastern Seaboard Industrial Estate Moo 4 Highway 331, T Pluakdaeng A Pluakdaeng, Rayong, 21140, Thailand
Tel.: (66) 38 656 051
Web Site: http://www.advaltech.com
Emp.: 100
Plastic Products Mfr & Distr
N.A.I.C.S.: 326199

Omni Plastics (Xiamen) Co. Ltd　　　(1)
No 33 Xiangxing Rd 1st Xiangyu Free Trade Zone, Xiamen, 361006, China
Tel.: (86) 592 574 7060
Injection Molding Plastic Products Mfr
N.A.I.C.S.: 326199

Omni Precision Sdn. Bhd.　　　(1)
No 9 Jalan Tampoi 7/4, 81200, Johor Bahru, Malaysia
Tel.: (60) 7 340 2100
Injection Molding Machine Mfr
N.A.I.C.S.: 333248
Gan Teong *(Gen Mgr)*

QSCH Termelo es Kereskedelmi Kft　　　(1)
Matyas kiraly u 67, H 7100, Szekzard, Hungary
Tel.: (36) 36 74 512580
Sales Range: $50-74.9 Million
Emp.: 180
Metal Stamping Mfr
N.A.I.C.S.: 332119

Styner+Bienz Formtech Ltd.　　　(1)
Freiburgstrasse 556, Niederwangen, 3172, Switzerland
Tel.: (41) 319808111
Web Site: http://www.advaltech.com
Emp.: 250
Injection Molding Machine Mfr
N.A.I.C.S.: 333248

Teuscher Kunststoff-Technik Ltd　　　(1)
Niklaus-Wengi-St 38, CH 2540, Grenchen, Switzerland
Tel.: (41) 326531935
Sales Range: $25-49.9 Million
Emp.: 35
Injection Molding Machine Mfr
N.A.I.C.S.: 333511

ADVAN GROUP CO., LTD.
4-32-14 Jingumae, Shibuya-ku, Tokyo, 150-0001, Japan
Tel.: (81) 334750281
Web Site: https://www.advan.co.jp
Year Founded: 1975
7463—(TKS)
Rev.: $134,196,220
Assets: $520,193,780
Liabilities: $192,443,540
Net Worth: $327,750,240
Earnings: $68,076,390
Emp.: 248
Fiscal Year-end: 03/31/24
Construction Materials Whslr
N.A.I.C.S.: 423610
Masaji Yamagata *(Founder & Chm)*

ADVANCE CREATE CO., LTD.
3-5-7 Kawara Machi, Chuo-Ku, Osaka, 541-0048, Japan
Tel.: (81) 120816316
Web Site:
　　https://www.advancecreate.co.jp
Year Founded: 1995
8798—(TKS)
Rev.: $72,055,670
Assets: $74,530,080
Liabilities: $41,611,210
Net Worth: $32,918,870

Advance Create Co., Ltd.—(Continued)

Earnings: $124,075
Emp.: 338
Fiscal Year-end: 09/30/23
Insurance Agency Services
N.A.I.C.S.: 524210
Yoshiharu Hamada (Pres)

ADVANCE DOOR SYSTEMS LTD

North Turningoff Hwy No1 East On Tower Road, Regina, S4N 4N0, SK, Canada
Tel.: (306) 781-0207
Web Site:
http://www.advancedoor.com
Rev.: $10,868,119
Emp.: 40
Door Mfr
N.A.I.C.S.: 321911
Brent Slater (Owner)

ADVANCE EQUITY HOLDING

1 Zlatovrah Str, 1164, Sofia, 1164, Bulgaria
Tel.: (359) 29882413
Web Site:
https://www.advancequity.bg
Year Founded: 2006
ADVE—(BUL)
Sales Range: Less than $1 Million
Asset Management Services
N.A.I.C.S.: 523940
Petar Kerezov (Chm)

ADVANCE GOLD CORP.

432 Royal Avenue, Kamloops, V2B 3P7, BC, Canada
Tel.: (250) 314-0186
Web Site:
https://advancelithiumcorp.com
Year Founded: 2007
AALI.H—(TSXV)
Assets: $696,253
Liabilities: $387,438
Net Worth: $308,815
Earnings: ($2,839,402)
Fiscal Year-end: 05/31/22
Gold Mining Services
N.A.I.C.S.: 212220
Marie Cupello (CFO & Sec)

ADVANCE INFORMATION MARKETING BERHAD

No 18 Jalan Balam, 51100, Kuala Lumpur, Malaysia
Tel.: (60) 340432699
Web Site: https://www.aim-net.com.my
Year Founded: 2004
AIM—(KLS)
Rev.: $727,654
Assets: $2,406,785
Liabilities: $564,520
Net Worth: $1,842,265
Earnings: ($940,234)
Fiscal Year-end: 12/31/22
Business Process Outsource Services
N.A.I.C.S.: 541512
Siew Wei Mak (Exec Dir)

Subsidiaries:

Angkara Setia Development Sdn. Bhd.   (1)
No 18 Jalan Balam Off Jalan Ipoh, 51100, Kuala Lumpur, Malaysia
Tel.: (60) 40432699
Loyalty Consulting Services
N.A.I.C.S.: 541613

PT. Cls System   (1)
Jl Kebon Jeruk VII No 2E Maphar, Taman Sari, Jakarta Barat, 11160, Indonesia
Tel.: (62) 212 268 6277
Web Site: https://www.cls-indo.com
Loyalty Consulting Services

N.A.I.C.S.: 541611

ADVANCE LIFESTYLES LIMITED

2nd Floor West Wing Electric Mansion Appasaheb Marathe Marg, Worli, Mumbai, 400025, Maharastra, India
Tel.: (91) 2242319900
Web Site: https://www.advanoo.net.in
521048—(BOM)
Assets: $10,653,490
Liabilities: $6,439,280
Net Worth: $4,214,210
Earnings: $128,709
Fiscal Year-end: 03/31/22
Real Estate Manangement Services
N.A.I.C.S.: 531390
Phulchand Agarwal (Chm & Mng Dir)

ADVANCE LOGISTICS INVESTMENT CORPORATION

17th Floor Jinbocho Mitsui Building, Chiyoda-ku, Tokyo, Japan
Tel.: (81) 335563912
Web Site: https://www.adl-reit.com
Year Founded: 2018
3493—(TKS)
Real Estate Investment Services
N.A.I.C.S.: 531190
Junichi Shoji (Exec Dir)

ADVANCE METALS LIMITED

Suite 706 Level 7 89 York Street, Sydney, 2000, NSW, Australia
Tel.: (61) 289644373
Web Site:
https://advancemetals.com.au
AVM—(ASX)
Rev.: $12,760
Assets: $3,978,764
Liabilities: $114,231
Net Worth: $3,864,533
Earnings: ($485,940)
Fiscal Year-end: 12/31/23
Metallurgical Coal Producer
N.A.I.C.S.: 324199
Mark Sykes (Mng Dir)

Subsidiaries:

Texas & Oklahoma Coal Company Ltd   (1)
Suite 2201 Wing On House 22nd Floor 71 Des Voeux Road, Central, China (Hong Kong)
Tel.: (852) 2 892 2996
Web Site: https://www.texascoal.com
Coal Exploration Services
N.A.I.C.S.: 213113
Dominic Hill (VP)

Subsidiary (US):

Texas & Oklahoma Coal Company (USA) LLC   (2)
3026 Mockingbird Ln Ste 312, Dallas, TX 75205
Tel.: (214) 800-2801
Coal Exploration Services
N.A.I.C.S.: 213113

ADVANCE METERING TECHNOLOGY LIMITED

C-4 to C-11 Hosiery Complex, Phase II Extension, Noida, 201 305, Uttar Pradesh, India
Tel.: (91) 1206958777
Web Site: https://www.pkrgroup.in
Year Founded: 2011
AMTL—(NSE)
Rev.: $2,726,823
Assets: $18,264,140
Liabilities: $5,178,774
Net Worth: $13,085,367
Earnings: ($365,736)
Emp.: 83
Fiscal Year-end: 03/31/22
Wind Electric Power Generation Services

N.A.I.C.S.: 221115
Pranav Kumar Ranade (Chm & Mng Dir)

Subsidiaries:

Advance Power & Trading GmbH   (1)
Josef-Breher-Weg 3, Pullach I Isartal, 82049, Munich, Germany
Tel.: (49) 89460885110
Web Site: http://www.ae-trading.com
Electric Power & Natural Gas Utility Distribution Services
N.A.I.C.S.: 221210

ADVANCE MULTITECH LTD.

36 Kothari Market Opp Hirabhai Market Kankaria, Ahmedabad, 380 022, Gujarat, India
Tel.: (91) 7925454795
Year Founded: 1991
Polyurethane Coated Fabric Mfr & Distr
N.A.I.C.S.: 325510
Arvind Kumar Goenka (Chm & Mng Dir)

ADVANCE PETROCHEMICALS LIMITED

36 Kothari Market Opp Hirabhai Market, Kankaria, Ahmedabad, 380 022, Gujarat, India
Tel.: (91) 8758998855
Web Site:
https://www.advancepetro.com
Year Founded: 1985
506947—(BOM)
Rev.: $3,826,832
Assets: $2,108,488
Liabilities: $1,757,042
Net Worth: $351,447
Earnings: $40,349
Emp.: 58
Fiscal Year-end: 03/31/22
Petrochemical Mfr & Distr
N.A.I.C.S.: 325110
Shailesh Singh Rajput (Exec Dir)

Subsidiaries:

ADVANCE PETROCHEMICALS LIMITED - AHMEDABAD WORKS   (1)
Pirana Road, Piplej, Ahmedabad, 382 405, Gujarat, India
Tel.: (91) 7929708156
Web Site: https://www.advancepetro.com
Petrochemical Products Mfr
N.A.I.C.S.: 325110

ADVANCE RESIDENCE INVESTMENT CORPORATION

17th Floor Jinbocho Mitsui Building 1-105 Kanda-Jinbocho, Chiyoda Ward, Tokyo, 101-0051, Japan
Tel.: (81) 120938469
Web Site: https://www.adr-reit.com
Year Founded: 2010
3269—(TKS)
Sales Range: $150-199.9 Million
Real Estate Investment Trust
N.A.I.C.S.: 525990
Kenji Kosaka (Exec Officer)

ADVANCE SYNERGY BERHAD

Synergy 9 9 Jalan Kajibumi U170 Temasya Glenmarie, Seksyen 22, 40000, Shah Alam, Selangor Darul Ehsan, Malaysia
Tel.: (60) 351928822
Web Site: https://www.asb.com.my
Year Founded: 1920
1481—(KLS)
Rev.: $51,450,159
Assets: $178,152,593
Liabilities: $57,227,090
Net Worth: $120,925,503
Earnings: ($9,403,386)
Emp.: 607

Fiscal Year-end: 12/31/22
Property Development Services
N.A.I.C.S.: 236117
Anton Syazi Ahmad Sebi (Deputy Chm-Grp)

Subsidiaries:

Advance Synergy Realty Sdn. Bhd.   (1)
Lot 6807 6808 Synergy Square Jalan Matang, 93050, Kuching, Sarawak, Malaysia
Tel.: (60) 82646617
Web Site: https://www.asrsynergy.com.my
Property Development Services
N.A.I.C.S.: 531311

Alangka-Suka Hotels & Resorts Sdn. Bhd.   (1)
B-16-8 Megan Avenue II 12 Jalan Yap Kwan Seng, PO Box 11369, 50744, Kuala Lumpur, Malaysia
Tel.: (60) 321622922
Web Site: http://www.holidayvilla.com.my
Home Management Services
N.A.I.C.S.: 721110

Subsidiary (Domestic):

Alor Setar Holiday Villa Sdn. Bhd.   (2)
Lot 162 163 Jalan Tunku Ibrahim Bandar, Mukim Kota Star, 05000, Alor Setar, Kedah Darul Aman, Malaysia   (100%)
Tel.: (60) 47349999
Web Site:
http://www.holidayvillaalorstar.com
Emp.: 120
Home Management Services
N.A.I.C.S.: 721110

Cherating Holiday Villa Berhad   (2)
Lot 1303 Mukim Sungai Karang, 26080, Kuantan, Pahang Darul Makmur, Malaysia
Tel.: (60) 95819500
Web Site: http://www.holidayvillahotels.com
Sales Range: $10-24.9 Million
Emp.: 65
Hotel & Resort Management Services
N.A.I.C.S.: 721110

Langkawi Holiday Villa Sdn. Bhd.   (2)
Jalan Teluk Baru Pantai Tengah, Mukim Kedawang Langkawi, 07000, Kedah, Malaysia
Tel.: (60) 49529999
Web Site: http://www.holidayvillahotels.com
Emp.: 200
Resort & Spa Operation Services
N.A.I.C.S.: 721110

Subsidiary (Non-US):

P.T. Diwangkara Holiday Villa Bali   (2)
Jl Hang Tuah 54, Denpasar, 80030, Bali, Indonesia
Tel.: (62) 361288577
Web Site: http://www.indosat.net.id
Sales Range: $10-24.9 Million
Emp.: 45
Home Management Services
N.A.I.C.S.: 721110
Tri Cahyadi (Gen Mgr)

Antara Holiday Villas Sdn. Bhd.   (1)
B-16-8 Megan Avenue II 12 Jalan Yap Kwan Seng, PO Box 11369, 50744, Kuala Lumpur, Malaysia
Tel.: (60) 321622922
Home Management Services
N.A.I.C.S.: 721110

Orient Escape Travel (Sabah) Sdn. Bhd.   (1)
Shop No 17 1st Floor Block K Sadong Jaya, Jalan Ikan Juara 1 Karamunsing, 88100, Kota Kinabalu, Sabah, Malaysia
Tel.: (60) 88 246 406
Travel & Tour Operating Agencies
N.A.I.C.S.: 561510

Orient Escape Travel Sdn. Bhd.   (1)
No 2 Unit D-11-1A Menara Suezcap 1 KL Gateway Jalan Kerinchi, Jalan P Ramlee, 59200, Kuala Lumpur, Malaysia
Tel.: (60) 379321622
Web Site: https://www.orientescape.com.my
Home Management Services
N.A.I.C.S.: 721110
Agnes Cheah (Exec Dir)

Osteria Gamberoni Sdn. Bhd. **(1)**
Ground Floor Yap Ah Shak House 17 Jalan
Yap Ah Shak, 50300, Kuala Lumpur, Malaysia
Tel.: (60) 326029727
Web Site: https://www.gamberoni.co
Restaurant Services
N.A.I.C.S.: 722511

Paydee Sdn. Bhd. **(1)**
Level 1 Synergy 9 9 Jalan Kajibumi U1/70,
Temasya Glenmarie, 40150, Shah Alam,
Selangor, Malaysia
Tel.: (60) 355618488
Web Site: https://www.paydee.co
Financial Payment Services
N.A.I.C.S.: 522320

Postpay Sdn. Bhd. **(1)**
3A-5-1 Plaza Sentral Jalan Stesen Sentral
5 Kuala Lumpur Sentral, 50470, Kuala Lumpur, Malaysia
Tel.: (60) 327105016
Web Site: https://postpay.asia
Post Pay Online Services
N.A.I.C.S.: 522320
Patrick Yap *(CEO)*

Sadong Development Sdn. Bhd. **(1)**
1st Floor Blok K Sadong Jaya Jln Ikan
Juara, Karamunsing, 88100, Kota Kinabalu,
Sabah, Malaysia
Tel.: (60) 88238995
Sales Range: $50-74.9 Million
Emp.: 2
Property Managing Services
N.A.I.C.S.: 531311
Liew Chaw Thai *(Mgr)*

Synergy Cards Sdn. Bhd. **(1)**
Level 2 East Wing Wisma Synergy No 72
Pesiaran Jubli Perak, Seksyen 22, 40000,
Shah Alam, Selangor, Malaysia
Tel.: (60) 351917788
Web Site: http://www.synergycards.com.my
Sales Range: $50-74.9 Million
Credit Card Issuing Services
N.A.I.C.S.: 522210

Synergy Tours Sdn. Bhd. **(1)**
Unit D-11-A1 Menara Suezcap 1 KL Gateway, No 2 Jalan Kerinchi Gerbang Kerinchi
Lestari, 59200, Kuala Lumpur, Malaysia
Tel.: (60) 327703515
Web Site: https://www.synergy-tours.com
Tour Operator
N.A.I.C.S.: 561520

Synergy Tours Sdn. Bhd.2002 **(1)**
Unit D-11-1A Menara Suezcap 1 KL Gateway No 2 Jalan Kerinchi, Gerbang Kerinchi
Lestari, 59200, Kuala Lumpur, Malaysia
Tel.: (60) 327703515
Web Site: http://www.synergy-tours.com
Sales Range: $25-49.9 Million
Travel & Tour Operating Agencies
N.A.I.C.S.: 561510

Unified Communications (OHQ) Sdn.
Bhd. **(1)**
Level 2 Synergy 9 9 Jalan Kajibumi U1/70,
Temasya Glenmarie, 40150, Shah Alam,
Selangor, Malaysia
Tel.: (60) 351632888
Web Site: http://www.unifiedcomms.com
Software Development Services
N.A.I.C.S.: 541511

Yap Ah Shak House Sdn. Bhd. **(1)**
17 Jalan Yap Ah Shak, 50300, Kuala Lumpur, Malaysia
Tel.: (60) 326031638
Web Site: https://www.yapahshakhouse.co
Business & Exceptional Services
N.A.I.C.S.: 561499

ADVANCE SYNTEX LIMITED
233/2 & 238/2 GIDC Por Raman-
Gamdi, Vadodara, 391 243, Gujarat,
India
Tel.: (91) 8048799423
Web Site:
https://www.advancesyntex.com
Year Founded: 1974
539982—(BOM)
Rev.: $2,322,895
Assets: $6,078,523
Liabilities: $4,597,179

Net Worth: $1,481,345
Earnings: ($208,181)
Emp.: 21
Fiscal Year-end: 03/31/23
Glitter Product Mfr & Distr
N.A.I.C.S.: 325180
Bhavan Dhirendra Vora *(Mng Dir & CFO)*

ADVANCE TERRAFUND REIT
1 Zlatovrah Street, 1164, Sofia, 1164,
Bulgaria
Tel.: (359) 24008332
Web Site:
https://www.advanceterrafund.bg
Year Founded: 2005
ATER—(BUL)
Rev.: $60,470,147
Assets: $195,286,944
Liabilities: $14,434,941
Net Worth: $180,852,003
Earnings: $56,760,843
Fiscal Year-end: 12/31/22
Real Estate Investment Services
N.A.I.C.S.: 531190
Radoslav Manolov *(CEO)*

ADVANCE ZINTECK LIMITED
1821 Ipswich Road, Rocklea, 4106,
QLD, Australia
Tel.: (61) 737262030   AU
Web Site:
https://www.advancezinctek.com
Year Founded: 1997
ANO—(ASX)
Rev.: $6,223,291
Assets: $25,200,988
Liabilities: $2,244,257
Net Worth: $22,956,731
Earnings: ($602,965)
Fiscal Year-end: 06/30/24
Specialty Chemicals Mfr
N.A.I.C.S.: 325998
Geoff Acton *(Bd of Dirs, Mng Dir & Co-Sec)*

ADVANCECON HOLDINGS
BERHAD
16 18 and 20 Jalan Pekaka 8/3
Seksyen 8 Kota Damansara, 47810,
Petaling Jaya, 47810, Selangor Darul
Ehsan, Malaysia
Tel.: (60) 361579563   MY
Web Site:
https://www.advancecon.com.my
Year Founded: 1997
5281—(KLS)
Rev.: $89,386,219
Assets: $137,973,389
Liabilities: $94,113,692
Net Worth: $43,859,697
Earnings: ($3,873,556)
Emp.: 1,353
Fiscal Year-end: 12/31/22
Civil Engineering Services
N.A.I.C.S.: 541330
Ang Kia Phum *(Founder & CEO)*

ADVANCED ANALOG TECH-
NOLOGY, INC.
7F-1 No 1 Taiyuan 2nd St, Tai Yuen
Hi-Tech Industrial Park Hsinchu, Zhu-
bei, 30288, Taiwan
Tel.: (886) 36209588
Web Site: https://www.aat-ic.com
Year Founded: 1999
3438—(TPE)
Rev.: $32,391,427
Assets: $49,387,174
Liabilities: $4,602,570
Net Worth: $44,784,604
Earnings: $3,378,732
Fiscal Year-end: 12/31/22
Semiconductor Product Mfr
N.A.I.C.S.: 334413
Shao-Tsung Liu *(Chm & CEO)*

Subsidiaries:

Chern Yih Electronics Ent.Co.,
Ltd. **(1)**
3F No 2 Zhongai St, Shulin Dist, New Taipei City, 238, Taiwan
Tel.: (886) 286882638
Information Technology Services
N.A.I.C.S.: 541519

Winking Technology Co., Ltd. **(1)**
Unit6 6/F Hope Sea Industrial Center NO
26 Lam Hing St, Kowloon Bay, Hong Kong,
China (Hong Kong)
Tel.: (852) 23312292
Information Technology Services
N.A.I.C.S.: 541519

ADVANCED BIOLOGICAL
LABORATORIES (ABL) S.A.
52-54 Avenue du Dix Septembre,
L-2550, Luxembourg, Luxembourg
Tel.: (33) 78364685
Web Site: https://www.ablsa.com
Research & Development in Biotech-
nology
N.A.I.C.S.: 541714

Subsidiaries:

ABL Diagnostics S.A. **(1)**
72c rue de Thionville, 57140, Woippy,
France
Tel.: (33) 78364685
Web Site: https://www.abldiagnostics.com
Software Publr
N.A.I.C.S.: 513210

ADVANCED BLOCKCHAIN AG
Scharnhorststrase 24, 10115, Berlin,
Germany
Tel.: (49) 4060918677
Web Site:
https://www.advancedblockchain.com
BWQ—(DUS)
Rev.: $139,657,228
Assets: $256,774,595
Liabilities: $2,696,987
Net Worth: $254,077,609
Earnings: ($6,886,690)
Fiscal Year-end: 12/31/20
Software Development Services
N.A.I.C.S.: 541511
Michael Geike *(Founder, Co-CEO & Mng Dir)*

ADVANCED BRAKING TECH-
NOLOGY LTD.
73 Inspiration Drive, Wangara, 6065,
WA, Australia
Tel.: (61) 800317543   AU
Web Site:
https://www.advancedbraking.com
ABV—(ASX)
Rev.: $10,207,666
Assets: $8,566,373
Liabilities: $2,645,566
Net Worth: $5,920,807
Earnings: $1,137,821
Emp.: 23
Fiscal Year-end: 06/30/24
Vehicle Braking Systems Mfr & Distr
N.A.I.C.S.: 336340
Louis Scheepers *(Mgr-Sales)*

Subsidiaries:

Advanced Braking Pty Ltd **(1)**
19 Creative Street, Osborne Park, Wan-
gara, 6065, WA, Australia
Tel.: (61) 800317543
Web Site:
https://www.advancedbraking.com
Sales Range: $25-49.9 Million
Emp.: 3
Automotive Braking System Mfr
N.A.I.C.S.: 336340
Martin John *(Pres)*

ADVANCED BUSINESS ANA-
LYTICS (M) SDN. BHD.

Suite C-12-08 Block C Level 12
Plaza Mont Kiara, 2 Jalan Kiara Mont
Kiara, 50480, Kuala Lumpur, Malaysia
Tel.: (60) 362032300   MY
Web Site: http://www.spss.com.my
Year Founded: 1999
Sales Range: $1-9.9 Million
Emp.: 9
Predictive Analytics & Data Mining
Software Distr
N.A.I.C.S.: 423430
Carol Kha *(Bus Mgr)*

ADVANCED BUSINESS SOFT-
WARE & SOLUTIONS LTD.
Ditton Park Riding Court Road,
Datchet, SL3 9LL, Berks, United
Kingdom
Tel.: (44) 845 160 6162
Web Site:
http://www.oneadvanced.com
Year Founded: 1996
HR & Payroll Software Publisher
N.A.I.C.S.: 541214
Gordon Wilson *(CEO)*

Subsidiaries:

ModSys International Ltd. **(1)**
6600 LBJ Fwy Ste 210, Dallas, TX 75240
Tel.: (206) 395-4152
Web Site: http://www.modernsystems.com
Software Tools; Database Modernization
N.A.I.C.S.: 541511
Austin Scott Miller *(Chm)*

Subsidiary (Non-US):

BluePhoenix Solutions Italia **(2)**
Piazza Central Commerciale 44, San Fe-
lice, 20090, Segrate, Milan, Italy
Tel.: (39) 027539111
Web Site: http://www.bphx.com
Sales Range: $25-49.9 Million
Emp.: 10
N.A.I.C.S.: 541511

BluePhoenix Solutions Nordic
Aps **(2)**
Borupvang 2 C Fl 1 Tv, Ballerup,
Denmark   **(100%)**
Tel.: (45) 44208000
Custom Computer Programming Services
N.A.I.C.S.: 541511

Subsidiary (Domestic):

BridgeQuest, Inc. **(2)**
8000 Regency Pkwy Ste 300, Cary, NC
27518-8514
Tel.: (919) 863-0318
Offshore Software Development Outsourcing Services
N.A.I.C.S.: 541512

Subsidiary (Non-US):

I-Ter/Informatica & Territorio
S.p.A. **(2)**
Via Veneto 43 - A, Riccione, Rimini,
Italy   **(100%)**
Tel.: (39) 0541666611
Custom Computer Programming Services
N.A.I.C.S.: 541511
Domenico Mezzapesa *(CEO)*

Liacom Systems Ltd. **(2)**
5 Hatzoref St, Holon, 58856, Israel   **(51%)**
Tel.: (972) 35573400
Web Site: http://www.liacom.co.il
Sales Range: $25-49.9 Million
Computer System Design Services
N.A.I.C.S.: 541512

ADVANCED CERAMIC X COR-
PORATION
No 16 Tzu Chiang Road, Hsinchu
Industrial Hsinchu, Hsien, 30352,
Taiwan
Tel.: (886) 35987008
Web Site: https://www.acxc.com.tw
Year Founded: 1998
3152—(TPE)
Rev.: $45,814

Advanced Ceramic X Corporation—(Continued)

Assets: $129,669
Liabilities: $18,540
Net Worth: $111,129
Earnings: $8,609
Emp.: 285
Fiscal Year-end: 12/31/22
Electronic Component Mfr & Distr
N.A.I.C.S.: 334419
Chien-Wen Kuo (Chm & Pres)

ADVANCED CHEMICAL IN-
DUSTRIES LIMITED

ACI Centre 245 Tejgaon Industrial
Area, Dhaka, 1208, Bangladesh
Tel.: (880) 28878603
Web Site: https://www.aci-bd.com
Year Founded: 1973
ACI—(CHT)
Rev.: $277,099,664
Assets: $601,175,956
Liabilities: $402,866,561
Net Worth: $198,309,395
Earnings: $16,263,566
Emp.: 11,077
Fiscal Year-end: 06/30/23
Pharmaceuticals Mfr
N.A.I.C.S.: 325412
Arif Dowla (Mng Dir)

Subsidiaries:

ACI Agrolinks Ltd.   (1)
ACI Centre 245, Tejgaon Industrial Area,
Dhaka, 1208, Bangladesh
Tel.: (880) 1313762225
Web Site: http://www.amianshrimp.com
Shrimp Mfr
N.A.I.C.S.: 311710
F. H. Ansarey (Mng Dir)

ACI Biotech Limited   (1)
Simple Tree Anarkali Level-13 Plot-03
Block- CWS A Holding, No 89 Gulshan Av-
enue, Dhaka, 1212, Bangladesh
Tel.: (880) 2550685511
Food Mfr & Distr
N.A.I.C.S.: 311991

ACI Chemicals Ltd.   (1)
Novo Tower 14th Floor 270, Tejgaon In-
dustrial Area, Dhaka, 1208, Bangladesh
Tel.: (880) 288709827
Web Site: http://www.aci-chemicals.com
Chemical Product Whslr
N.A.I.C.S.: 424690

ACI Edible Oils Ltd.   (1)
Novo Tower Level-14 270, Tejgaon Indus-
trial Area, Dhaka, Bangladesh
Tel.: (880) 288709827
Web Site: https://www.aci-bd.com
Edible Oil Distr
N.A.I.C.S.: 424490

ACI Foods Limited   (1)
ACI Centre 245, Tejgaon Industrial Area,
Dhaka, 1208, Bangladesh
Tel.: (880) 28878603
Web Site: https://www.aci-bd.com
Food Mfr & Distr
N.A.I.C.S.: 311991

ACI Formulations Limited   (1)
ACI Centre 245 Tejgaon Industrial Area,
Dhaka, 1208, Bangladesh
Tel.: (880) 28878603
Web Site: https://www.aci-bd.com
Rev.: $49,270,015
Assets: $75,044,766
Liabilities: $38,938,917
Net Worth: $36,105,849
Earnings: $2,817,422
Emp.: 982
Fiscal Year-end: 06/30/2022
Herbicide Mfr
N.A.I.C.S.: 325320
Arif Dowla (Mng Dir)

ACI HealthCare Ltd.   (1)
Novo Tower Level-6, Tejgaon Industrial
Area, Dhaka, 1208, Bangladesh
Tel.: (880) 28834121
Pharmaceutical Product Mfr & Distr
N.A.I.C.S.: 325412

ACI Logistics Limited   (1)
Novo Tower Level-14 270, Tejgaon Indus-
trial Area, Dhaka, 1208, Bangladesh
Tel.: (880) 288709827
Web Site: https://www.aci-bd.com
Agricultural Products Import & Distr
N.A.I.C.S.: 424910
F. H. Ansarey (Mng Dir)

ACI Pure Flour Limited   (1)
Novo Tower 14 th Floor, 270 Tejgaon Indus-
trial Area, Dhaka, 1208, Bangladesh
Tel.: (880) 288709827
Web Site: https://www.aciflour.com
Wheat Flour Mfr
N.A.I.C.S.: 311824
Anis Ud Dowla (Chm)

ACI Salt Limited   (1)
ACI Centre 245, Tejgaon Industrial Area,
Dhaka, 1208, Bangladesh
Tel.: (880) 255068511
Salt Mfr
N.A.I.C.S.: 311942

Creative Communication Ltd.   (1)
House 18/A Road 123 Gulshan-1, Dhaka,
1212, Bangladesh
Tel.: (880) 29842593
Web Site: http://www.cclbd.co
Marketing & Advertising Services
N.A.I.C.S.: 541613

Infolytx Bangladesh Limited   (1)
244 5th Ave Ste B288, New York, NY
10001
Tel.: (646) 789-5101
Web Site: https://www.aci-bd.com
Healtcare Services
N.A.I.C.S.: 621999
Badrul Husain (CEO)

Premiaflex Plastics Ltd.   (1)
ACI Centre 245 Tejgaon I/A, Tejgaon Indus-
trial Area, Dhaka, 1208, Bangladesh
Tel.: (880) 2887860310
Web Site: https://www.premiaflex.com
Emp.: 550
Packaging Material Whslr
N.A.I.C.S.: 424130
Anisur Rahman (Bus Dir)

ADVANCED CONNECTION
TECHNOLOGY INC.

10F No 69 Sec 2 Zhongzheng E Rd,
Danshui Dist, New Taipei City, 251,
Taiwan
Tel.: (886) 288091060
Web Site: https://www.actt.co
Year Founded: 1994
3492—(TPE)
Rev.: $23,550,668
Assets: $28,679,705
Liabilities: $10,289,372
Net Worth: $18,390,332
Earnings: $1,606,947
Fiscal Year-end: 12/31/22
Electronic Parts Mfr & Distr
N.A.I.C.S.: 334419
Danny Ma (Chm)

ADVANCED DIGITAL BROAD-
CAST HOLDINGS SA

Route de Lausanne 319, 1293, Belle-
vue, Switzerland
Tel.: (41) 225928400
Web Site:
    http://www.adbholdings.com
Year Founded: 1995
Sales Range: $350-399.9 Million
Emp.: 866
Digital Television Broadcast
N.A.I.C.S.: 516120
Belinda Wong (Exec VP-Fin)

Subsidiaries:

ADB Broadband S.p.A.   (1)
Viale Sarca 222, 20126, Milan, Italy
Tel.: (39) 02 66172
Web Site: http://adbglobal.com
Broadband Sales & Research Facility
N.A.I.C.S.: 517810

ADB Services S.A.   (1)

Ave De Tournay 7, Pregny, 1292, Geneva,
Switzerland
Tel.: (41) 227990799
Web Site: http://www.adbholdings.com
Emp.: 50
Digital Television Equipments Retailer
N.A.I.C.S.: 423620
Andrew N. Rybicki (Chm)

Advanced Digital Broadcast Hong
Kong Ltd.   (1)
Unit No 2704 W Tower Shun Tak Ctr 168-
200 Connaught Rd, Central, China (Hong
Kong)
Tel.: (852) 23245222
Digital Television Equipments Retailer
N.A.I.C.S.: 423620

Advanced Digital Broadcast Inc.   (1)
10901 W 120th Ave Ste 230, Broomfield,
CO 80021-3426
Tel.: (303) 474-8600
Web Site: http://www.adbhoding.com
Sales Range: $25-49.9 Million
Emp.: 13
Set Top Box Distr
N.A.I.C.S.: 423620

Advanced Digital Broadcast Italia
S.r.l   (1)
Via Cassanese 224, 20090, Segrate,
Milano, Italy
Tel.: (39) 02 8907 8154
Web Site: http://www.adbglobal.com
Digital Television Equipments Retailer
N.A.I.C.S.: 423620

Advanced Digital Broadcast Ltd.   (1)
15F 205 Sec 3 Pei-Hsin Road, Hsin Tien,
231, Taiwan
Tel.: (886) 289131500
Sales Range: $75-99.9 Million
Emp.: 100
Digital Television Equipment Sales & Sup-
port Services
N.A.I.C.S.: 423620
Charlene Lu (Dir-HR)

Advanced Digital Broadcast Polska
Sp. z.o.o.   (1)
Trasa Polnocna 16, Zielona Gora, 65-119,
Lubusz, Poland
Tel.: (48) 684515151
Web Site: http://www.adbglobal.com
Emp.: 100
Digital Television Equipment Sales & Tech-
nical Support Services
N.A.I.C.S.: 423620
Jamusz C. Szajna (Mng Dir)

Advanced Digital Broadcast S.A.   (1)
Avenue de Tournay 7, Pregny-Chambesy,
Geneva, 1292, Switzerland
Tel.: (41) 227990799
Web Site: http://www.adbglobal.com
Digital Television Equipment Sales & Sup-
port Services
N.A.I.C.S.: 423620

Advanced Digital Broadcast Spain
S.L.U.   (1)
Edificio America II Calle de Procion 7,
Bloque 2 1 E, 28023, Madrid, Spain
Tel.: (34) 917080690
Web Site: http://www.centromedeco.com
Sales Range: $25-49.9 Million
Emp.: 22
Digital Television Equipment Sales & Sup-
port Services
N.A.I.C.S.: 517810

ADVANCED DIGITAL CHIPS
INC.

72-9 Beolmal-ro 3rd floor, Dongan-gu,
Anyang, 431-810, Gyeonggi-do, Ko-
rea (South)
Tel.: (82) 7040441400
Web Site: https://www.adc.co.kr
Year Founded: 1996
054630—(KRS)
Rev.: $18,228,916
Assets: $65,874,365
Liabilities: $43,437,656
Net Worth: $22,436,709
Earnings: $(4,459,199)
Emp.: 154
Fiscal Year-end: 12/31/22

Semiconductor Product Mfr
N.A.I.C.S.: 334413
Mi-Sun Kim (CEO)

ADVANCED DIGITAL HEALTH
MEDICINA PREVENTIVA S.A.

Av Das Nacoes Unidas 8501 17st
floor, Sao Paulo, 05425-070, Brazil
Tel.: (55) 1134346548   BR
Web Site: http://www.advanced-
dh.com
ADHM3—(BRAZ)
Sales Range: Less than $1 Million
Biotechnology Research Services
N.A.I.C.S.: 541715
Daniel Lindenberg Badke (CEO)

ADVANCED DYNAMICS COR-
PORATION LTD.

1700 Marie Victorin, Saint-Bruno, J3V
6B9, QC, Canada
Tel.: (450) 653-7220
Web Site:
    http://www.advanceddynamics.com
Year Founded: 1965
Emp.: 200
Engineeering Services
N.A.I.C.S.: 541330
Kevin Williams (VP-Bus Dev)

ADVANCED ENERGY MAN-
AGEMENT LTD.

222 Edinburgh Drive, Dartmouth, E1E
4C7, NS, Canada
Tel.: (506) 857-0818
Web Site: http://www.aemltd.com
Year Founded: 1985
Rev.: $11,737,568
Emp.: 40
Heating & Air Conditioning Equipment
Distr
N.A.I.C.S.: 423730
Rino Levesque (Founder)

ADVANCED ENERGY MINER-
ALS INC.

500 Boulevard Cartier Ouest Suite
249, Laval, H7V 5B7, QC, Canada
Tel.: (418) 786-5492   QC
Web Site: https://aemcanada.com
ORTH—(CNSX)
Chemicals Mfr
N.A.I.C.S.: 325180
Charles Taschereau (Pres)

ADVANCED ENERGY SYS-
TEMS LIMITED

285 Goodwood Road, Kings Park,
5034, SA, Australia
Tel.: (61) 882714001   AU
Sales Range: Less than $1 Million
Real Estate Development Services
N.A.I.C.S.: 531390
Chenghui Xu (Chm, CEO & Mng Dir)

ADVANCED ENZYME TECH-
NOLOGIES LIMITED

5th Floor A-Wing Sun Magnectica
Near LIC Service Road Louiswadi,
Thane, 400604, Maharashtra, India
Tel.: (91) 2241703200   In
Web Site:
    https://www.advancedenzymes.com
Year Founded: 1989
540025—(BOM)
Rev.: $73,137,110
Assets: $173,028,629
Liabilities: $17,365,940
Net Worth: $155,662,689
Earnings: $16,322,943
Emp.: 322
Fiscal Year-end: 03/31/22
Enzyme Mfr & Distr
N.A.I.C.S.: 325199
Beni Prasad Rauka (CFO)

Subsidiaries:

Advanced Bio-Agro Tech Limited (1)
Off No-201 2nd Floor S N 6/1/1 Deron Hills,
Opposite Bata Showroom Baner Road,
Pune, 411 045, India
Tel.: (91) 2027291020
Web Site: https://www.abtlenzymes.com
Enzyme Mfr & Distr
N.A.I.C.S.: 325199
O. P. Singh (Mng Dir)

Advanced Enzymes USA, Inc. (1)
4880 Murrieta St, Chino, CA 91710
Tel.: (909) 613-1660
Enzyme Mfr & Distr
N.A.I.C.S.: 325199

Enzyme Innovation, Inc. (1)
13591 Yorba Ave, Chino, CA 91710
Tel.: (909) 203-4620
Web Site:
    https://www.enzymeinnovation.com
Enzyme Mfr & Distr
N.A.I.C.S.: 325199

Evoxx Technologies GmbH (1)
Creative-Campus-Allee 12, 40789, Mon-
heim am Rhein, Germany
Tel.: (49) 2173409940
Web Site: https://evoxx.com
Biotechnology Research & Development
Services
N.A.I.C.S.: 541714
Michael Puls (Mng Dir & Head-Research &
Development)

JC Biotech Private Limited (1)
Plot No 3 Sagar Society Road No 2 Banjara
Hills, Hyderabad, 500 034, Telangana,
India   (95.72%)
Tel.: (91) 4023542124
Web Site: https://www.jcbiotech.com
Enzyme Mfr & Distr
N.A.I.C.S.: 325199
S. Chandra Sekhar (Mng Dir)

**Scitech Specialities Private
Limited** (1)
501 DLH Park SV Road, Goregaon West,
Mumbai, 400 062, India
Tel.: (91) 2241750000
Web Site: https://scitech.net.in
Pharmaceuticals Product Mfr
N.A.I.C.S.: 325412

ADVANCED FIBER RE-SOURCES (ZHUHAI) LTD
No 399 Chuangxin 3rd Road Tangjia,
Zhuhai, 519080, China
Tel.: (86) 7563898088
Web Site: https://www.fiber-
    resources.com
Year Founded: 2000
300620—(CHIN)
Rev.: $99,989,133
Assets: $281,801,722
Liabilities: $41,886,410
Net Worth: $239,915,312
Earnings: $8,399,745
Emp.: 2,000
Fiscal Year-end: 12/31/23
Power Optical Component Mfr & Distr
N.A.I.C.S.: 334516
X. L. Wang (Chm, CEO & Member-
Mgmt Bd)

Subsidiaries:

**Advanced Fiber Resources (HK)
Ltd.** (1)
Room 1002 10/F Ho Lik Centre 66A Sha
Tsui Road, Tsuen Wan, New Territories,
China (Hong Kong)
Tel.: (852) 24932026
Optical Component Distr
N.A.I.C.S.: 423690

Arcadia Optronix Inc. (1)
399 Chuangxin 3rd Road, Tangjia, Zhuhai,
519080, China
Tel.: (86) 7563898079
Optoelectronic Device Mfr & Distr
N.A.I.C.S.: 334413

Vlink Optics Corporation (1)

2nd Floor Building F2- B ChangFeng Indus-
trial Park Liuxian Third Road, Baoan Dis-
trict, Shenzhen, 518101, China
Tel.: (86) 7552 302 9655
Web Site: https://www.vlinkoptics.com
Packaging Technology Mfr
N.A.I.C.S.: 333993

ADVANCED HEALTH INTELLI-GENCE LTD
AHI—(NASDAQ)
Rev.: $339,559
Assets: $8,170,372
Liabilities: $1,615,320
Net Worth: $6,555,052
Earnings: ($15,382,676)
Emp.: 19
Fiscal Year-end: 06/30/22
Software Development Services
N.A.I.C.S.: 513210
Katherine Iscoe (Co-Founder)

ADVANCED HOLDINGS LTD.
21 Woodlands Close 06 23 Primz
Bizhub, Singapore, 737854, Singa-
pore
Tel.: (65) 63200102
Web Site:
    https://www.advancedholdings.com
Year Founded: 1993
BLZ—(CAT)
Rev.: $6,340,983
Assets: $32,620,617
Liabilities: $7,252,140
Net Worth: $25,368,477
Earnings: ($3,365,144)
Emp.: 27
Fiscal Year-end: 12/31/23
Holding Company; Process Equip-
ment Designer, Mfr & Whslr
N.A.I.C.S.: 551112
Kar King Wong (Founder & Mng Dir-
Advanced Grp)

Subsidiaries:

ATOM Instrument LLC (1)
4140 World Houston Pkwy Ste 180, Hous-
ton, TX 77032
Tel.: (713) 461-0034
Web Site: http://atominstrument.com
All Other Support Services
N.A.I.C.S.: 561990

**Advanced CAE (ME) Control System
L.L.C.** (1)
10th Floor C 2 Tower Al Bateen King Abdul-
lah Al Saud Plot W 35, PO Box 113100,
Abu Dhabi, United Arab Emirates
Tel.: (971) 25632382
Measuring Equipment Maintenance Ser-
vices
N.A.I.C.S.: 811210

Advanced CAE Ltd. (1)
No 238 Feng Cun Road, Qingcun Town
Fengxian District, Shanghai, 201414, China
Tel.: (86) 216 027 0066
Web Site: https://www.advcae.com
Chemical & Petrochemical, Oil & Gas,
Power Generation & Micro-Electronics Pro-
cess Equipment Designer & Supplier
N.A.I.C.S.: 334513

**Advanced CAE Saudi Arabia Com-
pany Ltd.** (1)
PO Box 37, Dammam, 31411, Saudi Arabia
Tel.: (966) 138356000
Process Analyzer System & Equipment Mfr
N.A.I.C.S.: 334513

Advanced CAE, Inc. (1)
501 Hickerson St Bldg 6, Conroe, TX 77301
Tel.: (936) 282-5050
Process Analyzer System & Equipment Mfr
N.A.I.C.S.: 334513

Advanced Controls Pte. Ltd. (1)
30 Woodlands Loop, Singapore, 738319,
Singapore
Tel.: (65) 6 854 9000
Web Site: https://www.advanceholding.com

Chemical & Petrochemical, Oil & Gas,
Power Generation & Micro-Electronics Pro-
cess Equipment Designer & Supplier
N.A.I.C.S.: 334513

Subsidiary (Non-US):

Advanced Controls (M) Sdn. Bhd (2)
Unit 706 Level 7 Amcorp Tower Amcorp
Trade Centre, No 18 Persiaran Barat,
46050, Petaling Jaya, Selangor, Malaysia
Tel.: (60) 376206585
Web Site: http://advancedholdings.com
Sales Range: $25-49.9 Million
Industrial Machinery Mfr & Distr
N.A.I.C.S.: 334514

Advanced Controls Co., Ltd. (2)
Room 612 JNK Digital Tower 111 Digital-ro
26-gil, Guro-Gu, Seoul, 08390, Korea
(South)
Tel.: (82) 25844207
Web Site: http://www.advancedholdings.com
Chemical & Petrochemical, Oil & Gas,
Power Generation & Micro-Electronics Pro-
cess Equipment Designer & Supplier
N.A.I.C.S.: 334513

Representative Office (Non-US):

**Advanced Controls Pte. Ltd. - Beijing
Representative Office** (2)
Ste C1018 Jun Feng Hua Ting Bldg No 69
BeiChen West Road, Chao Yang District,
Beijing, 100029, PR, China
Tel.: (86) 1058772833
Chemical & Petrochemical, Oil & Gas,
Power Generation & Micro-Electronics Pro-
cess Equipment Designer & Supplier
N.A.I.C.S.: 334513

**Advanced Engineering Holdings Pte.
Ltd.** (1)
21 Woodlands Close 06-23 Primz Bizhub,
Singapore, 737854, Singapore   (100%)
Tel.: (65) 63200102
Holding Company; Industrial Equipments
Mfr
N.A.I.C.S.: 551112

Subsidiary (Domestic):

Advanced CAE Pte. Ltd. (2)
30 Woodlands Loop, Singapore, 738319,
Singapore
Tel.: (65) 6 854 9000
Web Site: https://advcae.com
Analyzers Mfr & Installation Services
N.A.I.C.S.: 334513
Kim Teck Quah (Mng Dir & Head-Ops-
Global)

Guided Wave Asia Pte. Ltd. (2)
21 Woodlands Close 06-23 Primz Bizhub,
Singapore, 737854, Singapore
Tel.: (65) 63200102
Emp.: 100
Optical Measurement Instruments Whslr
N.A.I.C.S.: 423490

Subsidiary (Non-US):

Guided Wave Europe BVBA (2)
Lange Lozanastraat 142 Bus 2, 2018, Ant-
werp, Belgium
Tel.: (32) 470101384
Web Site: http://guided-wave.com
Sales Range: $50-74.9 Million
Electronic Devices Sales
N.A.I.C.S.: 423490

**Advanced Environmental Technolo-
gies Pte. Ltd.** (1)
30 Woodlands Loop, Singapore, 738319,
Singapore   (100%)
Tel.: (65) 68549000
Web Site: http://advancedholdings.com
Holding Company; Oilfield Equipments Mfr
& Distr
N.A.I.C.S.: 551112

Advanced Green Energy Pte Ltd (1)
30 Woodlands Loop, Singapore, 738319,
Singapore
Tel.: (65) 68549000
Web Site: http://www.advancedholdings.com
Oil Field Equipment Mfr
N.A.I.C.S.: 333132

**Advanced Process Equipment (Thai-
land) Co., Ltd.** (1)

188/83 Sukhumvit Road, Mueng Rayong,
Map Ta Phut, 21150, Rayong, Thailand
Tel.: (66) 386092556
Analyser Distr
N.A.I.C.S.: 423830

P.T. Advanced Agri Indonesia (1)
Rukan Puri Mutiara Blok BC No 3 Kel
Sunter Agung Kec, Tanjung Priok DKI Ja-
karta, Jakarta Utara, 14350, Indonesia
Tel.: (62) 2129461411
Petrochemical Product Mfr & Distr
N.A.I.C.S.: 325110

ADVANCED INFO SERVICE PLC
414 Phaholyothin Rd, Phayathai,
Bangkok, 10400, Thailand
Tel.: (66) 20295000   TH
Web Site: https://www.ais.th
Year Founded: 1990
AVIFY—(OTCIQ)
Rev.: $5,194,095,949
Assets: $12,497,297,280
Liabilities: $10,003,602,893
Net Worth: $2,493,694,387
Earnings: $799,959,684
Emp.: 8,335
Fiscal Year-end: 12/31/23
Telecommunication Servicesb
N.A.I.C.S.: 517112
Hui Weng Cheong (Pres & COO)

Subsidiaries:

**AD Venture Public Company
Limited** (1)
Room 2101 21St Floor No 1126/2 Vanit
Building 2 New Petchaburi Road, Makkasan
Subdistrict Ratchathewi District, Bangkok,
10400, Thailand
Tel.: (66) 22646288
Mobile Digital Marketing Services
N.A.I.C.S.: 541613

AIN GlobalComm Co., Ltd. (1)
Web Site: http://www.ain.co.th
Telecommunication Servicesb
N.A.I.C.S.: 517810

**Advanced Broadband Network Com-
pany Limited** (1)
414 Phaholyothin Road, Samsen Nai Sub-
district Phaya Thai District, Bangkok,
10400, Thailand
Tel.: (66) 20295000
Training Services
N.A.I.C.S.: 611430

Subsidiary (Domestic):

**Amata Network Company
Limited** (2)
702/2 Moo 1, Klongtamru Muang, Pattaya,
Chonburi, Thailand
Tel.: (66) 20295055
Fiber Optic Cable Mfr
N.A.I.C.S.: 335921

**Advanced Contact Center Co.,
Ltd.** (1)
414 Phaholyothin Road Samsen Nai,
Phayathai, Bangkok, 10400, Thailand
Tel.: (66) 2 029 5000
Web Site: http://www.acc-contactcenter.com
Contact Center Solutions
N.A.I.C.S.: 561439

**Advanced Digital Distribution Com-
pany Limited** (1)
414 Phaholyothin Road Samsen Nai,
Phayathai, Bangkok, 10400, Thailand
Non-Life Insurance Services
N.A.I.C.S.: 524128

Advanced Magic Card Co., Ltd. (1)
414 Phaholyothin Road Samsen Nai, Phaya
Thai, Bangkok, 10400, Thailand
Cash Cards Distr
N.A.I.C.S.: 522210

**Advanced Wireless Network Co.,
Ltd.** (1)
414 Phaholyothin Road, Samsen Nai
Phayathai, Bangkok, 10400,
Thailand   (99.99%)
Tel.: (66) 20295000

Advanced Info Service Plc—(Continued)

Web Site: https://www.awn.co.th
Network Operator
N.A.I.C.S.: 517112

Holding (Non-US):

**CS LoxInfo Public Company
Limited** (2)
(98.96%)
Tel.: (66) 22638000
Rev.: $101,852,869
Assets: $79,080,935
Liabilities: $32,873,633
Net Worth: $46,207,303
Earnings: $11,825,137
Fiscal Year-end: 12/31/2019
Internet Services
N.A.I.C.S.: 517810
Somchai Kittichaikoolkit (Mng Dir-Acting &
Head-Enterprise Sls Grp C)

Subsidiary (Domestic):

**Teleinfo Media Public Company
Limited** (3)
1126/2 Vanit Bldg 2 28th Fl Room Number
2803 2804 New Phetchaburi Road, Makkasan Ratchathewi, Bangkok, 10400, Thailand
Tel.: (66) 22628888
Web Site: https://www.teleinfomedia.co.th
Telephone Directory Publishing & Advertising Services
N.A.I.C.S.: 513140

Subsidiary (Domestic):

**Triple T Broadband Public Company
Limited** (2)
200 Moo 4 Chaengwattana Rd, Pak Kret,
11120, Nonthaburi, Thailand
Tel.: (66) 21002100
Web Site: https://fiber.3bb.co.th
Internet Service Provider
N.A.I.C.S.: 517810

Subsidiary (Domestic):

Triple T Internet Co., Ltd. (3)
200 Moo 4 Chaeng Watthana Road,
Pakkret District, Nonthaburi, 11120, Thai-
land
Tel.: (66) 21002100
Web Site: http://www.3bb.co.th
Internet Service Provider
N.A.I.C.S.: 517810

Digital Phone Co., Ltd. (1)
414 Phaholyothin Road, Samsen Nai
Phayathai, Bangkok, Thailand
Tel.: (66) 20295000
Mobile Phone Network Provider
N.A.I.C.S.: 517112

Fax Lite Co., Ltd. (1)
1291/1 Phaholyothin Road, Phayathai,
Bangkok, Thailand
Tel.: (66) 20295000
Building Acquisition Services
N.A.I.C.S.: 531390

MIMO Tech Company Limited (1)
1291/1 Phaholyothin Rd, Samsenni
Phayathai, Bangkok, 10400, Thailand
Tel.: (66) 20295000
Web Site: https://www.mimotech.co.th
Information Technology Development Ser-
vices
N.A.I.C.S.: 541511

MMO Tech Co., Ltd. (1)
1291/1 Phaholyothin Roag, Samsennai
Phayathai, Bangkok, Thailand
Tel.: (66) 2299 6000
Information Technology & Content Aggrega-
tion Services
N.A.I.C.S.: 541511

Saha Advance Network Co., Ltd. (1)
414 Phaholyothin Road, Samsen Nai
Phayathai, Bangkok, Thailand
Tel.: (66) 20295055
Wireless Network Services
N.A.I.C.S.: 517112

**SingTel Strategic Investments Pte
Ltd.** (1)
31 Exeter Road Comcentre, Singapore,
239732, Singapore

Tel.: (65) 68383388
Web Site: https://www.singtel.com
Cellular & Wireless Telecommunications
Services
N.A.I.C.S.: 517112

**Super Broadband Network Co.,
Ltd.** (1)
414 Phaholyothin Road, Samsen Nai
Phayathai, Bangkok, Thailand
Tel.: (66) 20295000
International Communications Network
N.A.I.C.S.: 517112

Wireless Device Supply Co., Ltd. (1)
414 Phaholyothin Road, Samsen Nai
Phayathai, Bangkok, 10400, Thailand
Tel.: (66) 20295000
Mobile Phones & Calling Cards Distr
N.A.I.C.S.: 423690
Somprasong Boonyachai (Chm)

**Yellow Pages Commerce Company
Limited** (1)
1126/2 Vanit Bldg 2 New Phetchaburi Road,
Makkasan Ratchathewi, Bangkok, 10400,
Thailand
Tel.: (66) 22628888
Advertising Services
N.A.I.C.S.: 541810

ADVANCED INFORMATION TECHNOLOGY PCL
37/2 Suthisan Winitchai Road Sam-
sen, Huai Khwang District Nok Sub-
district, Bangkok, 10310, Thailand
Tel.: (66) 22759400
Web Site: https://www.ait.co.th
Year Founded: 1992
AIT—(THA)
Rev.: $190,345,012
Assets: $192,125,711
Liabilities: $73,802,733
Net Worth: $118,322,978
Earnings: $14,703,132
Emp.: 620
Fiscal Year-end: 12/31/23
Systems Integration & Services
N.A.I.C.S.: 541512
Thana Chaiprasit (Chm)

ADVANCED INTEGRATED MANUFACTURING CORP. LTD.
23 Ubi Crescent, Singapore, 408579,
Singapore
Tel.: (65) 62388882
Web Site: http://www.aimcorp.com.sg
Sales Range: $50-74.9 Million
Electronics Manufacturing Services
N.A.I.C.S.: 334418
Jeannie Poh Yit Liang (Mgr-Grp
Matls)

Subsidiaries:

**Advanced Manufacturing Corp Sdn.
Bhd.** (1)
PT1866 Tingkat Perusahaan 6 Prai Free
Industrial Zone, 13600, Perai, Penang, Ma-
laysia
Tel.: (60) 43902882
Web Site: http://www.aimcorp.com.sg
Emp.: 46
Electronic Components Mfr
N.A.I.C.S.: 334418

**Advanced Manufacturing Corporation
Pte. Ltd.** (1)
23 Ubi Crescent, Singapore, Singapore
Tel.: (65) 62388882
Electronic Components Mfr
N.A.I.C.S.: 334419

ADVANCED INTERNATIONAL MULTITECH CO., LTD.
No 26 Zhonglin Rd, Xiaogang Dist,
Kaohsiung, Taiwan
Tel.: (886) 78721410
Web Site:
https://www.adgroup.com.tw
Year Founded: 1987
8938—(TPE)
Rev.: $669,817,872

Assets: $525,822,937
Liabilities: $283,910,171
Net Worth: $241,912,766
Earnings: $78,173,936
Emp.: 8,315
Fiscal Year-end: 12/31/22
Sporting Equipment Mfr
N.A.I.C.S.: 339920
Chien Cheng (Chm)

Subsidiaries:

Launch Technologies Co., Ltd. (1)
No 38 Jingjian Road Pingtung Export Pro-
cessing Zone, Qianjinli Pingtung, Ping-tung,
Taiwan
Tel.: (886) 87510505
Web Site: https://www.launchtech.com.tw
Emp.: 480
Golf Equipment Mfr
N.A.I.C.S.: 339920

ADVANCED INVESTMENTS GROUP
82 Grey Street, Bassendean, 6054,
WA, Australia
Tel.: (61) 892790600
Web Site: http://www.braziron.com
Iron Ore Mining & Exploration Ser-
vices
N.A.I.C.S.: 212210
Samuel James Morton (CEO & Sec)

ADVANCED LEISURE TECH-NOLOGIES PLC
Suite 38 Pinewood Studios, Pin-
ewood Road, Iver Heath, SL0 0NH,
Bucks, United Kingdom
Tel.: (44) 8702430908
Web Site:
http://www.venuesolutionsplc.com
Sales Range: $1-9.9 Million
Emp.: 28
Venue Management Software & Ser-
vices
N.A.I.C.S.: 513210
Stephen Thomson (Chm)

ADVANCED LITHIUM ELEC-TROCHEMISTRY (KY) CO., LTD.
No 2-1 Zinghua Road, Taoyuan,
33068, Taiwan
Tel.: (886) 33646655
Web Site: https://www.aleees.com
Year Founded: 2005
5227—(TPE)
Rev.: $22,121,877
Assets: $40,647,563
Liabilities: $18,323,547
Net Worth: $22,324,016
Earnings: ($12,447,206)
Emp.: 169
Fiscal Year-end: 12/31/22
Oxide Cathode Material Mfr
N.A.I.C.S.: 335910
Shengshi Zhang (Chm & Gen Mgr)

Subsidiaries:

**Advanced Lithium Electrochemistry
(HK) Co., Limited** (1)
Unit 706 Haleson Building No 1 Jubilee St,
Central, China (Hong Kong)
Tel.: (852) 33646655
Lithium Battery Mfr & Distr
N.A.I.C.S.: 335910

Aleees AU Pty. Ltd. (1)
62-64 Burwood Rd, Burwood, 2134, NSW,
Australia
Tel.: (61) 88633646655
Lithium Battery Mfr
N.A.I.C.S.: 335910

Aleees EU SARL (1)
28 rue de l'Amiral Hamelin, 75116, Paris,
France
Tel.: (33) 88633646655
Lithium Battery Mfr
N.A.I.C.S.: 335999

Aleees UK, Ltd. (1)
42-46 Station Road, Edgware, HA8 7AB,
United Kingdom
Tel.: (44) 88633646655
Lithium Battery Mfr
N.A.I.C.S.: 335999

ADVANCED MANUFACTURING CONTROL SYSTEMS LTD.
City East Plaza Floor 6 Block C
Ballysimon Co, Limerick, Crecora,
Ireland
Tel.: (353) 61 390 600
Web Site: http://www.amcsgroup.com
Emp.: 500
Waste & Recycling Software Devel-
opment Services
N.A.I.C.S.: 541511
Jimmy Martin (Founder & CEO)

Subsidiaries:

AMCS Corporation (1)
119 S 5th St, Oxford, PA 19363
Tel.: (800) 962-9264
Software Distr
N.A.I.C.S.: 423430

AMCS France SAS (1)
13 rue Berthelot, 59000, Lille, France
Tel.: (33) 359057439
Software Distr
N.A.I.C.S.: 423430

AMCS LTD (1)
2 Kings Inch Way, Renfrew, PA4 8YU,
United Kingdom
Tel.: (44) 8450503300
Software Distr
N.A.I.C.S.: 423430

AMCS Sweden AB (1)
Smedstorpsgatan 10, Skara, Sweden
Tel.: (46) 101550800
Software Distr
N.A.I.C.S.: 423430

Dossier Systems, Inc. (1)
6 Terri Ln Ste 700, Burlington, NJ 08016
Tel.: (609) 747-8800
Web Site:
http://www.dossiersystemsinc.com
Fleet Maintenance & Management Software
Services
N.A.I.C.S.: 541519
Jack Boetefuer (CEO)

PC Scale, Inc. (1)
119 S 5th St, Oxford, PA 19363
Tel.: (610) 932-4006
Web Site: http://www.pcscaletower.com
Emp.: 25
Solid Waste & Recycling Software Mfr
N.A.I.C.S.: 541511
Donald P. Tefft (Pres & CEO)

ADVANCED MEDIA, INC.
42F Sunshine60 3-1-1 Higashi Ikebu-
kuro, Toshima-ku, Tokyo, 1706042,
Japan
Tel.: (81) 359581031
Web Site: https://www.advanced-
media.co.jp
Year Founded: 1997
3773—(TKS)
Rev.: $39,666,610
Assets: $104,603,250
Liabilities: $30,194,480
Net Worth: $74,408,770
Earnings: $6,643,050
Emp.: 267
Fiscal Year-end: 03/31/24
Voice Recognition & Voice Verifica-
tion Systems Mfr
N.A.I.C.S.: 334419
Kiyoyuki Suzuki (Pres & CEO)

Subsidiaries:

Amivoice Thai Co., Ltd. (1)
50 GMM Grammy Place 18th Floor Room
1802 Sukhumvit 21 Road, Klong Toey Nuea
Wattana, Bangkok, 10110, Thailand
Tel.: (66) 216349903
Web Site: https://www.amivoicethai.com

Software Development Services
N.A.I.C.S.: 513210

**Shorthand center Tsukuba Co.,
Ltd.**   **(1)**
301 Nakayama Building 3-4-20 Toride, To-
ride, Ibaraki, Japan
Tel.: (81) 29 786 8801
Web Site: https://s-c-t.jp
Microphone Equipment Mfr
N.A.I.C.S.: 334310

ADVANCED MEDICAL INSTI-
TUTE INC.
Level 4 80 William Street, Sydney,
2011, NSW, Australia
Tel.: (61) 2 9640 5253   **NV**
Web Site:
   http://www.amiaustralia.com.au
Sales Range: $10-24.9 Million
Emp.: 184
Erectile Dysfunction & Premature
Ejaculation Treatment Programs
N.A.I.C.S.: 621111
Jacov Vaisman *(Pres & CEO)*

ADVANCED MEDICAL SOLU-
TIONS GROUP PLC
Premier Park 33 Road One Winsford
Industrial Estate, Winsford, CW7 3RT,
Cheshire, United Kingdom
Tel.: (44) 1606863500   **UK**
Web Site: https://www.admedsol.com
Year Founded: 1993
AMS—(AIM)
Rev.: $160,674,165
Assets: $368,133,652
Liabilities: $57,249,958
Net Worth: $310,883,694
Earnings: $20,229,082
Fiscal Year-end: 12/31/23
Designer, Developer & Producer of
High Performance Polymers for the
Healthcare & Specialized Non-
Medical Markets
N.A.I.C.S.: 325211
Christopher Meredith *(CEO)*

Subsidiaries:

Advanced Medical Solutions (Plym-
outh) Ltd.   **(1)**
Western Wood Way Langage Science Park,
Plympton, PL7 5BG, Devon, United
Kingdom   **(100%)**
Tel.: (44) 1752 209955
Web Site: http://www.admedsol.com
Sales Range: $25-49.9 Million
Emp.: 39
Developer & Mfr of Medical Cyanoacrylate
Technologies
N.A.I.C.S.: 339999

Advanced Medical Solutions (UK)
Ltd.   **(1)**
Premier Park 33 Road One, Winsford, CW7
3RT, Cheshire, United Kingdom   **(100%)**
Tel.: (44) 1606863500
Web Site: http://www.admedsol.com
Sales Range: $75-99.9 Million
Emp.: 170
Holding Company
N.A.I.C.S.: 551112

Advanced Medical Solutions (US)
Inc   **(1)**
170 Pine St, Norwell, MA 02061
Tel.: (781) 467-9764
Medical Equipment Whslr
N.A.I.C.S.: 423450

Advanced Medical Solutions B.V. **(1)**
Munnikenheiweg 35, 4879 NE, Etten-Leur,
Netherlands   **(100%)**
Tel.: (31) 76 503 9420
Web Site: http://www.admesol.com
Sales Range: $50-74.9 Million
Emp.: 30
Foam Product Mfr & Distr
N.A.I.C.S.: 326150
Pieter van Hoof *(Gen Mgr)*

Advanced Medical Solutions Israel
(Sealantis) Limited   **(1)**

Malat Building Technion City, Josepho Cen-
ter for Industrial Research, Haifa, Israel
Tel.: (972) 48291051
Wound Care Product Mfr & Distr
N.A.I.C.S.: 339112

Advanced Medical Solutions Ltd.   **(1)**
Premier Park 33 Road One Winsford Indus-
trial Estate, Winsford, CW7 3RT, Cheshire,
United Kingdom   **(100%)**
Tel.: (44) 1606863500
Web Site: http://www.admedsol.com
Sales Range: $50-74.9 Million
Emp.: 250
Developer & Manufacturer of Woundcare
Dressings
N.A.I.C.S.: 339113

Raleigh Adhesive Coatings
Limited   **(1)**
Raleigh Hall Industrial Estate, Eccleshall,
Stafford, ST21 6JL, United Kingdom
Tel.: (44) 1785850357
Web Site: https://www.raleighcoatings.com
Wound Care Product Mfr & Distr
N.A.I.C.S.: 339112

Resorba Medical GmbH   **(1)**
Am Flachmoor 16, 90475, Nuremberg, Ger-
many
Tel.: (49) 912891150
Surgical Dressing & Medical Grade Material
Mfr
N.A.I.C.S.: 339113
Frank Stiebert *(Mgr-Ops)*

Resorba ooo   **(1)**
Fadeeva str 5, 125047, Moscow, Russia
Tel.: (7) 959783627
Surgical Dressing & Medical Grade Material
Mfr
N.A.I.C.S.: 339113

Resorba s.r.o.   **(1)**
Haltravska 578, 34401, Plzen, Czech Re-
public
Tel.: (420) 379724233
Surgical Dressing & Medical Grade Material
Mfr
N.A.I.C.S.: 339113

ADVANCED MICRO-
FABRICATION EQUIPMENT,
INC.
188 Taihua Road 5001 Huadong
Road, Jinqiao Export Processing
Zone South Area Pudong, Shanghai,
201201, China
Tel.: (86) 2161001199
Web Site: http://www.amec-inc.com
Year Founded: 2004
688012—(SHG)
Rev.: $867,234,382
Assets: $2,980,386,935
Liabilities: $512,633,114
Net Worth: $2,467,753,821
Earnings: $247,273,482
Emp.: 1,800
Fiscal Year-end: 12/31/23
Semiconductor Poduct Mfr & Distr
N.A.I.C.S.: 334413
Gerald Yin *(Chm & CEO)*

Subsidiaries:

AMEC International Pte Ltd.   **(1)**
10 Ang Mo Kio Street 65 02-14 TechPoint,
Singapore, 569059, Singapore
Tel.: (65) 68583113
Micro-Fabrication Equipment Mfr
N.A.I.C.S.: 334413

AMEC Japan Co., Inc.   **(1)**
Shinagawa Center Building 8F 3-23-17 Ta-
kanawa, Minato-ku, Tokyo, 108-0074, Japan
Tel.: (81) 354757505
Semiconductor Product Mfr & Distr
N.A.I.C.S.: 334413

AMEC KML Inc.   **(1)**
28-85 Gajang Industry East Road, Osan,
18103, Gyeonggi-Do, Korea (South)
Tel.: (82) 3180772800
Semiconductor Equipment Mfr & Distr
N.A.I.C.S.: 334413

AMEC Korea Limited   **(1)**

376-2 Gajang- Dong, Osan, 447-210,
Gyeonggi-do, Korea (South)
Tel.: (82) 318 077 2800
Semiconductor Product Mfr & Distr
N.A.I.C.S.: 334413

AMEC Nanchang Ltd.   **(1)**
699 Tianxiang Avenue Nanchang High-tech
Industrial Development Zone, Nanchang,
330095, Jiangxi, China
Tel.: (86) 79182111199
Semiconductor Equipment Mfr & Distr
N.A.I.C.S.: 334413

AMEC North America, Inc.   **(1)**
1901 S Bascom Ave Ste 1005, Campbell,
CA 95008
Tel.: (408) 412-8458
Semiconductor Product Mfr & Distr
N.A.I.C.S.: 334413

AMEC Taiwan Ltd.   **(1)**
7F-1 No 1 Sec 3 Gongdao 5th Rd, Hsinchu,
30069, Taiwan
Tel.: (886) 35723111
Semiconductor Equipment Mfr & Distr
N.A.I.C.S.: 334413

AMEC Xiamen Ltd.   **(1)**
Unit 101 888 Tonglong Second Road Torch
Hi-Tech Industrial Zone, Xiang'an, Xiamen,
361100, China
Tel.: (86) 5927105282
Semiconductor Equipment Mfr & Distr
N.A.I.C.S.: 334413

ADVANCED NANO PRODUCTS
CO., LTD.
78 Geumhoangol-gil Bugang-myeon,
Sejong, 30077, Korea (South)
Tel.: (82) 442756962
Web Site: http://www.anapro.com
121600—(KRS)
Rev.: $61,292,616
Assets: $163,954,660
Liabilities: $11,402,465
Net Worth: $152,552,195
Earnings: $14,711,186
Emp.: 270
Fiscal Year-end: 12/31/22
Chemical Coatings & Powders Mfr
N.A.I.C.S.: 325998
Changwoo Park *(Pres & CEO)*

Subsidiaries:

ANP USA Inc.   **(1)**
7041 Koll Center Pkwy Ste 225, Pleasan-
ton, CA 94566
Tel.: (925) 461-3212
Printed Electronic & Solar Cell Mfr
N.A.I.C.S.: 334413

Advanced Nano Products Co., Ltd. -
Daejeon Facility   **(1)**
243-2 Techno jungang-ro, Yuseong-gu,
Daejeon, 34027, Korea (South)
Tel.: (82) 427106966
Printed Electronic & Solar Cell Mfr
N.A.I.C.S.: 334413

ADVANCED ONCOTHERAPY
PLC
Third Floor 4 Tenterden Street, Lon-
don, W1S 1TE, United Kingdom
Tel.: (44) 2036178728   **UK**
Web Site:
   http://www.advancedtherapy.com
AVO—(AIM)
Assets: $191,833,227
Liabilities: $108,510,727
Net Worth: $83,322,500
Earnings: ($40,042,876)
Emp.: 174
Fiscal Year-end: 12/31/21
Pharmaceuticals Mfr
N.A.I.C.S.: 325412
Michael Jeffrey Sinclair *(Chm)*

Subsidiaries:

The Women's Cancer Centre
Limited   **(1)**
54 Baker Street, London, W1U 7BU, United
Kingdom

Tel.: (44) 20 7034 1949
Cancer Treatment Services
N.A.I.C.S.: 622110

ADVANCED OPTOELEC-
TRONIC TECHNOLOGY INC.
No 13 Gongye 5th Road Hsinchu In-
dustrial Park, Hukou Township, Hsin-
chu, 303, Taiwan
Tel.: (886) 35976988
Web Site: https://www.aot.com.tw
Year Founded: 1999
3437—(TAI)
Rev.: $75,373,542
Assets: $100,679,674
Liabilities: $21,274,333
Net Worth: $79,405,340
Earnings: ($4,447,550)
Emp.: 770
Fiscal Year-end: 12/31/22
Surface Mount Device LED Products
Mfr
N.A.I.C.S.: 334413
Jung-Hsi Fang *(Chm & CEO)*

ADVANCED PACKAGING
TECHNOLOGY (M) BHD
Lot 2 Jln P/2A Kawasan MIEL Bangi
Industrial Estate, 43650, Bandar Baru
Bangi, Selangor Darul Ehsan, Malay-
sia
Tel.: (60) 389257101
Web Site:
   https://www.advancedpack.com.my
ADVPKG—(KLS)
Rev.: $6,093,521
Assets: $8,970,062
Liabilities: $1,863,943
Net Worth: $7,106,119
Earnings: ($276,335)
Emp.: 96
Fiscal Year-end: 12/31/21
Packaging Materials Mfr
N.A.I.C.S.: 327213
Shiak Wan Leong *(Co-Sec)*

ADVANCED PETROCHEMICAL
COMPANY
Jubail Industrial City, PO Box 11022,
Jubail, 31961, Saudi Arabia
Tel.: (966) 133566000
Web Site:
   https://www.advancedpetrochem.com
Year Founded: 2005
2330—(SAU)
Rev.: $786,154,113
Assets: $2,196,602,053
Liabilities: $1,231,800,560
Net Worth: $964,801,493
Earnings: $77,958,406
Emp.: 325
Fiscal Year-end: 12/31/22
Propylene Mfr
N.A.I.C.S.: 325110
Khalifa Abdullatif Al Mulhem *(Chm)*

ADVANCED PHARMACEUTI-
CAL PACKAGING CO.
Industrial Zone 118 B4, 10th of Ra-
madan City, 1534, Egypt
Tel.: (20) 15 368619
Web Site: http://www.app-eg.com
Year Founded: 1995
Glass Products Mfr
N.A.I.C.S.: 327213
Mamdouh Hussein Sadiq *(Chm &
Mng Dir)*

ADVANCED POWER ELEC-
TRONICS CORP.
12F-1 and 2 No 5 Taiyuan 1st ST,
Hsin-chu, 302082, Taiwan
Tel.: (886) 36215899   **TW**
Web Site: https://www.a-
   power.com.tw
Year Founded: 1998

Advanced Power Electronics Corp.—(Continued)

8261—(TAI)
Rev.: $93,239,213
Assets: $192,860,224
Liabilities: $19,181,529
Net Worth: $173,678,695
Earnings: $10,780,797
Emp.: 149
Fiscal Year-end: 12/31/23
Transistors & Related Products Mfr & Distr
N.A.I.C.S.: 334290
Fu-Chi Teng *(Chm, Vice Chm, Co-Pres, COO & Gen Mgr)*

ADVANCED SEMICONDUCTOR MANUFACTURING CORPORATION LIMITED
385 Hongying Road, Shanghai, 200233, China
Tel.: (86) 2164851900
Web Site: http://www.asmcs.com
Semiconductor Devices Mfr
N.A.I.C.S.: 334413
Wenjing Luo *(CFO)*

ADVANCED SOLTECH SWEDEN AB
Box 3083, 103 61, Stockholm, Sweden
Tel.: (46) 842503151
Web Site: https://gigasun.se
Year Founded: 2014
7ST0—(DEU)
Rev.: $20,517,950
Assets: $190,464,095
Liabilities: $137,103,693
Net Worth: $53,360,402
Earnings: ($7,142,937)
Emp.: 19
Fiscal Year-end: 12/31/23
Solar Electric Power Generation Services
N.A.I.C.S.: 221114
Frederic Telander *(Chm)*

ADVANCED SYSTEMS AUTOMATION LIMITED
33 Ubi Ave 3 08 69 Vertex, Singapore, 408868, Singapore
Tel.: (65) 65128310
Web Site: https://www.asa.com.sg
Year Founded: 1986
5TY—(CAT)
Rev.: $52,093
Assets: $14,823,081
Liabilities: $16,259,034
Net Worth: ($1,435,953)
Earnings: ($2,955,708)
Fiscal Year-end: 12/31/20
Semiconductor Equipment Mfr
N.A.I.C.S.: 334413
Searn Por Theng *(Sec)*

Subsidiaries:

ASA Multiplate Sdn Bhd　　(1)
Plot 52 Hilir Sungai Keluang Dua, Bayan Lepas Industrial Park Phase 4, 11900, Penang, Malaysia
Tel.: (60) 46415911
Electronic Components Mfr
N.A.I.C.S.: 334413

Emerald Precision Engineering Sdn. Bhd.　　(1)
No 20 22 Jalan Istimewa 5 Taman Perindustrian Cemerlang, Ulu Tiram, 81800, Johor, Malaysia
Tel.: (60) 78633300
Web Site:
　https://www.emeraldprecision.com
Electronic Components Mfr
N.A.I.C.S.: 334413

Microfits (Beijing) Technology Co., Ltd.　　(1)

No 15-1A Jingsheng South Street 4 Jinqiao Science Industrial Park, Tongzhou Park Zhongguancun Science Park Tongzhou District, Beijing, 101102, China
Tel.: (86) 106 059 5188
Web Site: https://www.microfits.com
Engineeering Services
N.A.I.C.S.: 541330

Pioneer Venture Pte Ltd　　(1)
Blk 3014 Ubi Road 1 02 280 282, Singapore, 408702, Singapore
Tel.: (65) 67461887
Plastics Product Mfr
N.A.I.C.S.: 326199

Yumei Technologies Sdn. Bhd.　　(1)
No 73-77 Jalan Industri 21 Kawasan Perindustrian, Alor Gajah Industrial Estate Alor Gajah, 78000, Melaka, Malaysia
Tel.: (60) 65565504
Diecast Component Mfr
N.A.I.C.S.: 333514

ADVANCED TECHNOLOGY & MATERIALS CO., LTD.
No 76 Xueyuan South Road, Haidian District, Beijing, 100081, China
Tel.: (86) 1062180969
Web Site: https://www.atmcn.com
Year Founded: 1998
000969—(SSE)
Rev.: $1,039,803,804
Assets: $1,530,303,840
Liabilities: $652,261,896
Net Worth: $878,041,944
Earnings: $29,637,036
Emp.: 300
Fiscal Year-end: 12/31/22
Metal Products Mfr
N.A.I.C.S.: 332999
Junfeng Li *(Chm & Sec-Party Committee)*

Subsidiaries:

AT&M Amorphous Technology Co., Ltd.　　(1)
No 76 Xueyuan Nanlu, Haidian District, Beijing, 100081, China
Tel.: (86) 312 712 8313
Advanced Metal Research & Development Services
N.A.I.C.S.: 541714

AT&M Biomaterials Co., Ltd.　　(1)
No 12 Yongcheng Beilu AT and M Yongfeng Industrial Base, Haidian District, Beijing, 100094, China
Tel.: (86) 105 874 2850
Advanced Metal Research & Development Services
N.A.I.C.S.: 541714

AT&M Environmental Engineering Technology Co., Ltd.　　(1)
No 76 Xueyuan Nanlu, Haidian District, Beijing, 100081, China
Advanced Metal Research & Development Services
N.A.I.C.S.: 541714

AT&M Star Electronic Component Co., Ltd.　　(1)
CISRI Base Huoju Nanjie, Zhuozhou, 72750, China
Tel.: (86) 3123973524
Metallic Product Mfr
N.A.I.C.S.: 332999

AT&M Venture Capital Investment (Shenzhen) Co., Ltd.　　(1)
No 76 Xueyuan Nanlu, Haidian District, Beijing, 100081, China
Tel.: (86) 106 218 0969
Advanced Metal Research & Development Services
N.A.I.C.S.: 541714

ATTL Advanced Materials Co., Ltd.　　(1)
Room 102 Unit 2 Buiding 4 TongRenJian LiuJiaYao, Fengtai District, Beijing, 100079, China
Tel.: (86) 1087659637
Web Site: http://www.attl.cn
Emp.: 1,000

Metallic Product Mfr
N.A.I.C.S.: 332999
Cai Rang *(Pres)*

Advanced Technology & Materials Co., Ltd. - Amorphous Metal Products Division　　(1)
No 10 Yongcheng Beilu Part B of AT&M Yongfeng Industrial Base, Haidian District, Beijing, 100094, China
Metallic Product Mfr
N.A.I.C.S.: 332999

Advanced Technology & Materials Co., Ltd. - Functional Materials Division　　(1)
No 30 Yuhua Road Part B of Tianzhu Airport Industry Zone, Shunyi District, Beijing, 101318, China
Tel.: (86) 80485810
Metallic Product Mfr
N.A.I.C.S.: 332999

Advanced Technology & Materials Co., Ltd. - International Trading Division　　(1)
No 76 Xueyuan Nanlu Haidian District, Beijing, 100081, China
Tel.: (86) 1062182822
Metallic Product Mfr
N.A.I.C.S.: 332999

Antai-heyuan Nuclear Energy Technology & Materials Co., Ltd.　　(1)
Part C No 10 Yongcheng Beilu AT and M Yongfeng Industrial Base, Haidian District, Beijing, 100094, China
Tel.: (86) 105 871 7382
Advanced Metal Research & Development Services
N.A.I.C.S.: 541714

Beijing AT&M Six Nine New Materials Co., Ltd.　　(1)
South District of CISRI No 13 Gaoliangqiao Xiejie, Haidian District, Beijing, 100081, China
Tel.: (86) 106 215 2801
Advanced Metal Research & Development Services
N.A.I.C.S.: 541714

Beijing ATAS Metal Materials Co., Ltd.　　(1)
No 10 Yongcheng Beilu Part C of AT&M Yongfeng Industrial Base, Haidian District, Beijing, 100094, China
Tel.: (86) 1058712755
Metallic Product Mfr
N.A.I.C.S.: 332999

Beijing Gang Yan Diamond Products Co., Ltd.　　(1)
Tel.: (86) 1069723307
Advanced Metal Research & Development Services
N.A.I.C.S.: 541714

Beijing Harmofinery Technology Co., Ltd.　　(1)
No 1811 B Building No 8 Beichen Donglu BeiChenHuiBinDaSha, Chaoyang District, Beijing, 100101, China
Advanced Metal Research & Development Services
N.A.I.C.S.: 541714

CISRI Da Hui Investment Co., Ltd.　　(1)
No 76 Xueyuan Nanlu, Haidian District, Beijing, 100081, China
Advanced Metal Research & Development Services
N.A.I.C.S.: 541714

Ganzhou JXTC Summit AT&M New Materials Co., Ltd.　　(1)
Xia No 58 ShuiXiMaFang, Zhanggong District, Ganzhou, 341000, Jiangxi, China
Tel.: (86) 797 825 1789
Advanced Metal Research & Development Services
N.A.I.C.S.: 541714

HXF Saw Co., Ltd.　　(1)
HXF Technology Park No 8 Dalian Road, Yichang, 443003, Hubei, China
Tel.: (86) 717 648 7477

Advanced Metal Research & Development Services
N.A.I.C.S.: 541714

Hebei Tianwei Huari Electric Co., Ltd.　　(1)
Tianwei Huari Technology Park China Electricity Valley High-tech Zone, Baoding, 071000, Hebei, China
Tel.: (86) 3128639101
High Power Transformer Mfr
N.A.I.C.S.: 335311

Heye Special Steel Co., Ltd.　　(1)
No 17ShiJiDaDao Street Economic and Technological development zone, Shijiazhuang, 052165, Hebei, China
Tel.; (86) 311 88382028
Web Site: http://www.hss-cn.com
Steel Product Mfr & Distr
N.A.I.C.S.: 332999
Yang Wenyi *(Chm)*

Subsidiary (Domestic):

HEYE & SUMMIT TOOLS CO., LTD　　(2)
320 Xiangjiangdao Gaoxinqu, Shijiazhuang, Hebei, China
Tel.: (86) 31185323224
Web Site:
　http://www.hsctools.globalimporter.net
Steel Products Mfr
N.A.I.C.S.: 332999

Highmag Technology (Shenzhen), Ltd.　　(1)
2/F Block 105 Luohu 1st High-ech Park No 72 Guowei Road, Luohu, Shenzhen, 518004, China
Tel.: (86) 75525850762
Web Site: https://www.highmagtech.com
Emp.: 300
Electronic Components Mfr
N.A.I.C.S.: 334419

Kunshan AT&MIK Co., Ltd.　　(1)
No 55 Yangqin Road, Kunshan, 215300, Jiangsu, China
Tel.: (86) 5123 687 1264
Advanced Metal Research & Development Services
N.A.I.C.S.: 541714

Shanghai Antai-Zhigao Amorphous Metal Co., Ltd.　　(1)
No 1455 Zhenchen Road, Shanghai, 200444, China
Tel.: (86) 2136162621
Metallic Product Mfr
N.A.I.C.S.: 332999

Tianjin Sainteagle Welding Co., Ltd.　　(1)
No 12 Quanzhou Road, Wuqing Development Area, Tianjin, 301700, China
Tel.: (86) 2282173565
Carbon Steel Equipment Mfr & Distr
N.A.I.C.S.: 331110

ADVANCED TECHNOLOGY & SYSTEMS CO., LTD.
JR Shinagawa E Bldg 8F, 2-18-1 Kounan, Minato-ku, Tokyo, 108-0075, Japan
Tel.: (81) 367175700
Web Site: http://www.adtx.com
Year Founded: 1993
Sales Range: $100-124.9 Million
Emp.: 50
Multimedia Products Including Disk Array Products (RAID), Mirror Drive Products & SCSI-IDE Converter Cards Mfr & Marketer
N.A.I.C.S.: 541512
Daisaku Maeda *(CEO)*

ADVANCED TECHNOLOGY COMPANY K.S.C.C.
Salmiya Block4 Salem Al Mubarak Street, PO Box 44558, ATC Tower opposite Laila Tower, Hawalli, 32060, Kuwait
Tel.: (965) 22247444
Web Site: https://www.atc.com.kw

Year Founded: 1981
ATC—(KUW)
Rev.: $537,879,411
Assets: $1,000,207,985
Liabilities: $774,533,726
Net Worth: $225,674,260
Earnings: $22,793,149
Emp.: 2,100
Fiscal Year-end: 12/31/22
Medical, Dental, Laboratory, Diagnostic, Pharmaceutical, Sterilization, Disinfection, Agriculture, Veterinary, Health, Fitness & Commercial Kitchen Equipment Importer & Supplier & Maintenance Services
N.A.I.C.S.: 423450
Fouad Mohammed Thunyan Al Ghanim *(Chm)*

ADVANCED VITAL ENZYMES PVT. LTD.

Unit No 424 4th Floor Lodha Supremus II, Road No 22 Wagle Estate, Thane, 400-604, India
Tel.: (91) 2249708404
Web Site:
http://www.vitalenzymes.com
Year Founded: 2005
Pharmaceutical Products Research & Development
N.A.I.C.S.: 325412

ADVANCEDADVT LIMITED

11 Buckingham Street, London, WC2N 6DF, United Kingdom   VG
Web Site:
https://www.advancedadvt.com
ADVT—(LSE)
Investment Services
N.A.I.C.S.: 523940
Vinodka Murria *(Chm)*

ADVANCER GLOBAL LIMITED

135 Jurong Gateway Road No 05-317, Singapore, 600135, Singapore
Tel.: (65) 66653855   SG
Web Site: https://www.advancer.sg
Year Founded: 2016
43Q—(SES)
Rev.: $49,292,585
Assets: $33,062,940
Liabilities: $9,122,169
Net Worth: $23,940,771
Earnings: ($3,192,456)
Emp.: 1,339
Fiscal Year-end: 12/31/23
Investment Holding Services
N.A.I.C.S.: 551112
Michelle Ying Li *(CFO)*

Subsidiaries:

AGS Integration Pte. Ltd.   (1)
18 Boon Lay Way 03-138, Singapore, 609966, Singapore
Tel.: (65) 62660300
Web Site: https://agsi.sg
Security System Services
N.A.I.C.S.: 561621

Advancer Smart Technology Pte. Ltd.   (1)
Blk 18 Boon Lay Way Tradehub21 05-130, Singapore, 609966, Singapore
Tel.: (65) 69622672
Web Site: https://advastech.com.sg
Building Management Services
N.A.I.C.S.: 541690

KH Security Pte. Ltd.   (1)
28 Sin Ming Lane 06-142, Midview, 573972, Singapore
Tel.: (65) 66599142
Web Site: https://khsecurity.sg
Emp.: 260
Security System Services
N.A.I.C.S.: 561621

Newman & Goh Property Consultants Pte. Ltd.   (1)
125A Lorong 2 02-134, Toa Payoh, Singapore, 311125, Singapore
Tel.: (65) 62569333
Web Site: http://www.newman-goh.com
Real Estate Services
N.A.I.C.S.: 531390

Prestige International Management Pte. Ltd.   (1)
583 Orchard Road 09-03 Forum, Singapore, 238884, Singapore
Tel.: (65) 68320733
Property & Casualty Insurance Services
N.A.I.C.S.: 524126

World Clean Facility Services Pte. Ltd.   (1)
No 2 Clementi Loop 03-02 Logis Hub, Clementi, Singapore, Singapore
Tel.: (65) 62718995
Web Site: http://www.worldcleanfs.com
Residential Cleaning Services
N.A.I.C.S.: 561720

ADVANCETC LIMITED

Level 5 Tower 8 Avenue 5 Horizon 2 Bangsar South City, 59200, Kuala Lumpur, Malaysia
Tel.: (60) 377223990   AU
Web Site:
https://www.advancetc.com
Year Founded: 2005
ATCLF—(OTCIQ)
Rev.: $3,153
Assets: $557,345
Liabilities: $928,625
Net Worth: ($371,280)
Earnings: ($1,447,088)
Fiscal Year-end: 12/31/20
Telecommunication Device Mfr
N.A.I.C.S.: 334220
Cheng Pheng Loi *(Co-Founder & CEO)*

ADVANCETEK ENTERPRISE CO., LTD.

8F No 218 Sec 3 Zhonghua Rd, Xinzhuang Dist, New Taipei City, 248, Taiwan
Tel.: (886) 82922288
Web Site:
http://www.advancetek.com.tw
1442—(TAI)
Rev.: $171,210,792
Assets: $572,428,933
Liabilities: $337,250,944
Net Worth: $235,177,989
Earnings: $56,358,970
Fiscal Year-end: 12/31/23
Construction Engineering Services
N.A.I.C.S.: 237990
Hung-Ying Wu *(Chm & Chief Strategy Officer)*

ADVANEX INC.

Tabata-Asuka Tower 6-1-1 Tabata, Kita-ku, Tokyo, 114-8581, Japan
Tel.: (81) 338225860
Web Site: https://www.advanex.co.jp
Year Founded: 1946
5998—(TKS)
Rev.: $175,488,890
Assets: $188,100,770
Liabilities: $133,310,480
Net Worth: $54,790,290
Earnings: $1,771,480
Emp.: 1,920
Fiscal Year-end: 03/31/24
Precision Springs & Precision Component Parts & Motors Mfr & Sales
N.A.I.C.S.: 332721
Eitaro Asada *(Chm, Pres, Chief Advisory Officer-Recruitment & Education Strategy & Dir-Rep)*

Subsidiaries:

ADVANEX (HK) LTD.   (1)
Room No 802B 8/F Empire Centre 68 Mody Road, Tsimshatsui East, Kowloon, China (Hong Kong)

Tel.: (852) 27088806
Web Site: http://www.advanex.co.jp
Precision Tools Distr
N.A.I.C.S.: 423830

ADVANEX PRECISION COMPONENTS (DALIAN) CO., LTD.   (1)
Dong Bei Street 3-29 Dalian Development Zone, Dalian, 116600, Liaoning, China
Tel.: (86) 411 87505525
Web Site: http://www.advanex.co.jp
Precision Springs Mfr & Distr
N.A.I.C.S.: 332613
Yecheng Lu *(Gen Mgr)*

ADVANEX PRECISION COMPONENTS (DONGGUAN) CO., LTD.   (1)
No 9 Xi-Hu Hi-Tech Information Industrial Park, Shilong Town, Dongguan, 523325, Guangdong, China
Tel.: (86) 76986186600
Web Site: http://www.advanex.co.jp
Precision Component Mfr
N.A.I.C.S.: 332721
Tsuneo Shibano *(Gen Mgr)*

Accurate Inc.   (1)
Minami Koshigaya 4 16 13, Koshigaya, 343-0845, Saitama, Japan
Tel.: (81) 489869621
Web Site: http://www.accurate.jp
Rev.: $6,915,755
Emp.: 35
Mechanical Components Sales
N.A.I.C.S.: 333613
Tsuchiya Kazunobu *(Pres & CEO)*

Advanex (Changzhou) Inc.   (1)
B3 No 12 Xinhui Road, Wujin, Changzhou, 213164, Jiangsu, China
Tel.: (86) 5198 128 2688
Electrical Equipment Mfr & Distr
N.A.I.C.S.: 335999

Advanex (Dalian) Inc.   (1)
Dong Bei Street 3-29, Dalian Development Zone, Dalian, 116600, China
Tel.: (86) 4118 750 5525
Electrical Equipment Mfr & Distr
N.A.I.C.S.: 335999

Advanex (Dongguan) Inc.   (1)
No 9 Xi-Hu, Hi-Tech Information Industrial Park Shilong Town, Dongguan, 523325, Guangdong, China
Tel.: (86) 7698 618 6600
Electrical Equipment Mfr & Distr
N.A.I.C.S.: 335999

Advanex (India) Private Limited   (1)
Building B-300 A Indospace Industrial Park Block-B Walajabad Road, Sriperumbudur Taluk Kanchipuram Dist, Oragadam, 631 604, India
Tel.: (91) 950 012 2267
Electrical Equipment Mfr & Distr
N.A.I.C.S.: 335999

Advanex (Singapore) Pte. Ltd.   (1)
2306 Bedok Reservoir Road, Singapore, 479224, Singapore
Tel.: (65) 6 448 8639
Electrical Equipment Mfr & Distr
N.A.I.C.S.: 335999

Advanex (Thailand) Ltd.   (1)
151 Moo 1 Tambol Bann-len Amphur, Bang Pa-In, Phra Nakhon Si Ayutthaya, 13160, Thailand
Tel.: (66) 35314200
Web Site: http://www.advanex.co.th
Precision Springs Mfr
N.A.I.C.S.: 332613

Advanex (Vietnam) Ltd.   (1)
No 18 Road 11, VSIP Bac Ninh Integrated Township and Industrial Park Tien Du District, Dai Dong, Bac Ninh, Vietnam
Tel.: (84) 222 362 6887
Electrical Equipment Mfr & Distr
N.A.I.C.S.: 335999

Advanex Americas, Inc.   (1)
5780 Cerritos Ave, Cypress, CA 90630
Tel.: (714) 995-4519
Web Site: http://www.advanexusa.com
Precision Springs & Wire Forms Mfr
N.A.I.C.S.: 331222
James Grueser *(Pres)*

Advanex Czech Republic s.r.o.   (1)
U Tabulky 3085 Homi Pocernice, 193 00, Prague, Czech Republic
Tel.: (420) 25 570 9420
Electrical Equipment Mfr & Distr
N.A.I.C.S.: 335999

Advanex Deutschland GmbH   (1)
Schifferstrasse 210, Regierungsbezirk Dusseldorf, 47059, Duisburg, Germany
Tel.: (49) 170 362 3358
Electrical Equipment Mfr & Distr
N.A.I.C.S.: 335999

Advanex Europe Ltd   (1)
Glaisdale Dr W, Bilborough, Nottingham, NG8 4JY, United Kingdom
Tel.: (44) 3300539110
Web Site: https://advanex.co.uk
Sales Range: $25-49.9 Million
Emp.: 70
Compression Springs, Tension Springs, Torsion Springs, Flat Springs, Power Springs, Spiral Springs, Wire Forms, Pressings, Assemblies & Associated Components Mfr
N.A.I.C.S.: 331222

Advanex Europe Ltd.   (1)
Mill Park Way off Station Road, Southwell, NG25 0ET, Nottingham, United Kingdom
Tel.: (44) 1636815555
Web Site: http://www.advanex.co.uk
Sales Range: $50-74.9 Million
Emp.: 175
Precision Springs Mfr & Distr
N.A.I.C.S.: 332613
Ian Beardsmore *(Mng Dir)*

Subsidiary (Domestic):

MOTOFIT LIMITED   (2)
Lath Lane Spon Lane South, Smethwick, B66 1EA, West Midlands, United Kingdom
Tel.: (44) 1215537222
Web Site: http://www.porticoproducts.com
Sales Range: $50-74.9 Million
Emp.: 4
Electrical Parts & Shutter Components Distr
N.A.I.C.S.: 423510
Karl Williams *(Gen Mgr)*

Advanex de Mexico S. de R.L. de C.V.   (1)
Parque Industrial FINSA 1 Carretara Estatal 100Km 2, 565 Business Center II Suite 2, El Marques, Queretaro, Mexico
Tel.: (52) 442 404 9700
Electrical Equipment Mfr & Distr
N.A.I.C.S.: 335999

FUJI MICRO CO., LTD.   (1)
Matsuura Building 2F Uchi-kanda 3-16-9, Chiyoda-ku, Tokyo, 101-0047, Japan
Tel.: (81) 335266121
Web Site: http://www.fuji-micro.co.jp
Rev.: $42,415,490
Emp.: 40
Motors Mfr & Distr
N.A.I.C.S.: 335312
Toshiyuki Saito *(Auditor)*

Subsidiary (Non-US):

Fuji Micro Electronics Co., Ltd.   (2)
118 Shitanxi Road Shijing, Guangzhou, 510430, Guangdong, China
Tel.: (86) 2086421716
Sales Range: $200-249.9 Million
Motor Assemblies Mfr
N.A.I.C.S.: 326220

KATO SPRING (SHANGHAI) CO., LTD.   (1)
Standard Building 54 No 199 North Ri Ying Road, Waigaoqiao Free Trade Zone, Shanghai, 200131, China
Tel.: (86) 2150461717
Web Site: http://www.kato.com.sg
Sales Range: $50-74.9 Million
Emp.: 200
Precision Springs Mfr
N.A.I.C.S.: 332613

PT. Advanex Precision Indonesia (1)
Block C1-16 Cikarang Selatan, Lippo Cikarang Industrial Estate, Bekasi, 17855, Jawa Barat, Indonesia
Tel.: (62) 21 897 4272
Electrical Equipment Mfr & Distr
N.A.I.C.S.: 335999

Advanex Inc.—(Continued)

ADVANI HOTELS & RESORTS (INDIA) LIMITED
18 Jolly Makers Chambers - II Nariman Point, Mumbai, 400 021, India
Tel.: (91) 2222850101
Web Site:
   http://oaravelabeachresort.com
ADVANIHOTR—(NSE)
Rev.: $3,846,241
Assets: $8,789,521
Liabilities: $2,886,229
Net Worth: $5,903,293
Earnings: ($557,090)
Emp.: 153
Fiscal Year-end: 03/31/21
Hotel & Resort Management Services
N.A.I.C.S.: 721110
Shankar Kulkarni (CFO)

ADVANSA PTY. LTD.
1/40 Birralee Rd Regency Park, Adelaide, 5010, SA, Australia
Tel.: (61) 8 8243 9100
Web Site:
   http://www.advansa.com.au
Year Founded: 1948
Hardware Whslr
N.A.I.C.S.: 423710

ADVANTAGE COMMUNICATIONS, INC.
265 Brackley Point Road, Charlottetown, C1E 2A3, PE, Canada
Tel.: (800) 269-4022
Web Site:
   http://www.advantagecall.com
Call Center
N.A.I.C.S.: 519290
Gregory Hough (CEO)

Subsidiaries:

First Kontact LLC   **(1)**
823 Anchorage Pl, Chula Vista, CA 91914-4534
Tel.: (619) 400-4136
Web Site: http://www.firstkontact.com
Landscaping Services
N.A.I.C.S.: 561730
Juan Gutierrez (CEO)

ADVANTAGE ENERGY LTD.
Millennium Tower Suite 2200 440 2 Avenue SW, Calgary, T2P 5E9, AB, Canada
Tel.: (403) 718-8000   **AB**
Web Site:
   https://www.advantageog.com
Year Founded: 1997
AAV—(TSX)
Rev.: $359,009,414
Assets: $1,560,640,777
Liabilities: $418,419,668
Net Worth: $1,142,221,109
Earnings: $321,794,007
Emp.: 42
Fiscal Year-end: 12/31/21
Oil & Gas Exploration Services
N.A.I.C.S.: 211120
Jay P. Reid (Sec)

ADVANTAGE PARTNERS LLP
17F Toranomon Towers 4-1-28 Toranomon, Minato-ku, Tokyo, 105 0001, Japan
Tel.: (81) 351570170
Web Site:
   http://www.advantagepartners.com
Year Founded: 1992
Privater Equity Firm
N.A.I.C.S.: 523999
Taisuke Sasanuma (Partner)

Subsidiaries:

ESG Holdings, Ltd.   **(1)**
12 Europa View, Sheffield, S9 1XH, South

Yorkshire, United Kingdom
Tel.: (44) 114 251 9210
Facility Management Services
N.A.I.C.S.: 561210
Gavin Freed (CEO)

PiPEDO HD, Inc.   **(1)**
2-9-11 Akasaka, Minato-ku, Tokyo, 107-0052, Japan
Tel.: (81) 355756601
Web Site: http://www.pipedohd.com
Rev.: $75,562,080
Assets: $90,382,160
Liabilities: $37,268,000
Net Worth: $53,114,160
Earnings: $10,677,040
Fiscal Year-end: 02/28/2022
Business To Business Web Solution Services
N.A.I.C.S.: 425120

Q'sai Co., Ltd.   **(1)**
1-7-16 Kusagae, Chuo-ku, Fukuoka, 810-8606, Japan
Tel.: (81) 927240831
Web Site: http://corporate.kyusai.co.jp
Sales Range: $50-74.9 Million
Emp.: 498
Health Food Products Mfr & Distr
N.A.I.C.S.: 311999
Satoshi Kambe (Pres)

Riraku Co., Ltd.   **(1)**
Osaka Bay Tower Office 18F 1-2-1 Benten, Osaka, Japan
Tel.: (81) 6 4400 5400
Web Site: http://www.relxle.com
Emp.: 311
Massage Salon Operator
N.A.I.C.S.: 812199
Takuho Nibe (Pres & CEO)

United Cinemas Co., Ltd.   **(1)**
Izumiakasaka Bldg 2-22-24 Akasaka, Minato-Ku, Tokyo, 107-0052,
Japan   **(100%)**
Tel.: (81) 332243200
Web Site: http://www.unitedcinemas.jp
Motion Picture Theater Operating Services
N.A.I.C.S.: 512131

Xacti Corporation   **(1)**
1-1 Sanyocho, Daito, 574-8534, Osaka,
Japan   **(100%)**
Tel.: (81) 72 870 6204
Web Site: http://www.xacti-co.com
Emp.: 507
Digital Cameras Mfr & Distr
N.A.I.C.S.: 333310
Takao Nishiyama (Pres & COO)

ADVANTAGE RISK MANAGEMENT CO.,LTD.
Nakameguro GT Tower 17F 2-1-1 Kamimeguro, Meguro-ku, Tokyo, 153-0051, Japan
Tel.: (81) 357943800
Web Site: https://www.armg.jp
Year Founded: 1999
8769—(TKS)
Rev.: $46,256,780
Assets: $43,262,450
Liabilities: $16,954,650
Net Worth: $26,307,800
Earnings: $3,338,050
Emp.: 164
Fiscal Year-end: 03/31/24
Psychological Health Care Services
N.A.I.C.S.: 621610
Takefumi Morimitsu (Mng Exec Officer)

ADVANTAGEWON OIL CORP.
47 Colborne Street Suite 307, Toronto, M5E 1P8, ON, Canada
Tel.: (416) 318-6501
Web Site: http://www.aoc-oil.com
AOC—(CNSX)
Assets: $909,616
Liabilities: $298,983
Net Worth: $610,633
Earnings: ($2,175,970)
Fiscal Year-end: 12/31/21
Oil & Gas Extraction Services
N.A.I.C.S.: 211120

Stephen Hughes (CEO)

ADVANTECH ADVANCED MICROWAVE TECHNOLOGIES INC.
657 Orly Avenue, Dorval, H9P 1G1, QC, Canada
Tel.: (514) 420-0045
Web Site:
   http://www.advantechwireless.com
Year Founded: 1985
Rev.: $20,314,800
Emp.: 171
Wireless Communication Equipment Mfr
N.A.I.C.S.: 334290
David Gelerman (CEO)

ADVANTECH CO., LTD.
No 1 Alley 20 Lane 26 Rueiguang Road, Neihu District, Taipei, 114519, Taiwan
Tel.: (886) 277323399
Web Site:
   https://www.advantech.com
Year Founded: 1983
2395—(TAI)
Rev.: $2,111,504,449
Assets: $2,258,290,637
Liabilities: $662,111,032
Net Worth: $1,596,179,605
Earnings: $352,834,710
Emp.: 2,628
Fiscal Year-end: 12/31/23
Holding Company; Integrated Computer Systems & Components Designer, Mfr & Distr
N.A.I.C.S.: 551112
K. Chen Liu (Chm)

Subsidiaries:

Advanixs Corporation   **(1)**
No 27 Wende Rd, Guishan Dist, Taoyuan, 33371, Taiwan
Tel.: (886) 28 177 7089
Web Site: https://www.advanixs.com
Computer System Design Services
N.A.I.C.S.: 541512
K. C. Liu (Chm)

Advantech Australia Pty. Limited **(1)**
22 Brindley St, Dandenong South, 3175, VIC, Australia   **(100%)**
Tel.: (61) 397970100
Web Site: http://www.advantech.net.au
Sales Range: $25-49.9 Million
Emp.: 4
Computer Related Products & Services
N.A.I.C.S.: 541519

Advantech Automation Corp.   **(1)**
4F No 108-3 Ming-Chuan Road, Shing-Tien District, Taipei, 231, Taiwan **(100%)**
Tel.: (886) 2 2218 4567
Web Site: http://www.advantech.com
Industrial Automation Computer, Computer Component & Software Mfr & Distr
N.A.I.C.S.: 334118

Advantech Brazil Ltda.   **(1)**
Rua Fagundes Filho 134 - 12 floor - Cj 121, Vila Monte Alegre, Sao Paulo, 04304-010, Brazil   **(43.28%)**
Tel.: (55) 1155925355
Web Site: http://www.advantechsg.com.br
Sales Range: $25-49.9 Million
Emp.: 30
Computer & Computer Peripheral Equipment & Software Whslr
N.A.I.C.S.: 423430

Advantech Co. Malaysia Sdn. Bhd.   **(1)**
No 117 & 119 Ground Floor Jalan Perniagaan Gemilang 1, Pusat Perniagaan Gemilang Bukit Mertajam, 14000, Penang, Seberang Jaya, Malaysia **(100%)**
Tel.: (60) 45379188
Web Site: http://www.advantech.com.my
Sales Range: $25-49.9 Million
Emp.: 20
Computer System Design Services
N.A.I.C.S.: 541512

Advantech Co. Singapore Pte. Ltd.   **(1)**
6 Serangoon North Avenue 5 03-08 East Lobby, Singapore, 554910, Singapore   **(100%)**
Tel.: (65) 64421000
Sales Range: $25-49.9 Million
Emp.: 32
Other Electronic Parts & Equipment Whslr
N.A.I.C.S.: 423690

Advantech Corporation   **(1)**
380 Fairview Way, Milpitas, CA 95035-3062
Tel.: (408) 519-3800
Web Site: http://www.buy.adventech.com
Emp.: 300
Computer & Computer Components Whslr
N.A.I.C.S.: 423430

Advantech Corporation (Thailand) Co., Ltd.   **(1)**
65/213 Unit 5 and 7 25th Floor Chamnanphenjati Business Center, Rama 9 Road Huaykwang, Bangkok, 10310, Thailand
Tel.: (66) 224883069
Holding Company
N.A.I.C.S.: 551112

Advantech Czech s.r.o.   **(1)**
Sokolska 71, 56204, Usti nad Orlici, Czech Republic
Tel.: (420) 465524421
Automatic Control Equipment Mfr
N.A.I.C.S.: 334513

Advantech Electronics, S.De R.L.De C.   **(1)**
Ave Baja California 245 Int 704 Col, Hipodromo Condesa Delegacion Cuauhtemoc, 06100, Mexico, Mexico
Tel.: (52) 5562752777
Holding Company
N.A.I.C.S.: 551112

Advantech Embedded ePlatform Group   **(1)**
No 33 Lane 365 Yang Guang St, Neihu Dist, Taipei, 114067, Taiwan
Tel.: (886) 27 732 3399
Web Site: http://www.advantech.com
Computer Circuit Board Designer & Mfr
N.A.I.C.S.: 334418

Advantech Europe Holding B.V   **(1)**
Science Park Eindhoven 5708, Science Park, 5692 ER, Son, Netherlands
Tel.: (31) 402677000
Web Site: http://www.advantech.nl
Emp.: 90
Holding Company; Regional Managing Office
N.A.I.C.S.: 551112
Dirk Finstel (Assoc VP-Embedded IoT)

Subsidiary (Domestic):

Advantech Europe B.V.   **(2)**
Science Park Eindhoven 5708, 5692 ER, Son en Breugel, Netherlands **(100%)**
Tel.: (31) 402677000
Web Site: http://www.advantech.nl
Computer & Computer Components Whslr & Technical Support Services
N.A.I.C.S.: 423430

Subsidiary (Non-US):

DLoG Gesellschaft fur elektronische Datentechnik mbH   **(2)**
Industriestrasse 15, 82110, Germering, Germany
Tel.: (49) 89 411 1910
Web Site: http://www.dlog.com
Sales Range: $25-49.9 Million
Emp.: 80
Industrial Computer Terminal Designer, Mfr & Distr
N.A.I.C.S.: 334118
Ke-Cheng Liu (Chm & CEO)

Advantech Japan Co., Ltd.   **(1)**
6-16-3 Asakusa, Taito-ku, Tokyo, 111-0032, Japan   **(100%)**
Tel.: (81) 368021021
Web Site: http://www.advantech.co.jp
Electrical Apparatus & Equipment Wiring Supplies & Construction Material Whslr
N.A.I.C.S.: 423610

Advantech Poland Sp z o.o.   **(1)**

Ul Dzialkowa 121b budynek F3, 02-234,
Warsaw, Poland
Tel.: (48) 223151100
Holding Company
N.A.I.C.S.: 551112

**Advantech Raiser India Private
Limited** **(1)**
79/2 City Center Hebbal Outer Ring Road,
Bengaluru, 560024, Karnataka, India
Tel.: (91) 7942555975
Web Site: https://www.advantechraiser.in
Emp.: 5,000
Computer Device Whslr
N.A.I.C.S.: 423430

**Advantech Technology (China) Com-
pany Ltd.** **(1)**
No 600 Han-pu Road, Yu-Shan, Kunshan,
Jiangsu, China **(100%)**
Tel.: (86) 51257775666
Relay & Industrial Control Mfr
N.A.I.C.S.: 335314

Advantech Turkey Teknoloji AS **(1)**
Seyrantepe Mah Ibrahim Karaoglanoglu Cd
No 71-73 Kat 2 Kagithane, 34418, Istanbul,
Turkiye
Tel.: (90) 2122220422
Computer Device Whslr
N.A.I.C.S.: 423430

**Advantech Vietnam Technology Com-
pany Limited** **(1)**
12A Floor VTC Online building NO 18 Tam
Trinh, Hai Ba Trung dist, Hanoi, Vietnam
Tel.: (84) 2433991155
Holding Company
N.A.I.C.S.: 551112
Hau Do *(Pres)*

B&B SmartWorx Limited **(1)**
Westlink Commercial Park Oranmore Co,
Galway, Ireland
Tel.: (353) 91792444
Holding Company
N.A.I.C.S.: 551112
Wan-Te Hus *(Pres)*

Subsidiary (Non-US):

Advantech B&B SmartWorx s.r.o. **(1)**
Sokolska 71, Usti nad Orlici, 562 04, Czech
Republic
Tel.: (420) 465524421
Holding Company
N.A.I.C.S.: 551112

Bit Flow Inc. **(1)**
300 Wildwood Ave, Woburn, MA 01801
Tel.: (781) 932-2900
Web Site: http://www.bitflow.com
Rev.: $1,727,000
Emp.: 11
Custom Computer Programming Services
N.A.I.C.S.: 541511
Avner Butnaru *(CEO)*

Cermate Software Inc. **(1)**
No 61 West 40th Avenue, Vancouver, V5Y
2P9, BC, Canada
Tel.: (604) 565-2784
Software Development Services
N.A.I.C.S.: 541511

**Cermate Technologies (Shanghai)
Inc.** **(1)**
Rm 1601 No 1 Lane 600, Tongda Building
Changning, Shanghai, 200051, China
Tel.: (86) 21235708002
Internet Services
N.A.I.C.S.: 517121

Cermate Technologies Inc. **(1)**
7F-1 No 168 Liancheng Rd, Zhonghe Dist,
New Taipei City, 235, Taiwan
Tel.: (886) 22 243 7000
Web Site: https://www.cermate.com
Internet Services
N.A.I.C.S.: 517121

PT Advantech International **(1)**
Plaza Aminta 6th floor suite 601, Jl TB Si-
matupang Kav 10, Jakarta, 12310, Indone-
sia
Tel.: (62) 217511939
Holding Company
N.A.I.C.S.: 551112

**Shenzhen Cermate Technologies
Inc.** **(1)**

4F D Building Sogood Science Park
Hangcheng Street, SanWei Community
Baoan District, Shenzhen, 518126, China
Tel.: (86) 75583562179
Internet Services
N.A.I.C.S.: 517121

ADVANTECH TECHNOLOGIES
LTD.
2 BSR Building 1 Ben Gurion St,
Bnei Brak, 51201, Israel
Tel.: (972) 3 5775050
Web Site: http://www.advantech.co.il
IT Services
N.A.I.C.S.: 541512

Subsidiaries:

NessPRO Italy S.p.A. - Milan **(1)**
Via A Volta 16, 20093, Cologno Monzese,
Italy **(100%)**
Tel.: (39) 022515181
Web Site: http://www.nesspro.it
Sales Range: $25-49.9 Million
Emp.: 26
Information Technology Services
N.A.I.C.S.: 541512
Pasquale Favale *(CEO)*

NessPRO Italy S.p.A. - Rome **(1)**
Via V Lamaro 21, 00173, Rome,
Italy **(100%)**
Tel.: (39) 06724331
Web Site: http://www.nesspro.it
Sales Range: $25-49.9 Million
Emp.: 98
Information Technology Services
N.A.I.C.S.: 541512
Pasquale Favale *(CEO)*

NessPRO Portugal **(1)**
Av de Liberdade 110, 1269-046, Lisbon,
Portugal **(100%)**
Tel.: (351) 213404500
Emp.: 14
Information Technology Solutions
N.A.I.C.S.: 541512

NessPRO Spain S.A. **(1)**
C/Mesena 22-3 x Planta, Madrid, 28033,
Spain **(100%)**
Tel.: (34) 916303737
Web Site: http://www.nesspro.es
Sales Range: $25-49.9 Million
Emp.: 50
IT Services
N.A.I.C.S.: 541512

ADVANTEST CORPORATION
Shin Marunouchi Center Bldg 1-6-2
Marunouchi, Chiyoda-ku, Tokyo, 100-
0005, Japan
Tel.: (81) 332147500 JP
Web Site: https://www.advantest.com
Year Founded: 1954
6857—(TKS)
Rev.: $3,215,811,270
Assets: $4,436,823,690
Liabilities: $1,586,737,110
Net Worth: $2,850,086,580
Earnings: $411,736,900
Emp.: 7,358
Fiscal Year-end: 03/31/24
Other Electronic Component Mfr
N.A.I.C.S.: 334519
Hans-Juergen Wagner *(Mng Exec
Officer)*

Subsidiaries:

Advanfacilities Co., Ltd. **(1)**
1-5 Shintone, Kazo, 349-1158, Saitama,
Japan **(100%)**
Tel.: (81) 480727002
Web Site: https://www.afc-advantest.co.jp
Emp.: 90
Facility Management Services
N.A.I.C.S.: 561210

**Advansoft Development
Corporation** **(1)**
336-1 Owa Meiwamachi, Oura, 370-0718,
Gunma, Japan
Tel.: (81) 276845831
Software Development Services
N.A.I.C.S.: 541511

Advantest (China) Co., Ltd. **(1)**
C Block Bldg 3 168 Huatuo Road, Zhangji-
ang Hi-Tech Park, Shanghai, 201203, China
Tel.: (86) 2161630000
Sales Range: $25-49.9 Million
Emp.: 150
Semiconductor Test Systems Mfr
N.A.I.C.S.: 334413

Subsidiary (Domestic):

Advantest (Suzhou) Co., Ltd. **(2)**
1F-2F Block F Suzhou International Science
Park No 1355 Jinjihu Avenue, Suzhou In-
dustrial Park, Suzhou, 215021, Jiangsu,
China **(100%)**
Tel.: (86) 51262568318
Web Site: http://www.advantest.com.cn
Sales Range: $25-49.9 Million
Emp.: 20
Provider of Electricity Measurement Instru-
ments
N.A.I.C.S.: 334514

Advantest (Europe) GmbH **(1)**
Stefan-George-Ring 2, 81929, Munich,
Germany **(100%)**
Tel.: (49) 89993120
Web Site: http://www.advantest.com
Sales Range: $25-49.9 Million
Emp.: 100
Semiconductor Testing Equipment Devel-
oper & Mfr
N.A.I.C.S.: 334413
Peter Wewerka *(Mng Dir)*

Subsidiary (Domestic):

Advantest - Boblingen **(2)**
Herrenberger Str 130, 71034, Boblingen,
Germany
Tel.: (49) 70314357000
Sales Range: $75-99.9 Million
Semiconductor Test Systems Mfr
N.A.I.C.S.: 334413
Hans-Juergen Wagner *(VP)*

Subsidiary (Non-US):

Advantest Europe R&D S.A.R.L. **(2)**
5 Ave De Quebec ZA, BP 203, 91941,
Courtaboeuf, Cedex, France **(100%)**
Tel.: (33) 169182500
Web Site: http://www.advantest.com
Sales Range: $25-49.9 Million
Emp.: 17
Provider of Electricity Measurement Instru-
ments
N.A.I.C.S.: 334513
Kakizaki Koji *(Mng Dir)*

Subsidiary (Domestic):

**Advantest Europe Systems
GmbH** **(2)**
Wasserburger Str 44, 83123, Amerang,
Germany
Tel.: (49) 8075 17 0
Web Site: http://www.advantest.de
Semiconductor Testing Equipment Devel-
oper & Mfr
N.A.I.C.S.: 334413

Advantest (M) Sdn. Bhd. **(1)**
Plot 5 Technoplex Medan Bayan Lepas
Phase IV, Bayan Lepas Industrial Park,
11900, Penang, Malaysia
Tel.: (60) 46163800
Automobile Equipment Mfr
N.A.I.C.S.: 333242

Advantest (Singapore) Pte. Ltd. **(1)**
10 Ang Mo Kio Street 65 04-11 Techpoint,
Singapore, 569059, Singapore **(100%)**
Tel.: (65) 63473888
Web Site: http://www.advantest.co.sg
Sales Range: $25-49.9 Million
Emp.: 82
Provider of Electricity Measurement Instru-
ments
N.A.I.C.S.: 334513

Subsidiary (Non-US):

Advantest (Malaysia) Sdn. Bhd. **(2)**
Plot 5 Technoplex Medan Bepas Bayan
Lepas Industrial Park Phase IV, 11900,
Penang, Malaysia **(100%)**
Tel.: (60) 46163800
Web Site: http://www.advantest.com

Sales Range: $25-49.9 Million
Emp.: 22
Provider of Electricity Measurement Instru-
ments
N.A.I.C.S.: 334513

Advantest (Thailand) Ltd. **(2)**
Vision Business Park Building2 2nd Floor
No 3 Soi Ramintra 55/8, Ramintra Road
Tha Raeng Bang Khen, Bangkok, 10230,
Thailand
Tel.: (66) 234700068
Semiconductor Devices Mfr
N.A.I.C.S.: 334413
Cheng Sui Yoong *(Mng Dir)*

Advantest Philippines, Inc. **(2)**
Unit 311 & 313 KACC Philmade Building
Lot 1 & 2 Jose Abad Santos cor, E Quirino
Street Clark Freeport Zone, Pampanga,
2023, Philippines **(100%)**
Tel.: (63) 454993007
Web Site: http://www.atasp.advantest.co.jp
Sales Range: $25-49.9 Million
Emp.: 14
Provider of Electricity Measurement Instru-
ments
N.A.I.C.S.: 334515

**Advantest-Engineering (Malaysia)
Sdn. Bhd.** **(2)**
Plot 5 Technoplex Medan Bayan Lepas Pk
bhafd IV, 11900, Penang,
Malaysia **(100%)**
Tel.: (60) 46413980
Web Site: http://www.advantest.com
Sales Range: $1-9.9 Million
Emp.: 23
Joint Venture of Advantest (65%) & Eng.
Technologi Holdings Bhd. (35%)
N.A.I.C.S.: 551112

Advantest Academy, KK. **(1)**
336-1 Ohwa Meiwa-machi, Ora-gun,
Gunma, 370-0718, Japan
Tel.: (81) 276703425
Semiconductor Devices Mfr
N.A.I.C.S.: 334413

Advantest America Inc. **(1)**
3061 Zanker Rd, San Jose, CA
95134 **(100%)**
Tel.: (408) 456-3600
Web Site: http://www.advantest.com
Sales Range: $25-49.9 Million
Emp.: 93
Semiconductor Testing Equipment Devel-
oper & Mfr
N.A.I.C.S.: 334413

Subsidiary (Domestic):

W2bi, Inc. **(2)**
220 Davidson Ave Ste 339, Somerset, NJ
08873
Tel.: (908) 688-1700
Sales Range: $1-9.9 Million
Emp.: 33
Prepackaged Software Mfr
N.A.I.C.S.: 513210

Advantest Canada, Inc. **(1)**
1555 boulevard de L Avenir Suite 306 La-
val, Quebec, H7S 2N5, QC, Canada
Tel.: (450) 663-3743
Automobile Equipment Mfr
N.A.I.C.S.: 333242

Advantest Component, Inc. **(1)**
48-4 Matsubara Kamiaiko, Aoba-ku, Sendai,
989-3124, Miyagi, Japan
Tel.: (81) 223929711
Web Site: https://www.aci-advantest.co.jp
Semiconductor Devices Mfr
N.A.I.C.S.: 334413

Plant (Domestic):

**Advantest Component, Inc. - Sendai
Factory** **(2)**
48-2 Matsubara Kami-Ayashi, Aoba-ku,
Sendai, 989-3124, Miyagi, Japan
Tel.: (81) 22 392 9711
Web Site: http://www.advantest.co.jp
Semiconductor Devices Mfr
N.A.I.C.S.: 334413

**Advantest Corporation - Gunma
Factory** **(1)**
54-1 Shinozuka, Ora-machi Ora-gun,

Advantest Corporation—(Continued)

Gunma, 370-0615, Japan
Tel.: (81) 276 88 7500
Web Site: http://www.advantest.co.jp
Electronic Measuring Instrument Mfr
N.A.I.C.S.: 334513

Advantest Corporation - Gunma Factory 2 (1)
3685-1 Akahori Ora-machi, Ora-gun, Gunma, 370-0614, Japan
Tel.: (81) 276 80 9700
Web Site: http://www.advantest.co.jp
Electronic Measuring Instrument Mfr
N.A.I.C.S.: 334513

Advantest Finance Inc (1)
Shin-Marunouchi Center Building
Marunouchi 1-6-2, Chiyoda-ku, Tokyo, 100-0005, Japan
Tel.: (81) 332147500
Web Site: https://www.advantest.com
Semiconductor Test System Rental Services
N.A.I.C.S.: 532490
Kazumasa Furuta (Pres)

Advantest France SAS (1)
Miniparc Polytec Bat Alizes 32 rue des Berges, 38000, Grenoble, France
Tel.: (33) 438030250
Automobile Equipment Mfr
N.A.I.C.S.: 333242

Advantest Green Corporation (1)
1-5 Shintone, Kazo, 349-1158, Saitama, Japan
Tel.: (81) 480726821
Web Site: https://www.afc-advantest.co.jp
Environmental Consulting Services
N.A.I.C.S.: 541620

Advantest Israel Ltd. (1)
Hamerton House Building C Floor 2 18 Aharon Bart Street, Petach Tikva, 4951448, Israel
Tel.: (972) 39789000
Automobile Equipment Mfr
N.A.I.C.S.: 333242

Advantest Italia S.r.l. (1)
Via Energy Park n 22 - Building 04 Sud, 20871, Vimercate, MB, Italy
Tel.: (39) 0396072850
Automobile Equipment Mfr
N.A.I.C.S.: 333242

Advantest Korea Co., Ltd. (1)
140 3gongdan 6-ro, Seobuk-gu, Cheonan, 31085, Chungcheongnam, Korea (South) **(100%)**
Tel.: (82) 41 901 3900
Web Site: http://www.advantest.com
Sales Range: $25-49.9 Million
Emp.: 90
Electricity Measurement Instruments
N.A.I.C.S.: 334514

Advantest Kyushu Systems Co., Ltd (1)
1-5-1 Higashida, Yahatahigashi-ku, Kitakyushu, 805-0071, Fukuoka, Japan
Tel.: (81) 936810200
Web Site: http://www.advantest.co.jp
Laboratory Research Instrument Distr
N.A.I.C.S.: 423450

Advantest Laboratories Ltd (1)
48-4 Matsubara Kami-Ayashi, Aoba-ku, Sendai, 989-3124, Miyagi, Japan
Tel.: (81) 223928731
Sales Range: $25-49.9 Million
Emp.: 10
Laboratory Research Equipment Mfr
N.A.I.C.S.: 334516

Advantest Media Service Corporation (1)
1-5 Shin-tone, Kazo, 349-1158, Saitama, Japan
Tel.: (81) 480 72 7021
Sales Range: $25-49.9 Million
Emp.: 22
Commercial Printing Services
N.A.I.C.S.: 323111
Takayuki Yamada (Gen Mgr)

Advantest Pre-Owned Solutions Co., Ltd. (1)
Shin-Marunouchi Center Building

Marunouchi 1-6-2, Chiyoda-ku, Tokyo, 100-0005, Japan
Tel.: (81) 332147500
Web Site: https://www.advantest.com
Financial Lending Services
N.A.I.C.S.: 522220

Advantest Sales & Support (M) Sdn. Bhd. (1)
l 2-5A Penang SME Centre Plot 105 Hilir Sungai Keluang 5 Phase 4, Bayan Lepas Industrial Park, 11900, Penang, Malaysia
Tel.: (60) 46163800
Automobile Equipment Mfr
N.A.I.C.S.: 333242

Advantest Shanghai Co., Ltd. (1)
Room1602A LuNeng Plaza No 18 Taigu Road, Waigaoqiao FreeZone, Shanghai, 200131, China
Tel.: (86) 2161630000
Semiconductor Mfr
N.A.I.C.S.: 334413

Advantest Systems Corporation (1)
336-1 Ohwa Meiwa-machi, Ora-gun, Gunma, 370-0718, Japan
Tel.: (81) 276 84 5831
Web Site: http://www.advantest.co.jp
Semiconductor Devices Mfr
N.A.I.C.S.: 334413

Advantest Taiwan, Inc. (1)
Tel.: (886) 35975888
Web Site: http://www.advantest.com.tw
Electric Equipment Mfr
N.A.I.C.S.: 335999

Advantest Technology (Shanghai) Co., Ltd. (1)
C Block Bldg 3 168 HuaTuo Road Zhangjiang Hi-Tech Park, Shanghai, 201203, China
Tel.: (86) 2161630000
Automobile Equipment Mfr
N.A.I.C.S.: 333242

Advantest Test Solutions, Inc. (1)
26211 Enterprise Way, Lake Forest, CA 92630
Tel.: (949) 523-6900
Automobile Equipment Mfr
N.A.I.C.S.: 333242
Richard Chanthavong (Dir-Ops)

Advantest Vietnam Co., Ltd. (1)
Room 801 Vietnam Business Center 57-59 Ho Tung Mau Street, MBen Nghe Ward District 1, Ho Chi Minh City, Vietnam
Tel.: (84) 862884255
Automobile Equipment Mfr
N.A.I.C.S.: 333242

Essai, Inc. (1)
48580 Kato Rd, Fremont, CA 94538
Tel.: (510) 580-1700
Web Site: http://www.essai.com
End-to-End Engineering, Manufacturing, Quality & Research Services
N.A.I.C.S.: 541330

Japan Engineering Co., Ltd. (1)
2-9-2 Ikuta, Tama-ku, Kawasaki, 214-0038, Kanagawa, Japan **(100%)**
Tel.: (81) 449311311
Web Site: http://www.jec.co.jp
Sales Range: $25-49.9 Million
Emp.: 53
Semiconductor Testing Equipment Developer & Mfr
N.A.I.C.S.: 334413
Hitoshi Sugae (Pres)

R&D Altanova, Inc. (1)
3601 S Clinton Ave, South Plainfield, NJ 07080
Tel.: (732) 549-4554
Web Site: https://rdaltanova.com
Semiconductor Device Mfr & Distr
N.A.I.C.S.: 334413

ADVANTEX MARKETING INTERNATIONAL INC.
2 - 157C Harwood Avenue North Suite 238, Ajax, L1Z 0B6, ON, Canada
Tel.: (905) 470-9558   ON
Web Site: http://www.advantex.com
Year Founded: 1994
Rev.: $1,360,930

Assets: $2,761,732
Liabilities: $10,851,980
Net Worth: ($8,090,248)
Earnings: ($2,118,288)
Fiscal Year-end: 06/30/22
Online & Offline Customer Relationship Marketing Programs
N.A.I.C.S.: 541870
Kelly E. Ambrose (Pres & Co-CEO)

Subsidiaries:

Advantex Dining Corporation (1)
493-6400 Roberts St, Burnaby, V5G 4C9, BC, Canada
Tel.: (604) 205-5022
Sales Range: $25-49.9 Million
Emp.: 5
Marketing Management Services
N.A.I.C.S.: 541613

Advantex Marketing Corporation (1)
600 Alden Rd Ste 606, Markham, L3R 0E7, ON, Canada
Tel.: (905) 470-9558
Marketing Management Services
N.A.I.C.S.: 541613

ADVANZ PHARMA CORP.
5770 Hurontario Street Suite 310, Mississauga, L5R 3G5, ON, Canada
Tel.: (905) 842-5150   ON
Web Site:
http://www.advanzpharma.com
Year Founded: 2010
CXRXF—(OTCIQ)
Emp.: 444
Holding Company; Biopharmaceutical Products Developer, Mfr & Distr
N.A.I.C.S.: 551112
Francesco Tallarico (Chief Legal Officer & Sec)

Subsidiaries:

Complete Medical Homecare, Inc. (1)
14309 W 95th St, Lenexa, KS 66215
Tel.: (913) 422-1666
Web Site:
http://www.completemedicalhomecare.com
Medical Equipment Distr
N.A.I.C.S.: 423450
David Nguyen (Controller)

Concordia Healthcare (USA) Inc. (1)
7190 SW 87th Ave, Miami, FL 33173
Tel.: (305) 514-5200
Medical Equipment Distr
N.A.I.C.S.: 423450

Concordia Healthcare Inc. (1)
277 Lakeshore Road East Suite 302, Oakville, L6J 1H9, ON, Canada
Tel.: (905) 842-5150
Web Site: http://www.concordiapharma.ca
Emp.: 50
Biopharmaceutical Developer, Mfr & Distr
N.A.I.C.S.: 325412

Concordia International Rx UK Ltd (1)
Capital House 85 King William Street, London, EC4N 7BL, United Kingdom
Tel.: (44) 208 588 9100
Web Site:
http://www.concordiarxinternational.com
Holding Company; Specialty Pharmaceutical Mfr
N.A.I.C.S.: 551112
Karl Belk (Sr VP-Global Pharmaceutical Ops)

Correvio SAS (1)
15 rue du Bicentenaire, 92800, Puteaux, France
Tel.: (33) 17 768 8917
Pharmaceuticals Product Mfr
N.A.I.C.S.: 325412

Pinnacle Biologics, Inc. (1)
311 S Wacker Dr, Chicago, IL 60606
Tel.: (847) 283-7690
Web Site: http://www.pinnaclebiologics.com
Emp.: 20
Pharmaceutical Product Mfr & Distr
N.A.I.C.S.: 325412

Andy Hoyt (Gen Mgr)

ADVANZ PHARMA CORP. LIMITED
11-15 Seaton Place, Saint Helier, JE4 0QH, Jersey
Tel.: (44) 2085889100
Web Site:
http://www.advanzpharma.com
Year Founded: 1963
Health Care Srvices
N.A.I.C.S.: 621610
Graeme Duncan (CEO)

Subsidiaries:

Abcur AB (1)
Bergaliden 11, 252 23, Helsingborg, Sweden
Tel.: (46) 42135770
Web Site: http://abcur.advanzpharma.com
Pharmaceuticals Product Mfr
N.A.I.C.S.: 325412

Boucher & Muir Pty Limited (1)
Level 9 76 Berry Street, North Sydney, 2060, NSW, Australia
Tel.: (61) 294316333
Web Site:
http://bnmgroup.advanzpharma.com
Pharmaceuticals Product Mfr
N.A.I.C.S.: 325412

Mercury Pharmaceuticals (Ireland) Limited (1)
17 Northwood House Northwood, Santry, Dublin, Ireland
Tel.: (353) 16971640
Pharmaceutical Product Mfr & Distr
N.A.I.C.S.: 325412

ADVENICA AB
Roskildevagen 1, PO Box 17075, 200 10, Malmo, Sweden
Tel.: (46) 703860032
Web Site: https://www.advenica.com
Year Founded: 1993
ADVE—(OMX)
Rev.: $11,090,225
Assets: $16,761,827
Liabilities: $7,602,536
Net Worth: $9,159,291
Earnings: ($186,106)
Emp.: 80
Fiscal Year-end: 12/31/22
Security System Services
N.A.I.C.S.: 561621
Helene Bittmann (VP-Sls)

ADVENIS
52 rue de Bassano, 75008, Paris, France
Tel.: (33) 427705400
Web Site: http://www.advenis.com
Investment & Financial Services
N.A.I.C.S.: 523999
Stephane Amine (CEO)

Subsidiaries:

Avenir Finance Corporate (1)
53 rue La Boetie, 75008, Paris, France
Tel.: (33) 170080805
Web Site:
http://www.corporate.avenirfinance.fr
Sales Range: $25-49.9 Million
Emp.: 50
Financial Management Services
N.A.I.C.S.: 541618

Avenir Finance Gestion (1)
53 Rue La Boetie, 75008, Paris, France
Tel.: (33) 1 70 08 08 08
Financial Management Services
N.A.I.C.S.: 541618

Avenir Finance Investment Managers (AFIM) (1)
53 Rue La Boetie, 75008, Paris, France
Tel.: (33) 170080800
Web Site: http://www.im.avenirfinance.fr
Sales Range: $50-74.9 Million
Emp.: 50
Mutual Funds Management

N.A.I.C.S.: 525910
Thibault Delahaye *(Chm)*

Avenir Finance Partenaires (1)
53 Rue La Boetie, Paris, France
Tel.: (33) 170080885
Web Site:
http://www.partenaires.avenirfinance.fr
Investment Advisory Services
N.A.I.C.S.: 523940

Avenir Finance Securities (1)
53 Rue La Boetie, 75008, Paris, France
Tel.: (33) 170080808
Web Site:
http://www.securities.avenirfinance.fr
Financial Management Services
N.A.I.C.S.: 541618

ADVENT COMPUTER SER-VICES LTD.
Swathi Towers K22 7th Floor 5 and 7
Durgabai Deshmukh Road, R A
Puram, Chennai, 600028, India
Tel.: (91) 4445580095
Web Site:
https://www.adventcomputer.in
531429—(BOM)
Rev.: $622
Assets: $2,502,678
Liabilities: $495,893
Net Worth: $2,006,785
Earnings: ($26,826)
Emp.: 4
Fiscal Year-end: 03/31/20
Information Technology Software Services
N.A.I.C.S.: 541512
Michael Arul *(Chm & Mng Dir)*

ADVENT PHARMA LIMITED
Rupayan Karim Tower Level-10 80
Kakrail VIP Road Ramna, Dhaka,
1000, Bangladesh
Tel.: (880) 248311655
Web Site:
https://www.adventpharmabd.com
Year Founded: 2007
ADVENT—(CHT)
Rev.: $5,743,237
Assets: $17,632,496
Liabilities: $3,316,006
Net Worth: $14,316,489
Earnings: $1,317,642
Emp.: 314
Fiscal Year-end: 06/30/21
Pharmaceutical Product Mfr & Distr
N.A.I.C.S.: 325412
A. K. M. Shafiqul Alam *(Chm)*

ADVENT-AWI HOLDINGS INC.
550 West Broadway Unit 719, Van-couver, V5Z 0E9, BC, Canada
Tel.: (604) 428-0028   Ca
Year Founded: 1984
AWI—(TSXV)
Rev.: $4,294,064
Assets: $13,041,342
Liabilities: $2,255,556
Net Worth: $10,785,786
Earnings: $117,908
Fiscal Year-end: 12/31/23
Cellular & Wireless Product Whslr
N.A.I.C.S.: 423690
Edgar Pang *(CFO)*

Subsidiaries:

Advent Marketing Inc. (1)
3340 Peachtree Rd NE, Atlanta, GA 30326
Tel.: (404) 964-7142
Cellular & Wireless Product Distr
N.A.I.C.S.: 423690

ADVENTURE INC.
Yebisu GardenPlaceTower 24F
4-20-3, Ebisu Shibuya-ku, Tokyo,
150-6024, Japan
Tel.: (81) 362770149
Web Site: https://adventurekk.com

6030—(TKS)
Rev.: $139,272,020
Assets: $184,951,700
Liabilities: $109,820,320
Net Worth: $75,131,380
Earnings: $4,665,000
Emp.: 126
Fiscal Year-end: 06/30/24
Online Travel Services
N.A.I.C.S.: 721199
Shunichi Nakamura *(CEO)*

Subsidiaries:

RADO Travel Service Co., Ltd. (1)
ID Building 4F 1-11-5 Oyodominami, Kita-ku, Osaka, Japan
Tel.: (81) 663455671
Web Site: https://www.rado.co.jp
Emp.: 31
Network Tour Planning & Implementation
Services
N.A.I.C.S.: 561510

ADVENTUS HOLDINGS LIM-ITED
52 Telok Blangah Road 03-06 Telok
Blangah House, Singapore, 098829,
Singapore
Tel.: (65) 63822110
Web Site:
https://www.adventusholdings.com
Year Founded: 2003
5EF—(SES)
Rev.: $2,554,041
Assets: $43,597,423
Liabilities: $33,531,945
Net Worth: $10,065,478
Earnings: ($5,841,199)
Emp.: 165
Fiscal Year-end: 12/31/23
Telecommunication Servicesb
N.A.I.C.S.: 517111
Bee Fong Lee *(Sec)*

ADVENTZ GROUP
Global Business Park Tower A 5th
Floor, Sector 26 MG Road, Gurgaon,
122002, India
Tel.: (91) 124 4827 800
Web Site: http://www.adventz.com
Sales Range: $1-4.9 Billion
Emp.: 5,000
Holding Company
N.A.I.C.S.: 551112
Saroj Kumar Poddar *(Chm)*

Subsidiaries:

Zuari Agro Chemicals Limited (1)
Jai Kisaan Bhawan Zuarinagar, Goa, 403
726, India
Tel.: (91) 8322592180
Web Site: https://www.zuari.in
Rev.: $336,635,795
Assets: $733,261,552
Liabilities: $646,068,573
Net Worth: $87,192,979
Earnings: ($17,232,524)
Emp.: 623
Fiscal Year-end: 03/31/2021
Fertilizer Mfr & Whslr
N.A.I.C.S.: 325311
Saroj Kumar Poddar *(Chm)*

Subsidiary (Domestic):

Zuari Agri Sciences Limited (2)
Jai Kisaan Bhawan, Zuarinagar, 403726,
Goa, India
Tel.: (91) 832 2592180
Production & Trading of Seeds & Crop Care
Products
N.A.I.C.S.: 424590

Zuari Fertilisers & Chemicals
Limited (2)
Jai Kisaan Bhawan, Zuarinagar, Goa, 403
726, India   (100%)
Tel.: (91) 832 2592180
Web Site: http://www.zuari.in
Fertilizer Mfr
N.A.I.C.S.: 325312

Joint Venture (Domestic):

Zuari Maroc Phosphates Limited (2)
Jai Kissan Bhawan, PO Zuarinagar, Goa,
403726, India   (50%)
Tel.: (91) 832 2592180
Fertilizer & Phosphate Chemicals Mfr
N.A.I.C.S.: 325199
Saroj Kumar Poddar *(Chm)*

Subsidiary (Domestic):

Paradeep Phosphates Ltd (3)
5th Floor Bayan Bhavan Pandit Jawaharlal
Nehru Marg, Bhubaneswar, 751 001,
India   (80.45%)
Tel.: (91) 6746666100
Web Site:
http://www.paradeepphosphates.com
Fertilizer & Phospate Mfr
N.A.I.C.S.: 325312
Suresh Krishnan *(Mng Dir)*

Zuari Global Ltd. (1)
B/h Bajaj Process Narol Chokdi, Zuarina-gar, 403 726, Goa, India
Tel.: (91) 8322592180
Web Site: https://www.adventz.com
Rev.: $134,116,560
Assets: $681,669,220
Liabilities: $407,886,652
Net Worth: $273,782,568
Earnings: ($13,722,850)
Emp.: 12
Fiscal Year-end: 03/31/2021
Chemical Fertiliser Mfr
N.A.I.C.S.: 325311
N. Suresh Krishnan *(Mng Dir)*

Subsidiary (Domestic):

Texmaco Infrastructure & Holdings
Limited (2)
Belgharia, Kolkata, 700 056, India
Tel.: (91) 3325691500
Web Site: https://www.texinfra.in
Rev.: $4,266,854
Assets: $91,628,355
Liabilities: $5,897,346
Net Worth: $85,731,009
Earnings: $1,511,451
Emp.: 33
Fiscal Year-end: 03/31/2021
Industrial Machinery Mfr
N.A.I.C.S.: 333248

Texmaco Rail & Engineering Ltd. (2)
Belgharia 24 Paragnas North, Kolkata, 700
056, West Bengal, India
Tel.: (91) 3325691500
Web Site: https://www.texmaco.in
Rev.: $233,944,552
Assets: $360,616,333
Liabilities: $205,120,243
Net Worth: $155,496,091
Earnings: $1,641,085
Emp.: 2,403
Fiscal Year-end: 03/31/2021
Soil Engineering Services
N.A.I.C.S.: 541330
Damodar Hazarimal Kela *(CEO-Steel
Foundry)*

ADVEO GROUP INTERNA-TIONAL, S.A.
Calle Miguel angel 11, 28010, Ma-drid, Spain
Tel.: (34) 902 216 400   ES
Web Site: http://www.adveo.com
Year Founded: 1976
AFN—(AIM)
Stationery Products Mfr & Retailer
N.A.I.C.S.: 322230
Eladio Bezares Munilla *(Vice Chm)*

Subsidiaries:

Spicers Administracion y Servicios,
S.L. (1)
Edificio Madison Ctra Nacional 340 122-A 2
Planta, 08960, Barcelona, Spain
Tel.: (34) 93 503 80 00
Web Site: http://www.spicers.es
Stationery & Office Products Distr
N.A.I.C.S.: 424120

Branch (Non-US):

Adveo Italia S. R. L. (2)
Viale dell'Industria 31, 29015, Castel San

Giovanni, Piacenza, Italy
Tel.: (39) 0523866411
Web Site: http://www.spicers.it
Emp.: 88
Stationery & Office Products Whslr
N.A.I.C.S.: 424120

Subsidiary (Non-US):

Spicers Belgium NV (2)
Europalaan 69, 9800, Deinze, Belgium
Tel.: (32) 93810505
Web Site: http://www.spicers.be
Stationery & Office Products Distr
N.A.I.C.S.: 424120

Spicers Deutschland GmbH (2)
Gretlade 1, 31319, Sehnde, Germany
Tel.: (49) 5132 929 0
Web Site: http://www.spicers.de
Stationery & Office Product Whslr
N.A.I.C.S.: 424120

Spicers France SAS (2)
Zone Industrielle de Paris Nord II 47 allee
des Impressionnistes, BP 55402, 95943,
Roissy-en-France, France
Tel.: (33) 1 49 38 83 00
Web Site: http://www.spicers.fr
Emp.: 100
Consumer Goods Distr
N.A.I.C.S.: 424990

ADVERITAS LIMITED
Suite 10 16 Brodie Hall Drive, Bent-ley Technology Park, Bentley, 6102,
WA, Australia
Tel.: (61) 894732500
Web Site:
https://www.adveritas.com.au
Year Founded: 2012
AV1—(ASX)
Rev.: $1,556,740
Assets: $5,462,162
Liabilities: $4,189,991
Net Worth: $1,272,170
Earnings: ($6,959,151)
Fiscal Year-end: 06/30/22
Investment Services
N.A.I.C.S.: 523999
Mathew Ratty *(CEO)*

Subsidiaries:

Appenture d.o.o (1)
Anina 2, 42000, Varazdin, Croatia
Tel.: (385) 42421270
Web Site: https://www.appenture.com
Information Technology Development Ser-vices
N.A.I.C.S.: 541519

ADVFN PLC
28 Ongar Business Centre, The
Gables Fyfield Road, Ongar, CM5
0GA, United Kingdom
Tel.: (44) 2038794460
Web Site: https://www.advfn.com
Year Founded: 1989
AFN—(AIM)
Rev.: $6,767,810
Assets: $8,953,378
Liabilities: $2,396,674
Net Worth: $6,556,704
Earnings: ($2,309,748)
Emp.: 40
Fiscal Year-end: 06/30/23
Online Financial News
N.A.I.C.S.: 513199
Michael J. Hodges *(Co-Founder &
Chm)*

Subsidiaries:

ALL IPO plc (1)
26 Throgmorton Street, London, EC2N
2AN, United Kingdom
Tel.: (44) 2070700991
Web Site: http://www.allipo.com
Sales Range: Less than $1 Million
Emp.: 10
Online Business Information Services
N.A.I.C.S.: 561499
Clem Chambers *(Mng Dir)*

ADVFN PLC—(Continued)

InvestorsHub.com Inc. **(1)**
Ste 801-137 3122 Mahan Dr, Tallahassee,
FL 32308-2502
Web Site:
https://www.investorshub.advfn.com
Software Operating Services
N.A.I.C.S.: 541714

Throgmorton Street Capital Ltd. **(1)**
28 Ongar Business Centre The Gables Fy-
field Road, Ongar, CM5 0GA, Essex, United
Kingdom **(100%)**
Tel.: (44) 203 011 2309
Web Site:
https://www.throgmortonstreetcapital.com
Sales Range: $50-74.9 Million
Emp.: 5
Boutique Investment Bank
N.A.I.C.S.: 523150
Clem Chambers (CEO)

ADVICE A/S
Gammel Kongevej 3E, 1610, Copen-
hagen, Denmark
Tel.: (45) 3342 2100
Web Site: http://www.adviceas.dk
Year Founded: 1991
Sales Range: $10-24.9 Million
Emp.: 100
Advetising Agency
N.A.I.C.S.: 541810
Ralf Lodberg (Partner & Mng Dir)

ADVICENNE S.A.
262 Rue du Faubourg Saint Honore,
75008, Paris, France
Tel.: (33) 185733620
Web Site:
https://www.advicenne.com
Year Founded: 2017
ADVIC—(EUR)
Rev.: $3,207,130
Assets: $15,202,946
Liabilities: $26,521,725
Net Worth: ($11,318,779)
Earnings: ($12,229,314)
Emp.: 26
Fiscal Year-end: 12/31/22
Pharmaceutical Product Mfr & Distr
N.A.I.C.S.: 325412
Luc-Andre Granier (Co-Founder)

ADVIK CAPITAL LTD
Plot No-84 Khasra No 143/84 Ground
Floor Extended Lal Dora Kanjhawla,
Delhi, 110 081, India
Tel.: (91) 1125952595 In
Web Site: http://www.advikgroup.com
539773—(BOM)
Rev.: $6,357,788
Assets: $2,280,492
Liabilities: $800,177
Net Worth: $1,480,315
Earnings: $64,674
Emp.: 6
Fiscal Year-end: 03/31/22
Financial Support Services
N.A.I.C.S.: 523999
Virender Kumar Agarwal (Chm & Mng
Dir)

Subsidiaries:

Advik Optoelectronics Limited **(1)**
Advik House Plot No 84 Kanjhawala Indus-
trial Area, 100 Feet Road North West Delhi
Kanjawala, New Delhi, 110081, India
Tel.: (91) 9136311500
Web Site: https://www.advikgroup.com
Light Mfr
N.A.I.C.S.: 335132
Virender Kumar Agarwal (Mng Dir)

ADVIK LABORATORIES LTD.
703 Arunachal Building 19 Barakhamba Road, Connaught Place,
New Delhi, 110001, India
Tel.: (91) 1142424884

Web Site: https://mpspharmaa.com
Rev.: $26,645
Assets: $1,542,857
Liabilities: $1,003,569
Net Worth: $539,289
Earnings: ($602,854)
Emp.: 15
Fiscal Year-end: 03/31/21
Laboratory Services
N.A.I.C.S.: 541380
Pooja Chuni (Compliance Officer &
Sec)

ADVINI S.A.
L'Enclos, 34725, Saint-Felix-de-
Lodez, France
Tel.: (33) 467888000
Web Site: https://www.advini.com
ADVI—(EUR)
Sales Range: $250-299.9 Million
Emp.: 544
Wine Producer
N.A.I.C.S.: 312130
Antoine Leccia (Chm-Exec Bd)

Subsidiaries:

AdVini Polska, Sp. z.o.o. **(1)**
Chalubinskiego 8, Warsaw, 00-613, Poland
Tel.: (48) 226250950
Sales Range: $25-49.9 Million
Emp.: 8
Wine Mfr & Distr
N.A.I.C.S.: 312130
Krzysztof Boguszewski (Gen Mgr)

Antoine Moueix SAS **(1)**
Route du Milieu, BP 40100, Saint-Emilion,
33500, France
Tel.: (33) 5 57 55 58 00
Web Site: http://www.advini.com
Wine Mfr
N.A.I.C.S.: 312130

Gassier SAS **(1)**
Chemin De La Colle Jas Du Luc, 13114,
Puylouubier, France
Tel.: (33) 4 42 66 38 74
Web Site: http://www.chateau-gassier.com
Sales Range: $25-49.9 Million
Emp.: 8
Wine Mfr
N.A.I.C.S.: 312130
Nadege Merlo (Mgr-Production)

L'Avenir **(1)**
L'Avenir Wine Estate - Klapmuts Road R44,
Stellenbosch, 7599, Western Cape, South
Africa
Tel.: (27) 21 889 5001
Emp.: 28
Wine Mfr & Distr
N.A.I.C.S.: 312130
Dirk Coetzee (Mgr)

Rigal SAS **(1)**
Chateau De Chambert Les Hauts Coteaux,
46700, Floressas, France
Tel.: (33) 565 307 010
Web Site: http://www.rigal.fr
Sales Range: $25-49.9 Million
Emp.: 15
Wine Mfr
N.A.I.C.S.: 312130
Anne Ulrich (Mgr-Quality)

ADVOCATE PRINTING & PUB-
LISHING CO. LTD.
181 Brown's Point Road, PO Box
1000, Pictou, B0K 1H0, NS, Canada
Tel.: (902) 485-1990
Web Site:
https://www.advocateprinting.com
Year Founded: 1891
Printing Publisher
N.A.I.C.S.: 323111
Sean Murray (Pres & CEO)

Subsidiaries:

Advocate Printing & Publishing Co.
Ltd. - Dartmouth Plant **(1)**
162 Trider Crescent, Dartmouth, B3B 1R6,
NS, Canada
Tel.: (902) 457-7468

Sales Range: $25-49.9 Million
Emp.: 100
Newspaper Printing Services
N.A.I.C.S.: 323111

ADVOKATFIRMAET PRICEWA-
TERHOUSECOOPERS AS
Color Line Stadion Sjomannsvegen
14, 0000, Alesund, Norway
Tel.: (47) 95 26 00 00 NO
Web Site: http://www.pwc.no
Emp.: 1,700
Accounting & Business Consulting
Services
N.A.I.C.S.: 541211

ADVOKATFIRMAET SCHJODT
AS
Ruselokkveien 14, PO Box 2444,
0201, Oslo, Norway
Tel.: (47) 22 01 88 00 NO
Web Site: http://www.schjodt.no
Law firm
N.A.I.C.S.: 541199
Erling Ueland (Mng Partner)

ADVTECH LIMITED
ADvTECH House Inanda Greens 54
Wierda Road West Wierda Valley,
Sandton, 2196, South Africa
Tel.: (27) 116768000
Web Site: http://www.advtech.co.za
ADH—(JSE)
Rev.: $428,050,154
Assets: $515,736,200
Liabilities: $216,298,782
Net Worth: $299,437,418
Earnings: $54,361,972
Emp.: 5,915
Fiscal Year-end: 12/31/23
Education Training & Staff Placement
Services
N.A.I.C.S.: 611710
J. Didier R. Oesch (CFO & Grp Dir-
Comml)

Subsidiaries:

ADvTECH Resourcing (Pty) Ltd **(1)**
No 3 Eglin Rd Sunninghill Park, Sunninghill
Park, Sandton, 2199, Gauteng, South Africa
Tel.: (27) 112342404
Web Site: http://www.advtech.co.za
Sales Range: $350-399.9 Million
Emp.: 1,500
Recruitment Consulting Services
N.A.I.C.S.: 541612

Division (Domestic):

ADvTECH Resourcing (Pty) Ltd -
Communicate Personnel Division **(2)**
7 Naivasha Road Entrance on Eglin Road,
Sunninghill Sandton, Johannesburg, 2157,
Gauteng, South Africa
Tel.: (27) 11 318 2101
Web Site: https://www.communicate.co.za
Sales Range: $10-24.9 Million
Emp.: 50
Staffing & Recruitment Solutions
N.A.I.C.S.: 561311

ADvTECH Resourcing (Pty) Ltd - IT
Edge Division **(2)**
Eva Park Block C Unit C112 C/O Beyers
Naude & Judges Ave, Blackheath, Johan-
nesburg, 2195, Gauteng, South Africa
Tel.: (27) 116783131
Web Site: http://www.itedge.co.za
Sales Range: $25-49.9 Million
Emp.: 5
Information Technology Professionals Re-
cruitment Services
N.A.I.C.S.: 561311

ADvTECH Resourcing (Pty) Ltd - In-
source.ICT Division **(2)**
First Fl Engen House Waterfall Ofc Park
Bekker Rd, Midrand, 1685, Gauteng, South
Africa
Tel.: (27) 113159451
Web Site: http://www.insource.co.za

Sales Range: $10-24.9 Million
Emp.: 45
Information Technology Staffing Solutions
N.A.I.C.S.: 561311

ADvTECH Resourcing (Pty) Ltd -
Network Recruitment Division **(2)**
Summit Place Office Park 4th Floor Building
6 221 Garsfontein Rd, Menlyn, Pretoria,
0181, Gauteng, South Africa
Tel.: (27) 12 040 4040
Web Site:
https://www.networkrecruitment.com
Sales Range: $10-24.9 Million
Emp.: 15
Recruitment Services
N.A.I.C.S.: 561311

ADvTECH Resourcing (Pty) Ltd - Pro
Rec Recruitment Division **(2)**
The Crescent S Block Entrance 2 3 Eglin
Rd, Sunninghill, Johannesburg, 2125, Gau-
teng, South Africa
Tel.: (27) 11 803 5708
Web Site: http://www.prorec.co.za
Sales Range: $25-49.9 Million
Emp.: 4
Recruitment Services
N.A.I.C.S.: 561311

ADvTECH Resourcing (Pty) Ltd -
Tech-Pro Personnel Division **(2)**
7 Naivasha Road Entrance on Eglin Road,
Sunninghill, Sandton, 2157, South Africa
Tel.: (27) 11 514 0463
Web Site: https://www.tech-pro.co.za
Sales Range: $25-49.9 Million
Emp.: 19
Supply Chain Management Recruitment
Services
N.A.I.C.S.: 541612

Subsidiary (Domestic):

ADvTECh House **(2)**
Inanda Greens 54 Wierda Road West
Wierda Valley, Sandton, 2196, South Africa
Tel.: (27) 11 676 8000
Web Site: https://www.advtech.co.za
Staffing & Recruitment Services
N.A.I.C.S.: 541612

Division (Domestic):

Kapele Appointments (Pty) Limited -
The Working Earth Division **(3)**
7 Naivasha Road Corner of Eglin Road,
Sunninghill, Sandton, 2157, Gauteng, South
Africa
Tel.: (27) 114759668
Web Site:
https://www.theworkingearth.co.za
Emp.: 35
Online Recruitment Services
N.A.I.C.S.: 561311

Kapele Appointments (Pty) Ltd -
Vertex-Kapele Division **(3)**
Unit 3 Ground Fl Northdowns Ofc Park 17
Georgian Crescent W, Bryanston, 2152,
Gauteng, South Africa
Tel.: (27) 11 514 0899
Emp.: 14
Human Resource Consulting Services
N.A.I.C.S.: 541612

Subsidiary (Domestic):

Cassel & Company **(2)**
7 Naivasha Road Corner of Eglin Road en-
trance in Eglin Road, Sunninghill, Johan-
nesburg, 2157, Gauteng, South Africa
Tel.: (27) 11 234 1432
Web Site: https://www.cassel.co.za
Sales Range: $10-24.9 Million
Emp.: 24
Staffing & Recruitment Solutions
N.A.I.C.S.: 561311

Africa HR Solutions Ltd. **(1)**
Socota Business Park Sayed Hossen
Street, Phoenix, Mauritius
Tel.: (230) 465 3100
Web Site: https://www.africa-hr.com
Payroll Outsourcing Services
N.A.I.C.S.: 541214
Sundesh Ramchurn (Mgr-Content & Digital
Mktg)

CA Financial Appointments (Pty)
Ltd. **(1)**

Black River Park North Block B Ground
Floor 2 Fir Street, Observatory, Cape Town,
7925, South Africa
Tel.: (27) 21 442 1100
Web Site: https://www.ca.co.za
Financial Services
N.A.I.C.S.: 541611
Pete Whitehouse *(Mng Dir)*

CA Global Finance (Pty) Ltd.   **(1)**
Ground Floor Burg House Belmont Park
Belmont Road, Rondebosch, Cape Town,
7700, South Africa
Tel.: (27) 21 659 9200
Web Site: https://www.ca-finance.com
Recruitment Consulting Services
N.A.I.C.S.: 561312

CA Global Headhunters (Pty)
Ltd.   **(1)**
Ground Floor Burg House Belmont Park
Belmont Road, Rondebosch, Cape Town,
7700, South Africa
Tel.: (27) 21 659 9200
Web Site: https://www.caglobalint.com
Recruitment Consulting Services
N.A.I.C.S.: 561312

CA Mining (Pty) Ltd.   **(1)**
Ground Floor Burg House Belmont Park
Belmont Road, Rondebosch, Cape Town,
7700, South Africa
Tel.: (27) 21 659 9200
Web Site: https://www.camining.com
Recruitment Consulting Services
N.A.I.C.S.: 561312
Vivienne Gower *(Mng Dir)*

CA Oil & Gas (Pty) Ltd.   **(1)**
Ground Floor Burg House Belmont Park
Belmont Road, Rondebosch, Cape Town,
7700, South Africa
Tel.: (27) 21 659 9200
Web Site: https://www.ca-oil.com
Recruitment Consulting Services
N.A.I.C.S.: 561312
Zade-Leo Stafford *(Mgr-Team)*

Charterhouse Private Schools (Pty)
Ltd.   **(1)**
10 Erasmus Road, Radiokop, Honeydew,
2040, South Africa
Tel.: (27) 11 475 6809
Web Site: https://www.charterhouse.co.za
Private School Operator
N.A.I.C.S.: 611110

Maragon Private Schools Avianto
(Pty) Ltd.   **(1)**
Villa Maragon 1739 Postnet Suite 90, Mulders-
drift, 1739, Johannesburg, South Africa
Tel.: (27) 100201460
School Operator
N.A.I.C.S.: 611699
Tiffany Waterston *(Head-Primary School)*

Maragon Private Schools Ruimsig
(Pty) Ltd.   **(1)**
Cnr Peter and Kuilstock Roads, Ruimsig,
1724, Johannesburg, South Africa
Tel.: (27) 119580707
School Operator
N.A.I.C.S.: 611699

Oxbridge Academy (Pty) Ltd.   **(1)**
The Vineyard Corner of Devon Valley and
Adam Tas Road, Stellenbosch, 7600, South
Africa
Tel.: (27) 21 883 2454
Web Site:
    https://www.oxbridgeacademy.edu.za
Academy Operator
N.A.I.C.S.: 611110

Star Schools (Pty) Ltd.   **(1)**
167 Smit St, Braamfontein, Johannesburg,
Gauteng, South Africa
Tel.: (27) 11 018 4800
Web Site: https://www.starschools.co.za
School Operator
N.A.I.C.S.: 611699

The Independent Institute of Educa-
tion (Pty) Ltd   **(1)**
ADvTECH House Inanda Greens 54 Wierda
Road West, Wierda Valley, 2196, Sandton,
South Africa
Tel.: (27) 11 676 8021
Web Site: https://www.iie.ac.za

Sales Range: $1-4.9 Billion
Educational Institute Management Services
N.A.I.C.S.: 923110

University of Africa Ltd.   **(1)**
Plot 2982 Bukavu Road, Thorn Park, Lu-
saka, 10101, Zambia
Tel.: (260) 21 123 0812
Web Site: https://www.keystoneuoa.com
Academy Operator
N.A.I.C.S.: 611110

ADWAYS INC.
5F Sumitomo Fudosan Shinjuku First
Tower 1-1 Nishi-Shinjuku 5-chome,
Shinjuku-ku, Tokyo, 1600023, Japan
Tel.: (81) 353316328
Web Site: https://www.adways.net
Year Founded: 2001
2489—(TKS)
Rev.: $89,355,798
Assets: $166,679,881
Liabilities: $70,208,127
Net Worth: $96,471,754
Earnings: $6,382,557
Emp.: 1,125
Fiscal Year-end: 12/31/23
Mobile Advertising Services
N.A.I.C.S.: 541810
Haruhisa Okamura *(Founder & CEO)*

Subsidiaries:

ADWAYS TECHNOLOGY CO.,
JSC.   **(1)**
5F Agribank Building 266 Doi Can Str, Ba
Dinh Dist, Hanoi, Vietnam
Tel.: (84) 4 3762 4015
Mobile Advertising Services
N.A.I.C.S.: 541810

Adways China Co., Ltd.   **(1)**
Room 2002 Hong Kong New World Tower
300 Huaihai Middle Road, Huangpu District,
Shanghai, 200021, China
Tel.: (86) 2164718181
Web Site: https://adways.com.cn
Digital Marketing Services
N.A.I.C.S.: 541613

Adways Frontier Inc.   **(1)**
6-10-1 Odorinishi 6th Floor Odorinishi 6
Building, Chuo-ku, Sapporo, 060-0042,
Hokkaido, Japan
Tel.: (81) 117968830
Web Site: https://adways-frontier.net
Internet Advertising Services
N.A.I.C.S.: 541810

Adways Interactive, Inc.   **(1)**
25 Taylor St, San Francisco, CA 94012
Tel.: (415) 852-2180
Mobile Advertising Services
N.A.I.C.S.: 541810

Adways Korea, Inc.   **(1)**
Room A12 5th floor 216, Teheran-ro
Gangnam-gu, Seoul, 06628, Korea (South)
Tel.: (82) 7044206699
Web Site: https://www.adways.kr
Mobile Advertising Services
N.A.I.C.S.: 541810

Adways Labs (Thailand) Co.,
Ltd.   **(1)**
973 President Tower Unit 10D 10th Floor
Ploenchit Road, Pathumwan, Bangkok,
10330, Thailand
Tel.: (66) 2 656 0727
Web Site: http://www.th-adwayslabs.com
Online Marketing Services
N.A.I.C.S.: 541810
Pravit Anuvatesirikeat *(Mng Dir)*

Adways Philippines Inc.   **(1)**
Unit 507 5/F Prime Land Bldg Prime St,
Madrigal Business Park Ayala Alabang,
Muntinlupa, 1780, Philippines
Tel.: (63) 253103538
Mobile Advertising Services
N.A.I.C.S.: 541810

Adways Ventures, Inc.   **(1)**
5F Sumitomo Fudousan Shinjuku First
Tower 5-1-1, Nishi-Shinjuku Shinjuku-ku,
Tokyo, 160 0023, Japan
Tel.: (81) 353316325
Advertising Services

N.A.I.C.S.: 541810

JS Adways Media Inc.   **(1)**
21F No 510 Section 5 Zhongxiao East
Road, Xinyi District, Taipei, 110, Taiwan
Tel.: (886) 266380188
Web Site: https://www.js-adways.com.tw
Software Development Services
N.A.I.C.S.: 541511

Mist Technologies Inc.   **(1)**
8-17-1 Sumitomo Realty and Development
Shinjuku Grand Tower 34th Floor, Nishi-
Shinjuku Shinjuku-ku, Tokyo, 160-6134,
Japan
Tel.: (81) 35 331 6324
Advertising Services
N.A.I.C.S.: 541810

PT. Adways Indonesia   **(1)**
UOB PLAZA 22nd Floor JI MH Thamrin No
10, Jakarta, 10230, Indonesia
Tel.: (62) 21 319 20035
Web Site: http://www.adways-
    indonesia.co.id
Digital Advertising Services
N.A.I.C.S.: 541810

Samurai Adways Inc.   **(1)**
2nd floor Sumitomo Fudosan Ueno Building
1-9-12 Kitaueno, Taito-ku, Tokyo, 110 0014,
Japan
Tel.: (81) 367759800
Web Site: https://samurai-adways.net
Advertising Services
N.A.I.C.S.: 541810

ADX ENERGY LIMITED
29 Bay Road, Claremont, 6010, WA,
Australia
Tel.: (61) 893814266
Web Site: https://www.adx-
    energy.com
ADX—(ASX)
Rev.: $8,976,369
Assets: $29,041,041
Liabilities: $18,318,662
Net Worth: $10,722,379
Earnings: ($2,867,458)
Fiscal Year-end: 12/31/23
Oil & Gas Exploration Services
N.A.I.C.S.: 211120
Peter Ironside *(Co-Sec)*

Subsidiaries:

ADX Energy Panonia Srl   **(1)**
13 Tudor Stefan Street, 011655, Bucharest,
Romania
Tel.: (40) 21 230 0881
Oil & Gas Exploration Services
N.A.I.C.S.: 213112

ADX VIE GmbH   **(1)**
Canovagasse 5, 1010, Vienna, Austria
Tel.: (43) 50 724 5666
Oil & Gas Exploration Services
N.A.I.C.S.: 213112

AuDAX Energy GmbH   **(1)**
Kundratstr 6 2 1, Vienna, 1100, Austria
Tel.: (43) 16410189
Web Site: http://www.audax.com.au
Oil & Gas Field Exploration Services
N.A.I.C.S.: 213112

AuDAX Energy Srl   **(1)**
Via Monte del Marmo 103, 00166, Rome,
Italy
Tel.: (39) 066 442 0055
Oil & Gas Exploration Services
N.A.I.C.S.: 213112

ADYA INC.
675 Cochrane Drive Suite 100 North
Tower, Markham, L3R 0B8, ON,
Canada
Tel.: (416) 800-9999
Year Founded: 1993
ADYA—(TSXV)
Rev.: $1,637,426
Assets: $384,597
Liabilities: $2,971,551
Net Worth: ($2,586,954)
Earnings: ($350,483)
Fiscal Year-end: 12/31/23

N.A.I.C.S.: 541810
Telecommunication Servicesb
N.A.I.C.S.: 517810
Kyle Appleby *(CFO)*

ADYEN N.V.
Simon Carmiggeltstraat 5-60, 1011
DJ, Amsterdam, Netherlands
Tel.: (31) 858888138   NI
Web Site: https://www.adyen.com
Year Founded: 2006
1N8—(BER)
Rev.: $2,056,957,981
Assets: $10,562,237,696
Liabilities: $7,084,090,140
Net Worth: $3,478,147,555
Earnings: $770,856,706
Emp.: 4,196
Fiscal Year-end: 12/31/23
Electronic Payment Process Services
N.A.I.C.S.: 522320
Ingo Uytdehaage *(Co-CEO)*

Subsidiaries:

Adyen India Tech Hub Pvt. Ltd.   **(1)**
Office No 16A WeWork Enam Sambhav C -
20 G Block Road, Bandra Kurla Complex,
Mumbai, 400 051, Maharashtra, India
Tel.: (91) 8002002432
Payment Processing Services
N.A.I.C.S.: 522320

Adyen International B.V.   **(1)**
Simon Carmiggeltstraat 6-50, 1011 DJ, Am-
sterdam, Netherlands
Tel.: (31) 858888138
Ecommerce Services
N.A.I.C.S.: 513210

Subsidiary (Non-US):

Adyen (China) Software Technology
Co. Ltd.   **(2)**
ZhongChuang Building 04-116 819 Nanjing
West Road, Shanghai, 200041, China
Tel.: (86) 2152919320
Ecommerce Services
N.A.I.C.S.: 541511

Adyen Australia Pty Limited   **(2)**
1/10-14 Waterloo Street, Surry Hills, Syd-
ney, 2010, NSW, Australia
Tel.: (61) 285203890
Ecommerce Services
N.A.I.C.S.: 541512

Adyen Canada Ltd.   **(2)**
1 University Avenue Floor 11 Suite 11-114,
Toronto, M5J 2P1, ON, Canada
Tel.: (647) 849-1378
Ecommerce Services
N.A.I.C.S.: 541513

Adyen GmbH   **(2)**
Friedrichstrasse 63, 10117, Berlin, Germany
Tel.: (49) 3030808105
Ecommerce Services
N.A.I.C.S.: 522291

Adyen Hong Kong Limited   **(2)**
10F Suite102 YF Life Tower 33 Lockhart
Road, Wanchai, China (Hong Kong)
Tel.: (852) 58082209
Ecommerce Services
N.A.I.C.S.: 522210

Adyen Iberia SLU   **(2)**
Calle Serrano 37, 28001, Madrid, Spain
Tel.: (34) 919014001
Ecommerce Services
N.A.I.C.S.: 522110

Subsidiary (US):

Adyen Inc.   **(2)**
274 Brannan St Ste 600, San Francisco,
CA 94107
Tel.: (415) 367-1502
Ecommerce Services
N.A.I.C.S.: 423620
Gayathri Rajan *(Sr VP-Data & AI Products)*

Subsidiary (Non-US):

Adyen Japan K.K.   **(2)**
Tel.: (81) 357787695
Ecommerce Services
N.A.I.C.S.: 423620

ADYEN N.V.

Adyen N.V.—(Continued)

Adyen Mexico, S.A. de C.V. (2)
Av Paseo de la Reforma 483 48th floor,
Cuauhtemoc, CP 06500, Mexico, Mexico
Tel.: (52) 5541642395
Ecommerce Services
N.A.I.C.S.: 522110

Adyen Nordic AB (2)
Kungsbron 16 12th Floor, 111 22, Stock-
holm, Sweden
Tel.: (46) 812400950
Ecommerce Services
N.A.I.C.S.: 522110

Adyen Singapore Pte. Ltd. (2)
109 North Bridge Road 10-22 Funan, Sin-
gapore, 179097, Singapore
Tel.: (65) 31634469
Ecommerce Services
N.A.I.C.S.: 522210

Adyen UK Limited (2)
12-13 Wells Mews, London, W1T 3HE,
United Kingdom
Tel.: (44) 2039364029
Ecommerce Services
N.A.I.C.S.: 522210

Adyen do Brazil Ltda. (2)
Avenida das Nacoes Unidas 30th and 31st
Floors Conjunto B, Sao Paulo, 14261, Bra-
zil
Tel.: (55) 1131974315
Ecommerce Services
N.A.I.C.S.: 522320

ADYTON RESOURCES COR-PORATION

2800 Park Place 666 Burrard St,
Vancouver, V6S 2Z7, BC, Canada
Tel.: (416) 365-3407　　　　　　Ca
ADYRF—(OTCIQ)
Assets: $9,607,648
Liabilities: $303,416
Net Worth: $9,304,232
Earnings: ($1,744,034)
Fiscal Year-end: 12/31/22
Asset Management Services
N.A.I.C.S.: 523940
Timothy Elgon Savile Crossley *(Act-
ing CEO)*

AE MULTI HOLDINGS BER-HAD

Lot 87 Kawasan Perusahaan Bakar
Arang, 8000, Sungai Petani, Kedah
Darul Aman, Malaysia
Tel.: (60) 4213715
Web Site:
https://www.amallionpcb.com
AEM—(KLS)
Rev.: $23,134,657
Assets: $35,292,338
Liabilities: $18,722,204
Net Worth: $16,570,134
Earnings: ($4,412,789)
Emp.: 226
Fiscal Year-end: 03/31/23
Printed Circuit Board Mfr
N.A.I.C.S.: 334412
Chao-Tung Yang *(CEO & Mng Dir)*

Subsidiaries:

AE Corporation (M) Sdn. Bhd. (1)
Lot 87 Persiaran Sebelas Kawasan Perusa-
haan Bakar Arang, 08000, Sungai Petani,
kedah Darul Amam, Malaysia
Tel.: (60) 44213715
Sales Range: $50-74.9 Million
Emp.: 226
Printed Circuit Board Mfr
N.A.I.C.S.: 334412
C. K. Yang *(Gen Mgr)*

Subsidiary (Non-US):

**Amallion Enterprise (Thailand) Corpo-
ration Ltd.** (2)
707 Moo 4 Bangpoo Industrial Estate,
Praksa Muang, Samut Prakan, 10280, Thailand
Tel.: (66) 270926013

Emp.: 260
Printed Circuit Board Mfr
N.A.I.C.S.: 334412

AEA INTERNATIONAL HOLD-INGS PTE. LTD.

331 North Bridge Road 17-00 Odeon
Towers, Singapore, 188720, Singa-
pore
Tel.: (65) 63387800　　　　　　SG
Web Site:
http://www.internationalsos.com
Year Founded: 1985
Emp.: 11,000
Holding Company; Emergency Re-
sponse Services
N.A.I.C.S.: 551112

Subsidiaries:

International SOS (France) S.A. (1)
1 Allee Pierre Burelle, 92593, Levallois-
Perret, Cedex, France
Tel.: (33) 155 633 232
Web Site: http://www.internationalsos.com
Emergency Response Services
N.A.I.C.S.: 561421
Philippe Arnaud *(Reg Pres & CEO-Eastern
Europe, Central Asia, Middle East & Africa)*

**International SOS Assistance,
Inc.** (1)
3600 Horizon Blvd Ste 300, Philadelphia,
PA 19053
Tel.: (215) 942-8000
Web Site: http://www.internationalsos.com
Emergency Response Services
N.A.I.C.S.: 561421

International SOS Pte. Ltd. (1)
331 North Bridge Road 17-00 Odeon Tow-
ers, Singapore, 188720, Singapore
Web Site: http://www.internationalsos.com
Emergency Response Services
N.A.I.C.S.: 561421

AEA-BRIDGES IMPACT CORP.

Boundary Hall Cricket Square, PO
Box 1093, Georgetown, KY1-1102,
Cayman Islands
Tel.: (345) 814 5825　　　　　　Ky
Web Site:
http://www.aeabridgesimpact.com
Year Founded: 2020
IMPX—(NYSE)
Rev.: $12,516,887
Assets: $401,526,175
Liabilities: $454,592,853
Net Worth: ($53,066,678)
Earnings: $4,822,073
Emp.: 3
Fiscal Year-end: 12/31/21
Investment Services
N.A.I.C.S.: 523999
John Garcia *(Chm & Co-CEO)*

AEBI SCHMIDT HOLDING AG

Schulstrasse 4, 8500, Frauenfeld,
Switzerland
Tel.: (41) 71 626 91 10
Web Site: http://www.aebi-
schmidt.com
Sales Range: $350-399.9 Million
Emp.: 1,583
Holding Company Services
N.A.I.C.S.: 551112
Gero Buttiker *(VP)*

Subsidiaries:

Aebi & Co. AG Maschinenfabrik (1)
Buchmattstrasse 56, 3401, Burgdorf, Swit-
zerland
Tel.: (41) 34 421 61 21
Web Site: http://www.aebi-schmidt.ch
Agricultural & Road Maintenance Equip-
ment Mfr, Sls & Service
N.A.I.C.S.: 333111

Aebi Schmidt Austria GmbH (1)
Schiesstand 4, 6401, Inzing, Tirol, Austria
Tel.: (43) 5238 53 590 20
Web Site: http://www.aebi-schmidt.at

Agricultural & Road Maintenance Equip-
ment Sales & Service
N.A.I.C.S.: 423440
Robert Harandi *(Mng Dir)*

Aebi Schmidt Belgium (1)
Boomsesteenweg 74, 2630, Aartselaar,
Belgium
Tel.: (32) 3450 91 40
Web Site: http://www.aebi-schmidt.be
Agricultural & Road Maintenance Equip-
ment Sales & Service
N.A.I.C.S.: 423440
Arjan P. Ester *(Dir-Netherlands & Belgium-
Markets & Sls Europe)*

**Aebi Schmidt Deutschland
GmbH** (1)
Albtalstrasse 36, 79837, Sankt Blasien,
Germany
Tel.: (49) 76 72 412 0
Web Site: http://www.aebi-schmidt.de
Agricultural & Road Maintenance Equip-
ment Mfr & Distr
N.A.I.C.S.: 333111
Jochen Schneider *(COO)*

Aebi Schmidt Iberica S.A. (1)
C/ de la Perdiz Parcelas 18 y 19, 45950,
Casarrubios del Monte, Toledo, Spain
Tel.: (34) 9 02 02 02 42
Web Site: http://www.aebi-schmidt.es
Agricultural & Road Maintenance Equip-
ment Sales & Service
N.A.I.C.S.: 423440

Aebi Schmidt International AG (1)
Leutschenbachstrasse 52, 8050, Zurich,
Switzerland
Tel.: (41) 44 308 58 80
Web Site: http://www.aebi-schmidt-
international.com
Agricultural & Road Maintenance Equip-
ment Sales & Service
N.A.I.C.S.: 423820

Aebi Schmidt Italia s.r.l. (1)
Via dei Pinali 11, Frazione Cimpello, 33080,
Fiume Veneto, Italy
Tel.: (39) 0434 951 711
Web Site: http://www.aebi-schmidt.it
Agricultural & Road Maintenance Equip-
ment Sales & Service
N.A.I.C.S.: 423830
Luca Firotto *(Gen Dir)*

Aebi Schmidt Nederland BV (1)
Handelsweg 8, 7451 PJ, Holten, Nether-
lands
Tel.: (31) 548 37 00 00
Web Site: http://www.aebi-schmidt.nl
Emp.: 221
Agricultural & Road Maintenance Equip-
ment Mfr, Sls & Service
N.A.I.C.S.: 333111
Harald Bloemers *(Mgr-Supply Chain)*

Aebi Schmidt Norge AS (1)
Gjerstadveien 171, 4993, Sundebru, Aust-
Agder, Norway
Tel.: (47) 37 11 92 00
Web Site: http://www.aebi-schmidt.com
Road Maintenance Equipment Mfr, Sls &
Service
N.A.I.C.S.: 333924
Henrik Mortensen *(Mgr-Fin & Acctg)*

Aebi Schmidt Polska Sp. z o. o. (1)
ul Skrajna 80A, 25 650, Kielce, Poland
Tel.: (48) 41 36 52 149
Web Site: http://www.aebi-schmidt.pl
Agricultural & Road Maintenance Equip-
ment Mfr, Sls & Service
N.A.I.C.S.: 333111

Aebi Schmidt Sweden AB (1)
Borgmaestaregatan 24, 596 34, Skanninge,
Sweden
Tel.: (46) 142 29 90 00
Web Site: http://www.aebi-schmidt.se
Agricultural & Road Maintenance Equip-
ment Sales & Service
N.A.I.C.S.: 423440
Christopher Sundell *(Mng Dir)*

Aebi Schmidt UK Limited (1)
Southgate Way, Orton Southgate, Peterbor-
ough, PE2 6GP, United Kingdom
Tel.: (44) 1733 363 300
Web Site: http://www.aebi-schmidt.co.uk

Agricultural & Road Maintenance Equip-
ment Sales & Service
N.A.I.C.S.: 423440
Katherine Daunt *(Mgr-Sls Support)*

DMI International B.V. (1)
Hesselink van Suchtelenweg 4, 6703 CT,
Wageningen, Netherlands
Tel.: (31) 317 465700
Web Site: http://www.dmi-report.com
Software Developer; Mobile Data for Road
Maintenance & Public Spaces
N.A.I.C.S.: 513210

LLC ASH Rus. (1)
Vishnevaya str 9, 125362, Moscow, Russia
Tel.: (7) 495 648 73 56
Web Site: http://www.aebi-schmidt-
international.com
Agricultural & Road Maintenance Equip-
ment Sales & Service
N.A.I.C.S.: 423440

Meyer Products LLC (1)
18513 Euclid Ave, Cleveland, OH 44112
Tel.: (216) 486-1313
Web Site: http://www.meyerproducts.com
Emp.: 125
Snow Plows & Salt Spreaders Mfr
N.A.I.C.S.: 336390
Andrew L. Outcalt *(CEO)*

Swenson Spreader LLC (1)
127 Walnut St, Lindenwood, IL 61049-1049
Tel.: (888) 825-7323
Web Site: http://www.swensonproducts.com
Emp.: 130
Snow & Ice Control Equipment Mfr
N.A.I.C.S.: 336390
William Hintzsche *(Dir-Ops)*

AEC EDUCATION PLC

102F Pasir Panjang Road #08-01,
Singapore, 118530, Singapore
Tel.: (65) 6412 0734
Web Site:
http://www.aeceducationplc.co.uk
Sales Range: $10-24.9 Million
Emp.: 150
Educational Support Services
N.A.I.C.S.: 611710
Richard Mace *(CEO)*

Subsidiaries:

AEC Bilingual Pte Ltd. (1)
167 Jalan Bukit Merah Tower 5 No 03-11,
150167, Singapore, Singapore
Tel.: (65) 63366905
Web Site: http://www.aec.edu.sg
Sales Range: $10-24.9 Million
Emp.: 80
Business School Operation Services
N.A.I.C.S.: 611310

AEC Edu Group Pte Ltd. (1)
167 Jalan Bukit Merah Connection 1 Tower
4 No 02-13, Singapore, 150167, Singapore
Tel.: (65) 64120700
Web Site: http://www.aec-college.edu.sg
Sales Range: $10-24.9 Million
Emp.: 60
Training & Educational Services
N.A.I.C.S.: 611710
David Ho *(Mng Dir)*

Subsidiary (Domestic):

AEC College Pte. Ltd. (2)
167 Jln Bukit Merah Connection 1 Tower 4
02-13, Singapore, 150167, Singapore
Tel.: (65) 64120700
Web Site: http://www.aec-college.edu.sg
Sales Range: $10-24.9 Million
Business Schools Management Services
N.A.I.C.S.: 611310

**AEC Resource Development Pte
Ltd.** (2)
167 Jalan Bukit Merah Connection 1 Tower
4 No 02-13, Singapore, Singapore
Tel.: (65) 64120700
Web Site: http://www.aec.edu.sg
Sales Range: $10-24.9 Million
Emp.: 40
Education Services
N.A.I.C.S.: 611710
David Ho *(CEO)*

Brighton Commercial Training Centre Pte Ltd. (2)
43 Mid Rd Boon Sing Bldg No 01-00, Singapore, Singapore
Tel.: (65) 62258030
Web Site: http://www.bristol.edu.sg
Sales Range: $10-24.9 Million
Emp.: 30
Educational Support Services
N.A.I.C.S.: 611710
Betty Chua (Mgr)

Smartworks Learning Centre Pte Ltd. (2)
167 Jalan Bukit Merah Connection 1 Tower 4 #02-13, 150167, Singapore, Singapore
Tel.: (65) 6412 0700
Web Site: http://www.aec.edu.sg
Education Training Services
N.A.I.C.S.: 923110

AEC SECURITIES PUBLIC COMPANY LIMITED
17th Floor Room 1701 1705-1707 Athenee Tower 63 Wireless Rd Lumpini, Pathumwan, Bangkok, 10330, Thailand
Tel.: (66) 2 659 3456
Web Site: http://www.aecs.com
Year Founded: 1971
Rev.: $8,541,878
Assets: $43,803,029
Liabilities: $17,733,233
Net Worth: $26,069,797
Earnings: ($8,914,917)
Emp.: 428
Fiscal Year-end: 12/31/19
Securities Brokerage Services
N.A.I.C.S.: 523150
Vallapa Sunakorn (COO)

AECC AERO ENGINE CONTROL CO., LTD.
No 792 Liangxi Road, Binhu District, Wuxi, 214063, Hubin, China
Tel.: (86) 51085700611
Web Site: https://www.aaec.com.cn
Year Founded: 2010
000738—(SSE)
Rev.: $693,806,256
Assets: $2,110,457,700
Liabilities: $497,674,476
Net Worth: $1,612,783,224
Earnings: $96,651,360
Emp.: 8,216
Fiscal Year-end: 12/31/22
Aircraft Components Mfr
N.A.I.C.S.: 332994
Miao Zhongming (Chm)

AECC AERO SCIENCE & TECHNOLOGY CO., LTD.
Chengfa Industrial Park Shulong Avenue, Xindu District, Chengdu, 610503, Sichuan, China
Tel.: (86) 2889358616
Web Site: https://ast.aecc.cn
Year Founded: 1999
600391—(SHG)
Rev.: $533,710,144
Assets: $897,636,561
Liabilities: $589,972,439
Net Worth: $307,664,122
Earnings: $6,543,581
Emp.: 3,400
Fiscal Year-end: 12/31/22
Aircraft Product Mfr & Distr
N.A.I.C.S.: 336412
Xiong Yi (Sec, VP, Deputy Gen Mgr & Dir)

AECC AVIATION POWER CO., LTD.
Fengcheng 10th Road, Waiyang District, Xi'an, 710021, Shaanxi, China
Tel.: (86) 43185883022
Web Site: https://hfdl.aecc.cn
Year Founded: 1958

600893—(SHG)
Rev.: $5,208,439,706
Assets: $12,631,214,143
Liabilities: $6,834,720,663
Net Worth: $5,796,493,480
Earnings: $177,996,565
Fiscal Year-end: 12/31/22
Aircraft Engine Mfr & Whslr
N.A.I.C.S.: 336412
Yang Sen (Chm & Sec)

AECC SHANGHAI COMMERCIAL AIRCRAFT ENGINE MANUFACTURING CO.
No 3998 Lianhua South Road, Minhang, Shanghai, 200241, China
Tel.: (86) 2133366666
Web Site: https://www.acae.com.cn
Year Founded: 2009
Aircraft Engine Mfr
N.A.I.C.S.: 336412

AECI LIMITED
AECI Place 24 The Woodlands Woodlands Drive Woodmead, Sandton, 2191, South Africa
ZA
Tel.: (27) 118068700
Web Site: https://www.aeciworld.com
Year Founded: 1930
AFE—(JSE)
Rev.: $2,042,250,000
Assets: $1,521,721,320
Liabilities: $845,818,260
Net Worth: $675,903,060
Earnings: $64,262,800
Emp.: 7,235
Fiscal Year-end: 12/31/23
Specialty Chemicals Mfr
N.A.I.C.S.: 325130
K. Mark Kathan (CFO & Dir-Fin)

Subsidiaries:

AEL Holdco Limited (1)
No 1 Platinum Drive Long Meadow Buss Estate, Edenvale, 1644, South Africa
Tel.: (27) 116060000
Mining Engineering Services
N.A.I.C.S.: 541330

African Explosives (Botswana) Limited (1)
Unit 2 Plot 117 Millenium Park, Gaborone, Botswana
Tel.: (267) 3938133
Web Site: http://www.aelminingservices.com
Emp.: 10
Commercial Explosive Mfr
N.A.I.C.S.: 325920
Ronald Joseph (Mng Dir)

African Explosives (Tanzania) Limited (1)
Plot 98 Block W Capri Point Industrial Area, Mwanza, Tanzania
Tel.: (255) 28 250 3311
Web Site: http://www.aelminingservices.com
Mining Explosives Mfr
N.A.I.C.S.: 325920
Julian Taylor (Gen Mgr)

African Explosives Holdings (Pty) Limited (1)
The Platform 1 Platinum Drive, Longmeadow Business Estate Modderfontein, Johannesburg, 1645, South Africa
Tel.: (27) 11 606 0000
Web Site: http://www.aelminningservices.com
Sales Range: $100-124.9 Million
Emp.: 200
Specialty Chemicals Mining Services
N.A.I.C.S.: 212390
Edwin Ludick (Gen Mgr)

African Explosives Limited (1)
Platform House 1 Platinum Drive, Longmeadow Business Estate, Modderfontein, 1645, Johannesburg, South Africa (100%)
Tel.: (27) 116060004
Web Site: http://www.explosives.co.za
Sales Range: $1-4.9 Billion
Emp.: 3,000
Explosives Mfr

N.A.I.C.S.: 325920
Rafael Fernandes (Exec Dir-Fin)

Atlas Consolidated Industries (Pty) Limited (1)
114 Terrace Rd, Edenvale, 1609, South Africa
Tel.: (27) 119221900
Industrial Chemicals Mfr
N.A.I.C.S.: 325998

Chemfit (Pty) Limited (1)
AECI Chem Park 200 Bergrivier Drive Chloorkop Ext 24, Chloorkop, Kempton Park, 1619, Gauteng, South Africa
Tel.: (27) 119221780
Web Site: http://www.chemfit-online.co.za
Chemicals Whslr & Distr
N.A.I.C.S.: 424690

Chemical Initiatives (Pty) Limited (1)
Building 24 The Woodlands Woodlands Drive, Woodmead, Sandton, 2191, South Africa
Tel.: (27) 118068700
Web Site: http://cheminit-online.co.za
Sales Range: $25-49.9 Million
Emp.: 27
Sulphur Based Chemicals Mfr & Whslr
N.A.I.C.S.: 325199

Chemiphos SA (Pty) Limited (1)
PO Box 4104, Halfway House, Midrand, 1685, Gauteng, South Africa
Tel.: (27) 119221600
Web Site: http://www.chemiphos.com
Sales Range: $25-49.9 Million
Emp.: 20
Phosphoric Acid Mfr & Whslr
N.A.I.C.S.: 325180

Chemserve Perlite (Pty) Limited (1)
Cnr Cullinan & Turk Street, Olifantsfontein, Johannesburg, South Africa
Tel.: (27) 879402999
Perlite Mineral Products Mfr
N.A.I.C.S.: 327999

Subsidiary (Domestic):

Senmin International (Pty) Limited (2)
Block 5 Level 2 Falconview House Constantia Office Park Cnr 14th Ave &, H Potgieter St Weltevredenpark, Roodepoort, 1725, Gauteng, South Africa
Tel.: (27) 11 246 6300
Web Site: http://www.senmin.co.za
Sales Range: $25-49.9 Million
Emp.: 19
Ore Beneficiation Chemicals Mfr & Distr
N.A.I.C.S.: 325998

Chemserve Systems (Pty) Limited (1)
200 Bergrivier Drive, PO Box 12055, Chloorkop, Kempton Park, 1624, Gauteng, South Africa (100%)
Tel.: (27) 119221600
Web Site: http://www.chemsystems.co.za
Sales Range: $50-74.9 Million
Emp.: 150
Chemical Products Mfr
N.A.I.C.S.: 424690
Hugo Basson (Mng Dir)

Cobito (Pty) Limited (1)
Unit 2 17 Galaxy Road Linbro Park, Germiston, 2065, South Africa
Tel.: (27) 118748960
Sales Range: $25-49.9 Million
Emp.: 6
Mining Engineering Services
N.A.I.C.S.: 541330
Mark Cox (Mng Dir)

Crest Chemicals (Pty) Limited (1)
247 15th Rd Randjespark, PO Box 4280, Midrand, 1685, Gauteng, South Africa
Tel.: (27) 112543300
Sales Range: $50-74.9 Million
Emp.: 200
Chemical Distr
N.A.I.C.S.: 424690

DetNet South Africa (Pty) Ltd. (1)
Block 1B Founders Hill Office Park Centenary Way, PO Box 10, Centenary Way, Modderfontein, 1645, South Africa (50%)
Tel.: (27) 11 657 7600

Web Site: https://www.detnet.com
Sales Range: $25-49.9 Million
Emp.: 90
Explosives Mfr
N.A.I.C.S.: 325920
Gys Landman (CEO)

Duco Speciality Coatings (Pty) Limited (1)
249 Flamming Street, Edenvale, 1614, South Africa
Tel.: (27) 116630300
Web Site: http://www.duco.co.za
Sales Range: $25-49.9 Million
Emp.: 24
Automotive Paint Finishes Distr
N.A.I.C.S.: 424950
Mulder Llewelyn (Mng Dir)

ImproChem (Pty) Limited (1)
1 Pinelands Hill Business Park Maxwell Drive Founders Hill, Spartan, Kempton Park, 1645, Gauteng, South Africa
Tel.: (27) 119710400
Web Site: http://www.improserv.co.za
Sales Range: $25-49.9 Million
Emp.: 85
Water Treatment & Management Services
N.A.I.C.S.: 924110

Industrial Oleochemical Products (Pty) Limited (1)
317 Chamberlain Road, Jacobs, Durban, 4026, KwaZulu-Natal, South Africa
Tel.: (27) 31 461 8680
Web Site: http://www.oleo.co.za
Sales Range: $50-74.9 Million
Emp.: 131
Fatty Acids Mfr
N.A.I.C.S.: 325199
Martin Godbold (Mng Dir)

Lake International Technologies (Pty) Limited (1)
29 Marconi Road Montague Gardens, Cape Town, 7441, South Africa
Tel.: (27) 873576552
Web Site: http://www.lake.co.za
N.A.I.C.S.: 311999

Much Asphalt (Proprietary) Limited (1)
Tel.: (27) 21 900 4400
Web Site: https://www.muchasphalt.com
Asphalt Product Mfr
N.A.I.C.S.: 324121

Subsidiary (Domestic):

Spray Pave (Pty) Limited (2)
7 Evans Street Alrode South, Alberton, 1451, South Africa (100%)
Tel.: (27) 11 868 5451
Web Site: https://www.spraypave.co.za
Bituminous Spray Products Distr
N.A.I.C.S.: 212114
Eddie Jansen Van Vuuren (Dir)

Nulandis (1)
ECI Chem Park Block No2 - 2nd Floor Bergrivier Drive Chloorkop, Kempton Park, 1619, South Africa
Tel.: (27) 11 823 8000
Web Site: http://www.nulandis.com
Emp.: 143
Chemical Products Mfr & Distr
N.A.I.C.S.: 325998

SANS Fibers Incorporated (1)
1422 Burtonwood Dr Ste 203, Gastonia, NC 28054-4712
Tel.: (704) 869-8311
Web Site: http://www.sansfibers.com
Sales Range: $50-74.9 Million
Emp.: 6
Nylon Yarn Distr
N.A.I.C.S.: 424990
Stephen Myers (Gen Mgr)

SANS Technical Fibers LLC (1)
1422 Burtonwood Dr Ste 203, Gastonia, NC 28054
Tel.: (704) 869-8311
Web Site: http://www.sansfibers.com
Sales Range: $25-49.9 Million
Texturised Yarn Mfr
N.A.I.C.S.: 313110

Schirm GmbH (1)
Geschwister-Scholl-Strasse 127, 39218,

AECI Limited—(Continued)

Schonebeck, Germany
Tel.: (49) 392 845 6199
Web Site: https://www.schirm.com
Emp.: 900
Pesticides & Agricultural Chemical Products
Mfr
N.A.I.C.S.: 325320
Alfred Ludorf *(Member-Mgmt Bd)*

Division (Domestic):

Schirm GmbH-Lubeck (2)
Mecklenburger Strasse 229, Lubreck,
23568, Lubeck, Germany
Tel.: (49) 4516196562
Web Site: http://www.schirm.com
Sales Range: $25-49.9 Million
Emp.: 120
Agricultural Pesticides & Chemical Mfr
N.A.I.C.S.: 325320
Michael Becker Michael has a account
(Mgr-Ops)

Schirm GmbH-Schonebeck (2)
Geschwister Scholl Strasse 127, Schone-
beck, 39218, Germany
Tel.: (49) 3928456199
Agricultural Pesticides & Chemical Mfr
N.A.I.C.S.: 325320
Maik Pusch *(Head-Supply Chain Mgmt)*

Subsidiary (US):

Schirm USA, Inc. (2)
2801 S Oak Grove Rd, Ennis, TX 75119
Tel.: (972) 921-8968
Agricultural & Household Pesticides Mfr
N.A.I.C.S.: 325320
Chad Kern *(Pres & CEO)*

**Simitri Specialty Chemicals (Pty)
Limited** (1)
200 Bergrivier Dr, PO Box 12055,
Chloorkop, Kempton Park, 1624, South
Africa
Tel.: (27) 119221717
Web Site: http://www.simitri.co.za
Specialty Chemicals Distr
N.A.I.C.S.: 424690

AECON GROUP INC.

20 Carlson Court Suite 105, Toronto,
M9W 7K6, ON, Canada
Tel.: (416) 297-2600
Web Site: https://www.aecon.com
Year Founded: 1867
ARE—(TSX)
Rev.: $3,111,379,454
Assets: $2,571,211,203
Liabilities: $1,856,546,792
Net Worth: $714,664,410
Earnings: $38,865,235
Emp.: 2,900
Fiscal Year-end: 12/31/21
Holding Company; Construction, En-
gineering, Procurement, Project Man-
agement, Development & Financing
& Facilities Management Services
N.A.I.C.S.: 236220
John M. Beck *(Founder & Chm)*

Subsidiaries:

AGI Traffic Technology, Inc. (1)
2960 Markham Rd, Scarborough, M1X 1E6,
ON, Canada
Tel.: (416) 742-8900
Sales Range: $50-74.9 Million
Emp.: 150
Construction of Building & Civil Engineering
Work
N.A.I.C.S.: 237310

Aecon Atlantic Industrial Inc. (1)
61 Estates Road, Dartmouth, B2Y 4K3, NS,
Canada
Tel.: (902) 482-6500
Web Site: http://www.aeconatlantic.com
Industrial Construction & Power Generation
Services
N.A.I.C.S.: 221118

Aecon Buildings (1)
20 Carlson Court Suite 105, Toronto, M9W
7K6, ON, Canada
Tel.: (416) 297-2600

Web Site: http://www.aecon.com
Sales Range: $25-49.9 Million
Emp.: 60
General Contracting, Construction Manage-
ment & Design-Build Services
N.A.I.C.S.: 236220

Branch (US):

Aecon Buildings (2)
19020 33rd Ave W Ste 240, Lynnwood, WA
98036
Tel.: (425) 774-2945
Web Site: http://www.usa.aecon.com
General Contracting, Construction Manage-
ment & Design-Build Services
N.A.I.C.S.: 236220

Aecon Concessions (1)
20 Carlson Court Suite 800, Toronto, M9W
7K6, ON, Canada
Tel.: (416) 293-7004
Infrastructure Development Services
N.A.I.C.S.: 541320

**Aecon Construction & Materials
Ltd.** (1)
20 Carlson Court Suite 105, Toronto, M9W
7K6, ON, Canada
Tel.: (416) 297-2600
Web Site: http://www.aecon.com
Sales Range: $25-49.9 Million
Emp.: 150
Provider of Construction Services
N.A.I.C.S.: 541330

Aecon Construction Group Inc. (1)
6284 104 Street NW, Edmonton, T6H 2L5,
AB, Canada
Tel.: (780) 430-4070
Construction Engineering Services
N.A.I.C.S.: 541330

**Aecon Construction Management
Inc.** (1)
1003 Ellwood Rd SW Suite 301, Edmonton,
T6X 0B3, AB, Canada
Tel.: (780) 791-5477
Civil Engineering Construction Services
N.A.I.C.S.: 237990

Aecon Constructors (1)
20 Carlson Court Suite 105, Toronto, M9W
7K6, ON, Canada
Tel.: (416) 297-2600
Web Site: http://www.aecon.com
Sales Range: $350-399.9 Million
Emp.: 500
Construction & Project Management of
Large Scale Energy Developments, Sub-
ways, Bridges, Dams, Tunnels, Highways &
Airports
N.A.I.C.S.: 237310

Aecon Industrial (1)
150 Sheldon Drive, Cambridge, N1R 7K9,
ON, Canada
Tel.: (519) 653-3200
Web Site: http://www.aecon.com
Sales Range: $25-49.9 Million
Emp.: 100
Industrial Construction & Fabrication for Me-
chanical & Electrical Installations
N.A.I.C.S.: 236210

Division (Domestic):

**Aecon Industrial - Western
Canada** (2)
53367 Range Road 232, Sherwood Park,
T8A 4V2, AB, Canada
Tel.: (780) 416-5700
Sales Range: $25-49.9 Million
Emp.: 50
Construction Contractor
N.A.I.C.S.: 237310
Stan Shewchuk *(Pres)*

Aecon Industrial Western Inc. (1)
53367 Range Rd 232, Sherwood Park, T8A
4V2, AB, Canada
Tel.: (780) 416-5700
Construction Management Services
N.A.I.C.S.: 237990

Aecon Infrastructure (1)
1003 Ellwood Road SW, Edmonton, T6X
0B3, AB, Canada
Tel.: (780) 430-4070
Web Site: http://www.aecon.com

Industrial Construction Services
N.A.I.C.S.: 236210

**Aecon Materials Engineering
Corp.** (1)
117 Ringwood Drive Unit 6, Stouffville, L4A
8C1, ON, Canada
Tel.: (905) 640-7772
Web Site: http://www.aecon.com
Sales Range: $25-49.9 Million
Emp.: 12
Construction Engineering Services
N.A.I.C.S.: 541330

Aecon Mining Inc. (1)
316 MacKay Crescent, Fort McMurray, T9H
4E4, AB, Canada
Tel.: (780) 791-5477
Web Site: http://www.aecon.com
Emp.: 300
Industrial Sand Mining Services
N.A.I.C.S.: 212322

Aecon Transportation West Ltd. (1)
9700 Endeavour Drive Southeast, Calgary,
T3S 0A1, AB, Canada
Tel.: (403) 293-9300
Web Site: http://www.aecon.com
Road Construction Engineering Services
N.A.I.C.S.: 237310

Aecon Utilities (1)
20 Carlson Court Suite 105, Toronto, M9W
7K6, ON, Canada
Tel.: (416) 297-2600
Web Site: http://www.aecon.com
Sales Range: $150-199.9 Million
Emp.: 500
Infrastructure Building Services
N.A.I.C.S.: 237120

Aecon Utility Engineering (1)
20 Carlson Crt Suite 800, Toronto, M9W
7K6, ON, Canada
Tel.: (416) 297-2600
Industrial Engineering & Designing Services
N.A.I.C.S.: 541330

**Bermuda Skyport Corporation
Limited** (1)
L F Wade International Airport 2 Kindley
Field Road, Saint Georges, DD03,
Bermuda (50.1%)
Tel.: (441) 4444400
Web Site: https://www.bermudaairport.com
Airport Services
N.A.I.C.S.: 488119
Aaron Adderley *(Pres)*

Bremar Construction Ltd. (1)
20 Carlson Court Suite 105, Toronto, M9W
7K6, ON, Canada
Tel.: (416) 297-2600
Web Site:
http://www.bremarconstruction.com
Utility Line Construction Services
N.A.I.C.S.: 237130
Mark Arnone *(VP)*

**Canadian Highways Infrastructure
Corporation** (1)
20 Carlson Ct Ste 800, Toronto, M9W 7K6,
ON, Canada
Tel.: (416) 293-8020
Sales Range: $25-49.9 Million
Emp.: 75
Development, Management, Finance, De-
sign, Construction & Operation of Toll High-
ways
N.A.I.C.S.: 237990

Canonbie Contracting Limited (1)
161 2055 Premier Way, Sherwood Park,
T8H 0G2, AB, Canada
Tel.: (780) 410-6900
Web Site: http://www.canonbie.ca
Sales Range: $25-49.9 Million
Emp.: 5
Building Electrical & Mechanical Equipment
Installation Services
N.A.I.C.S.: 238210

Construction Armbro BFC Inc. (1)
2540 Daniel Johnson Blvd Ste 1106, Laval,
H7T 2S3, QC, Canada
Tel.: (450) 687-4221
Sales Range: $25-49.9 Million
Emp.: 8
Construction & Project Management of
Large Scale Energy Developments, Sub-
ways, Bridges, Dams, Tunnels, Highways &
Airports

N.A.I.C.S.: 237310

Groupe Aecon Quebec Ltee (1)
2015 rue Peel Bureau 600, Montreal, H3A
1T8, QC, Canada
Tel.: (514) 352-0100
Web Site: http://www.aeconquebec.com
Construction Engineering Services
N.A.I.C.S.: 541330

Karson Asphalt Paving Inc. (1)
3725 Carp Road, Carp, K0A 1L0, ON,
Canada
Tel.: (613) 839-2816
Web Site: http://www.karson.ca
Asphalt Paving Mixture Mfr
N.A.I.C.S.: 324121
Peter Pelletier *(Gen Mgr)*

Karson Konstruction Limited (1)
3232 Carp Road 3232, Box 264, Carp, K0A
1L0, ON, Canada
Tel.: (613) 839-2816
Road Construction Engineering Services
N.A.I.C.S.: 237310
Steve McEachen *(Mgr-Construction & Ops)*

Lockerbie & Hole Inc. (1)
14940 121 A Ave, Edmonton, T5V 1A3, AB,
Canada
Tel.: (780) 452-1250
Web Site: http://www.lockerbiehole.com
Sales Range: $300-349.9 Million
Emp.: 315
Mechanical, Electrical, Instrumentation, Pipe
Fabrication, Module Assembly, Boiler Erec-
tion, Insulation & Civil Construction Contrac-
tor
N.A.I.C.S.: 236220

Subsidiary (Domestic):

**Lockerbie & Hole Contracting
Limited** (2)
7335 Flint Road Southeast, Calgary, T2H
1G3, AB, Canada
Tel.: (403) 571-2121
Web Site: http://www.LockerbieHole.com
Sales Range: $25-49.9 Million
Emp.: 16
Construction Contractor
N.A.I.C.S.: 237310

**Lockerbie & Hole Contracting
Limited** (2)
401 Salter Street, New Westminster, V3M
5Y1, BC, Canada
Tel.: (604) 777-5950
Web Site: http://www.lockerbiehole.com
Sales Range: $25-49.9 Million
Emp.: 40
Construction Contractor
N.A.I.C.S.: 237310

**Lockerbie & Hole Contracting
Limited** (2)
401 Salter St New Westminster, Vancouver,
V3M 5Y1, BC, Canada
Tel.: (250) 370-2999
Web Site: http://www.Lockerbiehole.com
Sales Range: $25-49.9 Million
Emp.: 30
Construction Contractor
N.A.I.C.S.: 237310

Miwel Construction Limited (1)
1631 Bethesda Sideroad, Richmond Hill,
L4E 0G8, ON, Canada
Tel.: (905) 888-5270
Web Site: http://www.aecon.com
Sales Range: $50-74.9 Million
Emp.: 200
Industrial Building Construction Services
N.A.I.C.S.: 236210

QX Ltd. (1)
4-4140A Sladeview Crescent, Mississauga,
L5L 6A1, ON, Canada
Tel.: (905) 828-9055
Web Site: http://www.qxtechnology.com
Sales Range: $150-199.9 Million
Emp.: 8
Wireless & Fibre Communication Equipment
Distr
N.A.I.C.S.: 423610

Tristar Electric Inc. (1)
6068 Netherhart Rd Unit 1, Mississauga,
L5T 1N3, ON, Canada
Tel.: (905) 670-1642

Web Site: http://www.tristarelectric.ca
Airport Lighting Installation Services
N.A.I.C.S.: 488119

AEDAS HOMES

Paseo de la Castellana 130 5th floo,
28046, Madrid, Spain
Tel.: (34) 917878198
Web Site:
   https://www.aedashomes.com
Year Founded: 2016
AEDAS—(BIL)
Rev.: $1,235,343,044
Assets: $2,171,590,617
Liabilities: $1,166,746,820
Net Worth: $1,004,843,797
Earnings: $117,600,713
Emp.: 305
Fiscal Year-end: 03/31/24
Real Estate Investment Services
N.A.I.C.S.: 531390
David Martinez Montero (CEO)

AEDES SIIQ S.P.A

Via Tortona 37, 20144, Milan, Italy
Tel.: (39) 0262431   IT
Web Site: http://www.aedes-siiq.com
Year Founded: 1905
AE—(ITA)
Sales Range: Less than $1 Million
Residential, Commercial & Industrial
Property Investment Services
N.A.I.C.S.: 531390
Giovanni Barbara (Chm)

AEDGE GROUP LIMITED

4009 Ang Mo Kio Ave 10 04-33 Tech
Place I, Singapore, 569738, Singapore
Tel.: (65) 64587645   SG
Web Site: https://www.aedge.com.sg
Year Founded: 2000
XVG—(CAT)
Rev.: $19,613,416
Assets: $14,184,154
Liabilities: $5,361,045
Net Worth: $8,823,108
Earnings: ($1,665,409)
Emp.: 501
Fiscal Year-end: 06/30/23
Engineeering Services
N.A.I.C.S.: 541330
Yeo Mui Hong (COO-Security &
Manpower)

AEDIFICA SA

Rue Belliard 40, PO Box 11, B-1040,
Brussels, Belgium
Tel.: (32) 26260770
Web Site: https://aedifica.eu
Year Founded: 2005
AED—(EUR)
Rev.: $346,808,699
Assets: $6,818,424,772
Liabilities: $2,865,559,113
Net Worth: $3,952,865,659
Earnings: $24,894,580
Emp.: 127
Fiscal Year-end: 12/31/23
Real Estate Investment Services
N.A.I.C.S.: 531390
Stefaan Gielens (CEO, Mng Dir &
Exec Dir)

Subsidiaries:

Aedifica Invest SA   (1)
Avenue Louise 33-1333, Brussels, 1050,
Belgium
Tel.: (32) 26260770
Web Site: http://www.aedifica.be
Sales Range: $25-49.9 Million
Emp.: 35
Real Estate Manangement Services
N.A.I.C.S.: 531390
Stefaan Gielens (Gen Mgr)

LV Charrieres Limited   (1)
La Rue Des Charrieres, Saint Peter, JE3

7ZQ, Jersey
Tel.: (44) 1534707020
Nursing & Residential Care Services
N.A.I.C.S.: 531110

Schloss Bensberg Management
GmbH   (1)
Im Schlosspark 10, 51429, Bergisch Glad-
bach, Germany
Tel.: (49) 22 04 830 0
Web Site: http://www.serviceresidenz-
   schlossbensberg.de
Real Estate Development Services
N.A.I.C.S.: 531390
Daniela Faust (Mgr-Residence)

AEERIS LIMITED

Level 8 210 George St, PO Box
1915, Kingscliff, 2000, NSW, Australia
Tel.: (61) 266745717
Web Site: https://www.aeeris.com
AER—(ASX)
Rev.: $2,280,385
Assets: $1,647,463
Liabilities: $556,189
Net Worth: $1,091,275
Earnings: ($397,889)
Fiscal Year-end: 06/30/24
Severe Weather & Natural Hazard
Alerting & Forecasting Technology
N.A.I.C.S.: 541519
Michael Bath (Ops Mgr-Natl)

Subsidiaries:

Early Warning Network Pty. Ltd.   (1)
PO Box 1915, Kingscliff, 2487, NSW, Aus-
tralia
Tel.: (61) 266745717
Web Site: http://www.ewn.com.au
Weather Warning Services
N.A.I.C.S.: 541990
Kerry Plowright (Chm, CEO & Mng Dir)

AEFFE SPA

Via Delle Querce 51, 47842, Castel
San Giovanni, Marignano, Italy
Tel.: (39) 0541965211
Web Site: http://www.aeffe.com
Sales Range: $300-349.9 Million
Emp.: 1,300
Men's Wear, Women's Wear, Shoes,
Lingerie, Swimwear, Leather Goods,
Eyewear, Perfume & Other Accesso-
ries
N.A.I.C.S.: 424350
Massimo Ferretti (Chm)

Subsidiaries:

Aeffe France S.a.r.l   (1)
6 rue Caffarelli, Paris, 75003,   (100%)
France
Tel.: (33) 144543935
Web Site: http://www.aeffe.com
Sales Range: $25-49.9 Million
Emp.: 15
Design, Production & Distr of Fashion &
Luxury Products
N.A.I.C.S.: 424350

Aeffe Retail S.p.A.   (1)
Via delle querce 51 San Giovanni In, Mari-
gnano, Rimini, 47842, Italy
Tel.: (39) 05 41 96 52 11
Clothing Accessory Distr
N.A.I.C.S.: 458110

Aeffe USA Inc   (1)
30 W 56th St, New York, NY
10019-3801   (100%)
Tel.: (212) 632-9300
Web Site: http://www.aeffeusa.com
Sales Range: $75-99.9 Million
Emp.: 200
Womens Childrens & Infants Clothing & Ac-
cessories Whslr
N.A.I.C.S.: 424350
Michelle Stein (Pres)

Fashoff UK Ltd   (1)
28-29 Conduit St, London, W1S 2YB,
United Kingdom   (100%)
Tel.: (44) 2073180500
Other Specialized Design Services
N.A.I.C.S.: 541490

Moschino France S.a.r.l   (1)
15 Place De La Republique, Paris,
France   (100%)
Tel.: (33) 153018410
Sales Range: $25-49.9 Million
Emp.: 12
Family Clothing Stores
N.A.I.C.S.: 458110

Moschino Retail GMBH   (1)
Friedrichstr 71, Berlin, 10117,
Germany   (100%)
Tel.: (49) 3020946155
Web Site: http://www.moschino.it
Sales Range: $25-49.9 Million
Emp.: 5
Family Clothing Stores
N.A.I.C.S.: 458110

Moschino S.P.A   (1)
28 Via San Gregorio, Milano, Milan,
Italy   (100%)
Tel.: (39) 026787731
Web Site: http://www.moschino.it
Sales Range: $25-49.9 Million
Emp.: 100
Family Clothing Stores
N.A.I.C.S.: 458110

Subsidiary (Non-US):

Moschino Korea Ltd.   (2)
Baegang Building 5th floor - 666 14 Sinsa-
dong, Gangnam-gu, Seoul, Korea (South)
Tel.: (82) 234442203
Online Apparel & Accessory Distr
N.A.I.C.S.: 458110

Nuova Stireria Tavoleto Srl   (1)
Via Dell Artigianato 4, Urbino, Italy   (100%)
Tel.: (39) 0722629185
Textile Mill
N.A.I.C.S.: 314999

Pollini France S.a.r.l.   (1)
352 Rue Saint Honore, Paris, 75001,
France   (100%)
Tel.: (33) 142601494
Web Site: http://www.pollini.com
Family Clothing Stores
N.A.I.C.S.: 458110

Pollini Retail S.r.l.   (1)
Via Erbosa I tratto n 92, Gatteo, Forli,
47043, Italy
Tel.: (39) 0541816311
Footwear Distr
N.A.I.C.S.: 459110

Pollini SpA   (1)
Via Bezzecca 5, 20135, Milan,
Italy   (100%)
Tel.: (39) 0541816311
Web Site: http://www.pollini.com
Design Services
N.A.I.C.S.: 541490

Subsidiary (Non-US):

Pollini Austria GmbH   (2)
Designer-Outlet-Strasse 1/Top 405, 7111,
Parndorf, Austria
Tel.: (43) 216622205
Footwear Distr
N.A.I.C.S.: 459110

Velmar S.P.A   (1)
Via delle Robinie 43, I-47842, Rimini,
Italy   (75%)
Tel.: (39) 0541825717
Web Site: http://www.velmar.it
Womens & Girls Cut & Sew Lingerie
Loungewear & Nightwear Mfr
N.A.I.C.S.: 315250

AEGA ASA

Thunes vei 2, 0274, Oslo, Norway
Tel.: (47) 95188154
Web Site: https://www.aega.no
82T0—(DEU)
Rev.: $2,849,293
Assets: $26,129,759
Liabilities: $16,781,639
Net Worth: $9,348,120
Earnings: ($2,131,380)
Emp.: 2
Fiscal Year-end: 12/31/22
Investment Services
N.A.I.C.S.: 523999

Fabio Buonsanti (COO)

Subsidiaries:

S.T.A. S.R.L.   (1)
Via Edison 15/17, Sedriano, 20018, Milan,
Italy
Tel.: (39) 0290260913
Web Site: https://sta-srl.it
Pollution Control Equipment Distr
N.A.I.C.S.: 423830

AEGEAN AIRLINES S.A.

Building 57 Athens International Air-
port, 19 019, Athens, Greece
Tel.: (30) 2103550000
Web Site: https://www.aegeanair.com
Year Founded: 1999
AGZNF—(OTCIQ)
Rev.: $1,817,442
Assets: $2,589,810
Liabilities: $2,140,226
Net Worth: $449,584
Earnings: $181,035
Emp.: 3,068
Fiscal Year-end: 12/31/23
Airline Services
N.A.I.C.S.: 481111
Dimitrios Gerogiannis (Mng Dir)

Subsidiaries:

Olympic Air S.A.   (1)
Athens International Airport El Venizelos
Building 57, Attiki, 19019, Spata, Greece
Tel.: (30) 2103550000
Web Site: https://www.olympicair.com
Freight & Passenger Air Transportation Ser-
vices
N.A.I.C.S.: 481112

AEGEK GROUP

7 Kavalieratou Taki Str, 151 25, Ath-
ens, Greece
Tel.: (30) 2106306000
Web Site: http://www.aegek.com
Sales Range: $25-49.9 Million
Emp.: 1,400
General Construction Services
N.A.I.C.S.: 237110
Athanasios Evmorfopoulos (VP)

Subsidiaries:

Astakos Terminal S.A.   (1)
18-20 Amarousiou Halandriou Str, 151 25,
Maroussi, Greece   (50%)
Tel.: (30) 2106194003
Sales Range: $50-74.9 Million
Emp.: 4
Real Estate Lessor Services
N.A.I.C.S.: 531110

AEGIS LOGISTICS LTD.

1202 Tower B Peninsula Business
Park G K Marg, Lower Parel W,
Mumbai, 400013, India
Tel.: (91) 2266663666
Web Site: https://www.aegisindia.com
Year Founded: 1956
AEGISCHEM—(NSE)
Rev.: $1,203,138,300
Assets: $977,707,185
Liabilities: $425,316,255
Net Worth: $552,390,930
Earnings: $69,710,550
Emp.: 443
Fiscal Year-end: 03/31/23
Logistics & Physical Distribution Ser-
vices
N.A.I.C.S.: 541614
Raj K. Chandaria (Chm & Mng Dir)

AEGON N.V.

Aegonplein 50, 2591 TV, Hague,
Netherlands
Tel.: (31) 703443210   NI
Web Site: https://www.aegon.com
Year Founded: 1983
AEG—(NYSE)
Rev.: $81,229,139,978

Aegon N.V.—(Continued)

Assets: $70,639,255,739
Liabilities: $666,608,457,119
Net Worth: $39,784,100,279
Earnings: $2,986,975,525
Emp.: 22,271
Fiscal Year-end: 12/31/21
Financial Investment Services
N.A.I.C.S.: 551112
Marco B. A. Keim *(Member-Mgmt Bd)*

Subsidiaries:

AEGON Espana S.A. **(1)**
Via de los Poblados 3 Parque Empresarial
Cristalia Edificio 4B, 28033, Madrid,
Spain **(99.98%)**
Tel.: (34) 915632000
Web Site: https://www.aegon.es
Sales Range: $350-399.9 Million
Emp.: 758
Provider of Life, Health & General Insur-
ance Products
N.A.I.C.S.: 524126

AEGON Magyarorszag Altalanos Biz-
tosito Zrt. **(1)**
Ulloi Ut 1, PO Box 1813, 1091, Budapest,
Hungary **(100%)**
Tel.: (36) 14774800
Web Site: https://www.alfa.hu
Sales Range: $100-124.9 Million
Emp.: 865
Personal & Group Life & Non-Life Insur-
ance, Savings & Pension Products
N.A.I.C.S.: 524128

AEGON UK plc **(1)**
Level 26 The Leadenhall Building 122
Leadenhall Street, London, EC3V 4AB,
United Kingdom **(100%)**
Tel.: (44) 1316668577
Web Site: http://www.aegon.co.uk
Sales Range: $1-4.9 Billion
Emp.: 3,000
Insured Pension, Personal Investment, Em-
ployee Benefits & Protection Products
N.A.I.C.S.: 524292
Gill Scott *(Dir-HR)*

Subsidiary (Domestic):

AEGON Scottish Equitable plc **(2)**
Edinburgh Park, Edinburgh, EH12 9SE,
United Kingdom
Tel.: (44) 1313399191
Web Site: http://www.aegon.co.uk
Sales Range: $1-4.9 Billion
Emp.: 3,000
Life Insurance & Investment Services
N.A.I.C.S.: 524113

Kames Capital **(2)**
3 Lochside Crescent, Edinburgh, EH12
9SA, United Kingdom **(100%)**
Tel.: (44) 8706090101
Web Site: http://www.kamescapital.com
Sales Range: $550-599.9 Million
Emp.: 2,000
Asset Management Services & Institutional
& Retail Asset Management Products
N.A.I.C.S.: 531390
Anne Copeland *(Mgr-Fund-Property)*

AEGON USA, Inc. **(1)**
4333 Edgewood Rd NE, Cedar Rapids, IA
52499-0010
Tel.: (319) 398-8511
Web Site: http://www.aegonins.com
Sales Range: $5-14.9 Billion
Emp.: 12,000
Insurance Services
N.A.I.C.S.: 524113

Subsidiary (Domestic):

AEGON Direct Marketing Services,
Inc. **(2)**
520 Pk Ave, Baltimore, MD 21201 **(100%)**
Tel.: (410) 685-5500
Life Insurance, Supplemental Health Insur-
ance Products & Fee-Based Programs Di-
rect Marketer
N.A.I.C.S.: 524298

AEGON USA Investment Management LLC **(2)**

6300 C St SW, Cedar Rapids, IA 52499-
0001
Tel.: (319) 398-8511
Sales Range: $1-4.9 Billion
Emp.: 3,500
Investment Services
N.A.I.C.S.: 523999

AEGON USA Realty Advisors,
LLC **(2)**
330 Madison Ave 22nd Fl, New York, NY
10001 **(100%)**
Tel.: (212) 251-0101
Web Site: http://www.aegonrealty.com
Sales Range: $25-49.9 Million
Emp.: 10
Real Estate Leasing & Financial Consulting
N.A.I.C.S.: 531210
Lynn Ambrosy *(Mng Dir)*

Branch (Domestic):

AEGON USA, Inc. **(2)**
2 E Chase St, Baltimore, MD
21202 **(100%)**
Tel.: (410) 685-2900
Web Site: http://www.aegonins.com
Insurance Holding Company
N.A.I.C.S.: 524113

Division (Domestic):

AEGON USA-Individual Division **(2)**
4333 Edgewood Rd NE, Cedar Rapids, IA
52499-0001
Tel.: (319) 398-8511
Web Site: http://www.aegonins.com
Sales Range: $600-649.9 Million
Emp.: 2,000
Provider of Insurance Services
N.A.I.C.S.: 523940

AEGON USA-Monumental
Division **(2)**
Two E Chase St, Baltimore, MD
21202-2505 **(100%)**
Tel.: (410) 685-2900
Web Site: http://www.aegonins.com
Sales Range: $200-249.9 Million
Emp.: 469
Life & Health Insurance
N.A.I.C.S.: 524113

Subsidiary (Domestic):

Monumental Life **(3)**
300 W Morgan St, Durham, NC 27701-2162
Tel.: (919) 687-8200
Fire Insurance Services
N.A.I.C.S.: 524113

Monumental Life Insurance
Company **(3)**
2 E Chase St, Baltimore, MD
21202-2505 **(100%)**
Tel.: (410) 685-2900
Web Site: http://www.monlife.com
Sales Range: $700-749.9 Million
Fire Insurance Services
N.A.I.C.S.: 524113

Division (Domestic):

AEGON USA-Special Markets Group-
Consumer Direct **(2)**
300 Eagle View Blvd, Exton, PA 19341
Tel.: (610) 648-5000
Sales Range: $150-199.9 Million
Emp.: 500
Provider of Insurance Marketing Services
N.A.I.C.S.: 524210

Subsidiary (Domestic):

AUSA Life Insurance Co. **(2)**
1111 N Charles St, Baltimore, MD
21201-5505 **(100%)**
Tel.: (410) 576-4571
Rev.: $188,546,097
Holding Company; Property Development
N.A.I.C.S.: 524113

Subsidiary (Domestic):

International Life Investors Insurance
Company **(3)**
4333 Edgewood Rd NE, Cedar Rapids, IA
52499 **(100%)**
Tel.: (319) 398-8511
Web Site: http://www.aegonins.com
Life Insurance

N.A.I.C.S.: 524113

Money Services Inc. **(3)**
4333 Edgewood Rd NE, Cedar Rapids, IA
52499-0001
Tel.: (319) 398-8511
Web Site: http://www.aegonins.com
Sales Range: $50-74.9 Million
Emp.: 1
Investment Advice
N.A.I.C.3.: 520940

Division (Domestic):

Aegon Companies of Florida **(2)**
570 Carillon Pkwy, Saint Petersburg, FL
33716 **(100%)**
Tel.: (727) 299-1800
Web Site: http://www.aegon.com
Sales Range: $600-649.9 Million
Emp.: 1,200
Investor Services
N.A.I.C.S.: 523150

Subsidiary (Domestic):

Creditor Resources, Inc. **(2)**
2839 Paces Ferry Rd Se Ste 750, Atlanta,
GA 30339-5763 **(100%)**
Tel.: (678) 402-2100
Sales Range: $75-99.9 Million
Emp.: 160
Credit Insurance Services
N.A.I.C.S.: 524210

Life Investors Insurance Company of
America **(2)**
4333 Edgewood Rd NE, Cedar Rapids, IA
52499-0001
Tel.: (319) 398-8511
Web Site: http://www.aegonins.com
Sales Range: $600-649.9 Million
Emp.: 2,400
Fire Insurance Services
N.A.I.C.S.: 524113

Stonebridge Casualty Insurance
Company **(2)**
51 JFK Pkwy, Short Hills, NJ
07078 **(100%)**
Tel.: (973) 564-5110
Sales Range: $50-74.9 Million
Emp.: 6
Reinsurance Services
N.A.I.C.S.: 524127

Transamerica Corporation **(2)**
4333 Edgewood Rd NE, Cedar Rapids, IA
52499-0001
Tel.: (319) 355-8511
Web Site: http://www.transamerica.com
Insurance Services
N.A.I.C.S.: 524298
Mark Mullin *(Chm)*

Subsidiary (Domestic):

Tag Resources LLC **(3)**
136 Fox Rd, Knoxville, TN 37922
Tel.: (865) 670-1844
Web Site: http://www.tagresources.com
Rev.: $2,905,000
Emp.: 7
Portfolio Management
N.A.I.C.S.: 523940
Troy Tisue *(Pres)*

Transamerica Advisors Life Insurance
Company **(3)**
4333 Edgewood Rd NE, Cedar Rapids, IA
52499-0001
Tel.: (800) 346-3677
Rev.: $216,840,000
Assets: $8,621,825,000
Liabilities: $7,578,384,000
Net Worth: $1,043,441,000
Earnings: $99,405,000
Fiscal Year-end: 12/31/2017
Fire Insurance Services
N.A.I.C.S.: 524113
Blake S. Bostwick *(Pres)*

Transamerica Brokerage Group **(3)**
1150 S Olive St, Los Angeles, CA
90015-2211 **(100%)**
Tel.: (213) 742-2111
Web Site: http://www.transamerica.com
Rev.: $102,222,647
Emp.: 26
Brokerage Services
N.A.I.C.S.: 524210

Transamerica Capital, Inc. **(3)**
4600 S Syracuse St Ste 1100, Denver, CO
80237-2743
Tel.: (720) 482-1500
Web Site:
http://www.transamericacapital.com
Sales Range: $100-124.9 Million
Emp.: 250
Insurance Services
N.A.I.C.S.: 525910

Transamerica Financial Advisors,
Inc. **(3)**
1150 S Olive St, Los Angeles, CA 90015-
2211
Tel.: (800) 322-7161
Web Site: http://www.tfa.transamerica.com
Sales Range: $50-74.9 Million
Emp.: 62
Investment Firm
N.A.I.C.S.: 523150

Division (Domestic):

TransAmerica Financial Advisors,
Inc. **(4)**
570 Carillon Pkwy, Saint Petersburg, FL
33716-1294 **(100%)**
Sales Range: $50-74.9 Million
Security Brokers
N.A.I.C.S.: 523940

Subsidiary (Domestic):

Transamerica Investment
Management **(3)**
Ste 820 11111 Santa Monica Blvd, Los An-
geles, CA 90025-3342 **(100%)**
Tel.: (310) 996-3200
Web Site: http://www.transamerica.com
Sales Range: $50-74.9 Million
Emp.: 50
Investment Management & Life Insurance
Services
N.A.I.C.S.: 523940

Transamerica Life Insurance
Company **(3)**
4333 Edgewood Rd NE, Cedar Rapids, IA
52499-0001
Tel.: (319) 398-8511
Web Site: http://www.aegonins.com
Sales Range: $1-4.9 Billion
Emp.: 3,000
Life Insurance
N.A.I.C.S.: 524113
Mark Bloom *(COO)*

Subsidiary (Domestic):

Transamerica Life Insurance of New
York **(4)**
4 Manhattanville Rd, Purchase, NY 10577-
2134
Tel.: (914) 697-8000
Web Site: http://www.transamerica.com
Rev.: $364,607,974
Emp.: 7
Life Insurance Carrier
N.A.I.C.S.: 532490

Subsidiary (Domestic):

Transamerica Retirement Solutions,
LLC **(3)**
440 Mamaroneck Ave, Harrison, NY 10528
Tel.: (914) 627-3000
Web Site: https://www.trsretire.com
Insurance Services
N.A.I.C.S.: 523940
Mark William Mullin *(CEO)*

AXENT/AEGON N.V. **(1)**
Euclideslaan 251, 3584 BV, Utrecht, Neth-
erlands
Tel.: (31) 302563760
Web Site: http://www.axentaegon.nl
Personal Life & Non-Life Insurance & Sav-
ings Products
N.A.I.C.S.: 524128

Aegon Cappital B.V. **(1)**
PO Box 554, 9700 AN, Groningen, Nether-
lands
Tel.: (31) 703444508
Web Site: http://www.aegoncappital.nl
Pension Services
N.A.I.C.S.: 525110

Aegon Emeklilik ve Hayat A.S. **(1)**

Kozyatagi Mah Sari Kanarya Street K2
Plaza No 14 Kat 2, Kadikoy, Istanbul, Tur-
kiye
Tel.: (90) 2165797979
Web Site: http://www.aegon.com.tr
Insurance Broker Services
N.A.I.C.S.: 524210

Aegon Magyarorszag Befektetesi
Alapkezelo Zartkoruen Mukodo
Reszvenytarsasag **(1)**
Ulloi ut 1, 1091, Budapest, Hungary
Tel.: (36) 614774814
Web Site: https://www.vigam.hu
Asset Management Services
N.A.I.C.S.: 523940

Aegon Pensii Societate de Adminis-
trare a Fondurilor de Pensii Private
S.A. **(1)**
Str Avram Iancu Nr 506-508 etaj 4, Floresti,
407280, Cluj-Napoca, Romania
Tel.: (40) 264302200
Web Site: https://www.aegon.ro
Insurance Broker Services
N.A.I.C.S.: 524210

Aegon Powszechne Towarzystwo
Emerytaine Spolka Akcyjna **(1)**
Al Jerozolimskie 162A, 02-342, Warsaw,
Poland
Tel.: (48) 224902080
Web Site: http://www.aegon.pl
Insurance Broker Services
N.A.I.C.S.: 524210

Aegon Towarzystwo Ubezpieczen na
Zycie Spolka Akcyjna **(1)**
Al Jerozolimskie 162A, 02-342, Warsaw,
Poland
Tel.: (48) 224902080
Web Site: http://www.aegon.pl
Insurance Broker Services
N.A.I.C.S.: 524210

Nedasco B.V. **(1)**
Displayweg 4, 3821 BT, Amersfoort, Nether-
lands
Tel.: (31) 334670800
Web Site: https://www.nedasco.nl
Emp.: 182
Insurance Broker Services
N.A.I.C.S.: 524210

Prime Times Newspaper **(1)**
394 W Ironwood Rd, Salt Lake City, UT
84115
Tel.: (801) 485-5511
Rev.: $130,000
Emp.: 4
Newspaper Publishing
N.A.I.C.S.: 513110

Robidus Groep B.V. **(1)**
Ankersmidplein 2, 1506 CK, Zaandam,
Netherlands
Tel.: (31) 889199000
Web Site: http://www.robidus.nl
Social Security Services
N.A.I.C.S.: 923130

Santander Generales Seguros y
Reaseguros, S.A. **(1)**
Avenida de Cantabria s/n Ciudad Grupo
Santander, Boadilla del Monte, 28660, Ma-
drid, Spain
Tel.: (34) 915123123
Web Site: https://www.santanderseguros.es
Insurance Broker Services
N.A.I.C.S.: 524210

Spaarbeleg Kas N.V. **(1)**
Nevelgaarde 60, 3436 ZZ, Nieuwegein,
Netherlands
Tel.: (31) 306074411
Sales Range: $50-74.9 Million
Emp.: 100
Provider of Insurance-Linked Savings Prod-
ucts
N.A.I.C.S.: 522180

TKP Pensioen B.V. **(1)**
Europaweg 27, 9723 AS, Groningen, Neth-
erlands
Tel.: (31) 505821990
Web Site: http://www.tkppensioen.nl
Pension Services
N.A.I.C.S.: 525110

Transamerica Life (Bermuda)
Ltd. **(1)**

Mintflower Place 5th floor West 8 Par-la-
Ville Road, Hamilton, HM 08, Bermuda
Tel.: (441) 7058282
Web Site:
　https://www.transamericalifebermuda.com
Insurance Broker Services
N.A.I.C.S.: 524210
Chirag Rathod (CEO)

AELIS FARMA SA
Neurocentre Magendie 146 rue Leo
Saignat, 33077, Bordeaux, France
Tel.: (33) 554542327
Web Site:
　https://www.aelisfarma.com
Year Founded: 2013
AELIS—(EUR)
Rev.: $12,154,603
Assets: $31,976,702
Liabilities: $30,961,372
Net Worth: $1,015,331
Earnings: $648,276
Emp.: 26
Fiscal Year-end: 12/31/21
Biotechnology Research & Develop-
ment Services
N.A.I.C.S.: 541714
Valerie Scappaticci (CFO)

AEM HOLDINGS LTD.
52 Serangoon North Avenue 4, Sin-
gapore, 555853, Singapore
Tel.: (65) 64831811
Web Site: https://www.aem.com.sg
AWX—(SES)
Rev.: $364,525,486
Assets: $535,883,511
Liabilities: $176,581,837
Net Worth: $359,301,674
Earnings: ($881,618)
Emp.: 2,576
Fiscal Year-end: 12/31/23
Electroplating Mfr
N.A.I.C.S.: 333248
Wai Kong Soh (Co-Sec & VP-Fin)

Subsidiaries:

AEM (HongKong) Pte Ltd **(1)**
Suite 2301 23 Floor World-Wide House 19
Des Voeux Road, Central, China (Hong
Kong)
Tel.: (852) 28620093
Packaging Machinery Mfr
N.A.I.C.S.: 333993

AEM (Suzhou) Co., Ltd. **(1)**
83 QunXin Yi Road Tong Yuan Road Su-
zhou Industrial Park, Suzhou Industrial
Park, Suzhou, 215006, Jiangsu, China
Tel.: (86) 51267603000
Semiconductor Making Machinery Mfr
N.A.I.C.S.: 333242

AEM Microtronics (M) Sdn. Bhd. **(1)**
Plot 155 Jalan Sungai Bayan Lepas FIZ
Phase I, Bayan Lepas, 11900, Penang,
Malaysia
Tel.: (60) 46407200
Sales Range: $50-74.9 Million
Emp.: 60
Packaging Machinery Import & Distr
N.A.I.C.S.: 423830
Goh Hoon Har (Mgr-Fin)

AEM Microtronics (Suzhou) Co.,
Ltd. **(1)**
83 Qunxing Yi Road, Suzhou Industrial
Park, Suzhou, 215006, Jiangsu, China
Tel.: (86) 51267603000
Testing Sensor Equipment Mfr
N.A.I.C.S.: 334413
Zuhaidah Omar (Bus Mgr-Operation & Field
Svc Engrg)

AEM Singapore Pte. Ltd. **(1)**
52 Serangoon North Ave 4, Singapore,
555853, Singapore
Tel.: (65) 64831811
Testing Sensor Equipment Mfr
N.A.I.C.S.: 334413
Loke Wai San (Chm)

Subsidiary (Domestic):

CEI Limited **(2)**

No 2 Ang Mo Kio Avenue 12, Singapore,
569707, Singapore
Tel.: (65) 64811882
Web Site: http://www.cei.com.sg
Rev.: $102,830,952
Assets: $52,730,629
Liabilities: $23,484,503
Net Worth: $29,246,126
Earnings: $5,283,587
Emp.: 616
Fiscal Year-end: 12/31/2019
Printed Circuit Board Assembly
N.A.I.C.S.: 334118
Ka Huat Tan (Mng Dir)

Subsidiary (Non-US):

CEI International Investments (VN)
Ltd. **(3)**
No 2 Street 6, Vietnam Singapore Industrial
Park, Thuan An, Binh Duong, Vietnam
Tel.: (84) 2743782728
Electronic Printed Circuit Board Equipment
Mfr
N.A.I.C.S.: 334419
Quyet Thang Phung (Engr-Mktg)

CEI International Investments (Viet-
nam) Limited **(3)**
No 2 Street 6 Vietnam Singapore Industrial
Park, Thuan An, Binh Duong, Vietnam
Tel.: (84) 2743782728
Printed Circuit Board Assembly Mfr
N.A.I.C.S.: 334418
Yee Chee Hong Sean (Gen Mgr)

PT Surya Teknologi Batam **(3)**
Printed Circuit Board Assembly Mfr
N.A.I.C.S.: 334418
Cheng Kung Ng (Gen Mgr)

AEM TesTech (Shanghai) Co.,
Ltd. **(1)**
Room 308B Building 1 No169 Shengxia
Road No 1658 Zhangdong Road, Pilot Free
Trade Zone, Shanghai, China
Tel.: (86) 2161656626
Semiconductor Integrated Circuit Mfr & Distr
N.A.I.C.S.: 334413

Afore Oy **(1)**
Vakiotie 5, Lieto, 21420, Turku, Finland
Tel.: (358) 22746040
Web Site: https://aforeoy.com
Testing Sensor Equipment Mfr
N.A.I.C.S.: 334516
Jari Ojala (Production Mgr)

CEI Pte. Ltd. **(1)**
No 2 Ang Mo Kio Ave 12, Singapore,
569707, Singapore
Tel.: (65) 64811882
Web Site: https://www.cei.com.sg
Printed Circuit Board Assembly Mfr
N.A.I.C.S.: 334418

DB Design Group, Inc. **(1)**
48507 Milmont Dr, Fremont, CA 94538
Tel.: (408) 834-1400
Web Site: http://www.dbdesign.com
Engineeering Services
N.A.I.C.S.: 541330

LaserOp Ltd. **(1)**
6 Hamagshimim St, PO Box 7760, Petah
Tiqwa, 49170, Israel
Tel.: (972) 39220353
Web Site: http://www.laserop.com
Laser Systems Mfr & Distr
N.A.I.C.S.: 334510

Mu-Test S.A.S. **(1)**
Batiment 9 Parc de Metrotech, 42650,
Saint-Jean-Bonnefonds, France
Tel.: (33) 477562549
Semiconductor Integrated Circuit Mfr & Distr
N.A.I.C.S.: 334413

Nestek Korea Co., Ltd. **(1)**
72 Jeongamsandan 2-GL, Jeongnam-
myeon, Hwaseong, Gyeonggi-Do, Korea
(South)
Tel.: (82) 318924676
Web Site: https://nes-tek.com
Semiconductor Integrated Circuit Mfr & Distr
N.A.I.C.S.: 334413

AEMA GROUPE
17-21 place Etienne Pernet, 75015,
Paris, France

Web Site: http://aemagroupe.fr
Insurance Related Services
N.A.I.C.S.: 524298
Pascal Michard (Pres)

Subsidiaries:

Aviva France **(1)**
80 Avenue de l Europe, 92270, Bois-
Colombes, France **(100%)**
Tel.: (33) 176625000
Web Site: http://www.aviva.fr
Sales Range: $1-4.9 Billion
Emp.: 3,000
Underwriter & Broker of Life Insurance
N.A.I.C.S.: 524128
Ines de Dinechin (CEO-Investors)

Subsidiary (Domestic):

Aviva Assurances SA **(2)**
13 Rue Du Moulin Bailly, Bois-Colombes,
Paris, 92271, France
Tel.: (33) 233389892
Web Site: http://www.aviva-assurances.com
Insurance Management Services
N.A.I.C.S.: 524298

Aviva Vie S.A. **(2)**
70 Avenue De l'Europe, 92270, Bois-
Colombes, France
Tel.: (33) 1 76 62 50 00
Web Site: http://www.aviva.fr
Emp.: 2,000
Insurance Management Services
N.A.I.C.S.: 524298

Societe Francaise de Gestion et dIn-
vestissement Sofragi SA **(2)**
37 avenue des Champs Elysees, 75008,
Paris, France
Tel.: (33) 156436250
Web Site: http://www.sofragi.fr
Financial Investment Services
N.A.I.C.S.: 523940

Union Financiere de France Banque
SA **(2)**
32 Avenue d and 039 Iena, 75783, Paris,
Cedex 16, France **(75%)**
Tel.: (33) 140696517
Web Site: http://www.uff.net
Sales Range: $200-249.9 Million
Financial Support Services
N.A.I.C.S.: 523940
Julien Brami (CEO)

AEMOS SDN BHD
Level 36 Menara Maxis, Kuala Lum-
pur City Centre, Kuala Lumpur,
50088, Malaysia
Tel.: (60) 326157250
Web Site: http://www.aemos-
　international.com
Sales Range: $10-24.9 Million
Emp.: 100
IT & Business Consultancy Services
N.A.I.C.S.: 541511
Sufineh Mahmood (Mng Dir)

AEMULUS HOLDINGS BER-
HAD
No 25 Jalan Sultan Azlan Shah
Bayan Lepas Free Industrial Zone
Phase 1, 11900, Bayan Lepas, Pen-
ang, Malaysia
Tel.: (60) 6046846000　　　　　**MY**
Web Site: https://www.aemulus.com
Year Founded: 2004
AEMULUS—(KLS)
Rev.: $5,463,253
Assets: $39,358,620
Liabilities: $9,909,459
Net Worth: $29,449,160
Earnings: ($11,897,243)
Fiscal Year-end: 09/30/23
Investment Holding Services
N.A.I.C.S.: 551112
Sang Beng Ng (CEO)

Subsidiaries:

Aemulus Corporation Sdn. Bhd. **(1)**
Tel.: (60) 46846000
Web Site: http://www.aemulus.com

Aemulus Holdings Berhad—(Continued)

Testing Equipment Mfr
N.A.I.C.S.: 334519

Branch (US):

Aemulus Corporation Sdn. Bhd. - San
Ramon Branch   (2)
2315 Magnolia Bridge Dr, San Ramon, CA
94582
Tel.: (805) 300-6482
Testing Equipment Mfr
N.A.I.C.S.: 334519

AENIX INFORMATIQUE S.A.
Domaine Technologique 4 Rue Rene
Razel, 91400, Paris, France
Tel.: (33) 169187650   FR
Web Site: http://www.aenix.fr
Year Founded: 1990
Rev.: $12,000,000
Emp.: 34
Industrial Logistics Consultation &
Implementation
N.A.I.C.S.: 541614
Anne Le Brun (Mgr-Personnel)

AENZA S.A.A.
Av Petit Thouars N 4957 Miraflores,
Surquillo, 15047, Lima, Peru
Tel.: (51) 12136565   Pe
Web Site: https://www.aenza.com.pe
Year Founded: 1933
AENZAC1—(LIM)
Rev.: $1,155,689,146
Assets: $1,594,440,623
Liabilities: $1,194,846,588
Net Worth: $399,594,035
Earnings: $37,915,368
Emp.: 12,787
Fiscal Year-end: 12/31/23
Engineering & Construction Services
N.A.I.C.S.: 541330
Javier Vaca Terron (Reg Mgr-Engrg &
Construction)

Subsidiaries:

Adexus S.A.   (1)
Miraflores 383 piso 3, Santiago, Chile
Tel.: (56) 226861000
Web Site: https://www.adexus.com
Software Services
N.A.I.C.S.: 541511

Concesion Canchaque S.A.C.   (1)
Av Petit Thouars N 4957, Lima, Peru
Tel.: (51) 932493730
Web Site:
   https://www.concesioncanchaque.pe
Highway Construction Services
N.A.I.C.S.: 237310

Cumbra Ingenieria S.A.   (1)
Av Petit Thouars Nro 4957 Int 501 Floor 5,
Miraflores, Lima, Peru
Tel.: (51) 12130502
Web Site:
   https://www.cumbraingenieria.com.pe
Engineering Services
N.A.I.C.S.: 541330

Cumbra Peru S.A.   (1)
Av Petit Thouars Nro 4957 Int 401, 15074,
Lima, Peru
Tel.: (51) 12130444
Web Site: https://www.cumbra.com.pe
Construction Services
N.A.I.C.S.: 236220

Morelco S.A.S.   (1)
Av Carrera 9 115-06 Ofc 2602 Edificio,
Tierra Firme, 110121, Bogota, Colombia
Tel.: (57) 15188880
Web Site: http://www.mgrelco.com.co
Construction Services
N.A.I.C.S.: 236220

NORVIAL S.A.   (1)
Av Petit Thouars N 4957, Miraflores, Lima,
Peru
Tel.: (51) 932493730
Web Site: https://www.norvial.com.pe

Sales Range: Less than $1 Million
Food Transportation Services
N.A.I.C.S.: 488490

Survial S.A.   (1)
Av Petit Thouars N 4957, Lima, Peru
Tel.: (51) 932493730
Web Site: https://www.survial.com.pe
Highway Construction Services
N.A.I.C.S.: 237310

Unna Energia S.A.   (1)
Av Petit Thouars, 4957, Lima, Peru
Tel.: (51) 2151500
Web Site: https://www.unna.com.pe
Emp.: 467
Gas & Oil Exploration Services
N.A.I.C.S.: 211130

AEOLUS TYRE CO., LTD.
No 48 Jiaodong South Road, Ji-
aozuo, 454003, Henan, China
Tel.: (86) 3913999011
Web Site:
   https://www.aeolustyre.com
Year Founded: 1965
600469—(SHG)
Rev.: $700,300,318
Assets: $1,013,965,458
Liabilities: $601,168,806
Net Worth: $412,796,653
Earnings: $11,866,805
Fiscal Year-end: 12/31/22
Automotive Tire Mfr
N.A.I.C.S.: 326211
Zhang Linlin (Sec)

AEON CO., LTD.
1-5-1 Nakase, Mihama-ku, Chiba,
261-8515, Chiba, Japan
Tel.: (81) 432126012   JP
Web Site: https://www.aeon.info
Year Founded: 1926
8267—(TKS)
Rev.: $67,734,719,130
Assets: $91,750,761,210
Liabilities: $76,952,506,120
Net Worth: $14,798,255,090
Earnings: $316,866,280
Emp.: 599,000
Fiscal Year-end: 02/29/24
Department Store Retailer
N.A.I.C.S.: 551112
Yuki Habu (Exec Officer-China &
Digital Bus & Exec VP)

Subsidiaries:

AEON (CAMBODIA) Co., Ltd.   (1)
132 Street Sothearos, Khan Chamkarmon,
Phnom Penh, Cambodia
Tel.: (855) 23988580
Web Site: http://www.aeoncambodia.com
General Merchandise Retailer
N.A.I.C.S.: 445110

AEON (Thailand) CO., LTD   (1)
78 Aeon Bldg 2nd Fl Chaengwattana Rd
Kwaeng Answaaree Khet, Bang Khen,
Bangkok, 10220, Thailand
Tel.: (66) 2970182530
Web Site:
Consumer Lending Services
N.A.I.C.S.: 522291

AEON AGRI CREATE Co., Ltd   (1)
1-5-1 Nakase, Mihama-ku, Chiba, 261-
8515, Japan
Tel.: (81) 43 212 6462
Web Site: http://www.aeon.jp
Sales Range: $25-49.9 Million
Cabbage Cultivation Services
N.A.I.C.S.: 115112
Shigeo Fuji (Pres)

AEON BIG (M) Sdn. Bhd.   (1)
3rd Floor AEON Taman Maluri Shopping
Centre Jalan Jejaka, Taman Maluri Cheras,
55100, Kuala Lumpur, Malaysia
Tel.: (60) 1300802366
Web Site: http://www.aeonbig.com.my
Hypermarkets Operator
N.A.I.C.S.: 445110
Nagahisa Oyama (Chm)

AEON BODY Co., Ltd   (1)

3-1-1 Lake Town Aeon Lake Town mori 2nd
floor, Koshigaya, 343-0828, Saitama, Japan
Tel.: (81) 489724336
Web Site: https://www.aeonbody.com
Sales Range: $25-49.9 Million
Emp.: 110
Cosmetic Product Retailer
N.A.I.C.S.: 456120

AEON Bank, Ltd.   (1)
Terrace Square 3-22 Kanda Nishikicho,
Chiyoda-ku, Tokyo, 101-0054, Japan
Tel.: (81) 120131089
Web Site: https://www.aeonbank.co.jp
N.A.I.C.S.: 522320
Shunsuke Shirakawa (Chm)

AEON CINEMAS Co., Ltd.   (1)
2965 Oazani Temple, Yamato-cho, Saga,
840-0201, Japan
Tel.: (81) 952648788
Web Site: http://www.aeoncinema.com
Motion Picture Exhibition Services
N.A.I.C.S.: 512132

AEON Co. (M) Bhd.   (1)
3rd Floor AEON Taman Maluri Shopping
Centre Jalan Jejaka Taman Maluri, Cheras,
55100, Kuala Lumpur, Malaysia
Tel.: (60) 392072005
Web Site: https://www.aeonretail.com.my
Rev.: $898,789,296
Assets: $1,137,035,924
Liabilities: $732,375,059
Net Worth: $404,660,865
Earnings: $24,996,082
Emp.: 9,868
Fiscal Year-end: 12/31/2023
Retailing & Property Management Services
N.A.I.C.S.: 449210
Hiroyuki Kotera (Deputy Mng Dir)

AEON Credit Service (M) Berhad (1)
Bangsar South City Level 18 UOA Corpo-
rate Tower Avenue 10, No 8 Jalan Kerinchi,
59200, Kuala Lumpur, Malaysia
Tel.: (60) 327729000
Web Site: https://www.aeoncredit.com.my
Rev.: $416,301,918
Assets: $2,747,134,759
Liabilities: $2,172,987,825
Net Worth: $574,146,935
Earnings: $92,298,216
Emp.: 3,000
Fiscal Year-end: 02/29/2024
Consumer Credit Card Services, Vehicle
Purchase & Personal Loan Financing
N.A.I.C.S.: 522291
Yit Chan Tai (Co-Sec)

AEON DELIGHT Co., Ltd.   (1)
Minami-Senba Heart Building 2-3-2 Minami-
Senba, Chuo-ku, Osaka, 542-0081,
Japan   (55.2%)
Tel.: (81) 343603558
Web Site: https://www.aeondelight.co.jp
Rev.: $2,302,973,800
Assets: $1,136,222,130
Liabilities: $397,359,050
Net Worth: $738,863,080
Earnings: $75,912,630
Emp.: 21,209
Fiscal Year-end: 02/29/2024
Building Management Services
N.A.I.C.S.: 561790
Nobuo Yamazato (COO-Grp FM Bus &
Exec VP)

Subsidiary (Non-US):

AEON DELIGHT (China) Co.,
Ltd.   (2)
Room1003A Building 1 Jinghope Plaza No
88 Huachi Street, Industrial Park, Suzhou,
215021, Jiangsu, China
Tel.: (86) 51267585099
Web Site: http://www.aeondelight.com.cn
Building Management Services
N.A.I.C.S.: 561790

Subsidiary (Domestic):

AEON DELIGHT Academy Co.,
Ltd.   (2)
1199 Azasendomae, Tamura-Cho, Naga-
hama, 526-0829, Shiga, Japan
Tel.: (81) 749646010
Web Site: https://www.aeondelight-
academy.co.jp
Emp.: 180

Research & Training Facility
N.A.I.C.S.: 611699
Daisuke Ninomiya (Pres)

AEON DELIGHT Security Co.,
Ltd.   (2)
Minamisemba Heart Building 9F 2-3-2 Mi-
namisemba, Chuo-ku, Osaka, 542-0081,
Japan
Tel.: (81) 662605112
Web Site: https://aeondelight-security.co.jp
Emp.: 1,808
Guards & Security Services
N.A.I.C.S.: 561612
Akihiro Kishi (Pres)

AEON Eaheart Co., Ltd.   (1)
1-5-1 Nakase AEON Tower 9F, Mihama-ku,
Chiba, 261-8515, Japan
Tel.: (81) 432126419
Web Site: http://www.aeoneaheart.co.jp
Sales Range: $10-24.9 Million
Restaurant Operating Services
N.A.I.C.S.: 722511
Koji Nakamura (Pres)

AEON East China (Suzhou) Co.,
Ltd.   (1)
Room 1606BC 16F Block A Wuzhong Yin-
zuo Building, Wuzhong Economic Develop-
ment Zon, Suzhou, China
Tel.: (86) 51268837201
Web Site: https://www.szaeon.com
Shopping Centre Services
N.A.I.C.S.: 812990

AEON FOOD SUPPLY Co., Ltd   (1)
24-6 Takase-cho, Funabashi, 273-0014,
Chiba, Japan
Tel.: (81) 474318396
Web Site: https://www.aeon-fs.com
Emp.: 1,830
Food Product Retailer
N.A.I.C.S.: 445298

AEON FOREST CO., LTD   (1)
1-9-11 Horidome-cho NEWS Nihonbashi
Horidome-cho Building 4F, Nihonbashi
Chiyoda-ku, Tokyo, 103-0012, Japan
Tel.: (81) 332498170
Web Site: https://www.the-body-shop.co.jp
Sales Range: $200-249.9 Million
Emp.: 618
Cosmetic Product Retailer
N.A.I.C.S.: 456120
Takeshi Fukumoto (Pres)

AEON GLOBAL SCM CO., LTD   (1)
1-5-1 Nakase, Mihama-Ku, Chiba, 261-
8515, Japan
Tel.: (81) 432126120
Web Site: https://aeonglobalscm.co.jp
Emp.: 284
General Merchandise Retailer
N.A.I.C.S.: 455219
Daisuke Tezuka (Pres)

AEON Housing Loan Service Co.,
Ltd.   (1)
BIZCORE Jimbocho 3F 3-9-2 Kanda
Ogawacho, Chiyoda-ku, Tokyo, 101-0052,
Japan
Tel.: (81) 352173550
Web Site: https://www.aeonhousingloan.jp
Emp.: 149
Financial Services
N.A.I.C.S.: 921130

AEON INSURANCE SERVICE CO.,
LTD   (1)
Aeon Tower 1-5-1 Nakase, Mihama Ward,
Chiba, 261-0023, Chiba, Japan
Tel.: (81) 120003227
Web Site: https://www.hokenmarket.net
General Insurance Services
N.A.I.C.S.: 524291

AEON Integrated Business Service
Co., Ltd   (1)
12F Aeon Tower 1-5-1 Nakase, Mihama
Ward, Chiba, 261-8515, Chiba, Japan
Tel.: (81) 432126371
Web Site: https://www.aeonibs.co.jp
Emp.: 360
Shopping Center
N.A.I.C.S.: 531120

AEON KYUSHU CO., LTD.   (1)
2-9-11 Hakataeki-Minami, Hakata-ku,

Hakata-ku, Fukuoka, 812-0016,
Japan **(62.7%)**
Tel.: (81) 924410611
Web Site: https://www.aeon-kyushu.info
Sales Range: Less than $1 Million
Emp.: 10,200
Retail Store Operator
N.A.I.C.S.: 459999
Yuji Shibata *(Pres)*

AEON Pet Co., Ltd. (1)
4-17-8 Minamiyawata J-pro Motoyawata
Building 1F, Ichikawa, 272-0023, Chiba,
Japan
Tel.: (81) 120995439
Web Site: https://www.aeonpet.com
Pet Foods Retailers
N.A.I.C.S.: 424490

AEON Retail Co., Ltd (1)
1-5-1 Nakase, Mihama Ward, Chiba, 261-
8515, Chiba, Japan
Tel.: (81) 432126500
Web Site: https://www.aeonretail.jp
Emp.: 72,859
General Merchandise Retailer
N.A.I.C.S.: 455219

AEON SAVEUR Co., Ltd. (1)
1-2-15 Horidome-cho Third Asahi Building
8F, Nihonbashi Chuo-ku, Tokyo, 103-0012,
Japan
Tel.: (81) 356517720
Web Site: https://www.picard-frozen.jp
Emp.: 201
Food Product Mfr & Distr
N.A.I.C.S.: 311991

AEON SUPERCENTER Co., Ltd. (1)
1-11-5 Saien, Morioka, 020-0024, Iwate,
Japan
Tel.: (81) 196058800
Web Site:
https://www.aeonsupercenter.co.jp
Emp.: 3,194
Supermarket Management Services
N.A.I.C.S.: 445110

AEON South China Co., Ltd. (1)
12th Floor Block A Shenfang Plaza No
3005 Renmin South Road, Luohu District,
Shenzhen, 518001, China
Tel.: (86) 75582215555
Web Site: http://www.aeonsc.com.cn
Grocery Products Retailer
N.A.I.C.S.: 445110

**AEON Stores (Hong Kong) Co.,
Limited** (1)
Units 07-11 26/F CDW Building 388 Castle
Peak Road, Tsuen Wan, New Territories,
China (Hong Kong) **(100%)**
Tel.: (852) 25653600
Web Site: https://www.aeonstores.com.hk
Rev.: $1,220,343,428
Assets: $769,783,545
Liabilities: $756,794,610
Net Worth: $12,988,935
Earnings: ($28,651,290)
Emp.: 5,600
Fiscal Year-end: 12/31/2022
Operator of General Merchandise Stores
N.A.I.C.S.: 455219
Yuki Habu *(Chm, Chm & Mng Dir)*

**AEON Topvalu (Hong Kong) Co.,
Limited** (1)
Room 07 19th Floor Zhongran Building, No
388 Castle Peak Road, Tsuen Wan, China
(Hong Kong)
Tel.: (852) 23756307
General Merchandise Retailer
N.A.I.C.S.: 445110

AEON Topvalu Co., Ltd. (1)
1-4 Nakase, Mihama Ward, Chiba, 261-
0023, Chiba, Japan **(88.7%)**
Tel.: (81) 432126123
Web Site: https://www.topvalu.net
Sales Range: $125-149.9 Million
Emp.: 330
General Merchandise Store Operator
N.A.I.C.S.: 455219

**AEON Topvalu Vietnam Company
Limited** (1)
10th Floor B1 Area Robot Tower No 308-
308C Dien Bien Phu, Ward 4 District 3, Ho
Chi Minh City, Vietnam
Tel.: (84) 2838328800

Web Site: https://www.aeon.com.vn
Food Product Mfr & Distr
N.A.I.C.S.: 311991

AEON Town Co., Ltd. (1)
10th floor AEON Tower Building 1-5-1 Na-
kase, Mihama-ku, Chiba, 261-8515, Chiba,
Japan
Tel.: (81) 432126369
Web Site: https://www.aeontown.co.jp
Emp.: 750
Shopping Mall Development Services
N.A.I.C.S.: 236220

AT Japan Co., Ltd (1)
1-5-1 Nakase, Mihama-Ku, Chiba, 261-
0023, Japan
Tel.: (81) 432126473
Supermarket Management Services
N.A.I.C.S.: 445110

Subsidiary (Domestic):

AEON COMPASS Co., Ltd. (2)
2-6-1 Nakase World Business Garden
Malibu East 5F, Mihama-ku, Chiba, 261-
7105, Chiba, Japan **(55%)**
Tel.: (81) 432974300
Web Site: https://www.aeoncompass.co.jp
Emp.: 260
Overseas Business Services; Overseas &
Domestic Travel
N.A.I.C.S.: 561499

**Aeon Allianz Life Insurance Co.,
Ltd.** (1)
Hulic Kudan Building 1-13-5 Kudankita,
Chiyoda-ku, Tokyo, 102-0073, Japan
Tel.: (81) 120503928
Web Site: https://www.aeon-allianz.co.jp
Fire Insurance Services
N.A.I.C.S.: 524113

Aeon Fantasy Co., Ltd. (1)
8F M-Bay Point Makuhari 1-6 Nakase,
Mihama-ku, Chiba, 261-0023, Japan
Tel.: (81) 432126203
Web Site: https://www.fantasy.co.jp
Rev.: $579,664,220
Assets: $370,828,270
Liabilities: $310,272,580
Net Worth: $60,555,690
Earnings: $9,316,260
Emp.: 7,641
Fiscal Year-end: 02/29/2024
Indoor Theme Park Operator
N.A.I.C.S.: 713120
Hitoshi Takahashi *(Auditor)*

Aeon Hokkaido Corporation (1)
1-10 Minami Hondori 21-chome, Shiroishi-
ku, Sapporo, 003-8630, Hokkaido,
Japan **(80.47%)**
Tel.: (81) 118654100
Web Site: https://www.aeon-hokkaido.jp
Sales Range: $1-4.9 Billion
Departmental Store Operator
N.A.I.C.S.: 455110
Hideki Aoyagi *(Pres & CEO)*

Aeon Mall Co., Ltd. (1)
1-5-1 Nakase, Mihama-ku, Chiba, 261-
8539, Japan
Tel.: (81) 432126450
Web Site: https://www.aeonmall.com
Assets: $11,735,743,770
Liabilities: $8,359,301,430
Net Worth: $3,376,442,340
Earnings: $144,628,910
Emp.: 5,507
Fiscal Year-end: 02/29/2024
Shopping Mall Operator
N.A.I.C.S.: 531120
Seiichi Chiba *(CFO & Chief Overseas Bus
Officer)*

Aeon Next Co., Ltd. (1)
1-5-1 Nakase, Mihama-ku, Chiba, 261-
0023, Japan
Tel.: (81) 432396601
Web Site: https://aeonnext.co.jp
Food Products Distr
N.A.I.C.S.: 424420

Aeon Ryukyu Co., Ltd. (1)
514-1 Aza-Kanegusuku, Haebaru Town
Shimajiri District, Okinawa, 901-1111, Japan
Tel.: (81) 988895464
Web Site: https://world.aeon-ryukyu.jp

Sales Range: $75-99.9 Billion
Emp.: 4,662
Supermarket Management Services
N.A.I.C.S.: 445110

Subsidiary (Domestic):

OPA Co., Ltd (2)
2-6-1 Nakase WBG Malibu East 22F, Mi-
hama Ward, Chiba, 261-7122,
Japan **(100%)**
Tel.: (81) 432133211
Web Site: https://www.opa.gr.jp
Commercial Buildings Owner & Operator;
Retail Development Services
N.A.I.C.S.: 925120

Aeon Tohoku Co., Ltd. (1)
1-6-25 Tsuchizaki, Kohoku, Akita, 011-0941,
Japan
Tel.: (81) 188470111
Web Site: https://aeontohoku.co.jp
Emp.: 17,347
General Merchandise Retailer
N.A.I.C.S.: 445110

Aeon Town Co., Ltd. (1)
10th floor AEON Tower Building 1-5-1 Na-
kase, Mihama-ku, Chiba, 261-8515, Chiba,
Japan
Tel.: (81) 432126369
Sales Range: $200-249.9 Million
Emp.: 750
Commercial Property Development Services
N.A.I.C.S.: 236210

Altyfoods Co. Ltd. (1)
2-7-52 Yokoe, Ibaraki, 567-0865, Osaka,
Japan
Tel.: (81) 726334830
Web Site: https://www.altyfoods.co.jp
Emp.: 1,249
Perishable Food Processing & Sales
N.A.I.C.S.: 311991
Akira Kida *(Pres)*

Aqutia Co., Ltd. (1)
Hulic Shinkyobashi Building 6F 4-3-3 Ha-
tchobori, Chuo-ku, Tokyo, 104-0032, Japan
Tel.: (81) 335526627
Web Site: https://www.kajitaku.com
Emp.: 150
Cleaning & Maintenance Services
N.A.I.C.S.: 561720

Big-A Company, Inc. (1)
Big-A Itabashi Oyama Store 2F 25-13
Oyamahigashi- cho, Itabashi-ku, Tokyo,
173-0014, Japan
Tel.: (81) 359432820
Web Site: http://www.biga.co.jp
Perishable Food Processor
N.A.I.C.S.: 311991
Hiroshi Miura *(Pres)*

Bio C' Bon Japon Co., Ltd. (1)
10-11 Nihonbashi Kodemmacho Nihonbashi
Fukawa Building 3F, Chuo-ku, Tokyo, 103-
0001, Japan
Tel.: (81) 335272033
Web Site: https://www.bio-c-bon.jp
General Merchandise Retailer
N.A.I.C.S.: 445110

Bon Belta Co., Ltd. (1)
2-1-10 Akasaka, Narita, 286-8521, Japan
Tel.: (81) 476262111
Web Site: https://www.bonbelta.co.jp
Hotel & Resort Services
N.A.I.C.S.: 721110

Can Do Co., Ltd. (1)
2-21-1 Kitashinjuku, Shinjuku-ku, Tokyo,
169-0074, Japan **(51.16%)**
Tel.: (81) 353315500
Web Site: https://www.cando-web.co.jp
Rev.: $569,731,130
Assets: $206,623,870
Liabilities: $130,902,670
Net Worth: $75,721,200
Earnings: ($8,266,940)
Emp.: 632
Fiscal Year-end: 02/29/2024
Retail Store Operator
N.A.I.C.S.: 445131
Kazuya Kido *(Pres)*

Cordon Vert CO., LTD (1)
3-7-35 Tsutsujigaoka Sompo Japan Sendai
Bldg 8 Fl, Miyagino-ku, Sendai, 983-0852,
Miyagi, Japan

Tel.: (81) 227243120
Web Site: http://www.cordonvert.jp
Sales Range: $25-49.9 Million
Emp.: 29
Liquor Import & Distr
N.A.I.C.S.: 311352
Hiroaki Yamauchi *(Pres)*

DO SERVICE CO., LTD. (1)
7-13-36 Minami-tsumori, Nishinari-ku,
Osaka, 557-0063, Japan **(40%)**
Tel.: (81) 6 6651 9357
Retail Facility Cleaning Services
N.A.I.C.S.: 561720
Rikuo Shimozono *(Chm)*

**Dong Hung Investment Development
Consultancy Joint Stock Company
Limited** (1)
230 Nguyen Tray, Nguyen Cu Trinh Ward
District 1, Ho Chi Minh City, Vietnam
Tel.: (84) 838370799
General Merchandise Retailer
N.A.I.C.S.: 445110

FeliCa Pocket Marketing Inc. (1)
8F Daiwa Nishi-Shimbashi Building 3-2-1
Nishi-Shimbashi, Minato-ku, Tokyo, 105-
0003, Japan
Tel.: (81) 364528800
Web Site: https://felicapocketmk.co.jp
Software Development Services
N.A.I.C.S.: 541511

General Services, Inc. (1)
3F Nibancho Kojimachi Square 1F,
Chiyoda-ku, Tokyo, 102-0084,
Japan **(51%)**
Tel.: (81) 3 3288 6661
Web Site: http://www.gsij.co.jp
Emp.: 15
Facility Services
N.A.I.C.S.: 561790
Hiroyuki Kitano *(Pres)*

**Guangdong AEON Teen Stores Co.,
Ltd.** (1)
5th Floor West Tower Fortune Plaza No 118
Tiyu East Road, Tianhe District,
Guangzhou, China
Tel.: (86) 2038911666
Web Site: https://www.aeon.com.cn
N.A.I.C.S.: 458110

Hakuseisha Co., Ltd. (1)
Orchid Place Ningyocho 3- chome 5F 3-5-4
Nihonbashi Ningyocho, Chuo-ku, Tokyo,
103-0013, Japan
Tel.: (81) 356524300
Web Site: https://www.hakuseisha.co.jp
Emp.: 2,390
Building Maintenance & Security Services
N.A.I.C.S.: 541350

Kagoshima Sunrise Farm K.K. (1)
1131-1 Nishiharagawacho, Kanoya, Ka-
goshima, Japan
Tel.: (81) 994435588
Web Site: http://www.daiei.co.jp
Cattle & Pig Farming
N.A.I.C.S.: 112111

Kajitaku Inc. (1)
6th floor Daiwa Kyobashi Building 4-3-3 Ha-
tchobori, Chuo-ku, Tokyo, 104-0032, Japan
Tel.: (81) 3 3552 6627
Web Site: http://www.kajitaku.com
Emp.: 229
Housework, Cleaning, Apartment Concierge
& Other Services
N.A.I.C.S.: 561790
Yuichi Shibutani *(Pres)*

Kankyouseibi Co., Ltd. (1)
1333 Iwasocho, Utsunomiya, 321-0973,
Tochigi, Japan
Tel.: (81) 286643711
Web Site: https://www.kankyouseibi.co.jp
Emp.: 3,930
Facility Management & Cleaning Services
N.A.I.C.S.: 561720

Kasumi Co., Ltd. (1)
599-1 Nishiohashi, Tsukuba, 305-8510, Iba-
raki, Japan
Tel.: (81) 298501850
Web Site: https://www.kasumi.co.jp
Sales Range: $1-4.9 Billion
Supermarket & Specialty Store Operator
N.A.I.C.S.: 445110

AEON Co., Ltd.—(Continued)

Hiromasa Kohama (Chm)

Subsidiary (Domestic):

The Maruetsu Inc. (2)
5-51-12 Higashi-Ikebukuro, Toshima-ku, To-kyo, 170-8401, Japan
Tel.: (81) 335901110
Web Site: https://www.maruetsu.co.jp
Sales Range: $1-4.9 Billion
Emp.: 3,864
Supermarket Operator
N.A.I.C.S.: 445110
Makoto Ueda (Chm)

Kohyo Co., Ltd. (1)
5-4-19 Shinsho, Yokkaichi, 510-0064, Mie, Japan
Tel.: (81) 593545411
Web Site: https://www.kohyoj.co.jp
Emp.: 176
Processed Seafoods Mfr
N.A.I.C.S.: 311412
Masahiro Otsuki (Pres)

Subsidiary (US):

Kohyo America, Inc. (2)
2370 W Carson St Ste 245, Torrance, CA 90501
Tel.: (424) 571-8000
Web Site: https://kohyoamerica.com
Emp.: 5
Farm Product Distr
N.A.I.C.S.: 424910
Miyuki Nagata (Dir-HR)

Subsidiary (Non-US):

Kohyo Holland B.V. (2)
Kruisweg 643, 2132 NC, Hoofddorp, Netherlands
Tel.: (31) 235624160
Web Site: https://www.kohyo.nl
Sales Range: $25-49.9 Million
Processed Seafoods Whslr
N.A.I.C.S.: 424460

MAXVALU HOKKAIDO CO., Ltd. (1)
21-1-10 Kita Hachijo-Nishi, Chuo-ku, Sapporo, 060-0008, Hokkaido, Japan **(57.42%)**
Tel.: (81) 11 6311358
Web Site: http://www.mv-hokkaido.co.jp
Supermarket Operator
N.A.I.C.S.: 445110
Nobunari Deto (Pres)

Affiliate (Domestic):

A to Z Service Co., Ltd. (2)
Shinjuku 6-chome Building 7F 6-24-16 Shinjuku, Shinjuku-ku, Tokyo, 162-0022, Japan
Tel.: (81) 3 5155 8301
Web Site: http://www.aeondelight.co.jp
Facility Management Services
N.A.I.C.S.: 561790
Hiroyuki Kishino (Pres)

Marunaka Co., Ltd. (1)
11 Mukaida nishimachi Kisshoin, Minami-ku, Kyoto, 601-8307, Japan
Tel.: (81) 753139114
Web Site: https://www.marunaka-japan.co.jp
Emp.: 50
Agricultural Machinery Retailer
N.A.I.C.S.: 423820
Yuichiro Manabe (Pres)

MaxValu Kyushu Co., Ltd. (1)
13-3-21 4F Ev Building Hakata-eki, Hakata-ku, Fukuoka, 812-0013, Japan **(77%)**
Tel.: (81) 92 433 1228
Web Site: http://www.mv-kyushu.co.jp
Supermarket Owner & Operator
N.A.I.C.S.: 445110
Tsutomu Sasaki (Chm & Pres)

Maxvalu Hokuriku Co., Ltd. (1)
4-133 Kuratsuki KC Building 8F, Kanazawa, Japan
Tel.: (81) 762677810
Web Site: https://www.mv-hokuriku.co.jp
General Merchandise Retailer
N.A.I.C.S.: 445110

Maxvalu Kanto Co., Ltd. (1)
5-30-3 Kameido, Koto-ku, Tokyo, Japan
Tel.: (81) 368925800

Web Site: https://www.mv-kanto.co.jp
General Merchandise Retailer
N.A.I.C.S.: 445110

Maxvalu Minami Tohoku Co., Ltd. (1)
3-3-3 Chuo, Aoba Ward, Sendai, 980-8442, Japan
Tel.: (81) 120284196
Web Site: https://www.mv-minamitohoku.co.jp
General Merchandise Retailer
N.A.I.C.S.: 445110

Maxvalu Tohoku Co., Ltd. (1)
1-6-25 Tsuchizakiminato-Kita, Akita, 011-0941, Japan **(70.13%)**
Tel.: (81) 18 8470111
Web Site: http://www.mv-tohoku.co.jp
Sales Range: $900-999.9 Million
Supermarket Store Operator
N.A.I.C.S.: 445110
Kazuaki Uchida (Pres & Sr Dir-Sls)

Maxvalu Tokai Co., Ltd. (1)
303-1 Shimo-Nagakubo Nagaizumi-cho, Surito-gun, Shizuoka, 411-0934, Japan **(69.28%)**
Tel.: (81) 559895050
Web Site: https://www.mv-tokai.co.jp
Rev.: $2,600,200,780
Assets: $944,707,050
Liabilities: $373,281,410
Net Worth: $571,425,640
Earnings: $58,939,170
Fiscal Year-end: 02/29/2024
Supermarket Store Operator
N.A.I.C.S.: 445110
Masaaki Sakudo (Pres, CEO & Dir)

Mega Sports Co., Ltd (1)
4th floor 1-3-33 Ariake, Koto-ku, Tokyo, 135-0063, Japan
Tel.: (81) 120354437
Web Site: https://www.megasports.jp
Sales Range: $450-499.9 Million
Sporting Goods Retailer
N.A.I.C.S.: 459110

Ministop Co., Ltd. (1)
AEON Tower 1-5-1 Nakase, Mihama-ku, Chiba, 261-8515, Japan
Tel.: (81) 432126471
Web Site: https://www.ministop.co.jp
Rev.: $560,507,040
Assets: $552,311,000
Liabilities: $263,882,710
Net Worth: $288,428,290
Earnings: ($3,318,120)
Emp.: 690
Fiscal Year-end: 02/29/2024
Convenience Store Operator
N.A.I.C.S.: 445131
Akihiro Fujimoto (Pres)

Miraiya Shoten Co., Ltd. (1)
7F Makuhari Building 1-6 Nakase, Mihama-ku, Chiba, 261-0023, Japan
Tel.: (81) 432981021
Web Site: http://www.miraiyashoten.co.jp
Book Retailer
N.A.I.C.S.: 459210

ORIGIN TOSHU CO., LTD (1)
KDX Chofu Building 5th floor Chofugaoka 1-18-1, Chofu, 182-0021, Tokyo, Japan
Tel.: (81) 120240424
Web Site: http://www.toshu.co.jp
Sales Range: $250-299.9 Million
Frozen Food Products Sales
N.A.I.C.S.: 424420
Hiroya Sawamura (Pres)

Orange Food Court (1)
2-2-20 Toyo Toyo Ekimae Bldg 4F, Koto, Tokyo, 135-0016, Japan
Tel.: (81) 356278201
Web Site: https://dipperdan.jp
Emp.: 635
Food Court Services
N.A.I.C.S.: 722513

Qingdao AEON Dongtai Co., Ltd. (1)
No 72 Xianggang Middle Road, Shinan District, Qingdao, 266071, Shandong, China
Tel.: (86) 53285719659
Web Site: http://www.qdaeon.com
Supermarket Stores
N.A.I.C.S.: 445110

R.O.U Co., Ltd. (1)

9th floor of Aeon Tower 1-5-1 Nakase, Mihama Ward, Chiba, 261-8515, Japan
Tel.: (81) 432126059
Web Site: https://www.rou-web.jp
Emp.: 269
Shopping Centre Services
N.A.I.C.S.: 812990

Reform Studio Co., Ltd. (1)
2-62-6 Nihonbashihama-cho, Chuo-ku, Tokyo, 103-0007, Japan
Tel.: (81) 336615575
Web Site: http://www.reform-s.com
Sales Range: $25-49.9 Million
Fashion Apparel & Shoe Retailer & Repair
N.A.I.C.S.: 458110
Kazuo Maki (Pres)

Research Institute For Quality Living Co., Ltd. (1)
1-4 Nakase Ion Tower Annex, Mihama-Ku, Chiba, 261-0023, Japan
Tel.: (81) 432126189
Web Site: https://www.riql.jp
Emp.: 328
Food Safety Regulation & Inspection Services
N.A.I.C.S.: 561990

SUNDAY Co., Ltd. (1)
6-22-10 Nejo, Hachinohe, 039-1166, Aomori, Japan
Tel.: (81) 178478511
Web Site: https://www.sunday.co.jp
Sales Range: Less than $1 Million
Household Product Retailer & Distr
N.A.I.C.S.: 423620

Shanghai Hualian Lawson Co., Ltd. (1)
3rd Floor Block D 1799 Wuzhong, Lu Minhang District, Vientiane, 201103, Lao People's Democratic Republic
Tel.: (856) 21 2351 3990
Web Site: http://www.lawson.com.cn
Convenience Store Operator
N.A.I.C.S.: 445131

Shimizu Shoji Co., Ltd. (1)
272 Sodojima-cho, Ogaki, 503-2201, Japan
Tel.: (81) 584710862
Web Site: https://www.yabashi.co.jp
Emp.: 32
Home Furnishing Product Mfr & Distr
N.A.I.C.S.: 314120

Tasmania Feedlot Pty. Ltd. (1)
14532 Midlands Highway, PO Box 58, Powranna, 7300, TAS, Australia
Tel.: (61) 363986244
Sales Range: $25-49.9 Million
Emp.: 40
General Merchandise Stores
N.A.I.C.S.: 455219
Andrew Thompson (Mng Dir)

The Bonte Inc. (1)
4-6-1 Oshima Daiei Oshima 5th floor, Koto-ku, Tokyo, Japan
Tel.: (81) 3 6892 2880
Web Site: http://www.daiei.co.jp
Emp.: 76
Bread & Pastry Production & Sales
N.A.I.C.S.: 445291
Hiroe Kihara (Pres)

The Daiei, Inc. (1)
2-2-20 Toyo, Koto-ku, Tokyo, 135-0016, Japan **(100%)**
Tel.: (81) 363887100
Web Site: https://www.daiei.co.jp
Sales Range: $5-14.9 Billion
Food, Clothing, Personal Care Products, Household Items & Other Goods Retailer; Restaurant & Department Store Operator
N.A.I.C.S.: 455110

Topvalu Collection Co., Ltd. (1)
1-4 Nakase Aeon Tower Annex 8F, Mihama-ku, Chiba, 261-0023, Japan
Tel.: (81) 570024400
Web Site: https://topvalucollection.jp
Women's Clothing Retailer
N.A.I.C.S.: 458110

United Super Markets Holdings, Inc. (1)
1 Kanda Aioi-cho, Chiyoda-ku, Tokyo, 101-0029, Japan **(51%)**
Tel.: (81) 335264761

Web Site: https://www.usmh.co.jp
Rev.: $5,010,198,130
Assets: $2,024,230,450
Liabilities: $958,957,950
Net Worth: $1,065,272,500
Earnings: $7,146,720
Fiscal Year-end: 02/29/2024
Holding Company; Supermarkets & Convenience Stores Operator
N.A.I.C.S.: 551112
Motohiro Fujita (Pres & CEO)

Welcia Holdings Co., Ltd. (1)
3F Kandasudacho Place 1-9 Kanda-Sudacho, Chiyoda-ku, Tokyo, 101-0041, Japan **(50.1%)**
Tel.: (81) 352075878
Web Site: https://www.welcia.co.jp
Rev.: $8,630,933,510
Assets: $3,912,687,400
Liabilities: $2,180,125,370
Net Worth: $1,732,562,030
Earnings: $187,537,590
Emp.: 4,172
Fiscal Year-end: 02/29/2024
Holding Company; Drug Stores & Pharmacies
N.A.I.C.S.: 551112
Norimasa Sato (Exec VP)

Welpark Co., Ltd. (1)
6-1-1 Sakaecho, Tachikawa, 190-0003, Tokyo, Japan
Tel.: (81) 425375274
Web Site: https://www.welpark.jp
Supermarket Management Services
N.A.I.C.S.: 445110

AEON FINANCIAL SERVICE CO., LTD
Terrace Square 3-22 Kandanishiki-cho, Chiyoda-ku, Tokyo, 101-8445, Japan
Tel.: (81) 352812056 JP
Web Site: https://www.aeonfinancial.co.jp
Year Founded: 1981
8570—(TKS)
Rev.: $3,442,960,720
Assets: $49,244,098,390
Liabilities: $45,172,197,950
Net Worth: $4,071,900,440
Earnings: $148,152,640
Emp.: 15,968
Fiscal Year-end: 02/29/24
Consumer Credit Card Services, Vehicle Purchase & Personal Loan Financing
N.A.I.C.S.: 522291
Masaki Suzuki (Chm)

Subsidiaries:

AEON Credit Service (Asia) Company Limited (1)
20th Floor Mira Place Tower A 132 Nathan Road, Tsim Sha Tsui, Kowloon, China (Hong Kong)
Tel.: (852) 28956262
Web Site: https://www.aeon.com.hk
Sales Range: $1-9.9 Million
Emp.: 300
Consumer Credit Card Services, Vehicle Purchase & Personal Loan Financing
N.A.I.C.S.: 522291

AEON METALS LIMITED
Level 7 Suite 32 88 Pitt Street, Sydney, 2000, NSW, Australia
Tel.: (61) 292322298
Web Site:
https://www.aeonmetals.com.au
AML—(ASX)
Rev.: $1,335
Assets: $70,924,489
Liabilities: $24,038,273
Net Worth: $46,886,216
Earnings: ($2,295,876)
Emp.: 5
Fiscal Year-end: 06/30/23
Copper Ore Mining Services
N.A.I.C.S.: 212230
Stephen J. Lonergan (Sec)

AEON MOTOR CO., LTD.
No 41 Nanzhou, Shanshang District, Tainan City, 74342, Taiwan
Tel.: (886) 65783988
Web Site:
   https://www.aeonmotor.com.tw
Year Founded: 1998
1599—(TPE)
Rev.: $105,675,109
Assets: $97,109,840
Liabilities: $34,034,456
Net Worth: $63,075,384
Earnings: $8,594,034
Fiscal Year-end: 12/31/22
Motorcycle, Scooter & ATV Mfr
N.A.I.C.S.: 336991
Chieh Lin Chung *(Chm)*

AEON REIT INVESTMENT CORPORATION
11410 Uchikanda, Chiyoda-ku, Tokyo, 101-0054, Japan
Tel.: (81) 352836360
Web Site: https://www.aeon-jreit.co.jp
Year Founded: 2012
3292—(TKS)
Sales Range: Less than $1 Million
Real Estate Related Services
N.A.I.C.S.: 531390
Nobuaki Seki *(Exec Dir)*

AEOON TECHNOLOGIES GMBH
Amerling 133, 6233, Kramsach, Austria
Tel.: (43) 533763207
Web Site: https://aeoon.com
Year Founded: 2011
Digital Textile Product Mfr
N.A.I.C.S.: 323111

AEOREMA COMMUNICATIONS PLC
101 New Cavendish Street, London, W1W 6XH, United Kingdom
Tel.: (44) 2072910444   UK
Web Site: https://www.aeorema.com
AEO—(AIM)
Rev.: $25,644,531
Assets: $11,400,378
Liabilities: $7,848,819
Net Worth: $3,551,559
Earnings: $379,170
Emp.: 63
Fiscal Year-end: 06/30/24
Business Communications Services
N.A.I.C.S.: 561499
Michael Hale *(Chm)*

Subsidiaries:

Eventful Limited   (1)
87 New Cavendish Street, London, W1W 6XD, United Kingdom
Tel.: (44) 2088794208
Web Site: https://www.eventful.co.uk
Event Management Services
N.A.I.C.S.: 561920

AEQUITA SE & CO. KGAA
Widenmayerstr 31, Munich, D-80538, Germany
Tel.: (49) 89 2620 4840 0
Web Site: http://www.aequita.de
Privater Equity Firm
N.A.I.C.S.: 523999
Axel Geuer *(Mng Partner)*

Subsidiaries:

Glassolutions BV   (1)
Windmolen 17, Overijssel, 7609, Almelo, Netherlands   (99.91%)
Tel.: (31) 334502800
Web Site: http://www.glassolutions.nl
Sales Range: $25-49.9 Million
Emp.: 100
Mfr of Glass Products
N.A.I.C.S.: 327211

AEQUUS PHARMACEUTICALS INC.
2820 200 Granville Street, Vancouver, V6C 1S4, BC, Canada
Tel.: (604) 336-7906   BC
Web Site:
   https://www.aequuspharma.ca
Year Founded: 2013
AQS—(OTCQB)
Rev.: $192,477
Assets: $820,236
Liabilities: $4,062,604
Net Worth: ($3,242,367)
Earnings: ($2,238,721)
Emp.: 11
Fiscal Year-end: 12/31/23
Pharmaceuticals Mfr
N.A.I.C.S.: 325412
Ann Fehr *(CFO)*

Subsidiaries:

TeOra Health Ltd.   (1)
PO Box 207, Penticton, V2A 6J9, BC, Canada
Tel.: (250) 460-2161
Pharmaceuticals Product Mfr
N.A.I.C.S.: 325412

AER ARANN EXPRESS LTD.
1 N Wood Ave Santry, Dublin, 9, Ireland
Tel.: (353) 18447700
Web Site:
   http://www.eddiestobart.com
Rev.: $113,487,140
Emp.: 100
Oil Transportation Services
N.A.I.C.S.: 481111
Julian Carr *(CEO)*

AERCAP HOLDINGS N.V.
AerCap House 65 St Stephen s Green, Dublin, D02 YX20, Ireland
Tel.: (353) 18192010   NL
Web Site: http://www.aercap.com
Year Founded: 1995
AER—(NYSE)
Rev.: $7,580,418,000
Assets: $71,274,559,000
Liabilities: $54,685,513,000
Net Worth: $16,589,046,000
Earnings: $3,136,091,000
Emp.: 679
Fiscal Year-end: 12/31/23
Aviation Services; Aircraft & Engine Leasing, Trading & Parts Sales; Aircraft Management & Maintenance Services
N.A.I.C.S.: 423860
Peter Anderson *(Chief Comml Officer)*

Subsidiaries:

AerCap B.V.   (1)
Station Stlein 965, 1117 CE, Schiphol, Netherlands   (100%)
Tel.: (31) 206559655
Sales Range: $25-49.9 Million
Emp.: 85
Aircraft Manufacturing
N.A.I.C.S.: 336411

AerCap Dutch Aircraft Leasing B.V.   (1)
Stationspleim 965, Schiphol, 1110 CE, Netherlands   (100%)
Tel.: (31) 206559655
Web Site:
   http://www.bulgaria.bnpparibas.com
Sales Range: $25-49.9 Million
Emp.: 85
Aircraft Manufacturing
N.A.I.C.S.: 336411

AerCap Group Services B.V.   (1)
Aercap House Stationsplein 965, 1117 CE, Schiphol, Netherlands
Tel.: (31) 206559655

Sales Range: $50-74.9 Million
Emp.: 85
Aircraft Leasing Services
N.A.I.C.S.: 532411
Aengus Kelly *(CEO)*

AerCap Ireland Limited   (1)
Aviation House Building Westpark, Shannon, V14 AN29, Co Claire, Ireland (100%)
Tel.: (353) 61706500
Web Site: https://www.aercap.com
Sales Range: $25-49.9 Million
Emp.: 80
Aircraft Manufacturing
N.A.I.C.S.: 336411

Subsidiary (US):

International Lease Finance Corporation   (2)
10250 Constellation Blvd Ste 1500, Los Angeles, CA 90067   (100%)
Tel.: (310) 788-1999
Web Site: http://www.ilfc.com
New & Used Commercial Jet Aircraft Leasing & Sales to Airlines
N.A.I.C.S.: 488190
Steven F. Udvar-Hazy *(Co-Founder)*

Subsidiary (Domestic):

AeroTurbine, Inc.   (3)
6800 S Lindbergh St, Stockton, CA 95206
Tel.: (209) 983-1112
Web Site: https://www.aeroturbineinc.com
Commercial Air, Rail & Water Transportation Equipment Rental & Leasing
N.A.I.C.S.: 532411

Subsidiary (Non-US):

AeroTurbine Asia Pte Ltd   (4)
8 Shenton Way 32-03 AXA Tower, Singapore, 068811, Singapore
Tel.: (65) 65931500
Web Site: http://www.aeroturbine.com
Commercial Air, Rail & Water Transportation Equipment Rental & Leasing
N.A.I.C.S.: 532411

AeroTurbine Europe Limited   (4)
Unit 7 Hogwood Industrial Estate Ivanhoe Road, Finchampstead, RG40 4QQ, United Kingdom
Tel.: (44) 1189739900
Commercial Air, Rail & Water Transportation Equipment Rental & Leasing
N.A.I.C.S.: 532411

AerCap Netherlands B.V.   (1)
Stetion Tlibn 965, 1117 CE, Schiphol, Netherlands   (100%)
Tel.: (31) 206559655
Web Site: http://www.aercap.com
Sales Range: $25-49.9 Million
Emp.: 95
Aircraft Manufacturing
N.A.I.C.S.: 336411

AerCap Singapore Pte. Ltd.   (1)
8 Marina View 39-05 Asia Square Tower 1, Singapore, 018960, Singapore
Tel.: (65) 64171699
Aircraft Leasing Services
N.A.I.C.S.: 532411
James Drudy *(VP-Technical)*

AerCap USA, Inc   (1)
100 NE 3rd Ave Ste 800, Fort Lauderdale, FL 33301-1156   (100%)
Tel.: (954) 760-7777
Web Site: http://www.aercap.com
Sales Range: $25-49.9 Million
Emp.: 18
Aircraft Manufacturing
N.A.I.C.S.: 336411
Corey Thombley *(Pres)*

AerFi Group Limited   (1)
G P A House, Kilrush, Ireland   (100%)
Tel.: (353) 61723800
Aircraft Manufacturing
N.A.I.C.S.: 336411

Aercap Financial Services (Ireland) Ltd   (1)
4450 Atlantic ave, 4450 Atlantic Ave, Shannon, Co Clare, Ireland   (100%)
Tel.: (353) 61 723 600
Web Site: http://www.aercap.com

Sales Range: $25-49.9 Million
Emp.: 65
Aircraft Financial & Leasing Services
N.A.I.C.S.: 525990

Toulouse Location S.A.R.L.   (1)
104 Avenue De Lombez, 31300, Toulouse, France   (100%)
Tel.: (33) 561427511
Aircraft Manufacturing
N.A.I.C.S.: 336411

AERGO CAPITAL LTD.
38 Wellington Road, Mount Street Crecent, Dublin, Ireland
Tel.: (353) 16761077
Web Site:
   http://www.aergocapital.com
Year Founded: 1999
Commercial Jet Aircraft Leasing Services
N.A.I.C.S.: 532411
Fred Browne *(Founder & CEO)*

Subsidiaries:

Safair Operations (Pty) Limited   (1)
Northern Perimeter Road Bonaero Park, Kempton Park, 1619, Johannesburg, South Africa
Tel.: (27) 119280000
Web Site: http://www.safairoperations.com
Aircraft Leasing Services
N.A.I.C.S.: 532411
Elmar Conradie *(CEO)*

AERIA INC.
Akasaka HM Building 4F 3-7-13 Akasaka, Minato-Ku, Tokyo, 107-0052, Japan
Tel.: (81) 335879574
Web Site: https://www.aeria.jp
Year Founded: 2002
3758—(TKS)
Rev.: $160,737,390
Assets: $149,918,050
Liabilities: $81,272,670
Net Worth: $68,645,380
Earnings: $3,403,200
Fiscal Year-end: 12/31/23
Online Game Development Services
N.A.I.C.S.: 541511
Yusuke Kobayashi *(Pres)*

Subsidiaries:

Air Internet Service Co., Ltd.   (1)
1-10-4 Kitashinagawa Yb Building 4F, Shinagawa-ku, Tokyo, 140-0001, Japan
Tel.: (81) 36 717 5710
Web Site: https://www.airnet.jp
Application Hosting Services
N.A.I.C.S.: 518210

Arithmetic Inc.   (1)
Hiroo Complex Building 2F 5-7-35 Hiroo, Shibuya-ku, Tokyo, 150-0012, Japan
Tel.: (81) 354229710
Web Site: http://www.arith-metic.jp
Emp.: 56
Software Development Services
N.A.I.C.S.: 513210
Yoshitaka Terashima *(CEO)*

Asgard Corporation   (1)
Takasha 1-266 No 1 Round Spot 6F, Meito-ku, Nagoya, 465-0095, Aichi-ken, Japan
Tel.: (81) 529908883
Web Site: http://www.asgard-japan.com
Software Development Services
N.A.I.C.S.: 513210

Liber Entertainment Inc.   (1)
6th Floor Maruishi Building 2 1-9-16 kajicho, Chiyoda-ku, Tokyo, 101-0044, Japan
Tel.: (81) 352075361
Web Site: http://liberent.co.jp
Software Development Services
N.A.I.C.S.: 513210
Daisuke Kuramoto *(Mgr)*

AERIS ENVIRONMENTAL LTD
5/26-34 Dunning Avenue, Rosebery, 2018, NSW, Australia
Tel.: (61) 283441315   AU

Aeris Environmental Ltd—(Continued)

Web Site: https://www.aeris.com.au
AEI—(ASX)
Rev.: $2,114,093
Assets: $1,834,691
Liabilities: $1,853,057
Net Worth: ($18,366)
Earnings: ($1,985,143)
Fiscal Year-end: 06/30/24
Environmental Services including Removal of Bacteria & Mold in Air-Conditioning, Cold Storage & Bulk Water Systems
N.A.I.C.S.: 541620
Peter Bush *(CEO)*

Subsidiaries:

Aeris Biological Systems Pty Ltd. **(1)**
5 26-34 Dunning Ave, Rosebery, 2018, NSW, Australia
Tel.: (61) 283441315
Web Site: http://www.aeris.com.au
Emp.: 3
Cold Storage Systems
N.A.I.C.S.: 493120

Aeris Environmental LLC **(1)**
28610 Hwy 290 Ste F09 242, Cypress, TX 77433
Web Site: https://aerisguard.com
Industrial Air Handling Product Mfr
N.A.I.C.S.: 333415

Aeris Hygiene Services Pty Ltd. **(1)**
5 26-34 Dunning Ave, Rosebery, 2018, NSW, Australia
Tel.: (61) 283441315
Web Site: http://www.aeriscoldstorage.com
Sales Range: $25-49.9 Million
Emp.: 3
Cold Storage Maintenance Services
N.A.I.C.S.: 493190
Peter Bush *(Gen Mgr)*

AERIS RESOURCES LIMITED

Tel.: (61) 730346200
Web Site:
   https://www.aerisresources.com.au
AIS—(ASX)
Rev.: $360,592,955
Assets: $375,766,679
Liabilities: $194,282,959
Net Worth: $181,483,719
Earnings: ($16,198,037)
Emp.: 628
Fiscal Year-end: 06/30/24
Copper & Gold Mining Services
N.A.I.C.S.: 212230
Andre Labuschagne *(Chm)*

Subsidiaries:

PT Indo Muro Kencana **(1)**
Graha Kirana Bldge 9th Fl, Aalan Yos Sudarso, Jakarta, Indonesia **(100%)**
Tel.: (62) 2165314710
Sales Range: $50-74.9 Million
Emp.: 3
Gold Mining
N.A.I.C.S.: 212220

Straits Mining Pty Ltd **(1)**
U 38 105 Colin Street, West Perth, 6005, NSW, Australia
Tel.: (61) 8 9480 0500
Copper Mining Services
N.A.I.C.S.: 212230

Tritton Resources Limited **(1)**
Level 1 35 Ventnor Avenue, 1641, West Perth, 6005, Australia **(58%)**
Tel.: (61) 894864422
Sales Range: $50-74.9 Million
Emp.: 100
Mining & Exploration Services
N.A.I.C.S.: 212290
Milan Jerkovic *(Chm)*

AERISON GROUP LIMITED

Level 1 56 Ord Street, West Perth, 6005, WA, Australia
Tel.: (61) 893525900   AU
Web Site: https://www.aerison.com

Year Founded: 1988
AE1—(ASX)
Rev.: $103,348,304
Assets: $65,454,079
Liabilities: $39,571,415
Net Worth: $25,882,664
Earnings: $4,105,246
Emp.: 213
Fiscal Year-end: 12/31/21
Construction Services
N.A.I.C.S.: 237120
Daniel Hibbs *(Owner)*

AERMONT CAPITAL LLP

55 St Jamess S, London, SW1A 1LA, United Kingdom
Tel.: (44) 2031022300   UK
Web Site: http://www.aermont.com
Year Founded: 2007
Real Estate Related Investment
N.A.I.C.S.: 531390
Leon Bressler *(Mng Partner)*

Subsidiaries:

Pinewood Group Limited **(1)**
Pinewood Road, Iver Heath, SL0 0NH, Bucks, United Kingdom
Tel.: (44) 1753651700
Web Site: http://www.pinewoodgroup.com
Film & Television Production Services
N.A.I.C.S.: 512110
David Godfrey *(Dir-Intl Ops)*

Subsidiary (Domestic):

Pinewood Studios Limited **(2)**
Pinewood Road, Iver Heath, SL0 0NH, Bucks, United Kingdom
Tel.: (44) 1753651700
Web Site: http://www.pinewoodgroup.com
Film Studio Operators
N.A.I.C.S.: 512110

Shepperton Studios Limited **(2)**
Studios Road, Shepperton, TW17 0QD, Mddx, United Kingdom
Tel.: (44) 1932562611
Motion Picture Studio Operators
N.A.I.C.S.: 512110

AERO AVIATION LTD.

13-2139 Pegasus Way NE, Calgary, T2E 8T2, AB, Canada
Tel.: (403) 250-7553
Web Site: https://www.aeroav.com
Year Founded: 1979
Rev.: $13,857,093
Emp.: 50
Aviation Services
N.A.I.C.S.: 488190
Don Pott *(VP)*

AERO D.D.

Ipavceva ulica 32 pp 430, Celje, 3000, Slovenia
Tel.: (386) 34235100
Web Site: http://www.aero.si
Year Founded: 1921
Sales Range: $25-49.9 Million
Emp.: 350
Photographic Equipment & Supplies Mfr
N.A.I.C.S.: 333310
Milena Brezigar *(Mng Dir)*

Subsidiaries:

AERO BALKAN, d.o.o. **(1)**
Pancevacki put 85, 11210, Belgrade, Serbia
Tel.: (381) 11 2711 220
Shoe Polish Mfr
N.A.I.C.S.: 325612

Aero Copy d.o.o. **(1)**
Ipavceva Ulica 32 pp 430, Celje, 3000, Slovenia
Tel.: (386) 34235100
Web Site: http://www.aero.si
Sales Range: $50-74.9 Million
Emp.: 200
Paper Mfr
N.A.I.C.S.: 322299

Aero Exclusive d.o.o. **(1)**
Kolodvorska 12, 71000, Sarajevo, Bosnia & Herzegovina
Tel.: (387) 33 205 393
Adhesive Mfr
N.A.I.C.S.: 325520

Aero Papirotti d.o.o. **(1)**
Ipavceva ulica 32 pp 430, 3000, Celje, Slovenia
Tel.: (386) 34235100
Web Site: http://www.aero.si
Sales Range: $25-49.9 Million
Emp.: 100
Paper Mfr
N.A.I.C.S.: 322299

Aero Zagreb d.o.o. **(1)**
Franje Lucica 23/3, 10000, Zagreb, Croatia
Tel.: (385) 1 6190069
Adhesive Mfr
N.A.I.C.S.: 325520

AERO INVENTORY PLC

30 Lancaster Rd, New Barnet, EN4 8AP, United Kingdom
Tel.: (44) 2084499263   UK
Web Site: http://www.aero-inventory.com
Sales Range: $400-449.9 Million
Emp.: 115
Procurement & Inventory Management Solution Services for Aerospace Industry
N.A.I.C.S.: 541614
Nigel Mccorkell *(Chm)*

Subsidiaries:

Aero Inventory (Canada) Inc **(1)**
394 Isabey Ste 250, Saint Laurent, H4T 1V3, QC, Canada
Tel.: (514) 764-9520
Sales Range: $25-49.9 Million
Emp.: 60
Aerospace Industry Services
N.A.I.C.S.: 335991

Aero Inventory (Hong Kong) Limited **(1)**
Units 01-06 6th Fl Airport Freight Forwarding Ctr, 2 Chun Wan Rd Chek Lap Kok, Hong Kong, China (Hong Kong)
Tel.: (852) 3657 2600
Procurement & Inventory Management Services
N.A.I.C.S.: 561110

Aero Inventory (Japan) KK **(1)**
Utility Ctr Bldg 4th Fl, 3-5-10 Haneda Airport Otaku, Tokyo, 144 0041, Japan
Tel.: (81) 357567700
Aerospace Industry Services
N.A.I.C.S.: 334511

Aero Inventory (UK) Limited **(1)**
30 Lancaster Road, New Barnet, EN4 8AP, Herts, United Kingdom
Tel.: (44) 2084499263
Web Site: http://www.aeroinv.com
Sales Range: $25-49.9 Million
Emp.: 60
Procurement & Inventory Management Services
N.A.I.C.S.: 561110

Aero Inventory (USA) Inc **(1)**
12257 Florence Ave, Santa Fe Springs, CA 90670
Tel.: (562) 236-5500
Sales Range: $25-49.9 Million
Emp.: 6
Aerospace Industry Services
N.A.I.C.S.: 334511

AERO WIN TECHNOLOGY CORPORATION

No 1 Lane 13 Xingong Road, Xinying District, Taipei, 730, Taiwan
Tel.: (886) 66535001
Web Site: https://www.aerowin.com
8222—(TAI)
Rev.: $14,055,467
Assets: $42,263,390
Liabilities: $18,180,346
Net Worth: $24,083,044

Earnings: $591,408
Emp.: 200
Fiscal Year-end: 12/31/22
Aircraft Part Mfr
N.A.I.C.S.: 336412
Kuo-Hao Tseng *(Chm)*

AEROC INTERNATIONAL AS

Valke-Manniku Tn 3, Tallinn, Estonia
Tel.: (372) 679 9080
Web Site: http://www.aeroc.eu
Sales Range: $10-24.9 Million
Emp.: 150
Holding Company; Aerated Concrete Products Mfr
N.A.I.C.S.: 327390
Ivar Papalavskis *(Chm)*

Subsidiaries:

AEROC JAMERA AS **(1)**
Vaike-Manniku tn 3, 44209, Tallinn, Estonia
Tel.: (372) 6799080
Web Site: http://www.aeroc.ee
Concrete Products Mfr
N.A.I.C.S.: 327390
Andres Kalvik *(Dir-Mktg)*

Aeroc Jamera Oy **(1)**
Fallaker 1, 02740, Espoo, Finland
Tel.: (358) 290092270
Web Site: http://www.aeroc.fi
Concrete Product Distr
N.A.I.C.S.: 423320
Sirpa Lehikoinen *(Mgr-Mktg)*

SIA AEROC **(1)**
Ropazu iela 10, 1039, Riga, Latvia
Tel.: (371) 67418412
Web Site: http://www.aeroc.lv
Concrete Product Mfr & Distr
N.A.I.C.S.: 327390
Aivars Tarziers-Mazurs *(Mgr-Production)*

UAB Aeroc **(1)**
Luksio g 32/ J Kubiliaus g 12, 08222, Vilnius, Lithuania
Tel.: (370) 52747393
Web Site: http://www.aeroc.lt
Concrete Product Distr
N.A.I.C.S.: 423320

AEROCOM GMBH & CO.

Adam-Riese-Strasse 16, Schwabisch Gmund, 73529, Germany
Tel.: (49) 717110450
Web Site: http://www.aerocom.de
Year Founded: 1956
Sales Range: $25-49.9 Million
Emp.: 170
Pneumatic Tube Systems Mfr
N.A.I.C.S.: 333922
Wolfram Pfitzer *(Mng Dir)*

Subsidiaries:

Aerocom France S.A.R.L. **(1)**
4 rue Hoelzel, 67400, Illkirch-Graffenstaden, France
Tel.: (33) 388664440
Web Site: http://www.aerocom-france.com
Pneumatic Tube Mfr
N.A.I.C.S.: 333922

Aerocom GCT S.r.l. **(1)**
Viale Europa 54/1, Lodivecchio, 26855, Lodi, Italy
Tel.: (39) 0371460046
Web Site: http://www.aerocom.it
Pneumatic Tube Mfr
N.A.I.C.S.: 333922
Simone Orsi *(Gen Mgr)*

Aerocom GmbH & Co. **(1)**
Lukasstr 17, 9008, Saint Gallen, Switzerland
Tel.: (41) 712435980
Pneumatic Tube Distr
N.A.I.C.S.: 423830

Aerocom Neumatica S. L. **(1)**
C / Pintor Roig i Soler 16, 08915, Barcelona, Spain
Tel.: (34) 934809437
Pneumatic Tube Distr
N.A.I.C.S.: 423830

AERODROM NIKOLA TESLA A.D.
Aerodorm Beograd 47 Surcin, Belgrade, Serbia
Tel.: (381) 117450652   RS
Web Site: https://www.antb.rs
Year Founded: 1961
AERO—(BEL)
Rev.: $12,310,788
Assets: $397,250,018
Liabilities: $132,924,192
Net Worth: $264,325,827
Earnings: $2,170,213
Emp.: 35
Fiscal Year-end: 12/31/23
Air Traffic Control Services
N.A.I.C.S.: 488111

AERODROME GROUP LTD.
Ha Psagot St 4, Petah Tikva, Israel
Tel.: (972) 722608093
Web Site: http://www.aerodrome-ops.com
ARDM—(TAE)
Rev.: $9,182,799
Assets: $16,134,971
Liabilities: $4,671,927
Net Worth: $11,463,044
Earnings: ($147,769)
Fiscal Year-end: 06/30/23
Aircraft System Services
N.A.I.C.S.: 488190
Zion Sapir (Chm)

Subsidiaries:

SGC Knowledge Transfer Ltd.   (1)
Ha-Psagot St 4, Petah Tikva, Israel
Tel.: (972) 35730370
Web Site: https://sgc.co.il
Training & Educational Services
N.A.I.C.S.: 611420

AERODROMI REPUBLIKE SRPSKE A.D.
Ljevcanska 141, 78250, Laktasi, Bosnia & Herzegovina
Tel.: (387) 51535210
Web Site: https://www.bnx.aero
Year Founded: 1998
AERD-R-A—(BANJ)
Sales Range: Less than $1 Million
Airplane Ticket & Tourist Arrangement Services
N.A.I.C.S.: 561599
Marina Todorovic (Chm-Supervisory Bd)

AEROFOAM METALS, INC.
3330 Ridgeway Dr Units 15 & 16, Mississauga, L5L 5, ON, Canada
Tel.: (905) 569-2376
Year Founded: 2004
AFML—(OTCIQ)
Sales Range: Less than $1 Million
Foamed Aluminum Product Mfr
N.A.I.C.S.: 331524

AEROMETREX LIMITED
51-53 Glynburn Rd, Glynde, Adelaide, 5070, SA, Australia
Tel.: (61) 883629911   AU
Web Site:
    https://www.aerometrex.com.au
Year Founded: 1980
AMX—(ASX)
Rev.: $21,333,028
Assets: $34,225,707
Liabilities: $8,940,671
Net Worth: $25,285,036
Earnings: ($458,948)
Fiscal Year-end: 06/30/22
Software Development Services
N.A.I.C.S.: 541511
Kaitlin Smith (Sec)

Subsidiaries:

Aerometrex Ltd.   (1)

5500 Greenwood Plaza Blvd 130, Greenwood Village, CO 80111
Tel.: (303) 502-5290
Aerial Mapping Services
N.A.I.C.S.: 541360

MetroMap Pty. Ltd.   (1)
51-53 Glynburn Road, Glynde, 5070, SA, Australia
Tel.: (61) 1300776652
Web Site: https://metromap.com.au
Aerial Imagery Product Distr
N.A.I.C.S.: 423410

AEROPLEX OF CENTRAL EUROPE LTD.
Ferenc Liszt International Airport, Budapest, 1185, Hungary
Tel.: (36) 1 296 8597
Web Site: http://www.aeroplex.com
Year Founded: 1992
Sales Range: $125-149.9 Million
Emp.: 350
Aircraft Maintenance & Overhaul
N.A.I.C.S.: 488119
Nardi Veltman (VP-Engrg & Maintenance)

AEROPORTO GUGLIELMO MARCONI DI BOLOGNA S.P.A.
Via Triumvirato 84, 40132, Bologna, Italy
Tel.: (39) 0516479680
Web Site: https://www.bologna-airport.it
Year Founded: 1981
ADB—(ITA)
Rev.: $145,213,684
Assets: $362,518,886
Liabilities: $158,212,821
Net Worth: $204,306,065
Earnings: $33,573,279
Emp.: 31
Fiscal Year-end: 12/31/22
Airport Operations
N.A.I.C.S.: 488119
Enrico Postacchini (Chm)

AEROPORTS DE MONTREAL
975 Romeo Vachon Blvd N, Dorval, H4Y 1H1, QC, Canada
Tel.: (514) 394-7377
Web Site: http://www.admtl.com
Year Founded: 1992
Sales Range: $250-299.9 Million
Emp.: 600
Airport Management Services
N.A.I.C.S.: 488119
Philippe Rainville (Pres & CEO)

AEROPORTS DE PARIS S.A.
1 rue de France, Tremblay-en-France, 93290, Paris, France
Tel.: (33) 170363950   FR
Web Site:
    https://www.parisaeroport.fr
Year Founded: 1945
ADP—(EUR)
Rev.: $5,930,282,754
Assets: $21,217,353,766
Liabilities: $15,500,755,450
Net Worth: $5,716,598,316
Earnings: $680,984,243
Emp.: 28,174
Fiscal Year-end: 12/31/23
Commercial Airport Operator
N.A.I.C.S.: 488119
Elise Hermant (Chief Comm Officer & Dir-Comm)

Subsidiaries:

Airport International Group P.S.C.   (1)
Alpha Building 2nd Floor, PO Box 39052, Amman, 11104, Jordan
Tel.: (962) 64453000
Web Site: https://www.aig.aero
N.A.I.C.S.: 541330

Alyzia   (1)
Roissypole Le Dome 4 rue de la Haye, BP 11911, 93731, Charles de Gaulle, France
Tel.: (33) 174371109
Web Site: http://www.alyzia.com
Rev.: $203,875,200
Emp.: 2,000
Airport Ground Handling Services
N.A.I.C.S.: 488119
Serge Sellan (Pres)

Subsidiary (Domestic):

ALYZIA SURETE   (2)
4 rue de la Haye, Le Vesinet, 95731, Yvelines, France
Tel.: (33) 148168330
Air Freight Transportation Services
N.A.I.C.S.: 488190

Hub Telecom   (1)
Roissypole Le Dome, 4 rue de la Haye, Roissy-en-France, 95732, Val-d Oise, France
Tel.: (33) 170038500
Web Site: http://www.hubtelecom.com
Sales Range: $150-199.9 Million
Emp.: 700
Telecommunication Servicesb
N.A.I.C.S.: 517810

Merchant Aviation LLC   (1)
382 Springfield Ave Ste 411, Summit, NJ 07901
Tel.: (908) 273-3600
Web Site: https://merchantaviation.com
Aviation Consulting Services
N.A.I.C.S.: 813319

AEROPUERTO INTERNACIONAL DE TOCUMEN S.A.
Jose Domingo Diaz Road Township of Tocumen, Panama, Panama
Tel.: (507) 2382600
Web Site:
    http://www.tocumenpanama.aero
TOCU—(PAN)
Rev.: $265,482,234
Assets: $2,249,957,982
Liabilities: $1,871,741,136
Net Worth: $378,216,846
Earnings: ($12,976,417)
Fiscal Year-end: 12/31/23
Airport Operation Support Services
N.A.I.C.S.: 488119

AEROSPACE CH UAV CO., LTD.
No 788 Haihao Road, Taizhou Bay Cluster, Taizhou, 100074, Zhejiang, China
Tel.: (86) 57688169999
Web Site: http://www.nykj.cc
Year Founded: 2001
002389—(SSE)
Rev.: $541,649,160
Assets: $1,382,743,440
Liabilities: $251,300,556
Net Worth: $1,131,442,884
Earnings: $43,056,468
Emp.: 300
Fiscal Year-end: 12/31/22
Polypropylene Smooth, Rough & Metallized Film for Capacitors
N.A.I.C.S.: 334416
Hu Meixiao (Chm)

AEROSPACE COMMMUNICATIONS HOLDINGS GROUP CO., LTD.
Aerospace Communications Build 138 Jiefang Road, Hangzhou, 310009, Zhejiang, China
Tel.: (86) 571 8703 4676
Web Site: http://www.aerocom.cn
Rev.: $581,622,266
Assets: $899,068,637
Liabilities: $838,149,107
Net Worth: $60,919,530
Earnings: ($196,019,625)
Fiscal Year-end: 12/31/19

Holding Company
N.A.I.C.S.: 551112
Dehai Yu (Chm & Pres-Interim)

AEROSPACE HI-TECH HOLDING GROUP CO., LTD.
15th and 16th Floor Haiying Technology Building No 1 Haiying Road, Science City Fengtai District, Beijing, 100070, China
Tel.: (86) 1083636130
Web Site: http://www.as-hitech.com
Year Founded: 1999
000901—(SSE)
Rev.: $805,933,908
Assets: $1,175,857,020
Liabilities: $546,269,724
Net Worth: $629,587,296
Earnings: $4,094,064
Fiscal Year-end: 12/31/22
Holding Company
N.A.I.C.S.: 551112
Xu Tao (Chm)

AEROSPACE INDUSTRIAL DEVELOPMENT CORPORATION
No 1 Hanxiang Road, Xitun District, Taichung, 407803, Taiwan
Tel.: (886) 427020001
Web Site: https://www.aidc.com.tw
Year Founded: 1969
2634—(TAI)
Rev.: $945,574,430
Assets: $1,335,351,874
Liabilities: $840,310,603
Net Worth: $495,041,272
Earnings: $50,881,187
Emp.: 5,407
Fiscal Year-end: 12/31/22
Aircrafts & Aircraft Engines & Parts Mfr
N.A.I.C.S.: 336411
Ho Paul (VP-Production)

Subsidiaries:

AIDC USA LLC   (1)
2999 North 44th St 514, Phoenix, AZ 85018
Tel.: (602) 535-5164
Aircraft Parts Distr
N.A.I.C.S.: 423860

AEROSPACE TECHNOLOGY OF KOREA, INC.
23-65 Gongdan 1-ro, Sanam-myeon, Sacheon, 52531, Gyeongnam-do, Korea (South)
Tel.: (82) 558507000
Web Site: https://www.astk.co.kr
Year Founded: 2001
067390—(KRS)
Rev.: $128,078,894
Assets: $309,283,143
Liabilities: $320,868,903
Net Worth: ($11,585,760)
Earnings: ($10,467,956)
Emp.: 250
Fiscal Year-end: 12/31/22
Aircraft Part Mfr
N.A.I.C.S.: 336413
Kim Hee Won (CEO)

AEROSTAR S.A.
No 9 Condorilor Street, 600302, Bacau, 600302, Romania
Tel.: (40) 234575070
Web Site: https://www.aerostar.ro
Year Founded: 1953
ARS—(BUC)
Rev.: $114,762,859
Assets: $160,702,062
Liabilities: $41,871,300
Net Worth: $118,830,762
Earnings: $20,027,988
Emp.: 1,876
Fiscal Year-end: 12/31/23

AEROSTAR S.A.—(Continued)

Aviation & Defense Systems Maintenance Services
N.A.I.C.S.: 488190
Doru Damaschin *(Vice Chm & Dir-Fin & Acctg)*

AEROSUN CORPORATION

No 188 Tianyuan Middle Road, Jiangning Economic and Technological Development Zone, Nanjing, 211100, Jiangsu, China
Tel.: (86) 2552826035
Web Site: http://www.aerosun.cn
Year Founded: 1999
600501—(SHG)
Rev.: $582,019,902
Assets: $884,671,758
Liabilities: $536,241,808
Net Worth: $348,429,950
Earnings: $10,629,221
Emp.: 2,490
Fiscal Year-end: 12/31/22
Automotive Products Mfr
N.A.I.C.S.: 336211
Zegang Deng *(Sec)*

Subsidiaries:

Chongqing Aerospace New Century Satellite Application Technology Co., Ltd. **(1)**
West Park Road No 98 Standard Plant Unit 1 01 2 502 Plant, Shapingba District, Chongqing, 401332, China **(93.07%)**
Tel.: (86) 2367463668
Aerospace Product & Parts Mfr
N.A.I.C.S.: 336411

AEROSVIT AIRLINES

58A T Chevchenko Blvd, 01032, Kiev, Ukraine
Tel.: (380) 444903490
Web Site: http://www.aerosvit.com
Year Founded: 1994
Sales Range: $150-199.9 Million
Emp.: 1,600
International Air Transportation Services
N.A.I.C.S.: 481111
Aron Mayberg *(Chm-Supervisory Bd)*

AEROWASH AB

Krickvagen 22, 80309, Gavle, Sweden
Tel.: (46) 840024000
Web Site: https://www.aerowash.com
Automated Washing Robot Mfr
N.A.I.C.S.: 333998
Niklas Adler *(CEO)*

AERTICKET AG

Boppstr 10, 10967, Berlin, Germany
Tel.: (49) 3069802144
Web Site: http://www.aerticket.de
Year Founded: 2002
Sales Range: $50-74.9 Million
Emp.: 430
Airline Ticket Commercial Whslr
N.A.I.C.S.: 425120
Rainer Klee *(Chm-Mgmt Bd)*

AERWINS TECHNOLOGIES INC.

Shibakoen Annex Bldg 6th Floor 1-8 Shibakoen 3-chome, Minato-ku, Tokyo, 105-0011, Japan
Tel.: (81) 364096761
Year Founded: 2021
AWIN—(NASDAQ)
Assets: $1,066,659
Liabilities: $19,547,304
Net Worth: ($18,480,645)
Earnings: ($9,516,032)
Emp.: 76
Fiscal Year-end: 12/31/23
Aircraft Mfr

N.A.I.C.S.: 336411
Katharyn Field *(Chm)*

Subsidiaries:

Aerwins Inc **(1)**
600 N Broad St Ste 5 No. 529, Middletown, DE 19709
Web Site: https://aerwins.us
Aircraft Mfr
N.A.I.C.S.: 336411

AES BRASIL ENERGIA SA

Av das Nacoes Unidas 12495 12o andar, Brooklin, Paulista, 04578-000, Sao Paulo, Brazil
Tel.: (55) 1141954927
Web Site: https://ri.aesbrasil.com.br
AESB3—(BRAZ)
Electric Power Distribution Services
N.A.I.C.S.: 221118

AESKU.DIAGNOSTICS GMBH & CO. KG

Mikroforum Ring 2, 55234, Wendelsheim, Germany
Tel.: (49) 673496220
Web Site: http://www.aesku.com
Year Founded: 2000
Scientific Research
N.A.I.C.S.: 541990
Torsten Matthias *(Mng Dir)*

Subsidiaries:

MBL International Corporation **(1)**
15A Constitution Way, Woburn, MA 01801
Tel.: (781) 939-6964
Web Site: http://www.mblintl.com
Biotechnology Research & Development Services
N.A.I.C.S.: 541714
Nalini Murdter *(Pres & CEO)*

AESO HOLDING LIMITED

The Pemberton 22-26 Bonham Strand 18/F, Sheung Wan, China (Hong Kong)
Tel.: (852) 3 971 0848
8341—(HKG)
Rev.: $16,128,820
Assets: $11,387,644
Liabilities: $8,882,208
Net Worth: $2,505,437
Earnings: ($729,253)
Emp.: 37
Fiscal Year-end: 03/31/21
Renovation Construction Services
N.A.I.C.S.: 236220
Siu Chung Chan *(Chm)*

AESSEAL PLC

Mill Close, Rotherham, S60 1BZ, United Kingdom
Tel.: (44) 1709369966
Web Site: https://www.aesseal.co.uk
Year Founded: 1979
Sales Range: $25-49.9 Million
Emp.: 1,700
Metal Products Mfr
N.A.I.C.S.: 332999
Chris Rea *(Founder & Mng Dir)*

Subsidiaries:

AESSEAL (M) Sdn Bhd **(1)**
No 9 Jalan MJ 13 Taman Industi Meranti Jaya, 47120, Puchong, Selangor, Malaysia
Tel.: (60) 380664778
Web Site: http://www.aesseal.com.my
Metal Seal Distr
N.A.I.C.S.: 423840
Ravi Kesavan *(Mgr-Sls)*

AESSEAL (Sweden) AB **(1)**
Virkesvagen 12, 120 30, Stockholm, Sweden
Tel.: (46) 855602870
Web Site: http://www.aesseal.se
Metal Seal Distr
N.A.I.C.S.: 423840

AESSEAL ARGENTINA SA **(1)**

Jose Ingenieros 4860 Munro, Vicente Lopez, B1605BHL, Buenos Aires, Argentina
Tel.: (54) 1147210875
Metal Seal Distr
N.A.I.C.S.: 423840

AESSEAL Australia Pty Ltd **(1)**
12 Counihan Road Seventeen Mile Rocks, Brisbane, 4073, QLD, Australia
Tel.: (61) 1800773454
Web Site: http://www.aesseal.com.au
Metal Seal Distr
N.A.I.C.S.: 423840

AESSEAL Benelux BV **(1)**
Nikkelstraat 27, 4823 AE, Breda, Netherlands
Tel.: (31) 765649292
Web Site: http://www.aesseal.nl
Metal Seal Distr
N.A.I.C.S.: 423840

AESSEAL Brasil Ltda **(1)**
Av Guido Caloi 1985 Galpao 3, 05802-140, Sao Paulo, Brazil
Tel.: (55) 1158915878
Metal Seal Distr
N.A.I.C.S.: 423840

AESSEAL Canada Inc. **(1)**
Unit 304 19292 60th Avenue, Surrey, V3S 3M2, BC, Canada
Tel.: (604) 535-7512
Web Site: http://www.aesseal.ca
Metal Seal Distr
N.A.I.C.S.: 423840

AESSEAL Caribbean Limited **(1)**
Corner Carli Bay Rd and Caspian Dr Point Lisas Industrial Estate, Couva, Trinidad & Tobago
Tel.: (868) 8684837881
Web Site: http://www.aesseal.tt
Metal Seal Distr
N.A.I.C.S.: 423840
Dallison Edghill *(Gen Mgr)*

AESSEAL Chile SA **(1)**
Santa Isabel 0962, Santiago, Chile
Tel.: (56) 2343022
Metal Seal Distr
N.A.I.C.S.: 423840

AESSEAL China Ltd. **(1)**
No 366 Jingu Zhonglu Yinzhou Investment & Business Incubation Centre, 315000, Ningbo, Zhejiang, China
Tel.: (86) 57488232888
Web Site: http://www.aesseal.com.cn
Metal Seal Distr
N.A.I.C.S.: 423840

AESSEAL Czech s.r.o. **(1)**
Turanka 115 South Moravian Region, 627 00, Brno, Czech Republic
Tel.: (420) 543212489
Web Site: http://www.aesseal.cz
Metal Seal Distr
N.A.I.C.S.: 423840

AESSEAL DANMARK A/S **(1)**
Kobenhavnsvej 222, 4600, Koge, Denmark
Tel.: (45) 56641400
Web Site: http://www.aesseal.dk
Metal Seal Distr
N.A.I.C.S.: 423840

AESSEAL Deutschland GmbH **(1)**
9 Heidigstrasse, 76709, Kronau, Baden-Wurttemberg, Germany
Tel.: (49) 72538090
Web Site: http://www.aesseal.de
Metal Seal Distr
N.A.I.C.S.: 423840

AESSEAL Finland Oy **(1)**
Korvenkylantie 10, PL 50, 40951, Muurame, Finland
Tel.: (358) 207417890
Web Site: http://www.aesseal.fi
Metal Seal Distr
N.A.I.C.S.: 423840
Tero Kaipio *(Reg Mgr)*

AESSEAL France SAS **(1)**
392 rue de l'Epinette ZA des monts de Flanders bat 5, 59850, Nieppe, France
Tel.: (33) 320172850
Web Site: http://www.aesseal.fr
Metal Seal Distr
N.A.I.C.S.: 423840

AESSEAL IBERICA S.L. **(1)**
Calle Plata 7 Poligon Industrial Riuclar, 43006, Tarragona, Spain
Tel.: (34) 977554330
Web Site: http://www.aesseal.es
Metal Seal Distr
N.A.I.C.S.: 423840

AESSEAL Inc. **(1)**
355 Dunavant Dr, Rockford, TN 37853
Tel.: (865) 531-0192
Web Site: http://www.aesseal.com
Metal Seal Mfr
N.A.I.C.S.: 339991

AESSEAL India Private Limited **(1)**
Gat No 85 At Post Varve Tal Bhor, 412 205, Pune, Maharashtra, India
Tel.: (91) 2113302222
Web Site: http://www.aesseal.in
Metal Seal Mfr
N.A.I.C.S.: 339991
Pankaj Raina *(Mgr-Sls)*

AESSEAL Italia s.r.l. **(1)**
17 B via Varese, 21013, Gallarate, Varese, Italy
Tel.: (39) 0331799952
Web Site: http://www.aesseal.it
Metal Seal Distr
N.A.I.C.S.: 423840
Roberto Stebini *(Gen Mgr)*

AESSEAL MEXICO S. DE R.L. DE C.V. **(1)**
5 de Mayo 26B, 54000, Tlalnepantla, Mexico
Tel.: (52) 5553845070
Metal Seal Distr
N.A.I.C.S.: 423840

AESSEAL Middle East FZE **(1)**
JAFZA Showrooms S3 B5 SR 08 Jebel Ali Free Zone, 263199, Dubai, United Arab Emirates
Tel.: (971) 48806868
Web Site: http://www.aesseal.ae
Metal Seal Distr
N.A.I.C.S.: 423840
Lee Canning *(Sr Engr-Sls)*

AESSEAL Norway AS **(1)**
Lilleakersveien 10 Lilleaker, Ullern, 0216, Oslo, Norway
Tel.: (47) 22736849
Web Site: http://www.aesseal.no
Metal Seal Distr
N.A.I.C.S.: 423840

AESSEAL PTY Ltd **(1)**
67 Loper Avenue Spartan Kempton Park, 1619, Johannesburg, Gauteng, South Africa
Tel.: (27) 114666500
Web Site: http://www.aesseal.co.za
Metal Seal Mfr
N.A.I.C.S.: 339991

AESSEAL Polska Sp. z o.o. **(1)**
Mazancowice 999, Mazancowice, 43-391, Bielsko-Biala, Poland
Tel.: (48) 334432300
Web Site: http://www.aesseal.pl
Metal Seal Distr
N.A.I.C.S.: 423840

AESSEAL Saudi Arabia Co. Ltd. **(1)**
Abu Ali Road, PO Box 2128, 31951, Jubail, Ash Sharqiyah, Saudi Arabia
Tel.: (966) 33617461
Metal Seal Distr
N.A.I.C.S.: 423840

AESSEAL TAIWAN CO., LTD **(1)**
1F No 53 Ting Chang Street, San Ming District Ren Wu, 80789, Kaohsiung, Taiwan
Tel.: (886) 73713990
Web Site: http://www.aesseal.tw
Metal Seal Distr
N.A.I.C.S.: 423840

AESSEAL Univeda LDA **(1)**
Estrada Consiglieri Pedroso 71 Fracco Q4 Queluz de Baixo, Barcarena, 2730-055, Queluz, Portugal
Tel.: (351) 217969212
Web Site: http://www.aesseal.pt
Metal Seal Distr
N.A.I.C.S.: 423840

AVT Reliability Ltd. **(1)**
Unit 2 Easter Court Europa Boulevard, War-

rington, WA5 7ZB, Cheshire, United Kingdom
Tel.: (44) 161 486 3737
Web Site: http://www.avtreliability.com
Pump Distr
N.A.I.C.S.: 423830

AVTPUMP ApS   (1)
Jegstrupvej 50B, 8361, Hasselager, Denmark
Tel.: (45) 70268805
Pump Distr
N.A.I.C.S.: 423830

Aesseal Colombia S.A.   (1)
La Castellana, 111 111, Bogota, Colombia
Tel.: (57) 15336182
Metal Seal Distr
N.A.I.C.S.: 423840

Aesseal Ireland Ltd   (1)
Units 13 & 14 Knockgriffin Ind Park, Middleton, Cork, Ireland
Tel.: (353) 214633477
Metal Seal Distr
N.A.I.C.S.: 423840
John Smiddy (Dir-Sls & Technical Support)

Aesseal sizdirmazlik sistemleri
tic.ltd.sti.   (1)
Yesilbaglar Mah Selvili sokak No 2 Helis Beyaz Ofis B, Pendik, Istanbul, Turkiye
Tel.: (90) 2163040237
Web Site: http://www.aesseal.com.tr
Metal Seal Distr
N.A.I.C.S.: 423840

AESTHETIC MEDICAL INTERNATIONAL HOLDINGS GROUP LIMITED

1122 Nanshan Boulevard, Nanshan District, Shenzhen, 518052, Guangdong, China
Tel.: (86) 75525598065   Ky
Web Site: https://ir.aihgroup.net
Year Founded: 1997
AIH—(NASDAQ)
Rev.: $102,664,642
Assets: $83,709,348
Liabilities: $102,995,423
Net Worth: ($19,286,075)
Earnings: ($11,660,200)
Emp.: 1,167
Fiscal Year-end: 12/31/22
Holding Company
N.A.I.C.S.: 551112
Pengwu Zhou (Co-Founder, Chm & CEO)

AETHER CATALYST SOLUTIONS, INC.

Unit 104 8337 Eastlake Drive, Burnaby, V5A 4W2, BC, Canada
Tel.: (604) 608-2886
Web Site: https://www.aethercatalyst.com
Year Founded: 2011
2QZ—(DEU)
Assets: $163,258
Liabilities: $115,105
Net Worth: $48,153
Earnings: ($396,341)
Fiscal Year-end: 12/31/22
Chemical Products Mfr
N.A.I.C.S.: 325998
Paul Woodward (Pres)

AETHER GLOBAL INNOVATIONS CORP.

Suite 700 - 1199 West Hastings Street, Vancouver, V6E 3T5, BC, Canada
Tel.: (604) 729-2500   BC
Web Site: https://aethergic.com
Year Founded: 2011
AETHF—(OTCIQ)
Assets: $172,358
Liabilities: $375,879
Net Worth: ($203,520)
Earnings: ($459,811)
Fiscal Year-end: 11/30/23

Investment Services
N.A.I.C.S.: 523999
Dana Wheeler (Pres & CEO)

AETHER INDUSTRIES LIMITED

Plot No 8203 Road No 8 GIDC Industrial Estate Sachin, Surat, 394230, Gujarat, India
Tel.: (91) 2616603000
Web Site: https://www.aether.co.in
Year Founded: 2013
543534—(BOM)
Rev.: $81,493,367
Assets: $105,081,113
Liabilities: $52,270,901
Net Worth: $52,810,212
Earnings: $14,868,809
Emp.: 719
Fiscal Year-end: 03/31/22
Pharmaceutical Product Mfr & Distr
N.A.I.C.S.: 325412

AETHERTEK TECHNOLOGY CO., LTD.

9F No 607 Ruiguang Rd, Neihu Dist, Taipei, Taiwan
Tel.: (886) 226582068
Web Site: https://www.aether-tek.com
3219—(TPE)
Rev.: $46,408,123
Assets: $64,490,761
Liabilities: $16,177,657
Net Worth: $48,313,104
Earnings: $6,157,584
Emp.: 500
Fiscal Year-end: 12/31/22
Electronic Products Mfr
N.A.I.C.S.: 337126
Jerry Chang (Chm & CEO)

AEVIS VICTORIA SA

Rue Georges-Jordil 4, 1700, Fribourg, Switzerland
Tel.: (41) 263500202
Web Site: https://www.aevis.com
Year Founded: 2002
AEVS—(SWX)
Rev.: $1,268,818,182
Assets: $1,985,283,814
Liabilities: $1,419,721,729
Net Worth: $565,562,084
Earnings: $65,201,774
Emp.: 3,902
Fiscal Year-end: 12/31/22
Investment Management Service
N.A.I.C.S.: 523999
Christian Wenger (Chm)

Subsidiaries:

AS Ambulances Services SA   (1)
rue du 31 Decembre 55, Geneva, 1207, Switzerland
Tel.: (41) 22 786 39 39
Web Site: http://www.asgge.ch
Emp.: 60
Ambulance Service
N.A.I.C.S.: 621910

Centre Medico-Chirurgical des Eaux-Vives SA   (1)
Rue du Nant 6, 1207, Geneva, Switzerland
Tel.: (41) 227374700
Web Site: https://www.swissmedical.net
Surgical Center Services
N.A.I.C.S.: 621493

Clinique Generale-Beaulieu SA   (1)
Chemin de Beau-Soleil 20, 1206, Geneva, Switzerland
Tel.: (41) 228395555
Web Site: https://www.swissmedical.net
Emp.: 385
Health Care Srvices
N.A.I.C.S.: 621999

Genolier Swiss Medical Network SA   (1)
Route du Muids 3, Case Postale, 1272, Genolier, Switzerland
Tel.: (41) 22 366 9990

Web Site: https://www.swissmedical.net
Medical Clinic Operator
N.A.I.C.S.: 622110

Grand Hotel Victoria-Jungfrau AG   (1)
Hoheweg 41-49, CH-3800, Interlaken, Switzerland
Tel.: (41) 338282828
Web Site: https://www.victoria-jungfrau.ch
Hotel Operator
N.A.I.C.S.: 721110
Mustafa Kattan (Asst Dir-Sls)

IRJB Institut de Radiologie du Jura Bernois SA   (1)
Fontenayes 17, 2610, Saint Imier, Switzerland
Tel.: (41) 32 942 2330
Web Site: https://www.irjb.ch
Radiology & Imaging Services
N.A.I.C.S.: 621512

Infracore SA   (1)
Rue Georges-Jordil 4, 1700, Fribourg, Switzerland
Tel.: (41) 26 350 0202
Web Site: https://www.infracore.ch
Real Estate Services
N.A.I.C.S.: 531390

Les Hauts de Genolier SA   (1)
Route du Muids 5, Case Postale 53, 1272, Genolier, Switzerland
Tel.: (41) 22 316 82 00
Web Site: http://www.leshautsdegenolier.ch
Health Care Srvices
N.A.I.C.S.: 623311
Valerie Dubois-Hequet (Gen Mgr)

Swiss Healthcare Properties AG   (1)
Zugerstrasse 74, 6340, Baar, Switzerland
Tel.: (41) 58 787 00 00
Web Site: http://www.shp.net
Real Estate Manangement Services
N.A.I.C.S.: 531390
Antoine Hubert (Chm)

Swiss Medical Centers Network S.A.   (1)
Raemistrasse 6, 8001, Zurich, Switzerland
Tel.: (41) 445555010
Web Site:
    https://www.swissmedicalcenter.com
Medical Healthcare Services
N.A.I.C.S.: 621498

Swiss Medical Network SA   (1)
Route du Muids 3, 1272, Genolier, Switzerland
Tel.: (41) 223669990
Hospital Operator
N.A.I.C.S.: 622110

VJC-Management AG   (1)
Hoheweg 41, 3800, Interlaken, Switzerland
Tel.: (41) 338282828
Web Site: http://www.vjc.ch
Hotel Operator
N.A.I.C.S.: 721110

Victoria-Jungfrau Collection AG   (1)
Hoheweg 41, 3800, Interlaken, Switzerland   (71.2%)
Tel.: (41) 33 828 2828
Web Site: https://www.victoria-jungfrau-
    collection.ch
Emp.: 200
Hotel
N.A.I.C.S.: 721110
Patrick Bachmann (Head-Fin)

AEVITAS, INC.

75 Wanless Court, Ayr, N0B 1E0, ON, Canada
Tel.: (519) 740-1333
Web Site: https://www.aevitas.ca
Year Founded: 1993
Emp.: 150
Waste Treatment & Disposal
N.A.I.C.S.: 562211
Tom Maxwell (Founder)

Subsidiaries:

Aevitas Specialty Services Corp.   (1)
663 Lycaste St, Detroit, MI 48214
Tel.: (313) 924-5175
Web Site: http://www.aevitas.us.com

Sales Range: $1-9.9 Million
Emp.: 25
Oil Recycling
N.A.I.C.S.: 423930
Robert T. Slater (Mgr-Indus Svcs)

AEW UK REIT PLC

Central Square 29 Wellington Street, Leeds, LS1 4DL, United Kingdom
Tel.: (44) 9522515
Web Site: https://www.aewukreit.com
Year Founded: 2015
AEWU—(LSE)
Rev.: $25,715,592
Assets: $288,456,462
Liabilities: $86,467,437
Net Worth: $201,989,025
Earnings: ($14,061,663)
Fiscal Year-end: 03/31/23
Real Estate Investment Trust Services
N.A.I.C.S.: 523991
Richard Tanner (Mng Dir)

AEWIN TECHNOLOGIES CO., LTD.

9F No 133 Sec 2 Datong Rd, Xizhi, New Taipei City, 22183, Taiwan
Tel.: (886) 286926677
Web Site: https://www.aewin.com
3564—(TPE)
Rev.: $77,017,040
Assets: $92,538,192
Liabilities: $52,542,038
Net Worth: $39,996,154
Earnings: $4,807,022
Fiscal Year-end: 12/31/22
Network Component Mfr & Distr
N.A.I.C.S.: 334210
Charles Lin (CEO)

Subsidiaries:

Aewin Tech Inc.   (1)
780 Montague Expy Ste 207, San Jose, CA 95131
Tel.: (408) 432-8008
Network Security Services
N.A.I.C.S.: 561621

AEXIS N.V.

392B Leuvensesteenweg, Brussels, 1932, Belgium
Tel.: (32) 27251644
Web Site: http://www.aexis.com
Sales Range: $25-49.9 Million
Emp.: 30
IT & Customer Service Management Solutions Distr, Supplier & Integrator
N.A.I.C.S.: 541512
Frank Peeters (Mng Dir)

Subsidiaries:

Aexis France   (1)
Immeuble Technologies 84-88 bd de la Mission Marchand, 92411, Courbevoie, France
Tel.: (33) 1 49 04 71 71
Web Site: http://www.aexis.fr
Information Technology Consulting Services
N.A.I.C.S.: 541512

Aexis Nederland   (1)
Plesmanstraat 2, 3833 LA, Leusden, Netherlands   (100%)
Tel.: (31) 334321540
Web Site: http://www.aexis.com
Sales Range: $25-49.9 Million
Emp.: 20
Business Intelligence Solutions
N.A.I.C.S.: 334610
David Witte (Mgr)

AF GRUPPEN ASA

Innspurten 15, 0663, Oslo, Norway
Tel.: (47) 22891100   NO
Web Site: http://www.afgruppen.com
Year Founded: 1985
AFG—(OSL)
Rev.: $2,882,412,710
Assets: $1,335,396,268

AF Gruppen ASA—(Continued)

Liabilities: $1,012,654,720
Net Worth: $322,741,548
Earnings: $106,318,123
Emp.: 5,975
Fiscal Year-end: 12/31/22
Civil Engineering Construction Services
N.A.I.C.S.: 237990
Sverre Haerem (CFO)

Subsidiaries:

AF AeronMollier AS (1)
Nulandsvika 8, 4405, Flekkefjord, Norway
Tel.: (47) 3 832 7800
Web Site: https://www.afgruppen.no
General Contracting Services
N.A.I.C.S.: 236220

AF Bygg Goteborg AB (1)
Theres Svenssons gata 9, S - 417 55,
Gothenburg, Sweden
Tel.: (46) 317624000
Construction Services
N.A.I.C.S.: 236220

AF Bygg Syd AB (1)
Tullkammarhuset Strandgatan 3, 302 50,
Halmstad, Sweden
Tel.: (46) 35 710 2000
Web Site: https://www.afgruppen.se
General Contracting Services
N.A.I.C.S.: 236220

AF Decom AS (1)
Innspurten 15, 0336, Oslo, Norway
Tel.: (47) 22891100
General Contracting Services
N.A.I.C.S.: 236220
Oyvind Omnes (Dir-Dept-South)

AF Energi & Miljoteknikk AS (1)
Innspurten 15, 0663, Oslo, Norway
Tel.: (47) 22891100
General Contracting Services
N.A.I.C.S.: 236220
Bjorn Stokkevag (Dir-Dept)

AF Energi og Miljo AS (1)
Innspurten 15, 0663, Oslo, Norway
Tel.: (47) 2 289 1100
Construction Services
N.A.I.C.S.: 236220

AF Energija Baltic UAB (1)
Savanoriu pr 276-208, LT-50200, Kaunas,
Lithuania
Tel.: (370) 52392300
Environmental Renewable Services
N.A.I.C.S.: 813312
Jurgita Stepsiene (Head-Engrg)

AF Gruppen Norge AS (1)
Innspurten 15, 0663, Oslo, Norway
Tel.: (47) 2 289 1100
Web Site: https://www.afgruppen.no
Civil Engineering Services
N.A.I.C.S.: 541330
Karin Engen (Officer-Grp Privacy)

AF Harnosand Byggreturer AB (1)
Saltvik 176, Alandsbro, 870 10, Harnosand,
Sweden
Tel.: (46) 611550590
Emp.: 50
Demolition Contracting Services
N.A.I.C.S.: 238910

Asane Byggmesterforretning AS (1)
Hesthaugveien 18, Ulset, 5119, Bergen,
Norway
Tel.: (47) 55393900
Web Site: https://www.aabf.no
Emp.: 130
Construction Services
N.A.I.C.S.: 236220

Bergbolaget I Gotaland AB (1)
Bockangsgatan 2, 571 38, Nassjo, Sweden
Tel.: (46) 38 055 5230
Web Site: https://www.bergbolaget.se
General Contracting Services
N.A.I.C.S.: 236220

Betonmast AS (1)
Schweigaardsgate 34 E, 0191, Oslo, Norway
Tel.: (47) 2 217 5480

Web Site: https://www.betonmast.no
Emp.: 700
General Contracting Services
N.A.I.C.S.: 236220

Betonmast Buskerud-Vestfold AS (1)
Horten Industripark Bygg 24 1 st Nedre vei
8, 3183, Horten, Norway
Tel.: (47) 22175480
General Contracting Services
N.A.I.C.S.: 236220

Betonmast Innlandet AS (1)
Ringvegen 16, 2816, Gjovik, Norway
Tel.: (47) 61168600
General Contracting Services
N.A.I.C.S.: 236220

Betonmast Ostfold AS (1)
Kalnesveien 1, 1712, Gralum, Norway
Tel.: (47) 22175480
General Contracting Services
N.A.I.C.S.: 236220

Betonmast Ringerike AS (1)
Verkstedveien 14, 3516, Honefoss, Norway
Tel.: (47) 22175480
General Contracting Services
N.A.I.C.S.: 236220

Betonmast Romerike AS (1)
Storgata 10 2nd floor, 2000, Lillestrom,
Norway
Tel.: (47) 22175480
General Contracting Services
N.A.I.C.S.: 236220

Betonmast Rosand AS (1)
Naeringsveien 18, 6530, Averoy, Norway
Tel.: (47) 71517900
General Contracting Services
N.A.I.C.S.: 236220

Betonmast Telemark AS (1)
Stromdaljordet 58, 3727, Skien, Norway
Tel.: (47) 35504850
General Contracting Services
N.A.I.C.S.: 236220

Betonmast Trondelag AS (1)
Falkenborgvegen 36 B, 7044, Trondheim,
Norway
Tel.: (47) 90980099
General Contracting Services
N.A.I.C.S.: 236220

Consolvo AS (1)
Ringveien 6, 3409, Tranby, Norway
Tel.: (47) 3 224 2060
Web Site: https://www.consolvo.no
General Contracting Services
N.A.I.C.S.: 236220

Eiqon AS (1)
Sankt Hallvardsvei 3, 3414, Lierstranda,
Norway
Tel.: (47) 40000074
Web Site: https://www.eiqon.no
Emp.: 330
Construction Services
N.A.I.C.S.: 236220

Fjerby AS (1)
Marenlundveien 6, 2020, Skedsmokorset,
Norway
Tel.: (47) 6 480 2650
Web Site: https://www.fjerby.no
Security System Services
N.A.I.C.S.: 561621

Fundamentering AS (1)
Lovasmyra 4, 7093, Tiller, Norway
Tel.: (47) 7 382 2630
Web Site: https://www.fas.no
Emp.: 80
General Contracting Services
N.A.I.C.S.: 236220

HMB Construction AB (1)
Kolonnvagen 7, 791 31, Falun, Sweden
Tel.: (46) 2 379 2030
Web Site: https://www.hmbcon.com
Emp.: 330
General Contracting Services
N.A.I.C.S.: 236220

HMB Construction Orebro AB (1)
Kolonnvagen 7, 791 31, Falun, Sweden
Tel.: (46) 2 379 2030
Web Site: https://www.hmbcon.com
Construction Services
N.A.I.C.S.: 236220

Haga & Berg Entreprenor AS (1)
Ryensvingen 1 4 etasje, 0680, Oslo, Norway
Tel.: (47) 2 271 7761
Web Site: https://www.hagaberg.no
General Contracting Services
N.A.I.C.S.: 236220

Helgesen Tekniske Bygg AS (1)
Reigstadvegen 1, 5281, Valestrandsfossen,
Norway
Tel.: (47) 56193400
Web Site: https://www.htb.no
Emp.: 72
Construction Services
N.A.I.C.S.: 236220

JR Anlegg AS (1)
Innspurten 15, 0663, Oslo, Norway
Tel.: (47) 2 289 1100
Web Site: https://www.jranlegg.no
Emp.: 34
Civil Engineering Services
N.A.I.C.S.: 541330

Jolsen Miljopark AS (1)
Jolsenveien 26, 2000, Lillestrom, Norway
Tel.: (47) 4 017 1755
Web Site: https://www.miljopark.no
Environmental Renewable Services
N.A.I.C.S.: 813312

Kanonaden Entreprenad AB (1)
Bockangsgatan 2, 571 38, Nassjo, Sweden
Tel.: (46) 380555250
Web Site: https://www.kanohaden.com
General Contracting Services
N.A.I.C.S.: 236220
Lennart Fransson (CFO)

Kirkestuen AS (1)
Nils Hansens vei 2C, 0666, Oslo, Norway
Tel.: (47) 4 812 2100
Web Site: https://www.kirkestuenas.no
General Contracting Services
N.A.I.C.S.: 236220

LAB Entreprenor AS (1)
Kanalveien 105 B, 5068, Bergen, Norway
Tel.: (47) 5 520 6200
Web Site: https://www.lab.no
General Contracting Services
N.A.I.C.S.: 236220

Lasse Holst AS (1)
Gressvikfloa 11, 1621, Gressvik, Norway
Tel.: (47) 69360300
Web Site: https://www.lasseholst.no
Construction Equipment Distr
N.A.I.C.S.: 423810

Mivent AS (1)
Nils Hansens vei 2c, 0666, Oslo, Norway
Tel.: (47) 40612827
Web Site: https://www.mivent.no
Construction Services
N.A.I.C.S.: 236220

Nes Miljopark AS (1)
Miljoparkvegen 112, Vormsund, 2160, Nes,
Norway
Tel.: (47) 90625322
General Contracting Services
N.A.I.C.S.: 236220

Oslo Brannsikring AS (1)
Tvetenveien 11, 0661, Oslo, Norway
Tel.: (47) 22884580
Web Site: https://www.oslobrannsikring.no
Emp.: 40
Construction Services
N.A.I.C.S.: 236220

Oslo Prosjektbygg AS (1)
Nils Hansens vei 2C, 0666, Oslo, Norway
Tel.: (47) 4 586 6290
Web Site: https://www.osloprosjektbygg.no
General Contracting Services
N.A.I.C.S.: 236220

Oslo Stillasutleie AS (1)
Nils Hansens vei 2C, 0666, Oslo, Norway
Tel.: (47) 2 325 3400
Web Site: https://www.oslostillasutleie.no
Scaffolding Rental Services
N.A.I.C.S.: 532490

Palmer Gotheim Skiferbrudd AS (1)
Vollalia, Oppdal, 7340, Roros, Norway
Tel.: (47) 7 240 0130
Web Site: https://www.palmergotheim.no

Civil Engineering Services
N.A.I.C.S.: 541330

Palplintar I Sverige AB (1)
Borrvagen 4, Nykvarn, 155 93, Stockholm,
Sweden
Tel.: (46) 855065050
Web Site: http://www.palplintar.se
Concrete Material Mfr
N.A.I.C.S.: 327390

Protector AS (1)
Ringveien 6, 3409, Tranby, Norway
Tel.: (47) 32220810
Web Site: https://www.protector-
technology.com
Information Technology Management Services
N.A.I.C.S.: 541519
Jan Eri (Mng Dir)

Protector KKS GmbH (1)
Robert- Bosch- Str 18, 71563, Affalterbach,
Germany
Tel.: (49) 7144888560
Web Site: https://www.protector-
technology.com
Information Technology Management Services
N.A.I.C.S.: 541519

Storo Blikkenslagerverksted AS (1)
Kakkelovnskroken 2, 0954, Oslo, Norway
Tel.: (47) 22154690
Web Site: https://www.blikkenslager.no
Emp.: 35
Plumbing & Roofing Services
N.A.I.C.S.: 238220

Strom Gundersen AS (1)
Papyrusveien 33, 3050, Mjondalen, Norway
Tel.: (47) 3 227 4350
Web Site: https://www.stromgundersen.no
General Contracting Services
N.A.I.C.S.: 236220

Strom Gundersen Vestfold AS (1)
Halfdan Wilhelmsens Alle 37, 3117, Tons-
berg, Norway
Tel.: (47) 9 969 1846
Web Site: https://www.sgvestfold.no
General Contracting Services
N.A.I.C.S.: 236220

TKC Prosjekt AS (1)
Nils Hansens vei 2C, 0666, Oslo, Norway
Tel.: (47) 97887745
Web Site: https://www.tkcprosjekt.no
Construction Services
N.A.I.C.S.: 236220

Thorendahl AS (1)
Nils Hansens vei 2C, 0666, Oslo, Norway
Tel.: (47) 2 325 3400
Web Site: https://www.thorendahl.no
General Contracting Services
N.A.I.C.S.: 236220

Vannmeisling AS (1)
Ringveien 6, 3409, Tranby, Norway
Tel.: (47) 9 705 8041
Web Site: https://www.vannmeisling.no
General Contracting Services
N.A.I.C.S.: 236220

AF LEGAL GROUP LTD. AU
Web Site:
https://www.australianlawyers.com
Year Founded: 2000
AFL—(ASX)
Rev.: $14,598,132
Assets: $15,831,448
Liabilities: $9,171,409
Net Worth: $6,660,039
Earnings: $1,068,384
Fiscal Year-end: 06/30/24
Holding Company; Family Lawyer &
Legal Services
N.A.I.C.S.: 551112
Chris McFadden (CEO)

AF1 CAPITAL CORP.
217 Queen Street West Suite 401,
Toronto, M5V 0R2, ON, Canada
Tel.: (416) 907-5644
Business Consulting Services
N.A.I.C.S.: 522299

Paul Norman *(Chm)*

AFAQ FOR ENERGY CO. PLC
Airport street Foreign Ministry, PO
Box 925988, Amman, 11110, Jordan
Tel.: (962) 65734030
Year Founded: 2008
MANE—(AMM)
Rev.: $869,967,588
Assets: $698,016,795
Liabilities: $514,927,452
Net Worth: $183,089,343
Earnings: ($15,441,503)
Fiscal Year-end: 12/31/20
Investment Management Service
N.A.I.C.S.: 523999
Yaser Almanaser *(Gen Mgr)*

**AFAQ HOLDING FOR INVEST-
MENT & REAL ESTATE DE-
VELOPMENT CO P.L.C.**
Amman-al jandaweel, PO Box 502,
Amman, 11623, Jordan
Tel.: (962) 65650902
MANR—(AMM)
Rev.: $46,993,175
Assets: $172,400,874
Liabilities: $101,065,427
Net Worth: $71,335,447
Earnings: ($27,457,766)
Emp.: 3
Fiscal Year-end: 12/31/20
Financial Investment Services
N.A.I.C.S.: 523999

AFARAK GROUP SE
Kaisaniemenkatu 4, 100, Helsinki,
Finland
Tel.: (358) 503721130
Web Site: https://www.afarak.com
AFAGR—(HEL)
Rev.: $214,430,175
Assets: $172,413,123
Net Worth: $113,087,632
Earnings: $51,367,365
Emp.: 600
Fiscal Year-end: 12/31/22
Mining & Mineral Production Services
N.A.I.C.S.: 212290
Thorstein Abrahamsen *(Chm)*

Subsidiaries:

Afarak South Africa (Pty) Ltd.   (1)
4th Floor 267 West Street, Centurion, South
Africa
Tel.: (27) 116683800
Chrome Mining & Minerals Mfr & Distr
N.A.I.C.S.: 333131

Afarak Trading Ltd.   (1)
2nd Floor Europa Centre John Lopez
street, Floriana, FRN 1400, Malta
Tel.: (356) 21221566
Chrome Mining & Minerals Distr
N.A.I.C.S.: 423520

Afarak doo   (1)
Koste Jovanovica No 76, 11000, Belgrade,
Serbia
Tel.: (381) 11 407 8160
Web Site: https://afarak.rs
Building Material & Refractory Material Mfr
N.A.I.C.S.: 327120

Elektrowerk Weisweiler GmbH   (1)
Durener Strasse, 52249, Eschweiler, Ger-
many
Web Site: https://www.elektrowerk.de
Sales Range: $25-49.9 Million
Emp.: 110
Electrometallurgical Product Mfr
N.A.I.C.S.: 331110
Christoph Schneider *(Mng Dir)*

Mogale Alloys (Pty) Ltd   (1)
Deep Shaft Road West Rand Consolidated
Mine, Krugersdorp, 1739, Gauteng, South
Africa
Tel.: (27) 116683800
Emp.: 300
Silico Manganese Mining Services

N.A.I.C.S.: 212290
Willem Smith *(Gen Mgr)*

Pohjolan Design-Talo Oy   (1)
Karhuojantie 2, 90460, Oulunsalo, Pohjois
Pohjanmaa, Finland
Tel.: (358) 207 463 940
Web Site: http://www.designtalo.fi
Residential Design & Building Services
N.A.I.C.S.: 236117

RCS Ltd   (1)
2nd Floor Europa Centre John Lopez
Street, Floriana, 1400, Malta
Tel.: (356) 27 030 462
Chemical Products Mfr
N.A.I.C.S.: 325998
Stefano Bonati *(Gen Mgr)*

Turk Maadin Sirketi A.S.   (1)
Barbaros Bulvari Eser Apt No 78/19 Bal-
mumcu, Besiktas, 34726, Istanbul, Turkiye
Tel.: (90) 2123475700
Web Site: https://www.turkmaadin.com
Sales Range: $200-249.9 Million
Emp.: 250
Mining of Chrome Ore
N.A.I.C.S.: 212210

AFAS ERP SOFTWARE B.V.
Philipsstraat 9, 3833 LC, Leusden,
Netherlands
Tel.: (31) 33 4341800
Web Site: http://www.afas.nl
Sales Range: $50-74.9 Million
Emp.: 350
Enterprise Resource Planning Soft-
ware Publisher
N.A.I.C.S.: 513210
Bas van der Veldt *(CEO)*

AFC AGRO BIOTECH LIMITED
House 87 89 Road 04 Block B Nike-
ton Gulshan 1, Dhaka, 1212, Bangla-
desh
Tel.: (880) 8836830   BD
Web Site:
     https://www.afcagrobiotech.com
Year Founded: 2010
AFCAGRO—(CHT)
Rev.: $8,141,817
Assets: $29,653,305
Liabilities: $5,339,331
Net Worth: $24,313,973
Earnings: $297,336
Fiscal Year-end: 06/30/22
Pharmaceuticals Product Mfr
N.A.I.C.S.: 325412
A. B. M. Ghulam Mostafa *(Chm)*

AFC AJAX NV
Johan Cruijff Boulevard 29, PO Box
12522, 1101 AX, Amsterdam, Nether-
lands
Tel.: (31) 881831900
Web Site: https://www.ajax.nl
AJAX—(EUR)
Rev.: $228,180,386
Earnings: $59,171,688
Emp.: 284
Fiscal Year-end: 06/30/19
Soccer Team Owner & Operator
N.A.I.C.S.: 711219

AFC ENERGY PLC
Unit 71 4 Dunsfold Park Stovolds Hill,
Cranleigh, GU6 8TB, Surrey, United
Kingdom
Tel.: (44) 1483276726   UK
Web Site: https://www.afcenergy.com
Year Founded: 2006
AFC—(AIM)
Rev.: $790,193
Assets: $68,807,892
Liabilities: $6,708,495
Net Worth: $62,099,397
Earnings: ($22,329,063)
Emp.: 84
Fiscal Year-end: 10/31/22
Fuel Cell Producer & Marketer
N.A.I.C.S.: 457210

Adam Bond *(CEO)*

**AFC-HD AMS LIFE SCIENCE
CO., LTD.**
3-6-36 Toyoda, Suruga-ku, Shizuoka,
422-8027, Japan
Tel.: (81) 542810585
Web Site: https://www.ams-life.co.jp
Year Founded: 1969
2927—(TKS)
Rev.: $187,750,700
Assets: $292,526,600
Liabilities: $205,707,840
Net Worth: $86,818,760
Earnings: $7,787,440
Fiscal Year-end: 08/31/24
Pharmaceuticals Mfr
N.A.I.C.S.: 325412
Tadahiko Asayama *(Chm)*

Subsidiaries:

Nihon Preventive Medical Laboratory
Co., Ltd.   (1)
3-6-36 Toyoda, Suruga Ward, Shizuoka,
Japan
Tel.: (81) 542815154
Web Site: https://www.nyk-labo.com
Medical Research Services
N.A.I.C.S.: 541714

AFCON HOLDINGS LTD.
4 HaTavor Alley, Petah Tikva,
4969104, Israel
Tel.: (972) 732001333
Web Site: https://www.afcon.co.il
Year Founded: 1949
AFHL—(TAE)
Rev.: $584,216,962
Assets: $505,278,727
Liabilities: $376,421,561
Net Worth: $128,857,166
Earnings: ($2,366,195)
Emp.: 1,300
Fiscal Year-end: 09/30/23
Industrial Automation Mfr
N.A.I.C.S.: 333998
Yaron Karisi *(CEO)*

AFENTRA PLC
High Holborn House 52-54 High Hol-
born, London, WC1V 6RL, United
Kingdom
Tel.: (44) 2074054133   UK
Web Site: https://afentraplc.com
Year Founded: 1983
AET—(AIM)
Rev.: $86,000
Assets: $52,867,000
Liabilities: $3,059,000
Net Worth: $49,808,000
Earnings: ($9,086,000)
Emp.: 10
Fiscal Year-end: 12/31/22
Oil & Gas Energy Services
N.A.I.C.S.: 213112
David Marshall *(CEO)*

Subsidiaries:

Sterling Energy (UK) Limited   (1)
52-54 High Holborn, London, WC1V 6RB,
United Kingdom
Tel.: (44) 20 7405 4133
Web Site: http://www.sterlingenergyuk.com
Sales Range: $50-74.9 Million
Oil & Gas Exploration Services
N.A.I.C.S.: 211120

AFERIAN PLC
Botanic House 100 Hills Road, Cam-
bridge, CB2 1PH, United Kingdom
Tel.: (44) 1223598197
Web Site: https://aferian.com
AFRN—(LSE)
Rev.: $47,821,000
Assets: $52,016,000
Liabilities: $29,719,000
Net Worth: $22,297,000
Earnings: ($63,502,000)

Emp.: 169
Fiscal Year-end: 11/30/23
Electronic Systems Design & Soft-
ware Services
N.A.I.C.S.: 334419
Donald Kevin McGarva *(CEO-Grp)*

Subsidiaries:

24i Media USA LLC   (1)
1633 Bayshore Hwy Ste 338, Burlingame,
CA 94010
Tel.: (408) 861-1400
Web Site: https://www.24i.com
Computer Programming Services
N.A.I.C.S.: 541511

Amino Communications AB   (1)
Finlandsgatan 40, SE 164 74, Kista, Swe-
den
Tel.: (46) 856251600
Sales Range: $25-49.9 Million
Emp.: 40
Digital Entertainment Services
N.A.I.C.S.: 334112

Amino Communications Limited   (1)
1010 Cambourne Business Park, Cam-
bourne, Cambridge, CB23 6DP, United
Kingdom
Tel.: (44) 1223641990
Web Site: http://www.amino.tv
Sales Range: $25-49.9 Million
Emp.: 90
Internet TV & In Home Multimedia Distribu-
tion Services
N.A.I.C.S.: 517121
Jamie Mackinlay *(Sr VP-Sls & Mktg-Global)*

Mautilus s.r.o.   (1)
U Vodarny 3032/2a, 616 00, Brno, Czech
Republic
Tel.: (420) 51 111 6550
Web Site: https://www.mautilus.com
Software Development Services
N.A.I.C.S.: 541511
Rehor Vykoupil *(CEO)*

AFFCO HOLDINGS LIMITED
Great South Road, Private Bag 3301,
Hamilton, Horotiu, New Zealand
Tel.: (64) 78292888
Web Site: http://www.affco.co.nz
Year Founded: 1904
Sales Range: $500-549.9 Million
Emp.: 24
Meat & Associated Products Proces-
sor & Marketer
N.A.I.C.S.: 445240
Sam Lewis *(Chm)*

Subsidiaries:

AFFCO Europe Limited   (1)
3rd Fl Intl House Dover Pl, Ashford, TN23
1HU, Kent, United Kingdom   (100%)
Tel.: (44) 1233640728
Web Site: http://www.affco.co.nz
Sales Range: $25-49.9 Million
Emp.: 2
Meat Markets
N.A.I.C.S.: 445240
Stephen Clapham *(Mgr)*

AFFCO Holdings Limited - Moerewa
Plant   (1)
Main Road, Moerewa, New Zealand
Tel.: (64) 94040082
Meat Processing Services
N.A.I.C.S.: 311612
Christian Prime *(Plant Mgr)*

AFFCO Holdings Limited Horotiu
Plant   (1)
Great South Road, Hamilton, New Zealand
Tel.: (64) 78299500
Meat Processing Services
N.A.I.C.S.: 311612
Rebecca Ogg *(Plant Mgr)*

AFFCO Holdings Limited Imlay
Plant   (1)
Imlay Place, Wanganui, New Zealand
Tel.: (64) 63492400
Meat Processing Services
N.A.I.C.S.: 311612
Troy Lambly *(Plant Mgr)*

AFFCO Holdings Limited—(Continued)

AFFCO Holdings Limited Invercargill Plant (1)
Kekeno Place Awarua, Invercargill, New Zealand
Tel.: (64) 32183617
Meat Processing Services
N.A.I.C.S.: 311612
Kevin Hamilton *(Plant Mgr)*

AFFCO Holdings Limited Malvern Plant (1)
Two Chain Road, Burnham, Christchurch, New Zealand
Tel.: (64) 33476681
Meat Processing Services
N.A.I.C.S.: 311612
Dean Burgess *(Plant Mgr)*

AFFCO Holdings Limited Manawatu Plant (1)
Campbell Road, Feilding, New Zealand
Tel.: (64) 63234199
Meat Processing Services
N.A.I.C.S.: 311612
Ann Nuku *(Plant Mgr)*

AFFCO Holdings Limited Rangiuru Plant (1)
State Highway 2, Te Puke, New Zealand
Tel.: (64) 75730034
Meat Processing Services
N.A.I.C.S.: 311612
Kevin Casey *(Plant Mgr)*

AFFCO Holdings Limited Wairoa Plant (1)
Brown Street, Wairoa, New Zealand
Tel.: (64) 68388139
Meat Processing Services
N.A.I.C.S.: 311612
Dean Tucker *(Plant Mgr)*

AFFCO Holdings Limited Wanganui Plant (1)
47 Bryce Street, Wanganui, New Zealand
Tel.: (64) 63490038
Meat Processing Services
N.A.I.C.S.: 311612
John Fitness *(Plant Mgr)*

AFFCO New Zealand Limited
Imlay Place Gonville, PO box 425, Wanganui, New Zealand (100%)
Tel.: (64) 63445179
Web Site: http://www.AFFCO.com
Sales Range: $200-249.9 Million
Meat Markets
N.A.I.C.S.: 445240

Land Meat New Zealand Limited (1)
Great S Rd Horotiu, Private Bag 3301, Hamilton, 3240, New Zealand (100%)
Tel.: (64) 78292888
Web Site: http://www.affco.co.nz
Sales Range: $50-74.9 Million
Emp.: 75
Meat & Meat Product Whslr
N.A.I.C.S.: 424470

South Pacific Meats Limited (1)
86 Kekeno Pl Awarua, 1774, Invercargill, New Zealand (70%)
Tel.: (64) 32183617
Web Site: http://www.affco.com
Sales Range: $250-299.9 Million
Livestock Whslr
N.A.I.C.S.: 424520
Kevin Hamilton *(Plant Mgr)*

AFFICHAGE ROMANIA SRL
Str Biharia Nr 67-77 Corp G Et 1, Metav Business Park, Bucharest, Romania
Tel.: (40) 213128313
Web Site: http://www.affichage.ro
Sales Range: $25-49.9 Million
Emp.: 30
Advertising Agencies
N.A.I.C.S.: 541810
Rene Rosanbarg *(Pres & CEO)*

AFFIMED N.V.
Gottlieb-Daimler Strasse 2, 68165, Mannheim, Germany
Tel.: (49) 621560030   NL

Web Site: https://www.affimed.com
AFMD—(NASDAQ)
Rev.: $8,930,499
Assets: $104,853,227
Liabilities: $42,467,084
Net Worth: $62,386,143
Earnings: ($114,329,808)
Emp.: 76
Fiscal Year-end: 12/31/23
Biopharmaceutical Mfr
N.A.I.C.S.: 325412
Adi Hoess *(CEO)*

Subsidiaries:

Affimed GmbH (1)
Im Neuenheimer Feld 582, Technologiepark, 69120, Heidelberg, Germany
Tel.: (49) 6221674360
Web Site: https://www.affimed.com
Medical Devices
N.A.I.C.S.: 621999
Adi Hoess *(CEO)*

Amphivena Therapeutics Inc. (1)
2 Tower Pl Ste 1000, South San Francisco, CA 94080
Tel.: (650) 499-3178
Web Site: http://www.amphivena.com
Medical Devices
N.A.I.C.S.: 621999
Curtis Ruegg *(Pres & CEO)*

AFFIN HOLDINGS BERHAD
17th Floor Menara AFFIN 80 Jalan Raja Chulan, 50200, Kuala Lumpur, Malaysia
Tel.: (60) 3 2055 9000
Web Site: http://www.affin.com.my
Rev.: $582,932,705
Assets: $17,236,864,432
Liabilities: $15,186,232,061
Net Worth: $2,050,632,371
Earnings: $104,500,880
Emp.: 166,000
Fiscal Year-end: 12/31/17
Commercial Banking Services
N.A.I.C.S.: 523150
Nimma Safira Khalid *(Chief Legal Officer & Sec)*

Subsidiaries:

AFFIN Moneybrokers Sdn. Bhd. (1)
25th Floor Menara Boustead Jalan Raja Chulan, 50200, Kuala Lumpur, Federal Territory, Malaysia
Tel.: (60) 321489222
Web Site: http://www.affinmoneybrokers.com.my
Sales Range: $50-74.9 Million
Emp.: 46
Money Broking Services
N.A.I.C.S.: 523160
Soon Kim Lim *(Gen Mgr)*

Affin Hwang Asset Management Berhad (1)
Suite 12-03 12th Floor Menara Keck Seng, 203 Jalan Bukit Bintang, 55100, Kuala Lumpur, Federal Territory, Malaysia (53%)
Tel.: (60) 321421881
Web Site: http://www.affinhwang.com
Sales Range: $100-124.9 Million
Emp.: 200
Investment Management Service
N.A.I.C.S.: 523999
Chee Wai Teng *(Mng Dir)*

Affin Hwang Futures Sdn. Bhd. (1)
20th Floor Plaza Masalam 2 Jalan Tengku Ampuan, Zabedah E9/E Section 9, 40100, Shah Alam, Selangor, Malaysia (100%)
Tel.: (60) 355193398
Web Site: http://www.affinhwang.com
Sales Range: $50-74.9 Million
Emp.: 20
Financial Futures Brokerage Services
N.A.I.C.S.: 523150
Serene Sit *(Gen Mgr)*

Affin Hwang Investment Bank Berhad (1)
Levels 2-5 7 & 8 Wisma Sri Pinang I & II, 60 Green Hall/42 Green Hall, 10200, Pen-

ang, Malaysia (100%)
Tel.: (60) 42636996
Web Site: http://www.affinhwang.com
Sales Range: $100-124.9 Million
Emp.: 200
Investment Banking & Stock Broking Services
N.A.I.C.S.: 523150
Keong Si Hark *(Head-Ops)*

AFFINAGE CHAMPAGNE ARDENNES
19 Route De Bazancourt, 51110, Isles-sur-Suippe, Marne, France
Tel.: (33) 326038060
Web Site: http://www.afica.fr
Rev.: $32,500,000
Emp.: 53
Copper Alloy Producer from Recycling Metals
N.A.I.C.S.: 212230
Eric Rousseaux *(Mng Dir)*

AFFINE S.A.
39 Rue Washington, 75008, Paris, France
Tel.: (33) 1 44 90 43 00   FR
Web Site: http://www.affine.fr
Rev.: $40,479,283
Assets: $1,000,748,543
Liabilities: $630,255,237
Net Worth: $370,493,307
Earnings: $8,581,469
Emp.: 36
Fiscal Year-end: 12/31/17
Commercial Property Investment & Management Services
N.A.I.C.S.: 531120
Alain Chaussard *(Vice Chm)*

AFFINITY ENERGY AND HEALTH LIMITED
Unit 2 100 Railway Road, Subiaco, Perth, 6008, WA, Australia
Tel.: (61) 8 93806790
Web Site: http://www.affinityenergy.com.au
Rev.: $93,239
Assets: $8,242,123
Liabilities: $4,798,791
Net Worth: $3,443,331
Earnings: $6,190,772
Fiscal Year-end: 06/30/18
Alternative Energy Researcher & Developer
N.A.I.C.S.: 541715
Bill Lee *(Sec)*

AFFINITY EQUITY PARTNERS (HK) LTD.
Suite 4002 40th Floor One Exchange Square 8 Connaught Place, Central, Hong Kong, China (Hong Kong)
Tel.: (852) 31028329   HK
Web Site: http://www.affinityequity.com
Privater Equity Firm
N.A.I.C.S.: 523999
Kok-Yew Tang *(Chm & Mng Partner)*

Subsidiaries:

Affinity Equity Partners (Australia) Pty. Ltd. (1)
Level 30 363 George Street, Sydney, 2000, NSW, Australia
Tel.: (61) 292990889
Web Site: http://www.affinityequity.com
Privater Equity Firm
N.A.I.C.S.: 523999
Brett Sutton *(Pres & Partner)*

Holding (Domestic):

Health Communication Network Pty Limited (2)
72 Christie Street, Saint Leonards, 2065, NSW, Australia
Tel.: (61) 2 9906 6633
Web Site: http://www.medicaldirector.com

Emp.: 200
Medical Software Development Services
N.A.I.C.S.: 541511

Holding (Non-US):

Tegel Foods Limited (2)
Level 3 100 Carlton Gore Road New Market, Private Bag 99-927, Newmarket, Auckland, 1023, New Zealand
Tel.: (64) 99779000
Web Site: http://www.togel.co.nz
Sales Range: $300-349.9 Million
Emp.: 1,550
Breeding, Hatching, Processing, Marketing & Distribution of Poultry Products; Animal Feed & Animal Health Products
N.A.I.C.S.: 112320
Phil Hand *(CEO)*

Affinity Equity Partners (S) Pte Ltd (1)
8 Temasek Boulevard 28-03 Suntec Tower 3, Singapore, 038 988, Singapore
Tel.: (65) 6238 2260
Investment Management Service
N.A.I.C.S.: 523940
Jeanne Stampe *(VP)*

Affinity Equity Partners Beijing Limited Liability Company (1)
Room 1506 Tower H Phoenix Place No 5 Jia ShuGuangXiLi, Chaoyang District, Beijing, 100028, China
Tel.: (86) 10 5638 3380
Investment Management Service
N.A.I.C.S.: 523940

Affinity Equity Partners Korea LLC (1)
22nd Fl Young Poong Bldg 41, Cheonggyecheon-ro, Jongro, Korea (South)
Tel.: (82) 8223808800
Web Site: https://www.affinityequity.com
Privater Equity Firm
N.A.I.C.S.: 523999
Min Byung-chul *(Mng Dir)*

Subsidiary (Domestic):

SK Rent A Car Co., Ltd. (2)
822 Seobusaet-gi, Guro-gu, Seoul, Korea (South)
Tel.: (82) 15441600
Web Site: http://www.skcarrental.com
Rev.: $956,075,844
Assets: $2,563,291,388
Liabilities: $2,167,261,433
Net Worth: $396,029,955
Earnings: $15,907,667
Emp.: 652
Fiscal Year-end: 12/31/2022
Car Rental Services
N.A.I.C.S.: 532111
Mong Ju Hyeon *(CEO)*

PT Affinity Equity Partners Indonesia (1)
The Energy Building 10th Floor SCBD Lot 11A Jl Jend Sudirman Kav 52-53, Jakarta, 12190, Indonesia
Tel.: (62) 21 2995 1665
Investment Management Service
N.A.I.C.S.: 523940

SERVEONE Co., Ltd. (1)
150 Ang Gyeongseo Building, Gangseo-gu, Seoul, Gangseo-gu, Korea (South) (60.1%)
Tel.: (82) 804538585
Web Site: http://www.serveone.co.kr
Construction & Facility Management
N.A.I.C.S.: 236220
Park Kyusok *(CEO)*

Subsidiary (Non-US):

Serveone Construction (NanJing) Co., Ltd (2)
No 1 LG Road LG Industrial Park Economy & Technical Devolpement Zone, Nanjing, 210046, China
Tel.: (86) 2585598572
Construction Engineering Services
N.A.I.C.S.: 541330

AFFINITY METALS CORP.
600 890 West Pender St, Vancouver, V6C 1J9, BC, Canada
Tel.: (604) 227-3554

Web Site: https://affinitymetals.ca
Year Founded: 1978
AFF—(TSXV)
Assets: $1,532,882
Liabilities: $695,641
Net Worth: $837,241
Earnings: ($423,561)
Fiscal Year-end: 06/30/24
Gold, Silver & Other Precious Metals
Mining Services
N.A.I.C.S.: 212220
Robert N. Edwards (Pres & CEO)

AFFINOR GROWERS INC.

4th Floor 595 Howe St, Vancouver,
V6C 2T5, BC, Canada
Tel.: (604) 356-0411　　　　Ca
Web Site:
　　https://www.affinorgrowers.com
AFI—(OTCIQ)
Assets: $1,387,012
Liabilities: $534,835
Net Worth: $852,177
Earnings: ($799,379)
Fiscal Year-end: 05/31/21
Vegetable & Medical Marijuana Pro-
ducer
N.A.I.C.S.: 325411
Nick Brusatore (CEO)

AFFIRMA CAPITAL LIMITED

6 Battery Road #29-04, Singapore,
049909, Singapore
Tel.: (65) 6500 7920　　　　Ky
Web Site: http://affirmacapital.com
Year Founded: 2019
Holding Company; Private Equity In-
vestment & Management Services
N.A.I.C.S.: 551112
Nainesh Jaisingh (Founding Partner
& CEO-Southeast Asia)

Subsidiaries:

Affirma Capital Managers (Singapore)
Pte. Ltd.　　　　　　　　　　(1)
6 Battery Road #29-04, Singapore, 049909,
Singapore
Tel.: (65) 6500 7920
Web Site: http://affirmacapital.com
Privater Equity Firm
N.A.I.C.S.: 523999
Nainesh Jaisingh (Founding Partner &
CEO)

Coffee Day Enterprises Limited　(1)
No 165 R V Road Near Minerva Circle,
Bengaluru, 560004, India
Tel.: (91) 8067212345
Web Site: https://www.coffeeday.com
Rev.: $362,135,865
Assets: $1,300,619,775
Liabilities: $626,648,295
Net Worth: $673,971,480
Earnings: $252,321,615
Emp.: 197
Fiscal Year-end: 03/31/2020
Holding Company; Coffee Shops Operator,
Commercial Coffee Dispensing Equipment
Mfr & Related Products Distr
N.A.I.C.S.: 551112
S. V. Ranganath (Chm-Interim)

Subsidiary (Domestic):

Coffee Day Global Limited　　(2)
23/2 Coffee Day Square Vittal Mallya Road,
Bengaluru, 560001, India
Tel.: (91) 80 4001 2345
Web Site: http://www.coffeeday.com
Coffee Shops Operator, Commercial Coffee
Dispensing Equipment Mfr & Related Prod-
ucts Distr
N.A.I.C.S.: 722515
V. G. Siddhartha (Founder, Chm & Mng Dir)

Division (Domestic):

Coffee Day Global Ltd. - Cafe Coffee
Day Division　　　　　　　　(3)
23/2 Coffee Day Square Vittal Mallya Road,
Bengaluru, 560001, India
Tel.: (91) 80 4001 2345
Web Site: http://www.cafecoffeeday.com

Coffeeshop Operator
N.A.I.C.S.: 722515
A. Venu Madhav (CEO)

Coffee Day Global Ltd. - Exports
Division　　　　　　　　　　(3)
23/2 Coffee Day Square Vittal Mallya Road,
Bengaluru, 560001, India
Tel.: (91) 80 4001 2345
Web Site: http://www.coffeedayexport.com
Coffee Bean Whslr
N.A.I.C.S.: 424590
Rajeev Gupta (Pres)

Coffee Day Global Ltd. - Fresh &
Ground Division　　　　　　　(3)
2/23 12th Cross Swimming Pool Extn,
Malleshwaram, Bengaluru, 560003, India
Tel.: (91) 80 2331 5458
Web Site: http://www.coffeedayfng.com
Coffee Mfr & Distr
N.A.I.C.S.: 311920
C. J. Jayanth (Pres)

Coffee Day Global Ltd. - Vending
Division　　　　　　　　　　(3)
23/2 Coffee Day Square Vittal Mallya Road,
Bengaluru, 560001, India
Tel.: (91) 80 4001 2345
Web Site:
　　http://www.coffeedaybeverages.com
Commercial Coffee Vending Machines Mfr
& Distr
N.A.I.C.S.: 333310
Shankar Narayan (Pres)

Endurance Technologies Limited　(1)
E-92 MIDC Industrial Area Waluj, Aurang-
abad, 431136, Maharashtra, India
Tel.: (91) 2402569600
Web Site: https://www.endurancegroup.com
Rev.: $897,860,282
Assets: $784,540,439
Liabilities: $298,308,192
Net Worth: $486,232,247
Earnings: $70,921,169
Emp.: 3,800
Fiscal Year-end: 03/31/2021
Automotive Components Mfr
N.A.I.C.S.: 336330
Anurang Jain (Mng Dir)

Subsidiary (Non-US):

Endurance Amann GmbH　　　(2)
Jahnstrasse 19, 74252, Massenbach-
hausen, Germany
Tel.: (49) 71389900
Web Site: http://www.amann-druckguss.de
Emp.: 232
Aluminium Die Casting Products Mfr
N.A.I.C.S.: 331523
Francesco Endurance (Mng Dir)

Endurance Overseas S.r.l.　　(2)
Via Arsenale 33, 10121, Turin, Italy
Tel.: (39) 011 5168111
Web Site:
　　http://www.enduranceoverseas.com
Emp.: 13
Holding Company
N.A.I.C.S.: 551112
Massimo Venuti (CEO)

Subsidiary (Domestic):

Endurance Engineering S.r.l.　(3)
Strada Del Cascinotto 135/A, 10156, Turin,
Italy
Tel.: (39) 011 2234910
Emp.: 69
Automotive Plastic Parts Mfr
N.A.I.C.S.: 326199
Samuele Gabutto (CEO)

Endurance F.O.A. S.p.A.　　　(3)
Via Regione Pozzo 26 Torino, 10034, Chi-
vasso, Italy
Tel.: (39) 011 9592455
Emp.: 190
Aluminium Die Casting Products Mfr
N.A.I.C.S.: 331523
Giovanni Anastasi (CEO)

Endurance Fondalmec S.p.A.　(3)
Via Del Boschetto 2/43 Lombardore, 10040,
Turin, Italy
Tel.: (39) 011 9958711
Emp.: 221
Machining Component Mfr

N.A.I.C.S.: 332710
Giovanni Anastasi (CEO)

Smoothies Korea Inc.　　　　(1)
13-17 Yeoeuido-dong, Yeongdeungpo-gu,
Seoul, 150-870, Korea (South)
Tel.: (82) 2 786 2100
Web Site: http://www.smoothieking.co.kr
Fruit Juice Bar Operator & Franchisor
N.A.I.C.S.: 722515
Sungwan Kim (CEO)

Subsidiary (US):

Smoothie King Co., Inc.　　　(2)
1412 N Hwy 190, Covington, LA 70433
Tel.: (985) 809-9722
Web Site: http://locations.smoothieking.com
Holding Company; Fruit Juice Bar & Nutri-
tional Supplement Store Franchisor & Op-
erator
N.A.I.C.S.: 551112
Rebecca Miller (Head-Field Mktg)

Subsidiary (Domestic):

Smoothie King Franchises, Inc.　(3)
121 Park Pl, Covington, LA 70433
Tel.: (985) 635-6973
Web Site:
　　http://www.smoothiekingfranchise.com
Sales Range: $1-9.9 Million
Emp.: 45
Fruit Juice Bar & Nutritional Supplement
Store Franchisor
N.A.I.C.S.: 533110
Steve Kuhnau (Co-Founder & CEO)

Tat Hong Holdings Ltd.　　　(1)
82 Ubi Avenue 4 #05-01 Edward Boustead
Centre, Singapore, 408832, Singapore
Tel.: (65) 6709 0300
Web Site: http://www.tathong.com
Holding Company; Cranes & Other Heavy
Equipment Rental Services & Sales
N.A.I.C.S.: 551112
Michael Sang Kuey Ng (CEO-ASEAN II)

Subsidiary (Non-US):

PT Tatindo HeavyEquipment　(2)
Jl Raya Cakung Cilincing No 200 KM 3 5,
Jakarta Timur, Jakarta, 13910, Indonesia
Tel.: (62) 21160825373
Web Site: http://www.tathong.com
Heavy Equipment Distr
N.A.I.C.S.: 423830

Shanghai Tat Hong Equipment Rental
Co., Ltd.　　　　　　　　　(2)
Floor 4 Building D Synnex Plaza No 1086
Tianshan West Rd, Changning District,
Shanghai, China
Tel.: (86) 2160825373
Web Site: http://www.tathong.com
Construction Equipment Rental Services
N.A.I.C.S.: 532412

Subsidiary (Domestic):

Tat Hong (V.N.) Pte Ltd　　　(2)
82 Ubi Avenue 4 05-03 Edward Bousted
Centre, Singapore, 408832, Singapore
Tel.: (65) 62690022
Investment Management Service
N.A.I.C.S.: 523999

Subsidiary (Non-US):

Tat Hong (Vietnam) Co., Ltd.　(3)
11/1 Nguyen Van MAi Street, Ward 4 Tan
Binh District, Ho Chi Minh City, Vietnam
Tel.: (84) 2838113101
Construction Equipment Rental Services
N.A.I.C.S.: 532412

Subsidiary (Non-US):

Tat Hong Equipment (China) Pte.
Ltd.　　　　　　　　　　　(2)
Floor 4 Building D Synnex Plaza No 1068
Tianshan West Rd, Changning District,
Shanghai, China
Tel.: (86) 2160825373
Web Site: http://www.tathong.com
Investment Management Service
N.A.I.C.S.: 523999

Subsidiary (Domestic):

Tat Hong Equipment Service Co.,
Ltd.　　　　　　　　　　　(3)

Level 4 Block D 1068 TianShan West Road,
Shanghai, 200335, China
Tel.: (86) 21 6082 5373
Web Site: http://www.tathongchina.com
Construction Management Services
N.A.I.C.S.: 236116
Kok San Yau (CEO)

Subsidiary (Domestic):

Tat Hong Heavy Equipment (Pte.)
Ltd.　　　　　　　　　　　(2)
33 Tuas Bay, Singapore, 637310, Singa-
pore
Tel.: (65) 63059801
Web Site: www.ecranes.com.sg
Heavy Equipment Repair & Maintenance
Services
N.A.I.C.S.: 811310

Subsidiary (Domestic):

Load Controls Systems Pte Ltd　(3)
8 Sungei Kadut Avenue, Singapore,
729645, Singapore
Tel.: (65) 63666338
Safe Load Indicators Distr
N.A.I.C.S.: 423610

Subsidiary (Non-US):

Tat Hong Heavy Equipment (Hong
Kong) Limited　　　　　　　(3)
Unit 7 15th Floor Block B Hi-Tech Industrial
Center 491501, Castle Peak Road, Tsuen
Wan, New Territories, China (Hong Kong)
Tel.: (852) 24700436
Web Site: http://www.tathong.com
Construction Equipment Rental Services
N.A.I.C.S.: 532412

Subsidiary (Domestic):

Tat Hong Machinery Pte Ltd　　(3)
82 UBI Avenue 4 05-03 Edward Bousted
Centre, Singapore, 40832, Singapore
Tel.: (65) 62690022
Web Site: http://www.tathong.com
Spare Parts Distr
N.A.I.C.S.: 423120

Subsidiary (Domestic):

Tat Hong Plant Leasing Pte Ltd　(2)
33 Tuay Bay Dr, Singapore, 729489, Singapore
Tel.: (65) 62690022
Heavy Equipment & Machinery Rental Services
N.A.I.C.S.: 532490

Subsidiary (Domestic):

Peng Koon Heavy Machinery Pte
Ltd　　　　　　　　　　　(3)
17 Sungei Kadut Ave, Singapore, 729653,
Singapore
Tel.: (65) 67781661
Web Site: http://www.tathong.com
Heavy Construction Equipment Whslr
N.A.I.C.S.: 423810

Tat Hong Heavylift Pte Ltd　　(3)
82 Ubi Avenue 4 Edward Boustead Centre,
Singapore, 408832, Singapore
Tel.: (65) 62690022
Construction Equipment Rental Services
N.A.I.C.S.: 532412

Subsidiary (Non-US):

Tutt Bryant Group Limited　　(2)
Ground Floor Quad 1 8 Parkview Drive,
Sydney, 2127, NSW, Australia
Tel.: (61) 296466060
Web Site: http://www.tuttbryant.com.au
Construction Equipment Distributors
N.A.I.C.S.: 238910

Subsidiary (Domestic):

BT Equipment Pty Limited　　(3)
6-8 Ferngrove Place, Granville, 2142, NSW,
Australia
Tel.: (61) 297807200
Web Site: http://www.tuttbryant.com.au
Sales Range: $25-49.9 Million
Construction Equipments & Cranes Distr
N.A.I.C.S.: 532412

Affirma Capital Limited—(Continued)

Division (Domestic):

Tutt Bryant Group Limited - Caradel Hire (3)
99 Robinson St, Goulburn, 2580, New South Wales, Australia
Tel.: (61) 248234111
Web Site: http://www.tuttbryant.com.au
Hire Equipment Services
N.A.I.C.S.: 532412

Tutt Bryant Group Limited - Crane Hire Division (3)
50 Great Eastern Hwy, Guildford, 6055, WA, Australia
Tel.: (61) 892300500
Web Site: http://www.tuttbryant.com.au
Crane Hire Services
N.A.I.C.S.: 333923

Division (Domestic):

Tutt Bryant Heavy Lift & Shift (4)
Denman Road, Muswellbrook, 2333, NSW, Australia
Tel.: (61) 395540300
Web Site: http://www.tuttbryant.com.au
Construction Equipment Rental Services
N.A.I.C.S.: 532412

Subsidiary (Domestic):

Tutt Bryant Heavy Lift & Shift (3)
Denman Rd, PO Box 470, Muswellbrook, 2333, NSW, Australia
Tel.: (61) 265416444
Web Site: http://www.tuttbryant.com.au
Crane Rental & Leasing Services
N.A.I.C.S.: 532412
Gail Teague (Reg Mgr)

Division (Domestic):

Tutt Bryant Hire (3)
300 Portarlington Road, Moolap, Geelong, 3221, VIC, Australia
Tel.: (61) 352486266
Web Site: http://www.tuttbryant.com.au
Sales Range: $25-49.9 Million
Emp.: 18
Equipment Hiring Services
N.A.I.C.S.: 532412

Tutt Bryant Hire Portsmith (3)
Cnr Lyons & Hartley Streets, Portsmith, Cairns, 4870, QLD, Australia
Tel.: (61) 74052 4488
Web Site: http://www.tuttbryant.com.au
Plant & Hire Equipment Services
N.A.I.C.S.: 532412

Varun Beverages Limited (1)
Plot No 31 Institutional Area Sector 44, Gurgaon, 122002, Haryana, India
Tel.: (91) 1244643100
Web Site: http://www.varunbeverages.com
Rev.: $1,987,731,146
Assets: $1,840,686,580
Liabilities: $982,026,636
Net Worth: $858,659,944
Earnings: $254,739,736
Emp.: 13,500
Fiscal Year-end: 12/31/2023
Beverage Mfr & Distr
N.A.I.C.S.: 312111
Ravi Kant Jaipuria (Founder & Chm)

Subsidiary (Non-US):

Varun Beverages (Nepal) Private Limited (2)
PO Box 2968, Sinamangal Koteshwar, Kathmandu, Nepal
Tel.: (977) 97714990584
Beverage Distr
N.A.I.C.S.: 424490

Varun Beverages Morocco S.A. (2)
Z I Bouskoura 27 182, PO Box 408, Casablanca, Morocco
Tel.: (212) 529052999
Beverage Distr
N.A.I.C.S.: 424490
Fouad Loutfi (Engr-Sys & Virtualization)

AFFIRMATIVE FINANCE LIMITED

7-9 St James Square, Manchester, M2 6XX, United Kingdom
Tel.: (44) 8701 123 111
Web Site: http://www.affirmativefinance.co.uk
Sales Range: $10-24.9 Million
Emp.: 20
Business Credit & Lending Services
N.A.I.C.S.: 522390

AFFLE (INDIA) LIMITED
8th floor Unitech Commercial Tower 2 Sector 45, Gurgaon, 122003, Haryana, India
Tel.: (91) 1244992914
Web Site: https://www.affle.com
Year Founded: 2005
542752—(BOM)
Rev.: $157,429,682
Assets: $249,372,123
Liabilities: $88,390,439
Net Worth: $160,981,685
Earnings: $29,305,458
Emp.: 541
Fiscal Year-end: 03/31/22
Online Shopping Operator
N.A.I.C.S.: 541614
Anuj Khanna Sohum (Co-Founder, Chm & CEO)

Subsidiaries:

Mediasmart Mobile S.L. (1)
Calle Garcia de Paredes 12 1 B, 28010, Madrid, Spain
Tel.: (34) 911993546
Mobile Advertisement Services
N.A.I.C.S.: 541810
Noelia Amoedo (CEO)

AFFLUENT FOUNDATION HOLDINGS LIMITED
Unit 903-905 9/F The Octagon No 6 Sha Tsui Road, Tsuen Wan, New Territories, China (Hong Kong)
Tel.: (852) 2 593 5900   Ky
Web Site: http://www.hcho.com.hk
Year Founded: 1996
1757—(HKG)
Rev.: $57,634,197
Assets: $26,049,833
Liabilities: $16,011,061
Net Worth: $10,038,771
Earnings: $84,095
Emp.: 149
Fiscal Year-end: 03/31/21
Building Construction Services
N.A.I.C.S.: 238110
Siu Cheong Chan (Chm & CEO)

AFFLUENT MEDICAL SAS
320 avenue Archimede Les pleiades III Batiment B, 13100, Aix-en-Provence, France
Tel.: (33) 442951220
Web Site: https://www.affluentmedical.com
Year Founded: 2011
AFME—(EUR)
Rev.: $1,351,143
Assets: $62,563,197
Liabilities: $27,763,550
Net Worth: $34,799,647
Earnings: ($17,278,949)
Emp.: 63
Fiscal Year-end: 12/31/23
Medical Device Mfr
N.A.I.C.S.: 339112
Benjamin Renault (Chief Dev Officer)

AFFLUENT PARTNERS HOLDINGS LIMITED
Office A 6/F Valiant Commercial Building, 22-24 Prat Avenue Tsim Sha Tsui, Kowloon, China (Hong Kong)
Tel.: (852) 3 611 2188   Ky

Web Site: http://www.affluent-partners.com
Year Founded: 2014
1466—(HKG)
Rev.: $8,080,210
Assets: $10,590,419
Liabilities: $5,964,293
Net Worth: $4,626,126
Earnings: ($1,994,289)
Emp.: 47
Fiscal Year-end: 03/31/22
Holding Company; Pearls & Jewellery Mfr & Whslr
N.A.I.C.S.: 551112
Alex Leung (Exec Dir)

Subsidiaries:

Man Sang Jewellery Company Limited (1)
Suite 2208-14 22/F Sun Life Tower The Gateway 15 Canton Road, Tsimshatsui, Kowloon, China (Hong Kong)
Tel.: (852) 23175300
Web Site: http://www.mansangjewellery.com
Pearl & Jewellery Products Mfr & Whslr
N.A.I.C.S.: 423940

Subsidiary (Domestic):

Arcadia Jewellery Limited (2)
Suite 2208-14 22/F Sun Life Tower The Gateway 15 Canton Road, Tsimshatsui, Kowloon, China (Hong Kong) (100%)
Tel.: (852) 23179138
Web Site: http://www.arcadia-jewellery.com
Sales Range: $25-49.9 Million
Emp.: 50
Pearl Jewelry Products Exporter, Whlsr & Mfr
N.A.I.C.S.: 423940

AFFORDABLE ROBOTIC & AUTOMATION LTD.
Gate No1209 Near Hotel Vijay Executive, Pune, 412308, India
Tel.: (91) 7720018901
Web Site: https://www.arapl.co.in
541402—(BOM)
Rev.: $11,088,277
Assets: $16,498,714
Liabilities: $9,228,123
Net Worth: $7,270,591
Earnings: $323,396
Emp.: 250
Fiscal Year-end: 03/31/22
Electric Equipment Mfr
N.A.I.C.S.: 334111
Milind Manohar Padole (Mng Dir)

AFG GROUP NIJMEGEN B.V.
Hulzenseweg 10 20, 6534 AN, Nijmegen, Netherlands
Tel.: (31) 24 352 25 70
Web Site: http://www.afggroup.nl
Sales Range: $10-24.9 Million
Emp.: 100
Fire Prevention Equipment Mfr
N.A.I.C.S.: 339999
Frans Vogelzangs (CEO)

Subsidiaries:

Flame Guard B.V. (1)
Hulzenseweg 10 20, 6534 AN, Nijmegen, Netherlands
Tel.: (31) 24 3789581
Web Site: http://www.flameguard.nl
Fire Resistant Materials Mfr
N.A.I.C.S.: 325998

AFGRI LIMITED
12 Byls Bridge Boulevard Highveld Ext 73, Centurion, South Africa
Tel.: (27) 11 063 2347
Web Site: http://www.afgri.co.za
Year Founded: 1923
Agricultural Services
N.A.I.C.S.: 111191
Chris Venter (CEO)

Subsidiaries:

AFGRI Animal Feeds (1)
23 Frank Rd Bldg 3 HP&D Office Pk, Private Bag X2001, Isando, 1600, South Africa
Tel.: (27) 113064300
Sales Range: $25-49.9 Million
Emp.: 40
Animal Feeds Production & Distribution
N.A.I.C.S.: 311119

AFGRI Animal Feeds Eastern Cape (Pty) Ltd. (1)
22 Buchner Street, Paterson, 6130, Eastern Cape, South Africa
Tel.: (27) 422851114
Sales Range: $25-49.9 Million
Emp.: 75
Animal Feed Mfr
N.A.I.C.S.: 311119
Raymond Du Plessis (Gen Mgr)

AFGRI Financial and Logistics Services (1)
No 12 Byls Breach Blvd Ext 74, PO Box 11054, Centurion, 0046, South Africa
Tel.: (27) 0126438000
Web Site: http://wwwafgri.co.za
Emp.: 500
Financial & Logistics Services for Agriculture Industry
N.A.I.C.S.: 523999
Chrs Genter (CEO)

Afgritech Limited (1)
Old Croft, Carlisle, CA3 9BA, United Kingdom
Tel.: (44) 1228554600
Web Site: http://www.carrsgroup.com
Other Animal Food Mfr
N.A.I.C.S.: 311119
Tim David (CEO)

Clark Cotton (1)
The Atrium 9th Floor 41 Stanley Road, PO Box 7787, Auckland Park, Johannesburg, 2000, South Africa
Tel.: (27) 11 726 7210
Cotton Producer & Processor
N.A.I.C.S.: 111920

Daybreak Superior Marketing (Pty) Ltd. (1)
31 Collet Street, Alberton, 1449, Gauteng, South Africa
Tel.: (27) 136611247
Sales Range: $50-74.9 Million
Emp.: 10
Broiler Chicken Whslr
N.A.I.C.S.: 424440

Dormanko Dertig (Pty) Ltd. (1)
3 Louw Street, Bethlehem, 9701, Free State, South Africa
Tel.: (27) 583031906
Sales Range: $25-49.9 Million
Emp.: 18
Farm & Garden Machinery Whslr
N.A.I.C.S.: 423820

Labworld (Pty) Ltd. (1)
123 Witch Hazel Ave Technopark, Highveld, Centurion, 0157, Gauteng, South Africa
Tel.: (27) 126859600
Web Site: http://www.labworld.co.za
Sales Range: $25-49.9 Million
Emp.: 32
Laboratory & Scientific Analytical Equipment Distr
N.A.I.C.S.: 423490

Nedin Pty. Ltd. (1)
6 Charolais Street, Potgietersrus, 601, Limpopo, South Africa
Tel.: (27) 154914338
Sales Range: $25-49.9 Million
Emp.: 145
Cottonseed Oil Mfr
N.A.I.C.S.: 311224
Johan Maritz (Mgr-Ops)

Partmaster (Pty) Ltd. (1)
42 Naude Street, Bethlehem, 9700, Free State, South Africa
Tel.: (27) 583076500
Web Site: http://www.partrite.co.za
Sales Range: $50-74.9 Million
Emp.: 60
Agricultural Machinery Parts Distr
N.A.I.C.S.: 423820

Chris Weyer *(Gen Mgr-Transmission)*

The South African Bank of Athens Ltd (1)
54 Wierda Vly Sandton, Johannesburg, 2000, South Africa **(99.82%)**
Tel.: (27) 11 634 4300
Web Site: http://www.bankofathens.co.za
Commercial Banking Services
N.A.I.C.S.: 522110
Spiro Georgopoulos *(CEO)*

AFI DEVELOPMENT PLC
165 Spyrou Araouzou Lordos Waterfront Building Office 505, 3035, Limassol, Cyprus
Tel.: (357) 25310975 CY
Web Site: http://www.afi-development.com
Year Founded: 2001
Rev.: $296,043,000
Assets: $1,419,425,000
Liabilities: $673,347,000
Net Worth: $746,078,000
Earnings: $31,537,000
Emp.: 1,217
Fiscal Year-end: 12/31/18
Holding Company; Residential & Commercial Real Estate Development & Related Services
N.A.I.C.S.: 551112
Tzvia Leviev-Eliazarov *(VP-AFI RUS LLC)*

Subsidiaries:

AFI RUS LLC (1)
16A bld 5 Berezhkovskaya Embankment, Moscow, 121059, Russia
Tel.: (7) 4952554952
Web Site: http://afi-development.com
Residential & Commercial Real Estate Development & Related Services
N.A.I.C.S.: 531390
Mark Groysman *(CEO)*

Subsidiary (Domestic):

Aristeya LLC (2)
8 Str 5 Nab Paveletskaya, Moscow, 115114, Russia **(100%)**
Tel.: (7) 4957969988
Real Estate Development & Related Services
N.A.I.C.S.: 531390

Regionalnoe AgroProizvodstvennoe Objedinenie LLC (2)
9 Korp 21 Ul Kosinskaya, Moscow, 111538, Russia **(100%)**
Tel.: (7) 4957969988
Real Estate Development & Related Services
N.A.I.C.S.: 531390
Maxim Sibirichev *(Project Mgr)*

AFICOM
10 Rue Bergers, 75015, Paris, France
Tel.: (33) 145753594
Web Site: http://www.aficom.fr
Rev.: $23,200,000
Emp.: 15
Drugs, Proprietaries & Sundries
N.A.I.C.S.: 424210
Francois Marchand *(Pres)*

AFIN TECHNOLOGIES LIMITED
24 Greek St, Stockport Greater, Manchester, SK3 8AB, United Kingdom
Tel.: (44) 161 393 3200 UK
Web Site: http://www.survey-me.com
Year Founded: 2011
Software Publisher
N.A.I.C.S.: 513210
Lee Evans *(CEO)*

Subsidiaries:

Afin Technologies, Inc. (1)
1601 Dove St Ste 190, Newport Beach, CA 92660
Tel.: (888) 551-6632

Web Site: http://www.survey-me.com
Software Publisher
N.A.I.C.S.: 513210

Subsidiary (Domestic):

Entertainment Publications, LLC (2)
1401 Crooks Rd Ste 150, Troy, MI 48084
Tel.: (248) 404-1000
Web Site: http://www.entertainment.com
Discount, Promotion & Coupon Book Publisher
N.A.I.C.S.: 513130
Lori Tarallo *(Mgr-Ops)*

AFINE INVESTMENTS LIMITED
Unit 4602 Greenways Strand, Cape Town, 7140, South Africa
Tel.: (27) 218537956 ZA
Web Site: https://www.afineinvestments.com
Year Founded: 2020
ANI—(JSE)
Rev.: $2,364,559
Assets: $21,556,741
Liabilities: $6,013,343
Net Worth: $15,543,398
Earnings: $3,627,713
Fiscal Year-end: 04/29/24
Investment Management Service
N.A.I.C.S.: 523999
Anton Loubser *(CEO)*

AFINUM MANAGEMENT GMBH
Theatinerstrasse 7, 80333, Munich, Germany
Tel.: (49) 89 255 433 01 De
Web Site: http://www.afinum.de
Year Founded: 2000
Private Equity Investments
N.A.I.C.S.: 523999
Thomas Buhler *(Mng Partner)*

AFKEM AG
Brusseler Strasse 15, 53842, Troisdorf, Germany
Tel.: (49) 2241253660
Web Site: http://www.afkem.ag
Year Founded: 2017
CHIA—(STU)
Sales Range: Less than $1 Million
Renewable Energy Services
N.A.I.C.S.: 221118
Christian Tietz *(Chm-Mgmt Bd & CEO)*

AFONE PARTICIPATIONS SA
11 place Francois Mitterrand, 49100, Angers, France
Tel.: (33) 2 41860504 FR
Web Site: http://www.afoneparticipations.com
Year Founded: 1997
Telecommunication Servicesb
N.A.I.C.S.: 517810
Philip Fournier *(Chm & Mng Dir)*

AFONWEN LAUNDRY LIMITED
Afonwen, Pwllheli, Gwynedd, LL53 6NQ, United Kingdom
Tel.: (44) 1766 810264
Web Site: http://www.afonwenlaundry.com
Year Founded: 1935
Sales Range: $10-24.9 Million
Emp.: 400
Laundry & Linen Hire Services
N.A.I.C.S.: 812320
Mark Woolfenden *(Mng Dir)*

Subsidiaries:

Whiteriver Laundry Ltd (1)
Unit 8 Millshaw Park Industrial Estate, Leeds, LS11 0LR, United Kingdom
Tel.: (44) 113 272 0700
Web Site: http://www.whiteriverlaundry.com
Laundry Services
N.A.I.C.S.: 812320

Luke Gledhill *(Mng Dir)*

AFORTI HOLDING SA
Ul Chalubinskiego 8, 00-613, Warsaw, Poland
Tel.: (48) 226475000
Web Site: https://www.aforti.pl
Year Founded: 2009
Financial Support Services
N.A.I.C.S.: 541611
Klaudiusz Sytek *(Pres)*

AFR NUVENTURE RESOURCES INC.
1600 - 925 West Georgia Street, Vancouver, V6C 3L2, BC, Canada
Tel.: (647) 966-3100 BC
Web Site: https://afrnuventure.com
Year Founded: 1980
AFR—(TSXV)
Assets: $69,743
Liabilities: $50,177
Net Worth: $19,566
Earnings: ($276,798)
Fiscal Year-end: 05/31/24
Mineral Exploration Services
N.A.I.C.S.: 213114
Errol Farr *(CFO)*

AFREECATV CO., LTD.
Pangyo 7 VentureVelly 1-2 15 Pangyo-ro 228 beon-gil, Bundang-Gu, Seongnam, 463400, Gyeonggi-do, Korea (South)
Tel.: (82) 16887022
Web Site: http://www.corp.afreecatv.com
067160—(KRS)
Rev.: $241,587,352
Assets: $356,751,236
Liabilities: $171,770,294
Net Worth: $184,980,942
Earnings: $45,821,648
Emp.: 766
Fiscal Year-end: 12/31/22
Internet Services
N.A.I.C.S.: 518210

AFRI-CAN MARINE MINERALS CORPORATION
1801 McGill College Avenue Suite 950, Montreal, H3A 2N4, QC, Canada
Tel.: (514) 846-2133
Web Site: http://www.afri-can.com
Sales Range: Less than $1 Million
Mineral Exploration Services
N.A.I.C.S.: 213114

AFRIC INDUSTRIES SA
Industrial Area of Mghogha Tetouan Road Lot 107 Street 3, Tangiers, Morocco
Tel.: (212) 539351235
Web Site: https://www.africindustries.com
Year Founded: 1980
AFI—(CAS)
Sales Range: $1-9.9 Million
Fabricated Metal Products Mfr
N.A.I.C.S.: 332999

AFRICA CAPITALWORKS HOLDINGS
Level 5 Alexander House 35 Cybercity, Ebene, 72201, Mauritius
Tel.: (230) 4030800 MU
Web Site: https://africacapitalworks.com
Investment Services
N.A.I.C.S.: 523999

Subsidiaries:

Cipla Quality Chemical Industries Limited (1)
Plot 1-7 1st Ring Road, PO Box 34871,

Luzira Industrial Park, Kampala, Uganda **(51.18%)**
Tel.: (256) 312341100
Web Site: https://www.ciplaqcil.co.ug
Emp.: 350
Pharmaceuticals Product Mfr
N.A.I.C.S.: 325412
Emmanuel Katongole *(Chm)*

AFRICA ENERGY CORP.
Suite 2000 - 885 West Georgia Street, Vancouver, V6C 3E8, BC, Canada
Tel.: (604) 689-7842 AB
Web Site: https://www.africaenergycorp.com
Year Founded: 2010
HPMCF—(OTCIQ)
Assets: $41,908,000
Liabilities: $464,000
Net Worth: $41,444,000
Earnings: ($4,518,000)
Emp.: 8
Fiscal Year-end: 12/31/19
Oil & Gas Exploration Services
N.A.I.C.S.: 211120
Garrett Soden *(CEO & Pres)*

AFRICA ISRAEL INVESTMENTS LTD.
4 Derech Hachoresh Street, Yehud, Israel
Tel.: (972) 35393535
Web Site: http://www.afigroup-global.com
Rev.: $1,325,374,863
Assets: $4,318,354,160
Liabilities: $3,845,468,318
Net Worth: $472,885,842
Earnings: ($10,483,595)
Emp.: 1,184
Fiscal Year-end: 12/31/18
Investment Services
N.A.I.C.S.: 523940
Lev Leviev *(Co-Chm)*

Subsidiaries:

20 Pine Street LLC (1)
20 Pine St, New York, NY 10005
Tel.: (212) 344-4000
Web Site: http://www.20pine.com
Sales Range: $50-74.9 Million
Emp.: 20
Real Estate Management Services
N.A.I.C.S.: 531390

A.I. Holdings (USA) Corp. (1)
40 Wall St Fl 56, New York, NY 10005
Tel.: (212) 471-3300
Investment Management Service
N.A.I.C.S.: 523940

ADUT s.r.o (1)
Vinohradska 151, 13000, Prague, Czech Republic
Tel.: (420) 235351377
Web Site: http://www.adut.cz
Sales Range: $25-49.9 Million
Emp.: 25
Business Support Services
N.A.I.C.S.: 561499

AFI Europe (Israel Branch) Ltd. (1)
Derech Hachoresh 4, Yehud, 56470, Israel
Tel.: (972) 35393576
Real Estate Services
N.A.I.C.S.: 531390

AFI Europe Bulgaria EOOD (1)
Dobrotitsa Despot Street Block 41, District Lagera, 1612, Sofia, Bulgaria
Tel.: (359) 24898180
Real Estate Services
N.A.I.C.S.: 531390

AFI Europe Czech Republic, s.r.o. (1)
Jancovcova 1037/49, Prague, 170 00, Czech Republic
Tel.: (420) 255743111
Web Site: http://www.afi-europe.com

Africa Israel Investments Ltd.—(Continued)

Sales Range: $50-74.9 Million
Emp.: 20
Real Estate Development Services
N.A.I.C.S.: 531390
Doron Klein (CEO)

AFI Europe Financing B.V. (1)
Herengracht 456, Amsterdam, 1017 CA,
Netherlands
Tel.: (31) 204218928
Web Site: http://www.afi-europe.eu
Financial Management Services
N.A.I.C.S.: 523999

AFI Europe Infrastructure B.V. (1)
Herengracht 456, 1017 EP, Amsterdam,
Netherlands
Tel.: (31) 20 4218928
Real Estate Manangement Services
N.A.I.C.S.: 531390

AFI Europe Management SRL (1)
4 Vasile Milea Blvd, 6th District, Bucharest,
Romania
Tel.: (40) 2141202220
Web Site: http://www.eu.afi-g.com
Sales Range: $25-49.9 Million
Emp.: 10
Real Estate Development Services
N.A.I.C.S.: 531390
David Hay (CEO)

AFI Europe N.V (1)
4 Derech Hachoresh St, Yehud, 56470,
Israel
Tel.: (972) 35393625
Sales Range: $75-99.9 Million
Emp.: 250
Other Miscellaneous Durable Goods Merchant Whslr
N.A.I.C.S.: 423990
Avi Barzilay (CEO)

AFI Germany GmbH (1)
Kronenstr 3, Berlin, 10117, Germany
Tel.: (49) 3028045095
Web Site: http://www.afi-europe.eu
Sales Range: $50-74.9 Million
Emp.: 3
Real Estate Manangement Services
N.A.I.C.S.: 531390
Doron Klein (Gen Mgr)

AFI Germany Investment GmbH (1)
Kronen Str 3, Berlin, 10117, Germany
Tel.: (49) 3028045095
Web Site: http://www.asi-europe.de
Sales Range: $50-74.9 Million
Emp.: 5
Investment Management Service
N.A.I.C.S.: 523999
Karin Shalev (COO)

AFI Management SIA (1)
Gertrudes Street 10/12-4, 1010 LV, Riga,
Latvia
Tel.: (371) 67846525
Web Site: http://eu.afi-g.com
Emp.: 1
Real Estate Manangement Services
N.A.I.C.S.: 531390
Joris Hoppener (COO)

AFI Management Sp. z o.o. (1)
Bobrzynskiego 37, 30-348, Krakow, Poland
Tel.: (48) 122627406
Real Estate Services
N.A.I.C.S.: 531390

AFI Palace Cotroceni (1)
Bulevardul Vasile Milea 4, Bucharest, Romania
Tel.: (40) 31 425 75 10
Web Site: http://www.en.aficotroceni.ro
Commercial Building Construction Services
N.A.I.C.S.: 236220

Africa Israel (East Europe) Investments B.V. (1)
Noordendijk 189, Dordrecht, 3311RN, Netherlands
Tel.: (31) 786481555
Real Estate Investment Trust
N.A.I.C.S.: 525990

Africa Israel (Finance) 1985 Ltd. (1)
4 Hachoresh Rd, Yehud, 56470, Israel
Tel.: (972) 35393535
Investment Management Service

N.A.I.C.S.: 523940

Africa Israel Hotels Ltd. (1)
3 Moshe Dayan St, 56450, Yehud, Israel
Tel.: (972) 35394477
Web Site: http://www.hiil.co.il
Sales Range: $10-24.9 Million
Emp.: 100
Hotel Operator
N.A.I.C.S.: 721110
Ron Yarin (Gen Mgr)

Africa Israel Industries Ltd. (1)
4 Derech Hachoresh St, Yehud, Israel
Tel.: (972) 86625105
Web Site: http://www.afigroup-global.com
Sales Range: $450-499.9 Million
Steel Products Mfr
N.A.I.C.S.: 332999

Africa Israel International Holdings Ltd. (1)
4 Derech Hachoresh Street, Yehud, 56470,
Israel
Tel.: (972) 35393586
Web Site: http://www.africa-israel.com
Sales Range: $100-124.9 Million
Emp.: 250
Miscellaneous Financial Investment Activities
N.A.I.C.S.: 523999

Africa Israel Properties Ltd. (1)
4 Derech Hachoresh St, Yehud, Israel
Tel.: (972) 35393535
Web Site: http://www.africa-israel.co.il
Sales Range: $75-99.9 Million
Emp.: 250
Other Holding Companies Offices
N.A.I.C.S.: 551112

Subsidiary (Non-US):

AFI Europe B.V. (2)
Herengracht 456, 1017 CA, Amsterdam,
Netherlands
Tel.: (31) 20 421 8928
Web Site: http://www.afi-europe.eu
Emp.: 4
Real Estate Investment Services
N.A.I.C.S.: 531390
Avraham Barzilay (CEO)

Subsidiary (Domestic):

Africa Israel International Properties (2002) Ltd. (2)
4 Hahoresh St, Yehud, 56470, Israel
Tel.: (972) 3 5393586
Web Site: http://www.afieurope.com
Emp.: 125
Real Estate Leasing & Rental Services
N.A.I.C.S.: 531390
Avraham Barzilay (Office Mgr)

Subsidiary (Non-US):

Flamingo Ltd. (2)
32 Gen Gurko Str Flr 4, Burgas, Bulgaria
Tel.: (359) 56 843819
Sales Range: $50-74.9 Million
Emp.: 3
Property Management Services
N.A.I.C.S.: 531311
George Ivanov (Mng Dir)

Africa Israel Residences Ltd. (1)
4 Derech Hachoresh St, Yehud, Israel
Tel.: (972) 35393535
Sales Range: $25-49.9 Million
Emp.: 53
Real Estate Manangement Services
N.A.I.C.S.: 561790

Africa Israel Trade & Agencies Ltd. (1)
4 Derech Hachoresh St, Yehud, Israel
Tel.: (972) 35393535
Web Site: http://www.africa-israel.co.il
Sales Range: $75-99.9 Million
Emp.: 250
Holding Company
N.A.I.C.S.: 551112

Airport City Belgrade d.o.o. (1)
88-90 Omladinskih brigada street, New Belgrade, Belgrade, 11070, Serbia
Tel.: (381) 11 2090 525
Web Site:
http://www.airportcitybelgrade.com

Sales Range: $25-49.9 Million
Emp.: 25
Commercial Building Construction Services
N.A.I.C.S.: 236220
Gili Dekel (Pres)

Subsidiary (Domestic):

Airport City Property Management d.o.o. (2)
Omladinskih Brigada 88-90, Belgrade,
11070, Serbia
Tel.: (381) 11 2090 525
Web Site:
http://www.airportcitybelgrade.com
Sales Range: $25-49.9 Million
Property Management Services
N.A.I.C.S.: 531312

Anninmuizas IPASUMS SIA (2)
Gertrudes St 1012, Riga, 1010, Latvia
Tel.: (371) 67277776
Sales Range: $50-74.9 Million
Emp.: 9
Real Estate Lending Services
N.A.I.C.S.: 531190
Ilona Striga (CEO)

B.R. Holdings SIA (1)
Gertrudes Iela 10 06, Riga, 1010, Latvia
Tel.: (371) 67846523
Sales Range: $50-74.9 Million
Emp.: 9
Investment Management Service
N.A.I.C.S.: 523999
Ilona Striga (Gen Mgr)

Business Park Varna AD (1)
Business Park Varna Building 8 Floor 4,
Varna, 9009, Bulgaria
Tel.: (359) 52 912 601
Web Site: http://www.bpv.bg
Sales Range: $50-74.9 Million
Emp.: 10
Real Estate Development Services
N.A.I.C.S.: 531390
Tsahi Tabakman (CEO)

Crown Plaza Ltd (1)
111 Yese Nof, 34454, Haifa, Israel (100%)
Tel.: (972) 48350835
Web Site: http://www.h-i.co.il
Hotel Operator
N.A.I.C.S.: 721110
Herzel Levi (Gen Mgr)

Czerwone Maki Project SP. Z.O.O. (1)
Bobrzynskiego 37, Krakow, 30-348, Poland
Tel.: (48) 122627641
Sales Range: $50-74.9 Million
Emp.: 2
Investment Management Service
N.A.I.C.S.: 523999
Sebastian Kiec (Pres)

Danya Cebus Ltd. (1)
Yoni Netanyahu 1c, Or Yehuda, Israel
Tel.: (972) 3 6340341
Web Site: http://www.danya-cebus.co.il
Sales Range: $800-899.9 Million
Building Construction Services
N.A.I.C.S.: 236116
Ronen Ginzburg (CEO)

Danya Dutch BV (1)
Watermanweg 100, 3067, Rotterdam, GG,
Netherlands
Tel.: (31) 102861922
Sales Range: $50-74.9 Million
Emp.: 6
Holding Company
N.A.I.C.S.: 551112

Givat Savyon Ltd. (1)
4 Derech Hachoresh St, Yehud, Israel
Tel.: (972) 35393535
Sales Range: $75-99.9 Million
Emp.: 250
Real Estate Services
N.A.I.C.S.: 531210

Gottex Models Ltd. (1)
Yoni Netanyahu St, New Industrial Zone,
Yehud, Israel
Tel.: (972) 35387777
Web Site: http://www.gottex.co.il
Sales Range: $25-49.9 Million
Emp.: 24
Swimsuit Designer, Mfr & Exporter

N.A.I.C.S.: 315990

Investments Africa Israel s.r.o (1)
Jankovcova 2, 17000, Prague, Czech Republic
Tel.: (420) 255743111
Web Site: http://www.afi-europe.com
Sales Range: $10-24.9 Million
Emp.: 20
All Other Business Support Services
N.A.I.C.S.: 561499
David Hay (CEO-Romania)

M.D.C. LTD (1)
Unit 1 Lambs Farm Business Park Basingstoke Road, Swallowfield, Reading, RG7
1PQ, United Kingdom
Tel.: (44) 1189448811
Web Site: http://www.mdc-ltd.com
Emp.: 6
Software Development Services
N.A.I.C.S.: 541511
Stefanie Spaude (Dir-Sls)

Novo Maar SP. Z.O.O. (1)
Bobrzynskiego 37, Krakow, 30-348, Poland
Tel.: (48) 122627406
Web Site: http://www.afi-europe.eu
Emp.: 6
Real Estate Development Services
N.A.I.C.S.: 531390
Sebastian Kiec (Gen Mgr)

Star Estate SRL (1)
4 B-Dul Vasile Milea Park I Bld, 61344, Bucharest, Romania
Tel.: (40) 214120220
Web Site: http://www.afi-europe.eu
Investment Management Service
N.A.I.C.S.: 523999
David Hay (CEO)

Tulip Management SRL (1)
4 B-Dul Vasile Milea Blvd, Bucharest,
61344, Romania
Tel.: (40) 214120220
Sales Range: $50-74.9 Million
Emp.: 15
Real Estate Property Renting Services
N.A.I.C.S.: 531190
David Hay (CEO)

Tulipa Rokytka s.r.o. (1)
Classic 7 Business Park Building C 4th
Floor Jankovcova 1037/49, 170 00, Prague,
Czech Republic
Tel.: (420) 800 123 200
Web Site: http://www.tuliparokytka.cz
Residential Building Construction Services
N.A.I.C.S.: 236116

Tulipa Vokovice s.r.o. (1)
Jankovtova 1037/49, 17 000, Prague,
Czech Republic
Tel.: (420) 255743111
Sales Range: $25-49.9 Million
Emp.: 20
Residential Building Construction Services
N.A.I.C.S.: 236116

AFRICA OIL CORPORATION
666 Burrard Street Suite 2500, Vancouver, V6C 2XB, BC, Canada
Tel.: (201) 817-1511
Web Site:
https://www.africaoilcorp.com
AOI—(OTCIQ)
Rev.: $8,378,000
Assets: $812,305,000
Liabilities: $45,602,000
Net Worth: $766,703,000
Earnings: ($156,769,000)
Emp.: 39
Fiscal Year-end: 12/31/19
Oil & Gas Exploration Services
N.A.I.C.S.: 211120
Keith C. Hill (Pres & CEO)

Subsidiaries:

Africa Oil Ethiopia B.V. (1)
Teleportboulevard 140-5, 1043 EJ, Amsterdam, Netherlands
Tel.: (31) 205405800
Oil & Gas Exploration Services
N.A.I.C.S.: 213112

Africa Oil Kenya B.V. (1)

Westlands Office Park, Nairobi, 63298, Kenya
Tel.: (254) 204456173
Oil & Gas Exploration Services
N.A.I.C.S.: 213112

Africa Oil Turkana B.V. (1)
Amaliastraat 5, 2514 JC, Hague, South Holland, Netherlands
Tel.: (31) 703717811
Oil & Gas Exploration Services
N.A.I.C.S.: 211120

Africa Oil UK Limited (1)
112 Jermyn St, St James's, London, SW1Y 6LS, United Kingdom
Tel.: (44) 2080171511
Oil & Gas Exploration Services
N.A.I.C.S.: 213112

AFRICA RISK CONSULTING LTD.
6 25 Farringdon St, Farringdon, London, EC4A 4AB, United Kingdom
Tel.: (44) 2070784080
Web Site:
https://www.africariskconsulting.com
Year Founded: 2006
Management Consulting Services
N.A.I.C.S.: 541618

AFRICAN & OVERSEAS ENTERPRISES LIMITED
263 Victoria Road, Salt River, Cape Town, 7925, South Africa
Tel.: (27) 214609400   ZA
Web Site:
https://www.rextrueform.com
AOO—(JSE)
Rev.: $45,418,528
Assets: $55,322,863
Liabilities: $32,078,335
Net Worth: $23,244,528
Earnings: $3,450,391
Emp.: 500
Fiscal Year-end: 06/30/22
Investment Management Service
N.A.I.C.S.: 523940
Catherine Elizabeth Anne Radowsky (Co-CEO)

AFRICAN ALLIANCE INSURANCE PLC
54 Awolowo Road Ikoyi, Lagos, Nigeria
Tel.: (234) 8066309476
Web Site:
https://www.africanallianceplc.com
Year Founded: 1960
AFRINSURE—(NIGE)
Rev.: $5,262,533
Assets: $39,580,871
Liabilities: $35,823,275
Net Worth: $3,757,596
Earnings: ($2,147,395)
Emp.: 172
Fiscal Year-end: 12/31/22
Investment Management Service
N.A.I.C.S.: 525990
Joyce Ojemudia (CEO & Mng Dir)

AFRICAN DAWN CAPITAL LIMITED
3rd Floor The Village at Horizon Corner of Sonop & Ontdekkers Roads, Horizon View, 1724, Johannesburg, 1724, Gauteng, South Africa
Tel.: (27) 114757705   ZA
Web Site: https://www.afdawn.co.za
Year Founded: 1998
ADW—(JSE)
Rev.: $577,742
Assets: $768,386
Liabilities: $2,934,019
Net Worth: ($2,165,633)
Earnings: ($852,987)
Emp.: 50
Fiscal Year-end: 02/28/23

Financial Services
N.A.I.C.S.: 522299
W. Jacques Groenewald (CEO)

Subsidiaries:

Elite Group Proprietary Limited (1)
3rd Floor Horizon Shopping Centre Cnr Sonop and Ontdekkers Road, Horizon View, Roodepoort, 1724, South Africa
Tel.: (27) 114757705
Web Site: https://www.elitegroup.co.za
Financial Services
N.A.I.C.S.: 523999

AFRICAN EAGLE RESOURCES PLC
64 New Cavendish Street, London, W1G 8TB, United Kingdom
Tel.: (44) 207002 5356   UK
Web Site:
http://www.africaneagle.co.uk
Sales Range: Less than $1 Million
Emp.: 7
Gold & Copper Exploration Services
N.A.I.C.S.: 212220
Robert Jonathan McLearon (Dir-Fin)

Subsidiaries:

Twigg Resources Limited (1)
1st Floor 6-7 Queen Street, London, EC4N 1SP, United Kingdom
Tel.: (44) 2072486059
Mineral Exploration Services
N.A.I.C.S.: 213115

Subsidiary (Non-US):

Twigg Gold Limited (2)
PO Box 1866, Mwanza, Tanzania
Tel.: (255) 282 500 727
Emp.: 1
Mineral Exploration Services
N.A.I.C.S.: 213115
Mark Stanley (Country Mgr)

AFRICAN ENERGY METALS INC.
Suite 401 - 750 West Pender Street, Vancouver, V6C 2I7, BC, Canada
Tel.: (604) 834-2968   BC
Web Site:
https://africanenergymetals.com
Year Founded: 2007
NDENF—(OTCQB)
Assets: $8,312
Liabilities: $2,765,701
Net Worth: ($2,757,389)
Earnings: ($4,134,088)
Fiscal Year-end: 12/31/19
Metal Mining Services
N.A.I.C.S.: 212290
J. Stephen Barley (CEO)

AFRICAN EQUITY EMPOWERMENT INVESTMTS LIMITED
Waterway House 3 Dock Rd Victoria & Alfred Waterfront, Cape Town, 8001, South Africa
Tel.: (27) 214271500   ZA
Web Site: http://www.aeei.co.za
Year Founded: 1997
AEE—(JSE)
Rev.: $38,775,547
Assets: $90,408,750
Liabilities: $26,599,616
Net Worth: $63,809,134
Earnings: ($64,261,927)
Emp.: 2,200
Fiscal Year-end: 08/31/23
Investment Management Service
N.A.I.C.S.: 525990
Khalid Abdulla (CEO)

Subsidiaries:

Atlantic Fishing Enterprises (Pty) Ltd (1)
Quay 7 East Pier, Cape Town, 8001, Western Cape, South Africa
Tel.: (27) 214190124

Web Site: http://www.premierfishing.co.za
Salmon Fishing Services
N.A.I.C.S.: 114119
Khalid Abdullah (CEO)

Digital Matter (Pty) Ltd (1)
1st Floor Unit 15 Royal Melbourne Fourways Golf Park Roos Street, Fourways, 2068, South Africa
Tel.: (27) 113173920
Sales Range: $25-49.9 Million
Emp.: 11
Mobility Networking Software Development Services
N.A.I.C.S.: 541511
Jeremy Williams (Mng Dir)

Events Social Marketing and Productions Afrika (Pty) Ltd (1)
93 Loop Street, Cape Town, 8001, Western Cape, South Africa
Tel.: (27) 214225651
Event Management Services
N.A.I.C.S.: 711310

Health System Technologies (Pty) Ltd (1)
67 Rosmead Avenue, Kenilworth, 7945, Western Cape, South Africa
Tel.: (27) 216831506
Web Site: https://healthsystems.co.za
Emp.: 50
Healthcare Information Technology Consulting Services
N.A.I.C.S.: 541512
Leon Wolmarans (Mgr-Bus Dev & Call Centre)

John Ovenstone Ltd (1)
Q7 East Pier, Cape Town, 8001, Western Cape, South Africa
Tel.: (27) 214190124
Fish & Seafood Distr
N.A.I.C.S.: 424460
Samier Samier (Gen Mgr)

Premier Fishing & Brands Ltd. (1)
No 3 South Arm Road Victoria Basin, Cape Town, 8002, South Africa   (56.23%)
Tel.: (27) 214271400
Web Site: http://www.premierfishing.co.za
Rev.: $25,089,302
Assets: $53,240,106
Liabilities: $13,138,869
Net Worth: $40,101,237
Earnings: $619,250
Emp.: 750
Fiscal Year-end: 08/31/2022
Food Mfr
N.A.I.C.S.: 311999
Mogamat Samir Saban (CEO)

Subsidiary (Domestic):

Emergent Energy Proprietary Limited (2)
Brickfield Canvas 35 Brickfield Rd, Woodstock, Cape Town, 7925, South Africa
Tel.: (27) 218284202
Web Site:
https://www.emergentenergy.co.za
Solar PV System Services
N.A.I.C.S.: 221114

Magic 828 Proprietary Limited (2)
12 Oxbow Crescent Office 10 The Estuaries, Century, Cape Town, 7700, Western Cape, South Africa
Tel.: (27) 210014828
Web Site: https://www.magic828.co.za
Radio Station Services
N.A.I.C.S.: 516110

Talhado Fishing Enterprises Proprietary Limited (2)
Store 315 Harbour, Port Elizabeth, 6001, South Africa
Tel.: (27) 415851652
Web Site: https://www.talhadofishing.co.za
Emp.: 393
Fishing Operation Services
N.A.I.C.S.: 114111
Malcolm Stanley (CEO)

Saratoga Software (Pty) Ltd (1)
4 Greenwich Grove Station Rd, Rondebosch, Cape Town, 7700, South Africa
Tel.: (27) 216584100
Web Site: https://saratogasoftware.com

Sales Range: $25-49.9 Million
Emp.: 41
Software Development Services
N.A.I.C.S.: 541511
Anthony Robinson (Deputy Chm-Exec Bd)

Sekpharma (Pty) Ltd (1)
4 Silverwood Close Steenberg Office Park Steenberg Boulevard, Tokai, Cape Town, Western Cape, South Africa
Tel.: (27) 217015764
Web Site: http://www.sekhealth.com
Pharmaceuticals Product Mfr
N.A.I.C.S.: 325412
Tessa Economakis (Mgr-Gauteng Reg)

Sekunjalo Aquaculture (Pty) Ltd (1)
Quay 7 East Pier, Cape Town, 8001, Western Cape, South Africa
Tel.: (27) 214271400
Aquaculture Maintenance Services
N.A.I.C.S.: 112519
Samier Saban (Gen Mgr)

Sekunjalo Medical Services (Pty) Ltd (1)
Ground Fl 4 Silverwood Close Steenberg Office Park, Steenberg Boulevard Tokai, Cape Town, 7945, South Africa
Tel.: (27) 217014788
Healtcare Services
N.A.I.C.S.: 621999

Sekunjalo Technology Solutions Group (Pty) Ltd (1)
Ground Floor Block D 5 Eglin Road Belvedere Place, Sunninghill, Johannesburg, 2191, South Africa
Tel.: (27) 112313620
Information Technology Consulting Services
N.A.I.C.S.: 541512
Khalid Abdulla (Chm)

AFRICAN EXPORT IMPORT BANK LIMITED
72 B El-Maahad El-Eshteraky Street, Heliopolis, Cairo, 11341, Egypt
Tel.: (20) 24564100   EG
Web Site:
http://www.afreximbank.com
Year Founded: 1993
Sales Range: $25-49.9 Million
Emp.: 41
Banking Services
N.A.I.C.S.: 522180
Philip Kamau (Sr Dir-Fin)

AFRICAN GOLD LTD.
Level 1 Suite 23 513 Hay Street, Subiaco, 6008, WA, Australia
Tel.: (61) 861436749   AU
Web Site: https://www.african-gold.com
Year Founded: 2018
A1G—(ASX)
Rev.: $4,413
Assets: $7,346,559
Liabilities: $627,948
Net Worth: $6,718,611
Earnings: ($1,179,536)
Fiscal Year-end: 12/31/23
Mineral Exploration Services
N.A.I.C.S.: 212390
Phillip Gallagher (Mng Dir)

AFRICAN INFRASTRUCTURE INVESTMENT MANAGERS
Ground Floor, Colinton House The Oval 1 Oakdale Road, Newlands, Cape Town, South Africa
Tel.: (27) 216701234   ZA
Web Site: https://aiimafrica.com
Year Founded: 1999
Emp.: 100
Investment Services
N.A.I.C.S.: 523999

Subsidiaries:

Commercial Cold Strorage Group Ltd. (1)
7 Toulon & Rotterdam Roads, Durban, 4001, South Africa

African Infrastructure Investment Managers—(Continued)

Tel.: (27) 312057277
Web Site: http://www.comcold.co.za
Emp.: 60
Cold Storage & Transportation Services
N.A.I.C.S.: 493120
Sharon Gabellone (Mgr-Admin)

AFRICAN MEDIA ENTERTAINMENT LIMITED

AME Office Park, No 5 8th Street
Houghton Estate, Johannesburg,
2198, South Africa
Tel.: (27) 105904554   ZA
Web Site: https://www.ame.co.za
AME—(JSE)
Rev.: $14,188,416
Assets: $17,866,105
Liabilities: $4,088,552
Net Worth: $13,777,554
Earnings: $2,279,386
Emp.: 218
Fiscal Year-end: 03/31/23
Radio Broadcasting Services
N.A.I.C.S.: 516110
Angela Jane Isbister (Exec Dir-Fin)

Subsidiaries:

Central Media Group Proprietary
Limited   (1)
Central Media Park 7 Christo Groenewald
Street, PO Box 7117, Wild Olive Estate,
Bloemfontein, 9300, South Africa
Tel.: (27) 515050900
Radio Station Broadcasting Services
N.A.I.C.S.: 516110
Mari Reynolds (Fin Dir)

MediaHeads 360 Proprietary
Limited   (1)
No 5 8th Street AME Office Park, Houghton
Estate, Johannesburg, 2198, South Africa
Tel.: (27) 105904553
Advertising Services
N.A.I.C.S.: 541810

Seyalemoya Communications (Pty)
Ltd   (1)
Central Media Park 7 Christo Groenewald
Avenue, Wild Olive Estate, Bloemfontein,
9301, South Africa
Tel.: (27) 51 505 0900
Web Site: https://www.ofm.co.za
Radio Broadcasting Services
N.A.I.C.S.: 516210
Nick Efstathiou (CEO)

Umoya Communications (Pty)
Ltd   (1)
5 Upper Valley Rd Baakens Valley, Port
Elizabeth, 6001, Eastern Cape, South Africa
Tel.: (27) 415059497
Web Site: https://www.algoafm.co.za
Radio Broadcasting Services
N.A.I.C.S.: 516110

United Stations Proprietary
Limited   (1)
no 5 8th Street Oxford Office Park, Houghton Estate, Johannesburg, South Africa
Tel.: (27) 105904554
Radio Station Broadcasting Services
N.A.I.C.S.: 516110
Dave Tiltmann (CEO)

AFRICAN MEDICAL INVESTMENT PLC

3rd Floor Exchange House, 54 62
Athol Street, Douglas, IM1 1JD, Isle
of Man
Tel.: (44) 20 7236 1177
Web Site: http://www.amiplc.com
Sales Range: $10-24.9 Million
Emp.: 286
Hospital Management, Emergency &
Evacuation Services
N.A.I.C.S.: 622110
Peter Botha (Chm & CEO)

AFRICAN MINERALS EXPLO-

RATION & DEVELOPMENT SICAR SCA

12F rue Guillaume Kroll, 1882, Luxembourg, Luxembourg
Tel.: (352) 26897093
Web Site: http://www.amedfunds.com
Year Founded: 2012
Mineral Project Investment Services
N.A.I.C.S.: 523999
David Twist (Founding Partner)

Subsidiaries:

AMED Management Services
Ltd   (1)
Third Floor 15-17 Grosvenor Gardens, London, SW1W 0BD, United Kingdom
Tel.: (44) 2037405210
Mineral Exploration Services
N.A.I.C.S.: 213115
Stephen Robert Harrup (Office Mgr)

Canada Fluorspar Inc.   (1)
1 Clarke's Pond Road, PO Box 337, St
Lawrence, Quebec, A0E 2V0, NL, Canada
Tel.: (709) 873-3331
Web Site: http://www.canadafluorspar.ca
Sales Range: Less than $1 Million
Mineral Properties Exploration Services
N.A.I.C.S.: 213114
Rajeev Amara (Chm)

AFRICAN PAINTS (NIGERIA) PLC.

Plot 51 Morison Crescent
Alausa/Oregun Industrial Estat, Ikeja,
21538, Nigeria
Tel.: (234) 1 477 5237
Paints Mfr
N.A.I.C.S.: 325510
Olugbenga Akinbiyi Akinnawo (Chm)

AFRICAN RAINBOW CAPITAL INVESTMENTS

Level 3 Alexander House 19 Cybercity, Ebene, Mauritius
Tel.: (230) 4030800
Web Site: https://www.arci.mu
AIL—(JSE)
Rev.: $54,460
Assets: $837,867,100
Liabilities: $108,920
Net Worth: $837,758,180
Earnings: $108,103,100
Emp.: 1
Fiscal Year-end: 12/31/23
Asset Management Services
N.A.I.C.S.: 523940
Johan Van Zyl (CEO)

AFRICAN RAINBOW MINERALS LIMITED

ARM House 29 Impala Road, Chislehurston, Sandton, 2196, South Africa
Tel.: (27) 117791300
Web Site: https://www.arm.co.za
AFBOF—(OTCIQ)
Rev.: $850,082,912
Assets: $3,386,495,421
Liabilities: $527,202,442
Net Worth: $2,859,292,979
Earnings: $492,189,398
Emp.: 13,477
Fiscal Year-end: 06/30/23
Metal & Coal Mining Services
N.A.I.C.S.: 212290
Michael P. Schmidt (CEO)

Subsidiaries:

Jesdene Limited   (1)
ARM House 29 Impala Road, Chislehurston, Sandton, 2196, South Africa
Tel.: (27) 117791300
Coal & Copper Mining Services
N.A.I.C.S.: 213113

Two Rivers Platinum (Proprietary)
Limited   (1)
2 Rivers Platinum Mine Dwarsriver Farm KT

372, Steelpoort, 1133, Mpumalanga, South
Africa
Tel.: (27) 132302800
Platinum Mining Services
N.A.I.C.S.: 212290
J. J. Joubert (Gen Mgr)

AFRICAN SUN LIMITED

Bally House Mount Pleasant Business Park Cnr Norfolk Road/870, Endeavor Crescent, Harare, Zimbabwe
Tel.: (263) 242338232   ZW
Web Site:
    http://www.africansunhotels.com
Year Founded: 1968
ASUN—(ZIM)
Rev.: $54,726,234
Assets: $142,332,546
Liabilities: $42,387,060
Net Worth: $99,945,486
Earnings: $521,045
Emp.: 837
Fiscal Year-end: 12/31/23
Home Management Services
N.A.I.C.S.: 721120
Edwin Timothy Shangwa (Mng Dir)

Subsidiaries:

African Sun Zimbabwe (Private)
Limited   (1)
Crowne Plaza Monomotapa 54 Park Lane,
Harare, Zimbabwe
Tel.: (263) 4700521
Web Site: http://www.africansun.com
Home Management Services
N.A.I.C.S.: 721110

The Victoria Falls Hotel   (1)
1 Mallett Drive, PO Box 10, Victoria Falls,
Zimbabwe   (50%)
Tel.: (263) 832844751
Web Site: http://www.victoriafallshotel.com
Sales Range: $50-74.9 Million
Emp.: 350
Hotel
N.A.I.C.S.: 721110
Farai Chimba (Gen Mgr)

AFRICINVEST

16 Bis Avenue de la Motte Picquet,
75007, Paris, France
Tel.: (33) 173043440
Web Site: http://www.africinvest.com
Year Founded: 1994
Rev.: $1,500,000,000
Privater Equity Firm
N.A.I.C.S.: 523940
Cherif Bouattour (Partner)

AFRIKA GOLD AG

Firststrasse 15, Feusisberg, 8835,
Schwyz, Switzerland
Tel.: (41) 447868661
Web Site: https://www.afrika-gold.ch
Year Founded: 2008
Gold Mining Services
N.A.I.C.S.: 212220
Jean-Christophe Probst (Chm & CEO)

AFRIKA4U

12 Bompart Street, Westdene,
Bloemfontein, 9301, South Africa
Tel.: (27) 775 882 1013   NV
Year Founded: 2017
Assets: $1,185
Liabilities: $5,755
Net Worth: ($4,570)
Earnings: ($11,957)
Emp.: 1
Fiscal Year-end: 08/31/18
Leather Product Distr
N.A.I.C.S.: 424350
Charl Fredrick Coertzen (Founder,
Chm, Pres, CEO, CFO, Treas & Sec)

AFRILAND FIRST BANK

1063 Independence Square, PO Box
11834, Yaounde, Cameroon

Tel.: (237) 222233068
Web Site:
    http://www.afrilandfirstbank.com
Year Founded: 1987
Sales Range: $10-24.9 Million
Emp.: 240
Banking Services
N.A.I.C.S.: 522110
Alphonse Nafack (Gen Mgr)

Subsidiaries:

CCEI BANK GE   (1)
Calle presidente Nasser Apdo 428, Malabo,
Equatorial Guinea
Tel.: (240) 92203
Web Site: http://www.cceibankge.com
Commercial Banking Services
N.A.I.C.S.: 522110

AFRIMAT LIMITED

Tyger Valley Office Park No 2, PO
Box 5278, Corner Willie van Schoor
Avenue and Old Oak Road Tyger Valley, Bellville, 7536, South Africa
Tel.: (27) 219178840   ZA
Web Site: https://www.afrimat.co.za
AFT—(JSE)
Rev.: $259,204,153
Assets: $300,020,702
Liabilities: $96,754,190
Net Worth: $203,266,511
Earnings: $35,144,066
Emp.: 2,668
Fiscal Year-end: 02/28/23
Construction Materials Supplier
N.A.I.C.S.: 236210
Andries J. van Heerden (CEO)

Subsidiaries:

Afrimat Concrete Products   (1)
15 Bloekom Street, Vryheid, 3100, KwaZulu
Natal, South Africa
Tel.: (27) 349809411
Web Site: http://www.afrimat.co.za
Stone Quarrying Services
N.A.I.C.S.: 212311

Afrimat Readymix (Cape) (Pty)
Limited   (1)
189 Blouberg Rd, Cape Town, 7441, Western Cape, South Africa
Tel.: (27) 215563255
Sales Range: $25-49.9 Million
Emp.: 98
Readymix Concrete Mfr
N.A.I.C.S.: 327320

Boublok (Pty) Limited   (1)
38 Samuel Walter St, PO Box 601, Worcester, 6850, Western Cape, South Africa
Tel.: (27) 233423639
Web Site: http://www.afrimat.co.za
Sales Range: $25-49.9 Million
Emp.: 47
Readymix Concrete Mfr
N.A.I.C.S.: 327320

Cape Lime Proprietary Limited   (1)
Karoovlakte, Vredendal, 8160, South Africa
Tel.: (27) 2011200
Web Site: https://www.capelime.co.za
Mineral Mining Services
N.A.I.C.S.: 213114
Natasha Mouton (Ops Mgr)

Denver Quarries (Pty) Limited   (1)
Mission Rd, Port Elizabeth, 6390, Eastern
Cape, South Africa
Tel.: (27) 413721122
Stone Quarrying Services
N.A.I.C.S.: 212311

Infrasors Holdings Limited   (1)
Lyttelton Dolomite Mine Botha Avenue,
Lyttelton, 0157, Pretoria, South
Africa   (91.28%)
Tel.: (27) 126645649
Web Site: http://www.infrasors.co.za
Sales Range: $25-49.9 Million
Emp.: 271
Dolomite & Silica Mining Services
N.A.I.C.S.: 212319

Subsidiary (Domestic):

Delf Sand (Pty) Limited   (2)

Portion 10 Farm Pienaarspoort, Pretoria,
0002, Gauteng, South Africa
Tel.: (27) 127362240
Web Site: http://www.ifrimith.com
Plaster Sand Distr
N.A.I.C.S.: 423320

Plant (Domestic):

Delf Silica Coastal (2)
Tongaat Industrial Park 9 Walter Reid Road,
Tongaat, 102, South Africa
Tel.: (27) 32 944 5870
Metal Mining Services
N.A.I.C.S.: 212290

Lancaster Pre-Cast (Pty) Limited (1)
15 Bloekom St, Vryheid, 3100, Kwazulu-
Natal, South Africa
Tel.: (27) 349809411
Web Site: http://www.afrimat.co.za
Emp.: 500
Readymix Concrete Mfr
N.A.I.C.S.: 327320
Pieter Dewit (Gen Mgr)

Maritzburg Quarries (Pty) Limited (1)
Cliffdale Rd, Hammarsdale, 3700, Kwazulu-
Natal, South Africa
Tel.: (27) 317362036
Sales Range: $50-74.9 Million
Emp.: 50
Stone Quarrying Services
N.A.I.C.S.: 212311

Rodag Properties (Pty) Limited (1)
15 Bloekom St, Vryheid, 3100, South Africa
Tel.: (27) 349809411
Web Site: http://www.afrimat.co.za
Property Management Services
N.A.I.C.S.: 531312
Pieter De Wit (Mng Dir)

AFRIQUE ENERGIE CORP.

TD Canada Trust Tower 161 Bay
Street 27th Floor, Toronto, ON,
Canada
Tel.: (416) 572-4059
Web Site: http://www.afrique-
energie.com
Oil & Gas Exploration & Production
Services
N.A.I.C.S.: 211120
Mark Lawson (Pres)

AFRIQUE TELECOM SA

7 rue plaine des Isles, 89000, Aux-
erre, France
Tel.: (33) 386942640
Web Site: http://www.afrique-
telecom.com
Telecommunication Services Provider
N.A.I.C.S.: 517111
Philippe Tintignac (Chm & CEO)

AFRISAM (SOUTH AFRICA)
(PTY) LTD.

Main Reef Road, Roodepoort, 1401,
Gauteng, South Africa
Tel.: (27) 116705500 ZA
Web Site: http://www.afrisam.co.za
Year Founded: 2007
Sales Range: $900-999.9 Million
Emp.: 1,800
Cement & Concrete Mfr
N.A.I.C.S.: 327310
Louise van der Bank (CIO)

AFRISTRAT INVESTMENT
HOLDINGS LIMITED

1st Floor Block F Southern Life Gar-
dens, 70 2nd Avenue Newton Park,
Port Elizabeth, 6055, Gqeberha,
South Africa
Tel.: (27) 878080100 ZA
Web Site:
https://www.whoownswhom.co.za
Year Founded: 1995
ECS—(JSE)
Rev.: $3,625,333
Assets: $48,147,455
Liabilities: $59,853,403

Net Worth: ($11,705,948)
Earnings: ($37,613,971)
Fiscal Year-end: 03/31/21
Investment Management Service
N.A.I.C.S.: 523940
Dirk P. van der Merwe (Fin Dir)

Subsidiaries:

Ecsponent South Africa (Pty) Ltd (1)
Acacia House Green Hill Village Office Park
Cnr, Botterklapper and Nentabos The Wil-
lows, Pretoria, South Africa
Tel.: (27) 878080100
Financial Services
N.A.I.C.S.: 523210

AFROCENTRIC INVESTMENT
CORPORATION LIMITED

37 Conrad Road Florida North,
Roodepoort, 1709, South Africa
Tel.: (27) 873609552 ZA
Web Site:
https://www.afrocentric.za.com
Year Founded: 2006
ACT—(JSE)
Rev.: $470,468,478
Assets: $293,615,532
Liabilities: $108,840,292
Net Worth: $184,775,241
Earnings: $15,572,725
Emp.: 4,775
Fiscal Year-end: 06/30/23
Investment Management Service
N.A.I.C.S.: 523940
Anna T. Mokgokong (Chm)

AFRY AB

Frosundaleden 2A, 169 75 Solna,
Stockholm, Sweden
Tel.: (46) 105050000 SE
Web Site: https://www.afry.com
Year Founded: 1895
AFRY—(OMX)
Rev.: $2,205,925,052
Assets: $2,622,158,532
Liabilities: $1,481,543,923
Net Worth: $1,140,614,609
Earnings: $91,226,690
Emp.: 17,340
Fiscal Year-end: 12/31/22
Holding Company; Technical Consult-
ing & Engineering Services
N.A.I.C.S.: 551112
Anders Narvinger (Chm)

Subsidiaries:

AF Advansia AS (1)
Forusparken 2 Inngang 02 3 etg, 4031, Sta-
vanger, Norway
Tel.: (47) 95937086
Technical Consulting Services
N.A.I.C.S.: 541690
Christopher Klepsland (Dir-Admin)

AF Advansia Nordvest AS (1)
Sofus Jorgensens Veg 5, 6415, Molde, Nor-
way
Tel.: (47) 92010849
Technical Consulting Services
N.A.I.C.S.: 541690

AF Consult do Brasil Ltda. (1)
Av Kennedy 914 Sala 61 Bairro Anchieta,
Sao Bernardo do Campo, 09726-253, Sao
Paulo, Brazil
Tel.: (55) 1136751775
Web Site: http://www.afconsult.com
Technical Consulting Services
N.A.I.C.S.: 541611

AF Engineering AS (1)
Nittedalsgaten 7, 2000, Lillestrom, Norway
Tel.: (47) 24101010
Technical Consulting Services
N.A.I.C.S.: 541690

AF Infrastructure Polska Sp. z
o.o. (1)
ul 28 Czerwca 1956 roku nr 406, 61-441,
Poznan, Poland
Tel.: (48) 616589367
Technical Consulting Services

N.A.I.C.S.: 541690

AF Mercados Energy Markets Inter-
national S.A. (1)
Avenida de Burgos 12 13th Floor, 28036,
Madrid, Spain
Tel.: (34) 915795242
Technical Consulting Services
N.A.I.C.S.: 541690

Subsidiary (Non-US):

AF-MERCADOS EMI Enerji
Muhendisligi AR-GE Kontrol ve Test
Hizmetleri Ltd. Sti. (2)
Mustafa Kemal Mah Dumlupinar Bul No 208
D Blok No 3, Cankaya, 06510, Ankara, Tur-
kiye
Tel.: (90) 3123859354
Technical Consulting Services
N.A.I.C.S.: 541690
Serhat Can (Country Mgr)

AF Norge AS (1)
Haslevangen 15, NO-0579, Oslo, (100%)
Norway
Tel.: (47) 24101010
Web Site: http://www.afconsult.no
Sales Range: $25-49.9 Million
Emp.: 100
Infrastructure Consulting Services
N.A.I.C.S.: 541690

AF Sandellsandberg Arkitekter
AB (1)
Dobelnsgatan 54, 113 52, Stockholm, Swe-
den
Tel.: (46) 850653100
Web Site: https://www.sandellsandberg.se
Architecture & Design Services
N.A.I.C.S.: 541310

AF-Automaatika OU (1)
Lesta 14, 13516, Tallinn, Estonia
Tel.: (372) 6718130
Technical Consulting Services
N.A.I.C.S.: 541690
Raul Borkmann (Mng Dir)

AF-Consult (Thailand) Ltd. (1)
Vanit II Building 22nd Floor 1126/2 New
Phetburi Road, Makkasan Rajchthewi,
10400, Bangkok, Thailand
Tel.: (66) 21081000
Technical Consulting Services
N.A.I.C.S.: 541690

AF-Consult AB (1)
Frosundaleden 2, SE-169 99, Stockholm,
Sweden (100%)
Tel.: (46) 105050000
Web Site: http://www.afconsult.com
Sales Range: $150-199.9 Million
Emp.: 950
Energy Industry Consulting & Engineering
Services
N.A.I.C.S.: 541690

Subsidiary (Non-US):

AF-Automatikka OU (2)
Lesta 14, 13516, Tallinn, Harju, Estonia
Tel.: (372) 6718130
Web Site: http://www.automaatika.ee
Sales Range: $10-24.9 Million
Emp.: 17
Industrial Automation Services
N.A.I.C.S.: 561990
Priit Tilga (Dir-Sls)

AF-Consult OY (2)
Puolikkotie 8 A 7th floor, 02230, Espoo,
Finland
Tel.: (358) 103311
Web Site: http://www.afconsult.com
Sales Range: $150-199.9 Million
Emp.: 200
Design, Engineering, Consulting & Project
Management Services
N.A.I.C.S.: 541690

Subsidiary (Non-US):

AF-Consult UAB (3)
Lvovo Str 25, 09320, Vilnius, Lithuania
Tel.: (370) 52107210
Web Site: http://www.afconsult.com
Sales Range: $25-49.9 Million
Emp.: 18
Engineering Consulting Services

N.A.I.C.S.: 541330

AF-Consult, LLC (3)
Malaya Pirogovskaya Str 14 Build 1,
119435, Moscow, Russia
Tel.: (7) 495 647 1051
Web Site: http://www.afconsult.com
Sales Range: $75-99.9 Million
Technical Consulting Services
N.A.I.C.S.: 541690

AF-Estivo AS (3)
Vaike Paala 1, Tallinn, 10129, Estonia
Tel.: (372) 6053150
Web Site: http://www.estivo.ee
Sales Range: Less than $1 Million
Emp.: 17
Design, Engineering, Consulting & Project
Management Services
N.A.I.C.S.: 541620
Juri Alasi (Mng Dir)

Subsidiary (Non-US):

AF-Consult Switzerland Ltd. (2)
Tafernstrasse 26, CH-5405, Baden, Switzer-
land
Tel.: (41) 564831212
Web Site: http://www.afconsult.com
Sales Range: $25-49.9 Million
Emp.: 230
Energy & Environmental Technology Engi-
neering & Consulting Services
N.A.I.C.S.: 541330

Subsidiary (Non-US):

AF-Colenco Thailand Ltd. (3)
UBC II Building 24th Floor 591 Sukhumvit
Road 33 North Klongton, Watthana, Bang-
kok, 10110, Thailand
Tel.: (66) 22610294
Web Site: http://www.colenco.ch
Sales Range: $25-49.9 Million
Emp.: 5
Environmental Engineering Services
N.A.I.C.S.: 541330

AF-Consult India Pvt. Ltd. (3)
Office No 2-5 Ground Floor Tower-1, Stellar
IT Park C-25 Sector-62, Noida, 201301,
Uttar Pradesh, India
Tel.: (91) 1204185500
Web Site: http://afry.com
Sales Range: $10-24.9 Million
Environmental Engineering Services
N.A.I.C.S.: 541330

Subsidiary (Non-US):

AF-Engineering Oy (2)
Vuolteenkatu 20, 33100, Tampere, Pirkan-
maa, Finland
Tel.: (358) 10 425 1600
Web Site: http://www.afconsult.com
Civil Engineering Services
N.A.I.C.S.: 541330

AF-Engineering s.r.o (2)
Krizikova 68, 612 00, Brno, Czech Republic
Tel.: (420) 532043051
Web Site: http://www.afconsult.com
Sales Range: $25-49.9 Million
Emp.: 8
Engineeering Services
N.A.I.C.S.: 541330

AF-Consult Czech Republic s.r.o. (1)
Magistru 1275/13, 140 00, Prague, Czech
Republic
Tel.: (420) 261393302
Technical Consulting Services
N.A.I.C.S.: 541690
Petr Kosan (Dir-Sls & Infrastructure)

AF-Consult Energy doo (1)
Knez Mihajlova 1-3, 11000, Belgrade, Ser-
bia
Tel.: (381) 116555533
Technical Consulting Services
N.A.I.C.S.: 541690
Dragan Gojgic (Country Mgr)

AF-Consult GmbH (1)
Mundenheimer Str 100, 67061, Lud-
wigshafen, Germany
Tel.: (49) 6215871170
Technical Consulting Services
N.A.I.C.S.: 541690

AF-Consult Italy S.r.l. (1)

AFRY AB—(Continued)

Via Albricci 7, 20122, Milan, Italy
Tel.: (39) 0284044303
Technical Consulting Services
N.A.I.C.S.: 541690

AF-Consult Ltd. (1)
Str Pirinska No 23 Unit 2 4th Floor MK,
Skopje, North Macedonia
Tel.: (389) 25511855
Technical Consulting Services
N.A.I.C.S.: 541690
Nikola Bitrak (Country Mgr)

AF-Hansen & Henneberg A/S (1)
Lyskar 3 Sal Ef, 2400, Herlev, Hovedsta-
den, Denmark
Tel.: (45) 38165000
Emp.: 90
Civil Engineering Services
N.A.I.C.S.: 541330

AF-Industry AB (1)
Frosundaleden 2, SE-169 99, Stockholm,
Sweden (100%)
Tel.: (46) 105059597
Sales Range: $400-449.9 Million
Emp.: 1,350
Industrial Automation, IT & Mechanical En-
gineering Consulting Services
N.A.I.C.S.: 541690

Subsidiary (Non-US):

AF A/S (2)
Engelsholmvej 26, DK-8940, Randers, SV,
Denmark
Tel.: (45) 43 43 14 00
Web Site: http://www.afconsult.com
Sales Range: $25-49.9 Million
Emp.: 100
Industrial Automation, IT & Mechanical En-
gineering Consulting Services
N.A.I.C.S.: 541690

AF Industrier AS (2)
Iilleakerveien 8, Lysaker, 0283,
Norway (100%)
Tel.: (47) 24101010
Web Site: http://www.afconsult.com
Sales Range: $25-49.9 Million
Emp.: 100
Industrial Automation, IT & Mechanical En-
gineering Consulting Services
N.A.I.C.S.: 541690
Ove Guttormsen (Mgr-Ops)

Subsidiary (Domestic):

OrbiTec AB (2)
Glansgatan 2, Jonkoping, 554 54, Smaland,
Sweden
Tel.: (46) 36162870
Sales Range: $10-24.9 Million
Emp.: 35
Technical Consulting Services
N.A.I.C.S.: 541690

AF-Ingemansson AB (1)
Frosundaleden 2, SE-169 99, Stockholm,
Sweden (100%)
Tel.: (46) 10 505 1014
Web Site: http://www.ingemansson.com
Sound & Vibration Technical Consulting
Services
N.A.I.C.S.: 541690

AFRY (Peru) S.A.C. (1)
Calle Las Begonias 441 Edificio Plaza Del
Sol Piso 7, San Isidro, 15046, Lima, Peru
Tel.: (51) 12249111
Renewable Energy Distr
N.A.I.C.S.: 221114

AFRY (Thailand) Ltd. (1)
Vanit Building II 22nd Floor Room No 2202-
2203, 1126/2 New Petchburi Road Mak-
kasan Rajchthewi, Bangkok, TH-10400,
Thailand
Tel.: (66) 21081000
Renewable Energy Distr
N.A.I.C.S.: 221114

AFRY ApS (1)
Viborgvej 1, 7400, Herning, Denmark
Tel.: (45) 70104100
Software Development Services
N.A.I.C.S.: 541511

AFRY Austria GmbH (1)

Kranichberggasse 4, 1120, Vienna, Austria
Tel.: (43) 1536050
Web Site: https://afry.com
Emp.: 260
Engineering & Advisory Services
N.A.I.C.S.: 541330

AFRY CZ s.r.o. (1)
Magistru 1275/13, 140 00, Prague, Czech
Republic
Tel.: (420) 277005500
Web Site: https://www.afrycz.cz
Emp.: 70
Engineering Design Services
N.A.I.C.S.: 541330

AFRY Canada Inc. (1)
5250 Ferrier Suite 700, Montreal, H4P 1L4,
QC, Canada
Tel.: (514) 341-3221
Engineering & Advisory Services
N.A.I.C.S.: 541330

AFRY Capital Limited (1)
Four Millbank, Westminster, London, SW1P
3JA, United Kingdom
Tel.: (44) 2074794000
Engineering Design Services
N.A.I.C.S.: 541330

AFRY Deutschland GmbH (1)
Marburger Strasse 10, 10789, Berlin, Ger-
many
Tel.: (49) 30213040
Web Site: https://afry.com
Engineering & Advisory Services
N.A.I.C.S.: 541330

AFRY Estonia OU (1)
Kassi 1, Tallinn, Estonia
Tel.: (372) 6718130
Engineering & Advisory Services
N.A.I.C.S.: 541330

AFRY Finland Oy (1)
Jaakonkatu 3, 01620, Vantaa, Finland
Tel.: (358) 103311
Web Site: https://afry.com
Engineering & Advisory Services
N.A.I.C.S.: 541330

AFRY India Private Limited (1)
Office no 2-5 Ground floor Tower-1 Stellar
IT Park, Noida, 201 301, Uttar Pradesh,
India
Tel.: (91) 1204185500
Engineering & Advisory Services
N.A.I.C.S.: 541330

AFRY Ireland Limited (1)
The Hyde Building The Park, Carrickmines,
Dublin, D18VC44, Ireland
Tel.: (353) 18455031
Engineering & Advisory Services
N.A.I.C.S.: 541330

AFRY Italy S.R.L. (1)
Via Pietro Chiesa 9, 16149, Genoa, Italy
Tel.: (39) 010291051
Engineering Design Services
N.A.I.C.S.: 541330

AFRY Malaysia Sdn. Bhd. (1)
14-06 Level 14 Menara Hap Seng 2 Plaza
Hap Seng No 1 Jalan P Ramlee, 50250,
Kuala Lumpur, Malaysia
Tel.: (60) 327131601
Renewable Energy Distr
N.A.I.C.S.: 221114

**AFRY Management Consulting Aus-
tria GmbH** (1)
Kranichberggasse 2, 1120, Vienna, Austria
Tel.: (43) 16411800
Engineering Design Services
N.A.I.C.S.: 541330

**AFRY Management Consulting
Inc.** (1)
295 Madison Ave Ste 300, New York, NY
10017
Tel.: (914) 643-2767
Engineering Design Services
N.A.I.C.S.: 541330

**AFRY Management Consulting
S.R.L.** (1)
Viale Francesco Restelli 3/1, 20124, Milan,
Italy
Tel.: (39) 0236596900
Engineering Design Services

N.A.I.C.S.: 541330

AFRY Poland Sp. Z.o.o. (1)
Ul Zeromskiego 52, 90-626, Lodz, Poland
Tel.: (48) 426380400
Engineering Design Services
N.A.I.C.S.: 541330

AFRY Rus LLC (1)
Ligovskiy prospect 266 build V, Saint Pe-
tersburg, 196006, Russia
Tel.: (7) 8123258090
Web Site: https://afry.com
Engineering & Advisory Services
N.A.I.C.S.: 541330

AFRY Solutions Spain, S.A.U. (1)
Plaza de Pinares 1-2nd Floor, PO Box
3002, 20001, San Sebastian, Spain
Tel.: (34) 943326110
Engineering Design Services
N.A.I.C.S.: 541330

AFRY Solutions UK Limited (1)
4th Floor West Point Springfield Road, Hor-
sham, RH12 2PD, United Kingdom
Tel.: (44) 1403211400
Engineering Design Services
N.A.I.C.S.: 541330

AFRY South-East Asia Ltd. (1)
Vanit Building II 22nd Floor Room No 2202-
2203, 1126/2 New Petchburi Road Mak-
kasan Rajchthewi, Bangkok, TH-10400,
Thailand
Tel.: (66) 21081000
Renewable Energy Distr
N.A.I.C.S.: 221114

AFRY Vietnam Ltd. (1)
5A Floor - BIDV Tower 194 Tran Quang
Khai street, Hoan Kiem, Hanoi, Vietnam
Tel.: (84) 2439330468
Emp.: 50
Engineering & Advisory Services
N.A.I.C.S.: 541330

Advansia AS (1)
Lilleakerveien 8, 0283, Oslo, Norway
Tel.: (47) 24101010
Web Site: https://www.advansia.no
Emp.: 700
Project Management Services
N.A.I.C.S.: 541611

**Afry Engineering India Private
Limited** (1)
Pride Icon Office No 306 3rd Floor Kharadi
Mundhva, Hadapsar Bypass Road, Pune,
411014, Maharashtra, India
Tel.: (91) 9515122710
Engineering Design Services
N.A.I.C.S.: 541330

Afry Eroterv Zrt. (1)
Infopark B, 1117, Budapest, Hungary
Tel.: (36) 14553600
Engineering Design Services
N.A.I.C.S.: 541330

Afry USA LLC (1)
2323 E Capitol Dr, Appleton, WI 54911
Tel.: (920) 954-2106
Engineering & Advisory Services
N.A.I.C.S.: 541330

Cecon AB (1)
Tolarp 21, 555 94, Jonkoping, Sweden
Tel.: (46) 705977415
Web Site: http://www.cecon.se
Microsoft Dynamic Software Development
Services
N.A.I.C.S.: 513210

Digifex AB (1)
Sodergatan 26, 211 34, Malmo, Sweden
Tel.: (46) 406656880
Web Site: http://www.digifex.se
3D Animation & Visual Effect Services
N.A.I.C.S.: 512191

Gottlieb Paludan Architects A/S (1)
Orientkaj 4 Nordhavn, 2150, Copenhagen,
Denmark
Tel.: (45) 41718200
Web Site: https://www.gottliebpaludan.com
Architecture & Design Services
N.A.I.C.S.: 541330
Brian Jorgensen (Mgr-Project)

IFEC Ingegneria SA (1)
Via C Pellandini 3, Bellinzona, 6500, Lu-

gano, Switzerland
Tel.: (41) 919362700
Web Site: https://www.ifec.ch
Engineering Consulting Services
N.A.I.C.S.: 541330

ITECO Nepal (Pvt.) Ltd. (1)
96 Sri Panchakanya Marg Minbhawan New
Baneshwor, Post Office Box 2147, Kath-
mandu, Nepal
Tel.: (977) 14106776
Web Site: https://www.iteconepal.com
Engineering Consulting Services
N.A.I.C.S.: 541330
Tuk Lal Adhikari (Mng Dir)

KSH Solutions Inc. (1)
1 Place Alexis Nihon 3400 de Maisonneuve
O, Montreal, H3Z 3B8, QC, Canada
Tel.: (514) 932-4611
Web Site: https://www.ksh.ca
Sales Range: $25-49.9 Million
Emp.: 150
Engineering & Consulting Services
N.A.I.C.S.: 541330
Martin J. Pereira (Pres)

Konsultbolag1 Syd AB (1)
Hallenborgs Gata 4, 211 74, Malmo, Swe-
den
Tel.: (46) 765487840
Supplementary Course Training Services
N.A.I.C.S.: 611430

Light Bureau Limited (1)
Unit 7F 5 Hewlett House Havelock Terrace,
London, SW8 4AS, United Kingdom
Tel.: (44) 7979595925
Web Site: https://www.lightbureau.co
Lighting Design Services
N.A.I.C.S.: 541490
Arve Olsen (Dir-Design)

Subsidiary (Non-US):

Light Bureau AS (2)
Lilleakerveien 8, 0283, Oslo, Norway
Tel.: (47) 45478101
Architectural Design Services
N.A.I.C.S.: 541310
Paul Traynor (CEO & Principal)

**Nordblads VVS-Konstruktioner
AB** (1)
Halleblrg Gata 1, Malmo, 21119, Scania,
Sweden
Tel.: (46) 105055250
Web Site: http://www.afconsult.com
Sales Range: $25-49.9 Million
Emp.: 50
Technical Consulting Services
N.A.I.C.S.: 541690

P.A.P A/S (1)
Langebrogade 1D, 1411, Copenhagen,
Denmark
Tel.: (45) 35245555
Web Site: http://www.pap.dk
Electricity Supply Services
N.A.I.C.S.: 221122
Philippe Tring (Dir)

P.T. AFRY Indonesia (1)
Graha CIMB Niaga 8th Floor Jl Jend
Sudirman Kav 58, Jakarta, 12190, Indone-
sia
Tel.: (62) 212526668
Renewable Energy Distr
N.A.I.C.S.: 221114

Poyry PLC (1)
Jaakonkatu 3, PO Box 4, 01621, Vantaa,
Finland (99.3%)
Tel.: (358) 103311
Web Site: http://www.poyry.com
Rev.: $625,642,278
Assets: $467,285,186
Liabilities: $311,683,172
Net Worth: $155,602,014
Earnings: $6,708,016
Emp.: 4,637
Fiscal Year-end: 12/31/2017
Holding Company; Consulting & Engineer-
ing Services
N.A.I.C.S.: 551112

Subsidiary (Non-US):

Aquatis spol s.r.o. (2)
Prazska 1827/66, 678 01, Blansko, Czech
Republic
Tel.: (420) 606 683 397

Energy Consulting Services
N.A.I.C.S.: 541690

CJSC Giprobum-Poyry **(2)**
266 Ligovsky Prospect, 196084, Saint Petersburg, Russia
Tel.: (7) 812 325 8090
Emp.: 100
Construction Engineering Services
N.A.I.C.S.: 541330

ETT Proyectos S.A. **(2)**
C/ General Ramirez de Madrid 8-6 a
Planta, 28020, Madrid, Spain
Tel.: (34) 91 534 13 95
Sales Range: $25-49.9 Million
Emp.: 27
Railway Engineering & Consulting Services
N.A.I.C.S.: 541330
Jose Luis Sadornil *(Gen Mgr)*

ETV-Eroterv Rt. **(2)**
Angyal Str 1-3, 1094, Budapest, Hungary
Tel.: (36) 14553600
Web Site: http://www.eroterv.hu
Sales Range: $10-24.9 Million
Emp.: 170
Engineeering Services
N.A.I.C.S.: 541330

Subsidiary (Domestic):

East Engineering Ltd Oy **(2)**
Jaakonkatu 3, Vantaa, 01620, Finland
Tel.: (358) 989473978
Web Site: http://www.poyry.fi
Sales Range: $25-49.9 Million
Emp.: 200
Engineeering Services
N.A.I.C.S.: 541330
Teenu Vuora *(Gen Mgr)*

Subsidiary (Non-US):

POYRY Infra S.A. **(2)**
25 de Mayo 457 - 10 Piso, C1002ABI, Buenos Aires, Argentina
Tel.: (54) 11 6091 1560
Sales Range: $25-49.9 Million
Emp.: 15
Construction Engineering Services
N.A.I.C.S.: 541330

PT. Poyry Indonesia
Graha Cimb Niaga 8th Floor Jl Jend
Sudirman Kav 58, Jakarta, 12190, Indonesia
Tel.: (62) 212526668
Web Site: http://www.poyry.com
Sales Range: $25-49.9 Million
Business Management Consulting Services
N.A.I.C.S.: 541611

Paul Keller Ingenieure AG **(2)**
Hochbordstrasse 9, 8600, Dubendorf, Switzerland
Tel.: (41) 43 355 29 00
Web Site: http://www.pkag.ch
Sales Range: $25-49.9 Million
Emp.: 5
Construction Engineering Services
N.A.I.C.S.: 541330
Martin E. Bachmann *(Chm)*

Poyry & Company LLC **(2)**
Tamimah Building Way No 3830 Al Nadha
Street Wattayah, PO Box 86, Al Qurum,
Muscat, 102, Oman
Tel.: (968) 2457 4500
Construction Engineering Services
N.A.I.C.S.: 541330

Subsidiary (US):

Poyry (Appleton) LLC **(2)**
2323 E Capitol Dr, Appleton, WI 54912-
8028
Tel.: (920) 954-2000
Web Site: http://www.poyryappletonllc.com
Construction Engineering Services
N.A.I.C.S.: 541330
Michael Hooyman *(Pres)*

Subsidiary (Non-US):

Poyry (Mexico) S.A., de C.V. **(2)**
Av Paseo De La Reforma 404 - 302 Col
Juarez Del Cuauhtemoc, 06600, Mexico,
Mexico
Tel.: (52) 55 5514 3949
Web Site: http://www.poyry.com

Sales Range: $25-49.9 Million
Construction Engineering Services
N.A.I.C.S.: 541330

Poyry (Montreal) Inc. **(2)**
5250 Ferrier Suite 700, Montreal, H4P 1L4,
QC, Canada
Tel.: (514) 341-3221
Web Site: http://www.poyry.ca
Sales Range: $25-49.9 Million
Forestry Engineering Services
N.A.I.C.S.: 541330

Poyry (Peru) S.A.C. **(2)**
Av Jose Galvez Barrenechea 223, San
Isidro, Lima, 27, Peru
Tel.: (51) 1 2249 111
Web Site: http://www.poyry.com
Sales Range: $25-49.9 Million
Emp.: 50
Engineeering Services
N.A.I.C.S.: 541330

Poyry (Vancouver) Inc. **(2)**
Suite 200 1550 Alberni Street, Vancouver,
V6G 1A5, BC, Canada
Tel.: (604) 689-0344
Sales Range: $25-49.9 Million
Emp.: 35
Construction Engineering Services
N.A.I.C.S.: 541330

Poyry Capital Limited **(2)**
Portland House Bressenden Place, London,
SW1E 5BH, United Kingdom
Tel.: (44) 20 7479 4000
Web Site: http://www.poyrycapital.com
Sales Range: $50-74.9 Million
Investment Banking Services
N.A.I.C.S.: 523150

**Poyry Consulting and Engineering
(India) Private Limited** **(2)**
Andheri Kurla Road, Andheri E, Mumbai,
400 059, India
Tel.: (91) 99 0209 7711
Web Site: http://www.poyry.com
Civil Engineering Construction Services
N.A.I.C.S.: 237990

Poyry Deutschland GmbH **(2)**
Heinrich-von-Stephan-Strasse 3-5, 68161,
Mannheim, Germany
Tel.: (49) 621 8790 00
Web Site: http://www.poyry.de
Construction Engineering Services
N.A.I.C.S.: 541330
Ralf Teuchert *(Reg Sls Mgr)*

Subsidiary (Domestic):

Poyry Deutschland GmbH **(3)**
Borsteler Chaussee 51, 22453, Hamburg,
Germany **(100%)**
Tel.: (49) 40692000
Web Site: http://www.poyry.de
Sales Range: $25-49.9 Million
Emp.: 60
Engineeering Services
N.A.I.C.S.: 541330

Subsidiary (Non-US):

**Poyry Energy Consulting (Italia)
S.r.l.** **(2)**
Viale Francesco Restelli 3/1, 20-124, Milan,
Italy **(100%)**
Tel.: (39) 0236596900
Web Site: http://www.poyry.com
Sales Range: $25-49.9 Million
Emp.: 12
Management Consulting Services
N.A.I.C.S.: 541618

**Poyry Energy Consulting (Schweiz)
AG** **(2)**
Herostrasse 12, 8037, Zurich, Switzerland
Tel.: (41) 442889090
Sales Range: $25-49.9 Million
Emp.: 500
Management Consulting Services
N.A.I.C.S.: 541618
Topias Schwarz *(Mng Dir)*

**Poyry Energy Consulting Group
AG** **(2)**
Herostarsse 12, Zurich, 8048, Switzerland
Tel.: (41) 442889090
Web Site: http://www.poyry.com

Sales Range: $25-49.9 Million
Emp.: 20
Energy Consulting Services
N.A.I.C.S.: 541690

Subsidiary (Domestic):

Poyry Energy Oy **(2)**
Jaakonkatu 3, PO Box 4, 01621, Vantaa,
Finland **(100%)**
Tel.: (358) 103311
Web Site: http://www.poyry.fi
Sales Range: $25-49.9 Million
Emp.: 150
Engineeering Services
N.A.I.C.S.: 541330

Subsidiary (Non-US):

Poyry Energy AG **(3)**
Herostrasse 12, 8048, Zurich,
Switzerland **(100%)**
Tel.: (41) 443555555
Web Site: http://www.ewi.ch
Sales Range: $75-99.9 Million
Emp.: 500
Management Consulting Services
N.A.I.C.S.: 541618

Poyry Energy GmbH **(3)**
Laaer-Berg-Strasse 43, 1100, Vienna, Austria
Tel.: (43) 1 536 05 0
Web Site: http://www.poyry.at
Sales Range: $75-99.9 Million
Emp.: 30
Energy Consultancy Services
N.A.I.C.S.: 541990
Thomas Kriesch *(Mng Dir)*

Poyry Energy Inc. **(3)**
8th Floor Kings Court I Building 2129 Chino
Roces Avenue, Makati, 1231, Manila, Philippines
Tel.: (63) 28112741
Web Site: http://www.poyry.com
Sales Range: $25-49.9 Million
Emp.: 40
Engineeering Services
N.A.I.C.S.: 541330
Nicky Gemperle *(Mng Dir)*

Poyry Energy Limited **(3)**
4th Floor West Point Springfield Road, Horsham, RH12 2PD, United Kingdom **(100%)**
Tel.: (44) 1403211400
Web Site: http://www.poyry.co.uk
Sales Range: $25-49.9 Million
Emp.: 50
Engineeering Services
N.A.I.C.S.: 541330

Poyry Energy Ltd. **(3)**
Herostrasse 12, Zurich, 8048,
Switzerland **(100%)**
Tel.: (41) 443555554
Web Site: http://www.poyry.com
Sales Range: $25-49.9 Million
Emp.: 500
Engineeering Services
N.A.I.C.S.: 541330
Richard Pinnock *(Pres)*

Poyry Energy Ltd. **(3)**
22nd Floor Room No 2202-2203 1126/2,
Makkasan Rajchthewi, 10400, Bangkok,
Thailand
Tel.: (66) 2 657 1000
Sales Range: $25-49.9 Million
Emp.: 10
Energy Consulting Services
N.A.I.C.S.: 541330
Petteri Harkki *(Pres)*

Poyry Energy Sdn. Bhd. **(3)**
14-06 Level 14 Menara Hap Seng 2 Plaza
Hap Seng, No 1 Jalan P Ramlee, 50250,
Kuala Lumpur, Malaysia
Tel.: (60) 327131601
Web Site: http://www.poyry.com
Sales Range: $25-49.9 Million
Emp.: 5
Engineeering Services
N.A.I.C.S.: 541330

Poyry Energy Srl **(3)**
Via Pietro Chiesa 9, 16149, Genoa,
Italy **(100%)**
Tel.: (39) 010291051
Web Site: http://www.poyry.it

Sales Range: $25-49.9 Million
Emp.: 20
Management Consulting Services
N.A.I.C.S.: 541618

Subsidiary (Non-US):

Poyry Eroterv Zrt. **(2)**
Infopark Setany 3 Infopark B, 1117, Budapest, Hungary
Tel.: (36) 1 455 3600
Web Site: http://www.poyry.hu
Sales Range: $125-149.9 Million
Emp.: 90
Eletric Power Generation Services
N.A.I.C.S.: 221118
Denes Jozsef *(Chm, Mng Dir & VP-Nuclear
Energy & Global Competence)*

Subsidiary (Domestic):

Poyry Finland Oy **(2)**
Jaakonkatu 3, PO Box 4, 1621, Vantaa,
Finland
Tel.: (358) 103311
Emp.: 10
Engineeering Services
N.A.I.C.S.: 541330
Alexis Fries *(CEO)*

Subsidiary (Non-US):

Poyry Infra AG **(2)**
Hornlistrasse 12, Zurich, 8048, Switzerland
Tel.: (41) 44 355 5555
Sales Range: $75-99.9 Million
Emp.: 500
Construction Engineering Services
N.A.I.C.S.: 541330
Rene Stettler *(Controller)*

Poyry Infra GmbH **(2)**
Siegburger Strasse 183 - 187, Cologne,
Germany
Tel.: (49) 2219128430
Sales Range: $25-49.9 Million
Emp.: 27
Engineeering Services
N.A.I.C.S.: 541330
Michael Diegmann *(Mng Dir)*

Poyry Infra GmbH **(2)**
Rainerstrasse 29, 5020, Salzburg,
Austria **(100%)**
Tel.: (43) 503130
Web Site: http://www.poyry.com
Sales Range: $25-49.9 Million
Emp.: 69
Measuring Instrument & Testing Electricity &
Electrical Signals Mfr
N.A.I.C.S.: 334515
Johannes Dolzlmuller *(Pres-Bus Unit-
Eastern Europe)*

Poyry Infra Ltd. **(2)**
Vanit Building II 22nd Floor 1126/2 New
Phetchburi Road, Makkasan Rajchthewi,
10400, Bangkok, Thailand
Tel.: (66) 2 650 3410 2
Sales Range: $25-49.9 Million
Emp.: 7
Construction Engineering Services
N.A.I.C.S.: 541330
Danaisak Panyawai *(Mng Dir)*

Poyry Infra Sp. z o.o. **(2)**
ul Krupnicza 5/1, 31-123, Krakow, Poland
Tel.: (48) 12 429 5375
Sales Range: $25-49.9 Million
Emp.: 5
Construction Engineering Services
N.A.I.C.S.: 541330
Jeroen Huiskamp *(Gen Mgr)*

Poyry Infra de Venezuela S.A. **(2)**
Edf EXA Piso 1 Ofc 109 Urb El Rosal Entre
Av Libertador, El Retiro y Alameda, Caracas, 1060, Venezuela
Tel.: (58) 2129536753
Web Site: http://www.poyry.com
Emp.: 2
Civil Engineering Construction Services
N.A.I.C.S.: 237990

Subsidiary (Domestic):

**Poyry Management Consulting
Oy** **(2)**
Jaakonkatu 3, PO Box 4, 1621, Vantaa,
Finland
Tel.: (358) 103311

AFRY AB—(Continued)

Emp.: 10
Engineering Consulting Services
N.A.I.C.S.: 541330
Jarkko Sairanen *(Pres)*

Subsidiary (Non-US):

Poyry Management Consulting (Australia) Pty. Ltd.   **(3)**
Level 13 390 Saint Kilda Road, Melbourne, 3004, VIC, Australia
Tel.: (61) 3 9863 3700
Web Site: http://www.poyry.com.au
Sales Range: $25-49.9 Million
Engineering Consulting Services
N.A.I.C.S.: 541330

Poyry Management Consulting
(Deutschland) GmbH   **(3)**
Lützstrasse 2, 85356, Munich, Germany
Tel.: (49) 8161 480 66
Sales Range: $25-49.9 Million
Emp.: 2
Engineering Consulting Services
N.A.I.C.S.: 541330
Markku Korpivaara *(Gen Mgr)*

Poyry Management Consulting (Dusseldorf) GmbH   **(3)**
Bennigsen-Platz 1, 40474, Dusseldorf, Germany
Tel.: (49) 211 175238 0
Engineering Consulting Services
N.A.I.C.S.: 541330

Poyry Management Consulting (Italia)
S.r.l.   **(3)**
Viale Francesco Restelli 3, 20123, Milan, Italy
Tel.: (39) 0236596900
Engineering Consulting Services
N.A.I.C.S.: 541330
Antonio Nodari *(Mng Dir)*

Poyry Management Consulting (NZ)
Limited   **(3)**
Level 5 HSBC Building 1 Queen Street, PO Box 105891, Auckland, 0001, New Zealand
Tel.: (64) 9 918 1081
Web Site: http://www.poyry.co.nz
Sales Range: $25-49.9 Million
Emp.: 10
Engineering Consulting Services
N.A.I.C.S.: 541330

Poyry Management Consulting (Norway) AS   **(3)**
Lille Grensen 5, 0159, Oslo, Norway
Tel.: (47) 45 40 50 00
Web Site: http://www.poyry.com
Sales Range: $25-49.9 Million
Engineering Consulting Services
N.A.I.C.S.: 541330

Poyry Management Consulting
(Schweiz) AG   **(3)**
Herostrasse 12, 8048, Zurich, Switzerland
Tel.: (41) 44 288 90 90
Emp.: 500
Engineering Consulting Services
N.A.I.C.S.: 541330
Marcel Winter *(Gen Mgr)*

Poyry Management Consulting (Singapore) Pte. Ltd.   **(3)**
Tel.: (65) 67333331
Engineering Consulting Services
N.A.I.C.S.: 541330

Poyry Management Consulting (Sweden) AB   **(3)**
Banergatan 16 6 Tr, 115 23, Stockholm, Sweden
Tel.: (46) 8 528 01 200
Sales Range: $25-49.9 Million
Emp.: 2
Engineering Consulting Services
N.A.I.C.S.: 541330
Mots Evinsn *(Mng Dir)*

Poyry Management Consulting (UK)
Limited   **(3)**
King Charles House Park End Street, Oxford, OX1 1JD, United Kingdom
Tel.: (44) 1865 722 660
Web Site: http://www.poyry.com
Emp.: 8
Engineering Consulting Services

N.A.I.C.S.: 541330

Subsidiary (US):

Poyry Management Consulting (USA)
Inc.   **(3)**
1355 Peachtree St NE Ste 1500, Atlanta, GA 30309
Tel.: (404) 351-5707
Engineering Consulting Services
N.A.I.C.S.: 541330

Subsidiary (Non-US):

Poyry Norway AS   **(2)**
Hundskinnveien 96, 1711, Sarpsborg, Norway
Tel.: (47) 69 97 34 00
Web Site: http://www.poyry.no
Electrical & Construction Engineering Services
N.A.I.C.S.: 237130

Poyry Poland Sp. z o.o.   **(2)**
Ul Zeromskiego 52, 90-626, Lodz, Poland   **(100%)**
Tel.: (48) 42 6380 400
Web Site: http://www.poyry.pl
Sales Range: $25-49.9 Million
Engineeering Services
N.A.I.C.S.: 541330
Marek Wilman *(Pres)*

Poyry SAS   **(2)**
55 rue de la Villette, 69425, Lyon, France
Tel.: (33) 4 7291 8370
Web Site: http://www.poyry.com
Engineeering Services
N.A.I.C.S.: 327910

Poyry Shandong Engineering Consulting Co., Ltd.   **(2)**
9f-block B Yinhe Building No 2008 Xinluo Avenue, High-tech Development Zone, Jinan, 250101, Shandong-Sheng, China
Tel.: (86) 53188516690
Web Site: http://www.poyry.cn
Engineering Consulting Services
N.A.I.C.S.: 541330

Poyry Silviconsult Engenharia
Ltda.   **(2)**
Rua General Carneiro 904, Curitiba, 80060-150, Brazil   **(100%)**
Tel.: (55) 41 3252 7665
Web Site: http://www.poyry.com
Sales Range: $25-49.9 Million
Emp.: 30
Environmental Consulting Services
N.A.I.C.S.: 541620
Jefferson Bueno Mendes *(Mng Dir)*

Poyry Sweden AB   **(2)**
Ruddammsgatan 30, Box 4018, 800 04, Gavle, Sweden
Tel.: (46) 264014100
Engineering Consulting Services
N.A.I.C.S.: 541690

ProTAK Systems AB   **(1)**
Sjogatan 1D, Ornskoldsvik, Sweden
Tel.: (46) 105056311
Web Site: https://protak.se
Web Based Software Production Services
N.A.I.C.S.: 541511

Profil-Bau Industrial Oy   **(1)**
Ensimmainen Savu 2, 01510, Vantaa, Finland
Tel.: (358) 207350710
Web Site: http://www.profilbauindustrial.fi
Electrical & Automation Design Services
N.A.I.C.S.: 541330
Ismo Lehti *(Mng Dir)*

Zert AB   **(1)**
Hamngatan 7, 921 31, Lycksele, Sweden
Tel.: (46) 95013230
Web Site: https://www.zert.se
Technical Documentation Consulting Services
N.A.I.C.S.: 561410

AFT CORPORATION LIMITED

Unit 7 6-8 Herbert Street, St Leonards, Sydney, 2065, NSW, Australia
Tel.: (61) 2 8484 0151
Web Site: http://www.aftcorp.net
Rev.: $149,074

Assets: $248,196
Liabilities: $182,635
Net Worth: $65,561
Earnings: ($287,220)
Fiscal Year-end: 12/31/17
Logistic Services
N.A.I.C.S.: 541614
Maurice Watson *(Co-Sec)*

AFT PHARMACEUTICALS LIMITED

Level 1 129 Hurstmere Road, Takapuna, 0622, Auckland, New Zealand
Tel.: (64) 94880232
Web Site:
    https://www.aftpharmshares.com
Year Founded: 1998
AFT—(NZX)
Rev.: $93,684,809
Assets: $88,554,426
Liabilities: $44,733,852
Net Worth: $43,820,574
Earnings: $6,372,010
Emp.: 114
Fiscal Year-end: 03/31/23
Pharmaceutical Development & Sales
N.A.I.C.S.: 325412
Marree Atkinson *(Co-Founder)*

AFTER YOU PCL

1319/9 Pattanakarn, Suanluang, Bangkok, 10250, Thailand
Tel.: (66) 23184488
Web Site:
    https://investor.afteryoupcl.com
Year Founded: 2007
AU—(THA)
Rev.: $35,932,553
Assets: $40,930,918
Liabilities: $12,251,578
Net Worth: $28,679,340
Earnings: $5,199,137
Emp.: 1,132
Fiscal Year-end: 12/31/23
Dessert & Beverage Bar Operator
N.A.I.C.S.: 722515
Maetup T. Suwan *(Mng Dir)*

AFTERMATH SILVER LTD.

1500-409 Granville St, Vancouver, V6C 1T2, BC, Canada
Tel.: (604) 484-7855   BC
Web Site: https://aftermathsilver.com
Year Founded: 2011
AAG.H—(OTCIQ)
Assets: $28,890,948
Liabilities: $8,425,546
Net Worth: $20,465,402
Earnings: ($5,397,112)
Emp.: 1
Fiscal Year-end: 05/31/21
Silver Mining Services
N.A.I.C.S.: 212220
Ralph Rushton *(Pres & CEO)*

AFYA LIMITED

No 119 Sala 504 Alameda Oscar Niemeyer, Vila da Serra Minas Gerais, Nova Lima, Brazil
Tel.: (55) 3135157500   Ky
Web Site: http://www.afya.com.br
Year Founded: 2019
AFYA—(NASDAQ)
Rev.: $447,761,208
Assets: $1,384,111,373
Liabilities: $759,268,497
Net Worth: $624,842,876
Earnings: $75,507,341
Emp.: 8,708
Fiscal Year-end: 12/31/22
Medical & Healthcare Education Services
N.A.I.C.S.: 611710
Virgilio Deloy Capobianco Gibbon *(CEO)*

Subsidiaries:

Cardiopapers Solucoes Digitais
Ltda.   **(1)**
Av Marques de Olinda 126 Sala 104, Recife, 50030-901, Brazil
Tel.: (55) 8140404140
Web Site: https://www.cardiopapers.com
Medical Education Services
N.A.I.C.S.: 611710

IClinic Desenvolvimento de Software
Ltda.   **(1)**
Av Presidente Castelo Branco N 2525 sala 317A terreo Complexo Lagoinha, Parque Cidade Industrial Lagoinha Ribeirao Preto, Sao Paulo, 14096-560, Brazil
Tel.: (55) 1121996980
Web Site: http://iclinic.com.br
Healthcare Software Development Services
N.A.I.C.S.: 541511

Instituto Educacional Santo Agostinho
S.A.   **(1)**
Avenida Osmane Barbosa n 937, Conjunto Residencial JK, Montes Claros, 39404-006, Minas Gerais, Brazil
Tel.: (55) 3836903690
Web Site: http://www.fasa.edu.br
Education Management Services
N.A.I.C.S.: 611710

AFYREN SA

9-11 rue Gutenberg, 63100, Clermont-Ferrand, France
Tel.: (33) 451088699
Web Site: https://www.afyren.com
Year Founded: 2012
ALAFY—(EUR)
Rev.: $3,646,665
Assets: $76,005,828
Liabilities: $9,311,461
Net Worth: $66,694,367
Earnings: ($10,345,349)
Emp.: 122
Fiscal Year-end: 12/31/23
Biotechnology Research & Development Services
N.A.I.C.S.: 541714
Fabrice Orecchioni *(COO)*

AG AJIKAWA CORPORATION

4 11 88 Takeshima Nishi Yodogawaku, Osaka, 555 0011, Japan
Tel.: (81) 664742050
Web Site: http://www.ag-ajikawa.co.jp
Year Founded: 1930
Sales Range: $25-49.9 Million
Emp.: 200
Mfr of Steel Transmission Towers; Galvanization, Plastic Powder Coating of Steel Structures; Hobby Products
N.A.I.C.S.: 331513
Hideki Yoshida *(Pres)*

Subsidiaries:

AG Industries, Inc.   **(1)**
18404 Cascade Ave S Ste 140, Seattle, WA 98188
Tel.: (425) 282-5460
Web Site: http://www.whitewings.com
Sales Range: $50-74.9 Million
Emp.: 3
Mfr of Toys, Hobby Items, Gifts, Optical Goods; Distributor of Transmission Line Steel Towers & Galvanized Steel Structures
N.A.I.C.S.: 423920

AG ANADOLU GRUBU HOLDING A.S.

Fatih Sultan Mehmet Mahallesi Balkan Caddesi No 58 Buyaka E Blok Kat 6, Tepeustu Umraniye, 34771, Istanbul, Turkiye
Tel.: (90) 2165788500   TR
Web Site:
    https://www.anadolugrubu.com.tr
Year Founded: 1950
AGHOL—(IST)
Rev.: $11,217,180,017

Assets: $15,158,921,014
Liabilities: $9,827,915,190
Net Worth: $5,331,005,824
Earnings: $174,991,451
Emp.: 56,950
Fiscal Year-end: 12/31/21
Holding Company; Beer & Malt Beverage Brewer & Marketer, Soft Drinks Bottler, Motor Vehicle Mfr, Commercial Banking & Retail Operations
N.A.I.C.S.: 551112
Hursit Zorlu *(CEO)*

Subsidiaries:

Anadolu Endustri Holding A.S. **(1)**
Umut Sokak No 12, Icerenkoy, 34752, Istanbul, Turkiye **(68%)**
Tel.: (90) 2165788500
Web Site: http://www.anadolugroup.com
Emp.: 100
Holding Company
N.A.I.C.S.: 551112

Subsidiary (Domestic):

Alternatif Yatirim A.S. **(2)**
Cumhuriyet Cad Elmadag Han No 8 K 2-3, Elmadag Han, 34367, Istanbul, Turkiye
Tel.: (90) 2123155800
Web Site: http://www.ayatirim.com.tr
Emp.: 16
Commercial Banking Services
N.A.I.C.S.: 522110
Cem Sipal *(Gen Mgr)*

Anadolu Araclar Ticaret A.S. **(2)**
Ankara Asfalti Uzeri Ptt Hastanesi Yani Umut Sokak No 12, 34752, Istanbul, Turkiye
Tel.: (90) 2165788500
Motor Vehicle Distr
N.A.I.C.S.: 423110
Bora Kocak *(Mng Dir)*

Anadolu Bilisim Hizmetleri A.S. **(2)**
Fatih Sultan Mehmet District Balkan Cad Buyaka E Blok No 58, Tepeustu Umraniye, Istanbul, 34169, Turkiye
Tel.: (90) 2165788500
Web Site: https://www.abh.com.tr
Emp.: 185
Enterprise Software Development Services
N.A.I.C.S.: 541511
Atakan Karaman *(Product Mgr-Dev)*

Subsidiary (Non-US):

Anadolu Endustri Holding und Co. KG **(2)**
Bayerstrasse 15, 80335, Munich, Bavaria, Germany
Tel.: (49) 89594421
Emp.: 3
Market Research Services
N.A.I.C.S.: 541613

Subsidiary (Domestic):

Anadolu Motor Uretim ve Pazarlama A.S. **(2)**
Esentepe Mahallesi Anadolu Caddesi No 5, Kartal, 34870, Istanbul, Turkiye **(60.58%)**
Tel.: (90) 2163895960
Web Site: http://www.anadolumotor.com.tr
Emp.: 162
Single Cylinder Diesel Engines Mfr & Distr
N.A.I.C.S.: 333618

Anadolu Restoran Isletmeleri Limited Sirketi **(2)**
Ozsezen Is Merkezi A Blok 122-9 Buyukdere Caddesi, Istanbul, Turkiye
Tel.: (90) 2123363400
Web Site: http://www.mcdonalds.com.tr
Restaurant Management Services
N.A.I.C.S.: 722511
Dilek Basarir *(Gen Mgr)*

Anadolu Varlik Yonetim A.S. **(2)**
Umut Sok No 12 Icerenkoey, Kadikoy, 34752, Istanbul, Turkiye
Tel.: (90) 2165788500
Emp.: 5
Asset Management Services
N.A.I.C.S.: 531390
Ali Baki Usta *(Gen Mgr)*

Celik Motor Ticaret A.S. **(2)**

Ataturk Mah Anadolu Caddesi Yanyol Sokak No 5, Sekerpinari, Kocaeli, Turkiye
Tel.: (90) 2626778800
Web Site: http://www.celikmotor.com
Emp.: 250
Car Dealer
N.A.I.C.S.: 441110

Efes Turizm Isletmeleri A.S. **(2)**
Yildiz Posta Caddesi No 38/2, Istanbul, 34349, Turkiye
Tel.: (90) 2122745510
Web Site: http://www.efestur.com
Emp.: 28
Travel & Tour Operating Agencies
N.A.I.C.S.: 561520
Serife Yilmaz *(Sec)*

Joint Venture (Domestic):

Migros Ticaret A.S. **(2)**
Ataturk Mah Turgut Ozal Bulvar No 7, 34758, Istanbul, Turkiye **(40.25%)**
Tel.: (90) 2165793000
Web Site: http://www.migroskurumsal.com
Rev.: $2,301,183,827
Assets: $1,125,044,185
Liabilities: $998,721,780
Net Worth: $126,322,404
Earnings: $79,684,607
Emp.: 44,520
Fiscal Year-end: 12/31/2022
Supermarket Chain Operator
N.A.I.C.S.: 445110
Omer Ozgur Tort *(CEO)*

Subsidiary (Non-US):

Oyex Handels GmbH **(2)**
Bayerstr 15, 80335, Munich, Germany
Tel.: (49) 71318970905
Web Site: http://www.oyex-gmbh.de
Industrial Machinery Whslr
N.A.I.C.S.: 423830

Garenta Ulasim Cozumleri A.S. **(1)**
Fatih Sultan Mehmet Mahallesi Balkan Caddesi No 58 Buyaka, E Blok Tepeustu Umraniye, 34771, Istanbul, Turkiye
Tel.: (90) 2166562600
Web Site: https://www.garenta.com.tr
Car Rental Services
N.A.I.C.S.: 532111

AG ANADOLU GRUBU HOLDING ANONIM SIRKETI

Balkan Street No 58 Buyaka E Block Tepeustu, Fatih Sultan Mehmet Neighborhood Umraniye, 34771, Istanbul, Turkiye
Tel.: (90) 2165788500
Web Site:
http://www.anadolugrubu.com.tr
Rev.: $7,603,105,489
Assets: $11,282,154,846
Liabilities: $7,293,520,819
Net Worth: $3,988,634,028
Earnings: $204,511,710
Fiscal Year-end: 12/31/19
Consumer Staple Food Distr
N.A.I.C.S.: 445298
Mehmet Hursit Zorlu *(CEO)*

Subsidiaries:

AND Anadolu Gayrimenkul Yatirimlari A.S. **(1)**
F Sultan Mehmet Mh Balkan Cd No 58 Buyaka E Bl, Tepeustu Umraniye, Istanbul, Turkiye
Tel.: (90) 2165741055
Web Site: http://www.andgayrimenkul.com.tr
Real Estate Development Services
N.A.I.C.S.: 531390

Ant Sinai ve Tic.Urunleri Paz. A.S **(1)**
Fatih Sultan Mehmet Mahallesi Balkan Caddesi No 58 Buyaka, E Blok, Tepeustu Umraniye, 34771, Istanbul, Turkiye
Tel.: (90) 8502001900
Beverage Spare Part Whslr
N.A.I.C.S.: 423830

AG CAPITAL

47 A Tsarigradsko Shosse Blvd, Sofia, 1124, Bulgaria
Tel.: (359) 2 810 31 06   **BG**
Web Site: http://www.agcapital.bg
Year Founded: 1993
Sales Range: $1-9.9 Million
Emp.: 300
Real Estate Investment Services
N.A.I.C.S.: 523999
Christo T. Iliev *(Chm)*

Subsidiaries:

BLD Asset Management EAD **(1)**
47A Tsarigradsko shosse Blvd 3rd Floor, 1124, Sofia, Bulgaria
Tel.: (359) 28051910
Real Estate Asst Management Services
N.A.I.C.S.: 523940

Bulgarian Land Development EAD **(1)**
47A Tsarigradsko Shose Blvd, 1124, Sofia, Bulgaria
Tel.: (359) 2 805 1910
Web Site: http://www.bld.bg
Sales Range: $25-49.9 Million
Commercial & Residential Real Estate Development & Construction Management Services
N.A.I.C.S.: 237210
Dimitar Safov *(Gen Mgr)*

FrontEx International EAD **(1)**
15 Henrik Ibsen Str, Sofia, Bulgaria
Tel.: (359) 24390463
Web Site: http://www.frontex.bg
Debt Collection Services
N.A.I.C.S.: 561440
Gabriela Dimitrova *(Head-Legal Collection Dept)*

AG DER DILLINGER HUTTENWERKE

Werkstrasse 1, 66763, Dillingen, Germany
Tel.: (49) 6831470
Web Site: http://www.dillinger.de
Sales Range: $1-4.9 Billion
Emp.: 8,200
Steel Plate Mfr
N.A.I.C.S.: 331221
Markus Lauer *(CFO)*

Subsidiaries:

Ancofer Stahlhandel GmbH **(1)**
Rheinstrabe 163, Mulheim an der Ruhr, 45478, Germany
Tel.: (49) 20858020
Web Site: http://www.ancofer.de
Sales Range: $75-99.9 Million
Emp.: 119
Steel Product Distr
N.A.I.C.S.: 423840

AncoferWaldram Steelplates B.V. **(1)**
Damweg 12, 4905 BS, Oosterhout, Netherlands
Tel.: (31) 162 491500
Web Site: http://www.ancoferwaldram.com
Sales Range: $25-49.9 Million
Emp.: 90
Steel Plate Mfr
N.A.I.C.S.: 331110
Joost Van Dijk *(Mng Dir)*

Dillinger Espana S.L.U. **(1)**
Calle Cronos 24 Bloque 1 Escalera 1 2 B-1, 28037, Madrid, Spain
Tel.: (34) 917 43 0942
Steel Plate Distr
N.A.I.C.S.: 423840

Dillinger France S.A. **(1)**
Rue du Comte Jean, Grande synthe, 59760, Hauts-de-Seine, France
Tel.: (33) 328293999
Web Site: http://www.dillinger-france.com
Heavy Steel Sheet Mfr
N.A.I.C.S.: 332322
Emmanuelle Belpaire *(Head-Sls)*

Dillinger Hutte Services B.V. **(1)**
Spui Boulevard 340 B, Dordrecht, 3311 GR, Netherlands
Tel.: (31) 6 53331666

Emp.: 2
Steel Plate Distr
N.A.I.C.S.: 423840
Rinus Heistek *(Gen Mgr)*

Dillinger Hutte Vertrieb GmbH **(1)**
Werkstr 1, Dillingen, 66763, Saarland, Germany
Tel.: (49) 6831972555
Steel Plate Distr
N.A.I.C.S.: 423840

Dillinger International S.A. **(1)**
39/41 Rue Louis Blanc, 92400, Courbevoie, France
Tel.: (33) 155242191
Heavy Steel Product Mfr
N.A.I.C.S.: 332312
Bernard Rohr *(CEO)*

Dillinger Italia S.R.L. **(1)**
Via PL da Palestrina 2, 20124, Milan, Italy
Tel.: (39) 0267481852
Heavy Steel Product Mfr
N.A.I.C.S.: 332312
Maurizio Chiari *(Mng Dir)*

Dillinger Middle East FZE **(1)**
Road 1241 Between Junction 12 & 13 Jebel Ali Free Zone, PO Box 17592, Dubai, 17592, United Arab Emirates
Tel.: (971) 4 883 3894
Web Site:
http://www.dillingermiddleeast.com
Steel Plate & Fabricated Metal Product Distr
N.A.I.C.S.: 423510
P. J. Narayanan *(Gen Mgr-Sls)*

Subsidiary (Non-US):

Dillinger India Steel Service Center Private Ltd. **(2)**
604 Maithili Signet Sector 30 A Opp Inorbit Mall, Vashi, Mumbai, 400705, India
Tel.: (91) 22 41230270
Web Site: http://www.dillinger-india-ssc.com
Sales Range: $25-49.9 Million
Emp.: 6
Steel Plate Distr
N.A.I.C.S.: 423840
Ranjit Menon *(Mgr-Sls)*

Dillinger Nederland B.V. **(1)**
Spuiboulevard 340b, 3311 GR, Dordrecht, Netherlands
Tel.: (31) 78 6127208
Web Site: http://www.dillinger.de
Steel Plate Distr
N.A.I.C.S.: 423840

Dillinger Norge AS **(1)**
Akersgata 41, 0158, Oslo, Norway
Tel.: (47) 23 31 83 30
Steel Plate Mfr
N.A.I.C.S.: 331110

Eurodecoupe S.A.S. **(1)**
17 Avenue de la Vertonne, 44124, Vertou, France
Tel.: (33) 2 40 80 29 29
Web Site: http://www.eurodecoupe.fr
Steel Plate Mfr
N.A.I.C.S.: 331110

Jebens GmbH **(1)**
Daimlerstrabe 35-37, 70825, Korntal-Munchingen, Germany
Tel.: (49) 711 80 02 0
Web Site: http://www.jebens.de
Steel Plate Mfr & Distr
N.A.I.C.S.: 331110

Saarlux Stahl GmbH & Co. KG **(1)**
Herzogstr 6a, Stuttgart, 70176, Baden-Wurttemberg, Germany
Tel.: (49) 71161460
Steel Plate Distr
N.A.I.C.S.: 423840

Steelwind Nordenham GmbH **(1)**
Blexer Reede 2, 26954, Nordenham, Germany
Tel.: (49) 473136320
Web Site: http://www.steelwind-nordenham.de
Monopile & Wind Turbine Mfr
N.A.I.C.S.: 333611
Alexander M. Morber *(Mng Dir)*

Trans-Overseas B.V. **(1)**

AG der Dillinger Huttenwerke—(Continued)

Scheepmakerij 148, Zwijndrecht, 3331 MA,
South Holland, Netherlands
Tel.: (31) 786201212
Web Site: http://www.transsaar.nl
Sales Range: $25-49.9 Million
Emp.: 5
Steel Plate Mfr
N.A.I.C.S.: 331110
Hans-Joachim Welsch (Mng Dir)

AG GROWTH INTERNATIONAL INC.

198 Commerce Drive, Winnipeg, R3P
0Z6, MB, Canada
Tel.: (204) 489-1855
Web Site: https://www.aggrowth.com
Year Founded: 1996
7AG—(DEU)
Rev.: $937,580,572
Assets: $1,246,683,651
Liabilities: $1,036,445,119
Net Worth: $210,238,532
Earnings: $8,259,312
Emp.: 4,258
Fiscal Year-end: 12/31/21
Grain Equipment Mfr
N.A.I.C.S.: 333111
Nicolle Parker (Sr VP-Fin & Integration Sys)

Subsidiaries:

AGI Brasil Industria e Comercio
S.A.   (1)
Alameda Santos 2441 cj 62, Sao Paulo,
01419-101, SP, Brazil
Tel.: (55) 1138943000
Bulk Material Handling Equipment Mfr
N.A.I.C.S.: 333248

AGI EMEA S.R.L.   (1)
Via Bertella 2, 40064, Ozzano dell'Emilia,
BO, Italy
Tel.: (39) 051798107
Web Site: https://www.aggrowth.com
Grain Storage & Handling Equipment Mfr
N.A.I.C.S.: 333111
Cristiano Carpin (VP-EMEA)

AGI Solutions Inc.   (1)
4411 Bee Ridge Rd Ste 328, Sarasota, FL
34233
Tel.: (941) 924-5402
Web Site: https://agisolutions.com
Pressure Sensitive Product Mfr
N.A.I.C.S.: 322220

AGI Suretrack LLC   (1)
8040 Bond St, Lenexa, KS 66214
Web Site: https://www.agisuretrack.com
Grain Storage & Handling Equipment Mfr
N.A.I.C.S.: 333111
John Lawrence (Sls Mgr-District)

Ag Growth Industries Limited
Partnership   (1)
198 Commerce Drive, Winnipeg, R3P 0Z6,
MB, Canada
Tel.: (204) 489-1855
Web Site: http://www.aggrowth.com
Sales Range: $25-49.9 Million
Emp.: 45
Farming Equipments Mfr
N.A.I.C.S.: 333111

Ag Growth International - Edwards
Grain Guard Division   (1)
215 Barons Street, Nobleford, T0L 1S0, AB,
Canada
Tel.: (403) 824-3997
Web Site: http://www.aggrowth.com
Grain Handling & Storage Equipments Mfr
N.A.I.C.S.: 333111

Ag Growth International - Westfield
Division   (1)
74 Hwy 205 E, PO Box 39, Rosenort, R0G
1W0, MB, Canada
Tel.: (204) 746-2396
Web Site: http://www.aggrowth.com
Sales Range: $100-124.9 Million
Portable Grain Augers Mfr
N.A.I.C.S.: 333120

Airlanco Inc.   (1)

PO Box 398, Falls City, NE 68355
Tel.: (402) 245-2325
Air Management Equipment Mfr
N.A.I.C.S.: 333413

Applegate Livestock Equipment,
Inc.   (1)
902 S State Rd 32, Union City, IN 47390
Tel.: (765) 964-4631
Web Site:
       http://www.applegatelivestockequipment.com
Sales Range: $25-49.9 Million
Emp.: 100
Livestock Handling & Containment Equipments Mfr
N.A.I.C.S.: 333111
Aaron Applegate (Mgr-Sls)

Batco Manufacturing Ltd.   (1)
201 Industrial Drive, Swift Current, S9H
5R4, SK, Canada
Tel.: (306) 773-7779
Web Site: http://www.aggrowth.com
Sales Range: $25-49.9 Million
Agricultural Machinery & Equipment Mfr
N.A.I.C.S.: 333922

CMC Industrial Electronics Ltd.   (1)
305 - 3602 Gilmore Way, Burnaby, V5G
4W9, BC, Canada
Tel.: (604) 421-4425
Bulk Material Handling Equipment Mfr
N.A.I.C.S.: 333248

CMC Industrial Electronics USA,
Inc.   (1)
4838 Pk Glen Rd, Saint Louis Park, MN
55416
Tel.: (604) 421-4425
Hazard Monitoring Equipment Mfr
N.A.I.C.S.: 334519

Danmare Group Inc.   (1)
8100 ON-27 Suite 402, Woodbridge, L4H
3N2, ON, Canada
Tel.: (905) 264-1592
Project Management Services
N.A.I.C.S.: 541611

Euro-Tramco B.V.   (1)
Spacelab 47D, 3824 MR, Amersfoort, Netherlands
Tel.: (31) 334567033
Bulk Material Handling Equipment Mfr
N.A.I.C.S.: 333248

Hansen Manufacturing Corp.   (1)
4511 N Northview Ave, Sioux Falls, SD
57107-0154
Tel.: (605) 332-3200
Web Site: http://www.aggrowth.com
Sales Range: $25-49.9 Million
Conveyors Mfr & Sales
N.A.I.C.S.: 333922

Improtech Ltd.   (1)
40 Wynford Drive Unit 310, Toronto, M3C
1J5, ON, Canada
Tel.: (416) 444-7031
Project Management Services
N.A.I.C.S.: 541611

Junge Control, Inc.   (1)
640 29th Ave SW, Cedar Rapids, IA 52404-
3419
Tel.: (319) 365-0686
Web Site: http://www.jungecontrol.com
Sales Range: $1-9.9 Million
Emp.: 17
Mfg Process Control Instruments
N.A.I.C.S.: 334513

Mepu Oy   (1)
Mynamaentie 59, 21900, Ylane, Western
Finland, Finland
Tel.: (358) 2 275 4444
Web Site: https://www.mepu.fi
Sales Range: $25-49.9 Million
Grain Handling & Heating Systems Mfr
N.A.I.C.S.: 333111

Plant (Domestic):

Mepu Oy. - Pyharanta factory   (2)
Vanha Turuntie 210, 27320, Pyharanta,
Western Finland, Finland
Tel.: (358) 28236368
Web Site: http://www.mepu.com
Sales Range: $25-49.9 Million
Emp.: 7
Grain Handling & Heating Systems Mfr

N.A.I.C.S.: 333111

Milltec Machinery Private Limited   (1)
No 51-A 1st Phase, KIADB Industrial Area
Bommasandra, Bengaluru, 560099, Karnataka, India
Tel.: (91) 8037302192
Web Site: https://www.milltec-ricemillmachinery.com
Emp.: 550
Rice Milling Machinery Mfr & Distr
N.A.I.C.S.: 311212

Mitchell Mill Systems USA Inc.   (1)
927 S Schifferdecker Ave, Joplin, MO
64801
Tel.: (417) 623-2224
Grain Storage & Handling Equipment Mfr
N.A.I.C.S.: 333111

NuVision Industries Inc.   (1)
223072 Rge Rd 260, PO Box 450, Carseland, T0J 0M0, AB, Canada
Tel.: (403) 934-3591
Web Site: http://www.nvind.ca
Grain Auger & Fertilizer Handling Products
Mfr
N.A.I.C.S.: 333111

Sabe S.A.S.   (1)
La Perrauderie, 85140, Chauche, France
Tel.: (33) 251418445
Web Site: https://www.sabe.fr
Rev.: $13,500,000
Emp.: 50
Bulk Material Handling Equipment Mfr
N.A.I.C.S.: 333248

Tramco Europe Limited   (1)
Mendham Business Park Hull Road Saltend, Hull, HU12 8DZ, United Kingdom
Tel.: (44) 1482782666
Bulk Material Handling Equipment Mfr
N.A.I.C.S.: 333248

Tramco Inc.   (1)
1020 E 19th St N, Wichita, KS 67214
Tel.: (316) 264-4604
Web Site: http://www.tramcoinc.com
Sales Range: $25-49.9 Million
Emp.: 90
Mfr of Conveyors & Conveying Equipment
N.A.I.C.S.: 333922

Union Iron Inc.   (1)
3550 E Mound Rd, Decatur, IL 62521
Tel.: (217) 429-5148
Web Site: http://www.aggrowth.com
Elevators & Conveyors Mfr
N.A.I.C.S.: 333921

Westeel   (1)
450 Desautels Street, Winnipeg, R2H 3E6,
MB, Canada
Tel.: (204) 233-7133
Web Site: http://www.westeel.com
Storage Tank Mfr
N.A.I.C.S.: 332999

Westfield Industries   (1)
11500 38th St S, Horace, ND 58047-9511
Tel.: (701) 588-9269
Web Site: http://www.grainaugers.com
Sales Range: $50-74.9 Million
Agricultural Machinery & Equipment Distr
N.A.I.C.S.: 423820

Yargus Manufacturing   (1)
12285 E Main St, Marshall, IL
62441   (100%)
Tel.: (217) 826-6352
Web Site: http://www.yargus.com
Sales Range: $1-9.9 Million
Manufactures & Designs Layco Brand Fertilizer & Industrial Material Handling Equipments
N.A.I.C.S.: 325314

AG INDUSTRIES LIMITED

1 Setchell Rd Roodekop, 1428, Johannesburg, South Africa
Tel.: (27) 117246000
Web Site: http://www.ag-industries.com
Sales Range: $400-449.9 Million
Emp.: 1,853
Glass & Aluminium Fabrication Distr
N.A.I.C.S.: 423390
Clive Paul Kalil (Exec Dir)

Subsidiaries:

AG Industries Vietnam Company
Limited   (1)
Hoa Rang Bldg 3rd Fl Ste 303 32-34 Ngo
Duc Ke St, Ben Nghe Ward Dist 1, Ho Chi
Minh City, Vietnam
Tel.: (84) 8 2220 0622
Sales Range: $25-49.9 Million
Emp.: 3
Aluminum Windows & Doors Sales
N.A.I.C.S.: 321911

AGI Aluminium (Pty) Limited   (1)
40 Corobrick Rd, Effingham Heights, Durban, 4051, Kwazulu-Natal, South Africa
Tel.: (27) 119081500
Aluminum Windows & Doors Sales
N.A.I.C.S.: 423310

AGI Glass (Pty) Limited   (1)
77 Park Ave S, Pretoria, 0157, Gauteng,
South Africa
Tel.: (27) 126610415
Glass & Wallpaper Whslr
N.A.I.C.S.: 423390

AGI Manufacturing (Pty) Limited   (1)
1 Setchell Rd, Roodekop, Germiston, 1401,
Gauteng, South Africa
Tel.: (27) 117246000
Aluminum & Glass Windows & Doors Mfr
N.A.I.C.S.: 332321

Aluminium Glass Industries (Mauritius) Limited   (1)
1 Concorde Ave La Tour Koenig, Pointe aux
Sables, Port Louis, Mauritius
Tel.: (230) 2342525
Sales Range: $25-49.9 Million
Emp.: 18
Aluminum & Glass Windows & Doors Distr
N.A.I.C.S.: 423310

KAB Allglass GmbH   (1)
Schmidts Breite 17, 21107, Hamburg, Germany
Tel.: (49) 407520190
Web Site: http://www.kab-allglass.de
Sales Range: $25-49.9 Million
Emp.: 20
Glass Warehousing & Distr
N.A.I.C.S.: 423390

Ralph's Mirror and Glass (Pty)
Limited   (1)
75 Zeiler Street, Pretoria, 0183, Gauteng,
South Africa
Tel.: (27) 123274598
Emp.: 35
Mirror & Glass Distr
N.A.I.C.S.: 423220
D.C. Ralph (Gen Mgr)

West Cape Safety Glass (Pty)
Limited   (1)
8 Hawkins Ave Epping Industria, Cape
Town, 7475, Western Cape, South Africa
Tel.: (27) 215317429
Sales Range: $25-49.9 Million
Emp.: 50
Safety Glass Mfr
N.A.I.C.S.: 327215

AGA FINANCIAL GROUP INC.

3500 De Maisonneuve Blvd West
Suite 2200, Westmount, H3Z 3C1,
QC, Canada
Tel.: (514) 935-5444   QC
Web Site: http://www.aga.ca
Year Founded: 1978
Sales Range: $75-99.9 Million
Emp.: 90
Insurance & Annuity Plan Brokerage
Services
N.A.I.C.S.: 524210
Martin Papillon (Pres & CEO)

AGA KHAN DEVELOPMENT NETWORK

1-3 Avenue de la Paix, 1202, Geneva, Switzerland
Tel.: (41) 229097200
Web Site: http://www.akdn.org
Emp.: 80,000

Health, Education, Culture & Economic Development Services Organization
N.A.I.C.S.: 926110
Aaron Sherinian (Head-Comm-Global)

Subsidiaries:

Acorn Packaging Inc. (1)
563 Queensway East, Mississauga, L5A 3X6, ON, Canada
Tel.: (905) 279-5256
Web Site: http://www.acornpkg.com
Packaging Products Mfr
N.A.I.C.S.: 326112
Tommy Dennis (Mng Dir)

Aga Khan Fund for Economic Development S.A.
1-3 Avenue de la Paix, 1202, Geneva, Switzerland
Tel.: (41) 229097200
Web Site: http://www.akdn.org
Economic Development
N.A.I.C.S.: 926110

Holding (Non-US):

Air Burkina SA (2)
29 Av de la Nation, BP 1459, Ouagadougou, 01, Burkina Faso
Tel.: (226) 50 49 23 40
Web Site: http://www.air-burkina.com
Sales Range: $50-74.9 Million
Emp.: 130
Oil Transportation Services
N.A.I.C.S.: 481111

IPDC Finance Limited (2)
Hosna Centre 4th Floor 106 Gulshan Avenue, Dhaka, 1212, Bangladesh (51.05%)
Tel.: (880) 55068929
Web Site: http://www.ipdcbd.com
Rev.: $64,583,751
Assets: $791,137,271
Liabilities: $729,083,608
Net Worth: $62,053,664
Earnings: $8,218,736
Emp.: 679
Fiscal Year-end: 12/31/2022
Financial Services
N.A.I.C.S.: 522220
Mominul Islam (CEO & Mng Dir)

Jubilee General Insurance Company Limited (2)
2nd Floor Jubilee Insurance House II Chundrigar Road, PO Box 4795, Karachi, 74000, Pakistan
Tel.: (92) 2132416022
Web Site: https://www.jubileegeneral.com.pk
Rev.: $33,997,971
Assets: $142,252,671
Liabilities: $86,146,998
Net Worth: $56,105,673
Earnings: $7,884,395
Emp.: 738
Fiscal Year-end: 12/31/2019
Insurance Services
N.A.I.C.S.: 524210
Azfar Arshad (COO)

Jubilee Holdings Limited (2)
Jubilee Insurance House Wabera Street, PO Box 30100, 00100, Nairobi, Kenya
Tel.: (254) 203281000
Web Site: https://www.jubileeinsurance.com
Rev.: $574,073,800
Assets: $1,327,358,605
Liabilities: $1,003,986,638
Net Worth: $323,371,967
Earnings: $37,197,033
Emp.: 1,122
Fiscal Year-end: 12/31/2020
Holding Company; Insurance, Investment & Other Financial Products & Services
N.A.I.C.S.: 551112
Philip Kimani (CFO)

Jubilee Life Insurance Company Limited (2)
74/1-A Lalazar M T Khan Road, Karachi, 74000, Pakistan (57.87%)
Tel.: (92) 111111554
Web Site: https://www.jubileelife.com
Rev.: $170,317,991
Assets: $675,800,605
Liabilities: $625,646,157

Net Worth: $50,154,448
Earnings: $7,454,212
Emp.: 2,031
Fiscal Year-end: 12/31/2022
Life Insurance Products & Services
N.A.I.C.S.: 524113
Javed Ahmed (CEO & Mng Dir)

Allpack Industries Ltd (1)
PO Box 3741, 00506, Nairobi, Kenya
Tel.: (254) 202014403
Web Site: http://www.allpack.co.ke
Chemical Products Mfr
N.A.I.C.S.: 325211
Dickson Ireri (Mgr-Quality Assurance)

Compagnie Aerienne du Mali (1)
Rondpoint Harlem, Kayes Plateau, Kayes, Mali
Tel.: (223) 66727676
Passenger Transportation Services
N.A.I.C.S.: 485999

Diamond Trust Bank Tanzania Ltd (1)
DTB Centre plot 991 Kahama Road Masaki, PO Box 115, Dar es Salaam, Tanzania
Tel.: (255) 222114892
Web Site: https://diamondtrust.co.tz
Commercial Banking Services
N.A.I.C.S.: 522110
Abdul Samji (Chm)

Diamond Trust Bank Uganda Ltd (1)
Arua Avenue Road Arua, Arua, Uganda
Tel.: (256) 414387000
Commercial Banking Services
N.A.I.C.S.: 522110
Abdul Samji (Chm)

Farmer's Choice Ltd (1)
PO Box 47791, 00100, Nairobi, Kenya
Tel.: (254) 2020130089
Web Site: http://www.farmerschoice.co.ke
Emp.: 1,400
Frozen Meat Mfr
N.A.I.C.S.: 311612

Faso Coton SA (1)
PO Box 534, Ouagadougou, Burkina Faso
Tel.: (226) 50343039
Ginned Cotton Mfr
N.A.I.C.S.: 115111

Fasoplast s.a. (1)
Thessi Dio Pefka, Aspropirgos Attica, 19300, Athens, Greece
Tel.: (30) 2105596333
Web Site: http://www.fasoplast.gr
Plastics Product Mfr
N.A.I.C.S.: 325211

Fumoa s.a. (1)
Km 3 5 - Bd du Centenaire de la Commune, PO Box 1349, Dakar, Senegal
Tel.: (221) 338310505
Web Site: http://www.fumoa.sn
Metal Drum Mfr
N.A.I.C.S.: 332439

Hotel Polana Ltda (1)
Av Julius Nyerere 1380, PO Box 1151, 00100, Maputo, Mozambique
Tel.: (258) 21241700800
Web Site: http://www.serenahotels.com
Home Management Services
N.A.I.C.S.: 721110

Industrial Promotion Services (West Africa) s.a. (1)
62 Boulevard Schoelcher, PO Box 3963, Cocody, Abidjan, Cote d'Ivoire
Tel.: (225) 22400800
Web Site: http://www.ips-wa.org
Emp.: 1,420
Business Management Services
N.A.I.C.S.: 561110
Mahamadou Sylla (CEO)

Industrial Promotion Services Ltd (1)
60 Columbia Way Suite 720, Markham, L3R 0C9, ON, Canada
Tel.: (905) 475-9400
Financial Investment Management Services
N.A.I.C.S.: 523940
Alex Mwathi (Project Mgr)

Industrial Promotion Services s.a. (1)
Avenue de la Paix 1-3, 1202, Geneva, Switzerland

Tel.: (41) 229097200
Business Management Services
N.A.I.C.S.: 561110

Ivoire Coton s.a. (1)
71 boulevard de Marseille face au CHU de Treichville 18, PO Box 3419, Abidjan, Cote d'Ivoire
Tel.: (225) 21210171
Web Site: http://www.ivoire-coton.com
Ginned Cotton Mfr
N.A.I.C.S.: 115111

Jubilee Insurance (Mauritius) Ltd (1)
Mezzanine Floor One Cathedral Square Pope Hennessy Street, Port Louis, Mauritius
Tel.: (230) 2022200
Fire Insurance Services
N.A.I.C.S.: 524113
Nizar N. Juma (Chm)

Kamyn Industries Ltd (1)
PO Box 82851, Mombasa, 80100, Kenya
Tel.: (254) 202170999
Web Site: http://www.kamyn.co.ke
Hosiery & Sock Mfr
N.A.I.C.S.: 315120
Vincent Mbalu (Mgr-Sls & Mktg)

Kenya Litho Ltd (1)
Off Mombasa Road, PO Box 40775, 00100, Nairobi, Kenya
Tel.: (254) 2020481779
Packaging Products Mfr
N.A.I.C.S.: 326112
Celsus Wekesa (Mgr-Production)

Kyrgyz Investment and Credit Bank Ltd (1)
21 Erkindik blvd, Bishkek, 720040, Kyrgyzstan
Tel.: (996) 312620101
Web Site: http://www.en.kicb.net
Commercial Banking Services
N.A.I.C.S.: 522110
Zakir Mahmood (Chm)

Leather Industries of Kenya Ltd (1)
Located along the Garissa Road, PO Box 79, 01000, Thika, Kenya
Tel.: (254) 202020934
Web Site: http://www.likenya.com
Leather Product Mfr
N.A.I.C.S.: 316990

Premier Food Industries Ltd (1)
Baba Dogo Road, PO Box 41476-001000, Nairobi, Kenya
Tel.: (254) 208011108
Web Site: http://www.peptang.com
Juice Mfr
N.A.I.C.S.: 311421
Dharmarajan Sundararaman (Gen Mgr)

Socembal sprl (1)
1286 av des inflammables, Kinshasa, Congo, Democratic Republic of
Tel.: (243) 819811328
Metal Drum Mfr
N.A.I.C.S.: 332439

T&T Honda Ltd (1)
888 Meridian Road NE, Calgary, T2A 2N8, AB, Canada
Tel.: (403) 291-1444
Web Site: http://www.tandthonda.ca
Automobile Parts Design & Testing Services
N.A.I.C.S.: 541420
Navroz Jessani (Gen Mgr)

TLL Printing & Packaging Ltd (1)
Changombe Industrial Area, PO Box 2557, Dar es Salaam, Tanzania
Tel.: (255) 2865182
Web Site: http://www.tllprinting.com
Packaging Products Mfr
N.A.I.C.S.: 326112
Harold Pereira (Mgr-Sls Promotion)

Telecom Development Company Afghanistan Ltd (1)
House 13 Main Street, Wazir Akbar Khan, Kabul, Afghanistan
Tel.: (93) 799977755
Web Site: http://www.roshan.af
Telecommunication Servicesb
N.A.I.C.S.: 517111
Karim Khoja (CEO)

The Jubilee Insurance Company Ltd (1)

Jubilee Insurance House Wabera St, PO Box 30376, 01000, Nairobi, Kenya
Tel.: (254) 203281000
Fire Insurance Services
N.A.I.C.S.: 524113
Nizar N. Juma (Chm)

The Jubilee Insurance Company of Tanzania Ltd (1)
Amani Place Ohio Street 4th Floor, PO Box 20524, Dar es Salaam, Tanzania
Tel.: (255) 222135121
Fire Insurance Services
N.A.I.C.S.: 524113
George Alande (CEO)

The Jubilee Insurance Company of Uganda Ltd (1)
Jubilee Insurance Centre Plot 14 Parliament Avenue, PO Box 10234, Kampala, Uganda
Tel.: (254) 414311701
Fire Insurance Services
N.A.I.C.S.: 524113
Nizar N. Juma (Chm)

Trefilkin sprl (1)
11Eme Rue Limete, Kinshasa, Congo, Democratic Republic of
Tel.: (243) 998113280
Steel Pole Mfr
N.A.I.C.S.: 331110

Tsavo Power Company Ltd (1)
IPS Building 9th Floor Kimathi Street, 01000, Nairobi, Kenya
Tel.: (254) 20318969
Eletric Power Generation Services
N.A.I.C.S.: 221118
Julius Riungu (CEO)

Wire Products Ltd (1)
Athi River Road Off addis ababa Road Industrial Area, PO Box 18281, 00500, Nairobi, Kenya
Tel.: (254) 557930
Web Site: http://www.wireprod.net
Emp.: 300
Wire Product Mfr
N.A.I.C.S.: 335929

AGABANG & COMPANY
207 Teheran-ro, Gangnam-gu, Seoul, 06141, Korea (South)
Tel.: (82) 25271300
Web Site:
https://www.agabangncompany.com
Year Founded: 1979
013990—(KRS)
Rev.: $133,702,170
Assets: $159,814,867
Liabilities: $35,232,251
Net Worth: $124,582,616
Earnings: $7,966,797
Fiscal Year-end: 12/31/22
Infant Apparel Store Operator
N.A.I.C.S.: 458110
Shin Sang-Guk (CEO)

AGALAWATTE PLANTATIONS PLC
No 361 Kandy Road, Nittambuwa, Sri Lanka
Tel.: (94) 332299000 LK
Year Founded: 1992
AGAL.N0000—(COL)
Rev.: $15,815,681
Assets: $21,883,958
Liabilities: $9,483,738
Net Worth: $12,400,219
Earnings: $1,639,258
Emp.: 3,672
Fiscal Year-end: 12/31/23
Holding Company; Rubber, Palm Oil & Tea Farming
N.A.I.C.S.: 551112
Amarasuriya A. S. (Chm)

AGAPE ATP CORPORATION
1705-1708 Level 17 Tower 2 Faber Towers Jalan Desa Bahagia Taman Desa, 58100, Kuala Lumpur, 58100, Malaysia
Tel.: (60) 327325716 NV

Agape ATP Corporation—(Continued)

Web Site:
https://www.agapeatpgroup.com
Year Founded: 2016
ATPC—(NASDAQ)
Rev.: $1,856,564
Assets: $2,791,749
Liabilities: $1,229,295
Net Worth: $1,562,454
Earnings: ($1,686,899)
Emp.: 30
Fiscal Year-end: 12/31/22
Holding Company
N.A.I.C.S.: 551112
Andrew Kam Fan Lee (CFO)

AGAR SCIENTIFIC LIMITED
Unit 7 M11 Business Link Parsonage
Lane, Stansted, CM24 8GF, Essex,
United Kingdom
Tel.: (44) 1279215506   UK
Web Site:
http://www.agarscientific.com
Year Founded: 1978
Sales Range: $1-9.9 Million
Microscopy Consumables & Accessories Mfr & Whslr
N.A.I.C.S.: 334516
Paul Balas (Mgr-Technical Sls)

AGARTHA REAL ESTATE SO-CIMI, S.A.U.
Calle Piemonte 23, 28004, Madrid,
Spain
Tel.: (34) 630794477   ES
Web Site:
http://www.agartharealestate.com
Year Founded: 2018
Rev.: $410,800
Assets: $23,656,862
Liabilities: $14,105,006
Net Worth: $9,551,856
Earnings: ($669,993)
Fiscal Year-end: 12/31/18
Real Estate Investment Trust Services
N.A.I.C.S.: 525990
Juan Portilla (CEO)

AGARWAL INDUSTRIAL COR-PORATION LTD.
Eastern Court Unit No 201-202 Plot
No 12 VN Purav Marg ST Road,
Chembur, Mumbai, 400071, Maharashtra, India
Tel.: (91) 2225291149
Web Site: https://www.aicltd.in
531921—(BOM)
Rev.: $218,671,717
Assets: $74,136,412
Liabilities: $33,928,740
Net Worth: $40,207,672
Earnings: $8,693,535
Emp.: 64
Fiscal Year-end: 03/31/22
Liquid Petroleum Gas Transportation
Services
N.A.I.C.S.: 488999
Jaiprakash Agarwal (Mng Dir)

Subsidiaries:

Bituminex Cochin Pvt Ltd   (1)
Ettikkara Road Near HOC Ambalamugal
PO, Cochin, 682 302, Kerala, India
Tel.: (91) 4842720259
Web Site: https://bituminexcochin.com
Bituminous Product Mfr
N.A.I.C.S.: 325998

AGAT EJENDOMME A/S
Vestre Havnepromenade 7 3rd floor,
DK-9000, Aalborg, Denmark
Tel.: (45) 88961010
Web Site: https://www.agat.dk
Year Founded: 1960

AGAT—(CSE)
Rev.: $34,538,641
Assets: $125,609,527
Liabilities: $77,527,456
Net Worth: $48,082,071
Earnings: ($7,249,208)
Emp.: 14
Fiscal Year-end: 01/31/24
Real Estate Development Services
N.A.I.C.S.: 531390

AGATOS S.P.A.
Via Cesare Ajraghi 30, 20156, Milan,
Italy
Tel.: (39) 0248376601   IT
Web Site: https://www.agatos.it
Year Founded: 2004
AGA—(ITA)
Sales Range: Less than $1 Million
Holding Company; Renewable Energy Plant Design, Construction &
Maintenance Services
N.A.I.C.S.: 551112
Leonardo Rinaldi (CEO)

Subsidiaries:

Agatos Energia Srl   (1)
Via Ajraghi 30, 20156, Milan, Italy
Tel.: (39) 02 4837 6601
Web Site: http://www.agatosenergia.it
Renewable Energy Plant Design, Construction & Maintenance Services
N.A.I.C.S.: 237130
Leonardo Rinaldi (Owner)

AGBA GROUP HOLDING LIM-ITED
AGBA Tower 68 Johnston Road, New
Mandarin Plaza Tsimshatsui East,
Wanchai, China (Hong Kong)
Tel.: (852) 36018000   VG
Web Site: https://www.agba.com
Year Founded: 2018
AGBA—(NASDAQ)
Rev.: $31,080,227
Assets: $101,221,333
Liabilities: $97,071,054
Net Worth: $4,150,279
Earnings: ($44,520,635)
Emp.: 152
Fiscal Year-end: 12/31/22
Investment Services
N.A.I.C.S.: 523999
Robert E. Diamond Jr. (Chm)

AGC INC.
1-5-1 Marunouchi, Chiyoda-ku, Tokyo, 100 8405, Japan
Tel.: (81) 332185741   JP
Web Site: https://www.agc.com
Year Founded: 1907
5201—(TKS)
Rev.: $13,341,618,764
Assets: $19,378,863,561
Liabilities: $8,448,318,467
Net Worth: $10,930,545,094
Earnings: $544,988,437
Emp.: 56,724
Fiscal Year-end: 12/31/23
Chemical Products Mfr
N.A.I.C.S.: 325998
Takuya Shimamura (Chm)

Subsidiaries:

AGC (China) Holdings Co., Ltd.   (1)
Unit 3511 China World Office 2 No 1 Jianguomenwai Ave, Chaoyang District, Beijing,
China
Tel.: (86) 1065058029
Web Site: http://www.agc.com
Sales Range: $50-74.9 Million
Investment Management Service
N.A.I.C.S.: 523940

AGC Advanced Business Experts
(Thailand) Ltd.   (1)
944 Mitrtown Office Tower 14th Floor Rama
4 Road, Wangmai Sub-District Pathumwan
District, Bangkok, 10330, Thailand

Tel.: (66) 20926487
N.A.I.C.S.: 327215

AGC Amenitech Co., Ltd.   (1)
4-24-11 Higashiueno Nbf Ueno Building 6f,
Taito-ku, Tokyo, 110-0015, Japan
Tel.: (81) 358066210
Emp.: 64
Information Technology Consulting Services
N.A.I.C.S.: 541512

AGC America, Inc.   (1)
11175 Cicero Dr Ste 400, Alpharetta, GA
30022-1167   (100%)
Tel.: (404) 446-4200
Web Site: http://www.us.agc.com
Sales Range: $50-74.9 Million
Emp.: 50
Holding Company; Glass Products &
Chemicals Manufacturing & Distributing
N.A.I.C.S.: 551112

Subsidiary (Domestic):

AGC Capital, Inc.   (2)
11175 Cicero Dr Ste 400, Alpharetta, GA
30022
Tel.: (404) 446-4272
Web Site: http://www.agc.com
Financial Management Services
N.A.I.C.S.: 523999

AGC Chemicals Americas, Inc.   (2)
55 E Uwchlan Ave Ste 201, Exton, PA
19341
Tel.: (610) 423-4300
Web Site: https://www.agcchem.com
Sales Range: $75-99.9 Million
Emp.: 120
Flat Glass & Chemical Products Mfr
N.A.I.C.S.: 327211

Plant (Domestic):

AGC Chemicals Americas, Inc. -
Thorndale Manufacturing Plant   (3)
255 S Bailey Rd, Downingtown, PA 19335
Tel.: (610) 380-6200
Web Site: https://www.agcchem.com
Chemical Products Mfr
N.A.I.C.S.: 325998

Subsidiary (Domestic):

AGC Electronics America, Inc.   (2)
4375 NW 59th Ave, Hillsboro, OR 97124-5852
Tel.: (503) 844-9689
Web Site: http://www.agcem.com
Electronic Machinery & Component Mfr &
Distr
N.A.I.C.S.: 334419

AGC Flat Glass North America,
Inc.   (2)
11175 Cicero Dr Ste 400, Alpharetta, GA
30022
Tel.: (404) 446-4200
Web Site: https://www.agc.com
Flat Glass & Rolled Glass Mfr
N.A.I.C.S.: 327211

Subsidiary (Domestic):

AGC Automotive Americas Co.   (3)
2300 Litton Ln Ste 100, Hebron, KY
41048   (100%)
Tel.: (859) 334-8900
Web Site: http://www.agc-automotive.com
Sales Range: $25-49.9 Million
Emp.: 75
Automotive Glass Mfr
N.A.I.C.S.: 327215

Plant (Domestic):

AGC Automotive   (4)
1465 W Sandusky Ave, Bellefontaine, OH
43311-0819
Tel.: (937) 599-3131
Automotive Glass Mfr
N.A.I.C.S.: 327215

Subsidiary (Domestic):

AGC Automotive Americas R&D,
Inc.   (4)
1401 S Huron St, Ypsilanti, MI 48197
Tel.: (734) 547-2370
Web Site: http://www.agc.com
Processed Automotive Glass Mfr

N.A.I.C.S.: 327215

AGC Automotive California, Inc.   (4)
19301 Pacific Gateway Dr Ste 200, Torrance, CA 90502
Tel.: (310) 817-8700
Web Site: http://www.agc.com
Automotive Glass Parts Whslr
N.A.I.C.S.: 423120
Toshiaki Yamashita (Pres)

Plant (Domestic):

AGC Flat Glass North America, Inc. -
AGC-Alvarado Plant   (3)
1201 Hwy 67 E, Alvarado, TX 76009
Tel.: (817) 477-1144
Web Site: http://www.afgglass.com
Glass Products Mfr
N.A.I.C.S.: 327215

AGC Flat Glass North America, Inc. -
AGC-Baton Rouge Plant   (3)
1414 Julia St, Baton Rouge, LA 70802
Tel.: (225) 344-9401
Web Site: http://www.afgglass.com
Glass Products Mfr
N.A.I.C.S.: 327215

Plant (Non-US):

AGC Flat Glass North America, Inc. -
AGC-Calgary Plant   (3)
4015 7th St S E, Calgary, T2G 2Y9, AB,
Canada
Tel.: (403) 243-2501
Flat Glass Mfr
N.A.I.C.S.: 327211

Plant (Domestic):

AGC Flat Glass North America, Inc. -
AGC-Carbondale Plant   (3)
100 Business Ctr Dr, Carbondale, PA 18407
Tel.: (800) 233-4170
Web Site: http://www.afgglass.com
Glass Products Mfr
N.A.I.C.S.: 327215

Plant (Non-US):

AGC Flat Glass North America, Inc. -
AGC-Edmonton Plant   (3)
9845 42nd Ave, Edmonton, T6E 0A3, AB,
Canada
Tel.: (780) 462-5252
Sales Range: $25-49.9 Million
Emp.: 40
Flat Glass Mfr
N.A.I.C.S.: 327211

Plant (Domestic):

AGC Flat Glass North America, Inc. -
AGC-Fall River Plant   (3)
575 Currant Rd, Fall River, MA 02720
Tel.: (508) 675-9220
Web Site: http://www.afgglass.com
Flat Glass Mfr
N.A.I.C.S.: 327211

AGC Flat Glass North America, Inc. -
AGC-Houston Plant   (3)
5909 Milwee St, Houston, TX 77292-4767
Tel.: (713) 686-2509
Glass Products Mfr
N.A.I.C.S.: 327215

AGC Flat Glass North America, Inc. -
AGC-Jacksonville Plant   (3)
6600 Suemac Pl, Jacksonville, FL 32254
Tel.: (904) 786-6611
Web Site: http://www.afgglass.com
Flat Glass Mfr
N.A.I.C.S.: 327211

AGC Flat Glass North America, Inc. -
AGC-Knoxville Plant   (3)
2522 Westcott Blvd, Knoxville, TN 37931
Tel.: (865) 691-2040
Web Site: http://www.afgglass.com
Sales Range: $25-49.9 Million
Emp.: 40
Glass Products Mfr
N.A.I.C.S.: 327215

AGC Flat Glass North America, Inc. -
AGC-Opelousas Plant   (3)
710 W Landry St, Opelousas, LA 70570
Tel.: (800) 489-3386

Web Site: http://www.afgglass.com
Glass Products Mfr
N.A.I.C.S.: 327215

Plant (Non-US):

**AGC Flat Glass North America, Inc. -
AGC-Regina Plant** (3)
500 10th Ave E, Regina, S4N 6G7, SK,
Canada
Tel.: (306) 525-2341
Web Site: http://www.afgglass.com
Sales Range: $25-49.9 Million
Emp.: 37
Flat Glass Mfr
N.A.I.C.S.: 327211

Plant (Domestic):

**AGC Flat Glass North America, Inc. -
AGC-Richmond Plant** (3)
6200 Gorman Rd, Richmond, VA 23231
Tel.: (804) 222-0120
Web Site: http://www.afgglass.com
Emp.: 40
Glass Products Mfr
N.A.I.C.S.: 327215

**AGC Flat Glass North America, Inc. -
AGC-Salt Lake City Plant** (3)
3515 S 300 W, Salt Lake City, UT 84115
Tel.: (801) 268-2521
Web Site: http://www.afgglass.com
Glass Products Mfr
N.A.I.C.S.: 327215

**AGC Flat Glass North America, Inc. -
AGC-San Antonio Plant** (3)
5807 Business Park, San Antonio, TX
78218
Tel.: (210) 653-7790
Web Site: http://www.afgglass.com
Glass Products Mfr
N.A.I.C.S.: 327215

Plant (Non-US):

**AGC Flat Glass North America, Inc. -
AGC-Winnipeg Plant** (3)
450 Deschambault St, Winnipeg, R2H 0K1,
MB, Canada
Tel.: (204) 233-0229
Web Site: http://www.afgglass.com
Sales Range: $25-49.9 Million
Emp.: 60
Glass Products Mfr
N.A.I.C.S.: 327215

Plant (Domestic):

**AGC Flat Glass North America, Inc. -
Abingdon Plant** (3)
18370 Oak Park Dr, Abingdon, VA 24210
Tel.: (276) 619-6000
Web Site: http://www.afgglass.com
Emp.: 55
Glass Products Mfr
N.A.I.C.S.: 327215

**AGC Flat Glass North America, Inc. -
Blue Ridge Plant** (3)
1400 Lincoln St, Kingsport, TN 37660
Tel.: (423) 229-7200
Web Site: http://www.afgglass.com
Flat Glass Mfr
N.A.I.C.S.: 327211

**AGC Flat Glass North America, Inc. -
Boardman Plant** (3)
365 McClurg Rd- Ste E, Boardman, OH
44512
Tel.: (330) 965-1000
Web Site: http://www.afgglass.com
Sales Range: $25-49.9 Million
Emp.: 60
Glass Products Mfr
N.A.I.C.S.: 327215

**AGC Flat Glass North America, Inc. -
Carbondale** (3)
Clidco Dr, Carbondale, PA 18407-0313
Tel.: (570) 282-6711
Web Site: http://www.afg.com
Sales Range: $25-49.9 Million
Emp.: 26
Laminated Glass Mfr
N.A.I.C.S.: 327215

**AGC Flat Glass North America, Inc. -
Greenland Plant** (3)

AGC Road Hwy 11 W, Church Hill, TN
37642
Tel.: (423) 357-2400
Web Site: http://www.afgglass.com
Flat Glass Mfr
N.A.I.C.S.: 327211

**AGC Flat Glass North America, Inc. -
Marietta** (3)
660 Campbell Ct, Lithia Springs, GA 30122
Tel.: (770) 434-2041
Sales Range: $25-49.9 Million
Emp.: 80
Glass Fabricator
N.A.I.C.S.: 327211
Rodger Ruff *(Sls Dir-North America)*

**AGC Flat Glass North America, Inc. -
Quakertown Plant** (3)
480 California Rd, Quakertown, PA 18951
Tel.: (215) 538-9424
Web Site: http://www.us.agc.com
Sales Range: $25-49.9 Million
Emp.: 40
Flat Glass Mfr
N.A.I.C.S.: 327211

**AGC Flat Glass North America, Inc. -
Richmond Plant** (3)
201 Duncannon Ln, Richmond, KY 40475
Tel.: (859) 625-9002
Web Site: http://www.afgglass.com
Sales Range: $50-74.9 Million
Emp.: 175
Flat Glass Mfr
N.A.I.C.S.: 327211

**AGC Flat Glass North America, Inc. -
Spring Hill Plant** (3)
20400 N Webster, Spring Hill, KS 66083
Tel.: (913) 592-6100
Web Site: http://www.afgglass.com
Flat Glass Mfr
N.A.I.C.S.: 327211

Joint Venture (Domestic):

SCHOTT Gemtron Corporation (3)
615 Hwy 68, Sweetwater, TN 37874-1911
Tel.: (423) 337-3522
Web Site: http://www.gemtron.net
Sales Range: $50-74.9 Million
Emp.: 250
Mfr of Tempered & Decorative Glass For
Uses Including Shower Doors, Ovens &
Shelving; Joint Venture of Schott Glaswerke
& AFG Industries, Inc.
N.A.I.C.S.: 327211
Christian Mias *(COO)*

Branch (Domestic):

SCHOTT Gemtron Corporation (4)
2000 Chestnut St, Vincennes, IN 47591-
1760
Tel.: (812) 882-2680
Web Site: http://www.gemtron.com
Sales Range: $75-99.9 Million
Glass Tempering & Tempered Glass; Ce-
ramics
N.A.I.C.S.: 327215

Joint Venture (Domestic):

Belletech Corp. (2)
700 W Lake Ave, Bellefontaine, OH 43311-
0790
Tel.: (937) 599-3774
Web Site: http://www.belletechcorp.com
Sales Range: $75-99.9 Million
Automotive Glass Assemblies; Owned 60%
by Asahi Glass Co., Ltd. & 40% by PPG
Industries, Inc.
N.A.I.C.S.: 327215

**AGC Asia Pacific (Vietnam) Co.,
Ltd.** (1)
Room 606 at 6th Floor Icon 4 Tower 243A
De La Thanh, Dong Da District, Hanoi, Viet-
nam
Tel.: (84) 961153084
Sheet Glass Mfr & Distr
N.A.I.C.S.: 327215

AGC Asia Pacific Pte., Ltd. (1)
Alexandra Road PSA Building 32-01, Singa-
pore, 119963, Singapore
Tel.: (65) 62735656
Web Site: https://agc-asiapacific.com
N.A.I.C.S.: 423490

Kohama Takuji *(Mng Dir)*

**AGC Automotive (Qinhuangdao)
Inc.** (1)
108 Qinhuang Western street ETDZ, Qin-
huangdao, Hebei, China
Tel.: (86) 355910000
Automotive Glass Mfr
N.A.I.C.S.: 327215

**AGC Automotive (Thailand) Co.,
Ltd.** (1)
700/366 Moo 6 Amata City Chonburi Indus-
trial Estate Bangna-Trad km57, Nong Mai
Daeng Muang, Chon Buri, 20000, Thailand
Tel.: (66) 38214840
Web Site: http://www.th.agc-automotive.com
Automotive Glass Product Distr
N.A.I.C.S.: 423120

AGC Automotive Canada, Inc. (1)
120 Artesian Ind Parkway, Bradford, L3Z
3G3, ON, Canada
Tel.: (905) 778-8224
Automotive Glass Mfr
N.A.I.C.S.: 327215

**AGC Automotive Foshan Co.,
Ltd** (1)
Huasha Road, Songxia C Area Nanhai Eco-
nomic Development Zone, Foshan, Guang-
dong, China
Tel.: (86) 7578 588 8000
Web Site: http://www.agc.com
Automotive Glass Distr
N.A.I.C.S.: 423120

AGC Automotive Philippines Inc. (1)
Bldg No 1 Daystar Sta Rosa Industrial Park
Brgy, Pulong, Santa Rosa, 4026, Laguna,
Philippines
Tel.: (63) 25208490
Automotive Glass Assembly Services
N.A.I.C.S.: 811122
Marilyn Encinares *(Pres)*

**AGC Automotive Window Systems
Co., Ltd.** (1)
16-12 Shiba 3-Chome, Minato-ku, Tokyo,
105-0014, Japan
Tel.: (81) 334522231
Web Site: https://www.agc-winsys.com
N.A.I.C.S.: 327215
Hideki Takahashi *(Chm)*

AGC Biologics A/S (1)
Vandtaarnsvej 83B, Soeborg, 2860, Copen-
hagen, Denmark
Tel.: (45) 7 020 9470
Web Site: http://www.agcbio.com
Biopharmaceutical Mfr & Developer
N.A.I.C.S.: 325414
Patricio E. Massera *(CEO)*

Branch (US):

AGC Biologics Inc. (2)
21511 23rd Dr SE, Bothell, WA 98021
Tel.: (425) 485-1900
Web Site: https://www.agcbio.com
Emp.: 1,300
Biopharmaceutical Mfr & Developer
N.A.I.C.S.: 325414
Patricio E. Massera *(CEO)*

AGC Biologics S.p.A (1)
Via Olgettina 58, 20132, Milan, Italy
Tel.: (39) 02212771
Web Site: http://www.agcbio.com
Cancer Biopharmaceutical Researcher &
Mfr
N.A.I.C.S.: 325412

AGC Ceramics Co., Ltd. (1)
6F Mita NN Building 4-1-23 Shiba, Minato-
ku, Tokyo, 108-0014, Japan
Tel.: (81) 354429172
Web Site: https://www.agcc.jp
Sales Range: $75-99.9 Million
Emp.: 270
Ceramic Product Whslr
N.A.I.C.S.: 423320
Masaru Ohta *(Pres)*

**AGC Chemicals (Thailand) Co., Ltd. -
Phrapradaeng Plant** (1)
202 Moo 1 Suksawat Road Pakklong Bang
Pla Kot Subdistrict, Phra Samut Chedi Dis-
trict, Samut Prakan, 10290, Thailand
Tel.: (66) 2 463 6345

Web Site: http://www.acth.co.th
Chemical Products Mfr
N.A.I.C.S.: 325998

**AGC Chemicals (Thailand) Co., Ltd. -
Rayong Plant** (1)
4 Soi G-12 Eastern Industrial Estate Pakorn
Songkrohrad Road, Tambol Mab Ta Put
Amphur Muang, Rayong, 21150, Thailand
Tel.: (66) 3 868 3573
Chemical Products Mfr
N.A.I.C.S.: 325998

**AGC Chemicals Asia Pacific Pte.
Ltd.** (1)
460 Alexandra Road 32-01 PSA Building,
Singapore, 119963, Singapore
Tel.: (65) 6273 5656
Chemical Products Distr
N.A.I.C.S.: 424690

**AGC Chemicals Trading (Shanghai)
Co., Ltd.** (1)
Unit 4008-09 40F Raffles City Changning
Office Tower 1, No 1133 Changning Road,
Shanghai, 200051, China
Tel.: (86) 2163862211
Web Site: https://www.agcsh.com
Sales Range: $25-49.9 Million
Emp.: 30
Specialty Chemical Whslr
N.A.I.C.S.: 424690

AGC Coat-Tech Co., Ltd. (1)
Comfort Yasuda Bldg 5FL 2-9 Kandanishiki-
cho, Chiyoda-ku, Tokyo, 101-0054, Japan
Tel.: (81) 352175100
Paint Mfr & Distr
N.A.I.C.S.: 325510
Hisanori Shinozaki *(Mng Dir)*

**AGC Display Glass Yonezawa Co.,
Ltd.** (1)
4-2837-11 Hachimanbara, Yonezawa, 992-
1128, Yamagata, Japan
Tel.: (81) 238288301
Web Site: https://y-ady.co.jp
Sales Range: $200-249.9 Million
Flat Panel Display Glass Mfr
N.A.I.C.S.: 327211

AGC Electronics Co., Ltd. (1)
1-8 Machiikedai, Koriyama, 963-0215, Fu-
kushima, Japan
Tel.: (81) 249591890
Web Site: https://www.agcel.co.jp
Electronic Component & Semiconductor Mfr
N.A.I.C.S.: 334413

**AGC Electronics Singapore Pte.
Ltd.** (1)
460 Alexandra Road 30-01 PSA Building,
Singapore, 119963, Singapore
Tel.: (65) 6273 5656
Sales Range: $50-74.9 Million
Emp.: 8
Glass & Electronic Materials Distr
N.A.I.C.S.: 423690
Takako Kanoh *(Gen Mgr)*

AGC Engineering Co., Ltd. (1)
WBG Marive West 19F 2-6-1 Nakase,
Mihama-ku, Chiba, 261-7119, Japan
Tel.: (81) 433503366
Web Site: https://www.agec.co.jp
Sales Range: $75-99.9 Million
Emp.: 159
Anti Pollution Plant Engineering Services
N.A.I.C.S.: 541330
Satoshi Sumita *(Pres & CEO)*

AGC Europe S.A. (1)
Avenue Jean Monnet 4, 1348, Louvain-la-
Neuve, Belgium
Tel.: (32) 2 409 3000
Web Site: http://www.agc-group.com
Glass Products Mfr
N.A.I.C.S.: 327215

Subsidiary (Domestic):

AGC Automotive Europe S.A (2)
Avenue Jean Monnet 4, 1348, Louvain-la-
Neuve, Belgium
Tel.: (32) 24093000
Web Site: https://www.agc-automotive.com
Sales Range: $50-74.9 Million
Emp.: 150
Automotive Glass Mfr
N.A.I.C.S.: 327215

AGC Inc.—(Continued)

Subsidiary (Non-US):

AGC Automotive Italy S.r.l (2)
Via Del Carpine 9, Roccasecca, 03038,
Frosinone, Italy
Tel.: (39) 0171 3401
Web Site: http://www.agc.com
Automotive Glass Mfr
N.A.I.C.S.: 327215

AGC Automotive U.K. Ltd. (2)
Unit B Edgemead Close Round Spinney,
Northampton, NN3 4RG, United Kingdom
Tel.: (44) 1604671150
Sales Range: $25-49.9 Million
Emp.: 100
Automotive Glass Mfr
N.A.I.C.S.: 327215

AGC Biologics GmbH (2)
Czernyring 22, 69115, Heidelberg, Germany
Tel.: (49) 622190260
Biopharmaceutical Mfr
N.A.I.C.S.: 541714
Dieter Kramer (Mng Dir)

AGC Chemicals Europe, Ltd. (2)
Hillhouse International Fleetwood Road
North, PO Box 4, Thornton, FY5 4QD, Lan-
cashire, United Kingdom
Tel.: (44) 1253209600
Web Site: http://www.agcce.com
Chemical Product Whslr
N.A.I.C.S.: 424690

Division (Non-US):

AGC Chemicals Europe, Ltd. (3)
World Trade Center Zuidplein 80, 1077 XV,
Amsterdam, Netherlands (100%)
Tel.: (31) 20 880 4170
Web Site: http://www.agcce.com
Sales Range: $25-49.9 Million
Emp.: 20
Fluorochemicals & Fluoropolymers Mfr
N.A.I.C.S.: 327211

Subsidiary (Non-US):

AGC Flat Glass Czech A.S. (2)
Sklarska C450, 416 74, Teplica, Czech Re-
public
Tel.: (420) 417501111
Sales Range: $50-74.9 Million
Emp.: 200
Float & Automotive Glass Mfr
N.A.I.C.S.: 327211
Zuzana Zimova (Mgr-Sls)

Subsidiary (Domestic):

AGC Flat Glass Europe (2)
Avenue Jean Monnet 4, 1348, Louvain-la-
Neuve, Belgium
Tel.: (32) 24093000
Web Site: http://www.agc-glass.eu
Sales Range: $125-149.9 Million
Emp.: 600
Mfr of Flat Glass
N.A.I.C.S.: 327211

Subsidiary (Non-US):

AGC Flat Glass Iberica S.A. (2)
Calle Mallorca 272-274 6 5a, 08037, Barce-
lona, Spain
Tel.: (34) 934670760
Flat Glass Distr
N.A.I.C.S.: 423390

AGC Flat Glass Italia S.r.l (2)
Via Genova 31, 12100, Cuneo, Italy
Tel.: (39) 01713401
Flat Glass Mfr
N.A.I.C.S.: 327211

AGC Flat Glass Nederland B.V. (2)
PO Box 6025, 4000 HA, Tiel, Netherlands
Tel.: (31) 34 467 9911
Web Site: http://www.agc.com
Sales Range: $50-74.9 Million
Flat Glass Mfr
N.A.I.C.S.: 327211

Subsidiary (Domestic):

AGC Glass Europe S.A. (2)
Avenue Jean Monnet 4, 1348, Louvain-la-
Neuve, Belgium
Tel.: (32) 2 409 3000

Web Site: https://www.agc-glass.eu
Sales Range: $1-4.9 Billion
Flat Glass Mfr & Distr
N.A.I.C.S.: 327211
Jean-Marc Meunier (CEO & Pres-
Automotive-Europe)

Subsidiary (Non-US):

NordGlass Sp. z o.o. (2)
ul Bohaterów Warszawy 11, 75-211, Koza-
lin, Poland
Tel.: (48) 94 34 65 739
Web Site: http://www.nordglass.pl
Emp.: 1,000
Automobile Spare Parts Mfr
N.A.I.C.S.: 441330
Norbert Nowe (Acct Mgr-Central-Eastern
Europe & Turkey)

Subsidiary (Non-US):

NordGlass Danmark A/S (3)
Roholmsvej 12F, 2620, Albertslund, Den-
mark
Tel.: (45) 43 61 30 80
Web Site: http://www.nordglass.pl
Automotive Spare Parts Distr
N.A.I.C.S.: 423120

NordGlass Distribuce s.r.o. (3)
Pekarenska 54, Ceske Budejovice, 370 04,
Czech Republic
Tel.: (420) 739 665 363
Web Site: http://www.nordglass.pl
Automotive Spare Parts Distr
N.A.I.C.S.: 423120

NordGlass Distribution GmbH (3)
An der Furth 6, 47906, Kempen, Germany
Tel.: (49) 2152 55 19 790
Web Site: http://www.nordglass.pl
Automotive Spare Parts Distr
N.A.I.C.S.: 423120
Holger Ebert (Mgr-Territory)

NordGlass France SARL (3)
4 rue du Maréchal de Lattre de Tassigny,
ZAC de la Cle Saint Pierre, 78990, Elan-
court, France
Tel.: (33) 16 138 1770
Web Site: https://www.nordglass.pl
Automotive Spare Parts Distr
N.A.I.C.S.: 423120

NordGlass Sverige AB (3)
Dalstigen port 2, 52337, Ulricehamn, Swe-
den
Tel.: (46) 321 68 60 80
Web Site: http://www.nordglass.pl
Automotive Spare Parts Distr
N.A.I.C.S.: 423120

AGC Fabritech Co., Ltd. (1)
8th Floor Tamachi Front Bldg 4-13-2 Shiba,
Minato-ku, Tokyo, 108-0014, Japan
Tel.: (81) 364537650
Web Site: https://www.agc-fabritech.com
Sales Range: $25-49.9 Million
Processed Glass Products Whslr
N.A.I.C.S.: 423930

AGC Finance Co., Ltd. (1)
1-5-1 Marunouchi Shin-marunouchi Build-
ing, Chiyoda-Ku, Tokyo, 100-6530, Japan
Tel.: (81) 332013305
Web Site: http://www.agc.com
Sales Range: $50-74.9 Million
Financial Management Services
N.A.I.C.S.: 523999

**AGC Flat Glass (Hong Kong) Co.,
Ltd.** (1)
Unit07 7th Floor Laws Commercial Plaza
788 Cheung Sha Wan Road, Kowloon,
China (Hong Kong)
Tel.: (852) 2 541 0789
Web Site: http://www.agc.com
Flat Glass Distr
N.A.I.C.S.: 423390

**AGC Flat Glass (Suzhou) Co.,
Ltd.** (1)
No 158 Wang- Jiang Road Suzhou Indus-
trial Park, Suzhou, 215121, China
Tel.: (86) 512 6285 2501
Automotive Float Glasses Mfr & Distr
N.A.I.C.S.: 327211

**AGC Flat Glass (Thailand) Public
Co., Ltd.** (1)

200 Moo 1 Suksawas Rd Pak Khlong Bang
Pla Kod, Phra Sumut Chedi, Samut Prakan,
10290, Thailand
Tel.: (66) 28155000
Web Site: https://www.agc-flatglass.co.th
Emp.: 799
Flat Glass Mfr
N.A.I.C.S.: 327211

Plant (Domestic):

**AGC Flat Glass (Thailand) Public
Co., Ltd. - Chon Buri Factory** (2)
700/22 Moo 6 Nong Mai Daeng, Mueang
Chon Buri, Chon Buri, 20000, Thailand
Tel.: (66) 3 821 3063
Web Site: http://www.agc-flatglass.co.th
Automobile Parts Mfr
N.A.I.C.S.: 336390

**AGC Flat Glass Asia Pacific Pte.
Ltd.** (1)
PSA Bldg 460 Alexandra Rd Fl 32 Ste 2,
Singapore, 119963, Singapore (100%)
Tel.: (65) 62735656
Web Site: http://www.agc-flatglass.sg
Sales Range: $50-74.9 Million
Emp.: 74
N.A.I.C.S.: 327211

**AGC Flat Glass Protech (Shenzhen)
Co., Ltd.** (1)
101 building E No 12 Hi-tech Avenue,
Baolong Longgang, Shenzhen, 518116,
Guangdong, China
Tel.: (86) 75526826802
Soda Lime Glass Mfr
N.A.I.C.S.: 327215

AGC Glass France S.A. (1)
100 rue Leon Gambetta-BP 1, 59168,
Boussois, France
Tel.: (33) 327694000
Automotive Glass Mfr
N.A.I.C.S.: 327215

AGC Glass Kenzai Co., Ltd. (1)
Global One UENO 4-24-11 Higashiueno,
Taito-Ku, Tokyo, 110-0015, Japan
Tel.: (81) 358066500
Building Glass Material Installation Services
N.A.I.C.S.: 238150

AGC Glass Products Co., Ltd (1)
Global One UENO 4-24-11 Higashiueno,
Taito-Ku, Tokyo, 110-0015, Japan
Tel.: (81) 358066300
Web Site: http://www.agc-group.com
Flat Glass Mfr & Distr
N.A.I.C.S.: 327211

AGC Green-Tech Co., Ltd (1)
4F Kotobuki Building 3-10-4 Iwamotocho,
Chiyoda-ku, Tokyo, 101-0032, Japan
Tel.: (81) 358335451
Fluororesin Film Distr
N.A.I.C.S.: 424610

**AGC Insurance Management Co.,
Ltd.** (1)
RBM Tsukiji Bldg 2-15-5 Shintomi, Chuo-ku,
Tokyo, 104-0041, Japan
Tel.: (81) 362225011
Insurance Management Services
N.A.I.C.S.: 524298

AGC Logistics Co., Ltd. (1)
Shin-marunouchi Building 30th Floor 1-5-1
Marunouchi, Chiyoda-ku, Tokyo, 100-6530,
Japan (100%)
Tel.: (81) 3 3218 5476
Web Site: http://www.agcl.co.jp
Sales Range: $200-249.9 Million
Logistics Consulting Servies
N.A.I.C.S.: 541614

AGC Matex Co., Ltd. (1)
1-2-27 Miyashita, Chuo-ku, Sagamihara,
252-0212, Kanagawa, Japan
Tel.: (81) 42 772 1171
Web Site: http://www.agm.co.jp
Plastic Products Mfr & Distr
N.A.I.C.S.: 326199

**AGC Micro Glass (Thailand) Co.,
Ltd** (1)
99/39 Saha Group Industrial Park Lamphun
Pa Sak, Mueang Lamphun, Lamphun,
51000, Thailand
Tel.: (66) 53584300

Web Site: https://www.amgt.co.th
Molded Aspherical Glass Lenses Mfr
N.A.I.C.S.: 327215

AGC Micro Glass Co., Ltd. (1)
3-22-28 Morooka, Hakata-ku, Fukuoka,
812-0894, Japan
Tel.: (81) 925028380
Aspherical Glass Lense Mfr & Distr
N.A.I.C.S.: 327215

AGC Mineral Co., Ltd. (1)
Shiba Boat Building 6F 3-1-15 Shiba,
Minato-ku, Tokyo, 105-0014, Japan
Tel.: (81) 354199010
Web Site: https://www.agc-mineral.co.jp
Silica Mining Services
N.A.I.C.S.: 212322

AGC Multi Material (Suzhou) Inc. (1)
107-112 Building No 8 TusCity 60 Weixin
Rd, Suzhou Industry Park, Suzhou, 215000,
China
Tel.: (86) 51262867162
N.A.I.C.S.: 327211

AGC Multi Material America, Inc. (1)
1420 W 12th Pl, Tempe, AZ 85281
Tel.: (480) 967-5600
Web Site: https://www.agc-
multimaterial.com
Electronic Components Mfr
N.A.I.C.S.: 335311

AGC Multi Material Europe SA (1)
Route Des Usines, 65300, Lannemezan,
France (100%)
Tel.: (33) 0562985290
Web Site: https://www.agc-
multimaterial.com
Electronic Components Mfr
N.A.I.C.S.: 334220

**AGC Multi Material Singapore Pte.
Ltd.** (1)
4 6 Gul Crescent, Singapore, 629520, Ju-
rong, Singapore
Tel.: (65) 68617117
N.A.I.C.S.: 327211

AGC Polycarbonate Co., Ltd. (1)
1 Asahi Taketoyo-cho, Chita, 470-2514,
Aichi, Japan
Tel.: (81) 569737181
Web Site: http://www.agc.com
Polycarbonate Sheet Mfr & Distr
N.A.I.C.S.: 326112

AGC Polymer Material Co., Ltd. (1)
1-3-8 Nihonbashi Ningyocho, Chuo-ku, To-
kyo, 103-0013, Japan
Web Site: http://www.agc-polymer.com
Polyurethane Coating Mfr
N.A.I.C.S.: 325510

AGC Research Institute, Inc. (1)
Shin-Marunouchi Bldg 1-5-1 Marunouchi,
Chiyoda-ku, Tokyo, 100-6530, Japan
Tel.: (81) 332185663
Engineering Research & Development Ser-
vices
N.A.I.C.S.: 541715

AGC Seimi Chemical Co., Ltd. (1)
3-2-10 Chigasaki, Chigasaki, 253-8585, Ka-
nagawa, Japan
Tel.: (81) 467824131
Web Site: http://www.seimichemical.co.jp
Emp.: 368
Liquid Crystal & Cathode Material Mfr
N.A.I.C.S.: 334419
Yasuhiko Ariyama (Pres)

Plant (Domestic):

**AGC Seimi Chemical Co., Ltd. -
Kashima Plant** (2)
2276-2 Nada Hirai, Kashima, 314-0012,
Ibaraki, Japan
Tel.: (81) 299 84 0808
Liquid Crystal & Cathode Material Mfr
N.A.I.C.S.: 334419

AGC Shanghai Co., Ltd. (1)
Unit 15A 398 Huai Hai Zhong Road, Lu
Wan District, Shanghai, 200020, China
Tel.: (86) 21 53830808
Business Support Services
N.A.I.C.S.: 561499

AGC Si-Tech Co., Ltd. (1)

13-1 Kitaminato-machi, Wakamatsu-ku, Ki-takyushu, 808-0027, Fukuoka, Japan
Tel.: (81) 937611135
Sales Range: $50-74.9 Million
Emp.: 122
Silica Products Mfr
N.A.I.C.S.: 325180

AGC Singapore Services Pte. Ltd. (1)
460 Alexandra Road 32-01 PSA Building, Singapore, 119963, Singapore
Tel.: (65) 6 273 5656
Web Site: http://www.agc.com
Financial Management Services
N.A.I.C.S.: 523999

AGC Sunsmile, Inc. (1)
1-1 Suehirocho, Tsurumi-Ku, Yokohama, 230-0045, Kanagawa, Japan
Tel.: (81) 455037132
Building Waste Management Services
N.A.I.C.S.: 562998

AGC Techno Glass (Thailand) Co., Ltd. (1)
700/322 Moo 6 Amata Nakorn Industrial Estate Bangna-Trad Rd K M 57, T Donhua-roh A Muang, Chon Buri, 20000, Thailand
Tel.: (66) 38214497
Glass Tableware & Products Mfr
N.A.I.C.S.: 327215

AGC Techno Glass Co., Ltd. (1)
3583-5 Kawashiri Yoshidacho, Haibara, 421-0302, Shizuoka, Japan
Tel.: (81) 548321211
Web Site: http://atgc.co.jp
Electronic Glass Products Mfr
N.A.I.C.S.: 327215

AGC Techno Glass Corporation (1)
1-50-1 Gyoda, Funabashi, 273-0044, Japan
Tel.: (81) 474212115
Glass Products Mfr
N.A.I.C.S.: 327215

AGC Technology Solutions (Kunshan) Co., LTD. (1)
618 Wanhua Garden Building 5 218 Qing-yang North Road, Zhoushi Town, Kunshan, 215300, Jiangsu, China
Tel.: (86) 5125 518 1759
Web Site: http://www.agc.com
Glass Plant Engineering Services
N.A.I.C.S.: 541330

AGC Technology Solutions (Thailand) Co., Ltd. (1)
2/555 Sor Tower 7th Floor MOO 15 Bangna-Trad Road, T Bangkaew A Bang-plee, Samut Prakan, 10540, Thailand
Tel.: (66) 2 316 1423
Web Site: http://www.agc.com
Glass Plant Engineering Services
N.A.I.C.S.: 541330

AGC Technology Solutions Co., Ltd. (1)
Cube-Kawasaki Bldg 1F 1-14 Nisshin-cho, Kawasaki-Ku, Kawasaki, 210-0024, Kanagawa, Japan
Tel.: (81) 44 230 5620
Web Site: http://www.agmc.co.jp
Emp.: 228
Glass Plant Engineering Services
N.A.I.C.S.: 541330
Isao Naruge (Pres)

AGC Technology Solutions Taiwan Inc. (1)
Rm 5 9F No 161 Gongyi Rd, West Dist, Taichung, 403516, Taiwan
Tel.: (886) 423280210
Glass Equipment Mfr
N.A.I.C.S.: 327211

AGC Vinythai Public Company Limited (1)
2 I-3 Road Map Ta Phut Industrial Estate, Map Ta Phut Subdistrict Mueang Rayong District, Rayong, 21150, Thailand
Tel.: (86) 38925000
Web Site: https://agcvinythai.com
N.A.I.C.S.: 325110
Yoshihisa Horibe (Chm)

AGC Wakasa Chemicals Co., Ltd. (1)

24-26-1 Hansei, Obama, 917-0044, Fukui, Japan
Pharmaceuticals Product Mfr
N.A.I.C.S.: 325412

Agc Advanced Electronics Display Glass (Shenzhen) Co., Ltd. (1)
1/F No 168 Keyu Road Changzhen Community, Yutang Subdistrict Guangming District, Shenzhen, 518132, Guangdong, China
Tel.: (86) 75581727188
LCD Product Mfr
N.A.I.C.S.: 327215

Agc Asia Pacific (India) Pvt. Ltd. (1)
Suit No 2 2nd Floor First India Place Sushant Lok-1 Block-B, Mehrauli Gurgaon Road, Gurgaon, 122 002, HR, India
Tel.: (91) 1244028913
Automotive Glass Fabrication Distr
N.A.I.C.S.: 424310

Agc Automotive (China) Co., Ltd. (1)
Qinhuangdao Plant 108 Qinhuang Western street Etdz, Qinhuangdao, Hebei, China
Tel.: (86) 3355910000
Automotive Glass Fabrication Distr
N.A.I.C.S.: 424310

Agc Automotive (Suzhou) Inc. (1)
No 158 Wang-Jiang Road, Industrial Park, Suzhou, 215121, China
Tel.: (86) 51262852501
Automotive Glass Fabrication Mfr & Distr
N.A.I.C.S.: 327215

Agc Automotive Glass Mexico S.A. de C.V. (1)
Carretera al Castillo KM 13 5 Interior 2 El Castillo, 45685, El Salto, Jalisco, Mexico
Tel.: (52) 36881551
Automotive Glass Product Mfr
N.A.I.C.S.: 327215

Agc Automotive Mexico S.de R.L. de C.V (1)
Av Asia 601 Col Laguna de San Vicente, Industrial Park Logistk II Villa de Reyes, 79525, San Luis Potosi, Mexico
Tel.: (52) 4448702831
Automotive Glass Product Mfr
N.A.I.C.S.: 327215

Agc Bor Glassworks OOO (1)
Steklozavodskoye shosse r Bor-3, Nizhe-gorodsky, 606443, Velikiy Novgorod, Russia
Tel.: (7) 8312200207
Web Site: https://www.agc.com
Automotive Glass Product Mfr
N.A.I.C.S.: 327215

Agc Chemicals Vietnam Co., Ltd. (1)
Cai Mep Industrial Zone, Tan Thanh District, Ho Chi Minh City, Ba Ria-Vung Tau, Vietnam
Tel.: (84) 2543895310
Caustic Soda Mfr & Distr
N.A.I.C.S.: 325180
Nguyen Anh Tuan (Mgr-IT)

Agc Display Glass (Chongqing) Inc. (1)
Room 17-8 No 279 YuNan Rd, Banan District, Chongqing, 401304, China
Tel.: (86) 2362586988
LCD Product Mfr
N.A.I.C.S.: 327215

Agc Display Glass (Huizhou) Co., Ltd. (1)
No 11 Yinguang Section Yingshan Road, Lilin Town Zhongkai Hi-tech Industrial Development Zone, Huizhou, Guangdong, China
Tel.: (86) 7525300060
LCD Product Mfr
N.A.I.C.S.: 327215

Agc Display Glass (Kunshan) Inc. (1)
No 88 Weishanhu Road, Economic Technical Development Zone, Kunshan, 215333, Jiangsu, China
Tel.: (86) 51250173000
LCD Product Mfr
N.A.I.C.S.: 327215

Agc Display Glass (Shenzhen) Inc. (1)

No 8 Keyu Road Hi-Tech Park TangWei Community, FengHuang Sub-District Guang Ming District, Shenzhen, 518132, China
Tel.: (86) 75521382288
LCD Product Mfr
N.A.I.C.S.: 327215

Agc Display Glass Ochang Co., Ltd. (1)
105 Gwahak saneop 3-ro Ochang-eup, Cheongwon-gu, Cheongju, 28122, Chungcheongbuk-do, Korea (South)
Tel.: (82) 432405500
Web Site: https://ado.agcdisplay.com
LCD Product Mfr
N.A.I.C.S.: 327215

Agc Display Glass Taiwan Inc. (1)
No 8 Kegung 7th road, Douliu, 64064, Yun-lin hsien, Taiwan
Tel.: (886) 55512211
Web Site: https://www.agct.com.tw
Emp.: 1,800
LCD Product Mfr
N.A.I.C.S.: 327215

Agc Electronics Taiwan Inc. (1)
Tel.: (886) 36587071
Electronic Material Mfr & Distr
N.A.I.C.S.: 334419

Agc Fine Techno Korea Co., Ltd. (1)
178 Cheomdangeop-ro Sandong-myeon, Gumi, 39168, Gyeongsangbuk-do, Korea (South)
Tel.: (82) 544780600
Web Site: https://www.afk.co.kr
LCD Product Mfr
N.A.I.C.S.: 327215

Agc France S.A. (1)
100 rue Leon Gambetta, BP 1, Boussois, 59168, Nordhouse, France
Tel.: (33) 327694000
Automotive Glass Product Mfr
N.A.I.C.S.: 327215

Agc Glass UK Ltd. (1)
Unit B Edgemead Close Round Spinney, Northampton, NN3 4RG, United Kingdom
Tel.: (44) 1604671150
Automotive Glass Product Mfr
N.A.I.C.S.: 327215
Ian Hill (Mgr-Program)

Agc Middle East & Africa Fzco (1)
No 209 Wing D HQ Building, PO Box 371681, Dubai Silicon Oasis Free Zone, Dubai, United Arab Emirates
Tel.: (971) 45015578
Automotive Glass Product Mfr
N.A.I.C.S.: 327215
Takashi Washio (Mgr-Bus Dev)

Agc Pharma Chemicals Europe, S.L.U. (1)
Cami de la Pomereda 13, Malgrat de Mar, 08380, Barcelona, Spain
Tel.: (34) 937669700
Pharmaceuticals Product Mfr
N.A.I.C.S.: 325412
Meritxell Torrecilla (Mgr-Pur)

Agc Plibrico Co., Ltd. (1)
6F Mita-NN Bldg 1-23 Shiba 4-chome, Minato-ku, Tokyo, 108-0014, Japan
Web Site: https://www.plibrico.co.jp
Emp.: 200
Monolithic Refractory Mfr
N.A.I.C.S.: 327120

Agc Precision Glass (Shenzhen) Inc. (1)
Room 1201 Haiwang Xingchen Building No 2 Lanxiang 1st Street, Nanshan District, Shenzhen, 518057, China
Tel.: (86) 75586636706
Glass Products Mfr
N.A.I.C.S.: 327215

Agc Soda Corp. (1)
700 AFG Rd, Church Hill, TN 37642
Tel.: (423) 229-7200
Soda Ash Product Distr
N.A.I.C.S.: 212390

Agc Vidros do Brasil Ltda. (1)
Estrada Municipal Doutor Jaime Eduardo Ribeiro Pereira 500 - Jardim, Vista Alegre, Guaratingueta, 12523-671, SP, Brazil
Tel.: (55) 1231277100

Web Site: https://www.agcbrasil.com
Emp.: 1,000
Automotive Glass Product Mfr
N.A.I.C.S.: 327215

Asahi Glass Co., Ltd. - Aichi Plant (Taketoyo) (1)
1 Asahi Taketoyo-cho, Chita, 470-2394, Aichi, Japan
Tel.: (81) 569 73 1110
Web Site: http://www.agc.com
Sales Range: $450-499.9 Million
Emp.: 1,147
Flat Glass Mfr
N.A.I.C.S.: 327211

Asahi Glass Co., Ltd. - Aichi Plant (Toyota) (1)
9-30-1 Umetsubocho, Toyota, 471-0064, Aichi, Japan
Tel.: (81) 565 32 7331
Flat Glass Mfr
N.A.I.C.S.: 327211

Asahi Glass Co., Ltd. - Chiba Plant (1)
10 Goikaigan, Ichihara, 290-8566, Chiba, Japan
Tel.: (81) 436 23 3121
Web Site: http://www.agc.com
Sales Range: $200-249.9 Million
Emp.: 1,173
Specialty Chemicals Mfr
N.A.I.C.S.: 325998

Asahi Glass Co., Ltd. - Kansai Plant (1)
2 Nishimukoujima-cho, Amagasaki, 660-0857, Hyogo, Japan
Tel.: (81) 6 6413 3325
Web Site: http://www.agc.com
Sales Range: $125-149.9 Million
Emp.: 314
Glass Products Mfr
N.A.I.C.S.: 327215

Asahi Glass Co., Ltd. - Kashima Plant (1)
25 Touwada, Kamisu, 314-0195, Ibaraki, Japan
Tel.: (81) 299 96 2215
Sales Range: $125-149.9 Million
Emp.: 499
Glass Products Mfr
N.A.I.C.S.: 327215

Asahi Glass Co., Ltd. - Keihin Plant (1)
1-1 Suehiro-cho, Tsurumi-ku, Yokohama, 230-0045, Japan
Tel.: (81) 45 503 7100
Web Site: http://www.agc.com
Sales Range: $200-249.9 Million
Emp.: 831
Glass Products Mfr
N.A.I.C.S.: 327215

Asahi Glass Co., Ltd. - Kitakyushu Plant (1)
5-1-1 Makiyama, Tobata-ku, Kitakyushu, 804-8520, Japan
Tel.: (81) 93 871 1551
Web Site: http://www.agc.com
Automotive Glass Mfr
N.A.I.C.S.: 327215

Asahi Glass Co., Ltd. - Sagami Plant (1)
426-1 Sumida Aikawamachi, Aiko-gun, Koza, 243-0301, Kanagawa, Japan
Tel.: (81) 46 286 1254
Web Site: http://www.agc.com
Emp.: 510
Automotive Safety Glass Mfr
N.A.I.C.S.: 327215

Asahi Glass Co., Ltd. - Takasago Plant (1)
5-6-1 Umei, Takasago, 676-8655, Hyogo, Japan
Tel.: (81) 794 47 1882
Web Site: http://www.agc.com
Sales Range: $125-149.9 Million
Emp.: 372
Liquid Crystal Display Glass Mfr
N.A.I.C.S.: 327215

Asahi India Glass Ltd. (1)
A-2/10 1st Floor WHS DDA Marble Market

AGC Inc.—(Continued)

Kirti Nagar, New Delhi, 110 015, India
Tel.: (91) 1149454900
Web Site: https://www.aisglass.com
Rev.: $335,446,020
Assets: $515,062,275
Liabilities: $320,738,145
Net Worth: $194,324,130
Earnings: $18,164,055
Emp.: 2,524
Fiscal Year-end: 03/31/2021
Automotive Glass Mfr
N.A.I.C.S.: 327211
Sanjay Ganjoo (COO-Architectural Glass)

Unit (Domestic):

Asahi India Glass, Ltd. - AIS (Auto)
Haryana Works. **(2)**
94 4 Kms Stone Delhi - Jaipur Highway
NH-8 Village Jaliawas, Tehsil Bawal, Re-
wari, 123 501, Haryana, India
Tel.: (91) 1284264367
Glass Products Mfr
N.A.I.C.S.: 327215

Asahi India Glass, Ltd. - AIS (Float)
Works **(2)**
Plot No F-76 to 81 SIPCOT Industrial Park
Irungattukottai Sriperumpdur, Taluk
Kancheepuram, Chennai, 602105,
Tamilnadu, India
Tel.: (91) 4447103442
Emp.: 150
Glass Products Mfr
N.A.I.C.S.: 327215
Rui Neves (Gen Mgr)

Asahi PD Glass Korea Co., Ltd.
5 Block Gumi 4th National Indusutrial Com-
plex Sandong-Myeon, Bonsan-Ri, Gumi,
Kyung-Buk, Korea (South)
Tel.: (82) 54 478 0001
Plasma Display Panel Glass Mfr
N.A.I.C.S.: 327215

CARGLASS YAMATO Co.,Ltd. **(1)**
1-1-11 Fukami Higashi, Yamato, 242-0012,
Kanagawa Prefecture, Japan
Tel.: (81) 462632665
Web Site: https://www.carglass-yamato.co.jp
N.A.I.C.S.: 811122
Isao Shimada (CEO)

Hankuk Electric Glass Co., Ltd. **(1)**
150 Gongdan-Dong, Gumi, Kyung-Buk, Ko-
rea (South)
Tel.: (82) 544681156
Web Site: http://www.heg.co.kr
Color Television Glass Mfr
N.A.I.C.S.: 327215

Hanwook Techno Glass Co., Ltd. **(1)**
78 Cheomdangieop-Ro Sandong-Myoen,
Gumi, Kyungbuk, Korea (South)
Tel.: (82) 544753953
Web Site: http://www.htg.co.kr
Display Glass Panel Mfr
N.A.I.C.S.: 327215

Hokkaido Soda Co., Ltd. **(1)**
134-122 Numanohata, Tomakomai, 059-
1364, Japan
Tel.: (81) 144557862
Web Site: http://www.hokkaido-soda.co.jp
Inorganic Chemical Mfr
N.A.I.C.S.: 325180

Kashima Berth Co., Ltd. **(1)**
5 Touwada, Kamisu, 314-0102, Ibaraki,
Japan
Tel.: (81) 299919100
Port Facility Services
N.A.I.C.S.: 488310

Kashima Chemical Co., Ltd. **(1)**
30 Towada, Kamisu, 314-0102, Ibaraki,
Japan **(78.75%)**
Tel.: (81) 299962271
Web Site: https://www.kashima-
chemical.com
Sales Range: $25-49.9 Million
Emp.: 63
Chemicals Mfr
N.A.I.C.S.: 325998

Kashima South Joint Power
Corp. **(1)**
33 Towada, Kamisu, 314-0102, Ibaraki,
Japan

Tel.: (81) 299964112
Web Site: http://www.nankyo.co.jp
Eletric Power Generation Services
N.A.I.C.S.: 221118

Keiyo Monomer Co., Ltd. **(1)**
11-6 Goiminamikaigan, Ichihara, 290-0045,
Chiba, Japan
Tel.: (81) 43 624 8535
Web Site: http://www.agc-group.com
Industrial Inorganic Chemical Mfr
N.A.I.C.S.: 325180

Kyoei Shoji Co., Ltd. **(1)**
Yurakucho Denki Building North Tower 13F
1-7-1 Yurakucho, Chiyoda-ku, Tokyo, 100-
0006, Japan
Tel.: (81) 352180150
Emp.: 110
Warehousing & Transportation Services
N.A.I.C.S.: 493110

La Foret Engineering Co., Ltd. **(1)**
Roppongi Annex 7f 6-7-6 Roppongi, Minato-
ku, Tokyo, 106-0032, Japan
Tel.: (81) 364066721
Web Site: http://www.himawari-net.co.jp
Sales Range: $75-99.9 Million
Solar-Light Collection & Transmission Sys-
tems Mfr & Sales
N.A.I.C.S.: 221121

MCIS Safety Glass Sdn. Bhd. **(1)**
Lot 1 Lorong Senawang 2/1 Senawang In-
dustrial Estate, 70450, Seremban, Negeri
Sembilan, Malaysia
Tel.: (60) 66775367
Web Site:
   http://www.mcissafetyglass.com.my
Emp.: 400
Automotive Glass Product Distr
N.A.I.C.S.: 423120
Mukhtar Mohamad (Gen Mgr)

Nelco Products Pte. Ltd. **(1)**
126 Pioneer Road, Singapore, 639585,
Singapore **(100%)**
Tel.: (65) 68617117
Copper-Clad Laminates, Epoxy Glass Lami-
nates & Impregnated Glass Fibre Cloth Mfr
& Distr
N.A.I.C.S.: 331420
Patrick Wong (Dir-IT / Materials)

Nelco Products, Inc. **(1)**
1411 E Orange Thorpe Ave, Fullerton, CA
92831 **(100%)**
Tel.: (714) 879-4293
Web Site: http://www.parknelco.com
Sales Range: $75-99.9 Million
Emp.: 140
Copper Clad Epoxy Laminates Mfr
N.A.I.C.S.: 326130

New England Laminates Co.,
Inc. **(1)**
1411 E Orangethorpe Ave, Fullerton, CA
92831-5227 **(100%)**
Tel.: (845) 567-6200
Sales Range: $25-49.9 Million
Emp.: 90
Copper Clad Epoxy Laminates Mfr
N.A.I.C.S.: 326130

Optical Coatings Japan **(1)**
Shin-Marunouchi Building 1-5-1
Marunouchi, Chiyoda-ku, Tokyo, 100-8405,
Japan
Tel.: (81) 33 218 7998
Web Site: https://www.ocj.co.jp
Sales Range: $50-74.9 Million
Emp.: 119
Film Coated Optical Products Mfr & Distr
N.A.I.C.S.: 333310

P.T. Asahimas Chemical **(1)**
World Trade Centre WTC 2 10th Floor Jl
Jend Sudirman Kav 29-31, Jakarta, 12190,
Indonesia
Tel.: (62) 215211181
Web Site: http://www.asc.co.id
Sales Range: $25-49.9 Million
Emp.: 70
Specialty Chemicals Mfr
N.A.I.C.S.: 325998

Plant (Domestic):

P.T. Asahimas Chemical - Cilegon
Factory **(2)**

Desa Gunung Sugih Jl Raya Anyer Km 122,
Cilegon, 42447, Baten, Indonesia
Tel.: (62) 25 460 1252
Web Site: http://www.asc.co.id
Chemical Products Mfr
N.A.I.C.S.: 325998

Siam Asahi Technoglass Co.,
Ltd. **(1)**
87/12 Moo 2 Sukhumvit Road, Laemcha-
bang Industrial Estate, Thung Sukhla, Si
Racha, 20230, Chon Buri, Thailand
Tel.: (66) 38490680
Web Site: http://www.agc.co.jp
Sales Range: $400-449.9 Million
Emp.: 1,400
Television Glass Bulbs Mfr
N.A.I.C.S.: 335999

Tokai Kogyo Co., Ltd. **(1)**
Shiba Boat Bldg 6F Shiba 3-1-15, Minato-
ku, Tokyo, 105-0014, Japan
Tel.: (81) 354199010
Web Site: http://www.tokai-kc.co.jp
Sales Range: $25-49.9 Million
Emp.: 50
Commercial Building Construction Services
N.A.I.C.S.: 236210

Vinythai Public Company Ltd. **(1)**
No 2 Map Ta Phut Industrial Estate I-3
Road Tumbol Map Ta Phut Amphoe,
Mueang Rayong, Rayong, 21150,
Thailand **(58.78%)**
Tel.: (66) 38925000
Web Site: http://www.vinythai.co.th
Rev.: $568,905,328
Assets: $879,693,679
Liabilities: $134,778,890
Net Worth: $744,914,790
Earnings: $72,395,720
Emp.: 525
Fiscal Year-end: 12/31/2020
Plastic & Chemical Products Sales
N.A.I.C.S.: 325998
Sompot Cheeranorawanich (Sec & VP-Corp
Affairs & Comm)

Subsidiary (Non-US):

Vinythai Holding Pte. Ltd. **(2)**
No 10 Collyer Quay 10-01 Ocean Financial
Centre, Singapore, 049315,
Singapore **(100%)**
Tel.: (65) 656 531 4187
Holding Company
N.A.I.C.S.: 551112
Bruno van der Wielen (Chm)

Zibo Agc Alumina Materials Co.,
Ltd. **(1)**
60 Wulinglu, Boshan, Zibo, 255200, Shan-
dong, China
Tel.: (86) 5334281441
Alumina Material Mfr
N.A.I.C.S.: 331313

Zibo Asahi Glass Alumina Materials
Co., Ltd. **(1)**
60 Wulinglu Boshan, Zibo, 255200, Shan-
dong, China
Tel.: (86) 533 428 1441
Glass Products Whslr
N.A.I.C.S.: 238150

AGDER ENERGI AS

Kjoita 18, 4630, Kristiansand, Norway
Tel.: (47) 38 60 70 00
Web Site: http://www.ae.no
Emp.: 1,100
Energy Production & Distr
N.A.I.C.S.: 221122

Subsidiaries:

Markedskraft ASA **(1)**
Langbryggen 9, 4801, Arendal, Norway
Tel.: (47) 94 78 16 88
Web Site: http://www.markedskraft.de
Electric Power Distribution Services
N.A.I.C.S.: 221122
Espen Zachariassen (CEO)

AGEAS SA/NV

Avenue du Boulevard 21, Box 7,
1210, Brussels, Belgium
Tel.: (32) 25575711   BE
Web Site: https://www.ageas.com

Year Founded: 1993
AGESF—(OTCIQ)
Rev.: $7,105,640,800
Assets: $106,736,946,698
Liabilities: $97,355,116,472
Net Worth: $9,381,830,225
Earnings: $1,299,260,404
Emp.: 50,000
Fiscal Year-end: 12/31/23
Fire Insurance Services
N.A.I.C.S.: 551112
Bart Karel August De Smet (Chm)

Subsidiaries:

AG Insurance N.V. **(1)**
Emile Jacqmainlaan 53, 1000, Brussels,
Belgium
Tel.: (32) 26648111
Web Site: http://www.aginsurance.be
Sales Range: $5-14.9 Billion
Life Insurance Products & Services
N.A.I.C.S.: 524113
Benny De Wyngaert (Mng Dir-Bankchannel
& Life Dev)

Subsidiary (Domestic):

AG Real Estate **(2)**
Avenue des Arts 58, 1000, Brussels, Bel-
gium
Tel.: (32) 26096800
Web Site: http://www.agrealestate.eu
Emp.: 250
Real Estate Investment, Development &
Management Services
N.A.I.C.S.: 531390
Serge Fautre (CEO)

Subsidiary (Domestic):

Interparking SA **(3)**
Rue Brederode 9, 1000, Brussels,
Belgium **(51%)**
Tel.: (32) 25495811
Web Site: http://www.interparking.be
Transportation Support Services
N.A.I.C.S.: 488999
Claude De Clercq (Founder)

Subsidiary (Non-US):

Contipark Parkgaragengesellschaft
mbH **(4)**
Rankestrasse 13, 10789, Berlin, Germany
Tel.: (49) 302500970
Web Site: http://www.contipark.de
Transportation Support Services
N.A.I.C.S.: 488490

Interparking France SA **(4)**
30 Rue de Gramont, 75002, Paris,
France **(100%)**
Tel.: (33) 970140111
Web Site: http://www.interparking-
france.com
Parking Lot Operator
N.A.I.C.S.: 488490
Marc Grasset (COO & Dir-Publication)

Interparking Hispania, S.A. **(4)**
C/ Valencia 93 3 2, 08029, Barcelona,
Spain
Tel.: (34) 934516624
Web Site: http://www.interparking.es
Parking Lot Operation Services
N.A.I.C.S.: 812930

Interparking Nederland B.V. **(4)**
Beursplein 37, 3011 AA, Rotterdam, Nether-
lands
Tel.: (31) 885421300
Web Site: http://www.interparking.nl
Transportation Support Services
N.A.I.C.S.: 488999

AG Insurance SA/NV **(1)**
53 Boulevard Emile Jacqmain, 1000, Brus-
sels, Belgium
Tel.: (32) 26640200
Web Site: https://www.aginsurance.be
N.A.I.C.S.: 524113
Heidi Delobelle (CEO)

Ageas France S.A. **(1)**
50 Place de l'Ellipse, 30024, Paris, Cedex,
France
Tel.: (33) 173605317
Web Site: http://www.ageas.fr

Sales Range: $250-299.9 Million
Life Insurance, Pension Products & Wealth
Management Services
N.A.I.C.S.: 524113
Bertrand Hau *(Mng Dir)*

Subsidiary (Domestic):

SicavOnline SA　　　　　　　　　　　　**(2)**
50 place de l'Ellipse, CS 50053, La De-
fense, 92985, Paris, Cedex,
France　　　　　　　　　　　　　　　**(65%)**
Tel.: (33) 170080808
Web Site: http://www.sicavonline.fr
Sales Range: $50-74.9 Million
Fund & Asset Management Services
N.A.I.C.S.: 525910

Ageas Insurance Limited　　　　　　**(1)**
Ageas House Hampshire Corporate Park
Templars Way, Eastleigh, SO53 3YA,
Hampshire, United Kingdom
Tel.: (44) 2380312323
Web Site: http://www.ageas.co.uk
Personal & Commercial Insurance Products
& Services
N.A.I.C.S.: 524298
Lyn Nicholls *(Dir-HR)*

Subsidiary (Domestic):

Groupama Insurance Company
Limited　　　　　　　　　　　　　　**(2)**
6th Floor One America Square 17 Cross-
wall, London, EC3N 2LB, United
Kingdom　　　　　　　　　　　　**(100%)**
Tel.: (44) 8708508510
Web Site: http://www.groupama.co.uk
Sales Range: $700-749.9 Million
Emp.: 600
Property & Casualty Insurance Products &
Services
N.A.I.C.S.: 524126

Ageas N.V.　　　　　　　　　　　　**(1)**
Archimedeslaan 6, 3584 BA, Utrecht, Neth-
erlands
Tel.: (31) 302266566
Web Site: http://www.ageas.com
Holding Company; Insurance Products &
Services
N.A.I.C.S.: 551112
Jozef G. De Mey *(Chm)*

Ageas UK Ltd.　　　　　　　　　　**(1)**
Ageas House Hampshire Corporate Park
Templars Way, Eastleigh, SO53 3YA,
Hampshire, United Kingdom
Tel.: (44) 8000234567
Web Site: https://www.ageas.co.uk
N.A.I.C.S.: 524113
Ant Middle *(CEO)*

Muang Thai Life Assurance Co.,
Ltd.　　　　　　　　　　　　　　　**(1)**
250 Rachadaphisek Rd, Huanykwang,
Bangkok, 10310, Thailand
Tel.: (66) 227610257
Web Site: http://www.muangthai.co.th
General Insurance Services
N.A.I.C.S.: 524210
Jozef G. De Mey *(Vice Chm)*

AGEHA INC.
Hatchobori 2127 Uniden Building 3rd
floor, Chuo-ku, Tokyo, 104-0032, Ja-
pan
Tel.: (81) 362803336
Web Site: https://www.ageha.tv
Year Founded: 2001
9330—(TKS)
Emp.: 131
Marketing Consulting Services
N.A.I.C.S.: 541613
Takehiro Minato *(Pres)*

AGELLAN CAPITAL PART-
NERS INC.
156 Front Street West Suite 303, To-
ronto, M5J 2L6, ON, Canada
Tel.: (416) 593-6800　　　　　　　　ON
Web Site:
　　http://www.agellancapital.com
Real Estate Investment Management
Services
N.A.I.C.S.: 523940

Frank Camenzuli *(Founder, Pres &
Principal)*

AGENCE EURO SERVICES
22 Rue Michelet, 92100, Boulogne-
Billancourt, Hauts De Seine, France
Tel.: (33) 148251188
Sales Range: $10-24.9 Million
Emp.: 45
Advertising Agencies
N.A.I.C.S.: 541810
Dominique Bruzzi *(Dir-Fin)*

AGENCE FRANCE-PRESSE
13 Place de la Bourse, 75002, Paris,
France
Tel.: (33) 140414646　　　　　　　FR
Web Site: http://www.afp.com
Year Founded: 1835
Sales Range: $300-349.9 Million
Emp.: 2,000
International News Services
N.A.I.C.S.: 516210
Patrice Monti *(Deputy Dir-Sls & Mktg)*

Subsidiaries:

AFP GmbH　　　　　　　　　　　　**(1)**
Unter den Linden 21, 10117, Berlin, Ger-
many
Tel.: (49) 30308760
Information Technology Services
N.A.I.C.S.: 541519

AFP-Services SA　　　　　　　　　**(1)**
36 Rue du Sentier, 75002, Paris, France
Tel.: (33) 140418847
Web Site: http://www.afp-services.com
Information Technology Services
N.A.I.C.S.: 541519
Fabrice Fries *(CEO & Dir-Publication)*

Inedit　　　　　　　　　　　　　　**(1)**
33 avenue Philippe Auguste, 75011, Paris,
France
Tel.: (33) 142610264
Editorial Engineering: Integration of Informa-
tion Technology for Media Companies
N.A.I.C.S.: 513199

SID Sportmarketing & Communica-
tion Services GmbH　　　　　　　**(1)**
Ursulaplatz 1, 50668, Cologne, Germany
Tel.: (49) 22199880300
Advertising Services
N.A.I.C.S.: 541810

Sport-Informations-Dienst GmbH und
Co. KG　　　　　　　　　　　　　**(1)**
Hammfelddamm 10, 41460, Neuss, Ger-
many
Tel.: (49) 213113100
Web Site: http://www.sid.de
German Language Internet Sports Service
N.A.I.C.S.: 516210

AGENCE MEESTERS
3 rue Jacques Coeur, 75004, Paris,
France
Tel.: (33) 144786030
Year Founded: 1981
Advertising Services
N.A.I.C.S.: 541810

AGENCE SCHILLING COMMU-
NICATION
2 place Cap Quest, BP 20169,
17005, La Rochelle, Cedex1, France
Tel.: (33) 5 46 50 15 15
Web Site: http://www.n-schilling.com
Year Founded: 1974
Sales Range: $10-24.9 Million
Emp.: 8
Public Relations
N.A.I.C.S.: 541820
Nicole Schilling *(Dir)*

AGENCIA EFE, S.A.
Espronceda 32, E-28036, Madrid,
Spain
Tel.: (34) 913467100
Web Site: http://www.efe.com

Sales Range: $150-199.9 Million
Emp.: 1,000
News Services
N.A.I.C.S.: 516210
Javier Munoz *(Mgr-Sports)*

Subsidiaries:

Agencia EFE, S.A.　　　　　　　　**(1)**
Coronel Santiago Bueras 188, Santiago,
Chile
Tel.: (56) 26324946
News Services
N.A.I.C.S.: 516210

Agencia EFE, S.A.　　　　　　　　**(1)**
Alicia Moreau de Justo 1720 1st Fl, Apart-
ment F, Buenos Aires, C1107AFJ, Argentina
Tel.: (54) 1143125521
Web Site: http://www.efe.com
Sales Range: $25-49.9 Million
Emp.: 20
News Services
N.A.I.C.S.: 516210
Mar Mirim *(Gen Mgr)*

Agencia EFE, S.A.　　　　　　　　**(1)**
Quintas Altas Cumbres centre Calles Coro,
Y San Cristobal Las Palmas, 1050, Cara-
cas, Venezuela
Tel.: (58) 2127935752
News Services
N.A.I.C.S.: 516210

Agencia EFE, S.A.　　　　　　　　**(1)**
Lafayette 69, Anzures Miguel Hidalgo,
Mexico, 11590, DF, Mexico
Tel.: (52) 5552554085
Web Site: http://www.efe.com.mx
Sales Range: $25-49.9 Million
Emp.: 20
News Services
N.A.I.C.S.: 516210
Rahul Cortes *(Gen Mgr)*

Agencia EFE, S.A.　　　　　　　　**(1)**
Gonzalez Olaechea 207, San Isidro, Lima,
Peru
Tel.: (51) 14412094
Web Site: http://www.efe.com
Sales Range: $25-49.9 Million
Emp.: 11
News Services
N.A.I.C.S.: 516210

Agencia EFE, S.A.　　　　　　　　**(1)**
Praia de Botafogo 228, Sala 605-B, Rio de
Janeiro, 22359-900, RJ, Brazil
Tel.: (55) 2125536355
Web Site: http://www.efe.com
Sales Range: $25-49.9 Million
Emp.: 30
News Services
N.A.I.C.S.: 516210
Jaine Ortega *(Gen Mgr)*

Agencia EFE, S.A.　　　　　　　　**(1)**
Carrera 16 39A-69, Bogota, Colombia
Tel.: (57) 12323528
News Services
N.A.I.C.S.: 516210

Agencie EFE　　　　　　　　　　　**(1)**
Residence Pl Rue de la Loi 155, Brussels,
1040, Belgium
Tel.: (32) 22854830
Web Site: http://www.efe.com
Sales Range: $25-49.9 Million
Emp.: 6
News Services
N.A.I.C.S.: 516210
Jose Antonio Vera *(Pres)*

EFE News Services (US) Inc.　　　**(1)**
5959 Blue Lagoon Dr Ste 308, Miami, FL
33126
Tel.: (305) 262-7575
Web Site: http://www.efe.com
News Services
N.A.I.C.S.: 516210
Ignacio Esteban *(VP)*

AGENCY59
1910 Yonge St 4th Fl, Toronto, M4S
1Z5, ON, Canada
Tel.: (416) 484-1959　　　　　　　　Ca
Web Site: http://www.agency59.ca
Year Founded: 1959
Rev: $10,000,000

Emp.: 50
Advetising Agency
N.A.I.C.S.: 541810
John McIntyre *(Partner & Writer)*

Subsidiaries:

Agency59 Response　　　　　　　**(1)**
1910 Yonge Street 4th Fl, Toronto, M4S
1Z5, ON, Canada
Tel.: (416) 484-1959
Web Site: http://www.agency59.ca
Emp.: 40
Business-To-Business, Consumer Market-
ing, Direct Response Marketing,
E-Commerce, Health Care, High Technol-
ogy, Seniors' Market, Strategic
Planning/Research, Sweepstakes, Travel &
Tourism
N.A.I.C.S.: 541810

AGENDA CORPORATION
03-06 32F, 118 Connaight Road
West, Hong Kong, China (Hong
Kong)
Tel.: (852) 22983888
Emp.: 250
Advertising Agencies
N.A.I.C.S.: 541613
Steve Hsia *(CEO)*

AGENDIA NV
Science Park 406, 1098 XH, Amster-
dam, Netherlands
Tel.: (31) 204621510
Web Site: http://www.agendia.com
Year Founded: 2003
Molecular Diagnostic Services
N.A.I.C.S.: 325413
Patrick J. Balthrop, Sr. *(Chm-
Supervisory Bd)*

Subsidiaries:

Agendia Inc.　　　　　　　　　　　**(1)**
22 Morgan, Irvine, CA 92618
Tel.: (888) 321-2732
Healtcare Services
N.A.I.C.S.: 621491
Elizabeth S. Hanna *(Chief Comml Officer &
Exec VP)*

AGENNIX AG
Fraunhoferstrasse 20, 82152, Martin-
sried, Germany
Tel.: (49) 8985652600　　　　　　　De
Web Site: http://www.agennix.com
Year Founded: 2009
Sales Range: $1-9.9 Million
Emp.: 65
Holding Company; Biopharmaceutical
Products Developer & Mfr
N.A.I.C.S.: 551112
Gregory H. Hamm *(Sr VP-HR & Corp
Integration)*

Subsidiaries:

Agennix Incorporated　　　　　　**(1)**
8 E Greenway Plz Ste 910, Houston, TX
77046　　　　　　　　　　　　**(100%)**
Tel.: (713) 552-1091
Web Site: http://www.agennix.com
Biopharmaceutical Products Developer &
Mfr
N.A.I.C.S.: 325414

Branch (Domestic):

Agennix Inc. - Princeton　　　　　**(2)**
101 College Rd E, Princeton, NJ 08540
Tel.: (609) 524-1000
Web Site: http://www.agennix.com
Biopharmaceutical Products Developer &
Mfr
N.A.I.C.S.: 541715

AGENT, INC.
5F Dogenzakadori 22512 Dogenzaka,
Shibuya-Ku, Tokyo, 150-0042, Japan
Tel.: (81) 337803911
Web Site: https://www.agent-
　　network.com

Agent, Inc.—(Continued)
Year Founded: 2004
7098—(TKS)
Rev.: $39,803,260
Assets: $16,930,920
Liabilities: $15,229,320
Net Worth: $1,701,600
Earnings: $56,720
Emp.: 145
Fiscal Year-end: 01/31/24
Application Development Services
N.A.I.C.S.: 541511
Koji Shinomiya *(Founder, Pres, CEO & COO)*

AGENZIA NAZIONALE PER L'ATTRAZIONE DEGLI INVES-TIMENTI E LO SVILLUPO D'IMPRESA SPA
Via Calabria 46, 00187, Rome, Italy
Tel.: (39) 0848886886
Web Site: http://www.invitalia.it
Sales Range: $1-4.9 Billion
Emp.: 106,000
Economic Development & Inward Investment Services
N.A.I.C.S.: 523999
Claudio Tesauro *(Chm & Pres)*

Subsidiaries:

Innovazione Italia S.p.A.   **(1)**
Via Boncompagni 16, Roma, Latina, Italy
Tel.: (39) 06420329
Management Consulting Services
N.A.I.C.S.: 541618

Invitalia Partecipazioni S.p.A.   **(1)**
Via Calabria 46, 00187, Rome, Italy
Tel.: (39) 0642 1601
Investment Management Service
N.A.I.C.S.: 523940

Italia Navigando S.p.A.   **(1)**
Via Calabria, Latina, 00187, Italy
Tel.: (39) 064203291
Web Site: http://www.italianavigando.it
Land Subdivision
N.A.I.C.S.: 237210

SI Factor LLC   **(1)**
13816 Lexington Pl, Broomfield, CO 80020-9377
Tel.: (303) 255-1242
Engineeering Services
N.A.I.C.S.: 541330

Strategia Italia Sgr SpA   **(1)**
Corso Vittorio Emanuele II 88, Milan, Italy
Tel.: (39) 0115575201
Open-End Investment Funds
N.A.I.C.S.: 525910

Sviluppo Italia Abruzzo S.p.A.   **(1)**
Mazzarino 108, L'Aquila, 67100, Rome, Italy
Tel.: (39) 086248581
Web Site: http://www.sviluppoitaliaabruzzo.it
Holding Company
N.A.I.C.S.: 551112

Sviluppo Italia Campania SpA   **(1)**
Via A Olivetti 1, Pozzuoli, Italy
Tel.: (39) 0815255111
Web Site:
   http://www.sviluppoitaliacampania.it
Management Consulting Services
N.A.I.C.S.: 541618

Sviluppo Italia Marche SpA   **(1)**
Via Ludovico Menicucci 6, 60121i, Ancona, Italy
Tel.: (39) 0715021444
Management Consulting Services
N.A.I.C.S.: 541618

Sviluppo Italia Molise SpA   **(1)**
Via Don Giuseppe Mucciardi 5, 86020, Naples, Italy
Tel.: (39) 0874774210
Management Consulting Services
N.A.I.C.S.: 541618

Sviluppo Italia Puglia SpA   **(1)**
Via Giovanni Amendola 168 5, Bari, Italy
Tel.: (39) 0805461637

Web Site: http://por.regione.puglia.it
Management Consulting Services
N.A.I.C.S.: 541618

AGES INDUSTRI AB
Kristian IV s Vag 3 Plan 13, SE-302 50, Halmstad, Sweden
Tel.: (46) 370333700
Web Site: http://www.ages.se
AGES.B—(OMX)
Rev.: $130,628,164
Assets: $122,171,560
Liabilities: $77,588,676
Net Worth: $44,582,884
Earnings: $3,129,643
Emp.: 524
Fiscal Year-end: 12/31/21
Aluminum Mfr
N.A.I.C.S.: 331313
Stefan Jonsson *(Chm)*

Subsidiaries:

AGES Falkenberg AB   **(1)**
Kabelvagen 10, 311 50, Falkenberg, Sweden
Tel.: (46) 346715000
Die Casting Aluminum Mfr
N.A.I.C.S.: 331524
Paula Gustafsson *(Mgr-Quality)*

AGES Horle AB   **(1)**
Box 436, 331 24, Varnamo, Sweden
Tel.: (46) 370333700
Die Casting Aluminum Mfr
N.A.I.C.S.: 331524
David Elg *(Sls Mgr)*

AGES Kulltorp AB   **(1)**
Gnosjovagen 10, Kulltorp, 335 96, Gnosjo, Sweden
Tel.: (46) 37083660
Die Casting Aluminum Mfr
N.A.I.C.S.: 331524
Tomas Karrman *(Mng Dir & Mgr-Quality)*

AGES Shared Services AB   **(1)**
Horle 3, 331 92, Varnamo, Sweden
Tel.: (46) 370650700.
Industrial Machinery Mfr & Distr
N.A.I.C.S.: 333248

AGES Varnamo AB   **(1)**
Silkesvagen 11, 331 53, Varnamo, Sweden
Tel.: (46) 370692330
Die Casting Aluminum Mfr
N.A.I.C.S.: 331524
Anders Linder *(Mng Dir)*

UB Verktyg AB   **(1)**
Mjolnarevagen 6, 331 73, Bor, Sweden
Tel.: (46) 370658880
Die Casting Tool Mfr
N.A.I.C.S.: 331523
David Claesson *(Mgr-Technical)*

AGESA HAYAT VE EMEKLILIK AS
Icerenkoy Mah Umut Sok Quick Tower Sitesi N 10-12/9 Atasehir, Umraniye, 34768, Istanbul, Turkiye
Tel.: (90) 2166333333
Web Site: https://www.agesa.com.tr
AGESA—(IST)
Rev.: $40,162,441
Assets: $2,706,755,851
Liabilities: $2,653,433,082
Net Worth: $53,322,769
Earnings: $27,013,766
Emp.: 1,712
Fiscal Year-end: 12/31/22
Life Insurance & Pensions
N.A.I.C.S.: 524113
Haluk Dincer *(Chm)*

AGESON BERHAD
83 & 85 Jalan SS 15/4C, 47500, Subang Jaya, Selangor Darul Ehsan, Malaysia
Tel.: (60) 356292600
Web Site: http://www.prinsiptek.com
AGES—(KLS)
Rev.: $102,805,313
Assets: $79,980,360

Liabilities: $31,529,559
Net Worth: $48,450,801
Earnings: ($28,659,918)
Fiscal Year-end: 12/31/22
Construction & Property Development Services
N.A.I.C.S.: 236115
Chin Kok Foong *(Exec Dir)*

AGF A S
Stadion Alle 70, Aarhus C, 8000, Arhus, Denmark
Tel.: (45) 89386000
Web Site: https://agf.dk
Year Founded: 1880
AGF.B—(CSE)
Rev.: $25,773,032
Assets: $30,435,097
Liabilities: $6,372,358
Net Worth: $24,062,740
Earnings: $3,287,465
Emp.: 115
Fiscal Year-end: 06/30/23
Sports & Event Facility Operator
N.A.I.C.S.: 711211
Lars Fournais *(Chm)*

AGF MANAGEMENT LIMITED
Cibc Square Tower One 81 Bay Street Suite 3900, Toronto, M5J 0G1, ON, Canada
Tel.: (416) 367-1900   ON
Web Site: https://www.agf.com
Year Founded: 1957
A3J—(DEU)
Rev.: $366,892,449
Assets: $1,070,932,715
Liabilities: $264,757,190
Net Worth: $806,175,525
Earnings: $52,136,615
Emp.: 634
Fiscal Year-end: 11/30/22
Investment Services
N.A.I.C.S.: 523999
W. Robert Farquharson *(Vice Chm)*

Subsidiaries:

AGF Asset Management Asia Ltd.   **(1)**
80 Raffles Place, Singapore, 049712, Singapore
Tel.: (65) 64381633
Sales Range: $50-74.9 Million
Emp.: 5
Open-End Investment Funds
N.A.I.C.S.: 525910
Eng Hock Ong *(Mng Dir)*

AGF Funds Inc.   **(1)**
55 Standish Court Suite 1050, Mississauga, L5R 0G3, ON, Canada   **(100%)**
Tel.: (905) 214-8203
Web Site: http://www.agf.com
Open-End Investment Funds
N.A.I.C.S.: 525910

AGF International Advisors Company Ltd.   **(1)**
2nd Floor Unit 12 Duke Lane Royal Hibernian Way, Dublin, D02 DX07, Ireland   **(100%)**
Tel.: (353) 16613466
Sales Range: $50-74.9 Million
Emp.: 18
Investment Advice
N.A.I.C.S.: 523940

Subsidiary (Domestic):

AGFIA Limited   **(2)**
34 Molesworth St, Dublin, Ireland
Tel.: (353) 1 661 3466
Web Site: http://www.agf.com
Sales Range: $50-74.9 Million
Emp.: 12
Investment Management Service
N.A.I.C.S.: 523999

AGF International Company Ltd.   **(1)**
34 Molesworth St, Dublin, Ireland   **(100%)**
Tel.: (353) 16613619
Web Site: http://www.agf.com

Sales Range: $50-74.9 Million
Emp.: 12
Life Insurance Pension Products
Management Services
N.A.I.C.S.: 523410

AGF Investments Inc.   **(1)**
CIBC SQUARE Tower One 81 Bay Street Suite 4000, Toronto, M5J 0G1, ON, Canada
Tel.: (416) 367-1900
Investment Management Service
N.A.I.C.S.: 523999

Subsidiary (Domestic):

Acuity Funds Ltd.   **(2)**
40 King St W, Toronto, M5H 3Y2, ON, Canada
Tel.: (416) 366-9933
Investment Management Service
N.A.I.C.S.: 523999

Acuity Investment Management Inc.   **(2)**
40 King St W Scotia Plaza Bldg, Toronto, M1L 3Y2, ON, Canada
Tel.: (416) 366-9933
Web Site: http://www.agf.com
Investment Management Service
N.A.I.C.S.: 523999

Doherty & Associates Ltd.   **(2)**
56 Sparks St Ste 700, Ottawa, K1P 5A9, ON, Canada
Tel.: (613) 238-6727
Web Site: https://www.doherty.ca
Sales Range: $50-74.9 Million
Emp.: 15
Investment Management Service
N.A.I.C.S.: 523999
Ian S. Sterling *(Pres)*

AGF Securities (Canada) Ltd.   **(1)**
Toronto Dominion Bank Twr Ste 3100 31st Fl 66 Welling, Toronto, M5K 1E9, ON, Canada   **(100%)**
Tel.: (416) 865-4176
Web Site: http://www.agf.com
Investment Banking & Securities Dealing
N.A.I.C.S.: 523150

Cypress Capital Management Ltd.   **(1)**
1055 Georgia St W Ste 1700, Vancouver, V6E 3P3, BC, Canada   **(100%)**
Tel.: (604) 659-1850
Web Site: http://cypresscap.com
Sales Range: $50-74.9 Million
Emp.: 20
Investment Banking & Securities Dealing
N.A.I.C.S.: 523150
Greg Bay *(Partner)*

Highstreet Asset Management Inc.   **(1)**
244 Pall Mall Street Suite 350, London, N6A 5P6, ON, Canada
Tel.: (519) 850-9500
Web Site: https://www.highstreet.ca
Sales Range: $50-74.9 Million
Emp.: 38
Investment Services
N.A.I.C.S.: 523999
Grant Wang *(Chief Investment Officer)*

InstarAGF Asset Management Inc.   **(1)**
Toronto-Dominion Bank Tower 66 Wellington Street West Suite 3410, PO Box 342, Toronto, M5K 1K7, ON, Canada
Tel.: (416) 815-6224
Web Site: https://instarinvest.com
Asset Management Firm
N.A.I.C.S.: 523940
Gregory J. Smith *(Pres & CEO)*

Holding (US):

AMPORTS, Inc.   **(2)**
10060 Skinner Lake Dr Ste 205, Jacksonville, FL 32246
Tel.: (904) 652-2962
Web Site: http://www.amports.com
Marine Port Terminals Operator & Cargo Handling Services
N.A.I.C.S.: 488320
Steve Taylor *(CEO)*

Subsidiary (Domestic):

AMPORTS Atlantic Terminal   **(3)**

2901 Childs St, Baltimore, MD 21226
Tel.: (410) 350-0400
Web Site: http://www.amports.com
Marine Cargo Handling
N.A.I.C.S.: 488320
George Molyneaux *(Gen Mgr)*

Subsidiary (Non-US):

AMPORTS Mexico Altamira
Terminal (3)
Validad Mar Caribe 210, Col Puerto Indus-
trial, Altamira, 89603, Mexico
Tel.: (52) 833 260 1147
Web Site: http://www.amports.com
Marine Freight Holding & Receiving Facility
N.A.I.C.S.: 488320

Subsidiary (Domestic):

Benicia Port Terminal Company (3)
1997 Elm Rd, Benicia, CA 94510-2307
Tel.: (707) 745-2394
Web Site: http://www.amports.com
Marine Cargo Handling
N.A.I.C.S.: 488320
Jim Triplett *(Sr VP-West Coast)*

Holding (Domestic):

Windmill Farms (2)
9760 Heron Rd, Ashburn, L0B 1A0, ON,
Canada
Tel.: (905) 985-5569
Web Site: http://www.windmillfarms.ca
Mushroom Farming
N.A.I.C.S.: 111411

Subsidiary (US):

Greenwood Mushrooms (3)
749 Norway Rd, Chadds Ford, PA 19317-
8222
Tel.: (610) 388-9500
Web Site:
    http://www.greenwoodmushrooms.com
Farming
N.A.I.C.S.: 111310
Louis Marson Jr. *(Owner)*

Subsidiary (Domestic):

Ostrom Mushroom Farms LLC (4)
8323 Steilacoom Rd SE, Lacey, WA 98513-
2057
Tel.: (360) 491-1410
Web Site:
    http://www.ostrommushrooms.com
Fruit & Vegetable Canning
N.A.I.C.S.: 311421
Dan Cunningham *(Engr-Maintenance)*

Kensington Capital Partners
Limited (1)
95 Saint Clair Avenue West Suite 905, To-
ronto, M4V 1N6, ON, Canada (51%)
Tel.: (416) 362-9000
Web Site: http://www.kcpl.ca
Privater Equity Firm
N.A.I.C.S.: 523999
Elaine Turnbull *(Mgr-Admin)*

P.J. Doherty & Associates Co.
Ltd. (1)
56 Sparks St, Ottawa, K1P 5A9, ON,
Canada (100%)
Tel.: (613) 238-6727
Web Site: http://www.doherty.ca
Sales Range: $50-74.9 Million
Emp.: 10
Open-End Investment Funds
N.A.I.C.S.: 525910

AGFA-GEVAERT N.V.

Septestraat 27, B-2640, Mortsel, Bel-
gium
Tel.: (32) 34442111 BE
Web Site: https://www.agfa.com
Year Founded: 1894
AGFB—(EUR)
Rev.: $1,899,417,224
Assets: $2,260,954,025
Liabilities: $1,521,692,208
Net Worth: $739,261,817
Earnings: ($15,109,001)
Emp.: 6,993
Fiscal Year-end: 12/31/21

Imaging Systems Mfr & Distr for
Printing, Graphic Arts, Motion Picture
& Medical Imaging Processes
N.A.I.C.S.: 333310
Luc Delagaye *(Pres-Offset Solutions)*

Subsidiaries:

AGFA DE MEXICO S.A. DE C.V. (1)
Insurgentes Sur 1196 Piso 17 y 18 Col,
CDMX Tlacoquemecatl del Valle, 03200,
Mexico, Mexico
Tel.: (52) 5554888500
Medical Equipment Repair & Maintenance
Services
N.A.I.C.S.: 811210

AGFA FINANCE INC. (1)
77 Belfield Rd, Etobicoke, Toronto, M9W
1G6, ON, Canada
Tel.: (416) 241-5409
Financial Management Services
N.A.I.C.S.: 523999

AGFA FINANCE NV (1)
Tel.: (32) 34447190
Web Site: https://www.agfa.com
Financial Management Services
N.A.I.C.S.: 523999

AGFA GRAPHICS ARGENTINA
S.A. (1)
Venezuela 4269, C1211ABE, Buenos Aires,
Argentina
Tel.: (54) 11 4958 9300
Sales Range: $25-49.9 Million
Emp.: 35
Printing Machinery Distr
N.A.I.C.S.: 423830

AGFA GRAPHICS AUSTRIA
GMBH (1)
Lehrbachgasse 2, 1121, Vienna, Austria
Tel.: (43) 1891120
Printing Machinery Distr
N.A.I.C.S.: 423830
Moritz Rogger *(Mng Dir)*

AGFA GRAPHICS GERMANY GMBH
& CO. KG (1)
Zweigniederlassung Dusseldorf Paul-
Thomas-Strasse 58, 40599, Dusseldorf,
Germany
Tel.: (49) 211229860
Printing Machinery Distr
N.A.I.C.S.: 423830

AGFA GRAPHICS LTD. (1)
Coal Road, Seacroft, Leeds, LS14 2AL,
United Kingdom
Tel.: (44) 1132514000
Sales Range: $50-74.9 Million
Emp.: 95
Printing Equipment Mfr & Distr
N.A.I.C.S.: 423830

AGFA GRAPHICS MIDDLE EAST
FZCO (1)
P110 East Wing 1 Dubai Airport Free Zone,
PO Box 36159, Dubai, United Arab Emir-
ates
Tel.: (971) 42996969
Sales Range: $25-49.9 Million
Emp.: 25
Printing Machinery Distr
N.A.I.C.S.: 423830
Panos Bartziokas *(Gen Mgr)*

AGFA GRAPHICS S.R.L. (1)
Via Gorki 69, Cinisello Balsamo, 20092,
Milan, Italy
Tel.: (39) 02300881
Web Site: https://www.agfagraphics.com
Sales Range: $25-49.9 Million
Emp.: 50
Printing Machinery Mfr & Distr.
N.A.I.C.S.: 333248

AGFA GRAPHICS SP. Z.O.O. (1)
Aleje Jerozolimskie 195 A, 02-222, Warsaw,
Poland
Tel.: (48) 22 3 111 900
Printing Equipment Mfr & Distr
N.A.I.C.S.: 333248

AGFA GRAPHICS SWITZERLAND
AG (1)
Stettbachstrasse 7, 8600, Dubendorf, Swit-
zerland
Tel.: (41) 448237111

Printing Machinery Distr
N.A.I.C.S.: 423830

AGFA HEALTHCARE AG (1)
Stettbachstrasse 7, Dubendorf, 8600, Swit-
zerland
Tel.: (41) 44 823 7111
Sales Range: $25-49.9 Million
Emp.: 50
Medical Equipment Mfr
N.A.I.C.S.: 334510
Moretz Roger *(CEO)*

AGFA HEALTHCARE ARGENTINA
S.A. (1)
Venezuela 4269, C1211ABE, Buenos Aires,
Argentina
Tel.: (54) 11 4958 9300
Medical Software Development Services
N.A.I.C.S.: 541511

AGFA HEALTHCARE AUSTRALIA
LIMITED (1)
12 Dalmore Drive, Scoresby, 3179, VIC,
Australia
Tel.: (61) 1300364612
Sales Range: $25-49.9 Million
Medical Device Distr
N.A.I.C.S.: 423450

AGFA HEALTHCARE BRAZIL IM-
PORTACAO E SERVICOS
LTDA. (1)
Alameda Vicente Pinzon 51, Sao Paulo,
04547130, Brazil
Tel.: (55) 11 5188 6444
Web Site: http://www.agfa.com
Sales Range: $50-74.9 Million
Emp.: 70
Medical Device Distr
N.A.I.C.S.: 423450
Jose Laska *(Country Mgr)*

AGFA HEALTHCARE COLOMBIA
LTDA. (1)
Carre 68D No 25B -86 Ofc 906, Bogota,
Colombia
Tel.: (57) 14578888
Web Site: https://www.agfahealthcare.com
Healthcare Software Development Services
N.A.I.C.S.: 541511

AGFA HEALTHCARE DENMARK
A/S (1)
Arne Jacobsens Alle 15, 2300, Copenha-
gen, Denmark
Tel.: (45) 33310047
Healthcare Software Development Services
N.A.I.C.S.: 541511
Mek Nielsen *(CEO)*

AGFA HEALTHCARE FINLAND OY
AB (1)
Lars Sonckin kaari 16, 02600, Espoo, Fin-
land
Tel.: (358) 92 510 7222
Web Site: http://www.agfahealthcare.com
Healthcare Software Development Services
N.A.I.C.S.: 541511

AGFA HEALTHCARE HONG KONG
LTD. (1)
Unit 1606-09 Prosperity Millennia Plaza 663
King's Road, North Point, China (Hong
Kong)
Tel.: (852) 28739321
Web Site: https://www.agfahealthcare.com
Sales Range: $25-49.9 Million
Medical Equipment Distr
N.A.I.C.S.: 423450

AGFA HEALTHCARE HUNGARY
KFT. (1)
Dohany utca 12-14, 1074, Budapest, Hun-
gary
Tel.: (36) 23801172
Web Site: http://www.agfa.com
Medical Equipment Repair & Maintenance
Services
N.A.I.C.S.: 811210

AGFA HEALTHCARE IMAGING
AGENTS GMBH (1)
Am Coloneum 4, Cologne, 50829, Germany
Tel.: (49) 221 5717712
Medical Instrument Distr
N.A.I.C.S.: 423450

AGFA HEALTHCARE INC. (1)

5975 Falbourne Street, Mississauga, L5R
3V8, ON, Canada
Tel.: (416) 241-1110
Web Site: https://www.agfahealthcare.com
Healthcare Software Development Services
N.A.I.C.S.: 541511

AGFA HEALTHCARE LUXEM-
BOURG S.A. (1)
Route De Longwy 74, Helfenterbruck, 8080,
Luxembourg, Bertrange, Luxembourg
Tel.: (352) 4420441
Web Site: https://www.agfahealthcare.com
Sales Range: $25-49.9 Million
Emp.: 2
Software Development Services
N.A.I.C.S.: 541511

AGFA HEALTHCARE NORWAY
AS (1)
Sandakerveien 121, 0484, Oslo, Norway
Tel.: (47) 67057670
Digital Imaging Equipment Distr
N.A.I.C.S.: 423450

AGFA HEALTHCARE SHANGHAI
LTD. (1)
15F No 388 West Nanjing Road CIRO's
Plaza, 200003, Shanghai, China
Tel.: (86) 21 24122000
Healthcare Software Development Services
N.A.I.C.S.: 541511

AGFA HEALTHCARE SINGAPORE
PTE. LTD. (1)
62 Ubi Road 1 08-22 Oxley Bizhub 2, Sin-
gapore, 408734, Singapore
Tel.: (65) 62140622
Healthcare Imaging Equipment Distr
N.A.I.C.S.: 423450

AGFA HEALTHCARE SOUTH AF-
RICA PTY. LTD. (1)
Offices nr C1 C2 C4 C5 El Ridge Office
Park, Cnr Elizabeth and Caravelle Roads
Bartlett, Boksburg, 1459, South Africa
Tel.: (27) 118970891
Web Site: https://www.agfahealthcare.com
Sales Range: $25-49.9 Million
Digital Imaging System Whslr
N.A.I.C.S.: 423450

AGFA HEALTHCARE SWEDEN
AB (1)
Kistagangen 20B, SE-164 40, Kista, Swe-
den
Tel.: (46) 87930100
Sales Range: $25-49.9 Million
Medical Device Mfr & Distr
N.A.I.C.S.: 334510

AGFA INDIA PRIVATE LTD. (1)
2nd Floor Plot No B-14 Road No-1 Wagle
Estate Near Mulund Check Naka, Thane
West, Mumbai, 400601, Maharashtra, India
Tel.: (91) 22 40642900
Digital Imaging System Distr
N.A.I.C.S.: 423410

AGFA INDUSTRIES KOREA
LTD. (1)
631-4 Sunggok-dong, Danwon-gu, Ansan,
425-833, Gyeonggi, Korea (South)
Tel.: (82) 31 490 9101
Web Site: http://www.agfa.com
Sales Range: $25-49.9 Million
Emp.: 39
Printing Machinery Mfr
N.A.I.C.S.: 333248

AGFA LIMITED (1)
John F Kennedy Drive Naas Road, PO Box
368, Dublin, Ireland
Tel.: (353) 14506733
Sales Range: $25-49.9 Million
Emp.: 2
Photographic Equipment Mfr & Distr
N.A.I.C.S.: 325992

AGFA SINGAPORE PTE. LTD. (1)
150 Cecil Street 14-01, Singapore, 069543,
Singapore
Tel.: (65) 62140103
Web Site: https://www.agfa.com
Sales Range: $50-74.9 Million
Emp.: 20
Printing Equipment Sales & Maintenance
Services
N.A.I.C.S.: 423440

Agfa-Gevaert N.V.—(Continued)

AGFA-GEVAERT A.E.B.E. (1)
Stylianou Gonata 16, PO Box 42017, Peristeri, Greece
Tel.: (30) 1 576 3200
Sales Range: $25-49.9 Million
Emp.: 47
Photographic Film Mfr
N.A.I.O.G.: 025002
Konstantinos Panis (Gen Mgr)

AGFA-GEVAERT DO BRASIL LTDA. (1)
Alameda vicente Pinzon 51 7 andar Edificio Central, Vila Olimpia, Sao Paulo, 04547-130, SP, Brazil
Tel.: (55) 1151886402
Sales Range: $75-99.9 Million
Emp.: 150
Photographic Equipment Distr
N.A.I.C.S.: 423410
Fabrizio Valentini (Pres)

AGFA-GEVAERT HEALTHCARE GMBH (1)
Geisenhausener Str 15, 81379, Munich, Germany
Tel.: (49) 8962074800
Web Site: https://www.agfahealthcare.com
Sales Range: $200-249.9 Million
Emp.: 220
Digital Imaging System Mfr & Distr
N.A.I.C.S.: 334510
Hans Joachim (Mng Dir)

AGFA-GEVAERT INTERNATIONAL NV (1)
Septestraat 27, Mortsel, 2640, Belgium
Tel.: (32) 34445065
Web Site: http://www.agfa.com
Emp.: 5,000
Photographic Equipment Distr
N.A.I.C.S.: 423410

AGFA-GEVAERT LIMITED (1)
12 Dalmore Drive, PO Box 9149, Scoresby, Melbourne, 3179, VIC, Australia
Tel.: (61) 397564100
Emp.: 100
Photographic Equipment Distr
N.A.I.C.S.: 423410
Dean Adams (Mng Dir-Health Care)

AGFA-GEVAERT LTDA. (1)
Entregar en Bodega 506 Piso -5 Balmoral 309 Depto 1401, 7560827, Las Condes, Santiago, Chile
Tel.: (56) 225957600
Emp.: 25
Photographic Imaging System Distr
N.A.I.C.S.: 423410
Hector Rojas Sanchez (Gen Mgr)

AGFA-GEVAERT S.A.U. (1)
Napoles 249 4th Fl, 08013, Barcelona, Spain
Tel.: (34) 93 476 78 00
Web Site: http://www.agfa.com
Sales Range: $25-49.9 Million
Emp.: 80
Software Development Services
N.A.I.C.S.: 541511

Agfa Corporation (1)
100 Challenger Rd, Ridgefield Park, NJ 07660 (100%)
Tel.: (201) 440-2500
Web Site: https://www.agfa.com
Sales Range: $25-49.9 Million
Emp.: 100
Mfr & Marketer Electronic Imaging Systems for Medical Pre-Press & Photography Processes; Mfr of Films, Laser Imaging Systems & Digital Radiography Systems
N.A.I.C.S.: 333310

Subsidiary (Domestic):

Agfa Materials Corporation (2)
1658 Bushy Park Rd, Goose Creek, SC 29445
Tel.: (407) 504-9584
Web Site: https://www.agfa.com
Emp.: 100
Imagesetters, Computer to Plate Recorders, Workflow Systems & Laser Images Mfr
N.A.I.C.S.: 334118
Al Balcewicz (Mgr-Mfg)

Harold M. Pitman Company, Inc. (2)
721 Union Blvd, Totowa, NJ 07512-2207
Tel.: (973) 812-0400
Web Site: http://www.pitman.com
Digital Imaging Services
N.A.I.C.S.: 541430

Agfa Gevaert B.V. (1)
Polakweg 10-11, 2288GG, Rijswijk, Netherlands (100%)
Tel.: (31) 704131211
Rev.: $137,000,000
Emp.: 70
Photographic Equipment & Supplies
N.A.I.C.S.: 333310

Agfa Graphics NV (1)
Septestraat 27, 2640, Mortsel, Belgium
Tel.: (32) 34442111
Emp.: 3,500
Prepress Solutions for Printing & Publishing Industries
N.A.I.C.S.: 323120
Stefaan Vanhooren (Pres)

Agfa HealthCare Equipments Portugal Lda. (1)
Edificio Neo Park Av Tomas Ribeiro N 43 Bloco 2-3 F, 2790-221, Carnaxide, Portugal
Tel.: (351) 214201380
Healtcare Services
N.A.I.C.S.: 621999

Agfa HealthCare France S.A. (1)
Immeuble Optima 27-35 rue Victor Hugo, 94853, Ivry-sur-Seine, Cedex, France
Tel.: (33) 172946800
Healtcare Services
N.A.I.C.S.: 621999

Agfa HealthCare IT UK Limited (1)
6-9 The Square Stockley Park, Uxbridge, London, UB11 1FW, Middlesex, United Kingdom
Tel.: (44) 8448922004
Healtcare Services
N.A.I.C.S.: 621999

Agfa HealthCare Kazakhstan LLP (1)
Timiryazeva St 42 Pavilion 15/109, 50040, Almaty, Kazakhstan
Tel.: (7) 7272695505
Healtcare Services
N.A.I.C.S.: 621999

Agfa HealthCare Mexico S.A. de C.V. (1)
Piso 17 Av Insurgentes Sur 1196, Tlacoquemecatl del Valle, 03200, Mexico, Mexico
Tel.: (52) 5554885450
Photo Sensitive Printing Plate Mfr
N.A.I.C.S.: 325992

Agfa HealthCare Middle East FZ-LLC (1)
Bldg 52 Unit No 307-308 Dubai Health Care City, PO Box 505038, Dubai, United Arab Emirates
Tel.: (971) 45631750
Healtcare Services
N.A.I.C.S.: 621999
Said Al Halaby (Mgr-Sls & Mktg)

Agfa HealthCare NV (1)
Septestraat 27, 2640, Mortsel, Belgium
Tel.: (32) 34442111
Diagnostic Imaging & Healthcare IT Solutions
N.A.I.C.S.: 541519
Geertrui De Smet (Mgr-Global Comm Healthcare)

Subsidiary (Non-US):

Agfa HealthCare UK Limited (2)
10th Floor Vantage West, Great West Road, Brentford, TW8 9AX, Mddx, United Kingdom
Tel.: (44) 2082315984
Web Site: https://www.agfa.com
Sales Range: $25-49.9 Million
Emp.: 50
Diagnostic Imaging & Healthcare IT Solutions
N.A.I.C.S.: 423430

Agfa HealthCare Saudi Arabia Company Limited LLC (1)
Office 326 Akaria no 2, PO Box 6847,

Olayia, Riyadh, 2567-12244, Saudi Arabia
Tel.: (966) 114190505
Healtcare Services
N.A.I.C.S.: 621999

Agfa HealthCare Spain, S.A.U. (1)
C/ Gaspar Fabregas i Rosas 81, Esplugas de Llobregat, 08950, Barcelona, Spain (100%)
Tel.: (34) 934767600
Web Site: https://www.agfa.com
Sales Range: $50-74.9 Million
Emp.: 200
Photographic Equipment & Supplies
N.A.I.C.S.: 333310

Agfa HealthCare Ukraine LLC (1)
Novokonstantinovskaya Str 13/10 Office 215, Kiev, Ukraine
Tel.: (380) 442055638
Healtcare Services
N.A.I.C.S.: 621999

Agfa HealthCare Vietnam Co. Ltd. (1)
Sailing Tower 11th Floor Unit 1101 111A Pasteur, Ben Nghe Ward District 1, Ho Chi Minh City, Vietnam
Tel.: (84) 2838245378
Healtcare Services
N.A.I.C.S.: 621999

Agfa Imaging Products (Shenzhen) Co., Ltd. (1)
7/F South Union Hotel 2002 Shennan East Road, Luohu, Shenzhen, 518001, China
Tel.: (86) 755 82135000
Emp.: 10
Photographic Equipment Mfr
N.A.I.C.S.: 333310

Agfa Materials Japan Ltd. (1)
15th floor Harumi Island Triton Square office Tower W 1-8-8 Harumi, Harumi Island Chuo-ku, Tokyo, 104-0053, Japan
Tel.: (81) 362213370
Web Site: https://www.agfa.jp
Imagesetters, Computer to Plate Recorders, Workflow Systems & Laser Images Mfr
N.A.I.C.S.: 334118

Agfa Materials Taiwan Co., Ltd. (1)
3F 237 Sung Chiang Road, 10483, Taipei, 10483, Taiwan
Tel.: (886) 225168899
Sales Range: $25-49.9 Million
Emp.: 11
Imagesetters, Computer to Plate Recorders, Workflow Systems & Laser Images Mfr
N.A.I.C.S.: 334118
Frederick Wang (Mgr-Country & Gen Mgr)

Agfa Sp. z.o.o. (1)
Oxygen Park Building B ul Jutrzenki 137A, 02-231, Warsaw, Poland
Tel.: (48) 223111900
Web Site: https://agfa-polska.pl
Healtcare Services
N.A.I.C.S.: 621999

Agfa-Gevaert AB (1)
Torshamnsgatan 32 C, PO Box 6, Kista, 16440, Stockholm, Sweden (100%)
Tel.: (46) 879301001
Web Site: http://www.agfa.com
Sales Range: $25-49.9 Million
Emp.: 100
Photographic Equipment & Supplies
N.A.I.C.S.: 333310

Agfa-Gevaert AG/SA (1)
Stettbachstrasse 7, PO Box 738, CH 8600, Dubendorf, Switzerland
Tel.: (41) 18237422
Sales Range: $25-49.9 Million
Emp.: 90
Photographic Equipment & Supplies
N.A.I.C.S.: 333310

Agfa-Gevaert Argentina S.A. (1)
Venezuela 4269, C1211 ABE, Buenos Aires, Argentina (100%)
Tel.: (54) 1149589300
Sales Range: $25-49.9 Million
Emp.: 70
Mfr of Photographic Supplies
N.A.I.C.S.: 333310

Agfa-Gevaert Colombia Ltda. (1)
Carrera 68 D No 25 B-86 of 906, Bogota, Colombia

Tel.: (57) 6014578888
Graphic Production Product Distr
N.A.I.C.S.: 423410

Agfa-Gevaert Investment Fund NV (1)
Septestraat 27, 2640, Mortsel, Belgium
Tel.: (32) 34442111
Web Site: http://www.agfa.com
Emp.: 3,800
Financial Management Services
N.A.I.C.S.: 523999

Agfa-Gevaert Japan, Ltd. (1)
1-6-1 Osaki Osaki New City Building Building No 1 5th Floor, Shinagawa-ku, Tokyo, 141-0032, Japan (94%)
Tel.: (81) 354878250
Web Site: https://www.agfa.co.jp
Sales Range: $25-49.9 Million
Emp.: 100
Wholesale Distribution of Cameras & Supplies
N.A.I.C.S.: 449210

Agfa-Gevaert Ltd. (1)
Bantage W Great W Rd, Brentford, TW8 9AX, Mddx, United Kingdom (100%)
Tel.: (44) 2082314983
Web Site: http://www.agfa.co.uk
Sales Range: $50-74.9 Million
Emp.: 200
Mfr of Photographic Equipment
N.A.I.C.S.: 333310

Agfa-Gevaert S.A. (1)
21 avenue de Colmar, 92565, Rueil-Malmaison, cedex, France (99.9%)
Tel.: (33) 147771000
Sales Range: $400-449.9 Million
Emp.: 120
Scanner & Medical Equipment Mfr & Sales
N.A.I.C.S.: 339112

Agfa-Gevaert S.p.A. (1)
Viamrssemo Gorci 69, I 20092, Milan, Italy (100%)
Tel.: (39) 02 3088 220
Sales Range: $100-124.9 Million
Emp.: 464
Photographic Equipment & Supplies
N.A.I.C.S.: 333310

Agfa-Gevaert de Venezuela S.A. (1)
Av Principal de la Castellana Ed Centro Letonia Torre ING Bank Piso 9, Urbanizacion La Castellana 62305, 1060, Caracas, Venezuela
Tel.: (58) 2122772000
Graphic Production Product Distr
N.A.I.C.S.: 423410

Agfa-Gevaert do Brasil Ltd. (1)
Alameda vicente Pinzon 51 7th floor Central Building, Vila Olimpia, Sao Paulo, 04547-130, Brazil
Tel.: (55) 115 188 6444
Web Site: http://www.agfa.com.br
Mfr of Imagesetters, Computer to Plate Recorders, Workflow Systems & Laser Imagers
N.A.I.C.S.: 334118

Bodoni Systems (1)
Unit 19 Orbital 25 Business Park Dwight Road Tolpits Lane, Watford, WD18 9DA, United Kingdom
Tel.: (44) 1923220530
Web Site: https://www.bodoni.co.uk
Colour Management Consultancy Services
N.A.I.C.S.: 541618

INSIGHT AGENTS FRANCE S.R.L. (1)
282 Avenue Marne, 59700, Marcq-en-Baroeul, France
Tel.: (33) 8 00 10 60 26
Sales Range: $25-49.9 Million
Emp.: 15
Software Development Services
N.A.I.C.S.: 541511

Inovelan S.A. (1)
169 rue Sadi Carnot, 59350, Saint-Andrelez-Lille, France
Tel.: (33) 320061617
Web Site: http://www.inovelan.fr
Software Publishing Services
N.A.I.C.S.: 513210

Ipagsa Technologies S.L.U. (1)

C/Sant Jordi 15, Rubi, 08191, Barcelona, Spain
Tel.: (34) 93 588 4500
Web Site: https://www.ipagsa.net
Graphic Art Printing Services
N.A.I.C.S.: 323111
Lorenzo Ferrari (Mng Dir)

LASTRA ATTREZZATURE S.R.L. (1)
Stabilimento Produzione Via Lombardia 6, 25025, Manerbio, Brescia, Italy
Tel.: (39) 0309937059
Sales Range: $25-49.9 Million
Emp.: 5
Printing Equipment Distr
N.A.I.C.S.: 423830

LUITHAGEN NV (1)
Tel.: (32) 34442111
Printing Equipment Distr
N.A.I.C.S.: 423830

NEW PROIMAGE AMERICA INC. (1)
103 Carnegie Ctr Ste 300, Princeton, NJ 08540-6235
Tel.: (609) 587-5222
Web Site: https://newproimage.com
Sales Range: $25-49.9 Million
Emp.: 20
Software Development Services
N.A.I.C.S.: 541511

NEW PROIMAGE LTD. (1)
Poleg Industrial Park 4 Hagavish St, PO Box 8764, Netanya, 42507, Israel
Tel.: (972) 732600300
Sales Range: $25-49.9 Million
Emp.: 24
Software Development Services
N.A.I.C.S.: 541511
Ilan Vinner (CEO)

PT Gevaert-Agfa HealthCare Indonesia (1)
Jl Kesehatan Raya No 23C Bintaro, Jakarta Selatan, 12330, Indonesia
Tel.: (62) 2173880411
Healtcare Services
N.A.I.C.S.: 621999
Romdhani Arsanto (Acct Mgr)

Smart Packaging Solutions SAS (1)
85 avenue de la Plaine ZI de Rousset-Peynier, 13790, Rousset, France
Tel.: (33) 4 42 53 84 40
Web Site: http://www.s-p-s.com
Emp.: 180
Imagesetters, Computer to Plate Recorders, Workflow Systems & Laser Images Mfr
N.A.I.C.S.: 334118

AGFEED INDUSTRIES, INC.
Rm A1001-1002 Tower 16 Hengmao Intl Center, 333 South Guangchang Road, Nanchang, 330003, Jiangxi, China
Tel.: (86) 7916669099   NV
Year Founded: 2005
Sales Range: $200-249.9 Million
Emp.: 532
Hog Raising & Pig Feed Mfr
N.A.I.C.S.: 311119
Edward Pazdro (Chief Acctg Officer)

Subsidiaries:

AgFeed Animal Nutrition Holdings, Inc. (1)
Suite A1001-1002 Tower 16, Hengmao International Center, Nanchang, 330003, Jiangxi, China
Tel.: (86) 791 6669090
Sales Range: $150-199.9 Million
Emp.: 508
Animal Nutrition Products
N.A.I.C.S.: 311119

AGGIE GREY'S HOTEL & BUNGALOWS
PO Box 67, Apia, Samoa (Western)
Tel.: (685) 22880
Web Site: http://www.aggiegreys.com
Sales Range: $25-49.9 Million
Emp.: 300

Hotel & Resort Owner & Operator
N.A.I.C.S.: 721110
Rosa Stowers (CFO)

AGGREGATED MICRO POWER HOLDINGS PLC
1 Dover Street, London, W1S 4LD, United Kingdom
Tel.: (44) 207 3827800   UK
Web Site: http://www.ampplc.co.uk
Year Founded: 2013
Rev.: $62,866,109
Assets: $53,073,074
Liabilities: $22,472,493
Net Worth: $30,600,581
Earnings: ($7,255,999)
Emp.: 141
Fiscal Year-end: 03/31/19
Energy Facilities Operator
N.A.I.C.S.: 221118
Richard Burrell (CEO)

AGGREGATO GLOBAL PTY. LTD.
PO Box 6170, North Sydney, 2059, NSW, Australia
Tel.: (61) 2 8458 9100   AU
Web Site:
  http://www.aggregatoglobal.com
Holding Company; Prepaid Telephone Cards & Mobile Telecommunications Services
N.A.I.C.S.: 551112
Vaughan Bowen (Chm)

Subsidiaries:

Aggregato Mobile Pty. Ltd. (1)
PO Box 6170, North Sydney, 2059, NSW, Australia
Tel.: (61) 2 8458 9100
Web Site: http://www.aggregato.com.au
Mobile Virtual Network Telecommunications Services
N.A.I.C.S.: 517121
Ilario Faenza (Mng Dir)

Aggregato Prepaid Pty. Ltd. (1)
PO Box 6170, North Sydney, 2059, NSW, Australia
Tel.: (61) 2 8458 9100
Prepaid Telephone Cards & Services
N.A.I.C.S.: 517121
Ilario Faenza (Mng Dir)

AGI GREENPAC LIMITED
301-302 Park Centra sector-30 National Highway - 8, Gurgaon, 122 001, Haryana, India
Tel.: (91) 1244779200
Web Site: https://agigreenpac.com
Year Founded: 1960
500187—(BOM)
Rev.: $256,695,607
Assets: $389,847,044
Liabilities: $221,466,377
Net Worth: $168,380,667
Earnings: $12,020,135
Emp.: 2,818
Fiscal Year-end: 03/31/21
Ceramic Sanitary Ware Mfr
N.A.I.C.S.: 332999
Sandip Somany (Vice Chm & Mng Dir)

Subsidiaries:

Hindustan Sanitaryware & Industries Ltd (CD I) (1)
Delhi Rohtak Road, Jhajjar Dist, Bahadurgarh, 124507, Haryana, India
Tel.: (91) 1276230485
Web Site: http://www.hindwarehomes.com
Sales Range: $25-49.9 Million
Emp.: 200
Sanitary Ware Mfr
N.A.I.C.S.: 332999
Pream Prakash Dagar (Gen Mgr)

Hindustan Sanitaryware & Industries Ltd (CD II) (1)
Somanypuram Brahmanapally Vlg, Bibina-

gar, Nalgonda, 508126, Andhra Pradesh, India
Tel.: (91) 8685651448
Web Site: http://www.hindwarehomes.com
Sales Range: $400-449.9 Million
Emp.: 1,300
Sanitary Ware Mfr
N.A.I.C.S.: 332999

AGI INFRA LTD.
SCO 1-5 AGI Urbana Jalandhar heights -II 66 Feet Rd, Jalandhar, 144022, Punjab, India
Tel.: (91) 1812921991
Web Site: https://www.agiinfra.com
539042—(BOM)
Rev.: $27,425,757
Assets: $83,196,504
Liabilities: $66,019,085
Net Worth: $17,177,419
Earnings: $4,971,439
Emp.: 220
Fiscal Year-end: 03/31/22
Commercial Building Construction Services
N.A.I.C.S.: 236220
Aarti Mahajan (Officer-Compliance & Sec)

AGILE CAPITAL
386 Main Road, Bryanston, Johannesburg, 2196, South Africa
Tel.: (27) 112173300
Web Site:
  http://www.agilecapital.co.za
Privater Equity Firm
N.A.I.C.S.: 523999
Tshego Sefolo (CEO)

AGILE CONTENT SA
C/Casanova 209 principal 1a, 08021, Barcelona, Spain
Tel.: (34) 938023800
Web Site:
  https://www.agilecontent.com
AGIL—(MAD)
Rev.: $113,220,002
Assets: $142,722,155
Liabilities: $86,842,919
Net Worth: $55,879,236
Earnings: $1,265,040
Emp.: 290
Fiscal Year-end: 12/31/23
Digital Content Development Services
N.A.I.C.S.: 513199

AGILE GROUP HOLDINGS LIMITED
33/F Agile Center 26Huaxia Road, Zhujiang New Town Tianhe District, Guangzhou, 510623, Guangdong, China (Hong Kong)
Tel.: (852) 2088839888
Web Site: https://www.agile.com.cn
Year Founded: 1992
AGPYF—(OTCIQ)
Sales Range: $10-24.9 Million
Holding Company
N.A.I.C.S.: 551112
Zhuo Lin Chen (Chm & Pres)

Subsidiaries:

Agile Education Group (1)
36/F Agile Center No 26 Huaxia Road, Zhujiang New Town Tianhe District, Guangzhou, Guangdong, China
Tel.: (86) 2088839848
Web Site: http://www.en.agile-edu.cn
Educational Support Services
N.A.I.C.S.: 611710
Chen Gang (Pres)

Agile Real Estate Construction Management Group Co., Ltd. (1)
28th Floor Agile Centre No 26 Huaxia Road, Zhujiang New Town Tianhe District, Guangzhou, 510623, Guangdong, China
Tel.: (86) 2087586848
Web Site: http://agile-pm.agile.com.cn

Real Estate Development Services
N.A.I.C.S.: 531390

Guangzhou Agile Hotel Co., Ltd. (1)
Agile Garden 398 Xingnan Avenue Yingbin Road, Guangzhou, China
Tel.: (86) 2039956848
Web Site: http://www.agilehotel.com.cn
Hotel Operator
N.A.I.C.S.: 721110

AGILE MEDIA NETWORK, INC.
3F 2-3-6 Shibadaimon, Minato-ku, Tokyo, 1050012, Japan
Tel.: (81) 364357130
Web Site: https://www.agilemedia.jp
Year Founded: 2007
6573—(TKS)
Rev.: $2,049,010
Assets: $2,474,410
Liabilities: $1,687,420
Net Worth: $786,990
Earnings: ($3,481,190)
Fiscal Year-end: 12/31/23
Online Advertising Agency Services
N.A.I.C.S.: 541890
Atsushi Noguchi (Auditor)

AGILITAS PRIVATE EQUITY LLP
5th Floor 105 Piccadilly, London, W1J 7NJ, United Kingdom
Tel.: (44) 203 384 0111
Web Site: http://www.agilitaspe.com
Privater Equity Firm
N.A.I.C.S.: 523999
Anne-Claire de Pompignan (Head-IR)

AGILITY
Sulaibia Beside Land Customs Clearing Area, PO Box 25418, Safat, 13115, Kuwait, 13115, Kuwait
Tel.: (965) 1809222   KW
Web Site: https://www.agility.com
Year Founded: 1979
AGLTY—(KUW)
Rev.: $4,402,795,225
Assets: $12,188,174,812
Liabilities: $6,031,183,498
Net Worth: $6,156,991,314
Earnings: $350,558,069
Emp.: 54,000
Fiscal Year-end: 12/31/23
Logistics & Warehousing Services
N.A.I.C.S.: 488999
Henadi Anwar Essa Al-Saleh (Chm)

Subsidiaries:

Agility Company L.L.C. (1)
Eastern Ring Road Southern Istanbul Street, PO Box No 55073, Riyadh, 32213, Saudi Arabia
Tel.: (966) 138169800
Web Site:
  http://www.directory.agilityportal.com
Sales Range: $150-199.9 Million
Logistics & Freight Forwarding Services
N.A.I.C.S.: 488510

Agility DGS UK Ltd. (1)
Froghall Rd, Froghall, Stoke-on-Trent, ST10 2HA, United Kingdom
Tel.: (44) 1538260900
Web Site: https://www.agilitystoke.com
Aviation Spares Distr
N.A.I.C.S.: 488119

Agility Holdings Inc. (1)
310 Commerce Ste 250, Irvine, CA 92602
Tel.: (714) 617-6300
Web Site: http://www.agility.com
Emp.: 80
Air & Sea Freight Transportation Services
N.A.I.C.S.: 481112
David Barlow (CFO)

Agility International Logistics Pte. Ltd. (1)
1 Changi North Way, Singapore, 498802, Singapore
Tel.: (65) 62209055
Web Site: https://www.agilitylogistics.com

Agility—(Continued)

Sales Range: $75-99.9 Million
Logistics & Distribution Services
N.A.I.C.S.: 541614

Agility Logistics Corp. (1)
310 Commerce Ste 250, Irvine, CA 92602
Tel.: (714) 617-6300
Web Site: http://www.agility.com
Logistics & Distribution Services
N.A.I.C.S.: 541614

Agility Logistics GmbH (1)
Heidenkampsweg 82, 20097, Hamburg, Germany
Tel.: (49) 40237130
Web Site: http://www.agility.com
Logistics & Distribution Services
N.A.I.C.S.: 561990

Agility Logistics Holdings Pte. Ltd. (1)
Trans-link Logistics Centre 7 Toh Tuck Link, Singapore, Singapore
Tel.: (65) 64639868
Logistics & Distribution Services
N.A.I.C.S.: 541614

Agility Logistics International B.V. (1)
Anthony Fokker Business Park Fokkerweg 300 Building 2A, 1438 AN, Oude Meer, Netherlands
Tel.: (31) 884360000
Web Site: https://www.agility.com
Sales Range: $25-49.9 Million
Logistics & Distribution Services
N.A.I.C.S.: 541614

Agility Logistics LLC (1)
30 Sobornosti Ave Office 399, 02154, Kiev, Ukraine
Tel.: (380) 676727668
Web Site:
　http://www.directory.agilityportal.com
Sales Range: $50-74.9 Million
Logistics & Freight Forwarding Services
N.A.I.C.S.: 488510

Agility Logistics Limited (1)
19/F Broadway Centre 93 Kwai Fuk Road, Kwai Chung, New Territories, China (Hong Kong)
Tel.: (852) 22118888
Logistics & Distribution Services
N.A.I.C.S.: 541614

Agility Project Logistics Inc. (1)
15993 Diplomatic Plz Dr, Houston, TX 77032-2118
Tel.: (713) 452-3500
Web Site: http://www.agilitylogistics.com
Sales Range: $75-99.9 Million
Logistics & Distribution Services
N.A.I.C.S.: 541614
Grant Wattman (Pres & CEO)

Division (Domestic):

Agility Project Logistics Inc. (2)
115 Canvasback Dr Ste 100, Saint Rose, LA 70087
Tel.: (504) 465-1000
Web Site: http://www.agility.com
Sales Range: $25-49.9 Million
Emp.: 19
Freight Forwarding Services
N.A.I.C.S.: 488510

GeoLogistics Corporation (1)
1251 E Dyer Rd, Santa Ana, CA 92705-5639
Tel.: (714) 513-3000
Sales Range: $1-4.9 Billion
Emp.: 759
Transportation & Business Management Services
N.A.I.C.S.: 488510

Global Clearing House Systems K.S.C.C. (1)
PO Box 202, Al Farwaniyah, 81013, Kuwait
Tel.: (965) 1809222
Web Site: https://www.gcskw.com
Emp.: 2,000
Logistic Services
N.A.I.C.S.: 488510
Wael S. Khalifa (Chief Strategy & Program Officer)

Metal & Recycling Company K.S.C.C. (1)

Tel.: (965) 24577773
Web Site: http://www.mrckw.com
Rev.: $39,869,918
Assets: $87,955,718
Liabilities: $54,808,944
Net Worth: $33,146,774
Earnings: $2,814,144
Emp.: 207
Fiscal Year-end: 12/31/2022
Scrap Metal Buying, Selling & Recycling Services
N.A.I.C.S.: 423510
Tarek Ibrahim Al-Mousa (Vice Chm & CEO)

National Aviation Services Company W.L.L. (1)
PO Box 301, Al Farwaniyah, 81014, Kuwait
Tel.: (965) 1842842
Web Site: http://www.nas.aero
Airport Services
N.A.I.C.S.: 488119
Mansour Al Kheziem (Gen Mgr)

Subsidiary (Non-US):

John Menzies plc (2)
2 Lochside Avenue Edinburgh Park, Edinburgh, EH12 9DJ, United Kingdom
Tel.: (44) 1312258555
Web Site: http://www.menziesaviation.com
Rev.: $1,119,032,824
Assets: $1,141,570,976
Liabilities: $1,202,668,376
Net Worth: ($61,097,400)
Earnings: ($174,331,248)
Emp.: 26,889
Fiscal Year-end: 12/31/2020
Book, Periodical & Newspaper Whslr
N.A.I.C.S.: 424920
John Geddes (Sec & Dir-Corp Affairs)

Subsidiary (Non-US):

Air Menzies International (Cape) Proprietary Ltd. (3)
New Agents Road Unit 6 Air Cargo Centre International Airport, Cape Town, 7525, South Africa
Tel.: (27) 219351731
Wholesale Airfreight & Express Services
N.A.I.C.S.: 492110
Milton French (VP)

Air Menzies International (India) Private Ltd. (3)
509 Ascot Centre International Airport Road Sahar Andheri East, Mumbai, 400099, India
Tel.: (91) 2261520400
Wholesale Airfreight & Express Services
N.A.I.C.S.: 492110
Sneha Sawant (Mgr-Ops)

Air Menzies International (NZ) Ltd. (3)
23 Tom Pearce Drive Auckland Airport, Auckland, New Zealand
Tel.: (64) 92564242
Wholesale Airfreight & Express Services
N.A.I.C.S.: 492110
Yvette Firth (Branch Mgr)

Air Menzies International SA Proprietary Ltd. (3)
Unit 3 Aviation Park 18 Pomona Road, Johannesburg, 1619, South Africa
Tel.: (27) 119793900
Wholesale Airfreight & Express Services
N.A.I.C.S.: 492110
Jenny Blake (Mgr-Import)

Subsidiary (Domestic):

Aircraft Service International Group, Inc. (3)
Hallswelle House, 1 Hallswelle Road, London, 11 0DH, NW, United Kingdom
Tel.: (407) 648-7373
Web Site:
　https://www.aviationservicesintgroup.com
Holding Company; Commercial Airline Ground Support Services
N.A.I.C.S.: 551112

Menzies Aviation Group (3)
4 New Sq Bedfont Lk, Feltham, TW14 8HA, Middlesex, United Kingdom (100%)
Tel.: (44) 2087506000
Web Site: http://www.menziesaviation.com
Sales Range: $10-24.9 Million
Emp.: 45

Aviation Support; Cargo Handling, Ground Transportation, Passenger & Ramp Handling, Maintenance, Security, Courier Services
N.A.I.C.S.: 492110
John Redmond (Sr VP-America)

Division (Domestic):

Air Menzies International (4)
5 The Enterprise Centre, Kelvin Lane, Crawley, RH10 9PT, West Sussex, United Kingdom (100%)
Tel.: (44) 1293517817
Web Site: http://www.airmenzies.com
Sales Range: $10-24.9 Million
Wholesale Express Courier & Airfreight Distributor
N.A.I.C.S.: 492110
Jonathan Clark (CEO)

Subsidiary (Non-US):

Skystar Airport Services Pty. Ltd. (4)
40 Sugarbird Lady Rd, Perth Airport, Perth, 6105, WA, Australia (100%)
Tel.: (61) 8 9477 060
Web Site:
　http://www.skystarairportservices.com.au
Sales Range: $150-199.9 Million
Emp.: 400
Airport Ground Support Services
N.A.I.C.S.: 488190

PWC Transport Company W.L.L. (1)
Sulaibiya Beside Land Customs Clearing Area, PO Box 25418, Safat, 13115, Kuwait, Kuwait
Tel.: (965) 1809222
Web Site: http://www.agilitylogistics.com
Sales Range: $25-49.9 Million
Emp.: 25
Freight Transportation Services
N.A.I.C.S.: 488510

Tristar Terminals Guam Inc. (1)
8210 Santa Rita Industrial Dr route 2 A, Agana Heights, GU 96928
Tel.: (671) 565-2300
Web Site: https://tristar-terminals-guam-inc.business.site
Terminal Logistics Services
N.A.I.C.S.: 541614

Tristar Transport LLC (1)
Plot B158 Al Aweer Ras Al Khor, PO Box 51328, Dubai, United Arab Emirates
Tel.: (971) 43331310
Web Site: http://www.tristar-transport.com
Sales Range: $125-149.9 Million
Emp.: 400
Bulk Liquid Transportation Services
N.A.I.C.S.: 484230
Eugene Mayne (CEO)

United Projects Company For Aviation Services K.S.C.P. (1)
Kuwait International Airport Mezzanine Parking Safat, PO Box 27068, Kuwait, 13131, Kuwait
Tel.: (965) 1833338
Web Site: https://www.upac.com.kw
Real Estate Management Services
N.A.I.C.S.: 531390

AGILITY HEALTH, INC.
42 Niagara Street Suite 3000, Hamilton, ON, Canada
Tel.: (905) 505-0770
Year Founded: 2010
Holding Company; Physical, Occupational & Speech Therapy Services
N.A.I.C.S.: 551112
Robert Lynn Herr (Chm)

AGILITY INC.
3rd Floor 490 Adelaide Street West, Toronto, M5V 1T2, ON, Canada
Tel.: (416) 591-2500
Web Site: http://www.agilitycms.com
Year Founded: 2002
Sales Range: $1-9.9 Million
Emp.: 10
Cloud Content Management System
N.A.I.C.S.: 513210
Jonathan Voight (Founder & CEO)

AGILLIC A/S
Masnedogade 22, 2100, Copenhagen, Denmark
Tel.: (45) 70252825
Web Site: https://www.agillic.com
Year Founded: 1999
AGILC—(CSE)
Rev.: $9,707,321
Assets: $6,984,610
Liabilities: $9,982,435
Net Worth: ($2,997,825)
Earnings: ($4,072,073)
Fiscal Year-end: 12/31/23
General Marketing Services
N.A.I.C.S.: 541613
Emre Gursoy (CEO)

AGINCOURT AUTOHAUS INC.
3450 Sheppard Avenue East, Toronto, M1T 3K4, ON, Canada
Tel.: (416) 291-6456
Web Site: http://www.agincourtvw.ca
Rev.: $29,039,613
Emp.: 100
New & Used Car Dealers
N.A.I.C.S.: 441110
Ken Laird (Pres)

AGIO PAPER & INDUSTRIES LIMITED
505 Diamond Prestige 41 A AJC Bose Road, Kolkata, 700 017, West Bengal, India
Tel.: (91) 3366286654
Web Site: https://www.agiopaper.com
Year Founded: 1984
516020—(BOM)
Rev.: $1,215
Assets: $3,264,903
Liabilities: $2,564,275
Net Worth: $700,627
Earnings: ($183,415)
Fiscal Year-end: 03/31/22
Paper Mfr
N.A.I.C.S.: 322120
Ankit Jalan (CEO)

Subsidiaries:

AGIO PAPER & INDUSTRIES LIMITED - Bilaspur Mill (1)
Village Dhenka, PO Darrighat-Masturi, Bilaspur, 495551, Chhattisgarh, India
Tel.: (91) 7752257010
Web Site: https://www.agiopaper.com
Paper Mfr
N.A.I.C.S.: 322120

AGIS-AGROINDUSTRIJA
Branimira Cosica 2/III, Novi Sad, Serbia
Tel.: (381) 21 442 377
Web Site: http://ww.agis.co.rs
Year Founded: 1989
AGIN—(BEL)
Sales Range: Less than $1 Million
Frozen Vegetable Mfr
N.A.I.C.S.: 311411
Paja Apic (Chm)

AGL ENERGY LIMITED
Level 24 200 George St, Sydney, 2000, NSW, Australia
Tel.: (61) 299212999
Web Site: https://www.agl.com.au
Year Founded: 1837
AGL—(ASX)
Rev.: $9,069,845,048
Assets: $10,457,398,461
Liabilities: $6,830,929,459
Net Worth: $3,626,469,002
Earnings: $469,417,733
Emp.: 3,795
Fiscal Year-end: 06/30/24
Solar Heating Services
N.A.I.C.S.: 221118
Brett Redman (CEO & Mng Dir)

Subsidiaries:

AGL ACT Retail Investments Pty Limited (1)
L 22 101 Miller St, North Sydney, 2060, Australia
Tel.: (61) 299212999
Web Site: http://www.agl.com.au
Elrtric Power Generation Services
N.A.I.C.S.: 221118
Andy Bexley *(Mng Dir)*

AGL Corporate Services Pty Limited (1)
Level 22 101 Miller St, North Sydney, 2060, NSW, Australia
Tel.: (61) 299212999
Elrtric Power Generation Services
N.A.I.C.S.: 221118

AGL Electricity (VIC) Pty Limited (1)
L 22 101 Miller St, Sydney, 2060, NSW, Australia
Tel.: (61) 299212999
Web Site: http://www.agl.com.au
Emp.: 200
Electric Power Distr
N.A.I.C.S.: 221122

AGL Energy Services Pty Limited (1)
L 22 101 Miller St, Sydney, 2060, NSW, Australia
Tel.: (61) 299212999
Emp.: 250
Energy Consulting Services
N.A.I.C.S.: 541690

AGL Hydro Partnership (1)
L 22 600 Bourke St, Melbourne, 3000, Australia
Tel.: (61) 357543222
Electric Power Distribution Services
N.A.I.C.S.: 221122

AGL Loy Yang Pty Ltd (1)
Bartons Lane, Traralgon, 3844, VIC, Australia
Tel.: (61) 3 5173 2000
Web Site: http://www.loyyangpower.com.au
Sales Range: $25-49.9 Million
Emp.: 500
Power Distr
N.A.I.C.S.: 221122

AGL Macquarie (1)
34 Griffiths Rd, Lambton, Newcastle, 2299, NSW, Australia
Tel.: (61) 249687499
Web Site: http://www.macgen.com.au
Sales Range: $150-199.9 Million
Emp.: 650
Power Station Operator
N.A.I.C.S.: 221112
Diane Moriarty *(CFO & Sec)*

AGL Power Generation Pty Limited (1)
L 22 101 Miller St, North Sydney, 2060, Australia
Tel.: (61) 299212999
Web Site: http://www.agl.com
Elrtric Power Generation Services
N.A.I.C.S.: 221118

AGL SA Generation Pty Limited (1)
Level 22 101 Miller Street, North Sydney, 2060, Australia
Tel.: (61) 299212999
Elrtric Power Generation Services
N.A.I.C.S.: 221118

AGL Sales (Queensland Electricity) Pty Limited (1)
Complex 1/303 Burwood Highway, Burwood East, Melbourne, 3151, VIC, Australia
Tel.: (61) 388056633
Web Site: http://www.powerdirect.com.au
Electric Power Distribution
N.A.I.C.S.: 221122

AGL Sales Pty Limited (1)
L 22 120 Spencer St, Melbourne, 3000, Australia
Tel.: (61) 386336000
Renewable Energy Project Development Services
N.A.I.C.S.: 237990

AGL Southern Hydro (NSW) Pty Limited (1)

L 22 120 Spencer St, Melbourne, 3000, VIC, Australia
Tel.: (61) 386336000
Elrtric Power Generation Services
N.A.I.C.S.: 221118

AGL Southern Hydro Pty Limited (1)
L 22 101 Miller St, Sydney, 2060, Australia
Tel.: (61) 299212999
Elrtric Power Generation Services
N.A.I.C.S.: 221118

AGL Torrens Island Holdings Pty Limited (1)
L 22 101 Miller St, North Sydney, 2060, NSW, Australia
Tel.: (61) 299212999
Web Site: http://www.agl.com.au
Sales Range: $1-4.9 Billion
Emp.: 2,000
Elrtric Power Generation Services
N.A.I.C.S.: 221118

AGL Torrens Island Pty Limited (1)
L 22 101 Miller St, North Sydney, 2060, NSW, Australia
Tel.: (61) 299212999
Web Site: http://www.agl.com
Elrtric Power Generation Services
N.A.I.C.S.: 221118
Michael Fraser *(CEO & Mng Dir)*

Connect Now Pty. Ltd. (1)
Locked Bag 14120, Melbourne, 8001, VIC, Australia
Tel.: (61) 1300554323
Web Site: https://www.connectnow.com.au
Emp.: 70
Moving Home Services
N.A.I.C.S.: 484210

Energy 360 Pty. Ltd. (1)
21b Buontempo Road, Carrum Downs, 3201, VIC, Australia
Tel.: (61) 397708545
Web Site: https://www.energy360.com.au
Biogas Plant Construction Services
N.A.I.C.S.: 237120

OVO Energy Pty. Limited (1)
L22 120 Spencer St, Melbourne, 3000, VIC, Australia
Tel.: (61) 1300937686
Web Site: https://www.ovoenergy.com.au
Renewable Green Energy Retailer
N.A.I.C.S.: 237130

Perth Energy Pty. Limited (1)
L 4 165 Adelaide Terrace, Perth, 6004, WA, Australia
Tel.: (61) 894200300
Web Site: http://www.perthenergy.com.au
Sales Range: $75-99.9 Million
Emp.: 2
Electric Power Distr
N.A.I.C.S.: 221122
Ky Cao *(Founder)*

Powerdirect Pty Ltd (1)
Level 3 699 Bourke Street, Docklands, 3008, VIC, Australia
Tel.: (61) 1300307966
Web Site: https://www.powerdirect.com.au
Sales Range: $75-99.9 Million
Emp.: 80
Electric Power Distr
N.A.I.C.S.: 221122

Sol Distribution Pty. Limited (1)
Warehouse 5 2 Percival Road, Smithfield, 2164, NSW, Australia
Tel.: (61) 1300660483
Web Site: https://www.sol-distribution.com.au
Renewable Energy Distr
N.A.I.C.S.: 221122

Southern Phone Company Limited (1)
6 Page Street, Moruya, 2537, NSW, Australia
Tel.: (61) 131464
Web Site: https://www.southernphone.com.au
Telecommunication Servicesb
N.A.I.C.S.: 517810

The Australian Gas Light Company (1)
72 Christie St, Saint Leonards, 2065, NSW, Australia (100%)

Tel.: (61) 99212999
Web Site: http://www.agl.com.au
Sales Range: $250-299.9 Million
Emp.: 300
Natural Gas Distr
N.A.I.C.S.: 221210

Western Energy Pty. Ltd. (1)
Suite 18 Level 11 809-811 Pacific Hwy, Chatswood, 2067, NSW, Australia
Tel.: (61) 290117674
Web Site: http://www.westonenergy.com.au
Gas Whslr
N.A.I.C.S.: 424720
Garbis Simonian *(Mng Dir)*

AGLAND CORP.
Highway 16W Range Road 14, Lloydminster, T9V 3A2, AB, Canada
Tel.: (780) 875-4471
Web Site: https://www.agland.ca
Year Founded: 1958
Emp.: 140
Agriculture Equipment Services
N.A.I.C.S.: 423820
Kenneth Garne Kay *(Pres)*

AGLUKON SPEZIALDUNGER GMBH & CO. KG
Heerdter Landstr 199, PO Box 19, 40549, Dusseldorf, Germany
Tel.: (49) 2115064237   De
Web Site: http://www.aglukon.com
Year Founded: 1928
Sales Range: $10-24.9 Million
Emp.: 75
Fertilizer Mfr
N.A.I.C.S.: 325311
Hans Ulrich Born *(Mng Dir)*

AGM GROUP HOLDINGS INC.
Room 1502-3 15/F Connuaght Commercial Building 185 Wanchai Road, Wanchai, China (Hong Kong)
Tel.: (852) 1065020507   VG
Web Site: https://www.agmprime.com
Year Founded: 2015
AGMH—(NASDAQ)
Rev.: $36,709,931
Assets: $88,020,889
Liabilities: $62,967,113
Net Worth: $25,053,776
Earnings: $3,551,695
Emp.: 22
Fiscal Year-end: 12/31/21
Online Financial Transaction Processing Services
N.A.I.C.S.: 522320
Wenjie Tang *(Founder & Co-CEO)*

AGMO HOLDINGS BERHAD
Level 38 MYEG Tower Empire City Damansara Jalan PJU 8, Damansara Perdana, 47820, Petaling Jaya, Selangor, Malaysia
Tel.: (60) 376648515
Web Site: https://www.agmo.group
Year Founded: 2017
AGMO—(KLS)
Rev.: $7,455,256
Assets: $11,041,700
Liabilities: $1,024,910
Net Worth: $10,016,790
Earnings: $1,658,800
Emp.: 215
Fiscal Year-end: 03/31/24
Holding Company
N.A.I.C.S.: 551112
Chin Seng Tham *(CTO)*

AGN AGROINDUSTRIAL, PROJETOS E PARTICIPACOES LTDA.
Avenida Juscelino Kubistchek 1830 Tower 1 12 andar, 04543-900, Sao Paulo, SP, Brazil
Tel.: (55) 11 3897 7349   BR
Investment Holding Company

N.A.I.C.S.: 551112

Subsidiaries:

B&A Mineracao S.A. (1)
Avenida do Contorno 5919 5 andar, Savassi, 30110-035, Belo Horizonte, Brazil
Tel.: (55) 31 2552 1588
Web Site: http://www.bamineracao.com
Holding Company; Fertilizer Minerals, Iron Ore & Copper Mining
N.A.I.C.S.: 551112
Roger Agnelli *(Chm)*

Subsidiary (Domestic):

B&A Fertilizers Limited (2)
Avenida do Contorno 5919 5 andar, Savassi, 30110-035, Belo Horizonte, Brazil
Tel.: (55) 31 2552 1588
Fertilizer Mineral Mining
N.A.I.C.S.: 212390

AGNI SYSTEMS LIMITED
Navana Tower 11th Floor Suite A 45 Gulshan Avenue Gulshan 1, Dhaka, 1212, Bangladesh
Tel.: (880) 9606100700
Web Site: https://www.agni.com
Year Founded: 1995
AGNISYSL—(CHT)
Rev.: $5,200,894
Assets: $12,505,292
Liabilities: $1,948,906
Net Worth: $10,556,385
Earnings: $746,112
Emp.: 325
Fiscal Year-end: 06/30/23
Internet Service Provider
N.A.I.C.S.: 517810
Javed Bukth *(Chm)*

AGNICO EAGLE MINES LIMITED
145 King Street East Ste 400, Toronto, M5C 2Y7, ON, Canada
Tel.: (416) 947-1212   ON
Web Site: https://www.agnicoeagle.com
Year Founded: 1972
AEM—(NYSE)
Rev.: $6,626,909,000
Assets: $28,684,949,000
Liabilities: $9,262,034,000
Net Worth: $19,422,915,000
Earnings: $1,941,307,000
Emp.: 10,155
Fiscal Year-end: 12/31/23
Gold Exploration & Mining Services
N.A.I.C.S.: 212220
Jean Robitaille *(Sr VP-Corp Dev, Bus Strategy & Technical Svcs)*

Subsidiaries:

Agnico Eagle Mexico S.A. de C.V. (1)
Ave Mirador 7724 Colinas del Valle, Fraccionamiento las Haciendas, CP 31217, Chihuahua, Mexico
Tel.: (52) 6141803100
Gold Mining
N.A.I.C.S.: 212220

Agnico-Eagle (USA) Limited (1)
230 S Rock Blvd Ste 31, Reno, NV 89502 (100%)
Tel.: (775) 828-6070
Web Site: http://www.agnico-eagle.com
Sales Range: $50-74.9 Million
Emp.: 4
Gold Mining
N.A.I.C.S.: 212220

Agnico-Eagle Mines Limited-Exploration Division (1)
1953 3 rd Ave W, Val d'Or, G9P 4M9, QC, Canada (100%)
Tel.: (819) 874-5980
Web Site: http://www.agnico-eagle.com
Sales Range: $100-124.9 Million
Emp.: 200
Gold Exploration
N.A.I.C.S.: 212220

Agnico Eagle Mines Limited—(Continued)

Agnico-Eagle Mines Limited-LaRonde Division (1)
10 200, Route De Preissac, Rouyn-Noranda, J0Y 1C0, QC, Canada (100%)
Tel.: (819) 759-3644
Web Site: http://www.agnicoeagle.com
Sales Range: $350-399.9 Million
Emp.: 900
Gold Mining
N.A.I.C.S.: 212220

Agnico-Eagle Mines Limited-Meadowbank (1)
Two Bentall Centre 555 Burrard St Ste 375, Vancouver, V7X 1M8, BC, Canada
Tel.: (604) 608-2557
Web Site: http://www.agnico-eagle.com
Sales Range: $25-49.9 Million
Emp.: 25
Mineral Exploration Services
N.A.I.C.S.: 327999

Agnico-Eagle Mines Mexico Cooperatie U.A. (1)
Amsteldijk 166 Suite 1 17, Amsterdam, 1079 LH, Netherlands
Tel.: (31) 206441805
Mineral Mining Services
N.A.I.C.S.: 213115

Subsidiary (Non-US):

Tenedora Agnico Eagle Mexico S.A. de C.V. (2)
Mirador 7724 Colinas Delvalle, 31217, Chihuahua, Mexico
Tel.: (52) 6354576000
Sales Range: $650-699.9 Million
Emp.: 1,200
Mineral Mining Services
N.A.I.C.S.: 213115
Marco Perea (Gen Mgr)

Agnico-Eagle Mines Sweden Cooperatie U.A. (1)
Tel.: (31) 206441805
Mineral Mining Services
N.A.I.C.S.: 213115

Subsidiary (Non-US):

Agnico-Eagle Finland Oy (2)
Tel.: (358) 163380700
Gold Mining Services
N.A.I.C.S.: 212220

Canadian Malartic Corporation (1)
100 Chemin du Lac Mourier, Malartic, J0Y 1Z0, QC, Canada
Tel.: (819) 757-2225
Web Site: https://www.malartic.agnicoeagle.com
Mining Operation Services
N.A.I.C.S.: 213114

Canadian Malartic Partnership (1)
100 Chemin du Lac Mourier, Malartic, J0Y 1Z0, QC, Canada
Tel.: (819) 757-2225
Web Site: http://www.canadianmalartic.com
Gold Ore Mining
N.A.I.C.S.: 212220

Fosterville Gold Mine Pty. Ltd. (1)
McCormicks Road, Fosterville, 3557, VIC, Australia
Tel.: (61) 354399000
Web Site: https://fgmcommunity.com.au
N.A.I.C.S.: 212220

Riddarhyttan Resources AB (1)
Aurorum 30, 977 75, Lulea, Sweden (75%)
Tel.: (46) 92075897
Web Site: http://www.riddarhyttan.se
Sales Range: Less than $1 Million
Emp.: 973
Metal Exploration Services
N.A.I.C.S.: 212220

TMAC Resources, Inc. (1)
181 University Avenue Suite 300, PO Box 33, Toronto, M5H 3M7, ON, Canada
Tel.: (416) 628-0216
Web Site: http://www.tmacresources.com
Rev.: $194,983,152
Assets: $425,932,584
Liabilities: $192,917,004

Net Worth: $233,015,580
Earnings: ($468,020,784)
Emp.: 286
Fiscal Year-end: 12/31/2019
Mineral Exploration & Gold Mining Serives
N.A.I.C.S.: 212290
Ronald P. Gagel (Sec & Exec VP-Corp Affairs)

AGNITE EDUCATION LIMITED
18 Kambar Street Shanthi Colony, Pallikaranai, Chennai, 600 100, India
Tel.: (91) 446555 2589
Web Site: http://www.agniteedu.com
Sales Range: Less than $1 Million
Emp.: 300
Software Products & Services
N.A.I.C.S.: 334610
K. Padmanabhan (Mng Dir)

Subsidiaries:

AlphaSoft Services Corporation (1)
2121 N California Blvd Ste 345, Walnut Creek, CA 94596
Tel.: (925) 952-6300
Web Site: http://www.alphasoftservices.com
Outsourced Software Development & Systems Integration Services
N.A.I.C.S.: 541511

Teledata Informatics Ltd. (1)
235 Main St Ste 520, White Plains, NY 10601-2421
Tel.: (914) 686-2100
Web Site: http://www.teledata-usa.com
Software Products & Services
N.A.I.C.S.: 334610

Subsidiary (Domestic):

Transworld Information Systems (2)
485A Route 1 S Ste 200, Iselin, NJ 08830-2719
Tel.: (732) 634-0550
Computer Related Consulting Services
N.A.I.C.S.: 423110

eSys Technologies Pte. Ltd. (1)
1 Changi North Street 1, Singapore, 498789, Singapore (51%)
Tel.: (65) 64910250
IT Products Distr
N.A.I.C.S.: 423430

AGNORA LTD
200 Mountain Road, Collingwood, L9Y 4V5, ON, Canada
Tel.: (705) 444-6654
Web Site: https://agnora.com
Glass, Ceramics & Concrete Mfg.
N.A.I.C.S.: 327110

Subsidiaries:

W C P, Inc. (1)
17730 Crusader Ave, Cerritos, CA 90703
Tel.: (562) 653-9797
Web Site: http://www.westcoastglass.com
Sales Range: $1-9.9 Million
Emp.: 95
Flat Glass Mfr
N.A.I.C.S.: 327211
Roberto Mora (Plant Mgr)

AGNUS HOLDINGS PVT. LTD.
Plot No. 30 Galaxy 1st Main Road J. P., Nagar Third Phase Bangalore, Karnataka, 560078, India
Tel.: (91) 8046570300
Year Founded: 2002
Holding Company
N.A.I.C.S.: 551112
Chandrappa Seetharmaiah (Dir)

AGORA A.D.
Nikole Tesle 139, Zabalj, Serbia
Tel.: (381) 23 511 647
Year Founded: 1997
Sales Range: Less than $1 Million
Emp.: 3
Construction & Civil Engineering Services
N.A.I.C.S.: 541330

AGORA HOLDINGS INC.
170 Rimrock Road Unit #2, North York, M3J 3A6, ON, Canada
Tel.: (855) 561-4541 UT
Web Site: http://www.agoraholdingsinc.com
Year Founded: 1983
AGHI—(OTCIQ)
Holding Company; Investment Services
N.A.I.C.S.: 551112
Danail Terziev (CEO)

AGORA HOSPITALITY GROUP CO., LTD.
7F Toranomon 2nd Wyco Building 5-2-6 Toranomon, Minato-ku, Tokyo, 105-0001, Japan
Tel.: (81) 334361860
Web Site: https://www.agora.jp
Year Founded: 2007
9704—(TKS)
Rev.: $51,820,810
Assets: $129,257,790
Liabilities: $91,390,100
Net Worth: $37,867,690
Earnings: ($1,056,410)
Emp.: 609
Fiscal Year-end: 12/31/23
Home Management Services
N.A.I.C.S.: 721110
Gary Yan Kuen Kwok (Pres & CEO)

AGORA S.A.
Czerska 8/10, 00-732, Warsaw, 00-732, Poland
Tel.: (48) 225556000
Web Site: https://www.agora.pl
AGO—(WAR)
Rev.: $279,635,985
Assets: $450,452,947
Liabilities: $281,125,710
Net Worth: $169,327,237
Earnings: ($26,544,491)
Emp.: 2,363
Fiscal Year-end: 12/31/22
Holding Company; Newspaper & Magazine Publisher; Radio Broadcasting Station Owner & Operator
N.A.I.C.S.: 551112
Andrzej Szlezak (Chm-Supervisory Bd)

Subsidiaries:

AdTaily Sp. z o o (1)
ul Starowislna 55/7, 31-038, Krakow, Poland
Tel.: (48) 668347783
Web Site: http://www.adtaily.pl
Sales Range: $25-49.9 Million
Emp.: 12
Online Advertising Services
N.A.I.C.S.: 541613
Jakub Krzych (Gen Mgr)

Adpol Sp. z o.o. (1)
Ul Szosa Bydgoska 56, 87-100, Torun, Poland
Tel.: (48) 669889077
Web Site: http://www.woodwindows.pl
Window & Door Mfr
N.A.I.C.S.: 332321
Adam Daszkowski (CEO)

Agora Poligrafia Sp. z o.o (1)
Towarowa 4, 43-100, Tychy, Poland
Tel.: (48) 32 325 22 01
Web Site: http://www.agora.pl
Sales Range: $50-74.9 Million
Emp.: 130
Newspaper Printing Services
N.A.I.C.S.: 322120

Agora TC Sp. z o.o. (1)
Czerska 8/10, Warsaw, 00-732, Poland (100%)
Tel.: (48) 60005556001
Web Site: http://www.agora.pl
Machinery Mfr
N.A.I.C.S.: 333310

Art Marketing Syndicate SA (1)
Jana Pawla Ii 14, 61139, Poznan, Poland (100%)
Tel.: (48) 225556400
Sales Range: $75-99.9 Million
Emp.: 300
Advertising Agencies
N.A.I.C.S.: 541810

Subsidiary (Domestic):

Akcent Media Sp. z o o. (2)
Ul Jana Pawla II 14, 61-139, Poznan, Poland (100%)
Tel.: (48) 618751024
Advertising Agencies
N.A.I.C.S.: 541810

Foodio Concepts Sp. z o.o. (1)
Sienkiewicza 82/84, 90-318, Lodz, Poland
Tel.: (48) 426303601
Web Site: http://www.foodioconcepts.pl
Restaurant Operators
N.A.I.C.S.: 722511

GRA Sp. z o. o. (1)
Jakuba 13, 87100, Torun, Poland (100%)
Tel.: (48) 523253820
Web Site: http://www.gra.fm
Sales Range: $25-49.9 Million
Emp.: 80
Advertising Agencies
N.A.I.C.S.: 541810

Subsidiary (Domestic):

IM 40 Sp. z o.o (2)
ul Czerska 14, Warsaw, 00-732, Poland
Tel.: (48) 225555100
Radio & Television Broadcasting Services
N.A.I.C.S.: 327910

Grupa Radiowa Agory Sp. z o.o. (1)
ul Czerska 8/10, 00-732, Warsaw, Poland
Tel.: (48) 225555100
Web Site: https://www.agora.pl
Newspaper Publishing Services
N.A.I.C.S.: 513110

Helios S.A. (1)
Al Politechniki 1, 90-590, Lodz, Poland
Tel.: (48) 422999272
Web Site: https://www.helios.pl
Multi Cinema Complex Management Services
N.A.I.C.S.: 512131
Tomasz Jagiello (Chm-Mgmt Bd & Gen Dir)

Subsidiary (Domestic):

Kinoplex Sp. z o.o (2)
Kosciuszki 17, Lodz, 90-418, Poland
Tel.: (48) 426303601
Web Site: http://www.kinoplex.gazeta.pl
Sales Range: $25-49.9 Million
Emp.: 14
Video Production Services
N.A.I.C.S.: 512110
Thomas Jagiello (Gen Mgr)

Inforadio Sp. z o. o. (1)
Ul Czerska 8/10, 00-732, Warsaw, Poland (66.1%)
Tel.: (48) 225555100
Radio Stations
N.A.I.C.S.: 516110

LLC Agora Ukraine (1)
vul Vel Vasylkivska 77, Kiev, 03150, Ukraine
Tel.: (380) 44 586 6100
Web Site: http://www.agora.ua
Internet Publishing & Advertising Services
N.A.I.C.S.: 541810

Next Film Sp. z o.o. (1)
ul Czerska 8/10, 00-732, Warsaw, Poland
Tel.: (48) 225555334
Web Site: https://next-film.pl
Polish Film Mfr
N.A.I.C.S.: 325612
Robert Kijak (Pres)

Plan A Sp. z o.o. (1)
ul Nugat 9 Lok U12, 02-677, Warsaw, Poland
Tel.: (48) 221881075
Web Site: https://www.e-plan.pl
Network Installation Services
N.A.I.C.S.: 238210

Polskie Badania Internetu Sp. z o. o.   **(1)**
Al Jerozolimskie 65-79 pok 11 31, 00-697, Warsaw, Poland
Tel.: (48) 226307268
Web Site: http://www.pbi.org.pl
Sales Range: $25-49.9 Million
Emp.: 5
Radio & Television Broadcasting & Wireless Communications Equipment Mfr
N.A.I.C.S.: 334220
Pawel Laskowski *(CEO)*

Radiowe Doradztwo Reklamowe Sp. z.o.o.   **(1)**
ul sw Marcin 80/82, 61-809, Poznan, Poland   **(100%)**
Tel.: (48) 8528623
Web Site: http://www.bor.com.pl
Radio Station Operator
N.A.I.C.S.: 516110

Trader.com (Polska) Sp. z o.o   **(1)**
Ul Czerska 8/10, 00-732, Warsaw, Poland
Tel.: (48) 225555740
Web Site: http://www.domiporta.pl
Newspaper Classifieds Publishing Services
N.A.I.C.S.: 513110

AGOSTINI'S LIMITED
18 Victoria Avenue, Port of Spain, Trinidad & Tobago
Tel.: (868) 6234871   TT
Web Site: https://www.agostinislimited.com
Year Founded: 1925
AGL—(TRI)
Rev.: $691,120,735
Assets: $621,733,414
Liabilities: $300,552,916
Net Worth: $321,180,498
Earnings: $58,010,565
Emp.: 2,885
Fiscal Year-end: 09/30/23
Fast Moving Consumer Goods Distr
N.A.I.C.S.: 423990
Anthony J. Agostini *(Mng Dir)*

Subsidiaries:

Agostini Marketing   **(1)**
3 Chootoo Rd, El Socorro, WI, Trinidad & Tobago
Tel.: (868) 2254236
Web Site: https://www.agostinibuild.com
Emp.: 100
Construction Materials Distr
N.A.I.C.S.: 423320

Subsidiary (Domestic):

Fastening & Building Systems Limited   **(2)**
3 Duncan Street, Port of Spain, Trinidad & Tobago
Tel.: (868) 623 9004
Construction Materials Distr
N.A.I.C.S.: 423390

Hand Arnold Trinidad Limited   **(1)**
Hand Arnold Commercial Complex Chootoo Road, El Socorro, San Juan, Trinidad & Tobago
Tel.: (868) 6748001
Web Site: https://www.handarnold.com
Grocery Product Distr
N.A.I.C.S.: 424490
Anthony J. Agostini *(Chm)*

Rosco Petroavance Limited   **(1)**
2-4 Rodriguez Avenue Cross Crossing, San Fernando, Trinidad & Tobago
Tel.: (868) 2254775
Web Site: http://roscopetro.com
Emp.: 40
Industrial Valve Whslr
N.A.I.C.S.: 423830
Wayne Bernard *(CEO)*

Rosco Procom Limited   **(1)**
2-4 Rodriguez Avenue Cross Crossing, San Fernando, Trinidad & Tobago
Tel.: (868) 2254775
Web Site: https://www.procomtt.com
Oil & Gas Distr
N.A.I.C.S.: 424720

Smith Robertson & Company Limited   **(1)**
18 Chootoo Rd Ext, Aranguez, El Socorro, Trinidad & Tobago
Tel.: (868) 6387762
Web Site: https://www.smithrobertsontt.com
Personal Care Product Distr
N.A.I.C.S.: 456120
A. J. Agostini *(Chm)*

SuperPharm Limited   **(1)**
Lot Nos 19-21 Union Park West, Marabella, San Fernando, Trinidad & Tobago
Tel.: (868) 6755666
Web Site: http://www.superpharm.co.tt
Pharmacy Operator
N.A.I.C.S.: 456110

AGP CORPORATION
Kuko Shisetsu 2 Sogo Bldg 1-7-1 Hanedakuko, Ota-Ku, Tokyo, 144-0041, Japan
Tel.: (81) 337471631
Web Site: http://www.agpgroup.co.jp
Year Founded: 1965
Emp.: 609
Aircraft Power Supply Maintenance & Airport Facilities & Equipment Services
N.A.I.C.S.: 811310
Eiichi Yamaguchi *(Pres)*

AGP MALAGA SOCIMI, S.A.
Alameda Principal 16, 29005, Malaga, Spain
Tel.: (34) 952363860
Web Site: https://www.agpsocimi.com
Year Founded: 2019
MLAGP—(EUR)
Rev.: $3,962,169
Assets: $66,778,005
Liabilities: $21,229,518
Net Worth: $45,548,487
Earnings: $1,514,770
Emp.: 9
Fiscal Year-end: 12/31/23
Real Estate Investment Services
N.A.I.C.S.: 531190

AGRA LIMITED
8 Bessemer Street, Private Bag 12011, Windhoek, Namibia
Tel.: (264) 61 290 9111
Web Site: http://www.agra.com.na
Sales Range: $100-124.9 Million
Emp.: 850
Agriculture Product Distr
N.A.I.C.S.: 424910
Abelene Boer *(Sr Mgr-Mktg)*

Subsidiaries:

A Rosenthal (Cape) (Pty) Ltd.   **(1)**
13 Loop St, Cape Town, South Africa
Tel.: (27) 21 4187790
Arms & Ammunition Distr
N.A.I.C.S.: 423990

A Rosenthal (Pty) Ltd.   **(1)**
Loop Street, Cape Town, 8001, South Africa
Tel.: (27) 21 421 6728
Arms & Ammunition Distr
N.A.I.C.S.: 423990

AGRA STAHLHANDELS-GMBH
Vilstalstrasse 84, 92245, Amberg, Germany
Tel.: (49) 9621917080
Web Site: http://www.agra-stahlhandel.com
Rev.: $18,227,254
Emp.: 5
Stainless Steel Plates & Aluminium Sheets Mfr
N.A.I.C.S.: 331315
Peter Gradl *(Mng Dir)*

AGRALYS SERVICES
Rue De Courtalain, La Chapelle Du Noyer, 28200, Orleans, Eure Et Loir, France

Tel.: (33) 237975900
Web Site: http://www.agralys.com
Rev.: $24,700,000
Emp.: 230
Management Consulting Services
N.A.I.C.S.: 541618
Francois Lagrange *(Dir-Admin)*

AGRAM D.D.
IV brigade HVO Stjepana Radica 7, 88320, Ljubuski, Bosnia & Herzegovina
Tel.: (387) 3 983 7500
Web Site: http://www.agram.ba
AGRLR—(SARE)
Rev.: $5,901,454
Assets: $13,576,548
Liabilities: $3,202,421
Net Worth: $10,374,127
Earnings: $1,120,656
Emp.: 143
Fiscal Year-end: 12/31/20
Technical Testing & Analysis Services
N.A.I.C.S.: 541690

AGRAM NEKRETNINE D.D.
Vukovarska 1, 88 000, Mostar, Bosnia & Herzegovina
Tel.: (387) 36394580
ERLMR—(SARE)
Rev.: $2,968,114
Assets: $19,204,114
Liabilities: $2,705,678
Net Worth: $16,498,436
Earnings: $1,910,922
Emp.: 2
Fiscal Year-end: 12/31/20
Real Estate Manangement Services
N.A.I.C.S.: 531210

AGRANA BETEILIGUNGS-AG
Friedrich-Wilhelm-Raiffeisen-Platz 1, 1020, Vienna, Austria
Tel.: (43) 1211370   AT
Web Site: https://www.agrana.com
Year Founded: 1988
AGB2—(MUN)
Rev.: $4,180,223,226
Assets: $3,189,544,055
Liabilities: $1,879,548,410
Net Worth: $1,309,995,645
Earnings: $71,663,240
Emp.: 9,047
Fiscal Year-end: 02/28/24
Sugar & Starch Mfr
N.A.I.C.S.: 311314
Hans-Joerg Gebhard *(Vice Chm-Supervisory Bd)*

Subsidiaries:

AGRANA Frucht GmbH & Co KG   **(1)**
Donau-City-Strasse 9, 1220, Vienna, Austria   **(100%)**
Tel.: (43) 1211370
Sales Range: $25-49.9 Million
Emp.: 150
Fruit Preparation & Concentrate Mfr & Distr
N.A.I.C.S.: 311411
Johann Marihart *(CEO)*

AGRANA Fruit Argentina S.A   **(1)**
Juramento 2089 Piso 8 Oficina 803, RA-C1428, Buenos Aires, RA-C1428, Argentina
Tel.: (54) 1147880505
Web Site: https://ar.agrana.com
Emp.: 100
Fruit & Vegetable Preparations
N.A.I.C.S.: 311411

AGRANA Fruit Australia Pty. Ltd.   **(1)**
200 George Downes Drive, Central Mangrove, 2250, NSW, Australia
Tel.: (61) 243731245
Web Site: https://au.agrana.com
Sales Range: $25-49.9 Million
Emp.: 50
Fruit & Vegetable Preparations
N.A.I.C.S.: 311411

AGRANA Fruit Austria GmbH   **(1)**

Muhlwaldstrasse 1, 8200, Gleisdorf, Austria
Tel.: (43) 311222260
Fruit & Vegetable Preparations
N.A.I.C.S.: 311411

AGRANA Fruit Dachang Co. Ltd.   **(1)**
No 3 Industrial Road Chaobai River Industrial Estate, Dachang Hui Autonomous County, Hebei, 06530, China
Tel.: (86) 3168933353
Web Site: http://cn.agrana.com
Sales Range: $25-49.9 Million
Emp.: 25
Fruit & Vegetable Preparations
N.A.I.C.S.: 311411

AGRANA Fruit Fiji Pty. Ltd.   **(1)**
Nayawa Road, PO Box 80, Sigatoka, Fiji
Tel.: (679) 6500162
Sales Range: $25-49.9 Million
Emp.: 30
Fruit & Vegetable Preparations
N.A.I.C.S.: 311411

AGRANA Fruit France S.A.   **(1)**
17 avenue du 8 mai 1945, BP 504, 77295, Mitry-Mory, Cedex, France
Tel.: (33) 164675600
Web Site: https://fr.agrana.com
Fruit & Vegetable Preparations
N.A.I.C.S.: 311411

AGRANA Fruit Istanbul Gida San Ve Tic A.S.   **(1)**
Buyukdere Cad Ozsezen is Merkezi A Blok No 122 Kat 4, Esentepe Sisli, 34394, Istanbul, Turkiye
Tel.: (90) 2123476000
Web Site: http://tr.agrana.com
Sales Range: $25-49.9 Million
Emp.: 50
Fruit & Vegetable Preparations
N.A.I.C.S.: 311411
Heinz Scharl *(Mng Dir)*

AGRANA Fruit Korea Co. Ltd.   **(1)**
Elport Hallavivaldi 409 46 Wiryeseoil-Ro, Sujeong-gu, Seongnam, 13636, Korea (South)
Tel.: (82) 24489100
Web Site: https://kr.agrana.com
Sales Range: $25-49.9 Million
Emp.: 10
Fruit & Vegetable Preparations
N.A.I.C.S.: 311411

AGRANA Fruit Mexico SA de CV   **(1)**
Martinez de Navarrete 83 B Col Gral Francisco Villa, Jacona, 59820, Michoacan, Mexico
Tel.: (52) 3515309600
Web Site: http://mx.agrana.com
Fruit & Vegetable Preparations
N.A.I.C.S.: 311411

AGRANA Fruit Polska Sp z.o.o.   **(1)**
ul Lawska 2, 07-410, Ostroleka, Poland
Tel.: (48) 297670602
Web Site: http://pl.agrana.com
Fruit & Vegetable Preparations
N.A.I.C.S.: 311411

AGRANA Fruit South Africa Pty. Ltd..   **(1)**
10 Brigid Road Diep River, Cape Town, 7945, South Africa
Tel.: (27) 215072010
Web Site: https://za.agrana.com
Sales Range: $25-49.9 Million
Emp.: 100
Fruit & Vegetable Preparations
N.A.I.C.S.: 311411
Philippe Gomez *(Sr Project Mgr)*

AGRANA Fruit US, Inc.   **(1)**
6850 Southpointe Pkwy, Brecksville, OH 44141
Tel.: (440) 546-1199
Web Site: https://www.us.agrana.com
Emp.: 80
Fruit & Vegetable Preparations
N.A.I.C.S.: 311411

AGRANA Sales & Marketing GmbH   **(1)**
Josef-Reither-Strasse 21-23, 3430, Tulln, Austria
Tel.: (43) 22726020
Organic Fruit Mfr
N.A.I.C.S.: 111336

AGRANA Beteiligungs-AG—(Continued)

AGRANA Starke GmbH **(1)**
Friedrich-Wilhelm-Raiffeisen-Platz 1, 1020,
Vienna, Austria **(100%)**
Tel.: (43) 1211370
Web Site: http://www.agrana.at
Starch Mills & Mfr
N.A.I.C.S.: 311999

Subsidiary (US):

**Marroquin Organic International,
Inc.** **(2)**
303 Potrero St Ste 18, Santa Cruz, CA
95060
Tel.: (831) 423-3442
Web Site: https://www.marroquin-organics.com
Sales Range: $1-9.9 Million
Supermarkets & Other Grocery, except
Convenience, Stores
N.A.I.C.S.: 445110
Klaus Zaglmayr (Sls Dir)

AGRANA Zucker GmbH **(1)**
Josef-Reither-Strasse 21-23, 3430, Tulln,
Austria **(100%)**
Tel.: (43) 22726020
Sales Range: $100-124.9 Million
Emp.: 400
Sugar Factory
N.A.I.C.S.: 311314
Martin Doppler (CEO)

AUSTRIA JUICE GmbH **(1)**
Krollendorf 45, A- 3365, Allhartsberg,
Austria **(50.01%)**
Tel.: (43) 744823040
Web Site: https://www.austriajuice.com
Emp.: 1,000
Juice Concentrate Mfr
N.A.I.C.S.: 311421
Franz Ennser (CEO)

Subsidiary (Non-US):

Lukta Polska Sp. z o.o **(2)**
ul Plantowa 231, 96-230, Biala Rawska,
Poland
Tel.: (48) 814 60 25
Sales Range: $25-49.9 Million
Fruit Juices Mfr & Whslr
N.A.I.C.S.: 311411

Subsidiary (Domestic):

Ybbstaler Fruit Austria GmbH **(1)**
Kroellendorf 45, 3365, Allhartsberg, Austria
Tel.: (43) 744823040
Web Site: https://www.austriajuice.com
Sales Range: $25-49.9 Million
Emp.: 60
Beverage Compounds Mfr & Whslr
N.A.I.C.S.: 312111

Subsidiary (Non-US):

Ybbstaler Fruit Polska Sp. z o.o **(2)**
Ul Plantowa 231, Biala Rawska, Poland
Tel.: (48) 825622150
Web Site: http://www.ybbstaler.pl
Emp.: 200
Fruit Juices Whslr
N.A.I.C.S.: 424490
Helmut Stoger (Gen Mgr)

**Agrana Fruit (Jiangsu) Company
Limited** **(1)**
Liaohe Road No 1013, Changzhou,
213000, China
Tel.: (86) 51988121868
Web Site: https://cn.agrana.com
Food & Beverage Mfr
N.A.I.C.S.: 311999

**Agrana Fruit Brasil Industria, Comer-
cio, Importacao e Exportacao
Ltda.** **(1)**
Av Vereador Jose Donatto 530, Cabreuva,
Sao Paulo, 13318-000, Brazil
Tel.: (55) 1144090970
Web Site: https://br.agrana.com
Food & Beverage Mfr
N.A.I.C.S.: 311999

Agrana Fruit Germany GmbH **(1)**
Lilienthalstrasse 1, D-78467, Konstanz,
Germany
Tel.: (49) 753158070
Web Site: https://de.agrana.com

Food & Beverage Mfr
N.A.I.C.S.: 311999
Kolja Stitz (Mng Dir)

Agrana Fruit Japan Co., Ltd. **(1)**
Shinagawa East One Tower 2-16-1 Konan,
Miato-ku, Tokyo, 108-0075, Japan
Tel.: (81) 368942388
Web Site: https://jp.agrana.com
Food & Beverage Mfr
N.A.I.C.S.: 311999

Agrana Fruit Luka TOV **(1)**
Pryvokzalna Street 2A, Luka-Meleshkivska
Village, 23234, Vinnytsia, Ukraine
Tel.: (380) 432553568
Web Site: https://ua.agrana.com
Food & Beverage Mfr
N.A.I.C.S.: 311999

Agrana Fruit S.A.S. **(1)**
17 Avenue du 8 Mai 1945, BP 504, 77295,
Mitry-Mory, Cedex, France
Tel.: (33) 164675600
Web Site: https://fr.agrana.com
Food & Beverage Mfr
N.A.I.C.S.: 311999

Agrana Fruit Services GmbH **(1)**
Friedrich-Wilhelm-Raiffeisen-Platz 1, 1020,
Vienna, Austria
Tel.: (43) 1211370
Food & Beverage Mfr
N.A.I.C.S.: 311999

Agrana Fruit Ukraine TOV **(1)**
Serhii Zulinskyi Street 32, 21022, Vinnytsia,
Ukraine
Tel.: (380) 432553501
Food & Beverage Mfr
N.A.I.C.S.: 311999

**Agrana Juice (Xianyang) Co.,
Ltd.** **(1)**
Xilang Dajie Nanduan, Xianyang, 713400,
Shaanxi, China
Tel.: (86) 2937665488
Food & Beverage Mfr
N.A.I.C.S.: 311999

**Agrana Research & Innovation Cen-
ter GmbH** **(1)**
Josef-Reither-Strasse 21-23, A-3430, Tulln,
Austria
Tel.: (43) 227260211403
Web Site: https://www.agrana-research.com
Emp.: 85
Food & Beverage Mfr
N.A.I.C.S.: 311999

Agrana Romania S.R.L. **(1)**
Sos Straulesti nr 178-180 Sector 1, RO-
013339, Bucharest, Romania
Tel.: (40) 372381000
Web Site: https://ro.agrana.com
Food & Beverage Mfr
N.A.I.C.S.: 311999

Agrana Trading EOOD **(1)**
18 Shipchenski Prohod Blvd Office 801,
1113, Sofia, Bulgaria
Tel.: (359) 29250003
Web Site: https://bg.agrana.com
Sugar Product Distr
N.A.I.C.S.: 424490

Austria Juice Germany GmbH **(1)**
Am Ockenheimer Graben 6, 55411, Bingen,
Germany
Tel.: (49) 6721915221045
Food & Beverage Mfr
N.A.I.C.S.: 311999

Austria Juice Romania S.r.l. **(1)**
Strada Metalurgiei nr 3, RO-730234, Vaslui,
Romania
Tel.: (40) 235361710
Food & Beverage Mfr
N.A.I.C.S.: 311999

Austria Juice Ukraine TOV **(1)**
Serhii Zulinskyi Street 32, 21022, Vinnytsia,
Ukraine
Tel.: (380) 432553601
Food & Beverage Mfr
N.A.I.C.S.: 311999

Biogaz Fejleszto Kft. **(1)**
Pecsi utca 10-14, 7400, Kaposvar, Hungary
Tel.: (36) 82321456
Web Site: https://www.biogazfejleszto.hu

Biogas Mfr
N.A.I.C.S.: 325120

**Dirafrost Frozen Fruit Industry
N.V.** **(1)**
Klaverbladstraat 11, 3560, Lummen, Bel-
gium
Tel.: (32) 13552701
Web Site: https://www.dirafrost.com
Sales Range: $25-49.9 Million
Emp.: 50
Fruit & Vegetable Preparations
N.A.I.C.S.: 311411

Dirafrost Maroc SARL **(1)**
km 15 Route de Rabat, BP 49, Louamra,
92000, Larache, Morocco
Tel.: (212) 538800080
Food & Beverage Mfr
N.A.I.C.S.: 311999

**Instantina Nahrungsmittel
Entwicklungs- und Produktionsgesell-
schaft m.b.h.** **(1)**
Friedrich-Wilhelm-Raiffeisen-Platz 1, 1020,
Vienna, Austria
Tel.: (43) 12113712410
Web Site: https://www.instantina.at
Emp.: 130
Coffee & Tea Mfr
N.A.I.C.S.: 311920
Klaus Muik (Mng Dir)

**Osterreichische Rubensamenzucht
Gesellschaft m.b.H.** **(1)**
Josef-Reither-Strasse 21-23, 3430, Tulln,
Austria
Tel.: (43) 227260211590
Emp.: 19
Food & Beverage Mfr
N.A.I.C.S.: 311999

SC AGRANA Romania SA **(1)**
Soseaua Straulesti nr 178-180 sector 1,
013339, Bucharest, Romania
Tel.: (40) 372381000
Web Site: http://ro.agrana.com
Sales Range: $200-249.9 Million
Sugar Mfr
N.A.I.C.S.: 311313

Slovenske Cukrovary s.r.o. **(1)**
Cukrovarska 726, 926 01, Sered, Slovakia
Tel.: (421) 317884120
Web Site: https://www.korunnycukor.sk
Sugar Products Mfr
N.A.I.C.S.: 311314

AGRANI INSURANCE COM-
PANY LIMITED

Saiham Sky View Tower 45 Bijoy Na-
gar 14th Floor, Dhaka, 1000, Bangla-
desh
Tel.: (880) 28391571
Web Site: https://www.agraniins.com
Year Founded: 2000
AGRANINS—(DHA)
Rev.: $319,246
Assets: $9,217,126
Liabilities: $2,908,910
Net Worth: $6,308,216
Earnings: $899,427
Emp.: 153
Fiscal Year-end: 12/31/23
Insurance Services
N.A.I.C.S.: 524298
Santosh Kumar Nandi (Deputy Mng
Dir)

AGRARINVEST AG

Christoph-Schnyder Strasse 2, PO
Box 33, CH-6210, Sursee, Switzer-
land
Tel.: (41) 44 200 36 66
Web Site: http://www.agrarinvest.com
Agricultural Investment
N.A.I.C.S.: 523999
Theo Haeni (Chm)

AGRARIUS AG

Robert-Bosch-Strasse 10, 61267,
Neu-Anspach, Germany
Tel.: (49) 60815856400
Web Site: http://www.agrarius.de

AU2—(DEU)
Sales Range: $1-9.9 Million
Agricultural Services
N.A.I.C.S.: 111998

AGRATIO URBAN DESIGN,
INC.

Kichijoji Branch 4F HULIC New
KICHIJOJI 177 Kichijoji Minamimachi,
Tokyo, 180-0004, Japan
Tel.: (81) 422272177
Web Site: https://www.agr-
urban.co.jp
3467—(TKS)
Rev.: $182,469,050
Assets: $165,494,570
Liabilities: $125,880,840
Net Worth: $39,613,730
Earnings: $5,770,530
Fiscal Year-end: 03/31/24
Detached House Construction Ser-
vices
N.A.I.C.S.: 236115
Ryuichi Obayashi (Pres & CEO)

AGRAVIS RAIFFEISEN AG

Industrieweg 110, 48155, Munster,
Germany
Tel.: (49) 2516820
Web Site: http://www.agravis.de
Year Founded: 2004
Sales Range: $5-14.9 Billion
Emp.: 6,323
Agricultural & Energy Co-operative
Services
N.A.I.C.S.: 813910
Andreas Rickmers (Head-Mgmt Bd)

Subsidiaries:

AGRAVIS Baustoffhandel GmbH **(1)**
Wierlings Hook 28, 48249, Dulmen, Ger-
many
Tel.: (49) 2594783000
Building Materials Distr
N.A.I.C.S.: 444180

AGRAVIS Ems-Jade GmbH **(1)**
Raiffeisenstrasse 12, Esens, 26427, Witt-
mund, Germany
Tel.: (49) 497191930
Animal Food Product Mfr
N.A.I.C.S.: 311119

**AGRAVIS Kornhaus Ostwestfalen
GmbH** **(1)**
Warburger Strasse 28, 33034, Brakel, Ger-
many
Tel.: (49) 527237030
Animal Feed Product Distr
N.A.I.C.S.: 424910

**AGRAVIS Mischfutter Emsland
GmbH** **(1)**
Darmer Hafenstrasse 8, 49808, Lingen,
Germany
Tel.: (49) 5918001411
Animal Food Product Mfr
N.A.I.C.S.: 311119

**AGRAVIS Mischfutter
Oldenburg/Ostfriesland GmbH** **(1)**
Stau 199-203, 26122, Oldenburg, Germany
Tel.: (49) 441218892122
Animal Feed Product Distr
N.A.I.C.S.: 424910

**AGRAVIS Mischfutter Ostwestfalen-
Lippe GmbH** **(1)**
Zum Industriehafen 20, 32423, Minden,
Germany
Tel.: (49) 5713991111
Animal Food Product Mfr
N.A.I.C.S.: 311119

**AGRAVIS Mischfutter Westfalen
GmbH** **(1)**
Industrieweg 105, 48155, Munster, Ger-
many
Tel.: (49) 2516822431
Animal Feed Product Distr
N.A.I.C.S.: 424910

AGRAVIS Niedersachsen-Sud GmbH (1)
Am Mittellandkanal 2, 31515, Wunstorf, Germany
Tel.: (49) 503151770
Animal Food Product Mfr
N.A.I.C.S.: 311119

AGRAVIS Raiffeisen AG - Hannover Head Office (1)
Plathnerstr 4A, 30175, Hannover, Germany
Tel.: (49) 511 8075 0
Web Site: http://www.agravis.de
Agricultural & Energy Co-operative
N.A.I.C.S.: 551114
Justin Pfitzenreuter *(Sr Trader-Grains)*

AGRAVIS Raiffeisen-Markt GmbH (1)
Rudolf-Diesel-Str 5, 54516, Wittlich, Germany
Tel.: (49) 6571951830
Farm Equipment Distr
N.A.I.C.S.: 423820

AGRAVIS Technik BvL GmbH (1)
Kopenhagener Strasse 1, Versen, 49716, Meppen, Germany
Tel.: (49) 59359393100
Farm Equipment Distr
N.A.I.C.S.: 423820

AGRAVIS Technik Center GmbH (1)
Kopenhagener Str 1, Versen, 49716, Meppen, Germany
Tel.: (49) 59359393300
Industrial Product Distr
N.A.I.C.S.: 423840

AGRAVIS Technik Heide-Altmark GmbH (1)
Hansestrasse 30, 29525, Uelzen, Germany
Tel.: (49) 58188911
Farm Equipment Distr
N.A.I.C.S.: 423820

AGRAVIS Technik Hessen-Pfalz GmbH (1)
Brautacker 8, 34560, Fritzlar, Germany
Tel.: (49) 5622 91485 0
Web Site: http://www.agravis.de
Agricultural Equipment Mfr
N.A.I.C.S.: 333111
Stefan Kremper *(Mng Dir)*

AGRAVIS Technik Lenne-Lippe GmbH (1)
Im Gewerbegebiet 2, 57368, Lennestadt, Germany
Tel.: (49) 272171710
Farm Equipment Distr
N.A.I.C.S.: 423820

AGRAVIS Technik Munsterland-Ems GmbH (1)
Weseler Strasse 2, 46325, Borken, Germany
Tel.: (49) 28619260
Farm Equipment Distr
N.A.I.C.S.: 423820

AGRAVIS Technik Polska Sp. z o.o. (1)
Pianowo 46, 64-000, Koscian, Poland
Tel.: (48) 696284360
Web Site: http://www.agravistechnik-polska.pl
Farm Equipment Distr
N.A.I.C.S.: 423820

AGRAVIS Technik Raiffeisen GmbH (1)
Am Kalbesbrook 13, 37154, Northeim, Germany
Tel.: (49) 555160080
Farm Equipment Distr
N.A.I.C.S.: 423820

AGRAVIS Technik Sachsen-Anhalt/Brandenburg GmbH (1)
Damasckeweg 22, 06366, Kothen, Germany
Tel.: (49) 349641250
Farm Equipment Distr
N.A.I.C.S.: 423820

AGRAVIS Technik Saltenbrock GmbH (1)
Zur Funte 4, Wellingholzhausen, 49326,

Melle, Germany
Tel.: (49) 542994110
Farm Equipment Distr
N.A.I.C.S.: 423820

AGRAVIS Versicherungsservice GmbH & Co. KG (1)
Plathnerstrasse 4 A, 30175, Hannover, Germany
Tel.: (49) 51180753440
Farm Equipment Distr
N.A.I.C.S.: 423820

Agrar Cargo Spedition GmbH (1)
Rosenstrasse, 01591, Riesa, Germany
Tel.: (49) 3525657220
Web Site: http://www.agrar-cargo.de
Agriculture Product Distr
N.A.I.C.S.: 424910

Agri Futura GmbH (1)
Obhauser Weg 9, 06268, Querfurt, Germany
Tel.: (49) 34771550
Logistic Services
N.A.I.C.S.: 488510

Animedica Latino America S.A. de C.V. (1)
Retomo del Anahuac 61 Lomas de las Palmas, 52788, Huixquilucan, Mexico
Tel.: (52) 5552900524
Nutritional Supplement Distr
N.A.I.C.S.: 456191

Baro Lagerhaus GmbH & Co. KG (1)
Hauptstr 100, Bulstringen, 39345, Bordeland, Germany
Tel.: (49) 390589710
Renewable Energy Services
N.A.I.C.S.: 221111

DGO Grobhandel GmbH (1)
Industriezubringer 32-38, 49661, Cloppenburg, Germany
Tel.: (49) 447188460
Agricultural Trading Services
N.A.I.C.S.: 926140

DoFu Donaufutter GmbH (1)
Europaring 21, 94315, Straubing, Germany
Tel.: (49) 9421929520
Animal Food Product Mfr
N.A.I.C.S.: 311119

Dr.E.Graub AG (1)
Rehhagstrasse 83, 3018, Bern, Switzerland
Tel.: (41) 319802727
Web Site: http://www.graeub.com
Pharmaceutical Product Mfr & Distr
N.A.I.C.S.: 325412

EQUOVIS GmbH (1)
Industrieweg 110, 48155, Munster, Germany
Tel.: (49) 2516822580
Web Site: http://www.equovis.de
Animal Feed Product Distr
N.A.I.C.S.: 424910

FGL Handelsgesellschaft mbH (1)
Thomas-Edison-Str, 15517, Furstenwalde, Germany
Tel.: (49) 33615530
Agricultural Trading Services
N.A.I.C.S.: 926140

FINVIS Business Services GmbH (1)
Industrieweg 110, 48155, Munster, Germany
Tel.: (49) 2516820
Web Site: http://www.finvis.de
Commercial Support Services
N.A.I.C.S.: 561499

FS Trucks GmbH (1)
Benzstrasse 15, 49076, Osnabruck, Germany
Tel.: (49) 541770960
Web Site: http://www.fs-trucks.de
Automobile Parts Distr
N.A.I.C.S.: 423120

Feuerstrater GmbH (1)
Westkirchener Strasse 25, 48361, Beelen, Germany
Tel.: (49) 258693240
Web Site: http://www.feuerstraeter-landtechnik.de

Farm Equipment Distr
N.A.I.C.S.: 423820

Futura Agrarhandel GmbH (1)
Kosserner Str 3, Grossbothen, 04668, Leipzig, Germany
Tel.: (49) 3438471245
Industrial Product Distr
N.A.I.C.S.: 423840

Georg Piening GmbH & Co. KG (1)
Braunschweiger Str 55, 38723, Seesen, Germany
Tel.: (49) 538193911
Web Site: http://www.piening.de
Oil & Gas Services
N.A.I.C.S.: 213112

Georg Piening Haustechnik und Energieservice GmbH (1)
Braunschweiger Str 55, 38723, Seesen, Germany
Tel.: (49) 5513834050
Web Site: http://www.piening-haustechnik.de
Bathroom Remodeler Services
N.A.I.C.S.: 236118

GiG Geflugelintegration GmbH (1)
Darmer Hafenstrasse 8, 49808, Lingen, Germany
Tel.: (49) 5918001465
Web Site: http://www.gig-raiffeisen.de
Animal Feed Product Distr
N.A.I.C.S.: 424910

Graincom GmbH (1)
Plathnerstr 4A, 30175, Hannover, Germany
Tel.: (49) 51180753787
Web Site: http://www.graincom.de
Agricultural Trading Services
N.A.I.C.S.: 926140

Gundelach GmbH (1)
Walter-Althoff-Strasse 6, Bockenem, 31167, Hildesheim, Germany
Tel.: (49) 5067917190
Web Site: http://www.holzhandlung-gundelach.de
Farm Equipment Distr
N.A.I.C.S.: 423820

HL Hamburger Leistungsfutter GmbH (1)
Konsul-Ritter-Str 3, 21079, Hamburg, Germany
Tel.: (49) 40766920
Web Site: http://www.hl-futter.de
Animal Feed Product Distr
N.A.I.C.S.: 424910
Arne Schramm *(Head-Sls)*

Industria Italiana Integratori Trei S.p.A. (1)
Via Affarosa 4, Rio Saliceto, 42010, Reggio Emilia, RE, Italy
Tel.: (39) 0522640711
Web Site: http://www.livisto.it
Pharmaceutical Product Mfr & Distr
N.A.I.C.S.: 325412
Sara Lugli *(Mktg Mgr)*

LIVISTO Group GmbH (1)
Im Sudfeld 9 Bosensell, 48308, Senden, Germany
Tel.: (49) 25363302111
Web Site: http://www.asiacontest.livisto.com
Pharmaceutical Product Mfr & Distr
N.A.I.C.S.: 325412
Armin Thur *(CEO)*

LIVISTO Sp. z o.o. (1)
Ul Chwaszczynska 198a, 81-571, Gdynia, Poland
Tel.: (48) 585722438
Web Site: http://www.livisto.pl
Pharmaceutical Product Mfr & Distr
N.A.I.C.S.: 325412

Landtechnik Steigra GmbH (1)
Am Schwedenring 8 - 10, Steigra, 06268, Bad Bramstedt, Germany
Tel.: (49) 344615100
Web Site: http://www.landtechnik-steigra.de
Farm Equipment Distr
N.A.I.C.S.: 423820

Lorenz Rubarth Landtechnik GmbH (1)
Herringsener Weg 1, Anrochte, 59609, Soest, Germany

Tel.: (49) 292791790
Web Site: http://www.lorenz-rubarth-landtechnik.de
Farm Equipment Distr
N.A.I.C.S.: 423820

Lotus Agrar GmbH (1)
Dynamostrasse 13, 68165, Mannheim, Germany
Tel.: (49) 62143855280
Web Site: http://www.lotusagrar.de
Commercial Support Services
N.A.I.C.S.: 561499

MRA GmbH (1)
Am Hasensprung 11, Muhlenbeck, 16567, Brandenburg, Germany
Tel.: (49) 333839980
Web Site: http://www.mra.info
Construction Services
N.A.I.C.S.: 236220

Menke Agrar GmbH (1)
Overweg 22, 59494, Soest, Germany
Tel.: (49) 292196540
Web Site: http://www.menke-agrar.de
Farm Equipment Distr
N.A.I.C.S.: 423820

Menke Agrar Polska Sp. z o.o. (1)
Pianowo 46, 64-000, Koscian, Poland
Tel.: (48) 618420582
Agricultural Services
N.A.I.C.S.: 115116

New-Tec Ost Vertriebsgesellschaft fur Agrartechnik mbH (1)
Muhlenweg 10, 14929, Treuenbrietzen, Germany
Tel.: (49) 337488310
Web Site: http://www.newtec.info
Farm Equipment Distr
N.A.I.C.S.: 423820

New-Tec West Vertriebsgesellschaft fur Agrartechnik mbH (1)
Alfred-Delp-Str 2-4, 31177, Harsum, Germany
Tel.: (49) 512798070
Farm Equipment Distr
N.A.I.C.S.: 423820

PROFUMA Spezialfutterwerke GmbH & Co. KG (1)
Siemensstrasse 10, 41542, Dormagen, Germany
Tel.: (49) 2133978770
Web Site: http://www.profuma.de
Animal Food Product Mfr
N.A.I.C.S.: 311119
Christoph Bernholz *(Exec Dir)*

Raiffeisen Lienen-Lengerich GmbH (1)
Lengericher Str 33, Lienen, 49536, Steinfurt, Germany
Tel.: (49) 5483721770
Web Site: http://www.raiffeisenlienen.de
Farm Equipment Distr
N.A.I.C.S.: 423820

TecVis GmbH (1)
Robert-Bosch-Strasse 31, Olfen, 59399, Coesfeld, Germany
Tel.: (49) 25959692300
Web Site: http://www.tecvis.de
Farm Equipment Distr
N.A.I.C.S.: 423820
Daniel Bengfort *(Mgr-Spare Part)*

Technik Center Alpen GmbH (1)
Weseler Str 28, 46519, Alpen, Germany
Tel.: (49) 280294800
Web Site: http://www.technik-center-alpen.de
Farm Equipment Distr
N.A.I.C.S.: 423820

TerraVis GmbH (1)
Industrieweg 110, 48155, Munster, Germany
Tel.: (49) 2516822055
Web Site: http://www.terravis-biogas.de
Biogas Services
N.A.I.C.S.: 221117
Sascha Thies *(Product Mgr)*

Terres Agentur GmbH (1)
Industrieweg 110, 48155, Munster, Germany
Tel.: (49) 2516822098

AGRAVIS Raiffeisen AG—(Continued)

Web Site: http://www.terresagentur.de
Graphic Design Services
N.A.I.C.S.: 541430

Terres Marketing- und Consulting GmbH (1)
Industrieweg 110, 48155, Munster, Germany
Tel.: (49) 2516822095
Web Site: http://www.myfarmvis.de
Consulting Services
N.A.I.C.S.: 541618

VERAVIS GmbH (1)
Industrieweg 110, 48155, Munster, Germany
Tel.: (49) 2516822571
Web Site: http://www.veravis.de
Consulting Services
N.A.I.C.S.: 541618

VOVIS Automobile GmbH (1)
Albersloher Weg 277, 48155, Munster, Germany
Tel.: (49) 251608020
Car Parts Distr
N.A.I.C.S.: 441330

VR Agrar Center Wittelsbacher Land GmbH (1)
Sielenbacher Strasse 1, Altomunster, 85250, Dachau, Germany
Tel.: (49) 82549203030
Web Site: http://www.vr-agrarcenter.de
Agricultural Services
N.A.I.C.S.: 115116

aniMedica GmbH (1)
Im Sudfeld 9 Bosensell, 48308, Senden, Germany
Tel.: (49) 253633020
Web Site: http://www.livisto.de
Veterinary Pharmaceutical Product Mfr & Distr
N.A.I.C.S.: 325412
Sandra Weser (Grp Dir-Product Dev)

aniMedica international GmbH (1)
Eschborner Landstrasse 42-50, 60489, Frankfurt, Germany
Tel.: (49) 697272760
Web Site: http://www.animedica.com
Nutritional Supplement Distr
N.A.I.C.S.: 456191
Joachim Simon (Bus Mgr)

AGRI-TECH (INDIA) LIMITED
Nath House Nath Road, Aurangabad, 431005, India
Tel.: (91) 2402376314
Web Site: http://www.agri-tech.in
537292—(NSE)
Rev.: $123,030
Assets: $16,243,198
Liabilities: $2,169,208
Net Worth: $14,073,990
Earnings: ($406,290)
Emp.: 3
Fiscal Year-end: 03/31/21
Feed
N.A.I.C.S.: 111120
Reshma Talbani (Officer-Compliance & Sec)

AGRI-TRADE HOLDINGS LIMITED
Level 28 1 Market Street, Sydney, 2000, NSW, Australia
Tel.: (61) 438 184 784   AU
Senior Citizen Housing Services
N.A.I.C.S.: 623312

AGRIA CORPORATION
12/F Phase 1Austin Tower 22-26A Austin Avenue, Tsim Sha Tsui, Kowloon, China (Hong Kong)
Tel.: (852) 2619 0033   Ky
Web Site: http://www.agriacorp.com
Rev.: $860,652,000
Assets: $536,590,000
Liabilities: $394,998,000
Net Worth: $141,592,000

Earnings: ($14,650,000)
Emp.: 1,938
Fiscal Year-end: 06/30/18
Agricultural Products Mfr, Researcher & Developer
N.A.I.C.S.: 111191
Alan Guanglin Lai (Chm)

Subsidiaries:

Agria Corporation (1)
2 Park Pl Ste 2, Bronxville, NY 10708 (100%)
Tel.: (914) 337-1117
Web Site: http://www.agriacorp.com
Agri-Solutions & Sheep Breeding Products
N.A.I.C.S.: 111199

PGG Wrightson Limited (1)
1 Robin Mann Place Christchurch Airport, Christchurch, 8053, New Zealand (44.3%)
Tel.: (64) 33720800
Web Site: http://www.pggwrightson.co.nz
Rev.: $583,547,847
Assets: $296,966,507
Liabilities: $195,733,852
Net Worth: $101,232,656
Earnings: ($10,477,273)
Emp.: 1,309
Fiscal Year-end: 06/30/2023
Rural Services; Irrigation & Pumping Services, Livestock Marketing & Supply, Seed & Grain, Farm Consultancy, Farm Finance & Insurance & Real Estate Services
N.A.I.C.S.: 424520
Julian Daly (Gen Mgr-Corp Affairs)

Subsidiary (Domestic):

Agri-Feeds Limited (2)
61A Hull Rd, PO Box 4180, Mount Maunganui S, Mount Maunganui, 3149, New Zealand
Tel.: (64) 75474540
Web Site: http://www.agrifeeds.co.nz
Sales Range: $25-49.9 Million
Emp.: 20
Animal Feed Mfr
N.A.I.C.S.: 311119
Greg Aspinall (Mgr-Sls-Natl)

Subsidiary (Non-US):

PGG Wrightson Seeds (Australia) Pty Limited (2)
7-9 Distribution Dr, Truganina, Melbourne, 3029, VIC, Australia
Tel.: (61) 393943400
Web Site:
    http://www.pggwrightsonseeds.com.au
Forage Seeds Production & Distr
N.A.I.C.S.: 111120
Cameron Henley (Mgr-Mktg & Sls-Natl)

Subsidiary (Domestic):

AusWest Seeds Pty Limited (3)
2-8 Tobias Street, Forbes, 2871, NSW, Australia
Tel.: (61) 268521500
Web Site: http://www.auswestseeds.com.au
Sales Range: $25-49.9 Million
Emp.: 21
Forage Seeds Whslr
N.A.I.C.S.: 424910
Frank McRae (Product Mgr-Dev)

Subsidiary (Domestic):

Stephen Pasture Seeds Pty Limited (4)
27 Wiltshire Ln, Ballarat, 3356, VIC, Australia
Tel.: (61) 353358055
Web Site:
    http://www.stephenpastureseeds.com.au
Sales Range: $25-49.9 Million
Emp.: 16
Pasture Seeds Whslr
N.A.I.C.S.: 424910
Jim Stephen (Mgr-Bus Dev)

Subsidiary (Non-US):

Wrightson Pas S.A. Limited (2)
Maximo Santos 4900, 12400, Montevideo, Uruguay
Tel.: (598) 23557753
Web Site: http://www.wrightsonpas.com.uy

Sales Range: $25-49.9 Million
Emp.: 50
Forage Seeds Production & Distr
N.A.I.C.S.: 111199
Marcelo Banchero (Mgr)

AGRIA GROUP HOLDING JSC
Business Center Dimyat 9 Floor 111 Kniaz Boris I Str, 9002, Varna, 9002, Bulgaria
Tel.: (359) 52554000
Web Site: https://www.agriabg.com
AGH—(BUL)
Rev.: $9,263,878
Assets: $107,476,548
Liabilities: $52,025,163
Net Worth: $55,451,385
Earnings: $4,877,497
Emp.: 657
Fiscal Year-end: 12/31/23
Professional, Scientific & Technical Activities
N.A.I.C.S.: 541990
Emil Veselinov Raykov (Chm & CEO)

Subsidiaries:

Kehlibar EOOD (1)
5 Oborishte St, Lyaskovets, 5140, Veliko Tarnovo, Bulgaria
Tel.: (359) 6 192 2117
Web Site: https://www.kehlibar.com
Sunflower Seed Oil Mfr
N.A.I.C.S.: 311224

Kristera AD (1)
Industrial Area, 7800, Popovo, Bulgaria
Tel.: (359) 608 4 78 58
Wheat Farming Services
N.A.I.C.S.: 111140

Kristera-Agro EOOD (1)
Business Center Dimyat 9 Floor 111 Kniaz Boris I Str, 9002, Varna, Bulgaria
Tel.: (359) 52554000
Wheat Farming Services
N.A.I.C.S.: 111140
Emil Raykov (Exec Dir)

AGRIBANK SECURITIES JOINT STOCK CORPORATION
The 5th Floor Artex Building No 172, Dong Da, Hanoi, Vietnam
Tel.: (84) 2462762666
Web Site:
    https://www.agriseco.com.vn
Year Founded: 2000
Security Brokerage Services
N.A.I.C.S.: 523150

AGRICO CANADA LIMITED
2896 Slough St Unit 6, Mississauga, L4T 1G3, ON, Canada
Tel.: (905) 672-5610
Web Site:
    http://www.agricocanada.com
Sales Range: $100-124.9 Million
Emp.: 55
Fertilizer Whslr
N.A.I.C.S.: 325314
Robert L Whitelaw (Pres)

AGRICOLA CERRO PRIETO S.A.
Calle Dean Valdivia 111 Oficina 901-B San Isidro, Lima, Peru
Tel.: (51) 1 6193900
Web Site: http://www.acpagro.com
Year Founded: 1999
Agriculture Product Farming Services
N.A.I.C.S.: 111998

AGRICOLA GROUP LTD
3-5 Alton Business Centre, Valley Lane, Ipswich, IP9 2AX, Wherstead, United Kingdom
Tel.: (44) 147323 22 22
Web Site: http://www.agricola.co.uk
Year Founded: 1998
Sales Range: $900-999.9 Million

Emp.: 961
Nutrition for Farm Animals
N.A.I.C.S.: 311119
Nicholas Ian Coleman (Sec)

Subsidiaries:

BOCM PAULS Ltd. (1)
3-5 Alton Business Centre, Valley Lane Wherstead, Ipswich, IP9 2AX, Suffolk, United Kingdom
Tel.: (44) 1473556500
Web Site: http://www.bocmpauls.co.uk
Sales Range: $900-999.9 Million
Emp.: 900
Animal Feed Mfr
N.A.I.C.S.: 311611

Division (Domestic):

Feedex Nutrition (2)
The Airfield Rougham, Bury St Edmunds, Thetford, IP309NH, Suffolk, United Kingdom (100%)
Tel.: (44) 1359272936
Web Site: http://www.feedex.co.uk
Sales Range: $10-24.9 Million
Emp.: 50
Animal Feed Mfr
N.A.I.C.S.: 311119
Bruce Colman (Gen Mgr)

AGRICOLA NACIONAL S.A.C.I.
Almirante Pastene No 300, Santiago, Chile
Tel.: (56) 4706800
Web Site: http://www.anasac.cl
ANASAC—(SGO)
Sales Range: Less than $1 Million
Seeds Mfr
N.A.I.C.S.: 111120

AGRICULTURAL BANK OF CHINA (MOSCOW) LIMITED
5 Lesnaya Street, 125047, Moscow, Russia
Tel.: (7) 4999295599
Web Site: http://www.ru.abchina.com
Year Founded: 2014
Rev.: $3,400,227
Assets: $180,212,281
Liabilities: $150,765,418
Net Worth: $29,446,864
Earnings: ($1,005,847)
Emp.: 100
Fiscal Year-end: 12/31/18
Commercial Banking Services
N.A.I.C.S.: 522110
Fu Ying (Chm-Mgmt Bd)

AGRICULTURAL BANK OF CHINA LIMITED
No 69 Jianguomen Nei Avenue, Dongcheng District, Beijing, 100005, China
Tel.: (86) 1085109619   CN
Web Site: https://www.abchina.com
Year Founded: 1979
601288—(SHG)
Rev.: $172,351,830,469
Assets: $5,615,913,926,814
Liabilities: $5,207,904,491,419
Net Worth: $408,009,435,396
Earnings: $38,002,816,787
Emp.: 451,003
Fiscal Year-end: 12/31/23
Banking Services
N.A.I.C.S.: 522110
Xuguang Zhang (Exec VP)

Subsidiaries:

ABC Ansai Rural Bank Limited Liability Company (1)
Majiagou Village Zhenwudong County, Ansai Town, Majiagou, 717400, Shaanxi, China
Tel.: (86) 9116229906
Commercial Banking Services
N.A.I.C.S.: 522110

ABC Financial Leasing Co., Ltd. (1)

5-6 F East Yanan Road, Huangpu District, Shanghai, 200120, China
Tel.: (86) 2168776699
Web Site: http://www.abcleasing.com
Commercial Banking Services
N.A.I.C.S.: 522110

ABC Hubei Hanchuan Rural Bank Limited Liability Company (1)
Jianshece Road Xinhe Power Plant, Hanchuan, 431600, Hubei, China
Tel.: (86) 7128412338
Commercial Banking Services
N.A.I.C.S.: 522110

ABC International Holdings Limited (1)
10 th Fl Agricultural Bank Of China Tower 50 Connaught Road Central, Queensway, Central, China (Hong Kong)
Tel.: (852) 36660000
Commercial Banking Services
N.A.I.C.S.: 522110

ABC-CA Fund Management Co., Ltd. (1)
50th Floor Agricultural Bank Building No 9 Yincheng Road, Pudong New District, Shanghai, 200122, China
Tel.: (86) 21 61095588
Web Site: http://www.abc-ca.com
Sales Range: $50-74.9 Million
Fund Management Services
N.A.I.C.S.: 523940

Agricultural Bank of China - Hong Kong (1)
25/F Agricultural Bank of China Tower 50 Connaught Road Central, Hong Kong, China (Hong Kong)
Tel.: (852) 28195599
Web Site: http://www.hk.abchina.com
Sales Range: $50-74.9 Million
Emp.: 1
Commercial Banking Services
N.A.I.C.S.: 522110

Agricultural Bank of China - Singapore (1)
7 Temasek Boulevard 30-01/02/03 Suntec Tower 1, Singapore, 038987, Singapore
Tel.: (65) 65355255
Web Site: http://www.sg.abchina.com
Sales Range: $50-74.9 Million
Emp.: 45
Commercial Banking Services
N.A.I.C.S.: 522110

Agricultural Bank of China - Tokyo (1)
503 Kishimoto Building 2-1 2-Chome, Marunouchi, Chiyoda-Ku, Tokyo, Japan
Tel.: (81) 332114628
Commercial Banking Services
N.A.I.C.S.: 522110

Agricultural Bank of China - UK (1)
7/F 1 Bartholomew Lane, London, EC2N 2AX, United Kingdom
Tel.: (44) 2073748900
Web Site: http://www.uk.abchina.com
Sales Range: $50-74.9 Million
Emp.: 30
Commercial Banking Services
N.A.I.C.S.: 522110

China Agricultural Finance Co., Ltd. (1)
26/F Agricultural Bank of China Tower 50 Connaught Road Central, Hong Kong, China (Hong Kong)
Tel.: (852) 28631916
Web Site: http://www.abchina.com.hk
Financial Investment & Management Services
N.A.I.C.S.: 523999

AGRICULTURAL DEVELOP-MENT BANK LIMITED
Ramshah Path, Kathmandu, Nepal
Tel.: (977) 14262605
Web Site: https://www.adbl.gov.np
Year Founded: 1968
ADBL—(NEP)
Rev.: $179,470,731
Assets: $1,992,831,385
Liabilities: $1,738,018,980

Net Worth: $254,812,406
Earnings: $10,038,650
Emp.: 2,391
Fiscal Year-end: 07/16/23
Banking Services
N.A.I.C.S.: 522110
Anil Kumar Upadhyay (CEO)

AGRICULTURAL ENGINEER-ING COMPANY FOR INVEST-MENTS
Roukn Aldeen Highway- Alraed Building 56, PO Box 13328, Damascus, Syria
Tel.: (963) 11 271 8027
Year Founded: 1988
Grain & Cotton Farming Services
N.A.I.C.S.: 111191

AGRICULTURAL LAND TRUST
Level 11 20 Hunter Street, Sydney, 2000, NSW, Australia
Tel.: (61) 282770000   AU
Web Site:
   http://www.agriculturallandtrust.com
Rev.: $13,405,908
Assets: $100,992,615
Liabilities: $84,155,501
Net Worth: $16,837,115
Earnings: $9,611,717
Fiscal Year-end: 06/30/19
Investment Management Service
N.A.I.C.S.: 523940
Justin Epstein (Chm)

AGRICULTURE PRINTING & PACKAGING JOINT STOCK COMPANY
72 Truong Chinh Phuong Mai, Dong Da, Hanoi, Vietnam
Tel.: (84) 36895605
Web Site:
   https://www.appprintco.com
INN—(HNX)
Rev.: $171,020,200
Assets: $99,274,900
Liabilities: $40,067,800
Net Worth: $59,207,100
Earnings: $8,255,200
Fiscal Year-end: 12/31/22
Printed Packaging Product Mfr
N.A.I.C.S.: 323111

Subsidiaries:

APP Hung Yen Company Limited (1)
Road C1 Pho Noi A Industrial Park, Lac Hong Commune Van Lam District, Hung Yen, Vietnam
Tel.: (84) 2213982136
Agricultural Packaging Product Mfr
N.A.I.C.S.: 311710

AGRIEURO CORP.
Sos Iancului Near 60 Appartment 1 Sector 2, Bucharest, 021727, Romania
Tel.: (40) 2126559818
Construction & Agricultural Equipment Distr
N.A.I.C.S.: 423820
Radu Cosmin Monda (CEO)

AGRIFOODS INTERNATIONAL COOPERATIVE LTD
124-10506 Fulton Drive Acheson, Edmonton, T7X 6A1, AB, Canada
Tel.: (780) 486-4115   Ca
Web Site: http://www.agrifoods.ca
Rev.: $14,000,000
Emp.: 100
Dairy Products Mfr
N.A.I.C.S.: 311511
Nancy Korva (Sr VP-Diary)

Subsidiaries:

Earth's Own Food Company Inc. (1)

PO Box 3018, Vancouver, V6B 3X5, BC, Canada
Web Site: http://www.earthsown.com
Food Product Mfr & Distr
N.A.I.C.S.: 311991

Happy Planet Foods, Inc. (1)
200-4190 Lougheed Hwy, Burnaby, V5C 6A8, BC, Canada
Tel.: (800) 811-3213
Web Site: http://www.happyplanet.com
Packaged Food Product Mfr & Distr
N.A.I.C.S.: 311411

Meadowfresh Diary Corporation (1)
1373 Kebet Way, Port Coquitlam, V3C 6G1, BC, Canada
Tel.: (604) 472-0786
Dairy Product Mfr & Distr
N.A.I.C.S.: 311511

Olympic Diary Products Inc. (1)
7178 Vantage Way, Delta, V4G 1K7, BC, Canada
Tel.: (877) 651-6389
Web Site: http://www.olympicdairy.com
Dairy Product Mfr & Distr
N.A.I.C.S.: 311511
Russ Rimmer (Mgr-Ops)

AGRIFORCE GROWING SYS-TEMS, LTD.
800-525 West 8th Avenue, Vancouver, V5Z 1C6, BC, Canada
Tel.: (604) 757-0952   BC
Web Site:
   https://www.agriforcegs.com
Year Founded: 2017
AGRI—(NASDAQ)
Assets: $21,846,893
Liabilities: $11,304,240
Net Worth: $10,542,653
Earnings: ($12,873,102)
Emp.: 15
Fiscal Year-end: 12/31/22
Agricultural Technology Services
N.A.I.C.S.: 541690
William John Meekison (Co-Chm)

AGRIMIN LIMITED
2C Loch Street, Nedlands, 6009, WA, Australia
Tel.: (61) 893895363
Web Site:
   https://www.agrimin.com.au
AMN—(ASX)
Rev.: $75,923
Assets: $63,777,867
Liabilities: $8,950,352
Net Worth: $54,827,515
Earnings: ($3,560,219)
Fiscal Year-end: 06/30/24
Potash Exploration Services
N.A.I.C.S.: 212390
Mark Savich (CEO)

Subsidiaries:

Southern Energy Corporation Pty Ltd (1)
L 21 500 Collins St, Melbourne, 3000, VIC, Australia
Tel.: (61) 386 104700
Mineral Exploration Services
N.A.I.C.S.: 213115

AGRIMINCO CORP.
69 Yonge St Suite 200, PO Box 84, Toronto, M5E 1K3, ON, Canada
Tel.: (416) 907-9422   ON
Web Site: http://www.agriminco.com
ETPHF—(OTCIQ)
Potash Mining Services
N.A.I.C.S.: 212390
George Roach (Chm)

AGRIMONY COMMODITIES LTD
701 7th Floor Kingston Tejpal Rd, Vile Parle East, Mumbai, 400057, India

Tel.: (91) 2226124294
Web Site:
   http://www.agrimonycommodities.com
537492—(BOM)
Rev.: $110,929
Assets: $1,926,650
Liabilities: $236,988
Net Worth: $1,689,662
Earnings: $25,805
Emp.: 3
Fiscal Year-end: 03/31/21
Natural Resources, Precious Metals, Textiles & Agricultural Products Trading
N.A.I.C.S.: 425120
Anandrao Gole (Chm & Mng Dir)

AGRINURTURE, INC.
54 National Road Dampol 2A Pulilan, Bulacan, 3005, Philippines
Tel.: (63) 8156320
Web Site: https://www.ani.com.ph
Year Founded: 1997
ANI—(PHI)
Rev.: $53,670,546
Assets: $94,104,092
Liabilities: $37,161,134
Net Worth: $56,942,958
Earnings: ($2,650,025)
Emp.: 397
Fiscal Year-end: 12/31/23
Fresh & Processed Fruits & Vegetables Supplier
N.A.I.C.S.: 424480
Antonio L. Tiu (Chm, Pres & CEO)

AGRIOS GLOBAL HOLDINGS LTD.
Suite 2250 1055 West Hastings Street, Vancouver, V6E 2E9, BC, Canada
Tel.: (604) 688-9588
Web Site:
   https://www.agriosglobal.com
AGGHF—(OTCEM)
Rev.: $3,295,632
Assets: $31,279,315
Liabilities: $8,129,883
Net Worth: $23,149,432
Earnings: ($4,628,630)
Fiscal Year-end: 03/31/19
Investment Holding Company Services
N.A.I.C.S.: 551112
Stephanie Wong (Mng Dir)

AGRIPOWER FRANCE SA
9 Rue de la Metallurgie, 44470, Carquefou, France
Tel.: (33) 228060590
Web Site: https://www.agripower-france.com
Year Founded: 2012
ALAGP—(EUR)
Sales Range: $1-9.9 Million
Renewable Energy Consulting Services
N.A.I.C.S.: 541690
Eric Lecoq (VP-Fin Comm & Dir-IR)

AGRIPURE HOLDINGS COM-PANY LIMITED
70 Moo 6, Klong 1 District, Khlong Luang, 12120, Pratum Thani, Thailand
Tel.: (66) 516094145
Web Site:
   https://www.apureholdings.com
Year Founded: 1986
APURE—(THA)
Rev.: $87,576,010
Assets: $87,175,672
Liabilities: $14,720,838
Net Worth: $72,454,834
Earnings: $11,344,791
Emp.: 163

Agripure Holdings Company Limited—(Continued)

Fiscal Year-end: 12/31/23
Holding Company
N.A.I.C.S.: 551112
Suredpon Jungrungruangkit *(Chm & Pres)*

Subsidiaries:

River Kwai International Food Indus-
try Company Limited　　　　　　(1)
70 Moo 6, Klong 1 District Klongluang, Pa-
thumthani, Thailand
Tel.: (66) 2516094145
Web Site: http://rkifood.com
Sweet Corn Product Distr
N.A.I.C.S.: 424490

Subsidiary (Domestic):

Agrifresh Company Limited　　　　(2)
99 Moo 1 Thanamtuen Khaupoon Road,
Kaengsian, Amphur Muang, 71000, Kan-
chanaburi, Thailand
Tel.: (66) 34910514
Web Site: http://www.agrifreshco.com
Vegetable & Fruit Product Distr
N.A.I.C.S.: 424480

Sweet Corn Products Company
Limited　　　　　　　　　　　　(2)
No 128/10 Moo 8 Prueksa Kanchanaburi
Village 7, Kaengsian, Amphur Muang,
71000, Kanchanaburi, Thailand
Tel.: (66) 345207989
Sweet Corn Product Retailer
N.A.I.C.S.: 424490

AGRITECH LIMITED

2nd Floor Asia Centre 8-Babar Block,
New Garden Town, Lahore, Pakistan
Tel.: (92) 4235860341　　　　　　PK
Web Site: https://agritech.com.pk
AGL—(PSX)
Rev.: $78,746,874
Assets: $300,919,170
Liabilities: $254,490,502
Net Worth: $46,428,668
Earnings: $3,856,309
Emp.: 979
Fiscal Year-end: 12/31/23
Fertilizer Mfr
N.A.I.C.S.: 325314
Muhammad Faisal Muzammil *(CEO)*

Subsidiaries:

National Fertilizer Corporation of
Pakistan (Private) Limited　　　　(1)
1st Floor Alfalah Building Tail Wing
Shahrah-e-Quaid-e-Azam, Lahore, Pakistan
Tel.: (92) 429920528388
Web Site: https://www.nfc.com.pk
Fertilizer Mfr & Distr
N.A.I.C.S.: 325311

AGRITERRA LTD.

St Peter's House Rue des Brehauts,
St Pierre du Bois, Saint Peter Port,
GY7 9RT, Guernsey
Tel.: (44) 8451086060　　　　　　GY
Web Site: http://www.agriterra-
ltd.com
AGTA—(AIM)
Rev.: $11,494,000
Assets: $26,638,000
Liabilities: $16,631,000
Net Worth: $10,007,000
Earnings: ($2,109,000)
Emp.: 174
Fiscal Year-end: 03/31/23
Agricultural Services
N.A.I.C.S.: 111998
Caroline Havers *(Chm)*

AGRO ALLIANZ LIMITED

Unity Tower 8-C PECHS Block-6, Ka-
rachi, 74000, Pakistan
Tel.: (92) 21 34373605
Web Site:
　http://www.agroallianz.com.pk
AAL—(KAR)

Sales Range: Less than $1 Million
Textile Mill Operator
N.A.I.C.S.: 314999

AGRO FINANCE REIT

5 Dunav Blvd, Plovdiv, 4003, Bulgaria
Tel.: (359) 32204939
Web Site: http://www.agrofinance.bg
Year Founded: 2000
AGF—(BUL)
Sales Range: Less than $1 Million
Investment Banking Services
N.A.I.C.S.: 523150
Svetla Boyanova *(Chm-Mgmt Bd)*

AGRO INDUSTRIAL EXPORTA-DORA, S.A. DE C.V.

Frente A La Estacion Del Ferrocarril
Sin Numero Sin Colonia, 45640, Tla-
jomulco de Zuniga, Jal, Mexico
Year Founded: 1973
AGRIEXP—(MEX)
Sales Range: Less than $1 Million
Food Product Mfr & Whslr
N.A.I.C.S.: 311411
Jose Ricardo Alcala Luna *(Chm, Dir
Gen & Mng Dir)*

AGRO PHOS INDIA LTD.

M87 Trade Centre 18 South Toko-
ganj, Indore, 452001, Madhya
Pradesh, India
Tel.: (91) 7312529490
Web Site: https://www.agrophos.com
Year Founded: 2002
AGROPHOS—(NSE)
Rev.: $16,004,625
Assets: $11,558,820
Liabilities: $5,147,415
Net Worth: $6,411,405
Earnings: $795,795
Emp.: 90
Fiscal Year-end: 03/31/22
Agricultural Chemical Mfr
N.A.I.C.S.: 325320
Raj Kumar Gupta *(Mng Dir)*

AGRO PUCALA S.A.A.

Elias Aguirre Street s/n Block 1, Pu-
cala, Chiclayo, Lambayeque, Peru
Tel.: (51) 74692860
Web Site: http://www.agropucala.com
PUCALAC1—(LIM)
Sales Range: Less than $1 Million
Cereal & Crop Framing Services
N.A.I.C.S.: 111998

AGRO-100 LTEE

1090 rang Sud St Thomas, Joliette,
J0K 3L0, QC, Canada
Tel.: (450) 759-8887
Web Site: http://www.agro-100.com
Year Founded: 1990
Rev.: $10,636,745
Emp.: 35
Fertilizer Mfr
N.A.I.C.S.: 325314
Jean-Marc Harnois *(Dir-R&D)*

AGRO-KANESHO CO., LTD.

Marunouchi Trust Tower Main Build-
ing 25th floor 1-8-3 Marunouchi,
Chiyoda-ku, Tokyo, 100 0005, Japan
Tel.: (81) 352248003
Web Site:
　https://www.agrokanesho.co.jp
Year Founded: 1959
4955—(TKS)
Rev.: $110,993,950
Assets: $193,259,220
Liabilities: $46,411,140
Net Worth: $146,848,080
Earnings: $4,289,450
Emp.: 308

Fiscal Year-end: 12/31/23
Agricultural Chemical Mfr & Distr
N.A.I.C.S.: 325320
Hironori Kushibiki *(Pres)*

Subsidiaries:

Kanesho Soil Treatment
SPRL/BVBA　　　　　　　　　　(1)
Avenue de Tervueren 270, 1150, Brussels,
Belgium
Tel.: (32) 2 763 4059
Web Site: https://kaneshost.com
Soil Treatment Product Distr
N.A.I.C.S.: 424910
Osamu Yamamoto *(Gen Mgr)*

AGROB IMMOBILIEN AG

Munchener Str 101, 85737, Ismaning,
Germany
Tel.: (49) 899968730　　　　　　De
Web Site: https://www.agrob-ag.de
AGR—(MUN)
Rev.: $13,378,904
Assets: $157,908,604
Liabilities: $122,220,486
Net Worth: $35,688,117
Earnings: $2,616,172
Emp.: 9
Fiscal Year-end: 12/31/23
Real Estate Investment & Manage-
ment Services
N.A.I.C.S.: 531390

AGROBACKA A.D.

Backa 3, 21420, Bac, Serbia
Tel.: (381) 21 770 060
Web Site: http://www.agrobacka.rs
Year Founded: 1989
Sales Range: Less than $1 Million
Emp.: 5
Perennial Plant Farming Services
N.A.I.C.S.: 111421
Dragan Gutic *(Exec Dir)*

AGROBACKA A.D.

Marsala Tita 8, Backa Topola, Serbia
Tel.: (381) 24715844　　　　　　RS
Web Site: https://www.agrobacka.net
Year Founded: 1969
AGBC—(BEL)
Rev.: $913,818
Assets: $2,609,141
Liabilities: $112,368
Net Worth: $2,496,773
Earnings: ($187,915)
Emp.: 28
Fiscal Year-end: 12/31/22
Cereal Mfr
N.A.I.C.S.: 311230
Predrag Kljakic *(Exec Dir)*

AGROENERGY INVEST REIT

Bul Patriarh Evtimiy 22 et 1, Sofia,
1000, Bulgaria
Tel.: (359) 28052020
AGI—(BUL)
Sales Range: Less than $1 Million
Financial Services
N.A.I.C.S.: 523999

AGROENERGY REIT

Patriarh Evtimiy No 22, Sofia, 1000,
Bulgaria
Tel.: (359) 29870520
Web Site: http://www.agroenergy.bg
AGRE—(BUL)
Sales Range: Less than $1 Million
Real Estate Investment Services
N.A.I.C.S.: 531210

AGROEXPORT PROIZVODNJA I PROMET A.D.

Kralja Milana 25, Belgrade, Serbia
Tel.: (381) 11 2626 069
Year Founded: 1952
AGRX—(BEL)
Sales Range: Less than $1 Million

Emp.: 1
Home Management Services
N.A.I.C.S.: 721110
Milos Pesic *(Dir)*

AGROFERT HOLDING, A.S.

Psaelska 2327/2, 149 00, Prague,
Czech Republic
Tel.: (420) 272192111
Web Site: http://www.agrofert.cz
Year Founded: 1993
Sales Range: $800-899.9 Million
Emp.: 120
Holding Company; Agriculture, Food
& Chemicals
N.A.I.C.S.: 551112
Jiri Haspeklo *(Mgr-Key Acct)*

Subsidiaries:

ACHP Levice a.s.　　　　　　　　(1)
Podhradie 31, 934 01, Levice, Slovakia
Tel.: (421) 366357122
Web Site: http://www.achplv.sk
Fertilizer Distr
N.A.I.C.S.: 424910

AFEED, a.s.　　　　　　　　　　(1)
Nadrazni 563/60, 693 01, Hustopece,
Czech Republic
Tel.: (420) 515 151 112
Web Site: http://www.afeed.cz
Animal Feed Mfr
N.A.I.C.S.: 311119

AGROPODNIK DOMAZLICE a.
s.　　　　　　　　　　　　　　(1)
Masarykova 523, 344 01, Prague, Czech
Republic
Tel.: (420) 379 724 621
Web Site: http://www.agropodnik.com
Fuel Distr
N.A.I.C.S.: 424690
Jan Kozak *(Mgr-Departmental)*

AGROTEC a.s.　　　　　　　　　(1)
Brnenska 74, Hustopece, 693 01, Czech
Republic
Tel.: (420) 519 402 111
Web Site: http://www.agrotec.cz
Farm Machinery & Equipment Distr
N.A.I.C.S.: 423820

AGROTECHNIC MORAVIA a.s.　(1)
Lipenska 1120/47, 772 11, Olomouc, Czech
Republic
Tel.: (420) 585 154 826
Web Site: http://www.agrotechnicmoravia.cz
Farm Machinery & Equipment Distr
N.A.I.C.S.: 423820

AgroZZN, a.s.　　　　　　　　　(1)
V Lubnici 2333, 269 26, Rakovnik, Czech
Republic
Tel.: (420) 313 283 111
Web Site: http://www.agrozzn.cz
Fertilizer Mfr
N.A.I.C.S.: 325312

Agrofert China Co Ltd　　　　　　(1)
905 Huixin Apartment Yayuncun, 100101,
Beijing, China
Tel.: (86) 1064993943
Web Site: http://www.agrofert.com.cn
Chemical & Allied Products Merchant Whslr
N.A.I.C.S.: 424690

Agrofert Hungaria Kft.　　　　　　(1)
Somloi Ut 31 II 5, 1118, Budapest, Hungary
Tel.: (36) 12791795
Web Site: http://www.agrofert.hu
Sales Range: $50-74.9 Million
Emp.: 3
Plastics Materials & Basic Forms & Shapes
Whslr
N.A.I.C.S.: 424610

Agrona, a. s.　　　　　　　　　　(1)
Nebanice 30, 350 02, Cheb, Czech Repub-
lic
Tel.: (420) 355 328 111
Animal Feed Mfr
N.A.I.C.S.: 311119

Animalco a.s.　　　　　　　　　　(1)
Na Kocince 1, 160 00, Prague, Czech Re-
public
Tel.: (420) 220 107 111

Web Site: http://www.animalco.cz
Emp.: 6
Livestock Breeding Services
N.A.I.C.S.: 115210
Juraj Seketa *(Gen Mgr)*

BMC, spol. s.r.o. **(1)**
Zlatomoravecka cesta, Prague, 949 01,
Czech Republic
Tel.: (420) 37 692 68 70
Web Site: http://www.bmcnitra.sk
Industrial Machinery & Equipment Distr
N.A.I.C.S.: 423830
Roman Novak *(Mgr-Mktg)*

Cerea, a.s. **(1)**
Delnicka 384, 531 25, Pardubice, Czech
Republic
Tel.: (420) 466 050 131
Web Site: http://www.cerea.cz
Farm Machinery & Equipment Distr
N.A.I.C.S.: 423820

Duslo, a.s. **(1)**
Administrativna budova ev c 1236, 927 03,
Sala, Slovakia
Tel.: (421) 31 775 1111
Web Site: http://www.duslo.sk
Fertilizer Mfr
N.A.I.C.S.: 325312
Petr Blaha *(Vice Chm & Gen Dir)*

Energetika Chropyne, a.s **(1)**
Komenskeho 75, 768 11, Chropyne, Czech
Republic
Tel.: (420) 573 329 111
Web Site: http://www.ech.cz
Electric Power Distribution Services
N.A.I.C.S.: 221122

Ethanol Energy a.s. **(1)**
Skolska 118, 285 71, Vrdy, Czech Republic
Tel.: (420) 327 300 523
Web Site: http://www.ethanolenergy.cz
Methanol Mfr
N.A.I.C.S.: 325193

Fatra, a.s. **(1)**
trida Tomase Bati 1541, 763 61, Napajedla,
Czech Republic
Tel.: (420) 577 501 111
Web Site: http://www.fatra.cz
Plastic Product Distr
N.A.I.C.S.: 424610
Pavel Cechmanek *(CEO)*

Fertagra Deutschland GmbH **(1)**
Schillerstrasse 12, 60313, Frankfurt, Germany
Tel.: (49) 69921889011
Plastics Materials & Basic Forms & Shapes
Whslr
N.A.I.C.S.: 424610
Alexej Brencic *(Mng Dir)*

GreenChem Holding B.V. **(1)**
Keizerstraat 17, 4811 HL, Breda, Netherlands
Tel.: (31) 76 581 27 27
Web Site: http://www.greenchem-adblue.com
Emp.: 20
Plastic Materials Mfr
N.A.I.C.S.: 325211
Pavel Hanus *(Gen Mgr)*

HYZA a.s. **(1)**
Odbojarov 2279/37, Topolcany, 955 92,
Slovakia
Tel.: (421) 385 372 211
Web Site: http://www.hyza.sk
Poultry Product Distr
N.A.I.C.S.: 424440

Hydina ZK as **(1)**
Napajdla 1, Kosice, 042 47, Slovakia
Tel.: (421) 55 6709101
Web Site: http://www.hydinazk.sk
Poultry Processing
N.A.I.C.S.: 112320

INTERTEC spol. s r.o. **(1)**
Hybesova 14, 69301, Hustopece, Czech
Republic
Tel.: (420) 519 402 842
Web Site: http://www.stkhustopece.cz
Automotive Emission Testing Services
N.A.I.C.S.: 811198

KMOTR-Masna Kromeriz a.s. **(1)**

Hulinska 2286/28, 767 01, Kromeriz, Czech
Republic
Tel.: (420) 573 500 611
Web Site: http://www.kmotr.cz
Meat Mfr
N.A.I.C.S.: 311615

Kostelecke uzeniny a.s. **(1)**
Kostelec 60, 588 61, Prague, Czech Republic
Tel.: (420) 567 577 111
Web Site: http://www.kosteleckeuzeniny.cz
Meat Mfr
N.A.I.C.S.: 311615

**Krahulik - MASOZAVOD Krahulci,
a.s.** **(1)**
Krahulci 10, 588 56, Telc, Czech Republic
Tel.: (420) 567 145 212
Web Site: http://www.krahulik.cz
Meat Mfr
N.A.I.C.S.: 311615

Lovochemie, a.s. **(1)**
Terezinska 57, 410 17, Lovosice, Czech
Republic
Tel.: (420) 416 561 111
Web Site: http://www.lovochemie.cz
Emp.: 500
Fertilizer Mfr
N.A.I.C.S.: 325311
Petr Cingr *(CEO)*

MAFRA, a.s. **(1)**
Karla Englise 519/11, 150 00, Prague,
Czech Republic
Tel.: (420) 225 063 310
Web Site: http://www.mafra.cz
Newspaper Publishers
N.A.I.C.S.: 513110

Mlekarna Hlinsko, a.s. **(1)**
Kouty 53, 539 01, Prague, Czech Republic
Tel.: (420) 469 363 111
Web Site: http://www.tatramleko.cz
Dairy Products Mfr
N.A.I.C.S.: 311514

NAVOS FARM TECHNIC s.r.o. **(1)**
Kralicky Haj 322, 79812, Prague, Czech
Republic
Tel.: (420) 582 345 371
Web Site: http://www.navosfarmtechnic.cz
Farm Machinery & Equipment Distr
N.A.I.C.S.: 423820

Nadace AGROFERT HOLDING **(1)**
Pyselska 2327/2, 149 00, Prague, Czech
Republic
Tel.: (420) 702 087 970
Web Site: http://www.nadace-agrofert.cz
Emp.: 7
Holding Company
N.A.I.C.S.: 551112
Zuzana Tornikidis *(Mng Dir)*

OLMA, a.s. **(1)**
Pavelkova 597/18, Holice, 779 00, Olomouc, Czech Republic
Tel.: (420) 585 103 211
Web Site: http://www.olma.cz
Dairy Products Mfr
N.A.I.C.S.: 311514
Simona Sokolova *(Pres & Mng Dir)*

OSEVA, a.s. **(1)**
Potocni 1436, 696 81, Bzenec, Czech Republic
Tel.: (420) 518 395 210
Web Site: http://www.oseva.eu
Seed Mfr
N.A.I.C.S.: 111998

PENAM, a.s. **(1)**
Cejl 38, Brno, 602 00, Czech Republic
Tel.: (420) 545 518 111
Web Site: http://www.penam.cz
Bakery Products Mfr
N.A.I.C.S.: 311812

Subsidiary (Non-US):

PENAM SLOVAKIA, a.s. **(2)**
Sturova 74/138, 949 35, Nitra, Slovakia
Tel.: (421) 37 651 7681
Web Site: http://www.penam.sk
Bakery Products Mfr
N.A.I.C.S.: 311812

PREOL, a.s. **(1)**

Terezinska 1214, 410 02, Lovosice, Czech
Republic
Tel.: (420) 416 564 800
Web Site: http://www.preol.cz
Fuel Mfr
N.A.I.C.S.: 324110
Andrea Sikorova *(Controller)*

Precheza, a.s. **(1)**
nabr Dr Edvarda Benese 1170/24, 750 02,
Prerov, Czech Republic **(98.4%)**
Tel.: (420) 581252111
Web Site: http://www.precheza.cz
Emp.: 600
Chemicals & Fertilizers Mfr
N.A.I.C.S.: 325311
Oldrich Konecny *(Dir-Fin)*

Subsidiary (Domestic):

DEZA, a.s. **(2)**
Masarykova 753, Valasske Mezirici, 757 28,
Czech Republic
Tel.: (420) 571691111
Web Site: http://www.deza.cz
Sales Range: $200-249.9 Million
Crude Benzol & Tar Processor
N.A.I.C.S.: 325180
Abynek Prusa *(CEO)*

Primagra, a.s. **(1)**
Nadrazni 310, 262 31, Prague, Czech Republic
Tel.: (420) 313 113 111
Web Site: http://www.primagra.cz
Fertilizer Distr
N.A.I.C.S.: 424910

Synthesia, a.s. **(1)**
Semtin 103, 53002, Pardubice, Czech Republic
Tel.: (420) 466 821 111
Web Site: http://www.synthesia.eu
Chemical Products Mfr
N.A.I.C.S.: 325130
Josef Liska *(Vice Chm & CEO)*

TAJBA, a.s. **(1)**
Zeleznicna 2, 044 14, Cana, Slovakia
Tel.: (421) 915986274
Web Site: http://www.tajba.sk
Fertilizer Distr
N.A.I.C.S.: 424910

UNILES, a.s. **(1)**
Jirikovska 832/16, 408 01, Rumburk, Czech
Republic
Tel.: (420) 412 332 182
Web Site: http://www.uniles.cz
Forestry Services
N.A.I.C.S.: 115310

Vodnanska drubez, a.s. **(1)**
Radomilicka 886, 389 01, Vodnany, Czech
Republic
Tel.: (420) 383 838 001
Web Site: http://www.vodnanskadrubez.cz
Veal Product Mfr
N.A.I.C.S.: 311615

ZZN Pelhrimov a. s. **(1)**
Nadrazni 805, 393 57, Pelhrimov, Czech
Republic
Tel.: (420) 565 323 533
Web Site: http://www.zznpe.cz
Animal Feed Mfr
N.A.I.C.S.: 311119

ZZN Polabi, a.s. **(1)**
K Vinici 1304, 280 02, Kolin, Czech Republic
Tel.: (420) 321 770 111
Web Site: http://www.zznpolabi.cz
Fertilizer Distr
N.A.I.C.S.: 424910

AGROGORICA D.D.
Kavciceva Ulica 66, Ljubljana, 1000,
Slovenia
Tel.: (386) 5 907 4790
Web Site: http://www.agog.si/
Fruit & Vegetable Framing Services
N.A.I.C.S.: 311411

AGROGUACHAL SA
Carretera Palmira Pradera Km 6 5,
Palmira, Colombia
Tel.: (57) 3108227446

Web Site:
http://www.agroguachal.com.co
AGROCHAL—(COLO)
Sales Range: Less than $1 Million
Sugar Cane Mfr
N.A.I.C.S.: 311314

AGROHERCEGOVINA A.D.
Nemanjica 50, 88280, Nevesinje, Republika Srpska, Bosnia & Herzegovina
Tel.: (387) 59601649
Web Site:
https://www.agrohercegovina.com
AGRH—(BANJ)
Sales Range: Less than $1 Million
Cereal Crop Farming Services
N.A.I.C.S.: 111998
Vesna Radosavljevic *(Member-Mgmt
Bd)*

**AGROINDUSTRIAL DEL
NOROESTE S. DE R.L. DE C.V.**
Calle 4a 3207 Col Santa Rosa, Chihuahua, 31050, Chih, Mexico
Tel.: (52) 614 415 9322
Web Site:
http://www.chihuahuacountry.com
Sales Range: $100-124.9 Million
Emp.: 1,450
Beef Processor
N.A.I.C.S.: 311612

Subsidiaries:

Norson Alimentos S de RL de
CV **(1)**
Blvd Capomo No 2 local 2 entre Berrendo,
PO Box 1223, Y Sierra Azul Colonia Nuevo,
83299, Hermosillo, Mexico **(50%)**
Tel.: (52) 6622595800
Web Site: http://www.norson.net
Sales Range: $100-124.9 Million
Emp.: 700
Pork Processing Services
N.A.I.C.S.: 311423
Jesus Huerta *(Pres)*

**AGROINDUSTRIAL LAREDO
SAA**
Av Trujillo s/n, Laredo La Libertad,
Trujillo, Peru
Tel.: (51) 44435217
Web Site:
http://www.agroindustriallaredo.com
Year Founded: 1997
LAREDOC1—(LIM)
Rev.: $115,006,342
Assets: $244,060,400
Liabilities: $87,524,627
Net Worth: $156,535,773
Earnings: $10,575,122
Fiscal Year-end: 12/31/23
Sugarcane & Agriculture Product Mfr
N.A.I.C.S.: 311314
Carlos Mauricio Arias Pena *(Chm)*

AGROINDUSTRIAS AIB S.A.
Av Ricardo Palma 894, Miraflores,
18, Lima, 18, Peru
Tel.: (51) 16144500
Web Site: https://www.aib.com.pe
Year Founded: 1987
AIBC1—(LIM)
Sales Range: Less than $1 Million
Food Products Mfr
N.A.I.C.S.: 311411

AGROKOMBINAT A.D.
Boricka 3, 73220, Rogatica, Bosnia &
Herzegovina
Tel.: (387) 58415247
Emp.: 100
Fiscal Year-end: 12/31/23
Veal Product Mfr
N.A.I.C.S.: 311612
Momcilo Forcan *(Chm)*

Agrokombinat a.d.—(Continued)

AGROKRAJINA A.D.
Vidovdanska 39, 78000, Banja Luka,
Bosnia & Herzegovina
Tel.: (387) 51218310
AGKR-R-A—(BANJ)
Rev.: $190,780
Assets: $2,588,127
Liabilities: $1,729,492
Net Worth: $858,635
Earnings: $16,989
Emp.: 5
Fiscal Year-end: 12/31/12
Chemical Product Whslr
N.A.I.C.S.: 424690
Radivoj Karalic (Chm-Mgmt Bd)

AGROLI GROUP
Aleea Combinatului nr 486, Crevedia,
Romania
Tel.: (40) 21 352 67 77
Web Site: http://www.agroli.ro
Holding Company; Poultry Production
N.A.I.C.S.: 551112
Rami Ghaziri (CEO)

Subsidiaries:

Avicola Crevedia   (1)
Aleea Combinatului nr 486 Crevedia-judetul
Dambovita, Targoviste, Romania
Tel.: (40) 21 352 67 77
Web Site: http://www.agroli.ro
Poultry Processing
N.A.I.C.S.: 311615

AGROMEC SA
Scolii str no 13, Ilfov, Ciorogarla, Ro-
mania
Tel.: (40) 736626380
AGCM—(BUC)
Rev.: $194,598
Assets: $265,009
Liabilities: $17,146
Net Worth: $247,863
Earnings: ($14,926)
Emp.: 6
Fiscal Year-end: 12/31/23
Real-Estate Prorperty Leasing Ser-
vices
N.A.I.C.S.: 531190

AGROMEC SA
Str Eremia Grigorescu 632, Harman,
Brasov, Romania
Tel.: (40) 268 367547
Sales Range: Less than $1 Million
Emp.: 23
Landscape & Gardening Services
N.A.I.C.S.: 541320
Bena Alexandru Voicu (Pres & Gen
Mgr)

AGROMEC SA
Str Oituz Nr 2, Bihor, Diosig, Roma-
nia
Tel.: (40) 259 350152
Sales Range: Less than $1 Million
Emp.: 5
Seed Processing Services
N.A.I.C.S.: 115114
Constantin Pantis (Pres & Gen Mgr)

AGROMEC SA
Sat Bibesti, Gorj, Saulesti, Romania
Tel.: (40) 253 472116
Sales Range: Less than $1 Million
Emp.: 3
Landscape & Gardening Services
N.A.I.C.S.: 541320
Virgil Valceanu (Gen Mgr)

AGROMEC TILEAGD SA
Str Garii 793, Bihor, Tileagd, Roma-
nia
Tel.: (40) 259 345371
Sales Range: Less than $1 Million
Emp.: 4

Building Materials Whslr
N.A.I.C.S.: 444180

AGROMEHANIKA AD
ul Dimitrie Tucovik br 24-1/2, Skopje,
North Macedonia
Tel.: (389) 23229642
Web Site:
http://www.agromehanika.eu.mk
Year Founded: 2003
AMEH—(MAC)
Assets: $814,470
Liabilities: $28,390
Net Worth: $786,080
Earnings: ($257,120)
Fiscal Year-end: 12/31/19
Agricultural Equipment Whslr
N.A.I.C.S.: 423820

AGROMINO A/S
Vester Farimagsgade 23, DK-1606,
Copenhagen, Denmark
Tel.: (45) 044 586 4445
Web Site: http://www.agromino.com
Year Founded: 2006
Rev.: $43,416,972
Assets: $126,445,632
Liabilities: $67,497,322
Net Worth: $58,948,311
Earnings: $2,981,067
Emp.: 1,065
Fiscal Year-end: 12/31/19
Agribusiness Manager; Soft Com-
modities Operator
N.A.I.C.S.: 926140
Petr Krogman (Chm)

Subsidiaries:

LLC Saare Farmer   (1)
Uleioe 1, 93501, Karla, Saaremaa, Estonia
Tel.: (372) 4538667
Wheat Farming Services
N.A.I.C.S.: 111140

TC Farming Ukraine Ltd.   (1)
Oneworld Parkview House 75 Prodromou
Avenue, 1307, Nicosia, Cyprus
Tel.: (357) 22496000
Web Site: http://www.oneworld.com
Emp.: 60
Wheat Farming Services
N.A.I.C.S.: 111140
George Hadjipavlou (Gen Mgr)

AGRONOMICS LTD.
18 Athol Street, Douglas, IM1 1JA,
Isle of Man
Tel.: (44) 1624620711
Web Site: https://agronomics.im
Year Founded: 2011
ANIC—(AIM)
Rev.: $37,494,729
Assets: $214,848,638
Liabilities: $2,456,568
Net Worth: $212,392,070
Earnings: $28,242,459
Fiscal Year-end: 06/30/23
Biopharma Investment Services
N.A.I.C.S.: 523999
Richard Reed (Chm)

AGROOPREMA ODZACI A.D.
Knez Mihajlova 37, Odzaci, Serbia
Tel.: (381) 25 744 901
Year Founded: 1997
Sales Range: Less than $1 Million
Automotive Part Whslr
N.A.I.C.S.: 423110

**AGROPECUARIA DE GUIS-
SONA, S. COOP. LTDA.**
Avenida Verge Del Claustre 32, Gui-
sona, 25210, Baleares, Spain
Tel.: (34) 973550100
Web Site: http://www.cag.es
Year Founded: 1959
Sales Range: $200-249.9 Million
Emp.: 138

Animal Feed & Agricultural Services
N.A.I.C.S.: 311611
Rosendo Camats Ribera (Dir-Fin)

AGROPLOD AD
6 29 November Str, 7310, Resen,
North Macedonia
Tel.: (389) 47455793
Web Site: http://www.agroplod.mk
Year Founded: 1967
AGR—(MAC)
Rev.: $622,691
Assets: $7,666,651
Liabilities: $2,516,607
Net Worth: $5,150,044
Earnings: $108
Fiscal Year-end: 12/31/19
Food Products Mfr
N.A.I.C.S.: 311423

AGROPRODUKT A.D.
Veljka Vlahovica 35, Kraljevo, Serbia
Tel.: (381) 36 234 483
Year Founded: 1981
Sales Range: Less than $1 Million
Milk Production Services
N.A.I.C.S.: 112120

AGROPROMCREDIT JSCB
27 Str 5 Ul Electrozavodskaya, Mos-
cow, 107023, Russia
Tel.: (7) 4957558008
Web Site: http://www.apkbank.ru
Sales Range: Less than $1 Million
Commercial Banking Services
N.A.I.C.S.: 522110

AGROPUR COOPERATIVE
4600 Armand-Frappier Street, Saint-
Hubert, J3Z 1G5, QC, Canada
Tel.: (450) 878-2333   Ca
Web Site: http://www.agropur.com
Year Founded: 1938
Sales Range: $5-14.9 Billion
Emp.: 8,300
Dairy Cooperative; Milk Production &
Dairy Products Mfr & Whslr
N.A.I.C.S.: 813910
Roger Massicotte (Pres)

Subsidiaries:

Agropur Cooperative - Cheese & In-
gredients Division   (1)
510 Principale St, Granby, J2G 7G2, QC,
Canada
Tel.: (450) 375-1991
Sales Range: $25-49.9 Million
Emp.: 150
Cheese Mfr
N.A.I.C.S.: 311513

Unit (Domestic):

Agropur Cooperative - Allegro   (2)
4600 Armand-Frappier Street, Saint-Hubert,
J3Z 1G5, QC, Canada
Tel.: (450) 443-4838
Web Site: http://www.myallegro.ca
Sales Range: $125-149.9 Million
Fine Cheese Mfr
N.A.I.C.S.: 311513

Agropur Cooperative - Division Natrel
& Fresh Products   (1)
101 Roland Therrien Blvd Ste 600, Lon-
gueuil, J4H 4B9, QC, Canada
Tel.: (450) 646-1010
Web Site: http://www.agropur.com
Sales Range: $50-74.9 Million
Emp.: 250
Dairy Products Mfr & Distr
N.A.I.C.S.: 311511

Agropur Inc.   (1)
3500 E Destination Dr, Appleton, WI 54915
Tel.: (920) 944-0990
Web Site: http://www.tregafoods.com
Rev.: $74,700,000
Emp.: 260
Cheese Mfr
N.A.I.C.S.: 311513
Bill Diedrich (CFO)

Plant (Domestic):

Agropur Inc. - Little Chute (Appleton)
Plant   (2)
2701 Freedom Rd, Appleton, WI 54913-
9315
Tel.: (920) 788-2115
Web Site: http://www.tregafoods.com
Cheese Mfr
N.A.I.C.S.: 311513

Dairytown Products Limited   (1)
49 Milk Board Road Roachville, Sussex,
E4G 2G7, NB, Canada
Tel.: (506) 432-1950
Web Site: http://www.dairytown.com
Dairy Products & Butter Mfr
N.A.I.C.S.: 311512

AGROS A.D.
Ribarska 2, Opovo, Serbia
Tel.: (381) 13 681 242
Year Founded: 1998
Sales Range: $1-9.9 Million
Emp.: 58
Cereal Crop Farming Services
N.A.I.C.S.: 111998
Jovan Rackov (Exec Dir)

**AGROS DEVELOPMENT COM-
PANY PROODOS PUBLIC LTD.**
4860 Agros, Limassol, Cyprus
Tel.: (357) 25521201
Web Site:
https://www.rodonhotelcyprus.com
AGRO—(CYP)
Rev.: $2,728,675
Assets: $15,770,032
Liabilities: $7,275,150
Net Worth: $8,494,882
Earnings: $2,414,327
Fiscal Year-end: 12/31/21
Hotel Operator
N.A.I.C.S.: 721110

AGROSALGA, S.L.
C Zurbano no 43 1 izqda, E-28010,
Madrid, Spain
Tel.: (34) 913103715
Sales Range: Less than $1 Million
Emp.: 50
Grains
N.A.I.C.S.: 424510
Manuel Bermejo (Gen Mgr)

Subsidiaries:

Agroexpansion, S.A.   (1)
Centro de Transportes Benavente, PO Box
152, Nave E, Oficina 2, 49600, Benavente,
Zamora, Spain
Tel.: (34) 980638365
Leaf Tobacco Products
N.A.I.C.S.: 459991

AGROSAVEZ A.D.
Staparski put bb, Sombor, Serbia
Tel.: (381) 25 463 410
Year Founded: 1992
AGSA—(BEL)
Sales Range: Less than $1 Million
Construction Materials Whslr
N.A.I.C.S.: 423390
Mirko Rakonjac (CEO)

AGROSEME PANONIJA A.D.
Cantavirski put b.b., Subotica, Serbia
Tel.: (381) 24 566 933
Web Site: http://www.agroseme.rs
Year Founded: 1999
Sales Range: $1-9.9 Million
Emp.: 20
Seed Processing Services
N.A.I.C.S.: 115114

AGROSUPER SA
Camino La Estrella N 401 Punta de
Cortes Sector, Rancagua, O'Higgins,
Chile
Tel.: (56) 722356800

Web Site: http://www.agrosuper.com
Year Founded: 1955
Emp.: 100
Chickens, Pork, Salmon & Processed Foods Producer & Distr
N.A.I.C.S.: 112320

Subsidiaries:

Empresas AquaChile SA (1)
Cardonal s/n Lote B, Puerto Montt, 5480000, Chile
Tel.: (56) 652433500
Web Site: http://www.aquachile.com
Emp.: 100
Production & Marketing of Farmed Fish
N.A.I.C.S.: 112511

AGROTECHIMPEX JOINT STOCK COMPANY
10th Khoroo Amgalan Subdistrict, Bayanzurkh District, Ulaanbaatar, Mongolia
Tel.: (976) 11 358597
ATI—(MONG)
Assets: $634,047
Liabilities: $622,515
Net Worth: $11,533
Earnings: ($25,852)
Fiscal Year-end: 12/31/19
Transportation Services
N.A.I.C.S.: 488999

AGROTON PUBLIC LTD
Ilinskaya Street 8 Bts Illins Kyy The Third Entrance Fourth Floor, Kiev, Ukraine
Tel.: (380) 445945159 UA
Web Site:
https://www.agroton.com.ua
Year Founded: 1992
AGT—(WAR)
Rev.: $67,556,000
Assets: $120,337,000
Liabilities: $18,768,000
Net Worth: $101,569,000
Earnings: $11,759,000
Emp.: 1,779
Fiscal Year-end: 12/31/20
Grain Growing, Livestock Farming & Food Processing Operations
N.A.I.C.S.: 111191
Iurii Zhuravlov (Founder & CEO)

Subsidiaries:

ALLC Shiykivske (1)
Vul Kalinina 4 Harkivska Obl, 63809, Shvaykovka, Ukraine
Tel.: (380) 575962216
Crop Farming Services
N.A.I.C.S.: 111998

CJSC Agroton (1)
50 let Oborony Luhanska 9, Luhans'k, 91045, Ukraine
Tel.: (380) 642345379
Web Site: http://www.agrotonlg.ua
Crop Farming & Land Cultivation Services
N.A.I.C.S.: 111998

AGROVET A.D.
Srpskih Vladara 65, 23270, Melenci, Serbia
Tel.: (381) 23731607
Web Site: https://www.agrovet.co.rs
Year Founded: 1991
Sales Range: $1-9.9 Million
Perennial Farming Services
N.A.I.C.S.: 111421

AGROVOJVODINA EXPORT - IMPORT A.D.
Bulevar oslobodenja 127, Novi Sad, Serbia
Tel.: (381) 212100731
Year Founded: 1946
AGEX—(BEL)
Sales Range: Less than $1 Million
Emp.: 22

Plumbing & Heating Equipment Whslr
N.A.I.C.S.: 423720
Nenad Rakic (Exec Dir)

AGROVOJVODINA KOMERC-SERVIS AD
Bulevar Oslobodenja 127, 21000, Novi Sad, Serbia
Tel.: (381) 21450568021
Web Site:
http://www.komercservis.co.rs
Raw Material Merchant Distr
N.A.I.C.S.: 424590

AGROVRSAC A.D.
Belocrkvanski put bb, Vrsac, Serbia
Tel.: (381) 13806073
Web Site:
https://www.agrovrsac.co.rs
Year Founded: 1990
Sales Range: $1-9.9 Million
Emp.: 55
Crop Farming & Livestock Production Services
N.A.I.C.S.: 112990

AGS AUTOMOTIVE SYSTEMS
200 Yorkland Blvd Suite 800, Toronto, M2J 5C1, ON, Canada
Tel.: (416) 438-6650
Web Site:
http://www.agsautomotive.com
Year Founded: 1947
Sales Range: $250-299.9 Million
Emp.: 1,200
Automotive Metal Stamping Plating Painting Plastics Sequencing & Assembly Services
N.A.I.C.S.: 336370

Subsidiaries:

AGS Automotive Systems - Cambridge Plant (1)
560 Conestoga Blvd, Cambridge, N1R 7L7, ON, Canada
Tel.: (519) 621-7953
Automobile Parts Mfr
N.A.I.C.S.: 336390

AGS Automotive Systems - Oshawa Plant (1)
901 Simcoe St S, Oshawa, L1H 4L2, ON, Canada
Tel.: (905) 571-2121
Automobile Parts Mfr
N.A.I.C.S.: 336390

AGS Automotive Systems - Sterling Heights Plant (1)
6640 Sterling Dr S 6690 & 6710 Sterling Dr N, Sterling Heights, MI 48312
Tel.: (586) 268-4888
Automobile Parts Mfr
N.A.I.C.S.: 336390

AGS Automotive Systems - Windsor Plant (1)
275 Eugenie St E, Windsor, N8X 2X9, ON, Canada
Tel.: (519) 969-5193
Automobile Parts Mfr
N.A.I.C.S.: 336390

AGS CORPORATION
4-3-25 Harigaya, Urawa-ku, Saitama, 3300075, Japan
Tel.: (81) 488256000
Web Site: https://www.ags.co.jp
Year Founded: 1971
3648—(TKS)
Rev.: $146,028,120
Assets: $137,620,200
Liabilities: $46,058,480
Net Worth: $91,561,720
Earnings: $6,186,960
Emp.: 1,050
Fiscal Year-end: 03/31/24
Computer Related Services
N.A.I.C.S.: 541519
Toshiki Hara (CEO)

Subsidiaries:

AGS Business Computer Co., Ltd. (1)
1-299-12 Kitabukurocho Fuji Saitama Shin-toshin Building West Building, Omiya-ku, Saitama, 330-0835, Japan
Tel.: (81) 486776020
Web Site: http://www.ags-bc.co.jp
Emp.: 131
Computer Software Consulting Services
N.A.I.C.S.: 541512

AGS Pro Service Co., Ltd. (1)
Sakura Urawa Building 4-2-11 Harigaya, Urawa-ku, Saitama, 330-0075, Japan (100%)
Tel.: (81) 488255462
Web Site: https://www.ags-ps.co.jp
Emp.: 565
Business Process Outsourcing Services
N.A.I.C.S.: 561449
Kozo Tanuma (Pres)

AGS System Advisory Co., Ltd. (1)
Hariketani 4-2-11 Sakura Urawa building, Urawa Ward, Saitama, 330-0075, Japan
Tel.: (81) 488256039
Web Site: http://www.ags-sa.co.jp
Information Technology Consulting Services
N.A.I.C.S.: 541512

AGS TRANSACT TECHNOLO-GIES LTD.
601-602 B-Wing Trade World Kamala City Senapati Bapat Marg, Lower Parel, Mumbai, 400 013, India
Tel.: (91) 22 6781 2000
Web Site: http://www.agsttl.com
Year Founded: 1992
ATM & Point-of-Sale Equipment & Solutions
N.A.I.C.S.: 561439
Ravi B. Goyal (Chm & Mng Dir)

AGSTAR PLC
No 93 Minuwangoda Road, Colombo, Sri Lanka
Tel.: (94) 114812424
Web Site: https://agstaragri.lk
Year Founded: 2002
AGST.X0000—(COL)
Rev.: $24,826,754
Assets: $29,793,191
Liabilities: $5,801,666
Net Worth: $23,991,524
Earnings: $5,523,021
Emp.: 152
Fiscal Year-end: 03/31/23
Chemical Fertiliser Mfr
N.A.I.C.S.: 325998
D. N. N. Lokuge (Founder & Chm)

AGT FOOD AND INGREDI-ENTS INC.
6200 E Primrose Green Dr, Regina, S4V 3L7, SK, Canada
Tel.: (306) 525-4490 ON
Web Site: http://www.agtfoods.com
Year Founded: 2004
Rev.: $1,382,312,271
Assets: $955,136,901
Liabilities: $660,197,064
Net Worth: $294,939,837
Earnings: ($29,412,493)
Emp.: 2,100
Fiscal Year-end: 12/31/17
Food & Food Ingredient Processing & Sales
N.A.I.C.S.: 111199
Murad Al-Katib (Pres & CEO)

Subsidiaries:

A. Poortman (London) Ltd. (1)
83-85 Mansell Street, London, E1 8AN, United Kingdom
Tel.: (44) 20 7264 5000
Food Ingredients Processing & Sales
N.A.I.C.S.: 311999

AGT Foods Australia Pty Ltd. (1)

22 Pysent Street, PO Box 838, Horsham, 3400, VIC, Australia
Tel.: (61) 3 5382 4908
Cereal Pulses Whslr
N.A.I.C.S.: 424490
Murid Alkatib (CEO)

Alliance Grain Traders (Tianjin) Co. Ltd. (1)
No 97 Huanhexi Road Airport Economic Area, Tianjin, China
Tel.: (86) 22 2352 1777
Food Ingredients Processing & Sales
N.A.I.C.S.: 311999

Alliance Pulse Processors Inc. (1)
South Tower Road Suite 1, Regina, S4N 7K9, SK, Canada
Tel.: (306) 525-4490
Web Site: http://www.alliancegrain.com
Sales Range: $10-24.9 Million
Emp.: 40
Crops Export Services
N.A.I.C.S.: 115114

Arbel Group (1)
Yeni Mahalle Cumhuriyet Bulvari No 73/4, Kazanli, 33281, Mersin, Turkiye
Tel.: (90) 324 241 1111
Food & Food Ingredient Processing & Sales
N.A.I.C.S.: 311999

Saskcan Horizon Trading Inc. (1)
PO Box 340, Aberdeen, S0K 0A0, SK, Canada
Tel.: (306) 253-4233
Web Site: http://www.saskcan.com
Sales Range: $25-49.9 Million
Emp.: 25
Cereal Pulses Whslr
N.A.I.C.S.: 424490

United Pulse Trading Inc. (1)
1611 E Century Ave Ste 102, Bismarck, ND 58503-0780
Tel.: (701) 751-1623
Web Site: http://www.agtfoods.com
Sales Range: $50-74.9 Million
Emp.: 15
Cereal Pulses Suppliers
N.A.I.C.S.: 424490
Eric Bartsch (Gen Mgr)

AGTHIA GROUP PJSC
Sky Tower 17th Floor Al Reem Island, PO Box 37725, Abu Dhabi, United Arab Emirates
Tel.: (971) 25960600
Web Site: https://www.agthia.com
Year Founded: 2004
AGTHIA—(ABU)
Rev.: $1,241,889,039
Assets: $1,807,969,966
Liabilities: $938,457,049
Net Worth: $869,512,918
Earnings: $81,566,109
Emp.: 11,726
Fiscal Year-end: 12/31/23
Food & Beverages Mfr
N.A.I.C.S.: 311999
Thorbjorn Thorbjornsen (Sr VP-Strategy)

Subsidiaries:

Agthia Group Egypt LLC (1)
7th industrial Area Al Menoufiya Governorate, 07198, Sadat City, Egypt
Tel.: (20) 482625500
Food Mfr & Distr
N.A.I.C.S.: 311999

Al Ain Food & Beverages PJSC (1)
PO Box 16020, Al Ain, United Arab Emirates
Tel.: (971) 37083700
Food Mfr & Distr
N.A.I.C.S.: 311999
Hanif Shaikh (Area Mgr-Sls)

Al Foah Company LLC (1)
PO Box 18454, 800 5551, Al Ain, United Arab Emirates
Tel.: (971) 37018888
Web Site: https://alfoah.com
Dates Product Mfr & Distr
N.A.I.C.S.: 311423

Agthia Group PJSC—(Continued)

Al Manal Purification & Bottling of Mineral Water LLC (1)
PO Box 413, Al Hamriya, 131, Muscat, Oman
Tel.: (968) 24504464
Bottled Drinking Water Mfr
N.A.I.C.S.: 311999

Al Nabil Food Industries LLC (1)
Abdullah Ghosheh St, Amman, Jordan
Tel.: (962) 64022004
Web Site: https://nabilfoods.com
Emp.: 800
Protein Food Product Mfr & Distr
N.A.I.C.S.: 311412

Baklawa Made Better Investments LLC (1)
Dubai Investment Park Jebel Ali, Dubai, United Arab Emirates
Tel.: (971) 48833940
Web Site: https://www.bmb-group.com
Sweet Mfr & Distr
N.A.I.C.S.: 311919

Grand Mills Company PJSC (1)
Mina Zayed Port, PO Box 46622, Abu Dhabi, United Arab Emirates
Tel.: (971) 26969111
Web Site: https://www.grandmillsuae.com
Health Food Supplement Distr
N.A.I.C.S.: 424210

AGUA Y SANEAMIENTOS AR-GENTINOS, S.A.
Calle Tucuman 752, Buenos Aires, 1049, Argentina
Tel.: (54) 1163190000
Web Site: http://www.aysa.com.ar
Sales Range: $1-4.9 Billion
Emp.: 3,800
Water Supply & Treatment Services
N.A.I.C.S.: 221310
Carlos Humberto Ben (Pres)

AGUIA RESOURCES LIMITED
Level 12 680 George Street, Sydney, 2000, NSW, Australia
Tel.: (61) 419960560
Web Site:
    https://www.aguiaresources.com.au
Year Founded: 2007
AGR—(ASX)
Rev.: $6,526
Assets: $24,894,357
Liabilities: $623,365
Net Worth: $24,270,991
Earnings: ($3,869,816)
Fiscal Year-end: 06/30/24
Mineral Mining Services
N.A.I.C.S.: 212290
Warwick Grigor (Chm)

Subsidiaries:

Aguia Metais Ltda (1)
Rua Ceara 390, Sao Pedro do Parana, 87955-000, Parana, Brazil
Tel.: (55) 34644000
Web Site: https://www.aguiametais.com.br
Metal Products Mfr
N.A.I.C.S.: 332999

AGUILA COPPER CORP.
1305 1090 West Georgia Street, Vancouver, V6E 3V7, BC, Canada
Tel.: (604) 685-9316
Web Site: http://www.aguilagold.com
Year Founded: 1997
AGL—(TSXV)
Rev.: $7,817
Assets: $1,928,934
Liabilities: $110,671
Net Worth: $1,818,262
Earnings: ($667,728)
Fiscal Year-end: 04/30/21
Mineral Exploration Services
N.A.I.C.S.: 213114
Nick DeMare (CEO & Interim & CFO)

AGUNG PODOMORO LAND TBK
APL Tower 43rd Floor Podomoro City Jl Let Jend S Parman Kav 28, Jakarta, 11470, Indonesia
Tel.: (62) 2129034567　　Id
Web Site:
    https://www.agungpodomoro.com
Year Founded: 2004
APLN—(INDO)
Rev.: $303,701,774
Assets: $1,839,591,202
Liabilities: $966,056,994
Net Worth: $873,534,207
Earnings: $75,623,849
Emp.: 1,008
Fiscal Year-end: 12/31/23
Real Estate Development Services
N.A.I.C.S.: 531390
Noer Indradjaja (Vice Chm)

Subsidiaries:

PT Kencana Unggul sukses (1)
Jl Pluit Karang Ayu, Jakarta, 14450, Indonesia
Tel.: (62) 21 662 1888
Web Site: https://www.greenbaypluit.com
Residential Apartment Services
N.A.I.C.S.: 531110

AGV GROUP LIMITED
22 Benoi Road, Singapore, 629892, Singapore
Tel.: (65) 67358222　　SG
Web Site:
    http://www.agvgroup.com.sg
Year Founded: 2012
1A4—(SES)
Rev.: $7,749,767
Assets: $14,764,193
Liabilities: $17,421,688
Net Worth: ($2,657,494)
Earnings: ($2,099,572)
Emp.: 110
Fiscal Year-end: 09/30/20
Investment Holding Services
N.A.I.C.S.: 551112
Albert Ang (Co-Founder)

Subsidiaries:

AGV Galvanizing (M) Sdn. Bhd. (1)
No Plo 151 Jalan Nibong 1/1 Kawasan Perindustrian Tanjung Langsat, 81700, Pasir Gudang, Johor, Malaysia
Tel.: (60) 72529288
Fabricated Metal Products Mfr
N.A.I.C.S.: 332999

AGV PRODUCTS CORP.
No 11 Kung Yeh Second Rd Min Hsiong Industrial Zone, Chiayi, Taiwan
Tel.: (886) 52211521
Web Site: https://www.agv.com.tw
Year Founded: 1971
1217—(TAI)
Rev.: $132,529,084
Assets: $395,368,833
Liabilities: $173,016,573
Net Worth: $222,352,259
Earnings: $6,571,045
Emp.: 607
Fiscal Year-end: 12/31/23
Food Products Mfr
N.A.I.C.S.: 311999
Chen Zhizhan (Pres)

AGVA CORPORATION LIMITED
Block 625 Aljunied Road, 04-07 Aljunied Industrial Complex, Singapore, 389836, Singapore
Tel.: (65) 6743 1232
Web Site: http://www.agvagroup.com
Year Founded: 1983
Media Storage Products, Lifestyle Accessories & Plastic Products Mfr
N.A.I.C.S.: 325211

Vic Tan (Officer-Sls)

Subsidiaries:

AGVA Singapore Pte Ltd (1)
63 Kaki Bukit Place, Singapore, 416234, Singapore
Tel.: (65) 67431232
Web Site: http://www.agvagroup.com
Sales Range: $25-49.9 Million
Emp.: 6
Electronic Products & Components Mfr
N.A.I.C.S.: 335999

AH INDUSTRIES A/S
Industrivej 4, Ribe, DK 6760, Denmark
Tel.: (45) 75577000　　DK
Web Site: http://www.ah-industries.com
Year Founded: 1987
Metal Component Mfr
N.A.I.C.S.: 332999
Mette Thomsen (Mgr-Grp Fin)

AH-VEST LIMITED
15 Misgund Road, PO Box 100, Eikenhof, Johannesburg, 1872, South Africa
Tel.: (27) 119489949　　ZA
Web Site: https://www.alljoy.co.za
Year Founded: 1988
AHL—(JSE)
Rev.: $11,028,847
Assets: $7,963,255
Liabilities: $5,533,202
Net Worth: $2,430,054
Earnings: $76,360
Fiscal Year-end: 06/30/23
Spice Mfr
N.A.I.C.S.: 311941
Ismail Ebrahim Darsot (Chm & CEO)

AHA CO., LTD.
67 Hwanggeum-ro 109beon-gil, Yangchon-eup, Gimpo, Gyeonggi-do, Korea (South)
Tel.: (82) 15440878
Web Site: https://www.i-aha.com
Year Founded: 1999
102950—(KRS)
Electronic Component Mfr & Distr
N.A.I.C.S.: 334419
Gu Ki-Do (CEO)

AHASOLAR TECHNOLOGIES LIMITED
207 Kalasagar Mall Nr Sattadhar Cross Road, Ghatlodia, Ahmedabad, 380061, Gujarat, India
Tel.: (91) 7940394029
Web Site: https://www.ahasolar.in
Year Founded: 2017
543941—(BOM)
Rev.: $2,531,020
Assets: $631,270
Liabilities: $147,852
Net Worth: $483,418
Earnings: $193,581
Fiscal Year-end: 03/31/23
Electrical Equipment Mfr & Distr
N.A.I.C.S.: 333414
Ranjan Baheti (CMO)

AHB HOLDINGS BERHAD
Suite 10 02 Level 10 The Gardens South Tower Mid Valley City, Lingkaran Syed Putra, 59200, Kuala Lumpur, Malaysia
Tel.: (60) 322980263
Web Site: http://www.ahb.com.my
AHB—(KLS)
Rev.: $2,159,563
Assets: $7,317,066
Liabilities: $1,382,339
Net Worth: $5,934,727
Earnings: ($1,924,129)
Fiscal Year-end: 09/30/22

Office Interior Products Sales
N.A.I.C.S.: 541410
Yoke Keong Yong (CEO & Mng Dir)

Subsidiaries:

AHB Distribution Sdn. Bhd. (1)
No 17 Jalan Industri PBP 11 Pusat Bandar, 47100, Puchong, Selangor, Malaysia
Tel.: (60) 3 8061 7171
Sales Range: $25-49.9 Million
Emp.: 30
Office Furniture Whslr
N.A.I.C.S.: 423210

AHB Technology Sdn. Bhd. (1)
17 Jalan Industri Pbp 11 Pusat Bandar Puchong, Puchong, 47100, Selangor, Malaysia
Tel.: (60) 358822882
Web Site: http://www.artwright.com
Sales Range: $50-74.9 Million
Emp.: 75
Office Equipment Whslr
N.A.I.C.S.: 423420
Yee Ping Chua (Gen Mgr & Sr Mgr)

AHC GROUP, INC.
2-11-9 Iwamotocho, Chiyoda-Ku, Tokyo, 101-0032, Japan
Tel.: (81) 362409550
Web Site: https://www.ahc.co.jp
Year Founded: 2010
7083—(TKS)
Rev.: $41,937,350
Assets: $37,194,140
Liabilities: $28,991,010
Net Worth: $8,203,130
Earnings: $475,030
Emp.: 1,500
Fiscal Year-end: 11/30/23
Restaurant Operators
N.A.I.C.S.: 722511
Yoshitaka Araki (Founder, Chm & Pres)

AHC LIMITED
Suite 30202 Lvl 2 Southport Central Tower 3 9 Lawson Street, Southport, 4215, QLD, Australia
Tel.: (61) 755732666
Web Site: http://www.ahc.com.au
Rev.: $1,792,774
Assets: $38,372,533
Liabilities: $16,103,534
Net Worth: $22,268,999
Earnings: ($113,701)
Emp.: 10
Fiscal Year-end: 06/30/19
Building Development
N.A.I.C.S.: 236116
Sheryl Anne Macleod (Exec Dir)

AHEARN & SOPER INC.
100 Woodbine Downs Boulevard, Etobicoke, Toronto, M9W 5S6, ON, Canada
Tel.: (416) 675-3999　　ON
Web Site: http://www.ahearn.com
Year Founded: 1881
Sales Range: $25-49.9 Million
Emp.: 150
Computer Scanner Printer & Label Applicator Mfr
N.A.I.C.S.: 334118

Subsidiaries:

Ahearn & Soper Inc. (1)
3375 Rue Griffith, Saint Laurent, H4T 1W5, QC, Canada
Tel.: (514) 341-7671
Sales Range: $25-49.9 Million
Emp.: 10
Industrial Barcode Equipment Including Barcode Computers, Scanners, Printers & Label Applicators Sales & Services
N.A.I.C.S.: 811210

Ahearn & Soper Inc. (1)
380 Jamieson Parkway Unit 4, Cambridge, N3C 4N4, ON, Canada
Tel.: (519) 885-2260

Web Site: http://www.ahearn.com
Sales Range: $25-49.9 Million
Emp.: 5
Industrial Barcode Equipment Including Barcode Computer Scanner Printer & Label Applicator Sale & Services
N.A.I.C.S.: 811210

Ahearn & Soper Inc. (1)
2915 19th Street Northeast Bay 1, Calgary, T2E 7A2, AB, Canada
Tel.: (403) 291-0300
Web Site: http://www.ahearn.com
Sales Range: $25-49.9 Million
Emp.: 5
Industrial Barcode Equipment Including Barcode Computers, Scanners, Printers & Label Applicators Sales & Services
N.A.I.C.S.: 811210

Ahearn & Soper Inc. (1)
6695 E Clyde Rd, Howell, MI 48855-8070
Tel.: (248) 489-1950
Web Site: http://www.ahern.com
Sales Range: $25-49.9 Million
Emp.: 60
Industrial Barcode Equipment Including Barcode Computers, Scanners, Printers & Label Applicators Mfr, Sales & Services
N.A.I.C.S.: 334118

Ahearn & Soper Inc. (1)
38 Antares Drive Suite 110, Ottawa, K2E 7V2, ON, Canada
Tel.: (613) 226-4520
Web Site: http://www.ahearn.com
Emp.: 3
Industrial Barcode Equipment Including Barcode Computers, Scanners, Printers & Label Applicators Sales
N.A.I.C.S.: 423430

AHEIM CAPITAL GMBH
Theatinerstrasse 7, 80333, Munich, Germany
Tel.: (49) 8945246790
Web Site: http://www.aheim.com
Private Equity Firm Services
N.A.I.C.S.: 523999
Frank Henkelmann (Mng Dir)

AHIMSA INDUSTRIES LIMITED
160 Devraj Industrial Park Village Piplaj Piplaj-Pirana Road, Ahmedabad, 382405, India
Tel.: (91) 9725817733
Web Site:
https://www.ahimsaind.com
AHIMSA—(NSE)
Rev.: $3,019,794
Assets: $3,248,827
Liabilities: $1,430,981
Net Worth: $1,817,845
Earnings: $12,605
Emp.: 21
Fiscal Year-end: 03/31/21
Plastic Materials Mfr
N.A.I.C.S.: 325211
Ashutosh Damubhai Gandhi (Founder & Mng Dir)

AHJIKAN CO., LTD.
7-3-9 Shoko-center, Nishi-ku, Hiroshima, 733-8677, Japan
Tel.: (81) 822774539
Web Site: https://www.ahjikan.co.jp
Year Founded: 1965
2907—(TKS)
Rev.: $332,086,400
Assets: $182,700,400
Liabilities: $77,971,560
Net Worth: $104,728,840
Earnings: $9,974,490
Emp.: 880
Fiscal Year-end: 03/31/24
Food Products Mfr
N.A.I.C.S.: 311991
Keiichi Ashikaga (Chm)

AHLADA ENGINEERS LIMITED
Survey No 66 - 68 Satyam St, Bahadurpally Village Satyam St Gandi

Maisamma, Hyderabad, 500043, Telangana, India
Tel.: (91) 9866500811
Web Site: https://www.ahlada.com
Year Founded: 2005
AHLADA—(NSE)
Rev.: $21,732,343
Assets: $31,744,610
Liabilities: $15,500,135
Net Worth: $16,244,476
Earnings: $1,390,695
Emp.: 258
Fiscal Year-end: 03/31/21
Steel Door Mfr
N.A.I.C.S.: 332321
Koduru Iswara Varaprasad Reddy (Chm)

AHLI BANK QPSC
Salwa ST, Doha, Qatar
Tel.: (974) 44205222
Web Site:
https://www.ahlibank.com.qa
ABQK—(QE)
Rev.: $503,275,815
Assets: $12,038,386,054
Liabilities: $10,404,924,334
Net Worth: $1,633,461,721
Earnings: $185,101,622
Emp.: 420
Fiscal Year-end: 12/31/19
Commericial Banking
N.A.I.C.S.: 522110
Mahmoud Yahya Malkawi (CEO-Acting)

AHLI BANK S.A.O.G.
Mina Al Fahal, PO Box 545, 116, Muscat, Oman
Tel.: (968) 24577177 OM
Web Site: https://www.ahlibank.com
Year Founded: 1997
ABOB—(MUS)
Rev.: $371,552,507
Assets: $8,619,301,786
Liabilities: $7,264,996,482
Net Worth: $1,354,305,304
Earnings: $94,682,979
Emp.: 943
Fiscal Year-end: 12/31/23
Banking Services
N.A.I.C.S.: 522110
Hamdan Ali Nasser Al Hinai (Chm)

AHLIA INSURANCE COMPANY (S.A.)
sec 904 st 80 house 10/1 Hai -AlWahda, Breha, Baghdad, Iraq
Tel.: (964) 7821760544
Web Site: http://www.aic-iraq.com
Year Founded: 2001
NAHF—(IRAQ)
Sales Range: Less than $1 Million
Insurance Management Services
N.A.I.C.S.: 524298
Yesar Farook Al-Mallak (Mng Dir)

AHLSELL AB
Liljeholmsvagen 30, Stockholm, 11798, Sweden
Tel.: (46) 86857000 SE
Web Site: http://www.ahlsell.com
Sales Range: $1-4.9 Billion
Emp.: 4,500
Holding Company; Installation Products, Tools & Machinery Distr
N.A.I.C.S.: 551112
Rikard Froberg (Head-Business Development)

Subsidiaries:

AS FEB (1)
Forelli 4, Tallinn, 10621, Estonia
Tel.: (372) 654 85 00
Web Site: http://www.feb.ee
Sanitary Ware Whslr
N.A.I.C.S.: 423720

Ahlsell ApS (1)
Abildager 24, 2605, Brondby, Denmark
Tel.: (45) 43241700
Web Site: https://www.ahlsell.com
Heating Equipment Retailer
N.A.I.C.S.: 423720

Ahlsell Danmark ApS (1)
Abildager 24, 2605, Brondby, Denmark
Tel.: (45) 43444299
Web Site: http://www.ahlsell.dk
Sales Range: $25-49.9 Million
Emp.: 55
Heating, Sanitation & Construction Services
N.A.I.C.S.: 238220
Henrik Lohse (Mgr-Sls)

Subsidiary (Domestic):

Sanistal A/S (2)
Handvaerkervej 14, 9000, Aalborg, Denmark (75.49%)
Tel.: (45) 96306000
Web Site: http://www.sanistaal.com
Rev.: $577,513,902
Assets: $324,428,578
Liabilities: $225,105,959
Net Worth: $99,322,619
Earnings: $2,773,176
Emp.: 1,185
Fiscal Year-end: 12/31/2021
Metal Tool Product Mfr
N.A.I.C.S.: 333515
Christian B. Lund (CEO)

Ahlsell Norway AS (1)
Kvaenv 4, PO Box 184, Stavanger, 4065, Norway
Tel.: (47) 69236150
Web Site: http://www.ahlsell.no
Sales Range: $50-74.9 Million
Emp.: 250
Tiles Mfr
N.A.I.C.S.: 326211

Ahlsell Oy (1)
Kallionopontie 1, Hyvinkaa, 05620, Finland
Tel.: (358) 205845000
Web Site: http://www.ahlsell.fi
Sales Range: $25-49.9 Million
Emp.: 12
Tiles Mfr
N.A.I.C.S.: 326211
Mika Salokangas (Mng Dir)

Ahlsell Sverige AB (1)
117 98 Stockholm Besoksadress Arstaangsvagen 11, 117 43, Stockholm, Sweden
Tel.: (46) 86857000
Web Site: https://www.ahlsell.se
Construction Product Distr
N.A.I.C.S.: 423390

Gelia Industri AB (1)
Industrigatan, PO Box 214, 467 40, Grastorp, Sweden
Tel.: (46) 51458800
Web Site: http://www.gelia.se
Sales Range: $25-49.9 Million
Emp.: 50
Tiles Mfr
N.A.I.C.S.: 326211
Mikael Olsson (Dir-Sls)

Tempcold Sp. z o. o. (1)
ul Burleska 3, 01-939, Warsaw, Poland
Tel.: (48) 22835550001
Web Site: https://www.tempcold.com.pl
Air Conditioning Services
N.A.I.C.S.: 238220

VVS Trading A/S (1)
Ellegardsvej 30, DK 6400, Sonderborg, Denmark
Tel.: (45) 74430200
Web Site: http://www.vvs-trading.dk
Sales Range: $50-74.9 Million
Emp.: 175
Tiles Mfr
N.A.I.C.S.: 326211

ZAO Ahlsell Spb (1)
Rentgena 5, Box 7001, 190000, Saint Petersburg, Russia
Tel.: (7) 8123252424
Web Site: http://www.ahlsell.ru
Sales Range: $25-49.9 Million
Emp.: 50
Tiles Mfr
N.A.I.C.S.: 326211

Alexander Boyarko (Mgr-Sls)

AHLSTROM CAPITAL OY
Etelaesplanadi 14, PO Box 169, 00131, Helsinki, Finland
Tel.: (358) 1088818 FI
Web Site:
http://www.ahlstromcapital.com
Equity Investment Firm
N.A.I.C.S.: 523999
Tero Telaranta (Dir-Industrial Investments)

Subsidiaries:

Ahlstrom-Munksjo Oyj (1)
Alvar Aallon katu 3 C, PO BOX 329, 00101, Helsinki, Finland (36%)
Tel.: (358) 108880
Web Site: http://www.ahlstrom-munksjo.com
Rev.: $3,295,736,392
Assets: $3,836,284,816
Liabilities: $2,381,311,712
Net Worth: $1,454,973,104
Earnings: $116,068,680
Emp.: 7,814
Fiscal Year-end: 12/31/2020
Fiber-based Materials Mfr; Specialty Paper Mfr
N.A.I.C.S.: 322120
Dan Adrianzon (Exec VP-Industrial Solutions)

Subsidiary (Non-US):

Ahlstrom Asia Holdings Pte Ltd (2)
14 Ann Siang Road 02-01, Singapore, 69694, Singapore
Tel.: (65) 6861 2700
Web Site: http://www.ahlstrom-munksjo.com
Investment Management Service
N.A.I.C.S.: 523999

Subsidiary (Non-US):

Ahlstrom-Munksjo Fibercomposites (Binzhou) Limited (3)
Ahlstrom Binzhou No 209 Huanghe 5 Road, Binzhou, 256600, Shangdong, China
Tel.: (86) 543 340 9777
Web Site: http://www.ahlstrom-munksjo.com
Paper Products Mfr
N.A.I.C.S.: 322299

Ahlstrom-Munksjo Korea Co., Ltd. (3)
7 Keum Li Yuga Myoun Talsung County, Daegu, 711-882, Korea (South)
Tel.: (82) 536600491
Web Site: http://www.ahlstrom-munksjo.com
Automotive Filter Papers Mfr & Sales
N.A.I.C.S.: 322211

Subsidiary (Domestic):

Ahlstrom Seoul Co. Ltd (4)
Room 601 Kanglim Building 448-7 Seongnae-dong, Gangdong-gu, Seoul, 134884, Korea (South)
Tel.: (82) 2 3452 7314
Web Site: http://www.ahlstrom-munksjo.com
Pulp Paper Products Mfr & Distr
N.A.I.C.S.: 322120

Subsidiary (Non-US):

Ahlstrom-Munksjo Paper (Taicang) Co., Ltd. (3)
No 90 Fada Rd, Taicang Economic Development Area, Taicang, 215413, Jiangsu, China
Tel.: (86) 51253986618
Web Site: http://www.ahlstrom-munksjo.com
Insulation & Specialty Paper Mfr
N.A.I.C.S.: 322120

Ahlstrom-Munksjo Paper Trading (Shanghai) Co., Ltd. (3)
Unit BC 11F/L East Tower No 666 East Beijing Road, Huangpu District, Shanghai, 200001, China
Tel.: (86) 2123307330
Insulation & Specialty Paper Mfr
N.A.I.C.S.: 322120

PT Ahlstrom Indonesia (3)
Haryono Square-3rd Floor Room 303 MT Haryono Kav 10, 13330, Jakarta Timur, Indonesia

Ahlstrom Capital Oy—(Continued)

Tel.: (62) 2129067150
Insulation & Specialty Paper Mfr
N.A.I.C.S.: 322120

Subsidiary (Non-US):

Ahlstrom Munksjo Fiber Composites India Private Ltd. (2)
Mundra Sez Textile & Apparel Park Plot No 7 Survey No 141, Mudra Kutch, Gujarat, 370 421, India
Tel.: (91) 2838 619100
Web Site: http://www.ahlstrom-munksjo.com
Fiber Composite Materials Mfr
N.A.I.C.S.: 322219

Ahlstrom Munksjo Fiber Composites India Private Ltd. (2)
Mundra Sez Textile and Apparel Park MI-TAP Plot No 7 Survey No 141, Mundra, Kutch, 370 421, Gujarat, India
Tel.: (91) 2838619100
Insulation & Specialty Paper Mfr
N.A.I.C.S.: 322120

Ahlstrom Research and Services SA (2)
Immeuble Perigares B 201 Rue Carnot, 94127, Fontenay-sous-Bois, France
Tel.: (33) 4 74 57 29 29
Paper Products Mfr
N.A.I.C.S.: 322299

Subsidiary (Domestic):

Ahlstrom Sales Helsinki Oy (2)
Alvar Aallon katu 3 C, PO Box 329, DI-00101, Helsinki, Finland
Tel.: (358) 10 8880
Specialty Papers & Packaging Materials Distr
N.A.I.C.S.: 424130

Subsidiary (Non-US):

Ahlstrom-Munksjo AB (2)
Barnarpsgatan 39 41, 553 33, Jonkoping, Sweden
Tel.: (46) 36303300
Insulation & Specialty Paper Mfr
N.A.I.C.S.: 322120

Ahlstrom-Munksjo Apprieu S.A.S. (2)
Centre De recherche Apprieu 40 Rue Du Grand Champ, Apprieu, 38140, Isere, France
Tel.: (33) 476937271
Insulation & Specialty Paper Mfr
N.A.I.C.S.: 322120

Ahlstrom-Munksjo Arches S.A.S. (2)
48 Route de Remiremont, Arches, 88380, Les Marches, France
Tel.: (33) 329326000
Insulation & Specialty Paper Mfr
N.A.I.C.S.: 327910

Ahlstrom-Munksjo Aspa Bruk AB (2)
Fabriksvagen, Aspabruk, 696 80, Orebro, Sweden
Tel.: (46) 58381500
Insulation & Specialty Paper Mfr
N.A.I.C.S.: 322120

Ahlstrom-Munksjo Brasil Ltda. (2)
Rua Armando Steck 770 Bairro Capivari, CEP 13290-000, Louveira, Brazil
Tel.: (55) 19 3878 9238
Mfr & Sales of Specialty Fiber-Based Materials
N.A.I.C.S.: 322120

Subsidiary (Domestic):

Ahlstrom Brasil Ltda. (3)
Rua Armando Steck 770-Bairro Capivari, 13290-000, Louveira, Brazil
Tel.: (55) 1938789238
Insulation & Specialty Paper Mfr
N.A.I.C.S.: 322120

Ahlstrom-Munksjo Brasil Industria e Comercio de Papeis Especiais Ltda. (3)
Rod Euryale De Jesus Zerbine S/N P 66 Km 84, Predio Industrial Paper Jardim Sao Gabriel, Jacarei, 12340-010, Sao Paulo, Brazil
Tel.: (55) 1221279300

Insulation & Specialty Paper Mfr
N.A.I.C.S.: 327910

Plant (Domestic):

Ahlstrom-Munksjo Oyj - Caieiras Plant (3)
Rod Pres Tancredo A Neves Km 34, PO Box 21, Caieiras, 07705-000, Sao Paulo, Brazil
Tel.: (55) 1144417800
Insulation & Specialty Paper Mfr
N.A.I.C.S.: 322120

Ahlstrom-Munksjo Oyj - Jacarei Plant (3)
Rod Euryale De Jesus Zerbine SN SP 66 Km 84 Jardim Sao Gabriel, Jacarei, 12340-010, Sao Paulo, Brazil
Tel.: (55) 1221279300
Insulation & Specialty Paper Mfr
N.A.I.C.S.: 322120

Ahlstrom-Munksjo Oyj - Louveira Plant (3)
Rua Armando Steck 770 Bairro Capivari, Louveira, 13290-000, Sao Paulo, Brazil
Tel.: (55) 1938789200
Insulation & Specialty Paper Mfr
N.A.I.C.S.: 322120

Subsidiary (Non-US):

Ahlstrom-Munksjo Brignoud SAS (2)
Rue Alfred Fredet, 38196, Brignoud, France
Tel.: (33) 4 7645 3515
Web Site: http://www.ahlstrom-munksjo.com
Paper Products Mfr
N.A.I.C.S.: 322299

Ahlstrom-Munksjo Chirnside Ltd. (2)
Chirnside, Duns, TD11 3JW, Berwickshire, United Kingdom
Tel.: (44) 1890818303
Web Site: http://www.ahlstrom-munksjo.com
Filters, Medical Fabrics, Life Science & Diagnostics, Wallcoverings, Tapes & Food & Beverage Packaging Mfr
N.A.I.C.S.: 322211

Plant (Domestic):

Ahlstrom-Munksjo Chirnside Limited - Manchester Plant (3)
Mount Sion Works Sion Street, Manchester, M26 3SB, United Kingdom
Tel.: (44) 1617255320
Insulation & Specialty Paper Mfr
N.A.I.C.S.: 322120

Subsidiary (Non-US):

Ahlstrom-Munksjo Falun AB (2)
Soldatvagen 14, 791 10, Falun, Sweden
Tel.: (46) 23705880
Web Site: http://www.ahlstrom-munksjo.com
Insulation & Specialty Paper Mfr
N.A.I.C.S.: 322120

Ahlstrom-Munksjo Germany Holding GmbH (2)
Nordlicher Stadtgraben 4, 73430, Aalen, Germany
Tel.: (49) 7361506111
Holding Company; Insulation & Specialty Paper Mfr
N.A.I.C.S.: 551112

Subsidiary (Domestic):

Ahlstrom-Munksjo Germany GmbH (3)
Niederschlag 1, 09471, Barenstein, Germany
Tel.: (49) 3 7347 830
Web Site: http://www.ahlstrom-munksjo.com
Holding Company; Paper Products Mfr & Distr
N.A.I.C.S.: 551112

Ahlstrom-Munksjo Paper GmbH (3)
Waldhauser Strasse 41, 73432, Aalen, Germany
Tel.: (49) 73615060
Insulation & Specialty Paper Mfr
N.A.I.C.S.: 322120

Subsidiary (Domestic):

Ahlstrom-Munksjo Glassfibre Oy (2)
Ahlstromintie 19, PO Box 140, 48601,

Kotka, Finland
Tel.: (358) 1088811
Web Site: http://www.ahlstrom-munksjo.com
Fiber Glass Products Mfr
N.A.I.C.S.: 327215

Subsidiary (Non-US):

Ahlstrom-Munksjo Tver LLC (3)
Promyshlennaya Str 11, Redkino, 171261, Tver, Russia
Tel.: (7) 4956441350
Web Site: http://www.ahlstrom-munksjo.com
Glass Products Mfr
N.A.I.C.S.: 327215

Subsidiary (Non-US):

Ahlstrom-Munksjo Italia S.p.A. (2)
Via Stura 98, 10075, Mathi, Torino, Italy
Tel.: (39) 0119260111
Paper Impregnation Processes & Making Masking Tape
N.A.I.C.S.: 322211

Ahlstrom-Munksjo Italia S.p.A. (2)
Localita Campoginepro 2 Frazione Gaville, 60041, Sassoferrato, Ancona, Italy
Tel.: (39) 073 29127
Web Site: http://www.ahlstrom-munksjo.com
Paper Products Mfr
N.A.I.C.S.: 322299

Ahlstrom-Munksjo Japan Inc. (2)
Estage Osaki Bldg 3-5-2 Osaki, Shinagawa-ku, Tokyo, 141-0032, Japan
Tel.: (81) 3 5776 3600
Paper Product Distr
N.A.I.C.S.: 424130

Ahlstrom-Munksjo La Gere S.A.S. (2)
Usine de La Gere Chemin Cartallier, 38780, Pont-l'Eveque, France
Tel.: (33) 4 7416 1010
Web Site: http://www.ahlstrom-munksjo.com
Packaging Paper Products Mfr
N.A.I.C.S.: 322220

Ahlstrom-Munksjo Malmedy SA (2)
Avenue de Pont de Warche 1, 4960, Malmedy, Belgium
Tel.: (32) 8079 5411
Web Site: http://www.ahlstrom-munksjo.com
Paper Products Mfr
N.A.I.C.S.: 322299

Ahlstrom-Munksjo Monterrey, S. de R.L. de C.V. (2)
Lazaro Cardenas 2400 Col Residencial San Agustin, San Pedro Garza Garcia Nuevo Leon, 07300, Mexico, Mexico
Tel.: (52) 81 8104 0442
Web Site: http://www.ahlstrom-munksjo.com
Paper & Cardboard Products Distr
N.A.I.C.S.: 424130

Subsidiary (US):

Ahlstrom-Munksjo Nonwovens LLC (2)
2 Elm St, Windsor Locks, CT 06096-2335
Tel.: (860) 654-8300
Web Site: http://www.ahlstrom-munksjo.com
Specialty Paper Products Mfr
N.A.I.C.S.: 322299

Subsidiary (Domestic):

Ahlstrom-Munksjo Filtration LLC (3)
215 Nebo Rd, Madisonville, KY 42431
Tel.: (270) 821-0140
Web Site: http://www.ahlstrom-munksjo.com
Automotive Filters Mfr
N.A.I.C.S.: 336110

Plant (Domestic):

Ahlstrom-Munksjo Filtration LLC - Mount Holly Springs Plant (4)
122 W Butler St, Mount Holly Springs, PA 17065
Tel.: (717) 486-3438
Web Site: http://www.ahlstrom-munksjo.com
Filtration Papers Mfr
N.A.I.C.S.: 322120

Ahlstrom-Munksjo Filtration LLC - Taylorville Plant (4)
1200 E Elm St, Taylorville, IL 62568
Tel.: (217) 824-9611

Web Site: http://www.ahlstrom-munksjo.com
Filtration Solutions
N.A.I.C.S.: 322120

Subsidiary (Domestic):

Ahlstrom-Munksjo NA Specialty Solutions LLC (3)
600 Thilmany Rd, Kaukauna, WI 54130
Tel.: (920) 766-8440
Web Site: http://www.ahlstrom-munksjo.com
Paper & Packaging Products Mfr
N.A.I.C.S.: 322120

Plant (Domestic):

Ahlstrom-Munksjo NA Specialty Solutions LLC - Nicolet Plant (4)
115 N 5th St, De Pere, WI 54115
Tel.: (920) 336-4211
Web Site: http://www.ahlstrom-munksjo.com
Insulation & Specialty Paper Mfr
N.A.I.C.S.: 322120

Ahlstrom-Munksjo NA Specialty Solutions LLC - Rhinelander Mill (4)
515 W Davenport St, Rhinelander, WI 54501-3328
Tel.: (715) 369-4100
Web Site: http://www.ahlstrom-munksjo.com
Paper Products Mfr
N.A.I.C.S.: 322299

Subsidiary (Domestic):

Ahlstrom-Munksjo Paper Inc. (3)
100 Erdman Way Ste S100, Leominster, MA 01453
Tel.: (978) 342-1080
Web Site: http://www.ahlstrom-munksjo.com
Decor Base Paper Mfr
N.A.I.C.S.: 322220

Subsidiary (Non-US):

Ahlstrom-Munksjo Paper S.A. (2)
Eldua Apartado 15, Berastegui, 20492, Tolosa, Spain
Tel.: (34) 943683032
Insulation & Specialty Paper Mfr
N.A.I.C.S.: 322120

Ahlstrom-Munksjo Rottersac S.A.S. (2)
Usine Rottersac, Lalinde, 24150, Dordogne, France
Tel.: (33) 553615400
Insulation & Specialty Paper Mfr
N.A.I.C.S.: 322120

Ahlstrom-Munksjo Rus LLC (2)
Ul Prechistenka 40/2 Building 1 6th Floor, 119034, Moscow, Russia
Tel.: (7) 4957853962
Insulation & Specialty Paper Mfr
N.A.I.C.S.: 322120

Ahlstrom-Munksjo Specialties S.A.S. (2)
15 Rue des Papetiers, 27500, Pont Audemer, Cedex, France
Tel.: (33) 2 3241 6100
Web Site: http://www.ahlstrom-munksjo.com
Paper Products Mfr
N.A.I.C.S.: 322299

Plant (Domestic):

Ahlstrom-Munksjo Specialties S.A.S. - Saint Severin Plant (3)
Usine Du Marchais, Saint-Severin, 16390, Saint-Yrieix-sur-Charente, France
Tel.: (33) 545985221
Web Site: http://www.ahlstrom-munksjo.com
Insulation & Specialty Paper Mfr
N.A.I.C.S.: 322120

Subsidiary (Non-US):

Ahlstrom-Munksjo Stalldalen AB (2)
Stallbergsvagen 30, Stalldalen, 71481, Sweden
Tel.: (46) 58029100
Web Site: http://www.ahlstrom-munksjo.com
Filters, Medical Fabrics, Life Science & Diagnostics, Wallcoverings, Tapes & Food & Beverage Packaging Mfr
N.A.I.C.S.: 322211

Subsidiary (Domestic):

Ahlstrom-Munksjo Tampere Oy   (2)
Aunankaari 4, 33840, Tampere, Finland
Tel.: (358) 10 888 14
Web Site: http://www.ahlstrom-munksjo.com
Paper Products Mfr
N.A.I.C.S.: 322299

Enics AG   (1)
Leutschenbachstr 95, 8050, Zurich, Switzerland
Tel.: (41) 56 299 44 00
Web Site: http://www.enics.com
Electronics Mfr
N.A.I.C.S.: 334419
Peter Back (VP-New Sls)

Subsidiary (Non-US):

Enics Raahe Oy   (2)
Pajunilityntie 43, 92120, Raahe, Finland
Tel.: (358) 8 2103 111
Web Site: http://www.enics.com
Electric Equipment Mfr
N.A.I.C.S.: 336320

AHLUWALIA CONTRACTS (INDIA) LIMITED
Plot No A-177 Okhla Industrial Area
Phase-I, New Delhi, 110020, India
Tel.: (91) 1149410502
Web Site: https://www.acilnet.com
532811—(BOM)
Rev.: $391,469,824
Assets: $340,341,497
Liabilities: $172,674,206
Net Worth: $167,667,291
Earnings: $26,477,833
Emp.: 2,300
Fiscal Year-end: 03/31/23
Construction Engineering Services
N.A.I.C.S.: 541330
Bikramjit Ahluwalia (Chm & Mng Dir)

Subsidiaries:

Ahlcon Ready Mix Concrete Pvt. Ltd.   (1)
Safdarjang Enclave, New Delhi, 110029, India
Tel.: (91) 1146003600
Web Site: http://www.ahlconrmc.com
Readymix Concrete Mfr
N.A.I.C.S.: 327320

Plant (Domestic):

Ahlcon Ready Mix Concrete Pvt. Ltd. - Bommenhalli Plant   (2)
Bommenhalli Village Bidarahalli Hobli Bangalore East Taluk, Urban District, Bengaluru, 560049, Karnataka, India
Tel.: (91) 80 28470444
Web Site: http://www.ahlconrmc.com
Readymix Concrete Mfr
N.A.I.C.S.: 327320

AHMAD HASSAN TEXTILE MILLS LIMITED
46 Hassan Parwana Colony, Multan, Pakistan
Tel.: (92) 614512362
Web Site: https://www.ahtml.com.pk
AHTM—(KAR)
Rev.: $52,227,276
Assets: $34,172,685
Liabilities: $20,200,858
Net Worth: $13,971,827
Earnings: $294,061
Emp.: 645
Fiscal Year-end: 06/30/19
Spinning & Weaving Mill
N.A.I.C.S.: 313220
Muhammad Aurangzeb (CEO)

AHMAD ZAKI RESOURCES BERHAD
Menara AZRB No 71 Persiaran Gurney, 54000, Kuala Lumpur, Malaysia
Tel.: (60) 326987171
Web Site: https://www.azrb.com

AZRB—(KLS)
Rev.: $80,517,249
Assets: $980,815,661
Liabilities: $970,602,540
Net Worth: $10,213,122
Earnings: ($21,986,667)
Emp.: 514
Fiscal Year-end: 06/30/23
Civil & Structural Construction Services
N.A.I.C.S.: 236115
Aman Raja Ahmad (Chm)

Subsidiaries:

EKVE Sdn Bhd   (1)
Menara AZRB No 71 Pesiaran Gurney, 54000, Kuala Lumpur, Malaysia
Tel.: (60) 26987171
Web Site: https://www.ekve.com.my
Highway Road Services
N.A.I.C.S.: 237310

TB Supply Base Sdn Bhd   (1)
Jalan Tok Bali Tok Bali, 16700, Pasir Puteh, Kelantan, Malaysia
Tel.: (60) 97789000
Web Site: https://www.tbsb.my
Oil & Gas Exploration Services
N.A.I.C.S.: 213112
Mustaffa Mohamad (Mng Dir)

AHMED MANSOOR AL-A'ALI CO.
PO Box 778, Manama, Bahrain
Tel.: (973) 17250521
Web Site: http://www.alaali.com
Sales Range: $600-649.9 Million
Emp.: 4,350
Nonresidential Construction Services
N.A.I.C.S.: 236220
Ahmed Mansoor Al A'ali (Chm)

Subsidiaries:

Comsip Al A'ali W.L.L.   (1)
PO Box 26949, Adliya, Bahrain
Tel.: (973) 17773006
Web Site: http://www.comsip.com.bh
Sales Range: $125-149.9 Million
Emp.: 400
Electrical Work & Instrumentation Mfr
N.A.I.C.S.: 238210

Subsidiary (Non-US):

Comsip Al A'ali W.L.L.   (2)
PO Box 23342, Doha, Qatar
Tel.: (974) 444 0232
Electrical Work
N.A.I.C.S.: 238210

AHMEDABAD STEELCRAFT LTD.
N T 604 ONE-42 Complex B/h Ashok Vatika Nr Jayantilal Park BRTS, Ambli Bopal Road, Ahmedabad, 380 058, India
Tel.: (91) 7929641996
Web Site: https://www.steelcraft.co.in
522273—(BOM)
Rev.: $413,925
Assets: $3,586,092
Liabilities: $96,228
Net Worth: $3,489,864
Earnings: ($30,853)
Emp.: 12
Fiscal Year-end: 03/31/21
Steel Fabricated Products Mfr
N.A.I.C.S.: 331210
Anand Vipinchandra Shah (CEO)

AHN-GOOK PHARMACEUTICAL CO., LTD.
613 Siheung-daero, Yeongdeungpo-gu, 150-953, Seoul, 150-953, Korea (South)
Tel.: (82) 232894221
Web Site: http://www.ahn-gook.com
Year Founded: 1959
001540—(KRS)
Rev.: $157,533,007

Assets: $171,740,837
Liabilities: $53,107,985
Net Worth: $118,632,852
Earnings: $5,273,418
Emp.: 325
Fiscal Year-end: 12/31/22
Pharmaceutic Product Mfr & Distr
N.A.I.C.S.: 325412
Jin Auh (Vice Chm & CEO)

AHNLAB, INC.
220 Pangyoyeok-ro, Bundang-gu, Seongnam, Gyeonggi, Korea (South)
Tel.: (82) 317228000
Web Site: https://www.ahnlab.com
Year Founded: 1995
053800—(KRS)
Rev.: $184,184,814
Assets: $289,045,908
Liabilities: $69,814,521
Net Worth: $219,231,387
Earnings: $26,721,146
Emp.: 1,295
Fiscal Year-end: 12/31/23
Security Solutions
N.A.I.C.S.: 541690

AHOKU ELECTRONIC COMPANY
5F No 88 Sec 1 Neihu Rd, Neihu Dist, Taipei, 114, Taiwan
Tel.: (886) 227991199
Web Site: https://www.ahoku.com.tw
Year Founded: 1983
3002—(TAI)
Rev.: $19,644,396
Assets: $60,464,827
Liabilities: $15,290,199
Net Worth: $45,174,628
Earnings: $195,755
Emp.: 1,200
Fiscal Year-end: 12/31/23
Power Devices Mfr
N.A.I.C.S.: 335931
Kuang-Hao Li (Chm & Pres)

Subsidiaries:

ACPA Technology Co., Ltd.   (1)
No 4 Ln 311 Sec 1 Jieshou Rd, Sanxia Dist, New Taipei City, 237, Taiwan
Tel.: (886) 28 671 6551
Web Site: https://www.acpa.com.tw
Electronic Components Mfr
N.A.I.C.S.: 334419

Ahoku Techland Electronics Ltd.   (1)
5 DaBanDi 1st Road ShaBen ChangAn, Dongguan, 523876, Guangdong, China
Tel.: (86) 76987088788
Power Devices & Electronic Components Mfr
N.A.I.C.S.: 334419

China Ahoku Techland Electronics Ltd.   (1)
5 DaBanDi 1st Rd ShaBen, ChangAn, Dongguan, GuangDong, China
Tel.: (86) 76987088788
Electronic Products Mfr
N.A.I.C.S.: 334111

Taiwan Ahoku Electronic Company   (1)
5F No 88 Sec 1 Neihu Rd, Neihu Dist, Taipei, 114, Taiwan
Tel.: (886) 22 799 1199
Electronic Products Mfr
N.A.I.C.S.: 334111

AHREN ACQUISITION CORP.
Boundary Hall Cricket Square, Georgetown, KY1-1102, Grand Cayman, Cayman Islands
Tel.: (345) 6464800033
Web Site: https://www.ahrenacq.com
Year Founded: 2021
AHRN—(NASDAQ)
Assets: $310,974,802
Liabilities: $313,844,169
Net Worth: ($2,869,367)

Earnings: $13,757,880
Fiscal Year-end: 12/31/22
Investment Management Service
N.A.I.C.S.: 523999

AHRENS GROUP PTY. LTD.
Wilhelm Rd, Kingsford, 5118, SA, Australia
Tel.: (61) 885210000
Web Site: http://www.ahrens.com.au
Year Founded: 1906
Emp.: 300
Construction Engineering Services
N.A.I.C.S.: 541330
Stefan Ahrens (Mng Dir)

AHRESTY CORPORATION
Nakano-sakaue Sunbright Twin 5F
2-46-1 Honcho, Nakano-ku, Tokyo, 164-0012, Japan
Tel.: (81) 363698660
Web Site: https://www.ahresty.co.jp
Year Founded: 1943
5852—(TKS)
Rev.: $1,046,058,940
Assets: $870,953,430
Liabilities: $529,765,060
Net Worth: $341,188,370
Earnings: ($50,890,390)
Emp.: 5,590
Fiscal Year-end: 03/31/24
Die Cast Aluminum Products Mfr
N.A.I.C.S.: 331523
Arata Takahashi (Pres & CEO)

Subsidiaries:

AHRESTY CORPORATION - Higashimatsuyama Plant   (1)
25-27 Oaza Miyako, Hiki-gun, Namegawa, 355-0812, Saitama, Japan
Tel.: (81) 493564421
Web Site: http://www.ahresty.com
Sales Range: $25-49.9 Million
Emp.: 100
Aluminium Die Casting Products Mfr
N.A.I.C.S.: 331523
Arata Takahashi (Pres)

AHRESTY CORPORATION - Kumagaya Plant   (1)
284-11 Miizugahara, Kumagaya, 360-8543, Saitama, Japan
Tel.: (81) 485335161
Web Site: http://www.ahresty.co.jp
Sales Range: $25-49.9 Million
Emp.: 60
Aluminium Secondary Ingot Products Mfr
N.A.I.C.S.: 331314

Ahresty Die Mold Hamamatsu Corporation   (1)
5-3-10 Sakuradai, Nishi-ku, Hamamatsu, 431-1104, Shizuoka, Japan
Tel.: (81) 534361711
Emp.: 100
Aluminium Die Casting Products Mfr
N.A.I.C.S.: 331523

Subsidiary (Non-US):

Thai Ahresty Die Co., Ltd.   (2)
Hi-Tech Industrial Estate 133 Moo1, Bhan Wha Sub-Dist Bang Pa-In Dist, Ayutthaya, 13160, Thailand
Tel.: (66) 3 535 0993
Web Site: http://www.tad.co.th
Die Cast Aluminum Mfr
N.A.I.C.S.: 331523

Ahresty Die Mold Kumamoto Corporation   (1)
12 Urakawachi, Matsubase-machi, Uki, 869-0521, Kumamoto, Japan
Tel.: (81) 964333536
Aluminium Products Mfr
N.A.I.C.S.: 331315

Ahresty Die Mold Tochigi Corporation   (1)
4060 Oaza Mibu Otsu, Mibu-machi Shimotsuga-gun, Tochigi, 321-0215, Japan
Tel.: (81) 282825111
Aluminium Products Mfr
N.A.I.C.S.: 331315

Ahresty Corporation—(Continued)

Ahresty India Private Limited (1)
Plot No-194 Sec-04 Phase-II Growth Center
Bawal, Distt. Rewari, 123 501, Haryana,
India
Tel.: (91) 1284268100
Web Site: https://www.ahresty.co.in
Emp.: 275
Aluminium Products Mfr
N.A.I.C.S.: 331315
Devinder Aggarwal (Acct Mgr)

Ahresty Kumamoto Corporation (1)
36 Urakawachi Matsubase-machi, Uki, 869-
0521, Kumamoto, Japan
Tel.: (81) 964333111
Die Casting Products Mfr
N.A.I.C.S.: 333517

Ahresty Mexicana, S.A. de C.V. (1)
Industria Automotriz 20 Complejo de Naves
Industriales, 98604, Guadalupe, Zacatecas,
Mexico
Tel.: (52) 4924914010
Die Cast Aluminum Mfr
N.A.I.C.S.: 331523

**Ahresty Precision Die Mold
(Guangzhou) Co., Ltd.** (1)
No 70 Xin Ye St, Yonghe Economic District
Economic Technological Development Dis-
trict, Guangzhou, 511356, China
Tel.: (86) 2082461670
Web Site: http://www.hfalst.com
Aluminium Products Mfr
N.A.I.C.S.: 331315

Ahresty Pretech Corporation (1)
3-8-38 Takaokahigashi, Naka-Ku, Ha-
mamatsu, 433-8117, Shizuoka, Japan
Tel.: (81) 534362121
Web Site: http://www.tokaiseiko.co.jp
Sales Range: $100-124.9 Million
Emp.: 300
Automotive & Motorcycle Components Mfr
N.A.I.C.S.: 336991

**Ahresty Techno Service
Corporation** (1)
938 Nagashima, Hamakita-ku, Hamamatsu,
434-0013, Shizuoka, Japan
Tel.: (81) 535841414
Web Site: http://www.ahresty-tec.jp
Sales Range: $25-49.9 Million
Emp.: 100
Die Casting Peripheral Equipment Mfr &
Distr
N.A.I.C.S.: 333517

Ahresty Tochigi Corporation (1)
4060 Oaza Mibu Otsu, Shimotsuga-gun,
Mibu, 321-0215, Tochigi, Japan
Tel.: (81) 282825111
Web Site: http://www.ahresty.co.jp
Die Casting Products Mfr
N.A.I.C.S.: 333517

Ahresty Wilmington Corporation (1)
2627 S S St, Wilmington, OH 45177
Tel.: (937) 382-6112
Aluminum Die-Castings Mfr
N.A.I.C.S.: 331523
Kazuhisa Kawata (Pres)

Ahresty Yamagata Corporation (1)
65 Arato Otsu, Nishiokitama-gun, Shirataka,
992-0832, Yamagata, Japan
Tel.: (81) 238855233
Aluminium Die Casting Products Mfr
N.A.I.C.S.: 331523

**Guangzhou Ahresty Casting Co.,
Ltd.** (1)
No 7 Xinfeng St, Yonghe Economic District
Economic & Technological Development
District, Guangzhou, 511356, China
Tel.: (86) 2032221638
Aluminium Products Mfr
N.A.I.C.S.: 331315

Hefei Ahresty Casting Co., Ltd. (1)
2295 Qinglongtan Rd Hefei Economic and
Technological Development Area, Hefei,
Anhui, China
Tel.: (86) 55163679389
Aluminium Products Mfr
N.A.I.C.S.: 331315
Hirofumi Kondo (Gen Mgr)

**Thai Ahresty Engineering Co.,
Ltd.** (1)

43 Thai CC Tower 204 Room 20th Floor
South Sathorn Rd, Yannawa Sathorn,
Bangkok, 10120, Thailand
Tel.: (66) 106626739928
Aluminium Products Mfr
N.A.I.C.S.: 331315

**AHSAY BACKUP SOFTWARE
DEVELOPMENT COMPANY
LIMITED**
28/F Ford Glory Plaza No 37 Wing
Hong Street Lai Chi Kok, Kowloon,
China (Hong Kong)
Tel.: (852) 35806900   Ky
Web Site: http://www.ahsay.com.hk
8290—(HKG)
Rev.: $5,722,455
Assets: $10,392,015
Liabilities: $6,868,425
Net Worth: $3,523,590
Earnings: ($294,780)
Emp.: 73
Fiscal Year-end: 12/31/22
Software Development Services
N.A.I.C.S.: 541511
King Fan Chong (Chm)

Subsidiaries:

**Ahsay Systems Corporation
Limited** (1)
28/F Ford Glory Plaza 37 Wing Hong
Street, Lai Chi Kok, Kowloon, China (Hong
Kong)
Tel.: (852) 3 580 8091
Web Site: https://www.ahsay.com
Backup Software Services
N.A.I.C.S.: 541511

CloudBacko Corporation (1)
28/f Ford Glory Plaza No 37 Wing Hong
Street, Lai Chi Kok, Kowloon, China (Hong
Kong)
Tel.: (852) 35806976
Web Site: http://www.cloudbacko.com
Backup Software Recovery Services
N.A.I.C.S.: 541519

Kintips Limited (1)
28th Floor Fu Yuen Plaza 37 Wing Hong
Street, Lai Chi Kok, Kowloon, China (Hong
Kong)
Tel.: (852) 37011411
Web Site: https://www.kintips.com
Software Development Services
N.A.I.C.S.: 541511

**AHT SYNGAS TECHNOLOGY
NV**
Diepenbroich 15, 51491, Overath,
Germany
Tel.: (49) 220695190
Web Site: https://www.aht-
cleantec.com
Turbine Generator Mfr
N.A.I.C.S.: 333611
Gero Bernhard Ferges (CEO)

**AHWAZ PIPE MILLS COM-
PANY**
8 Second St Ahmad Ghasir St Shahid
Beheshti Ave, PO Box 15875-3385,
15146 38713, Tehran, Iran
Tel.: (98) 21 88736959
Web Site: http://www.apm-ir.com
Year Founded: 1967
Steel Pole Mfr
N.A.I.C.S.: 331210

**AHWAZ ROLLING & PIPE
MILLS CO.**
9th km Ahwaz-Khoramshahr Road,
Ahvaz, 61335, Iran
Tel.: (98) 611 3310460
Web Site: http://www.arpcosteel.com
Year Founded: 1966
Steel Pole Mfr
N.A.I.C.S.: 331210
Ali Khani (Mgr-Pur & Contracts)

**AI BATNAH HOTELS COM-
PANY SAOG**
Al-Tareef, PO Box 132, 321, Sohar,
Oman
Tel.: (968) 26841111
Web Site:
http://www.soharbeach.com
Year Founded: 1992
DAI IO—(MUS)
Rev.: $764,557
Assets: $7,865,072
Liabilities: $3,982,023
Net Worth: $3,883,049
Earnings: ($1,492,190)
Fiscal Year-end: 12/31/21
Hotel Operator
N.A.I.C.S.: 721110

**AI CHAMPDANY INDUSTRIES
LIMITED**
25 Princep Street, Kolkata, 700072,
India
Tel.: (91) 3322377880
Web Site: https://www.jute-world.com
Year Founded: 1873
532806—(BOM)
Rev.: $9,871,503
Assets: $43,340,388
Liabilities: $33,747,578
Net Worth: $9,592,811
Earnings: ($2,379,932)
Emp.: 2,816
Fiscal Year-end: 03/31/21
Jute Product Mfr & Whslr
N.A.I.C.S.: 313110
N. Pujara (Mng Dir)

AI CLAIMS SOLUTIONS PLC
Indemnity House Sir Frank Whittle
Way, Blackpool, FY4 2FB, Lancs,
United Kingdom
Tel.: (44) 844 571 3333   UK
Web Site:
http://www.aiclaimssolutions.com
Sales Range: $150-199.9 Million
Emp.: 471
Holding Company; Automotive Insur-
ance Claims Management Services
N.A.I.C.S.: 551112
Peter J. Harrison (Dir-Fin)

Subsidiaries:

Ai Claims Solutions (UK) Limited (1)
Indemnity House Sir Frank Whittle Way,
Blackpool, FY4 2FB, Lancs, United King-
dom
Tel.: (44) 844 571 3333
Web Site: http://www.aiclaimssolutions.com
Automotive Insurance Claims Management
Services
N.A.I.C.S.: 524291

AI CO., LTD.
KDX Kasuga Building 10F 1-15-15
Nishikata, Bunkyo Ward, Tokyo, 113-
0024, Japan
Tel.: (81) 368018461
Web Site: https://www.ai-j.jp
Year Founded: 2003
4388—(TKS)
Voice Synthesis System Development
N.A.I.C.S.: 541715
Shinichi Hiroi (Pres)

Subsidiaries:

FueTrek Co., Ltd. (1)
Shin-osaka Prime Tower 18F 6-1-1 Nishina-
kajima, Yodogawa-ku, Osaka, 532-0011,
Japan
Tel.: (81) 648063112
Web Site: https://www.fuetrek.co.jp
Rev.: $15,391,200
Assets: $37,442,240
Liabilities: $11,161,040
Net Worth: $26,281,200
Earnings: $1,287,440
Emp.: 108
Fiscal Year-end: 03/31/2022

Software Development Services
N.A.I.C.S.: 541511
Yasutaka Urakawa (Pres & CEO)

Subsidiary (Domestic):

ATR-Trek Co., Ltd. (2)
Shin-Osaka Prime Tower 18F 6-1-1 Nishi-
nakajima, Yodogawa-ku, Osaka, 532-0011,
Japan
Tel.: (81) 66 838 3160
Web Site: https://www.atr-trek.co.jp
Information Technology Services
N.A.I.C.S.: 541511
Toshiaki Fukada (CEO)

SuperOne Co., Ltd. (2)
8-1-2 PMO Nishi-Shinjuku 604, Nishi-
Shinjuku Shinjuku-ku, Tokyo, 160-0023,
Japan
Tel.: (81) 362068290
Web Site: https://www.super-one.net
Software Development Services
N.A.I.C.S.: 541511

**AI CONVERSATION SYSTEMS
LTD.**
1 Sycamore Street, PO Box 11,
Savyon, 56530, Israel
Tel.: (972) 37343100
Web Site: http://www.a-i.com
Year Founded: 1978
AICS,M—(TAE)
Assets: $618,870
Liabilities: $568,034
Net Worth: $50,836
Earnings: ($863,931)
Fiscal Year-end: 12/31/23
Offices of Other Holding Companies
N.A.I.C.S.: 551112
Chen Buskilla (CTO)

AI CROSS, INC.
Atago East Building 13F 3-16-11
Nishi-shinbashi, Minato-ku, Tokyo,
105-0003, Japan
Tel.: (81) 5017453021
Web Site: https://www.aicross.co.jp
Year Founded: 2015
4476—(TKS)
Rev.: $23,070,860
Assets: $15,059,160
Liabilities: $3,155,050
Net Worth: $11,904,110
Earnings: $1,106,040
Fiscal Year-end: 12/31/23
Software Development Services
N.A.I.C.S.: 541511
Soh Suzuki (CTO)

**AI ENERGY PUBLIC COM-
PANY LIMITED**
55/2 Moo 8 Sethakit 1 Rd Khlong
maduea, Krathum Baen, Samut Sak-
hon, 74110, Thailand
Tel.: (66) 34877488
Web Site: https://www.aienergy.co.th
AIE—(THA)
Rev.: $239,990,489
Assets: $74,519,334
Liabilities: $13,147,354
Net Worth: $61,371,980
Earnings: $1,175,468
Fiscal Year-end: 12/31/23
Biodiesel Producer & Distr
N.A.I.C.S.: 324199
Narong Thareratanavibool (Chm)

Subsidiaries:

AI Logistics Company Limited (1)
254 Seri Thai Road, Kannayaow, Bangkok,
10230, Thailand
Tel.: (66) 2 540 2528
Logistics Consulting Servies
N.A.I.C.S.: 541614

**AI Ports and Terminals Company
Limited** (1)
23/1 Moo 7 Thajeen, Amphur Muang,
74000, Samut Sakhon, Thailand
Tel.: (66) 34 497 184
Web Site:

Cost Management Services
N.A.I.C.S.: 488320

AI HOLDINGS CORP.
12-8 Nihombashi Hisamatsu-cho,
Chuo-ku, Tokyo, 103-0005, Japan
Tel.: (81) 332496335
Web Site: http://www.aiholdings.co.jp
3076—(TKS)
Information & Security Equipment Mfr
N.A.I.C.S.: 335999
Akihiko Ohshima *(Pres)*

Subsidiaries:

IWATSU ELECTRIC Co Ltd   (1)
1-7-41 Kugayama, Suginami-ku, Tokyo,
168-8501, Japan
Tel.: (81) 353705474
Web Site: https://www.iwatsu.co.jp
Rev.: $224,401,760
Assets: $352,748,880
Liabilities: $107,273,760
Net Worth: $245,475,120
Earnings: $5,759,600
Emp.: 1,258
Fiscal Year-end: 03/31/2022
Communication Equipment Mfr
N.A.I.C.S.: 334220
Toru Nishido *(Pres & CEO)*

Subsidiary (Non-US):

Iwatsu (Malaysia) Sdn. Bhd.   (2)
No 660 Kawasan Perusahaan, Taman Tu-
anku Jaafar Sungai Gadut, 71450, Serem-
ban, Negeri Sembilan, Malaysia
Tel.: (60) 66777611
Web Site: https://www.iwatsu.com.my
Sales Range: $50-74.9 Million
Emp.: 193
Telecommunications Equipment Mfr
N.A.I.C.S.: 334210
Tomokazu Ishiyama *(Mng Dir)*

Iwatsu Hong Kong, Ltd.   (2)
Ste No 8B-9 18 F Tower 2 33 Canton Rd,
Tsim Sha Tsui Kowloon, Hong Kong, China
(Hong Kong)
Tel.: (852) 23759998
Web Site: http://www.iwatsu.co.jp
Sales Range: $25-49.9 Million
Emp.: 6
Telecommunications Equipment Mfr
N.A.I.C.S.: 334210

AI INSIDE, INC.
Shibuya Dai-Ichiseimei Bldg 4F 3-8-
12, Shibuya-ku, Tokyo, 1500002, Ja-
pan
Tel.: (81) 354685041
Web Site: https://www.inside.ai
Year Founded: 2015
4488—(TKS)
Application Development Services
N.A.I.C.S.: 541511
Taku Toguchi *(Pres & CEO)*

AI KARAAUYL JSC
Tole bi 63, Almalinsky district,
050040, Almaty, Kazakhstan
Tel.: (7) 7273317707
Web Site: https://www.ai-karaaul.kz
Year Founded: 2000
AKRL—(KAZ)
Sales Range: Less than $1 Million
Ore Mining Services
N.A.I.C.S.: 212220
Ishmukhamedov Erzhan *(Pres & CEO)*

AI TOPPER & CO
287 Clarence Street, Sydney, 2000,
NSW, Australia
Tel.: (61) 292611900
Web Site: http://www.aitopper.com.au
Year Founded: 1954
Leather Product Distr
N.A.I.C.S.: 424990
Brian Topper *(Mng Dir)*

AI-MEDIA TECHNOLOGIES LIMITED
Level 1 103 Miller St, North Sydney,
2060, NSW, Australia
Tel.: (61) 88707722
Web Site: https://www.ai-media.tv
Year Founded: 2003
AIM—(ASX)
Rev.: $44,228,137
Assets: $62,192,508
Liabilities: $11,503,003
Net Worth: $50,689,505
Earnings: ($895,430)
Fiscal Year-end: 06/30/24
Live & Recorded Captioning, Speech
Analytics Provider; Cloud-Based
Technology Platform
N.A.I.C.S.: 518210
Anthony Abrahams *(Co-Founder, CEO & Exec Dir)*

Subsidiaries:

Caption IT, LLC   (1)
1017 Peonies Dr, De Pere, WI 54115-7694
Tel.: (920) 336-7232
Web Site: https://www.captionit.net
Court Reporting & Stenotype Services
N.A.I.C.S.: 561492
Jared Janssen *(Dir-Sls & Ops)*

EEG Enterprises, Inc.   (1)
586 Main St, Farmingdale, NY 11735
Tel.: (516) 293-7472
Web Site: http://www.eegent.com
Radio & Television Broadcasting & Wireless
Communications Equipment Mfr
N.A.I.C.S.: 334220
Philip McLaughlin *(Pres)*

AIA ENGINEERING LTD.
11-12 Sigma Corporates B/h HOF
Showroom Off S G Highway,
Sindhubhavan Road Bodakdev,
Ahmedabad, 380054, Gujarat, India
Tel.: (91) 7966047800
Web Site:
https://www.aiaengineering.com
532683—(BOM)
Rev.: $508,167,305
Assets: $699,640,469
Liabilities: $49,431,550
Net Worth: $650,208,918
Earnings: $84,577,857
Emp.: 1,287
Fiscal Year-end: 03/31/22
Engineeering Services
N.A.I.C.S.: 541330
Bhadresh Kantilal Shah *(Mng Dir)*

Subsidiaries:

Vega Industries (Middle East)
F.Z.C.   (1)
A1-304/314 Ajman Free Zone, PO Box
4275, Ajman, United Arab Emirates
Tel.: (971) 67420241
Cement Mfr
N.A.I.C.S.: 327310

Welcast Steels Ltd.   (1)
Plot No 15 Phase I Peenya Industrial Area,
Bengaluru, 560 058, India   (74.85%)
Tel.: (91) 8028394058
Web Site: https://www.welcaststeels.com
Rev.: $11,833,472
Assets: $5,856,860
Liabilities: $1,417,566
Net Worth: $4,439,294
Earnings: ($67,076)
Emp.: 127
Fiscal Year-end: 03/31/2022
Grinding Media Balls Mfr
N.A.I.C.S.: 327910

AIA GROUP LIMITED
35/F AIA Central 1 Connaught Road,
Central, China (Hong Kong)
Tel.: (852) 28326030
Web Site: https://www.aia.com
Year Founded: 1919
AAGIY—(OTCIQ)
Rev.: $19,110,000,000

Assets: $303,048,000,000
Liabilities: $264,498,000,000
Net Worth: $38,550,000,000
Earnings: $320,000,000
Emp.: 25,405
Fiscal Year-end: 12/31/22
Financial Investment Services
N.A.I.C.S.: 551112
Mitchell New *(Gen Counsel)*

Subsidiaries:

AIA (Vietnam) Life Insurance Com-
pany Limited   (1)
15th Floor Saigon Center Building Tower 2
67 Le Loi Street, Ben Nghe Ward District 1,
Ho Chi Minh City, Vietnam
Tel.: (84) 2838122777
Web Site: https://www.aia.com.vn
Insurance Agency Services
N.A.I.C.S.: 524210

AIA Company, Limited   (1)
AIA Wealth Select Centre 12/F AIA Tower
183 Electric Road, PO Box 456, North
Point, Hong Kong, China (Hong
Kong)   (100%)
Tel.: (852) 22328888
Web Site: https://www.aia.com.hk
Sales Range: $350-399.9 Million
Emp.: 600
Life, Medical, Casualty & Other Specialty
Insurance Products & Services
N.A.I.C.S.: 524298
Alger Fung *(CEO)*

Subsidiary (Non-US):

AIA Australia Limited   (2)
PO Box 6111, Melbourne, 3004, VIC, Aus-
tralia
Tel.: (61) 1800333613
Web Site: https://www.aia.com.au
Financial Insurance Services
N.A.I.C.S.: 524210
Damien Mu *(CEO & Mng Dir)*

AIA Bhd.   (2)
Menara AIA 99 Jalan, Ampang, 50450,
Kuala Lumpur, Malaysia
Tel.: (60) 1300881899
Web Site: https://www.aia.com.my
Emp.: 2,400
Insurance Agency Services
N.A.I.C.S.: 524210
Ben Ng *(CEO)*

AIA Singapore Private Limited   (2)
3 Tampines Grande 09-01 AIA Tampines,
Singapore, 528799, Singapore
Tel.: (65) 62488000
Web Site: https://www.aia.com.sg
Insurance Agency Services
N.A.I.C.S.: 524210
Wong Sze Keed *(CEO)*

AIA Everest Life Company
Limited   (1)
12/F AIA Tower 183 Electric Road, North
Point, 999077, China (Hong Kong)
Tel.: (852) 22328888
Web Site: https://www.aia.com.hk
N.A.I.C.S.: 524113

AIA Life Insurance Co. Ltd.   (1)
AIA Tower 16 Tongil-Ro 2-Gil, Jung-gu,
Seoul, 04511, Korea (South)
Tel.: (82) 237074800
Web Site: https://www.aia.co.kr
N.A.I.C.S.: 524113
Nathan Michael Chop *(CEO)*

AIA New Zealand Limited   (1)
AIA House 74 Taharoto Road, Takapuna,
North Shore, 0622, New Zealand
Tel.: (64) 94879000
Web Site: https://www.aia.co.nz
Financial Insurance Services
N.A.I.C.S.: 524210
Nick Stanhope *(CEO)*

BPI AIA Life Assurance
Corporation   (1)
15/F BPI Philam Life Makati 6811 Ayala Av-
enue, Makati, 1226, Philippines
Tel.: (63) 277537490
Web Site: https://www.bpi-aia.com.ph
N.A.I.C.S.: 524113
Karen Custodia *(CEO)*

PT. AIA Financial   (1)
Jl Gen Sudirman Kav 48A, South Jakarta,
12930, Indonesia
Tel.: (62) 1500980
Web Site: https://www.aia-financial.co.id
Financial Insurance Services
N.A.I.C.S.: 524210

Stable Vision Corporation Sdn
Bhd   (1)
Tel.: (60) 333426068
Life Insurance & Employee Benefits Prod-
ucts & Services
N.A.I.C.S.: 524113

The Philippine American Life & Gen-
eral Insurance Company   (1)
Clock In BGC 3F C2 Building 7th Avenue
Bonifacio High Street Central, Bonifacio
Global City, Taguig, 1634, Philippines
Tel.: (63) 85282000
Web Site: https://www.aia.com.ph
Insurance & Financial Services
N.A.I.C.S.: 524128
Gary Ogilvie *(CFO)*

Joint Venture (Non-US):

BPI-Philam Life Assurance
Corporation   (2)
                                      (51%)
Sales Range: $500-549.9 Million
Life Insurance Products & Services
N.A.I.C.S.: 524113
Spencer Yap *(CFO)*

AIAI GROUP CORPORATION
Arca Central 16F 1-2-1 Kinshicho,
Sumida-ku, Tokyo, 130-0013, Japan
Tel.: (81) 362841607
Web Site: https://aiai-group.co.jp
Year Founded: 2007
6557—(TKS)
Rev.: $78,116,980
Assets: $77,052,770
Liabilities: $65,518,320
Net Worth: $11,534,450
Earnings: $2,333,330
Fiscal Year-end: 03/31/24
Social Welfare Services
N.A.I.C.S.: 525120
Sadamatsu Sei *(Pres & CEO)*

Subsidiaries:

AIAI Child Care Co., Ltd.   (1)
Arca Central 16F, 1-2-1 Kinshicho, Sumida-
ku,, Tokyo, 130-0013, Japan
Tel.: (81) 362841607
Web Site: https://nursery.aiai-cc.co.jp
Child Day Care Services
N.A.I.C.S.: 624410

AIAS INVESTMENT PUBLIC LTD.
Thalassines Esperides 6 Pervolia,
Larnaca, Cyprus
Tel.: (357) 22 374536
AIAS—(CYP)
Sales Range: Less than $1 Million
Financial Services
N.A.I.C.S.: 523999
Zenios Demetriou *(Chm)*

AIB GROUP PLC
10 Molesworth Street, PO Box 452,
Dublin, 2, Ireland
Tel.: (353) 16600311   IE
Web Site: https://aib.ie
Year Founded: 1966
AIBGY—(ISE)
Rev.: $579,399,142
Assets: $12,583,943,449
Liabilities: $10,244,887,655
Net Worth: $2,339,055,794
Earnings: $339,560,717
Emp.: 696
Fiscal Year-end: 12/31/23
Financial Investment Services
N.A.I.C.S.: 551111
Helen Dooley *(Gen Counsel)*

AIB Group plc—(Continued)

Subsidiaries:

AIB Capital Markets plc **(1)**
AIB Bankcentre Ballsbridge, Dublin, 4,
Ireland **(100%)**
Tel.: (353) 18740222
Web Site: http://www.aib.ie
Sales Range: $700-749.9 Million
Emp.: 2,000
International Banking, Treasury, Investment
Management & Corporate Banking
N.A.I.C.S.: 522299
Jerry McCrohan (Mng Dir)

AIB Corporate Banking Limited **(1)**
AIB Bankcentre Ballsbridge, Dublin, Ireland
Tel.: (353) 1 660 0311
Web Site: http://www.aibcorporate.ie
Sales Range: $50-74.9 Million
Emp.: 130
Commercial Banking Services
N.A.I.C.S.: 522110
Conor P. Daly (Head-Food, Drink, Leisure,
Media & Education Div)

AIB Corporate Finance Ltd. **(1)**
Bankcentre Ballsbridge, Dublin, 4,
Ireland **(100%)**
Tel.: (353) 16670233
Web Site: http://www.aibcf.ie
Sales Range: $50-74.9 Million
Emp.: 15
Advice on Mergers, Acquisitions, Disposals
& Fund Raising
N.A.I.C.S.: 522299
Alan Doherty (Mng Dir)

AIB Finance & Leasing Ltd. **(1)**
Bankcentre Ballsbridge, Sandyford, Dublin,
4, Ireland **(100%)**
Tel.: (353) 16603011
Web Site: http://www.aib.ie
Sales Range: $200-249.9 Million
Emp.: 350
Business & Consumer Asset Financing
N.A.I.C.S.: 523910

AIB Holdings (NI) Limited **(1)**
4 Queen s Square, PO Box 4, Belfast, BT1
3DJ, United Kingdom
Tel.: (44) 28 9032 5599
Investment Management Service
N.A.I.C.S.: 523999

AIB Insurance Services Limited **(1)**
AIB Bankcentre Ballsbridge, Dublin, 4, Ire-
land
Tel.: (353) 16600311
Insurance Brokerage Services
N.A.I.C.S.: 524210

**AIB International Consultants
Ltd.** **(1)**
Bankcentre Ballsbridge, Dublin, 4,
Ireland **(100%)**
Tel.: (353) 16600311
Web Site: http://www.aib.ie
Sales Range: $25-49.9 Million
Emp.: 200
Business Consulting Services
N.A.I.C.S.: 541611

AIB International Finance **(1)**
Bankcentre Ballsbridge, Dublin, Ireland
Tel.: (353) 16600311
Financial Management Services
N.A.I.C.S.: 523999

**AIB Mortgage Bank Unlimited
Company** **(1)**
10 Molesworth Street, 2, Dublin, D02 R126,
Ireland
Tel.: (353) 16600311
N.A.I.C.S.: 522310

AIB Securities Services Ltd. **(1)**
Block L3 Bank Centre ballsbridge, Dublin,
4, Ireland **(100%)**
Tel.: (353) 18740222
Web Site: http://www.aibbny.ie
Sales Range: $50-74.9 Million
Emp.: 60
Custody Services
N.A.I.C.S.: 523991

**Allied Irish Banks (Holdings & Invest-
ments) Limited** **(1)**
Bankcentre Ballsbridge, Dublin, 4, Ireland

Tel.: (353) 16600311
Web Site: http://www.aib.ie
Investment Management Service
N.A.I.C.S.: 523999
Richard A. Pym (Chm)

Allied Irish Finance Limited **(1)**
Bankcentre Ballsbridge, Dublin, Ireland
Tel.: (353) 16600311
Financial Management Services
N.A.I.C.S.: 523999

EBS Mortgage Finance **(1)**
EBS Building Society 2 Burlington Road,
Dublin, Ireland
Tel.: (353) 1 665 9000
Web Site: http://www.ebs.ie
Mortgage Insurance Services
N.A.I.C.S.: 524126
David J. Duffy (CEO)

EBS d.a.c. **(1)**
10 Molesworth Street, PO Box 76, Dublin,
D02 R126, Ireland
Tel.: (353) 16658075
Web Site: https://www.ebs.ie
Sales Range: $200-249.9 Million
Emp.: 40
Financial Management Services
N.A.I.C.S.: 523999
Fergus J. Murphy (CEO)

Goodbody Stockbrokers UC **(1)**
Ballsbridge Park, Ballsbridge, Dublin,
Ireland **(100%)**
Tel.: (353) 16670400
Web Site: http://www.goodbody.ie
Sales Range: $100-124.9 Million
Emp.: 300
Investment Services
N.A.I.C.S.: 523999
Roy Barrett (Mng Dir)

Haven Mortgages Ltd. **(1)**
2 Burlington Road, Dublin, Ireland
Tel.: (353) 16658011
Web Site: http://www.havenmortgages.ie
Mortgage Loan Services
N.A.I.C.S.: 522310
Kieran Tansey (Mng Dir)

Payzone Ireland Limited **(1)**
Payzone House 4 Heather Rd, Sandyford
Indus Estate, Dublin, 18, Ireland
Tel.: (353) 12076000
Web Site: http://www.payzone.ie
Sales Range: $1-4.9 Billion
Automatic Teller Machine & Payment Net-
works
N.A.I.C.S.: 522320
Jim Deignan (Mng Dir)

AIB-VINCOTTE BELGIUM VZW
Jan Olieslagerslaan 35, 1800, Vil-
voorde, Belgium
Tel.: (32) 26745711
Web Site: http://www.aib-vincotte.be
Sales Range: $200-249.9 Million
Emp.: 2,500
Business Management & Consulting
Services
N.A.I.C.S.: 541611
Michel Vandegard (CMO)

AIBIT CO., LTD.
Digital Road 9, Geumcheon-gu,
Seoul, 99 307, Korea (South)
Tel.: (82) 2 3282 1900
Web Site: http://aibit.co.kr
Year Founded: 1979
Rev.: $32,164,463
Assets: $58,518,169
Liabilities: $15,129,159
Net Worth: $43,389,011
Earnings: ($9,618,342)
Emp.: 89
Fiscal Year-end: 12/31/19
Semiconductor Devices Mfr
N.A.I.C.S.: 334413
Jun Yil Park (CEO)

AIC MINES LIMITED
Suite 3 130 Hay Street, Subiaco,
6008, WA, Australia
Tel.: (61) 862690110 **AU**

Web Site:
https://www.aicmines.com.au
A1M—(ASX)
Rev.: $60,722,090
Assets: $76,298,733
Liabilities: $23,809,354
Net Worth: $52,489,378
Earnings: $16,210,282
Emp.: 56
Fiscal Year-end: 12/31/22
Precious & Base Metal Exploration &
Mining
N.A.I.C.S.: 213114
Audrey Ferguson (Sec)

Subsidiaries:

AIC Resources Limited **(1)**
A8 Level 1 435 Roberts Road, Subiaco,
6008, WA, Australia
Tel.: (61) 862690110
Web Site: http://www.aicmines.com.au
Mineral Exploration Services
N.A.I.C.S.: 213114

**AICA KOGYO COMPANY, LIM-
ITED**
JP Tower Nagoya 26F 1-1-1 Meieki
Nakamura-Ku, Nagoya, 450-6326,
Aichi, Japan
Tel.: (81) 525333156 **JP**
Web Site: http://www.aica.co.jp
Year Founded: 1936
R5Y—(DEU)
Rev.: $1,564,091,250
Assets: $1,816,024,790
Liabilities: $649,075,560
Net Worth: $1,166,949,230
Earnings: $100,042,350
Emp.: 5,007
Fiscal Year-end: 03/31/24
Wood Product & Adhesive Mfr
N.A.I.C.S.: 321999
Kenji Ebihara (Pres)

Subsidiaries:

**AICA Asia Laminates Holding Co.,
Ltd.** **(1)**
Unit 2202 22nd Fl 42 Tower 65 Soi
Sukhumvit 42 Sukhumvit Rd, Prakanong
Klongtoey, Bangkok, 10110, Thailand
Tel.: (66) 2 059 7184
Web Site: https://www.aica-al.com
High Pressure Laminate Product Mfr
N.A.I.C.S.: 326130

**AICA Asia Pacific Holding Pte.
Ltd.** **(1)**
43 Shipyard Road, Singapore, 628135,
Singapore
Tel.: (65) 62650388
Industrial Resin Mfr
N.A.I.C.S.: 325211

AICA Bangkok Co., Ltd. **(1)**
156/2 Moo 17 Bangna-Trad Rd KM 23,
Bang Sao Thong, 10540, Samutprakarn,
Thailand
Tel.: (66) 27051974
Web Site: http://www.aicabangkok.com
Emp.: 42
Industrial Adhesive Product Mfr.
N.A.I.C.S.: 325520

AICA Harima Kogyo Co., Ltd. **(1)**
395 Yokoo, Hojo-cho, Kasai, Japan
Tel.: (81) 790420631
Web Site: https://aica-harima.co.jp
Melamine Resins Material Mfr & Distr
N.A.I.C.S.: 325211

AICA Hatyai Co., Ltd. **(1)**
417/115 Karnchanavanich Rd, Patong
Hatyai, Hat Yai, 90230, Songkhla, Thailand
Tel.: (66) 74 291 5723
Web Site: https://www.aica-hatyai.com
Formaldehyde Resin Mfr
N.A.I.C.S.: 325211
Adrian Loo (Mgr-Factory)

AICA Kogyo Co., Ltd. **(1)**
GIC Bld 3B Floor 9 Nguyen Huu Canh St,
Binh Thanh Dist, Ho Chi Minh City, Vietnam
Tel.: (84) 2835106102

Decorative Laminate Product Mfr.
N.A.I.C.S.: 326130

AICA Laminates India Pvt. Ltd. **(1)**
Jet Air House 4th Floor 13 Community Cen-
tre Yusuf Sarai, New Delhi, 110 049, India
Tel.: (91) 112 656 2430
Web Site: https://www.aicasunmica.com
Panel Mfr
N.A.I.C.S.: 321992
J. L. Aluja (COO)

Plant (Domestic):

**AICA Laminates India Pvt. Ltd. -
Rudrapur Factory** **(2)**
Plot No 23-26 & 45 to 48 Sector-5 IIE SID-
CUL, Rudrapur, 263 153, India
Tel.: (91) 5944 250196
Laminated Sheet Mfr
N.A.I.C.S.: 326130

**AICA Laminates Vietnam Co.,
Ltd.** **(1)**
Road 4 Nhon Trach 3 IP- Phase 2, Long
Tho Commune, Nhon Trach, Dong Nai,
Vietnam
Tel.: (84) 2513686717
High Pressure Laminate Product Mfr
N.A.I.C.S.: 326130

AICA Malaysia Sdn. Bhd. **(1)**
Lot 115, Senawang Industrial Estate,
70450, Seremban, Negeri Sembilan, Malay-
sia
Tel.: (60) 196221465
Adhesive Product Mfr
N.A.I.C.S.: 325520

AICA NZ Ltd. **(1)**
149 Corbett Road, Bell Block, New Plym-
outh, 4373, New Zealand
Tel.: (64) 6 968 1800
Web Site: https://www.aicanz.co.nz
Emp.: 25
Industrial Resin Mfr
N.A.I.C.S.: 325211

AICA Singapore Pte. Ltd. **(1)**
43 Shipyard Road, Singapore, 628135,
Singapore
Tel.: (65) 62673105
Decorative Laminate Product Mfr
N.A.I.C.S.: 326130

AICA Tech Kenzai Co., Ltd. **(1)**
6-5-15 Toyotama Kita Tokyo Aica Tokyo
Building 2F, Nerima-ku, Tokyo, 176-0012,
Japan
Tel.: (81) 359120740
Web Site: https://www.aica-tech.co.jp
Emp.: 172
Building Materials Distr
N.A.I.C.S.: 423390

**AICA Trading (Shanghai) Co.,
Ltd.** **(1)**
24 Floor 01-03 JingNan Shipyard Bldg No
600 LuBan Road, LuWan District, Shang-
hai, 200125, China
Tel.: (86) 21 5466 6133
Web Site: http://www.aica-china.com
Adhesive Mfr
N.A.I.C.S.: 325520

Aica Adtek Sdn. Bhd. **(1)**
7 Jalan Korporat/KU9, Kawasan Perindus-
trian Meru, 42200, Klang, Selangor Darul
Ehsan, Malaysia
Tel.: (60) 333927608
Web Site: https://www.aica-adtek.com.my
Adhesive Mfr & Distr
N.A.I.C.S.: 325520

Aica Dong Nai Co., Ltd. **(1)**
Go Dau Industrial Park, Phuoc Thai Com-
mune, Long Thanh, Dong Nai, Vietnam
Tel.: (84) 2513841411
Web Site: https://aica-dongnai.com
Adhesive Product Mfr
N.A.I.C.S.: 325520

Aica Nanjing Co., Ltd. **(1)**
59 ChongFu Road, Nanjing Chemical In-
dustry Park, Nanjing, 210047, China
Tel.: (86) 2558676818
Adhesive Mfr & Distr
N.A.I.C.S.: 325520

Aica Thai Chemical Ltd. **(1)**
116 Moo 11 Tanon Suksawad Road T Naik-

longbangplakod A Prasamutjayde, Samut Prakan, 10290, Thailand
Tel.: (66) 281555145
Web Site: https://www.aica-tcc.com
Chemical Product Mfr & Distr
N.A.I.C.S.: 325998

Dynea (Guangdong) Co., Ltd. (1)
Jinli Town, Gaoyao, Guangdong, 526105, China
Tel.: (86) 7588579988
Paper Overlay Whslr
N.A.I.C.S.: 424130

Dynea (Nanjing) Co., Ltd. (1)
59 ChongFu Road, Nanjing Chemical Industry Park Luhe, Nanjing, 210047, China
Tel.: (86) 2558676818
Adhesive Product Whslr
N.A.I.C.S.: 424690

Dynea (Shanghai) Co., Ltd. (1)
Room 212 No 118 Futebei Road Waigaoqiao Free Trade Zone, Shanghai, China
Tel.: (86) 2158693060
Adhesive Product Whslr
N.A.I.C.S.: 424690

Kunshan AICA Kogyo Co., Ltd. (1)
No 501 Yu Jin Xiang Road Economic Development Zone, Kunshan, Jiangsu, China
Tel.: (86) 51257721777
Adhesive & Sealant Product Mfr
N.A.I.C.S.: 325520

Maica Laminates Sdn. Bhd. (1)
Lot 226 Batu 7 1/2 Jalan Padang Serai, Lunas, 09600, Kedah, Malaysia
Tel.: (60) 4 484 8496
Web Site: https://www.maica.com.my
Decorative Laminate Product Mfr
N.A.I.C.S.: 326130

NISHI TOKYO CHEMIX Corporation (1)
1-6 Kandanishikicho, Chiyoda-ku, Tokyo, 101-0054, Japan
Tel.: (81) 352077011
Web Site: https://www.nishi-tokyo.co.jp
Emp.: 50
Electronic Components Mfr & Distr
N.A.I.C.S.: 334413

P.T. AICA Indonesia (1)
Jl Ir H Juanda No 318, Bekasi, 17113, West Java, Indonesia
Tel.: (62) 21 880 1391
Web Site: https://www.aica.co.id
Melamine Resin Mfr
N.A.I.C.S.: 325211

PT. Techno Wood Indonesia (1)
Sector 1A Block K-5A-B Kawasan Industri Indotaisei Koto Bukit Indah, Cikampek, Karawang, 41373, Jawa Barat, Indonesia
Tel.: (62) 264350151
Web Site:
https://www.technowoodindonesia.com
Decorative Polyester Plywood Product Mfr
N.A.I.C.S.: 321211

PT.AICA Indria (1)
Jl Rawa Terate I/3, Pulogadung Industrial Estate, Jakarta, 13920, Indonesia
Tel.: (62) 214606202
Web Site: https://www.lem-fox.com
Adhesive Product Mfr
N.A.I.C.S.: 325520
Alvino Rizaldy (Plant Mgr)

Shenyang AICA-HOPE Kogyo Co., Ltd. (1)
No 100-11 Jianshe Road, Dadong District, Shenyang, 110122, China
Tel.: (86) 2489873619
Adhesive Mfr & Distr
N.A.I.C.S.: 325520

Sois Mendinni Industrial Technology (Shanghai) Co., Ltd. (1)
Room 301 No 1471 Gumei Road, Shanghai, 201102, China
Tel.: (86) 2154666133
High Pressure Laminate Product Mfr
N.A.I.C.S.: 326130

TAIWAN AICA KOGYO Co., Ltd. (1)
No 1562 Zhongzheng West Road, Hsinchu County, Zhubei, 302046, Taiwan
Tel.: (886) 3 556 6799

Web Site: https://www.aica.com.tw
Industrial Resin Mfr & Distr
N.A.I.C.S.: 325211

Wilsonart (Shanghai) Co., Ltd. (1)
1688 Songhua Road, Qingpu District, Shanghai, 201706, China (51%)
Tel.: (86) 2167001688
Decorative Laminated Products & Adhesives Mfr & Distr
N.A.I.C.S.: 337110

Wilsonart (Thailand) Company Limited (1)
622 18/5 floor Emporium Tower Sukhumvit Road, Klong Ton Sub-district Klong Toey District, Bangkok, 10110, Thailand (50.99%)
Tel.: (66) 2 681 1505
Web Site: https://www.wilsonart.co.th
Decorative Laminated Products & Adhesives Mfr & Distr
N.A.I.C.S.: 337110

Wilsonart Asia Limited (1)
Room 1608 16th Floor Hong Kong Center No 778-784 Changsha Wan Road, Kowloon, China (Hong Kong)
Tel.: (852) 23703899
Web Site: https://www.wilsonartasia.com
Home Decorative Product Distr
N.A.I.C.S.: 423220

Wilsonart Australia Pty Ltd (1)
Pigott Stinson Level 3 10 Barrack Street, Sydney, 2000, NSW, Australia (100%)
Tel.: (61) 1300 910 957
Web Site: http://www.wilsonart.com.au
Decorative Laminated Products & Adhesives Mfr & Distr
N.A.I.C.S.: 337110

AICHI CORPORATION

1152-10 Ryoke, Ageo, 362-8550, Saitama, Japan
Tel.: (81) 487811111
Web Site: https://www.aichi-corp.co.jp
Year Founded: 1962
6345—(NGO)
Rev.: $351,035,766
Assets: $627,166,108
Liabilities: $86,769,417
Net Worth: $540,396,690
Earnings: $34,820,459
Emp.: 1,046
Fiscal Year-end: 03/31/24
Industrial Truck Mfr & Whslr
N.A.I.C.S.: 333924
Toshiya Yamagishi (Pres, Pres & CEO)

Subsidiaries:

Aichi Aus Pty Ltd (1)
Unit 34 121 Kerry Road, Archerfield, 4108, QLD, Australia
Tel.: (61) 415457923
Work Platform Mfr
N.A.I.C.S.: 333923

Aichi Europe B.V. (1)
DeKreek 14, 4906 BB, Oosterhout, Netherlands
Tel.: (31) 162 480260
Industrial Truck Distr
N.A.I.C.S.: 423110

Aichi NZ Limited (1)
19 Ngapara Street, Otago, Alexandra, New Zealand
Tel.: (64) 3 440 2203
Web Site: https://www.aichinz.com
Insulation Material Distr
N.A.I.C.S.: 423330

Zhejiang AICHI Industrial Machinery Co., Ltd. (1)
No 180 Jinqiao Street, Economic and Technological Development Area, Hangzhou, 310018, Zhejiang, China
Tel.: (86) 57181996301
Web Site: http://www.aichi-zhe.com
Industrial Truck Distr
N.A.I.C.S.: 423110

AICHI ELECTRIC CO., LTD.

1 Aichi cho, Kasugai, 486-8666, Aichi, Japan
Tel.: (81) 568351211 JP
Web Site: http://www.aichidenki.jp
Year Founded: 1942
Sales Range: $400-449.9 Million
Emp.: 727
Electric Power Transformer Mfr
N.A.I.C.S.: 335311
Toru Sato (Pres)

Subsidiaries:

AICHI KINZOKU KOGYO CO., LTD. (1)
3-13-18 Odetatori-cho, Kasugai, Aichi, Japan
Tel.: (81) 568814181
Electric Power Transformer Mfr & Distr
N.A.I.C.S.: 335311

AIKOKIKI MFG. CO., LTD. (1)
1-2 Aichi-cho, Kasugai, Aichi, Japan
Tel.: (81) 568351680
Electric Power Transformer Mfr & Distr
N.A.I.C.S.: 335311

Aichi Electric & Electronic Products Division (1)
1 Aichi-cho, Kasugai, 486-8666, Aichi, Japan
Tel.: (81) 568351211
Web Site: http://www.aichidenki.jp
Sales Range: $200-249.9 Million
Small Motor & Motor Applied Apparatus Mfr
N.A.I.C.S.: 335312
Maghui Hideo (Mgr)

Aichi Electric Development & Environment Division (1)
2 Aichi-cho, Kasugai, 486-8666, Aichi, Japan
Tel.: (81) 568351211
Research & Product Development Services
N.A.I.C.S.: 541715
Yamaga Isao (Pres)

Aichi Electric Power Products Division (1)
2 Aichi-cho, Kasugai, 486-8666, Aichi, Japan
Tel.: (81) 568351211
Transformer & Switchgear Mfr
N.A.I.C.S.: 335311

ENA AICHI ELECTRIC CO., LTD. (1)
1780 Okada Iiji-cho, Ena, Gifu, Japan
Tel.: (81) 573223311
Electric Power Transformer Mfr & Distr
N.A.I.C.S.: 335311

GIFU AICHI ELECTRIC CO., LTD. (1)
195 Kinzokudanchi, Kagamihara, Gifu, Japan
Tel.: (81) 583821131
Electric Power Transformer Mfr & Distr
N.A.I.C.S.: 335311

KOTOBUKI KOGYO CO., LTD. (1)
3-13-35 Odetatori-cho, Kasugai, Aichi, Japan
Tel.: (81) 568814135
Electric Power Transformer Mfr & Distr
N.A.I.C.S.: 335311

NAGANO AICHI ELECTRIC CO., LTD. (1)
1280 Kawanakajimamachi hara, Nagano, Nagano, Japan
Tel.: (81) 262920885
Electric Power Transformer Mfr & Distr
N.A.I.C.S.: 335311

SHIROTORI AICHI ELEC CO., LTD. (1)
1393 Nakatsuya Shirotori-cho, Gujo, Gifu, Japan
Tel.: (81) 575824111
Electric Power Transformer Mfr & Distr
N.A.I.C.S.: 335311

Suzhou Aichi Technology Co., Ltd. (1)
112 Tong Sheng Road Suzhou Ind Park, Suzhou, 215126, Jiangsu, China
Tel.: (86) 51267325138
Automobile Parts Distr

N.A.I.C.S.: 423120

AICHI FINANCIAL GROUP CO., LTD.

3-14-12 Sakae, Naka-ku, Nagoya, 460-8678, Aichi, Japan
Tel.: (81) 522626512 JP
Web Site: https://www.aichi-fg.co.jp
Year Founded: 2020
73890—(TKS)
Rev.: $585,972,746
Assets: $45,136,677,154
Liabilities: $42,629,039,930
Net Worth: $2,507,637,223
Earnings: $54,806,724
Emp.: 882
Fiscal Year-end: 03/31/24
Bank Holding Company
N.A.I.C.S.: 551111
Yukinori Ito (Pres & CEO)

Subsidiaries:

The Aichi Bank, Ltd. (1)
3-14-12 Sakae, Naka-ku, Nagoya, 460-8678, Aichi, Japan
Tel.: (81) 522513211
Web Site: https://www.aichibank.co.jp
Rev.: $515,905,280
Assets: $36,669,117,760
Liabilities: $34,284,043,200
Net Worth: $2,385,074,560
Earnings: $41,294,880
Emp.: 1,692
Fiscal Year-end: 03/31/2021
Banking Services
N.A.I.C.S.: 522110
Shinichi Koide (Chm)

Subsidiary (Domestic):

Aigin Business Service Co., Ltd. (2)
3-14-12 Sakae, Naka-ku, Nagoya, 460-0008, Japan
Tel.: (81) 522629580
Web Site: https://www.aichibank.co.jp
Sales Range: $25-49.9 Million
Emp.: 80
Business Support Services
N.A.I.C.S.: 561499

Aigin Computer Service Co., Ltd. (2)
2-17-21 Nishiki, Naka-ku, Nagoya, 460-0003, Japan
Tel.: (81) 522181184
Sales Range: $25-49.9 Million
Emp.: 9
Computer Services
N.A.I.C.S.: 541519

Aigin DC Card Co., Ltd. (2)
4-22-20 Meieki 5th floor Aichi Bank Nagoya Ekimae Building, Nakamura-ku, Nagoya, 450-0002, Japan
Tel.: (81) 525510510
Web Site: https://www.aigindc.co.jp
Credit Card Services
N.A.I.C.S.: 522210
Haruhiko Ando (Pres)

Aigin Lease Co., Ltd. (2)
14-12 Sakae 3-chome, Naka-ku, Nagoya, 460-8678, Japan
Tel.: (81) 522513211
Sales Range: $50-74.9 Million
Emp.: 23
Equipment Rental & Leasing Services
N.A.I.C.S.: 532490

The Chukyo Bank, Ltd. (1)
3-33-13 Sakae, Naka-ku, Nagoya, 460-8681, Aichi, Japan
Tel.: (81) 522626111
Web Site: https://www.chukyo-bank.co.jp
Rev.: $304,397,280
Assets: $20,395,789,040
Liabilities: $19,324,300,160
Net Worth: $1,071,488,880
Earnings: $22,583,440
Emp.: 1,247
Fiscal Year-end: 03/31/2021
Banking Services
N.A.I.C.S.: 522110

AICHI STEEL CORPORATION

1 Wanowari Arao-machi Tokai-shi, Tokai, 476-8666, Aichi, Japan

Aichi Steel Corporation—(Continued)

Tel.: (81) 526041111
Web Site: https://www.aichi-steel.co.jp
Year Founded: 1940
5482—(TKS)
Rev.: $1,959,970,760
Assets: $2,928,943,880
Liabilities: $1,197,057,780
Net Worth: $1,731,886,100
Earnings: $43,579,730
Emp.: 4,572
Fiscal Year-end: 03/31/24
Speciality Steel, Forged Products, Electronic & Magnetic Parts Mfr & Whslr
N.A.I.C.S.: 331513
Takahiro Fujioka *(Pres)*

Subsidiaries:

Aichi Ceratec Corporation **(1)**
No 2 After Myojingo Kusumura-cho, Nishio, Aichi, Japan
Tel.: (81) 563596485
Web Site: http://www.aicera.co.jp
Emp.: 68
Industrial Furnace Product Mfr
N.A.I.C.S.: 333994

Aichi Europe GmbH **(1)**
Immermannstr 65b, 40210, Dusseldorf, Germany
Tel.: (49) 2111793430
Web Site: http://www.aichi-europe.de
Electromagnetic Product Mfr
N.A.I.C.S.: 335999

Aichi Forge (Thailand) Co., Ltd. **(1)**
150/68 Moo 9, Pinthong Industrial Estate II Nongkham, Si Racha, 20110, Chonburi, Thailand
Tel.: (66) 383472906
Web Site: http://www.aichi.co.th
Emp.: 354
Forging Component Mfr
N.A.I.C.S.: 332111
Sadamu Sakamoto *(Mng Dir)*

Aichi Forge Philippines, Inc. **(1)**
Brgy Pulong Sta Cruz, Santa Rosa, 4026, Laguna, Philippines
Tel.: (63) 288922260
Web Site: http://www.afp.ph
Forging Component Mfr
N.A.I.C.S.: 332111
Tomonori Kurosaki *(Pres)*

Aichi Forge USA, Inc. **(1)**
596 Triport Rd, Georgetown, KY 40324
Tel.: (502) 863-7575
Web Site: https://www.aichiforge.com
Automotive Parts Mfr & Distr
N.A.I.C.S.: 336390

Aichi Forging Company of Asia, Inc. **(1)**
Barrio Pulong Santa Cruz, Santa Rosa, 1043 AP, Laguna, Philippines **(62%)**
Tel.: (63) 28922260
Sales Range: $10-24.9 Million
Emp.: 270
Specialty Steel, Forged Products, Electronic & Magnetic Parts Mfr & Sales
N.A.I.C.S.: 331110

Aichi Information System Corporation **(1)**
3-5 Sumiyoshi-cho, Kariya, 448-0852, Aichi, Japan
Tel.: (81) 566217231
Web Site: https://www.asc21.net
Emp.: 260
Software Development Services
N.A.I.C.S.: 541511

Aichi Korea Corporation **(1)**
22 Teheran-ro 51-gil, Gangnam-gu, Seoul, 06148, Korea (South)
Tel.: (82) 25396065
Electronic Components Distr
N.A.I.C.S.: 449210

Aichi Magfine Czech s.r.o **(1)**
Heyrovskeho 488, 462 10, Liberec, Czech Republic
Tel.: (420) 488100299

Electromagnetic Product Mfr
N.A.I.C.S.: 335999

Aichi Magfine Technology (Pinghu) Co., Ltd. **(1)**
588 Xinghe Road Economic Development Zone, Pinghu, 314200, Zhejiang, China
Tel.: (86) 57385276222
Electronic Device & Magnetic Product Whslr
N.A.I.C.S.: 423690

Aichi Steel Logistics Co., Ltd. **(1)**
Tel.: (81) 562331431
Web Site: http://www.asl21.net
Emp.: 200
Cargo Transportation Services
N.A.I.C.S.: 488510

Aichi Techno Metal Fukaumi Co., Ltd. **(1)**
1483 Yoshidashimonakano, Tsubame, 959-0215, Niigata, Japan
Tel.: (81) 256923171
Web Site: http://www.atm-fukaumi.com
Emp.: 35
Rolling & Secondary Machinery Mfr
N.A.I.C.S.: 333519
Ryushin Endo *(Pres)*

Aichi USA Inc. **(1)**
596 Triport Rd, Georgetown, KY 40324-9529 **(100%)**
Tel.: (502) 863-2233
Sales Range: $50-74.9 Million
Emp.: 8
Sales of Hot Forged Products & Rolled Steel Bars
N.A.I.C.S.: 551112

Subsidiary (Domestic):

Aichi Forge & Gear Works, LLC **(2)**
596 Triport Rd, Georgetown, KY 40324-9529
Tel.: (502) 863-7575
Web Site: http://www.aichiforge.com
Sales Range: $75-99.9 Million
Mfr & Sales of Hot Forged Products
N.A.I.C.S.: 332111

Aiko Service Co., Ltd. **(1)**
52 Kamihirai Arao-cho, Tokai, 476-0003, Aichi, Japan
Tel.: (81) 526013100
Web Site: https://www.aiko-service.co.jp
Emp.: 400
Travel Agency Services
N.A.I.C.S.: 561510

Asdex Corporation **(1)**
1-23 Nanei-cho Fujie, Higashiura-cho, Chita, 470-2105, Aichi-ken, Japan
Tel.: (81) 562822480
Forging Die Product Mfr
N.A.I.C.S.: 333514

Omi Mining Co., Ltd. **(1)**
1780 Nagaoka, Maibara, 521-0242, Shiga Prefecture, Japan
Tel.: (81) 749550551
Web Site: https://www.omi-mining.co.jp
Limestone Mining Services
N.A.I.C.S.: 212312

PT. Aichi Forging Indonesia **(1)**
Jl Pegangsaan Dua Blok AI Km I 6 Kodya, Kelapa Gading, Jakarta Utara, 14240, Indonesia
Tel.: (62) 2146835191
Forging Product Mfr
N.A.I.C.S.: 332111

Shanghai Aichi Forging Co., Ltd. **(1)**
No 3300 Jiaan-Road, Shanghai, 201814, China
Tel.: (86) 2169574000
Forging Product Mfr
N.A.I.C.S.: 332111

Tokai Specialty Steel Co. Ltd. **(1)**
5-3 Tokai-machi, Tokai, 476-0015, Aichi-ken, Japan
Tel.: (81) 526037327
Crude Specialty Steel Mfr
N.A.I.C.S.: 331110

Zhejiang Aichi Mechanical & Electrical Co., Ltd. **(1)**
588 Xinghe Road Economic Development Zone, Pinghu, 314200, Zhejiang, China
Tel.: (86) 57385298888

Motor Magnet & Magnetic Product Mfr
N.A.I.C.S.: 335314

AICHI TOKEI DENKI CO., LTD.
Sennen 1-2-70, Atsuta-Ku, Nagoya, 456-8691, Japan
Tel.: (81) 526615151
Web Site: https://www.aichitokei.co.jp
Year Founded: 1898
7723—(NGO)
Rev.: $338,453,820
Assets: $405,675,473
Liabilities: $113,908,128
Net Worth: $291,767,345
Earnings: $20,971,253
Emp.: 1,739
Fiscal Year-end: 03/31/24
Gas Measuring Equipment Mfr & Whslr
N.A.I.C.S.: 333912
Hoshika Toshiyuki *(Chm)*

AID PARTNERS TECHNOLOGY HOLDINGS LIMITED
22/F New World Tower II 18 Queens Road, Central, China (Hong Kong)
Tel.: (852) 3468 5222 Ky
Web Site: http://www.aid8088.com
Rev.: $1,507,405
Assets: $65,315,361
Liabilities: $27,708,952
Net Worth: $37,606,409
Earnings: $(19,217,712)
Emp.: 40
Fiscal Year-end: 12/31/19
Investment Holding Company
N.A.I.C.S.: 551112
Suet Ngan Chan *(Sec)*

AIDA ENGINEERING, LTD.
2-10 Ohyama-cho, Midori-Ku, Sagamihara, 2525181, Kanagawa, Japan
Tel.: (81) 427725231
Web Site: https://www.aida.co.jp
Year Founded: 1917
6118—(TKS)
Rev.: $480,824,620
Assets: $834,148,950
Liabilities: $290,007,140
Net Worth: $544,141,810
Earnings: $18,560,880
Emp.: 2,020
Fiscal Year-end: 03/31/24
Press Machines Mfr
N.A.I.C.S.: 333248
Kimikazu Aida *(Pres, CEO & Chm)*

Subsidiaries:

AIDA (Thailand) Co., Ltd. **(1)**
19/19 Moo 6 Wat-Sriwarinoi Rd T Srisajorrakaeyai, A Bangsaothong, Samut Prakan, 10570, Thailand
Tel.: (66) 2 136 3900
Printing Machinery Equipment Mfr & Distr
N.A.I.C.S.: 323111

AIDA BUSINESS CORP. **(1)**
2-10 Ohyama-cho Midori Ward, Sagamihara, 252-0146, Kanagawa, Japan
Tel.: (81) 427794810
Web Site: http://www.aida.co.jp
Sales Range: $350-399.9 Million
Emp.: 700
Used Machine Sales Services
N.A.I.C.S.: 532420

AIDA Engineering (M) Sdn. Bhd. **(1)**
Plo 524 Jalan Keluli, 81700, Pasir Gudang, Johor, Malaysia
Tel.: (60) 7 251 6688
Metal Automation Equipment Mfr & Distr
N.A.I.C.S.: 333248

AIDA Engineering China Co., LTD. **(1)**
Hua Jing Rd 9 Waigaoqiao Free Trade Zone, Pudong New Area, Shanghai, 200131, China
Tel.: (86) 2150462066

Sales Range: $25-49.9 Million
Emp.: 100
Metal Stamping Presses Mfr
N.A.I.C.S.: 333248

AIDA Engineering de Mexico, S. de R. L. de C.V. **(1)**
Av Hercules 401-B Nave Industrial 7 Poligono Empresarial Santa Rosa, Santa Rosa Jauregui, 76220, Queretaro, Mexico
Tel.: (52) 442 291 1320
Clutch & Brake Repair Services
N.A.I.C.S.: 811198

AIDA Europe GmbH **(1)**
Josef-Eggler Strasse 8, 88250, Weingarten, Germany
Tel.: (49) 75 156 0929
Web Site: https://www.aida-europe.com
Printing Machinery Equipment Mfr & Distr
N.A.I.C.S.: 323111

AIDA Greater Asia Philippines, Inc. **(1)**
Unit 101B Coherco Financial Tower Trade St Cor Investment Drive, Madrigal Business Park Ayala Alabang, Muntinlupa, 1780, Philippines
Tel.: (63) 28 771 1561
Printing Machinery Equipment Mfr & Distr
N.A.I.C.S.: 323111

AIDA Hong Kong, LTD. **(1)**
Unit 901-902 9/F 29 Austin Road, Tsimshatsui, Kowloon, China (Hong Kong)
Tel.: (852) 27360118
Web Site: http://www.aida.com.hk
Metal Stamping Presses Mfr
N.A.I.C.S.: 333517

AIDA India Pvt. Ltd. **(1)**
No 48 Ground Floor DLF Star Tower Silokhera Sector 30, Gurgaon, 122001, Haryana, India
Tel.: (91) 124 471 6888
Printing Machinery Equipment Mfr & Distr
N.A.I.C.S.: 323111

AIDA Manufacturing (Asia) Sdn. Bhd. **(1)**
Plo 524 Jalan Keluli, 81700, Pasir Gudang, Johor, Malaysia
Tel.: (60) 7 251 6688
Printing Machinery Equipment Mfr & Distr
N.A.I.C.S.: 323111

AIDA Maroc Sarl **(1)**
Lot 81 Ilot C5 Zone Franche d' Exportation, 90100, Tangiers, Morocco
Tel.: (212) 53 939 5325
Printing Machinery Equipment Mfr & Distr
N.A.I.C.S.: 323111

AIDA PRESSEN GmbH **(1)**
Steuerungsbau Sdfeld 9d, Kamen, 59174, Germany
Tel.: (49) 23074386420
Web Site: http://www.aida-global.com
Sales Range: $25-49.9 Million
Emp.: 8
Metal Stamping Presses Mfr
N.A.I.C.S.: 333517
Troy Daniel Robert *(Mng Dir)*

AIDA Stamping Technology (India) Pvt Ltd. **(1)**
No 48 Ground Floor DLF Star Tower Sector 30, Silokhera, Gurgaon, 122001, Haryana, India
Tel.: (91) 1244716888
Web Site: http://www.aida.com.sg
Sales Range: $25-49.9 Million
Emp.: 13
Metal Stamping Presses Mfr
N.A.I.C.S.: 333517
C. L. Goh *(Mgr)*

AIDA Stamping Technology (Thailand) Co., Ltd. **(1)**
41 23 Moo 6 Bangna-Trad Km 16 5 Tambol Bangchalong, Bang Phli, 10540, Samut Prakan, Thailand
Tel.: (66) 23370197
Web Site: http://www.aida.com.sg
Sales Range: $25-49.9 Million
Metal Stamping Presses Mfr
N.A.I.C.S.: 333517

AIDA Vietnam Co., Ltd. **(1)**

Room 108 Industrial Park Center, Thang Long Industrial Park Kim Chung Commune, Dong Anh District, Hanoi, Vietnam
Tel.: (84) 243 885 3388
Printing Machinery Equipment Mfr & Distr
N.A.I.C.S.: 323111

AIDA do Brasil Comercio de Maquinas Ltda. (1)
Rua Arnaldo Batista de Almeida 63 Centro Empresarial, Indaiatuba, 13347-433, Sao Paulo, Brazil
Tel.: (55) 193 500 4600
Printing Machinery Equipment Mfr & Distr
N.A.I.C.S.: 323111

Access Ltd. (1)
1080 Kozu-machi, Hakusan, 924-0821, Ishikawa, Japan
Tel.: (81) 762748200
Web Site: http://www.kkaccess.co.jp
Sales Range: $50-74.9 Million
Emp.: 104
Metal Processing Machines Mfr & Sales
N.A.I.C.S.: 333248

Aida Canada Inc. (1)
122 Commerce Park Drive Units B and C, Barrie, L4N 8W8, ON, Canada
Tel.: (705) 734-9692
Web Site: http://www.aida-global.com
Sales Range: $25-49.9 Million
Emp.: 4
Metal Stamping Presses Mfr
N.A.I.C.S.: 332119
Steve Mirrles (Mgr-Svc)

Aida Germany Gmbh (1)
Sudfeld 9d, 59174, Kamen, Germany
Tel.: (49) 23074386420
Metal Stamping Press Mfr & Distr
N.A.I.C.S.: 336370

Aida Greater Asia Pte. Ltd. (1)
No1 Bukit Batok Crescent 02-60 Wcega Plaza, Singapore, 658064, Singapore
Tel.: (65) 73555
Web Site: https://www.aida.com.sg
Metal Stamping Press Mfr
N.A.I.C.S.: 336370

Aida Press Machinery Systems Co., Ltd. (1)
No 409 Jimei Road Chenqiao Street, Gangzha District, Nantong, China
Tel.: (86) 5135 100 6588
Printing Machinery Equipment Mfr & Distr
N.A.I.C.S.: 323111

OOO AIDA (1)
Frunze Street 14B Office 230, 445037, Togliatti, Russia
Tel.: (7) 8482270376
Printing Machinery Equipment Mfr & Distr
N.A.I.C.S.: 323111

PT AIDA Stamping Technology Indonesia (1)
Ruko Mall Bekasi Fajar Blok B No 22 Kawasan Industri MM2100, Cikarang Barat, Bekasi, 17520, West Java, Indonesia
Tel.: (62) 2189982432
Web Site: http://www.aida.com.sg
Sales Range: $25-49.9 Million
Emp.: 20
Metal Stamping Presses Mfr
N.A.I.C.S.: 333517

PT. AIDA Indonesia (1)
Jl Science Boulevard Blok A2/9 Kawasan Industri Jababeka V Kel, Cikarang Timur, Bekasi, 17530, Indonesia
Tel.: (62) 212 962 6688
Printing Machinery Equipment Mfr & Distr
N.A.I.C.S.: 323111

REJ Co., Ltd. (1)
2-3-2 Fukuura, Kanazawa-ku, Yokohama, 236-8641, Kanagawa, Japan (80%)
Tel.: (81) 45 701 1770
Web Site: https://www.rej.jp
Industrial Control Mfr
N.A.I.C.S.: 334519
Kubo Kazuhiro (Pres)

AIDA PHARMACEUTICALS, INC.
31 Dingjiang Road, Jianggan District, Hangzhou, 310016, China

Tel.: (86) 57185802712 NV
AIDA—(OTCIQ)
Sales Range: Less than $1 Million
Pharmaceuticals Product Mfr
N.A.I.C.S.: 325412
Biao Jin (Chm & CEO)

AIDALA MUNAI JSC
Dostyk Ave 38, Medeu district, 050010, Almaty, Kazakhstan
Tel.: (7) 273390299
ADLA—(KAZ)
Assets: $3,302
Liabilities: $83,150
Net Worth: ($79,848)
Earnings: ($11,516)
Fiscal Year-end: 12/31/23
Oil & Gas Exploration Services
N.A.I.C.S.: 213112
Zholdybaev Dosbol (Pres & CEO)

AIDIGONG MATERNAL & CHILD HEALTH LIMITED
room e 28 / F Enhao International Center 1 Changyue Road, Kowloon, China (Hong Kong)
Tel.: (852) 26206623 BM
Web Site: http://www.aidigong.hk
Year Founded: 1990
0286—(HKG)
Rev.: $86,693,115
Assets: $284,519,310
Liabilities: $166,529,535
Net Worth: $117,989,775
Earnings: ($22,712,850)
Emp.: 1,561
Fiscal Year-end: 12/31/22
Investment Holding Company; Health Management
N.A.I.C.S.: 551112
Wing Cheung Wong (Sec)

Subsidiaries:

eClinix Holdings Limited (1)
13/F No 8 Hart Road, Tsim Sha Tsui, Kowloon, China (Hong Kong)
Tel.: (852) 29838388
Web Site: http://www.eclinix.com.hk
Health Care Srvices
N.A.I.C.S.: 621999

AIDMA MARKETING COMMUNICATION CORPORATION
1331 Toyodacho, Toyama, 931-8313, Japan
Tel.: (81) 764397878
Web Site: https://www.e-aidma.co.jp
9466—(TKS)
Rev.: $38,582,570
Assets: $30,280,410
Liabilities: $10,728,030
Net Worth: $19,552,380
Earnings: $1,044,380
Emp.: 190
Fiscal Year-end: 03/31/24
Marketing Consulting Services
N.A.I.C.S.: 541613
Takashi Ebitani (Founder)

AIER EYE HOSPITAL GROUP CO., LTD.
North Tower Aier Ophthalmology Building No 188 Section 1, Furong South Road Tianxin District, Changsha, 410015, Hunan, China
Tel.: (86) 73185179288
Web Site: https://www.aierchina.com
Year Founded: 2003
300015—(CHIN)
Rev.: $2,868,714,021
Assets: $4,251,785,413
Liabilities: $1,431,297,756
Net Worth: $2,820,487,657
Earnings: $473,097,051
Emp.: 50,000
Fiscal Year-end: 12/31/23
Ophthalmology Medical Services

N.A.I.C.S.: 621111

Subsidiaries:

Clinica Baviera S.A. (1)
Tel.: (34) 917819880
Web Site: https://www.clinicabaviera.com
Sales Range: Less than $1 Million
Healtcare Services
N.A.I.C.S.: 621610
Eduardo Baviera Sabater (CEO)

AIFARM LTD.
Unit 503 5/F Silvercord Tower 2 30 Canton Road TST, Kowloon, China (Hong Kong)
Tel.: (852) 91235575 NV
Web Site: http://www.ecoenergytechasia.com
Year Founded: 2015
AIFM—(OTCBB)
Rev.: $37
Assets: $88,274
Liabilities: $3,481,646
Net Worth: ($3,393,372)
Earnings: ($547,089)
Emp.: 3
Fiscal Year-end: 12/31/19
Garden Equipment Mfr
N.A.I.C.S.: 333111
Yuen May Cheung (Founder, Pres & CEO)

Subsidiaries:

EcoAgri Asia Ltd. (1)
Room 2001A Fullin Plaza No 87 Fuzhou Road, Qingdao, 266071, China
Tel.: (86) 53266009446
Potato Starch Mfr
N.A.I.C.S.: 311999

AIFINYO AG
Friedrichstrasse 94, 10117, Berlin, Germany
Tel.: (49) 35189693310
Web Site: https://www.aifinyo.de
Year Founded: 2012
EBEN—(DEU)
Rev.: $57,137,658
Assets: $69,409,620
Liabilities: $50,537,880
Net Worth: $18,871,740
Earnings: $1,236,792
Emp.: 71
Fiscal Year-end: 12/31/22
Asset Management Services
N.A.I.C.S.: 523999

AIFORIA TECHNOLOGIES OYJ
Pursimiehenkatu 29-31 D, 00150, Helsinki, Finland
Tel.: (358) 207349130
Web Site: https://www.aiforia.com
Year Founded: 2013
AIFORIA—(HEL)
Rev.: $2,590,114
Assets: $30,423,052
Liabilities: $11,094,323
Net Worth: $19,328,729
Earnings: ($13,954,241)
Emp.: 73
Fiscal Year-end: 12/31/23
Software Development Services
N.A.I.C.S.: 541511
Jukka Tapaninen (CEO)

AIFUL CORPORATION
381-1 Takasago-cho Gojo-Agaru Karasuma-Dori, Shimogyo-ku, Kyoto, 600-8420, Japan
Tel.: (81) 752012000 JP
Web Site: https://www.aiful.co.jp
Year Founded: 1967
8515—(TKS)
Rev.: $1,078,150,490
Assets: $8,370,732,140
Liabilities: $7,039,398,820
Net Worth: $1,331,333,320
Earnings: $144,216,980

Emp.: 2,470
Fiscal Year-end: 03/31/24
Consumer Finance, Mortgage Loan, Guaranteed Loan & Real Estate Services
N.A.I.C.S.: 522310
Yoshitaka Fukuda (Chm)

Subsidiaries:

AG Crowdfunding Co.,Ltd. (1)
Banzai Building 8F 2-31-19 Shiba, Minato-ku, Tokyo, 105-0014, Japan
Tel.: (81) 357300513
Web Site: https://www.ag-crowdfunding.com
Financial Investment Services
N.A.I.C.S.: 523999

AG Guarantee Co., Ltd. (1)
Banzai Building 6F 2-31-19 Shiba, Minato-ku, Tokyo, 105-0014, Japan
Tel.: (81) 357652099
Web Site: https://www.aifulguarantee.co.jp
Collection Agency Services
N.A.I.C.S.: 561440

AG Loan Services Corporation (1)
1-1 Nishioji-cho, Kusatsu, 525-0037, Shiga, Japan
Tel.: (81) 775030200
Web Site: https://www.a-g-sv.com
Financial Collection Services
N.A.I.C.S.: 561440

AG Medical Corporation (1)
Banzai Building 2-31-19 Shiba, Minato-ku, Tokyo, 105-0014, Japan
Tel.: (81) 354847511
Web Site: https://www.agmedical.co.jp
Financial Services
N.A.I.C.S.: 522320

AG Smile Leaseback Corporation (1)
1-1 Nishiojicho, Kusatsu, 525-0037, Japan
Tel.: (81) 775615151
Web Site: https://agsmileleaseback.co.jp
Fund Management Services
N.A.I.C.S.: 523999

AG Stock Center Corporation (1)
6861-4 Iimuro Asacho, Asakita Ward, Hiroshima, 731-1142, Japan
Tel.: (81) 828350363
Web Site: https://aifulstockcenter.co.jp
Warehouse Logistics Services
N.A.I.C.S.: 493110

AIFUL Business Finance Corporation (1)
2-31-19 Shiba, Minato-ku, Tokyo, 105-0014, Japan
Tel.: (81) 120290051
Web Site: https://www.aiful-bf.co.jp
Emp.: 130
Financial Services
N.A.I.C.S.: 523999

AIFUL Guarantee Co., Ltd. (1)
Banzai Building 6F 2-31-19 Shiba, Minato-ku, Tokyo, 105-0014, Japan
Tel.: (81) 357652099
Web Site: http://www.aifulguarantee.co.jp
Storage Agency Services
N.A.I.C.S.: 531130

AIFUL Partners Corporation (1)
Banzai Building 8th Floor 2-31-19 Shiba, Minato-ku, Tokyo, 105-0014, Japan
Tel.: (81) 343342006
Web Site: http://www.aiful-p.com
Consumer Finance Services
N.A.I.C.S.: 522291

AIFUL Stock Center Corporation (1)
4 of 6861 Imuro Asa-cho, Asakita-ku, Hiroshima, 731-1142, Japan
Tel.: (81) 828350363
Web Site: http://www.aifulstockcenter.co.jp
Warehousing Services
N.A.I.C.S.: 493190

AIRA & AIFUL Public Company Limited (1)
No 90 CW Tower Floor 33 34 Room No B 3301-2 B 3401-2, Ratchadaphisek Road Huai Khwang Subdistrict Huai Khwang District, Bangkok, 10310, Thailand
Tel.: (66) 21175000
Web Site: https://www.aira-aiful.co.th

AIFUL Corporation—(Continued)

Financial Services
N.A.I.C.S.: 523999
Wichian Mektrakam *(Chm)*

AsTry Loan Services Corporation (1)
Banzai Building 8F 31-19 Shiba 2-chome,
Minato-ku, Tokyo, 105-0014, Japan
Tel.: (81) 343342000
Web Site: http://www.astry-s.co.jp
Loan Services
N.A.I.C.S.: 561790

Life Card Co., Ltd. (1)
1-3-20 Edanishi, Aoba-ku, Yokohama, 225-
0014, Kanagawa, Japan
Tel.: (81) 459147003
Web Site: http://www.lifecard.co.jp
Financial Services
N.A.I.C.S.: 523999

New Frontier Partners Co Ltd (1)
5F 1-2-2 Yuurakuchou Chuo-ku, Tokyo, 100
0006, Japan
Tel.: (81) 345036400
Web Site: http://www.nf-partners.co.jp
Venture Capital Funding Services
N.A.I.C.S.: 523999
Toshihito Hayano *(Pres)*

**Sumishin Life Card Company,
Limited** (1)
Banzai Building 3F 2-31-19 Shiba, Minato-
ku, Tokyo, 105-0014, Japan
Tel.: (81) 354440675
Web Site: http://www.sumishinlifecard.co.jp
Financial Insurance Services
N.A.I.C.S.: 524210

Tryto Corporation (1)
Aiful Honsha Bldg 9f 381-1, Karasumadori
Gojo Shimogyo K, Kyoto, Japan
Tel.: (81) 753535035
Financial Services
N.A.I.C.S.: 523999

WIDE Corporation (1)
15F The First Tower III 602
Dongtangiheung-ro, Hwaseong, 18469,
Gyeonggi-do, Korea (South)
Tel.: (82) 312181600
Web Site: https://www.widecorp.com
Sales Range: $25-49.9 Million
Emp.: 81
Image Quality Assurance Systems Mfr
N.A.I.C.S.: 334515
Hodae Hwang *(Pres & CEO)*

AIGAN CO., LTD.
4-9-12 Daido Tennoji-ku, Tennoji-ku,
Osaka, 543-0052, Japan
Tel.: (81) 667723383
Web Site: https://online-
shop.aigan.co.jp
Year Founded: 1961
9854—(TKS)
Rev.: $96,889,380
Assets: $93,062,190
Liabilities: $13,061,360
Net Worth: $80,000,830
Earnings: ($1,196,410)
Emp.: 311
Fiscal Year-end: 03/31/24
Optical Store Operator
N.A.I.C.S.: 456130

AII DATA PROCESSING LTD.
64 Kiril i Metodii Street, Sofia, 1202,
Bulgaria
Tel.: (359) 28012600
Web Site: http://www.aiidatapro.com
Year Founded: 1999
Sales Range: $25-49.9 Million
Emp.: 250
Information Services, Data Process-
ing & Business Services
N.A.I.C.S.: 518210
Radostina Jilevska *(CFO)*

AIICO INSURANCE PLC
Plot PC 12 Churchgate Street Victo-
ria Island, Lagos, Nigeria
Tel.: (234) 12792930
Web Site: https://www.aiicoplc.com

Year Founded: 1963
AIICO—(NIGE)
Rev.: $65,341,653
Assets: $200,097,351
Liabilities: $166,782,517
Net Worth: $33,314,834
Earnings: $5,590,594
Emp.: 481
Fiocal Year-end: 12/31/22
Asset Management Services
N.A.I.C.S.: 523940
Kundan Sainani *(Chm)*

Subsidiaries:

AIICO Capital Limited (1)
Plot 12 AIICO Plaza Churchgate Street Vic-
toria Island, PO Box 2577, Lagos, Nigeria
Tel.: (234) 9167429986
Web Site: https://www.aiicocapital.com
Financial Investment Services
N.A.I.C.S.: 523940

AIICO Multishield Limited (1)
322 Ikorodu Road Anthony B/Stop, Anthony
Village, Lagos, Nigeria
Tel.: (234) 12930823
Web Site: https://www.aiicomultishield.com
Healtcare Services
N.A.I.C.S.: 621999
Leke Oshunniyi *(CEO & Mng Dir)*

AIK BAACKA TOPOLA A.D.
61 Marsala Tita St, 24300, Backa To-
pola, Serbia
Tel.: (381) 24 712300
Web Site: http://www.aikbt.rs
Year Founded: 1974
Sales Range: $1-9.9 Million
Animal Feed Mfr
N.A.I.C.S.: 311119

AIK FOTBOLL AB
Evenemangsgatan 31, 16979, Solna,
Sweden
Tel.: (46) 87359650
Web Site: https://www.aikfotboll.se
Sports Club Operator
N.A.I.C.S.: 711211
Hakan Strandlund *(CEO, CFO & Fin
Dir)*

**AIKBEE RESOURCES BER-
HAD**
B-8-7 Megan Ave 1 189 Jalan Tun
Razak, 50400, Kuala Lumpur, Malay-
sia
Tel.: (60) 321616322
Web Site: http://www.aikbee.com.my
Sales Range: $10-24.9 Million
Molding Timbers Mfr
N.A.I.C.S.: 321215
Mohd Zaki Hamzah *(Exec Dir)*

Subsidiaries:

**Aikbee Timbers (Sabah) Sdn.
Bhd.** (1)
Batu 6 1/2 Jalan Kepong, 52000, Kuala
Lumpur, Malaysia
Tel.: (60) 362511122
Timber Logging Services
N.A.I.C.S.: 113110
Lim Chong Kee *(Mgr)*

**AIKCHOL HOSPITAL PUBLIC
COMPANY LIMITED**
No 68/ 3 Moo 2 Phrayasatcha Rd,
Ban Suan Subdistrict Mueang Chon-
buri District, Chon Buri, 20000, Thai-
land
Tel.: (66) 38939999
Web Site: https://www.aikchol.com
Year Founded: 1978
AHC—(THA)
Rev.: $53,396,723
Assets: $71,331,027
Liabilities: $10,731,298
Net Worth: $60,599,729
Earnings: $5,510,267
Emp.: 1,197

Fiscal Year-end: 12/31/23
Health Care Srvices
N.A.I.C.S.: 621999
Phortchana Manoch *(Vice Chm)*

AIKO CORPORATION
205-2 Nishi-Odomo, Odawara, 250-
0293, Kanagawa, Japan
Tel.: (01) 46 5372111
Web Site: http://www.aiko-denki.co.jp
Year Founded: 1959
99090—(JAS)
Rev.: $111,122,060
Assets: $61,750,780
Liabilities: $38,156,370
Net Worth: $23,594,410
Earnings: $1,916,530
Fiscal Year-end: 03/31/20
Lighting Equipment Whslr
N.A.I.C.S.: 423610
Tamotsu Kondo *(Pres)*

AILLERON SA
Oxygen Park Jutrzenki 137 Street,
02-231, Warsaw, Poland
Tel.: (48) 122523400
Web Site: https://www.ailleron.com
Year Founded: 2011
ALL—(WAR)
Rev.: $115,121,697
Assets: $110,687,754
Liabilities: $57,449,949
Net Worth: $53,237,805
Earnings: $5,306,148
Fiscal Year-end: 12/31/23
Software Development Services
N.A.I.C.S.: 541511
Marcin Dabrowski *(Member-Mgmt Bd
& Gen Mgr-Fintech Div)*

AILLEURS EXACTEMENT
38 bis rue du fer-a-Moulin, 75005,
Paris, France
Tel.: (33) 155435000
Year Founded: 1985
Sales Range: $10-24.9 Million
Emp.: 56
Advertising Agencies, Consumer Mar-
keting, Direct Marketing, Travel &
Tourism
N.A.I.C.S.: 541810
Evelyn Soum *(Owner, Chm & CEO-
Ailleurs exactement, S & F Paris)*

AILSEN LIMITED.
Finch Close Lenton Lane, Notting-
ham, NG7 2NN, United Kingdom
Tel.: (44) 1159869686
Web Site: http://www.ailsen.ltd.uk
Year Founded: 1975
Rev.: $12,208,631
Emp.: 35
Building Services
N.A.I.C.S.: 561790
Paul Phillips *(Dir-Fin)*

**AIM INDUSTRIAL GROWTH
FREEHOLD & LEASEHOLD
REIT**
Unit 803 8th floor Tower B GPF Wit-
thayu Building, No 93/1 Witthayu
Road Lumpini Pathumwan, Bangkok,
10330, Thailand
Tel.: (66) 225404412
Web Site: https://www.aimirt.com
AIMIRT—(THA)
Rev.: $26,619,522
Assets: $323,095,917
Liabilities: $108,750,560
Net Worth: $214,345,357
Earnings: $15,352,651
Fiscal Year-end: 12/31/23
Real Estate Investment Trust Ser-
vices
N.A.I.C.S.: 523991
Amorn Chulaluksananukul *(CEO)*

AIM VACCINE CO., LTD.
Unit 2505-2507 Tower A 25/F Gem-
dale Plaza 91 Jianguo Road, Chaoy-
ang District, Beijing, China
Tel.: (86) 1085950689   CN
Web Site: https://www.aimbio.com
Year Founded: 2011
6660—(HKG)
Rev.: $193,668,624
Assets: $1,359,859,173
Liabilities: $461,909,612
Net Worth: $897,949,561
Earnings: ($35,334,822)
Emp.: 1,576
Fiscal Year-end: 12/31/22
Vaccine Mfr & Distr
N.A.I.C.S.: 325414
Ling Liu *(Chief Investment Officer)*

AIM3 VENTURES, INC.
77 King Street West Suite 400, To-
ronto, M5K 0A1, ON, Canada
Tel.: (416) 818-4972
AIMC.P.—(TSXV)
Assets: $588,910
Liabilities: $13,399
Net Worth: $575,511
Earnings: ($26,516)
Fiscal Year-end: 12/31/19
Asset Management Services
N.A.I.C.S.: 523940
Zachary Goldenberg *(CEO)*

AIMCO PESTICIDES LIMITED
Aimco House Akhand Jyoti 8th Road,
Santacruz East, Mumbai, 400 055,
India
Tel.: (91) 2267604000
Web Site:
https://www.aimcopesticides.com
Year Founded: 1987
524288—(BOM)
Rev.: $42,701,609
Assets: $22,794,722
Liabilities: $15,902,851
Net Worth: $6,891,871
Earnings: $1,455,035
Emp.: 135
Fiscal Year-end: 03/31/22
Agrochemical Manufacturing, Formu-
lation & Marketing of Insecticides,
Fungicides & Herbicides
N.A.I.C.S.: 325320
Pradeep Pushkarrai Dave *(Co-Chm)*

**AIMCORE TECHNOLOGY CO.,
LTD.**
No 10 Guangfu N Road, Hsinchu In-
dustrial Zone, Hsinchu, 30351, Tai-
wan
Tel.: (886) 35986336
Web Site:
https://www.aimcore.com.tw
Year Founded: 2000
3615—(TPE)
Rev.: $35,357,440
Assets: $106,136,573
Liabilities: $29,481,818
Net Worth: $76,654,754
Earnings: $1,599,287
Fiscal Year-end: 12/31/22
Glass Material Mfr
N.A.I.C.S.: 327215
Yeh Chwei-Jing *(Chm)*

AIMECHATEC LTD.
5-2 Koyodai, Ryugasaki, 301-0852,
Ibaraki, Japan
Tel.: (81) 297629111
Web Site: https://www.ai-mech.com
6227—(TKS)
Rev.: $95,918,620
Assets: $141,654,280
Liabilities: $73,514,180
Net Worth: $68,140,100
Earnings: $690,420

Emp.: 252
Fiscal Year-end: 06/30/24
Electronic Components Mfr
N.A.I.C.S.: 334419

Subsidiaries:

Nanjing AIMECHATEC Ltd. **(1)**
No1 Ruixin, Hushu Sub-district Jiangning
District, Nanjing, 211121, Jiangsu, China
Tel.: (86) 2584236700
Emp.: 36
Flat Panel Display Mfr & Distr
N.A.I.C.S.: 334118

AIMER CO., LTD.
Building No 218 & 219 Area 2,
Lizezhong Park Wangjing Develop-
ment Zone Chaoyang District, Beijing,
100102, China
Tel.: (86) 1064390009
Web Site: http://www.aimer.com.cn
Year Founded: 1981
603511—(SHG)
Rev.: $463,374,953
Assets: $720,016,577
Liabilities: $89,266,783
Net Worth: $630,749,794
Earnings: $28,792,347
Emp.: 10,000
Fiscal Year-end: 12/31/22
Clothing Apparel Mfr & Distr
N.A.I.C.S.: 315250
Rongming Zhang (Chm & Gen Mgr)

AIMFLEX BERHAD
12-2 Jalan Persiaran Teknologi Ta-
man, 81400, Senai, Johor, Malaysia
Tel.: (60) 75955545 MY
Web Site:
https://www.aimflex.com.my
Year Founded: 2007
AIMFLEX—(KLS)
Rev.: $18,747,150
Assets: $24,672,371
Liabilities: $5,454,072
Net Worth: $19,218,300
Earnings: $1,170,350
Emp.: 267
Fiscal Year-end: 12/31/21
Automation Product Mfr & Distr
N.A.I.C.S.: 336320
Lee Yong Ho (Head-Ops & Mfg Auto-
mation)

Subsidiaries:

Bizit Systems & Solutions Pte.
Ltd. **(1)**
2 Kallang Avenue CT Hub 04-03, Singa-
pore, 339407, Singapore
Tel.: (65) 64420411
Web Site: http://www.bizits.com
Software Services
N.A.I.C.S.: 541511

Bizit Systems (M) Sdn. Bhd. **(1)**
V03-08-23A Lingkaran SV Sunway Velocity
Jalan Peel, 55100, Kuala Lumpur, Malaysia
Tel.: (60) 327105044
Web Site: http://www.bizits.com
Wireless Communication Device Distr
N.A.I.C.S.: 423690

Owin Industrial Sdn. Bhd. **(1)**
No 3 Lorong Nagasari 2 Taman Nagasari,
13600, Perai, Penang, Malaysia
Tel.: (60) 135966403
Web Site: https://www.owin.com.my
Precision Parts Mfr
N.A.I.C.S.: 332721

Union Tech Automation Sdn.
Bhd. **(1)**
No 2 Lintang Beringin, 11960, Penang, Ma-
laysia
Tel.: (60) 46264487
Web Site: https://www.uniontech.com.my
Automation Equipment Mfr
N.A.I.C.S.: 333310

AIMHIGH GLOBAL CORP.
10F Sinyeong Bldg Yeongdong-daero

731, Gangnam-gu, Seoul, 6072, Ko-
rea (South)
Tel.: (82) 2 316 2200
Web Site: http://www.ahg.co.kr
Rev.: $21,860,212
Assets: $142,311,458
Liabilities: $8,243,082
Net Worth: $134,068,376
Earnings: ($19,813,282)
Emp.: 28
Fiscal Year-end: 12/31/17
Electronic Components Mfr
N.A.I.C.S.: 334419

AIMIA FOODS LIMITED
Penny Lane, Haydock, WA11 0QZ,
Merseyside, United Kingdom
Tel.: (44) 1942272900 UK
Web Site:
https://www.aimiafoods.com
Year Founded: 1981
Emp.: 300
Food & Beverage Mfr
N.A.I.C.S.: 311999
Rob Unsworth (Chm)

AIMIA INC.
1010 Saint Catherine Street West
Suite 200, Montreal, H3B 5L1, QC,
Canada
Tel.: (514) 497-8973 Ca
Web Site: https://www.aimia.com
Year Founded: 2008
AIMFF—(OTCIQ)
Rev.: $246,320,144
Assets: $1,167,944,104
Liabilities: $727,633,632
Net Worth: $440,310,472
Earnings: $142,415,632
Emp.: 15
Fiscal Year-end: 12/31/23
Consumer Loyalty Management &
Promotion Services
N.A.I.C.S.: 561499
Joshua Chandler (Treas, VP & Head-
Global)

Subsidiaries:

Aeroplan Canada Inc **(1)**
Pointe Claire Dorval Station, PO Box
21000, Dorval, QC, Canada
Tel.: (902) 367-8445
Web Site: http://www.aeroplan.com
Loyalty Management Services
N.A.I.C.S.: 541611

Aimia Acquisition UK Limited **(1)**
80 Strand, London, WC2R ONN, United
Kingdom
Tel.: (44) 2071524700
Sales Range: $75-99.9 Million
Emp.: 400
Marketing Consulting Services
N.A.I.C.S.: 541613

Subsidiary (Domestic):

LMG Insight & Communication **(2)**
80 Strand, London, WC2R ONN, United
Kingdom
Tel.: (44) 2071524700
Web Site: http://www.aimia.com
Sales Range: $75-99.9 Million
Emp.: 300
Business Management Services
N.A.I.C.S.: 561110

Nectar 360 Limited **(2)**
33 Holborn, London, EC1N 2HT, United
Kingdom
Tel.: (44) 2076956000
Emp.: 700
Consumer Loyalty Program Operating Ser-
vices
N.A.I.C.S.: 541613
Jan Pieter Lips (CEO)

Air Miles Middle East **(1)**
PO Box 43004, Dubai, United Arab Emir-
ates
Tel.: (971) 43913400
Web Site: http://www.uae.airmilesme.com
Loyalty Management Services

N.A.I.C.S.: 541611

Carlson Marketing **(1)**
1405 Xenium Ln N, Plymouth, MN 55441
Tel.: (763) 445-3000
Sales Range: $900-999.9 Million
Emp.: 3,000
Marketing & Advertising Agency
N.A.I.C.S.: 541613

Branch (Domestic):

Carlson Marketing Group **(2)**
5887 Glenridge Dr NE Ste 375, Atlanta, GA
30328
Tel.: (404) 847-8700
N.A.I.C.S.: 541613

Carlson Marketing Group **(2)**
30 W Hubbard St Ste 400, Chicago, IL
60610
Tel.: (312) 670-2464
N.A.I.C.S.: 541613

Carlson Marketing Group **(2)**
2800 Livernois Ste 600, Troy, MI 48083
Tel.: (248) 824-7600
Emp.: 100
N.A.I.C.S.: 541613

Carlson Marketing Group **(2)**
205 Lexington Ave 6th Fl, New York, NY
10016
Tel.: (212) 252-5815
N.A.I.C.S.: 541613

Carlson Marketing Group **(2)**
160 Spear St 7th Fl, San Francisco, CA
94105
Tel.: (415) 844-2200
N.A.I.C.S.: 541611

Subsidiary (Non-US):

Carlson Marketing Group **(2)**
Priorijdreef 19, Dreve de Prieure, 1160,
Brussels, Belgium
Tel.: (32) 2 661 21 11
Emp.: 15
N.A.I.C.S.: 541810

Branch (Domestic):

Carlson Marketing Group **(2)**
400 Wilson Blvd Ste 500, Arlington, VA
22203
Tel.: (703) 682-7338
N.A.I.C.S.: 541810

Subsidiary (Non-US):

Carlson Marketing Group **(2)**
Level 2 Suite 203, 153-161 Park St S, Mel-
bourne, 3205, VIC, Australia
Tel.: (61) 3 9093 7111
Emp.: 9
N.A.I.C.S.: 541810

Carlson Marketing Group (Aust.) Pty.
Limited **(2)**
Level 2 33 Saunders St, Pyrmont, 2009,
NSW, Australia
Tel.: (61) 299215000
Emp.: 200
Marketing Solutions
N.A.I.C.S.: 541613

Carlson Marketing Group HK
Ltd. **(2)**
27th Fl ING Tower Sheung wan, Wanchai,
China (Hong Kong)
Tel.: (852) 2213 5805
N.A.I.C.S.: 541613

Carlson Marketing Group
Interact **(2)**
Menara Jamsostek Jl Jenderal, Gatot Sub-
roto Kav 38, Jakarta, 12710, Indonesia
Tel.: (62) 21 831 3023
N.A.I.C.S.: 541613

Carlson Marketing Group Ltd. **(2)**
2845 Mathieson Blvd E, Mississauga, L4W
5K2, ON, Canada
Tel.: (905) 214-8699
Emp.: 350
Results Marketing Strategies
N.A.I.C.S.: 541613

Branch (Domestic):

Carlson Marketing Canada **(3)**

759 Victoria Square Suite 105, Montreal,
H2Y 2J7, QC, Canada
Tel.: (514) 288-9889
Emp.: 90
N.A.I.C.S.: 541613

Subsidiary (Non-US):

Carlson Marketing Group NZ
Limited **(2)**
Ground Fl 109 Carlton Gore Rd, Newmar-
ket, Auckland, New Zealand
Tel.: (64) 95241120
Emp.: 35
N.A.I.C.S.: 541810

Carlson Marketing Group Sdn.
Bhd. **(2)**
9th Fl Bangunan Mas Jalan Sultan Ismail,
50250, Kuala Lumpur, Malaysia
Tel.: (60) 3 6195 1000
N.A.I.C.S.: 541613

Kognitiv Singapore Pte. Ltd **(2)**
W15 Beach Rd 2nd Floor, Singapore,
189677, Singapore
Tel.: (65) 62200005
Emp.: 40
N.A.I.C.S.: 541613

Kognitiv UK Ltd **(2)**
1st Floor Cannon Green, London, EC4R
0AA, United Kingdom
Tel.: (44) 2088750875
Emp.: 60
N.A.I.C.S.: 541810

Branch (Domestic):

Carlson Marketing Group (UK)
Ltd. **(3)**
Belgrave House 1 Greyfriars, Northampton,
NN1 2LQ, United Kingdom
Tel.: (44) 1604 234 300
Emp.: 300
Advertising Agencies
N.A.I.C.S.: 541810

Unit (Domestic):

Relationship Travel & Event
Solutions **(3)**
Carlson Court 116 Putney Bridge Rd, Lon-
don, SW15 2NQ, United Kingdom
Tel.: (44) 20 8875 0875
N.A.I.C.S.: 541810

bbCarlson **(3)**
Carlson Court 116 Putney Bridge Rd, Lon-
don, SW15 2NQ, United Kingdom
Tel.: (44) 20 8875 3875
N.A.I.C.S.: 541810

Excellence In Motivation, Inc. **(1)**
6 N Main St Ste 370, Dayton, OH 45402
Tel.: (937) 222-2900
Web Site: http://www.eim-inc.com
Sales Range: $10-24.9 Million
Emp.: 175
Administrative Management & General
Management Consulting Service
N.A.I.C.S.: 541611

Giovanni Bozzetto S.p.A. **(1)**
Tel.: (39) 035996711
Web Site: http://www.bozzetto-group.com
Sales Range: $500-549.9 Million
Emp.: 5,000
Textile Mfr
N.A.I.C.S.: 313310
Roberto Curreri (CEO)

Subsidiary (Non-US):

BGB Giovanni Bozzetto, S.A. **(2)**
Pol Industrial de Lantaron C/ Antepardo 7,
Salcedo, 01213, Alava, Spain
Tel.: (34) 945333105
Chemicals Mfr
N.A.I.C.S.: 325199

BOZZETO KIMYA SA. VE TIC.
A.S. **(2)**
1275 Ada 16 Parsel Turan Mah, Izmir, Tur-
kiye
Tel.: (90) 2325112278
Chemical Products Distr
N.A.I.C.S.: 424690

Bozzetto GmbH **(2)**
Baekerpfad 25, 47805, Krefeld, Germany

Aimia Inc.—(Continued)

Tel.: (49) 215 138 1822
Chemicals Mfr
N.A.I.C.S.: 325199

Subsidiary (US):

Bozzetto Inc.   (2)
2507 S Elm Eugene St, Greensboro, NC
27406
Tel.: (336) 333-3672
Chemical Products Distr
N.A.I.C.S.: 424690
Randall Cox (Pres)

Subsidiary (Non-US):

Bozzetto Kimya San.Ve Tic .
A.S.   (2)
Bozzetto Kimya Zafer Mah Akcay Cd Plaza
Artkiy No 142, Izmir, Turkiye
Tel.: (90) 232 436 5444
Chemicals Mfr
N.A.I.C.S.: 325199

Bozzetto Polska Sp. z o.o.   (2)
Ul Koksownicza 28, 41-800, Zabrze, Poland
Tel.: (48) 323761440
Chemical Products Distr
N.A.I.C.S.: 424690

Giovanni Bozzetto (Shanghai) Chemi-
cal Trading Co., Ltd.   (2)
Suit 605 No 50 Lane 2080 Lain Hua Road,
Shanghai, 201103, China
Tel.: (86) 215 445 0616
Chemicals Mfr
N.A.I.C.S.: 325199

P.T. BOZZETTO INDONESIA   (2)
Tel.: (62) 225947176
Chemical Products Distr
N.A.I.C.S.: 424690

Smart Button Associates, Inc.   (1)
1501 Casho Mill Rd Ste 14, Newark, DE
19711
Tel.: (302) 283-0200
Web Site: http://www.smartbutton.com
Sales Range: $25-49.9 Million
Emp.: 15
Customer Relationship Marketing Software
Mfr
N.A.I.C.S.: 541511

AIMING INC.

5th Floor Sumitomo Fudosan Shin-
juku Minamiguchi Building, 5-31-11
Sendagaya Shibuya-ku, Tokyo, 151-
0051, Japan
Tel.: (81) 353338424
Web Site: https://www.aiming-
    inc.com
Year Founded: 2011
3911—(TKS)
Rev.: $129,030,910
Assets: $52,437,640
Liabilities: $18,575,800
Net Worth: $33,861,840
Earnings: ($15,789,430)
Emp.: 720
Fiscal Year-end: 12/31/23
Online Game Developer
N.A.I.C.S.: 513210
Tadashi Shiiba (Pres & CEO)

Subsidiaries:

Aiming Global Service, Inc.   (1)
6th Flr King's Court Building, Makati, Metro
Manila, Philippines
Tel.: (63) 28100239
Web Site: http://www.aiming-inc.com.ph
Online Game Development Services
N.A.I.C.S.: 513210
Analyn Galoso (Officer-Acctg)

AIML RESOURCES INC.

Suite 203 645 Fort St, Victoria, V8W
1G2, BC, Canada
Tel.: (778) 405-0882   BC
Web Site: https://www.aiml-
    innovations.com
Year Founded: 1983
FIX—(CNSX)

Assets: $2,811,530
Liabilities: $1,177,709
Net Worth: $1,633,821
Earnings: ($2,211,371)
Fiscal Year-end: 04/30/21
Diamonds & Gold Exploration
N.A.I.C.S.: 212220
John F. Cook (Pres, CEO & Sec)

AIMS APAC REIT

1 Raffles Place, Singapore, 48616,
Singapore
Tel.: (65) 63091050
Web Site: https://aimsapacreit.com
O5RU—(SES)
Rev.: $131,367,914
Assets: $1,716,650,609
Liabilities: $653,831,789
Net Worth: $1,062,818,821
Earnings: $41,519,081
Emp.: 34
Fiscal Year-end: 03/31/24
Trust Management Services
N.A.I.C.S.: 523940
Wee Lih Koh (CEO)

AIMS FINANCIAL GROUP

Level 16 Central Square 323 Cas-
tlereagh Street, Sydney, 2000, NSW,
Australia
Tel.: (61) 292172727
Web Site: http://www.aims.com.au
Year Founded: 1991
Sales Range: $25-49.9 Million
Emp.: 50
Financial & Investment Services
N.A.I.C.S.: 523150
George Wang (Chm & CEO)

AIMS PROPERTY SECURITIES FUND

Level 41 259 George Street, Sydney,
2000, NSW, Australia
Tel.: (61) 292172727
Web Site: https://www.aims.com.au
BVP—(SES)
Rev.: $4,274,640
Assets: $95,330,062
Liabilities: $95,126
Net Worth: $95,234,936
Earnings: $3,053,099
Fiscal Year-end: 06/30/22
Investment Management Service
N.A.I.C.S.: 525990
George Wang (Chm)

AIMVALLEY B.V.

Utrechtseweg 38, 1213 TV, Hilver-
sum, Netherlands
Tel.: (31) 356891900   NI
Web Site: http://www.aimvalley.com
Year Founded: 2003
Telecommunication Products Mfr
N.A.I.C.S.: 334210
Hwan Park (Chm)

AIN HOLDINGS INC.

5-2-4-30 Higashi Sapporo Shiroishi-
ku, Sapporo, 003-0005, Hokkaido,
Japan
Tel.: (81) 118141000
Web Site: http://www.ainj.co.jp
Year Founded: 1969
9627—(TKS)
Rev.: $2,642,836,640
Assets: $1,648,593,490
Liabilities: $753,526,780
Net Worth: $895,066,710
Earnings: $75,360,610
Emp.: 15,114
Fiscal Year-end: 04/30/24
Pharmacy & Drug Store Management
& Franchising Services
N.A.I.C.S.: 456110
Kiichi Otani (Chm & Pres)

Subsidiaries:

AIN TOKAI Inc.   (1)
Soa Bldg 2, 1 2 3 Izumi Higashi, Nagoya,
461 0001, Aichi, Japan
Tel.: (81) 529553111
Web Site: http://www.aint.jp
Sales Range: $100-124.9 Million
Emp.: 300
Drug Stores Management Services
N.A.I.C.S.: 456110

Ayura Laboratories Inc.   (1)
1-5 Yoyogi 2-chome JR Nam Shijuku Build-
ing 10F, Shibuya-ku, Tokyo, 151-0053, Ja-
pan
Tel.: (81) 353331128
Web Site: http://www.ayura.co.jp
Cosmetic Product
N.A.I.C.S.: 456120

Daitiku Co., Ltd.   (1)
Hunan 24 2 Chuo ku, 950 1151, Niigata,
Japan
Tel.: (81) 252880228
Web Site: http://www.daichiku.co.jp
Sales Range: $50-74.9 Million
Emp.: 240
Drug Stores Management Services
N.A.I.C.S.: 456110

Heartland Medical Corporation   (1)
No 16 Second Fl, Jonan cho 1 chome,
Yamagata, Yamagata, Japan
Tel.: (81) 236463222
Web Site: http://www.m-heartland-aing.jp
Sales Range: $50-74.9 Million
Emp.: 93
Medical Drugs & Health Care Related Prod-
ucts Sales
N.A.I.C.S.: 423450

AINAVO HOLDINGS CORPO-RATION

2-6-6 Motoasakusa, Taito-ku, Tokyo,
111-0041, Japan
Tel.: (81) 338533391
Web Site: https://www.ainavo.co.jp
Year Founded: 1955
7539—(TKS)
Rev.: $610,342,650
Assets: $311,974,180
Liabilities: $140,545,070
Net Worth: $171,429,110
Earnings: $9,032,660
Fiscal Year-end: 09/30/23
Holding Company
N.A.I.C.S.: 551111

AINO HEALTH AB

Skeppargatan 8, 114 52, Stockholm,
Sweden
Tel.: (46) 20482482
Web Site:
    https://www.ainohealth.com
AINO—(OMX)
Rev.: $1,864,808
Assets: $1,623,161
Liabilities: $1,832,027
Net Worth: ($208,866)
Earnings: ($1,401,182)
Emp.: 22
Fiscal Year-end: 12/31/22
Health Care Srvices
N.A.I.C.S.: 621610
Jyrki Eklund (CEO)

Subsidiaries:

Aino Health Management Oy   (1)
Pitajanmaentie 14 4 krs, 00380, Helsinki,
Finland
Tel.: (358) 103239500
Healtcare Services
N.A.I.C.S.: 621999

AIOBIO CO., LTD.

8F 38 Teheran-ro 4-gil, Gangnam-gu,
Seoul, Korea (South)
Tel.: (82) 25615101
Web Site: https://www.aiobio.co.kr
Year Founded: 2011
447690—(KRS)

Medical Device Mfr
N.A.I.C.S.: 339112
Yoon Hong-Cheol (CEO)

AIOLOS INC

2150 Islington Avenue, Etobicoke,
M9P 3V4, ON, Canada
Tel.: (416) 674-3017
Web Site: http://www.aiolos.com
Rev.: $51,123,631
Emp.: 50
Wind Tunnels Mfr
N.A.I.C.S.: 541330
Gary Elfstrom (VP)

AION THERAPEUTIC INC.

703 45 Sheppard Ave East, Toronto,
M2N 5W9, ON, Canada
Tel.: (416) 460-3000
Web Site:
    http://www.aiontherapeutic.com
AION—(CNSX)
Assets: $1,254,388
Liabilities: $943,460
Net Worth: $310,928
Earnings: ($6,465,660)
Fiscal Year-end: 04/30/21
Medical Products Mfr
N.A.I.C.S.: 325411
Stephen D. Barnhill (Chm)

AION-TECH SOLUTIONS LIM-ITED

My Home Hub 9th Floor Block - I
Hitech City, Madhapur, Hyderabad,
500081, Telangana, India
Tel.: (91) 4066284999
Web Site: https://aiontech.ai
Year Founded: 1994
GOLDTECH—(NSE)
Rev.: $12,844,104
Assets: $13,285,054
Liabilities: $3,852,781
Net Worth: $9,432,273
Earnings: $62,244
Emp.: 143
Fiscal Year-end: 03/31/23
Information Technology Consulting
Services
N.A.I.C.S.: 541512
Vithal V. S. S. N. K. Popuri (CFO)

Subsidiaries:

Staytop Systems Inc   (1)
1525 McCarthy Blvd Ste 1133, Milpitas, CA
95035
Tel.: (408) 538-5990
Information Technology Consulting Services
N.A.I.C.S.: 541512

AIP FOUNDATION

12B Ngoc Khanh Street, Ba Dinh Dis-
trict, 100000, Hanoi, Vietnam
Tel.: (84) 2437710700
Web Site: https://www.aip-
    foundation.org
Year Founded: 1999
Road Safety Education Services
N.A.I.C.S.: 813319

AIPHONE CO., LTD.

10th floor Meiji Yasuda Life Nagoya
Building 1-1 Shin-Sakae-cho, Naka-
ku, Nagoya, 460-0004, Aichi, Japan
Tel.: (81) 522288181   JP
Web Site: https://www.aiphone.co.jp
Year Founded: 2005
6718—(TKS)
Rev.: $405,417,740
Assets: $518,329,760
Liabilities: $89,254,830
Net Worth: $429,074,930
Earnings: $30,703,450
Emp.: 1,999
Fiscal Year-end: 03/31/24
Electronic Communications Equip-
ment Mfr & Whslr

N.A.I.C.S.: 334419
Shusaku Ichikawa *(Chm & CEO)*

Subsidiaries:

AIPHONE COMMUNICATIONS (VIETNAM) CO., LTD. (1)
No 25 6 Street Vietnam Singapore Industrial Park II VSIP II, Hoa phu Ward, Thu Dau Mot, Binh Duong, Vietnam
Tel.: (84) 6503628031
Intercom Device Mfr
N.A.I.C.S.: 334419

AIPHONE PTE. LTD. (1)
Oxley Bizhub 2 62 Ubi Road 1 05-14, Singapore, 408734, Singapore
Tel.: (65) 65341135
Web Site: https://www.aiphone.com.sg
Intercom Device Distr
N.A.I.C.S.: 423690

AIPHONE Shanghai CO., LTD. (1)
11F/A3 No 1336 Huashan Road, Shanghai, 200052, China
Tel.: (86) 216 251 8271
Web Site: http://www.aiphone.com.cn
Intercom Device Distr
N.A.I.C.S.: 423690

AIPHONE UK LIMITED (1)
Unit 25 Mitre Bridge Industrial Estate Mitre Way, London, W10 6AU, United Kingdom
Tel.: (44) 2075076250
Intercom Device Distr
N.A.I.C.S.: 423690
Wyatt Taylor *(Mng Dir)*

Abdul Mohsin Bader Al Khorafi Est. Co. For Gen. Trading & Contracting WLL (1)
Al Qibla Ahmed Al Jaber St Group Tower 2nd Floor - Block 9 Safat, PO Box 757, Kuwait, 13008, Kuwait
Tel.: (965) 2 246 1722
Security Intercom Device Services
N.A.I.C.S.: 561612

Agencias Pan Americanas, S de R.L. de C.V. (1)
PO Box 420, Tegucigalpa, Honduras
Tel.: (504) 390411
Security Intercom Device Services
N.A.I.C.S.: 561612

Aiphone Corporation (1)
6670 185th Ave NE, Redmond, WA 98052
Tel.: (425) 455-0510
Intercom Device Distr
N.A.I.C.S.: 423690
Bradley Kamcheff *(Mgr-Mktg)*

Aiphone Pty Ltd. (1)
Unit 11A 2 Eden Park Drive, Macquarie Park, 2113, NSW, Australia
Tel.: (61) 280364507
Web Site: https://www.aiphone.com.au
Intercom Device Distr
N.A.I.C.S.: 423690
Roy Torii *(Mng Dir)*

Aiphone S.A.S. (1)
ZAC du Bois Chaland-6 rue des Pyrenees, Evry, 91056, Lisses, Cedex, France
Tel.: (33) 16 911 4600
Web Site: https://www.aiphone.fr
Electronic Security Equipment Mfr
N.A.I.C.S.: 334419

Bethlehem Advanced Technologies Co., Ltd. (1)
Manger Sq, PO Box 75, Bethlehem, South Africa
Tel.: (27) 9702 277 6633
Security Intercom Device Services
N.A.I.C.S.: 561612

Comptoir Commercial International N.V. (1)
Louiza-Marialei 8 bus 5, 2018, Antwerp, Belgium
Tel.: (32) 3 232 7864
Web Site: https://www.ccinv.be
Electronic Security Equipment Mfr
N.A.I.C.S.: 334419

Creative Hardware For Integrated Products SAL (1)
Media Center Bldg, Ashrafieh, Beirut, Lebanon

Tel.: (961) 157 3573
Security Intercom Device Services
N.A.I.C.S.: 561612

Diqu Tech Private Limited (1)
Basavanagudi, Bengaluru Urban, Bengaluru, India
Tel.: (91) 802 662 2637
Web Site: https://diqutech.com
Security Intercom Device Services
N.A.I.C.S.: 561612

Egypt & Middle East Import-Export Ltd. Co. (1)
PO Box 1765, Cairo, Egypt
Tel.: (20) 2 574 9205
Security Intercom Device Services
N.A.I.C.S.: 561612

Electrocom S.A. (1)
5a AV A 13-30 Zona 9, Guatemala, Guatemala
Tel.: (502) 331 2431
Security Intercom Device Services
N.A.I.C.S.: 561612

Eltek Distribution SRL (1)
1/II Pipera Bvd, Ilfov, 077190, Voluntari, Romania
Security Intercom Device Services
N.A.I.C.S.: 561612

Eros Electricals LLC (1)
Eros House Al Barsha 1, PO Box 1184, Dubai, United Arab Emirates
Tel.: (971) 4 209 8888
Web Site: https://www.erosgroup.com
Electronic Product Distr
N.A.I.C.S.: 423690
Yousuf Badri *(Mng Dir & Chm)*

Geotron CIA. Ltda. (1)
Av Shyris N44-59 and Rio Coca, Quito, Pichincha, Ecuador
Tel.: (593) 2 226 4330
Web Site: https://geotron.com.ec
Security Intercom Device Services
N.A.I.C.S.: 561612

HA-HO Kft. (1)
Roppentyu u 69, 1139, Budapest, Hungary
Tel.: (36) 1 350 2098
Web Site: https://www.ha-ho.hu
Communication Devices Mfr
N.A.I.C.S.: 334220

Heyderhoff GmbH (1)
Rehhecke 25, 40885, Ratingen, Germany
Tel.: (49) 2 102 9180
Web Site: https://www.heyderhoff.de
Electrical Products Distr
N.A.I.C.S.: 423690

Hyper Advance Sdn. Bhd. (1)
Unit 4 03 and 4 04 Level 4 BICMA Lot 2 Jalan 51A/243, 46100, Petaling Jaya, Selangor, Malaysia
Tel.: (60) 37 877 6537
Web Site: https://www.hyper-advance.com
Electrical Products Distr
N.A.I.C.S.: 423690

Intel, S.A. (1)
Carretera La Uruca Diagonal a Subestacion de la Cia N de F y L, PO Box 466-1007, San Jose, Costa Rica
Tel.: (506) 233 1333
Security Intercom Device Services
N.A.I.C.S.: 561612

Internationaal Handelskantoor B.V. (1)
Marconistraat 21, 2809 PH, Gouda, Netherlands
Tel.: (31) 18 258 1275
Web Site: https://www.ihkbv.nl
Communication Devices Mfr
N.A.I.C.S.: 334220

Kaj Larsen Communication A/S (1)
Risboge 6 Hojrup, 6640, Lunderskov, Denmark
Tel.: (45) 5 687 9200
Web Site: https://www.kajlarsen.dk
Door Phone System Mfr
N.A.I.C.S.: 334210

Khai Quoc Trading & Technology Development Co., Ltd. (1)
No 15 Lot 12B Trung Yen 10 Road, Cau Giay Dist, Hanoi, Vietnam

Tel.: (84) 243 733 6620
Security Intercom Device Services
N.A.I.C.S.: 561612

Mega Hertz Technologies Sdn. Bhd. (1)
No 1-2B Jalan PJU 1/3F Sunwaymas Commercial Centre, 47301, Petaling Jaya, Selangor, Malaysia
Tel.: (60) 37 880 9671
Web Site: https://mhertz.com.my
Security Intercom Device Services
N.A.I.C.S.: 561612

Moritani S.A. (1)
Av Republica de Panama No 3990, Surquillo, Lima, Peru
Tel.: (51) 221 2070
Construction Materials Distr
N.A.I.C.S.: 423320

Nik. M. Kourakos & Co., Ltd. (1)
33 Tsimiski Str, 11472, Athens, Greece
Tel.: (30) 210 363 8747
Security Intercom Device Services
N.A.I.C.S.: 561612

Novel Limited (1)
Acibadem Cad No 77-4, Kadikoy, 34718, Istanbul, Turkiye
Tel.: (90) 216 428 0921
Security Intercom Device Services
N.A.I.C.S.: 561612

Optimus S.A. (1)
C/ Barcelona 101, 17003, Girona, Spain
Tel.: (34) 97 220 3300
Web Site: https://www.optimusaudio.com
Intercom Equipment Mfr & Distr
N.A.I.C.S.: 334290

Oy Hedengren Security AB (1)
Lauttasaarentie 50, 00200, Helsinki, Finland
Tel.: (358) 968 2841
Security Intercom Device Services
N.A.I.C.S.: 561612

Primex Ltda. (1)
Calle 21 de Mayo N 690, PO Box 2879, Santa Cruz, Bolivia
Tel.: (591) 333 5068
Web Site: https://www.primex-ltda.com
Screwdriver Tool Mfr
N.A.I.C.S.: 333991

Qatar Boom Electrical Engineering W.L.L. (1)
PO Box 24845, Doha, Qatar
Tel.: (974) 4 005 3988
Web Site: https://qb-engineering.com
Engineeering Services
N.A.I.C.S.: 541330

Rodhe Security, S.A. de C.V. (1)
Iztaccihuatl 158 Col Florida, 01030, Mexico, Mexico
Tel.: (52) 556 308 4067
Web Site: https://www.rodhe.com.mx
Information Technology Services
N.A.I.C.S.: 541511

Scharfstein S.A. (1)
Av Sta Maria 0510, Providencia, Chile
Tel.: (56) 22 550 0000
Web Site: https://www.scharfstein.cl
Networking Services
N.A.I.C.S.: 541512

Shenzhen Jinhang Industry Co., Ltd. (1)
Room 1311 Block A International, Chamber of Commerce Building Fuhua 1st Road Futian District, Shenzhen, China
Tel.: (86) 7558 369 6666
Web Site: https://www.jinhang.com.cn
Security Services
N.A.I.C.S.: 561621

Shenzhen Totech Technologies Co., Ltd. (1)
Room 801 Block A International Chamber of Commerce Building, Fuhua 1st Road Futian District, Shenzhen, China
Tel.: (86) 7558 293 1122
Web Site: https://www.totech.cn
Electronic Security Equipment Mfr
N.A.I.C.S.: 334419

Sin Chew Alarm Company Limited (1)
No 408-412 10th Floor unit A Strand Rd,

Latha Township, Yangon, Myanmar
Tel.: (95) 96 886 8857
Security Intercom Device Services
N.A.I.C.S.: 561612

Standard Audio AB (1)
Turbingatan 2, 195 60, Arlandastad, Sweden
Tel.: (46) 85 900 0500
Web Site: https://www.standardaudio.se
Audio Visual Equipment Distr
N.A.I.C.S.: 423690

Tech & House S.A. (1)
Via Brazil calle 2da al lado de Comasa, Panama, Panama
Tel.: (507) 263 9611
Security Intercom Device Services
N.A.I.C.S.: 561612

Technology of Energy & Controls Co., Ltd. (1)
PO Box 3919, Dammam, 32426, Saudi Arabia
Tel.: (966) 3 832 9960
Security Intercom Device Services
N.A.I.C.S.: 561612

Tecnodiesel S.A.S. (1)
Cra 10 No 9-53 Av Ferrocarril La Popa, Dosquebradas, Colombia
Tel.: (57) 6 330 6102
Web Site: https://www.tecnodiesel.com.co
Power Generator Distr
N.A.I.C.S.: 423610

Teo Hong Phaisan Co., Ltd. (1)
95 Naradhiwas Rajnagarindra Rd, Chong Nonsri Yannawa, Bangkok, 10120, Thailand
Tel.: (66) 2 678 1595
Web Site: https://www.teohong.net
Security System Services
N.A.I.C.S.: 561621

Tezao s.r.o. (1)
Cihlarska 727/2, 190 00, Prague, Czech Republic
Tel.: (420) 28 388 0555
Web Site: https://www.tezao.cz
Electrical Equipment Whslr
N.A.I.C.S.: 423610

Tslelay Gitit Ltd. (1)
PO Box 10049, Tel Aviv, 61100, Israel
Tel.: (972) 3 544 3121
Security Intercom Device Services
N.A.I.C.S.: 561612

Vieceli & Furlan Associados Industria e Comercio Ltda. (1)
Av Independencia 7815-Jardim Primavera, Vinhedo, Sao Paulo, 13280-000, Brazil
Tel.: (55) 193 886 2654
Web Site: https://www.vieceliefurlan.com.br
Research & Development Services
N.A.I.C.S.: 541715

Zahra Security Systems & Electricals LLC (1)
Al Quoz Industrial Area 1 Behind Al Khaleej Times Near, PO 10239, Topaz Bldg Opp Mosq, Dubai, United Arab Emirates
Tel.: (971) 4 347 4422
Security Intercom Device Services
N.A.I.C.S.: 561612

AIPTEK INTERNATIONAL INC.
1st Floor 9th Floor No 215 Section 2 Chang'an East Road, Songshan Dist, Taipei, 10552, Taiwan
Tel.: (886) 227771215
Web Site: https://www.aiptek.com.tw
6225—(TAI)
Rev.: $1,751,006
Assets: $3,441,316
Liabilities: $324,896
Net Worth: $3,116,420
Earnings: $285,228
Fiscal Year-end: 12/31/23
Camera & Camcorder Mfr
N.A.I.C.S.: 334220

Subsidiaries:

AIPTEK International GmbH (1)
Halskestr 29, 47877, Willich, Germany
Tel.: (49) 2154923550
Web Site: http://www.aiptek.de

AIPTEK International Inc.—(Continued)

Electronic Gadgets Distr
N.A.I.C.S.: 423620

AIQ LIMITED

84 Eccleston Square Victoria, London, KY1-1106, United Kingdom
Tel.: (44) 2039118716   Ky
Web Site: http://www.aiqhub.com
Year Founded: 2017
AIQ—(LSE)
Rev.: $263,792
Assets: $234,306
Liabilities: $836,178
Net Worth: ($601,873)
Earnings: ($640,609)
Emp.: 42
Fiscal Year-end: 10/31/23
Online Transaction Services
N.A.I.C.S.: 522320
Li Chun Chung (Exec Dir)

Subsidiaries:

Alchemist Codes Sdn. Bhd.   (1)
Unit 3-3 Level 3 UOA Corporate Tower A
No 8 Jalan Kerinchi, 59200, Kuala Lumpur,
Selangor, Malaysia
Tel.: (60) 32 242 3926
Web Site: https://www.alcodes.net
Software Developer Services
N.A.I.C.S.: 541511
Charles Yong (CEO)

Alcodes International Limited   (1)
Room 47 Smart-Space FinTech Level 4
Core E, Cyberport 3 100 Cyberport Road,
Hong Kong, China (Hong Kong)
Tel.: (852) 65480068
Web Site: https://www.alcodeshk.com
Software Operating Services
N.A.I.C.S.: 541714

AIR ARABIA PJSC

Sharjah Freight Center Cargo near
Sharjah International Airport, PO Box
132, Sharjah, United Arab Emirates
Tel.: (971) 65088977   AE
Web Site: https://www.airarabia.com
Year Founded: 2003
AIRARABIA—(DFM)
Rev.: $1,633,562,972
Assets: $3,995,465,096
Liabilities: $1,943,872,277
Net Worth: $2,051,592,819
Earnings: $421,394,038
Emp.: 2,515
Fiscal Year-end: 12/31/23
Scheduled Air Passenger Transportation Services
N.A.I.C.S.: 481111
Adel Abdulla Ali (CEO)

AIR BALTIC CORPORATION AS

Riga International Airport Tehnikas 3,
1053, Riga, Latvia
Tel.: (371) 6 7207069
Web Site: http://www.airbaltic.com
Year Founded: 1995
Rev.: $569,958,346
Assets: $1,087,648,347
Liabilities: $1,049,671,655
Net Worth: $37,976,692
Earnings: ($10,206,404)
Emp.: 1,500
Fiscal Year-end: 12/31/19
Oil Transportation Services
N.A.I.C.S.: 481111
Martin Gauss (Chm & CEO)

Subsidiaries:

airBaltic Training   (1)
Pilotu Iela 6 Riga International Airport, Riga,
1053, Latvia
Tel.: (371) 676 68 512
Web Site: http://www.airbaltictraining.com
Flight Training Services
N.A.I.C.S.: 611512

AIR BERLIN PLC & CO. LUFTVERKEHRS KG

Saatwinkler Damm 42 43, D-13627,
Berlin, Germany
Tel.: (49) 3034343434
Web Site:
   http://www.airberlingroup.com
Year Founded: 1978
ABI—(DEU)
Sales Range: $5-14.9 Billion
Emp.: 9,113
Oil Transportation Services
N.A.I.C.S.: 481111
James Hogan (Vice Chm)

Subsidiaries:

AB Dritte Flugzeugvermietungs
GmbH   (1)
Saatwinkler Damm 42-43, 13627, Berlin,
Germany
Tel.: (49) 3041013473
Management Consulting Services
N.A.I.C.S.: 541618

AB Erste Flugzeugvermietungs
GmbH   (1)
Saatwinkler Damm 42-43, 13627, Berlin,
Germany
Tel.: (49) 3034345500
Management Consulting Services
N.A.I.C.S.: 541618

AB Vierte Flugzeugvermietungs
GmbH   (1)
Saatwinkler Damm 42-43, 13627, Berlin,
Germany
Tel.: (49) 3034345500
Management Consulting Services
N.A.I.C.S.: 541618

AB Zweite Flugzeugvermietungs
GmbH   (1)
Saatwinkler Damm 42-43, 13627, Berlin,
Germany
Tel.: (49) 3034345500
Management Consulting Services
N.A.I.C.S.: 541618

Air Berlin Gmbh & Co. Funfte
Flugzeugvermietungs Ohg   (1)
Zeppelinstr 3, 12529, Brandenburg, Germany
Tel.: (49) 1801737800
Management Consulting Services
N.A.I.C.S.: 541618

Air Berlin Luftfahrttechnischer Betrieb
GmbH   (1)
Saatwinkler Damm 42-43, 13627, Berlin,
Germany
Tel.: (49) 1805737800
Web Site: http://www.airberlin.com
Management Consulting Services
N.A.I.C.S.: 541618

CHS Cabin and Handling Service
GmbH   (1)
Heinrichstr 169 A, 40239, Dusseldorf, Germany
Tel.: (49) 211964920
Management Consulting Services
N.A.I.C.S.: 541618

Subsidiary (Domestic):

CHS Cabin and Handling Service
Bayern GmbH   (2)
Postfach 24 14 44, 85356, Munich, Germany
Tel.: (49) 2119649228
Full-Service Restaurants
N.A.I.C.S.: 722511

CHS Cabin and Handling Service
Sud-West GmbH   (2)
Terminal 2 Postfach 64, 60549, Frankfurt,
Germany
Tel.: (49) 2119649220
Personal Services
N.A.I.C.S.: 812990

Euconus Flugzeugleasinggesellschaft
mbH   (1)
Zeppelinstr 3, 13657, Brandenburg, Germany
Tel.: (49) 3034345524

Management Consulting Services
N.A.I.C.S.: 541618

AIR CANADA

7373 Cote-Vertu Blvd West, Ville
Saint Laurent, H4S 1Z3, QC,
Canada   AB
Web Site: https://www.aircanada.com
Year Founded: 1956
ADH2—(DEU)
Rev.: $16,128,388,860
Assets: $22,307,010,416
Liabilities: $21,718,992,391
Net Worth: $588,018,025
Earnings: $1,681,317,870
Emp.: 39,000
Fiscal Year-end: 12/31/23
Commercial Airlines
N.A.I.C.S.: 481111
Jon Turner (VP-Maintenance)

Subsidiaries:

Touram Limited Partnership   (1)
1440 Saint Catherine St W Ste 600, Montreal, H3G 1R8, QC, Canada   (100%)
Tel.: (514) 876-0700
Web Site:
   http://www.aircanadavacations.com
Rev.: $135,000,000
Emp.: 354
Air Transportation Chartering, Tour Productions & Operations
N.A.I.C.S.: 561520
Hugo Coulombe (VP-Finance)

AIR CHANGE INTERNATIONAL LIMITED

2 Ashford Avenue, Milperra, 2214,
NSW, Australia
Tel.: (61) 2 8774 1400   AU
Web Site:
   http://www.airchange.com.au
Year Founded: 2000
Sales Range: $10-24.9 Million
Air Conditioning Mfr & Sales
N.A.I.C.S.: 333415
Alan S. Jones (Chm)

Subsidiaries:

Air Change Pty Ltd   (1)
12 Parraweena Rd, Caringbah, 2229, NSW,
Australia
Tel.: (61) 295314699
Web Site: http://www.air-change.com
Sales Range: $25-49.9 Million
Emp.: 50
Heating, Ventilation & Air Conditioning Systems Mfr
N.A.I.C.S.: 333415

AIR CREEBEC INC.

101 7th Street, PO Box 430, Val d'Or,
J9P 4P4, QC, Canada
Tel.: (819) 825-8375
Web Site: http://www.aircreebec.ca
Year Founded: 1979
Rev.: $29,500,000
Emp.: 180
Oil Transportation Services
N.A.I.C.S.: 481112
Matthew Happyjack (Pres)

AIR FRANCE-KLM S.A.

7 Rue du Cirque, 75008, Paris,
France
Tel.: (33) 141565656   FR
Web Site:
   https://www.airfranceklm.com
Year Founded: 1933
AFLYY—(OTCIQ)
Rev.: $13,618,725,120
Assets: $37,106,358,560
Liabilities: $43,760,962,960
Net Worth: ($6,654,604,320)
Earnings: ($8,699,623,920)
Emp.: 82,167
Fiscal Year-end: 12/31/20
Oil Transportation Services
N.A.I.C.S.: 481111

Anne-Marie Couderc (Chm)

Subsidiaries:

AIRPORT MEDICAL SERVICES
C.V.   (1)
Stationsplein-No 236, Schiphol, 1117 CJ,
Netherlands
Tel.: (31) 206494364
Web Site: http://www.klmhealthservice.com
Sales Range: $25-49.9 Million
Emp.: 200
Air Transportation Health Care Services
N.A.I.C.S.: 488119
Paula Knape (Gen Mgr)

AMSTERDAM SCHIPHOL
PIJPLEIDING C.V.   (1)
Oude Vijfhuizerweg 6, Schiphol, 1118 LV,
Netherlands
Tel.: (31) 206493063
Oil Transportation Services
N.A.I.C.S.: 488190

Aero Maintenance Group LLC   (1)
2200 NW 84th Ave, Miami, FL 33122
Tel.: (305) 436-5464
Web Site:
   http://www.aeromaintenancegroup.com
Aircraft Component Repair & Maintenance
Services
N.A.I.C.S.: 811198
Jerome Colombel (CFO)

Air France   (1)
7 Megalou Alexandrou & Karaiskaki Str,
164 52, Athens, Argyroupoli,
Greece   (100%)
Tel.: (30) 2109980222
Web Site: http://www.airfrance.gr
Sales Range: $25-49.9 Million
Emp.: 42
Airline Transportation Services
N.A.I.C.S.: 481111
Jean-Cyril Spinetta (Chm)

Air France C.S. Participation   (1)
45 Rue De Paris, 95747, Roissy-en-France,
France   (100%)
Tel.: (33) 141567800
Web Site: http://www.airfrance.fr
Rev.: $31,560,757
Emp.: 10,000
N.A.I.C.S.: 481111
Frederic Gagey (Pres)

Air France Klm Component Services
Co. Ltd.   (1)
Building 2 7975 Beiqing Route, Qingpu District, Shanghai, China
Tel.: (86) 13818985619
Aircraft Components Mfr
N.A.I.C.S.: 336413

Air France SA   (1)
45 rue de Paris, Tremblay-en-France
Roissy Charles de Gaulle, 95747, Roissy-en-France, Cedex, France
Tel.: (33) 141567800
Web Site: https://wwws.airfrance.fr
Emp.: 42,000
Oil Transportation Services
N.A.I.C.S.: 488190

Air France, USA   (1)
125 W 55th St 2nd Fl, New York, NY 10019
Tel.: (212) 830-4000
Web Site: http://www.airfrance.com
Sales Range: $125-149.9 Million
Emp.: 400
International Air Transportation (Passenger
& Cargo)
N.A.I.C.S.: 481111
Eric Schramm (Exec VP-Ops & Mgr-Accountable)

BLUE CROWN B.V.   (1)
Amsterdamseweg 55, Amstelveen, 1182
GP, Netherlands
Tel.: (31) 206499959
Emp.: 6
Airline Transportation Services
N.A.I.C.S.: 488190

Barfield, Inc.   (1)
4101 NW 29th St, Miami, FL
33142-5617   (100%)
Tel.: (305) 894-5300
Sales Range: $50-74.9 Million
Emp.: 220

Avionics, Aircraft Instrument & Electronic Components Testing, Maintenance & Repair Services
N.A.I.C.S.: 811210
John Rogers *(Sr VP-Sls)*

BlueLink (1)
57 rue Ledru-Rollin, 94200, Ivry-sur-Seine, Cedex, France
Tel.: (33) 1 58 68 24 60
Web Site: http://www.bluelinkservices.com
Sales Range: $75-99.9 Million
Emp.: 2,000
Airline Customer Service Management Services
N.A.I.C.S.: 488119
Stephan Laluque *(Dir-Information Sys)*

BlueLink International CZ s. r. o. (1)
Olivova 4, Prague, 110 00, Czech Republic
Tel.: (420) 296 341 311
Web Site: http://www.bluelinkservices.com
Airport Luggage Claim Management Services
N.A.I.C.S.: 488119
Vincent Leonardi *(Mgr-Prague)*

Bluelink International Australia Pty. Ltd. (1)
2/55 Murray Street, Pyrmont, 2009, NSW, Australia
Tel.: (61) 285846500
Multi-lingual & Multimedia Services
N.A.I.C.S.: 541840
Keith Barreto *(Head-Ops & Comml Dev)*

Bluelink International Chile SPA. (1)
Av Presidente Kennedy 5735 Torre Poniente Piso 10 of 1002, Las Condes, Santiago, Chile
Tel.: (56) 225809671
Multi-lingual & Multimedia Services
N.A.I.C.S.: 541840
Aldo Maldonado Perez *(Mgr-HR)*

Bluelink International Strasbourg SA (1)
18 rue Livio, 67100, Strasbourg, France
Tel.: (33) 369744200
Multi-lingual & Multimedia Services
N.A.I.C.S.: 541840
Marion Obritin *(Mgr-Work Force)*

Brit Air (1)
Aeroport Cf 27925, Morlaix, 29679, France (100%)
Tel.: (33) 298621022
Web Site: http://www.britair.com
Sales Range: $300-349.9 Million
Emp.: 1,300
Regional Airline Operator
N.A.I.C.S.: 561599

Subsidiary (Domestic):

Centre de Formation Aeronautique ICARE (2)
Aeroport, 29600, Morlaix, France (99.96%)
Tel.: (33) 298881010
Web Site: http://www.icare.fr
Sales Range: $25-49.9 Million
Emp.: 35
Airline Training Services
N.A.I.C.S.: 488119
Marc Lamidey *(Chm)*

CRMA Sarl (1)
ZA de la Clef de Saint Pierre 14 avenue Gay Lussac, 78990, Elancourt, France
Sales Range: $50-74.9 Million
Emp.: 400
Aircraft Component Repair & Maintenance Services
N.A.I.C.S.: 811198
Jimmy Hilleraud *(VP-Sls & Mktg)*

CYGNIFIC B.V. (1)
Tel.: (31) 202013000
Web Site: http://www.cygnific.com
Sales Range: $150-199.9 Million
Emp.: 700
Airline Travel Agency Services
N.A.I.C.S.: 561599

City Jet Ltd (1)
(100%)
Tel.: (353) 18700110
Web Site: http://www.cityjet.com
Sales Range: $75-99.9 Million
Emp.: 500
Regional Airline Operator

N.A.I.C.S.: 561599

Compagnie d'Exploitaition des Services Auxiliaires Aeriens (1)
10-14 rue de Rome, BP 19701, Tremblay, 95726, Roissy-en-France, Cedex, France
Tel.: (33) 148648585
Sales Range: $550-599.9 Million
Emp.: 10,000
Airport & Airline Catering & Cabin Cleaning Services
N.A.I.C.S.: 488119
Alexis Frantz *(CEO)*

Subsidiary (Domestic):

ACNA (2)
22 Ave Des Nations, 93420, Villepinte, France
Tel.: (33) 149388282
Web Site: http://www.acna.fr
Rev.: $970,500,000
N.A.I.C.S.: 481111

Branch (Domestic):

ACNA (3)
Orly Sud 182, 94542, Orly, France
Tel.: (33) 141752223
Web Site: http://www.servair.fr
Sales Range: $125-149.9 Million
Emp.: 300
Airport & Airline Services
N.A.I.C.S.: 488119

Subsidiary (Domestic):

Aeroform (3)
22 Ave Des Nations Le Rousseau, PO Box 2, BP 85931, Villepinte, France
Tel.: (33) 148177380
Web Site: http://www.servair.fr
Rev.: $3,000,000
Emp.: 18
Airport & Airline Services
N.A.I.C.S.: 488119

LogAir (3)
ZAC du Parc, 12 rue Saint Exupery, 77290, Compans, France
Tel.: (33) 160217219
Airport & Airline Services
N.A.I.C.S.: 488119

Passerelle (3)
Zone Boutiquaires Terminal 2 Hall AC, 95724, Roissy-en-France, Cedex, France
Tel.: (33) 148165437
Sales Range: $50-74.9 Million
Emp.: 140
Airport & Airline Services
N.A.I.C.S.: 488119

Servantage (3)
8 Chemin des Glirettes, 95000, Le Thillay, France
Tel.: (33) 130180341
Sales Range: $25-49.9 Million
Emp.: 50
Airport & Airline Services
N.A.I.C.S.: 488119

Subsidiary (Domestic):

Cremonini (2)
83 Rue Du Chalolais, 75010, Paris, France
Tel.: (33) 59754611
Sales Range: $100-124.9 Million
Emp.: 360
N.A.I.C.S.: 481111

Subsidiary (US):

European Catering Services Inc. (2)
1209 N Orange St, Wilmington, DE 19801
N.A.I.C.S.: 481111

Subsidiary (Domestic):

Jet Chef (2)
Zone d'Aviation d'Affaires, Aeroport du Bourget, 93350, Le Bourget, France
Tel.: (33) 1 48646326
Web Site: http://www.jetchef.fr
Sales Range: $25-49.9 Million
Emp.: 157
Air Transportation Catering Services
N.A.I.C.S.: 722320

Orly Air Traiteur (2)
1 Rue Du Pont Des Pierres, 91422, Wissous, France

Tel.: (33) 149758200
Web Site: http://www.servair.fr
Sales Range: $10-24.9 Million
Emp.: 800
N.A.I.C.S.: 481111

Subsidiary (Non-US):

Societe de Restauration Industrielle (2)
Zone de Fret Nord Aeroport Pole Caraibes, 97139, Abymes, Guadeloupe
Tel.: (590) 211714
N.A.I.C.S.: 481111

European Pneumatic Component Overhaul & Repair (Epcor) BV (1)
Bellsingel 41, 1119 NT, Schiphol-Rijk, Netherlands
Tel.: (31) 203161730
Web Site: http://www.epcor.nl
Mechanical Component Maintenance & Repair Services
N.A.I.C.S.: 811310
Sander Zwart *(Mgr-Customer Support)*

Executive Health Management BV (1)
The Red Office second floor Wegalaan 42, 2132 JC, Hoofddorp, Netherlands
Tel.: (31) 235541540
Web Site: https://www.ehm.nl
Healtcare Services
N.A.I.C.S.: 621610
Miranda Van Nieuwpoort *(Mgr-Comml)*

Global Logistics System Europe Company for Cargo Information Services GmbH (1)
Lyoner St 36, 60528, Frankfurt am Main, Germany
Tel.: (49) 69669060
Web Site: http://www.traxon.com
Sales Range: $25-49.9 Million
Emp.: 30
Support Activities for Air Transportation
N.A.I.C.S.: 488190
Felix Keck *(Mng Dir)*

INTERNATIONAL AIRLINE SERVICES AMERICAS L.P. (1)
11200 Fuqua St Ste 100, Houston, TX 77089
Tel.: (713) 275-9090
Web Site: https://www.ias-global.com
Emp.: 6
Airline Transportation Services
N.A.I.C.S.: 488190
Rafael J. Alcala *(Gen Mgr)*

INTERNATIONAL AIRLINE SERVICES EUROPE LIMITED (1)
6th Floor 25 Farringdon Street, London, EC4A 4AB, United Kingdom
Tel.: (44) 1135140002
Airline Transportation Services
N.A.I.C.S.: 488190
Nathalie Mouton *(Mgr-Sls-Global & Mktg)*

INTERNATIONAL AIRLINE SERVICES LIMITED (1)
Bridge Ho 4 Borough High St, London, SE1 9QQ, United Kingdom
Tel.: (44) 2073789133
Airline Transportation Services
N.A.I.C.S.: 488190

INTERNATIONAL MARINE AIRLINE SERVICES LIMITED (1)
Bridge House 4 Borough High Street, London, SE1 9QQ, United Kingdom
Tel.: (44) 2074038112
Oil Transportation Services
N.A.I.C.S.: 488190
Bernard Rafferty *(Gen Mgr)*

KES AIRPORT EQUIPMENT FUELLING B.V. (1)
Pakhuisstraat 1, Postbus 7700, 1117 ZL, Schiphol, Netherlands
Tel.: (31) 206492236
Sales Range: $75-99.9 Million
Emp.: 146
Aircraft Fueling Distr
N.A.I.C.S.: 424720
Andrea Schittmann *(Gen Mgr)*

KLM CATERING SERVICES SCHIPHOL B.V. (1)

Havenmeesterweg 1 Gebouw 540, 1118 CB, Schiphol, Netherlands
Tel.: (31) 206494707
Web Site: https://www.kcs.nl
Emp.: 1,300
Airline Catering Services
N.A.I.C.S.: 722320

KLM FINANCIAL SERVICES B.V. (1)
Amsterdamseweg 55, Amstelveen, 1182 GP, Netherlands
Tel.: (31) 206491359
Financial Management Services
N.A.I.C.S.: 523999
Bas Brouns *(VP-Aircraft Financing)*

KLM HEALTH SERVICES B.V. (1)
Stationsplein N O 236 KLM Health Services Building 133, Postbus 7700, Schiphol-Oost, 1117 CJ, Amsterdam, Netherlands
Tel.: (31) 206495187
Web Site: http://www.klmhealthservices.nl
Health Care Srvices
N.A.I.C.S.: 621999

KLM LUCHTVAARTSCHOOL B.V. (1)
Burg J G Legroweg 43, 9761 TA, Eelde, Netherlands
Tel.: (31) 503098300
Web Site: https://klmflightacademy.nl
Emp.: 50
Flight Training Services
N.A.I.C.S.: 611512
Viktor Simpson *(Gen Mgr)*

KLM OLIEMAATSCHAPPIJ B.V. (1)
Amsterdamseweg 55, Amstelveen, Amsterdam, 1182 GP, Netherlands
Tel.: (31) 206499123
Web Site: http://www.klm.com
Petroleum Product Distr
N.A.I.C.S.: 424720
Peter Elberse *(Gen Mgr)*

KLM Royal Dutch Airlines (1)
Amsterdamseweg 55, 1182 GP, Amstelveen, Netherlands (100%)
Tel.: (31) 206499123
Web Site: http://www.klm.nl
Sales Range: $5-14.9 Billion
Emp.: 30,000
Scheduled Air Transport; Freight Arrangements
N.A.I.C.S.: 481111
Kornelis J. Storm *(Chm-Supervisory Bd)*

Subsidiary (Domestic):

KLM Cityhopper (2)
Schiphol Airport, PO Box 7700, 1117 ZL, Amsterdam, Netherlands (100%)
Tel.: (31) 206492227
Web Site: http://www.klm.com
Rev.: $256,000,000
Emp.: 1,000
Domestic & Regional Airline
N.A.I.C.S.: 481111
E. G. Kreiken *(Mng Dir)*

Division (US):

KLM Royal Dutch Airlines (2)
565 Taxter Rd 3rd Fl, Elmsford, NY 10523
Tel.: (914) 784-2000
Web Site: http://www.klm.com
Sales Range: $25-49.9 Million
Emp.: 60
International Airline Services
N.A.I.C.S.: 481111
Jan Willem Smeulers *(VP-North America)*

Subsidiary (Non-US):

KLM UK ENGINEERING LIMITED (2)
Liberator Road Norwich Airport, Norwich, NR6 6ER, Norfolk, United Kingdom
Tel.: (44) 1603254400
Web Site: https://www.klmukengineering.com
Emp.: 400
Aircraft Repair & Maintenance Services
N.A.I.C.S.: 811198
Graham Casbourne *(Dir-Bus Dev & Sls)*

KLM UK Ltd. (2)
Leeds Bradford International Airport, Leeds, LS19 7TU, United Kingdom

Air France-KLM S.A.—(Continued)
Tel.: (44) 8712310000
Web Site: http://www.klmuk.com
Rev.: $589,000,000
Emp.: 1,400
Scheduled International & Charter Airline
N.A.I.C.S.: 481111

Subsidiary (Domestic):

Transavia Airlines C.V.   **(2)**
Schiphol Airport, PO Box 7777, 1118 ZM,
Schiphol, Netherlands
Tel.: (31) 202146032
Web Site: https://www.transavia.com
Sales Range: $600-649.9 Million
Emp.: 1,482
Oil Transportation Services
N.A.I.C.S.: 488190
Onno P. M. van den Brink *(Pres & CEO)*

Klm Equipment Services BV   **(1)**
Pakhuisstraat 1 Luchthaven, 1118 DJ, Schiphol, Netherlands
Web Site: http://www.kes-gse.nl
Logistic Services
N.A.I.C.S.: 488510
Frans De Saegher *(Fin Mgr)*

LYON MAINTENANCE   **(1)**
Lyon Saint Eiupery Airport, Box 386, 69145,
Lyon, France
Tel.: (33) 4 72 22 80 65
Emp.: 50
Aircraft Equipment Maintenance Services
N.A.I.C.S.: 811198
Patrice Brocard *(Gen Mgr)*

Martinair Holland N.V.   **(1)**
Piet Guilonardweg 17, Schiphol, 1117 EE,
Amsterdam, Netherlands   **(100%)**
Tel.: (31) 206492038
Web Site: https://www.martinair.com
Sales Range: $1-4.9 Billion
Emp.: 3,647
International Charter Airline
N.A.I.C.S.: 481112
Adriaan den Heijer *(Mng Dir)*

Regional Compagnie Aerienne
Europeenne   **(1)**
Aeroport De Nantes Atlantique, Bouguenais, 44345, France   **(100%)**
Tel.: (33) 240135300
Web Site: http://www.hop.fr
Sales Range: $350-399.9 Million
Emp.: 1,700
Regional Airline Operator
N.A.I.C.S.: 561599

Regional Jet Center BV   **(1)**
Hangar 73 Westerkimweg 1 Oost, 1118 ZS,
Schiphol, Netherlands
Tel.: (31) 206491891
Web Site: https://www.rjc.nl
Emp.: 300
Mechanical Component Maintenance & Repair Services
N.A.I.C.S.: 811310
M. Eijk *(Mng Dir)*

SKYCHEF LTD   **(1)**
Seychelles International Airport, PO Box
450, Victoria, Seychelles
Tel.: (248) 438 17 63
Airport Restaurant Operating Services
N.A.I.C.S.: 722511

SoDExl
Zone Cargo 6 2 Rue de Voyelles, CS 16
041, Tremblay-en-France, 95723, Roissy-
en-France, Cedex, France   **(100%)**
Tel.: (33) 686810803
Sales Range: $10-24.9 Million
Emp.: 400
International Express Parcel Service; Joint
Venture of Groupe Air France (60%), TAT
S.A. (20%) & La Poste (20%)
N.A.I.C.S.: 492110

Societe Nouvelle Air Ivoire S.A.   **(1)**
Pl de la Republique, Abidjan, Cote
d'Ivoire   **(76%)**
Tel.: (225) 20251561
Web Site: http://www.airivoire.com
Sales Range: $25-49.9 Million
Emp.: 50
Airline Operator
N.A.I.C.S.: 488119

Societe de Construction et de Reparation de Materiel Aeronautique   **(1)**
14 avenue Gay Lussac, 78990, Elancourt,
France   **(100%)**
Tel.: (33) 130683701
Sales Range: $125-149.9 Million
Emp.: 350
Maintenance of Aircraft Parts
N.A.I.C.S.: 488119

TRANSAVIA AIRLINES B.V.   **(1)**
Piet Guilonardweg 15 Transport Building
Schiphol Centrum, Amsterdam, 1117 EE,
Netherlands
Tel.: (31) 206046555
Airline Transportation Services
N.A.I.C.S.: 488190

TRANSAVIA FRANCE S.A.S.   **(1)**
3 allee Helene Boucher, 91550, Paray-
Vielle-Poste, France
Tel.: (33) 892058888
Web Site: https://www.transavia.com
Emp.: 40
Oil Transportation Services
N.A.I.C.S.: 488190
Nathalie Stubler *(CEO)*

AIR GREENLAND A/S
PO Box 1012, 3900, Nuuk, Greenland
Web Site:
      http://www.airgreenland.com
Year Founded: 1960
Sales Range: $125-149.9 Million
Emp.: 600
Scheduled, Charter & Freight Airline
Services
N.A.I.C.S.: 481112
Hans Peter Hansen *(Dir-Charter & Cargo)*

Subsidiaries:

Greenlands Rejsebureau A/S   **(1)**
Wilders Plads 13A 1, 1403, Copenhagen,
Denmark
Tel.: (45) 33 13 10 11
Web Site: http://www.greenland-travel.dk
Travel Agency Services
N.A.I.C.S.: 561510

Hotel Arctic A/S   **(1)**
PO Box 1501, DK 3952, Ilulissat, Greenland
Tel.: (299) 0299 94 41
Web Site: http://www.hotelarctic.com
Hotel & Conference Center Operator
N.A.I.C.S.: 721110
Erik Bjerregaard *(Gen Mgr)*

AIR INDIA LIMITED
Air India Bldg 218 Backbay Reclamation, Nariman Pt, Mumbai, 400 021,
India
Tel.: (91) 2222796666
Web Site: http://www.airindia.in
Year Founded: 1932
Sales Range: $1-4.9 Billion
Emp.: 16,274
International Airline
N.A.I.C.S.: 481111
A. S. Soman *(Exec Dir-Trng)*

Subsidiaries:

Air India   **(1)**
570 Lexington Ave 15th Fl, New York, NY
10022
Tel.: (212) 407-1300
Web Site: http://www.airindia.com
Sales Range: $25-49.9 Million
Emp.: 100
International Airline Svcs
N.A.I.C.S.: 561599
K. M. Unni *(Head-Airframes)*

Air India Charters Ltd.   **(1)**
1st Floor Inflight Service Department Opp-
Indian Oil Depot Sahar, Andheri-East, Mumbai, 400 099, India
Tel.: (91) 2228318825
Oil Transportation Services
N.A.I.C.S.: 481111
Pushpinder Singh *(COO)*

Airline Allied Services Limited   **(1)**
First Floor Domestic Arrival Termina - I B
IGI Airport, New Delhi, India
Tel.: (91) 11 2567 5654
Oil Transportation Services
N.A.I.C.S.: 481111

HOTEL CORPORATION OF INDIA
LIMITED   **(1)**
Indira Gandi International Airport, New
Delhi, 110037, India
Tel.: (91) 11 25652223
Web Site: http://www.centaurhotels.com
Hotel Operator
N.A.I.C.S.: 721110
Chetan Kak *(VP)*

AIR MALAWI LIMITED
PO Box 84, Blantyre, Malawi.
Tel.: (265) 1820811
Web Site: http://www.airmalawi.com
Year Founded: 1967
Sales Range: $75-99.9 Million
Emp.: 441
Government Operated Airline Services
N.A.I.C.S.: 481111
Patrick Chilambe *(CEO)*

AIR MARINE SA
305 Avenue de Mont de Marsan,
Leognan, 33850, Bordeaux, France
Tel.: (33) 35542920
Web Site: http://www.air-marine.fr
MLAIM—(EUR)
Sales Range: $1-9.9 Million
Aerial Geophysical Surveying Services
N.A.I.C.S.: 541360
Gilles Olichon *(Chm & Co-CEO)*

AIR MARSHALL ISLANDS, INC.
uluga, Majuro, 96960, Marshall Islands
Tel.: (692) 6253731
Web Site:
      http://www.airmarshallislands.com
Sales Range: $25-49.9 Million
Emp.: 100
Oil Transportation Services
N.A.I.C.S.: 481111
Thomas Heine *(Chm)*

AIR MAURITIUS LIMITED
Air Mauritius Centre President John
Kennedy Street, Port Louis, Mauritius
Tel.: (230) 2077070
Web Site:
      http://www.airmauritius.com
Year Founded: 1967
AIRM—(MAU)
Rev.: $1,257,689
Assets: $13,699,484
Liabilities: $20,329,165
Net Worth: ($6,629,681)
Earnings: ($1,463,676)
Emp.: 2,000
Fiscal Year-end: 03/31/21
Airline Services
N.A.I.C.S.: 481111
Donald Emmanuel Payen *(Exec VP-Customer, Product & Digitalisation)*

Subsidiaries:

Air Mauritius South Africa (Pty)
Limited   **(1)**
Grayston Ridge Office Park, Ground Floor
Block A, Sandton, South Africa
Tel.: (27) 114444600
Web Site: http://www.airmauritius.com
Sales Range: $25-49.9 Million
Emp.: 13
Other Support Activities for Air Transportation
N.A.I.C.S.: 488190

Airmate Ltd   **(1)**
10th Floor Wing A Cyber Tower, Ebene,
Reduit, Mauritius   **(100%)**

Tel.: (230) 4030165
Web Site: http://www.airmate.mu
Sales Range: $25-49.9 Million
Emp.: 65
Other Airport Operations
N.A.I.C.S.: 488119

Mauritius Helicopter Ltd.   **(1)**
SSR International Airport, Plaine Magnien,
Mauritius
Tel.: (230) 6033754
Helicopter Services
N.A.I.C.S.: 481211

AIR NAMIBIA (PTY) LTD.
2729 Dr Wkoon Street, PO Box 731,
Windhoek, Namibia
Tel.: (264) 612996000
Web Site:
      http://www.airnamibia.com.na
Year Founded: 1946
Sales Range: $75-99.9 Million
Emp.: 500
Oil Transportation Services
N.A.I.C.S.: 481111
Theo Namases *(Mng Dir)*

AIR NEW ZEALAND LIMITED
185 Fanshawe Street, Auckland,
1010, New Zealand
Tel.: (64) 93362400   NZ
Web Site:
      https://www.airnewzealand.co.nz
Year Founded: 1939
AIR—(NZX)
Rev.: $3,785,885,167
Assets: $5,499,401,914
Liabilities: $4,255,980,861
Net Worth: $1,243,421,053
Earnings: $246,411,483
Emp.: 11,474
Fiscal Year-end: 06/30/23
Domestic & International Air Passenger & Cargo Services; Aviation Overhaul & Maintenance Services
N.A.I.C.S.: 481111
Janice Dawson *(Deputy Chm)*

Subsidiaries:

Air Nelson Limited   **(1)**
Private Bag 32, Nelson, 7011, New Zealand
Tel.: (64) 35478700
Web Site: http://www.airnelson.co.nz
Oil Transportation Services
N.A.I.C.S.: 488190

Air New Zealand (Australia) Pty
Limited   **(1)**
L 11 151 Clarence St, Sydney, 2000, NSW,
Australia
Tel.: (61) 282359999
Web Site: http://www.airnz.com.au
Oil Transportation Services
N.A.I.C.S.: 488190

Subsidiary (Domestic):

TAE Pty Limited   **(2)**
L1 Tae House 52 Mcdougall St, Milton,
4064, QLD, Australia
Tel.: (61) 733674811
Web Site: http://www.tae.com.au
Aerospace Engineering Services
N.A.I.C.S.: 541330

Subsidiary (Domestic):

TAE Aviation Pty Limited   **(3)**
Hangar 1C James Schofield Dr, Adelaide,
5850, SA, Australia
Tel.: (61) 881500200
Web Site: http://www.tae.com.au
Sales Range: $25-49.9 Million
Emp.: 60
Aerospace Engineering Services
N.A.I.C.S.: 541330
Andrew Sanderson *(Gen Mgr)*

TAE Gas Turbines Pty Limited   **(3)**
1 Jet Place, Bundamba, 4304, QLD, Australia
Tel.: (61) 738136800
Web Site: https://www.taeaerospace.com
Aerospace Engineering Services

N.A.I.C.S.: 541330

Air New Zealand Aircraft Holdings Limited (1)
Air New Zealand House 185 Fanshawe Street, Auckland, 1010, New Zealand
Tel.: (64) 93362400
Web Site: http://www.airnewzealand.co.nz
Oil Transportation Services
N.A.I.C.S.: 481212

Air New Zealand Cargo Services (1)
185 sainshiwe Street, 1010, Auckland, New Zealand (100%)
Tel.: (64) 93362400
Web Site: http://www.airnewzealand.co.nz
Sales Range: $1-4.9 Billion
Emp.: 3,000
Cargo & Transport Services
N.A.I.C.S.: 481111
Mark Street (Gen Mgr)

Air New Zealand Engineering Services (1)
5 Geoffrey Roberts Road Mangere, Private Bag 92007, Auckland, 1142, New Zealand (100%)
Tel.: (64) 93362400
Web Site: http://www.airnewzealand.co.nz
Sales Range: $50-74.9 Million
Emp.: 200
Aviation Overhaul & Maintenance
N.A.I.C.S.: 488119
Mark Street (Head-Customer Loyalty)

Air New Zealand Ltd. (U.S.A.) (1)
222 N Setulveda Ste 920, El Segundo, CA 90245-5000
Tel.: (310) 648-7000
Web Site: http://www.airnewzealand.com
Sales Range: $25-49.9 Million
Emp.: 80
Operator of Commercial & Cargo Air Lines
N.A.I.C.S.: 561510
Cam Wallace (Chief Comml & Sls Officer)

Altitude Aerospace Interiors Limited (1)
Ground Floor Isitt House 1 Leonard Isitt Drive, Mangere, Auckland, New Zealand
Tel.: (64) 92563242
Web Site: http://www.altitude-ai.com
Aerospace Engineering Services
N.A.I.C.S.: 541330

Blue Pacific Tours (1)
Room 404 Shin Kokusai Building, 3 4 1 Marunouchi Chiyoda Ku, Tokyo, 100 0005, Japan (100%)
Tel.: (81) 332118071
Web Site: http://www.bpt.co.jp
Sales Range: $25-49.9 Million
Emp.: 20
N.A.I.C.S.: 481111

Eagle Air Maintenance Limited (1)
Boyd Road Hamilton Airport, Hamilton, 3282, New Zealand
Tel.: (64) 78571000
Web Site: http://www.eagleair.co.nz
Sales Range: $25-49.9 Million
Emp.: 80
Oil Transportation Services
N.A.I.C.S.: 481212
Martin Vincent (Mgr-Fin)

Eagle Airways Limited (1)
Boyd Road Hamilton Airport R D 2, Hamilton, 3282, New Zealand
Tel.: (64) 78571000
Web Site: http://www.eagleair.co.nz
Sales Range: $25-49.9 Million
Emp.: 75
Oil Transportation Services
N.A.I.C.S.: 481212
Myles Perry (Gen Mgr)

Mount Cook Airline Limited (1)
Unit 3 Aviation House 12 Orchard Road, Christchurch, 8544, New Zealand
Tel.: (64) 33581200
Emp.: 20
Oil Transportation Services
N.A.I.C.S.: 481211

AIR NIGERIA DEVELOPMENT LIMITED
9th Floor Etiebets Place 21 Mobolaji Bank Anthony Way, Ikeja, Lagos, Nigeria
Tel.: (234) 1 2711144　　　NG
Web Site: http://www.myairnigeria.com
Year Founded: 2004
Sales Range: $150-199.9 Million
Emp.: 1,000
Commercial Air Transportation
N.A.I.C.S.: 481111
Erwin Zeiler (Head-Aircraft Maintenance)

AIR PACIFIC LIMITED
Nasoso Rd Nadi Airport, Nadi, Fiji
Tel.: (679) 6737357
Web Site: http://www.airpacific.com
Sales Range: $250-299.9 Million
Emp.: 800
Oil Transportation Services
N.A.I.C.S.: 481111
Watson Seeto (Sr Gen Mgr-Airport, Inflight Svcs & Freight)

AIR SEYCHELLES LTD.
Pointe Lorue, PO Box 386, Victoria, Mahe, Seychelles
Tel.: (248) 391002　　　Sc
Web Site: http://www.airseychelles.com
Year Founded: 1971
Sales Range: $100-124.9 Million
Emp.: 800
Oil Transportation Services
N.A.I.C.S.: 481111
Lekha Nair (Dir-Fin)

AIR TAHITI
PO Box 314, Papeete, French Polynesia
Tel.: (689) 482847
Web Site: http://www.airtahiti.aero
Sales Range: $150-199.9 Million
Emp.: 970
Oil Transportation Services
N.A.I.C.S.: 481111
Christian Vernaudon (Mng Dir)

AIR VANUATU LTD
Air Vanuatu House, Rue de Paris, Port-Vila, Vanuatu
Tel.: (678) 23838
Web Site: http://www.airvanuatu.com
Sales Range: $25-49.9 Million
Emp.: 200
Oil Transportation Services
N.A.I.C.S.: 481111
Joseph Laloyer (Mng Dir)

AIR WATER INC.
2-12-8 Minami Semba, Chuo-ku, Osaka, 542-0081, Japan
Tel.: (81) 662521337
Web Site: https://www.awi.co.jp
Year Founded: 1929
AWTRF—(OTCQB)
Rev.: $7,205,233,380
Assets: $7,827,094,650
Liabilities: $4,625,818,710
Net Worth: $3,201,275,940
Earnings: $287,782,290
Emp.: 20,109
Fiscal Year-end: 03/31/23
Gases for Industrial, Medical & Food Processing Operations
N.A.I.C.S.: 325120
Hirohisa Hiramatsu (Auditor)

Subsidiaries:

Air Water (Thailand) Co., Ltd. (1)
700/352 M 6 T Donhuaroh A, Muang, Chon Buri, 20000, Thailand
Tel.: (66) 3 846 8130
Web Site: https://www.airwater.co.th
Metal Surface Treatment Services
N.A.I.C.S.: 332811

Air Water America Inc. (1)
135 US Hwy 202 206 Ste 12, Bedminster, NJ 07921
Tel.: (908) 719-6560
Engineering Services
N.A.I.C.S.: 541330

Subsidiary (Domestic):

American Gas Products, LLC. (2)
24 Vine St, Everett, MA 02149-4514
Tel.: (617) 381-1020
Web Site: http://agpgas.com
Sales Range: $1-9.9 Million
Emp.: 20
Chemical & Allied Product Whslr
N.A.I.C.S.: 424690
Jim Hermetet (VP-Sls)

Air Water Asia Pte. Ltd. (1)
No 2 Tampines Industrial Drive Power Partners Building 05-01, Singapore, Singapore
Tel.: (65) 6 797 9940
Industrial Gas Distribution Services
N.A.I.C.S.: 221210

Air Water BellPearl Inc. (1)
20-16 Higashi Shinsaibashi 1-chome, Chuo-ku, Osaka, 542-0083, Japan
Tel.: (81) 662521802
Emp.: 50
Phenolic Resins Mfr
N.A.I.C.S.: 325211

Air Water Carbonic Inc. (1)
4-21-3 Shinbashi Tokyu Building 10th Floor, Minato-ku, Tokyo, 105-0004, Japan
Tel.: (81) 33 431 9131
Web Site: https://www.awci.co.jp
Emp.: 130
Liquid Nitrogen Gas Mfr & Distr
N.A.I.C.S.: 325120

Air Water ECOROCA Inc. (1)
3440-9 Wakaho-hoshina, Nagano, 381-0102, Japan
Tel.: (81) 33 433 2771
Web Site: https://www.ecoroca.com
Emp.: 51
Construction Material Mfr & Distr
N.A.I.C.S.: 327120
Kazuya Watanabe (Pres)

Air Water Inc. - Hokkaido (1)
1 2 Kita 3 Jo Nishi, Chuo Ku, Sapporo, 060 0003, Japan
Tel.: (81) 112122821
Web Site: http://www.awi.co.jp
Industrial Gas Mfr
N.A.I.C.S.: 325120

Air Water Inc. - Kashima Plant (1)
No 3 Hikari, Kashima, 314-0014, Ibaraki, Japan
Tel.: (81) 299843511
Organic Chemical Mfr
N.A.I.C.S.: 325411

Air Water India Private Limited (1)
DLF IT Park-1 Tower-A 11th Floor Block-AF Action Area-1, New Town Rajarhat, Kolkata, 700156, West Bengal, India
Tel.: (91) 336 637 3900
Industrial Gas Distribution Services
N.A.I.C.S.: 221210

Air Water Link Inc. (1)
132-1 Takeda Mukaishiro-cho, Fushimi-ku, Kyoto, 612-8418, Japan
Tel.: (81) 75 694 1052
Web Site: https://www.awlink.co.jp
Emp.: 234
Medical Equipment Mfr & Distr
N.A.I.C.S.: 339112

Air Water Mach (Dalian) Co., Ltd. (1)
31-4 Aigang Road, Free Trade Zone, Dalian, Liaoning, China
Tel.: (86) 4116 677 8055
Metal Product Mfr & Distr
N.A.I.C.S.: 332312

Air Water Mach Inc. (1)
4009-1 Azusagawa Yamato, Matsumoto, 390-1701, Nagano, Japan
Tel.: (81) 26 378 5556
Web Site: https://www.awimach.com
Rubber Product Mfr & Distr
N.A.I.C.S.: 326291
Yasuhiko Tsuzuki (Pres)

Air Water Mach Rubber Products (Fujian) Co., Ltd. (1)
Honglu Rongqiao Economic and Technological Development Zone, Fuqing, Fujian, China
Tel.: (86) 5918 538 2951
Rubber Molded Product Mfr & Distr
N.A.I.C.S.: 326291

Air Water Materials Inc. (1)
2-13-7 Hamamatsucho, Minato-ku, Tokyo, Japan
Tel.: (81) 33 578 7200
Web Site: https://www.aw-mt.com
Emp.: 240
Semiconductor Material Mfr & Distr
N.A.I.C.S.: 334413
Kazuyuki Tomoto (Pres)

Air Water NV (Shanghai) Co., Ltd. (1)
No 555-2 Dong Zhou Road, Song Jiang District, Shanghai, China
Tel.: (86) 216 787 7565
Metal Surface Treatment Services
N.A.I.C.S.: 332811

Air Water NV Inc. (1)
8 Nakahama-cho, Amagasaki, 660-0091, Hyogo, Japan
Tel.: (81) 66 412 5355
Web Site: https://www.awnv.co.jp
Metal Surface Hardening Treatment Services
N.A.I.C.S.: 332811

Air Water Philippines, Inc. (1)
Unit B Winsouth One No 140 East Main Avenue Loop, Phase6 Laguna Techno-park, Binan, Laguna, Philippines
Tel.: (63) 49 541 2759
Industrial Gas Distribution Services
N.A.I.C.S.: 221210

Air Water Plant & Engineering, Inc. (1)
2-6-40 Chikko-Shinmachi, Nishi-ku, Sakai, 592-8331, Osaka, Japan
Tel.: (81) 72 244 8801
Web Site: https://www.awpe.co.jp
Industrial Gas Distribution Services
N.A.I.C.S.: 221210
Shigeki Otsuka (Pres)

Air Water Safety Service Inc. (1)
03-02-2016 Takatsukadai, Nishiku-ku, Kobe, 651-2271, Japan
Tel.: (81) 78 992 1400
Web Site: https://www.awb.co.jp
Ventilator Mfr
N.A.I.C.S.: 333415
Yuji Sakai (Pres & CEO)

Air Water Sol (Shanghai) Trading Co. Ltd. (1)
Room 903 5F Shang Chuang Building 450 Cao Yang Road, Putuo District, Shanghai, China
Tel.: (86) 216 224 2906
Aerosol Product Mfr & Distr
N.A.I.C.S.: 332431

Air Water Sol Inc. (1)
47-1 Kanda Higashimatsushita-cho Daiwa Kanda East Building 7th Floor, Chiyoda-ku, Tokyo, 101-0042, Japan
Tel.: (81) 35 207 3201
Web Site: https://www.airwatersol.com
Emp.: 645
Aerosol Product Mfr & Distr
N.A.I.C.S.: 332431

Air Water Special Gas Co., Ltd. (1)
Xiangxing Road Building 96, Xiang'an District, Xiamen, Fujian, China
Tel.: (86) 592 727 8521
Industrial Gas Distribution Services
N.A.I.C.S.: 221210

Air Water Vietnam Co., Ltd. (1)
Floor 5 Miss Ao Dai Building 21 Nguyen Trung Ngan Street, Ben Nghe Ward District 1, Ho Chi Minh City, Vietnam
Tel.: (84) 254 392 3360
Web Site: https://www.airwatervn.com
Industrial Gas Distribution Services
N.A.I.C.S.: 221210
Miyoshi Naoki (CEO)

Air Water, Inc. - Tokyo (1)

Air Water Inc.—(Continued)

3-18-19 Toranomon, Minato-ku, Tokyo, 105-0001, Japan
Tel.: (81) 335787801
Web Site: http://www.awi.co.jp
Sales Range: $25-49.9 Million
Emp.: 100
Industrial Gas Mfr
N.A.I.C.S.: 325120

Aquaintec Corporation (1)
3311-1 Higashiyokoji, Kikugawa, 439-0022, Shizuoka, Japan
Tel.: (81) 53 725 7540
Web Site: https://www.aquaintec.co.jp
Water Treatment Machinery Mfr & Distr
N.A.I.C.S.: 312112

Critical Power Solutions Pte. Ltd. (1)
2 Tampines Industrial Drive Power Partners Building, Singapore, Singapore
Tel.: (65) 6 755 5635
Power Generation Services
N.A.I.C.S.: 221114

Critical Systems Services Pte. (1)
Ltd.
2 Tampines Industrial Drive Power Partners Building, Singapore, Singapore
Tel.: (65) 6 555 6116
Industrial Gas Distribution Services
N.A.I.C.S.: 221210

Daito Chemical Co., Ltd. (1)
364-1 Oritate, Gifu, 501-1132, Japan
Tel.: (81) 58 239 1333
Web Site: https://www.daito-chemical.com
Chemical Product Mfr & Distr
N.A.I.C.S.: 325998

Denken-Highdental Co., Ltd. (1)
24-3 Kisshoin Ishiharakyomichi-cho, Minami-ku, Kyoto, 601-8356, Japan
Tel.: (81) 75 672 2101
Web Site: https://www.denken-highdental.co.jp
Emp.: 120
Dental Equipment Mfr & Distr
N.A.I.C.S.: 339114
Hiroshi Okuno *(Pres)*

Dohmeyer Holding BVBA (1)
Kerkstraat 108, 9050, Gent, Belgium
Tel.: (32) 9 241 5222
Web Site: https://www.dohmeyer.com
Cryogenic Refrigeration Mfr
N.A.I.C.S.: 333248

Ecofroz S.A. (1)
Panamericana Sur km 40, Machachi, Ecuador
Tel.: (593) 2 231 6293
Web Site: https://www.ecofroz.com
Emp.: 1,035
Frozen Vegetable Mfr & Distr
N.A.I.C.S.: 311411

Ellenbarrie Industrial Gases Ltd. (1)
3A Ripon Street, Kolkata, 700 016, India
Tel.: (91) 3322291923
Web Site: https://www.ellenbarrie.com
Sales Range: $10-24.9 Million
Industrial Gas Mfr & Distr
N.A.I.C.S.: 325120
Padam Kumar Agarwala *(Mng Dir)*

Epoch Technology Co., Ltd. (1)
Room 501 C Building No 1618 Yi-Shan Road, Shanghai, China
Tel.: (86) 216 433 8211
Chemical Products Distr
N.A.I.C.S.: 424690

FILWEL Co., Ltd. (1)
3-1 Kanebo-cho, Hofu, 747-0823, Yamaguchi, Japan
Tel.: (81) 83 525 6812
Web Site: https://www.filwel.co.jp
Artificial Leather Mfr & Distr
N.A.I.C.S.: 315250
Kazuhiko Nakamura *(Pres)*

Globalwide International Pte. Ltd. (1)
84 Kaki Bukit Industrial Terrace, Singapore, 416164, Singapore
Tel.: (65) 6 448 8280
Web Site: https://www.globalwide-intl.org
Interior Design & Construction Services
N.A.I.C.S.: 236220

Globalwide M&E Pte. Ltd. (1)
84 Kaki Bukit Industrial Terrace, Singapore, Singapore
Tel.: (65) 6 448 8280
Hospital Equipment & Design Services
N.A.I.C.S.: 541430

Gold Kogyo Laguna Philippines, Inc. (1)
Unit 3 7 Mountain Drive Lisp II Barangay La Mesa, Calamba, Laguna, Philippines
Tel.: (63) 49 544 5396
Plastic Product Mfr & Distr
N.A.I.C.S.: 326199

Gold-Pak Co., Ltd. (1)
4-13-14 Higashi-Shinagawa Glass Cube Shinagawa, Shinagawa-ku, Tokyo, 140-0002, Japan
Tel.: (81) 36 711 4320
Web Site: https://www.gold-pak.com
Emp.: 736
Vegetable Juice Mfr & Distr
N.A.I.C.S.: 311411

Healthcare-Tech Corporation (1)
7F 2-12-3 Nishi-Gotanda, Shinagawa-ku, Tokyo, 141 0031, Japan (60%)
Tel.: (81) 3 5437 3535
Web Site: http://www.healthcare-tech.co.jp
Emp.: 303
Nutritional Supplements Import & Distr
N.A.I.C.S.: 424210
Takaya Higuchi *(Pres)*

Hitec Holding B.V. (1)
Bedrijvenpark Twente 40, 7602 KB, Almelo, Netherlands
Tel.: (31) 54 658 9589
Industrial Gas Distribution Services
N.A.I.C.S.: 221210

Hitec Power Protection (Beijing) Co., (1)
Ltd.
3-18-A408 Bai Jia Zhuang Road, Chaoyang District, Beijing, China
Tel.: (86) 215 072 2038
Industrial Gas Distribution Services
N.A.I.C.S.: 221210

Hitec Power Protection (Malaysia) (1)
Sdn. Bhd.
Level 3 and 4 Wisma Suria Jalan Teknokrat 6 Cyber 5, 63000, Cyberjaya, Selangor, Malaysia
Tel.: (60) 38 318 2346
Industrial Gas Distribution Services
N.A.I.C.S.: 221210

Hitec Power Protection B.V. (1)
Bedrijvenpark Twente 40, 7602 KB, Almelo, Netherlands
Tel.: (31) 54 658 9589
Web Site: https://www.hitec-ups.com
Electric Equipment Mfr
N.A.I.C.S.: 335999

Hitec Power Protection Iberica (1)
S.L.
Pol Molid'en Serra C/ Baix Alt Penedes nave 4, Santa Oliva, 43710, Tarragona, Spain
Tel.: (34) 97 766 8902
Industrial Gas Distribution Services
N.A.I.C.S.: 221210

Hitec Power Protection Ltd. (1)
1740 Solihull Parkway, Birmingham Business Park, Birmingham, B37 7YD, United Kingdom
Tel.: (44) 192 648 4535
Industrial Gas Distribution Services
N.A.I.C.S.: 221210

Hitec Power Protection Taiwan (1)
Ltd.
No 226-1 Wuhe Street, Qionglin Township, Hsinchu, 307, Taiwan
Tel.: (886) 3 593 1197
Industrial Gas Distribution Services
N.A.I.C.S.: 221210

Hitec Vastgoed B.V. (1)
Bedrijvenpark Twente 40, 7602 KB, Almelo, Netherlands
Tel.: (31) 54 658 9589
Real Estate Manangement Services
N.A.I.C.S.: 531390

Inotec Taiwan Co., Ltd. (1)

6F 156-2 Sung Chiang Road, Taipei, 106468, Taiwan
Tel.: (886) 22 562 8885
Chemical Products Distr
N.A.I.C.S.: 424690

Inoueki (Malaysia) Sdn. Bhd. (1)
C-06-02 Level 6 Block C Plaza Mont Kiara No 2, Jalan Kiara Mont Kiara, 50480, Kuala Lumpur, Malaysia
Tel.: (60) 36 201 0517
Chemical Products Distr
N.A.I.C.S.: 424690

Inoueki (Thailand) Co., Ltd. (1)
340 Pracha Uthit Road, Donmuang, Bangkok, 10210, Thailand
Tel.: (66) 2 503 7512
Semiconductor Material Distr
N.A.I.C.S.: 423690

Inoueki Philippines, Inc. (1)
Panorama Building 5 and 6 South Science Avenue Laguna Technopark, Santa Rosa, 4206, Laguna, Philippines
Tel.: (63) 49 502 1514
Chemical Products Distr
N.A.I.C.S.: 424690

Inoueki Singapore Pte. Ltd. (1)
3 Ubi Avenue 3 03-03 Crocodile House, Singapore, 408857, Singapore
Tel.: (65) 6 746 0669
Industrial Gas Distribution Services
N.A.I.C.S.: 221210

KDF U.S., Inc. (1)
1673 E 28th St, Signal Hill, CA 90755
Tel.: (310) 320-6633
Dental Equipment Distr
N.A.I.C.S.: 423450

Kawasaki Kasei Chemicals Ltd. (1)
Muza Kawasaki Central Tower 6F 1310 Omiya-cho, Saiwai-ku, Kawasaki, 212-0014, Kanagawa, Japan (50.1%)
Tel.: (81) 44 266 6351
Web Site: http://www.kk-chem.co.jp
Emp.: 248
Chemical Products Mfr
N.A.I.C.S.: 325199
Nobuhiko Kobayashi *(Pres)*

Plant (Domestic):

Kawasaki Kasei Chemicals Ltd. - Kawasaki Plant (2)
1-2 Chidoricho, Kawasaki-ku, Kawasaki, 210-0865, Kanagawa, Japan
Tel.: (81) 44 266 6351
Web Site: http://www.kk-chem.co.jp
Chemical Products Mfr
N.A.I.C.S.: 325199

Misawa Medical Industry Co., (1)
Ltd.
1320 - 5 Nagatoro, Kasama, 309-1712, Ibaraki, Japan
Tel.: (81) 29 677 8901
Web Site: https://www.misawa-medical.co.jp
Emp.: 278
Medical Equipment Mfr & Distr
N.A.I.C.S.: 339112
Chieko Takeuchi *(Mgr)*

NSCC Air Water, Inc. (1)
1-13-1 Nihonbashi Nittetsu Nihonbashi Building General Reception 13F, Chuo-ku, Tokyo, 103-0027, Japan
Tel.: (81) 33 548 8571
Web Site: https://www.nscc-awi.co.jp
Emp.: 29
Industrial Gas Distribution Services
N.A.I.C.S.: 221210

Nichiro Sunpack Co., Ltd. (1)
18-1-1 Kita Nishimachi Nishi-ku, Sapporoshi, 063-0061, Hokkaido, Japan
Tel.: (81) 116633741
Bottled Water Mfr
N.A.I.C.S.: 312112

Nihon Dennetsu Co., Ltd. (1)
3788 Misatoyutaka, Azumino, 399-8102, Nagano, Japan
Tel.: (81) 26 387 8282
Web Site: https://www.nichinetu.co.jp
Heating Equipment Mfr & Distr
N.A.I.C.S.: 333414
Hiroyuki Matsuda *(Pres & CEO)*

Nippon Helium Inc. (1)
3-10-1 Shiohama, Kawasaki, 210-0826, Japan
Tel.: (81) 44 281 2211
Web Site: https://www.nippon-helium.co.jp
Industrial Gas Distribution Services
N.A.I.C.S.: 221210
Hirofumi Matsuyama *(Pres & CEO)*

PT. Indonesia Air Water (1)
Sahid Sudirman Center Lt 50-F Jl Jend Sudirman No 86, Jakarta Pusat, 10220, Indonesia
Tel.: (62) 212 788 9294
Industrial Gas Distribution Services
N.A.I.C.S.: 221210

Pacific Petro Import & Export Trading (1)
Joint Stock Company
99 Ich Thanh Street, Truong Thanh Ward District 9, Ho Chi Minh City, Vietnam
Tel.: (84) 283 730 0896
Industrial Gas Distribution Services
N.A.I.C.S.: 221210

Plecia Co., Ltd. (1)
5-32-1 Tomuro, Atsugi, 243-0031, Kanagawa, Japan
Tel.: (81) 46 295 9530
Web Site: https://www.plecia.co.jp
Emp.: 1,000
Baked Goods Mfr & Distr
N.A.I.C.S.: 311812

Power Partners Pte. Ltd. (1)
2 Tampines Industrial Drive Power Partners Building, Singapore, 528532, Singapore
Tel.: (65) 6 555 6116
Web Site: https://www.powerpartners-awi.com
Engineeéring Services
N.A.I.C.S.: 541330

Printec Co., Ltd. (1)
1866-3 Sakai, Atsugi, 243-0022, Kanagawa, Japan (100%)
Tel.: (81) 462273888
Web Site: http://www.printec.co.jp
Sales Range: $25-49.9 Million
Emp.: 40
Manufactures & Sells High Performance Semiconductor Substrates & LED Adhesives
N.A.I.C.S.: 333242

Sayama Corporation (1)
6-10-12 Higashi-jujo, Kita-ku, Tokyo, 114-0001, Japan
Tel.: (81) 33 903 2181
Web Site: https://www.sayama.com
Pressure Equipment Mfr & Distr
N.A.I.C.S.: 334513
Hiroshi Watanabe *(Sr Gen Mgr)*

Shanghai Air Water International (1)
Trading Co., Ltd.
Room A2B 15/F Huaxin Haixin Building 666 Fu Zhou Road, Shanghai, China
Tel.: (86) 215 852 9330
International Trade Agency Services
N.A.I.C.S.: 561920

Shanghai Air Water Medical Gas Co., (1)
Ltd.
No 336 Jiu-yuan Road, Qingpu Industrial Zone Qingpu District, Shanghai, China
Tel.: (86) 216 922 5828
Industrial Gas Distribution Services
N.A.I.C.S.: 221210

Shanghai Dongpeng Safety Co., (1)
Ltd.
579-A-7 Dong Xing Road, Songjiang Industrial Qu Songjiang District, Shanghai, China
Tel.: (86) 216 774 0601
Medical Equipment Mfr & Distr
N.A.I.C.S.: 339112

Sun-up Recycling Co., Ltd. (1)
79/2 Moo 4 T Thepparat A Ban Pho, Chachoengsao, 24140, Thailand
Tel.: (66) 3 859 5508
Recycled Organic Product Mfr & Distr
N.A.I.C.S.: 325199

Suzhou Air Water Trading Co., (1)
Ltd.
Room 1217 Gold River International Center No 88 Shi Shan Road, Suzhou New District, Jiangsu, China

Tel.: (86) 5126 818 5381
Industrial Gas Distribution Services
N.A.I.C.S.: 221210

Taiwan Air Water Mach Tech. Co., Ltd. (1)
3F No 247 Dong Sec 1 Guangming 6th Rd, Hsinchu, Zhubei, 302, Taiwan
Tel.: (886) 3 658 0301
Industrial Gas Distribution Services
N.A.I.C.S.: 221210

Taiwan Kyusuyuya Co., Ltd. (1)
6th FL No 156-2 Song-Jiang Road, Taipei, 10429, Taiwan
Tel.: (886) 22 568 3111
Restaurant Management Services
N.A.I.C.S.: 561110

Taiwan Nichinetu Co., Ltd. (1)
10F No101 Sec2 Nanjing E Rd, Zhongshan Dist, Taipei, 10457, Taiwan
Tel.: (886) 22 568 3896
Electric Heating Equipment Distr
N.A.I.C.S.: 423730

Tateho Chemical Dalian Co., Ltd. (1)
No 41 North-East 2nd St, Dalian Economic and Technical Development Zone, Dalian, 116600, China
Tel.: (86) 4118 764 3530
Industrial Gas Distribution Services
N.A.I.C.S.: 221210

Tateho Chemical Industries Co., Ltd. (1)
974 Kariya, Ako, 678-0239, Hyogo, Japan
Tel.: (81) 79 142 5041
Web Site: http://www.tateho.co.jp
Sales Range: $125-149.9 Million
Emp.: 380
Industrial Chemicals Mfr
N.A.I.C.S.: 325998

Tateho Ozark Technical Ceramics, Inc. (1)
402 Ware St, Webb City, MO 64870
Tel.: (417) 673-2463
Ceramic Products Mfr
N.A.I.C.S.: 327110

Taylor-Wharton America Inc. (1)
1411 Transport Dr, Baytown, TX 77523
Tel.: (281) 738-2863
Temperature Equipment Mfr & Distr
N.A.I.C.S.: 334513

Ying Kou Abe Harness Co., Ltd. (1)
19 Xifei Street, Xicheng District, Yingkou, Liaoning, China
Tel.: (86) 417 481 4540
Web Site: https://www.ykyah.com
Motor Vehicle Parts Mfr
N.A.I.C.S.: 336390

Zhejiang Kawamoto Health Care Products Co., Ltd. (1)
No 508 Xiuxin Road, Xiuzhou Industrial Park, Jiaxing, 314032, Zhejiang, China
Tel.: (86) 5738 371 1886
Web Site: https://en.skawamoto.com
Sanitary Material Mfr & Distr
N.A.I.C.S.: 325612

AIRA CAPITAL PUBLIC COMPANY LIMITED
319 Chamchuri Square Building 17th and 20th Floors Phayathai Road, Pathumwan, Bangkok, 10330, Thailand
Tel.: (66) 20802888
Web Site: https://www.aira.co.th
Year Founded: 2010
AIRA—(THA)
Rev.: $28,589,430
Assets: $276,694,288
Liabilities: $150,428,756
Net Worth: $126,265,532
Earnings: ($5,103,450)
Emp.: 1,000
Fiscal Year-end: 12/31/23
Holding Company; Securities Dealing
N.A.I.C.S.: 551112
Prasert Bunsumpun *(Chm)*

Subsidiaries:

AIRA Securities Public Company Limited (1)

319 Chamchuri Square Building 17th and 20th Floors Phayathai Road, Pathumwan, Bangkok, 10330, Thailand
Tel.: (66) 20802888
Web Site: https://www.aira.co.th
Financial Security Management Services
N.A.I.C.S.: 522291

AIRA FACTORING PUBLIC COMPANY LIMITED
188 Spring Tower Building Floor 12A Unit 6-10, Phaya Thai Road, Bangkok, 10330, Thailand
Tel.: (66) 26576222
Web Site:
https://www.airafactoring.co.th
Year Founded: 1997
AF—(THA)
Rev.: $7,039,611
Assets: $73,110,133
Liabilities: $57,567,094
Net Worth: $15,543,039
Earnings: $199,045
Emp.: 86
Fiscal Year-end: 12/31/23
Financial Investment Services
N.A.I.C.S.: 523999
Vuthipong Anurattada *(Asst Mng Dir-Credit & Mktg Grp 1)*

Subsidiaries:

AIRA Advisory Co., Ltd. (1)
319 Chamchuri Square Building 17th Floor Phayathai Road, Pathumwan, Bangkok, 10330, Thailand
Tel.: (66) 20802925
Web Site: https://www.airaadvisory.co.th
Financial Investment Services
N.A.I.C.S.: 523999

AIRA Leasing Plc (1)
188 Spring Tower Building 21st Floor Phaya Thai Road, Thung Phaya Thai Subdistrict Ratchathewi District, Bangkok, 10400, Thailand
Tel.: (66) 21175800
Web Site: https://www.airaleasing.co.th
Financial Investment Services
N.A.I.C.S.: 523999

AIRAN LIMITED
408 Kirtiman Complex C G Road, Ahmedabad, Gujarat, India
Tel.: (91) 7926462233
Web Site:
https://www.airanlimited.com
Year Founded: 1990
543811—(BOM)
Rev.: $12,720,926
Assets: $18,423,036
Liabilities: $3,192,039
Net Worth: $15,230,998
Earnings: $1,369,081
Emp.: 1,712
Fiscal Year-end: 03/31/22
Commercial Banking Services
N.A.I.C.S.: 522110
Sandeepkuma Agrawal *(Mng Dir)*

Subsidiaries:

Airan Australia Pty Limited (1)
Level 1 Suite 1a 33 Queen Street, Brisbane, 4000, QLD, Australia
Tel.: (61) 482088866
Account Outsourcing Services
N.A.I.C.S.: 541219

Airan Global Private Limited (1)
807-808 IFSC Block 13-B Zone-1, SEZ Area of GIFT City, Gandhinagar, 382355, India
Tel.: (91) 8511155101
Web Site: https://www.airanglobal.com
Account Outsourcing Services
N.A.I.C.S.: 541219

Cqub Infosystem Private Limited (1)
07 Kirtiman Complex B/h Rambrant C G Road, Ahmedabad, 380006, Gujarat, India
Tel.: (91) 8511155333
Web Site: http://www.cqub.com
Application Development Services

N.A.I.C.S.: 541511

AIRASIA X BERHAD
RedQ Jalan Pekeliling 5 Lapangan Terbang Antarabangsa, 64000, Kuala Lumpur, Selangor Darul Ehsan, Malaysia
Tel.: (60) 386600007   MY
Web Site: http://www.airasiax.com
Year Founded: 2006
AAX—(KLS)
Rev.: $534,835,132
Assets: $664,036,614
Liabilities: $639,449,312
Net Worth: $24,587,302
Earnings: $70,159,788
Emp.: 1,336
Fiscal Year-end: 12/31/23
Air Transportation Distr
N.A.I.C.S.: 481111
Moses Devanayagam *(Sr Dir)*

Subsidiaries:

Asian Aviation Centre of Excellence Sdn Bhd (1)
Lot PT25B Jalan S5 Southern Support Zone KLIA, 64000, Sepang, Selangor, Malaysia
Tel.: (60) 387778060
Web Site: http://www.aace.asia
Flight Training Services
N.A.I.C.S.: 611512

AIRBATH GROUP PLC
Rotterdam Road Sutton Fields Industrial Estate, Kingston upon Hull, HU7 0XD, United Kingdom
Tel.: (44) 1482327704
Web Site: http://www.airbath.co.uk
Year Founded: 2001
Sales Range: $25-49.9 Million
Emp.: 192
Baths & Bathing Accessories Mfr
N.A.I.C.S.: 326191
Gary Stevens *(Mng Dir)*

AIRBOSS OF AMERICA CORP.
16441 Yonge Street, Newmarket, L3X 2G8, ON, Canada
Tel.: (905) 751-1188   ON
Web Site: https://airboss.com
2S1—(DEU)
Rev.: $426,025,000
Assets: $356,656,000
Liabilities: $207,799,000
Net Worth: $148,857,000
Earnings: ($41,749,000)
Emp.: 1,197
Fiscal Year-end: 12/31/23
Rubber Based Products Developer & Mfr
N.A.I.C.S.: 326299
P. Grenville Schoch *(Chm & CEO)*

Subsidiaries:

AirBoss Defense Group Ltd. (1)
970 Rue Landry, Acton Vale, J0H 1A0, QC, Canada
Tel.: (450) 546-2776
Survival Products & Equipment Sales & Support Services
N.A.I.C.S.: 334511
Patrick Callahan *(CEO)*

AirBoss Defense Group, LLC (1)
8261 Preston Ct, Jessup, MD 20794
Tel.: (301) 352-8800
Web Site: https://www.adg.com
Medical Equipment Mfr & Distr
N.A.I.C.S.: 334517
Daren Olsen *(CTO)*

AirBoss Flexible Products LLC (1)
2600 Auburn Ct, Auburn Hills, MI 48326-3201
Tel.: (248) 852-5500
Web Site: http://www.flexible-products.com
Molded Rubber Mfr
N.A.I.C.S.: 326299

AirBoss Rubber Compounding (1)

101 Glasgow St, Kitchener, N2G 4X8, ON, Canada (100%)
Tel.: (519) 576-5565
Web Site:
http://www.airbossrubbercompounding.com
Sales Range: $50-74.9 Million
Emp.: 300
Custom Rubber Compounds Mfr
N.A.I.C.S.: 326299

AirBoss Rubber Compounding (NC) Inc. (1)
500 AirBoss Pkwy, Scotland Neck, NC 27874
Tel.: (252) 826-4919
Web Site:
http://www.airbossrubbersolutions.com
Rubber Compounding
N.A.I.C.S.: 326299

AirBoss-Defense (1)
28 Unit B boul de l'Aeroport, Bromont, J2L 1S6, QC, Canada
Tel.: (450) 534-9979
Rubber Protective Gear Mfr
N.A.I.C.S.: 326299
Earl Laurie *(Exec VP)*

Subsidiary (US):

AirBoss-Defense Inc. (2)
93 Gonyeau Road, Milton, VT 05468
Tel.: (802) 891-5950
Rubber Products Mfr
N.A.I.C.S.: 326299
Andrew Bessy *(Plant Mgr)*

Subsidiary (Domestic):

Critical Solutions International, Inc. (3)
2284 Clements Ferry Rd Ste A, Charleston, SC 29492
Tel.: (843) 800-0033
Web Site: http://www.c-s-i.com
Land Mine & Improvised Explosive Device Detection Equipment Mfr
N.A.I.C.S.: 334511

Innovative Elastomers, Inc. (1)
320 Bryant Blvd, Rock Hill, SC 29732
Tel.: (803) 324-7979
Web Site: http://www.aceelastomer.com
Sales Range: $1-9.9 Million
Emp.: 20
Rubber Product Mfr for Mechanical Use
N.A.I.C.S.: 326291
Russell Foster *(CEO)*

SunBoss Chemicals Corp. (1)
101 Glasgow Street, Kitchener, N2G 4X8, ON, Canada
Tel.: (519) 576-5565
Web Site: https://www.sunboss.ca
Chemical Products Mfr
N.A.I.C.S.: 325998

AIRBUS SE
Mendelweg 30, 2333 CS, Leiden, Netherlands
Tel.: (31) 715245600   NI
Web Site: https://www.airbus.com
Year Founded: 2000
AIR—(MAD)
Rev.: $61,303,914,880
Assets: $135,223,082,800
Liabilities: $127,293,565,360
Net Worth: $7,929,517,440
Earnings: ($1,435,812,560)
Emp.: 131,349
Fiscal Year-end: 12/31/20
Airplanes, Helicopters, Tactical Missiles & Space/Strategic Systems Mfr
N.A.I.C.S.: 336411
Christian Scherer *(Chief Comml Officer & Head-Airbus Intl)*

Subsidiaries:

ATLAS ELEKTRONIK GmbH (1)
Sebaldsbruecker Heerstr 235, 28309, Bremen, Germany (49%)
Tel.: (49) 42145702
Web Site: https://www.atlas-elektronik.com
Sales Range: $450-499.9 Million
Emp.: 2,000
Maritime Combat System Developer & Mfr

Airbus SE—(Continued)

N.A.I.C.S.: 334511

Subsidiary (Non-US):

ATLAS ELEKTRONIK Finland Oy   **(2)**
Lars Sonckin kaari 16, 02600, Espoo, Finland
Tel.: (358) 207790181
Web Site: https://www.finland.atlas-elektronik.com
Emp.: 12
Combat & Mission Management Systems for Ships
N.A.I.C.S.: 541512
Jaakko Savisaari (CEO)

ATLAS ELEKTRONIK UK Ltd.   **(2)**
Dorset Innovation Park, Winfrith Newburgh, Dorchester, DT2 8ZB, Dorset, United Kingdom
Tel.: (44) 1305212400
Web Site: https://www.uk.atlas-elektronik.com
Sales Range: $25-49.9 Million
Emp.: 200
Maritime Defense Electronic System Designer & Mfr
N.A.I.C.S.: 334511

ATLAS MARIDAN Aps   **(2)**
Rungsted Havn 1D, Rungsted Kyst, 2960, Horsholm, Denmark
Tel.: (45) 45674050
Web Site: https://www.maridan.atlas-elektronik.com
Sales Range: $25-49.9 Million
Emp.: 5
Autonomous Underwater Vehicle Designer & Mfr
N.A.I.C.S.: 334511
Allan Bertelsen (Mng Dir)

ATLAS NAVAL SYSTEMS MALAYSIA SDN BHD   **(2)**
18 Lumut Waterfront Villa, Jalan Titi Panjang, 32200, Perak, Malaysia
Tel.: (60) 56804330
Web Site: http://www.atlashydro.atlas-elektronik.com
Maritime Combat System Developer & Mfr
N.A.I.C.S.: 334511

Subsidiary (US):

ATLAS North America, LLC   **(2)**
120 Newsome Dr Ste H, Yorktown, VA 23692-1309
Tel.: (757) 463-0670
Web Site: https://www.na.atlas-elektronik.com
Emp.: 30
Defense Products & Vehicles Distr
N.A.I.C.S.: 334511

Subsidiary (Domestic):

Hagenuk Marinekommunikation GmbH   **(2)**
Hamburger Chaussee 25, 24220, Flintbeck, Germany
Tel.: (49) 43477140
Web Site: https://www.hmk.atlas-elektronik.com
Emp.: 130
Marine Integrated Communication System Mfr
N.A.I.C.S.: 334220

Subsidiary (Non-US):

SONARTECH ATLAS Pty. Ltd.   **(2)**
Unit G01 Ground Floor 16 Giffnock Avenue, Macquarie Park, 2113, NSW, Australia
Tel.: (61) 284847400
Web Site: https://www.sonartech.atlas-elektronik.com
Sales Range: $25-49.9 Million
Emp.: 40
Sonar System Designer & Mfr
N.A.I.C.S.: 334511

Airbus Bank GmbH   **(1)**
Prannerstrasse 8, 80333, Munich, Germany
Tel.: (49) 892901400
Web Site: http://www.airbusbank.com
Real Estate Finance Services
N.A.I.C.S.: 522292

Dominik Asam (Chm-Supervisory Bd)

Airbus Defence & Space GmbH   **(1)**
Robert-Koch-Str 1, Taufkirchen, 82024, Ottobrunn, Germany
Tel.: (49) 896070
Web Site: http://www.space-airbusds.com
Researcher & Developer of Aerospace Defense Technology & Propulsion Systems
N.A.I.C.S.: 336411
Jean-Pierre Talamoni (Head-Mktg & Sls)

Division (Domestic):

Airbus Defence & Space GmbH - Cassidian Division   **(2)**
Landshuter Strasse 26, 85716, Unterschleissheim, Germany
Tel.: (49) 89 3179 0
Web Site: http://www.cassidian.com
Military Aircraft & Space Vehicles, Electronic Components & Support Equipment Designer & Mfr
N.A.I.C.S.: 336413

Subsidiary (Domestic):

Airbus DS Optronics GmbH   **(3)**
Carl-Zeiss-Strasse 22, 73447, Oberkochen, Germany
Tel.: (49) 7364 9557 0
Web Site: http://www.airbusds-optronics.com
Researcher & Developer of Aerospace Defense Technology & Propulsion Systems
N.A.I.C.S.: 336411

Subsidiary (Non-US):

Airbus DS Optronics (Pty) Ltd.   **(4)**
Nellmapius Drive, Irene, 0046, South Africa
Tel.: (27) 12 674 0215
Web Site: http://www.airbusds-optronics.com
Engineering Services
N.A.I.C.S.: 541330

Subsidiary (Domestic):

Cassidian Air Systems GmbH.   **(3)**
Rechliner Strasse, Manching, 85077, Germany
Tel.: (49) 84 59 81 0
Defense & Security Services
N.A.I.C.S.: 541690

Subsidiary (Non-US):

Cassidian Belgium N.V.   **(3)**
Siemenslaan 16, 8020, Oostkamp, Belgium
Tel.: (32) 50831811
Aircraft Engineering Services
N.A.I.C.S.: 541330

Subsidiary (Domestic):

Cassidian Communications GmbH   **(3)**
Worthstrasse 85, 89077, Ulm, Germany
Tel.: (49) 7313920
Web Site: http://www.cassidian.com
Emp.: 2,000
Researcher & Developer of Aerospace Defense Technology & Propulsion Systems
N.A.I.C.S.: 334511

Subsidiary (Non-US):

Cassidian Defesa e Segurança do Brasil Ltda.   **(3)**
Rua Joaquim Floriano 960 - 12 Andar Itaim Bibi, 04534 004, Sao Paulo, Brazil
Tel.: (55) 11 3093 9799
Defense & Security Services
N.A.I.C.S.: 541690

Subsidiary (Domestic):

ODEBRECHT-CASSIDIAN DEFESA S.A   **(4)**
Rua Hungria 1240 - 5 Andar Edificio Riverside, Jardim Europa, 01455 000, Sao Paulo, Brazil
Tel.: (55) 11 2144 9501
Aircraft Engineering Services
N.A.I.C.S.: 541330

Subsidiary (Non-US):

Cassidian Finland Oy   **(3)**
Mattilanniemi 6, 40100, Jyvaskyla, Finland

Tel.: (358) 104080000
Web Site: http://www.cassidian.com
Engineering Services
N.A.I.C.S.: 541330

Cassidian Hong Kong Limited   **(3)**
Unit 905-909 Level 9 Tower 1 Millennium City 1 388 Kwun Tong Road, Kwun Tong, Kowloon, China (Hong Kong)
Tel.: (852) 2285 9511
Web Site: http://www.eads.com
Engineering Services
N.A.I.C.S.: 541330

Cassidian Mexico S.A de C.V.   **(3)**
Insurgentes Sur 1106 Piso 8 Colonia Noche Buena, 3720, Mexico, Mexico
Tel.: (52) 55 54 88 83 40
Aerospace Engineering Services
N.A.I.C.S.: 541330
Fred Gallart (Gen Mgr)

Subsidiary (Domestic):

Cassidian Real Estate Manching GmbH & Co. KG   **(3)**
Emil-Riedl-Weg 6, Pullach, 82049, Germany
Tel.: (49) 896070
Real Estate Development Services
N.A.I.C.S.: 531390

Cassidian Real Estate Ulm/Unterschleissheim GmbH & Co. KG   **(3)**
Landshuter Strasse 26, 85716, Unterschleissheim, Germany
Tel.: (49) 896070
Web Site: http://www.cassidian.com
Industrial Real Estate Investment & Development Services
N.A.I.C.S.: 531390

Subsidiary (Non-US):

Cassidian S.A.S.   **(3)**
Metapole 1 Boulevard Jean Moulin, 78990, Elancourt, France
Tel.: (33) 1 61 38 50 00
Web Site: http://www.cassidian.com
Network Security System Mfr
N.A.I.C.S.: 334290

Subsidiary (Domestic):

Cassidian CyberSecurity SAS   **(4)**
1 boulevard Jean Moulin, 78990, Elancourt, France
Tel.: (33) 1 61 38 50 00
Emp.: 3,000
Computer Security Services & Solutions
N.A.I.C.S.: 513210
Francois Lavaste (CEO)

Subsidiary (Non-US):

Cassidian Solutions S.A.U.   **(3)**
Barajas Park Edificio A1, 28042, Madrid, Spain
Tel.: (34) 917461440
Web Site: http://www.eadscassidian.com
Electronic Components Mfr
N.A.I.C.S.: 334418

Subsidiary (Domestic):

CTC GmbH   **(2)**
Airbus-Strasse 1, 21684, Stade, Germany
Tel.: (49) 4141 938 500
Web Site: http://www.ctc-gmbh.com
Carbon Fiber Reinforced Polymer Mfr
N.A.I.C.S.: 335991
Marc Fette (Member-Mgmt Bd)

DADC Luft- und Raumfahrt Beteiligungs AG   **(2)**
Willy-Messerschmitt-Str, 85521, Ottobrunn, Germany
Tel.: (49) 896070
Defense & Security Services
N.A.I.C.S.: 541690

Dornier GmbH   **(2)**
Prinzregentenplatz 11, Munich, 81675, Bavaria, Germany
Tel.: (49) 894194030
Sales Range: $25-49.9 Million
Emp.: 16
Industrial Machinery Mfr
N.A.I.C.S.: 333248
Dirk Ruettgers (CEO)

Subsidiary (Domestic):

Dornier Consulting GmbH   **(3)**
Burogebaude 10, Graf von Soden Strasse, 88090, Immehstaad, Germany
Tel.: (49) 754585440
Web Site: http://www.dornier-consulting.com
Sales Range: $25-49.9 Million
Transportation, Infrastructure & Environmental Engineering Consulting
N.A.I.C.S.: 541330
Jurgen R. Koffler (Pres & CEO)

Dornier MedTech Europe GmbH   **(3)**
Argelsrieder Feld 7, Wesseling, 82234, Germany
Tel.: (49) 81538880
Web Site: http://www.dornier.com
Medical Instruments
N.A.I.C.S.: 339112

Subsidiary (US):

American Dornier Machinery Corporation   **(4)**
4101 Performance Rd, Charlotte, NC 28214-8091
Tel.: (704) 394-6192
Web Site: http://www.american-dornier.com
Sales Range: $25-49.9 Million
Emp.: 30
Weaving Goods & Supplies
N.A.I.C.S.: 459130
Peter Dornier (Pres)

Dornier Medtech America   **(4)**
1155 Roberts Blvd NW, Kennesaw, GA 30144-3617
Tel.: (770) 426-1315
Web Site: http://www.dornier.com
Sales Range: $25-49.9 Million
Emp.: 68
Distribution of Medical Equipment
N.A.I.C.S.: 423450
Brian Walsh (Gen Mgr)

Subsidiary (Domestic):

wpm Projektmanagement GmbH   **(3)**
Schulze-Delitzsch-Strasse 38, 70565, Stuttgart, Germany
Tel.: (49) 7111842951
Web Site: http://www.wpm-icl.com
Sales Range: $25-49.9 Million
Engineering Services
N.A.I.C.S.: 541330

Subsidiary (Domestic):

EADS Real Estate Taufkirchen GmbH & Co. KG   **(2)**
Emil-Riedl-Weg 6 I Isartal, Pullach, 82049, Bavaria, Germany
Tel.: (49) 896070
Real Estate Development Services
N.A.I.C.S.: 531390

FLUGZEUG-UNION SUD GMBH   **(2)**
Rudolf-Diesel-Str 26, Ottobrunn, 85521, Germany
Tel.: (49) 89 607 25931
Web Site: http://www.fus.de
Sales Range: $25-49.9 Million
Emp.: 60
Defense & Aircraft Machinery Mfr
N.A.I.C.S.: 336413
Ralf Schluter (Mng Dir)

Gesellschaft fur Flugzieldarstellung mbH   **(2)**
Flugplatz Hohn, 24806, Hohn, Germany
Tel.: (49) 4335 92 020
Web Site: http://www.gfd-hohn.de
Emp.: 100
Air Charter Services
N.A.I.C.S.: 481219
Stefan Mueller (Mng Dir)

MCG Marlink Comm Gmbh   **(2)**
Johann-Mohr-Weg 2, Hamburg, 22763, Germany
Tel.: (49) 40 41 00 48 0
Web Site: http://www.marlink.com
Sales Range: $25-49.9 Million
Emp.: 3
Communication Service
N.A.I.C.S.: 517810
Frank Reichenbach (Country Mgr)

Matra Holding GmbH   **(2)**

Berliner Str 56, Kehl, 77694, Germany
Tel.: (49) 7851 74810
Investment Management Service
N.A.I.C.S.: 523940

MilSat Services GmbH (2)
Airbus-Allee 1, Bremen, 28199, Germany
Tel.: (49) 8960733668
Web Site: http://www.milsatservices.de
Data Information Management Services
N.A.I.C.S.: 541618
Stefan Gramolla (Gen Mgr)

Premium AEROTEC GmbH (2)
Haunstetter Str 225, 86179, Augsburg, Germany
Tel.: (49) 821 801 0
Web Site: http://www.premium-aerotec.com
Rev.: $1,717,807,000
Emp.: 8,000
Aircraft Parts Mfr & Distr
N.A.I.C.S.: 336413
Kai Horten (Pres & CEO)

Plant (Domestic):

Premium AEROTEC GmbH - Augsburg Plant (3)
Haunstetter Str 225, 86179, Augsburg, Germany
Tel.: (49) 821 801 0
Web Site: http://www.premium-aerotec.com
Sales Range: $700-749.9 Million
Emp.: 4,000
Aircraft Part Mfr
N.A.I.C.S.: 336413

Premium AEROTEC GmbH - Bremen Plant (3)
Airbus-Allee 1, 28199, Bremen, Germany
Tel.: (49) 421 538 0
Sales Range: $75-99.9 Million
Emp.: 410
Aircraft Part Mfr
N.A.I.C.S.: 336413

Premium AEROTEC GmbH - Nordenham Plant (3)
Bergstr 4, 26954, Nordenham, Germany
Tel.: (49) 4731 3620
Web Site: http://www.premium-aerotec.com
Sales Range: $700-749.9 Million
Emp.: 3,000
Fuselage Shell Mfr
N.A.I.C.S.: 336413

Premium AEROTEC GmbH - Varel Plant (3)
Riesweg 151-155, Varel, 26316, Germany
Tel.: (49) 4451 121 0
Web Site: http://www.premium-aerotec.com
Sales Range: $350-399.9 Million
Emp.: 2,100
Aircraft Part Mfr
N.A.I.C.S.: 336413
Gerd Weber (Mng Dir)

Subsidiary (Non-US):

Premium AEROTEC SRL (3)
Str Aeroportului Nr 9 Ghimbav, Ghimbav, Brasov, 507075, Romania
Tel.: (40) 368 081 002
Web Site: http://www.premium-aerotec.com
Emp.: 700
Aircraft Part Mfr
N.A.I.C.S.: 336413
Hans Joachim von Wrurmb (Gen Mgr)

Plant (Domestic):

Premium AEROTEC SRL - Brasov Plant (4)
Str Aeroportului Nr 9, 507075, Ghimbav, Brasov, Romania
Tel.: (40) 368 081 002
Web Site: http://www.premium-aerotec.com
Sales Range: $100-124.9 Million
Emp.: 500
Aircraft Mfr
N.A.I.C.S.: 336411
Hans-Joachim von Wurmb (Mgr)

Subsidiary (Domestic):

RST Rostock System-Technik GmbH (2)
Friedrich-Barnewitz-Strasse 9, 18119, Rostock, Germany
Tel.: (49) 381 56 0

Web Site: http://www.rst-rostock.com
Sales Range: $25-49.9 Million
Emp.: 150
Project Management Consulting Services
N.A.I.C.S.: 541618

TESAT-Spacecom GmbH & Co. KG (2)
Gerberstrasse 49, Backnang, 71522, Germany
Tel.: (49) 71919300
Web Site: http://www.tesat.de
Satellite Communication Services
N.A.I.C.S.: 517810
Peter Schlote (CEO)

Subsidiary (Domestic):

TESAT-Spacecom Geschaftsfuhrung GmbH (3)
Gerberstrasse 49, Backnang, 71522, Germany
Tel.: (49) 71919300
Emp.: 1,200
Satellite Communication Equipment Mfr
N.A.I.C.S.: 334290
Marc Steckling (CEO)

Airbus Defence & Space Limited (1)
Floor 2 Wellington House 125-30 Strand, London, WC2R 0AP, United Kingdom
Tel.: (44) 2073957800
Aircraft Product Mfr
N.A.I.C.S.: 336411

Airbus Defence & Space S.A. (1)
Paseo John Lennon S/N, 28906, Getafe, Madrid, Spain
Tel.: (34) 914433000
Aircraft Product Mfr
N.A.I.C.S.: 336411

Airbus Group Limited (1)
125-130 Strand Wellington House, London, WC2R 0AP, United Kingdom
Tel.: (44) 2073957801
Web Site: https://www.airbus.com
Aerospace Engineering Services
N.A.I.C.S.: 541330
Guillaume Faury (CEO)

Subsidiary (Domestic):

DMC International Imaging Ltd. (2)
Tycho House 20 Stephenson Road Surrey Research Park, Guildford, GU2 7YE, United Kingdom
Tel.: (44) 1483 804299
Web Site: http://www.dmcii.com
Sales Range: $25-49.9 Million
Emp.: 50
Satellite Imaging Equipment Sales & Maintenance Services
N.A.I.C.S.: 423690

Turbo-Union Ltd. (2)
Gyps Patch Ln, PO Box 3, Filton, BS12 7QE, United Kingdom
Tel.: (44) 179791234
Aircraft Part Mfr
N.A.I.C.S.: 336413

Airbus Group, Inc. (1)
2550 Wasser Ter Ste 9000, Herndon, VA 20171
Tel.: (703) 466-5600
Web Site: http://northamerica.airbus-group.com
Sales Range: $75-99.9 Million
Emp.: 130
Holding Company; Regional Managing Office
N.A.I.C.S.: 551112
Charles H. Coolidge (VP-Air Force Programs)

Subsidiary (Domestic):

EADS Sodern North America, Inc. (2)
10455 Pacific Ctr Ct, San Diego, CA 92121
Tel.: (858) 457-2000
Optical & Space Instrument Mfr
N.A.I.C.S.: 333310

EADS Supply & Services, Inc. (2)
7646 Standish Pl, Rockville, MD 20855
Tel.: (301) 424-8096
Web Site: http://northamerica.airbus-group.com
Avionics Hardware & Systems Acquisition

N.A.I.C.S.: 561499

Spot Image Corporation, Inc. (2)
14595 Avion Pkwy Ste 500, Chantilly, VA 20151
Tel.: (703) 715-3100
Rev.: $3,404,000
Emp.: 15
Aerospace Engineering Services
N.A.I.C.S.: 541330

i-cubed, LLC (2)
1600 Prospect Pkwy, Fort Collins, CO 80525
Tel.: (970) 482-4400
Web Site: http://www.i3.com
Geospatial Mapping Services
N.A.I.C.S.: 541370

Airbus Helicopters Espana, S. A. (1)
Carretera Pe, 02006, Albacete, Spain
Tel.: (34) 967850798
N.A.I.C.S.: 336413

Airbus Helicopters Holding SAS (1)
Aeroport International Marseille Provence, 13752, Marignane, Cedex, France
Tel.: (33) 442858585
Web Site: http://www.airbushelicopters.com
Holding Company; Helicopter Mfr, Support & Training Services
N.A.I.C.S.: 551112
Herve Berriet (CEO)

Subsidiary (Domestic):

Airbus Helicopters S.A.S. (2)
Aeroport International Marseille Provence, 13725, Marignane, Cedex, France (100%)
Tel.: (33) 442858585
Web Site: http://www.airbushelicopters.com
Sales Range: $5-14.9 Billion
Emp.: 1,100
Helicopter Mfr
N.A.I.C.S.: 336411
Matthieu Louvot (Exec VP-Programmes)

Subsidiary (Non-US):

Airbus Helicopters Canada (3)
1100 Gilmore Rd, PO Box 250, Fort Erie, L2A 5M9, ON, Canada
Tel.: (905) 871-7772
Web Site: https://www.airbushelicopters.ca
Sales Range: $25-49.9 Million
Emp.: 200
Mfr & Distribution of Helicopters & Parts
N.A.I.C.S.: 336411

Airbus Helicopters Deutschland GmbH (3)
Industriestrasse 4, 86609, Donauworth, Germany
Tel.: (49) 906710
Emp.: 5,000
Aircraft Product Mfr
N.A.I.C.S.: 336411

Airbus Helicopters Malaysia Sdn Bhd (3)
Helicopter Centre Malaysia International Aerospace Centre, Sultan Abdul Aziz Shah Airport, 47200, Subang Jaya, Selangor, Malaysia
Tel.: (60) 3 7848 7600
Web Site: http://www.airbushelicopters.asia
Sales Range: $10-24.9 Million
Emp.: 40
Fleet Services
N.A.I.C.S.: 488190

Airbus Helicopters Romania SA (3)
40 Hermann Oberth, Ghimbav, 507075, Brasov, Romania
Tel.: (40) 268303000
Web Site: http://www.airbus.com
Emp.: 190
Helicopters Products Distr & Marketer
N.A.I.C.S.: 488190
Serge Durand (Mng Dir)

Subsidiary (Domestic):

Airbus Helicopters Training Services (3)
Aeroport International Marseille Provence, 13725, Marignane, Cedex, France
Tel.: (33) 4 42 85 20 89
Web Site:
    http://www.airbushelicopterservices.com
Training & Educational Support Services

N.A.I.C.S.: 611512
Herve Berriet (CEO)

Subsidiary (US):

Airbus Helicopters, Inc. (3)
2701 N Forum Dr, Grand Prairie, TX 75052
Tel.: (972) 641-0000
Web Site:
    http://www.airbushelicoptersinc.com
Sales Range: $300-349.9 Million
Emp.: 560
Helicopters Mfr & Marketing
N.A.I.C.S.: 336411
Treg Manning (VP-Sls & Mktg-North America)

Subsidiary (Non-US):

Australian Aerospace Limited (3)
65-75 Pandanus Avenue, Brisbane Airport, Brisbane, 4008, QLD, Australia
Tel.: (61) 7 3637 3000
Web Site: http://www.ausaero.com.au
Sales Range: $25-49.9 Million
Helicopter Mfr & Distr
N.A.I.C.S.: 336411
Jimmy Nel (Bus Mgr-Support)

Subsidiary (Domestic):

Australian Aerospace Composites Pty Ltd. (4)
65-75 Pandanus Ave Brisbane Airport, Brisbane, 4007, QLD, Australia
Tel.: (61) 736373000
Aerospace Operation Services
N.A.I.C.S.: 488190

Subsidiary (Non-US):

EUROCOPTER CHINA CO LTD (3)
22D Jin An Bldg N 908 Dongdaming Road, Shanghai, 200082, China
Tel.: (86) 21 6595 6101
Web Site:
    http://www.airbushelicopterschina.com
Sales Range: $25-49.9 Million
Emp.: 55
Aircraft Machinery Distr
N.A.I.C.S.: 423830
Bruno Boulnois (Pres)

Subsidiary (Domestic):

General Aviation Maintenance & Engineering Co., Ltd (4)
Shenzhen Heliport N 21 Qilin Road, Nan Shan District, Shenzhen, 518051, China
Tel.: (86) 755 267 26 492
Aircraft Equipment Maintenance Services
N.A.I.C.S.: 488190

Subsidiary (Non-US):

EUROCOPTER KHDS Limited (3)
539-14 Yesu-Ri Jeongdong-Myeon, Sacheon, 664-932, Gyeongsangnam-do, Korea (South)
Tel.: (82) 55 855 2323
Rev.: $53,648,434
Emp.: 22
Aerospace Technical Consulting Services
N.A.I.C.S.: 541690
Guillaume Faury (Pres & CEO)

EUROCOPTER VOSTOK (3)
Yakimanskaya Emb 4 Bld 1, 119180, Moscow, Russia
Tel.: (7) 495 663 1556
Web Site: http://www.eurocopter.ru
Sales Range: $25-49.9 Million
Emp.: 29
Helicopter Mfr
N.A.I.C.S.: 336411

Eurocopter Chile SA (3)
Av Jose Arrieta La Reina, Santiago, Chile
Tel.: (56) 24134300
Web Site: http://www.eurocopter.cl
Sales Range: $1-9.9 Million
Emp.: 100
Distr of Eurocopter Products & Services
N.A.I.C.S.: 336413
Alexandre Ceccacci (Mng Dir)

Eurocopter Deutschland GmbH (3)
Industriestr 4, Donauworth, 86609, Bayern, Germany
Tel.: (49) 906710
Aerospace Training Center Operator

Airbus SE—(Continued)

N.A.I.C.S.: 611512

Subsidiary (Domestic):

MOTORFLUG BADEN-BADEN GmbH **(4)**
Flugstrassee 12, Baden-Baden, 76532, Germany
Tel.: (49) 7229 30 14 0
Web Site: http://www.motorflug.com
Sales Range: $75-99.9 Million
Emp.: 150
Aircraft Parts Sales & Maintenance Services
N.A.I.C.S.: 423860
Cliff Wooley (Mgr-Technical Avionics)

Subsidiary (Domestic):

SPAERO TRADE GmbH **(5)**
Baden-Airpark Summersite Ave C-312, 77836, Rheinmunster, Germany
Tel.: (49) 7229 301416
Web Site: http://www.spaero.de
Aircraft Parts Distr
N.A.I.C.S.: 423860
Michaela Eisberg (Mng Dir)

Subsidiary (Non-US):

Eurocopter Espana SA **(3)**
Carretera Del Barrio De La Fortuna 10, Cuatro Vientos, 28044, Madrid, Spain
Tel.: (34) 913797200
Sales Range: $1-9.9 Million
Emp.: 15
Marketer & Retailer of Eurocopter Products & Services
N.A.I.C.S.: 336411

Eurocopter India Pvt Ltd **(3)**
Worldmark 1 5th Floor West Wing, Hera City, New Delhi, 110 037, India
Tel.: (91) 11 4580 1100
Rev.: $4,360,587
Emp.: 21
Aircraft Parts Distr
N.A.I.C.S.: 423860
Xavier Hay (CEO)

Eurocopter Japan Co. **(3)**
Roppongi Hills Mori Tower 19F 6-10-1 Roppongi Minato-ku, Tokyo, 107 0062, Japan
Tel.: (81) 357756262
Web Site: http://www.eurocopter.co.jp
Sales Range: Less than $1 Million
Emp.: 280
Eurocopter Support Network Services
N.A.I.C.S.: 336411
Stephane Ginoux (Pres & CEO)

Subsidiary (Domestic):

Eurocopter Japan RG Co, Ltd. **(4)**
Roppongi Hills Mori Tower 19F 6-10-1 Roppongi, Minato-Ku, Tokyo, 106 6119, Japan
Tel.: (81) 3 5414 3346
Aircraft Parts Distr
N.A.I.C.S.: 423860

Subsidiary (Non-US):

Eurocopter Philippines Inc. **(3)**
2 Manila Domestic Airport, PO Box 2, Pasay, 1300, Philippines
Tel.: (63) 28538857
Sales Range: $1-9.9 Million
Emp.: 50
Distribution of Eurocopter Products & Services
N.A.I.C.S.: 336411

Eurocopter South East Asia Pte. Ltd. **(3)**
12 Seletar Aerospace Link, Singapore, 797553, Singapore
Tel.: (65) 65927110
Web Site: http://www.airbushelicopters.asia
Sales Range: $25-49.9 Million
Emp.: 180
Distr of Eurocopter Products & Services
N.A.I.C.S.: 336411

Eurocopter Southern Africa Pty. Ltd. **(3)**
Hangar 27 Lanseria Airport, PO Box 135, Lanseria, 1748, South Africa
Tel.: (27) 117998300
Web Site: http://www.eurocopter.co.za

Sales Range: $1-9.9 Million
Emp.: 82
Distribution & Customization of Eurocopter Products & Services
N.A.I.C.S.: 336411
Fabrice Cagnat (Mng Dir)

Eurocopter UK Ltd. **(3)**
Langford Lane, Kidlington, OX5 1QZ, Oxfordshire, United Kingdom
Tel.: (44) 1865 852400
Web Site: http://www.eurocopter.co.uk
Sales Range: $50-74.9 Million
Emp.: 250
Helicopter Charter Services
N.A.I.C.S.: 481211
David Lewis (Dir-Sls-Natl Resilience)

Eurocopter de Mexico S.A. **(3)**
Hangar N 1 Zona G de Hangares, Aeropuerto International, Mexico, 15620, Mexico
Tel.: (52) 5557167555
Web Site: http://www.eurocopter.com.mx
Sales Range: $25-49.9 Million
Emp.: 400
Helicopters & Parts
N.A.I.C.S.: 336411

Subsidiary (Domestic):

HELISIM **(3)**
Helisim Aeroport International Marseille, 13725, Marignane, France
Tel.: (33) 4 42 77 39 00
Web Site: http://www.helisim.fr
Sales Range: $10-24.9 Million
Emp.: 50
Aerospace Training Center Operator
N.A.I.C.S.: 611512
Christian Cochini (CEO)

Subsidiary (Non-US):

Helibras **(3)**
Av Santos Dumont Rua Santos Dumont 200 Distrito Industrial, Itajuba, 37504-900, Minas Gerais, Brazil
Tel.: (55) 3521434000
Web Site: http://www.helibras.com.br
Sales Range: $25-49.9 Million
Emp.: 359
Helicopters & Parts
N.A.I.C.S.: 336411
Richard Marelli (Mng Dir)

Airbus Operations SAS **(1)**
316 Route de Bayonne, 31060, Toulouse, Cedex 9, France
Tel.: (33) 561935555
N.A.I.C.S.: 336413

Airbus Operations, S.L. **(1)**
Paseo John Lennon, 28906, Getafe, Madrid, Spain
Tel.: (34) 916242322
N.A.I.C.S.: 336413

Airbus S.A.S. **(1)**
1 rond-point Maurice Bellonte, 31707, Blagnac, Cedex, France **(100%)**
Tel.: (33) 561933333
Web Site: http://www.airbus.com
Sales Range: $25-49.9 Billion
Emp.: 48,000
Military & Commercial Aircraft Mfr
N.A.I.C.S.: 336411

Subsidiary (US):

Airbus Americas, Inc. **(2)**
2550 Wasser Ter Ste 9100, Herndon, VA 20171
Tel.: (703) 834-3400
Web Site: http://www.airbus.com
Sales Range: $350-399.9 Million
Emp.: 1,200
Jet Aircraft & Airplanes Mfr & Distr
N.A.I.C.S.: 336411
C. Jeffrey Knittel (Chm & CEO)

Subsidiary (Domestic):

Airbus Military North America **(3)**
2550 Wasser Ter Ste 9000, Herndon, VA 20171
Tel.: (703) 466-5600
Web Site: http://www.eadsnorthamerica.com
Aircraft Parts Sales & Maintenance Services
N.A.I.C.S.: 423860

Metron Aviation, Inc. **(3)**
45300 Catalina Ct Ste 101, Dulles, VA 20166
Tel.: (703) 456-0123
Web Site: http://www.metronaviation.com
Emp.: 60
Air Traffic Management Services
N.A.I.C.S.: 488111
Alan Bloodgood (Sr VP & Gen Mgr-Comml Products & Solutions)

Subsidiary (Non-US):

Airbus China **(2)**
Beijing Tianzhu Airport Industrial Zone, Tianwei Erjie, Beijing, 101312, Shunyi County, China
Tel.: (86) 1080486161
Web Site: http://www.airbus.com
Airplane Distr
N.A.I.C.S.: 532411
George Xu (CEO)

Subsidiary (Domestic):

Airbus Corporate Jet Centre S.A.S. **(2)**
316 Route De Bayonne, Toulouse, 31000, France
Tel.: (33) 5 61 18 39 35
Airbus Cabin Outfitting Services
N.A.I.C.S.: 488190
Benoit Defforge (Mng Dir & Head-Cabin Completions)

Subsidiary (Non-US):

Airbus Deutschland GmbH **(2)**
Kreetslag 10, PO Box 950109, 21129, Hamburg, Germany
Tel.: (49) 4074370
Web Site: http://www.airbus.com
Sales Range: $600-649.9 Million
Emp.: 18,000
Aircraft Mfr
N.A.I.C.S.: 336411

Subsidiary (Domestic):

Airbus Operations GmbH **(3)**
Kreetslag 10, Hamburg, 21129, Germany
Tel.: (49) 40 743 70
Aircraft Mfr
N.A.I.C.S.: 336411

Airspares **(3)**
Weg Beim Jaeger 150, PO Box 630107, Hamburg, 22335, Germany
Tel.: (49) 4050760
Web Site: http://www.airspares.com
Sales Range: $200-249.9 Million
Emp.: 600
Aircraft Parts Distr
N.A.I.C.S.: 423860

KID-Systeme GmbH **(3)**
Lueneburger Schanze 30, Buxtehude, 21614, Germany
Tel.: (49) 40 743 7 16 33
Web Site: http://www.kid-systeme.de
Emp.: 30
Aircraft Cabin Electronic Component Mfr
N.A.I.C.S.: 336413
Patrick Schrot (Exec Dir)

Subsidiary (Non-US):

Airbus Japan KK **(2)**
ERK Mori Building, 1 12 32 Akasaka Minato Ku, Tokyo, 107 6035, Japan
Tel.: (81) 355738400
Web Site: http://www.airbusjapan.com
Airplane Distr
N.A.I.C.S.: 532411

Airbus Operations Ltd. **(2)**
Chester Road Broughton, Chester, CH4 0DR, United Kingdom
Tel.: (44) 1244 520444
Aircraft Mfr
N.A.I.C.S.: 336411

Subsidiary (Domestic):

Airbus Prosky S.A.S. **(2)**
1 Rond-Point Maurice Bellonte, 31707, Blagnac, France
Tel.: (33) 561933333
Web Site: http://www.airbusprosky.com
Aircraft Development & Research Services
N.A.I.C.S.: 541715

Sylvie Sureda-Perez (Head-Mktg)

Subsidiary (Non-US):

Airbus Real Estate Premium AEROTEC Nord GmbH & Co. KG **(2)**
Emil-Riedl-Weg 6 I Isartal Bayern, Pullach, 82049, Germany
Tel.: (49) 407 4370
Web Site: http://www.airbus.com
Real Estate Development Services
N.A.I.C.S.: 531390

Subsidiary (Domestic):

Airbus Transport International S.N.C. **(2)**
12 Rue Gabriel Clerc Cedex, Blagnac, 31700, France
Tel.: (33) 5 62 11 81 96
Aircraft Fleet Management Services
N.A.I.C.S.: 488190

Subsidiary (Non-US):

Airbus UK **(2)**
Gulf Cruz Lane Filton House Filton, PO Box 77, Bristol, BS99 7AR, United Kingdom
Tel.: (44) 79693831
Web Site: http://www.airbus.com
Sales Range: $1-4.9 Billion
Emp.: 7,000
Airplane Component Mfr
N.A.I.C.S.: 336413
Katherine Bennett (Sr VP)

PFW Aerospace GmbH **(2)**
Am Neuen Rheinhafen 10, 67346, Speyer, Germany **(74.9%)**
Tel.: (49) 62326160
Web Site: http://www.pfw.aero
Sales Range: $250-299.9 Million
Emp.: 2,200
Aircraft Components Mfr
N.A.I.C.S.: 336412
Philippe Olivier (Chm-Supervisory Bd)

Satair A/S **(2)**
Amager Landevej 147A, Kastrup, 2770, Denmark
Tel.: (45) 32470100
Web Site: http://www.satair.com
Sales Range: $400-449.9 Million
Emp.: 488
Supplier of Aircraft Parts & Service Solutions
N.A.I.C.S.: 336413
Morten Olsen (COO & Head-Global Sls)

Subsidiary (Non-US):

Satair China **(3)**
CASC Airbus No 5 Tianzhu Donglu Tianzhu Airport Industrial Zone, PO Box 3412, 101312, Beijing, China
Tel.: (86) 10 8048 6340
Aircraft Parts Distr
N.A.I.C.S.: 423860

Satair Pte. Ltd. **(3)**
27 Loyang Way, Singapore, 508728, Singapore
Tel.: (65) 65430977
Web Site: http://www.satair.com
Aircraft Parts Distr
N.A.I.C.S.: 423860

Satair UK **(3)**
Purdeys Way Purdeys Industrial Estate, Rochford, SS4 1NE, Essex, United Kingdom
Tel.: (44) 1702560700
Aircraft Parts Distr
N.A.I.C.S.: 423860

Subsidiary (US):

Satair USA Inc. **(3)**
3993 Tradeport Blvd, Atlanta, GA 30354
Tel.: (404) 675-6333
Web Site: http://www.satair.com
Sales Range: $25-49.9 Million
Emp.: 50
Aircraft Equipments & Parts Distr
N.A.I.C.S.: 423860

Branch (Domestic):

Satair USA Inc. - Miami **(4)**
11255 NW 106th St Bldg 1 Ste 6, Miami, FL 33178
Tel.: (305) 863-7620

Web Site: http://www.satair.com
Sales Range: $10-24.9 Million
Distr & Retailer of Hydraulic Equipment &
Supplies
N.A.I.C.S.: 423830

Airbus Safran Launchers SAS (1)
51-61 Route de Verneuil, 78130, Les
Mureaux, Cedex, France
Tel.: (33) 139061234
Web Site: https://www.ariane.group
Emp.: 450
Space Launcher Research & Development
Services
N.A.I.C.S.: 336415
Alain Charmeau *(CEO)*

Subsidiary (Domestic):

Arianespace SAS (2)
Boulevard de l'Europe, BP 177,
Courcouronnes, 91006, Evry, Cedex,
France
Tel.: (33) 16 087 6000
Web Site: https://www.arianespace.com
Emp.: 300
Commercial Space Transportation Services
N.A.I.C.S.: 481212
Louis Laurent *(Sr VP)*

Subsidiary (Non-US):

Arianespace Singapore Pte, Ltd. (3)
No 3 Shenton Way No 18-09A Shenton
House, Singapore, 068805, Singapore
Tel.: (65) 62236426
Web Site: http://www.arianespace.com
Commercial Space Transportation Services
N.A.I.C.S.: 481212
Vivian Quenet *(Mng Dir & Head-Sls-Asia
Pacific)*

Subsidiary (US):

Arianespace, Inc. (3)
5335 Wisconsin Ave NW Ste 520, Washing-
ton, DC 20015
Tel.: (202) 628-3936
Web Site: http://www.arianespace.com
Emp.: 5
Commercial Space Transportation Services
N.A.I.C.S.: 481212
Wiener Kernisan *(Pres)*

Astrium Holding S.A.S. (1)
12 Rue Pasteur, 75116, Suresnes, France
Tel.: (33) 1 39 06 25 60
Emp.: 200
Holding Company
N.A.I.C.S.: 551112
Francois Auque *(Mng Dir)*

Subsidiary (Domestic):

Airbus Defence and Space SAS (2)
31 rue des Cosmonautes ZI du Palays,
31402, Toulouse, Cedex 4, France
Tel.: (33) 562 19 62 19
Web Site: http://www.space-airbusds.com
Sales Range: $15-24.9 Billion
Emp.: 40,000
Satellite Design, Assembly Integration &
Test Services
N.A.I.C.S.: 517410
Sabine Klauke *(Chief Technical Officer)*

Subsidiary (Non-US):

**ASTRIUM Space Transportation
GmbH** (3)
Airbus-Allee 1, Bremen, 28199, Germany
Tel.: (49) 421 539 0
Engineeering Services
N.A.I.C.S.: 541330

**Airbus Defence and Space
Limited** (3)
Anchorage Rd, Portsmouth, PO3 5PU,
United Kingdom
Tel.: (44) 2392705705
Spacecraft Platforms Mfr
N.A.I.C.S.: 336414

Astrium (UK) Limited (3)
Anchorage Road, Portsmouth, PO3 5PU,
Hampshire, United Kingdom
Tel.: (44) 2392705705
Aeronautical Engineering Services
N.A.I.C.S.: 541330

Astrium GmbH (3)

Airbus-Allee 1, 28199, Bremen, Germany
Tel.: (49) 42159300
Web Site: http://www.astrium.eads.net
Engineeering Services
N.A.I.C.S.: 541330

Subsidiary (US):

Astrium North America, Inc. (3)
16055 Space Center Blvd Ste 480, Hous-
ton, TX 77062
Tel.: (281) 461-8409
Web Site: http://www.astrium-na.com
Sales Range: $25-49.9 Million
Emp.: 21
Engineeering Services
N.A.I.C.S.: 541512

Subsidiary (Domestic):

Marlink, Inc. (4)
11777 S Sam Houston Pkwy W Ste C,
Houston, TX 77031
Tel.: (713) 910-3352
Web Site: http://www.marlink.com
Satellite Telecommunication Services
N.A.I.C.S.: 517410

Subsidiary (Domestic):

Astrium Space Transportation (3)
66 Route De Verneuil, Les Mureaux, 78133,
France
Tel.: (33) 1 39 06 12 34
Oil Transportation Services
N.A.I.C.S.: 488190
Alain Charmeau *(Gen Mgr)*

Subsidiary (Non-US):

**Computadoras, Redes e Ingenieria
SA** (3)
C/ Torres Quevedo 9 PTM, Tres Cantos,
28760, Madrid, Spain
Tel.: (34) 918068600
Web Site: http://www.crisa.es
Sales Range: $75-99.9 Million
Emp.: 400
Aviation Electronic Equipment Mfr
N.A.I.C.S.: 336413
Fernando del Ray Garcia *(Mng Dir)*

Dutch Space B.V. (3)
Mendelweg 30, Leiden, 2333, Zuid-Holland,
Netherlands
Tel.: (31) 715245000
Web Site: http://www.dutchspace.nl
Sales Range: $50-74.9 Million
Emp.: 250
Aircraft Part Mfr
N.A.I.C.S.: 336413
Rob van Hassel *(Mgr-Sls)*

Infoterra Limited (3)
Europa House Southwood Crescent, Farn-
borough, GU14 0NL, United Kingdom
Tel.: (44) 252362000
Web Site: http://www.infoterra-global.com
Sales Range: $25-49.9 Million
Emp.: 60
Supplying & Processing Remotely Sensed
Data & Imagery Acquired from Earth Obser-
vation Satellites
N.A.I.C.S.: 517410

Subsidiary (Non-US):

Infoterra GmbH (4)
Claude-Dornier-Str Immenstaad Am
Bodensee, Immenstaad, 88090, Baden-
Wurttemberg, Germany
Tel.: (49) 754589969
Sales Range: $25-49.9 Million
Information Technology Consulting Services
N.A.I.C.S.: 541512
Corinna Prietzsch *(Mgr-Trng)*

Infoterra Magyarorszag Kft. (4)
Malom Udvar Soroksari Ut 48, 1095, Buda-
pest, Hungary
Tel.: (36) 1 323 3750
Sales Range: $25-49.9 Million
Emp.: 37
Aircraft Engineering Services
N.A.I.C.S.: 541330
Olga Kadar *(Gen Mgr)*

**Infoterra Servicios de Geoinformacion
SA** (4)
Paseo De La Catellana 149 1a, 28046, Ma-
drid, Spain

Tel.: (34) 91 449 0149
Geospatial Mapping Services
N.A.I.C.S.: 541370

Subsidiary (Non-US):

Jena-Optronik GmbH (3)
Otto-Eppenstein-Strasse 3, 07745, Jena,
Germany (100%)
Tel.: (49) 3641200110
Web Site: http://www.jena-optronik.de
Sales Range: $50-74.9 Million
Emp.: 250
Opto-Electronic Instruments & Sensory
Equipment Mfr
N.A.I.C.S.: 334511
Peter Kapell *(CEO)*

ND Satcom GmbH (3)
Graf-von-Soden-Strasse, 88090, Immen-
staad, Baden-Wurttemberg, Germany
Tel.: (49) 75459390
Web Site: http://www.ndsatcom.com
Emp.: 150
Telecommunication Servicesb
N.A.I.C.S.: 517410
Michael Weixler *(Dir-Tech)*

Subsidiary (Domestic):

ND SatCom Defence GmbH (4)
Graf-Von-Soden-Str Immenstaad Am
Bodensee, Immenstaad, 88090, Baden-
Wurttemberg, Germany
Tel.: (49) 75459390
Communication Equipment Distr
N.A.I.C.S.: 423690

ND SatCom Products GmbH (4)
Graf-Von-Soden-Str Immenstaad Am
Bodensee, Immenstaad, 88090, Baden-
Wurttemberg, Germany
Tel.: (49) 75459390
Telecommunication Servicesb
N.A.I.C.S.: 517810

Subsidiary (Non-US):

**ND SatCom Satellite Communication
Systems (Beijing) Co. Ltd.** (4)
Rm 3110 Tengda Bldg No 168 Xizhimenwai
St, Chaoyang District, Beijing, 100004,
China
Tel.: (86) 10 6590 6869
Engineering & Telecommunication Services
N.A.I.C.S.: 541330

Subsidiary (US):

ND Satcom, Inc. (4)
3801 E Plano Pkwy Ste 200, Plano, TX
75074
Tel.: (214) 231-3400
Web Site: http://www.ndsatcom.com
Satellite Communication Equipment Distr
N.A.I.C.S.: 423690
David Bowne *(VP)*

Subsidiary (Non-US):

Paradigm Services Ltd. (3)
Portsmouth Site Anchorage Road, Ports-
mouth, P03 5PU, Hampshire, United King-
dom
Tel.: (44) 1438282828
Satellite Communication Services
N.A.I.C.S.: 517410

Surrey Satellite Technology Ltd. (3)
Tycho House 20 Stephenson Road Surrey
Research Park, Guildford, GU2 7YE, Sur-
rey, United Kingdom
Tel.: (44) 1483 803803
Web Site: http://www.sstl.co.uk
Emp.: 500
Satellite Telecommunication Services
N.A.I.C.S.: 517410
Sarah Parker *(Grp Mng Dir)*

Subsidiary (Domestic):

Surrey Satellite Services Ltd. (4)
20 Stephenson Road, Guildford, GU2 7YE,
United Kingdom
Tel.: (44) 1483803803
Sales Range: $100-124.9 Million
Emp.: 500
Satellite Communication Services
N.A.I.C.S.: 517810

Subsidiary (Domestic):

Vizada SAS (3)
137 rue du Faubourg St Denis, 75010,
Paris, France
Tel.: (33) 1 53 35 95 00
Web Site: http://www.vizada.com
Sales Range: $650-699.9 Million
Emp.: 700
Satellite-Based Mobility Communication
Services
N.A.I.C.S.: 517410
Bertrand Pivin *(Chm)*

Subsidiary (Non-US):

Vizada AS (4)
Lysaker Torg 45, 1327, Lysaker, Norway
Tel.: (47) 22 58 20 50
Satellite-Based Mobility Communication
Services
N.A.I.C.S.: 517410

Vizada B.V. (4)
Binckhorstlaan 151-A, 2516 BA, Hague,
Netherlands
Tel.: (31) 70 3001818
Telecommunication Servicesb
N.A.I.C.S.: 517810

Vizada GmbH (4)
Konrad-Adenauer-Ufer 41-45, Cologne,
50668, Germany
Tel.: (49) 221 995 91 0
Web Site: http://www.vizada.com
Emp.: 50
Telecommunication Servicesb
N.A.I.C.S.: 517810
Eric Beranger *(CEO)*

Vizada Networks Ltd. (4)
Alpha House New Bagamoyo Rd, PO Box
105905, Dar es Salaam, Tanzania
Tel.: (255) 22 276 1341
Telecommunication Servicesb
N.A.I.C.S.: 517810

Vizada RO Hong Kong (4)
35F Central Plaza 18 Harbour Rd, Wan-
chai, China (Hong Kong)
Tel.: (852) 6386 5490
Satellite-Based Mobility Communication
Services
N.A.I.C.S.: 517410

Vizada RO Singapore (4)
131 Neil Road, 088860, Singapore, Singa-
pore
Tel.: (65) 64027003
Sales Range: $25-49.9 Million
Emp.: 30
Satellite Communications
N.A.I.C.S.: 517410

Subsidiary (Non-US):

EADS Canada, Inc. (2)
Constitution Square I 360 Albert Street
Suite 530, Ottawa, K1R 7X7, ON, Canada
Tel.: (613) 230-3902
Web Site: http://www.eads.com
Sales Range: $25-49.9 Million
Emp.: 10
Aircraft Security System Mfr
N.A.I.C.S.: 336413

Subsidiary (Domestic):

Composites Atlantic Limited (3)
71 Hall St, PO Box 1150, Lunenburg, B0J
2C0, NS, Canada
Tel.: (902) 634-8448
Web Site:
http://www.compositesatlantic.com
Sales Range: $10-24.9 Million
Aircraft Parts & Equipment
N.A.I.C.S.: 336413
Claude Baril *(Pres)*

**EADS Composites Atlantic
Limited** (3)
71 Hall Street, PO Box 1150, Lunenburg,
B0J 2C0, NS, Canada
Tel.: (902) 634-8448
Web Site:
http://www.compositesatlantic.com
Sales Range: $75-99.9 Million
Aircraft Composite Mfr
N.A.I.C.S.: 336413
Vince Dixon *(VP-Supply Chain)*

Airbus SE—(Continued)

Affiliate (Domestic):

Starsem (2)
2 rue Francois Truffaut, 91042, Evry, Cedex, France
Tel.: (33) 169870110
Web Site: http://www.starsem.com
Sales Range: $25-49.9 Million
Emp.: 12
Commercial Rocket Launch Services
N.A.I.C.S.: 927110
Alexei Riabtsev (VP-Fin)

Avions de Transport Regional (1)
1 Allee Pierre Nadot, 31712, Blagnac, France (50%)
Tel.: (33) 562216221
Web Site: http://www.atr-aircraft.com
Sales Range: $1-4.9 Billion
Emp.: 1,000
Turboprop Commuter Aircraft Mfr
N.A.I.C.S.: 336411
Jean-Pierre Cousserans (Sr VP-Customer Svcs)

Construcciones Aeronauticas, S.A. (1)
Avenida Aragon 404, 28022, Madrid, 28022, Spain
Tel.: (34) 915857000
Web Site: http://www.airbusdusgroup.com
Sales Range: $1-4.9 Billion
Emp.: 7,400
Military & Commercial Aircraft Mfr
N.A.I.C.S.: 336411

Subsidiary (US):

EADS Casa (2)
8100 Airbus Military Dr, Mobile, AL 36608
Tel.: (251) 338-0700
Sales Range: $25-49.9 Million
Emp.: 29
Mfr & Sales of Aircraft
N.A.I.C.S.: 423860
Hamed Baher (Engr-Avionics)

EADS Chile (1)
Av Isidora Goyenechea 3356 60, 3356, Las Condes, Santiago, Chile
Tel.: (56) 2 333 4333
Engineeering Services
N.A.I.C.S.: 541330

EADS China (1)
11th Fl Tower B Ping An International Financial Center N 1-3 Xinyuan, South Road Chaoyang District, Beijing, 100027, China
Tel.: (86) 10 6461 1266
Web Site: http://www.eads.com
Aerospace Engineering Services
N.A.I.C.S.: 541330

EADS France S.A.S. (1)
37 bd de Montmorency, 75016, Paris, France
Tel.: (33) 1 42 24 24 24
Aircraft Components Mfr
N.A.I.C.S.: 336413
Klaus Richter (Chief Procurement Officer)

Subsidiary (Domestic):

APSYS (2)
22 Gallieni, 92150, Suresnes, France
Tel.: (33) 142045000
Web Site: http://www.apsys.eads.net
Sales Range: $100-124.9 Million
Emp.: 350
Sensor Systems & Instruments for Aircraft
N.A.I.C.S.: 334511
Christian Forestier (CEO)

Subsidiary (Non-US):

APSYS Risk Engineering UK Limited (3)
Unit 3 Dyce Avenue Kirkhill Estate, Aberdeen, AB21 0LQ, United Kingdom
Tel.: (44) 1224 452 880
Web Site: http://www.apsysoilandgas.com
Emp.: 4
Software Development Services
N.A.I.C.S.: 541511
Pierre Secher (Bus Mgr & Product Mgr)

APSYS UK (3)
Building 07V New Filton House, Filton, Bristol, BS997AR, United Kingdom

Tel.: (44) 117 936 0201
Aircraft Management Services
N.A.I.C.S.: 488190

Subsidiary (Domestic):

Aerolia S.A.S. (2)
13 rue Marie Louise BP73216, BP 73216, 31027, Toulouse, France
Tel.: (33) 5 81 91 40 00
Web Site: http://www.aerolia.com
Emp.: 500
Aircraft Part Mfr
N.A.I.C.S.: 336413
Cedric Gautier (CEO)

Plant (Domestic):

Aerolia S.A.S. - Meaulte Facility (3)
Bp 70210, BP 70210, 80302, Albert, France
Tel.: (33) 322643000
Web Site: http://wwwaerolia.com
Sales Range: $350-399.9 Million
Aircraft Part Mfr
N.A.I.C.S.: 336413

Aerolia S.A.S. - Saint-Nazaire Facility (3)
Boulevard des Apprentis, BP 50301, 44605, Saint Nazaire, France
Tel.: (33) 2 53 48 50 00
Web Site: http://www.aerolia.com
Sales Range: $150-199.9 Million
Aircraft Part Mfr
N.A.I.C.S.: 336413

Aerolia S.A.S. - Toulouse Facility (3)
13 Rue Marie Louise Dissard, BP 73216, 31027, Toulouse, France
Tel.: (33) 5 81 91 40 00
Web Site: http://www.aerolia.com
Sales Range: $75-99.9 Million
Emp.: 400
Aircraft Machinery Mfr
N.A.I.C.S.: 336413

Subsidiary (Domestic):

Aerospatiale Matra ATR (2)
37 Blvd De Montmorency, 75781, Paris, France
Tel.: (33) 42242424
Web Site: http://www.eads.net
Sales Range: $1-9.9 Million
Emp.: 110
Engineeering Services
N.A.I.C.S.: 541330

Airbus Defence & Space SAS (2)
51-61 Route de Verneuil, 78 130, Les Mureaux, Cedex, France
Tel.: (33) 139061234
Web Site: http://www.space-airbusds.com
Sales Range: $25-49.9 Million
Emp.: 100
Defense & Space Engineering Services
N.A.I.C.S.: 541330

CILAS SA (2)
8 Avenue Buffon Z I La Source, BP 6319, 45063, Orleans, France
Tel.: (33) 2 38 64 15 55
Web Site: http://www.cilas.com
Sales Range: $50-74.9 Million
Emp.: 170
Communication Service
N.A.I.C.S.: 517810
Philippe Lucherini (CEO)

Composites Aquitaine S.A. (2)
19 route de Lacanau, 33160, Salaunes, France
Tel.: (33) 5 56 68 55 00
Web Site:
    http://www.composites-aquitaine.com
Rev.: $64,748,110
Emp.: 530
Aircraft & Defense Machinery Mfr
N.A.I.C.S.: 336413
J. M. Leonard (Pres)

EADS ATR S.A. (2)
5 Avenue Georges Guynemer, Colomiers, 31770, Haute-Garonne, France
Tel.: (33) 562216221
Oil Transportation Services
N.A.I.C.S.: 488190

EADS Composites Aquitaine (2)
16 route de Lacanau, 33160, Salaunes, France

Tel.: (33) 556685500
Web Site: http://www.stelia-aerospace.com
Sales Range: $75-99.9 Million
Emp.: 400
Engineeering Services
N.A.I.C.S.: 541330

EADS Defense & Security Networks (2)
Rue Jean Pierre Timbaud, BP 26, 78063, Bois-d'Arcy, France
Tel.: (33) 134608020
Web Site: http://www.eads-telecom.com
Telephony & Contact Center Solutions
N.A.I.C.S.: 517111

Unit (Domestic):

EADS France S.A.S. - Innovation Works (2)
5 Quai Marcel Dassault, 92150, Suresnes, France
Tel.: (33) 1 46 97 30 00
Web Site: http://www.eads.com
Aerospace Engineering Services
N.A.I.C.S.: 541330

Subsidiary (Domestic):

EADS Multicoms (2)
6 Allee Latecoere, PO Box 280, F 78147, Velizy-Villacoublay, France
Tel.: (33) 134584900
Satellite Communications Carrier
N.A.I.C.S.: 517410

EADS Systems & Defense Electronics (2)
1 Blvd Jean Moulin ZAC de la Clef Saint Pierre, 78990, Elancourt, France
Tel.: (33) 161385000
Sales Range: $75-99.9 Million
Emp.: 2,500
Engineeering Services
N.A.I.C.S.: 541330
Herve Juillou (Mng Dir)

Get Electronique S.A.S. (2)
14 rue Henri Regnault - Zac De La Chartreuse, Castres, 81100, France
Tel.: (33) 563728200
Web Site: http://www.get-electronique.fr
Emp.: 100
Voltage Regulator Mfr & Distr
N.A.I.C.S.: 334419
Jean-Yves Barbier (Mgr-Sls)

IFR France S.A.S. (2)
8 Av G Guynemer CS 30324, 31773, Colomiers, France
Tel.: (33) 5 62 74 75 00
Web Site: http://www.ifrskeyes.com
Sales Range: $25-49.9 Million
Emp.: 80
Aircraft Maintenance Services
N.A.I.C.S.: 488119

Nucletudes (2)
3 avenue du Hoggar, 91940, Les Ulis, France
Tel.: (33) 160926100
Web Site: http://www.nucletudes.com
Sales Range: $25-49.9 Million
Emp.: 50
Engineeering Services
N.A.I.C.S.: 541330
Laurent Bouaziz (CEO)

SECA (Societe d'Exploitation et de Construction Aeronautiques) (2)
1 Boulevard du 19 Mars 1962, BP 50064, 95503, Gonesse, France
Tel.: (33) 130185336
Web Site: http://www.seca.eads.net
Sales Range: $125-149.9 Million
Emp.: 300
Aircraft Engines
N.A.I.C.S.: 336411
Thierry Poulard (Dir-Customer Support)

SMPE Group (2)
12 Qui Henri IV, 75004, Paris, France
Tel.: (33) 148046666
Web Site: http://www.smpe.com
Sales Range: $25-49.9 Million
Emp.: 200
Engineeering Services
N.A.I.C.S.: 541330

Sodern S.A. (2)

20 Avenue Descartes, BP 23, 94451, Limiel Brevannes, France
Tel.: (33) 1 45 95 70 00
Web Site: http://www.sodern.fr
Rev.: $77,962,010
Emp.: 330
Attitude Sensor, Space Instrumentation & Defense Optronics Mfr & Distr
N.A.I.C.S.: 334511

Spot Image S.A.S. (2)
5 Rue des Satellites, Toulouse, 31030, France
Tel.: (33) 5 62 19 40 40
Data Information Management Services
N.A.I.C.S.: 519290

EADS India Pvt Ltd (1)
Teri University Campus Plot N 10 Vasant Kunj Institutional Area, New Delhi, 110070, India
Tel.: (91) 114 580 1100
Aerospace Engineering Services
N.A.I.C.S.: 541330
Yves Guillaume (CEO)

EADS Indonesia (1)
One Pacific Place Building 12th Floor Suite 1207 Sudirman Central, Business District Lot 3-5 Jl, Jakarta, 12190, Indonesia
Tel.: (62) 21 57 97 36 15
Aerospace Engineering Services
N.A.I.C.S.: 541330
Laurent Godin (Gen Mgr)

EADS KOREA CO., LTD. (1)
3rd Fl Volvo Building 130 Hannam-Dong, Yongsan-Gu, Seoul, 140-210, Korea (South)
Tel.: (82) 2 798 49 25
Web Site: http://www.eads.com
Aerospace Engineering Services
N.A.I.C.S.: 541330

EADS Norway NUF (1)
Aker Brygge Stranden 1A 6th Floor, 0250, Oslo, Norway
Tel.: (47) 22 00 95 50
Web Site: http://www.eads.com
Aircraft Parts Distr
N.A.I.C.S.: 423860

EADS Secure Networks (1)
Centro Direzionale Lombardo, Via Roma 108, 20060, Milan, Cassina De' Pecchi, Italy
Tel.: (39) 02 952551
Telecommunication Installer & Services
N.A.I.C.S.: 517112

EADS South Africa Pty. Ltd. (1)
Ground Fl Block D Cambridge Park 5 Bauhinia Road Entrance Oak Ave, Highveld Techno Park, Centurion, 169, South Africa
Tel.: (27) 12 686 8900
Emp.: 7
Aerospace Engineering Services
N.A.I.C.S.: 541330

EADS TAIWAN CO., LTD (1)
14th Fl Bank Tower Suite 1403 205 Tun Hua North Road, Taipei, 105, Taiwan
Tel.: (886) 2 2712 1594
Defense & Security Services
N.A.I.C.S.: 541690

EADS Thailand (1)
999/9 The Offices At Central World Unit 3607 - 3609 36th Floor, Rama I Road Pathumwan, Bangkok, 10330, Thailand
Tel.: (66) 2 610 4300
Web Site: http://www.eads.com
Sales Range: $25-49.9 Million
Emp.: 20
Aerospace Engineering Services
N.A.I.C.S.: 541330

EADS Turkey (1)
Sedat Simavi Sokak No 56/5, Cankaya, Ankara, 06540, Turkiye
Tel.: (90) 312 439 89 64
Aerospace Engineering Services
N.A.I.C.S.: 541330

Eads Mexico, S.A. de C.V. (1)
Campos Eliseos No 345 Piso 8 Edificio Omega, Polanco, 11560, Mexico
Tel.: (52) 55 4777 5100
Aerospace Engineering Services
N.A.I.C.S.: 541330

Eads Singapore Pte Ltd (1)
16 Collyer Quay 08-00, Singapore, 049318,
Singapore
Tel.: (65) 6325 0380
Aerospace Engineering Services
N.A.I.C.S.: 541330

**Eurockot Launch Services
GmbH** (1)
Airbus-Allee 1, 28199, Bremen,
Germany (51%)
Tel.: (49) 42143722509
Web Site: http://www.eurockot.com
Sales Range: $50-74.9 Million
Emp.: 9
Commercial Rocket Launch Services
N.A.I.C.S.: 927110
Elena Brandt *(Mgr-Future Programs)*

Eurofighter GmbH (1)
Am Soldnermoos 17, 85399, Hallbergmoos,
Germany (46%)
Tel.: (49) 0811800
Web Site: http://www.eurofighter.com
Sales Range: $25-49.9 Million
Emp.: 100
Fighter-Aircraft Mfr; Joint Venture of EADS
Deutschland GmbH (33%), BAE Systems
Plc (33%), Alenia Aeronautica SpA (21%) &
EADS Construcciones Aeronauticas SA
(13%)
N.A.I.C.S.: 336411
Theodor Benien *(VP-Comm)*

**European Aeronautic Defense And
Space Co.** (1)
Chelm Ul 19, Warsaw, 00-021, Poland
Tel.: (48) 226270528
Sales Range: $1-9.9 Million
Emp.: 4
Engineering & Construction Services
N.A.I.C.S.: 541330

Korean Helicopter Development Support Ltd. (1)
539-14 Yesu-Ri Jeongdong-Myeon, Sacheon, 664 932, Gyeongsangnam-do, Korea (South)
Tel.: (82) 558552323
Rev.: $53,648,434
Emp.: 22
Helicopter Technical Assistance & Support
Services
N.A.I.C.S.: 488190

MBDA Holdings S.A.S. (1)
37 Boulevard de Montmorency, 75016,
Paris, France (37.5%)
Tel.: (33) 142242424
Web Site: http://www.mbda-systems.com
Holding Company; Guided Missiles &
Missile Systems Mfr
N.A.I.C.S.: 551112
Antoine Bouvier *(CEO)*

Subsidiary (Non-US):

MBDA Deutschland GmbH (2)
Hagenauer Forst 27, Schrobenhausen,
86529, Germany
Tel.: (49) 8252 99 0
Aircraft Machinery Mfr
N.A.I.C.S.: 336413
Thomas Homberg *(Mng Dir)*

Subsidiary (Domestic):

Bayern-Chemie Gesellschaft fur Flugchemische Antriebe mbH (3)
Liebigstrasse 17, PO Box 11, 84544, Aschau, Germany
Tel.: (49) 86386010
Web Site: http://bayern-chemie.com
Sales Range: $50-74.9 Million
Emp.: 160
Rocket Propulsion Systems Mfr
N.A.I.C.S.: 336415

TDW-Gesellschaft fur verteidigungstechnische Wirksysteme GmbH (3)
Hagenauer Forst 27, 86529, Schrobenhausen, Germany
Tel.: (49) 8252 99 0
Web Site: http://www.eads.com
Sales Range: $200-249.9 Million
Emp.: 1,000
Aircraft Part Mfr
N.A.I.C.S.: 336413
Thomas Homberg *(Gen Mgr)*

Subsidiary (Domestic):

MBDA France SAS (2)
1 ave Reaumur, 92350, Le Plessis-Robinson, France
Tel.: (33) 171541000
Web Site: http://www.mbda-systems.com
Sales Range: $25-49.9 Million
Emp.: 100
Missiles & Missile Systems
N.A.I.C.S.: 336412

Joint Venture (Domestic):

EUROSAM (3)
Centre d'affaires de la Boursidiere Batiment
Kerguelen, Le Plessis-Robinson, 92357,
France
Tel.: (33) 1 4187 1416
Web Site: http://www.eurosam.com
Emp.: 70
Missile Defense Systems Mfr
N.A.I.C.S.: 336414
Michelle Vigneras *(Mng Dir)*

ROXEL S.A.S. (3)
La Boursidi Immeuble Jura, 92357, Le
Plessis-Robinson, France (50%)
Tel.: (33) 141 07 82 95
Web Site: http://www.roxelgroup.com
Propulsion System Mfr
N.A.I.C.S.: 336415

Subsidiary (Domestic):

ROXEL France (4)
Route D Ardon, 45240, La Ferte-Saint-Aubin, France
Tel.: (33) 238516666
Sales Range: $100-124.9 Million
Emp.: 300
Rocket Propulsion Systems Mfr
N.A.I.C.S.: 335312

Subsidiary (Non-US):

MBDA Italia SpA (2)
Via Monte Flavio 45, 00131, Rome, Italy
Tel.: (39) 06 87711
Web Site: http://www.mbda-systems.com
Missile Systems Mfr
N.A.I.C.S.: 336414

MBDA UK Ltd. (2)
Six Hills Way, Stevenage, SG1 2DA, United
Kingdom
Tel.: (44) 1438312422
Web Site: http://www.mbda.co.uk
Sales Range: $350-399.9 Million
Emp.: 2,000
Missile Mfr
N.A.I.C.S.: 336414

Branch (Domestic):

MBDA UK (3)
Six Hills Way, Stevenage, SG1 2DA, Hertfordshire, United Kingdom
Tel.: (44) 1438752000
Web Site: http://www.mbda.co.uk
Emp.: 4,000
Missile Mfr
N.A.I.C.S.: 336414
Chris Allam *(Mng Dir)*

NAVBLUE (1)
295 Hagey Blvd Suite 200, Waterloo, N2L
6R5, ON, Canada (100%)
Tel.: (519) 747-0616
Web Site: http://www.navblue.aero
Flight Operations Software Solutions
N.A.I.C.S.: 513210
Marc Lemeilleur *(CEO)*

Subsidiary (Non-US):

NAVBLUE UK (2)
Hersham Place Technology Park Molesey
Road, Walton-on-Thames, KT12 4RZ, Surrey, United Kingdom
Tel.: (44) 1932704200
Web Site: http://www.navblue.aero
Flight & Support Operations Software
N.A.I.C.S.: 513210

Nahuelsat S.A. (1)
Bouchard 1680 12th Fl, Capital Federal,
1106, Buenos Aires, Argentina
Tel.: (54) 158112600
Web Site: http://www.nahuelsat.com.ar

Sales Range: $25-49.9 Million
Emp.: 50
Communication Equipment Mfr
N.A.I.C.S.: 334290

OOO EADS (1)
40/2 Ul Bolshaya Ordynka, Moscow,
119017, Russia
Tel.: (7) 4957975368
Sales Range: $25-49.9 Million
Emp.: 20
Air Charter Services
N.A.I.C.S.: 481219
Gorskaya Stanislava *(Office Mgr)*

Panavia Aircraft GmbH (1)
Am Soeldnermoos 17, 85399, Hallbergmoos, Germany (42.5%)
Tel.: (49) 811800
Web Site: http://www.panavia.de
Sales Range: $25-49.9 Million
Emp.: 100
Military Aircraft Designer & Mfr
N.A.I.C.S.: 336411

Safe Air Limited (1)
Blenheim Airport, PO Box 244, Blenheim,
7240, New Zealand
Tel.: (64) 35728416
Web Site: http://www.safeair.co.nz
Aviation Engineering Services
N.A.I.C.S.: 541330
Doug Keesing *(Mgr-Safe Air-Australia)*

Subsidiary (Non-US):

Safe Air Australia Pty Limited (2)
7 Plane tree Avenue, Dingley, 3172, Melbourne, Victoria, Australia
Tel.: (61) 395518766
Web Site: http://www.safeair.co.nz
Repair & Maintenance Services
N.A.I.C.S.: 811114
Doug Keesing *(Ops Mgr)*

Space Engineering S.p.A. (1)
Via dei Berio 91, Rome, 00155, Italy
Tel.: (39) 06 22595 1
Web Site: http://www.space.it
Sales Range: $50-74.9 Million
Emp.: 150
Telecommunications & Radar System Mfr
N.A.I.C.S.: 334290
Raimondo Lo Forti *(Pres)*

**AIRDRIE CHRYSLER DODGE
JEEP**
139 East Lake Crescent, Airdrie, T4A
2H7, AB, Canada
Tel.: (403) 948-2600
Web Site:
http://www.airdriedodge.com
Year Founded: 1984
Sales Range: $50-74.9 Million
New & Used Car Dealers
N.A.I.C.S.: 441110

AIREA PLC
Victoria Mills, The Green, Ossett,
WF5 0AN, West Yorkshire, United
Kingdom
Tel.: (44) 1924262525
Web Site: https://www.aireaplc.com
AIEA—(AIM)
Rev.: $26,637,213
Assets: $34,686,948
Liabilities: $15,821,762
Net Worth: $18,865,186
Earnings: $970,714
Emp.: 104
Fiscal Year-end: 12/31/23
Flooring Solution Sales & Mfr
N.A.I.C.S.: 449121
Paul Stevenson *(Fin Dir & Sec)*

Subsidiaries:

Burmatex Limited (1)
Victoria Mills The Green, Ossett, WF5 0AN,
West Yorkshire, United Kingdom
Tel.: (44) 1924262525
Web Site: https://www.burmatex.co.uk
Sales Range: $50-74.9 Million
Emp.: 200
Carpet Designing & Manufacturing Services
N.A.I.C.S.: 321999

Subsidiary (Non-US):

Burmatex Sp. z.o.o. (2)
ul Ostrowska 364, 61 312, Poznan, Poland
Tel.: (48) 61 870 58 70
Web Site: http://www.burmatex.pl
Carpet Mfr
N.A.I.C.S.: 321999

Ryalux Carpets Limited (1)
Mossfield Mill Chesham Fold Rd, Bury, BL9
6JZ, Lancashire, United Kingdom
Tel.: (44) 1617623030
Web Site: http://www.ryalux.com
Carpet Mfr & Distr
N.A.I.C.S.: 314110

AIRESIS S.A.
Chemin du Pierrier 1, 1815, Clarens,
Switzerland
Tel.: (41) 219898250
Web Site: https://www.airesis.com
Year Founded: 1814
AIRE—(SWX)
Rev.: $165,988,914
Assets: $183,975,610
Liabilities: $192,442,350
Net Worth: ($8,466,741)
Earnings: ($4,303,769)
Emp.: 10
Fiscal Year-end: 12/31/22
Holding Company; Sporting Equipment Retailer
N.A.I.C.S.: 551112
Marc-Henri Beausire *(Chm & CEO)*

Subsidiaries:

A2I SA (1)
Chemin du Pierrier 1, CH-1815, Clarens,
Montreux, Switzerland (100%)
Tel.: (41) 219898250
Web Site: http://www.airesis.com
Sports Mfr & Distr
N.A.I.C.S.: 339920

AIREX INC.
5 Sandhill Court Unit C, Brampton,
L6T 5J5, ON, Canada
Tel.: (905) 790-8667
Web Site: http://www.airex.ca
Year Founded: 1982
Rev.: $17,000,000
Emp.: 70
Air Conditioning Product Mfr
N.A.I.C.S.: 333415
Enzo Iantorno *(Pres)*

AIRIQ, INC.
1099 Kingston Rd, Pickering, L1W
3W9, ON, Canada
Tel.: (905) 831-6444
Web Site: https://www.airiq.com
Year Founded: 1997
IQ—(TSXV)
Rev.: $4,073,281
Assets: $6,728,226
Liabilities: $893,846
Net Worth: $5,834,380
Earnings: $641,944
Fiscal Year-end: 03/31/24
Wireless Location-Based Fleet Management Services
N.A.I.C.S.: 561990

AIRKENYA AVIATION LTD.
Wilson Airport, PO Box 30357,
00100, Nairobi, Kenya
Tel.: (254) 203916000
Web Site: http://www.airkenya.com
Year Founded: 1985
Sales Range: $25-49.9 Million
Emp.: 160
Scheduled Air Transportation Services
N.A.I.C.S.: 481111
Dino M. Bisleti *(Gen Mgr)*

Subsidiaries:

AeroLink Uganda Limited (1)

AirKenya Aviation Ltd.—(Continued)

PO Box 689, Entebbe, Uganda
Tel.: (256) 317333000
Web Site: http://www.aerolinkuganda.com
Travel Arrangement Services
N.A.I.C.S.: 561599
Anthony Njoroge (Country Mgr)

Regional Air Services   (1)
PO Box 14755, Arusha, Tanzania
Tel.: (255) 784285753
Web Site: http://www.regionaltanzania.com
Emp.: 37
Travel Arrangement Services
N.A.I.C.S.: 561599

AIRKIT S.A.
Avenue Loopold III 25, 7134, Binche,
Belgium
Tel.: (32) 64 27 32 21
Sales Range: $1-9.9 Million
Industrial Automation, Home Automation Systems & Heating Pumps Mfr &
Sales
N.A.I.C.S.: 334513
Adriano Costantini (Chm & CEO)

**AIRLUX ELECTRICAL CO.,
LTD.**
2-20 Nan-Yuan Road, Zhongli Dist,
Hsien, 320, Taiwan
Tel.: (886) 34511761   TW
Web Site:
  https://www.airluxgroup.com
Year Founded: 1976
4609—(TPE)
Rev.: $5,435,419
Assets: $23,065,566
Liabilities: $16,690,273
Net Worth: $6,375,293
Earnings: $119,720
Fiscal Year-end: 12/31/22
Home Appliance Mfr
N.A.I.C.S.: 335220

**AIRMATE (CAYMAN) INTER-
NATIONAL CO. LIMITED**
No 11 Shin Chung Road, An Ping
Industrial District, T'ainan, Taiwan
Tel.: (886) 75527655988
Web Site: http://www.airmate-
  china.com
1626—(TAI)
Rev.: $288,305,131
Assets: $275,923,303
Liabilities: $175,404,121
Net Worth: $100,519,182
Earnings: $14,795,266
Fiscal Year-end: 12/31/22
Electrical Fans, Heaters, Cookers &
Other Home Appliances Mfr
N.A.I.C.S.: 335220

Subsidiaries:

Airmate China International
Limited   (1)
Palm Grove House, PO Box 438, Tortola,
Road Town, Virgin Islands (British)
Tel.: (284) 75527655988
Household Appliances Mfr & Distr
N.A.I.C.S.: 337121

Airmate Electrical Appliances (Jiujiang) Co., Limited
No 1 Tonggang East Road, Chengxi Port
District Economic & Technological Development Zone, Jiangxiang, China
Tel.: (86) 7922286888
Household Appliances Mfr & Distr
N.A.I.C.S.: 337121

Airmate International Holdings
Limited   (1)
Craigmuir Chambers, PO Box 71, Tortola,
Road Town, Virgin Islands (British)
Tel.: (284) 75527655988
Household Appliances Mfr & Distr
N.A.I.C.S.: 337121

Airmate e-Commerce (Shenzhen)
Co,, Ltd.   (1)

Huangfengling Industrial Zone Shiyan
Street, Baoan District, Shenzhen, Guangdong, China
Tel.: (86) 75527655988
Household Appliances Mfr & Distr
N.A.I.C.S.: 337121

Waon Development Limited   (1)
Flat 1006-1007 10/F Fortress Tower 250
Kings Road, North Point, Hong Kong, China
(Hong Kong)
Tel.: (852) 25783303
Household Appliances Mfr & Distr
N.A.I.C.S.: 337121

WeiWu Technology (Foshan City)
Co., Ltd.   (1)
Huangfengling Industrial Zone Shiyan
Street, Baoan District, Shenzhen, Guangdong, China
Tel.: (86) 75527655988
Household Appliances Mfr & Distr
N.A.I.C.S.: 337121

AIRNET TECHNOLOGY INC.
Suite 301 No 26 Dongzhimenwai
Street, Dongcheng District, Beijing,
100027, China
Tel.: (86) 1084508818   Ky
Web Site: https://ir.airnetgroup.cn
Year Founded: 2007
ANTE—(NASDAQ)
Rev.: $2,969,000
Assets: $115,149,000
Liabilities: $101,796,000
Net Worth: $13,353,000
Earnings: ($13,335,000)
Emp.: 39
Fiscal Year-end: 12/31/22
Air Travel Media Network
N.A.I.C.S.: 561599
Herman Man Guo (Chm, CEO &
CFO-Interim)

AIRO LAM LIMITED
Nananpur Approach Road, Dalpur
Village Ta Prantij Dist S K, Ahmedabad, 383120, Gujarat, India
Tel.: (91) 2770240572
Web Site: https://www.airolam.com
Year Founded: 2008
AIROLAM—(NSE)
Rev.: $23,244,285
Assets: $21,751,084
Liabilities: $14,074,037
Net Worth: $7,677,047
Earnings: $895,071
Emp.: 500
Fiscal Year-end: 03/31/22
Industrial Machinery Equipment Distr
N.A.I.C.S.: 423830
Pravinbhai Nathabhai Patel (Chm &
Mng Dir)

AIROIL FLAREGAS PVT. LTD.
204 Sumer Kendra Pandurang
Budhkar Marg Worli, Mumbai, 400
018, India
Tel.: (91) 2224965031   In
Web Site:
  http://www.airoilflaregas.com
Year Founded: 1984
Sales Range: $75-99.9 Million
Emp.: 500
Industrial Combustion Equipment Developer & Mfr
N.A.I.C.S.: 333994
Hasu Sheth (Mng Dir)

Subsidiaries:

Airoil Flaregas Pvt. Ltd. - Indrad
Works   (1)
Survey No 788 & 793 Opp Torrent Laboratories Kalol-Mehsana Highway, Indrad Kadi,
Mehsana, 383 341, Gujarat, India
Tel.: (91) 2764233495
Combustion Equipment Mfr
N.A.I.C.S.: 334513

**AIRPORT FACILITIES CO.,
LTD.**
Sogo Building No 5 1-6-5 Haneda
Airport, Ota-ku, Tokyo, 144-0041,
Japan
Tel.: (81) 337470251
Web Site: https://www.afc.jp
Year Founded: 1970
8864 (TKS)
Rev.: $171,529,500
Assets: $730,147,210
Liabilities: $328,490,560
Net Worth: $401,656,650
Earnings: $13,352,200
Emp.: 124
Fiscal Year-end: 03/31/24
Real Estate Manangement Services
N.A.I.C.S.: 531120
Toshiyuki Nagayoshi (Exec VP)

**AIRPORTS OF THAILAND
PUBLIC COMPANY LIMITED**
333 Cherdwutagard Road, Srikan
Don Mueang, Bangkok, 10210, Thailand
Tel.: (66) 25351192
Web Site:
  https://www.airportthai.co.th
Year Founded: 1903
AOT—(OTCIQ)
Rev.: $492,034,761
Assets: $5,054,943,762
Liabilities: $2,235,632,924
Net Worth: $2,819,310,838
Earnings: ($301,846,932)
Emp.: 8,176
Fiscal Year-end: 09/30/22
Airline Services
N.A.I.C.S.: 488119
Shanalai Chayakul (Co-Sec)

Subsidiaries:

Suvarnabhumi Airport Hotel Company
Limited   (1)
999 Moo 1, Nong Prue Subdistrict, Bang
Phli, 10540, Samut Prakan, Thailand
Tel.: (66) 2 132 1888
Web Site:
  http://www.suvarnabhumiairport.com
Home Management Services
N.A.I.C.S.: 561110
Sirote Duangratana (Gen Mgr)

AIRPORTS VANUATU LTD
Bauerfield Airport, PO Box 131, Port-
Vila, Vanuatu
Tel.: (678) 25111
Web Site: http://www.airports.vu
Year Founded: 2000
Sales Range: $25-49.9 Million
Emp.: 200
Airport Management & Operation
N.A.I.C.S.: 488119
Benson Kanas (CFO)

**AIRSHIP & BALLOON COM-
PANY LTD.**
82 Henbury Road, Bristol, BS10 7AA,
United Kingdom
Tel.: (44) 7971154717
Web Site:
  http://www.airshipandballoon.com
Sales Range: $10-24.9 Million
Emp.: 30
Hot Air Balloon Operator
N.A.I.C.S.: 541890
Nick Langley (Mng Dir)

AIRSPRUNG GROUP PLC
Canal Road, Trowbridge, BA14 8RQ,
Wiltshire, United Kingdom
Tel.: (44) 1225754411
Web Site: http://www.airsprung-
  group.co.uk
Sales Range: $50-74.9 Million
Emp.: 600

Mfr of Mattresses, Beds & Upholstered Furniture
N.A.I.C.S.: 337910
Tony Lisanti (CEO)

Subsidiaries:

Airsprung Furniture Limited   (1)
Canal Road, Trowbridge, BA14 8RQ, Wiltshire, United Kingdom
Tel.: (44) 1225754411
Web Site: http://www.airsprung.com
Sales Range: $100-124.9 Million
Emp.: 500
Bed & Upholstered Furniture Mfr
N.A.I.C.S.: 337126

Collins & Hayes Furniture Ltd.   (1)
Menzies Road, Ponswood, Saint Leonards,
TN38 9XF, E Sussex, United Kingdom
Tel.: (44) 1424720027
Web Site: http://www.collinsandhayes.com
Sales Range: $10-24.9 Million
Emp.: 160
Upholstered Furniture Mfr
N.A.I.C.S.: 337121
David Backler (Dir-Fin)

**AIRSYS COMMUNICATIONS
TECHNOLOGY LIMITED**
35 City Industrial Park Southern
Road, Southampton, SO15 1HG,
United Kingdom
Tel.: (44) 2380718700
Web Site: http://www.airsys.co.uk
Year Founded: 1992
Sales Range: $10-24.9 Million
Emp.: 20
Communication Devices Distr
N.A.I.C.S.: 517112
Paula Cooper (Mgr-Sls & Product)

**AIRTAC INTERNATIONAL
GROUP**
No 28 Kanxi Rd, Xinshi Dist, Tainan
City, 74148, Taiwan
Tel.: (886) 227197538
Web Site: https://global.airtac.com
Year Founded: 1988
1590—(TAI)
Rev.: $975,419,434
Assets: $1,898,321,162
Liabilities: $505,326,708
Net Worth: $1,392,994,453
Earnings: $227,784,255
Fiscal Year-end: 12/31/23
Control Systems Mfr
N.A.I.C.S.: 335314
Shih-Chung Wang (Chm, Chm, Gen
Mgr & Gen Mgr)

Subsidiaries:

ATC (Italia) S.R.L.   (1)
Via Manzoni 20, 20020, Magnago, MI, Italy
Tel.: (39) 0331307204
Web Site: http://www.assofluid.it
Pneumatic Product Mfr & Distr
N.A.I.C.S.: 333998

Airtac (China) Co., Ltd.   (1)
No 8 Huisheng Rd, Fenghua, 315500, Zhejiang, China
Tel.: (86) 57488989999
Pneumatic Mfr & Distr
N.A.I.C.S.: 333998

Airtac (Fujian) Intelligent Equipment
Co., Ltd.   (1)
Unit 802 No 1 Kengping Road, Guankou
Town Jimei District, Xiamen, Fujian, China
Tel.: (86) 5926381281
Pneumatic Equipment Mfr & Distr
N.A.I.C.S.: 333912

Airtac (Jiangsu) Automation Co.,
Ltd.   (1)
No 188 Ruike Road, Yushan Town, Kunshan, Jiangsu, China
Tel.: (86) 51255181853
Pneumatic Mfr & Distr
N.A.I.C.S.: 333912

Airtac (Tianjin) Intelligent Technology
Co., Ltd.   (1)

Room 803 Gate 1 Building 7 No 1 Huixue Road, Xinhua Intl University Science & Technology Park Jingwu Town Xiqing, Tianjin, China
Tel.: (86) 2283990572
Pneumatic Equipment Mfr & Distr
N.A.I.C.S.: 333912

Airtac Co., Ltd. (1)
3-6-3 Kusune Higashi, Osaka, 577-0006, Japan
Tel.: (81) 643076039
Web Site: http://global.airtac.com
Pneumatic Product Mfr & Distr
N.A.I.C.S.: 333998

Airtac Industrial (Malaysia) Sdn. Bhd. (1)
20-01 Jalan Ekoperniagan 1/3 Taman Ekoperniaagan, 81100, Johor Bahru, Johor, Malaysia
Tel.: (60) 75568989
Pneumatic Equipment Mfr & Distr
N.A.I.C.S.: 333912

Airtac Industrial Co., Ltd. (1)
11/12 Moo 9 Bangchalong, Bang Phli, 10540, Samutprakarn, Thailand
Tel.: (66) 202335157
Web Site: http://global.airtac.com
Pneumatic Product Mfr & Distr
N.A.I.C.S.: 333998

Airtac USA Corporation (1)
21201 Park Row Dr, Katy, TX 77449
Tel.: (281) 394-7177
Web Site: http://global.airtac.com
Pneumatic Product Mfr & Distr
N.A.I.C.S.: 333998

Guangdong Airtac Intelligent Equipment Co., Ltd. (1)
No 13 Building 7 23 Degree Cultural and Creative Park, 88 South Ring Road Liunan District Guangxi, Liuzhou, China
Tel.: (86) 752 398 9888
Pneumatic Equipment Mfr & Distr
N.A.I.C.S.: 333912

Ningbo Airtac Automatic Industrial Co., Ltd. (1)
No 88 Siming E Rd, High Tech Area of Fenghua City, Ningbo, 315500, Zhejiang, China
Tel.: (86) 57488950001
Pneumatic Mfr & Distr
N.A.I.C.S.: 333998

AIRTASKER LIMITED
Level 20 109 Pitt Street, Sydney, 2000, NSW, Australia AU
Web Site: https://www.airtasker.com
Year Founded: 2011
ART—(ASX)
Rev.: $28,800,287
Assets: $33,232,705
Liabilities: $14,255,721
Net Worth: $18,976,984
Earnings: ($8,422,768)
Emp.: 150
Fiscal Year-end: 06/30/23
Software Development Services
N.A.I.C.S.: 541511
Timothy Fung (Founder)

AIRTEC PNEUMATIC GMBH
Westerbachstr 7, 61476, Kronberg, Germany
Tel.: (49) 617395620
Web Site: http://www.airtec.de
Year Founded: 1975
Rev.: $25,998,559
Emp.: 140
Machinery Products Mfr
N.A.I.C.S.: 333310

Subsidiaries:

AIRTEC PNEUMATIC SWEDEN AB (1)
Gerfasts vag 6, 283 50, Osby, Sweden
Tel.: (46) 47912600
Web Site: http://www.airtec.se
Industrial Control Accessory Distr
N.A.I.C.S.: 423610

AIRTEC Pneumatic C.C. (1)
Acreage Gardens No 70 5th street Wynberg, Sandton, South Africa
Tel.: (27) 112622506
Industrial Control Accessory Distr
N.A.I.C.S.: 423610

AIRTEC Pneumatic Engineering BV (1)
Hammerstraat 26, 8161 PH, Epe, Netherlands
Tel.: (31) 578627866
Web Site: http://www.airtec.nl
Industrial Control Accessory Mfr
N.A.I.C.S.: 335314

AIRTEC Pneumatics Inc (1)
730 Racquet Club Drive, Addison, IL 60101
Tel.: (630) 543-0265
Industrial Control Accessory Distr
N.A.I.C.S.: 423610

AIRTEC Pneumatics UK Ltd. (1)
Unit 18B Shaw Lane Ind Estate Ogden Road, Doncaster, DN2 4SQ, South Yorkshire, United Kingdom
Tel.: (44) 1302769000
Industrial Control Accessory Distr
N.A.I.C.S.: 423610

Air-Com Pneumatyka Automatyka s.c. (1)
Ul Wroclawska 44, 55-095, Wroclaw, Dlugoleka, Poland
Tel.: (48) 717994581
Web Site: http://www.air-com.pl
Industrial Control Accessory Distr
N.A.I.C.S.: 423610

Airtec France SARL (1)
15 rue du General Walter, 67230, Obenheim, France
Tel.: (33) 388252886
Web Site: http://www.airtec-france.fr
Industrial Control Accessory Distr
N.A.I.C.S.: 423610

AIRTECH JAPAN, LTD.
1-14-9 Iriya, Taito-ku, Tokyo, 110-8686, Japan
Tel.: (81) 338726611
Web Site: https://www.airtech.co.jp
Year Founded: 1973
6291—(TKS)
Sales Range: Less than $1 Million
Air Purification Equipment Mfr
N.A.I.C.S.: 333413
Shinya Hirasawa (Pres)

Subsidiaries:

AIRTECH JAPAN, LTD. - CLEAN SUPPLY FACTORY (1)
8-12 2 Chome Aoyagi, Soka, 340-0002, Saitama, Japan
Tel.: (81) 48 931 9445
Air Purification Equipment Mfr
N.A.I.C.S.: 333413

AIRTECH JAPAN, LTD. - GUNMA FACTORY (1)
250-1 simofurei-cho, Isesaki, 379-2214, Gunma, Japan
Tel.: (81) 270 63 3700
Air Purification Equipment Mfr
N.A.I.C.S.: 333413

AIRTECH JAPAN, LTD. - KAZO FACTORY (1)
5-12 Shanasaki, Kazo, 347-0032, Saitama, Japan
Tel.: (81) 480 67 0200
Air Purification Equipment Mfr
N.A.I.C.S.: 333413

AIRTECH JAPAN, LTD. - SOKA FACTORY (1)
10-20 2chome Aoyagi, Soka, 340-0002, Saitama, Japan
Tel.: (81) 48 936 3033
Air Purification Equipment Mfr
N.A.I.C.S.: 333413

AIRTECH SYSTEM CO., LTD. (1)
No 58-1 Kuang Fu Rd, Hsin Chu Indusrial Park, Hsin-chu, Taiwan
Tel.: (886) 3 610 5668
Air Purification Equipment Distr

N.A.I.C.S.: 423620

Airtech Equipment Pte. Ltd. (1)
No 7 Kaki Bukit Place Eunos Techpark, Singapore, 416185, Singapore
Tel.: (65) 6 746 6194
Web Site: https://www.airtech.com.sg
Biosafety Equipment Mfr
N.A.I.C.S.: 325414

Hemair Systems India Ltd. (1)
No 296/7/6 and 7/7 I D A Bollaram Miyapur, Hyderabad, 502 325, Andhra Pradesh, India
Tel.: (91) 402 301 8900
Web Site: https://www.hemairsystems.com
Central Air Cooling System Mfr
N.A.I.C.S.: 333415

Pea GmbH (1)
Neuwieder Strasse 80, Engers, 56566, Neuwied, Germany
Tel.: (49) 262 290 5980
Web Site: https://www.pea-gmbh.de
Emp.: 50
Engineering Equipment Mfr
N.A.I.C.S.: 333248

Pyramid Airtech Pvt. Ltd. (1)
Unit No 15 And 16 Electronic Sadan1, Bhosari, Pune, 411026, India
Tel.: (91) 202 746 4644
Cleanroom Air System Mfr & Distr
N.A.I.C.S.: 333415

Suzhou Antai Air Tech Co., Ltd. (1)
No 2 Weixin Rd SIP, Suzhou, Jiangsu, China
Tel.: (86) 5126 531 9495
Web Site: https://www.airtechsat.com
Laboratory Product Mfr
N.A.I.C.S.: 334516

Thelong Airtech Joint Stock Company (1)
No 144 Viet Hung Str Group 3, Viet Hung Ward Long Bien Dist, Hanoi, Vietnam
Tel.: (84) 243 873 7717
Web Site: https://www.thelong.com.vn
Clean Room Equipment Mfr
N.A.I.C.S.: 339113

Woolee Airtech Korea Co., Ltd. (1)
Woori Building 1507-1, Seocho-dong Seocho-gu, Seoul, Korea (South)
Tel.: (82) 2 598 0333
Web Site: https://www.wooleeeng.co.kr
Fan Filter Equipment Mfr
N.A.I.C.S.: 333413

AIRTEL AFRICA PLC
53-54 Grosvenor Street, London, W1K 3HU, United Kingdom UK
Tel.: (44) 2074939315
Web Site: https://www.airtel.africa
Year Founded: 2010
AIRTELAFRI—(NIGE)
Rev.: $5,268,000,000
Assets: $11,166,000,000
Liabilities: $7,358,000,000
Net Worth: $3,808,000,000
Earnings: $750,000,000
Emp.: 4,000
Fiscal Year-end: 03/31/23
Telecommunication Servicesb
N.A.I.C.S.: 517810
Anthony Shiner (Chief Comml Officer)

Subsidiaries:

Airtel Congo RDC S.A. (1)
130B Ave Kango Gombe 1, BP 1201, Kinshasa, Congo, Democratic Republic of
Tel.: (243) 997301448
Telecommunication Servicesb
N.A.I.C.S.: 532490

Airtel Money Tanzania Limited (1)
Airtel House Corner of AH Mwinyi Road Morrocco, PO Box 9623, Dar es Salaam, Tanzania
Tel.: (255) 784103001
Web Site: https://www.airtel.co.tz
Telecommunication Servicesb
N.A.I.C.S.: 532490

Airtel Money Transfer Limited (1)
Parkside Towers Mombasa Road, PO Box 73146, 00200, Nairobi, Kenya

Tel.: (254) 734110000
Web Site: https://www.airtelkenya.com
Mobile Communications Services
N.A.I.C.S.: 532490

AIRTEX MANUFACTURING PARTNERSHIP
1401 Hastings Crescent SE, Calgary, T2G 4C8, AB, Canada
Tel.: (403) 287-2590
Web Site: https://www.engineeredair.com
Year Founded: 1964
Sales Range: $100-124.9 Million
Emp.: 1,000
Heating Equipment Mfr
N.A.I.C.S.: 333414
Brian Neufeld (Gen Mgr)

Subsidiaries:

Airtex Manufacturing Partnership - Calgary Heat Transfer Plant (1)
6324 10th Street SE, Calgary, T2H 2K7, AB, Canada
Tel.: (403) 279-2282
Air Conditioning System Mfr
N.A.I.C.S.: 333415

Airtex Manufacturing Partnership - Edmonton Factory (1)
6130-97th Street, Edmonton, T6E 3J4, AB, Canada
Tel.: (780) 430-0310
Air Conditioning System Mfr
N.A.I.C.S.: 333415

Airtex Manufacturing Partnership - Newmarket Factory (1)
1175 Twinney Drive, Newmarket, L3Y 9C8, ON, Canada
Tel.: (905) 898-1114
Air Conditioning System Mfr
N.A.I.C.S.: 333415

AIRTIFICIAL INTELLIGENCE STRUCTURES SA
General Diaz Porlier 49, 28001, Madrid, Spain
Tel.: (34) 911211700
Web Site: https://www.airtificial.com
Year Founded: 1970
AI—(MAD)
Sales Range: Less than $1 Million
Collaborative Robotics & Artificial Intelligence
N.A.I.C.S.: 541512
Jose Luis Perez del Pulgar Barragan (Member-Mgmt Bd)

Subsidiaries:

Stereocarto, S.L. (1)
Paseo de la Habana N 200, 28036, Madrid, Spain
Tel.: (34) 913431940
Web Site: http://www.stereocarto.com
Sales Range: $25-49.9 Million
Emp.: 30
Aerial Geophysical Surveying Services
N.A.I.C.S.: 541360
Alfonso Molina Gomez (Gen Mgr)

Subsidiary (Domestic):

Cartografia General, S.A. (2)
Plz Doctor Laguna 10, Madrid, 28009, Spain
Tel.: (34) 915046496
Sales Range: $25-49.9 Million
Emp.: 15
Aerial Photography & Cartography & Topography Services
N.A.I.C.S.: 541370

HIFSA (2)
Peseo De La Hevana 200, 28236, Madrid, Spain
Tel.: (34) 91 443 02 86
Web Site: http://www.hifsa.com
Sales Range: $10-24.9 Million
Aerial Photography Services
N.A.I.C.S.: 541922

AIRTOUCH SOLAR LTD

Airtouch Solar Ltd—(Continued)

Hatzoref 5 Industrial area Holon 2nd
floor, Holon, 5885633, Israel
Tel.: (972) 732100660
Web Site:
https://www.airtouchsolar.com
ARTS—(TAE)
Rev.: $4,409,468
Assets. $15,296,893
Liabilities: $7,463,532
Net Worth: $7,833,360
Earnings: ($5,434,629)
Fiscal Year-end: 06/30/23
Solar Panel Mfr
N.A.I.C.S.: 335999
Yanir Allouche *(Founder & Chm)*

AIRTRIP CORP.

Atago green Hills MORI tower 19F
251 Atago, Minato-ku, Tokyo, 105-
6219, Japan
Tel.: (81) 334316191
Web Site: https://www.airtrip.co.jp
6191—(TKS)
Rev.: $164,218,580
Assets: $216,854,740
Liabilities: $122,649,910
Net Worth: $94,204,830
Earnings: $10,557,010
Emp.: 823
Fiscal Year-end: 09/30/23
Online Travel Agency Services
N.A.I.C.S.: 561510
Hideki Yoshimura *(Co-Founder &
Chief Growth Officer)*

Subsidiaries:

Inbound Platform Corp.   **(1)**
5th Floor SW Shimbashi Building 6-14-5
Shimbashi, Minato-ku, Tokyo, 105-0004,
Japan
Tel.: (81) 33 437 3129
Web Site: https://www.inbound-platform.com
Wi-Fi Router Rental Services
N.A.I.C.S.: 532120
Shin O. *(CEO)*

AIRTRONA INTERNATIONAL, INC.

1040 South Service Road, Stoney
Creek, L8E 6G3, ON, Canada
Tel.: (289) 656-1264   **NV**
Year Founded: 2006
Gold Mining & Exploration Services
N.A.I.C.S.: 212220

AIRVANCE GROUP

383 rue des barronieres, 02700, Bey-
nost, France
Tel.: (33) 478558695
Web Site:
http://www.airvancegroup.com
Year Founded: 2020
Emp.: 1,950
Heating, Ventilation & Air Condition-
ing Products Mfr & Distr
N.A.I.C.S.: 333415
Olivier Dolbeau *(Chm-Mgmt Bd)*

Subsidiaries:

France Air Management SA   **(1)**
Rue des Barronnieres Beynost, 01708, Miri-
bel, Cedex, France
Tel.: (33) 472881111
Web Site: http://www.france-air-group.com
Air Handling Systems Design Distr
N.A.I.C.S.: 423730
Laurent Dolbeau *(Mng Dir)*

Subsidiary (Non-US):

SIG Air Handling Hungary Kft   **(2)**
Factory Street 2 BITEP Industrial Park,
2040, Budaors, Hungary
Tel.: (36) 23444133
Web Site: http://www.sigairhandling.hu
Air & Refrigeration Product Distr
N.A.I.C.S.: 423730

Subsidiary (Non-US):

SIG Air Handling N.V.   **(3)**
Hoogstraat 180, 1930, Zaventem, Belgium
Tel.: (32) 27253180
Air Handling Services
N.A.I.C.S.: 238220

SIG Air Handling Romania Srl   **(3)**
Sos Odaii 307-309 Sector 1, 013604, Bu-
charest, Romania
Tel.: (40) 318242111
Web Site: http://www.sigairhandling.ro
Ventilation & Air Conditioning Distr
N.A.I.C.S.: 423730

AIRWAY MEDIX SA

ul Szara 10, 00-420, Warsaw, Poland
Tel.: (48) 224084480
Web Site: https://airway-medix.com
Year Founded: 2010
AWM—(WAR)
Rev.: $3,049
Assets: $1,870,173
Liabilities: $5,225,610
Net Worth: ($3,355,437)
Earnings: ($832,317)
Fiscal Year-end: 12/31/23
Biotechnology Research & Develop-
ment Services
N.A.I.C.S.: 541714
Marek Orlowski *(Chm-Mgmt Bd)*

AISAN INDUSTRY CO., LTD.

1-1-1 Kyowa-cho, Obu, 474-8588,
Aichi, Japan
Tel.: (81) 562471131
Web Site: https://www.aisan-ind.co.jp
Year Founded: 1938
7283—(TKS)
Rev.: $2,077,760,960
Assets: $1,801,548,890
Liabilities: $879,070,510
Net Worth: $922,478,380
Earnings: $77,627,840
Emp.: 10,904
Fiscal Year-end: 03/31/24
Automotive Parts Mfr & Sales
N.A.I.C.S.: 336390
Kazuhiko Nishimura *(Exec Officer)*

Subsidiaries:

Aikyo Sangyo Co., Ltd.   **(1)**
7-1-1 Kyoei-cho, Obu, 474-8505, Aichi, Ja-
pan
Tel.: (81) 562485331
Web Site: https://aikyosangyo.co.jp
Emp.: 300
Transportation Services
N.A.I.C.S.: 541614

Aisan (Fhoshan) Auto Parts Co.,
Ltd   **(1)**
5 Xinhui Road Wusha, Daliang Town
Shunde, Foshan, 528333, Guangdong,
China   **(95%)**
Tel.: (86) 75729960580
Web Site: http://www.aisan-ind.co.jp
Sales Range: $100-124.9 Million
Emp.: 278
Motor Vehicle Parts Mfr
N.A.I.C.S.: 336390

Aisan (Foshan) Auto Parts Co.,
Ltd.   **(1)**
5 Xinhui Road, Wusha Daliang Town
Shunde, Foshan, 528333, China
Tel.: (86) 75729960580
Automotive Parts Mfr & Distr
N.A.I.C.S.: 336390

Aisan (Tianjin) Auto Parts Co.,
Ltd   **(1)**
No 169 Xijiu Road Pilot Free Trade Zone
Airport Industrial Park, Tianjin, 300308,
China   **(96.3%)**
Tel.: (86) 2224893048
Web Site: http://www.aisan-ind.co.jp
Sales Range: $50-74.9 Million
Emp.: 112
Motor Vehicle Parts
N.A.I.C.S.: 336390

Aisan Autopartes Mexico, S.A. de
C.V.   **(1)**
San Miguelito Poniente Circuito No 106
Colinas de San Luis Cd Satelite, 78423,
San Luis Potosi, Mexico
Tel.: (52) 4442989400
Web Site: https://en.aisanmexico.com
Automotive Parts Mfr & Distr
N.A.I.C.S.: 336390

Aisan Bitron Louny S.r.o.   **(1)**
Osvoboditelu 896, 44001, Louny, Czech
Republic   **(95%)**
Tel.: (420) 415930530
Sales Range: $100-124.9 Million
Emp.: 257
Fluid Power Pump & Motor Mfr
N.A.I.C.S.: 333996

Aisan Computer Services Corp.   **(1)**
7-3-3 Kyoei-cho, Obu, 474-8580, Aichi, Ja-
pan
Tel.: (81) 562487333
Automotive Parts Mfr & Distr
N.A.I.C.S.: 336390

Aisan Corporation Asia Pacific
Limited   **(1)**
1126/1 Vanit Place1 10th Floor Unit 1003
New Petchburi Road, Makkasan
Ratchathewi, Bangkok, 10400, Thailand
Tel.: (66) 26504550
Automobile Parts Distr
N.A.I.C.S.: 423120

Aisan Corporation Europe S.A.   **(1)**
Belgicastraat 13, 1930, Zaventem,
Belgium   **(100%)**
Tel.: (32) 25414756
Web Site: http://www.aisan-ind.co.jp
Sales Range: $25-49.9 Million
Emp.: 4
Automotive Parts & Accessories Stores
N.A.I.C.S.: 441330
Koji Banno *(Mng Dir)*

Aisan Corporation Gauangzhou Co.,
Ltd   **(1)**
Room 1809 Grand Tower Site 1 of 228,
Tianhe Rd Tianhe Qu, Guangzhou, 510620,
China   **(100%)**
Tel.: (86) 2038330920
Automotive Parts & Accessories Stores
N.A.I.C.S.: 441330

Aisan Corporation of America,
Inc.   **(1)**
24387 Halsted Rd, Farmington Hills, MI
48335   **(100%)**
Tel.: (248) 522-9717
Web Site: http://www.aisan-ind.co.jp
Industrial Machinery & Equipment Whslr
N.A.I.C.S.: 423830

Aisan Industry Co., Ltd - ANJO
Plant   **(1)**
100 Kitayama Higashibata-cho, Anjo, Aichi,
Japan
Tel.: (81) 566920611
Sales Range: $200-249.9 Million
Emp.: 965
Engine Valve Mfr
N.A.I.C.S.: 336310

Aisan Industry Co., Ltd. - TOYOTA
Plant   **(1)**
635-30 Komugio Nishihirose-cho, Toyota,
470-0309, Aichi, Japan
Tel.: (81) 565 46 0021
Web Site: http://www.aisan-ind.co.jp
Sales Range: $200-249.9 Million
Emp.: 539
Automobile Parts Mfr
N.A.I.C.S.: 336390

Aisan Industry Czech s.r.o.   **(1)**
Industrial 2727, 440 01, Louny, Czech Re-
public
Tel.: (420) 415930500
Web Site: http://www.aisan.cz
Electric Fuel Pump Mfr
N.A.I.C.S.: 336320
Katsumi Takeuchi *(Mng Dir)*

Aisan Industry France SA   **(1)**
1 Rue Des Grands Champs, 58000, Nevers, France   **(100%)**
Tel.: (33) 386718210
Web Site: https://www.aisanindustryfrance.fr

Sales Range: $50-74.9 Million
Emp.: 200
Pump & Pumping Equipment Mfr
N.A.I.C.S.: 333914
Franco Orsi *(Mng Dir)*

Aisan Industry India Pvt. Ltd.   **(1)**
Plot Nos B4-B5, ELCINA Electronics Manu-
facturing Cluster Salarpur Industrial Area,
Alwar, 3010 109, Rajasthan, India
Tel.: (91) 72300/638
Automotive Parts Mfr & Distr
N.A.I.C.S.: 336390

Aisan Industry Kentucky, LLC   **(1)**
65 Clarence Dr, Mount Sterling, KY 40353
Tel.: (859) 497-2040
Automotive Parts Mfr & Distr
N.A.I.C.S.: 336390

Aisan Industry Louny s.r.o.   **(1)**
Prumyslova 2725, 440 01, Louny, Czech
Republic
Tel.: (420) 415 930 530
Web Site: http://www.aisan.cz
Sales Range: $100-124.9 Million
Emp.: 300
Automobile Parts Mfr
N.A.I.C.S.: 336390
Kunio Kadowaki *(Pres)*

Aisan Kumamoto Co., Ltd.   **(1)**
393-1 Kitamuta, Tamana, 865-0046, Japan
Tel.: (81) 968763911
Web Site: https://www.aisan-
kumamoto.co.jp
Emp.: 41
Automotive Parts Mfr & Distr
N.A.I.C.S.: 336390

Aisan Sales India Pvt. Ltd.   **(1)**
Suite 615 Level 6 Wing B Two Horizon
Center, Golf Course Road DLF5 Sector 43,
Gurgaon, 122 002, Haryana, India
Tel.: (91) 415397200
Automobile Parts Distr
N.A.I.C.S.: 423120

D&H Co., Ltd.   **(1)**
5/F Daeho Bldg 207-30 Geoje 1 Il-Dong,
Yeonje-Gu, Pusan, 611071, Korea (South)
Tel.: (82) 515037089
Automotive Parts Mfr & Distr
N.A.I.C.S.: 336390

Franklin Precision Industry, Inc.   **(1)**
3220 Bowling Green Rd, Franklin, KY
42134
Tel.: (270) 598-4300
Web Site: http://www.fpik.com
Sales Range: $125-149.9 Million
Emp.: 650
Throttle Bodies, Carbon Canisters & Fuel
Pump Modules Mfr
N.A.I.C.S.: 336211
Takehiro Nakajima *(Pres)*

Hyundam (Zhangjiagang) Automobile
Parts Co., Ltd.   **(1)**
31 Chang Xing Road, Jiangsu Zhangjia-
gang Economic Development Zone North
District, Zhangjiagang, 215699, China
Tel.: (86) 51288838851
Automotive Parts Mfr & Distr
N.A.I.C.S.: 336390

Hyundam Industrial Co., Ltd.   **(1)**
29 Yeokri-gil Yeongin-myeon Asan-si,
Chung Cheong Nam-do, Yesan, Korea
(South)   **(91%)**
Tel.: (82) 415397200
Sales Range: $200-249.9 Million
Emp.: 583
Fluid Power Pump & Motor Mfr
N.A.I.C.S.: 333996

Hyundam Slovakia s.r.o.   **(1)**
M R Stefanika 71, 010 01, Zilina, Slovakia
Tel.: (421) 417231194
Sales Range: $25-49.9 Million
Emp.: 60
Automotive Parts Mfr & Distr
N.A.I.C.S.: 336390

Hyundam Tech Co., Ltd.   **(1)**
142-1 Yeimsung-ri Yeomchi-up, Asan,
Chungnam, Korea (South)
Tel.: (82) 415391990
Automobile Parts Mfr
N.A.I.C.S.: 336390

IHD Industries Pvt. Ltd. (1)
B-25 26 SIPCOT Industrial Park, Irrungattu-
kottai Kancheepuram Dist Sriperumbudur,
Chennai, 602 105, Tamilnadu,
India (100%)
Tel.: (91) 4427156863
Web Site: https://hyundam.co.in
Fluid Power Pump & Motor Mfr
N.A.I.C.S.: 333996
Seung Yong Song (Mng Dir)

Nichialloy Co., Ltd. (1)
170-1 Aonoyama Higashibatacho, Anjo,
444-121, Aichi, Japan
Tel.: (81) 566782110
Web Site: https://www.nichialloy.co.jp
Emp.: 100
Automotive Parts Mfr & Distr
N.A.I.C.S.: 336390

P.T. Aisan Nasmoco Industri (1)
East Jakarta Industrial Park Plot 9L, Cika-
rang Selatan, Bekasi, 17550, West Java,
Indonesia
Tel.: (62) 218971577
Emp.: 1,300
Automobile Parts Mfr
N.A.I.C.S.: 336390
Yunus Anis (Gen Mgr)

Shenyang Xuantan Automobile Parts
Co., Ltd. (1)
No 1A2 No 4 Street Shenyang Economic,
Technological Development Zone, She-
nyang, 110000, Liaoning, China (100%)
Tel.: (86) 2425377151
Web Site: https://www.hyundam.com.cn
Engineeering Services
N.A.I.C.S.: 541330

TK Carburettor Co., Ltd. (1)
5-10 Kotobuki-cho, Toyota, 471-0834, Aichi,
Japan
Tel.: (81) 565282311
Web Site: https://www.teikei.co.jp
Emp.: 192
Automotive Parts Mfr & Distr
N.A.I.C.S.: 336390

AISAN TECHNOLOGY CO.,
LTD.
AT Bldg 3-7-14 Nishiki, Naka-ku, Na-
goya, Aichi, Japan
Tel.: (81) 529507500
Web Site: https://www.aisantec.co.jp
Year Founded: 1970
4667—(TKS)
Rev.: $36,209,580
Assets: $56,826,170
Liabilities: $15,117,070
Net Worth: $41,709,100
Earnings: $2,247,400
Fiscal Year-end: 03/31/24
CAD System Development Services
N.A.I.C.S.: 513210
Atsushi Kato (Pres)

AISEI PHARMACY CO., LTD.
Marunouchi Mitsui Bldg 2-2-2
Marunouchi, Chiyoda-ku, Tokyo, 100-
0005, Japan
Tel.: (81) 332400222
Web Site: https://www.aisei.co.jp
Year Founded: 1984
Emp.: 4,289
Pharmacy Owner & Operator
N.A.I.C.S.: 456110
Emi Fujii (Pres & CEO)

AISHA STEEL MILLS LIMITED
1 F Arif Habib Centre 23 MT Khan
Road, Karachi, Pakistan
Tel.: (92) 2132468317   PK
Web Site: https://www.aishasteel.com
Year Founded: 2005
ASL—(PSX)
Rev.: $111,890,945
Assets: $136,871,229
Liabilities: $80,420,221
Net Worth: $56,451,008
Earnings: ($11,568,325)
Emp.: 643
Fiscal Year-end: 06/30/23

Steel Products Mfr
N.A.I.C.S.: 331110
Khawar A. Siddiqui (Gen Mgr-Sls &
Mktg)

Subsidiaries:

Arif Habib Consultancy (Pvt.)
Limited (1)
23 M T Khan Road, Karachi, 744000, Paki-
stan
Tel.: (92) 213241521345
Web Site: https://www.arifhabib.com.pk
Investment Advisory Services
N.A.I.C.S.: 523940

Pakarab Fertilizers Limited (1)
Khayaban-e-Jinnah, Lahore, 110, Pakistan
Tel.: (92) 42111328462
Web Site: https://fatima-group.com
Fertilizer Mfr & Distr
N.A.I.C.S.: 325311

Pakistan Opportunities Limited (1)
Arif Habib Centre 23 M T Khan Road, Kara-
chi, Pakistan
Tel.: (92) 213246071719
Web Site: https://pakistanopportunities.com
Financial Services
N.A.I.C.S.: 522320

AISHIDA CO., LTD.
Central M-6 2/F Hi Tech Industrial
Park, Nanshan District, Shenzhen,
518057, China
Tel.: (86) 755 86028268
Web Site:
    http://www.szsuccess.com.cn
Year Founded: 2004
002289—(SSE)
Rev.: $29,261,088
Assets: $56,986,713
Liabilities: $12,943,395
Net Worth: $44,043,318
Earnings: $1,864,593
Emp.: 5,000
Fiscal Year-end: 12/31/19
Liquid Crystal Display Modules
N.A.I.C.S.: 334419
Yang Zhang (Chm)

Subsidiaries:

Shenzhen Success Electronics Co.,
Ltd. - Yu Shun Electronics
Factory (1)
Block 21-23 ChangxingIndustrial Estate II
Changzhen Community, Gongming Sub-
district Guangming NewDistrict, Shenzhen,
518132, China
Tel.: (86) 75527179881
Liquid Crystal Display Mfr
N.A.I.C.S.: 334419

AISHIDA CO., LTD.
No 2 Keji Road Economic Develop-
ment Zone, Wenling, 317500, Zheji-
ang, China
Tel.: (86) 57686199005
Web Site: http://www.chinaasd.com
Year Founded: 1993
002403—(SSE)
Rev.: $412,770,384
Assets: $720,531,396
Liabilities: $442,886,184
Net Worth: $277,645,212
Earnings: ($11,053,692)
Fiscal Year-end: 12/31/22
Non-Stick Cookware, Pressure Cook-
ers & Stainless Steel Cookware Mfr
N.A.I.C.S.: 332215
Chen Helin (Chm & Gen Mgr)

Subsidiaries:

ZHEJIANG ASD HOUSEHOLD
EQUIPMENT CO., LTD (1)
No 18 Qiantang Road Jiashan Economic
Development Zone, Hangzhou, China
Tel.: (86) 57389118696
Household Equipment Mfr
N.A.I.C.S.: 332215

AISIN CORPORATION
2-1 Asahi-machi, Kariya, 448-8650,
Aichi, Japan
Tel.: (81) 566248441   JP
Web Site: https://www.aisin.com
Year Founded: 1949
ASEKF—(OTCIQ)
Rev.: $32,452,171,770
Assets: $30,690,335,760
Liabilities: $14,812,924,070
Net Worth: $15,877,411,690
Earnings: $600,273,930
Emp.: 115,140
Fiscal Year-end: 03/31/24
Automotive Parts & Housing-Related
Equipment Mfr
N.A.I.C.S.: 336390

Subsidiaries:

AD Green Co., Ltd. (1)
129 Akiba Takaokahonmachi, Toyota, 473-
0922, Aichi, Japan
Tel.: (81) 565528771
Web Site: http://www.aisin.com
Greening & Exterior Refurbishing Services
N.A.I.C.S.: 541320
Fumio Fujimori (Pres)

AD Nobi Co., Ltd. (1)
4-23-2 Chiyoda, Naka-Ku, Nagoya, 460-
0012, Aichi, Japan
Tel.: (81) 0566636282
Web Site: https://www.aisin-ad.co.jp
Emp.: 11
Condominiums Building Services
N.A.I.C.S.: 236117
Ryo Ozaki (Pres & CEO)

ADVICS Co., Ltd. (1)
2 1 Showa-cho, Kariya, 448-8688, Aichi,
Japan
Tel.: (81) 566 56 5900
Web Site: http://www.advics.co.jp
Emp.: 10,310
Brake Systems & Components Research,
Development & Mfr
N.A.I.C.S.: 336340
Takahiro Goshima (Exec VP)

Subsidiary (Non-US):

ADVICS ASIA PACIFIC CO.,
LTD. (2)
235 Moo 7 Simahaphot, Tha Tum District,
Prachin Buri, Thailand
Tel.: (66) 37 414 093
Rev.: $358,650,720
Emp.: 26
Automobile Component Distr
N.A.I.C.S.: 423120

Subsidiary (US):

ADVICS MANUFACTURING INDI-
ANA, L.L.C. (2)
10550 James Adams St, Terre Haute, IN
47802
Tel.: (812) 298-1617
Web Site: http://www.advics.co.jp
Automotive Brake Components Mfr
N.A.I.C.S.: 336340

ADVICS North America, Inc. (2)
45300 Polaris Ct, Plymouth, MI
48170 (100%)
Tel.: (734) 414-5100
Sales Range: $50-74.9 Million
Emp.: 70
Brake Systems Mfr & Seller
N.A.I.C.S.: 336340

Division (Domestic):

ADVICS Manufacturing Ohio,
Inc. (3)
1650 Kingsview Dr, Lebanon, OH
45036 (100%)
Tel.: (513) 932-7878
Web Site: http://www.advics-ohio.com
Sales Range: $100-124.9 Million
Braking Systems Mfr
N.A.I.C.S.: 336340

SAFA, LLC (3)
1621 Lukken Industrial Dr W, Lagrange, GA
30240-5703 (100%)
Tel.: (706) 812-0007

Web Site: http://www.aisin.com
Wire Harnesses Mfr
N.A.I.C.S.: 332618
Catherine Bowen (Mgr-HR)

Subsidiary (Non-US):

PT. ADVICS INDONESIA (2)
East Jakarta Industrial Park EJIP Plot 5J
Cikarang Selatan, Jawa Barat, Bekasi,
17550, Indonesia
Tel.: (62) 218970973
Web Site: http://www.advics.co.jp
Rev.: $21,672,200
Emp.: 14
Automobile Component Distr
N.A.I.C.S.: 423120
Tetsuhiro Tomita (Gen Mgr)

AI Dream Life Support Co., Ltd. (1)
4-188 Hantsukicho, Obu, 474-0037, Aichi,
Japan
Tel.: (81) 562 47 7190
Web Site: https://www.aisin-ad.co.jp
Senior Citizen Home Services
N.A.I.C.S.: 623312

AISIN AI (THAILAND) CO., LTD. (1)
Wellgrow Industrial Estate Phase2 80 Moo5
Km36 Bangna Trad Tambol Bang, Amphur
Bangpakong, Chachoengsao, 24180, Thai-
land
Tel.: (66) 38 570 062
Automotive Parts Mfr & Distr
N.A.I.C.S.: 336390

AISIN ASIA PACIFIC CO., LTD (1)
1 Soi Bangna Trad 25 Bang Na Trad Road,
Bangna, Bangkok, 10260, Thailand
Tel.: (66) 23986308
Automobile Parts Mfr
N.A.I.C.S.: 336390

AISIN AUTOMOTIVE CASTING TEN-
NESSEE, INC. (1)
221 Frank L Diggs Dr, Clinton, TN 37716
Tel.: (865) 457-4581
Web Site: http://www.aisinworld.com
Sales Range: $100-124.9 Million
Emp.: 480
Aluminum Casting Mfr
N.A.I.C.S.: 331315
Robin Watson (Mgr-HR)

AISIN CANADA, INC (1)
180 Wright Blvd, Stratford, N4Z 1H3, ON,
Canada
Tel.: (519) 271-1575
Web Site: https://www.aisincanada.com
Automotive Parts Mfr & Distr
N.A.I.C.S.: 336390

AISIN CHEMICAL (THAILAND) CO.,
LTD. (1)
5/6 Moo 11 Rojana Industrial Park, Ban
Khai, Rayong, 21120, Thailand
Tel.: (66) 389619516
Automobile Brake Pads Mfr
N.A.I.C.S.: 336390

AISIN Corporation - Handa Electron-
ics Plant (1)
4-29 Nitto-cho, Handa, 475-0033, Aichi,
Japan
Tel.: (81) 569246810
Web Site: https://www.aisin.com
Electronic Components Mfr
N.A.I.C.S.: 334419

AISIN Corporation - Nishio Engine
Component Plant (1)
80 Kowari Minaminakane-cho, Nishio, 445-
0801, Aichi, Japan
Tel.: (81) 563576300
Web Site: https://www.aisin.com
Oil & Water Pump Mfr
N.A.I.C.S.: 333914

AISIN EUROPE MANUFACTURING
CZECH s. r. o. (1)
Cizovska 456, 397 01, Pisek, Czech Re-
public
Tel.: (420) 382 909 111
Web Site: http://www.aisin.co.cz
Sales Range: $125-149.9 Million
Emp.: 440
Automotive Parts Mfr & Distr
N.A.I.C.S.: 336390
Susumu Takase (Exec Dir)

AISIN Corporation—(Continued)

AISIN LIGHT METALS, LLC (1)
10900 Redco Dr, Marion, IL 62959
Tel.: (618) 997-7900
Web Site: http://www.aisinillinois.com
Aluminum Automotive Parts Mfr
N.A.I.C.S.: 331315
Katsunori Maeda (Pres)

**AISIN MFG. AGUASCALIENTES, S.
A. DE C.V.** (1)
Av Mexico 208 Parque Industrial San Fran-
sisco, 20300, Mexico, Aguascalientes,
Mexico
Tel.: (52) 4659673236
All Other Motor Vehicle Parts Manufacturing
N.A.I.C.S.: 336390

**AISIN OTOMOTIV PARCALARI
SANAYI VE TICARET A. S.** (1)
10 Mermerciler Organize Sanayi Bolgesi 1
Sanayi Caddesi, Istanbul, Turkiye
Tel.: (90) 2165932130
Automobile Parts Mfr
N.A.I.C.S.: 336390

AISIN SIN'EI CO., LTD. (1)
2-8-12 Konan-machi, Hekinan, 447-8508,
Aichi, Japan
Tel.: (81) 566 48 7000
Web Site: http://www.aisin-sinei.co.jp
Rev.: $325,584,000
Emp.: 632
Automobile Parts Mfr
N.A.I.C.S.: 336390

**AISIN TECHNICAL CENTER OF
AMERICA, INC.** (1)
15300 Centennial Dr, Northville, MI 48168
Tel.: (734) 453-5551
Web Site: http://www.aisintca.com
Automotive Product Development Services
N.A.I.C.S.: 488970
Yoshiaki Kato (Pres)

AKKM Co., Ltd. (1)
132-246 Yukoku Dogaen,, Kira-cho, Nishio,
Japan
Tel.: (81) 566626870
Web Site: http://www.akk-m.co.jp
Emp.: 123
Greening & Landscaping Design Services
N.A.I.C.S.: 561730

AS Brake Systems, Inc. (1)
1-1-1 Koyakita, Itami, 664-0016, Hyogo,
Japan
Tel.: (81) 727712400
Web Site: http://www.asbrake.co.jp
Brake System Mfr
N.A.I.C.S.: 336340

AW EUROPE S.A. (1)
Avenue de l'Industrie 19, 1420, Braine-
l'Alleud, Belgium
Tel.: (32) 2 389 12 00
Web Site: http://www.aw-europe.be
Car Navigation Systems Mfr & Distr
N.A.I.C.S.: 336390

AW-I'S Co., Ltd. (1)
38 Ikenoue-cho Creative Center M3F, Echi-
zen, 915-8520, Fukui, Japan
Tel.: (81) 778 25 7860
Web Site: http://www.aw-is.co.jp
Sales Range: $25-49.9 Million
Emp.: 109
Molded Metal Parts Mfr
N.A.I.C.S.: 336390
Keika Akira (Pres)

Aichi Giken Co., Ltd. (1)
50-1 Kojiritsuki Hitotsugi-cho, Kariya, 448-
0003, Aichi, Japan
Tel.: (81) 566 23 2731
Web Site: http://www.aichigiken.co.jp
Automobile Parts Mfr
N.A.I.C.S.: 336390

Aisin (Australia) Pty. Ltd. (1)
593 599 Somarville Road Sunshine, Mel-
bourne, 3020, VIC, Australia (100%)
Tel.: (61) 383119100
Web Site: http://www.aisin.com
Sales Range: $50-74.9 Million
Emp.: 100
Import, Export & Sale of Automotive Parts,
Household Sewing Machines & Apparel
N.A.I.C.S.: 336340

Kazuhiko Asai (Mng Dir)

Aisin AW Industries Co., Ltd. (1)
38 Ikenokami Cho, Takefu, 915 8520, Fu-
kui, Japan (59%)
Tel.: (81) 778256611
Sales Range: $200-249.9 Million
Emp.: 3,915
Mfr & Sale of Automatic Transmission Parts
N.A.I.C.S.: 336350

Aisin Asia Pte. Ltd. (1)
10 Anson Rd Unit 31-08 International Plz,
Singapore, 79903, Singapore
Tel.: (65) 62220592
Web Site: http://www.aisin.com.sg
Sales Range: $25-49.9 Million
Emp.: 30
Import, Export & Sale of Automotive Parts,
Household Sewing Machines & Apparel
N.A.I.C.S.: 336340
Mark Shiiya (Mng Dir)

Aisin Chemical Co., Ltd. (1)
1141 1 Okawagahara, Fujioka Eiino Cho,
Toyota, 470 0492, Aichi, Japan
Tel.: (81) 565766661
Web Site: http://www.aisin-chem.co.jp
Sales Range: $10-24.9 Million
Emp.: 1,234
Molded Plastic Automotive Parts, Automo-
tive Friction Materials, Paints, Adhesives &
Molding Sand Adhesives Mfr
N.A.I.C.S.: 441330
Kanichi Shimizu (Pres)

Subsidiary (US):

**AISIN CHEMICAL INDIANA,
LLC** (2)
1004 Industrial Way, Crothersville, IN 47229
Tel.: (812) 793-2888
Web Site: http://www.aisinworld.com
Sales Range: $25-49.9 Million
Emp.: 40
Wet Friction Material Mfr
N.A.I.C.S.: 336390
Tim Carter (Gen Mgr)

Aisin Collabo Co., Ltd. (1)
2-3 Showacho Aishin Seiki Jimu Honkannai,
Kariya, 448-8650, Aichi, Japan
Tel.: (81) 566249833
Web Site: https://ai-collabo.co.jp
Emp.: 917
Human Resource Consulting Services
N.A.I.C.S.: 541612
Katsuhiro Sugiura (Mng Dir)

Aisin Comcruise Co., Ltd. (1)
Nagoya Cross Court 3F 4-10-4 Meieki,
Nakamura-ku, Nagoya, 450-0002, Aichi,
Japan
Tel.: (81) 52 533 7051
Web Site: http://www.aisin-comcruise.com
Sales Range: $50-74.9 Million
Emp.: 702
Software Development Services
N.A.I.C.S.: 541511
Yoshiaki Kato (Pres)

Aisin Development Co., Ltd. (1)
3-3 Aioi-cho, Kariya, 448-8525, Aichi, Japan
Tel.: (81) 566278700
Web Site: http://www.aisin-ad.co.jp
Sales Range: $350-399.9 Million
Emp.: 343
Civil Engineering, Construction, Gardening
& Horticulture & Insurance Services
N.A.I.C.S.: 237990
Tsuno Ito (Pres)

Aisin Engineering Co., Ltd. (1)
RF Kariya Ekimae Building 1-1-1 Aioi-Cho,
Kariya, 448-8605, Aichi, Japan
Tel.: (81) 566 62 8170
Web Site: http://www.ai-e.co.jp
Rev.: $188,373,600
Emp.: 1,594
Computer Peripheral Equipment Mfr
N.A.I.C.S.: 334118
Suzuki Mitsuyuki (Pres)

**Aisin Europe Manufacturing (UK)
Ltd.** (1)
Unit 1 Bell Heath Way Woodgate Business
Park, Birmingham, B32 3BZ, United
Kingdom (100%)
Tel.: (44) 1214215688
Web Site: https://www.aisin.com

Emp.: 139
Automotive Parts Mfg.
N.A.I.C.S.: 321911

Aisin Europe S.A. (1)
Ave De I Indus 21, Parc Indus, 1420,
Braine-l'Alleud, 1420, Belgium
Tel.: (32) 23870707
Web Site: http://www.aisin-europe.com
Sales Range: $25-49.9 Million
Emp.: 90
Marketing of Automotive Parts
N.A.I.C.S.: 441330
Nakamura Akira (Gen Mgr)

Aisin Hokkaido Co., Ltd. (1)
32-5 Kashiwabara, Tomakomai, 059-1362,
Hokkaido, Japan
Tel.: (81) 144 53 7111
Web Site: http://www.ai-h.co.jp
Aluminum Casting Products Mfr & Distr
N.A.I.C.S.: 331523

Aisin Holdings of America, Inc. (1)
15300 Centennial Dr, Northville, MI 48170
Tel.: (734) 453-5551
Web Site: http://www.aisinworld.com
Sales Range: $75-99.9 Million
Emp.: 200
Holding Company
N.A.I.C.S.: 551112

Subsidiary (Domestic):

**AISIN ELECTRONICS ILLINOIS,
LLC** (2)
11200 Redco Dr, Marion, IL 62959
Tel.: (618) 997-9800
Web Site: http://www.aisinillinois.com
Electric Equipment Mfr
N.A.I.C.S.: 334419
Akito Yamauchi (Pres)

Aisin World Corp. of America (2)
46501 Commerce Ctr Dr, Northville, MI
48170
Tel.: (734) 453-5551
Web Site: http://www.aisinworld.com
Automotive Components Supplier
N.A.I.C.S.: 423120
Don Whitsitt (Pres)

Subsidiary (Domestic):

AW North Carolina, Inc. (3)
4112 Old Oxford Hwy, Durham, NC 27712
Tel.: (919) 479-6550
Web Site: http://www.aw-nc.com
Sales Range: $150-199.9 Million
Emp.: 950
Automotive Transmission Component Mfr
N.A.I.C.S.: 336350
Susumu Kasai (Pres)

**AW Transmission Engineering U.S.A.,
Inc.** (3)
14920 Keel St, Plymouth, MI 48170
Tel.: (734) 454-1710
Web Site: http://www.awtec.com
Sales Range: $50-74.9 Million
Emp.: 180
Transmission Remanufacturing
N.A.I.C.S.: 336350

Aisin Automotive Casting, LLC (3)
4870 E Hwy 552, London, KY 40744-9430
Tel.: (606) 878-6523
Web Site: http://www.aisinauto.com
Sales Range: $100-124.9 Million
Emp.: 500
Mfr of Auto Parts
N.A.I.C.S.: 331523
Hisashi Hatta (Treas & Sec)

Aisin Drivetrain, Inc. (3)
1001 Industrial Way, Crothersville, IN
47229-9415
Tel.: (812) 793-2427
Web Site: http://www.aisindrive.com
Sales Range: $125-149.9 Million
Emp.: 375
Mfr Torque Converters & Transmissions for
Heavy Industrial Trucks & Brake Assembly
Components
N.A.I.C.S.: 336350
Scott Turpin (Pres)

Aisin Electronics, Inc. (3)
199 Frank W Cir, Stockton, CA
95206-4002 (100%)
Tel.: (209) 983-4988

Web Site: http://www.aisin.com
Sales Range: $50-74.9 Million
Emp.: 160
Mfr of Automotive Parts for Electronic Com-
ponents
N.A.I.C.S.: 335314
Shawn Maguire (Mgr-Production Control &
Pur Dept)

Aisin USA Manufacturing Inc. (3)
1700 E 4th St, Seymour, IN
47274-4309 (100%)
Tel.: (812) 523-1969
Web Site: http://www.aisinusa.com
Sales Range: $350-399.9 Million
Emp.: 1,750
Mfr of Automotive Parts
N.A.I.C.S.: 336390
Darrell Tolley (Mgr-Supplier Engrg Dev Unit
& Tech Dept)

IMRA America, Inc. (3)
1044 Woodridge Ave, Ann Arbor, MI
48105-9748 (100%)
Tel.: (734) 930-2560
Web Site: http://www.imra.com
Sales Range: $25-49.9 Million
Emp.: 90
Fibre Optics Research
N.A.I.C.S.: 541910
Gyu C. Cho (VP-Tech Dev & Laser Res)

Aisin Infotex Co., Ltd. (1)
3-11-34 Mita, Minato-Ku, Tokyo, 108-0073,
Aichi, Japan
Tel.: (81) 3 5730 9300
Web Site: http://www.aisinix.com
Software Consulting Services
N.A.I.C.S.: 541512

Aisin Keikinzoku Co., Ltd. (1)
12-3 Nagonoe Imizu, Toyama, 934-8588,
Japan
Tel.: (81) 766828800
Web Site: http://www.aisin-ak.co.jp
Sales Range: $550-599.9 Million
Emp.: 1,700
Mfr & Sale of Die-Cast Aluminum Products,
Aluminum Mold Cast Products & Aluminum
Products
N.A.I.C.S.: 331523
Yoshifumi Kawahara (Pres)

Aisin Kiko Co., Ltd. (1)
70-6 Ikegami Oaza Tomokuni Kira Cho,
Nishio, 444 0504, Aichi, Japan
Tel.: (81) 563 35 3850
Web Site: https://www.aisin.com
Sales Range: $400-449.9 Million
Emp.: 1,200
Manufacture & Development of Functional
Automatic Transmission Components,
Drivetrain-Related & Body-Related Compo-
nents
N.A.I.C.S.: 336330

Aisin Kyushu Casting Co., Ltd (1)
1227-1 Jonammachimainohara,
Shimomashiki-gun, Kumamoto, 861-4214,
Japan
Tel.: (81) 964281611
Aluminum Die-Castings Mfr
N.A.I.C.S.: 331523

Aisin Kyushu Co., Ltd. (1)
500-1 Nishi Amainohara Jonan Machi,
Shimomashiki-gun, Kumamoto, Japan
Tel.: (81) 964 28 8181
Web Site: http://www.aisin-kyushu.co.jp
Automobile Parts Mfr
N.A.I.C.S.: 336390
Hiroshi Takahi (CEO)

Aisin Machine Tech Co. Ltd. (1)
80-1 Nishiotsubo Higashibata-cho, Anjo,
444-1213, Aichi, Japan
Tel.: (81) 5669267021
Web Site: https://www.aisin.com
Equipment Mfr & Maintenance Services
N.A.I.C.S.: 335999

Aisin Maintenance Co., Ltd. (1)
3-3 Aioicho, Kariya, 448-0027, Aichi, Japan
Tel.: (81) 566626771
Automotive Parts Repair & Maintenance
Services
N.A.I.C.S.: 811198

Aisin Metaltech Co., Ltd. (1)
615 Fukujima Nyuzenmachi, Shimoniikawa-
Gun, Toyama, 939-0645, Japan
Tel.: (81) 765 72 5511

Web Site: http://www.aisin-metaltech.jp
Automobile Parts Mfr
N.A.I.C.S.: 336390

Aisin Mexicana S.A. De. C.V.   (1)
Calle Texas 100 Oriente, Parque Industrial
Nacional Cienega de Flores, 65550,
Mexico, NL, Mexico
Tel.: (52) 8183197733
Web Site: http://www.aisin.com
Sales Range: $100-124.9 Million
Emp.: 500
Mfr & Sale of Automotive Parts
N.A.I.C.S.: 336340

Aisin Seiki Co., Ltd. - Anjo Plant   (1)
1-11-2 Mikawaanjo-cho, Anjo, 446-8524,
Aichi, Japan
Tel.: (81) 566 76 9111
Web Site: http://www.aisin.com
Sales Range: $100-124.9 Million
Emp.: 400
Air Conditioner Mfr
N.A.I.C.S.: 336390
Katsumi Yamada (Mgr-Quality)

**Aisin Seiki Co., Ltd. - Handa
Plant**   (1)
4-29 Nitto-cho, Handa, 475-0033, Aichi,
Japan
Tel.: (81) 569 24 6710
Web Site: http://www.aisin.com
Sales Range: $200-249.9 Million
Emp.: 828
Automotive Brake System Mfr
N.A.I.C.S.: 336340

**Aisin Seiki Co., Ltd. - Kinuura
Plant**   (1)
2-8-12 Kohnan-machi, Hekinan, 447-0824,
Aichi, Japan
Tel.: (81) 566 46 3800
Web Site: http://www.aisin.com
Sales Range: $200-249.9 Million
Emp.: 560
Door Handles & Sunroofs Mfr
N.A.I.C.S.: 336390

**Aisin Seiki Co., Ltd. - Machinery &
Equipment Plant**   (1)
80 Kowari Minaminakane-cho, Nishio, 445-
0801, Aichi, Japan
Tel.: (81) 563 57 6660
Sales Range: $100-124.9 Million
Emp.: 328
Automotive Assembling Component Mfr
N.A.I.C.S.: 336330

**Aisin Seiki Co., Ltd. - Nishio Die-
casting Plant**   (1)
80 Kowari Minaminakane-cho, Nishio, 445-
0801, Aichi, Japan
Tel.: (81) 563 57 6200
Sales Range: $200-249.9 Million
Emp.: 993
Transmission & Transaxle Case Mfr
N.A.I.C.S.: 332999

**Aisin Seiki Co., Ltd. - Ogawa
Plant**   (1)
1 Kukui Ogawa-cho, Anjo, 444-1162, Aichi,
Japan
Tel.: (81) 563 57 6701
Sales Range: $200-249.9 Million
Emp.: 724
Automatic Transmission Mfr
N.A.I.C.S.: 336350

**Aisin Seiki Co., Ltd. - Shinkawa
Plant**   (1)
4-75 Rokuken-cho, Hekinan, 447-0861,
Aichi, Japan
Tel.: (81) 566 41 3321
Sales Range: $100-124.9 Million
Emp.: 423
Automobile Parts Mfr
N.A.I.C.S.: 336390

**Aisin Seiki Co., Ltd. - Shintoyo
Plant**   (1)
1 Tennoh Takaokashin-machi, Toyota, 473-
0921, Aichi, Japan
Tel.: (81) 565 54 8611
Web Site: http://www.aisin.com
Sales Range: $400-449.9 Million
Emp.: 1,356
Automobile Parts Mfr
N.A.I.C.S.: 336390

Aisin Sinwa Co., Ltd.   (1)

2458 Nyuzen Nyuzen-Cho, Shimoshinkawa-
Gun, Toyama, 939 0626, Japan
Tel.: (81) 765725811
Web Site: http://www.aisin-sinwa.co.jp
Sales Range: $100-124.9 Million
Emp.: 456
Cast Components for Automobiles, Indus-
trial Machinery, Home Electric Appliances,
Agricultural Equipment & Forged Automo-
tive Components Mfr
N.A.I.C.S.: 441330
Katsushi Nakajima (Pres)

Aisin Takaoka Co., Ltd.   (1)
1 Tennoh Takaokashin Machi, Toyota, 473
8501, Aichi, Japan
Tel.: (81) 565541123
Web Site: http://www.at-takaoka.co.jp
Sales Range: $800-899.9 Million
Automotive Parts Mfr & Sale
N.A.I.C.S.: 441330
Haruhiko Amakusa (Pres)

Subsidiary (US):

ATTC MANUFACTURING, INC.   (2)
10455 State Rd 37, Tell City, IN 47586
Tel.: (812) 547-5060
Web Site: http://www.attcmanufacturing.com
Sales Range: $75-99.9 Million
Emp.: 500
Automobile Parts Mfr
N.A.I.C.S.: 336390
Frank Yuda (Mgr-Trng)

Intat Precision, Inc.   (2)
2148 N State Rd 3, Rushville, IN
46173   (98%)
Tel.: (765) 932-5323
Web Site: http://www.intat.com
Emp.: 400
Gray & Ductile Iron Castings for Automotive
Industry
N.A.I.C.S.: 331511
Sandeep Deshpande (Gen Mgr)

Subsidiary (Non-US):

**Takaoka Lioho (Tianjin) Industries
Co., Ltd**   (2)
Tianjin BeiChen Economic Development
Area ShuanChenZhongLu, Tianjin, China
Tel.: (86) 22 8699 5950
Web Site: http://www.atl.com.cn
Automobile Parts Mfr
N.A.I.C.S.: 336390

Aisin Tohoku Co., Ltd.   (1)
6 Moriyama Nishine Kanegasaki-Cho,
Iwate, 029-4503, Japan
Tel.: (81) 197 44 2663
Web Site: http://www.aisin-tohoku.co.jp
Exhaust System Parts Mfr
N.A.I.C.S.: 336390

At India Auto Parts Pvt. Ltd.   (1)
No 33 & 34 Ramanagara Bidadi Industrial
Area, Karnataka, 562109, India
Tel.: (91) 80492000
Web Site: https://atiautoparts.co.in
Industrial Machinery Parts Mfr
N.A.I.C.S.: 335999

Awquis Japan Co., Ltd...   (1)
3-2-7 Shimizucho, Takahama, 444-1312,
Aichi, Japan
Tel.: (81) 566527751
Air Terrain Vehicles Repair & Rebuilding
Services
N.A.I.C.S.: 811198

CVTEC Co., Ltd.   (1)
2-2-65 Midorigahama, Tahara, 444-3401,
Aichi, Japan
Tel.: (81) 531 24 1329
Web Site: http://www.cvtec.co.jp
Industrial Belts Mfr
N.A.I.C.S.: 333922

**Elite Sewing Machine Mfg. Co.,
Ltd.**   (1)
3 3rd Road Taichung Industrial Park, Taic-
hung, Taiwan
Tel.: (886) 423591111
Web Site: http://www.twelite.com.tw
Rev.: $102,256,853
Emp.: 658
Household Sewing Machines & Automotive
Parts Mfr & Sales
N.A.I.C.S.: 335220

Equos Research Co., Ltd.   (1)
1-18-13 Sotokanda Chiyoda-ku, Chiyoda-
ku, Tokyo, 101-0021, Japan
Tel.: (81) 3 3255 9766
Web Site: http://www.equos.co.jp
Sales Range: $25-49.9 Million
Emp.: 45
Automobile Parts Mfr
N.A.I.C.S.: 336390
Syouji Yokoyama (Pres)

FT TECHNO EUROPE GmbH   (1)
Schleussnerstrasse 56, Neu-Isenburg,
63263, Hesse, Germany
Tel.: (49) 61023678951
Web Site: http://www.fttechno-europe.de
Sales Range: $25-49.9 Million
Emp.: 1
Automotive Parts Repair Services
N.A.I.C.S.: 811198
Masao Kawauchi (Gen Mgr)

FT TECHNO OF AMERICA, LLC   (1)
1750 Smith Rd, Fowlerville, MI 48836
Tel.: (517) 223-6777
Web Site: http://www.ftt-a.com
Sales Range: $25-49.9 Million
Emp.: 16
Vehicle Performance Testing Services
N.A.I.C.S.: 488999
Tetsuya Takano (VP)

FT Techno Inc.   (1)
918-11 Sakashita Mitsukuricho, Toyota,
470-0424, Aichi, Japan
Tel.: (81) 565 75 1441
Web Site: http://www.fttechno.co.jp
Automotive Parts Repair & Maintenance
Services
N.A.I.C.S.: 811198

**HOSEI BRAKE INDUSTRY CO.,
LTD.**   (1)
10 Michigami Kazue-cho, Toyota, 470-1293,
Aichi, Japan
Tel.: (81) 565 21 1213
Web Site: http://www.hosei.co.jp
Emp.: 1,280
Brake System Mfr
N.A.I.C.S.: 336340
Shizuo Shimanuki (Pres)

Plant (Domestic):

**HOSEI BRAKE INDUSTRY CO.,
LTD. - Okazaki Factory**   (2)
183 Ogoya-nishi Hashime-cho, Okazaki,
444-0909, Aichi, Japan
Tel.: (81) 564 32 3425
Web Site: http://www.hosei.co.jp
Brake System Mfr
N.A.I.C.S.: 336340

**HOSEI BRAKE INDUSTRY CO.,
LTD. - Takahama Factory**   (2)
1-2 Shinden-cho, Takahama, 444-1301,
Aichi, Japan
Tel.: (81) 566 53 0101
Web Site: http://www.hosei.co.jp
Brake System Mfr
N.A.I.C.S.: 336340

Hekinan Unso Co., Ltd.   (1)
3 Tenno Takaokashinmachi, Toyota, 473-
0921, Aichi, Japan
Tel.: (81) 565527728
Web Site: http://www.hekiun.co.jp
Truck Transportation Services
N.A.I.C.S.: 488999
Fumihiko Ishiguro (Pres)

IMRA Europe S.A.   (1)
220 Rue Albert Caquot Sophia Antipolis,
Valbonne, 06914, France   (100%)
Tel.: (33) 493957373
Web Site: http://www.imra-europe.com
Sales Range: $50-74.9 Million
Emp.: 25
N.A.I.C.S.: 336340
Koji Kiryu (Pres)

IMRA Material R&D Co., Ltd.   (1)
2-1 Asahimachi, Kariya, 448-0032, Aichi,
Japan
Tel.: (81) 566249380
Automobile Parts Mfr
N.A.I.C.S.: 336390

Konan Kogyo Co., Ltd.   (1)
18 Kotobuki, Ikoma-cho, Toyota, 473-0928,

Aichi, Japan
Tel.: (81) 566211450
Web Site: https://www.aisin.com
Automobile Product Distr
N.A.I.C.S.: 423120

Kotobuki Industry Co., Ltd.   (1)
148 Yokoyama Ikomacho, Toyota, 473-
0928, Aichi, Japan
Tel.: (81) 565 57 2011
Web Site: http://www.kotobukigiken.co.jp
Door Hinge & Window Regulator Mfr
N.A.I.C.S.: 336390

Liberty Mexicana S.A. de C.V.   (1)
Km 15 100 Carretera Mexico Laredo, Santa
Clara, 554000, Estado De Mexico,
Mexico   (100%)
Tel.: (52) 5555692333
Sales Range: $25-49.9 Million
Emp.: 94
Mfr of Sewing Machines for Home & Indus-
trial Use
N.A.I.C.S.: 335220

P.T. Aisin Indonesia   (1)
East Jakarta Industrial Park Plot 5J South,
Cikarang, Bekasi, 17550,
Indonesia   (100%)
Tel.: (62) 8970909
Web Site: https://www.aisinindonesia.co.id
Sales Range: $300-349.9 Million
Emp.: 1,000
N.A.I.C.S.: 336370

Sanetsu Transport Co., Ltd.   (1)
1230-1 Nyuzen-machi, Shimoniikawa-gun,
Toyama, 939-0653, Japan
Tel.: (81) 765 72 2121
Web Site: http://www.sanetsu-u.com
Truck Transportation Services
N.A.I.C.S.: 488999

Shinko Seiki Co., Ltd.   (1)
708-8 Ishimaru, Takaoka, 934-0095,
Toyama, Japan
Tel.: (81) 766 84 8196
Web Site: http://www.shinko-seiki.co.jp
Industrial Mold Mfr
N.A.I.C.S.: 331511

Shiroki Corporation   (1)
35-1 Shimono Ichiba Chigiri-cho, Toyokawa,
442-8501, Aichi, Japan
Tel.: (81) 533 84 4691
Web Site: http://www.shiroki.co.jp
Sales Range: $1-4.9 Billion
Automobile Parts Mfr
N.A.I.C.S.: 336390
Takuo Matsui (Pres)

Subsidiary (Domestic):

Kyushu Shiroki Co., Ltd.   (2)
2142-1 Kukioka Maedaaza, Yawatahigashi-
ku, Kitakyushu, 805-0058, Japan
Tel.: (81) 936636325
Web Site: https://www.aisin.com
Motor Vehicle Parts Mfr
N.A.I.C.S.: 336390

Subsidiary (Non-US):

**Shiroki Corporation (Thailand)
Ltd.**   (2)
Amatanakorn Industrial Estate 700/325 Moo
6 Bangna-Trad Road, Bangpakong Km 57
T Donhuaroh A Muangchonburi, Chon Buri,
20000, Thailand
Tel.: (66) 38 458 850 2
Web Site: http://www.shiroki.co.th
Automotive Component Mfr & Distr
N.A.I.C.S.: 339999

Subsidiary (US):

Shiroki North America, Inc.   (2)
1111 West Broad St, Smithville, TN 37166
Tel.: (615) 597-8870
Web Site: http://www.shiroki-na.com
Emp.: 329
Automotive Component Mfr & Distr
N.A.I.C.S.: 336390
James Austin (Head-Info Sys)

Subsidiary (Domestic):

Shiroki-GA, LLC   (3)
1300 Veterans Dr, Dalton, GA 30721-8692
Tel.: (706) 217-6440
Web Site: http://www.shiroki-na.com

AISIN Corporation—(Continued)

Emp.: 334
Automotive Component Mfr & Distr
N.A.I.C.S.: 336390
Ginger Sels *(Plant Mgr)*

Shiroki-GT, LLC (3)
165 Spicer Dr, Gordonsville, TN 38563
Tel.: (615) 683-3500
Web Site: http://www.shiroki-na.com
Emp.: 147
Automotive Component Mfr & Distr
N.A.I.C.S.: 336390

Subsidiary (Domestic):

Shiroki Seikei Co., Ltd. (2)
42-1 Misasaki Nagakusacho, Toyokawa,
442-0003, Japan
Tel.: (81) 533842521
Web Site: http://www.aisin.com
Machine Tool Mfr & Distr
N.A.I.C.S.: 333517

Siam Aisin Co., Ltd. (1)
235 Moo 7 Tha Tum District, Simahaphot,
Prachin Buri, 25140, Thailand
Tel.: (66) 37208612
Web Site: http://www.siamaisin.co.ch
Sales Range: $600-649.9 Million
Emp.: 2,000
N.A.I.C.S.: 336340

**Tangshan Aisin Automotive Parts Co.,
Ltd**
No 297 Weiguo North Road High Tech De-
velopment Zone, Tangshan, 063020, Hebei,
China
Tel.: (86) 3153852168
Automobile Parts Mfr
N.A.I.C.S.: 336390

Tangshan Aisin Gear Co., Ltd. (1)
Feng Run Qu, Hebei, Tangshan, Hebei,
China
Tel.: (86) 3153086114
Web Site: http://www.tagc.com.cn
Auto Parts Development, Design, Manufac-
turing & Sales
N.A.I.C.S.: 336340

Technova, Inc. (1)
Imperial Hotel Tower 13F 1 1 Uchisaiwaicho
1 Chome, Chiyoda Ku, Tokyo, 100 0011,
Japan **(100%)**
Tel.: (81) 335082280
Web Site: http://www.technova.co.jp
Sales Range: $50-74.9 Million
Emp.: 20
N.A.I.C.S.: 336340
Atsushi Kamei *(Pres)*

**Tianjin Aisin Automobile Parts Co.,
Ltd.**
8 BeiCang Road, Tianjin, BeiChan District,
China
Tel.: (86) 22 2681 1524
Web Site: http://www.aisinworld.com
Sales Range: $300-349.9 Million
Emp.: 620
Manufacture & Sale of Automotive Parts
N.A.I.C.S.: 336340
Masahiko Komuro *(Pres)*

Tonamino Kogyo Co., Ltd. (1)
320-1 Shogawamachi Goka, Tonami, 932-
0313, Toyama, Japan
Tel.: (81) 763 82 5225
Web Site: http://www.tonamino.co.jp
Automobile Parts Mfr
N.A.I.C.S.: 336390

YCK (THAILAND) CO., LTD. (1)
74/4 Moo 7 Bangbuathong Suphanburi
Road Laharn, Amphur Bangbuathong, Non-
thaburi, 11110, Thailand
Tel.: (66) 2925 5164
Automobile Parts Mfr
N.A.I.C.S.: 336390

Yamagata Clutch Co., Ltd. (1)
43 Shonan Shimo-Yamazoe, Tsuruoka, 997-
0341, Yamagata, Japan
Tel.: (81) 235572881
Automobile Parts Mfr
N.A.I.C.S.: 336390

AISINO CORPORATION
No 18A Xingshikou Road Haidian

District, Beijing, 100195, China
Tel.: (86) 1088896666
Web Site: http://www.aisino.com
Year Founded: 2000
600271—(SHG)
Rev.: $3,602,815,883
Assets: $3,493,865,188
Liabilities: $925,198,420
Net Worth: $2,568,666,769
Earnings: $156,997,351
Emp.: 18,000
Fiscal Year-end: 12/31/21
Information Technology Services
N.A.I.C.S.: 541512
Tianhui Ma *(Chm)*

Subsidiaries:

**Beijing Aerospace Golden Card
Co.** (1)
Aisino Science Park 18A Xingshikou Road,
Haidian District, Beijing, 100195, China
Tel.: (86) 1088896951
Tax Preparation Services
N.A.I.C.S.: 541213

SmartTech Production Ltd. (1)
Unit 908-911 9/F 61-63 Au Pui Wan Street,
Yale Industrial Centre, Fotan, China (Hong
Kong)
Tel.: (852) 26739918
Web Site: http://www.smarttech.com.hk
Plastic Card Product Mfr
N.A.I.C.S.: 326199

AIT CORPORATION
15F Sakaisuji-Honmachi-Center Bldg
2-1-6 Honmachi, Chuo-ku, Osaka,
541-0053, Japan
Tel.: (81) 662603450
Web Site: https://www.ait-jp.com
Year Founded: 1988
9381—(TKS)
Rev.: $580,132,080
Assets: $227,634,880
Liabilities: $90,817,760
Net Worth: $136,817,120
Earnings: $22,912,560
Emp.: 200
Fiscal Year-end: 02/28/22
Freight Forwarding & Ship Brokerage
Services
N.A.I.C.S.: 488510
Hidekazu Yagura *(Pres & CEO)*

Subsidiaries:

AIT (HKG) Limited (1)
Unit 601 6/F Mirror Tower 61 Mody Road
TST East, Kowloon, China (Hong Kong)
Tel.: (852) 29560081
Logistics & Distribution Services
N.A.I.C.S.: 541614

**Ait International Logistics (Shanghai)
Co., Ltd.** (1)
Room No 1206 No 500 Guangdong Road,
Shanghai, China
Tel.: (86) 2163621088
Logistic Services
N.A.I.C.S.: 541614

**Ait International Logistics (Taiwan)
Co., Ltd.** (1)
3F No 146 Song Jiang Rd, ZhongShan
Dist, Taipei, 10458, Taiwan
Tel.: (886) 225421122
Logistic Services
N.A.I.C.S.: 541614

Aitc Logistics (Vietnam) Co., Ltd. (1)
8f Phuoc Thanh Bldg 199 Dien Bien Phu
Phuong 15, Quan Binh Thanh, Ho Chi Minh
City, Vietnam
Tel.: (84) 2838408225
Logistic Services
N.A.I.C.S.: 541614

Nisshin Transportation Co., Ltd. (1)
1-27-12 Nishikujo, Konohana-ku, Osaka,
554-0012, Japan
Tel.: (81) 64624809
Logistics Transportation Services
N.A.I.C.S.: 488510

AITHENUTRIGENE CO.
630ho 42 Changeop-ro, Sujeong-gu,
Seongnam, Gyeonggi-do, Korea
(South)
Tel.: (82) 16665950
Web Site:
    https://en.aithenutrigene.com
Year Founded: 2012
311960—(KRS)
Medical Device Mfr
N.A.I.C.S.: 339112

**AITKEN CHEVROLET BUICK
GMC**
51 Queensway E, Simcoe, N3Y 4M5,
ON, Canada
Tel.: (519) 426-1680
Web Site: http://www.aitkenchev.ca
Year Founded: 1922
Rev.: $12,751,926
Emp.: 70
New & Used Car Dealers
N.A.I.C.S.: 441110
Bradly D. Scherer *(Mng Partner)*

AITKEN SPENCE PLC
Aitken Spence Tower 305 Vauxhall
Street, 2, Colombo, 2, Sri Lanka
Tel.: (94) 112308308   LK
Web Site:
    https://www.aitkenspence.com
SPEN—(COL)
Rev.: $326,568,100
Assets: $713,483,872
Liabilities: $426,489,375
Net Worth: $286,994,498
Earnings: $26,884,488
Emp.: 7,408
Fiscal Year-end: 03/31/23
Tourism, Cargo Handling, Printing &
Packaging, Plantations, Property De-
velopment & Management Services;
Manufacture of Clothing
N.A.I.C.S.: 561520
Deshamanya H. S. Jayawardena
(Chm)

Subsidiaries:

Aitken Spence Cargo (Pvt) Ltd. (1)
3rd Floor The Landmark Building 385 Galle
Road, 03, Colombo, Sri Lanka
Tel.: (94) 115301303
Web Site: http://www.aoecargo.lk
Logistic & Freight Forwarding Services
N.A.I.C.S.: 488510

**Aitken Spence Elevators (Pvt)
Ltd** (1)
9th Floor AitkenSpence Tower 2 Vauxhall
St, Colombo, Sri Lanka
Tel.: (94) 776189639
Web Site: https://aitkenspenceelevators.lk
Elevator Mfr
N.A.I.C.S.: 333921

**Aitken Spence Hotel Holdings
PLC** (1)
No 315 Vauxhall Street, 2, Colombo, 2, Sri
Lanka
Tel.: (94) 112308308
Web Site:
    https://www.aitkenspencehotels.com
Rev.: $130,716,550
Assets: $540,223,364
Liabilities: $391,012,935
Net Worth: $149,710,429
Earnings: $5,502,503
Emp.: 2,943
Fiscal Year-end: 03/31/2022
Home Management Services
N.A.I.C.S.: 721110
Chrishanthus Mohan Susith Jayawickrama
(Co-Mng Dir)

**Aitken Spence Hotel Managements
(Pvt) Ltd.** (1)
Tel.: (94) 112308408
Hotel Services
N.A.I.C.S.: 721110
Stasshani Jayawardena *(Chm)*

Aitken Spence Shipping Ltd. (1)

315 Vauxhall Street, Colombo, Sri Lanka
Tel.: (94) 112308100
Logistic Services
N.A.I.C.S.: 488510

**Aitken Spence Technologies (Pvt)
Ltd.** (1)
Aitken Spence Tower I 305 Vauxhall Street,
Colombo, 2, Sri Lanka
Tel.: (94) 11 230 8308
Web Site:
    https://www.aitkenspencetech.com
Software Development Services
N.A.I.C.S.: 541511
Dhammika Dasa *(CEO)*

Fiji Ports Terminal Ltd. (1)
Kings Wharf Usher St, Suva, Fiji
Port Terminal Services
N.A.I.C.S.: 488310
Hasmukh Patel *(Chm)*

Global Parcel Delivery (Pvt) Ltd. (1)
316 K Cyril C Perera Mawatha, 13, Co-
lombo, Sri Lanka
Tel.: (94) 115308444
Web Site: https://www.gpd.lk
Global Delivery Services
N.A.I.C.S.: 492110

AIV GMBH + CO. KG
Tatschenweg 1, 74078, Heilbronn,
Germany
Tel.: (49) 71315930
Web Site: http://www.aiv.de
Year Founded: 1976
Rev.: $19,181,725
Emp.: 90
Cabling & Accessory Distr
N.A.I.C.S.: 517111
Christian Trapl *(Mng Dir)*

**AIXIN LIFE INTERNATIONAL,
INC.**
Hongxing International Business
Building 2 14th FL, No 69 Qingyun
South Ave Jinjiang District, Chengdu,
Sichuan, China
Tel.: (86) 2886691072   CO
Year Founded: 1987
AIXN—(OTCQX)
Rev.: $2,708,560
Assets: $5,050,884
Liabilities: $5,517,072
Net Worth: ($466,188)
Earnings: ($6,369,245)
Emp.: 163
Fiscal Year-end: 12/31/22
Blank Check Company; Nutritional
Products Mfr
N.A.I.C.S.: 424490
Quanzhong Lin *(Pres, CEO, Founder
& Chm)*

Subsidiaries:

**Chengdu AiXin Zhonghong Biological
Technology Co., Ltd.** (1)
Hongxing Intl Business Bldg 2 14th Floor
No 69 Qingyun South Ave, Jinjiang District,
Chengdu, Sichuan, China **(100%)**
Tel.: (86) 313 673 2526
Nutritional Products Marketer & Whslr
N.A.I.C.S.: 424210
Quanzhong Lin *(Chm & CEO)*

AIXTRON SE
Dornkaulstr 2, 52134, Herzogenrath,
Germany
Tel.: (49) 240790300
Web Site: https://www.aixtron.com
Year Founded: 1983
AIXA—(MUN)
Rev.: $695,305,636
Assets: $1,136,699,094
Liabilities: $278,583,672
Net Worth: $858,115,422
Earnings: $160,259,847
Emp.: 1,029
Fiscal Year-end: 12/31/23
Semiconductor Devices Mfr
N.A.I.C.S.: 334413

Bernd Schulte *(Co-Pres & Member-Exec Bd)*

Subsidiaries:

AIXTRON Inc. **(1)**
1139 Karlstad Dr, Sunnyvale, CA 94089-2117
Tel.: (408) 747-7120
Sales Range: $25-49.9 Million
Emp.: 100
Capital Equipment & Processes Designer, Mfr & Marketer For Advanced Semiconductor Manufacturing
N.A.I.C.S.: 332410
Randy Singh *(VP-Fin)*

APEVA SE **(1)**
Dornkaulstr 2, 52134, Herzogenrath, Germany
Tel.: (49) 240790300
Web Site: http://www.apeva.de
Semiconductor Equipment Mfr
N.A.I.C.S.: 333242
Kim Schindelhauer *(Chm)*

Aixtron China Ltd. **(1)**
Rm 1101 Nan Fung Tower No 1568 Huashan Road, Shanghai, 200052, China
Tel.: (86) 2164453226
Semiconductor Equipment Mfr
N.A.I.C.S.: 333242
Tony Weng *(Mgr-Sourcing)*

Aixtron KK **(1)**
9F Daiwa Shinagawa North Bld 1-8-11 Kitashinagawa, Shinagawa-ku, Tokyo, 140-0001, Japan
Tel.: (81) 357810931
Semiconductor Equipment Mfr
N.A.I.C.S.: 333242

Aixtron Korea Co. Ltd. **(1)**
201 2F GWell Estate 160 Dongtanbanseok-ro, Hwaseong, 18454, Gyeonggi-do, Korea (South)
Tel.: (82) 313713000
Semiconductor Equipment Mfr
N.A.I.C.S.: 333242

Aixtron Ltd. **(1)**
Anderson Road Buckingway Business Park, Swavesey, Cambridge, CB24 4FQ, United Kingdom
Tel.: (44) 1223519444
Semiconductor Equipment Mfr
N.A.I.C.S.: 333242
Matt Benham *(Ops Mgr)*

Aixtron Taiwan Co. Ltd. **(1)**
6F-1 No 3 Lane 91 Dong Mei Road, Hsinchu, 30070, Taiwan
Tel.: (886) 35712678
Semiconductor Equipment Mfr
N.A.I.C.S.: 333242

AIZAWA SECURITIES GROUP CO., LTD.
Tokyo Shiodome Building 1-9-1 Higashi-Shimbashi, Minato-ku, Tokyo, 105-7307, Japan
Tel.: (81) 368527744
Web Site: https://www.aizawa-group.jp
Year Founded: 1918
8708—(TKS)
Rev.: $125,457,800
Assets: $820,426,590
Liabilities: $432,703,820
Net Worth: $387,722,770
Earnings: $19,664,750
Fiscal Year-end: 03/31/24
Security Services
N.A.I.C.S.: 561621
Takuya Aizawa *(Pres)*

Subsidiaries:

AIZAWA Investments Co., Ltd. **(1)**
Tokyo Shiodome Building 1-9-1 Higashi-Shimbashi, Minato-ku, Tokyo, 105-7307, Japan
Tel.: (81) 368527742
Web Site: https://www.aizawa-inv.co.jp
Real Estate Related Business Services
N.A.I.C.S.: 531390

Aizawa Asset Management Co., Ltd. **(1)**
7th Floor Tokyo Shiodome Building 1-9-1 Higashi-Shimbashi, Minato-ku, Tokyo, 105-7307, Japan
Tel.: (81) 362639690
Web Site: https://www2.aizawa-am.co.jp
Investment Advice Services
N.A.I.C.S.: 525110

Asuka Asset Management Co., Ltd. **(1)**
7th Floor Tokyo Shiodome Building 1-9-1 Higashi-Shimbashi, Minato-ku, Tokyo, 105-7307, Japan
Tel.: (81) 335009800
Web Site: https://www.aizawa-am.co.jp
Investment Management Service
N.A.I.C.S.: 523940
Toshihiro Hirao *(Pres)*

Japan Securities Incorporated **(1)**
7th floor Tower 1 Capital Place Building 29 Lieu Giai, Ngoc Khanh Ward Ba Dinh District, Hanoi, Vietnam
Tel.: (84) 2437911818
Web Site: https://www.japan-sec.vn
Financial Services
N.A.I.C.S.: 523999
Tsuyoshi Imai *(Chm & Gen Dir)*

Life Design Partners Co., Ltd. **(1)**
Tokyo Shiodome Building 1-9-1 Higashi-Shimbashi, Minato-ku, Tokyo, 105-7307, Japan
Tel.: (81) 368527743
Web Site: https://www.l-d-p.co.jp
Fire Insurance Services
N.A.I.C.S.: 524113

AJ ADVANCE TECHNOLOGY PUBLIC COMPANY LIMITED
427/2 Rama 2 Road Kwang Samaedum Khet Bangkhuntian, Bangkok, 10150, Thailand
Tel.: (66) 24516888
Web Site: http://www.ajthai.com
Year Founded: 2001
AJA—(THA)
Rev.: $9,525,134
Assets: $25,796,145
Liabilities: $3,705,208
Net Worth: $22,090,936
Earnings: ($1,111,278)
Emp.: 63
Fiscal Year-end: 12/31/23
Electric Appliances Importer & Distr
N.A.I.C.S.: 423620
Chirakom Kitiyakara *(Chm)*

Subsidiaries:

Reisen Energy Co., Ltd. **(1)**
Tashan Industry Zone, Meilin Sub-District Ninghai County, Ningbo, Zhejiang, China
Tel.: (86) 57459953588
Web Site: https://en.risenenergy.com
Emp.: 10,000
Solar Cell Mfr & Distr
N.A.I.C.S.: 334413

AJ BELL PLC.
4 Exchange Quay Salford Quays, Manchester, M5 3EE, United Kingdom
Tel.: (44) 3454089100   UK
Web Site: https://www.ajbell.co.uk
AJB—(LSE)
Rev.: $360,214,336
Assets: $386,203,672
Liabilities: $113,489,441
Net Worth: $272,714,231
Earnings: $112,700,670
Fiscal Year-end: 09/30/24
Pension Services
N.A.I.C.S.: 524292
Michael Summersgill *(CFO & Member-Mgmt Bd)*

Subsidiaries:

AJ Bell Media Limited **(1)**
1st Floor 49 Southwark Bridge Road, London, SE1 9HH, United Kingdom

Tel.: (44) 2073784424
Web Site: https://www.media.ajbell.co.uk
Financial Services
N.A.I.C.S.: 523940

AJ Bell Securities Limited **(1)**
4 Exchange Quay Salford Quays, Manchester, M5 3EE, Kent, United Kingdom
Tel.: (44) 345 408 9100
Web Site: https://www.ajbell.co.uk
Emp.: 900
Securities Dealing
N.A.I.C.S.: 523150

MoneyAM Limited **(1)**
1st Floor 49 Southwark Bridge Road, London, SE1 9HH, United Kingdom
Tel.: (44) 3454089100
Web Site: https://media.ajbell.co.uk
Financial Services
N.A.I.C.S.: 523940

AJ NETWORKS CO LTD
AJ Building Jeongui-ro 8-gil, Songpa-gu, Seoul, 05836, Korea (South)
Tel.: (82) 15880053
Web Site:
https://www.ajnetworks.co.kr
Year Founded: 2000
095570—(KRS)
Rev.: $926,817,932
Assets: $1,136,268,600
Liabilities: $858,702,159
Net Worth: $277,566,441
Earnings: $6,726,233
Emp.: 561
Fiscal Year-end: 12/31/22
Equipment Rental Services
N.A.I.C.S.: 532420
Son Sam-Dal *(CEO)*

AJ POWER LIMITED
1 Charlestown Drive Carn Industrial Area, Craigavon, BT63 5GA, United Kingdom
Tel.: (44) 28 3836 1000
Web Site: http://www.ajpower.net
Year Founded: 2003
Sales Range: $50-74.9 Million
Emp.: 74
Diesel Generator Mfr
N.A.I.C.S.: 335312
Ashley Pigott *(Founder & Mng Dir)*

AJACCIO AUTOMOBILES
Vignetta Campo Dell Oro, 20090, Ajaccio, Corse, France
Tel.: (33) 495239090
Rev.: $21,300,000
Emp.: 66
New & Used Car Dealers
N.A.I.C.S.: 441110
Francois Fanchi *(Dir-Admin)*

AJANTA PHARMA LIMITED
Ajanta House Charkop Kandivili West, Mumbai, 400 067, India
Tel.: (91) 2266061000
Web Site:
https://www.ajantapharma.com
532331—(BOM)
Rev.: $471,835,455
Assets: $553,586,670
Liabilities: $108,004,260
Net Worth: $445,582,410
Earnings: $97,280,820
Emp.: 7,234
Fiscal Year-end: 03/31/22
Pharmaceuticals Product Mfr
N.A.I.C.S.: 325412
Yogesh M. Agrawal *(Co-Mng Dir)*

Subsidiaries:

Ajanta Pharma (Mauritius) Limited **(1)**
BPML Building, Goodlands, Mauritius
Tel.: (230) 2830334
Pharmaceuticals Product Mfr
N.A.I.C.S.: 325412

Ajanta Pharma Philippines Inc. **(1)**
1702 AXA Life Center 1286 Sen Gil Puyat Avenue corner Tindalo Street, San Antonio Village, Makati, 12000, Metro Manila, Philippines
Tel.: (63) 28447350
Web Site: https://www.ajantapharma.com.ph
Pharmaceuticals Product Mfr
N.A.I.C.S.: 325412
Sam Gioskos *(Pres)*

Ajanta Pharma USA Inc. **(1)**
1 Grande Commons 440 US Hwy 22 E Ste 150, Bridgewater, NJ 08807
Tel.: (908) 252-1165
Web Site:
https://www.ajantapharmausa.com
Pharmaceutical Drug Mfr
N.A.I.C.S.: 325412
Ramesh Jhawar *(Pres)*

AJANTA SOYA LIMITED
12th Floor Bigjos Tower Netaji Subhash Place, Wazirpur District Centre, Delhi, 110034, India
Tel.: (91) 1142515151
Web Site:
https://www.ajantasoya.com
Year Founded: 1992
519216—(BOM)
Rev.: $184,316,046
Assets: $36,110,611
Liabilities: $19,294,712
Net Worth: $16,815,899
Earnings: $5,760,204
Emp.: 89
Fiscal Year-end: 03/31/22
Edible Oil Mfr
N.A.I.C.S.: 311224
Sushil Goyal *(Mng Dir)*

AJAX RESOURCES PLC
Salisbury House London Wall, London, EC2M 5PS, United Kingdom
Tel.: (44) 2081466289   UK
Web Site:
https://www.ajaxresources.com
Year Founded: 2021
AJAX—(LSE)
Miscellaneous Financial Investment Activities
N.A.I.C.S.: 523999
Ippolito Cattaneo *(CEO)*

AJCON GLOBAL SERVICES LTD.
408 Express Zone A Wing Cello Sonal Realty Near Oberoi Mall, Western Express Highway Goregaon East, Mumbai, 400063, India
Tel.: (91) 2267160400
Web Site:
https://www.ajcononline.com
511692—(BOM)
Rev.: $5,690,972
Assets: $4,759,236
Liabilities: $1,883,291
Net Worth: $2,875,946
Earnings: $298,048
Emp.: 35
Fiscal Year-end: 03/31/22
Financial Advisory Services
N.A.I.C.S.: 523940
Ashok Kumar Ajmera *(Chm & Mng Dir)*

Subsidiaries:

Kanchanmanik Securities Private Limited **(1)**
101 Samarth Lt PN Kotnis Road Off Hinduja Hospital Mahim W, Mumbai, 400016, India
Tel.: (91) 2267160400
Financial Services
N.A.I.C.S.: 523940

AJEL LTD.
106 Link Plaza Commercial Complex New Link Road Oshiwara, Jogesh-

AJEL LTD.

Ajel Ltd.—(Continued)

wari West, Mumbai, 400 102, Maharashtra, India
Tel.: (91) 912226398888
Web Site: https://www.ajel.in
530713—(BOM)
Rev.: $565,992
Assets: $3,170,725
Liabilities: $1,201,007
Net Worth: $1,889,688
Earnings: $12,938
Emp.: 18
Fiscal Year-end: 03/31/22
Information Technology Consulting Services
N.A.I.C.S.: 541512
Srinivasa Reddy Arikatla (Chm & Mng Dir)

Subsidiaries:

Ajel Technologies Inc **(1)**
45 Brunswick Ave Ste 222, Edison, NJ 08817
Tel.: (732) 476-6000
Web Site: http://www.ajel.com
Information Technology Services
N.A.I.C.S.: 541511

AJIAL REAL ESTATE ENTERTAINMENT COMPANY K.S.C.C.

Al Andalus Mall 16th Floor Hawally, PO Box 22448, Safat, Kuwait, 13085, Kuwait
Tel.: (965) 1886889
Web Site: https://www.ajial-realestate.com
Year Founded: 1996
AREEC—(KUW)
Rev.: $19,376,593
Assets: $556,410,624
Liabilities: $123,659,976
Net Worth: $432,750,648
Earnings: $13,014,641
Emp.: 30
Fiscal Year-end: 12/31/22
Real Estate & Entertainment Services
N.A.I.C.S.: 531390

AJINEXTEK CO., LTD.

27 Seongseo Industrial Complex-ro 11-gil, Dalseo-gu, Daegu, 42714, Korea (South)
Tel.: (82) 535933700
Web Site: https://www.ajinextek.com
Year Founded: 1995
059120—(KRS)
Rev.: $27,375,392
Assets: $38,662,994
Liabilities: $5,192,355
Net Worth: $33,470,638
Earnings: $1,250,196
Emp.: 94
Fiscal Year-end: 12/31/22
Semiconductor Devices Mfr
N.A.I.C.S.: 334413

AJINOMOTO COMPANY, INC.

15-1 Kyobashi 1-chome, Chuo-ku, Tokyo, 104-8315, Japan
Tel.: (81) 352508111 **JP**
Web Site: https://www.ajinomoto.com
Year Founded: 1909
2802—(TKS)
Rev.: $9,513,316,910
Assets: $11,729,411,950
Liabilities: $5,885,748,910
Net Worth: $5,843,663,040
Earnings: $575,869,810
Emp.: 34,862
Fiscal Year-end: 03/31/24
Food Products Distr
N.A.I.C.S.: 424490
Masaya Tochio (Sr VP & Gen Mgr-Corp Svc Div-Global)

Subsidiaries:

AJINOMOTO FOODS EUROPE
S.A.S **(1)**

32 rue de Guersant, 75017, Paris, France
Tel.: (33) 143180586
Sales Range: $25-49.9 Million
Emp.: 8
Food Products Mfr
N.A.I.C.S.: 311999

Subsidiary (Non-US):

Ajinomoto Foods Europe SAS **(2)**
Ludwig-Erhard-Strasse 20, 20459, Hamburg, Germany **(100%)**
Tel.: (49) 403749360
Web Site: http://www.ajinomoto.de
Sales Range: $25-49.9 Million
Fruits, Vegetables & Dressings
N.A.I.C.S.: 311421

AJINOMOTO KOREA, INC. **(1)**
7th floor Hanju Building 7 Gukjegeumyung-ro 2-gil, Yeongdeungpo-gu, Seoul, 137-810, Korea (South)
Tel.: (82) 2 3443 0010
Web Site: http://www.ajinomoto.co.kr
Emp.: 16
Food Products Mfr & Distr
N.A.I.C.S.: 311999

AJINOMOTO LOGISTICS CORPORATION **(1)**
Tel.: (81) 355423636
Logistics Consulting Servies
N.A.I.C.S.: 541614
Hiroyuki Tanaka (Pres & CEO)

AJINOMOTO TAIWAN INC. **(1)**
15F-2 No 178 Fu-Hsing N Rd, Taipei, Taiwan
Tel.: (886) 2 8712 2069
Web Site: http://www.ajinomoto.com.tw
Food Products Mfr
N.A.I.C.S.: 311999

Ajinomoto (China) Co., Ltd. **(1)**
Rm A-1008 North of SOHO Shangdu 8 Dongdaqiao Rd, Chaoyang, Beijing, 100020, China
Tel.: (86) 1065880220
Web Site: http://www.ajinomoto.com.cn
Food Mfr & Marketer
N.A.I.C.S.: 311421

Ajinomoto (Malaysia) Berhad **(1)**
No 1 Persiaran Teknologi 6 Techpark 2 Enstek, Petaling, 71760, Kuala Lumpur, Malaysia **(100%)**
Tel.: (60) 7377000
Web Site: https://www.ajinomoto.com.my
Sales Range: $100-124.9 Million
Emp.: 400
Spices & Flavorings
N.A.I.C.S.: 311421

Ajinomoto (Singapore) Pte. Ltd. **(1)**
460 Alexandra Road 13-04/05/06 mTower, Singapore, 119963, Singapore **(100%)**
Tel.: (65) 62572022
Web Site: http://www.ajinomoto.com.sg
Sales Range: $25-49.9 Million
Emp.: 50
Spices & Flavorings
N.A.I.C.S.: 311421

Ajinomoto Bakery Co., Ltd. **(1)**
Tel.: (81) 352508370
Web Site: http://www.ajinomoto-bakery.co.jp
Bakery Product Mfr & Distr
N.A.I.C.S.: 311812

Ajinomoto Betagro Frozen Foods (Thailand) Co., Ltd. **(1)**
Betagro Twr N Pk 323 Vibhavadi Rangsit Rd, Bangkok, 10210, Thailand **(50%)**
Tel.: (66) 29550555
Web Site: http://www.betagro.com
Sales Range: $25-49.9 Million
Frozen Process Chicken Production
N.A.I.C.S.: 311412

Ajinomoto Betagro Specialty Foods (Thailand) Co., Ltd. **(1)**
323 Moo 6, Lak si, Bangkok, 10210, Thailand **(51%)**
Tel.: (66) 28338000
Frozen Food Products Mfr & Distr
N.A.I.C.S.: 311412

Ajinomoto Bioitalia S.p.A. **(1)**
Via Gramsci 1, 45013, Bottrighe, Italy **(100%)**
Tel.: (39) 0426995311

Web Site: http://www.ajinomoto-europe.com
Sales Range: $25-49.9 Million
Emp.: 90
N.A.I.C.S.: 311421

Ajinomoto Biolatina Industria e Comercio Ltda. **(1)**
Rua Joaquim Tavora 541, 04015 001, Sao Paulo, SP, Brazil **(90%)**
Tel.: (55) 1155796971
Web Site: http://www.lisina.com.br
Sales Range: $25-49.9 Million
Emp.: 15
N.A.I.C.S.: 311421

Ajinomoto Cambrooke, Inc. **(1)**
4 Copeland Dr, Ayer, MA 01432
Tel.: (508) 782-2300
Web Site: https://www.cambrooke.com
Protein Food & Supplement Distr
N.A.I.C.S.: 424490
Howard Lossing (CEO)

Ajinomoto Co., (Hong Kong) Ltd. **(1)**
2102 21st Floor Bangkok Bank Building 14-20 Bonham Strand West, Sheung Wan, Hong Kong, China (Hong Kong) **(100%)**
Tel.: (852) 25342888
Web Site: https://www.ajinomoto.com.hk
Sales Range: $25-49.9 Million
Emp.: 6
Spices & Flavorings
N.A.I.C.S.: 311421

Ajinomoto Co., (Thailand) Ltd. **(1)**
487/1 Si Ayutthaya Road, Khwaeng Thanon Phaya Thai Khet Ratchathewi, Bangkok, 10400, Thailand **(82.52%)**
Web Site: http://www.ajinomoto.co.th
Sales Range: $25-49.9 Million
Emp.: 40
Spices & Flavorings
N.A.I.C.S.: 311421

Subsidiary (Domestic):

Wan Thai Foods Industry Co., Ltd. **(2)**
2/4 Soi Serithai 58, Minburi, Bangkok, 10510, Thailand
Tel.: (66) 25170944
Web Site: http://www.yumyumfoods.com
Sales Range: $100-124.9 Million
Canned Fruit & Vegetable Juice Mfr
N.A.I.C.S.: 311421

Ajinomoto Communications Co., Inc. **(1)**
2-9-1 Hatchobori RBM Higashiyaesu Building, Chuo-ku, Tokyo, 104-0032, Japan
Tel.: (81) 335551771
Web Site: https://www.ajicom.co.jp
Emp.: 528
Marketing Services
N.A.I.C.S.: 541613

Ajinomoto Euro-Aspartame S.A. **(1)**
ZIP Des Huttes Rte De La Grande Hernesse Port 7516, 59820, Gravelines, France **(100%)**
Tel.: (33) 328227400
Web Site: http://www.Aji-Aspartame.eu
Sales Range: $25-49.9 Million
Emp.: 100
Artificial Sweetener Mfr
N.A.I.C.S.: 311421
Ag Tammiram (Pres)

Ajinomoto Eurolysine S.A.S. **(1)**
153 Rue De Courcelles, 75817, Paris, France **(50%)**
Tel.: (33) 1 44 40 1212
Web Site: http://www.ajinomoto-eurolysine.com
Sales Range: $25-49.9 Million
Emp.: 25
Mfr of Amino Acids for Animal & Human Nutritional Products
N.A.I.C.S.: 325180
Daniel Bercovici (Pres)

Ajinomoto Europe S.A.S **(1)**
32 rue Guersant, 75017, Paris, Cedex, France **(100%)**
Tel.: (33) 0147669863
Web Site: https://www.ajinomoto-europe.com
Sales Range: $25-49.9 Million
Emp.: 11
Spices & Flavorings

N.A.I.C.S.: 311421

Ajinomoto Fine-Techno Co., Inc. **(1)**
1-2 Suzuki-cho, Kawasaki-ku, Kawasaki, 210-0801, Japan
Tel.: (81) 442212370
Web Site: https://www.aft-website.com
Emp.: 365
Electronic Material Mfr & Distr
N.A.I.C.S.: 334419
Tadahiko Yokota (Chm)

Ajinomoto Foods North America, Inc. **(1)**
4200 Concours St Ste 100, Ontario, CA 91764
Tel.: (909) 477-4700
Web Site: https://www.ajinomotofoods.com
Emp.: 2,800
Frozen Food Mfr
N.A.I.C.S.: 311412
T. Komura (Chief Comml Officer)

Ajinomoto Frozen Foods (Thailand) Co., Ltd. **(1)**
Hi-Tech Industrial Estate 59 Moo 2 Tambol Banpo, Amphoe Ban Pa-in, Ayutthaya, 13160, Thailand
Tel.: (66) 6320669709
Processed Food Mfr
N.A.I.C.S.: 311999

Ajinomoto Frozen Foods Co., Inc. **(1)**
7-14-13 Nichichi Ginza Building, Ginza Chuo-ku, Tokyo, 104-0061, Japan
Tel.: (81) 363678600
Web Site: https://www.ffa.ajinomoto.com
Emp.: 2,900
Frozen Food Mfr & Distr
N.A.I.C.S.: 311412

Ajinomoto General Foods, Inc. **(1)**
3 20 2 Nishishinjuku Tokyo Opera City 40f, Tokyo, 160-0023, Japan
Tel.: (81) 353027500
Mobile Food Services
N.A.I.C.S.: 722330

Ajinomoto Genexine Co., Ltd. **(1)**
105 Jisikgiban-ro, yeonsu-gu, Incheon, Korea (South)
Tel.: (82) 322102600
Web Site: http://en.ajinomotogenexine.com
Cell Research & Development Services
N.A.I.C.S.: 541714

Ajinomoto Health & Nutrition North America, Inc. **(1)**
250 E Devon Ave, Itasca, IL 60143
Tel.: (630) 931-6800
Web Site: https://www.ajihealthandnutrition.com
Food Solution & Research Development Services
N.A.I.C.S.: 311999
Jiro Sakamoto (Pres)

Subsidiary (Domestic):

More Than Gourmet, Inc. **(2)**
929 Home Ave, Akron, OH 44310 **(50.1%)**
Tel.: (330) 762-6652
Web Site: http://www.morethangourmet.com
Spice & Extract Mfr
N.A.I.C.S.: 311942

Ajinomoto Healthy Supply Co., Inc. **(1)**
1-19-8 Kyobashi OM Building 6th Floor, Kyobashi Chuo-ku, Tokyo, 104-0031, Japan
Tel.: (81) 335670051
Web Site: https://www.ahs.ajinomoto.com
Food Raw Material Distr
N.A.I.C.S.: 424490

Ajinomoto India Private Limited **(1)**
Plot No 14 One Hub Chennai, Manambathi Post Panchanthiruthi Village, Chengalpattu, 603105, Tamil Nadu, India
Tel.: (91) 4471900900
Web Site: http://www.ajinomoto.co.in
Processed Food Mfr
N.A.I.C.S.: 311999

Ajinomoto Interamericana Industria e Comercio Ltda. **(1)**
Rua Vergueiro 1737, Villa Mariana, Sao Paulo, 04101-000, SP, Brazil **(100%)**
Tel.: (55) 1150806700

Web Site: http://www.ajinomoto.com.br
Sales Range: $100-124.9 Million
Emp.: 300
Flavoring & Spices
N.A.I.C.S.: 311421

Ajinomoto Kohjin Bio Co., Ltd. (1)
5-1-3 Chiyoda, Sakado, 350-0214, Saitama,
Japan
Tel.: (81) 492998982
Web Site: https://www.ajikb.co.jp
Regenerative Medicine Mfr
N.A.I.C.S.: 325412

Ajinomoto North America, Inc. (1)
400 Kelby St, Fort Lee, NJ 07024
Tel.: (201) 292-3200
Mfr & Sale of Amino Acids & Foods for Pro-
cessed Food Manufacturers
N.A.I.C.S.: 311999
Tomoya Yoshizumi (Pres)

Subsidiary (Domestic):

Ajinomoto Althea, Inc (2)
11040 Roselle St, San Diego, CA 92121
Tel.: (858) 882-0123
Web Site: http://www.altheatech.com
Sales Range: $75-99.9 Million
Emp.: 220
Biological Product Contract Research &
Manufacturing Services
N.A.I.C.S.: 325412
Francois Ferre (Co-Founder & Chm)

Ajinomoto AminoScience LLC (2)
4020 Ajinomoto Dr, Raleigh, NC 27610-
2911
Tel.: (919) 231-0100
Web Site: http://www.ajiusa.com
Sales Range: $50-74.9 Million
Mfr of Amino Acids
N.A.I.C.S.: 325199

Ajinomoto Windsor, Inc. (2)
4200 Concours St Ste 100, Ontario, CA
91764
Tel.: (909) 477-4700
Web Site: http://www.ajinomoto-usa.com
Emp.: 1,900
Seasonings & Frozen Foods Mfr & Distr
N.A.I.C.S.: 311411
Julie Marcelo (Mgr-HR)

Unit (Domestic):

Bernardi Italian Foods (3)
301 W Third St, Toluca, IL 61369 (100%)
Tel.: (815) 452-2361
Sales Range: $25-49.9 Million
Emp.: 275
Mfr of Frozen Precooked Pasta Products
N.A.I.C.S.: 311412
Steve Leins (Gen Mgr)

Subsidiary (Domestic):

Golden Tiger (3)
6711 S Alameda St, Los Angeles, CA
90001-2123
Tel.: (323) 582-2872
Sales Range: $25-49.9 Million
Emp.: 160
Mfr of Chinese Egg Rolls & Appetizers
N.A.I.C.S.: 311412

Unit (Domestic):

The Original Chili Bowl (3)
9016 E 46th St, Tulsa, OK 74145-4822
Tel.: (918) 628-0225
Web Site:
　　http://www.theoriginalchilibowl.com
Sales Range: $25-49.9 Million
Emp.: 85
Frozen Chili & Barbecue Meat Specialties
Mfr
N.A.I.C.S.: 311412

**Ajinomoto Pharmaceuticals Europe
Ltd.** (1)
Aubrey House 10 15, Queen St, London,
EC4N 1TX, United Kingdom
Tel.: (44) 2072360160
Web Site: http://www.ajinomoto-europe.com
N.A.I.C.S.: 311421

**Ajinomoto Philippines
Corporation** (1)
V Corporate Center 125 L P Leviste Street,
Salcedo Village, Makati, 1227, Metro Ma-

nila, Philippines
Tel.: (63) 88956081
Web Site: https://www.ajinomoto.com.ph
Sales Range: $50-74.9 Million
Emp.: 200
Spices & Flavorings Mfr
N.A.I.C.S.: 311421

Ajinomoto Poland Sp. z o.o. (1)
Klimczaka Street 1, 02-797, Warsaw, Po-
land
Tel.: (48) 22 460 0070
Web Site: https://www.ajinomoto.com.pl
Sales Range: $25-49.9 Million
Emp.: 18
Vegetables & Fruits
N.A.I.C.S.: 311421
Sergiusz Matusiak (Member-Mgmt Bd &
VP)

Ajinomoto Trading, Inc. (1)
11th Floor Tradepia Odaiba 3-1 Daiba
2-chome, Minato-ku, Tokyo, 135-0091, Ja-
pan
Tel.: (81) 335284411
Web Site: http://www.ajitrade.com
Emp.: 70
Food Plant Machinery Distr
N.A.I.C.S.: 423830

**Ajinomoto Treasury Management,
Inc.** (1)
1-15-1 Kyobashi, Chuo-Ku, Tokyo, 104-
0031, Japan
Tel.: (81) 352508676
Treasury Management Services
N.A.I.C.S.: 541618

Ajinomoto Vietnam Co., Ltd. (1)
Bien Hoa Industrial Park 1 Le Van Duyet
Street, An Binh Ward, Bien Hoa, Dong Nai,
Vietnam (100%)
Tel.: (84) 2513831289
Web Site: https://www.ajinomoto.com.vn
Sales Range: $200-249.9 Million
Emp.: 900
Spices & Flavorings Mfr
N.A.I.C.S.: 311421

**Ajinomoto de Mexico, S. de R.L. de
C.V.** (1)
Calle Hamburgo 206 - Int 102, Col Juarez
Alc Cuauhtemoc, 06600, Mexico, Mexico
Tel.: (52) 5555331530
Web Site: https://www.ajinomotomexico.com
Food Products Distr
N.A.I.C.S.: 424490

Ajinomoto del Peru S.A. (1)
Av Republica de Panama 2455, 13, Lima,
Peru (100%)
Tel.: (51) 14706050
Web Site: https://www.ajinomoto.com.pe
Sales Range: $100-124.9 Million
Emp.: 300
Spices & Flavorings Mfr
N.A.I.C.S.: 311421

**Ajinomoto do Brasil Ind. e Com. de
Alimentos Ltda.** (1)
Oriento S/N Laranja Paulista, Sao Paulo,
18500-000, Brazil
Tel.: (55) 1532839000
Web Site: http://www.ajinomoto.com.br
Food Products Mfr & Distr
N.A.I.C.S.: 311999

**Ajinomoto-Genetika Research
Institute** (1)
1-1 1st Dorozhny proezd, 117545, Moscow,
Russia (100%)
Tel.: (7) 4957803266
Web Site: http://en.agri.ru
Sales Range: $25-49.9 Million
Emp.: 100
Food Production & Research
N.A.I.C.S.: 311999

**California Manufacturing Co.,
Inc.** (1)
Km 18 East Service Road, South Super-
highway, Paranaque, 1702, Metro Manila,
Philippines
Tel.: (63) 28238021
N.A.I.C.S.: 311421

Chuanhua Ajinomoto Co., Ltd. (1)
Qingbaijiang, Chengdu, 610301, Sichuan,
China
Tel.: (86) 2883604305

N.A.I.C.S.: 311421
Delica Ace Co., Ltd. (1)
1345 Yoshida, Ageo, 362-0013, Saitama,
Japan
Tel.: (81) 487781711
Web Site: http://www.delicaace.co.jp
Cooked Food Mfr & Distr
N.A.I.C.S.: 311991

GeneDesign, Inc. (1)
7-7-29 Saitoasagi, Ibaraki, 567-0085,
Osaka, Japan
Tel.: (81) 726405180
Web Site: http://www.ajioligos.com
Emp.: 100
Genetic Engineering Research & Develop-
ment Services
N.A.I.C.S.: 541714

Hokkaido Ajinomoto Co., Inc. (1)
Tel.: (81) 116438411
Web Site:
　　http://www.hokkaido.ajinomoto.co.jp
Food Service
N.A.I.C.S.: 541890

**Kawaken Fine Chemicals Co.,
Ltd.** (1)
2-3-3 Nihombashi Horidome-cho, Chuo-ku,
Tokyo, 103-0012, Japan
Tel.: (81) 336625891
Web Site: https://www.kawakenfc.co.jp
Emp.: 384
Chemicals Mfr
N.A.I.C.S.: 325199
Yoichi Tani (Pres)

Lianhua Ajinomoto Co., Ltd. (1)
Rm 2201 Lianwei Rd, Xiangcheng, 10020,
Henan, China
Tel.: (86) 1065880110
Web Site: http://www.ajinomoto.com.cn
Sales Range: $25-49.9 Million
Emp.: 20
Fruit & Vegetable Canning
N.A.I.C.S.: 311421

**Lianyungang Ajinomoto Frozen Foods
Co., Ltd.** (1)
Songatiao Industrial Zone, Haizhoy District,
Lianyungang, Jiangsu, China
Tel.: (86) 51885150741
Web Site: http://www.lyg-ajinomoto.com
Processed Food Mfr
N.A.I.C.S.: 311999

**Lianyungang Ajinomoto Ruyi Foods
Co., Ltd.** (1)
Dingzi Road East, Xinpu, Lianyungang,
222002, Jiangsu, China
Tel.: (86) 51885150741
Frozen Food Mfr & Distr
N.A.I.C.S.: 424420

**Maruchan Ajinomoto India Private
Limited** (1)
Plot No 15 Onehub Chennai, Manambathi
Post Panchanthiruthi Village Chengalpattu
District, Kanchipuram, 603105, Tamil Nadu,
India
Tel.: (91) 4471800200
Web Site: http://www.maruchan-
ajinomoto.com
Processed Food Mfr
N.A.I.C.S.: 311999

NRI System Techno, Ltd. (1)
4-4-1 Minato Mirai, Nishi-ku, Yokohama,
220-0012, Kanagawa, Japan
Tel.: (81) 453368000
Web Site: https://www.nri-st.co.jp
Emp.: 342
Software Services
N.A.I.C.S.: 541511
Shin Kanai (Pres)

Nissin-Ajinomoto Alimentos Ltda. (1)
Rodovia Bandeirantes Km 57, 18140-000,
Ibiuna, SP, Brazil (50%)
Tel.: (55) 15 3145 5900
Web Site: http://www.ajinomoto.com
Sales Range: $25-49.9 Million
Emp.: 100
Instant Noodles Mfr
N.A.I.C.S.: 311423

P.T. Ajinomoto Indonesia (1)
Jl Rear Admiral Yos Sudarso No 77-78
Sunter, Jakarta, 14350, Indonesia (100%)

Tel.: (62) 2165304455
Web Site: https://www.ajinomoto.co.id
Sales Range: $50-74.9 Million
Emp.: 150
Fruit & Vegetable Canning
N.A.I.C.S.: 311421

Promasidor Holdings Limited (1)
32 Bruton Road, Bryanston, 2021, South
Africa
Tel.: (27) 115401900
Web Site: https://promasidor.com
N.A.I.C.S.: 311999

S.A. Ajinomoto OmniChem N.V. (1)
Cooppallaan 91 Ind Zone 7, 9230, Wet-
teren, Belgium
Tel.: (32) 9 365 3333
Web Site: https://www.ajinomoto-
omnichem.com
Sales Range: $75-99.9 Million
Emp.: 160
Pharmaceutical Industry Fine Chemicals &
Intermediates Mfr & Whslr
N.A.I.C.S.: 325998
Peter Stuyck (Mng Dir)

**Sazonadores del Pacifico C.
Ltda.** (1)
Km 11 5 Via a Daule El Sauce Industrial
Park, Guayaquil, Ecuador
Tel.: (593) 42103719
Web Site:
　　http://www.sazonadoresdelpacifico.com
Processed Food Mfr
N.A.I.C.S.: 311999

**Shanghai Ajinomoto Amino Acid Co.,
Ltd.** (1)
718 Lok Road, Shanghai, Songjiang,
China (100%)
Tel.: (86) 21 577 40370
Web Site: http://www.ajinomoto.com.cn
Sales Range: $50-74.9 Million
Emp.: 153
Mfr & Sale of Amino Acids for Pharmaceuti-
cals & Foods
N.A.I.C.S.: 325180
Jun Yu Guo (Gen Mgr)

**Shanghai Ajinomoto Seasoning Co.,
Ltd.** (1)
3000 Shen Gang Rd, Songjiang, Shanghai,
201611, China
Tel.: (86) 2167600909
Processed Food Product Mfr
N.A.I.C.S.: 311999

Shanghai Amoy Foods Co. Ltd. (1)
Room 1439 2/F No 148 Lane 999 Xiner
Road, Baoshan District, Shanghai, 200439,
China
Tel.: (86) 2158995838
Web Site: http://www.amoy.com
Sales Range: $25-49.9 Million
Emp.: 100
Sauces & Frozen Products Mfr
N.A.I.C.S.: 311941

Taiso Commerce, Inc. (1)
10 Fl No 68 Changshan N Rd, Taipei, 104,
Taiwan (70%)
Tel.: (886) 225210150
Web Site: http://www.taiso.com.tw
Sales Range: $1-9.9 Million
Emp.: 20
N.A.I.C.S.: 311421

West African Seasoning Co., Ltd. (1)
37 Creek Road, Apapa, Lagos, Nigeria
Tel.: (234) 8178548548
Web Site: http://ajinomoto.com.ng
Food & Beverage Mfr
N.A.I.C.S.: 311421

**Xiamen Ajinomoto Life Ideal Foods
Co., Ltd.** (1)
Ting Yang Maxiang, Xiangan, Xiamen,
China
Web Site: http://www.xmryali.com
Processed Food Mfr
N.A.I.C.S.: 311999

**ZAO Ajinomoto-Genetika Research
Institute** (1)
1-1 1st Dorozhny Proezd, Moscow, 117545,
Russia
Tel.: (7) 4957803266
Web Site: https://en.agri.ru
N.A.I.C.S.: 541714

Ajinomoto Company, Inc.—(Continued)

Konstantin Rybak *(Pres)*

AJIS CO., LTD.

4-544-4 Makuhari-cho, Hanamigawa-
ku, Chiba, 262032, Japan
Tel.: (81) 433500888
Web Site: https://www.ajis.jp
Year Founded. 1978
4659—(TKS)
Rev.: $198,266,950
Assets: $188,973,290
Liabilities: $33,241,690
Net Worth: $155,731,600
Earnings: $12,625,100
Emp.: 875
Fiscal Year-end: 03/31/24
Inventory Management Services
N.A.I.C.S.: 561990

Subsidiaries:

AJIS (THAILAND) Co., Ltd.　　(1)
33/4 The Ninth Tower Tower A 35th Floor
Rama 9 Road, Khwaeng Huaykwang Khet
Huaykwang, Bangkok, 10310, Thailand
Tel.: (66) 27161122
Web Site: https://www.ajis.co.th
Inventory Management Services
N.A.I.C.S.: 561990

AJIS Hokkaido Co., Ltd.　　(1)
5F Marukin Headquarters Building 3-18 Mi-
nami 3-jo Higashi, Chuo-ku, Sapporo, 060-
0053, Japan
Tel.: (81) 112223072
Web Site: https://www.ajis-hokkaido.co.jp
Emp.: 1,038
Warehouse Management & Distribution
Services
N.A.I.C.S.: 493110

AJIS Kyushu Co., Ltd.　　(1)
AJIS Kyushu Head Office Building 2-24-10
Kanenokuma, Hakata-ku, Fukuoka, 812-
0863, Japan
Tel.: (81) 925833110
Web Site: https://www.ajisk.co.jp
Warehouse Management & Distribution
Services
N.A.I.C.S.: 493110

AJIS Malaysia Sdn Bhd.　　(1)
C-1-23 8 Avenue Jalan Sungai Jernih 8/1
Seksyen 8, 46050, Petaling Jaya, Selangor,
Malaysia
Tel.: (60) 379555563
Web Site: https://www.ajis.jp
Data Processing Services
N.A.I.C.S.: 518210

AJIS Philippines, Inc.　　(1)
30-B Unit Chatham House 116 Valero Cor
V A Rufino Streets, Salcedo, Makati, Philip-
pines
Tel.: (63) 28891200
Web Site: https://www.ajisph.com
Inventory Services
N.A.I.C.S.: 541614

AJIS Retail Support Co., Ltd.　　(1)
4-544-4 Makuhari-cho, Hanamigawa-cho,
Chiba, 262-0032, Japan
Tel.: (81) 433500888
Warehouse Management & Distribution
Services
N.A.I.C.S.: 493110

AJIS Shikoku Co., Ltd.　　(1)
51-21 Matsunawa-cho, Takamatsu, 760-
0079, Kagawa Prefecture, Japan
Tel.: (81) 878144555
Web Site: https://www.ajis-shikoku.co.jp
Emp.: 800
Warehouse Management & Distribution
Services
N.A.I.C.S.: 493110

AJIS USA, Inc.　　(1)
530 Technology Dr Ste 100 & 200, Irvine,
CA 92618
Tel.: (949) 504-5547
Web Site: https://ajisretailsolutions.com
Marketing Consulting Services
N.A.I.C.S.: 541613

Ajis (Hong Kong) Co., Limited　　(1)
Rm C 9/F Hop Hing Industrial Bldg 704

Castle Peak Rd Kln, Hong Kong, China
(Hong Kong)
Tel.: (852) 23104628
Web Site: https://www.ajis.com.hk
Inventory Management Services
N.A.I.C.S.: 561990

Ajis Merchandising Service Co.,
Ltd.　　(1)
3-7727-1 Makuharicho, Hanamigawa Ward,
Chiba, 262-0032, Japan　　(88.09%)
Tel.: (81) 432132006
Emp.: 132
Marketing Consulting Services
N.A.I.C.S.: 541613

Lowp Co., Ltd.　　(1)
4F 5 Ichigayasanai, Shinjuku, Tokyo, 162-
0846, Japan
Tel.: (81) 368249020
Web Site: https://www.lowp.jp
Media Advertising Services
N.A.I.C.S.: 541840

Nip's System Center Co., Ltd.　　(1)
7F Imon Hakata Building East 2-2-1 Sum-
iyoshi, Hakata-ku, Fukuoka, 812-0018, Ja-
pan
Tel.: (81) 922601397
Web Site: https://www.nipssc.co.jp
Emp.: 55
Software Operating Services
N.A.I.C.S.: 541714

AJISEN CHINA HOLDINGS LTD.

6F Ajisen Group Building Block B No
24-26 Sze Shan Street, Yau Tong,
Kowloon, 200021, China (Hong
Kong)
Tel.: (852) 39727788　Ky
Web Site: http://www.ajisen.com.hk
0538—(HKG)
Rev.: $200,742,797
Assets: $543,149,194
Liabilities: $132,996,989
Net Worth: $410,152,205
Earnings: ($21,954,067)
Emp.: 2,813
Fiscal Year-end: 12/31/22
Holding Company
N.A.I.C.S.: 551112
Wai Poon *(Chm & CEO)*

AJIYA BERHAD

Suite 9D Level 9 Menara Ansar 65
Jalan Trus, 80000, Johor Bahru, Jo-
hor, Malaysia
Tel.: (60) 79434211
Web Site: https://www.ajiya.com
AJIYA—(KLS)
Rev.: $66,350,023
Assets: $123,950,882
Liabilities: $16,030,763
Net Worth: $107,920,118
Earnings: $12,132,279
Emp.: 127
Fiscal Year-end: 11/30/23
Metal Doors & Window Frames Mfr
N.A.I.C.S.: 332321
Wah Kiang Chan *(Mng Dir)*

Subsidiaries:

ARI Utara Sdn. Bhd.　　(1)
Lot 28 Taman Perindustrian Bukit Makmur,
08000, Sungai Petani, Kedah,
Malaysia　　(80%)
Tel.: (60) 44422899
Sales Range: $25-49.9 Million
Emp.: 50
Construction Materials Mfr
N.A.I.C.S.: 339999
Sing Huat Tee *(Exec Dir)*

Ajiya STI Sdn. Bhd.　　(1)
No 4 Jalan Sungai Pelubung 32/149
Seksyen 32, 40460, Shah Alam, Selangor,
Malaysia
Tel.: (60) 351210011
Construction Materials Mfr
N.A.I.C.S.: 327331

Ajiya Safety Glass Sdn. Bhd.　　(1)

Lot 575 1 KM Lebuh Raya Segamat-
Kuantan, 85000, Segamat, Johor, Malaysia
Tel.: (60) 79313133
Glass Materials Mfr
N.A.I.C.S.: 327212

Subsidiary (Domestic):

ASG Marketing Sdn. Bhd.　　(2)
No 6 Jalan PPU 3 Taman Perindustrian Pu-
chong Utama, 47100, Puchong, Selangor,
Malaysia
Tel.: (60) 380623939
Sales Range: $25-49.9 Million
Emp.: 100
Safety Glass Distr
N.A.I.C.S.: 424990

AJMAN BANK PJSC

A & amp F Towers Khalifa Street, PO
Box 7770, Ajman, United Arab Emir-
ates
Tel.: (971) 67479999　AE
Web Site: http://www.ajmanbank.ae
Year Founded: 2008
Rev.: $346,855,154
Assets: $6,431,176,296
Liabilities: $5,747,297,941
Net Worth: $683,878,355
Earnings: $22,975,068
Fiscal Year-end: 12/31/19
Commercial Banking Services
N.A.I.C.S.: 522110
Ammar Humaid Al Nuaimi *(Chm)*

AJMERA REALTY & INFRA IN-DIA LIMITED

2nd Floor Citi Mall New Link Road
Andheri West, Mumbai, 400 053,
India
Tel.: (91) 2266984000
Web Site: https://ajmera.com
513349—(BOM)
Rev.: $66,764,402
Assets: $275,521,059
Liabilities: $164,770,529
Net Worth: $110,750,531
Earnings: $6,195,148
Emp.: 187
Fiscal Year-end: 03/31/22
Real Estate Manangement Services
N.A.I.C.S.: 531390
Rajnikant Shamalji Ajmera *(Chm & Mng Dir)*

AJN RESOURCES, INC.

Suite 1400 - 1199 West Hastings
Street, Vancouver, V6E 3T5, BC,
Canada
Tel.: (778) 218-9638
Web Site:
　　https://www.ajnresources.com
AJN—(CNSX)
Assets: $1,364,517
Liabilities: $1,351,576
Net Worth: $12,941
Earnings: ($1,052,671)
Fiscal Year-end: 07/31/23
Financial Consulting Services
N.A.I.C.S.: 541611
Klaus Eckhof *(Pres & CEO)*

AJOONI BIOTECH LIMITED

D-118 Industrial Area Phase-7, Mo-
hali, 160059, Punjab, India
Tel.: (91) 9888333506
Web Site:
　　https://www.ajoonibiotech.com
AJOONI—(NSE)
Rev.: $696,915,779
Assets: $382,558,899
Liabilities: $168,926,531
Net Worth: $213,632,369
Earnings: $5,092,157
Emp.: 47
Fiscal Year-end: 03/12/21
Animal Feed Mfr
N.A.I.C.S.: 311119
Jasjot Singh *(Mng Dir & CFO)*

AJU IB INVESTMENT CO., LTD.

201 Teheran-ro, Gangnam-gu, Seoul,
Korea (South)
Tel.: (82) 234519200
Web Site: http://www.ajuib.co.kr
27360—(KRS)
Rev.: $3,827,811
Assets: $294,898,563
Liabilities: $102,584,212
Net Worth: $192,314,351
Earnings: $1,610,830
Fiscal Year-end: 12/31/22
Asset Management Services
N.A.I.C.S.: 523940
Yang Jung-Kyoo *(Vice Chm)*

AJU STEEL CO., LTD.

321 4-Gongdan-Ro, Gumi,
Gyeongsangbuk-do, Korea (South)
Tel.: (82) 547143000
Web Site: https://www.ajusteel.co.kr
Year Founded: 1995
139990—(KRS)
Emp.: 548
Steel Surface Mfr
N.A.I.C.S.: 331110
Lee Hak-Yeon *(CEO)*

Subsidiaries:

AJU EGL Co., Ltd.　　(1)
664 Bongsan-ro, Bongsan-myeon, Gim-
cheon, Gyeongsangbuk-do, Korea (South)
Tel.: (82) 54 714 3630
Semi Finished Metal Product Mfr
N.A.I.C.S.: 332999

AJU MCM Co., Ltd.　　(1)
Gongdan-ro 286 Waegwan-eup, 39909,
Chilgok, Gyeongsangbuk-do, Korea (South)
Tel.: (82) 54 974 5500
Web Site: https://www.ajumcm.com
Metal Sheet Mfr
N.A.I.C.S.: 332322
Jung Won-Chang *(CEO)*

AJWA FUN WORLD & RE-SORT LIMITED

A Tower 1st floor Kunj Plaza Palace
Road, Vadodara, 390 001, Gujarat,
India
Tel.: (91) 2652434864
Web Site: https://www.ajwaworld.com
Year Founded: 1992
526628—(BOM)
Rev.: $76,645
Assets: $888,984
Liabilities: $1,238,724
Net Worth: ($349,740)
Earnings: ($159,487)
Emp.: 22
Fiscal Year-end: 03/31/22
Amusement Park Operator
N.A.I.C.S.: 713990
Rajeshkumar Chunilal Jain *(Chm & Mng Dir)*

AJWA GROUP FOR FOOD IN-DUSTRIES HOLDING LTD. CO.

Al Balad Al Mahamal Tower King
Abdulaziz St, PO Box 16645, Jeddah,
21474, Saudi Arabia
Tel.: (966) 26420552
Web Site: http://www.ajwagroup.com
Year Founded: 1992
Sales Range: $450-499.9 Million
Emp.: 5,000
Food Products Processor & Distr
N.A.I.C.S.: 424490
Ahmad Al Towairji *(Grp-Gen Mgr)*

Subsidiaries:

Ajwa Edible Oil Company
Limited　　(1)
King Abdulaziz Port, PO Box 8421, Dam-
mam, Saudi Arabia
Tel.: (966) 3 859 0069
Oil Distr

N.A.I.C.S.: 424990

Gulf Vegetable Oil Company (Nabati) (1)
King Abdul Aziz, Al Khobar, 31482, Saudi Arabia
Tel.: (966) 38590061
Web Site: http://www.ajwa.com
Sales Range: $25-49.9 Million
Emp.: 225
Edible Oils Processor & Distr
N.A.I.C.S.: 311224

Misr Gulf Oil Processing Co. (1)
95C El Merghany Street, Heliopolis Horreya, PO Box 2788, Cairo, Egypt
Tel.: (20) 2 417 8182
Sales Range: $150-199.9 Million
Emp.: 720
Edible Oils Processor, Packer, Sales & Distr
N.A.I.C.S.: 311224

Saudi Tunisian Company (1)
Zone Industrielle Bir El Kassaa, En Face Mache du Gros, Ben Arous, 2013, Tunis, Tunisia
Tel.: (216) 7138 8888
Sales Range: $25-49.9 Million
Emp.: 55
Edible Oils Processor & Distr
N.A.I.C.S.: 311224

AJWAN GULF REAL ESTATE CO. (K.S.C.C.)
Mirqab-Block1-Abdullah Al Mubarak Street Star Tower-Third Floor, PO Box 24932, 13110, Kuwait, Kuwait
Tel.: (965) 2 299 6543
Web Site: http://www.ajwangulf.net
Year Founded: 2002
AJWAN—(KUW)
Rev.: $717,564
Assets: $29,121,733
Liabilities: $7,375,908
Net Worth: $21,745,826
Earnings: ($13,351,871)
Emp.: 6
Fiscal Year-end: 12/31/20
Real Estate Manangement Services
N.A.I.C.S.: 531390
Yousif H. Mh Boodai (Chm)

AK ALTYNALMAS JSC
10/1 Elebekova Street Venus Business Center, Almaty, Kazakhstan
Tel.: (7) 273500200
Web Site: https://www.altynalmas.kz
Year Founded: 1993
ALMS—(KAZ)
Rev.: $710,797,429
Assets: $1,322,569,530
Liabilities: $1,092,354,491
Net Worth: $230,215,038
Earnings: $149,882,822
Emp.: 2,000
Fiscal Year-end: 12/31/20
Gold Ore Mining Services
N.A.I.C.S.: 212220
Diyar Kanashev (Pres & CEO)

AK FAKTORING AS
Buyukdere Cad ozsezen Business Center C Blok No 126 Kat 9, Esentepe/Sisli, 34394, Istanbul, Turkiye
Tel.: (90) 2125273131
Web Site: http://www.akfactoring.com.tr
AKSFA—(IST)
Sales Range: Less than $1 Million
Financial Management Services
N.A.I.C.S.: 551112
Inan Altinbas (Chm)

AK HOLDINGS, INC.
188 Yanghwa-ro, Mapo-gu, Seoul, 08392, Korea (South)
Tel.: (82) 27682923
Web Site: http://www.aekyunggroup.co.kr

Year Founded: 1970
006840—(KRS)
Rev.: $2,905,365,209
Assets: $3,838,324,915
Liabilities: $2,854,771,532
Net Worth: $983,553,384
Earnings: ($91,310,213)
Emp.: 24
Fiscal Year-end: 12/31/22
Holding Company
N.A.I.C.S.: 551112
Jang-hwan Lee (Exec Dir)

Subsidiaries:

AMPLUS Asset Development Inc. (1)
17F 18F Gwangil Plaza Building 1337-32 Seocho 2-dong, Seocho-gu, 137-860, Seoul, Korea (South)
Tel.: (82) 221795000
Web Site: https://www.amplus.co.kr
Emp.: 37
Real Estate Development Services
N.A.I.C.S.: 531110

Aekyung Chemical Co., Ltd. (1)
Tel.: (82) 260783000
Web Site: https://www.aekyungchemical.co.kr
Rev.: $1,669,327,089
Assets: $946,542,215
Liabilities: $388,054,712
Net Worth: $558,487,504
Earnings: $46,133,354
Emp.: 715
Fiscal Year-end: 12/31/2022
Petrochemical, Resins & Dye Mfr
N.A.I.C.S.: 325110
Kyoungwon Pyo (CEO)

Subsidiary (Non-US):

AK VINA Co., Ltd. (2)
Go Dau Industrial Zone, Long Thanh, Dong Nai, Vietnam
Tel.: (84) 613543732
Chemical Product Mfr & Distr
N.A.I.C.S.: 325998
In Jong Yu (Mgr-Ops)

Aekyung (Ningbo) Chemical Co., Ltd. (2)
Tai Xing Lu Zhenhai Qu, Zhenhaj District, Ningbo, Zhejiang Sheng, China
Tel.: (86) 57486453188
Chemical Product Mfr & Distr
N.A.I.C.S.: 325998

Aekyung HongKong Co., Ltd (2)
Rms 1905-8 19/F Kai Tak Commercial Building 161 Connaught Road, Central, China (Hong Kong)
Tel.: (852) 25378382
Sales Range: $25-49.9 Million
Emp.: 4
Petrochemical Mfr
N.A.I.C.S.: 324110
M. H. Cho (Mgr)

Subsidiary (Domestic):

Honglk Co., Ltd (2)
413-834 344-9 11 Dongpae-dong, P'aju, Gyeonggi-do, Korea (South)
Tel.: (82) 31 946 2100
Chemical Product Mfr & Distr
N.A.I.C.S.: 325998

Aekyung Industrial Co., Ltd. (1)
188 Yanghwa-ro, Mapo-gu, Seoul, 04051, Korea (South)
Tel.: (82) 800241357
Personal Care Product Mfr
N.A.I.C.S.: 325620

AK MEDICAL HOLDINGS LIMITED
2nd Floor Xingye Building No 10 Baifuquan Road, Science and Technology Park Changping District, Beijing, 102200, China
Tel.: (86) 1080109581
Web Site: http://www.ak-medical.net
Year Founded: 2003
1789—(HKG)
Rev.: $147,707,399

Assets: $389,538,677
Liabilities: $74,514,632
Net Worth: $315,024,044
Earnings: $28,749,989
Emp.: 1,023
Fiscal Year-end: 12/31/22
Medical Product Mfr & Distr
N.A.I.C.S.: 339113
Zhijiang Li (Co-Founder, Chm & CEO)

Subsidiaries:

JRI Orthopaedics Limited (1)
18 Churchill Way 35A Business Park, Chapeltown, Sheffield, S35 2PY, United Kingdom
Tel.: (44) 114 345 3200
Web Site: https://www.jri-ltd.com
Orthopaedic Implants & Surgical Equipment Mfr
N.A.I.C.S.: 339113
Stephen Ayres (Fin Dir)

AK RETAIL HOLDINGS LIMITED
Newcombe House Bakewell Road Orton Southgate, Peterborough, PE2 6XU, United Kingdom
Tel.: (44) 3448 204 204   UK
Year Founded: 2004
Holding Company
N.A.I.C.S.: 551112

Subsidiaries:

Long Tall Sally Ltd. (1)
The Lansdowne Building 2 Lansdowne Road, Croydon, CR9 2ER, United Kingdom
Tel.: (44) 207 1111 595
Web Site: http://www.longtallsally.com
Women's Clothing & Footwear Retailer
N.A.I.C.S.: 458110
Andrew Shapin (CEO)

AKA GROUP LIMITED
115 Shaftesbury Avenue, London, WC2H 8AF, United Kingdom
Tel.: (44) 20 7836 4747
Web Site: http://www.akauk.com
Year Founded: 1995
Sales Range: $75-99.9 Million
Emp.: 194
Internet Publishing Services
N.A.I.C.S.: 516210
Tom Ellis (Coord-Studio & Print)

AKANDA CORP.
1a 1b Learoyd Road, New Romney, TN28 8XU, United Kingdom
Tel.: (44) 2034889514   Ca
Web Site: https://www.akandacorp.com
Year Founded: 2021
AKAN—(NASDAQ)
Rev.: $2,619,682
Assets: $38,996,777
Liabilities: $12,096,616
Net Worth: $26,900,161
Earnings: ($11,657,674)
Emp.: 46
Fiscal Year-end: 12/31/22
Cannabis Product Mfr & Distr
N.A.I.C.S.: 325412
Katharyn Field (Exec Dir)

AKANKSHA POWER & INFRASTRUCTURE LIMITED
87/4 MIDC Satpur, Nashik, 422007, Maharashtra, India
Tel.: (91) 18002334062
Web Site: https://www.apipl.co.in
Year Founded: 2008
AKANKSHA—(NSE)
Rev.: $5,652,792
Assets: $5,772,332
Liabilities: $3,838,053
Net Worth: $1,934,279
Earnings: $343,869
Emp.: 434

Fiscal Year-end: 03/31/23
Electrical Equipment Mfr & Distr
N.A.I.C.S.: 331110

AKAR AUTO INDUSTRIES LTD.
304 Abhay Steel House Baroda Street Carneac Bunder, Mumbai, 400 009, Maharastra, India
Tel.: (91) 2223484886   In
Web Site: https://akarauto.com
Year Founded: 1989
530621—(BOM)
Rev.: $25,909,952
Assets: $21,755,124
Liabilities: $18,260,806
Net Worth: $3,494,318
Earnings: ($387,496)
Emp.: 398
Fiscal Year-end: 03/31/21
Precision Engineering Products Mfr
N.A.I.C.S.: 332216
Sunil Todi (Mng Dir)

AKARI THERAPEUTICS, PLC
75/76 Wimpole Street, London, W1G 9RT, United Kingdom
Tel.: (44) 2080040261   UK
Web Site: https://www.akaritx.com
Year Founded: 2004
AKTX—(NASDAQ)
Rev.: $5,340,146
Assets: $13,831,612
Liabilities: $12,040,866
Net Worth: $1,790,746
Earnings: ($17,748,062)
Emp.: 15
Fiscal Year-end: 12/31/22
Biopharmaceutical Mfr
N.A.I.C.S.: 325412
Samir R. Patel (Interim Pres & Interim CEO)

Subsidiaries:

Peak Bio, Inc. (1)
Tel.: (925) 463-4800
Web Site: https://peak-bio.com
Rev.: $367,877
Assets: $2,596,415
Liabilities: $20,753,364
Net Worth: ($18,156,949)
Earnings: ($12,825,917)
Fiscal Year-end: 12/31/2024
Biotechnology Research Services
N.A.I.C.S.: 541714
Samir R. Patel (Pres & Sec)

AKARY FOR INDUSTRIES & REAL ESTATE INVESTMENTS PLC
Wasfi Attal St - Building 105, PO Box 1728, Gardens, Amman, 11118, Jordan
Tel.: (962) 6 5563887
Year Founded: 1964
Assets: $507,925
Liabilities: $123,528
Net Worth: $384,397
Earnings: ($133,270)
Emp.: 29
Fiscal Year-end: 12/31/18
Woolen Yarn Mfr
N.A.I.C.S.: 313110

AKASAKA DIESELS LIMITED
4th fl Shin-Kokusai Bldg 3-4-1 Marunouchi, Chiyoda-ku, Tokyo, 100-0005, Japan
Tel.: (81) 368609081
Web Site: https://www.akasaka-diesel.jp
Year Founded: 1910
6022—(TKS)
Sales Range: Less than $1 Million
Emp.: 282
Diesel Engine Mfr & Whslr
N.A.I.C.S.: 333618
Akira Sugimoto (Pres)

Akasaka Diesels Limited—(Continued)

Subsidiaries:

Akasaka Diesels Limited - Nakaminato Factory **(1)**
4-3-1 Nakaminato, Yaizu, 425-0021, Shizuoka, Japan
Tel.: (81) 54 627 2121
Web Site: https://www.akasaka-diesel.jp
Emp.: 282
Diesel Engine Mfr
N.A.I.C.S.: 333618
Haruhisa Akasaka *(Gen Mgr)*

Akasaka Diesels Limited - Toyoda Factory **(1)**
670 Yanagi Araya, Yaizu, 425-0074, Shizuoka, Japan
Tel.: (81) 54 627 5091
Diesel Engine Mfr
N.A.I.C.S.: 333618

AKASH INFRA PROJECTS LTD.

Builders Of Reliable Roads Regd Office 2 Ground Floor, Abhishek Building Opp Hotel Haveli Sector No 11, Gandhinagar, 382011, Gujarat, India
Tel.: (91) 7923227006
Web Site: https://akashinfra.com
Year Founded: 1997
AKASH—(NSE)
Rev.: $13,065,152
Assets: $20,113,330
Liabilities: $9,218,077
Net Worth: $10,895,253
Earnings: $317,049
Emp.: 41
Fiscal Year-end: 03/31/22
Construction Services
N.A.I.C.S.: 236220
Ambusinh P. Gol *(Executives)*

AKASTOR ASA

Building B Oksenoyveien 10, 1366, Lysaker, Norway
Tel.: (47) 21525800   NO
Web Site: https://www.akastor.com
AKAST—(OSL)
Rev.: $27,722,072
Assets: $594,549,971
Liabilities: $204,278,247
Net Worth: $390,271,723
Earnings: ($25,755,968)
Emp.: 2,200
Fiscal Year-end: 12/31/23
Investment Holding Company; Oil & Gas Services
N.A.I.C.S.: 551112
Karl Erik Kjelstad *(CEO)*

Subsidiaries:

AGR (Australia) Pty Ltd **(1)**
Level 2 16 Milligan Street, Perth, 6000, WA, Australia
Tel.: (61) 448077019
Software Development Services
N.A.I.C.S.: 541511

AGR Group Americas, Inc. **(1)**
11450 Compaq Ctr W Dr Ste 210, Houston, TX 77070
Tel.: (832) 998-8769
Software Development Services
N.A.I.C.S.: 541511

Agr Energy Services AS **(1)**
Karenslyst Alle 4 Skoyen, 0278, Oslo, Norway
Tel.: (47) 99201479
Web Site: https://agr.com
Reservoir & Integrated Field Management Services
N.A.I.C.S.: 213112

Bronco Manufacturing LLC **(1)**
4953 S 48th W Ave, Tulsa, OK 74107-7202
Tel.: (918) 446-7196
Web Site: http://www.broncomfg.com
Drilling Rigs Mfr
N.A.I.C.S.: 333132
Max Mantooth *(CEO)*

DDW Offshore AS **(1)**
Oksenoyveien 10, 1366, Lysaker, Norway
Tel.: (47) 24134191
Web Site: https://www.ddwoffshore.com
Tug Supply Vessel Mfr
N.A.I.C.S.: 336611
Bruce Lethuillier *(Mng Dir)*

Frontica Engineering AS **(1)**
Butangen 20, 4639, Kristiansand, Norway
Tel.: (47) 40022430
Web Site: http://www.frontica.com
Emp.: 100
Offshore Drilling Services
N.A.I.C.S.: 213111
Bjorg Hansen *(Sr VP-HR)*

MHWirth AS **(1)**
Butangen 20, 4639, Kristiansand, Norway
Tel.: (47) 38057000
Web Site: http://www.mhwirth.com
Sales Range: $75-99.9 Million
Emp.: 550
Drilling Equipment & Facilities Supplier
N.A.I.C.S.: 333132

Subsidiary (Non-US):

MHWirth (Singapore) Pte. Ltd. **(2)**
25 Benoi Lane, Singapore, 627800, Singapore
Tel.: (65) 62626633
Sales Range: $25-49.9 Million
Emp.: 35
Drilling Equipment & Facilities Supplier
N.A.I.C.S.: 333132
Jackson Koh *(Dir)*

Subsidiary (Domestic):

MHWirth AS **(2)**
Maskinveien 9, 4033, Stavanger, Norway
Tel.: (47) 38057000
Web Site: https://hmhw.com
Drilling Equipment & Facilities Supplier
N.A.I.C.S.: 333132

Subsidiary (Non-US):

MHWirth Azerbaijan **(2)**
Salyan Highway 15th km 5, Lokbatan District, AZ 1045, Baku, Azerbaijan
Tel.: (994) 125650960
Web Site: https://hmhw.com
Drilling Equipment & Facilities Supplier
N.A.I.C.S.: 333132

MHWirth India Pvt. Ltd. **(2)**
Unit no. 2 A Win 09th Floor Lodha I-Think Techno Campus, Thane, 400607, Maharashtra, India
Tel.: (91) 98492611
Web Site: https://hmhw.com
Drilling Equipment & Facilities Supplier
N.A.I.C.S.: 333132

Subsidiary (US):

MHWirth LLC **(2)**
3300 N Sam Houston Pkwy E, Houston, TX 77032
Tel.: (281) 449-2000
Web Site: https://hmhw.com
Drilling Equipment Mfr
N.A.I.C.S.: 333132

Subsidiary (Non-US):

MHWirth UK Ltd. **(2)**
Fyvie Bldg Howe Moss Avenue, Dyce, Aberdeen, AB21 0GP, United Kingdom
Tel.: (44) 1224750900
Sales Range: $1-9.9 Million
Emp.: 25
Drilling Equipment & Facilities Supplier
N.A.I.C.S.: 333132

MHWirth Canada Inc. **(1)**
Suite 511 215 Water Street Atlantic Place, Saint John's, A1C 6C9, NL, Canada
Tel.: (709) 733-5134
Drilling Equipment Mfr & Whslr
N.A.I.C.S.: 333132

MHWirth GmbH **(1)**
Kolner Strasse 71-73, 41812, Erkelenz, Germany
Tel.: (49) 2431830
Drilling Equipment Mfr & Whslr
N.A.I.C.S.: 333132

MHWirth Offshore Petroleum Engineering (Shanghai) Co. Ltd. **(1)**
Unit 18A Tower B ShinMay Union Square 506 Shang Cheng Road, Pudong New District, Shanghai, 200120, China
Tel.: (86) 2161099175
Drilling Equipment Mfr & Whslr
N.A.I.C.S.: 333132

MHWirth Pty Ltd **(1)**
96 Raubers Road, Northgate, Brisbane, 4013, QLD, Australia
Tel.: (61) 731649000
Drilling Equipment Mfr & Whslr
N.A.I.C.S.: 333132

MHWirth do Brasil Equipamentos Ltda **(1)**
Rua Sergio Roberto Franco s/n Quadra 03 parte Fazenda Boa Vista, Imboassica, Macae, 27932-354, RJ, Brazil
Tel.: (55) 2221413163
Drilling Equipment Mfr & Whslr
N.A.I.C.S.: 333132

PT Step Oiltools **(1)**
Graha Inti Fauzi 12th Floor Jl Warung Buncit Raya No 22 RT 2/RW 7, Pejaten Barat Kec Ps Minggu, Jakarta Selatan, 12510, Jakarta, Indonesia
Tel.: (62) 217943352
Oil & Gas Operation Services
N.A.I.C.S.: 213112

Step Oiltools (Australia) Pty Ltd **(1)**
50 Kurnall Road, Welshpool, Perth, 6106, WA, Australia
Tel.: (61) 894556662
Oil & Gas Operation Services
N.A.I.C.S.: 213112

Step Oiltools (Thailand) Ltd. **(1)**
252/124 Unit E-F 26th Floor Muang Thai Phatra Complex B, Ratchadaphisek Rd Huaykwang Sub-District Huaykwang District, Bangkok, 10310, Thailand
Tel.: (66) 2693061011
Oil & Gas Operation Services
N.A.I.C.S.: 213112

Step Oiltools (UK) Ltd. **(1)**
Unit 3 Blackness Road, Blackness Industrial Centre Altens, Aberdeen, AB12 3LH, United Kingdom
Tel.: (44) 1224937188
Oil & Gas Operation Services
N.A.I.C.S.: 213112

Step Oiltools AS **(1)**
Maskinveien 9, Stavanger, 4033, Norway
Tel.: (47) 1224937188
Oil & Gas Operation Services
N.A.I.C.S.: 213112

Step Oiltools GmbH **(1)**
Bockhorner Weg 6, 29683, Bad Fallingbostel, Germany
Tel.: (49) 516298580
Solid Control Equipment Mfr
N.A.I.C.S.: 333132

Step Oiltools LLC **(1)**
Sadovnicheskaya 14 str Bld 2, 115035, Moscow, Russia
Tel.: (7) 4952580777
Oil & Gas Operation Services
N.A.I.C.S.: 213112

Step Oiltools LLP **(1)**
Microdistrict 1 GSK Khazar ARTEK Base, Aktau, 130000, Mangistau, Kazakhstan
Tel.: (7) 7292203291
Oil & Gas Operation Services
N.A.I.C.S.: 213112

Step Oiltools Pte Ltd **(1)**
7500A Beach Road 16-307/ 312 The Plaza, Singapore, 199591, Singapore
Tel.: (65) 63963872
Oil & Gas Operation Services
N.A.I.C.S.: 213112

AKATSUKI CORP.

4F Yashima Gakuen Building 2-12-13 Shinjuku, Shinjuku-ku, Tokyo, 160-0022, Japan
Tel.: (81) 368210606
Web Site: https://www.akatsuki-corp.com

Year Founded: 1950
8737—(TKS)
Rev.: $308,561,410
Assets: $608,979,300
Liabilities: $498,268,410
Net Worth: $110,710,890
Earnings: $16,776,180
Fiscal Year-end: 03/31/24
Holding Company
N.A.I.C.S.: 551112
Hideaki Shimane *(Pres)*

AKATSUKI EAZIMA CO., LTD.

2770-5 Semba-cho, Tokyo, 310-0851, Ibaraki, Japan
Tel.: (81) 292445111
Web Site: http://www.eazima.co.jp
Year Founded: 1953
1997—(TKS)
Sales Range: $75-99.9 Million
Air Conditioner Maintenance Services
N.A.I.C.S.: 811198

AKATSUKI, INC.

8F oak meguro 2-13-30 Kamiosaki Shinagawa-Ku, Tokyo, 141-0021, Japan
Tel.: (81) 364510277
Web Site: http://www.aktsk.jp
Year Founded: 2010
3932—(TKS)
Rev.: $158,454,920
Assets: $344,004,230
Liabilities: $78,209,520
Net Worth: $265,794,710
Earnings: $8,513,680
Fiscal Year-end: 03/31/24
Mobile Application Development Services
N.A.I.C.S.: 541511
Tetsuro Koda *(Co-Founder & CEO)*

Subsidiaries:

Akatsuki Entertainment USA, Inc. **(1)**
5225 Wilshire Blvd Ste 707, Los Angeles, CA 90036
Tel.: (323) 904-3776
Web Site: http://aktsk-ent.com
Feature Film Production Services
N.A.I.C.S.: 512110
Annmarie Sairrino Bailey *(Pres)*

AKB AVANGARD OAO

st Bolshaya Yakimanka 1, Moscow, 115035, Russia
Tel.: (7) 4952349898   RU
Web Site: https://www.avangard.ru
Year Founded: 1994
AVAN—(MOEX)
Sales Range: Less than $1 Million
Banking Services
N.A.I.C.S.: 522110

AKBANK T.A.S.

Sabanci Center 4, Levent, 34330, Istanbul, Türkiye
Tel.: (90) 2123855555   TR
Web Site: https://www.akbank.com
Year Founded: 1948
AKBNK—(IST)
Rev.: $7,147,727,047
Assets: $37,066,184,955
Liabilities: $30,128,559,528
Net Worth: $6,937,625,427
Earnings: $2,053,906,040
Emp.: 12,670
Fiscal Year-end: 12/31/23
Commercial Banking Services
N.A.I.C.S.: 522110
Eyup Engin *(Vice Chm & Vice Chm)*

Subsidiaries:

Ak Asset Management **(1)**
Ak Porfoy Yonetimi A S Sabanci Center Hazine Binasi Kat 1 4 Levent, Besiktas, 34330, Istanbul, Türkiye
Tel.: (90) 2123852700

Web Site: http://www.akportfoy.com.tr
Sales Range: $50-74.9 Million
Emp.: 30
Portfolio Management & Financial Advisory Services
N.A.I.C.S.: 523940

Ak Finansal Kiralama A.S. (1)
Sabanci Center Kule 2 Kat 8-9, Levent, 343304, Istanbul, Turkiye
Tel.: (90) 2123869600
Web Site: http://www.aklease.com
Sales Range: $50-74.9 Million
Financial Lending Services
N.A.I.C.S.: 532411

Ak Portfoy Yonetimi A.S. (1)
Konaklar Mahallesi Selvili Sokak Sabanci Center Kule 2 Kat 12, Besiktas, 34330, Istanbul, Turkiye
Tel.: (90) 2123852700
Web Site: https://www.akportfoy.com.tr
Investment Management Service
N.A.I.C.S.: 523940

Ak Securities (1)
Sabanci Center 4 Levent, 34330, Istanbul, Turkiye
Tel.: (90) 2123349500
Web Site: http://www.akyatirim.com.tr
Sales Range: $50-74.9 Million
Emp.: 60
International Banking & Securities Trading
N.A.I.C.S.: 523150

Ak Yatirim Menkul Degerler A.S. (1)
Sabanci Center 4 Levent, 34330, Istanbul, Turkiye
Tel.: (90) 2123349494
Web Site: http://www.akyatirim.com.tr
Sales Range: $50-74.9 Million
Investment Management Service
N.A.I.C.S.: 523940
Alphan Akiz (Exec VP)

Ak Yatirim Ortakligi A.S. (1)
Ak B Tipi Yatirim Ortakligi AS Inonu Cad No 42, Gumussuyu, Istanbul, 34437, Turkiye
Tel.: (90) 2123349585
Web Site:
http://www.akyatirimortakligi.com.tr
Sales Range: $50-74.9 Million
Emp.: 100
Investment Management Service
N.A.I.C.S.: 523940
Mert Erdogmus (Gen Mgr)

Akbank (Dubai) Limited (1)
Gate Bldg Level 15 Ofc No 5, PO Box 506828, Dubai, 506828, United Arab Emirates
Tel.: (971) 44486466
Web Site: http://www.akbank.ae
Sales Range: $50-74.9 Million
Emp.: 5
Commercial Banking Services
N.A.I.C.S.: 522110

Akbank AG (1)
Taunsgor 2, 60311, Frankfurt am Main, Germany
Tel.: (49) 6929717131
Web Site: http://www.akbank.de
Sales Range: $25-49.9 Million
Emp.: 30
Commercial Banking Services
N.A.I.C.S.: 522110
K. Banu Ejder Ozcan (Chm-Mgmt Bd & CEO)

Akbank International N.V. (1)
Amstelplein 1, 1096 HA, Amsterdam, Netherlands   (100%)
Tel.: (31) 880063950
Sales Range: $1-9.9 Million
Emp.: 30
Banking
N.A.I.C.S.: 523150

Akode Elektronik Para ve Odeme Hizmetleri A.S. (1)
Selvili Sok Sabanci Center Tower 2 Apt No 2/2, Konaklar Mah Besiktas, Istanbul, Turkiye
Tel.: (90) 8504770867
Web Site: http://www.akode.com
Online Payment Services
N.A.I.C.S.: 522320

AKBAR GROUP

No 1 First Floor Services Club Ext Bldg, Mereweather Road, Karachi, 75520, Pakistan
Tel.: (92) 21 568 0307
Web Site:
http://www.akbargroup.com.pk
Year Founded: 1976
Investment Holding Company
N.A.I.C.S.: 551112
M. I. Akbar (Founder & Chm)

Subsidiaries:

Fauji Akbar Portia Marine Terminals Limited (1)
10 2nd Floor Services Club Extension Bldg, Mereweather Road, Karachi, 75520, Pakistan   (19.8%)
Tel.: (92) 21 3567 8985
Web Site: http://www.fapterminals.com
Grain, Oilseeds & Fertilizer Port Terminal Operator
N.A.I.C.S.: 488310
Hassan Sobuctageen (COO)

Premier Aviation Services (Pvt.) Ltd. (1)
Services Club Extn Building Mereweather Road, Karachi, Pakistan
Tel.: (92) 21 35674684
Aviation Services
N.A.I.C.S.: 481112

AKD CAPITAL LIMITED

511 5th Floor Continental Trade Centre Block 8, Main Clifton Rd, Karachi, Pakistan
Tel.: (92) 2135302963
Web Site: https://www.akdcapital.com
AKDHL—(PSX)
Rev.: $4,317
Assets: $60,865
Liabilities: $32,482
Net Worth: $28,383
Earnings: ($17,850)
Emp.: 3
Fiscal Year-end: 06/30/23
Investment Management Service
N.A.I.C.S.: 523940
Nessar Ahmed (CEO)

Subsidiaries:

Akd Securities Limited (1)
602 Continental Trade Centre Clifton Block 8, Karachi, Pakistan
Tel.: (92) 111253111
Web Site: http://www.akdsecurities.net
Security Brokerage Services
N.A.I.C.S.: 523150
Muhammad Farid Alam (CEO)

AKD SA

40 rue Francois 1er, 75008, Paris, France
Tel.: (33) 1 48 73 14 78
Web Site: http://www.akd.fr
Year Founded: 2005
Sales Range: $1-9.9 Million
Emp.: 14
Cosmetics
N.A.I.C.S.: 325620
Alain Legout (Chm & CEO)

AKDENIZ FAKTORING A.S.

Bulgurlu Mahallesi Gurpinar Cad No 15, Uskudar, 34660, Istanbul, Turkiye
Tel.: (90) 2162284000
Web Site:
http://www.akdenizfaktoring.com
Year Founded: 1993
AKDFA—(IST)
Sales Range: Less than $1 Million
Financial Management Services
N.A.I.C.S.: 551112
Isfendiyar Zulfikari (Chm & Gen Mgr)

AKDENIZ YATIRIM HOLDING AS

Mahmutbey Mah Tasocagi Yolu Cad Balance Gunesli No 19/6 D 16,

Bagcilar, Istanbul, Turkiye
Tel.: (90) 2124658870
Web Site:
https://www.akdenizguvenlik.com.tr
AKYHO—(IST)
Rev.: $3,459,372
Assets: $24,626,269
Liabilities: $4,578,181
Net Worth: $20,048,088
Earnings: ($1,674,289)
Fiscal Year-end: 12/31/23
Security Services
N.A.I.C.S.: 561612
Necmeddin Simsek (Chm)

AKEBONO BRAKE INDUSTRY CO., LTD.

19-5 Nihonbashi Koami-cho, Chuo-ku, Tokyo, 1038534, Japan
Tel.: (81) 336685171   JP
Web Site: https://www.akebono-brake.com
Year Founded: 1929
7238—(TKS)
Rev.: $1,099,249,610
Assets: $994,639,750
Liabilities: $594,952,880
Net Worth: $399,686,870
Earnings: $22,817,720
Emp.: 5,548
Fiscal Year-end: 03/31/24
Automotive Brakes & Accessories Mfr
N.A.I.C.S.: 336340
Takeshi Saito (Exec Officer)

Subsidiaries:

A&M Casting (Thailand) Co., Ltd. (1)
Ratchaburi Industrial Estate 155/63 Moo 4 T Chet Samian A, Photharam, Ratchaburi, 70120, Thailand
Tel.: (66) 618201780
Automotive Component Mfr & Whslr
N.A.I.C.S.: 336340

Akebono 123 Co., Ltd. (1)
5-4-71 Higashi, Hanyu, 348-8508, Saitama, Japan
Tel.: (81) 485601231
Packing & Printing Services
N.A.I.C.S.: 323111

Akebono Advanced Engineering (UK) Ltd. (1)
415 Wharfedale Road Winnersh Triangle, Wokingham, RG41 5RA, Berkshire, United Kingdom
Tel.: (44) 1189445100
Brake Parts Mfr
N.A.I.C.S.: 336340
Hideki Takayama (Mgr)

Akebono Advanced Engineering Co., Ltd. (1)
5-4-71 Higashi, Hanyu, 348-8508, Saitama, Japan
Tel.: (81) 485601452
Motor Vehicle Brake System Mfr
N.A.I.C.S.: 336340

Akebono Brake (Thailand) Co., Ltd. (1)
700/880 Moo 1 Tambol Panthong, Amphur Panthong, Chon Buri, 20160, Thailand
Tel.: (66) 38185082
Brake Parts Distr
N.A.I.C.S.: 423120

Akebono Brake Astra Vietnam Co., Ltd. (1)
Plot F-3 Thang Long Industrial Park II, Lieu Xa Commune Yen My District, Hung Yen, Vietnam
Tel.: (84) 2213974477
Motor Vehicle Brake System Mfr & Whslr
N.A.I.C.S.: 336340

Akebono Brake Corporation (1)
310 Ring Rd, Elizabethtown, KY 42701
Tel.: (270) 234-5500
Web Site: http://www.akebonobrakes.com
Sales Range: $1-4.9 Billion
Emp.: 2,000
Brake Components Mfr
N.A.I.C.S.: 336340

Andy Abascal (Mgr-Sls-Mexico, Central & South America Reg)

Plant (Domestic):

Akebono Brake - Clarksville Plant (2)
780 International Blvd, Clarksville, TN 37040-5327
Tel.: (931) 553-6500
Web Site: http://www.akebonobrakes.com
Sales Range: $25-49.9 Million
Emp.: 250
Brake Components Mfr
N.A.I.C.S.: 336340

Akebono Brake - Elizabethtown Plant (2)
300 Ring Rd, Elizabethtown, KY 42701   (100%)
Tel.: (270) 737-4906
Sales Range: $350-399.9 Million
Emp.: 1,100
Disc & Drum Brake Assemblies & Components
N.A.I.C.S.: 336340
Doug Morgan (Plant Mgr)

Division (Domestic):

Akebono R&D Engineering Center (2)
34385 W Twelve Mile Rd, Farmington Hills, MI 48331
Tel.: (248) 489-7400
Web Site: http://www.akebonobrakes.com
Emp.: 250
Brake Systems Engineering & Research
N.A.I.C.S.: 541715
Hadrian Rori (Exec VP)

Akebono Brake Europe N.V. (1)
Pegasuslaan 5, 1831, Diegem, Flemish Brabant, Belgium
Tel.: (32) 27092034
Web Site: http://www.akebono-brake.com
Automobile Parts Distr
N.A.I.C.S.: 423120

Akebono Brake Fukushima Manufacturing Co., Ltd. (1)
10 Shinjuku Narita Aza, Koori-machi O-aza Date-gun, Fukushima, Japan
Automotive Brake Components Mfr
N.A.I.C.S.: 336340

Akebono Brake Iwatsuki Manufacturing Co., Ltd. (1)
1190 Oaza-Kanamuro, Iwatsuki-ku, Saitama, 339-8601, Japan
Tel.: (81) 487944111
Motor Vehicle Brake System Mfr
N.A.I.C.S.: 336340

Akebono Brake Mexico S.A. de C.V. (1)
Av Mineral De Valenciana 186 Fracc, Industrial Santa Fell Guanajuato Puerto Interior, 36275, Silao, Guanajuato, Mexico
Tel.: (52) 4727489116
Motor Vehicle Brake System Mfr
N.A.I.C.S.: 336340

Akebono Brake Sanyo Manufacturing Co., Ltd. (1)
1966-8 Kushiro, Soja, 710-1201, Okayama, Japan
Tel.: (81) 866962111
Motor Vehicle Brake System Mfr
N.A.I.C.S.: 336340

Akebono Brake Slovakia s.r.o. (1)
Bratislavska 581, 911 05, Trencin, Slovakia
Tel.: (421) 323215411
Motor Vehicle Brake System Mfr & Whslr
N.A.I.C.S.: 336340

Akebono Brake Yamagata Manufacturing Co., Ltd. (1)
161-3 Chuo Kogyo Danchi, Sagae, 991-0061, Yamagata, Japan
Tel.: (81) 237831111
Motor Vehicle Brake System Mfr
N.A.I.C.S.: 336340

Akebono Cooperation (Thailand) Co., Ltd. (1)
President Hotel and Tower 11rd Floor Room 11 D971 973 Phloenchit road, Lumpini Pathm wan, Bangkok, 10330, Thailand

Akebono Brake Industry Co., Ltd.—(Continued)

Tel.: (66) 25650015
Administrative Support Services
N.A.I.C.S.: 561110

Akebono Corporation (1)
No 8 Hefeng 1st Street, Yonghe Economic
Zone of Guangzhou Development District,
Guangzhou, 511356, China
Tel.: (86) 2082986818
Motor Vehicle Brake System Mfr
N.A.I.C.S.: 336340

**Akebono Corporation
(Guangzhou)** (1)
No 8 Hefeng 1st Street Yonghe Economic
Zone, Guangzhou Development District,
Guangzhou, Guangdong, China
Tel.: (86) 2082986818
Sales Range: $25-49.9 Million
Emp.: 100
Drum & Disc Brakes Mfr
N.A.I.C.S.: 336340

Akebono Corporation (Suzhou) (1)
TingLan Road No 168 Chang Yang Street,
Industrial Park, Suzhou, 215021, Jiangsu,
China
Tel.: (86) 512 6283 1577
Emp.: 180
Disc Brake Pads Mfr & Whslr
N.A.I.C.S.: 336340

Akebono Europe GmbH (1)
Auf der Heide 11-13, Limburg-Dietkirchen,
65553, Limburg, Germany
Tel.: (49) 64317798510
Brake Component Whslr
N.A.I.C.S.: 423120

Akebono Europe S.A.S (Arras) (1)
Site Artoipole 244 Allee d'Espagne, 62118,
Monchy-le-Preux, Pas-de-Calais, France
Tel.: (33) 321244800
Sales Range: $25-49.9 Million
Emp.: 90
Brake Components Mfr
N.A.I.C.S.: 336340
Marc Landou (Mgr-HR)

**Akebono Europe S.A.S
(Gonesse)** (1)
6 Avenue Pierre Salvi, BP 90111, 95505,
Gonesse, Val-d'Oise, France
Tel.: (33) 134451770
Sales Range: $25-49.9 Million
Emp.: 50
Brake Components Import & Distr
N.A.I.C.S.: 423120

**Akebono Research & Development
Centre Ltd.** (1)
5-4-71 Higashi, Hanyu, 348-8511, Saitama,
Japan
Tel.: (81) 485601421
Research & Development Services
N.A.I.C.S.: 541720

Alocs Corporation (1)
255-1 Ainohara, Iwatsuki-ku, Saitama, 339-
0071, Japan
Tel.: (81) 487941321
Logistic Services
N.A.I.C.S.: 541614

NeoStreet Inc. (1)
5-4-71 Higashi, Hanyu, 348-8501, Saitama,
Japan
Tel.: (81) 485600590
Online Store Services
N.A.I.C.S.: 531120

P.T. Tri Dharma Wisesa
J Pegangsaan Dua Block A1, Km 1 6 Ke-
lapa Gading, Jakarta, Indonesia **(50%)**
Tel.: (62) 214602755
Motor Vehicle Brake Component Marketing
N.A.I.C.S.: 423120

**PT. Akebono Brake Astra
Indonesia** (1)
Jl Pegangsaan Dua Blok A1 Km 1 6, Ke-
lapa Gading, Jakarta, 14250, Indonesia
Tel.: (62) 2146830075
Web Site: https://www.akebono-astra.co.id
Motor Vehicle Brake System Mfr & Whslr
N.A.I.C.S.: 336340

AKELIUS RESIDENTIAL AB

Rosenlundsgatan 50, Box 38149, 100
64, Stockholm, Sweden
Tel.: (46) 107223100
Web Site: http://www.akelius.com
AKEL.D—(OMX)
Rev.: $33,057,360
Assets: $668,294,728
Liabilities: $387,058,994
Net Worth: $281,235,735
Earnings: ($25,810,551)
Emp.: 674
Fiscal Year-end: 12/31/23
Residential Property Owner & Man-
ager
N.A.I.C.S.: 531311
Ralf Spann (CEO)

Subsidiaries:

Akelius Lagenheter AB (1)
Rosenlundsgatan 50, Box 38149, 100 64,
Stockholm, Sweden
Tel.: (46) 856613000
Construction Services
N.A.I.C.S.: 236220

AKEMI CHEMISCH TECHNIS-
CHE SPEZIALFABRIK GMBH

Lechstrasse 28, 90451, Nuremberg,
Germany
Tel.: (49) 911642960
Web Site: http://www.akemi.de
Year Founded: 1933
Rev.: $19,818,967
Emp.: 100
Adhesive Mfr
N.A.I.C.S.: 325520
Torsten Hamann (Mng Dir)

Subsidiaries:

**AKEMI Brasil Industria e Comercio
Ltda.** (1)
Av Marchal Castelo Branco no 350 Jardim
Tres Marias, 06790-070, Taboao da Serra,
Sao Paulo, Brazil
Tel.: (55) 11413880100
Adhesive Distr
N.A.I.C.S.: 424690

**AKEMI TECHNOLOGY INDIA PRI-
VATE LIMITED** (1)
Plot 276 Kachanayakanahalli Sub Layout
Phase 1 Bommasandra, Jigani Hobli Anekal
Taluk, Bengaluru, 560105, Karnataka, India
Tel.: (91) 9243626777
Adhesive Distr
N.A.I.C.S.: 424690

AKENERJI ELEKTRIK URETIM
A.S.

Miralay Sefik Bey Sokak No 15
Akhan Kat 3-4 Gumussuyu, 34437,
Istanbul, Turkiye
Tel.: (90) 2122498282
Web Site: https://www.akenerji.com.tr
Year Founded: 1989
AKENR—(IST)
Rev.: $526,525,031
Assets: $697,400,912
Liabilities: $520,499,043
Net Worth: $176,901,869
Earnings: ($48,510,785)
Emp.: 288
Fiscal Year-end: 12/31/22
Electricity Power Generation & Distri-
bution Services
N.A.I.C.S.: 221111

AKER ASA

Oksenoyveien 10, NO-1366, Lysaker,
Norway
Tel.: (47) 24130000   NO
Web Site: http://www.akerasa.com
Year Founded: 1841
AKER—(OSL)
Rev.: $1,339,091,077
Assets: $8,197,949,381
Liabilities: $3,506,281,175
Net Worth: $4,691,668,206
Earnings: ($175,318,677)

Emp.: 29,300
Fiscal Year-end: 12/31/23
Investment & Asset Management
Services
N.A.I.C.S.: 523940
Kjell Inge Rokke (Chm)

Subsidiaries:

Aker BioMarine ASA (1)
Oksenoyveien 10, PO Box 496, 1327, Ly-
saker, Norway
Tel.: (47) 24130000
Web Site: http://www.akerbiomarine.com
Sales Range: $75-99.9 Million
Biotechnology Products Research & Devel-
opment Services
N.A.I.C.S.: 541714
Matts Johansen (CEO)

Aker Capital AS (1)
Fjordalleen 16, 0250, Oslo, Norway
Tel.: (47) 2413 0000
Investment Holding Company
N.A.I.C.S.: 551112

Aker Horizons ASA (1)
Oksenoyveien 8, NO-1366, Lysaker, Nor-
way
Tel.: (47) 24130100
Web Site: https://www.akerhorizons.com
Rev.: $378,180,181
Assets: $2,677,047,751
Liabilities: $2,068,833,355
Net Worth: $608,214,396
Earnings: ($713,302,676)
Emp.: 792
Fiscal Year-end: 12/31/2023
Investment Management
N.A.I.C.S.: 523940
Kristian Rokke (CEO)

Philly Shipyard, Inc. (1)
2100 Kitty Hawk Ave, Philadelphia, PA
19112-1808
Tel.: (215) 875-2600
Web Site: https://www.phillyshipyard.com
Ship Building & Repairing Services
N.A.I.C.S.: 336611
Kristian Rokke (Chm)

AKER BP ASA

Fornebuporten Building B, Okse-
noyveien 10, 1366, Lysaker, Norway
Tel.: (47) 51353000   NO
Year Founded: 2001
AKRBF—(OTCQX)
Rev.: $13,669,900,000
Assets: $39,046,500,000
Liabilities: $26,684,300,000
Net Worth: $12,362,200,000
Earnings: $1,335,700,000
Emp.: 2,562
Fiscal Year-end: 12/31/23
Petroleum Exploration, Development
& Extraction
N.A.I.C.S.: 211120
Oyvind Eriksen (Chm)

AKER CARBON CAPTURE
ASA

Oksenoyveien 8, 1366, Lysaker, Nor-
way
Tel.: (47) 24130100   NO
Web Site:
https://www.akercarboncapture.com
Year Founded: 2020
ACC—(OSL)
Rev.: $148,263,532
Assets: $155,882,875
Liabilities: $91,043,045
Net Worth: $64,839,830
Earnings: ($15,778,034)
Emp.: 146
Fiscal Year-end: 12/31/23
Software Development Services
N.A.I.C.S.: 541511
Egil Fagerland (CEO)

AKER SOLUTIONS ASA

Oksenoyveien 8, NO-1366, Lysaker,
Norway

Tel.: (47) 67513000   NO
Web Site:
http://www.akersolutions.com
Year Founded: 2014
AKSO—(OSL)
Rev.: $3,564,743,888
Assets: $4,055,385,241
Liabilities: $2,192,206,406
Net Worth: $1,863,178,835
Earnings: ($1,474,578)
Emp.: 11,473
Fiscal Year-end: 12/31/23
Holding Company; Oil & Gas Field
Products, Engineering & Operations
Support Services
N.A.I.C.S.: 551112
Oyvind Eriksen (Deputy Chm)

Subsidiaries:

Aker Egersund AS (1)
Hovlandsveien 160, 4374, Egersund,
Norway **(100%)**
Tel.: (47) 5 146 9000
Web Site: https://www.akersolutions.com
Sales Range: $75-99.9 Million
Emp.: 470
Modules, Steel Jackets & Flare Booms Mfr
for Offshore Installations
N.A.I.C.S.: 331513

**Aker Engineering & Technology
AS** (1)
Snaroyveien 36, N 1364, Fornebu,
Norway **(100%)**
Tel.: (47) 67595050
Web Site: http://www.akersolutions.com
Sales Range: $150-199.9 Million
Emp.: 800
Technology, Development, Studies & Engi-
neering, Project Management, Procurement
& Construction Support Services for Off-
shore Oil & Gas Projects
N.A.I.C.S.: 541330

**Aker Engineering Malaysia Sdn
Bhd** (1)
Level 16 Integra Tower The Intermark, 348
Jalan Tun Razak, 50400, Kuala Lumpur,
Malaysia
Tel.: (60) 323818388
Web Site: https://www.akersolutions.com
Sales Range: $25-49.9 Million
Emp.: 80
Engineering & Design Services for the Oil,
Gas, Hydrocarbon & Process Industries
N.A.I.C.S.: 541330

Aker Solutions Finland Oy (1)
Fritilantie 11, 28400, Ulvila, Finland
Tel.: (358) 25319200
Engineeering Services
N.A.I.C.S.: 541330

Aker Solutions Inc. (1)
2103 CityWest Blvd Ste 800, Houston, TX
77042-3755 **(100%)**
Tel.: (713) 685-5700
Web Site: https://www.akersolutions.com
Sales Range: $350-399.9 Million
Emp.: 15,000
Wellhead Equipment, Subsea Trees, Pro-
duction Control Systems Mfr & Designer
N.A.I.C.S.: 333132

Aker Solutions do Brasil Ltda. (1)
Rua Francisco Sobania 1300 CIC, Curitiba,
81460-130, PR, Brazil **(100%)**
Tel.: (55) 41 2102 4350
Sales Range: $150-199.9 Million
Emp.: 1,000
Engineering & Construction Services
N.A.I.C.S.: 237990
Marea Peralta (Pres)

Aker Subsea AS (1)
Snaroyveien 36, 1364, Fornebu,
Norway **(100%)**
Tel.: (47) 6751 3000
Sales Range: $75-99.9 Million
Emp.: 250
Petroleum Sub-Surface Consultancy Spe-
cializing in Geological & Geophysical Inter-
pretation, Petrophysics, Reservoir Modelling
& Technology & Operation & Wellside Geol-
ogy
N.A.I.C.S.: 211120
Tom Munkejord (Sr VP-Norway)

Kvaerner Canada Ltd. (1)
Suite 305 Atlantic Place 215 Water Street,
Saint John's, A1C 6C9, NL, Canada
Tel.: (709) 738-7659
Engineeering Services
N.A.I.C.S.: 541330
Bill Fanning (Pres & Country Mgr)

Kvaerner LLC (1)
Gasheka 7 str Office 320, Moscow, Russia
Tel.: (7) 4956647711
Engineering Services
N.A.I.C.S.: 541330

Unitech Power Systems AS (1)
Jattavagveien 18, PO Box 47, N-4064, Stavanger, Norway
Tel.: (47) 51958900
Web Site: https://www.unitech.no
Emp.: 45
Electrical Power System Investigation Services
N.A.I.C.S.: 561611

AKESO, INC.
Kaifaqu Shennong Road No 6,
Zhongshan, Guangdong, China
Tel.: (86) 76089873936   Ky
Web Site: http://www.akesobio.com
Year Founded: 2012
9926—(HKG)
Pharmaceutical Product Mfr & Distr
N.A.I.C.S.: 325412
Michelle Xia (Pres & CEO)

AKFEN GAYRIMENKUL YATIRIM ORTAKLIGI A.S.
Levent Loft Buyukdere Cad No 201 C
Blok Kat 8, Levent, 34390, Istanbul,
Turkiye
Tel.: (90) 2123718700
Web Site:
https://www.akfengyo.com.tr
Year Founded: 1997
AKFGY—(IST)
Rev.: $37,080,228
Assets: $791,805,913
Liabilities: $257,298,193
Net Worth: $534,507,720
Earnings: $24,761,652
Emp.: 43
Fiscal Year-end: 12/31/23
Real Estate Investment Services
N.A.I.C.S.: 531390
Cuneyt Baltaoglu (Coord-Projects-Russia)

AKFEN HOLDING A.S.
Koza Sok No 22, Gaziosmanpasa,
06700, Ankara, Turkiye
Tel.: (90) 3124081000
Web Site: http://www.akfen.com.tr
Year Founded: 1976
Sales Range: Less than $1 Million
Holding Company; Infrastructure Investment Services
N.A.I.C.S.: 551112
Hamdi Akin (Chm)

Subsidiaries:

Akfen Insaat Turizm Ve Ticaret
A.S. (1)
Koza Sokak 22, Gaziosmanpasa, 6700, Ankara, Turkiye
Tel.: (90) 312 408 10 00
Web Site: http://www.akfen.com.tr
Construction Engineering Services
N.A.I.C.S.: 541330
Hamdi Akin (Gen Mgr)

AKG EXIM LTD.
Unit No 23702nd Floor Tower-B
Spazedge Tower Sector-47 Sohna
Road, Pitampura, Gurgaon, 122018,
Haryana, India
Tel.: (91) 1244267873
Web Site: https://www.akg-global.com
AKG—(NSE)
Rev.: $143

Assets: $49
Liabilities: $20
Net Worth: $29
Earnings: $2
Fiscal Year-end: 03/31/21
Export Trading Services
N.A.I.C.S.: 522299
Mahima Goel (Mng Dir)

AKHURST MACHINERY LIMITED
1669 Foster's Way, Delta, V3M 6S7,
BC, Canada
Tel.: (604) 540-1430
Web Site: https://www.akhurst.com
Year Founded: 1938
Rev.: $22,953,467
Emp.: 85
Industrial Equipment Distr
N.A.I.C.S.: 423830
Eric M. Stebner (Pres)

Subsidiaries:

Akhurst Machinery Inc. (1)
1124 Fir Ave PMB Ste 104, Blaine, WA
98230
Tel.: (604) 540-1430
Industrial Equipment Distr
N.A.I.C.S.: 423830

AKI INDIA LIMITED
D-115 Defence Colony Jajmau,
Kanpur, 208010, Uttar Pradesh, India
Tel.: (91) 8400392705
Web Site: https://groupaki.com
Year Founded: 1994
542020—(BOM)
Leather Product Mfr
N.A.I.C.S.: 316990

AKIBA HOLDINGS CO., LTD.
Yoko Tsukiji Building 2-1-17 Tsukiji,
Chuo-Ku, Tokyo, 104-0045, Japan
Tel.: (81) 335415068
Web Site: https://www.akiba-holdings.co.jp
Year Founded: 1968
6840—(TKS)
Rev.: $104,755,280
Assets: $75,803,480
Liabilities: $50,725,140
Net Worth: $25,078,340
Earnings: $1,930,120
Emp.: 241
Fiscal Year-end: 03/31/24
Memory Product Mfr
N.A.I.C.S.: 334419

AKIBANK PJSC
88a Mira Avenue, Naberezhnye
Chelny, 423818, Russia
Tel.: (7) 8552773388
Web Site: http://www.akibank.ru
Year Founded: 1993
Sales Range: Less than $1 Million
Commercial Banking Services
N.A.I.C.S.: 522110

AKIKAWA FOODS & FARMS CO., LTD.
10317 Niho Shimo, Yamaguchi,
7530303, Japan
Tel.: (81) 839290630
Web Site:
https://www.akikawabokuen.com
Year Founded: 1979
1380—(TKS)
Rev.: $48,861,120
Assets: $46,600,500
Liabilities: $32,144,430
Net Worth: $14,456,070
Earnings: $647,780
Emp.: 473
Fiscal Year-end: 03/31/24
Meat & Processed Food Mfr
N.A.I.C.S.: 112320
Tadashi Akikawa (Pres)

AKIN FAKTORING HIZMETLERI A.S.
Husrev Gerede Cad No 126 Kat 5,
Tevikiye, 80200, Istanbul, Turkiye
Tel.: (90) 2122369930   TR
Web Site:
http://www.akinfaktoring.com.tr
Financial Transaction Services
N.A.I.C.S.: 522320

AKIN TEKSTIL A.S.
Cirpici Kosuyolu Sok No 5/1-2-3-4,
Osmaniye Mah Bakirkoy, 34144, Istanbul, Turkiye
Tel.: (90) 2125436440
Web Site:
https://www.akintekstil.com.tr
Year Founded: 1956
ATEKS—(IST)
Rev.: $58,164,875
Assets: $126,688,772
Liabilities: $46,776,175
Net Worth: $79,912,597
Earnings: ($551,405)
Fiscal Year-end: 12/31/23
Yarn Mfr
N.A.I.C.S.: 313110
Ragip Akin (Chm)

AKIS GAYRIMENKUL YATIRIM ORTAKLIGI A.S.
Acbadem Mahallesi Cecen Sokak No
25 Akasya AVM, Acibadem/Uskudar,
34660, Istanbul, Turkiye
Tel.: (90) 2123930100
Web Site: https://www.akisgyo.com
Year Founded: 2005
AKSGY—(IST)
Rev.: $27,175,146
Assets: $428,190,353
Liabilities: $125,040,177
Net Worth: $303,150,176
Earnings: $171,843,333
Emp.: 263
Fiscal Year-end: 12/31/22
Real Estate Investment Services
N.A.I.C.S.: 523999
Ahmet Cemal Dorduncu (Deputy Chm)

Subsidiaries:

Akyasam Yonetim Hizmetleri
A.S. (1)
Acibadem Mah Cecen Sok Akasya Evleri B
Blok No 25/B, Uskudar, Istanbul, Turkiye
Tel.: (90) 216 325 0372
Web Site: https://www.akyasam.com.tr
Real Estate Services
N.A.I.C.S.: 531210

Saf Gayrimenkul Yatirim Ortakligi
A.S. (1)
Ankara Devlet Yolu Haydarpasa Yonu 4 Km
Cecen Sokak Acibadem, Uskudar, 34660,
Istanbul, Turkiye (100%)
Tel.: (90) 2163250372
Web Site: https://www.safgyo.com
Real Estate Investment Services
N.A.I.C.S.: 523999
Ahmet Cemal Dorduncu (Chm)

AKITA DRILLING LTD.
1000 333-7th Ave SW, Calgary, T2P
2Z1, AB, Canada
Tel.: (403) 292-7979   AB
Web Site: https://www.akita-drilling.com
Year Founded: 1992
AKT.A—(TSX)
Rev.: $86,119,641
Assets: $193,672,189
Liabilities: $90,814,103
Net Worth: $102,858,086
Earnings: ($16,420,057)
Emp.: 1,000
Fiscal Year-end: 12/31/21
Contract Oil & Gas Well Drilling Services

N.A.I.C.S.: 213111
Karl A. Ruud (Pres & CEO)

Subsidiaries:

Akita Drilling USA Corp. (1)
9811 Katy Frwy Ste 225, Houston, TX
77024
Tel.: (281) 994-4600
Drilling Rigs Operation Services
N.A.I.C.S.: 213112
Charlie Proulx (Sr VP)

AKIYAMA INTERNATIONAL COMPANY LTD.
2 34 11 Takara Machi, Tokyo, 124-0005, Japan
Tel.: (81) 336935191   JP
Web Site: http://www.akiyama-international.com
Year Founded: 1948
Sales Range: $5-14.9 Billion
Emp.: 200
Printing Press Mfr
N.A.I.C.S.: 333248
Kazuhiko Hamada (Gen Mgr-Intl Sls)

Subsidiaries:

Akiyama International Corp
(USA) (1)
13311 E 166th St, Cerritos, CA 90703
Tel.: (562) 404-4767
Web Site: http://www.akiyama.com
Sales Range: $25-49.9 Million
Emp.: 20
Printing Press Mfr
N.A.I.C.S.: 333248

Subsidiary (Domestic):

Akiyama Corporation America (2)
13311 East 166th St, Cerritos, CA 90703
Tel.: (562) 404-4767
Web Site: http://www.akiyama.com
Sales Range: $25-49.9 Million
Emp.: 20
Printing Trades Machinery, Equipment & Supplies
N.A.I.C.S.: 423830

AKKHIE PRAKARN PUBLIC COMPANY LIMITED
792 Moo 2 Soi 1C/1 Bangpoo Industrial Estate Sukhumwit Rd, Bangpoo
Mai, Bang Pu Mai Mueang Samut
Prakarn, Samut Prakan, 10280, Thailand
Tel.: (66) 23230714
Web Site: https://www.akkhie.com
AKP—(THA)
Rev.: $10,523,802
Assets: $20,917,623
Liabilities: $3,123,371
Net Worth: $17,794,252
Earnings: $492,040
Emp.: 187
Fiscal Year-end: 12/31/23
Hazardous Waste Services
N.A.I.C.S.: 562211
Uthai Jantima (Chm)

AKKO INVEST NYRT.
Tel.: (36) 703284738
Web Site: https://www.akkoinvest.hu
Year Founded: 2019
AKKO—(BUD)
Rev.: $127,882
Assets: $22,780,521
Liabilities: $2,594,018
Net Worth: $20,186,502
Earnings: ($77,598)
Fiscal Year-end: 12/31/19
Investment Management Service
N.A.I.C.S.: 523940
Zoltan Prutkay (Chm)

Subsidiaries:

NEO Property Services Zrt. (1)
Mariassy Suite 7, Budapest, 1095, Hungary
Tel.: (36) 1 299 2150

AKKO Invest Nyrt.—(Continued)

Web Site:
http://www.neopropertyservices.hu
Sales Range: $150-199.9 Million
Emp.: 650
Real Estate Management Services
N.A.I.C.S.: 531390
Gabor Landi (Dir-Mktg & Sls)

AKM INDUSTRIAL COMPANY LIMITED
Rooms 2708-11 27th Floor West
Tower Shun Tak Centre, 168-200
Connaught Road, Central, China
(Hong Kong)
Tel.: (852) 28507999
Web Site:
http://www.akmcompany.com
1639—(HKG)
Rev.: $216,225,039
Assets: $316,672,083
Liabilities: $124,390,118
Net Worth: $192,281,965
Earnings: $15,401,502
Emp.: 1,499
Fiscal Year-end: 12/31/20
Flexible Printed Circuit Mfr
N.A.I.C.S.: 334412
Zheng Feng Xiong (Chm)

Subsidiaries:

AKM Electronic Technology (Suzhou) Company Limited (1)
188 Lushan Road National New and Hi-Tech Industrial Development Zone, Suzhou, China
Tel.: (86) 51282259651
Flexible Printed Circuit Mfr & Distr
N.A.I.C.S.: 334418
Chai Zhi Qiang (Chm)

AKM Electronics Industrial (Panyu) Ltd (1)
63 South of the Huanshi Road Information Technology Park, Nansha District, Guangzhou, China
Tel.: (86) 2039050288
Flexible Printed Circuit Mfr & Distr
N.A.I.C.S.: 334418
Chai Zhi Qiang (Chm)

AKM Electronics Technology (Suzhou) Company Limited (1)
188 Lushan Road National New & Hi-Tech Industrial Development Zone, Suzhou, China
Tel.: (86) 51282259651
Flex Printed Circuit Mfr
N.A.I.C.S.: 334412
Feng Genhai (Mgr-SMT Ops)

AKM LACE AND EMBROTEX PRIVATE LIMITED
X/6024 Ram Gali Subhash Mohalla
Gandhi Nagar, Delhi, 110031, India
Tel.: (91) 9899173704
Web Site: http://www.akmlace.com
Year Founded: 2009
540718—(BOM)
Rev.: $346,474
Assets: $1,293,136
Liabilities: $255,040
Net Worth: $1,038,096
Earnings: ($3,688)
Emp.: 2
Fiscal Year-end: 03/31/21
Textile Product Mfr & Distr
N.A.I.C.S.: 313310
Anoop Kumar Mangal (Mng Dir)

AKMERKEZ GAYRIMENKUL YATIRIM ORTAKLIGI A.S.
Kultur mah Nispetiye Cad Akmerkez
No 56/1, Besiktas, Istanbul, Turkiye
Tel.: (90) 2122820170
Web Site: https://www.akmgyo.com
Year Founded: 1989
AKMGY—(IST)
Rev.: $16,358,102
Assets: $35,362,833

Liabilities: $1,057,150
Net Worth: $34,305,684
Earnings: $12,854,520
Emp.: 6
Fiscal Year-end: 12/31/21
Real Estate Investment Services
N.A.I.C.S.: 523999
Raif Ali Dinckok (Chm)

AKO STONEWOOD INC.
2183 Shawanaga Trail, Mississauga, L5H 3X6, ON, Canada
Tel.: (905) 990-1670
Rev.: $12,400,000
Emp.: 28
Flooring Contractors
N.A.I.C.S.: 238330
Mary Grace Ferrari (Owner)

AKOBO MINERALS AB
Sodra Allegatan 13, 41301, Gothenburg, Sweden
Tel.: (46) 92804014
Web Site:
https://www.akobominerals.com
Year Founded: 2009
AKOBO—(EUR)
Assets: $10,542,051
Liabilities: $798,346
Net Worth: $9,743,705
Earnings: ($1,203,769)
Emp.: 41
Fiscal Year-end: 12/31/22
Gold Exploration Services
N.A.I.C.S.: 212220
Jorgen Evjen (CEO)

AKORA RESOURCES LIMITED
12 Anderson Street, Princes Hill, Ballarat, 3350, VIC, Australia
Tel.: (61) 419449833
Web Site: https://www.akoravy.com
Year Founded: 2009
AKO—(ASX)
Rev.: $6,888
Assets: $7,348,761
Liabilities: $115,188
Net Worth: $7,233,573
Earnings: ($1,039,949)
Fiscal Year-end: 12/31/23
Iron Ore Mining Services
N.A.I.C.S.: 212210
John Michael Madden (Sec)

AKRITAS S.A.
3 Sokratis Economou Str, 68100, Alexandroupoli, Greece
Tel.: (30) 2551089810
Web Site: https://www.akritas.gr
Year Founded: 1977
Sales Range: $25-49.9 Million
Emp.: 298
Reconstituted Wood Mfr
N.A.I.C.S.: 321219
Georgios A. Sarantis (Vice Chm)

Subsidiaries:

EMOS LTD (1)
Uzundjovska St 7-9, Sofia, Bulgaria
Tel.: (359) 2 981 38 46
Sales Range: $50-74.9 Million
Emp.: 7
Timber Mfr & Distr
N.A.I.C.S.: 321215

AKS CORPORATION PUBLIC COMPANY LIMITED
102 Rimklongbangkapi Road Jaturatid Road, Bangkapi Huai Khwang District, Bangkok, 10310, Thailand
Tel.: (66) 20335555
Web Site: https://akscorporation.co.th
Year Founded: 1982
AKS—(THA)
Rev.: $27,849,957
Assets: $198,139,154
Liabilities: $120,360,215

Net Worth: $77,778,939
Earnings: ($7,136,006)
Emp.: 261
Fiscal Year-end: 12/31/23
Real Estate Property Development Services
N.A.I.C.S.: 531390
Khan Prachaubmoh (Chm)

Subsidiaries:

MSCW Co., Ltd. (1)
199/9 Soi Sukhumvit 16 Sammitr Sukhumvit Road, Klongtoey Subdistrict Klongtoey District, Bangkok, 10110, Thailand
Tel.: (66) 20968782
Web Site: https://msmoneyspeed.com
Financial Institution Services
N.A.I.C.S.: 522320

AKSA AKRILIK KIMYA SANAYII A.S.
Merkez Mahallesi Ali Raif Dinckok Caddesi No 2 Taskopru Ciftlikkoy, Yalova, Istanbul, Turkiye
Tel.: (90) 2263532545
Web Site: https://www.aksa.com
Year Founded: 1968
AKSA—(IST)
Rev.: $539,118,902
Assets: $352,647,341
Liabilities: $175,342,342
Net Worth: $177,304,999
Earnings: $105,698,383
Emp.: 1,416
Fiscal Year-end: 12/31/22
Textile Products Mfr
N.A.I.C.S.: 314999
Ahmet Cemal Dorduncu (Vice Chm)

Subsidiaries:

Aksa Egypt Acrylic Fiber Industry SAE (1)
Merkez Ofis 4th Industrial Zone Plot 19, New Borg El-Arab, Alexandria, Egypt
Tel.: (20) 34594850
Textile Products Distr
N.A.I.C.S.: 424990

DowAksa Ileri Kompozit Malzemeler San. Ltd. Sti. (1)
Miralay Sefik Bey Sk Akhan No 15, 34437, Istanbul, Turkiye
Tel.: (90) 212 251 4500
Web Site: https://www.dowaksa.com
Carbon-Fiber Material Distr
N.A.I.C.S.: 424690
Douglas Parks (CEO)

DowAksa Switzerland Gmbh (1)
Bachtobelstrasse 3, 8810, Horgen, Switzerland
Tel.: (41) 44 728 2353
Carbon-Fiber Material Mfr
N.A.I.C.S.: 335991

DowAksa USA LLC (1)
2820 E Fort Lowell Rd, Tucson, AZ 85716
Carbon-Fiber Material Mfr
N.A.I.C.S.: 335991

Fitco BV (1)
Bergweg 133 A, Rotterdam, 3037 EE, Zuid-Holland, Netherlands
Tel.: (31) 104158240
Textile Products Distr
N.A.I.C.S.: 424990

LLC NCC-Alabuga (1)
b 4/1 SH-2 St SEZ Alabuga, Yelabuga Municipal District, 423600, Yelabuga, Russia
Tel.: (7) 8555759000
Web Site: https://alabuga.ru
Finance Investment Services
N.A.I.C.S.: 523999
Timur Shagivaleev (CEO)

Nanotechnology Centre of Composites LLC (1)
42 bld 5 Volgogradsky Prosp, 109316, Moscow, Russia
Tel.: (7) 4957754694
Web Site: https://www.nccrussia.com
Lab Equipment Mfr
N.A.I.C.S.: 334516

Alexei Rannev (CEO)

AKSA ENERJI URETIM A.S.
Ruzgarlibahce Mahallesi Ozalp Cikmazi No10, Kavacik, 34805, Istanbul, Turkiye
Tel.: (90) 2166810000
Web Site:
https://www.akcaonerji.com.tr
Year Founded: 1997
AKSEN—(IST)
Rev.: $1,409,649,100
Assets: $1,026,470,862
Liabilities: $440,887,212
Net Worth: $585,583,650
Earnings: $150,887,308
Emp.: 1,234
Fiscal Year-end: 12/31/22
Electric Power Generation
N.A.I.C.S.: 221112
Saban Cemil Kazanci (Chm & CEO)

AKSH OPTIFIBRE LIMITED
A-35 2nd Floor Mohan Co-operative Industrial Estate, Mathura Road, New Delhi, 110044, India
Tel.: (91) 1149991700
Web Site:
https://www.akshoptifibre.com
Year Founded: 1986
532351—(BOM)
Rev.: $43,802,768
Assets: $65,467,393
Liabilities: $51,329,938
Net Worth: $14,137,455
Earnings: ($56,688)
Fiscal Year-end: 03/31/22
Fiber Optic Cable Mfr
N.A.I.C.S.: 335921
Gaurav Mehta (Sec)

AKSHAR SPINTEX LIMITED
102/2 Plot No 2 Kalavad-Ranuja Road Kalavad Shitla, At Haripar, Jamnagar, 361013, Gujarat, India
Tel.: (91) 7574887001
Web Site:
https://www.aksharspintex.in
AKSHAR—(NSE)
Rev.: $18,826,298
Assets: $10,434,142
Liabilities: $4,886,577
Net Worth: $5,547,565
Earnings: ($377,327)
Emp.: 195
Fiscal Year-end: 03/31/23
Textile Products Mfr
N.A.I.C.S.: 314999
Pratik Raiyani (CFO)

AKSHARCHEM (INDIA) LIMITED
Akshar House ChhatralKadi Road Indrad, Mehsana, 382 715, Gujarat, India
Tel.: (91) 2764233007
Web Site:
https://www.aksharchemindia.com
Year Founded: 1989
524598—(BOM)
Rev.: $52,006,200
Assets: $55,415,451
Liabilities: $17,233,739
Net Worth: $38,181,712
Earnings: $2,172,370
Emp.: 200
Fiscal Year-end: 03/31/22
Specialty Chemical Mfr & Distr
N.A.I.C.S.: 325998
Paru M. Jaykrishna (Founder, Chm & Co-Mng Dir)

AKSIGORTA A.S.
Poligon Avenue Buyaka 2 Site No 8
Tower 1 Floor 0-6 Umraniye, 34771, Istanbul, Turkiye

Tel.: (90) 2162808888
Web Site:
　https://www.aksigorta.com.tr
Year Founded: 1960
AKGRT—(IST)
Rev.: $362,785,208
Assets: $715,449,462
Liabilities: $605,874,965
Net Worth: $109,574,497
Earnings: $38,966,615
Emp.: 743
Fiscal Year-end: 12/31/23
General Insurance Services
N.A.I.C.S.: 524210
Ugur Gulen (Gen Mgr)

AKSO HEALTH GROUP
Room 515 Floor 5 Jia No 92-4 to 24
Jianguo Road, Chaoyang District,
Beijing, 100020, China
Tel.: (86) 1053709902　　　　Ky
Web Site: https://ahgtop.com
Year Founded: 2013
AHG—(NASDAQ)
Rev.: $2,414,338
Assets: $142,018,117
Liabilities: $3,593,923
Net Worth: $138,424,194
Earnings: ($9,516,577)
Emp.: 9
Fiscal Year-end: 03/31/24
Finance & Banking Services
N.A.I.C.S.: 522291
Xiaobo An (Founder, Chm & CEO)

AKSU ENERJI VE TICARET A.S.
Mimarsinan Cad Miralay Office Building Floor 2 No 77, Pirimehmet Mah,
32300, Isparta, Turkiye
Tel.: (90) 2462326044
Web Site:
　https://www.aksuenerji.com.tr
Year Founded: 1985
AKSUE—(IST)
Electric Power Generation & Distribution Services
N.A.I.C.S.: 221118
Ali Ihsan Beyhan (Chm)

AKTEK GIYIM SAN. VE TIC. A.S.
Cirpici Veliefendi Yolu No 49, Osmaniye Bakirkoy, 34144, Istanbul,
Turkiye
Tel.: (90) 2125436440　　　　TR
Real Estate Development Services
N.A.I.C.S.: 531390

AKTIA BANK PLC
PL 207 Arkadiankatu 46, 00101, Helsinki, Finland
Tel.: (358) 102475000
Web Site: https://www.aktia.com
Year Founded: 1825
AKTIA—(HEL)
Rev.: $274,452,838
Assets: $13,375,000,000
Liabilities: $12,621,973,883
Net Worth: $753,026,117
Earnings: $55,669,113
Emp.: 891
Fiscal Year-end: 12/31/22
Banking Services
N.A.I.C.S.: 522110
Juha Hammaren (Deputy CEO & Exec VP)

Subsidiaries:

Aktia Fund Management Company
Ltd.　　　　　　　　　　　　　　(1)
Arkadiankatu 4-6, PO Box 695, 00101, Helsinki, Finland
Tel.: (358) 102475000
Financial Services
N.A.I.C.S.: 523940

Aktia Life Insurance Ltd.　　　　(1)
Lemminkaisenkatu 14 A 4th Floor, PO Box 800, 20520, Turku, Finland
Tel.: (358) 102478300
Financial Services
N.A.I.C.S.: 523940

Aktia Wealth Management Ltd.　(1)
Arkadiankatu 4-6, 00100, Helsinki, Finland
Tel.: (358) 80002471
Investment Banking Services
N.A.I.C.S.: 523150

AKTIESELSKABET SCHOUW & CO.
Chr Filtenborgs Plads 1, DK-8000,
Arhus, C, Denmark
Tel.: (45) 86112222　　　　　　DK
Web Site: https://www.schouw.dk
SCHO—(CSE)
Rev.: $4,722,403,091
Assets: $4,115,842,630
Liabilities: $2,489,907,540
Net Worth: $1,625,935,090
Earnings: $143,681,903
Emp.: 15,000
Fiscal Year-end: 12/31/22
Holding Company
N.A.I.C.S.: 551112
Jens Bjerg Sorensen (Pres)

Subsidiaries:

AQ1 Systems Pty. Ltd.　　　　　(1)
2 McKay Avenue, Glenorchy, 7010, TAS,
Australia
Tel.: (61) 362346677
Web Site: https://aq1systems.com
Optical Glass Mfr & Distr
N.A.I.C.S.: 334610

AQ1 Systems S.A.　　　　　　　(1)
Ciudad del Saber 154 B Calle Gustavo Lara
Ciudad de, Panama, Panama
Tel.: (507) 62623956
Engineeering Services
N.A.I.C.S.: 541330

BioMar Group A/S　　　　　　　(1)
Mylius-Erichsensvej 35, 7330, Brande,
Denmark　　　　　　　　　　(100%)
Tel.: (45) 97180722
Web Site: https://www.biomar.com
Emp.: 1,500
Fish Feed Producer
N.A.I.C.S.: 114119
Carlos Diaz (CEO)

Subsidiary (Domestic):

BioMar A/S　　　　　　　　　　(2)
Mylius-Erichsensvej 35, 7330, Brande,
Denmark　　　　　　　　　　(68%)
Tel.: (45) 9 718 0722
Web Site: https://www.biomar.com
Fish Feed Mfr & Whslr
N.A.I.C.S.: 311119

Subsidiary (Non-US):

BioMar OOO　　　　　　　　　　(3)
Leningrad region Strelninskoe highway 4,
Lomonosovsky district, 188514, Ropsha,
Russia
Tel.: (7) 8123092211
Web Site: http://www.biomar.com
Fish Feeding Food Distr
N.A.I.C.S.: 424910

BioMar Sp. z.o.o.　　　　　　　(3)
ul Wspolna 23, 95-200, Pabianice, Poland
Tel.: (48) 422270214
Web Site: https://biomar.pl
Medical Dressing Materials Distr
N.A.I.C.S.: 423450

Oy BioMar Ab　　　　　　　　　(3)
Ratorpsvagen 41C, 01640, Vantaa, Finland
Tel.: (358) 400 157 662
Web Site: http://www.biomar.com
Fish Feeding Services
N.A.I.C.S.: 112511
Henrik Arvonen (Mgr-Sls)

Subsidiary (Non-US):

BioMar AS　　　　　　　　　　(2)
Bolstadsvei 24, 8430, Myre, Norway

Tel.: (47) 76119200
Web Site: https://www.biomar.com
Sales Range: $25-49.9 Million
Emp.: 14
Fish Food Production
N.A.I.C.S.: 311710
Havard Jorgensen (Mng Dir-Trondheim)

BioMar Chile SA　　　　　　　　(2)
Bernardino 1981, Los Lagos, Puerto Montt,
Chile
Tel.: (56) 652320600
Web Site: https://www.biomar.com
Sales Range: $600-649.9 Million
Fish Feed Mfr
N.A.I.C.S.: 114119

BioMar Hellenic SA　　　　　　(2)
2nd Industrial Zone of Volos Block No 6,
37500, Velestino, Greece
Tel.: (30) 242 506 1500
Web Site: https://www.biomar.com
Sales Range: $25-49.9 Million
Emp.: 34
Fish & Seafood Whslr
N.A.I.C.S.: 424460
Panos Lagos (Mng Dir-Sls & Mktg Dir)

BioMar Ltd.　　　　　　　　　　(2)
North Shore Road, Grangemouth Docks,
Grangemouth, FK3 8UL, United Kingdom
Tel.: (44) 1324665585
Web Site: https://www.biomar.com
Sales Range: $25-49.9 Million
Emp.: 50
Fish & Seafood Whslr
N.A.I.C.S.: 424460

BioMar S.A.S.　　　　　　　　　(2)
60 Rue Pierre-Georges Debouchaud, Zone
Industrielle, 16440, Nersac, France
Tel.: (33) 545903500
Web Site: https://www.biomar.com
Sales Range: $10-24.9 Million
Emp.: 50
Fresh & Frozen Seafood Processing
N.A.I.C.S.: 311710

Subsidiary (Non-US):

BioMar Iberia S.A.　　　　　　　(3)
A-62 Km 99 Apdo 16, 34210, Duenas, ES,
Spain
Tel.: (34) 979761404
Emp.: 15
Fish Feed Distr
N.A.I.C.S.: 424910
Fernando Alonso (Dir-Fin)

BioMar Srl　　　　　　　　　　　(3)
Via Lombardia n 3/C, 31050, Monastier di
Treviso, Treviso, Italy
Tel.: (39) 0422 898933
Fish Feeding Food Distr
N.A.I.C.S.: 424910

Borg Automotive A/S　　　　　　(1)
Tel.: (45) 86801177
Web Site: http://www.borgautomotive.com
Emp.: 1,500
Automotive Parts Mfr & Distr
N.A.I.C.S.: 336390
Kim Kruse Andersen (CEO)

Borg Automotive Reman Spain
S.L.U.　　　　　　　　　　　　(1)
Calle Italia 52-54, Imarcoain, 31119, Navarra, Spain
Tel.: (34) 948314435
Auto Spare Parts Mfr & Distr
N.A.I.C.S.: 336390

Borg Automotive Sp.z.o.o.　　　(1)
ul Zytnia 5/7, 98-220, Zdunska Wola, Poland
Tel.: (48) 438232306
Web Site: http://www.borgautomotive.pl
Automotive Parts Mfr & Distr
N.A.I.C.S.: 336390
Mariusz Owczarek (Mgr-Pur)

Borg Automotive Spain S.L.U.　(1)
Calle Italia 52-54, Imarcoain, 31119, Navarra, Spain
Tel.: (34) 948314435
Automotive Parts Mfr & Distr
N.A.I.C.S.: 336390

Borg Automotive UK Ltd.　　　　(1)
Newman Park Western Way, Wednesbury,
WS10 7BJ, W Mids, United Kingdom

Tel.: (44) 1215025800
Automotive Parts Mfr & Distr
N.A.I.C.S.: 336390

Car Parts Industries Belgium SA　(1)
Avenue Konrad Adenauer 19, 1401, Nivelles, Belgium
Tel.: (32) 67400250
Web Site: http://www.carpartsindustries.eu
Automotive Parts Mfr & Distr
N.A.I.C.S.: 336390
Benoit Rampelbergh (Dir-Sls)

Dansk Afgratningsteknik A/S　　(1)
Stalvej 18, 6900, Skjern, Denmark
Tel.: (45) 96800840
Web Site: https://www.afgratning.dk
Metal Product Maintenance Services
N.A.I.C.S.: 213114

Fibertex Nonwovens A/S　　　　(1)
Svendborgvej 16, 9220, Aalborg, Denmark
Tel.: (45) 96353535
Web Site: http://www.fibertex.com
Sales Range: $25-49.9 Million
Industrial Nonwoven Fabric Mfr
N.A.I.C.S.: 313230

Subsidiary (Non-US):

Elephant Nonwovens - Nao Tecidos
U.P., Lda.　　　　　　　　　　(2)
Rua Conde Moser 86 - 2, Estoril, 2765-428,
Cascais, Portugal
Tel.: (351) 214646210
Fiber Non Woven Products Whslr
N.A.I.C.S.: 313230

Fibertex Elephant Espana, S.L.　(2)
Sociedad Unipersonal Ctra Sant Cugat a
Rubi 40 2-3a, 08174, Sant Cugat del Valles,
Spain
Tel.: (34) 935830550
Non-Woven Fabric Product Distr
N.A.I.C.S.: 424310

Fibertex France S.A.R.L.　　　　(2)
218 Chaussee Jules Cesar, Beauchamp,
95252, Taverny, Cedex, France
Tel.: (33) 139959520
Industrial & Technical Nonwoven Fabric Mfr
N.A.I.C.S.: 313230

Fibertex Naotecidos Ltda.　　　　(2)
Estrada Vicinal Octavio Pilon KM 2 3 Bairro
Sao Francisco, Cerquilho, Sao Paulo,
18527-450, Brazil
Tel.: (55) 1533848400
Nonwoven Product Mfr
N.A.I.C.S.: 313230

Fibertex Nonwovens S.A.　　　　(2)
3-5 rue de la Croix Renaudeau ZI de la
Pierre Blanche, BP 49, Chemille, 49120,
France　　　　　　　　　　　(100%)
Tel.: (33) 241715555
Sales Range: $50-74.9 Million
Emp.: 120
Nonwoven Fabric Mfr
N.A.I.C.S.: 313230
Jorgen Bech Madsen (Chm-Exec Bd)

Fibertex Nonwovens Tekstil Sanayi
ve Ihracat A.S.　　　　　　　　(2)
COSB Gazi Osman Pasa Mah 6 Cadde No
2/4, Cerkezkoy, 59500, Tekirdag, Turkiye
Tel.: (90) 2827254008
Nonwoven Fabric Product Mfr & Distr
N.A.I.C.S.: 313230

Subsidiary (Domestic):

Fibertex Personal Care A/S　　　(2)
Svendborgvej 2, 9220, Aalborg, Denmark
Tel.: (45) 72299722
Web Site: https://fibertexpersonalcare.com
Sales Range: $75-99.9 Million
Emp.: 680
Personal Care Nonwoven Fabric Mfr
N.A.I.C.S.: 313230
Anders Sogaard (Dir-Ops)

Subsidiary (US):

Fibertex Personal Care
Corporation　　　　　　　　　(2)
733 Commerce Pl, Asheboro, NC 27203
Tel.: (336) 799-1323
Printed Nonwoven Fabric Mfr
N.A.I.C.S.: 313230
Daniel Lee Ellingson (Dir-Sls & Bus Dev)

Aktieselskabet Schouw & Co.—(Continued)

Subsidiary (Non-US):

Fibertex Personal Care Sdn Bhd **(2)**
Jalan Mekanikal 1 Nilai 3 Industrial Park,
71800, Nilai, Negeri Sembilan, Malaysia
Tel.: (60) 67982400
Sales Range: $25-49.9 Million
Emp.: 260
Non Woven Fabric Material Mfr
N.A.I.C.S.: 313230
Peter Andersen (CEO)

Fibertex South Africa Ltd. **(2)**
16 Van Eck Avenue, Hammarsdale, 3700,
KwaZulu Natal, South Africa
Tel.: (27) 317367100
Web Site: http://www.geotextilesafrica.co.za
Nonwoven Fabric Product Mfr & Distr
N.A.I.C.S.: 313230

Fibertex, a.s. **(2)**
Prumyslova 2179/20, 568 23, Svitavy,
Czech Republic
Tel.: (420) 461 573 211
Sales Range: $25-49.9 Million
Emp.: 20
Textile Woven & Yarn Mfr
N.A.I.C.S.: 313230
Bjarne Knudsen (Mng Dir)

Fibertex Personal Care AG **(1)**
Trift 10, 38871, Ilsenburg, Germany
Tel.: (49) 3945216900
Web Site: https://fibertexpersonalcare.com
Nonwoven Fabric Mfr
N.A.I.C.S.: 313230

GPV Estonia AS **(1)**
Valga mnt 7a, 61504, Elva, Estonia
Tel.: (372) 51947327
Electronic Components Mfr
N.A.I.C.S.: 334419

GPV Group A/S **(1)**
Lysholt Alle 11, 7100, Vejle, Denmark
Tel.: (45) 72191919
Web Site: https://gpv-group.com
Electronic Components Mfr
N.A.I.C.S.: 334419

GPV International A/S **(1)**
Haandvaerkervej 3-5, 6880, Tarm, DK, Den-
mark
Tel.: (45) 72191919
Web Site: https://www.gpv-group.com
Sales Range: $100-124.9 Million
Emp.: 80
Mechanical & Electronic Products Designer
& Mfr
N.A.I.C.S.: 334419
Bo Lybaek (CEO & Member-Exec Bd)

Subsidiary (Non-US):

**GPV Americas Mexico S.A.P.I de
CV** **(2)**
Carretera Al C U C B A Numero 175 Interior
27, Fraccionamiento Pinar Industrial III La
Venta del Astillero Zapopan, 45221, Guada-
lajara, Jalisco, Mexico
Emp.: 184
Electronic Products Mfr
N.A.I.C.S.: 334418

GPV Asia (Hong Kong), Ltd. **(2)**
Unit C-F 11/Floor Hollywood Centre 77-91
Queen's Road West, Hong Kong, China
(Hong Kong)
Tel.: (852) 28519914
Electronic Component Sourcing Services
N.A.I.C.S.: 561499

GPV Asia (Thailand) Co., Ltd. **(2)**
834 Moo4 Bangpoo Industrial Estate Soi 11
12 Sukhumvit Road, Muang Dis, Praeksa,
10280, Samutprakarn, Thailand
Tel.: (66) 27092550
Emp.: 1,470
Electronic Products Mfr
N.A.I.C.S.: 334418

GPV Austria Cable GmbH **(2)**
Bahnhofstrasse 50/1, Rottenmann, 8786,
Salzburg, Austria
Tel.: (43) 3614 31 040
Emp.: 73
Cable Assemblies Mfr
N.A.I.C.S.: 334418

GPV Austria GmbH **(2)**
Untermuhlberg 1, 4890, Frankenmarkt, Aus-
tria
Tel.: (43) 7684 88 040
Emp.: 124
Cable Assemblies Mfr
N.A.I.C.S.: 334418

GPV Germany GmbH **(2)**
Daimlerring 33/35, 31135, Hildesheim, Ger-
many
Tel.: (49) 5121 750 990
Emp.: 176
Electronic Components Mfr
N.A.I.C.S.: 334419

GPV Lanka (Private), Ltd. **(2)**
Baseline Road, Daluwakotuwa Koch-
chikade, 11540, Colombo, Sri Lanka
Tel.: (94) 314871500
Emp.: 1,100
Electronic Components Mfr
N.A.I.C.S.: 334419

GPV Slovakia s.r.o. **(2)**
Priemyselna 1214, Sulekovo, 92003, Hlo-
hovec, Slovakia
Tel.: (421) 333214000
Emp.: 230
Electronic Components Mfr
N.A.I.C.S.: 334419

GPV Switzerland SA **(2)**
Via Pra Mag 6, 6850, Mendrisio, Switzer-
land
Tel.: (41) 916408484
Emp.: 300
Electronics Components & Assemblies Mfr
N.A.I.C.S.: 334419

GPV Zhongshan Co., Ltd. **(2)**
No 6 Maonan Road, South China Modern
Traditional Chinese Medicine City Nanlang,
Zhongshan, 528451, Guangdong, China
Tel.: (86) 76023752700
Emp.: 19
Electronic Components Mfr
N.A.I.C.S.: 334419

GPV Slovakia (Nova) s.r.o. **(1)**
Trencianska 19, 01851, Nova Dubnica, Slo-
vakia
Tel.: (421) 918328294
Emp.: 720
Electronic Components Mfr
N.A.I.C.S.: 334419

GPV Sweden AB **(1)**
Kontraktsvagen 1, 721 69, Vasteras, Swe-
den
Tel.: (46) 21179300
Emp.: 400
Electronic Components Mfr
N.A.I.C.S.: 334419

Hydra-Grene A/S **(1)**
Baekgaardsvej 36, 6900, Skjern, Denmark
Tel.: (45) 97 35 05 99
Web Site: http://www.hydra.dk
Emp.: 15
Hydraulic Component Distr
N.A.I.C.S.: 423830
Soren Nielsen (Head-Product Mgmt)

Subsidiary (Non-US):

**Hydra Grene Hydraulics Equipment
Accessory (Tianjin) Co. Ltd** **(2)**
Room 1704 DiYang Tower No H2 Dong San
Huan Bei Lu, Chaoyang District, Beijing,
100027, China
Tel.: (86) 10 8453 7125
Sales Range: $25-49.9 Million
Emp.: 12
Hydraulic Equipment Distr
N.A.I.C.S.: 423830
Lichun Xun (Vice Gen Mgr)

**Hydra Grene India Private
Limited** **(2)**
Shed No 208 Sidco Industrial Es, Ambattur,
600098, Chennai, India
Tel.: (91) 44 4202 2556
Sales Range: $25-49.9 Million
Emp.: 8
Hydraulic Machinery Distr
N.A.I.C.S.: 423830
Venkatesh Kumar (Country Mgr)

Specma AB **(2)**
J A Wettergrens Gata 7, 401 22, Gothen-
burg, Sweden **(100%)**
Tel.: (46) 31891700
Web Site: http://www.hydraspecma.com
Sales Range: $75-99.9 Million
Emp.: 12
Hydraulic Component Mfr & Distr
N.A.I.C.S.: 332912
Morten Kjaer Graakjaer (CEO)

Subsidiary (Non-US):

Samwon Tech (Europe) Ltd **(3)**
Unit 1-2 Northfield Way Aycliffe Business
Park, Newton Aycliffe, DL5 6EJ, Durham,
United Kingdom
Tel.: (44) 13 2530 7130
Web Site:
　http://www.samwontecheurope.com
Hydraulic Pipe Fitting Mfr
N.A.I.C.S.: 332996
Charl Erasmus (Dir-Comml)

Specma Do Brasil Ltda **(3)**
Rua Antonio Zielonka Nr 700 Estancia, Vila
Taruma, 83323-210, Pinhais, Brazil
Tel.: (55) 41 3669 6569
Web Site: http://www.specmagroup.com
Hydraulic Equipment Mfr
N.A.I.C.S.: 332912
Bruno Santos (Mng Dir)

**Specma Hydraulic Shanghai Co
Ltd.** **(3)**
Area A 1st floor 11th Building No 600 South
Xin Yuan Road, Lingang New City Pudong
District, Shanghai, 201306, China
Tel.: (86) 21 6828 4598
Web Site: http://www.wiro.se
Industrial Machinery Mfr
N.A.I.C.S.: 333248

Subsidiary (US):

Specma Hydraulic U.S. Inc. **(3)**
4358 FM1518, Selma, TX 78154
Tel.: (210) 249-3967
Web Site: http://www.wiro.se
Hydraulic Pipe Fitting Mfr
N.A.I.C.S.: 332912

Subsidiary (Domestic):

Specma Hydraulikhuset AB **(3)**
Ruskvadersgatan 7, 418 34, Gothenburg,
Sweden
Tel.: (46) 31647990
Web Site: http://www.hydraspecma.se
Fittings, Pipes & Hose Assemblies for Hy-
draulics Designer & Mfr
N.A.I.C.S.: 332912

Subsidiary (Domestic):

Specma Component AB **(4)**
Svedjevagen 10, 931 36, Skelleftea, Swe-
den
Tel.: (46) 910733200
Web Site: http://www.specmagroup.com
Hydraulic Components Mfr
N.A.I.C.S.: 333998
Magnus Andersson (Mng Dir)

Division (Domestic):

**Specma Hydraulic - OEM
Division** **(4)**
Groenvagen 1, Landvetter, 438 91, Gothen-
burg, Sweden
Tel.: (46) 3 189 1700
Web Site: http://www.specmahydraulic.se
Hydraulic Components, Piping, Hose &
Fluid Conveyance Systems Mfr & Distr
N.A.I.C.S.: 423830
Anders Langnas (CFO)

**Specma Hydraulic - System
Division** **(4)**
Ruskvadersgatan 7, 418 34, Gothenburg,
Sweden
Tel.: (46) 31647990
Web Site:
　http://www.specmahydraulikhuset.se
Hydraulic Components Marketer
N.A.I.C.S.: 423990

Subsidiary (Non-US):

Specma Oy **(3)**
Linnoitustie 3, 02600, Espoo, Finland
Tel.: (358) 207509300
Web Site: http://www.specma.fi

**Fluid Components & Hydraulic Hose As-
semblies Mfr**
N.A.I.C.S.: 332912
Catherine Juva (Mgr-IT)

Specma Sp. z.o.o. **(3)**
Przemyslowa 14, 73-100, Stargard Szc-
zecinski, Poland
Tel.: (48) 31891700
Web Site: http://www.specmahydraulic.se
Hydraulic Pipe Fitting Mfr
N.A.I.C.S.: 332996

Subsidiary (Domestic):

Specma Wiro AB **(3)**
Turbinvagen 8, PO Box 247, Bergsatters
industriomrade, 591 23, Motala, Sweden
Tel.: (46) 1 415 2020
Web Site: http://www.wiro.se
Metal Hoses, PTFE-Hoses, High Pressure
Hoses & Compensators Mfr & Distr
N.A.I.C.S.: 332999
Claes Lofgren (Mgr-Sls)

HydraSpecma Components AB **(1)**
Svedjevagen 10, 931 36, Skelleftea, Swe-
den
Tel.: (46) 910733200
Fluid Control Component Distr
N.A.I.C.S.: 423830

HydraSpecma Do Brazil Ltda. **(1)**
Rua Antonio Zielonka nr 700, Estancia, Pin-
hais, 83323-210, Brazil
Tel.: (55) 4136696569
Fluid Control Component Mfr & Distr
N.A.I.C.S.: 332912

**HydraSpecma Hydraulic Systems
(Tianjin) Co., Ltd.** **(1)**
No 9 Factory No 3 Xinye Avenue, West-
TEDA, Tianjin, 300462, China
Tel.: (86) 15900315984
Fluid Control Component Mfr & Distr
N.A.I.C.S.: 332912

HydraSpecma Hydraulikhuset AB **(1)**
Ruskvadersgatan 7, 418 34, Gothenburg,
Sweden
Tel.: (46) 31647990
Fluid Control Component Mfr & Distr
N.A.I.C.S.: 332912

HydraSpecma India Private Ltd. **(1)**
GB130A Thriveni Nagar Hiranandani Parks,
Greenbase Industrial & Logistics Park Va-
dakkupattu Village Kundrathur,
Kanchipuram, 603-204, Tamil Nadu, India
Tel.: (91) 9840809366
Fluid Control Component Mfr & Distr
N.A.I.C.S.: 332912

HydraSpecma Norge AS **(1)**
Tankveien 6, Svege Industripark, 4400,
Flekkefjord, Norway
Tel.: (47) 41326049
Fluid Control Component Mfr & Distr
N.A.I.C.S.: 332912

HydraSpecma Oy **(1)**
Linnoitustie 3, 02600, Espoo, Finland
Tel.: (358) 207509200
Lubrication System Product Mfr
N.A.I.C.S.: 324191

HydraSpecma Samwon Ltd. **(1)**
Unit 20 Parsons Court Welbury Way, Ayc-
liffe Business Park Durham, Newton Ayc-
liffe, DL5 6ZE, United Kingdom
Tel.: (44) 1325307130
Fluid Control Component Mfr
N.A.I.C.S.: 332912

HydraSpecma USA Inc. **(1)**
875 N Michigan Ave Ste 3950, Chicago, IL
60611
Tel.: (312) 239-6332
Fluid Control Component Mfr & Distr
N.A.I.C.S.: 332912

HydraSpecma Wiro AB **(1)**
Turbinvagen 8, Box 247, Bergsatters Indus-
triomrade, 591 23, Motala, Sweden
Tel.: (46) 705557374
Fluid Control Component Mfr
N.A.I.C.S.: 332912

Schouw & Co. Finans A/S **(1)**
Chr Filtenborgs Plads 1, 8000, Arhus, Denmark

Tel.: (45) 87345800
Web Site: http://www.schouw.dk
Emp.: 10
Financial Management Services
N.A.I.C.S.: 523999

AKTIF BANK SUKUK VARLIK KIRALAMA A.S.

Esentepe Mah Kore Sehitleri Cad
Aktif Bank Genel Mudurluk No 8/1,
Sisli, 34394, Istanbul, Turkiye
Tel.: (90) 2123408345
Web Site: http://www.aktifvks.com.tr
AKTVK—(IST)
Sales Range: Less than $1 Million
Financial Brokerage Services
N.A.I.C.S.: 523160
Serdar Sumer (Chm)

AKTIF YATIRIM BANKASI A.S.

No 8/1 Sisli Aktif Bank Genel Mu-
durluk Esentepe, Mahalleli Kore Se-
hitleri Caddesi, 34394, Istanbul, Tur-
kiye
Tel.: (90) 2123408000
Web Site: http://www.aktifbank.com.tr
AKTIF—(IST)
Rev.: $89,851,153
Assets: $1,514,063,968
Liabilities: $1,347,839,570
Net Worth: $166,224,398
Earnings: $62,307,949
Fiscal Year-end: 12/31/22
Finance & Banking Services
N.A.I.C.S.: 522110
Ahmet Calik (Chm)

Subsidiaries:

E-Kent Gecis Sistemleri ve Biletleme
Teknolojileri A.S. (1)
Esentepe Mh Kore Sehitleri Cd No 4 Propa
Plaza Kat 7, Sisli, 34394, Istanbul, Turkiye
Tel.: (90) 2123408914
Web Site: http://www.e-kent.com.tr
Investment Banking Services
N.A.I.C.S.: 523150
Zeynep Tosun Bilgic (Mgr-Bus Dev)

Kazakhstan Ijara Company Joint
Stock Company (1)
Office 63 51/78 Kabanbaybatyr str, 050010,
Almaty, Kazakhstan
Tel.: (7) 7272281818
Web Site: https://www.kic.kz
Leasing Financial Services
N.A.I.C.S.: 523999

Mukafat Portfoy Yonetimi A.S. (1)
Kore Sehitleri Cad No 8/1 Kat 5 Esentepe,
Sisli, 34394, Istanbul, Turkiye
Tel.: (90) 2123763200
Web Site: http://www.aktifportfoy.com.tr
Asset Management Services
N.A.I.C.S.: 523940
Osman Gencer (Chm)

N Kolay Odeme Kurulu u A.S. (1)
Maltepe Mah Davutpasa Cad Cebe Ali Bey
Sok No 7, Zeytinburnu, Istanbul, Turkiye
Tel.: (90) 2129550015
Web Site: https://www.nkolayislem.com.tr
Financial Payment Services
N.A.I.C.S.: 522320
Haluk Yum (Gen Mgr)

Pavo Teknik Servis Elektrik Elektronik
Sanayi ve Ticaret A.S (1)
Esentepe Mahallesi Kore Sehitleri Cad No
55 Aktuna Is Merkezi K 2, Zincirlikuyu Sisli,
Istanbul, Turkiye
Tel.: (90) 8506110444
Web Site: http://www.pavo.com.tr
Financial Payment Services
N.A.I.C.S.: 522320

Sigortayeri Sigorta ve Reasurans
Brokerligi A.S. (1)
Esentepe Mahallesi Kore Sehitleri Cad No
8/1 Kat 5, Zincirlikuyu Sisli, 34394, Istanbul,
Turkiye
Tel.: (90) 2123408581
Web Site: https://www.sigortayeri.com
Insurance Services
N.A.I.C.S.: 524210

Zeynep Turker (Deputy Gen Mgr)

UPT Odeme Hizmetleri A.S. (1)
Maltepe Mah Cebe Ali Bey sok No 7 Kat 2,
Zeytinburnu, Istanbul, Turkiye
Tel.: (90) 8507240878
Web Site: http://www.upt.com.tr
Financial Payment Services
N.A.I.C.S.: 522320
Mehmet Usta (Chm)

AKTIO HOLDINGS CORPORA-TION

Asahi Bldg 7F Nihonbashi 3-12-2,
Chuo-ku, Tokyo, 103-0027, Japan
Tel.: (81) 3 6880 9001
Web Site: http://www.aktio.co.jp
Year Founded: 2013
Holding Company
N.A.I.C.S.: 551112

Subsidiaries:

Aktio Corporation (1)
Asahi Bldg 7F 3-12-2 Nihonbashi, Chuo-ku,
Tokyo, 103-0027, Japan
Tel.: (81) 3 6854 1411
Web Site: http://www.aktio.co.jp
Construction Equipment Rental Services &
Sales
N.A.I.C.S.: 423810
Mitsuo Konuma (Chm & CEO)

Subsidiary (Non-US):

Aktio Malaysia Sdn Bhd (2)
Lot 33132 Jalan KB 2/15 Balakong, Seri
Kembangan, 43300, Selangor Darul Ehsan,
Malaysia
Tel.: (60) 3 8964 1313
Web Site: http://www.aktio.com.my
Construction Equipment Rental & Sales
N.A.I.C.S.: 532412

Aktio Pacific Pte. Ltd. (2)
No 11 Pioneer Sector 1, Jurong, Singapore,
628422, Singapore
Tel.: (65) 6861 6777
Web Site: http://www.aktio.com.sg
Construction Equipment Rental, Sales &
Service
N.A.I.C.S.: 532412

Aktio Taiwan Co., Ltd. (2)
No 106 Sec 2 Chang an E Rd, Zhongshan
District, Taipei, 104, Taiwan
Tel.: (886) 2 2503 2193
Construction Equipment Rental
N.A.I.C.S.: 532412

Aktio Thailand Co., Ltd. (2)
88/8 Moo 3 Debaratna Road Km 23 T
Bangsaothong, King A Bangsaothong, Bang
Sao Thong, 10570, Samutprakarn, Thailand
Tel.: (66) 2 338 6700
Web Site: http://www.aktio.co.th
Emp.: 465
Construction Equipment Sale & Rental Ser-
vice
N.A.I.C.S.: 532412
Toyokazu Menda (Pres)

Subsidiary (Domestic):

Chigasaki Rental Co., Ltd. (2)
1171 Hagizono, Chigasaki, 253-0071, Kana-
gawa, Japan
Tel.: (81) 467 84 4633
Construction Equipment Rental
N.A.I.C.S.: 532412

Koyo Kenki Lease Co., Ltd. (2)
Kudamacho 797, Kofu, 400-0815, Yama-
nashi, Japan
Tel.: (81) 55 237 7801
Construction Equipment Rental
N.A.I.C.S.: 532412

Kyosei Rentemu Co., Ltd. (2)
1-14 Nishi 18 jyo kita, Obihiro, 080-0048,
Hokkaido, Japan (94.33%)
Tel.: (81) 155 331380
Web Site: http://www.kyosei-rentemu.co.jp
Construction Machinery Rental Services
N.A.I.C.S.: 532412

Subsidiary (Non-US):

PT. Aktio Equipment Indonesia (2)
Jl Kapuk Blok F23 No 6 Unit No 2 Delta

Silikon 3, Lippo Cikarang, Bekasi, Indonesia
Tel.: (62) 21 2808 5182
Construction Equipment Rental
N.A.I.C.S.: 532412

Subsidiary (Domestic):

SHINTECHNO Corporation (2)
Asahi Bldg 8F Nihonbashi 3-12-2, Chuo-ku,
Tokyo, 103-0027, Japan
Tel.: (81) 3 6854 1210
Web Site: http://www.shin-techno.co.jp
Electric Equipment Rental
N.A.I.C.S.: 532490
Hisashi Miura (Pres)

SRS Co., Ltd. (2)
Asahi Bldg 8F Nihonbashi 3-12-2, Chuo-ku,
Tokyo, 103-0027, Japan (100%)
Tel.: (81) 3 3517 3360
Web Site: http://www.srscorp.co.jp
Sales Range: $75-99.9 Million
Emp.: 362
Construction Machinery Rental Services
N.A.I.C.S.: 532412

Sainichi Co., Ltd. (2)
125-1 Chikumazawa, Iruma-gun, Miyoshi,
354-0063, Saitama, Japan
Tel.: (81) 49 257 0777
Construction Equipment Rental
N.A.I.C.S.: 532412

Sokuto Co., Ltd. (2)
1338-2 Nishiyokamachi, Saga, 840-0034,
Saga, Japan
Tel.: (81) 952 26 0117
Construction Equipment Rental
N.A.I.C.S.: 532412

SANSHIN CORPORATION (1)
7F Yanagibashi First Bldg 2-19-6 Yanag-
ibashi, Taito-Ku, Tokyo, 111-0052,
Japan (95.93%)
Tel.: (81) 3 58253700
Web Site: http://www.sanshin-corp.co.jp
Construction Engineering Services
N.A.I.C.S.: 541330
Kazumi Ohsawa (Pres)

Tomec Corporation (1)
Kawatsuma Kawagishimae 1362, Sashima-
gun, Goka, 306-0314, Ibaraki, Japan
Tel.: (81) 280 84 3860
Web Site: http://www.tomec.jp
Construction Equipment Mfr, Sales, Rental
& Repair Services
N.A.I.C.S.: 423810
Miya Tadao (Pres)

AKTIV PROPERTIES REIT

Plovdiv 37 Nestor Abadjiev Street
floor 2, Plovdiv, Bulgaria
Tel.: (359) 32604710
Web Site:
https://www.aktivproperties.com
5AX—(BUL)
Rev.: $8,966,603
Assets: $13,043,372
Liabilities: $88,750
Net Worth: $12,954,623
Earnings: $772,410
Fiscal Year-end: 12/31/19
Real Estate Manangement Services
N.A.I.C.S.: 531390
Dimitar Georgiev Rusev (Chm)

AKTOBE METALWARE PLANT JSC

Yeset batyr 9 B, Medeu district,
031100, Kromtau, Kazakhstan
Tel.: (7) 132773602
AKZM—(KAZ)
Rev.: $3,654,203
Assets: $2,951,496
Liabilities: $1,481,177
Net Worth: $1,470,320
Earnings: $56,498
Fiscal Year-end: 12/31/20
Petroleum Product Merchant Distr
N.A.I.C.S.: 424720
Asanov Sultan (CEO)

AKTOBE OIL EQUIPMENT PLANT JSC

42/4 312 Strelkovaya divisiya ave,
030000, Aktobe, Kazakhstan
Tel.: (7) 132536753
AZNO—(KAZ)
Rev.: $18,658,719
Assets: $17,098,103
Liabilities: $7,742,930
Net Worth: $9,355,173
Earnings: $1,078,165
Fiscal Year-end: 12/31/23
Oil & Gas Field Machinery Equipment
Mfr
N.A.I.C.S.: 333132

AKTOBE REFINERY LLP

401 plot Sazdinskom C/o, Aktobe,
030000, Kazakhstan
Tel.: (7) 132741061
Web Site:
http://www.en.aktoberefinery.kz
AKNP—(KAZ)
Rev.: $1,603,722
Assets: $3,268,772
Liabilities: $1,679,159
Net Worth: $1,589,613
Earnings: $1,265,064
Fiscal Year-end: 12/31/19
Oil Refining Services
N.A.I.C.S.: 324110
Erasyl Serik (Gen Dir)

AKTOBE-TEMIR-VS JSC

Zhonys Ukubayev 56 2, Badamsha
village Kargaly district, 030500, Ak-
tobe, Kazakhstan
Tel.: (7) 7132717078
ATVS—(KAZ)
Assets: $76,864
Liabilities: $6,947,276
Net Worth: ($6,870,412)
Earnings: ($1,174,027)
Fiscal Year-end: 12/31/20
Mineral Product Mfr & Distr
N.A.I.C.S.: 327992
Irgebayev Keneskhan (CEO & Gen
Dir)

AKUMPLAST JSC

Tel.: (359) 58602793
Web Site:
https://www.akumplast.com
Year Founded: 1985
AKUM—(BUL)
Sales Range: Less than $1 Million
Plastics Product Mfr
N.A.I.C.S.: 326199
Temenuga Atanasova (Dir-IR)

AKWEL

975 Route des Burgondes, 1410,
Bellegarde-sur-Valserine, France
Tel.: (33) 450569898 FR
Web Site: https://www.akwel-
automotive.com
Year Founded: 1972
AKW—(EUR)
Rev.: $1,056,105,218
Assets: $923,013,605
Liabilities: $285,845,021
Net Worth: $637,168,583
Earnings: $11,843,350
Emp.: 8,528
Fiscal Year-end: 12/31/22
Automotive & Heavy Goods Vehicle
Component Mfr
N.A.I.C.S.: 335999
Andre Coutier (Chm-Supervisory Bd)

Subsidiaries:

AKWEL Sweden AB (1)
Susvindsvagen 28, PO Box 1114, 432 15,
Varberg, Sweden
Tel.: (46) 340628600
Vehicle Components Mfr
N.A.I.C.S.: 336350

AKWEL Wuhan Auto Parts Co.,
Ltd. (1)

AKWEL—(Continued)

Phoenix Mountain Industrial Zone, Caidian District, Wuhan, 430100, China
Tel.: (86) 2769601810
Vehicle Components Mfr
N.A.I.C.S.: 336350

Akwel Automotive Pune India Private Limited (1)
Gat N 057/10/2 Off, Taluka Klied Dist, Pune, 410 501, Maharashtra, India
Tel.: (91) 2135678502
Automobile Parts Mfr
N.A.I.C.S.: 336390
Vijay Kaushik *(Mng Dir)*

Akwel Bursa Turkey Otomotive A.S (1)
Ceviz Cd No 17 Minarelicavus Osb, Nilufer, 16140, Bursa, Turkiye
Tel.: (90) 2242806800
Automobile Parts Mfr
N.A.I.C.S.: 336390
Demirci Yildiray *(Mgr-Quality)*

Akwel Cadillac USA Inc. (1)
603 W 7th St, Cadillac, MI 49601
Tel.: (231) 775-6571
Automobile Parts Mfr
N.A.I.C.S.: 336390
Ryan Schook *(Mgr-Engrg)*

Akwel Chippenham UK Limited (1)
5/6 Westpoint Business Park Bumpers Farm, Chippenham, SN14 6RB, Wiltshire, United Kingdom
Tel.: (44) 1249707300
Industrial Equipment Distr
N.A.I.C.S.: 423840
Leigh Hambly *(Sls Dir)*

Akwel Chongqing Auto Parts Co, Ltd (1)
516 Jiarong Road, Yubei District, Chongqing, 401122, China
Tel.: (86) 2363213900
Automobile Parts Mfr
N.A.I.C.S.: 336390

Akwel Cordoba Argentina SA (1)
Lote 22 Parque Industrial Ferreyra, X5925XAD, Cordoba, Argentina
Tel.: (54) 3514503400
Automobile Parts Mfr
N.A.I.C.S.: 336390

Akwel El Jadida Morocco Sarl (1)
Lot 108 Zone industrielle El Jadida, 24020, El Jadida, Morocco
Tel.: (212) 523377424
Automobile Parts Mfr
N.A.I.C.S.: 336390
Ahlame El Benaissi *(Mgr-QSEE)*

Akwel Gebze Turkey Otomotive Sanayi Limited Sirketi (1)
Nonu Mah Balcik Koyu Yolu UzeriGEPOSB 4 Cadde N 41 Sokak, Gebze, 41400, Kocaeli, Turkiye
Tel.: (90) 2626788300
Rubber Product Distr
N.A.I.C.S.: 423990

Akwel Germany Services GmbH (1)
Valterweg 24-25, Eppstein, 65817, Hessen, Germany
Tel.: (49) 61985854110
Automobile Parts Mfr
N.A.I.C.S.: 336390
Kai Brauer *(Sls Dir)*

Akwel Japan Services Co., Ltd. (1)
Bunsyoukudan Building 8F 1/4/5 Kudannminami, Chiyoda-ku, Tokyo, 102-0074, Japan
Tel.: (81) 362615408
Automobile Parts Mfr
N.A.I.C.S.: 336390
Kenji Takayama *(Pres)*

Akwel Jundiai Brazil Ltda. (1)
Avenida Juvenal Arantes 2500 Galpoes 3 a 5 Jardim Carolina, Jundiai, 13212-354, Sao Paulo, Brazil
Tel.: (55) 1148159500
Automobile Parts Mfr
N.A.I.C.S.: 336390
Edimar Oliveira *(Gen Mgr-Plant)*

Akwel Mateur Tunisia Sarl (1)
Zone Industrielle Ennaser Route De,

Tabarka Mateur, 7030, Bizerte, Tunisia
Tel.: (216) 70017080
Automobile Parts Mfr
N.A.I.C.S.: 336390
Raafat Hamza *(Mgr-Industrialisation & Engrg)*

Akwel Ningbo China Co, Ltd (1)
No 688 Yangmei North Road, Henghe Town, Cixi, 315318, Zhejiang, China
Tel.: (86) 57463197884
Automobile Parts Mfr
N.A.I.C.S.: 336390

Akwel Orizaba Mexico S.A. de C.V. (1)
Oriente 12 No 1151 Col Centro, 94300, Orizaba, Mexico
Tel.: (52) 2727242855
Automobile Parts Mfr
N.A.I.C.S.: 336390
Daniel Trueba *(Mgr-Engrg)*

Akwel Paredes de Coura (Portugal) Unipessoal Lda (1)
Zona Industrial de Castanheira Lugar de Corredouras, Paredes de Coura, 4940 105, Tondela, Portugal
Tel.: (351) 961422866
Automobile Parts Mfr
N.A.I.C.S.: 336390
Ricardo Lima *(Mgr-Maintenance)*

Akwel Rudnik Czech Republic A.S (1)
Rudnik 472, 543 72, Trutnov, Czech Republic
Tel.: (420) 499407111
Automobile Parts Mfr
N.A.I.C.S.: 336390
Lenka Jaklova *(Mgr-HR)*

Akwel Sant Just Spain S.L. (1)
Blasco de Garay 5-7, Sant Just Desvern, 08960, Barcelona, Spain
Tel.: (34) 934707960
Automobile Parts Mfr
N.A.I.C.S.: 336390
Francis Pouteau *(Mgr-Production Unit)*

Akwel Sweden AB (1)
Susvindsvagen 28, PO Box 1114, 432 15, Varberg, Sweden **(100%)**
Tel.: (46) 340628600
Web Site: http://www.autotube.se
Sales Range: $75-99.9 Million
Emp.: 265
Motor Vehicle Parts Mfr
N.A.I.C.S.: 336390
Christian Fredriksson *(Mgr-Sls & Technical)*

Akwel Timisoara Romania Srl (1)
Calea Aviatorilor nr 16, Timis, 307200, Ghiroda, Romania
Tel.: (40) 256309555
Automobile Parts Mfr
N.A.I.C.S.: 336390
Flori Burca *(Fin Mgr)*

Akwel Tondela (Portugal), Lda (1)
Zona Industrial Da Adica, 3460-070, Tondela, Portugal
Tel.: (351) 232819800
Automobile Parts Mfr
N.A.I.C.S.: 336390
Filipa Madureira *(Mgr-HR)*

Akwel USA Inc. (1)
39750 Grand River Ave, Novi, MI 48375
Tel.: (248) 848-9599
Automobile Parts Mfr
N.A.I.C.S.: 336390
Chad Halpin *(Sls Mgr)*

Akwel Vannes France S.A.S. (1)
18 Rue Dutenos le Verger, 56000, Vannes, France
Tel.: (33) 297267000
Automobile Parts Mfr
N.A.I.C.S.: 336390

Akwel Vigo Spain S.L. (1)
Camino del Caramuxo 37, 36213, Vigo, Pontevedra, Spain
Tel.: (34) 986821700
Automobile Parts Mfr
N.A.I.C.S.: 336390

Gold Seal Avon Polymers Private Limited (1)
Gold Seal House Opp Ceat Tyres Ltd,

Bhandup, Mumbai, 400 078, India
Tel.: (91) 2225663498
Web Site: http://www.goldseal.in
Rubber Product Distr
N.A.I.C.S.: 423990

Mgi Coutier UK Ltd. (1)
Midpoint Park Kingsbury Road, Minworth, Sutton Coldfield, B76 1AF, United Kingdom
Tel.: (44) 1213136300
Automobile Parts Mfr
N.A.I.C.S.: 336390

Sinfa Cables Sarl (1)
Lot 105 Zone Industriale, Casablanca, Moulay Rachid, Morocco
Tel.: (212) 522727880
Automobile Parts Mfr
N.A.I.C.S.: 336390

AKYUREK TUKETIM URUNLERI PAZARLAMA DAGITIM VE TICARET AS

Tekstilkent Koza Plaza B Blok 24, Esenler, Istanbul, Turkiye
Tel.: (90) 212 438 47 67
Web Site:
http://www.akyurekpazarlama.com.tr
Food Products Distr
N.A.I.C.S.: 424490

AKZO NOBEL N.V.

AkzoNobel Center Christian Neefestraat 2, 1077 WW, Amsterdam, Netherlands
Tel.: (31) 889697809 **NI**
Web Site:
https://www.akzonobel.com
Year Founded: 1792
AKZOY—(OTCQX)
Rev.: $11,972,623,912
Assets: $16,272,215,479
Liabilities: $11,251,793,798
Net Worth: $5,020,421,681
Earnings: $428,303,345
Emp.: 33,965
Fiscal Year-end: 12/31/23
Holding Company; Paints, Coatings, Healthcare Products & Chemicals Mfr
N.A.I.C.S.: 325510
Maarten de Vries *(CFO & Member-Mgmt Bd)*

Subsidiaries:

Akzo Nobel (1)
2505 De La Metropole St, Longueuil, J4G 1E5, QC, Canada
Tel.: (514) 527-5111
Sales Range: $200-249.9 Million
Emp.: 1,000
Architectural Paint & Metal Coating Mfr
N.A.I.C.S.: 325510

Akzo Nobel (Australia) Pty Ltd (1)
2 Capelli Road, Wingfield, Adelaide, 5013, SA, Australia
Tel.: (61) 8 8359 4333
Paint & Coating Mfr
N.A.I.C.S.: 325510
Blake Andrew *(Office Mgr)*

Akzo Nobel (C) Holdings B.V. (1)
Velperweg 76, Arnhem, 6824 BM, Netherlands
Tel.: (31) 26366 44 33
Investment Management Service
N.A.I.C.S.: 523940

Akzo Nobel (Shanghai) Co. Ltd. (1)
No 137 Jiang Tian East Road Song Jiang Industrial Zone, Shanghai, 201600, China
Tel.: (86) 21 57745700
Web Site: http://www.sc.akzonobel.com
Sales Range: $125-149.9 Million
Emp.: 400
Paint & Coating Mfr
N.A.I.C.S.: 325510

Akzo Nobel AB (1)
Sickla industrivag 6, Nacka, Sweden
Tel.: (46) 8 743 40 00
Paint & Coating Mfr
N.A.I.C.S.: 325510

Akzo Nobel Aerospace Coatings GmbH (1)
Sachsenkamp 3rd floor 5, 20097, Hamburg, Germany
Tel.: (49) 40 5268380
Aerospace Coating Mfr
N.A.I.C.S.: 325510

Akzo Nobel Aerospace Coatings Ltd (1)
Unit 1 Meridian West Meridian Business Park, Leicester, LE19 1WX, United Kingdom
Tel.: (44) 116 223 4123
Web Site: http://www.akzonobel.com
Aerospace Coating Mfr
N.A.I.C.S.: 325510

Akzo Nobel Argentina S.A. (1)
Buenos Aires Av Paseo Colon 221 5th Floor, C1063ACC, Buenos Aires, Argentina
Tel.: (54) 1143432011
Paint & Coating Mfr
N.A.I.C.S.: 325510
Rozolso Selro *(Pres)*

Akzo Nobel Asia Co., Ltd. (1)
22F Eco City 1788 West Nan Jing Road, Shanghai, 200040, China
Tel.: (86) 21 2220 5000
Web Site: http://www.akzonobel.com
Organic Chemical Distr
N.A.I.C.S.: 424690

Akzo Nobel Assurantie N.V. (1)
Oude Velperweg 76, Arnhem, 6824 BM, Netherlands
Tel.: (31) 26 3664433
Emp.: 600
Paint & Coating Mfr
N.A.I.C.S.: 325510
Peter De Haan *(Mng Dir)*

Akzo Nobel Automotive and Aerospace Coatings Mexico S.A. de C.V. (1)
Roberto Fulton No 2, Tlalnepantla, 54030, Mexico
Tel.: (52) 5558640715
Aerospace Coating Mfr
N.A.I.C.S.: 325510

Akzo Nobel Baltics AS (1)
Kastani Street 7, 79514, Rapla, Estonia
Tel.: (372) 4892321
Paint & Coating Distr
N.A.I.C.S.: 424950

Akzo Nobel Baltics SIA (1)
Ciekurkalna 1 gara linija 11, Riga, 1026, Latvia
Tel.: (371) 6736 84 91
Sales Range: $50-74.9 Million
Emp.: 10
Paint & Coating Distr
N.A.I.C.S.: 424950

Akzo Nobel Baltics, UAB (1)
Savanoriu prospekt 178, Vilnius, 03154, Lithuania
Tel.: (370) 523 11 132
Web Site: http://www.akzonobel.com
Paint & Coating Mfr
N.A.I.C.S.: 325510

Akzo Nobel Boya Sanayi Ve Ticaret AS (1)
Akcay Caddesi Ege Serbest Bolgesi Gaziemir 144, 35410, Izmir, Turkiye **(100%)**
Tel.: (90) 232 2522700
Sales Range: $50-74.9 Million
Emp.: 210
Powder Coating Mfr
N.A.I.C.S.: 325510

Akzo Nobel Bygglim AB (1)
Fiskartorpsvagen 2, Box 11550, 681 29, Kristinehamn, Sweden
Tel.: (46) 55088700
Paint & Coating Mfr
N.A.I.C.S.: 325510

Akzo Nobel Canada Inc. (1)
2505 De la Metropole, Longueuil, J4G 1E5, QC, Canada
Tel.: (450) 670-7426
Web Site: http://www.akzonobel.com
Paint & Coating Mfr
N.A.I.C.S.: 325510

Akzo Nobel Car Refinishes (Ireland) Ltd (1)
Unit 1d Avonbeg Industrial Estate Longmile Road, Dublin, Ireland
Tel.: (353) 1 4501344
Sales Range: $25-49.9 Million
Emp.: 8
Automotive Coating Mfr
N.A.I.C.S.: 325510
Jon Amor *(Mgr-Sls)*

Akzo Nobel Car Refinishes (Singapore) Pte. Ltd. (1)
510 Thomson Road 16-03 SLF Building, Singapore, 298135, Singapore
Tel.: (65) 6254 8477
Web Site: http://www.wandarefinish.asia
Car Refinish Paint Mfr
N.A.I.C.S.: 325510

Akzo Nobel Car Refinishes (Suzhou) Co. Ltd (1)
Xiang Yang Road 125, 215009, Suzhou, China
Tel.: (86) 512 68257828
Automotive Coating Mfr
N.A.I.C.S.: 325510

Akzo Nobel Car Refinishes A/S (1)
Baldersbuen 31, Hedehusene, 2640, Denmark
Tel.: (45) 46 565666
Automotive Coating Mfr
N.A.I.C.S.: 325510

Akzo Nobel Car Refinishes AB (1)
Mediavagen 1, 135 27, Tyreso, Sweden
Tel.: (46) 850304100
Web Site: http://www.akzonobel.com
Sales Range: $25-49.9 Million
Emp.: 20
Automotive Coating Distr
N.A.I.C.S.: 424950

Akzo Nobel Car Refinishes AG (1)
Adetswilerstrasse 4, Postfach 8623, 8344, Baretswil, Switzerland
Tel.: (41) 449314444
Emp.: 40
Paint & Coating Distr
N.A.I.C.S.: 424950

Akzo Nobel Car Refinishes Australia Pty Ltd (1)
269 Williamstown Road Port, Melbourne, 3207, Australia
Tel.: (61) 3 96441711
Emp.: 35
Automotive Coating Mfr
N.A.I.C.S.: 325510

Akzo Nobel Car Refinishes India Pvt Ltd (1)
62P Hoskote Industrial Area, Bengaluru, 562114, India
Tel.: (91) 80 2204 7000
Sales Range: $25-49.9 Million
Emp.: 39
Automotive Coating Mfr & Distr
N.A.I.C.S.: 325510

Akzo Nobel Car Refinishes Korea Co. Ltd (1)
Yang Jae-Dong 423-4, SeoCho-Ku, 137-897, Seoul, Korea (South)
Tel.: (82) 2577 7233
Web Site: http://www.akzonobel.com
Automotive Coating Mfr
N.A.I.C.S.: 325510

Akzo Nobel Car Refinishes SAS (1)
Rue Jean Casse - ZI les Bas Pres, Montataire, 60160, France
Tel.: (33) 3 44 28 53 00
Automotive Coating Mfr
N.A.I.C.S.: 325510

Akzo Nobel Car Refinishes SL (1)
Feixa Llarga 14-20 P I Zona Franca, Barcelona, 8040, Spain
Tel.: (34) 932670800
Emp.: 200
Automotive Coating Mfr
N.A.I.C.S.: 325510

Akzo Nobel Cellulosic Specialties Inc. (1)
281 Fields Ln, Brewster, NY 10509 (100%)
Tel.: (845) 276-8230

Web Site: http://www.cs.akzonobel.com
Rev.: $2,400,000
Emp.: 12
Chemicals & Adhesives Mfr
N.A.I.C.S.: 424690

Akzo Nobel Center Energie B.V. (1)
Oude Velperweg 76, Arnhem, 6824 BM, Netherlands
Tel.: (31) 26 3664433
Emp.: 15
Paint & Coating Mfr
N.A.I.C.S.: 325510
Klein Baltink *(Asst Mgr)*

Akzo Nobel Chang Cheng Coatings (Guangdong) Co Ltd (1)
Luo Tian da Dao Road Yan Chuan Chun Village, Songgang Town, 518105, Shenzhen, China
Tel.: (86) 755 2714 8450
Powder Coating Mfr
N.A.I.C.S.: 325510

Akzo Nobel Chang Cheng Coatings (Suzhou) Co Ltd (1)
Xiang Yang Road 125, Suzhou, 215011, China
Tel.: (86) 512 68257828
Powder Coating Mfr
N.A.I.C.S.: 325510

Akzo Nobel Chang Cheng Limited (1)
W15 District 11 Floor 17 Flemington Tower 182 Le Dai Hanh Street, Tan Phu District, 70000, Ho Chi Minh City, Vietnam
Tel.: (84) 8 3 8221612
Web Site: http://www.akzonobel.com
Powder Coating Mfr
N.A.I.C.S.: 325510

Akzo Nobel ChangCheng Coating (Langfang) Co., Ltd. (1)
Quanxing Road 32, 065001, Langfang, China
Tel.: (86) 316 5919519
Powder Coating Mfr
N.A.I.C.S.: 325510

Akzo Nobel Coatings (Dongguan) Co. Ltd. (1)
Dalingshan Science and Industrial Park, Dongguan, 523816, China
Tel.: (86) 769 85620333
Web Site: http://www.akzonobel.com
Sales Range: $125-149.9 Million
Emp.: 300
Coil & Extrusion Coating Mfr
N.A.I.C.S.: 325510

Akzo Nobel Coatings (Jiaxing) Co. Ltd (1)
No 1 Dongsheng Road Jeda, Jiashan, Jiaxing, 314100, Zhejiang, China
Tel.: (86) 57384252001
Coil & Extrusion Coating Mfr
N.A.I.C.S.: 325510

Akzo Nobel Coatings (Tianjin) Co., Ltd. (1)
110 Tai Hua Road Teda, Tianjin, 300457, China
Tel.: (86) 22 2529 3001
Paint & Coating Mfr
N.A.I.C.S.: 325510

Akzo Nobel Coatings A.E. (1)
Parodos Kolokotronis 10, Kryoneri, 14568, Athens, Greece
Tel.: (30) 2106220621
Web Site: http://www.sikkenscr.gr
Sales Range: $25-49.9 Million
Emp.: 20
Paint & Coating Mfr
N.A.I.C.S.: 325510

Akzo Nobel Coatings AG (1)
Taschmattstrasse 16, 6015, Lucerne, Switzerland
Tel.: (41) 41 268 14 14
Web Site: http://www.akzonobel.com
Paint & Coating Mfr
N.A.I.C.S.: 325510

Subsidiary (Domestic):

Jordan Peinture SA (2)
2 Chemin de la Colice, Crissier, 1023, Lau-

sanne, Switzerland
Tel.: (41) 216376655
Web Site: http://www.jordan-peinture.ch
Paint Varnish & Supplies Merchant Whslr
N.A.I.C.S.: 424950

Akzo Nobel Coatings AS (1)
Floisbonnvieen 6 1412 Sofiemyr, 1412, Kolbotn, Norway
Tel.: (47) 66819400
Web Site: http://www.akzonobel.com
Sales Range: $50-74.9 Million
Emp.: 70
Paint & Coating Distr
N.A.I.C.S.: 424950

Akzo Nobel Coatings B.V. (1)
Rijksstraatweg 31, Sassenheim, 2171 AJ, Netherlands (100%)
Tel.: (31) 713086944
Sales Range: $1-4.9 Billion
Emp.: 1,200
Holding Company for Coatings & Resins
N.A.I.C.S.: 325510

Akzo Nobel Coatings GmbH (1)
Zetschegasse 9, Vienna, 1230, Austria
Tel.: (43) 1 767 4488 322
Web Site: http://www.akzonobel.com
Paint & Coating Distr
N.A.I.C.S.: 424950

Akzo Nobel Coatings GmbH (1)
Kruppstrasse 30, 70469, Stuttgart, Germany
Tel.: (49) 711 8951 0
Web Site: http://www.akzonobel.com
Paint & Coating Mfr
N.A.I.C.S.: 325510

Akzo Nobel Coatings India Private Ltd (1)
2B - 2nd floor shyams garden No 10 Khader Nawaz Khan Road, Nawaz Khan Road, 600 034, Chennai, India
Tel.: (91) 44 42903737
Emp.: 10
Paint & Coating Mfr
N.A.I.C.S.: 325510

Akzo Nobel Coatings International B.V. (1)
Rijksstraatweg 31, Sassenheim, 2171 AJ, Netherlands (100%)
Tel.: (31) 713086944
Sales Range: $400-449.9 Million
Emp.: 1,200
Mfr of Paints, Stains, Synthetic Resins
N.A.I.C.S.: 325510

Akzo Nobel Coatings K.K. (1)
3-20 Yoshino-cho, Suita, 564-0054, Osaka, Japan
Tel.: (81) 6 6330 1151
Web Site: http://www.akzonobel.com
Paint & Coating Mfr
N.A.I.C.S.: 325510

Akzo Nobel Coatings Oy (1)
Malmarintie 20, 01380, Vantaa, Finland
Tel.: (358) 108 419 500
Web Site: http://www.akzonobel.com
Paint & Coating Mfr
N.A.I.C.S.: 325510

Akzo Nobel Coatings SrL (1)
Bd Regiei nr 6D bl 4 parter sector 6, Bucharest, 060204, Romania
Tel.: (40) 721240584
Paint & Coating Distr
N.A.I.C.S.: 424950

Akzo Nobel Coatings Trading Ltd (1)
98/21 Moo 11 Phuddamonthon 5 Rd Raikhing, Sam Phran, 73210, Thailand
Tel.: (66) 2811 8421
Paint & Coaitng Mfr
N.A.I.C.S.: 325510

Akzo Nobel Coatings Vietnam Limited (1)
Lot 107 Amata Industrial Park, Bien Hoa, 70000, Dong Nai, Vietnam
Tel.: (84) 61 3936 389
Sales Range: $25-49.9 Million
Emp.: 80
Paint & Coating Mfr
N.A.I.C.S.: 325510

Akzo Nobel Coatings Zrt (1)
Vacist 45, 1037, Budapest, Hungary

Tel.: (36) 1 430 3950
Emp.: 30
Paint & Coating Mfr
N.A.I.C.S.: 325510

Akzo Nobel Coatings sp. z o.o. (1)
Ul Cybernetyki 7B, 02-677, Warsaw, Poland
Tel.: (48) 22 321 0621
Web Site: http://www.akzonobel.com
Automotive Paint Distr
N.A.I.C.S.: 424950

Akzo Nobel Coatings, S.L. (1)
Felix Llarga 14, 08040, Barcelona, Spain
Tel.: (34) 934842730
Paint & Coating Mfr
N.A.I.C.S.: 325510

Akzo Nobel Coil Coatings SA (1)
Zi Les Bas Pres, Montataire, 60761, France
Tel.: (33) 3 44 31 38 89
Coil Coating Mfr
N.A.I.C.S.: 325510

Akzo Nobel Cross Linking Peroxides (Ningbo) Co. Ltd (1)
No 501 Hongyuan Road Houhaitang Industrial Estate, Zhenhai, Ningbo, 315200, China
Tel.: (86) 574 8625 2484
Chemical Products Mfr
N.A.I.C.S.: 325998

Akzo Nobel Deco A/S (1)
Holmbladsgade 70, Copenhagen, 2300, Denmark
Tel.: (45) 32 698000
Web Site: http://www.akzonobel.com
Sales Range: $25-49.9 Million
Emp.: 40
Paint & Coating Mfr
N.A.I.C.S.: 325510

Akzo Nobel Deco GmbH (1)
Vetales Strasse 198-226, 50827, Cologne, Germany
Tel.: (49) 2103 77800
Web Site: http://www.akzonobel.com
Sales Range: $125-149.9 Million
Emp.: 500
Decorative Paints Mfr
N.A.I.C.S.: 325510

Akzo Nobel Decorative Coatings A/S (1)
Torshovgt 3, 0476, Oslo, Norway
Tel.: (47) 22806150
Web Site: http://www.akzonobel.com
Decorative Coatings Mfr
N.A.I.C.S.: 325510

Akzo Nobel Decorative Coatings Sverige AB (1)
Staffanstorpsvagen 50, 205 17, Malmo, Sweden
Tel.: (46) 40 355000
Sales Range: $125-149.9 Million
Emp.: 500
Paint & Coating Mfr
N.A.I.C.S.: 325510

Akzo Nobel Decorative Coatings Turkey B.V. (1)
Oude Velperweg 76, 6824 BM, Arnhem, Netherlands
Tel.: (31) 26 3664433
Paint & Coating Mfr
N.A.I.C.S.: 325510

Akzo Nobel Decorative International (1)
Bonsiepen 5, 45136, Essen, Germany
Tel.: (49) 201 565 860
Web Site: http://www.akzonobel.com
Sales Range: $50-74.9 Million
Emp.: 3
Decorative Paint Distr
N.A.I.C.S.: 424950

Akzo Nobel Decorative Paints (1)
Rijkstraatweg 31, PO Box 3, 2170 BA, Sassenheim, Netherlands
Tel.: (31) 205027555
Web Site: http://www.akzonobel.com
Rev.: $6,519,820,200
Emp.: 1,200
Decorative Coatings Mfr
N.A.I.C.S.: 325510
Amit Jain *(Dir-North & Central Europe)*

Subsidiary (Domestic):

Akzo Nobel Decorative Coatings bv (2)

Akzo Nobel N.V.—(Continued)

Rijkstraatweg 31, 2171 AJ, Sassenheim,
Netherlands
Tel.: (31) 713086944
Web Site: http://www.akzonobel.com
Rev.: $3,552,907,100
Decorative Coatings Mfr
N.A.I.C.S.: 325510

Plant (Domestic):

Akzo Nobel Decorative Coatings
B.V. (3)
Ambachtsweg 1, 2964 LG, Groot-Ammers,
Netherlands
Tel.: (31) 0184606464
Web Site: http://www.akzonobel.com
Sales Range: $25-49.9 Million
Emp.: 100
Mfr of Decorative Coatings
N.A.I.C.S.: 325510

Akzo Nobel Decorative Coatings
B.V. (3)
Markkade 50, 4815 HJ, Breda,
Netherlands (100%)
Tel.: (31) 765251000
Web Site: http://www.akzonobel.com
Sales Range: $25-49.9 Million
Emp.: 40
Mfr of Paints
N.A.I.C.S.: 325510

Akzo Nobel Decorative Coatings
B.V. (3)
Zevenakkersweg 4, Wapenveld, 8191 AA,
Netherlands (100%)
Tel.: (31) 384471911
Web Site: http://www.deco.akzonobel.com
Sales Range: $50-74.9 Million
Emp.: 130
Mfr of Coatings
N.A.I.C.S.: 325510

Joint Venture (Non-US):

Akzo Nobel Industrial Finishes
AB (2)
Odensvivagen 32, SE 594 32, Gamleby,
Sweden
Tel.: (46) 49314100
Sales Range: $50-74.9 Million
Emp.: 120
Mfr of Coatings; Joint Venture of Akzo No-
bel N.V. (75%) & Nippon Paint Company
(25%)
N.A.I.C.S.: 325510

Akzo Nobel Nippon Paint Espania
SA (2)
14-20 Feixa Llarga, Zona Franca, 08040,
Barcelona, Spain (75%)
Tel.: (34) 93 484 2541
Sales Range: $25-49.9 Million
Emp.: 6
Mfr of Coatings; Joint Venture of Akzo No-
bel N.V. (75%) & Nippon Paint Company
(25%)
N.A.I.C.S.: 325510

Akzo Nobel Nippon Paint GmbH (2)
Lochnerstrasse 12, D 90441, Nuremberg,
Germany
Tel.: (49) 91166880
Sales Range: $50-74.9 Million
Emp.: 150
Mfr of Coatings; Joint Venture of Akzo No-
bel N.V. (75%) & Nippon Paint Company
(25%)
N.A.I.C.S.: 325510

Akzo Nobel Nippon Paint Limited (2)
Hollins Rd, PO Box 37, Darwen, BB3 0BG,
Lancashire, United Kingdom
Tel.: (44) 254760760
Web Site: http://www.akzonobel-ic.co.uk
Sales Range: $25-49.9 Million
Emp.: 20
Mfr & Sales of Coatings; Joint Venture of
Akzo Nobel N.V. (75%) & Nippon Paint
Company (25%)
N.A.I.C.S.: 325510

Akzo Nobel Nippon Paint Srl (2)
Via Emilia 2, 26861, Fombio, Lo, Italy
Tel.: (39) 0377410390
Web Site: http://www.akzonobel.it
Sales Range: $25-49.9 Million
Emp.: 11

Mfr of Coatings; Joint Venture of Akzo Nobel N.V. (75%) & Nippon Paint Company
(25%)
N.A.I.C.S.: 325510

Subsidiary (Non-US):

Akzo Nobel Paints (Singapore) Pte
Limited (2)
3 Changi Business Park Vista 05-01, Singa-
pore, 486051, Singapore
Tel.: (65) 62650677
Emp.: 120
Paints Mfr
N.A.I.C.S.: 325510

Akzo Nobel Paints (Thailand) Ltd.,
Eka Bangkok Branch (2)
283/61-63 12fl Home Place Office Building
Soi Sukhumvit 55 Thonglor, 10110, Bang-
kok, Thailand
Tel.: (66) 2 7299299
Web Site: http://www.akzonobel.com
Sales Range: $50-74.9 Million
Emp.: 200
Decorative Paints Mfr
N.A.I.C.S.: 325510

Akzo Nobel Paints Belgium
NV/SA (2)
Gustave Levisstraat 2, Vilvoorde, 1800,
Belgium
Tel.: (32) 2 254 22 11
Sales Range: $125-149.9 Million
Emp.: 450
Paint & Coating Mfr
N.A.I.C.S.: 325510

Akzo Nobel Paints Taiwan
Limited (2)
52 Tung Yuan Rd Jhongli Ind Park, Chung-
li, 32063, Taiwan
Tel.: (886) 34523116
Paints Mfr
N.A.I.C.S.: 325510

Akzo Nobel Paints Vietnam Ltd (2)
12 Floor 72 Le Thanh Ton St District 1, Dis-
trict 1, Ho Chi Minh City, 70000, Vietnam
Tel.: (84) 8 3822 1612
Emp.: 150
Paint Distr
N.A.I.C.S.: 424950

AkzoNobel (2)
Lambroek Straat 5 D, 1831, Diegem, Bel-
gium
Tel.: (32) 27159595
Sales Range: $50-74.9 Million
Emp.: 35
Deco Paints Marketing & Sales
N.A.I.C.S.: 325510

AkzoNobel (2)
Vyskocilova 1481/4, Prague, 140 00, Czech
Republic
Tel.: (420) 261399100
Web Site: http://www.international-pc.com
Paint Distr
N.A.I.C.S.: 325510

AkzoNobel Decorative Paints (2)
Wexham Road, Slough, SL2 5DS, Berk-
shire, United Kingdom
Tel.: (44) 1753500000
Web Site: http://www.AkzoNobel.com
Sales Range: $150-199.9 Million
Emp.: 500
Lubricant Mfr
N.A.I.C.S.: 325510

Subsidiary (Domestic):

AkzoNobel (3)
Needham Rd, Stowmarket, IP14 2QP, Suf-
folk, United Kingdom
Tel.: (44) 1449778000
Sales Range: $75-99.9 Million
Emp.: 100
Decorative Paints Mfr
N.A.I.C.S.: 325510

International Paint Ltd (3)
Stoneygate Lane Felling, Gateshead, NE10
0JY, Tyne and Wear, United Kingdom
Tel.: (44) 1914696111
Sales Range: $1-4.9 Billion
Emp.: 60
Marine & Protective Coatings
N.A.I.C.S.: 325510

Subsidiary (Non-US):

AkzoNobel Ltd. (2)
Parque Ind Pl 24, 3942, Santa Cruz, Bolivia
Tel.: (591) 33467069
Web Site: http://www.pinturascoral.com.bo
Sales Range: $75-99.9 Million
Emp.: 19
Decorative Paints Mfr
N.A.I.C.S.: 325510

AkzoNobel Paints (Asia Pacific) Pte
Ltd (2)
1 Maritime Sq Harbourfront Centre, Ste 09-
80, Singapore, 099253, Singapore
Tel.: (65) 62959361
Web Site: http://www.akzonobel.com
Sales Range: $25-49.9 Million
Emp.: 100
Decorative Paints Mfr & Whslr
N.A.I.C.S.: 325510

AkzoNobel Paints (Singapore) Pte
Ltd. (2)
22 Soon Lee Rd, Jurong, 628082, Singa-
pore
Tel.: (65) 62676100
Web Site: http://www.dulux.com.sg
Sales Range: $25-49.9 Million
Emp.: 80
Decorative Paints Whslr
N.A.I.C.S.: 325510

AkzoNobel Paints Espana (2)
Pol Ind Domensys II, Agricultura 7 10,
08720, Vilafranca del Penedes, Spain
Tel.: (34) 938191000
Web Site: http://www.akzo.com
Sales Range: $75-99.9 Million
Emp.: 60
Decorative Paints Mfr
N.A.I.C.S.: 325510

AkzoNobel Paints Sp. z o.o. (2)
6 D UI Wybrzeze Gdynskie, 01-531, War-
saw, Poland
Tel.: (48) 223212020
Sales Range: $100-124.9 Million
Emp.: 72
Decorative Paints & Packaging Coatings
Sales
N.A.I.C.S.: 424950

AkzoNobel SA (2)
Centre d' Affaires Objectif, 2 rue Louis Ar-
mand, Asnieres, 92607, France
Tel.: (33) 146883000
Sales Range: $550-599.9 Million
Emp.: 900
Decorative Paints Supplier
N.A.I.C.S.: 424950

Subsidiary (Domestic):

Alabastine Holland BV (2)
Hogesteeg 27 E, PO Box 5, 5324 ZG, Am-
merzoden, Netherlands
Tel.: (31) 735999333
Web Site: http://www.alabastine.nl
Sales Range: $125-149.9 Million
Emp.: 80
Deco Paints Mfr
N.A.I.C.S.: 325510

Subsidiary (Non-US):

Dulux Paints Ireland Ltd. (2)
Unit J South City Business Park Killinarden
Tallaght, Killinarden Tallaght, Dublin, 24,
Ireland
Tel.: (353) 14556099
Web Site: http://www.dulux.ie
Sales Range: $100-124.9 Million
Emp.: 65
Decorative Paints Supplier
N.A.I.C.S.: 424950

International Paint (Akzo Nobel Chile)
Ltda (2)
R U T 76 048 140-8 Puerto Madero 9710,
Oficina 47-Pudahuel, Santiago, Chile
Tel.: (56) 2 544 8452
Sales Range: $50-74.9 Million
Emp.: 10
Paint & Coating Distr
N.A.I.C.S.: 424950

International Paint (Belgium) NV (2)
G Levisstraat 2, Vilvoorde, 1800, Vlaams-
Brabant, Belgium

Tel.: (32) 3 644 0066
Web Site: http://www.international-pc.com
Sales Range: $25-49.9 Million
Emp.: 50
Marine Paint & Coating Mfr
N.A.I.C.S.: 325510

International Paint (East Russia)
Ltd (2)
002 Office Kirova Street 23, 090008, Vladi-
vostok, Russia
Tel.: (7) 4232 346647
Emp.: 23
Paint & Coating Mfr
N.A.I.C.S.: 325510

International Paint (Hellas) S.A. (2)
599 Vouliagmenis Ave, Argyroupolis, 16452,
Greece
Tel.: (30) 210 4295 140
Sales Range: $25-49.9 Million
Emp.: 19
Marine Paint & Surface Coating Mfr
N.A.I.C.S.: 325510

International Paint (Hong Kong)
Limited (2)
Unit 2005 20/F 148 Electric Rd, North Point,
China (Hong Kong)
Tel.: (852) 25 08 7700
Emp.: 8
Paint & Coating Mfr
N.A.I.C.S.: 325510
Patrick Tang (CEO)

International Paint (Korea) Ltd (2)
17th Floor National Pension Bldg 1422-8,
YeonSan-dong YeonJe-gu, Busan, 611-705,
Korea (South)
Tel.: (82) 51 580 6111
Web Site: http://www.international-pc.com
Sales Range: $25-49.9 Million
Emp.: 100
Paint & Coating Mfr
N.A.I.C.S.: 325510

Plant (Domestic):

International Paint (Korea) Ltd -
Chilseo Factory (3)
Gongdandong-gil Chilseo-myeon 17,
HamAn-gun, Busan, 52002,
Gyeongsangnam-do, Korea (South)
Tel.: (82) 55 586 2310
Web Site: http://www.international-pc.com
Marine Paint & Coating Mfr
N.A.I.C.S.: 325510

Subsidiary (Non-US):

International Paint (Research)
Ltd (2)
841-5 Hannae-ri Yeoncho-myeon, Geoje,
656-813, Gyeongsangnam-do, Korea
(South)
Tel.: (82) 55 632 6284
Emp.: 40
Marine Paint & Coating Mfr
N.A.I.C.S.: 325510
Soonho Lee (Gen Mgr)

International Paint (Taiwan) Ltd (2)
20 Yu Ming St Ta Fa Industrial District, Ka-
ohsiung, 831, Taiwan
Tel.: (886) 7 787 3959
Emp.: 120
Paint & Coating Mfr
N.A.I.C.S.: 325510
Philip Yang (Mgr-Supply Chain)

International Paint France S.A. (2)
Route Frontonas, 38290, La Verpilliere,
France
Tel.: (33) 4 74 94 56 28
Paint & Coating Mfr
N.A.I.C.S.: 325510

International Paint Italia SPA (2)
Via de Marini 61/14, Genoa, Italy
Tel.: (39) 0 10 6595 71
Web Site: http://www.international-pc.com
Marine Coating Mfr
N.A.I.C.S.: 325510

International Paint Japan K.K. (2)
10F Kobe Ito-machi Building 121 Ito-machi,
Chuo-ku, Kobe, 650-0032, Hyogo, Japan
Tel.: (81) 78 321 6871
Web Site: http://www.international-pc.com

Sales Range: $25-49.9 Million
Emp.: 10
Marine Paint & Coating Mfr
N.A.I.C.S.: 325510

Subsidiary (US):

International Paint LLC (2)
2270 Morris Ave, Union, NJ 07083
Tel.: (908) 686-1300
Web Site: http://www.yachtpaint.com
Sales Range: $25-49.9 Million
Emp.: 85
International Marine Coatings, Protective
Coatings, Interlux Yacht Finishes, Intergard
Epoxy Coatings, Inter-Zinc Zinc Silicates,
Interthane Polyeurethanes, Intl. Antifouling
Coatings, Powder Coatings
N.A.I.C.S.: 444120

Subsidiary (Non-US):

**International Paint Pazarlama Limited
Sirketi**
Kozyatagi Mah Saniye Ermutlu Sokak Sas-
maz Plaza, No 8 K 4 Kozyatagi, İstanbul,
34742, Turkiye
Tel.: (90) 216 445 44 40
Web Site: http://www.international-pc.com
Sales Range: $25-49.9 Million
Emp.: 40
Paint & Coating Mfr
N.A.I.C.S.: 325510

International Paint Sdn Bhd (2)
Jalan Keluli 6 Plo 762A, 81700, Pasir Gu-
dang, Johor, Malaysia
Tel.: (60) 7 2541112
Web Site: http://www.akzonobel.com
Marine Paint & Coating Mfr
N.A.I.C.S.: 325510

**International Paint Singapore Pte
Ltd** (2)
3 Neythal Road, Jurong Town, Singapore,
628570, Singapore
Tel.: (65) 62615033
Web Site: http://www.international-pc.com
Sales Range: $50-74.9 Million
Emp.: 200
Paint & Coating Mfr
N.A.I.C.S.: 325510

International Paint Iberia, Lda (2)
Aptdo 37 Estrada Nacional 10 Quinta da
Bassaqueira, Azeitao, 2925-511, Portugal
Tel.: (351) 21 219 91 00
Web Site: http://www.international-pc.com
Sales Range: $25-49.9 Million
Emp.: 20
Marine Paint & Coating Mfr
N.A.I.C.S.: 325510

**International Paint of Shanghai Co
Ltd** (2)
Xin Jin Qiao Road 1515, Pudong, Shang-
hai, 201206, China
Tel.: (86) 2161006808
Web Site: http://www.akzonobel.com
Marine Paint & Coating Mfr
N.A.I.C.S.: 325510

International Paints (Canada) Ltd (2)
7885 N Fraser Way, Burnaby, V5J 5M7,
BC, Canada
Tel.: (604) 291-8242
Emp.: 12
Paint & Coating Distr
N.A.I.C.S.: 424950

International Peinture S.A. (2)
2 Ave Foch, Le Havre, 76600, France
Tel.: (33) 2 35 22 13 50
Web Site: http://www.international-pc.com
Sales Range: $25-49.9 Million
Emp.: 47
Yacht Paint & Coating Mfr
N.A.I.C.S.: 325510

**SA Alba (Deco Paints Latin
America)** (2)
Ruta Panamericana KM 37 5, B 1619 IEA,
Buenos Aires, Garin, Argentina
Tel.: (54) 3327447777
Decorative Coatings Mfr
N.A.I.C.S.: 325510

Subsidiary (Non-US):

Pinturas Inca S.A. (3)

7897 Camino Carlos A Lopez, Montevideo,
16900, Uruguay
Tel.: (598) 2 320 891
Decorative Paints Mfr
N.A.I.C.S.: 325510

Tintas Coral Ltda (3)
Av Papa Jopo XXIII 2100, Sertaozinho,
Maua, 09370-800, SP, Brazil
Tel.: (55) 1145435511
Web Site: http://www.tintascoral.com.br
Decorative Paints Mfr
N.A.I.C.S.: 325510

Subsidiary (Non-US):

Unitecta Italiana S.p.A. (2)
Via Martelli 8, Zibido San Giacomo, 20080,
Milan, Italy
Tel.: (39) 029 00 23913
Sales Range: $50-74.9 Million
Emp.: 27
Decorative Paints Mfr
N.A.I.C.S.: 325510

**Akzo Nobel Decorative Paints Bel-
gium nv** (1)
Gustaaf Levisstraat 2, Vilvoorde, 1800, Bel-
gium
Tel.: (32) 2 254 2211
Sales Range: $125-149.9 Million
Emp.: 400
Paint & Coating Mfr
N.A.I.C.S.: 325510

**Akzo Nobel Decorative Paints Sp. Z
o.o** (1)
Ul Wybrzeze Gdynskie 6 d, 01-531, War-
saw, Mazowieckie, Poland
Tel.: (48) 22 321 20 45
Decorative Paints Mfr
N.A.I.C.S.: 325510

**Akzo Nobel Distribution Ouest
S.A.S.** (1)
Service Client 2 Boulevard des Breton-
nieres, 49182, Saint Barthelemy-d'Anjou,
France
Tel.: (33) 2 41 37 50 00
Paint Supplies Distr
N.A.I.C.S.: 424950

Akzo Nobel Distribution SAS (1)
23 Rue Georges Bonnet Ville, 26000, Va-
lence, France
Tel.: (33) 4 75 82 05 10
Sales Range: $25-49.9 Million
Emp.: 6
Paint & Coating Mfr
N.A.I.C.S.: 325510
Dorris Bustin *(Gen Mgr)*

**Akzo Nobel Distribution Ile de France
S.A.S.** (1)
2-4 Avenue De L'Industrie Ville, 69969, Cor-
bas, France
Tel.: (33) 4 72 21 90 56
Paint & Coating Mfr
N.A.I.C.S.: 325510

**Akzo Nobel Energie Hengelo
B.V.** (1)
Boortorenweg 27, Hengelo, 7554RS, Neth-
erlands
Tel.: (31) 742 44 91 11
Paint & Coating Mfr
N.A.I.C.S.: 325510
Peter De Jong *(Mgr-Plant)*

Akzo Nobel Energy B.V. (1)
Welplaatweg 12 Havennr 4150, Rotterdam,
3197 KS, Netherlands
Tel.: (31) 10 438 9240
Electric Power Generation & Distribution
Services
N.A.I.C.S.: 221118

**Akzo Nobel Engineering & Opera-
tional Solutions B.V.** (1)
Oude Velperweg 76, 6824 BM, Arnhem,
Netherlands
Tel.: (31) 26 3664433
Paint & Coating Mfr
N.A.I.C.S.: 325510

**Akzo Nobel Farben
Beteiligungs-GmbH** (1)
Kruppstr 46, Stuttgart, 70469, Baden-
Wurttemberg, Germany
Tel.: (49) 71189510

Paint & Coating Mfr
N.A.I.C.S.: 325510
Volker Wenger *(Mng Dir)*

**Akzo Nobel Faser
Pensionsverwaltungs-GmbH** (1)
Kasinostr 19-21, 100149, Wuppertal, Ger-
many
Tel.: (49) 202322539
Paint & Coating Mfr
N.A.I.C.S.: 325510

Akzo Nobel GmbH (1)
Kasinostrasse 19-21, Wuppertal, 42103,
Germany
Tel.: (49) 202 322571
Sales Range: $25-49.9 Million
Emp.: 6
Paint & Coating Mfr
N.A.I.C.S.: 325510

**Akzo Nobel Holding Duitsland
B.V.** (1)
Velperweg 76, Arnhem, 6824 BM, Nether-
lands
Tel.: (31) 26 366 4433
Investment Management Service
N.A.I.C.S.: 523940

**Akzo Nobel Holding Osterreich
GmbH** (1)
Aubergstr 7, Elixhausen, 5161, Salzburg,
Austria
Tel.: (43) 662 48989 0
Emp.: 60
Investment Management Service
N.A.I.C.S.: 523940

Akzo Nobel Inc. (1)
525 W Van Buren, Chicago, IL 60607
Tel.: (312) 544-7000
Sales Range: $50-74.9 Million
Emp.: 100
Mfr of Healthcare Products, Coatings &
Chemicals
N.A.I.C.S.: 325199
Jeff Jirak *(Dir-Powder Coatings Bus)*

Akzo Nobel Inda, S.A. de C.V. (1)
Privada Andres Guajardo 320 Parque In-
dustrial Apodaca I, Apodaca, 66600, Nuevo
Leon, Mexico
Tel.: (52) 8182869800
Web Site: http://www.interpon.mx
Powder Coating Mfr
N.A.I.C.S.: 325510

Akzo Nobel India Limited (1)
Geetanjali Apartment 1st Floor 8-B Middle-
ton Street, Kolkata, 700 071, India
Tel.: (91) 3322267462
Web Site: https://www.akzonobel.co.in
Rev.: $432,882,450
Assets: $353,753,400
Liabilities: $181,831,650
Net Worth: $171,921,750
Earnings: $39,598,650
Emp.: 1,467
Fiscal Year-end: 03/31/2022
Paints, Chemicals & Starch Mfr
N.A.I.C.S.: 325510
Amit Jain *(Chm)*

Subsidiary (Domestic):

Centak Chemicals Ltd. (2)
15-17 2nd Floor Gold Field Plaza 45, Sasson Road Pune Station, Pune, 411001, Maharashtra, India
Tel.: (91) 20 2612 2136
Chemical Products Mfr
N.A.I.C.S.: 325998

**Akzo Nobel Industrial Coatings
AB** (1)
Odensvivagen 32, Gamleby, 594 32, Swe-
den
Tel.: (46) 493 14100
Sales Range: $50-74.9 Million
Emp.: 170
Industrial Coating Mfr
N.A.I.C.S.: 325510

**Akzo Nobel Industrial Coatings
Ltd** (1)
Unit 04A Mercer Way Shadsworth Business
Park, Blackburn, BB1 2QZ, Lancashire,
United Kingdom
Tel.: (44) 1254 687 950

Sales Range: $25-49.9 Million
Emp.: 12
Industrial Coating Distr
N.A.I.C.S.: 424950

**Akzo Nobel Industrial Coatings
Mexico SA de CV** (1)
Anillo Periferico 205 km 16 64, 66000, Villa
de Garcia, Nuevo Leon, Mexico
Tel.: (52) 81 1365 3000
Sales Range: $25-49.9 Million
Emp.: 5
Coil & Extrusion Coating Mfr
N.A.I.C.S.: 325510

**Akzo Nobel Industrial Coatings
SA** (1)
Poligono Industrial Can Prunera 9, 08759,
Vallirana, Spain
Tel.: (34) 93 680 69 00
Industrial Coating Mfr
N.A.I.C.S.: 325510

**Akzo Nobel Industrial Coatings Sdn
Bhd** (1)
Lot 1&2 Jalan Gangsa, Pasir Gudang,
81700, Johor, Malaysia
Tel.: (60) 7 254 1122
Emp.: 50
Industrial Coating Mfr
N.A.I.C.S.: 325510

**Akzo Nobel Industrial Coatings Sp. z
o.o.** (1)
Ul Duninowska 9, 87-800, Wloclawek, Po-
land
Tel.: (48) 54 4121921
Sales Range: $25-49.9 Million
Emp.: 20
Industrial Coating Mfr
N.A.I.C.S.: 325510

**Akzo Nobel Industrial Finishes
GmbH** (1)
Lochnerstrasse 12, 90441, Nuremberg,
Germany
Tel.: (49) 911 66880
Industrial Coating Mfr
N.A.I.C.S.: 325510

**Akzo Nobel Industrial Paints,
S.L.** (1)
Poligono Industrial Can Prunera s/n Apar-
tado de Correos 9, 08759, Vallirana, Barce-
lona, Spain
Tel.: (34) 936806900
Web Site: http://www.interpon.com
Sales Range: $50-74.9 Million
Emp.: 150
Industrial Paints Mfr
N.A.I.C.S.: 325510

Akzo Nobel Industries Limited (1)
8 Callaway Pl, Wetherill Park, 2164, NSW,
Australia
Tel.: (61) 2 9616 6900
Emp.: 30
Paint & Coating Mfr
N.A.I.C.S.: 325510
Peter Black *(Dir-Functional)*

**Akzo Nobel Insurance Management
B.V.** (1)
Oude Velperweg 76, 6824 BM, Arnhem,
Netherlands
Tel.: (31) 26 3664433
Sales Range: $700-749.9 Million
Emp.: 1,100
General Insurance Services
N.A.I.C.S.: 524298

Akzo Nobel Kemipol A.S. (1)
Kemalpasa OSB Mahllesi Izmir-Ankara Yolu
Ansizca Kume Evleri No 287, Kemalpasa,
35730, Izmir, Turkiye
Tel.: (90) 2328770030
Web Site: http://www.akzonobel.com
Sales Range: $50-74.9 Million
Emp.: 181
Paint & Coating Mfr
N.A.I.C.S.: 325510

Akzo Nobel Lakokraska Ltd (1)
Sovkhoznaya Street 38, 142603, Orekhovo-
Zuyevo, Russia
Tel.: (7) 4954117350
Sales Range: $50-74.9 Million
Powder Paint Mfr
N.A.I.C.S.: 325510

Akzo Nobel N.V.—(Continued)

Akzo Nobel Limited (1)
Portland House, London, SW1E 5BG,
United Kingdom
Tel.: (44) 1254 704951
Paint & Coating Mfr
N.A.I.C.S.: 325510

Akzo Nobel Ltda. (1)
Rodovia Akzo Nobel 707 Itupeva, Sao
Paulo, 13295-000, Brazil
Tel.: (55) 11 4591 8939
Chemical Products Mfr
N.A.I.C.S.: 325998

Akzo Nobel Management B.V. (1)
Velperweg 76, Arnhem, 6824 BM, Nether-
lands
Tel.: (31) 263664433
Investment Management Service
N.A.I.C.S.: 523940

Akzo Nobel Nederland BV (1)
Velperweg 76, 6824 BM, Arnhem, Nether-
lands
Tel.: (31) 26 366 4433
Sales Range: $450-499.9 Million
Emp.: 1,100
Specialty Chemicals Mfr
N.A.I.C.S.: 325998

**Akzo Nobel Packaging Coatings
S.A.** (1)
Poligono Domenys II c/Agricultura 7-10,
Vilafranca del Penedes, 8720, Spain
Tel.: (34) 93 819 1000
Sales Range: $25-49.9 Million
Emp.: 60
Paint & Coating Mfr
N.A.I.C.S.: 325510

**Akzo Nobel Packaging Coatings
S.A.S.** (1)
182 Rue Ludovic Becquet, 76320, Saint
Pierre-les-Elbeuf, France
Tel.: (33) 2 32 96 43 00
Web Site: http://www.akzonobel.com
Marine & Automotive Coating Mfr & Distr
N.A.I.C.S.: 325510

**Akzo Nobel Paints (Puerto Rico)
Inc.** (1)
630 Calle Feria Av 65 Infanteria Km 13 4,
Carolina, PR 00988
Tel.: (787) 641-8900
Paint & Coating Mfr
N.A.I.C.S.: 325510

Akzo Nobel Paints LLC (1)
16651 W Sprague Rd, Strongsville, OH
44136
Tel.: (440) 826-5100
Adhesive Mfr & Distr
N.A.I.C.S.: 325520

Akzo Nobel Pakistan Limited (1)
346 Ferozepur Road, PO Box 273, Lahore,
54600, Pakistan
Tel.: (92) 42111551111
Web Site: http://ww.akzonobel.pk
Rev.: $54,689,420
Assets: $54,196,747
Liabilities: $11,730,441
Net Worth: $42,466,307
Earnings: $3,534,871
Emp.: 217
Fiscal Year-end: 12/31/2019
Paintings & Coatings Mfr
N.A.I.C.S.: 325510

Akzo Nobel Pensions GmbH (1)
Kasinostr 19-21, 42103, Wuppertal, Ger-
many
Tel.: (49) 202 322539
Pension Fund Services
N.A.I.C.S.: 325510

**Akzo Nobel Performance
Coatings** (1)
Strawinskylaan 2555, PO Box 75730, 1070
AS, Amsterdam, Netherlands
Tel.: (31) 205027555
Web Site: http://www.akzonobel.com
Sales Range: $5-14.9 Billion
Emp.: 21,000
Performance Coatings Mfr
N.A.I.C.S.: 325998

Plant (Non-US):

Akzo Coatings Ltda -Tintas (2)

Rua Assumpta Sabatini Rossi 1650, San
Bernardo Do Campo, 09842 000, Sao
Paulo, Brazil (100%)
Tel.: (55) 1143461818
Web Site: http://www.akzonobel.com
Sales Range: $50-74.9 Million
Emp.: 200
Performance Coatings, Marine & Protective
Coatings Sales & Marketing
N.A.I.C.S.: 325510

Subsidiary (Non-US):

Akzo Nobel Aerospace Coatings (2)
Cironvallazione Nomemtona 180 B, 00162,
Rome, Italy
Tel.: (39) 0697749411
Sales Range: $25-49.9 Million
Emp.: 38
Mfr of Adhesive & Coating Systems
N.A.I.C.S.: 325520

Subsidiary (Domestic):

Akzo Nobel Car Refinishes bv (2)
Rijksstraatweg 31, 2171 AJ, Sassenheim,
Netherlands (100%)
Tel.: (31) 713086944
Web Site: http://www.akzonobel.com
Sales Range: $450-499.9 Million
Emp.: 1,200
Car Refinish Production & Research & De-
velopment
N.A.I.C.S.: 325510

Subsidiary (US):

Akzo Nobel Coatings Inc. (2)
2031 Nelson Miller Pkwy, Louisville, KY
40223 (100%)
Tel.: (502) 254-0470
Web Site: http://www.akzonobel.com
Sales Range: $25-49.9 Million
Emp.: 25
Industrial Finishes Mfr
N.A.I.C.S.: 325510

Plant (Domestic):

Akzo Nobel Coatings Inc. (3)
1000 Industrial Park Dr, Clinton, MS 39056-
3210
Tel.: (601) 924-7222
Web Site: http://www.akzonobel.com
Paints & Coatings
N.A.I.C.S.: 325510

Akzo Nobel Coatings Inc. (3)
1550 Progress Dr, Springfield, OH 45505-
4456
Tel.: (937) 322-2671
Sales Range: $25-49.9 Million
Emp.: 12
Paint & Coating Services
N.A.I.C.S.: 325510

Akzo Nobel Coatings Inc. (3)
1 E Water St, Waukegan, IL 60085-5635
Tel.: (847) 623-4200
Paint & Coatings
N.A.I.C.S.: 325510

Akzo Nobel Coatings Inc. (3)
1313 Windsor Ave, Columbus, OH 43211-
2851
Tel.: (614) 294-3361
Chemical Coatings Mfr
N.A.I.C.S.: 325510

Akzo Nobel Coatings Inc. (3)
1629 Vanderbilt Rd, Birmingham, AL 35234-
1413
Tel.: (205) 323-5201
Web Site: http://www.akzonobel-ccna.com
Sales Range: $25-49.9 Million
Mfr of Coil Coatings
N.A.I.C.S.: 325510

Akzo Nobel Coatings Inc. (KY) (3)
4730 Critten Dr, Louisville, KY
40209 (100%)
Tel.: (502) 367-6111
Web Site: http://www.akzonobel-if.com
Sales Range: $25-49.9 Million
Mfr of Plastic & Wood Adhesive & Coating
Products
N.A.I.C.S.: 325520

Akzo Nobel Coatings Inc. (MI) (3)

1845 Maxwell St, Troy, MI
48084-4510 (100%)
Tel.: (248) 637-0400
Resins & Coatings
N.A.I.C.S.: 325510

Subsidiary (Non-US):

Akzo Nobel Coatings Ltd. (2)
110 Woodbine Downs Blvd Ste 4, Etobi-
coke, M9W 5S6, ON, Canada (100%)
Tel.: (416) 674-6633
Sales Range: $25-49.9 Million
Emp.: 30
Mfg., Marketing & Sales of Coatings
N.A.I.C.S.: 325510

Akzo Nobel Coatings S.p.A. (2)
Dascoli 11, 28040, Dormelletto,
Italy (100%)
Tel.: (39) 02486051
Mfr of Protective Coatings
N.A.I.C.S.: 325510

Akzo Nobel Coatings SA (2)
Juan Zufriategui 4501, Villa Martelli, 1603,
Buenos Aires, Argentina (100%)
Tel.: (54) 1147093109
Sales Range: $25-49.9 Million
Emp.: 50
Performance Coatings Mfr
N.A.I.C.S.: 325510

Akzo Nobel Coatings SA (2)
64 Blvd Moulay Slimaine, PO Box 10610,
Casablanca, 20300, Morocco
Tel.: (212) 22678787
Web Site: http://www.akzonobel.ma
Sales Range: $125-149.9 Million
Emp.: 450
Coating Mfr
N.A.I.C.S.: 325510

**Akzo Nobel Package Coatings
GmbH** (2)
Dusseldorfer Strasse 96-100, 40721,
Hilden, Germany
Tel.: (49) 2103771
Sales Range: $50-74.9 Million
Emp.: 180
Package Coatings Marketing, Sales, Re-
search & Mfr
N.A.I.C.S.: 325510

**Akzo Nobel Packaging Coatings
Ltd.** (2)
Holden Works Bordelsey Green Rd,
Bordesley Greed Road, Birmingham, B9
4TQ, United Kingdom
Tel.: (44) 121 766 6601
Web Site: http://www.akzonobel.com
Specialized Coatings Sales & Mfr
N.A.I.C.S.: 325510

Subsidiary (US):

**Akzo Nobel Decorative Paints,
USA** (3)
15885 Sprague Rd, Strongsville, OH 44136
Tel.: (330) 650-4070
Web Site: http://www.flood.com
Sales Range: $50-74.9 Million
Emp.: 500
Interior & Exterior Wood Care Products Mfr
N.A.I.C.S.: 325510

Subsidiary (Non-US):

AkzoNobel (3)
182 Rue Ludovic Becquet, 76320, Saint
Pierre-les-Elbeuf, France
Tel.: (33) 232964300
Sales Range: $25-49.9 Million
Emp.: 70
Packaging Coatings Research, Marketing &
Mfr
N.A.I.C.S.: 322220

Subsidiary (Non-US):

**Akzo Nobel Powder Coatings
Ltd.** (2)
Stoneygate Lane, Felling, Gateshead, NE10
0JY, Tyne and Wear, United Kingdom
Tel.: (44) 1914696111
Sales Range: $1-4.9 Billion
Emp.: 1,000
Chemical Coatings
N.A.I.C.S.: 325510

Subsidiary (Non-US):

Lucoat Powder Coatings tld (3)
203-5 Ba Shihwa Industrial Complex,
676-12 Seonggok-dong Danwon-gu, Ansan,
425836, Korea (South)
Tel.: (82) 314321100
Web Site: http://www.interpon.com
Sales Range: $25-49.9 Million
Emp.: 50
Powder Coatings Whslr
N.A.I.C.S.: 325613

Subsidiary (Non-US):

**AkzoNobel Coatings Vietnam
Ltd.** (2)
Flemington Tower 17th Floor 182 Le Dai
Hanh, District 11, Ho Chi Minh City, Nhuan
District, Vietnam
Tel.: (84) 839629666
Web Site: http://www.international-pc.com
Decorative Paints Marketing & Whslr
N.A.I.C.S.: 325510

Akzo Nobel Peru S.AC. (1)
Cal Campo Primavera Cap Laredo 0 Table-
ros Peruanos, Trujillo, Peru
Tel.: (51) 44435453
Paint & Coating Mfr
N.A.I.C.S.: 325510

**Akzo Nobel Polymer Chemicals
(Ningbo) Co., Ltd.** (1)
No 1801 Mid-Haitian Rd Xiepu Town, Zhen-
hai District, Ningbo, 315204, China
Tel.: (86) 574 86621239
Chemical Products Mfr
N.A.I.C.S.: 325998

**Akzo Nobel Powder Coatings
(Chengdu) Co., Ltd.** (1)
Building 9C Dragon fly industrial park,
610100, Chengdu, China
Tel.: (86) 28 8484 7422
Powder Coating Mfr
N.A.I.C.S.: 325510

**Akzo Nobel Powder Coatings
(Langfang) Co. Ltd.** (1)
No 32 Quanxing Street Langfang Economic
& Technical Development Zone, Langfang,
065001, Hebei, China
Tel.: (86) 316 5919519
Web Site: http://www.interpon.com
Powder Coating Mfr
N.A.I.C.S.: 325510

**Akzo Nobel Powder Coatings
(Ningbo) Co., Ltd.** (1)
Ningchuan Road, Wuxiang Town, Ningbo,
315111, Zhejiang, China
Tel.: (86) 574 5680 1404
Sales Range: $125-149.9 Million
Emp.: 300
Powder Coating Mfr
N.A.I.C.S.: 325510
Eddie Wang (Gen Mgr)

**Akzo Nobel Powder Coatings (Su-
zhou) Co., Ltd.** (1)
125 Xiang Yang Road Suzhou New District,
Suzhou, 215011, China
Tel.: (86) 512 6825 7828
Powder Coating Mfr
N.A.I.C.S.: 325510

**Akzo Nobel Powder Coatings (Viet-
nam) Co., Ltd.** (1)
Road No 2 Nhon Trach Industrial Zone,
Nhon Trach, 7000, Dong Nai, Vietnam
Tel.: (84) 613560730
Emp.: 130
Powder Coating Mfr
N.A.I.C.S.: 325510

**Akzo Nobel Powder Coatings
A.E.** (1)
10 Kolokotroni str, Krioneri Attikis, 14568,
Athens, Greece
Tel.: (30) 210 8160 160
Sales Range: $25-49.9 Million
Emp.: 14
Powder Coating Mfr
N.A.I.C.S.: 325510
Vaggelis Manolopoulos (Mgr-Technical Sup-
port)

**Akzo Nobel Powder Coatings
B.V.** (1)

Rijksstraatweg 31, Sassenheim, 2171 AJ,
Netherlands
Tel.: (31) 713086944
Emp.: 35
Powder Coating Mfr
N.A.I.C.S.: 325510

**Akzo Nobel Powder Coatings
Fze** **(1)**
Plot n FZS2AC 9 10, PO Box 262203,
Jebel Ali Free Zone, Dubai, United Arab
Emirates
Tel.: (971) 4 8862181
Powder Paint Mfr
N.A.I.C.S.: 325510

**Akzo Nobel Powder Coatings
GmbH** **(1)**
Markwiesen Strasse 50, Reutlingen, 72770,
Germany
Tel.: (49) 71215190
Emp.: 80
Powder Coating Mfr
N.A.I.C.S.: 325510

**Akzo Nobel Powder Coatings
GmbH** **(1)**
Zur Alten Ruhr 4, D 59755, Arnsberg, Ger-
many
Tel.: (49) 293262990
Web Site: http://www.interpol.de
Sales Range: $25-49.9 Million
Emp.: 130
Powder Coating Mfr
N.A.I.C.S.: 325510
Salvatore Alfieri *(Mgr)*

**Akzo Nobel Powder Coatings Korea
Co., Limited** **(1)**
203-5Ba Shihwa Industrial Complex 676-12,
Seonggok-Dong Danwon-gu, Ansan, Korea
(South)
Tel.: (82) 31 434 1100
Powder Coating Mfr
N.A.I.C.S.: 325510

**Akzo Nobel Powder Coatings
SNC** **(1)**
Rue de la Gaudree - ZI La Gaudree,
91410, Dourdan, France
Tel.: (33) 1 60 81 81 81
Powder Coating Mfr
N.A.I.C.S.: 325510

**Akzo Nobel Powder Coatings South
Africa (Proprietary) Limited** **(1)**
14 Union Street, Alberton, 1449, South Af-
rica
Tel.: (27) 11 907 8195
Web Site: http://www.interpon.com
Emp.: 90
Powder Coating Mfr
N.A.I.C.S.: 325510

**Akzo Nobel Protective Coatings (Su-
zhou) Co. Ltd** **(1)**
No 129 Hongxi Road, Suzhou, 215151,
China
Tel.: (86) 51 2825 1299
Protective Coating Mfr & Distr
N.A.I.C.S.: 325510

**Akzo Nobel Representative Offices
B.V.** **(1)**
Oude Velperweg 76, Arnhem, 6824 BM,
Netherlands
Tel.: (31) 26 3664433
Paint & Coating Mfr
N.A.I.C.S.: 325510
Peter de Haan *(Office Mgr)*

Akzo Nobel S.A.S. **(1)**
34 Avenue Leon Jouhaux, Antony, 92164,
France
Tel.: (33) 1 46 11 51 15
Chemical Product Mfr & Distr
N.A.I.C.S.: 325998

Akzo Nobel Salt B.V. **(1)**
Stationsplein 77, Amersfoort, 3811, Nether-
lands
Tel.: (31) 33 4676767
Web Site: http://www.akzonobelsalt.com
Salt Mfr & Distr
N.A.I.C.S.: 325998

Akzo Nobel Sino Coatings B.V. **(1)**
Rijksstraatweg 31, Sassenheim, 2171 AJ,
Netherlands
Tel.: (31) 71 3086944

Paint & Coating Mfr
N.A.I.C.S.: 325510

Akzo Nobel Sourcing B.V. **(1)**
Oude Velperweg 76, Arnhem, 6824 BM,
Netherlands
Tel.: (31) 26 3664433
Chemical Products Mfr
N.A.I.C.S.: 325998
Peter Haan *(Mng Dir)*

**Akzo Nobel Surface Chemistry
AB** **(1)**
Stenunge Alle 3, Stenungsund, 44485,
Sweden
Tel.: (46) 303 850 00
Chemical Products Distr
N.A.I.C.S.: 424690

**Akzo Nobel Swire Paints
(Guangzhou) Limited** **(1)**
Guangzhou Economic & Technological De-
velopment Zone, Beiwei Industrial District,
Guangzhou, 510730, China
Tel.: (86) 20 8221 7755
Paint & Coating Mfr
N.A.I.C.S.: 325510

Akzo Nobel Swire Paints Limited **(1)**
Suite 2806 Island Place Tower 510 King's
Road, North Point, China (Hong Kong)
Tel.: (852) 2823 1388
Web Site: http://www.ici.com.hk
Paints Mfr
N.A.I.C.S.: 325510

**Akzo Nobel Tintas para Automoveis
Lda** **(1)**
Carregado Park - Q Carregado, Carregado,
Lisbon, 2580-512, Portugal
Tel.: (351) 263856060
Sales Range: $25-49.9 Million
Emp.: 9
Paint & Coating Mfr
N.A.I.C.S.: 325510
Nunu Andrada *(Mgr)*

Akzo Nobel UK Ltd **(1)**
Bressenden Place, Portland House, Lon-
don, SW1E 5BG, United Kingdom **(100%)**
Tel.: (44) 2079329900
Web Site: http://www.internationalpaint.com
Sales Range: $25-49.9 Million
Emp.: 40
Mfr of Protective Coatings
N.A.I.C.S.: 325510

**Akzo Nobel Wilton Applied Research
Group** **(1)**
Wilton Centre, Wilton, Redcar, TS10 4RF,
United Kingdom
Tel.: (44) 642435880
Web Site: http://www.ici.com
Sales Range: $25-49.9 Million
Emp.: 60
Provider of Technological Services.
N.A.I.C.S.: 541512

Akzo Nobel Wood Coatings Ltd **(1)**
155 Rose Glen Rd N, Port Hope, L1A 3V6,
ON, Canada
Tel.: (905) 885-6388
Web Site: http://www.chemcraft.com
Emp.: 100
Wood Coating Distr
N.A.I.C.S.: 424950

**Akzo Nobel Wood Finishes and
Adhesives** **(1)**
Sickla Industrivag 6, 13134, Nacka,
Sweden **(100%)**
Tel.: (46) 8 7434000
Web Site: http://www.akzonobel.com
Sales Range: $50-74.9 Million
Emp.: 150
Adhesives, Sealants, Leveling Compounds,
Paints & Wood-Processing Resins
N.A.I.C.S.: 325520

**Akzo Nobel industrial Coatings Korea
Ltd.** **(1)**
5ba-203 Sihwa Industrial Complex 676-12,
Seonggok-Dong Danwon-gu, Ansan, 425-
836, Korea (South)
Tel.: (82) 31 432 1100
Powder Coating Mfr
N.A.I.C.S.: 325510

**Akzo Noble Finance United States
Inc** **(1)**

1105 N Market St, Wilmington, DE 19801
Tel.: (302) 478-1820
Financial Management Services
N.A.I.C.S.: 523999

**AkzoNobel (Asia Pacific) Pte.
Ltd.** **(1)**
1 Maritime Square Harbourfront Centre, 09-
80, Singapore, 099253, Singapore
Tel.: (65) 62959361
Web Site: http://www.akzonobel.com
Rev.: $912,112,400
Decorative Coatings Mfr
N.A.I.C.S.: 325510

AkzoNobel Deco GmbH **(1)**
Vitalisstrabe 198-226, Duesseldorfer
Strasse 96 100, 40721, Cologne, Germany
Tel.: (49) 210377800
Sales Range: $50-74.9 Million
Emp.: 200
Decorative Paints Research, Development,
Sales & Marketing
N.A.I.C.S.: 325510

AkzoNobel India Ltd. **(1)**
DLF Cyber Terraces Building No 5 Tower A
20th Fl, DLF Cyber City Phase III, Gurgaon,
122 002, Haryana, India
Tel.: (91) 124 2540400
Web Site: http://www.akzonobel.com
Sales Range: $150-199.9 Million
Emp.: 1,200
Supplier of Paints & Chemical Products
N.A.I.C.S.: 325998
Jayakumar Krishnaswamy *(Mng Dir)*

Subsidiary (Domestic):

AkzoNobel India Ltd. **(2)**
DLF Epitome Building No 5 Tower A 20th
Floor DLF Cyber City Phase III, 122 002,
Gurgaon, Haryana, India
Tel.: (91) 1242540400
Sales Range: $25-49.9 Million
Emp.: 82
Decorative Paints Marketer, Researcher &
Mfr
N.A.I.C.S.: 325510

ICI India Ltd.-Paints Division **(2)**
DLF Plaza Tower 10th Floor, DLF Qutab
Enclave Phase 1, Gurgaon, 122 002, Hary-
ana, India
Tel.: (91) 1242540400
Web Site: http://www.akzonobel.com
Decorative Paints Mfr
N.A.I.C.S.: 325510

AkzoNobel Polska Sp. Zo.o. **(1)**
3 ul Przemyslowa, 08 440, Pilawa, Poland
Tel.: (48) 257866100
Web Site: http://www.akzonobel.com
Sales Range: $100-124.9 Million
Emp.: 300
Decorative Paints Mfr
N.A.I.C.S.: 325510

AkzoNobel Sdn Bhd **(1)**
Unit 3-1 Lvl 3 Bldg A Peremba Sq, Saujana
Resort Section U 2, Shah Alam, 40150, Se-
langor, Malaysia
Tel.: (60) 85655650
Sales Range: $100-124.9 Million
Emp.: 300
Decorative Paints Mfr
N.A.I.C.S.: 325510

AkzoNobel Surface Chemistry **(1)**
909 Mueller Dr, Chattanooga, TN 37406-
0401
Tel.: (423) 629-1405
Sales Range: $50-74.9 Million
Emp.: 150
Specialty Chemicals Mfr
N.A.I.C.S.: 325180

Balakom Slovakia s.r.o. **(1)**
Bytcicka 89, 01009, Zilina, Slovakia
Tel.: (421) 415 640 612
Web Site: http://www.resicoat.com
Sales Range: $25-49.9 Million
Emp.: 100
Powder Coating Mfr
N.A.I.C.S.: 325510

Carbide Sweden AB **(1)**
Stockviksvagen 20 Stockviksverken,
Sundsvall, 85467, Sweden
Tel.: (46) 60 13 40 00
Chemical Product Mfr & Distr

N.A.I.C.S.: 325998

Carelaa B.V. **(1)**
Velperweg 76, Arnhem, 6824 BM, Nether-
lands
Tel.: (31) 26 3662488
Paint & Coating Mfr
N.A.I.C.S.: 325510

Casco Adhesives (Asia) Pte Ltd **(1)**
14 Sungei Kadut Way, Singapore, 728788,
Singapore
Tel.: (65) 6762 2088
Sales Range: $25-49.9 Million
Emp.: 45
Adhesive Distr
N.A.I.C.S.: 424690

Casco Adhesives AB **(1)**
Smedjegatan 32, Nacka, SE-100 61, Stock-
holm, Sweden **(100%)**
Tel.: (46) 87434000
Web Site: http://www.cascoadhesives.com
Sales Range: $50-74.9 Million
Emp.: 160
Industrial Wood Adhesives & Resins Mfr
N.A.I.C.S.: 325520

Subsidiary (Non-US):

PT Casco Persada **(2)**
Jalan Industri Utara 1 Blok SS No 18-19,
Kawasan Industri Cikarang, Bekasi, 17550,
Indonesia
Tel.: (62) 218935858
Web Site: http://www.cascoadhesives.com
Sales Range: $25-49.9 Million
Emp.: 100
Industrial Finishes Mfr
N.A.I.C.S.: 325510

Casco Adhezivi d.o.o. **(1)**
Spruha 19, 1236, Trzin, Slovenia
Tel.: (386) 1 721 99 85
Adhesive Distr
N.A.I.C.S.: 424690

Casco Byglim A/S **(1)**
Tempovej 16, 2750, Ballerup, Denmark
Tel.: (45) 702 77 703
Web Site: http://www.casco.dk
Sales Range: $50-74.9 Million
Emp.: 6
Adhesive Distr
N.A.I.C.S.: 424690
Ann-Cathrine Anki Andersson *(Controller-
Sls & Bus)*

Commenda Adria D.O.O. **(1)**
23 Franje Lucica, Zagreb, 10090, Croatia
Tel.: (385) 13475688
Web Site: http://www.akzonobel.hr
Sales Range: $25-49.9 Million
Emp.: 17
Decorative Paint Distr
N.A.I.C.S.: 424950

**Compania Mexicana de Pinturas in-
ternational SA De CV** **(1)**
Ernesto Monroy S/N, Toluca, 50223, Mexico
Tel.: (52) 7225222300
Paint & Coating Mfr
N.A.I.C.S.: 325510

Cuprinol Limited **(1)**
Wexham Road, Slough, SL2 5DS, Berk-
shire, United Kingdom
Tel.: (44) 1753550000
Web Site: http://www.cuprinol.co.uk
Sales Range: $200-249.9 Million
Emp.: 700
Woodcare Products & Damp Proofers Mfr
N.A.I.C.S.: 325510

De Sikkens Grossier B.V. **(1)**
Handelsweg 26, 1525 RG, West-
Knollendam, Netherlands
Tel.: (31) 756 47 62 00
Paint & Coating Mfr
N.A.I.C.S.: 325510

Decorative Ouest S.A.S. **(1)**
2 Boulevard Des Bretonnieres, BP 40115,
49124, Saint Barthelemy-d'Anjou, France
Tel.: (33) 2 41 37 50 00
Paint & Coating Mfr
N.A.I.C.S.: 325510

Dulux Botswana (Pty) Limited **(1)**
Plot 1240 Haile Selassie Rd, Gaborone,
Botswana

Akzo Nobel N.V.—(Continued)

Tel.: (267) 395 1011
Emp.: 57
Paint & Coating Mfr
N.A.I.C.S.: 325510

Dulux Limited (1)
PO Box 30013, Blantyre, Malawi
Tel.: (265) 1 871 767
Paint & Coating Distr
N.A.I.C.S.: 424950

Dulux Paints ZA (1)
56 Emerald Parkway, PO Box 123704, Al-
rode, Greenstone Hill, 7099, South Africa
Tel.: (27) 11 861 1000
Web Site: http://www.dulux.co.za
Paint & Coating Mfr
N.A.I.C.S.: 325510

Dulux Swaziland (Pty) Limited (1)
10th St Matsapha Industrial Site, Box 1020,
Matsapha, H100, Eswatini
Tel.: (268) 2518 4091
Paints Mfr.
N.A.I.C.S.: 325510
Zanele Nxumalo (Gen Mgr)

E. Beffa S.A. (1)
rue des Draizes 4, 2000, Neuchatel, Swit-
zerland
Tel.: (41) 32 737 70 50
Paint Supplies Distr
N.A.I.C.S.: 424950

ES Sadolin AS (1)
Kastani Street 7, Rapla, 79514, Estonia
Tel.: (372) 48 92 321
Web Site: http://www.sadolin.ee
Paint & Coating Mfr & Distr
N.A.I.C.S.: 325510
Tiit Romulus (Mgr-Logistic)

Expancel Inc. (1)
2240 Northmont Pkwy, Duluth, GA 30096-
5895
Tel.: (770) 813-9126
Web Site: http://www.expancel.com
Sales Range: $25-49.9 Million
Emp.: 30
Manufacture of Chemical & Allied Products
N.A.I.C.S.: 424690
Eddie Bowers (CEO)

Fabryo Corporation srl (1)
SOS Oltenitei No 202 B, 77160, Popesti-
Leordeni, Jud Ilfov, Romania
Tel.: (40) 21 405 50 00
Web Site: http://www.fabryo.com
Paint, Varnish, Plaster & Other Wall-
Covering Products Mfr
N.A.I.C.S.: 325510

Hammerite Products Limited (1)
Wexham Road, Slough, SL2 5DS, Berk-
shire, United Kingdom
Tel.: (44) 3332227171
Web Site: http://www.hammerite.co.uk
Metal Paint Mfr
N.A.I.C.S.: 325510

**Imperial Chemical Industries
PLC** (1)
Portland House 26th Fl, Bressenden Pl,
London, SW1E 5BG, United Kingdom
Tel.: (44) 2079329900
Emp.: 31,070
Paints, Foods, Fragrances & Personal Care
Products Mfr
N.A.I.C.S.: 325199

Subsidiary (Non-US):

ICI Holdings (Australia) Pty Ltd (2)
8 Kellaway Pl, Wetherill Park, 2164, NSW,
Australia
Tel.: (61) 2 9616 6980
Investment Management Service
N.A.I.C.S.: 523940

ICI Omicron B.V. (2)
Velperweg 76, Arnhem, 6824 BM, Nether-
lands
Tel.: (31) 263664514
Paint & Coating Mfr
N.A.I.C.S.: 325510

ICI Packaging Coatings Ltda. (2)
Avenida Dos Estados 4826, Utinga, 09220-
900, Santo Andre, SP, Brazil

Tel.: (55) 44639000
Web Site: http://www.ici.com
Sales Range: $50-74.9 Million
Emp.: 140
Mfr of Packaging Coatings
N.A.I.C.S.: 322220

ICI Paints CZ spol.s.r.o. (2)
3 Matechova, 142 00, Prague, Czech Re-
public
Tel.: (420) 241 440 385
Decorative Paint Distr
N.A.I.C.S.: 325510

ICI Paints Deco France SA (2)
ZI Les Bas Pres, BP 70113, Montataire,
60761, France
Tel.: (33) 3 44 64 91 00
Paint & Coating Mfr
N.A.I.C.S.: 325510

ICI Paints Mercosur B.V. (2)
Velperweg 76, Arnhem, 6824 BM, Nether-
lands
Tel.: (31) 26 366 4514
Paint & Coating Mfr
N.A.I.C.S.: 325510

**ICI South Pacific Holdings Pty
Ltd** (2)
L 39 101 Collins St, Melbourne, 3000, VIC,
Australia
Tel.: (61) 3 9679 3111
Investment Management Service
N.A.I.C.S.: 523940

ICI Swire Paints (Shanghai) Ltd. (2)
3 F K Wah Centre, 1010 Huai Hai road,
200031, Shanghai, China
Tel.: (86) 2154050909
Sales Range: $50-74.9 Million
Emp.: 200
Decorative Paints Whslr
N.A.I.C.S.: 424950

ICI Theta B.V. (2)
Blaak 40, 3011 TA, Rotterdam, Netherlands
Tel.: (31) 735999333
Paint & Coating Mfr
N.A.I.C.S.: 325510

International Coatings Ltd (1)
Stoneygate Lane Felling, Gateshead, NE10
0JY, Tyne & Wear, United Kingdom
Tel.: (44) 191 469 6111
Web Site: http://www.international-pc.com
Sales Range: $200-249.9 Million
Emp.: 1,000
Marine Paint & Coating Mfr
N.A.I.C.S.: 325510

International Coatings Pte Ltd (1)
56 Comport St, Cairns, 4870, QLD, Austra-
lia
Tel.: (61) 7 4035 1160
Emp.: 3
Paint & Coating Mfr
N.A.I.C.S.: 325510
James Bond (Gen Mgr)

International Farbenwerke GmbH (1)
3rd floor - 5 Sachsenkamp, 20097, Ham-
burg, Germany
Tel.: (49) 407 200 30
Marine Coating Mfr
N.A.I.C.S.: 325510

International Farg AB (1)
Holmedalen 3, Box 44, 424 22, Angered,
Sweden
Tel.: (46) 31928500
Emp.: 50
Marine Paint & Coating Mfr
N.A.I.C.S.: 325510

International Maling A/S (1)
Floisbonnvegen 6, 1411, Kolbotn, Norway
Tel.: (47) 66 81 94 81
Marine Paint & Coating Mfr
N.A.I.C.S.: 325510

**International Paint (Nederland)
B.V.** (1)
Kleidijk 88, Rhoon, 3161 HJ, Netherlands
Tel.: (31) 10 503 3500
Web Site: http://www.international-pc.com
Emp.: 30
Paint & Coating Distr
N.A.I.C.S.: 424950

International Paint Inc. (1)

6001 Antoine Dr, Houston, TX 77091-3503
Tel.: (713) 682-1711
Rev.: $114,300,000
Emp.: 200
Mfr of Paints
N.A.I.C.S.: 325510
Ian Walton (CEO)

J.P. Mcdougall & Co. Limited (1)
Manchester Road, Timperley West, Altrin-
cham, WA14 5PG, Cheshire, United King-
dom
Tel.: (44) 1619 683 160
Web Site:
http://www.duluxdecoratorcentre.co.uk
Emp.: 200
Paint & Coating Retailer
N.A.I.C.S.: 444120

Kayaku Akzo Corporation (1)
4-1-28 Kudankita, Chiyoda-Ku, Tokyo, 102-
0073, Japan
Tel.: (81) 3 3234 0801
Web Site: http://www.kayakuakzo.co.jp
Sales Range: $50-74.9 Million
Emp.: 100
Chemical Product Mfr & Distr
N.A.I.C.S.: 325199

**Keum Jung Akzo Nobel Peroxides
Ltd** (1)
24 5 km Wai Huan Xian West Side, Be-
ichen District, Tianjin, 300400, China
Tel.: (86) 22 2681 3188
Chemical Products Mfr & Distr
N.A.I.C.S.: 325998

Maricogen A/S (1)
Hadsundvej 17, Mariager, 9550, Denmark
Tel.: (45) 96 68 78 88
Sales Range: $50-74.9 Million
Emp.: 160
Paint & Coating Mfr
N.A.I.C.S.: 325510

National Starch Personal Care (1)
10 Finderne Ave, Bridgewater, NJ 08807-
3355
Tel.: (908) 685-5000
Web Site:
http://www.personalcarepolymers.com
Sales Range: $550-599.9 Million
Emp.: 1,200
Sales of Industrial Chemicals, Paints, Spe-
cialty Chemicals & Surfactants Mfr
N.A.I.C.S.: 325211
John D. G. McAdam (CEO)

New Nautical Coatings, Inc. (1)
14805 49th St N, Clearwater, FL 33762
Tel.: (727) 523-8053
Web Site: http://www.seahawkpaints.com
Paint & Coating Mfr
N.A.I.C.S.: 325510

Nobel Industries Holding B.V. (1)
Velperweg 76, 6824 BM, Arnhem, Nether-
lands
Tel.: (31) 263664433
Investment Management Service
N.A.I.C.S.: 523940

Nobel Industries USA Inc. (1)
525 W Van Buren St, Chicago, IL 60607
Tel.: (312) 544-7000
Rev.: $99,500,000
Emp.: 100
Mfr of Healthcare Products, Coatings &
Chemicals
N.A.I.C.S.: 325199

Nordsjo Butiker AB (1)
De la Gardievegan 8, 531 50, Lidkoping,
Sweden
Tel.: (46) 13355340
Web Site: http://www.nordsjoideisign.se
Paint Retailer
N.A.I.C.S.: 444120

OOO Akzo Nobel (1)
Meridian Commercial Tower Smolnaya Str
24D, Moscow, 125445, Russia
Tel.: (7) 495 9602890
Web Site: http://www.akzonobel.com
Sales Range: $75-99.9 Million
Emp.: 200
Chemical Product Mfr & Distr
N.A.I.C.S.: 325998

**OOO Akzo Nobel Wood
Coatings** (1)

Pulkovskoe Shosse 40 block 4 office C
6070 Technopark Technopolis, 196158,
Saint Petersburg, Russia
Tel.: (7) 8126769144
Sales Range: $25-49.9 Million
Emp.: 13
Wood Coating Mfr
N.A.I.C.S.: 325510

OOO Petrokom-Lipetsk (1)
1 Trubniy proezd, Lipetsk, 398036, Russia
Tel.: (7) 4742 38 49 54
Coil Coating Mfr
N.A.I.C.S.: 325510

**PT Akzo Nobel Car Refinishes
Indonesia** (1)
Jalan Pulogadung 37, 13015, Jakarta, Indo-
nesia
Tel.: (62) 21 4610191
Web Site: http://www.akzonobel.com
Sales Range: $50-74.9 Million
Emp.: 200
Automotive Coating Mfr
N.A.I.C.S.: 325510

PT Eka Chemicals Indonesia (1)
Jalan Rembang Industri III/32, 67152, Pasu-
ruan, Indonesia
Tel.: (62) 343 740127
Web Site: http://www.akzonobel.com
Chemical Products Mfr
N.A.I.C.S.: 325998

Pacific Oleochemicals Sdn Bhd. (1)
Plo 285 Jln Pekeliling Timur, Pasir Gudang,
81707, Johor Darul Takzim, Malaysia
Tel.: (60) 7 251 8000
Web Site: http://www.pacificoleo.com
Emp.: 250
Renewable Vegetable Raw Materials Prod-
ucts Mfr
N.A.I.C.S.: 311225

Panter B.V. (1)
Frt St Michielstr 23, 5922 XC, Venlo, Neth-
erlands
Tel.: (31) 77 3821609
Paint & Coating Mfr
N.A.I.C.S.: 325510

**Peintures Couleurs Decoration
S.A.S.** (1)
87 Route de Cormeilles, 78500, Sartrou-
ville, France
Tel.: (33) 1 30 86 83 83
Web Site: http://www.peinture-couleurs-
decoration.fr
Sales Range: $25-49.9 Million
Emp.: 6
Paint & Coating Retailer
N.A.I.C.S.: 444120
Hughes Lumeter (Mng Dir)

Pinturas Coral De Bolivia Ltda (1)
Parque Industrial P I 24, Santa Cruz, Bo-
livia
Tel.: (591) 33467069
Sales Range: $25-49.9 Million
Emp.: 18
Paint & Coating Distr
N.A.I.C.S.: 424950

**Proquimio Produtos Quimicos Opo-
terapicos Ltda.** (1)
Avenida Marginal Esquerda Do Rio Tiete
5101, Caixa Postal 11225, Aldeia Velha,
06410-240, Barueri, SP, Brazil (100%)
Tel.: (55) 1141967979
Sales Range: $50-74.9 Million
Emp.: 150
Mfr of Raw Materials for the Pharmaceutical
Industry
N.A.I.C.S.: 325412

Remmert Holland B.V. (1)
Velperweg 76, 6824 BM, Arnhem, Nether-
lands
Tel.: (31) 26 3665337
Paint & Coating Mfr
N.A.I.C.S.: 325510

Rhone Sud Est Decoration S.A. (1)
19 Cours De La Liberte N 19-21, 69003,
Lyon, France
Tel.: (33) 4 78 60 16 37
Paint & Coating Mfr
N.A.I.C.S.: 325510

Sadolin Farveland A/S (1)

Holmbladsgade 70, Copenhagen, 2300,
Denmark
Tel.: (45) 32 69 80 00
Web Site: http://www.sadolinfarveland.dk
Paint & Varnish Distr
N.A.I.C.S.: 424950

Sadvel SA **(1)**
64 Blvd Moulay Slimane, Casablanca, Mo-
rocco
Tel.: (212) 5 22 67 87 67
Paint & Coating Distr
N.A.I.C.S.: 424950
Lahcen Chatir *(Gen Mgr)*

Sales Support Group Limited **(1)**
Manchester Rd West, Altrincham, WA14
5PG, United Kingdom
Tel.: (44) 1753 550000
Sales Management Consulting Services
N.A.I.C.S.: 541613

Salinco V.O.F. **(1)**
Boortorenweg 27, 7554 RS, Hengelo, Neth-
erlands
Tel.: (31) 74244 30 96
Sales Range: $50-74.9 Million
Emp.: 40
Eletric Power Generation Services
N.A.I.C.S.: 221118

Schramm Coatings GmbH **(1)**
Kettelerstrasse 100, Offenbach, 63075,
Germany
Tel.: (49) 69 8603 0
Sales Range: $75-99.9 Million
Emp.: 250
Plastic & Metal Coating Product Distr
N.A.I.C.S.: 424690
Petrus Broks *(Mng Dir)*

Schramm Coatings Iberica SA **(1)**
Pl Can Comelles Suc c Fornal 10, 08292,
Esparraguera, Spain
Tel.: (34) 937 776 241
Web Site: http://www.schrammcoatings.com
Paint & Coating Distr
N.A.I.C.S.: 424950

Schramm Holding AG **(1)**
Kettelerstrasse 100, 63075, Offenbach,
Germany **(100%)**
Tel.: (49) 6986030
Web Site: http://www.schramm-holding.com
Sales Range: $150-199.9 Million
Emp.: 791
Coating Mfr
N.A.I.C.S.: 325510
Kyung Seok Chae *(Chief Strategy Officer)*

Schramm SSCP (Hanoi) Co Ltd. **(1)**
Lot I2-1 Que Vo, Bac Ninh, Vietnam
Tel.: (84) 1262366025
Chemical Products Distr
N.A.I.C.S.: 424690

Schramm SSCP (Thailand) Co.,
Ltd. **(1)**
7/206 M 6 Mabyangporn, Pluakdang, Ray-
ong, 21140, Thailand
Tel.: (66) 38 650 430 1
Chemical Products Distr
N.A.I.C.S.: 424690

Scottish Agricultural Industries
Limited **(1)**
West Mains of Ingleston, Newbridge, EH28
8ND, Midlothian, United Kingdom
Tel.: (44) 131 335 3100
Paint & Coating Mfr
N.A.I.C.S.: 325510

Server Boya Matbaa Murekkepleri ve
Vernik Sanayi ve Ticaret A.S. **(1)**
Istanbul Kimyacilar Organize Sanayi Bolgesi
Kristal Sok No 4, Tuzla, 34956, Istanbul,
Turkiye
Tel.: (90) 216 593 10 30
Web Site: http://www.serverboya.com
Sales Range: $25-49.9 Million
Emp.: 40
Paint & Coating Mfr
N.A.I.C.S.: 325510
Ugur Yenier *(Mgr-Sls)*

Sikkens Verkoop B.V. **(1)**
Korte Huifakkerstraat 12, 4815 PS, Breda,
Netherlands
Tel.: (31) 765222112
Web Site: http://www.sikkens.nl

Sales Range: $50-74.9 Million
Emp.: 2
Paint Supplies Distr
N.A.I.C.S.: 424950

Societe Tunisienne de Peintures As-
tral S.A. **(1)**
GP1 Route de Sousse Km 5 5, Megrine,
2033, Tunisia
Tel.: (216) 71 434 700
Web Site: http://www.astral-tn.com
Sales Range: $50-74.9 Million
Emp.: 150
Paint & Coating Mfr
N.A.I.C.S.: 325510

Soliant, LLC **(1)**
1872 Hwy 9 Bypass W, Lancaster, SC
29720-4702
Tel.: (803) 285-9401
Web Site: http://www.paintfilm.com
Sales Range: $50-74.9 Million
Emp.: 80
Mfr of Coating, Laminating & Film Products
N.A.I.C.S.: 322220

Suzhou Eka Trade Co. Ltd **(1)**
Suzhou Industrial Park No 302, Suzhou,
215122, China
Tel.: (86) 512 62582276
Web Site: http://www.akzonoble.com
Emp.: 60
Paint & Coating Mfr
N.A.I.C.S.: 325510

Techni-Coat Germany GmbH **(1)**
Imkerstrass 3, Kirchhorst, 30916, Isernha-
gen, Germany
Tel.: (49) 5136 977 36 0
Web Site: http://www.techni-coat.de
Paints Mfr
N.A.I.C.S.: 325510

Techni-Coat International N.V. **(1)**
Franseweg 31, Kalmthout, 2920, Belgium
Tel.: (32) 3 620 21 20
Plastic Coating Product Distr
N.A.I.C.S.: 424610

Tekyar Teknik Yardim A. S. **(1)**
Tavsanli Koyu Eynarca Mevkii Dilovasi,
Gebze, Turkiye
Tel.: (90) 262 7547470
Paint & Coating Mfr
N.A.I.C.S.: 325510

Tianjin Akzo Nobel Peroxides Co.
Ltd **(1)**
24 5 km Wai Huan Xin west Side, Beichen
District, Tianjin, 300400, China
Tel.: (86) 22 2681 3188
Chemical Products Mfr
N.A.I.C.S.: 325998

Van Noordenne Verf B.V. **(1)**
Transportweg 29, 3371 MA, Hardinxveld-
Giessendam, Netherlands
Tel.: (31) 184 675895
Paint & Coating Mfr
N.A.I.C.S.: 325510

Vivechrom Dr. Stefanos D. Pateras
S.A. **(1)**
Thesi Vathi Pigadi, Mandra Attica, 19600,
Greece
Tel.: (30) 210 5538700
Web Site: http://www.vivechrom.gr
Sales Range: $125-149.9 Million
Emp.: 265
Paint & Varnish Mfr
N.A.I.C.S.: 325510

Xylazel S.A. **(1)**
Prado Budino S/N Poligono Las Gandaras,
Porrino, 36400, Spain
Tel.: (34) 986343424
Web Site: http://www.xylazel.com
Paint & Coating Mfr
N.A.I.C.S.: 325510

ZAO Akzo Nobel Dekor **(1)**
Severnaya Promzona Pokrovsky proezd 9,
143900, Balashikha, Moscow, Russia
Tel.: (7) 4957950160
Paint & Coating Mfr
N.A.I.C.S.: 325510

Interquim S.A. **(1)**
Cl 10 S 50 Ff-28 Of 402, Medellin, Colom-
bia
Tel.: (57) 4 3618888

Sales Range: $50-74.9 Million
Emp.: 114
Paint & Coating Mfr
N.A.I.C.S.: 325510

AL ABDULLATIF INDUSTRIAL
INVESTMENT COMPANY
2nd New Industrial City New Al Kharj
Road, PO Box 859, Riyadh, 11421,
Saudi Arabia
Tel.: (966) 112658888
Web Site: http://www.carpets.com
Year Founded: 1981
2340—(SAU)
Rev.: $124,120,832
Assets: $341,606,178
Liabilities: $40,233,137
Net Worth: $301,373,042
Earnings: ($6,612,495)
Emp.: 2,905
Fiscal Year-end: 12/31/20
Carpet Mfr
N.A.I.C.S.: 314110
Suleiman Omar Suleiman Al Abdul-
latif *(Chm)*

Subsidiaries:

Adfa blanket company **(1)**
Street 236, PO Box 859, New Industrial
Area, Riyadh, 11421, Saudi Arabia
Tel.: (966) 112656600
Web Site: https://www.adfablankets.com
Fabric Material Mfr & Distr
N.A.I.C.S.: 313310

Eastern Textile Company **(1)**
New Industrial city, PO Box 859, Riyadh,
11421, Saudi Arabia
Tel.: (966) 112654538
Web Site: https://www.etex.com
Fabric Material Mfr & Distr
N.A.I.C.S.: 313310

National Spinning Company Ltd.
Co. **(1)**
2nd Industrial city, Post Box No 859, Ri-
yadh, 11421, Saudi Arabia
Tel.: (966) 12652200
Web Site: https://www.nscyarns.com
Yarn Mfr
N.A.I.C.S.: 313110

AL AHLIA ENTERPRISES PLC
11 August St - Khorma Building, PO
Box 830554, Al-Shmisani, Amman,
11183, Jordan
Tel.: (962) 5688471
Year Founded: 1993
ABLA—(AMM)
Sales Range: $10-24.9 Million
Emp.: 189
Superstore Management Services
N.A.I.C.S.: 455211

AL AHLIAH TRANSPORT
COMPANY
Pullman Garage, Hama, Syria
Tel.: (963) 33 2473260
Year Founded: 1992
Bus Transportation Services
N.A.I.C.S.: 488490
Ahmad Mamdouh Al Asfar *(Chm)*

AL AHLY FOR DEVELOPMENT
& INVESTMENT
7 Lazoughly St- Garden city, Cairo,
Egypt
Tel.: (20) 225780791
Web Site: https://www.adi-alahly.com
Year Founded: 1995
Financial Investment Services
N.A.I.C.S.: 523999
Fahd Shobokshi *(Chm)*

AL AIN AHLIA INSURANCE
COMPANY
Al Ain Ahlia Insurance Co Bldg Airport
Road, PO Box 3077, Abu Dhabi,
United Arab Emirates

Tel.: (971) 26119999
Web Site:
  https://www.alaininsurance.com
ALAIN—(EMI)
Rev.: $328,582,607
Assets: $751,439,899
Liabilities: $432,809,111
Net Worth: $318,630,788
Earnings: $20,681,915
Emp.: 226
Fiscal Year-end: 12/31/20
General Insurance Services
N.A.I.C.S.: 524210
Mohammed Juan Rashed Al Badi Al
Dhaeri *(Chm)*

AL AMEEN INSURANCE COM-
PANY
Sec 903 St 17 Bld 12 Al-Masbeh,
Baghdad, Iraq
Tel.: (964) 7188956
Year Founded: 2000
NAME—(IRAQ)
Sales Range: Less than $1 Million
Insurance Management Services
N.A.I.C.S.: 524298

AL AMEEN REAL ESTATE IN-
VESTMENT CO.
Al-Hamra Hotel, Jadriah, Baghdad,
Iraq
Tel.: (964) 7906479228
Year Founded: 1999
SAEI—(IRAQ)
Sales Range: Less than $1 Million
Real Estate Investment Services
N.A.I.C.S.: 523999

AL AMIN FOR INVESTMENT
P.L.C.
Shmeisani, PO Box 940216, Amman,
Jordan
Tel.: (962) 6 5677377
Year Founded: 1989
AAFI—(AMM)
Sales Range: Less than $1 Million
Emp.: 3
Investment Management Service
N.A.I.C.S.: 523999
Asa'd Addese *(Gen Mgr)*

AL ANWAR CERAMIC TILES
CO. SAOG
Suite No 301 Beach One Building
Way No 2601 Shatti Al Qurum, PO
Box 143, 118, Muscat, 118, Oman
Tel.: (968) 98511248
Web Site: https://www.alshams.org
Year Founded: 1998
AACT—(MUS)
Rev.: $51,435,337
Assets: $110,583,000
Liabilities: $12,865,068
Net Worth: $97,717,933
Earnings: $5,246,003
Emp.: 309
Fiscal Year-end: 12/31/19
Ceramic Tile Mfr
N.A.I.C.S.: 327120

AL BADIA FOR GENERAL
TRANSPORTATION
Al-Nahdha Garage, Baghdad, Iraq
Tel.: (964) 8865612
Year Founded: 1994
SBAG—(IRAQ)
Sales Range: Less than $1 Million
Transportation Services
N.A.I.C.S.: 488999

AL BARAKA BANKING
GROUP B.S.C.
Bahrain Bay, PO Box 1882, Manama,
Bahrain
Tel.: (973) 17541122   **BH**
Web Site: https://www.albaraka.com

Al Baraka Banking Group B.S.C.—(Continued)

Year Founded: 1978
BARKA—(BAH)
Rev.: $1,138,732,000
Assets: $24,981,834,000
Liabilities: $8,882,235,000
Net Worth: $16,099,599,000
Earnings: $239,454,000
Emp.: 10,663
Fiscal Year-end: 12/31/22
Banking Services
N.A.I.C.S.: 522110
Abdulla A. Saudi (Vice Chm)

Subsidiaries:

Al Baraka Bank (Pakistan)
Limited **(1)**
Al Baraka House 162 Bangalore Town Main
Shahrah-e-Faisal, Karachi, Pakistan
Tel.: (92) 21 3431 5851
Web Site: http://www.albaraka.com.pk
Commercial Banking Services
N.A.I.C.S.: 522110
Adnan Ahmed Yousif (Chm)

Al Baraka Bank Egypt **(1)**
62 Mohy El-Din Abu El-Ezz St, PO Box
504, Dokki, 12311, Giza, 12311, Egypt
Tel.: (20) 233383482
Web Site: http://www.albaraka-bank.com.eg
Rev.: $258,961,044
Assets: $2,116,658,280
Liabilities: $1,911,285,045
Net Worth: $205,373,235
Earnings: $46,771,529
Emp.: 1,000
Fiscal Year-end: 12/31/2023
Commercial Banking Services
N.A.I.C.S.: 522110
Adnan Ahmed Yousif (Pres & CEO-Al Baraka Banking Grp)

Al Baraka Bank Lebanon SAL **(1)**
Justinian street BAC Center 12th floor, PO
Box 113/5683, Sanayeh, Beirut,
Lebanon **(98.71%)**
Tel.: (961) 1748061
Web Site: http://www.al-baraka.com
Sales Range: $100-124.9 Million
Emp.: 112
Banking Services
N.A.I.C.S.: 522110

Al Baraka Bank Ltd. **(1)**
2 Kingsmead Boulevard Kingsmead Office
Park Stalwart Simelane Street, Stanger
Street, Durban, 4001,
South Africa **(62.15%)**
Tel.: (27) 313649000
Web Site: http://www.albaraka.co.za
Sales Range: $50-74.9 Million
Emp.: 70
Banking Services
N.A.I.C.S.: 522110

Al Baraka Bank Sudan **(1)**
(82.08%)
Web Site: http://www.albaraka.com.sd
Sales Range: $350-399.9 Million
Emp.: 640
Banking Services
N.A.I.C.S.: 522110
Abdelrahman Ahmed Osman (Vice Chm)

Al Baraka Bank Syria **(1)**
9 Tulaytulah Street Al Malki Square, Damascus, Syria
Tel.: (963) 113321980
Web Site: http://www.albarakasyrio.com
Banking Services
N.A.I.C.S.: 522110

Al Baraka Bank Tunisia **(1)**
88 Avenue Hedi Chaker, 1002, Tunis, Tunisia
Tel.: (216) 71186500
Web Site: http://www.albarakabank.com.tn
Commercial Banking Services
N.A.I.C.S.: 522110
Abdul-Elah Sabbahi (Chm)

Al Baraka Islamic Bank E.C. **(1)**
AlBaraka Tower, PO Box 1882, Bahrain
Bay, Manama, Bahrain
Tel.: (973) 13300401
Web Site: http://albaraka.bh
Banking Services

N.A.I.C.S.: 522110
Mohammed Al-Mutaweh (CEO)

Albaraka Turkish Finance House **(1)**
Saray Mahallesi Dr Adnan Buyukdeniz Caddesi No 6, Umraniye, 34768, Istanbul, Turkiye
Tel.: (90) 216666010
Web Site: http://www.albarakaturt.com.tr
Banking Services
N.A.I.C.S.: 522110

BTI Bank Company **(1)**
157 Avenue Hassan II, Casablanca, Morocco
Tel.: (212) 801050404
Web Site: https://btibank.ma
Banking Services
N.A.I.C.S.: 522110

Banque Al Baraka D'Algerie
S.P.A. **(1)**
Hai Bouteldja Houidef villa n 1 rocade sud,
16000, Ben Aknoun, Algeria
Tel.: (213) 23381270
Web Site: https://www.albaraka-bank.dz
Financial Banking Services
N.A.I.C.S.: 522320

Banque Al Baraka d'Algerie **(1)**
Hai Bouteldja Houidef villa no 1 rocade sud,
Ben Aknoun, Algiers, Algeria
Tel.: (213) 23381270
Web Site: http://www.albaraka-bank.com
Sales Range: $200-249.9 Million
Emp.: 381
Banking Services
N.A.I.C.S.: 522110

Egyptian Saudi Finance Bank **(1)**
60 Mohie Elddin Abu El Ezz Street, PO Box
455, Dokki, Cairo, Egypt
Tel.: (20) 27481222
Sales Range: $100-124.9 Million
Emp.: 200
Banking Services
N.A.I.C.S.: 522110

Future Applied Computer Technology
Company **(1)**
Wasfi Al-Tal Street Jordan Islamic Bank
Building 23 5TH Floor, PO Box 926785,
Amman, 11190, Jordan
Tel.: (962) 65515155
Web Site: https://www.fact.com.jo
Emp.: 60
Software Development Services
N.A.I.C.S.: 541511

Itqan Capital **(1)**
Ahmed Al Attas Street Al Zahraa Commercial Center, PO Box 8021, Al Zahraa District, Jeddah, 21482, Saudi Arabia
Tel.: (966) 122638787
Web Site: http://itqancapital.com
Investment Banking Services
N.A.I.C.S.: 523150
Abdulaziz Mohammed Yamani (Chm)

Jordan Islamic Bank **(1)**
PO Box 926225, Shmeisani, Amman,
11190, Jordan **(66.01%)**
Tel.: (962) 65666325
Web Site:
https://www.jordanislamicbank.com
Rev.: $272,832,332
Assets: $6,832,874,971
Liabilities: $2,081,866,162
Net Worth: $4,751,008,808
Earnings: $73,514,487
Emp.: 2,433
Fiscal Year-end: 12/31/2020
Banking Services
N.A.I.C.S.: 522110
Musa Abdulaziz Shihadeh (Co-Chm)

Sanable Alkhair for Financial
Investment **(1)**
Housing Bank Complex Queen Noor St 91,
Amman, 11193, Jordan
Tel.: (962) 65653046
Emp.: 15
Commercial Banking Services
N.A.I.C.S.: 522110
Ausama Khtab (Gen Mgr)

AL BATEK FINANCIAL INVESTMENT CO.

Sadoon Against The Ministry Of Agriculture Building, The Bank Of Babylon The Fifth Floor, Baghdad, Iraq
Tel.: (964) 1 7182265
Year Founded: 2001
Financial Investment Services
N.A.I.C.S.: 523999

AL BATINAH DEVELOPMENT & INVESTMENT HOLDING CO. SAOG

PO Box 68, Rewi Commercial Area,
117, Muscat, Oman
Tel.: (968) 24856658
Web Site: http://www.albatinah.com
Year Founded: 1997
DBIH—(MUS)
Rev.: $370,407
Assets: $6,028,341
Liabilities: $1,129,855
Net Worth: $4,898,486
Earnings: ($566,771)
Emp.: 3
Fiscal Year-end: 12/31/23
Real Estate Development Services
N.A.I.C.S.: 531390

Subsidiaries:

National Cans & Packing Industry
LLC **(1)**
Road No 18 Rusayl Industrial Estate, PO
Box 102, 124, Muscat, Oman
Tel.: (968) 24446650
Web Site: http://www.ncpioman.com
Sales Range: $100-124.9 Million
Emp.: 460
Can Mfr
N.A.I.C.S.: 332431
Salah Hilal Al Ma'awali (Chm)

AL BATINAH POWER CO SAOG

Bareeq Al Shatti P C 103 Muscat
Grand Mall Flat No 501, PO Box 39,
Building No 5 Level 1 South-East
Street No 35 Al Khuwair, Muscat,
Oman
Tel.: (968) 24393300
Web Site:
https://www.albatinahpower.com
BATP—(MUS)
Rev.: $134,855,361
Assets: $655,903,101
Liabilities: $404,646,408
Net Worth: $251,256,694
Earnings: $28,823,730
Fiscal Year-end: 12/31/21
Eletric Power Generation Services
N.A.I.C.S.: 221118
Yusuke Koseki (CFO)

AL BILAD SECURITIES & INVESTMENT CO.

Building No 2 Al Rawashdeh Complex 1 Paris Street Sweifieh, PO Box
3275, Amman, 11181, Jordan
Tel.: (962) 65105900
Web Site:
https://www.biladcapital.com
Year Founded: 2006
BLAD—(AMM)
Rev.: $616,073
Assets: $13,183,469
Liabilities: $2,432,562
Net Worth: $10,750,907
Earnings: ($705,898)
Emp.: 12
Fiscal Year-end: 12/31/20
Portfolio Management & Brokerage
Services
N.A.I.C.S.: 523940
Sameer Al-Rawashdeh (Mng Dir)

AL BUHAIRA NATIONAL INSURANCE COMPANY P.S.C.

Al Buhaira Tower Khalid Lagoon Bu-

haira Corniche, PO Box 6000,
Sharjah, United Arab Emirates
Tel.: (971) 65174444
Web Site: http://www.albuhaira.com
Year Founded: 1978
ABNIC—(EMI)
Rev.: $245,353,524
Assets: $534,817,634
Liabilities: $349,400,992
Net Worth: $185,356,642
Earnings: $6,814,899
Emp.: 346
Fiscal Year-end: 12/31/21
Insurance Services
N.A.I.C.S.: 524298
Nader T. Qaddumi (Gen Mgr)

AL DANUBE BUILDING MATERIALS TRADING CO., LLC

PO Box 18022, Jebel Ali, United Arab
Emirates
Tel.: (971) 48871234
Web Site: http://www.aldanube.com
Year Founded: 1993
Sales Range: $100-124.9 Million
Emp.: 900
Building Materials Distr
N.A.I.C.S.: 444180
Anis Sajan (Mng Dir)

AL DAWLIYAH FOR HOTELS & MALLS PLC

Alal Al-Fasi st, PO Box 942175,
Shmeisany, Amman, 11194, Jordan
Tel.: (962) 5680106
Web Site: https://dawliyah-jo.com
Year Founded: 1994
MALL—(AMM)
Rev.: $5,135,050
Assets: $85,958,098
Liabilities: $14,485,167
Net Worth: $71,472,931
Earnings: ($3,825,414)
Emp.: 8
Fiscal Year-end: 12/31/20
Construction Engineering Services
N.A.I.C.S.: 541330

AL DUCA D'AOSTA SPA

Via Volturno 7, 30173, Maestre, VE,
Italy
Tel.: (39) 0412620111
Web Site:
http://www.alducadaosta.com
Year Founded: 1902
Sales Range: $10-24.9 Million
Emp.: 125
Clothing Retailer
N.A.I.C.S.: 458110
Matteo Ceccato (Pres)

AL EID FOOD CO

Block 2 Building 100, PO Box 41081,
Ardiya Industrial Area, Hawalli,
85851, Kuwait
Tel.: (965) 24335300
Web Site: https://www.aleidfood.com
Year Founded: 1994
ALEID—(KUW)
Rev.: $15,418,522
Assets: $102,847,564
Liabilities: $28,893,880
Net Worth: $73,953,684
Earnings: $8,463,434
Emp.: 105
Fiscal Year-end: 12/31/22
Food Products Distr
N.A.I.C.S.: 424490
Fahad Al-Mutairi (Chm)

AL ENTKAEYA FOR INVESTMENT & REAL ESTATE DEVELOPMENT CO. PLC

Al Wakalat Street Al Hourani Complex, PO Box 14412, Sweifieh, Amman, 11814, Jordan

Tel.: (962) 65818225
Year Founded: 2007
ENTK—(AMM)
Assets: $2,382,920
Liabilities: $545,802
Net Worth: $1,837,118
Earnings: ($24,908)
Fiscal Year-end: 12/31/20
Real Estate Development Services
N.A.I.C.S.: 531390

AL FAHIM GROUP

Mussafah Industrial Area Street 10
Area 5, PO Box 279, Abu Dhabi,
United Arab Emirates
Tel.: (971) 26567000
Web Site: http://www.alfahim.com
Year Founded: 1954
Sales Range: $350-399.9 Million
Emp.: 1,300
Holding Company
N.A.I.C.S.: 551112
Ahmed Abdul Jalil Al Fahim *(Chm)*

Subsidiaries:

Emirates Motor Co.   **(1)**
PO Box 279, Abu Dhabi, United Arab Emir-
ates
Tel.: (971) 2 444 000
Web Site: http://www.emc.mercedes-
benz.com
New & Used Car Sales
N.A.I.C.S.: 441110
Bilal Al Ribi *(Gen Mgr-Comml Vehicles Div)*

Subsidiary (Domestic):

Central Motors & Equipment LLC   **(2)**
PO Box 71343, Abu Dhabi, United Arab
Emirates
Tel.: (971) 24017700
Web Site: http://www.cmeuae.ae
Automobile Parts Distr
N.A.I.C.S.: 423120
Sumit Chordia *(Head-Bus)*

Eastern Motors LLC   **(2)**
PO Box 16050, 16050, Al Ain, United Arab
Emirates
Tel.: (971) 3 715 7444
Web Site: http://www.alfahim.ae
New Car Dealers
N.A.I.C.S.: 441110
Nassim Mourani *(Gen Mgr)*

Emirates Property Investment
Co.   **(1)**
PO Box 101, Abu Dhabi, United Arab Emir-
ates
Tel.: (971) 800 37426
Web Site: http://www.epico.ae
Property Development & Real Estate
N.A.I.C.S.: 531210
Jason Gibb *(Gen Mgr)*

Marjan Industrial Development
Co.   **(1)**
Liwa Street, PO Box 6644, Abu Dhabi,
United Arab Emirates
Tel.: (971) 26222114
Web Site: http://www.alfahim.com
Mechanical, Electrical & Oil Equipment
Contractors
N.A.I.C.S.: 238210

Safar Travel Services   **(1)**
Liwa Street, PO Box 507, Abu Dhabi,
United Arab Emirates
Tel.: (971) 26225225
Web Site: http://www.safar.ae
Sales Range: $10-24.9 Million
Emp.: 30
Travel & Cargo Services
N.A.I.C.S.: 561510

Western Motors LLC   **(1)**
Hamdan St, PO Box 46193, Mussafa, Abu
Dhabi, United Arab Emirates
Tel.: (971) 25546333
Web Site: http://www.alfahim.ae
Sales Range: $75-99.9 Million
Emp.: 180
Automobile Distr, Motor Vehicle Supplies &
Parts Whslr
N.A.I.C.S.: 423110

AL FAISALIAH GROUP

PO Box 16460, Riyadh, 11464, Saudi
Arabia
Tel.: (966) 14610077
Web Site: http://www.alfaisaliah.com
Year Founded: 1970
Sales Range: $650-699.9 Million
Emp.: 5,270
Electrical & Electronic Equipment,
Computers, Communications &
Broadcast Products, Petrochemicals,
Dairy & Agricultural Products Trading
Services
N.A.I.C.S.: 425120

Subsidiaries:

Al Faisaliah Electronics Services **(1)**
PO Box 16460, Riyadh, 11464, Saudi Ara-
bia
Tel.: (966) 14407799
Sales Range: $25-49.9 Million
Emp.: 133
Computer Maintenance, Network Services
& Cabling
N.A.I.C.S.: 541519

Al Faisaliah Medical Systems   **(1)**
Olaya Road Al Nemer Center, PO Box
62961, Riyadh, 11595, Saudi Arabia
Tel.: (966) 12119999
Web Site: http://www.alfaisaliah.com
Sales Range: $50-74.9 Million
Emp.: 100
Medical Equipment Distr
N.A.I.C.S.: 423450

Al Safi Danone Co.   **(1)**
PO Box 15025, Riyadh, 11443, Saudi Ara-
bia
Tel.: (966) 1 211 9999
Web Site: http://www.alsafidanone.com.sa
Dairy Products; Owned by Group Danone
SA & Al Faisaliah Group
N.A.I.C.S.: 112120

Modern Electronics Company
Ltd.   **(1)**
Business Gate Building 8 East Ring Road -
Exit 8, Qurtubah District, Riyadh, Saudi
Arabia
Tel.: (966) 92 000 7669
Emp.: 500
Electronic Product Distr
N.A.I.C.S.: 423690

Modern Electronics Establishment
(MEE)   **(1)**
King Fahd Highway near Riyadh Bank, PO
Box 2769, Al Khobar, 31952, Saudi Arabia
Tel.: (966) 38949078
Web Site: http://www.mee.com.sa
Computer & Electronic Product Mfr
N.A.I.C.S.: 334118

Modern Media Systems   **(1)**
4210 Abdulmalik Ibn Marwan Street, Al
Maathar District, Riyadh, Saudi Arabia
Tel.: (966) 11 463 3312
Web Site: http://www.mms.com.sa
Television Broadcasting Services
N.A.I.C.S.: 516120
Mohammed Mazheruddin *(Mgr-Sls)*

AL FAJAR AL ALAMIA COM-
PANY SAOG

Qurum City Center Sultanate of
Oman, PO Box 78, 102, Al-Ghubra,
Oman
Tel.: (968) 24614707   OM
Web Site: https://www.alfajar.co.om
Year Founded: 1997
AFAI—(MUS)
Rev.: $26,435,802
Assets: $129,959,858
Liabilities: $93,976,614
Net Worth: $35,983,243
Earnings: ($15,803,252)
Emp.: 72
Fiscal Year-end: 06/30/23
Industrial Explosive Mfr & Whslr
N.A.I.C.S.: 325920
Saleem Qassim Ahmed Al Zawawi
(Chm)

Subsidiaries:

Technical Drilling and Blasting Co.
LLC   **(1)**
Post Box 2482, Fujairah, United Arab Emir-
ates
Tel.: (971) 92227657
Web Site: https://www.tdb.ae
Explosive Mfr & Distr
N.A.I.C.S.: 325920

AL FATH TRADING CO. LTD.

El Siteen El Gharpy St Behind Sham-
lan Station, PO Box 15196, Sana'a,
Yemen
Tel.: (967) 1402246   YE
Pharmaceuticals Product Mfr
N.A.I.C.S.: 325412

AL FIRDOUS HOLDINGS
(P.J.S.C.)

PO Box 25233, Dubai, United Arab
Emirates
Tel.: (971) 4 3739826
Web Site:
   http://www.alfirdousholdings.info
Year Founded: 1998
Sales Range: $1-9.9 Million
Holding Company
N.A.I.C.S.: 551112
Khalid Zayed Saqer Al Nahian *(Chm)*

AL FUJAIRAH NATIONAL IN-
SURANCE COMPANY (P.S.C.)

8th Floor Insurance Bldg Hamad Bin
Abdullah St, PO Box 277, Fujairah,
United Arab Emirates
Tel.: (971) 92233355
Web Site: https://www.afnic.ae
Year Founded: 1976
AFNIC—(ABU)
Rev.: $64,718,728
Assets: $186,688,087
Liabilities: $106,433,041
Net Worth: $80,255,046
Earnings: ($3,930,213)
Fiscal Year-end: 12/31/22
Insurance Services
N.A.I.C.S.: 524298
Abdul Ghaffour Behroozian *(Chm)*

AL GASSIM INVESTMENT
HOLDING CO.

King Fahd Road West, PO Box 2210,
Qassim, Buraidah, 51451, Saudi Ara-
bia
Tel.: (966) 163823500
Year Founded: 1985
6020—(SAU)
Rev.: $2,948,910
Assets: $113,837,093
Liabilities: $34,562,392
Net Worth: $79,274,701
Earnings: $1,932,355
Emp.: 25
Fiscal Year-end: 12/31/22
Agricultural Investment Services
N.A.I.C.S.: 523999
Ahmed Sulaiman Almuzaini *(Chm)*

AL GHURAIR GROUP

Salahuddin Road, Dubai, United Arab
Emirates
Tel.: (971) 4 2623377
Web Site: http://www.alghurair.com
Year Founded: 1960
Sales Range: $5-14.9 Billion
Emp.: 25,000
Holding Company
N.A.I.C.S.: 551112
Abdulrahman Saif Al Ghurair *(Chm)*

Subsidiaries:

ADEKA Al Ghurair Additives LLC **(1)**
Plot No 37B4, PO Box 40306, Abu Dhabi,
United Arab Emirates
Tel.: (971) 2 5508361

Web Site: http://www.adeka-alghurair.com
Chemical Products Mfr
N.A.I.C.S.: 325411
Toshinori Yukino *(CEO)*

Arabian Can Industry LLC   **(1)**
PO Box 26595, Jebel Ali Industrial Area 1,
Dubai, United Arab Emirates
Tel.: (971) 4 8801166
Web Site: http://www.arabiancan.com
Emp.: 150
Metal Tank Mfr
N.A.I.C.S.: 339999
Majid Saif Al Ghurair *(Mng Dir)*

Arabian Packaging Co. LLC   **(1)**
PO Box 10337, Jebel Ali Industrial Area 2,
Dubai, United Arab Emirates
Tel.: (971) 4 801 5500
Web Site: http://www.arabpack.com
Plastics Films Mfr
N.A.I.C.S.: 326112

Gulf Extrusions Co. (LLC)   **(1)**
PO Box 5598, Dubai, United Arab Emirates
Tel.: (971) 48846146
Web Site: http://www.gulfex.com
Industrial Building Construction Services
N.A.I.C.S.: 236210

Royal Engineering Fabrication Com-
pany LLC   **(1)**
PO Box 120145, Dubai, United Arab Emir-
ates
Tel.: (971) 4 884 9710
Web Site: http://www.refcometals.com
Fabricated Metal Products Mfr
N.A.I.C.S.: 332313

Taghleef Industries L.L.C.   **(1)**
Jebel Ali Industrial Area 1, PO Box 56391,
Dubai, United Arab Emirates
Tel.: (971) 4 880 1100
Web Site: http://www.ti-films.com
Sales Range: $75-99.9 Million
Emp.: 30
Polypropylene & Biodegradable Packaging
& Label Film Mfr
N.A.I.C.S.: 326112

Subsidiary (Non-US):

Taghleef Industries GmbH   **(2)**
Reutig 2, 56357, Holzhausen an der Haide,
Germany   **(100%)**
Tel.: (49) 6772 9676 011
Web Site: http://www.ti-films.com
Polypropylene Packaging Film Distr
N.A.I.C.S.: 424610

Subsidiary (US):

Taghleef Industries Inc.   **(2)**
2751 Centerville Rd Ste 400, Wilmington,
DE 19808
Tel.: (302) 326-5500
Web Site: http://www.ti-films.com
Polypropylene Packaging Films Mfr & Whslr
N.A.I.C.S.: 326112

Subsidiary (Non-US):

Taghleef Industries Canada Inc.   **(3)**
3362 Chemin de la Baronnie, Varennes,
J3X 1T2, QC, Canada   **(100%)**
Tel.: (302) 326-5500
Web Site: http://www.ti-films.com
Sales Range: $25-49.9 Million
Emp.: 100
Polypropylene Packaging Film Mfr & Whslr
N.A.I.C.S.: 326112

Subsidiary (Non-US):

Taghleef Industries Pty. Ltd.   **(2)**
11 Moloney Drive, Wodonga, 3690, VIC,
Australia   **(100%)**
Tel.: (61) 2 6022 0220
Web Site: http://www.ti-films.com
Emp.: 60
Polypropylene & Biodegradable Packaging
Film Mfr
N.A.I.C.S.: 326112
Elie Jarrous *(CEO)*

Taghleef Industries S.A.E.   **(2)**
Industrial Zone 4 Street 59, 6th of October
City, Cairo, Egypt
Tel.: (20) 2 38289400
Plastic Film Distr
N.A.I.C.S.: 424610

Al Ghurair Group—(Continued)

Taghleef Industries S.A.O.C. (2)
PO Box 38, Sohar Industrial Estate, 327,
Sohar, Oman
Tel.: (968) 2675 1823
Web Site: http://www.ti-films.com
Sales Range: $50-74.9 Million
Emp.: 250
Polypropylene Packaging & Label Film Mfr
N.A.I.C.S.: 326112
Sundeep Mudgai (Reg Mgr)

Taghleef Industries S.L.U. (2)
C/ Cronos 20 Ed 1 3a Floor, 28037, Madrid,
Spain
Tel.: (34) 953598100
Web Site: http://www.ti-films.com
Printable & Over-Laminated Films Mfr &
Sales
N.A.I.C.S.: 326112

Taghleef Industries S.L.U. (2)
Avenida de Iberoamerica 56, Alcala la Real,
23680, Jaen, Spain
Tel.: (34) 953 59 81 00
Plastic Film Distr
N.A.I.C.S.: 424610

Taghleef Industries S.p.A. (2)
Via E Fermi 46, 33058, San Giorgio di
Nogaro, Udine, Italy
Tel.: (39) 0431 627 111
Web Site: http://www.ti-films.com
Polypropylene & Biodegradable Packaging
Film Mfr & Wlsl
N.A.I.C.S.: 326112

Subsidiary (Non-US):

Taghleef Industries Kft (3)
PO Box 259, 3581, Tiszaujvaros, Hungary
Tel.: (36) 49 521 954
Web Site: http://www.ti-films.com
Polypropylene & Biodegradable Packaging
Film Mfr & Wlsl
N.A.I.C.S.: 326112
Antar Bazso (Gen Mgr)

AL GHURAIR INVESTMENT LLC

PO Box 6999, Dubai, United Arab
Emirates
Tel.: (971) 4 20 29777 AE
Web Site: http://www.al-ghurair.com
Year Founded: 1960
Investment Holding Company
N.A.I.C.S.: 551112
Abdul Aziz Al Ghurair (CEO)

Subsidiaries:

**Al Ghurair Construction & Founda-
tions Saudi LLC** (1)
King Abdul Aziz Road Center Etoile En-
trance C Second floor, PO Box 54798,
Alzahrah Neighborhood, Jeddah, 21524,
Saudi Arabia
Tel.: (966) 26926294
Construction Engineering Services
N.A.I.C.S.: 237990

**Al Ghurair Construction & Readymix
Saudi LLC** (1)
PO Box 259223, 11351, Riyadh, Saudi Ara-
bia
Tel.: (966) 14629200
Readymix Concrete Mfr
N.A.I.C.S.: 327320

**Al Ghurair Construction - Aluminum
India Private Limited** (1)
No 02 Rajdeo Compound Film City Road,
Gokuldham market Malad East, Mumbai,
400 097, India
Tel.: (91) 2228420591
Construction Materials Distr
N.A.I.C.S.: 423390

**Al Ghurair Construction - Foundations
LLC** (1)
PO Box 78659, Dubai, United Arab Emir-
ates
Tel.: (971) 42330115
Construction Engineering Services
N.A.I.C.S.: 237990

**Al Ghurair Construction - Readymix
LLC** (1)

PO Box 158, Dubai, United Arab Emirates
Tel.: (971) 43502100
Readymix Concrete Mfr
N.A.I.C.S.: 327320

**Al Ghurair Construction - Readymix
WLL** (1)
PO Box 55319, Doha, Qatar
Tel.: (974) 44666695
Readymix Conoroto Mfr
N.A.I.C.S.: 327320

**Al Ghurair Construction Aluminum
Qatar** (1)
C Ring Road Al Hitmi Village Business Cen-
ter, PO Box 55309, Building 2 - Third Floor,
Doha, Qatar
Tel.: (974) 44214919
Construction Materials Mfr
N.A.I.C.S.: 327120

Al Ghurair Construction LLC (1)
PO Box 1550, Dubai, United Arab Emirates
Tel.: (971) 42858485
Construction Engineering Services
N.A.I.C.S.: 237990
Shakil Rajguru (VP-Fin)

**Al Ghurair Energy Trading
DMCC** (1)
PO Box 82674, Dubai, United Arab Emir-
ates
Tel.: (971) 42055207
Oil & Gas Exploration Services
N.A.I.C.S.: 213111

**Al Ghurair Foods - Animal Nutrition
LLC** (1)
PO Box 16808, Dubai, United Arab Emir-
ates
Tel.: (971) 48816800
Animal Feed Product Distr
N.A.I.C.S.: 424910

Al Ghurair Foods LLC (1)
PO Box 780, Dubai, United Arab Emirates
Tel.: (971) 43939633
Food Products Distr
N.A.I.C.S.: 424490

**Al Ghurair Printing and Publishing
LLC** (1)
PO Box 5613, Dubai, United Arab Emirates
Tel.: (971) 43312317
Magazine Publisher
N.A.I.C.S.: 513120

Al Ghurair Resources LLC (1)
PO Box 5326, Dubai, United Arab Emirates
Tel.: (971) 43120153
Food Products Distr
N.A.I.C.S.: 424490

Al Ghurair Retail LLC (1)
PO Box 80547, Dubai, United Arab Emir-
ates
Tel.: (971) 42234223
Web Site: http://www.agretail.ae
Cosmetic Product Distr
N.A.I.C.S.: 456120
Keith Flanagan (Gen Mgr)

Edible Oil Company (D) LLC (1)
PO Box 17799, Dubai, United Arab
Emirates (70%)
Tel.: (971) 48811160
Emp.: 80
Other Oilseed Processing
N.A.I.C.S.: 311224
Sreekumar Brahmanandan (Dir)

Khaleej National Flour Mills (1)
PO Box 1309, Port Sudan, Sudan
Tel.: (249) 311825937
Food Products Mfr
N.A.I.C.S.: 311211

**National Flour Mills - Lebanon
WLL** (1)
PO Box 1503, Al Bahsas, Tripoli, Lebanon
Tel.: (961) 6411230
Food Products Mfr
N.A.I.C.S.: 311211

Serendib Flour Mills (Pvt) Ltd. (1)
245/52 Old Avissawella Road, Orugoda-
watta, Wellampitiya, Sri Lanka
Tel.: (94) 117777026
Food Products Mfr
N.A.I.C.S.: 311211

AL GROUP LIMITED

Unit A 35/F EGL Tower 83 Hung To
Road, Kwun Tong, China (Hong
Kong)
Tel.: (852) 23116022
Web Site: http://www.al-grp.com
Year Founded: 1999
8360—(HKG)
Rev.: $14,116,345
Assets: $8,448,319
Liabilities: $8,223,765
Net Worth: $224,554
Earnings: ($5,471,332)
Emp.: 31
Fiscal Year-end: 12/31/21
Interior Design Services
N.A.I.C.S.: 541410
Chung Ping Yau (Co-Founder &
Dir-Design)

AL HABTOOR GROUP LLC

Al Wasl Road Al Safa 2, PO Box
25444, Dubai, United Arab Emirates
Tel.: (971) 43941444
Web Site: http://www.habtoor.com
Year Founded: 1970
Sales Range: $5-14.9 Billion
Emp.: 40,000
Construction Services
N.A.I.C.S.: 236220
Khalaf Ahmad Al Habtoor (Founder &
Chm)

Subsidiaries:

Al Habtoor Leighton Group (1)
PO Box 320, Dubai, United Arab Emirates
Tel.: (971) 42857551
Web Site: http://www.hlgroup.com
Sales Range: $1-4.9 Billion
Emp.: 15,000
Construction & Engineering Services
N.A.I.C.S.: 236220
Khalif Al Habtoot (Chm)

**Al Habtoor Motors Company
LLC** (1)
PO Box 19879, Dubai, United Arab Emir-
ates
Tel.: (971) 4 269 1110
Web Site: http://www.alhabtoor-motors.com
Motor Vehicle Distr
N.A.I.C.S.: 423110
Ahmed Al Habtoor (CEO)

Diamondlease LLC (1)
PO Box 32689, Dubai, United Arab Emir-
ates
Tel.: (971) 4 885 2677
Web Site: http://www.diamondlease.com
Automobile Rental Services
N.A.I.C.S.: 532111
Colin Jobe (Mng Dir)

AL HAMAD CONTRACTING COMPANY LLC

PO Box 6275, Sharjah, United Arab
Emirates
Tel.: (971) 65349666
Web Site: http://www.al-hamad.com
Year Founded: 1985
Sales Range: $50-74.9 Million
Emp.: 3,250
Building Contractors
N.A.I.C.S.: 236220
Thamin Sulaiman Fakhouri (Mng Dir)

Subsidiaries:

**Al Hamad Industrial Company
LLC** (1)
PO Box 4713, Ajman, United Arab Emirates
Tel.: (971) 67438212
Nonresidential Construction
N.A.I.C.S.: 236210

Dubai Civil Engineering Est (1)
PO Box 21706, Dubai, United Arab Emir-
ates
Tel.: (971) 042574441
Special Trade Contracting
N.A.I.C.S.: 238990

**Global Pioneer Aluminium Industrial
FZE** (1)
PO Box 31291, Al Jazeera Al Hamra, Ras
al Khaimah, United Arab Emirates
Tel.: (971) 7 244 7668
Aluminium Products Mfr
N.A.I.C.S.: 327999

Select Glass Industries LLC (1)
Industrial Area 56 Al Jazeera Al Hamra, PO
Box 32388, Ras al Khaimah, United Arab
Emirates
Tel.: (971) 7 2445195
Web Site: http://www.selectglass.ae
Glass Mfr
N.A.I.C.S.: 327211
Nashat Sahawneh (Chm)

AL HAMMADI HOLDING COMPANY

PO Box 55004, Riyadh, 11534, Saudi
Arabia
Tel.: (966) 112329999
Web Site:
https://www.alhammadi.com
Year Founded: 1985
4007—(SAU)
Rev.: $299,265,971
Assets: $661,737,919
Liabilities: $205,648,680
Net Worth: $456,089,239
Earnings: $68,613,830
Emp.: 3,245
Fiscal Year-end: 12/31/22
Hospital Operations
N.A.I.C.S.: 622110
Saleh Mohammed Al Hammadi
(Chm)

AL HASSAN ENGINEERING COMPANY S.A.O.G.

PO Box 1948, 112, Ruwi, Oman
Tel.: (968) 24810575
Web Site: https://www.al-hassan.com
Year Founded: 1998
HECI—(MUS)
Rev.: $57,118,637
Assets: $53,077,015
Liabilities: $170,630,629
Net Worth: ($117,553,614)
Earnings: $37,879,281
Emp.: 5,300
Fiscal Year-end: 12/31/20
Construction & Contracting Services
N.A.I.C.S.: 237990
Shawqi Hamdan Sajwani (CEO)

Subsidiaries:

Al Hamas Trading Company LLC (1)
PO Box 19546, Dubai, United Arab Emir-
ates
Tel.: (971) 14 3350020
Web Site: http://www.al-hassan.com
Engineering Services
N.A.I.C.S.: 541330

Al Hassan Electricals LLC (1)
PO Box 1948, 112, Ruwi, Oman
Tel.: (968) 24825281
Web Site: http://www.llc.al-hassan.com
Engineering Services
N.A.I.C.S.: 541330
Abbas Jamal (CEO)

**Al Hassan Engineering Co. Abu
Dhabi LLC** (1)
PO Box 47943, Abu Dhabi, United Arab
Emirates
Tel.: (971) 25513858
Engineering Services
N.A.I.C.S.: 541330

**Al Hassan Engineering Co. Dubai
LLC** (1)
PO Box 47943, Dubai, United Arab Emir-
ates
Tel.: (971) 43350020
Sales Range: $25-49.9 Million
Emp.: 40
Engineering Services
N.A.I.C.S.: 541330

Al Hassan Engineering Co.
SAOG **(1)**
PO Box 1948, Ruwi, 112, Oman
Tel.: (968) 24810575
Web Site: http://www.al-hassan.com
Emp.: 2,000
Engineeering Services
N.A.I.C.S.: 541330

Al Hassan Lighting & Fans Industries
LLC **(1)**
P. O. Box 1948, 112, Ruwi, Oman
Tel.: (968) 24810575
Web Site: http://www.al-hassan.com
Lighting Equipment Mfr
N.A.I.C.S.: 335139

Al Hassan Power Industries **(1)**
PO Box 130 Madinat Al Sultan Qaboos, PO
Box 130, Madinat Qaboos, 115, Muscat,
Oman
Tel.: (968) 24591283
Web Site: http://wwwal-hassan.com
Sales Range: $25-49.9 Million
Emp.: 200
Engineering Services
N.A.I.C.S.: 541330
Mani Khadem *(Gen Mgr)*

Al Hassan Switchgear
Manufacturing **(1)**
PO Box 130, Madinat Qaboos, 115, Muscat,
Oman
Tel.: (968) 24591283
Web Site: http://www.llc.al-hassan.com
Sales Range: $25-49.9 Million
Emp.: 200
Engineeering Services
N.A.I.C.S.: 541330

Al Sahwa Trading Co, LLC **(1)**
Khaleefa St, PO Box 45491, Abu Dhabi,
United Arab Emirates
Tel.: (971) 26273270
Web Site: http://www.al-hassan.com
Sales Range: $25-49.9 Million
Emp.: 8
Engineering Services
N.A.I.C.S.: 541330
Thomas John *(Mgr)*

Hi-Tech Services & Supplies LLC **(1)**
PO Box 2992, Ruwi, 112, Oman
Tel.: (968) 24810575
Web Site: http://www.al-hassan.com
Engineeering Services
N.A.I.C.S.: 541330
Hassan Ali Salamn *(Pres)*

Noor Al Khaleej LLC **(1)**
PO Box 45261, Abu Dhabi, United Arab
Emirates
Tel.: (971) 12 6273270
Web Site: http://www.al-hassan.com
Engineeering Services
N.A.I.C.S.: 541330

AL HASSAN GHAZI IBRAHIM SHAKER

As Sahafah, Riyadh, Saudi Arabia
Tel.: (966) 112638900
Web Site: https://www.shaker.com.sa
Year Founded: 1950
1214—(SAU)
Rev.: $248,377,744
Assets: $383,382,523
Liabilities: $209,614,849
Net Worth: $173,767,674
Earnings: $2,698,684
Emp.: 648
Fiscal Year-end: 12/31/20
Electronic Products Mfr
N.A.I.C.S.: 334419
Abdulelah Abdullah Abunayyan *(Chm)*

Subsidiaries:

Energy Management Services Inter-
national LLC **(1)**
PO Box 2457, Amman, 11953, Jordan
Tel.: (962) 655380856
Renewable Energy Services
N.A.I.C.S.: 221111

AL IMTIAZ INVESTMENT GROUP COMPANY- K.S.C.

Al Dhow Tower Khaled Bin Al Waleed
St, PO Box 29050, Sharq Safat, Ku-
wait, 13151, Kuwait
Tel.: (965) 1822282 KW
Web Site: https://www.alimtiaz.com
Year Founded: 2005
ALIMTIAZ—(KUW)
Rev.: $226,968,615
Assets: $830,993,903
Liabilities: $219,020,283
Net Worth: $611,973,620
Earnings: ($8,824,437)
Emp.: 48
Fiscal Year-end: 12/31/22
Financial Investment Services
N.A.I.C.S.: 523999
Abdullah Dekheel Jassar Al-Jassar
(Deputy Chm)

Subsidiaries:

Dimah Capital Investment
Company-K.S.C. **(1)**
Khaled Bin Al Waleed St Al Dhow Tower
Floor 7, Al-Sharq, Kuwait
Tel.: (965) 22955700
Web Site: https://dimah.com.kw
Investment Management Service
N.A.I.C.S.: 523940

Majd Food Company-K.S.C. **(1)**
Khalid Ibn Alwaleed St-Dhow Tower-25th
Floor, Sharq, Kuwait, Kuwait
Tel.: (965) 22301333
Web Site: https://majdifood.com
Food Product Mfr & Distr
N.A.I.C.S.: 311999

AL JABER GROUP

Petroleum Services Area Plot 1 & 1A,
PO Box 2175, Abu Dhabi, United
Arab Emirates
Tel.: (971) 25554300
Web Site: http://www.aljaber.com
Year Founded: 1970
Sales Range: $1-4.9 Billion
Emp.: 50,000
Holding Company
N.A.I.C.S.: 551112
Panicos Euripides *(CEO)*

Subsidiaries:

AJECOBOND - Al Jaber Aluminium
Composite LLC **(1)**
PO Box 41073, Abu Dhabi, United Arab
Emirates
Tel.: (971) 2 5501777
Panel Mfr
N.A.I.C.S.: 332311

Al Jaber & Partners - Construction &
Energy Projects W.L.L. **(1)**
GRIDCO III Building-P Floor C-Ring Road,
PO Box 23007, Doha, Qatar
Tel.: (974) 44411880
Construction Services
N.A.I.C.S.: 236220

Al Jaber Aluminum Extrusion
L.L.C. **(1)**
PO Box 41073, Abu Dhabi, United Arab
Emirates
Tel.: (971) 25553707
Aluminum Mfr for Architectural & Industrial
Applications
N.A.I.C.S.: 331318
Nabil Salman *(Gen Mgr)*

Al Jaber Bitumen LLC **(1)**
PO Box 8602, Abu Dhabi, United Arab
Emirates
Tel.: (971) 2 5553562
Web Site: http://www.aljaber.com
Emp.: 28
Asphalt Paving Contract Services
N.A.I.C.S.: 237310
Raed Joudeh *(Gen Mgr)*

Al Jaber Building L.L.C. **(1)**
Sector 6 & 7 St, PO Box 2175, Abu Dhabi,
United Arab Emirates
Tel.: (971) 25554376
Web Site: http://www.aljaber.com
Residential Construction
N.A.I.C.S.: 236116

Jihad Khaled *(Mng Dir)*

Al Jaber Carpentry & Decor
L.L.C. **(1)**
PO Box 41073, Abu Dhabi, United Arab
Emirates
Tel.: (971) 25547075
Web Site: http://www.aljaber.com
Sales Range: $100-124.9 Million
Emp.: 300
Carpentry Services
N.A.I.C.S.: 238350

Al Jaber Catering Services L.L.C **(1)**
PO Box 2175, Abu Dhabi, United Arab
Emirates
Tel.: (971) 25020472
Construction Services
N.A.I.C.S.: 236220

Al Jaber Contracting Ltd. **(1)**
Tatweer Towers Tower 4 8th Floor King Fa-
had Road, PO Box 14119, Al Muhamedi-
yah, Riyadh, 11424, Saudi Arabia
Tel.: (966) 114945900
Web Site: https://www.aljaberksa.com
Construction Contracting Services
N.A.I.C.S.: 236220
Obaid Khaleefa Al Jaber Al Marri *(Chm)*

Al Jaber Delta Energy Services &
General Construction **(1)**
PO Box 2175, Abu Dhabi, United Arab
Emirates
Tel.: (971) 22040350
Building Construction
N.A.I.C.S.: 236117

Al Jaber Energy Services **(1)**
Al Jaber Yard, PO Box 47467, Mussafah
Industrial Area, Abu Dhabi, 47647, United
Arab Emirates
Tel.: (971) 25546550
Web Site: http://www.ajes.ae
Sales Range: $1-4.9 Billion
Emp.: 10,000
Mechanical, Electrical & Contracting Ser-
vices
N.A.I.C.S.: 238210
Ronald Metcalf *(Mng Dir)*

Al Jaber Fusion-Bonded Epoxy Coat-
ing Plant **(1)**
PO Box 41073, Abu Dhabi, United Arab
Emirates
Tel.: (971) 25541050
Sales Range: $50-74.9 Million
Emp.: 180
Concrete Reinforcement Bars
N.A.I.C.S.: 327390

Al Jaber Heavy Lift **(1)**
Corniche Side 5th R/A, Mussafah, 2175,
Abu Dhabi, United Arab Emirates
Tel.: (971) 2 5825454
Web Site: http://www.ajhl.com
Emp.: 560
Fleet Forwarding Services
N.A.I.C.S.: 488510
Alex Mulins *(Exec Dir)*

Subsidiary (Non-US):

Al Jaber Heavy Lift & Transport
Pte.Ltd **(2)**
21 Pandan Crescent, Singapore, 128471,
Singapore
Tel.: (65) 67775 2411
Fleet Forwarding Services
N.A.I.C.S.: 488510

Al Jaber Heavy Lift & Transport
LLC **(1)**
PO Box 2175, Abu Dhabi, United Arab
Emirates
Tel.: (971) 25825454
Web Site: https://www.ajhl.com
Marine Transportation Services
N.A.I.C.S.: 488820
Marwan Farhat *(Mng Dir)*

Al Jaber Iron & Steel Foundry
LLC **(1)**
PO Box 8602, Abu Dhabi, United Arab
Emirates
Tel.: (971) 2 5541524
Steel Products Mfr
N.A.I.C.S.: 331513

Al Jaber Landscape LLC **(1)**

PO Box 2175, Abu Dhabi, United Arab
Emirates
Tel.: (971) 25020169
Construction Services
N.A.I.C.S.: 236220

Al Jaber Leasing Services L.L.C. **(1)**
PO Box 2175, Abu Dhabi, United Arab
Emirates
Tel.: (971) 8005544
Construction Services
N.A.I.C.S.: 236220

Al Jaber Lighting LLC **(1)**
PO Box 109091, Abu Dhabi, United Arab
Emirates
Tel.: (971) 2 5557810
Web Site: http://www.aljaber.com
Emp.: 13
LED Bulb Distr
N.A.I.C.S.: 423610
M. Sivakumar *(Mgr-Technical)*

Al Jaber Precision Engineering
Establishment **(1)**
PO Box 2175, Abu Dhabi, United Arab
Emirates
Tel.: (971) 25020602
Web Site: http://www.ajeprecision.com
Sales Range: $200-249.9 Million
Emp.: 600
Mfr of High Precision Engineering Compo-
nents & Units, Specializing in Matching,
Gearing, Heat Treatment, Plasma Coating,
CNC, Steel Fabrication & Inspection Ser-
vices
N.A.I.C.S.: 332999

Al Jaber Protective Coating
L.L.C. **(1)**
PO Box 41073, Abu Dhabi, United Arab
Emirates
Tel.: (971) 25541050
Web Site: http://www.aljaber.com
Sales Range: $50-74.9 Million
Emp.: 250
Epoxy Coatings for Reinforcement Steel
Bars
N.A.I.C.S.: 325510

Al Jaber Shipping Agency & Marine
Works LLC **(1)**
7 Musaffah, PO Box 2175, Abu Dhabi,
United Arab Emirates
Tel.: (971) 250 20 427
Web Site: http://www.aljabershipping.com
Shipping Logistics
N.A.I.C.S.: 541614
Janus Jerome *(Engr-Contracts)*

Al Jaber Signs L.L.C. **(1)**
M 20 Plot No 5 12 & 23, PO Box 2175, Abu
Dhabi, 41073, United Arab
Emirates **(100%)**
Tel.: (971) 25553707
Web Site: http://www.aljaber.com
Sales Range: $400-449.9 Million
Emp.: 2,500
Supply, Erection & Maintenance of Various
Road & Street Fixtures
N.A.I.C.S.: 332999
Nabil Salman *(Mng Dir)*

Al Jaber Steel Products L.L.C. **(1)**
Mussaffh St, PO Box 2175, Abu Dhabi,
2175, United Arab Emirates
Tel.: (971) 25020705
Sales Range: $50-74.9 Million
Emp.: 220
Steel Structures Mfr
N.A.I.C.S.: 332111
Sarkis Karkamazian *(Gen Mgr)*

Al Jaber Trading LLC **(1)**
Salahuddin Road Al Muraqqabat Deira, PO
Box 1940, Dubai, United Arab Emirates
Tel.: (971) 4 2667700
Commodity Trading Services
N.A.I.C.S.: 523160

Al Jaber Trailers, Steel and Metal
Works Establishment **(1)**
PO Box 2175, Abu Dhabi, United Arab
Emirates
Tel.: (971) 25554300
Designer & Fabricator of Custom Made
Equipment & Components for the Construc-
tion & Transportation Industry
N.A.I.C.S.: 333120

Al Jaber Group—(Continued)

Al Jaber Transport & General Contracting Co. (1)
Mussafah Indsutrial Area St No 17 Sector 21, PO Box 2175, Abu Dhabi, United Arab Emirates
Tel.: (971) 25554300
Sales Range: $25-49.9 Million
Road Construction & Infrastructure Development
N.A.I.C.S.: 237310

Subsidiary (Non-US):

Al Jaber & Partners L.L.C. (2)
PO Box 23007, Doha, Qatar
Tel.: (974) 4411880
Web Site: http://www.aljaber.com
Construction Services
N.A.I.C.S.: 237310

Al Jaber Tunneling & Mechanical Works Est (1)
PO Box 9755, Abu Dhabi, United Arab Emirates
Tel.: (971) 25553335
Web Site: http://www.aljaber.com
Tunneling, Sewage Pipes & Water Pipes Networks
N.A.I.C.S.: 237110

Deutsche Babcock Al Jaber W.L.L. (1)
Al Matar Center Al Matar Street Zone 45 Building No 272, Gate 2 First Floor Office No 121, Doha, Qatar
Tel.: (974) 44651900
Web Site: https://www.debaj.com.qa
Engineeering Services
N.A.I.C.S.: 541330
Chidambaranathan Thirumeni (CEO)

GLOBAL PROCESS SYSTEMS LLC (1)
Media One Tower Levels 37 & 36 Media City, PO Box 30593, Dubai, United Arab Emirates
Tel.: (971) 444 86800
Web Site: http://www.globalprocesssystems.com
Oil & Gas Engineering Services
N.A.I.C.S.: 213112

GLOBAL PROCESS SYSTEMS PTE LTD (1)
5 Temasek Boulevard 10-03 Suntec Tower Five, Singapore, 038985, Singapore
Tel.: (65) 659 34299
Oil & Gas Engineering Services
N.A.I.C.S.: 213112

GLOBAL PROCESS SYSTEMS SDN BHD (1)
Menara Binjai Level 22 No 2 Jalan Binjai, 50450, Kuala Lumpur, Malaysia
Tel.: (60) 3 914 53000
Oil & Gas Engineering Services
N.A.I.C.S.: 213112
Bryan Yen Fei Lee (Engr-Proposal)

Hytec Abu Dhabi L.L.C. (1)
Musaffah M 39, PO Box 8616, Abu Dhabi, United Arab Emirates
Tel.: (971) 25515657
Web Site: https://www.hytec.ae
Piling & Foundation Equipment Mfr & Distr
N.A.I.C.S.: 333120

INE TECHNOLOGIES SDN BHD (1)
Level 8 Menara See Hoy Chan No 374, Jalan Tun Razak, 50400, Kuala Lumpur, Malaysia
Tel.: (60) 39145 3100
Instrumentation & Controlling Mfr
N.A.I.C.S.: 334519
Steven Chadwick (Gen Mgr)

Middle East Equipment & Trading (1)
Po Box No-29151, PO Box 29151, Abu Dhabi, United Arab Emirates
Tel.: (971) 25559559
Web Site: http://www.aljaber.com
Sales Range: $25-49.9 Million
Emp.: 100
Sells Used Equipment & Refurbished Construction Plants, Machines & Equipment
N.A.I.C.S.: 459510

Toxido Pest Control LLC (1)
Mussafah Industrial Area, Mussafah, Abu Dhabi, United Arab Emirates
Tel.: (971) 2 5828454
Pest Control Services
N.A.I.C.S.: 561710

Trakker Middle East LLC (1)
18th Floor Sidra Tower Building Shk Zayed Road, Tecom, Dubai, United Arab Emirates
Tel.: (971) 524706292
Web Site: https://trakker.ae
Vehicle Tracking Services
N.A.I.C.S.: 513199

Veolia Environmental Services Emirates LLC (1)
PO Box 9755, Abu Dhabi, United Arab Emirates
Tel.: (971) 125511557
Construction Services
N.A.I.C.S.: 236220

Xtramix Concrete Solution Mix LLC (1)
PO Box 32020, Abu Dhabi, United Arab Emirates
Tel.: (971) 2 5511118
Web Site: http://www.xtramix.ae
Readymix Concrete Mfr
N.A.I.C.S.: 327320

AL JAMIL FOR INVESTMENT COMPANY
Um Uthainah, PO Box 2036, Amman, Jordan
Tel.: (962) 6 5522508
Year Founded: 2006
JMIL—(AMM)
Sales Range: $1-9.9 Million
Emp.: 15
Financial Investment Services
N.A.I.C.S.: 523999
Hani Jamil Barakat (Gen Mgr)

AL JAZEERA STEEL PRODUCTS COMPANY S.A.O.G.
Sohar Industrial Estate, PO Box 40, 327, Sohar, 327, Oman
Tel.: (968) 26751763
Web Site:
https://www.jazeerasteel.com
Rev.: $269,392,808
Assets: $174,976,656
Liabilities: $66,277,846
Net Worth: $108,698,810
Earnings: $798,795
Emp.: 645
Fiscal Year-end: 12/31/19
Steel Pipes & Tubes Mfr
N.A.I.C.S.: 331210
Arun Kumar Sinha (CMO)

AL JAZEERA SUDANESE JORDANIAN BANK
Africa St Khartoum Tower of the Sudanese Jordanian Jazira Bank, Khartoum, Sudan
Tel.: (249) 187 051000
Web Site:
http://www.aljazeerabank.com.sd
Year Founded: 2006
JSJB—(KHAR)
Sales Range: $10-24.9 Million
Banking Services
N.A.I.C.S.: 522110
Aymen Hazzaa Barakat Al Majali (Chm)

AL JAZIRA TAKAFUL TA'AWUNI COMPANY
Al Musadia Plaza 3 Al Madinah Road, Jeddah, Saudi Arabia
Tel.: (966) 126688877
Web Site: http://www.ajt.com.sa
Year Founded: 2010
8012—(SAU)
Rev.: $45,609,119
Assets: $707,117,984
Liabilities: $482,754,033

Net Worth: $224,363,951
Earnings: $7,560,059
Emp.: 142
Fiscal Year-end: 12/31/22
Insurance Services
N.A.I.C.S.: 524298
Sager Abdullatif Nadershah (CEO)

Subsidiaries:

Solidarity Saudi Takaful Company (1)
Al.Takhasusi Street Al.Thumammah Opposite Jarir Bookstore North East, PO Box 85770, Al Nada district, Riyadh, 11612, Saudi Arabia
Tel.: (966) 11 2994555
Web Site: http://www.solidaritytakaful.com
Sales Range: $75-99.9 Million
Emp.: 140
Insurance Management Services
N.A.I.C.S.: 524298
Bader Khalid Al Anzi (CEO)

AL JOUF CEMENT COMPANY
Delmar Center Building - First Floor - Office No 8, Riyadh, Saudi Arabia
Tel.: (966) 920020208
Web Site: http://www.joufcem.com.sa
Year Founded: 2006
3091—(SAU)
Rev.: $67,154,118
Assets: $522,715,060
Liabilities: $219,748,937
Net Worth: $302,966,122
Earnings: $8,237,279
Emp.: 520
Fiscal Year-end: 12/31/22
Cement Product Mfr & Whslr
N.A.I.C.S.: 327310
Mohammad Saeed Al-Attiyah (Chm & CEO)

AL KATHIRI HOLDING CO
Prince Yazid bin Abdullah bin Abdulrahman AlMalqa, PO Box 33722, Almalqa, Riyadh, 11458, Saudi Arabia
Tel.: (966) 920004192
Web Site:
https://www.alkathiriholding.com
Year Founded: 2008
3008—(SAU)
Rev.: $34,447,059
Assets: $80,256,904
Liabilities: $45,248,016
Net Worth: $35,008,888
Earnings: ($1,098,097)
Emp.: 332
Fiscal Year-end: 12/31/23
Concrete Distr
N.A.I.C.S.: 423320

AL KHALEEJ INVESTMENT P.J.S.C.
PO Box 5662, Ras al Khaimah, Al Nakheel, United Arab Emirates
Tel.: (971) 65320737   AE
Web Site: https://www.kico.ae
Year Founded: 1982
KICO—(ABU)
Rev.: $4,594,185
Assets: $76,388,493
Liabilities: $1,446,704
Net Worth: $74,941,790
Earnings: $518,820
Emp.: 52
Fiscal Year-end: 12/31/23
Investment & Financial Services
N.A.I.C.S.: 523940
Abdul Rahman Jasem Obaid Salem Al Abdouli (Mng Dir)

AL KHALEEJ TAKAFUL INSURANCE COMPANY Q.P.S.C.
Grand Hamad Street, PO Box 4555, Doha, Qatar
Tel.: (974) 44041111   QA
Web Site: https://www.alkhaleej.com

Year Founded: 1978
AKHI—(QE)
Rev.: $17,909,745
Assets: $278,812,798
Liabilities: $119,366,704
Net Worth: $159,446,094
Earnings: $9,263,073
Fiscal Year-end: 12/31/20
Insurance Services
N.A.I.C.S.: 524298
Abdulla Ahmed Al Ahmed Al-Thani (Chm)

Subsidiaries:

Qatar Takaful Company S.O.C. (1)
Nr Lulu Hypermarket D Ring Rd, PO Box 23553, Doha, Qatar
Tel.: (974) 44299000
General Insurance Services
N.A.I.C.S.: 524210

AL KHALILI UNITED ENTERPRISES LLC
CR 2435, Muscat, 112, Oman
Tel.: (968) 2481630
Web Site: http://www.alkhalili.com
Sales Range: $1-4.9 Billion
Emp.: 3,000
Wholesale Trading Services; Construction, Electrical, Hardware & IT Products
N.A.I.C.S.: 425120
Ayub Khan (CEO)

AL KHAZER FOR CONSTRUCTION MATERIALS, REAL ESTATE INVESTMENTS & GENERAL CONTRACTING
Al-Zuhoor St Opposite To Prophet Younis Market, Dargazliya, Mosul, Iraq
Tel.: (964) 816600
Year Founded: 1989
IKHC—(IRAQ)
Sales Range: Less than $1 Million
Real Estate Investment Services
N.A.I.C.S.: 523999

AL KHAZNA INSURANCE COMPANY P.S.C.
Al Khazna Tower Najdha Street, PO Box 73343, Abu Dhabi, United Arab Emirates
Tel.: (971) 26969700
Web Site: https://www.alkhazna.com
Year Founded: 1996
AKIC—(ABU)
Rev.: $5,337,860
Assets: $105,081,831
Liabilities: $102,687,560
Net Worth: $2,394,270
Earnings: ($8,435,198)
Emp.: 150
Fiscal Year-end: 12/31/20
Insurance Services
N.A.I.C.S.: 524298
Ehsan Hasbani (Head-Motor)

Subsidiaries:

Al Khazna Insurance Company - Abu Dhabi Traffic (1)
Najda Street, PO Box 73343, Abu Dhabi, United Arab Emirates   (100%)
Tel.: (971) 24493497
Web Site: http://www.alkhazna.com
Insurance Services
N.A.I.C.S.: 524298

Al Khazna Insurance Company - Al Ain Branch (1)
Oud Al Tuba St, PO Box 20755, Al Ain, United Arab Emirates   (100%)
Tel.: (971) 37661700
Sales Range: $350-399.9 Million
Insurance Services
N.A.I.C.S.: 524298

Al Khazna Insurance Company - Al Ain Traffic **(1)**
Al Khazna Tower Oud Al Tuba Street, PO Box 20755, Al Ain, United Arab Emirates
Tel.: (971) 3 766 1700
Web Site: http://www.alkhazna.com
Insurance Services
N.A.I.C.S.: 524298

Al Khazna Insurance Company - Al Mussafah **(1)**
Villa No 86 Opp Al Nahyan Campus Delma Street No 13, PO Box 73343, Abu Dhabi, United Arab Emirates
Tel.: (971) 26969700
Web Site: http://www.alkhazna.com
Sales Range: $50-74.9 Million
Emp.: 88
Insurance Services
N.A.I.C.S.: 524298
Samir Alwazan (CEO)

Al Khazna Insurance Company - Al Mussafah Light Vehicle **(1)**
PO Box 73343, Abu Dhabi, United Arab Emirates
Tel.: (971) 25544561
Insurance Services
N.A.I.C.S.: 524298

Al Khazna Insurance Company - Al Wagan **(1)**
The Mair Road, PO Box 20755, Al Ain, United Arab Emirates **(100%)**
Tel.: (971) 37352065
Web Site: http://www.alkhazna.com
Sales Range: $1-9.9 Million
Insurance Services
N.A.I.C.S.: 524298
Fatih Yaswen (Gen Mgr)

Al Khazna Insurance Company - Beda Zayed **(1)**
PO Box 73343, Abu Dhabi, United Arab Emirates
Tel.: (971) 28844290
Web Site: http://www.alkhazna.com
Insurance Services
N.A.I.C.S.: 524298

Al Khazna Insurance Company - Dubai **(1)**
Al Mana Building Al Ittihad Road Near ENOC Petrol Station, PO Box 8953, Dubai, United Arab Emirates **(100%)**
Tel.: (971) 4 217 3333
Web Site: http://www.alkhazna.com
Sales Range: $50-74.9 Million
Emp.: 15
Insurance Services
N.A.I.C.S.: 524298

AL KINDI OF VETERINARY VACCINES CO.
Abu-Graib, Baghdad, Iraq
Tel.: (964) 5112154
Year Founded: 1990
IKLV—(IRAQ)
Sales Range: Less than $1 Million
Veterinary Medical Product Mfr
N.A.I.C.S.: 325412

AL KUHAIMI METAL INDUS-TRIES LTD.
PO Box 545, Dammam, 31421, Saudi Arabia
Tel.: (966) 38472777
Web Site: http://www.alkuhaimi.com
Year Founded: 1975
Sales Range: $125-149.9 Million
Emp.: 700
Metal Door Mfr
N.A.I.C.S.: 332321
Mohammed Ahmed Al Kuhaimi (Chm)

AL MADAR INVESTMENT CO K.S.C.P
14th Floor Al-Salam Tower, Fahed Al-Salem Street Salhiyah, Kuwait, Kuwait
Tel.: (965) 22061000
Web Site: https://www.almadar-fi.com
Year Founded: 1998

MADAR—(KUW)
Rev.: $131,704
Assets: $90,542,107
Liabilities: $13,916,689
Net Worth: $76,625,418
Earnings: $166,261
Emp.: 27
Fiscal Year-end: 12/31/22
Investment Management & Advisory Services
N.A.I.C.S.: 523150
Ahmed A. Al-Bahar (CEO)

AL MADINA INSURANCE COMPANY SAOG
Office No 301/302 Bldg No 6 3rd Floor Muscat Grand Mall, PO Box 80, Al-Ghubra, 136, Oman
Tel.: (968) 22033 888
Web Site: http://www.almadinatakaful.com
Rev.: $40,294,458
Assets: $250,053,892
Liabilities: $194,185,454
Net Worth: $55,868,438
Earnings: $713,646
Fiscal Year-end: 12/31/19
Fire, Marine & Casualty Insurance Services
N.A.I.C.S.: 524298
Mohammed Ali Al Barwani (Chm)

AL MADINA TAKAFUL CO. SAOG
Office No 301/302 Bldg No 6 3rd Floor Muscat Grand Mall, Al-Ghubra, Oman
Tel.: (968) 22033888
Web Site: https://www.almadinatakaful.com
Year Founded: 2006
AMAT—(MUS)
Rev.: $41,774,714
Assets: $320,108,924
Liabilities: $263,248,326
Net Worth: $56,860,599
Earnings: $399,242
Emp.: 158
Fiscal Year-end: 12/31/23
Insurance Services
N.A.I.C.S.: 524210
Mohammed Ali Al Barwani (Chm)

AL MAHA PETROLEUM PROD-UCTS MARKETING COMPANY S.A.O.G.
PO Box 57, 116, Muscat, 116, Oman
Tel.: (968) 24610200
Web Site: https://www.almaha.com.om
MHAS—(MUS)
Rev.: $864,820,731
Assets: $334,768,814
Liabilities: $227,661,864
Net Worth: $107,106,950
Earnings: $2,236,145
Emp.: 321
Fiscal Year-end: 12/31/20
Petroleum Products Marketer & Distr
N.A.I.C.S.: 424720
Ahmed Bakhit Al Shanfari (Head-Mktg Div)

AL MAMOURA REAL ESTATE INVESTMENTS CO.
Building 26 St 35 Dist 929 Arasat Al Hindya, Baghdad, Iraq
Tel.: (964) 7810681558
Web Site: https://www.mamorairaq.com
Year Founded: 1993
SMRI—(IRAQ)
Sales Range: Less than $1 Million
Real Estate Services
N.A.I.C.S.: 531390

AL MANAR FINANCING & LEASING CO.
Al Qiblah Block 13 Street 23 Building 19 Floor 29, PO Box 22828, Safat, Kuwait, 13089, Kuwait
Tel.: (965) 22983000
Web Site: https://www.almanar.com.kw
Year Founded: 2003
ALMANAR—(KUW)
Rev.: $6,537,798
Assets: $133,397,653
Liabilities: $43,927,125
Net Worth: $89,470,529
Earnings: $4,806,474
Emp.: 38
Fiscal Year-end: 12/31/22
Financial Lending Services
N.A.I.C.S.: 522220
Faisal Abdel Aziz Abdullah Al-Nassar (Chm)

AL MANSOUR COMPANY FOR PHARMACEUTICAL INDUS-TRIES
Abo Ghareib - High Way Road Before Bilady Milk Factory, Baghdad, Iraq
Tel.: (964) 7726664777
Web Site: https://mpi-iq.com
Year Founded: 1989
IMAP—(IRAQ)
Sales Range: Less than $1 Million
Pharmaceuticals Product Mfr
N.A.I.C.S.: 325412
Ali Khaleel (CEO)

AL MASANE AL KOBRA MIN-ING COMPANY
Building 7847 Unit 2, Najran, 66244-3181, Saudi Arabia
Tel.: (966) 175292264
Web Site: https://www.amak.com.sa
Year Founded: 2008
1322—(SAU)
Rev.: $155,384,270
Assets: $412,710,451
Liabilities: $87,367,913
Net Worth: $325,342,538
Earnings: $33,683,814
Emp.: 459
Fiscal Year-end: 12/31/22
Gold Ore Mining Services
N.A.I.C.S.: 212220
Muhammed M. Aballala (Chm)

AL MASAOOD OIL INDUSTRY SUPPLIES & SERVICES CO.
PO Box 4352, Abu Dhabi, United Arab Emirates
Tel.: (971) 26267666
Web Site: http://www.almasaoodoiss.com
Year Founded: 1971
Sales Range: $25-49.9 Million
Emp.: 500
Oil, Construction & Engineering Services
N.A.I.C.S.: 213112
Rahma Al Masaood (Chm)

AL MAWARID MANPOWER CO.
Rawdah, Riyadh, 13211, Saudi Arabia
Tel.: (966) 920027202
Web Site: https://www.mawarid.com.sa
Year Founded: 2012
1833—(SAU)
Rev.: $26,995,116
Assets: $107,984,997
Liabilities: $45,860,799
Net Worth: $62,124,198
Earnings: $14,839,223
Emp.: 188

Fiscal Year-end: 12/31/22
Human Resource Consulting Services
N.A.I.C.S.: 541612
Ahmad Mohammad Al-Rukban (Chm)

AL MEERA CONSUMER GOODS COMPANY Q.S.C.
PO Box 3371, Doha, Qatar
Tel.: (974) 40119111
Web Site: https://www.almeera.com.qa
Year Founded: 2004
MERS—(QE)
Rev.: $778,193,823
Assets: $798,703,656
Liabilities: $337,783,702
Net Worth: $460,919,953
Earnings: $49,415,803
Fiscal Year-end: 12/31/23
Foodstuff & Consumer Goods Com-modities Whlsr
N.A.I.C.S.: 445298
Abdulla Abdulaziz Abdullah Turki Al-Subaie (Chm)

AL MOUWASAT MEDICAL SERVICES COMPANY
PO Box 282, Dammam, 31411, Saudi Arabia
Tel.: (966) 138200000
Web Site: https://www.mouwasat.com
Year Founded: 1974
4002—(SAU)
Rev.: $537,122,237
Assets: $1,242,922,704
Liabilities: $422,676,549
Net Worth: $820,246,155
Earnings: $168,694,216
Emp.: 4,084
Fiscal Year-end: 12/31/22
Hospitals, Medical Centers, Medicine Warehouses & Pharmacies Owner, Manager & Operator
N.A.I.C.S.: 622110
Mohammed Sultan Al-Subaie (Chm)

AL MOWASAT HEALTHCARE COMPANY K.S.C.C.
982 Salmiya Plot 2 Block 3 Ave 79, Kuwait, 22010, Kuwait
Tel.: (965) 2576 5550
Web Site: http://www.newmowasat.com
Sales Range: $75-99.9 Million
Emp.: 1,000
Holding Company; Hospital Opera-tions & Real Estate Development Services
N.A.I.C.S.: 551112

AL MUDON INTERNATIONAL REAL ESTATE COMPANY - KPSC
Kuwait qibla Fahad al Salem street al Nasser tower 7 floor, PO Box 13042, Safat, 2376, Kuwait, Kuwait
Tel.: (965) 22258985   KW
Year Founded: 1996
ALMUDON—(KUW)
Rev.: $7,293
Assets: $12,301,049
Liabilities: $413,313
Net Worth: $11,887,736
Earnings: $31,626
Emp.: 6
Fiscal Year-end: 12/31/20
Real Estate Manangement Services
N.A.I.C.S.: 531390
Abdullah Sami Al-Joaan (Vice Chm & CEO)

AL OMANIYA FINANCIAL SER-VICES (SAOG)

Al Omaniya Financial Services (SAOG)—(Continued)

PO Box 1087, 114, Jibroo, 114, Oman
Tel.: (968) 24724700 **OM**
Web Site: https://www.aofsoman.com
AOFS—(MUS)
Rev.: $38,318,660
Assets: $031,549,201
Liabilities: $461,930,642
Net Worth: $169,618,620
Earnings: $8,885,762
Emp.: 157
Fiscal Year-end: 12/31/19
Financial Services
N.A.I.C.S.: 523999
Khalid Said Al Wahaibi (Chm)

AL QUDS READYMIX

PO Box 710078, Amman, 11171, Jordan
Tel.: (962) 64202575
Web Site: https://www.qrm.jo
Year Founded: 1996
AQRM—(AMM)
Rev.: $6,139,830
Assets: $18,683,133
Liabilities: $8,509,185
Net Worth: $10,173,948
Earnings: ($726,302)
Emp.: 80
Fiscal Year-end: 12/31/20
Readymix Concrete Mfr
N.A.I.C.S.: 327320
Ayman Haza'a Al-Majali (Chm)

AL RAJHI BANK

Olaya St, PO Box 28, Riyadh, 11411, Saudi Arabia
Tel.: (966) 920003344 **SA**
Web Site:
http://www.alrajhibank.com.sa
Year Founded: 1976
1120—(SAU)
Rev.: $7,519,432,342
Assets: $203,270,503,133
Liabilities: $176,547,390,215
Net Worth: $26,723,112,918
Earnings: $4,572,943,608
Emp.: 15,820
Fiscal Year-end: 12/31/22
Banking Services
N.A.I.C.S.: 522110
Abdullah Sulaiman Al Rajhi (Chm)

Subsidiaries:

Al Rajhi Bank - Jordan Ltd. **(1)**
Abdul Hameed Sharaf Street Building Number 67, Shmeissani, Jordan
Tel.: (962) 65100818
Web Site: https://www.alrajhibank.com.jo
Banking Services
N.A.I.C.S.: 522110

Al Rajhi Bank - Kuwait WLL **(1)**
Gulf Street Ahmad Tower, Sharq, Kuwait, Kuwait
Tel.: (965) 24954343
Web Site: https://www.alrajhibank.com.kw
Banking & Trading Services
N.A.I.C.S.: 523999

Al Rajhi Bank - Malaysia Sdn. Bhd. **(1)**
Ground Floor East Block Wisma Golden Eagle Realty 142-B Jalan Ampang, 50450, Kuala Lumpur, Malaysia
Tel.: (60) 323326000
Web Site: https://www.alrajhibank.com.my
Banking Services
N.A.I.C.S.: 522110

Al Rajhi Banking & Investment Corporation Bhd **(1)**
16 Fl Menara Chan Jalan Ampang, Kuala Lumpur, 50450, Malaysia **(100%)**
Tel.: (60) 323017000
Web Site: http://www.alrajhibank.com.my
Sales Range: $100-124.9 Million
Emp.: 150

Miscellaneous Financial Investment Activities
N.A.I.C.S.: 523999

Al Rajhi Capital Company **(1)**
8467 King Fahd Road, PO 5561, Al Muruj Dist, Riyadh, 12263-2743, Saudi Arabia
Tel.: (966) 920005856
Web Site: https://www.alrajhi-capital.com
Investment Banking Services
N.A.I.C.S.: 523150
Waleed AlRashed AlHumaid (CEO)

Al Rajhi Development Company Ltd. **(1)**
PO Box 4301, Riyadh, Saudi Arabia **(99%)**
Tel.: (966) 14761581
Web Site:
http://www.alrajhidevelopment.com
Sales Range: $25-49.9 Million
Emp.: 100
Support Activities for Transportation
N.A.I.C.S.: 488999

AL RAJHI COMPANY FOR CO-OPERATIVE INSURANCE

3485-at Thummamah Road, PO Box 67791, Ar Rabie Dist, Riyadh, 11517, Saudi Arabia
Tel.: (966) 114409666
Web Site:
https://www.alrajhitakaful.com
Year Founded: 2008
8230—(SAU)
Rev.: $663,825,623
Assets: $1,446,785,762
Liabilities: $1,103,331,023
Net Worth: $343,454,739
Earnings: $23,894,947
Emp.: 974
Fiscal Year-end: 12/31/22
Insurance Management Services
N.A.I.C.S.: 524298
Abdullah Sulaiman Al Rajhi (Chm)

AL RAMZ CAPITAL LLC

Sky Tower Al Reem Island, PO Box 3200, Abu Dhabi, United Arab Emirates
Tel.: (971) 2 6262626 **AE**
Web Site: http://www.alramzuae.ae
Year Founded: 1998
Emp.: 50
Securities Brokerage
N.A.I.C.S.: 523150
Ayman Ghoneim (Dir-Bus & Ops)

Subsidiaries:

Al Ramz Corporation Investment & Development Company PJSC **(1)**
Sky Tower 22nd Floor, PO Box 32000, Dubai, United Arab Emirates
Tel.: (971) 26262626
Web Site: https://www.alramz.ae
Real Estate Development Services
N.A.I.C.S.: 531390
Khalifa Mohamed Al Kindi (Chm)

AL RAWABI DAIRY COMPANY L.L.C.

Al Khawaneej No 2 Al Aweer Aleyas Road, PO Box 50368, Dubai, United Arab Emirates
Tel.: (971) 42892123
Web Site:
http://www.alrawabidairy.com
Sales Range: $550-599.9 Million
Emp.: 900
Dairy Products Mfr
N.A.I.C.S.: 311511
Ahmed El Tigani (CEO)

AL SAFAT REAL ESTATE COMPANY K.P.S.C.

Beirut St In Front Of Al-Qadsia Sporting Club - 12 Floor, Hawalli, Kuwait
Tel.: (965) 1877777 **KW**
Year Founded: 2003

SAFRE—(KUW)
Rev.: $8,332,108
Assets: $142,649,462
Liabilities: $32,943,764
Net Worth: $109,705,698
Earnings: $7,288,204
Fiscal Year-end: 12/31/23
Real Estate Manangement Services
N.A.I.O.O.: 501090
Jassem Hamad Jasssem Al-Ghanim (Chm)

AL SALAM BANK - SUDAN

Al Jame'a Street Ma'amoun Al Burair Group Building, Khartoum, Sudan
Tel.: (249) 183747000 **Sd**
Web Site: http://www.alsalam-bank.net
Year Founded: 2004
ALSALAMS—(DFM)
Rev.: $8,005,652
Assets: $124,641,360
Liabilities: $61,815,835
Net Worth: $62,825,526
Earnings: $1,734,528
Emp.: 148
Fiscal Year-end: 12/31/19
Commercial Banking Services
N.A.I.C.S.: 522110
Mohammed Omeir Yousef (Chm)

AL SALAM BANK-BAHRAIN B.S.C.

Burj Al Khair 3, PO Box 18282, Al Seef District, 436, Manama, Bahrain
Tel.: (973) 97317005500 **BH**
Web Site:
https://www.alsalambank.com
Year Founded: 2006
SALAM.BAH—(DFM)
Rev.: $740,779,352
Assets: $13,653,536,004
Liabilities: $5,130,444,589
Net Worth: $8,523,091,415
Earnings: $127,799,883
Emp.: 509
Fiscal Year-end: 12/31/23
Commercial Banking Services
N.A.I.C.S.: 522110
Mohammed Burhan Arbouna (Head-Shari'a Compliance)

Subsidiaries:

Al Salam Asia-Pacific Pte Ltd. **(1)**
80 Raffles Place UOB Plaza 2 17-23, Singapore, 48624, Singapore
Tel.: (65) 6236 9602
Private Equity Investment Services
N.A.I.C.S.: 523999

Al Salam Bank Seychelles Limited **(1)**
Maison Esplanade Francis Rachel Street, Mahe, Victoria, Seychelles
Tel.: (248) 4385600
Web Site:
https://www.alsalamseychelles.com
Finance Investment Services
N.A.I.C.S.: 523999
Alhur Al Suwaidi (Chm)

BMI Bank BSC **(1)**
Bahrain World Trade Center, PO Box 350, Manama, Bahrain
Tel.: (973) 175 08080
Web Site: http://www.bmibank.com.bh
Sales Range: $100-124.9 Million
Emp.: 180
Commericial Banking
N.A.I.C.S.: 522110
Habib Ahmed Kassim (Deputy Chm)

AL SALAM GROUP HOLDING COMPANY KSCC

Murgab-Alsoor Street - Jasim Alasfoor Tower, Mirqab, Kuwait, Kuwait
Tel.: (965) 2 296 0777
Web Site:
http://www.alsalamholding.com

ALSALAM—(KUW)
Rev.: $571,861
Assets: $94,700,413
Liabilities: $9,977,979
Net Worth: $84,722,435
Earnings: ($25,972,500)
Emp.: 15
Fiscal Year-end: 12/31/20
Investment Services
N.A.I.C.S.: 523999
Sara Ali Darweesh Al-Shemali (CEO)

AL SHAFAR GROUP

Karama Trade Crt Rd Close to Burjuman Opp Fpnney Schafar Bldg, PO Box 2185, Dubai, 2185, United Arab Emirates
Tel.: (971) 4 3969999
Web Site: http://www.alshafar.ae
Year Founded: 1960
Sales Range: $500-549.9 Million
Emp.: 3,000
Holding Company for Special Trade Contractors
N.A.I.C.S.: 551112
Ahmed Abdullah Shafar (Co-Chm)

Subsidiaries:

Al Shafar Development **(1)**
Office No 107 First Floor Al Shafar Building, Karama Bur Dubai, Dubai, United Arab Emirates
Tel.: (971) 4 397 1999
Web Site:
http://www.alshafardevelopment.com
Holding Company
N.A.I.C.S.: 551112
Nasser Abdul Salam Ahmed Ali (Gen Mgr)

Parkway International Contracting L.L.C. **(1)**
Al Karama Area Al Shafar & Sons Building, PO Box 211924, Dubai, 211924, United Arab Emirates
Tel.: (971) 4 357 8166
Web Site: http://www.parkwayic.com
Emp.: 2,000
Construction Engineering Services
N.A.I.C.S.: 541330
Tarek Zoabi (Gen Mgr)

Powerpoint Electrical & Mechanical Works L.L.C. **(1)**
PO Box 31377, Dubai, United Arab Emirates
Tel.: (971) 4 3966771
Web Site: http://www.powerpointuae.com
Emp.: 1,200
Electromechanical Engineering Services
N.A.I.C.S.: 541330
Ahmed Abdulla Al Shafar (Chm)

Quick Sign LLC **(1)**
Near Aladin Custom Ras Al Khor Industriul Area 2, Dubai, United Arab Emirates
Tel.: (971) 4 333 6133
Web Site: http://www.quicksign.ae
Sign Board Mfr
N.A.I.C.S.: 339950

AL SHAHEER CORP.

Suite G/5/5 3rd Floor Mansoor Tower Clifton Block 9, Karachi, Pakistan
Tel.: (92) 2138781100
Web Site: https://www.ascfoods.com
Year Founded: 2008
ASC—(PSX)
Rev.: $24,768,520
Assets: $39,779,671
Liabilities: $15,110,366
Net Worth: $24,669,305
Earnings: ($6,518,533)
Emp.: 658
Fiscal Year-end: 06/30/23
Food Mfr
N.A.I.C.S.: 311999
Kamran Khalili (CEO)

AL SHAMS HOUSING & URBANIZATION

26 Sherif St Imobilia Bldg, Cairo, Egypt
Tel.: (20) 2 23925844
Web Site:
http://www.alshamscompany.com
Year Founded: 1946
ELSH.CA—(EGX)
Sales Range: Less than $1 Million
Real Estate Development Services
N.A.I.C.S.: 531390
Mahmoud Maghawari Mohamed *(Chm & Mng Dir)*

AL SHARQ INVESTMENTS PROJECTS(HOLDING) P.L.C.
Wasfi Altal st building no 115, PO Box 941166, Amman, 11194, Jordan
Tel.: (962) 65510940
Year Founded: 1994
AIPC—(AMM)
Rev.: $2,859,392
Assets: $28,001,199
Liabilities: $1,193,648
Net Worth: $26,807,550
Earnings: ($1,773,362)
Emp.: 3
Fiscal Year-end: 12/31/20
Tour Management Services
N.A.I.C.S.: 561520

AL SORAYAI GROUP
PO Box 1563, Jeddah, 21441, Saudi Arabia
Tel.: (966) 26918222
Web Site: http://www.al-sorayai.com
Sales Range: $400-449.9 Million
Emp.: 2,200
Carpets, Rugs, Fabrics, Blinds, Curtains, Blankets, Mattresses & Furniture Mfr, Distr, Importer & Sales
N.A.I.C.S.: 314110
Saleh Nasseer Al Sorayai *(Chm)*

AL SUWADI POWER COMPANY SAOG
Bareeq Al Shatti-103 Level 1 south east Muscat Grand Mall Bldg No 5, PO Box 39, Street No 35 Al Khuwair, Muscat, Oman
Tel.: (968) 24393300
Web Site:
https://www.alsuwadipower.com
SUWP—(MUS)
Rev.: $213,760,452
Assets: $746,470,868
Liabilities: $481,970,909
Net Worth: $264,499,959
Earnings: $29,370,459
Emp.: 7
Fiscal Year-end: 12/31/21
Eletric Power Generation Services
N.A.I.C.S.: 221118
Charles Paul Dexter *(Chm)*

AL TAJAMOUAT FOR CATERING & HOUSING COMPANY, PLC.
PO Box 14, Amman, 11636, Jordan
Tel.: (962) 64022928
Web Site: https://www.altajamouat-ch.com
Year Founded: 2003
JNTH—(AMM)
Rev.: $2,369,308
Assets: $13,644,587
Liabilities: $1,271,056
Net Worth: $12,373,531
Earnings: $3,195
Emp.: 48
Fiscal Year-end: 12/31/20
Catering & Housekeeping Services
N.A.I.C.S.: 561720

AL TAJAMOUAT FOR TOURISTIC PROJECTS CO. PLC

Taj Mall - Abdoun, PO Box 5376, Amman, 11183, Jordan
Tel.: (962) 5921122
Year Founded: 1994
TAJM—(AMM)
Rev.: $14,947,135
Assets: $187,833,860
Liabilities: $42,123,509
Net Worth: $145,710,352
Earnings: ($530,327)
Emp.: 122
Fiscal Year-end: 12/31/20
Investment Management Service
N.A.I.C.S.: 523999

AL TAYER GROUP LLC
Garhoud Atrium 2nd St, PO Box 2623, 2623, Dubai, United Arab Emirates
Tel.: (971) 42011111
Web Site: https://www.altayer.com
Year Founded: 1979
Holding Company
N.A.I.C.S.: 551112

Subsidiaries:

Al Tayer Stocks LLC   (1)
30th 31st Floor API Trio Office Towers Al Barsha 1, PO Box 2623, Garhoud, Dubai, 2623, United Arab Emirates   **(51%)**
Tel.: (971) 45034888
Web Site: http://www.altayerstocks.com
Sales Range: $50-74.9 Million
Emp.: 150
Interior-Contracting; Plastering, Furnishing & Electrical & Mechanical Systems Installation
N.A.I.C.S.: 236220

AL WATHBA NATIONAL INSURANCE COMPANY P.S.C.
Al Wathba Insurance Building Najda Street, PO Box 45154, Abu Dhabi, United Arab Emirates
Tel.: (971) 600544040
Web Site: https://www.awnic.com
Year Founded: 1997
AWNIC—(EMI)
Rev.: $68,060,666
Assets: $427,252,105
Liabilities: $218,777,627
Net Worth: $208,474,478
Earnings: $1,624,277
Emp.: 150
Fiscal Year-end: 12/31/19
Insurance Services
N.A.I.C.S.: 524298
Saif Mohammed Butti Al-Hamed *(Chm)*

AL WIAAM FOR FINANCIAL INVESTMENT CO.
Alwatheq Sequare- United Bank Building - 2 Floor, Baghdad, Iraq
Tel.: (964) 7706348675
Year Founded: 2000
VWIF—(IRAQ)
Sales Range: Less than $1 Million
Financial Investment Services
N.A.I.C.S.: 523999

AL YAMAMAH STEEL INDUSTRIES COMPANY
New Akaria Building Salah Udin Al Ayoubi St, Malaz Area, Riyadh, Saudi Arabia
Tel.: (966) 14770512
Web Site: https://www.yamsteel.com
1304—(SAU)
Rev.: $415,820,216
Assets: $477,507,874
Liabilities: $312,100,079
Net Worth: $165,407,795
Earnings: ($44,032,626)
Emp.: 1,192
Fiscal Year-end: 06/30/23
Metal Products Mfr

N.A.I.C.S.: 331110
Yousef Saeed Mohammed Ba-Zaid *(CEO)*

AL YOUSEF GROUP
PO Box 200, 100, Muscat, Oman
Tel.: (968) 24613000
Web Site:
http://www.alyousefgroup.com
Investment Holding Company
Mohamed Musa Al-Yousef *(Chm)*

Subsidiaries:

Al Anwar Holdings S.A.O.G   (1)
Villa No 897 Way No 3013 Shatti Al Qurum, PO Box 468, Near Al Sarooj Filling Station, 131, Muscat, 131, Oman
Tel.: (968) 24692503
Web Site: https://www.alanwar.om
Rev.: $4,646,995
Assets: $126,840,355
Liabilities: $45,521,845
Net Worth: $81,318,510
Earnings: $919,528
Emp.: 7
Fiscal Year-end: 03/31/2023
Investment Holding Company
N.A.I.C.S.: 551112
Masoud Humaid Malik Al Harthy *(Chm)*

Holding (Domestic):

Falcon Insurance Company SAOC   (2)
2nd Floor Sultan Centre, PO Box 2279, Qurum, Ruwi, 112, Oman
Tel.: (968) 24660900
Web Site:
http://www.falconinsurancesaoc.com
General Insurance Services
N.A.I.C.S.: 524210
A. R. Srinivasan *(Gen Mgr)*

National telephone Services Co. LLC   (1)
PO Box 2786, Ruwi, 112, Oman
Tel.: (968) 24709281
Web Site: http://www.nts.com.om
Telecommunication Engineering Services
N.A.I.C.S.: 517810
Vinay Misra *(CEO)*

Oman Sharpoorji Construction Co. LLC (1)
PO Box 1347, 112, Ruwi, Oman
Tel.: (968) 24590297
Web Site: http://www.osco.com.om
Construction Engineering Services
N.A.I.C.S.: 541330
Kumar Mahadevan *(Mng Dir)*

Truckoman LLC   (1)
PO Box 367, Mina Al Fahal, 116, Muscat, Oman
Tel.: (968) 2456 5248
Web Site: http://www.truckoman.com
Emp.: 1,000
Logistics Consulting Servies
N.A.I.C.S.: 541614
Chris Fidler *(Grp Gen Mgr)*

AL YUSR INDUSTRIAL CONTRACTING COMPANY WLL
Al Jubayl Industrial City, PO BOX 10270, Al Jubayl, 31961, Saudi Arabia
Tel.: (966) 3 341 5224
Web Site: http://www.aytb.com
Year Founded: 1979
Sales Range: $1-4.9 Billion
Emp.: 4,000
Support Activities for Oil & Gas Operations
N.A.I.C.S.: 213112
Abdulmohsen Ogaili *(CEO)*

AL ZAWRAA FINANCIAL INVESTMENT PLC
Al-Nidal St White Palace Bld Sec 103 St 11, Baghdad, Iraq
Tel.: (964) 7199511
Year Founded: 2000

VZAF—(IRAQ)
Sales Range: Less than $1 Million
Financial Investment Services
N.A.I.C.S.: 523999

AL ZAYANI INVESTMENTS WLL
Zayani House, PO Box 5553, Manama, Bahrain
Tel.: (973) 17531177
Web Site: http://www.alzayani.com
Year Founded: 2001
Sales Range: $25-49.9 Million
Emp.: 50
Equity Investment Firm
N.A.I.C.S.: 523999
Hamid Rashid Al Zayani *(Founder & Partner)*

Subsidiaries:

Zayani Leasing W.L.L.   (1)
PO Box 1185, Manama, Bahrain
Tel.: (973) 1770 2333
Web Site: http://www.zayanileasing.com
Emp.: 35
Automobile Leasing Services
N.A.I.C.S.: 532112
Nawaf K. Al Zayani *(Mng Dir)*

Zayani Motors WLL   (1)
Building 4 Road 15 Block 635, Manama, Bahrain
Tel.: (973) 17703703
Web Site: http://www.zmotors.com
Emp.: 190
Automobile Leasing Services
N.A.I.C.S.: 532112
Mohammed Zaki *(Gen Mgr)*

Subsidiary (Domestic):

Orient Motors WLL   (2)
Block 939 Road 3901 Building 78, Manama, Bahrain
Tel.: (973) 17772555
Web Site: http://www.ombahrain.com
New Car Dealers
N.A.I.C.S.: 441110
Ebrahim Mohammed *(Mgr-Sls)*

Zayani Properties WLL   (1)
Zayani House Diplomatic Area, PO Box 5553, Manama, Bahrain
Tel.: (973) 17 532244
Real Estate Management Services
N.A.I.C.S.: 531390
Haitham Mustafa *(Gen Mgr)*

AL-'AQAR HEALTHCARE REIT
Unit 1-19-02 Level 19 Block 1 V SQUARE Jalan Utara, 46200, Petaling Jaya, Selangor Darul Ehsan, Malaysia
Tel.: (60) 379321692   MY
Web Site: https://www.alaqar.com.my
Year Founded: 2006
5116—(KLS)
Rev.: $23,330,935
Assets: $395,146,208
Liabilities: $189,598,107
Net Worth: $205,548,101
Earnings: $12,727,801
Emp.: 25
Fiscal Year-end: 12/31/22
Real Estate Investment Management Services
N.A.I.C.S.: 531120
Azman Ismail *(CEO)*

AL-ABBAS SUGAR MILLS LIMITED
Pardesi House Survey No 2/1 R Y 16 Old Queens Road, Karachi, 74000, Pakistan
Tel.: (92) 21111111224
Web Site: https://www.aasml.com
Year Founded: 1991
AABS—(KAR)
Rev.: $46,141,711
Assets: $41,297,253
Liabilities: $20,513,757

AL-ABBAS SUGAR Mills Limited—(Continued)

Net Worth: $20,783,496
Earnings: $7,161,138
Emp.: 2,003
Fiscal Year-end: 09/30/19
Sugarcane Cultivation & Production
Services
N.A.I.C.S.: 111930
Zuhair Abbas (Sec)

Subsidiaries:

Al-Abbas Sugar Mills Limited -
Dhabeji Plant   (1)
Main National Highway, Dhabeji, Sindh,
Pakistan
Tel.: (92) 2134420201
Sugar Products Mfr
N.A.I.C.S.: 311314

Al-Abbas Sugar Mills Limited - Mir-
wah Plant   (1)
Mirpur Khas-Digri Road Mirpur Khas, Mir-
wah Gorchani, Sindh, Pakistan
Tel.: (92) 2338962346
Sugar Products Mfr
N.A.I.C.S.: 311314

AL-ABID SILK MILLS LIMITED
A-34/A SITE Manghopir Road, Kara-
chi, Pakistan
Tel.: (92) 212560040
Web Site: https://www.alabid.com
Year Founded: 1968
AASM—(PSX)
Rev.: $1,143,828
Assets: $9,785,743
Liabilities: $9,706,143
Net Worth: $79,601
Earnings: $316,961
Emp.: 5
Fiscal Year-end: 06/30/23
Textile Products Mfr
N.A.I.C.S.: 314120
Naseem A. Sattar (CEO)

AL-ABRAJ HOLDING COM-
PANY KSCC
PO Box 3066, Hawally, Kuwait,
32031, Kuwait
Tel.: (965) 22254241
Year Founded: 1999
Sales Range: $50-74.9 Million
Holding Company; Investment Ser-
vices
N.A.I.C.S.: 551112
Jamal Ahmad Al-Kandari (Chm)

AL-AHLEIA SWITCHGEAR
COMPANY K.S.C.C.
Safat, PO Box 25876, Kuwait, 13119,
Kuwait
Tel.: (965) 1822600
Web Site: http://www.ahleiasg.com
Year Founded: 1982
Sales Range: $100-124.9 Million
Emp.: 2,400
High & Low Voltage Switchgear Mfr
N.A.I.C.S.: 335313
Nasrallah S. H. Behbehani (Chm)

Subsidiaries:

Al-Ahleia Switchgear Company
K.S.C.C. - Unit - 4   (1)
Block 9 Street 92 Plot 148, Kuwait, Kuwait
Tel.: (965) 1822400
Industrial Equipment Distr
N.A.I.C.S.: 423120

Al-Ahleia Switchgear Company
K.S.C.C. - Unit - 5   (1)
Block 8 Street 84 Plot 181 182 & 184, Ku-
wait, Kuwait
Tel.: (965) 24723016
Industrial Equipment Distr
N.A.I.C.S.: 423120

Al-Ahleia Switchgear Company
K.S.C.C. - Unit - 6   (1)
Block S Street 101 Plot 119, Kuwait, Kuwait

Tel.: (965) 1822600
Industrial Equipment Distr
N.A.I.C.S.: 423120

AL-AHLIA VEGETABLE OIL
COMPANY
Ieppo Highway Iron factory diversion,
1807 Location Kamhana, Hama,
Cyria
Tel.: (963) 33 2524510
Web Site: http://www.avoco-sy.com
Year Founded: 1996
AVOC—(DSE)
Sales Range: Less than $1 Million
Vegetable Oil Mfr & Whslr
N.A.I.C.S.: 311225
Mohammed Hasan Al-Assiri (Chm)

AL-AHLYIA FOR AGRICUL-
TURAL PRODUCTION
Sec 902 -St 32- H 1, Hai Al-Wahdad
-Al-Wathew Sequare, Baghdad, Iraq
Tel.: (964) 7197379
Year Founded: 1994
AAHP—(IRAQ)
Sales Range: Less than $1 Million
Fish Farming Services
N.A.I.C.S.: 112511

AL-AMAL FINANCIAL INVEST-
MENT COMPANY
Tel.: (962) 65671485
Web Site: https://www.alamal.com.jo
Year Founded: 1980
AMAL—(AMM)
Rev.: $2,353,164
Assets: $17,209,960
Liabilities: $810,828
Net Worth: $16,399,132
Earnings: $1,102,683
Emp.: 13
Fiscal Year-end: 12/31/20
Securities Brokerage Services
N.A.I.C.S.: 523150
Omar Zuhair Abed Alfatah Malhas
(Chm)

AL-AMAN INVESTMENT COM-
PANY K.S.C.C.
Al-Daw Tower-Sharq-khaled Bin Al-
Waled St Block 7 Blding, PO Box
12466, 1 Floor 11-12-13 Shamiya,
Kuwait, 71655, Kuwait
Tel.: (965) 1822626
Web Site: http://www.alaman.com.kw
ALAMAN—(KUW)
Sales Range: $1-9.9 Million
Emp.: 25
Investment Services; Owned 45% by
Securities House K.S.C.C.
N.A.I.C.S.: 523999
Wafaa M. W. Badawy (Exec VP-Res
& Consulting)

AL-AQARIYA TRADING IN-
VESTMENT COMPANY
Al-Masyoun, PO Box 662, Ramallah,
Palestine
Tel.: (970) 22986916
Web Site: https://www.aqariya.ps
Year Founded: 2004
AQARIYA—(PAL)
Rev.: $5,337,082
Assets: $19,149,389
Liabilities: $7,583,791
Net Worth: $11,565,598
Earnings: $833,870
Fiscal Year-end: 12/31/23
Real Estate Investment Services
N.A.I.C.S.: 531390
Ayoub Wael Zurub (Chm)

AL-ARAFAH ISLAMI BANK
PLC
Al-Arafah Tower 63 Purana Paltan,
Dhaka, 1000, Bangladesh

Tel.: (880) 244850005   BD
Web Site: https://www.aibl.com
ALARABANK—(CHT)
Rev.: $286,155,568
Assets: $5,241,441,620
Liabilities: $4,999,188,670
Net Worth: $242,252,951
Earnings: $21,544,033
Emp.: 5,104
Fiscal Year-end: 12/31/23
Retail Banking & Investment Services
N.A.I.C.S.: 522110
Mohammed Abdus Salam (Vice Chm)

AL-AZHAR TEXTILE MILLS
LIMITED
76-A Gulgasht Colony, Multan, Paki-
stan
Tel.: (92) 61 6211119
Textile Mill Operator
N.A.I.C.S.: 313110

AL-BABTAIN GROUP
PO Box 766, Safat, Kuwait, 13008,
Kuwait
Tel.: (965) 826000
Web Site: http://www.babtain.com
Year Founded: 1948
Sales Range: $250-299.9 Million
Emp.: 1,038
Consumer Goods Importer & Distr;
Investment Services
N.A.I.C.S.: 423110
Saleh A. Al-Babtain (Vice Chm &
CEO)

Subsidiaries:

Al-Babtain Body Manufacturing
Co.   (1)
Street 94 Block 8, South Subhan, Safat,
Kuwait, Kuwait
Tel.: (965) 474 2279
Truck Body Mfr
N.A.I.C.S.: 333924

Kuwait Paint Co.   (1)
Shuwaikh Industrial Area, PO Box 42255,
Safat, Kuwait, 70653, Kuwait
Tel.: (965) 4832644
Web Site: http://www.babtain.com
Sales Range: $25-49.9 Million
Emp.: 96
Paints Mfr
N.A.I.C.S.: 325510
Essam Bahnasy (Mgr-Tech)

National Computer Services   (1)
PO Box 766, Safat, Kuwait, Kuwait
Tel.: (965) 4755127
Web Site: http://www.nts-me.com
Sales Range: $25-49.9 Million
Emp.: 32
Computer Installation & Maintenance Ser-
vices
N.A.I.C.S.: 541519

AL-BABTAIN POWER & TELE-
COMMUNICATION COMPANY
PO Box 88373, Riyadh, 11662, Saudi
Arabia
Tel.: (966) 112411222
Web Site: https://www.al-
babtain.com.sa
Year Founded: 1950
2320—(SAU)
Rev.: $664,113,956
Assets: $780,842,992
Liabilities: $535,434,741
Net Worth: $245,408,251
Earnings: $38,128,632
Emp.: 1,502
Fiscal Year-end: 12/31/23
Electric Power Transmission & Distri-
bution Services
N.A.I.C.S.: 221121
Jawad Jamel Ismail Shehadeh (CEO)

AL-BAGHLI SPONGE MANU-
FACTURING COMPANY

Div No 415 Block No 1 Main Street
Sabhan Industrial Area S, Al Rai
Area, Kuwait, 13160, Safat, Kuwait
Tel.: (965) 24761444
Web Site: http://www.albaghli-
united.com
Year Founded: 1972
Sales Range: $75-99.9 Million
Emp.: 300
Foam Products Importer & Mfr
N.A.I.C.S.: 326140

AL-BAHA INVESTMENT AND
DEVELOPMENT CO.
Al Baha City Kirig Fahd Road, PO
Box 448, Riyadh, 22888, Saudi Ara-
bia
Tel.: (966) 117223333
Web Site:
    https://www.albahacompany.com
Year Founded: 1992
4130—(SAU)
Rev.: $3,070,691
Assets: $105,659,821
Liabilities: $44,511,671
Net Worth: $61,148,151
Earnings: $2,158,344
Emp.: 3
Fiscal Year-end: 12/31/22
Tour Management Services
N.A.I.C.S.: 238910
Land Reclamation Services
N.A.I.C.S.: 238910
Ibrahim Abdullah Rashed Kulib (CEO)

AL-BILAD MEDICAL SER-
VICES CO.
Istiklal St - Istiklal Hospital, PO Box
1493, Amman, 11821, Jordan
Tel.: (962) 65652600
Web Site: http://istiklal.jo
Year Founded: 1997
ABMS—(AMM)
Rev.: $19,060,114
Assets: $49,993,143
Liabilities: $12,923,630
Net Worth: $37,069,513
Earnings: $809,571
Emp.: 739
Fiscal Year-end: 12/31/20
General Hospital Services
N.A.I.C.S.: 622110
Ahmed Mohammed Al-Ahmad (Gen
Mgr)

AL-DAR NATIONAL REAL ES-
TATE COMPANY K.S.C.C.
Ahmed Al Jaber Street-Dar Al Awadhi
Complex-26th Floor, PO Box 22242,
Safat, 13060, Kuwait, Kuwait
Tel.: (965) 22411016
Web Site: http://www.adnrec.com
Year Founded: 2000
Sales Range: $1-9.9 Million
Real Estate Services
N.A.I.C.S.: 531390

AL-DAWAA MEDICAL SER-
VICES COMPANY
Eastern Cement Towers King Fahd
Road, Al Rawabi, Al Khobar, Saudi
Arabia
Tel.: (966) 920000838
Web Site: https://www.al-
dawaa.com.sa
Year Founded: 1993
4163—(SAU)
Rev.: $1,432,407,015
Assets: $1,198,979,697
Liabilities: $906,968,542
Net Worth: $292,011,155
Earnings: $81,442,110
Emp.: 6,359
Fiscal Year-end: 12/31/22
Health Care Srvices
N.A.I.C.S.: 621610
Waleed Al-Jaafari (Mng Dir)

AL-DEERA HOLDING CO. K.S.C.C.

Derwazat AlAbdulrazzak SoukAlKuwait Building Block A Floor 8, PO Box 4839, Safat, 13049, Kuwait, 13049, Kuwait
Tel.: (965) 22493955
Web Site:
https://www.aldeeraholding.com
Year Founded: 1998
ALDEERA—(KUW)
Rev.: $4,315,291
Assets: $80,641,080
Liabilities: $38,255,179
Net Worth: $42,385,901
Earnings: $2,129,988
Emp.: 19
Fiscal Year-end: 12/31/22
Investment & Financial Services
N.A.I.C.S.: 523999
Rami A. Habli (Exec VP-Investments)

AL-DORRA PETROLEUM SERVICES KSCC

Al Mirqab Abdullah Al Mubarak St Al-Nafisi Tower 6th Fl, PO Box 26583, Safat, Kuwait, 13126, Kuwait
Tel.: (965) 22954560
Web Site: http://www.al-dorra.com
Sales Range: $25-49.9 Million
Emp.: 15
Oil & Gas Services
N.A.I.C.S.: 213112
Waleed Al Houti (Chm)

AL-EQBAL INVESTMENT CO. (PLC)

Building No 39 Sa ad Ibn Abi Waqqas Street, PO Box 911145, Amman, 11191, Jordan
Tel.: (962) 65561333
Web Site: https://www.eqbal-invest.com
Year Founded: 1989
EICO—(AMM)
Rev.: $315,601,098
Assets: $605,862,324
Liabilities: $335,752,620
Net Worth: $270,109,704
Earnings: $63,509,036
Emp.: 726
Fiscal Year-end: 12/31/19
Cigarette & Tobacco Mfr
N.A.I.C.S.: 312230
Manuel Stotz (Chm)

Subsidiaries:

Al Fakher for Tobacco Trading & Agencies LLC (1)
PO Box 20037, Ajman, United Arab Emirates
Tel.: (971) 67400366
Web Site: http://www.alfakher.com
Tobacco Mfr
N.A.I.C.S.: 312230

AL-FARIS NATIONAL COMPANY FOR INVESTMENT & EXPORT PLC

Mecca Towers Mecca Al Mukarramah St, PO Box 414, Amman, 11953, Jordan
Tel.: (962) 65629999
Web Site:
https://www.optimizasolutions.com
Year Founded: 2005
CEBC—(AMM)
Rev.: $27,596,374
Assets: $47,147,085
Liabilities: $27,047,380
Net Worth: $20,099,705
Earnings: $632,594
Emp.: 252
Fiscal Year-end: 12/31/20
Information Technology Consulting Services

N.A.I.C.S.: 541512
Saif Khouri (COO)

AL-FUTTAIM PRIVATE COMPANY LLC

Dubai Festival City Festival Tower Level 28, Dubai, United Arab Emirates
Tel.: (971) 47062222
Web Site: http://www.al-futtaim.ae
Sales Range: $1-4.9 Billion
Emp.: 10,000
Diverse Trading Company; Automotive; Electronics; Insurance; Real Estate; Retail
N.A.I.C.S.: 561499
Omar Al Futtaim (Vice Chm)

Subsidiaries:

AFTRON Electronics (1)
PO Box 28657, Dubai, United Arab Emirates
Tel.: (971) 4 2103784
Web Site: http://www.aftron.com
Household Appliance Whslr
N.A.I.C.S.: 423620
Anil Kumar Neelakandhan (Mgr-Natl Sls)

Al-Futtaim ACE Company L.L.C (1)
PO Box 7880, Dubai, United Arab Emirates
Tel.: (971) 4 206 6700
Web Site: http://www.aceuae.com
Household Product Distr
N.A.I.C.S.: 423620
Kathryn Brown (Mgr-Internal Comm & Design)

Al-Futtaim Automall (1)
Sheikh Zayed Road, Dubai, United Arab Emirates
Tel.: (971) 4 3472212
Web Site: http://www.automalluae.com
Used Car Dealers
N.A.I.C.S.: 441120
Mohamed Abdul Malique (Mgr-Svc)

Al-Futtaim Electronics (1)
PO Box 5559, Dubai, United Arab Emirates
Tel.: (971) 4 3599979
Household Appliance Whslr
N.A.I.C.S.: 423620
Ankit Agrawal (Asst Product Mgr)

Al-Futtaim Engineering Company LLC (1)
Airport Road, PO Box 159, Dubai, United Arab Emirates
Tel.: (971) 4 2119111
Web Site: http://www.engineeringuae.com
Air Conditioning Installation Services
N.A.I.C.S.: 238220
Srinivasa Chakravarthy (Asst Mgr)

Al-Futtaim Group Real Estate (1)
Dubai Festival City, PO Box 49776, Dubai, United Arab Emirates
Tel.: (971) 4 213 6213
Real Estate Development Services
N.A.I.C.S.: 531390

Al-Futtaim Motors Company LLC (1)
Marsa Automotive Park Dubai Festival City, PO Box 11052, Dubai, 11502, United Arab Emirates
Tel.: (971) 4 2066000
Web Site: http://www.alfuttaimmotors.ae
Automotive Part Whslr
N.A.I.C.S.: 423120
Emad Salaheldin (Mgr-Bus Dev)

Al-Futtaim Panatech Company LLC (1)
PO Box 531, Dubai, United Arab Emirates
Tel.: (971) 4 2103333
Web Site: http://www.panasonicuae.com
Household Appliance Whslr
N.A.I.C.S.: 423620
Shaun Sullivan (Gen Mgr)

Al-Futtaim Technologies LLC (1)
21st Floor Festival Tower Dubai Festival City, PO Box 5866, Dubai, United Arab Emirates
Tel.: (971) 43977800
Web Site:
http://www.alfuttaimtechnologies.com
Emp.: 150

Information Technology Consulting Services
N.A.I.C.S.: 541512
Venkataraghavan Narayana (Gen Mgr)

Al-Futtaim Trading Enterprises Company L.L.C (1)
PO Box 5628, Dubai, United Arab Emirates
Tel.: (971) 4 2954246
Web Site: http://www.tradingenterprises.ae
Emp.: 1,200
New Car Dealers
N.A.I.C.S.: 441110
Shishir Jain (Mgr-Sls Accessories)

Al-Futtaim Travel (1)
101 Business Point Behind Nissan Showroom, Deira, Dubai, United Arab Emirates
Tel.: (971) 4 231 9200
Web Site: http://www.alfuttaimtravel.ae
Travel Agency
N.A.I.C.S.: 561510
William Horsley (Gen Mgr)

Al-Futtaim Watches and Jewellery (1)
PO Box 7916, Dubai, United Arab Emirates
Tel.: (971) 4 2224142
Web Site: http://www.watches.ae
Jewelry Retailer
N.A.I.C.S.: 458310
Anas Khan (Mgr-Mktg)

Emirates Investment Bank P.J.S.C. (1)
Level 15 Festival Tower Dubai Festival City, PO Box 5503, Dubai, United Arab Emirates (50.26%)
Tel.: (971) 42317777
Web Site: https://www.eibank.com
Rev.: $31,424,254
Assets: $1,236,224,968
Liabilities: $905,598,466
Net Worth: $330,626,502
Earnings: $29,281,203
Emp.: 81
Fiscal Year-end: 12/31/2023
Banking Services
N.A.I.C.S.: 522110
Omar Abdulla Al Futtaim (Chm)

Orient Insurance PJSC (1)
Orient Building Al Badia Business Park, PO Box 27966, Dubai Festival City, Dubai, United Arab Emirates
Tel.: (971) 42531300
Web Site: https://www.insuranceuae.com
Rev.: $1,734,947,476
Assets: $3,253,044,317
Liabilities: $2,072,125,111
Net Worth: $1,180,919,206
Earnings: $173,194,023
Emp.: 1,700
Fiscal Year-end: 12/31/2023
Insurance Services
N.A.I.C.S.: 524298
Jack Jenner (COO-Grp)

Plug-Ins Electronix (1)
PO Box 2798, Dubai, United Arab Emirates
Tel.: (971) 4 2825995
Web Site: http://www.pluginsuae.com
Household Appliance Whslr
N.A.I.C.S.: 423620
Sadiq Pasha (Supvr-IT Sls)

AL-GHAZI TRACTORS LIMITED

Tractor House 102-B 16th East Street DHA Phase I Off, Korangi Road, Karachi, Pakistan
Tel.: (92) 2135318901
Web Site:
https://www.alghazitractors.com
Year Founded: 1983
AGTL—(KAR)
Rev.: $90,110,979
Assets: $35,261,467
Liabilities: $29,441,529
Net Worth: $5,819,937
Earnings: $6,296,079
Emp.: 436
Fiscal Year-end: 12/31/19
Tractor Mfr
N.A.I.C.S.: 333924
Bernd Schwendtke (Chm)

AL-HAJ GROUP OF COMPANIES

5 7 15 Mezzanine Floor Marine Centre Block 2 Clifton, Karachi, 75600, Sindh, Pakistan
Tel.: (92) 21 35875606 7
Web Site: http://www.alhajgroup.com
Holding Company
N.A.I.C.S.: 551112
Taj Mohammad Afridi (CEO & Mng Dir)

Subsidiaries:

Al-Haj Enterprises (Private) limited (1)
5 7 15 Mezzanine Floor Marine Centre Block 2 Clifton, Karachi, 75600, Sindh, Pakistan
Tel.: (92) 21 3587 5606
Web Site: http://www.alhajgroup.com
Petroleum & Natural Gas Exploration
N.A.I.C.S.: 213112
Taj Mohammad Afridi (Chm)

Al-Haj FAW Motors Private Limited (1)
Main national Highway, Zulfiqarabad, Karachi, Sindh, Pakistan
Tel.: (92) 21 111 092 111
Web Site: http://www.alhajfaw.com
Heavy & Light Trucks Dealer & Assembly
N.A.I.C.S.: 423110
Hilal Khan Afridi (CEO)

AL-HAJ TEXTILE MILLS LIMITED

66 Dilkusha C/A 4th Floor, Dhaka, 1000, Bangladesh
Tel.: (880) 2223390929 BD
Web Site:
https://www.alhajtextilemills.com
Year Founded: 1962
AL-HAJTEX—(DHA)
Rev.: $4,077,079
Assets: $10,807,049
Liabilities: $8,343,667
Net Worth: $2,463,382
Earnings: $235,117
Emp.: 90
Fiscal Year-end: 06/30/22
Cotton Yarn Mfr
N.A.I.C.S.: 313110
Abdullah Bokhari (Chm)

AL-HAMARA'A INSURANCE COMPANY

Arrest Al-Hindia Dist 929 St 23 Bldg 27, Baghdad, Iraq
Tel.: (964) 17177573
Web Site:
https://www.alhamraains.com
Year Founded: 2001
NHAM—(IRAQ)
Sales Range: Less than $1 Million
Insurance Management Services
N.A.I.C.S.: 524298

AL-HASAWI INDUSTRIAL GROUP

Al-Rai Industrial Area Street No 12 Building No 1196, PO Box 1175, Safat, 13012, Kuwait, Kuwait
Tel.: (965) 24769100
Web Site: http://www.alhasawi.com
Year Founded: 1960
Sales Range: $125-149.9 Million
Emp.: 830
Refrigerators, Water Coolers, Split A/C Units, Cold Stores, Transport Refrigeration Boxes & Water Heaters Mfr & Distr
N.A.I.C.S.: 335220
Abdul Karim Al Hasawi (Founder)

Subsidiaries:

Alhasawi Factories for Water Heaters W.L.L. (1)
PO Box 1175, Kuwait, 13012, Kuwait
Tel.: (965) 24769100
Water Heater Mfr

Al-Hasawi Industrial Group—(Continued)

N.A.I.C.S.: 335220

AL-HASSAN G.I. SHAKER COMPANY

PO Box 5124, 11411, Riyadh, Saudi Arabia
Tel.: (966) 14011450
Web Site: http://www.shaker.com.sa
Year Founded: 1950
Sales Range: $200-249.9 Million
Emp.: 728
Air Conditioning Products & Home Appliances Importer & Distr
N.A.I.C.S.: 423730
Hussein G.I. Shaker *(Chm & CEO)*

AL-HEJAILAN GROUP

PO Box 9175, Riyadh, 11413, Saudi Arabia
Tel.: (966) 114761414
Web Site: http://www.hejailan.com
Year Founded: 1980
Emp.: 2,000
Holding Services
N.A.I.C.S.: 551110
Faisal Al-Hejailan *(CEO)*

Subsidiaries:

Armetal Metal Industries Company Ltd.   (1)
PO Box 172, Riyadh, 11383, Saudi Arabia
Tel.: (966) 11 2441615
Web Site: http://www.armetal.com
Metal Cutting & Fabrication Services
N.A.I.C.S.: 332312

Biolab Arabia Ltd.   (1)
PO Box 76126, Al Khobar, 31952, Saudi Arabia
Tel.: (966) 13 894 5662
Web Site: http://www.biolabarabia.com
Waste Treatment Services
N.A.I.C.S.: 221310
Karthikeyan Krishnamoorthy *(Mgr-IT)*

Plant (Domestic):

Biolab Arabia Ltd. - Jubail Factory   (2)
Jubail Industrial City, PO Box 10918, Al Jubayl, 31961, Saudi Arabia
Tel.: (966) 13 340 3180
Waste Treatment Services
N.A.I.C.S.: 221310

Enjaz Energy & Projects Co.   (1)
Al Tuwairqi Tower 8th Floor, PO Box 76126, Al Khobar, 31952, Saudi Arabia
Tel.: (966) 138945662
Web Site: http://www.enjazenergy.com
Waste Water Treatment Services
N.A.I.C.S.: 221320
Mohammad Faraz Rabbani *(Mgr-Fin & Comml)*

Mustang Al-Hejailan DAR PI   (1)
Al-Butain Tower Prince Turki Bin Abdul Aziz Street, PO Box 3863, Al Khobar, 31952, Saudi Arabia
Tel.: (966) 13 8697100
Web Site: http://www.mustanghdp.com
Architectural Design & Engineering Services
N.A.I.C.S.: 541310

Saudi Arabian Integrated Logistic Systems   (1)
PO Box 90872, Riyadh, 11623, Saudi Arabia
Tel.: (966) 11 479 4147
Web Site: http://www.sails.net
Emp.: 25
Business Support Services
N.A.I.C.S.: 541611
Ahmad Merai *(Mgr-Ops)*

Swedtel International Co.   (1)
Single Business Tower Sheikh Zayed Road, PO Box 9435, Dubai, United Arab Emirates
Tel.: (971) 4 328 9568
Web Site: http://www.swedtel.com
Wireless Telecommunication Services
N.A.I.C.S.: 517112

Subsidiary (Non-US):

Swedtel Arabia Ltd   (2)
PO Box 68367, Riyadh, 11527, Saudi Arabia
Tel.: (966) 11 473 5990
Wireless Telecommunication Services
N.A.I.C.S.: 517112

Swedtel International AB   (2)
Svanholmsvagen 37, Stocksund, Stockholm, 182 75, Sweden
Tel.: (46) 8 688 11 00
Wireless Telecommunication Services
N.A.I.C.S.: 517112
Lennart Broman *(CEO)*

Swedtel SEA Sdn. Bhd   (2)
Level 16 1 Sentral Jalan Stesen Sentral 5 KL, 50470, Kuala Lumpur, Malaysia
Tel.: (60) 3 2092 9479
Wireless Telecommunication Services
N.A.I.C.S.: 517112

AL-JAZEERA SATELLITE NETWORK

PO Box 23123, Doha, Qatar
Tel.: (974) 489 6000
Web Site: http://english.aljazeera.net
Year Founded: 1996
Sales Range: $1-4.9 Billion
Emp.: 3,000
Media Holding Company; Satellite Television & Online News, Documentary & Sports Network Owner & Operator
N.A.I.C.S.: 551112
Hamad bin Khalifa al-Thani *(Owner & Chm)*

Subsidiaries:

Al Jazeera America, LLC   (1)
435 Hudson St, New York, NY 10014
Tel.: (212) 207-4742
Web Site: http://america.aljazeera.com
Sales Range: $50-74.9 Million
Emp.: 170
Cable Television & Online News Network Operator
N.A.I.C.S.: 516210
Terry Baker *(Exec VP-Brdcst Production)*

Al Jazeera English   (1)
PO Box 23127, Doha, Qatar
Tel.: (974) 4890777
Web Site: http://english.aljazeera.net
Sales Range: $250-299.9 Million
Emp.: 1,000
English-Language Satellite Television & Internet Broadcasting News Network Operator
N.A.I.C.S.: 516210
Hamad Thamer Mohammed Al Thani *(Chm)*

Al Jazeera Media Network   (1)
PO Box 23127, Doha, Qatar
Tel.: (974) 4489 7446
Web Site: http://www.aljazeera.com
Television Broadcasting Services
N.A.I.C.S.: 516120
Muhammad Waseem Shakoor *(Engr-Brdcst)*

Aljazeera Balkans d.o.o.   (1)
Trg djece Sarajeva 1, Sarajevo, Bosnia & Herzegovina
Tel.: (387) 33 897 200
Television Broadcasting Services
N.A.I.C.S.: 516120

AL-JOUF AGRICULTURAL DEVELOPMENT COMPANY

Al-Jouf Bisetta, PO Box 321, Sakakah, Saudi Arabia
Tel.: (966) 146466664
Web Site: https://www.aljouf.com.sa
Year Founded: 1988
6070—(SAU)
Rev.: $91,186,946
Assets: $242,293,262
Liabilities: $64,307,245
Net Worth: $177,986,017
Earnings: $13,615,588
Fiscal Year-end: 12/31/22
Vegetable Farming Services
N.A.I.C.S.: 111998

Abdulaziz Mishal Abdulaziz Al Saud *(Chm)*

AL-KHAIR GADOON LIMITED

Al-Khair House 43-T Gurumangat Rd, T Gulberg 2, Lahore, 54660, Pakistan
Tel.: (92) 3424311111
Web Site: https://alkhairfoam.com
Year Founded: 1980
AKGL—(PSX)
Rev.: $4,985,057
Assets: $3,561,382
Liabilities: $1,998,852
Net Worth: $1,562,529
Earnings: $141,633
Fiscal Year-end: 06/30/21
Foam Products Mfr
N.A.I.C.S.: 326150
Mohammad Saeed Sheikh *(CEO)*

AL-KOUT INDUSTRIAL PROJECTS COMPANY K.S.C.C.

Al-Kout Industrial Projects 18th Floor Al Hamra Tower, Al Hamra Tower Abdul Aziz Al Saqr Street Sharq, Kuwait, Kuwait
Tel.: (965) 22286668
Web Site:
    https://www.alkoutprojects.com
ALKOUT—(KUW)
Rev.: $124,891,472
Assets: $134,951,864
Liabilities: $29,470,698
Net Worth: $105,481,166
Earnings: $32,394,654
Emp.: 256
Fiscal Year-end: 12/31/22
Salt & Chlorine Products Mfr & Sales
N.A.I.C.S.: 325180
Ali Abdul Aziz Behbehani *(VP-HR & Admin)*

Subsidiaries:

Cisco Trading Company   (1)
Jasim Tower Floor 11 Soor Street, Kuwait, Kuwait
Tel.: (965) 22960200
Web Site: https://www.ciscotrading.com
Chemical Products Distr
N.A.I.C.S.: 424690

AL-MADINA FOR FINANCE & INVESTMENT COMPANY KSCC

East - Behbehani Tower - 16th Floor, PO Box 2799, Safat, 13028, Kuwait, Kuwait
Tel.: (965) 22252207
Web Site:
    http://www.almadinainvest.com
Year Founded: 1980
ALMADINA—(DFM)
Rev.: $13,764,236
Assets: $91,572,807
Liabilities: $37,796,587
Net Worth: $53,776,220
Earnings: $11,453,801
Emp.: 26
Fiscal Year-end: 12/31/20
Investment & Financial Services
N.A.I.C.S.: 523999
Mohamed Darweish AlShamali *(Vice Chm)*

AL-MAL INVESTMENT COMPANY KSCC

Mazaya Tower 3 Floor 13 Al Mirqab Khalid Ibn Al weed Street, PO Box 26308, Safat, Kuwait, 13124, Kuwait
Tel.: (965) 2 225 4800
Web Site: http://www.almal.com.kw
ALMAL—(KUW)
Rev.: $1,493,762
Assets: $47,575,039
Liabilities: $23,289,791
Net Worth: $24,285,248

Earnings: ($664,909)
Emp.: 17
Fiscal Year-end: 12/31/20
Investment Services
N.A.I.C.S.: 523999

AL-MAL SECURITIES & SERVICES LIMITED

406 4th Floor Trade Centre I I Chundrigar Road, Karachi, Pakistan
Tel.: (92) 21 2211325
Emp.: 16
Investment Banking Services
N.A.I.C.S.: 523150

AL-MAMOURA COMPANY FOR REAL ESTATE INVESTMENT

Arsat Al-handia 929/35/26 Al-Elwiah, PO Box 4377, Baghdad, Iraq
Tel.: (964) 1 7781117
Web Site:
    http://www.mamorairaq.com
Year Founded: 1993
Real Estate Investment Services
N.A.I.C.S.: 531390
Basim Abdul El-Wahab Kammona *(Mgr-Direct)*

AL-MANARA INSURANCE PLC CO.

Shmeisani - Shaker Bin Zaid Street, PO Box 935818, Amman, 11193, Jordan
Tel.: (962) 62227777
Web Site:
    https://www.almanarainsurance.com
Year Founded: 1974
ARSI—(AMM)
Rev.: $22,522,752
Assets: $32,190,183
Liabilities: $25,401,844
Net Worth: $6,788,339
Earnings: ($299,945)
Emp.: 86
Fiscal Year-end: 12/31/22
Insurance Services
N.A.I.C.S.: 524298

AL-MASAKEN INTERNATIONAL FOR REAL ESTATE DEVELOPMENT CO. - K.S.C.

Sharq AlHamra Business Tower 34th floor, PO Box 24079, Safat, Kuwait, 13101, Kuwait
Tel.: (965) 1888811
Web Site:
    https://www.masakenint.com
Year Founded: 1991
MASAKEN—(KUW)
Rev.: $934,486
Assets: $60,054,074
Liabilities: $40,707,374
Net Worth: $19,346,700
Earnings: ($136,686)
Emp.: 7
Fiscal Year-end: 12/31/22
Real Estate Management Services
N.A.I.C.S.: 531390
Nabil Ghassan Ahmad Al Khalid *(CEO)*

AL-MASSALEH REAL ESTATE COMPANY K.S.C.C.

Universal Tower Ahmad Al-Jaber Street Sharq, PO Box 719, Safat, 13008, Kuwait, 13008, Kuwait
Tel.: (965) 1887000
Web Site: https://almassaleh.com
MASSALEH—(KUW)
Rev.: $15,821,109
Assets: $299,185,479
Liabilities: $249,168,342
Net Worth: $50,017,137
Earnings: $5,164,432
Emp.: 40
Fiscal Year-end: 12/31/22

Real Estate Services
N.A.I.C.S.: 531390
Mehdi Rajab Malaki *(Vice Chm)*

Subsidiaries:

Taameer Real Estate Investment Co,
KSCC **(1)**
sharq - Ahmed Al jaber street -AL eaneffer-
sal tower- Floor14, PO Box 29295, 13153,
Kuwait, Kuwait
Tel.: (965) 22496321
Web Site: http://www.altaameer.com.kw
Rev.; $1,206,513
Assets: $73,876,577
Liabilities: $32,164,971
Net Worth: $41,711,606
Earnings: ($5,571,982)
Emp.: 30
Fiscal Year-end: 12/31/2022
Real Estate Investment Services
N.A.I.C.S.: 531390
Ziad A. AlDuaij *(Chm)*

Subsidiary (Non-US):

Taameer Hospitality for Hotel Man-
agement S.A. **(2)**
50 Mohamed Mazhar Street Office # 3, El
Zamalek, Cairo, Egypt
Tel.: (20) 2 2736 4873
Home Management Services
N.A.I.C.S.: 531390

Taameer Hotel Management Com-
pany & Consultancy S.A. **(2)**
85 avenue des FAR, Fes, 30000, Morocco
Tel.: (212) 5 3594 8000
Web Site: http://www.altaameer.com.kw
Home Management Services
N.A.I.C.S.: 531390

Taameer Lebanon Holding
Company-S.A.L. **(2)**
Ramada Downtown Hotel Chateaubriand St
Minet El Hosn Sector, Beirut, 00961, Leba-
non
Tel.: (961) 1990299
Web Site:
   http://www.ramadadowntownbeirut.com
Emp.: 50
Real Estate & Design Consulting Services
N.A.I.C.S.: 531390
Yasmine Maalouf *(Gen Mgr)*

Subsidiary (Domestic):

Star Tower S.A.L. **(3)**
Minet El Hosn Chateaubriand Street, PO
Box 11215, Beirut, Lebanon
Tel.: (961) 1 990299
Web Site: http://www.ramadalebanon.com
Hotel Operator
N.A.I.C.S.: 721110
Yanmint Maanous *(Gen Mgr)*

Taameer Hospitality-S.A.L. **(3)**
Beirut Downtown Ramada hotel Building
Ground Floor, PO Box 11-215, Downtown,
Beirut, Lebanon
Tel.: (961) 1995990
Web Site: http://www.ramadalebanon.com
Sales Range: $10-24.9 Million
Emp.: 77
Home Management Services
N.A.I.C.S.: 721110
Yasmine Maalouf *(Gen Mgr)*

**AL-MAZAYA HOLDING COM-
PANY K.S.C.P.**
Kuwait Mazaya Tower 01 25th Floor
Al Murqab, PO Box 3546, Safat, Ku-
wait, 13036, Kuwait
Tel.: (965) 858885
Web Site:
   https://www.mazayaholding.com
Year Founded: 1998
MAZAYA—(KUW)
Rev.: $49,331,242
Assets: $660,119,656
Liabilities: $454,924,456
Net Worth: $205,195,200
Earnings: ($43,408,905)
Emp.: 37
Fiscal Year-end: 12/31/22

Holding Company; Real Estate Ser-
vices
N.A.I.C.S.: 551112
Rashid Yaccoub Al Nafisi *(Chm)*

Subsidiaries:

First Dubai Real Estate Development
Company K.S.C. **(1)**
Kuwait Mazaya Tower 01 24th Floor, PO
Box 3546, Al Murqab, Kuwait, 13036, Ku-
wait
Tel.: (965) 22063335
Web Site: https://www.1stdubai.com
Real Estate Services
N.A.I.C.S.: 531210
Abdulaziz Al Loughani *(Chm)*

First Dubai for Real Estate Develop-
ment Company K.S.C.C. **(1)**
Kuwait Mazaya Tower 01 24th Floor Al
Murqab, PO Box 3546, Safat, 13036, Ku-
wait, Kuwait **(67%)**
Tel.: (965) 1858885
Web Site: https://www.1stdubai.com
Rev.: $7,302,974
Assets: $297,853,440
Liabilities: $55,507,387
Net Worth: $242,346,053
Earnings: ($15,923,654)
Emp.: 39
Fiscal Year-end: 12/31/2022
Real Estate Services
N.A.I.C.S.: 531390
Salwa Malhas *(COO)*

Med Cell Medical Co. K.S.C.C. **(1)**
Mazaya Towers 3B Khalid Ibn Al Waleed St,
Kuwait, Kuwait
Tel.: (965) 22063371
Web Site: https://medcellkwt.com
Diagnostic Services
N.A.I.C.S.: 621512

AL-MOSUL FOR FUNFAIRS
Left Side Near Nineveh Bridge, Mo-
sul, Iraq
Tel.: (964) 1 816934
Year Founded: 1992
Amusement Park Operator
N.A.I.C.S.: 713110
Ahmed Abdel Razaq *(Exec Dir)*

**AL-MUNTASER TRADING &
CONTRACTING CO. W.L.L.**
Saleh Al-Mutawa Building Eighth
Floor Behind, Next to Public Authority
for Minor Affairs PAMA Area 30 Al-
Sharq, Kuwait, Kuwait
Tel.: (965) 22410861 **KW**
Web Site: http://www.muntaser.com
Year Founded: 1977
Sales Range: $250-299.9 Million
Emp.: 300
Oil & Gas Refining & Petrochemical
Power Generation Water Desalination
& Wastewater Treatment Services
N.A.I.C.S.: 213112

Subsidiaries:

Al-Muntaser Trading & Contracting
Co. W.L.L. - Contracting Division **(1)**
KFH Building 206 Behind Fisheries Building
1st Floor Office No 04, Suhada Street
Sharq, Kuwait, 13120, Kuwait
Tel.: (965) 2241 3249
Web Site: http://www.muntaser.com
Sales Range: $75-99.9 Million
Oil & Gas Pipeline Engineering Services
N.A.I.C.S.: 541330
Sanjay Punj *(Office Mgr)*

**AL-NAWADI HOLDING COM-
PANY - KPSC**
Sharq-Gulf Street - Near Souk Sharq,
PO Box 775, Dasman, 15458, Ku-
wait, Kuwait
Tel.: (965) 22922555 **KW**
Web Site:
   http://www.alnawadiholding.com
Year Founded: 2004
Rev.: $30,831,245

Assets: $326,203,597
Liabilities: $133,459,123
Net Worth: $192,744,474
Earnings: $15,574,391
Fiscal Year-end: 12/31/18
Holding Company
N.A.I.C.S.: 551112
Mitab Jaber Al-Ahmed Al-Sabah
(Deputy Chm)

**AL-NOOR SUGAR MILLS LIM-
ITED**
96-A Sindhi Muslim Housing Society,
Karachi, 7440, Pakistan
Tel.: (92) 2134550161 **PK**
Web Site: https://www.alnoorsugar.co
Year Founded: 1969
ALNRS—(PSX)
Rev.: $47,208,103
Assets: $65,163,116
Liabilities: $37,520,025
Net Worth: $27,643,092
Earnings: $1,062,501
Emp.: 679
Fiscal Year-end: 09/30/23
Sugar Mfr
N.A.I.C.S.: 311314
Mohammad Yasin Mughal *(Sec)*

**AL-OMRAN INDUSTRIAL
TRADING CO.**
Astoria Complex Second Floor King
Abdulaziz Road, PO Box 40569, Exit
5 Opposite The Kingdom Schools,
Riyadh, 11511, Saudi Arabia
Tel.: (966) 112305566
Year Founded: 2003
4141—(SAU)
Rev.: $34,782,671
Assets: $64,389,800
Liabilities: $22,057,488
Net Worth: $42,332,312
Earnings: ($3,773,452)
Emp.: 409
Fiscal Year-end: 12/31/23
Electric Equipment Mfr
N.A.I.C.S.: 335999
Abdul Rahman Mohammed Nasser
Omran *(CEO & Mng Dir)*

**AL-OSAIS INTERNATIONAL
HOLDING COMPANY**
PO Box 1083, Dammam, 31431,
Saudi Arabia
Tel.: (966) 38113333
Web Site: http://www.alosais.com
Year Founded: 1972
Sales Range: $800-899.9 Million
Emp.: 3,000
Holding Company
N.A.I.C.S.: 551112
Ghurm A. Moraisel *(Pres)*

Subsidiaries:

Al Arabi Steel Structure Manufactur-
ing Co. **(1)**
Dammam Second Industrial City, PO Box
14044, Dammam, 31424, Saudi Arabia
Tel.: (966) 38123070
Web Site: http://www.asfsteel.com
Sales Range: $50-74.9 Million
Emp.: 160
Structural Steel Frames, Girders, Structural
Beams & Miscellaneous Steel Structures
Mfr
N.A.I.C.S.: 332312

Al-Berri United Food Co. Ltd. **(1)**
PO Box 29, Al Jubayl, 31951, Saudi Arabia
Tel.: (966) 33612827
Web Site: http://www.alberri.com
Sales Range: $50-74.9 Million
Emp.: 120
Importer & Supplier of Frozen Food Prod-
ucts
N.A.I.C.S.: 424420
Hashim G. Moraisel *(Gen Mgr)*

Al-Osais Contracting Co. **(1)**

PO Box 1083, Dammam, 31431, Saudi
Arabia
Tel.: (966) 3 811 3333
Web Site: http://www.alosais.com
Residential & Commercial Construction
N.A.I.C.S.: 236220
Ahmed M. Alabdulaali *(Mng Dir)*

Al-Osais Hiring Co. **(1)**
PO Box 1083, Dammam, 31431, Saudi
Arabia
Tel.: (966) 38110196
Web Site: http://www.alosais.com
Sales Range: $150-199.9 Million
Emp.: 600
Employment Services
N.A.I.C.S.: 561311

Al-Osais Industrial & Structural Sup-
ply Co. **(1)**
PO Box 13376, Dammam, Saudi Arabia
Tel.: (966) 38112225
Web Site: http://www.alosais.com
Industrial & Construction Consumables &
Materials Supplier
N.A.I.C.S.: 423390

Al-Osais MCM Co. Ltd. **(1)**
PO Box 9724, Dammam, 31431, Saudi
Arabia
Tel.: (966) 38116372
Web Site: http://www.al-osais.com
Sales Range: $25-49.9 Million
Emp.: 50
Construction & Civil Engineering Services
N.A.I.C.S.: 541330

Al-Osais Petroleum Services Co. **(1)**
PO Box 14044, Dammam, 31424, Saudi
Arabia
Tel.: (966) 38203390
Web Site: http://www.alosais.com
Motor Fuel Retail
N.A.I.C.S.: 457120
Abdullah Musbeh *(Gen Mgr)*

Al-Osais Real Estate Co. **(1)**
PO Box 1083, Dammam, 31431, Saudi
Arabia
Tel.: (966) 38113333
Web Site: http://www.al-osais.com
Sales Range: $75-99.9 Million
Emp.: 100
Ownership of Land, Buildings & Rentals;
Property Management Services
N.A.I.C.S.: 531210

Al-Osais Transportation & Road Con-
struction Co. **(1)**
Airport Rd Al-Osais Petroleum Crossing 91,
Dammam, 14044, Saudi Arabia
Tel.: (966) 38203390
Web Site: http://www.al-osais.com
Road Construction & Maintenance; Quar-
ries; Asphalt Production
N.A.I.C.S.: 237310
Abdullah Musbeh *(VP)*

Arabian Pipeline & Services Co.
Ltd. **(1)**
PO Box 234, Al Jubayl, 31951, Saudi Ara-
bia
Tel.: (966) 33620556
Web Site: http://www.anabeeb.com
Sales Range: $400-449.9 Million
Emp.: 2,000
Pipeline Construction
N.A.I.C.S.: 237120
Hashim Moraisel *(Gen Mgr)*

Baseelah Mechanical Works **(1)**
PO Box 8275, Dammam, 31482, Saudi
Arabia
Tel.: (966) 38111555
Sales Range: $100-124.9 Million
Emp.: 500
Heating, Ventilation & Air Conditioning De-
sign & Installation
N.A.I.C.S.: 238220
Tariq G. Moraisel *(Gen Mgr)*

MGA Trading Est. **(1)**
PO Box 9377, Dammam, 31413, Saudi
Arabia
Tel.: (966) 38584783
Web Site: http://www.mgat.com
Sales Range: $50-74.9 Million
Emp.: 20
Electrical, Construction & Industrial Material
& Equipment Supplier

Al-Osais International Holding
Company—(Continued)

N.A.I.C.S.: 423390

Middle East Resources Co. (1)
PO Box 13376, Dammam, 31493, Saudi
Arabia
Tel.: (966) 38120999
Web Site: http://www.mercowax.com
Sales Range: $25-49.9 Million
Emp.: 22
Development & Manufacturing of Petroleum
& Industrial Chemical Products
N.A.I.C.S.: 324199

AL-OTHAIM HOLDING COMPANY

Eastern Roundabout Street Exit 14,
PO Box 28090, Al Rabwah Area, Riyadh, 11437, Saudi Arabia
Tel.: (966) 12540000   SA
Web Site:
  http://www.othaimholding.com
Year Founded: 1956
Investment Holding Company
N.A.I.C.S.: 551112
Abdullah Saleh Al-Othaim (Chm &
CEO)

Subsidiaries:

Abdullah Al-Othaim Investment &
Real Estate Development
Company   (1)
Eastern Roundabout Street Exit 14, PO Box
28090, Al Rabwah Area, Riyadh, 11437,
Saudi Arabia   (81.3%)
Tel.: (966) 12415503
Web Site: http://www.othaimmalls.com
Real Estate Investment Trust; Shopping
Centers Developer, Owner & Lessor
N.A.I.C.S.: 525990

AL-OULA COMPANY

PO Box 2227, 211, Salalah, 211,
Oman
Tel.: (968) 23135765
Web Site: http://www.aloula.com
Year Founded: 1999
DMGI—(MUS)
Rev.: $413,710
Assets: $929,418
Liabilities: $5,025,276
Net Worth: ($4,095,859)
Earnings: ($3,837,487)
Fiscal Year-end: 12/31/20
Marble & Granite Distr
N.A.I.C.S.: 444180
Mohammed Alotaibi (CEO-Acting)

Subsidiaries:

Al Oula Middle East LLC   (1)
Sudan St, Cairo, Egypt
Tel.: (20) 102 629 8926
Event & Conference Services
N.A.I.C.S.: 561920
Ahamad Shaqqur (CEO)

AL-QADIR TEXTILE MILLS LIMITED

6-KM Jhelum Road, Chakwal, Pakistan
Tel.: (92) 543 540831   PK
Web Site: http://www.aqtextile.com
Textile Spinning Mill Operator
N.A.I.C.S.: 313110

AL-QAIM TEXTILE MILLS LIMITED

Awan House Faisal Colony Talagang
Road, Chakwal, 48800, Pakistan
Tel.: (92) 54 356 9705
Textile Spinning Mill Operator
N.A.I.C.S.: 313110

AL-RAKAEZ PLC

Al madeenah street - eyas hotel
building, PO Box 928482, Amman,
11190, Jordan

Tel.: (962) 5548961
Web Site: https://www.npsc.com
Year Founded: 2006
RICS—(AMM)
Rev.: $935,888
Assets: $17,438,315
Liabilities: $2,240,512
Net Worth: $15,197,803
Earnings: ($1,027,525)
Emp.: 73
Fiscal Year-end: 12/31/20
Real Estate Development Services
N.A.I.C.S.: 531390

Subsidiaries:

Al-Jazeera Trading FZCo.
Islamic Bank Complex Wasfi Al-Tal St, Amman, 972 34, Jordan
Tel.: (962) 6 5517311
Web Site: http://www.aljazeera-trading.com
Tire Import & Distr
N.A.I.C.S.: 423130

AL-RUBAIYAT COMPANY

7575 Medina Road North, PO Box
5967, Tahlia Street, Jeddah, 21432,
Saudi Arabia
Tel.: (966) 126606699
Web Site: http://www.rubaiyat.com
Sales Range: $75-99.9 Million
Emp.: 300
Clothing Retailer
N.A.I.C.S.: 458110

AL-SADEER HOTEL

Al-Anduls Sequare, Baghdad, Iraq
Tel.: (964) 1 7188166
Year Founded: 1990
Home Management Services
N.A.I.C.S.: 721110

AL-SAFAT INVESTMENT COMPANY K.S.C.C.

Al Safat Tower Beirut St Hawalli, PO
Box 20133, Safat, Kuwait, 13062,
Kuwait
Tel.: (965) 1877777
Web Site:
  https://www.alsafatinvest.com
Year Founded: 1983
ALSAFAT—(KUW)
Sales Range: $1-9.9 Million
Investment Services
N.A.I.C.S.: 523150
Abdullah Ahmed Al Shaheen (CEO)

AL-SAFWA GROUP HOLDING CO. K.P.S.C.

Beirut Street 11th Floor, PO Box
26552, Hawally, Kuwait, 13126, Kuwait
Tel.: (965) 22675110
Sales Range: $125-149.9 Million
Holding Company
N.A.I.C.S.: 551112
Adel Yousef Saleh Al-Saqabi (CEO)

Subsidiaries:

Al Safat United Food Company
K.S.C.   (1)
PO Box 27660, Kuwait, 13137, Kuwait
Tel.: (965) 22659629
Fine Dining Restaurant Operation Services
N.A.I.C.S.: 722511

Danah Al Safat Foodstuff Company
K.S.C.   (1)
Alia center 7th floor Al Shuhada street Al
Salhiah, PO Box 22044, Safat, Kuwait,
13081, Kuwait
Tel.: (965) 2 290 9845
Web Site: http://www.danahalsafat.com
Rev.: $2,824,408
Assets: $17,426,212
Liabilities: $10,457,172
Net Worth: $6,969,100
Earnings: ($28,089,937)
Emp.: 16
Fiscal Year-end: 12/31/2019

Shrimp Fishing, Processing & Marketing
Services
N.A.I.C.S.: 114112
Fahad Abdul Rahman Al Mukhaizeim (Chm)

Shuaiba Industrial Company
K.S.C.C.   (1)
Subhan Industrial Area Block 3 St 31 Bldg
150 Subhan, PO Box 10088, Shuaiba, Kuwait, 65451, Kuwait
Tel.: (965) 24711350
Web Site: https://www.sic-kwt.com
Rev.: $47,263,853
Assets: $77,718,233
Liabilities: $17,061,695
Net Worth: $60,656,537
Earnings: $4,371,338
Emp.: 309
Fiscal Year-end: 12/31/2022
Paper Packaging Mfr, Importer & Exporter
N.A.I.C.S.: 322120
S. Farid Ahmed (Pres)

AL-SAGR NATIONAL INSURANCE COMPANY

Al Sagr National Insurance Building
Diplomatic Area Al Seef Road, PO
Box 14614, Bur Dubai, Dubai, United
Arab Emirates
Tel.: (971) 47028500   AE
Web Site: https://www.alsagrins.ae
Year Founded: 1979
ASNIC—(DFM)
Rev.: $225,194,689
Assets: $231,590,018
Liabilities: $174,582,945
Net Worth: $57,007,072
Earnings: $1,755,813
Emp.: 324
Fiscal Year-end: 12/31/23
Insurance Services
N.A.I.C.S.: 524298
Faraj Omari (Exec VP-Motor)

Subsidiaries:

Al Sagr Cooperative Insurance
Company   (1)
First floor Abdulrahman Al Turki Building
King Khalid Street, PO Box 3501, Mohammed bin Saud District, Al Khobar, 31952,
Saudi Arabia
Tel.: (966) 920001043
Web Site: https://www.alsagr.com
Rev.: $110,929,311
Assets: $177,614,032
Liabilities: $142,865,382
Net Worth: $34,748,650
Earnings: ($19,596,390)
Emp.: 248
Fiscal Year-end: 12/31/2022
Insurance Agency Services
N.A.I.C.S.: 524210
Abdulrahman Ali Al Turki (Chm)

Jordan Emirates Insurance
Company   (1)
PO Box 925383, Amman, 11190, Jordan
Tel.: (962) 6 568 1444
Web Site: http://www.joemirates.com
Insurance Services
N.A.I.C.S.: 524210

Union Insurance Co. P.S.C.   (1)
Ground & Mezzanine Floors Ajman Building
Sheikh Khalifa bin Zayed Road, PO Box
1225, Ajman, United Arab Emirates
Tel.: (971) 6 746 6996
Web Site: http://www.unioninsurance.ae
Insurance Services
N.A.I.C.S.: 524210
Abdul Muttaleb M. Al Jaedi (CEO)

AL-SALAM REAL ESTATE INVESTMENT TRUST

Level 14 Menara KOMTAR Johor
Bahru City Centre, 80000, Johor
Bahru, Johor, Malaysia
Tel.: (60) 72267692   MY
Web Site:
  https://www.alsalamreit.com.my
ALSREIT—(KLS)
Rev.: $15,195,780
Assets: $276,214,548

Liabilities: $140,810,194
Net Worth: $135,404,353
Earnings: $13,844,666
Emp.: 99
Fiscal Year-end: 12/31/22
Trust Management Services
N.A.I.C.S.: 523940
Suhaimi Saad (Head-Ops)

AL-SALAMA INSURANCE CO., LTD.

PO Box 1448, Khartoum, Sudan
Tel.: (249) 83795614   Sd
Year Founded: 1992
Insurance Products & Services
N.A.I.C.S.: 524298
Ali MuhammadAl Hassan (Chm)

AL-SALBOOKH TRADING COMPANY K.S.C.

Office 19 6th Floor Panasonic Tower
Fahad Al Salem Street Al Qibla, Kuwait, Kuwait
Tel.: (965) 22598854
Web Site: http://www.salbookh-group.com
Year Founded: 1973
SALBOOKH—(KUW)
Rev.: $640,791
Assets: $13,500,010
Liabilities: $12,505,012
Net Worth: $994,998
Earnings: ($11,837,317)
Emp.: 31
Fiscal Year-end: 12/31/22
Crushed Stone Whslr
N.A.I.C.S.: 423320

AL-SANABEL INTERNATIONAL FOR ISLAMIC INVESTMENT (HOLDING) PLC

38 Abdullah Ghosheh Street Office
401, PO Box 1223, Amman, 11821,
Jordan
Tel.: (962) 65819495
Web Site:
  https://www.sanabelintl.com
Year Founded: 2006
SANA—(AMM)
Rev.: $83,144
Assets: $22,976,251
Liabilities: $1,927,987
Net Worth: $21,048,264
Earnings: ($249,465)
Emp.: 7
Fiscal Year-end: 12/31/20
Investment Banking Services
N.A.I.C.S.: 523150

AL-SAWANI GROUP

PO Box 1223344, Jeddah, 2145,
Saudi Arabia
Tel.: (966) 26912612
Web Site: http://www.al-sawani.com
Sales Range: $150-199.9 Million
Emp.: 650
Department Stores
N.A.I.C.S.: 455110

AL-SHAMEKHA FOR REAL ESTATE & FINANCIAL INVESTMENTS CO., LTD.

Jabal Al-Hussein - Firas Circle, PO
Box 921196, Amman, 11192, Jordan
Tel.: (962) 5662104
Year Founded: 1974
VFED—(AMM)
Rev.: $172,737
Assets: $3,239,383
Liabilities: $335,508
Net Worth: $2,903,875
Earnings: ($27,852)
Emp.: 5
Fiscal Year-end: 12/31/20
Real Estate & Financial Investment
Services

N.A.I.C.S.: 531390

AL-THEMAR INTERNATIONAL HOLDING CO. (K.S.C.)

Dhajeej Area Bldg 58 Mezzanine, PO Box 1161, Farwaniya Safat, 13012, Kuwait, Kuwait
Tel.: (965) 25333114
Year Founded: 1982
Sales Range: $10-24.9 Million
Holding Company
N.A.I.C.S.: 551112

AL-TUWAIRQI GROUP

Dammam Ksobar Rd Bar Al Rakkah, PO Box 7600, 31472, Dammam, Saudi Arabia
Tel.: (966) 38579922
Web Site:
http://www.altuwairqi.com.sa
Year Founded: 1977
Sales Range: $400-449.9 Million
Emp.: 3,000
Diversified Holding & Trading Company; Steel Products Mfr & Building Materials Distr
N.A.I.C.S.: 551112
Hilal Hussain Al Tuwairqi *(Chm)*

Subsidiaries:

Al Ittefaq Steel Products
Company   (1)
PO Box 7600, Dammam, 31472, Saudi Arabia
Tel.: (966) 38121143
Web Site: http://www.altuwairqu.com.sa
Sales Range: $200-249.9 Million
Emp.: 750
Steel Producer
N.A.I.C.S.: 331110

Al Tuwairqi Trading &
Contracting   (1)
PO Box 2705, Dammam, 31461, Saudi Arabia
Tel.: (966) 38579922
Web Site: http://altuwairqi.tripod.com
Sales Range: $200-249.9 Million
Emp.: 600
Contracting & Manufacturing Services
N.A.I.C.S.: 236220

Al-Faisal Steel Products
Company   (1)
PO Box 2705, 31461, Dammam, Saudi Arabia
Tel.: (966) 38122212
Steel Investment Foundries
N.A.I.C.S.: 331512

Direct Reduction Iron Company   (1)
PO Box 7600, 31472, Dammam, Saudi Arabia
Tel.: (966) 38122966
Iron & Steel Forging
N.A.I.C.S.: 332111

National Steel Company Limited   (1)
PO Box 7600, 31472, Dammam, Saudi Arabia
Tel.: (966) 38122966
Electronic & Precision Equipment Repair & Maintenance
N.A.I.C.S.: 811210

The International Electrical Products
Company (TIEPCO)   (1)
PO Box 2705, 31461, Dammam, Saudi Arabia
Tel.: (966) 3 857 9922
Web Site: http://www.altuwairqi.com.sa
Switchgear & Switchboard Apparatus Mfr
N.A.I.C.S.: 335313

AL-WATANIA INSURANCE COMPANY YSC

Palace Road Nasser Ali Zayid Building, PO Box 15497, Sana'a, Yemen
Tel.: (967) 1272713
Web Site:
http://www.alwataniains.com
Year Founded: 1993
Sales Range: $150-199.9 Million

Emp.: 20
Insurance Services
N.A.I.C.S.: 524298
Al-Haj Yousef Abdulwadood Saeed *(Chm)*

AL-WATANIAH TOWERS COMPANY

34 Al-Bireh Municipality St, Al-Bireh, Palestine
Tel.: (970) 22983800
Web Site: https://www.abraj-pal.com
Year Founded: 1995
ABRAJ—(PAL)
Rev.: $1,639,465
Assets: $28,830,849
Liabilities: $2,675,494
Net Worth: $26,155,355
Earnings: $1,016,350
Fiscal Year-end: 12/31/23
Real Estate Development Services
N.A.I.C.S.: 531390

AL-WAZZAN HOLDING GROUP

PO Box 1251, Safat, Kuwait, 13013, Kuwait
Tel.: (965) 1881000
Sales Range: $350-399.9 Million
Emp.: 3,000
Holding Company
N.A.I.C.S.: 551112
Salah Mohammad Al-Wazzan *(CEO)*

Subsidiaries:

Mushrif Trading & Contracting Company K.S.C.P.   (1)
Area 1 Street 7 Plot 1666 Al Rai, PO Box 32514, Rumaithiya, Kuwait, 25556, Kuwait
Tel.: (965) 24766172
Web Site: http://www.mushrif.com
Heavy Civil Building & Infrastructure Contractor
N.A.I.C.S.: 237990
Faisal Belhoul *(Deputy Chm)*

AL-ZAMIN INVESTBANK

101-108 Kassam Court, BC-9 Block 5, Clifton, Karachi, 75600, Pakistan
Tel.: (92) 21 5876651
Web Site: http://www.alzamin.com.pk
Sales Range: $1-9.9 Million
Emp.: 144
Financial Services
N.A.I.C.S.: 522320
Zafar Iqbal *(Chm)*

AL-ZARQA EDUCATIONAL & INVESTMENT CO. P.L.C.

Al-Zarqa, PO Box 3331, Commercial Area, Zarqa, 13111, Jordan
Tel.: (962) 3986946
Year Founded: 1992
ZEIC—(AMM)
Rev.: $25,992,081
Assets: $71,434,290
Liabilities: $26,969,257
Net Worth: $44,465,032
Earnings: $1,234,316
Emp.: 13
Fiscal Year-end: 12/31/20
Educational Support Services
N.A.I.C.S.: 611710

ALA SPA

Mostra d'Oltremare, 54 Viale J F Kennedy, 80125, Naples, Italy
Tel.: (39) 0813036311
Web Site:
http://www.alacorporation.com
Year Founded: 2015
Investment Services
N.A.I.C.S.: 523999
Gennaro di Capua *(CEO)*

Subsidiaries:

Specialist Technologies Ltd.   (1)

1 Lyon Road, Walton-on-Thames, KT12 3PU, Surrey, United Kingdom
Tel.: (44) 1932251500
Web Site: http://www.stag-aerospace.com
Sales Range: $10-24.9 Million
Aerospace Component Mfr & Distr
N.A.I.C.S.: 336413
Thibaut de Bouillane *(Dir-Sls)*

Subsidiary (Domestic):

Arnold Wragg Ltd.   (2)
Unit 2 Parkway One Business Centre, Parkway Drive, Sheffield, S9 4WU, South Yorkshire, United Kingdom
Tel.: (44) 1142519050
Web Site: http://www.arnold-wragg.com
Sales Range: $1-9.9 Million
Emp.: 30
Fasteners, Threaded Components & Mechanical Component Mfr
N.A.I.C.S.: 332722
Paul Drunton *(Mng Dir)*

Flitetec Ltd   (2)
Unit 9 28 Plantation Road, Amersham, HP6 6HD, Buckinghamshire, United Kingdom
Tel.: (44) 1494 43 24 44
Molded Plastic Product Mfr
N.A.I.C.S.: 326199

Subsidiary (Non-US):

Spectech France SAS   (2)
281 Allee de Lagace, ZA de la Faisanderie, 40090, Saint-Avit, France
Tel.: (33) 5 58 85 20 00
Emp.: 38
Aircraft Parts Distr
N.A.I.C.S.: 333618
Pascal Lefevre *(CEO)*

ALACRITY SECURITIES LIMITED

101 Hari Darshan B-Wing Bhogilal Fadia Road, Kandivali West, Mumbai, 400 067, India
Tel.: (91) 2228073460
Web Site:
https://www.alacritysec.com
Year Founded: 1995
535916—(BOM)
Rev.: $17,450,976
Assets: $4,901,248
Liabilities: $2,480,054
Net Worth: $2,421,193
Earnings: $276,113
Fiscal Year-end: 03/31/21
Securities & Financial Services
N.A.I.C.S.: 523150
Pooja Heemanshu Mehta *(Exec Dir)*

ALADDIN BLOCKCHAIN TECHNOLGIES

280 High Holborn, London, WC1V 7EE, United Kingdom
Tel.: (44) 2030775700
Web Site:
http://www.edisongroup.com
Financial Support Services
N.A.I.C.S.: 541611
James Brotherton *(Fin Dir-Tyman)*

ALAM GROUP OF COMPANIES

Casements Complex Plot 86/90 5th Street Industrial Area, PO Box 4641, Kampala, 4641, Uganda
Tel.: (256) 414233577
Web Site: https://www.alam-group.com
Year Founded: 1965
Sales Range: $25-49.9 Million
Emp.: 2,500
Holding Company; Construction, Manufacturing, Real Estate & Related Services
N.A.I.C.S.: 551112
Manzur Alam *(Chm)*

Subsidiaries:

Alam Constructions Ltd.   (1)

Plot 86/90 Casements Complex 5th St, Industrial Area, Kampala, Uganda
Tel.: (256) 41234000
Sales Range: $100-124.9 Million
Emp.: 150
Construction Services
N.A.I.C.S.: 238990

Ama Ply Ltd.   (1)
PO Box 4641, Kampala, Uganda
Tel.: (256) 41340199
Web Site: http://www.alam-group.com
Wood Flooring Products
N.A.I.C.S.: 321912

Crocodile Tool Company (Uganda)
Ltd.   (1)
Plot 13/19 Eden Road, PO Box 1391, Jinja, Uganda
Tel.: (256) 43123109
Web Site: http://www.alam-group.com
Sales Range: $50-74.9 Million
Emp.: 60
Farm Hand Tools & Hoes Mfr
N.A.I.C.S.: 332323

Ekono Homes Ltd.   (1)
Plot 86/90 5th Street Ind Area Casement Complex, PO Box 2288, Kampala, Uganda
Tel.: (256) 392884944
Web Site: http://www.ekonoprefabs.com
Residential Builder
N.A.I.C.S.: 236220

Inns of Uganda   (1)
Plot 86/90 Casements Complex 5th St, Industrial Area, Kampala, Uganda
Tel.: (256) 41234000
Home Management Services
N.A.I.C.S.: 721199

Oxygas Ltd.   (1)
Plot 501, Nakawa Industrial Area, Kampala, Uganda
Tel.: (256) 41505865
Web Site: http://www.alam-group.com
Sales Range: $25-49.9 Million
Emp.: 50
Industrial & Medical Oxygen & Dissolved Acetylene
N.A.I.C.S.: 325120

Rhino Footwear Ltd.   (1)
Plot 86/90 Fifth Street, Industrial Area, Kampala, Uganda
Tel.: (256) 755841364
Web Site: https://rhinofootwear.co.ug
Shoe Mfr
N.A.I.C.S.: 316210

Roofclad Ltd.   (1)
Plot 86/90 Casements Complex 5th St, Industrial Area, Kampala, Uganda
Tel.: (256) 41234000
Wire Products & Security Systems Mfr
N.A.I.C.S.: 332618
Abid Alam *(Mng Dir)*

SIAMMCO Ltd.   (1)
Cementry Road, Soroti, Uganda
Tel.: (256) 4561361
Agricultural Implements & Machinery Mfr
N.A.I.C.S.: 332323

Steel Rolling Mills Ltd.   (1)
PO Box 22431, Masese, Jinja, Uganda
Tel.: (256) 43120987
Sales Range: $100-124.9 Million
Emp.: 400
Steel Products Producer
N.A.I.C.S.: 331513

Sugar & Allied Industries Limited   (1)
Plot 86/90 5th Street, Industrial Area, Kampala, Uganda
Tel.: (256) 414233577
Web Site: https://sail.co.ug
Brown Sugar Mfr & Distr
N.A.I.C.S.: 311314

ALAM MARITIM RESOURCES BERHAD

No 38F Level 3 Jalan Radin Anum Bandar Baru Sri Petaling, 57000, Kuala Lumpur, Malaysia
Tel.: (60) 390582244
Web Site: http://www.alam-maritim.com.my

Alam Maritim Resources Berhad—(Continued)

ALAM—(KLS)
Rev.: $65,736,173
Assets: $48,479,362
Liabilities: $61,034,100
Net Worth: ($12,554,738)
Earnings: $3,002,688
Emp.: 128
Fiscal Year-end: 06/30/23
Offshore Supply Vessels & Services
N.A.I.C.S.: 488330
Shaharuddin Warno *(COO-Grp)*

Subsidiaries:

Alam Maritim (M) Sdn. Bhd.　　　**(1)**
No 38F Level 2 Jalan Radin Anum, Bandar
Baru Sri Petaling, 57000, Kuala Lumpur,
Malaysia
Tel.: (60) 390582244
Web Site: http://www.alam-maritim.com.my
Sales Range: $25-49.9 Million
Ship Repair & Maintenance Services
N.A.I.C.S.: 336611

Subsidiary (Domestic):

Alam Food Industries (M) Sdn.
Bhd.　　　**(2)**
K-7865 Rumah Kedai 1 1/2 Tingkat Kam-
pong Bukit Kuang, 24000, Kemaman,
Terengganu, Malaysia
Tel.: (60) 98504845
Web Site: http://www.alam-maritim.com.my
Sales Range: $10-24.9 Million
Catering Services
N.A.I.C.S.: 722320

Alam Hidro (M) Sdn. Bhd.　　　**(2)**
No 38 D & E Level 4 Bandar Baru Sri Pet-
aling, 57000, Kuala Lumpur, Malaysia
Tel.: (60) 390562155
Web Site: http://www.alam-maritim.com.my
Sales Range: $25-49.9 Million
Construction Engineering Services
N.A.I.C.S.: 541330

Eastar Offshore Pte. Ltd.　　　**(1)**
19 Bukit Batok Street 22, Singapore,
659588, Singapore
Tel.: (65) 66655369
Web Site: http://www.eastaroffshores.com
Sales Range: $25-49.9 Million
Emp.: 22
Remotely Operated Underwater Vehicles
Mfr & Distr
N.A.I.C.S.: 339999

Subsidiary (Domestic):

Alam Subsea Pte. Ltd.　　　**(2)**
19 Bukit Batok St 22, Singapore, 659588,
Singapore
Tel.: (65) 66655322
Web Site: http://www.alamsubsea.com
Sales Range: $25-49.9 Million
Emp.: 20
Remotely Operated Vehicle Mfr & Support
Services
N.A.I.C.S.: 339999

Workboat International DMCCO　　　**(1)**
124 Al Arti Plaza, PO Box 119181, Karama,
Dubai, United Arab Emirates
Tel.: (971) 43571555
Oil & Gas Marine Consulting Services
N.A.I.C.S.: 541330

ALAMOS GOLD INC.
181 Bay Street Suite 3910, Toronto,
M5J 2T3, ON, Canada
Tel.: (416) 368-9932　　　ON
Web Site:
　　https://www.alamosgold.com
Year Founded: 2003
AGI—(NYSE)
Rev.: $821,200,000
Assets: $3,674,200,000
Liabilities: $953,100,000
Net Worth: $2,721,100,000
Earnings: $37,100,000
Emp.: 1,919
Fiscal Year-end: 12/31/22
Gold Exploration & Mining
N.A.I.C.S.: 212220

Paul J. Murphy *(Chm)*

Subsidiaries:

Manitou Gold Inc.　　　**(1)**
82 Richmond St East, Toronto, M5C 1P1,
ON, Canada
Tel.: (705) 698-1962
Web Site: https://www.manitougold.com
Rev.: $79,173
Assets: $2,250,993
Liabilities: $847,884
Net Worth: $1,403,109
Earnings: ($1,713,666)
Fiscal Year-end: 12/31/2019
Gold Mining Services
N.A.I.C.S.: 212220
Richard Murphy *(Pres & CEO)*

Minera Santa Rita, S, de R.L. de
C.V.　　　**(1)**
Lamberto Hernandez No 278, Caborca,
83600, Sonora, Mexico
Tel.: (52) 6373272094
Gold & Silver Ore Mining Services
N.A.I.C.S.: 212220
Hector Araiza *(Gen Mgr)*

Oro de Altar, S.A. de C.V.　　　**(1)**
Calle Paseo Rio Sonora Nte 42 211-A, Co-
lonia Centenario, Hermosillo, Sonora,
Mexico
Tel.: (52) 662 372 7094
Investment Management Service
N.A.I.C.S.: 523940

**ALAN ALLMAN ASSOCIATES
SA**
LAmiral 15 Rue Rouget de Lisle-Hall
2, 92130, Issy-les-Molineaux,
France
Tel.: (33) 153839560
Web Site: https://www.alan-
　　allman.com
Year Founded: 1954
AAA—(EUR)
Rev.: $403,578,762
Assets: $420,123,634
Liabilities: $346,727,012
Net Worth: $73,396,622
Earnings: $7,335,247
Emp.: 3,838
Fiscal Year-end: 12/31/23
Management Consulting Services
N.A.I.C.S.: 541618
Florent Sainsot *(COO)*

Subsidiaries:

Comitem S.A.S.　　　**(1)**
9-15 rue Rouget de Lisle, 92130, Issy-les-
Moulineaux, France
Tel.: (33) 174905040
Web Site: https://www.comitem.com
Computer Related Services
N.A.I.C.S.: 541519

Digitalum N.V.　　　**(1)**
Eurostraat 1, 3500, Hasselt, Belgium
Tel.: (32) 28978539
Web Site: https://www.digitalum.eu
Emp.: 50
Online Shopping Services
N.A.I.C.S.: 531120

Ec Solutions Inc.　　　**(1)**
3200 Highway Laval West, Laval, H7T 2H6,
QC, Canada
Web Site: https://www.e-c-solutions.com
Information Technology Management Ser-
vices
N.A.I.C.S.: 561311

Gdg Info Et Gestion Inc.　　　**(1)**
330 St-Vallier Street E 023, Quebec, G1K
9C5, QC, Canada
Tel.: (418) 647-0006
Web Site: https://www.gdginc.com
Information Technology Consulting Services
N.A.I.C.S.: 541512

Les Solutions Victrix Inc.　　　**(1)**
630 Rue Sherbrooke O, Montreal, H3A
1E4, QC, Canada
Tel.: (514) 879-1919
Web Site: https://www.victrix.ca

Information Technology Management Services
N.A.I.C.S.: 561311

Noverka Conseil Inc.　　　**(1)**
630 Sherbrooke W Street Suite 1100, Mon-
treal, H3A 1E4, QC, Canada
Tel.: (514) 849-7072
Web Site: https://www.noverkaconseil.com
Information Technology Consulting Services
N.A.I.C.S.: 541512

Privatum N.V.　　　**(1)**
Klaverbladstraat 7a Bus 5, 3560, Lummen,
Belgium
Tel.: (32) 13323649
Web Site: https://www.privatum.be
Computer Related Services
N.A.I.C.S.: 541519

Source Evolution Inc.　　　**(1)**
2000 Peel Street Suite 540, Montreal, H3A
2W5, QC, Canada
Tel.: (514) 354-6565
Web Site: https://sourcevolution.com
Information Technology Consulting Services
N.A.I.C.S.: 541512

Teccweb Inc.　　　**(1)**
22 King St S Suite 300, Waterloo, N2J 1N8,
ON, Canada
Tel.: (905) 637-9255
Web Site: https://teccweb.com
Computer Related Services
N.A.I.C.S.: 541519

**ALAN HICKINBOTHAM PTY.
LTD.**
25 North Terrace, Hackney, 5069,
SA, Australia
Tel.: (61) 883660000
Web Site:
　　http://www.hickinbotham.com.au
Year Founded: 1954
Residential Building Construction
Services
N.A.I.C.S.: 236116
Michael Hickinbotham *(Mng Dir)*

ALAN NUTTALL LTD.
Orchard House Dodwells Road,
Hinckley, LE10 3BZ, Leicestershire,
United Kingdom
Tel.: (44) 1455638300
Web Site: http://www.nuttalls.co.uk
Year Founded: 1988
Sales Range: $100-124.9 Million
Emp.: 489
Display Cabinet Mfr
N.A.I.C.S.: 337211
Alan Nuttall *(Founder)*

**ALAN SCOTT INDUSTRIES
LIMITED**
Unit No 302 Kumar Plaza 3rd Floor
Near Kalina Masjid, Kalina Kurla
Road Santacruz East, Mumbai,
400029, India
Tel.: (91) 2261786000
Web Site:
　　https://www.thealanscott.com
Year Founded: 1994
539115—(BOM)
Rev.: $260,671
Assets: $759,695
Liabilities: $338,460
Net Worth: $421,234
Earnings: ($8,441)
Emp.: 14
Fiscal Year-end: 03/31/22
Socks Mfr
N.A.I.C.S.: 316210
Soketu Parikh *(Chm & Mng Dir)*

**ALANDALUS PROPERTY
COMPANY**
PO Box 260020, Riyadh, Saudi Ara-
bia
Tel.: (966) 114700735
Web Site:
　　https://www.alandalus.com.sa

Year Founded: 2006
4320—(SAU)
Rev.: $57,621,178
Assets: $547,928,790
Liabilities: $214,516,059
Net Worth: $333,412,731
Earnings: $23,275,223
Emp.: 96
Fiscal Year-end: 12/31/22
Real Estate Investment Services
N.A.I.C.S.: 531390
Abdulsalam Abdulrahman Al-Aqeel
(Chm)

ALANDSBANKEN ABP
Nygatan 2, AX-22100, Mariehamn,
Finland
Tel.: (358) 20429011
Web Site:
　　http://www.alandsbanken.com
ALBBV—(HEL)
Rev.: $198,078,998
Assets: $6,364,903,950
Liabilities: $6,023,408,159
Net Worth: $341,495,791
Earnings: $39,693,503
Emp.: 935
Fiscal Year-end: 12/31/22
Banking Services
N.A.I.C.S.: 522110
Peter Wiklof *(CEO & Mng Dir)*

Subsidiaries:

Alandsbanken Asset Management
Ab　　　**(1)**
Bulevardi 3, 00120, Helsinki,
Finland　　　**(100%)**
Tel.: (358) 20 429 3600
Web Site: https://www.alandsbanken.fi
Commercial Banking Services
N.A.I.C.S.: 522110
Peter Wiklof *(Gen Mgr)*

Alandsbanken Equities Research
Ab　　　**(1)**
Bulevardi 3, 00120, Helsinki, Finland
Tel.: (358) 2042 9011
Web Site: http://www.alandsbanken.fi
Commercial Banking Services
N.A.I.C.S.: 522110
Peter Wikstroem *(Gen Mgr)*

Alandsbanken Fondbolag Ab　　　**(1)**
Nygatan 9, 22100, Mariehamn, Finland
Tel.: (358) 20429088
Commercial Banking Services
N.A.I.C.S.: 522110
Tom Pettersson *(Mng Dir)*

Alandsbanken Sverige AB　　　**(1)**
Stureplan 19, Mailbox 10781, 111 45,
Stockholm, Sweden
Tel.: (46) 8 791 4800
Web Site: https://www.alandsbanken.se
Sales Range: $100-124.9 Million
Emp.: 130
Banking Services
N.A.I.C.S.: 522110

Crosskey Banking Solutions Ab
Ltd.　　　**(1)**
Elverksgatan 10, 22100, Mariehamn, Fin-
land
Tel.: (358) 20429022
Web Site: https://www.crosskey.fi
Sales Range: $100-124.9 Million
Commercial Banking Services
N.A.I.C.S.: 522110
Thomas Lundberg *(Mng Dir)*

ALANG MARINE LTD.
303 Panchkalayan Kalanala, Bhavna-
gar, 364001, Gujarat, India
Tel.: (91) 278426825
Web Site:
　　https://www.alangmaritime.com
Year Founded: 1991
Shipbuilding & Repair Services
N.A.I.C.S.: 336611

**ALANKIT CORPORATE SER-
VICES LIMITED**

205-208 Anarkali Complex Jhande-
walan Extension, New Delhi, 110
055, India
Tel.: (91) 114 154 0028
Year Founded: 1989
531082—(NSE)
Rev.: $16,168,616
Assets: $22,579,134
Liabilities: $9,151,410
Net Worth: $13,427,723
Earnings: $1,511,628
Emp.: 2,650
Fiscal Year-end: 03/31/21
Commodity Trading Services
N.A.I.C.S.: 523160
Ankit Agarwal *(Chm & Mng Dir)*

ALANTRA PARTNERS, SA
Calle de Jose Ortega y Gasset 29,
28006, Madrid, Spain
Tel.: (34) 917458484
Web Site: https://www.alantra.com
Year Founded: 1997
ALNT—(BAR)
Rev.: $204,754,388
Assets: $530,651,286
Liabilities: $131,468,153
Net Worth: $399,183,133
Earnings: $12,054,311
Emp.: 668
Fiscal Year-end: 12/31/23
Private Equity Investment Services
N.A.I.C.S.: 523999
Santiago Bergareche Busquet *(Vice
Chm)*

ALAPIS HOLDING INDUS-
TRIAL & COMMERCIAL SA
Aftokratoros Nikolaou St 2, Athens,
17671, Greece
Tel.: (30) 21301750000
Pharmaceutical Product Mfr & Distr
N.A.I.C.S.: 325411
Aristotelis Charalampakis *(Chm)*

ALARA RESOURCES LIMITED
Suite 1 02 110 Erindale Road, Bal-
catta, 6021, WA, Australia
Tel.: (61) 892404211
Web Site:
     https://www.alararesources.com
AUQ—(ASX)
Rev.: $3,672,824
Assets: $114,817,009
Liabilities: $101,058,469
Net Worth: $13,758,540
Earnings: ($7,094,748)
Emp.: 475
Fiscal Year-end: 06/30/24
Exploration of Resource
N.A.I.C.S.: 213114
Justin Richard *(CEO & Mng Dir)*

ALARGAN INTERNATIONAL
REAL ESTATE CO. K.S.C.C.
ARGAN Business Park Free Trade
Zone Shuwaikh Block F25 - F41, PO
Box 8904, Salmiyah, 22060, Kuwait,
22060, Kuwait
Tel.: (965) 22263222
Web Site: https://www.alargan.com
ARGAN—(KUW)
Rev.: $8,523,689
Assets: $770,598,953
Liabilities: $512,318,311
Net Worth: $258,280,643
Earnings: $2,515,769
Emp.: 85
Fiscal Year-end: 12/31/22
Real Estate Services
N.A.I.C.S.: 531390
Khaled Khudair Al-Mashaan *(Vice
Chm)*

Subsidiaries:

Alargan Bahrain W.L.L.   (1)

Building 2376 Road 5756 Block 457, PO
Box 21186, Bu Quwah, Manama, Bahrain
Tel.: (973) 17563600
Real Estate Management & Development
Services
N.A.I.C.S.: 531311

Alargan Towel Investment Company
LLC   (1)
Qurm Gardens Building Commercial Wing
Penthouse, Opposite Qurm national park Al
Qurm, Muscat, Oman
Tel.: (968) 22009353
Real Estate Manangement Services
N.A.I.C.S.: 531390

ALARIS EQUITY PARTNERS
INCOME TRUST
Suite 250 333 24th Avenue SW, Cal-
gary, T2S 3E6, AB, Canada
Tel.: (403) 260-1457   Ca
Web Site:
     https://www.alarisequitypartners.com
Year Founded: 2006
ADLRF—(OTCIQ)
Rev.: $182,173,455
Assets: $1,113,721,957
Liabilities: $388,185,294
Net Worth: $725,536,664
Earnings: $104,544,854
Fiscal Year-end: 12/31/23
Investment Services
N.A.I.C.S.: 525910
Stephen W. King *(Co-Founder, Pres
& CEO)*

ALARIS HOLDINGS LIMITED
1 Travertine Avenue N1 Business
Park, Old Johannesburg Road Centu-
rion, Pretoria, 0157, Gauteng, South
Africa
Tel.: (27) 110345300
Web Site:
     http://www.alarisholdings.com
ALH—(JSE)
Rev.: $29,804,761
Assets: $28,735,042
Liabilities: $8,268,465
Net Worth: $20,466,577
Earnings: $3,513,609
Emp.: 202
Fiscal Year-end: 06/30/23
Antenna & Digital Television Broad-
casting Equipment Mfr
N.A.I.C.S.: 334220
Juergen Dresel *(CEO)*

Subsidiaries:

Alaris Antennas Proprietary
Limited   (1)
1 Travertine Avenue N1 Business Park Old
Johannesburg Road, Centurion, 0157, Gau-
teng, South Africa
Tel.: (27) 110345300
Web Site: https://antennas.alaris.tech
Broadband Antenna Mfr & Distr
N.A.I.C.S.: 334220

Cojot Oy   (1)
Paivankakkarantie 10, 02270, Espoo, Fin-
land
Tel.: (358) 94522334
Web Site: https://cojot.alaris.tech
Broadband Antenna Mfr & Distr
N.A.I.C.S.: 334220

Kuhne Electronic GmbH   (1)
Scheibenacker 3, 95180, Berg, Germany
Tel.: (49) 9293800640
Web Site: https://www.kuhne-electronic.de
Electronic Microwave Component Mfr &
Distr
N.A.I.C.S.: 334419

Linwave Technology Limited   (1)
Marlin Building 4 Sadler Rd, Lincoln, LN6
3RS, United Kingdom
Tel.: (44) 1522681811
Web Site: https://linwave.alaris.tech
Microwave Product Distr
N.A.I.C.S.: 423620

mWAVE Industries, LLC   (1)

33R Main St Unit 1, Windham, ME 04062
Tel.: (207) 892-0011
Web Site: https://mwave.alaris.tech
Rev.: $2,000,000
Emp.: 15
Radio Television Broadcasting & Wireless
Communications Equipment Mfr
N.A.I.C.S.: 334220
Peter Farnum *(Mng Dir)*

ALARKO GAYRIMENKUL
YATIRIM ORTAKLIGI AS
Muallim Naci Cad 69 Ortakoy, Istan-
bul, Turkiye
Tel.: (90) 2123103300   TR
Web Site:
     https://www.alarkoyatirim.com.tr
Year Founded: 1996
ALGYO—(IST)
Rev.: $17,487,254
Assets: $619,625,024
Liabilities: $45,254,948
Net Worth: $574,370,077
Earnings: $68,853,036
Emp.: 20
Fiscal Year-end: 12/31/22
Real Estate Manangement Services
N.A.I.C.S.: 531390
Umit Nuri Yildiz *(Deputy Chm &
Deputy Vice Chm)*

ALARKO HOLDING A.S.
Muallim Naci Cad No 69 Ortakoy,
34347, Istanbul, Turkiye
Tel.: (90) 2123103300
Web Site: https://www.alarko.com.tr
Year Founded: 1954
ALARK—(IST)
Rev.: $273,384,212
Assets: $966,860,941
Liabilities: $348,859,553
Net Worth: $618,001,387
Earnings: $172,772,677
Emp.: 4,722
Fiscal Year-end: 12/31/21
Portfolio Management Services
N.A.I.C.S.: 523940
Izzet Garih *(Chm)*

Subsidiaries:

Alarko Carrier Sanayi ve Ticaret
A.S.   (1)
Gebze Organized Industrial Zone Sahabet-
tin Bilgisu Street, 41480, Istanbul, Turkiye
Tel.: (90) 2626486000
Web Site: https://www.alarko-carrier.com.tr
Rev.: $171,478,269
Assets: $159,772,162
Liabilities: $92,292,652
Net Worth: $67,479,509
Earnings: $9,754,345
Emp.: 641
Fiscal Year-end: 12/31/2021
Circulation Pumps, Pressure Tanks & Boil-
ers Mfr
N.A.I.C.S.: 333414
Niv Garih *(Chm)*

Alsim Alarko S.R.L.   (1)
Strada Mircea Vulcanescu No 49 Sector 1,
Bucharest, Romania
Tel.: (40) 314380441
Engineering Services
N.A.I.C.S.: 541330

Alsim Alarko San. Tes. ve Tic.
A.S.   (1)
Emirhan Cad No 113 / C Barbaros Plaza
Kat 2, Dikilitas Besiktas, 34349, Istanbul,
Kocaeli, Turkiye
Tel.: (90) 2129535700
Web Site: http://www.alsimalarko.com.tr
Construction Engineering Services
N.A.I.C.S.: 541330

Altek Alarko Elektrik Sant. Tes. Isl. ve
Tic. A.S.   (1)
Muallim Naci Cad 69, Ortakoy, 34347, Is-
tanbul, Turkiye
Tel.: (90) 2122523154
Web Site: http://www.altek.alarko.com.tr
Electric Power Distr
N.A.I.C.S.: 221122

Attas Alarko Turistik Tesisler A.S.   (1)
Nispetiye Caddesi Ahular Sokak No 6,
Etiler, Istanbul, 34337, Turkiye
Tel.: (90) 212 362 30 00
Web Site: http://hillside.com.tr
Tourism Facility Management Services
N.A.I.C.S.: 561520

ALARUM TECHNOLOGIES
LTD.
30 Haarba a Street, PO BOX 174, Tel
Aviv, 6473926, Israel
Tel.: (972) 98666110   II
Web Site: http://www.safe-t.com
Year Founded: 1989
ALAR—(NASDAQ)
Rev.: $26,521,000
Assets: $20,066,000
Liabilities: $6,885,000
Net Worth: $13,181,000
Earnings: ($5,525,000)
Emp.: 2
Fiscal Year-end: 12/31/23
Data Management Services
N.A.I.C.S.: 541513
Amir Mizhar *(Co-Founder & Pres)*

Subsidiaries:

Safe-T USA Inc.   (1)
51 John F Kennedy Pkwy 1st Fl W, Short
Hills, NJ 07078
Tel.: (561) 843-1428
Web Site: https://safe-t.us
Computer Security Services
N.A.I.C.S.: 561621

ALASKA ENERGY METALS
CORPORATION
Suite 2300 1177 W Hastings St, Van-
couver, V6E 2K3, BC, Canada
Tel.: (604) 638-3164   BC
Web Site:
     https://www.millrockresources.com
AKEMF—(OTCIQ)
Rev.: $864,893
Assets: $3,757,070
Liabilities: $753,938
Net Worth: $3,003,132
Earnings: ($3,288,174)
Fiscal Year-end: 12/31/19
Metal Mining Services
N.A.I.C.S.: 212290
Gregory A. Beischer *(Pres & CEO)*

Subsidiaries:

Millrock Exploration Corp.   (1)
719 E 11th Ave, Anchorage, AK 99501
Tel.: (907) 677-7479
Gold Ore Mining Services
N.A.I.C.S.: 212220

ALASKA HYDRO CORPORA-
TION
2633 Carnation Street, North Vancou-
ver, V7H 1H6, BC, Canada
Tel.: (604) 916-9185
Web Site:
     https://www.alaskahydro.com
Year Founded: 2006
Sales Range: Less than $1 Million
Renewable Energy Acquisition & De-
velopment Services
N.A.I.C.S.: 221111
Cliff Grandison *(Pres-Interim & CEO)*

Subsidiaries:

Cascade Creek LLC   (1)
3633 Alderwood Ave, Bellingham, WA
98225
Tel.: (360) 738-9999
Web Site: http://www.thomasbayhydro.com
Hydroelectric Power Generation Services
N.A.I.C.S.: 221111

ALATAU ZHARYK COMPANY
JSC
24b Manas str, Almaty, 050008, Kazakhstan

ALATAU ZHARYK COMPANY JSC

Alatau Zharyk Company JSC—(Continued)

Tel.: (7) 27 356 99 99
Electric Power Generation & Distribution Services
N.A.I.C.S.: 221118

ALATNICA A.D.

Bore Stankovic 9, Bujanovac, Serbia
Tel.: (381) 63 410 439
Year Founded: 1998
Sales Range: Less than $1 Million
Machine Tools Mfr
N.A.I.C.S.: 333517

ALAYA CARE INC.

151 Yonge Street Suite 1000, Toronto, M5C 2W7, ON, Canada
Tel.: (647) 477-4174
Web Site: http://www.alayacare.com
Year Founded: 2014
Healthcare Software Publisher
N.A.I.C.S.: 513210
Adrian Schauer *(Founder & CEO)*

Subsidiaries:

Delta Health Technologies, LLC **(1)**
400 Lakemont Park Blvd, Altoona, PA 16602-5967
Tel.: (800) 444-1651
Web Site: http://www.deltahealthtech.com
Healthcare Software Publisher
N.A.I.C.S.: 513210
Tony Ott *(CEO)*

ALB-GOLD TEIGWAREN GMBH

Im Grindel 1, 72818, Trochtelfingen, Germany
Tel.: (49) 71 24 9291 0   De
Web Site: http://www.alb-gold.de
Sales Range: $25-49.9 Million
Spaetzle & Pasta Mfr
N.A.I.C.S.: 311824
Irmgard Freidler *(CEO)*

Subsidiaries:

Al Dente Pasta Company **(1)**
9815 Main St, Whitmore Lake, MI 48189
Tel.: (734) 449-8522
Web Site: http://www.aldentepasta.com
Sales Range: $1-9.9 Million
Pasta Mfr
N.A.I.C.S.: 311824
Nanette Carson *(Gen Mgr)*

ALBA FRUCT SA

Str Motilor 106, Alba, Alba Iulia, Romania
Tel.: (40) 258 834896
Year Founded: 1991
Sales Range: Less than $1 Million
Fruit & Vegetable Whslr
N.A.I.C.S.: 424480

ALBA GRUPO MARCH

Castello 77-5th floor, 28006, Madrid, Spain
Tel.: (34) 914363710   ES
Web Site:
   http://www.corporacionalba.es
Year Founded: 1986
Sales Range: $10-24.9 Million
Emp.: 23
Financial Services
N.A.I.C.S.: 561499
Juan March Delgado *(Co-Chm)*

Subsidiaries:

Banca March S.A. **(1)**
Av Alejandro Rossello 8, 07002, Palma de Mallorca, Balearic Islands, Spain
Tel.: (34) 971779111
Web Site: http://www.bancamarch.es
Sales Range: $700-749.9 Million
Emp.: 1,171
Full Banking Services
N.A.I.C.S.: 522110

Alberto del Cid Picado *(Mgr-Treasury & Foreign Exchange)*

Affiliate (Non-US):

Balboa Finance S.A. **(2)**
6 Rue Ceard, CH-1204, Geneva, Switzerland   **(30%)**
Tel.: (41) 223108922
Personal Financing Services
N.A.I.C.S.: 522210

Branch (Non-US):

Banca March-London **(2)**
30 Eastcheap, London, EC3M 1HD, United Kingdom
Tel.: (44) 2072207488
Web Site: http://www.bancamarch.co.uk
Emp.: 4
Full Banking Services
N.A.I.C.S.: 522110

Subsidiary (Domestic):

March - Unipsa Correduria de Seguros, S.A.U **(2)**
C/ Lagasca 88 2 Planta, Madrid, 28001, Spain
Tel.: (34) 91 781 1515
Full Banking Services
N.A.I.C.S.: 522110

Subsidiary (Domestic):

March-JLT Correduria de Seguros, SA **(3)**
Calle de Lagasca 88, Madrid, 28001, Spain   **(100%)**
Tel.: (34) 917 81 15 15
Web Site: http://www.march-jlt.es
Insurance Consulting & Risk Management Services
N.A.I.C.S.: 524298
Carlos Navarro *(Mng Dir)*

Subsidiary (Domestic):

March Correduria de Seguros S.A. **(2)**
Avenida A Rossello 8, 07002, Palma de Mallorca, Spain   **(80.37%)**
Tel.: (34) 971779368
Web Site: http://www.marchunidsa.es
Insurance Brokers
N.A.I.C.S.: 524298
Pedro Ballesteros *(Mng Dir)*

March Patrimonios S.A. **(2)**
Avda A Rossello 8, Palma de Mallorca, 07002, Baleares, Spain   **(100%)**
Tel.: (34) 971779256
Investment Fund
N.A.I.C.S.: 523940

Corporacion Financiera Alba S.A. **(1)**
Castello 77 5th planta, 28006, Madrid, 28006, Spain   **(53.18%)**
Tel.: (34) 914363710
Web Site: http://www.cf-alba.com
Sales Range: $1-9.9 Million
Emp.: 196,967
Investment Holding Company
N.A.I.C.S.: 551112
Juan March Delgado *(Co-Chm)*

ALBA MINERAL RESOURCES PLC

6th Floor 60 Gracechurch Street, London, EC3V 0HR, United Kingdom
Tel.: (44) 2039500725
Web Site:
   https://www.albaminerals.com
ALBA—(AIM)
Assets: $16,000,730
Liabilities: $629,982
Net Worth: $15,370,748
Earnings: ($3,536,861)
Emp.: 11
Fiscal Year-end: 11/30/22
Mineral Exploration Services
N.A.I.C.S.: 213115
George Frangeskides *(Chm)*

ALBA SE

Stollwerckstrasse 9A, D-51149, Cologne, Germany
Tel.: (49) 220391470
Web Site: https://alba.info
Year Founded: 1968
ABA—(DEU)
Rev.: $343,592,008
Assets: $220,421,680
Liabilities: $71,431,725
Net Worth: $148,989,955
Earnings: ($1,909,703)
Emp.: 416
Fiscal Year-end: 12/31/23
Metal Recycling & Waste Treatment Services
N.A.I.C.S.: 423510
Axel Schweitzer *(Chm & CEO)*

Subsidiaries:

ALBA Berlin GmbH **(1)**
Flottenstr 9, 13407, Berlin, Germany
Tel.: (49) 3035182351
Web Site: https://berlin.alba.info
Waste Disposal Management Services
N.A.I.C.S.: 562998

ALBA Braunschweig GmbH **(1)**
Frankfurter Strasse 251, 38122, Braunschweig, Germany
Tel.: (49) 53188620
Web Site: https://alba-bs.de
Emp.: 260
Waste Disposal Management Services
N.A.I.C.S.: 562998

ALBA China Recycling Solutions Ltd. **(1)**
Room 1401 Air China Century Plaza No 40 Xiaoyun Road, Chaoyang, Beijing, 100027, China
Tel.: (86) 1056436666
Waste Disposal Management Services
N.A.I.C.S.: 562998
Kate Yan *(Fin Mgr-Asia)*

ALBA Cottbus GmbH **(1)**
Dissenchener Str 50, 03042, Cottbus, Germany
Tel.: (49) 3557508700
Waste Disposal Management Services
N.A.I.C.S.: 562998

ALBA Dolny Slask Sp. z o.o. **(1)**
Ul Piasta 16, 58304, Walbrzych, Poland
Tel.: (48) 748434220
Waste Disposal Management Services
N.A.I.C.S.: 562998
Witek Senczuk *(Pres)*

ALBA Ekoplus Sp. z o.o. **(1)**
Ul Brukowa 27, 91341, Lodz, Poland
Tel.: (48) 691991586
Waste Disposal Management Services
N.A.I.C.S.: 562998

ALBA Electronics Recycling GmbH **(1)**
Heilbronner Strasse 13, 75031, Eppingen, Germany
Tel.: (49) 7262612100
Web Site: http://aer.alba.info
Waste Disposal Services
N.A.I.C.S.: 562119

ALBA Europe Holding plc & Co. KG **(1)**
Knesebeckstr 56-58, 10719, Berlin, Germany
Tel.: (49) 30351823260
Web Site: http://www.albaclick.de
Waste Disposal Services
N.A.I.C.S.: 562119

ALBA Ferrous Trading GmbH **(1)**
Dieselstrasse 52, 60314, Frankfurt, Germany
Tel.: (49) 694126944050
Waste Disposal Management Services
N.A.I.C.S.: 562998

ALBA Heilbronn-Franken plc & Co. KG **(1)**
Benzstr 17, 74076, Heilbronn, Germany
Tel.: (49) 7131952020
Web Site: https://heilbronn-franken.alba.info
Waste Disposal
N.A.I.C.S.: 562119

Beate Lang *(Acct Mgr)*

ALBA Integrated Waste Solutions (Hong Kong) Limited **(1)**
Lots P2-P4 Eco Park 133 Lung Mun Road Area 38, New Territories, Tuen Mun, China (Hong Kong)
Tel.: (852) 23712822
Web Site: http://www.weee.com.hk
Waste Disposal Management Services
N.A.I.C.S.: 562998
Donald Lim *(Ops Mgr)*

ALBA Logistik GmbH **(1)**
Hultschiner Damm 335, 12623, Berlin, Germany
Tel.: (49) 3035182351
Waste Disposal Management Services
N.A.I.C.S.: 562998

ALBA MPGK Sp. z o.o. **(1)**
Ul Starocmentarna 2, 41300, Dabrowa Gornicza, Poland
Tel.: (48) 322625029
Waste Disposal Management Services
N.A.I.C.S.: 562998
Marcin Pelz *(Mgr-Transportation & Fleet)*

ALBA MPO Sp. z o.o. **(1)**
Ul Kluczewska 2, 32300, Olkusz, Poland
Tel.: (48) 322410081
Waste Disposal Management Services
N.A.I.C.S.: 562998

ALBA Metall Nord GmbH **(1)**
Werkstrasse 1, 18069, Rostock, Germany
Tel.: (49) 381809060
Web Site: http://metall-nord.alba.info
Waste Disposal Management Services
N.A.I.C.S.: 562998
Norman Broja *(Mgr-OPEX Anlagen)*

ALBA Metall Sud Franken GmbH **(1)**
Schweinfurter Strasse 6-8, 97526, Sennfeld, Germany
Tel.: (49) 972165060
Waste Disposal Management Services
N.A.I.C.S.: 562998

ALBA Metall Sud Rhein-Main GmbH **(1)**
Carl-Benz-Strasse 1, 60314, Frankfurt am Main, Germany
Tel.: (49) 694167450
Waste Disposal Management Services
N.A.I.C.S.: 562998

ALBA Niedersachsen-Anhalt GmbH **(1)**
Frankfurter Strasse 251, 38122, Braunschweig, Germany
Tel.: (49) 5318862222
Web Site: http://nisa.alba.info
Waste Disposal Management Services
N.A.I.C.S.: 562998

ALBA Nord GmbH **(1)**
Ziegeleiweg 12, 19057, Schwerin, Germany
Tel.: (49) 3854811327
Web Site: https://nord.alba.info
Waste Disposal Management Services
N.A.I.C.S.: 562998

ALBA Nordbaden GmbH **(1)**
Industriestrasse 1, 76189, Karlsruhe, Germany
Tel.: (49) 721500060
Web Site: https://nordbaden.alba.info
Waste Disposal Management Services
N.A.I.C.S.: 562998

ALBA PGK Sp. z o.o. **(1)**
Ul Wojkowicka 14 A, 41250, Czeladz, Poland
Tel.: (48) 322651289
Waste Disposal Management Services
N.A.I.C.S.: 562998

ALBA PTS Sp. z o.o. **(1)**
Ul Bytkowska 15, 41503, Chorzow, Poland
Tel.: (48) 322495680
Waste Disposal Management Services
N.A.I.C.S.: 562998

ALBA Poludnie Polska Sp. z o.o. **(1)**
Ul Starocmentarna 2, 41300, Dabrowa Gornicza, Poland
Tel.: (48) 323969200
Waste Disposal Management Services
N.A.I.C.S.: 562998

ALBA Rising Green Fuel (Hong Kong) Ltd. **(1)**
49/F The Pinnacle Building No 17 Zhujiang West Road, Guangzhou, 510620, China
Tel.: (86) 2038609166
Waste Disposal Management Services
N.A.I.C.S.: 562998

ALBA Sachsen GmbH **(1)**
Ruckmarsdorfer Strasse 31, 04179, Leipzig, Germany
Tel.: (49) 3414481352
Waste Disposal Management Services
N.A.I.C.S.: 562998

ALBA Sud GmbH & Co. KG **(1)**
Anton-Schmidt-Strasse 25, 71332, Waiblingen, Germany
Tel.: (49) 715117130
Web Site: https://sued.alba.info
Waste Disposal Management Services
N.A.I.C.S.: 562998
Wolfgang Russe (CEO)

ALBA Supply Chain Management GmbH **(1)**
Franz-Josef-Schweitzer-Platz 1, 16727, Velten, Germany
Tel.: (49) 3035182234
Waste Disposal Management Services
N.A.I.C.S.: 562998

ALBA TAV Betriebs GmbH **(1)**
Am Alten Flugplatz 1, 19288, Ludwigslust, Germany
Tel.: (49) 387425070
Web Site: https://tav.alba.info
Waste Disposal Management Services
N.A.I.C.S.: 562998

ALBA Uckermark GmbH **(1)**
Kuhheide 15, Schwedt, 16303, Brandenburg, Germany
Tel.: (49) 3332538401
Waste Disposal Management Services
N.A.I.C.S.: 562998

ALBA Utility Scrap Solutions GmbH **(1)**
Waterworks 6, 18147, Rostock, Germany
Tel.: (49) 381673140
Waste Disposal Management Services
N.A.I.C.S.: 562998

ALBA W&H Smart City Pte. Ltd. **(1)**
18 Tuas Ave 10, Singapore, 639142, Singapore
Tel.: (65) 64508160
Web Site: https://www.alba-wh.sg
Waste Disposal Management Services
N.A.I.C.S.: 562998
Nettie Lee (Mgr-Customer Svcs)

ALBA Wertstoffmanagement GmbH **(1)**
Franz-Josef-Schweitzer-Platz 1, 16727, Velten, Germany
Tel.: (49) 30351829836
Waste Disposal Management Services
N.A.I.C.S.: 562998

ALBA Zenica d.o.o. **(1)**
Sarajevska bb, 72000, Zenica, Bosnia & Herzegovina
Tel.: (387) 32442841
Web Site: https://alba.ba
Waste Disposal Management Services
N.A.I.C.S.: 562998

ALL Abfall-Logistik Leipzig GmbH **(1)**
Max-Liebermann-Str 97, 04157, Leipzig, Germany
Tel.: (49) 3419039541
Waste Disposal Management Services
N.A.I.C.S.: 562998

ATO Abfallwirtschaft Torgau-Oschatz GmbH **(1)**
Gewerbering 51, 04860, Torgau, Germany
Tel.: (49) 3421773000
Web Site: https://www.ato-online.de
Emp.: 54
Waste Disposal Management Services
N.A.I.C.S.: 562998

AWU Abfallwirtschafts-Union Oberhavel GmbH **(1)**
Breite Strasse 47a, 16727, Velten, Germany

Tel.: (49) 33043760
Web Site: https://www.awu-oberhavel.de
Waste Disposal Management Services
N.A.I.C.S.: 562998

AWU Logistik OPR GmbH **(1)**
Gewerbering 34, Rheinsberg, 16831, Brandenburg, Germany
Tel.: (49) 3393138699
Waste Disposal Management Services
N.A.I.C.S.: 562998

AWU Ostprignitz-Ruppin GmbH **(1)**
Ahornallee 10, Markisch Linden OT Werder, 16818, Brandenburg, Germany
Tel.: (49) 339205020
Web Site: https://www.awu-opr.de
Waste Disposal Management Services
N.A.I.C.S.: 562998

BRAL Reststoff-Bearbeitungs GmbH **(1)**
Marzahner Strasse 36, 13053, Berlin, Germany
Tel.: (49) 309824235
Web Site: https://www.bral.berlin
Food Waste Disposal Services
N.A.I.C.S.: 562119

ERV GmbH **(1)**
Veltener Str 24, Germendorf, 16515, Oranienburg, Germany
Tel.: (49) 3301207090
Web Site: https://www.erv-info.de
Waste Disposal Management Services
N.A.I.C.S.: 562998

Grunske Metall-Recycling GmbH & Co. KG **(1)**
Veltener Strasse 32, Germendorf, 16515, Oranienburg, Germany
Tel.: (49) 330157370
Web Site: https://www.grunske.net
Waste Disposal Management Services
N.A.I.C.S.: 562998

HAW Havellandische Abfallwirtschaftsgesellschaft mbH **(1)**
Schwanebecker Weg 4, Neukammer, 14641, Nauen, Germany
Tel.: (49) 332174620
Web Site: https://haw-mbh.de
Waste Disposal Management Services
N.A.I.C.S.: 562998

Interseroh Austria GmbH **(1)**
Ungargasse 33, 1030, Vienna, Austria
Tel.: (43) 171420050
Web Site: http://www.interseroh.at
Waste Disposal Management Services
N.A.I.C.S.: 562998
Franz Sauseng (Co-CEO)

Interseroh Organizacja Odzysku Opakowan S.A. **(1)**
Ul Wiertnicza 165, 02-952, Warsaw, Poland
Tel.: (48) 227421022
Web Site: http://www.interseroh.pl
Waste Disposal Management Services
N.A.I.C.S.: 562998
Anna Grom (Chm)

Interseroh Product Cycle GmbH **(1)**
Spenger Strasse 15, 49328, Melle, Germany
Tel.: (49) 5226592900
Waste Disposal Management Services
N.A.I.C.S.: 562998
Trott Alexander (Mgr-Sls & Logistics)

Interseroh Service Italia S.r.l. **(1)**
Via Leonardo Bistolfi 49, 20134, Milan, Italy
Tel.: (39) 0283634982
Web Site: http://www.interseroh.it
Waste Disposal Management Services
N.A.I.C.S.: 562998
Roberto Magnaghi (Mng Dir)

Interseroh Services d. o. o. **(1)**
Fra Andela Zvizdovica 1 B Tower 7 Floor, 71000, Sarajevo, Bosnia & Herzegovina
Tel.: (387) 33295778
Waste Disposal Management Services
N.A.I.C.S.: 562998

Interzero d.o.o **(1)**
Beograjska ulica 4, 1000, Ljubljana, Slovenia
Tel.: (386) 15609150
Web Site: https://interzero.si
Waste Disposal Management Services

N.A.I.C.S.: 562998
Darja Figelj (Gen Mgr)

KVB Kunststoffverwertung Brandenburg GmbH **(1)**
Seefichtenstrasse 15, 15890, Eisenhuttenstadt, Germany
Tel.: (49) 3035182455
Waste Disposal Management Services
N.A.I.C.S.: 562998

RDB Plastics GmbH **(1)**
Nortorfer Strasse 2, Aukrug, 24613, Rendsburg, Germany
Tel.: (49) 487320340
Web Site: https://www.rdb-plastics.com
Waste Disposal Management Services
N.A.I.C.S.: 562998
Peter Maerz (Mng Dir)

Repasack GmbH **(1)**
Nerotal 4, 65193, Wiesbaden, Germany
Tel.: (49) 6115323030
Waste Disposal Management Services
N.A.I.C.S.: 562998
Marion Nickel (Acct Mgr)

SR Service GmbH **(1)**
Petridamm 26, 18146, Rostock, Germany
Tel.: (49) 3814593111
Web Site: http://www.stadtentsorgung-rostock.de
Waste Disposal Management Services
N.A.I.C.S.: 562998

Sonderabfall Service Sudwest - 3S GmbH **(1)**
Anton-Schmidt-Strasse 25, 71332, Waiblingen, Germany
Tel.: (49) 71511713800
Web Site: https://www.3s-sonderabfall.de
Waste Disposal Management Services
N.A.I.C.S.: 562998

TVF Altwert GmbH **(1)**
Dissenchener Strasse 50, 03042, Cottbus, Germany
Tel.: (49) 35549382820
Web Site: https://tvf-altwert.de
Emp.: 120
Waste Disposal Management Services
N.A.I.C.S.: 562998

Umwelt-Service Nordschwarzwald GmbH **(1)**
Gaaullee 5, 72202, Nagold, Germany
Tel.: (49) 745260067050
Web Site: https://www.usn-info.de
Waste Disposal Management Services
N.A.I.C.S.: 562998

WPO Alba S.A. **(1)**
Ul Szczecinska 5, 54517, Wroclaw, Poland
Tel.: (48) 713375116
Waste Disposal Management Services
N.A.I.C.S.: 562998

ALBAAD MASSUOT YITZHAK LTD.
MP Sde Gat, Masu'ot Yitzhak, 79858, Israel
Tel.: (972) 88607222   II
Web Site: https://www.albaad.com
Year Founded: 1985
ALBA—(TAE)
Rev.: $472,573,276
Assets: $437,243,535
Liabilities: $325,835,331
Net Worth: $111,408,204
Earnings: $8,564,995
Emp.: 1,700
Fiscal Year-end: 12/31/23
Toilet Preparation Manufacturing
N.A.I.C.S.: 325620
Gadi Choresh (Pres-Non-Woven Div)

Subsidiaries:

Albaad Deutschland GmbH **(1)**
Am Langenhorster Bahnhof 23, 48607, Ochtrup, Germany
Tel.: (49) 255393300
Paper Product Mfr & Distr
N.A.I.C.S.: 322211

ALBARAKA TURK KATILIM BANKASI A.S.

Saray Mah Dr Adnan Buyukdeniz, Cad No 6 Umraniye, 34768, Istanbul, Turkiye
Tel.: (90) 2166660101
Web Site:
  https://en.albarakaturk.com.tr
Year Founded: 1984
ALBRK—(IST)
Rev.: $340,352,767
Assets: $4,539,332,613
Liabilities: $4,250,602,307
Net Worth: $288,730,305
Earnings: $57,313,864
Emp.: 2,695
Fiscal Year-end: 12/31/22
Banking Services
N.A.I.C.S.: 522110
Meliksah Utku (CEO & Gen Mgr)

Subsidiaries:

Albaraka Portfoy Yonetimi A.S. **(1)**
Saray Mahallesi Dr Adnan Buyukdeniz Caddesi No 6 Kat 10, Umraniye, 34768, Istanbul, Turkiye
Tel.: (90) 2166660050
Web Site: http://www.albarakaportfoy.com.tr
Portfolio Management Services
N.A.I.C.S.: 523940

Deger Varlik Kiralama A.S. **(1)**
Saray Mh Dr Adnan Buyukdeniz Cd No 6, Umraniye, 34768, Istanbul, Turkiye
Tel.: (90) 2166660303
Web Site: https://degervarlik.com
Asset Management Services
N.A.I.C.S.: 532490

Insha GmbH **(1)**
Hardenbergstrasse 32, 10623, Berlin, Germany
Tel.: (49) 30255585575
Web Site: https://www.getinsha.com
Mobile Banking Services
N.A.I.C.S.: 522110
Yakup Sezer (Mng Dir)

ALBATRON TECHNOLOGY CO., LTD.
6F No 716 Chung Cheng Rd, Chung-Ho Dist, New Taipei City, Taiwan
Tel.: (886) 282273277
Web Site:
  https://www.albatron.com.tw
Year Founded: 1984
5386—(TPE)
Rev.: $97,583,685
Assets: $25,310,571
Liabilities: $11,038,958
Net Worth: $14,271,613
Earnings: $1,589,876
Fiscal Year-end: 12/31/22
Broadcasting Equipment Mfr
N.A.I.C.S.: 334220
Jack Ko (CEO)

ALBENA TOUR LTD
33-35 St Ivan Rilski str, 1000, Sofia, Bulgaria
Tel.: (359) 885853097
Web Site: https://albenatour.bg
Home Management Services
N.A.I.C.S.: 721110

ALBERCO CONSTRUCTION LTD.
14 Rayborn Crs Riel Business Park, Saint Albert, T8N 4B1, AB, Canada
Tel.: (780) 459-7110
Web Site: https://www.alberco.com
Year Founded: 1962
Rev.: $28,521,500
Emp.: 30
Bridge Construction Services
N.A.I.C.S.: 237310

ALBERCO HOLDING B.V.
PO Box 351, 8912 AX, Leeuwarden, Netherlands

Alberco Holding B.V.—(Continued)

Tel.: (31) 582330660
Web Site: http://www.steensma.com
Sales Range: $50-74.9 Million
Emp.: 120
Holding Company
N.A.I.C.S.: 551112
Alfred Bruin (CEO)

Subsidiaries:

Steensma B.V.   (1)
Galvanistraat 1, 8912 AX, Leeuwarden,
Netherlands
Tel.: (31) 881632000
Web Site: http://www.steensma.com
Sales Range: $10-24.9 Million
Emp.: 60
Food Ingredients & Raw Materials Producer
& Exporter
N.A.I.C.S.: 311999
R. De Jong (Mng Dir)

ALBERT BALLIN KG
Ballindamm 25, 20095, Hamburg,
Germany
Tel.: (49) 4030010
Web Site: http://www.hapag-
  lloyd.com
Year Founded: 2009
Holding Company; Owned by Kuhne
Holding AG, Signal Iduna Gruppe,
HSH Nordbank, M.M. Warburg Bank
& HanseMerkur
N.A.I.C.S.: 551112

Subsidiaries:

Hapag-Lloyd AG   (1)
Ballindamm 25, Hamburg, 20095, Germany
Tel.: (49) 4030010
Web Site: http://www.hapag-lloyd.com
Sales Range: $5-14.9 Billion
Emp.: 1,600
Maritime Freight Shipping Services
N.A.I.C.S.: 483111
Michael Behrendt (Chm-Supervisory Bd)

Subsidiary (Non-US):

Adriatikagent Internationla Shipping
Agency d.o.o.   (2)
Cesta Dveh Cesarjev 403, 1000, Ljubljana,
Slovenia
Tel.: (386) 01 4769821
Container Shipping ervices
N.A.I.C.S.: 483111

Agencia Maritima Remar S.R.L.   (2)
Estrella 692 Lider 4 Floor 8 Ste 81, Asun-
cion, Paraguay
Tel.: (595) 21 497715
Container Shipping ervices
N.A.I.C.S.: 483111

Agencia Naviera Europa S.A.   (2)
Edif Plaza Maritima 4 Calle Entre, 1 Y 2
Ave Barrio Guamilito, San Pedro Sula, Hon-
duras
Tel.: (504) 2544 0450
Container Shipping ervices
N.A.I.C.S.: 483111

Agencias Continental S.A.   (2)
Edif Eurocentro Ave Abel Bravo, Obarrio,
Panama, Panama
Tel.: (507) 300 1400
Container Shipping ervices
N.A.I.C.S.: 483111

Alson's Shipping Ltd.   (2)
3 Abercromby Street, Port of Spain, Trini-
dad & Tobago
Tel.: (868) 6252201 5
Container Shipping ervices
N.A.I.C.S.: 483111
Chris Maraj (Gen Mgr)

Aquamarine Shipping Co. Ltd.   (2)
Room 8D Penthouse Building No 24-26
Race Course Condo, South Race Course
Street, 11201, Yangon, Myanmar
Tel.: (95) 1 542725
Container Shipping ervices
N.A.I.C.S.: 483111

Arkas Algerie S.p.A.   (2)

7 Route de Sidi Yahia Lot B 16 016 Hydra
Ville, 16 016 Hydra, 16040, Algiers, Algeria
Tel.: (213) 21 43 58 82
Container Shipping ervices
N.A.I.C.S.: 483111

Arkas Shipping & Transport S.A.   (2)
Liman Cadessi Arkas Binasi N 38, Alsan-
cak, Tripoli, Libya
Tel.: (218) 21 340 25 28
Container Shipping ervices
N.A.I.C.S.: 483111

B ianchi & Co. (1916) Ltd.   (2)
Palazza Marina, 143 Saint Christopher
Street, Valletta, Malta
Tel.: (356) 21232241
Container Shipping ervices
N.A.I.C.S.: 483111

Blue Funnell Angola   (2)
AV 4 de Fevererio, 1214, Luanda, Angola
Tel.: (244) 2 310007
Container Shipping ervices
N.A.I.C.S.: 483111

CSAV Agenciamiento Maritimo
SpA   (2)
Plaza Sotomayor 50, Valparaiso, Chile
Tel.: (56) 322203000
Freight Forwarding & Shipping Services
N.A.I.C.S.: 488510

CSAV Agency France S.A.S.   (2)
112 Boulevard des Dames, 13002, Mar-
seille, France
Tel.: (33) 486678300
Freight Forwarding & Shipping Services
N.A.I.C.S.: 488510

CSAV Agency Italy, S.p.A.   (2)
Via Scarsellini 147, 16149, Genoa, Italy
Tel.: (39) 0108997611
Freight Forwarding & Shipping Services
N.A.I.C.S.: 488510

Division (US):

CSAV Agency LLC   (2)
99 Wood Ave S Ste 900, Iselin, NJ 08830
Tel.: (732) 635-2600
Freight Forwarding & Shipping Services
N.A.I.C.S.: 488510
Percy Bilimoria (Acct Mgr)

Subsidiary (Non-US):

CSAV Agency Ltd.   (2)
Suite 504-1166 Alberni St, Vancouver, V6E
3Z3, BC, Canada
Tel.: (604) 646-0120
Freight Forwarding & Shipping Services
N.A.I.C.S.: 488510

CSAV Argentina S.A.   (2)
Carlos Pellegrini 1363 4 piso, C1011AAA,
Buenos Aires, Argentina
Tel.: (54) 1153557700
Web Site: http://www.csavgroup.com.ar
Freight Forwarding & Shipping Services
N.A.I.C.S.: 488510

CSAV Denizcilik Acentasi A.S.   (2)
Iskele Meydani Albay Faik Sozdener Sokak
n 9/12, Kadikoy, 34710, Istanbul, Turkiye
Tel.: (90) 2164442728
Freight Forwarding & Shipping Services
N.A.I.C.S.: 488510

CSAV Group (China) Shipping Co.
Ltd.   (2)
19/F Hongyi Plaza No 288 Jiu Jiang Road,
Shanghai, 200001, China
Tel.: (86) 2123211600
Web Site: http://www.csavagency-cn.com
Freight Forwarding & Shipping Services
N.A.I.C.S.: 488510
Allen Zhang Xiaoguang (Mgr-Pricing)

CSAV Group (Hong Kong) Ltd.   (2)
Units 2506-10 25/F Tower 2 Ever Gain
Plaza 88 Container Port, Kwai Chung,
China (Hong Kong)
Tel.: (852) 28577868
Freight Forwarding & Shipping Services
N.A.I.C.S.: 488510

CSAV Group Agencies (India) Pvt
Ltd
Solitaire Corporate Park Office No - 1121-
1122 Second Floor, Building No 11 Andheri

Kurla Road Chakala Andheri (E), Mumbai,
400093, India
Tel.: (91) 2240509000
Web Site: http://www.csavagency-in.com
Freight Forwarding & Shipping Services
N.A.I.C.S.: 488510
Asgar S. T. Bharuchwala (Gen Mgr-IT &
Comm)

CSAV Group Agencies (Taiwan)
Ltd.   (2)
Room 701A 7F No 50 Sec 1 Sinsheng
South Road, Jhongjheng, Taipei, Taiwan
Tel.: (886) 223959990
Freight Forwarding & Shipping Services
N.A.I.C.S.: 488510

CSAV Group Agencies Uruguay
S.A.   (2)
Montevideo Juncal 1385 5th floor, Montevi-
deo, 11000, Uruguay
Tel.: (598) 29163003
Freight Forwarding & Shipping Services
N.A.I.C.S.: 488510

CSAV Group Agency Colombia
Ltda.   (2)
Calle 100 No 8A-49 Piso 8, Bogota, Colom-
bia
Tel.: (57) 12966313
Freight Forwarding & Shipping Services
N.A.I.C.S.: 488510

Subsidiary (Domestic):

CSAV North & Central Europe
GmbH   (2)
Ericusspitze 2 - 4, 20457, Hamburg, Ger-
many
Tel.: (49) 4030014100
Freight Forwarding & Shipping Services
N.A.I.C.S.: 488510
Eckart Ahrens (Mgr-Container Control &
Empty Logistic)

Subsidiary (Non-US):

CSAV North & Central Europe
N.V.   (2)
Sint Pietersvliet 7, 2000, Antwerp, Belgium
Tel.: (32) 32200511
Freight Forwarding & Shipping Services
N.A.I.C.S.: 488510

CSAV UK & Ireland Limited   (2)
New Kestrel House Unit 23/24 M11 Busi-
ness Link Parsonage Lane, Stansted,
CM24 8GF, United Kingdom
Tel.: (44) 1279818855
Freight Forwarding & Shipping Services
N.A.I.C.S.: 488510

Cargo Marine Ltd.   (2)
Rear Port Area, AMA Building, Ashdod,
Israel
Tel.: (972) 8 8527543
Container Shipping ervices
N.A.I.C.S.: 483111

Catoni 7 Co.   (2)
3 8 Lessia Ukranka Street Apartment 8,
0108, Tbilisi, Georgia
Tel.: (995) 32 989230
Container Shipping ervices
N.A.I.C.S.: 483111

Coconut Products Ltd.   (2)
Level 1 Carpenter House, Waigani Drive
Sec 136 Allotment 4 Hohola, Port Moresby,
Papua New Guinea
Tel.: (675) 3255166
Container Shipping ervices
N.A.I.C.S.: 483111

Companhia Libra de Navegacao
S.A.   (2)
Alameda Rio Negro 585 - 5 CJ 5/52 Alpha-
ville, Barueri, Sao Paulo, 06454-000, Brazil
Tel.: (55) 1140032728
Freight Forwarding & Shipping Services
N.A.I.C.S.: 488510

Delta Transport (Pvt.) Ltd.   (2)
P 38 Ground Floor Chenab Market, Madina
Town Susan Road, Faisalabad, Pakistan
Tel.: (92) 41 8728378
Container Shipping ervices
N.A.I.C.S.: 483111

Division (US):

Florida Vessel Management LLC   (2)

401 E Jackson St Ste 3300, Tampa, FL
33602
Tel.: (813) 276-4600
Freight Forwarding & Shipping Services
N.A.I.C.S.: 488510

Subsidiary (Non-US):

GAC Shipping Nigeria Limited   (2)
2-4 Edde Street Apapa, PMB 1285, Lagos,
Nigeria
Tel.: (234) 12910303
Container Shipping ervices
N.A.I.C.S.: 483111

GBX Logistics Ltd.   (2)
Ayub Trade Center 3rd Floor, 1269 B SK
Mujin Road Agrabad Commercial Area,
Chittagong, Bangladesh
Tel.: (880) 31 2516868
Web Site: http://www.hlcl.com
Container Shipping ervices
N.A.I.C.S.: 483111

Global Maritime Services Ltd.   (2)
Pozitano 9 Str Entr A Fl 6 Office 20, 1303,
Sofia, Bulgaria
Tel.: (359) 2 950 3530
Web Site: http://www.gmsvar.com
Container Shipping ervices
N.A.I.C.S.: 483111
Dimitar Dobrev (Gen Mgr)

Grindrod Ships Agencies Lda   (2)
51 Praca Dos Trabalhadores 4th Floor, Ma-
puto, Mozambique
Tel.: (258) 21 325891
Container Shipping ervices
N.A.I.C.S.: 483111

Haji Abdullah Alireza & Co. Ltd.   (2)
Shipping Department, Dammam, 31411,
Saudi Arabia
Tel.: (966) 3 8324133
Container Shipping ervices
N.A.I.C.S.: 483111

Hapac-Lloyd (Schweiz) AG   (2)
Messeplatz 10 Messe Tower / 21 Floor,
4058, Basel, Switzerland
Tel.: (41) 61 63822 33
Container Shipping ervices
N.A.I.C.S.: 483111

Hapag-Lloyd (Africa) Pty. Ltd.   (2)
13 Waterford News, Waterford Place Cen-
tury City Blvd, 7441, Cape Town, South
Africa
Tel.: (27) 21 527 5800
Container Shipping ervices
N.A.I.C.S.: 483111

Division (US):

Hapag-Lloyd (America) Inc.   (2)
399 Hoes Ln, Piscataway, NJ 08854
Tel.: (732) 562-1800
Container Shipping ervices
N.A.I.C.S.: 483111
Stanley Silver (Dir-Controlling)

Subsidiary (Non-US):

Hapag-Lloyd (Australia) Pty. Ltd.   (2)
Unit 3 463 Nudgee Road, Hendra, Bris-
bane, 4011, QLD, Australia
Tel.: (61) 7 38682137
Container Shipping ervices
N.A.I.C.S.: 483111

Hapag-Lloyd (Canada) Inc.   (2)
6708 Bayne St 2nd Fl, Fairview Cover Con-
tainer Terminal, Halifax, B3K 0A8, NS,
Canada
Tel.: (877) 893-4426
Liner Shipping Services
N.A.I.C.S.: 483111

Hapag-Lloyd (China) Ltd.   (2)
6/F Manhattan Place 23 Wang Tai Road,
Kowloon, China (Hong Kong)
Tel.: (852) 27681600
Freight Forwarding & Shipping Services
N.A.I.C.S.: 488510
Baniel Tse Sr. (Mgr-Ops)

Hapag-Lloyd (China) Shipping
Ltd.   (2)
8F Citic Plaza, No 1350 North Sichuan
Road, 200080, Shanghai, China
Tel.: (86) 21 26066000

Container Shipping Servicesfre
N.A.I.O.S.: 483111

Hapag-Lloyd (Eastwind) Pte. Ltd. **(2)**
Area-South East Asia 200 Cantonment
Road 08-03, Southpoint Buliding, Singa-
pore, 089763, Singapore
Tel.: (65) 62236119
Freight Forwarding & Shipping Services
N.A.I.C.S.: 488510
Chris Schmid *(Mng Dir)*

Hapag-Lloyd (France) SAS **(2)**
99 Quai Du Docteur Dervaux, F-92600,
Paris, France
Tel.: (33) 1 40802250
Container Shipping ervices
N.A.I.C.S.: 483111

Hapag-Lloyd (Ireland) Ltd. **(2)**
3rd Floor Russell House Stokes Place Saint
Stephen's Green, Dublin, D02 DF28, Ire-
land
Tel.: (353) 1 4052542
Web Site: http://www.hlag.com
Emp.: 20
Container Shipping ervices
N.A.I.C.S.: 483111
John Oboien *(Office Mgr)*

Hapag-Lloyd (Italy) S.R.L. **(2)**
V Le Cassala 22, 20143, Milan, Italy
Tel.: (39) 02 581571
Freight Forwarding & Shipping Services
N.A.I.C.S.: 488510
Emanuela Lomazzi *(Office Mgr)*

Hapag-Lloyd (Japan) K.K. **(2)**
4 87 Ichibancho Chiyoda-Ku, Hapag-Lloyd
House, Tokyo, 102-0082, Japan
Tel.: (81) 3 52126155
Web Site: http://www.hapag-lloyd.com
Container Shipping ervices
N.A.I.C.S.: 483111
Satoru Nakamura *(Dir-Customer Svc)*

**Hapag-Lloyd (Malaysia) Sdn.
Bhd.** **(2)**
Level 20 Nucleus Tower No 10 Jalan Pju
7/6, Mutiara Damansara, 47800, Kuala
Lumpur, Selangor, Malaysia
Tel.: (60) 3 2245 8888
Web Site: http://www.hapag-lloyd.com
Emp.: 40
Container Shipping ervices
N.A.I.C.S.: 483111
Andy Van Den Abeele *(Mng Dir)*

Hapag-Lloyd (New Zealand) Ltd. **(2)**
74 Taharoto road Smales Farm Level 3 Air
New Zealand Buliding, Takapuna, Auckland,
0622, New Zealand
Tel.: (64) 94883366
Freight Forwarding & Shipping Services
N.A.I.C.S.: 488510
Davina Kemp *(Mgr-Import Documentation)*

Hapag-Lloyd (Philippines) Inc. **(2)**
5th Fl 777 Victory Holding Corp 888 Plare-
del St Umapad, AC Cortes Avenue, Man-
daue, 6014, Philippines
Tel.: (63) 32 346 7716
Web Site: http://www.hapag-lloyd.com
Emp.: 4
Container Shipping ervices
N.A.I.C.S.: 483111
Andy Vanden Abeele *(Mng Dir)*

Hapag-Lloyd (Thailand) Ltd. **(2)**
127-29 Panjathani Tower 24th Floor, Nonsee Road Chong Nonsee Yannawa, Bangkok, 10120, Thailand
Tel.: (66) 2 6854200
Container Shipping ervices
N.A.I.C.S.: 483111

Hapag-Lloyd (UK) Ltd. **(2)**
Hapag Lloyd House 48A Cambridge road,
Essex, Barking, IG11 8HH, United Kingdom
Tel.: (44) 2085074000
Freight Forwarding & Shipping Services
N.A.I.C.S.: 488510
Andrew Allen *(Dir-Ops)*

Hapag-Lloyd (Vietnam) **(2)**
4th Floor 1 C Ngo Quyen Street, Hoen
Kiem District, Hanoi, Vietnam
Tel.: (84) 4 39366206
Container Shipping ervices
N.A.I.C.S.: 483111
Dinny Chuy *(Country Mgr)*

Hapag-Lloyd (korea) Ltd. **(2)**
Metro Twr 11th Fl toegyero 1oth Str jungjgu
4, 51 Sogong Dong Jung-Gu, Seoul,
004637, Korea (South)
Tel.: (82) 2 37063000
Emp.: 80
Container Shipping ervices
N.A.I.C.S.: 483111
Estapan Perez *(Mng Dir)*

Hapag-Lloyd Agency LLC **(2)**
Al-Fajer complex B Rm 105 Oud Metha Rd,
Suite 107-108 Oud Metha Road, Dubai,
124474, United Arab Emirates
Tel.: (971) 4 3871300
Web Site: http://www.hapag-lloyd.com
Container Shipping ervices
N.A.I.C.S.: 483111

Hapag-Lloyd Antwerpen **(2)**
Kattendijkdok Westkaai 21, 2000, Antwerp,
Belgium
Tel.: (32) 3 5450 611
Container Shipping ervices
N.A.I.C.S.: 483111

Hapag-Lloyd Argentina S.R.L. **(2)**
Bouchard 557 23rd Fl, C1106ABG, Buenos
Aires, Argentina
Tel.: (54) 11 4323 1000
Container Shipping ervices
N.A.I.C.S.: 483111

Hapag-Lloyd Austria GmbH **(2)**
Gonzagogasse 1 1 11, A-1010, Vienna,
Austria
Tel.: (43) 1 53448 0
Container Shipping ervices
N.A.I.C.S.: 483111

Hapag-Lloyd Brazil **(2)**
Avenida Luis Carlos Berrini 1645, Brooklyn
Novo, 04571-011, Sao Paulo, Brazil
Tel.: (55) 11 5504 9555
Container Shipping ervices
N.A.I.C.S.: 483111

Hapag-Lloyd Chile Ag. Mar. Ltda. **(2)**
Ave El Bosque Norta 500 Piso 14, 755-
0092, Santiago, Chile
Tel.: (56) 2 24819400
Container Shipping ervices
N.A.I.C.S.: 483111

Hapag-Lloyd Colombia Ltda. **(2)**
Carrera 9A 99-02 Oficina 502B, Bogota,
Colombia
Tel.: (57) 1 632 6030
Container Shipping ervices
N.A.I.C.S.: 483111

Hapag-Lloyd Costa Rica S.A. **(2)**
Oficentro La Sabana, Torre 7 Piso 6, 1000,
San Jose, Costa Rica
Tel.: (506) 2519 5900
Liner Shipping Services
N.A.I.C.S.: 483111

Hapag-Lloyd Denamrk **(2)**
Roejelskaer15, DK-2840, Holte, Denmark
Tel.: (45) 45465 600
Container Shipping ervices
N.A.I.C.S.: 483111

**Hapag-Lloyd Denizasiri Nakliyat
A.S.** **(2)**
Kibris Sehitleri Cad No 136/1 Kat 4, Alsan-
cak, Izmir, 35220, Türkiye
Tel.: (90) 2324553636
Web Site: http://www.denizasiri.com.tr
Freight Forwarding & Shipping Services
N.A.I.C.S.: 488510

**Hapag-Lloyd Global Services Pvt.
Ltd.** **(2)**
Plot No 1501 One Indian Bulls Center
Senapati Bapat Road Elphinstone, Parel,
Mumbai, 400013, India
Tel.: (91) 2249461775
Freight Forwarding & Shipping Services
N.A.I.C.S.: 488510
Kartik Narayanaswamy *(Mgr-Customer Svc
Ops)*

Hapag-Lloyd Guatamala S.A. **(2)**
Blvd Vista Hermosa 24-00 Zona 15 Vista
Hermosa II, Edif Reforma 10 Ofic 601A,
Guatemala, Guatemala
Tel.: (502) 2205 4000
Container Shipping ervices
N.A.I.C.S.: 483111

Hapag-Lloyd Lanka (Pvt.) Ltd. **(2)**
Level 1 Aitken Spence Tower II, No 315
Vauxhall Street, 02, Colombo, Sri Lanka
Tel.: (94) 112499505
Container Shipping ervices
N.A.I.C.S.: 483111

**Hapag-Lloyd Mexico S.A. De
C.V.** **(2)**
Sierra De Las Palomas 125 Interior,
Bosques Del Prado Sur, 20130, Aguascali-
entes, Mexico
Tel.: (52) 449 9965434
Container Shipping ervices
N.A.I.C.S.: 483111

**Hapag-Lloyd Overseas Transport
(Hellas) SA** **(2)**
33 Akti Miaouli Street 2 Defteras Merrar-
chias Str, GR-18535, Piraeus, Greece
Tel.: (30) 210 4596000
Web Site: http://www.hapag-lloyd.com
Container Shipping ervices
N.A.I.C.S.: 483111
Alexandros Kutulogianis *(Gen Mgr)*

**Hapag-Lloyd Overseas Transport
S.A.** **(2)**
Kasap Sokak, Arkas Binasi 2 4, TR-34394,
Istanbul, Türkiye
Tel.: (90) 212 3180044
Container Shipping ervices
N.A.I.C.S.: 483111

Hapag-Lloyd Peru S.A.C. **(2)**
Amador Merino Reyna 267 Ste 901, San
Isidro, Peru
Tel.: (51) 1 3174100
Container Shipping ervices
N.A.I.C.S.: 483111

Hapag-Lloyd Polska SP. z.o.o. **(2)**
Ul Wspolna 35 12, 00 519, Warsaw, Poland
Tel.: (48) 22 52278 00
Container Shipping ervices
N.A.I.C.S.: 483111

Hapag-Lloyd Portugal Lda. **(2)**
Avenida D. Carlos I 44 5, 1990, Lisbon,
Portugal
Tel.: (351) 213943000
Container Shipping ervices
N.A.I.C.S.: 483111

Hapag-Lloyd Pte. Ltd. **(2)**
200 Cantonment Road 08-03, Southpoint
Building, Singapore, 089763, Singapore
Tel.: (65) 62236119
Container Shipping ervices
N.A.I.C.S.: 483111

Hapag-Lloyd Rotterdam **(2)**
Waalhaven OZ 79, 3087 BM, Rotterdam,
Netherlands
Tel.: (31) 10 240 4400
Container Shipping ervices
N.A.I.C.S.: 483111

Hapag-Lloyd Spain S.L. **(2)**
C Comtal 32-1, E-08002, Barcelona, Spain
Tel.: (34) 933436000
Container Shipping ervices
N.A.I.C.S.: 483111

Hapag-Lloyd Sweden AB **(2)**
Marieholsgatan 1, S-415 02, Gothenburg,
Sweden
Tel.: (46) 31 3378 200
Container Shipping ervices
N.A.I.C.S.: 483111

Hapag-Lloyd Taiwan Ltd. **(2)**
11F 285 Chung Hsiao East Road Sec 4,
Taipei, 106, Taiwan
Tel.: (886) 2 21731600
Web Site: http://www.hapag-lloyd.com
Container Shipping ervices
N.A.I.C.S.: 483111

Hapag-Lloyd Venezuela, C.A. **(2)**
Av Fransisco De Miranda Edificio, Parque
Cristol Piso 6 OFc 6-11, 1060, Caracas,
Venezuela
Tel.: (58) 2122 2781000
Container Shipping ervices
N.A.I.C.S.: 483111

Division (US):

Hapag-Lloyd(America) LLC **(2)**

Caribbean Business 3350 SW 148th Ave,
Miramar, FL 33027
Tel.: (954) 447-7100
Freight Forwarding & Shipping Services
N.A.I.C.S.: 488510
Diego Garcia *(Dir-Bus Admin)*

Subsidiary (Non-US):

Harbour Link Shipping Sdn. Bhd. **(2)**
Lot 11620 Unit 4 Ground Floor Block A,
Scouts HQ Jln Gadong, BA1779, Bandar
Seri Begawan, Brunei Darussalam
Tel.: (673) 2 456618
Container Shipping ervices
N.A.I.C.S.: 483111

Hub Dacia S.R.L. **(2)**
157B Barbu Vacarescu Street Sector 2,
R-020276, Bucharest, Romania
Tel.: (40) 21 2088700
Container Shipping ervices
N.A.I.C.S.: 483111

Hub Dunav d.o.o. **(2)**
21 Boze Jankovica 1st Floor Suite 2,
11000, Belgrade, Serbia
Tel.: (381) 11 3988003
Container Shipping ervices
N.A.I.C.S.: 483111

Hub Levant Limited **(2)**
Baghdad Street, Montana Building 3rd
Floor, Lattakia, Syria
Tel.: (963) 41 469194
Container Shipping ervices
N.A.I.C.S.: 483111

**Humberto Alvarez Sucesores De Ni-
caragua S.A.** **(2)**
Carretera Norte De Los Semaforos, De La
Sebasta 1 Km Al Norte, Managua, Nicara-
gua
Tel.: (505) 2263 1400
Container Shipping ervices
N.A.I.C.S.: 483111

ISS Shipping India Pvt. Ltd. **(2)**
4th Floor Office 402, Loha Bhavan NR Old
High Court, ICICI Bank Lane Income Tax,
Ahmedabad, 380006, Gujarat, India
Tel.: (91) 99989 45698
Container Shipping ervices
N.A.I.C.S.: 483111

**Inchcape Shipping Services (Cambo-
dia) Ltd.** **(2)**
Ground Floor Regency Complex C Street
217 Number 18-20A 168, Vithei Preah
Monireth, 12000, Phnom Penh, Cambodia
Tel.: (855) 23 424 731 6
Web Site:
http://www.inchcapeshippingservices.com
Container Shipping ervices
N.A.I.C.S.: 483111
Heang Lin *(Gen Mgr)*

Inchcape Shipping Services LLC **(2)**
Al Noor Street Way Number 3109, Buildign
Number 483 Ground Floor, 112, Muscat,
Ruwi, Oman
Tel.: (968) 24701294
Container Shipping ervices
N.A.I.C.S.: 483111

Inchcape Shipping Services WLL **(2)**
Bulldign 1378 Office 22 2nd Floor,
Buashurah, Sitra, Bahrain
Tel.: (973) 17 747445
Container Shipping ervices
N.A.I.C.S.: 483111

Marine Trading Ltd. **(2)**
Black Rock Main Road, Saint Michael,
Bridgetown, Barbados
Tel.: (246) 4291292
Container Shipping ervices
N.A.I.C.S.: 483111

Medlevant Shipping S.A.E. **(2)**
9 Hussein Hassab Street, From El Sultan
Hussein, Alexandria, Egypt
Tel.: (20) 3 4885600
Container Shipping ervices
N.A.I.C.S.: 483113

Subsidiary (Domestic):

Norddeutscher Lloyd GmbH **(2)**
Gustav-Deetjen-Allee 26, 28215, Bremen,
Germany

Albert Ballin KG—(Continued)
Tel.: (49) 4030010
Freight Forwarding & Shipping Services
N.A.I.C.S.: 488510

Subsidiary (Non-US):

OCS Kaliningrad (2)
Portovaya 24, 236003, Kaliningrad, Russia
Tel.: (7) 4012092255
Container Shipping ervices
N.A.I.C.S.: 483111

OCS Ocean Container Services Ltd. (2)
Sadama 17, 10111, Tallinn, Estonia
Tel.: (372) 6 4018 02
Web Site: http://en.ocs.agency
Emp.: 75
Container Shipping ervices
N.A.I.C.S.: 483111

OCS Ocean Container Services Ltd. (2)
Okeaninu Konteineriu Servisas, 18 6
Birutes Street, 91210, Klaipeda, Lithuania
Tel.: (370) 46 3811 96
Container Shipping ervices
N.A.I.C.S.: 483111

Ocean Container Service (OCS) (2)
Ganibu Gambis, 1005, Riga, Latvia
Tel.: (371) 6 77839 49
Container Shipping ervices
N.A.I.C.S.: 483111

Oil & Marine Agencies (O.M.A.) SARL (2)
Concession Otam, Zone Portuire Port De Peche, Lome, Togo
Tel.: (228) 2 71 2776
Container Shipping ervices
N.A.I.C.S.: 483111

Oil and Marine Agencies (Ghana) Ltd. (2)
2nd Floor North Wing, Atlantic Plaza Community 1, Tema, Ghana
Tel.: (233) 303 203 945
Container Shipping ervices
N.A.I.C.S.: 483111
Francesco Leuzzi (Gen Mgr)

Oil and Marine Agencies SARL (2)
08 BP 799, Cotonou, Benin
Tel.: (229) 21 315288
Container Transport Services
N.A.I.C.S.: 483111
Geldas Atengehou (Mgr)

Ot Hapag-Lloyd Finland AB (2)
Porkkalankatu 20 C, 00180, Helsinki, Finland
Tel.: (358) 9 689131
Container Shipping ervices
N.A.I.C.S.: 483111

Overseas Transport Ukraine Ltd. (2)
Office 4 Ul Uspenskaya 39, 65125, Odessa, Ukraine
Tel.: (380) 48 7342174 75
Container Shipping ervices
N.A.I.C.S.: 483111

PT Samudera Indonesia, TBK. (2)
Cyber 2 Tower Level # A E F, JL Hr Rasuna Said Block X5 No 13, Jakarta, 12950, Indonesia
Tel.: (62) 21 2934 3600
Container Shipping ervices
N.A.I.C.S.: 483111

Papeete Seirland Transports (PST) (2)
Immeuble Franco-Oceanienne, Fare-Ute, Papeete, French Polynesia
Tel.: (689) 549700
Container Shipping ervices
N.A.I.C.S.: 483111

Perez Y Cia Jamaica Ltd. (2)
6-12 Newport Boulevard Newport Centre, Kingston, 13, Jamaica
Tel.: (876) 9012994
Web Site: http://www.perezycia.ja.com
Container Shipping ervices
N.A.I.C.S.: 483111
Leonie Mendel (Mng Dir)

Qatar Maritime & Mercantile Intl. Co. (2)

Bldg 244 C-Ring Rd, Al Mudhaf Near Musium R B, Doha, 24724, Qatar
Tel.: (974) 44329810
Container Shipping ervices
N.A.I.C.S.: 483111

Quay Cargo Services Ltd. (2)
1st Fl unit 6 Victoria business park, Belfast, BT39JL, United Kingdom
Tel.: (44) 28 90371195
Web Site: http://www.quaycargo.co.uk
Emp.: 16
Container Shipping ervices
N.A.I.C.S.: 483111
Gary Stewart (Mng Dir)

SAM Shipping & Clearing Co. Ltd. (2)
Meena Street, Hodeidah, Hodeidah, Yemen
Tel.: (967) 3 203544/46/47
Container Shipping ervices
N.A.I.C.S.: 483111

Saget Maroc/Worms S.M. Group (2)
Port Agadir Immeuble Le Dauphin, Agadir, Morocco
Tel.: (212) 522 48 47 30
Container Shipping ervices
N.A.I.C.S.: 483111

Servicios Corporativos Portuarios S.A. de C.V. (2)
Periferico Sur No 4829 Piso 5 Parques Del Pedregal, Tlalpan, Mexico, 14010, Mexico
Tel.: (52) 5554478166
Cost Management Services
N.A.I.C.S.: 488320

Societe Maritime Genmar SarL (2)
Zone Portuire Rades, 2040, Tunis, Tunisia
Tel.: (216) 71 469070
Container Shipping ervices
N.A.I.C.S.: 483111

Tourism & Shipping Services SarL (2)
386 Pasteur Street, Gemmayze, Beirut, Lebanon
Tel.: (961) 1 570771
Web Site: http://www.hapag-lloyd.com
Container Shipping ervices
N.A.I.C.S.: 483111

Trans Global S.R.L. (2)
Calle 9 de Obrajes Edif El Zodiaco, Pio 1 of 101, La Paz, Bolivia
Tel.: (591) 2 2786881
Container Shipping ervices
N.A.I.C.S.: 483111

Transmeres S.A. De C.V. (2)
79 Ave Sur Colonia Escalon, EDF Plaza Cristol, San Salvador, El Salvador
Tel.: (503) 22065400
Liner Shipping Services
N.A.I.C.S.: 483111

Transoceana Cia. Ltda. (2)
Malecon 1401 E Illingworth 3rd Fl, Guayaquil, Ecuador
Tel.: (593) 4 2598380
Container Shipping ervices
N.A.I.C.S.: 483111

United Arab Shipping Company (S.A.G.) (2)
UASC Building Old Airport Rd Beside Zain Bldg, PO Box 20722, Kuwait, 13068, Safat, Kuwait
Tel.: (965) 2494 3300
Sales Range: $750-799.9 Million
Emp.: 700
Shipping & Transportation Services
N.A.I.C.S.: 488390
Jorn Hinge (Pres & CEO)

Affiliate (Non-US):

Arabian Chemical Carriers Ltd. Co. (3)
569 NSCSA Bldg, PO Box 8931, Riyadh, 11492, Saudi Arabia
Tel.: (966) 14785454
Web Site: http://www.nscsa.com.sa
Sales Range: $1-9.9 Million
Emp.: 7
Petrochemical Transportation Services; Owned 50% by National Shipping Company of Saudi Arabia & 50% by United Arab Shipping Company

N.A.I.C.S.: 488330

Subsidiary (Non-US):

UAA Denmark (3)
18-20 Snorresgade, 2300, Copenhagen, Denmark
Tel.: (45) 32571600
Web Site: http://www.uasc.com
Marine Shipping Services
N.A.I.C.S.: 488510

UAA Finland (3)
Itamerenkatu 1, 00180, Helsinki, Finland
Tel.: (358) 9 4150 5401
Marine Shipping Services
N.A.I.C.S.: 488510

UAASC Norway (3)
Vollsveien 13H, 1326, Lysaker, Norway
Tel.: (47) 67115490
Marine Shipping Services
N.A.I.C.S.: 488510

UASC (Italy) SRL (3)
Piazza G Alessi 1/3, 16128, Genoa, Italy
Tel.: (39) 010 59631
Marine Shipping Services
N.A.I.C.S.: 488510
Lorenzo Bertolini (Mgr-Sls Support)

UASAC (UK) Ltd. (3)
Gredley House 1-11 Broadway, Stratford, London, E15 4BQ, United Kingdom
Tel.: (44) 20 8221 7888
Web Site: http://www.uasa.com
Marine Shipping Services
N.A.I.C.S.: 488510

UASAC CEE (Austria) GMBH (3)
Clemens Holzmeister Strasse 4, 1100, Vienna, Austria
Tel.: (43) 664 883 85 381
Web Site: http://www.uasaccoee.net
Emp.: 7
Marine Shipping Services
N.A.I.C.S.: 488510
Imrich Lelkes (Gen Mgr)

UASAC CEE (Hungary) Kft. (3)
Nepfurdo utca 22, 1138, Budapest, Hungary
Tel.: (36) 1 270 9335
Marine Shipping Services
N.A.I.C.S.: 488510

UASAC CEE (Slovakia) s.r.o. (3)
Pribinova 4, 81109, Bratislava, Slovakia
Tel.: (421) 2 3231 0921
Marine Shipping Services
N.A.I.C.S.: 488510

UASAC Denizcilik Nakliyat A.S. (3)
Ahi Evran Cad Polaris Plaza No 21 Kat12, Maslak, Sisli, 34398, Istanbul, Turkiye
Tel.: (90) 212 3677700
Marine Shipping Services
N.A.I.C.S.: 488510
John McKinstry (Gen Mgr)

UASAC France SAS (3)
Immeuble Cap Azur 67 rue Chevalier Paul, 13002, Marseille, France
Tel.: (33) 4 91 99 83 10
Marine Shipping Services
N.A.I.C.S.: 488510

UASAC Iberia S.L. (3)
Dr J J Domine 18-2, 46011, Valencia, Spain
Tel.: (34) 96 3993100
Marine Shipping Services
N.A.I.C.S.: 488510

UASAC Polska (3)
Pulaskiego 6, 81-368, Gdynia, Poland
Tel.: (48) 58 735 4555
Marine Shipping Services
N.A.I.C.S.: 488510
Rafal Moll (Mgr-Comml)

UASC Agencies Ghana (3)
Gateway house Fishing harbour road, PO Box 214, Tema, CO124, Ghana
Tel.: (233) 303 219 224
Marine Shipping Services
N.A.I.C.S.: 488510

UASC Agencies Nigeria (3)
34 Wharf Road, Apapa, Nigeria
Tel.: (234) 709 810 7434
Marine Shipping Services
N.A.I.C.S.: 488510

United Arab Agencies AB (3)
Marieholmsgatan 1, 41502, Gothenburg, Sweden
Tel.: (46) 31 7782250
Marine Shipping Services
N.A.I.C.S.: 488510

United Arab Agencies Australia Pty Ltd (3)
10th Floor 64 Millor Stroot, Sydney, 2060, NSW, Australia
Tel.: (61) 2 9410 8888
Emp.: 40
Marine Shipping Services
N.A.I.C.S.: 488510

Subsidiary (US):

United Arab Agencies, Inc. (3)
511 South Ave, Cranford, NJ 07016
Tel.: (908) 272-0050
Web Site: http://www.uasc.net
Water Transportation Services
N.A.I.C.S.: 488510
Anil Vitarana (Pres)

Subsidiary (Non-US):

United Arab Shipping Agencies (Pakistan) Pvt. Ltd. (3)
First Floor Bahria Complex-1 M T Khan Road, Karachi, Pakistan
Tel.: (92) 21 35644678
Marine Shipping Services
N.A.I.C.S.: 488510

United Arab Shipping Agencies Co. (Saudia) Ltd. (3)
Kanoo Tower King Saud Street, PO Box 2563, Dammam, 31461, Saudi Arabia
Tel.: (966) 38355666
Web Site: http://www.uasc.net
Water Transportation Services
N.A.I.C.S.: 488390

United Arab Shipping Agencies Co. (Saudia) Ltd. (3)
New Al Akariah Siteen St 3rd floor, Apt 4103, Riyadh, 11452, Saudi Arabia
Tel.: (966) 14786775
Web Site: http://www.uasac.net
Sales Range: $25-49.9 Million
Emp.: 14
Water Transportation Services
N.A.I.C.S.: 488390

United Arab Shipping Agencies Co. (Saudia) Ltd. (3)
Kanoo Tower Madinah Road Kilo 7, PO Box 6757, Jeddah, 21452, Saudi Arabia
Tel.: (966) 22632828
Web Site: http://www.uasc.net
Water Transportation Services
N.A.I.C.S.: 488390

United Arab Shipping Agencies Company (3)
Hay Al Saadoon Mahalh No 101 Street 87 UASC Building, Floor, PO Box 2086, Baghdad, Iraq
Tel.: (964) 1 7174336
Marine Shipping Services
N.A.I.C.S.: 488510

United Arab Shipping Agencies Company (Emirates) (3)
City Avenue Building 4th Floor Opp City Centre Residence, Dubai, United Arab Emirates
Tel.: (971) 42952525
Container Shipping ervices
N.A.I.C.S.: 483111

United Arab Shipping Agencies Company W.L.L. (3)
Building 876 Room 4216 Block 342, Algurayfa, Manama, Bahrain
Tel.: (973) 17 291291
Marine Shipping Services
N.A.I.C.S.: 488510

United Arab Shipping Agency (India) Pvt Ltd (3)
801/A Godrej Coliseum Somaiya Hospital Road, Sion, Mumbai, 400 022, India
Tel.: (91) 22 67978000
Marine Shipping Services
N.A.I.C.S.: 488510

United Arab Shipping Agency Co. (M)
Sdn Bhd   **(3)**
Suite 6 01 Level 6 IMS 2 88 Jalan Batai
Laut 4 Taman Intan, 41300, Klang, Malaysia
Tel.: (60) 3 3342 2998
Marine Shipping Services
N.A.I.C.S.: 488510

United Arab Shipping Agency Com-
pany (BENELUX) B.V.   **(3)**
Waalhaven Oostzijde 83, 3087 BM, Rotter-
dam, Netherlands
Tel.: (31) 10 8514400
Marine Shipping Services
N.A.I.C.S.: 488510

United Arab Shipping Agency Com-
pany (Deutschland) GmbH   **(3)**
Am Sandtorkai 41, 20457, Hamburg, Ger-
many
Tel.: (49) 40 300 608 100
Marine Shipping Services
N.A.I.C.S.: 488510

United Arab Shipping Agency Com-
pany (Hong Kong) Limited   **(3)**
Unit 1801 - 1807 18/F Tower 2 Ever Gain
Plaza 88 Container Port Road, Kwai Chung,
Hong Kong, China (Hong Kong)
Tel.: (852) 2579 3793
Marine Shipping Services
N.A.I.C.S.: 488510

United Arab Shipping Agency Com-
pany (Ningbo) Ltd.   **(3)**
Room 5-5 China Hong Center No 717
Zhongxing Road, Ningbo, 315040, Zheji-
ang, China
Tel.: (86) 574 2789 5900
Marine Shipping Services
N.A.I.C.S.: 488510

United Arab Shipping Agency Com-
pany (Qatar) WLL   **(3)**
Jaidah Tower - 5th floor, PO Box 6636,
Doha, Qatar
Tel.: (974) 44322158
Marine Shipping Services
N.A.I.C.S.: 488510

United Arab Shipping Agency Com-
pany (Shanghai) Ltd.   **(3)**
Unit A-C 9/F 686 Jiu Jiang Road, Shanghai,
200001, China
Tel.: (86) 21 23215300
Marine Shipping Services
N.A.I.C.S.: 488510

United Arab Shipping Agency Com-
pany (Shenzhen) Ltd.   **(3)**
Room3101 Pangling Square 2002 Jiabin
Road, Luohu District, Shenzhen, 518005,
Guangdong, China
Tel.: (86) 755 22949700
Marine Shipping Services
N.A.I.C.S.: 488510

United Arab Shipping Agency Com-
pany (Singapore)   **(3)**
10 Hoe Chiang Road #12-05 Keppel Tow-
ers, Singapore, 089315, Singapore **(100%)**
Tel.: (65) 627 55788
Sales Range: $25-49.9 Million
Emp.: 40
Shipping, Freight & E-commerce Services
N.A.I.C.S.: 483111

United Arab Shipping Agency Com-
pany (Taiwan) Ltd.   **(3)**
13th Floor World Trade Building 50 Hsin
Sheng South Road, Taipei, Taiwan
Tel.: (886) 2 23934261
Marine Shipping Services
N.A.I.C.S.: 488510

United Arab Shipping Agency Com-
pany (Thailand) Ltd.   **(3)**
24/F Times Square Building 246 Sukhumvit
Road, Klongtoey, Bangkok, 10110, Thailand
Tel.: (66) 2 2537550
Marine Shipping Services
N.A.I.C.S.: 488510

United Arab Shipping Agency Com-
pany (Vietnam) Limited   **(3)**
Unit 1401 14th Floor Gemadept Tower 2Bis-
4-6, Le Thanh Ton Street District 1, Ho Chi
Minh City, Vietnam
Tel.: (84) 8 3521 8833

Marine Shipping Services
N.A.I.C.S.: 488510

United Arab Shipping Company   **(3)**
Al Garhoud Rd, PO Box 55586, Deira,
Dubai, United Arab Emirates
Tel.: (971) 42952626
Emp.: 800
Water Transportation Services
N.A.I.C.S.: 488390
Jorn Hinge (CEO)

United Arab Shipping Company   **(3)**
Tourist Club Area Omar Bin Zayd Bldg 3rd
Foor 304, PO Box 2190, Sheikh Hamdan
St, Abu Dhabi, 2190, United Arab
Emirates   **(100%)**
Tel.: (971) 26332111
Sales Range: $25-49.9 Million
Emp.: 15
Water Transportation Services
N.A.I.C.S.: 488390
George Aboud (Mgr-Fin)

United Arab Shipping Company   **(3)**
Jaidah Tower 5th Fl, PO Box 6636, Doha,
Qatar   **(100%)**
Tel.: (974) 4322158
Sales Range: $25-49.9 Million
Emp.: 10
Water Transportation Services
N.A.I.C.S.: 488390

United Arab Shipping Company   **(3)**
Cardinal Ct 23 Thomas More St, London,
E1W 1XZ, United Kingdom   **(100%)**
Tel.: (44) 2073696700
Sales Range: $25-49.9 Million
Emp.: 35
Water Transportation Services
N.A.I.C.S.: 488390

United Arab Shipping Company   **(3)**
Hay Al Saadoon Mahalah 101 St 87, UASC
Bldg Fl 4, Baghdad, Iraq   **(100%)**
Tel.: (964) 17174336
Web Site: http://www.uasc.net
Sales Range: $25-49.9 Million
Emp.: 12
Water Transportation Services
N.A.I.C.S.: 488390

Subsidiary (Domestic):

United Arab Shipping Company   **(3)**
Airport Rd, PO Box 3636, Safat, 13037,
Kuwait, Kuwait
Tel.: (965) 4842160
Sales Range: $50-74.9 Million
Emp.: 200
Water Transportation Services
N.A.I.C.S.: 488390

Subsidiary (Non-US):

United Shipping Agencies Ltd   **(3)**
No 123 9th Floor Bauddhaloka Mawatha,
Colombo, 4, Sri Lanka
Tel.: (94) 11 2506081
Emp.: 16
Marine Shipping Services
N.A.I.C.S.: 488510
Romesh De Livera (Mng Dir)

United Shipping Co. Ltd.   **(3)**
Marine Center Bldg Suite 608 118, 2-Ka
Nam dae Moon-Ro, Chung-gu, Seoul, 100-
770, Korea (South)
Tel.: (82) 2 3788 6700
Marine Shipping Services
N.A.I.C.S.: 488510

Subsidiary (Non-US):

VR Shipping (Aruba) N.V.   **(2)**
Caya GF Betico Croes 220 Unit 12, Cayena
Mall, Oranjestad, Aruba
Tel.: (297) 5824124
Container Shipping ervices
N.A.I.C.S.: 483111

VR Shipping NV   **(2)**
Scarlet Building, Fokkerweg 26, Willemstad,
Curacao
Tel.: (599) 9 4614700
Container Shipping ervices
N.A.I.C.S.: 483111

Vassilopoulos Shipping Ltd.   **(2)**
20 Strovolos Ave 2011, Nicosia, 1687, Cyprus

Tel.: (357) 22710000
Container Shipping ervices
N.A.I.C.S.: 483111

WSS Alarbab Shipping Co.   **(2)**
University Area Buildign Number 1 5, Ka-
bashi Issa Street, Khartoum, Sudan
Tel.: (249) 311 834153
Container Shipping ervices
N.A.I.C.S.: 483111

Luis A. Ayala Colon Sucrs Inc.   **(1)**
3091 Santiago De Los Cabelleros Ave,
Ponce, PR 00716
Tel.: (787) 848-9000
Container Shipping ervices
N.A.I.C.S.: 483111

ALBERT DAVID LTD
D Block 3rd Floor Gillander House
Netaji Subhas Road, Kolkata, 700
001, West Bengal, India
Tel.: (91) 3322302330
Web Site:
   https://www.albertdavidindia.com
ALBERTDAVD—(NSE)
Rev.: $48,725,149
Assets: $57,793,254
Liabilities: $15,263,567
Net Worth: $42,529,687
Earnings: $4,937,874
Emp.: 1,300
Fiscal Year-end: 03/31/23
Pharmaceuticals Mfr
N.A.I.C.S.: 325412
A. K. Kothari (Chm)

Subsidiaries:

Albert David Ltd. - Kolkatta Unit   **(1)**
5/11 D Gupta Lane, Kolkata, 700 050, West
Bengal, India
Tel.: (91) 3325571131
Web Site: https://www.albertdavidindia.com
Sales Range: $125-149.9 Million
Medicinal Product Mfr
N.A.I.C.S.: 325412
T. Neogi (Assoc VP-Quality Assurance)

**ALBERT GREIFENBERG
GMBH & CO. KG**
Gottwaldstr 17, D-45525, Hattingen,
Germany
Tel.: (49) 232450080
Web Site: http://www.albert-
   greifenberg.de
Year Founded: 1952
Rev.: $65,811,184
Emp.: 161
Pipe Connection Parts Mfr
N.A.I.C.S.: 332919
Tristan Colombet (CEO)

**ALBERT LABS INTERNA-
TIONAL CORP.**
6996 Merritt Ave, Burnaby, V5J 4R6,
BC, Canada
Tel.: (778) 819-0740   BC
Web Site: https://albertlabs.com
Year Founded: 2009
ALBLF—(OTCIQ)
Assets: $120,971
Liabilities: $390,837
Net Worth: ($269,866)
Earnings: ($5,214,459)
Fiscal Year-end: 12/31/22
Seismic Devices Mfr
N.A.I.C.S.: 334513
Navchand Jagpal (CFO & Dir)

**ALBERT PASVAHL (GMBH &
CO.)**
Oehleckerring 23, 22419, Hamburg,
Germany
Tel.: (49) 40 53 28 52 0
Web Site: http://www.pasvahl.de
Year Founded: 1933
Rev.: $12,414,600
Emp.: 25

Connection Elements & Accessories
Mfr
N.A.I.C.S.: 332722
Horst Blanchebarbe (Mng Dir)

**ALBERT SCHUCK GMBH &
CO. KG**
Industriestr 20-22, Stockstadt, 63811,
Germany
Tel.: (49) 602720890
Web Site: http://www.albertschuck.de
Year Founded: 1934
Rev.: $28,967,400
Emp.: 195
General Freight Trucking Services
N.A.I.C.S.: 484110

**ALBERT TECHNOLOGIES LIM-
ITED**
37 Menachem Begin Rd, Tel Aviv,
Israel
Tel.: (972) 35377137
Web Site: http://www.adgorithms.com
Year Founded: 2009
Rev.: $1,733,000
Assets: $14,337,000
Liabilities: $3,749,000
Net Worth: $10,588,000
Earnings: ($13,020,000)
Emp.: 100
Fiscal Year-end: 12/31/17
Artificial Intelligence Marketing Ser-
vices
N.A.I.C.S.: 541613
Or Shani (Founder & CEO)

ALBERTA HEALTH SERVICES
14th Floor North Tower 10030-107
Street NW, Edmonton, T5J 3E4, AB,
Canada
Tel.: (780) 342-2000
Web Site:
   https://www.albertahealthservices.ca
Health Services
N.A.I.C.S.: 923120
Verna Yiu (Pres & CEO)

**ALBERTA INVESTMENT MAN-
AGEMENT CORPORATION**
1100-10830 Jasper Ave, Edmonton,
T5J 2B3, AB, Canada
Tel.: (780) 392-3600   AB
Web Site:
   http://www.aimco.alberta.ca
Year Founded: 2008
Rev.: $70,000,000,000
Emp.: 250
Investment Management Service
N.A.I.C.S.: 524292
Angela Fong (Chief Corp & HR Offi-
cer)

Subsidiaries:

Environmental Resources Manage-
ment Limited   **(1)**
2nd Floor Exchequer Court 33 St Mary Axe,
London, EC3A 8AA, United Kingdom
Tel.: (44) 20 3206 5200
Web Site: http://www.erm.com
Emp.: 300
Environmental Consulting Services
N.A.I.C.S.: 541620
Shawn Doherty (Dir-Digital Bus &
Transformation-US)

Subsidiary (US):

The ERM Group, Inc.   **(2)**
75 Vly Stream Pkwy Ste 200, Malvern, PA
19355
Tel.: (484) 913-0300
Web Site: http://www.erm.com
Sales Range: $900-999.9 Million
Emp.: 4,500
Environmental Engineering & Consulting
Services
N.A.I.C.S.: 541620
Rachel Agnew (Sr Engr-Honolulu)

London City Airport Limited   **(1)**

Alberta Investment Management Corporation—(Continued)

London City Airport City Aviation House, Royal Docks, London, E16 2PB, United Kingdom
Tel.: (44) 20 7646 0088
Web Site: http://www.londoncityairport.com
Airport Operator
N.A.I.C.S.: 488119
Alison FitzGerald (COO)

Porterbrook Leasing Company Limited (1)
Ivatt House 7 The Point Pinnacle Way, Pride Park, Derby, DE24 8ZS, United Kingdom
Tel.: (44) 1332285050
Web Site: https://www.porterbrook.co.uk
Rolling Stock Leasing Services
N.A.I.C.S.: 532411

Puget Energy, Inc. (1)
355 110th Ave NE, Bellevue, WA 98004
Tel.: (425) 454-6363
Web Site: https://www.pugetenergy.com
Rev.: $4,221,162,000
Assets: $17,187,514,000
Liabilities: $5,560,052,000
Net Worth: $11,627,462,000
Earnings: $414,345,000
Emp.: 3,250
Fiscal Year-end: 12/31/2022
Holding Company; Electric Power & Gas Distr
N.A.I.C.S.: 551112
Steven W. Hooper (Chm)

Subsidiary (Domestic):

Puget Sound Energy, Inc. (2)
355 110th Ave NE, Bellevue, WA 98004
Tel.: (425) 454-6363
Web Site: https://www.pse.com
Rev.: $4,216,173,000
Assets: $15,200,242,000
Liabilities: $5,542,394,000
Net Worth: $9,657,848,000
Earnings: $490,952,000
Emp.: 3,250
Fiscal Year-end: 12/31/2022
Electric Power & Natural Gas Distribution & Generation Services
N.A.I.C.S.: 221122
Steven W. Hooper (Chm)

Subsidiary (Domestic):

Puget Western, Inc. (3)
19515 North Creek Pkwy Ste 310, Bothell, WA 98011-8200
Tel.: (425) 487-6550
Web Site: http://www.pugetwestern.com
Sales Range: $25-49.9 Million
Emp.: 5
Real Estate Holding & Developing
N.A.I.C.S.: 237210
Joel Molander (Pres)

ALBERTA PENSION SERVICES CORPORATION
5103 Windermere Blvd SW, Edmonton, T6W 0S9, AB, Canada
Tel.: (780) 427-2782   AB
Web Site: http://www.apsc.ca
Year Founded: 1995
Emp.: 500
Pension Fund Administration Services
N.A.I.C.S.: 524292
Colin P. MacDonald (Chm)

Subsidiaries:

Local Authorities Pension Plan (1)
5103 Windermere Blvd SW, Edmonton, T6W 0S9, AB, Canada
Tel.: (780) 427-5447
Web Site: http://www.lapp.ca
Emp.: 6
Pension Funds
N.A.I.C.S.: 525110
Gosia Talanczuk (VP)

ALBERTA TEACHERS RETIREMENT FUND
600 Barnett House 11010 142 St

NW, Edmonton, T5N 2R1, AB, Canada
Tel.: (780) 451-4166
Web Site: http://www.atrf.com
Year Founded: 1939
Pension Plans Administrator
N.A.I.C.S.: 525110
Rod Matheson (CEO)

ALBERTA TREASURY BRANCHES
ATB Financial Suite 2100 10020 100 Street NW, Edmonton, T5J 0N3, AB, Canada
Tel.: (780) 408-7000
Web Site: http://www.atb.com
Year Founded: 1938
Rev.: $1,369,224,298
Assets: $41,337,517,360
Liabilities: $38,725,374,482
Net Worth: $2,612,142,878
Earnings: $218,710,954
Emp.: 4,542
Fiscal Year-end: 03/31/18
Financial Services
N.A.I.C.S.: 525990
Curtis Stange (Pres & CEO)

Subsidiaries:

ATB Capital Markets Inc. (1)
Suite 410 585 8 Avenue SW, Calgary, T2P 1G1, AB, Canada
Tel.: (403) 539-8600
Web Site: https://atbcapitalmarkets.com
Investment Banking Services
N.A.I.C.S.: 523150
Darren Eurich (CEO & Sr VP)

ATB Securities Inc. (1)
919 11 Ave SW Suite 800, Calgary, T2R 1P3, AB, Canada
Tel.: (403) 813-1046
Financial Management Services
N.A.I.C.S.: 523999

ALBERTON ACQUISITION CORPORATION
Room 1001 10/F Capital Center, 151 Gloucester Road, Wanchai, China (Hong Kong)
Tel.: (852) 2 117 1621   VG
Web Site: http://www.albertoncorp.com
Year Founded: 2018
ALAC—(NASDAQ)
Rev.: $113,013
Assets: $14,870,460
Liabilities: $9,831,761
Net Worth: $5,038,699
Earnings: ($615,039)
Emp.: 3,200
Fiscal Year-end: 12/31/21
Investment Services
N.A.I.C.S.: 523999
Keqingre Liu (CFO & Sec)

ALBINI & PITIGLIANI S.P.A.
Viale G Marconi 46, 59100, Prato, Italy
Tel.: (39) 05745730
Web Site: http://www.albinipitigliani.it
Sales Range: $75-99.9 Million
Emp.: 400
Freight Forwarding Services
N.A.I.C.S.: 488510
Sandro Pitigliani (Pres)

Subsidiaries:

AL-PI Polonia Sp. z o.o. (1)
ul Sosnowiec 23a, 95-010, Strykow, Poland
Tel.: (48) 42 714 58 01
Web Site: http://www.alpipolonia.pl
Logistics & Warehousing Services
N.A.I.C.S.: 493110

ALPI ADRIATICA srl (1)
Via G Ansaldo 5, Civitanova Marche, 62012, Macerata, Italy
Tel.: (39) 0733 898694

Freight Forwarding Services
N.A.I.C.S.: 488510

ALPI BELGIUM N.V.S.A. (1)
Havenlaan Av Du Port 108 110, 1000, Brussels, Belgium
Tel.: (32) 2 4262255
Freight Forwarding Services
N.A.I.C.S.: 488510

ALPI EXPRESS NORD srl (1)
Via P Mascagni 1, 20122, Milan, Italy
Tel.: (39) 02 95025650
Freight Forwarding Services
N.A.I.C.S.: 488510
Francesco Sini (Mng Dir)

ALPI KOREA Ltd (1)
696 Tungchon-dong, Kangso-ku, Seoul, Korea (South)
Tel.: (82) 2 36628093
Freight Forwarding Services
N.A.I.C.S.: 488510

ALPI LATVIA SIA (1)
Rankas iela 4a, Riga, 1005, Latvia
Tel.: (371) 67382105
Freight Forwarding Services
N.A.I.C.S.: 488510
Valdis Martuleavs (Dir-Facility)

ALPI LISBOA LDA (1)
Estrada Ligeiras Armazem A1, 2735-337, Lisbon, Portugal
Tel.: (351) 21 4267160
Freight Forwarding Services
N.A.I.C.S.: 488510

ALPI LUCCA srl (1)
Via E Fermi 8/a, Altopascio, 55011, Lucca, Italy
Tel.: (39) 0583 297277
Freight Forwarding Services
N.A.I.C.S.: 488510

ALPI Netherlands B.V. (1)
Symon Spiersweg 13, 1506 RZ, Zaandam, Netherlands
Tel.: (31) 75 750 2600
Web Site: http://www.alpi.nl
Emp.: 22
Logistics Consulting Servies
N.A.I.C.S.: 541614
Maarten den Heijer (Mgr-Sls)

ALPI OLIMPIKA LTD. (1)
85 Vas Mira Str Thessi Draseza, PO Box 39, Mandra, 19600, Athens, Greece
Tel.: (30) 210 5552905
Web Site: http://www.alpiolympika.gr
Logistics Consulting & Freight Forwarding Services
N.A.I.C.S.: 541614

ALPI SERVIZIO MODA s.r.l. (1)
Via di Gonfienti 2, 59100, Prato, Italy
Tel.: (39) 0574 516022
Freight Forwarding Services
N.A.I.C.S.: 488510

ALPI SUISSE S.A. (1)
Via d'Argine, 6930, Bedano, Switzerland
Tel.: (41) 91 960 21 11
Freight Forwarding Services
N.A.I.C.S.: 488510

ALPI USA PACIFIC INC. (1)
360 N Sepulveda Blvd Ste 1015, Los Angeles, CA 90245
Tel.: (310) 333-0829
Freight Forwarding Services
N.A.I.C.S.: 488510

ALPI USA, Inc. (1)
700 Nicholas Blvd Ste 411, Elk Grove Village, IL 60007
Tel.: (847) 364-5342
Web Site: http://www.alpiusa.com
Sales Range: $25-49.9 Million
Emp.: 9
Foreign Freight Forwarding
N.A.I.C.S.: 488510
Piero Albini (Pres)

Albini & Pitigliani Sverige AB (1)
Segloravagen 504 64, Boras, Sweden
Tel.: (46) 33 22 21 80
Web Site: http://www.albini.se
Freight Forwarding Services
N.A.I.C.S.: 488510
Torbjorn Hagderg (Mng Dir)

Alpi Air & Sea A/S (1)
Vejlevej 5, 7400, Herning, Denmark
Tel.: (45) 9928 7800
Freight Forwarding Services
N.A.I.C.S.: 488510

Alpi Eesti OU (1)
Loomae tee 8, Lehmja Rae vald, 75306, Harjumaa, Estonia
Tel.: (372) 610 7061
Web Site: http://www.alpieesti.ee
Freight Forwarding Services
N.A.I.C.S.: 488510
Tiit Roosve (Mgr-Quotations)

Alpi Express S.r.l. (1)
Via Gora del Pero 44/3, 59100, Prato, Italy
Tel.: (39) 0574 625104
Web Site: http://www.alpiexpress.it
Freight Forwarding Services
N.A.I.C.S.: 488510

Alpi Laghi S.R.L. (1)
Via Peneporto, San Fermo Della Battaglia, 22020, Como, Italy
Tel.: (39) 031 535311
Web Site: http://www.alpilaghi.it
Freight Forwarding Services
N.A.I.C.S.: 488510
Luca Guarisco (Gen Mgr)

Alpi Levante Srl (1)
Via Callano 112 - z i, 76121, Bari, Italy
Tel.: (39) 0883 535197
Web Site: http://www.alpilevante.it
Freight Forwarding Services
N.A.I.C.S.: 488510
Marco Bollino (Gen Mgr)

Alpi Livorno Srl (1)
Via Giovanni March N 14/a, 57121, Livorno, Italy
Tel.: (39) 0586 444 329
Web Site: http://www.alpilivorno.it
Emp.: 10
Logistics Consulting Servies
N.A.I.C.S.: 541614
Franco Franceschi (Pres)

Alpi Logistics Inc (1)
120 Tices Ln, East Brunswick, NJ 08816
Tel.: (732) 390-1234
Freight Forwarding Services
N.A.I.C.S.: 488510

Alpi Nord Est S.r.l. (1)
Via Sommacampagna 22/A, 37137, Verona, Italy
Tel.: (39) 045 8628511
Freight Forwarding Services
N.A.I.C.S.: 488510

Alpi Padana S.r.l. (1)
Via Provinciale per Reggio 63, Lemizzone di Correggio, 42015, Reggio Emilia, Italy
Tel.: (39) 0522 623111
Web Site: http://www.alpipadana.it
Freight Forwarding Services
N.A.I.C.S.: 488510
Artioli Luigi (Mgr-Logistic)

Alpi Portugal Lda. (1)
Av Jose Ramos Maia 130, Touguinho, 4480-575, Porto, Portugal
Tel.: (351) 252 650 200
Web Site: http://www.alpiportugal.pt
Freight Forwarding Services
N.A.I.C.S.: 488510
Manuel Almeida (Gen Mgr)

Alpi Suomi Oy (1)
Teknikonkatu 3 B, 15520, Lahti, Finland
Tel.: (358) 3 877 700
Web Site: http://www.alpisuomi.fi
Freight Forwarding & Warehousing Services
N.A.I.C.S.: 488510
Maila Lehtinen (Mng Dir)

Alpi Tirrenica s.r.l. (1)
Strada Consortile zona ASI, Teverola, 81030, Caserta, Italy
Tel.: (39) 081 5137084
Web Site: http://www.alpitirrenica.it
Freight Forwarding Services
N.A.I.C.S.: 488510

Alpi UK Ltd (1)
Suite 106 Colnbrook Cargo Centre Old Bath Road, Colnbrook, Slough, SL3 0NW, Berkshire, United Kingdom
Tel.: (44) 1753 210060

Web Site: http://www.alpiuk.com
Freight Forwarding Services
N.A.I.C.S.: 488510
Thomas Mercuri (Gen Mgr)

ALBION CAPITAL
1 King's Arms Yard, London, EC2R
7AF, United Kingdom
Tel.: (44) 2076011850
Web Site: http://www.albion.capital
Year Founded: 1996
Venture Capital Trust Management
Services
N.A.I.C.S.: 523999
Patrick Reeve (Mng Partner)

ALBION CROWN VCT PLC
1 Benjamin Street, London, EC1M
5QL, United Kingdom
Tel.: (44) 2074227830   UK
CRWN—(LSE)
Rev.: $1,842,770
Assets: $126,172,902
Liabilities: $3,518,706
Net Worth: $122,654,196
Earnings: $993,428
Fiscal Year-end: 06/30/24
Investment Advisory Services
N.A.I.C.S.: 523940

ALBION DEVELOPMENT VCT PLC
Albion Capital Group LLP 1 Benjamin
Street, London, EC1M 5QL, United
Kingdom
Tel.: (44) 2076011850
Web Site: https://www.albion.capital
AADV—(LSE)
Portfolio Management & Investment
Advice
N.A.I.C.S.: 523940
Ole Bettum (Mgr-Fund)

ALBION RESOURCES LIMITED
216 St George's Terrace, Perth,
6005, WA, Australia
Tel.: (61) 894810389   AU
Web Site:
  https://www.albionresources.com.au
Year Founded: 2015
ALB—(ASX)
Rev.: $51,929
Assets: $2,135,010
Liabilities: $32,217
Net Worth: $2,102,793
Earnings: ($521,000)
Fiscal Year-end: 06/30/23
Metal Exploration Services
N.A.I.C.S.: 213114
Colin Locke (Chm)

ALBION TECHNOLOGY & GENERAL VCT PLC
1 Benjamin Street, London, EC1M
5QL, United Kingdom   UK
Year Founded: 2000
AATG—(LSE)
Rev.: $1,462,264
Assets: $146,326,915
Liabilities: $1,059,022
Net Worth: $145,267,894
Earnings: $27,002,335
Fiscal Year-end: 12/31/21
Investment Management Service
N.A.I.C.S.: 523999

ALBION VENTURE CAPITAL TRUST PLC
1 Benjamin St, Farringdon, London,
EC1M 5QL, United Kingdom
Tel.: (44) 2076011850   UK
Web Site: https://www.albion.vc
AAVC—(LSE)
Rev.: $1,964,150
Assets: $79,106,286
Liabilities: $831,861

Net Worth: $78,274,426
Earnings: ($6,214,340)
Fiscal Year-end: 03/31/24
Miscellaneous Financial Investment
Activities
N.A.I.C.S.: 523999
Andrew Elder (Deputy Mng Partner)

ALBIS CO., LTD.
3-4 Mitoda Distribution Center, Imizu,
Toyama, 939-0402, Japan
Tel.: (81) 766567200
Web Site: https://www.albis.co.jp
Year Founded: 1968
7475—(TKS)
Rev.: $646,444,780
Assets: $328,146,840
Liabilities: $120,288,780
Net Worth: $207,858,060
Earnings: $10,212,450
Emp.: 3,422
Fiscal Year-end: 03/31/24
Supermarket Owner & Operator
N.A.I.C.S.: 445110
Yoshihara Kinuhiko (Mng Exec Officer, Gen Mgr-CS Dept & Deputy Gen Mgr-Sales)

ALBIS LEASING AG
Ifflandstrasse 4, 22087, Hamburg,
Germany
Tel.: (49) 40808100100
Web Site: https://www.albis-
  leasing.de
Year Founded: 1986
ALG—(DEU)
Rev.: $23,534,508
Assets: $257,565,987
Liabilities: $222,231,108
Net Worth: $35,334,879
Earnings: $4,989,492
Emp.: 104
Fiscal Year-end: 12/31/23
Financial Lending Services
N.A.I.C.S.: 522220

Subsidiaries:

ALBIS HiTec Leasing GmbH   (1)
Ifflandstrasse 4, 22087, Hamburg, Germany
Tel.: (49) 40808100400
Leasing Financial Services
N.A.I.C.S.: 525990

Subsidiary (Domestic):

ALBIS Service GmbH   (2)
Ifflandstrasse 4, 22087, Hamburg, Germany
Tel.: (49) 40808100600.
Leasing Financial Services
N.A.I.C.S.: 525990

ALBIS OPTOELECTRONICS AG
Moosstrasse 2a, Rueschlikon, 8803,
Zurich, Switzerland
Tel.: (41) 445525300
Web Site: http://www.albisopto.com
Year Founded: 2003
Sales Range: $10-24.9 Million
Emp.: 16
Optical Component Mfr
N.A.I.C.S.: 333310
Vincent Grundlehner (CEO)

ALBORZ CABLE COMPANY
East Brazil St - after the Court of Accounts - Laleh Alley - No 3, PO Box
15875-3644, Tehran, Iran
Tel.: (98) 2188666790
Web Site: https://alborzcable.ir
Year Founded: 1983
KALZ1—(THE)
Sales Range: Less than $1 Million
Emp.: 197
Cable Products Mfr
N.A.I.C.S.: 332618

ALBORZ DAROU PHARMA-

CEUTICAL COMPANY
No 66-Alborz Building-Khalid Eslamboli St, Tehran, 15117 36897, Iran
Tel.: (98) 21 88721517
Year Founded: 1976
DALZ—(THE)
Sales Range: $1-9.9 Million
Emp.: 370
Pharmaceuticals Product Mfr
N.A.I.C.S.: 325412
Abdulmejeed Choraghali (Chm)

ALBORZ INSURANCE COMPANY
No 1320 corner of Aban Alley above
Dastgardi Zafar St Shariati St, District
3, Tehran, Iran
Tel.: (98) 211574
Web Site: http://en.alborzins.com
Year Founded: 1959
BALB—(THE)
Sales Range: Less than $1 Million
Insurance Services
N.A.I.C.S.: 524298

ALBORZ INVESTMENT COMPANY
No 5 Aviz Alley Alvand Street Arzhantin Square, Tehran, Iran
Tel.: (98) 2188201940
Web Site: http://www.alborzinvest.ir
Year Founded: 1966
ALBZ—(THE)
Sales Range: Less than $1 Million
Emp.: 3,000
Holding Company
N.A.I.C.S.: 551112

Subsidiaries:

Alborz Bulk Raw Materials
Company   (1)
2nd Floor No2 Nik Khah Dead End beginning of Nejatollahi Ave, Enghelab Ave,
1599914713, Tehran, Iran
Tel.: (98) 2188940140
Pharmaceuticals Product Mfr
N.A.I.C.S.: 325412

Ati Pharmed Pharmaceutical
Company   (1)
No 17 Dashte Behesh St Saadat Abad,
Tehran, Iran
Tel.: (98) 2122069696
Web Site: http://www.atipharmed.com
Pharmaceuticals Product Mfr
N.A.I.C.S.: 325412

Etela Alborz Investment
Company   (1)
2nd Floor No 30 Alley 3 Khaled Eslambi
Ave, 1411853695, Tehran, Iran
Tel.: (98) 2188729469
Pharmaceuticals Product Mfr
N.A.I.C.S.: 325412

Iran Darou Company   (1)
End of Kermani Ave, Moallem Blvd,
1371658111, Tehran, Iran
Tel.: (98) 2166628848
Pharmaceuticals Product Mfr
N.A.I.C.S.: 325412

Pakhsh Alborz Company   (1)
343 between Jomhoori and Nofeloshato
Hafez Ave, 1131614351, Tehran, Iran
Tel.: (98) 2166705799
Pharmaceuticals Product Mfr
N.A.I.C.S.: 325412

Sobhan Darou Company   (1)
No 295 West Dr Fatemi St, Post Box
14185565, 1411853695, Tehran, Iran
Tel.: (98) 2166568181
Web Site: http://www.sobhandarou.com
Pharmaceuticals Product Mfr
N.A.I.C.S.: 325412
Marmam Rahmatipasand (Mgr-R&D)

Sobhan Oncology Pharmaceutical
Company   (1)
No5 Aviz Alley Alvand STArgentina Sq, Tehran, Iran
Tel.: (98) 2183879000

Web Site: http://www.sobhanoncology.com
Pharmaceuticals Product Mfr
N.A.I.C.S.: 325412

Tolid Darou Pharmaceutical
Company   (1)
Shahid Yadegar Ave beginning of Saveh
Road, 1371616314, Tehran, Iran
Tel.: (98) 2161170
Pharmaceuticals Product Mfr
N.A.I.C.S.: 325412

ALBOURNE PARTNERS LIMITED
16 Palace Street, London, SW1E
5JD, United Kingdom
Tel.: (44) 207 346 7000
Web Site: http://www.albourne.com
Year Founded: 1994
Sales Range: $50-74.9 Million
Emp.: 200
Investment Advisor & Consulting
N.A.I.C.S.: 523940
Clare Cotton (CFO)

Subsidiaries:

Albourne America LLC   (1)
655 Montgomery St Ste 1910, San Francisco, CA 94111
Tel.: (415) 283-1300
Management Consulting Services
N.A.I.C.S.: 541618
David Hutchings (Head-Private Equity)

Albourne Partners (Asia) Limited   (1)
Unit C 22/F On Hing Building 1-9 On Hing
Terrace, Central, China (Hong Kong)
Tel.: (852) 28682254
Management Consulting Services
N.A.I.C.S.: 541618

Albourne Partners (Singapore) Pte.
Ltd.   (1)
Soho2 The Central 12 Eu Tong Sen Street
07-166/167, Singapore, 59819, Singapore
Tel.: (65) 65369541
Management Consulting Services
N.A.I.C.S.: 541618

Albourne Partners Deutschland
AG   (1)
Richard-Strauss-Strasse 71, 81679, Munich,
Germany
Tel.: (49) 8989067870
Management Consulting Services
N.A.I.C.S.: 541618

Albourne Partners Japan Limited   (1)
Akasaka Tokyu Building 7F 2-14-3 Nagatacho, Chiyoda-ku, Tokyo, 100-0014, Japan
Tel.: (81) 355211777
Management Consulting Services
N.A.I.C.S.: 541618

ALBUS A.D.
Privrednikova 10, Novi Sad, Serbia
Tel.: (381) 21442830
Web Site: https://www.albus.rs
Year Founded: 1871
ALBS—(BEL)
Rev.: $6,789,971
Assets: $9,875,558
Liabilities: $4,815,846
Net Worth: $5,059,712
Earnings: $440,448
Emp.: 85
Fiscal Year-end: 12/31/23
Soap & Detergent Mfr
N.A.I.C.S.: 325611
Jelena Macesic (Gen Mgr)

ALCADON GROUP AB
Segelbatsvagen 2, 112 64, Stockholm, Sweden
Tel.: (46) 86573600
Web Site:
  https://www.alcadongroup.se
Year Founded: 1988
ALCA—(OMX)
Rev.: $147,617,803
Assets: $148,073,000
Liabilities: $85,370,573

Alcadon Group AB—(Continued)

Net Worth: $62,702,427
Earnings: $3,546,040
Emp.: 164
Fiscal Year-end: 12/31/23
Telecommunication Product Mfr & Distr
N.A.I.C.S.: 334210
Jonas Martensson *(Vice Chm)*

Subsidiaries:

Alcadon ApS   (1)
Mollevej 9 E1, 2990, Nivaa, Denmark
Tel.: (45) 45707077
Web Site: https://www.alcadon.dk
Emp.: 21
Optic Cable Whslr
N.A.I.C.S.: 423460

Alcadon GmbH   (1)
Wahlerstrasse 14, 40472, Dusseldorf, Germany
Tel.: (49) 21187587503
Web Site: https://www.alcadon.de
Emp.: 13
Optic Cable Whslr
N.A.I.C.S.: 423460

Networks Centre (Scotland) Limited   (1)
Units 3C/3D 42 Payne Street Port Dundas, Glasgow, G4 OLE, United Kingdom
Tel.: (44) 1415791234
Optic Cable Whslr
N.A.I.C.S.: 423460

Networks Centre B.V.   (1)
De Boomgaard 9-7, 1243 HV, 's-Graveland, Netherlands
Tel.: (31) 357994230
Power Generation Services
N.A.I.C.S.: 562213

Networks Centre Ltd.   (1)
Networks Centre Bentley House Wiston Business Park London Road, Pulborough, Ashington, RH20 3DJ, West Sussex, United Kingdom
Tel.: (44) 1403754233
Optic Cable Whslr
N.A.I.C.S.: 423460

ALCALIBER S.A
Paseo de Recoletos 16 Planta 2, 28001, Madrid, Spain
Tel.: (34) 915754667
Web Site: https://www.alcaliber.com
Year Founded: 1973
Pharmaceuticals Product Mfr
N.A.I.C.S.: 325412
Juan Abello Gallo *(Chm)*

ALCANTARA GROUP
G/F Alsons Building 2286 Chino Roces Extension, 1231, Makati, Philippines
Tel.: (63) 2 9823000
Web Site:
   http://www.alcantaragroup.com
Holding Company; Power Generation, Energy & Mining, Agribusiness, Forestry, Transportation, Construction & Real Estate
N.A.I.C.S.: 551112
Nicasio I. Alcantara *(Pres)*

Subsidiaries:

Alsons Consolidated Resources, Inc.   (1)
Alsons Building 2286 Chino Roces Ext, Makati, 1231, Philippines
Tel.: (63) 289823000
Web Site: https://www.acr.com.ph
Rev.: $224,298,039
Assets: $865,755,738
Liabilities: $511,274,152
Net Worth: $354,481,586
Earnings: $41,257,845
Emp.: 417
Fiscal Year-end: 12/31/2023
Investment Holding Company & Oil Exploration
N.A.I.C.S.: 523940

Roberto V. San Jose *(Sec)*

Subsidiary (Non-US):

Indophil Resources NL   (2)
Level 3 411 Collins Street, Melbourne, 3000, VIC, Australia
Tel.: (61) 386205800
Web Site: http://www.indophil.com
Mining Exploration Services
N.A.I.C.S.: 213114
Richard Laufmaan *(CEO & Mng Dir)*

Subsidiary (Domestic):

Southern Philippines Power Corporation   (2)
3rd Floor Solid House Building, 2285 Chino Roces Ext, Makati, 1231, Philippines
Tel.: (63) 28120294
Power Generation Services
N.A.I.C.S.: 221111

Alsons Development and Investment Corporation   (1)
A Bonifacio, Davao, Philippines
Tel.: (63) 822217697
Real Estate Investment Services
N.A.I.C.S.: 531210

ALCATEL-LUCENT TELETAS TELEKOMUNIKASYON AS
Barbaros Mah Mor Sumbul Sk Nidakule Block No 7/3F Internal Door No 1, Atasehir, 34776, Istanbul, Turkiye
Tel.: (90) 5051910316
ALCTL—(IST)
Rev.: $99,618,546
Assets: $106,950,962
Liabilities: $46,610,788
Net Worth: $60,340,174
Earnings: $3,940,412
Fiscal Year-end: 12/31/21
Transmission Equipment Mfr
N.A.I.C.S.: 333613
Eric Jean- Edouard Decourchelle *(Chm)*

ALCEA TECHNOLOGIES INC.
2197 Riverside Drive Suite 204, Ottawa, K1H 7X3, ON, Canada
Tel.: (613) 563-9595
Web Site: http://www.alceatech.com
Year Founded: 1997
Sales Range: $1-9.9 Million
Emp.: 12
IT Staffing Services; Software Publisher
N.A.I.C.S.: 561320
Susan Norton *(Co-Founder)*

Subsidiaries:

FIT Tracking Solutions   (1)
2197 Riverside Drive Suite 204, Ottawa, K1H 7X3, ON, Canada
Tel.: (613) 563-9595
Web Site:
   http://www.fittrackingsolutions.com
Software Publisher
N.A.I.C.S.: 513210

ALCEON GROUP PTY LTD.
Level 16 20 Hunter Street, Sydney, 2000, NSW, Australia
Tel.: (61) 2 8023 4000
Web Site: http://www.alceon.com.au
Private Investment Firm
N.A.I.C.S.: 523999
Morris Symonds *(Co-Founder & Partner)*

Subsidiaries:

EziBuy Ltd.   (1)
Private Bag 11000, Palmerston North, 4442, New Zealand
Tel.: (64) 508500500
Web Site: http://www.ezibuy.co.nz
Online & Clothing Store
N.A.I.C.S.: 458110
Richard Facioni *(Chm)*

Mosaic Brands Ltd   (1)
Ground Floor 61 Dunning Avenue, Rosebery, 2018, NSW, Australia   (77.5%)
Tel.: (61) 285777777
Web Site:
   https://www.mosaicbrandslimited.com.au
Rev.: $330,652,934
Assets: $211,689,284
Liabilities: $255,807,630
Net Worth: ($44,110,040)
Earnings: $177,582
Emp.: 212
Fiscal Year-end: 07/02/2023
Women's Apparel & Accessories Sales
N.A.I.C.S.: 424350
Scott Graham Evans *(CEO & Mng Dir)*

ALCHEMIA S.A.
ul Jagiellonska 76, 03-301, Warsaw, Poland
Tel.: (48) 22 658 64 52
Web Site: http://www.alchemiasa.pl
Year Founded: 1811
Assets: $201,340
Liabilities: $66,472
Net Worth: $134,868
Earnings: ($352)
Fiscal Year-end: 12/31/16
Rolled Steel Products Mfr
N.A.I.C.S.: 331210
Karina Wsciubiak-Hanko *(Chm-Supervisory Bd)*

ALCHEMIST CORPORATION LIMITED
R-4 Unit 103 First Floor Khirki Extention Main Road, Malviya Nagar, New Delhi, 110 017, India
Tel.: (91) 01129544474
Web Site: http://www.alchemist-corp.com
Year Founded: 1993
531409—(BOM)
Rev.: $205
Assets: $2,403,738
Liabilities: $293,885
Net Worth: $2,109,853
Earnings: ($24,720)
Fiscal Year-end: 03/31/23
Metal & Fabric Product Whslr
N.A.I.C.S.: 335929
Sohan Lal *(Mng Dir)*

Subsidiaries:

Kautilya Infotech Limited   (1)
B-103 Thakur Bhawan Behind Appolo Tyres Office Bhawar Kua Square AB Rd, Indore, 452001, Madhya Pradesh, India
Tel.: (91) 9669379370
Web Site: http://www.kautilyainfotech.com
Digital Marketing Services
N.A.I.C.S.: 541613
Aakash Savkare *(Founder)*

ALCHEMIST LTD
23 Alchemist House Nehru Place, New Delhi, 110019, India
Tel.: (91) 01140600800
Web Site: http://www.alchemist.co.in
Rev.: $3,966,129
Assets: $111,013,755
Liabilities: $132,452,643
Net Worth: ($21,438,888)
Earnings: ($7,118,864)
Emp.: 189
Fiscal Year-end: 03/31/19
Holding Company
N.A.I.C.S.: 551112
Bikram Bhattacharya *(Exec Dir)*

Subsidiaries:

Alchemist Aviation Pvt. Ltd.   (1)
Sonari Airport, Jamshedpur, 831011, Jharkhand, India
Tel.: (91) 6572301516
Web Site: http://www.alchemistaviation.com
Sales Range: $10-24.9 Million
Emp.: 40
Aviation Training Schools
N.A.I.C.S.: 611512

S. K. Upadhyay *(Mgr)*

ALCHEMIST REALTY LTD.
Building No 23 Nehru Place, New Delhi, 110019, India
Tel.: (91) 11 40600800
Web Site:
   http://www.alchemistrealty.com
Rev.: $339,270
Assets: $46,099,372
Liabilities: $46,537,774
Net Worth: ($438,402)
Earnings: ($2,483,917)
Emp.: 19
Fiscal Year-end: 03/31/19
Real Estate Support Services
N.A.I.C.S.: 531390
Vinay Kumar Mittal *(Mng Dir)*

ALCHEMY PARTNERS LLP
21 Palmer Street, London, SW1H 0AD, United Kingdom
Tel.: (44) 2072409596
Web Site:
   http://www.alchemypartners.com
Year Founded: 2002
Sales Range: $25-49.9 Million
Emp.: 30
Investment Management Service
N.A.I.C.S.: 523940
Robert Barnes *(Co-Founder)*

Subsidiaries:

Parkdean Holidays Limited   (1)
2nd Floor One Gosforth Park Way Gosforth Business Park, Newcastle upon Tyne, NE12 8ET, United Kingdom
Tel.: (44) 3443353507
Web Site: http://www.parkdeanresorts.co.uk
Sales Range: $200-249.9 Million
Camping Destinations
N.A.I.C.S.: 721214
Steve Richards *(CEO)*

Parkdean Resorts UK Limited   (1)
2nd Floor One Gosforth Park Way, Gosforth Business Park, Newcastle upon Tyne, NE12 8ET, United Kingdom
Tel.: (44) 191 256 0795
Web Site: http://www.parkdeanresorts.co.uk
Caravan Parks Owner & Operator
N.A.I.C.S.: 721214
John Waterworth *(CEO)*

ALCHEMY RESOURCES LIMITED
Suite 8 8 Clive Street, West Perth, 6005, WA, Australia
Tel.: (61) 894814400
Web Site:
   https://www.alchemyresources.com.au
ALY—(ASX)
Rev.: $104,323
Assets: $9,008,345
Liabilities: $160,047
Net Worth: $8,848,298
Earnings: ($988,853)
Fiscal Year-end: 06/30/24
Gold & Copper Exploration Services
N.A.I.C.S.: 212220
Bernard Crawford *(Sec)*

ALCHERA INC.
Gb2 Building C 7F 25 Pangyo-Ro 256Beon-Gil, Bundang-Gu, Seongnam, Gyeonggi-Do, Korea (South)
Tel.: (82) 316978961
Web Site: https://www.alchera.ai
Year Founded: 2016
347860—(KRS)
Rev.: $18,925,216
Assets: $45,288,683
Liabilities: $18,825,520
Net Worth: $26,463,163
Earnings: ($10,687,167)
Emp.: 211
Fiscal Year-end: 12/31/22
Software Development Services
N.A.I.C.S.: 541511

Hoe Sun Kim *(CFO)*

ALCHIMIE SA
43-45 avenue Victor Hugo Le Parc
des Portes de Paris Batiment 264,
93534, Aubervilliers, France
Tel.: (33) 892976423
Web Site: https://www.alchimie.com
Year Founded: 1998
ALCHI—(EUR)
Video Broadcasting Services
N.A.I.C.S.: 516120
Pauline Grimaldi D'Esdra *(CEO)*

ALCHIP TECHNOLOGIES, LIMITED
9F No 12 Wenhu Street, Neihu District, Taipei, 114, Taiwan
Tel.: (886) 227992318
Web Site: http://www.alchip.com
ALCHP—(LUX)
Rev.: $429,140,606
Assets: $617,144,264
Liabilities: $210,614,107
Net Worth: $406,530,157
Earnings: $57,320,858
Emp.: 564
Fiscal Year-end: 12/31/22
Semiconductor Devices Mfr
N.A.I.C.S.: 334413
Kinying Kwan *(Chm)*

Subsidiaries:

Alchip Investment Inc.　　　　　(1)
Portcullis TrustNet Chambers 4th Floor Ellen Skelton Building 3076, Sir Francis
Drake Highway Road Town, Tortola, Virgin
Islands (British)
Tel.: (284) 227992318
Semiconductor Design Services
N.A.I.C.S.: 541512

Alchip Technologies (Shanghai)
Limited　　　　　　　　　　　(1)
Building 11 No 1221 East Pingzhuang Rd
Lingang Special area, Shanghai Pilot Free
Trade Zone, Shanghai, China
Tel.: (86) 2152350999
Software Development Services
N.A.I.C.S.: 541511

Alchip Technologies, (Chongqing)
Inc.　　　　　　　　　　　　　(1)
Floor 7 No 142 Yunhan Avenue, Beibei District, Chongqing, 400714, China
Tel.: (86) 2386970666
Software Development Services
N.A.I.C.S.: 541511

Alchip Technologies, (Guangzhou)
Inc.　　　　　　　　　　　　　(1)
Room 01 12F Building A Grandtek No 18
Science Avenue, Huangpu District,
Guangzhou, China
Tel.: (86) 2089819302
Software Development Services
N.A.I.C.S.: 541511

Alchip Technologies, Inc.　　　　(1)
1900 McCarthy Blvd Ste 106, Milpitas, CA
95035
Tel.: (408) 943-8296
Semiconductor Design Services
N.A.I.C.S.: 541512

Alchip Technologies, KK　　　　(1)
10F Shin-Yokohama Square Building 2-3-12
Shin-Yokohama, Kouhoku, Yokohama, 222-
0033, Kanagawa, Japan
Tel.: (81) 454701090
Silicon Semiconductor Product Mfr
N.A.I.C.S.: 334413

Alchip Technologies, Limited　　(1)
Bank of America Tower 12 Harcourt Road,
Central, China (Hong Kong)
Tel.: (852) 25222922
Computer Design Services
N.A.I.C.S.: 541512

Subsidiary (Non-US):

Alchip Technologies, (Hefei) Inc.　(2)
6F Building C4 No 800 Wangjiang West
Road, Hefei, China

Tel.: (86) 55165655001
Semiconductor Design Services
N.A.I.C.S.: 541512

Alchip Technologies, (JiNan) Inc.　(2)
1F Building B Qilu Software Park No 1000
ShunHua Road, High-tech Development
Zone, Jinan, China
Tel.: (86) 53189017990
Semiconductor Design Services
N.A.I.C.S.: 541512

Alchip Technologies, (Wuxi) Inc.　(2)
4F Building A5 No 777 Jianzhuxi Road,
Binhu District, Wuxi, 214063, Jiangsu,
China
Tel.: (86) 51085120332
Semiconductor Design Services
N.A.I.C.S.: 541512

Chiptopia (Shanghai) Technology Co.,
Ltd.　　　　　　　　　　　　　(1)
Room 06 11F No 212 Zhaojiangbang Road,
HuangPu District, Shanghai, 200020, China
Tel.: (86) 13761232125
Software Development Services
N.A.I.C.S.: 541511

ALCIDION GROUP LIMITED
Level 10 9 Yarra Street, South Yarra,
3141, VIC, Australia
Tel.: (61) 380606177
Web Site: https://www.alcidion.com
ALC—(ASX)
Rev.: $24,744,257
Assets: $76,428,953
Liabilities: $18,376,068
Net Worth: $58,052,884
Earnings: ($5,620,326)
Emp.: 145
Fiscal Year-end: 06/30/24
Health Information Services
N.A.I.C.S.: 561499
Raymond Howard Blight *(Co-Founder)*

Subsidiaries:

Alcidion NZ Limited　　　　　　(1)
Level 22 The SAP Tower 151 Queen Street,
Auckland, 1010, New Zealand
Tel.: (64) 93733703
Computer Software Services
N.A.I.C.S.: 541511

Alcidion UK Limited　　　　　　(1)
Suite 3 185 Fleet Road, Fleet, GU51 3BL,
Hampshire, United Kingdom
Tel.: (44) 1749685238
Computer Software Services
N.A.I.C.S.: 541511

ExtraMed Limited　　　　　　　(1)
Suite 3 185 Fleet Road, Fleet, GU51 3BL,
Hampshire, United Kingdom
Tel.: (44) 1749685238
Web Site: https://extramed.co.uk
Software Digital Development Services
N.A.I.C.S.: 541512

Silverlink PCS Software Limited　(1)
The Catalyst 3 Science Square Newcastle
Helix, Newcastle upon Tyne, NE4 5TG,
United Kingdom
Tel.: (44) 3304037310
Web Site: https://silverlinksoftware.com
Patient Administration Systems Software
Services
N.A.I.C.S.: 541512

ALCO HELLAS S.A.
Thesi Kirillo, 193 00, Aspropyrgos,
Greece
Tel.: (30) 2115595223
Web Site: http://www.alco.gr
Sales Range: $300-349.9 Million
Emp.: 1,378
Aluminum Mfr
N.A.I.C.S.: 331313

Subsidiaries:

ALCO ROM TRADE SRL　　　　(1)
Visili Suite No 3-5, Bucharest, Romania
Tel.: (40) 214246042

Sales Range: $25-49.9 Million
Emp.: 9
Aluminum Frames Distr
N.A.I.C.S.: 331318

GARTNER EXTRUSION GMBH　(1)
Peterswoerther Str 1a, 89432, Gundelfingen, Baden-Wurttemberg, Germany
Tel.: (49) 907380000
Web Site: http://www.gartner-extrusion.de
Sales Range: $100-124.9 Million
Emp.: 300
Aluminum Extrusion Product Mfr
N.A.I.C.S.: 331313

GUTMANN AG　　　　　　　　(1)
Nuernberger Strasse 57, 91781, Weissenburg, Germany
Tel.: (49) 91419920
Web Site: http://www.gutmann.de
Sales Range: $200-249.9 Million
Emp.: 630
Aluminium Products Mfr
N.A.I.C.S.: 331313
Charalambos Gotsis *(Chm)*

Subsidiary (Domestic):

NORDALU GMBH　　　　　　　(2)
Oderstrasse 78-82, 24539, Neumunster,
Schleswig-Holstein, Germany
Tel.: (49) 43218890
Sales Range: $25-49.9 Million
Emp.: 180
Aluminium Products Mfr
N.A.I.C.S.: 331313
Olaf Tjerkstra *(CEO)*

GUTMANN ALUMINIUM DRAHT
GMBH　　　　　　　　　　　(1)
Nuernberger Str 57-81, 91781, Weissenburg, Bavaria, Germany
Tel.: (49) 91419920
Web Site: http://www.gutmann-wire.de
Sales Range: $25-49.9 Million
Emp.: 100
Aluminium Product Distr
N.A.I.C.S.: 332812

ALCO HOLDINGS LIMITED
11/F Metropole Square 2 On Yiu
Street, Sha Tin, China (Hong Kong)
Tel.: (852) 2 562 6121
Web Site: http://www.alco.com.hk
0328—(HKG)
Rev.: $76,264,842
Assets: $107,540,557
Liabilities: $142,742,166
Net Worth: ($35,201,609)
Earnings: ($76,690,734)
Emp.: 625
Fiscal Year-end: 03/31/22
Electronic Products Mfr
N.A.I.C.S.: 334419
Wilson Wai Sing Leung *(Chm &
CEO)*

Subsidiaries:

Advance Packaging Limited　　　(1)
11F Zung Fu Indus Bldg 1067 Kings Rd,
Quarry Bay, China (Hong Kong)
Tel.: (852) 25626121
Web Site: http://www.alco.com.hk
Sales Range: $50-74.9 Million
Emp.: 100
Packaging Plastic Products Mfr & Sales
N.A.I.C.S.: 326150
Bond Yip *(Mgr-Mktg)*

Alco Digital Devices Limited　　(1)
11F Zung Fu Indus Bldg 1067 Kings Rd,
Quarry Bay, China (Hong Kong)
Tel.: (852) 28800698
Web Site: http://www.alco.com.hk
Sales Range: $50-74.9 Million
Emp.: 100
Software Development & Electronic Products Distr
N.A.I.C.S.: 423620
Bond Yit *(Gen Mgr)*

Alco Electronics (Shenzhen)
Limited　　　　　　　　　　　(1)
23F Huangcheng Plz No 7 Futian S Rd,
Futian Dist, Shenzhen, 518045, Guangdong, China

Tel.: (86) 75583694800
Consumer Electronics Distr
N.A.I.C.S.: 423620

Alco Electronics Limited　　　　(1)
11 Fl Zung Fu Indus Bldg 1067 Kings Rd,
Quarry Bay, China (Hong Kong)
Tel.: (852) 28800698
Web Site: http://www.alco.com.hk
Sales Range: $50-74.9 Million
Emp.: 150
Consumer Electronics Mfr
N.A.I.C.S.: 334310
Bond Yip *(Mgr-Sls & Mktg)*

Alco International Limited　　　(1)
11 Fl Zung Fu Indus Bldg 1067 Kings Rd,
Quarry Bay, China (Hong Kong)
Tel.: (852) 28800698
Web Site: http://www.alco.com.hk
Sales Range: $25-49.9 Million
Emp.: 100
Consumer Electronics Whslr
N.A.I.C.S.: 423620
Bond Yip *(Gen Mgr-Mktg)*

Alco Properties Limited　　　　(1)
11 F Zung Fu Indus Bldg 1067 Kings Rd,
Quarry Bay, China (Hong Kong)
Tel.: (852) 25626121
Web Site: http://www.alco.com.hk
Sales Range: $75-99.9 Million
Emp.: 150
Property Management Services
N.A.I.C.S.: 531311
Wilson Leung *(CEO)*

Asia Dragon International
Limited　　　　　　　　　　　(1)
11F Zung Fu Indus Bldg 1067 Kings Rd,
Quarry Bay, China (Hong Kong)
Tel.: (852) 25626121
Sales Range: $50-74.9 Million
Emp.: 100
Consumer Electronics Whslr
N.A.I.C.S.: 423620
Willson Leung *(Mng Dir)*

Commusonic Industries Limited　(1)
11F Zung Fu Indus Bldg 1067 Kings Rd,
Quarry Bay, China (Hong Kong)
Tel.: (852) 25626121
Web Site: http://www.alco.com.hk
Sales Range: $50-74.9 Million
Emp.: 150
Consumer Electronics Mfr & Sales
N.A.I.C.S.: 334310
Catherine Cheung *(Mgr-HR)*

Multimedia Devices Limited　　(1)
5 11F Zung Fu Indus Bldg 1067 Kings Rd,
Quarry Bay, China (Hong Kong)
Tel.: (852) 28800698
Sales Range: $50-74.9 Million
Emp.: 100
Consumer Electronics Whslr
N.A.I.C.S.: 423620
Catherine Cheung *(Mgr-Admin)*

Nexstgo Company Limited　　　(1)
Room 3201-5 32/F Enterprise Square Two
3 Sheung Yuet Road, Kowloon Bay, Kowloon, China (Hong Kong)
Tel.: (852) 37250611
Web Site: https://www.nexstgo.com
Information Technology Services
N.A.I.C.S.: 541519
Wilson Leung *(Co-Founder & Chm)*

Taiwan Nexstgo Limited　　　　(1)
10F-1 No 188 Baoqiao Rd, Xindian Dist,
New Taipei City, 23145, Taiwan
Tel.: (886) 229172168
Information Technology Services
N.A.I.C.S.: 541519

**ALCO PLASTIC PRODUCTS
LIMITED**
10 67 Kings Road 11/F Zung Fu Indl
Bldg, Quarry Bay, China (Hong Kong)
Tel.: (852) 24228777　　　　　HK
Sales Range: $10-24.9 Million
Plastic Products Mfr & Sales
N.A.I.C.S.: 326199
Francis Kwok Wai Lau *(Owner)*

ALCO VENTURES INC.

Alco Ventures Inc.—(Continued)

9747 199A St, Langley, V1M 2X7, BC, Canada
Tel.: (604) 888-7655
Web Site:
http://www.alcoventures.com
Year Founded: 1970
Rev.: $15,959,663
Emp.: 125
Aluminium Railing Systems Mfr
N.A.I.C.S.: 336510
Peter Siemens (*Mgr-Mirage Retractable Screen Sys*)

ALCOHOL COUNTERMEASURE SYSTEMS CORP.

60 International Boulevard, Toronto, M9W 6J2, ON, Canada
Tel.: (416) 619-3500
Web Site: http://www.acs-corp.com
Year Founded: 1976
Sales Range: $10-24.9 Million
Emp.: 400
Alcohol Interlocks & Breath Alcohol Testers Mfr
N.A.I.C.S.: 334519

ALCOM SA TIMISOARA

Str Proclamatia de la Timisoara Nr 7, Timis, Timisoara, Romania
Tel.: (40) 734557730
Web Site:
https://www.alcomtimisoara.ro
ALCQ—(BUC)
Rev.: $709,631
Assets: $6,300,745
Liabilities: $115,702
Net Worth: $6,185,043
Earnings: $171,366
Emp.: 4
Fiscal Year-end: 12/31/23
Commercial Space Rental Services
N.A.I.C.S.: 531120

ALCOMET AD

II Industrial Zone, 9700, Shumen, 9700, Bulgaria
Tel.: (359) 54858601
Web Site: https://www.alcomet.eu
Year Founded: 1981
6AM—(BUL)
Rev.: $198,793,478
Assets: $220,585,872
Liabilities: $94,852,458
Net Worth: $125,733,415
Earnings: $4,900,140
Emp.: 1,088
Fiscal Year-end: 12/31/19
Modern Production Equipment Services
N.A.I.C.S.: 811310
Fikret Ince (*Chm-Supervisory Bd*)

ALCON INC.

Rue Louis-d'Affry 6, 1701, Fribourg, Switzerland
Tel.: (41) 8172930450   CH
Web Site: https://www.alcon.com
Year Founded: 1945
ALC—(NYSE)
Rev.: $9,455,000,000
Assets: $29,614,000,000
Liabilities: $8,990,000,000
Net Worth: $20,624,000,000
Earnings: $974,000,000
Emp.: 25,315
Fiscal Year-end: 12/31/23
Optical Related Goods Mfr
N.A.I.C.S.: 339115
Timothy C. Stonesifer (*CFO & Sr VP*)

Subsidiaries:

Aerie Pharmaceuticals, Inc.   (1)
4301 Emprevor Blvd Ste 400, Durham, NC 27703
Tel.: (919) 237-5300

Web Site: http://www.aeriepharma.com
Rev.: $194,134,000
Assets: $431,391,000
Liabilities: $448,724,000
Net Worth: ($17,333,000)
Earnings: ($74,810,000)
Emp.: 376
Fiscal Year-end: 12/31/2021
Pharmaceuticals Mfr
N.A.I.C.S.: 325412
Casey C. Kopczynski (*Chief Scientific Officer*)

Alcon Ophthalmika GmbH   (1)
Am Tabor 44/5 OG/Top 3 05 C, 1020, Vienna, Austria
Tel.: (43) 159669700
Web Site: https://www.alcon.at
Ophthalmology Surgical Product Mfr
N.A.I.C.S.: 339112

ALCONIX CORPORATION

12th floor Sanno Park Tower 11-1 Nagatacho 2-chome, Chiyoda-ku, Tokyo, 100 6112, Japan
Tel.: (81) 335967400
Web Site: https://www.alconix.com
Year Founded: 1981
3036—(TKS)
Rev.: $1,156,095,610
Assets: $1,208,902,900
Liabilities: $770,329,400
Net Worth: $438,573,500
Earnings: $10,562,780
Emp.: 3,227
Fiscal Year-end: 03/31/24
Aluminum, Copper, Nickel, Titanium, Tungsten, Molybdenum, Rare Metal & Rare Earth Related Products Importer, Exporter & Sales
N.A.I.C.S.: 423510
Masato Takei (*Pres & CEO*)

Subsidiaries:

Advanced Material Japan Corporation   (1)
12F Sanno Park Tower 2-11-1 Nagata-cho, Chiyoda-ku, Tokyo, 100-6112, Japan
Tel.: (81) 335072301
Web Site: http://www.amjc.co.jp
Sales Range: $25-49.9 Million
Emp.: 30
Rare Metals Mfr
N.A.I.C.S.: 332999
Satoshi Fukuda (*CEO*)

Advanced Material Trading Pte Ltd.   (1)
91 Tanglin Road 04-01 Tanglin Place, Singapore, 247918, Singapore
Tel.: (65) 68361030
Web Site: http://www.amt.sg
Non Ferrous Metal Product Mfr
N.A.I.C.S.: 331491

Alconix (Malaysia) Sdn. Bhd.   (1)
Level23 Menara Imc No 8 Jalan Sultan Ismail, 50250, Kuala Lumpur, Malaysia
Tel.: (60) 320313750
Web Site: http://www.alconix.com
Sales Range: $25-49.9 Million
Emp.: 6
Metals Mfr
N.A.I.C.S.: 332999
Tatsuya Himuti (*Mng Dir*)

Alconix (Shanghai) Corp.   (1)
Room No1507 Ruijin Building 205 Maoming South Road, Huangpu District, Shanghai, 200131, China
Tel.: (86) 2154662666
Web Site: http://www.alconix.com
Sales Range: $25-49.9 Million
Emp.: 15
Metals Mfr
N.A.I.C.S.: 332999

Alconix (Taiwan) Corporation   (1)
7F-6 No 191 Fusing N Rd, Songshan District, Taipei, 105, Taiwan
Tel.: (886) 227122926
Web Site: http://www.alconix.com
Sales Range: $25-49.9 Million
Emp.: 3
Metals Mfr
N.A.I.C.S.: 332999

Alconix (Thailand) Ltd.   (1)
Thaniya Plaza Building 11th floor 52 Silom Road, Bangkok, 10500, Thailand
Tel.: (66) 22312375
Web Site: http://www.alconix.co.th
Sales Range: $25-49.9 Million
Emp.: 11
Metals Mfr
N.A.I.C.S.: 332999
Tanaka Yutaka (*Pres*)

Alconix Europe Gmbh   (1)
Immermann Strasse 9, 40210, Dusseldorf, Germany
Tel.: (49) 21150080810
Web Site: http://www.alconix.com
Sales Range: $25-49.9 Million
Emp.: 4
Metals Mfr
N.A.I.C.S.: 332999

Alconix Hong Kong Corp.,Ltd.   (1)
Web Site: http://www.alconix.com
Emp.: 10
Metals Mfr
N.A.I.C.S.: 332999

Alconix Korea Corporation   (1)
19F 1901 50 Eulji-ro, Jung-Gu, Seoul, 04539, Korea (South)
Tel.: (82) 27796524
Non Ferrous Metal Product Mfr & Distr
N.A.I.C.S.: 331491

Alconix Logistics (Thailand) Ltd.   (1)
Thaniya Plaza Building 11th Floor 52 Silom Road, Bangkok, Thailand
Tel.: (66) 22312375
Metal Product Mfr & Distr
N.A.I.C.S.: 331523

Alconix Mitaka Corporation   (1)
14th Floor Yodoyabashi Square 2-6-18 Kitahama, Chuo-ku, Osaka, 541-0041, Japan
Tel.: (81) 661212962
Web Site: https://www.alconix-mitaka.com
Emp.: 60
Non Ferrous Metal Product Mfr
N.A.I.C.S.: 331491

Alconix Sanshin Corporation   (1)
Sanno Park Tower 12th floor 2-11-1 Nagatacho, Chiyoda-ku, Tokyo, 100-6112, Japan
Tel.: (81) 335967470
Web Site: http://www.alconix.com
Metals Mfr
N.A.I.C.S.: 332999

Alconix USA, Inc.   (1)
25 NorthWest Point Blvd Ste 810, Elk Grove Village, IL 60007
Tel.: (847) 717-7407
Non Ferrous Metal Product Mfr & Distr
N.A.I.C.S.: 331491

Alconix Vietnam Co., Ltd.   (1)
15/F Oriental Tower 324 Tay Son Street, Nga Tu So Ward Dong Da District, Hanoi, Vietnam
Tel.: (84) 2439440290
Non Ferrous Metal Product Mfr & Distr
N.A.I.C.S.: 331491

Aluminum & Copper Recycling Center Corporation   (1)
2-7-3 Deyashikinishi-machi, Hirakata, 573-0003, Osaka, Japan
Tel.: (81) 728475931
Aluminum & Copper Scrap Product Mfr
N.A.I.C.S.: 331492

Fuji Alconix Mexico S.A. De C.V.   (1)
Calle Europa 309 A Parque Logistik, Villa de Reyes, 79526, San Luis Potosi, Mexico
Tel.: (52) 4445006203
Web Site: https://fujialconix.com.mx
Metal Product Mfr & Distr
N.A.I.C.S.: 331523

Fuji Carbon Manufacturing Co.   (1)
1-11 Nishiki-machi, Anjo, 446-0035, Aichi, Japan
Tel.: (81) 566730620
Web Site: http://www.fuji-carbon.co.jp
Emp.: 200
Carbon Products Mfr
N.A.I.C.S.: 335991

Fuji Press Co. Ltd.   (1)
118 Ida Kitazaki-cho, Obu, 474-0001, Aichi, Japan

Tel.: (81) 562475126
Web Site: https://www.fuji-press.co.jp
Emp.: 280
Automobile Parts Mfr
N.A.I.C.S.: 336390

Fujine Sangyo Co., Ltd.   (1)
745-3 Matsunaga, Numazu, 410-0874, Japan
Tel.: (81) 559212131
Web Site: https://www.fujine.com
Emp.: 130
Air Conditioning Product Mfr & Distr
N.A.I.C.S.: 333415

Guangdong Chuangfu Metal Manufacturing Co., Ltd.   (1)
No 168 Lunjiao Yang Road, Shunde District, Foshan, 528308, Guangdong, China
Tel.: (86) 75727722333
Web Site: https://www.gd-chuangfu.com
Automobile Parts Mfr
N.A.I.C.S.: 336390
Ouyang Tianzhuo (*Chm*)

Guangzhou Alconix (Shanghai) Corp.   (1)
Room02 Floor26 Goldlion Digital Network Centre No 138 Tiyu Dong Road, Tianhe District, Guangzhou, China
Tel.: (86) 2022836005
Non Ferrous Metal Product Mfr & Distr
N.A.I.C.S.: 331491

Hayashi Metal Corp.   (1)
4-8-15 Kawaguchi, Nishi-ku, Osaka, 550-0021, Japan
Tel.: (81) 665832575
Web Site: http://www.alconix.com
Sales Range: $25-49.9 Million
Emp.: 27
Metal Whslr
N.A.I.C.S.: 423510
Mitsuo Sugie (*Mng Dir*)

Heiwa Kinzoku Co., Ltd.   (1)
14F Yodoyabashi Square 2-6-18 Kitahama, Chuo-ku, Osaka, 541-0041, Japan
Tel.: (81) 661212301
Web Site: http://www.heiwa-web.co.jp
Emp.: 35
Non Ferrous Metal Product Mfr
N.A.I.C.S.: 331491

K'MAC Co., Ltd.   (1)
2-6-8 Tagawa, Yodogawa-ku, Osaka, 532-0027, Japan
Tel.: (81) 663001047
Web Site: https://www.kmacnet.co.jp
Emp.: 317
Automotive Components Mfr
N.A.I.C.S.: 336390
Hiroaki Nakajima (*Chm*)

Marktec Corporation   (1)
17-35 Omori Nishi 4-chome, Ota-ku, Tokyo, 143-0015, Japan
Tel.: (81) 337624453
Web Site: https://www.marktec.co.jp
Non Destructive Inspection Device Mfr.
N.A.I.C.S.: 334519
Keigo Nishimoto (*Pres & CEO*)

Ohba Seiken Co. Ltd.   (1)
170 Aza-Fukazawa Terasawa-cho, Toyohashi, 441-3124, Aichi, Japan
Tel.: (81) 532213121
Web Site: http://www.ohba-seiken.co.jp
Emp.: 253
Automobile Parts Mfr
N.A.I.C.S.: 336390
Takumi Fujii (*CEO*)

Ohkawa Corp.   (1)
2-11-20 Sakura-Shinmachi, Setagaya, Tokyo, 154-0015, Japan   (100%)
Tel.: (81) 334293223
Web Site: http://www.odsinc.co.jp
Sales Range: $1-9.9 Million
Emp.: 122
Metals Mfr
N.A.I.C.S.: 332999
Hiroyuki Nakayama (*Pres & CEO*)

Shenzhen Alconix (Shanghai) Corp.   (1)
Room 801 Phase 1 Times Square Excellence Fuhua Road, Futian District, Shenzhen, 518017, Guangdong, China
Tel.: (86) 75525904105

Non Ferrous Metal Product Mfr & Distr
N.A.I.C.S.: 331491

Tokai Yogyo Co., Ltd. (1)
1-29 Imae Hanamoto-cho, Toyota, 470-
0334, Aichi, Japan
Tel.: (81) 565432311
Web Site: https://www.tokai-yogyo.co.jp
Emp.: 40
Welding Equipment Mfr
N.A.I.C.S.: 333992
Naoki Otake (Pres)

ALCOR MICRO CORPORATION LTD.
9th Floor No 66 Sanchong Road,
Nangang District, Taipei, 115, Taiwan
Tel.: (886) 226535000
Web Site:
https://www.alcormicro.com
Year Founded: 1999
8054—(TPE)
Rev.: $65,084,369
Assets: $211,854,664
Liabilities: $40,842,734
Net Worth: $171,011,930
Earnings: ($8,200,987)
Emp.: 400
Fiscal Year-end: 12/31/23
Semiconductor Equipment Mfr
N.A.I.C.S.: 333242
Chang Chi-Tung (Chm & CEO)

Subsidiaries:

Alcor Micro (Shenzhen) Corporation
Ltd. (1)
Room 1502 Building B No 6 Gaoxinan
Road, TCL Industrial Research Institute
Building Nanshan District, Shenzhen,
518057, China
Tel.: (86) 7558 302 4167
Semiconductor Product Mfr
N.A.I.C.S.: 334413

Syncomm Corporation Ltd. (1)
10th Floor No 101 Section 2 Gongdao 5th
Road, Hsinchu, Taiwan
Tel.: (886) 3 516 9188
Semiconductor Product Mfr
N.A.I.C.S.: 334413

ALCORLINK CORP.
5F No 209 Building B Sec 1 Nangang
Rd, Nangang Dist, Taipei, 115, Taiwan
Tel.: (886) 226559980
Web Site: http://www.alcorlink.com
Year Founded: 2015
6594—(TPE)
Rev.: $16,584,548
Assets: $19,443,771
Liabilities: $5,378,077
Net Worth: $14,065,694
Earnings: $1,200,274
Fiscal Year-end: 12/31/20
Electronic Product Distr
N.A.I.C.S.: 423690
Dennis Chang (Chm)

ALCUIN CAPITAL PARTNERS LLP
65 Sloane Street, London, SW1X
9SH, United Kingdom
Tel.: (44) 203 178 4089
Web Site:
http://www.alcuincapital.com
Sales Range: $25-49.9 Million
Emp.: 8
Investment Management Service
N.A.I.C.S.: 523940
Mark Storey (Co-Founder)

Subsidiaries:

Krispy Kreme UK Ltd. (1)
Unit 4 Albany Park Frimley Road, Camberley, GU16 7PQ, United Kingdom
Tel.: (44) 1276 60 11 70
Web Site: http://www.krispykreme.co.uk
Owns & Operates Bakeries
N.A.I.C.S.: 311811

Richard Cheshire (Mng Dir)

ALCUMUS HOLDINGS LTD
1st Fl Unit 9 Bell Business Park
Smeaton Close, Aylesbury, HP19
8JR, Bucks, United Kingdom
Tel.: (44) 330127130
Web Site:
http://www.alcumusgroup.com
Year Founded: 1979
Holding Company; Risk Management
Services
N.A.I.C.S.: 551112
Alyn Franklin (CEO)

ALD AUTOMOTIVE
1-3 Rue Eugene et Armand Peugeot,
92500, Rueil-Malmaison, France
Tel.: (33) 18002095253
Web Site: https://www.ayvens.com
ALD—(EUR)
Rev.: $5,184,437,729
Assets: $33,834,448,521
Liabilities: $26,394,992,445
Net Worth: $7,439,456,076
Earnings: $1,303,582,992
Emp.: 7,529
Fiscal Year-end: 12/31/22
Fleet Management Services
N.A.I.C.S.: 532112
Tim Albertsen (CEO)

Subsidiaries:

ALD Automotive AG (1)
Thurgauerstrasse 54, 8050, Zurich, Switzerland
Tel.: (41) 582723234
Web Site: http://www.aldautomotive.ch
Vehicle Leasing Services
N.A.I.C.S.: 532112
Martin Kossler (Gen Mgr)

ALD Automotive Algerie SPA (1)
30 rue Djaffer Slimane, Cheraga, Algiers,
Algeria
Tel.: (213) 21994700
Web Site: http://www.aldautomotive.dz
Leasing Services
N.A.I.C.S.: 532490
Mounir Bensaci (Dir-Procurement & Facilities)

ALD Automotive D.O.O. (1)
Bulevar Zorana Dindica 48 B, Novi Beograd, 11070, Serbia
Tel.: (381) 116556255
Web Site: http://www.aldautomotive.rs
Vehicle Leasing Services
N.A.I.C.S.: 532112
Nikola Dzodic (Ops Mgr)

ALD Automotive D.O.O. ZA. (1)
Veliko Polje Betinska 1, 10010, Zagreb,
Croatia
Tel.: (385) 16659755
Web Site: http://www.aldautomotive.hr
Vehicle Leasing Services
N.A.I.C.S.: 532112
Ivanka Krajnc (Mgr-Acct)

ALD Automotive EOOD (1)
Business Park Sofia Building 11 B 4th
Floor, 1766, Sofia, Bulgaria
Tel.: (359) 28026120
Web Site: http://www.aldautomotive.bg
Emp.: 42
Leasing Services
N.A.I.C.S.: 532490
Olena Tymofiyiva (CEO)

ALD Automotive Eesti AS (1)
Sopruse pst 145, Tallinn, 13417, Estonia
Tel.: (372) 6308960
Web Site: http://www.aldautomotive.ee
Leasing Services
N.A.I.C.S.: 532490
Risto Ojassaar (Sls Mgr)

ALD Automotive Fuhrparkmanagement und Leasing GmbH (1)
Rivergate Handelskai 92 Gate 1 3 OG,
1200, Vienna, Austria
Tel.: (43) 152652250
Web Site: http://www.aldautomotive.at
Vehicle Leasing Services

N.A.I.C.S.: 532112
Martin Kossler (Gen Mgr)

ALD Automotive Limitada. (1)
Av Del Valle 524 Office 603 Ciudad Empresarial, Huechuraba, Santiago, Chile
Tel.: (56) 6002452600
Web Site: http://www.aldautomotive.cl
Leasing Services
N.A.I.C.S.: 532490
Julien Bourdonnec (Gen Mgr)

ALD Automotive Magyarorszag Autopark - kezelo es Finanszirozo KFT (1)
Vaci ut 76, 1133, Budapest, Hungary
Tel.: (36) 18025800
Web Site: http://www.aldautomotive.hu
Leasing & Management Services
N.A.I.C.S.: 532112

ALD Automotive OOO (1)
Warsaw highway 25A building 6, 117105,
Moscow, Russia
Tel.: (7) 4955102858
Web Site: http://www.aldautomotive.ru
Emp.: 130
Vehicle Leasing Services
N.A.I.C.S.: 532112
Roman Voskanov (Mgr-Acct)

ALD Automotive Operational Leasing DOO (1)
Letaliska cesta 29a, 1000, Ljubljana, Slovenia
Tel.: (386) 13007820
Web Site: http://www.aldautomotive.si
Leasing & Management Services
N.A.I.C.S.: 532112

ALD Automotive Peru S.A.C. (1)
Av 28 de Julio 1005 interior 701 Edificio
Paso 28 de Julio, Miraflores, Lima, Peru
Tel.: (51) 16176800
Web Site: http://www.aldautomotive.pe
Leasing Services
N.A.I.C.S.: 532490
Gerardo Manuel Vasquez Chirinos (Comml Dir)

ALD Automotive Polska Sp z o.o. (1)
Zajecza 2B, 00-351, Warsaw, Poland
Tel.: (48) 226999999
Web Site: http://www.aldautomotive.pl
Leasing & Management Services
N.A.I.C.S.: 532112
Tomasz Mucha (Mgr-IT)

ALD Automotive Private Limited (1)
9th Floor B Wing Ashar IT Park Road No
16Z, Wagle Industrial Estate Thane West,
Mumbai, 400604, India
Tel.: (91) 2261933200
Web Site: http://www.aldautomotive.in
Leasing & Management Services
N.A.I.C.S.: 532112
Bhavin Marolia (Asst Mgr)

ALD Automotive S.A. (1)
Rua Apeninos 222 10 andar, Aclimacao,
Sao Paulo, 01533-000, Brazil
Tel.: (55) 1131474710
Web Site: http://www.aldautomotive.com.br
Vehicle Leasing Services
N.A.I.C.S.: 532112
Fernando Martins (CIO-Latam)

ALD Automotive S.A. (1)
1-3 Pindou and Poseidonos Ave, 183 44,
Moschato, Greece
Tel.: (30) 2104840000
Web Site: http://www.aldautomotive.gr
Leasing & Management Services
N.A.I.C.S.: 532112

ALD Automotive S.A. de C.V. (1)
Av Miguel de Cervantes Saavedra 193 Int
803 Col Granada, 11520, Mexico, Mexico
Tel.: (52) 25813270
Web Site: http://www.aldautomotive.com.mx
Leasing & Management Services
N.A.I.C.S.: 532112

ALD Automotive S.A.S (1)
Calle 99 7A-51 Office 601, Bogota, Colombia
Tel.: (57) 14431040
Web Site: http://www.aldautomotive.co
Leasing Services

N.A.I.C.S.: 532490
Mauricio Serna Lozano (Comml Dir)

ALD Automotive S.A.U (1)
Carretera de Pozuelo num 32, Majadahonda, 28220, Madrid, Spain
Tel.: (34) 913336717
Web Site: http://www.aldautomotive.es
Leasing & Management Services
N.A.I.C.S.: 532112

ALD Automotive SIA (1)
Karla Ulmana gatve 119, Riga, LV-2167,
Latvia
Tel.: (371) 67783377
Web Site: http://www.aldautomotive.lv
Leasing Services
N.A.I.C.S.: 532490
Maris Rozensteins (Sls Mgr)

ALD Automotive SRL (1)
Floreasca Business Park 169A Calea Floreasca nr 169A Buidling A, 2nd Floor, Bucharest, 011171, Romania
Tel.: (40) 213014959
Web Site: http://www.aldautomotive.ro
Leasing Services
N.A.I.C.S.: 532490
Cristina Ilie (Mgr-Acct)

ALD Automotive Slovakia S.R.O (1)
Panonska cesta 47 Petrzalka, 851 04, Bratislava, Slovakia
Tel.: (421) 268298800
Web Site: http://www.aldautomotive.sk
Leasing Services
N.A.I.C.S.: 532490
Jakub Kralovic (Mgr-Fleet)

ALD Automotive Turizm Ticaret Anonim Sirketi (1)
Ruzgarlibahce Mah Kavak Sok Kavacik Ticaret Merkezi Blok No 18, Kavacik-Beykoz,
Istanbul, Türkiye
Tel.: (90) 4448830
Web Site: http://www.aldautomotive.com.tr
Leasing & Management Services
N.A.I.C.S.: 532112

ALD Automotive Ukraine Limited Liability Company (1)
8 Illinska Street Entrance 11 3rd Floor,
Kiev, 04070, Ukraine
Tel.: (380) 442476969
Web Site: http://www.aldautomotive.ua
Leasing Services
N.A.I.C.S.: 532490
Pierre-Vladimir Joliot (Gen Mgr)

Merrion Fleet Management Limited (1)
Stillorgan Business Park 15/16 Holly Avenue, Stillorgan, Dublin, A94 XA72, Ireland
Tel.: (353) 12061118
Web Site: http://www.merrionfleet.ie
Leasing Services
N.A.I.C.S.: 532490
David Hurley (Owner)

NF Fleet A/S (1)
Helgeshoj Alle 34, DK-2630, Taastrup, Denmark
Tel.: (45) 33558000
Web Site: https://ffleet.dk
Leasing Services
N.A.I.C.S.: 532490
Ole Elm Christiansen (Gen Mgr)

NF Fleet AB (1)
Eldarvagen 6, 187 75, Taby, Sweden
Tel.: (46) 850112380
Web Site: https://nffleet.se
Leasing Services
N.A.I.C.S.: 532490
Katarina Bjurkell (Mgr-Acct)

NF Fleet AS (1)
Holtet 45, 1368, Stabekk, Norway
Tel.: (47) 67108740
Web Site: https://nffleet.no
Leasing Services
N.A.I.C.S.: 532490

NF Fleet OY (1)
Ohtolankatu 4, 01511, Vantaa, Finland
Tel.: (358) 10404505
Web Site: https://nffleet.fi
Leasing Services
N.A.I.C.S.: 532490
Sanna Polvikoski Andersen (Mgr-Customer Svc)

ALD Automotive—(Continued)

UAB ALD Automotive (1)
Ukmerges str 308, LT-12110, Vilnius, Lithuania
Tel.: (370) 52477760
Web Site: http://www.aldautomotive.lt
Leasing Services
N.A.I.C.S.: 532490
Raimonda Ausre (Sls Mgr)

ALDACHANIE
6 Rue Des Freres Lumiere, 60200, Compiegne, Oise, France
Tel.: (33) 344203621
Rev.: $21,100,000
Emp.: 49
Miscellaneous General Merchandise Stores,
N.A.I.C.S.: 444180
Patrick De Bosschere (Pres)

ALDAMAN FOR INVESTMENTS PLC
Matalqah Center, PO Box 942430, Shmeisani, Amman, 11194, Jordan
Tel.: (962) 5622365
Year Founded: 1993
DMAN—(AMM)
Rev.: $891,435
Assets: $16,630,986
Liabilities: $2,438,986
Net Worth: $14,192,000
Earnings: ($746,970)
Emp.: 17
Fiscal Year-end: 12/31/20
Investment Management Service
N.A.I.C.S.: 523999

ALDAR PROPERTIES PJSC
Al Raha Beach, PO Box 51133, Abu Dhabi, United Arab Emirates
Tel.: (971) 26725327
Web Site: http://www.aldar.com
ALDAR—(ABU)
Rev.: $3,856,149,552
Assets: $19,839,900,880
Liabilities: $9,442,317,349
Net Worth: $10,397,583,531
Earnings: $1,202,626,692
Emp.: 3,000
Fiscal Year-end: 12/31/23
Real Estate Investment & Development Services
N.A.I.C.S.: 531190
Mohamed Khalifa Al Mubarak (Chm)

Subsidiaries:

Addar Real Estate Services LLC (1)
PO Box 51133, Abu Dhabi, United Arab Emirates
Tel.: (971) 2 633 6886
Asset & Real Estate Development & Management Services
N.A.I.C.S.: 531390

Al Jimi Mall LLC (1)
Hamdan Bin Mohammad Street Al Jimi, PO Box 16427, Abu Dhabi, Al Ain, Abu Dhabi, United Arab Emirates
Tel.: (971) 60 056 5464
Web Site: https://www.aljimimall.com
Sales Range: $25-49.9 Million
Emp.: 16
General Stores
N.A.I.C.S.: 455219

Aldar Education - Sole Proprietorship LLC (1)
PO Box 128484, Abu Dhabi, United Arab Emirates
Tel.: (971) 28132111
Web Site: https://www.aldareducation.com
Educational Support Services
N.A.I.C.S.: 923110

Asteco Property Management LLC (1)
First Floor L1 - 031 Yas Mall Yas Island, PO Box 73300, Abu Dhabi, United Arab Emirates
Tel.: (971) 600547773

Web Site: https://www.asteco.com
Real Estate Services
N.A.I.C.S.: 531390

ALDEBARAN RESOURCES, INC.
200 Burrard Street, Vancouver, V6C 3L6, BC, Canada
Tel.: (604) 605-0000
Web Site: https://www.aldebaranresource.com
ADBRF—(OTCQX)
Rev.: $471,878
Assets: $125,257,899
Liabilities: $3,156,044
Net Worth: $122,101,854
Earnings: ($432,789)
Fiscal Year-end: 06/30/24
Metal Exploration Services
N.A.I.C.S.: 213114
Adam Greening (Sr VP)

Subsidiaries:

Aldebaran Argentina S.A. (1)
Lateral Este Av Circunvalacion 198 sur 5411, Santa Lucia, A4408FEM, San Juan, Argentina
Tel.: (54) 2644254793
Copper & Gold Mining Services
N.A.I.C.S.: 212290

ALDER FUND I AB
Sturegatan 34, 114 36, Stockholm, Sweden
Tel.: (46) 8 440 65 45   SE
Web Site: http://www.alder.se
Year Founded: 2008
Investment Management Service
N.A.I.C.S.: 523999
Dag Broman (Co-Founder & Partner)

Subsidiaries:

Alder II AB (1)
Sturegatan 34, 114 36, Stockholm, Sweden
Tel.: (46) 8 440 65 45
Web Site: http://www.alder.se
Investment Services
N.A.I.C.S.: 523999
Henrik Lindholm (Mgr-Investment)

Holding (Domestic):

Scanacon AB (2)
Bergkallavagen 36C, 192 79, Sollentuna, Sweden
Tel.: (46) 8 564 823 00
Web Site: http://www.scanacon.com
Chemical Products Distr
N.A.I.C.S.: 424690
Stig Lundstrom (CEO)

Subsidiary (Non-US):

Scanacon (Shanghai) Environmental Technologies., Ltd. (3)
Room 1901 No 107 Zunyi Road, Changning District, Shanghai, China
Tel.: (86) 2162375309
Chemical Products Distr
N.A.I.C.S.: 424690

Scanacon Asia Ltd. (3)
Suite D 6/F Ho Lee Commercial Building 38-44 D'Aguilar Street, Central, China (Hong Kong)
Tel.: (852) 66812912698
Chemical Products Distr
N.A.I.C.S.: 424690

ALDERAN RESOURCES LIMITED
Suite 23 513 Hay Street, Subiaco, 6008, WA, Australia
Tel.: (61) 861436711   AU
Web Site: https://www.alderanresources.com
Year Founded: 2013
AL8—(ASX)
Rev.: $6,633
Assets: $3,367,281
Liabilities: $157,115
Net Worth: $3,210,166

Earnings: ($4,248,761)
Emp.: 6
Fiscal Year-end: 06/30/24
Support Activities for Metal Mining
N.A.I.C.S.: 213114
Frank David Hegner (VP-Ops)

ALDERON IRON ORE CORP.
Suite 1240 1140 West Pender St, Vancouver, V6E 4G1, BC, Canada
Tel.: (604) 681-8030
Web Site: http://www.alderonironore.com
AXXDF—(OTCIQ)
Sales Range: $1-9.9 Million
Iron Ore Mining
N.A.I.C.S.: 212210
Kate-Lynn Genzel (CFO)

ALDES AERAULIQUE SAS
20 Boulevard Joliot Curie, 69694, Venissieux, Cedex, France
Tel.: (33) 4 7877 1515   FR
Web Site: http://www.aldes.com
Year Founded: 1925
Sales Range: $200-249.9 Million
Emp.: 1,300
Heating, Ventilation, Air Conditioning & Plumbing Equipment Designer, Mfr, Whslr & Services
N.A.I.C.S.: 333415
Stanislas Lacroix (Chm-Mgmt Bd)

Subsidiaries:

EXHAUSTO A/S (1)
Odensevej 76, 5550, Langeskov, Denmark
Tel.: (45) 65 66 12 34
Web Site: http://www.exhausto.com
Industrial Fans Mfr
N.A.I.C.S.: 333413
Marianne Skov Esbech (Asst Mgr-Export)

Subsidiary (Non-US):

EXHAUSTO AB (2)
Ostra Hindbyvagen 26B, 21374, Malmo, Sweden
Tel.: (46) 010 211 7100
Web Site: http://www.exhausto.se
Heat Exchanger Distr
N.A.I.C.S.: 423620

EXHAUSTO GmbH (2)
Mainzer Str 43, 55411, Bingen, Germany
Tel.: (49) 6721 9178 111
Web Site: http://www.exhausto.de
Industrial Fans Mfr
N.A.I.C.S.: 333413

ALDHAFRA INSURANCE COMPANY P.S.C
PO Box 319, Abu Dhabi, United Arab Emirates
Tel.: (971) 26949444   AE
Web Site: https://www.aldhafrainsurance.ae
Year Founded: 1979
DHAFRA—(ABU)
Rev.: $87,295,221
Assets: $357,922,941
Liabilities: $231,642,767
Net Worth: $126,280,173
Earnings: $11,245,657
Emp.: 182
Fiscal Year-end: 12/31/23
Insurance Services
N.A.I.C.S.: 524298
Kamal Sartawi (Gen Mgr)

ALDI EINKAUF SE & CO. OHG
Eckenberg Strasse 16, Postfach 13 01 110, 45307, Essen, Germany
Tel.: (49) 20185930
Web Site: http://www.aldi.com
Sales Range: $50-74.9 Billion
Emp.: 133,000
Discount Grocery Retailer
N.A.I.C.S.: 445110
Dietmar Stewan (CFO)

Subsidiaries:

Aldi Food Inc. (1)
1200 N Kirk Rd, Batavia, IL 60510-1443
Tel.: (630) 879-8100
Web Site: http://www.aldi.com
Sales Range: $25-49.9 Million
Emp.: 80
Retailer of Groceries
N.A.I.C.S.: 445110

Subsidiary (Domestic):

Southeastern Grocers, Inc. (2)
8928 Prominence Pkwy Ste 200, Jacksonville, FL 32256
Tel.: (904) 783-5000
Web Site: https://www.segrocers.com
Sales Range: $5-14.9 Billion
Emp.: 40,000
Offices of Other Holding Companies
N.A.I.C.S.: 551112
D. Mark Prestidge (Exec VP)

Subsidiary (Domestic):

BI-LO, LLC (3)
5050 Edgewood Ct, Jacksonville, FL 32254
Tel.: (904) 783-5000
Web Site: http://www.bi-lo.com
Sales Range: $1-4.9 Billion
Supermarket Chain Operator
N.A.I.C.S.: 445110
Bruce Steadman (Grp VP-Center Store)

J.H. Harvey Co., LLC (3)
727 S Davis St, Nashville, GA 31639-2673
Tel.: (229) 686-7654
Web Site: http://www.harveyssupermarkets.com
Sales Range: $350-399.9 Million
Emp.: 3,000
Supermarket Operator
N.A.I.C.S.: 445110
Barry Robinson (VP-Consumer Affairs)

Winn-Dixie Stores, Inc. (3)
5050 Edgewood Ct, Jacksonville, FL 32254-3601
Tel.: (904) 783-5000
Web Site: http://www.winn-dixie.com
Sales Range: $1-4.9 Billion
Holding Company: Supermarkets Owner, Operator & Grocery Distr
N.A.I.C.S.: 551112

Subsidiary (Domestic):

Winn-Dixie Logistics, Inc. (4)
5050 Edgewood Ct, Jacksonville, FL 32254
Tel.: (904) 783-5000
Grocery Truck Transportation, Warehousing & Logistics Services
N.A.I.C.S.: 484121
Cassi Canaday (Supvr-Fleet)

Division (Domestic):

Winn-Dixie Stores, Inc. - Jacksonville Division (4)
1722 S 8th St, Fernandina Beach, FL 32034
Tel.: (904) 277-2539
Web Site: http://www.winn-dixie.com
Sales Range: $25-49.9 Million
Emp.: 100
Retail Grocery Stores
N.A.I.C.S.: 445110

Winn-Dixie Stores, Inc. - Orlando Division (4)
3015 Coastline Dr, Orlando, FL 32808-3801   (100%)
Tel.: (407) 578-4000
Web Site
http://www
Sales Range: $25-49.9 Million
Emp.: 100
Operators of Retail Grocery Stores
N.A.I.C.S.: 445110

TACT Holding (1)
538 Mission St, South Pasadena, CA 91030-3036
Tel.: (626) 441-1177
Sales Range: $900-999.9 Million
Emp.: 4,500
Holding Company
N.A.I.C.S.: 445110

Subsidiary (Domestic):

Trader Joe's Co. (2)

604 W Huntington Dr, Monrovia, CA
91016-6346 **(100%)**
Tel.: (626) 358-8884
Web Site: http://www.traderjoes.com
Rev.: $8,000,000,000
Emp.: 3,500
Specialty Market
N.A.I.C.S.: 445110

ALDORO RESOURCES LIMITED
Suite 11 & 12 Level 2 23 Railway Rd,
Subiaco, 6008, WA, Australia
Tel.: (61) 272294628 **AU**
Web Site:
https://www.aldororesources.com
Year Founded: 2017
ARN—(ASX)
Rev.: $707,183
Assets: $7,620,763
Liabilities: $111,605
Net Worth: $7,509,158
Earnings: ($1,192,764)
Fiscal Year-end: 06/30/24
Mineral Exploration Services
N.A.I.C.S.: 213114
Sarah Smith *(Sec)*

ALDREES PETROLEUM & TRANSPORT SERVICES COMPANY
PO Box 609, Riyadh, 11421, Saudi
Arabia
Tel.: (966) 112355555
Web Site: https://www.aldrees.com
Year Founded: 1920
4200—(SAU)
Rev.: $3,294,515,128
Assets: $1,683,930,702
Liabilities: $1,388,144,986
Net Worth: $295,785,716
Earnings: $64,478,581
Emp.: 8,111
Fiscal Year-end: 12/31/22
Petroleum & Transportation Services
N.A.I.C.S.: 488510

Subsidiaries:

Mohammad Saad Aldrees & Sons
Company Limited **(1)**
PO Box 609, 11421, Riyadh, Saudi
Arabia **(100%)**
Tel.: (966) 1 235 5555
Web Site: http://www.aldrees.com
Sales Range: $750-799.9 Million
Emp.: 2,000
Crude Petroleum & Natural Gas Extraction
N.A.I.C.S.: 211120

ALDRICH RESOURCES BHD
B-21-1 Level 21 Tower B Northpoint
Mid Valley City No 1, Medan Syed
Putra Utara, 59200, Kuala Lumpur,
Selangor, Malaysia
Tel.: (60) 397702200 **MY**
Web Site: https://aldrich.my
Year Founded: 2001
ALRICH—(KLS)
Rev.: $1,669,928
Assets: $5,866,536
Liabilities: $990,680
Net Worth: $4,875,856
Earnings: ($93,188)
Fiscal Year-end: 12/31/22
Information Technology Services
N.A.I.C.S.: 541512
Abdul Rani Achmed Abdullah *(Exec Dir)*

Subsidiaries:

ASAP Sdn. Bhd. **(1)**
F-06-3 Plaza Kelana Jaya Jalan SS7/13A,
Kelana Jaya, 47301, Petaling Jaya, Selangor, Malaysia
Tel.: (60) 376295515
Web Site: http://www.asap.com.my
Business Development Services
N.A.I.C.S.: 541511
Aziz Rashid *(VP)*

Aldpro Corporate Services Sdn.
Bhd. **(1)**
Level 5 Block B Dataran PHB Saujana Resort Section U2, 40150, Shah Alam, Selangor, Malaysia
Tel.: (60) 378900638
Poll Administration Services
N.A.I.C.S.: 541910

Boardroom.com Sdn. Bhd. **(1)**
B-21-1 Level 21 Tower B Northpoint Mid
Valley City No 1, Medan Syed Putra Utara,
59200, Kuala Lumpur, Malaysia
Tel.: (60) 397702200
Web Site: https://boardroom.com
Management Consulting Services
N.A.I.C.S.: 541611

ALDRIDGE MINERALS INC.
10 King Street East Suite 300, Toronto, M5C 1C3, ON, Canada
Tel.: (416) 477-6980 **Ca**
Web Site: http://www.aldridge.com.tr
Year Founded: 1994
Sales Range: Less than $1 Million
Mineral Exploration Services
N.A.I.C.S.: 213114
James O'Neill *(CFO)*

ALDUS PTY. LTD.
1 Rhodes Street West Ryde, Sydney,
2114, NSW, Australia
Tel.: (61) 290499200
Web Site:
http://www.aldustronics.com.au
Year Founded: 1949
Product Branding Application Services; Printing, Labelling & Coding
N.A.I.C.S.: 561910
Frank Floriano *(CEO)*

Subsidiaries:

API Foilmakers Limited **(1)**
50 Lothian Road Festival Square, Edinburgh, EH3 9WJ, United Kingdom
Tel.: (44) 1506 438611
Web Site: http://www.apifoilmakers.com
Stamping Foil Mfr
N.A.I.C.S.: 331315
Will Oldham *(Mng Dir)*

Subsidiary (Domestic):

API Foils Holdings Limited **(2)**
Firth Road Houstoun Industrial Estate, West
Lothian, Livingston, EH54 5DJ, United
Kingdom **(100%)**
Tel.: (44) 1506438611
Web Site: http://www.apifoils.com
Emp.: 120
Metal Stamping
N.A.I.C.S.: 332119
Colin Void *(Gen Mgr)*

Subsidiary (Non-US):

API Foils (New Zealand) Limited **(3)**
PO Box 11182, Ellerslie, Auckland, 1542,
New Zealand **(100%)**
Tel.: (64) 95799262
Web Site: http://apigroup.com
Metals Service Center
N.A.I.C.S.: 423510

API Foils Pty Limited **(3)**
Unit 10 197 Power Street, Glendenning,
2761, NSW, Australia
Tel.: (61) 29 625 9500
Metals Service Center
N.A.I.C.S.: 423510

API Foils SAS **(3)**
14 Boulevard Arago 14 A 16, Z1 Villemilan,
91320, Wissous, France
Tel.: (33) 169754321
Web Site: http://www.apigroup.com
Emp.: 25
Foils & Laminates Product Distr
N.A.I.C.S.: 423510
Dino Kyriakopoulos *(CEO)*

ALE GROUP HOLDING LIMITED
Unit 1005 10/F Tower A New Mandarin Plaza 14 Science Museum Road,

Tsim Sha Tsui, Hong Kong, China
(Hong Kong)
Tel.: (852) 36202688 **VG**
Web Site: https://ir.alecs.com.hk
Year Founded: 2014
ALEH—(NASDAQ)
Rev.: $1,531,105
Assets: $3,230,881
Liabilities: $351,995
Net Worth: $2,878,886
Earnings: $672,585
Emp.: 6
Fiscal Year-end: 03/31/24
Holding Company
N.A.I.C.S.: 551112

ALEA INZENIRING DOO
Glavni trg 12, 3000, Celje, Slovenia
Tel.: (386) 3 428 27 10
Accounting Services
N.A.I.C.S.: 541219

ALEADRI-SCHINNI PARTICIPACOES E REPRESENTACOES S.A.
Av Primo Schincariol 2 300 Itaim, Itu,
13312-900, SP, Brazil
Tel.: (55) 11 2118 9500
Holding Company
N.A.I.C.S.: 551112
Alexandre Schincariol *(Co-CEO)*

ALEAFIA HEALTH INC.
85 Basaltic Rd, Concord, L4K 1G4,
ON, Canada
Tel.: (416) 860-5665 **BC**
Web Site: https://www.aleafiainc.com
Year Founded: 2007
AH—(TSXV)
Rev.: $12,512,439
Assets: $353,814,071
Liabilities: $59,671,885
Net Worth: $294,142,186
Earnings: ($30,308,861)
Emp.: 173
Fiscal Year-end: 12/31/19
Medical Clinic
N.A.I.C.S.: 621511
Nicholas Bergamini *(VP-IR)*

Subsidiaries:

Emblem Corp. **(1)**
36 York Mills Road Suite 500, Toronto, M2P
2E9, ON, Canada
Tel.: (844) 546-3633
Web Site: http://emblemcorp.com
Sales Range: $1-9.9 Million
Medical Cannabis Producer
N.A.I.C.S.: 621999
Daniel Saperia *(COO)*

ALEATOR ENERGY LIMITED
18 40 St Quentin Avenue, Claremont,
6010, WA, Australia
Tel.: (61) 8 9385 0700 **AU**
Web Site:
http://www.aleatorenergy.com.au
Sales Range: Less than $1 Million
Oil & Gas Exploration Services
N.A.I.C.S.: 211120
Lewis Cross *(Chm)*

Subsidiaries:

Golden Eagle Exploration LLC
USA **(1)**
1616 17th St Ste 600, Denver, CO 80202
Tel.: (303) 628-5429
Industrial Gas Distr
N.A.I.C.S.: 424690

Technology Resource Company
Limited **(1)**
59 Fitzgerald St, Northbridge, Perth, 6003,
WA, Australia
Tel.: (61) 863827000
Web Site: http://www.techresources.com.au
Engineering Recruitment Consulting Services
N.A.I.C.S.: 541612

Matthew Iustini *(CEO)*

ALECTA PENSIONSFORSAKRING, OMSESIDIGT
Regeringsgatan 107, Stockholm,
10373, Sweden
Tel.: (46) 8 441 60 00
Web Site: http://www.alecta.se
Year Founded: 1917
Sales Range: $1-4.9 Billion
Emp.: 380
Pension Management
N.A.I.C.S.: 524292
Magnus Landare *(Head-Legal Affairs)*

Subsidiaries:

Alecta Real Estate USA, LLC **(1)**
235 Pine St Ste 1200, San Francisco, CA
94104-2733
Tel.: (415) 321-6120
Real Estate Development Services
N.A.I.C.S.: 531390

Subsidiary (Domestic):

Alecta Real Estate Investment,
LLC **(2)**
1 Embarcadero Ctr Ste 2350, San Francisco, CA 94111
Tel.: (415) 321-6100
Real Estate Development Services
N.A.I.C.S.: 531390

Hillsboro Club, LLC **(2)**
2323 NW 188th Ave, Hillsboro, OR 97124
Tel.: (503) 690-8100
Real Estate Development Services
N.A.I.C.S.: 531390

Hillsboro Terrace, LLC **(2)**
19000 NW Evergreen Pkwy, Hillsboro, OR
97124
Tel.: (503) 645-8311
Web Site:
http://www.theterracesaptstanaspourne.com
Emp.: 8
Real Estate Development Services
N.A.I.C.S.: 531390
Shawna Mulvaney *(Gen Mgr)*

Alfab Jonkoping 5 AB **(1)**
Regeringsgatan 107, Stockholm, Stockholm, 103 73, Sweden
Tel.: (46) 8 4419372
Real Estate Development Services
N.A.I.C.S.: 531390

Alfab Valutan 13 AB **(1)**
Alecta Pensionsforsakringar, Stockholm,
103 73, Sweden
Tel.: (46) 850894980
Real Estate Development Services
N.A.I.C.S.: 531390

World Trade Center Stockholm
AB **(1)**
Klarabergsviadukten 70 / Kungsbron 1,
Stockholm, Sweden
Tel.: (46) 8 700 45 00
Web Site: http://www.wtc.se
Property Leasing Services
N.A.I.C.S.: 531120

ALECTO MINERALS PLC
47 Charles Street, London, W1J 5EL,
United Kingdom
Tel.: (44) 20 3137 8862
Web Site:
http://www.alectominerals.com
Sales Range: Less than $1 Million
Emp.: 10
Mineral Resources Exploration
N.A.I.C.S.: 212220
Kevin John Ludolph Van Wou *(CEO)*

ALEEDA INC.
7115 Tonken Road, Mississauga, L5S
1R7, ON, Canada
Tel.: (905) 696-9525 **ON**
Web Site: http://www.aleedainc.com
Year Founded: 2006
Sales Range: $10-24.9 Million
Emp.: 20
Beauty Care Products Mfr

Aleeda Inc.—(Continued)

N.A.I.C.S.: 456120
Juvenal Alvarez *(Chm)*

ALEF S.A.

Av Presidente Wilson 231 - 28
Andar/parte, 20030021, Rio de Ja-
neiro, Brazil
Tel.: (55) 2138043700
Web Site: http://www.alefnet.com.br
Year Founded: 1997
ALEF3B—(BRAZ)
Sales Range: Less than $1 Million
Financial Investment Services
N.A.I.C.S.: 523999

ALEF-BANK CJSC JSCB

5 Moldavskaya st, 121467, Moscow,
Russia
Tel.: (7) 4954117747
Web Site: http://www.alefbank.com
Year Founded: 1992
Sales Range: Less than $1 Million
Commercial Banking Services
N.A.I.C.S.: 522110
Kolesnikova Irina Alekseevna *(Deputy Chm-Mgmt Bd)*

ALEFARM BREWING A/S

Lunikvej 2B, 2670, Greve, Denmark
Tel.: (45) 53564606
Web Site: https://shop.alefarm.dk
Year Founded: 2015
ALEFRM—(NASDAQ)
Beverage Product Mfr
N.A.I.C.S.: 312120
Jens Erik Thorndahl *(Chm)*

ALEKSA SANTIC U RESTRUK-TURIRANJU A.D.

Solunskih dobrovoljaca 3, 25212,
Aleksa Santic, Serbia
Tel.: (381) 25 838 100
Web Site: http://www.aleksasantic.rs
Year Founded: 1986
Sales Range: $1-9.9 Million
Emp.: 220
Cereal Crop Farming Services
N.A.I.C.S.: 111998

ALELION ENERGY SYSTEMS AB

Sorredsbacken 4, 418 78, Gothen-
burg, Sweden
Tel.: (46) 31866200
Web Site: http://www.alelion.com
2FZ—(BER)
Rev.: $12,932,805
Assets: $18,743,256
Liabilities: $6,958,242
Net Worth: $11,785,014
Earnings: ($8,379,989)
Emp.: 37
Fiscal Year-end: 12/31/19
Lithium Battery Mfr
N.A.I.C.S.: 335910
Asa Nordstrom *(CEO)*

ALEMBIC LIMITED

Alembic Road, Vadodara, 390 003,
Gujarat, India
Tel.: (91) 2652280550
Web Site:
    https://www.alembiclimited.com
Year Founded: 1907
ALEMBICLTD—(NSE)
Rev.: $22,849,772
Assets: $359,261,557
Liabilities: $18,477,923
Net Worth: $340,783,634
Earnings: $11,765,508
Emp.: 305
Fiscal Year-end: 03/31/22
Pharmaceuticals Product Mfr
N.A.I.C.S.: 325412
Chirayu R. Amin *(Chm)*

Subsidiaries:

Alembic Glass Industries Ltd. **(1)**
Alembic Road, Vadodara, 390 016, Gujarat,
India
Tel.: (91) 2652281097
Web Site: http://www.yera.com
Sales Range: $125-149.9 Million
Emp.: 400
Household Glassware Mfr
N.A.I.C.S.: 327212

Alembic Pharmaceuticals Limited **(1)**
Alembic Road, Vadodara, 390 003, Gujarat,
India
Tel.: (91) 2656637000
Web Site:
    https://www.alembicpharmaceuticals.com
Rev.: $737,528,610
Assets: $915,775,770
Liabilities: $224,134,365
Net Worth: $691,641,405
Earnings: $160,812,015
Emp.: 12,160
Fiscal Year-end: 03/31/2021
Pharmaceuticals Product Mfr
N.A.I.C.S.: 325412
Chirayu Ramanbhai Amin *(Chm & CEO)*

Shreno Ltd **(1)**
Alembic Road, Vadodara, 390003, Gujarat,
India **(100%)**
Tel.: (91) 2652280550
Web Site: http://www.shrenoengg.com
Pressed & Blown Glass & Glassware Mfr
N.A.I.C.S.: 327212

Plant (Domestic):

Shreno Ltd - Factory Unit-1 **(2)**
3/23-24 Gorwa Industrial Estate, Vadodara,
390003, Gujarat, India
Tel.: (91) 265 228 2284
Sales Range: $50-74.9 Million
Emp.: 120
Industrial Machinery Mfr & Distr
N.A.I.C.S.: 333241

Shreno Ltd - Factory Unit-2 **(2)**
4/22-23 Baroda Industrial Estate Gorwa,
Vadodara, 390 016, Gujarat, India
Tel.: (91) 2652280190
Web Site: http://www.shrenoengg.com
Industrial Machinery Mfr & Sistr
N.A.I.C.S.: 333241

ALEPH GROUP, INC.

22nd Street 21 Villa 2B Umm Suqeim
2, Dubai, United Arab Emirates
Tel.: (971) 4 264 8999   Ky
Web Site:
    https://www.graphexgroup.com
Year Founded: 2021
Rev.: $36,999,000
Assets: $96,287,000
Liabilities: $88,792,000
Net Worth: $7,495,000
Earnings: $17,654,000
Emp.: 1,064
Fiscal Year-end: 12/31/21
Holding Company
N.A.I.C.S.: 551112
Christian Gaston Taratuta *(CEO)*

ALERIO GOLD CORP.

409 Granville Street Suite 1000, Van-
couver, V6C 1T2, BC, Canada
Tel.: (604) 825-2995
Web Site: https://www.aleriogold.com
ALE—(DEU)
Assets: $12,107,445
Liabilities: $801,635
Net Worth: $11,305,810
Earnings: ($688,658)
Fiscal Year-end: 08/31/23
Mineral Exploration Services
N.A.I.C.S.: 213115
Jonathan Challis *(CEO)*

ALERION CLEAN POWER S.P.A.

Via Renato Fucini, 420133, Milan,
NO, Italy
Tel.: (39) 027788901   IT

Web Site: https://www.alerion.it
Year Founded: 1981
ARN—(ITA)
Rev.: $222,657,026
Assets: $1,583,919,859
Liabilities: $1,223,256,430
Net Worth: $360,663,429
Earnings: $75,061,265
Emp.: 169
Fiscal Year-end: 12/31/23
Eletric Power Generation Services
N.A.I.C.S.: 221118

ALESAYI TRADING CORPO-RATION

Kilo 11 Makkah Road, Jeddah,
21431, Saudi Arabia
Tel.: (966) 26202000
Web Site: http://www.alesayi-motors.com
Sales Range: $125-149.9 Million
Emp.: 1,000
Automotive Distr
N.A.I.C.S.: 441110
Faeed Omar Alesayi *(Chm)*

ALESSANDRO ROSSO GROUP S.P.A.

Viale Fulvio Testi 121, 20162, Milan,
MI, Italy
Tel.: (39) 02 87387 201   IT
Web Site: http://arossogroup.com
Year Founded: 2002
Sales Range: $100-124.9 Million
Emp.: 250
Holding Company; Incentive Travel,
Team Building Events, Convention
Organization & Tour Operation Ser-
vices
N.A.I.C.S.: 551112
Alessandro Rosso *(Founder, Chm, Pres & CEO)*

Subsidiaries:

Alessandro Rosso Incentive S.r.l. **(1)**
Via Privata Alessandro Antonelli 3, 20139,
Milan, MI, Italy
Tel.: (39) 02 87387 201
Web Site: http://www.arossogroup.com
Incentive Travel & Team Building Services
N.A.I.C.S.: 561599

Best Tours S.p.A. **(1)**
Via Tito Speri 8, 20154, Milan, MI,
Italy **(100%)**
Tel.: (39) 02 33633 1
Web Site: http://www.besttours.it
Tour Operator
N.A.I.C.S.: 561520
Alessandro Rosso *(Pres)*

Subsidiary (Domestic):

Best Tours Italia S.p.A. **(2)**
Via Tito Speri 8, 20154, Milan, MI,
Italy **(100%)**
Tel.: (39) 02 33633 1
Web Site: http://www.besttours.it
Tour Operator
N.A.I.C.S.: 561520

ALEX MACINTYRE & ASSOCI-ATES LTD.

1390 Government Road West, PO
Box 517, Kirkland Lake, P2N 3J5,
ON, Canada
Tel.: (705) 567-6663
Web Site:
    http://www.macintyremining.com
Year Founded: 1958
Rev.: $32,404,535
Emp.: 150
Mining Services
N.A.I.C.S.: 212290
Syd McDougall *(Pres)*

ALEX PHARM LTD.

Dmitrievskaya st 17 a/2, 01054, Kiev,
Ukraine

Tel.: (380) 445372222   UA
Pharmaceuticals Product Mfr
N.A.I.C.S.: 325412

ALEX WILSON COLDSTREAM LTD.

32 Colonization Ave, PO Box 3009,
Dryden, P8N 2Y9, ON, Canada
Tel.: (807) 223-2381
Web Site: http://awclprinting.ca
Year Founded: 1940
Rev.: $15,000,000
Emp.: 34
Stock Products & Custom Orders
Printers
N.A.I.C.S.: 323111
Roy Wilson *(Pres & CEO)*

ALEXANDER FORBES GROUP HOLDINGS LIMITED

Alexforbes 115 West Street, Sandton,
2196, South Africa
Tel.: (27) 112690000   ZA
Web Site:
    https://www.alexforbes.com
Year Founded: 1935
AFH—(JSE)
Rev.: $267,165,891
Assets: $22,373,545,883
Liabilities: $22,131,147,891
Net Worth: $242,397,992
Earnings: $36,544,534
Emp.: 2,467
Fiscal Year-end: 03/31/24
Financial Management, Insurance &
Risk Management Services
N.A.I.C.S.: 523999
Lynn Stevens *(CMO)*

Subsidiaries:

Alexander Forbes Channel Islands
Limited **(1)**
2 - 6 Church Street, PO Box 336, Saint He-
lier, JE2 3NN, Jersey
Tel.: (44) 1534837837
Financial Services
N.A.I.C.S.: 523999
Niall Doran *(Mng Dir)*

Alexander Forbes Consulting Actuar-
ies Nigeria Limited **(1)**
235 Muri Okunola Street, PO Box 74686,
Victoria Island, 234, Lagos, Nigeria
Tel.: (234) 1 271 1080
Financial Services
N.A.I.C.S.: 523999

Alexander Forbes Limited **(1)**
115 West Street, 61 Katherine Street San-
down, Sandton, 2196, South Africa **(90%)**
Tel.: (27) 115056000
Web Site: https://www.alexforbes.com
Sales Range: $450-499.9 Million
Emp.: 2,467
Financial Management, Insurance & Risk
Services
N.A.I.C.S.: 523999
Edward Kieswetter *(CEO)*

Subsidiary (Domestic):

Alexander Forbes Community
Trust **(2)**
Alexander Forbes Place, 90 Rivonia Road
Sandown, Sandton, 2196, South Africa
Tel.: (27) 116693000
Web Site: http://www.alexanderforbes.co.za
Community Development & Investment Ser-
vices
N.A.I.C.S.: 523999

Alexander Forbes Compensation
Technologies (Pty) Ltd **(2)**
1st Floor Block East Hatfield Gardens,
Grosvenor and Arcadia Streets, Pretoria,
0028, South Africa
Tel.: (27) 124319700
Web Site: http://www.afct.co.za
Sales Range: $75-99.9 Million
Emp.: 120
Healthcare Solutions & Accident Insurance
Compensation Services
N.A.I.C.S.: 524298

Lynne Marais *(Reg Mgr)*

Branch (Non-US):

Alexander Forbes International
Ltd.　　　　　　　　　　　　　(2)
3rd Floor 1 Royal Exchange, London, EC3V
3LN, United Kingdom
Tel.: (44) 20 7847 3375
Web Site: http://www.alexanderforbes.co.uk
Sales Range: $25-49.9 Million
Emp.: 30
Direct Insurance Brokers
N.A.I.C.S.: 524210
Lisa Whice *(Office Mgr)*

Caveo Fund Solutions Proprietary
Limited　　　　　　　　　　　(1)
115 West Street, Sandton, 2196, Johannes-
burg, South Africa
Tel.: (27) 11 505 6200
Web Site: https://www.caveo.co.za
Fund Management Services
N.A.I.C.S.: 523940

Euroguard Insurance Company PCC
Limited　　　　　　　　　　　(1)
Suite 931 a/b Europort, PO Box 703, Gi-
braltar, Gibraltar
Tel.: (350) 20052699
General Insurance Services
N.A.I.C.S.: 524298
Richard Buchanan *(Dir-Ops)*

Guardrisk Allied Products & Services
Proprietary Limited　　　　　(1)
Alexander Forbes Place 90 Rivonia Road,
Johannesburg, 2196, Gauteng, South Africa
Tel.: (27) 116691000
Financial Services
N.A.I.C.S.: 523999

LCP Libera AG　　　　　　　(1)
Birsstrasse 320, 4010, Basel, Switzerland
Tel.: (41) 612057400
Web Site: https://libera.ch
General Insurance Services
N.A.I.C.S.: 524298

Senior Finance Proprietary
Limited　　　　　　　　　　　(1)
61 Katherine Street, Sandton, 2196, South
Africa
Tel.: (27) 86 073 6467
Web Site: https://www.seniorsfinance.co.za
Financial Services
N.A.I.C.S.: 523999
Ali Bacher *(Chm)*

Superflex, Ltd.　　　　　　　(1)
400 S 2nd St, Elizabeth, NJ 07206
Tel.: (718) 768-1400
Web Site: https://superflex.com
Electrical Products Mfr
N.A.I.C.S.: 335999
Yigal Elbaz *(Pres)*

ALEXANDER MARINE CO., LTD.
1 Jinfu Road, Qian-Zhen Dist, Kaoh-
siung, 80668, Taiwan
Tel.: (886) 78314126
Web Site:
　　https://www.oceanalexander.com.tw
Year Founded: 1978
8478—(TAI)
Rev.: $206,844,918
Assets: $358,397,220
Liabilities: $167,024,455
Net Worth: $191,372,765
Earnings: $68,067,200
Emp.: 761
Fiscal Year-end: 12/31/23
Boat Building Product Mfr
N.A.I.C.S.: 336612
Ching-Cheng Chueh *(Chm)*

ALEXANDER SCHNEIDER LTD.
8a Hatsoran St, PO Box 8449, Sapir
Industrial Park, Netanya, 4250608,
Israel
Tel.: (972) 98924444　　　　II
Web Site: http://www.schneider.co.il
Year Founded: 1963

Sales Range: $10-24.9 Million
Emp.: 100
Electronic Parts & Equipment Distr
N.A.I.C.S.: 423690
Yigal Schneider *(Gen Mgr)*

ALEXANDER STAMPS & COIN LTD.
SF-7 Silver Rock Complex Near
Dairy Teen Rasta Makarpura Road,
Vadodara, 390014, India
Tel.: (91) 2656569067
511463—(BOM)
Rev.: $103,726
Assets: $2,335,187
Liabilities: $160,183
Net Worth: $2,175,005
Earnings: $5,651
Fiscal Year-end: 03/31/21
Stamp Coin Collection Services
N.A.I.C.S.: 339940
Vineet Dubey *(CFO)*

ALEXANDER TECH CORP.
1586 Noah Bend, London, N6G 0T2,
ON, Canada
Tel.: (519) 619-4370　　　　DE
Year Founded: 2005
Assets: $11,879
Liabilities: $317,253
Net Worth: ($305,374)
Earnings: ($61,344)
Fiscal Year-end: 04/30/24
Investment Services
N.A.I.C.S.: 523999

ALEXANDRIA CONTAINER & CARGO HANDLING COMPANY
Quay 23/25-Port Of Alexandria, Alex-
andria, Egypt
Tel.: (20) 34800633
Web Site: https://www.alexcont.com
Year Founded: 1984
ALCN.CA—(EGX)
Rev.: $91,820,852
Assets: $180,551,156
Liabilities: $13,721,475
Net Worth: $166,829,680
Earnings: $65,511,853
Fiscal Year-end: 06/30/23
Container & Cargo Handling Services
N.A.I.C.S.: 488320
Yasser Mohamed Morsy Heikal *(Exec
Mng Dir)*

ALEXANDRIA GROUP OYJ
Etelaesplanadi 22 A 4th floor, 00130,
Helsinki, Finland
Tel.: (358) 941351300
Web Site: https://www.alexandria.fi
Year Founded: 1996
ALEX—(HEL)
Rev.: $47,554,918
Assets: $49,762,667
Liabilities: $11,966,001
Net Worth: $37,796,666
Earnings: $8,897,229
Emp.: 90
Fiscal Year-end: 12/31/23
Asset Management Services
N.A.I.C.S.: 523999
Jan Akesson *(CEO)*

ALEXANDRIA MINERAL OILS CO.
El-Sad El-Ali Street Wady El-Kamar
Alex 2 Haras Gomhory Buildings, El
max Abas el-Aqad st 7th floor, Nasr,
Egypt
Tel.: (20) 3105646
Web Site: https://www.amoceg.com
Year Founded: 1997
AMOC.CA—(EGX)
Rev.: $461,847,363
Assets: $231,761,131

Liabilities: $113,731,234
Net Worth: $118,029,897
Earnings: $29,717,020
Fiscal Year-end: 12/31/23
Petroleum Product Mfr
N.A.I.C.S.: 324191
Amr Lotfy *(Chm & CEO)*

ALEXANDRIA NATIONAL COMPANY FOR FINANCIAL INVESTMENT
73 Al Fouad St Horrya Rd, Alexan-
dria, Egypt
Tel.: (20) 3 4946099
Web Site: http://www.anffi.net
Year Founded: 1996
ANFI.CA—(EGX)
Sales Range: Less than $1 Million
Financial Investment Services
N.A.I.C.S.: 523999
Laila Khairy *(Chm & Mng Dir)*

ALEXANDRIA SPINNING & WEAVING CO.
El Bar el Kebly El Mahmoudeia El
Nozha, Alexandria, Egypt
Tel.: (20) 33818046
Web Site: https://www.spinalex.com
Year Founded: 1959
SPIN.CA—(EGX)
Sales Range: Less than $1 Million
Emp.: 1,700
Cotton Yarn Mfr
N.A.I.C.S.: 313110
Refaat Helal *(Chm & Mng Dir)*

ALEXIUM INTERNATIONAL GROUP LIMITED
Tel.: (61) 893843160　　　　AU
Web Site:
　　http://www.alexiuminternational.com
AXIIF—(OTCIQ)
Rev.: $8,174,937
Assets: $6,423,905
Liabilities: $4,848,222
Net Worth: $1,575,683
Earnings: ($3,360,271)
Fiscal Year-end: 06/30/22
Business Management Services
N.A.I.C.S.: 561499
Robert Brookins *(CEO)*

Subsidiaries:

Alexium Inc　　　　　　　　　(1)
350 W Phillips Rd, Greer, SC 29650
Tel.: (864) 254-9923
Web Site:
　　https://www.alexiuminternational.com
Commercial Licensing Services
N.A.I.C.S.: 926150

ALFA
Av Caracas N 35-55, Bogota, Colom-
bia
Tel.: (57) 3311531
Web Site: http://alfa.com.co
Year Founded: 1954
Sales Range: Less than $1 Million
Floor & Wall Tile Mfr & Distr
N.A.I.C.S.: 327120

Subsidiaries:

OPA International Corporation　(1)
7122 NW 50th St, Miami, FL 33166
Tel.: (305) 594-3922
Web Site: http://www.alfagres.us
Floor & Wall Tile Distr
N.A.I.C.S.: 327910
Carlos A. Boggio *(Pres)*

Branch (Domestic):

OPA International Corporation -
Houston　　　　　　　　　　　(2)
9612 W Tidwell Rd, Houston, TX 77041
Tel.: (214) 349-6700
Web Site: http://www.alfagres.us
Floor & Wall Tile Distr

N.A.I.C.S.: 423320

ALFA ACCIAI SPA
Via San Polo, 25134, Brescia, Italy
Tel.: (39) 03023911　　　　　IT
Web Site: http://www.alfaacciai.it
Sales Range: $500-549.9 Million
Emp.: 814
Concrete Reinforcing Steel Mfr
N.A.I.C.S.: 331110
Ettore Lonati *(Pres)*

Subsidiaries:

Acciaierie Di Sicilia S.p.A.　　(1)
1a Stradale Passo Cavaliere; 95121, Cata-
nia, Italy
Tel.: (39) 0957487811
Web Site: http://www.acciaieriedisicilia.it
Emp.: 200
Steel Reinforcements Mfr
N.A.I.C.S.: 332111

TSR Recycling GmbH & Co. KG　(1)
Hafenstr 98, 46242, Bottrop, Germany
Tel.: (49) 204170600
Web Site: http://www.tsr.eu
Steel Scrap & Non-Ferrous Metals Recy-
cling
N.A.I.C.S.: 423930

Subsidiary (Non-US):

HKS Metals B.V.　　　　　　　(2)
Graanweg 18, 4782 PP, Moerdijk,
Netherlands　　　　　　　　　(100%)
Tel.: (31) 886065200
Web Site: http://www.hks.nl
Emp.: 2,600
Holding Company; Scrap Metal Recycling
Services
N.A.I.C.S.: 551112

Subsidiary (Domestic):

HKS Scrap Metals B.V.　　　　(3)
Graanweg 18, 4782 PP, Moerdijk, Nether-
lands
Tel.: (31) 886065000
Web Site: http://www.hksmetals.eu
Sales Range: $25-49.9 Million
Emp.: 70
Scrap Metal Recycling
N.A.I.C.S.: 562920
Wouter Kusters *(Mng Dir)*

ALFA FINANCE HOLDING AD
7 Sheinovo str, Sofia, 1504, Bulgaria
Tel.: (359) 24893741　　　　BG
Web Site: http://www.alfafinance.bg
Investment Management Service
N.A.I.C.S.: 523940
Ivo Prokopiev *(Chm-Mgmt Bd &
CEO)*

Subsidiaries:

Broker Ins Ltd.　　　　　　　　(1)
3 Karnigradska str, Sofia, 1000, Bulgaria
Tel.: (359) 29 86 79 11
Web Site: http://www.brokerins.bg
Insurance Brokerage Services
N.A.I.C.S.: 524210
Stefan Enchev *(Mng Partner)*

Bulbrokers AD　　　　　　　　(1)
7 Sheynovo Street 1 floor, Sofia, Bulgaria
Tel.: (359) 2 4893 712
Web Site: http://www.bulbrokers.com
Financial Investment Services
N.A.I.C.S.: 523999
Ivan Nenkov *(Chm)*

Landmark Property Management
Jsc　　　　　　　　　　　　　(1)
7 Sheinovo St, Sofia, Sofia, Bulgaria
Tel.: (359) 2 4898 700
Web Site: http://www.landmark.bg
Real Estate Manangement Services
N.A.I.C.S.: 531390
Martin Voev *(Exec Dir)*

Solarpro Holding AD　　　　　(1)
7 Sheinovo Str, Sofia, 1504,
Bulgaria　　　　　　　　　　　(93.05%)
Tel.: (359) 2 422 41 52
Web Site: http://www.solarpro.bg
Photovoltaic Panel Mfr

Alfa Finance Holding AD—(Continued)

N.A.I.C.S.: 339999
Daniela Peeva *(Mgr-IR)*

ALFA FINANCIAL SOFTWARE HOLDINGS PLC

Moor Place 1 Fore Street Avenue, London, EC2Y 9DT, United Kingdom
Tel.: (44) 2075881800   UK
Web Site:
    http://www.alfasystems.com
Year Founded: 1990
ALFA—(LSE)
Rev.: $112,078,720
Assets: $113,156,400
Liabilities: $54,692,260
Net Worth: $58,464,140
Earnings: $25,999,030
Fiscal Year-end: 12/31/21
Financial Software Services
N.A.I.C.S.: 541511
Andrew Denton *(CEO)*

Subsidiaries:

Alfa Financial Software Limited   **(1)**
Moor Place 1 Fore Street Avenue, London, EC2Y 9DT, United Kingdom
Tel.: (44) 207 588 1800
Software Development Services
N.A.I.C.S.: 541511
Gillian Bray *(Mgr-Human Resources)*

CHP Consulting Inc   **(1)**
124 E Hudson Ave, Royal Oak, MI 48067
Software Development Services
N.A.I.C.S.: 541511

ALFA GROUP

11 Bolshoi Savvinsky Pereulok Office No 351 Floor 5 Entrance 3, Moscow, 119435, Russia
Tel.: (7) 495 787 00 77
Web Site: http://www.alfagroup.org
Year Founded: 1989
Financial Services & Holdings
N.A.I.C.S.: 523999
Mikhail Fridman *(Chm)*

Subsidiaries:

ABH Holdings S.A.   **(1)**
3 Boulevard du Prince Henri, L1724, Luxembourg, Luxembourg
Tel.: (352) 264 70 621
Web Site: http://www.abhh.lu
Financial Holding Company
N.A.I.C.S.: 551112
Petr Aven *(Chm)*

Subsidiary (Non-US):

PJSC Ukrsotsbank   **(2)**
29 Kovpaka Street, 03150, Kiev, Ukraine   **(99.9%)**
Tel.: (380) 44 2054555
Web Site: http://en.ukrsotsbank.com
Banking Services
N.A.I.C.S.: 522110

Alfa Capital LLC   **(1)**
Sadovaya-Kudrinskaya Street 32 Building 1 Bronnaya Plaza Centre, 107078, Moscow, Russia
Tel.: (7) 4957973152
Web Site: http://www.alfacapital.ru
Commercial Banking Services
N.A.I.C.S.: 522110
Irina Krivosheeva *(CEO)*

ALFA ICA (INDIA) LTD.

Alfa-Palazzo Satellite Road Near Shiv Ranjani X Road Satellite Road, Jodhpur, Ahmedabad, 380015, Gujarat, India
Tel.: (91) 7926754030
Web Site: https://www.alfaica.com
530973—(BOM)
Rev.: $10,979,637
Assets: $6,130,392
Liabilities: $3,590,182
Net Worth: $2,540,210
Earnings: $222,140

Emp.: 63
Fiscal Year-end: 03/31/22
Laminated Sheet Mfr
N.A.I.C.S.: 326130
Rishi Tikmani *(Exec Dir)*

ALFA LAVAL AB

Rudeboksvagen 1, SE-226 55, Lund, Sweden
Tel.: (46) 46366500   SE
Web Site: https://www.alfalaval.com
Year Founded: 1883
ALFA—(OMX)
Rev.: $6,313,459,317
Assets: $8,168,840,849
Liabilities: $4,458,276,328
Net Worth: $3,710,564,520
Earnings: $633,450,484
Emp.: 21,321
Fiscal Year-end: 12/31/23
Foodstuff, Beverage, Pharmaceutical, Chemical, Oil & Water Industrial Heating, Cooling, Separating & Transporting Products Mfr & Environmental Engineering Solutions
N.A.I.C.S.: 333248
Dennis Jonsson *(Chm)*

Subsidiaries:

AO Alfa Laval Potok   **(1)**
st Sovetskaya 73, Microdistrict, Bolshevo, 141060, Russia
Tel.: (7) 4952321250
Web Site: https://www.alfalaval.ru
Gas Fired Steam Boiler Mfr
N.A.I.C.S.: 332410

Alfa Laval (Taicang) Technologies Co. Ltd.   **(1)**
No 100 Chenmenjing Road, Chengxiang Town, Taicang, China
Tel.: (86) 4009976911
Heat Transfer Product Mfr & Distr
N.A.I.C.S.: 333415

Alfa Laval Holding AB   **(1)**
Rudeboksvagen 1, Lund, 221 00, Sweden
Tel.: (46) 46367000
Web Site: http://www.alfalaval.com
Emp.: 50
Investment Management Service
N.A.I.C.S.: 523940

Subsidiary (Non-US):

Aalborg Industries d.o.o.   **(2)**
Zoraniceva 61, Solin, 21210, Croatia
Tel.: (385) 21 688 520
Web Site: http://www.alfalaval.com
Sales Range: $25-49.9 Million
Emp.: 6
Marine Steam Boiler Mfr
N.A.I.C.S.: 332410

Subsidiary (Domestic):

Ageratec AB   **(2)**
St Herrebro, 605 97, Norrkoping, Sweden
Tel.: (46) 853065800
Web Site: http://www.ageratec.com
Sales Range: $25-49.9 Million
Emp.: 20
Processed Biodiesel Mfr
N.A.I.C.S.: 324110

Subsidiary (Non-US):

Alfa Laval (China) Ltd.   **(2)**
338 Kings Road North Point Room 1206-1209 12th Floor, Chinachem Exchange Square, Hong Kong, China (Hong Kong)
Tel.: (852) 285 770 00
Web Site: http://www.alfalaval.cn
Sales Range: $50-74.9 Million
Emp.: 110
Equipment Service Center
N.A.I.C.S.: 811412
Jan Debruyn *(Pres)*

Subsidiary (Non-US):

Alfa Laval (Jiangyin) Manufacturing Co Ltd   **(3)**
465 Renmin Road Qiaoqi, Xiake Town, Jiangyin, 214408, Jiangsu, China
Tel.: (86) 51086561280

Heat Exchanger Mfr
N.A.I.C.S.: 332410

Subsidiary (Domestic):

Alfa Laval Flow Equipment (Kunshan) Co Ltd   **(4)**
Baishu Road Kunshan Economic & Technical Development Zone, Suzhou, 215301, China
Tel.: (86) 512 577 145 04
Pumping Equipment Mfr
N.A.I.C.S.: 333914

Subsidiary (Non-US):

Alfa Laval (Shanghai) Technologies Co Ltd   **(2)**
25th Floor Admiralty Plaza No 98 Huaihai Middle Road, Shanghai, 200021, China
Tel.: (86) 2153858000
Emp.: 400
Air Conditioning & Heating Equipment Mfr
N.A.I.C.S.: 333415

Liyang Sifang Stainless Steel Products Co., Ltd   **(3)**
No 1 Xin'an South Road, Daitou Town, Liyang, 213300, Jiangsu, China
Tel.: (86) 51987366198
Web Site: https://en.lysf.com
Emp.: 1,000
Sanitary Fluid Pump & Valve Mfr
N.A.I.C.S.: 333914

Tranter Heat Exchangers (Beijing) Co Ltd   **(3)**
No 5 Anqing Avenue Area B Tianzhu Airport Development Zone, 101318, Beijing, China
Tel.: (86) 1064379490
Web Site: http://www.tranter.com
Sales Range: $25-49.9 Million
Emp.: 110
Heat Exchanger Mfr
N.A.I.C.S.: 332410

Subsidiary (Non-US):

Alfa Laval (India) Ltd   **(2)**
India customer center Mumbai-Pune road, Dapodi, Pune, 411 012, Maharashtra, India   **(88.77%)**
Tel.: (91) 2066119100
Web Site: https://www.alfalaval.in
Sales Range: $150-199.9 Million
Emp.: 1,045
Industrial Equipment Mfr
N.A.I.C.S.: 333248
Rajita Kumar *(Head-Comm & Brand)*

Alfa Laval (Kunshan) Manufacturing Co Ltd   **(2)**
299 Yuyang Road, Yushan Town, Kunshan, 215301, Jiangsu, China
Tel.: (86) 51257714504
Web Site: http://www.alfalaval.cn
Heat Exchanger Mfr
N.A.I.C.S.: 332410

Alfa Laval (Portugal) Lda   **(2)**
Alfrapark Edificio F Alfragide, 2614-519, Amadora, Portugal
Tel.: (351) 214166400
Web Site: http://www.alfalaval.pt
Sales Range: $25-49.9 Million
Emp.: 14
Heating Equipment Mfr
N.A.I.C.S.: 333415

Alfa Laval (Pty) Ltd   **(2)**
Unit E3 Isando Business Park Cnr Gewel and Hulley Street, Isando, 1600, South Africa
Tel.: (27) 11 230 3600
Web Site: https://www.alfalaval.co.za
Sales Range: $25-49.9 Million
Emp.: 50
Heat Exchanger Mfr
N.A.I.C.S.: 332410

Alfa Laval (Thailand) Ltd.   **(2)**
13/F 1/26-27 Bangna Thani Building Soi 34 Bangna-Trad Road, Bangna, Bangkok, 10260, Thailand
Tel.: (66) 23994419
Web Site: https://www.alfalaval.co.th
Sales Range: $25-49.9 Million
Emp.: 60
N.A.I.C.S.: 322212

Alfa Laval A/O   **(2)**
Sovetskaya Str 73, RU 141 070, Kaliningrad, Russia
Tel.: (7) 0952321250
Web Site: http://www.alfalaval.com
Sales Range: $25-49.9 Million
Emp.: 50
N.A.I.C.S.: 322212

Alfa Laval AEBE   **(2)**
20th km Lavrion Avenue, Thesis Karella Attica, 19400, Koropi, Greece
Tel.: (30) 210 668 3500
Web Site: https://www.alfalaval.gr
Sales Range: $25-49.9 Million
Emp.: 22
Industrial Equipment & Machinery Distr
N.A.I.C.S.: 423830

Alfa Laval Aalborg A/S   **(2)**
Gasvaerksvej 21, PO Box 844, 9000, Aalborg, Denmark
Tel.: (45) 99304000
Web Site: https://www.alfalaval.dk
Emp.: 600
Industrial & Marine Boiler Mfr
N.A.I.C.S.: 332410

Subsidiary (Non-US):

Aalborg Industries Ltda   **(3)**
Avenida Ver Isaias Prieto 46, Itu, 13304-780, Sao Paulo, Brazil
Tel.: (55) 11 4025 6000
Industrial Machinery Equipment Mfr & Whlsr
N.A.I.C.S.: 333248

Alfa Laval (Qingdao) Co. Ltd   **(3)**
86 Guangzhou Road North, Jiaozhou, 266300, Shandong, China
Tel.: (86) 53292299330
Web Site: http://www.alfalaval.com
Power Boiler & Heat Exchanger Mfr
N.A.I.C.S.: 332410

Alfa Laval Aalborg (FPS) Pte Ltd   **(3)**
11 Joo Koon Circle, Jurong, 629043, Singapore
Tel.: (65) 62 61 98 98
Boiler & Heat Exchanger Mfr
N.A.I.C.S.: 332410
Isa Ahmad *(Mgr-Sls-Spare Parts)*

Alfa Laval Aalborg BV   **(3)**
Ohmweg 8, 3208 KE, Spijkenisse, Netherlands
Tel.: (31) 181 650 500
Web Site: http://www.aalborg-industries.com
Heating Equipment Mfr & Distr
N.A.I.C.S.: 333414

Alfa Laval Aalborg Ltd   **(3)**
5th Floor Saesam Bldg 1485-1 Ja-Dong, Haeundae-Ku, Busan, 612-842, Korea (South)
Tel.: (82) 51 703 6162
Web Site: http://www.aalborg-industries.com
Sales Range: $25-49.9 Million
Emp.: 50
Boiler & Heat Exchanger Mfr
N.A.I.C.S.: 332410

Alfa Laval Aalborg Nijmegen BV   **(3)**
St Hubertusstraat 10, Nijmegen, 6503 GD, Netherlands
Tel.: (31) 24 352 31 00
Web Site: http://www.alfalaval.com
Emp.: 80
Inert Gas Generator Distr
N.A.I.C.S.: 423830

Alfa Laval Aalborg Oy   **(3)**
Kaivopuistontie 33, PO Box 9, 26100, Rauma, Finland
Tel.: (358) 10 838 3800
Web Site: https://www.alfalaval.fi
Industrial Boiler Mfr
N.A.I.C.S.: 332410

Alfa Laval HaiPhong Co. Ltd   **(3)**
An Hong Marine Industrial Zone, An Duong District, Haiphong, Vietnam
Tel.: (84) 313 594 116
Web Site: http://www.alfalaval.com
Sales Range: $25-49.9 Million
Emp.: 200
Power Boiler Mfr
N.A.I.C.S.: 332410

Subsidiary (Non-US):

Alfa Laval Aalborg Industria e Comercio Ltda.   **(2)**

Rua Divino Espirito Santo 1 100, Bairro Ca-
rangola Petropolis, Rio de Janeiro, 25715-
410, Brazil
Tel.: (55) 2422339963
Web Site: http://www.aalborg-industries.com
Sales Range: $125-149.9 Million
Emp.: 380
Marine Boiler Installation Services & Mfr
N.A.I.C.S.: 238220

Alfa Laval Aalborg Pty Ltd   (2)
10 Lucca Road, North Wyong, Wyong,
2259, NSW, Australia
Tel.: (61) 243990000
Web Site: http://www.aalborg-industries.com
Sales Range: $25-49.9 Million
Emp.: 58
Marine Boiler Mfr
N.A.I.C.S.: 332410

Alfa Laval Australia Pty Ltd   (2)
14 Healey Circuit, Locked Bag 40, Hunting-
wood, 2148, NSW, Australia
Tel.: (61) 288222700
Web Site: https://www.alfalaval.com.au
Sales Range: $25-49.9 Million
Emp.: 50
Fluid Handling Equipment Mfr
N.A.I.C.S.: 332912

Alfa Laval Copenhagen A/S   (2)
                                     (100%)
Web Site: https://www.alfalaval.com
Sales Range: $150-199.9 Million
Emp.: 600
Technology Services
N.A.I.C.S.: 311224

Subsidiary (Domestic):

Alfa Laval Corporate AB   (2)
Rudeboksvagen 1, 226 55, Lund, Sweden
Tel.: (46) 46366500
Heat Exchanger Mfr & Distr
N.A.I.C.S.: 332410

Subsidiary (Non-US):

**Definox (Beijing) Stainless Steel
Equipment Ltd**   (3)
No 18 East Road - An Ning Zhuang Qu-
inghe, Beijing Haidian District, Beijing,
100085, China
Tel.: (86) 1062934909
Sales Range: $25-49.9 Million
Industrial Valve Mfr
N.A.I.C.S.: 332911

Subsidiary (Non-US):

Alfa Laval Dis Ticaret Ltd Sti   (2)
Yakacik Caddesi No 17, Samandira Kartal,
34885, Istanbul, Türkiye
Tel.: (90) 2163117900
Sales Range: $25-49.9 Million
Emp.: 45
Paper Products
N.A.I.C.S.: 322212
Tayfun Aydemir *(Gen Mgr)*

Alfa Laval EOOD   (2)
Brodisce 26, 1236, Trzin, Slovenia
Tel.: (386) 15637522
Web Site: https://www.alfa-laval.si
Sales Range: $50-74.9 Million
Emp.: 6
Building Materials Distr
N.A.I.C.S.: 423390

Subsidiary (Domestic):

Alfa Laval Europe AB   (2)
Rudeboksvagen 1, Box 93, 226 55, Lund,
Sweden
Tel.: (46) 46367500
Heat Exchanger Mfr
N.A.I.C.S.: 332410
Lars Torstensson *(Gen Mgr)*

Subsidiary (Non-US):

Alfa Laval France SAS   (2)
97 Allee Alexandre Borodine, Saint Priest,
France
Tel.: (33) 469 16 77 00
Web Site: http://local.alfalaval.com
Heating Equipment Mfr & Whlsr
N.A.I.C.S.: 333414

Subsidiary (Domestic):

Alfa Laval HES SA   (3)

Route du Stade ZI du Moulin, Pontcharra,
69490, France
Tel.: (33) 474055350
Web Site: http://www.alfalaval.fr
Water Heater Equipment Mfr
N.A.I.C.S.: 333415

Alfa Laval Moatti SAS   (3)
The Clef Saint-Pierre 10 Rue du Marechal
de Lattre de Tassigny, 78997, Elancourt,
Cedex, France
Tel.: (33) 130818181
Web Site: https://www.alfalaval.fr
Oil Filter Machinery Mfr
N.A.I.C.S.: 333998

Alfa Laval Spiral SAS   (3)
10 rue Alfred Masse, 58028, Nevers,
France
Tel.: (33) 386598300
Power Boiler & Heat Exchanger Mfr
N.A.I.C.S.: 332410

Subsidiary (Non-US):

Alfa Laval Vicarb SAS   (3)
Tel.: (33) 476565050
Emp.: 245
Heat Exchanger Mfr
N.A.I.C.S.: 332410

Subsidiary (Domestic):

Definox SAS   (3)
ZAC de Tabari Sud 2 3 Rue des Papetiers,
44190, Clisson, France
Tel.: (33) 228039850
Stainless Valve Mfr
N.A.I.C.S.: 332911

Subsidiary (Non-US):

Alfa Laval Groningen BV   (2)
Peizerweg 97, Groningen, 9700 AA, Nether-
lands
Tel.: (31) 50 5217 555
Emp.: 100
Heat Exchanger Mfr
N.A.I.C.S.: 332410

Alfa Laval Holding BV   (2)
Baarschot 2, 4817 ZZ, Breda, Netherlands
Tel.: (31) 765791200
Investment Management Service
N.A.I.C.S.: 523940

Subsidiary (Non-US):

Alfa Laval Holding GmbH   (3)
Wilhelm-Bergner-Strasse 7, Glinde, 21503,
Germany
Tel.: (49) 40727403
Emp.: 200
Heat Exchanger Mfr
N.A.I.C.S.: 332410

Subsidiary (Domestic):

Alfa Laval Mid Europe GmbH   (4)
Wilhelm-Bergner-Strasse 7, 21509, Glinde,
Germany
Tel.: (49) 40727403
Sales Range: $50-74.9 Million
Emp.: 200
Designer, Mfr & Distr of Process Lines &
Components for Heat Transfer, Separation
& Fluid Handling
N.A.I.C.S.: 333248

Subsidiary (Non-US):

Alfa Laval Mid Europe GmbH   (4)
Strasse 2 M7/1 IZ-NO-Sud, 2355, Wiener
Neudorf, Austria   (100%)
Tel.: (43) 22366820
Sales Range: $10-24.9 Million
Emp.: 25
Mfr of Barn Equipment
N.A.I.C.S.: 332323
Martin Leodolter *(Mgr-Site)*

Subsidiary (Domestic):

Tranter Warmetauscher GmbH   (5)
Kammeringstrasse 18, 2353, Guntramsdorf,
Austria
Tel.: (43) 223656623
Web Site: http://www.tranter.com
Emp.: 6
Plate Heat Exchanger Mfr
N.A.I.C.S.: 332410
Harald Rottenschlager *(Mgr-Sls)*

Subsidiary (Non-US):

Alfa-Laval Mid Europe AG   (4)
Richtiarkade 18, 8304, Wallisellen,
Switzerland   (100%)
Tel.: (41) 448071414
Sales Range: $25-49.9 Million
Emp.: 19
Farm Equipment
N.A.I.C.S.: 333111

Subsidiary (US):

Alfa Laval USA Inc.   (3)
5400 International Trade Dr, Richmond, VA
23231
Tel.: (804) 222-5300
Web Site: https://www.alfalaval.com
Heat Exchanger Mfr
N.A.I.C.S.: 332410
Jo Vanhoren *(Pres-North America)*

Subsidiary (Domestic):

Alfa Laval US Holding Inc.   (4)
5400 International Trade Dr, Richmond, VA
23231
Tel.: (804) 222-5300
Food Processing Machinery Mfr
N.A.I.C.S.: 333241

Subsidiary (Domestic):

AGC Heat Transfer Inc.   (5)
10129 Piper Ln, Bristow, VA 20136
Tel.: (703) 257-1660
Web Site: https://www.agcheattransfer.com
Heat Exchanger Mfr & Whslr
N.A.I.C.S.: 332410
George Tholl *(Dir-R&D-Portland)*

Plant (Domestic):

**AGC Heat Transfer Inc. - Western
Factory**   (6)
3109 NE 230th Ave, Fairview, OR 97024
Tel.: (503) 774-7342
Web Site: http://www.agcheattransfer.com
Sales Range: $75-99.9 Million
Heat Exchanger Mfr
N.A.I.C.S.: 332410
George Tholl *(Dir-R&D)*

Subsidiary (Domestic):

Alfa Laval Inc.   (5)
5400 International Trade Dr, Richmond, VA
23231
Tel.: (804) 222-5300
Web Site: https://www.alfalaval.us
Sales Range: $25-49.9 Million
Emp.: 100
Food Product Machinery Mfr
N.A.I.C.S.: 333241

Subsidiary (Domestic):

Alfa Laval Aalborg Inc.   (6)
3118 Commerce Pkwy, Miramar, FL 33025
Tel.: (954) 435-5999
Web Site: http://www.aalborg-industries.com
Sales Range: $25-49.9 Million
Emp.: 13
Marine Heating Boiler Services & Whlsr
N.A.I.C.S.: 423720

Alfa Laval Flow Inc.   (6)
9560 - 58th Pl Ste 300, Kenosha, WI 53144
Tel.: (262) 605-2600
Web Site: http://www.alfalaval.us
Sales Range: $25-49.9 Million
Emp.: 50
Rotary Lube, Peristaltic, Gear & Diaphragm
Pumps
N.A.I.C.S.: 423830

Branch (Domestic):

Alfa Laval Inc. - Kenosha   (6)
9560 58th Pl Ste 300, Kenosha, WI 53144
Tel.: (262) 605-2600
Web Site: https://www.alfalaval.us
Sales Range: $50-74.9 Million
Emp.: 100
Flow Equipment Mfr & Retailer
N.A.I.C.S.: 423830

Alfa Laval Inc. - Product Center   (6)
111 Parker St, Newburyport, MA 01950-
4011
Tel.: (978) 465-5777

Web Site: https://www.alfalaval.us
Sales Range: $25-49.9 Million
Emp.: 25
Scraped Surface Heat Exchanger Distr
N.A.I.C.S.: 423730

Subsidiary (Domestic):

Alfa Laval Sharples   (6)
955 Mearns Rd, Warminster, PA 18974-
2811
Tel.: (215) 443-4000
Sales Range: $25-49.9 Million
Emp.: 80
Mfr of Centrifuges
N.A.I.C.S.: 541613
John Atanasio *(Branch Pres)*

Branch (Domestic):

Alfa Laval, Inc.   (6)
955 Mearns Rd, Warminster, PA 18974
Tel.: (215) 443-4000
Web Site: https://www.alfalaval.com
Emp.: 90
Mfr & Distr of Industrial, Environmental &
Marine Separators & Decanters
N.A.I.C.S.: 541613

Subsidiary (Domestic):

Autorad, Inc.   (5)
2050 N Ruby St, Melrose Park, IL 60160
Tel.: (708) 345-5400
Web Site: http://www.stanref.com
Sales Range: $25-49.9 Million
Emp.: 185
Refrigerants
N.A.I.C.S.: 333415

Subsidiary (Domestic):

Ketema LP   (6)
2300 W Marshall Dr, Grand Prairie, TX
75051-3509
Tel.: (972) 647-2626
Sales Range: $25-49.9 Million
Emp.: 50
Mfr of Whitlock Hi-Transfer Heat Exchang-
ers for Standard & Custom Heat Transfer
Applications; ACME
N.A.I.C.S.: 333415

Subsidiary (Domestic):

Definox Inc.   (5)
16720 W Victor Rd, New Berlin, WI 53151
Tel.: (262) 797-5730
Web Site: http://www.definox.com
Sales Range: $25-49.9 Million
Emp.: 5
Stainless Valve Mfr
N.A.I.C.S.: 332919

Gamajet Cleaning Systems, Inc.   (5)
735 Fox Chase Rd Ste 108, Coatesville, PA
19320
Tel.: (610) 408-9940
Web Site: http://www.gamajet.com
Emp.: 20
Other Commercial & Service Industry Ma-
chinery Mfr
N.A.I.C.S.: 333310
Robert E. Delaney *(Pres)*

Hutchison Hayes Separation Inc.   (5)
3520 E Sam Houston Pkwy N, Houston, TX
77015
Tel.: (713) 455-9600
Web Site: http://hutch-hayes.com
Separation Equipment Whslr
N.A.I.C.S.: 423830
Mike Dunson *(Pres & CEO)*

Niagara Blower Company   (5)
673 Ontario St, Buffalo, NY 14207
Tel.: (716) 875-2000
Web Site: http://www.niagarablower.com
Sales Range: $50-74.9 Million
Emp.: 120
Mfr of Process Equipment for Industry &
Heat Transfer
N.A.I.C.S.: 333415

Tranter Inc.   (5)
1900 Old Burk Hwy, Wichita Falls, TX
76306
Tel.: (940) 723-7125
Web Site: http://www.tranter.com

Alfa Laval AB—(Continued)

Sales Range: $25-49.9 Million
Emp.: 200
Heat Exchanger & Gasket Mfr
N.A.I.C.S.: 332410

Tranter PHE, Inc. (5)
1900 Old Burk Hwy, Wichita Falls, TX
76307
Tel.: (940) 723-7125
Web Site: http://www.tranter.com
Sales Range: $125-149.9 Million
Emp.: 227
Welded & Gasketed Plate Heat Exchangers
Mfr
N.A.I.C.S.: 332410
Scott Poenitzsch (VP & Gen Mgr)

Subsidiary (Non-US):

Tranter HES GmbH (6)
Hohe-Flum-Strasse 31, Schopfheim, 79650,
Germany
Tel.: (49) 7622 66689 0
Sales Range: $25-49.9 Million
Emp.: 70
Spiral Heat Exchanger Mfr & Whlsr
N.A.I.C.S.: 332410

Tranter Heat Exchangers Canada
Inc. (6)
4080 78 Ave NW, Edmonton, T6B 3M8, AB,
Canada
Tel.: (780) 465-4582
Heat Exchanger Mfr
N.A.I.C.S.: 332410

Tranter India Pvt Ltd (6)
Gat no 127/128 Dhingrajwadi, Tal Shirur,
Pune, 412 208, Maharashtra, India
Tel.: (91) 2137677000
Emp.: 150
Heat Exchanger Mfr
N.A.I.C.S.: 332410

Tranter International AB (6)
Maria Skolgata 79 B, Stockholm, SE 118
53, Sweden (100%)
Tel.: (46) 84424970
Web Site: http://www.tranter.com
Sales Range: $25-49.9 Million
Emp.: 100
Heat Exchanger Mfr
N.A.I.C.S.: 332410
Manfred Maierhofer (Dir-Sls)

Subsidiary (Non-US):

Tranter SAS (7)
39 Rue Des Peupliers, 92000, Nanterre,
France
Tel.: (33) 147517572
Heat Exchanger Mfr
N.A.I.C.S.: 332410
Frederic Candelier (Mgr-Sls)

Subsidiary (Non-US):

Tranter Solarice GmbH (6)
Am Kalkfeld 7, Artern, 06556, Germany
Tel.: (49) 3466 339540
Web Site: http://www.solarice.de
Sales Range: $25-49.9 Million
Emp.: 4
Air Conditioning Equipment Mfr
N.A.I.C.S.: 333415

Subsidiary (Non-US):

Alfa Laval Holdings Ltd (2)
7 Doman Road, Camberley, GU153 DN,
Surrey, United Kingdom
Tel.: (44) 127663383
Emp.: 150
Investment Management Service
N.A.I.C.S.: 523940

Alfa Laval Iberia S.A. (2)
C/ Francisco Gervas 4 2 planta, Alcoben-
das, 28108, Madrid, Spain
Tel.: (34) 913790600
Sales Range: $50-74.9 Million
Emp.: 200
Mfr of Separators; Pumps; Heat Exchang-
ers; Fresh-Water Distillers; Electrically
Heated Boilers; Oil Heaters; Static Separa-
tors
N.A.I.C.S.: 333241

Alfa Laval K.K. (2)

2-12-23 Konan Meishan Takahama Building
10th floor, Minato-ku, Tokyo, 108-0075, Ja-
pan
Tel.: (81) 35 462 2442
Web Site: https://www.alfalaval.jp
Sales Range: $50-74.9 Million
Emp.: 200
N.A.I.C.S.: 322212

Alfa Laval Kft. (2)
Aliz utca 4, 1117, Budapest,
Hungary (100%)
Tel.: (36) 18899700
Web Site: https://www.alfalaval.hu
Sales Range: $1-9.9 Million
Emp.: 20
Heat Transfer & Fluid Handling Mfr
N.A.I.C.S.: 332410

Alfa Laval Kolding A/S (2)
Albuen 31, 6000, Kolding, Denmark
Tel.: (45) 44576200
Web Site: https://www.alfalaval.dk
Sales Range: $200-249.9 Million
Emp.: 600
Industrial Machinery Mfr
N.A.I.C.S.: 333248

Subsidiary (Domestic):

Alfa Laval Nakskov A/S (3)
Stavangervej 10, 4900, Nakskov, Denmark
Tel.: (45) 70204900
Web Site: http://local.alfalaval.com
Sales Range: $25-49.9 Million
Emp.: 86
Industrial Machinery Mfr
N.A.I.C.S.: 333248

Alfa Laval Tank Equipment A/S (3)
Baldershoj 19, Ishoj, 2635, Denmark
Tel.: (45) 43 55 86 00
Sales Range: $25-49.9 Million
Emp.: 55
Industrial Tank Mfr
N.A.I.C.S.: 332420

Subsidiary (Non-US):

Alfa Laval Korea Ltd. (2)
10 Toegye-ro, Jung-gu Seoul Metro Tower
10th Floor Alfa Laval Korea, Seoul, 04637,
Korea (South)
Tel.: (82) 234060600
Web Site: https://www.alfalaval.kr
Sales Range: $25-49.9 Million
Emp.: 18
Paper Products
N.A.I.C.S.: 322212

Alfa Laval Krakow Sp.z.o.o. (2)
Zawila 56, 30390, Krakow, Poland
Tel.: (48) 122529999
Sales Range: $25-49.9 Million
Emp.: 100
Heat Exchanger Mfr
N.A.I.C.S.: 332410

Alfa Laval LKM A/S (2)
Albuen 31, Kolding, 6000,
Denmark (100%)
Tel.: (45) 79322200
Web Site: http://www.alfalaval.dk
Sales Range: $150-199.9 Million
Emp.: 500
Mfr of Stainless Steel Fittings & Tank Ac-
cessories
N.A.I.C.S.: 332420

Alfa Laval Limited (2)
7 Doman Road, Camberley, GU15 3DN,
Surrey, United Kingdom
Tel.: (44) 127 663 3833
Web Site: https://www.alfalaval.co.uk
Sales Range: $25-49.9 Million
Emp.: 100
Mfr of Vacuum Pumps & Separations for
Industrial & Marine Purposes
N.A.I.C.S.: 333914

Subsidiary (Domestic):

Alfa Laval Finance Co Ltd (3)
7 Doman Road, Camberley, GU15 3DN,
Surrey, United Kingdom
Tel.: (44) 127663383
Financial Management Services
N.A.I.C.S.: 523999

Branch (Domestic):

Alfa Laval Limited (3)

---

7 Doman Road, Camberley, GU15 3DN,
Surrey, United Kingdom
Tel.: (44) 127663383
Web Site: https://www.alfalaval.co.uk
Sales Range: $25-49.9 Million
Emp.: 200
Pumps Mfr
N.A.I.C.S.: 333914

Alfa Laval Ltd. (3)
7 Doman Road, Camberley, GU15 3DN,
Surrey, United Kingdom
Tel.: (44) 127 663 3833
Web Site: https://www.alfalaval.co.uk
Sales Range: $25-49.9 Million
Emp.: 3
Paper Product Sales
N.A.I.C.S.: 322212

Subsidiary (Non-US):

Alfa Laval Ltd (2)
2 Yanko Sakazov Str Kv, Druzhba, Sliven,
8806, Bulgaria
Tel.: (359) 44 674 114
Web Site: http://www.alfalaval.com
Sales Range: $25-49.9 Million
Emp.: 3
Plate Heat Exchanger Mfr
N.A.I.C.S.: 332410

Subsidiary (Domestic):

Alfa Laval Lund AB (2)
Rude boks vagen 1, PO Box 74, Lund, 221
00, Skane, Sweden
Tel.: (46) 46 366 500
Web Site: http://www.alfalaval.com
Sales Range: $150-199.9 Million
Emp.: 1,000
Heat Exchanger Mfr
N.A.I.C.S.: 332410

Subsidiary (Non-US):

Alfa Laval Makine Sanayii ve Ticaret
Ltd Sti (2)
Fatih Mh Yakacik Cad No 23, Samandira,
34885, Istanbul, Turkiye
Tel.: (90) 2163117900
Web Site: https://www.alfalaval.com.tr
Emp.: 55
Heat Exchanger Mfr
N.A.I.C.S.: 332410

Alfa Laval Middle East Ltd (2)
Building No 13 Street No 6 Community No
364, Al Quoz Industrial Area, Dubai, United
Arab Emirates
Tel.: (971) 4 372 0800
Web Site: https://www.alfalaval.ae
Heat Exchanger Mfr
N.A.I.C.S.: 332410
Nibu Rahim (Mgr-Wastewater Industry)

Alfa Laval NV (2)
Baarschot 2, Breda, 4817 ZZ, Netherlands
Tel.: (31) 765791200
Emp.: 150
Real Estate Managment Services
N.A.I.C.S.: 531390

Subsidiary (Non-US):

Alfa Laval Ltda (3)
Av Mutinga 4935 Building A Vila Jaguara,
Sao Paulo, 05110-903, Brazil
Tel.: (55) 1151886000
Web Site: https://www.alfalaval.com.br
Air Conditioner & Refrigerator Mfr & Whlsr
N.A.I.C.S.: 333415

Subsidiary (Domestic):

Alfa Laval Nederland BV (3)
Baarschot 2, Breda, 4817ZZ, Netherlands
Tel.: (31) 765 79 12 00
Financial Management Services
N.A.I.C.S.: 523999

Subsidiary (Domestic):

Helpman Capital BV (4)
Peizerweg 97, Groningen, 9727AJ, Nether-
lands
Tel.: (31) 505 21 75 55
Web Site: http://www.helpman.com
Emp.: 60
Financial Management Services
N.A.I.C.S.: 523999

Subsidiary (Non-US):

Alfa Laval S.A. (3)
Argentine Republic 5212 triangle area Mal-
vinas Argentinas, Tigre, 1648, Buenos Ai-
res, Argentina
Tel.: (54) 9116 045 1377
Web Site: https://www.alfalaval.lat
Sales Range: $25-49.9 Million
Emp.: 100
Mfr of Separators, Milking Machines, Plate
Heat Exchangers
N.A.I.C.S.: 333241

Alfa Laval S.A. de C.V. (3)
Gustavo Baz No 352, Col La Loma, 54060,
Tlalnepantla, Estado de Mexico, Mexico
Tel.: (52) 5530032700
Web Site: http://www.alfalaval.mx
Sales Range: $50-74.9 Million
Emp.: 75
Industrial Equipment & Machinery Sales,
Service & Distr
N.A.I.C.S.: 423830

Alfa-Laval Inc. (3)
101 Milner Avenue, Scarborough, M1S 4S6,
ON, Canada
Tel.: (416) 299-6101
Web Site: https://www.alfalaval.ca
Sales Range: $50-74.9 Million
Emp.: 60
Sales of Tanks, Cooling Tanks & Cheese-
making Equipment
N.A.I.C.S.: 423830

Subsidiary (Non-US):

Alfa Laval New Zealand Ltd. (2)
307 Sandwich Road, PO Box 20424, Te
Rapa, Hamilton, 3200, New Zealand
Tel.: (64) 7 849 6025
Web Site: https://www.alfalaval.co.nz
Emp.: 20
Fluid Handling Equipment Mfr
N.A.I.C.S.: 332912

Alfa Laval Nordic A/S (2)
Billingstadsletta 13, 1396, Billingstad, Nor-
way
Tel.: (47) 66858000
Web Site: https://www.alfalaval.no
Sales Range: $50-74.9 Million
Emp.: 69
Heating & Filtering Equipment Distr
N.A.I.C.S.: 423720

Subsidiary (Domestic):

Alfa Laval Nordick AB (2)
Hans Stahles vag 7, 147 80, Tumba, Swe-
den
Tel.: (46) 853065600
Web Site: https://www.alfalaval.se
Emp.: 200
Mfr of Centrifugal Separators & Decanter
Centrifuges, Desalination Plant
N.A.I.C.S.: 333415

Subsidiary (Non-US):

Alfa Laval Olmi SpA (2)
Viale Europa 43, Suisio, 24040, Bergamo,
Italy
Tel.: (39) 035999111
Web Site: https://www.alfalaval.it
Heat Exchanger Mfr
N.A.I.C.S.: 332410

Alfa Laval Oy (2)
Self - goverment streets 6, PO Box 51,
02600, Espoo, Finland
Tel.: (358) 9804041
Web Site: http://www.alfalaval.fi
Sales Range: $10-24.9 Million
Emp.: 40
N.A.I.C.S.: 322212

Subsidiary (Domestic):

Alfa Laval Vantaa OY (2)
Ansatie 3, 01740, Vantaa, Finland
Tel.: (358) 9 894 41
Web Site: http://www.alfalaval.fi
Emp.: 150
Air Conditioning & Heating Equipment Mfr
N.A.I.C.S.: 333415
Voutilainen Jarmo (Fin Dir)

Subsidiary (Non-US):

Alfa Laval Packinox (2)

14 rue de Bassano, 75116, Paris,
France **(100%)**
Tel.: (33) 15 367 4141
Web Site: https://www.alfalaval.fr
Emp.: 9
Mfr of Plate Exchangers
N.A.I.C.S.: 332313

Subsidiary (Non-US):

Packinox Moscow **(3)**
15/13 Petrovska Street Apt 19, 103031,
Moscow, Russia
Tel.: (7) 4952342837
Web Site: http://www.packinox.com
Distr of Plate Exchangers
N.A.I.C.S.: 423490

Subsidiary (Non-US):

Alfa Laval Philippines, Inc. **(2)**
4th Floor Molave Building 2231 Chino Ro-
ces Avenue, Makati, 1231, Metro Manila,
Philippines **(100%)**
Tel.: (63) 288127596
Sales Range: $25-49.9 Million
Emp.: 20
Paper Products
N.A.I.C.S.: 322212

Alfa Laval Polska Sp. zoo **(2)**
Ul Marynarska 15, 02-674, Warsaw,
Poland **(100%)**
Tel.: (48) 223366464
Web Site: https://www.alfalaval.pl
Sales Range: $25-49.9 Million
Emp.: 16
Spare Parts, Separators, Gaskets Mfr
N.A.I.C.S.: 333248

Alfa Laval Polska Sp. zoo **(2)**
Ul Jedrzejowska 85, 93-636, Lodz, Poland
Tel.: (48) 69 542 6600
Web Site: https://www.alfalaval.pl
Sales Range: $25-49.9 Million
Emp.: 50
N.A.I.C.S.: 322212

Alfa Laval S.A. **(2)**
Calle 100 19A - 30 Floor 4, Bogota, Colom-
bia
Tel.: (57) 6012916330
Web Site: https://www.alfalaval.com.co
Sales Range: $25-49.9 Million
Emp.: 25
Heat Transfer Mfr & Distr
N.A.I.C.S.: 332410

Alfa Laval S.A. **(2)**
Av Jose Larco 1232 Miraflores Lima We-
Work Favor solicitar cita, Lima, Peru
Web Site: http://www.alfaval.com.pe
Purifier & Separator Whlsr
N.A.I.C.S.: 423830
Tom Erixon *(Pres & CEO)*

Alfa Laval S.A.C.I. **(2)**
San Sebastian No 2839 Oficina 401, PO
Box 122, Las Condes, Santiago,
Chile **(100%)**
Tel.: (56) 223530300
Web Site: http://www.alfalaval.lat
Sales Range: $10-24.9 Million
Emp.: 25
Mfr of Equipment, Systems & Services for
Heat Transfer & Treatment, Fluid Handling
& Liquid/Solid Separations
N.A.I.C.S.: 332811

Alfa Laval S.A.S **(2)**
Lyon Technology Park Sequoia Building 3,
97 Alley Alexander Borodin, 69792, Saint
Priest, Cedex, France **(100%)**
Tel.: (33) 46 916 7700
Web Site: https://www.alfalaval.fr
Sales Range: $200-249.9 Million
Emp.: 750
Mfr of Processing Equipment; Separators;
Heat Exchangers
N.A.I.C.S.: 333415

Alfa Laval S.R.L. **(2)**
Str Baratiei Nr 35 Sector 3, 030197, Bucha-
rest, Romania
Tel.: (40) 21 310 0730
Web Site: https://www.alfalaval.ro
Sales Range: $25-49.9 Million
Emp.: 15
Heat Transfer & Fluid Handling Distr
N.A.I.C.S.: 333996

Alfa Laval S.p.A. **(2)**
Via Delle Albere 5, Alonte, 36040, Vicenza,
Italy
Tel.: (39) 0444725411
Sales Range: $100-124.9 Million
Emp.: 350
Mfr Separators
N.A.I.C.S.: 333241

Subsidiary (Domestic):

Alfa Laval Parma Srl **(3)**
Via Martiri Liberazione 12, 43126, Parma,
Italy
Tel.: (39) 052 130 2811
Web Site: https://www.astepo.com
Emp.: 13
Food Processing Machinery Mfr
N.A.I.C.S.: 333241

Subsidiary (Non-US):

Framo Flatey AS **(3)**
Flatoyvegen 24, 5918, Frekhaug, Norway
Tel.: (47) 55999400
Pumping Equipment Mfr
N.A.I.C.S.: 333914

Subsidiary (Domestic):

Tranter Srl **(3)**
Via Ercolano 24, 20052, Monza, Italy
Tel.: (39) 039282821
Heat Exchanger Equipment Mfr
N.A.I.C.S.: 332410

Subsidiary (Non-US):

Alfa Laval SIA **(2)**
Svitrigailos st 11B, 03228, Vilnius,
Lithuania **(100%)**
Tel.: (370) 52133566
Web Site: https://www.alfalaval.lt
Sales Range: $25-49.9 Million
Emp.: 6
Paper Products
N.A.I.C.S.: 322212

Alfa Laval SIA **(2)**
Kr Valdemara str 33 - 9, Riga, 1010, Latvia
Tel.: (371) 6 782 8508
Web Site: https://www.alfalaval.lv
Sales Range: $25-49.9 Million
Emp.: 8
Heating Equipment Distr
N.A.I.C.S.: 423720

Alfa Laval Singapore Pte. Ltd. **(2)**
11 Joo Koon Circle, Jurong, 629043, Singa-
pore
Tel.: (65) 65592828
Web Site: https://www.alfalaval.sg
Sales Range: $25-49.9 Million
Emp.: 50
Mfr of Equipment, Systems & Services for
Heat Transfer & Treatment, Fluid Handling
& Liquid/Solid Separations
N.A.I.C.S.: 332811

Alfa Laval Slovakia spol, s.r.o. **(2)**
Racianska 153/A, 831 54, Bratislava,
Slovakia **(100%)**
Tel.: (421) 24 445 5093
Web Site: https://www.alfalaval.sk
Sales Range: $25-49.9 Million
Emp.: 10
Industrial Engineering Services
N.A.I.C.S.: 541330

**Alfa Laval South East Europe
Ltd.** **(2)**
Bul Cherni vrah 1 Floor 6, 1421, Sofia, Bul-
garia
Tel.: (359) 29555666
Sales Range: $25-49.9 Million
Emp.: 14
N.A.I.C.S.: 322212
Peter Scegel *(Mgr)*

Alfa Laval Spol S.R.O. **(2)**
Voctarova 2449/5, 180 00, Prague, Czech
Republic
Tel.: (420) 234710700
Web Site: https://www.alfalaval.cz
Sales Range: $25-49.9 Million
Emp.: 50
Heating Equipment Distr
N.A.I.C.S.: 423720

Subsidiary (Domestic):

Alfa Laval Thermal A/S **(2)**

Rudeboksvagen 1, PO Box 74, Lund,
22655, Sweden
Tel.: (46) 366500
Rev.: $305,640,000
Emp.: 1,800
Provider of Heat Exchangers for Heating,
Ventilation & Engineering Industry
N.A.I.C.S.: 332410
Lars Renstron *(Gen Mgr)*

**Alfa Laval Treasury International
AB** **(2)**
Rudeboksvagen 1, 22655, Lund, Sweden
Tel.: (46) 46367000
Web Site: http://www.alfalaval.com
Investment Management Service
N.A.I.C.S.: 523999

Alfa Laval Tumba AB **(2)**
Hans Stahles vag 7, 147 80, Tumba, Swe-
den
Tel.: (46) 853065000
Web Site: http://www.alfalaval.se
Sales Range: $125-149.9 Million
Emp.: 550
N.A.I.C.S.: 322212

Subsidiary (Non-US):

Alfa Laval Ukraine **(2)**
Novokostyantynivska Street 13/10 office
213, 04080, Kiev, Ukraine
Tel.: (380) 442055667
Web Site: https://www.alfalaval.ua
Sales Range: $25-49.9 Million
Emp.: 20
Heat Exchanger Mfr & Distr
N.A.I.C.S.: 332410

Alfa Laval Venezolana S.A. **(2)**
Apartado Postal 47723, Caracas, 1041,
Venezuela **(100%)**
Tel.: (58) 2127010500
Sales Range: $25-49.9 Million
Emp.: 12
Machinery for Liquid/Solid Separation &
Fluid Handling
N.A.I.C.S.: 333111

Alfa Laval Vietnam LLC **(2)**
3rd Floor Petroland Tower 12 Tan Trao St,
Tan Phu Ward District 7, 72908, Ho Chi
Minh City, Vietnam
Tel.: (84) 2854111400
Industrial Machinery Mfr
N.A.I.C.S.: 333248

Alfa Laval, Taiwan **(2)**
1st Floor 9th Floor No 16 Lane 35 Jihu
Road, Neihu District, Taipei, 114754,
Taiwan **(100%)**
Tel.: (886) 266001166
Web Site: https://www.alfalaval.tw
Sales Range: $25-49.9 Million
Emp.: 33
Paper Products
N.A.I.C.S.: 322212

Alfa-Laval (Malaysia) Sdn Bhd **(2)**
Lot No 4 Jalan Anggerik Mokara 31/54, Yel-
low City, 40460, Shah Alam, Selangor, Ma-
laysia
Tel.: (60) 35 122 2880
Web Site: https://www.alfalaval.my
Sales Range: $25-49.9 Million
Emp.: 60
Paper Products
N.A.I.C.S.: 322212

Alfa-Laval (N.Z.) Ltd. **(2)**
307 Sandwich Road, Te Rapa, Hamilton,
3200, New Zealand
Tel.: (64) 7 849 6025
Web Site: https://www.alfalaval.co.nz
Sales Range: $25-49.9 Million
Emp.: 31
Mfr of Equipment, Systems & Services for
Heat Transfer & Treatment, Fluid Handling
& Liquid/Solid Separations
N.A.I.C.S.: 332811

Alfa-Laval Benelux B.V. **(2)**
Baarschot 2, 4817 ZZ, Breda, Netherlands
Tel.: (31) 765791200
Web Site: https://www.alfalaval.nl
Sales Range: $50-74.9 Million
Emp.: 120
Tanks & Cooling Tanks Mfr
N.A.I.C.S.: 332420

Alfa-Laval Benelux N.V. **(2)**

Bazellaan 5, 1140, Brussels,
Belgium **(100%)**
Tel.: (32) 27283811
Sales Range: $25-49.9 Million
Emp.: 50
Paper Products
N.A.I.C.S.: 322212

Alfa-Laval Iran Co. **(2)**
Unit 10 22nd Floor Negar Tower Vanak Sq,
19687, Tehran, Iran
Tel.: (98) 2188641821
Web Site: http://www.alfalaval.com
Sales Range: $25-49.9 Million
Emp.: 20
Mfr of Equipment, Systems & Services for
Heat Transfer & Treatment, Fluid Handling
& Liquid/Solid Separations
N.A.I.C.S.: 333414

DeLaval S.A. **(2)**
Anabel Segura 7, 28108, Alcobendas, Ma-
drid, Spain
Tel.: (34) 91 490 4473
Web Site: https://www.delaval.com
Sales Range: $25-49.9 Million
Emp.: 35
Milking Systems, Equipment & Products
N.A.I.C.S.: 311511

DeLaval SIA **(2)**
Maskavas iela 240-3, Riga, 1063,
Latvia **(100%)**
Tel.: (371) 6 778 2460
Web Site: https://www.delaval.com
Sales Range: $1-9.9 Million
Emp.: 24
Milk Production Farming Services
N.A.I.C.S.: 112120

Framo AS **(2)**
Florvagvegen 39, PO Box 23, Florvag,
5329, Bergen, Norway
Tel.: (47) 5 599 9000
Web Site: https://www.framo.com
Pumping Equipment Mfr
N.A.I.C.S.: 333914

Subsidiary (Domestic):

Framo Fusa AS **(3)**
Venjanesvegen 217, Fusa, 5641, Horda-
land, Norway
Tel.: (47) 55999600
Pumping Equipment Mfr
N.A.I.C.S.: 333914

Framo Holsney AS **(3)**
Rosslandsvegen 933, 5918, Frekhaug, Nor-
way
Tel.: (47) 55997500
Pumping Equipment Mfr
N.A.I.C.S.: 333914

Subsidiary (US):

Framo Houston Inc. **(3)**
3002 E 13th St, La Porte, TX 77571
Tel.: (281) 884-4800
Pumping Equipment Mfr
N.A.I.C.S.: 333914

Subsidiary (Non-US):

Framo Korea Ltd. **(3)**
RM 608 Centum SH Valley 35 Centum
Dong-Ro, Haeundae-Gu, Busan, 48059,
Korea (South)
Tel.: (82) 517436942
Pumping Equipment Mfr
N.A.I.C.S.: 333914

Framo Nederland BV **(3)**
Edisonweg 18, PO Box 305, 3200 AH,
Spijkenisse, Netherlands
Tel.: (31) 181650300
Pumping Equipment Mfr
N.A.I.C.S.: 333914

Subsidiary (Non-US):

Framo Nippon KK **(4)**
Kotsu Building 5F 5-15-5 Shinbashi, Minato-
ku, Tokyo, 105-0004, Japan
Tel.: (81) 357762405
Pumping Equipment Mfr
N.A.I.C.S.: 333914

Subsidiary (Domestic):

Framo Services AS **(3)**
Florvagvegen 39, PO Box 44, Florvag,

Alfa Laval AB—(Continued)
5329, Bergen, Norway
Tel.: (47) 55999200
Pumping Equipment Mfr
N.A.I.C.S.: 333914

Subsidiary (Non-US):

Framo Shanghai Ltd.　　(3)
Building NO 5 123 Lane 1165 Jin Du Road,
Min Hang District, Shanghai, 201108, China
Tel.: (86) 2161155000
Pumping Equipment Mfr
N.A.I.C.S.: 333914

Framo Singapore Pte. Ltd.　　(3)
17 Tuas View Circuit, Singapore, 637575,
Singapore
Tel.: (65) 62102400
Pumping Equipment Mfr
N.A.I.C.S.: 333914

Framo do Brasil Ltda.　　(3)
Rua Gerson Ferreira 61-lote 56, Ramos,
Rio de Janeiro, 21030-151, Brazil
Tel.: (55) 2125077898
Pumping Equipment Mfr
N.A.I.C.S.: 333914

Subsidiary (Non-US):

Kenus LLP　　(2)
Tole bi 301, Almaty, 050000, Kazakhstan
Tel.: (7) 727 223 15 78
Heating & Air Conditioning Installation Services
N.A.I.C.S.: 238220

LHE Co. Ltd.　　(2)
Hallim-Ro 515beon-Gil, PO Box 50848,
Hallim-Myeon, Gimhae, 203-42,
Gyeongsangnam-do, Korea (South)
Tel.: (82) 553400100
Web Site: https://www.lhe.co.kr
N.A.I.C.S.: 332410
HagBum Kim (Pres)

Subsidiary (US):

MCD Gaskets Inc.　　(2)
10 000 N Central Ste 400, Dallas, TX
75231
Tel.: (804) 997-5289

Subsidiary (Non-US):

OAO Alfa Laval Potok　　(2)
18-ya line of Vasylievsky ostrov Business
center, 199178, Saint Petersburg, Russia
Tel.: (7) 8123247272
Web Site: http://www.alfalaval.com
Heat Exchanger Mfr
N.A.I.C.S.: 332410

Onnuri Industrial Machinery Co.
Ltd　　(2)
Free Trade Zone 2 654-4 Bongam-Dong,
Masan Hoewon-Gu, Changwon, 630-803,
Kyeongnam, Korea (South)
Tel.: (82) 55 286 5177
Web Site: http://www.onnurico.com
Sales Range: $25-49.9 Million
Emp.: 40
Industrial Machinery Mfr & Distr
N.A.I.C.S.: 333248

PT Alfa Laval Indonesia　　(2)
Graha Inti Fauzi - 4th Floor Jl Buncit Raya
No 22, Jakarta Selatan, 12510, Jakarta,
Indonesia
Tel.: (62) 217 918 2288
Web Site: https://www.alfalaval.id
Heating Equipment Mfr & Distr
N.A.I.C.S.: 333414

SIA Alfa Laval Eesti filiaal　　(2)
Paernu Mnt 130, Tallinn, 11317, Estonia
Tel.: (372) 6 55 80 23
Web Site: http://local.alfalaval.com
Heat Exchanger Mfr
N.A.I.C.S.: 332410

Wuxi MCD Gasket Co., Ltd.　　(2)
81 RenMin Road, Qiaoqi Xuxiake Town,
Jiangyin, 214408, Jiangsu Province, China
Tel.: (86) 51086578866
N.A.I.C.S.: 339991

Alfa Laval Italy S.R.L.　　(1)
Via Pusiano 2, 20900, Monza, Italy

Tel.: (39) 0392704444
Heat Transfer Product Mfr & Distr
N.A.I.C.S.: 333415

Alfa Laval New Zeeland Pty. Ltd.　　(1)
307 Sandwich Road, Hamilton, 3200, New
Zealand
Tel.: (64) 78496025
Heat Transfer Product Mfr & Distr
N.A.I.C.S.: 333415

Alfa Laval Niagara Inc.　　(1)
Ste 120, Buffalo, NY 14221
Tel.: (716) 875-2000
Environmental Engineering Services
N.A.I.C.S.: 541330

Alfa Laval Nijmegen B.V.　　(1)
Kerkenbos 1016, 6546 BA, Nijmegen, Netherlands
Tel.: (31) 243523100
Web Site: https://www.alfalaval.nl
Gas Fired Steam Boiler Mfr
N.A.I.C.S.: 332410

Alfa Laval Technologies AB　　(1)
Box 38, 372 21, Ronneby, Sweden
Tel.: (46) 46366500
N.A.I.C.S.: 423610

Alfa Laval Technologies Equipment
and Service Solutions LLC　　(1)
PO Box 79077, Abu Dhabi, United Arab
Emirates
Tel.: (971) 26228850
Heat Transfer Product Mfr & Distr
N.A.I.C.S.: 333415

Alfa Laval d.o.o.　　(1)
Brodisce 26, 1236, Trzin, Slovenia
Tel.: (386) 15637522
Web Site: https://www.alfa-laval.si
Gas Fired Steam Boiler Mfr
N.A.I.C.S.: 332410

Desmet Rosedowns Ltd.　　(1)
Cannon Street, Kingston upon Hull, HU2
0AD, United Kingdom
Tel.: (44) 1482329864
Web Site: https://www.desmet.com
Industrial Equipment Whsr
N.A.I.C.S.: 423830

Framo Flatoy AS　　(1)
Flatoyvegen 24, 5918, Frekhaug, Norway
Tel.: (47) 55999400
Gas Pumping Equipment Mfr & Distr
N.A.I.C.S.: 333914

Framo Holsnoy AS　　(1)
Rosslandsvegen 933, 5918, Frekhaug, Norway
Tel.: (47) 55997500
Piping System Mfr
N.A.I.C.S.: 327332

LiftUP AS　　(1)
Hagensvej 21, 9530, Stovring, Denmark
Tel.: (45) 96863020
Web Site: https://www.liftup.dk
N.A.I.C.S.: 333923
Flemming Eriksen (Co-Founder)

MCD S.A.S.　　(1)
Lieu-dit le vieux chateau, 02300, Guny,
France
Tel.: (33) 323526767
Web Site: https://groupmcd.com
Emp.: 200
Industrial Machinery Mfr & Distr
N.A.I.C.S.: 333248

PSM Instrumentation Ltd.　　(1)
Unit 3 Burrell Road, Haywards Heath, RH16
1TW, West Sussex, United Kingdom
Tel.: (44) 1444410040
Web Site: https://psminstrumentation.com
Pressure Sensor Mfr
N.A.I.C.S.: 334519

Scanjet Asia Pacific Pte. Ltd.　　(1)
No 3 Ang Mo Kio Street 62 01-45, Singapore, 569139, Singapore
Tel.: (65) 62417138
Pressure Sensor Mfr
N.A.I.C.S.: 334519

Scanjet Marine & Systems AB　　(1)
Datavagen 6A, Askim, 436 32, Gothenburg,
Sweden
Tel.: (46) 313387530
Web Site: https://scanjet.net

Document Scanner Mfr
N.A.I.C.S.: 333310

Stolz S.A.S.　　(1)
82 route de Boisjean, 62170, Wailly-
Beaucamp, France
Tel.: (33) 321900505
Web Site: https://www.stolz.fr
Feed Mill Mfr
N.A.I.C.S.: 311119

Stolz Sequipag S.A.S.　　(1)
82 route de Boisjean, 62170, Wailly-
Beaucamp, France
Tel.: (33) 321900505
Web Site: https://www.stolz.fr
Industrial Equipment Mfr
N.A.I.C.S.: 333248

StormGeo AS　　
Nordre Nostekaien 1, 5011, Bergen, Norway
Tel.: (47) 5 570 6170
Web Site: https://www.stormgeo.com
Sales Range: $50-74.9 Million
Emp.: 320
Commercial Weather Service
N.A.I.C.S.: 541620
Gard Hauge (CTO)

Subsidiary (US):

Applied Weather Technology,
Inc.　　(2)
140 Kifer Ct, Sunnyvale, CA 94086
Tel.: (408) 731-8600
Web Site: http://www.awtworldwide.com
Sales Range: $1-9.9 Million
Emp.: 13
Maritime Weather Routing Solutions
N.A.I.C.S.: 513210
Haydn Jones (CEO)

Subsidiary (Non-US):

StormGeo AB　　(2)
Kormakargrand 6 4tr, 111 22, Stockholm,
Sweden
Tel.: (46) 841005510
Web Site: http://www.stormgeo.com
Environmental Consulting Activities
N.A.I.C.S.: 541620
Johan Groth (Mng Dir)

StormGeo FZ LLC　　(2)
Office 1907 Business Central Tower A, PO
Box 102628, Dubai Media City, Dubai,
102628, United Arab Emirates
Tel.: (971) 43678257
Web Site: https://www.stormgeo.com
Environmental Consulting Services
N.A.I.C.S.: 541620
Daniel Mathew (Mng Dir)

StormGeo Germany　　(2)
Gasstrasse 18 Haus 6a, 22761, Hamburg,
Germany
Tel.: (49) 408 221 1872
Web Site: https://www.stormgeo.com
Emp.: 4
Environmental Consulting Activities
N.A.I.C.S.: 541620
Anna Hilden (Mgr-Global Industry-Offshore
Wind)

StormGeo Korea　　(2)
Room 908 Hanaro Bldg 25 Insadong 5-gil,
Jongno-gu, Seoul, 03162, Korea (South)
Tel.: (82) 2 739 3464
Web Site: http://www.stormgeo.com
Environmental Consulting Activities
N.A.I.C.S.: 541620
Ick-Soo Mok (Mng Dir)

StormGeo Limited　　(2)
Unit 6 Kingshill Park Venture Drive, Arnhall
Business Park, Westhill, AB32 6FL, Aberdeenshire, United Kingdom
Tel.: (44) 1224766580
Environmental Consulting Activities
N.A.I.C.S.: 541620

StormGeo Singapore　　(2)
16 Science Park Dr 04-02 Dnv Gl Technology Center, Singapore, 118227, Singapore
Tel.: (65) 6 224 7068
Web Site: http://www.stormgeo.com
Environmental Consulting Activities
N.A.I.C.S.: 541620
Duncan Wyse (Sls Mgr)

StormGeo do Brasil　　(2)
Rua Sete de Setembro 98 9 andar sala 909
Centro, Rio de Janeiro, Brazil
Tel.: (55) 2197 412 4929
Web Site: http://www.stormgeo.com
Environmental Consulting Activities
N.A.I.C.S.: 541620
Kieran Nash (Mng Dir)

StormGeo Brasil AS　　(1)
Nordre Nostekaien 1, 5011, Bergen, Norway
Tel.: (47) 55706170
Web Site: https://www.stormgeo.com
Weather Intelligence Analytic Services
N.A.I.C.S.: 541990

StormGeo Denmark A/S　　(1)
Maskinvej 5, 2860, Soborg, Denmark
Tel.: (45) 39536000
Renewable Energy Generation Services
N.A.I.C.S.: 221118

StormGeo Japan KK　　(1)
10th Floor Meisan Takayama Bldg 2-12-23,
Kohnan Minato-ku, Tokyo, 108-0075, Japan
Tel.: (81) 368695553
Weather Intelligence Analytic Services
N.A.I.C.S.: 541990

StormGeo PH Inc.　　(1)
7/F Dohle Haus Manila 30-38 Sen Gil Puyat
Ave, Brgy San Isidro, Makati, 1234, Philippines
Tel.: (63) 285597877
Weather Intelligence Analytic Services
N.A.I.C.S.: 541990

StormGeo Pte. Ltd.　　(1)
16 Science Park Dr 04-02 DNV, Technology
Center, Singapore, 118227, Singapore
Tel.: (65) 62247068
Weather Analytic Services
N.A.I.C.S.: 541990

UAB StormGeo　　(1)
K Kalinausko gatve 2 b 4th Floor, LT03107,
Vilnius, Lithuania
Tel.: (370) 55706170
Marine Shipping Services
N.A.I.C.S.: 541990

ALFA TRANSFORMERS LTD.
No 3337 Mancheswar Industrial Estate, Bhubaneswar, 751010, Orissa,
India
Tel.: (91) 6742580484
Web Site: https://www.alfa.in
517546—(BOM)
Rev.: $4,018,901
Assets: $4,929,479
Liabilities: $2,959,661
Net Worth: $1,969,818
Earnings: $138,446
Fiscal Year-end: 03/31/23
Transformer Mfr
N.A.I.C.S.: 335311
Dillip Kumar Das (Mng Dir)

ALFA WOOD BULGARIA S.A.
Industrial area, Dolni Chiflik, 9120,
Bulgaria
Tel.: (359) 52 685 806
Web Site: http://www.alfawood.bg
Wood Processing
N.A.I.C.S.: 321999

ALFA, S.A.B. DE C.V.
Ave Gomez Morin 1111 South, Col
Carrizalejo San Pedro, 66254, Garza
Garcia, NL, Mexico
Tel.: (52) 8187481111　　MX
Web Site: https://www.alfa.com.mx
Year Founded: 1974
ALFFF—(OTCIQ)
Rev.: $15,486,176,200
Assets: $13,528,008,890
Liabilities: $10,772,157,220
Net Worth: $2,755,851,670
Earnings: $373,455,830
Emp.: 83,400
Fiscal Year-end: 12/31/21
Refined Petroleum Mfr
N.A.I.C.S.: 324110

Armando Garza Sada *(Chm)*

Subsidiaries:

Alfa Corporativo, S.A. de C.V.　(1)
Av Gomez Morin No 1111 Sur Carrizalejo,
Garza Garcia, 66200, Nuevo Leon, Mexico
Tel.: (52) 8187481111
Petrochemical Mfr
N.A.I.C.S.: 325110

Alpek Polyester Brasil S.A.　(1)
Rodovia PE60 Km10 Zona Industrial 3B
zi-3b s/n, Ipojuca, 55590-000, Pernambuco,
Brazil
Tel.: (55) 8133114950
Web Site: https://alpekpolyester.com.br
Plastics Material & Resin Mfr
N.A.I.C.S.: 325211

**Alpek Polyester Pernambuco S.
A.　(1)**
Rodovia PE 60 KM 10 Zona Industrial 3B
Suape, Ipojuca, 55590-000, Pernambuco,
Brazil
Tel.: (55) 8133435200
Plastics Material & Resin Mfr
N.A.I.C.S.: 325211

Alpek Polyester UK Ltd.　(1)
Davies Office, Redcar, TS10 4XZ, United
Kingdom
Tel.: (44) 1642451000
Plastics Material & Resin Mfr
N.A.I.C.S.: 325211

Alpek, S.A. de C.V.　(1)
Ave Gomez Morin 1111 Sur Col Carrizalejo,
San Pedro, Garza Garcia, 66254, NL,
Mexico　**(100%)**
Tel.: (52) 8187481111
Web Site: http://www.alpek.com
Sales Range: $1-4.9 Billion
Emp.: 6,550
Petrochemical Group Involved in Raw Material for Polyester, Fibers & Polymers & Plastics & Chemicals
N.A.I.C.S.: 324110
Jose de Jesus Valdez *(CEO)*

Subsidiary (Domestic):

Akra Polyester, S.A. de C.V.　(2)
Ave Ruiz Cortines y Privada El Roble SN,
Col Pedro Lozano, Monterrey, 64400,
Nuevo Leon, Mexico
Tel.: (52) 81 8389 3100
Web Site: http://www.akra.com
Polyester Filament & Polymers Mfr & Distr
N.A.I.C.S.: 325110

Alpek Polyester S.A. de C.V.　(2)
Avenida Ricardo Margain 444 Torre Equus
Sur Piso 16, San Pedro Garza Garcia,
66265, Nuevo Leon, Mexico　**(100%)**
Tel.: (52) 8187481500
Web Site: http://www.petrotemex.com
Petrochemical Mfr
N.A.I.C.S.: 325110

Subsidiary (Domestic):

**DAK Resinas Americas Mexico, S.A.
de C.V.　(3)**
Predio Buenavista de Torres Km 29 Barrancas, Cosoleacaque Veracruz, 96345,
Mexico, Mexico
Tel.: (52) 9212116000
Web Site: http://www.dakamericas.com.mx
Resin Product Mfr
N.A.I.C.S.: 325211

Subsidiary (Domestic):

Indelpro, S.A. de C.V.　(2)
Boulevard Petrocel KM 0 5 Colonia, Puerto
Industrial, 89603, Altamira, Tamaulipas,
Mexico
Tel.: (52) 8335001600
Web Site: http://www.indelpro.com
Sales Range: $50-74.9 Million
Polypropylene Resin Mfr
N.A.I.C.S.: 325211

Joint Venture (Domestic):

Polioles S.A. de C.V.　(2)
Fernando Montes de Oca No 71 Col Condesa, Del Cuauhtemoc, 06140, Mexico, DF,
Mexico　**(50%)**
Tel.: (52) 559 140 0500

Web Site: https://www.polioles.com.mx
Emp.: 360
Petrochemicals Mfr & Whslr
N.A.I.C.S.: 325110

Braedt, S. A.　(1)
Av Michael Faraday 111, Ate, Peru
Tel.: (51) 12011490
Web Site: http://www.braedt.com.pe
Veal Product Mfr
N.A.I.C.S.: 311612

Colombin Bel, S.A. de C.V.　(1)
Camino Viejo a Tonala 1729 Cd Aztlan,
Tonala, 45400, Guadalajara, Jalisco,
Mexico
Tel.: (52) 3338128940
Web Site: http://www.colombinbel.com
Polyurethane Foam Mfr
N.A.I.C.S.: 326150

Plant (Domestic):

**Colombin Bel, S.A. de C.V. - SANTA
CATARINA PLANT　(2)**
Galeana 201 Sector Industrial El Lechugal,
66350, Santa Catarina, Nuevo Leon,
Mexico
Tel.: (52) 81 87 48 88 00
Web Site: http://colombinbel.com
Polyurethane Foam Mfr
N.A.I.C.S.: 326150

**Colombin Bel, S.A. de C.V. - TLAL-
NEPANTLA PLANT　(2)**
Fernando Montes de Oca Num 20 Fracc
Industrial San Nicolas, 54030, Tlalnepantla,
Mexico
Tel.: (52) 55 91 40 02 22
Web Site: http://colombinbel.com
Polyurethane Foam Mfr
N.A.I.C.S.: 326150

DAK Americas LLC　(1)
5925 Carnegie Blvd Ste 500, Charlotte, NC
28209
Tel.: (704) 940-7500
Web Site: http://www.dakamericas.com
Sales Range: $300-349.9 Million
Emp.: 697
Terephthalic Acid, Polyester Resin & Polyester Staple Fiber Products Mfr
N.A.I.C.S.: 325220

Subsidiary (Non-US):

Alpek Polyester Argentina S.A.　(2)
Av De Libertador 767 - Piso 4, B1638BEG,
Vicente Lopez, Buenos Aires, Argentina
Tel.: (54) 1152970800
Web Site: http://www.dakamericas.com
Resin Product Mfr
N.A.I.C.S.: 325211

Subsidiary (Domestic):

DAK Americas Mississippi Inc.　(2)
Pearl River Site 3303 Port & Harbor Dr,
Bay Saint Louis, MS 39520
Tel.: (228) 533-4000
Web Site: http://www.dakamericas.com
PVC Resin Mfr
N.A.I.C.S.: 325211

Nemak, S.A.　(1)
Libramiento Arco Vial Km 3 8, 66000, Villa
de Garcia, Mexico
Tel.: (52) 8187485200
Web Site: http://www.nemak.com
Sales Range: $350-399.9 Million
Emp.: 2,500
Aluminum Cylinder Head & Block Castings
Producer
N.A.I.C.S.: 331523
Armando Tamez *(CEO)*

Subsidiary (Non-US):

Nemak Argentina, S.R.L.　(2)
Ruta Nacional N 36 KM 747, San Agustin,
5191, Cordoba, Argentina
Tel.: (54) 3547 491009
Web Site: http://www.nemak.com
Sales Range: $25-49.9 Million
Emp.: 200
Industrial Machinery Mfr
N.A.I.C.S.: 333248

Nemak Europe GmbH　(2)
THE SQUAIRE 17 Am Flughafen, 60549,
Frankfurt, Germany　**(100%)**

Tel.: (49) 696953760
Web Site: http://www.nemak.com
Aluminum Mold Mfr
N.A.I.C.S.: 331524

Subsidiary (Domestic):

Modellbau Schonheide GmbH　(3)
Lindenstrasse 36, 08304, Schonheide, Germany
Tel.: (49) 37755 61 0
Web Site: http://www.mbschoenheide.de
Sales Range: $50-74.9 Million
Telecommunication Servicesb
N.A.I.C.S.: 517810
Frank Mockel *(Mng Dir)*

Subsidiary (Non-US):

Nemak Czech Republic, S.r.o.　(3)
Havran 137, 434 40, Most, Czech Republic
Tel.: (420) 605 630 102
Web Site: http://www.nemak.com
Sales Range: $50-74.9 Million
Emp.: 240
Industrial Mold Mfr
N.A.I.C.S.: 333511

Subsidiary (Domestic):

Nemak Dillingen GmbH　(3)
Marie Curie Strasse, 66763, Dillingen, Germany
Tel.: (49) 68319060
Sales Range: $150-199.9 Million
Emp.: 800
Industrial Mold Mfr
N.A.I.C.S.: 333511
Klaus Lellig *(Gen Mgr)*

Subsidiary (Non-US):

Nemak Gyor Kft　(3)
Ipari Park Nyirfa Sor, 9027, Gyor, Gyor-
Moson-Sopron, Hungary
Tel.: (36) 96520100
Web Site: http://www.nemakgyorkft-
c.cegbongeszo.hu
Aluminum Casting Mfr
N.A.I.C.S.: 331523

Nemak Linz GmbH　(3)
Zeppelinstrasse 24, 4030, Linz, Austria
Tel.: (43) 732 300 103 0
Web Site: http://www.nemak.com
Sales Range: $75-99.9 Million
Semi Permanent Mold Mfr
N.A.I.C.S.: 333511

Nemak Poland Sp. z.o.o.　(3)
ul Komorowicka 53, 43-300, Bielsko-Biala,
Poland
Tel.: (48) 334847000
Web Site: http://www.nemak.com
Sales Range: $150-199.9 Million
Aluminum Casting Product Mfr
N.A.I.C.S.: 331523

Nemak Slovakia, S.r.o.　(3)
Ladomerska Vieska 394, 965 01, Ziar nad
Hronom, Slovakia
Tel.: (421) 456 702 111
Web Site: http://www.nemak.com
Industrial Machinery Mfr
N.A.I.C.S.: 333248

Subsidiary (Domestic):

Nemak Wernigerode GmbH　(3)
Giesserweg 10, 38855, Wernigerode, Germany
Tel.: (49) 3943 652 0
Web Site: http://www.nemak.com
Sales Range: $150-199.9 Million
Suspension Parts Mfr
N.A.I.C.S.: 336330

Plant (US):

Nemak Wisconsin-Taylor Facility　(2)
3101 S Taylor Dr, Sheboygan, WI 53082-
1024
Tel.: (920) 458-7724
Web Site: http://www.nemak.com
Sales Range: $500-549.9 Million
Global Designer & Mfr of Die-Cast Aluminum Automotive Components & Assemblies
N.A.I.C.S.: 336390

Subsidiary (Domestic):

Nemak, S.A. de C.V.　(2)

Libramiento Arco Vial Km 3 8, 66000, Villa
de Garcia, Nuevo Leon, Mexico
Tel.: (52) 8187485200
Automotive Aluminum Component Mfr
N.A.I.C.S.: 331314

Subsidiary (US):

**Camen International Trading,
Inc.　(3)**
13713 N Unitec Dr Unitec Industrial Ctr,
Laredo, TX 78045
Tel.: (956) 728-8336
Supply Chain Management Services
N.A.I.C.S.: 561499

Petrocel - Temex, S.A. de C.V.　(1)
Carretera Tampico Mante km 17.5, Altamira,
Tamaulipas, CP89600, Mexico
Tel.: (52) 332292200
Polyester Products Mfr
N.A.I.C.S.: 325998

Planetario ALFA　(1)
Av Roberto Garza Sada No 1000, Garza
Garcia, 66254, Nuevo Leon, Mexico
Tel.: (52) 81 83 03 00 01
Web Site: http://www.planetarioalfa.org.mx
Science & Technology Museum Services
N.A.I.C.S.: 712110

Praimit, S. A. de C. V.　(1)
Apolo 516 Interior 18 Parque Industrial Kalos del Poniente, 66367, Santa Catarina,
NL, Mexico
Tel.: (52) 8113654165
Web Site: https://www.vigar.mx
N.A.I.C.S.: 424470

**Productora de Tereft de Altamira,
S.A. de C.V　(1)**
Carretera Tampico Mante Km 17 5, Altamira, 89600, Tamaulipas, Mexico
Tel.: (52) 833 229 2200
Textile Products Mfr
N.A.I.C.S.: 314999

Sigma Alimentos, S.A. de C.V.　(1)
Ave Gomez Morin 1111, 66254, Garza Garcia, NL, Mexico　**(100%)**
Tel.: (52) 8187489000
Web Site: http://www.sigma-alimentos.com
Sales Range: $50-74.9 Million
Refrigerated & Frozen Food Mfr & Distr
N.A.I.C.S.: 311991
Rodrigo Fernandez *(CEO)*

Subsidiary (Domestic):

**Alimentos Finos de Occidente, S.A.
de C.V.　(2)**
Av Fracisco Villa No 68 La Estrella, Lazaro
Cardenas, 60990, Michoacan, Mexico
Tel.: (52) 7535327161
Food Products Mfr
N.A.I.C.S.: 311999

Subsidiary (Non-US):

Campofrio Food Group, S.A.　(2)
Avda Europa 24 Parque Empresarial La
Moraleja, 28108, Alcobendas, Spain
Tel.: (34) 914842700
Web Site:
　　http://www.campofriofoodgroup.com
Rev: $2,094,487,805
Assets: $2,644,052,824
Liabilities: $1,749,398,239
Net Worth: $894,654,584
Earnings: $59,490,381
Emp.: 6,793
Fiscal Year-end: 12/31/2016
Pork Processor
N.A.I.C.S.: 311999
Paulino Jose Rodriguez Mendivil *(Vice
Chm)*

Subsidiary (Non-US):

Aoste Filiale (Suisse) Sarl　(3)
Rue Jacques-Grosselin 8, Carouge, 1227,
Geneva, Switzerland
Tel.: (41) 223017626
Web Site: http://www.aoste.ch
Emp.: 4
Food Products Mfr
N.A.I.C.S.: 311999
Lober Mauer *(Gen Mgr)*

CESARE FIORUCCI S.p.a　(3)
Viale Cesare Fiorucci 11 Loc Santa

ALFA, S.A.B. de C.V.—(Continued)

Palomba, 71, Pomezia, Roma, Italy
Tel.: (39) 06 911 931
Web Site: http://www.fioruccifood.it
Specialty Food Mfr & Distr
N.A.I.C.S.: 311412
Alberto Alfieri *(CEO)*

CFG Deutschland GmbH   **(3)**
Balcke-Durr-Allee 2, 40882, Hatingen, Germany
Tel.: (49) 210287540
Web Site: http://www.cfgdeutschland.de
Sales Range: $25-49.9 Million
Veal Product Mfr
N.A.I.C.S.: 311612

Plant (Non-US):

Campofrio Food Group, S.A. - Manufacturing Pitesti   **(3)**
Pitesti Abatorului Street no 30 jud, Arges, Romania
Tel.: (40) 248 615 252
Web Site: http://www.carolefoods.ro
Emp.: 1,000
Processed Meat Mfr
N.A.I.C.S.: 311612

Campofrio Food Group, S.A. - Manufacturing Tulcea   **(3)**
Tulcea Str Prislav no 177 jud, Tulcea, Romania
Tel.: (40) 240 517 940
Processed Meat Mfr
N.A.I.C.S.: 311612

Subsidiary (Non-US):

Campofrio Food Groupe France Holding SAS   **(3)**
523 Cours du Troisieme Millenaire Parc Mail, 69800, Saint Priest, France
Tel.: (33) 472148500
Web Site:
     http://www.campofriofoodgroup.com
Sales Range: $750-799.9 Million
Emp.: 3,000
Veal Product Mfr
N.A.I.C.S.: 311612

Campofrio Portugal, S.A.   **(3)**
Estrada Nacional 249 km 14, 2725397, Mem Martins, Portugal   **(100%)**
Tel.: (351) 219179400
Web Site: http://www.campofrio.pt
Sales Range: $25-49.9 Million
Emp.: 30
Meat & Meat Product Whslr
N.A.I.C.S.: 424470

Subsidiary (Domestic):

Carnes Selectas 2000 S.A.   **(3)**
Calle Bureba Pg Ind Gamonal Villimar S/n, Burgos, 09007, Spain
Tel.: (34) 947490100
Processed Meat Product Mfr
N.A.I.C.S.: 311999

Subsidiary (Non-US):

Imperial Meat Products N.V.   **(3)**
Grote Baan 200, 9920, Lovendegem, Belgium
Tel.: (32) 93700211
Web Site: http://www.imperial.be
Sales Range: $25-49.9 Million
Emp.: 670
Meat & Meat Products Producer
N.A.I.C.S.: 311612

Industrias de Carnes Nobre S.A.   **(3)**
PO Box 23, 2040-998, Aveiro, Portugal
Tel.: (351) 243909200
Web Site: http://www.nobre.pt
Sales Range: $450-499.9 Million
Emp.: 700
Meat Products Producer
N.A.I.C.S.: 311612
Paolo Soares *(CEO)*

LUIGI UGOLOTTI S.r.l.   **(3)**
Stabilimento di Felino Via Calestano 68, 43035, Felino, Parma, Italy
Tel.: (39) 05 21 85 90 11
Food Products Distr
N.A.I.C.S.: 424420

Stegeman B.V.   **(3)**

Jan Meesterweg 2, 8131 PM, Wijhe, Netherlands
Tel.: (31) 570505505
Web Site: https://www.stegeman.nl
Sales Range: $150-199.9 Million
Veal Product Mfr
N.A.I.C.S.: 311612

Subsidiary (Non-US):

Caroli Foods Group S. R. L.   **(2)**
Str Intrarea Abatorului nr 30, Arges, Pitesti, Romania
Tel.: (40) 248615252
Web Site: http://www.carolifoods.ro
Sausage Product Mfr
N.A.I.C.S.: 311612

Subsidiary (Domestic):

Grupo Chen, S. de R.L. de C.V.   **(2)**
Av Gomez Morin No 1111 Carrizalejo, Garza Garcia, 66254, Nuevo Leon, Mexico
Tel.: (52) 8187489000
Web Site: http://www.chen.com.mx
Food Products Mfr
N.A.I.C.S.: 311999

Subsidiary (US):

Mexican Cheese Producers, Inc.   **(2)**
11718 State Rd 23, Darlington, WI 53530
Tel.: (608) 776-8555
Web Site: http://www.mexican-cheese.com
Sales Range: $25-49.9 Million
Cheese Mfr
N.A.I.C.S.: 311513

Subsidiary (Domestic):

Sigma Alimentos Noreste, S.A. de C.V
Avenida Gomez Morin 1111 Colonia Carrizalejo, Garza Garcia, 66254, Nuevo Leon, Mexico
Tel.: (52) 8187489000
Packaged Frozen Food Whslr
N.A.I.C.S.: 424420

Subsidiary (US):

Sigma Foods Inc.   **(2)**
110 Cypress Station Dr Ste 202, Houston, TX 77090
Tel.: (281) 999-6361
Web Site: http://www.sigmafoodsusa.com
Sales Range: $25-49.9 Million
Emp.: 30
Refrigerated & Frozen Food Mfr & Distr
N.A.I.C.S.: 424420
Helio Castano *(VP)*

Subsidiary (Domestic):

Bar-S Foods Co.   **(3)**
2140 S 7th Ave Ste B-160, Phoenix, AZ 85007
Tel.: (602) 258-2265
Web Site: http://www.bar-sfoods.com
Emp.: 4,500
Meat & Poultry Products Mfr
N.A.I.C.S.: 311612

Styropek Do Brasil LTD.   **(1)**
Rua George Ohm 230 - Tower A 15th Floor Conj 151-152, Cidade Moncoes, Sao Paulo, 04576-020, Brazil
Tel.: (55) 1149350820
Expandable Polystyrene Mfr
N.A.I.C.S.: 326140

Styropek Mexico, S. A. de C. V.   **(1)**
Fernando Montes de Oca 71 Col Condesa, Del Cuauhtemoc, 06140, Mexico, Mexico
Tel.: (52) 5591400521
Web Site: http://www.styropek.com
Expandable Polystyrene Mfr
N.A.I.C.S.: 326140

Styropek S. A.   **(1)**
Libertador 767 Floor 4, Vicente Lopez, 1638, Buenos Aires, Argentina
Tel.: (54) 1151694610
Expandable Polystyrene Mfr
N.A.I.C.S.: 326140

Terza, S.A. de C.V.   **(1)**
Carretera a Monclova Km 11 5, 66550, El Carmen, Mexico
Tel.: (52) 8187484900
Web Site: http://www.terza.com

Sales Range: $25-49.9 Million
Emp.: 200
Carpet Mfr; Owned by Alfa, S.A.B. de C.V. & Shaw Industries
N.A.I.C.S.: 314110

Versax, S.A. de C.V.   **(1)**
Ave Gomez Morin 1111, Colonel Carrizalejo, San Pedro, Garza Garcia, NL 66254, Mexico   **(100%)**
Tel.: (52) 8187481152
Sales Range: $1-4.9 Billion
Emp.: 6,500
Autoparts, Carpets & Home Building Materials
N.A.I.C.S.: 313110

ALFA-PLAM A.D.
Radnicka 1, 17500, Vranje, Serbia
Tel.: (381) 17421121
Web Site: https://www.alfaplam.rs
Year Founded: 1948
ALFA—(BEL)
Sales Range: Less than $1 Million
Emp.: 1,000
Heating Device Mfr
N.A.I.C.S.: 333414

ALFA-WASSERMANN S.P.A.
Via Ragazzi del 99 5, 40133, Bologna, Italy
Tel.: (39) 051 6489511
Web Site:
     http://www.alfawassermann.it
Sales Range: $150-199.9 Million
Emp.: 650
Mfr of Pharmaceuticals, Medicinal & Botanical Products
N.A.I.C.S.: 325412
Stefano Golinelli *(CEO)*

Subsidiaries:

ALFA WASSERMANN (BEIJING) MARKET RESEARCH & MANAGEMENT CO. Ltd.   **(1)**
Oriental Kenzo Office Bldg Room No F-G 20th Fl No 48 Dong Zhi Men Wai, Dong Cheng District, Beijing, 100027, China
Tel.: (86) 10 8447 7552
Pharmaceutical Research & Development Services
N.A.I.C.S.: 541715

ALFA WASSERMANN CZECH s. r. o.   **(1)**
Ke Stvanici 656/3, 186 00, Prague, Czech Republic
Tel.: (420) 277011888
Pharmaceutical Product Mfr & Whslr
N.A.I.C.S.: 325412

ALFA WASSERMANN MAGHREB s.a.r.l.   **(1)**
Rue Lac Victoria 8211 Res Lac des Cygnes Appt A1, Les Berge Du Lac, 1053, Tunis, Tunisia
Tel.: (216) 71 860 224
Web Site:
     http://www.alfawassermann.com.tn
Pharmaceutical Product Mfr & Whslr
N.A.I.C.S.: 325412

ALFA WASSERMANN PHARMA SAS   **(1)**
67 rue Anatole France, 92300, Levallois-Perret, France
Tel.: (33) 1 41 27 25 10
Pharmaceutical Product Mfr & Whslr
N.A.I.C.S.: 325412
Ribot-Mariotte Emmanuelle *(Gen Mgr)*

ALFA WASSERMANN PRODUTOS FARMACEUTICOS, LDA.   **(1)**
Edificio Malhoa Plaza Av Jose Malhoa n 2 Escritorio 2 2, 1070-325, Lisbon, Portugal
Tel.: (351) 21 722 6110
Pharmaceutical Product Mfr & Whslr
N.A.I.C.S.: 325412
Anabela Ventura *(Mgr-Technical & Regulatory Affairs)*

ALFA WASSERMANN S.A. de C.V.   **(1)**
Av Insurgentes Sur No 2453 Piso 5 Oficina 501 Col Tizapan San Angel De, Alvaro

Obregon, Mexico, 01090, Mexico
Tel.: (52) 55 54 81 47 00
Web Site:
     http://www.alfawassermann.com.mx
Pharmaceutical Product Mfr & Whslr
N.A.I.C.S.: 325412

ALFA WASSERMANN S.p.A. - ALANNO MANUFACTURING DIVISION   **(1)**
Via Enrico Fermi n 1 Alanno, Pescara, 65020, Italy
Tel.: (39) 085 8571226
Web Site:
     http://www.alfawassermannmanufacturing.it
Pharmaceuticals Product Mfr
N.A.I.C.S.: 325412

ALFA WASSERMANN S.p.A. - MILANO INTERNATIONAL DIVISION   **(1)**
Viale Sarca 223, Milan, 20100, Italy
Tel.: (39) 02 64 222 1
Web Site: http://www.alfawassermann.it
Pharmaceutical Product Mfr & Whslr
N.A.I.C.S.: 325412
Luca Frassini *(Area Mgr)*

Alfa Wassermann Polska Sp.Z o.o.   **(1)**
Aleje Jerozolimskie 96, 00-807, Warsaw, Poland
Tel.: (48) 228240364
Web Site: http://www.alfawassermann.pl
Sales Range: $25-49.9 Million
Emp.: 16
Pharmaceutical Preparation Mfr
N.A.I.C.S.: 325412
Kaparrzna Jasimska Suninska *(Pres)*

Alfa Wassermann Srl   **(1)**
Bd Unirii 20 ap 61 Sector 4, Bucharest, Romania
Tel.: (40) 31805352627
Web Site: http://www.alfawassermann.it
Medicinal & Botanical Mfr
N.A.I.C.S.: 325411
Carmela Negulescu *(Mng Dir)*

Alfa Wassermann Tunisie Sarl   **(1)**
Rue Lac Victoria, Res Lac des Cygnes Appt A1 Les, 1053, Tunis, Tunisia
Tel.: (216) 71860224
Web Site:
     http://www.alfawassermann.com.tn
Sales Range: $25-49.9 Million
Emp.: 15
Pharmaceutical Preparation Mfr
N.A.I.C.S.: 325412
Slem Chouchane *(Mgr)*

Alfa-Wassermann B.V.   **(1)**
Pompmolenlaan 24, Woerden, 3447 GK, Netherlands
Tel.: (31) 348487300
Web Site:
     http://www.alfawassermannus.com
Sales Range: $25-49.9 Million
Emp.: 20
Medical Dental & Hospital Equipment & Supplies Whslr
N.A.I.C.S.: 423450
Ira S. Nordlicht *(Pres & CEO)*

Alfa-Wassermann Inc.   **(1)**
4 Henderson Dr, West Caldwell, NJ 07006-6608
Tel.: (973) 882-8630
Web Site:
     http://www.alfawassermannus.com
Medical Diagnostic Systems Mfr & Distr
N.A.I.C.S.: 339112
Peter J. Napoli *(COO)*

BAMA-GEVE, S.L.U.   **(1)**
Avenida Diagonal 490 4, 08006, Barcelona, Spain
Tel.: (34) 93 415 48 22
Web Site: http://www.bamageve.es
Pharmaceuticals Product Mfr
N.A.I.C.S.: 325412
Joan Buxo *(Product Mgr-Grp)*

Biosaude - Produtos Farmaceuticos, Lda.   **(1)**
Edificio Malhoa Pl No 2 Escritoio 2-2, Lisbon, 1070-325, Portugal
Tel.: (351) 217226110
Sales Range: $25-49.9 Million
Emp.: 44
Drugs & Druggists Sundries Whslr

N.A.I.C.S.: 424210
Goao Albergaria (Mng Dir)

OOO ALFA WASSERMANN (1)
Derbenevskaya naberezhnaya 11 bild A
sector 2 office 74, 115114, Moscow, Russia
Tel.: (7) 495 913 68 39
Web Site: http://www.alfawassermann.ru
Pharmaceutical Product Mfr & Whslr
N.A.I.C.S.: 325412

ALFAGOMMA S.P.A.
Via Torri Bianche 1, 20059, Vi-
mercate, Italy
Tel.: (39) 03960161
Web Site: http://www.alfagomma.com
Sales Range: $400-449.9 Million
Emp.: 2,000
Holding Company
N.A.I.C.S.: 551112
Antonio Maruca (CIO)

Subsidiaries:

Alfagomma (Ningbo) Co Ltd (1)
296 Kaiyuan Road, Investment Pioneering
Centre, Ningbo, 315022, Jiangbei, China
Tel.: (86) 57488157288
Rubber Products Mfr
N.A.I.C.S.: 326299

Alfagomma America Inc. (1)
3520 West Ave, Burlington, IA 52601
Tel.: (319) 758-9224
Web Site: http://www.alfagomma.com
Rubber Product Distr
N.A.I.C.S.: 423840
Massimo Eritale (Gen Mgr)

Alfagomma Australia Pty Ltd (1)
12 Healey Circuit, Huntingwood, 2148,
NSW, Australia
Tel.: (61) 2 9853 0950
Web Site: http://www.alfagomma.com.au
Sales Range: $50-74.9 Million
Emp.: 40
Rubber Products Mfr
N.A.I.C.S.: 326299

Alfagomma Canada, Inc. (1)
6540 Abrams, Montreal, H4S 1Y2, QC,
Canada
Tel.: (514) 333-5577
Sales Range: $25-49.9 Million
Emp.: 50
Rubber Products Mfr
N.A.I.C.S.: 326299
Ignazeo Blanco (Gen mgr)

Alfagomma Do Brasil Ltda (1)
Rodovia BR 491 - Km 69 Distrito Industrial
1, 37810-000, Guaranesia, Minas Gerais,
Brazil
Tel.: (55) 35 3555 0400
Rubber Product Distr
N.A.I.C.S.: 423840

Alfagomma Fracne Paris IDF (1)
23 Allee des Impressionnistes Le Sisley,
93420, Villepinte, France
Tel.: (33) 1 48 17 21 21
Web Site: http://www.alfagomma.com
Rubber Products Mfr
N.A.I.C.S.: 326299

Alfagomma Germany GmbH (1)
Friedrich Der Grosse 10, D 44628, Herne,
Germany (100%)
Tel.: (49) 232314730
Rubber Products Mfr
N.A.I.C.S.: 326299

Alfagomma Hellas S.A. (1)
72 Mikalis St, 18540, Piraeus, Greece
Tel.: (30) 4119909
Rubber Products Mfr
N.A.I.C.S.: 326299

Alfagomma International BV (1)
LJ Costerstraat 52, 5916 PS, Venlo, Neth-
erlands
Tel.: (31) 77 354 59 0
Rubber Products Mfr
N.A.I.C.S.: 326299

Alfagomma Korea Co. Ltd. (1)
1018-5 Yongso-Ri, Yangkam-Myun
Hwasung-Kun, Songtan, Korea (South)
Tel.: (82) 313528671
Rubber Products Mfr

N.A.I.C.S.: 326299
Jonggin Choi (Gen Mgr)

Alfagomma Pacific Pte Ltd (1)
19 Joo Koon Crescent, Singapore, 629017,
Singapore
Tel.: (65) 63639511
Web Site: http://www.alfagomma.com
Emp.: 20
Rubber Products Mfr
N.A.I.C.S.: 326299
Melody Teng (Mgr-Fin)

Alfagomma South Africa Pty Ltd (1)
17 Quark Crescent, Linbro Business Park,
Sandton, 2065, South Africa
Tel.: (27) 112010900
Sales Range: $25-49.9 Million
Emp.: 18
Rubber Products Mfr
N.A.I.C.S.: 326299

Alfagomma UK Ltd. (1)
43 Wilcock Road, Old Boston Trading Es-
tate, Haydock, WA11 9TG, United Kingdom
Tel.: (44) 1942407680
Rubber Products Mfr
N.A.I.C.S.: 326299

Hiflex Denmark A/S (1)
PO Box 2605, Brondby, DK-2605,
Denmark (100%)
Tel.: (45) 43254020
Web Site: http://www.dunlophiflex.dk
Sales Range: $25-49.9 Million
Emp.: 14
Rubber Hose Whslr
N.A.I.C.S.: 326220

ALFANAR TRADING CO.
PO Box 301, Riyadh, 11411, Saudi
Arabia
Tel.: (966) 12415566
Web Site:
http://www.alfanartrading.com
Year Founded: 1976
Sales Range: $25-49.9 Million
Emp.: 1,000
Electrical Products Mfr & Contracting
Services
N.A.I.C.S.: 238210

Subsidiaries:

Heinrich Kopp GmbH (1)
Alzenauer Strasse 68, 63796, Kahl, Ger-
many
Tel.: (49) 6188 400
Web Site: http://www.kopp.eu
Emp.: 280
Electrical Equipment Developer, Mfr & Distr
N.A.I.C.S.: 335999
Stephan Dorrschuck (Mng Dir)

ALFASIGMA S.P.A
Via Ragazzi del '99, 5, 40133, Bolo-
gna, Italy
Tel.: (39) 0516489511
Web Site: https://www.alfasigma.com
Year Founded: 1948
Pharmaceuticals Mfr
N.A.I.C.S.: 325412
Francesco Balestrieri (CEO)

Subsidiaries:

Intercept Pharmaceuticals, Inc. (1)
305 Madison Ave, Morristown, NJ 07960
Tel.: (646) 747-1000
Web Site: https://www.interceptpharma.com
Rev.: $285,710,000
Assets: $553,711,000
Liabilities: $460,634,000
Net Worth: $93,077,000
Earnings: $221,816,000
Emp.: 341
Fiscal Year-end: 12/31/2022
Biopharmaceutical Mfr
N.A.I.C.S.: 325412
Francesco Balestrieri (Pres)

ALFASTRAKHOVANIE PLC
Shabolovka Str 31B, 115162, Mos-
cow, Russia
Tel.: (7) 4957880999
Web Site: http://www.alfastrah.ru

Emp.: 100
Fire Insurance Services
N.A.I.C.S.: 524113
Bershadsky Mikhail Vladimirovich
(Pres)

**ALFAVISION OVERSEAS (IN-
DIA) LIMITED**
1-A Press Complex AB Road, Indore,
452001, Madhya Pradesh, India
Tel.: (91) 9977200123
Web Site:
https://www.alfavisionoverseas.com
Year Founded: 1994
531156—(BOM)
Rev.: $24,572,661
Assets: $15,797,504
Liabilities: $13,959,753
Net Worth: $1,837,751
Earnings: $195,770
Fiscal Year-end: 03/31/21
Real Estate Development Services
N.A.I.C.S.: 531390
Vishnu Prasad Goyal (Chm & Mng
Dir)

ALFEN N.V.
Hefbrugweg 28, 1332, Almere, Neth-
erlands
Tel.: (31) 365493400
Web Site: http://www.alfen.com
Year Founded: 1937
ALFEN—(EUR)
Rev.: $541,516,746
Assets: $425,041,864
Liabilities: $232,241,305
Net Worth: $192,800,558
Earnings: $31,863,461
Emp.: 931
Fiscal Year-end: 12/31/23
Electric Power Distribution Services
N.A.I.C.S.: 221122
Ard Van Der Kleij (Acct Mgr)

Subsidiaries:

Alfen Belgie BV (1)
Traktaatweg 9, 9000, Gent, Belgium
Tel.: (32) 92291200
Electric Vehicle Charging Station Operator
N.A.I.C.S.: 457120

Alfen Elkamo Oy Ab (1)
Permonkaarre 107, PO Box 18, 68601, Pi-
etarsaari, Finland
Tel.: (358) 67889550
Web Site: https://www.alfenelkamo.fi
Electrical & Electronic Product Mfr
N.A.I.C.S.: 335999

ALFESCA HF.
Kringlan no 7, 103, Reykjavik, Iceland
Tel.: (354) 4777000
Web Site: http://www.alfesca.com
Year Founded: 1932
Sales Range: $750-799.9 Million
Frozen & Fresh Fish & Saltfish Prod-
ucts Distr & Marketer
N.A.I.C.S.: 311710
Olafur J. Olafsson (Chm)

Subsidiaries:

Blini S.A. (1)
77 boulevard Haussmann, 75008, Paris,
France (100%)
Tel.: (33) 1 5330 7270
Web Site: http://www.blini.fr
Sales Range: $50-74.9 Million
Emp.: 150
Seafood & Bakery Products
N.A.I.C.S.: 311710

Lyons Seafoods Limited (1)
Fairfield House Fairfield Rd, Warminster,
BA12 9DA, Wiltshire, United Kingdom
Tel.: (44) 1985224300
Web Site: http://www.lyons-seafoods.com
Sales Range: $100-124.9 Million
Emp.: 280
Mfr of Frozen Chilled Seafood
N.A.I.C.S.: 311710

Ole Norgaard (CEO)

**ALFIO BARDOLLA TRAINING
GROUP SPA**
Via Ripamonti n 89, 20141, Milan,
Italy
Tel.: (39) 0800199335
Web Site:
https://www.alfiobardolla.com
ABTG—(ITA)
Sales Range: Less than $1 Million
Educational Training & Support Ser-
vices
N.A.I.C.S.: 611710
Alfio Bardolla (Founder)

**ALFONS HAAR MASCHINEN-
BAU GMBH & CO. KG**
Fangdieckstrasse 67, 22547, Ham-
burg, Germany
Tel.: (49) 40 83391 0 De
Web Site: http://www.alfons-haar.de
Year Founded: 1949
Industrial Packaging Machinery Mfr
N.A.I.C.S.: 333993
Thomas Haar (Member-Mgmt Bd)

Subsidiaries:

Alfons Haar Incorporated (1)
150 Advanced Dr, Springboro, OH 45066
Tel.: (937) 560-2031
Packaging Machinery Distr
N.A.I.C.S.: 423830

Alfons Haar Limited (1)
Unit N1 Gildersome Spur, Leeds, LS27 7JZ,
United Kingdom
Tel.: (44) 1132522663
Web Site: http://www.alfonshaar.co.uk
Industrial Machinery Mfr
N.A.I.C.S.: 333998

Alfons Haar Svenska AB (1)
Sjodalsvagen 21, 141 46, Huddinge, Swe-
den
Tel.: (46) 87112590
Packaging Machinery Distr
N.A.I.C.S.: 423830

Beta Fueling Systems, LLC (1)
1209 Freeway Dr, Reidsville, NC 27320-
7103
Tel.: (336) 342-0306
Web Site: http://www.betafueling.com
Fueling Equipment Mfr & Whslr
N.A.I.C.S.: 333924
Jon DeLine (Pres & CEO)

Haar Australia Pty Ltd (1)
PO Box 233, Seddon, 3011, VIC, Australia
Tel.: (61) 415993500
Web Site: http://www.alfons-haar.com.au
Packaging Machinery Distr
N.A.I.C.S.: 423830
Nick Symons (Engr-Application)

Haar CZ s,r.o. (1)
Jiriho ze Vtelna 1731, Horni Pocernice, 193
00, Prague, Czech Republic
Tel.: (420) 281012652
Web Site: http://www.alfons-haar.cz
Packaging Machinery Mfr
N.A.I.C.S.: 333993

Haar France SAS (1)
13 Rue Rene Cassin, 95228, Herblay,
France
Tel.: (33) 139976466
Web Site: http://www.haarfrance.fr
Packaging Machinery Mfr
N.A.I.C.S.: 333993

Haar Nederland CV (1)
van Polanenweg 1, 2921 LT, Krimpen aan
de ijssel, Netherlands
Tel.: (31) 180518055
Web Site: http://www.haarnederland.nl
Industrial Machinery Mfr
N.A.I.C.S.: 333998

Haar Peninsular S.L. (1)
Poligono Industrial Cubilete KM 0 500, Ajal-
vir, 28864, Madrid, Spain
Tel.: (34) 918874167
Packaging Machinery Distr
N.A.I.C.S.: 423830

Alfons Haar Maschinenbau GmbH & Co.
KG—(Continued)

Luis Garcia Perla *(Gen Mgr)*

Haar Polska SP. Z O.O. (1)
ul Olszanicka 38A, 30-241, Krakow, Poland
Tel.: (48) 126226070
Web Site: http://www.haar.pl
Industrial Machinery Mfr
N.A.I.C.S.: 333998

Haar Salzburg GmbH & Co. KG (1)
Eugen-Muller-Strasse 39, 5020, Salzburg,
Austria
Tel.: (43) 6624325940
Packaging Machinery Distr
N.A.I.C.S.: 423830

ALFONSINO S.P.A.
Via Lamberti 15, 81100, Caserta, Italy
Web Site:
https://www.alfonsino.delivery
Year Founded: 2016
ALFO—(EUR)
Information Technology Services
N.A.I.C.S.: 541512
Carmen Iodice *(CEO)*

ALFONSO GALLARDO S.A.
Ctra de Badajoz 32, 06380, Jerez de
los Caballeros, Badajoz, Spain
Tel.: (34) 924 759 000   ES
Web Site: http://www.grupoag.es
Sales Range: $1-4.9 Billion
Emp.: 3,000
Steel Products & Concrete Mfr
N.A.I.C.S.: 332111

Subsidiaries:

Ferralca, S.A. (1)
C/ Luis Sauquillo 68, 28944, Fuenlabrada,
Spain
Tel.: (34) 91 690 45 50
Steel Products Mfr
N.A.I.C.S.: 331221

Siderurgica Balboa, S.A. (1)
Ctra de Badajoz 32, 06380, Jerez de los
Caballeros, Spain
Tel.: (34) 924759000
Web Site: http://www.grupoag.es
Sales Range: $200-249.9 Million
Emp.: 600
Corrugated Steel Mfr
N.A.I.C.S.: 331221
Sebastian Garcia *(Mng Dir)*

ALFOT TECHNOLOGIES CO., LTD.
No 8 19th Rd, Taichung Industrial
Park, Taichung, 40850, Taiwan
Tel.: (886) 423592768
Web Site: https://www.alfot.com
Year Founded: 1983
4553—(TAI)
Aluminum Forging Product Mfr
N.A.I.C.S.: 332112
Shu-Yuan Liao *(Chm)*

ALFRED HERBERT (INDIA) LTD.
13/3 Strand Road, Kolkata, 700 001,
India
Tel.: (91) 3322484801
Web Site:
https://www.alfredherbert.co.in
505216—(BOM)
Rev.: $533,852
Assets: $15,155,800
Liabilities: $792,150
Net Worth: $14,363,649
Earnings: $279,770
Emp.: 8
Fiscal Year-end: 03/31/23
Industrial Machine Tool Distr
N.A.I.C.S.: 423830
Aditya Vikram Lodha *(Chm)*

ALFRED KARCHER GMBH & CO. KG
Alfred Karcher Strasse 28-40, 71364,
Winnenden, Germany
Tel.: (49) 7195140   De
Web Site: http://www.karcher.com
Year Founded: 1953
Sales Range: $1-4.9 Billion
Emp.: 10,000
Cleaning Equipment Mfr
N.A.I.C.S.: 561740
Hartmut Jenner *(Chm-Mgmt Bd & CEO)*

Subsidiaries:

Alfred Karcher Ges.m.b.H. (1)
Lichtblaustrasse 7, 1220, Vienna, Austria
Tel.: (43) 1250600
Web Site: http://www.karcher.at
Cleaning Equipment Mfr
N.A.I.C.S.: 561740

Alfred Karcher Vertriebs-GmbH (1)
Friedrich-List-Strasse 4, 71364, Winnenden,
Germany
Tel.: (49) 71959030
Web Site: http://www.kaercher.de
Sales Range: $300-349.9 Million
Emp.: 2,500
Cleaning Equipment Services
N.A.I.C.S.: 561740
Hartmut Jenner *(Chm)*

C-Tech Industries de Mexico, S. de
R.L. de C.F. (1)
Avenida Avante #831Parque Industrial, Es-
tado Nuevo Leon, Guadalupe, Apodaca,
Mexico
Tel.: (52) 55 5357 0428
Web Site: http://www.karcher.com.mx
Cleaning Equipment Mfr
N.A.I.C.S.: 561740

Karcher (Japan) Co., Ltd. (1)
3-2 Matsuzakadaira Taiwa-Cho, Kurokawa-
Gun, Miyagi, 981-3408, Japan
Tel.: (81) 223443140
Web Site: http://www.karcher.co.jp
Sales Range: $25-49.9 Million
Emp.: 80
Cleaning Equipment Mfr
N.A.I.C.S.: 561740
Hachiro Sato *(Pres)*

Karcher (Shanghai) Cleaning Sys-
tems Co., Ltd. (1)
Part F 2nd Floor Building 17 No 33 Xi Ya
Road, Shanghai, 200131, Pudong, China
Tel.: (86) 2150768018
Web Site: http://www.karcher.de
Cleaning Equipment Mfr
N.A.I.C.S.: 561740

Karcher (UK) Ltd. (1)
Karcher House Beaumont Road, Banbury,
OX16 1TB, United Kingdom
Tel.: (44) 1295 752 000
Web Site: http://www.karcher.co.uk
Cleaning Equipment Mfr & Distr
N.A.I.C.S.: 333310

Karcher AB (1)
Tagenevagen 31, Hisings Karra, 425 37,
Gothenburg, Sweden
Tel.: (46) 31 57 73 00
Web Site: http://www.karcher.se
Cleaning Equipment Mfr & Distr
N.A.I.C.S.: 333310

Karcher AG (1)
Industriestrasse 16, 8108, Dallikon, Switzer-
land
Tel.: (41) 844 850 863
Web Site: http://www.kaercher.ch
Cleaning Equipment Mfr & Distr
N.A.I.C.S.: 333310
Stefan Obernosterer *(Dir-Sls)*

Karcher AS (1)
Stanseveien 31, 0976, Oslo, Norway
Tel.: (47) 24177700
Web Site: http://www.kaercher.de
Cleaning Equipment Mfr & Distr
N.A.I.C.S.: 333310

Karcher Anlagenvermietungs
GmbH (1)
Alfred-Karcher-Strasse 28-40, 71364,
Winnenden, Germany
Tel.: (49) 7195143030

Cleaning Equipment Mfr
N.A.I.C.S.: 561740

Karcher B.V. (1)
2320 Hoogstraten, Hoogstraten, Belgium
Tel.: (32) 33400711
Web Site: http://www.karcher.com
Cleaning Equipment Mfr
N.A.I.C.S.: 561740

Karcher Canada, Inc. (1)
Millcreek Road Unit 67, Mississauga, L5N
2N2, ON, Canada
Tel.: (905) 672-8233
Sales Range: $25-49.9 Million
Emp.: 6
Cleaning Equipment Mfr
N.A.I.C.S.: 561740

Karcher Cleaning Systems A.E. (1)
Moratini 18 Metamorphosis, 14452, Athens,
Greece
Tel.: (30) 2102316153
Web Site: http://www.karcher.gr
Sales Range: $10-24.9 Million
Emp.: 30
Cleaning Equipment Mfr
N.A.I.C.S.: 561740
Fransis Lazaros *(Mng Dir)*

Karcher Cleaning Systems Sdn.
Bhd. (1)
5 Jalan Perintis U1/52 Kawasan Perindus-
trian Temasya Glenmarie, 40150, Shah
Alam, Selangor, Malaysia
Tel.: (60) 3 55670 510
Web Site: http://www.karcher.com.my
Emp.: 50
Cleaning Equipment Mfr & Distr
N.A.I.C.S.: 333310
Francis Fam *(Mgr-Sls)*

Karcher Co., Ltd. (South Korea) (1)
872-2 Sinjeong-Dong, Seoul, 158 856,
Yangcheon-Gu, Korea (South)
Tel.: (82) 23226588
Web Site: http://www.karcher.gr
Cleaning Equipment Mfr
N.A.I.C.S.: 561740

Karcher FZE (1)
Jebel Ali Free Zone, PO Box 17416, Dubai,
United Arab Emirates
Tel.: (971) 4 8861177
Web Site: http://www.karcher.ae
Cleaning Equipment Mfr & Distr
N.A.I.C.S.: 333310
R. Nouira *(Mng Dir)*

Karcher Floor Care, Inc. (1)
1351 W Stanford Ave, Englewood, CO
80110
Tel.: (303) 783-5815
Rev.: $74,400,000
Emp.: 350
Carpet/Floor Care Equipment Mfr
N.A.I.C.S.: 333310
Hannes Saeubert *(CEO)*

Subsidiary (Domestic):

Graco Manufacturing Co. Inc. (2)
1 T and G Way, Blackwood, NJ 08012
Tel.: (856) 228-1800
Web Site: http://www.gracomfg.com
Sales Range: $1-9.9 Million
Emp.: 30
Commercial Cleaning Equipment
N.A.I.C.S.: 333310

Windsor Industries, Inc. (2)
1351 W Stanford Ave, Englewood, CO
80110
Tel.: (303) 762-1800
Web Site: http://www.windsorind.com
Sales Range: $1-9.9 Million
Emp.: 350
Mfr of Commercial Floor Cleaning Machines
N.A.I.C.S.: 333310
Deborah Koepke *(Mgr-HR)*

Karcher Hungaria Kft. (1)
Tormasret ut 2, 2051, Biatorbagy, Hungary
Tel.: (36) 23 530 0
Web Site: http://www.karcher.de
Cleaning Equipment Mfr
N.A.I.C.S.: 561740

Karcher Industria e Comercio
Ltda. (1)
Via Miguel Melhado Campos 600, Industrial

District, Vinhedo, 13288-003, Sao Paulo,
Brazil
Tel.: (55) 1938849100
Sales Range: $75-99.9 Million
Emp.: 500
Cleaning Equipment Mfr
N.A.I.C.S.: 561740
Abilio Cepera *(Mng Dir)*

Karcher Leasing GmbH (1)
Alfred-Karcher-Strasse 28-40, 71364,
Winnenden, Germany
Tel.: (49) 7195143030
Web Site: http://www.karcher.de
Cleaning Equipment Mfr
N.A.I.C.S.: 561740

Karcher Limited (1)
Unit 05 13/F Nanyang Plaza 57 Hung To
Road, Kwun Tong, Kowloon, China (Hong
Kong)
Tel.: (852) 2 357 5863
Web Site: http://www.karcher.com.hk
Cleaning Equipment Mfr & Distr
N.A.I.C.S.: 333310

Karcher Ltd (1)
Unit 4 EP Money Business Pk Wakinstown
Avenue, Clondalkin, Dublin, Ireland
Tel.: (353) 14097777
Web Site: http://www.karcher.de
Emp.: 7
Cleaning Equipment Mfr
N.A.I.C.S.: 561740
Paul Carrol *(Mng Dir)*

Karcher Mexico, S.A. de C.V. (1)
Boulevard Manuel Avila Camacho No 520
Colonia Industrial Atoto, 53519, Naucalpan,
Mexico
Tel.: (52) 55 5357 0428
Web Site: http://www.karcher.com.mx
Cleaning Equipment Mfr & Distr
N.A.I.C.S.: 333310

Karcher N.V. (1)
Industrieweg 12, 2320, Hoogstraten, Bel-
gium
Tel.: (32) 33400711
Web Site: http://www.karcher.de
Cleaning Equipment Mfr
N.A.I.C.S.: 561740

Karcher North America (1)
4275 NW Pacific Rim Blvd, Camas, WA
98607
Tel.: (360) 833-1600
Web Site: http://www.karcher.com
Sales Range: $75-99.9 Million
Emp.: 600
High-Pressure Cleaning Equipment Mfr
N.A.I.C.S.: 333998
Hannes Saubert *(CEO)*

Unit (Domestic):

Landa Water Cleaning Systems (2)
4275 NW Pacific Rim Blvd, Camas, WA
98607
Tel.: (360) 833-9100
Web Site: http://www.karcherna.com
Sales Range: $50-74.9 Million
Emp.: 300
Industrial Pressure Washers & Water
Cleaning Systems Mfr
N.A.I.C.S.: 333310

The Hotsy Corporation (2)
4275 NW Pacific Rim Blvd, Camas, WA
98607
Tel.: (360) 834-0983
Web Site: http://www.hotsy.com
Sales Range: $50-74.9 Million
Emp.: 160
High Pressure Cleaning Equipment & Re-
lated Chemical Mfr
N.A.I.C.S.: 333310

Karcher Oy (1)
Yrittajantie 17, 01800, Klaukkala, Finland
Tel.: (358) 9 87919 191
Web Site: http://www.karcher.de
Cleaning Equipment Mfr
N.A.I.C.S.: 561740

Karcher Poland Ltd. Sp. z o.o. (1)
Ul Stawowa 138-140 31-346, Krakow, Po-
land
Tel.: (48) 126397105
Web Site: http://www.karcher.pl
Cleaning Equipment Services

N.A.I.C.S.: 561740

Karcher Pty. Ltd. (1)
40 Koornang Road, Scoresby, 3179, Australia
Tel.: (61) 397652300
Web Site: http://www.karcher.com.au
Sales Range: $10-24.9 Million
Emp.: 50
Cleaning Equipment Mfr
N.A.I.C.S.: 561740
Markus Haefeli (Mng Dir)

Karcher Rengoringssystemer A/S (1)
Islevdalvej 98, 2610, Rodovre, Denmark
Tel.: (45) 70206667
Web Site: http://www.karcher.dk
Sales Range: $25-49.9 Million
Emp.: 15
Cleaning Equipment Mfr
N.A.I.C.S.: 561740

Karcher Residential Solutions, Inc. (1)
750 W. Hampden Ave, Englewood, CO 80110
Tel.: (303) 738-2400
Web Site: http://www.karcherresidential.com
Cleaning Equipment Mfr
N.A.I.C.S.: 561740

Karcher S.A.S. (1)
5 Avenue des Coquelicots, 94865, Bonneuil, France
Tel.: (33) 143996770
Web Site: http://www.karcher.de
Sales Range: $25-49.9 Million
Emp.: 170
Cleaning Equipment Mfr
N.A.I.C.S.: 561740

Karcher S.p.A. (1)
Via Amerigo Vespucci 19, Gallarate, 21013, Varese, Italy
Tel.: (39) 0332 417 400
Web Site: http://www.karcher.de
Cleaning Equipment Mfr
N.A.I.C.S.: 561740

Karcher Servis Ticaret A.S. (1)
Binbasi Resat Mah Akcay Cad No 3B Gaziemir, 307 Sokak No 6, Izmir, Turkiye
Tel.: (90) 2322520708
Web Site: http://www.karcher.com.tr
Sales Range: $25-49.9 Million
Emp.: 60
Cleaning Equipment Mfr
N.A.I.C.S.: 561740
Delikanli Umut (Mng Dir)

Karcher South East Asia Pte Ltd. (1)
3 Depot Close 01-01, Links Express Distripark, Singapore, 109840, Singapore
Tel.: (65) 68971811
Web Site: http://www.karcher.sg
Emp.: 45
Cleaning Equipment Mfr
N.A.I.C.S.: 561740
Kenneth Eng (Mng Dir)

Karcher Spol. s r.o. (1)
155 00 Praha 5, Prague, Czech Republic
Tel.: (420) 2 3552 1665
Web Site: http://www.karcher.de
Cleaning Equipment Mfr
N.A.I.C.S.: 561740

Karcher Ukraine (1)
Kilzeva doroga str 9, 03134, Kiev, Ukraine
Tel.: (380) 44 2507576
Web Site: http://www.karcher.com.ua
Cleaning Equipment Mfr & Distr
N.A.I.C.S.: 333310
Nataliya Budarina (Mgr-Mktg)

Karcher, S.A. (1)
Pol Industrial Font del Radium, Calle Doctor Trueta 6-7, 08400, Barcelona, Spain
Tel.: (34) 932651616
Cleaning Equipment Mfr
N.A.I.C.S.: 561740

ALFRED RAITH GMBH
2 Industriestrasse 10, 68766, Hockenheim, Germany
Tel.: (49) 620530510
Web Site: http://www.alfra.de
Year Founded: 1973
Sales Range: $10-24.9 Million

Building Machinery Mfr
N.A.I.C.S.: 333120
Markus A. Doring (Mng Partner)

Subsidiaries:

ALFRA Russland Overtime JSC (1)
nab Chernoy Rechki 41 i, 197342, Saint Petersburg, Russia
Tel.: (7) 8123273486
Web Site: http://www.alfra.ru
Machine Tool Distr
N.A.I.C.S.: 423710

ALFRA UK, LTD. (1)
Vicarage Road, Sheffield, S9 3RH, South Yorkshire, United Kingdom
Tel.: (44) 1142438800
Web Site: http://www.alfra.co.uk
Machine Tool Distr
N.A.I.C.S.: 423710
Ian Smith (Mng Dir)

ALFRA USA, LLC (1)
120 Prairie Lk Rd Unit-B, East Dundee, IL 60118
Tel.: (847) 844-8900
Machine Tool Distr
N.A.I.C.S.: 423710
Ron Tomson (Mgr-Div)

Mehring AG (1)
Grossmattstrasse 24, 8964, Rudolfstetten, Switzerland
Tel.: (41) 566338053
Web Site: http://www.mehring.ch
Engine Distr
N.A.I.C.S.: 423830

ALFRED SCHELLENBERG GMBH
An den Weiden 31, Siegen, 57041, Germany
Tel.: (49) 271890560
Web Site: http://www.schellenberg.de
Year Founded: 1984
Rev.: $27,879,825
Emp.: 120
Shutter Accessories Whslr
N.A.I.C.S.: 423310
Sascha Schellenberg (Mng Dir)

ALFRED TRONSER GMBH
Quellenweg 14, 7533, Engelsbrand, Germany
Tel.: (49) 70827980
Web Site: http://www.tronser.de
Year Founded: 1951
Rev.: $17,932,200
Emp.: 108
Electronic Components Mfr
N.A.I.C.S.: 334416
Alfred Tronser (Founder)

Subsidiaries:

Tronser, Inc. (1)
3066 John A Trush Jr Blvd, Cazenovia, NY 13035
Tel.: (315) 655-9528
Emp.: 20
Capacitor Mfr
N.A.I.C.S.: 334416
James K. Biando (Mgr-Mfg)

ALFRESA HOLDINGS CORPORATION
1-1-3 Otemachi, Chiyoda-ku, Tokyo, 100-0004, Japan
Tel.: (81) 352195102
Web Site: https://www.alfresa.com
Year Founded: 2003
2784—(TKS)
Rev.: $18,894,685,000
Assets: $9,568,801,250
Liabilities: $6,396,933,260
Net Worth: $3,171,867,990
Earnings: $195,378,380
Emp.: 15,578
Fiscal Year-end: 03/31/24
Holding Company
N.A.I.C.S.: 551112
Taizo Kubo (Chm)

Subsidiaries:

Alfresa Corporation (1)
7 Kanda Mitoyocho, Chiyoda-ku, Tokyo, 101-8512, Japan
Tel.: (81) 332923331
Web Site: https://www.alfresa.co.jp
Emp.: 5,862
Medical Device Distr
N.A.I.C.S.: 423450

Alfresa Fine Chemical Corporation (1)
1-10-1 Mukaihama, Akita, 010-1601, Japan
Tel.: (81) 188637701
Web Site: http://www.alfresa-fc.co.jp
Emp.: 134
Pharmaceuticals Product Mfr
N.A.I.C.S.: 325412

Alfresa Healthcare Corporation (1)
3-11-5 Nihonbashi-Honcho, Chuo-ku, Tokyo, 103-0023, Japan   (100%)
Tel.: (81) 336396281
Web Site: https://www.alfresa-hc.com
Sales Range: $150-199.9 Million
Emp.: 384
Whslr of OTC Pharmaceuticals, Dairy Products for Infants, Quasi Drugs & Sundries
N.A.I.C.S.: 424210
Hisashi Katsuki (Pres)

Alfresa Medical Service Corporation (1)
2-3-14 Kudan-minami, Chiyoda-ku, Tokyo, 102-0074, Japan
Tel.: (81) 368432330
Web Site: http://www.alfresa-ms.co.jp
Sales Range: $150-199.9 Million
Emp.: 1,208
Pharmaceutical Product Whslr
N.A.I.C.S.: 424210

Alfresa Nikken Sangyo Corporation (1)
4-20 Imamachi, Gifu, 500-8023, Japan
Tel.: (81) 665325621
Web Site: http://www.nk-gifu.co.jp
Sales Range: $150-199.9 Million
Emp.: 456
Pharmaceutical Product Whslr
N.A.I.C.S.: 424210

Alfresa Pharma Corporation (1)
2-2-9 Kokumachi, Chuo-Ku, Osaka, 540-8575, Japan   (100%)
Tel.: (81) 669410300
Web Site: https://www.alfresa-pharma.co.jp
Sales Range: $1-9.9 Million
Emp.: 1,074
Manufacture, Import, Export & Marketing of Pharmaceuticals, Diagnostic Products, Medical Devices & Pharmaceutical Raw materials
N.A.I.C.S.: 325412

Alfresa Shinohara Chemicals Corporation (1)
9-41 Minamigoza, Kochi, 781-9506, Japan
Tel.: (81) 888825000
Web Site: https://www.e-shinohara.co.jp
Medical Device Distr
N.A.I.C.S.: 423450

Alfresa System Corporation (1)
1-1 Kandanishikicho, Chiyoda-ku, Tokyo, 101-0054, Japan
Tel.: (81) 352827260
Web Site: https://www.alfresa-system.com
Sales Range: $25-49.9 Million
Emp.: 51
Software Support Services
N.A.I.C.S.: 541512

Apollo Medical Holdings Inc. (1)
2-45-8 Minami-Otsuka Nissei Otsuka Ekimae Building 8th Floor, Toshima-ku, Tokyo, 170-0005, Japan
Tel.: (81) 359771189
Web Site: http://www.islands.co.jp
Pharmaceuticals Product Mfr
N.A.I.C.S.: 325412

CS Yakuhin Co., Ltd. (1)
3-2-26 Marunouchi, Naka-Ku, Nagoya, 460-0002, Aichi, Japan
Tel.: (81) 529628201
Web Site: http://www.cs-yakuhin.com
Sales Range: $200-249.9 Million
Emp.: 1,000
Pharmaceutical Product Whslr

N.A.I.C.S.: 325412
Ryuji Arakawa (Pres)

Kowa Pharmaceuticals Co., Ltd. (1)
1-46-1 Kikutamachi Oroshi, Koriyama, 963-8676, Fukushima, Japan
Tel.: (81) 24 959 6611
Web Site: http://www.kowa-yakuhin.co.jp
Emp.: 467
Pharmaceutical Product Whslr
N.A.I.C.S.: 424210
Yasuo Takita (Pres)

Meisho Co., Ltd. (1)
Ha 1 Muryoji-cho, Kanazawa, 920-0392, Ishikawa, Japan
Tel.: (81) 762664141
Web Site: https://www.mshhs.jp
Emp.: 398
Pharmaceutical Product Whslr
N.A.I.C.S.: 424210
Kenji Orimoto (Co-Pres & CEO)

Nihon Apoch Co., Ltd. (1)
6-20 Wakitahoncho 3F Kubota Building, Kawagoe, 350-1123, Saitama, Japan
Tel.: (81) 492467333
Web Site: http://www.apoch.co.jp
Pharmaceuticals Product Mfr
N.A.I.C.S.: 325412

Qingdao Nesco Medical Co., Ltd. (1)
Building A Yihe International No 10 Hong Kong Middle Road, Qingdao, 266107, Shandong, China
Tel.: (86) 53266888123
Web Site: https://www.nescoqd.com.cn
Sales Range: $25-49.9 Million
Emp.: 60
Surgical Sutures Mfr
N.A.I.C.S.: 339113
Sonoda Norihisa (Mgr-Sls)

Ryuyaku Co., Ltd. (1)
5-6-5 Makiminato, Urasoe, 901-2686, Okinawa, Japan
Tel.: (81) 988781111
Web Site: https://www.ryuyaku.co.jp
Emp.: 183
Wholesale Distribution of Pharmaceuticals & Medical Equipment
N.A.I.C.S.: 424210
Tadashi Inamine (Mng Dir)

Seiwa Sangyo Co., Ltd. (1)
4-57-7 Higashi Komatsugawa, Edogawa-ku, Tokyo, 132-0033, Japan
Tel.: (81) 3 3654 4151
Web Site: http://www.seiwa-sangyo.co.jp
Sales Range: $25-49.9 Million
Emp.: 20
Commercial Washing, Drying & Sterilization Equipment Mfr, Whslr, Leasing & Maintenance Services
N.A.I.C.S.: 333310

Shikoku Alfresa Corporation (1)
1255-10 Fuke Kou, Kokubunji-cho, Takamatsu, 769-0193, Kagawa, Japan
Tel.: (81) 878025000
Web Site: http://www.s-alfresa.com
Sales Range: $600-649.9 Million
Emp.: 551
Wholesale Pharmaceutical Sales Management Including Medical Equipment & Diagnostic Reagents
N.A.I.C.S.: 424210

TS Alfresa Corporation (1)
1-2-19 Shoko Center, Nishi-ku, Hiroshima, 733-8633, Japan
Tel.: (81) 825010222
Web Site: https://www.ts-alfresa.net
Emp.: 1,166
Medical Device Distr
N.A.I.C.S.: 423450

Tohoku Alfresa Corporation (1)
1-46-1 Kikuta-cho, Koriyama, 963-8676, Fukushima, Japan
Tel.: (81) 249596611
Web Site: http://www.tohoku-alfresa.co.jp
Emp.: 948
Medical Device Distr
N.A.I.C.S.: 423450

ALGAR TELECOM S.A.
Rua Jose Alves Garcia 415, 38400-668, Uberlandia, MG, Brazil

Algar Telecom S.A.—(Continued)

Tel.: (55) 3432562978
Web Site:
    http://www.algartelecom.com.br
Year Founded: 1954
Rev.: $948,556,650
Assets: $1,097,034,225
Liabilities: $726,960,630
Net Worth: $370,073,595
Earnings: $81,385,800
Fiscal Year-end: 12/31/18
Telecommunication Servicesb
N.A.I.C.S.: 517112
Jean Carlos Borges (CEO)

ALGERIE TELECOM SPA

Route Nationale 5, Cinq Maisons Mo-
hammadia, 16130, Algiers, Algeria
Tel.: (213) 21823838
Web Site:
    http://www.algerietelecom.dz
Sales Range: $1-4.9 Billion
Emp.: 23,000
Telecommunication Servicesb
N.A.I.C.S.: 517112
Kebbal Tayeb (Chm & Interim CEO)

ALGERNON PHARMACEUTI-CALS, INC.

Suite 400 - 601 West Broadway, Van-
couver, V5Z 4C2, BC, Canada
Tel.: (604) 398-4175
Web Site:
    https://www.algernonpharma.com
Year Founded: 2015
AGNPF—(OTCQB)
Rev.: $9,330
Assets: $7,930,467
Liabilities: $799,736
Net Worth: $7,130,731
Earnings: ($6,050,216)
Emp.: 1
Fiscal Year-end: 08/31/21
Pharmaceuticals Product Mfr
N.A.I.C.S.: 325412
Christopher J. Moreau (CEO)

ALGOE

9 Bis Route De Champagne, PO Box
60208, 69134, Ecully, Cedex, France
Tel.: (33) 987876900
Web Site: http://www.algoe.fr
Year Founded: 1959
Sales Range: $50-74.9 Million
Emp.: 200
Management Consulting Services
N.A.I.C.S.: 541611
Gerard Debrinay (CEO)

Subsidiaries:

Algoe Executive   (1)
23 rue Louis-le-Grand, 75002, Paris, France
Tel.: (33) 1 53 02 26 86
Web Site: http://www.algoe-executive.com
Human Resource Consulting Services
N.A.I.C.S.: 561312
Palacin Philp (Mng Dir)

ALGOL OY

Karapellontie 6, PO Box 13, Espoo,
02611, Finland
Tel.: (358) 950991   FI
Web Site: http://www.algol.fi
Year Founded: 1894
Sales Range: $10-24.9 Million
Emp.: 450
Industrial & Pharmaceutical Supplier
N.A.I.C.S.: 325412
Alexander Bargum (Mng Dir &
Member-Exec Bd)

Subsidiaries:

Algol Chemicals AB   (1)
Lastgatan 8, 254 64, Helsingborg, Sweden
Tel.: (46) 42 203 850
Pharmaceutical Product Whslr
N.A.I.C.S.: 424210

Algol Chemicals AS   (1)
PO Box 221, 1326, Lysaker, Norway
Tel.: (47) 67 819 310
Web Site: http://www.algol.si
Emp.: 2
Pharmaceutical Product Whslr
N.A.I.C.S.: 424210
Earic Karsttsen (Mgr)

Algol Chemicals ApS   (1)
Hammervej 2, 2970, Horsholm, Denmark
Tel.: (45) 43 473 002
Pharmaceutical Product Whslr
N.A.I.C.S.: 424210

Algol Chemicals OU   (1)
Vaike-Paala 1, 11415, Tallinn, Estonia
Tel.: (372) 6 056 010
Web Site: http://www.algolchemicals.com
Emp.: 6
Pharmaceutical Product Whslr
N.A.I.C.S.: 424210
Alexander Bargum (Gen Mgr)

Algol Chemicals SIA   (1)
Asarisi 3, Marupe District, Riga, 2167,
Latvia   (100%)
Tel.: (371) 67615321
Web Site: http://www.algol.lv
Provider of Storage Services
N.A.I.C.S.: 493110
Alvils Brants (Pres)

Algol Diagnostics A/S   (1)
Lyngso Alle 3, 2970, Horsholm, Denmark
Tel.: (45) 4517 0600
Web Site: http://www.algoldiagnostics.dk
Medical Supplies Distr
N.A.I.C.S.: 423450

Algol Technics Oy   (1)
Karapellontie 6, PO Box 13, 02611, Espoo,
Finland
Tel.: (358) 950991
Web Site: http://www.algol.fi
Emp.: 350
Technical Trade
N.A.I.C.S.: 611519
Alexander Bargum (Mng Dir)

Algol Techniques   (1)
Karapellontie 6, Espoo, 2610,
Finland   (100%)
Tel.: (358) 950991
Web Site: http://www.algol.fi
Production & Sales of Materials Handling
Equipment
N.A.I.C.S.: 238290
Viktor Jardinan (Gen Mgr)

Algol-Eesti OU   (1)
Vana-Narva mnt 21, Beterb Ori Rd 44,
11415, Tallinn, Estonia   (50%)
Tel.: (372) 66056010
Web Site: http://www.algol.ee
Sales Office & Storage Depot
N.A.I.C.S.: 493190

Histolab Products AB   (1)
Sodra Langebergsgatan 36, 421 32, Goth-
enburg, Sweden
Tel.: (46) 31 709 30 30
Web Site: http://www.histolab.se
Pharmaceutical Product Whslr
N.A.I.C.S.: 423450

IOOO Algol Chemicals   (1)
Fabritsius Srt 8B Premisis 2 Office No 50,
220007, Minsk, Belarus
Tel.: (375) 172 183 387
Pharmaceutical Product Whslr
N.A.I.C.S.: 424210

Suomen Unipol Oy   (1)
Karapellontie 8, 02610, Espoo,
Finland   (60%)
Tel.: (358) 96823260
Web Site: http://www.unipol.fi
Emp.: 4
Wholesale Trade of Industrial Chemicals &
Plastic Raw Materials
N.A.I.C.S.: 424690
Markku Ekholm (Mng Dir)

TOV Algol Chemicals   (1)
28 Chervonopraporna Street, 03083, Kiev,
Ukraine
Tel.: (380) 44 501 9805
Pharmaceutical Product Whslr
N.A.I.C.S.: 424210

UAB Algol Chemicals   (1)
Europe Ave 32, Kaunas, 46326, Lithuania
Tel.: (370) 37373220
Web Site: http://www.algolchemicals.lt
Sales Office & Storage Depot
N.A.I.C.S.: 493110
Vaedotas Kizelevicius (Gen Mgr)

ZAO Algol Chemicals   (1)
Obukhozskoy Oborony 70/2 Office 301,
Saint Petersburg, 192029, Russia   (100%)
Tel.: (7) 8123090100
Web Site: http://www.algolchemicals.ru
Sales Office & Storage Depot
N.A.I.C.S.: 493110
Ivanov Uri (Mng Dir)

ALGOLTEK TECHNOLOGY CO., LTD.

No 55 Gaotie 2nd Rd, Hsinchu
County, Zhubei, 302, Taiwan
Tel.: (886) 36675345
Web Site:
    https://www.algoltek.com.tw
Year Founded: 2010
6684—(TPE)
Rev.: $13,423,225
Assets: $29,828,378
Liabilities: $3,942,313
Net Worth: $25,886,064
Earnings: $1,176,375
Fiscal Year-end: 12/31/22
Semiconductor Equipment Mfr
N.A.I.C.S.: 333242
Eric Hu (Chm)

ALGOMA CENTRAL CORPO-RATION

63 Church Street Suite 600, Saint
Catharines, L2R 3C4, ON, Canada
Tel.: (905) 687-7888
Web Site: https://www.algonet.com
Year Founded: 1899
ACH—(DEU)
Rev.: $546,763,514
Assets: $1,014,999,079
Liabilities: $427,282,387
Net Worth: $587,716,692
Earnings: $62,576,794
Emp.: 1,551
Fiscal Year-end: 12/31/23
Marine Transport Company
N.A.I.C.S.: 488390
Duncan N. R. Jackman (Chm)

Subsidiaries:

Algoma Central Corporation - Fraser
Marine & Industrial Division   (1)
1 Chestnut St, Port Colborne, L3K 1R3,
ON, Canada
Tel.: (905) 834-4549
Web Site:
    http://www.frasermarineandindustrial.com
Sales Range: $25-49.9 Million
Emp.: 7
Ship Building & Repairing Services
N.A.I.C.S.: 336611

Algoma Central Properties, Inc.   (1)
421 Bay St 608, PO Box 7000, Sault Sainte
Marie, P6A 1X3, ON, Canada   (100%)
Tel.: (705) 946-7220
Emp.: 20
Transportation Services
N.A.I.C.S.: 488190
Ken Sorenson (Pres)

Algoma Shipping Inc.   (1)
152 Conant St, Beverly, MA 01915
Tel.: (978) 232-4800
Web Site: http://www.algonet.com
Emp.: 4
Freight Forwarding Services
N.A.I.C.S.: 488510

Algoma Tankers   (1)
63 Church St Ste 600, Saint Catharines,
L2R 3C4, ON, Canada   (100%)
Tel.: (905) 687-7888
Web Site: http://www.algonet.com
Sales Range: $25-49.9 Million
Emp.: 90
Sea Transportation-Freight

N.A.I.C.S.: 483111

Fraser Marine & Industrial   (1)
1 Chestnut Street, Port Colborne, L3K1R3,
ON, Canada   (100%)
Tel.: (905) 834-4549
Web Site:
    http://www.frasermarineandindustrial.com
Sales Range: $10-24.9 Million
Emp.: 85
N.A.I.C.S.: 488210

LAKEN SHIPPING CORPORATION
SMT (USA) INC.   (1)
1 Cleveland Ctr 1250 Old River Rd Ste 2 N,
Cleveland, OH 44113
Tel.: (216) 771-1999
Ship Repair & Maintenance Services
N.A.I.C.S.: 336611

Marbulk Canada Inc.   (1)
152 Conant St, Beverly, MA 01915   (50%)
Tel.: (978) 299-1090
Holding Company
N.A.I.C.S.: 551112

Subsidiary (Domestic):

Marbulk Shipping Inc.   (2)
152 Conant St, Beverly, MA 01915
Tel.: (978) 232-4810
Provider of International Dry Bulk Shipping
N.A.I.C.S.: 483113

ALGOMA INC.

105 West Street, Sault Sainte Marie,
P6A 7B4, ON, Canada
Tel.: (705) 945-2351   ON
Web Site: http://www.algoma.com
Year Founded: 1901
Rolled Sheet & Plate Steel Mfr
N.A.I.C.S.: 331221
Michael Dennis Garcia (CEO)

ALGOMA STEEL GROUP INC.

105 West Street, Sault Sainte Marie,
P6A 7B4, ON, Canada
Tel.: (705) 945-2351   BC
Web Site: https://ir.algoma.com
Year Founded: 2021
ASTL—(NASDAQ)
Rev.: $2,046,643,100
Assets: $1,808,794,960
Liabilities: $731,738,440
Net Worth: $1,077,056,520
Earnings: $219,875,100
Emp.: 2,847
Fiscal Year-end: 03/31/23
Holding Company; Raw Steel & Steel
Products Mfr
N.A.I.C.S.: 551112
Michael Dennis Garcia (CEO)

Subsidiaries:

Algoma Steel Inc.   (1)
105 West Street, Sault Sainte Marie, P6A
7B4, ON, Canada   (100%)
Tel.: (705) 945-2351
Web Site: https://algoma.com
Steel Mfrs
N.A.I.C.S.: 331513

ALGONQUIN POWER & UTILI-TIES CORP.

354 Davis Road, Oakville, L6J 2X1,
ON, Canada
Tel.: (905) 465-4500
Web Site:
    https://www.algonquinpower.com
Year Founded: 1988
AQN—(NYSE)
Rev.: $2,698,015,000
Assets: $18,373,961,000
Liabilities: $11,749,553,000
Net Worth: $6,624,408,000
Earnings: $20,318,000
Emp.: 3,946
Fiscal Year-end: 12/31/23
Renewable Energy Services
N.A.I.C.S.: 221210
Kenneth Moore (Chm)

Subsidiaries:

AAGES Devco Services S.A. **(1)**
Campus Palmas Altas Calle Energia Solar
1, 41014, Seville, Spain
Tel.: (34) 95 493 7000
Web Site: http://www.aa-ges.com
Energy & Water Infrastructure Services
N.A.I.C.S.: 221118
Armando Zuluaga Zilbermann *(CEO)*

Joint Venture (Non-US):

Liberty Group Limited **(2)**
27 Serpentine Road, Pembroke, HM DX,
Bermuda
Tel.: (441) 2986100
Web Site: http://www.liberty.bm
Sales Range: $200-249.9 Million
Holding Company; Electric Power Genera-
tion & Energy Distribution Services
N.A.I.C.S.: 551112
Wayne M. Caines *(Pres)*

Subsidiary (Non-US):

BTS Limited **(3)**
Grevgatan 34, 114 53, Stockholm, Sweden
Tel.: (46) 858707000
Web Site: https://bts.com
Investment Management Service
N.A.I.C.S.: 541611
Henrik Ekelund *(Founder)*

Subsidiary (Domestic):

**Bermuda Electric Light Company
Limited** **(3)**
27 Serpentine Road, Pembroke, HM 07,
Bermuda
Tel.: (441) 2955111
Web Site: https://www.belco.bm
Electric Power Distribution
N.A.I.C.S.: 221122

Subsidiary (Domestic):

BELCO Properties Limited **(4)**
PO Box HM 1026, Hamilton, Bermuda
Tel.: (441) 2955111
Residential Property Managers
N.A.I.C.S.: 531311

Subsidiary (Domestic):

PureNERGY Renewables, Ltd **(3)**
25 Serpentine Road, Pembroke, HM 07,
Bermuda
Tel.: (441) 2992808
Web Site: http://www.purenergy.bm
Sales Range: $25-49.9 Million
Emp.: 4
Wind Turbine Mfr
N.A.I.C.S.: 333611

Liberty Utilities Co. **(1)**
36 5th St, Fall River, MA 02720
Tel.: (508) 324-7811
Web Site: http://www.libertyutilities.com
Sales Range: $300-349.9 Million
Emp.: 420
Natural Gas Distr
N.A.I.C.S.: 221210
Travis Johnson *(VP-Ops)*

Subsidiary (Non-US):

**Enbridge Gas New Brunswick
Inc.** **(2)**
440 Wilsey Road Suite 101, Fredericton,
E3B 7G5, NB, Canada
Tel.: (506) 457-7703
Web Site: http://naturalgasnb.com
Natural Gas Distribution Services
N.A.I.C.S.: 221210

Liberty Utilities (Canada) Corp. **(2)**
2845 Bristol Circle, Oakville, L6H 7H7, ON,
Canada
Tel.: (905) 465-4500
Web Site: http://www.libertyutilities.com
Water, Electricity & Gas Utility Services
N.A.I.C.S.: 221122

Subsidiary (US):

Granite State Electric Company **(3)**
11 Northeastern Blvd, Salem, NH
03079-1953 **(100%)**
Tel.: (603) 890-7120

Sales Range: $50-74.9 Million
Emp.: 45
Electric Power & Natural Gas Distr
N.A.I.C.S.: 221122

**Liberty Utilities (Pine Bluff Water)
Inc.** **(3)**
1100 State St, Pine Bluff, AR 71601
Tel.: (870) 534-2721
Web Site: http://www.libertyutilities.com
Sales Range: $50-74.9 Million
Emp.: 37
Water Supply & Treatment
N.A.I.C.S.: 221310

Unit (US):

Liberty Utilities West **(3)**
701 National Ave, Tahoe Vista, CA 96148
Web Site: http://www.libertyutilities.com
Electric Power Distribution Services
N.A.I.C.S.: 221122

Subsidiary (US):

**The Empire District Electric
Company** **(3)**
602 S Joplin Ave, Joplin, MO
64801 **(100%)**
Tel.: (417) 625-5100
Emp.: 749
Electric Power Generation & Water Distr
N.A.I.C.S.: 221122

Subsidiary (Domestic):

Empire District Industries, Inc. **(4)**
602 S Joplin Ave, Joplin, MO 64801
Tel.: (417) 625-5100
Emp.: 750
Fiber Optic Mfr
N.A.I.C.S.: 335921

Subsidiary (Domestic):

Liberty Utilities Apple Valley **(2)**
21760 Ottawa Rd, Apple Valley, CA 92308
Tel.: (760) 247-6484
Web Site: http://california.libertyutilities.com
Water Utility
N.A.I.C.S.: 221310

**Liberty Utilities Energy Solutions (Ap-
pliance) Corp.** **(2)**
45 N Main St Ste 1, Fall River, MA 02720
Tel.: (508) 676-7598
Natural Gas Pipeline Operator
N.A.I.C.S.: 486210

**New York American Water Company,
Inc.** **(2)**
60 Brooklyn Ave, Merrick, NY 11566
Tel.: (856) 782-2316
Waste Water Treatment Services
N.A.I.C.S.: 221320
Walter J. Lynch *(COO)*

St. Lawrence Gas Company, Inc. **(1)**
33 Stearns St, Massena, NY 13662
Tel.: (315) 769-3511
Web Site: http://www.stlawrencegas.com
Natural Gas Distribution
N.A.I.C.S.: 486210

St. Leon Wind Energy LP **(1)**
354 Davis Rd, Oakville, L6H 7H7, ON,
Canada
Tel.: (204) 744-2315
Web Site: http://www.algonquinpower.com
Emp.: 800
Eletric Power Generation Services
N.A.I.C.S.: 221111

Valley Power Limited Partnership **(1)**
5302 34th Ave, Drayton Valley, T7A 1S3,
AB, Canada
Tel.: (780) 542-7196
Sales Range: $25-49.9 Million
Emp.: 22
Electrical Contractor
N.A.I.C.S.: 238210
Terry McCool *(Mng Dir)*

ALGOQUANT FINTECH LIM-
ITED
4/11 1st Floor Asaf Ali Road, New
Delhi, 110002, India
Tel.: (91) 9910032394 In

Web Site:
https://www.algoquantfintech.com
Year Founded: 1962
505725—(BOM)
Rev.: $711,212
Assets: $3,456,322
Liabilities: $710,740
Net Worth: $2,745,582
Earnings: $509,114
Emp.: 13
Fiscal Year-end: 03/31/21
Hand Tools Mfr & Distr
N.A.I.C.S.: 332216
Shravan Kumar Mandelia *(Mng Dir)*

ALHAMBRA RESOURCES LTD
Suite 3A 4015 - 1St Street SE, Cal-
gary, T2G 4X7, Canada
Tel.: (403) 228-2855 AB
Web Site:
http://www.alhambraresources.com
Year Founded: 1993
Sales Range: $1-9.9 Million
Emp.: 15
Gold Exploration & Development
N.A.I.C.S.: 212220
John J. Komarnicki *(Chm & CEO)*

ALHAMRANI GROUP
Aba Alkhail St, Jeddah, 21431, Saudi
Arabia
Tel.: (966) 26065555
Web Site:
http://www.alhamranigroup.com
Sales Range: $800-899.9 Million
Emp.: 3,000
Holding Company
N.A.I.C.S.: 551112
Abdullah Ali Alhamrani *(Chm & CEO)*

Subsidiaries:

**Alhamrani Company For Investment
In Trade Limited** **(1)**
PO Box 7656, 21452, Jeddah, Saudi
Arabia **(100%)**
Tel.: (966) 26634204
Sales Range: $250-299.9 Million
Emp.: 600
Automobile & Motor Vehicle Whslr
N.A.I.C.S.: 423110

Alhamrani Company for Industry **(1)**
PO Box 5260, 21422, Jeddah, Saudi
Arabia **(100%)**
Tel.: (966) 26065555
Web Site: http://www.aci.alhamrani.net
Building Material Dealers
N.A.I.C.S.: 444180

Alhamrani Industrial Group Ltd **(1)**
PO Box 7172, 21462, Jeddah, Saudi
Arabia **(100%)**
Tel.: (966) 26360390
Web Site: http://www.aig.alhamrani.net
Packaging Machinery Mfr
N.A.I.C.S.: 333993

**Alhamrani Real Estate Development
Company** **(1)**
Junction of Sari St Madinah Rd, PO Box
54736, 21524, Jeddah, Saudi
Arabia **(100%)**
Tel.: (966) 26978080
Web Site: http://www.intertrade.com.sa
Sales Range: $50-74.9 Million
Emp.: 60
Real Estate Property Lessors
N.A.I.C.S.: 531190

Alhamrani United Company **(1)**
Al Hamra, PO Box 701, Madinah Rd,
21421, Jeddah, Saudi Arabia **(100%)**
Tel.: (966) 26696690
Web Site: http://www.nissan.com.sa
Motor Vehicle Supplies & New Parts Whslr
N.A.I.C.S.: 423120

**Alhamrani Universal Company
Ltd** **(1)**
PO Box 1229, 21431, Jeddah, Saudi
Arabia **(100%)**
Tel.: (966) 26065555
Web Site: http://www.universal.com.sa

Investment Banking & Securities Dealing
N.A.I.C.S.: 523150

**Alhamrani-Fuchs Petroleum Saudi
Arabia Ltd.** **(1)**
Tahlia St, PO Box 7103, Jeddah, 21462,
Saudi Arabia
Tel.: (966) 26635666
Web Site: http://www.fuchs.com.sa
Sales Range: $75-99.9 Million
Emp.: 75
Mfr of Lubricants
N.A.I.C.S.: 324191

**Mohamed A. Alhamrani & Co Inter-
trade Co (Ltd)** **(1)**
Jeddah Junction of Sari St, Madinah Rd,
21524, Jeddah, Saudi Arabia **(100%)**
Tel.: (966) 26978080
Web Site: http://www.alhamrani.net
Motor Vehicle Supplies & New Parts Whslr
N.A.I.C.S.: 423120

ALI ABDULLAH AL TAMIMI
COMPANY
PO Box 172, Dammam, 31411, Saudi
Arabia
Tel.: (966) 138075700
Web Site: http://www.al-tamimi.com
Year Founded: 1953
Sales Range: $1-4.9 Billion
Emp.: 9,000
Holding Company
N.A.I.C.S.: 551112
Tariq A. Tamimi *(Pres)*

Subsidiaries:

**High Seas Marine & Industrial Ser-
vices Co. Ltd.** **(1)**
Building no 3311 Prince Mohammad Bin
Abdul Aziz Street, PO Box 1450, King
Abdullah Bin Abdul Aziz Road Al - Dana,
Ras Tanura, 31941, Saudi Arabia
Tel.: (966) 136682570
Web Site: http://www.highseas.com.sa
Marine Shipping Services
N.A.I.C.S.: 488510
Ibrahim A. Al-Saeed *(Mng Dir)*

Kuwait Pearls Catering Co. **(1)**
PO Box 12253, Kuwait, 71653, Kuwait
Tel.: (965) 24754256
Web Site: http://kuwait-pearls-catering-
co.kuwaitbd.com
Catering Services
N.A.I.C.S.: 722320

**Masdar Al Hayat for Food Industries,
Ltd.** **(1)**
Masdar Al Hayat for Food Industries Ltd
Industrial Zone No 2, PO Box 355011, Ri-
yadh, 11383, Saudi Arabia
Tel.: (966) 112656000
Web Site: http://www.masdar.sa
Food Products Mfr
N.A.I.C.S.: 311919

Tamimi & Saihaiti Transport Co. **(1)**
PO Box 1246, Al Khobar, 31952, Saudi
Arabia
Tel.: (966) 38824457
Web Site: http://www.taseco.com.sa
Bus Transportation Services
N.A.I.C.S.: 485113
Abdullah Cordova *(Mgr-Ops)*

**Tamimi Power and Industrial
Group** **(1)**
PO Box 172, Dammam, 31411, Saudi Ara-
bia
Tel.: (966) 3 847 4050
Web Site:
http://www.tamimipowergroup.com
Industrial Support Services
N.A.I.C.S.: 213112

Affiliate (Domestic):

Aquilex Arabia, Ltd. **(2)**
Jubail Road Dammam 2nd Industrial City,
Al Khobar, 31952, Saudi Arabia
Tel.: (966) 3 8681037
Machinery Maintenance, Repair & Overhaul
Services
N.A.I.C.S.: 811310

Ali Abdullah Al Tamimi Company—(Continued)

Tamimi Tape Manufacturing Co. Ltd (1)
PO Box 31952, Al Khobar, Saudi Arabia
Tel.: (966) 138951128
Tiles Mfr
N.A.I.C.S.: 322230

ALI ASGHAR TEXTILE MILS LTD.
Ellahi Tower Plot 6 Sector No 25 Adjacent Getz Pharma Astola Project, Korangi Industrial Area, Karachi, Pakistan
Tel.: (92) 21350627967
Web Site: https://www.aatml.com.pk
AATML—(KAR)
Rev.: $71,956
Assets: $2,655,513
Liabilities: $600,428
Net Worth: $2,055,085
Earnings: ($82,986)
Emp.: 24
Fiscal Year-end: 06/30/19
Cotton Yarn Mfr
N.A.I.C.S.: 313110
Muhammad Suleman (CFO)

ALI BIN ALI ESTABLISHMENT
ABA Tower Airport Road, PO Box 75, Ummguilena, Doha, 00974, Qatar
Tel.: (974) 44469888
Web Site: http://www.alibinali.com
Year Founded: 1945
Sales Range: $350-399.9 Million
Emp.: 1,500
Holding Company
N.A.I.C.S.: 551112
Adel Ali Bin Ali (Chm)

Subsidiaries:

Ali Bin Ali & Partners (1)
Opposite Gulf Cinema C Ring Road, PO Box 1993, Doha, Qatar
Tel.: (974) 489 5666
Sales Range: $75-99.9 Million
Emp.: 125
Grocery Distr
N.A.I.C.S.: 424410
Wadih Kazan (Gen Mgr)

Ali Bin Ali Technology Solutions (1)
Bldg 289 St 230 C Ring Road, New Salata, Doha, Qatar
Tel.: (974) 44056704
Web Site: http://www.abats.com.qa
Graphic Design Services
N.A.I.C.S.: 541430

ALI CORPORATION
5th Floor No 83 Section 1, Chongqing South Road, Taipei, 100, Taiwan
Tel.: (886) 266365566
Web Site: https://www.ali.com.tw
Year Founded: 1993
3041—(TAI)
Rev.: $47,279,308
Assets: $83,159,191
Liabilities: $30,711,991
Net Worth: $52,447,200
Earnings: ($55,313,612)
Emp.: 639
Fiscal Year-end: 12/31/23
Integrated Circuit Chips Research & Development, Design, Testing, Mfr & Distr
N.A.I.C.S.: 334413
Sophia Liang (Chm & CEO)

Subsidiaries:

ALi (China) Corporation (1)
206 Room Block A, Unisplendour Information Harbor Nanshan District, Shenzhen, 518052, Guangdong, China
Tel.: (86) 75525195788
Integrated Circuit Chips Research & Development, Design, Testing, Mfr & Distr
N.A.I.C.S.: 334413

ALi (Hsinchu) Corporation (1)
6F No 1 Jinshan 8th St, Hsinchu, 300, Taiwan
Tel.: (886) 3 578 0589
Web Site: http://www.ali.com.tw
Integrated Circuit Chips Research & Development, Design, Testing, Mfr & Distr
N.A.I.C.S.: 334413

ALi (Shanghai) Corporation (1)
6F-A Building 3 No 7 Guiqing Road, Shanghai, 200233, China
Tel.: (86) 21 6485 5058
Web Site: http://www.ali.com.tw
Integrated Circuit Chips Research & Development, Design, Testing, Mfr & Distr
N.A.I.C.S.: 334413

ALi (Zhuhai) Corporation (1)
4F Bldg 3 No 1 Software Road, Tangjia, Zhuhai, Guangdong, China
Tel.: (86) 7563392000
Web Site: https://www.ali.com.tw
Integrated Circuit Chips Research & Development, Design, Testing, Mfr & Distr
N.A.I.C.S.: 334413

ALitech India LLP (1)
Unit No B- 201-202 UTC Urbtech Trade Centre Tower-A Block- B B-35, Sec -132, Noida, 201304, Uttra Pradesh, India
Tel.: (91) 1206137444
Software Development Services
N.A.I.C.S.: 541511

Abilis Systems Sarl (1)
3 chemin Pre Fleuri, Plan-les-Ouates, 1228, Geneva, Switzerland
Tel.: (41) 22 816 19 00
Web Site: http://www.abilis.com
Sales Range: $25-49.9 Million
Emp.: 48
Electronic Components Mfr
N.A.I.C.S.: 334413

Subsidiary (US):

Abilis Systems LLC (2)
ASU Research Park Transamerica Bldg 7855 S River Pkwy Ste 116, Tempe, AZ 85284
Tel.: (480) 882-8639
Web Site: http://www.abilis.com
Electronic Component Sales
N.A.I.C.S.: 423690
Kiet Van Kuru (Gen Mgr)

ALI HOLDING S.R.L
Via Gobetti 2A Villa Fiorita, 20063, Milan, Italy
Tel.: (39) 029219
Web Site: https://www.aligroup.it
Emp.: 100
Holding Company
N.A.I.C.S.: 551112

Subsidiaries:

Ali S.p.A. (1)
Via Gobetti 2A Villa Fiorita, Cernusco sul Naviglio, 20063, Milan, Italy
Tel.: (39) 02921991
Web Site: http://www.aligroup.it
Sales Range: $800-899.9 Million
Emp.: 4,200
Designs, Manufactures, Supplies & Services Equipment for the Foodservice Industry
N.A.I.C.S.: 333241
Luciano Berti (Chm)

Subsidiary (US):

Aladdin Temp-Rite, LLC (2)
250 E Main St, Hendersonville, TN 37075 (100%)
Tel.: (615) 537-3600
Web Site: http://www.aladdintemprite.com
Sales Range: $75-99.9 Million
Emp.: 200
Mfr of Insulated Food Service Systems for Hospitals, Correctional Facilities & Institutions
N.A.I.C.S.: 423450
Debbie Witt (Mgr-Adv & PR)

Subsidiary (Non-US):

Aladdin Temp-Rite Canada (3)

3701 Lakeshore Blvd W, PO Box 48559, Toronto, NAW 1P5, ON, Canada (100%)
Tel.: (905) 562-9467
Web Site: http://www.aladdintemprite.com
Sales Range: $10-24.9 Million
Emp.: 10
Food Service Solutions
N.A.I.C.S.: 722330

Subsidiary (Domestic):

Aladdin Temp-Rite Puerto Rico (3)
PO Box 19411, San Juan, PR 00910 (100%)
Tel.: (787) 788-5700
Web Site: http://www.aladdintemprite.com
Sales Range: $10-24.9 Million
Emp.: 5
Providers of Food Service Solutions
N.A.I.C.S.: 722330
Jose Garcia (Gen Mgr)

Subsidiary (Non-US):

Ali Comenda S.A. (2)
17-19 Avenue Gaston Monmousseau, 93240, Stains, France
Tel.: (33) 1 48 21 63 25
Web Site: http://www.comenda.fr
Dishwasher Mfr
N.A.I.C.S.: 335220

Ali Foodservice Equipment (Shanghai) Co., Ltd. (2)
361 Hong Zhong Road, Shanghai, 201103, China
Tel.: (86) 21 5109 8033
Web Site: http://www.aligroup.cn
Dishwasher Distr
N.A.I.C.S.: 423620

Subsidiary (Domestic):

Alphatech ALI S.p.A. (2)
Via Schiaparelli 15 - Z I San Giacomo di Vegli, 31029, Vittorio Veneto, Italy
Tel.: (39) 0438 912588
Web Site: http://www.alphatech-ali.it
Cooking Equipment Mfr & Whslr
N.A.I.C.S.: 333310

Ambach Ali S.p.A. (2)
Sulla Strada del Vino Localita Ganda 1, 39052, Bolzano, Italy
Tel.: (39) 0471 662213
Web Site: http://www.ambach.com
Food Product Machinery Mfr
N.A.I.C.S.: 333241

Baron ALi SPA (2)
Via del Boscon n 424, 32100, Belluno, Italy
Tel.: (39) 0437 855411
Web Site: http://www.baronprofessional.com
Food Product Machinery Mfr
N.A.I.C.S.: 333241

Subsidiary (Non-US):

Bertrand-Puma (2)
ZI Saint-Eloi, 58000, Nevers, France
Tel.: (33) 3 86 71 88 00
Web Site: http://www.bertrand-puma.fr
Food Product Equipment Mfr & Distr
N.A.I.C.S.: 333241

Burlodge Ltd. (2)
C60 Barwell Business Park Leatherhead Road, Chessington, KT9 2NY, Surrey, United Kingdom
Tel.: (44) 20 8879 5700
Web Site: http://www.burlodgeuk.com
Emp.: 80
Food Product Equipment Mfr & Distr
N.A.I.C.S.: 333241
Peter Stansfield (Mng Dir)

Subsidiary (Non-US):

Burlodge Canada Ltd. (3)
10 Edvac Drive, Brampton, L6S 5P2, ON, Canada
Tel.: (905) 790-1881
Web Site: http://www.burlodgeca.com
Emp.: 15
Cooking Equipment Distr
N.A.I.C.S.: 423440
Paul Gauntley (Pres)

Burlodge S.r.l. (3)
Via Ca Bertoncina 43, Seriate, 24048, Bergamo, Italy

Tel.: (39) 035 452 4900
Web Site: http://www.burlodgeit.com
Cooking Equipment Distr
N.A.I.C.S.: 423440
Ellen Speranza (Mng Dir)

Burlodge SAS (3)
40 Boulevard de Nesles, 77420, Champs-sur-Marne, France
Tel.: (33) 1 60 17 66 74
Web Site: http://www.burlodgefr.com
Cooking Equipment Distr
N.A.I.C.S.: 423440

Subsidiary (US):

Burlodge USA Inc. (3)
3760 Industrial Dr, Winston Salem, NC 27115-4088
Tel.: (336) 776-1010
Web Site: http://www.burlodgeusa.com
Emp.: 4
Cooking Equipment Distr
N.A.I.C.S.: 423440
Paul Gauntley (Pres)

Subsidiary (Non-US):

CFI (2)
ZA Lavaveix-les-Mines, 23150, Ahun, France
Tel.: (33) 4 7557 5500
Web Site: http://www.froid-cfi.fr
Food Product Machinery Mfr
N.A.I.C.S.: 333241

Subsidiary (US):

CMA Dishmachines (2)
12700 Knott St, Garden Grove, CA 92841
Tel.: (714) 898-8781
Web Site: http://www.cmadishmachines.com
Dishwasher Mfr & Distr
N.A.I.C.S.: 335220
John Lacey (Dir-Sls)

Subsidiary (Domestic):

Carpigiani Group (2)
via Emilia 45, 40011, Anzola dell'Emila, Italy
Tel.: (39) 051 6505 111
Web Site: http://www.carpigiani.com
Food Product Machinery Mfr
N.A.I.C.S.: 333241
Andrea Occari (Mgr-Pur & Plng)

Subsidiary (Non-US):

CARPIGIANI DEUTSCHLAND GMBH (3)
Echterdinger Str 111, Bernhausen, 70794, Filderstadt, Germany
Tel.: (49) 711 7089264
Cooking Equipment Distr
N.A.I.C.S.: 423440

CARPIGIANI FRANCE S.A. (3)
15/19 Rue Leon Geoffroy Parcd Act, 94400, Vitry-sur-Seine, France
Tel.: (33) 1 468 10591
Ice Making Equipment Distr
N.A.I.C.S.: 423740

CARPIGIANI NEDERLAND (3)
Beatrix de Rijkweg 7, 5657 EG, Eindhoven, Netherlands
Tel.: (31) 40 235 35 35
Web Site: http://www.carpigiani.nl
Cooking Equipment Distr
N.A.I.C.S.: 423440

CARPIGIANI SHANGHAI (3)
Room 601 Huading Building Zhongshan Xi Road No2368, Shanghai, 200235, China
Tel.: (86) 21 64846659
Ice Making Machinery Distr
N.A.I.C.S.: 423740

Carpigiani Centro Sudamerica, SA (3)
Tucuman 994 - 1er Piso CABA, 1049, Buenos Aires, Argentina
Tel.: (54) 11 43310550
Web Site: http://www.carpigiani.com
Food Product Machinery Mfr & Distr
N.A.I.C.S.: 333241

Carpigiani Centro Suramerica do Brasil Ltda (3)
Al Franca 447 - J Paulista, Sao Paulo, 01422-000, Brazil

Tel.: (55) 11 20618207
Web Site: http://www.carpigiani.com
Ice Cream Machine Mfr & Distr
N.A.I.C.S.: 423740

Carpigiani Japan Co., Ltd. (3)
Toei Mishuku Building 5F 1-13-1 Mishuku,
Setagaya, Tokyo, 154-0005, Japan
Tel.: (81) 3 5779 8850
Ice Making Machinery Distr
N.A.I.C.S.: 423740

Carpigiani Solutions (3)
Skladochnaja Str 1 st 18 of 205, 127018,
Moscow, Russia
Tel.: (7) 495 580 3360
Cooking Equipment Distr
N.A.I.C.S.: 423440

Carpigiani UK Ltd (3)
Carpigiani House Coldnose Road, Rother-
was, Hereford, HR2 6JL, United Kingdom
Tel.: (44) 1432 346 018
Web Site: http://www.carpigiani.co.uk
Emp.: 30
Ice Making Machinery Distr
N.A.I.C.S.: 423740
Paul Ingram (Mng Dir)

Sencotel S.L. (3)
Tramuntana n 10, 46716, Rafelcofer, Spain
Tel.: (34) 962 801 112
Web Site: http://www.sencotel.es
Food Product Machinery Mfr
N.A.I.C.S.: 333241

Subsidiary (US):

Champion Industries, Inc. (2)
3765 Champion Blvd, Winston Salem, NC
27105
Tel.: (336) 661-1556
Web Site:
   http://www.championindustries.com
Dishwasher Mfr & Distr
N.A.I.C.S.: 335220
Filippo Berti (CEO)

Subsidiary (Domestic):

Comenda Ali SpA. (2)
Via Galileo Galilei 8, 20060, Cassina de'
Pecchi, Italy
Tel.: (39) 02 952281
Web Site: http://www.comenda.eu
Dishwasher Mfr & Distr
N.A.I.C.S.: 335220

DIHR Ali S.p.A. (2)
Via del Lavoro 28, 31033, Castelfranco
Veneto, Italy
Tel.: (39) 0423 7344
Web Site: http://www.dihr.com
Dishwasher Mfr
N.A.I.C.S.: 335220

Subsidiary (Non-US):

Dawson Mmp Limited (2)
Wath Rd, Barnsley, S74 8HJ, South York-
shire, United Kingdom
Tel.: (44) 1226 350450
Dishwasher Distr
N.A.I.C.S.: 423620
Andrew Shearing (Reg Mgr-Sls)

Subsidiary (Domestic):

Fimi Ali S.p.a. (2)
Via Puglie 14/16, 20098, San Giuliano Mila-
nese, Italy
Tel.: (39) 02 98281146
Web Site: http://www.fimi-inox.it
Cooking Equipment Distr
N.A.I.C.S.: 423440

Subsidiary (Non-US):

Friginox (2)
Villevallier, 89330, Saint-Julien-du-Sault,
France
Tel.: (33) 3 86 91 10 58
Web Site: http://www.friginox.com
Refrigerated Cabinet Mfr
N.A.I.C.S.: 333415

Subsidiary (Domestic):

Friulinox Ali Spa (2)
Via Treviso 4, Taiedo di Chions, 33083,
Pordenone, Italy
Tel.: (39) 0434 635411

Web Site: http://www.friulinox.com
Emp.: 80
Refrigerated Equipment Mfr & Distr
N.A.I.C.S.: 333415
Simone Froli (Gen Counsel)

Grandimpianti I.l.e. Ali SpA. (2)
Via Masiere 211/c, Sospirolo, 32037, Bel-
luno, Italy
Tel.: (39) 0437 848 711
Web Site: http://www.grandimpianti.com
Industrial Laundry Equipment Mfr
N.A.I.C.S.: 333310

Subsidiary (Non-US):

Hackman Oyj Abp (2)
Ahjonkaarre, 04220, Kerava, Finland
Tel.: (358) 204 3913
Web Site: http://www.hackman.com
Food Product Machinery Mfr
N.A.I.C.S.: 333241

Subsidiary (Domestic):

Hiber Ali SpA (2)
Via Cal Larga 8 - Z I San Giacomo di Veg-
lia, 31029, Vittorio Veneto, Italy
Tel.: (39) 0438 911940
Web Site: http://www.hiber.it
Catering Equipment Mfr
N.A.I.C.S.: 333310

Hoonved Ali SpA (2)
Via U Foscolo 1, Venegono Superiore,
21040, Varese, Italy
Tel.: (39) 0331 856111
Web Site: http://www.hoonved.com
Washing Machine Whslr
N.A.I.C.S.: 423440

Subsidiary (Non-US):

Krefft Grobkuchentechnik GmbH (2)
Lochfeldstrasse 28, 76437, Rastatt, Ger-
many
Tel.: (49) 72 22 15 977 40
Web Site: http://www.krefft.de
Catering Equipment Mfr
N.A.I.C.S.: 333310

Subsidiary (Domestic):

Kromo Ali SpA (2)
Via Mestre 3, 31033, Castelfranco Veneto,
Italy
Tel.: (39) 0423 734580
Web Site: http://www.kromo-alf.com
Washing Equipment Mfr
N.A.I.C.S.: 333310

Mareno Ali S.P.A (2)
via Conti Agosti 231, Mareno di Piave,
31010, Treviso, Italy
Tel.: (39) 0438 4981
Web Site: http://www.mareno.it
Emp.: 229
Cooking Equipment Mfr
N.A.I.C.S.: 333310
Fabrizio Rocco (Gen Mgr)

Subsidiary (Non-US):

Moffat Pty Ltd (2)
740 Springvale Road, Mulgrave, 3170, VIC,
Australia
Tel.: (61) 3 9518 3888
Web Site: http://www.moffat.com.au
Cooking Equipment Distr
N.A.I.C.S.: 423440

Subsidiary (Non-US):

Blue Seal Limited (3)
Unit 67 Gravelly Business Park Gravelly,
Birmingham, B24 8TQ, United Kingdom
Tel.: (44) 121 327 5575
Web Site: http://www.blue-seal.co.uk
Cooking Equipment Distr
N.A.I.C.S.: 423440

Moffat Ltd (3)
45 Illinois Drive Izone Business Hub,
Rolleston, 7675, New Zealand
Tel.: (64) 3 389 1007
Web Site: http://www.moffat.co.nz
Cooking Equipment Distr
N.A.I.C.S.: 423440

Subsidiary (Domestic):

OEM - Ali S.p.A (2)

Viale Lombardia 33, Bozzolo, Mantua, Italy
Tel.: (39) 0376 910511
Web Site: http://www.oemali.com
Cooking Equipment Mfr
N.A.I.C.S.: 333310
Ermes Torresan (CEO)

Polaris Ali SpA. (2)
Via Cavalieri di Vittorio V 25, Sedico,
32036, Belluno, Italy
Tel.: (39) 0437 8551
Web Site: http://www.polarisgroup.it
Industrial Refrigeration Equipment Mfr
N.A.I.C.S.: 333415

Promac Italia Srl (2)
Via Cremona 1, Legnano, 20025, Milan,
Italy
Tel.: (39) 0331 455102
Web Site: http://www.promacitalia.com
Coffee Machine Mfr
N.A.I.C.S.: 333310
Guido Petti (Gen Mgr)

Rancilio Group S.p.A. (2)
Viale della Repubblica 40, Villastanza di
Parabiago, 20015, Milan, Italy
Tel.: (39) 0331 408200
Web Site: http://www.ranciliogroup.com
Coffee Machine Mfr
N.A.I.C.S.: 333310
Silvia Nebuloni (Dir-HR)

Subsidiary (Non-US):

EGRO Suisse AG (3)
Bahnhofstrasse 66, 5605, Dottikon, Switzer-
land
Tel.: (41) 566169595
Web Site: http://www.egrosuisse.ch
Emp.: 50
Coffee Machine Mfr
N.A.I.C.S.: 333310
Michael Wehrli (CEO)

**Rancilio Group Deutschland
GmbH** (3)
Talstrasse 27, 97990, Weikersheim, Ger-
many
Tel.: (49) 7934 99 29 30
Web Site: http://www.ranciliogroup.com
Emp.: 10
Coffee Machine Whslr
N.A.I.C.S.: 423440
G. Rancilio (Mng Dir)

Rancilio Group Espana s.a. (3)
Gran Via de Carlos III 84 3 Edificio Trade,
08028, Barcelona, Spain
Tel.: (34) 902 884 275
Web Site: http://www.ranciliogroup.com
Coffee Machine Mfr & Distr
N.A.I.C.S.: 423440

Subsidiary (US):

**Rancilio Group North America
Inc.** (3)
1340 Internationale Pkwy Ste 200,
Woodridge, IL 60517
Tel.: (630) 914-7900
Web Site: http://www.ranciliogroupna.com
Coffee Machine Whslr
N.A.I.C.S.: 423440
Chris Gittens (Reg Mgr-Sls)

Subsidiary (Non-US):

Rancilio Group Portugal Lda (3)
Rua Vicente Goncalves n 14-Armaz-2
Parque Industrial do Seixal, Aldeia de Paio
Pires-Seixal, 2840-048, Lisbon, Portugal
Tel.: (351) 21 493 52 58
Coffee Machine Whslr
N.A.I.C.S.: 423440

Subsidiary (Non-US):

Rosinox SAS (2)
23 Rue Felix Chedin, 18020, Bourges,
France (100%)
Tel.: (33) 248702828
Web Site: http://www.rosinox.com
Sales Range: $50-74.9 Million
Emp.: 120
Mfr of Household Appliances
N.A.I.C.S.: 335220

Scotsman Industries (S) Pte Ltd. (2)
1 Commonwealth Lane 09-22 One Commonwealth, Singapore, 149544, Singapore

Tel.: (65) 6738 5393
Emp.: 4
Ice Making Machinery Distr
N.A.I.C.S.: 423740
Andrea Tronci (Gen Mgr)

Subsidiary (US):

Scotsman Industries, Inc. (2)
775 Corporate Woods Pkwy, Vernon Hills,
IL 60061
Tel.: (847) 215-4500
Web Site:
   http://www.scotsmanindustries.com
Sales Range: $400-449.9 Million
Emp.: 800
Holding Company; Commercial Ice-Making
Equipment Mfr & Distr
N.A.I.C.S.: 551112
Richard Zuehlsdorf (VP-Procurement)

Subsidiary (Non-US):

CastelMAC, S.p.A. (3)
Via del Lavoro 9, 31033, Castelfranco
Veneto, Treviso, Italy
Tel.: (39) 0423 738311
Web Site: http://www.castelmac.it
Sales Range: $50-74.9 Million
Emp.: 140
Commercial Ice Machines & Refrigeration
Systems Mfr
N.A.I.C.S.: 333415
Sabio Dotto (CFO)

Subsidiary (Domestic):

Mile High Equipment LLC (3)
11100 E 45th Ave, Denver, CO 80239-3006
Tel.: (303) 371-3737
Web Site: http://www.iceomatic.com
Sales Range: $50-74.9 Million
Emp.: 200
Commercial Ice-Making Equipment Mfr
N.A.I.C.S.: 333415
Gary Mick (Pres)

Group (Domestic):

Scotsman Group LLC (3)
775 Corporate Woods Pkwy, Vernon Hills,
IL 60061-3112
Tel.: (847) 215-4500
Web Site: http://www.scotsman-ice.com
Sales Range: $25-49.9 Million
Emp.: 100
Commercial Ice-Making Equipment Mfr
N.A.I.C.S.: 333310
Jeff Biel (Dir-Mktg)

Subsidiary (Non-US):

Frimont, S.p.A. (4)
Via Puccini 22, 20010, Bettolino di Po-
gliano, MI, Italy
Tel.: (39) 0293960208
Web Site: http://www.frimont.it
Sales Range: $50-74.9 Million
Emp.: 250
Commercial Ice Machines & Refrigeration
Systems Mfr
N.A.I.C.S.: 333310
Emanuele Lanzani (Mng Dir)

**Scotsman Ice Systems (Shanghai)
Co., Ltd.** (4)
Room 405-407 Jing An China Tower 1701
West Beijing Road, Shanghai, 200040,
China
Tel.: (86) 21 61313200
Web Site: http://www.scotsman-ice.com
Sales Range: $25-49.9 Million
Emp.: 80
Commercial Ice Making Equipment Mfr
N.A.I.C.S.: 333310
Richeo Zhou (Gen Mgr)

Subsidiary (Non-US):

Stierlen GmbH (2)
Lochfeldstr 30, 76437, Rastatt, Germany
Tel.: (49) 7222 9047 0
Web Site: http://www.stierlen.de
Emp.: 25
Dishwasher Mfr & Distr
N.A.I.C.S.: 335220
Richard Krictmann (Gen Mgr)

Temp-Rite International GmbH (2)
Theodor-Barth-Str 29, 28307, Bremen, Germany

Ali Holding S.r.l—(Continued)

Tel.: (49) 4 21 4 86 92 0
Catering Equipment Distr
N.A.I.C.S.: 423440

Temp-Rite International Holding B.V. (2)
Goeseelsstraat 30, 4817 MV, Breda, Netherlands
Tel.: (31) 76 542 43 43
Web Site: http://www.temp-rite.nl
Holding Company
N.A.I.C.S.: 551112

Temp-Rite International Kft. (2)
Krisztina Krt 83-85, 1016, Budapest, Hungary
Tel.: (36) 1 212 70 43
Web Site: http://www.temprite.t-online.hu
Catering Equipment Distr
N.A.I.C.S.: 423440

The AFE Group Ltd. (2)
Bryggen Road, North Lynn Industrial Estate, King's Lynn, PE30 2HZ, Norfolk, United Kingdom (100%)
Tel.: (44) 1553817554
Web Site: http://www.theafegroup.com
Sales Range: $500-549.9 Million
Emp.: 250
Holding Company; Commercial Cooking Equipment Mfr
N.A.I.C.S.: 551112
Tim Smith (CEO)

Subsidiary (US):

ACP Inc. (3)
225 49th Ave Dr SW, Cedar Rapids, IA 52404
Tel.: (319) 368-8120
Web Site: http://www.acpsolutions.com
Sales Range: $25-49.9 Million
Emp.: 100
Commercial Microwave & Accelerated Cooking Ovens Mfr & Distr
N.A.I.C.S.: 333310

Belshaw Brothers, Inc. (3)
814 44th St NW Ste 103, Auburn, WA 98001 (100%)
Tel.: (206) 322-5474
Web Site: http://www.belshaw.com
Sales Range: $25-49.9 Million
Emp.: 100
Commercial & Industrial Bakery & Donut Production Equipment Mfr
N.A.I.C.S.: 333241
Frank Chandler (Pres)

Subsidiary (Non-US):

Bongard S.A. (3)
32 Route de Wolfisheim, Holtzheim, 67810, France (100%)
Tel.: (33) 388780023
Web Site: http://www.bongard.fr
Sales Range: $125-149.9 Million
Commercial Bakery Equipment Mfr
N.A.I.C.S.: 333241
Martin Thomas (Dir-Pur)

Eloma GmbH (3)
Otto-Hahn-Strasse 10, D-82216, Maisach, Bavaria, Germany (100%)
Tel.: (49) 81413950
Web Site: http://www.eloma.com
Sales Range: $75-99.9 Million
Commercial Combi-Steamer & Baking Oven Mfr & Distr
N.A.I.C.S.: 333310
Mark Joseph Muller (Mng Dir)

Esmach S.p.A. (3)
Via Vittorio Veneto 143, Grisignano di Zocco, Vicenza, Italy (100%)
Tel.: (39) 0444419777
Web Site: http://www.esmach.it
Commercial Cooking Mixers, Dividers & Proofing Cabinets Mfr & Distr
N.A.I.C.S.: 333310

Subsidiary (Domestic):

Falcon Foodservice Equipment (3)
Wallace View Hillfoots Rd, Stirling, FK9 5PY, United Kingdom (100%)
Tel.: (44) 1786455200
Web Site: http://www.falconfoodservice.com

Sales Range: $75-99.9 Million
Commercial Cooking Ranges, Grills, Steamers, Fryers & Kettles Mfr & Distr
N.A.I.C.S.: 333310
Alan Turnbull (Dir-Engrg)

Miller's Vanguard Ltd. (3)
1 Chesham Fold Road, Bury, BL9 6LE, Lancashire, United Kingdom (100%)
Tel.: (44) 1617647374
Web Site: http://www.millersvanguard.co.uk
Sales Range: $25-49.9 Million
Emp.: 250
Commercial Foodservice Equipment Maintenance & Repair Services
N.A.I.C.S.: 811412
Stephen Nicklin (Dir-Sls)

Mono Equipment Ltd. (3)
Queensway, Swansea West Industrial Pk, Swansea, SA5 4EB, United Kingdom (100%)
Tel.: (44) 1792561234
Web Site: http://www.monoequip.com
Sales Range: $25-49.9 Million
Emp.: 120
Commercial Modular, Convection, Rack & Deck Ovens & Dough Handling Equipment Mfr & Distr
N.A.I.C.S.: 333310
Andrew Jones (Mng Dir)

Subsidiary (Non-US):

Pavailler S.A.S.
Rue Benoit Frachon, BP 54, Portes-les-Valence, 26802, France
Tel.: (33) 475575500
Web Site: http://www.pavailler.com
Sales Range: $25-49.9 Million
Emp.: 100
Commercial Bakery Equipment Mfr
N.A.I.C.S.: 333241

Subsidiary (Domestic):

Serviceline (3)
Maxwell Road, Stevenage, SG1 2DW, Herts, United Kingdom (100%)
Tel.: (44) 1438363000
Web Site: http://www.service-line.co.uk
Sales Range: $25-49.9 Million
Emp.: 80
Commercial Foodservice Equipment Maintenance Services
N.A.I.C.S.: 811412
Steve Elliott (Mng Dir)

Subsidiary (US):

Victory Refrigeration Company LLC (3)
3779 Champion Blvd, Winston Salem, NC 27105 (100%)
Web Site: http://www.victoryrefrigeration.com
Sales Range: $25-49.9 Million
Emp.: 150
Commercial Refrigerators, Freezers & Other Foodservice Equipment Mfr
N.A.I.C.S.: 333415

Division (Domestic):

Williams Refrigeration Ltd. (3)
Bryggen Road, North Lynn Industrial Estate, King's Lynn, PE30 2HZ, United Kingdom (100%)
Tel.: (44) 1553817000
Web Site: http://www.williams-refrigeration.com
Sales Range: $25-49.9 Million
Emp.: 200
Commercial Refrigeration Equipment Mfr & Distr
N.A.I.C.S.: 333415

Subsidiary (Non-US):

Williams Refrigeration Australia Pty. Ltd. (4)
38-42 Gaine Road, Dandenong, 3175, VIC, Australia (100%)
Tel.: (61) 387874747
Web Site: http://www.williamsref.com.au
Sales Range: $25-49.9 Million
Emp.: 50
Commercial Refrigeration Equipment Mfr & Distr
N.A.I.C.S.: 333415

Brag Dunn (Mng Dir)

Subsidiary (Non-US):

Washtech (2)
414 Rosebank Road Evendale, Avondale, Auckland, 1026, New Zealand
Tel.: (64) 9 829 0930
Web Site: http://www.washtech.co.nz
Emp.: 70
Industrial Washing Machine Mfr & Distr
N.A.I.C.S.: 333310
Gary Brent (Gen Mgr)

Wexiodisk AB (2)
Mardvagen 4, 35245, Vaxjo, Sweden
Tel.: (46) 470 77 1 2 00
Web Site: http://www.wexiodisk.com
Emp.: 170
Dishwasher Mfr & Distr
N.A.I.C.S.: 335220
Magnus Ericsson (Mgr-Quality)

Welbilt, Inc. (1)
2227 Welbilt Blvd, New Port Richey, FL 34655
Tel.: (727) 375-7010
Web Site: http://www.welbilt.com
Rev.: $1,153,400,000
Assets: $2,141,600,000
Liabilities: $1,868,600,000
Net Worth: $273,000,000
Earnings: ($7,400,000)
Emp.: 4,400
Fiscal Year-end: 12/31/2020
Holding Company; Foodservice Equipment Mfr & Distr
N.A.I.C.S.: 551112

Subsidiary (Non-US):

Crem International (Shanghai) Co., Ltd. (2)
Building A No 521-551 Kangyi Road Kangqiao Industrial Zone, Pudong New Area, Shanghai, 201315, China
Tel.: (86) 2168187010
Coffee Maker Mfr & Distr
N.A.I.C.S.: 335210

Crem International AB (2)
Rontgenvagen 2, 171 54, Solna, Sweden
Tel.: (46) 57047700
Coffee Maker Mfr & Distr
N.A.I.C.S.: 335210

Crem International GmbH (2)
Werner-von-Siemens-Str 2-6 Gebaude 5108, 766 46, Bruchsal, Germany
Tel.: (49) 1608985865
Coffee Maker Mfr & Distr
N.A.I.C.S.: 335210

Crem International Spain, S.L. (2)
C/ Comerc n 4 Pol Ind Alcodar, 46701, Gandia, Spain
Tel.: (34) 962878875
Coffee Maker Mfr & Distr
N.A.I.C.S.: 335210

Crem International UK Ltd. (2)
Unit 3b Bridgewater Court Bentley Wood Way Network 65 Business Park, Preston, BB11 5ST, Lancashire, United Kingdom
Tel.: (44) 1282458473
Coffee Maker Mfr & Distr
N.A.I.C.S.: 335210

Subsidiary (Domestic):

Manitowoc Foodservice Companies, LLC (2)
2227 Welbilt Blvd, New Port Richey, FL 34655
Tel.: (727) 375-7010
Web Site: http://www.manitowocfoodservice.com
Sales Range: $1-4.9 Billion
Holding Company; Foodservice Equipment Mfr & Distr
N.A.I.C.S.: 551112
Andreas Georg Weishaar (Sr VP-Strategy, Mktg & HR)

Subsidiary (Domestic):

Enodis Corporation (3)
2227 Welbilt Blvd, New Port Richey, FL 34655
Tel.: (727) 375-7010

Web Site: http://www.manitowocfoodservice.com
Commercial Food Service Equipment Mfr
N.A.I.C.S.: 333310

Subsidiary (Domestic):

Cleveland Range LLC (4)
760 Beta Dr Ste C, Mayfield Heights, OH 44143
Tel.: (216) 481-4900
Web Site: http://www.clevelandrange.com
Commercial Cooking & Warming Equipment Mfr
N.A.I.C.S.: 333310

Subsidiary (Non-US):

Cleveland Range, Ltd. (5)
8251 Keele Street, Concord, L4K 1Z1, ON, Canada
Tel.: (905) 660-4747
Web Site: https://www.clevelandrange.com
Commercial Cooking Equipment Mfr
N.A.I.C.S.: 333241

Subsidiary (Domestic):

Delfield Company (4)
980 S Isabella Rd, Mount Pleasant, MI 48858-9256
Tel.: (989) 773-7981
Web Site: http://www.delfield.com
Commercial Refrigeration Equipment Mfr
N.A.I.C.S.: 333310

Frymaster, L.L.C. (4)
8700 Line Ave, Shreveport, LA 71106-6800
Tel.: (318) 865-1711
Web Site: http://www.frymaster.com
Restaurant Equipment Mfr
N.A.I.C.S.: 333241
Todd Phillips (VP & Gen Mgr)

Unit (Domestic):

Kolpak (4)
2915 Tennessee Ave N, Parsons, TN 38363
Tel.: (731) 847-5328
Web Site: http://www.kolpak.com
Freezers & Refrigerators for Food Service Industry Mfr
N.A.I.C.S.: 333415
Clint Reed (Mng Dir & VP)

Subsidiary (Domestic):

Manitowoc Ice, Inc. (4)
2110 S 26th St, Manitowoc, WI 54220
Tel.: (920) 682-0161
Web Site: http://www.manitowocice.com
Commercial Ice Machines & Storage Bins Mfr
N.A.I.C.S.: 333415
Lee Wichlacz (Sr VP-Global Product & Engrg & Mng Dir)

Subsidiary (Non-US):

Enodis France SA (3)
23 Rue Condorcet ZAC Des Radars, 91700, Fleury Merogis, France
Tel.: (33) 1 69 02 25 25
Web Site: http://www.enodis.fr
Commercial Food Service Equipment Mfr
N.A.I.C.S.: 333241
Francois Houpert (Founder & Pres)

Fo Shan Manitowoc Foodservice Co. (3)
Songgang Industrial Zone, Songgang Town, Foshan, 528234, Guangdong, China
Tel.: (86) 75785222886
Kitchen Equipment Mfr
N.A.I.C.S.: 333310
Peng Sam (Mgr-IE&QA)

Garland Commercial Ranges, Ltd. (3)
1177 Kamato Road, Mississauga, L4W 1X4, ON, Canada
Tel.: (905) 624-0260
Web Site: https://www.garland-group.com
Commercial Cooking & Ventilation Equipment Mfr
N.A.I.C.S.: 333310

Subsidiary (Domestic):

Manitowoc FSG Manufactura Mexico, S. De R.L. De C.V. (3)
Calle Tampico 1601, Guadalupe, 67140, Mexico

Tel.: (52) 8181314711
Kitchen Equipment Mfr
N.A.I.C.S.: 333310

Newton Food Equipment Co. Ltd. (3)
Floor 5 Kamthorn Building 897/1 Rama III
Rd Bangpongpang, Bangkok, 10120, Thailand
Tel.: (66) 2 088 0440
Web Site: http://www.newton.co.th
Cube Ice & Ice Dispensers Mfr & Distr
N.A.I.C.S.: 333241

Subsidiary (Non-US):

Spengler GmbH & CO. KG (2)
Werner-von-Siemens-Str 2-6 Gebaude
5108, 766 46, Bruchsal, Germany
Tel.: (49) 57047700
Coffee Maker Mfr & Distr
N.A.I.C.S.: 335210

WELBILT (Shanghai) Foodservice Co., Ltd. (2)
5A (200051) Building 5 No 255 Yangzhai
Road, Changning District, Shanghai, China
Tel.: (86) 2161526100
Food & Beverage Equipment Mfr & Distr
N.A.I.C.S.: 333241

WELBILT Asia Pacific Private Limited (2)
627A Aljunied Road 05-03 Biztech Centre,
Singapore, 389842, Singapore
Tel.: (65) 64200 800
Web Site: http://www.welbiltasia.com
Kitchen Equipment Mfr & Whslr
N.A.I.C.S.: 335220

Welbilt (Halesowen) Limited (2)
Chancel Way, Halesowen Industrial Estate,
Halesowen, B73 5TA, West Midlands,
United Kingdom
Tel.: (44) 1215012566
Web Site:
http://www.multiplexbeverage.com
Commercial Beverage Dispensing Equipment Mfr
N.A.I.C.S.: 333241

Welbilt Deutschland GmbH (2)
Auf Der Weih 11, 35745, Herborn, Germany
Tel.: (49) 277258050
Web Site: http://www.welbiltde.com
Commercial Food Service Equipment Mfr
N.A.I.C.S.: 333241

Subsidiary (Domestic):

Convotherm Elektrogerate GmbH (3)
Talstrasse 35, 82436, Eglfing,
Germany (100%)
Tel.: (49) 884767110
Web Site: http://www.convotherm.de
Sales Range: $75-99.9 Million
Commercial Food Service Equipment Mfr
N.A.I.C.S.: 333241

Subsidiary (Non-US):

Welbilt International Ltd. (2)
Bahnhofstrasse 25, 9100, Herisau, Switzerland
Tel.: (41) 715607000
Web Site: http://www.inducs.com
Induction Heating Equipment Mfr
N.A.I.C.S.: 333994
Daniele Romano (Dir-Sls & Ops)

Welbilt M.E. - FZE (2)
Light Industrial Units Phase 3 Industrial
Area, Dubai, United Arab Emirates
Tel.: (971) 4326 3313
Web Site: http://www.welbiltemea.com
Kitchen Equipment Mfr & Whslr
N.A.I.C.S.: 335220
Rakesh Tiwari (Reg Mgr-Accounts & Distr)

Welbilt UK Limited (2)
Ashbourne House The Guildway Old Portsmouth Road, Guildford, GU3 1LR, United
Kingdom
Tel.: (44) 1483 464 900
Web Site: http://www.welbilt.uk
Commercial Food Service Equipment Mfr
N.A.I.C.S.: 333241

Subsidiary (Domestic):

Merrychef Limited (3)

Ashbourne House The Guildway Old Portsmouth Road, Guildford, GU3 1LR, United
Kingdom (100%)
Tel.: (44) 1483464900
Web Site: http://www.merrychef.com
Cookware Mfr & Distr
N.A.I.C.S.: 332215

ALI ZAID AL-QURAISHI & BROTHERS CO.
King Khaled Street, PO Box 339, Al
Tobaishi District, Dammam, 31411,
Saudi Arabia
Tel.: (966) 138333339
Web Site: http://www.alquraishi.com
Year Founded: 1958
Sales Range: $100-124.9 Million
Emp.: 970
Leisure Goods Household Product
TimePiece Office Furniture Telecommunication Equipment Electronics
Electrical Equipment & Motor Vehicle
Markets Distr
N.A.I.C.S.: 423690
Yousef Al Quraishi (Co-CEO & Mng Dir)

Subsidiaries:

Al Quraishi Electric Services of Saudi Arabia (1)
PO Box 7386, Dammam, 31462, Saudi
Arabia
Tel.: (966) 38572537
Electrical Apparatus & Materials
N.A.I.C.S.: 423610

Al Quraishi Furniture Corp. (1)
PO Box 1848, Riyadh, 11441, Saudi Arabia
Tel.: (966) 1 477 5335
Importation, Selling & Installation of Westinghouse Furniture
N.A.I.C.S.: 337211

Al Quraishi Leisure Services (1)
PO Box 1796, Jeddah, Saudi Arabia
Tel.: (966) 26970779
Sales Range: $50-74.9 Million
Emp.: 100
Markets & Distributes Consumer Goods,
Recreational Products & Toys
N.A.I.C.S.: 423920

Al Quraishi Marketing Co. Ltd. (1)
PO Box 50995, Jeddah, 21533, Saudi Arabia
Tel.: (966) 26700053
Marketing for Household Products & Cleaners
N.A.I.C.S.: 561740

Al Quraishi Services (1)
PO Box 7121, Jeddah, 21462, Saudi Arabia
Tel.: (966) 26700053
Sells & Distributes Tobacco Products
N.A.I.C.S.: 312230

Al Sabah Trading & Contracting Inc. (1)
PO Box 11793, Jeddah, 21463, Saudi Arabia
Tel.: (966) 26434175
Trading Company
N.A.I.C.S.: 236220

Integrated Systems Co. Ltd. (1)
Al-Hamra District, Jeddah, KSA, Saudi Arabia
Tel.: (966) 26650836
Web Site: http://www.isystems-sa.com
Computer Programming
N.A.I.C.S.: 541511

Teamwork Saudi Arabia Ltd. (1)
POBox 10747, Riyadh, Saudi Arabia
Tel.: (966) 14771519
Construction Company
N.A.I.C.S.: 236210

Waha Electric Supply Company of Saudi Arabia (1)
First Industrial City of Damman, PO Box
2389, Dammam, 31451, Saudi Arabia
Tel.: (966) 38474242
Web Site: http://www.wescosa.com
Produces High Voltage Oil-Insulated & Low
Voltage Dry-Type Transformers

N.A.I.C.S.: 334416

ALIANTA INVESTMENTS GROUP SA
Bd Republicii Nr 55 Mansarda Camera 1, Bistrita-Nasaud, Bistrita, Romania
Tel.: (40) 263 235 175
Sales Range: Less than $1 Million
Emp.: 1
Real Estate Prorperty Leasing Services
N.A.I.C.S.: 531190

ALIAXIS S.A./N.V.
Avenue Arnaud Fraiteur 15-23, 1050,
Brussels, Belgium
Tel.: (32) 27755050
Web Site: http://www.aliaxis.com
Year Founded: 2003
Rev.: $3,491,243,060
Assets: $3,832,795,881
Liabilities: $2,255,439,475
Net Worth: $1,577,356,406
Earnings: $206,396,917
Emp.: 15,511
Fiscal Year-end: 12/31/19
Plastic Plumbing Products for Construction, Industrial & Public Utilities
Applications Mfr
N.A.I.C.S.: 326191
Alex Mestres (CEO-Americas Div)

Subsidiaries:

Abu-Plast GmbH (1)
Am Bahnhof 20, 96472, Rodental,
Germany (100%)
Tel.: (49) 956393210
Web Site: http://www.abu.de
Sales Range: $50-74.9 Million
Emp.: 150
Sanitary
N.A.I.C.S.: 322291

Akatherm B.V. (1)
Industrieterrein 11, 5981 NK, Panningen,
Netherlands
Tel.: (31) 77 30 88 650
Web Site: http://www.akatherm.com
Plastic Tank Mfr
N.A.I.C.S.: 326122

Akatherm International B.V. (1)
Industrieterrein 11, 5981 NK, Panningen,
Netherlands (100%)
Tel.: (31) 773088650
Web Site: http://www.akatherm.nl
Sales Range: $75-99.9 Million
Emp.: 75
Sewage & Surface Drainage Provider
N.A.I.C.S.: 221320

Subsidiary (Non-US):

Akatherm FIP GmbH (2)
Steinzeugstrasse 50, 68229, Mannheim,
Germany (100%)
Tel.: (49) 6214862901
Web Site: http://www.akatherm-fip.de
Sales Range: $75-99.9 Million
Emp.: 50
Sewage & Surface Drainage Provider
N.A.I.C.S.: 221320
Corrado Mazzacano (Mng Dir)

VigotecAkatherm N.V. (2)
Schoonmansveld 52, 2870, Puurs,
Belgium (100%)
Tel.: (32) 38600190
Web Site: http://www.vigotec.be
Sales Range: $50-74.9 Million
Emp.: 47
Sewage & Surface Drainage
N.A.I.C.S.: 221320

Aliaxis (1)
Viate Del Lavoro 21-25, Zona Ind Loc
Ponte, Vicenza, 36020, Italy (100%)
Tel.: (39) 0444795276
Sales Range: $25-49.9 Million
Emp.: 60
Soil & Waste Removal
N.A.I.C.S.: 562119

Aliaxis Holding Italia Spa (1)

Via Madonna Dei Prati 5/a, Zola Predosa,
Bologna, 40069, Italy
Tel.: (39) 0516 17 51 11
Holding Company
N.A.I.C.S.: 551112

Aliaxis Holdings UK Ltd (1)
Dickley Lane, Maidstone, ME17 2DE, Kent,
United Kingdom
Tel.: (44) 1622 858888
Holding Company
N.A.I.C.S.: 551112

Aliaxis Nederland B.V. (1)
Industrieterrein 11, 5981 NK, Panningen,
Netherlands
Tel.: (31) 773088650
Web Site: https://aliaxis.nl
Water Distribution Services
N.A.I.C.S.: 221310

Aliaxis Services S.A. (1)
1 Rue de l'Amandier, BP 65, 78540, Vernouillet, France
Tel.: (33) 139796000
Web Site: http://www.aliaxis.com
Injected Plastic Building Materials Mfr
N.A.I.C.S.: 326199

Aliaxis Utilities & Industry AG (1)
Straubstrasse 13, 7323, Wangs, Switzerland
Tel.: (41) 817254170
Web Site: https://www.aliaxis-ui.ch
Water Distribution Services
N.A.I.C.S.: 221310

Arnomij B.V. (1)
Delfweg 48, 2211, Noordwijkerhout,
Netherlands (100%)
Tel.: (31) 252416950
Web Site: http://www.arnomij.nl
Sales Range: $75-99.9 Million
Emp.: 20
Sewage & Surface Drainage Provider
N.A.I.C.S.: 221320

Ashirvad Pipes Pvt. Ltd (1)
4-B Attibele Industrial Area Hosur Road,
Bengaluru, 562 107, Karnataka, India
Tel.: (91) 9902333333
Web Site: http://www.ashirvad.com
Plastic Pipe Mfr & Distr
N.A.I.C.S.: 326122

Astore Valves & Fittings S.r.l. (1)
Localita Pian di Parata, 16015, Casella,
Italy
Tel.: (39) 01096211
Web Site: http://www.astore.it
Sales Range: $25-49.9 Million
Emp.: 43
Plastic Pipes & Plumbing Fixtures
N.A.I.C.S.: 326191
Lucio Ricciotti (Mng Dir)

Canplas Industries Ltd. (1)
500 Veterans Drive, Barrie, L4M 4V3, ON,
Canada (100%)
Tel.: (705) 726-3361
Web Site: http://www.canplas.com
Sales Range: $125-149.9 Million
Mfr of Plastic Fittings
N.A.I.C.S.: 326122

Canplas USA LLC (1)
11402 E 53rd Ave Ste 200, Denver, CO
80239
Tel.: (303) 373-1918
Plastic Plumbing Product Mfr
N.A.I.C.S.: 326122

Chemvin Plastics Ltd (1)
102 Portage Road, Avondale, Auckland,
New Zealand
Tel.: (64) 9 270 0065
Web Site: http://www.chemvin.co.nz
Plastic Materials Mfr
N.A.I.C.S.: 325211

Dalpex S.p.a. (1)
Via della Fiera 13 15, 57021, Venturina,
Italy
Tel.: (39) 0565 856 611
Web Site: http://www.dalpex.com
Sales Range: $125-149.9 Million
Emp.: 120
Water Supply System Solutions
N.A.I.C.S.: 221310

Durman Colombia SAS (1)

Aliaxis S.A./N.V.—(Continued)

Km 27 via Fontibon Facatativa Los, Alpes 400Mts Via Arley - Colegio Lote 3, Cundinamarca, Colombia
Tel.: (57) 8200200
Web Site: https://durman.com.co
Pipe Mfr & Distr
N.A.I.C.S.: 326122

Durman Esquivel Guatemala S.A. (1)
Carret al Pacifico Km 19 5, Villa Nueva, Guatemala
Tel.: (502) 66361111
Plastic Tank Mfr
N.A.I.C.S.: 326122

Durman Esquivel Puerto Rico Corp. (1)
Parque Industrial Rayo, Sabana Grande, 00637, Guatemala, Guatemala
Tel.: (502) 6636 1111
Plastic Tank Mfr
N.A.I.C.S.: 326122

Durman Esquivel S.A. (1)
Via Interamericana David, David, Panama
Tel.: (507) 7755656
Plastic Pipe Mfr & Distr
N.A.I.C.S.: 326122

Durman Esquivel de Mexico S.A. de CV (1)
Camino La Palma estaciaon El Ahorcado, Pedro Escobedo, Mexico, Queretaro, Mexico
Tel.: (52) 448 275 2100
Web Site: http://www.durman.com.mx
Plastic Tank Mfr
N.A.I.C.S.: 326122

Dux Industries Ltd (1)
32 Mahia Road, Manurewa, Auckland, 2102, New Zealand
Tel.: (64) 9 279 2850
Web Site: http://www.dux.co.nz
Plastic Plumbing Product Mfr & Distr
N.A.I.C.S.: 326122
Jeff La Haye (Gen Mgr)

Dynex Extrusions Ltd (1)
310-316 Rosebank Rd, PO Box 19-133, Avondale, Auckland, 1746, New Zealand
Tel.: (64) 9 820 2800
Web Site: http://www.dynex.co.nz
Plastic Plumbing Product Mfr
N.A.I.C.S.: 326122

Formatura Inezione Polimeri Spa (1)
Loc Pian di Parata, 16015, Casella, Italy
Tel.: (39) 010 9621 1
Web Site: http://www.fipnet.it
Plastic Plumbing Product Mfr
N.A.I.C.S.: 326122

Friatec AG (1)
Steinzeugstrasse 50, PO Box 710261, Steinzeugstrasse, 68229, Mannheim, Germany (100%)
Tel.: (49) 6214860
Web Site: http://www.friatec.de
Sales Range: $450-499.9 Million
Emp.: 1,200
Pipe Systems Products for Water, Gas & Industrial Applications Including Pumps & Valves
N.A.I.C.S.: 486990

Division (Domestic):

Friatec Ag-Ceramics Division (2)
Steinzeugstrasse, 68229, Mannheim, Germany (100%)
Tel.: (49) 6214861339
Web Site: http://www.friatec.de
Pipe Systems Products for Water, Gas & Industrial Applications Including Pumps & Valves
N.A.I.C.S.: 486990

Friatec Ag-Technical Plastics Division (2)
Sterinzeugstrasse 50, 68229, Mannheim, Germany (100%)
Tel.: (49) 6214861447
Web Site: http://www.friatec.de
Sales Range: $200-249.9 Million
Emp.: 800
Pipe Systems Products for Water, Gas & Industrial Applications Including Pumps & Valves

N.A.I.C.S.: 486990

Friatec Building Services (2)
Steinzeugstrasse, 68229, Mannheim, Germany
Tel.: (49) 6214860
Web Site: http://www.friatec.de
Pipe Systems Products for Water, Gas & Industrial Applications Including Pumps & Valves
N.A.I.C.S.: 486990

Subsidiary (Non-US):

Friatec DPL (2)
ZA La Grande Borne, Nemours, 77793, France (100%)
Tel.: (33) 164452364
Web Site: http://www.firatecdpl.com
Sales Range: $25-49.9 Million
Emp.: 17
Pipe Systems Products for Water, Gas & Industrial Applications Including Pumps & Valves
N.A.I.C.S.: 486990

Friatec SARL (2)
Route De Montereau, BP 83, Nemours, 77793, France (100%)
Tel.: (33) 164452302
Web Site: http://www.aliaxis.com
Sales Range: $25-49.9 Million
Emp.: 29
Pipe Systems Products for Water, Gas & Industrial Applications Including Pumps & Valves
N.A.I.C.S.: 332996

Subsidiary (Domestic):

Sed Flow Control GmbH (2)
Am Schafbaum 2, 74906, Bad Rappenau, Germany
Tel.: (49) 72649210
Web Site: http://sed.samsongroup.com
Sales Range: $25-49.9 Million
Emp.: 120
Pipe Systems Products for Water, Gas & Industrial Applications
N.A.I.C.S.: 486990
Valentin Mall (Mng Dir)

GPS GmbH & Co KG (2)
Aschaffenburger Str 73, 63773, Goldbach, Germany
Tel.: (49) 6021 7932158
Web Site: http://www.gpsbau.de
Construction Contractor Services
N.A.I.C.S.: 236116

GPS Holding Germany GmbH (1)
Steinzeugstrasse 50, 68229, Mannheim, Germany
Tel.: (49) 621 4814403
Holding Company
N.A.I.C.S.: 551112
Klaus Wolf (Gen Mgr)

Gie ETEX Plastics Gestion (1)
3 Rue De lAmandier, BP 65, 78540, Vernouillet, France (100%)
Tel.: (33) 39796060
Sales Range: $1-4.9 Billion
Emp.: 5,800
N.A.I.C.S.: 425120

Girpi S.A. (1)
Rue Robert Ancel, CS 90133, 76700, Harfleur, France (100%)
Tel.: (33) 232796000
Web Site: http://www.girpi.com
Sales Range: $50-74.9 Million
Injection of Plastic Fittings & Accessories
N.A.I.C.S.: 326199

Glynwed Pacific Holdings Pty Ltd (1)
47-59 Deeds Rd, Plympton, 5037, SA, Australia
Tel.: (61) 883009200
Holding Company
N.A.I.C.S.: 551112

Glynwed Pipe Systems Ltd. (1)
St Peter's Road, ppe29, Huntingdon, PE29 7DA, United Kingdom (100%)
Tel.: (44) 1480442600
Web Site: http://www.gpsuk.com
Sales Range: $100-124.9 Million
Emp.: 130
Thermoplastic Pipes, Valves, Fittings, Metal Couplings & Rubber Components for Pipe Lines & Systems Mfr & Distr

N.A.I.C.S.: 332919
Jonathan Brian (Product Mgr)

Subsidiary (Non-US):

GPS Iberica S.L. (2)
Ctra N 152 Km-14 9 Pol Ind, Sta Perpetua De Magoda, 08130, Barcelona, Spain (100%)
Tel.: (34) 935449240
Web Site: http://www.glynwed.es
Sales Range: $25-49.9 Million
Emp.: 27
Thermoplastic Pipes, Valves, Fittings, Metal Couplings & Rubber Components for Pipe Lines & Systems Mfr
N.A.I.C.S.: 332996

Glynwed A/S (2)
Sandvadsvej 1, 4600, Koge, Denmark (100%)
Tel.: (45) 46772575
Web Site: http://www.glynwed.dk
Thermoplastic Pipes, Valves, Fittings, Metal Couplings & Rubber Components for Pipe Lines & Systems Mfr
N.A.I.C.S.: 332996

Glynwed AB (2)
Stormbyvagen 6, 163 55, Spanga, Sweden (100%)
Tel.: (46) 84466910
Web Site: http://www.glynwed-se.com
Sales Range: $25-49.9 Million
Emp.: 15
Thermoplastic Pipes, Valves, Fittings, Metal Couplings & Rubber Components for Pipe Lines & Systems Mfr
N.A.I.C.S.: 332996

Glynwed AG (2)
Straubstrasse 13, 7323, Neuhausen, Switzerland (100%)
Tel.: (41) 817254170
Web Site: http://www.glynwed.ch.ch
Sales Range: $25-49.9 Million
Emp.: 60
Thermoplastic Pipes, Valves, Fittings, Metal Couplings & Rubber Components for Pipe Lines & Systems Mfr
N.A.I.C.S.: 332996

Glynwed B.V. (2)
Steenpad 5, 4797 SG, Willemstad, Curacao (100%)
Tel.: (599) 168473651
Web Site: http://www.glynwed.nl
Thermoplastic Pipes, Valves, Fittings, Metal Couplings & Rubber Components for Pipe Lines & Systems Mfr
N.A.I.C.S.: 332996
Marc Sweere (Mgr-Site)

Glynwed N.V. (2)
Industriezone Blauwesteen, Heiveldekens 20, Kontich, 2550, Belgium (100%)
Tel.: (32) 34582400
Web Site: http://www.glynwed.be
Sales Range: $25-49.9 Million
Emp.: 17
Thermoplastic Pipes, Valves, Fittings, Metal Couplings & Rubber Components for Pipe Lines & Systems Mfr
N.A.I.C.S.: 332996

Glynwed Pipe Systems (Asia) Pte. Ltd. (2)
15A 12 Ave 18 Unit No 0301, Singapore, 638905, Singapore (100%)
Tel.: (65) 62869555
Web Site: http://www.glynwedasia.com
Sales Range: $25-49.9 Million
Emp.: 21
Thermoplastic Pipes, Valves, Fittings, Metal Couplings & Rubber Components for Pipe Lines & Systems Mfr
N.A.I.C.S.: 332996
Florence Yeo (Gen Mgr)

Glynwed S.A.S. (2)
ZAE Route de Beziers, Meze, 34140, France (100%)
Tel.: (33) 467516330
Web Site: http://www.glynwed.fr
Emp.: 80
Thermoplastic Pipes, Valves, Fittings, Metal Couplings & Rubber Components for Pipe Lines & Systems Mfr
N.A.I.C.S.: 332996

Glynwed Srl (2)
Via Aldo Moro 12 12a, 20080, Milan, Carpiano, Italy (100%)
Tel.: (39) 029850901
Web Site: http://www.glynwed.it
Sales Range: $25-49.9 Million
Emp.: 25
Thermoplastic Pipes, Valves, Fittings, Metal Couplings & Rubber Components for Pipe Lines & Systems Mfr
N.A.I.C.S.: 332996

Glynwed s.r.o. (2)
Nitrianska 18, SK 917 01, Trnava, Czech Republic (100%)
Tel.: (420) 33 5514 626
Web Site: http://www.glynwed.sk
Thermoplastic Pipes, Valves, Fittings, Metal Couplings & Rubber Components for Pipe Lines & Systems Mfr
N.A.I.C.S.: 332996

Rhine Ruhr Pumps & Valves (Pty.) Ltd. (2)
354 Angus Cresent Northlands Bussiness Park New Market Road, Northriding, 2162, South Africa (90%)
Tel.: (27) 117965075
Web Site: http://www.rrpumps.co.za
Sales Range: $25-49.9 Million
Emp.: 10
Thermoplastic Pipes, Valves, Fittings, Metal Couplings & Rubber Components Mfr & Distr for Pipe Lines & Systems
N.A.I.C.S.: 332919

Hamilton Kent Inc (1)
77 Carlingview Dr, Toronto, M9W 5E6, ON, Canada
Tel.: (416) 675-9873
Web Site: http://www2.hamiltonkent.com
Plastic Tank Mfr
N.A.I.C.S.: 326122
Jason Maristanez (Mgr-Product Dev)

Hunter Plastics Ltd. (1)
Nathan Way W Thamesmead Bus Pk, London, SE28 0AE, United Kingdom (100%)
Tel.: (44) 2088559851
Web Site: http://www.hunterplastics.co.uk
Sales Range: $25-49.9 Million
Emp.: 30
Drainage Solution Services
N.A.I.C.S.: 425120

IPEX, Inc. (1)
3 Place du Commerce Suite 101 Ile-des-Soeurs, Verdun, H3E 1H7, QC, Canada (100%)
Tel.: (514) 769-2200
Web Site: http://www.ipexinc.com
Sales Range: $25-49.9 Million
Mfr of Plastic Pipes & Fittings
N.A.I.C.S.: 326122

Subsidiary (US):

IPEX USA Manufacturing/Distribution (2)
10100 Rodney St, Pineville, NC 28134-7538 (100%)
Tel.: (704) 889-2431
Web Site: http://www.ipexamerica.com
Sales Range: $50-74.9 Million
Thermoplastic Piping Systems Mfr
N.A.I.C.S.: 326122

Innoage PEI S.a.m. (1)
Immeubie Les Industries, 2 Rue Du Gabian, Monaco, 98007, Cedex, Monaco
Tel.: (377) 92055000
Web Site: http://www.innoage.com
Emp.: 10
Public Utilities
N.A.I.C.S.: 926130

Innoge PE Industries S.A.M. (1)
2 Rue du Gabian, PO Box 289, 98007, Monaco, Monaco
Tel.: (377) 9205 5000
Web Site: http://www.innogaz.com
Plastic Plumbing Product Mfr
N.A.I.C.S.: 326122

Ipex Branding Inc (1)
3 Place du Commerce Suite 101, Ile-des-Soeurs, Verdun, H3E 1H7, QC, Canada
Tel.: (514) 769-2200
Web Site: http://www.ipexinc.com
Plastic Tank Mfr

N.A.I.C.S.: 326122

Ipex Electrical Inc (1)
1425 North Service Rd E Unit 3, Oakville,
L6H 1A7, ON, Canada
Tel.: (289) 881-0120
Web Site: http://www.ipexinc.com
Plastic Tank Mfr
N.A.I.C.S.: 326122

Ipex Management Inc (1)
2081 Logan Ave, Winnipeg, R2R 0J1, MB,
Canada
Tel.: (204) 633-3111
Web Site: http://www.ipexna.com
Plastic Tank Mfr
N.A.I.C.S.: 326122

Ipex USA LLC (1)
10100 Rodney St, Pineville, NC 28134
Tel.: (704) 889-2431
Web Site: https://ipexna.com
Plastic Pipes Distr
N.A.I.C.S.: 423720

Jimten S.A. (1)
Calle del Yen, 03114, Alicante, Spain
Tel.: (34) 965109044
Web Site: http://www.jimten.com
Sales Range: $25-49.9 Million
Mfr of Soil & Waste, Rain Gutter Systems,
Utilities, Hot & Cold Water, Industry, Sani-
tary, Sewage, Ventilation, Irrigation, Floor
Drainage Plastic Products
N.A.I.C.S.: 115112

Marley Alutec Ltd. (1)
Unit 1 G-H Hudson Road, Elms Farm In-
dustrial Estate, Bedford, MK41 0LZ, United
Kingdom (100%)
Tel.: (44) 1234 359438
Web Site: http://www.marleyalutec.co.uk
Sales Range: $50-74.9 Million
Emp.: 35
Mfr of Roofing Tiles, Blocks, Floor Cover-
ings, Plastic Rainwater Gutters, Under-
ground Drainage Pipe Products, Plastic
Moldings & Ventilation Equipment
N.A.I.C.S.: 327120
Drummond McKenzie (Mgr-Area Sls-
Scotland)

Marley Deutschland GmbH (1)
Adolf-Oesterheld-Str 28, Postfach 11 40,
31515, Wunstorf, Germany (100%)
Tel.: (49) 5031530
Web Site: http://www.marley.de
Sales Range: $125-149.9 Million
Emp.: 400
Mfr of Roof Tiles, Blocks, Floor Coverings,
Plastic Rainwater Guttering, Pipes Under-
ground Drainage Products, Plastic Moldings
& Ventilation Equipment
N.A.I.C.S.: 327120

Marley Magyarorszag Rt (1)
Palanki Ut 6, 7100, Szekszard,
Hungary (100%)
Tel.: (36) 74529800
Web Site: http://www.marley.hu
Sales Range: Less than $1 Million
Emp.: 80
Mfr of Roof Tiles, Blocks, Floor Coverings,
Plastic Rainwater Guttering, Pipes Under-
ground Drainage Products, Plastic Moldings
& Ventilation Equipment
N.A.I.C.S.: 327120
Peter Polgar (Dir-Fin)

Marley New Zealand (1)
32 Mahia Rd, Private Bag 802, Manureva,
Auckland, 2102, New Zealand (100%)
Tel.: (64) 92792799
Web Site: http://www.marley.co.nz
Sales Range: $1-9.9 Million
Emp.: 317
Mfr of Roof Tiles, Blocks, Floor Coverings,
Plastic Rainwater Guttering, Pipes Under-
ground Drainage Products, Plastic Moldings
& Ventilation Equipment
N.A.I.C.S.: 327120

Marley Pipe Systems Pty Ltd (1)
1 Bickley Road Pretoriusstad, Nigel, 1491,
South Africa (100%)
Tel.: (27) 0117398600
Web Site:
    http://www.marleypipesystems.co.za
Sales Range: $125-149.9 Million
Emp.: 500

Mfr of Roof Tiles, Blocks, Floor Coverings,
Plastic Rainwater Guttering, Pipes Under-
ground Drainage Products, Plastic Moldings
& Ventilation Equipment
N.A.I.C.S.: 327120

Marley Polska Sp. z.o.o. (1)
Ul Postepu 12 Wjazd Od Ulicy Marynarskie
15, 02 676, Warsaw, Poland (100%)
Tel.: (48) 228432131
Web Site: http://www.marley.com.pl
Sales Range: $10-24.9 Million
Emp.: 50
Mfr of Roof Tiles, Blocks, Floor Coverings,
Plastic Rainwater Guttering, Pipes Under-
ground Drainage Products, Plastic Moldings
& Ventilation Equipment
N.A.I.C.S.: 327120

Material de Aireacion S.A. (1)
Pl Zudibiarte sn, 01409, Vitoria, Spain
Tel.: (34) 945898200
Sales Range: $50-74.9 Million
Emp.: 70
Polyethylene Pipe Mfr
N.A.I.C.S.: 486210

Multi Fittings Corporation (1)
4507 LeSaint Ct, Fairfield, OH 45014
Tel.: (513) 942-9910
Plastic Plumbing Product Mfr
N.A.I.C.S.: 326122

Nicoll Belgium S.A. (1)
Parc Industriel des Hauts-Sarts 1ere Av-
enue 106, 4040, Herstal, Belgium (70%)
Tel.: (32) 42488940
Web Site: http://www.nicoll.be
Sales Range: $25-49.9 Million
Emp.: 16
Sanitary; Soil & Waste Removal
N.A.I.C.S.: 562998
Gozes Engelen (Mng Dir)

Nicoll Eterplast S.A. (1)
Peribebuy 1492, Tablada, B1766AAJ, Bue-
nos Aires, Argentina (100%)
Tel.: (54) 11 4441 4450
Web Site: http://www.nicoll.com.ar
Construction & Structural Engineering &
PVC Pipe Fittings
N.A.I.C.S.: 237990

Nicoll Industria Plastica Ltda (1)
Avenida Rui Barbosa 11792, Sao Jose dos
Pinhais, 83025-613, Brazil
Tel.: (55) 41 3208 1900
Web Site: http://www.nicoll.com.br
Plastic Tank Mfr
N.A.I.C.S.: 326122

Nicoll Peru S.A. (1)
Ca Venancio Avila 1990 Urb Chacra Rios,
Cercado de Lima, Lima, Peru
Tel.: (51) 1 219 4500
Web Site: http://www.nicoll.com.pe
Plastic Tank Mfr
N.A.I.C.S.: 326122

Nicoll Polska Sp. z o.o. (1)
Ul Energetyczna 6, 56-400, Olesnica, Po-
land
Tel.: (48) 713995600
Web Site: http://www.nicoll.pl
Sewer System & Sanitary Plastic Mfr
N.A.I.C.S.: 326199

Nicoll S.A. (1)
37 Rue Pierre Et Marie Curie, BP 10966,
49000, Cholet, France
Tel.: (33) 241637383
Web Site: http://www.nicoll.fr
Sales Range: $50-74.9 Million
Mfr of Soil & Waste, Rain Gutter Systems,
Sanitary, Sewage, Ventilation & Floor Drain-
age Products
N.A.I.C.S.: 325211

Nicoll S.A. (1)
Peribebuy 1492 - Tablada, B1766AAJ, Bue-
nos Aires, Argentina
Tel.: (54) 11 4441 4450
Web Site: http://www.nicoll.com.ar
Plastic Tank Mfr
N.A.I.C.S.: 326122

Nicoll S.r.l. (1)
Via Gorizia, S Lucia di Piave, 31025, Ven-
ice, Veneto, Italy
Tel.: (39) 0438700899
Web Site: http://www.nicoll-italia.com

Sales Range: $10-24.9 Million
Emp.: 30
Sanitary; Soil & Waste Removal
N.A.I.C.S.: 562998

Nicoll SpA (1)
Via Gorizia 7, S Lucia Di Piave, Treviso,
31025, Italy (100%)
Tel.: (39) 0438 4697
Web Site: http://www.europlast.it
Sales Range: $10-24.9 Million
Emp.: 50
Soil & Waste, Ventilation & Floor Drainage
Products Mfr
N.A.I.C.S.: 562998

Nicoll Uruguay S.A. (1)
Cno Maldonado 7475, 14200, Montevideo,
Uruguay
Tel.: (598) 25120000
Web Site: http://www.nicoll.com.uy
Plastic Tank Mfr
N.A.I.C.S.: 326122

Nicoll e.p.e. (1)
9 Shinon St, Acharnes, 136 77,
Greece (100%)
Tel.: (30) 2102465560
Web Site: http://www.nicoll.com.gr
Sales Range: $75-99.9 Million
Emp.: 10
Sewage & Surface Drainage
N.A.I.C.S.: 221320
Eleni Vassilakou (Mgr)

Paling Industries Sdn. Bhd. (1)
Lot 10072 Persiaran Mahogani Utama 2,
Seksyen 4 Bandar Utama Batang Kali,
44300, Batang Kali, Malaysia (60%)
Tel.: (60) 60636888
Web Site: http://www.paling.com.my
Sales Range: $25-49.9 Million
Emp.: 170
Sanitary; Soil & Waste Removal
N.A.I.C.S.: 562998
Chew Thong Boon (Gen Mgr-Sls)

Philmac Pty. Ltd. (1)
47-59 Deeds Road, Plympton, 5037, SA,
Australia
Tel.: (61) 883009200
Web Site: http://www.philmac.com.au
Sales Range: $50-74.9 Million
Plastic Pipe Fittings
N.A.I.C.S.: 326122

RX Plastics Limited (1)
19 Maronan Road, Tinwald, Ashburton,
7740, New Zealand
Tel.: (64) 3 307 9081
Web Site: http://www.rxplastics.co.nz
Plastic Pipe Mfr & Distr
N.A.I.C.S.: 326122
Phil Gatehouse (Mgr-Export & Technical)

Redi S.p.A. (1)
Via Madonna Dei Prati 5 A, Zola Predosa,
40069, Bologna, Italy (100%)
Tel.: (39) 0516175111
Web Site: http://www.redi.it
Sales Range: $50-74.9 Million
Mfr of Polypropylene & PVC Soil, Waste &
Underground Systems for Civil & Industrial
Use
N.A.I.C.S.: 325211

Riuvert S.A. (1)
Ctra De Ocana 125, 03114, Alicante, Spain
Tel.: (34) 965617125
Web Site: http://www.riuvert.es
Sales Range: $125-149.9 Million
Emp.: 150
Soil & Waste Removal; Sewage & Surface
Drainage
N.A.I.C.S.: 221320

**Sanitaire Accessoires Services
S.A.S.** (1)
15 Ave Jean Moulin, PO Box 14, 69720,
Saint Laurent-de-Mure, France (100%)
Tel.: (33) 472483900
Web Site: http://www.nicoll.fr
Sales Range: $50-74.9 Million
Mfr of Sanitary Products
N.A.I.C.S.: 322291

Sanitartechnik Eisenberg GmbH (1)
Gewerbegebiet In Der Wiesen 8, 07607,
Eisenberg, Germany (100%)
Tel.: (49) 366915980

Web Site: http://www.sanit.com
Mfr of Sanitary Plastic Products
N.A.I.C.S.: 322291

Sicoac (1)
Industrial Area, 1009, Jebel Jeloud,
Tunisia (40%)
Tel.: (216) 71391075
Web Site: http://www.sicoac.com.tn
Sales Range: $25-49.9 Million
Emp.: 100
Extrusion of Pipes in Polyvinyl Chloride
(PVC) & in Polyethylene (PE)
N.A.I.C.S.: 331318

Straub Werke AG (1)
Straubstrasse 13, 7323, Wangs, Switzer-
land
Tel.: (41) 81 725 41 00
Web Site: http://www.straub.ch
Pipe Coupling Mfr
N.A.I.C.S.: 332996
De Toffol Remo (Mgr-Key Acct)

**Universal Hardware & Plastic Factory
Limited** (1)
Unit A and D 22 Fl Nathan Commercial
Bldg, 430 436 Nathan Rd, Kowloon, China
(Hong Kong) (100%)
Tel.: (852) 23322878
Web Site: http://www.anchorhk.com
Sales Range: $50-74.9 Million
Emp.: 12
N.A.I.C.S.: 425120

Vinidex Pty Ltd. (1)
Level 4 26 College St, Darlinghurst, 2010,
NSW, Australia
Tel.: (61) 131169
Web Site: https://www.vinidex.com.au
Pipe Mfr & Distr
N.A.I.C.S.: 326122

Vinilit S.A. (1)
Av Pdte Jorge Alessandri Rodrrguez,
Casilla 251, 10900, San Bernardo, Chile
Tel.: (56) 25924000
Web Site: http://www.vinilit.cl
Sales Range: Less than $1 Million
Plastic Pipe & Fitting Mfr; Joint Venture of
S.A. Etex Group N.V. (60%) & Aliaxis
S.A./N.V. (40%)
N.A.I.C.S.: 425120

Wefatherm GmbH (1)
Adolf-Oesterheld-Str 28, 31515, Wunstorf,
Germany
Tel.: (49) 503153700
Web Site: http://www.wefatherm.de
Plastic Tank Mfr
N.A.I.C.S.: 326122

**Zhongshan Universal Enterprises
Ltd** (1)
No 1 Xingdong Road, Dongfeng Town,
Zhongshan, 528425, Guangdong, China
Tel.: (86) 76022788600
Web Site: http://www.anchorhk.com
Plastic Tank Mfr
N.A.I.C.S.: 326122

ALIBABA GROUP HOLDING LIMITED
969 West Wen Yi Road, Yu Hang
District, Hangzhou, 311121, China
Tel.: (86) 57185022088
Web Site:
    https://www.alibabagroup.com
Year Founded: 1999
BABA—(NYSE)
Rev.: $130,697,629,020
Assets: $259,775,675,130
Liabilities: $93,972,885,600
Net Worth: $165,802,789,530
Earnings: $9,537,169,290
Emp.: 254,941
Fiscal Year-end: 03/31/22
Holding Company; Online & Mobile
Commerce Services
N.A.I.C.S.: 551112
Jack Yun Ma (Co-Founder)

Subsidiaries:

Alibaba Group Holding Limited -
Hangzhou Office (1)
699 Wangshang Road, Binjiang District,

Alibaba Group Holding Limited—(Continued)

Hangzhou, 310052, China
Tel.: (86) 57185022088
Web Site: https://www.alibabagroup.com
Executive Office
N.A.I.C.S.: 921140

Subsidiary (Domestic):

Alibaba.com Limited (2)
699 Wang Shang Road, Binjiang District,
Hangzhou, 310052, China (100%)
Tel.: (86) 57185022088
Web Site: https://www.alibaba.com
Emp.: 12,878
Online International Business-to-Business
Marketplaces & Consumer Websites Operator
N.A.I.C.S.: 425120

Subsidiary (Non-US):

AGTech Holdings Limited (3)
Unit 3912 39/F Tower Two Times Square,
Causeway Bay, China (Hong Kong)
Tel.: (852) 25061668
Web Site: http://www.agtech.com
Rev.: $20,849,488
Assets: $406,084,759
Liabilities: $26,456,120
Net Worth: $379,628,640
Earnings: ($14,117,377)
Emp.: 292
Fiscal Year-end: 12/31/2020
Gaming Technology Services
N.A.I.C.S.: 713290
John Ho Sun (Chm & CEO)

Subsidiary (Domestic):

**Alibaba Technology (Shanghai) Co.,
Ltd.** (3)
Rm 3601 3604 Zhaofeng Plz, 1027 Chang
Ning Rd, Shanghai, 200050, China (100%)
Tel.: (86) 2152559888
Online Provider of Business Networking
Services
N.A.I.C.S.: 561499

Subsidiary (Non-US):

Alibaba.com Hong Kong Limited (2)
26/F Tower One Times Square 1 Matheson
Street, Causeway Bay, Hong Kong,
310013, China (Hong Kong) (100%)
Tel.: (852) 22155100
Web Site: http://www.alibaba.com
Sales Range: $500-549.9 Million
Emp.: 2,000
Operator of International Online Business to
Business Marketplaces & Consumer Websites
N.A.I.C.S.: 425120

Subsidiary (US):

Alibaba.com, Inc. (3)
3945 Freedom Cir Ste 600, Santa Clara,
CA 95054 (100%)
Tel.: (408) 748-1200
Web Site: http://www.alibaba.com
Sales Range: $10-24.9 Million
Emp.: 30
Business Networking Services
N.A.I.C.S.: 541611

Auctiva Corporation (3)
360 E 6th St, Chico, CA
95928-5631 (100%)
Tel.: (530) 892-9191
Web Site: https://www.auctiva.com
Sales Range: $25-49.9 Million
Emp.: 12
e-Commerce Solutions
N.A.I.C.S.: 513210
Jeff Schlicht (Founder)

Vendio Services, Inc. (3)
2800 Campus Dr, San Mateo, CA
94403 (100%)
Tel.: (650) 293-3500
Web Site: http://www.vendio.com
Sales Range: $25-49.9 Million
Emp.: 50
e-Commerce Solutions
N.A.I.C.S.: 513210

Subsidiary (Domestic):

AutoNavi Holdings Limited (2)

16/F Section A Focus Square No 6 Futong
East Avenue Wangjing, Chaoyang District,
Beijing, 100102, China (100%)
Tel.: (86) 10 8410 7000
Sales Range: $125-149.9 Million
Holding Company; Digital Map Content,
Navigation & Location-Based Software
N.A.I.C.S.: 551112
Congwu Cheng (Co-Founder & CEO)

Subsidiary (Domestic):

AutoNavi Software Co., Ltd. (3)
16/F Section A Focus Square No 6 Futong
East Avenue Wangjing, Chaoyong District,
Beijing, 100102, China
Tel.: (86) 1084107016
Web Site: http://www.autonavi.com
Navigation Software Development Services
N.A.I.C.S.: 513210

Subsidiary (Domestic):

**Intime Retail (Group) Company
Limited** (2)
Building 3 No 1063 Tonghui Riverside Cre-
ative, Chaoyang District, Beijing, 100124,
China (98%)
Tel.: (86) 1087159349
Web Site: http://www.intime.com.cn
Holding Company; Department Store Op-
erator
N.A.I.C.S.: 455110
Xiaodong Chen (CEO)

Subsidiary (Non-US):

**South China Morning Post Publishers
Ltd** (2)
19/F Tower 1 Times Square 1 Matheson
Street, Causeway Bay, Hong Kong, China
(Hong Kong)
Tel.: (852) 26808888
Web Site: https://www.scmp.com
Newspaper Publishers
N.A.I.C.S.: 513110
Romanus Ng (Sr VP-Adv & Mktg Solutions)

Subsidiary (Domestic):

Taobao (2)
Alibaba Xixi Park No 969 Wenyi West
Road, Yuhang District, Hangzhou, 311100,
China (100%)
Tel.: (86) 57188157858
Web Site: https://world.taobao.com
Internet Retail Website Operator
N.A.I.C.S.: 423620

Yahoo! (China) Limited (2)
9/F Tower A Winterless Center, No 1 West
Da Wang Lu, Chaoyang District, Beijing,
100026, China
Tel.: (86) 10 6598 6666
Web Site: http://cn.yahoo.com
Internet Search Portal Operator
N.A.I.C.S.: 519290

Youku Tudou Inc. (2)
11/F SinoSteel Plaza 8 Haidian Street,
Haidian District, Beijing, 100080, China
Tel.: (86) 1058851881
Web Site: http://www.youku.com
Sales Range: $650-699.9 Million
Emp.: 2,797
Internet Television Broadcasting Services
N.A.I.C.S.: 516120
Dele Liu (Pres)

Sun Art Retail Group Limited (1)
5F Manulife Place 348 Kwun Tong Road,
Hong Kong, China (Hong Kong) (78.7%)
Tel.: (852) 29801888
Web Site: https://www.sunartretail.com
Rev.: $11,746,144,800
Assets: $9,002,167,200
Liabilities: $5,604,908,400
Net Worth: $3,397,258,800
Earnings: $10,951,200
Emp.: 107,785
Fiscal Year-end: 03/31/2023
Hypermarket Owner & Operator
N.A.I.C.S.: 445110
Ming-Tuan Huang (CEO)

Subsidiary (Non-US):

**Auchan (China) Investment Co.,
Ltd.** (2)
No 1750 Chang Yang Road, Shanghai,

200090, China
Tel.: (86) 2165436543
Food Retailer
N.A.I.C.S.: 445110

**Beijing Auchan Hypermarkets Co.,
Ltd.** (2)
7-01-162-HM and 7-02-166-HM No 15 Xin-
ning Avenue, Daxing District, Beijing, China
Tel.: (86) 1052592347
Food Retailer
N.A.I.C.S.: 445110

**Chengdu Auchan Hypermarkets Co.,
Ltd.** (2)
No 88 Taihe Road, Gaoxin District,
Chengdu, 610041, Sichuan, China
Tel.: (86) 2866323009
Food Retailer
N.A.I.C.S.: 445110

**Feiniu E-commerce Hong Kong
Limited** (2)
2f No 2 Pengjiang Rd, Shanghai, 200246,
China (100%)
Tel.: (86) 2136699521
Ecommerce Services
N.A.I.C.S.: 423620

**Hangzhou Auchan Hypermarket Co.,
Ltd.** (2)
No 213 Da Guan Road, Hangzhou, 310015,
Zhejiang, China
Tel.: (86) 57158105618
Food Retailer
N.A.I.C.S.: 445110

**Huzhou Auchan Hypermarkets Co.,
Ltd.** (2)
No 238 Jingyi Road, Changxing Town, Hu-
zhou, 313100, Zhejiang, China
Tel.: (86) 5726620777
Food Retailer
N.A.I.C.S.: 445110

**Jiaxing Auchan Hypermarkets Co.,
Ltd.** (2)
No 1468 East Zhonghuan Road, Nanhu
District, Jiaxing, 314000, Zhejiang, China
Tel.: (86) 57389970976
Food Retailer
N.A.I.C.S.: 445110

**Meizhou Auchan Hypermarkets Co.,
Ltd.** (2)
No 139 Renmin Road, Xingning District,
Meizhou, 514500, Guangdong, China
Tel.: (86) 7538688111
Food Retailer
N.A.I.C.S.: 445110

**Nanjing Auchan Hypermarkets Co.,
Ltd.** (2)
No 151 Han Zhong Men Road, Nanjing,
200029, Jiangsu, China
Tel.: (86) 2586580282
Food Retailer
N.A.I.C.S.: 445110

**Ningbo Auchan Hypermarkets Co.,
Ltd.** (2)
No 160 Cui Bai Road, Haishu District,
Ningbo, 315012, Zhejiang, China
Tel.: (86) 57427907345
Food Retailer
N.A.I.C.S.: 445110

**Suzhou Auchan Hypermarkets Co.,
Ltd.** (2)
No 181 Zhongxin Avenue West, Suzhou,
215021, Jiangsu, China
Tel.: (86) 51267611616
Food Retailer
N.A.I.C.S.: 445110

**Taizhou Auchan Hypermarkets Co.,
Ltd.** (2)
No 455 Donghai Road, Jiaojiang District,
Taizhou, 318000, Zhejiang, China
Tel.: (86) 57688673186
Food Retailer
N.A.I.C.S.: 445110

**Yangzhou Auchan Hypermarkets Co.,
Ltd.** (2)
No 425 Jiangyang Road, Yangzhou,
225009, Jiangsu, China
Tel.: (86) 51485582678
Food Retailer

N.A.I.C.S.: 445110

**Zhenjiang Auchan Hypermarkets Co.,
Ltd.** (2)
No 68 Xuefu Road, Jingkou District, Zhenji-
ang, 212000, Jiangsu, China
Tel.: (86) 51185575377
Food Retailer
N.A.I.C.S.: 445110

**ALIBABA HEALTH INFORMA-
TION TECHNOLOGY LIMITED**
26/F Tower One Times Square 1
Matheson Street, Causeway Bay,
China (Hong Kong)
Tel.: (852) 2 583 9333 BM
Web Site: http://www.alihealth.cn
0241—(HKG)
Rev.: $3,152,696,547
Assets: $2,941,933,670
Liabilities: $785,927,006
Net Worth: $2,156,006,665
Earnings: ($40,744,821)
Emp.: 1,849
Fiscal Year-end: 03/31/22
Investment Management Service
N.A.I.C.S.: 523940
Shunyan Zhu (Chm & CEO)

**ALIBABA PICTURES GROUP
LTD**
26/F Tower One Times Square 1
Matheson Street, Causeway Bay,
China (Hong Kong)
Tel.: (852) 2215 5428
Web Site:
http://ir.alibabapictures.com
Rev.: $441,090,579
Assets: $2,416,059,470
Liabilities: $242,159,839
Net Worth: $2,173,899,631
Earnings: ($43,028,170)
Emp.: 1,184
Fiscal Year-end: 03/31/19
Holding Company
N.A.I.C.S.: 551112
Luyuan Fan (Chm & CEO)

ALIBERICO, S.L.
C/ De Orense 16-5th Floor, 28020,
Madrid, Spain
Tel.: (34) 91 417 6907 ES
Web Site: http://www.aliberico.com
Year Founded: 1987
Emp.: 1,200
Aluminium Material Mfr
N.A.I.C.S.: 331313
Clemente Gonzalez Soler (Pres)

Subsidiaries:

Alucoat Conversion, S.A. (1)
Camino de San Luis s/n Apartado de
Correos 27, 23700, Linares, Spain
Tel.: (34) 953 607 190
Web Site: http://www.alucoat-
conversion.com
Lacquered Aluminum Coil Mfr
N.A.I.C.S.: 331315
Jose Manuel Gonzalez (Gen Mgr)

Alucoil S.A. (1)
Pol Ind de Bayas Calle Ircio parcelas R72 a
R77, 09200, Miranda de Ebro, Spain
Tel.: (34) 947 333 320
Web Site: http://www.alucoil.com
Rolled & Extruded Aluminum Products Mfr
N.A.I.C.S.: 331318
Belin Martin (Mng Dir)

Iberfoil Aragon S.L.U. (1)
Avenida de Huesca 25, 22600, Sabinanigo,
Huesca, Spain
Tel.: (34) 974484155
Web Site: http://www.iberfoil.com
Aluminum Foil Mfr
N.A.I.C.S.: 331315
Aurora Rodriguez (Mng Dir)

**ALICANTO MINERALS LIM-
ITED**

Level 2 8 Richardson Street, West Perth, 6005, WA, Australia
Tel.: (61) 862799425
Web Site: https://www.alicantominerals.com.au
Year Founded: 2011
AQI—(ASX)
Rev.: $25,211
Assets: $1,966,247
Liabilities: $270,688
Net Worth: $1,695,559
Earnings: ($3,652,661)
Fiscal Year-end: 06/30/24
Gold Ore & Silver Ore Mining
N.A.I.C.S.: 212220
Jamie Byrde *(Co-Sec)*

Subsidiaries:

StrataGold Guyana Inc.   (1)
63 Middle St, North Cummingsburg, Georgetown, Guyana
Tel.: (592) 227 2116
Web Site: http://www.stratagoldguyana.com
Gold Mining Services
N.A.I.C.S.: 212220

ALICE EVENEMENTS
110 Avenue Victor Hugo, 92514, Boulogne-Billancourt, Cedex, France
Tel.: (33) 146251160
Web Site: http://www.alice-evenements.com
Rev.: $21,100,000
Emp.: 35
Travel Agencies
N.A.I.C.S.: 561510
Didier Pachoud *(Dir-Fin)*

ALICE QUEEN LIMITED
Level 2 568 Chapel Street, South Yarra, 3141, VIC, Australia
Tel.: (61) 386691408
Web Site: https://alicequeen.com.au
AQX—(ASX)
Rev.: $3,852
Assets: $400,128
Liabilities: $358,723
Net Worth: $41,405
Earnings: ($1,505,077)
Fiscal Year-end: 06/30/24
Other Metal Ore Mining
N.A.I.C.S.: 212290
Andrew Buxton *(Mng Dir)*

ALICON CASTALLOY LIMITED
Gat No 1426 Village Shikrapur Taluka, Shirur District, Pune, 412 208, Maharashtra, India
Tel.: (91) 2066027480
Web Site: https://www.alicongroup.co.in
531147—(BOM)
Rev.: $191,735,162
Assets: $148,452,554
Liabilities: $81,860,865
Net Worth: $66,591,689
Earnings: $7,018,980
Emp.: 3,864
Fiscal Year-end: 03/31/23
Aluminum Casting Services
N.A.I.C.S.: 331524
Rajeev Sikand *(CEO)*

Subsidiaries:

Illichmann Castalloy S.R.O   (1)
Partizanska 81, 966 81, Zarnovica, Slovakia
Tel.: (421) 456830333
Aluminum Casting Mfr
N.A.I.C.S.: 331524

Subsidiary (Non-US):

Illichmann Castalloy GmbH   (2)
Laxenburger Strasse 15, 1100, Vienna, Austria
Tel.: (43) 12350313100
Aluminum Casting Mfr
N.A.I.C.S.: 331524

ALICORN LIMITED
Morelands, 5-27 Old St,, London, EC1V 9HL, United Kingdom
Tel.: (44) 2045422223
Web Site: https://alicorn-vp.com
Private Equity
N.A.I.C.S.: 523940

ALICROS S.P.A.
Via Davide Campari 9/B, 20099, Sesto San Giovanni, Italy
Tel.: (39) 0262694051   IT
Web Site: http://www.alicros.com
Emp.: 10
Investment Holding Services
N.A.I.C.S.: 551112
Luca Garavoglia *(Mng Dir)*

Subsidiaries:

Davide Campari-Milano N.V.   (1)
Via Sacchetti 20, 20099, Sesto San Giovanni, MI, Italy   (51%)
Tel.: (39) 0262251
Web Site: https://www.camparigroup.com
Rev.: $3,520,505,072
Assets: $6,482,948,414
Liabilities: $3,594,539,175
Net Worth: $2,888,409,238
Earnings: $357,759,551
Emp.: 4,146
Fiscal Year-end: 12/31/2022
Wine & Liquor Mfr
N.A.I.C.S.: 312130
Robert Kunze-Concewitz *(CEO & Mng Dir)*

Subsidiary (US):

Campari America LLC   (2)
1255 Battery St Ste 500, San Francisco, CA 94111
Tel.: (415) 315-8000
Web Site: http://www.campariamerica.com
Sales Range: $75-99.9 Million
Emp.: 200
Alcoholic Beverages Mfr
N.A.I.C.S.: 424820
Gerard Ruvo *(Chm & CEO)*

Unit (Domestic):

Wild Turkey Distillery   (3)
1417 Versailles Rd, Lawrenceburg, KY 40342
Tel.: (502) 839-4544
Web Site: http://www.wildturkeybourbon.com
Sales Range: $125-149.9 Million
Emp.: 25
Distiller of Bourbon
N.A.I.C.S.: 312140
Matthew McConaughey *(Dir-Creative-Bourbon Brand)*

Subsidiary (Domestic):

Campari S.p.A.   (2)
Frazione Valpone 79, I 12043, Canale, Italy
Tel.: (39) 0173967111
Wine & Spirits Mfr
N.A.I.C.S.: 312130

Subsidiary (Non-US):

Societe des Produits Marnier-Lapostolle S.A.   (2)
91 Boulevard Haussmann, 75008, Paris, France
Tel.: (33) 142664311
Web Site: http://en.grand-marnier.com
Cognac & Other Distilled Liquor Mfr & Whslr
N.A.I.C.S.: 312140
Jacques Marnier-Lapostolle *(Pres)*

ALIEN METALS LTD.
16 Berkeley St, London, W1J 8DZ, United Kingdom
Tel.: (44) 2039074060   VG
Web Site: http://www.alienmetals.uk
Year Founded: 2006
UFO—(AIM)
Assets: $13,057,000
Liabilities: $786,000
Net Worth: $12,271,000
Earnings: ($2,258,000)

Emp.: 5
Fiscal Year-end: 12/31/21
Silver Mining
N.A.I.C.S.: 212220
Bill Brodie Good *(CEO & Dir-Technical)*

Subsidiaries:

Arian Silver Mexico S.A. de C.V.Mexico   (1)
Mina El Eden 128 Lomas de Bernardez, Guadalupe, 98610, Zacatecas, Mexico
Tel.: (52) 4929279410
Web Site: http://ariansilver.net
Sales Range: $25-49.9 Million
Emp.: 8
Silver Products Mfr
N.A.I.C.S.: 339910

ALIF MANUFACTURING COMPANY LTD.
Bilquis Tower 9th Floor House 06, Road 46 Gulshan 02, Dhaka, 1212, Bangladesh
Tel.: (880) 258815227
Web Site: https://www.amcl.com.bd
Year Founded: 1995
ALIF—(DHA)
Rev.: $16,783,799
Assets: $38,552,498
Liabilities: $2,744,539
Net Worth: $35,807,959
Earnings: $1,205,990
Fiscal Year-end: 06/30/23
Cotton Yarn Mfr
N.A.I.C.S.: 313110
Md. Azizul Islam *(Chm)*

ALIGNA AG
Bernhard-Wicki-Strasse 5, 80636, Munich, Germany
Tel.: (49) 89810290   De
Web Site: http://www.aligna.de
Year Founded: 1998
Sales Range: $25-49.9 Million
Emp.: 5
Holding Company
N.A.I.C.S.: 551112
Wilfried Riggers *(Chm-Supervisory Bd)*

Subsidiaries:

DeltaSelect GmbH   (1)
Pettenkofer Ste 22, 80336, Munich, Germany
Tel.: (49) 89810290
Web Site: http://www.deltaselect.de
Sales Range: $25-49.9 Million
Pharmaceutical Preparations
N.A.I.C.S.: 325412

ALIGNED GENETICS, INC.
FL 2 & 3 28 Simindaero 327beon-gil, Dongan-gu, Anyang, 14055, Gyeonggi-do, Korea (South)
Tel.: (82) 314784185
Web Site: https://www.logosbio.com
Year Founded: 2008
238120—(KRS)
Rev.: $10,548,228
Assets: $28,303,440
Liabilities: $6,175,697
Net Worth: $22,127,743
Earnings: $1,789,225
Emp.: 53
Fiscal Year-end: 12/31/22
Laboratory Equipment Mfr
N.A.I.C.S.: 334516

ALIGNVEST MANAGEMENT CORPORATION
70th Floor First Canadian Place 100 King Street West, Toronto, M5X 1C7, ON, Canada
Tel.: (416) 360-6390
Web Site: http://www.alignvest.com
Investment Brokerage
N.A.I.C.S.: 523999

Andy Moysiuk *(Partner)*

Subsidiaries:

Alignvest Aquisition II Corp.   (1)
1027 Yonge Street Suite 200, Toronto, M4W 2K9, ON, Canada
Tel.: (416) 360-6390
Web Site: https://www.alignvest.com
Aquisition Company
N.A.I.C.S.: 523999
Lee Lau *(Co-Founder)*

Subsidiary (Non-US):

Sagicor Financial Corporation Limited   (2)
Cecil F De Caires Building, Wildey, Saint Michael, Barbados
Tel.: (246) 467 7500
Web Site: http://www.sagicor.com
Rev.: $1,484,261,000
Assets: $7,325,424,000
Liabilities: $6,189,963,000
Net Worth: $1,135,461,000
Earnings: $102,950,000
Fiscal Year-end: 12/31/2018
Holding Company; Insurance, Pension & Investment Services
N.A.I.C.S.: 551112
Dodridge D. Miller *(Pres & CEO-Grp)*

Subsidiary (Domestic):

Sagicor Asset Management Inc.   (3)
Sagicor Corporate Center, Wildey, Saint Michael, Barbados
Tel.: (246) 467 7500
Sales Range: $50-74.9 Million
Emp.: 20
General Insurance Services
N.A.I.C.S.: 524126

Subsidiary (Non-US):

Sagicor Finance Inc.   (3)
Sagicor Financial Centre, PO Box 1699, Choc Estate, Castries, Saint Lucia
Tel.: (758) 452 4272
Web Site: http://www.sagicor.com
Sales Range: $75-99.9 Million
Emp.: 9
Investment Management Service
N.A.I.C.S.: 523150
Rae Atkinson *(Gen Mgr)*

Subsidiary (Domestic):

Sagicor Funds Incorporated   (3)
Sagicor Corporate Centre, Wildey, Saint Michael, Barbados
Tel.: (246) 467 7500
Mutual Fund Services
N.A.I.C.S.: 523940

Sagicor General Insurance Inc.   (3)
St Michael, PO Box 150, Wildey, BP 11000, Barbados
Tel.: (246) 4677500
Web Site: http://www.sagicorgeneral.com
Emp.: 6
General Insurance Services
N.A.I.C.S.: 524298
Keston Howell *(CEO)*

Subsidiary (Non-US):

Sagicor Group Jamaica Limited   (3)
28-48 Barbados Avenue, Kingston, Jamaica
Tel.: (876) 929 8920
Web Site: http://www.sagicorjamaica.com
Financial Holding Company
N.A.I.C.S.: 551111
Christopher W. Zacca *(Pres & CEO)*

Subsidiary (Domestic):

Employee Benefits Administrators Ltd.   (4)
28-48 Barbados Avenue, Kingston, Jamaica
Tel.: (876) 929 8920
General Insurance Services
N.A.I.C.S.: 524298
Richard Byles *(Chm)*

Sagicor Bank Jamaica Limited   (4)
Sagicor Bank Building 60 Knutsford Boulevard, Kingston, 5, Jamaica
Tel.: (876) 929 5583
Web Site: http://www.gopancaribbean.com
Commercial Banking Services

N.A.I.C.S.: 522110
Philip Armstrong (Pres)

Sagicor Insurance Brokers
Limited   (4)
28-48 Barbados Avenue, Kingston, Jamaica
Tel.: (876) 936 7494
Insurance Brokerage Services
N.A.I.C.S.: 524210

Sagicor Investments Jamaica
Limited   (4)
85 Hope Road, Kingston, 5, Jamaica
Tel.: (876) 9469490
Web Site:
    http://www.sagicorinvestmentsja.com
Sales Range: $50-74.9 Million
Emp.: 292
Investment Banking Services
N.A.I.C.S.: 523150
Tara Nunes (Gen Mgr)

Subsidiary (Domestic):

Sagicor Life Inc.   (3)
1st Ave Belleville, Wildey, Bridgetown,
Barbados   (100%)
Tel.: (246) 467 7500
Web Site: http://www.sagicor.com
Emp.: 500
Life Insurance Carrier & Services
N.A.I.C.S.: 524113
Jacinto Martinez (VP-Sls & Mktg-Trinidad &
Tobago)

Subsidiary (US):

Sagicor Life Insurance Company   (4)
4343 N Scottsdale Ste 300, Scottsdale, AZ
85251
Tel.: (480) 425-5100
Web Site: http://www.sagicorlifeusa.com
Sales Range: $75-99.9 Million
Emp.: 100
Life Insurance Carrier & Services
N.A.I.C.S.: 524113
Bart Catmull (Pres & COO)

Subsidiary (Non-US):

Sagicor Life Jamaica Limited   (4)
Sagicor Corporate Centre 28-48 Barbados
Avenue, Kingston, 5, Jamaica
Tel.: (876) 9298920
Web Site: http://www.sagicorjamaica.com
Sales Range: $200-249.9 Million
Life Insurance Products & Services
N.A.I.C.S.: 524113
Willard Brown (Exec VP-Employee Benefits
Div)

Sagicor Life of the Cayman Islands
Limited   (4)
103 S Church Street, PO Box 1087,
Georgetown, KY1-1102, Cayman Islands
Tel.: (345) 949 8211
Sales Range: $50-74.9 Million
Emp.: 36
General Insurance Management Services
N.A.I.C.S.: 524210
Richard Owen Byles (Pres)

Subsidiary (Non-US):

Sagicor Life Inc.   (3)
Sagicor Financial Centre 16 Queen's Park
West, Port of Spain, Trinidad & Tobago
Tel.: (868) 628 1636
Web Site: http://www.sagicorlife.com
Emp.: 300
General Insurance Services
N.A.I.C.S.: 524126
Robert Trestrail (Exec VP & Gen Mgr)

Sagicor Panama SA   (3)
Ave Samuel Lewis Edificio Plaza Obarrio
Piso 2 local 201, Panama, Panama
Tel.: (507) 2231511
Web Site: http://www.sagicorpanama.com
General Insurance Services
N.A.I.C.S.: 524298

Sagicor Syndicate Holdings
Limited   (3)
1 Great Tower Street Fenchurch Street,
London, EC3R 5AA, United Kingdom
Tel.: (44) 2030036800
Web Site:
    http://www.sagicorunderwriting.com

Sales Range: $100-124.9 Million
Emp.: 150
General Insurance Services
N.A.I.C.S.: 524126

Subsidiary (US):

Sagicor USA, Inc.   (3)
4010 Boy Scout Blvd, Tampa, FL 33607
Tel.: (813) 286-2222
Web Site: http://www.sagicor.com
Sales Range: $50-74.9 Million
Emp.: 60
Holding Company
N.A.I.C.S.: 551112
Dodridge Miller (Pres & CEO)

Subsidiary (Domestic):

Sagicor Claims Management,
Inc.   (4)
1 Ridge Gate Rd Ste 225, Temecula, CA
92590
Tel.: (951) 676-7016
Property & Casualty Insurance Claims Man-
agement Services
N.A.I.C.S.: 524126

Sagicor International Management
Services, Inc.   (4)
4010 Boy Scout Blvd, Tampa, FL 33607
Tel.: (813) 287-1602
Web Site: http://www.sagicor-
    international.com
Sales Range: $25-49.9 Million
Emp.: 40
General Insurance Services
N.A.I.C.S.: 524113
Dodridge Miller (Pres)

Subsidiary (Non-US):

Sagicor Underwriting Limited   (3)
1 Great Tower St, London, EC3R 5AA,
United Kingdom
Tel.: (44) 2030036969
Web Site:
    http://www.amtrustunderwriting.com
Sales Range: $100-124.9 Million
Emp.: 190
General Insurance Services
N.A.I.C.S.: 524126
Adrian Harris (Gen Mgr)

Sagicor at Lloyd's Limited   (3)
1 Great Tower St, London, EC3R 5AA,
United Kingdom
Tel.: (44) 2030036800
Web Site: http://www.sagicoratlloyds.com
Emp.: 150
General Insurance Services
N.A.I.C.S.: 524126

ALIJARAH HOLDING QSC
Qatar D Ring Road, PO Box 24141,
Doha, Qatar
Tel.: (974) 44100400
Web Site: https://www.alijarah.com
NLCS—(QE)
Rev.: $32,642,646
Assets: $224,035,036
Liabilities: $33,507,116
Net Worth: $190,527,920
Earnings: $3,502,986
Fiscal Year-end: 12/31/20
Holding Company
N.A.I.C.S.: 551112
Falah Jassim Jabr Al-Thani (Chm)

ALIMENTA S.A.
154 Rte De Suisse, Versoix, 1290,
Geneva, Switzerland
Tel.: (41) 227750200
Web Site: http://www.alimenta.com
Emp.: 10
Producer of Food Products
N.A.I.C.S.: 445298
Dikran S. Izmirlian (Pres)

ALIMENTATION COUCHE-
TARD INC.
4204 Boul Industriel, Laval, H7L 0E3,
QC, Canada
Tel.: (450) 662-6632   QC

Web Site: https://www.couche-
    tard.com
Year Founded: 1980
ATD—(OTCIQ)
Rev.: $71,856,700,000
Assets: $29,049,200,000
Liabilities: $16,484,700,000
Net Worth: $12,564,500,000
Earnings: $3,090,900,000
Emp.: 128,000
Fiscal Year-end: 04/30/23
Department Store Retailer
N.A.I.C.S.: 455110
Alain Bouchard (Founder & Chm)

Subsidiaries:

Circle K Stores Inc.   (1)
PO Box 52085, Phoenix, AZ 85072
Tel.: (602) 728-8000
Web Site: https://www.circlek.com
Sales Range: $200-249.9 Million
Emp.: 600
Convenience Store Operator
N.A.I.C.S.: 445131

Dion's Quik Marts Inc.   (1)
638 United St, Key West, FL 33040
Tel.: (305) 296-2000
Web Site: http://www.dionsbest.com
Sales Range: $10-24.9 Million
Emp.: 100
Convenience Store
N.A.I.C.S.: 449110
Susie Banks (Controller)

Holiday Stationstores, LLC   (1)
4567 American Blvd W, Bloomington, MN
55437
Tel.: (952) 830-8700
Web Site:
    https://www.holidaystationstores.com
Gas Stations
N.A.I.C.S.: 457110

Mac's Convenience Stores, Inc.   (1)
305 Milner Avenue 4th Floor, Toronto, M1B
3V4, ON, Canada   (100%)
Tel.: (416) 291-4441
Web Site: http://www.macs.ca
Sales Range: $50-74.9 Million
Emp.: 150
Convenience & Specialty Retail Store
Owner & Operator
N.A.I.C.S.: 457110

Branch (Domestic):

Mac's Convenience Stores, Inc.   (2)
85 Patterson Rd, Barrie, L4N 3V9, ON,
Canada
Tel.: (705) 737-5112
Web Site: http://www.macs.ca
Rev.: $81,989,000
Emp.: 13
Convenience Store
N.A.I.C.S.: 445131

Topaz Energy Group Limited   (1)
Beech Hill, Clonskeagh, Dublin, 4, Ireland
Tel.: (353) 12028888
Web Site: http://www.topaz.ie
Commercial Fuel, Lubricants & Home Heat-
ing Oil Refiner & Distr
N.A.I.C.S.: 457210
Margaret Barron (Mktg Dir)

ALIMENTATION DU FLORIVAL
10 Rue Theodore Deck, 68500,
Guebwiller, Haut Rhin, France
Tel.: (33) 389621462
Rev.: $21,400,000
Emp.: 58
Grocery Stores
N.A.I.C.S.: 445110
Rene Kohler (Pres)

ALIMENTOS MARAVILLA S.A.
Calzada Roosevelt 43-28 Zone 7,
Guatemala, Guatemala
Tel.: (502) 24216300
Web Site:
    http://www.alimentosmaravilla.com
Sales Range: $100-124.9 Million
Emp.: 350

Fruits, Vegetables & Related Prod-
ucts
N.A.I.C.S.: 424480
Jorge Castillo Love (CEO)

ALIMENTS FONTAINE SANTE,
INC.
450 Rue Deslauriers, Saint-Laurent,
Montreal, H4N 1V8, QC, Canada
Tel.: (888) 627-2683
Web Site:
    http://www.fontainesante.com
Year Founded: 1990
Hummus, Dips & Salads Mfr
N.A.I.C.S.: 311941
Pat Carvell (CFO)

Subsidiaries:

Garden Fresh Gourmet, LLC   (1)
1220 E 9 Mile Rd, Ferndale, MI 48220
Tel.: (248) 336-8486
Web Site:
    http://www.gardenfreshgourmet.com
Sales Range: $100-124.9 Million
Emp.: 500
Mayonnaise, Dressing & Other Prepared
Sauce Mfr
N.A.I.C.S.: 311941
Jack Aronson (Pres)

ALIMENTS KRISPY KERNELS
INC
2620 rue Watt, Sainte-Foy, G1P 3T5,
QC, Canada
Tel.: (418) 658-1515
Web Site:
    http://www.krispykernels.com
Year Founded: 1945
Rev.: $32,589,347
Emp.: 300
Nuts, Peanuts & Snacks Distr
N.A.I.C.S.: 311919
Dennis Jalbert (Owner)

ALINA HOLDINGS PLC
Eastleigh Court Bishopstrow, Warm-
inster, BA12 9HW, United Kingdom
Tel.: (44) 2073558800   UK
Web Site: https://www.alina-
    holdings.com
ALNA—(LSE)
Rev.: $443,070
Assets: $8,851,300
Liabilities: $1,155,011
Net Worth: $7,696,289
Earnings: ($171,674)
Emp.: 2
Fiscal Year-end: 12/31/22
Retail Property Real Estate Invest-
ment Trust
N.A.I.C.S.: 525990
William Heaney (Sec)

ALINCO INCORPORATED
Yodoyabashi Daibiru 4-4-9 Ko-
raibashi, Chuo-ku, Osaka, 541-0043,
Japan
Tel.: (81) 676362222
Web Site: https://www.alinco.co.jp
Year Founded: 1970
5933—(TKS)
Rev.: $382,560,360
Assets: $451,562,150
Liabilities: $249,666,310
Net Worth: $201,895,840
Earnings: $13,140,680
Emp.: 1,437
Fiscal Year-end: 03/31/24
Construction Equipment Mfr & Distr
N.A.I.C.S.: 333120

Subsidiaries:

Alinco (Thailand) Co., Ltd.   (1)
30/49 Moo 1 Sinsakhon Industrial Estate
Tambol Khok Kham, Amphur Muang,
74000, Samut Sakhon, Thailand
Tel.: (66) 34119255
Emp.: 80

Equipment Rental Services
N.A.I.C.S.: 532490
Masanori Matsui *(Mng Dir)*

Alinco Scaffolding (Thailand) Co., Ltd. (1)
Metropolis Building 12thFl 725 Sukhumvit Rd, Klongton Nua Wattana, Bangkok, 10110, Thailand
Tel.: (66) 22586151
Web Site: https://www.alincoscaffold.co.th
Emp.: 44
Steel Scaffolding Rental Services
N.A.I.C.S.: 532490
Kotaro Sakura *(Pres)*

Alinco Scaffolding Rental Service Co., Ltd. (1)
No 721 Taishan Road, New District, Suzhou, Jiangsu, China
Tel.: (86) 18351636861
Web Site: https://alincosz.cn
Emp.: 18
Steel Scaffolding Rental Services
N.A.I.C.S.: 532490

ALINEA SAS
Avenue de la Baumonne ZI des Paluds Zone Commerciale, Auchan, 13400, Aubagne, Cedex, France
Tel.: (33) 969323551
Web Site: http://www.alinea.com
Year Founded: 1989
Home Furnishing Distr
N.A.I.C.S.: 423220
Alexis Mulliez *(Pres)*

ALINK INTERNET, INC.
337 Yamabukicho, Shinjuku-Ku, Tokyo, 162-0801, Japan
Tel.: (81) 359468779
Web Site: http://www.alink.ne.jp
Year Founded: 2013
7077—(TKS)
Media Advertising Services
N.A.I.C.S.: 541840
Hiroto Ikeda *(Founder & CEO)*

ALINMA BANK
9033 King Fahad Road Olaya Unit 8, PO Box 66674, Riyadh, 12214 - 2370, Saudi Arabia
Tel.: (966) 112185555   SA
Web Site: https://www.alinma.com
Year Founded: 2006
1150—(SAU)
Rev.: $2,123,199,573
Assets: $53,442,535,395
Liabilities: $44,943,318,491
Net Worth: $8,499,216,904
Earnings: $959,642,714
Emp.: 2,862
Fiscal Year-end: 12/31/22
Commercial Banking Services
N.A.I.C.S.: 522110
Abdullah Ali Al-Khalifa *(CEO)*

Subsidiaries:

Alinma Investment Company (1)
Al Anoud Tower 2 King Fahad Road, PO Box 55560, Riyadh, 11544, Saudi Arabia
Tel.: (966) 8004413333
Web Site:
  https://www.alinmainvestment.com
N.A.I.C.S.: 523999
Abdullah Ali Al-Khalifa *(Vice Chm)*

Alinma Tokio Marine Co. (1)
King Fahad Road Alanoud Tower 2 Floor 21, Riyadh, Saudi Arabia
Tel.: (966) 11 212 9307
Web Site: http://www.atmc.com.sa
Rev.: $84,234,685
Assets: $174,692,001
Liabilities: $120,962,514
Net Worth: $53,729,487
Earnings: ($1,550,665)
Emp.: 178
Fiscal Year-end: 12/31/2020
Insurance & Reinsurance Services
N.A.I.C.S.: 524113
Abdulmohsen Abdulaziz Al Fares *(Chm)*

Esnad Company (1)
6376 dinars Al-Ansari, PO Box 1850, District 3209, Riyadh, 13266, Saudi Arabia
Tel.: (966) 115114799
Web Site:
  https://www.esnadcontracting.com
N.A.I.C.S.: 541330
Mohamed Messfer Almahari *(Chm)*

ALINMA RETAIL REIT FUND
Kingdom Tower 49th Floor King Fahd Road, PO Box 2076, Riyadh, 11451, Saudi Arabia
Tel.: (966) 112110737
Web Site: http://www.swicorp.com
Year Founded: 1987
4345—(SAU)
Rev.: $14,424,539
Assets: $261,603,160
Liabilities: $9,224,708
Net Worth: $252,378,451
Earnings: $270,311
Fiscal Year-end: 12/31/20
Investment Management Service
N.A.I.C.S.: 525990
Kamel Lazaar *(Founder)*

ALIOR BANK S.A.
ul Lopuszanska 38 D, 02-232, Warsaw, Poland
Tel.: (48) 225552323
Web Site: https://www.aliorbank.pl
ALORY—(OTCIQ)
Rev.: $1,731,247
Assets: $22,899,932,360
Liabilities: $20,549,934,907
Net Worth: $2,349,997,453
Earnings: $515,784
Fiscal Year-end: 12/31/23
Commericial Banking
N.A.I.C.S.: 522110
Agata Strzelecka *(Deputy CEO & Member-Mgmt Bd)*

Subsidiaries:

Alior Leasing Sp. z o.o. (1)
ul Weglowa 9, 40-106, Katowice, Poland
Tel.: (48) 327456456
Web Site: https://www.aliorleasing.pl
Vehicle Financing Services
N.A.I.C.S.: 522220

Subsidiary (Domestic):

Serwis Ubezpieczeniowy Sp. z o.o. (2)
ul Grazynskiego 12, 43-300, Bielsko-Biala, Poland
Tel.: (48) 338165116
Web Site: http://www.serwis-
  ubezpieczeniowy.pl
Automobile Insurance Services
N.A.I.C.S.: 524126

Alior TFI SA (1)
ul Lopuszanska 38D, 02-232, Warsaw, Poland
Tel.: (48) 224638888
Web Site: https://www.aliortfi.com
Investment Management Service
N.A.I.C.S.: 523940

ALIRAN IHSAN RESOURCES BERHAD
2-2 Persiaran 65C Pekeliling Bus Ctr Jalan Pahang Barat, 53000, Kuala Lumpur, Malaysia
Tel.: (60) 340241152
Web Site: http://www.airb.com.my
Sales Range: $25-49.9 Million
Emp.: 290
Water Treatment & Water Works Construction Services
N.A.I.C.S.: 221310
Mohd Fadhil Halim *(Dir-Ops)*

ALISON HAYES
361B-363b Liverpool Rd, London, N1 1NL, United Kingdom
Tel.: (44) 2077008800

Web Site:
  http://www.alisonhayes.co.uk
Sales Range: $50-74.9 Million
Emp.: 90
Ladies Clothing Design & Mfr
N.A.I.C.S.: 315250
Robert Chamberlain *(Chm)*

ALISRA FOR EDUCATION & INVESTMENT CO. PLC
PO Box 22 & 33, Amman, Jordan
Tel.: (962) 64711710
Year Founded: 1991
AIFE—(AMM)
Rev.: $20,346,783
Assets: $54,922,964
Liabilities: $7,988,333
Net Worth: $46,934,631
Earnings: $3,382,121
Fiscal Year-end: 12/31/20
Higher Education Services
N.A.I.C.S.: 923110
Ali Ghalayini *(Gen Mgr)*

ALISTHE INVESTMENTS PTY LTD
Level 1 420 Hay St, Subiaco, 6008, WA, Australia
Tel.: (61) 893882655
Real Estate & Construction Holding Company
N.A.I.C.S.: 551112
Harry A. Xydas *(Chm)*

Subsidiaries:

Doric Group Holdings Pty Ltd (1)
Level 1 420 Hay Street, Subiaco, 6008, WA, Australia
Tel.: (61) 893882655
Web Site: http://www.doricgroup.com.au
Sales Range: $100-124.9 Million
Emp.: 100
Property Developer
N.A.I.C.S.: 531390
Harry A. Xydas *(Chm)*

ALITA RESOURCES LIMITED
Lakeside Corporate Building Unit 6 24 Parkland Road, Osborne Park, 6017, WA, Australia
Tel.: (61) 893888826   AU
Web Site:
  http://www.allianceminerals.com.au
Year Founded: 2010
40F—(CAT)
Sales Range: $25-49.9 Million
Metal Exploration & Mining Development
N.A.I.C.S.: 213114
Jenna Mazza *(Sec)*

ALITALIA - COMPAGNIA AEREA ITALIANA S.P.A.
Piazza Almerico da Schio 3, 00054, Fiumicino, RM, Italy
Tel.: (39) 06 65631   IT
Web Site: http://www.alitalia.com
Airline Operator
N.A.I.C.S.: 481111
Roberto Colaninno *(Chm)*

Subsidiaries:

Air One S.p.A. (1)
Piazza Almerico da Schio 3, 00054, Fiumicino, RM, Italy
Tel.: (39) 06 65631
Web Site: http://www.flyairone.com
Passenger Air Transportation Services
N.A.I.C.S.: 481111

ALITER CAPITAL LLP
14 Brook's Mews, London, W1K 4DG, United Kingdom
Tel.: (44) 2039559910   UK
Web Site: https://www.alitercap.com
Year Founded: 2016
Privater Equity Firm
N.A.I.C.S.: 523999

Greig Brown *(Partner)*

Subsidiaries:

ITM Communications Ltd. (1)
41 Alston Drive Bradwell Abbey, Milton Keynes, MK13 9HA, Bucks, United Kingdom
Tel.: (44) 1908318844
Web Site: http://www.itm.uk.com
Information & Communication Technology Support Services
N.A.I.C.S.: 541512

ALITHYA GROUP, INC.
1100 boul Robert Bourassa Suite 400, Montreal, H3B 3A5, QC, Canada
Tel.: (514) 285-5552
Web Site: https://www.alithya.com
Year Founded: 1992
ALYA—(TSX)
Rev.: $362,801,950
Assets: $307,673,044
Liabilities: $178,247,026
Net Worth: $129,426,017
Earnings: ($12,307,010)
Emp.: 3,000
Fiscal Year-end: 03/31/24
Information Technology Management Services
N.A.I.C.S.: 541512
Ghyslain Rivard *(Founder)*

Subsidiaries:

Alithya Canada Inc. (1)
725 Boulevard Lebourgneuf Bureau 525, Quebec, G2J 0C4, QC, Canada
Tel.: (418) 650-2866
Web Site: https://www.alithya.com
Information Technology Services
N.A.I.C.S.: 541511

Alithya USA, Inc. (1)
2500 Northwinds Pkwy Ste 600, Alpharetta, GA 30009 (100%)
Tel.: (770) 772-3121
Sales Range: $100-124.9 Million
Staffing, Information Technology, Professional Consulting & Solution Services
N.A.I.C.S.: 541511
Russell Smith *(Pres)*

Subsidiary (Domestic):

Edgewater Technology (Delaware), Inc. (2)
1050 Perimeter Rd, Manchester, NH 03103
Tel.: (603) 644-2445
Sales Range: $100-124.9 Million
Business Advisory & Technical Consulting Services
N.A.I.C.S.: 541618
Marshall McCausland *(VP-Mgmt Info Sys)*

Edgewater Technology-Ranzal & Associates (2)
108 Corporate Park Dr Ste 105, White Plains, NY 10604
Tel.: (914) 253-6600
Web Site: http://www.ranzal.com
Sales Range: $100-124.9 Million
Retailer of Business Intelligence Software
N.A.I.C.S.: 513210
Veda Gagliardi *(Sr VP-Sls-Global)*

ALJ FINANSMAN A.S.
Merkez Mah Erenler Cad No 18-20 Ofis 4, Cekmekoy, 34782, Istanbul, Turkiye
Tel.: (90) 2166430400
Web Site: http://www.aljfinans.com.tr
ALJF—(IST)
Financial Investment Services
N.A.I.C.S.: 523999
Nilufer Gunhan *(Chm)*

ALKA DIAMOND INDUSTRIES LIMITED
626 Panchratna MP Road Opera House, Mumbai, 400004, India
Tel.: (91) 22 23636534

ALKA DIAMOND INDUSTRIES LIMITED—(Continued)

Web Site:
http://www.alkadiamond.com
Year Founded: 1989
Assets: $1,857,824
Liabilities: $516,854
Net Worth: $1,340,970
Earnings: ($10,178)
Fiscal Year-end: 03/31/18
Diamond Distr
N.A.I.C.S.: 423940
Gopal M. Javda (*Chm & Mng Dir*)

ALKA INDIA LIMITED
Unit 102 1st Floor Morya Landmark II
New Link Road, Near Infinity Mall
Andheri W, Mumbai, 400053, Maharashtra, India
Tel.: (91) 2249720369
Web Site: https://www.alkaindia.in
Year Founded: 1993
530889—(BOM)
Rev.: $14,046
Assets: $3,319,980
Liabilities: $472,345
Net Worth: $2,847,636
Earnings: ($18,550)
Emp.: 7
Fiscal Year-end: 03/31/22
Textile Products Mfr
N.A.I.C.S.: 313310
Ramakant Gokulchand Sharma (*Exec Dir*)

ALKA SECURITIES LIMITED
10 Maitri N S Road No 10, JVPD
Scheme Juhu, Mumbai, 400049, Maharashtra, India
Tel.: (91) 9819424948
Web Site:
https://www.aslventure.com
532166—(BOM)
Sales Range: Less than $1 Million
Financial Services
N.A.I.C.S.: 523999
Mahendra Pandey (*CEO & CFO*)

ALKALI METALS LIMITED
Plot B5 BlockIII IDA Uppal, Hyderabad, 500 039, India
Tel.: (91) 4023445962
Web Site:
https://www.alkalimetals.com
Year Founded: 1968
ALKALI—(NSE)
Rev.: $12,463,378
Assets: $13,584,384
Liabilities: $6,475,110
Net Worth: $7,109,275
Earnings: $475,129
Emp.: 108
Fiscal Year-end: 03/31/22
Sodium Derivatives, Pyridine Derivatives & Various Fine Chemicals Mfr
N.A.I.C.S.: 325998
Y. S. R. Venkata Rao (*Mng Dir*)

ALKALOID A.D. SKOPJE
Blvd Aleksandar Makedonski 12,
1000, Skopje, North Macedonia
Tel.: (389) 23104007
Web Site:
https://www.alkaloid.com.mk
Year Founded: 1936
ALK—(MAC)
Rev.: $200,516,712
Assets: $245,505,834
Liabilities: $59,571,831
Net Worth: $185,934,003
Earnings: $18,335,596
Emp.: 2,227
Fiscal Year-end: 12/31/19
Pharmaceuticals, Herbal Materials, Cosmetics, Chemical Products & Coating Agents

N.A.I.C.S.: 325412
Zhivko Mukaetov (*Chm-Mgmt Bd & CEO*)

Subsidiaries:

ALK & KOS Shpk (1)
Magjistralja Prishtine-Shkup km i shtate, Laplje Selo Gracanice, 10500, Pristina, Kosovo
Tel.: (383) 44447733
Pharmaceutical Products Distr
N.A.I.C.S.: 424210

ALK&KOS Sh.p.k. (1)
Magjistralja Prishtine-Shkup, Laplje Selo, 10000, Pristina, Kosovo, Serbia
Tel.: (381) 38 606 0081
Web Site: http://www.alkaloid.com.mk
Sales Range: $25-49.9 Million
Emp.: 20
Pharmaceutical Products Distr
N.A.I.C.S.: 424210
Dritan Ismaili (*Gen Mgr*)

ALKA-LAB DOO (1)
Celovska cesta 40a, 1000, Ljubljana, Slovenia
Tel.: (386) 17771120
Pharmaceuticals Product Mfr
N.A.I.C.S.: 325412

Alkaloid Buchurest SRL (1)
Hermes Business Campus Building C 1st floor Blvd Dimitrie Pompeiu 5-7, 2nd District, 020335, Bucharest, Romania
Tel.: (40) 372923141
Cosmetic & Chemical Product Mfr
N.A.I.C.S.: 325411

Alkaloid DOO (Podgorica) (1)
Tel.: (382) 20246207
Web Site: https://www.alkaloid.com.mk
Pharmaceutical Products Distr
N.A.I.C.S.: 424210

Alkaloid DOO (Sarajevo) (1)
Isevica sokak 6, 71000, Sarajevo, Bosnia & Herzegovina
Tel.: (387) 33713571
Web Site: https://www.alkaloid.com.mk
Emp.: 1,832
Pharmaceutical Products Distr
N.A.I.C.S.: 424210

Alkaloid DOO (Zagreb) (1)
Grada Vukovara 226, 10000, Zagreb, Croatia
Tel.: (385) 16 311 920
Sales Range: $25-49.9 Million
Emp.: 30
Pharmaceutical Products Distr
N.A.I.C.S.: 424210
Neven Sukarovski (*Reg Dir-Sls*)

Alkaloid ILAC TLS (1)
Vizyon park A1/9 29 ekim cad Yenibosna merkez mah, Bahcelievler, Istanbul, Türkiye
Tel.: (90) 2126031070
Pharmaceuticals Product Mfr
N.A.I.C.S.: 325412

Alkaloid INT DOO (1)
Slandrova ulica 4, Crnuce, 1231, Ljubljana, Slovenia
Tel.: (386) 13004290
Pharmaceuticals Product Mfr
N.A.I.C.S.: 325412

Alkaloid Kiev CO, LTD. (1)
Street Kyrylivska 15/1A office 4, 04080, Kiev, Ukraine
Tel.: (380) 443906066
Web Site: http://www.alkaloid.com.ua
Pharmaceuticals Product Mfr
N.A.I.C.S.: 325412

Alkaloid Kons DOOEL (1)
12 Aleksandar Makedonski, 1000, Skopje, North Macedonia
Tel.: (389) 23204430
Web Site: http://www.alkaloid.com
Sales Range: $25-49.9 Million
Emp.: 42
Pharmaceutical Products Distr
N.A.I.C.S.: 424210

Alkaloid Sh.p.k. (Tirana) (1)
Tel.: (355) 42422955
Web Site: http://www.alkaloid.al
Pharmaceutical Products Distr

N.A.I.C.S.: 424210

Alkaloid USA LLC (1)
6530 W Campus Oval Ste 280, New Albany, OH 43054
Tel.: (614) 939-9488
Emp.: 1
Pharmaceutical Products Distr
N.A.I.C.S.: 424210

Alkaloid Veledrogerija DOO (1)
Ul Prahovska 3, 11000, Belgrade, Serbia
Tel.: (381) 113679070
Pharmaceuticals Product Mfr
N.A.I.C.S.: 325412

Alkaloid d.o.o. (1)
Ul Prahovska 3, 11000, Belgrade, Serbia
Tel.: (381) 113679070
Web Site: https://www.alkaloid.rs
Pharmaceutical Distr & Sales
N.A.I.C.S.: 424210
Zivko Mukaetov (*CEO*)

Alkaloid e.d.o.o (1)
Tel.: (359) 28081081
Web Site: https://www.alkaloid.com.mk
Pharmaceutical Distr & Sales
N.A.I.C.S.: 424210

Alkaloid-Farm d.o.o. (1)
Slandrova ulica 4, Crnuce, 1231, Ljubljana, Slovenia
Tel.: (386) 13004290
Sales Range: $50-74.9 Million
Emp.: 8
Pharmaceutical Distr & Sales
N.A.I.C.S.: 424210

Alkaloidpharma SA (1)
Tel.: (41) 263234190
Web Site: https://www.alkaloid.com.mk
Sales Range: $550-599.9 Million
Pharmaceutical Distr & Sales
N.A.I.C.S.: 424210

OOO Alkaloid RUS (1)
Tel.: (7) 4955029297
Sales Range: $50-74.9 Million
Emp.: 55
Pharmaceutical Products Distr
N.A.I.C.S.: 424210

ALKAN SAS
Rue du 8 Mai 1945, 94460, Valenton, France
Tel.: (33) 1 4510 8600   FR
Web Site: http://www.alkan.fr
Year Founded: 1923
Emp.: 160
Military Aircraft Carriage, Release & Ejection Systems Mfr
N.A.I.C.S.: 336413
Lionel Levy (*CFO*)

ALKANE RESOURCES LIMITED
Level 4 66 Kings Park Road, West Perth, 6005, WA, Australia
Tel.: (61) 892275677
Web Site: https://www.alkane.com.au
ALKEF—(OTCIQ)
Rev.: $126,429,012
Assets: $272,523,823
Liabilities: $66,515,252
Net Worth: $206,008,570
Earnings: $53,825,614
Emp.: 200
Fiscal Year-end: 06/30/22
Support Activities for Nonmetallic Minerals (except Fuels) Mining
N.A.I.C.S.: 213115
David Ian Chalmers (*Dir-Technical*)

ALKEM LABORATORIES LTD.
Devashish Building Alkem House, Senapati Bapat Road Lower Parel, Mumbai, 400013, India
Tel.: (91) 2239829999
Web Site: https://www.alkemlabs.com
Year Founded: 1973
ALKEM—(NSE)
Rev.: $1,473,768,660
Assets: $1,920,444,435

Liabilities: $712,783,890
Net Worth: $1,207,660,545
Earnings: $224,627,130
Emp.: 16,966
Fiscal Year-end: 03/31/22
Pharmaceutical Manufacturing
N.A.I.C.S.: 325412
Rajesh Dubey (*CFO*)

Subsidiaries:

Alkem Laboratories (Pty) Limited (1)
Route 21 Corporate Park 121 Sovereign Drive Block A Office 202, Irene Ext 30, Centurion, 0157, South Africa
Tel.: (27) 817914369
Pharmaceuticals Product Mfr
N.A.I.C.S.: 325412

Ascend GmbH (1)
Wilhelm-Spaeth-Str 2, 90461, Nuremberg, Germany
Tel.: (49) 9111488750
Web Site: https://www.ascend.de
Wireless Internet Services
N.A.I.C.S.: 517111
Christian Heckel (*Mng Dir*)

Ascend Laboratories LLC (1)
339 Jefferson Rd Ste 101, Parsippany, NJ 07054
Tel.: (201) 476-1977
Web Site:
https://www.ascendlaboratories.com
Pharmaceuticals Product Mfr
N.A.I.C.S.: 325412
John Dillaway (*Exec VP*)

Ascend Laboratories Sdn. Bhd. (1)
Redberry City Lot 2A Jalan 13/2, 46200, Petaling Jaya, Selangor, Malaysia
Tel.: (60) 374955600
Web Site: http://www.ascensionlab.com
Web Development Services
N.A.I.C.S.: 541511

Ascend Laboratories SpA (1)
Av Apoquindo 4700 17th Floor, Las Condes, Santiago, Chile
Tel.: (56) 232455980
Web Site: https://www.ascendlabs.cl
Pharmaceuticals Product Mfr
N.A.I.C.S.: 325412

Cachet Pharmaceuticals Private Limited (1)
415 Shah Nahar Dr E Moses Road, Worli, Mumbai, 400018, India
Tel.: (91) 2240829999
Web Site: https://www.cachetindia.com
Pharmaceuticals Product Mfr
N.A.I.C.S.: 325412
Satish Kumar Singh (*Mng Dir*)

Enzene Biosciences Limited (1)
Plot Number 165/1/26 Priyadarshini Society 26 Internal Rd, Next to Gujjar Bharath gas Bhosari MIDC, Pune, 411026, Maharashtra, India
Tel.: (91) 2067184200
Web Site: https://www.enzene.com
Pharmaceuticals Product Mfr
N.A.I.C.S.: 325412

Indchemie Health Specialities Private Limited (1)
510 Shah & Nahar Industrila Estate Dr E Moses Road, Worli, Mumbai, 400018, India
Tel.: (91) 2268424800
Web Site: https://www.indchemie.in
Pharmaceuticals Product Mfr
N.A.I.C.S.: 325412

Pharmacor Pty Limited (1)
Suite 803 Level 8 Tower A The Zenith 821 Pacific Higway, Chatswood, 2067, NSW, Australia
Tel.: (61) 1300138805
Web Site: https://www.pharmacor.com.au
Pharmaceutical Product Mfr & Distr
N.A.I.C.S.: 325412

S & B Pharma Inc. (1)
405 S Motor Ave, Azusa, CA 91702
Tel.: (626) 334-2908
Web Site: https://noracpharma.com
Pharmaceuticals Product Mfr
N.A.I.C.S.: 325412
Randall Wong (*Dir-Quality Assurance & Regulatory Affairs*)

ALKEMY CAPITAL INVESTMENTS PLC

167-169 Great Portland Street Fifth Floor, London, W1W 5PF, United Kingdom
Tel.: (44) 2073170636   UK
Web Site:
https://www.alkemycapital.co.uk
Year Founded: 2021
ALK—(LSE)
Rev.: $1,588
Assets: $622,342
Liabilities: $1,285,166
Net Worth: ($662,824)
Earnings: ($2,254,592)
Emp.: 2
Fiscal Year-end: 01/31/24
Miscellaneous Financial Investment Activities
N.A.I.C.S.: 523999
Sam Quinn (Sec)

Subsidiaries:

Tees Valley Lithium Limited   (1)
167-169 Great Portland Street Fifth Floor, London, W1W 5PF, United Kingdom
Tel.: (44) 2073170636
Web Site: https://teesvalleylithium.co.uk
Lithium Chemical Mfr
N.A.I.C.S.: 325180

ALKEMY SPA

Via San Gregorio 34, 20124, Milan, Italy
Tel.: (39) 02928941
Web Site: https://www.alkemy.com
Year Founded: 2012
ALK—(ITA)
Rev.: $115,016,188
Assets: $131,375,998
Liabilities: $84,531,621
Net Worth: $46,844,377
Earnings: $6,058,709
Emp.: 899
Fiscal Year-end: 12/31/22
Digital Marketing Services
N.A.I.C.S.: 541613
Vittorio Massone (Vice Chm)

Subsidiaries:

Design Group Italia Corp.   (1)
84 Withers St 1st Fl, Brooklyn, NY 11211
Tel.: (347) 951-4350
Design Services
N.A.I.C.S.: 541430

Design Group Italia I.D. S.R.L.   (1)
Via Aleardo Aleardi 12, 20154, Milan, Italy
Tel.: (39) 0222175400
Web Site: https://www.designgroupitalia.com
Design Services
N.A.I.C.S.: 541430

Innocv Solutions S.L.   (1)
Po de Recoletos 27 Centro, 28001, Madrid, Spain
Tel.: (34) 911923832
Web Site: https://www.innocv.com
Software Development Services
N.A.I.C.S.: 541511

Kreativa New Formula D.o.o.   (1)
Kneza Mihaila 1/II, 11000, Belgrade, Serbia
Tel.: (381) 116556822
Web Site: http://www.knf.rs
Digital Marketing Services
N.A.I.C.S.: 541613

Nunatac S.r.l   (1)
Via S Gregorio 34, 20124, Milan, MI, Italy
Tel.: (39) 0286996848
Web Site: http://www.nunatac.biz
Database Management Services
N.A.I.C.S.: 518210

ALKERMES PLC

Connaught House 1 Burlington Road, Dublin, 4, Ireland
Tel.: (353) 17728000   IE
Web Site: https://www.alkermes.com
ALKS—(NASDAQ)
Rev.: $1,663,405,000
Assets: $2,136,223,000
Liabilities: $933,537,000
Net Worth: $1,202,686,000
Earnings: $355,757,000
Emp.: 2,100
Fiscal Year-end: 12/31/23
Pharmaceuticals Mfr
N.A.I.C.S.: 325412
Michael J. Landine (Sr VP-Corp Dev)

Subsidiaries:

Alkermes Pharma Ireland Limited   (1)
Monksland, Athlone, N37 EA09, County Westmeath, Ireland
Tel.: (353) 906495000
Pharmaceutical Drug Mfr
N.A.I.C.S.: 325412
Richie Paul (Sr Dir-Intellectual Property)

Alkermes, Inc.   (1)
900 Winter St, Waltham, MA 02451
Tel.: (781) 609-6000
Web Site: http://www.alkermes.com
Sales Range: $300-349.9 Million
Emp.: 600
Developer of Pharmaceutical Products Based on Specialized Drug Delivery Systems
N.A.I.C.S.: 325412
Richard F. Pops (Founder, Chm & CEO)

Subsidiary (Domestic):

Alkermes Controlled Therapeutics, Inc.   (2)
852 Winter St, Waltham, MA 02451
Tel.: (617) 494-0171
Pharmaceuticals Product Mfr
N.A.I.C.S.: 325412

Plant (Domestic):

Alkermes, Inc. - Wilmington Facility   (2)
265 Olinger Cir, Wilmington, OH 45177
Tel.: (937) 382-5642
Web Site: http://www.alkermes.com
Sales Range: $125-149.9 Million
Emp.: 320
Pharmaceuticals Product Mfr
N.A.I.C.S.: 325412

ALKHALEEJ TRAINING & EDUCATION COMPANY

Al-Ulaya Main Road, behind Jarir bookstore, Riyadh, Saudi Arabia
Tel.: (966) 920024824
Web Site: https://alkhaleej.com.sa
Year Founded: 1993
4290—(SAU)
Rev.: $234,874,774
Assets: $512,737,146
Liabilities: $319,017,558
Net Worth: $193,719,588
Earnings: $1,070,937
Emp.: 4,500
Fiscal Year-end: 12/31/22
Computer Training Services
N.A.I.C.S.: 611420
Abdulaziz Hammad Al-Bulaihid (Chm)

Subsidiaries:

Franklin Covey Middle East Company Ltd.   (1)
Al Saqr Business Tower 1402 Sheikh Zayed Road, PO Box 53703, Dubai, United Arab Emirates
Tel.: (971) 43322244
Educational Consultancy Services
N.A.I.C.S.: 611710

Lingyophone Company Ltd.   (1)
3rd Floor CI Tower St George's Square, New Malden, KT3 4HG, United Kingdom
Tel.: (44) 2036036534
Web Site: https://www.linguaphone.co.uk
Language Course Provider
N.A.I.C.S.: 611630

ALKIM ALKALI KIMYA A.S.

Inonu Caddesi No 13 Taksim, 34437, Istanbul, Turkiye
Tel.: (90) 2122922266
Web Site: https://www.alkim.com
Year Founded: 1948
ALKIM—(IST)
Rev.: $86,390,773
Assets: $53,860,319
Liabilities: $15,326,771
Net Worth: $38,533,547
Earnings: $20,622,667
Emp.: 494
Fiscal Year-end: 12/31/22
Sodium Sulfate Mfr
N.A.I.C.S.: 325180
Galip Cavdar (Mgr-Mining Ops)

ALKIM KAGIT SANAYI VE TICARET A.S.

Kemalpasa OSB Kirovasi Mevkii, Kemalpasa, 35730, Izmir, Turkiye
Tel.: (90) 2328770606
Web Site:
https://www.alkimkagit.com.tr
Year Founded: 1948
ALKA—(IST)
Rev.: $65,268,729
Assets: $40,356,466
Liabilities: $13,068,740
Net Worth: $27,287,726
Earnings: $7,474,604
Fiscal Year-end: 12/31/19
Photocopy Paper Mfr
N.A.I.C.S.: 322120
Ferit Kora (Chm)

ALKIS H. HADJIKYRIACOS (FROU FROU BISCUITS) PUBLIC LTD.

115 Grigori Afxentiou Avenue Kokkinotrimithia Industrial Area, 2660, Nicosia, Cyprus
Tel.: (357) 22835090
Web Site:
https://www.froufrou.com.cy
Year Founded: 1964
FBI—(CYP)
Rev.: $23,836,800
Assets: $93,729,678
Liabilities: $22,133,254
Net Worth: $71,596,425
Earnings: $1,432,090
Emp.: 200
Fiscal Year-end: 12/31/22
Biscuits & Snack Foods Mfr
N.A.I.C.S.: 311813

Subsidiaries:

Frou Frou Cereals Ltd   (1)
Kokkinotrimithia, PO Box 15029, Nicosia, 2660, Cyprus
Tel.: (357) 22835090
Web Site: http://www.froufrou.com.cy
Sales Range: $25-49.9 Million
Emp.: 200
Cereals Mfr & Trading Services
N.A.I.C.S.: 311230
Micheal Hadjikyriacos (Gen Mgr)

Frou Frou Investments Ltd   (1)
PO Box 15029, Kokkinotrimithia, 2660, Nicosia, Cyprus
Tel.: (357) 22835090
Web Site: http://www.froufrou.com.cy
Sales Range: $100-124.9 Million
Emp.: 200
Investment Management Service
N.A.I.C.S.: 523940
Alkis H. Hadjikyriacos (Mng Dir)

ALKOSIGN LIMITED

Plot No 12-A Kalyan Bhiwandi Industrial Area MIDC Saravali, Bhiwandi, 421311, Maharashtra, India
Tel.: (91) 7391040250
Web Site: https://www.alkosign.com
Year Founded: 2020
543453—(BOM)
Industry Machinery Mfr

N.A.I.C.S.: 333310
Poorvi Gattani (Compliance Officer & Sec)

ALKYL AMINES CHEMICALS LIMITED

401-407 Nirman Vyapar Kendra Sector 17, Vashi, Navi Mumbai, 400 703, Maharashtra, India
Tel.: (91) 2267946600
Web Site:
https://www.alkylamines.com
Year Founded: 1979
506767—(BOM)
Rev.: $231,537,688
Assets: $217,046,930
Liabilities: $57,488,477
Net Worth: $159,558,454
Earnings: $31,211,448
Emp.: 700
Fiscal Year-end: 03/31/23
Specialty Chemicals Distr
N.A.I.C.S.: 424690
Yogesh M. Kothari (Chm & Mng Dir)

ALL ABOUT, INC.

6F Ebisu Subaru Bldg 1-20-8 Ebisu, Shibuya-Ku, Tokyo, 150-0013, Japan
Tel.: (81) 363621300
Web Site: https://corp.allabout.co.jp
Year Founded: 1993
2454—(TKS)
Rev.: $103,796,830
Assets: $54,036,750
Liabilities: $24,490,050
Net Worth: $29,546,700
Earnings: ($3,014,160)
Emp.: 130
Fiscal Year-end: 03/31/24
Online Advertisement Services
N.A.I.C.S.: 541810

ALL ACTIVE ASSET CAPITAL LTD.

c/o Codan Trust Company BVI Ltd Commerce House Wickhams Cay 1, PO Box 3140, Road Town, Tortola, VG1110, Virgin Islands (British)
Tel.: (284) 3756 0124   VG
Web Site: http://www.aaacap.com
Year Founded: 2012
Rev.: $13,887
Assets: $1,492,149
Liabilities: $84,187
Net Worth: $1,407,962
Earnings: ($672,427)
Fiscal Year-end: 12/31/18
Investment Services
N.A.I.C.S.: 523999
Rodger Sargent (Exec Dir)

ALL COSMOS BIO-TECH HOLDING CORPORATION

190 Elgin Avenue Grand Cayman, Georgetown, KY1-9005, Cayman Islands
Tel.: (345) 6072523788
Web Site: http://www.allcosmos.com
Year Founded: 1999
4148—(TAI)
Rev.: $92,435,557
Assets: $120,139,143
Liabilities: $28,108,864
Net Worth: $92,030,279
Earnings: $6,190,817
Emp.: 529
Fiscal Year-end: 12/31/23
Fertilizer (Mixing Only) Manufacturing
N.A.I.C.S.: 325314
Tony Peng (Chm & CEO)

Subsidiaries:

All Cosmos Industries Sdn. Bhd.   (1)
PLO 650 Jalan Keluli 7, Pasir Gudang Industrial Estate, 81700, Pasir Gudang, Johor, Malaysia
Tel.: (60) 72523788

All Cosmos Bio-Tech Holding
Corporation—(Continued)

Web Site: https://allcosmos.com
Agricultural Product Mfr
N.A.I.C.S.: 325320

GK Bio International Sdn. Bhd. (1)
42-2 Jalan PJU 5/11, kota damansara,
47810, Petaling Jaya, Selangor, Malaysia
Tel.: (60) 361421139
Web Site: http://www.mygkb.com
Bio-Chemical Fertilizer Mfr
N.A.I.C.S.: 325311
Howard Heng (Specialist-Bus Dev)

PT All Cosmos Indonesia (1)
Ira Building Jl Cactus Raya Blok J No1
Komp Perumahan, Taman Setia Budi Indah,
Medan, 20131, Sumatera Utara, Indonesia
Tel.: (62) 618201288
Bio-Chemical Compound Fertilizer Retailer
N.A.I.C.S.: 424690

**Sabah Softwoods Hybrid Fertiliser
Sdn. Bhd.** (1)
Lot 50 and 51 Phase 2 Jalan Tengah Nipah
5 5 KM, 91100, Lahad Datu, Sabah, Malaysia
Tel.: (60) 89863280
Web Site: http://www.sshf.com.my
Bio-Chemical Fertilizer Mfr
N.A.I.C.S.: 325311
Jamalul Kiram (Co-Chm)

ALL IN GAMES SA
Bohaterow Wrzesnia 82, 31621, Krakow, Poland
Tel.: (48) 575999037
Web Site:
　https://www.allingames.com
Year Founded: 2018
ALG—(WAR)
Rev.: $1,007,879
Assets: $5,180,391
Liabilities: $9,832,848
Net Worth: ($4,652,457)
Earnings: ($1,658,178)
Emp.: 100
Fiscal Year-end: 12/31/23
Computer Game Development Services
N.A.I.C.S.: 541511
Piotr Zygadlo (Chm)

ALL IN WEST! CAPITAL CORPORATION
400 - 360 Main Street, Winnipeg,
R3C 3Z3, MB, Canada
Tel.: (204) 947-1200
Web Site: http://www.allinwest.com
Sales Range: $1-9.9 Million
Emp.: 20
Real Estate Services
N.A.I.C.S.: 531390

Subsidiaries:

**Marwest Management Canada
Ltd.** (1)
300-360 Main St, Winnipeg, R3C 3Z3, MB,
Canada
Tel.: (204) 947-1200
Web Site: http://www.marwest.ca
Sales Range: $50-74.9 Million
Emp.: 10
Real Estate Management Services
N.A.I.C.S.: 531390
John Bruce (Sr Mgr-Property)

ALL INSPIRE DEVELOPMENT PUBLIC COMPANY LIMITED
4345 Bhiraj Tower At Bitec 18th Floor
Sukhumvit Road, Bangna, Bangkok,
10260, Thailand
Tel.: (66) 2 029 9988　　　　TH
Web Site: http://www.allinspire.co.th
Year Founded: 2013
ALL—(THA)
Rev.: $42,984,330
Assets: $263,198,573
Liabilities: $196,289,062
Net Worth: $66,909,511

Earnings: ($11,568,843)
Fiscal Year-end: 12/31/21
Real Estate Development Services
N.A.I.C.S.: 531390
Thanakorn Thanawarith (CEO)

ALL INVEST SECURITIES LTD.
4 Diagorou Kermia Building Floor 5
Flat 503, 1097, Nicosia, Cyprus
Tel.: (357) 22673725
Investment Services
N.A.I.C.S.: 523940

ALL METAL SERVICES LTD.
Unit 6 Horton Road Industrial Park
West Drayton, London, UB7 8JD,
Middlesex, United Kingdom
Tel.: (44) 1895 444066
Web Site: http://www.allmetal.co.uk
Year Founded: 1974
Sales Range: $200-249.9 Million
Emp.: 306
Metal Products Mfr
N.A.I.C.S.: 331210
Mark Roberts (Mgr-Intl Sls)

ALL ORE MINERACAO PARTICIPACOES S.A.
Rua Leopoldo Couto de Magalhaes
Jr 758 - 2nd floor cj 22 Itaim Bibi,
04542-000, Sao Paulo, Brazil
Tel.: (55) 1137774250
Web Site: http://www.allore.com.br
Iron Products Mfr & Distr
N.A.I.C.S.: 331110
Heinz-Gerd Stein (Chm)

ALL POINTS NORTH PLC
Cumbria House Suite 8 Gilwilly Road,
Penrith, CA11 9FF, Cumbria, United
Kingdom
Tel.: (44) 1768865959
Web Site:
　http://www.allpointsnorthplc.com
Sales Range: $1-9.9 Million
Real Estate Agents & Brokers
N.A.I.C.S.: 531210
Kevin Philbin (Sec)

ALL RESPONSE MEDIA
12 St John Sq, London, EC1M 4NL,
United Kingdom
Tel.: (44) 2070171450
Web Site:
　http://www.allresponsemedia.com
Year Founded: 1995
Emp.: 130
N.A.I.C.S.: 541810
Andy Sloan (CEO)

ALL RING TECH CO., LTD.
1 Luko 10th Rd Lujhu Kaohsiung,
Hsien, Taiwan
Tel.: (886) 76071828
Web Site: https://www.allring-
tech.com.tw
Year Founded: 1996
6187—(TPE)
Rev.: $70,309,633
Assets: $130,217,147
Liabilities: $54,180,565
Net Worth: $76,036,582
Earnings: $15,603,258
Emp.: 35
Fiscal Year-end: 12/31/22
Automated Machinery Mfr
N.A.I.C.S.: 333248
Lu Ching-Lai (Chm)

ALL SAINTS COMMERCIAL PLC
27/28 Eastcastle Street, London,
W1W 8DH, United Kingdom
Tel.: (44) 1912114120
Web Site: http://www.allsaints.com
Real Estate Management Services

N.A.I.C.S.: 531210

ALL WEATHER WINDOWS LTD.
18550 118A Avenue NW, Edmonton,
T5S 2K7, AB, Canada
Tel.: (780) 451-0670
Web Site:
　http://www.allweatherwindows.com
Year Founded: 1978
Sales Range: $125-149.9 Million
Windows & Doors Mfr
N.A.I.C.S.: 321911

ALLA PUBLIC COMPANY LIMITED
933 935 937 939 Soi On nut 46 On
nut Road, Suanluang, Bangkok,
10250, Thailand
Tel.: (66) 23220777
Web Site: https://www.alla.co.th
Year Founded: 1992
ALLA—(THA)
Rev.: $24,719,436
Assets: $33,740,407
Liabilities: $6,606,315
Net Worth: $27,134,092
Earnings: $3,162,902
Emp.: 470
Fiscal Year-end: 12/31/23
Industrial Machinery Equipment Distr
N.A.I.C.S.: 423830
Weerachai Ngamdeevilaisak (Chm)

Subsidiaries:

Onvalla Company Limited (1)
50 Moo 20, Lam Luk Ka Lam Luk Ka, Pathumthani, 12150, Thailand
Tel.: (66) 219353805
Web Site: https://www.onvalla.com
Handling Equipment Mfr
N.A.I.C.S.: 333998

ALLAN CRAWFORD ASSOCIATES LIMITED
5805 Kennedy Road, Mississauga,
L4Z 2G3, ON, Canada
Tel.: (905) 890-2010
Web Site: http://www.aca.ca
Year Founded: 1959
Rev.: $27,967,838
Emp.: 65
Electronic Instrument Distr
N.A.I.C.S.: 423690
Allan Crawford (Chm)

ALLAN INTERNATIONAL HOLDINGS LIMITED
Tel.: (852) 21037288
Web Site: https://www.allan.com.hk
0684—(HKG)
Rev.: $101,016,104
Assets: $182,190,699
Liabilities: $39,984,187
Net Worth: $142,206,512
Earnings: ($3,481,815)
Emp.: 2,000
Fiscal Year-end: 03/31/22
Electric Appliances Mfr
N.A.I.C.S.: 335210
Alex Wing Kong Li (Dir-Quality Assurance)

Subsidiaries:

Allan Electric Mfg., Limited (1)
12 Fl Zung Fu Indus Bldg 1067 Kings Rd,
Quarry Bay, China (Hong Kong)
Tel.: (852) 21037288
Web Site: http://www.allan.com.hk
Sales Range: $50-74.9 Million
Emp.: 100
Household Electrical Appliance Mfr
N.A.I.C.S.: 335210
Michelle Wing Tong Tsang (Gen Mgr)

**Allan Mould Manufacturing
Limited** (1)
12 F Zung Fu Indus Bldg 1067 Kings Rd,

Quarry Bay, China (Hong Kong)
Tel.: (852) 21037288
Web Site: http://www.allan.com.hk
Emp.: 100
Plastic Container Mfr
N.A.I.C.S.: 322299

Allan Plastic Mfg., Limited (1)
12 F Zung Fu Indus Bldg 1067 Kings Rd,
Quarry Bay, China (Hong Kong)
Tel.: (852) 21037288
Web Site: http://www.allan.com.hk
Sales Range: $125-149.9 Million
Emp.: 500
Plastics Product Mfr
N.A.I.C.S.: 326199

**Conan Electric Manufacturing
Limited** (1)
12 F Zung Fu Indus Bldg 1067 Kings Rd,
Quarry Bay, China (Hong Kong)
Tel.: (852) 21037288
Web Site: http://www.allan.com.hk
Emp.: 100
Household Electrical Appliance Whslr
N.A.I.C.S.: 423620
Carrie Ka Lee Kwok (Dir-Mfg)

Global Express (HK) Limited (1)
12 F Zung Fu Indus Bldg 1067 Kings Rd,
Quarry Bay, China (Hong Kong)
Tel.: (852) 21037288
Consumer Electronics Whslr
N.A.I.C.S.: 423620

**Karan Electric Manufacturing
Limited** (1)
12 F Zung Fu Indus Bldg 1067 Kings Rd,
Quarry Bay, China (Hong Kong)
Tel.: (852) 21037288
Web Site: http://www.allan.com.hk
Sales Range: $50-74.9 Million
Emp.: 100
Consumer Electronics Whslr
N.A.I.C.S.: 423620
Simon Shu Chun Cheung (Mgr-Sls)

**Warran Electric Manufacturing
Limited** (1)
12 F Zung Fu Indus Bldg 1067 Kings Rd,
Quarry Bay, China (Hong Kong)
Tel.: (852) 21037288
Web Site: http://www.allam.com.hk
Emp.: 100
Electrical Contracting Services
N.A.I.C.S.: 238210
Eric Li (Dir-Sls)

ALLAN R. NELSON ENGINEERING (1997) INC.
2nd Floor 17510-102 Avenue, Edmonton, T5S 1K2, AB, Canada
Tel.: (780) 483-3436
Web Site: https://www.arneng.ab.ca
Year Founded: 1966
Sales Range: $25-49.9 Million
Emp.: 15
Mechanical Engineering Services
N.A.I.C.S.: 541330

Subsidiaries:

Encore Electronics, Inc. (1)
4400 Rte 50, Saratoga Springs, NY 12866
Tel.: (518) 584-5354
Web Site: http://www.encore-elec.com
Sales Range: $25-49.9 Million
Measuring & Testing Instruments for Electricity & Electrical Signals
N.A.I.C.S.: 334515
Sheri Steele (Office Mgr-HR)

ALLAN WINDOW TECHNOLOGIES LTD.
131 Caldari Road Unit 1, Concord,
L4K 3Z9, ON, Canada
Tel.: (905) 738-8600
Web Site:
　http://www.allanwindows.com
Year Founded: 1959
Rev.: $39,299,117
Emp.: 360
Doors & Windows Mfr
N.A.I.C.S.: 332321
Brian J. Cohen (Pres-Bus Dev-US)

Subsidiaries:

Global Architectural Metals Inc (1)
123 Centre St, Welland, L3B 5N9, ON, Canada
Tel.: (905) 714-4321
Web Site:
http://www.globalarchitectural.com
Architectural Components Mfr
N.A.I.C.S.: 332323
Kyra Moate *(Coord-Health & Safety)*

ALLANASONS PRIVATE LIMITED
Allana Centre A R J Allana Marg 113 / 115 M G Road Fort, Mumbai, 400 001, India
Tel.: (91) 22 2262 8000   In
Web Site: http://www.allana.com
Year Founded: 1865
Sales Range: Less than $1 Million
Food Product Mfr & Distr
N.A.I.C.S.: 311612

ALLAND ET ROBERT
125 Rue Grande, 27940, Rouen, France
Tel.: (33) 232775177
Web Site: http://www.allandetrobert.fr
Rev.: $20,700,000
Emp.: 33
Durable Goods
N.A.I.C.S.: 423990
Xavier Maison *(Dir)*

ALLANNIC FRERES SA
ZI de Kerpont 1371 rue Dominique Francois Arago, 56850, Caudan, France
Tel.: (33) 297769600
Web Site:
http://allannic.lorient.mercedes.fr
Rev.: $21,200,000
Emp.: 23
Automotive Repair Services
N.A.I.C.S.: 811114
Frederic Blin *(Mgr-Sls)*

ALLANSON INTERNATIONAL INC.
33 Cranfield Road, Toronto, M4B 3H2, ON, Canada
Tel.: (416) 755-1191
Web Site: http://www.allanson.com
Rev.: $27,272,343
Emp.: 90
Electrical Products Mfr
N.A.I.C.S.: 335999
Nigel Isaac *(Mgr-Program Sls)*

ALLAWASAYA TEXTILE & FINISHING MILLS LTD.
Allawasaya Square Mumtazabad industrial Area Vehari Road, Multan, Pakistan
Tel.: (92) 614233624
Web Site:
https://www.allawasaya.com
Year Founded: 1958
AWTX—(PSX)
Rev.: $13,583,476
Assets: $14,277,044
Liabilities: $8,257,554
Net Worth: $6,019,489
Earnings: ($592,749)
Emp.: 986
Fiscal Year-end: 06/30/23
Textile Mfr
N.A.I.C.S.: 313310
Muhammad Jamil *(Exec Dir)*

ALLCAP ASSET MANAGEMENT LTD
10 Earlsfort Terrace, Dublin, Ireland
Tel.: (353) 18974921
Web Site: http://www.allcap.com
Year Founded: 2003

Sales Range: $25-49.9 Million
Emp.: 25
Asset Management Advisory & Consulting Services
N.A.I.C.S.: 523940
Jana Becher *(Mng Dir)*

ALLCARGO LOGISTICS LIMITED
6th Floor Allcargo House CST Road, Santacruz E, Mumbai, 400 098, India
Tel.: (91) 2266798100
Web Site:
https://www.allcargologistics.com
532749—(BOM)
Rev.: $2,745,616,965
Assets: $1,333,618,650
Liabilities: $849,668,820
Net Worth: $483,949,830
Earnings: $131,667,900
Emp.: 959
Fiscal Year-end: 03/31/22
Freight Transportation Arrangement
N.A.I.C.S.: 488510
S. Suryanarayanan *(Exec Dir-Strategy & Fin)*

Subsidiaries:

Avvashya CCI Logistics Private Limited (1)
Avvashya House CST Road, Kalina Santacruz E, Mumbai, 400098, Maharashtra, India
Tel.: (91) 226 679 8100
Web Site: https://avvashyacci.com
Emp.: 400
Logistic Services
N.A.I.C.S.: 541614
Shashi Kiran Shetty *(Chm)*

Contech Logistics Solutions Private Limited (1)
SBL House No 54 Montieth Road, Egmore, Chennai, 600 008, India
Tel.: (91) 4449782293
Web Site: https://contechlogistics.com
Logistic Services
N.A.I.C.S.: 541614

Deolix S.A. (1)
Tel.: (598) 29170603
Sales Range: $25-49.9 Million
Emp.: 5
Freight Forwarding Services
N.A.I.C.S.: 488510
Ricardo Biernacki *(Gen Mgr)*

ECU Trucking, Inc. (1)
2401 NW 69th St, Miami, FL 33147
Web Site: https://www.ecutrucking.com
Container Trucking Services
N.A.I.C.S.: 484110

ECU Worldwide CEE S.R.L. (1)
4 Intrarea Veronica Micle Street 1st Floor Ap 2, District 1, 010046, Bucharest, Romania
Tel.: (40) 744591220
Logistic Services
N.A.I.C.S.: 541614

ECUHOLD N.V. (1)
Schomhoeveweg No 15, Antwerp, 2030, Belgium
Tel.: (32) 35412466
Sales Range: $75-99.9 Million
Emp.: 150
Holding Company
N.A.I.C.S.: 551112
Ivan Lardenoit *(Mng Dir)*

Subsidiary (Non-US):

Conecli International S.A. (2)
De Mc Donald Sabana 200 Este 75 Sur Frente A Condominios Fasaro, PO Box 1018-1000, Sabana Sur, San Jose, Costa Rica
Tel.: (506) 2 296 6748
Freight Forwarding Services
N.A.I.C.S.: 488510

Subsidiary (Domestic):

E.C.B N.V. (2)

Schomhoeveweg 15, 2030, Antwerp, Belgium
Tel.: (32) 3 542 33 61
Web Site:
http://www.europeancustombrokers.be
Sales Range: $25-49.9 Million
Emp.: 20
Freight Forwarding Services
N.A.I.C.S.: 488510
Koen Hendrickx *(Mgr-Customs)*

ECU Air N.V. (2)
Building 709 - B, Brucargo, Brussels, 1931, Belgium
Tel.: (32) 27515051
Web Site: http://www.ecuair.net
Sales Range: $25-49.9 Million
Emp.: 10
Air Freight Forwarding Services
N.A.I.C.S.: 481112
Rakesh Shah *(Mgr-Fin)*

Subsidiary (Non-US):

ECU Australia Pty Ltd. (2)
Tel.: (61) 383368600
Sales Range: $25-49.9 Million
Emp.: 20
Freight Forwarding Services
N.A.I.C.S.: 488510

Subsidiary (Domestic):

ECU International N.V. (2)
Schomhoeveweg 15, 2030, Antwerp, Belgium
Tel.: (32) 35443800
Web Site: http://www.ecuworldwide.com
Sales Range: $50-74.9 Million
Emp.: 150
Freight Forwarding Services
N.A.I.C.S.: 488510

Subsidiary (Non-US):

ECU Line Abu Dhabi LLC (2)
Tel.: (971) 26339597
Web Site: http://www.ecuworldwide.net
Sales Range: $25-49.9 Million
Emp.: 3
Freight Forwarding Services
N.A.I.C.S.: 488510
Varuna Wirasinha *(Mng Dir)*

ECU Line Algerie S.A.R.L. (2)
Tel.: (213) 660733453
Sales Range: $25-49.9 Million
Emp.: 10
Freight Forwarding Services
N.A.I.C.S.: 488510

ECU Logistics S.A. (2)
Tel.: (54) 1153530200
Freight Forwarding Services
N.A.I.C.S.: 488510

ELV Multimodal C.A. (2)
Avenida Sucre Torre Centro Parque Boyaca Piso 16-Oficina 164, Los Dos Caminos, Caracas, 1070, Miranda, Venezuela
Tel.: (58) 2122859320
Sales Range: $25-49.9 Million
Emp.: 10
Freight Forwarding Services
N.A.I.C.S.: 488510

Ecu Line (Thailand) Co.Ltd. (2)
Sales Range: $25-49.9 Million
Emp.: 60
Freight Forwarding Services
N.A.I.C.S.: 488510
Viraj Nobnomtham *(Gen Mgr-Sls)*

Ecu Line Chile S.A. (2)
Tel.: (56) 24306600
Sales Range: $25-49.9 Million
Emp.: 36
Freight Forwarding Services
N.A.I.C.S.: 488510
Miroslava Damjanic *(Mgr-Ops)*

Ecu Line China Ltd. (2)
9F Bldg B Silverbay Tower 469 WuSong Rd, Shanghai, 200 080, China
Tel.: (86) 2163643399
Freight Forwarding Services
N.A.I.C.S.: 488510

Ecu Line Cote d'Ivoire Sarl (2)
10 Rue Pierre Et Marie Curie Zone 4C 18, BP 2528, Abidjan, Cote d'Ivoire

Tel.: (225) 21257179
Freight Forwarding Services
N.A.I.C.S.: 488510

Ecu Line Del Ecuador S.A. (2)
Freight Forwarding Services
N.A.I.C.S.: 488510

Ecu Line Doha W.L.L. (2)
Al Attiyah Building Office 12 First floor Building 340 Zone 24, PO Box 24064, Street 230 C-Ring Road, Doha, Qatar
Tel.: (974) 44438491
Sales Range: $25-49.9 Million
Emp.: 10
Freight Forwarding Services
N.A.I.C.S.: 488510
Vijayan Krishnan *(Country Mgr)*

Ecu Line Egypt Ltd. (2)
31 Omar Bakeer St 9th Fl Flat 802, Heliopolis, Cairo, Egypt
Sales Range: $25-49.9 Million
Emp.: 14
Freight Forwarding Services
N.A.I.C.S.: 488510

Ecu Line Guatemala S.A. (2)
Sales Range: $25-49.9 Million
Emp.: 15
Freight Forwarding Services
N.A.I.C.S.: 488510

Ecu Line Japan Ltd. (2)
Sales Range: $10-24.9 Million
Emp.: 30
Logistic Services
N.A.I.C.S.: 541614
Don Hasegawa *(Pres)*

Ecu Line Maroc S.A. (2)
Tel.: (212) 522402727
Sales Range: $25-49.9 Million
Emp.: 30
Freight Forwarding Services
N.A.I.C.S.: 488510

Ecu Line Middleeast LLC (2)
Jebel Ali Free Zone, PO Box 28430, Jebel Ali, Dubai, United Arab Emirates
Tel.: (971) 48175666
Sales Range: $25-49.9 Million
Emp.: 30
Freight Forwarding Services
N.A.I.C.S.: 488510

Ecu Line Philippines Inc. (2)
Sales Range: $25-49.9 Million
Emp.: 30
Freight Forwarding Services
N.A.I.C.S.: 488510

Ecu Line Romania S.R.L. (2)
Emp.: 8
Freight Forwarding Services
N.A.I.C.S.: 488510

Ecu Line Rotterdam B.V. (2)
Nieuwesluisweg 240, 3197 KV, Rotterdam, Netherlands
Tel.: (31) 104950444
Sales Range: $25-49.9 Million
Emp.: 25
Freight Forwarding Services
N.A.I.C.S.: 488510
Dammis Witter *(Mgr-Fin)*

Ecu Line S.A. (Pty) Ltd. (2)
Sales Range: $25-49.9 Million
Emp.: 30
Freight Forwarding Services
N.A.I.C.S.: 488510
Yvonne Palm *(Mng Dir)*

Ecu Line Singapore Pte. Ltd. (2)
Tel.: (65) 62203373
Sales Range: $25-49.9 Million
Emp.: 80
Freight Forwarding Services
N.A.I.C.S.: 488510
Zalina Bte Saini *(Mgr-Import)*

Ecu Line Spain S.L. (2)
Tel.: (34) 934120061
Freight Forwarding Services
N.A.I.C.S.: 488510

Ecu Nordic Oy (2)
Unioninkatu 22, 00130, Helsinki, Finland
Tel.: (358) 942412324
Web Site: http://www.eculine.com

Allcargo Logistics Limited—(Continued)

Sales Range: $25-49.9 Million
Emp.: 5
Freight Forwarding Services
N.A.I.C.S.: 488510

Ecu Worldwide (Malaysia) Sdn Bhd   (2)
No 43-01 Jalan Molek 3/20, Taman Molek, 81100, Johor, Malaysia
Tel.: (60) 73500249
Freight Forwarding Services
N.A.I.C.S.: 488510
Claudio Scandella *(CEO)*

Ecu-Line (Germany) GmbH   (2)
Tel.: (49) 402388900
Sales Range: $25-49.9 Million
Emp.: 50
Freight Forwarding Services
N.A.I.C.S.: 488510
Thomas Heydorn *(Mng Dir)*

Ecu-Line Canada Inc.   (2)
1804 Alstep Dr Unit 2, Toronto, L5S 1W1, ON, Canada
Tel.: (905) 677-8334
Sales Range: $25-49.9 Million
Emp.: 10
Freight Forwarding Services
N.A.I.C.S.: 488510
Mike McCarthy *(Gen Mgr)*

Ecu-Line Czech S.r.o.   (2)
Freight Forwarding Services
N.A.I.C.S.: 488510

Ecu-Line De Colombia S.A   (2)
Tel.: (57) 14139640
Freight Forwarding Services
N.A.I.C.S.: 488510

Ecu-Line Guangzhou Ltd.   (2)
Tel.: (86) 2083649778
Sales Range: $25-49.9 Million
Emp.: 30
Freight Forwarding Services
N.A.I.C.S.: 488510
Candy Wong *(Branch Mgr)*

Ecu-Line Hong Kong Ltd.   (2)
Freight Forwarding Services
N.A.I.C.S.: 488510

Ecu-Line Malta Ltd.   (2)
10 Timberwharf, Marsa, MRS1443, Malta
Tel.: (356) 21340731
Sales Range: $25-49.9 Million
Emp.: 20
Freight Forwarding Services
N.A.I.C.S.: 488510
Simon Bajada *(Country Mgr)*

Subsidiary (Domestic):

Ecu-Line N.V.   (2)
Schouwkenstraat 15, B 2030, Antwerp, Belgium
Tel.: (32) 35412466
Sales Range: $100-124.9 Million
Emp.: 300
Freight Transportation Services
N.A.I.C.S.: 483211

Subsidiary (US):

Econocaribe Consolidators Inc.   (3)
2401 NW 69th St, Miami, FL 33147-6883
Tel.: (305) 693-5133
Sales Range: $50-74.9 Million
Emp.: 220
Freight Transportation Arrangement
N.A.I.C.S.: 488510
John Abisch *(Pres)*

Ecu International   (3)
9130 S Dadeland Blvd Ste, Miami, FL 33156
Tel.: (305) 670-1877
Rev.: $16,000,000
Emp.: 150
Freight Consolidation
N.A.I.C.S.: 333994
John Abisch *(Gen Mgr)*

Subsidiary (Non-US):

Ecu-Line Panama S.A.   (2)
Tel.: (507) 2361775

Sales Range: $25-49.9 Million
Emp.: 15
Freight Forwarding Services
N.A.I.C.S.: 488510

Ecu-Line Peru S.A.   (2)
Tel.: (51) 16195120
Freight Forwarding Services
N.A.I.C.S.: 488510

Flamingo Line El Salvador S.A. De C.V.   (2)
Sales Range: $25-49.9 Million
Emp.: 4
Freight Forwarding Services
N.A.I.C.S.: 488510

Rotterdam Freight Station B.V.   (2)
Haven nummer 5044 Nieuwesluisweg 240, Botlek, 3197 KV, Rotterdam, Netherlands
Tel.: (31) 102961860
Web Site:
    https://www.rotterdamfreightstation.nl
Sales Range: $25-49.9 Million
Emp.: 14
Warehousing & Freight Forwarding Services
N.A.I.C.S.: 488510
Rik van Riet *(Mng Dir)*

ELWA Ghana Ltd.   (1)
Plot 23/25 Commercial Warehouse Area Near Main Harbour, PO Box 855, Tema Harbour Area, Tema, Ghana
Tel.: (233) 303224603
Freight Forwarding Services
N.A.I.C.S.: 488510
Richard Mensah *(Mng Dir & VP-Sls & Fin)*

Ecu Worldwide (Cyprus) Ltd.   (1)
Corner Omonias and Aeginis no 1 Psilos Court 3rd Floor, PO Box 56027, 3052, Limassol, 3052, Cyprus
Tel.: (357) 25560292
Logistic Services
N.A.I.C.S.: 541614

Ecu Worldwide (Kenya) Ltd.   (1)
Inchcape House 3rd Floor Archbishop Makarios CLS Off MOI Avenue, PO Box 94066, 80107, Mombasa, Kenya
Tel.: (254) 412223035
Logistic Services
N.A.I.C.S.: 541614

Ecu Worldwide (Mauritius) Ltd.   (1)
MFD Business Centre Freeport Zone 5 Mer Rouge, Port Louis, Mauritius
Tel.: (230) 2063945
Logistic Services
N.A.I.C.S.: 541614

Ecu Worldwide (Poland) Sp Zoo   (1)
Ul Janka Wisniewskiego 31, 81-355, Gdynia, Poland
Tel.: (48) 586606495
Logistic Services
N.A.I.C.S.: 541614

Ecu Worldwide (South Africa) Pty Ltd   (1)
Block B - 1st Floor Southern Life Gardens 70 2nd Ave Newton Park, Port Elizabeth, 6055, South Africa
Tel.: (27) 114529435
Logistic Services
N.A.I.C.S.: 541614

Ecu Worldwide Italy S.r.l.   (1)
Societa con Socio Unico Via Pammatone 2 - int 15-16, 16121, Genoa, Italy
Tel.: (39) 0104694162
Logistic Services
N.A.I.C.S.: 541614

Ecu Worldwide Lanka (Private) Ltd.   (1)
1st Floor 110-114 Braybrook Place, 02, Colombo, Sri Lanka
Tel.: (94) 722330544
Logistic Services
N.A.I.C.S.: 541614

Ecu Worldwide Logistics do Brazil Ltda   (1)
Praca dos Expedicionarios n 19 cj 31 Bairro Gonzaga, Santos, 11065-500, Sao Paulo, Brazil
Tel.: (55) 1332266000
Logistic Services
N.A.I.C.S.: 541614

Ecu Worldwide Mexico SA de CV   (1)
Clavel 113 Fraccionamiento Villa de las Flores Altamira, 89603, Tamaulipas, Mexico
Tel.: (52) 5541694570
Logistic Services
N.A.I.C.S.: 541614

Ecu Worldwide New Zealand Ltd.   (1)
64 Richard Pearse Drive Airport Oaks, Auckland, New Zealand
Tel.: (64) 92550299
Logistic Services
N.A.I.C.S.: 541614

Ecu Worldwide Turkey Tasimacilik Limited Sirketi   (1)
Aydinevler Mah Sanayi Cad Centrum Plaza No 3 A Blok Kat 6, Maltepe, 34854, Istanbul, Turkiye
Tel.: (90) 2165756000
Logistic Services
N.A.I.C.S.: 541614

Ecu-Line Paraguay SA   (1)
Malutin No AD6 138 - 1er Piso C/ Avda Mcal Lopez, 1808, Asuncion, Paraguay
Tel.: (595) 981547023
Logistic Services
N.A.I.C.S.: 541614

Ecu-Line Saudi Arabia LLC   (1)
Al Muhammadiyah plaza 4th Floor Office No 45, PO Box 104071, Jeddah, Saudi Arabia
Tel.: (966) 126501193
Logistic Services
N.A.I.C.S.: 541614

Hindustan Cargo Ltd.   (1)
Flat No C Old No 113 New No 80 Sterling Road, Nungambakam, Chennai, 600034, Tamil Nadu, India
Tel.: (91) 44 459 11500
Web Site: http://www.hindustancargoltd.in
Sales Range: $25-49.9 Million
Emp.: 40
Freight Forwarding Services
N.A.I.C.S.: 488510
Deepal Shah *(CEO)*

PT Ecu Worldwide Indonesia   (1)
The Emerald Tower 6th floor Jl Boulevard Barat XB-3 RT 002 / RW004, Kelapa Gading, Jakarta, 14240, Indonesia
Tel.: (62) 2124520192
Logistic Services
N.A.I.C.S.: 541614

Societe Ecu-Line Tunisie Sarl   (1)
Tec Center N 40 Rue de Jerissa Z I Saint Gobain Megrine, 2014, Tunis, 2014, Tunisia
Tel.: (216) 71434087
Logistic Services
N.A.I.C.S.: 541614

ALLCORE S.P.A.
Via San Gregorio 55, 20124, Milan, Italy
Tel.: (39) 0800960599
Web Site: https://allcore.it
Year Founded: 2016
CORE—(EUR)
Emp.: 450
Management Consulting Services
N.A.I.C.S.: 541618
Gianluca Massini Rosati *(Chm)*

ALLEANZA HOLDINGS CO., LTD.
Sekinoue 58 Taiheiji, Fukushima, 960-8151, Japan
Tel.: (81) 245636818   JP
Web Site: https://www.alleanza-hd.co.jp
Year Founded: 2016
3546—(TKS)
Rev.: $1,061,479,350
Assets: $626,174,620
Liabilities: $406,561,870
Net Worth: $219,612,750
Earnings: $16,817,480
Fiscal Year-end: 02/29/24

Holding Company; Home Centers & Other Retail Stores Operator
N.A.I.C.S.: 551112
Wagano Morisaku *(Pres & Co-CEO)*

Subsidiaries:

Daiyu Eight Co., Ltd.   (1)
58 Jisekinojo Taiheiji, Fukushima, 960-8151, Fukushima, Japan
Tel.: (81) 245452215
Web Site: https://www.daiyu8.co.jp
Emp.: 529
Home Centers & Other Stores Operator
N.A.I.C.S.: 444110

ALLEGIANCE COAL LIMITED
Suite 107 109 Pitt Street, Sydney, 2000, NSW, Australia
Tel.: (61) 292335579
Web Site:
    http://www.allegiancecoal.com.au
AHQ—(ASX)
Rev.: $59,897,342
Assets: $134,106,171
Liabilities: $111,438,674
Net Worth: $22,667,497
Earnings: ($74,750,207)
Fiscal Year-end: 06/30/22
Coal Exploration
N.A.I.C.S.: 212115
Jonathan Reynolds *(Fin Dir)*

Subsidiaries:

Telkwa Coal Limited   (1)
1415 Hankin Avenue Suite D, Telkwa, Prince George, V0J 2X0, BC, Canada   **(100%)**
Tel.: (778) 643-2843
Web Site: http://www.telkwacoal.com
Mining Services
N.A.I.C.S.: 213114
Mark Gray *(Chm & Mng Dir)*

ALLEGIANT GOLD LTD.
400-1681 Chestnut Street, Vancouver, V6J 4M6, BC, Canada
Tel.: (604) 634-0970
Web Site:
    https://www.allegiantgold.com
Year Founded: 2017
AUXXF—(OTCQX)
Assets: $23,234,801
Liabilities: $476,310
Net Worth: $22,758,491
Earnings: ($2,230,201)
Fiscal Year-end: 09/30/21
Metal Exploration Services
N.A.I.C.S.: 213114
Peter Gianulis *(Pres & CEO)*

Subsidiaries:

Allegiant Gold (U.S.) Ltd.   (1)
573 E 2nd St, Reno, NV 89502
Tel.: (775) 324-1226
Gold Exploration Services
N.A.I.C.S.: 212220

ALLEGION PUBLIC LIMITED COMPANY
Block D Iveagh Court Harcourt Road, Dublin, D02 VH94, Ireland
Tel.: (353) 12546200   IE
Web Site: http://www.allegion.com
Year Founded: 2013
ALLE—(NYSE)
Rev.: $3,650,800,000
Assets: $4,311,500,000
Liabilities: $2,993,200,000
Net Worth: $1,318,300,000
Earnings: $540,400,000
Emp.: 12,200
Fiscal Year-end: 12/31/23
Holding Company; Locking Mechanisms Mfr & Distr
N.A.I.C.S.: 551112
Tracy L. Kemp *(Chief Information & Digital Officer & Sr VP)*

Subsidiaries:

AXA Stenman Industries B.V. **(1)**
Energiestraat 2, 3903 AV, Veenendaal,
Netherlands
Tel.: (31) 8536111
Web Site: http://www.axasecurity.com
Hardware Mfr & Distr
N.A.I.C.S.: 332510
Peter Van Vlijmen *(CEO)*

AXA Stenman Nederland B.V. **(1)**
Energiestraat 2, PO Box 47, 3903 AV,
Veenendaal, Netherlands
Tel.: (31) 318536111
Web Site: http://www.axasecurity.com
Hardware Mfr & Distr
N.A.I.C.S.: 332510

Subsidiary (Non-US):

**AXA Stenman Deutschland
GmbH** **(2)**
Johann-Krane-Weg 37, 48149, Munster,
Germany
Tel.: (49) 2512101620
Web Site: http://www.axasecurity.com
Hardware Mfr & Distr
N.A.I.C.S.: 332510
John Stanley *(Mng Dir)*

AXA Stenman France S.A.S. **(2)**
Usine de beaulieu, PO Box 50, 58502, Cl-
amecy, France
Tel.: (33) 386270701
Web Site: http://www.axasecurity.com
Hardware Mfr & Distr
N.A.I.C.S.: 332510

AXA Stenman Poland Sp.z.o.o. **(2)**
Technologiczna 8, 42-400, Zawiercie, Po-
land
Tel.: (48) 326100100
Web Site: http://www.axahomesecurity.pl
Hardware Material Mfr & Distr
N.A.I.C.S.: 332510

Allegion (Australia) Pty Limited **(1)**
64 Parramatta Rd Underwood, Brisbane,
4119, QLD, Australia
Tel.: (61) 732088900
Web Site: http://www.allegion.com.au
Security & Safety Product Mfr
N.A.I.C.S.: 334290

Allegion Canada Inc. **(1)**
1076 Lakeshore Rd East, Mississauga, L5E
1E4, ON, Canada
Web Site: https://www.allegion.ca
Security & Safety Product Mfr
N.A.I.C.S.: 334290

Allegion Fu Hsing Limited **(1)**
29/F Fortis Twr 77 - 79 Gloucester Rd, Wan
Chai, Chai Wan, China (Hong Kong)
Tel.: (852) 25287300
Security & Safety Product Mfr
N.A.I.C.S.: 334290

Allegion International AG **(1)**
Tafernhof Mellingerstrasse 207, 5405,
Baden, Switzerland
Tel.: (41) 564845111
Household Electronic Product Whslr
N.A.I.C.S.: 423620

**Allegion Security Technologies
(China) Co., Ltd.** **(1)**
10F L'Avenue 99 Xianxia Road, Shanghai,
200051, China
Tel.: (86) 400 920 1818
Locking Mechanisms Mfr & Distr; Regional
Managing Office
N.A.I.C.S.: 332510
William Feng Yu *(Reg Pres-Asia Pacific)*

**Allegion US Holding Company
Inc.** **(1)**
11819 N Pennsylvania St, Carmel, IN
46032
Tel.: (317) 810-3700
Web Site: https://us.allegion.com
Holding Company; Locking Mechanisms Mfr
N.A.I.C.S.: 551112

Plant (Domestic):

Allegion US **(2)**
7127 Crossroads Blvd Ste 101, Brentwood,
TN 37027
Tel.: (615) 376-2664

Web Site: http://us.allegion.com
Sales Range: $25-49.9 Million
Emp.: 10
Security & Safety Products Mfr & Distr
N.A.I.C.S.: 332510

Unit (Domestic):

**Ingersoll-Rand Security Technologies
Consultants** **(2)**
488 E Santa Clara St Ste101, Arcadia, CA
91006-7230
Tel.: (626) 359-5555
Sales Range: $10-24.9 Million
Emp.: 8
Mfr of Locks or Lock Sets
N.A.I.C.S.: 561621

LCN Closers **(2)**
121 W Railroad Ave, Princeton, IL 61356
Tel.: (815) 875-3311
Web Site: http://www.lcnclosers.com
Sales Range: $75-99.9 Million
Emp.: 300
Premium Door Mechanisms Mfr & Distr
N.A.I.C.S.: 332510

Subsidiary (Domestic):

Schlage Lock Company LLC **(2)**
3899 HANCOCK Expy, Colorado City, CO
80911
Tel.: (317) 810-3700
Web Site: https://www.schlage.com
Sales Range: $1-4.9 Billion
Emp.: 2,712
Locking Mechanisms Mfr & Distr
N.A.I.C.S.: 332510

Unit (Domestic):

Schlage Electronic Security **(3)**
11819 N Pennsylvania St, Carmel, IN
46032-4555
Tel.: (860) 584-9158
Web Site: http://www.ingersollrand.com
Sales Range: $100-124.9 Million
Emp.: 140
Electronic Security Systems
N.A.I.C.S.: 561621

Branch (Domestic):

Schlage Lock Co. **(3)**
3899 Hancock Expy, Colorado Springs, CO
80911
Tel.: (719) 390-5071
Web Site: http://www.schlage.com
Sales Range: $300-349.9 Million
Emp.: 800
Mfr of Locks or Lock Sets
N.A.I.C.S.: 561622

Subsidiary (Domestic):

Zero International, Inc. **(3)**
415 Concord Ave, Bronx, NY 10455
Tel.: (718) 585-3230
Web Site: http://www.zerointernational.com
Sales Range: $1-9.9 Million
Emp.: 50
Mfr of Sealing Systems for Doors & Win-
dows
N.A.I.C.S.: 339991

Subsidiary (Domestic):

Von Duprin LLC **(2)**
2720 Tobey Dr, Indianapolis, IN 46219
Tel.: (317) 429-2000
Web Site: http://www.vonduprin.com
Sales Range: $25-49.9 Million
Emp.: 35
Supplier For Builders Hardware
N.A.I.C.S.: 332510

**Allegion plc - Europe, Middle East,
India & Africa Main Office** **(1)**
Via Oberdan 42, 48018, Faenza, RA, Italy
Tel.: (39) 0546677111
Regional Managing Office; Locking Mecha-
nisms Mfr & Distr
N.A.I.C.S.: 551114
Lucia Veiga Moretti *(Reg Pres-Europe,
Middle East, India & Africa)*

Subsidiary (Non-US):

Allegion (UK) Limited **(1)**
35 Rocky Lane, Aston, Birmingham, B6
5RQ, West Midlands, United Kingdom

Tel.: (44) 1213802401
Web Site: https://www.allegion.co.uk
Emp.: 75
Locking Mechanisms Mfr & Distr
N.A.I.C.S.: 332510

Allegion A/S **(2)**
Mirabellevej 3, Randers, 8930, Denmark
Tel.: (45) 86 42 75 22
Web Site: http://www.randi.dk
Locking Mechanisms Mfr & Distr
N.A.I.C.S.: 332510
Torben Jensen *(Mng Dir)*

Allegion B.V. **(2)**
Energiestaat 2, 3900 AA, Veenendaal,
Netherlands
Tel.: (31) 347325858
Emp.: 20
Locking Mechanisms Mfr & Distr
N.A.I.C.S.: 332510
Daniel Naegels *(Mgr-Sls)*

**Allegion Emniyet ve Guvenlik Sistem-
leri Sanayi A.S.** **(2)**
Kayisdagi Cad Karaman Ciftlik Yolu No 47
Kar Plaza Kat 12, Atasehir, 34752, Istanbul,
Turkiye
Tel.: (90) 216 5726351
Web Site: http://www.itokilit.com.tr
Emp.: 15
Locking Mechanisms Mfr & Distr
N.A.I.C.S.: 332510

Allegion NV **(2)**
Pontbeekstraat 2, 1702, Groot-Bijgaarden,
Belgium
Tel.: (32) 2 5830999
Web Site:
   http://www.interflex.ingersollrand.com
Locking Mechanisms Mfr & Distr
N.A.I.C.S.: 332510
Kirk S. Hachigian *(Chm)*

SimonsVoss Technologies AG **(2)**
Feringastrasse 4, 85774, Unterfohring, Ger-
many
Tel.: (49) 89992280
Web Site: http://www.simons-voss.com
Emp.: 300
Digital Locking & Access Control Systems
Mfr
N.A.I.C.S.: 334419
Bernhard Sommer *(Chm & CEO)*

**Fire and Security Hardware Pty
Limited** **(1)**
Unit 24/30-32 Perry st, Matraville, 2036,
NSW, Australia
Tel.: (61) 800098094
Web Site: https://www.fshlocking.com.au
Security & Safety Product Mfr
N.A.I.C.S.: 334290

Isonas, Inc. **(1)**
4750 Walnut St Ste 110, Boulder, CO,
80301
Tel.: (303) 567-6516
Web Site: http://www.isonas.com
All Other Miscellaneous Electrical Equip-
ment & Component Mfr
N.A.I.C.S.: 335999
Tom Gambon *(Gen Mgr)*

**Normbau Beschlage und Ausstat-
tungs GmbH** **(1)**
Schwarzwaldstrasse 15, 77871, Renchen,
Germany
Tel.: (49) 78437040
Web Site: https://www.normbau.de
Architechtural Hardware Mfr
N.A.I.C.S.: 332510

Randi A/S **(1)**
Mirabellevej 3, 8930, Randers, Denmark
Tel.: (45) 86427522
Web Site: https://www.randi.dk
Architechtural Hardware Mfr
N.A.I.C.S.: 332510

**Republic Doors and Frames,
LLC** **(1)**
155 Republic Dr, McKenzie, TN 38201
Tel.: (731) 352-3383
Web Site: https://www.republicdoor.com
Steel Door & Frame Mfr
N.A.I.C.S.: 332321

**SimonsVoss Security Technologies
(Asia) Pte. Ltd.** **(1)**

178 Paya Lebar Rd 04-10 Paya Lebar 178,
Singapore, 409030, Singapore
Tel.: (65) 62277318
Web Site: http://www.simonsvossasia.com
Security Control System Mfr & Distr
N.A.I.C.S.: 334290
Jason Paul Kurek *(Mng Dir)*

SimonsVoss Technologies AB **(1)**
Ostermalmstorg 1, Stockholm, 114 42, Swe-
den
Tel.: (46) 850256663
Digital Locking System Distr
N.A.I.C.S.: 423610

SimonsVoss Technologies BV **(1)**
The Base B Evert van de Beekstraat 1-104,
1118 CL, Schiphol, Netherlands
Tel.: (31) 206541882
Access Control System Mfr & Distr
N.A.I.C.S.: 334290
Harry Dansberg *(Mgr-Acct)*

SimonsVoss Technologies FZE **(1)**
PO Box 184220, Dubai, United Arab Emir-
ates
Tel.: (971) 48815835
Digital Locking System Distr
N.A.I.C.S.: 423610

SimonsVoss Technologies GmbH **(1)**
Feringastrasse 4, 85774, Unterfohring, Ger-
many
Tel.: (49) 89992280
Web Site: https://www.simons-voss.com
Digital Locking System Mfr
N.A.I.C.S.: 332510
Bernhard Sommer *(Chm)*

**SimonsVoss Technologies
Limited** **(1)**
Empingham House Office 5 Uppingham
Gateway, Uppingham, LE15 9NY, United
Kingdom
Tel.: (44) 1132515036
Digital Locking System Distr
N.A.I.C.S.: 423610

SimonsVoss Technologies SAS **(1)**
Immeuble Les Portes de Paris 1/3 Rue du
Rempart, 93160, Noisy-le-Grand, France
Tel.: (33) 148151480
Security Control System Mfr & Distr
N.A.I.C.S.: 334290
William Priou *(Mgr-Admin & Fin)*

**Stanley Access Technologies,
LLC** **(1)**
600 Myrtle St, New Britain, CT 06053
Tel.: (860) 677-2861
Web Site:
   http://www.stanleyaccesstechnologies.com
Sales Range: $150-199.9 Million
Automatic Door Operating Equipment Distr
N.A.I.C.S.: 423310
Jeremy Morton *(Pres)*

TGP Canada Enterprises, ULC **(1)**
8699 Escarpment Way Unit 5, Milton, L9T
0J5, ON, Canada
Tel.: (800) 426-0279
Construction Glass Distr
N.A.I.C.S.: 423390

Technical Glass Products DMCC **(1)**
Reef Tower 29th Floor, PO Box 5003317,
Dubai, United Arab Emirates
Tel.: (971) 44487579
Web Site: https://www.fireglass.com
Construction Glass Distr
N.A.I.C.S.: 423390
Karam Hamadeh *(Mgr-Middle East Terri-
tory)*

Technical Glass Products, Inc. **(1)**
881 Callendar Blvd, Painesville, OH 44077
Tel.: (440) 639-6399
Web Site: https://www.technicalglass.com
Flat Glass Mfr
N.A.I.C.S.: 327211

Trelock Asia Pacific Limited **(1)**
36/F Times Sq Twr 2, Causeway Bay,
China (Hong Kong)
Tel.: (852) 25170231
Bicycle Lock Distr
N.A.I.C.S.: 423710

Trelock GmbH **(1)**
Johann-Krane-Weg 37, 48149, Munster,
Germany

Allegion Public Limited Company—(Continued)

Tel.: (49) 251919990
Web Site: https://www.trelock.de
Bicycle Lock Mfr
N.A.I.C.S.: 336991

Zero Seal Systems Limited (1)
Units 43 - 45 Ladford Covert, Seighford,
Stafford, ST18 9QG, United Kingdom
Tel.: (44) 1785282910
Web Site: https://www.zeroplus.co.uk
Architectural Hardware Mfr & Distr
N.A.I.C.S.: 321911

ALLEGRA ORTHOPAEDICS LTD.
Level 8 18-20 Orion Road, Lane
Cove, 2066, NSW, Australia
Tel.: (61) 291199200
Web Site:
　　https://www.allegraorthopaedic.com
AMT—(ASX)
Rev.: $461,595
Assets: $1,944,874
Liabilities: $2,945,661
Net Worth: ($1,000,786)
Earnings: ($1,392,821)
Fiscal Year-end: 06/30/23
Medical Devices & Surgical Tools Mfr
N.A.I.C.S.: 339112
Jenny Swain *(CEO)*

ALLEGRO FUNDS PTY. LTD.
Level 1 Plaza Building 95 Pitt Street,
Sydney, 2000, NSW, Australia
Tel.: (61) 282288700　　　　AU
Web Site:
　　http://www.allegrofunds.com.au
Year Founded: 2004
Private Equity Services
N.A.I.C.S.: 523999
Chester Moynihan *(Co-Founder & Partner)*

Subsidiaries:

Custom Bus Australia Pty. Ltd. (1)
44 Biloela Street, Villawood, 2163, NSW,
Australia
Tel.: (61) 2 9914 3800
Web Site:
　　http://www.customcoaches.com.au
Sales Range: $10-24.9 Million
Emp.: 120
Bus Designer & Mfr
N.A.I.C.S.: 336211
Mark Burgess *(CEO)*

Pizza Pan Group Pty. Ltd. (1)
61 Epping Road, Sydney, 2113, NSW, Aus-
tralia
Tel.: (61) 1300 749 924
Web Site: http://www.pizzahut.com.au
Pizzeria Franchisor
N.A.I.C.S.: 533110
Peter Rodwell *(Chm)*

Slater & Gordon Limited (1)
Level 12 485 La Trobe Street, Melbourne,
3000, VIC, Australia
Tel.: (61) 396026888
Web Site: http://www.slatergordon.com.au
Rev.: $155,875,992
Assets: $320,727,134
Liabilities: $182,464,318
Net Worth: $138,262,816
Earnings: $11,086,769
Emp.: 800
Fiscal Year-end: 06/30/2021
Law firm
N.A.I.C.S.: 541110
John Somerville *(CEO)*

Subsidiary (Non-US):

Slater & Gordon (UK) LLP (2)
50-52 Chancery Lane, London, WC2A 1HL,
United Kingdom　　　　　　　(100%)
Tel.: (44) 20 7657 1555
Web Site: http://www.slatergordon.co.uk
Emp.: 166
Law firm
N.A.I.C.S.: 541110
Alison Jackson-Carter *(Head-Media & Comm)*

Subsidiary (Domestic):

**Slater Gordon Solutions Legal
Limited** (3)
Dempster Building Brunswick Business
Park, Atlantic Way, Liverpool, Merseyside,
United Kingdom
Tel.: (44) 151 236 9594
Web Site:
　　http://www.slatergordonsolutionslegal.com
Personal Injury Legal Claims Services
N.A.I.C.S.: 922130

Subsidiary (Non-US):

Trilby Misso Lawyers Limited (2)
　　　　　　　　　　　　　　(100%)
Tel.: (61) 130 073 1582
Web Site: https://trilbymissolawyers.com.au
Sales Range: $25-49.9 Million
Emp.: 175
Law firm
N.A.I.C.S.: 541110

ALLEGRO WIRELESS CANADA INC.
2350 Matheson Blvd E, Mississauga,
L4W 5G9, ON, Canada
Tel.: (905) 624-2924
Web Site:
　　http://www.allegrowireless.com
Sales Range: $10-24.9 Million
Mobile Information Solutions
N.A.I.C.S.: 541512
Savino Griesi *(Co-Founder & CEO)*

ALLEN OVERY SHEARMAN STERLING LLP
One Bishops Square, London, E1
6AD, United Kingdom
Tel.: (44) 2030880000
Web Site:
　　https://www.aoshearman.com
Year Founded: 1930
Emp.: 1,942
Law firm
N.A.I.C.S.: 541110
Adam S. Hakki *(Co-Chm & Partner)*

Subsidiaries:

Shearman & Sterling LLP (1)
599 Lexington Ave, New York, NY 10022
Tel.: (212) 848-4000
Web Site: http://www.shearman.com
Sales Range: $750-799.9 Million
Emp.: 1,001
Legal Advisory Services
N.A.I.C.S.: 541110
Stuart J. Baskin *(Partner)*

ALLER HOLDING A/S
Havneholmen 33, 1561, Copenha-
gen, Denmark
Tel.: (45) 72342900
Web Site: http://www.allerholding.dk
Year Founded: 1873
Sales Range: $100-124.9 Million
Emp.: 400
Holding Company
N.A.I.C.S.: 551112
Bettina Aller *(Co-CEO)*

Subsidiaries:

Aller Media AB (1)
Landskronavagen 23, 251 85, Helsingborg,
Sweden
Tel.: (46) 424443000
Web Site: http://www.aller.se
Magazine Advertising Services
N.A.I.C.S.: 541810
Karin Sodersten *(Acct Mgr)*

Aller Media AS (1)
PO Box 1169, 107, Oslo, Sentrum, Norway
Tel.: (47) 21301100
Web Site: http://www.aller.no
Holding Company
N.A.I.C.S.: 551112
Roger Hansen *(Mng Dir)*

Subsidiary (Domestic):

Allers Familie-Journal A/S (2)
PO Box 1169, Oslo, 107, Norway (100%)
Tel.: (47) 21301000
Web Site: http://www.aller.no
Sales Range: $50-74.9 Million
Emp.: 180
Weekly Magazine Publisher
N.A.I.C.S.: 513120
Roger Hansen Henne *(Dir-Admin)*

Scandinavia Online AS (2)
PO Box 858 Sentrum, N 0104, Oslo,
Norway　　　　　　　　　　(100%)
Tel.: (47) 21508000
Web Site: http://www.sol.no
News Website
N.A.I.C.S.: 517810

Aller Media Oy (1)
Pursimiehenkatu 29-31 A, 00150, Helsinki,
Finland
Tel.: (358) 986217000
Web Site: http://www.aller.fi
Magazine Advertising Services
N.A.I.C.S.: 541810
Pauli Aalto-Setala *(CEO)*

Aller Tryk A/S (1)
Helgeshoj Alle 36, 2630, Taastrup, Denmark
Tel.: (45) 43505400
Web Site: http://www.allertryk.dk
Publishing & Printing Services
N.A.I.C.S.: 513130

ALLER-RETOUR
2550 Daniel Johnson Blvd suite 600,
Laval, H7T 2L1, QC, Canada
Tel.: (450) 682-1888
Web Site: http://www.aller-retour.com
Rev.: $20,000,000
Emp.: 25
Travel Agencies
N.A.I.C.S.: 561510
Luc Imbeault *(Mgr-Admin)*

ALLERTHAL-WERKE AG
Friesenstrasse 50, 50670, Cologne,
Germany
Tel.: (49) 221820320　　　　De
Web Site: https://www.allerthal.de
ATW—(BER)
Asset Management Services
N.A.I.C.S.: 523940
Alfred Schneider *(CEO)*

ALLFUNDS GROUP PLC
2 Fitzroy Place 8 Mortimer Street,
London, W1T 3JJ, United Kingdom
Tel.: (44) 2077585008　　　　UK
Web Site: https://www.allfunds.com
Year Founded: 2000
ALLFG—(EUR)
Rev.: $3,002,169,221
Assets: $6,011,464,494
Liabilities: $3,474,329,808
Net Worth: $2,537,134,686
Earnings: $92,495,144
Emp.: 1,031
Fiscal Year-end: 12/31/23
Asset Management Services
N.A.I.C.S.: 523999
Juan Alcaraz *(CEO)*

ALLGEIER SE
Einsteinstrasse 172, D-81677, Mu-
nich, Germany
Tel.: (49) 899984210　　　　De
Web Site: https://www.allgeier.com
AEIN—(MUN)
Rev.: $539,593,733
Assets: $579,266,821
Liabilities: $426,292,517
Net Worth: $152,974,305
Earnings: $14,438,620
Emp.: 3,531
Fiscal Year-end: 12/31/23
Holding Company; Information Tech-
nology Consulting & Support Services
N.A.I.C.S.: 551112

Carl Georg Durschmidt *(Chm-Exec Bd)*

Subsidiaries:

Allgeier (Schweiz) AG (1)
Seestrasse 97, 8800, Thalwil, Switzerland
Tel.: (41) 44 722 75 55
Web Site: http://www.allgeier.ch
Information Technology Management Ser-
vices
N.A.I.C.S.: 541512

Allgeier Core GmbH (1)
Westerbachstrasse 32, Kronberg im Tau-
nus, 61476, Darmstadt, Germany
Tel.: (49) 78120358800
Web Site: http://www.allgeier-core.com
Software Development Services
N.A.I.C.S.: 541511
Heike Bauer *(Mgr-HR)*

Allgeier CyRis GmbH (1)
Hans-Bredow-Str 60, 28307, Bremen, Ger-
many
Tel.: (49) 42143841875
Web Site: https://www.allgeier-cyris.com
Information Technology Services
N.A.I.C.S.: 541519

Allgeier DMS Solutions (1)
Leuvensesteenweg 633C B, 1930,
Zaventem, Belgium
Tel.: (32) 2 709 01 00
Web Site: http://www.allgeier-dms.net
Information Technology Management Ser-
vices
N.A.I.C.S.: 541512

Allgeier Education GmbH (1)
Kaiserswerther Str 229, 40474, Dusseldorf,
Germany
Tel.: (49) 21154556354
Web Site: http://www.allgeier-education.com
Digital Training Services
N.A.I.C.S.: 611430

Allgeier Engineering GmbH (1)
Wilhelm-Wagenfeld-Strasse 28, 80807, Mu-
nich, Germany
Tel.: (49) 89124148748
Web Site: https://www.allgeier-
engineering.com
Emp.: 200
Automotive Products Mfr
N.A.I.C.S.: 336110
Rebekka Bing *(Mgr-HR)*

Allgeier Enterprise Services SE (1)
Bauhausplatz 4, 80807, Munich, Germany
Tel.: (49) 89356200
Information Technology Services
N.A.I.C.S.: 541519

Allgeier Experts GmbH (1)
Bauhausplatz 4, 80807, Munich, Germany
Tel.: (49) 89919292030
Web Site: https://www.aex-experts.com
Staffing & Recruiting Services
N.A.I.C.S.: 561311

Allgeier Experts Go GmbH (1)
Gustav-Stresemann-Ring 12-16, 65189,
Wiesbaden, Germany
Tel.: (49) 61144560
Information Technology Services
N.A.I.C.S.: 541519

Allgeier Experts Holding GmbH (1)
Bauhausplatz 4, 80807, Munich, Germany
Tel.: (49) 89919292030
Web Site: https://www.aex-experts.com
Information Technology Services
N.A.I.C.S.: 541519

Allgeier Experts Pro GmbH (1)
Bauhausplatz 4, 80807, Munich, Germany
Tel.: (49) 89356200
Information Technology Services
N.A.I.C.S.: 541519
Andreas Gmeinwieser *(Mgr-Recruiting Temp IT)*

Allgeier Experts SE (1)
Gustav-Stresemann-Ring 12-16, 65189,
Wiesbaden, Germany
Tel.: (49) 61144560
Web Site: http://www.allgeier-experts.com
Human Resource Consulting Services
N.A.I.C.S.: 541612

Allgeier GRC GmbH (1)
Schauenburger Strasse 116, 24118, Kiel, Germany
Tel.: (49) 43153033990
Web Site: https://allgeier-grc.de
Information Technology Services
N.A.I.C.S.: 541511

Allgeier IT Services GmbH (1)
Bauhausplatz 4, 80807, Munich, Germany
Tel.: (49) 4488528080
Web Site: https://www.allgeier-its.com
Information Technology Services
N.A.I.C.S.: 541519

Allgeier IT Solutions AG (1)
Wehrlestr 12, 81679, Munich, Bogen-hausen, Germany
Tel.: (49) 9984210
Web Site: http://www.allgeier.com
Emp.: 10
Information Technology Consulting Services
N.A.I.C.S.: 541512
Carl Duersdhmidt (Mng Dir)

Allgeier IT Solutions GmbH (1)
Hans-Bredow-Strasse 60, 28307, Bremen, Germany
Tel.: (49) 421 43841 0
Web Site: http://www.allgeier-it.de
Emp.: 120
Information Technology Management Services
N.A.I.C.S.: 541512
Hans Moggert (Acct Mgr-Technical)

Allgeier Inovar GmbH (1)
Hans-Bredow-Str 60, D-28307, Bremen, Germany
Tel.: (49) 421438410
Web Site: https://www.allgeier-inovar.de
Information Technology Services
N.A.I.C.S.: 541519

Allgeier Ltd. (1)
Sotiri Tsangari Street 4, CY-1095, Nicosia, Cyprus
Tel.: (357) 22119476
Emp.: 10
Information Technology Consulting Services
N.A.I.C.S.: 541512
Stephane Horta (CEO)

Allgeier Public SE (1)
Bauhausplatz 4, 80807, Munich, Germany
Tel.: (49) 61144560
Web Site: https://www.allgeier-public.eu
Emp.: 3,300
Information Technology Services
N.A.I.C.S.: 541519

Allgeier S.A. (1)
Rue de l Industrie 20, 8399, Windhof, Luxembourg
Tel.: (352) 27 39 32 1
Information Technology Management Services
N.A.I.C.S.: 541512

Allgeier secion GmbH (1)
Paul-Dessau-Strasse 8, 22761, Hamburg, Germany
Tel.: (49) 403890710
Web Site: https://www.secion.de
Information Technology Security Services
N.A.I.C.S.: 561311

Bsh It Solutions GmbH (1)
Hans-Bredow-Str 60, 28307, Bremen, Germany
Tel.: (49) 4488528080
Web Site: http://www.allgeier-bsh.com
Information Technology Services
N.A.I.C.S.: 541519
Marc Oleschkewitz (Co-CEO)

CUBE Management GmbH (1)
Max-von-Eyth-Strasse 3, 85737, Ismaning, Germany
Tel.: (49) 9401 93 18 0
Web Site: http://www.cube-mm.de
Information Technology Consulting Services
N.A.I.C.S.: 541512

Cloudical Deutschland GmbH (1)
Edisonstr 63, 12459, Berlin, Germany
Tel.: (49) 30959996450
Web Site: https://cloudical.io
Cloud Data Migration Services
N.A.I.C.S.: 541511

Evora IT Solutions GmbH (1)
Altrottstr 31, 69190, Walldorf, Germany
Tel.: (49) 15117126873
Information Technology Services
N.A.I.C.S.: 541511

Evora IT Solutions Group GmbH (1)
Altrottstr 31, 69190, Walldorf, Germany
Tel.: (49) 15154417835
Information Technology Services
N.A.I.C.S.: 541511

Evora IT Solutions Pvt. Ltd. (1)
4th and 5th Floor No 29 HAL Old Airport Road, Kodihalli Murugeshpalya, Bengaluru, 560-017, India
Tel.: (91) 9880980199
Information Technology Services
N.A.I.C.S.: 541511

It-novum Schweiz GmbH (1)
Seestrasse 97, 8800, Thalwil, Switzerland
Tel.: (41) 447227555
Information Technology Consulting Services
N.A.I.C.S.: 518210

Mgm Security Partners GmbH (1)
Taunusstr 23, 80807, Munich, Germany
Tel.: (49) 89358680880
Web Site: https://www.mgm-sp.com
Software Development Services
N.A.I.C.S.: 541511
Thomas Schreiber (Founder & Mng Dir)

Mgm Technology Partners Eurl (1)
26 Allee Aloyzi Kospicki, 38000, Grenoble, France
Tel.: (33) 456600087
Software Development Services
N.A.I.C.S.: 541511

Mgm Technology Partners Portugal, Unipessoal Lda. (1)
Avenida dos Aliados 168 3rd floor, 4000-065, Porto, Portugal
Tel.: (351) 911990558
Information Technology Services
N.A.I.C.S.: 541519

Mgm Technology Partners Schweiz AG (1)
General-Guisan-Strasse 6, 6303, Zug, Switzerland
Tel.: (41) 89358680855
Software Development Services
N.A.I.C.S.: 541511

Mgm Technology Partners USA Corp. (1)
200 Daingerfield Rd Ste 301, Alexandria, VA 22314
Tel.: (571) 529-5252
Software Development Services
N.A.I.C.S.: 541511

Mgm Technology Partners Vietnam Co., Ltd. (1)
7 Phan Chau Trinh, Hai Chau District, Da Nang, Vietnam
Tel.: (84) 2363531773
Software Development Services
N.A.I.C.S.: 541511

MySign AG (1)
Agency & Software House Neuhardstrasse 38, 4600, Olten, Switzerland
Tel.: (41) 628368010
Web Site: https://www.mysign.ch
Online Marketing Services
N.A.I.C.S.: 561320

Nagarro AS (1)
Kongens Gate 14, 0153, Oslo, Norway
Tel.: (47) 40001766
Software Development Services
N.A.I.C.S.: 541511

Nagarro GmbH (1)
Am Europlatz 2, 1120, Vienna, Austria
Tel.: (43) 140958900
Software Development Services
N.A.I.C.S.: 541511

Nagarro Inc. (1)
1737 N 1st St Ste 590, San Jose, CA 95112
Tel.: (408) 436-6170
Software Development Services
N.A.I.C.S.: 541511

Subsidiary (Non-US):

Nagarro Software GmbH (2)

Westerbachstrasse 32, Kronberg, 61476, Frankfurt am Main, Germany
Tel.: (49) 69274015880
Web Site: http://www.nagarro.com
Emp.: 4
Software Development Services
N.A.I.C.S.: 541511
Balkrishna Dubey (Mng Dir)

Nagarro Software S.A. (2)
Torres IOS Campestre Av Ricardo Margain 575 Parque Corporativo, 66267, Garza Garcia, Mexico
Tel.: (52) 81 1253 7200
Software Development Services
N.A.I.C.S.: 541511

Nagarro K.K. (1)
1st Floor Office Vera Nihonbashi hakozaki 27-9 Nihonbashi Hakozaki-cho, Chuo-Ku, Tokyo, 103-0015, Japan
Tel.: (81) 368617699
Software Development Services
N.A.I.C.S.: 541511

Nagarro Pty. Ltd. (1)
Level 12 One Pacific Highway, North Sydney, 2060, NSW, Australia
Tel.: (61) 407821342
Software Development Services
N.A.I.C.S.: 541511

Nagarro Sdn. Bhd. (1)
Unit 37-2 Level 37 Q Sentral No 2A Jalan Stesen 2, Kuala Lumpur Sentral, 50470, Kuala Lumpur, Malaysia
Tel.: (60) 322988417
Software Development Services
N.A.I.C.S.: 541511

Nagarro Software A/S (1)
Sondre Ringvej 55, 2605, Brondby, Denmark
Tel.: (45) 42206488
Software Development Services
N.A.I.C.S.: 541511

Nagarro Software Ab (1)
Jan Stenbecks Torg 17, 164 40, Kista, Sweden
Tel.: (46) 87513548
Software Development Services
N.A.I.C.S.: 541511

Nagarro Software Pvt. Ltd. (1)
13 Subedar Major Laxmi Chand Road Udyog Vihar Sector 18, Gurgaon, 122015, India
Tel.: (91) 1244221111
Software Development Services
N.A.I.C.S.: 541511

Nagarro Software SAS (1)
19 Boulevard Malesherbes, 75008, Paris, France
Tel.: (33) 155273544
Software Development Services
N.A.I.C.S.: 541511

Nagarro Software Srl (1)
Coriolan Brediceanu Street 10 Building D, Timisoara, Romania
Tel.: (40) 256699000
Software Development Services
N.A.I.C.S.: 541511

Objectiva Software Solutions (Beijing) Co., Ltd. (1)
Room 401 Bailian Plaza No 17 Jianhua Road S Jianwai Street, Chaoyang District, Beijing, 100022, China
Tel.: (86) 1065666918
Software Development Services
N.A.I.C.S.: 541511

Objectiva Software Solutions (Xi'An) Co., Ltd. (1)
F3 G1 Building GLP I-Park No 211 Tiangu 8th Road High-tech Zone, Xi'an, 710077, China
Tel.: (86) 2968913000
Software Development Services
N.A.I.C.S.: 541511
Gary Yuan (Head-ODC & Dir-Delivery)

Objectiva Software Solutions, Inc. (1)
12770 El Camino Real Ste 300, San Diego, CA 92130
Tel.: (858) 809-5950
Web Site: http://www.objectivasoftware.com

Software Outsourcing Services
N.A.I.C.S.: 541511
Nasser Barghouti (CEO)

Subsidiary (Non-US):

Objectiva China (2)
Room 401 Bailian Plaza No 17 Jianhua Road S Jianwai Street, Chaoyang District, Beijing, 100022, China
Tel.: (86) 1065666918
Web Site: http://www.objectivasoftware.com
Software Publishing & Development
N.A.I.C.S.: 513210
Yiping Tan (COO)

Oxygen Consultancy (1)
Esentepe Mah Kore Sehitleri Cad Cesur Apartmani No 30/4, Sisli, Istanbul, Turkiye
Tel.: (90) 2122758757
Web Site: http://www.oxygen-tr.com
Consulting Services
N.A.I.C.S.: 541611
Zeynep Dogrul Asar (Gen Mgr)

Pooliestudios GmbH (1)
Rolandstrasse 83, 50677, Cologne, Germany
Tel.: (49) 22163061113
Web Site: https://www.pooliestudios.com
Management Consulting Services
N.A.I.C.S.: 541611

SOFTCON AG (1)
Aidenbachstr 42, 81379, Munich, Germany
Tel.: (49) 897850000
Web Site: http://www.softcon.de
Information Technology Consulting Services
N.A.I.C.S.: 541512
Alexandra Schmack (Co-Mng Dir)

Subsidiary (Non-US):

SOFTCON IT Service S.r.l. (2)
P-ta Consiliul Europei Nr 1 Et 7, Timisoara, 300627, Romania
Tel.: (40) 25 643 0286
Web Site: http://www.nagarro.com
Emp.: 33
Software Development Services
N.A.I.C.S.: 541511
Marconi Alin (Mgr)

Secion GmbH (1)
Paul-Dessau-Strasse 8, 22761, Hamburg, Germany
Tel.: (49) 403890710
Web Site: http://www.secion.de
Network Security Services
N.A.I.C.S.: 561621

Solutions 4 Mobility LLC (1)
412 Al Yasmeen Building Near Abu Hail Metro Station Salahuddin Street, PO Box 21300, Deira, Dubai, United Arab Emirates
Tel.: (971) 42627300
Web Site: http://www.s4m.ae
Software Development Services
N.A.I.C.S.: 541511
Bachar Kassar (Mng Dir)

TOPjects GmbH (1)
Stefan George Ring 6, 81929, Munich, Germany
Tel.: (49) 89 993910 0
Web Site: http://www.topjects.de
Information Technology Management Services
N.A.I.C.S.: 541512
Lothar Reeg (Mgr-Recruiting)

Subsidiary (Domestic):

SKYTEC AG (2)
Feringastrasse 12b, Unterfohring, 85774, Germany
Tel.: (49) 89 744 927 625
Web Site: http://www.skytecag.de
Information Technology Consulting Services
N.A.I.C.S.: 541512
Paula Lavinia Kroner (Mgr-Res & Dev)

Terna GmbH (1)
Grabenweg 3a, 6020, Innsbruck, Austria (100%)
Tel.: (43) 512 362060 0
Web Site: http://www.terna.com
Sales Range: Less than $1 Million
Emp.: 860
Business Software Publisher
N.A.I.C.S.: 513210

Allgeier SE—(Continued)

Christian Kranebitter *(Member-Mgmt Bd)*

U.N.P. - Software GmbH (1)
Grabenstrasse 17, 40213, Dusseldorf, Germany
Tel.: (49) 2118289850
Web Site: https://www.unp.de
Emp.: 70
Information Technology Consulting Services
N.A.I.C.S.: 541512

U.N.P.-Hrsolutions GmbH (1)
Grabenstrasse 17, 40213, Dusseldorf, Germany
Tel.: (49) 2118289850
Software Development Services
N.A.I.C.S.: 541511

VJii Productions AG (1)
Rosengasse 43, 4600, Olten, Switzerland
Tel.: (41) 625111170
Web Site: https://www.vjii.ch
Video Production Services
N.A.I.C.S.: 512110

b+m Informatik AG (1)
Rotenhofer Weg 20, 24109, Melsdorf, Germany
Tel.: (49) 4340 404 0
Web Site: http://www.bminformatik.de
Software Development Services
N.A.I.C.S.: 541511

iQuest GmbH & Co KG (1)
Wilhelm-Leuschner Strasse 72, D-60329, Frankfurt am Main, Germany
Tel.: (49) 69 90020760
Web Site: http://www.iquestint.com
Sales Range: $75-99.9 Million
Emp.: 400
Software Publisher
N.A.I.C.S.: 513210
Cornelius Brody *(CEO)*

Subsidiary (Non-US):

iQuest Schweiz AG (2)
Luegislandstrasse 105, 8051, Zurich, Switzerland
Tel.: (41) 444556939
Software Development Services
N.A.I.C.S.: 541511

iQuest Technologies Kft (2)
Vorosmarty u 28/c II 5, 1201, Budapest, Hungary
Tel.: (36) 12878252
Software Development Services
N.A.I.C.S.: 541511

iQuest Technologies SRL (2)
6-8 Motilor Street, 400001, Cluj-Napoca, Romania
Tel.: (40) 372343400
Software Development Services
N.A.I.C.S.: 541511

it-novum GmbH (1)
Office Park 1 Top B02, 1300, Vienna, Austria
Tel.: (43) 122787139
Web Site: http://www.it-novum.com
Information Technology Consulting Services
N.A.I.C.S.: 541519
Peter Lipp *(Mgr-Sls)*

mgm integration partners GmbH (1)
Ludwig-Erhard-Strasse 31, 84034, Landshut, Germany
Tel.: (49) 8761725320
Web Site: https://mgm-ip.de
Information Technology Services
N.A.I.C.S.: 541511

mgm technology partners GmbH (1)
Taunusstr 23, 80807, Munich, Germany
Tel.: (49) 893586800
Web Site: https://www.mgm-tp.com
Software Development Services
N.A.I.C.S.: 541511
Hamarz Mehmanesh *(CEO & Mng Dir)*

Subsidiary (Domestic):

SF Software & Friends GmbH (2)
Neumarkt 2, Leipzig, 04109, Germany
Tel.: (49) 341 21586 0
Software Development Services
N.A.I.C.S.: 541511

Subsidiary (Non-US):

mgm technology partners s.r.o. (2)
Letenske namesti 4/157, 170 00, Prague, Czech Republic
Tel.: (420) 239005107
Software Development Services
N.A.I.C.S.: 541511

publicplan GmbH (1)
Kennedydamm 24, 40476, Dusseldorf, Germany
Tel.: (49) 21163550180
Web Site: https://www.publicplan.de
Software Development Services
N.A.I.C.S.: 541511

ALLGENS MEDICAL TECHNOLOGY CO., LTD.
A305 Floor 3 No 5 Development Road, Haidian, Beijing, 102609, China
Tel.: (86) 1056330935
Web Site: https://www.allgensmed.cn
Year Founded: 2004
688613—(SHG)
Rev.: $34,440,836
Assets: $204,873,969
Liabilities: $18,743,288
Net Worth: $186,130,681
Earnings: $13,368,509
Fiscal Year-end: 12/31/22
Medical Product Mfr & Distr
N.A.I.C.S.: 339112
Eric Gang Hu *(Chm)*

ALLGREEN PROPERTIES LTD.
1 Kim Seng Promenade Ste 07-01 Great World City, Singapore, 237994, Singapore
Tel.: (65) 67332822
Web Site: http://www.allgreen.com.sg
Sales Range: $700-749.9 Million
Emp.: 100
Property Development & Investment, Hospitality, Project & Property Management Services
N.A.I.C.S.: 531390
Oon Kwong Kuok *(Chm)*

Subsidiaries:

Allgreen Properties (Tianjin) Pte. Ltd. (1)
1 Kim Seng Promenade 05-02 Great World City, Singapore, 237994, Singapore
Tel.: (65) 67332822
Web Site: http://www.allgreen.com.sg
Real Estate Asset Management Services
N.A.I.C.S.: 531390
Ong Wendy *(Mgr-Sls)*

Allgreen Properties (Vietnam) Pte. Ltd. (1)
1 Kim Seng Promenade 05-02, Singapore, 237994, Singapore
Tel.: (65) 67332822
Web Site: http://www.allgreen.com.sg
Property Development Services
N.A.I.C.S.: 531390

Arcadia Development Pte. Ltd. (1)
1 Kim Seng Promenade 05-02 Great World City, Singapore, 237994, Singapore
Tel.: (65) 67332822
Web Site: http://www.allgreen.com.sg
Residential Property Development Services
N.A.I.C.S.: 236115
Khor Thongmeng *(Gen Mgr)*

Cuscaden Properties Pte Ltd (1)
163 Tanglin Road, Singapore, 247933, Singapore (55.4%)
Tel.: (65) 67364922
Hotel & Motels
N.A.I.C.S.: 721110

Leo Property Management Private Limited (1)
Hex 05- 02 1 Kim Seng Promenade, Great World City, Singapore, 237994, Singapore (100%)
Tel.: (65) 67373822
Web Site: http://www.allgreen.com.sg

Sales Range: $25-49.9 Million
Other Real Estate Property Lessors
N.A.I.C.S.: 531190
Yong Oon Chen *(Dir-Sls)*

Midpoint Properties Limited (1)
Great World City 1 Kim Seng Promenade, No 05-02, 237994, Singapore, Singapore (100%)
Tel.: (65) 68397950
Web Site: http://www.GreatWorld.com.sg
Other Real Estate Property Lessors
N.A.I.C.S.: 531190

Tanglin Place Development Pte Ltd (1)
91 Tanglin Road 01-00 Tanglin Place, Singapore, 247918, Singapore
Tel.: (65) 67346386
Sales Range: $25-49.9 Million
Emp.: 22
Residential Property Development Services
N.A.I.C.S.: 236115
Evelyn Soh *(Sr Mgr)*

Worldwide Apartment Services Pte Ltd (1)
1 Kim Seng Promenade, Singapore, Singapore (100%)
Tel.: (65) 67332822
Web Site: http://www.allgreen.com.sg
Sales Range: $50-74.9 Million
Emp.: 60
Other Real Estate Property Lessors
N.A.I.C.S.: 531190

Wyndham Supplies Pte Ltd (1)
1 Kinseng Promenade C-02, Great World City, Singapore, 237994, Singapore (100%)
Tel.: (65) 67332822
Web Site: http://www.allgreen.com.sg
Lumber Plywood Millwork & Wood Panel Whslr
N.A.I.C.S.: 423310
Goh Soo Siah *(CEO)*

ALLGREENTECH INTERNATIONAL PLC
Tricor Suite 4th Floor 50 Mark Lane, London, EC3R 7QR, United Kingdom
Tel.: (44) 2032162000   UK
Web Site:
http://www.allgreentechplc.com
Sales Range: $50-74.9 Million
Emp.: 227
Investment Holding Company
N.A.I.C.S.: 523999
Navin S. Sidhu *(CEO)*

Subsidiaries:

Malaysian Mega Galvaniser Sdn. Bhd. (1)
5th Floor West Wing Quattro West, No 4 Lorong Persiaran Barat, 46200, Petaling Jaya, Selangor, Malaysia (50%)
Tel.: (60) 3 7957 1115
Web Site: http://www.megagalvanizer.com
Metals Galvanizing Services
N.A.I.C.S.: 423510

Violed International Pte. Ltd (1)
55 Ubi Avenue 1 04-01, Singapore, 408935, Singapore
Tel.: (65) 68421623
Financial Management Services
N.A.I.C.S.: 523999

ALLIANCE AIRLINES
81 Pandanus Avenue, PO Box 1126, Airport, Brisbane, 4009, QLD, Australia
Tel.: (61) 732121212
Web Site:
https://www.allianceairlines.com.au
AQZ—(ASX)
Rev.: $345,254,013
Assets: $520,579,793
Liabilities: $287,075,344
Net Worth: $233,504,449
Earnings: $24,342,031
Emp.: 1,082
Fiscal Year-end: 06/30/23
Oil Transportation Services

N.A.I.C.S.: 481111
Scott McMillan *(Mng Dir)*

Subsidiaries:

Jet Engine Leasing Pty Ltd (1)
Lot 12 Pandanus Avenue, Eagle Farm, 4009, QLD, Australia
Tel.: (61) 732121212
Sales Range: $50-74.9 Million
Emp.: 200
Passenger Air Transportation Services
N.A.I.C.S.: 481111

ALLIANCE DEVELOPPEMENT CAPITAL SIIC SE
avenue de l Astronomie 9, 1210, Saint-Josse-ten-Noode, Brussels, Belgium
Tel.: (32) 22294150   FR
Web Site: https://www.adcsiic.eu
Year Founded: 1923
ALDV—(EUR)
Sales Range: Less than $1 Million
Residential Real Estate Management Services
N.A.I.C.S.: 531311
Alain Dumenil *(Chm & CEO)*

ALLIANCE ENERGY LTD.
3230 Faithful Avenue, Saskatoon, S7K 8H3, SK, Canada
Tel.: (306) 242-5802   SK
Web Site: http://www.alliance-energy.com
Year Founded: 1983
Emp.: 200
Electrical Contracting & Maintenance Services
N.A.I.C.S.: 238210
Chad Waldner *(Co-CEO)*

Subsidiaries:

Alliance Energy Ltd. - Regina Office (1)
504 Henderson Drive, Regina, S4N 5X2, SK, Canada
Tel.: (306) 721-6484
Web Site: http://www.alliance-energy.com
Electrical Contracting & Maintenance Services
N.A.I.C.S.: 238210

ALLIANCE FINANCE COMPANY PLC
Tel.: (94) 115573600
Web Site:
https://www.alliancefinance.lk
ALLI—(COL)
Rev.: $41,693,341
Assets: $174,506,529
Liabilities: $150,653,140
Net Worth: $23,853,389
Earnings: $1,862,288
Emp.: 1,411
Fiscal Year-end: 03/31/23
Leasing & Financial Services
N.A.I.C.S.: 551112
Romani de Silva *(Deputy Chm & Mng Dir)*

ALLIANCE FINANCIAL GROUP BERHAD
3rd Floor Menara Multi-Purpose Capital Square, No 8 Jalan Munshi Abdullah, 50100, Kuala Lumpur, Malaysia
Tel.: (60) 0326043333   MY
Web Site: http://www.alliancefg.com
Sales Range: $450-499.9 Million
Commercial Financing Services
N.A.I.C.S.: 522110
Wei Yen Lee *(Sec)*

Subsidiaries:

Alliance Bank Malaysia Bhd (1)
Menara Multi Purpose Capital Square 8, Jalan Munshi Abdullah, Kuala Lumpur, 50100, Malaysia
Tel.: (60) 3 2694 8800

Web Site: http://www.alliancebank.com.my
Banking Services
N.A.I.C.S.: 523150

Subsidiary (Domestic):

Alliance Investment Bank Bhd **(2)**
Menara Multi-Purpose Capital Square 8,
Jalan Munshi Abdullah, Kuala Lumpur,
50100, Wilayah Persekutuan, Malaysia
Tel.: (60) 3 2692 7788
Web Site:
    http://www.allianceinvestmentbank.com
Banking Services
N.A.I.C.S.: 523150

Subsidiary (Domestic):

HwangDBS Vickers Research Sdn.
Bhd. **(3)**
Suite 26 03 26th Floor Menara Keck Seng,
203 Jalan Bukit Bintang, 55100, Kuala
Lumpur, Federal Territory, Malaysia
Tel.: (60) 327112222
Sales Range: $50-74.9 Million
Emp.: 15
Stock Analysis & Research Services
N.A.I.C.S.: 523210
Wong Ming Tek *(Mng Dir)*

ALLIANCE GLOBAL GROUP, INC.
7/F 1880 Eastwood Avenue East-
wood City CyberPark 188E Rodri-
guez Jr Ave, Bagumbayan, 1110,
Quezon City, 1110, Philippines
Tel.: (63) 287092038   **PH**
Web Site:
    https://www.allianceglobalinc.com
Year Founded: 1993
ALGGF—(OTCIQ)
Rev.: $3,697,028,661
Assets: $14,129,151,276
Liabilities: $7,005,065,193
Net Worth: $7,124,086,083
Earnings: $547,972,015
Emp.: 30,326
Fiscal Year-end: 12/31/23
Investment Holding Company; Real
Estate, Food & Beverage, Fast Food
Restaurants, Tourism & Gaming
N.A.I.C.S.: 551112
Andrew L. Tan *(Chm)*

Subsidiaries:

Emperador Inc. **(1)**
7/F 1880 Eastwood Avenue Eastwood City
CyberPark, Bagumbayan, Quezon City,
1110, Metro Manila, Philippines **(87.55%)**
Tel.: (63) 87092222
Web Site:
    https://www.emperadorbrandy.com
Rev.: $1,185,226,333
Assets: $2,685,008,886
Liabilities: $962,378,366
Net Worth: $1,722,630,521
Earnings: $161,485,549
Emp.: 3,013
Fiscal Year-end: 12/31/2023
Holding Company; Distilled Spirits Mfr &
Whslr
N.A.I.C.S.: 551112
Winston S. Co *(Pres & CEO)*

Subsidiary (Domestic):

Emperador Distillers, Inc **(2)**
7th Floor Bldg 1880 Eastwood Ave Cyber
Park, Rodriguez Jr Avenue Bagumbayan,
Quezon City, 1110, Philippines
Tel.: (63) 27092222
Sales Range: $150-199.9 Million
Emp.: 600
Brandy Mfr
N.A.I.C.S.: 312130

Subsidiary (Domestic):

The Bar Beverage, Inc **(3)**
7th Floor 1880 Building Eastwood Ave East-
wood City, Libis, Quezon City, 1110, Philip-
pines
Tel.: (63) 2 709 2222
Alcoholic Beverages Mfr
N.A.I.C.S.: 312140
Katherine Dan *(Gen Mgr)*

Subsidiary (Non-US):

Whyte & Mackay Group Limited **(2)**
Dalmore House 310 St Vincent Street,
Glasgow, G2 5RG, Scotland, United King-
dom
Tel.: (44) 141 248 5771
Web Site: http://www.whyteandmackay.com
Holding Company; Distilled Spirits Mfr &
Whslr
N.A.I.C.S.: 551112

Subsidiary (Domestic):

Whyte & Mackay Limited **(3)**
Dalmore House 310 St Vincent Street,
Glasgow, G2 5RG, Scotland, United King-
dom
Tel.: (44) 1412485771
Web Site: http://www.whyteandmackay.com
Sales Range: $300-349.9 Million
Distilled Spirits Mfr & Whslr
N.A.I.C.S.: 312140
Steven Pearson *(Mktg Dir-Global)*

First Oceanic Property Management,
Inc **(1)**
7/F Paseo Ctr 8757 Paseo De Roxas,
Makati, 1200, Philippines
Tel.: (63) 28300443
Web Site: http://www.firstoceanic.com.ph
Real Estate Manangement Services
N.A.I.C.S.: 531311
Rogie A. Santos *(VP)*

Great American Foods, Inc **(1)**
433 Airport Blvd Ste 404, Burlingame, CA
94010-2014
Tel.: (650) 282-4444
Web Site: http://www.pik-nik.com
Emp.: 10
Food Products Mfr
N.A.I.C.S.: 311919
Alex Gabaldon *(Pres)*

Megaworld Corporation **(1)**
30th Floor Alliance Global Tower 36th Street
cor 11th Avenue Uptown, Bonifacio, Taguig,
1634, Philippines
Tel.: (63) 79052800
Web Site: https://www.megaworldcorp.com
Rev.: $1,258,971,830
Assets: $7,954,729,873
Liabilities: $3,248,259,827
Net Worth: $4,706,470,046
Earnings: $350,285,625
Emp.: 6,204
Fiscal Year-end: 12/31/2023
Real Estate Services
N.A.I.C.S.: 531110
Andrew L. Tan *(Founder, Chm, Pres & CEO)*

Subsidiary (Domestic):

Empire East Land Holdings, Inc. **(2)**
Gilmore Heights 2F Castilla Street corner
Granada St, Uptown Bonifacio, Quezon
City, 1112, Philippines
Tel.: (63) 6328103333
Web Site: http://www.empire-east.com
Rev.: $106,295,394
Assets: $944,465,740
Liabilities: $340,829,966
Net Worth: $603,635,774
Earnings: $10,918,800
Emp.: 654
Fiscal Year-end: 12/31/2020
Real Estate Services
N.A.I.C.S.: 236118
Andrew L. Tan *(Chm)*

Global-Estate Resorts, Inc. **(2)**
9/F Eastwood Global Plaza, Palm Tree Av-
enue Eastwood City Bagumbayan, Quezon
City, Philippines
Tel.: (63) 253184374
Web Site: https://geri.com.ph
Rev.: $103,711,180
Assets: $1,125,655,847
Liabilities: $375,381,331
Net Worth: $750,274,517
Earnings: $31,089,615
Emp.: 825
Fiscal Year-end: 12/31/2021
Real Estate Services
N.A.I.C.S.: 531390
Monica T. Salomon *(Pres & COO)*

Suntrust Properties, Inc. **(2)**

GF One World Square McKinley Hill Fort
Bonifacio, Taguig, 1630,
Philippines **(100%)**
Tel.: (63) 28567015
Web Site: http://www.suntrust.com.ph
Sales Range: $75-99.9 Million
Real Estate Management Services
N.A.I.C.S.: 531210
Andrew L. Tan *(Chm & Pres)*

Oceanic Realty Group International,
Inc **(1)**
Penthouse Paseo Center 8757 Paseo de
Roxas, Corner Sedeneo & Valero Street,
Makati, 1200, Philippines
Tel.: (63) 26678913
Real Estate Manangement Services
N.A.I.C.S.: 531311

Travellers International Hotel Group,
Inc. **(1)**
10/F Newport Entertainment & Commercial
Centre Newport Boulevard, Newport City,
Pasay, 1309, Metro Manila, Philippines
Tel.: (63) 2 908 8000
Web Site: http://www.travellers.com.ph
Rev.: $422,660,333
Assets: $1,728,409,033
Liabilities: $843,735,869
Net Worth: $884,673,164
Earnings: $4,833,959
Emp.: 4,785
Fiscal Year-end: 12/31/2017
Holding Company; Hotel & Casino Operator
N.A.I.C.S.: 551112
Walter L. Mactal *(Pres, CEO, Mng Dir,
CFO, Chief Admin Officer & Chief Legal
Officer)*

ALLIANCE GROUP LIMITED
51 Don Street, Invercargill, 9810,
New Zealand
Tel.: (64) 32142700   **NZ**
Web Site: http://www.alliance.co.nz
Rev.: $1,151,247,828
Assets: $363,605,395
Liabilities: $134,878,382
Net Worth: $228,727,013
Earnings: $3,340,287
Emp.: 5,000
Fiscal Year-end: 09/30/19
Processor of Sheep, Lambs, Cattle,
Deer & Pigs
N.A.I.C.S.: 112410
Murray James Taggart *(Chm)*

Subsidiaries:

Alliance Group (NZ) Ltd **(1)**
Unit 6 Shepherdess Walk Buildings, Lon-
don, N1 7LG, United Kingdom
Tel.: (44) 20 7566 5000
Web Site: http://www.alliance.co.nz
Emp.: 12
Meat & Meat Product Distr
N.A.I.C.S.: 424470

Alliance Group Limited - Dannevirke
Plant **(1)**
Carlson Street, Dannevirke, Manawatu,
4930, New Zealand
Tel.: (64) 6 374 4350
Web Site: http://www.alliance.co.nz
Emp.: 200
Meat Processing Services
N.A.I.C.S.: 311612

Alliance Group Limited - Levin
Plant **(1)**
Hamaria Rd, PO Box 417, Levin, New Zea-
land
Tel.: (64) 6 366 0420
Meat Processing Services
N.A.I.C.S.: 311612

Alliance Group Limited - Lorneville
Plant **(1)**
205 State Highway 99 Underwood, PO Box
1410, Invercargill, 9840, New Zealand
Tel.: (64) 3 215 6400
Meat Processing Services
N.A.I.C.S.: 311612

Alliance Group Limited - Makarewa
Plant **(1)**
Makarewa Junction, Private Bag, Invercar-
gill, New Zealand

Tel.: (64) 3 235 7625
Meat Processing Services
N.A.I.C.S.: 311612

Alliance Group Limited - Mataura
Plant **(1)**
McQueen Avenue, PO Box 1, Mataura,
New Zealand
Tel.: (64) 3 203 6500
Meat Processing Services
N.A.I.C.S.: 311612

Alliance Group Limited - Nelson
Plant **(1)**
Main Road Stoke, Nelson, 7011, New Zea-
land
Tel.: (64) 3 543 9660
Emp.: 200
Meat Processing Services
N.A.I.C.S.: 311612

Alliance Group Limited - Pukeuri
Plant **(1)**
Pukeuri Works Road, Oamaru, 9444, New
Zealand
Tel.: (64) 3 437 3800
Web Site: http://www.alliance.co.nz
Emp.: 1,000
Meat Processing Services
N.A.I.C.S.: 311612

Alliance Group Limited - Smithfield
Plant **(1)**
Bridge Road, Timaru, 7910, New Zealand
Tel.: (64) 3 684 2100
Web Site: http://www.alliance.co.nz
Emp.: 500
Meat Processing Services
N.A.I.C.S.: 311612

New Zealand Holdings (UK) Ltd **(1)**
140-142 St John St, London, EC1V 4UB,
United Kingdom
Tel.: (44) 2075665000
Web Site: http://www.nzfarmers.co.uk
Holding Company
N.A.I.C.S.: 551111

Waitaki International Ltd **(1)**
C 51 Don Street, Invercargill, New Zealand
Tel.: (64) 34331800
Holding Company
N.A.I.C.S.: 551111

ALLIANCE GROWERS CORP.
Suite 500 - 666 Burrard Street, Van-
couver, V6C 3P6, BC, Canada
Tel.: (778) 331-4266   **BC**
Web Site:
    https://www.otcmarkets.com
Year Founded: 2014
ALGWF—(OTCIQ)
Sales Range: Less than $1 Million
Medical Marijuana Grower & Mfr
N.A.I.C.S.: 325411
Dennis Petke *(Pres & CEO)*

ALLIANCE HEALTHCARE GROUP LIMITED
25 Bukit Batok Crescent 07-01 to
07-13 The Elitist, Singapore, 658066,
Singapore
Tel.: (65) 66977700   **SG**
Web Site:
    https://alliancehealthcare.com.sg
Year Founded: 1994
MIJ—(CAT)
Rev.: $42,982,333
Assets: $48,127,232
Liabilities: $30,525,906
Net Worth: $17,601,326
Earnings: $1,489,103
Emp.: 320
Fiscal Year-end: 06/30/23
Healtcare Services
N.A.I.C.S.: 621491
Barry Lip Mong Thng *(Chm & CEO)*

Subsidiaries:

Alliance Medinet Pte. Ltd. **(1)**
25 Bukit Batok Crescent 07-12 The Elitist,
Singapore, 658066, Singapore
Tel.: (65) 66640241
Web Site: https://www.alliancemedinet.com

Alliance Healthcare Group Limited—(Continued)

Healtcare Services
N.A.I.C.S.: 621999

Elite Orthopaedics Pte. Ltd. (1)
3 Mount Elizabeth 12-10 Mount Elizabeth
Medical Centre, Singapore, 228510, Singapore
Tel.: (65) 68368000
Healtcare Services
N.A.I.C.S.: 621999

Ho Kok Sun Colorectal Pte. Ltd. (1)
3 Mount Elizabeth Mount Elizabeth Medical
Centre 04-08, Singapore, 228510, Singapore
Tel.: (65) 67372778
Web Site: https://www.hkscolorectal.com.sg
Healtcare Services
N.A.I.C.S.: 621999

Lim Jit Fong Colorectal Pte. Ltd. (1)
09-09 Gleneagles Medical Centre 6 Napier
Road, Singapore, 258499, Singapore
Tel.: (65) 6 476 0181
Web Site: https://www.colorectal-
surgery.com.sg
Healtcare Services
N.A.I.C.S.: 621999

My ENT Specialist Pte. Ltd. (1)
38 Irrawaddy Road 09-24, Singapore,
329563, Singapore
Tel.: (65) 63975280
Web Site: https://www.myentspecialist.sg
Vocal Cord Surgery Services
N.A.I.C.S.: 561730

**My Family Clinic (Angsana
Breeze@Yishun) Pte. Ltd.** (1)
Blk 507 Yishun Ave 4 01-05, Singapore,
760507, Singapore
Tel.: (65) 67530178
Healtcare Services
N.A.I.C.S.: 621999

My Family Clinic (CCK) Pte. Ltd. (1)
Blk 475 Choa Chu Kang Ave 3 Sunshine
Place 02-01, Singapore, 680475, Singapore
Tel.: (65) 67674566
Healtcare Services
N.A.I.C.S.: 621999

**My Family Clinic (Clementi 325) Pte.
Ltd.** (1)
325 Clementi Ave 5 01-139, Singapore,
120325, Singapore
Tel.: (65) 67784608
Healtcare Services
N.A.I.C.S.: 621999

**My Family Clinic (Clementi) Pte.
Ltd.** (1)
Blk 420A Clementi Ave 1 01-05 Casa Clem-
enti, Singapore, 121420, Singapore
Tel.: (65) 66942574
Healtcare Services
N.A.I.C.S.: 621999

**My Family Clinic (Hougang Central)
Pte. Ltd.** (1)
Blk 804 Hougang Central 01-118, Singa-
pore, 530804, Singapore
Tel.: (65) 63852117
Medical Clinic Centre Services
N.A.I.C.S.: 621491

My Family Clinic (PN) Pte. Ltd. (1)
Blk 638 Jurong West St 61 02-09 Pioneer
Mall, Singapore, 640638, Singapore
Tel.: (65) 68611182
Healthcare Solution Services
N.A.I.C.S.: 621491

**My Family Clinic (Punggol Central)
Pte. Ltd.** (1)
Blk 301 Punggol Central 01-02, Singapore,
820301, Singapore
Tel.: (65) 68537351
Healtcare Services
N.A.I.C.S.: 621999

My Family Clinic (RV) Pte. Ltd. (1)
11 Rivervale Crescent 02-11A Rivervale
Mall, Singapore, 545082, Singapore
Tel.: (65) 68811978
Healthcare Solution Services
N.A.I.C.S.: 621491

My Family Clinic (SJ) Pte. Ltd. (1)

Blk 628 Senja Road 01-04 Senja Grand,
Singapore, 670628, Singapore
Tel.: (65) 63140638
Healtcare Services
N.A.I.C.S.: 621999

**My Family Clinic (Segar) Pte.
Ltd.** (1)
Blk 485 Segar Road 01-508, Singapore,
670485, Singapore
Tel.: (65) 67107269
Healtcare Services
N.A.I.C.S.: 621999

**My Family Clinic (St George) Pte.
Ltd.** (1)
2 St George's Road, Singapore, 328023,
Singapore
Tel.: (65) 62922128
Web Site: https://www.myfamilyclinic.com.sg
Healtcare Services
N.A.I.C.S.: 621999

My Family Clinic (TH) Pte. Ltd. (1)
25 Bukit Batok Crescent 07-12, Singapore,
658066, Singapore
Tel.: (65) 66977700
Web Site: https://www.myfamilyclinic.com.sg
Healtcare Services
N.A.I.C.S.: 621999

My Family Clinic (TPY) Pte. Ltd. (1)
Blk 79D Toa Payoh Central 01-53, Singa-
pore, 314079, Singapore
Tel.: (65) 62380301
Medical Clinic Centre Services
N.A.I.C.S.: 621491

My Family Clinic (WD) Pte. Ltd. (1)
Blk 768 Woodlands Ave 6 02-07 Woodlands
Mart, Singapore, 730768, Singapore
Tel.: (65) 68840658
Web Site: https://www.myfamilyclinic.com.sg
Healtcare Services
N.A.I.C.S.: 621999

**My Family Clinic (Woodlands Glen)
Pte. Ltd.** (1)
Blk 573 Woodlands Drive 16 01-09 Wood-
lands Glen, Singapore, 730573, Singapore
Tel.: (65) 67321520
Healtcare Services
N.A.I.C.S.: 621999

ALLIANCE INSURANCE (PSC)
2nd Floor Warba Center, PO Box
5501, Deira, Dubai, United Arab
Emirates
Tel.: (971) 46051111 AE
Web Site: https://www.alliance-
uae.com
Year Founded: 1975
ALLIANCE—(DFM)
Rev.: $83,049,957
Assets: $359,746,656
Liabilities: $207,208,928
Net Worth: $152,537,728
Earnings: $14,673,995
Emp.: 245
Fiscal Year-end: 12/31/23
Insurance Services
N.A.I.C.S.: 524298
Ahmed Saeed Al Maktoum (Chm)

**ALLIANCE INTEGRATED
METALIKS LIMITED**
DSC 327 Second Floor DLF South
Court Saket, Manjusha Building
Nehru Place, New Delhi, 110017,
India
Tel.: (91) 1140517610
Web Site: https://www.aiml.in
534064—(BOM)
Rev.: $10,145,444
Assets: $58,355,565
Liabilities: $103,900,797
Net Worth: ($45,545,232)
Earnings: ($13,521,731)
Emp.: 62
Fiscal Year-end: 03/31/21
Power Plant Construction Services
N.A.I.C.S.: 237990
Daljit Singh Chahal (Exec Dir)

**ALLIANCE INTERNATIONAL
EDUCATION LEASING HOLD-
INGS LIMITED**
Unit 2602 26/F One Hennessy No 1
Hennessy Road, Wan Chai, Hong
Kong, China (Hong Kong)
Tel.: (852) 29607000 Ky
Web Site: https://www.aiel-
holdings.com
Year Founded: 2014
1563—(HKG)
Rev.: $56,503,235
Assets: $639,597,514
Liabilities: $241,564,062
Net Worth: $398,033,452
Earnings: $57,012,505
Emp.: 1,692
Fiscal Year-end: 12/31/22
Holding Company
N.A.I.C.S.: 551112
Luqiang Li (CEO)

ALLIANCE MAGNESIUM INC.
9160 Leduc Blvd Suite 410, Bros-
sard, J4Y 0E3, QC, Canada
Web Site:
http://www.alliancemagnesium.com
Magnesium Production Technology
Developer
N.A.I.C.S.: 213115
Joel Fournier (CEO)

ALLIANCE MINING CORP.
888 Dunsmuir Street Suite 888, Van-
couver, V6C 3K4, BC, Canada
Tel.: (604) 488-3900 Ca
Web Site:
https://www.alliancemining.com
Year Founded: 2002
ALM—(TSXV)
Assets: $3,566
Liabilities: $2,345,972
Net Worth: ($2,342,407)
Earnings: ($498,437)
Fiscal Year-end: 12/31/23
Metal Ore Mining Services
N.A.I.C.S.: 212290
Christopher R. Anderson (Pres &
CEO)

ALLIANCE NICKEL LIMITED
Level 1 Suite 102 45 Stirling High-
way, Nedlands, 6009, WA, Australia
Tel.: (61) 61822718
Web Site:
https://www.gmeresources.com.au
AXN—(ASX)
Rev.: $759,042
Assets: $34,892,678
Liabilities: $807,199
Net Worth: $34,085,479
Earnings: ($1,099,768)
Fiscal Year-end: 06/30/24
Minerals Exploration
N.A.I.C.S.: 213115
Mark Edward Pitts (Sec)

ALLIANCE OIL COMPANY LTD.
Sivtsev Vrazhek 39, Moscow,
119002, Russia
Tel.: (7) 4957771808
Web Site:
http://www.allianceoilco.com
Sales Range: $1-4.9 Billion
Emp.: 7,512
Oil & Gas Exploration Services
N.A.I.C.S.: 211120
Arsen E. Idrisov (Mng Dir)

Subsidiaries:

AO NNK-Amurnefteproduct (1)
Ul Pervomayskaya 1A Amur Region, Bla-
goveshchensk, 675002, Russia
Tel.: (7) 4162221300
Web Site: http://www.anp.aoil.ru
Petroleum Product Distr
N.A.I.C.S.: 424720

AO NNK-Primornefteproduct (1)
Fontannaya St 55, Vladivostok, Russia
Tel.: (7) 4232456814
Web Site: http://www.pnp.aoil.ru
Petroleum Product Retailer
N.A.I.C.S.: 457210

LLC Alliance Oil Company MC (1)
39 Sivtsev Vrazhek Lane, 119002, Moscow,
Russia
Tel.: (7) 495 777 18 08
Petroleum Product Distr
N.A.I.C.S.: 424720

ALLIANCE PHARMA PLC
Avonbridge House Bath Road, Chip-
penham, SN15 2BB, Wiltshire, United
Kingdom
Tel.: (44) 1249466966
Web Site:
https://www.alliancepharma.com
APH—(AIM)
Rev.: $207,897,189
Assets: $667,356,980
Liabilities: $310,139,550
Net Worth: $357,217,430
Earnings: $1,162,325
Emp.: 285
Fiscal Year-end: 12/31/22
Pharmaceuticals Producut Sales
N.A.I.C.S.: 424210
John Dawson (Founder)

Subsidiaries:

Alliance Pharma S.r.l. (1)
Viale Restelli 5, 20124, Milan, Italy
Tel.: (39) 02304601
Web Site: https://kelocote.it
Pharmaceuticals Product Mfr
N.A.I.C.S.: 325412

**Alliance Pharmaceuticals (Thailand)
Co., Ltd.** (1)
4-15 Moo 5 Rama II Rd, Samae Dam
Bangkhuntien, Bangkok, 10150, Thailand
Tel.: (66) 2 513 7856
Web Site: https://alliancepharma.co.th
Pharmaceuticals Product Mfr
N.A.I.C.S.: 325412
Niwes Phancharoenworakul (Chm)

Alliance Pharmaceuticals GmbH (1)
Niederkasseler Lohweg 175, 40547, Dus-
seldorf, Germany
Tel.: (49) 2113 878 9182
Health Care Srvices
N.A.I.C.S.: 621610

Alliance Pharmaceuticals Limited (1)
Avonbridge House Bath Road, Chippen-
ham, SN15 2BB, Wiltshire, United Kingdom
Tel.: (44) 1249466966
Sales Range: $25-49.9 Million
Emp.: 90
Medicinal Product Mfr
N.A.I.C.S.: 325412

Opus Healthcare Limited (1)
United Drug House Magna Drive Magna
Business Park Citywest Road, Dublin, Ire-
land
Tel.: (353) 66 718 1636
Web Site: https://www.opus-healthcare.ie
Pharmaceuticals Product Mfr
N.A.I.C.S.: 325412

**ALLIANCE RESOURCES LIM-
ITED**
Ste 3 51-55 City Road, Southbank,
3006, VIC, Australia
Tel.: (61) 396979090
Web Site:
http://www.allianceresources.com.au
AGS—(ASX)
Rev.: $42,907
Assets: $14,899,331
Liabilities: $505,685
Net Worth: $14,393,645
Earnings: ($1,055,044)
Fiscal Year-end: 06/30/21
Mineral Exploration Services
N.A.I.C.S.: 213115
Kevin Malaxos (Mng Dir)

Subsidiaries:

Alliance (SA) Pty. Ltd.   (1)
Ste 3 51-55 City Rd, Southbank, 3006, VIC, Australia
Tel.: (61) 396979090
Web Site:
http://www.allianceresources.com.au
Sales Range: $50-74.9 Million
Emp.: 1
Mineral Exploration Services
N.A.I.C.S.: 213115
Steve Johnson (Mng Dir)

ALLIANCE SELECT FOODS INTERNATIONAL, INC.
Suite 3104 A West Tower PSEC Exchange Rd, Ortigas Business District, Pasig, 1605, Metro Manilla, Philippines
Tel.: (63) 277473798   PH
Web Site:
https://www.alliancefoods.com
Year Founded: 2003
FOOD—(PHI)
Rev.: $34,579,904
Assets: $36,427,712
Liabilities: $19,675,596
Net Worth: $16,752,116
Earnings: ($3,492,852)
Emp.: 124
Fiscal Year-end: 12/31/22
Canned Tuna Proccessor
N.A.I.C.S.: 311710
Alvin Y. Dee (Vice Chm)

Subsidiaries:

PT International Alliance Food Indonesia   (1)
Jl Raya Madidir Lorong Union Kel Madidir Unet Lingkungan II Kec, Madidir Kota, Bitung, Indonesia
Tel.: (62) 43834573
Tuna Processing Canning Export Services
N.A.I.C.S.: 114111

Spence & Co., Ltd.   (1)
76 Campanelli Industrial Dr, Brockton, MA 02301
Tel.: (508) 427-5577
Web Site: https://www.spenceltd.com
Salmoon Products Distr
N.A.I.C.S.: 424460
Francis Martin Dee Gonzales (Treas & Sec)

ALLIANCE TRUST PLC
River Court 5 West Victoria Dock Road, Dundee, DD1 3JT, United Kingdom
Tel.: (44) 1382938320   UK
Web Site:
https://www.alliancetrust.co.uk
Year Founded: 1888
ATST—(LSE)
Rev.: $357,582,716
Assets: $4,627,431,540
Liabilities: $549,791,064
Net Worth: $4,077,640,476
Earnings: $312,365,210
Emp.: 4
Fiscal Year-end: 12/31/20
Investment Trust Management Services
N.A.I.C.S.: 523991
Gregor Stewart (Chm)

Subsidiaries:

Alliance Trust Investments Limited   (1)
8 West Marketgait, Dundee, DD1 1QN, United Kingdom
Tel.: (44) 1382321000
Web Site:
http://www.alliancetrustinvestments.com
Sales Range: $50-74.9 Million
Emp.: 200
Specialist Fund Management Services
N.A.I.C.S.: 523940
Rod Davidson (Head-Fixed Income)

ALLIANCES
16 Rue Ali Abderrazak, Casablanca, Morocco
Tel.: (212) 22993480
Web Site: https://alliancesdarna.ma
Year Founded: 1994
ADI—(CAS)
Sales Range: $200-249.9 Million
Real Estate Development Services
N.A.I.C.S.: 531390
Alami Lazrak (Pres & CEO)

ALLIANDER N.V.
Utrechtseweg 68, 6812 AH, Arnhem, Netherlands
Tel.: (31) 885426363   NI
Web Site: http://www.alliander.com
Year Founded: 2009
Rev.: $2,206,124,200
Assets: $9,844,689,260
Liabilities: $5,114,400,620
Net Worth: $4,730,288,640
Earnings: $283,324,580
Emp.: 5,703
Fiscal Year-end: 12/31/19
Electric & Gas Grid Network Management Services
N.A.I.C.S.: 221121

Subsidiaries:

Alliander AG   (1)
Rudower Chaussee 13, 12489, Berlin, Germany
Tel.: (49) 30409020
Web Site: http://www.alliander.de
Emp.: 7,000
Gas & Electricity Transmission Services
N.A.I.C.S.: 221122

Alliander Finance B.V.   (1)
Utrechtseweg 68, NL-6812 AH, Arnhem, Netherlands   (100%)
Tel.: (31) 268442266
Financial Support Services
N.A.I.C.S.: 561499

Endinet B.V.   (1)
Wekkerstraat 25, 5652 AN, Eindhoven, 5652 AN, Netherlands
Tel.: (31) 40 238 9333
Web Site: http://www.endinet.nl
Electricity Transmission Services
N.A.I.C.S.: 221122

Liander N.V.   (1)
Utrechtseweg 68, 6812 AH, Arnhem, Netherlands   (100%)
Tel.: (31) 885426444
Web Site: http://www.liander.nl
Sales Range: $1-4.9 Billion
Energy Network Construction & Maintenance Services
N.A.I.C.S.: 237130

Liandon B.V.   (1)
Dijkgraaf 24, NL-6921 RL, Duiven, Gelderland, Netherlands   (100%)
Tel.: (31) 268447400
Web Site: http://www.liandon.com
Sales Range: $200-249.9 Million
Emp.: 700
Private Energy Grid Design, Construction & Management Services
N.A.I.C.S.: 541990

Subsidiary (Domestic):

Liandon Meetbedrijf N.V.   (2)
Coenensparkstraat 25, 7202 AN, Zutphen, Netherlands   (100%)
Tel.: (31) 57559 7203
Private Energy Grid Monitoring Services
N.A.I.C.S.: 541990

Stam Heerhugowaard Holding B.V   (1)
Pascalstraat 17, 1704 RD, Heerhugowaard, 1704 RD, Noord-Holland, Netherlands
Tel.: (31) 72 5762200
Electric Power Transmission Services
N.A.I.C.S.: 221122

ALLIANZ AYUDHYA CAPITAL PUBLIC COMPANY LIMITED

No 898 Ploenchit Tower Building 7th Floor Ploenchit Road, Lumpini Pathumwan, Bangkok, 10330, Thailand
Tel.: (66) 23057374
Web Site: https://www.ayud.co.th
AYUD—(THA)
Rev.: $298,832,534
Assets: $674,089,732
Liabilities: $305,558,743
Net Worth: $368,530,989
Earnings: $27,236,166
Emp.: 760
Fiscal Year-end: 12/31/23
Insurance Services
N.A.I.C.S.: 524126
Bryan James Smith (Pres & CEO)

Subsidiaries:

Allianz Ayudhya Assurance Pcl.   (1)
Floor 1 Ploenchit Tower 898 Ploen Chit Road, 898 Ploenchit Road, Bangkok, 10330, Thailand   (20.17%)
Tel.: (66) 23057000
Web Site: https://www.allianz.co.th
Life Insurance Products & Services
N.A.I.C.S.: 524113
Patchara Taveechaiwattana (Chief Market Mgmt Officer & Member-Mgmt Bd)

My Health Services (Thailand) Co., Ltd.   (1)
898 Ploenchit Tower Ploenchit Road, Lumpini Sub-district Pathumwan District, Bangkok, 10330, Thailand
Tel.: (66) 26770900
Patient Healthcare Services
N.A.I.C.S.: 621999

ALLIANZ GLOBAL INVESTORS LUXEMBOURG S.A.
6A route de Treves, Senningerberg, Luxembourg
Tel.: (352) 4634631
Web Site: https://lu.allianzgi.com
Year Founded: 1998
Investment Management Service
N.A.I.C.S.: 523999

ALLIANZ SE
Koniginstrasse 28, 80802, Munich, Germany
Tel.: (49) 8938000   De
Web Site: https://www.allianz.com
Year Founded: 1890
ALV—(MUN)
Assets: $1,085,296,283,380
Liabilities: $1,020,745,277,390
Net Worth: $64,551,005,990
Earnings: $9,428,153,670
Emp.: 157,883
Fiscal Year-end: 12/31/23
Holding Company; Industrial, Life, Health & Specialty Insurance & Asset Management Products & Services
N.A.I.C.S.: 551112
Michael Diekmann (Chm-Supervisory Bd)

Subsidiaries:

ACP GmbH & Co. Beteiligungen KG   (1)
Theresienstr 6-8, 80333, Munich, Germany
Tel.: (49) 89 38000
Investment Management Service
N.A.I.C.S.: 523999

ACP Vermogensverwaltung GmbH & Co. KG Nr. 4a   (1)
Theresienstr 6-8, 80333, Munich, Germany
Tel.: (49) 89 38000
Asset Management Services
N.A.I.C.S.: 523940

ACP Vermogensverwaltung GmbH & Co. KG Nr. 4c   (1)
Theresienstr 6-8, 80333, Munich, Germany
Tel.: (49) 89 38000
Asset Management Services
N.A.I.C.S.: 523940

ADAC Autoversicherung AG   (1)
Hansastrasse, 80686, Munich, Germany
Tel.: (49) 8976760
Fire Insurance Services
N.A.I.C.S.: 524126

ADIG Fondsvertrieb GmbH   (1)
Seidlstrasse 24-24a, 80335, Munich, Germany
Tel.: (49) 89 12 20 74 44
Web Site: http://www.adig.de
Sales Range: $50-74.9 Million
Emp.: 7
Mutual Fund Management Services
N.A.I.C.S.: 523940

AGA Assistance (India) Private Limited   (1)
1st Floor DLF Square M-Block Jacaranda Marg Phase-II, Gurgaon, 122 002, Haryana, India
Tel.: (91) 124 4343800
Web Site: http://www.allianz-assistance.in
Emp.: 250
Travel Insurance Services
N.A.I.C.S.: 524298
Puneet Sachdeva (CFO)

AGA Assistance Australia Pty Ltd.   (1)
74 High Street, PO Box 162, Toowong, Brisbane, 4066, QLD, Australia
Tel.: (61) 7 3305 7000
Web Site: http://www.allianz-assistance.com.au
Emp.: 500
Travel Assistance Services
N.A.I.C.S.: 923130

AGA Service Company Corp.   (1)
9950 Mayland Dr, Richmond, VA 23233
Web Site:
https://www.allianztravelinsurance.com
Travel Insurance Services
N.A.I.C.S.: 524126

AGCS Americas   (1)
225 W Washington St, Chicago, IL 60606-3484
Tel.: (312) 224-3300
Sales Range: $350-399.9 Million
Emp.: 800
General Insurance Services
N.A.I.C.S.: 524210
Hugh Burgess (Pres & CEO)

AGCS Argentina   (1)
San Martin 550, Buenos Aires, Argentina
Tel.: (54) 11 43203800
General Insurance Services
N.A.I.C.S.: 524210

AGCS Australia   (1)
2 Market Street, Sydney, 2000, NSW, Australia
Tel.: (61) 2 82585447
General Insurance Services
N.A.I.C.S.: 524210

AGCS Lebanon   (1)
Allianz SNA Bldg - Hazmieh, PO Box 16-6528, Beirut, Lebanon
Tel.: (961) 5 956600
General Insurance Services
N.A.I.C.S.: 524210

AGCS Marine Insurance Company   (1)
777 San Marin Dr, Novato, CA 94998
Tel.: (415) 899-2000
Marine Insurance Services
N.A.I.C.S.: 524298

AGCS North America   (1)
130 Adelaide Street West Suite 1600, Toronto, M5H 3P5, ON, Canada
Tel.: (416) 915-4247
Sales Range: $100-124.9 Million
Emp.: 125
General Insurance Services
N.A.I.C.S.: 524210

AGCS Resseguros Brasil S.A.   (1)
Rua Eugenio de Medeiros 303 1st Floor, Pinheiros, 05425-000, Sao Paulo, Brazil
Tel.: (55) 1135270200
Insurance Services
N.A.I.C.S.: 524126

AGCS Singapore   (1)
12 Marina View #14-01 Asia Square Tower 2, Singapore, 018961, Singapore

Allianz SE—(Continued)
Tel.: (65) 6 2972529
Web Site: http://www.allianz.com
Insurance Management Services
N.A.I.C.S.: 524298

AGCS South Africa Limited **(1)**
Firs 2nd Floor 32A Cradock Avenue, Rose-
bank, 2196, South Africa
Tel.: (27) 11 2147900
Web Site: http://www.agcs.allianz.com
General Insurance Services
N.A.I.C.S.: 524298
Kevin Barnes (CFO)

AGF S.A. **(1)**
87 Rue De Richelieu, 75113, Paris, Cedex
02, France **(58%)**
Tel.: (33) 144862000
Web Site: http://www.agf.fr
Emp.: 31,855
Life & Health Insurance, Property & Liability
Insurance, Reinsurance & Credit Insurance
N.A.I.C.S.: 524113

Subsidiary (Domestic):

AGF 2X, S.A. **(2)**
87 Rue Richelieu, 75113, Paris, France
Tel.: (33) 1 44 86 20 00
General Insurance Services
N.A.I.C.S.: 524210

Subsidiary (Non-US):

**AGF Allianz Chile Compania de Se-
guros Generales S.A.** **(2)**
Hendaya 60 Piso 10, Las Condes, San-
tiago, Chile
Tel.: (56) 2 330 2000
Web Site: http://www.agf.cl
Insurance Provider
N.A.I.C.S.: 524128

**AGF Assurances Luxembourg
S.A.** **(2)**
14 Bd Franklin-Roosevelt, L-2450, Luxem-
bourg, Luxembourg
Tel.: (352) 4723461
Web Site: http://www.agf.lu
Sales Range: $25-49.9 Million
Emp.: 50
Insurance Services
N.A.I.C.S.: 524298

AGF Brasil Seguros SA **(2)**
Rua Luis Coelho 26 - 8 andar, 01309-900,
Sao Paulo, SP, Brazil
Tel.: (55) 1131716000
Insurance Services
N.A.I.C.S.: 524128

AGF Burkina Assurances **(2)**
99 Avenue de l'UEMOA, Ouagadougou,
Burkina Faso **(52%)**
Tel.: (226) 50 30 62 04
Insurance Services
N.A.I.C.S.: 524298

AGF Burkina Assurances Vie **(2)**
Avenue Leo Frobenius, BP 398, Ouagadou-
gou, Burkina Faso **(70%)**
Tel.: (226) 50306204
Insurance Services
N.A.I.C.S.: 524298

AGF Cameroun Assurances **(2)**
1124 Rue Manga Bell, BP 105, Douala,
Cameroon **(71%)**
Tel.: (237) 3429203
Insurance Services
N.A.I.C.S.: 524298

Subsidiary (Non-US):

AGF Centrafrique Assurances **(3)**
Boulevard du General de Gaulle, BP 343,
Bangui, Central African Republic **(83%)**
Tel.: (236) 21613666
Insurance Services
N.A.I.C.S.: 524298
Bruno Ribeiron (Mgr)

Subsidiary (Non-US):

AGF Cameroun Assurances Vie **(2)**
1124 Rue Manga Bell, BP 105, Douala,
Cameroon **(76%)**
Tel.: (237) 33429203

Sales Range: $50-74.9 Million
Emp.: 100
Insurance Services
N.A.I.C.S.: 524298

Subsidiary (Domestic):

AGF Capital Investissement 2 **(2)**
117 Avenue des Champs-Elysees, Paris,
75008, France
Tel.: (33) 1 58 18 56 56
Investment Management Service
N.A.I.C.S.: 523999
Grossmann Baviere (Gen Mgr)

Subsidiary (Non-US):

**AGF Cote d'Ivoire Assurances
Vie** **(2)**
2 Bb Roume 01, BP 1741, Abidjan, Cote
d'Ivoire **(70%)**
Tel.: (225) 20304000
Web Site: http://www.agf-coteivoire.com
Insurance Services
N.A.I.C.S.: 524298

AGF Life Luxembourg S.A **(2)**
14 Blvd Franklin-Roosevelt, L-2450, Luxem-
bourg, Luxembourg
Tel.: (352) 4723461
Web Site: http://www.allianz.lu
Sales Range: $50-74.9 Million
Emp.: 60
Life Insurance
N.A.I.C.S.: 524113

AGF Senegal Assurances Vie **(2)**
Avenue Abdoulaye Fadiga X rue de Thann,
BP 2610, Dakar, Senegal **(96%)**
Tel.: (221) 8494400
Insurance Services
N.A.I.C.S.: 524298

Adriatica de Seguros C.A. **(2)**
Avenida Andres Bello Edf Adriatica De Se-
guros CA, Caracas, 1011 A, Distrito Capital,
Venezuela **(100%)**
Tel.: (58) 2125080477
Sales Range: $150-199.9 Million
Emp.: 300
Insurance Provider
N.A.I.C.S.: 524113

Subsidiary (Domestic):

Arcalis **(2)**
20 Place de Seine, 92086, Paris, Cedex,
France
Tel.: (33) 144862000
Web Site: http://www.allianz.fr
Emp.: 4,000
Financial Services
N.A.I.C.S.: 525990

Banque AGF **(2)**
164 rue Ambroise Croizat, F-93288, Saint
Denis, Cedex, France
Tel.: (33) 155877000
Web Site: http://www.banqueagf.fr
Financial Services
N.A.I.C.S.: 525990

Calypso **(2)**
410 la Courtine, 75002, Noisy-le-Grand,
France
Tel.: (33) 144862000
Web Site: http://www.allianz.fr
Insurance & Financial Services
N.A.I.C.S.: 524298

Subsidiary (Non-US):

Club Marine Ltd. **(2)**
40 The Esplanade, Brighton, 3186, VIC,
Australia
Tel.: (61) 385911950
Web Site: http://www.clubmarine.com.au
Sales Range: $50-74.9 Million
Emp.: 30
Insurance Services
N.A.I.C.S.: 524298

**Compania Colombiana de Inversion
Colseguros S.A.** **(2)**
Carrera 13 A N 29-24 piso 19, 1951, Bo-
gota, Colombia
Tel.: (57) 15616336
Web Site: http://www.colseguros.com
Insurance Services
N.A.I.C.S.: 524298

**Hauteville Insurance Company
Ltd.** **(2)**
34 Lscanichers, Saint Peter Port, GY1 2LT,
Guernsey
Tel.: (44) 1481724212
Sales Range: $50-74.9 Million
Emp.: 2
Insurance Services
N.A.I.C.S.: 524298

Hunter Premium Funding Ltd. **(2)**
Level 7 360 Elizabeth St, Melbourne, 3000,
Australia
Tel.: (61) 392243000
Web Site: http://www.hpf.com.au
Sales Range: $150-199.9 Million
Emp.: 400
Investment Fund Services
N.A.I.C.S.: 525910
Bradley Bartlem (CEO)

Subsidiary (Domestic):

Mondial Assistance Group **(2)**
54 Rue Ge Lorgemer, F-75394, Paris,
France
Tel.: (33) 0153255325
Sales Range: $1-4.9 Billion
Emp.: 8,100
Assistance & Travel Insurance Services;
Owned 50% by AGF S.A. & 50% by Ri-
unione Adriatica di Sicurta S.p.A. (Both
Companies Owned by Allianz AG)
N.A.I.C.S.: 524298

Subsidiary (Non-US):

AGA Assistance Australia Pty Ltd **(3)**
74 High Street, Toowong, 4066, QLD, Aus-
tralia
Tel.: (61) 7 3305 7000
Web Site: http://www.allianz-
assistance.com.au
Sales Range: $150-199.9 Million
Emp.: 400
Assistance & Travel Insurance Services
N.A.I.C.S.: 524298

**AGA Services (Thailand) Co.,
Ltd.** **(3)**
7th Floor Citylink Tower 1091/335 Soi
Petchburi 35, New Petchburi Rd Makasan
Rajathevi, Bangkok, 10400, Thailand
Tel.: (66) 23058555
Web Site: http://www.allianz-
assistance.co.th
Emp.: 400
Insurance Services
N.A.I.C.S.: 524298

Subsidiary (US):

Allianz Global Assistance Inc. **(3)**
9950 Mayland Dr, Richmond, VA 23233
Tel.: (804) 285-3300
Web Site: http://www.allianzassistance.com
Sales Range: $50-74.9 Million
Emp.: 800
Travel Insurance Agents & Brokers
N.A.I.C.S.: 524210
Daniel Durazo (Dir-External Comm)

Branch (Domestic):

World Access Service Corp. **(4)**
2805 N Parham Rd, Richmond, VA 23230-
2942
Tel.: (804) 673-3573
Web Site: http://www.worldaccess.com
Insurance Brokers
N.A.I.C.S.: 524210

Subsidiary (Domestic):

**ELVIA Societe d'Assurances de
Voyages** **(3)**
36 rue du general de gaulle, F-93173, Bag-
nolet, Cedex 08, France
Tel.: (33) 0142990299
Web Site: http://www.monderlassistance.fr
Sales Range: $5-14.9 Billion
Emp.: 50,000
Travel & Property Insurance Services
N.A.I.C.S.: 524126

Subsidiary (Non-US):

Allianz Global Assistance **(4)**
Hertistrasse 2, CH-8304, Wallisellen, Switzerland

Tel.: (41) 442833222
Web Site: http://www.allianz-assistance.ch
Sales Range: $25-49.9 Million
Emp.: 50
Travel & Property Insurance Services
N.A.I.C.S.: 524126

Allianz Global Assistance **(4)**
Poeldijkstraat 4, 1059 VM, Amsterdam,
Netherlands
Tel.: (31) 205618711
Web Site: http://www.allianz-global-
assistance.nl
Sales Range: $50-74.9 Million
Emp.: 250
Travel Insurance & Personal Services
N.A.I.C.S.: 524126
Willem Snijders (Mng Dir)

**Allianz Global Assistance (AGA) In-
ternational S.A.** **(4)**
Ludmillastrasse 26, D-81543, Munich, Ger-
many
Tel.: (49) 89 6 24 24 460
Web Site: http://www.allianz-assistance.de
Sales Range: $125-149.9 Million
Emp.: 178
Travel & Property Insurance Services
N.A.I.C.S.: 524126

ELVIA Reiseversicherung AG **(4)**
Pottendorfer Strasse 25 27, 1120, Vienna,
Austria
Tel.: (43) 01525030
Web Site: http://www.mondeal-assistance-
austria.at
Sales Range: $50-74.9 Million
Emp.: 150
Travel & Property Insurance Services
N.A.I.C.S.: 524126
Christoph Heissenberger (Mng Dir)

Mondial Assistance Portugal **(4)**
Avenida do Brazil 56 3rd Floor, Lisbon,
1700 073, Portugal
Tel.: (351) 217806200
Web Site: http://www.allianz-
assiatance.com.pt
Sales Range: $50-74.9 Million
Emp.: 150
Travel & Property Insurance Services
N.A.I.C.S.: 524126
Miguel Mallo Do Rego (Mng Dir)

Subsidiary (Non-US):

Mondial Assistance Singapore **(3)**
143 Cecil Street 13-01 GB Building, Singa-
pore, 069542, Singapore
Tel.: (65) 63954800
Web Site: http://www.mondial-
assistance.com.sg
Sales Range: $50-74.9 Million
Emp.: 50
Assistance & Travel Insurance Services
N.A.I.C.S.: 524298

Subsidiary (Non-US):

**Phenix Compagnie
D'Assurances** **(2)**
4 Ave de la Gare, CH-1001, Lausanne,
Switzerland
Tel.: (41) 213400404
Sales Range: $25-49.9 Million
Emp.: 70
Insurance Services
N.A.I.C.S.: 524298

**Societe Nationale d'Assurances
s.a.l.** **(2)**
Immeuble SNA Hazmieh, PO Box 16-6528,
Beirut, 16, Lebanon
Tel.: (961) 5956600
Web Site: http://www.allianzsna.com
Sales Range: $25-49.9 Million
Financial Services
N.A.I.C.S.: 524298

AMOS Austria GmbH **(1)**
Hietzinger Kai 101-105, 1130, Vienna, Aus-
tria
Tel.: (43) 1 87807 0
Information Technology Consulting Services
N.A.I.C.S.: 541512

APKV US Private REIT GP LLC **(1)**
1209 Orange St, Wilmington, DE 19801
Tel.: (302) 658-7581
Investment Management Service

N.A.I.C.S.: 523999

APKV US Private REIT LP   (1)
1209 Orange St, Wilmington, DE 19801
Tel.: (302) 658-7581
Investment Management Service
N.A.I.C.S.: 523999

AS Selecta s.r.o.   (1)
Mileticova 40, 821 08, Bratislava, Slovakia
Tel.: (421) 2 555 67 736
Web Site: http://www.selectavending.sk
Welding Machine Distr
N.A.I.C.S.: 423440

AUG. PRIEN Immobilien PE Verwaltung BrahmsQuartier GmbH   (1)
Charlottenstr 3, Stuttgart, 70182, Germany
Tel.: (49) 1724077047
Real Estate Manangement Services
N.A.I.C.S.: 531390

AWP Assistance UK Ltd.   (1)
102 George Street, Croydon, CR9 6HD, Surrey, United Kingdom
Tel.: (44) 2086812525
N.A.I.C.S.: 524113

AWP Australia Pty. Ltd.   (1)
310 Ann St, Brisbane, 4000, QLD, Australia
Tel.: (61) 733057000
Web Site: https://www.allianz-partners.com
Insurance Services
N.A.I.C.S.: 524210

AWP France SAS   (1)
7 rue Dora Maar, CS 60001, 93488, Saint-Ouen-l'Aumone, France
Tel.: (33) 140255555
Insurance Services
N.A.I.C.S.: 524210

AWP P&C S.A.   (1)
Bahnhofstrasse 16, Aschheim, 85609, Munich, Germany
Tel.: (49) 892620830
N.A.I.C.S.: 524113

AZ Jupiter 4 B.V.   (1)
Keizersgracht 484, 1017 EH, Amsterdam, North Holland, Netherlands
Tel.: (31) 205569715
Investment Management Service
N.A.I.C.S.: 523999

AZ Jupiter 8 B.V.   (1)
Tel.: (31) 205569715
Investment Management Service
N.A.I.C.S.: 523999

AZ Jupiter 9 B.V.   (1)
Keizersgracht 484, North Holland, 1017 EH, Amsterdam, Netherlands
Tel.: (31) 205569715
Investment Management Service
N.A.I.C.S.: 523999

AZ Vers US Private REIT GP LLC   (1)
1209 Orange St, Wilmington, DE 19801
Tel.: (302) 658-7581
Investment Management Service
N.A.I.C.S.: 523999

AZ Vers US Private REIT LP   (1)
55 Greens Farms Rd, Westport, CT 06881
Tel.: (203) 221-8500
Investment Management Service
N.A.I.C.S.: 523999

AZ-Arges Vermogensverwaltungsgesellschaft mbH   (1)
Koninginstr 28, 80802, Munich, Germany
Tel.: (49) 8938000
Asset Management Services
N.A.I.C.S.: 523940

AZ-Argos 50 Vermogensverwaltungsgesellschaft mbH & Co. KG   (1)
Koninginstr 28, Munich, 80802, Bayern, Germany
Tel.: (49) 893 8000
Asset Management Services
N.A.I.C.S.: 523940

AZ-Argos 51 Vermogensverwaltungsgesellschaft mbH & Co. KG   (1)
Koninginstr 28, Munich, 80802, Bayern, Germany
Tel.: (49) 893 8000
Asset Management Services

N.A.I.C.S.: 523940

AZ-Argos 56 Vermogensverwaltungsgesellschaft mbH   (1)
koninginstrasse 28, 80802, Munich, Bayern, Germany
Tel.: (49) 89 3800 0
Asset Management Services
N.A.I.C.S.: 523940

AZ-SGD Private Equity Fonds GmbH   (1)
Theresienstr 6-8, Munich, 80333, Bayern, Germany
Tel.: (49) 89380070
Web Site:
    http://www.allianzcapitalpartners.com
Emp.: 100
Investment Management Service
N.A.I.C.S.: 523999

Adeus Aktienregister-Service GmbH   (1)
Strahlenbergerstrassa 13, Offenbach, 60301, Germany
Tel.: (49) 692562703
Web Site: http://www.adeus.de
Sales Range: $50-74.9 Million
Emp.: 19
Financial Services
N.A.I.C.S.: 525990

Aequitas GmbH Allianz Equity - Alternative Strategies   (1)
Seidlstr 24-24a, 80333, Munich, Bayern, Germany
Tel.: (49) 89 38000
Financial Management Services
N.A.I.C.S.: 523999

AllSecur B.V.   (1)
Stationsplein 50, PO Box 1951, 's-Hertogenbosch, 5211, Netherlands
Tel.: (31) 73 5485000
Web Site: http://www.allsecur.nl
Fire Insurance Services
N.A.I.C.S.: 524126

AllSecur Deutschland AG   (1)
Theodor-Stern-Kai 1, 60596, Frankfurt am Main, Germany
Tel.: (49) 69 99999 111
Web Site: http://www.allsecur.de
Automobile Insurance Services
N.A.I.C.S.: 524126

Allegiance Marketing Group LLC   (1)
5500 Village Blvd Ste 200, West Palm Beach, FL 33407
Tel.: (800) 330-1997
Web Site: http://www.amgadvisor.com
Marketing Consulting Services
N.A.I.C.S.: 541613
Chuck Segal *(Officer-Suitability)*

Allianz   (1)
35 Rue De Laeken, 1000, Brussels, Belgium   **(100%)**
Tel.: (32) 22146111
Web Site: http://www.allianz.be
Sales Range: $300-349.9 Million
Emp.: 800
Insurance Services
N.A.I.C.S.: 524128
Robert Franssen *(Gen Dir)*

Subsidiary (Domestic):

Allianz Belgium S.A.   (2)
35 Rue De Laeken, 1000, Brussels, 1000, Belgium   **(100%)**
Tel.: (32) 22146111
Web Site: http://www.allianz.be
Sales Range: $350-399.9 Million
Emp.: 800
Insurance Provider
N.A.I.C.S.: 524128

Subsidiary (Non-US):

Fenix Directo Compania de Seguros y Reaseguros S.A.   (2)
Calle Ramirez de Arellano 35, 28043, Madrid, Spain
Tel.: (34) 910789888
Web Site: https://www.allianzdirect.es
Direct Insurance & Reinsurance Services
N.A.I.C.S.: 524298

Allianz (UK) Limited   (1)

57 Ladymead, Guildford, GU1 1DB, United Kingdom
Tel.: (44) 1483568161
Web Site: http://www.allianz.co.uk
Emp.: 1,200
General Insurance Services
N.A.I.C.S.: 524298

Allianz AVI 1 Fonds   (1)
Mainzer Landstrasse 11-13, Frankfurt am Main, 60329, Germany
Tel.: (49) 18 03 30 33 11
Mutual Fund Management Services
N.A.I.C.S.: 523940

Allianz AVM B Fonds   (1)
Mainzer Landstrasse 11-13, 60329, Frankfurt am Main, Germany
Tel.: (49) 18 03 30 33 11
Mutual Fund Management Services
N.A.I.C.S.: 523940

Allianz AZL Vermogensverwaltung GmbH   (1)
Tel.: (49) 8938000
Web Site: http://www.allianz.de
Financial Management Services
N.A.I.C.S.: 523999

Allianz Actio France   (1)
87 Rue De Richelieu, Paris, 75002, France
Tel.: (33) 1 44 86 20 00
Mutual Fund Management Services
N.A.I.C.S.: 523940

Allianz Actions Aequitas   (1)
87 Rue De Richelieu, Paris, 75113, France
Tel.: (33) 1 44 86 20 00
Mutual Fund Management Services
N.A.I.C.S.: 523940

Allianz Actions Euro Value   (1)
87 Rue De Richelieu, Paris, 75002, France
Tel.: (33) 1 44 86 20 00
Mutual Fund Management Services
N.A.I.C.S.: 523940

Allianz Actions France   (1)
87 Rue De Richelieu, Paris, 75002, France
Tel.: (33) 1 44 86 20 00
Web Site: http://www.allianz.fr
Mutual Fund Management Services
N.A.I.C.S.: 523940

Allianz Actions France MidCap   (1)
87 Rue De Richelieu, Paris, 75002, France
Tel.: (33) 1 44 86 20 00
Mutual Fund Management Services
N.A.I.C.S.: 523940

Allianz Actions Japon   (1)
87 Rue de Richelieu, Paris, 75002, France
Tel.: (33) 1 44 86 20 00
Mutual Fund Management Services
N.A.I.C.S.: 523940

Allianz Africa S.A.   (1)
1 cours Michelet, CS 30051, 92076, Paris, Cedex, France
Tel.: (33) 158851500
General Insurance Services
N.A.I.C.S.: 524210

Allianz Alapkezelo Zrt.   (1)
Konyves Kalman krt 48-52, 1087, Budapest, Hungary
Tel.: (36) 12372399
Insurance Services
N.A.I.C.S.: 524126
Laszlo Szentasko *(Sr Portfolio Mgr)*

Allianz Alternative Assets Holding GmbH   (1)
Koninginstr 19, 80802, Munich, Germany
Tel.: (49) 893 80 00
Web Site: http://www.allianz.de
Investment Management Service
N.A.I.C.S.: 523999

Allianz Argentina Compania de Seguros S.A.   (1)
Corrientes 299, C1043AAC, Buenos Aires, Argentina
Tel.: (54) 11 4320380001
Web Site: http://www.allianz.com.ar
General Insurance Services
N.A.I.C.S.: 524210

Allianz Asset Management of America L.P   (1)

680 Newport Centre Dr Ste 250, Newport Beach, CA 92660
Tel.: (949) 219-2000
Asset Management Services
N.A.I.C.S.: 523940

Allianz Australia Advantage Ltd.   (1)
GPO Box 4049, Sydney, 2001, NSW, Australia
Tel.: (61) 1300368764
General Insurance Services
N.A.I.C.S.: 524210

Allianz Australia Insurance Limited   (1)
GPO Box 4049, GPO Box 4049, Sydney, 2001, NSW, Australia
Tel.: (61) 289889581
Emp.: 2,800
General Insurance Services
N.A.I.C.S.: 524210

Allianz Australia Life Insurance Limited   (1)
L 12 2 Market St, Sydney, 2000, NSW, Australia
Tel.: (61) 131000
Fire Insurance Services
N.A.I.C.S.: 524113

Allianz Australia Limited   (1)
2 Market Street, Sydney, 2000, NSW, Australia   **(100%)**
Tel.: (61) 730239322
Web Site: http://www.allianz.com.au
Sales Range: $1-4.9 Billion
Emp.: 2,900
Insurance Services
N.A.I.C.S.: 524128
Vicky Drakousis *(Chief HR Officer)*

Subsidiary (Non-US):

Allianz New Zealand Ltd.   (2)
Level 1 152 Fanshawe St, PO Box 794, Auckland, 1010, New Zealand   **(100%)**
Web Site: http://www.allianz.co.nz
Sales Range: $50-74.9 Million
Emp.: 50
Personal, Commercial & Corporate Insurance
N.A.I.C.S.: 524128

Affiliate (Non-US):

Assurances Generales du Laos   (2)
2nd Floor Vientiane Commercial Bank Building, 33 Lane Xang Avenue, Vientiane, Lao People's Democratic Republic
Tel.: (856) 21217600
Web Site: http://www.agl-allianz.com
Sales Range: $50-74.9 Million
Emp.: 90
Insurance Services; Owned 51% by AGF S.A. & 49% by the Government of Laos
N.A.I.C.S.: 524298

Astree Assurances   (2)
45 Avenue Khereddine Pacha, 1002, Tunis, Tunisia
Tel.: (216) 71792211
Sales Range: $25-49.9 Million
Emp.: 150
Insurance Services
N.A.I.C.S.: 524298

Subsidiary (Non-US):

Axioma Insurance (Cyprus) Ltd   (2)
Iris House 2nd Floor Office no 4 John Kennedy St, PO Box 54350, 3106, Lemesos, Cyprus
Tel.: (357) 25588788
Insurance & Financial Services
N.A.I.C.S.: 524298

Allianz Australia Services Pty Limited   (1)
2 Market St, Sydney, 2000, NSW, Australia
Tel.: (61) 293906262
Financial Management Services
N.A.I.C.S.: 523999

Allianz Australia Workers Compensation (NSW) Limited   (1)
Level 12 2 Market Street, Sydney, 2000, NSW, Australia
Tel.: (61) 1300 130 664
Employee Benefit Services
N.A.I.C.S.: 525190

Allianz SE—(Continued)

Allianz Australia Workers Compensation (SA) Limited (1)
89 Pirie St, Adelaide, 5000, SA, Australia
Tel.: (61) 8 8394 8111
Employee Benefit Services
N.A.I.C.S.: 525190

Allianz Australia Workers Compensation (Victoria) Limited (1)
Level 5 360 Elizabeth Street, Melbourne, 3001, VIC, Australia
Tel.: (61) 3 9234 3800
Employee Benefit Services
N.A.I.C.S.: 525190

Allianz Automotive Services GmbH (1)
Einsteinring 28, Aschheim, 85609, Munich, Germany
Tel.: (49) 89 2000 48 000
Web Site: http://www.allianz-warranty.com
Vehicle Insurance Services
N.A.I.C.S.: 524298

Allianz Autowelt GmbH (1)
Kunigistr 28, 80802, Munich, Germany
Tel.: (49) 899233450
Web Site: http://www.allianz-autowelt.de
Sales Range: $50-74.9 Million
Emp.: 8
Insurance Services
N.A.I.C.S.: 524298

Allianz Aviation Managers LLC (1)
317 Madison Ave Ste 1110, New York, NY 10017
Tel.: (646) 472-1400
Web Site: http://www.allianz.com
General Insurance Services
N.A.I.C.S.: 524210

Allianz Ayudhya Assurance Pcl. (1)
Floor 1 Ploenchit Tower 898 Ploen Chit Road, 898 Ploenchit Road, Bangkok, 10330, Thailand
Tel.: (66) 23057000
Web Site: https://www.allianz.co.th
Life Insurance Products & Services
N.A.I.C.S.: 524113
Patchara Taveechaiwattana (Chief Market Mgmt Officer & Member-Mgmt Bd)

Allianz Ayudhya General Insurance Public Company Limited (1)
898 Ploenchit Tower 1st Floor Ploenchit Road, Lumpini Pathumwan, Bangkok, 10330, Thailand
Tel.: (66) 1292
Finance & Insurance Services
N.A.I.C.S.: 524210

Allianz Bank Financial Advisors S.p.A. (1)
Piazzale Lodi 3, 20137, Milan, Italy
Tel.: (39) 02 7216 8000
Web Site: http://www.allianzbank.it
Commercial Banking Services
N.A.I.C.S.: 522110

Allianz Benelux S.A. (1)
Koning Albert II-laan 32, 1000, Brussels, Belgium
Tel.: (32) 22146111
Web Site: https://allianz.be
Emp.: 1,000
Insurance Services
N.A.I.C.S.: 524210

Allianz Beratungs- und Vertriebs-AG (1)
Konigstr 28, 80802, Munich, Germany
Tel.: (49) 8938000
Insurance Consulting Services
N.A.I.C.S.: 524298

Allianz Biznes Sp. z o.o. (1)
Rodziny Hiszpaskich 1, 02-685, Warsaw, Poland
Tel.: (48) 22 567 50 00
Financial Management Services
N.A.I.C.S.: 523999

Allianz Bulgaria Holding (1)
Str Srebarna 16, 1407, Sofia, Bulgaria
Tel.: (359) 70013014
Web Site: https://www.allianz.bg
Sales Range: $700-749.9 Million
Emp.: 1,400
Insurance Services

N.A.I.C.S.: 524298

Allianz Bulgaria Pension Company AD (1)
19B Tzar Boris III Blvd, Sofia, 1612, Bulgaria
Tel.: (359) 29334800
Pension Fund Management Services
N.A.I.C.S.: 523940

Alllariz Burkina Assurances Vie (1)
Avenue de l'UEMOA 01, BP 398, Ouagadougou, 01bp398, Burkina Faso
Tel.: (226) 50306204
Fire Insurance Services
N.A.I.C.S.: 524113
Chyerry Droussou (Mng Dir)

Allianz C.P. General Insurance Co., Ltd. (1)
CP Twr 19 Fl 313 Silom Rd Bangrak, Bangkok, 10500, Thailand
Tel.: (66) 26389000
Web Site: http://www.allianzcp.com
Sales Range: $50-74.9 Million
Emp.: 100
Insurance Services; Owned by Allianz AG & by Charoen Pokphang Group
N.A.I.C.S.: 524298
Pakit Iamopus (Pres & CEO)

Allianz Cameroun Assurances SA (1)
Rue Manga Bell, BP 105, Douala, Cameroon
Tel.: (237) 233502000
Insurance Services
N.A.I.C.S.: 524126
Eric Yakam (Mgr-Investment)

Allianz Cameroun Assurances Vie S.A. (1)
Immeuble Allianz BP 1124 Rue Manga Bell, Douala, Cameroon
Tel.: (237) 233502000
Web Site: https://www.allianz.cm
Emp.: 100
Finance & Insurance Services
N.A.I.C.S.: 524210

Allianz Capital Partners GmbH (1)
Seidlstrasse 24-24a, 80335, Munich, Germany
Tel.: (49) 8938007010
Web Site:
   http://www.allianzcapitalpartners.com
Sales Range: $50-74.9 Million
Emp.: 50
Industrial, Life, Health & Specialty Insurance; Asset Management Services
N.A.I.C.S.: 524298
Rainer Husmann (CFO, COO & Member-Mgmt Bd)

Subsidiary (Domestic):

Allianz Capital Partners Verwaltungs GmbH (2)
Theresienstrasse 6-8, 80333, Munich, Germany
Tel.: (49) 8938000
Office Administrative Services
N.A.I.C.S.: 561110

Allianz Private Equity Partners GmbH (2)
Gheresien St No 6-8, 80333, Munich, Germany
Tel.: (49) 89380019900
Web Site:
   http://www.allianzcapitalpartners.com
Sales Range: $50-74.9 Million
Financial Services
N.A.I.C.S.: 523999

Joint Venture (Non-US):

Gas Connect Austria GmbH (2)
Floridsdorfer Hauptstrasse 1, Floridsdorfer Hauptstrasse 1, 1210, Vienna, Austria (29.4%)
Tel.: (43) 1275000
Web Site: https://www.gasconnect.at
Sales Range: $75-99.9 Million
Emp.: 240
Petroleum Services
N.A.I.C.S.: 213112
Harald Stindl (Mng Dir)

NET4GAS, s.r.o. (2)

N.A.I.C.S.: 524298

Na Hrebenech II 1718/8, 140 21, Prague, Czech Republic
Tel.: (420) 220221111
Web Site: http://www.net4gas.cz
Sales Range: $50-74.9 Million
Natural Gas Transportation Services
N.A.I.C.S.: 486210
Andreas Rau (CEO & Mng Dir)

Porterbrook Leasing Company Limited (2)
Ivatt House 7 The Point Pinnacle Way, Pride Park, Derby, DE24 8ZS, United Kingdom
Tel.: (44) 1332285050
Web Site: https://www.porterbrook.co.uk
Rolling Stock Leasing Services
N.A.I.C.S.: 532411

Allianz Capital Partners of America LLC (1)
1633 Broadway, New York, NY 10105
Tel.: (212) 739-3600
Infrastrcuture Management Services
N.A.I.C.S.: 561110

Allianz Centrafrique Assurances (1)
Boulevard Du General De Gaulle, BP 343, Bangui, Central African Republic
Tel.: (236) 21613666
General Insurance Services
N.A.I.C.S.: 524210

Allianz China General Insurance Company Ltd. (1)
Room 10 34/F Guangzhou International Finance Center, Guangzhou, 510623, China
Tel.: (86) 20 8396 6788
Web Site: http://www.allianz.cn
Emp.: 180
General Insurance Services
N.A.I.C.S.: 524298
Victor Jiang (Chief Transformation Officer)

Subsidiary (Non-US):

Commercial Bank Allianz Bulgaria Ad (2)
79 Maria Louisa Boulevard, 1202, Sofia, Bulgaria
Tel.: (359) 29215404
Web Site: http://www.bank.allianz.bg
Sales Range: $100-124.9 Million
Emp.: 918
Banking Services
N.A.I.C.S.: 522110

Allianz China Life Insurance Co., Ltd. (1)
Unit 5107 CITIC Plaza 233 Tianhe Beilu, Guangzhou, 510613, China
Tel.: (86) 2038911889
Web Site: http://www.allianz.com.cn
Fire Insurance Services
N.A.I.C.S.: 524113

Subsidiary (Non-US):

AGCS Hong Kong (2)
Suites 403-11 4/F Cityplaza Phase Four 12 Tai Koo Wan Road Tai Koo, Shing Island East, Hong Kong, China (Hong Kong) (100%)
Tel.: (852) 25216651
Web Site: http://www.allianz.com.hk
Sales Range: $150-199.9 Million
Emp.: 100
Insurance Services
N.A.I.C.S.: 524298

Allianz Insurance Management Asia Pacific Pte. Ltd. (1)
12 Marina View 1401 Asia Square Tower 2, Singapore, 018961, Singapore (100%)
Tel.: (65) 62978802
Web Site: http://www.allianz.com
Sales Range: $50-74.9 Million
Emp.: 100
N.A.I.C.S.: 524128

Allianz Compagnia Italiana Finanziamenti S.p.A. (1)
Corso Italia 23, Milan, 20122, Italy
Tel.: (39) 0272161
Securities Brokerage Services
N.A.I.C.S.: 523150

Allianz Compania de Seguros y Reaseguros SA (1)

Calle Tarragona 109, 08014, Barcelona, Spain (100%)
Web Site: http://www.allianz.es
Sales Range: $150-199.9 Million
Emp.: 300
Insurance Provider
N.A.I.C.S.: 524128

Allianz Cote d'Ivoire Assurances (1)
2 Bld Roume 01, PO Box 1741, Abidjan, Cote d'Ivoire
Tel.: (225) 20304000
Web Site: http://www.allianz.com
Insurance Services
N.A.I.C.S.: 524298

Allianz Cote d'Ivoire Assurances Vie SA (1)
2 bld Roume, BP 1741, Abidjan, Cote d'Ivoire
Tel.: (225) 20304000
Insurance Services
N.A.I.C.S.: 524126

Allianz DGD Fonds (1)
Mainzer Landstrasse 11-13, Frankfurt am Main, 60329, Germany
Tel.: (49) 18 03 30 33 11
Mutual Fund Management Services
N.A.I.C.S.: 523940

Allianz Deutschland AG (1)
Konigstrasse 28, 80802, Munich, Germany
Tel.: (49) 8938000
Holding Company; General Insurance Services
N.A.I.C.S.: 551112
Klaus-Peter Rohler (CEO)

Allianz Direct New Europe Sp. z o.o. (1)
ul Rodziny Hiszpanskich 1, Warsaw, 02-685, Poland
Tel.: (48) 22 567 6767
General Insurance Services
N.A.I.C.S.: 524210

Allianz Direct S.p.A. (1)
Piazza Tre Torri 3, 20145, Milan, Italy
Tel.: (39) 0230459009
Web Site: https://www.allianzdirect.it
Insurance Services
N.A.I.C.S.: 524210

Allianz Direct Versicherungs-AG (1)
Konigstrasse 28, 80802, Munich, Germany
Tel.: (49) 8988997091
Insurance Services
N.A.I.C.S.: 524126

Allianz Direct s.r.o. (1)
Ke Stvanici 656/3, Prague, 186 00, Czech Republic
Tel.: (420) 844 855 866
Web Site: http://www.allianzdirect.cz
General Insurance Services
N.A.I.C.S.: 524210

Allianz Dresdner Bauspar AG (1)
Am Sonnenplatz 1, 61116, Bad Vilbel, Germany (100%)
Tel.: (49) 891796167
Sales Range: $200-249.9 Million
Emp.: 300
N.A.I.C.S.: 524128

Allianz Dresdner Pension Consult GmbH (1)
Marienstr 50, D-70178, Stuttgart, Germany
Tel.: (49) 71166396096
Web Site: http://www.adpc.allianz.de
Sales Range: $50-74.9 Million
Emp.: 26
Pension Services
N.A.I.C.S.: 525110

Allianz Elementar Versicherungs AG (1)
Hietzinger Kai 101-105, PO Box 2000, A-1130, Vienna, Austria
Tel.: (43) 001878072010
Web Site: http://www.allianz.at
Sales Range: $1-4.9 Billion
Emp.: 3,000
Insurance Services
N.A.I.C.S.: 524298

Subsidiary (Non-US):

Allianz Elementar Lebensversicherungs AG (2)

(100%)
Web Site: http://www.allianz.at
Sales Range: $1-4.9 Billion
Emp.: 3,000
Life Insurance
N.A.I.C.S.: 524113

Allianz Elementar
Versicherungs-Aktiengesellschaft (1)
Insurance Services
N.A.I.C.S.: 524126

Allianz Equity Investments Ltd. (1)
57 Ladymead, Guildford, GU1 1DB, United
Kingdom
Tel.: (44) 1483 568 161
Financial Management Services
N.A.I.C.S.: 523999

Allianz Europe B.V. (1)
Keizersgracht 484, PO Box 9444, 1017 EH,
Amsterdam, Netherlands
Tel.: (31) 205618711
Holding Company
N.A.I.C.S.: 551112

Subsidiary (Non-US):

Allianz Saudi Fransi Cooperative In-
surance Company (2)
Khorais Road Khaleej Bridge, PO Box
3540, Riyadh, 11481, Saudi Arabia **(51%)**
Tel.: (966) 11 821 3000
Web Site: http://www.allianzsf.com
Insurance Services
N.A.I.C.S.: 524298

Allianz Sigorta A.S. (2)
Allianz Tower Kucukbakkalkoy Mahallesi
Kayisdagi Cad No 1, Atasehir, 34750, Istan-
bul, Turkiye **(84%)**
Tel.: (90) 2165566666
Web Site: http://www.allianzsigorta.com.tr
Sales Range: Less than $1 Million
Emp.: 700
Health, Property & Casualty Insurance
Products & Services
N.A.I.C.S.: 524298
Oliver Baete *(Vice Chm)*

Subsidiary (Domestic):

Allianz Hayat ve Emeklilik A.S. (3)
Allianz Tower Kucukbakkalkoy Mahallesi
Kayisdagi Cad No 1, Atasehir, 34750, Istan-
bul, Turkiye
Tel.: (90) 2165566666
Web Site: http://www.allianzemeklilik.com.tr
Sales Range: Less than $1 Million
Emp.: 700
Life Insurance & Pension Products & Ser-
vices
N.A.I.C.S.: 524298

Allianz Finance III B.V. (1)
Keizersgracht 484, Amsterdam, 1017 EH,
Netherlands
Tel.: (31) 20 5569715
Financial Management Services
N.A.I.C.S.: 523999

Allianz Finance Pty Ltd. (1)
Level 9 2 Market Street, Sydney, 2000,
NSW, Australia
Tel.: (61) 2 8258 6073
Financial Management Services
N.A.I.C.S.: 523999

Allianz Fire and Marine Insurance
Japan Ltd. (1)
Anzen Bldg 1-6-6 Motoakasaka, Minato-ku,
Tokyo, 107 0051, Japan **(100%)**
Tel.: (81) 345887500
Web Site: http://www.allianz.co.jp
Sales Range: $50-74.9 Million
Emp.: 100
Insurance Provider
N.A.I.C.S.: 524128
Michael Maicher *(Pres)*

Allianz France (1)
87 rue de Richelieu, 75002, Paris, France
Tel.: (33) 144862000
Web Site: http://www.allianz.fr
Insurance & Financial Services
N.A.I.C.S.: 524298
Clarisse Kopff *(CFO)*

Allianz France Infrastructure 1 (1)
87 Rue de Richelieu, 75002, Paris, France
Tel.: (33) 1 44 86 20 00

Financial Management Services
N.A.I.C.S.: 523999

Allianz General Insurance Company
S.A. (1)
Athinon Ave 110 Bldg C, GR 10442, Ath-
ens, Greece **(100%)**
Tel.: (30) 2106905500
Web Site: http://www.allianz.gr
Sales Range: Less than $1 Million
Insurance Provider
N.A.I.C.S.: 524128

Allianz General Laos Ltd. (1)
33 Lane Xang Avenue 2nd Floor ANZ Build-
ing, PO Box 4223, Vientiane, Lao People's
Democratic Republic
Tel.: (856) 21215903
Web Site: http://www.agl-allianz.com
Health Insurance Services
N.A.I.C.S.: 524114
Guy Apovy *(CEO)*

Allianz Global Assistance -
Canada (1)
4273 King St E, Kitchener, N2P 2E9, ON,
Canada
Tel.: (519) 742-2800
Web Site: http://www.allianz-assistance.ca
Travel Insurance Services
N.A.I.C.S.: 524210
Gino Riola *(VP-Sls)*

Allianz Global Assistance S.A.S. (1)
37 Rue Taitbout, Paris, 75009, France
Tel.: (33) 1 5325 5325
Web Site: http://www.allianz-global-
assistance.com
Travel Insurance & Medical Assistance Ser-
vices
N.A.I.C.S.: 524298

Allianz Global Assistance USA (1)
9950 Maryland Dr, Richmond, VA 23233
Tel.: (800) 628-4908
Web Site: http://www.allianzassistance.com
General Insurance Services
N.A.I.C.S.: 524210
Michael J. Nelson *(CEO)*

Allianz Global Benefits GmbH (1)
Reinsburgstrasse 19, 70178, Stuttgart,
Germany **(100%)**
Tel.: (49) 7116631900
Web Site:
http://www.allianzglobalbenefits.com
Employee Benefits Network
N.A.I.C.S.: 524298
Cyril Samson *(Mng Dir)*

Allianz Global Corporate &
Specialty (1)
Saridar Building 92 Al Tahrir Street Dokki,
Dokki, Giza, Egypt
Tel.: (20) 2 37605445 717
General Insurance Services
N.A.I.C.S.: 524210

Allianz Global Corporate &
Specialty (1)
Nordic Region Office Pilestraede 58, 1112,
Copenhagen, Denmark
Tel.: (45) 32700001
General Insurance Services
N.A.I.C.S.: 524210

Allianz Global Corporate &
Specialty (1)
Mannerheimintie 12 B, Helsinki, 81737,
Finland
Tel.: (358) 9 25166432
General Insurance Services
N.A.I.C.S.: 524210
Ilkka Ilmonen *(Gen Mgr)*

Allianz Global Corporate &
Specialty (1)
Corso Italia 23, Milan, 20122, Italy
Tel.: (39) 02 72162225
Web Site: http://www.agcs.allianz.com
General Insurance Services
N.A.I.C.S.: 524210

Allianz Global Corporate &
Specialty (1)
Carrera 13 A N 29-24 Piso 17 Torre Allianz
Santa Fe De, Bogota, Colombia
Tel.: (57) 1 5600601
General Insurance Services
N.A.I.C.S.: 524210

Allianz Global Corporate &
Specialty (1)
Toedistrasse 61, 8002, Zurich, Switzerland
Tel.: (41) 44 285 1616
General Insurance Services
N.A.I.C.S.: 524210

Allianz Global Corporate &
Specialty (1)
ul Rodziny Hiszpanskich 1, 02-685, War-
saw, Poland
Tel.: (48) 22 567 4000
General Insurance Services
N.A.I.C.S.: 524210

Allianz Global Corporate & Specialty
AG (1)
Fritz Schaeffer St 9, 81724, Munich,
Germany **(100%)**
Tel.: (49) 8938000
Web Site: http://www.agcs.allianz.com
Sales Range: $1-4.9 Billion
Emp.: 3,000
Property & Casualty Insurance Products &
Services
N.A.I.C.S.: 524126
Chris Fischer Hirs *(CEO)*

Subsidiary (Non-US):

Allianz Global Corporate & Specialty
(France) S.A. (2)
Tour Opus 12 77 Esplanade du General de
Gaulle, Paris, 75444, La Defense, France
Tel.: (33) 1 5885 9550
Web Site: http://www.agcs.allianz.com
Sales Range: $1-4.9 Billion
Emp.: 3,000
Property & Casualty Insurance Products &
Services
N.A.I.C.S.: 524126
Shanil Williams *(Head-Fin Lines-Global)*

Unit (Non-US):

Allianz Global Corporate & Specialty -
Australia (2)
Level 12 2 Market St, Sydney, 2000, NSW,
Australia
Tel.: (61) 293906994
Web Site: http://www.agcs.allianz.com
Property & Casualty Insurance Products &
Services
N.A.I.C.S.: 524126

Allianz Global Corporate & Specialty -
Austria (2)
Hietzinger Kai 101-105, A 1130, Vienna,
Austria
Tel.: (43) 1 87807 88700
Web Site: http://www.allianz.at
Sales Range: $400-449.9 Million
Emp.: 600
Property & Casualty Insurance Products &
Services
N.A.I.C.S.: 524126
Andreas Schmitt *(Head-Market Mgmt-*
Austria)

Allianz Global Corporate & Specialty -
Belgium (2)
Uitbreidingstraat 86, 2600, Antwerp,
Berchem, Belgium
Tel.: (32) 3 304 1600
Web Site: http://www.agcs.allianz.com
Sales Range: $50-74.9 Million
Emp.: 35
Property & Casualty Insurance Products &
Services
N.A.I.C.S.: 524126
Ronald Jorssen *(Head-Risk Consulting-*
Belgium)

Allianz Global Corporate & Specialty -
Ireland (2)
Elmtech Merrion Rd, Dublin, 4, Ireland
Tel.: (353) 16133000
Web Site: http://www.allianz.ie
Sales Range: $200-249.9 Million
Emp.: 500
Property & Casualty Insurance Products &
Services
N.A.I.C.S.: 524126

Allianz Global Corporate & Specialty -
Singapore (2)
12 Marina View 14-01 Asia Square Tower 2,
08-01 Centennial Tower, Singapore,
018961, Singapore

Tel.: (65) 6297 2529
Web Site: http://www.agcs.allianz.com
Sales Range: $75-99.9 Million
Emp.: 70
Property & Casualty Insurance Products &
Services
N.A.I.C.S.: 524126

Allianz Global Corporate & Specialty -
UK (2)
60 Gracechurch St, London, EC3V 0HR,
United Kingdom
Tel.: (44) 20 3451 3000
Web Site: http://www.agcs.allianz.com
Sales Range: $100-124.9 Million
Emp.: 200
Property & Casualty Insurance Products &
Services
N.A.I.C.S.: 524126
Elke Vagenende *(Head-Market Mgmt)*

Subsidiary (US):

Allianz Global Risks US Insurance
Company (2)
225 W Washington St Ste 1800, Chicago,
IL 60606 **(100%)**
Tel.: (312) 224-3300
Web Site: http://www.agcs.allianz.com
Sales Range: $400-449.9 Million
Emp.: 800
Property & Casualty Insurance Products &
Services
N.A.I.C.S.: 524126
Wanda Phillips *(Head-Entertainment-North*
America)

Subsidiary (Non-US):

AIM Underwriting Limited (3)
1600-130 Adelaide Street, Toronto, M5H
3P5, ON, Canada
Tel.: (416) 849-4542
Insurance Underwriting Services
N.A.I.C.S.: 524127

Unit (Non-US):

Allianz Global Corporate & Specialty -
Canada (3)
130 Adelaide St W Suite 1600, Toronto,
M5H 3P5, ON, Canada
Tel.: (416) 915-4247
Web Site: https://www.allianz.com
Sales Range: $75-99.9 Million
Emp.: 100
Property & Casualty Insurance Products &
Services
N.A.I.C.S.: 524126

Subsidiary (Non-US):

Allianz Risk Transfer AG (2)
Lavaterstrasse 67, 8002, Zurich, Switzer-
land
Tel.: (41) 442851818
Web Site: http://www.art-allianz.com
Sales Range: $900-999.9 Million
Emp.: 40
Financial & Insurance Services
N.A.I.C.S.: 525990

Subsidiary (Non-US):

AGCS Dubai (3)
Dubai International Financial Center Gate
Village 8, Dubai, 7659, United Arab Emir-
ates
Tel.: (971) 4 7026666
Web Site: http://www.allianz.com
Emp.: 20
Reinsurance Services
N.A.I.C.S.: 524130
Sajan Baburajan *(Mgr-Claims)*

Allianz Risk Transfer (Bermuda)
Limited (3)
Tel.: (441) 2954722
Web Site: http://www.art-allianz.com
Sales Range: $75-99.9 Million
Emp.: 10
Financial & Insurance Services
N.A.I.C.S.: 525990

Subsidiary (US):

Allianz Risk Transfer, Inc. (3)
1330 Avenue of the Americas 19th Fl, New
York, NY 10019
Tel.: (646) 840-5000

Allianz SE—(Continued)

Web Site: http://www.art-allianz.com
Sales Range: $50-74.9 Million
Emp.: 15
Financial & Insurance Services
N.A.I.C.S.: 525990
Bill Scaldaferri (Pres & CEO)

Allianz Global Corporate & Specialty South Africa Ltd. (1)
The Firs 2nd Floor 32A Cradock Avenue, Rosebank, 2196, South Africa
Tel.: (27) 871950581
Fire Insurance Services
N.A.I.C.S.: 524210
Thusang Mahlangu (CEO)

Allianz Global Corporate & Specialty, National Insurance Company (1)
Unit 12 & 13 Block A Regent Square Simpang 150, Kampong Kiajong, BE1318, Brunei Darussalam
Tel.: (673) 242 6888
Web Site: http://www.allianz.com
Sales Range: $50-74.9 Million
Emp.: 38
General Insurance Services
N.A.I.C.S.: 524298
Parag Bavishi (Deputy Head-Alternative Risk Transfer Div-Americas)

Allianz Global Investors (France) S.A. (1)
87 rue de Richelieu, 75444, Paris, France
Tel.: (33) 144862000
Web Site: http://www.allianzgi.fr
Sales Range: $75-99.9 Million
Emp.: 250
Financial Services
N.A.I.C.S.: 525990
Franck Dixmier (Dir Gen)

Allianz Global Investors AG (1)
Seidl str 24-24A, 80335, Munich, Germany
Tel.: (49) 89122070
Web Site: http://www.allianzglobalinvestors.com
Sales Range: $200-249.9 Million
Emp.: 400
Investment & Financial Services
N.A.I.C.S.: 523999
Malie Conway (Chief Investment Officer-Fixed Income-Global)

Subsidiary (Domestic):

Allianz Climate Solutions GmbH (2)
Koeniginstrasse 28, 80802, Munich, Germany
Tel.: (49) 89380012203
Web Site: http://www.acs.allianz.com
General Insurance Services
N.A.I.C.S.: 524298
Simone Ruiz-Vergote (Mng Dir & Head-Climate Advisory)

Subsidiary (US):

Allianz Global Investors (2)
680 Newport Center Dr Ste 250, Newport Beach, CA 92660-6309
Tel.: (949) 219-2200
Web Site: http://www.adam-us.com
Sales Range: $75-99.9 Million
Emp.: 120
Investment Management
N.A.I.C.S.: 523940
Spencer Garrett Rhodes (Mgr-Alternative Investments Global Bus)

Allianz Global Investors (2)
555 Mission St Ste 1700, San Francisco, CA 94105 (100%)
Tel.: (415) 954-5400
Web Site: http://www.us.allianzgi.com
Sales Range: $150-199.9 Million
Emp.: 350
Investment Advisory Services
N.A.I.C.S.: 523940
David Owen (Gen Mgr)

Subsidiary (Non-US):

Allianz Global Investors (Luxembourg) S.A. (2)
6A Rte de Treves Senningerbrg, 2633, Luxembourg, Luxembourg (100%)
Tel.: (352) 4634631

Web Site: http://www.allianzglobalinvestors.lu
Sales Range: $50-74.9 Million
Emp.: 55
International Banking; Asset Management
N.A.I.C.S.: 522299

Allianz Global Investors (Schweiz) AG (2)
Hohlstriffe 552, 8048, Zurich, Switzerland
Tel.: (41) 583580542
Web Site: http://www.allianzglobalinvestors.com
Investment & Financial Services
N.A.I.C.S.: 523999

Allianz Global Investors (UK) Ltd. (2)
199 Bishopsgate, London, EC2M 3TY, United Kingdom
Tel.: (44) 2070651407
Web Site: http://www.allianzglobalinvestors.co.uk
Sales Range: $75-99.9 Million
Emp.: 170
Investment & Financial Services
N.A.I.C.S.: 523999
Mike Riddell (Portfolio Mgr-Fixed Income)

Subsidiary (US):

Allianz Global Investors Distributors LLC (2)
1633 Broadway, New York, NY 10019-7585
Tel.: (212) 739-3000
Web Site: http://www.allianzinvestors.com
Sales Range: $100-124.9 Million
Emp.: 115
Mutual Fund
N.A.I.C.S.: 523150

Subsidiary (Domestic):

Allianz Global Investors GmbH (2)
Seidlstrasse 24-24a, 80335, Munich, Germany
Tel.: (49) 89122070
Web Site: https://de.allianzgi.com
Investment Management Service
N.A.I.C.S.: 523940
Elizabeth Corley (Mng Dir)

Subsidiary (Non-US):

Rogge Global Partners Ltd. (3)
Sion Hall 56 Victoria Embankment, London, EC4Y 0DZ, United Kingdom (100%)
Tel.: (44) 2078428420
Web Site: http://www.roggeglobal.com
Fixed Income Trading Services
N.A.I.C.S.: 523150
Olaf Rogge (Founder)

Subsidiary (Non-US):

Allianz Global Investors Hong Kong Limited (2)
Suite 2003B 21 Fl Cheung Kong Center, Central, China (Hong Kong)
Tel.: (852) 22388688
Web Site: http://www.allianzglobalinvestors.com.hk
Sales Range: $75-99.9 Million
Emp.: 200
Investment & Financial Services
N.A.I.C.S.: 523999
Philip Tso (Head-Institutional Solutions-Asia Pacific)

Subsidiary (Non-US):

Allianz Global Investors Securities Investment Consulting Co. Ltd. (3)
7th Fl 378 Fu-Hsing N Rd, Taipei, 104, Taiwan
Tel.: (886) 225022989
Sales Range: $100-124.9 Million
Emp.: 200
Investment & Financial Services
N.A.I.C.S.: 523999

Allianz Global Investors Singapore Ltd. (3)
79 Robinson Road 09-03, Singapore, 068897, Singapore
Tel.: (65) 63118000
Web Site: http://www.allianzglobalinvestors.com.sg

Sales Range: $50-74.9 Million
Emp.: 30
Investment & Financial Services
N.A.I.C.S.: 523999

Allianz Global Investors Taiwan Ltd. (3)
Sales Range: $75-99.9 Million
Emp.: 200
Investment & Financial Services
N.A.I.C.S.: 523999

RCM Capital Management Pty Ltd (3)
Level 57 MLC Centre 19 29 Martin Pl, Sydney, 2000, NSW, Australia
Tel.: (61) 292382070
Web Site: http://www.rcm.com
Investment & Financial Services
N.A.I.C.S.: 523999

Subsidiary (Domestic):

Allianz Global Investors Kapitalanlagegesellschaft mbH (2)
Mainzer Landstrasse 11-13, 60329, Frankfurt am Main, Germany
Tel.: (49) 1803303311
Web Site: http://www.allianzglobalinvestors.de
Investment Advisory Services
N.A.I.C.S.: 523940
Thomas Hammer (Head-Reg Acct Mgmt)

Subsidiary (US):

AllianzGI Capital LLC (2)
600 W Broadway Ste 2900, San Diego, CA 92101-3398
Tel.: (619) 687-8000
Web Site: http://www.allianzgic.com
Sales Range: $75-99.9 Million
Emp.: 150
Provider of Investment Advice
N.A.I.C.S.: 523940

Joint Venture (Non-US):

Guotai Junan Allianz Fund Management Co., Ltd. (2)
9th Floor 1318 DBS Building Shanghai Lujiazui Rd, Shanghai, 200121, China
Tel.: (86) 2138784766
Web Site: http://www.vip-funds.com
Fund Management Services; Owned 33% by Allianz Global Investors AG & 67% by Guotai Junan Securities Co., Ltd.
N.A.I.C.S.: 525910

Subsidiary (US):

NFJ Investment Group LP (2)
2100 Ross Ave Ste 700, Dallas, TX 75201-2739
Tel.: (214) 754-1780
Web Site: http://www.nfjinvestmentgroup.com
Sales Range: $25-49.9 Million
Emp.: 45
Investment Advice
N.A.I.C.S.: 523940
John L. Johnson (Mng Dir & Founder)

Pacific Investment Management Company LLC (2)
650 Newport Ctr Dr Ste 100, Newport Beach, CA 92660
Tel.: (949) 720-6000
Web Site: http://www.pimco.com
Investment Advice
N.A.I.C.S.: 523940
David N. Fisher (Mng Dir & Co-Head-Wealth Management Strategic Acco-U.S. Global)

Subsidiary (Domestic):

Columbia Property Trust, Inc. (3)
315 Park Ave S, New York, NY 10010
Tel.: (212) 687-0800
Web Site: http://www.columbia.reit
Rev.: $300,566,000
Assets: $4,086,518,000
Liabilities: $1,402,924,000
Net Worth: $2,683,594,000
Earnings: $115,710,000
Emp.: 160
Fiscal Year-end: 12/31/2020
Real Estate Investment Services
N.A.I.C.S.: 531390

Wendy W. Gill (Chief Acctg Officer & Sr VP)

Subsidiary (Domestic):

Columbia Property Trust Operating Partnership, L.P. (4)
315 Park Ave S, New York, NY 10010
Tel.: (212) 687-0800
Rev.: $248,937,000
Assets: $3,986,579,000
Liabilities: 31,726,100,000
Net Worth: $2,260,413,000
Earnings: $12,901,000
Fiscal Year-end: 12/31/2019
Real Estate Investment Services
N.A.I.C.S.: 531210
E. Nelson Mills (Pres & CEO)

Normandy Real Estate Management, LLC (4)
53 maple Ave, Morristown, NJ 07960-5219
Tel.: (973) 898-1160
Web Site: http://www.normandyrealty.com
Sales Range: $1-9.9 Million
Emp.: 65
Alternative Investment Services
N.A.I.C.S.: 523999

Division (Domestic):

PIMCO Advisory (3)
840 Newport Ctr Dr Ste 100, Newport Beach, CA 92660
Tel.: (949) 720-6426
Web Site: http://www.pimco.com
Analyzes, Designs & Manages Asset-Liability Solutions
N.A.I.C.S.: 523940
Rod Dubitsky (Exec VP)

Subsidiary (Non-US):

PIMCO Asia Ltd. (3)
24th Floor Units 2402 2403 & 2405 Nine Queen's Road, Central, China (Hong Kong)
Tel.: (852) 3650 7700
Web Site: http://www.pimco.com
Investment Management Service
N.A.I.C.S.: 523999
Eric J. Mogelof (Head-Asia Pacific)

PIMCO Asia Pte. Ltd. (3)
501 Orchard Road #09-03 Wheelock Place, Singapore, 238880, Singapore
Tel.: (65) 6564918000
Web Site: http://www.pimco.com.sg
Bond Investment Services
N.A.I.C.S.: 523999

Subsidiary (Non-US):

PIMCO Australia Pty Ltd. (4)
Level 19 363 George Street, Sydney, 2000, NSW, Australia
Tel.: (61) 292791771
Web Site: http://www.pimco.com
Sales Range: $25-49.9 Million
Emp.: 30
Bond Investment Services
N.A.I.C.S.: 523999
Scott Delaney (Sr VP & Head-Ops)

PIMCO Japan Ltd. (4)
4-1-28 Toranomon Tower Office 18th Fl, Tokyo, 105-0001, Japan
Tel.: (81) 357778150
Web Site: http://www.japan.pimco.com
Sales Range: $25-49.9 Million
Emp.: 80
Bond Investment Services
N.A.I.C.S.: 523999

Subsidiary (Non-US):

PIMCO Canada Corp. (3)
199 Bay Street Suite 2050, PO Box 363, Toronto, M5L 1G2, ON, Canada
Tel.: (416) 368-3350
Web Site: https://www.pimco.com
Sales Range: $50-74.9 Million
Emp.: 18
Bond Investment Services
N.A.I.C.S.: 523999

PIMCO Europe Ltd. (3)
11 Baker Street, London, W1U 3AH, United Kingdom
Tel.: (44) 2036401000
Web Site: http://www.pimco.co.uk
Bond Investment Services
N.A.I.C.S.: 523999

Philippe Bodereau *(Portfolio Mgr & Head-Fin Res-Global)*

Subsidiary (Non-US):

PIMCO (Switzerland) LLC (4)
Dreikoenigstrasse 31a, Zurich, 8002, Switzerland
Tel.: (41) 442083867
Web Site: http://www.pimco.com
Sales Range: $75-99.9 Million
Emp.: 4
Risk & Investments Services
N.A.I.C.S.: 523999
Daniel Huk *(VP & Mgr-Acct)*

PIMCO Deutschland GmbH (4)
Seidlstr 24-24a, Munich, 80335, Germany
Tel.: (49) 89 1220 80
Web Site: http://de.pimco.com
Investment Management Service
N.A.I.C.S.: 523999
Frank Witt *(Chm)*

Subsidiary (Domestic):

PIMCO Global Advisors LLC (3)
650 Newport Centre Dr, Newport Beach, CA 92660
Tel.: (949) 219-2200
Web Site: http://www.pimco.com
Investment Advisory Services
N.A.I.C.S.: 523940

PIMCO Investments LLC (3)
1633 Broadway, New York, NY 10019
Tel.: (212) 739-3000
Web Site: http://www.pimco.com
Sales Range: $150-199.9 Million
Emp.: 400
Partnership Holding Company for Investment Management Services
N.A.I.C.S.: 525990
Sean McCarthy *(Exec VP & Head-Municipal Credit Res)*

Subsidiary (Non-US):

Primacy Underwriting Management Pty Limited (2)
357 Collins St Level 20, Melbourne, 3000, VIC, Australia
Tel.: (61) 3 9603 1050
Web Site: http://www.pum.com.au
Insurer of Crop & Forestry Businesses
N.A.I.C.S.: 524126

Subsidiary (Domestic):

cominvest Asset Management GmbH (2)
Platz Der Einheit 1, 60327, Frankfurt am Main, Germany
Tel.: (49) 6913010
Web Site: http://www.cominvest.de
Sales Range: $300-349.9 Million
Investment Trust
N.A.I.C.S.: 523991

Subsidiary (Non-US):

Cominvest Investment Luxembourg S.A. (3)
25 Rue Edward Steichen, L 2540, Luxembourg, Luxembourg
Tel.: (352) 25111
Investment Advisory Services
N.A.I.C.S.: 523940

Subsidiary (Domestic):

risklab GmbH (2)
Seidlstr 24 - 24a, 80335, Munich, Germany
Tel.: (49) 89 1220 7750
Web Site: http://www.risklab.com
Sales Range: $25-49.9 Million
Emp.: 33
Asset Management Services
N.A.I.C.S.: 523940

Allianz Global Investors Asia Pacific GmbH (1)
27th Floor ICBC Tower 3 Garden Road, Central, China (Hong Kong)
Tel.: (852) 2238 8888
Web Site: http://www.allianzgi.com
Financial Management Services
N.A.I.C.S.: 523999

Allianz Global Investors Asia Pacific Limited (1)

27/F ICBC Tower 3 Garden Road, Central, China (Hong Kong)
Tel.: (852) 2238 8888
Web Site: http://www.allianzgi.hk
Sales Range: $200-249.9 Million
Emp.: 300
Investment Management Service
N.A.I.C.S.: 523999

Allianz Global Investors Asset Management (Shanghai) Limited (1)
Room 1403 Level 14 Shanghai Tower 501 Yincheng Middle Road, Lujiazui Pudong New Area, Shanghai, 200120, China
Tel.: (86) 2160588900
Finance & Insurance Services
N.A.I.C.S.: 524210

Allianz Global Investors Capital LLC (1)
680 Nwport Ctr Dr Ste 250, Newport Beach, CA 92660
Tel.: (949) 219-2200
Investment Management Service
N.A.I.C.S.: 523999

Allianz Global Investors Fund Management LLC (1)
1633 Broadway 41st Fl, New York, NY 10019
Tel.: (212) 739-3000
Investment Management Service
N.A.I.C.S.: 523999
Peter Kocmond *(Dir-Retirement Product Mgmt)*

Allianz Global Investors Ireland Ltd. (1)
15/16 Fitzwilliam Place, Dublin, Ireland
Tel.: (353) 1 489 6820
Investment Management Service
N.A.I.C.S.: 523999

Allianz Global Investors Italia S.p.A (1)
Piazza Velasca 7/9, 20122, Milan, Italy
Tel.: (39) 02 802 003 70
Web Site: http://www.allianzgi.it
Asset Management Services
N.A.I.C.S.: 523940
Elizabeth Corley *(Pres)*

Allianz Global Investors Japan Co., Ltd. (1)
19th floor Ark Hills South Tower 1-4-5 Roppongi, Minato-ku, Tokyo, 106-0032, Japan
Tel.: (81) 362290200
Web Site: https://jp.allianzgi.com
Emp.: 20
Investment Management Service
N.A.I.C.S.: 523940

Allianz Global Investors Managed Accounts LLC (1)
1633 Broadway, New York, NY 10019-7585
Tel.: (212) 739-3000
Web Site: http://www.allianzinvestors.com
Financial Advisory Services
N.A.I.C.S.: 523940

Subsidiary (Domestic):

Allianz Life Insurance Company of North America (2)
5701 Golden Hills Dr, Minneapolis, MN 55416-1297 **(100%)**
Tel.: (763) 765-6500
Web Site: http://www.allianzlife.com
Sales Range: $5-14.9 Billion
Emp.: 1,647
Life Insurance, Annuity Products, Long Term Care Insurance & Broker-Dealer Services
N.A.I.C.S.: 524113
Walter R. White *(Pres & CEO)*

Subsidiary (Domestic):

Allianz Life Insurance Company of New York (3)
1633 Broadway 42nd Fl, New York, NY 10019-7585
Tel.: (212) 586-7733
Fire Insurance Services
N.A.I.C.S.: 524113

Allianz of New York (3)
1 Madison 38 Fl, New York, NY 10005-3310

Web Site: http://www.allianzlife.com
Rev.: $105,780,312
Emp.: 4
Life Insurance Carrier
N.A.I.C.S.: 524210

Questar Capital Corporation (3)
5701 Golden Hills Dr, Minneapolis, MN 55416-0177
Tel.: (888) 446-5872
Web Site: http://www.questarcapital.com
Securities Brokerage & Financial Services
N.A.I.C.S.: 523150
Matt Dian *(COO, Supervision Officer & VP)*

Tax Planning Seminars Inc. (3)
Two Echelon Plz 221 Laurel Rd Ste 220, Voorhees, NJ 08043-2315 **(100%)**
Tel.: (856) 772-6200
Sales Range: $25-49.9 Million
Emp.: 12
Management Consulting Services
N.A.I.C.S.: 541611

Subsidiary (Domestic):

Fireman's Fund Insurance Company (2)
777 San Marin Dr, Novato, CA 94998-0001 **(100%)**
Tel.: (415) 899-2000
Web Site: http://www.firemansfund.com
Sales Range: $1-4.9 Billion
Emp.: 4,500
Commercial & Personal Property & Liability Insurance Services
N.A.I.C.S.: 524126
Jay Dipasupil *(VP-Pro Liability)*

Subsidiary (Domestic):

Associated Indemnity Corp. (3)
777 San Marin Dr, Novato, CA 94998-0001 **(100%)**
Tel.: (415) 899-2000
Web Site: http://www.ffic.com
Sales Range: $700-749.9 Million
Emp.: 1,400
Commercial & Personal Property & Liability Insurance Services
N.A.I.C.S.: 524113

Fireman Fund Specialties (3)
33 W Monroe St Ste 1200, Chicago, IL 60603 **(100%)**
Tel.: (312) 346-6400
Web Site: http://www.firemanfund.com
Sales Range: $150-199.9 Million
Emp.: 200
Surplus Lines Brokerage & Underwriting
N.A.I.C.S.: 524126
Joseph Harbeck *(Dir-HR)*

Fireman's Fund Financial Services, LLC (3)
55 Greens Farms Rd, Westport, CT 06880
Tel.: (203) 221-8500
Investment Management Service
N.A.I.C.S.: 523999

Fireman's Fund Indemnity Corporation (3)
777 San Marin Dr, Novato, CA 94998
Tel.: (415) 899-2000
Investment Management Service
N.A.I.C.S.: 523999

Fireman's Fund Insurance Co. of Georgia (3)
11475 Great Oaks Way Ste 200, Alpharetta, GA 30022-2440 **(100%)**
Tel.: (678) 393-4000
Web Site: http://www.firemansfund.com
Sales Range: $50-74.9 Million
Emp.: 50
Insurance Services
N.A.I.C.S.: 524126

Fireman's Fund Insurance Co. of Hawaii, Inc. (3)
1003 Bishop St Ste 1900, Honolulu, HI 96813 **(100%)**
Tel.: (808) 523-6500
Web Site: http://www.firemansfund.com
Insurance Services
N.A.I.C.S.: 524210

Fireman's Fund Insurance Co. of New Jersey (3)
150 Allen Rd, Liberty Corner, NJ 07938

Tel.: (908) 542-5600
Web Site: http://www.firemansfund.com
Sales Range: $50-74.9 Million
Emp.: 50
Insurance Services
N.A.I.C.S.: 524210

Fireman's Fund Insurance Co. of Texas (3)
500 N Akard St Lincoln Plz Ste 400, Dallas, TX 75201-2519
Tel.: (214) 220-4000
Web Site: http://www.ffic.com
Insurance Services
N.A.I.C.S.: 524126

Fireman's Fund Insurance Company (3)
33 W Monroe St Ste 1200, Chicago, IL 60603 **(100%)**
Tel.: (800) 227-1700
Web Site: http://www.firemansfund.com
Sales Range: $150-199.9 Million
Emp.: 435
Insurance Services
N.A.I.C.S.: 524126

Fireman's Fund Insurance Company of Louisiana, Corp. (3)
777 San Marine Dr, Novato, CA 94998
Tel.: (504) 734-2221
Investment Management Service
N.A.I.C.S.: 523999

Fireman's Fund McGee Underwriters (3)
75 Wall St, New York, NY 10005
Tel.: (212) 524-8600
Web Site: http://www.allianz.com
Insurance Management Services
N.A.I.C.S.: 524298

International Film Guarantors LLC (3)
2828 Donald Douglas Loop N 2nd Fl, Santa Monica, CA 90405
Tel.: (310) 309-5660
Web Site: http://www.ifgbonds.com
Media Insurance Services
N.A.I.C.S.: 524298

Interstate Fire & Casualty Company (3)
33 W Monroe St Ste 1200, Chicago, IL 60603
Tel.: (415) 899-2482
Property & Casualty Insurance Services
N.A.I.C.S.: 524126

Interstate Insurance Group (3)
33 W Monroe St Ste 1300, Chicago, IL 60603
Tel.: (312) 346-6400
Sales Range: $50-74.9 Million
Emp.: 100
Insurance Services
N.A.I.C.S.: 524298

Life Sales LLC (3)
773 San Marin Dr 2160, Novato, CA 94945
Tel.: (800) 486-5400
Web Site: http://www.lifesales.net
Fire Insurance Services
N.A.I.C.S.: 524113

Allianz Global Investors Nominees (UK) Ltd. (1)
199 Bishopsgate, London, EC2M 3AD, United Kingdom
Tel.: (44) 20 7859 9000
Web Site:
http://www.allianzglobalinvestors.co.uk
Investment Management Service
N.A.I.C.S.: 523999
Andreas Utermann *(CEO)*

Allianz Global Investors Solutions LLC (1)
600 W Broadway Ste 3400, San Diego, CA 92101
Tel.: (619) 687-2799
Investment Management Service
N.A.I.C.S.: 523999

Allianz Global Investors U.S. LLC (1)
1633 Broadway, New York, NY 10019-7585
Tel.: (212) 739-3300
Finance & Insurance Services
N.A.I.C.S.: 524210

Allianz SE—(Continued)

Allianz Global Life Ltd. (1)
Maple House Temple Road, Blackrock,
Dublin, Ireland
Tel.: (353) 12422300
Web Site: https://www.allianzgloballife.com
Fire Insurance Services
N.A.I.C.S.: 524113
Carsten Quitte (Chm)

Allianz Group Greece (1)
Athinon Ave 110 Building C, 104 42, Athens, Greece
Tel.: (30) 210 6999999
Web Site: http://www.allianz.gr
Sales Range: $100-124.9 Million
Emp.: 200
General Insurance Services
N.A.I.C.S.: 524210

Allianz Hayat ve Emeklilik AS (1)
Baglarbasi Kisikli Cad No 13, Altunizade,
34662, Istanbul, Türkiye
Tel.: (90) 216 5566666
Web Site: http://www.allianz.com.tr
General Insurance Services
N.A.I.C.S.: 524210

Allianz Hellas Insurance Company S.A. (1)
Athinon Avenue 110 Building C, Athens,
10442, Greece
Tel.: (30) 210 69 05 644
Health Insurance Services
N.A.I.C.S.: 524114

Allianz Hellas Single Member Insurance S.A. (1)
Athinon Ave 110 Building C, 104 42, Athens, Greece
Tel.: (30) 2106905500
Finance & Insurance Services
N.A.I.C.S.: 524210

Allianz Holding France SAS (1)
87 Rue de Richelieu, 75002, Paris, France
Tel.: (33) 9 78 97 80 08
Investment Management Service
N.A.I.C.S.: 523999

Allianz Holding eins GmbH (1)
Hietzinger Kai 101-105, Vienna, 1130, Austria
Tel.: (43) 187807
Investment Management Service
N.A.I.C.S.: 523999

Allianz Holdings plc (1)
57 Ladymead, Guildford, GU1 1DB, United Kingdom
Investment Management Service
N.A.I.C.S.: 523999

Allianz Hungaria Biztosito Zrt. (1)
Konyves Kalman krt 48-52, 1087, Budapest, Hungary
Tel.: (36) 14211421
Insurance Services
N.A.I.C.S.: 524210
Koppany Ocskan (Dir-Bus Dev)

Allianz IARD S.A. (1)
87 Rue De Richelieu, Paris, 75113, France
Tel.: (33) 1 44 86 20 00
General Insurance Services
N.A.I.C.S.: 524210

Allianz Immobilien GmbH (1)
Charlottenstrasse 3, 70182, Stuttgart,
Germany (100%)
Tel.: (49) 7116630
Web Site: http://www.allianz-real-estate-germany.de
Sales Range: $50-74.9 Million
Emp.: 100
Real Estate Company
N.A.I.C.S.: 531210

Allianz Insurance Company Lanka Limited (1)
103/7 Galle Road, Colombo, 00300, Sri Lanka
Tel.: (94) 11 2393393
Web Site: http://www.allianz.com
General Insurance Services
N.A.I.C.S.: 524210
Surekha Alles (Mng Dir)

Allianz Insurance Company of Kenya Limited (1)
Allianz Plaza 96 Riverside Drive, PO Box
66257, 00800, Nairobi, Kenya
Tel.: (254) 709566000
Web Site: http://www.allianz.co.ke
Insurance & Asset Management Services
N.A.I.C.S.: 523940
Hussein Dzila (Fin Mgr)

Allianz Insurance Company of Singapore Pte Ltd (1)
12 Marina View Asia Square Tower 2, Singapore, 018961, Singapore (100%)
Tel.: (65) 62972529
Web Site: http://www.allianz.com.sg
Sales Range: $50-74.9 Million
Emp.: 100
Insurance
N.A.I.C.S.: 524298

Allianz Insurance Company-Egypt S.A.E. (1)
Saridar Building 92 Tahrir Street, Dokki,
12311, Cairo, Egypt
Tel.: (20) 2 3760 5445
Web Site: http://www.allianz.com.eg
General Insurance Services
N.A.I.C.S.: 524210

Allianz Insurance Lanka Limited (1)
Levels 25-27 One Galle Face Tower 1A
Centre Road Galle Face, 02, Colombo, Sri Lanka
Tel.: (94) 112300400
Web Site: https://www.allianz.lk
Finance & Insurance Services
N.A.I.C.S.: 524210

Allianz Insurance Laos Co. Ltd. (1)
33 Lane Xang Avenue Allianz Building, PO
Box 4223, Vientiane, Laos
Tel.: (856) 212159031
Web Site: https://www.azlaos.com
Insurance Services
N.A.I.C.S.: 524210

Allianz Insurance Luxembourg (1)
14 Bld F D Roosevelt, Luxembourg, 2450,
Luxembourg
Tel.: (352) 472 3461
Web Site: http://www.allianz.lu
Emp.: 100
General Insurance Services
N.A.I.C.S.: 524210

Allianz Insurance New Zealand (1)
Level 1 152 Fanshawe St, PO Box 794,
Auckland, New Zealand
Tel.: (64) 9 3542900
General Insurance Services
N.A.I.C.S.: 524210

Allianz Insurance PLC (1)
57 Ladymead, Guildford, GU1 1DB, Surrey,
United Kingdom (100%)
Tel.: (44) 1483568161
Web Site: https://www.allianz.co.uk
Sales Range: $550-599.9 Million
Emp.: 1,000
Insurance Products & Services
N.A.I.C.S.: 524298
Jon Dye (CEO)

Subsidiary (Domestic):

Allianz Business Services Limited (2)
Caton Road, Lancaster, LA1 3PE, United Kingdom
Tel.: (44) 1524597949
Web Site:
http://www.allianzbusinessservices.co.uk
General Insurance Services
N.A.I.C.S.: 524298

Subsidiary (Non-US):

Allianz Cornhill Information Services Private Ltd. (2)
3rd Floor Chandragiri Technopark, Kariavattom, Trivandrum, 695 581, Kerala, India
Tel.: (91) 471 2335550
Web Site: http://www.acis.co.in
Sales Range: $150-199.9 Million
Emp.: 600
Information Technology Consulting Services
N.A.I.C.S.: 541512

Allianz Inversiones S.A. (1)
Carrera 13a 29-24 Local 102 Torre Allianz,
Bogota, Colombia

Tel.: (57) 15600600
N.A.I.C.S.: 523999

Allianz Invest Kapitalanlagegesellschaft mbH (1)
Wiedner Belt 9-13, 1100, Vienna, Austria
Tel.: (43) 15055480
Web Site: https://www.allianzinvest.at
Sales Range: $50-74.9 Million
Emp.: 60
Banking, Trading & Compensation
N.A.I.C.S.: 522299
Christian Raneerger (Mng Dir)

Allianz Investment Company LLC (1)
55 Greens Farms Rd, Westport, CT 06881
Tel.: (203) 221-8500
Web Site: http://www.allianz.com
Investment Management Service
N.A.I.C.S.: 523999

Allianz Investment Management LLC (1)
5701 Golden Hills Dr, Minneapolis, MN
55416-1297
Web Site: https://www.allianzim.com
Investment Advisory Services
N.A.I.C.S.: 523940
Johan Grahn (Asst VP-Portfolio Mgmt)

Allianz Investment Management SE (1)
Koeniginstrasse 28, 80802, Munich, Germany
Tel.: (49) 8938000
Insurance Brokerage Services
N.A.I.C.S.: 524210

Allianz Investment Properties Ltd. (1)
57 Ladymead, Guildford, GU1 1DB, United Kingdom
Tel.: (44) 1483 568161
Web Site: http://www.allianz.co.uk
Emp.: 1,200
Real Estate Management Services
N.A.I.C.S.: 531390

Allianz Investmentbank AG (1)
Hietzinger Kai 101-105, 1130, Vienna, Austria
Tel.: (43) 150554800
Web Site: http://www.allianzinvest.at
Sales Range: $50-74.9 Million
Emp.: 60
Financial Services
N.A.I.C.S.: 523999

Allianz Jingdong General Insurance Company Ltd. (1)
Room 10 34/F Main Tower Guangzhou International Finance Center, No 5 Zhujiang
Xi Road Zhujiang New Town, Guangzhou,
510613, China
Tel.: (86) 2083966788
Finance & Insurance Services
N.A.I.C.S.: 524210

Allianz Kunde und Markt GmbH (1)
Koniginstr 28, 80802, Munich, Germany
Tel.: (49) 8938000
Finance & Insurance Services
N.A.I.C.S.: 524210

Allianz LAD Fonds (1)
Mainzer Landstrasse 11-13, Frankfurt am
Main, 60329, Germany
Tel.: (49) 18 03 30 33 11
Mutual Fund Management Services
N.A.I.C.S.: 523940

Allianz LEBENCO Fonds (1)
Mainzer Landstrasse 11-13, Frankfurt am
Main, 60329, Germany
Tel.: (49) 18 03 30 33 11
Mutual Fund Management Services
N.A.I.C.S.: 523940

Allianz Lebensversicherungs-AG (1)
Reinsburgstrasse 19, 70178, Stuttgart,
Germany (91%)
Tel.: (49) 7116630
Web Site: http://www.allianz.de
Sales Range: $700-749.9 Million
Emp.: 2,000
Life Insurance
N.A.I.C.S.: 524113

Allianz Lietuva gyvybes draudimas UAB (1)

Lvivo g 25 3 BURES, LT-09320, Vilnius,
Lithuania
Tel.: (370) 52690169
Web Site: https://www.allianz.lt
Finance & Insurance Services
N.A.I.C.S.: 524210

Allianz Life (Bermuda) Ltd. (1)
105 Allianz SNA Bldg 56 Jisr el Bacha, PO
Box 16-6516, Beirut, Hazmieh, Lebanon
Tel.: (961) 5450642
N.A.I.C.S.: 524113

Allianz Life Assurance Company-Egypt S.A.E. (1)
92 Tahrir Street Saridar Building, Dokki,
Giza, Egypt
Tel.: (20) 237605445
Fire Insurance Services
N.A.I.C.S.: 524113

Allianz Life Financial Services LLC (1)
5701 Golden Hills Dr, Minneapolis, MN
55416-1297
N.A.I.C.S.: 524113

Allianz Life Insurance Company (1)
3rd Samotechny Pereulok 3, 127473, Moscow, Russia (100%)
Tel.: (7) 4959376996
Web Site: http://www.allianz.ru
Sales Range: $100-124.9 Million
Emp.: 150
Fire Insurance Services
N.A.I.C.S.: 524113
Wermer L. Lellinger (Pres & CEO)

Subsidiary (Domestic):

Allianz Risk Audit (2)
3rd Samotechny Pereulok 3, 127473, Moscow, Russia
Tel.: (7) 4959376996
Web Site: http://www.allianz.ru
Sales Range: $75-99.9 Million
Emp.: 140
Insurance Services
N.A.I.C.S.: 524298

Allianz Life Insurance Company S.A. (1)
Athinon 110 bld C, 10442, Athens,
Greece (100%)
Tel.: (30) 2106905500
Web Site: http://www.allianz.gr
Life Insurance Provider
N.A.I.C.S.: 524113

Allianz Life Insurance Company of Ghana Limited (1)
Volta Place 35 Patrice Lumumba Road Airport Residential Area, 600 Meters From National Service Secretariat PMB CT 353
Cantonments, Accra, Ghana
Tel.: (233) 308249090
Web Site: https://www.allianz-gh.com
N.A.I.C.S.: 524113
Gideon O. Ataraire (CEO)

Allianz Life Insurance Japan Ltd. (1)
Anzen Building 6-6 Motoakasaka 1-chome,
Minato-ku, Tokyo, 107-0051, Japan
Tel.: (81) 3 45881500
Web Site: http://life.allianz.co.jp
Fire Insurance Services
N.A.I.C.S.: 524113

Allianz Life Insurance Lanka Ltd. (1)
Levels 25-27 One Galle Face Tower 1A
Centre Road, Galle Face, 02, Colombo, Sri Lanka
Tel.: (94) 112303300
Web Site: https://www.allianz.lk
Emp.: 470
General Insurance Services
N.A.I.C.S.: 524210

Allianz Life Insurance Malaysia Berhad (1)
Web Site: http://www.allianz.com.my
Sales Range: $50-74.9 Million
Emp.: 50
Fire Insurance Services
N.A.I.C.S.: 524113
Joseph Kumar Gross (CEO)

Allianz Life Luxembourg S.A. (1)
14 Boulevard FD Roosevelt, 2450, Luxembourg, Luxembourg

Tel.: (352) 4723461
Web Site: https://www.allianz.lu
Fire Insurance Services
N.A.I.C.S.: 524113

Allianz Madagascar (1)
13 Rue Indira Gandhi, BP 8619, Antanana-
rivo, 101, Madagascar
Tel.: (261) 20 2257900
Fire Insurance Services
N.A.I.C.S.: 524113

Allianz Malaysia Berhad (1)
Level 29 Menara Allianz Sentral 203 Jalan
Tun Sambathan, Kuala Lumpur Sentral,
50470, Kuala Lumpur, Malaysia
Tel.: (60) 322641188
Web Site: https://www.allianz.com.my
Rev.: $1,591,682,153
Assets: $5,851,763,033
Liabilities: $4,826,085,165
Net Worth: $1,025,677,868
Earnings: $118,428,008
Emp.: 155,000
Fiscal Year-end: 12/31/2021
General Insurance Services
N.A.I.C.S.: 524126
Siew Gek Ng *(Sec)*

Allianz Mali Assurances (1)
Avenue de la Nation, BP E4447, Bamako,
Mali (70%)
Tel.: (223) 20224165
Web Site: http://www.allianz-africa.com
Sales Range: $50-74.9 Million
Emp.: 24
Insurance Services
N.A.I.C.S.: 524298

**Allianz Managed Operations & Ser-
vices SE** (1)
Gutenbergstrasse 8, 85774, Unterfohring,
Germany
Tel.: (49) 89 3800 0
Information Technology Consulting Services
N.A.I.C.S.: 541512

Allianz Maroc S.A. (1)
166-168 Boulevard Mohamed Zerktouni,
20060, Casablanca, Morocco
Tel.: (212) 522499700
Web Site: https://www.allianz.ma
Insurance & Asset Management Services
N.A.I.C.S.: 523940
Fatima Zahra Fatene *(Head-HR)*

Allianz Mexico S.A. (1)
Blvd MA Camacho 164 Col, Lomas De Bar-
rilaco, 11010, Mexico, Mexico (100%)
Tel.: (52) 52013000
Web Site: http://www.allianz.com.mx
Insurance
N.A.I.C.S.: 524113

**Allianz Mexico S.A. Compania de
Seguros** (1)
Blvd Manuel A Camacho 164 Col Lomas de
Barrilaco, 11010, Mexico, Mexico
Tel.: (52) 5555403000
Fire Insurance Services
N.A.I.C.S.: 524210

Allianz Nederland Groep NV (1)
Coolsingel 120, 3011 AG, Rotterdam, Neth-
erlands
Tel.: (31) 104541911
Web Site: http://www.allianz.nl
Sales Range: $1-4.9 Billion
Emp.: 1,500
Insurance & Financial Services
N.A.I.C.S.: 524298

Subsidiary (Domestic):

**Allianz Global Corporate & Specialty -
Netherlands** (2)
school single, PO Box 441, 3000 AK, Rot-
terdam, Netherlands
Tel.: (31) 10 454 1336
Web Site: http://www.allianz.nl
Sales Range: $800-899.9 Million
Emp.: 40
Property & Casualty Insurance Products &
Services
N.A.I.C.S.: 524126

Allianz Nederland (2)
Buizerdlaan 12, 3435 SB, Nieuwegein,
Netherlands
Tel.: (31) 306077651

Web Site: http://www.allianz.nl
Sales Range: $50-74.9 Million
Emp.: 100
Financial Services
N.A.I.C.S.: 523991

**Allianz Nederland Asset Management
B.V.** (2)
Coolsingel 134, PO Box 40, 3430 AA, Rot-
terdam, Netherlands (100%)
Tel.: (31) 30 607 7651
Web Site: http://www.allianz.nl
Sales Range: $300-349.9 Million
Emp.: 500
Asset Management & Insurance Services
N.A.I.C.S.: 524128

**Allianz Nederland Levensverzekering
NV** (2)
Coolsingel 139, PO Box 9, 3430 AA, Rotter-
dam, Netherlands
Tel.: (31) 302814242
Web Site: http://www.allianz.nl
Sales Range: $200-249.9 Million
Emp.: 1,000
Insurance & Financial Services
N.A.I.C.S.: 524298
Sjoerd Laarberg *(Gen Mgr)*

**Allianz Nederland Schadeverzekering
NV** (2)
Coolsingel 139, Rotterdam, 3012 AG, Neth-
erlands
Tel.: (31) 104541911
Web Site: http://www.allianz.nl
Sales Range: $200-249.9 Million
Emp.: 1,100
Insurance & Financial Services
N.A.I.C.S.: 524298

Allianz Risk Consultants B.V. (2)
Coolsingel 139, 3012 AG, Rotterdam, Neth-
erlands
Tel.: (31) 104541840
Web Site: http://www.arc-allianz.com
Financial Services
N.A.I.C.S.: 525990

ITEB B.V. (2)
Coolsingel 139, 2800 AA, Rotterdam, Neth-
erlands
Tel.: (31) 182569421
Web Site: http://www.iteb.nl
Sales Range: $50-74.9 Million
Emp.: 90
Financial Services
N.A.I.C.S.: 525990

London Verzekeringen N.V. (2)
Coolsingel 139, 3012 AG, Rotterdam, Neth-
erlands
Tel.: (31) 882772602
Web Site: http://www.london.nl
Insurance Services
N.A.I.C.S.: 524298

Universal Leven N.V. (2)
Coolsingel 139, PO Box 9, 3435 SB, Rotter-
dam, Netherlands
Tel.: (31) 306986140
Web Site: http://www.allianz.nl
Sales Range: $50-74.9 Million
Emp.: 20
Financial Services
N.A.I.C.S.: 525990
Barbara Kwant *(Product Mgr)*

**Allianz New Europe Holding
GmbH** (1)
Hietzinger Kai 101-105, Vienna, 1130, Aus-
tria
Tel.: (43) 1 87 8070
Investment Management Service
N.A.I.C.S.: 523999

Allianz Nigeria Insurance plc (1)
95 Broad Street, Lagos, Nigeria
Tel.: (234) 8002554269
Web Site: https://www.allianz.ng
Insurance Services
N.A.I.C.S.: 524210

Allianz Northern Ireland Ltd (1)
Allianz House 21 Linenhall St, Belfast, BT2
8AB, Northern Ireland, United Kingdom
Tel.: (44) 2890895600
Sales Range: $50-74.9 Million
Emp.: 100
Insurance Services
N.A.I.C.S.: 524298

**Allianz ONE - Business Solutions
GmbH** (1)
Koniginstrasse 28, 80802, Munich, Ger-
many
Tel.: (49) 8938000
Finance & Insurance Services
N.A.I.C.S.: 524210

Allianz PNB Life Insurance Inc. (1)
9th Floor Allied Bank Center 6754 Ayala
Avenue Corner Legaspi Street, PO Box
3191, Makati, Philippines
Tel.: (63) 88184357
Web Site: https://www.allianzpnblife.ph
Fire Insurance Services
N.A.I.C.S.: 524210
Lucio Tan *(Chm)*

**Allianz Partners Deutschland
GmbH** (1)
Bahnhofstrasse 16, Aschheim, 85609, Mu-
nich, Germany
Tel.: (49) 892620830
Web Site: https://www.allianz-partners.com
Insurance Services
N.A.I.C.S.: 524126

Allianz Partners S.A.S. (1)
7 rue Dora Maar, 93400, Saint-Ouen-
l'Aumone, France
Tel.: (33) 153058600
Web Site: https://www.allianz-partners.fr
Insurance Services
N.A.I.C.S.: 524210

Allianz Pension Consult GmbH (1)
Marienstrasse 50, Stuttgart, 70178, Ger-
many
Tel.: (49) 711 663 96096
Web Site: http://www.apc.allianz.de
Sales Range: $50-74.9 Million
Emp.: 35
Pension Fund Management Services
N.A.I.C.S.: 523940

**Allianz Pensionsfonds
Aktiengesellschaft** (1)
Reinsburgstrasse 19, Baden-Wurttemberg,
70178, Stuttgart, Germany
Tel.: (49) 8938000
Pension Fund Management Services
N.A.I.C.S.: 525110

Allianz Pensionskasse AG (1)
Hietzinger Kai 1012-105, A-1130, Vienna,
Austria
Tel.: (43) 1878074952
Web Site: http://www.allianzpk.at
Sales Range: $50-74.9 Million
Emp.: 20
Pension Management Services
N.A.I.C.S.: 525110

Allianz Pojistovna A/S (1)
Kestani 656, 186 00, Prague, Czech
Republic (100%)
Tel.: (420) 224405111
Web Site: http://www.allianz.cz
Sales Range: $100-124.9 Million
Emp.: 200
Insurance Provider
N.A.I.C.S.: 524128
Dusan Quis *(Chm-Mgmt Bd)*

**Allianz Polska Services Sp. z
o.o.** (1)
ul Rodziny Hiszpanskiego 1, 02-685, Warsaw, Poland
Tel.: (48) 225674000
General Insurance Services
N.A.I.C.S.: 524210

Allianz Popular S.L. (1)
C/ Ramirez de Arellano 35, 28043, Madrid,
Spain
Tel.: (34) 914360300
Fire Insurance Services
N.A.I.C.S.: 524210

Allianz Portugal (1)
Rua Andrade Corvo 32, P 1069014, Lisbon,
Codex, Portugal (100%)
Tel.: (351) 213165300
Web Site: http://www.allianz.pt
Sales Range: $50-74.9 Million
Emp.: 100
Insurance Provider
N.A.I.C.S.: 524128

**Allianz Private Equity Partners Ver-
waltungs GmbH** (1)

Theresienstr 6-8, Munich, 80333, Germany
Tel.: (49) 8938000
Financial Advisory Services
N.A.I.C.S.: 523940

**Allianz Private
Krankenversicherungs-AG** (1)
Fritz-Schaeffer-Strasse 9, D-81727, Munich,
Germany
Tel.: (49) 8967850
Web Site: http://www.allianz.com
Sales Range: $200-249.9 Million
Emp.: 300
Insurance & Financial Services
N.A.I.C.S.: 524298

**Allianz Private Krankenversicherungs-
Aktien
gesellschaft** (1)
Koniginstr 28, 80802, Munich, Germany
Tel.: (49) 8938000
Insurance Services
N.A.I.C.S.: 524126

Allianz Properties Limited (1)
57 Ladymead, Guildford, GU1 1DB, Surrey,
United Kingdom
Tel.: (44) 1483568161
Real Estate Development Services
N.A.I.C.S.: 531390
Stuart John Robertson *(Chief Acct)*

Allianz ProzessFinanz GmbH (1)
Koeniginstrasse 28, Munich, 80802, Ger-
many
Tel.: (49) 89380018370
Web Site: http://www.allianz-profi.de
Sales Range: $50-74.9 Million
Emp.: 2
Financial Services
N.A.I.C.S.: 525990
Karola Wollner *(CEO)*

Allianz Real Estate Asia Pacific (1)
12 Marina View 14-01 Asia Square Tower 2,
Singapore, 018961, Singapore
Tel.: (65) 63958607
Web Site: http://wwwallianz-realestate.com
Real Estate Manangement Services
N.A.I.C.S.: 531390
Vincent Chew *(Gen Mgr)*

**Allianz Real Estate Germany
GmbH** (1)
Charlottenstrasse 3, 70182, Stuttgart, Ger-
many
Tel.: (49) 711 663 0
Real Estate Manangement Services
N.A.I.C.S.: 531390

Allianz Real Estate GmbH (1)
Seidlstrasse 24-24a, 80335, Munich, Ger-
many
Tel.: (49) 8938000
Web Site: https://pimcoprimerealestate.com
Real Estate Services
N.A.I.C.S.: 531190

Allianz Reinsurance America Inc. (1)
1465 N MacDowell Blvd Ste 201, Petaluma,
CA 94954
Tel.: (415) 899-2000
Fire Insurance Services
N.A.I.C.S.: 524210

**Allianz Renewable Energy Manage-
ment GmbH** (1)
Feldscheide 2, Sehestedt, 24814,
Schleswig-Holstein, Germany
Tel.: (49) 435799770
Eletric Power Generation Services
N.A.I.C.S.: 221118
Gordon Johnston *(Gen Mgr)*

Allianz Risk Consulting GmbH (1)
Koniginstr 28, Munich, 80802, Germany
Tel.: (49) 89203051000
General Insurance Services
N.A.I.C.S.: 524210

**Allianz Risk Transfer (UK)
Limited** (1)
Allianz House 60 Gracechurch Street, Lon-
don, EC3V 0HR, United Kingdom
Tel.: (44) 20 3451 3000
General Insurance Services
N.A.I.C.S.: 524210
Toni Mead *(Mgr-HR)*

Allianz Risk Transfer AG (1)
Im alten Riet 102, 9494, Schaan, Liechtenstein

Allianz SE—(Continued)

Tel.: (423) 2358500
Fire Insurance Services
N.A.I.C.S.: 524210
Thomas Schatzman *(CFO)*

Allianz Risk Transfer N.V. **(1)**
Keizersgracht 482, Amsterdam, 1017 EG, Netherlands
Tel.: (31) 20 520 3823
Web Site: http://www.allianz.com
Emp.: 6
General Insurance Services
N.A.I.C.S.: 524210

Allianz S.p.A. **(1)**
Largo Ugo Irneri, 34123, Trieste, Italy
Tel.: (39) 0 40 7781 111
Web Site: http://www.allianz.it
Emp.: 5,500
Insurance Products & Financial Services
N.A.I.C.S.: 524298
Giacomo Campora *(CEO)*

Subsidiary (Domestic):

Aviva Italia S.p.A **(2)**
Via Scarsellini 14, 20161, Milan, Italy
Tel.: (39) 0227751
Web Site: http://www.avivaitalia.it
Insurance Services
N.A.I.C.S.: 524298

Genialloyd SpA **(2)**
Viale Mansa 2, 20127, Milan, Italy **(99.9%)**
Tel.: (39) 0228351
Web Site: http://www.genialloyd.it
Sales Range: $150-199.9 Million
Emp.: 500
Insurance Services
N.A.I.C.S.: 524298

Investitori Sgr S.P.A. **(2)**
Piazza Erculea 15, Milan, 20122, Italy
Tel.: (39) 0272162500
Web Site: http://www.investitori.it
Emp.: 20
Private Banking Services
N.A.I.C.S.: 523999
Emanule Vizzini *(CFO)*

RAS Asset Management SGR S.p.A. **(2)**
Piazza Velasca 7/9, 20122, Milan, Italy
Tel.: (39) 02 802001
Asset Management Services
N.A.I.C.S.: 525990

RAS Tutela Giudiziaria S.p.A. **(2)**
Corso Italia 23, I 20122, Milan, Italy **(100%)**
Tel.: (39) 02 582801
Insurance Provider
N.A.I.C.S.: 524128

Allianz SNA Sal **(1)**
Allianz SNA Bldg Hazmieh, PO Box 16-6528, Beirut, 16-6528, Lebanon
Tel.: (961) 5 956600
Web Site: http://www.allianzsna.com
General Insurance Services
N.A.I.C.S.: 524210

Allianz SOA Fonds **(1)**
Mainzer Landstrasse 11-13, Frankfurt am Main, 60329, Germany
Tel.: (49) 18 03 30 33 11
Mutual Fund Management Services
N.A.I.C.S.: 523940

Allianz Saude S.A. **(1)**
Tel.: (55) 1140015060
Health Insurance Services
N.A.I.C.S.: 524114

Allianz Seguros S.A. **(1)**
Rua Eugenio de Medeiros 303, 01309-900, Sao Paulo, SP, Brazil
Tel.: (55) 1131564340
General Insurance Services
N.A.I.C.S.: 524210
Jose Miguel Echevarria *(Dir-Comml-North)*

Allianz Seguros de Vida S.A. **(1)**
Carrera 13a 29-24 Local 102 Torre Allianz, Bogota, Colombia
Tel.: (57) 15600600
Fire Insurance Services
N.A.I.C.S.: 524210

Allianz Senegal Assurances **(1)**

Avenue Abdoulaye Fadiga X rue de Thann, BP 2610, Dakar, Senegal **(83%)**
Tel.: (221) 338494400
Web Site: http://www.allianz-africa.com
Sales Range: $50-74.9 Million
Emp.: 50
Insurance Services
N.A.I.C.S.: 524298

Allianz Senegal Assurances Vie **(1)**
Avenue Abdoulaye Fadiga X Rue de Thann, 2610, Dakar, Senegal
Tel.: (221) 33 8494400
Web Site: http://www.allianztusn.com
General Insurance Services
N.A.I.C.S.: 524210

Allianz Senegal dommages **(1)**
Avenue Abdoulaye Fadiga X Rue De Thann, Dakar, Senegal
Tel.: (221) 338494400
Web Site: http://www.allianz-sn.com
Emp.: 60
General Insurance Services
N.A.I.C.S.: 524210

Allianz Senegal vie **(1)**
Avenue Abdoulaye Fadiga X Rue de Thann, BP 2610, Dakar, Senegal
Tel.: (221) 33 849 44 00
General Insurance Services
N.A.I.C.S.: 524210

Allianz Service Center GmbH **(1)**
Nymphenburger Str 110-112, Munich, 80636, Germany
Tel.: (49) 8918943580
General Insurance Services
N.A.I.C.S.: 524210

Allianz Services Private Ltd. **(1)**
Ganga Technopark Campus Phase III, Trivandrum, 695581, Kerala, India
Tel.: (91) 4716613555
N.A.I.C.S.: 524113

Allianz Slovenska Poistovna, a.s. **(1)**
Dostojevskeho Rad 4, 815 74, Bratislava, 815 74, Slovakia
Tel.: (421) 250122222
Web Site: http://www.allianzsp.sk
Sales Range: $600-649.9 Million
Insurance Products & Services
N.A.I.C.S.: 524113
Todor Todorov *(Chm)*

Allianz Slovenska dochodkova spravcovsa spolocnost, a.s. **(1)**
Racianska 62, Bratislava, 831 02, Slovakia
Tel.: (421) 2 57 10 6811
Web Site: http://www.asdss.sk
Emp.: 29
Pension Fund Management Services
N.A.I.C.S.: 525110
Miroslav Suchy *(Head-Sls & Mktg)*

Allianz South America Holding B.V. **(1)**
Keizersgracht 484, 1017 EH, Amsterdam, Netherlands
Tel.: (31) 205569715
Investment Management Service
N.A.I.C.S.: 523940

Allianz Sp. z o.o. **(1)**
Ul Rodziny Hiszpanskich 1, 02-685, Warsaw, Poland
Tel.: (48) 224224224
Web Site: https://www.allianz.pl
Finance & Insurance Services
N.A.I.C.S.: 524210

Allianz Subalpina Holding S.p.A. **(1)**
Via Vittorio Alfieri 22, 10121, Turin, Italy
Tel.: (39) 0115161111
Holding Company
N.A.I.C.S.: 551112

Allianz Suisse Versicherungen **(1)**
Bleicherweg 19, CH 8022, Zurich, Switzerland **(100%)**
Tel.: (41) 433119911
Web Site: http://www.allianz-suisse.ch
Sales Range: $1-4.9 Billion
Emp.: 3,953
Property, Casualty, Life & Health Insurance & Financial Services
N.A.I.C.S.: 524126

Subsidiary (Domestic):

Alba Allgemeine Versicherungs-Gesellschaft AG **(2)**

St Alban-Anlage 56, PO Box 101, CH-4020, Basel, Switzerland
Tel.: (41) 612953111
Web Site: http://www.alba.ch
Sales Range: $75-99.9 Million
Emp.: 250
Insurance Services
N.A.I.C.S.: 524298

Allianz Suisse Immobilien AG **(2)**
Postfach, Zurich, 8604, Switzerland
Tel.: (41) 583580111
Web Site: http://www.allianz.ch
Sales Range: $25-49.9 Million
Emp.: 45
Financial Services
N.A.I.C.S.: 523999

Allianz Suisse Insurance Company **(2)**
Hohlstrasse 552, 8048, Zurich, Switzerland
Tel.: (41) 583587111
Web Site: http://www.allianz-suisse.ch
Sales Range: $150-199.9 Million
Emp.: 500
Insurance Products & Services
N.A.I.C.S.: 524298
Hansjoerg Leibundgut *(Mgr-Comm)*

Allianz Suisse Versicherungen - Allianz Suisse Leben **(2)**
Bleicherweg 19, 8022, Zurich, Switzerland
Tel.: (41) 442095111
Web Site: http://www.allianz-suisse.ch
Sales Range: $1-4.9 Billion
Financial Services
N.A.I.C.S.: 525990

CAP Rechtsschutz Versicherung **(2)**
Neue Winterthurerstrasse 88, 8304, Wallisellen, Switzerland
Tel.: (41) 583580900
Web Site: http://www.cap.ch
Sales Range: $50-74.9 Million
Emp.: 100
Insurance & Financial Services
N.A.I.C.S.: 524298
Eugster Daniel *(CEO)*

Allianz Suisse Versicherungs-Gesellschaft AG **(1)**
Richtiplatz 1, 8304, Wallisellen, Switzerland
Tel.: (41) 583587111
Web Site: http://www.allianz.ch
Insurance Service Provider
N.A.I.C.S.: 524126
Gregor Huber *(Head-Corp Insurance)*

Allianz Taiwan Life Insurance Company Ltd. **(1)**
5th Floor No 100 Section 5 Xinyi Road, Xinyi District, Taipei, Taiwan
Tel.: (886) 800007668
Web Site: https://www.allianz.com.tw
Sales Range: $700-749.9 Million
Emp.: 1,200
Insurance Services
N.A.I.C.S.: 524298

Allianz Takaful B.S.C.(c) **(1)**
Al Raya Bldg Bldg 1025 Road 3621, Seef District, 436, Manama, Bahrain
Tel.: (973) 17 568 222
Web Site: http://www.allianz.com.bh
Life & Health Insurance Services
N.A.I.C.S.: 524113

Allianz Togo Assurances **(1)**
21 Avenue Duisburg Bd du 13 Janvier, BP 3703, Lome, Togo **(94%)**
Tel.: (228) 221 9773
Web Site: http://www.allianz-africa.com
Financial Services
N.A.I.C.S.: 524298

Allianz US Private REIT LP **(1)**
55 Greens Farms Rd, Westport, CT 68806
Tel.: (203) 221-8500
General Insurance Services
N.A.I.C.S.: 524210

Allianz Underwriters Insurance Company, Corp. **(1)**
3400 Riverside Dr Ste 300, Burbank, CA 91505-4669
Tel.: (818) 972-8000
Insurance Underwriting Services
N.A.I.C.S.: 524127

Allianz Versicherungs AG **(1)**

Koeninginstrasse 28, 80802, Munich, 80802, Germany **(100%)**
Tel.: (49) 8938000
Web Site: http://www.allianz.de
Sales Range: $1-4.9 Billion
Emp.: 6,000
Property & Casualty Insurance
N.A.I.C.S.: 524126

Subsidiary (Domestic):

Allianz Handwerker Services GmbH **(2)**
Bahnhofstrasse 16, 85609, Aschheim, Germany
Tel.: (49) 89517190
Web Site: http://www.allianz-services.de
Sales Range: $50-74.9 Million
Emp.: 230
Building Restoration & Construction
N.A.I.C.S.: 236210
Rudiger Hermann *(Mng Dir)*

Branch (Domestic):

Allianz Versicherungs AG **(2)**
PO Box, 10900, Berlin, Germany **(100%)**
Tel.: (49) 01802100101
Web Site: http://www.allianz.de
Sales Range: $600-649.9 Million
Emp.: 2,500
Property & Casualty Insurance
N.A.I.C.S.: 524126

Allianz Versicherungs-AG **(2)**
Uhlandstrasse 2, 70182, Stuttgart, Germany **(100%)**
Tel.: (49) 71121730
Web Site: http://www.allianz-stuttgart.de
Sales Range: $600-649.9 Million
Emp.: 1,500
Insurance Provider
N.A.I.C.S.: 524128

Allianz Versicherungs-AG **(2)**
Kaiser Wilhelm Ring 31, D 50672, Cologne, Germany **(100%)**
Tel.: (49) 22157312437
Web Site: http://www.allianz.de
Sales Range: $600-649.9 Million
Emp.: 2,000
Insurance Provider
N.A.I.C.S.: 524128

Branch (Non-US):

Allianz Versicherungs-AG (Dubai Branch) **(2)**
Alatar Business Tower 29th Fl Office No 2 Sheikh Zayed Rd, PO Box 7659, Dubai, 7659, United Arab Emirates **(100%)**
Tel.: (971) 43329929
Web Site: http://www.allianz.ae
Sales Range: $50-74.9 Million
Emp.: 25
Insurance Provider
N.A.I.C.S.: 524128

Subsidiary (Domestic):

esa Euroship Assekuradeurgesellschaft mbH & Co. KG **(2)**
Friedrichsplatz 2, 74177, Bad Friedrichshall, Germany
Tel.: (49) 71369513414
Web Site: http://www.esa-allianz.de
Sales Range: $75-99.9 Million
Emp.: 120
Financial Services
N.A.I.C.S.: 524298
Walter Szabados *(Mng Dir)*

Allianz Viva S.p.A. **(1)**
Piazza Tre Torri 3, 20145, Milan, Italy
Tel.: (39) 0289040764
Web Site: https://www.allianzviva.it
Insurance Services
N.A.I.C.S.: 524210

Allianz Vorsorgekasse AG **(1)**
Wiedner Belt 9-13, 1100, Vienna, Austria
Tel.: (43) 5900980181
Web Site: https://www.allianzvk.at
Property & Casualty Life Insurance Services
N.A.I.C.S.: 524126

Allianz Worldwide Care Limited **(1)**
18 B Beckett Way Park West Business Campus Nangor Road, Dublin, 12, Ireland
Tel.: (353) 16301300

Web Site:
http://www.allianzworldwidecare.com
Sales Range: $100-124.9 Million
Emp.: 200
Health Insurance Services
N.A.I.C.S.: 524114
Duncan Wright *(Mgr-Bus Dev-United Kingdom)*

Allianz Yasam ve Emeklilik A.S. (1)
Allianz Tower Kucukbakkalkoy Mahallesi
Kayisdagi Cad No 1, Atasehir, 34750, Istanbul, Turkiye
Tel.: (90) 2165566666
Property & Casualty Life Insurance Services
N.A.I.C.S.: 524126
Ali Can *(Head-Sls)*

Allianz Zagreb d.d. (1)
Heinzelova 70, 10000, Zagreb, 10000, Croatia
Tel.: (385) 13670367
Web Site: http://www.allianz.hr
Insurance Services
N.A.I.C.S.: 524298

Allianz Zentrum fuer Technik GmbH (1)
Koenigin Str 28, 85737, Ismaning, Germany
Tel.: (49) 8938000
Web Site: http://www.allianz-azt.de
Sales Range: $50-74.9 Million
Emp.: 100
Loss Prevention & Corporate Risk Management Services
N.A.I.C.S.: 524298

Allianz business services s.r.o. (1)
Karloveska 6C, 842 02, Bratislava, Slovakia
Tel.: (421) 2 6929 4442
Web Site: http://www.allianz-services.sk
Financial Management Services
N.A.I.C.S.: 523999
Miroslav Kocan *(Gen Mgr)*

Allianz of America, Inc. (1)
55 Greens Farms Rd, Westport, CT 06880-6149 **(100%)**
Tel.: (203) 221-8500
Sales Range: $50-74.9 Million
Emp.: 42
Holding Company; Insurance Products & Services
N.A.I.C.S.: 551112
Jacqueline Hunt *(Chm)*

Allianz of Asia-Pacific and Africa GmbH (1)
Koniginstr 28, 80802, Munich, Germany
Tel.: (49) 8938000
General Insurance Services
N.A.I.C.S.: 524210

Allianz penzijni fond a.s. (1)
Ke Stvanici 656/3, 186 00, Prague, Czech Republic
Tel.: (420) 2 24405789
Pension Fund Management Services
N.A.I.C.S.: 525110

Allianz penzijni spolecnost a.s. (1)
Ke Stvanici 656/3, 186 00, Prague, Czech Republic
Tel.: (420) 241170000
Finance & Insurance Services
N.A.I.C.S.: 524210

Allianz plc (1)
Allianz House Elmpark Merrion Road, Dublin, 4, Ireland **(100%)**
Tel.: (353) 16133000
Web Site: http://www.allianz.ie
Emp.: 650
Holding Company; Insurance Products & Services
N.A.I.C.S.: 551112

Subsidiary (Domestic):

Allianz Re Dublin Ltd. (2)
Allianz House Elmpark Merrion Road, Dublin, Ireland
Tel.: (353) 15125400
Web Site: http://www.allianz.ie
Sales Range: $50-74.9 Million
Emp.: 16
Reinsurance Services
N.A.I.C.S.: 524130

Allianz-Slovenska DSS a.s. (1)
Pribinova 19, 811 09, Bratislava, Slovakia

Tel.: (421) 250122222
Web Site: https://www.asdss.sk
N.A.I.C.S.: 524113
Miroslav Kotov *(Chm)*

Allianz-Tiriac Asigurari S.A. (1)
80-84 Caderea Bastiliei St, 010616, Bucharest, Romania
Tel.: (40) 212082105
Web Site: http://www.allianztiriac.ro
Insurance Services
N.A.I.C.S.: 524298

Allianz-Tiriac Pensii Private (1)
Ion Slatineanu 6, 010602, Bucharest, Romania
Tel.: (40) 21 207 2100
Web Site: http://pensii.allianztiriac.ro
Sales Range: $50-74.9 Million
Emp.: 81
Pension Fund Management Services
N.A.I.C.S.: 525110

Allvest GmbH (1)
Konigstrasse 28, 80802, Munich, Germany
Tel.: (49) 8948929990
Web Site: https://www.allvest.de
Investment Fund Services
N.A.I.C.S.: 525910

American Automobile Insurance Company, Corp. (1)
777 San Marin Dr, Novato, CA 94998
Tel.: (415) 899-2000
Automobile Insurance Services
N.A.I.C.S.: 524126
Lori Dickerson Fouché *(Pres)*

American Financial Marketing Inc. (1)
400 Hwy 169 S Ste 200, Saint Louis Park, MN 55426
Tel.: (763) 593-0905
Web Site: http://www.afmus.com
General Insurance Services
N.A.I.C.S.: 524210
Tom Wade *(Co-Founder & Partner)*

Ann Arbor Annuity Exchange Inc. (1)
45 Research Dr, Ann Arbor, MI 48103
Tel.: (800) 321-3924
Web Site: http://www.annuity-exchange.com
Emp.: 30
General Insurance Services
N.A.I.C.S.: 524210
Meghan Eiler *(Coord-New Bus)*

Approfrais S.A. (1)
Rue Jean Monnet, BP 1802, 27000, Evreux, France
Tel.: (33) 232381409
General Insurance Services
N.A.I.C.S.: 524210

Assistance Courtage d'Assurance et de Reassurance S.A. (1)
87 Rue De Richelieu, 75002, Paris, France
Tel.: (33) 1 45 67 60 68
General Insurance Services
N.A.I.C.S.: 524210

Assurance Vie et Prevoyance (AVIP) S.A. (1)
Tour Neptune 20 place de Seine Case Postale 2401, La Defense, Paris, 92086, France
Tel.: (33) 1 58 85 95 00
Web Site: http://www.avip.fr
General Insurance Services
N.A.I.C.S.: 524210

Assurances Medicales SA (1)
4 rue des messageries, 57000, Metz, France
Tel.: (33) 387565554
Health Insurance Services
N.A.I.C.S.: 524114

Autobahn Tank & Rast GmbH (1)
Andreas Hermes Strasse 729, 53175, Bonn, Germany
Tel.: (49) 2289220
Web Site: http://www.tank.rast.de
Gas Station Operator
N.A.I.C.S.: 457110
Karl-H. Rolfes *(CEO)*

Subsidiary (Domestic):

AXXE Reisegastronomie GmbH (2)

Clevischer Ring 127, 51063, Cologne, Germany
Tel.: (49) 2219647670
Web Site: http://www.axxe.de
Motorway Restaurant & Hotel Services
N.A.I.C.S.: 722511
Wolfgang Fritze *(Mng Dir)*

BAWAG Allianz Mitarbeitervorsorgekasse AG (1)
Hietzinger Kai 101-105, 1130, Vienna, Austria
Tel.: (43) 1 878075357
Web Site: http://www.allianz.com
Financial Management Services
N.A.I.C.S.: 523999

Bajaj Allianz General Insurance Co. Ltd. (1)
1st Floor GE Plaza Airport Road, Yerwada, Pune, 411006, Maharashtra, India
Tel.: (91) 2056026666
Web Site: http://www.bajajallianz.co.in
Sales Range: $250-299.9 Million
Emp.: 1,371
Insurance Services; Owned by Allianz AG & by Bajaj Auto Limited
N.A.I.C.S.: 524298

Subsidiary (Domestic):

Bajaj Allianz Life Insurance Co. Ltd. (2)
Ground Floor GE Plaza Airport Road, Yerwada, Pune, 411006, Maharashtra, India
Tel.: (91) 2066026666
Web Site: http://www.bajajallianz.com
Fire Insurance Services
N.A.I.C.S.: 524113
Chandramohan Mehra *(CMO)*

Bankhaus W. Fortmann & Sohne KG (1)
Lange Str 12, 26122, Oldenburg, Germany
Tel.: (49) 441 21002 0
Web Site: http://www.fortmann.de
Commercial Banking Services
N.A.I.C.S.: 522110

Beykoz Gayrimenkul Yatirim Insaat Turizm Sanayi ve Ticaret A.S. (1)
Allianz Tower Kucukbakkalkoy Mah Kayisdagi Cad No 1, Atasehir, 34750, Istanbul, Turkiye
Tel.: (90) 2165566351
Web Site: https://www.allianzteknik.com.tr
N.A.I.C.S.: 524113

Bilan Services S.N.C. (1)
25 Boulevard Des Bouvets, 92000, Nanterre, France
Tel.: (33) 1 41 97 05 05
General Insurance Services
N.A.I.C.S.: 524210

BrahmsQ Objekt GmbH & Co. KG (1)
Charlottenstr 3, Stuttgart, Baden-Wurttemberg, Germany
Tel.: (49) 40771250
Investment Management Service
N.A.I.C.S.: 523999

Brasil de Imoveis e Participacoes Ltda. (1)
Luis Coelho 26, Sao Paulo, 01309-000, Brazil
Tel.: (55) 1131716687
Investment Management Service
N.A.I.C.S.: 523999

Bureau d'Expertises Despretz S.A. (1)
Boulevard Du Souverain 360 / 2, 1160, Brussels, Belgium
Tel.: (32) 2 649 27 30
Web Site: http://www.bdexp.be
General Insurance Services
N.A.I.C.S.: 524210

Burgel Beteiligungs GmbH (1)
Gasstr 18, Hamburg, 22761, Germany
Tel.: (49) 40 8 98 03 0
Investment Management Service
N.A.I.C.S.: 523999

Burgel Erfurt Beteiligungsgesellschaft mbH (1)
Schillerstr 62, Erfurt, 99096, Germany
Tel.: (49) 361 340980

Web Site: http://www.buergel.de
Investment Management Service
N.A.I.C.S.: 523999

Burgel Erfurt GmbH & Co. KG (1)
Schillerstrasse 62, Erfurt, 99096, Germany
Tel.: (49) 361 3 40 98 0
Credit Information Services
N.A.I.C.S.: 519290

Burgel Internationale Inkassogesellschaft GmbH (1)
Gasstr 18, Hamburg, 22761, Germany
Tel.: (49) 40 89803 0
Debt Collection Services
N.A.I.C.S.: 561440

Burgel Wirtschaftsinformationen GmbH & Co. KG (1)
Gasstrasse 18, 22761, Hamburg, Germany
Tel.: (49) 40 89 80 3 0
Web Site: http://www.buergel.de
Debt Collection Services
N.A.I.C.S.: 561440

Subsidiary (Domestic):

Supercheck GmbH (2)
Sulzburgstrasse 218, Cologne, 50937, Germany
Tel.: (49) 221 42060 740
Web Site: http://www.supercheck.de
Address Investigation Services
N.A.I.C.S.: 812990

Burgel Wirtschaftsinformationen Verwaltungs-GmbH (1)
Gasstr 18, Hamburg, 22761, Germany
Tel.: (49) 40 89 80 30
Business Management Consulting Services
N.A.I.C.S.: 541618

Cedulas Colon de Capitalizacion Colseguros S.A. (1)
Cr 13 A 29 24 Loc 102, Bogota, Colombia
Tel.: (57) 15600600
Investment Management Service
N.A.I.C.S.: 523999

Challenging Financial Careers Insurance Marketing Corp., LLC (1)
17011 Beach Blvd Ste 1500, Huntington Beach, CA 92647
Tel.: (714) 960-6122
General Insurance Services
N.A.I.C.S.: 524210

Chateau Larose Trintaudon S.A. (1)
Route de Pauillac D 206 Cs 30200, 33112, Saint-Laurent-Medoc, France
Tel.: (33) 5 56594192
Web Site: http://www.chateau-larose-trintaudon.fr
Wine Mfr
N.A.I.C.S.: 312130

Chicago Insurance Company, Corp. (1)
33 W Monroe St Fl 12, Chicago, IL 60603
Tel.: (312) 346-6400
Web Site: http://www.firemensfund.com
General Insurance Services
N.A.I.C.S.: 524210

Companhia de Seguros Allianz Portugal S.A. (1)
Rua Andrade Corvo 32, 1069-014, Lisbon, Portugal
Tel.: (351) 213108300
Web Site: https://www.allianz.pt
Sales Range: $200-249.9 Million
Emp.: 500
Insurance Products & Services
N.A.I.C.S.: 524298

ControlExpert Colombia SAS (1)
Av Cra 15 No 93A-84 Business Building 93 Office 303, Bogota, Colombia
Tel.: (57) 17559304
Web Site: https://www.controlexpert.com
N.A.I.C.S.: 541618

ControlExpert GmbH (1)
Marie-Curie-Strasse 3, 40764, Langenfeld, Germany
Tel.: (49) 2173849840
Web Site: https://www.controlexpert.com
Software Development Services
N.A.I.C.S.: 541511

ControlExpert Holding GmbH (1)

Allianz SE—(Continued)

Marie-Curie-Strasse 3, 40764, Langenfeld,
Germany
Tel.: (49) 2173849840
Web Site: https://www.controlexpert.com
N.A.I.C.S.: 524292
Sebastian Lins *(Mng Dir)*

Corn Investment Ltd. **(1)**
199 Bishopsgate, London, EC2M 3TY,
United Kingdom
Tel.: (44) 2035356769
Web Site: https://www.corninvests.com
N.A.I.C.S.: 523999

CreditRas Vita S.p.A. **(1)**
Corso Italia 23, Milan, 20122, Italy
Tel.: (39) 02 7216 1
Web Site: http://www.creditrasvita.it
Fire Insurance Services
N.A.I.C.S.: 524113

**D.A.S. poistovna pravnej ochrany,
a.s.** **(1)**
Sumavska 34, PO Box 162, SK 821 08,
Bratislava, Slovakia
Tel.: (421) 249101010
Web Site: http://www.das.sk
Insurance Services
N.A.I.C.S.: 524298

DONATOR Beratungs GmbH **(1)**
Theresienstr 6-8, 80333, Munich, Germany
Tel.: (49) 89 3800 0
Management Consulting Services
N.A.I.C.S.: 541611

Darta Saving Life Assurance Ltd. **(1)**
Maple House Temple Road, Blackrock,
Dublin, Ireland
Tel.: (353) 12422300
Web Site: https://www.allianzdarta.ie
General Insurance Services
N.A.I.C.S.: 524298

**Deutsche
Lebensversicherungs-AG** **(1)**
Merlitzstrasse 8, 12489, Berlin,
Germany **(100%)**
Tel.: (49) 305389364710
Web Site: https://dlvag.allianz.de
Sales Range: $50-74.9 Million
Emp.: 40
Life Insurance Provider
N.A.I.C.S.: 524113

Diamond Point a.s. **(1)**
Ke Stvanici 656/3, Karlin, 186 00, Prague,
8, Czech Republic
Tel.: (420) 225095851
Web Site: https://diamondpoint.cz
N.A.I.C.S.: 523999
Venelin Yanakiev *(Chm)*

EF Solutions LLC **(1)**
84 Lake Caroline Dr, Ruther Glen, VA
22546-5213
Tel.: (804) 448-5567
Investment Management Service
N.A.I.C.S.: 523999

ESA Cargo & Logistics GmbH **(1)**
Friedrichplatz 2, 74177, Bad Friedrichshall,
Germany
Tel.: (49) 7136 9513 0
Web Site: http://esa.allianz.de
Logistics Consulting Servies
N.A.I.C.S.: 541614

**EURO-Pro Gesellschaft fur Data Pro-
cessing mbH** **(1)**
Lindenhof 1-3, 61279, Gravenwiesbach,
Germany
Tel.: (49) 6086 3988 0
Web Site: http://www.europro.de
Data Processing Services
N.A.I.C.S.: 518210

**EUROGRAFICA
Systemplanungs-GmbH** **(1)**
Alois-Senefelder-Allee 1, Augsburg, 86153,
Germany
Tel.: (49) 821 21736 0
Business Management Consulting Services
N.A.I.C.S.: 541618

**Elix Vintage Residencial SOCIMI
S.A.** **(1)**
Serrano 51 4 o-D, 28006, Madrid, Spain
Tel.: (34) 918380044

Web Site: https://www.elixvrs.com
Real Estate Asset Management Services
N.A.I.C.S.: 531390

Euler Hermes Acmar SA **(1)**
37 Bd Abdellatif Ben Kaddour, Casablanca,
Morocco
Tel.: (212) 522790330
Credit Insurance Services
N.A.I.C.S.: 524126

**Euler Hermes Collections Sp. z
o.o.** **(1)**
Al Jerozolimskie 98, 00-807, Warsaw, Po-
land
Financial Banking Services
N.A.I.C.S.: 522110

Euler Hermes Group SA **(1)**
1 Place des Saisons, La Defense, F-92048,
Paris, Cedex, France **(100%)**
Tel.: (33) 184115000
Web Site: http://www.eulerhermes.com
Rev.: $3,074,844,331
Assets: $7,982,058,698
Liabilities: $7,061,624,272
Net Worth: $920,434,426
Earnings: $377,858,948
Emp.: 5,843
Fiscal Year-end: 12/31/2017
Financial Services
N.A.I.C.S.: 524298
Wilfried Verstraete *(Chm-Mgmt Bd)*

Subsidiary (Non-US):

Acredia Versicherung AG **(2)**
Himmelpfortgasse 29, 1010, Vienna, Austria
Tel.: (43) 5 01 02 1111
Credit Insurance Services
N.A.I.C.S.: 524210

**COSEC Companhia de Seguro de
Creditos, S.A.** **(2)**
Avenida da Republica no 58, 1069-057, Lis-
bon, Portugal
Tel.: (351) 21 791 3700
Credit Insurance Services
N.A.I.C.S.: 524298

Subsidiary (Domestic):

Euler Gestion **(2)**
1 Rue Euler, Paris, 75008, France
Tel.: (33) 140 705 050
Investment Management Service
N.A.I.C.S.: 523999

Subsidiary (US):

Euler Hermes ACI **(2)**
800 Red Brook Blvd, Owings Mills, MD
21117 **(55%)**
Tel.: (410) 753-0753
Web Site: http://www.eulerhermes.us
Sales Range: $75-99.9 Million
Emp.: 110
Holding Company
N.A.I.C.S.: 524126
James Daly *(CEO & Head-Americas)*

Subsidiary (Non-US):

Euler Hermes Aktiengesellschaft **(2)**
Gaastrasse 27, 22761, Hamburg, Germany
Tel.: (49) 4088349090
Web Site: https://www.agaportal.de
Insurance Services
N.A.I.C.S.: 524298

Euler Hermes Australia Pty Ltd. **(2)**
Allianz Building 2 Market Street, Sydney,
2000, NSW, Australia
Tel.: (61) 2 8258 5108
Financial Services
N.A.I.C.S.: 525990

**Euler Hermes Cescob Service
s.r.o.** **(2)**
Molakova 576/11, Prague, 186 00, Czech
Republic
Tel.: (420) 266109552
Financial Management Services
N.A.I.C.S.: 523999

**Euler Hermes Cescob uverova pojis-
tovna a.s.** **(2)**
Molakova 576/11, 186 00, Prague, Czech
Republic
Tel.: (420) 266109521
Web Site: http://www.eulerhermes.com

Emp.: 50
General Insurance Services
N.A.I.C.S.: 524298
Julius Kudla *(CEO)*

Euler Hermes Collections GmbH **(2)**
Zeppelinstr 48, 14471, Potsdam, Germany
Tel.: (49) 33127890000
Web Site: http://www.eulerhermes-
collections.de
Sales Range: $25-49.9 Million
Emp.: 100
Debt Collection Services
N.A.I.C.S.: 561440

**Euler Hermes Collections UK
Limited** **(2)**
1 Canada Square, London, E14 5DX,
United Kingdom
Tel.: (44) 2078602756
Web Site: http://www.eulerhermes.co.uk
Debt Collection Services
N.A.I.C.S.: 561440

Euler Hermes Colombia **(2)**
Calle 72 6-44 Piso 3 Edificio APA, Bogota,
Colombia
Tel.: (57) 571 3264640
Web Site: http://www.co.eulerhermes.com
Credit Insurance Services
N.A.I.C.S.: 524126
John-Paul Bahamondez *(Gen Mgr)*

**Euler Hermes Consulting (Shanghai)
Co., Ltd.** **(2)**
Unit 2103 Taiping Finance Tower N 488,
Middle Yincheng Road Pudong New Area,
Shanghai, 200120, China
Tel.: (86) 21 6030 5900
Insurance Services
N.A.I.C.S.: 524298

**Euler Hermes Credit Insurance Nor-
dic AB** **(2)**
Klara Veadukten, Stockholm, 11164, Swe-
den
Tel.: (46) 855513600
Web Site: http://www.eulerhermes.se
Sales Range: $50-74.9 Million
Emp.: 50
Credit Insurance Services
N.A.I.C.S.: 524128

**Euler Hermes Credit Management
OOO** **(2)**
Office C08 4-th Dobrynnskly per 8, 119049,
Moscow, Russia
Tel.: (7) 4959812833
Credit Insurance Services
N.A.I.C.S.: 524298

**Euler Hermes Credit Management
Services Ireland Ltd.** **(2)**
3rd Floor Mespil Court 39a Mespil Road,
Dublin, Ireland
Tel.: (353) 1 660 1667
Insurance & Credit Management Services
N.A.I.C.S.: 524298

**Euler Hermes Credit Services (JP)
Ltd.** **(2)**
Kyobashi Nisshoku Bldg 7F 8-7 Kyobashi
1-chome, Chuo-ku, Tokyo, 104-0031, Japan
Tel.: (81) 3 3538 5403
Sales Range: $50-74.9 Million
Emp.: 7
Insurance Management Services
N.A.I.C.S.: 524298

Euler Hermes Danmark **(2)**
Amerika Plads 19, 2100, Copenhagen,
Denmark
Tel.: (45) 88333388
Web Site: http://www.eulerhermes.dk
Emp.: 70
Insurance Management Services
N.A.I.C.S.: 524298
Peter Hecht *(Gen Mgr)*

Euler Hermes Deutschland AG **(2)**
Friedensallee 254, 22763, Hamburg, Ger-
many
Tel.: (49) 40 88340
Web Site: http://www.eulerhermes.de
Sales Range: $200-249.9 Million
Emp.: 300
Credit Information Services
N.A.I.C.S.: 522299
Silke Grimm *(Member-Mgmt Bd)*

Euler Hermes Emporiki S.A. **(2)**
16 Laodikias Str & 1-3 Nymfeou Str, Ilissia,
Athens, 11528, Greece
Tel.: (30) 210 69000 00
Credit Insurance Services
N.A.I.C.S.: 524126
Vassilis Christidis *(CEO)*

Euler Hermes Europe SA **(2)**
Avenue des Arts Kunstlaan 56, 1000, Brus-
sels, Belgium
Tel.: (32) 2 289 3111
Financial Services
N.A.I.C.S.: 525990

**Euler Hermes Forderungsmanage-
ment GmbH** **(2)**
Friedensallee 254, Hamburg, 22763, Ger-
many
Tel.: (49) 40 88 34 0
Web Site: http://www.eulerhermes-risk.com
Sales Range: $300-349.9 Million
Emp.: 1,300
Debt Collection Services
N.A.I.C.S.: 561440
Diane Koy *(Mng Dir)*

**Euler Hermes Hellas Credit Insurance
SA** **(2)**
16 Laodiktas Street & 1-3 Nymfeou Street,
11528, Athens, Greece
Tel.: (30) 210 6900 000
Credit Insurance Services
N.A.I.C.S.: 524298

Euler Hermes Holdings UK plc **(2)**
1 Canada Sq, London, E14 5DX, United
Kirgdom
Tel.: (44) 20 7512 9333
General Insurance Services
N.A.I.C.S.: 524298

**Euler Hermes Hong Kong Services
ltd.** **(2)**
Suites 403-11 4/F Cityplaza 4, 12 Taikoo
Wan Road Island East, Hong Kong, China
(Hong Kong)
Tel.: (852) 3665 8001
Credit Insurance Services
N.A.I.C.S.: 524298

Euler Hermes India Pvt. Ltd. **(2)**
5th Floor Vaibhav Chambers Opp Income
Tax Office, Bandra Kurla Complex Bandra
East, Mumbai, 400 051, India
Tel.: (91) 22 6623 2525
Credit Insurance Services
N.A.I.C.S.: 524298

Euler Hermes Ireland **(2)**
Arch Blackrock Business Park Carysfort
Avenue Blackrock, Dublin, Ireland
Tel.: (353) 1 200 0400
Web Site: http://www.eulerhermes.ie
General Insurance Services
N.A.I.C.S.: 524298

**Euler Hermes Magyar Koveteleske-
zelo Kft.** **(2)**
Kiscelli U 104, Budapest, 1036, Hungary
Tel.: (36) 14 53 90 00
Financial Management Services
N.A.I.C.S.: 523999

**Euler Hermes Management UK
Limited** **(2)**
1 Canada Sq, London, E14 5DX, United
Kingdom
Tel.: (44) 20 7512 9333
Business Management Consulting Services
N.A.I.C.S.: 541618

Euler Hermes New Zealand Ltd. **(2)**
Level 1 152 Fanshawe Street, Auckland,
1010, New Zealand
Tel.: (64) 9 354 2995
Credit Insurance Services
N.A.I.C.S.: 524298

Euler Hermes Norge **(2)**
Holbergsgate 21, Oslo, 0130, Norway
Tel.: (47) 23 25 60 00
Web Site: http://www.eulerhermes.no
General Insurance Services
N.A.I.C.S.: 524298

**Euler Hermes North America Insur-
ance Company** **(2)**
1155 Rene-Levesque Blvd West Suite
2810, Montreal, H3B 2L2, QC, Canada

Tel.: (514) 476-9656
Insurance Services
N.A.I.C.S.: 524298

Euler Hermes Rating Deutschland GmbH (2)
Friedensallee 254, Hamburg, 22763, Germany
Tel.: (49) 40 88 34 64 0
Web Site: http://www.ehrg.de
Emp.: 16
Marketing Consulting Services
N.A.I.C.S.: 541613

Euler Hermes Rating GmbH (2)
Friedensallee 254, 22763, Hamburg, Germany
Tel.: (49) 40 834 640
Credit Services
N.A.I.C.S.: 522299

Euler Hermes Reinsurance AG (2)
Toedistrasse 65, 8002, Zurich, Switzerland
Tel.: (41) 442836565
Emp.: 60
Reinsurance Services
N.A.I.C.S.: 524130
Stefan Ruf *(Gen Mgr)*

Euler Hermes Risk Services UK Limited (2)
1 Canada Square, London, E14 5DX, United Kingdom
Tel.: (44) 20 7512 9333
Web Site: http://www.eulerhermes.com
Financial Management Services
N.A.I.C.S.: 523999

Euler Hermes Risk Yonetimi ve Danismanlik Hizmetleri Limited Sirketi (2)
Iz Plaza Giz Ayazaga Yolu No 9 Kat 14, Maslak, 34398, Istanbul, Turkiye
Tel.: (90) 212 2907610
Web Site: http://www.allianz.com
Insurance Management Services
N.A.I.C.S.: 524298

Subsidiary (Domestic):

Euler Hermes SFAC (2)
1 rue Euler, 75008, Paris, France
Tel.: (33) 140705050
Web Site: http://www.eulerhermes.com
Sales Range: $150-199.9 Million
Emp.: 500
Financial Services
N.A.I.C.S.: 525990

Euler Hermes SFAC Recouvrement S.A.S. (2)
1 Rue Euler, 75008, Paris, France
Tel.: (33) 1 40 70 50 50
Debt Collection Services
N.A.I.C.S.: 561440

Subsidiary (Non-US):

Euler Hermes Seguros de Credito SA (2)
Avenida Paulista 2 421-3 andar, Jardim Paulista, Sao Paulo, 01311-300, SP, Brazil
Tel.: (55) 11 3065 2260
Credit Insurance Services
N.A.I.C.S.: 524298

Euler Hermes Services AG (2)
Richtistrasse, Wallisellen, 8304, Switzerland
Tel.: (41) 442836565
Credit Insurance Services
N.A.I.C.S.: 524126

Euler Hermes Services B.V. (2)
Pettelaarpark 20, Postbus 7051, 's-Hertogenbosch, 5216 PD, Netherlands
Tel.: (31) 73 688 99 99
Web Site: http://www.eolis.nl
Sales Range: $100-124.9 Million
Emp.: 120
General Insurance Services
N.A.I.C.S.: 524298

Euler Hermes Services Belgium S.A. (2)
15 Rue Montoyer, Brussels, 1000, Belgium
Tel.: (32) 22893111
Sales Range: $100-124.9 Million
Emp.: 180
Insurance Management Services
N.A.I.C.S.: 524298

Euler Hermes Services India Private Limited (2)
4th Floor Voltas House 23 J N Heredia Marg Ballard Estate, Mumbai, 400 001, India
Tel.: (91) 22 66232525
Web Site: http://www.allianz.com
Sales Range: $50-74.9 Million
Emp.: 18
Financial Management Services
N.A.I.C.S.: 523999

Euler Hermes Servicii Financiare S.R.L. (2)
6 Petru Maior, 011264, Bucharest, Romania
Tel.: (40) 21 3020300
Web Site: http://www.eulerhermes.ro
Sales Range: $50-74.9 Million
Emp.: 30
Insurance Management Services
N.A.I.C.S.: 524298

Euler Hermes Servicios S.A. (2)
Blvd Manuel Avila Camacho 164-8, Mexico, Mexico
Tel.: (52) 55 5201 7900
Credit Insurance Services
N.A.I.C.S.: 524126

Euler Hermes Sigorta A.S. (2)
Buyukdere Cad No: 100-102 Maya Akar Center Kat: 7, Esentepe Sisli, 34394, Istanbul, Turkiye
Tel.: (90) 2122907610
Credit Insurance Services
N.A.I.C.S.: 524298

Euler Hermes Singapore Services Pte Ltd. (2)
79 Robinson Road 09-01, Singapore, 068897, Singapore
Tel.: (65) 65893700
Web Site: http://www.eulerhermes.sg
Credit Insurance Services
N.A.I.C.S.: 524298

Euler Hermes Suomi (2)
Mannerheimintie 105, Helsinki, 280, Finland
Tel.: (358) 1 08508500
Web Site: http://www.eulerhermes.fi
General Insurance Services
N.A.I.C.S.: 524298

Euler Hermes Sverige (2)
Klarabergsviadukten 90, Box 729, Stockholm, 11164, Sweden
Tel.: (46) 8 555 136 00
Web Site: http://www.eulerhermes.se
Financial Management Services
N.A.I.C.S.: 523999

Euler Hermes Trade Credit Limited (2)
Level 1 152 Fanshawe St, Auckland, 1010, New Zealand
Tel.: (64) 9 3542995
Credit Insurance Services
N.A.I.C.S.: 524126

Euler Hermes Trade Credit Underwriting Agents Pty Ltd (2)
Level 9 Forecourt Allianz Building 2 Market Street, Sydney, 2000, NSW, Australia
Tel.: (61) 2 8258 5108
Credit Underwriting Services
N.A.I.C.S.: 524126

Subsidiary (US):

Euler Hermes UMA Inc (2)
600 S 7th St, Louisville, KY 40201-1672
Tel.: (502) 583-3600
Debt Collection Services
N.A.I.C.S.: 561440

Subsidiary (Domestic):

Euler Hermes World Agency SASU (2)
8 Rue Euler, 75008, Paris, France
Tel.: (33) 1 40 70 50 83
Credit Insurance Services
N.A.I.C.S.: 524126

Euler SFAC Asset Management (2)
1 Rue Euler, 75008, Paris, France
Tel.: (33) 1 40 70 50 50
Asset Management Services
N.A.I.C.S.: 523940

Euler Hermes Hong Kong Service Limited (1)
Suites 403-11 4/F 12 Taikoo Wan Road, Taikoo Shing, China (Hong Kong)
Tel.: (852) 36658994
Credit Insurance Services
N.A.I.C.S.: 524126
Shirley Li *(Mktg Mgr)*

Euler Hermes Korea Non-life Broker Company Limited (1)
Level 22 Seoul Finance Center 136 Sejong daero, Jung-gu, Seoul, Korea (South)
Tel.: (82) 221791300
Credit Insurance Services
N.A.I.C.S.: 524126

Euler Hermes Seguros S.A. (1)
Rua Eugenio de Mederios 303-4 andar, Sao Paulo, 05425-000, SP, Brazil
Tel.: (55) 1130652260
Web Site: https://www.allianz-trade.com
Finance & Insurance Services
N.A.I.C.S.: 524210

Euler Hermes Service AB (1)
Sveavagen 98, Box 729, 101 34, Stockholm, Sweden
Tel.: (46) 855513600
Credit Insurance Services
N.A.I.C.S.: 524126
Pekka Puotunen *(CEO)*

Euler Hermes Services Italia S.r.l. (1)
Via R Matarazzo 19, 00139, Rome, Italy
Tel.: (39) 0687001
Insurance Services
N.A.I.C.S.: 524210

Euler Hermes Servicos de Gestao de Riscos Ltda. (1)
Rua Eugenio de Mederios 303 4o andar, Sao Paulo, Brazil
Tel.: (55) 1130652260
Health Insurance Services
N.A.I.C.S.: 524210

Euro Garantie AG (1)
Bannholzstrasse 12, 8608, Bubikon, Switzerland
Tel.: (41) 848 488 228
General Insurance Services
N.A.I.C.S.: 524210

FAI Allianz Ltd. (1)
L 14 2 Market St, Sydney, 2000, NSW, Australia
Tel.: (61) 1300368764
General Insurance Services
N.A.I.C.S.: 524210

Generation Vie S.A. (1)
Tour Neptune - 20 place de Seine, 92400, Courbevoie, France
Tel.: (33) 1403267487
Health Insurance Services
N.A.I.C.S.: 524114

Global Transport & Automotive Insurance Solutions Pty Limited (1)
Level 6 55 Chandos Street, St Leonards, Sydney, 2065, NSW, Australia
Tel.: (61) 2 9966 8820
Web Site: http://www.gtins.com.au
Automobile Insurance Services
N.A.I.C.S.: 524126

Grundstucksgesellschaft der Vereinten Versicherungen mbH (1)
Koniginstrasse 28, 80802, Munich, Bayern, Germany
Tel.: (49) 89 38000
General Insurance Services
N.A.I.C.S.: 524298

Grupo Multiasistencia S.A. (1)
C/Ronda de Poniente 7, Tres Cantos, 28760, Madrid, Spain
Tel.: (34) 918045656
Web Site: http://www.multiasistencia.com
Insurance Claims Management Services
N.A.I.C.S.: 524291
Javier Bartolome *(CEO)*

HELVIASS Verzekeringen B.V. (1)
Coolsingel 139, 3012 AG, Rotterdam, Netherlands
Tel.: (31) 205618560
Web Site: http://www.helviass.nl

General Insurance Services
N.A.I.C.S.: 524298

Havelaar et Van Stolk B.V. (1)
Coolsingel 139, 3012 AG, Rotterdam, Netherlands
Tel.: (31) 10 281 67 77
Web Site: http://www.havelaar.com
General Insurance Services
N.A.I.C.S.: 524210

Home & Legacy Insurance Services Limited (1)
500 Avebury Boulevard Lower Ground Floor, Milton Keynes, MK9 2LA, Buckinghamshire, United Kingdom
Tel.: (44) 20 3118 7777
Web Site: http://www.homeandlegacy.co.uk
General Insurance Services
N.A.I.C.S.: 524210
Adrian Ewington *(Dir-Underwriting & Markets)*

ICON Immobilien GmbH & Co. KG (1)
Muhlenkamp 59, 22303, Hamburg, Germany
Tel.: (49) 4065052990
Web Site: https://www.icon-immobilien.de
N.A.I.C.S.: 531210

IDS GmbH-Analysis and Reporting Services (1)
Koeniginstrasse 28, 80802, Munich, Germany
Tel.: (49) 8000008670
Web Site: https://www.idsdata.com
Investment Management Service
N.A.I.C.S.: 523940

Immovalor Gestion S.A. (1)
B218 87 Rue De Richelieu, 75113, Paris, France
Tel.: (33) 155271700
Web Site: http://www.immovalor.fr
Asset Management Services
N.A.I.C.S.: 523940

International Film Guarantors Ltd. (1)
19 Margaret Street, London, W1W 8RR, United Kingdom
Tel.: (44) 20 7636 8855
Web Site: http://www.ifgbonds.com
Media Insurance Services
N.A.I.C.S.: 524298

Jota-Vermogensverwaltungsgesellschaft mbH (1)
Koniginstrasse 28, 80802, Munich, Germany
Tel.: (49) 89 38000
Asset Management Services
N.A.I.C.S.: 523940

Ken Tame & Associates Pty Ltd (1)
Shop 15 79-83 High St 79 High St, Kew, Melbourne, 3101, VIC, Australia
Tel.: (61) 3 9853 5555
Web Site: http://www.kentame.com.au
Insurance Brokerage Services
N.A.I.C.S.: 524210

Legal & General Insurance Ltd. (1)
1 Coleman Street, London, EC2R 5AA, United Kingdom (100%)
Tel.: (44) 3709003131
Web Site: http://www.legalandgeneral.com
Sales Range: $700-749.9 Million
Emp.: 1,800
Treasury Operations
N.A.I.C.S.: 522299
Bernie Hickman *(CEO)*

Liverpool Victoria Friendly Society Limited (1)
County Gates, Bournemouth, BH1 2NF, United Kingdom (69.9%)
Tel.: (44) 1202292333
Web Site: http://www.lv.com
Sales Range: $1-4.9 Billion
Emp.: 5,500
Insurance & Financial Services Organization
N.A.I.C.S.: 813910
Richard Rowney *(CEO)*

Subsidiary (Domestic):

Liverpool Victoria Insurance Company Limited (2)

Allianz SE—(Continued)

County Gates, Bournemouth, BH1 2NF,
Dorset, United Kingdom
Tel.: (44) 1202292333
Web Site: http://www.lv.com
Sales Range: $1-4.9 Billion
Insurance Products & Services
N.A.I.C.S.: 524298
Mike Rogers (CEO)

Subsidiary (Domestic):

LV Insurance Management
Limited   (3)
69 Park Lane, Croydon, CR9 1BG, United
Kingdom
Tel.: (44) 84 5640 5100
Fire Insurance Services
N.A.I.C.S.: 524113

Lloyd Adriatico S.p.A.   (1)
Largo Ugo Irneri 1, 34123, Trieste,
Italy   (100%)
Tel.: (39) 0407781111
N.A.I.C.S.: 524128

MAWISTA GmbH   (1)
Esslinger Str 83, 73207, Plochingen, Ger-
many
Tel.: (49) 7024469510
Web Site: https://www.mawista.com
Health Care Insurance Services
N.A.I.C.S.: 524210

MONDIAL ASSISTANCE GmbH   (1)
Pottendorfer Strasse 25-27, Vienna, 1120,
Austria
Tel.: (43) 1 52503 0
Web Site: http://www.allianz-assistance.at
Emp.: 180
General Insurance Services
N.A.I.C.S.: 524298
Christof Heissenberger (Gen Mgr)

MONDIAL ASSISTANCE IRELAND
LIMITED   (1)
511 Q House Furze Rd, Sandyford, Dublin,
18, Ireland
Tel.: (353) 1 6373667
Web Site: http://www.mondial-assistance.ie
Sales Range: $50-74.9 Million
Emp.: 35
Travel Insurance Services
N.A.I.C.S.: 524298

Magdeburger Sigorta A.S.   (1)
Baglarbasi Kisikli Cad No 13 Altunizade,
34662, Istanbul, Turkiye
Tel.: (90) 216 556 66 66
Web Site: http://www.magdeburger.com.tr
General Insurance Services
N.A.I.C.S.: 524210

Managed Insurance Operations
B.V.   (1)
Coolsingel 139, Rotterdam, 3001DA, Neth-
erlands
Tel.: (31) 88 577 32 00
Web Site: http://www.mio-insurance.nl
Emp.: 50
General Insurance Services
N.A.I.C.S.: 524210
T. Baken (Gen Mgr)

Medexpress JSIC   (1)
Gorokhovaya St 14/26, 191186, Saint Pe-
tersburg, Russia
Tel.: (7) 8124949411
Web Site: http://www.medexpress.ru
Emp.: 100
Financial Management Services
N.A.I.C.S.: 523999

Medi24 AG   (1)
Bolligenstrasse 54, 3006, Bern, Switzerland
Tel.: (41) 313400500
Web Site: http://www.medi24.ch
Emp.: 120
Personal Health Advice Services
N.A.I.C.S.: 621999
Lebrecht Gerber (Chm & CEO)

Menzis   (1)
Weestblaak 67, NL 3600 AB, Rotterdam,
Netherlands
Tel.: (31) 102706300
N.A.I.C.S.: 524128

Mondial Assistance Agent de Asigurare SRL   (1)

Calea Floreasca Nr 169 Sector 1, Bucha-
rest, 014459, Romania
Tel.: (40) 21 312 22 36
Web Site: http://www.mondial-assistance.ro
General Insurance Services
N.A.I.C.S.: 524210

Mondial Assistance Asia Pacific
Ltd.   (1)
12 Marina View Asia Tower Sq 2 Unit 13-
04, Singapore, 18961, Singapore
Tel.: (65) 35 3585
Web Site: http://www.mondial-assistance-
asiapacific.com
Sales Range: $50-74.9 Million
Emp.: 35
Travel Insurance & Assistance Services
N.A.I.C.S.: 524298

Mondial Assistance Belgium   (1)
Rue des Hirondelles 2, 1000, Brussels,
Belgium
Tel.: (32) 2 2906411
Web Site: http://www.mondial-assistance.be
Sales Range: $75-99.9 Million
Emp.: 100
Travel Insurance & Medical Assistance Ser-
vices
N.A.I.C.S.: 524298

Mondial Assistance Brazil   (1)
Alameda Santos 745 2 Andar - Cj 22,
01419-001, Sao Paulo, Brazil
Tel.: (55) 11 30652599
Web Site: http://www.mondial-
assistance.com.br
Travel Insurance Services
N.A.I.C.S.: 524128

Mondial Assistance France   (1)
7 Rue Dora Maar, 75008, Paris, France
Tel.: (33) 153058600
Travel Insurance Services
N.A.I.C.S.: 524128
Michael Rouviere (Project Mgr)

Mondial Assistance Greece   (1)
10 Premetis St, 173 42, Athens, Greece
Tel.: (30) 210 99 88 100
Web Site: http://www.mondial-assistance.gr
Travel Insurance Services
N.A.I.C.S.: 524298

Mondial Assistance OOO   (1)
Timiryazevskaya Str 1, Moscow, 127422,
Russia
Tel.: (7) 495 661 47 22
Web Site: http://www.mondial-assistance.ru
Travel Insurance Services
N.A.I.C.S.: 524298

Mondial Assistance Reunion S.A.   (1)
11 rue Roland Garros Residence Les Char-
milles, Saint Denis, France
Tel.: (33) 262 90 99 95
Web Site: http://www.mondial-assistance.re
General Insurance Services
N.A.I.C.S.: 524298

Mondial Assistance SARL   (1)
Timiryazvskaya St 1, Moscow, 127422,
Russia
Tel.: (7) 495 6614722
Web Site: http://www.mondial-assistance.ru
General Insurance Services
N.A.I.C.S.: 524210

Mondial Assistance Sigorta Aracilik
Hizmetleri Limited Sirketi, LS   (1)
Unsal Carsi K 6/215 1 Halaskargazi Cad-
desi, Istanbul, 34662, Turkiye
Tel.: (90) 2164743576
Insurance Management Services
N.A.I.C.S.: 524298
Erik Heusel (Gen Mgr)

Mondial Assistance Sp. z o.o.   (1)
Ul Domaniewska 50B, 02-672, Warsaw,
Poland
Tel.: (48) 22 522 25 00
Web Site: http://www.mondial-assistance.pl
Travel Insurance Services
N.A.I.C.S.: 524298

Mondial Assistance Turkey   (1)
Buyukdere C Enka Binasi 108 Kat 10
Esentepe, Istanbul, 34394, Turkiye
Tel.: (90) 212 3374337
Web Site: http://www.mondial-
assistance.com.tr
Travel & Medical Assistance Services

N.A.I.C.S.: 923130

Mondial Assistance s.r.o   (1)
Jankovcova 1596/14b, Prague, 17000,
Czech Republic
Tel.: (420) 283 002 711
Web Site: http://www.mondial-assistance.cz
Travel Insurance & Medical Assistance Ser-
vices
N.A.I.C.S.: 524298
Miroslav Dolezal (Gen Mgr)

Mondial Assistance/Auto Assist Co.,
Ltd.   (1)
29th Floor Grand Amarin Tower 1550 New
Petchaburi Road, Makasan Rajathevi,
Bangkok, 10400, Thailand
Tel.: (66) 2 305 8555
Web Site: http://www.autoassist.co.th
Travel Insurance & Assistance Services
N.A.I.C.S.: 524298

Mondial Service Italia S.r.l   (1)
Via Ampere Andrea Maria 30, 20131, Milan,
Italy
Tel.: (39) 02 236951
Insurance Management Services
N.A.I.C.S.: 524298

Mondial Service- Belgium S.A.   (1)
Rue Des Hirondelles 2, Brussels, 1030,
Belgium
Tel.: (32) 2 2906411
Web Site: http://www.allianz-global-
assistance.be
Emp.: 100
Financial Management Services
N.A.I.C.S.: 523999

Mondial Services (India) Pvt. Ltd.   (1)
1st Floor DLF Square M-Block - Jacaranda
Marg Phase-II, Gurgaon, 122 002, Haryana,
India
Tel.: (91) 124 4343800
Web Site: http://www.allianz-assistance.com
General Insurance Services
N.A.I.C.S.: 524298

Mondial Servicios S.A. de C.V.   (1)
Boulevard Adolfo Lopez Mateos 379 Col
Atlamaya, 01760, Mexico, Mexico
Tel.: (52) 5553773800
Sales Range: $50-74.9 Million
Emp.: 70
Insurance Management Services
N.A.I.C.S.: 524298
Hugo Esquivel (Branch Mgr)

Munchener und Magdeburger Agrar-
versicherung Aktiengesellschaft   (1)
Albert-Schweitzer-Str 62-64, Munich, 81735,
Germany
Tel.: (49) 89 678297 0
Web Site: http://www.mmagrar.de
Emp.: 70
Agricultural Insurance Services
N.A.I.C.S.: 524126
Olif Bogenreader (Gen Mgr)

Munsterlandische Bank Thie & Co.
KG   (1)
Alter Steinweg 1, 48143, Munster, Germany
Tel.: (49) 251 48 47 1 0
Web Site: http://www.mlb.de
Credit Information Services
N.A.I.C.S.: 522299

NEM Insurance Ireland Limited   (1)
South Leinster Street 7-9, Dublin, Ireland
Tel.: (353) 1 702 30 00
General Insurance Services
N.A.I.C.S.: 524210

NEXtCARE Claims Management
LLC   (1)
EIFFEL 2 Building 1st Floor Umm Al Sheif
Sheikh Zayed Road, PO Box 80864, Near
to the First Gulf Bank Metro station, Dubai,
United Arab Emirates
Tel.: (971) 42708800
Web Site: http://www.nextcarehealth.com
Health Insurance Management Services
N.A.I.C.S.: 524292
Jihad Francis (Chief Bus Dev Officer)

NEXtCARE Holding WLL   (1)
Office 131 bldg 79 Road 2802 seef block
428 capitalplus tower, PO Box 18442, Seef
District 410, Manama, Bahrain
Tel.: (973) 17382721

Web Site: http://www.nextcarehealth.com
Emp.: 10
Investment Management Service
N.A.I.C.S.: 523940
Layla Redha (Gen Mgr)

Subsidiary (Non-US):

NEXtCARE Egypt LLC   (2)
17 Al Ahram Street Building B Floor 7 Roxy
Heliopolis, Cairo, Egypt
Tel.: (20) 2 24182564
Web Site: http://www.nextcarehealth.com
Insurance Management Services
N.A.I.C.S.: 524298

NEXtCARE Lebanon SAL   (1)
Saifi Area Pasteur Street Pasteur 40 Build-
ing, Beirut, Lebanon
Tel.: (961) 1 577200
Web Site: http://www.nextcarehealth.com
Health Insurance Services
N.A.I.C.S.: 524114

NEXtCARE UAE, AGHS LLC   (1)
EIFFEL- 2 Building 1st Floor Sheikh Zayed
Road Umm Al Sheif, PO Box 80864, Deira,
Dubai, 80864, United Arab Emirates
Tel.: (971) 4 2095200
Web Site: http://www.nextcarehealth.com
Health Insurance Services
N.A.I.C.S.: 524114

National Surety Corporation   (1)
777 San Marin Dr, Novato, CA 94998
Tel.: (415) 899-2000
Property & Casualty Insurance Services
N.A.I.C.S.: 524126

Neoasistencia Manoteras S.L.   (1)
Av Las Americas 4, 28823, Coslada, Spain
Tel.: (34) 916745002
Financial Management Services
N.A.I.C.S.: 523999

OJSC ROSNO   (1)
Ozerkovskaya Nab 30, 115184, Moscow,
Russia   (97%)
Tel.: (7) 4952323333
Web Site: http://www.allianz.com
Sales Range: $650-699.9 Million
Emp.: 6,000
Insurance Services
N.A.I.C.S.: 524298

Subsidiary (Domestic):

Allianz ROSNO Asset
Management   (2)
Paveletskaya Square 2 Building 1, 115054,
Moscow, Russia
Tel.: (7) 4957373773
Web Site: http://www.allianzinvest.ru
Sales Range: $150-199.9 Million
Emp.: 50
Asset Management Services
N.A.I.C.S.: 523940

Allianz ROSNO Life   (2)
Ozerkovskaya Nab 30, Moscow, 115184,
Russia
Tel.: (7) 4952323333
Web Site: http://www.allianzrosnolife.ru
Fire Insurance Services
N.A.I.C.S.: 524113

Subsidiary (Non-US):

Allianz Ukraine SLC   (2)
210 G Dehtyarivska St, Kiev, 4119, Ukraine
Tel.: (380) 444590058
Web Site: http://www.allianz.ua
Sales Range: $75-99.9 Million
Emp.: 200
Insurance Services
N.A.I.C.S.: 524298

OLB-Beteiligungsgesellschaft
mbH   (1)
Stau 17, 26122, Oldenburg, Germany
Tel.: (49) 441 2210
Investment Management Service
N.A.I.C.S.: 523999

OLB-Immobiliendienst-GmbH   (1)
Alexanderstrasse 113, Oldenburg, 26121,
Germany
Tel.: (49) 441 95072 14
Web Site: http://www.olb.de
Emp.: 8
Real Estate Management Services

N.A.I.C.S.: 531390
Thomas Schmedes (Office Mgr)

OLB-Service GmbH (1)
Stau 15-17, 26122, Oldenburg, Germany
Tel.: (49) 4412212000
Web Site: http://www.olb.de
Emp.: 4,000
Financial Management Services
N.A.I.C.S.: 523999
Thomas Bretzger (Gen Mgr)

OY Selecta AB (1)
Konalantie 47 B, 00390, Helsinki, Finland
Tel.: (358) 20 721 0300
Web Site: http://www.selecta.com
Coffee Machine Mfr
N.A.I.C.S.: 333241

Objekt Burchardplatz GmbH & Co. KG
Charlottenstr 3, 70182, Stuttgart, Germany
Tel.: (49) 711 6630
Real Estate Management Services
N.A.I.C.S.: 531390

Ontario Limited (1)
834 Yonge St, Toronto, M4W 2H1, ON, Canada
Tel.: (416) 901-6863
Financial Management Services
N.A.I.C.S.: 523999

P.T. Asuransi Allianz Life Indonesia (1)
Summitmas II 19th Fl, Jl Jend Sudirman Kav 61 62, 12190, Jakarta, Indonesia (100%)
Tel.: (62) 2152998888
Web Site: http://www.allianz.co.id
Sales Range: $200-249.9 Million
Emp.: 400
Insurance Provider
N.A.I.C.S.: 524128

P.T. Asuransi Allianz Utama Indonesia (1)
Summitmas II 9th Fl Jl Jend Sudirman Kav 61 62, Jakarta, 12190, Indonesia (100%)
Tel.: (62) 212522470
Web Site: http://www.allianz.co.id
Sales Range: $100-124.9 Million
Emp.: 200
Insurance Provider
N.A.I.C.S.: 524128

PIMCO (Schweiz) GmbH (1)
Brandschenkestrasse 41, 8002, Zurich, Switzerland
Tel.: (41) 445124910
Web Site: http://www.pimco.ch
Investment Management Service
N.A.I.C.S.: 523940
Marc Schumacher (Acct Mgr)

PIMCO Europe GmbH (1)
Seidlstr 24-24a, 80335, Munich, Germany
Tel.: (49) 89262096000
Asset Management Services
N.A.I.C.S.: 523940

PIMCO Global Advisors (Ireland) Ltd. (1)
3rd Floor Harcourt Building Harcourt Street, 2, Dublin, D02 F721, Ireland
Tel.: (353) 28229248
N.A.I.C.S.: 523999

PIMCO Taiwan Ltd. (1)
40th Floor No 68 Section 5 Zhongxiao East Road, Xinyi District, Taipei, 11065, Taiwan
Tel.: (886) 287295500
Investment Management Service
N.A.I.C.S.: 523999
Mitch Wang (Gen Mgr)

PT manroland Indonesia (1)
Management Building 2nd Floor Jl Buncit Raya Kav 100, Jakarta, 12510, Indonesia
Tel.: (62) 2179199818
Web Site: http://www.manroland-sheetfed.com
Printing Machinery Mfr
N.A.I.C.S.: 333248

PTE Allianz Polska SA (1)
ul Rodziny Hiszpanskich 1, 02-685, Warsaw, Poland
Tel.: (48) 225674000
Pension Fund Services
N.A.I.C.S.: 525110

Personalized Brokerage Service LLC (1)
6001 SW 6th Ave Ste 330, Topeka, KS 66615
Tel.: (800) 225-4896
Web Site: http://www.pbsworksforme.com
Insurance Brokerage Services
N.A.I.C.S.: 524210
Patrick K. Seelye (Pres)

Pet Plan Ltd. (1)
Great West House GW2 Great West Road, Brentford, TW8 9DX, Middlesex, United Kingdom
Tel.: (44) 845 077 1934
Web Site: http://www.petplan.co.uk
Art Insurance Services
N.A.I.C.S.: 524128

Popular Gestion SGIIC, S.A. (1)
Labastida 11, 28034, Madrid, Spain
Tel.: (34) 915208200
Investment Management Service
N.A.I.C.S.: 523999

Progress-Garant Insurance Company OJSC (1)
Seleznevskaya St 32, Moscow, 127473, Russia
Tel.: (7) 495 7816666
General Insurance Services
N.A.I.C.S.: 524210

Quality 1 AG (1)
Bannholzstrasse 12, 8608, Bubikon, Switzerland
Tel.: (41) 55 254 30 00
Web Site: http://www.quality1.ch
General Insurance Services
N.A.I.C.S.: 524210

Questar Agency Inc. (1)
5701 Golden Hills Dr, Minneapolis, MN 55416-1297
Tel.: (763) 765-7937
General Insurance Services
N.A.I.C.S.: 524210

RB Fiduciaria S.p.A (1)
Piazzale Lodi N 3, 20137, Milan, Italy
Tel.: (39) 02 72128236
Investment Management Service
N.A.I.C.S.: 523999

RCM (UK) Ltd. (1)
199 Bishopsgate, London, EC2M 3TY, United Kingdom
Tel.: (44) 2078 599 000
Web Site: http://www.rcm.co.uk
Emp.: 160
Investment Management Service
N.A.I.C.S.: 523999

RHEA, S.A. (1)
Rue Beaumont 11, Luxembourg, 1219, Luxembourg
Tel.: (352) 22 34 22 31
Financial Management Services
N.A.I.C.S.: 523999

ROSNO Insurance Company OJSC (1)
Ozerkovskaya Nab 30, Moscow, 115184, Russia
Tel.: (7) 495 2323333
General Insurance Services
N.A.I.C.S.: 524210

Risikomanagement und Softwareentwicklung GmbH (1)
Hietzinger Kai 101-105, 1130, Vienna, Austria
Tel.: (43) 1 878 072 191
Information Technology Consulting Services
N.A.I.C.S.: 541512

Roster Financial LLC (1)
1000 Voorhees Dr Ste B, Voorhees, NJ 08043
Tel.: (800) 933-6632
Web Site: http://www.rosterfinancial.com
Financial Management Services
N.A.I.C.S.: 523999
Tom Yacovino (Pres)

SA CARENE ASSURANCE (1)
92 Rue De Richelieu, Paris, 75002, France
Tel.: (33) 1 42 46 52 52
General Insurance Services
N.A.I.C.S.: 524210

Faucier Gilles (Mgr)

SA Vignobles de Larose (1)
Route de Pauillac, 33112, Saint-Laurent-Medoc, France
Tel.: (33) 556594172
Web Site: http://www.vignoblesdelarose.com
Men & Women Product Whslr
N.A.I.C.S.: 424350

SIFCOM Assurances (1)
BP 8484, Abidjan, Cote d'Ivoire
Tel.: (225) 21757575
General Insurance Services
N.A.I.C.S.: 524210

SITIA Beteiligungs- und Verwaltungs GmbH (1)
Unter Sachsenhausen 4, 50667, Cologne, Germany
Tel.: (49) 22114501
Web Site: http://www.allianz.com
Investment Advice Services
N.A.I.C.S.: 523940

SOCIEDAD MUNDIAL DE ASISTENCIA S.A. (1)
Ramirez de Arellano 35, Madrid, Spain
Tel.: (34) 91 325 54 40
General Insurance Services
N.A.I.C.S.: 524298

Saint-Barth Assurances S.a r.l. (1)
2 Rue Roi Oscar II, 97133, Saint Barthelemy-d'Anjou, France
Tel.: (33) 8 99 54 42 84
General Insurance Services
N.A.I.C.S.: 524210

Seine GmbH (1)
Hochstrasse 20, 45721, Haltern, Germany
Tel.: (49) 23642062
Web Site: https://www.seine-elektro.de
N.A.I.C.S.: 541511

Selecta A/S (1)
Krondalvej 9C, 2610, Rodovre, Denmark
Tel.: (45) 44 50 34 50
Web Site: http://www.selecta.dk
Welding Machine Distr
N.A.I.C.S.: 423440

Selecta AS (1)
Kabelgaten 39, PO Box 67, 0508, Oslo, Norway
Tel.: (47) 98 28 50 50
Web Site: http://www.selecta.no
Coffee Maker Mfr
N.A.I.C.S.: 333241

Selecta Ag (1)
Industrie Neuhof 78, 3422, Kirchberg, Switzerland
Tel.: (41) 844 848 844
Web Site: http://www.selecta.ch
Welding Machine Distr
N.A.I.C.S.: 423440

Selecta Betriebsverpflegungs GmbH (1)
Iz No-Sud Strasse 16 Objekt 70/3, Wiener Neudorf, 2355, Austria
Tel.: (43) 2236 660 500 0
Web Site: http://www.selecta.at
Welding Machine Distr
N.A.I.C.S.: 423440

Selecta Deutschland GmbH (1)
Otto Volger Strasse 15, 65843, Sulzbach, Germany
Tel.: (49) 61 96 956 100
Web Site: http://www.selectavending.de
Vending Machine Mfr
N.A.I.C.S.: 333310

Selecta Eesti Osauhing (1)
Tookoja 1, 11313, Tallinn, Estonia
Tel.: (372) 6363895
Web Site: http://www.selecta.ee
Coffee Machine Mfr
N.A.I.C.S.: 333241

Selecta Group B.V. (1)
Keizersgracht 484, 1017 EH, Amsterdam, Netherlands
Tel.: (31) 205569715
Investment Management Service
N.A.I.C.S.: 523999
Gabriel Pirona (CFO)

Selecta Holding AB (1)

Arstaagsvagen 13, Stockholm, 117 60, Sweden
Tel.: (46) 8 57 85 85 85
Investment Management Service
N.A.I.C.S.: 523999

Selecta Holding GmbH (1)
Konigsteiner Str 10, 65812, Bad Soden am Taunus, Germany
Tel.: (49) 6196 95 61 00
Investment Management Service
N.A.I.C.S.: 523940

Selecta Holding Ltd. (1)
1st Floor Spinnaker House Lime Tree Way Hampshire Int Bus, Basingstoke, RG24 8GG, Hampshire, United Kingdom
Tel.: (44) 1256340600
Emp.: 50
Investment Management Service
N.A.I.C.S.: 523999
Dylan Jones (Mng Dir)

Selecta Hungary Automatauzemelteto KFT (1)
Fehervari Ut 84/A, Budapest, 1119, Hungary
Tel.: (36) 13829091
Web Site: http://www.selecta.hu
Emp.: 20
Welding Machine Distr
N.A.I.C.S.: 423440

Selecta Infratechniek B.V. (1)
Pittsburghstraat 57, 3047 BL, Rotterdam, Netherlands
Tel.: (31) 10 415 40 75
Web Site: http://www.selectaholding.com
Emp.: 250
Pipeline Construction Engineering Services
N.A.I.C.S.: 237120

Selecta Olland B.V. (1)
Koeweistraat 10, Waardenburg, 4181 CD, Netherlands
Tel.: (31) 41865 78 00
Web Site: http://www.selectavending.nl
Sales Range: $50-74.9 Million
Emp.: 200
Vending Machine Mfr
N.A.I.C.S.: 333310
N. Bron (Mgr-Mktg)

Selecta Purchasing AG (1)
Hinterbergstrasse 20, Steinhausen, 6330, Switzerland
Tel.: (41) 41 727 72 72
Welding Machine Distr
N.A.I.C.S.: 423440

Selecta S.A. (1)
18 Rue Goubet, Paris, 75019, France
Tel.: (33) 144845960
Web Site: http://www.selecta.fr
Financial Management Services
N.A.I.C.S.: 523999

Selecta TMP AG (1)
Hinterbergstrasse 20, Cham, 6330, Switzerland
Tel.: (41) 41 7277272
Welding Machine Distr
N.A.I.C.S.: 423440

Selecta UK Ltd. (1)
Stanley House Park Lane Castle Vale, Birmingham, B35 6LJ, United Kingdom
Tel.: (44) 844 7360 209
Web Site: http://www.selecta.co.uk
Vending Machine Operators
N.A.I.C.S.: 445132

Siac Services Srl (1)
Via Friuli 33, Dalmine, 24044, Italy
Tel.: (39) 035565421
General Insurance Services
N.A.I.C.S.: 524210

Signa 12 Verwaltungs GmbH (1)
Benrather Strasse 18, 40213, Dusseldorf, Germany
Tel.: (49) 21116640000
Investment Management Service
N.A.I.C.S.: 523999

Societa Agricola San Felice S.p.A. (1)
Localita San Felice, Castelnuovo Berardenga, 53019, Italy
Tel.: (39) 0577 399 203
Web Site: http://www.agricolasanfelice.it

Allianz SE—(Continued)

Emp.: 104
Wine Mfr
N.A.I.C.S.: 312130
Fabrizio Nencioni *(Dir-Sls & Mktg)*

Spherion Objekt GmbH & Co. KG (1)
Charlottenstr 3, 70182, Stuttgart, Germany
Tel.: (49) 7116630
Web Site: http://www.allianz.de
Real Estate Management Services
N.A.I.C.S.: 531390

Syncier GmbH (1)
Koniginstrasse 28, 80802, Munich, Germany
Tel.: (49) 89244174910
Web Site: http://www.syncier.com
Emp.: 230
Insurance Services
N.A.I.C.S.: 524126
Andreas Nolte *(Mng Dir)*

The American Insurance Company, Corp. (1)
777 San Marin Dr Ste 2160, Novato, CA 94945-1352
Tel.: (415) 899-2000
General Insurance Services
N.A.I.C.S.: 524210

The Annuity Store Financial & Insurance Services LLC (1)
1451 River Park Dr Ste 130, Sacramento, CA 95815
Tel.: (800) 825-6094
Web Site: http://www.theannuitystore.com
General Insurance Services
N.A.I.C.S.: 524210
Richard J. Marasco *(Pres)*

The Navakij Insurance Co., Ltd. (1)
18th Fl S 26th Fl Sathorn Nakorn Bldg Sathorn Thani Complex, 100 North Sathorn Rd, Bangkok, 10500, Thailand **(100%)**
Tel.: (66) 26367900
Web Site: http://www.navakij.co.th
Sales Range: $1-9.9 Million
Insurance Services
N.A.I.C.S.: 524128
Suchin Wanglee *(Chm)*

Top Versicherungs-Vermittler Service GmbH (1)
Hietzinger Kai 101-105, 1130, Vienna, Austria
Tel.: (43) 19094444
Web Site: http://www.tvvs.at
Insurance Brokerage Services
N.A.I.C.S.: 524210

Top Versicherungsservice GmbH (1)
Hietzinger Kai 101-105, 1130, Vienna, Austria
Tel.: (43) 5 9009 0
General Insurance Services
N.A.I.C.S.: 524210

Top Vorsorge-Management GmbH (1)
Hietzinger Kai 101-105, Vienna, 1130, Austria **(75%)**
Tel.: (43) 1 54 622 567
Financial Management Services
N.A.I.C.S.: 523999

Towarzystwo Ubezpieczen Euler Hermes S.A. (1)
Domaniewska 50B Str, 02-672, Warsaw, Poland
Tel.: (48) 22 385 46 55
General Insurance Services
N.A.I.C.S.: 524210

Towarzystwo Ubezpieczen i Reasekuracji Allianz Polska S.A. (1)
ul Rodziny Hiszpanskich 1, 02-685, Warsaw, Poland
Tel.: (48) 225674000
Web Site: http://www.allianz.pl
Insurance & Financial Products & Services
N.A.I.C.S.: 524126

Subsidiary (Domestic):

PTE Allianz Polska S.A. (2)
ul Rodziny Hiszpanskich 1, 02-685, Warsaw, Poland

Tel.: (48) 224 224 224
Web Site: http://www.allianz.pl
Sales Range: $50-74.9 Million
Emp.: 30
Pension & Retirment Fund Management Services
N.A.I.C.S.: 524292
Marek Jandzinski *(CEO)*

TFI Allianz Polska S.A. (2)
Ul Rodziny Hiszpanskich 1, 02-685, Warsaw, Poland
Tel.: (48) 225674000
Web Site: http://www.allianz.pl
Investment & Asset Management Services
N.A.I.C.S.: 523940

TU Allianz Zycie Polska S.A. (2)
ul Rodziny Hiszpanskich 1, 02-685, Warsaw, Poland
Tel.: (48) 225674000
Web Site: http://www.allianz.pl
Life & Health Insurance Products & Services
N.A.I.C.S.: 524298

Trafalgar Insurance Public Limited Company (1)
57 Ladymead, Guildford, GU1 1DB, Surrey, United Kingdom
Tel.: (44) 1483 568161
General Insurance Services
N.A.I.C.S.: 524210

Travel Care Inc. (1)
6600 W Broad St Ste 100, Richmond, VA 23230-1709
Tel.: (804) 673-1517
Travel Insurance Services
N.A.I.C.S.: 524128

UAB Selecta (1)
Mindaugo G 42, Vilnius, 01311, Lithuania
Tel.: (370) 5 240 43 43
Web Site: http://www.selecta.lt
Emp.: 40
Coffee Machine Mfr
N.A.I.C.S.: 333241

UfS Beteiligungs-GmbH (1)
Koninginstr 28, 80802, Munich, Germany
Tel.: (49) 7136 951330
Investment Management Service
N.A.I.C.S.: 523999

Vereinte Spezial Krankenversicherung Aktiengesellschaft (1)
Fritz-Schaffer-Str 9, 81737, Munich, Germany
Tel.: (49) 89 38 00 0
General Insurance Services
N.A.I.C.S.: 524298

VertBois S.a r.l. (1)
2 Avenue Charles De Gaulle, 1653, Luxembourg, Luxembourg
Tel.: (352) 26 43 20 18
Real Estate Management Services
N.A.I.C.S.: 531390

Villa La Pagliaia S.r.l. (1)
Loc San Felice, 53019, Castelnuovo Berardenga, Italy
Tel.: (39) 0577 3991
Wine Mfr
N.A.I.C.S.: 312130

Volkswagen Autoversicherung AG (1)
Gifhorner Str 57, 38112, Braunschweig, Germany
Tel.: (49) 53139397430
Web Site: https://www.volkswagen-autoversicherung.de
Insurance Services
N.A.I.C.S.: 524126

Willemsbrug B.V. (1)
Boterdiep 11, 3077 AW, Rotterdam, Netherlands
Tel.: (31) 10 4790000
Financial Management Services
N.A.I.C.S.: 523999

Windpark Emmendorf GmbH & Co.KG (1)
Bevenser Str 7, 29579, Emmendorf, Germany
Tel.: (49) 5875 560
Eletric Power Generation Services
N.A.I.C.S.: 221118

Windpark Kesfeld Heckhuscheid GmbH & Co. KG (1)
Schauenburgerstr 24, Pinneberg, 25421, Germany
Tel.: (49) 4101408890
Windpark Construction & Operation Services
N.A.I.C.S.: 237130
Mike Pearson *(Mng Dir)*

Windpark Kirf GmbH & Co, KG (1)
Schauenburgerstr 24, Pinneberg, 25421, Schleswig-Holstein, Germany
Tel.: (49) 4101408890
Web Site: http://www.enxco.de
Sales Range: $25-49.9 Million
Emp.: 3
Windpark Management Services
N.A.I.C.S.: 237130

Windpark Quitzow GmbH & Co. KG (1)
Windmuehlenbert, 24814, Sehestedt, Germany
Tel.: (49) 435799770
Eletric Power Generation Services
N.A.I.C.S.: 221118
Torsten Levsen *(Gen Mgr)*

Windpark Redekin GmbH & Co KG (1)
Berliner Chaussee 50Berliner Chaussee 50, 39307, Genthin, Germany
Tel.: (49) 3933 93220
Eletric Power Generation Services
N.A.I.C.S.: 221118

Windpark Werder Zinndorf GmbH & Co. KG (1)
Windmuhlenberg, 24814, Sehestedt, Germany
Tel.: (49) 435799770
Emp.: 1
Eletric Power Generation Services
N.A.I.C.S.: 221118

esa Allianz (1)
Friedrichsplatz 2, 74177, Bad Friedrichshall, Germany
Tel.: (49) 7136 95130
Web Site: http://www.esa-allianz.de
Sales Range: $50-74.9 Million
Emp.: 40
General Insurance Services
N.A.I.C.S.: 524298

esa EuroShip GmbH (1)
Friedrichsplatz 2, Bad Friedrichshall, 74177, Germany
Tel.: (49) 7136 9513 0
Web Site: http://www.esa-allianz.de
General Insurance Services
N.A.I.C.S.: 524210

ppi Media US, Inc. (1)
401 N Michigan Ave Ste 1200, Chicago, IL 60611
Tel.: (855) 828-0008
Newspaper Publishers
N.A.I.C.S.: 513110

rehacare GmbH (1)
Kapuzinerstrasse 9D, Munich, 80337, Germany
Tel.: (49) 89200045120
Web Site: http://www.rehacare.net
Medical Management Consulting Services
N.A.I.C.S.: 541611

ALLIANZ TECHNOLOGY TRUST PLC
29 Wellington Street Link Group 10th Floor Central Square, Leeds, LS1 4DL, United Kingdom
Tel.: (44) 3706640300   De
Web Site:
    https://www.allianztechnology.com
Year Founded: 1995
ATT—(LSE)
Assets: $1,134,000,615
Liabilities: $3,035,340
Net Worth: $1,130,965,275
Earnings: ($595,215,720)
Emp.: 1,718
Fiscal Year-end: 12/31/22
Investment Trust Management Services

N.A.I.C.S.: 523940
Robert Jeens *(Chm)*

ALLIED ARCHITECTS, INC.
Unosawa Tokyu Building 4F 1-19-15 Ebisu, Shibuya-ku, Tokyo, 150-0013, Japan
Tel.: (81) 364082791
Web Site: https://www.aainc.co.jp
Year Founded: 2005
6081—(TKS)
Rev.: $29,380,960
Assets: $29,132,810
Liabilities: $7,182,170
Net Worth: $21,950,640
Earnings: ($1,035,140)
Emp.: 194
Fiscal Year-end: 12/31/23
Social Media Marketing Consulting Services
N.A.I.C.S.: 541613
Masahide Nakamura *(Pres, Pres & CEO)*

Subsidiaries:

Allied Tech Base Co., Ltd. (1)
9th Floor Office Building 2 Sun Square Building No 21 Le Duc Tho, My Dinh 2 Nam Tu Liem, Hanoi, Vietnam
Tel.: (84) 2423466663
Web Site: http://www.alliedtechbase.com
Marketing Services
N.A.I.C.S.: 541613
Motoaki Iwamoto *(CEO)*

Allied Tech Camp Co., Ltd. (1)
102 Nguyen Dinh Chinh Phuong 15, Q Phu Nhuan, Ho Chi Minh City, Vietnam
Tel.: (84) 917901691
Web Site: https://www.alliedtechcamp.com
Social Media Marketing Services
N.A.I.C.S.: 541840

Digital Change Inc. (1)
6F MT Building 3-6-16 Kamimeguro, Meguro-ku, Tokyo, 153-0051, Japan
Tel.: (81) 364539611
Web Site: https://www.digitalchange.co.jp
Advertising Media Operation Services
N.A.I.C.S.: 541810

Next Batter's Circle Inc. (1)
Unosawa Tokyu Building 7F 1-19-15 Ebisu, Shibuya-ku, Tokyo, 150-0013, Japan
Tel.: (81) 364082791
Web Site: https://www.nextbatterscircle.co.jp
Digital Marketing Human Resource Consultancy Services
N.A.I.C.S.: 541612

Othello Inc. (1)
1-19-15 Ebisu Unosawa Building 7F, Shibuya-ku, Tokyo, 150-0013, Japan
Tel.: (81) 364082809
Web Site: https://www.othellooo.com
Marketing Services
N.A.I.C.S.: 541613

ALLIED BIOTECH CORP.
13th Floor No 71 Section 2 Tun Hua South Rd, Daan District, Taipei, 10682, Taiwan
Tel.: (886) 227030209
Web Site: https://www.altratene.com
Year Founded: 2002
1780—(TAI)
Food Products Mfr
N.A.I.C.S.: 333241
Ching-Hui Lin *(Pres)*

ALLIED BLENDERS AND DISTILLERS PVT. LTD.
394/C Ground Fl Lamington Chambers, Lamington Rd, Mumbai, 400 004, India
Tel.: (91) 2267779777
Web Site: http://www.abdindia.com
Rev.: $186,703,860
Liquor Producer & Distr
N.A.I.C.S.: 312140

Kishore Rajaram Chhabria *(Chm)*

ALLIED COMPUTERS INTER-NATIONAL ASIA LTD.
Office No 8 5th Floor Block - A Aidun Building 1st Floor, Dhobi Talao Lane, Mumbai, 400002, Maharashtra, India
Tel.: (91) 02265281804 In
Web Site: https://www.aciasialtd.com
Year Founded: 2002
Rev.: $5,566,857
Assets: $41,468,771
Liabilities: $11,547,735
Net Worth: $29,921,036
Earnings: $18,871
Fiscal Year-end: 03/31/18
Computer System Design Services
N.A.I.C.S.: 541512
Hirji Kanji Patel *(Mng Dir)*

ALLIED COOPERATIVE IN-SURANCE GROUP
7143 Prince Turki Bin Abdulaziz Al Awwal Rd 7143 hitten Dist, Riyadh, 13512, Saudi Arabia
Tel.: (966) 122255444
Web Site: https://www.acig.com.sa
8150—(SAU)
Rev.: $137,346,221
Assets: $161,954,406
Liabilities: $123,124,650
Net Worth: $38,829,756
Earnings: ($244,501)
Emp.: 258
Fiscal Year-end: 12/31/22
Cooperative Insurance Services
N.A.I.C.S.: 524113
Hesham Mohammed Al Shareef *(CEO)*

ALLIED CORP.
200-460 Doyle Ave, Kelowna, V1Y OC2, BC, Canada NV
Web Site: https://www.allied.health
Year Founded: 2013
ALID—(OTCQB)
Rev.: $96,180
Assets: $2,114,841
Liabilities: $9,663,305
Net Worth: ($7,548,464)
Earnings: $3,976,184
Fiscal Year-end: 08/31/24
Health Care Srvices
N.A.I.C.S.: 621610
Calum Hughes *(Founder, Chm & CEO)*

Subsidiaries:

Tactical Relief, LLC **(1)**
145 E Elm St, New Albany, IN 47150
Tel.: (502) 905-4052
Web Site: http://www.tacticalrelief.com
Cannabis Product Mfr & Distr
N.A.I.C.S.: 325411

ALLIED CRITICAL METALS CORP.
Suite 1518 800 West Pender Street, Vancouver, V6C 2V6, BC, Canada
Tel.: (604) 720-2730
Web Site: https://alliedcritical.com
Metal Mining Exploration Service
N.A.I.C.S.: 212290
Roy Bonnell *(CEO)*

ALLIED DIGITAL SERVICES LIMITED
Premises No 13A 13th Floor Earnest House Backbay Reclamation, Nariman Point, Mumbai, 400021, India
Tel.: (91) 2266816400
Web Site: https://www.allieddigital.net
Year Founded: 1984
532875—(BOM)
Rev.: $66,508,260
Assets: $94,631,355

Liabilities: $18,686,850
Net Worth: $75,944,505
Earnings: $8,331,960
Emp.: 1,450
Fiscal Year-end: 03/31/22
Computer Services
N.A.I.C.S.: 541519
Prakash D. Shah *(Exec Dir)*

Subsidiaries:

Allied Digital Services LLC **(1)**
680 Knox St Ste 200, Torrance, CA 90502
Tel.: (310) 431-2375
Web Site: https://www.allieddigital.net
Sales Range: $75-99.9 Million
Emp.: 400
Business Management Services
N.A.I.C.S.: 561110
Kashif Rasheed *(Gen Mgr)*

ALLIED FARMERS LIMITED
201 Broadway, PO Box 304, Hawera, 4640, New Zealand
Tel.: (64) 67656199
Web Site: https://www.alliedfarmers.co.nz
ALF—(NZX)
Rev.: $16,231,459
Assets: $20,870,215
Liabilities: $9,672,249
Net Worth: $11,197,967
Earnings: $2,558,612
Emp.: 6
Fiscal Year-end: 06/30/23
Livestock Trading, Finance & Real Estate Services
N.A.I.C.S.: 541890
Richard Perry *(Chm)*

ALLIED GOLD CORPORATION
Bay Adelaide Centre-North Tower 40 Temperance Street, Toronto, M5H 0B4, ON, Canada
Tel.: (416) 869-5300 ON
Web Site: https://www.alliedgold.com
Year Founded: 2021
AAUC—(TSX)
Assets: $12,153
Liabilities: $191,330
Net Worth: ($179,177)
Earnings: ($115,308)
Emp.: 1,930
Fiscal Year-end: 12/31/22
Gold Exploration & Mining Services
N.A.I.C.S.: 212220
Basie Maree *(COO)*

ALLIED GROUP LIMITED
22nd Floor Allied Kajima Building 138 Gloucester Road, Wanchai, China (Hong Kong)
Tel.: (852) 25192288 HK
Web Site: https://www.alliedgroup.com.hk
ALEDY—(OTCIQ)
Rev.: $793,562,348
Assets: $15,517,312,942
Liabilities: $5,992,410,800
Net Worth: $9,524,902,142
Earnings: $1,028,912,154
Emp.: 4,177
Fiscal Year-end: 12/31/21
Investment Holding Company
N.A.I.C.S.: 551112
Seng Hui Lee *(CEO)*

Subsidiaries:

AG Capital Limited **(1)**
22 F Allied Kajima Bldg 138 Gloucester Rd, Wanchai, China (Hong Kong)
Tel.: (852) 25192288
Securities Trading & Money Lending Services
N.A.I.C.S.: 522291

Allied Properties (H.K.) Limited **(1)**
22nd Floor Allied Kajima Building 138 Gloucester Road, Wanchai, China (Hong Kong) **(74.99%)**

Tel.: (852) 25192288
Web Site: https://www.alliedproperties.com.hk
Sales Range: $500-549.9 Million
Emp.: 5,271
Property Investment & Development Services
N.A.I.C.S.: 523940
Seng Hui Lee *(CEO)*

Subsidiary (Domestic):

Sun Hung Kai & Co. Limited **(2)**
40/F Lee Garden One 33 Hysan Avenue, Causeway Bay, China (Hong Kong) **(72.74%)**
Tel.: (852) 37482888
Web Site: https://www.shkco.com
Rev.: $529,584,000
Assets: $5,471,624,250
Liabilities: $2,213,221,500
Net Worth: $3,258,402,750
Earnings: ($150,054,750)
Emp.: 1,608
Fiscal Year-end: 12/31/2022
Holding Company; Investment & Financial Services
N.A.I.C.S.: 551112
Seng Huang Lee *(Chm & Exec Dir)*

Subsidiary (Domestic):

Everbright Securities Digital Finance (HK) Limited **(3)**
28/F Lee Garden One 33 Hysan Avenue, Causeway Bay, Hong Kong, China (Hong Kong)
Tel.: (852) 28225001
Web Site: https://www.ebshk.com
Online Securities Trading, Broking & Other Financial Services
N.A.I.C.S.: 518210
Lee Seng Huang *(Chm)*

Subsidiary (Non-US):

Sun Hung Kai Investment Services Limited - Macau Branch **(3)**
Shop E Macau Chamber Of Commerce Building, No 165 Rua de Xangai, Macau, China (Macau)
Tel.: (853) 2878 1212
Web Site: http://www.shkf.com
Securities Brokerage & Financial Services
N.A.I.C.S.: 523150

Branch (Non-US):

Sun Hung Kai Investment Services Limited - Shenzhen Branch **(3)**
Unit 711A 7F Tower A Tian an Cyber Times Square No 6 Tairan Road 4, Futian District, Shenzhen, 518000, China
Tel.: (86) 755 8347 5079
Web Site: http://www.shkf.com
Securities Brokerage & Financial Services
N.A.I.C.S.: 523150

Conrad Security Limited **(1)**
Room 3501 China Network Center 333 Lockhart Road, Wanchai, China (Hong Kong)
Tel.: (852) 3 571 9992
Web Site: https://www.conrad-security.com.hk
Professional & Rigorous Security Services
N.A.I.C.S.: 561612

Polyking Services Limited **(1)**
22/F China Online Centre 333 Lockhart Road, Wanchai, China (Hong Kong)
Tel.: (852) 2 527 0632
Web Site: https://www.polyking.com.hk
Commercial Building Cleaning & Maintenance Services
N.A.I.C.S.: 561720

Protech Property Management Limited **(1)**
Room 3501 China Online Centre 333 Lockhart Road, Wanchai, China (Hong Kong)
Tel.: (852) 2 598 8990
Web Site: https://www.ppml.com.hk
Property Management Services
N.A.I.C.S.: 531311

SHK Finance Limited **(1)**
20/F Allied Kajima Building 138 Gloucester Road, Wanchai, China (Hong Kong)
Tel.: (852) 28922892

Web Site: http://www.shkfinance.com.hk
Professional Loan Services
N.A.I.C.S.: 522291

Sun Hung Kai Credit Limited **(1)**
Room 1701 17/F Office Tower Two Grand Plaza 625 Nathan Road, Mongkok, Kowloon, China (Hong Kong)
Tel.: (852) 2 996 2688
Web Site: https://www.shkcredit.com.hk
Mortgage Loan Services
N.A.I.C.S.: 522310

United Asia Finance Limited **(1)**
21/F United Kashima Building 138 Gloucester Road, Wanchai, China (Hong Kong)
Tel.: (852) 2 681 8888
Web Site: https://www.uaf.com.hk
Loan Services
N.A.I.C.S.: 522310

Yirongzhan Fintech (Shenzhen) Limited **(1)**
2001 West Tower Phase II Innovation and Technology Plaza, Tianan Cyber City Futian District, Shenzhen, 518000, Guangdong, China
Tel.: (86) 7558 829 8491
Web Site: https://www.yirongzhan.com
Technical Consulting Services
N.A.I.C.S.: 541690

ALLIED HERBALS LIMITED
13-B 3rd Floor Netaji Subhash Marg, Daryaganj, New Delhi, 110 002, India
Tel.: (91) 11 41513567
Web Site: http://www.rajdhanileasing.com
Year Founded: 1985
Personal Care Products Whslr
N.A.I.C.S.: 424210

ALLIED HOLDINGS LTD.
Suite 300 515 West Penderstreet, Vancouver, V6B 6H5, BC, Canada
Tel.: (604) 669-5335
Holding Company
N.A.I.C.S.: 551112
Peter Y. L. Eng *(Chm & CEO)*

Subsidiaries:

Allied Hotel Properties Inc. **(1)**
Suite 300 515 West Pender Street, Vancouver, V6B 6H5, BC, Canada
Tel.: (604) 669-5335
Rev.: $670,414
Assets: $26,317,464
Liabilities: $1,892,335
Net Worth: $24,425,128
Earnings: ($1,065,465)
Fiscal Year-end: 12/31/2020
Hotel & Real Estate Management Services
N.A.I.C.S.: 531390

Subsidiary (Domestic):

Allied Don Valley Hotel Inc. **(2)**
175 Wynford Drive, Toronto, M3C 1J3, ON, Canada
Tel.: (416) 449-4111
Home Management Services
N.A.I.C.S.: 721110

ALLIED INTERNATIONAL LTD.
10 Rue des Moulins, 75001, Paris, France
Tel.: (33) 144550570
Web Site: http://www.allied-international.com
Sales Range: $10-24.9 Million
Emp.: 10
Destination Management Services
N.A.I.C.S.: 561599
Karine Berberian *(Mng Dir)*

Subsidiaries:

Allied Arabia **(1)**
PO Box 502068, Media city bld 8 off 51, Dubai, United Arab Emirates
Tel.: (971) 44230880
Web Site: http://www.alliedpoa.com
Sales Range: $10-24.9 Million
Emp.: 3
Travel Arrangement Services

Allied International Ltd.—(Continued)
N.A.I.C.S.: 721199

Allied France (1)
10 Rue Des, Moulins, 75001, France
Tel.: (33) 144550570
Web Site: http://www.alliedpra.com
Travel Arrangement Services
N.A.I.C.S.: 561599
Karine Derberian (Mng Dir)

Allied Spain (1)
Gran via de lef corts Catalnis No 649 office
1, 08009, Barcelona, Spain
Tel.: (34) 934677780
Web Site: http://www.alliedpra.com
Travel Arrangement Services
N.A.I.C.S.: 561599

Allied UK (1)
Greville House Hatton Road, Bedfont,
Heathrow, TW14 9PX, Mddx, United King-
dom
Tel.: (44) 2088444000
Travel Arrangement Services
N.A.I.C.S.: 561599

AlliedPRA Monaco (1)
11 bis Rue Grimaldi, 98000, Monaco, Mo-
naco
Tel.: (377) 97976464
Web Site: http://www.alliedpra.com
Travel Arrangement Services
N.A.I.C.S.: 561599
Miek Egberts (Mng Dir)

ALLIED PLASTIC SKYLIGHT
707 Arrow Road, North York, M9M
2L4, ON, Canada
Tel.: (416) 749-7070
Web Site:
  https://www.allied2000.com
Sales Range: $10-24.9 Million
Emp.: 15
Plastics Product Mfr
N.A.I.C.S.: 326199
Ron Bruhm (Owner)

Subsidiaries:

Architectural Plastics Limited (1)
707 Arrow Road, Weston, M9M 2L4, ON,
Canada
Tel.: (416) 748-3000
Web Site:
  http://www.architecturalskylights.com
Plastics Product Mfr
N.A.I.C.S.: 326199

Reliable Toy Corporation (1)
707 Arrow Rd, Weston, M9M 2L4, ON,
Canada (100%)
Tel.: (416) 762-1111
Toy Mfr
N.A.I.C.S.: 339930
Tod Bruhm (Gen Mgr & Mgr-Adv)

Viceroy Rubber Limited (1)
707 Arrow Rd, Weston, M9M 2L4, ON,
Canada
Tel.: (416) 762-1111
Web Site: http://www.viceroyrubber.com
Mechanical Use Rubber Product Mfr
N.A.I.C.S.: 326291
Todd Bruhm (Gen Mgr)

ALLIED PROPERTIES REAL ESTATE INVESTMENT TRUST
134 Peter Street Suite 1700, Toronto,
M5V 2H2, ON, Canada
Tel.: (416) 977-9002　　　　ON
Web Site: https://www.alliedreit.com
Year Founded: 2003
AP.UN—(TSX)
Rev.: $445,028,140
Assets: $8,123,736,075
Liabilities: $3,096,983,155
Net Worth: $5,026,752,920
Earnings: $346,668,164
Emp.: 355
Fiscal Year-end: 12/31/21
Investment Trust Services
N.A.I.C.S.: 523150
Michael R. Emory (Founder, Pres &
CEO)

Subsidiaries:

Allied Properties Management Lim-
ited Partnership (1)
70 Arthur Street Suite 200, Winnipeg,
R3B1G7, MB, Canada
Tel.: (204) 942-8400
Sales Range: $50-74.9 Million
Emp.: 7
Property Managing Services
N.A.I.C.S.: 531311
Michael Emory (Pres)

ALLIED SUSTAINABILITY & ENVIRONMENTAL CONSUL-TANTS GROUP LIMITED
27/F Overseas Trust Bank Building
160 Gloucester Road, Wanchai,
China (Hong Kong)
Tel.: (852) 2 815 7028　　　　Ky
Web Site: http://asecg.com
8320—(HKG)
Rev.: $5,200,474
Assets: $12,726,199
Liabilities: $2,605,396
Net Worth: $10,120,803
Earnings: $446,142
Emp.: 58
Fiscal Year-end: 03/31/21
Environmental Consulting Services
N.A.I.C.S.: 541620
Grace May Han Kwok (Chm & Com-
pliance Officer)

Subsidiaries:

Light Plus Design Limited (1)
27/F Overseas Trust Bank Building 160
Gloucester Road, Wanchai, China (Hong
Kong)
Tel.: (852) 28157028
Web Site: https://aivexdesign.com
Lighting Design Services
N.A.I.C.S.: 541490

ALLIED TECHNOLOGIES LTD.
2 Venture Drive #16-09 Vision Ex-
change, Singapore, 608526, Singa-
pore
Tel.: (65) 65602011
Web Site: http://www.allied-
tech.com.sg
A13—(SES)
Rev.: $91,420,374
Assets: $89,853,893
Liabilities: $42,039,471
Net Worth: $47,814,423
Earnings: ($22,662,397)
Fiscal Year-end: 12/31/19
Stamped Metal & Electronics Parts
Mfr
N.A.I.C.S.: 334419
Keith Ho (Asst Mgr-Sls)

Subsidiaries:

Allied Precision Manufacturing (M)
Sdn. Bhd. (1)
No 9 Jalan Bioteknologi 3 Kawasan Perin-
dustrian Silc, Nusajaya, 79200, Johor, Ma-
laysia
Tel.: (60) 73523031
Metal Stamping Mfr
N.A.I.C.S.: 336370

Allied Precision Technologies (M)
Sdn. Bhd. (1)
No 1A Jalan Nobat 7, Taman Perindustrian
Bukit Rambai, 75250, Melaka, Malaysia
Tel.: (60) 62801888
Precision Product Mfr
N.A.I.C.S.: 332721
Lee Sze Shiuan (Asst Mgr-Fin)

Allied Tech (S) Pte. Ltd. (1)
2 Venture Drive 16-09 Vision Exchange,
Singapore, 608526, Singapore
Tel.: (65) 65602011
Precision Metal Part Mfr
N.A.I.C.S.: 332721
Keith Ho (Asst Mgr-Sls)

Allied Technologies Holdings Pte.
Ltd. (1)
2 Venture Drive 16-09 Vision Exchange,
Singapore, 608526, Singapore
Tel.: (65) 65602011
Web Site: http://www.allied-tech.com.sg
Business Management Consulting Services
N.A.I.C.S.: 541611
Keith Ho (Asst Mgr-Sls)

Subsidiary (Non-US):

Allied Precision (Thailand) Co.,
Ltd. (2)
138/6 Moo 4 Phetchakasem Road T
Srapang, Khao Yoi, 76140, Petchaburi,
Thailand
Tel.: (66) 32706362
Metal Stamped Product Mfr & Distr
N.A.I.C.S.: 332119

Allied Technologies (Saigon) Co.,
Ltd. (2)
Lot 14 Saigon Hi-Tech Park Le Van Viet
Street, District 9, Ho Chi Minh City, Vietnam
Tel.: (84) 837335663
Metal Stamped Product Mfr & Distr
N.A.I.C.S.: 332119
Lee Ko Shin (Sls Mgr)

Suzhou Allied Tech Co., Ltd. (2)
Room 1108 Litong Building No 158 Wu-
zhong East Road, Wuzhong District, Su-
zhou, China
Tel.: (86) 51266215766
Metal Parts & Tool Mfr & Distr
N.A.I.C.S.: 333515

ALLIED TELESIS HOLDINGS K.K.
2nd TOC Bldg 7-21-11 Nishi-
Gotanda, Shinagawa-ku, Tokyo, 141-
0031, Japan
Tel.: (81) 354376000
Web Site: https://www.allied-
telesis.co.jp
Year Founded: 2004
6835—(TKS)
Rev.: $314,689,650
Assets: $322,559,550
Liabilities: $198,718,520
Net Worth: $123,841,030
Earnings: $7,721,010
Emp.: 909
Fiscal Year-end: 12/31/23
Telecom Equipment Mfr
N.A.I.C.S.: 334220
Sachie Oshima (VP)

Subsidiaries:

Allied Telesis (Hong Kong) Ltd. (1)
Unit 1908 19/F Elite Centre 22 Hung To
Road Kwun Tong, Kowloon, China (Hong
Kong)
Tel.: (852) 22636566
Web Site: http://www.alliedtelesis.com.hk
Mobile Communications Services
N.A.I.C.S.: 334220

Allied Telesis Capital Corp. (1)
3041 Orchard Pkwy, San Jose, CA 95134
Tel.: (408) 519-8700
Web Site: http://www.alliedtelesis.com
Sales Range: $50-74.9 Million
Emp.: 150
Internet Protocol Technology Services
N.A.I.C.S.: 517810
Keith Southard (CEO)

Allied Telesis Inc. (1)
3041 Orchard Pkwy, San Jose, CA 95134
Tel.: (408) 519-8700
Web Site: http://www.alliedtelesis.com
Sales Range: $25-49.9 Million
Emp.: 150
Network Management Services
N.A.I.C.S.: 541618
Kenneth Torp (Sr VP-Middle East)

Allied Telesis International S.L.U (1)
Calle Retama 7 - 6 Planta, 28045, Madrid,
Spain
Tel.: (34) 915591055
Web Site: http://www.alliedtelesis.es
Network Management Services
N.A.I.C.S.: 541511

Allied Telesis International Services
Ltd. (1)
11 Pine Court Kembrey Park, Swindon,
SN2 8AD, Wiltshire, United Kingdom
Tel.: (44) 1793501400
Web Site: http://www.alliedtelesis.com
Emp.: 9
Computer Support Services
N.A.I.C.S.: 541511
Chris Alliott (Mgr-Sls)

Allied Telesis Labs (Philippines)
Inc. (1)
2th Floor Unit 3 Arthaland Century Pacific
Tower 5th Avenue, 30th Street E-Square
Fort Bonifacio Global City, Taguig, 1634,
Metro Manila, Philippines
Tel.: (63) 28153130
Web Site: http://www.alliedtelesis.com
Sales Range: $25-49.9 Million
Emp.: 50
Computer Hardware Services
N.A.I.C.S.: 541511

Allied Telesis Labs S.R.L. (1)
Via Tiziano n 32, 20147, Milan, Italy
Tel.: (39) 0200694519
Web Site: http://www.alliedtelesis.com
Sales Range: $25-49.9 Million
Emp.: 20
Network Support Services
N.A.I.C.S.: 541512

Allied Telesis R&D Center K.K. (1)
2nd TOC Building 7-21-11 Nishigotanda,
Shinagawa-ku, Tokyo, 141-0031, Japan
Tel.: (81) 354376000
Web Site: http://www.allied-telesis.co.jp
Sales Range: $25-49.9 Million
Emp.: 100
Business Research & Development Ser-
vices
N.A.I.C.S.: 541720
Taki Oshima (CEO)

Allied Telesis, Inc. (1)
Kyobo Bldg 17F 1 Jongro-1 Ga, Jongro-gu,
Seoul, Korea (South)
Tel.: (82) 27347454
Web Site: http://www.alliedtelesyn.co.kr
Network Management Services
N.A.I.C.S.: 541618

Allied Telesyn (China) Ltd. (1)
Tianchen Building No 12 Chaoyangmen
North St Room 1503 Timeson Tower, Cha-
oyan Chaoyang District, Beijing, 100020,
China
Tel.: (86) 1085252299
Web Site: http://www.alliedtelesis.com.cn
Sales Range: $25-49.9 Million
Emp.: 20
Network Management Services
N.A.I.C.S.: 541513

Allied Telesyn International (Asia)
Pte. Ltd. (1)
719 A3 Fl Zone D2 KPN Tower Rama 9 Rd,
Bangkapi Huaykwang, Bangkok, 10320,
Thailand
Tel.: (66) 27170242
Sales Range: $25-49.9 Million
Emp.: 10
Network Management Services
N.A.I.C.S.: 541512

Allied Telesyn International
GmbH (1)
Karl-Hammerschmidt-Strasse 34 Dornach,
85609, Aschheim, Germany
Tel.: (49) 894354940
Web Site: http://www.alliedtelesis.com
Sales Range: $25-49.9 Million
Emp.: 15
Network Management Services
N.A.I.C.S.: 541512
Roy Bann (Sr VP)

Allied Telesyn International Ltd. (1)
11 Pine Court Kembrey Park, Swindon,
SN2 8AD, Wiltshire, United Kingdom
Tel.: (44) 1793501400
Web Site: http://www.alliedtelesis.com
Sales Range: $25-49.9 Million
Emp.: 30
Networking Hardware Devices Mfr
N.A.I.C.S.: 334118

Allied Telesyn International S.A. (1)
12 Avenue de Scandinavie Parc Victoria, Le

Toronto Courtaboeuf, 91940, Les Ulis, France
Tel.: (33) 160921525
Web Site: http://www.alliedtelesis.fr
Sales Range: $25-49.9 Million
Emp.: 15
Computer Peripheral Whslr
N.A.I.C.S.: 423430

Allied Telesyn International S.R.L. **(1)**
Via I Vivanti 151, 00144, Rome, Italy
Tel.: (39) 0652244329
Web Site: http://www.alliedtelesis.it
Sales Range: $25-49.9 Million
Emp.: 35
Data Communication Products Whslr
N.A.I.C.S.: 334210

Allied Telesyn South Asia Pte. Ltd. **(1)**
11 Tai Seng Link, Singapore, 534182, Singapore
Tel.: (65) 63833832
Web Site: http://www.alliedtelesis.com.sg
Sales Range: $25-49.9 Million
Emp.: 20
Network Management Services
N.A.I.C.S.: 541511

Allied Telesyn Vertriebsgesellschaft m.b.H. **(1)**
Business Park Vienna, Wienerbergstr. 7
13th Floor, 1100, Vienna, Austria
Tel.: (43) 1 876 2441
Web Site: http://www.alliedtelesis.at
Sales Range: $50-74.9 Million
Emp.: 6
Communication Equipment Whslr
N.A.I.C.S.: 423490

ALLIGATOR BIOSCIENCE AB
Medicon Village Scheelevagen 2, SE-223 81, Lund, Sweden
Tel.: (46) 465408200
Web Site:
https://www.alligatorbioscience.se
Year Founded: 2001
ATORX—(OMX)
Rev.: $3,478,135
Assets: $15,883,560
Liabilities: $7,542,874
Net Worth: $8,340,686
Earnings: ($18,114,492)
Emp.: 53
Fiscal Year-end: 12/31/22
Biotechnology Research & Development Services
N.A.I.C.S.: 541714
Peter Ellmark *(Chief Scientific Officer)*

Subsidiaries:

Atlas Therapeutics AB **(1)**
Ideon Science Park Scheelevagen 15, 223 63, Lund, Sweden
Tel.: (46) 854595850
Web Site: https://www.atlasantibodies.com
Antibodies Mfr
N.A.I.C.S.: 325412

ALLIGATOR ENERGY LIMITED
Suite 2 128 Bowen Street, Spring Hill, 4000, QLD, Australia
Tel.: (61) 738393904
Web Site:
https://www.alligatorenergy.com.au
AGE—(ASX)
Rev.: $747,218
Assets: $45,497,191
Liabilities: $1,524,751
Net Worth: $43,972,440
Earnings: ($2,304,837)
Emp.: 42
Fiscal Year-end: 06/30/24
Other Metal Ore Mining
N.A.I.C.S.: 212290
Michael Meintjes *(Sec)*

ALLIS ELECTRIC CO., LTD.
12F No 19-11 Sanchong Road, Nangang District, Taipei, 11501, Taiwan
Tel.: (886) 226553456

Web Site: https://www.allis.com.tw
Year Founded: 1968
1514—(TAI)
Rev.: $310,127,592
Assets: $367,403,139
Liabilities: $212,546,020
Net Worth: $154,857,118
Earnings: $25,094,378
Emp.: 377
Fiscal Year-end: 12/31/23
Electric Equipment Mfr
N.A.I.C.S.: 238210

Subsidiaries:

AEC International S.r.l. **(1)**
Via Nerviano 55, 20045, Lainate, MI, Italy
Tel.: (39) 0294158991
Ups System Mfr
N.A.I.C.S.: 335999

AIR KING Industrial Co., Ltd. **(1)**
Tel.: (886) 227893886
Sales Range: $75-99.9 Million
Emp.: 500
Environmental & Electrical Engineering Services
N.A.I.C.S.: 541330

ALLIS COMMUNICATIONS Co., Ltd. **(1)**
10-3 Floor No 31-1 Lane 169 Kang-Ning Street, Hsi-chieh, Taipei, Taiwan
Tel.: (886) 2 2695 2378
Web Site: http://www.alliscom.com.tw
Rev.: $2,000,000
Emp.: 100
Cellular Antenna Mfr
N.A.I.C.S.: 334220

Allis Electric (S) Pte. Ltd. **(1)**
34 Woodlands Sector2 Woodland Connection, Singapore, 737689, Singapore
Tel.: (65) 65183064
Switchgear Product Mfr & Distr
N.A.I.C.S.: 335313

Impact Power, Inc. **(1)**
12655 W Jefferson Blvd 4th Fl, Los Angeles, CA 90066
Tel.: (949) 977-9198
Web Site: http://www.impactpwr.com
Electronic Products Mfr
N.A.I.C.S.: 334220

LE MIN Industrial Co., Ltd. **(1)**
20 Lane 268 Hsinshu Rd, Hsinchuang, 242, Taipei Hsien, Taiwan
Tel.: (886) 22 203 6203
Web Site: http://www.allis.com.tw
Metal Forging Materials Mfr
N.A.I.C.S.: 332111

TAIWAN MARINE Electric Co., Ltd. **(1)**
20 Lane 268 Hsinshu Road, Hsinchuang, New Taipei City, Taiwan
Tel.: (886) 22 205 1006
Web Site: https://www.tmc1006.com.tw
Electric Device Mfr
N.A.I.C.S.: 334419

ALLIS PARTICIPACOES S.A.
Av Brigadeiro Faria Lima 155 - 15 Andar, 1452002, Sao Paulo, SP, Brazil
Tel.: (55) 11 3382 6528
Web Site: http://www.allis.com.br
Year Founded: 2007
Human Resource & Outsourcing Services
N.A.I.C.S.: 541612
Alexandre Milani de Oliveira Campos *(Dir-IR)*

ALLIUM MEDICAL SOLUTIONS LTD.
2 Ha Eshel St Caesarea Industrial Park South, PO Box 3081, Caesarea, 3088900, Israel
Tel.: (972) 46277166
Web Site: https://www.allium-medical.com
Year Founded: 2001
ALMD—(TAE)

Assets: $16,347,285
Liabilities: $882,719
Net Worth: $15,464,567
Earnings: $392,872
Emp.: 40
Fiscal Year-end: 12/31/23
Surgical & Medical Instrument Manufacturing
N.A.I.C.S.: 339112
Eitan Hod *(VP-RA & Quality Assurance)*

ALLKEM LIMITED
Riparian Plaza Level 35 71 Eagle Street, Brisbane, 4000, QLD, Australia
Tel.: (61) 730643600
Web Site: https://www.allkem.co
AKE—(ASX)
Rev.: $84,760,000
Assets: $1,348,694,000
Liabilities: $623,603,000
Net Worth: $725,091,000
Earnings: ($89,474,000)
Emp.: 300
Fiscal Year-end: 06/30/21
Lithium, Potash & Boron Exploration
N.A.I.C.S.: 212390
Neil Kaplan *(CFO & Co-Sec)*

Subsidiaries:

Advantage Lithium Corp. **(1)**
789-999 West Hastings, Vancouver, V6C 2W2, BC, Canada **(100%)**
Tel.: (604) 423-4499
Web Site: http://www.advantagelithium.com
Lithium Chemical Mfr
N.A.I.C.S.: 325180
Callum Grant *(CEO)*

Galaxy Resources Limited **(1)**
Level 4/21 Kintail Road, Applecross, 6153, WA, Australia
Tel.: (61) 892151700
Web Site: http://www.gxy.com
Rev.: $69,514,000
Assets: $316,096,000
Liabilities: $75,261,000
Net Worth: $240,835,000
Earnings: ($283,742,000)
Fiscal Year-end: 12/31/2019
Lithium Mineral Mining
N.A.I.C.S.: 212390
Anthony Peter Tse *(Exec Dir)*

Subsidiary (Non-US):

Galaxy Lithium (Canada) Inc. **(2)**
2000 Peel St Suite 720, Montreal, H3A 2W5, QC, Canada
Tel.: (514) 558-1855
Lithium Concentrate Mfr
N.A.I.C.S.: 325180

Galaxy Lithium (Sal de Vida) S.A. **(2)**
Mamerto Medina 17 2nd Floor, San Fernando, 4700, Argentina
Tel.: (54) 3834452446
Lithium Mfr
N.A.I.C.S.: 325180

ALLMED MEDICAL PRODUCTS CO., LTD.
No 18 Qixing Avenue, Majiadian, Yichang, 443200, Hubei, China
Tel.: (86) 75588299832
Web Site: https://www.allmed-china.com
Year Founded: 2002
002590—(SSE)
Rev.: $591,154,200
Assets: $806,950,404
Liabilities: $367,360,812
Net Worth: $439,589,592
Earnings: $57,114,720
Fiscal Year-end: 12/31/22
Medical Product Mfr & Distr
N.A.I.C.S.: 339112
Jinhai Cui *(Chm & Pres)*

ALLOS SA
Rua Dias Ferreira 190 3rd floor, Leblon, 22431-050, Rio de Janeiro, Brazil
Tel.: (55) 2121767272 BR
Web Site:
http://www.alianscesonae.com.br
Year Founded: 2003
ALSO3—(BRAZ)
Rev.: $153,335,716
Assets: $2,093,136,294
Liabilities: $628,752,279
Net Worth: $1,464,384,015
Earnings: $38,925,434
Fiscal Year-end: 12/31/20
Shopping Center Development & Management Services
N.A.I.C.S.: 236220
Carlos Alberto Correa *(CFO)*

Subsidiaries:

Aliansce Mall e Midia Ltda **(1)**
Av Dr Cardoso de Melo 1184 - 13 andar, Vila Olimpia, Sao Paulo, Brazil
Tel.: (55) 1133714133
Grocery Product Distr
N.A.I.C.S.: 445110

Aliansce Shopping Centers SA **(1)**
Rua Dias Ferreira 190 / 3rd andar, Leblon, Rio de Janeiro, Brazil
Tel.: (55) 2121767272
Web Site: http://www.aliansce.com.br
Shopping Center Management Services
N.A.I.C.S.: 531312
Renato Rique *(Founder & Chm)*

BR Malls Participacoes S.A. **(1)**
Av Borges de Medeiros 633 1 andar-Leblon, Rio de Janeiro, 22430-041, RJ, Brazil
Tel.: (55) 2131389900
Shopping Mall Operator
N.A.I.C.S.: 531120
Ruy Kameyama *(CEO)*

Subsidiary (Domestic):

BR Malls Servicos Compartilhados Ltda. **(2)**
Av D Helder Camara 5474, Pilares, 20771-004, Rio de Janeiro, Brazil
Tel.: (55) 21 2583 9814
Shopping Mall Operator
N.A.I.C.S.: 531120

Campo Grande Parking Ltda. **(2)**
Afonso Pena 4909 Santa Fe, Campo Grande, 79031-900, Brazil
Tel.: (55) 67 33271468
Car Parking Management Services
N.A.I.C.S.: 812930

Companhia Fluminense de Administracao e Comercio **(2)**
Rua Miguel Frias 77 s 1914 Icarai, Niteroi, 24220-008, Brazil
Tel.: (55) 21 2622 1934
Shopping Mall Operator
N.A.I.C.S.: 531120

SAS Sociedade Administradora de Centros Comerciais Ltda. **(2)**
Rua Domingos De Morais 2564, Sao Paulo, 04035-001, Brazil
Tel.: (55) 1150831159
Shopping Mall Operator
N.A.I.C.S.: 531120

Boulevard Shopping Belem S.A **(1)**
Av Visc de Souza Franco 776, Reduto, Belem, 66053-000, Para, Brazil
Tel.: (55) 9132990500
Web Site: http://boulevardbelem.com.br
Grocery Product Distr
N.A.I.C.S.: 445110

ALLOT LTD.
22 Hanagar Street Industrial Zone B, Hod Hasharon, 4501317, Israel
Tel.: (972) 97619200 IL
Web Site: https://www.allot.com
Year Founded: 1996
ALLT—(NASDAQ)
Rev.: $122,737,000
Assets: $212,953,000

Allot Ltd.—(Continued)

Liabilities: $110,980,000
Net Worth: $101,973,000
Earnings: ($32,030,000)
Emp.: 523
Fiscal Year-end: 12/31/22
Computer Software & Networking
Equipment Mfr
N.A.I.C.S.: 513210
Yigal Jacoby (Founder & Chm)

Subsidiaries:

Allot Communications (Asia Pacific)
Pte. Ltd.   (1)
6 Ubi Road 1, Singapore, 408726,
Singapore   (100%)
Tel.: (65) 68413020
Web Site: http://www.allot.com
Sales Range: $25-49.9 Million
Emp.: 50
Software Development & Sales
N.A.I.C.S.: 423430

Allot Communications Inc.   (1)
300 Trade Ctr Ste 4680, Woburn, MA
01801
Tel.: (781) 939-9300
Web Site: http://www.allot.com
Sales Range: $25-49.9 Million
Emp.: 20
Computer Software Developer
N.A.I.C.S.: 513210

Allot Communications UK
Limited   (1)
Quatro House Lyon Way, Frimley, Guildford,
GU16 7ER, Surrey, United
Kingdom   (100%)
Tel.: (44) 1483397750
Web Site: http://www.allot.com
Sales Range: $50-74.9 Million
Emp.: 6
Software Developer
N.A.I.C.S.: 423430

ALLOY COMPUTER PRODUCTS (AUSTRALIA) PTY. LTD.

Unit 4 585 Blackburn Road, Notting
Hill, 3168, VIC, Australia
Tel.: (61) 385629000   AU
Web Site: http://www.alloy.com.au
Sales Range: $25-49.9 Million
Emp.: 30
Networking & Communication Product Mfr
N.A.I.C.S.: 334220
John Williams (CEO)

Subsidiaries:

Alloy Computer Products LLC   (1)
1226 Alderwood Ave, Sunnyvale, CA 94089
Tel.: (408) 740-4016
Web Site: http://www.alloycp.com
Communication Equipment Mfr & Distr
N.A.I.C.S.: 334220
John Williams (CEO)

ALLOY STEEL INTERNATIONAL, INC.

93 Mulgul Road, Malaga, 6090, WA,
Australia
Tel.: (61) 892483188
Web Site: http://www.alloysteel.net
AYSI—(OTCIQ)
Rev.: $29,036,000
Assets: $28,852,000
Liabilities: $2,101,000
Net Worth: $26,751,000
Earnings: $4,443,000
Emp.: 70
Fiscal Year-end: 09/30/19
Arcoplate Mfr
N.A.I.C.S.: 331110
Steven Kostecki (CEO & Mng Dir)

Subsidiaries:

Alloy Steel International, Inc.
Mooresville Branch   (1)
207 Byers Creek Rd, Mooresville, NC
28117

Tel.: (704) 664-3223
Arcoplate Distr
N.A.I.C.S.: 423510

ALLREAL HOLDING AG

Lindbergh-Allee 1, Glattpark, 8152,
Opfikon, Switzerland
Tel.: (41) 443191111
Web Site: https://www.allreal.ch
Year Founded: 1999
ALLN—(SWX)
Rev.: $556,541,020
Assets: $6,307,206,208
Liabilities: $3,429,268,293
Net Worth: $2,877,937,916
Earnings: $171,507,761
Emp.: 227
Fiscal Year-end: 12/31/22
Real Estate & Portfolio Services
N.A.I.C.S.: 531210
Roger Herzog (CEO)

Subsidiaries:

Allreal Finance AG   (1)
Grabenstrasse 25, 6340, Baar, Switzerland
Tel.: (41) 417113303
Web Site: http://www.allreal.ch
Sales Range: $150-199.9 Million
Emp.: 300
Real Estate Financial Services
N.A.I.C.S.: 531390

Allreal Generalunternehmung AG   (1)
Eggbuhlstrasse 15, 8050, Zurich, Switzerland
Tel.: (41) 443191111
Sales Range: $75-99.9 Million
Emp.: 250
Real Estate Financial Services
N.A.I.C.S.: 531390

Allreal Home AG   (1)
Eggbuhlstrasse 15, 8050, Zurich, Switzerland
Tel.: (41) 443191111
Sales Range: $75-99.9 Million
Emp.: 300
Real Estate Financial Services
N.A.I.C.S.: 531390
Roter Herzog (CEO)

Allreal Office AG   (1)
Eggbuhlstrasse 15, 8050, Zurich, Switzerland
Tel.: (41) 443191111
Emp.: 300
Real Estate Financial Services
N.A.I.C.S.: 531390
Bruno Bettoni (Mng Dir)

Allreal Toni AG   (1)
Lindbergh-Allee 1, Glattpark, 8152, Zurich,
Switzerland
Tel.: (41) 443191111
Real Estate Financial Services
N.A.I.C.S.: 531390

Allreal Vulkan AG   (1)
Lindbergh-Allee 1, Glattpark, 8152, Zurich,
Switzerland
Tel.: (41) 443191111
Web Site: http://www.allreal.ch
Sales Range: $150-199.9 Million
Emp.: 300
Real Estate Financial Services
N.A.I.C.S.: 531390

Allreal West AG   (1)
Lindbergh-Allee 1, Glattpark, 8152, Zurich,
Switzerland
Tel.: (41) 443191111
Web Site: https://www.allreal.ch
Sales Range: $75-99.9 Million
Emp.: 250
Real Estate Financial Services
N.A.I.C.S.: 531390

Apalux AG   (1)
Eggbuhlstrasse 15, 8050, Zurich, Switzerland
Tel.: (41) 443191111
Real Estate Financial Services
N.A.I.C.S.: 531390

Bulachguss AG   (1)
Lindbergh-Allee 1 Glattpark, 8152, Zurich,
Switzerland

Tel.: (41) 44 319 1111
Real Estate Services
N.A.I.C.S.: 531390

ALLSAFE JUNGFALK GMBH & CO. KG

Gerwigstrasse 31, 78234, Engen,
Germany
Tol.: (10) 773360020
Web Site: http://www.allsafe-
group.com
Year Founded: 1964
Sales Range: $50-74.9 Million
Emp.: 270
Winches, Fasteners & Cargo Nets
Mfr
N.A.I.C.S.: 333923

Subsidiaries:

Ancra Japan Ltd.   (1)
Nisheki Yokohama Building 9th Floor 1-1-8
Sakuragi-Cho Naku-ku, Yokohama, 231-
0062, Japan   (100%)
Tel.: (81) 456818171
Web Site: http://www.ancra.jp
Sales Range: $25-49.9 Million
Emp.: 50
Mfr of Winches, Fasteners & Cargo Nets
N.A.I.C.S.: 333923
Taizo Nakamura (Chm)

allsafe JUNGFALK Australia   (1)
2/148 Karimbla Road, Miranda, 2228, NSW,
Australia
Tel.: (61) 415078100
Trailer Distr
N.A.I.C.S.: 423110
David Bailey (Country Mgr)

allsafe JUNGFALK Benelux   (1)
Bastion 1 5, 5491 AN, Sint-Oedenrode,
Netherlands
Tel.: (31) 413483087
Trailer Distr
N.A.I.C.S.: 423110
Frank Beljaards (Country Mgr)

ALLSHIPS LTD.

80 Kifissias Avenue, Maroussi,
15125, Athens, Greece
Tel.: (30) 210 809 0570   MH
Year Founded: 1998
Sales Range: Less than $1 Million
Emp.: 2
Ship Repair Services
N.A.I.C.S.: 336611
George Economou (Chm & Pres)

ALLSTAR HEALTH BRANDS, INC.

3250 Bloor Street, Toronto, M8X 2X9,
ON, Canada
Tel.: (905) 513-0000   NV
Web Site:
https://www.allstarhealthbrands.com
Year Founded: 2012
ALST—(OTCIQ)
Sales Range: Less than $1 Million
Emp.: 4
Pharmaceuticals Mfr
N.A.I.C.S.: 325412
Neil Mellor (Sr VP-Sls & Ops)

ALLTAINER AB

Stora Avagen 21, Askim, 436 34,
Gothenburg, Sweden
Tel.: (46) 763111911
Web Site: https://www.alltainer.com
Year Founded: 2019
70H—(DEU)
Construction Engineering Services
N.A.I.C.S.: 541330
Jakob Kesj (CEO)

ALLTEK TECHNOLOGY CORPORATION

9F No 360 Ruei Guang Rd, Neihu,
Taipei, 114, Taiwan
Tel.: (886) 226275859

Web Site: https://www.alltek.com
Year Founded: 1991
3209—(TAI)
Rev.: $1,831,940,871
Assets: $621,146,090
Liabilities: $458,430,867
Net Worth: $162,715,223
Earnings: $19,602,668
Emp.: 606
Fiscal Year-end: 12/31/23
Wireless Communication Equipment
Distr
N.A.I.C.S.: 517112
Yi-Wen Wu (Chm & Deputy Chm)

Subsidiaries:

Alder Optomechanical Corp.   (1)
No 171 Tianjin St, Pingzhen Dist, Taoyuan,
32458, Taiwan
Tel.: (886) 34393588
Web Site: https://www.alder.com.tw
Electronic Parts Mfr & Distr
N.A.I.C.S.: 334419

Alltek Marine Electronics Corp.   (1)
14F-2 No 237 Sec 1 Datong Rd, Xizhi District, New Taipei City, 22161, Taiwan
Tel.: (886) 286918568
Web Site: https://www.alltekmarine.com
Electric Equipment Mfr
N.A.I.C.S.: 334419

Alltek Technology (Singapore) Pte.
Ltd.   (1)
8 Boon Lay Way 08-10 8 Tradehub 21, Singapore, 609964, Singapore
Tel.: (65) 6 425 0088
Web Site: https://www.alltek.sg
Sales Range: $25-49.9 Million
Emp.: 3
Voice & Telecommunication Services
N.A.I.C.S.: 517810

Pantek Technology Corp.   (1)
7F No 605 Ruei-Guang Rd, Nei-Hu Dist,
Taipei, 11492, Taiwan
Tel.: (886) 226272211
Web Site: https://www.pantek.com.tw
Electronic Parts Mfr & Distr
N.A.I.C.S.: 334419

ALLTERCO JSCO

103 Cherni Vrah Blvd, 1407, Sofia,
Bulgaria
Tel.: (359) 29887435
Web Site: https://www.allterco.com
Year Founded: 2010
SLYG—(BUL)
Rev.: $158,150,227
Assets: $137,796,244
Liabilities: $19,511,116
Net Worth: $118,285,128
Earnings: $35,559,033
Emp.: 195
Fiscal Year-end: 12/31/23
Telecommunication Servicesb
N.A.I.C.S.: 517810
Mirche Atanasovski (Chief Comml
Officer)

Subsidiaries:

Allterco Europe Gmbh   (1)
Lothstr 5, 80335, Munich, Germany
Tel.: (49) 89150018490
IoT Product Development Services
N.A.I.C.S.: 541420

ALLTEX INDUSTRIES LTD.

Suite 5B House 1 Road 27 Banani
Block K, Banani, Dhaka, Bangladesh
Tel.: (880) 248810664
Web Site: https://www.alltexbd.com
Year Founded: 1986
ALLTEX—(CHT)
Rev.: $8,940,979
Assets: $44,124,952
Liabilities: $38,444,644
Net Worth: $5,680,308
Earnings: $128,200
Emp.: 306
Fiscal Year-end: 06/30/22

Textile Mfr
N.A.I.C.S.: 313310
Afsar Uddin Ahmad *(Chm)*

ALLTOP TECHNOLOGY CO., LTD.
3F No 102 Sec 3 Jhongshan Rd, Jhonghe Dist, New Taipei City, Taiwan
Tel.: (886) 222251688
Web Site:
   https://www.alltopconnector.com
Year Founded: 1998
3526—(TPE)
Rev.: $72,222,055
Assets: $128,070,037
Liabilities: $49,392,177
Net Worth: $78,677,860
Earnings: $17,324,391
Fiscal Year-end: 12/31/22
Electric Equipment Mfr
N.A.I.C.S.: 335311

Subsidiaries:

Alltop Electronics (Suzhou) Ltd. **(1)**
No 59 Zhenxi Road, ChangFu Industrial Park Sha Xi Town, Taicang, JiangSu, China
Tel.: (86) 51253290598
Electrical Connector Distr
N.A.I.C.S.: 423610

ALLTRONICS HOLDINGS LIMITED
Unit 408 4/F Citicorp Centre 18 Whitfield Road, Causeway Bay, Hong Kong, China (Hong Kong)
Tel.: (852) 29775666
Web Site:
   http://www.alltronics.com.hk
0833—(HKG)
Rev.: $213,640,924
Assets: $175,221,781
Liabilities: $108,366,545
Net Worth: $66,855,235
Earnings: $8,659,975
Emp.: 2,944
Fiscal Year-end: 12/31/21
Electronic Products Mfr
N.A.I.C.S.: 334419
Kin Hung So *(Exec Dir)*

Subsidiaries:

Allcomm (H.K.) Limited **(1)**
Unit 408 4/F Citicorp Centre 18 Whitfield Road, Causeway Bay, Hong Kong, China (Hong Kong)
Tel.: (852) 29775666
Electronic Components Mfr
N.A.I.C.S.: 334419

Alltronics Manufacturing (Shenzhen) Limited **(1)**
Tang Xia Yong 2nd Industrial Area, Song Gang Town Baoan District, Shenzhen, 518105, Guang Dong, China
Tel.: (86) 75529866628
Electronic Equipment Distr
N.A.I.C.S.: 423690

Alltronics Tech. Mftg. Limited **(1)**
Unit 408 4/F Citicorp Centre 18 Whitfield Road, Causeway Bay, Hong Kong, China (Hong Kong)
Tel.: (852) 29775666
Electronic Components Mfr
N.A.I.C.S.: 334419

Dynamic Progress International Limited **(1)**
Unit 807 8/F Hopeful Factory Centre 10 - 16 Wo Shing Street, Fo Tan, Sha Tin, China (Hong Kong)
Tel.: (852) 27080033
Web Site: http://www.dynamic-progress.com.hk
Electronic Components Mfr
N.A.I.C.S.: 334419

Southchina Engineering & Manufacturing Limited **(1)**
7A 40 Shek Pai Wan Rd, Aberdeen, China (Hong Kong)

Tel.: (852) 25538185
Web Site: http://www.scem.com.hk
Electronic Components Mfr
N.A.I.C.S.: 334419

ALLU GROUP OY
Jokimaentie 1, 16320, Pennala, Finland
Tel.: (358) 3882140
Year Founded: 1985
Construction Materials Mfr
N.A.I.C.S.: 333120

ALLUP SILICA LIMITED
Tel.: (61) 861851744   AU
Web Site: https://www.allupsilica.com
Year Founded: 2013
APS—(ASX)
Rev.: $61,116
Assets: $2,910,855
Liabilities: $208,473
Net Worth: $2,702,382
Earnings: ($1,073,167)
Fiscal Year-end: 06/30/23
Silica Exploration Services
N.A.I.C.S.: 212322
Andrew Haythorpe *(Chm)*

ALLWELLNESS HOLDINGS GROUP LIMITED
Factory 2 3-11 Hallmark Street, Pendle Hill, 2145, NSW, Australia
Tel.: (61) 298962266
Web Site:
   http://www.allwellness.com.au
Year Founded: 2015
AWH—(NSXA)
Rev.: $85,964
Assets: $568,771
Liabilities: $825,786
Net Worth: ($257,015)
Earnings: ($269,399)
Fiscal Year-end: 06/30/20
Healthcare Product Distr
N.A.I.C.S.: 424210
Yong Zhang *(Exec Dir)*

ALLWIN TELECOMMUNICATION CO., LTD.
No 6 Gaoge Road, Hunnan District, Shenyang, 110179, Liaoning, China
Tel.: (86) 2483781111
Web Site: https://syallwin.com
Year Founded: 2000
002231—(SSE)
Rev.: $26,763,048
Assets: $81,440,424
Liabilities: $32,322,888
Net Worth: $49,117,536
Earnings: ($7,466,472)
Fiscal Year-end: 12/31/22
Network Equipment Mfr
N.A.I.C.S.: 335929
Fang Du *(Chm & Pres)*

ALLWINNER TECHNOLOGY CO., LTD.
No 9 Technology Road 2 High-Tech Zone, Zhuhai, 519080, Guangdong, China
Tel.: (86) 7563818333   CN
Web Site:
   https://www.allwinnertech.com
300458—(CHIN)
Rev.: $212,583,852
Assets: $499,682,196
Liabilities: $84,422,520
Net Worth: $415,259,676
Earnings: $29,632,824
Fiscal Year-end: 12/31/22
Multi-Core Application Processors & Smart Power Management ICs Mfr
N.A.I.C.S.: 334413
Jianhui Zhang *(Chm)*

ALM EQUITY AB
Regeringsgatan 59, SE-111 56, Stockholm, Sweden
Tel.: (46) 856230300
Web Site: https://www.almequity.se
Year Founded: 2006
ALM—(OMX)
Rev.: $646,454,429
Assets: $1,078,797,756
Liabilities: $539,679,864
Net Worth: $539,117,892
Earnings: ($53,949,254)
Emp.: 134
Fiscal Year-end: 12/31/22
Real Estate Development & Investment Services
N.A.I.C.S.: 237210
Maria Wideroth *(Chm)*

ALM. BRAND A/S
Midtermolen 7, DK 2100, Copenhagen, Denmark
Tel.: (45) 35474747
Web Site: https://www.almbrand.dk
Year Founded: 1792
ALMB—(CSE)
Rev.: $1,212,542,142
Assets: $5,580,298,361
Liabilities: $3,588,574,901
Net Worth: $1,991,723,459
Earnings: $73,215,552
Emp.: 2,298
Fiscal Year-end: 12/31/22
Commercial Banking Services
N.A.I.C.S.: 522110
Jorgen Hesselbjerg Mikkelsen *(Chm)*

ALMA MARITIME LIMITED
Vouliagmenis Avenue 88, Elliniko, 16777, Greece
Tel.: (30) 2111024000   MH
Web Site:
   http://www.almamaritime.com
Year Founded: 2008
Sales Range: $25-49.9 Million
Emp.: 14
Deep Sea Freight Transportation Services
N.A.I.C.S.: 483111
Stamatis Molaris *(Chm & CEO)*

ALMA MARKET S.A.
ul Pilotow 6, 30-964, Krakow, Poland
Tel.: (48) 126276320   PL
Web Site: http://www.almamarket.pl
Year Founded: 1991
Consumer Good Retailer
N.A.I.C.S.: 445298
Rafal Dylag *(Chm-Mgmt Bd)*

Subsidiaries:

Alma Development Sp. z o.o. **(1)**
Pilotow 6, 30-964, Krakow, Lesser Poland, Poland
Tel.: (48) 126276115
Real Estate Property Development Services
N.A.I.C.S.: 531210

Krakowski Kredens Sp. z o.o. **(1)**
ul Grodzka 7, 31-006, Krakow, Poland
Tel.: (48) 123705801
Web Site: http://www.krakowskikredens.pl
Sales Range: $400-449.9 Million
Emp.: 2,007
Convenience Food Products Retailer
N.A.I.C.S.: 445131
Ewa Lewek *(Mng Dir)*

Paradise Group Sp. z o.o. **(1)**
ul Grodzka 7, 31-006, Krakow, Lesser Poland, Poland
Tel.: (48) 124218280
Web Site: http://www.paradisegroup.pl
Luxury Fashion Apparels Retailer
N.A.I.C.S.: 458110

ALMA MEDIA CORPORATION
Alvar Aallon katu 3 C Alma House, FI-00100, Helsinki, Finland
Tel.: (358) 10665000   FI

Year Founded: 1998
ALMA—(HEL)
Rev.: $333,261,386
Assets: $534,426,937
Liabilities: $312,216,706
Net Worth: $222,210,231
Earnings: $77,595,510
Emp.: 1,679
Fiscal Year-end: 12/31/22
Media Holding Company; Newspaper, Magazine & Internet Publishing & Graphic Services
N.A.I.C.S.: 551112
Kai Telanne *(Pres & CEO)*

Subsidiaries:

AS Kinnisvaraportaal **(1)**
Parnu mnt 141, 11314, Tallinn, Harjumaa, Estonia
Tel.: (372) 6660360
Web Site: http://www.city24.ee
Emp.: 11
Real Estate Portal Services
N.A.I.C.S.: 519290
Karin Noppel-Kokerov *(Mgr)*

Alma 360 Custom Media **(1)**
Konalantie 6-8 B 3rd Floor, Helsinki, 370, Finland
Tel.: (358) 1066 5102
Web Site: http://www.alma360.fi
Sales Range: $25-49.9 Million
Emp.: 5
Newspaper & Magazine Publishing Services
N.A.I.C.S.: 513110
Markku Rimpilaeinen *(Mgr-Dev)*

Alma Intermedia Oy **(1)**
Pohjoesranta 11e, Pori, 28100, Finland
Tel.: (358) 25221400
Sales Range: $25-49.9 Million
Emp.: 24
Online Directory & Telemarketing Services
N.A.I.C.S.: 561422

Alma Media Interactive Oy **(1)**
Itainenkatu 11, PO Box 327, FIN 33101, Tampere, Finland **(100%)**
Tel.: (358) 106338200
Web Site: http://www.etuovi.com
Sales Range: $25-49.9 Million
Emp.: 20
N.A.I.C.S.: 516120

Alma Media Ventures Oy **(1)**
Etelaesplanadi 20, Helsinki, 130, Finland
Tel.: (358) 10665000
Newspaper Publishing Services
N.A.I.C.S.: 513110

Alma Mediapartners Oy **(1)**
Alma House Alvar Aallon katu 3 C, 00100, Helsinki, Finland **(100%)**
Tel.: (358) 10665000
Web Site: https://www.almamedia.fi
Emp.: 1,530
Advertising Agency Services
N.A.I.C.S.: 541810

Alma Talent Oy **(1)**
Alvar Aallon katu 3 C, 00100, Helsinki, Finland
Tel.: (358) 10665101
Web Site: https://www.almatalent.fi
Journal Publisher, Direct Marketer, TV Content Producer & Pre-Media Services
N.A.I.C.S.: 513120
Juha-Petri Loimovuori *(Mng Dir)*

Subsidiary (Domestic):

Suoramarkkinointi Mega Oy **(2)**
Salomonkatu 17 B 11th floor, 00100, Helsinki, Finland
Tel.: (358) 985677700
Web Site: https://www.sm-mega.fi
Telemarketing Services
N.A.I.C.S.: 561422
Joni Haverinen *(Dir-Sls & Mktg)*

Subsidiary (Non-US):

Telemarket SIA **(2)**
Valguma street 4a, Riga, 1048, Latvia
Tel.: (371) 67611665
Web Site: https://www.telemarketing.lv
Emp.: 200
Telemarketing Services

Alma Media Corporation—(Continued)

N.A.I.C.S.: 561422
Inna Ponne *(Project Mgr)*

Alpress Oy (1)
Etelaesplanadi 14, PO Box 140, FIN 00101,
Helsinki, Finland (100%)
Tel.: (358) 950771
Sales Range: $25-49.9 Million
Emp.: 30
Newspaper & Magazine Publishing
N.A.I.C.S.: 513110

Subsidiary (Domestic):

Kainuun Sanomain Kirjapaino Oy (2)
Kauppakatu 11, PO Box 150, 87100, Ka-
jaani, Finland (100%)
Tel.: (358) 106657205
Web Site: http://www.kainuunsanomat.fi
Sales Range: $25-49.9 Million
Television Broadcasting Services
N.A.I.C.S.: 516120

Lapin Kansa Oy (2)
Rovakatu 32, 96200, Rovaniemi,
Finland (100%)
Tel.: (358) 85377620
Web Site: http://www.lapinkansa.fi
Sales Range: $50-74.9 Million
Emp.: 200
Television Broadcasting
N.A.I.C.S.: 516120

Suomen Paikallissanomat Oy (2)
Ita inenkatu 11 33210, PO Box 327, 33101,
Tampere, Finland (100%)
Tel.: (358) 32666111
Web Site: http://www.stsp.fi
Sales Range: $25-49.9 Million
Emp.: 100
N.A.I.C.S.: 516120

Bovision AB (1)
Svenosknabbevegen 26, 393 51, Kalmar,
Sweden
Tel.: (46) 480 47 75 50
Online Business Portal Services
N.A.I.C.S.: 519290

City24 Polska Sp. z.o.o. (1)
ul E Ciolka 11A Lok 306, 01-445, Warsaw,
Poland
Tel.: (48) 22 533 62 27
Web Site: http://www.citydom24.pl
Sales Range: $25-49.9 Million
Emp.: 4
Online Property Advertising Services
N.A.I.C.S.: 541810
Monika Horeczy *(Gen Mgr)*

**Digitaalinen asuntokauppa DIAS
Oy** (1)
Salomonkatu 1, 00100, Helsinki, Finland
Tel.: (358) 102011190
Web Site: https://www.dias.fi
Housing Utility Services
N.A.I.C.S.: 624229

Etua Oy (1)
Alvar Aallon katu 3 C, 00100, Helsinki, Fin-
land
Tel.: (358) 923163611
Web Site: https://www.etua.fi
Financial Services
N.A.I.C.S.: 523999

Forssa Print (1)
Teerivuorenkatu 5, 33300, Tampere,
Finland (36%)
Tel.: (358) 106185111
Web Site: http://www.actaprint.fi
Sales Range: $125-149.9 Million
Emp.: 300
Commercial Printing
N.A.I.C.S.: 323111

Kauppalehti Oy (1)
Alvar Aallon katu 3 C, PO Box 189, 00101,
Helsinki, Finland (100%)
Tel.: (358) 10665101
Web Site: http://www.kauppalehti.fi
Sales Range: $75-99.9 Million
Emp.: 499
Business News & Information Syndicate &
Publisher
N.A.I.C.S.: 513110
Juha-Petri Loimovuori *(Mng Dir)*

Kotikokki.net Oy (1)

Simonkatu 12 A 4B, Helsinki, 00100, Fin-
land
Tel.: (358) 405920671
Web Site: http://www.kotikokki.net
Online Directory Publishing Services
N.A.I.C.S.: 513140

Kustannus Oy Aamulehti (1)
Itainenkatu 11, PO Box 327, Tampere,
33210, Finland (100%)
Tel.: (358) 32666111
Web Site: http://www.aamulehti.fi
Sales Range: $100-124.9 Million
Emp.: 200
Television Broadcasting
N.A.I.C.S.: 516120

Kustannusosakeyhtio Iltalehti (1)
Alvar Aallon katu 3 C 00100, Helsinki, 110,
Finland
Tel.: (358) 1066 5100
Newspaper Publishing & Online Portal Ser-
vices
N.A.I.C.S.: 513110
Kari Kivela *(Mng Dir)*

LMC s.r.o. (1)
Lighthouse Towers Jankovcova 1569/2c,
170 00, Prague, Czech Republic
Tel.: (420) 224810055
Web Site: https://www.lmc.eu
Internet Provider Services
N.A.I.C.S.: 517810

Mascus A/S (1)
Agro Food Park 15, 8200, Arhus, Denmark
Tel.: (45) 33 39 47 97
Online Advertising & Online Vehicle Retail
Services
N.A.I.C.S.: 541890
Charlotte Villum Jensen *(Country Mgr &
Mgr-Sls)*

Monster Oy (1)
Alvar Aallon katu 3 C, 00100, Helsinki, Fin-
land
Tel.: (358) 106652180
Web Site: http://www.monster.fi
Sales Range: $25-49.9 Million
Emp.: 2
Online Recruitment Services
N.A.I.C.S.: 513140

Objektvision AB (1)
Skeppsbrogatan 47, 392 31, Kalmar, Swe-
den
Tel.: (46) 480477560
Sales Range: $25-49.9 Million
Emp.: 12
Online Property Advertising Services
N.A.I.C.S.: 541810
Peter Bergstrom *(CEO)*

SIA City24 (1)
Gustava Zemgala gatve 78-1, Riga, 1039,
Latvia
Tel.: (371) 67491017
Web Site: https://www.city24.lv
Emp.: 4
Real Estate Advertising Services
N.A.I.C.S.: 541810

Suomalainen Lehtitaino Oy (1)
Ilmalankatu 2C, PO Box 139, 240, Helsinki,
Finland (100%)
Tel.: (358) 950782
Web Site: http://www.alprint.fi
Graphic Services
N.A.I.C.S.: 541430

Subsidiary (Domestic):

Acta Print Tampere (2)
Hietalahdenranta 17, Tampere, 00180, Fin-
land
Tel.: (358) 106185111
Web Site: http://www.actaprint.fi
Commercial Printing
N.A.I.C.S.: 323111
Seppo Aaltonen *(Mng Dir)*

Alprint Rovaniemi (2)
Veitikantie 2 8, FIN 6100, Rovaniemi, Fin-
land
Tel.: (358) 16320011
Web Site: http://www.lapinkansa.fi
Sales Range: $50-74.9 Million
Emp.: 200
Newspapers
N.A.I.C.S.: 513110

**Suomen Business Viestinta SBV
Oy** (1)
Munkkiniemen Puistotie 25, Helsinki, 00330,
Finland
Tel.: (358) 10665106
Web Site: http://www.sbv.fi
Sales Range: $25-49.9 Million
Emp.: 50
Advertising Agency Services
N.A.I.C.S.: 541810

Suomen Tukkuautot Oy (1)
Alvar Aallon katu 3C, PO Box 368, 00101,
Helsinki, Finland
Tel.: (358) 50 449 4999
Web Site: https://www.tukkuautot.fi
Car Dealing Services
N.A.I.C.S.: 441110

**Suunnittelutoimisto TTNK Helsinki
Oy** (1)
Palvelukeskus, PL 900, 33101, Tampere,
Finland
Tel.: (358) 4076 11349
Digital Marketing Communication Services
N.A.I.C.S.: 541613

UAB City24 (1)
J Tumo-Vaizganto Str 8-2, 1108, Vilnius,
Lithuania
Tel.: (370) 52487488
Web Site: http://www.city24.lt
Sales Range: $25-49.9 Million
Emp.: 3
Real Estate Internet Portal Services
N.A.I.C.S.: 519290
Skaiste Kiausaite *(Mgr-Customer Support)*

ALMA METALS LIMITED
Suite 1 245 Churchill Avenue, Subi-
aco, 6008, WA, Australia
Tel.: (61) 864655500
Web Site:
   https://www.energyresources.com
ALM—(ASX)
Rev.: $5,676
Assets: $3,672,205
Liabilities: $228,867
Net Worth: $3,443,338
Earnings: ($2,082,955)
Emp.: 21
Fiscal Year-end: 06/30/24
Other Community Housing Services
N.A.I.C.S.: 624229
Charles Frazer Tabeart *(Exec Dir-
Investor Relations-Business Develop-
ment & CEO)*

ALMA TALENT AB
Fleminggatan 7, 112 26, Stockholm,
Sweden
Tel.: (46) 87966650
Web Site: http://www.almatalent.se
Publishing Services; Online & Digital
Advertising
N.A.I.C.S.: 541810
Ulf Magnusson *(CEO)*

Subsidiaries:

Alma Talent Media AB (1)
Fleminggatan 7, 112 26, Stockholm, Swe-
den
Tel.: (46) 87966650
Web Site: http://www.almatalent.se
Publishing & Online Advertising Services
N.A.I.C.S.: 541810

**ALMA TELECOMMUNICA-
TIONS KAZAKHSTAN JSC**
Aitiev 23, Almaly district, 050026, Al-
maty, Kazakhstan
Tel.: (7) 272500510
Web Site: http://www.almatv.kz
ALTV—(KAZ)
Rev.: $11,253,153
Assets: $69,153,571
Liabilities: $23,692,030
Net Worth: $45,461,541
Earnings: $3,410,166
Fiscal Year-end: 12/31/19
Wireless Telecommunication Services
N.A.I.C.S.: 517112

Dmitriy Basin *(Chm, CEO & Gen Dir)*

ALMAC CO., LTD.
148 Gongdan-ro, Seongsan-gu,
Changwon, Gyeongsangnam-do, Ko-
rea (South)
Tel.: (82) 552600400
Web Site: https://www.almac.co.kr
Year Founded: 2001
354320—(KRS)
Emp.: 151
Pharmaceuticals Product Mfr
N.A.I.C.S.: 325412
Shin Sang-ho *(CEO)*

**ALMAC SCIENCES GROUP
LTD.**
Almac House 20 Seagoe Industrial
Estate, Craigavon, BT63 5QD, United
Kingdom
Tel.: (44) 2838332200
Web Site:
   http://www.almacgroup.com
Year Founded: 1968
Sales Range: $650-699.9 Million
Emp.: 5,000
Developer & Marketer of Pharmaceu-
tical Products
N.A.I.C.S.: 541715
Alan Armstrong *(Chm & CEO)*

Subsidiaries:

Almac Clinical Services (1)
9 Charlestown Rd, Seagoe Industrial Es-
tate, Craigavon, BT63 5PW, United King-
dom
Tel.: (44) 2838362436
Web Site: http://www.almacgroup.com
Sales Range: $550-599.9 Million
Emp.: 1,100
Management Services for Manufacture,
Packaging, Labeling, Release, Distribution,
Return & Analysis of Clinical Trial Supplies
N.A.I.C.S.: 325412
Robert Dunlop *(Pres & Mng Dir)*

Almac Clinical Technologies (1)
25 Fretz Rd, Souderton, PA 18964
Tel.: (215) 660-8500
Web Site: http://www.almacgroup.com
Sales Range: $200-249.9 Million
Emp.: 800
Interactive Support Services & Online Data
Collection for Clinical Trials
N.A.I.C.S.: 541690
Jim Murphy *(Pres)*

Almac Diagnostics (1)
19 Seagoe Industrial Estate, Craigavon,
BT63 5QD, United Kingdom
Tel.: (44) 2838337575
Web Site: http://www.almacgroup.com
Sales Range: $25-49.9 Million
Emp.: 100
Diagnostic Services
N.A.I.C.S.: 621511

Almac Pharma Services (1)
22 Seagoe Industrial Estate, Craigavon,
BT63 5QD, United Kingdom
Tel.: (44) 2838363363
Sales Range: $50-74.9 Million
Emp.: 200
Pharmaceutical Development, Analysis,
Manufacturing & Packaging Services
N.A.I.C.S.: 325412
Graeme McBurney *(Mng Dir)*

**Almac Pharmaceutical Services
K.K.** (1)
29F Toranomon Hills Mori Tower 1-23-1,
Toranomon Minato-ku, Tokyo, 105-6329,
Japan
Tel.: (81) 342339178
Pharmaceutical Preparation Mfr
N.A.I.C.S.: 325412

**Almac Pharmaceutical Services Pte.
Ltd.** (1)
9 Changi South Street 3, Singapore,
486361, Singapore
Tel.: (65) 63090720
Web Site: http://www.almacgroup.com

Emp.: 30
Pharmaceutical Products Distr
N.A.I.C.S.: 424210
Alan Armstrong *(Chm & CEO)*

Almac Sciences (1)
Almac House, 20 Seagoe Industrial Estate,
Craigavon, BT63 5QD, United Kingdom
Tel.: (44) 2838332200
Web Site: http://www.css-almac.com
Sales Range: $400-449.9 Million
Emp.: 2,500
Chemical Research & Development Services for Pharmaceutical Industry
N.A.I.C.S.: 541715
Stephen Barr *(Pres & Mng Dir)*

Arran Chemical Company (1)
Monksland Industrial Estate, Athlone, N37
DN24, Co Roscommon, Ireland
Tel.: (353) 906445700
Web Site: https://arranchemical.ie
Chemicals Mfr
N.A.I.C.S.: 325199
Rhona Fitzgerald *(Mgr-Supply Chain)*

Galen Limited (1)
Seagoe Industrial Estate, Craigavon, BT63
5UA, United Kingdom
Tel.: (44) 2838334974
Web Site: http://www.galen.co.uk
Sales Range: $25-49.9 Million
Emp.: 40
Pharmaceutical Product Marketing Services
N.A.I.C.S.: 424210
Ken Ross *(VP-Comml Ops)*

Galen Pharma Ireland Limited (1)
Finnabair Industrial Estate, Dundalk, Co
Louth, Ireland
Tel.: (353) 429320718
Pharmaceutical Preparation Mfr
N.A.I.C.S.: 325412

POA Pharma Scandinavia AB (1)
Banevaenget 13 1, 3460, Birkerod, Denmark
Tel.: (45) 31174300
Pharmaceutical Product Mfr & Distr
N.A.I.C.S.: 325412

ALMACENAJES, S.A.
Via Fernandez de Cordoba Vista Hermosa Calle Principal Corregimiento,
Apartado Postal 0816-03585,
Panama, Panama
Tel.: (507) 224 1111
Web Site:
http://www.almacenajes.net
ALMC—(PAN)
Sales Range: $1-9.9 Million
Emp.: 53
Warehousing & Storage Services
N.A.I.C.S.: 493110
Carlos Valencia Correa *(Pres)*

ALMACENES METALURGICOS, S.A.U.
Pol Ind Sector Autopista C Galileo 1
C 17 Km 14 5, Parets del Valles,
08150, Barcelona, Spain
Tel.: (34) 933 06 86 00   ES
Web Site: http://www.almesa.com
Steel Pole Mfr
N.A.I.C.S.: 331210

ALMADEN MINERALS LTD.
Suite 210 1333 Johnston Street, Vancouver, V6H 3R9, BC, Canada
Tel.: (604) 689-7644
Web Site:
https://www.almadenminerals.com
AAU—(NYSEAMEX)
Rev.: $198,597
Assets: $61,057,118
Liabilities: $6,441,710
Net Worth: $54,615,408
Earnings: ($9,267,327)
Emp.: 5
Fiscal Year-end: 12/31/22
Mineral, Gold & Silver Mining Services
N.A.I.C.S.: 212290

James Duane Poliquin *(Founder & Chm)*

ALMANA NETWORKS SOLUTIONS
Financial Square Building No 1 1st
Floor Office No 5 C-Ring Road, PO
Box 55229, Doha, 55229, Qatar
Tel.: (974) 44073000
Web Site:
http://www.almananetworks.com
Year Founded: 2005
Emp.: 170
Computer & Communications Systems Design Services
N.A.I.C.S.: 541512
Swaraj Bontula *(CEO)*

ALMARAI COMPANY LTD.
Exit 7 Northern Ring Road, PO Box
8524, Al-Izdihar, Riyadh, 11492,
Saudi Arabia
Tel.: (966) 114700005   SA
Web Site: https://www.almarai.com
Year Founded: 1976
2280—(SAU)
Rev.: $5,219,460,072
Assets: $9,650,450,607
Liabilities: $4,902,063,725
Net Worth: $4,748,386,882
Earnings: $547,001,466
Emp.: 42,000
Fiscal Year-end: 12/31/23
Food Products Distr
N.A.I.C.S.: 424430
Andrew Mackie *(Exec VP-Farming)*

Subsidiaries:

Continental Farmers Group PLC (1)
33/37 Athol Street, Douglas, IM1 1LB, Isle
of Man
Tel.: (44) 1624647647
Web Site:
http://www.continentalfarmersgroup.com
Emp.: 414
Farming
N.A.I.C.S.: 111199
Mark C. Laird *(CEO)*

**Hail Agricultural Development
Company** (1)
PO Box 106, 81411, Hail, Saudi Arabia
Tel.: (966) 65200011
Web Site: http://www.hadco.com.sa
Sales Range: $50-74.9 Million
Emp.: 3,000
Wheat, Alfalfa, Yellow Corn, Dates, Grapes,
Chicken, Poultry Feed & Animal Feed
N.A.I.C.S.: 111998

**International Company for Agricultural
Industries Projects (Beyti) (SAE)** (1)
Plot 88 1st 70th Street 5th Settlement,
16964, New Cairo, Egypt
Tel.: (20) 8006444444
Web Site: https://www.beytiegypt.com
N.A.I.C.S.: 311421

**Teeba Investment for Developed
Food Processing Company** (1)
PO Box 35076, Amman, 11180, Jordan
Tel.: (962) 65009090
Web Site: https://teeba.jo
N.A.I.C.S.: 311421
Shadi Qatati *(CEO)*

ALMAST OJSC
28 Rubinyants St, 0035, Yerevan,
Armenia
Tel.: (374) 10243060
Web Site:
http://www.almastcompany.com
Year Founded: 1964
ALMS—(ARM)
Sales Range: Less than $1 Million
Diamond Cutting Tool Mfr
N.A.I.C.S.: 339910

ALMATINSKIE
ELEKTRICHESKIE SETI JSC

7 Dostyk ave, Almaty, 050002, Kazakhstan
Tel.: (7) 727 254 03 31
Eletric Power Generation Services
N.A.I.C.S.: 221118

ALMATYTEMIR JSC
2 Auezov Street, 050026, Almaty,
Kazakhstan
Tel.: (7) 727 379 19 76
Web Site: http://www.almatytemir.kz
ALTM—(KAZ)
Rev.: $1,150,096,500
Assets: $6,513,168,870
Liabilities: $3,775,106,610
Net Worth: $2,738,062,260
Earnings: $164,051,550
Fiscal Year-end: 12/31/19
Storehouse Facilities Leasing; Metal
Product Sales
N.A.I.C.S.: 531130

ALMAVIVA S.P.A.
Via di Casal Boccone 188-190,
Rome, Italy
Tel.: (39) 0639931   IT
Web Site: https://www.almaviva.it
Information Technology Services
N.A.I.C.S.: 551112

Subsidiaries:

Iteris, Inc. (1)
1250 S Capital of Texas Hwy Bldg 1 Ste
330, Austin, TX 78746
Tel.: (512) 716-0808
Web Site: https://www.iteris.com
Rev.: $171,987,000
Assets: $123,445,000
Liabilities: $53,538,000
Net Worth: $69,907,000
Earnings: $3,131,000
Emp.: 454
Fiscal Year-end: 03/31/2024
Traffic Control & Safety Machine Vision
Systems & Sensors Mfr
N.A.I.C.S.: 335314
Todd Kreter *(Sr VP & Gen Mgr-Advanced
Sensor Technologies)*

Subsidiary (Domestic):

Iteris, Inc. - Grand Forks (2)
4324 University Ave Ste B, Grand Forks,
ND 58203
Tel.: (218) 779-2320
Web Site: https://www.iteris.com
Weather Forecasting Services
N.A.I.C.S.: 541990

Trafficcast International, Inc (2)
2801 Coho St, Madison, WI 53713
Tel.: (608) 268-3946
Web Site: http://www.trafficcast.com
Rev.: $3,200,000
Emp.: 35
Computer System Design Services
N.A.I.C.S.: 541512
Jerome Chen-Chan *(Exec VP-Engrg &
R&D)*

ALMAWAVE S.P.A.
Via di Casal Boccone 188-190,
00137, Rome, Italy
Tel.: (39) 0639931
Web Site: https://www.almawave.com
Year Founded: 2008
AIW—(ITA)
Rev.: $65,569,047
Assets: $130,416,161
Liabilities: $53,322,663
Net Worth: $77,093,498
Earnings: $10,280,384
Emp.: 446
Fiscal Year-end: 12/31/23
Information Technology Services
N.A.I.C.S.: 541512
Antonio Amati *(VP)*

Subsidiaries:

Almawave do Brasil Ltda. (1)
344 Edificio Italia 30 Andar - CJ 301 Centro, Sao Paulo, 01046-010, Brazil

Tel.: (55) 1135149566
Emp.: 59
Big Data & Knowledge Management Services
N.A.I.C.S.: 518210

Pervoice S.p.A. (1)
Via alla Cascata 56/C, 38123, Trento, Italy
Tel.: (39) 04611812800
Web Site: https://www.pervoice.com
Emp.: 50
Speech Recognition Development Services
N.A.I.C.S.: 541930

Sistemi Territoriali S.R.L. (1)
Via Pietro Di Lupo Parra Sud 144, Cascina
- Loc, 56021, San Prospero, PI, Italy
Tel.: (39) 050768711
Web Site: https://www.sister.it
Artificial Intelligence Analysis & Big Data
Services
N.A.I.C.S.: 541715

**The Data Appeal Company
S.p.A.** (1)
Via del Tiratoio 1, 50124, Florence, Italy
Tel.: (39) 0800090319
Web Site: https://datappeal.io
Artificial Intelligence Research & Development Services
N.A.I.C.S.: 541715

ALMEDA VENTURES LP
Azrieli Center Triangle Building 45th
Flr 132 Menachem Begin Road, Tel
Aviv, 67023, Israel
Tel.: (972) 97885599
Web Site:
http://www.almedaventures.com
AMDA—(TAE)
Rev.: $5,526
Assets: $7,103,743
Liabilities: $111,894
Net Worth: $6,991,850
Earnings: ($437,077)
Fiscal Year-end: 12/31/23
Medical Equipment Distr
N.A.I.C.S.: 423450
Irit Yaniv *(CEO & Partner)*

ALMEDAHLS OY
Rahkasammaleenkatu 6, 20780, Kaarina, Finland
Tel.: (358) 22766366
Web Site: http://www.almedahls.fi
Year Founded: 1846
Sales Range: $25-49.9 Million
Emp.: 175
Textile Mfr
N.A.I.C.S.: 314999
Riitta Norrdgard *(Mgr-IT, Fin & Personnel)*

Subsidiaries:

Almedahl-Kinna AB (1)
Box 265, SE 511 23, Kinna, Sweden
Tel.: (46) 320209500
Web Site: http://www.almedahl-kinna.se
Sales Range: $25-49.9 Million
Emp.: 100
Textile Mfr
N.A.I.C.S.: 314120
Gry Hege Solsnes *(Gen Mgr)*

Subsidiary (Domestic):

Ahmedahls AB (2)
PO Box 265, 511 23, Kinna, Sweden
Tel.: (46) 320794000
Web Site: http://www.almedahls.se
Sales Range: $25-49.9 Million
Emp.: 20
Household Textile Mfr
N.A.I.C.S.: 314120
Gry Hege Solsnes *(CEO)*

ALMEDIO, INC.
KS Kunitachi Bld 7F 1-4-12 Higashi,
Kunitachi-shi, Tokyo, 186-0002, Japan
Tel.: (81) 425110500
Web Site: https://www.almedio.co.jp
Year Founded: 1981

Almedio, Inc.—(Continued)

7859—(TKS)
Rev.: $76,391,770
Assets: $64,487,160
Liabilities: $14,575,050
Net Worth: $49,912,110
Earnings: $15,388,080
Emp.: 310
Fiscal Year-end: 03/31/24
Test Tapes & Discs Mfr, Research,
Developer & Sales; CDs & DVDs Mfr
& Sales
N.A.I.C.S.: 541380
Shinichi Urushiyama (Exec Officer)

Subsidiaries:

A Drink Trade Co., Ltd.   (1)
Tianmu West Road 218 Room 1008 2nd
Building, Jingan District, Shanghai, China
Tel.: (86) 2162373290
Beverage Vending Machine Operator
N.A.I.C.S.: 445132

Alcera (suzhou) Co., Ltd.   (1)
No 8 Yexin Rd, Jungian Wujiang Economic
and Technology Development Zone, Su-
zhou, 215200, China
Tel.: (86) 51263496667
Kiln Furniture Mfr
N.A.I.C.S.: 327120

ALMENDRAL S.A.

Isidora Goyenechea 3642 Piso 4, Las
Condes, Santiago, Chile
Tel.: (56) 3344815
Web Site: http://www.almendral.cl
Year Founded: 1981
ALMENDRAL—(SGO)
Sales Range: Less than $1 Million
Holding Company; Financial Invest-
ment Services
N.A.I.C.S.: 551112
Luis Felipe Gazitua Achondo (Chm &
Pres)

Subsidiaries:

Empresa Nacional de Telecomunica-
ciones S.A.   (1) (54.76%)
Amunategui 20, Santiago, Chile
Tel.: (56) 3600123
Web Site: http://www.entel.cl
Rev.: $2,998,005,827
Assets: $6,602,508,798
Liabilities: $4,768,180,182
Net Worth: $1,834,328,616
Earnings: $539,009,052
Emp.: 11,967
Fiscal Year-end: 12/31/2022
Mobile Phones & Internet Services
N.A.I.C.S.: 517810
Antonio Buchi Buc (CEO)

ALMIRALL, S.A.

Ronda General Mitre 151, 08022,
Barcelona, Spain
Tel.: (34) 932913000
Web Site: https://www.almirall.com
Year Founded: 1944
ALM—(VAL)
Rev.: $987,433,492
Assets: $2,621,685,617
Liabilities: $1,006,275,527
Net Worth: $1,615,410,090
Earnings: ($42,470,471)
Emp.: 1,904
Fiscal Year-end: 12/31/23
Pharmaceutical Developer
N.A.I.C.S.: 325412
Jorge Gallardo Ballart (Chm)

Subsidiaries:

Almirall - Produtos Farmaceuticos
Lda.   (1)
Rua do Central Park Edificio 3 numero 6
4B, 2795-242, Linda-a-Velha, Portugal
Tel.: (351) 214155750
Pharmaceuticals Product Mfr
N.A.I.C.S.: 325412
Almirall ApS   (1)

Vandtarnsvej 77, 2860, Soborg, Denmark
Tel.: (45) 70257575
Pharmaceuticals Product Mfr
N.A.I.C.S.: 325412
Karsten Kjaergaard (Dir-Mktg)

Almirall B.V.   (1)
Papendorpseweg 100, 3528 BJ, Utrecht,
Netherlands
Tel.: (31) 307991155
Web Site: http://www.almirall.nl
Pharmaceuticals Product Mfr
N.A.I.C.S.: 325412

Almirall GmbH   (1)
Breitenfurter Str 113 Top 101, 1120, Vienna,
Austria
Tel.: (43) 15953960
Emp.: 20
Pharmaceuticals Product Mfr
N.A.I.C.S.: 325412
Gunter Schaden (Gen Mgr)

Almirall Hermal GmbH   (1)
Scholtzstrasse 3, 21465, Reinbek, Germany
Tel.: (49) 40727040
Web Site: https://www.almirall.de
Sales Range: $100-124.9 Million
Dermatological Pharmaceuticals Mfr
N.A.I.C.S.: 325412

Almirall Limited   (1)
Harman House 1 George Street, Uxbridge,
UB8 1QQ, Middlesex, United Kingdom
Tel.: (44) 2071602500
Web Site: https://www.almirall.co.uk
Pharmaceuticals Product Mfr
N.A.I.C.S.: 325412

Almirall sp. z o.o.   (1)
Ul Pileckiego 63, 02-781, Warsaw, Poland
Tel.: (48) 223300257
Pharmaceuticals Product Mfr
N.A.I.C.S.: 325412

Almirall, S.A. de C.V.   (1)
Periferico Sur 3325 Piso 1 Colonia San Je-
ronimo Lidice, 10200, Mexico, Mexico
Tel.: (52) 5999 8600
Pharmaceuticals Product Mfr
N.A.I.C.S.: 325412

Almirall, S.p.A.   (1)
Via Messina 38 Torre C, 20154, Milan, Italy
Tel.: (39) 02346181
Web Site: https://www.almirall.it
Pharmaceuticals Product Mfr
N.A.I.C.S.: 325412
Biagio Vigano (Dir-HR)

Almirall, SAS   (1)
Immeuble Le Barjac 1 boulevard Victor,
75015, Paris, France
Tel.: (33) 1 46 46 19 20
Pharmaceuticals Product Mfr
N.A.I.C.S.: 325412
Rita Ananikian (Office Mgr)

Aqua Pharmaceutical Holdings
Inc.   (1)
707 Eagle view Blvd, Exton, PA 19341
Tel.: (610) 644-7000
Web Site: http://www.aquapharm.com
Emp.: 25
Holding Company
N.A.I.C.S.: 551112
Jim DeMaioribus (VP-Mktg)

ALMOGIM HOLDINGS LTD.

2 Hatish Street, PO Box 2058, Tirat
Karmel, 3912001, Israel
Tel.: (972) 48577080
Web Site: https://www.almogim.co.il
ALMA—(TAE)
Rev.: $80,105,538
Assets: $395,293,819
Liabilities: $328,620,799
Net Worth: $66,673,020
Earnings: $3,388,037
Emp.: 100
Fiscal Year-end: 12/31/23
Offices of Other Holding Companies
N.A.I.C.S.: 551112

ALMONDZ GLOBAL SECURI-
TIES LIMITED

F 33/3 Okhla Industrial Area Phase II,
New Delhi, 110020, India
Tel.: (91) 1143500700
Web Site:
https://www.almondzglobal.com
531400—(BOM)
Rev.: $9,848,693
Assets: $34,355,180
Liabilities: $9,336,136
Net Worth: $25,019,044
Earnings: $2,530,983
Emp.: 143
Fiscal Year-end: 03/31/22
Securities Brokerage Services
N.A.I.C.S.: 523150
Jagdeep Singh (Exec Dir)

Subsidiaries:

Almondz Capital Markets Pvt.
Ltd.   (1)
6th Floor Dinsha Vachha Road Opp K C
College, Churchgate, Mumbai, 400020,
India
Tel.: (91) 2267526699
Securities Brokerage Services
N.A.I.C.S.: 523150

Almondz Commodities Pvt. Ltd.   (1)
Level 5 Grande Palladium 175 CST Road
Off BKC Kalina Santarcruz East, Church-
gate, Mumbai, 400 098, India
Tel.: (91) 2266437600
Web Site: http://www.almondz.com
Emp.: 75
Commodity Brokerage Services
N.A.I.C.S.: 523160
Ashit Kothi (VP)

Almondz Insurance Brokers Pvt.
Ltd.   (1)
Ground and First Floor Worldmark 1 Asset
Area 11 Aerocity, Hospitality District Indira
Gandhi International Airport Delhi, New
Delhi, 110 037, India
Tel.: (91) 1149288888
Web Site: http://www.almondzin.com
Insurance Brokerage Services
N.A.I.C.S.: 524210

Almondz Reinsurance Brokers Pri-
vate Limited   (1)
2nd Floor 3 Scindia House Janpath, New
Delhi, 110001, India
Tel.: (91) 1141514666
Web Site: http://www.almondz.com
Insurance Brokerage Services
N.A.I.C.S.: 524210

ALMONTY INDUSTRIES INC.

100 King Street West Suite 5700,
Toronto, M5X 1C7, ON, Canada
Tel.: (647) 438-9766   BC
Web Site: http://www.almonty.com
Year Founded: 2009
AII—(ASX)
Rev.: $16,997,659
Assets: $177,704,448
Liabilities: $141,075,285
Net Worth: $36,629,163
Earnings: ($6,672,959)
Emp.: 413
Fiscal Year-end: 12/31/23
Tungsten Exploration Services
N.A.I.C.S.: 212290
Lewis Black (Chm, Pres & CEO)

ALMUNEEF CO.

Building No 5065 Unit No 1, Al-
Manakh District, Riyadh, 14314,
Saudi Arabia
Tel.: (966) 112227262
Web Site: https://www.almuneef.com
Year Founded: 2009
9569—(SAU)
Rev.: $65,677,245
Assets: $30,063,128
Liabilities: $4,882,081
Net Worth: $25,181,047
Earnings: $4,688,085
Emp.: 226
Fiscal Year-end: 12/31/23

Electrical Contracting Services
N.A.I.C.S.: 238210
Hamad Murshid Nasser Al Muneef Al
Hajri (Chm)

ALMY D.O.O.

Vranducka bb Poslovna zona Pecuj,
7200, Zenica, Bosnia & Herzegovina
Tel.: (387) 32456266
Web Site: http://www.almy.ba
Year Founded: 1989
Other Miscellaneous Durable Goods
Merchant Wholesalers
N.A.I.C.S.: 423990
Almir Begic (Dir)

Subsidiaries:

Metalno d.d.   (1)
Sarajevska no 364, 72000, Zenica, Bosnia
& Herzegovina
Steel Structural Mfr
N.A.I.C.S.: 331110
Sisic Semiz (Chm & CEO)

ALNA AB

Lvovo St 105A, Vilnius, Lithuania
Tel.: (370) 52785500
Web Site: http://www.alna.lt
Year Founded: 1989
Sales Range: $25-49.9 Million
Emp.: 250
IT Services
N.A.I.C.S.: 541512
Justina Milaknyte (Chm)

Subsidiaries:

Alna Intelligence UAB   (1)
A Gostauto 40B, Vilnius, 03163, Lithuania
Tel.: (370) 5 210 28 20
Web Site: http://www.alna.lt
Sales Range: $25-49.9 Million
Emp.: 90
Information Technology Consulting Services
N.A.I.C.S.: 541512
Algirdas Sukys (Mgr-IT Svc)

Alna Software UAB   (1)
A Gostauto 40B, 01112, Vilnius, Lithuania
Tel.: (370) 5 239 73 00
Web Site: http://www.alna.lt
Sales Range: $25-49.9 Million
Emp.: 100
Software Development Services
N.A.I.C.S.: 541511

BPO House   (1)
A Domasevicus Str 9, 01400, Vilnius,
Lithuania
Tel.: (370) 5 278 55 00
Web Site: http://www.alna.lt
Business Process Outsourcing Services
N.A.I.C.S.: 561499
Tomas Milaknis (CEO)

DocLogix JSC   (1)
Lvovo str 105A, LT-08104, Vilnius, Lithuania
Tel.: (370) 5 274 58 53
Web Site: http://www.doclogix.com
Sales Range: $25-49.9 Million
Emp.: 50
Document Management Software Develop-
ment & Whslr
N.A.I.C.S.: 541511
Jaroslav Gil (Gen Mgr)

SIA Unitree   (1)
Brivibas Gatve 223, Riga, 1039, Latvia
Tel.: (371) 6 7024878
Web Site: http://www.unitree.lv
Emp.: 7
System Integration & Networking Services
N.A.I.C.S.: 541512
Lornakims Maksim (Gen Mgr)

ALNA TRADING & EXPORTS
LTD.

Allana House Allana Road Colaba,
Mumbai, 400 001, India
Tel.: (91) 2222811000
Web Site: https://www.alna.co.in
Year Founded: 1981
506120—(BOM)
Rev.: $874

Assets: $266,120
Liabilities: $150
Net Worth: $265,970
Earnings: ($7,794)
Fiscal Year-end: 03/31/22
Frozen Food Product Mfr
N.A.I.C.S.: 311412
Prakashchandra Khulbe (Compliance Officer & Sec)

ALNOX S.R.O

Vrsovicka 1525/1D, 10 Vrsovice, 101 00, Prague, Czech Republic
Tel.: (420) 257 325 181
Web Site: http://www.alnox.cz
Year Founded: 2003
Kitchen Cabinet Mfr
N.A.I.C.S.: 337126

ALOE PRIVATE EQUITY SAS

34 Boulevard Malesherbes, 75008, Paris, France
Tel.: (33) 1 45 53 32 13
Web Site: http://www.aloe-group.com
Privater Equity Firm
N.A.I.C.S.: 523999
Vivek Tandon (Co-Founder & Gen Partner)

ALOIS DALLMAYR KG

Dienerstr 14-15, 80331, Munich, Germany
Tel.: (49) 8921350
Web Site: http://www.dallmayr.com
Year Founded: 1700
Sales Range: $125-149.9 Million
Emp.: 3,800
Coffee Mfr; Delicatessen; Vending Machines Network
N.A.I.C.S.: 311920
Wolfgang Wille (Gen Partner)

Subsidiaries:

Alois Dallmayr Automaten-Service GmbH Herxheim (1)
Karcherstr 16, 66539, Neunkirchen, Germany
Tel.: (49) 727698500
Vending Machine Whslr
N.A.I.C.S.: 423440

Alois Dallmayr Gastro-Service GmbH & Co KG (1)
Dienerstrasse 14-15, 80331, Munich, Germany
Tel.: (49) 8921350
Web Site: http://www.dallmayr.de
Coffee Whslr
N.A.I.C.S.: 424490
George Randlkofe (Gen Mgr)

Alois Dallmayr Kaffee OHG (1)
Dienerstr 14-15, Munich, 80333, Germany
Tel.: (49) 89 2135 0
Roast Coffee Mfr & Whslr
N.A.I.C.S.: 311920

Dallmayr Automaten-Service GmbH (1)
Stiftswaldstr 4, 67657, Kaiserslautern, Germany
Tel.: (49) 631 3407972
Vending Machine Whslr
N.A.I.C.S.: 423440

Heimbs Kaffee GmbH & Co. KG (1)
Rebenring 30, Braunschweig, 38106, Germany
Tel.: (49) 531 3 80 02 0
Web Site: http://www.heimbs.de
Coffee & Tea Mfr & Whslr
N.A.I.C.S.: 311920

ALON ISRAEL OIL COMPANY LTD.

France Bldg Europark, PO Box 10, Yakum, 60972, Israel
Tel.: (972) 99618500
Web Site: http://www.alon.co.il
Energy, Retail & Infrastructures Holding Company

N.A.I.C.S.: 551112
Avigdor Kaplan (CEO)

Subsidiaries:

Alon Natural Gas Exploration Ltd. (1)
Biniyan Tsarfat Td 10 Iyurop'ark Iyakum, Yakum, 60792, Israel
Tel.: (972) 733242742
Rev.: $46,399,000
Assets: $228,834,000
Liabilities: $152,239,000
Net Worth: $76,595,000
Earnings: $21,456,000
Fiscal Year-end: 12/31/2020
Financial Investment Services
N.A.I.C.S.: 523999

ALONY HETZ PROPERTIES AND INVESTMENTS LTD.

Amot Atrium Tower 2 Jabotinsky St, Ramat Gan, 5250501, Israel
Tel.: (972) 37521115
Web Site: https://www.alony-hetz.com
ALHE—(TAE)
Rev.: $406,179,979
Assets: $9,846,005,368
Liabilities: $6,160,896,101
Net Worth: $3,685,109,267
Earnings: $91,798,709
Emp.: 494
Fiscal Year-end: 12/31/22
Real Estate Construction, Property Development & Leasing Services
N.A.I.C.S.: 531190
Nathan Hetz (Founder, Pres & CEO)

Subsidiaries:

Alony Hetz Global Ltd. (1)
7 Jabotinsky, Ramat Gan, 52520, Israel
Tel.: (972) 37521115
Web Site: http://www.alony-hetz.com
Sales Range: $50-74.9 Million
Emp.: 15
Real Estate Property Development Services
N.A.I.C.S.: 531210
Naama Emanuel (Controller)

ALORO MINING CORP.

Suite 250 - 750 West Pender Street, PO Box 201, Vancouver, V6C 2T7, BC, Canada
Tel.: (604) 689-5722   BC
Web Site:
    https://www.aloromining.com
Year Founded: 2004
WLRMF—(OTCIQ)
Assets: $1,162,608
Liabilities: $1,018,969
Net Worth: $143,638
Earnings: ($265,232)
Fiscal Year-end: 12/31/22
Metal Minerals Mining & Exploration Services
N.A.I.C.S.: 212290
Thomas A. Doyle (Pres & CEO)

ALOYS F. DORNBRACHT GMBH & CO. KG

Kobbingser Muhle 6, 58640, Iserlohn, Germany
Tel.: (49) 23714330
Web Site: http://www.dornbracht.com
Year Founded: 1950
Rev.: $165,941,820
Emp.: 800
Bathroom & Kitchen Fitting Mfr
N.A.I.C.S.: 332919
Matthias Dornbracht (Mng Dir)

Subsidiaries:

Dombracht Austria GmbH (1)
IZ No-Sud Strasse 7 Objekt 58 D Top 6, 2355, Wiener Neudorf, Austria
Tel.: (43) 2236677360
Bathroom Accessory Distr
N.A.I.C.S.: 423220

Dornbracht (Shanghai) Commercial Ltd. (1)
No 899 Lingling Rd, 28K-L Cross Region Plaza, Shanghai, 200030, China
Tel.: (86) 2163606930
Bathroom Accessory Distr
N.A.I.C.S.: 423220
Harry Fan (Mgr-Technical)

Dornbracht Americas Inc. (1)
1700 Executive Dr S Ste 600, Duluth, GA 30096
Tel.: (800) 774-1181
Bathroom Accessory Distr
N.A.I.C.S.: 423220

Dornbracht Asia Pacific Ltd. (1)
Room 1305 Sino Favour Centre 1 On Yip Street, Chai Wan, China (Hong Kong)
Tel.: (852) 25056254
Bathroom Accessory Distr
N.A.I.C.S.: 423220

Dornbracht Espana S.L. (1)
Folgueroles 17-25, 08022, Barcelona, Spain
Tel.: (34) 932723910
Bathroom Accessory Distr
N.A.I.C.S.: 423220

Dornbracht France SARL (1)
2 rue de la Roquette, 75011, Paris, France
Tel.: (33) 140211070
Bathroom Accessory Distr
N.A.I.C.S.: 423220
Marie Bellenger (Coord-Mktg)

Dornbracht India Private Limited (1)
1102 Wing-A Cello Triumph I B Patel road, Opp Laghu Udyog Goregaon East, Mumbai, 400063, India
Tel.: (91) 2226853900
Bathroom Accessory Distr
N.A.I.C.S.: 423220

Dornbracht International Holding GmbH (1)
PO Box 114268, Dubai, United Arab Emirates
Tel.: (971) 43806611
Bathroom Accessory Distr
N.A.I.C.S.: 423220
Haitham Ghannam (Reg Mgr-Sls)

Dornbracht Italia s.r.l. (1)
Via Morimondo 2/5, 20143, Milano, Italy
Tel.: (39) 028183431
Bathroom Accessory Distr
N.A.I.C.S.: 423220
Massimo Caucino (Project Mgr-Sls)

Dornbracht Nederland BV (1)
Rivium Boulevard 21, 2909 LK, Capelle aan den IJssel, Netherlands
Tel.: (31) 105243400
Bathroom Accessory Distr
N.A.I.C.S.: 423220
Kor Bos (Dir-Sls & Mktg)

Dornbracht Nordic A/S (1)
Masteskurene skur 7 Galionsvej 33, 1437, Copenhagen, Denmark
Tel.: (45) 50845400
Bathroom Accessory Distr
N.A.I.C.S.: 423220
Inge-Hanne Tegnander (Project Mgr)

Dornbracht Schweiz AG (1)
Letziweg 9, 4663, Aarburg, Switzerland
Tel.: (41) 627872030
Bathroom Accessory Distr
N.A.I.C.S.: 423220
Guy Roy Dornbracht (Project Mgr & Area Mgr-Sls)

Dornbracht South East Asia Pte Ltd. (1)
Level 18 Republic Plaza II 9 Raffles Place, Singapore, 48619, Singapore
Tel.: (65) 68236813
Bathroom Accessory Distr
N.A.I.C.S.: 423220

Dornbracht Turkey (1)
Karanfil Caddesi Karanfil Araligi Sogak No 6 2 Levent, 34330, Istanbul, Turkiye
Tel.: (90) 2122849495
Bathroom Accessory Distr
N.A.I.C.S.: 423220
Turgut Sarikaya (Mng Dir)

Dornbracht UK Ltd. (1)

Unit 8 & 9 Bow Court, Fletchworth Gate, Coventry, CV5 6SP, United Kingdom
Tel.: (44) 2476717129
Bathroom Accessory Distr
N.A.I.C.S.: 423220

ALOYS INC.

6F Marcus Bldg 4-5 Yanghyeon-Ro 405Beon-Gil, Jungwon-gu, Seong-nam, 13438, Gyeonggi-do, Korea (South)
Tel.: (82) 7086805501
Web Site: https://www.aloys.co.kr
Year Founded: 2018
297570—(KRS)
Rev.: $22,046,802
Assets: $31,906,844
Liabilities: $7,934,995
Net Worth: $23,971,849
Earnings: $4,666,958
Emp.: 36
Fiscal Year-end: 12/31/22
Communication Equipment Mfr
N.A.I.C.S.: 334220
Han Geunam (CFO)

ALP GROUP

Plot No. 32, Sector-18 HUDA, Gurgaon, Delhi, 122015, India
Tel.: (91) 1244731500
Web Site: https://alpgroup.in
Year Founded: 1985
Polymer & Silicon Mfr
N.A.I.C.S.: 326140

Subsidiaries:

ALP Overseas Pvt. Ltd. (1)
Plot No. 32 Sector-18 HUDA Gurgaon, Delhi, 122015, India
Tel.: (91) 01244731500
Web Site: https://www.alpoverseas.com
Polymer & Silicon Mfr
N.A.I.C.S.: 326140

ALP USA, Inc. (1)
545 Johnson Ave Ste 4, Bohemia, NY 11716-2698
Fabricated Rubber Products
N.A.I.C.S.: 326299

Subsidiary (Domestic):

SoffSeal, Inc. (2)
104 May Dr, Harrison, OH, 45030
Tel.: (513) 367-0028
Web Site: http://www.soffseal.com
Emp.: 35
Fabricated Rubber Products & Weather-stripping Mfr
N.A.I.C.S.: 326299
Donna Anderson (CEO)

ALPA LABORATORIES LTD

33/2 Pigdamber A B Road Rau, Indore, 453446, Madhya Pradesh, India
Tel.: (91) 7314294567
Web Site: https://www.alpalabs.in
532878—(BOM)
Rev.: $16,795,383
Assets: $21,190,164
Liabilities: $4,573,856
Net Worth: $16,616,309
Earnings: $1,923,517
Emp.: 393
Fiscal Year-end: 03/31/22
Pharmaceuticals Product Mfr
N.A.I.C.S.: 325412
Mahendra Singh Chawla (Chm)

ALPA LUMBER INC

7630 Airport Road, Mississauga, L4T 4G6, ON, Canada
Tel.: (905) 612-1222
Web Site: https://alpastairs.com
Sales Range: $500-549.9 Million
Emp.: 1,500
Lumber Product Whslr
N.A.I.C.S.: 423310

Alpa Lumber Inc—(Continued)

Subsidiaries:

Gillies Lumber Inc. **(1)**
777 Industrial Road, Cambridge, N3H 5C6,
ON, Canada
Tel.: (519) 653-3219
Web Site: http://gillieslumber.ca
Wooden Stairs, Railings & Roof Trusses Mfr
& Lumber Products Whslr
N.A.I.C.S.: 423310

ALPAGEL GAP

83 Avenue d'Embrun, Cedex, 05010,
Gap, Hautes Alpes, France
Tel.: (33) 492514868
Web Site: http://alpes.relaisdor.fr
Rev.: $20,500,000
Emp.: 49
Packaged Frozen Goods
N.A.I.C.S.: 424420
Bernard Costorier *(Dir)*

ALPEN CO., LTD.

Alpen Marunouchi Tower 9-40
2-chome Marunouchi, Naka-ku, Na-
goya, 460-8637, Aichi, Japan
Tel.: (81) 525590120
Web Site: https://store.alpen-group.jp
Year Founded: 1972
3028—(TKS)
Rev.: $1,573,261,920
Assets: $1,255,718,480
Liabilities: $526,485,680
Net Worth: $729,232,800
Earnings: $10,779,260
Fiscal Year-end: 06/30/24
Sports Products Mfr & Sales; Man-
agement of Ski Resorts & Golf
Courses
N.A.I.C.S.: 339920
Takehito Suzuki *(Exec VP)*

Subsidiaries:

Japana Co., Ltd. **(1)**
2-9-40 Marunouchi 2-chome, Naka-ku, Na-
goya, 460-0002, Aichi, Japan
Tel.: (81) 525591011
Web Site: http://www.japana.co.jp
Sporting Goods Mfr
N.A.I.C.S.: 423910

Subsidiary (Non-US):

Wuxi Japana Sports Goods Co.,
Ltd. **(2)**
1 Lingjiang Rd Development Zone for High
& New Tech Wuxi Of China, Wuxi, 214028,
Jiangsu, China
Tel.: (86) 510 85216314
Web Site: http://www.wxjpn.com
Ski & Snowboard Garments & Gloves Mfr
N.A.I.C.S.: 339920
Hirose Toshihiu *(Gen Mgr)*

Kissmark Japan Co., Ltd. **(1)**
Alpine Marunochi Tower 2 9 40 Marunouchi
Naka-ku, Naka-Ku, 460-0002, Nagoya,
Aichi, Japan
Tel.: (81) 525591035
Web Site: http://www.kissmark.co.jp
Sales Range: $25-49.9 Million
Emp.: 10
Sporting & Athletic Goods Mfr
N.A.I.C.S.: 339920

Royal Hills Co., Ltd. **(1)**
Alpine Marunouchi Tower 20F 2 9 40
Marunouchi, Naka-Ku, Nagoya, 460-8637,
Aichi, Japan
Tel.: (81) 525591040
Web Site: http://www.alpen-group.jp
Sales Range: $75-99.9 Million
Emp.: 3,000
Golf & Skiing Managing Services
N.A.I.C.S.: 711310

Sports Logistics Co., Ltd. **(1)**
12 Tsukamotogonishi Hozumitsukamoto,
Chiakicho, Ichinomiya, 491-0803, Aichi,
Japan
Tel.: (81) 586812161

Sales Range: $25-49.9 Million
Emp.: 60
Logistic Services
N.A.I.C.S.: 541614
Hattori Humitoshi *(CEO)*

ALPER CONSULTORIA E COR-RETORA DE SEGUROS S.A.

Gilbert Sabino 215-13 andar Pin-
heiros, Sao Paulo, 05425-020, Brazil
Tel.: (55) 1131752900
Web Site:
   https://www.brasilinsurance.com.br
Year Founded: 2010
APER3—(BRAZ)
Rev.: $57,061,009
Assets: $146,945,707
Liabilities: $63,128,115
Net Worth: $83,817,591
Earnings: ($1,240,950)
Fiscal Year-end: 12/31/23
Insurance Brokerage Services
N.A.I.C.S.: 524298
Marcos Aurelio Couto *(Pres & CEO)*

Subsidiaries:

BASE BRASIL B.I. Corretora de Se-
guros Ltda.
Avenida Presidente Vargas 3131 s/n sl
1605, Rio de Janeiro, Brazil
Tel.: (55) 21 4007 1315
Insurance Brokerage Services
N.A.I.C.S.: 524210

PROMOVE Corretora de Seguros
Ltda. **(1)**
Rua Alvaro Alvim 1061 Vila Pauliceia,
09693-000, Sao Bernardo do Campo, Sao
Paulo, Brazil
Tel.: (55) 11 2588 2100
Web Site:
   http://www.promoveseguros.com.br
Insurance Brokerage Services
N.A.I.C.S.: 524210

YORK BRUKAN B.I. Assessoria Ad-
ministracao e Corretagem de Se-
guros Ltda.
Av 09 de Julho 5 049 - Conj - 1a, Jd Pau-
lista, 01407 200, Sao Paulo, Brazil
Tel.: (55) 11 3032 6003
Sales Range: $50-74.9 Million
Emp.: 22
Insurance Brokerage Services
N.A.I.C.S.: 524210
Marcio Chaves *(Gen Mgr)*

ALPERIA SPA

via Dodiciville 8, 39100, Bolzano,
Italy
Tel.: (39) 0471 986 111
Web Site: http://www.alperiagroup.eu
Year Founded: 2015
Energy Services Provider
N.A.I.C.S.: 221122
Johann Wohlfarter *(CEO)*

Subsidiaries:

Gruppo Green Power S.p.A. **(1)**
via Varotara 57, 30035, Mirano, Venice,
Italy **(71.88%)**
Tel.: (39) 041930125
Web Site:
   http://www.gruppogreenpower.com
Rev.: $19,486,770
Assets: $8,757,381
Liabilities: $1,718,824
Net Worth: $7,038,558
Earnings: ($2,886,920)
Fiscal Year-end: 12/31/2019
Power Generation
N.A.I.C.S.: 221111
Giangiacomo Indri Raselli *(Pres)*

ALPES PROVENCE AGNEAUX

10 Allee des Romarins, BP 5, 04201,
Sisteron, France
Tel.: (33) 492613350
Web Site:
   http://alpagneau.pagesperso-
   orange.fr
Sales Range: $10-24.9 Million

Emp.: 27
Meat Packing Plants
N.A.I.C.S.: 311611
Francois Monge *(Pres)*

ALPHA ADRIATIC D.D.

Carrarina 6, 52100, Pula, Croatia
Tel.: (385) 52211544
Web Site: https://alphaadriatic.com
Year Founded: 1986
ULPL—(ZAG)
Sales Range: Less than $1 Million
Marine Cargo Handling Services
N.A.I.C.S.: 488320

ALPHA AND OMEGA SEMI-CONDUCTOR LIMITED

Clarendon House 2 Church Street,
Hamilton, HM 11, Bermuda
Tel.: (441) 8309742   **BM**
Web Site: https://www.aosmd.com
Year Founded: 2000
AOSL—(NASDAQ)
Rev.: $657,274,000
Assets: $1,145,013,000
Liabilities: $253,406,000
Net Worth: $891,607,000
Earnings: ($11,081,000)
Emp.: 2,332
Fiscal Year-end: 06/30/24
Holding Company: Semiconductors &
Related Devices
N.A.I.C.S.: 551112
Wenjun Li *(COO)*

Subsidiaries:

Agape Package Manufacturing
(Shanghai) Ltd. **(1)**
Ste B1 Building Dongkai Industrial Park,
Songjiang, Shanghai, 201614, China
Tel.: (86) 2157856600
Semiconductor Assembly & Testing Ser-
vices
N.A.I.C.S.: 334413

Alpha & Omega Semiconductor
(Hong Kong) Limited **(1)**
Room 701 Tesbury Center 28 Queen's
Road East, Wanchai, China (Hong Kong)
Tel.: (852) 75583517733
Semiconductor Devices Mfr
N.A.I.C.S.: 334413

Alpha & Omega Semiconductor
(Shenzhen) Limited **(1)**
East 10/F Matsunichi Building 9996 Shen-
nan Blvd, Shenzhen, 518057, China
Tel.: (86) 75583517733
Semiconductor & Related Device Mfr
N.A.I.C.S.: 334413

Alpha and Omega Semiconductor
(Shanghai) Co., Ltd. **(1)**
Room 1002-1005 Tower 1 Kerry EverBright
City 218, Tianmu West Road Bldg A,
Shanghai, 200070, China
Tel.: (86) 2163533218
Semiconductor Devices Mfr
N.A.I.C.S.: 334413

Alpha and Omega Semiconductor
(Shenzhen) Co., Ltd. **(1)**
Tel.: (86) 75583517733
Semiconductor Devices Mfr & Whslr
N.A.I.C.S.: 334413

Alpha and Omega Semiconductor
(Taiwan) Ltd. **(1)**
9/F No 292 Yangguang Street, Neihu Dis-
trict, Taipei, 11491, Taiwan
Tel.: (886) 287515616
Semiconductor Devices Mfr & Whslr
N.A.I.C.S.: 334413

Alpha and Omega Semiconductor
Incorporated **(1)**
475 Oakmead Pkwy, Sunnyvale, CA
94085 **(100%)**
Tel.: (408) 830-9742
Web Site: https://www.aosmd.com
Emp.: 120
Software Mfr & Distr
N.A.I.C.S.: 513210

Jireh Semiconductor
Incorporated **(1)**
3131 NE Brookwood Pkwy, Hillsboro, OR
97124
Tel.: (503) 681-6307
Emp.: 275
Integrated Semiconductor Chips Mfr
N.A.I.C.S.: 334413

ALPHA ASSOCIES CONSEIL SAS

43 Avenue Hoche, 75008, Paris,
France
Tel.: (33) 156602020
Web Site:
   http://www.groupealpha.com
Sales Range: $25-49.9 Million
Emp.: 25
Privater Equity Firm
N.A.I.C.S.: 523999
Olaf Kordes *(Partner)*

Subsidiaries:

APEF Management Company 5
Limited **(1)**
22 Grenville Street, PO Box 87, Saint He-
lier, JE4 8PX, Channel Islands, Jersey
Tel.: (44) 1534 609 000
Web Site: http://www.groupealpha.com
Investment Management Service
N.A.I.C.S.: 523940

Calligaris S.p.A. **(1)**
Via Trieste 12, Manzano, 33044, Udine,
Italy **(80%)**
Tel.: (39) 0432 748211
Web Site: http://www.calligaris.it
Furniture Mfr
N.A.I.C.S.: 423210
Stefano Rosa Uliana *(CEO)*

EUROPART Holding GmbH **(1)**
Martinstrabe 13, 58135, Berlin, Germany
Tel.: (49) 2331 3564 0
Web Site: http://www.europart.net
Commercial Vehicle Workshops; Truck,
Trailer, Transporter & Bus Fleets Operator
N.A.I.C.S.: 485113
Olaf Giesen *(CEO)*

Subsidiary (Non-US):

Europart i Sverige AB **(2)**
Flygaregatan 4, 212 39, Malmo, Sweden
Tel.: (46) 40 89930
Web Site: http://www.europart.net
Industrial Activities & Related Operations
N.A.I.C.S.: 336212

Savio Macchine Tessili S.p.A. **(1)**
via Udine 105, 33170, Pordenone, Italy
Tel.: (39) 0434 3971
Web Site: http://www.saviotechnologies.com
Sales Range: $600-649.9 Million
Emp.: 1,500
Mfr Machinery Mfr
N.A.I.C.S.: 333998

Subsidiary (Non-US):

BMS bvba **(2)**
Vlamingstraat 16, 8560, Wevelgem, Bel-
gium
Tel.: (32) 56 26 26 11
Web Site: http://www.visionbms.com
Mfr Equipment Mfr
N.A.I.C.S.: 333998
Johan Schepens *(Pres)*

Subsidiary (Non-US):

BMS Vision Ltd. **(3)**
Capricorn Park Blakewater Road, Black-
burn, BB1 5QR, United Kingdom **(100%)**
Tel.: (44) 1254662244
Web Site: http://www.visionbms.com
Mfr Equipment Mfr
N.A.I.C.S.: 333998
David Robson *(Mng Dir)*

Subsidiary (US):

BMSVision LLC **(3)**
4420 Taggart Creek Rd Ste 112, Charlotte,
NC 28208-5414
Tel.: (704) 392-9371
Web Site: http://www.visionbms.com

Electronic Inspecting Devices Mfr
N.A.I.C.S.: 423440
Dany Claeys (VP)

Subsidiary (Non-US):

Loepfe Brothers Ltd. **(2)**
Kastellstrasse 10, PO Box 582, CH 8623,
Wetzikon, Switzerland **(100%)**
Tel.: (41) 434881111
Web Site: http://www.loepfe.com
Sales Range: $25-49.9 Million
Textile Machinery Mfr
N.A.I.C.S.: 333998
Ralph Mennicke (CEO)

Sedo Treepoint GmbH **(2)**
Neuwies 1, 35794, Mengerskirchen,
Germany **(10%)**
Tel.: (49) 6476310
Web Site: http://www.sedo-treepoint.com
Sales Range: $1-9.9 Million
Textile Manufacturing Equipment Mfr
N.A.I.C.S.: 333998
Maurizio Wermelinger (Gen Mgr)

ALPHA BULGARIA JSC
133 Vitosha Blvd, 1408, Sofia, Bulgaria
Tel.: (359) 888542757
Web Site: https://www.alpha-bulgaria.com
ALFB—(BUL)
Sales Range: Less than $1 Million
Investment Services
N.A.I.C.S.: 523999
Goran Svensson (Exec Dir)

ALPHA CO., LTD.
709-6 Kuwano, Naka-Ku, Okayama,
702-8002, Japan
Tel.: (81) 862774511
Web Site: https://www.popalpha.co.jp
Year Founded: 1984
4760—(TKS)
Rev.: $38,091,280
Assets: $26,584,280
Liabilities: $17,982,020
Net Worth: $8,602,260
Earnings: $827,260
Fiscal Year-end: 08/31/24
Biopharmaceutical Product Mfr
N.A.I.C.S.: 325412
Kaoru Asano (Chm)

ALPHA COGNITION INC.
439 Helmcken Street, Vancouver,
V6B 2E6, BC, Canada
Tel.: (604) 564-9244 BC
Web Site:
https://www.alphacognition.com
Year Founded: 2000
ACOGF—(OTCIQ)
Rev.: $6,804
Assets: $2,452,170
Liabilities: $7,164,774
Net Worth: ($4,712,604)
Earnings: ($13,772,567)
Emp.: 4
Fiscal Year-end: 12/31/23
Biotechnology Research & Development Services
N.A.I.C.S.: 541714
Denis Kay (Chief Scientific Officer)

ALPHA COPPER CORP.
595 Burrard Street, Vancouver, V7X
1L4, BC, Canada
Tel.: (647) 407-2515
Web Site: https://alphacopper.com
ALCU—(OTCIQ)
Assets: $1,011,792
Liabilities: $71,250
Net Worth: $940,542
Earnings: ($289,263)
Fiscal Year-end: 09/30/21
Mineral Exploration Services
N.A.I.C.S.: 213115

ALPHA CORPORATION
1-6-8 Fukuura, Kanazawa-ku, Yokohama, 236-0004, Kanagawa, Japan
Tel.: (81) 457878400
Web Site: https://www.kk-alpha.com
Year Founded: 1923
3434—(TKS)
Rev.: $492,735,840
Assets: $449,136,280
Liabilities: $216,299,030
Net Worth: $232,837,250
Earnings: $11,911,220
Emp.: 4,304
Fiscal Year-end: 03/31/24
Automobile Parts Mfr
N.A.I.C.S.: 332510
Nobuyuki Oi (Auditor)

Subsidiaries:

ALPHA (GUANGZHOU) AUTOMOTIVEPARTS CO., LTD. **(1)**
No 11 CheCheng Road, Huadu Auto City,
Guangzhou, 510800, China
Tel.: (86) 2086733318
Automobile Parts Distr
N.A.I.C.S.: 423120

ALPHA Corporation - Gumma Plant **(1)**
648 Kondo-cyo, Tatebayashi, Gunma, Japan
Tel.: (81) 276 73 2131
Automobile Parts Mfr
N.A.I.C.S.: 336390

ALPHA HOUSING HARDWARE (THAILAND) CO., LTD. **(1)**
111 Moo 10 Soi Wat Banchang Rojana
Road, Lamta-sao Wangnoi, Ayutthaya,
13170, Thailand
Tel.: (66) 35275121
Automobile Parts Distr
N.A.I.C.S.: 423120

ALPHA INDUSTRY (Thailand) CO., LTD. **(1)**
238 Moo 7 Thatoom, Amphur Srimahaphot,
Prachin Buri, 25140, Thailand
Tel.: (66) 37208726
Automobile Parts Distr
N.A.I.C.S.: 423120
Khun Suwit Thongrord (Sr Mgr)

ALPHA TECHNOLOGY CORPORATION **(1)**
1450 McPherson Park Dr Ste 200, Howell,
MI 48844-0168
Tel.: (517) 546-9700
Automobile Parts Mfr & Distr
N.A.I.C.S.: 336390

Alpha Industry Queretaro, S.A. de C.V. **(1)**
Circuito El Marques Sur 16, Fracc parque
Industrial El Marques, 76246, El Marques,
Queretaro, Mexico
Tel.: (52) 4422274600
Web Site: https://alpha-queretaro.com
Automobile Parts Distr
N.A.I.C.S.: 423120

Kyushu Alpha Co., Ltd. **(1)**
402 Osagi oaza, Yukuhashi, Fukuoka, 824-0058, Japan
Tel.: (81) 930235520
Automobile Parts Mfr
N.A.I.C.S.: 336390

ALPHA DHABI HOLDING PJSC
The Landmark Tower Al Markaziyah
West - Abu Dhabi Corniche, 65th
Floor, Abu Dhabi, United Arab Emirates
Tel.: (971) 97124940001
Web Site: https://alphadhabi.com
ALPHADHABI—(ABU)
Rev.: $12,367,071,045
Assets: $38,219,559,132
Liabilities: $17,530,336,846
Net Worth: $20,689,222,286
Earnings: $3,616,602,674
Emp.: 95,000
Fiscal Year-end: 12/31/23
Investment Holding Company
N.A.I.C.S.: 551112

Subsidiaries:

ANEWA Engineering Private Limited **(1)**
16th Floor Manjeera Trinity Corporate Jntu -
Hitech City Road, Hyderabad, 500072, Telangana, India
Tel.: (91) 4040326770
Web Site: https://anewa.in
Emp.: 1,200
Civil & Structural Engineering Services
N.A.I.C.S.: 541330

Abu Dhabi United Hospitality - Sole Proprietorship LLC **(1)**
Al Sadyat Island, Abu Dhabi, United Arab Emirates
Tel.: (971) 24455886
Restaurant Management & Catering Services
N.A.I.C.S.: 722511

Al Forsan Tadbeer Center LLC **(1)**
414 Sheikh Rashid Bin Saeed St - Al Hisn -
W4, Abu Dhabi, United Arab Emirates
Tel.: (971) 507846532
Web Site: https://alforsantadbeerauh.ae
Building Construction & Design Services
N.A.I.C.S.: 541310

Al Maha Modular Industries LLC **(1)**
PO Box 111059, Abu Dhabi, United Arab Emirates
Tel.: (971) 25097300
Web Site: https://almahamodular.ae
Structural Steel & Pipe Mfr
N.A.I.C.S.: 332312

Al Wathba A Luxury Collection Desert Resort & Spa - Sole Proprietorship LLC **(1)**
Al Wathba South, 56620, Abu Dhabi, United Arab Emirates
Tel.: (971) 22044444
Hotel & Resort Operator
N.A.I.C.S.: 721120

Barari Natural Resources LLC **(1)**
22nd Floor Nation Towers Corniche Road,
PO Box 59769, Abu Dhabi, United Arab Emirates
Tel.: (971) 26818980
Web Site: https://barari.ae
Park Management & Maintenance Services
N.A.I.C.S.: 561110

Dicon Investment LLC **(1)**
The Metropolis Tower, Business Bay, Dubai,
United Arab Emirates
Tel.: (971) 542895543
Web Site: https://diconinvestments.com
Investment Management Service
N.A.I.C.S.: 523940

Emirates Gateway Securities Services LLC **(1)**
Prestige Tower 17 - 19th Floor Beside Capital Mall, PO 111184, Mohamed Bin Zayed
City 79th St, Abu Dhabi, United Arab Emirates
Tel.: (971) 25588249
Web Site: https://wwww.egssuae.ae
Integrated Security Services
N.A.I.C.S.: 561621

Emirates Safety Laboratory LLC **(1)**
240 AlAwir Road Warsan 3 Mushraif, PO
Box 231908, Dubai, United Arab Emirates
Tel.: (971) 45201800
Web Site: https://emirateslaboratory.com
Building Construction & Design Services
N.A.I.C.S.: 541310

Etihad International Hospitality LLC - Sole Proprietorship LLC **(1)**
Office No CO 45 Emirates Palace Hotel
Corniche Road, 42013, Abu Dhabi, United Arab Emirates
Tel.: (971) 26711320
Web Site: https://etihadhospitality.ae
Hospitality & Facility Management Services
N.A.I.C.S.: 561210

Hi-Tech Concrete Products LLC **(1)**
PO Box 109200, Abu Dhabi, United Arab Emirates
Tel.: (971) 25509112
Web Site: https://hitechconcrete.ae
Building Construction & Design Services
N.A.I.C.S.: 541310

Le Noir Cafe - Sole Proprietorship LLC **(1)**
The St Regis Sadiyat, Abu Dhabi, United Arab Emirates
Tel.: (971) 24484859
Web Site: https://www.lenoircafe.com
Restaurant Management & Catering Services
N.A.I.C.S.: 722511

Mais Interior Design LLC **(1)**
Office 201 H Sheikh Omar Bin Zayed Al
Nahyan Tower, Al Zahiyah, Abu Dhabi,
United Arab Emirates
Tel.: (971) 26343669
Web Site: https://maisinterior.com
Emp.: 800
Building Interior Design Services
N.A.I.C.S.: 541410

Mawarid Holding Investment LLC **(1)**
22nd Floor Nation Towers Office Entrance
Corniche St, Abu Dhabi, United Arab Emirates
Tel.: (971) 23015555
Web Site: https://mawaridhi.com
Emp.: 11,000
Building Construction & Design Services
N.A.I.C.S.: 541310

Mawarid Hotels and hospitality LLC **(1)**
22nd Floor Nation Towers Corniche Road,
PO Box 113260, Abu Dhabi, United Arab Emirates
Tel.: (971) 23015555
Hotel & Tourist Resort Operator
N.A.I.C.S.: 721120

NPCC Engineering Limited **(1)**
3rd Floor Jolly Board Tower 1 I - Think
Techno Campus Nehru Nagar, Kanjurmarg
East, Mumbai, 400042, Maharashtra, India
Tel.: (91) 2240390505
Web Site: https://www.npcc.ae
Emp.: 1,000
Mechanical & Civil Engineering Services
N.A.I.C.S.: 541330

NT Energies LLC **(1)**
Guardian Tower - Sheikh Sultan Bin Zayed
First And Dhafeer Street, PO Box 7657,
Abu Dhabi, United Arab Emirates
Tel.: (971) 26116000
Construction Engineering Services
N.A.I.C.S.: 541330

National Petroleum Construction Co. (Saudi) Ltd. **(1)**
Novotel Business Park Tower 3 3th Floor
Khaldiya, PO Box 31705, Al Khobar, 31952,
Saudi Arabia
Tel.: (966) 138824999
Construction Engineering Services
N.A.I.C.S.: 541330

National Projects and Construction LLC **(1)**
PO Box 7865, Abu Dhabi, United Arab Emirates
Tel.: (971) 25097200
Web Site: https://npc.ae
Emp.: 6,000
Building & Infrastructure Construction Services
N.A.I.C.S.: 541310

Phoenix Timber Factory LLC **(1)**
PO Box 42779, Abu Dhabi, United Arab Emirates
Tel.: (971) 25513390
Web Site: https://phoenixtimber.ae
Wooden Furniture & Door Mfr
N.A.I.C.S.: 321911

Pure Health Holding LLC **(1)**
6th Floor Al Dar Headquarters Building Al
Raha Beach, Abu Dhabi, United Arab Emirates
Tel.: (971) 44473338
Web Site: https://purehealth.ae
Hospitals & Health Care Services
N.A.I.C.S.: 622110

Reem Emirates Aluminum LLC **(1)**
Sector No M-41 Plot No 7FR6 8FR6
ICAD-1, PO Box 36863, Mussafah, Abu
Dhabi, United Arab Emirates
Tel.: (971) 25994200
Web Site: https://reememirates.ae

Alpha Dhabi Holding PJSC—(Continued)

Aluminum & Glass Mfr
N.A.I.C.S.: 332321

Reem Ready Mix LLC **(1)**
Reem Island, PO Box 113718, Abu Dhabi,
United Arab Emirates
Tel.: (971) 24174600
Web Site: https://reemreadymix.com
Ready Mix Concrete & Cement Distr
N.A.I.C.S.: 424690

Sandstorm Motor Vehicles Manufacturing LLC **(1)**
Dubai Investment Park - 2, Dubai, United
Arab Emirates
Tel.: (971) 42612672
Web Site: https://www.sandstorm-auto.com
Automobile Equipment Mfr
N.A.I.C.S.: 336330

St. Regis Saadiyat Island Resort - Abu Dhabi **(1)**
Saadiyat Island, PO Box 54345, Abu Dhabi,
United Arab Emirates
Tel.: (971) 24988888
Hotel & Resort Operator
N.A.I.C.S.: 721120

Telal Resort LLC **(1)**
Remah Al Ain, PO Box 200800, Abu Dhabi,
United Arab Emirates
Tel.: (971) 87020000
Web Site: https://www.telalresort.ae
Hotel & Resort Operator
N.A.I.C.S.: 721120

Trojan Construction Group - Sole Proprietorship LLC **(1)**
PO Box 111059, Abu Dhabi, United Arab
Emirates
Tel.: (971) 25097300
Web Site: https://trojanconstruction.group
Emp.: 36,000
Building Construction & Design Services
N.A.I.C.S.: 541310

Trojan General Contracting LLC **(1)**
PO Box 111059, Abu Dhabi, United Arab
Emirates
Tel.: (971) 25097300
Web Site: https://trojan.ae
Emp.: 12,800
Real Estate & Construction Services
N.A.I.C.S.: 531390

Twasol Business Men Service LLC **(1)**
Muraqqabat Road Opposite To Coral Deira
Hotel, PO Box 88531, Dubai, United Arab
Emirates
Tel.: (971) 47044900
Web Site: https://twasol.ae
Hospitality & Facility Management Services
N.A.I.C.S.: 561210

ALPHA DIVISIONS PUBLIC COMPANY LIMITED
98 Athakravi Building 1 Floor 5 Soi
Aree Sukhumvit Road, Klong Tan
Sub-district Klong Toei District, Bangkok, 10110, Thailand
Tel.: (66) 20775853
Web Site: http://www.dussthai.com
ALPHAX—(THA)
Rev.: $6,183,151
Assets: $173,496,343
Liabilities: $12,938,465
Net Worth: $160,557,878
Earnings: ($3,110,988)
Fiscal Year-end: 12/31/23
Faucets, Water Supply Products &
Sanitary Wares Mfr & Importer
N.A.I.C.S.: 332913

ALPHA DX GROUP LIMITED
29 Tai Seng Avenue 07-07 Natural
Cool Lifestyle Hub, Singapore,
534119, Singapore
Tel.: (65) 65124255   **SG**
Year Founded: 2003
VVL—(CAT)
Rev.: $9,714,725
Assets: $21,841,001

Liabilities: $7,519,225
Net Worth: $14,321,776
Earnings: ($6,213,422)
Fiscal Year-end: 12/31/21
Investment Holding Company; Petroleum Exploration & Production
N.A.I.C.S.: 551112
Lim Kok Meng *(Sec)*

ALPHA EXPLORATION LIMITED
Level 6 Room 602 SA Building Warsay Street, 189, Asmara, Eritrea
Tel.: (291) 1111202   **VG**
Web Site: https://www.alpha-exploration.com
Year Founded: 2011
ALEX—(TSXV)
Rev.: $31,172
Assets: $15,914,846
Liabilities: $1,145,467
Net Worth: $14,769,379
Earnings: ($758,904)
Fiscal Year-end: 12/31/23
Support Activities for Nonmetallic
Minerals (except Fuels) Mining
N.A.I.C.S.: 213115
Denitsa Doncheva *(CFO)*

Subsidiaries:

Alpha Exploration Eritrea Limited **(1)**
Level 6 Room 602 SA Building Warsay
Street, PO Box 1114, 189, Asmara, Eritrea
Tel.: (291) 1111202
Gold Mining Services
N.A.I.C.S.: 213114

ALPHA GRAPHIC INDIA LTD.
B-7/403 Natraj Township Part-II Parsuram Nagar Society Road, Sayajigund, Vadodara, 390005, Gujarat,
India
Tel.: (91) 2652971681
Industrial Machinery Equipment Distr
N.A.I.C.S.: 423840
Alkaben A. Jadhav *(Mng Dir)*

ALPHA GRISSIN S.A.
Attica 16km Lavriou Av, 190 02, Peania, Greece
Tel.: (30) 2126875400
AGRI—(ATH)
Sales Range: $25-49.9 Million
Emp.: 93
Holding Company; Technonology,
Real Estate, Energy
N.A.I.C.S.: 551112
Dimitrios Parthenis *(Vice Chm, Mng
Dir & Head-Economic Svcs)*

ALPHA GROUP CO., LTD.
10/F Poly Center No 5 Lin Jiang
Road, Zhujiang New Town,
Guangzhou, 510623, China
Tel.: (86) 20 38983278
Web Site: http://www.gdalpha.com
Emp.: 4,392
Toy & Animation Game Mfr
N.A.I.C.S.: 339930
Cai Dongqing *(Chm)*

Subsidiaries:

Alpha Animation & Culture Co., Ltd. -
Chenghai Factory **(1)**
Auldey Industrial Area Wenguan Rd,
Chenghai, Guangzhou, China
Tel.: (86) 754 8586 2278
Toy & Animation Game Mfr
N.A.I.C.S.: 339930

Baby Trend, Inc. **(1)**
1607 S Campus Ave, Ontario, CA 91761
Tel.: (800) 328-7363
Web Site: http://www.babytrend.com
Baby Furniture, Strollers, Car Seats &
Walkers Whslr
N.A.I.C.S.: 423210
Brad Mattarocci *(Gen Mgr)*

ALPHA GROUP INC.
14F Tokyo Tatemono Higashi Shibuya
Building 26-20 Higashi 1-chome,
Shibuya-Ku, Tokyo, 150-0011, Japan
Tel.: (81) 354697300
Web Site: https://www.alpha-grp.co.jp
Year Founded: 1997
3322—(TKS)
Rev.: $91,958,320
Assets: $64,024,460
Liabilities: $31,688,340
Net Worth: $32,336,120
Earnings: $2,650,610
Emp.: 258
Fiscal Year-end: 03/31/24
Office Equipment Distr
N.A.I.C.S.: 423420
Yoshioka Shinichiro *(Founder, Chm,
Pres & CEO)*

ALPHA GROUP INTERNATIONAL PLC
Brunel Building 2 Canalside Walk,
London, W2 1DG, United Kingdom
Tel.: (44) 2038000120   **UK**
Web Site:
   https://www.alphagroup.com
Year Founded: 2009
ALPH—(AIM)
Rev.: $122,108,678
Assets: $366,571,909
Liabilities: $187,190,174
Net Worth: $179,381,735
Earnings: $48,492,290
Emp.: 400
Fiscal Year-end: 12/31/22
Foreign Currency Exchange Services
N.A.I.C.S.: 523160
Morgan Tillbrook *(CEO)*

Subsidiaries:

Alpha FX Europe Limited **(1)**
171 Old Bakery St, Valletta, Malta
Tel.: (356) 2038549265
Foreign Exchange Risk Management Services
N.A.I.C.S.: 522390

ALPHA GROWTH PLC
35 Berkeley Square, Mayfair, London,
W1J 5BF, United Kingdom
Tel.: (44) 2039598600   **UK**
Web Site: https://www.algwplc.com
ALGW—(LSE)
Rev.: $4,760,997
Assets: $584,653,865
Liabilities: $576,185,757
Net Worth: $8,468,108
Earnings: $4,012,343
Emp.: 3
Fiscal Year-end: 12/31/22
Financial Consulting Services
N.A.I.C.S.: 541611
Gobind Sahney *(Chm & CEO)*

Subsidiaries:

Alpha Growth Management Inc. **(1)**
500 Newport Ctr Dr Ste 680, Newport
Beach, CA 92660
Tel.: (949) 326-9796
Investment Management Service
N.A.I.C.S.: 541611

Providence Life Assurance Company
Ltd. **(1)**
Rosebank Centre 5th Floor 11 Bermudiana
Road, Pembroke, HM 08, Bermuda
Tel.: (441) 2925535
Web Site:
   https://www.providencelifeassurance.com
Financial Services
N.A.I.C.S.: 524113

ALPHA HOLDINGS, INC.
2F 3F 4F 225-12 Pangyoyeok-ro,
Bundang-gu, Seongnam, Gyeonggi-do, Korea (South)
Tel.: (82) 316080800

Web Site: https://alpha-holdings.co.kr
Year Founded: 2002
117670—(KRS)
Rev.: $69,053,967
Assets: $77,055,210
Liabilities: $28,572,701
Net Worth: $48,482,508
Earnings: ($30,687,250)
Emp.: 128
Fiscal Year-end: 12/31/22
Semiconductor Chip Mfr
N.A.I.C.S.: 334413
Jin Kyu Choi *(CEO)*

ALPHA HPA LIMITED
Level 2 66 Hunter Street, Sydney,
2000, NSW, Australia
Tel.: (61) 293003310   **AU**
Web Site: https://alphahpa.com.au
A4N—(ASX)
Rev.: $4,366,637
Assets: $178,483,560
Liabilities: $13,436,162
Net Worth: $165,047,398
Earnings: ($16,680,716)
Fiscal Year-end: 06/30/24
Mineral Exploration Services
N.A.I.C.S.: 213115
Norman Alfred Seckold *(Chm)*

ALPHA INSURANCE LIMITED
Level 1 Kina Haus Douglas Street,
Port Moresby, Papua New Guinea
Tel.: (675) 321 2611
Web Site:
   http://www.alphainsurancepng.com
Emp.: 100
Insurance Services
N.A.I.C.S.: 524210
Bruce Avenell *(Mng Dir)*

Subsidiaries:

TOWER Insurance (PNG)
Limited **(1)**
Level 2 Harbourside West Stanley Esplanade, PO Box 136, Port Moresby, 136,
Papua New Guinea
Tel.: (675) 3211388
Web Site:
   http://www.towerinsurance.com.pg
Sales Range: $50-74.9 Million
General Insurance Services
N.A.I.C.S.: 524114
Stefan Hansen *(Gen Mgr)*

ALPHA MICROELECTRONICS CORP.
9/F1 295 Kuang Fu Road Section 2,
Hsinchu, Taiwan
Tel.: (886) 35736660
Web Site: https://www.ealpha.com.tw
Year Founded: 1992
8024—(TPE)
Rev.: $13,957,978
Assets: $25,522,528
Liabilities: $3,132,258
Net Worth: $22,390,270
Earnings: $3,100,585
Fiscal Year-end: 12/31/22
Semiconductor & Related Device Mfr
N.A.I.C.S.: 334413

ALPHA NETWORKS INC.
No 8 Li-Hsin 7th Rd Hsinchu Science
Park, Hsinchu, 300094, Taiwan
Tel.: (886) 35636666
Web Site:
   https://www.alphanetworks.com
Year Founded: 2003
3380—(TAI)
Rev.: $924,562,279
Assets: $778,274,048
Liabilities: $342,351,405
Net Worth: $435,922,643
Earnings: $20,925,046
Emp.: 1,619
Fiscal Year-end: 12/31/23
Network & Digital Products Mfr

N.A.I.C.S.: 334210
Peter Chen *(Vice Chm)*

Subsidiaries:

Aespula Technology Inc. **(1)**
4th Floor-2 No 76 Section 2 Jiafeng South
Road, Hsinchu County, Zhubei, Taiwan
Tel.: (886) 36576031
Web Site: https://www.aespula.com
Software Development Services
N.A.I.C.S.: 541511

Alpha Networks (Changshu) Co.,
Ltd. **(1)**
No 6 Yintong Road, National New And Hi-
Tech Industrial Development Zone, Chang-
shu, Jiangsu, China
Tel.: (86) 51252156789
Telecommunications Equipment Mfr
N.A.I.C.S.: 334290

Alpha Networks (Chengdu) Co.,
Ltd. **(1)**
Building D15 No 168 Guangfu Road Cheng-
fei Highway, Industrial Centralization Devel-
opment Zone QingYang Dist, Chengdu,
China
Tel.: (86) 2887323668
Telecommunications Equipment Mfr
N.A.I.C.S.: 334290

Alpha Networks (Dongguan) Co.,
Ltd. **(1)**
Xingang Road, Xin'an Area ChangAn,
Dongguan, Guangdong, China
Tel.: (86) 76985318000
Telecommunications Equipment Mfr
N.A.I.C.S.: 334290

Alpha Networks Inc. **(1)**
1551 McCarthy Blvd Ste 201, Milpitas, CA
95035
Tel.: (408) 844-8850
Web Site: http://www.alphanetworks.com
Sales Range: $25-49.9 Million
Emp.: 20
Networking Components Distr
N.A.I.C.S.: 423690
Hender Hsing *(Pres)*

Alpha Networks Vietnam Company
Limited **(1)**
Lot CN03 Dong Van 4 Industrial Park, Dai
Cuong Commune Kim Bang District, Ha
Nam, Vietnam
Tel.: (84) 2263967700
Telecommunications Equipment Mfr
N.A.I.C.S.: 334290

Alpha Solutions Co., Ltd. **(1)**
10F 8-8-15 Nishigotanda, Shinagawa-ku,
Tokyo, 141-0031, Japan
Tel.: (81) 354349678
Sales Range: $25-49.9 Million
Emp.: 4
Computer Peripheral Equipments Mfr &
Distr
N.A.I.C.S.: 334210

Alpha Technical Services Inc. **(1)**
7 Cushing, Irvine, CA 92618
Tel.: (949) 486-5500
Telecommunications Equipment Mfr
N.A.I.C.S.: 334290

Alpha Technical and Services
Inc. **(1)**
7 Cushing, Irvine, CA 92618
Tel.: (949) 486-5500
Web Site: http://www.alphanetworks.com
Sales Range: $25-49.9 Million
Emp.: 25
Networking Components Distr
N.A.I.C.S.: 423690

Dongguan Youxun Electronics Co.,
Ltd. **(1)**
Xin'an Area, Chang An, Dongguan, 523000,
Guangdong, China
Tel.: (86) 76985318000
Web Site: http://www.alphanetworks.com
Networking Components Mfr
N.A.I.C.S.: 334210

Mirac Networks (Dongguan) Co.,
Ltd. **(1)**
Xingang Road, Xin'an Area Chang An,
Dongguan, Guandong, China
Tel.: (86) 76986072000

Web Site: http://www.alphanetworks.com
Networking Components Mfr
N.A.I.C.S.: 334111

ALPHA PEAK LEISURE INC.
160-170 6751 Graybar Road, Rich-
mond, V6W 1H3, BC, Canada
Tel.: (604) 488-8253   BC
Year Founded: 2011
Rev.: $369,640
Assets: $4,399,090
Liabilities: $2,901,874
Net Worth: $1,497,215
Earnings: ($2,550,579)
Fiscal Year-end: 12/31/18
Investment Services
N.A.I.C.S.: 523999
Zachary Goldenberg *(CEO)*

ALPHA PRO TECH, LTD.
60 Centurian Drive Suite 112,
Markham, L3R 9R2, ON, Canada
Tel.: (905) 479-0654   DE
Web Site:
     https://www.alphaprotech.com
Year Founded: 1989
APT—(NYSEAMEX)
Rev.: $61,981,000
Assets: $64,803,000
Liabilities: $4,045,000
Net Worth: $60,758,000
Earnings: $3,282,000
Emp.: 122
Fiscal Year-end: 12/31/22
Protective Apparel Mfr for Cleanroom,
Industrial, Medical & Dental & Phar-
maceutical Industries
N.A.I.C.S.: 423450
Lloyd Hoffman *(Pres & CEO)*

Subsidiaries:

Alpha Pro Tech-Nogales **(1)**
1287 W Fairway Dr, Nogales, AZ 85621-
3889
Tel.: (520) 281-0127
Web Site: http://www.alphaprotech.com
Rev.: $21,130,000
Emp.: 450
Surgical Appliances & Supplies
N.A.I.C.S.: 339113

Alpha ProTech Engineered Products,
Inc. **(1)**
301 S Blanchard St, Valdosta, GA 31601
Tel.: (229) 242-1931
Medical Equipment Mfr
N.A.I.C.S.: 339114
Lloyd Hoffman *(CEO)*

ALPHA REAL TRUST LIMITED
Floor 2 Trafalgar Court, PO Box 286,
Les Banques, Saint Peter Port, GY1
4LY, Guernsey
Tel.: (44) 1481742742   GY
Web Site:
     https://www.alpharealtrustltd.com
ARTL—(LSE)
Rev.: $9,296,895
Assets: $167,501,894
Liabilities: $12,104,267
Net Worth: $155,397,627
Earnings: ($1,172,684)
Fiscal Year-end: 03/31/24
Real Estate Investment Services
N.A.I.C.S.: 531210
David Jeffreys *(Chm)*

ALPHA RHEINTAL BANK AG
Bahnhofstrasse 2, Postfach, CH-
9435, Heerbrugg, Switzerland
Tel.: (41) 717479595
Web Site:
     http://www.alpharheintalbank.ch
Banking Services
N.A.I.C.S.: 523150
Reto Monsch *(CEO)*

Subsidiaries:

Bankhaus Jungholz AG **(1)**

Poststrasse 6, 9000, Saint Gallen, Switzer-
land
Tel.: (41) 712284100
Web Site: http://www.bankhaus-jungholz.ch
Private Banking Services
N.A.I.C.S.: 523150
Thomas Krammer *(Member-Mgmt Bd)*

**ALPHA SERVICES AND HOLD-
INGS S.A.**
40 Stadiou Street, 102 52, Athens,
Greece
Tel.: (30) 2103260000   GR
Web Site: http://www.alpha.gr
ALPHA—(LUX)
Rev.: $1,782,268,509
Assets: $78,452,541,550
Liabilities: $70,586,478,524
Net Worth: $7,866,063,026
Earnings: $707,250,162
Emp.: 8,137
Fiscal Year-end: 12/31/23
Banking Services
N.A.I.C.S.: 522110
Spyros N. Filaretos *(Gen Mgr-Growth
& Innovation)*

Subsidiaries:

ABC Factors A.E. **(1)**
48 Michalakopoulou Street, 11528, Athens,
Greece
Tel.: (30) 2107266800
Web Site: https://www.abcfactors.gr
Financial Management Services
N.A.I.C.S.: 523999
Maria M. Raikou *(Mng Dir & Gen Mgr)*

APE Commercial Property A.E, **(1)**
Panepistimiou 43, 10564, Athens, Greece
Tel.: (30) 2103436700
Banking Services
N.A.I.C.S.: 522110

Alpha Asset Management
A.E.D.A.K. **(1)**
45 Panepistimiou, 10564, Athens, Greece
Tel.: (30) 2103266505
Web Site: https://www.alphamutual.gr
Mutual Fund Management Services
N.A.I.C.S.: 525910
Spiros A. Andronikakis *(Vice Chm)*

Alpha Astika Akinita S.A. **(1)**
24 Stadiou str, 10564, Athens,
Greece   **(93.14%)**
Tel.: (30) 2103263929
Web Site:
     https://www.alpharealestateservices.gr
Emp.: 63
Real Estate Development Services
N.A.I.C.S.: 531390
Themistokles I. Corcontzelos *(Chm)*

Alpha Bank Cyprus Limited **(1)**
Alpha Bank Building 3 Lemesou Ave 4th
floor, Aglantzia, 2112, Nicosia,
Cyprus   **(100%)**
Tel.: (357) 22877477
Web Site: https://www.alphabank.com.cy
Rev.: $87,179,981
Assets: $2,912,266,481
Liabilities: $2,557,791,596
Net Worth: $354,474,885
Earnings: $11,804,444
Emp.: 683
Fiscal Year-end: 12/31/2019
Commercial Banking Services
N.A.I.C.S.: 522110
Andreas M. Michaelides *(Chm)*

Alpha Bank London Ltd **(1)**
Capital House 85 King William Street, Lon-
don, EC4N 7BL, United Kingdom
Tel.: (44) 2073326767
Web Site: https://alphabanklondon.co.uk
Commercial Banking Services
N.A.I.C.S.: 522110
Mark Austen *(Chm)*

Alpha Finance A.E.P.E.Y **(1)**
5 Merlin Street, Athens, 106 71, Greece
Tel.: (30) 210 367 7500
Financial Investment Services
N.A.I.C.S.: 523999
Paris Vasiliadis *(Mng Dir & VP)*

Alpha Finance Romania S.A. **(1)**

Calea Dorobantilor no 237B 2nd floor, Dis-
trict 1, 010566, Bucharest, Romania
Tel.: (40) 214557205
Web Site: https://www.alphafinance.ro
Sales Range: $1-9.9 Million
Emp.: 10
Investment & Banking Services
N.A.I.C.S.: 523999

Alpha Group Jersey Ltd **(1)**
5 Wests Centre, Saint Helier, Jersey
Tel.: (44) 1534733113
Financial Banking Services
N.A.I.C.S.: 522110

Alpha Insurance Ltd **(1)**
Kennedy Avenue Stasinou Street, 1640,
Nicosia, Cyprus
Tel.: (357) 22379999
Web Site: https://www.altiusinsurance.net
General Insurance Services
N.A.I.C.S.: 524210

Alpha Leasing A.E. **(1)**
103 Athens Ave, 10447, Athens, Greece
Tel.: (30) 2103367900
Web Site: https://www.alphaleasing.gr
Leasing Services
N.A.I.C.S.: 523910
Tilemachos D. Georgakis *(Chm)*

Alpha Leasing Romania IFN S.A. **(1)**
Piata Gheorghe Cantacuzino nr 6 sector 2,
Bucharest, 020026, Romania
Tel.: (40) 21455590001
Web Site: https://www.alphaleasing.ro
Leasing & Financial Services
N.A.I.C.S.: 523999

Alpha Real Estate Management &
Investments S.A. **(1)**
Tel.: (30) 2103263980
Financial Investment Services
N.A.I.C.S.: 523999
Lazaros A. Papagaryfallou *(Chm)*

Alpha Real Estate Services LLC **(1)**
3 Limassol Avenu, CY-2112, Nicosia, Cy-
prus
Tel.: (357) 22888874
Web Site:
     https://www.aresproperties.com.cy
Property Management Services
N.A.I.C.S.: 531311
Georgios Pimenides *(CEO)*

Alpha Ventures A.E. **(1)**
1 Korai Street, 10252, Athens, Greece
Tel.: (30) 2103262700
Private Equity Fund Management Services
N.A.I.C.S.: 523940
Christos N. Karampelas *(Mng Dir)*

Alphalife A.A.E.Z. **(1)**
Pesmazoglou 12-14, 10564, Athens,
Greece
Tel.: (30) 2103266904
Web Site: https://www.alphalife.gr
Underwriting Insurance Services
N.A.I.C.S.: 524128

Asmita Gardens Srl **(1)**
Str Gladitei no 42 block T6 Floor 20 apt
2003 sector 4, Bucharest, Romania
Tel.: (40) 217808301
Web Site: http://www.asmitagardens.ro
Apartment Rental Services
N.A.I.C.S.: 531390

Ionian Hotel Enterprises S.A. **(1)**
Vas Sófias 46, 11528, Athens, Greece
Tel.: (30) 210 7281770
Web Site: http://www.ionianhe.gr
Home Management Services
N.A.I.C.S.: 721110
Achilles Konstantakopoulos *(Chm)*

SKY Cac Limited **(1)**
1 Megalou Alexandrou, Latsia, 2235, Nico-
sia, Cyprus
Tel.: (357) 22696765
Web Site: https://www.skycac.com
N.A.I.C.S.: 522299

ALPHA SYSTEMS INC.

Alpha Systems Inc.—(Continued)

6-6-1 Kami-kodanaka, Nakahara-ku, Kawasaki, 211-0053, Japan
Tel.: (81) 334865111
Web Site: https://www.alpha.co.jp
Year Founded: 1972
4719—(TKS)
Sales Range: $300-349.9 Million
Emp.: 2,826
Communications Equipment & Systems Mfr
N.A.I.C.S.: 334290
Ken-ichi Kuroda *(Pres)*

ALPHA TAU MEDICAL LTD.
Kiryat Hamada 5, Jerusalem, 9777605, Israel
Tel.: (972) 35774115   Il
Web Site: https://www.alphatau.com
Year Founded: 2015
DRTS—(NASDAQ)
Assets: $120,149,000
Liabilities: $14,492,000
Net Worth: $105,657,000
Earnings: ($33,762,000)
Emp.: 100
Fiscal Year-end: 12/31/22
Medical Device Mfr
N.A.I.C.S.: 339112
Amnon Gat *(COO)*

ALPHA TECHNOLOGY GROUP LIMITED
Unit B 12 F 52 Hung To Road Kwun Tong, Kowloon, China (Hong Kong)
Tel.: (852) 65428077   VG
Web Site:
   https://alphatechnologys.com
Year Founded: 2022
ATGL—(NASDAQ)
Emp.: 18
Information Technology Services
N.A.I.C.S.: 541512
Anthony Chun Ho Tsang *(Exec Officer)*

ALPHA TRUST
1 Aristeidou St, 145 61, Kifissia, Greece
Tel.: (30) 2106289100
Web Site: https://www.andromeda.eu
ANDRO—(ATH)
Assets: $26,214,576
Liabilities: $260,378
Net Worth: $25,954,198
Earnings: ($1,218,230)
Emp.: 2
Fiscal Year-end: 12/31/22
Asset Management Services
N.A.I.C.S.: 523940
Phaedon-Theodore Tamvakakis *(Vice Chm)*

ALPHA UNIVERSAL MANAGEMENT PLC
30 Percy Street, London, W1T 2DB, United Kingdom
Tel.: (44) 207 467 1700
Web Site: http://www.aumplc.com
Year Founded: 2006
Investment Management Service
N.A.I.C.S.: 523999
Gobind Sahney *(Chm & Mng Dir)*

ALPHA WASTEWATER, INC.
Suite 1500 - 701 West Georgia Street, Vancouver, V7Y 1C6, BC, Canada
Tel.: (604) 601-8503   NV
Web Site:
   https://www.alphawastewater.com
Year Founded: 1997
AWWI—(OTCIQ)
Wastewater Treatment
N.A.I.C.S.: 562219
Charles James Mayer *(Chm)*

ALPHACOM HOLDINGS, INC.
14th floor Connaught Harbour Front House 35 Connaught Road West, Sheung Wan, China (Hong Kong)
Tel.: (852) 2811 8186   NV
Year Founded: 2013
Technology Development & Acquisition
N.A.I.C.S.: 513210
Astrid Lorena Buitrago Millan *(Pres, CEO, CFO, Treas & Sec)*

ALPHAGEN INTELLIGENCE CORP.
1930-1177 West Hastings Street, Vancouver, V6E 4T5, BC, Canada
Tel.: (604) 398-3379   BC
Web Site: https://www.alphagen.co
Year Founded: 2019
APETF—(OTCIQ)
Rev.: $156,462
Assets: $2,897,512
Liabilities: $957,509
Net Worth: $1,940,003
Earnings: ($6,589,637)
Fiscal Year-end: 06/30/22
Software Development Services
N.A.I.C.S.: 541511
Brian Wilneff *(CEO)*

ALPHAGEO INDIA LTD
Plot No 1Sagar Society Road No 2 Banjara Hills, Hyderabad, 500034, Andhra Pradesh, India
Tel.: (91) 4023550502
Web Site:
   https://www.alphageoindia.com
ALPHAGEO—(NSE)
Rev.: $21,862,932
Assets: $42,326,220
Liabilities: $5,239,703
Net Worth: $37,086,518
Earnings: $1,663,744
Emp.: 152
Fiscal Year-end: 03/31/22
Seismic Survey Services
N.A.I.C.S.: 541360
Dinesh Alla *(Chm & Co-Mng Dir)*

ALPHAKAT GMBH
Schulstrasse 8, 96155, Buttenheim, Germany
Tel.: (49) 9545208
Web Site: http://www.alphakat.de
Sales Range: $25-49.9 Million
Emp.: 5
Synthetic Energy Products Mfr
N.A.I.C.S.: 325212
Christian Koch *(CEO)*

ALPHALOGIC INDUSTRIES LIMITED
207 2nd Floor Kohinoor B-Zone Besides Vijay Sales, Old Mumbai-Pune Highway Chinchwad, Pune, 411019, India
Tel.: (91) 8297740000
Web Site:
   https://www.alphalogicindustry.com
Year Founded: 2020
543937—(BOM)
Storage Facility Services
N.A.I.C.S.: 493190
Anshu Goel *(Mng Dir)*

ALPHALOGIC TECHSYS LTD.
405 Pride Icon Kharadi Bypass Road, Pune, 411014, Maharashtra, India
Tel.: (91) 7276701155
Web Site:
   https://www.alphalogicinc.com
Year Founded: 2008
542770—(BOM)
Rev.: $1,930,247
Assets: $3,384,149
Liabilities: $819,205

Net Worth: $2,564,944
Earnings: $282,596
Emp.: 20
Fiscal Year-end: 03/31/22
Software Development Services
N.A.I.C.S.: 541511
Anshu Goel *(Mng Dir)*

ALPHAMIN RESOURCES CORP.
Suite 1 Perrieri Office Suites C2302 Level 3, Office Block C La Croisette, 30517, Grand Baie, Mauritius
Tel.: (230) 2694166   Ca
Web Site:
   https://www.alphaminresources.com
Year Founded: 1981
AFMJF—(OTCIQ)
Rev.: $288,504,726
Assets: $516,760,050
Liabilities: $151,248,065
Net Worth: $365,511,985
Earnings: $57,964,155
Fiscal Year-end: 12/31/23
Support Activities for Metal Mining
N.A.I.C.S.: 213114
Eoin O'Driscoll *(CFO)*

ALPHANAM JOINT STOCK COMPANY
33A Ba Trieu Street, Hoan Kiem District, Hanoi, Vietnam
Tel.: (84) 439367979
Web Site:
   http://www.alphanam.com.vn
Sales Range: $50-74.9 Million
Emp.: 1,300
Heavy Electrical & Mechanical Specialized Equipment Mfr
N.A.I.C.S.: 335999
Tuan Hai Nguyen *(Chm-Mgmt Bd & Gen Dir)*

Subsidiaries:

Alphanam E&C Joint Stock Company   (1)
No 47 Vu Trong Phung Street, Thanh Xuan District, Hanoi, Vietnam
Tel.: (84) 435587979
Web Site: http://www.alphanam.com.vn
Rev.: $71,388,115
Assets: $116,130,781
Liabilities: $102,328,839
Net Worth: $13,801,943
Earnings: $836,335
Emp.: 120
Fiscal Year-end: 12/31/2021
Power Transmission Lines & Electrical Systems Mfr
N.A.I.C.S.: 237130

ALPHANCO VENTURE CORP.
2110 28th Street, West Vancouver, V7V 4M3, BC, Canada
Tel.: (604) 925-0551
AVC.P—(TSXV)
Rev.: $2,632
Assets: $311,177
Liabilities: $2,323
Net Worth: $308,854
Earnings: ($8,078)
Fiscal Year-end: 07/31/20
Business Consulting Services
N.A.I.C.S.: 522299
Joanne Yan *(CEO & CFO)*

ALPHAPHARM PTY LTD
Level 1 13 The Bond 30-34 Hickson Road Bistro Nearest Point, Sydney, 2000, NSW, Australia
Tel.: (61) 292983999
Web Site:
   http://www.alphapharm.com.au
Sales Range: $400-449.9 Million
Emp.: 700
Medicines Research, Developing & Mfr
N.A.I.C.S.: 325412

Heather Bresch *(CEO)*

ALPHAPOLIS CO., LTD.
19th floor Yebisu Garden Place Tower 4-20-3 Ebisu, Shibuya-ku, Tokyo, 150-6019, Japan
Tel.: (81) 362771602
Web Site:
   https://www.alphapolis.co.jp
Year Founded: 2000
9467—(TKS)
Sales Range: $10-24.9 Million
Emp.: 54
Novels & Comics Internet Publisher
N.A.I.C.S.: 513130
Yusuke Kajimoto *(Pres & Dir)*

ALPHAWAVE IP GROUP PLC
85 Gresham Street, London, EC2V 7NQ, United Kingdom
Tel.: (44) 2077175877   UK
Web Site: https://awavesemi.com
Year Founded: 2017
AWE—(LSE)
Emp.: 100
Semiconductor & Related Device Manufacturing
N.A.I.C.S.: 334413
Rahul Mathur *(CFO)*

ALPHAWEST SERVICES PTY LTD
1 Lyonpark Road, Macquarie Park, 1670, NSW, Australia
Tel.: (61) 292635888
Web Site:
   http://www.alphawest.com.au
Sales Range: $75-99.9 Million
Emp.: 800
Technology, Software, Business Processes & Services
N.A.I.C.S.: 513210
Rob Parcell *(CEO)*

ALPHAX FOOD SYSTEM CO., LTD.
128 Chizaki, Sanyo-Onoda, 756-0039, Yamaguchi, Japan
Tel.: (81) 836395151
Web Site: https://www.afs.co.jp
Year Founded: 1993
3814—(TKS)
Sales Range: Less than $1 Million
Application Provider Services
N.A.I.C.S.: 541511
Takamori Tamura *(Chm, Pres, CEO & Dir-Rep)*

ALPHINAT INC.
2000 Peel Suite 680, Montreal, H3A 2W5, QC, Canada
Tel.: (514) 398-9799
Web Site: https://www.alphinat.com
Year Founded: 2004
APHTF—(OTCEM)
Rev.: $1,104,249
Assets: $452,442
Liabilities: $892,099
Net Worth: ($439,657)
Earnings: $119,805
Fiscal Year-end: 08/31/23
Software Development Services
N.A.I.C.S.: 541511

ALPHONSE CHARPIOT ET COMPAGNIE
18 bis Avenue du General de Gaulle, BP 29, 90100, Delle, France
Tel.: (33) 384367878
Web Site: http://www.charpiot.com
Year Founded: 1920
Rev.: $21,500,000
Emp.: 181
Freight Transportation Arrangement
N.A.I.C.S.: 488510
Monique Schepard *(Mgr-Pur)*

ALPICO HOLDINGS CO., LTD.
2-1-1 Igawajo, Matsumoto, 390-8518,
Nagano, Japan
Tel.: (81) 263 26 7000   JP
Web Site: http://www.alpico.co.jp
Year Founded: 2008
Holding Company; Transportation,
Tourism & Hospitality Services
N.A.I.C.S.: 551112
Yoshio Horigome *(Pres)*

Subsidiaries:

ALPICO Kotsu Co., Ltd.   (1)
2-1-1 Igawajo, Matsumoto, 390-8518, Na-
gano, Japan
Tel.: (81) 263 26 7000
Web Site: http://www.alpico.co.jp
Emp.: 1,150
Mixed Mode & Bus Transit Services
N.A.I.C.S.: 485111
Ryuji Furuta *(Pres)*

ALPICO Taxi Co., Ltd.   (1)
1-25 Minami 1-chome, Matsumoto, 390-
0832, Nagano, Japan
Tel.: (81) 263 87 0555
Web Site: http://www.alpico.co.jp
Emp.: 530
Taxi Service
N.A.I.C.S.: 485310
Hiroaki Kobayashi *(Pres)*

Matsuya Co., Ltd.   (1)
3-6-1 Ginza, Chuo-ku, Tokyo, 104 8130,
Japan
Tel.: (81) 335671211
Web Site: https://www.matsuya.com
Rev.: $292,469,590
Assets: $488,316,660
Liabilities: $298,191,220
Net Worth: $190,125,440
Earnings: $18,653,790
Emp.: 552
Fiscal Year-end: 02/29/2024
Department Store Operator & Mail Order
Services
N.A.I.C.S.: 455110
Yasunori Obinata *(Exec Operating Officer &
VP-Admin Div & Corp Plng Dept)*

Subsidiary (Domestic):

A Table Matsuya Co., Ltd.   (2)
No 2 No 1 Akashi-cho, Chuo-ku, Tokyo,
104-0044, Japan
Tel.: (81) 335457850
Web Site: http://www.atable-matsuya.com
Event Dining Hall Management & Catering
Services
N.A.I.C.S.: 722310
Mitsuru Takakura *(Pres)*

Unit (Domestic):

Matsuya Co., Ltd. - Asakusa   (2)
1-4-1 Hanakawado, Taito-ku, Tokyo, 111
0033, Japan
Tel.: (81) 338421111
Web Site: http://www.matsuya.com
Department Stores
N.A.I.C.S.: 455110

Matsuya Co., Ltd. - Ginza   (2)
3-6-1 Ginza, Chuo-ku, Tokyo, 104-8130,
Japan
Tel.: (81) 335671211
Web Site: http://www.matsuya.com
Department Stores
N.A.I.C.S.: 455110

**ALPINA CAPITAL PARTNERS
LLP**
Niddry Lodge 51 Holland Street, Lon-
don, W8 7JB, United Kingdom
Tel.: (44) 2037619680
Web Site:
   http://www.alpinapartners.com
Rev.: $300,000,000
Privater Equity Firm
N.A.I.C.S.: 523940
Florian Strehle *(Partner)*

Subsidiaries:

Virtalis Inc.   (1)
1952 Woodman Ctr Dr, Dayton, OH 45420-
1165

Tel.: (937) 534-9600
Web Site: http://www.virtalis.com
Software Publisher
N.A.I.C.S.: 513210
Guenter Dahm *(CEO)*

**ALPINA PRODUCTOS ALI-
MENTICIOS S.A.**
Km 3 Via Briceno Sopo Administra-
tive Building Alpina, Cundinamarca,
Colombia
Tel.: (57) 4238600   Co
Web Site: http://www.alpina.com
Sales Range: $700-749.9 Million
Emp.: 6,200
Dairy, Food & Beverage Mfr & Distr
N.A.I.C.S.: 311514
Carlos A. Mejia Bonilla *(CFO & VP-
Bus Dev)*

Subsidiaries:

Alpina Foods, Inc.   (1)
5011 AG Park Dr W, Batavia, NY 14020
Tel.: (585) 343-2805
Web Site: http://www.alpinaus.com
Emp.: 50
Yogurt Mfr
N.A.I.C.S.: 311514
David Corbelli *(Reg Mgr-Sls)*

ALPINA, D.D.
Strojarska Ulica 2, 4226, Ziri, Slove-
nia
Tel.: (386) 45158000
Web Site: http://www.alpina.si
Year Founded: 1947
Sales Range: $75-99.9 Million
Emp.: 500
Sales & Footwear Mfr & Distr
N.A.I.C.S.: 316210

Subsidiaries:

ALPINA BH, d.o.o.   (1)
Zmaja od Bosne 7-7A, Sarajevo, 71000,
Bosnia & Herzegovina
Tel.: (387) 33 590 462
Sales Range: $25-49.9 Million
Emp.: 41
Sporting Goods & Supplies Mfr
N.A.I.C.S.: 339920

ALPINA BROMY, d.o.o.   (1)
Vukovo bb, 74260, Tesanj, Bosnia & Herze-
govina
Tel.: (387) 32 667 270
Sporting Goods & Supplies Mfr
N.A.I.C.S.: 339920

ALPINA CRO, d.o.o.   (1)
Radnicka Cesta 80, Zagreb, Croatia
Tel.: (385) 13665761
Sporting Goods & Supplies Mfr
N.A.I.C.S.: 339920

ALPINA SIRO, S.R.L.   (1)
Str I C Bratianu NR 24, Medias, 551003,
Romania
Tel.: (40) 269 844 810
Sales Range: $50-74.9 Million
Emp.: 140
Sporting Goods & Supplies Mfr
N.A.I.C.S.: 339920

ALPINA SPORTS Corp.   (1)
93 Etna Rd, Lebanon, NH 03766
Tel.: (603) 448-3101
Sales Range: $25-49.9 Million
Emp.: 10
Sporting Goods & Supplies Mfr
N.A.I.C.S.: 339920
Gary Flemming *(Pres)*

ALPINA YUG, d.o.o.   (1)
Bulevar umetnosti 4, Belgrade, 11071, Ser-
bia
Tel.: (381) 11 21 31 140
Sporting Goods & Supplies Mfr
N.A.I.C.S.: 339920

TOV ALPINA UA   (1)
Bud 13 Kv 127 Vul Romena Rollana, Kiev,
Ukraine
Tel.: (380) 444535583
Sporting Goods & Supplies Mfr
N.A.I.C.S.: 339920

ALPINE AEROTECH LTD.
1260 Industrial Rd, Kelowna, V1Z
1G5, BC, Canada
Tel.: (250) 769-6344
Web Site:
   http://www.alpineaerotech.com
Year Founded: 1990
Rev.: $10,259,504
Emp.: 100
Aircraft Products & Service Provider
N.A.I.C.S.: 488190
Neil Baycroft *(Gen Mgr)*

ALPINE BAU GMBH
Alte Bundesstrasse 10, 5071,
Salzburg, Austria
Tel.: (43) 66285820   AT
Web Site: http://www.alpine.at
Year Founded: 1965
Sales Range: $5-14.9 Billion
Emp.: 15,000
Construction Company
N.A.I.C.S.: 237990
Jiri Pech *(Chm-Supervisory Bd)*

Subsidiaries:

ALPINE Mayreder Construction Co.,
Ltd.   (1)
37 Maizidian Street 1080 Sunflower Tower,
Chaoyang District, Beijing, 100026, China
Tel.: (86) 10 852 75116
Construction Engineering Services
N.A.I.C.S.: 541330

ALPINE-Energie Holding AG   (1)
Wolfentalstrasse 29, 88400, Biberach an
der Riss, Germany
Tel.: (49) 7351 579 0
Construction Engineering Services
N.A.I.C.S.: 541330

ALTEC Umwelttechnik GmbH   (1)
Industriepark Euronova, 9601, Arnoldstein,
Austria   (56%)
Tel.: (43) 42552728
Web Site: http://www.altec.at
Soil Decontamination Services
N.A.I.C.S.: 562211
Horst Strassegger *(Mgr-Ops)*

Alpine Bau Deutschland AG   (1)
Fuholzener Strasse 12, 85386, Eching,
Germany
Tel.: (49) 89327110
Web Site: http://www.alpine-bau.de
Sales Range: $100-124.9 Million
Emp.: 315
Construction Company
N.A.I.C.S.: 237310

Beton- und Monierbau Gesellschaft
m.b.H.   (1)
Bernhard-Hofel-Strasse 11, 6020,
Innsbruck, Austria
Tel.: (43) 51233110
Web Site: http://www.alpine-bemo.com
Rev.: $131,211,700
Emp.: 200
Tunneling & Underground Structure Con-
struction
N.A.I.C.S.: 237310

HAZET Bauunternehmung
GmbH   (1)
Oberlaaer Strasse 276, 1230, Vienna, Aus-
tria
Tel.: (43) 159946
Web Site: http://www.hazet.at
Construction Engineering Services
N.A.I.C.S.: 541330

Klocher Baugesellschaft m.b.H.   (1)
Kloch 23, Kloch, 8493, Austria
Tel.: (43) 347572310
Construction Engineering Services
N.A.I.C.S.: 541330

Konrad Beyer & Co Spezialbau
GmbH   (1)
Dietrich-Keller-Str 20, 8074, Raaba, Austria
Tel.: (43) 316 212 0
Web Site: http://www.k-beyer.at
Construction Engineering Services
N.A.I.C.S.: 541330

Okotechna Entsorgungs- und
Umwelttechnik GmbH   (1)
Waldmuhlgasse 31, 2380, Perchtoldsdorf,
Austria
Tel.: (43) 187682740
Web Site: http://www.oekotechna.at
Environmental Engineering & Consulting
Services
N.A.I.C.S.: 541330
Josef Zauner *(Mng Dir)*

ZAO "ALPINE-GAZ"   (1)
1 Koloboski Per House 13 Building 1,
127051, Moscow, Russia
Tel.: (7) 495 984 58 88
Construction Engineering Services
N.A.I.C.S.: 541330

ALPINE HOLDING GMBH
Alte-Bundesstrasse 10, Wals, 5071,
Salzburg, Austria
Tel.: (43) 66285820
Web Site: http://www.alpine.at
Year Founded: 1965
Sales Range: $1-4.9 Billion
Emp.: 15,294
Holding Company
N.A.I.C.S.: 551112
Dietmar Aluta-Oltyan *(Chm-
Supervisory Bd)*

**ALPINE HOUSING DEVELOP-
MENT CORPORATION LTD.**
002 Alpine Arch 10 Langford Road,
Bengaluru, 560 027, Karnataka, India
Tel.: (91) 8040473500
Web Site:
   https://www.alpinehousing.com
526519—(BOM)
Rev.: $6,209,876
Assets: $21,527,415
Liabilities: $11,486,052
Net Worth: $10,041,363
Earnings: $284,111
Emp.: 45
Fiscal Year-end: 03/31/22
Construction Engineering Services
N.A.I.C.S.: 237990
Syed Abdul Kabeer *(Chm & Co-Mng
Dir)*

Subsidiaries:

Alpine Housing Development Corpo-
ration Ltd. - Alpine Alloys
Division   (1)
263 narasapura bye-pass NH-4, district ko-
lar, Bengaluru, 562122, Karnataka, India
Tel.: (91) 8152 290410
Sales Range: $25-49.9 Million
Emp.: 20
Iron Casting Mfr
N.A.I.C.S.: 331513

ALPINE SELECT AG
Gotthardstrasse 31, CH-6000, Zug,
Switzerland
Tel.: (41) 417204411
Web Site: https://www.alpine-
   select.ch
ALPN—(SWX)
Rev.: $6,794,628
Assets: $84,395,056
Liabilities: $2,104,825
Net Worth: $82,290,231
Earnings: ($514,618)
Emp.: 3
Fiscal Year-end: 12/31/23
Portfolio Management & Investment
Advice
N.A.I.C.S.: 523940
Raymond J. Baer *(Chm)*

ALPIQ HOLDING AG
Ch de Mornex 10, 1003, Lausanne,
Switzerland
Tel.: (41) 213412111   CH
Web Site: http://www.alpiq.com
ALPH—(SWX)
Rev.: $4,277,623,040

Alpiq Holding AG—(Continued)

Assets: $7,588,301,440
Liabilities: $3,808,052,480
Net Worth: $3,780,248,960
Earnings: ($279,064,960)
Emp.: 1,218
Fiscal Year-end: 12/31/19
Holding Company; Energy Genera-
tion & Distribution Services
N.A.I.C.S.: 551112
Michael Wider *(Deputy CEO,
Member-Exec Bd & Head-
Generation)*

Subsidiaries:

Alpiq AG   **(1)**
Bahnhofquai 12, 4600, Olten, Switzerland
Tel.: (41) 622867111
Web Site: http://www.alpiq.com
Sales Range: $5-14.9 Billion
Holding Company; Energy Companies &
Power Plants
N.A.I.C.S.: 335311

Subsidiary (Domestic):

Aare Energie AG   **(2)**
Solothurnerstrasse 21, Postfach, 4601, Ol-
ten, Switzerland
Tel.: (41) 622055656
Web Site: http://www.aen.ch
Sales Range: $75-99.9 Million
Emp.: 75
Energy Services
N.A.I.C.S.: 221122

Advens AG   **(2)**
Katharina-Sulzer-Platz 12, 8400, Winterthur,
Switzerland
Tel.: (41) 52 244 03 30
Web Site: http://www.advens.ch
Engineering Consulting Services
N.A.I.C.S.: 541330

Alpiq Central Europe AG   **(2)**
Bahnhofqaui 12, 4601, Olten, 4601,
Switzerland   **(100%)**
Tel.: (41) 622867777
Web Site: http://www.alpiq.com
Sales Range: $75-99.9 Million
Emp.: 500
Electric Power Trading
N.A.I.C.S.: 221122

Subsidiary (Non-US):

Alpiq Csepel Kft.   **(2)**
Kalvin Ter 12, 1085, Budapest, Hungary
Tel.: (36) 14291030
Web Site: http://www.alpiq.hu
Sales Range: $150-199.9 Million
Emp.: 40
Hot Water, Natural Gas & Sewage Utility
Services
N.A.I.C.S.: 221310
Briglovics Gabor *(Gen Mgr)*

Subsidiary (Domestic):

Alpiq Csepeli Eromu Kft   **(3)**
Szinesfem Utca 3, 1211, Budapest, Hun-
gary
Tel.: (36) 1 278 5440
Sales Range: $100-124.9 Million
Emp.: 80
Electric Power Generator & Distribution
Services
N.A.I.C.S.: 221118
Ambrovics Denes *(Deputy Gen Mgr)*

Alpiq Csepeli Szolgaltato Kft.   **(3)**
Hoeromu Utca 3, 1211, Budapest, Hungary
Tel.: (36) 1 278 3800
Sales Range: $75-99.9 Million
Emp.: 56
Eletric Power Generation Services
N.A.I.C.S.: 221118
Varga Csaba *(Grp Dir-Production)*

Subsidiary (Non-US):

Alpiq Deutschland GmbH   **(2)**
Im Breitspiel 7, Heidelberg, 69126, Ger-
many
Tel.: (49) 62219401
Emp.: 2
Eletric Power Generation Services

N.A.I.C.S.: 221118
Hans Genghnrl *(Gen Mgr)*

Subsidiary (Domestic):

Alpiq Anlagentechnik GmbH   **(3)**
Im Breitspiel 7, 69126, Heidelberg, Ger-
many
Tel.: (49) 62219410
Web Site: http://www.energie-und-
   kraftanlagen.de
Sales Range: $1-4.9 Billion
Emp.: 4,956
Infrastructure Engineering Services
N.A.I.C.S.: 237130

Subsidiary (Non-US):

Caliqua Anlagentechnik GmbH   **(4)**
IZ-NO-Sud Strasse 2d Objekt 57, 2355,
Wiener Neudorf, Austria
Tel.: (43) 2236 65920 0
Web Site: http://www.caliqua.at
Sales Range: $25-49.9 Million
Emp.: 200
Air Conditioning Equipment Installation Ser-
vices
N.A.I.C.S.: 238220
Wolf Dirnbacher *(Mng Dir)*

Subsidiary (Domestic):

Kraftanlagen Power Plants
GmbH   **(4)**
Ridlerstr 31c, Munich, 80339, Germany
Tel.: (49) 8962370
Web Site: http://www.ka-muenchen.de
Emp.: 35
Power Plant Construction Engineering Ser-
vices
N.A.I.C.S.: 237130

Subsidiary (Domestic):

Kraftanlagen Hamburg GmbH   **(5)**
Fangdieckstrasse 68, 22547, Hamburg,
Germany
Tel.: (49) 40547160
Web Site: http://www.ka-hamburg.de
Sales Range: $50-74.9 Million
Emp.: 140
Energy Services
N.A.I.C.S.: 221122
Jens Pokoiewski *(Gen Mgr)*

Kraftanlagen Heidelberg GmbH   **(5)**
Im Breitspiel 7, 69126, Heidelberg, Ger-
many
Tel.: (49) 6221940
Web Site: http://www.ka-heidelberg.de
Sales Range: $25-49.9 Million
Emp.: 400
Power Distr
N.A.I.C.S.: 221122

Subsidiary (Non-US):

Kraftanlagen Romania S.R.L.   **(5)**
Bulevardul Bucuresti Nr 66, 100520,
Ploiesti, Judetul Prahova, Romania
Tel.: (40) 34440995
Web Site: http://www.ka-romania.ro
Sales Range: $25-49.9 Million
Emp.: 200
Power Plant Construction Services
N.A.I.C.S.: 237130

Subsidiary (Domestic):

Biogas neu Kosenow GmbH & Co
KG   **(3)**
Neuer Wall 54, 20354, Hamburg, Germany
Tel.: (49) 40 809063100
Eletric Power Generation Services
N.A.I.C.S.: 221118

Digi Communication Systeme
GmbH   **(3)**
August-Horch-Strasse 4, D-38518, Gifhorn,
Germany
Tel.: (49) 53715880
Web Site: http://www.ga-netztechnik.de
Sales Range: $200-249.9 Million
Emp.: 650
Telecommunication Servicesb
N.A.I.C.S.: 517121

ECM Ing.Unternehmen fur Energie-
und Umwelttechnik GmbH   **(3)**
Burgkirchenerstrasse 64-66, 84489,
Burghausen, Germany

Tel.: (49) 867796720
Web Site: http://www.ec-muenchen.de
Sales Range: $25-49.9 Million
Emp.: 60
Engineering & Chemical Processor
N.A.I.C.S.: 541330

ECM Ingenieur-Unternehmen fur
Energie- und Umwelttechnik
GmbH   **(3)**
Ridlerstrasse 31a, 80339, Munich, Germany
Tel.: (49) 89 62 37 101
Web Site: http://www.ec-muenchen.de
Engineeering Services
N.A.I.C.S.: 541330

Elektro Stiller GmbH   **(3)**
Chemnitzer Strasse 3, 30952, Ronneburg,
Germany
Tel.: (49) 511946960
Web Site: http://www.elektro-stiller.de
Sales Range: $1-9.9 Million
Emp.: 77
Transport & Logistic Services
N.A.I.C.S.: 541614

FINOW Rohrsysteme GmbH   **(3)**
Angermunder Strasse 101, 16225, Eber-
swalde, Germany
Tel.: (49) 3334 57 0
Web Site: http://www.finow.de
Emp.: 100
Steel Pipe Component Mfr
N.A.I.C.S.: 331210

Frankenluk AG   **(3)**
Podeldorfer Str 86, Bamberg, 96052, Ger-
many
Tel.: (49) 9511820
Web Site: http://www.frankenluk.de
Sales Range: $250-299.9 Million
Emp.: 40
Eletric Power Generation Services
N.A.I.C.S.: 221118

Franz Lohr GmbH   **(3)**
Steinbeisstrasse 10, 88214, Ravensburg,
Germany
Tel.: (49) 7518810
Web Site: http://www.franz-lohr.de
Sales Range: $25-49.9 Million
Emp.: 230
Public Utilities
N.A.I.C.S.: 221122

GA-com Telekommunikation und
Telematik GmbH   **(3)**
Rotestrasse 24, D-74321, Bietigheim-
Bissingen, Germany
Tel.: (49) 7142969122
Web Site: http://www.ga-com.de
Sales Range: $50-74.9 Million
Emp.: 225
Telecommunications & Telemarketing Prod-
ucts
N.A.I.C.S.: 561422

GAH Pensions GmbH   **(3)**
Im Breitspiel 7, 69126, Heidelberg, Ger-
many
Tel.: (49) 6221 9401
Electric Power Distribution Services
N.A.I.C.S.: 221122
Hans Genthner *(Mng Dir)*

Ingenieurburo Kiefer & Voss
GmbH   **(3)**
Wetterkreuz 3, Erlangen, 91058, Germany
Tel.: (49) 9131 78 77 0
Web Site: http://www.ibkv.de
Sales Range: $25-49.9 Million
Emp.: 100
Power Plant Construction Engineering Ser-
vices & Piping Supplies Distr
N.A.I.C.S.: 237130
Stefan Barnert *(Gen Mgr)*

K+M Fahrleitungstechnik GmbH   **(3)**
Malerstrasse 22, 38550, Isenbuttel, Ger-
many
Tel.: (49) 5374 91909 0
Road & Rail Transport Infrastructure Sup-
port Services
N.A.I.C.S.: 488490

Martin Bohsung GmbH   **(3)**
Im Bonholz 7, 71277, Rutesheim, Germany
Tel.: (49) 7152 33116 0
Web Site: http://www.bohsung.de
Emp.: 40

Pipeline Construction Engineering Services
N.A.I.C.S.: 237120

te-com Telekommunikations-Technik
GmbH   **(3)**
Eugen-Adolff-Strasse 122, 71522,
Backnang, Germany
Tel.: (49) 719132970
Web Site: http://www.te-com.de
Sales Range: $100-124.9 Million
Emp.: 500
Telecommunications & Marketing Services
N.A.I.C.S.: 517121

Subsidiary (Domestic):

Alpiq EcoPower Ltd.   **(2)**
Bahnhofquai 12, 4600, Olten,
Switzerland   **(100%)**
Tel.: (41) 622867111
Web Site: http://www.alpiq.com
Emp.: 600
Hydro Power Plant Operation & Construc-
tion
N.A.I.C.S.: 221111

Subsidiary (Domestic):

Alpiq EcoPower Switzerland Ltd.   **(3)**
Bahnhofquai 12, 4601, Olten, Switzerland
Tel.: (41) 62 286 71 11
Hydroelectric Power Generation Services
N.A.I.C.S.: 221111
Gerhard Danioth *(Mng Dir)*

Subsidiary (Domestic):

Alpiq EnerTrans AG   **(2)**
Oltnerstrasse 61, Niedergosgen, 5013,
Switzerland   **(100%)**
Tel.: (41) 62 858 82 00
Web Site: http://www.alpiq-enertrans.ch
Sales Range: $75-99.9 Million
Emp.: 150
Electrical Grid Construction, Operation &
Maintenance, Switchgear Systems Mfr &
Distr
N.A.I.C.S.: 221121
Rudolf Meier *(Mng Dir)*

Subsidiary (Non-US):

Alpiq Energia Espana S.A.U.   **(2)**
Edificio Iberia Mart I Calle de Orense 34,
28020, Madrid, Spain
Tel.: (34) 902020276
Emp.: 7
Electric Power Generation & Distribution
Services
N.A.I.C.S.: 221118
Andres Romaro *(CEO)*

Alpiq Energie France S.A.S.   **(2)**
27 rue des Poissonniers, 92522, Neuilly-
sur-Seine, Cedex, France
Tel.: (33) 153438420
Web Site: http://www.alpiq.fr
Emp.: 50
Energy Services
N.A.I.C.S.: 221122

Subsidiary (Domestic):

Alpiq Production France Management
S.A.S.   **(3)**
15 Rue Louis Le Grand, 75002, Paris,
France
Tel.: (33) 1 53 43 49 36
Web Site: http://www.alpiq.com
Sales Range: $25-49.9 Million
Emp.: 8
Business Management Consulting Services
N.A.I.C.S.: 541611

Subsidiary (Non-US):

Alpiq Energija BH d.o.o.   **(2)**
Kaptol 5/2, 71000, Sarajevo, Bosnia & Her-
zegovina
Tel.: (387) 33 260 135
Sales Range: $75-99.9 Million
Emp.: 2
Electric Power Distribution Services
N.A.I.C.S.: 221122
Ermina Arnautovic *(Gen Mgr)*

Alpiq Energija Hrvatska d.o.o.   **(2)**
Vijenac 7 Tuskanac, Zagreb, 10000, Hr-
vatska, Croatia
Tel.: (385) 1 4813 579
Web Site: http://www.alpiq.com.hr

Electric Power Distr
N.A.I.C.S.: 221122

Alpiq Energy Hellas S.A. (2)
Karistou 5, Ambelokipi, 11523, Athens,
Greece
Tel.: (30) 210 6998 201
Sales Range: $75-99.9 Million
Emp.: 2
Electric Power Distribution Services
N.A.I.C.S.: 221122

Subsidiary (Domestic):

Atel Hellas S.A. (3)
iera Odos 150, 12242, Athens, Greece
Tel.: (30) 2103467384
Web Site: http://www.alpiq.com
Electric Power Distr Owned 76% by Atel &
24% by Zeritis Group
N.A.I.C.S.: 221122

Subsidiary (Non-US):

Alpiq Energy SE (2)
al Armii Ludowej 26, 00-609, Warsaw, Po-
land
Tel.: (48) 225796525
Web Site: http://www.alpiq.pl
Sales Range: $50-74.9 Million
Emp.: 12
Electricity Trading
N.A.I.C.S.: 221118

Alpiq Energy SE (2)
Jungmannova 26/15, 110 00, Prague,
Czech Republic
Tel.: (420) 221720111
Web Site: http://www.alpiq.cz
Sales Range: $75-99.9 Million,
Emp.: 100
International Electricity Trading
N.A.I.C.S.: 221121

Subsidiary (Domestic):

Alpiq Zlin s.r.o. (3)
Trida Tomase Bati 650, 760 01, Zlin, Czech
Republic
Tel.: (420) 577524855
Web Site: http://www.generation.alpiq.cz
Sales Range: $100-124.9 Million
Emp.: 160
Heat Generation, Electrical Energy & Com-
pressed Air
N.A.I.C.S.: 221122

GA Energo technik s.r.o. (3)
Na Strilne AB, Orlik-Bolevec, 330 11, Plzen,
Czech Republic
Tel.: (420) 373 303 111
Web Site: http://www.gaenergo.cz
Sales Range: $100-124.9 Million
Emp.: 33
Electric Power Structure Construction Ser-
vices
N.A.I.C.S.: 237130
Zdenek Zidek *(Gen Mgr)*

Subsidiary (Domestic):

Alpiq Finanzbeteiligungen Ltd. (2)
Bahnhofquai 12, Olten, 4600, Switzerland
Tel.: (41) 622867111
Investment Management Service
N.A.I.C.S.: 523999

Alpiq Grid Ltd. (2)
Chemin de Mornex 10, 1001, Lausanne,
Switzerland
Tel.: (41) 21 341 21 11
Web Site: http://www.alpiq.ch
Electric Power Distribution Services
N.A.I.C.S.: 221122

Alpiq Hydro Aare AG (2)
Aarburgerstrasse 264, 4618, Boningen,
Switzerland **(100%)**
Tel.: (41) 627876911
Web Site: http://www.alpiq.ch
Sales Range: $50-74.9 Million
Emp.: 25
Hydroelectric Power Generation
N.A.I.C.S.: 221111

Subsidiary (Non-US):

Alpiq Italia S.r.l. (2)
Via Montalbino 3/5, Milan, 20159, Italy
Tel.: (39) 02 366981
Web Site: http://www.alpiq.com.it

Electric Power Generation & Distribution
Services
N.A.I.C.S.: 221118

Subsidiary (Domestic):

Alpiq Energy Italy S.p.A. (3)
Via Marostica 1, Milan, 20146, Italy
Tel.: (39) 02366981
Web Site: http://www.alpiq.it
Sales Range: $10-24.9 Million
Emp.: 50
Electricity Distr
N.A.I.C.S.: 221122

Alpiq Narzole S.r.l. (3)
Via Montalbino 3/5, Milan, 20159, Italy
Tel.: (39) 02366981
Eletric Power Generation Services
N.A.I.C.S.: 221118

Alpiq Vercelli S.r.l. (3)
48 Via Ara Ettore, 13100, Vercelli, Italy
Tel.: (39) 016129 991
Electric Power Structure Construction Ser-
vices
N.A.I.C.S.: 237130

Energit S.p.A. (3)
Via Edward Jenner 19/21, 09121, Cagliari,
Italy
Tel.: (39) 0707521422
Web Site: http://energit.it
Emp.: 6
Electric Power Distribution Services
N.A.I.C.S.: 221122

Idrovalsesia S.r.l. (3)
Via Montalbino 3/5, Milan, 20159, Italy
Tel.: (39) 02366981
Eletric Power Generation Services
N.A.I.C.S.: 221118

Subsidiary (Domestic):

Alpiq Management Ltd. (2)
Bahnhofquai 12, Olten, 4600, Switzerland
Tel.: (41) 62 286 75 60
Web Site: http://www.alpiq.cz
Emp.: 500
Business Management Consulting Services
N.A.I.C.S.: 541611

Subsidiary (Non-US):

Alpiq Norway AS (2)
Dronning Eufemias Gate 16 9th floor, PO
Box 26, 0191, Oslo, Norway
Tel.: (47) 21645562
Web Site: http://www.alpiq.no
Sales Range: $25-49.9 Million
Emp.: 30
Energy Consulting Services
N.A.I.C.S.: 541690

Subsidiary (Domestic):

Alpiq EcoPower Scandinavia AS (3)
Dronning Eufemias Gate 6, 191, Oslo, Nor-
way
Tel.: (47) 22 81 47 00
Hydroelectric Power Generation Services
N.A.I.C.S.: 221111

Energipartner AS (3)
Christian Frederiks Plasse 6, 0154, Oslo,
Norway
Tel.: (47) 22814700
Web Site: http://www.energipartner.no
Sales Range: $10-24.9 Million
Emp.: 30
Independent Energy Consulting & Portfolio
Management Company
N.A.I.C.S.: 221122

Subsidiary (Domestic):

Alpiq Reseau SA Lausanne (2)
Chemin de Mornex 10, 1001, Lausanne,
Switzerland **(100%)**
Tel.: (41) 213412111
Web Site: http://www.alpiq.ch
Electrical Grid Construction, Operation &
Maintenance
N.A.I.C.S.: 221121

Alpiq Suisse SA (2)
Ch De Mornex 10, CP 570, 1001, Lau-
sanne, Switzerland **(100%)**
Tel.: (41) 213412111
Web Site: http://www.alpiq.com
Emp.: 200

Hydro Power, Thermal Energy & Renewable Energy Generation
N.A.I.C.S.: 221111

Alpiq Swisstrade Ltd. (2)
Bahnhofquai 12, Olten, 4601, Switzerland
Tel.: (41) 62 286 71 11
Web Site: http://www.alpiq.com
Emp.: 450
Securities Brokerage Services
N.A.I.C.S.: 523150

Alpiq Trading Ltd. (2)
Bahnhofquai 12, Olten, 4600, Switzerland
Tel.: (41) 622867111
Web Site: http://www.alpiq.com
Emp.: 500
Electric Power Distribution Services
N.A.I.C.S.: 221122

Avenis SA (2)
Chemin de Mornex 10, 1003, Lausanne,
Switzerland
Tel.: (41) 21 341 28 00
Sales Range: $125-149.9 Million
Emp.: 20
Electric Power Distribution Services
N.A.I.C.S.: 221122

Birs Wasserkraft AG (2)
Bahnhofstrasse 21, Grellingen, 4203, Swit-
zerland
Tel.: (41) 622867111
Web Site: http://www.alpiq.com
Emp.: 500
Electric Power Generation & Distribution
Services
N.A.I.C.S.: 221118
Jafmin Staiblin *(CEO)*

**Energie Electrique du Simplon
SA** (2)
12 Place de la Gare, Lausanne, 1001, Swit-
zerland
Tel.: (41) 21 341 21 11
Hydroelectric Power Generation Services
N.A.I.C.S.: 221111
Michael Wider *(Gen Mgr)*

Entegra Wasserkraft AG (2)
Rosenbergstrasse 72, 9000, Saint Gallen,
Switzerland
Tel.: (41) 81 511 11 70
Sales Range: $75-99.9 Million
Emp.: 5
Hydroelectric Power Generation Services
N.A.I.C.S.: 221111

Subsidiary (Non-US):

GA Austria GmbH (2)
Gewerbestrasse 5, 4072, Alkoven, Austria
Tel.: (43) 7274 7333 0
Electric Power Structure Construction Ser-
vices
N.A.I.C.S.: 237130

GA-Magyarorszag Kft. (2)
Topark Utca 1/A, 2045, Torokbalint, Hun-
gary
Tel.: (36) 23 501 100
Sales Range: $50-74.9 Million
Emp.: 120
Electric Power Structure Construction Ser-
vices
N.A.I.C.S.: 237130

Subsidiary (Domestic):

Grande Dixence SA (2)
Rue des Creusets 41, 1950, Sion, Switzer-
land
Tel.: (41) 27 328 43 11
Web Site: http://www.grande-dixence.ch
Sales Range: $75-99.9 Million
Emp.: 4
Eletric Power Generation Services
N.A.I.C.S.: 221118

Hydro-Solar Energie AG (2)
Bachmatten 9, 4435, Niederdorf, Switzer-
land
Tel.: (41) 61 963 00 33
Web Site: http://www.hydro-solar.ch
Emp.: 13
Hydroelectric Power Generation Services
N.A.I.C.S.: 221111
N. Sriram *(Gen Mgr)*

Subsidiary (Non-US):

Kraftszer Kft. (2)

4-6 Pap Karoly str, 1139, Budapest, Hun-
gary
Tel.: (36) 14657031
Web Site: http://kraftszer.hu
Sales Range: $10-24.9 Million
Emp.: 200
Designing, Engineering, Environmental Pro-
tection, Operation & Maintenance of Power
Plants
N.A.I.C.S.: 221122

Subsidiary (Domestic):

Kraftszer Vallalkozasi Kft. (3)
4-6 Pap Karoly str, 1139, Budapest, Hun-
gary
Tel.: (36) 1 465 7031
Web Site: http://www.kraftszer.hu
Power Plant Construction Engineering Ser-
vices
N.A.I.C.S.: 237130

Subsidiary (Domestic):

Nant de Drance SA (2)
Chemin du Gilloud 3, 1920, Martigny, Swit-
zerland
Tel.: (41) 27 720 47 30
Eletric Power Generation Services
N.A.I.C.S.: 221118

Alpiq Energia Bulgaria EOOD (1)
2 Pozitano Square-Floor 7, Triaditza Dis-
trict, 1000, Sofia, Bulgaria
Tel.: (359) 24008085
Power Generation Services
N.A.I.C.S.: 221118

**Alpiq Energie Deutschland
GmbH** (1)
Kantstrasse 21, 10623, Berlin, Germany
Tel.: (49) 3040674013
Web Site: http://www.alpiq.de
Renewable Energy Services
N.A.I.C.S.: 221118

Alpiq Energija Skopje DOOEL (1)
Str Mirce Acev 2/3rd Floor, 1000, Skopje,
North Macedonia
Tel.: (389) 23136530
Power Generation Services
N.A.I.C.S.: 221118

Alpiq Energy Ukraine LLC (1)
25-B P Sagaydachnogo str Office 415,
04070, Kiev, Ukraine
Tel.: (380) 444985274
Power Generation Services
N.A.I.C.S.: 221118

Alpiq RomIndustries SRL (1)
Strada Nicolae G Caramfil nr 41 Etajele 3 4
si 5 Sector 1, 014142, Bucharest, Romania
Tel.: (40) 212093232
Web Site: http://www.alpiq.ro
Power Generation Services
N.A.I.C.S.: 221118

ALPITOUR S.P.A.
Via Lugaro 15, 10126, Turin, Italy
Tel.: (39) 0110171111   IT
Web Site: http://www.alpitour.it
Sales Range: $1-4.9 Billion
Emp.: 3,500
Tourism Services
N.A.I.C.S.: 561520
Gabriele Burgio *(Chm & CEO)*

**ALPLA-WERKE ALWIN LEH-
NER GMBH & CO. KG**
Mockenstrasse 34, 6971, Hard, Aus-
tria
Tel.: (43) 5574602200
Web Site: http://www.alpla.com
Year Founded: 1955
Sales Range: $1-4.9 Billion
Emp.: 20,900
Mfr of Plastics
N.A.I.C.S.: 326199
Guntar Lehanar *(CEO)*

Subsidiaries:

ALPLA (Guangzhou) Plastic Co.,
Ltd. (1)
No 168 Bi Gang Xin Cun Road East Zone,
Economic & Technology Development

Alpla-Werke Alwin Lehner GmbH & Co.
KG—(Continued)

Zone, 510735, Guangzhou, China
Tel.: (86) 202 2017399
Plastic Packaging Product Distr
N.A.I.C.S.: 424610

ALPLA (Hefei) Plastic Co., Ltd (1)
Shinan Road 16 Hefei Hi-Tech Zone,
230088, Hofei, China
Tel.: (86) 222 3970701
Plastic Packaging Product Distr
N.A.I.C.S.: 424610

**ALPLA (Jiangsu) Plastic Co.,
Ltd.** (1)
No 8 West Xiexin Road Taicang Port Development Zone, 215434, Taicang, China
Tel.: (86) 512 33022618
Plastic Packaging Product Distr
N.A.I.C.S.: 424610
Sarah Duan (Supvr-Customer Svc)

**ALPLA (Shanghai) Plastic Co.,
Ltd** (1)
Room 1 Floor 17th Building A No 391 Guiping Road Caohejing, High-Tech Park Xuhui District, 200233, Shanghai, China
Tel.: (86) 216 4858383
Plastic Packaging Product Distr
N.A.I.C.S.: 424610

ALPLA (Tianjin) Plastic Co., Ltd. (1)
Xiqing Economic Development Area Hong Yuan Street, 300385, Tianjin, China
Tel.: (86) 139 20018011
Plastic Packaging Product Distr
N.A.I.C.S.: 424610

ALPLA Avellaneda S.A. (1)
Calle 20 y 9 Ruta 8 km 60 1629 Pilar, Buenos Aires, 1629, Argentina
Tel.: (54) 230 4467800
Web Site: http://www.alpla.com
Emp.: 250
Plastic Packaging Product Distr
N.A.I.C.S.: 424610
Christian Schellmann (Plant Mgr)

ALPLA BH d.o.o. Citluk (1)
Idustrijska zona, 88260, Citluk, Bosnia &
Herzegovina
Tel.: (387) 36 656524
Plastic Packaging Product Distr
N.A.I.C.S.: 424610

ALPLA Belgium N.V. (1)
Westerring 13, 9700, Oudenaarde, Belgium
Tel.: (32) 55300250
Web Site: http://www.alpla.com
Emp.: 100
Plastic Packaging Product Distr
N.A.I.C.S.: 424610
Didier Deveen (Mng Dir)

ALPLA Caribe Inc. (1)
Santo Domingo Oeste Autopista Duarte Km 14 Los Alcarrizos, Santo Domingo, Dominican Republic
Tel.: (809) 560 1991277
Plastic Packaging Product Distr
N.A.I.C.S.: 424610

ALPLA Colombia Ltda. (1)
Urbanizacion Industrial San Carlos km 4 autopista, Bogota, Colombia
Tel.: (57) 182 32233
Plastic Packaging Product Distr
N.A.I.C.S.: 424610
Bernardo Baader (Country Mgr)

ALPLA D.O.O (1)
Vojvodici 19 Novaki Samoborski, 10431, Sveta Nedelja, Croatia
Tel.: (385) 133 71187
Plastic Packaging Product Distr
N.A.I.C.S.: 424610

ALPLA France SAS (1)
4 Rue du Clos Thomas Parc d'Activites Euro Val de Loire, 41330, Fosse, France
Tel.: (33) 254 525650
Web Site: http://www.alpla.com
Emp.: 130
Plastic Packaging Product Distr
N.A.I.C.S.: 424610
Ludovic Louis (Mgr-Production)

ALPLA Iberica S.A. (1)
Pol Ind El Romeral, 46340, Requena, Spain

Tel.: (34) 962 323003
Plastic Packaging Product Distr
N.A.I.C.S.: 424610
Josep Manzanera (Mgr-Second Tool)

ALPLA India Private Ltd. (1)
Plot No 100 EPIP Phase II Thana, 173205, Baddi, Himachal Pradesh, India
Tel.: (91) 988 5196900
Plastic Packaging Product Distr
N.A.I.C.S.: 424610
Vagish Dixit (Mng Dir)

ALPLA Italia S.R.L (1)
Strada delle cinque miglia 76, 00042, Anzio, Italy
Tel.: (39) 069 86081
Web Site: http://www.alpla.com
Emp.: 150
Plastic Packaging Product Distr
N.A.I.C.S.: 424610
Andrea Romano (Mgr-Ops)

ALPLA LLC (1)
Academica Zhukova 12 Dzerzhinsky, Dzerzhinsky, 140090, Moscow, Russia
Tel.: (7) 4952216379
Plastic Packaging Product Distr
N.A.I.C.S.: 424610

**ALPLA Muanyag Csomagoloipari
Kft** (1)
Buzavirag u 8, 2800, Tatabanya, Hungary
Tel.: (36) 345 12570
Plastic Packaging Product Distr
N.A.I.C.S.: 424610

ALPLA NDM Sp.z.o.o (1)
ul Przemyslowa 2, 05-100, Nowy Dwor Mazowiecki, Poland
Tel.: (48) 227 1349 44
Plastic Packaging Product Distr
N.A.I.C.S.: 424610

ALPLA Nederland B.V. (1)
Groot-Mijdrecht-Straat 39, 3641, Mijdrecht, Netherlands
Tel.: (31) 297 231100
Web Site: http://www.alpla.com
Emp.: 50
Plastic Packaging Product Distr
N.A.I.C.S.: 424610
Theo Stenekes (Controller-Fin)

**ALPLA Opakowania z Tworzyw
Sztucznych Spolka z.o.o.** (1)
ul Lubiejewska 63 Oddzia, 07-300, Ostrow Mazowiecka, Poland
Tel.: (48) 296 442844
Plastic Packaging Product Distr
N.A.I.C.S.: 424610
Dariusz Stasiewicz (Engr-IT Sys)

**ALPLA Packaging (Vietnam) Co.,
Ltd.** (1)
Block B2 B4 Street D4 Dong Nam Industrial Zone, 70700, Ho Chi Minh City, Vietnam
Tel.: (84) 123 4249115
Plastic Packaging Product Distr
N.A.I.C.S.: 424610

ALPLA Packaging Ltd. (1)
No 257 Village No 7 Tha Tum, Sub-district, 25140, Tambol Dong-Kee-Lek, Prachin Buri, Thailand
Tel.: (66) 372 74148
Plastic Packaging Product Distr
N.A.I.C.S.: 424610

**ALPLA Plastik Sanayi Ve Ticaret
Ltd.** (1)
Kocaeli Pelitli koyu yolu uzeri Cardakbayyry Mevkii, 41490, Gebze, Turkiye
Tel.: (90) 262 7513210
Plastic Packaging Product Distr
N.A.I.C.S.: 424610

ALPLA Tashkent LRS (1)
Ziroat Street Bektemir Region Binokor Village, 700083, Tashkent, Uzbekistan
Tel.: (998) 712 5875 86
Plastic Packaging Product Distr
N.A.I.C.S.: 424610

ALPLA UK Limited (1)
Yew Tree Way Stonecross Business Park Golborne, Warrington, WA3 3JD, United Kingdom
Tel.: (44) 194 2407440
Plastic Packaging Product Distr
N.A.I.C.S.: 424610

Paul Vickers (Mgr-Production)

ALPLA Waidhofen GmbH (1)
Brunnerstr 40, 3830, Waidhofen, Austria
Tel.: (43) 284 252572
Plastic Packaging Product Distr
N.A.I.C.S.: 424610

**ALPLA Werke Lehner GmbH & Co
KG** (1)
Struthweg, 35285, Gemunden, Germany
Tel.: (49) 64536481110
Plastic Packaging Product Distr
N.A.I.C.S.: 424610

ALPLA de Venezuela S.A. (1)
Carretera Nacional Guacara-Mariara, 2018, San Joaquin, Venezuela
Tel.: (58) 245 5520210
Plastic Packaging Product Distr
N.A.I.C.S.: 424610

ALPLA spol. s.r.o. (1)
Petrovice 8, 25751, Petrovice, Czech Republic
Tel.: (420) 317 784101
Plastic Packaging Product Distr
N.A.I.C.S.: 424610

Alpla Honduras SA (1)
Km 1 Carretera Puerto Cortes Barrio Las Brisas Honduras, San Pedro Sula, Honduras
Tel.: (504) 450 82457
Plastic Packaging Product Distr
N.A.I.C.S.: 424610

Alpla Inc. (1)
289 Hwy 155 S, McDonough, GA 30253
Tel.: (770) 914-1407
Rev.: $10,600,000
Emp.: 480
Plastics Bottle Mfr
N.A.I.C.S.: 326160
Jodok Schaeffler (Gen Mgr-US)

Alpla Mexico S.A. DE C.V. (1)
Autopista Celaya-Queretaro km 16 S/N Carretera Ce, 38160, Apaseo el Grande, Mexico
Tel.: (52) 442 2942390
Plastic Packaging Product Distr
N.A.I.C.S.: 424610
Uli Renner (Gen Mgr)

**BrasALPLA Amazonia Industria de
Embalagens Ltda.** (1)
Avenida Buriti 5828 Distrito Industrial, Manaus, 69075-000, Brazil
Tel.: (55) 922 1232600
Plastic Packaging Product Distr
N.A.I.C.S.: 424610

BrasALPLA Brasil Industria de Embalagens Ltda. (1)
Rua Rosangela Mariana Limas 265 Villa Dr Cardoso, 06654-550, Itapevi, Sao Paulo, Brazil
Tel.: (55) 112 1041400
Plastic Packaging Product Distr
N.A.I.C.S.: 424610
Rogerio Mariano dos Santos (Mgr-Ops)

**BrasALPLA Pernambuco - Industria
de Embalagens Ltda.** (1)
Rodovia Washington Luiz - km 107 N 17777, 25240-005, Cabo de Santo Agostinho, Rio de Janeiro, Brazil
Tel.: (55) 213 0941410
Plastic Packaging Product Distr
N.A.I.C.S.: 424610

IberoALPLA Portugal LDA (1)
Estrada de Nazare 224 Aparto 9 Leiria, 2431, Marinha Grande, Portugal
Tel.: (351) 244 545120
Plastic Packaging Product Distr
N.A.I.C.S.: 424610

Lubecker Kunststoffwerk GmbH (1)
Niels-Bohr-Ring 18, 23568, Lubeck, Germany
Tel.: (49) 451 388700
Plastic Packaging Product Distr
N.A.I.C.S.: 424610

PET Recycling Team GmbH (1)
Madersperger Str 6, Wollersdorf-Steinabruckl, 2752, Austria
Tel.: (43) 262 2433330
Web Site: http://www.petrecyclingteam.at

Material Recycling Services
N.A.I.C.S.: 562920
Erich Happenhofer (CEO)

PRT Radomsko sp. z o.o. (1)
ul Geodetow 8, 97-500, Radomsko, Poland
Tel.: (48) 443 072601
Web Site: http://www.petrecyclingteam.eu
Emp.: 80
Plastic Packaging Product Distr
N.A.I.C.S.: 424610
Martin Jablonski (Mng Dir)

S.C. ALPLA PLASTIC S.R.L. (1)
Biruintei Bulevard No 130, 907230, Pantelimon, Romania
Tel.: (40) 316 204949
Plastic Packaging Product Distr
N.A.I.C.S.: 424610

**ZAMIL ALPLA Plastic - Middle East,
Limited** (1)
Dammam 2nd Industrial Area, PO Box 1748, 31952, Al Khobar, Saudi Arabia
Tel.: (966) 381 21114
Plastic Packaging Product Distr
N.A.I.C.S.: 424610
Shoaib Shaikh (Mgr-Mktg & Sls)

ALPOS, D.D.

Cesta Kozjanskega Odreda 29b,
3230, Sentjur pri Celju, Slovenia
Tel.: (386) 37462750
Web Site: http://www.alpos.si
Sales Range: $150-199.9 Million
Emp.: 980
Steel Pipes & Other Products Mfr
N.A.I.C.S.: 331210
Mirjan Bevc (Head-Mgmt & Gen Mgr)

Subsidiaries:

ALPOS Oprema Trgovin d.o.o. (1)
Hajduk Veljkova 11, 21000, Novi Sad, Serbia
Tel.: (381) 21301608
Sales Range: $25-49.9 Million
Emp.: 2
Steel Pole Mfr
N.A.I.C.S.: 331210

Alpos Alu, d.o.o. (1)
Cesta Leona Dobrotinska 2, 3230, Sentjur pri Celju, Slovenia
Tel.: (386) 37462750
Web Site: http://www.alu.alpos.si
Sales Range: $25-49.9 Million
Emp.: 100
Aluminium Ladders Mfr
N.A.I.C.S.: 332999
Damjana Kozlevca (Gen Mgr)

Alpos Handels GmbH (1)
Paradeisergasse 92, 9020, Klagenfurt, Austria
Tel.: (43) 463502171
Web Site: http://www.alpos.si
Furniture Mfr
N.A.I.C.S.: 332510
Stane Flander (Gen Mgr)

**Alpos Mizarska Proizvodnja,
d.o.o.** (1)
Cesta Leona Dobrotinska 2, 3230, Sentjur pri Celju, Slovenia
Tel.: (386) 3 7463 182
Furniture Mfr
N.A.I.C.S.: 332510

Alpos Pohistvo, d.o.o. (1)
Cesta Leona Dobrotinska 2, 3230, Sentjur pri Celju, Slovenia
Tel.: (386) 37463123
Sales Range: $50-74.9 Million
Emp.: 115
Metal Furnitures Mfr
N.A.I.C.S.: 332510

Alpos Posebne Storitve, d.o.o. (1)
Cesta Leona Dobrotinska 2, 3230, Sentjur pri Celju, Slovenia
Tel.: (386) 37462702
Sales Range: $50-74.9 Million
Emp.: 158
Metal Production & Textile Services
N.A.I.C.S.: 332510

Alpos Proizvodnja Orodij, d.o.o. (1)
Cesta Kozjanskega Odreda 25, 3230,

Sentjur pri Celju, Slovenia
Tel.: (386) 37463406
Sales Range: $25-49.9 Million
Emp.: 25
Cylinder Mfr
N.A.I.C.S.: 333995

Alpos Rohr Und Metallhandel Deutschland GmbH (1)
Schorner Strasse 10, 82065, Baierbrunn, Germany
Tel.: (49) 896252686
Web Site: http://www.alpos.de
Sales Range: $25-49.9 Million
Emp.: 10
Steel Pole Mfr
N.A.I.C.S.: 332322
R Rieger *(CEO)*

Alpos Sp. z.o.o. (1)
Ul Fabryczna 3, 67-320, Malomice, Zagan, Poland
Tel.: (48) 683769313
Web Site: http://www.alpos.pl
Furniture Mfr
N.A.I.C.S.: 332510

Alpos d.d. (1)
Predovecka 13, HR - 1000, Zagreb, Croatia
Tel.: (385) 98237897
Web Site: http://www.alpos.si
Furniture Mfr
N.A.I.C.S.: 332510

Alpos d.o.o. Aleksinac (1)
Naselje Aleksinacki Rudnik Bb, 18220, Aleksinac, Serbia
Tel.: (381) 18804700
Web Site: http://pohistvo.alpos.si
Steel Pole Mfr
N.A.I.C.S.: 332322

Alpos, Industrija Kovinsklh Izdelkov On Opreme, d.d. (1)
Cesta Kozjanskega Odreda 25, 3230, Sentjur pri Celju, Slovenia
Tel.: (386) 37463100
Sales Range: $50-74.9 Million
Emp.: 200
Steel Pole Mfr
N.A.I.C.S.: 331210

ZAO Alpos (1)
Moskovsky Prospect 111, 196084, Saint Petersburg, Russia
Tel.: (7) 812 369 3960
Web Site: http://www.alpos.ru
Furniture Production & Services
N.A.I.C.S.: 332510

ALPRINT S.A.
Henry Ford 1000, Maipu, Santiago, Chile
Tel.: (56) 2 5352171
Web Site: http://www.alprint.cl
Sales Range: $10-24.9 Million
Emp.: 27
Mfr of Aluminum Flexible Packaging Products
N.A.I.C.S.: 322220
Maria Eugenia Tellez *(Gen Mgr)*

ALPRO A.D.
Njegoseva bb, 75440, Vlasenica, Republika Srpska, Bosnia & Herzegovina
Tel.: (387) 65644651
Web Site: https://www.alpro-vl.com
Year Founded: 1977
ALPR—(BANJ)
Sales Range: $10-24.9 Million
Emp.: 132
Architectural Aluminium Product Mfr
N.A.I.C.S.: 339999

ALPS ALPINE CO., LTD.
1-7 Yukigayaotsukamachi, Ota-ku, Tokyo, 145 8501, Japan
Tel.: (81) 337261211 JP
Web Site: https://www.alpsalpine.com
Year Founded: 1948
6770—(TKS)
Rev.: $6,372,634,900
Assets: $4,983,867,290

Liabilities: $2,387,300,650
Net Worth: $2,596,566,640
Earnings: ($197,070,540)
Emp.: 28,693
Fiscal Year-end: 03/31/24
Electronic Components Mfr
N.A.I.C.S.: 334419
Toshihiro Kuriyama *(Chm, Pres, Pres & CEO)*

Subsidiaries:

ALCOM ELECTRONICOS DE MEXICO, S.A. DE C.V. (1)
Avenida Industrial Del Norte Lote 5 - 1, Parque Industrial Del Norte Cd, 88736, Reynosa, Tamaulipas, Mexico
Tel.: (52) 8999210800
Electronic Components Mfr
N.A.I.C.S.: 334419

ALPS (SHANGHAI) INTERNA-TIONAL TRADING CO., LTD. (1)
Room No 5A Tomson Commercial Bldg 710 Dongfang RD, Pudong, Shanghai, 200122, China
Tel.: (86) 21 5820 3213
Web Site: http://www.alps.com
Electronic Component & Audio Equipment Distr
N.A.I.C.S.: 423690

ALPS COMMUNICATION DEVICES TECHNOLOGY(SHANGHAI) CO., LTD. (1)
Room No 5A Tomson Commercial Bldg 710 Dongfang Road, Pudong New Area, Shanghai, 200122, China
Tel.: (86) 215 081 7575
Web Site: http://www.alps.com
Emp.: 87
Communication Devices Mfr
N.A.I.C.S.: 334290

ALPS ELECTRIC (THAILAND) CO., LTD. (1)
B B Building 19th floor Room No 1901 54 Sukhumvit 21 Road Asoke, Kwaeng North Klongtoey Khet Wattana, Bangkok, 10110, Thailand
Tel.: (66) 20231600
Web Site: http://www.alps.com
Electronic Components Distr
N.A.I.C.S.: 423690

ALPS ELECTRIC CZECH, s.r.o. (1)
Sebranice 240 Sebranice u, 679 31, Boskovice, Czech Republic
Tel.: (420) 516490111
Web Site: https://www.alps.cz
Sales Range: $100-124.9 Million
Emp.: 400
Electromechanical Component Mfr
N.A.I.C.S.: 334419

ALPS ELECTRONICS TAIWAN CO., LTD. (1)
2F No 130 Sec 3 Nanjing E Rd, Zhongshan District, Taipei, 10488, Taiwan
Tel.: (886) 28 772 5969
Web Site: http://www.alps.com
Electronic Components Distr
N.A.I.C.S.: 423690

ALPS GREEN DEVICES CO., LTD. (1)
1-7 Yukigaya-otsukamachi, Ota-ku, Tokyo, 145-8501, Japan
Tel.: (81) 3 5499 3101
Web Site: http://www.alpsgd.com
Sales Range: $25-49.9 Million
Emp.: 90
Power Control Devices Mfr
N.A.I.C.S.: 335999

Alpine Customer Service (USA), Inc. (1)
2150 195th St, Torrance, CA 90501
Tel.: (310) 783-7230
Electric Device Mfr
N.A.I.C.S.: 334419

Alpine Do Brasil Ltda (1)
Avenida Joao Paulo I 1776 Modulo E Jardim Santa Barbara, Embu das Artes, Sao Paulo, 06817-000, Brazil
Tel.: (55) 1122961135
Web Site: https://www.alpinebrasil.com.br

Electric Device Mfr
N.A.I.C.S.: 334419

Alpine Electronics (China) Company Limited (1)
R2-4F China Merchants Tower No 116 Jiangou Street, Chaoyang District, Beijing, 100022, China
Tel.: (86) 10 6566 0308
Web Site: http://www.alpine.com.cn
Emp.: 50
Mfr of Semiconductors & Related Devices
N.A.I.C.S.: 334413

Alpine Electronics (Europe) GmbH (1)
Ohmstrasse 4, 85716, Unterschleissheim, Germany (100%)
Tel.: (49) 893214210
Web Site: http://www.alpine.de
Sales Range: $25-49.9 Million
Emp.: 50
Provider of Electricity Measurement Instruments
N.A.I.C.S.: 334413

Alpine Electronics Australia Pty. Limited (1)
161 165 Princes Hwy, Hallam, 3803, VIC, Australia (100%)
Tel.: (61) 387871200
Web Site: http://www.alpine.com.au
Sales Range: $25-49.9 Million
Emp.: 14
N.A.I.C.S.: 334413
Joey Thompson *(Mng Dir)*

Alpine Electronics France S.A.R.L. (1)
184 allee des Erables Roissy Charles de Gaulle, PO Box 52016, Villepinte, Cedex, France (99%)
Tel.: (33) 148638989
Web Site: http://www.alpine-electronics.fr
Sales Range: $25-49.9 Million
Emp.: 20
Mfr of Semiconductors & Related Devices
N.A.I.C.S.: 334413

Alpine Electronics GmbH (1)
Ohmstrasse 4, 85716, Unterschleissheim, Germany (100%)
Tel.: (49) 893242640
Web Site: http://www.alpine.de
Sales Range: $50-74.9 Million
Emp.: 170
Mfr of Semiconductors & Related Devices
N.A.I.C.S.: 334413

Alpine Electronics Manufacturing of Europe Ltd. (1)
2051 Biatorbagy, Vendel Park, 2051, Budapest, Hungary
Tel.: (36) 23534111
Web Site: http://www.alpine.com
Sales Range: $200-249.9 Million
Emp.: 1,000
Audio Product Mfr
N.A.I.C.S.: 334310

Alpine Electronics Marketing Inc. (1)
1-7 Yukiya Otsukacho, Ota-ku, Tokyo, 145-0067, Japan (100%)
Tel.: (81) 570006636
Web Site: http://www.alpine.co.jp
Emp.: 150
Semiconductor & Related Devices
N.A.I.C.S.: 334413

Alpine Electronics de Espana, S.A. (1)
C/Portal de Gamarra 36, 36 Pabellon 32, 01013, Vitoria, Alava, Spain (100%)
Tel.: (34) 945283588
Web Site: http://www.alpine.es
Sales Range: $25-49.9 Million
Emp.: 19
Provides GIS-Related Solutions
N.A.I.C.S.: 334413

Alpine Electronics of America, Inc. (1)
19145 Gramercy Pl, Torrance, CA 90501-1128
Tel.: (310) 326-8000
Web Site: http://www.alpine-usa.com
Sales Range: $150-199.9 Million
Emp.: 356
Mfr & Importer of Mobile Electronics

N.A.I.C.S.: 423620
Koichi Endo *(CTO-Product Dev)*

Alpine Electronics of Canada, Inc. (1)
777 Supertest Road, Toronto, M3J 2M9, ON, Canada (100%)
Tel.: (416) 736-6211
Web Site: http://www.alpine-usa.com
Sales Range: $25-49.9 Million
Emp.: 10
N.A.I.C.S.: 334413
Steven Robert Hash *(Sr Mgr)*

Alpine Electronics of Middle East, FZCO (1)
Warehouse No XA-05 Round 08 Blue-Shed Area North, PO Box 18012, Jebel Ali Free Zone, Dubai, United Arab Emirates
Tel.: (971) 48808089
Electric Device Mfr
N.A.I.C.S.: 334419

Alpine Electronics of Silicon Valley, Inc. (1)
3151 Jay St Ste 101, Santa Clara, CA 95054
Tel.: (408) 703-6800
Electric Device Mfr
N.A.I.C.S.: 334419

Alpine Electronics of U.K. Limited (1)
Alpine House Fletchamstead Highway Earlplace Business Park, Coventry, CV4 9TW, United Kingdom (100%)
Tel.: (44) 2476719500
Web Site: http://www.alpine.co.uk
Sales Range: $25-49.9 Million
Emp.: 50
Mfr of Semiconductors & Related Devices
N.A.I.C.S.: 334413

Alpine Electronics, Inc. (1)
1-1-8 Nishi-Gotanda, Shinagawa-ku, Tokyo, 141-8501, Japan (40.9%)
Tel.: (81) 334941101
Web Site: http://www.alpine.com
Rev.: $2,444,495,280
Assets: $1,936,958,880
Liabilities: $550,755,360
Net Worth: $1,386,203,520
Earnings: $82,814,880
Emp.: 13,175
Fiscal Year-end: 03/31/2018
Electronic Components & Audio Products
N.A.I.C.S.: 334419
Masami Aihara *(VP-Actuators Bus)*

Alpine Italia S.P.A. (1)
Via C Colombo 8, 20090, Trezzano sul Naviglio, MI, Italy (100%)
Tel.: (39) 02484781
Web Site: http://italy.alpine-europe.com
Sales Range: $25-49.9 Million
Emp.: 20
Mfr of Heaters & Associated Products
N.A.I.C.S.: 334413

Alpine Manufacturing, Inc. (1)
3-10 Yoshima Industrial Park, Iwaki, 970-1144, Fukushima, Japan (100%)
Tel.: (81) 246366969
Web Site: https://www.alpine-manufacturing.jp
Sales Range: $100-124.9 Million
Emp.: 300
Sales of Electrical Appliances
N.A.I.C.S.: 449210
Yoshihugu Kanno *(Pres)*

Alpine Of Asia Pacific India PVT., LTD. (1)
Plot No 11 Sector 31 Ecotech-1, Kasna Industrial Area, Noida, 201308, Uttar Pradesh, India
Tel.: (91) 1204204625
Electric Device Mfr
N.A.I.C.S.: 334419

Alpine Precision, Inc. (1)
48 1 Akai Aza Tanmachi Taira, Iwaki, 979 3131, Fukushima, Japan (100%)
Tel.: (81) 246210008
Web Site: http://www.alpine.com
N.A.I.C.S.: 334413

Alpine Technology Manufacturing (Thailand) Co., Ltd. (1)
210 Moo 13 Suwansorn Road Tambol

Alps Alpine Co., Ltd.—(Continued)

Dong-Khee-Lek, Amphur Muang, 25000,
Prachinburi, Thailand
Tel.: (66) 37403330
Electric Device Mfr
N.A.I.C.S.: 334419

**Alpine Technology Manufacturing,
Inc.** (1)
61-1 Ohara Aza Shinbori Onahama, Iwaki,
971 8111, Fukushima, Japan (100%)
Tel.: (81) 246545161
Web Site: http://www.atmi.co.jp
Sales Range: $50-74.9 Million
Emp.: 130
N.A.I.C.S.: 334413

Alps Accounting Centre (1)
1-7 Yukigaya-otsukamachi, Ota-ku, Tokyo,
145-8501, Japan
Tel.: (81) 33 726 1211
Web Site: http://www.alps.co.jp
N.A.I.C.S.: 334413

Alps Alpin Asia Co., Ltd. (1)
The 9th Towers Tower B 24th Floor Unit
TNB01-03 33/4 Rama 9 Road, Huay
Kwang, Bangkok, 10310, Thailand
Tel.: (66) 20909596
Electric Device Mfr
N.A.I.C.S.: 334419

Alps Alpine North America, Inc. (1)
3151 Jay St Ste 101, Santa Clara, CA
95054
Tel.: (408) 361-6400
Electric Device Mfr
N.A.I.C.S.: 334419

Alps Alpine Vietnam Co., Ltd. (1)
Unit 3 4th Floor Office Building No 165 Thai
Ha str, Lang Ha ward Dong Da Dist, Hanoi,
Vietnam
Tel.: (84) 2432171486
Electric Device Mfr
N.A.I.C.S.: 334419

**Alps Electric (India) Private
Limited** (1)
4th Floor Tower One Vatika Business Park
Sector-49 Sohna Road, Gurgaon, 122001,
Haryana, India
Tel.: (91) 8448188416
Electric Device Mfr
N.A.I.C.S.: 334419

Alps Electric (Ireland) Limited (1)
Clara Road, Millstreet Town, Cork, P51
XC56, Ireland (100%)
Tel.: (353) 297 0677
Web Site: http://www.alps.ie
Emp.: 450
Electronic Surveillance Equipment Rental
Services
N.A.I.C.S.: 334413

**Alps Electric (Malaysia) Sdn.
Bhd.** (1)
Nilai Industrial Estate, PO Box 10643,
71800, Nilai, Negeri Sembilan,
Malaysia (100%)
Tel.: (60) 67991515
Web Site: http://www.alpselectric.com
Sales Range: $800-899.9 Million
Emp.: 3,000
Paper & Film Substrate Release Liners Mfr
N.A.I.C.S.: 334413

Plant (Domestic):

**Alps Electric (Malaysia) Sdn.Bhd. -
JENGKA PLANT** (2)
LOT3 industrial Estate Phase2, 26400,
Bandar Pusat Jengka, Pahang Darul
Makmur, Malaysia
Tel.: (60) 9 4663388
Web Site: http://www.alps.com
Electronic Components Mfr
N.A.I.C.S.: 334419

**Alps Electric (North America),
Inc.** (1)
1500 Atlantic Blvd, Auburn Hills, MI 48326-
1500
Tel.: (248) 391-9950
Web Site: https://www.alps.com
Sales Range: $25-49.9 Million
Emp.: 100
Mfr of Automotive On-Board Electronics

N.A.I.C.S.: 811114
Masataka Kataoka (Pres)

Alps Electric (S) Pte. Ltd. (1)
28 GENTING LANE 09-06 Platinum 28,
Singapore, 349585, Singapore (60%)
Tel.: (65) 6 226 2933
Web Site: http://www.alps.com
Sales Range: $150-199.9 Million
Emp.: 12
Book & Magazine Publisher
N.A.I.C.S.: 334413

**Alps Electric (Singapore), Pte.
Ltd.** (1)
28 Genting Lane 09-06 Platinum 28, Singa-
pore, 349585, Singapore (100%)
Tel.: (65) 62262933
Web Site: http://www.alps.com
Sales Range: $25-49.9 Million
Emp.: 42
Electronic Components Mfr & Distr
N.A.I.C.S.: 334413

Alps Electric (USA), Inc. (1)
3151 Jay St Ste 101, Santa Clara, CA
95054
Tel.: (408) 361-6400
Sales Range: $25-49.9 Million
Emp.: 50
N.A.I.C.S.: 334413

**Alps Electric Co., Ltd. - FURUKAWA
PLANT** (1)
6-3-36 Furukawanakazato, Osaki, 989-
6181, Miyagi, Japan
Tel.: (81) 229 23 5111
Web Site: http://www.alps.com
Electronic Components Mfr
N.A.I.C.S.: 334419

**Alps Electric Co., Ltd. - KAKUDA
PLANT** (1)
6-1 Nishida Kakuda-aza, Kakuda, 981-
1595, Miyagi, Japan
Tel.: (81) 224631211
Electronic Components Mfr
N.A.I.C.S.: 334419

**Alps Electric Co., Ltd. - NAGAOKA
PLANT** (1)
1-3-5 Higashitakami, Nagaoka, 940-8572,
Niigata, Japan
Tel.: (81) 258244111
Web Site: http://www.alps.com
Electronic Components Mfr
N.A.I.C.S.: 334419

**Alps Electric Co., Ltd. - ONAHAMA
PLANT** (1)
41-25 Yanagimachi Noda-aza Onahama,
Iwaki, 971-8126, Fukushima, Japan
Tel.: (81) 246586464
Electronic Components Mfr
N.A.I.C.S.: 334419

**Alps Electric Co., Ltd. - TAIRA
PLANT** (1)
39-1 Sakuhata Oyasaku Yoshima-machi,
Iwaki, 970-1193, Fukushima, Japan
Tel.: (81) 246 36 4511
Web Site: http://www.alps.com
Electronic Components Mfr
N.A.I.C.S.: 334419

**Alps Electric Co., Ltd. - WAKUYA
PLANT** (1)
230 Shibue, Tohda-gun, Miyagi, 981-1595,
Japan
Tel.: (81) 229 43 2711
Web Site: http://www.alps.com
Electronic Components Mfr
N.A.I.C.S.: 334419

Alps Electric Europa GmbH (1)
Hansaallee 203, D 40549, Dusseldorf,
Germany (100%)
Tel.: (49) 21159770
Web Site: http://www.alps.com
Sales Range: $25-49.9 Million
Emp.: 80
N.A.I.C.S.: 334413
Yoichero Kaga (Pres)

Alps Electric Europe GmbH (1)
Gruvgatan 37, 421 30, Vastra Frolunda,
Sweden (100%)
Tel.: (46) 317583300
Web Site: http://www.alps.com

Sales Range: $25-49.9 Million
Emp.: 40
Electronic Component Sales
N.A.I.C.S.: 334413

Alps Electric Europe GmbH (1)
Schiessstrasse 43, 40549, Dusseldorf, Ger-
many
Tel.: (49) 21159770
Web Site: http://www.alps.com
Sales Range: $50-74.9 Million
Emp.: 100
Electrical Component Distr
N.A.I.C.S.: 423610
Wilfried Baumann (Pres)

Plant (Domestic):

**Alps Electric Europe GmbH - Dort-
mund Plant** (2)
Giselherstrasse 4, 44319, Dortmund, Ger-
many
Tel.: (49) 23121880
Emp.: 150
Electronic Components Mfr
N.A.I.C.S.: 334413
Detlev Mucke (Gen Mgr)

Alps Electric Korea Co., Ltd. (1)
33 Hanamsandan 5beon-ro, Gwangsan-gu,
Gwangju, 62217, Korea (South) (100%)
Tel.: (82) 629502114
Web Site: https://www.alpsalpine.com
Sales Range: $200-249.9 Million
Emp.: 800
Book & Magazine Publisher
N.A.I.C.S.: 334413
Kim Kyunam (CEO)

**Alps Electronics Hong Kong
Limited** (1)
Unit No 1 9th Floor Mirror Tower 61 Mody
Road, Tsim Sha Tsui East, Kowloon, China
(Hong Kong) (100%)
Tel.: (852) 2 313 1111
Web Site: http://www.alps.com
Sales Range: $25-49.9 Million
Emp.: 75
Electronic Components Mfr & Sales
N.A.I.C.S.: 334419

**Alps Logistics (Guang Dong) Co.,
Ltd.** (1)
Wangshuishan Chongtoucun Changanzhen,
Dongguan, 523856, Guangdong, China
Tel.: (86) 76938956888
Web Site: http://www.alps-logistics.jp
International Forwarding Service of Air &
Sea Cargo
N.A.I.C.S.: 488320

**Alps Precision (Malaysia) Sdn.
Bhd.** (1)
PT 10643 Nilai Industrial Estate Nalai Post
Office, 71800, Nilai, Negeri Sembilan Daru,
Malaysia
Tel.: (60) 67991515
Web Site: http://www.alps.com.my
Sales Range: $800-899.9 Million
Emp.: 3,000
N.A.I.C.S.: 334413

**Alps de Mexico S. DE R.L. DE
C.V.** (1)
Lote 5-1, Avenida Industrial Del Norte
Parque Industrial Del Norte, 88736, Rey-
nosa, Tamaulipas, Mexico
Tel.: (52) 8999210800
Electric Device Mfr
N.A.I.C.S.: 334419

Alps(China)Co., Ltd. (1)
28F East Tower Hanwei Plaza No 7 Guan-
ghua Road, Chaoyang District, Beijing,
100004, China (100%)
Tel.: (86) 1065393690
Sales Range: $25-49.9 Million
Emp.: 25
Electrical Components Mfr & Distr
N.A.I.C.S.: 334413

Cirque Corporation (1)
2463 S 3850 W, Salt Lake City, UT 84120-
2335
Tel.: (801) 467-1100
Web Site: http://www.cirque.com
Sales Range: $25-49.9 Million
Emp.: 28
Input Technology Products Developer
N.A.I.C.S.: 541512

**DANDONG ALPS ELECTRONICS
CO., LTD.** (1)
No 71-1 Jihuan Road, Tangchi Industrial
Zone Zhenxing District, Dandong, 118303,
Liaoning, China
Tel.: (86) 415 618 9243
Web Site: http://www.alps.com
Electronic Components Mfr & Distr
N.A.I.C.S.: 334419

**DONGGUAN ALPS ELECTRONICS
CO., LTD.** (1)
NO 51 Chang'an Xingfa South Street,
Chang'an Town, Dongguan, 523000,
Guangdong, China
Tel.: (86) 76985536840
Electronic Component Mfr & Distr
N.A.I.C.S.: 334419

**Dalian Alpine Electronics Co.,
Ltd.** (1)
No 2 Yingbin Road, Jinzhou Economic De-
velopment Zone, Dalian, 116100, Liaoning,
China
Tel.: (86) 4118 769 8716
Web Site: http://www.alpine.com
Automobile Communications & Navigation
Equipment Mfr
N.A.I.C.S.: 334413

Dalian Alps Electronics Co. Ltd. (1)
No 6 Hanzheng Road Jinzhou, Economic
Development Zone, Dalian, China
Tel.: (86) 41187675102
Web Site: http://www.alpsco.jp
Electronic Products
N.A.I.C.S.: 334419

**Dan Dong Alpine Electronics,
Inc.** (1)
No 14 Guozhen Rd, Dandong, 51001, Lia-
oning, China (100%)
Tel.: (86) 4156167836
Sales Range: $200-249.9 Million
Emp.: 800
N.A.I.C.S.: 334413

Faital S.p.A. (1)
Via B Buozzi 12, 20090, San Donato Mila-
nese, Italy
Tel.: (39) 025277031
Electric Device Mfr
N.A.I.C.S.: 334419

Greina Technologies, Inc. (1)
1959 S 4130 W Ste H, Salt Lake City, UT
84104
Tel.: (801) 975-6468
Web Site: http://www.rfranging.com
Tracking Device & Product Mfr
N.A.I.C.S.: 334511
Daniel Lee (Co-Founder & CTO)

**NISHIKI ELECTRONICS CO.,
LTD.** (1)
28 Mae Eguri Nishikimachi, Iwaki, 974-
8232, Fukushima, Japan
Tel.: (81) 246 631167
Electronic Components Mfr & Distr
N.A.I.C.S.: 334419

Ningbo Alps Electronics Co., Ltd. (1)
No 299 Jinyuan Road, Zhenhai District,
Ningbo, 315221, Zhejiang, China (100%)
Tel.: (86) 57486599700
Electric Device Mfr
N.A.I.C.S.: 334419

**Taicang Alpine Electronics Co.,
Ltd.** (1)
No 1 Guangzhou West Road, Economic
Development Zone, Taicang, Jiangsu, China
Tel.: (86) 51253568111
Electric Device Mfr
N.A.I.C.S.: 334419

Tianjin Alps Electronics Co., Ltd. (1)
No1 Wei 7 Road Micro-Electronics Indus-
trial Park Jingang Road, Tianjin, 300385,
China
Tel.: (86) 22 839 82577
Web Site: http://www.alps.com
Mfr & Sales of Electronic Components
N.A.I.C.S.: 334419

Tohoku Alps, Co., Ltd. (1)
1 7 Yukigaya Otsuka Cho, Ota Ku, Tokyo,
145 8501, Japan (100%)
Tel.: (81) 337261211
Web Site: http://www.alps.com

Sales Range: $1-4.9 Billion
Emp.: 6,000
N.A.I.C.S.: 334413

Wuxi Alps Electronics Co., Ltd.　(1)
No 5 Xingchuang 4 Road, Singapore Industrial Park, Wuxi, 214028, Jiangsu, China
Tel.: (86) 51085281211
Electric Device Mfr
N.A.I.C.S.: 334419

ALPS INDUSTRIES LIMITED
Plot No 15B G T Road Chaudhary Mor, Sahibabad, Ghaziabad, 201010, India
Tel.: (91) 1204161700
Web Site:
https://www.alpsindustries.com
530715—(BOM)
Rev.: $41,813,199
Assets: $6,209,289
Liabilities: $103,628,561
Net Worth: ($97,419,272)
Earnings: ($11,318,484)
Emp.: 1,334
Fiscal Year-end: 03/31/22
Fashion Accessories, Home Furnishing & Automotive Fabrics Mfr
N.A.I.C.S.: 315990
Sandeep Agarwal *(Mng Dir)*

ALPS LOGISTICS CO., LTD.
1756 Nippa-cho, Kohoku-ku, Yokohama, 223-0057, Kanagawa, Japan
Tel.: (81) 455314133
Web Site: https://www.alps-logistics.com
Year Founded: 1964
9055—(TKS)
Rev.: $785,558,840
Assets: $677,663,810
Liabilities: $244,669,150
Net Worth: $432,994,660
Earnings: $23,597,700
Emp.: 5,867
Fiscal Year-end: 03/31/24
Transportation Services
N.A.I.C.S.: 484121
Koji Fukiyama *(Sr VP & Gen Mgr-Bus Div)*

ALRAI MEDIA GROUP COMPANY K.S.C.
Ardyah Store Plot 1 Block 292, PO Box 2292, Safat, 13023, Kuwait, Kuwait
Tel.: (965) 2 224 4500
Web Site:
http://www.alraimediagroup.com
Year Founded: 2002
ALRAI—(KUW)
Rev.: $24,001,461
Assets: $58,243,288
Liabilities: $24,195,584
Net Worth: $34,047,704
Earnings: ($11,650,262)
Emp.: 867
Fiscal Year-end: 12/31/19
Newspaper Printing & Distribution Services
N.A.I.C.S.: 323111
Mohammed Abdullah Ali Aljumah *(Chm)*

ALROS PRODUCTS LIMITED
350 Wildcat Rd, Toronto, M3J 2N5, ON, Canada
Tel.: (416) 633-2231
Web Site: http://www.polytarp.com
Year Founded: 1957
Rev.: $38,960,490
Emp.: 120
Polyethylene Products Supplier
N.A.I.C.S.: 326113
Marty Benkiel *(Mgr-Construction & GSD)*

ALROSA CO. LTD.

ul Lenina 6, Mirny, 678174, Russia
Tel.: (7) 4113630180
Web Site: http://www.alrosa.ru
Year Founded: 1992
Sales Range: $1-4.9 Billion
Emp.: 30,000
Diamond Exploration, Mining, Polishing & Whslr
N.A.I.C.S.: 212390
Ivan Kirillovich Demyanov *(VP)*

Subsidiaries:

Arcos Hong Kong Ltd.　(1)
64th Floor Central Plaza, Harbour Rd No 18, Wanchai, China (Hong Kong)
Tel.: (852) 25219229
Web Site: http://www.alrosa.ru
Sales Range: $50-74.9 Million
Emp.: 3
Jewelry, Watch, Precious Stone & Precious Metal Whslr
N.A.I.C.S.: 423940
Timur Yigorov *(Mng Dir)*

Arcos Limited　(1)
2nd Floor 86 Hatton Garden, London, EC1N8QQ, United Kingdom
Tel.: (44) 2078313004
Sales Range: $50-74.9 Million
Emp.: 5
Activities for Nonmetallic Minerals
N.A.I.C.S.: 213115

ALROV PROPERTIES & LODGINGS LTD.
The Alrov Tower 46 Rothschild Blvd, Tel Aviv, 66883, Israel
Tel.: (972) 37147777
Web Site: https://www.alrov.co.il
ALRPR—(TAE)
Rev.: $355,133,300
Assets: $4,872,584,259
Liabilities: $2,913,033,523
Net Worth: $1,959,550,736
Earnings: ($61,619,283)
Fiscal Year-end: 12/31/23
Other Activities Related to Real Estate
N.A.I.C.S.: 531390
Alfred Akirov *(Chm)*

Subsidiaries:

Australian Wool Industries Ltd.　(1)
Level 3 24 York Street, Sydney, 2000, NSW, Australia
Tel.: (61) 282953100
Web Site: https://www.wool.com
Wool Fabric Mfr & Distr
N.A.I.C.S.: 313220

Epic Suisse AG　(1)
Seefeldstrasse 5a, 8008, Zurich, Switzerland
Tel.: (41) 443888100
Web Site: https://www.epic.ch
Real Estate Manangement Services
N.A.I.C.S.: 531390
Roni Greenbaum *(Chm)*

Epic Suisse Property Management GmbH　(1)
Chemin du Levant 23, 1005, Lausanne, Switzerland
Tel.: (41) 443888100
Real Estate Development Services
N.A.I.C.S.: 531390

European Property Investment Corporation Limited　(1)
11 St Christophers Place, London, W1U 1NG, United Kingdom
Tel.: (44) 2074866671
Web Site: https://www.epicgroup.eu
Real Estate Investment Services
N.A.I.C.S.: 531390

ALS LIMITED
32 Shand Street, Stafford, 4053, QLD, Australia
Tel.: (61) 732437222　　　　AU
Web Site: https://www.alsglobal.com
Year Founded: 1863

ALQ—(ASX)
Rev.: $1,605,007,509
Assets: $2,409,988,932
Liabilities: $1,629,588,587
Net Worth: $780,400,344
Earnings: $9,780,270
Emp.: 19,565
Fiscal Year-end: 03/31/24
Consumer Products; Industrial Chemicals, Including Hygienic; Laboratory Services
N.A.I.C.S.: 325998
Michael Pearson *(Sec)*

Subsidiaries:

ACIRL Quality Testing Services Pty Ltd　(1)
7 Brisbane Road, Riverview, 4303, QLD, Australia
Tel.: (61) 738105200
Web Site: http://www.alsglobal.com
Emp.: 6
Inspection & Testing Services
N.A.I.C.S.: 926150
Wes Membrey *(Gen Mgr)*

ALS Burkina SARL　(1)
Porte 629 Blvd Tansoba Tabkom Zone Kossodo Secteur 25 Kossodo 11, BP 235, Ouaga CMS 11, Ouagadougou, Burkina Faso
Tel.: (226) 5 035 6077
Laboratory Services
N.A.I.C.S.: 541380

ALS Chemex (Guangzhou) Ltd.　(1)
48 Hongmian Avenue, Huadu District, Guangzhou, 51800, China
Tel.: (86) 203 687 5966
Laboratory Services
N.A.I.C.S.: 541380

ALS Chita Laboratory LLC　(1)
35a Traktovaya Street, Zabaykalsky Krai, 672014, Chita, Russia
Tel.: (7) 3022283050
Laboratory Services
N.A.I.C.S.: 541380

ALS Denmark AS　(1)
Bakkegardsvej 406 A, 3050, Humlebaek, Denmark
Tel.: (45) 4 925 0770
Web Site: https://www.alsglobal.dk
Emp.: 80
Laboratory Services
N.A.I.C.S.: 541380

ALS Dominican Republic SAS　(1)
Av Isabel Aguiar Corner of Calle I, Herrera Industrial Zone Oeste National District, Santo Domingo, 11113, Dominican Republic
Tel.: (809) 537 0695
Laboratory Services
N.A.I.C.S.: 541380

ALS Food & Pharmaceutical Polska Sp. z o.o.　(1)
Rubiez 46E, 61-612, Poznan, Poland
Tel.: (48) 61 423 6016
Web Site: https://www.alsglobal.pl
Emp.: 12,000
Laboratory Services
N.A.I.C.S.: 541380

ALS Ghana Limited　(1)
Plot 1-4 Block A New Brofoyedu, Kumasi, Ghana
Tel.: (233) 54 444 4449
Laboratory Services
N.A.I.C.S.: 541380

ALS Inspection Mozambique Service, Lda.　(1)
Rua Joe Slovo 1st Floor 102 Joaquim Laper Street, Maputo, Mozambique
Tel.: (258) 82 494 8370
Laboratory Services
N.A.I.C.S.: 541380

ALS Inspection Netherlands BV　(1)
Geyssendorfferweg 58, Zuid Holland, 3088 GK, Rotterdam, Netherlands
Tel.: (31) 10 428 7888
Laboratory Services
N.A.I.C.S.: 541380

ALS Inspection South Korea Limited　(1)

Second Floor 11 Singyeong-gil, Onsan-eup Ulju-Gun, Ulsan, 689-890, Korea (South)
Tel.: (82) 52 237 2033
Laboratory Services
N.A.I.C.S.: 541380

ALS Inspection UK Limited　(1)
1 and 2 Caddick Road Knowsley Business Park, Merseyside, Prescot, L34 9HP, United Kingdom
Tel.: (44) 151 548 7777
Laboratory Services
N.A.I.C.S.: 541380

ALS Italia S.r.l.　(1)
Via Viatta 1, 33080, Zoppola, PN, Italy
Tel.: (39) 043 463 8200
Web Site: https://www.alsglobal.it
Emp.: 100
Laboratory Services
N.A.I.C.S.: 541380

ALS Laboratories (UK) Ltd.　(1)
7-8 Aspen Court Centurion Business Park Bessemer Way, Rotherham, S60 1FB, United Kingdom
Tel.: (44) 135 469 7028
Web Site: https://www.als-testing.co.uk
Laboratory Services
N.A.I.C.S.: 541380

ALS Laboratory Group Norway AS　(1)
Drammensveien 264, 0283, Oslo, Norway
Tel.: (47) 2 213 1800
Web Site: https://www.alsglobal.no
Chemistry Laboratory Services
N.A.I.C.S.: 541380

ALS SK, s.r.o.　(1)
Kirejevska 1678, Rimavska Sobota, 97901, Slovakia
Tel.: (421) 94 855 5851
Web Site: https://www.mikrolab.sk
Metallurgical Testing Services
N.A.I.C.S.: 541380

ALS Scandinavia AB　(1)
Aurorum 10, 977 75, Lulea, Sweden
Tel.: (46) 92 028 9900
Web Site: https://www.alsglobal.se
Laboratory Services
N.A.I.C.S.: 541380

ALS Services PLC　(1)
Nifas Silk Subcity Wereda 09 House No 1659, Addis Ababa, 22898, Oromia, Ethiopia
Tel.: (251) 11 471 7299
Laboratory Services
N.A.I.C.S.: 541380

ALS Testing Services India Private Limited　(1)
No 65 Bommasandra Jigani Link Road Kiadb Industrial Area, Bengaluru, 560105, India
Tel.: (91) 8061116000
Laboratory Testing Services
N.A.I.C.S.: 621511

ALS Testing Services NZ Limited　(1)
36B Seaview Road, Seaview Wellington, Lower Hutt, 5010, New Zealand
Tel.: (64) 4 586 6202
Laboratory Services
N.A.I.C.S.: 541380

Aquimisa S.L.　(1)
C/ Hoces del Duraton n 30-34 Pl El Montalvo II, 37008, Salamanca, Spain
Tel.: (34) 92 319 3343
Web Site: https://www.aquimisa.com
Food & Beverage Services
N.A.I.C.S.: 722310

Australian Laboratory Group (Zambia) Limited　(1)
Stand No 1318 Lukuasu Road Industrial Area, Ndola, Copperbelt, Zambia
Tel.: (260) 97 937 6284
Laboratory Services
N.A.I.C.S.: 541380

Australian Laboratory Services (ALS) (Cambodia) Co., Ltd.　(1)
No 75 National Road No 4 Group 5 Sangkat Chom Chao, Phnom Penh, Cambodia
Tel.: (855) 9 943 4534
Laboratory Services

ALS Limited—(Continued)
N.A.I.C.S.: 541380

Australian Laboratory Services Pty. Ltd. (1)
32 Shand St, Stafford, Brisbane, 4053, QLD, Australia **(100%)**
Tel.: (61) 732437222
Web Site: http://www.alsglobal.com.au
Sales Range: $75-99.9 Million
Emp.: 350
Laboratory Services
N.A.I.C.S.: 541380
Greg Afflick (Controller-Fin)

Subsidiary (Non-US):

ALS Canada Ltd (2)
393 University Avenue Suite 1701, Toronto, M5G 1E6, ON, Canada
Tel.: (416) 497-2267
Web Site: https://als.ca
Analytical Laboratories Operators
N.A.I.C.S.: 541380
Arthur J. Hudson (Founder)

ALS Chemex South Africa (Proprietary) Ltd (2)
53 Angus Crescent, Long Meadow Business Park, Edenvale, 1610, Gauteng, South Africa
Tel.: (27) 116080555
Web Site: http://www.alsglobal.com
Emp.: 70
Testing Laboratories
N.A.I.C.S.: 541380
Martin Stone (Gen Mgr)

ALS Chemex de Mexico S.A. de C.V. (2)
FCO Silva Romero Antes Jazmin 1140 Sector Reforma, Col San Carlos, 44460, Guadalajara, Jalisco, Mexico
Tel.: (52) 3336197438
Web Site: http://www.alsglobal.com
Sales Range: $10-24.9 Million
Emp.: 15
Chemical Testing Laboratory Services
N.A.I.C.S.: 541380
Ray Mundo Solorcano (Gen Mgr)

Unit (Domestic):

ALS Coal - Collie (2)
Lot 2073 Collins Street, Collie, 6225, WA, Australia
Tel.: (61) 897343622
Web Site: http://www.alsglobal.com
Emp.: 20
Oil & Gas Exploration Services
N.A.I.C.S.: 213112
Clayton Flynn (Bus Mgr)

Subsidiary (Non-US):

ALS Czech Republic s.r.o (2)
Na Harfa 336/9, 190 00, Prague, Czech Republic
Tel.: (420) 226226228
Web Site: http://www.alsglobal.cz
Sales Range: $75-99.9 Million
Emp.: 300
Testing Laboratories
N.A.I.C.S.: 541380

Subsidiary (US):

ALS Environmental (2)
1317 S 13th Ave, Kelso, WA 98626-2845
Tel.: (360) 577-7222
Web Site: http://www.alsglobal.com
Testing Laboratory Services
N.A.I.C.S.: 541715

ALS Environmental (2)
301 Fulling Mill Rd, Middletown, PA 17057-3500
Tel.: (717) 944-5541
Web Site: http://www.alsglobal.com
Testing Laboratory Services
N.A.I.C.S.: 541380

Subsidiary (Non-US):

ALS Finland OY (2)
Ruosilankuja 3 A, 00390, Helsinki, Finland
Tel.: (358) 10 470 1200
Web Site: http://www.alsglobal.fi
Testing Laboratory Services
N.A.I.C.S.: 541380

Subsidiary (US):

ALS Group USA, Corp (2)
3352 128th Ave, Holland, MI 49424-9263
Tel.: (616) 399-6070
Web Site: http://www.alsglobal.com
Sales Range: $10-24.9 Million
Emp.: 50
Testing Laboratories
N.A.I.C.S.: 541380

Subsidiary (Domestic):

ALS Industrial Holdings Pty. Ltd. (2)
109 Bannister Road, Canning Vale, 6155, WA, Australia **(100%)**
Tel.: (61) 8 9232 0300
Sales Range: $50-74.9 Million
Holding Company; Industrial Testing & Engineering Services
N.A.I.C.S.: 551112

Subsidiary (Domestic):

ALS Industrial Australia Pty. Ltd. (3)
109 Bannister Road, Canning Vale, 6155, WA, Australia
Tel.: (61) 892320400
Web Site: http://www.alsglobal.com
Industrial Testing & Engineering Services
N.A.I.C.S.: 541330

Subsidiary (Non-US):

ALS Laboratory Group (Thailand) Co. Ltd (2)
615 Ramkhamheang Road Bang Kapi, Bangkok, 10240, Thailand
Tel.: (66) 27158700
Food Product Testing Services
N.A.I.C.S.: 541380

Subsidiary (Domestic):

ALS Metallurgy Holdings Pty. Ltd. (2)
6 MacAdam Place, Balcatta, 6021, WA, Australia
Tel.: (61) 893442416
Web Site: http://www.alsglobal.com
Sales Range: $25-49.9 Million
Emp.: 200
Metallurgical & Mineral Testing Consulting Services
N.A.I.C.S.: 213115
Greg Kilmister (Mng Dir)

Unit (Domestic):

ALS Metallurgy - Burnie (3)
39 River Rd, Burnie, 7320, TAS, Australia
Tel.: (61) 364316333
Metallurgical Testing Laboratory
N.A.I.C.S.: 541380
John Glen (Mgr)

Subsidiary (Non-US):

ALS Patagonia S.A (2)
Los Ebanistas 8521 Parque Industrial, La Reina, Santiago, Chile
Tel.: (56) 24345060
Analytical Laboratory Services
N.A.I.C.S.: 541380

ALS Peru S.A. (2)
Calle Uno Mz D Lt 1 A, Callao, 01, Peru
Tel.: (51) 15745700
Web Site: http://www.alsglobal.com
Emp.: 20
Laboratory Testing Services
N.A.I.C.S.: 541380
Gilliand Ortiz (Gen Mgr)

ALS Poland Sp. z.o.o (2)
Marokanska 4H, Warsaw, 00-001, Poland
Tel.: (48) 228551031
Emp.: 5
Testing Laboratories
N.A.I.C.S.: 541380
Artur Wajda (Mng Dir)

ALS Taiwan Co. Ltd (2)
530-1 Chung Shan Rd Fl 10 Sec 2, Chungho, Taipei, 23557, Taiwan
Tel.: (886) 282281355
Web Site: http://www.alstaiwan.com.tw
Sales Range: $25-49.9 Million
Emp.: 70
Laboratory Testing Services
N.A.I.C.S.: 541380

ALS Technichem (HK) Pty Ltd (2)
11 F Chung Shun Knitting Ctr 1-3 Wing Yip St, Kwai Chung, China (Hong Kong)
Tel.: (852) 26101044
Sales Range: $25-49.9 Million
Emp.: 90
Testing Laboratories
N.A.I.C.S.: 541380
Richard Fung (Gen Mgr)

ALS Technichem (Singapore) Pte Ltd (2)
121 Genting Lane 04-01 ALS Building, Singapore, 349572, Singapore
Tel.: (65) 65890118
Web Site: http://www.alsglobal.com
Emp.: 100
Laboratory Testing Services
N.A.I.C.S.: 541380
Yao Kai Wen (Gen Mgr)

ALS Testing Services (Thailand) Co. Ltd (2)
75/37 Moo 11 Tumbol Khlong Nueng Amphoe, Khlong Luang, Pathum Thani, Thailand
Tel.: (66) 29081681
Food Product Testing Services
N.A.I.C.S.: 541380

Subsidiary (US):

ALS USA, Inc (2)
4977 Energy Way, Reno, NV 89502-4105
Tel.: (775) 356-5395
Web Site: https://www.alsglobal.com
Sales Range: $50-74.9 Million
Emp.: 100
Mining & Mineral Exploration Services
N.A.I.C.S.: 213113

Subsidiary (Domestic):

Ecowise Environmental Pty Ltd (2)
16B Lithgow St, PO Box 1834, Fyshwick, 2609, Australia
Tel.: (61) 262025400
Web Site: http://www.ecowise.com.au
Environmental Management Services
N.A.I.C.S.: 541620

Subsidiary (Non-US):

Witlab (Proprietary) Ltd (2)
1 Gryhoak Str Extension 23 Tasbet Prk Mpumalanga, Witbank, 1034, South Africa
Tel.: (27) 136928000
Web Site: http://www.alsglobal.com
Mineral Exploration Services
N.A.I.C.S.: 213115
Grahan Condie (Mng Dir)

Australian Laboratory Services Suriname N.V. (1)
Parasolmierstraat no 2528 Loods 2 Geyersvlijt, Paramaribo, Suriname
Tel.: (597) 453057
Laboratory Services
N.A.I.C.S.: 541380

Controlvet - Seguranca Alimentar, SA (1)
Zona Industrial de Tondela ZIM II Lote 6, 3460-070, Tondela, Portugal
Tel.: (351) 23 281 7817
Web Site: https://www.controlvet.com
Laboratory Services
N.A.I.C.S.: 541380

Ecowise Australia Pty Ltd (1)
22 Dalmore Dr, Scoresby, 3179, VIC, Australia
Tel.: (61) 387568000
Web Site: http://www.ecowise.com.au
Emp.: 100
Agricultural Support Services
N.A.I.C.S.: 115310
Geoff Anderson (Gen Mgr)

Group de Laboratoire ALS Mail SARL (1)
Koulouba-Sogonafing B P E, Bamako, 2670, Mali
Tel.: (223) 2 021 3137
Laboratory Services
N.A.I.C.S.: 541380

Laboratorio de Control ARJ, S. A. de C. V. (1)
Chicle N 134 Col Granjas Mexico Del Izta-

calco, 08400, Mexico, Mexico
Tel.: (52) 555 650 0600
Web Site: https://www.arj.mx
Environmental Services
N.A.I.C.S.: 541620

OMAC Laboratories Limited (1)
IDA Business Park Dublin Road, Loughrea, Galway, H62 PN80, Ireland
Tel.: (353) 9 184 1741
Laboratory Services
N.A.I.C.S.: 541380

Pandee Services Pty Ltd (1)
28 Gray Street, Kilkenny, 5009, SA, Australia
Tel.: (61) 8 8347 1999
Web Site: http://www.pandee.com.au
Logistics Consulting & Distribution Services
N.A.I.C.S.: 541614

Reservoir Group Limited (1)
Muirtonside Whirecairns, Aberdeen, AB23 8UP, United Kingdom
Tel.: (44) 1651863000
Web Site: http://www.reservoirgroup.com
Holding Company; Oil & Gas Drilling, Completion & Production Technologies Mfr & Services
N.A.I.C.S.: 551112
Pascal Bartette (Mng Dir)

Subsidiary (Domestic):

Corpro Group Limited (2)
Muirtonside, Whitecairns, Aberdeen, AB23 8UP, United Kingdom
Tel.: (44) 1651 863 000
Web Site: http://www.corpro-group.com
Holding Company; Oil & Gas Drilling & Geological Surveying Services
N.A.I.C.S.: 551112
Doug Kinsella (Mng Dir)

Subsidiary (Non-US):

Quest Coring Inc. (3)
8 26313 Township Road 531A, Acheson, T7X 5A3, AB, Canada
Tel.: (780) 955-2288
Oil & Gas Drilling Services
N.A.I.C.S.: 213111
Steve McCallum (Mgr-Intl Ops)

Subsidiary (US):

Empirica LLC (2)
6510 Guhn Road, Houston, TX 77040
Tel.: (713) 466-7400
Web Site: http://www.alsglobal.com
Sales Range: $75-99.9 Million
Emp.: 135
Oil & Gas Surface Logging & Other Support Services
N.A.I.C.S.: 213112
Jordan Dawson (Dir-Ops)

Subsidiary (Domestic):

Interica Limited (2)
First Floor North Suite Sackville House Brooks Close, Lewes, BN7 2FZ, East Sussex, United Kingdom
Tel.: (44) 1825745100
Web Site: http://www.interica.com
Sales Range: $25-49.9 Million
Emp.: 40
Information Management Software & Consultancy Services
N.A.I.C.S.: 541511

Subsidiary (Domestic):

Interica Limited (3)
5 Swan Business Park Sandpit Road, Dartford, DA1 5ED, Kent, United Kingdom
Tel.: (44) 1322285921
Web Site: http://www.interica.com
Sales Range: $1-9.9 Million
Emp.: 40
Geotechnical Asset & Information Management Services
N.A.I.C.S.: 541990
Simon Kendall (CEO)

Subsidiary (US):

Interica, Inc. (3)
16000 Barkers Point Ln Ste 120, Houston, TX 77079
Tel.: (832) 981-6577

Web Site: https://interica.com
Sales Range: $1-9.9 Million
Emp.: 4
Information Management Software & Consultancy Services
N.A.I.C.S.: 541511

Subsidiary (US):

Mudlogging Systems, Inc. **(2)**
2521 Weslo Ct, Grand Junction, CO 81505
Tel.: (970) 243-3044
Web Site: http://www.mudlogsys.com
Emp.: 10
Digital Gas Detection Systems & Software Mfr
N.A.I.C.S.: 333132
Andy Kelley *(Pres)*

Subsidiary (Domestic):

Omega Well Monitoring **(2)**
Kirkhill Industrial Estate, Dyce, AB21 7DU, AB, United Kingdom
Tel.: (44) 1224772763
Web Site: http://www.omegawell.com
Sales Range: $1-9.9 Million
Emp.: 10
Oil & Gas Downhole Memory Tools & Surveying Gauges Designer, Mfr & Whslr
N.A.I.C.S.: 333132
Neil Matheson *(Mng Dir)*

Subsidiary (Non-US):

Omega Well Monitoring **(3)**
105 1437-47th Ave NE, Calgary, T2E 6N7, AB, Canada
Tel.: (403) 232-1400
Web Site: http://www.reservoirgroup.com
Emp.: 20
Oil & Gas Downhole Measurement Tools Designer, Mfr & Whslr
N.A.I.C.S.: 333132
Camila Nazer *(Gen Mgr)*

York Analytical Laboratories, Inc **(1)**
120 Research Dr, Stratford, CT 06615
Tel.: (800) 306-9675
Web Site: http://www.yorklab.com
Sales Range: $1-9.9 Million
Research & Development in Biotechnology
N.A.I.C.S.: 541714
Michael J. Beckerich *(Pres & CEO)*

ALSAIF STORES FOR DEVELOPMENT & INVESTMENT COMPANY

Emam Saud bin Abdulaziz bin Mohammed Street, Altaawon, Riyadh, Saudi Arabia
Tel.: (966) 112293562
Web Site:
   https://www.alsaifgallery.com
Year Founded: 1993
4192—(SAU)
Rev.: $191,936,245
Assets: $250,921,966
Liabilities: $143,577,440
Net Worth: $107,344,526
Earnings: $26,182,432
Emp.: 1,084
Fiscal Year-end: 12/31/23
Investment Management Service
N.A.I.C.S.: 523999
Suleiman Mohammed Al-Saif *(Chm)*

ALSEA, S.A.B. DE C.V.

Avenida Revolucion No 1267 Torre Corporativa Piso 21 Colonia Los Alpes, Delegation Alvaro Obregon, CP 01040, Mexico, Mexico
Tel.: (52) 5575832000   MX
Web Site: https://www.alsea.net
ALSEA—(MEX)
Rev.: $1,935,164,763
Assets: $4,194,425,143
Liabilities: $3,810,671,755
Net Worth: $383,753,388
Earnings: ($195,824,674)
Emp.: 60,000
Fiscal Year-end: 12/31/20
Fresh Pizzas Mfr
N.A.I.C.S.: 311991

Xavier Mangino Duenas *(Sec-Technical)*
Subsidiaries:

Distribuidora e Importadora Alsea, S. A. de C. V. **(1)**
Avenue Tlahuac 6768, Santiago, Zapotiltic, 13300, Jalisco, Mexico
Tel.: (52) 5558623000
Fast Food Restaurants Services
N.A.I.C.S.: 722513

Especialistas en Restaurantes de Comida Estilo Asiatica, S. A. de C. V. **(1)**
Boulevard Pureta De Hierro 5225 Sn, Puebla, 72500, Mexico
Tel.: (52) 3336113294
Sales Range: $10-24.9 Million
Emp.: 90
Fast Food Distr
N.A.I.C.S.: 722513

Fast Food Sudamericana, S. A. **(1)**
Avenida Del Libertador 1295 Edificio Libertador Park Piso 30, Vicente Lopez, 1638, Buenos Aires, Argentina
Tel.: (54) 1155307000
Web Site: http://www.burgerking.com.ar
Fast Food Store Operation Services
N.A.I.C.S.: 722513
Pablo de los Heros *(Gen Mgr)*

Food Service Project, SL **(1)**
Camino de la Zarzuela 1, Madrid, Spain
Tel.: (34) 913829800
Restaurant Operators
N.A.I.C.S.: 722511
Rafael Herrero *(Mgr)*

Subsidiary (Domestic):

Grupo Vips **(2)**
Calle Pedro de Valdivia, 28006, Madrid, Spain
Tel.: (34) 91 590 66 82
Web Site: http://www.grupovips.com
Emp.: 8,000
Holding Company; Restaurant Operator
N.A.I.C.S.: 551112
Placido Arango *(Pres)*

Subsidiary (Domestic):

Starbucks Coffee Espana S.L. **(3)**
C/ Maria de Molina 41, 28006, Madrid, Spain **(100%)**
Tel.: (34) 902423423
Web Site: http://www.starbucks.es
Cafeteria Operator
N.A.I.C.S.: 722515

Operadora de Franquicias Alsea, S. A. de C. V. **(1)**
Jose Maria Pino Suarez SN La Merced Centro Cuauhtemoc, 06090, Mexico, Mexico **(80%)**
Tel.: (52) 4493122226
Fast Food Franchise Operator
N.A.I.C.S.: 722513

Starbucks Coffee Argentina S.R.L. **(1)**
Av del Libertador 1295 Vicente Lopez, Buenos Aires, B1638BEL, Argentina
Tel.: (54) 1155307000
Web Site: http://www.starbucks.com.ar
Cafeteria Operator
N.A.I.C.S.: 722515

ALSHAMEL INTERNATIONAL HOLDING COMPANY K.S.C.P.

Sharq-Khaled Bin Al-Waleed St Kipco Tower Floor 30, PO Box 28406, Safat, 13145, Kuwait, Kuwait
Tel.: (965) 22976000   KW
Year Founded: 1996
Holding Company
N.A.I.C.S.: 551112

ALSINCO SA

Nafpliou Str 8, Metamorfosi, 14452, Athens, Greece
Tel.: (30) 210 284 3076
Web Site: http://www.alsinco.gr
Year Founded: 1992

Emp.: 32
Footwear & Apparel Retailer
N.A.I.C.S.: 424340
George Avramidis *(Founder, Pres & CEO)*

ALSTAR OILFIELD CONTRACTORS LTD.

310-East River Road, Hinton, T7V 2G3, AB, Canada
Tel.: (780) 865-5938
Web Site:
   http://www.alstaroilfield.com
Year Founded: 1969
Sales Range: $10-24.9 Million
Emp.: 120
Oil Filed Construction Services
N.A.I.C.S.: 213112
Scott Fofonoff *(Pres)*

ALSTOM S.A.

48 rue Albert Dhalenne, 93400, Saint-Ouen, France
Tel.: (33) 157068778   FR
Web Site: https://www.alstom.com
Year Founded: 1988
ALO—(EUR)
Rev.: $17,814,590,978
Assets: $33,883,013,166
Liabilities: $24,060,004,317
Net Worth: $9,823,008,850
Earnings: ($142,456,292)
Emp.: 78,419
Fiscal Year-end: 03/31/23
Railroad Rolling Mfr
N.A.I.C.S.: 335312
Gian Luca Erbacci *(Sr VP-Europe)*

Subsidiaries:

ALSTOM Algerie Societe par Actions **(1)**
Cooperative Immobiliere-El-Amel Lots N 3 Et 4 Said Hamdine, Bp 47, Bir Mourad Rai, 16000, Algiers, Algeria
Tel.: (213) 21605745
Railroad Rolling Stock & Component Mfr
N.A.I.C.S.: 336510

ALSTOM Argentina S.A. **(1)**
Av L N Alem 896 7 Floor, C1001AAQ, Buenos Aires, Argentina
Tel.: (54) 1148919600
N.A.I.C.S.: 813312

ALSTOM Baltics SIA **(1)**
Mukusalas Iela 42A, Riga, 1004, Latvia
Tel.: (371) 26006013
Railroad Rolling Stock & Component Mfr
N.A.I.C.S.: 336510

ALSTOM Czech Republic A.S. **(1)**
Vaclavske Namesti 47, 110 00, Prague, 1, Czech Republic
Tel.: (420) 487802119
Emp.: 1,100
Railroad Rolling Stock & Component Mfr
N.A.I.C.S.: 336510

ALSTOM Ferroviaria Portugal, S.A.
Rua Odette De Saint-Maurice 3L Piso 0 Escritorio A, 1700-921, Lisbon, Portugal
Tel.: (351) 214969100
Railroad Rolling Stock & Component Mfr
N.A.I.C.S.: 336510

ALSTOM Flertex S.A.S. **(1)**
41 Rue Jean Jaures, 92232, Gennevilliers, Cedex, France
Tel.: (33) 146139320
Web Site: https://flertex.fr
Railway Metal Friction Material Mfr
N.A.I.C.S.: 332312

ALSTOM Hungary Kft. **(1)**
Vaci Ut 152-158, 1138, Budapest, Hungary
Tel.: (36) 706506950
Emp.: 650
Railroad Rolling Stock & Component Mfr
N.A.I.C.S.: 336510

ALSTOM Investment Company Limited **(1)**
10F Cura International Center No 500

Hongqiao Road, Xuhui District, Shanghai, 200030, China
Tel.: (86) 2161033888
Railroad Equipment Distr
N.A.I.C.S.: 423860

ALSTOM Israel Ltd. **(1)**
8 Shaul Hamelech Blvd Amot Mishpat Bldg 1st Floor, Tel Aviv, 6473307, Israel
Tel.: (972) 723387430
Railroad Rolling Stock & Component Mfr
N.A.I.C.S.: 336510

ALSTOM Kazakhstan LLP **(1)**
Tel.: (7) 7172620740
Railroad Equipment Mfr
N.A.I.C.S.: 336510

ALSTOM Khadamat S.A. **(1)**
113 Ostad Motahari Ave, 15769-18911, Tehran, Iran
Tel.: (98) 2188742779
Railroad Equipment Distr
N.A.I.C.S.: 423860

ALSTOM Korea Transport Ltd. **(1)**
19Fl 358 Gangnam-daero, Gangnam-gu, Seoul, 06241, Korea (South)
Tel.: (82) 221616200
Railroad Equipment Distr
N.A.I.C.S.: 423860

ALSTOM Netherlands B.V. **(1)**
Vliegend Hertlaan 45 8th Floor, 3526 KT, Utrecht, Netherlands
Tel.: (31) 857991030
Emp.: 450
Railroad Rolling Stock & Component Mfr
N.A.I.C.S.: 336510

ALSTOM Panama, S.A. **(1)**
PH Capital Plaza Piso 6 Oficina 602 Costa del Este, Panama, Panama
Tel.: (507) 3773800
N.A.I.C.S.: 336510

ALSTOM Polska Spolka Akcyjna **(1)**
Ul Emilii Plater 53, 00-113, Warsaw, Poland
Tel.: (48) 225406600
Emp.: 4,000
Railroad Rolling Stock & Component Mfr
N.A.I.C.S.: 336510

ALSTOM Proyectos de Transporte, SRL **(1)**
Av Reyes Catolicos Casi Esq Maximo Gomez Antigua Cementera, Santo Domingo, Dominican Republic
Tel.: (809) 3345019
Railroad Rolling Stock & Component Mfr
N.A.I.C.S.: 336510

ALSTOM Schienenfahrzeuge AG **(1)**
Victor-von-Bruns Strasse 19, 8212, Neuhausen am Rheinfall, Switzerland
Tel.: (41) 525339210
Railroad Equipment Distr
N.A.I.C.S.: 423860

ALSTOM Services Italia S.p.A. **(1)**
Via Nomentana 41, 00161, Rome, Italy
Tel.: (39) 0683531801
Railroad Equipment Mfr
N.A.I.C.S.: 336510

ALSTOM Signalling, Limited Liability Company **(1)**
Bolsunovska 13-15 Str 8th Floor, 01014, Kiev, Ukraine
Tel.: (380) 444904549
Railroad Rolling Stock & Component Mfr
N.A.I.C.S.: 336510

ALSTOM Transport (Thailand) Co., Ltd. **(1)**
118/1 USA Bldg 4th Fl Unit 4M Vibhavadi Rangsit Rd, Chomphon Chatuchak, Bangkok, 10900, Thailand
Tel.: (66) 20214928
Railroad Equipment Distr
N.A.I.C.S.: 423860

ALSTOM Transport Australia Pty Limited **(1)**
Level 4 16 Giffnock Avenue, North Ryde, Sydney, 2113, NSW, Australia
Tel.: (61) 288706000
Railroad Equipment Distr
N.A.I.C.S.: 423860

ALSTOM Transport Austria GmbH **(1)**

Alstom S.A.—(Continued)

Hermann-Gebauer-Strasse 5, 1220, Vienna, Austria
Tel.: (43) 13950926044
Emp.: 800
Railroad Rolling Stock & Component Mfr
N.A.I.C.S.: 336510

ALSTOM Transport Azerbaijan LLC (1)
75 Rasul Rza Winterpark Plaza 17th floor, AZ1014, Baku, Azerbaijan
Tel.: (994) 124040738
Web Site: https://www.alstom.com
Emp.: 30
Railroad Equipment Distr
N.A.I.C.S.: 423860

ALSTOM Transport Canada Inc. (1)
1050 Cote du Beaver Hall 18th Floor, Montreal, H2Z 0A5, QC, Canada
Tel.: (514) 764-1725
Railroad Equipment Distr
N.A.I.C.S.: 423860

ALSTOM Transport Hungary Zrt. (1)
Vaci ut 152-156, 1138, Budapest, Hungary
Tel.: (36) 709842770
Railroad Equipment Distr
N.A.I.C.S.: 423860

ALSTOM Transport India Limited (1)
601-B 6th Floor Tower -1, Konnectus - Bhavbhuti Marg, New Delhi, 110001, India
Tel.: (91) 1166196700
Railroad Equipment Distr
N.A.I.C.S.: 423860
Bernard Delpit (CFO & Exec VP)

ALSTOM Transport Norway AS (1)
Drammensveien 165, 0277, Oslo, Norway
Tel.: (47) 22892600
Web Site: https://www.alstom.com
Emp.: 80
Railroad Equipment Distr
N.A.I.C.S.: 423860

ALSTOM Transport Systems (Malaysia) Sdn. Bhd. (1)
Level 25 Axiata Tower No 9 Jalan Stesen Sentral 5 Kuala Lumpur Sentral, 50470, Kuala Lumpur, Malaysia
Tel.: (60) 322764756
Emp.: 80
Railroad Rolling Stock & Component Mfr
N.A.I.C.S.: 336510

ALSTOM Transport Vietnam Inc. (1)
Suite 902 Capital Tower 109 Tran Hung Dao Street, Hoan Kiem District, 100000, Hanoi, Vietnam
Tel.: (84) 437475304
Railroad Equipment Distr
N.A.I.C.S.: 423860

ALSTOM Transportation Colombia S.A.S. (1)
Cra 7 No 71-21 Piso 5 Torre A, 110221, Bogota, Colombia
Tel.: (57) 13582405
Railroad Rolling Stock & Component Mfr
N.A.I.C.S.: 336510

ALSTOM Transportation Germany GmbH (1)
Ernst-Reuter-Platz 6, 10587, Berlin, Germany
Tel.: (49) 30166361300
Emp.: 9,600
Railroad Rolling Stock & Component Mfr
N.A.I.C.S.: 336510

ALSTOM Ulasim Anonim Sirketi Ankara Subesi (1)
Altunizade Mah Mahir Iz Cad No 9/1, Uskudar, 34662, Istanbul, Turkiye
Tel.: (90) 2164002100
Railroad Equipment Distr
N.A.I.C.S.: 423860

Alstom (Shared Services) Philippines, Inc. (1)
5F South Park Plaza Paseo De Magallanes Commercial Complex, Manila, Makati, 1232, Philippines
Tel.: (63) 28860777
Railroad Rolling Stock & Component Mfr
N.A.I.C.S.: 336510

Alstom Holdings (1)
3th Ave Andre Malraux, 92300, Levallois-Perret, Cedex, France
Tel.: (33) 141492000
Holding Company
N.A.I.C.S.: 551112

Subsidiary (Non-US):

Alstom (China) Investment Co. Ltd (2)
5 F Entrance C Qian Kun Plaza 6 West Street, San Li Tun District, Beijing, 100027, China
Tel.: (86) 1084609000
Web Site: http://www.cn.alstom.com
Holding Company
N.A.I.C.S.: 551112

Alstom Algerie S.p.A. (2)
153 Rue Ali Khodja El Biar Hydra, Algiers, Algeria
Tel.: (213) 21929719
Gas Turbine Mfr & Distr
N.A.I.C.S.: 333611

Alstom Asia Pacific Sdn. Bhd. (2)
5th Floor Chulan Tower 3 Jalan Conlay, Kuala Lumpur, 50450, Malaysia
Tel.: (60) 3 2055 6000
Emp.: 50
Power Plant Construction Engineering Services
N.A.I.C.S.: 237130
Ling Fang (Sr VP-Asia Pacific)

Subsidiary (Domestic):

Alstom Services Sdn. Bhd. (3)
5th Floor Chulan Tower 3 Jalan Conlay, Kuala Lumpur, 50450, Malaysia
Tel.: (60) 3 2055 6000
Emp.: 50
Industrial Equipment Distr
N.A.I.C.S.: 423830

Subsidiary (Non-US):

Alstom Australia Ltd (2)
Level 4 16 Giffnock Avenue, North Ryde, 2113, NSW, Australia (100%)
Tel.: (61) 28 870 6000
Web Site: https://www.alstom.com
Sales Range: $75-99.9 Million
Emp.: 1,600
Energy Generation & Distribution Equipment Mfr, Railroad Equipment Mfr & IT Services
N.A.I.C.S.: 333611

Alstom Austria GmbH (2)
Clemens-Holzmeister-Strasse 4, 1109, Vienna, Austria
Tel.: (43) 1608880
Web Site: http://alstom.echonet.at
Sales Range: $50-74.9 Million
Emp.: 80
Electric Power Generation & Transmission Services
N.A.I.C.S.: 221118
Josef Reisel (CEO & Exec Dir)

Alstom Belgium SA (2)
50-52 rue Cambier Dupret, 6001, Charleroi, Belgium
Tel.: (32) 71445411
Sales Range: $200-249.9 Million
Emp.: 1,000
Holding Company
N.A.I.C.S.: 551112

Subsidiary (Domestic):

Alstom Transport Belgium (3)
South Center Titanium Place, Marcel Broodthaers 8, B 6001, Charleroi, Belgium
Tel.: (32) 71445607
Sales Range: $150-199.9 Million
Emp.: 800
Sales, Marketing & Mfr of Rail & Locomotive Products
N.A.I.C.S.: 336510

Subsidiary (Non-US):

Alstom Brasil Ltda. (2)
Virgilio Wey Street 150 Agua Branca, Sao Paulo, 05036-050, SP, Brazil
Tel.: (55) 1136178000
Sales Range: $400-449.9 Million
Emp.: 700
Electrical Transformer Mfr

N.A.I.C.S.: 334416

Alstom Chile S.A (2)
Edificio Birmann Sanchez Fontecilla 310 of 101, Santiago, Chile (100%)
Tel.: (56) 22908500
Web Site: http://www.alstom.cl
Sales Range: $100-124.9 Million
Emp.: 200
Power Generation, Distribution & Transmission Services; Railroad Equipment Mfr
N.A.I.C.S.: 221122

Alstom Danmark A/S (2)
Ringager 2A, DK-2605, Brondby, Denmark (100%)
Tel.: (45) 46900100
Sales Range: $25-49.9 Million
Emp.: 22
Sales & Marketing of Rail & Locomotive Products
N.A.I.C.S.: 336510

Alstom Deutschland AG (2)
Boveristrasse 22, D 68309, Mannheim, Germany (100%)
Tel.: (49) 6213290
Web Site: http://www.de.alstom.com
Sales Range: $25-49.9 Million
Emp.: 1
Energy &Transport Infrastructure Services
N.A.I.C.S.: 333611

Subsidiary (Domestic):

Alstom Carbon Capture GmbH (3)
Lorenz-Schott-Strasse 4, 55252, Mainz-Kastel, Germany
Tel.: (49) 61347120
Eltric Power Generation Services
N.A.I.C.S.: 221118
Kai Uwe Krauel (Gen Mgr)

Alstom Transport Deutschland GmbH (3)
Linke-Hofmann-Busch Strasse 1, 38239, Salzgitter, Germany
Tel.: (49) 53419000
Web Site: http://www.de.alstom.com
Transport Systems Developer, Designer & Mfr
N.A.I.C.S.: 336510

Affiliate (Domestic):

Alstom Lokomotiven Service GmbH (4)
Tangermunderstrasse 23A, D 29576, Stendal, Germany
Tel.: (49) 0393125400
Web Site: http://www.transport.alstom.com
Sales Range: $25-49.9 Million
Emp.: 175
Locomotive Refurbishment Services: Joint Venture of Alstom (51%) & Deutsche Bahn AG (49%)
N.A.I.C.S.: 336510

Subsidiary (Non-US):

Alstom Espana IB (2)
Calle Martinez Villergas 49-edificio V, 28027, Madrid, Spain (100%)
Tel.: (34) 913345800
Sales Range: $1-4.9 Billion
Emp.: 3,100
Holding Company
N.A.I.C.S.: 551112

Subsidiary (Domestic):

Alstom Transporte SA (3)
Castellana 257 Planta 6, 28046, Madrid, Spain (100%)
Tel.: (34) 913345700
Web Site: http://www.es.alstom.com
Sales Range: $100-124.9 Million
Emp.: 300
Locomotive, Train Control Systems & Parts Mfr & Service
N.A.I.C.S.: 336510

Subsidiary (Non-US):

Alstom Finland Oy (2)
Martinkylantie 43, 1720, Vantaa, Finland
Tel.: (358) 10 3037 100
Sales Range: $300-349.9 Million
Emp.: 50
Electric Power Generation & Transmission Services

N.A.I.C.S.: 221118
Sari Luhanka (Country Dir-Comm)

Alstom Gulf Area (2)
Crescent Twr 4 Fl, Al Buhaira Corniche Rd, 25448, Sharjah, United Arab Emirates (100%)
Tel.: (971) 65563971
Web Site: http://www.alstom.com
Sales Range: $25-49.9 Million
Emp.: 10
Energy Generation & Distribution Equipment; Thermal & Nuclear Powerplant Turbogenerators; Industrial Equipment; Railroad Equipment
N.A.I.C.S.: 333611

Alstom Hong Kong Ltd. (2)
Unit 1011-12 10F New Kowloon Plaza 38 Tai Kok Tsui Road, Kowloon, China (Hong Kong)
Tel.: (852) 27246300
Sales Range: $100-124.9 Million
Emp.: 10
Electric Power Generation & Transmission Services
N.A.I.C.S.: 221118

Alstom K.K. (2)
3-4 Minatojima Chuo Ku, Nakamachi 2 Chome, Chuo Ku, 650 0046, Kobe, Japan
Tel.: (81) 78 303 5790
Web Site: http://www.jp.alstom.com
Energy Generation & Distribution Equipment; Thermal & Nuclear Powerplant Turbogenerators; Industrial Equipment; Railroad Equipment; Shipbuilding
N.A.I.C.S.: 333611

Subsidiary (Domestic):

Nihon Kengyo K.K. (3)
2-3 Shindenasahimachi, Daito, 574-0053, Osaka, Japan
Tel.: (81) 728721581
Eltric Power Generation Services
N.A.I.C.S.: 221118

Subsidiary (Non-US):

Alstom Konstal S.A. (2)
ul Metalowcow 9, 41-500, Chorzow, Poland
Tel.: (48) 323491266
Eltric Power Generation Services
N.A.I.C.S.: 221118

Alstom LLC (2)
18 Shchipok Str Building 2, 115093, Moscow, Russia
Tel.: (7) 495 231 29 49
Sales Range: $550-599.9 Million
Emp.: 60
Electric Power Generation & Transmission Services
N.A.I.C.S.: 221118
Philippe Pegorier (Pres)

Subsidiary (Domestic):

Alstom Hydro (3)
18 Shchipok Str Building 2, Moscow, 115093, Russia
Tel.: (7) 4959899909
Sales Range: $75-99.9 Million
Emp.: 10
Hydroelectric Power Generation & Transmission Services
N.A.I.C.S.: 221111

Subsidiary (Non-US):

Alstom Ltd. (2)
The Place 175 High Holborn, London, WC1V 7AA, United Kingdom
Tel.: (44) 2074389230
Web Site: https://www.alstom.com
Emp.: 6,000
General Management
N.A.I.C.S.: 561110
Nick Crossfield (Mng Dir)

Subsidiary (Domestic):

Alstom Transport Regional Trains (3)
Hoole Bridge Hoole Road, Chester, CH2 3DJ, United Kingdom
Tel.: (44) 1244 605873
Sales Range: $25-49.9 Million
Train Repair & Maintenance Services
N.A.I.C.S.: 488210

Angelo Cuffaro *(Mng Dir)*

Subsidiary (Non-US):

Alstom Mexico SA de CV   **(2)**
Montes Urales No 727, Col Lomas de
Chapultepec, 11000, Mexico,
Mexico   **(100%)**
Tel.: (52) 5511010700
Sales Range: $25-49.9 Million
Emp.: 30
Holding Company
N.A.I.C.S.: 551112

Subsidiary (Domestic):

Alstom Transporte SA de CV   **(3)**
Montesurales No 727 Lomis de Chapulte-
pec, 11520, Mexico, Mexico   **(100%)**
Tel.: (52) 5511010700
Sales Range: $25-49.9 Million
Locomotive, Train Control Systems & Parts
Mfr & Service
N.A.I.C.S.: 336510

Subsidiary (Non-US):

Alstom N.V.   **(2)**
Koopmansstraat 7, 2288 BC, Rijswijk, Neth-
erlands
Tel.: (31) 704132833
Holding Company
N.A.I.C.S.: 551112

Alstom Nederland BV   **(2)**
Koopmansstraat 7, 2288 BC, Rijswijk,
Netherlands   **(50%)**
Tel.: (31) 74132833
Sales Range: $25-49.9 Million
Emp.: 50
Equipment for Power Generation; Transmis-
sion & Distribution, Railway Systems, Ship-
building
N.A.I.C.S.: 485112

Subsidiary (Domestic):

Alstom Transport B.V.   **(3)**
Koopmansstraat 7, 2288 BC, Rijswijk,
Netherlands   **(100%)**
Tel.: (31) 704132830
Sales Range: $50-74.9 Million
Motors, Generators, Traction Drive Sys-
tems, Crane Drive Systems, Power Sup-
plies, Servicing/Refurbishing
N.A.I.C.S.: 335312
Leon Linden *(Gen Mgr)*

Alstom Transport BV   **(3)**
Ringdijk 390C, 2983 GS, Ridderkerk, Neth-
erlands
Tel.: (31) 180453999
Web Site: https://www.alstom.com
Railroad Electrical Equipment Mfr
N.A.I.C.S.: 336510

Subsidiary (Non-US):

Alstom New Zealand Ltd   **(2)**
2A Simsey Place Te Rapa, 3200, Hamilton,
New Zealand   **(100%)**
Tel.: (64) 795 79260
Sales Range: $25-49.9 Million
Emp.: 12
Holding Company
N.A.I.C.S.: 551112
Grant Taylor *(Mgr-Fin & Ops)*

Subsidiary (Domestic):

**Alstom Transport New Zealand
Ltd**   **(3)**
Gate 1, Hellaby's Road, Private Box 22430,
Otahuhu, Auckland, New Zealand
Tel.: (64) 92720540
Locomotive Maintenance Services
N.A.I.C.S.: 336510

Subsidiary (Non-US):

Alstom Norway AS   **(2)**
Drammensveien 165, 0277, Oslo, Norway
Tel.: (47) 22127000
Sales Range: $150-199.9 Million
Emp.: 20
Electric Power Generation & Transmission
Services
N.A.I.C.S.: 221118
Eric Staurset *(Pres & Mng Dir)*

Subsidiary (Domestic):

Alstom Vannkraft AS   **(3)**
Drammensveien 165, 277, Oslo, Norway
Tel.: (47) 22127000
Emp.: 40
Hydroelectric Power Generation Services
N.A.I.C.S.: 221111
Nils Ottesen *(Mng Dir)*

Subsidiary (Non-US):

**Alstom Renewable Power Canada
Inc.**   **(2)**
1350 Chemin St-Roch, Sorel-Tracy, J3R
5P9, QC, Canada
Tel.: (450) 746-6500
Sales Range: $100-124.9 Million
Emp.: 300
Wind Turbine Mfr
N.A.I.C.S.: 333611

Alstom S&E Africa (Pty) Ltd   **(2)**
Country Club Estates 21 Woodlands Drive,
Woodmead, 2191, South Africa
Tel.: (27) 11 518 8100
Web Site: http://www.alstom.com
Sales Range: $150-199.9 Million
Emp.: 200
Electric Power Generation & Transmission
Services
N.A.I.C.S.: 221118
Jerome Boyet *(Pres)*

Subsidiary (Domestic):

Alstom Ubunye (Pty) Ltd.   **(3)**
Marivale Road, Vosterkroon, Nigel, 1490,
South Africa   **(51%)**
Tel.: (27) 11 733 0000
Electric Locomotives, Freight Wagons &
Rail Cars Designer & Mfr
N.A.I.C.S.: 336510

Subsidiary (Non-US):

Alstom S.p.A.   **(2)**
Via O Moreno 23, 12038, Savigliano, CN,
Italy
Tel.: (39) 0172716306
Web Site: http://www.alstom.com
Holding Company
N.A.I.C.S.: 551112

Subsidiary (Domestic):

Alstom Ferroviaria S.p.A.   **(3)**
Via Ottavio Moreno 23, 12038, Savigliano,
CN, Italy
Tel.: (39) 0172718111
Web Site: https://www.alstom.com
Locomotive Mfr
N.A.I.C.S.: 336510

Branch (Domestic):

**Alstom Ferroviaria S.p.A. -
Bologna**   **(4)**
Via Di Corticella 75, 40128, Bologna, Italy
Tel.: (39) 051 416 3594
Web Site: https://www.alstom.com
Locomotive, Train Control Systems & Parts
Mfr & Service
N.A.I.C.S.: 336510

**Alstom Ferroviaria S.p.A. -
Modugno**   **(4)**
Via dei Gladioli 5, 70123, Modugno, BA,
Italy
Tel.: (39) 080 538 0812
Web Site: https://www.alstom.com
Train Detection & Signalling Systems De-
veloper
N.A.I.C.S.: 335999

Subsidiary (Non-US):

Alstom Slovakia, s.r.o.   **(2)**
Prievozska 4, 821 09, Bratislava, Slovakia
Tel.: (421) 232 251 001
Eletric Power Generation Services
N.A.I.C.S.: 221118

Alstom Switzerland Ltd   **(2)**
Brown Boveri Str 7, 5401, Baden,
Switzerland   **(100%)**
Tel.: (41) 562057733
Web Site: http://www.alstom.ch
Sales Range: $800-899.9 Million
Emp.: 3,000

Power Generation Systems & Equipment
Design, Engineering & Manufacture
N.A.I.C.S.: 333611
Walter Granicher *(Pres-Power Svcs)*

Alstom Taiwan Ltd   **(2)**
408 Rui Guang Road 8F-5, Neihu District,
Taipei, 11492, Taiwan
Tel.: (886) 226525900
Web Site: http://www.alstom.com.tw
Emp.: 80
Electric Power Generation & Transmission
Services
N.A.I.C.S.: 221113

Alstom Transport AB   **(2)**
PO Box 739, 10135, Stockholm, Sweden
Tel.: (46) 87236581
Web Site: http://www.transport.alstom.com
Sales Range: $25-49.9 Million
Emp.: 100
Locomotive Mfr
N.A.I.C.S.: 336510

Subsidiary (US):

Alstom Transportation Inc.   **(2)**
1025 John St, West Henrietta, NY 14586
Tel.: (585) 783-2000
Web Site: http://www.transport.alstom.com
Rail Transport Control Sys
N.A.I.C.S.: 334290

Subsidiary (Domestic):

Alstom Signaling Inc.   **(3)**
1025 John St, West Henrietta, NY 14586
Tel.: (585) 783-2000
Web Site:
  http://www.alstomsignalingsolutions.com
Sales Range: $150-199.9 Million
Emp.: 657
Mfr & Whslr of Transportation Control
Equipment for Railroad & Rail Mass Transit
Systems
N.A.I.C.S.: 334290

Alstom Signaling Operation, LLC   **(3)**
120 S Central Ave, Clayton, MO 63105
Tel.: (816) 650-3112
Web Site: http://www.getransportation.com
Emp.: 75
Railroad Signaling Devices
N.A.I.C.S.: 334290

Branch (Domestic):

Alstom Transportation Inc   **(3)**
1 Transit Dr, Hornell, NY 14843
Tel.: (607) 324-4595
Web Site: http://www.transport.alstom.com
Sales Range: $25-49.9 Million
Emp.: 200
Railroad Stock Mfr
N.A.I.C.S.: 336510

Subsidiary (Non-US):

Alstom Vietnam Ltd.   **(2)**
Suite 902 Capital Tower 109 Tran Hung
Dao Street, Hoan Kiem, 100000, Hanoi,
Vietnam
Tel.: (84) 437475304
Emp.: 2
Electric Power Generation & Transmission
Services
N.A.I.C.S.: 221118
Hoang Ngoc Tuan *(Gen Dir)*

Alstom s.r.o.   **(2)**
Olomoucka 7/9, 656 66, Brno, Czech Re-
public
Tel.: (420) 545101111
Emp.: 20
Eletric Power Generation Services
N.A.I.C.S.: 221118
Jiri Filip *(Country Mgr-Transport)*

Joint Venture (Non-US):

CASCO Signal Ltd.   **(2)**
11F Building 2 Shibei One Center No 21
Lane 1401 Jiangchang Road, Jing'an Dis-
trict, Shanghai, 200070, China
Tel.: (86) 2156637080
Web Site: https://www.casco.com.cn
Sales Range: $25-49.9 Million
Emp.: 2,000
Engineering Services
N.A.I.C.S.: 541330

Joint Venture (US):

GE Grid Solutions LLC   **(2)**
7000 West Bert Kouns Industrial Loop,
Shreveport, LA 71129
Tel.: (678) 844-6777
Web Site: http://www.gegridsolutions.com
Emp.: 20,000
Electricity Distribution
N.A.I.C.S.: 221122
Reinaldo Garcia *(CEO)*

Subsidiary (Non-US):

Nomad Digital Limited   **(2)**
6th Floor One Trinity Broad Chare,
Newcastle upon Tyne, NE1 2HF, United
Kingdom
Tel.: (44) 2070966966
Web Site: https://www.nomad-digital.com
Transportation Communication Equipment &
Services
N.A.I.C.S.: 517112
Reece Donovan *(CEO)*

Subsidiary (Non-US):

Nomad Digital BV   **(3)**
Waarderweg 33 B1-B5, 2031 BN, Haarlem,
Netherlands
Tel.: (31) 23 551 0031
Web Site: https://www.nomad-digital.com
Fleet Management Services
N.A.I.C.S.: 488210

Nomad Digital GmbH   **(3)**
Hafenstrasse 24b, 31137, Hildesheim, Ger-
many
Web Site: https://www.nomad-digital.com
Fleet Management Services
N.A.I.C.S.: 488210

Subsidiary (US):

Nomad Digital Inc.   **(3)**
Ste 201 9707 Key W Ave, Rockville, MD
20850
Tel.: (240) 479-4633
Web Site: https://nomad-digital.com
Fleet Management Services
N.A.I.C.S.: 488210

Subsidiary (Non-US):

Nomad Digital Pty Limited   **(3)**
Level 4 190 St Georges Terrace, Perth,
6000, WA, Australia
Tel.: (61) 862311440
Fleet Management Services
N.A.I.C.S.: 532411
Moin Majid *(Gen Mgr)*

**Bombardier Transportation
GmbH**   **(1)**
Schoneberger Ufer 1, 10785, Berlin, 10785,
Germany
Tel.: (49) 30986070
Sales Range: $1-4.9 Billion
Emp.: 31,570
Rail Vehicles for Urban & Mainline Opera-
tions, Modernization of Rolling Stock & Op-
erations & Maintenance Services
N.A.I.C.S.: 336510
Claas Belling *(Head-External Comm-Global)*

Subsidiary (Non-US):

**Bombardier Transpaortation Israel
Ltd.**   **(2)**
11 Menachem Begin Street, PO Box 3463,
Ramat Gan, 52136, Israel
Tel.: (972) 3 612 1106
Sales Range: $25-49.9 Million
Emp.: 15
Railway Transportation Services
N.A.I.C.S.: 488210
Yael Dror *(Gen Mgr)*

**Bombardier Transport France
S.A.S.**   **(2)**
1 Place Des Ateliers, 59154, Crespin,
France
Tel.: (33) 327235300
Sales Range: $350-399.9 Million
Emp.: 2,000
Mfr of Double-Decker, Self-Propelled Com-
muter Cars, Subway Cars, Turbo Trains &
Cars for the French High-Speed TGV train
N.A.I.C.S.: 336510

Alstom S.A.—(Continued)

Division (Domestic):

Bombardier Transport France S.A.S. - Services Division (3)
Les Collines de l Arche Immeuble Opera E, 92057, Paris, France
Tel.: (33) 1 41 45 0808
Emp.: 1
Railroad Rolling Stock Mfr
N.A.I.C.S.: 336510

Subsidiary (Domestic):

Bombardier Transport (Bahn-technologie) Germany GmbH (2)
Kablower Weg 89, 12526, Berlin, Germany (100%)
Tel.: (49) 3067931509
Sales Range: $25-49.9 Million
Emp.: 160
Light Rail & Locomotives Mfr
N.A.I.C.S.: 333618
Germar Wacker (Head-Mainline & Metros Segment-Central & Eastern Europe)

Subsidiary (Non-US):

Bombardier Transportation (China) Ltd. (2)
Room 2003-2005 Suite A China Shine Plaza No 9 Lin He Xi Road, Tian He District, Guangzhou, 510610, Guangdong, China
Tel.: (86) 2038108791
Web Site: http://www.cn.bombardier.com
Emp.: 40
Transport Equipment Parts & Accessories Mfr
N.A.I.C.S.: 336360

Bombardier Transportation (Holdings) UK Ltd. (2)
Derby Carriage Works, Derby, DE24 8AD, United Kingdom
Tel.: (44) 1332344666
Sales Range: $400-449.9 Million
Emp.: 180
Railroad Equipment Mfr
N.A.I.C.S.: 336510
Andy Derbyshire (Gen Dir)

Bombardier Transportation (Malaysia) Sdn. Bhd. (2)
Level 25 Axiata Tower No 9 Jalan Stesen, Sentral 5, Kuala Lumpur Sentral, 50470, Kuala Lumpur, Malaysia
Tel.: (60) 322722386
Emp.: 80
Transportation Services
N.A.I.C.S.: 488999

Bombardier Transportation (Netherland) B.V. (2)
De Ruyterkade 6, Amsterdam, 1013 AA, Netherlands
Tel.: (31) 203445720
Sales Range: $25-49.9 Million
Emp.: 41
Transportation Services
N.A.I.C.S.: 488999
Roger Hall (Mgr-Sls)

Bombardier Transportation (Obsluga Klienta) Polska Sp. z.o.o. (2)
ul Aleksandrowska 67/93, 91-205, Lodz, Poland
Tel.: (48) 42 613 2666
Web Site: http://www.bombardier.com
Transportation Equipment Mfr
N.A.I.C.S.: 336999

Subsidiary (Domestic):

Bombardier Transportation (Propulsion & Controls) Germany GmbH (2)
Am Rathenaupark, 16761, Brandenburg, Germany
Tel.: (49) 3302890
Sales Range: $50-74.9 Million
Emp.: 250
Railroad Rolling Stock Mfr
N.A.I.C.S.: 336510
Ragnar Joris (Principal-Legal Council)

Subsidiary (Non-US):

Bombardier Transportation (Rail Engineering) Polska Sp. z o.o. (2)

ul Ogrodowa 58, 00-876, Warsaw, Poland
Tel.: (48) 22 520 2122
Web Site: http://www.bombardier.com
Sales Range: $25-49.9 Million
Emp.: 50
Railroad Rolling Stock Mfr
N.A.I.C.S.: 336510

Bombardier Transportation (Rolling Stock) UK Ltd (?)
Derby Carriage Works Litchurch Lane, Derby, DE24 8AD, United Kingdom
Tel.: (44) 1332257500
Web Site: http://www.btros.co.uk
Sales Range: $50-74.9 Million
Emp.: 200
Railroad Equipment Mfr.
N.A.I.C.S.: 336510

Bombardier Transportation (Shared Services) Philippines Inc. (2)
14th Floor TGU Tower JM Del Mar Avenue corner Salinas Drive, Asiatown IT Park Apas, Cebu, 6000, Philippines
Tel.: (63) 325051914
Web Site: http://www.bombardier.com
Sales Range: $100-124.9 Million
Emp.: 300
Financial Management Services
N.A.I.C.S.: 523999

Subsidiary (Domestic):

Bombardier Transportation (Signal) Germany GmbH (2)
Wolfenbutteler Strasse 86 / Oberbergstr 5, Braunschweig, 38102, Germany
Tel.: (49) 5312240
Sales Range: $75-99.9 Million
Emp.: 15
Electric & Electronic Component Mfr.
N.A.I.C.S.: 327910
Johann Konigshofer (Gen Mgr)

Subsidiary (Non-US):

Bombardier Transportation (Switzerland) Ltd. (2)
Brown Boveri-Strasse 5, 8050, Zurich, Switzerland
Tel.: (41) 44 318 33 33
Web Site: http://www.bombardier-transportation.ch
Sales Range: $250-299.9 Million
Emp.: 900
Rail Transportation Equipment Distr
N.A.I.C.S.: 423860

Bombardier Transportation (ZWUS) Polska Sp. z o.o. (2)
Ul Modelarska 12, 40-142, Katowice, Poland
Tel.: (48) 32 730 5000
Sales Range: $125-149.9 Million
Emp.: 50
Rail Transportation Services
N.A.I.C.S.: 488210
Slawomir Nalewajka (Pres)

Bombardier Transportation AB (2)
Ostra Ringvagan 2, 72173, Vasteras, Sweden
Tel.: (46) 21317000
Web Site: http://www.bombardier.com
Sales Range: $350-399.9 Million
Emp.: 2,000
Railway Equipment & Weather Data Systems Mfr
N.A.I.C.S.: 335312

Bombardier Transportation AG (2)
Zurcher Strasse 39, 8401, Winterthur, Switzerland
Tel.: (41) 522641010
Web Site: http://www.transportation.bombardier.com
Sales Range: $25-49.9 Million
Emp.: 50
Locomotives & Gears Mfr
N.A.I.C.S.: 333618

Bombardier Transportation Australia Pty. Ltd. (2)
3rd Floor North Tower John Oxley Center 339 Coronation Drive, Milton, Brisbane, 4064, QLD, Australia
Tel.: (61) 738582400
Sales Range: $25-49.9 Million
Emp.: 6
Rail Transportation Services

N.A.I.C.S.: 488210
Per Allmer (Pres-Western Europe, Middle East, Africa, South East Asia &)

Bombardier Transportation Austria GmbH (2)
Hermann Gebauer Strasse 5, 1220, Vienna, Austria
Tel.: (43) 1251100
Sales Range: $200-249.9 Million
Emp.: 65
Light Rail Vehicle Mfr & Distr
N.A.I.C.S.: 333618
Christian Diewald (Gen Mgr)

Bombardier Transportation Belgium (2)
Vaartdijkstraat 5, 8200, Brugge, Belgium (100%)
Tel.: (32) 50401111
Web Site: http://www.bombardier.com
Sales Range: $250-299.9 Million
Emp.: 800
Mfr of Locomotives, Railway Freight & Passenger Cars, Subway Cars & Light Rail Vehicles
N.A.I.C.S.: 336510

Bombardier Transportation Brasil Ltda. (2)
Av Das Nacoes Unidas 4 777 Conjunto 7 A, Sao Paulo, 05477-000, Brazil
Tel.: (55) 1135384700
Transportation Equipment Mfr
N.A.I.C.S.: 336999

Bombardier Transportation Czech Republic A/S (2)
Svatopluka Cecha 1205, 470 01, Ceska Lipa, Czech Republic
Tel.: (420) 487802111
Web Site: https://bombardier.trudo.cz
Sales Range: $150-199.9 Million
Emp.: 1,000
Component Mfr for Rolling Stock
N.A.I.C.S.: 333618

Bombardier Transportation Denmark A/S (2)
Toldbodgade 39, 8900, Randers, Denmark
Tel.: (45) 86425300
Web Site: http://www.dk.bombardier.com
Sales Range: $25-49.9 Million
Emp.: 4
Railroad Rolling Stock Renovation
N.A.I.C.S.: 336510

Bombardier Transportation Equipment (Suzhou) Co., Ltd. (2)
1 Qiming Road Free Trade Zone Suzhou Industrial Park, Suzhou, 215121, Jiangsu, China
Tel.: (86) 512 6733 3200
Emp.: 22
Propulsion & Controls Machinery Mfr
N.A.I.C.S.: 333248
Monika David (Gen Mgr)

Bombardier Transportation Holdings (Thailand) Ltd. (2)
3354 / 16-19 Manorom Bldg 2nd Floor Rama 4 Rd, Klongton Klontoey, 10110, Bangkok, Thailand
Tel.: (66) 26728290
Web Site: http://www.bombardier.com
Investment Management Service
N.A.I.C.S.: 523940

Bombardier Transportation Hungary Kft. (2)
Szabadsag ut 51, 3143, Matranovak, Hungary
Tel.: (36) 32 548 310
Emp.: 620
Railroad Rolling Stock Mfr
N.A.I.C.S.: 336510

Bombardier Transportation Korea Ltd. (2)
4th Fl Samwha Bldg 21 Sokong-dong, Joong-ku, 100-070, Seoul, Korea (South)
Tel.: (82) 27766133
Sales Range: $25-49.9 Million
Emp.: 2
Railroad Rolling Stock Mfr
N.A.I.C.S.: 336510
Wonhee Lee (Dir-Fin)

Bombardier Transportation North America Inc. (2)

1101 Parent Street, Saint-Bruno, J3V 6E6, QC, Canada
Tel.: (450) 441-2020
Transportation Services
N.A.I.C.S.: 488999

Subsidiary (Non-US):

Bombardier Mexico, S.A. De C.V. (3)
Isaac Newton 1650, Parque Industrial AJ Bermudez, Chihuahua, 32470, Mexico (100%)
Tel.: (52) 6923700
Sales Range: $100-124.9 Million
Emp.: 350
Transportation Aerostructures & Engineering
N.A.I.C.S.: 333618

Subsidiary (US):

Bombardier Transportation (Holdings) USA Inc. (3)
1501 Lebanon Church Rd, Pittsburgh, PA 15236-1406 (100%)
Tel.: (412) 655-5700
Sales Range: $1-9.9 Million
Production of Railroad Vehicles & Equipment
N.A.I.C.S.: 336510
Frank Swartz (Engr-Software Safety Sys)

Subsidiary (Domestic):

Bombardier Mass Transit Corporation (4)
71 Wall St, Plattsburgh, NY 12901-3755
Tel.: (518) 566-0150
Sales Range: $100-124.9 Million
Emp.: 350
Locomotive Mfr
N.A.I.C.S.: 333618
Dave Black (Gen Mgr)

Bombardier Transit Corporation (4)
261 Mountain View Dr, Burlington, VT 05446 (100%)
Tel.: (802) 764-5232
Web Site: http://www.bombardiertransportation.as com
Sales Range: $25-49.9 Million
Emp.: 4
Manufactures of Rail Cars
N.A.I.C.S.: 541690

Branch (Domestic):

Bombardier Transportation (4)
5727 Northwest 7th St Box 294, Miami, FL 33126
Tel.: (305) 871-4220
N.A.I.C.S.: 541310

Subsidiary (Domestic):

Bombardier Transportation Canada (3)
1101 Parent St, Saint-Bruno, J3V 6E6, QC, Canada
Tel.: (450) 441-2020
Rev.: $1,158,210,048
Emp.: 600
Mfr of Passenger Rail & Freight Cars; Urban, Suburban & Intercity Vehicles as Well as TurnKey Rail Systems Worldwide
N.A.I.C.S.: 336510

Division (Domestic):

Bombardier Transportation Canada - Transit Systems (4)
5095 Taylor Kidd Blvd County Rd 23, Millhaven, K7M 6J9, ON, Canada
Tel.: (613) 384-3100
Sales Range: $50-74.9 Million
Emp.: 220
Street Car Engineering Design Services
N.A.I.C.S.: 333618

Subsidiary (Non-US):

Bombardier Transportation Norway AS (2)
Stasjonsveien 1, PO Box 83, 2011, Strommen, Norway
Tel.: (47) 63809600
Web Site: http://www.bombardier.com
Transportation Equipment Mfr
N.A.I.C.S.: 336999

Bombardier Transportation Polska Sp. z.o.o. (2)
ul Fabryczna 12, 53-609, Wroclaw, Poland
Tel.: (48) 713562000
Web Site: http://www.bombardier.com
Sales Range: $100-124.9 Million
Emp.: 500
Transportation Equipment Mfr
N.A.I.C.S.: 336999

Bombardier Transportation Portugal, S.A. (2)
Edificio Art, 1998-028, Lisbon, Portugal
Tel.: (351) 214969110
Sales Range: $25-49.9 Million
Emp.: 10
Railway Equipment Mfr
N.A.I.C.S.: 335999

Bombardier Transportation Romania SRL (2)
90 Calea 13 Septembrie Grand Offices 2nd Floor Sector 5, 50726, Bucharest, Romania
Tel.: (40) 21 403 44 25
Sales Range: $25-49.9 Million
Emp.: 3
Transportation Services
N.A.I.C.S.: 488999
Mircea Marian *(Country Mgr)*

Bombardier Transportation SA (2)
Zone Industrielle A 26, CH 1844, Villeneuve, Switzerland (100%)
Tel.: (41) 21 967 0505
Web Site:
 http://www.transportbombardier.com
Sales Range: $75-99.9 Million
Emp.: 300
Locomotives & Gears Mfr
N.A.I.C.S.: 333618

Bombardier Transportation Shared Services Romania SRL (2)
Power Business Center Calea Dorobantilor Nr 18-20, 400117, Cluj-Napoca, Romania
Tel.: (40) 264 502 900
Emp.: 450
Transportation Services
N.A.I.C.S.: 488999
Eva Elges *(Gen Mgr)*

Bombardier Transportation South Africa (Pty.) Ltd (2)
22 Milkyway Avenue Linbro Business Park Marlboro Drive, Johannesburg, 2196, Gauteng, South Africa
Tel.: (27) 119978899
Web Site: http://www.bombardier.com
Sales Range: $25-49.9 Million
Emp.: 22
Transportation Services
N.A.I.C.S.: 488999

Bombardier Transportation UK Ltd. (2)
Litchurch Lane, Derby, DE24 8AD, United Kingdom (100%)
Tel.: (44) 1332344666
Web Site:
 http://www.transportation.bombardier.com
Sales Range: $25-49.9 Million
Emp.: 1,800
Transportation Equipment
N.A.I.C.S.: 488510

Bombardier-Wien Schienenfahrzeuge AG (2)
Donaufelder Strasse 73 79, 1211, Vienna, Austria
Tel.: (43) 125110
Sales Range: $150-199.9 Million
Emp.: 600
Light Rail Vehicles Mfr
N.A.I.C.S.: 541611

Btren Mantenimiento Ferroviario S.A. (1)
Complejo Miniparc III Edf K C/ Calendula 93 Soto De La Moraleja, Alcobendas, 28109, Madrid, Spain
Tel.: (34) 916585493
Web Site: https://www.btren.es
Railway Testing & Maintenance Services
N.A.I.C.S.: 811310

Center D'essais Ferroviaires SA (1)
Rue Fresnel, BP 9, Petite-Foret, 59494, Hauts-de-Seine, France
Tel.: (33) 327323024

Web Site: https://www.c-e-f.fr
N.A.I.C.S.: 336510

Centre d'Essais Ferroviaires SAS (1)
Rue Fresnel Bp 9, 59494, Petite-Foret, France
Tel.: (33) 327323025
Web Site: https://www.c-e-f.fr
Railway Testing & Maintenance Services
N.A.I.C.S.: 811310

Electrovoz Kurastyru Zauyty LLP (1)
184 A street b 10 Industrial Park, 010000, Nur-Sultan, Kazakhstan
Tel.: (7) 7172938502
Web Site: http://www.ekz.com.kz
Railroad Equipment Mfr
N.A.I.C.S.: 336510
Julien Naudy *(Gen Dir)*

Gibela Rail Transport Consortium (Pty) Ltd (1)
2 Shosholoza Avenue Dunnottar, Ekurhuleni, Nigel, 1496, South Africa
Tel.: (27) 106000651
Web Site: https://www.gibela-rail.com
Rail Transport Services
N.A.I.C.S.: 482111
Hector Danisa *(CEO)*

Irvia Mantenimiento Ferroviario, S.A. (1)
Tel.: (34) 913345780
Web Site: http://irvia.es
Rail Maintenance Services
N.A.I.C.S.: 488210

Lorelec Sarl (1)
ZI Carrefour de l'EUROPE - Rue Jean Prouve, 57600, Morsbach, France
Tel.: (33) 387911090
Web Site: https://www.lorelec.net
Electrical Installation Services
N.A.I.C.S.: 238210

Nomad Digital Belgium S.A. (1)
Leuvensesteenweg 350, 3190, Boortmeerbeek, Belgium
Tel.: (32) 4402070966966
Business Management Consulting Services
N.A.I.C.S.: 541611

Nomad Digital France SARL (1)
Bureau 108 & 109 Tour Pacific 11 Cours Valmy, Puteaux, 92 800, Paris, France
Tel.: (33) 2070966966
N.A.I.C.S.: 541511

Nomad Digital Italia S.R.L. (1)
Deposito Alstom NTV Via Boscofangone, Nola, 80035, Naples, Italy
Tel.: (39) 0813151062
N.A.I.C.S.: 541511

Nomad Tech, Lda. (1)
Parque Oficinal De Guifoes Rua Do Ferroviario - Gatoes, Guifoes, 4460-020, Matosinhos, Portugal
Tel.: (351) 220969065
Web Site: https://www.nomadtech.pt
N.A.I.C.S.: 541330
Augusto Costa Franco *(Gen Mgr-Software Engineering & Power Systems)*

PT ALSTOM Transport Indonesia (1)
Office Beyond 206-207 - Jl Cimanuk No 6, Bandung, 40115, Indonesia
Tel.: (62) 224205225
Engineeering Services
N.A.I.C.S.: 541330

Rail Engineering Sp. Z o.o. (1)
Aleja Solidarnosci 171, 00-877, Warsaw, Poland
Tel.: (48) 222430700
Web Site: https://www.railre.pl
Emp.: 100
Railroad Design & Engineering Services
N.A.I.C.S.: 237990

Stationone S.A.S. (1)
69-73 Boulevard Victor Hugo, 93400, Saint-Ouen-sur-Seine, France
Tel.: (33) 663308439
Web Site: https://www.station-one.com
Railway Metal Friction Material Mfr
N.A.I.C.S.: 332312

VGT Vorbereitungsgesellschaft Transporttechnik GmbH (1)

Tangermunder Str 23A, 39576, Stendal, Germany
Tel.: (49) 15254511214
Web Site: http://www.vgt-bahn.de
Railroad Services
N.A.I.C.S.: 488210

ALSTONE TEXTILES (INDIA) LTD.
47 18 Basement Rajendra Place Metro Station, New Delhi, 110060, India
Tel.: (91) 1147476072 In
Web Site:
 https://www.alstonetextiles.in
Year Founded: 1985
539277—(BOM)
Assets: $16,962,732
Liabilities: $9,732
Net Worth: $16,953,000
Earnings: ($11,971)
Emp.: 2
Fiscal Year-end: 03/31/21
Textile Products Mfr
N.A.I.C.S.: 314999
Deepak Kumar Bhojak *(Mng Dir)*

ALSTRIA OFFICE REIT-AG
Steinstrasse 7, D-20095, Hamburg, Germany
Tel.: (49) 40226341300 De
Web Site: https://www.alstria.de
Year Founded: 2006
AOX—(MUN)
Rev.: $211,976,156
Assets: $4,677,671,202
Liabilities: $2,892,106,284
Net Worth: $1,785,564,918
Earnings: ($721,235,542)
Emp.: 184
Fiscal Year-end: 12/31/23
Real Estate Investment Trust
N.A.I.C.S.: 525990
Olivier Elamine *(CEO & Member-Mgmt Bd)*

Subsidiaries:

DO Deutsche Office AG (1)
Backerbreitergang 75, 20355, Hamburg, Germany (94.6%)
Tel.: (49) 40 226 341 300
Web Site: http://www.deutsche-office.de
Rev.: $116,152,919
Assets: $1,878,257,419
Liabilities: $1,106,193,538
Net Worth: $772,063,881
Earnings: ($85,998,546)
Fiscal Year-end: 12/31/2015
Real Estate Investment Trust
N.A.I.C.S.: 525990
Olivier Elamine *(Vice Chm-Supervisory Bd)*

ALSUWAIKET TRADING & CONTRACTING CO.
Prince Mohammed St Cross No 23, PO Box 321, Al Khobar, 31952, Saudi Arabia
Tel.: (966) 138985000
Web Site: http://www.alsuwaiket.com
Sales Range: $900-999.9 Million
Emp.: 750
Holding Company Oil & Gas Industrial Travel Trading Agricultural & Catering Services
N.A.I.C.S.: 551112

Subsidiaries:

AlSuwaiket Agriculture Division (1)
PO Box 691, Dhahran, 31932, Saudi Arabia
Tel.: (966) 501422680
Agricultural Services
N.A.I.C.S.: 111998

AlSuwaiket Education Division (1)
PO Box 691, Dhahran, 31932, Saudi Arabia
Tel.: (966) 38575603
Education Services
N.A.I.C.S.: 923110
Mobarak A. AlSuwaiket *(Chm)*

AlSuwaiket Furniture & Home Furnishing Division (1)
PO Box 654, Dhahran, 31932, Saudi Arabia
Tel.: (966) 38592170
Sales Range: $50-74.9 Million
Emp.: 100
Homefurnishings
N.A.I.C.S.: 423220

AlSuwaiket Trading & Contracting Co. - Construction Division (1)
PO Box 89644, Riyadh, 11692, Saudi Arabia
Tel.: (966) 479 2680
Oil & Gas Pipeline Drilling & Construction Services
N.A.I.C.S.: 237120

AlSuwaiket Trading & Contracting Co. - Trading Division (1)
PO Box 4228, Al Khobar, 31952, Saudi Arabia
Tel.: (966) 385 91088
Oil & Gas Pipeline Drilling & Construction Services
N.A.I.C.S.: 237120

AlSuwaiket Travel & Tourism Division (1)
PO Box 654, Dhahran, 31932, Saudi Arabia
Tel.: (966) 38944100
Web Site: http://www.travellers-sa.com
Sales Range: $25-49.9 Million
Emp.: 55
Travel & Tourism Services
N.A.I.C.S.: 561510
Mobarak A. AlSuwaiket *(Chm)*

ALT CO., LTD.
82-19 Gwahaksaneop 1-ro Oksanmyeon, Heungdeok-gu Namchon-ri Ochang Scientific Industrial Zone, Cheongju, 28122, Chungbuk, Korea (South)
Tel.: (82) 437112500
Web Site: https://alt-s.kr
Year Founded: 2003
172670—(KRS)
Rev.: $33,992,561
Assets: $141,035,910
Liabilities: $87,842,031
Net Worth: $53,193,879
Earnings: $10,937,490
Emp.: 176
Fiscal Year-end: 12/31/22
Software Development Services
N.A.I.C.S.: 541511
Duck-Hyung Lee *(CEO)*

ALT TELECOM PCL
52/1 Moo 5 Bangkruay-Sainoi Road, Bangsithong Bangkruay, Nonthaburi, 11130, Thailand
Tel.: (66) 28638999
Web Site: https://alt.co.th
Year Founded: 2001
ALT—(THA)
Rev.: $42,811,263
Assets: $105,978,792
Liabilities: $58,905,791
Net Worth: $47,073,001
Earnings: $641,832
Emp.: 279
Fiscal Year-end: 12/31/23
Telecommunications Equipment Mfr
N.A.I.C.S.: 334290
Preeyaporn Tangpaosak *(Pres)*

Subsidiaries:

Innova Telecommunication Company Limited (1)
365 Bond Street Rd, Bangpood, Pak Kret, 11120, Nonthaburi, Thailand
Tel.: (66) 250 339 4749
Web Site: https://www.innovatelecom.co.th
Telecommunications Equipment Mfr
N.A.I.C.S.: 334220

ALTA BANKA A.D.
Bulevar Zorana Djindjica 121, PO Box 59, 11070, Belgrade, Serbia

ALTA banka a.d.—(Continued)

Tel.: (381) 112205 500
Web Site: http://www.jubmes.rs
Year Founded: 1997
JMBN—(BEL)
Sales Range: $1-9.9 Million
Emp.: 130
Banking Services
N.A.I.C.S.: 522110
Rajko Peric (Member-Exec Bd)

ALTA COMPANY
Lot II-3 Group CN 2 Rod No 11 Road
08 Tan Binh Industrial Park, Tay
Thanh Ward Tan Phu District, Ho Chi
Minh City, Vietnam
Tel.: (84) 2822108685
Web Site: https://www.alta.com.vn
Year Founded: 1989
ALT—(HNX)
Rev.: $12,513,717
Assets: $13,461,729
Liabilities: $4,375,275
Net Worth: $9,086,454
Earnings: $289,183
Fiscal Year-end: 12/31/23
Printing & Packaging Products Mfr &
Distr
N.A.I.C.S.: 326112

Subsidiaries:

Au Lac Software Development Com-
pany Limited   (1)
86/33 Au Co, Ward 9 Tan Binh District, Ho
Chi Minh City, Vietnam
Tel.: (84) 2822436888
Web Site: https://altasoftware.vn
Software Development Services
N.A.I.C.S.: 541511

Au Lac Technology Applications Plas-
tics Company Limited   (1)
Lot II-3 Group CN2 11th Drive, Tan Binh
Industrial Park Tay Thanh Ward Tan Phu
Dist, Ho Chi Minh City, Vietnam
Tel.: (84) 2838162884
Information Technology Services
N.A.I.C.S.: 541511

ALTA FLIGHTS (CHARTERS) INC.
3767 56 Avenue East Edmonton In-
ternational Airport, Edmonton, T5J
2T2, AB, Canada
Tel.: (780) 890-1333
Web Site: http://www.altaflights.com
Year Founded: 1986
Rev.: $20,861,440
Emp.: 40
Oil Transportation Services
N.A.I.C.S.: 481212
Bob Lamoureux (Pres)

ALTA S.A.
ul Poznanska 37, 00-689, Warsaw,
Poland
Tel.: (48) 222508840
Web Site: https://www.altasa.pl
AAT—(WAR)
Rev.: $140,498
Assets: $52,173,780
Liabilities: $212,907
Net Worth: $51,960,874
Earnings: $1,927,083
Emp.: 19
Fiscal Year-end: 12/31/23
Investment Management Service
N.A.I.C.S.: 523940
Halina Rogalska (Dir-Fin)

ALTA SKUPINA D.D.
Zelezna Cesta 18, 1000, Ljubljana,
Slovenia
Tel.: (386) 80 10 60
Web Site: http://www.alta.si
Year Founded: 2009
Emp.: 100

Investment Banking & Securities
Dealing
N.A.I.C.S.: 523150
Jasna H. Brdnik (Dir-Projects)

Subsidiaries:

Medvesek Pusnik Borzno posredni-
ska hisa d.d. Ljubljana   (1)
Gradnikove brigade 11, 1000, Ljubljana,
Slovenia
Tel.: (386) 15864450
Web Site: http://www.medvesekpusnik.si
Sales Range: $10-24.9 Million
Emp.: 35
Private Banking, Stock Exchange Trading,
Securities Broking, Tax & Investment Con-
sulting Services
N.A.I.C.S.: 523150

ALTA-FAB STRUCTURES LTD.
504-13 Avenue, Nisku, T9E 7P6, AB,
Canada
Tel.: (780) 955-7733
Web Site: http://www.altafab.com
Year Founded: 1973
Rev.: $46,167,768
Emp.: 300
Modular Building Mfr
N.A.I.C.S.: 332311
Hank Van Weelden (CEO)

ALTAGAS LTD.
1700 355 4th Avenue SW, Calgary,
T2P 0J1, AB, Canada
Tel.: (403) 691-7575   Ca
Web Site: https://www.altagas.ca
Year Founded: 1994
ATGFF—(OTCIQ)
Rev.: $9,695,762,000
Assets: $17,509,366,000
Liabilities: $11,643,568,000
Net Worth: $5,865,798,000
Earnings: $513,994,000
Emp.: 2,893
Fiscal Year-end: 12/31/23
Natural Gas Facilities & Services
N.A.I.C.S.: 221210
Randy W. Toone (Pres-Midstream &
Exec VP)

Subsidiaries:

AltaGas Operating Partnership   (1)
355 4th Avenue Southwest Suite 1700, Cal-
gary, T2P 0J1, AB, Canada   (100%)
Tel.: (403) 691-7575
Web Site: http://www.atlagas.com
Sales Range: $100-124.9 Million.
Emp.: 250
Crude Petroleum & Natural Gas Extraction
N.A.I.C.S.: 211120

AltaGas Utility Group Inc.   (1)
355 4th Avenue SW Suite 540, Calgary,
T2P 0J1, AB, Canada
Tel.: (780) 986-5215
Natural Gas Distr
N.A.I.C.S.: 221210

Subsidiary (Domestic):

AltaGas Utilities, Inc.   (2)
5509 45th St, Leduc, T9E 6T6, AB,
Canada   (100%)
Tel.: (780) 986-5215
Web Site: http://www.altagasutilities.com
Sales Range: $75-99.9 Million
Emp.: 220
Transmission of Natural Gas
N.A.I.C.S.: 486210
Graeme Feltham (Pres)

Blythe Energy, LLC   (1)
301 Hobsonway, Blythe, CA 92225
Tel.: (760) 922-2957
Sales Range: $10-24.9 Million
Emp.: 15
Electric Power Generation
N.A.I.C.S.: 221118

ECNG Energy Limited
Partnership   (1)
Ste 1700 355 4th Ave SW, Calgary, T2P
0J1, AB, Canada   (100%)

Tel.: (403) 691-7575
Web Site: http://www.ecng.com
Sales Range: $350-399.9 Million
Emp.: 600
Crude Petroleum & Natural Gas Extraction
N.A.I.C.S.: 211120

Pacific Northern Gas Ltd.   (1)
Suite 950 1185 West Georgia Street, Van-
couver, V6E 4F6, BC, Canada
Tel.: (604) 691-5680
Web Site: http://www.png.ca
Sales Range: $75-99.9 Million
Emp.: 102
Natural Gas Transmission, Distr & Retail
Sales
N.A.I.C.S.: 221210
Janet P. Kennedy (VP-Regulatory Affairs &
Gas Supply)

Petrogas Energy Corporation   (1)
1700 355 4th Avenue SW, Calgary, T2P
0J1, AB, Canada
Tel.: (403) 266-1985
Web Site:
     http://www.petrogasmarketing.com
Natural Gas Distribution Services
N.A.I.C.S.: 221210

SEMCO Energy, Inc.   (1)
1411 3rd St Ste A, Port Huron, MI 48060
Tel.: (810) 987-2200
Web Site: https://www.semcoenergy.com
Sales Range: $600-649.9 Million
Emp.: 570
Natural Gas Distribution
N.A.I.C.S.: 221210

Subsidiary (Domestic):

ENSTAR Natural Gas Company   (2)
3000 Spenard Rd, Anchorage, AK 99503-
3606
Tel.: (907) 277-5551
Web Site: http://www.enstarnaturalgas.com
Sales Range: $100-124.9 Million
Emp.: 150
Natural Gas Distribution
N.A.I.C.S.: 221210

SEMCO Energy Ventures, Inc.   (2)
PO Box 5004, Port Huron, MI 48060
Tel.: (810) 987-2200
Energy Investment Activities
N.A.I.C.S.: 523999

WGL Holdings, Inc.   (1)
1000 Main Ave SW, Washington, DC 20024
Tel.: (703) 750-2000
Web Site: https://www.wgl.com
Holding Company; Natural Gas Distr
N.A.I.C.S.: 551112
Douglas I. Bonawitz (CFO, Treas & Sr VP)

Subsidiary (Domestic):

Hampshire Gas Company   (2)
114 Hampshire Gas Dr, Romney, WV
26757   (100%)
Tel.: (304) 822-5664
Web Site: http://www.wgl.com
Natural Gas Storage Facilities
N.A.I.C.S.: 486210

Washington Gas Light Company   (2)
1000 Maine Ave SW, Washington, DC
20024
Tel.: (703) 750-4440
Web Site: http://www.washingtongas.com
Natural Gas Distr
N.A.I.C.S.: 221210
Douglas I. Bonawitz (CFO, Treas & Sr VP)

Subsidiary (Domestic):

Washington Gas Resources
Corp.   (3)
1000 Maine Ave SW, Washington, DC
20024
Tel.: (703) 750-2000
Holding Company for Washington Gas Light
Companies Unregulated, Nonutility Opera-
tions
N.A.I.C.S.: 523999

Subsidiary (Domestic):

WGL Energy Services, Inc.   (4)
8614 Westwood Center Dr Ste 1200, Vienna, VA 22182-2260
Tel.: (703) 333-3900

Web Site: http://www.wglenergy.com
Commercial & Residential Service Provider
N.A.I.C.S.: 334512

Washington Gas Energy Services,
Inc.   (4)
8614 Westwood Ctr Ste 1200, Vienna,
VA 22182-2260
Tel.: (703) 333-3900
Natural Gas & Electricity Supplier
N.A.I.C.S.: 221122

Washington Gas Energy Systems,
Inc.   (4)
8614 Westwood Ctr Dr Ste 1200, Vienna,
VA 22182-2260
Tel.: (703) 333-3900
Design, Builds & Owns Custom Energy
Solutions
N.A.I.C.S.: 221118

ALTAI RESOURCES INC.
895 Don Mills Road Two Morneau
Shepell Centre Suite 900, Toronto,
M3C 1W3, ON, Canada
Tel.: (416) 383-1328   ON
Web Site:
     https://www.altairesources.com
Year Founded: 1955
1IA—(DEU)
Rev.: $179,730
Assets: $4,118,765
Liabilities: $323,682
Net Worth: $3,795,084
Earnings: ($112,015)
Fiscal Year-end: 12/31/21
Minerals Exploration
N.A.I.C.S.: 213115
Niyazi Kacira (Chm & Pres)

ALTAIR RESOURCES INC.
1305 1090 West Georgia Street, Van-
couver, V6E 3V7, BC, Canada
Tel.: (604) 685-9316   BC
Web Site:
     https://www.altairresources.com
Year Founded: 2005
AVX—(TSXV)
Assets: $47,413
Liabilities: $1,358,155
Net Worth: ($1,310,741)
Earnings: ($2,414,537)
Fiscal Year-end: 03/31/22
Mineral Exploration Services
N.A.I.C.S.: 213114
Nick DeMare (CFO & Interim & Sec)

ALTALEY MINING CORPORA-TION
1111 Melville Street Suite 1000, Van-
couver, V6E 3V6, BC, Canada
Tel.: (604) 684-8071   BC
Web Site:
     http://www.telsonmining.com
Year Founded: 1986
ATLY—(OTCIQ)
Rev.: $34,766,870
Assets: $41,401,387
Liabilities: $62,296,868
Net Worth: ($20,895,481)
Earnings: ($9,093,223)
Fiscal Year-end: 12/31/20
Gold & Silver Mining Services
N.A.I.C.S.: 212220
Ralph Shearing (Pres & CEO)

ALTAMIN LIMITED
Level 3 Suite 3.5 9 Bowman Street,
South Perth, 6151, WA, Australia
Tel.: (61) 893215000   AU
Web Site:
     https://www.altamin.com.au
AZI—(ASX)
Rev.: $101,008
Assets: $2,540,686
Liabilities: $422,695
Net Worth: $2,117,991
Earnings: ($2,463,098)
Emp.: 14

Fiscal Year-end: 06/30/24
Uranium Exploration Services
N.A.I.C.S.: 212290
Alexander Burns (Chm)

Subsidiaries:

Energia Minerals (Italia) S.R.L. **(1)**
Via Roma 492, Oltre il Colle, 24013, Bergamo, Italy
Tel.: (39) 034567950
Metal Exploration Services
N.A.I.C.S.: 213114

ALTAMIR S.C.A.

1 rue Paul Cezanne, 75008, Paris, France
Tel.: (33) 634323897
Web Site: https://www.altamir.fr
LTA—(EUR)
Rev.: $354,353,453
Assets: $1,314,051,338
Liabilities: $179,386,877
Net Worth: $1,134,664,461
Earnings: $274,428,157
Emp.: 15,000
Fiscal Year-end: 12/31/19
Privater Equity Firm
N.A.I.C.S.: 523999
Maurice Tchenio (Chm & CEO)

ALTAMIRA GOLD CORP.

Suite 1500-409 Granville Street, Vancouver, V6C 1T2, BC, Canada
Tel.: (604) 676-5661   BC
Web Site: https://altamiragold.com
Year Founded: 1994
EQTRF—(OTCIQ)
Rev.: $11,859
Assets: $15,494,708
Liabilities: $357,799
Net Worth: $15,136,908
Earnings: ($1,238,323)
Fiscal Year-end: 02/28/22
Gold Mining Services
N.A.I.C.S.: 212220
Elvis Alves (Project Mgr)

ALTAMIRA THERAPEUTICS LTD.

Tel.: (441) 2955950
Web Site:
https://altamiratherapeutics.com
CYTO—(NASDAQ)
Rev.: $283,358
Assets: $8,530,221
Liabilities: $1,369,780
Net Worth: $7,160,440
Earnings: ($8,059,909)
Emp.: 10
Fiscal Year-end: 12/31/23
Biopharmaceutical Mfr
N.A.I.C.S.: 325412
Thomas Meyer (CEO, Founder & Chm)

Subsidiaries:

Auris Medical Ltd. **(1)**
The Black Church St Marys Place, Dublin, D07 P4AX, Ireland
Tel.: (353) 766154675
Web Site: https://altamiratherapeutics.com
Pharmaceuticals Product Mfr
N.A.I.C.S.: 325412

ALTAN NEVADA MINERALS LIMITED

c/o 1700 666 Burrard Street, Vancouver, V6C 2X8, BC, Canada
Tel.: (619) 322-1788   BC
Web Site: http://www.altnev.com
Year Founded: 2008
HHH—(TSXV)
Rev.: $17
Assets: $1,145,043
Liabilities: $462,890
Net Worth: $682,153
Earnings: ($320,954)

Fiscal Year-end: 12/31/23
Gold Exploration Services
N.A.I.C.S.: 212220
John L. C. Jones (Chm)

ALTAN RIO MINERALS LIMITED

800 - 1199 West Hastings St, Vancouver, V6E 3T5, BC, Canada
Tel.: (619) 322-1788   BC
Web Site: http://www.altanrio.com
Year Founded: 2010
GHML—(TSXV)
Rev.: $3,065,595
Assets: $7,267,245
Liabilities: $893,643
Net Worth: $6,373,602
Earnings: ($726,301)
Fiscal Year-end: 12/31/23
Investment Services
N.A.I.C.S.: 523999
John L. C. Jones (Chm)

ALTAPEX CORPORATION

1741 Blvd Edouard Laurin, Saint Laurent, H4L 5E9, QC, Canada
Tel.: (514) 937-1700
Web Site: http://www.altapex.com
Year Founded: 1992
Rev.: $12,010,500
Emp.: 12
Construction Services
N.A.I.C.S.: 236220
Leonardo Soares (Founder, Pres & CEO)

ALTAREA SCA

87 rue de Richelieu, 75002, Paris, France
Tel.: (33) 156262400
Web Site: https://www.altarea.com
ALTA—(EUR)
Rev.: $226,850,853
Assets: $9,807,576,085
Liabilities: $5,534,426,937
Net Worth: $4,273,149,147
Earnings: $352,687,244
Emp.: 2,139
Fiscal Year-end: 12/31/22
Commercial & Residential Real Estate Investment Services
N.A.I.C.S.: 525990
Christian de Gournay (Chm-Supervisory Bd)

Subsidiaries:

ALTAREA Espana SL **(1)**
C/ Orense 85 - Edificio, Lexington, Madrid, 28020, Spain
Tel.: (34) 913822101
Web Site: http://www.altareacogedim.com
Sales Range: $50-74.9 Million
Emp.: 5
Real Estate Manangement Services
N.A.I.C.S.: 531210
Asun Sanchez (Mgr-Mktg)

ALTAREA France SAS **(1)**
87 rue de Richelieu, 75002, Paris, France
Tel.: (33) 156262400
Web Site: http://www.altarea.com
Sales Range: $150-199.9 Million
Emp.: 400
Real Estate Manangement Services
N.A.I.C.S.: 531210

ALTAREA Italia s.r.l. **(1)**
Viale Sarca 336, 20122, Milan, Italy
Tel.: (39) 024333141
Sales Range: $25-49.9 Million
Emp.: 40
Real Estate Manangement Services
N.A.I.C.S.: 531210

Alta CRP Aubergenville SNC **(1)**
Rte Quarante Sous, 78410, Aubergenville, Yvelines, France
Tel.: (33) 139297240
Sales Range: $50-74.9 Million
Emp.: 2
Real Estate Manangement Services

N.A.I.C.S.: 531210

Altarea COGEDIM Citalis **(1)**
8 Avenue Delcasse, Paris, 75008, France
Tel.: (33) 153892120
Web Site: http://www.altareacogedim.it
Emp.: 500
Real Estate Manangement Services
N.A.I.C.S.: 531210
Alain Taravella (Gen Mgr)

Altareit SCA **(1)**
87 Rue de Richelieu, FR-75002, Paris, France
Tel.: (33) 156262400
Web Site: https://www.altareit.com
Rev.: $2,664,422,122
Assets: $4,143,282,924
Liabilities: $3,252,345,734
Net Worth: $890,937,190
Earnings: ($359,752,732)
Emp.: 1,617
Fiscal Year-end: 12/31/2023
Real Estate Support Services
N.A.I.C.S.: 531390
Alain Taravella (Chm)

COGEDIM Midi-Pyrenees **(1)**
46 Boulevard De Strasbourg, Toulouse, 31000, Haute-Garonne, France
Tel.: (33) 534414900
Sales Range: $25-49.9 Million
Emp.: 30
Real Estate Manangement Services
N.A.I.C.S.: 531210
Benoit Michaud (Mng Dir)

COGEDIM Savoies-Leman SNC **(1)**
Parc de la Bouvarde Allee du Parmelan, 74370, Metz-Tessy, Haute-Savoie, France
Tel.: (33) 450058060
Web Site: http://www.altarea-cogedim.com
Sales Range: $50-74.9 Million
Emp.: 30
Real Estate Manangement Services
N.A.I.C.S.: 531210

Centostazioni S.p.A. **(1)**
Via Bartolomeo Eustachio 8, 00161, Rome, Italy   **(59.99%)**
Tel.: (39) 06 440711
Web Site: http://www.centostazioni.it
Railway Station Redevelopment, Enhancement & Management Services
N.A.I.C.S.: 561210
Luca Preziosi (CEO)

Cogedim Residences Services SNC **(1)**
87 rue de Richelieu, 75002, Paris, France
Tel.: (33) 805234200
Web Site: https://www.cogedim-club.fr
Senior Residency Services
N.A.I.C.S.: 623312
Naoiel Khalfaoui (Office Mgr)

Cogedim SAS **(1)**
8 avenue Delcasse, 75008, Paris, France
Tel.: (33) 970255255
Web Site: http://www.cogedim.com
Real Estate Services
N.A.I.C.S.: 531390

Pitch Promotion SNC **(1)**
87 rue de Richelieu, 75002, Paris, France
Tel.: (33) 142683333
Web Site: https://pitchimmo.fr
Real Estate Services
N.A.I.C.S.: 531390
Margot Antoni (Mgr-Land Dev)

SCCV Clef de Sol **(1)**
Zone Scolaire Groupe Malbosc Avenue De Fes, Montpellier, 34080, Herault, France
Tel.: (33) 467412790
Real Estate Manangement Services
N.A.I.C.S.: 531210

SNC COGEDIM Atlantique **(1)**
11 rue Arthur III, Nantes, 44200, France
Tel.: (33) 251860020
Web Site: http://www.cogedim.com
Sales Range: $50-74.9 Million
Emp.: 15
Real Estate Manangement Services
N.A.I.C.S.: 531210
Gerone Belmzoas (Gen Mgr)

SNC COGEDIM Grand Lyon **(1)**
235 Cours Lafayette, 69006, Lyon, Rhone, France

Tel.: (33) 4 72 75 40 80
Web Site: http://www.altareacogedim.com
Sales Range: $50-74.9 Million
Emp.: 50
Real Estate Investment Trust
N.A.I.C.S.: 525990

SNC COGEDIM Grenoble **(1)**
56 Vdjanbegta, 38300, Grenoble, France
Tel.: (33) 476896989
Sales Range: $50-74.9 Million
Emp.: 15
Real Estate Manangement Services
N.A.I.C.S.: 531210

SNC COGEDIM Mediterranee **(1)**
400 promenade des Anglais, 6200, Nice, Alpes-Maritimes, France
Tel.: (33) 492478000
Web Site: http://www.altareacogedim.com
Sales Range: $25-49.9 Million
Emp.: 50
Real Estate Property Development Services
N.A.I.C.S.: 531210
Jean-Marie Ebel (Co-Pres)

SNC COGEDIM Provence **(1)**
26 rue Grignan, 13001, Marseille, Bouches-du-Rhone, France
Tel.: (33) 496176320
Sales Range: $50-74.9 Million
Emp.: 40
Real Estate Manangement Services
N.A.I.C.S.: 531210
Dominique Gougard (Mgr)

SNC COGEDIM Vente **(1)**
8 Avenue Delcasse, 75008, Paris, France
Tel.: (33) 1 60 79 86 70
Real Estate Manangement Services
N.A.I.C.S.: 531210

SNC Cogedim Aquitaine **(1)**
92 rue Lucien Faure, 33300, Bordeaux, France
Tel.: (33) 556001370
Real Estate Services
N.A.I.C.S.: 531390

SNC Cogedim Est **(1)**
30 avenue du Rhin, 67100, Strasbourg, France
Tel.: (33) 388561655
Real Estate Services
N.A.I.C.S.: 531390

SNC Cogedim Gestion **(1)**
30 cours de ile Seguin - Horizons Building, 92100, Boulogne-Billancourt, France
Tel.: (33) 809103030
Rental Services
N.A.I.C.S.: 532310

SNC Cogedim Languedoc Roussillon **(1)**
Immeuble DoraMar - 50 rue Ray Charles, 34000, Montpellier, France
Tel.: (33) 499549800
Real Estate Services
N.A.I.C.S.: 531390
Florence Robert (Comml Dir)

SNC Cogedim Midi-Pyrenees **(1)**
10 rue des Trente-Six Ponts, 31400, Toulouse, France
Tel.: (33) 534414900
Real Estate Services
N.A.I.C.S.: 531390
Alexandre Ubeda (Deputy Dir-Land Dev)

SNC Cogedim Paris Metropole **(1)**
87 rue de Richelieu, 75002, Paris, France
Tel.: (33) 156262400
Real Estate Services
N.A.I.C.S.: 531390
Vanessa Bravo (Office Mgr)

SNC Cogedim Savoies-Leman **(1)**
Allee de la Mandallaz, 74370, Metz-Tessy, France
Tel.: (33) 450058060
Real Estate Services
N.A.I.C.S.: 531390
Chloe Mathieu (Mgr-Land Dev)

Salle Wagram **(1)**
5 Bis rue de Montenotte, 75017, Paris, France
Tel.: (33) 155378686
Web Site: http://www.sallewagram.com
Event Management Services

Altarea SCA—(Continued)

N.A.I.C.S.: 711310

ALTAS PARTNERS LP
79 Wellington St West Suite 3500,
P.O. Box 357, Toronto, M5K 1K7, ON,
Canada
Tel.: (416) 306-9800
Web Site:
　http://www.altaspartners.com
Year Founded: 2012
Investment Firm
N.A.I.C.S.: 523999
Andrew Sheiner (CEO & Mng Part-
ner)

Subsidiaries:

DuBois Chemicals, Inc.　　　　　**(1)**
3630 E Kemper Rd, Sharonville, OH 45241-
2011
Tel.: (513) 554-4200
Web Site: http://www.duboischemicals.com
Specialty Chemical Mfr & Whslr
N.A.I.C.S.: 325998

Subsidiary (Domestic):

CIMCOOL Industrial Products
LLC　　　　　　　　　　　　　　　**(2)**
3000 Disney St, Cincinnati, OH
45209　　　　　　　　　　　　**(100%)**
Tel.: (513) 458-8100
Web Site: http://www.cimcool.com
Emp.: 100
Metalworking Fluids Mfr & Whslr
N.A.I.C.S.: 325998
Jack Teat (Pres)

Subsidiary (Non-US):

CIMCOOL Europe B.V.　　　　　**(3)**
Schiedamsedijk 20, 3134 KK, Vlaardingen,
Netherlands　　　　　　　　　**(100%)**
Tel.: (31) 104600660
Web Site: http://www.cimcool.net
Sales Range: $25-49.9 Million
Holding Company; Metalworking Fluids Mfr
& Whslr
N.A.I.C.S.: 551112

Subsidiary (Domestic):

CIMCOOL Industrial Products
B.V.　　　　　　　　　　　　　　　**(4)**
Schiedamsedijk 20, Vlaardingen, 3134 KK,
Netherlands　　　　　　　　　**(100%)**
Tel.: (31) 10 460 0660
Web Site: http://www.cimcool.net
Metalworking Fluids Mfr & Marketer
N.A.I.C.S.: 325998

Tecta America Corp.　　　　　　**(1)**
9450 W Bryn Mawr Ave Ste 500, Rose-
mont, IL 60018
Tel.: (847) 581-3888
Web Site: http://www.tectaamerica.com
Holding Company; Roofing Services
N.A.I.C.S.: 551112
Dave Reginelli (Pres & CEO)

Subsidiary (Domestic):

A C Hathorne Co　　　　　　　　**(2)**
252 Avenue C, Williston, VT 05495
Tel.: (802) 862-6473
Web Site: http://www.achathorne.com
Other Building Finishing Contractors
N.A.I.C.S.: 238390
Shane Raymond (Gen Mgr)

Anthony Roofing Ltd.　　　　　　**(2)**
2555 White Oak Cir, Aurora, IL 60502
Tel.: (630) 898-4444
Web Site: http://www.anthonyroofing.com
Rev.: $22,160,012
Emp.: 70
Roofing Contractors
N.A.I.C.S.: 238160
Tony Clausen (Pres)

Blackmore & Buckner Roofing,
LLC.　　　　　　　　　　　　　　**(2)**
9750 E 150th St Noblesville, Indianapolis,
IN 46060
Tel.: (317) 263-0708
Web Site:
　http://www.blackmorebuckner.com

Sales Range: $10-24.9 Million
Emp.: 100
Roofing
N.A.I.C.S.: 238160
Steaven Buckner (Pres)

CEI Roofing Colorado, LLC　　**(2)**
1881 W 13th Ave, Denver, CO 80204
Tel.: (303) 573-5953
Web Site:
　http://www.ceiroofingcolorado.com
Rev.: $13,800,000
Emp.: 95
Roofing Contractors
N.A.I.C.S.: 238160

CEI Roofing Texas, LLC　　　　**(2)**
720 Bastrop Hwy Ate 308, Austin, TX 78741
Tel.: (512) 389-2611
Roofing Services
N.A.I.C.S.: 238160

Branch (Domestic):

CEI Roofing - Texas　　　　　　**(3)**
2510 Cockrell Ave, Dallas, TX 75215
Tel.: (214) 352-3032
Web Site: http://www.tectaamerica.com
Roofing Contractors
N.A.I.C.S.: 238160
Jim Renard (Pres)

Subsidiary (Domestic):

Childers Roofing & Sheetmetal,
Inc.　　　　　　　　　　　　　　**(2)**
10416 New Berlin Rd, Jacksonville, FL
32226
Tel.: (904) 696-8550
Rev.: $1,860,000
Emp.: 15
Other Building Finishing Contractors
N.A.I.C.S.: 238390
Butch Childers (Pres)

Chris Andersen Roofing & Erecting.,
Co.　　　　　　　　　　　　　　**(2)**
95 New Brunswick Ave, Hopelawn, NJ
08861
Tel.: (732) 826-1250
Web Site: https://www.tectaamerica.com
Other Building Finishing Contractors
N.A.I.C.S.: 238390
Nabil Elmachtoub (Pres)

Commercial Roofing, Inc.　　　　**(2)**
2300 Maple Dr, Plover, WI 54467
Tel.: (715) 341-2178
Web Site: http://www.tectaamerica.com
Roofing, Siding & Sheetmetal Work Con-
tractors
N.A.I.C.S.: 238160
Shawn Herzog (Pres)

Eagle Cornice Co. Inc.　　　　　**(2)**
89 Pettaconsett Ave, Cranston, RI 02920
Tel.: (401) 781-5978
Web Site: http://www.eaglecornice.com
Roofing Contractors
N.A.I.C.S.: 238160
J. Lawrence Brillon (Pres)

Empire Roofing, Inc.　　　　　　**(2)**
5301 Sun Valley Dr, Fort Worth, TX 76119
Tel.: (817) 572-2250
Web Site: http://www.empireroofing.com
Sales Range: $1-9.9 Million
Emp.: 100
Roofing Contractors
N.A.I.C.S.: 238160
Matt Kelley (VP)

FJA Christiansen Roofing Co.,
Inc.　　　　　　　　　　　　　　**(2)**
2101 W Purdue St, Milwaukee, WI 53209-
0350
Tel.: (414) 445-4141
Web Site: http://www.tectaamerica.com
Sales Range: $25-49.9 Million
Emp.: 110
Commercial Roofing Contractors
N.A.I.C.S.: 238160
Andrew Sherifi (Treas)

General Works, LLC　　　　　　**(2)**
588 Monroe Rd, Sanford, FL 32771
Tel.: (386) 775-6320
Web Site:
　http://www.generalworksroofing.com
Sales Range: $10-24.9 Million
Emp.: 100
Roofing Contractors

N.A.I.C.S.: 238160

J.P. Patti Tecta America, LLC　　**(2)**
365 Jefferson St, Saddle Brook, NJ 07663-
0539
Tel.: (973) 478-6200
Sales Range: $10-24.9 Million
Emp.: 130
Roofing Services
N.A.I.C.S.: 238160
James Wisse (Pres)

Katchmark Construction Inc.　　**(2)**
3856 Dulles South Ct, Chantilly, VA 20151
Tel.: (703) 817-0200
Web Site: http://www.katchmark.com
Rev.: $2,480,000
Emp.: 20
Other Building Finishing Contractors
N.A.I.C.S.: 238390

Mahaney Group　　　　　　　　**(2)**
2822 N Mead St, Wichita, KS 67219-4241
Tel.: (316) 262-4768
Web Site: http://www.mahaneyroofing.com
Roofing Contractors
N.A.I.C.S.: 238160
Doug Hoover (Acct Mgr)

Margo, Inc.　　　　　　　　　　**(2)**
125 Pocahontas St, Petersburg, VA 23803
Tel.: (804) 733-8815
Sales Range: $10-24.9 Million
Emp.: 100
Roofing Services
Rev.: $12,010,000
N.A.I.C.S.: 238160

Pieros Construction Co, Inc.　　**(2)**
58 Tannery Rd, Somerville, NJ 08876
Tel.: (908) 534-4451
Web Site: https://pierosroofing.com
Sales Range: $1-9.9 Million
Emp.: 48
Roofing Contractors
N.A.I.C.S.: 238160
Jean Pieros (VP)

Pinkston-Hollar Construction Services
Inc.　　　　　　　　　　　　　　**(2)**
2214 S Lincoln St, Amarillo, TX 79109
Tel.: (281) 446-7770
Web Site: http://www.constrservices.com
Rev.: $22,635,700
Emp.: 70
Roofing Contractors
N.A.I.C.S.: 238160
Robert L. Pinkston (Chm & CEO)

Pioneer Roofing, LLC　　　　　**(2)**
151 Maple St, Johnson Creek, WI 53038
Tel.: (920) 699-2731
Web Site: http://www.pioneerroofing.net
Sales Range: $1-9.9 Million
Emp.: 30
Roofing, Siding, And Sheetmetal Work, Nsk
N.A.I.C.S.: 238160
Brian Monogue (Accountant)

Pro-Tec Roofing, Inc.　　　　　**(2)**
520 11th Ave SE, Watertown, SD 57201
Tel.: (605) 882-4060
Sales Range: $1-9.9 Million
Emp.: 25
Contractor Specializing In Roofing & Sheet
Metal
N.A.I.C.S.: 238160

Roof Services JGM Corporation　**(2)**
3056 Holland Rd, Virginia Beach, VA 23453
Tel.: (757) 468-4443
Web Site: http://www.roofservicescom.com
Roofing Industry; Commercial Flat Roofing
& Composite Metal Roofing
N.A.I.C.S.: 238160
John Babcock (Pres)

Roof Systems of Maine　　　　　**(2)**
332 Target Industrial Cir, Bangor, ME
04401-1134
Tel.: (207) 947-0195
Web Site:
　http://www.roofsystemsofmaine.com
Rev.: $7,440,000
Emp.: 110
Roofing & Siding Services to Commercial,
Residential, Industrial & Institutional Appli-
cations
N.A.I.C.S.: 238160
Lee Corro (Pres)

Schwickert's Tecta America of
Mankato LLC　　　　　　　　　**(2)**

221 Minnesota St, Mankato, MN 56002-
0487
Tel.: (507) 387-3106
Web Site: http://www.schwickerts.com
Sales Range: $10-24.9 Million
Emp.: 350
Commercial Roofing Contractors
N.A.I.C.S.: 238160
Kim L. Schwickert (Chm & COO)

Subsidiary (Domestic):

Schwickert's Tecta America LLC　**(3)**
330 Poplar St, Mankato, MN 56001
Tel.: (507) 387-3101
Web Site: http://www.schwickerts.com
Roofing Services
N.A.I.C.S.: 238160
Kim L. Schwickert (CEO)

Branch (Domestic):

Schwickert's Tecta America LLC -
Stewartville　　　　　　　　　**(4)**
204 Schumann Dr NW, Stewartville, MN
55976
Tel.: (507) 281-0611
Web Site: http://www.schwickerts.com
Sales Range: $25-49.9 Million
Emp.: 80
Roofing Contractors
N.A.I.C.S.: 238160

Subsidiary (Domestic):

Stock Roofing Company, LLC　　**(2)**
7731 Main St NE, Fridley, MN 55432
Tel.: (763) 780-3561
Web Site: http://www.stockroofing.com
Sales Range: $10-24.9 Million
Emp.: 70
Roofing Services
N.A.I.C.S.: 238160

Tecta America Arizona, LLC　　**(2)**
1824 W Bdwy Rd, Phoenix, AZ 85041
Tel.: (602) 246-8661
Roofing Services
N.A.I.C.S.: 238160
Chuck Chapman (Pres)

Tecta America Carolinas, LLC　**(2)**
13615 E Independence Blvd, Indian Trail,
NC 28079
Tel.: (704) 882-1200
Web Site: http://www.tectaamerica.com
Emp.: 70
Roofing Services
N.A.I.C.S.: 238160
Randy Winecoff (Pres)

Tecta America Colorado, LLC　**(2)**
1881 W 13th Ave, Denver, CO 80204
Tel.: (303) 573-5953
Roofing Services
N.A.I.C.S.: 238160
Brad Topham (Mgr-Svc)

Tecta America Dakotas, LLC　　**(2)**
1810 N 6th St, Grand Forks, ND 58208
Tel.: (701) 775-5369
Web Site: http://www.grsnd.com
Sales Range: $10-24.9 Million
Emp.: 80
Commercial Roofing Contractors
N.A.I.C.S.: 238160
Kevin Pederson (Mgr-Svc)

Division (Domestic):

Greenberg Roofing, Inc.　　　　**(3)**
701 4th Ave NE, Minot, ND 58701
Tel.: (701) 839-1751
Web Site: http://www.grsnd.com
Roofing Services
N.A.I.C.S.: 238160
Kevin Pederson (Mgr-Ops & Svc)

Greenberg Roofing, Inc.　　　　**(3)**
2315 7th Ave N, Fargo, ND 58102
Tel.: (701) 232-4632
Web Site:
　http://www.tectaamericadakotas.com
Emp.: 40
Roofing Services
N.A.I.C.S.: 238160
Davey Hovland (Mgr-Svc)

Subsidiary (Domestic):

Target Roofing Inc.　　　　　　**(3)**

307 5th St SE, Devils Lake, ND 58301
Tel.: (701) 662-8137
Roofing Contractors
N.A.I.C.S.: 238160
Kenny Lybeck *(Pres & Mgr-Project)*

Division (Domestic):

Tecta America Dakotas, LLC -
Jamestown　　　　　　　　　　　(3)
105 7th Ave SE, Jamestown, ND 58401
Tel.: (701) 252-2403
Web Site: http://www.tectaamerica.com
Roofing Services & Warehousing
N.A.I.C.S.: 238160

Subsidiary (Domestic):

Tecta America East LLC　　　　(2)
5220 Pennington Ave, Baltimore, MD 21226
Tel.: (410) 319-0300
Web Site: http://www.tectaamerica.com
Sales Range: $10-24.9 Million
Emp.: 50
Roofing Services
N.A.I.C.S.: 238160

Branch (Domestic):

Tecta America East LLC -
Fruitland　　　　　　　　　　　(3)
302 S Division St, Fruitland, MD 21826
Tel.: (410) 219-7980
Web Site: http://www.tectaamerica.com
Roofing Contractors
N.A.I.C.S.: 238160

Tecta America East LLC - Glen
Rock　　　　　　　　　　　　　(3)
342 Commerce Dr, Glen Rock, PA 17327
Tel.: (717) 235-0507
Web Site: http://www.tectaamerica.com
Roofing Services
N.A.I.C.S.: 238160
Chris Mummert *(Dir-Roofing Ops)*

Tecta America East LLC -
Jessup　　　　　　　　　　　　(3)
7340 Montevideo Rd, Jessup, MD 20794
Tel.: (410) 799-1972
Web Site: http://www.tectaamerica.com
Sales Range: $10-24.9 Million
Emp.: 50
Roofing Services
N.A.I.C.S.: 238160

Subsidiary (Domestic):

Tecta America Illinois Roofing,
LLC　　　　　　　　　　　　　(2)
4813 Kingston, Drive Lisle, IL 60532
Tel.: (630) 554-2200
Web Site: http://www.tectaamerica.com
Roofing Services
N.A.I.C.S.: 238160
Michael Ward *(Pres)*

Subsidiary (Domestic):

BB&W Associates, Inc　　　　(3)
11305 NE Marx St, Portland, OR 97220
Tel.: (503) 786-0616
Web Site: http://www.abcroofingco.com
Other Building Finishing Contractors
N.A.I.C.S.: 238390
Micky Washburn *(COO)*

Subsidiary (Domestic):

Tecta America Metro New York,
LLC　　　　　　　　　　　　　(2)
38 Roosevelt Ave, Belleville, NJ 07109
Tel.: (973) 450-9555
Web Site: http://www.tectaamerica.com
Emp.: 20
Roofing Services
N.A.I.C.S.: 238160
Raquel Bolognini *(Office Mgr)*

Tecta America New England,
LLC　　　　　　　　　　　　　(2)
2 Sterling Rd, North Billerica, MA 01862
Tel.: (978) 436-9990
Web Site: http://www.tectaamerica.com
Emp.: 50
Roofing Services
N.A.I.C.S.: 238160
Jay Maschmeier *(Sr VP)*

Tecta America Sacramento Inc.　(2)

3257 Fitzgerald Rd, Rancho Cordova, CA
95742
Tel.: (916) 635-9921
Web Site: http://www.tectaamerica.com
Sales Range: $25-49.9 Million
Emp.: 50
Roofing Contractors
N.A.I.C.S.: 238160
Michael G. McClain *(Pres)*

Tecta America South Florida　(2)
1431 SW 30th Ave, Deerfield Beach, FL
33442
Tel.: (954) 419-9339
Web Site: http://www.tectaamerica.com
Sales Range: $10-24.9 Million
Emp.: 80
Roofing Services
N.A.I.C.S.: 238160
Tim Eberly *(Pres)*

Tecta America Southern California,
Inc.　　　　　　　　　　　　　(2)
1217 E Wakeham Ave, Santa Ana, CA
92705
Tel.: (714) 973-6233
Roofing Services
N.A.I.C.S.: 238160
Dan Klein *(Sec-Operating Unit & Project
Mgr)*

Tecta America West Florida, LLC　(2)
5429 56th St N, Tampa, FL 33619
Tel.: (813) 621-1700
Web Site: http://www.tectaamerica.com
Sales Range: $25-49.9 Million
Emp.: 30
Roofing Contractors
N.A.I.C.S.: 238160
Norm Kirkpatrick *(Pres)*

Tecta America Zero Company
LLC　　　　　　　　　　　　　(2)
6225 Wiehe Rd, Cincinnati, OH 45237
Tel.: (513) 541-1848
Web Site: http://www.tectaamerica.com
Emp.: 120
Roofing Services
N.A.I.C.S.: 238160
Jonathan Wolf *(Pres)*

Branch (Domestic):

Tecta America Zero Company LLC -
Columbus　　　　　　　　　　(3)
1230 Goodale Blvd, Columbus, OH 43212
Tel.: (614) 291-9747
Web Site: http://www.tectaamerica.com
Sales Range: $1-9.9 Million
Emp.: 11
Roofing Contractors
N.A.I.C.S.: 238160
Josh Beer *(Gen Mgr)*

Tecta America Zero Company LLC -
Louisville　　　　　　　　　　(3)
4045 McCollum Ct, Louisville, KY 40218
Tel.: (502) 456-5848
Web Site: http://www.tectaamerica.com
Emp.: 40
Roofing Services
N.A.I.C.S.: 238160
Pat Dorsey *(Pres)*

Subsidiary (Domestic):

The Melanson Company Inc　　(2)
353 W St, Keene, NH 03431
Tel.: (603) 352-4232
Web Site: http://www.melanson.com
Sales Range: $10-24.9 Million
Emp.: 110
Roofing Contractors
N.A.I.C.S.: 238160
Robert W. Therrien *(Pres)*

Tuscano-Maher Roofing, Inc.　(2)
373 Moween Rd, Saltsburg, PA 15681
Tel.: (724) 639-9687
Web Site: http://www.tmrroofing.com
Rev.: $5,200,000
Emp.: 49
Roofing Contractors
N.A.I.C.S.: 238160
Mike Maher *(Pres)*

Weatherguard Tecta America,
LLC　　　　　　　　　　　　　(2)
2003 Chrisler Ave, Schenectady, NY 12303
Tel.: (518) 356-5000

Web Site: http://www.tectaamerica.com
Emp.: 40
Roofing Services
N.A.I.C.S.: 238160
Edward Lawless *(VP)*

Western Roofing Service, Inc.　(2)
15002 Wicks Blvd, San Leandro, CA 94577
Tel.: (415) 648-6472
Web Site: http://www.westroof.com
Sales Range: $25-49.9 Million
Emp.: 150
Roofing Services
N.A.I.C.S.: 238160

Subsidiary (Domestic):

Western Roofing Service, Inc.　(3)
9500 Aurora Ave N, Seattle, WA 98103-
3219
Tel.: (425) 881-9190
Sales Range: $25-49.9 Million
Emp.: 50
Roofing Services
N.A.I.C.S.: 238160

Subsidiary (Domestic):

Wolfe Roofing, a Tecta America Com-
pany, LLC　　　　　　　　　　(2)
3907 Pottsville Pike, Reading, PA 19605
Tel.: (610) 921-1060
Web Site: http://www.wolferoofing.com
Commercial & Industrial Roofing Contractor
N.A.I.C.S.: 238160
Gary D. Wolfe *(Chm & CEO)*

ALTASCIENCES COMPANY INC.
575 Armand-Frappier Blvd, Laval,
H7V 4B3, QC, Canada
Tel.: (450) 973-6077　　　　　　QC
Web Site:
http://www.altasciences.com
Year Founded: 2017
Pharmaceutical & Biotechnology Ser-
vices
N.A.I.C.S.: 325412
Steve Mason *(Co-COO)*

Subsidiaries:

Altasciences Clinical Los Angeles,
Inc.　　　　　　　　　　　　　(1)
5630 Cerritos Ave, Cypress, CA 90630
Tel.: (714) 252-0700
Sales Range: $25-49.9 Million
Emp.: 246
Clinical Research Services
N.A.I.C.S.: 621511
Kenneth T. Kim *(Founder & Chief Medical
Officer)*

Subsidiary (Domestic):

Medelis, Inc.　　　　　　　　　(2)
30 Burton Hills Blvd Ste 210, Nashville, TN
37215
Tel.: (615) 297-6105
Web Site: http://www.medelis.com
Research & Development in Biotechnology
N.A.I.C.S.: 541714
E. Laughlin Flanagan *(Chm & CEO)*

Calvert Laboratories, Inc.　　(1)
1225 Crescent Green Ste 460, Cary, NC
27518　　　　　　　　　　　(100%)
Tel.: (919) 854-4453
Web Site: http://www.calvertlabs.com
Pharmaceutical Research & Development
Laboratory
N.A.I.C.S.: 541715
Charles B. Spainhour *(Chief Scientific Offi-
cer)*

ALTAVIA S.A.
10 Rue Blanqui, 93400, Saint-Ouen,
France
Tel.: (33) 149480000
Web Site: http://www.altavia-
paris.com
Year Founded: 1983
Sales Range: $10-24.9 Million
Emp.: 55
Marketing & Publishing Services
N.A.I.C.S.: 541613

Laurent Gampel *(Deputy CEO)*

Subsidiaries:

Altavia Advertising Co., Ltd.　(1)
No Jia-6 Gongti Bei Road Unit 2202-2203
22nd floor, Zhong Yu Plaza Chaoyang, Bei-
jing, 100027, China
Tel.: (86) 10 6539 3621
Advetising Agency
N.A.I.C.S.: 541810
Jing Legrand *(CEO)*

Altavia Belgium SA　　　　　(1)
Avenue Louise - Louizalaan 287/5,
Bruxelles, 1050, Brussels, Belgium
Tel.: (32) 2 639 68 68
Marketing Consulting Services
N.A.I.C.S.: 541613
Christel Mayalian *(COO)*

Altavia Ceska SRO　　　　　(1)
Pocernicka 96, 108 00, Prague, Czech Re-
public
Tel.: (420) 296 411 541
Web Site: http://www.altavia.cz
Marketing Consulting Services
N.A.I.C.S.: 541613
Rodolph Crozier *(Gen Mgr)*

Altavia Deutschland GmbH　(1)
Am Wehrhahn 100, 40211, Dusseldorf, Ger-
many
Tel.: (49) 211 54 26 88 0
Marketing Consulting Services
N.A.I.C.S.: 541613
Peter Schober *(Gen Mgr)*

Altavia HTT Ltd　　　　　　　(1)
4 Park Square Newton Chambers Road,
Thorncliffe Park Chapeltown, Sheffield, S35
2PH, United Kingdom
Tel.: (44) 114 220 3760
Emp.: 20
Marketing Consulting Services
N.A.I.C.S.: 541613
Nick White *(Mng Dir)*

Altavia Hellas AE　　　　　　(1)
103 Ethnikis Antistaseos street, N Psychiko,
15451, Athens, Greece
Tel.: (30) 210 67 73 900
Marketing Consulting Services
N.A.I.C.S.: 541613
Rania Athanasoulia *(Gen Mgr)*

Altavia Hungaria KFT　　　　(1)
Karolyi Istvan u 10, Budapest, 1047, Hun-
gary
Tel.: (36) 1 688 2325
Web Site: http://www.altavia.hu
Emp.: 6
Marketing Consulting Services
N.A.I.C.S.: 541613
Laszlo Orosz *(Mgr-Production)*

Altavia Iberica CFA　　　　　(1)
Calle Orense n 16 1 planta, 28020, Madrid,
Spain
Tel.: (34) 91 121 38 38
Marketing Consulting Services
N.A.I.C.S.: 541613
Erick Bilinski *(Gen Mgr)*

Altavia Iletisim AS　　　　　(1)
Otim Yolu Pazar Sok Bareli Plaza No 2-4 K
3, Gayrettepe, 34287, Istanbul, Turkiye
Tel.: (90) 212 2135050
Marketing Consulting Services
N.A.I.C.S.: 541613

Altavia Italia Srl　　　　　　(1)
Alzaia Naviglio Pavese 78/3, 20142, Milan,
Italy
Tel.: (39) 02303043
Marketing Consulting Services
N.A.I.C.S.: 541613
Paolo Mamo *(Gen Mgr)*

Altavia Lille SAS　　　　　　(1)
23 rue du Molinel, BP 369, 59026, Lille, Ce-
dex, France
Tel.: (33) 3 20 51 15 15
Marketing Consulting Services
N.A.I.C.S.: 541613

Altavia Optitrans S.A.S.　　　(1)
19 Chemin de la plaine, 69390, Vourles,
France
Tel.: (33) 4 78 86 86 70
Web Site: http://www.altavia-optitrans.com

Altavia S.A.—(Continued)

Emp.: 1,000
Logistics Consulting Servies
N.A.I.C.S.: 541614
Patricia Seprez *(Pres)*

Altavia Polska Sp. z o.o. **(1)**
ul Mlynarska 48, 01-171, Warsaw, Poland
Tel.: (48) 22 535 55 41
Marketing Consulting Services
N.A.I.C.S.: 541613

Altavia Romania Communication SRL **(1)**
Str Sergent Constantin Apostol nr 10 Cladirea Besta - parter Sector 6, Bucharest, Romania
Tel.: (40) 742582842
Marketing Consulting Services
N.A.I.C.S.: 541613
Radu Paun *(Dir-Ops)*

Altavia Rus, ooo **(1)**
ul Yablochkova 21/3, Yablochkova, 127322, Moscow, Russia
Tel.: (7) 4959846445
Web Site: http://www.altavia.ru
Marketing Consulting Services
N.A.I.C.S.: 541613
Andrey Ivanov *(Gen Mgr)*

Altavia Swiss SA **(1)**
Industriestrasse 47, Postfach 4461, 6304, Zug, Switzerland
Tel.: (41) 41 726 42 24
Marketing Consulting Services
N.A.I.C.S.: 541613

Cosmic Communication SA **(1)**
6 rue Royale, Paris, 75008, France
Tel.: (33) 144585858
Web Site: http://www.agencecosmic.com
Emp.: 40
Marketing Consulting Services
N.A.I.C.S.: 541613
Sydney Palti *(Pres)*

SAS Altavia Saint-Etienne **(1)**
1 rue Pablo Picasso, 42 000, Saint-Etienne, France
Tel.: (33) 4 77 92 82 82
Marketing Consulting Services
N.A.I.C.S.: 541613
Pierre Artru *(CEO)*

ALTAWEST GROUP
11 Rue de Fontenay, 92340, Bourg-la-Reine, France
Tel.: (33) 140848834 **FR**
Web Site: http://www.altawest.net
Year Founded: 2005
Emp.: 1,200
OEM & Energy, Environmental, Process Industries Service Solutions
N.A.I.C.S.: 335311
Philippe Garelli *(Chm)*

Subsidiaries:

Inova Groupe **(1)**
1 rue Eugene et Armand Peugeot, CS 80002, F 92508, Rueil-Malmaison, Cedex, France **(100%)**
Tel.: (33) 147100350
Web Site: http://www.inova-groupe.com
Sales Range: $50-74.9 Million
Emp.: 80
Construction, Maintenance & Operation of Waste-to-Energy & Biomass Power Plants
N.A.I.C.S.: 541330

Jeumont Electric **(1)**
367 rue de l'Industrie, PO Box 20109, 59572, Jeumont, France
Tel.: (33) 3 61 99 96 00
Web Site: http://www.jeumontelectric.com
Sales Range: $100-124.9 Million
Emp.: 650
Industrial Machines Design, Maintains & Mfr
N.A.I.C.S.: 333248

Subsidiary (Domestic):

JEUMONT Electric Maintenance **(2)**
5 rue du Chateau de Bel Air, BP 80 203, Carquefou, 44472, Nantes, Cedex, France
Tel.: (33) 2 40 25 13 55
Web Site: http://www.je-maintenance.com

Emp.: 90
Power Generator Repair & Maintenance Services
N.A.I.C.S.: 811310
Benoit Leroux *(Gen Mgr)*

Subsidiary (Non-US):

JEUMONT Electric Middle East **(2)**
Airport Road Fetouh Al Khair Centre Tower 3 0 floor, PO Box 44183, Abu Dhabi, United Arab Emirates
Tel.: (971) 50 666 1907
Power Generator Distr
N.A.I.C.S.: 423610

Subsidiary (Domestic):

Jeumont Drives Systems SAS **(2)**
15 rue Armand Japy, 25460, Etupes, France
Tel.: (33) 3 63 70 00 50
Power Generator Distr
N.A.I.C.S.: 423610

Subsidiary (Non-US):

Jeumont Electric India Private Limited **(2)**
615-616 6th Floor B Wing Bonanza Sahar Plaza Andheri Kurla Road, Andheri East, Mumbai, 400059, India
Tel.: (91) 22 40151264
Web Site: http://www.jeumontelectric.in
Power Generator Mfr & Distr
N.A.I.C.S.: 333611

Subsidiary (Domestic):

Sarelem **(2)**
5 Rue Du Chateau De Bel Air, PO Box 80203, 44472, Carquefou, France **(100%)**
Tel.: (33) 240251355
Web Site: http://www.sarelem.fr
Sales Range: $25-49.9 Million
Emp.: 100
Renovator of Electrical Equipment
N.A.I.C.S.: 335999

Leroux & Lotz Maintys Sas **(1)**
Agence Rhone-alpes 4950 Route Nationale 7, 26 800, Etoile-sur-Rhone, France
Tel.: (33) 4 75 58 69 40
Web Site: http://www.llmaintys.com
Industrial Boiler Mfr & Distr
N.A.I.C.S.: 332410

Leroux & Lotz Technologies SA **(1)**
10 rue des Usines, BP 88509, 44185, Nantes, Cedex, France
Tel.: (33) 2 40 95 96 97
Web Site: http://www.lerouxlotz.com
Emp.: 150
Industrial Boiler Mfr
N.A.I.C.S.: 332410

Timolor Leroux Et Lotz SAS **(1)**
32 rue Ingenieur Verriere, 56100, Lorient, France
Tel.: (33) 297 871 500
Web Site: http://www.timolor.com
Emp.: 200
Ship Building & Repairing Services
N.A.I.C.S.: 336611

ALTE LEIPZIGER VERSICHERUNG AG
Alte Leipziger-Platz 1, 61440, Oberursel, Germany
Tel.: (49) 61716600
Web Site: http://www.alte-leipziger.de
Year Founded: 1819
Sales Range: $450-499.9 Million
Emp.: 1,700
Commercial Liability Technical & Transport Insurance Services
N.A.I.C.S.: 524128
Gesa Adolphs *(Mgr-PR)*

Subsidiaries:

Alte Leipziger Autoversicherung **(1)**
Alte Leipziger Platz 1, Oberursel, 61440, Taunus, Germany **(100%)**
Tel.: (49) 6171662030
Web Site: http://www.alte-leipziger.com
Sales Range: $700-749.9 Million
Emp.: 1,200
Automobile Insurance

N.A.I.C.S.: 524128
Walter Botermann *(Gen Mgr)*

Rechtsschutz Union Versicherungs-AG **(1)**
Sonnenstrasse 33, 80331, Munich, Germany **(25.01%)**
Tel.: (49) 8954853605
Web Site: http://www.rechtsschutzunion.de
Insurance
N.A.I.C.S.: 524128

ALTEA GREEN POWER S.P.A.
Via Chivasso 15 A, 10098, Rivoli, TO, Italy
Tel.: (39) 0110195120
Web Site:
https://www.alteagreenpower.it
Year Founded: 2000
AGP—(ITA)
Rev.: $19,128,183
Assets: $42,184,969
Liabilities: $22,928,999
Net Worth: $19,255,970
Earnings: $5,430,690
Emp.: 29
Fiscal Year-end: 12/31/23
Natural Gas Distribution Services
N.A.I.C.S.: 221210
Giovanni Di Pascale *(CEO & Founder)*

ALTEC HOLDINGS S.A.
Patmou 12, 15123, Maroussi, Greece
Tel.: (30) 210 6872348
Web Site: http://www.altec.gr
Year Founded: 1988
Sales Range: $300-349.9 Million
Emp.: 374
Holding Company
N.A.I.C.S.: 551112
Athanasoulis X. Athanasios *(Chm & CEO)*

ALTECH BATTERIES LIMITED
Suite 8 295 Rokeby Road, Subiaco, 6008, WA, Australia
Tel.: (61) 861681555
Web Site:
https://www.altechgroup.com
Year Founded: 2007
ATC—(ASX)
Rev.: $359,082
Assets: $75,384,035
Liabilities: $651,668
Net Worth: $74,732,367
Earnings: ($4,445,763)
Emp.: 11
Fiscal Year-end: 06/30/22
All Other Miscellaneous Chemical Product & Preparation Manufacturing
N.A.I.C.S.: 325998
Iggy Tan *(Mng Dir)*

ALTECH CO., LTD.
2nd floor Sumitomo Irifune Building 1-1-1 irifune 2-chome, Chuo-ku, Tokyo, 104-0042, Japan
Tel.: (81) 355426760 **JP**
Web Site: https://www.altech.co.jp
Year Founded: 1976
9972—(TKS)
Rev.: $126,428,880
Assets: $152,754,050
Liabilities: $68,950,250
Net Worth: $83,803,800
Earnings: ($7,274,340)
Emp.: 466
Fiscal Year-end: 11/30/23
Industrial Machinery & Equipment Sales
N.A.I.C.S.: 423830
Norihiro Chono *(Pres & CEO)*

Subsidiaries:

Altech Asia Pacific Vietnam Co., Ltd. **(1)**
4th Floor-DC Tower No 111D Ly Chinh

Thang Street, Vo Thi Sau Ward District 3, Ho Chi Minh City, Vietnam
Tel.: (84) 283 848 3901
Industrial Machinery Equipment Distr
N.A.I.C.S.: 423830
Kenichi Kitazawa *(Pres)*

Altech Engineering Co., Ltd. **(1)**
Sumitomo Fudosan Yotsuya Bldg 1F 13-4 Araki-cho, Shinjuku-ku, Tokyo, 160-0007, Japan
Tel.: (81) 353630864
Web Site:
http://www.altech-engineering.com
Rev.: $6,517,688
Emp.: 45
Industrial Equipment Repair & Maintenance Services
N.A.I.C.S.: 811310
Hiroyuki Inoue *(Exec Officer)*

Altech IT Inc. **(1)**
Intec 88 Bldg 8F 20-21 Araki-cho, Shinjuku-ku, Tokyo, 160-0007, Japan
Tel.: (81) 353633007
Web Site: http://www.altech-it.com
Sales Range: $25-49.9 Million
Emp.: 40
Software Development & Sales
N.A.I.C.S.: 513210

Subsidiary (Non-US):

Altech New Materials (Suzhou) Co., Ltd. **(2)**
Dongxin Road No 199, Xukou Town Wuzhong District, Suzhou, 215164, China
Tel.: (86) 5126 621 6000
Web Site: http://www.altech.co.jp
Manufacture & Sales of Preforms for Aseptic Filling, Caps & Other Packaging Materials
N.A.I.C.S.: 333993

Altech New Material Co., Ltd. **(1)**
68-12 Oguro Maruoka-cho, Maruoka-cho, Sakai, 910-0315, Fukui, Japan **(100%)**
Tel.: (81) 77 668 1170
Web Site: http://www.altech.co.jp
Recycled Plastic Pallets Mfr & Sales
N.A.I.C.S.: 326199

Altech New Materials (Fukui) Co., Ltd. **(1)**
68-12 Oguro Maruoka-cho, Sakai, 910-0315, Fukui, Japan
Tel.: (81) 77 668 1170
Web Site: https://altech-fukui.co.jp
Emp.: 45
Plastic Product Mfr & Distr
N.A.I.C.S.: 326199

Altech Shanghai Co., Ltd. **(1)**
Rm2006-2007Chang Fang International Plaza No 555Lou Shan Guan Road, Chang Ning District, Shanghai, 200050, China
Tel.: (86) 2161363802
Web Site: https://www.altechchina.com
Sales Range: $25-49.9 Million
Emp.: 10
Packing Devices Mfr
N.A.I.C.S.: 339991

PT. Altech **(1)**
GD Marga Guna Grand 2nd Floor Jl Marge Guna Raya No 9 Gandaria Selatan, Cilandak, Jakarta Selatan, 12420, Indonesia
Tel.: (62) 217 590 1140
Web Site: http://www.altech.co.jp
Preforms Mfr & Distr
N.A.I.C.S.: 326121

PT. Altech Asia Pacific Indonesia **(1)**
GD Marga Guna Grand 2nd Floor Jl Marge Guna Raya No 9, Cilandak Gandaria Selatan, Jakarta Selatan, 12420, Indonesia
Tel.: (62) 217 590 1140
Industrial Machinery Equipment Distr
N.A.I.C.S.: 423830
Masanori Tsukahara *(Pres)*

ALTECH CORPORATION
Queen s Tower C 18F 2-3-5 Minatomirai, Nishi-ku, Yokohama, 220-6218, Kanagawa, Japan
Tel.: (81) 456403700
Web Site: https://www.alpsgiken.co.jp
Year Founded: 1968

4641—(TKS)
Rev.: $327,671,440
Assets: $177,427,250
Liabilities: $57,847,310
Net Worth: $119,579,940
Earnings: $26,204,640
Emp.: 6,107
Fiscal Year-end: 12/31/23
Staffing Services
N.A.I.C.S.: 561330
Masashi Sugai *(Corp Officer)*

Subsidiaries:

Alps Agri Career Corporation **(1)**
Altech Corporation Building No 2 4F
1-16-18 Nishihashimoto, Midori-ku, Sagami-
hara, 252-0131, Kanagawa, Japan
Tel.: (81) 427382955
Web Site: https://www.agri-career.co.jp
Agriculture Staffing Services
N.A.I.C.S.: 561320
Nobuyuki Wataabe *(Chm)*

Alps Business Service
Corporation **(1)**
1-16-18 Nishihashimoto Alps Giken 2nd
Building 6F, Midori-ku, Sagamihara, 252-
0131, Kanagawa, Japan
Tel.: (81) 427743339
Business Support Services
N.A.I.C.S.: 561499

Alps Care Heart Corporation **(1)**
1-16-18 Nishihashimoto Alps Giken 2nd
Building 2nd Floor, Midori-ku, Sagamihara,
252-0131, Kanagawa, Japan
Tel.: (81) 427193252
Long-term Care Services
N.A.I.C.S.: 623110

Alps Career Designing
Corporation **(1)**
11F MG Ichigaya Building 1-9, Chiyoda-ku,
Tokyo, 101-0052, Japan
Tel.: (81) 3 3230 3334
Web Site: http://www.alpscd.co.jp
Employment Placement Services
N.A.I.C.S.: 561311
Yoshiro Kiuchi *(Pres)*

Alpsgiken Myanmar Co., Ltd. **(1)**
No 15/17 Room No 4B 4th Floor Yangon
Insein Road, Hleden Kamayaut Township,
Yangon, Myanmar
Tel.: (95) 977 955 1712
Engineering Equipment Mfr
N.A.I.C.S.: 333248
Keiji Mashimo *(Pres)*

Alpsgiken Taiwan Co., Ltd. **(1)**
Room E 5F No 146 Shung Chiang Road,
Taipei, 10458, Taiwan
Tel.: (886) 225319933
Engineering Equipment Mfr
N.A.I.C.S.: 333248
Atsushi Imamura *(Chm)*

Altech Shine Co., Ltd. **(1)**
5F No 146 Shung Chiang Road, Taipei,
10458, Taiwan
Tel.: (886) 2 2531 9933
Web Site: http://www.altechshine.com.tw
Employment Placement Services
N.A.I.C.S.: 561311
Takahiko Ichimura *(Chm)*

Digital Spice Corporation **(1)**
Matsuki Building 2F 1821 Shiga Akanuma,
Suwa, 392-0012, Nagano, Japan
Tel.: (81) 266562266
Web Site: https://www.digital-spice.co.jp
Emp.: 113
Software Development Services
N.A.I.C.S.: 541511
Kazunori Tashiro *(Pres)*

Pana R&D Co., Ltd. **(1)**
6F Tagosin Building 2-23-3 Higashi,
Shibuya-ku, Tokyo, 150-0011, Japan
Tel.: (81) 35 467 5611
Web Site: https://www.panard.co.jp
Automobile Equipment Services
N.A.I.C.S.: 811310

ALTECHNA UAB
Savanoriu Ave 176B, 03154, Vilnius,
Lithuania

Tel.: (370) 52725738   LT
Web Site: https://www.altechna.com
Year Founded: 1996
Laser Optics & Optomechanical As-
semblies Mfr
N.A.I.C.S.: 333310
Antanas Laurutis *(CEO)*

Subsidiaries:

Alpine Research Optics Corp. **(1)**
6810 Winchester Cir, Boulder, CO 80301
Tel.: (303) 444-3420
Web Site: http://www.arocorp.com
Sales Range: $1-9.9 Million
Emp.: 54
Optical Instruments & Lenses Mfr
N.A.I.C.S.: 333310
Rolf Easto *(Mgr-Mktg)*

ALTECO MEDICAL AB
Hostbruksvagen 8, 226 60, Lund,
Sweden
Tel.: (46) 46328600
Web Site:
   https://www.altecomedical.se
Year Founded: 2002
Medical Equipment Mfr
N.A.I.C.S.: 339112
Anders Althin *(Chm)*

ALTEK CORPORATION
No 12 Li-Hsin Road HsinchuScience-
Based Industrial Park, Hsin-chu, Tai-
wan
Tel.: (886) 35784567
Web Site: https://www.altek.com.tw
Year Founded: 1996
3059—(TAI)
Rev.: $297,565,246
Assets: $518,086,183
Liabilities: $219,751,848
Net Worth: $298,334,336
Earnings: $13,404,558
Emp.: 439
Fiscal Year-end: 12/31/23
Digital Camera Mfr
N.A.I.C.S.: 334118
Alex Hsia *(Founder, Chm, Pres &
CEO)*

Subsidiaries:

Altek Lab Inc. **(1)**
1411 W 190th St Ste 475, Gardena, CA
90248
Tel.: (310) 225-5688
Photographic Equipment Mfr
N.A.I.C.S.: 333310
Qinghua Fu *(Sr Mgr)*

ALTEN S.A.
40 Avenue Andre Morizet, 92100,
Boulogne-Billancourt, Cedex, France
Tel.: (33) 146087200
Web Site: https://www.alten.com
Year Founded: 1988
ATE—(EUR)
Sales Range: $1-4.9 Billion
Engineering & Technology Consulting
Services
N.A.I.C.S.: 541330
Gerald Attia *(Deputy CEO-Sls, Work-
packages & Intl Zone 2)*

Subsidiaries:

ALTEN Austria Sud GmbH **(1)**
Liebenauer Hauptstrasse 246, 8041, Graz,
Austria
Tel.: (43) 316 401 4850
Web Site: https://www.alten.at
Innovative Engineering Services
N.A.I.C.S.: 541330
Corvin Mieling *(Mgr)*

ALTEN Belgium SPRL **(1)**
Chaussee de Charleroi 112, 1060, Brussels,
Belgium
Tel.: (32) 2 774 8811
Web Site: https://www.alten.be
Innovative Engineering Services
N.A.I.C.S.: 541330

Camille Lojou *(Mgr-Coach Bus)*

ALTEN Calsoft Labs India Private
Ltd. **(1)**
7th Floor Tower D IBC Knowledge Park 4/1
Bannerghatta Main Road, Bengaluru,
560029, India
Tel.: (91) 8040343000
Innovative Engineering Services
N.A.I.C.S.: 541330
Lokesh Ashok *(Sr Mgr-Sls)*

ALTEN Calsoft Labs, Inc. **(1)**
2903 Bunker Hill Ln Ste 107, Santa Clara,
CA 95054
Tel.: (408) 755-3000
Web Site: http://www.altencalsoftlabs.com
Computer Related Services
N.A.I.C.S.: 541519

Subsidiary (Domestic):

Premier Logic, LLC **(2)**
3655 N Point Pkwy Ste 650, Alpharetta, GA
30005
Tel.: (678) 736-6950
Web Site: http://www.premierlogic.com
Software Developer & Support Services
N.A.I.C.S.: 513210
Chad Osgood *(CEO)*

ALTEN Canada Inc. **(1)**
1100 Rene-Levesque West Suite 1350,
Montreal, H3B 4N4, QC, Canada
Tel.: (514) 360-1058
Web Site: https://www.alten.ca
Technical Consulting Services
N.A.I.C.S.: 541690
Jonathan Hardy *(Acct Mgr)*

ALTEN China Ltd. **(1)**
Room 1003-4 Floor 10 Capital Square No
268 Hengtong Rd, Jingan District, Shang-
hai, 200070, China
Tel.: (86) 215 228 5991
Web Site: https://www.altenchina.com
Technical Consulting Services
N.A.I.C.S.: 541690
Sherry Zhao *(Exec Dir-Bus)*

ALTEN Delivery Center IASI
SRL **(1)**
54 Rue Mitropolit Varlaam NBC 8th Floor,
Iasi, Romania
Tel.: (40) 372401467
Emp.: 160
Technical Consulting Services
N.A.I.C.S.: 541690
Oana Lungu *(Dir-HR)*

ALTEN GMBH **(1)**
Rosenauer Strasse 27 Eingang 1 3 OG,
96450, Coburg, Germany
Tel.: (49) 95 615 5330
Web Site: http://www.alten-engineering.com
Sales Range: $25-49.9 Million
Emp.: 45
Automotive Engineering Services
N.A.I.C.S.: 541330

ALTEN ITALIA SPA **(1)**
Via Gaetano Crespi 12, 20134, Milan, Italy
Tel.: (39) 023 657 1000
Web Site: https://www.alten.it
Business Development Consulting Services
N.A.I.C.S.: 561499

ALTEN LTD **(1)**
The Whitehouse 9A Belvedere Road, South
Bank, London, SE1 8AB, United Kingdom
Tel.: (44) 8456585770
Web Site: http://www.alten.co.uk
Sales Range: $25-49.9 Million
Emp.: 150
Engineering Consulting Services
N.A.I.C.S.: 541330

ALTEN Luxembourg SARL **(1)**
20 rue Eugene Ruppert, 2453, Luxem-
bourg, Luxembourg
Tel.: (352) 26493440
Technical Consulting Services
N.A.I.C.S.: 541690
Sihem Dimassi *(Bus Mgr)*

ALTEN Nederland BV **(1)**
Fascinatio Boulevard 582, 2909 VA, Capelle
aan den IJssel, Netherlands
Tel.: (31) 10 463 7700
Web Site: https://www.alten.nl
Technical Consulting Services

N.A.I.C.S.: 541690
Arnold Schutter *(Mgr-Bus & Technical Software)*

ALTEN Polska Sp. z o.o. **(1)**
ul Panska 73 Panska Corner 3rd Floor, 00-
834, Warsaw, Poland
Tel.: (48) 22 314 7547
Web Site: https://www.altenpolska.pl
Technical Consulting Services
N.A.I.C.S.: 541690
Dawid Blaszczyk *(Mgr-Bus Dev)*

ALTEN SI-TECHNO ROMANIA
SRL **(1)**
Sector 2 73 Bd Dacia, Bucharest, 020062,
Romania
Tel.: (40) 213100337
Information Technology Consulting Services
N.A.I.C.S.: 541512

ALTEN SIR AND TELECOM **(1)**
130 rue de Silly, 92514, Boulogne-
Billancourt, France
Tel.: (33) 146087500
Web Site: http://www.alten.fr
Sales Range: $100-124.9 Million
Emp.: 500
Telecommunication Servicesb
N.A.I.C.S.: 517810

ALTEN Spain SA **(1)**
Cristalia Business Park C/ Via de los Pobla-
dos 3 Ed 5 - Plta 2, 28033, Madrid, Spain
Tel.: (34) 91 791 0000
Web Site: https://www.alten.es
Emp.: 2,400
Technical Consulting Services
N.A.I.C.S.: 541690
Stefania Piras *(Bus Mgr)*

ALTEN Sweden AB **(1)**
Theres Svenssons gata 15, Gothenburg,
417 55, Sweden
Tel.: (46) 317251000
Web Site: http://www.alten.se
Sales Range: $900-999.9 Million
Emp.: 1,200
Mechanical Design & Engineering Services
N.A.I.C.S.: 541330
Martin Segerstrom *(Head-Ops)*

ALTEN Switzerland Sarl AG **(1)**
Riedstrasse 11, 6330, Cham, Switzerland
Tel.: (41) 41 790 3714
Web Site: https://www.alten.ch
Innovative Engineering Services
N.A.I.C.S.: 541330
Alexandre Gitz *(Mgr-Engrg Bus)*

ALTEN Technology GmbH **(1)**
Fangdieckstrasse 66, 22547, Hamburg,
Germany
Tel.: (49) 40 853 9900
Web Site: http://www.alten-technology.com
Innovative Engineering Services
N.A.I.C.S.: 541330
Pierre Bonhomme *(CEO)*

ANOTECH ENERGY SA **(1)**
112 avenue Kleber, BP 77536, 75016,
Paris, France
Tel.: (33) 15 817 7525
Web Site: https://www.anotech-energy.com
Oil & Gas Exploration Services
N.A.I.C.S.: 213112

AXEN SARL **(1)**
2 R Seze, Bordeaux, Gironde, France
Tel.: (33) 556815397
Engineeering Services
N.A.I.C.S.: 541330

Aixial GmbH **(1)**
Mainzer Landstrasse 49, 60329, Frankfurt
am Main, Germany
Tel.: (49) 1718107832
Technical Consulting Services
N.A.I.C.S.: 541690

Aixial S.R.O. **(1)**
Pernerova 149/35, 186 00, Prague, Czech
Republic
Tel.: (420) 237836505
Technical Consulting Services
N.A.I.C.S.: 541690
Adam Svobodnik *(Country Mgr)*

Aixial SAS **(1)**
4 rue Danjou - Batiment B, 92513,
Boulogne-Billancourt, Cedex, France

Alten S.A.—(Continued)

Tel.: (33) 14 608 8900
Web Site: https://www.aixial.com
Emp.: 800
Technical Consulting Services
N.A.I.C.S.: 541690
Yoann Allias (Sr Mgr-Data)

Aixial SPRL (1)
112 Chaussee de Charleroi, 1060, Brussels, Belgium
Tel.: (32) 27748811
Technical Consulting Services
N.A.I.C.S.: 541690
Guillaume De Munter (Bus Mgr)

Algor, S.L. (1)
Calle Zurbano 8, Madrid, 28010, Spain
Tel.: (34) 913190124
Engineeering Services
N.A.I.C.S.: 541330

Alte Oy (1)
Rautaruukintie 155, 92100, Raahe, Finland
Tel.: (358) 20 786 3300
Web Site: https://www.alten.fi
Technical Consulting Services
N.A.I.C.S.: 541690
Veli Pekka Kalm (Dir-Technical)

Alten Italia (1)
Via Gaetano Crespi 12, 20134, Milan, BS, Italy
Tel.: (39) 023 657 1000
Web Site: https://www.alten.it
Information Technology Consulting Services
N.A.I.C.S.: 541512

Alten PCS (1)
Eemnesserweg 26, 3741 GA, Baarn, Netherlands
Tel.: (31) 356926969
Web Site: http://www.altenpts.nl
Sales Range: $25-49.9 Million
Emp.: 170
Software Consulting Services
N.A.I.C.S.: 541690
Eric Haesen (Mng Dir)

Alten Sud Ouest SAS (1)
Buroparc 3 Rue de la Decouverte, BP 47533, 31675, Labege, France
Tel.: (33) 562882121
Sales Range: $75-99.9 Million
Emp.: 300
Engineeering Services
N.A.I.C.S.: 541330

Anotech Do Brasil Ltda (1)
Av Churchill 109 Salas 703/704 Centro, Rio de Janeiro, 20020-050, Brazil
Tel.: (55) 2125320437
Oil & Gas Exploration Services
N.A.I.C.S.: 213112
Sebastien Prat (Ops Mgr)

Anotech Energy Doha LLC (1)
Office 1603 16th Floor Palm Tower B Majlis Al Taawon Street-West Bay, PO Box 23012, Doha, Qatar
Tel.: (974) 44789210
Oil & Gas Exploration Services
N.A.I.C.S.: 213112
Pierre Gonsolin (Sr Acct Mgr)

Anotech Energy Nigeria Limited (1)
South Atlantic Petroleum Towers 7A Plot 01 Adeola Odeku Street, Victoria Island, Lagos, Nigeria
Tel.: (234) 8170281488
Oil & Gas Exploration Services
N.A.I.C.S.: 213112
Emilomo Jennifer Oyibokja (Mgr-Personnel Admin)

Anotech Energy Singapore Pte. Ltd. (1)
160 Robinson Road SBF Center 21-04, Singapore, 068914, Singapore
Tel.; (65) 69701351
Oil & Gas Exploration Services
N.A.I.C.S.: 213112
Joe Han Lim (Bus Mgr)

Anotech Energy USA Inc. (1)
16225 Park Ten Place Ste 420, Houston, TX 77084
Tel.: (281) 994-5900
Oil & Gas Exploration Services
N.A.I.C.S.: 213112

Jennifer Schindewolf (Mgr-HR)

Atexis France SAS (1)
10/12 Boulevard Pythagore, 13127, Vitrolles, France
Tel.: (33) 44 239 3635
Web Site: https://www.atexis.com
Innovative Engineering Services
N.A.I.C.S.: 541330
Etienne Oswald (Sls Dir)

Atexis GmbH (1)
Fangdieckstr 66, 22547, Hamburg, Germany
Tel.: (49) 405475264100
Innovative Engineering Services
N.A.I.C.S.: 541330
Stefan Eskierski (Head-Quality & Mgr-Continuous Improvement)

Atexis SRL (1)
Calea Chisinaului nr 23 Cladirea Tester, 700265, Iasi, Romania
Tel.: (40) 232406118
Innovative Engineering Services
N.A.I.C.S.: 541330
Oana Georgiana Embach (Asst Mgr)

Atexis Spain SL (1)
Edificio Morera y Vallejo II Calle de la aviacion Na 14 Planta 3a, Poligono Industrial Calonge, 41007, Seville, Spain
Tel.: (34) 954467255
Innovative Engineering Services
N.A.I.C.S.: 541330

Avenir Conseil Formation SA (1)
65 avenue Edouard Vaillant, 92773, Boulogne-Billancourt, France
Tel.: (33) 14 608 8200
Web Site: https://www.avenir-conseil.fr
Emp.: 270
Management Consulting Services
N.A.I.C.S.: 541618
Nathalie Heroux Ambolet (CEO)

B2I AUTOMOTIVE (1)
1 Rue Galvani Bat C, 91300, Massy, France
Tel.: (33) 1 46 84 41 00
Web Site: http://www.b2i-automotive.com
Sales Range: $25-49.9 Million
Emp.: 200
Automotive Engineering Services
N.A.I.C.S.: 541330

BURKE NEWCO S.L. (1)
Paseo Castellana 139-3, Madrid, 28046, Spain
Tel.: (34) 915715550
Engineeering Services
N.A.I.C.S.: 541330

Beone Stuttgart GmbH (1)
Curiestrasse 5, 70563, Stuttgart, Germany
Tel.: (49) 7116 569 3300
Web Site: https://www.beone-stuttgart.de
Management Consulting Services
N.A.I.C.S.: 541618
Andreas Koch (Bus Mgr-Unit)

CLEAR Consult GmbH (1)
Am Weichselgarten 21, 91058, Erlangen, Germany
Tel.: (49) 911981996500
Web Site: http://www.clear-consult.de
Technical Consulting Services
N.A.I.C.S.: 541690

CLEAR INTEC Sp. z o.o (1)
ul Czeslawa Klosia 7, 02-466, Warsaw, Poland
Tel.: (48) 22 880 0963
Web Site: https://www.clear-intec.com
Information Technology & Services
N.A.I.C.S.: 541511
David Gaszyna (CEO)

Calsoft Labs UK Private Ltd. (1)
3-5 Crutched Friars, London, EC3N 2HT, United Kingdom
Tel.: (44) 2074620120
Innovative Engineering Services
N.A.I.C.S.: 541330

Comiq Oy (1)
Kaisaniemenkatu 1C 5 Fl, 00100, Helsinki, Finland
Tel.: (358) 104405150
Web Site: http://www.comiq.fi
Information Technology Services

N.A.I.C.S.: 541511
Taija Kjerin (Mgr-Test)

Cresttek LLC (1)
565 Metroplace S Ste 420, Dublin, OH 43017
Tel.: (614) 408-3330
Web Site: https://www.cresttek.com
Automotive Engineering Services
N.A.I.C.S.: 541330

DIXID (1)
1 rue Ampere, 22300, Lannion, France
Tel.: (33) 296484428
Web Site: http://www.dixid.com
Software Development Services
N.A.I.C.S.: 541511

E-TIC Sistemes S.L.U. (1)
Carrer Balmes 7 4a Planta, 08007, Barcelona, Spain
Tel.: (34) 934874906
Web Site: http://www.etics.es
Information Technology Services
N.A.I.C.S.: 541511
Esther Lopez Bas (Bus Mgr)

ELITYS CONSULTING SARL (1)
115 Boulevard Stalingrad, 69100, Villeurbanne, France
Tel.: (33) 4 37 42 13 33
Web Site: http://www.elitys.fr
Engineering Consultancy Services
N.A.I.C.S.: 541330

Extia (1)
1 avenue de la Cristallerie Batiment A 6eme etage, 92310, Sevres, France
Tel.: (33) 14 699 9191
Web Site: http://www.extia.fr
Engineering Consulting Services
N.A.I.C.S.: 541330

Imp Poland sp. z o.o. (1)
Pilsudskiego 12, 50-049, Wroclaw, Poland
Tel.: (48) 713766910
Web Site: http://www.altens.com
Sales Range: $25-49.9 Million
Emp.: 20
Engineeering Services
N.A.I.C.S.: 541330
Martin Novak (Gen Mgr)

Kepler Rominfo SA (1)
Bd Ghica Tei nr 108, 023705, Bucharest, Romania
Tel.: (40) 212331080
Web Site: http://www.kepler-rominfo.com
Information Technology Services
N.A.I.C.S.: 541511

LMACP SA (1)
96 rue du clery, 75002, Paris, France
Tel.: (33) 54545345454
Web Site: http://www.lmacp.com
Information Technology Services
N.A.I.C.S.: 541511
Jeremie Freund (CEO)

Larix AS (1)
Lyskaer 8b, 2730, Herlev, Denmark
Tel.: (45) 7 027 2221
Web Site: https://www.larix.dk
Statistical Consulting Services
N.A.I.C.S.: 541618
Klaus Juel Olsen (Founder, CEO & Mng Dir)

Larix Sweden AB (1)
Medicon Village Scheeletorget 1, 223 81, Lund, Sweden
Tel.: (46) 70272221
Statistical Consulting Services
N.A.I.C.S.: 541618

MI-GSO GmbH (1)
Elsenheimerstrasse 55 A, 80687, Munich, Germany
Tel.: (49) 89436667789
Management Consulting Services
N.A.I.C.S.: 541618

MI-GSO SA (1)
Batiment Turcat II 7 rue Alain Fournier, 31300, Toulouse, France
Tel.: (33) 53 442 7700
Web Site: https://www.migso-pcubed.com
Management Consulting Services
N.A.I.C.S.: 541618
Maxime Bernard (Mgr-Talent Acquisition)

Optimissa Capital Markets Consulting S.A. de C.V. (1)
Av Chapultepec 480 Floor 12 Col Roma Norte, 06700, Mexico, Mexico
Tel.: (52) 5547392290
Marketing Consulting Services
N.A.I.C.S.: 541613
Julio Cesar Montoya (Project Mgr)

Optimissa Ltd (1)
35 New Broad St, London, EC2M 1NH, United Kingdom
Tel.: (44) 2030093027
Marketing Consulting Services
N.A.I.C.S.: 541613

Optimissa Portugal Unipessoal, Lda (1)
Av Duque de Loule 123 Fraccao 31, 1050-089, Lisbon, Portugal
Tel.: (351) 210497750
Marketing Consulting Services
N.A.I.C.S.: 541613
Francisco Barrocas Lourido (Country Mgr)

Optimissa Servicios Profesionales SL (1)
Jose Echegaray 14 Las Rozas Parque Empresarial, 28232, Madrid, Spain
Tel.: (34) 916404659
Management Consulting Services
N.A.I.C.S.: 541618

Orion Engineering BV (1)
Hurksestraat 43, 5652 AH, Eindhoven, Netherlands
Tel.: (31) 40 211 6777
Web Site: https://www.orionengineering.nl
Emp.: 450
Engineeering Services
N.A.I.C.S.: 541330
Marjolein Van Breugel (Mgr-Div)

PVR Technologies Inc. (1)
501 Allendale Rd Ste 201, King of Prussia, PA 19406
Tel.: (610) 337-1935
Web Site: https://pvrtech.com
Technical Consulting Services
N.A.I.C.S.: 541690
Kiran Kumar (Mgr-Payroll)

Pcubed Australia Pty Ltd (1)
Level 17 9 Castlereagh Street, Sydney, 2000, NSW, Australia
Tel.: (61) 1300791530
Management Consulting Services
N.A.I.C.S.: 541618
Phil Barclay (Mgr-NSW Bus)

Positech SRL (1)
Via Gaetano Crespi 12, 20134, Milan, Italy
Tel.: (39) 024 547 7718
Web Site: https://www.positech.it
Innovative Engineering Services
N.A.I.C.S.: 541330
Marcello Barba (Mgr-HR)

Premier Logic India Private Ltd. (1)
Stellar IT Park C-25 Sector-62 3rd Floor Western Side of Tower-2, Noida, 201301, Uttar Pradesh, India
Tel.: (91) 1204179653
Information Technology Services
N.A.I.C.S.: 541511
Dinesh Jhamb (Mng Dir)

Quick Release Automotive Ltd. (1)
1386 London Road, Leigh-on-Sea, SS9 2UJ, Essex, United Kingdom
Tel.: (44) 7523505474
Web Site: http://www.quickrelease.co.uk
Emp.: 200
Automotive Engineering Services
N.A.I.C.S.: 541330
Nick Solly (COO)

SACC Inc. (1)
2903 Bunker Hill Ln Ste 107, Santa Clara, CA 95054
Tel.: (408) 755-3000
Web Site: http://www.saccinc.com
Emp.: 25
Software Development Services
N.A.I.C.S.: 541511

SD PARTNERS LIMITED (1)
The Whitehouse 9a Belvedere Road, London, SE1 8AB, United Kingdom
Tel.: (44) 2074019399

Web Site: http://www.sd-partners.com
Sales Range: $25-49.9 Million
Emp.: 100
Information Technology Consulting Services
N.A.I.C.S.: 541512

Servicios De Desarrollo Orientado A Soluciones SL (1)
Luis Fuentes Bejarano 60 Edificio Nudo Norte primera planta, 41020, Seville, Spain
Tel.: (34) 95 511 4933
Web Site: https://www.sdos.es
Technical Consulting Services
N.A.I.C.S.: 541690

Shangai Shuangje Technology Co., Ltd. (1)
No 299 Anhong Road, Huangdu Town Jiading District, Shanghai, 201804, China
Tel.: (86) 213 959 3329
Web Site: https://www.sjtc.com.cn
Emp.: 200
Automobiles Design Services
N.A.I.C.S.: 541420

Si2Chip Technologies Private Ltd. (1)
2nd Floor Gayatri Tech Park No 183, EPIP Industrial Area Whitefield, Bengaluru, 560 066, India
Tel.: (91) 806 818 7000
Web Site: https://www.si2chip.com
Emp.: 100
Innovative Engineering Services
N.A.I.C.S.: 541330
Ashok Mishra (Co-Founder & Mng Dir)

StatMinds LLC (1)
501 Allendale Rd 2nd fl Ste 202, King of Prussia, PA 19406
Tel.: (484) 213-3337
Web Site: https://www.statminds.com
Technical Consulting Services
N.A.I.C.S.: 541690
J. Steve (Mgr-Bus Dev)

Techalten Portugal, Lda (1)
Avenida D Joao II 46-1A Ed D Joao II, 1990-095, Lisbon, Portugal
Tel.: (351) 21 584 2574
Web Site: https://www.alten.pt
Technical Consulting Services
N.A.I.C.S.: 541690
Marco Nuno Ferreira (Mng Dir)

Techno Like US Co., Ltd. (1)
Tamachi East Wing 6F Shibaura 3-5-39, Shibaura Minato-ku, Tokyo, 108-0023, Japan
Tel.: (81) 364352394
Web Site: http://www.tec-likeus.co.jp
Emp.: 150
Innovative Engineering Services
N.A.I.C.S.: 541330
Syuichi Aikawa (CEO)

Wafer Space Semiconductors Technologies Pvt. Ltd. (1)
No 3/E Monarch Ramani 5th Floor 7th C Main, 3rd Industrial Block Koramangala, Bengaluru, 560034, India
Tel.: (91) 804 672 0000
Web Site: https://www.waferspace.com
Semiconductor Devices Mfr
N.A.I.C.S.: 334413
Rahul Malvi (Founder & CEO)

X-DIN Inc. (1)
7874 Thorndike Rd, Greensboro, NC 27409
Tel.: (757) 340-1401
Web Site: https://www.xdin.com
Engineering Consulting Services
N.A.I.C.S.: 541330

cPrime Inc. (1)
4100 E 3rd Ave Ste 205, Foster City, CA 94404
Tel.: (877) 753-2760
Web Site: http://www.cprime.com
IT Project Management, Consulting & Staffing Services
N.A.I.C.S.: 541690
Monte Montoya (VP-Mktg & Sls)

ALTEO LIMITED
Tel.: (230) 4029050
Web Site: https://alteo.mu
ALTG—(MAU)
Rev.: $110,702,776

Assets: $790,097,900
Liabilities: $313,649,150
Net Worth: $476,448,750
Earnings: $43,530,955
Emp.: 1,549
Fiscal Year-end: 06/30/22
Sugarcane Farming Services
N.A.I.C.S.: 111930
Christian Marot (COO-Agricultural Activities)

Subsidiaries:

Sukari Investment Company Limited (1)
Industrial Area, Nairobi, Kenya
Tel.: (254) 722131814
Web Site:
http://www.sukariinvestmentltd.co.ke
Sugar Whslr
N.A.I.C.S.: 424490

ALTEOGEN INC.
62 1628beon-gil Yuseong-daero, Yuseong-gu, Daejeon, 34054, Korea (South)
Tel.: (82) 423848780
Web Site: https://www.alteogen.com
Year Founded: 2008
196170—(KRS)
Rev.: $22,757,012
Assets: $193,937,208
Liabilities: $79,085,417
Net Worth: $114,851,790
Earnings: ($7,961,544)
Emp.: 132
Fiscal Year-end: 12/31/22
Biopharmaceutical Mfr
N.A.I.C.S.: 325412
Soon Jae Park (CEO)

Subsidiaries:

Altos Biologics Co., Ltd. (1)
8th floor 15 Teheran-ro 84-gil, Gangnam-gu, Seoul, Korea (South)
Tel.: (82) 220399520
Web Site: https://altosbiologics.com
Biopharmaceutical Product Mfr
N.A.I.C.S.: 325412

Ceres F&D Inc. (1)
100 BioValley 2-ro, Jecheon, 27159, Chungcheongbuk-do, Korea (South)
Tel.: (82) 436528404
Web Site: https://www.ceresfnd.com
Biopharmaceutical Product Mfr & Distr
N.A.I.C.S.: 325412

ALTERATION EARTH PLC
Keystone Law 48 Chancery Lane, London, WC2A 1JF, United Kingdom
Tel.: (44) 2045018549   UK
Web Site:
https://www.altearthplc.com
Year Founded: 2021
ALTE—(LSE)
Assets: $1,473,601
Liabilities: $61,717
Net Worth: $1,411,885
Earnings: ($194,328)
Fiscal Year-end: 09/30/22
Investment Management Service
N.A.I.C.S.: 523999

ALTERCO S.A.
ul Smiala 59, 01-526, Warsaw, Poland
Tel.: (48) 730 054 682
Web Site: http://www.alterco.eu
Real Estate Development Services
N.A.I.C.S.: 531390

ALTERE SECURITIZADORA S.A.
Av Amador Bueno Da Veiga 1230 Sala 702 Parte, Penha, Sao Paulo, 03636-100, Brazil
Tel.: (55) 1130410212

Web Site:
http://www.alteresec.com.br
Year Founded: 1998
Emp.: 100
Real Estate Development Services
N.A.I.C.S.: 531210
Felipe Wallace Simonsen (CEO)

ALTERI PARTNERS LLP
20 Balderton Street, London, W1K 6TL, United Kingdom
Tel.: (44) 207 318 0570   UK
Web Site: http://www.alteri-investors.com
Corporate Debt Restructuring & Investment services
N.A.I.C.S.: 523999
Gavin George (CEO)

Subsidiaries:

Austin Reed Limited (1)
Waverley Mills, Langholm, DG13 0EB, United Kingdom   (100%)
Tel.: (44) 1387 380 611
Web Site: http://www.austinreed.com
Men's & Women's Branded Apparel Licensing & Store Operator
N.A.I.C.S.: 458110

Brantano Retail Limited (1)
Interlink Way West Interlink Business Park, Bardon, Coalville, LE67 1LD, Leics, United Kingdom
Tel.: (44) 1530 516146
Web Site: http://www.brantano.co.uk
Footwear Retailer
N.A.I.C.S.: 458210
David Short (Mng Dir)

ALTERITY THERAPEUTICS LIMITED
Tel.: (61) 393494906   AU
Web Site:
https://www.alteritytherapeutics.com
Year Founded: 1997
ATH—(ASX)
Rev.: $2,863,050
Assets: $12,836,367
Liabilities: $3,622,921
Net Worth: $9,213,446
Earnings: ($12,769,407)
Emp.: 10
Fiscal Year-end: 06/30/24
Pharmaceutical Development Services
N.A.I.C.S.: 325412
Geoffrey Paul Kempler (Founder & Chm)

Subsidiaries:

Alterity Therapeutics Inc. (1)
39899 Balentine Dr Ste 360, Newark, CA 94560
Tel.: (650) 300-2141
Therapy Services
N.A.I.C.S.: 621340

ALTERN ENERGY LIMITED
Descon Headquarter 18Km Ferozepur Road, Lahore, Pakistan
Tel.: (92) 4235990034
Web Site:
https://www.alternenergypk.com
ALTN—(PSX)
Rev.: $60,661,135
Assets: $120,966,121
Liabilities: $11,393,281
Net Worth: $109,572,840
Earnings: $26,053,937
Emp.: 5
Fiscal Year-end: 06/30/23
Eletric Power Generation Services
N.A.I.C.S.: 221116
Taimur Dawood (Chm)

ALTERNATE HEALTH CORP.
Suite 200 99 Yorkville Avenue, Toronto, M5R 3K5, ON, Canada
Tel.: (416) 607-5757

Web Site: https://www.sedar.com
Cannabis Product Mfr
N.A.I.C.S.: 325412
Howard W. Mann (Founder & CEO)

Subsidiaries:

Blaine Labs, Inc. (1)
11037 Lockport Pl, Santa Fe Springs, CA 90670
Tel.: (800) 307-8818
Web Site: http://www.blainelabs.com
Hospital Equipment Whslr
N.A.I.C.S.: 423450
Michael Doe (Founder & CEO)

ALTERNATIF FINANSAL KIRALAMA AS
Vadistanbul Bulvar Ayazaga Mah Cendere Cad109M 2D Blok K 3, Istanbul, 34485, Turkiye
Tel.: (90) 2123157200
Financial Lending Services
N.A.I.C.S.: 533110
Kaan Gur (Co-Chm)

ALTERNATIVE CREDIT INVESTMENTS PLC
11-12 Hanover Square, London, W1S 1JJ, United Kingdom
Tel.: (44) 2037286750   UK
Web Site: http://www.p2pgi.com
Year Founded: 2013
Rev.: $153,428,081
Assets: $1,433,091,946
Liabilities: $502,330,868
Net Worth: $930,761,078
Earnings: $38,992,835
Fiscal Year-end: 12/31/18
Investment Management Service
N.A.I.C.S.: 523940

ALTERNATIVE EARTH RESOURCES INC.
1500-409 Granville Street, Vancouver, V6C 1T2, BC, Canada
Tel.: (604) 688-1553   BC
Web Site: http://www.alternative-earth.com
Geothermal Power Services
N.A.I.C.S.: 221118
Brian D. Fairbank (Pres & CEO)

Subsidiaries:

Blue Mountain Power Company Inc., (1)
409 Granville Street Suite 1500, Vancouver, V6C1T2, BC, Canada
Tel.: (604) 688-1553
Web Site: http://www.alternative-earth.com
Sales Range: $25-49.9 Million
Emp.: 2
Geothermal Leasing & Drilling Services
N.A.I.C.S.: 237110
Bryan Fairbank (Pres & CEO)

NGP Blue Mountain I LLC (1)
595 Double Eagle Crt Ste 2001, Reno, NV 89521
Tel.: (775) 786-3399
Sales Range: $25-49.9 Million
Emp.: 25
Geothermal Power Plant Construction
N.A.I.C.S.: 237130
Brian D. Fairbank (Pres)

ALTERNATIVE INCOME REIT PLC
The Scalpel 18th Floor 52 Lime Street, London, EC3M 7AF, United Kingdom
Tel.: (44) 2045511240   UK
Web Site:
https://www.alternativeincomereit.com
Year Founded: 2017
AIRE—(LSE)
Rev.: $9,984,833
Assets: $137,561,931
Liabilities: $55,255,308
Net Worth: $82,306,623

Alternative Income REIT PLC—(Continued)

Earnings: $2,979,019
Fiscal Year-end: 06/30/24
Real Estate Investment Trust Services
N.A.I.C.S.: 531190

ALTERNATIVE INVESTMENT TRUST

Level 11 20 Hunter Street, Sydney, 2000, NSW, Australia
Tel.: (61) 282770000   **AU**
Web Site:
http://www.alternativetrust.com
Year Founded: 2005
AIQ—(ASX)
Rev.: $3,618,700
Assets: $31,545,935
Liabilities: $98,455
Net Worth: $31,447,480
Earnings: $3,399,622
Fiscal Year-end: 12/31/22
Investment Management Service
N.A.I.C.S.: 523940
Frank Tearle (Co-Sec)

ALTERNERGY HOLDINGS CORPORATION

Level 3B 111 Paseo de Roxas Bldg
Paseo de Roxas Avenue, Legaspi Village, Makati, 1229, Philippines
Tel.: 277594327
Web Site: https://www.alternergy.com
Year Founded: 2009
ALTER—(PHI)
Rev.: $3,055,846
Assets: $86,858,935
Liabilities: $38,314,145
Net Worth: $48,544,790
Earnings: $677,537
Emp.: 60
Fiscal Year-end: 06/30/23
Holding Company
N.A.I.C.S.: 551112
Gerry P. Magbanua (Pres)

ALTERNERGY LIMITED

Swan Business Centre 9 Fishers Lane Chiswick, London, W4 1RX, United Kingdom
Tel.: (44) 20 8996 9560
Web Site: http://www.alternergy.co.uk
Year Founded: 2006
Sales Range: $50-74.9 Million
Emp.: 20
Solar Energy Product Whslr
N.A.I.C.S.: 423690
Rajiv Bhatia (Founder)

ALTERON REIT VARNA

bul Knyaz Boris I N 7 et 2, 9010, Varna, Bulgaria
Tel.: (359) 52653830
2AL—(BUL)
Sales Range: Less than $1 Million
Real Estate Services
N.A.I.C.S.: 531390
Diyan Georgiev (Dir-Investor Relations)

ALTHEA GROUP HOLDINGS LIMITED

Suite 2 Level 37 360 Elizabeth Street, Melbourne, 3000, VIC, Australia
Tel.: (61) 1300702020   **AU**
Web Site:
https://www.altheagroupholding.com
Year Founded: 2016
AGH—(ASX)
Rev.: $16,361,088
Assets: $31,518,550
Liabilities: $12,108,626
Net Worth: $19,409,924
Earnings: ($8,948,947)

Emp.: 100
Fiscal Year-end: 06/30/23
Offices of Other Holding Companies
N.A.I.C.S.: 551112
David Sauer (Gen Counsel)

ALTIA CONSULTORES SA

calle Vulcano No 3, Oleiros, 15172, A Coruna, Spain
Tel.: (34) 981138847
Web Site: https://www.altia.es
Year Founded: 1994
ALC—(MAD)
Sales Range: $25-49.9 Million
Emp.: 365
Computer & IT Consulting Services
N.A.I.C.S.: 541519
Adela Perez Verdugo (VP)

ALTIA OYJ

Porkkalankatu 22, PO Box 350, 00101, Helsinki, Finland
Tel.: (358) 207013013
Web Site: http://www.altia.fi
Year Founded: 1977
Sales Range: $550-599.9 Million
Emp.: 1,108
Mfr, Distr & Marketer of Finnish Wines & Spirits
N.A.I.C.S.: 312130
Hannu Tuominen (Sr VP-Indus Svcs & Supply Chain)

Subsidiaries:

Alakari Wines Ltd   **(1)**
Salmisaarenranta 7h, Helsinki, Finland   **(100%)**
Tel.: (358) 91332720
Other Grocery & Related Products Whslr
N.A.I.C.S.: 424490

Alpha Beverages Oy   **(1)**
Porkkalankatu 22, 00101, Helsinki, Finland   **(80.1%)**
Tel.: (358) 207013011
Web Site: http://www.viinimaa.fi
Sales Range: $25-49.9 Million
Emp.: 11
Winery Production
N.A.I.C.S.: 312130
Kari Kilpinen (Gen Mgr)

Altia Eesti AS   **(1)**
Tammi tee 30, Laabi kula Tabasalu, 76901, Harjumaa, Estonia   **(100%)**
Tel.: (372) 6712100
Web Site: http://www.altia.ee
Sales Range: $50-74.9 Million
Emp.: 80
Beer & Ale Whslr
N.A.I.C.S.: 424810
Kristel Mets (Mng Dir)

Altia Norway Services AS   **(1)**
Hoffsveien 70 C, 342, 0213, Oslo, Norway   **(100%)**
Tel.: (47) 21501800
Web Site: http://www.altiacorporation.com
Sales Range: $50-74.9 Million
Emp.: 70
Wine & Distilled Alcoholic Beverage Whslr
N.A.I.C.S.: 424820

Altia Sweden AB   **(1)**
Sandhamnsgatan 63 A, Stockholm, 10251, Sweden   **(100%)**
Tel.: (46) 859811000
Web Site: http://www.altiacorporation.com
Sales Range: $75-99.9 Million
Emp.: 60
Wine & Distilled Alcoholic Beverage Whslr
N.A.I.C.S.: 424820

Subsidiary (Domestic):

Altia Sweden Services AB   **(2)**
Samdhamnsgatan 63A, PO Box 27084, 10251, Stockholm, Sweden   **(100%)**
Tel.: (46) 859811100
Web Site: http://www.altiacorporation.com
Sales Range: $25-49.9 Million
Emp.: 100
Management Consulting Services
N.A.I.C.S.: 541618

Bibendum AB   **(2)**
Sandhamnsgatan 63 A, 10252, Stockholm, Sweden   **(100%)**
Tel.: (46) 859811100
Web Site: http://www.bibendum.se
Sales Range: $25-49.9 Million
Emp.: 90
Beer & Ale Whslr
N.A.I.C.S.: 424810

Philipson & Soderberg AB   **(2)**
Sandhamnsgatan 63 C, 10052, Stockholm, Sweden   **(100%)**
Tel.: (46) 859811200
Web Site: http://www.philipson-soderberg.se
Sales Range: $25-49.9 Million
Emp.: 70
Beer & Ale Whslr
N.A.I.C.S.: 424810
Carl-Johan Elg (Dir-Comml)

Best Buys International AS   **(1)**
Harbitzalle 2B, 0275, Oslo, Norway   **(100%)**
Tel.: (47) 21501880
Wine & Distilled Alcoholic Beverage Whslr
N.A.I.C.S.: 424810

BevCo AB   **(1)**
Sandhamnsgatan 63 C, PO Box 27084, SE-10251, Stockholm, Sweden   **(100%)**
Tel.: (46) 855779009
Web Site: http://www.altiacorporation.com
Sales Range: $50-74.9 Million
Emp.: 1
Beer & Ale Whslr
N.A.I.C.S.: 424810
Johan Wikren (Mng Dir)

Bibendum AS   **(1)**
Harbitzalleen 2A, 0275, Oslo, Norway   **(100%)**
Tel.: (47) 21501800
Web Site: http://www.altiacorporation.com
Sales Range: $50-74.9 Million
Emp.: 15
Wine & Distilled Alcoholic Beverage Whslr
N.A.I.C.S.: 424820
Idar Sorensen (Area Mgr-Sls)

Interbev AS   **(1)**
Harbitzalleen 2 A, Oslo, 275, Norway   **(100%)**
Tel.: (47) 21501820
Web Site: http://www.altiacorporation.com
Sales Range: $10-24.9 Million
Emp.: 15
Drinking Places (Alcoholic Beverages)
N.A.I.C.S.: 722410
Froee Hellmann (Mng Dir)

OY Wennerco Ab   **(1)**
Porkkalankatu 22 A, Helsinki, 350, Finland   **(100%)**
Tel.: (358) 207013012
Web Site: http://www.wennerco.fi
Sales Range: $25-49.9 Million
Emp.: 20
Beer & Ale Whslr
N.A.I.C.S.: 424810
Janne Halttunen (Office Mgr)

SIA Mobil Plus ADV   **(1)**
Kuldigas iela 36A, 1083, Riga, Latvia   **(100%)**
Tel.: (371) 67628884
Web Site: http://www.altiacorporation.com
Sales Range: $50-74.9 Million
Emp.: 100
Wine & Distilled Alcoholic Beverage Whslr
N.A.I.C.S.: 424810
Normunds Ozolins (Dir-Comml)

Strom AS   **(1)**
Harbitzalleem 2A, Oslo, 0213, Norway   **(100%)**
Tel.: (47) 21501860
Web Site: http://www.strom.no
Sales Range: $50-74.9 Million
Emp.: 10
Wine & Distilled Alcoholic Beverage Whslr
N.A.I.C.S.: 424820
Piilhelge Kiraknes (Mng Dir)

ALTICAST CORP.

6th Floor Park Bldg 16 Banpo-daero 27-gil, Seocho-gu, Seoul, 06655, Korea (South)
Tel.: (82) 220077700

Web Site: https://www.alticast.com
Year Founded: 1999
085810—(KRS)
Rev.: $33,353,316
Assets: $76,521,473
Liabilities: $16,953,554
Net Worth: $59,567,919
Earnings: ($4,518,189)
Emp.: 146
Fiscal Year-end: 12/31/21
Interactive Television Software Solutions
N.A.I.C.S.: 513210
Dong In Lee (Sr Dir)

ALTICE EUROPE N.V.

Prins Bernhardplein 200, 1097 JB, Amsterdam, Netherlands
Tel.: (31) 27858901   **Nl**
Web Site: http://www.altice.net
ALLVF—(OTCIQ)
Rev.: $4,311,217,926
Assets: $86,473,154,042
Liabilities: $87,325,311,646
Net Worth: ($852,157,604)
Earnings: ($133,202,032)
Emp.: 47,143
Fiscal Year-end: 03/31/18
Holding Company; Cable Television & Other Telecommunication Products & Services
N.A.I.C.S.: 551112
Jurgen Van Breukelen (Chm)

Subsidiaries:

Altice Luxembourg S.A.   **(1)**
3 Boulevard Royal, 2449, Luxembourg, Luxembourg
Tel.: (352) 27 858 901
Web Site: http://www.altice.net
Cable Television & Other Telecommunication Products & Services
N.A.I.C.S.: 517111

Fundacao Portugal Telecom   **(1)**
Rua de Entrecampos 28, 1749-076, Lisbon, Portugal
Tel.: (351) 21 500 35 00
Web Site: http://www.fundacao.telecom.pt
Business Management Consulting & Support Services
N.A.I.C.S.: 541611

Orange Dominicana SA   **(1)**
Avenida Nunez de Caceres No 8 Torre Orange, Bella Vista, Santo Domingo, Dominican Republic
Tel.: (809) 8591000
Web Site: http://www.orange.com.do
Sales Range: $600-649.9 Million
Fixed-Line & Mobile Telecommunication Services
N.A.I.C.S.: 517111

PT Contact - Telemarketing e Servicos de Informacao, S.A.   **(1)**
Av Afonso Costa 4, 1900-034, Lisbon, Portugal
Tel.: (351) 215015000
Web Site: http://www.ptcontact.pt
Telecommunication Servicesb
N.A.I.C.S.: 517810

PT Inovacao - Altice Labs   **(1)**
Rua Eng Jose Ferreira Pinto Basto, 3810-106, Aveiro, Portugal
Tel.: (351) 234403200
Web Site: http://www.alticelabs.com
Telecommunications Research & Development
N.A.I.C.S.: 517810
Alcino Lavrador (Gen Mgr)

PT Portugal, SGPS, S.A.   **(1)**
Av Fontes Pereira de Melo 40, 1069-300, Lisbon, Portugal
Tel.: (351) 215 002 000
Web Site: http://www.telecom.pt
Sales Range: $250-299.9 Million
Holding Company; Wireless Telecommunications Services
N.A.I.C.S.: 551112

Subsidiary (Non-US):

Cabo Verde Telecom S.A.   **(2)**

Rua Cabo Verde Telecom, CP 220, Praia, Cape Verde
Tel.: (238) 2609200
Web Site: http://www.cvtelecom.cv
Data Communication Services
N.A.I.C.S.: 517112

Elta - Empresa de Listas Telefonicas de Angola **(2)**
Rua Cirilo Da Conceicao Silva N 41, Luanda, Angola
Tel.: (244) 222 337 481
Web Site: http://www.eltangola.com
Telephone Directory Publishing Services
N.A.I.C.S.: 513140

Subsidiary (Domestic):

Portugal Telecom - Associacao de Cuidados de Saude **(2)**
Rua de Entrecampos n 28 Bloco A, 1749-076, Lisbon, Portugal
Tel.: (351) 21 311 6600
Web Site: http://www.ptacs.pt
Health Plan Management Services
N.A.I.C.S.: 524114

Tricom S.A. **(1)**
Avenida Lope de Vega 95, Santo Domingo, Dominican Republic **(88%)**
Tel.: (809) 4766000
Web Site: http://www.tricom.net
Sales Range: $200-249.9 Million
Emp.: 1,725
Telecommunication Servicesb
N.A.I.C.S.: 517410

ALTIFORT FRANCE SAS
2 rue du Marais, Ham, 80400, Picardie, France
Tel.: (33) 563781264   FR
Web Site: http://www.altifort.com
Year Founded: 2014
Mechanical & Industrial Engineering Services
N.A.I.C.S.: 541330
Stanislas Vigier *(Pres)*

Subsidiaries:

GEA Westfalia Separator Production France SAS **(1)**
18 Avenue De l Europe, Chateau-Thierry, 02400, France
Tel.: (33) 3 2384 8900
Beverage Separator Machinery Mfr
N.A.I.C.S.: 333241

ALTIMA PARTNERS LLP
6th Floor The Adelphi 1-11 John Adam Street, London, WC2N 6HT, United Kingdom
Tel.: (44) 20 7968 6400
Web Site:
http://www.altimapartners.com
Year Founded: 2004
Investment Advisory & Fund Management Services
N.A.I.C.S.: 523940

Subsidiaries:

Banjalucka Pivara a,d., Banja Luka **(1)**
Slatinska 8, 78000, Banja Luka, Bosnia & Herzegovina
Tel.: (387) 51334100
Web Site: http://www.banjaluckapivara.com
Rev.: $27,382,192
Assets: $44,635,087
Liabilities: $21,710,021
Net Worth: $22,925,066
Earnings: ($716,135)
Emp.: 289
Fiscal Year-end: 12/31/2019
Beer Brewery Operator
N.A.I.C.S.: 312120

ALTIMA RESOURCES LTD.
Suite 303 595 Howe Street, Vancouver, V6C 2T5, BC, Canada
Tel.: (604) 336-8610
Web Site: https://altimaresources.ca
ARH—(TSXV)
Sales Range: Less than $1 Million

Emp.: 6
Oil & Natural Gas Exploration Services
N.A.I.C.S.: 211120
Richard Barnett *(CFO & Sec)*

ALTIN YUNUS TURISTIK TESISLER A.S.
3215 Sokak No 38, Altin Yunus Mahallesi Cesme, 35930, Izmir, Turkiye
Tel.: (90) 2327231250
Web Site:
https://www.altinyunus.com.tr
Year Founded: 1974
AYCES—(IST)
Sales Range: Less than $1 Million
Home Management Services
N.A.I.C.S.: 721110
Emine Feyhan Yasar *(Chm & Mng Dir)*

ALTINA CAPITAL CORP.
2500 - 700 West Georgia Street, Vancouver, V7Y 1B3, BC, Canada
Tel.: (604) 319-9000
Year Founded: 2019
ALTN.P—(TSXV)
Rev.: $105,087
Assets: $94,726
Liabilities: $25,836
Net Worth: $68,891
Earnings: $71,410
Fiscal Year-end: 12/31/23
Business Consulting Services
N.A.I.C.S.: 522299
Mirza Rahimani *(CEO & CFO)*

ALTINYAG KOMBINALARI AS
Cinarli Mah Ozan Abay Cad No 10 Ege Perla Kat 12 D 123, Konak, Izmir, Turkiye
Tel.: (90) 2323768451
Web Site: http://www.altinyag.com.tr
Year Founded: 1962
Vegetable Oil Mfr
N.A.I.C.S.: 311225
Mehmed Nureddin Cevik *(Chm)*

ALTIPLANO METALS INC.
250 Southridge NW Suite 300, Edmonton, T6H 4M9, AB, Canada
Tel.: (780) 437-6624   BC
Web Site:
https://www.apnmetals.com
Year Founded: 2010
9AJ1—(DEU)
Rev.: $3,195,114
Assets: $3,904,601
Liabilities: $2,446,824
Net Worth: $1,457,777
Earnings: ($1,155,376)
Fiscal Year-end: 03/31/24
Metal Mining Services
N.A.I.C.S.: 212290
John Williamson *(Chm & Chm)*

ALTISOURCE PORTFOLIO SOLUTIONS S.A.
40 Avenue Monterey, L-2163, Luxembourg, Luxembourg
Tel.: (352) 27614900   LU
Web Site: http://www.altisource.com
ASPS—(NASDAQ)
Rev.: $153,120,000
Assets: $195,005,000
Liabilities: $313,879,000
Net Worth: ($118,874,000)
Earnings: ($53,418,000)
Emp.: 1,496
Fiscal Year-end: 12/31/22
Real Estate & Mortgage Portfolio Management Services
N.A.I.C.S.: 523940
William B. Shepro *(Chm & CEO)*

Subsidiaries:

Altisource Solutions, Inc. **(1)**
1000 Abernathy Rd NE Ste 200, Bldg 400 Northpark Town Ctr, Atlanta, GA 30328
Tel.: (770) 612-7007
Portfolio Management Services
N.A.I.C.S.: 523940
Ashley Bean *(VP-Real Estate Svcs)*

Subsidiary (Domestic):

Springhouse, L.L.C. **(2)**
6404 International Pkwy Ste 1000, Plano, TX 75093
Tel.: (502) 384-0727
Web Site: http://www.springhouseamc.com
Real Estate Manangement Services
N.A.I.C.S.: 531320
Phil Huff *(Pres & CEO)*

The Mortgage Partnership of America, L.L.C. **(2)**
2 City Pl Ste 30, Saint Louis, MO 63141
Tel.: (314) 292-7920
Portfolio Management Services
N.A.I.C.S.: 523940

CastleLine Holdings, LLC **(1)**
535 Madison Ave 30th Fl, New York, NY 10022
Tel.: (212) 897-2346
Web Site: http://www.castleline.com
Business Risk Management Services
N.A.I.C.S.: 541611

PTS-Texas Title, Inc. **(1)**
6404 International Pkwy Ste 2050, Plano, TX 75093
Tel.: (469) 917-1000
Mortgage Brokerage Services
N.A.I.C.S.: 522310

Pointillist, Inc. **(1)**
321 Summer St, Boston, MA 02210
Web Site: http://www.pointillist.com
Computer Software Development Services
N.A.I.C.S.: 541511
Ron Rubbico *(Co-Founder & CEO)*

ALTITUDE GROUP PLC
7th Floor 32 Eyre St Sheffield City Centre, Sheffield, S1 4QZ, United Kingdom
Tel.: (44) 8448802751
Web Site: https://www.altitudeplc.com
ALT—(AIM)
Rev.: $23,297,410
Assets: $17,215,073
Liabilities: $5,503,658
Net Worth: $11,711,416
Earnings: $484,302
Emp.: 78
Fiscal Year-end: 03/31/23
Promotional Merchandise, Marketing & Exhibitions
N.A.I.C.S.: 541890
Nichole Stella *(CEO)*

Subsidiaries:

AIM Smarter LLC **(1)**
315 Walnut St Ste 1432, Philadelphia, PA 19107
Web Site: https://aimsmarter.com
Advertising Services
N.A.I.C.S.: 541810
Nichole Stella *(CEO)*

Promoserve Business Systems Limited **(1)**
Unit 1 Acorn Business Park Woodseats Close, Sheffield, S8 0TB, United Kingdom
Tel.: (44) 8445090030
Web Site: http://www.customerfocus.co.uk
Sales Range: $25-49.9 Million
Emp.: 10
Business Management Software Development Services
N.A.I.C.S.: 541511
Andy Barton *(COO)*

Ross Promotional Products Limited **(1)**
Tel.: (44) 1412211030
Sales Range: $25-49,9 Million
Emp.: 12
Promotional Merchandise Mfr

N.A.I.C.S.: 339999

Trade Only Inc. **(1)**
1810 Ave Rd Ste 300, Toronto, M5M 3Z2, ON, Canada
Tel.: (416) 221-4619
Web Site: http://www.tradeonly.com
Business Management Software Development Services
N.A.I.C.S.: 541511
Graham Anderson *(CTO)*

Trade Only Limited **(1)**
Unit 4 Rhodes Business Park Manchester Old Road, Middleton, M24 4NE, Manchester, United Kingdom
Tel.: (44) 844 880 2751
Web Site: http://www.tradeonly.com
Catalog & Magazine Publishing Services
N.A.I.C.S.: 513120
Nigel Bailey *(Dir-Event)*

ALTIUM LIMITED
The Zenith Tower B Level 6 821 Pacific Highway, Chatswood, 2067, NSW, Australia
Tel.: (61) 294747890
Web Site: https://www.altium.com
Year Founded: 1985
ALU—(ASX)
Rev.: $220,812,000
Assets: $381,450,000
Liabilities: $106,596,000
Net Worth: $274,854,000
Earnings: $55,345,000
Emp.: 791
Fiscal Year-end: 06/30/22
Computer Softwares Mfr
N.A.I.C.S.: 513210
Aram Mirkazemi *(CEO)*

Subsidiaries:

Altium B.V. **(1)**
Plotterweg 31, Amersfoort, 3824 ME, Netherlands
Tel.: (31) 334558584
Web Site: http://www.tasking.com
Sales Range: $25-49.9 Million
Emp.: 35
Electronic Products Mfr
N.A.I.C.S.: 334416
Peter Mwrnm *(Gen Mgr)*

Altium Europe GmbH **(1)**
Philipp-Reis-Strasse 3, 76137, Karlsruhe, Germany
Tel.: (49) 721 824 4300
Web Site: http://www.altium.com
Sales Range: $25-49.9 Million
Emp.: 40
Electronic Products Mfr & Sls
N.A.I.C.S.: 334417

Altium Information Technology (Shanghai) Co., Ltd. **(1)**
Room 2107-2018 No 1601 West Nanjing Road The Park Plaza, Jing An District, Shanghai, 200122, China
Tel.: (86) 216 015 2200
Web Site: https://www.altium.com
Sales Range: $50-74.9 Million
Emp.: 200
Electronic Products Mfr
N.A.I.C.S.: 334417

Altium Japan KK **(1)**
7F Tamachi Dai16 Fujishima Building 4-13-4, Shiba Minato-ku, Tokyo, 108-0014, Japan
Tel.: (81) 364350682
Web Site: http://www.altium.com
Printed Circuit Board Mfr
N.A.I.C.S.: 334418

Altium Netherlands BV **(1)**
Goorseweg 5, Markelo, 7475 BB, Hengelo, Netherlands
Tel.: (31) 54 733 4045
Software Publisher
N.A.I.C.S.: 513210

Altium UK Limited **(1)**
4 Millers House Roydon Road, Stanstead Abbotts, Ware, SG12 8HN, United Kingdom
Tel.: (44) 192 087 6250
Software Publisher
N.A.I.C.S.: 513210

Altium Limited—(Continued)

Gumstix Inc. (1)
48501 Warm Springs Blvd Ste 103, Fremont, CA 94539
Tel.: (778) 654-7502
Web Site: https://www.gumstix.com
Computer Hardware Mfr
N.A.I.C.S.: 332510
W. Gordon Kruberg (Pres & CEO)

Octopart Inc. (1)
29 W 38th St 14th Fl, New York, NY 10018
Tel.: (917) 525-2600
Web Site: https://octopart.com
Electronic Components Mfr
N.A.I.C.S.: 334419

ALTIUS MINERALS CORPORATION

2nd Floor 38 Duffy Place, Saint John's, A1B 4M5, NL, Canada
Tel.: (709) 576-3440　　　　　　AB
Web Site:
　https://www.altiusminerals.com
Year Founded: 1997
ALS—(TSX)
Rev.: $46,981,390
Assets: $461,240,111
Liabilities: $160,981,490
Net Worth: $300,258,621
Earnings: ($20,505,906)
Emp.: 15
Fiscal Year-end: 12/31/20
Mineral Exploration & Development
N.A.I.C.S.: 213114
Brian Francis Dalton (Pres & CEO)

Subsidiaries:

Altius Resources, Inc. (1)
66 Kentmount Rd Ste 202, Saint John's, A1B 3V7, NL, Canada
Tel.: (709) 576-3440
Web Site: http://www.altiusminerals.com
Gold & Copper Exploration Services
N.A.I.C.S.: 213114
Brian Francis Dalton (Pres & CEO)

ALTO MARKETING

Off 3 Universal Marina Crableck Ln Sarisbury Green, Southampton, SO31 7AL, Hampshire, United Kingdom
Tel.: (44) 1489557672
Web Site: http://www.alto-marketing.com
Year Founded: 2002
Sales Range: $10-24.9 Million
Emp.: 15
Advertising Agencies
N.A.I.C.S.: 541810
David Robinson (Founder & Mng Dir)

ALTO METALS LIMITED

Suite 9/12-14 Thelma St, West Perth, 6005, WA, Australia
Tel.: (61) 893812808
Web Site:
　https://www.altometals.com.au
Year Founded: 2012
AME—(ASX)
Rev.: $48,015
Assets: $22,185,631
Liabilities: $667,414
Net Worth: $21,518,217
Earnings: ($1,266,526)
Fiscal Year-end: 06/30/24
Other Metal Ore Mining
N.A.I.C.S.: 212290
Matthew Bowles (Exec Dir)

ALTO PLASTICS LTD.

19 Keeling Road, Auckland, New Zealand
Tel.: (64) 98360225
Web Site: http://www.alto.co.nz
Sales Range: $250-299.9 Million
Emp.: 110
Rigid Plastics Packaging Products

N.A.I.C.S.: 326199

ALTON SPORTS CO., LTD.

8F 25 Pangyo-ro 256beon-gil, Bundang-gu, Seongnam, Gyeonggi-do, Korea (South)
Tel.: (82) 317279100
Web Site:
　https://www.altonsports.co.kr
Year Founded: 1994
123750—(KRS)
Rev.: $39,360,807
Assets: $31,926,572
Liabilities: $11,149,860
Net Worth: $20,776,712
Earnings: ($542,231)
Emp.: 76
Fiscal Year-end: 12/31/22
Bicycle Mfr
N.A.I.C.S.: 336991
Shin-sung Kim (Pres & CEO)

Subsidiaries:

Alton Sports co., Ltd. - China Plant (1)
Tianyu Scientific and technological Park, Jinghai District, Tianjin, China
Tel.: (86) 2259526880
Bicycle Mfr
N.A.I.C.S.: 336991

Alton Sports co., Ltd. - Yangju Plant (1)
82 Chilbongsan-ro 120beon-gil, Yangju, 482-090, Gyeonggi-do, Korea (South)
Tel.: (82) 318586770
Bicycle Mfr
N.A.I.C.S.: 336991

ALTONA RARE EARTHS PLC

Eccleston Yards 25 Eccleston Place, London, SW1W 9NF, United Kingdom
Tel.: (44) 2070248390　　　　　UK
Web Site: https://www.altonare.com
Assets: $15,964,137
Liabilities: $137,610
Net Worth: $15,826,527
Earnings: ($460,050)
Emp.: 6
Fiscal Year-end: 06/30/17
Coal Exploration Services
N.A.I.C.S.: 213113
Cedric Simonet (CEO)

Subsidiaries:

Arckaringa Energy Pty Ltd (1)
Level 9 420 King William St, Adelaide, 5000, SA, Australia
Tel.: (61) 8 8110 2500
Eletric Power Generation Services
N.A.I.C.S.: 221118

ALTOR

Parc Industriel de Tabari, PO Box 9417, 44190, Clisson, France
Tel.: (33) 240361667
Web Site: http://www.altor-industrie.com
Rev.: $23,800,000
Emp.: 140
Plastics Products
N.A.I.C.S.: 326199
Gautier Jean Francois (Mgr-Export)

Subsidiaries:

Altor Industrie (1)
Lincoln House 4th floor 300 High Holborn, London, WC1V 7JH, United Kingdom
Tel.: (44) 207 924 46 99
Web Site: http://www.altor-industrie.co.uk
Emp.: 130
Plastics Product Mfr
N.A.I.C.S.: 326199
Rodolphe Lampe (Mgr-Sls-UK Export)

ALTOR EQUITY PARTNERS AB

Jakobsgatan 6, 111 52, Stockholm, Sweden

Tel.: (46) 86789100　　　　　　SE
Web Site: https://www.altor.com
Year Founded: 2003
Privater Equity Firm
N.A.I.C.S.: 523999
Harald Mix (Partner)

Subsidiaries:

AGR Group ASA (1)
Karenslyst Alle 4 Skoyen, PO Box 444, 0213, Oslo, Norway　　　　(76%)
Tel.: (47) 24061000
Web Site: http://www.agr.com
Sales Range: $200-249.9 Million
Emp.: 306
Oil & Natural Gas Operations Support Services
N.A.I.C.S.: 213112
Tove Magnussen (Sr VP-HSEQ-ER Center-Norway)

Altor Equity Partners A/S (1)
Christian IX s Gade 7 III, 1111, Copenhagen, Denmark
Tel.: (45) 3336 7300
Privater Equity Firm
N.A.I.C.S.: 523999

Altor Equity Partners OY (1)
Pohjoisesplanadi 25 B, 00100, Helsinki, Finland
Tel.: (358) 9 6829 470
Web Site: http://www.altor.com
Emp.: 3
Privater Equity Firm
N.A.I.C.S.: 523999

BYGGmax Group AB (1)
Armegatan 38, 17171, Solna, Sweden
Tel.: (46) 851493060
Web Site: http://www.byggmax.se
Rev.: $683,544,541
Assets: $609,551,640
Liabilities: $388,415,896
Net Worth: $221,135,744
Earnings: $29,316,174
Emp.: 1,387
Fiscal Year-end: 12/31/2022
Building Material Retailer
N.A.I.C.S.: 444110

C-Map USA, Inc. (1)
133 Falmouth Rd, Mashpee, MA 02649
Tel.: (508) 539-4350
Web Site: http://commercialmarine.c-map.com
Digital Marine Mapmaking
N.A.I.C.S.: 541370
Sean Fernback (CEO)

Carnegie Investment Bank AB (1)
Regeringsgatan 56, 103 38, Stockholm, Sweden
Tel.: (46) 858868800
Web Site: http://www.carnegie.se
Emp.: 620
Investment Banking Services
N.A.I.C.S.: 523150
Anders Johnsson (Chm)

Subsidiary (Domestic):

Carnegie Fonder AB (2)
Regeringsgatan 56, 103 38, Stockholm, Sweden
Tel.: (46) 812155000
Web Site: http://www.carnegiefonder.se
Sales Range: $25-49.9 Million
Emp.: 320
Mutual Fund Management Services
N.A.I.C.S.: 525910

Subsidiary (US):

Carnegie Inc. (2)
20 W 55th St 10th Fl, New York, NY 10019-5373
Tel.: (212) 262-5800
Web Site: http://www.carnegieinc.com
Sales Range: $50-74.9 Million
Emp.: 17
Investment Banking Services
N.A.I.C.S.: 523150

Dustin AB (1)
Augustendalsv 7, Box 27304, 131 26, Nacka, Sweden
Tel.: (46) 8 553 44 553
Web Site: http://www.dustin.se

Sales Range: $500-549.9 Million
Internet Retailer of Computer Equipment
N.A.I.C.S.: 449210

Ferrosan A/S (1)
Sydmarken 5, Soborg, 2860, Denmark　　　　　　　　　　　(70%)
Tel.: (45) 39692111
Web Site: http://www.ferrosan.com
Sales Range: $200-249.9 Million
Developer, Producer & Marketer of Pharmaceuticals
N.A.I.C.S.: 325412

Subsidiary (Non-US):

Ferrosan International A/S (2)
25 Rue d'Hauteville, 75 010, Paris, France
Tel.: (33) 153249140
Web Site: http://www.ferrosan.com
Developer, Producer & Marketer of Pharmaceuticals
N.A.I.C.S.: 325412

Ferrosan Norge AS (2)
Trollasveien 6, PO Box 443, N-1411, Kolbotn, Norway
Tel.: (47) 66995780
Web Site: http://www.ferrosan.com
Developer, Producer & Marketer of Pharmaceuticals
N.A.I.C.S.: 325412

Ferrosan Poland Sp. z.o.o. (2)
ul Wlodarzewska 45D, PL 02 384, Warsaw, Poland
Tel.: (48) 226687676
Developer, Producer & Marketer of Pharmaceuticals
N.A.I.C.S.: 325412

Ferrosan S.R.L (2)
Calea Turziy 178C, Cluj-Napoca, 40595, Romania
Tel.: (40) 264453232
Emp.: 117
Developer, Producer & Marketer of Pharmaceuticals
N.A.I.C.S.: 325412

Ferrosan do Brasil Ltda. (2)
Rua Americo Brasiliense No 271 CJ 608, Chacara Sto Antonio, Sao Paulo, 0471 5005, Brazil
Tel.: (55) 1121641400
Web Site: http://www.imaging.com.br
Sales Range: $25-49.9 Million
Emp.: 25
Developer, Producer & Marketer of Pharmaceuticals
N.A.I.C.S.: 325412

Oy Ferrosan AB (2)
Vavarsvagen 11, FIN 02630, Espoo, Finland
Tel.: (358) 95259050
Web Site: http://www.ferrosan.fi
Sales Range: $25-49.9 Million
Emp.: 17
Developer, Marketer & Producer of Pharmaceuticals
N.A.I.C.S.: 325412

Haarslev Industries A/S (1)
Bogensevej 85, 5471, Sonderso, Funen, Denmark
Tel.: (45) 63831100
Web Site: http://www.haarslev.com
Sales Range: $200-249.9 Million
Emp.: 650
Mfr of Processing Equipment for the Meat, Pet Food, Fish, Oil, Environmental Protection & Biofuel Industries
N.A.I.C.S.: 333248

Subsidiary (US):

Haarslev Inc. (2)
9700 NW Conant Ave, Kansas City, MO 64153
Tel.: (816) 799-0808
Web Site: http://www.haarslev.com
Sales Range: $25-49.9 Million
Emp.: 20
Sales of Processing Equipment for the Meat, Pet Food, Fish, Oil, Environmental Protection & Biofuel Industries
N.A.I.C.S.: 423830

Subsidiary (Non-US):

Haarslev Industries (2)

Level 13 Platinum Techno Park 17 & 18
Sector 30 Vashi, Navi Mumbai, 400705,
India
Tel.: (91) 22 6121 4949
Sales of Processing Equipment for the
Meat, Pet Food, Fish, Oil, Environmental
Protection & Biofuel Industries
N.A.I.C.S.: 423830

Haarslev Industries GmbH (2)
Hohenbudberger Strasse 33, 47829,
Krefeld, Germany
Tel.: (49) 2151494690
Web Site: http://www.haarslev.com
Sales Range: $25-49.9 Million
Emp.: 4
Mfr & Sales of Processing Equipment for
the Meat, Pet Food, Fish, Oil, Environmen-
tal Protection & Biofuel Industries
N.A.I.C.S.: 423830
Juergen Hess (Mng Dir)

Haarslev Industries Ltd. (2)
10 Beatrice Tinsley Crescent, Albany, Auck-
land, 632, New Zealand
Tel.: (64) 9415 2330
Web Site: http://www.haarslev.com
Emp.: 10
Sales of Processing Equipment for the
Meat, Pet Food, Fish, Oil, Environmental
Protection & Biofuel Industries
N.A.I.C.S.: 423830

Haarslev Industries Ltda. (2)
Rua Cyro Correia Pereira 3210, Cidade In-
dustrial de Curitiba, Curitiba, 81460-050,
PR, Brazil
Tel.: (55) 41 3389 0055
Web Site: http://www.haarslev.com.br
Mfr of Processing Equipment for the Meat,
Pet Food, Fish, Oil, Environmental Protec-
tion & Biofuel Industries
N.A.I.C.S.: 333248

Haarslev Industries S.A.U. (2)
Poligon Ind Font del Radium Alfred Nobel
16, Granollers, Barcelona, 8403, Spain
Tel.: (34) 9 3840 4500
Mfr of Processing Equipment for the Meat,
Pet Food, Fish, Oil, Environmental Protec-
tion & Biofuel Industries
N.A.I.C.S.: 333248
Joaquim Latorre (Mgr-Plng-Global)

Haarslev Industries SAC (2)
Av Comercial no 13 Urb Las Praderas de
Lurin, Lurin, Lima, Peru
Tel.: (51) 1720 7272
Mfr of Processing Equipment for the Meat,
Pet Food, Fish, Oil, Environmental Protec-
tion & Biofuel Industries
N.A.I.C.S.: 333248

Haarslev Industries Sdn Bhd (2)
2A Jalan Anggerik Vanilla W31/W Kota Ke-
muning, Shah Alam, 40460, Selangor Darul
Eshan, Malaysia
Tel.: (60) 3 5122 3763
Web Site: http://www.haarslev.com
Emp.: 25
Sales of Processing Equipment for the
Meat, Pet Food, Fish, Oil, Environmental
Protection & Biofuel Industries
N.A.I.C.S.: 423830

Haarslev Machinery Xuzhou Co. (2)
18 Miaoshan Road Jinshanqiao Economic
Development Zone, Xuzhou, Jiangsu, China
Tel.: (86) 516 8773 2999
Web Site: http://www.haarslev.com
Mfr of Processing Equipment for the Meat,
Pet Food, Fish, Oil, Environmental Protec-
tion & Biofuel Industries
N.A.I.C.S.: 333248

Haarslev UK Ltd. (2)
Haarslev House West Pimbo Business
Park, Paddock Road, Skelmersdale, WN8
9PL, Lancs, United Kingdom
Tel.: (44) 1695455500
Web Site: http://www.haarslevuk.com
Mfr & Sales of Processing Equipment for
the Meat, Pet Food, Fish, Oil, Environmen-
tal Protection & Biofuel Industries
N.A.I.C.S.: 423830

OOO Haarslev Industries (2)
Prospect Lenina 107/49 Office 304, Pod-
olsk, 142100, Russia
Tel.: (7) 4955439410

Sales of Processing Equipment for the
Meat, Pet Food, Fish, Oil, Environmental
Protection & Biofuel Industries
N.A.I.C.S.: 423830

Norican Group ApS (1)
Hojager 8, DK-2630, Taastrup, Denmark
Tel.: (45) 44 50 50 50
Web Site: http://www.noricangroup.com
Emp.: 5,000
Holding Company; Industrial Machinery &
Molding Equipment Mfr & Distr
N.A.I.C.S.: 551112
Bo Bugge (CIO)

Subsidiary (Non-US):

DISA Industrie AG (2)
Kasernenstrasse 1, CH-8184, Bachen-
bulach, Switzerland
Tel.: (41) 44 815 4000
Web Site: http://www.noricangroup.com
Foundry Equipment Mfr & Sales
N.A.I.C.S.: 332999

Subsidiary (Domestic):

DISA Industries A/S (2)
Hojager 8, DK-2630, Taastrup, Denmark
Tel.: (45) 4450 5050
Web Site: http://www.disagroup.com
Emp.: 5,000
Industrial Machinery Mfr
N.A.I.C.S.: 333248
Peter Holm Larsen (Pres & COO)

Subsidiary (Non-US):

Disa India Ltd (2)
6th Floor Unit No S-604 World Trade Cen-
ter Brigade Gateway Campus, 26/1 Dr Raj-
kumar Road Malleswaram Rajajinagar, Ben-
galuru, 560 055, India (74.82%)
Tel.: (91) 8022496700
Web Site: https://www.disagroup.com
Rev.: $36,356,775
Assets: $45,997,770
Liabilities: $17,878,770
Net Worth: $28,119,000
Earnings: $5,267,535
Emp.: 250
Fiscal Year-end: 03/31/2022
Foundry & Surface Preparation Equipment
Mfr
N.A.I.C.S.: 333248
Amar Nath Mohanty (CFO)

Subsidiary (US):

**Simpson Technologies
Corporation** (2)
751 Shoreline Dr, Aurora, IL 60504-6194
Tel.: (630) 978-0044
Web Site: http://www.simpsongroup.com
Sales Range: $10-24.9 Million
Emp.: 120
Foundry Sand Mixing, Preparing, Reclaim-
ing & Handling Equipment; Vibratory
Screens
N.A.I.C.S.: 333248
Henry W. Dienst (Chm)

Subsidiary (Non-US):

Simpson Technologies GmbH (3)
Blegistrasse 21, 6340, Baar, Switzerland
Tel.: (41) 41 711 15 55
Web Site: http://www.simpsongroup.com
Industrial Machinery Mfr
N.A.I.C.S.: 333248
Andre Klimm (Sr Mgr-Sls & Svc-Alfeld)

**Wesman Simpson Technologies Pvt.
Ltd.** (3)
Wesman Center 8 Mayfair Road, Kolkata,
700019, India
Tel.: (91) 33 4002 0300
Industrial Machinery Mfr
N.A.I.C.S.: 333248

Subsidiary (Non-US):

Wheelabrator Group Ltd. (2)
66 Circumstantial Pat, Altrincham, WA14
5GL, United Kingdom
Tel.: (44) 161 928 6388
Web Site: http://www.noricangroup.com
Surface Preparation Services; Shot Peening
& Wheel Blast Equipment Mfr
N.A.I.C.S.: 333248

NorthStar Battery Co. LLC (1)
4000 Continental Way, Springfield, MO
65803
Tel.: (417) 575-8200
Web Site: http://www.northstarbattery.com
Sales Range: $200-249.9 Million
Battery Mfr
N.A.I.C.S.: 335910
Hans Liden (CEO)

Northstar Marine Electronics (1)
30 Sudbury Rd, Acton, MA 01720
Tel.: (978) 897-6600
Web Site: http://www.northstarcmc.com
Sales Range: $25-49.9 Million
Emp.: 45
Electronic Navigation Equipment Mfr
N.A.I.C.S.: 334511

OptiGroup AB (1)
Kronogardsgatan 3, Molndal, 431 33, Swe-
den
Tel.: (46) 105170000
Web Site: http://www.papyrus.com
Sales Range: $1-4.9 Billion
Holding Company; Paper, Office Supplies &
Industrial Packaging Whslr
N.A.I.C.S.: 551112
Soren Gaardboe (Pres & CEO)

Subsidiary (Non-US):

Papyrus A/S (2)
Bredebjergvej 1, Taastrup, DK-2630, Co-
penhagen, Denmark
Tel.: (45) 70223838
Web Site: http://www.papyrus.com
Paper, Office Supplies & Industrial Packag-
ing Whslr
N.A.I.C.S.: 424110

Papyrus AS (2)
Betooni 6, 14115, Tallinn, Estonia
Tel.: (372) 6788670
Web Site: http://www.papyrus.com
Emp.: 10
Paper, Office Supplies & Industrial Packag-
ing Whslr
N.A.I.C.S.: 424110

Papyrus Finland Oy (2)
Koivuvaarankuja 2, Vantaa, 1640, Finland
Tel.: (358) 20774949
Web Site: http://www.papyrus.com
Sales Range: $50-74.9 Million
Emp.: 15
Paper, Office Supplies & Industrial Packag-
ing Whslr
N.A.I.C.S.: 424110
Petra Jaaskelainen (Mgr-Pur)

Papyrus Groep Nederland b.v. (2)
Bijsterhuizen Noord 2202, 6604 LD,
Wijchen, Netherlands
Tel.: (31) 886565222
Web Site: http://www.papyrus.com
Sales Range: $75-99.9 Million
Emp.: 170
Paper, Office Supplies & Industrial Packag-
ing Whslr
N.A.I.C.S.: 424110

Papyrus Hungaria Zrt. (2)
Konyves Kalman korut 11/c, HU-1097, Bu-
dapest, Hungary
Tel.: (36) 14529800
Web Site: http://www.papyrus.com
Sales Range: $50-74.9 Million
Paper Office Supply & Industrial Packaging
Whslr
N.A.I.C.S.: 424110
Jeno Szilagyi (Mng Dir-Czech Republic)

Papyrus Norge AS (2)
Soren Bulls vei 2, NO-1051, Oslo, Norway
Tel.: (47) 22904590
Web Site: http://www.papyrus.com
Sales Range: $25-49.9 Million
Emp.: 40
Paper, Office Supplies & Industrial Packag-
ing Whslr
N.A.I.C.S.: 424110

Papyrus SIA (2)
Dzelzavas iela 120, LV-1021, Riga, Latvia
Tel.: (371) 731 3022
Web Site: http://www.papyrus.com
Paper, Office Supplies & Industrial Packag-
ing Whslr
N.A.I.C.S.: 424110

Papyrus Schweiz AG (2)
Zurcherstrasse 68, CH-8800, Thalwil, Swit-
zerland
Tel.: (41) 585805800
Web Site: http://www.papyrus.com
Sales Range: $250-299.9 Million
Paper, Office Supplies & Industrial Packag-
ing Whslr
N.A.I.C.S.: 424110

Papyrus Sp. z o.o. (2)
Woloska 5 Budynek Taurus, 02-675, War-
saw, Poland
Tel.: (48) 224490200
Web Site: http://www.papyrus.com
Sales Range: $50-74.9 Million
Paper Office Supply & Industrial Packaging
Distr
N.A.I.C.S.: 424110
Eric Jasse (Mng Dir)

Subsidiary (Domestic):

Papyrus Sverige AB (2)
Kronogardsgatan 3, Molndal, 431 23, Swe-
den
Tel.: (46) 105170000
Web Site: http://www.papyrus.com
Sales Range: $150-199.9 Million
Paper, Office Supplies & Industrial Packag-
ing Whslr
N.A.I.C.S.: 424110
Soren Gaardboe (CEO)

Subsidiary (Non-US):

UAB Papyrus Lietuva (2)
R Kalantos St 59, 52304, Kaunas, Lithuania
Tel.: (370) 37400330
Web Site: http://www.papyrus.com
Paper, Office Supplies & Industrial Packag-
ing Whslr
N.A.I.C.S.: 424110
Vilija Rugieniute (Gen Dir)

Permascand Top Holding AB (1)
Folkets Husvagen 50, 841 99, Ljungaverk,
Sweden
Tel.: (46) 69135500
Web Site: https://www.permascand.com
Rev.: $52,229,335
Assets: $48,967,222
Liabilities: $15,579,011
Net Worth: $33,388,211
Earnings: $745,783
Emp.: 219
Fiscal Year-end: 12/31/2022
Electrification & Renewables, Industrial so-
lutions & Water treatment
N.A.I.C.S.: 221122
Per Lindgren (Chm)

QNTM Group AB (1)
Biblioteksgatan 29, 114 35, Stockholm,
Sweden
Tel.: (47) 96510101
Web Site: https://qntmgroup.com
Software & Technology Solutions Services
N.A.I.C.S.: 518210
Eivind Roald (CEO)

Subsidiary (Non-US):

ACTITO S.A. (2)
Avenue Athena 1, 1348, Louvain-la-Neuve,
Belgium
Tel.: (32) 10458514
Web Site: http://www.actito.com
Digital Marketing Platform Services
N.A.I.C.S.: 541613
Benoit De Nayer (Co-Founder & Co-CEO)

Subsidiary (Non-US):

SmartFocus Holdings Ltd. (3)
Fourth Floor The Space One Thomas More
Square, London, E1W 1YN, United King-
dom
Tel.: (44) 20 7554 4500
Web Site: http://www.smartfocus.com
Emp.: 80
Software Publisher
N.A.I.C.S.: 513210
Robert Mullen (CEO)

Subsidiary (Domestic):

PredictiveIntent Ltd. (4)
The Enterprise Pavilion, Poole, BH12 5HH,
Dorset, United Kingdom
Tel.: (44) 1202 832030

Altor Equity Partners AB—(Continued)

Web Site: http://www.predictiveintent.com
Software Publisher
N.A.I.C.S.: 513210
Stuart Swift (CTO)

Subsidiary (US):

SmartFocus US Inc. (4)
545 5th Ave Ste 1000, New York, NY 10017
Tel.: (212) 257-6018
Web Site: http://www.smartfocus.com
Sales Range: $50-74.9 Million
Emp.: 600
Software Publisher
N.A.I.C.S.: 513210
Charles Wells (Chief Product Officer & Sr VP)

Subsidiary (Non-US):

SmartFocus Germany GmbH (5)
Grosse Bleichen 34, 20354, Hamburg, Germany
Tel.: (49) 40 30 60 3 0
Software Publisher
N.A.I.C.S.: 513210

Realia Group Oy (1)
Valimotie 9, 00380, Helsinki, Finland
Tel.: (358) 20 780 3780
Property Management & Brokerage Services
N.A.I.C.S.: 531390
Matti Bergendahl (Pres & CEO)

Subsidiary (Domestic):

Realia Management Oy (2)
Valimotie 17-19, 00380, Helsinki, Finland
Tel.: (358) 20 780 3760
Web Site: http://www.realiamanagement.fi
Real Estate Management
N.A.I.C.S.: 531390
Lea Jokinen (VP)

Relacom AB (1)
Hemvarnsgatan 9, Solna, 17154, Sweden
Tel.: (46) 855390000
Web Site: http://www.relacom.com
Sales Range: $1-4.9 Billion
Computer Network Design Services
N.A.I.C.S.: 541512
Thord Hansson Rivedal (Mgr-HR)

Skis Rossignol S.A.S. (1)
1998 Rue Louis Bawran, Saint Jean, 38430, Moirans, Cedex, France
Tel.: (33) 438038038
Web Site: http://www.rossignol.com
Skis, Snowboards & Winter Outerwear Mfr & Retailer
N.A.I.C.S.: 339920
Bruno Cercley (Pres & CEO)

Subsidiary (Non-US):

Rossignol GmbH (2)
Rotchu Strasse 19, CH 6331, Hunenberg, Switzerland
Tel.: (41) 416180180
Web Site: http://www.rossignol.com
Retailer & Distr of Skis, Snowboards & Winter Outerwear
N.A.I.C.S.: 339920
Simon Boner (Country Mgr)

Rossignol Lange SRL (2)
Via S Gaeteno 243, 31044, Montebelluna, Italy
Tel.: (39) 0423616611
Web Site: http://www.rossignol.com
Sales Range: $100-124.9 Million
Emp.: 90
Mfr of Skis, Snowboards, Winter Outerwear & Ice Skates
N.A.I.C.S.: 339920
Garbujo Giuseppe (Dir-Ops)

Rossignol Osterreich GmbH (2)
Valiergasse 62 1, Innsbruck, 6020, Austria
Tel.: (43) 512364585
Web Site: http://www.rossignol.com
Sales Range: $25-49.9 Million
Emp.: 10
Distr of Skis, Snowboards & Winter Outerwear
N.A.I.C.S.: 339920

Rossignol SCI SARL (2)

Via Gentile 3, 20157, Milan, Italy
Tel.: (39) 02 39 03 05 33
Retailer & Distr of Skis, Snowboards & Winter Outerwear
N.A.I.C.S.: 339920

Subsidiary (US):

Rossignol Ski Company, Inc. (2)
1413 Center Dr, Park City, UT 84098
Tel.: (435) 252-3300
Web Site: http://www.rossignol.com
Sales Range: $25-49.9 Million
Emp.: 40
Mfr & Distr of Skis, Snowboards & Winter Outerwear
N.A.I.C.S.: 339920

Subsidiary (Non-US):

Groupe Rossignol Canada Inc. (3)
955 Rue Andre Line, Granby, J2J 1J6, QC, Canada
Tel.: (450) 378-9971
Web Site: http://www.rossignol.com
Sales Range: $75-99.9 Million
Emp.: 40
Ski & Snowboard Equipment Distr
N.A.I.C.S.: 339920
Carol Adams (Sls Mgr-Bike Div)

Subsidiary (Non-US):

Rossignol Ski Deutschland GmbH (2)
Zielstattstr 11, 81379, Munich, Germany
Tel.: (49) 897244850
Web Site: http://www.rossignol.de
Sales Range: $25-49.9 Million
Emp.: 6
Skis, Snowboards & Winter Outerwear Distr
N.A.I.C.S.: 339920

Subsidiary (Domestic):

Skis Dynastar S.A.S. (2)
1412 Ave De Geneve, 74700, Sallanches, France
Tel.: (33) 450912930
Web Site: http://www.my-dynastar.com
Sales Range: $75-99.9 Million
Emp.: 400
Mfr of Skis
N.A.I.C.S.: 339920

Subsidiary (Non-US):

Skis Rossignol de Espana S.A. (2)
Poligono Industrial Santa Maria De Artes, Artes, 08271, Barcelona, Spain
Tel.: (34) 938305000
Web Site: http://www.rossignol.com
Sales Range: $25-49.9 Million
Emp.: 100
Distr of Skis, Snowboards & Winter Outerwear
N.A.I.C.S.: 339920

Transcom WorldWide AB (1)
Halsingegatan 40 15th floor, PO Box 45033, SE-104 30, Stockholm, Sweden (98%)
Tel.: (46) 8 120 800 80
Web Site: http://www.transcom.com
Rev.: $621,801,989
Assets: $551,431,453
Liabilities: $430,501,968
Net Worth: $120,929,485
Earnings: ($35,408,307)
Emp.: 24,330
Fiscal Year-end: 12/31/2018
Holding Company; Customer Relationship Management, Sales, Technical Support & Credit Management Services
N.A.I.C.S.: 551112
Fredrik Cappelen (Chm)

Subsidiary (Non-US):

Dr Finsterer und Konigs Inkasso GmbH (2)
Tackweg 33, 47918, Tonisvorst, Germany
Tel.: (49) 215199530
Web Site: http://www.inkasso-gmbh.de
Sales Range: $25-49.9 Million
Emp.: 150
Administrative Management & General Management Consulting Services
N.A.I.C.S.: 541611

Transcom A/S (2)

Marienbergvej 132, 4760, Vordingborg, Denmark
Tel.: (45) 77555000
Web Site: http://www.transcom.dk
Sales Range: $25-49.9 Million
Emp.: 120
Business Support Services
N.A.I.C.S.: 561499

Subsidiary (Domestic):

Transcom AB (2)
Skrantahojdsvagen 42, 69178, Karlskoga, Sweden
Tel.: (46) 586795000
Web Site: http://www.transcom.com
Sales Range: $300-349.9 Million
Emp.: 1,500
Business Support Services
N.A.I.C.S.: 561499
Henrik Olsson (Country Mgr)

Subsidiary (Non-US):

Transcom Norge AS (2)
Sivlokka 6, PO Box 1422, Fredrikstad, 1602, Rolvsoy, Norway (100%)
Tel.: (47) 69302000
Web Site: http://www.transcom.com
Sales Range: $75-99.9 Million
Emp.: 400
Personal Care Services
N.A.I.C.S.: 812199
Ole Sommer Erichson (Mgr)

Transcom WorldWide Belgium SA (2)
99 Ave Du Parc Industriel, 4041, Herstal, Belgium
Tel.: (32) 42486300
Web Site: http://www.transcom.com
Sales Range: $25-49.9 Million
Emp.: 15
Business Support Services
N.A.I.C.S.: 561499

Transcom WorldWide Czech Republic s.r.o. (2)
Doudlebska 5-1699, Prague, 1400, Czech Republic
Tel.: (420) 221507800
Collection Agencies
N.A.I.C.S.: 561440

Transcom WorldWide France SAS (2)
14 Rue Des Freres Caudron, Velizy-Villacoublay, France
Tel.: (33) 139454545
Business Support Services
N.A.I.C.S.: 561499

Transcom WorldWide Rostock GmbH (2)
Trelleborger Str 5, 18107, Rostock, Germany
Tel.: (49) 3811231300
Web Site: http://www.transcom.com
Sales Range: $75-99.9 Million
Emp.: 450
Business Support Services
N.A.I.C.S.: 561499
Marcus Golonka (Pres)

Transcom WorldWide S.p.A. (2)
Centro Direzionale Summit Via Brescia 28 D3, Cernusco Sul Naviglio, I 20063, Milan, Italy
Tel.: (39) 029261200
Web Site: http://www.transcom.com
Business Support Services
N.A.I.C.S.: 812199

Transcom WorldWide Spain SL (2)
Avenida Europa 26 - Ed Atica 5, Pozuelo De Alarcon, Madrid, 28224, Spain
Tel.: (34) 987081200
Web Site: http://www.transcom.com
Advertising Agency Services
N.A.I.C.S.: 541810

Transcom WorldWide Vilnius UAB (2)
Zirmunu 139, 09120, Vilnius, Lithuania
Tel.: (370) 52363311
Web Site: http://www.transcom.com
Emp.: 560
Business Support Services
N.A.I.C.S.: 561499
Katien Lolse (Country Mgr)

Transcom WorldWide d.o.o. (2)
Olajnica 19, Vukovar, 32000, Osijek, Croatia
Tel.: (385) 32455700
Business Support Services
N.A.I.C.S.: 561499

Subsidiary (Domestic):

Transvoice AB (2)
Rolamams Yagem 17, Stockholm, Sweden (100%)
Tel.: (46) 81208000
Web Site: http://www.transcom.com
Sales Range: $25-49.9 Million
Emp.: 25
Business Support Services
N.A.I.C.S.: 561499

Trioworld Industrier AB (1)
Parkgatan 10, PO Box 143, 333 23, Smalandsstenar, Sweden
Tel.: (46) 371 345 00
Web Site: http://www.trioworld.com
Packaging & Hygiene Film Mfr
N.A.I.C.S.: 322220
Andreas Malmberg (CEO)

Subsidiary (Domestic):

Bengt Lundin AB (2)
Box 992, 671 29, Arvika, Sweden
Tel.: (46) 570 72 71 00
Packaging Product Distr
N.A.I.C.S.: 423840

Subsidiary (Non-US):

Trioplanex France SAS (2)
80 Rue de la Republique, BP 6, 80610, Saint-Ouen, France
Tel.: (33) 322 39 44 44
Web Site: http://www.trioworld.com
Packaging Film Mfr
N.A.I.C.S.: 322220

Subsidiary (Domestic):

Trioplast Landskrona AB (2)
Lodjursgatan 5, Box 345, 261 44, Landskrona, Sweden
Tel.: (46) 418 43 79 00
Web Site: http://www.trioworld.com
Packaging Film Mfr
N.A.I.C.S.: 322220

Subsidiary (Non-US):

Trioplast Nyborg A/S (2)
Tasingevej 1, 5800, Nyborg, Denmark (100%)
Tel.: (45) 63313000
Web Site: http://www.trioworld.com
Develops, Manufactures & Distributes Packaging Materials for Industrial & Agricultural Use
N.A.I.C.S.: 333993

Subsidiary (Domestic):

Trioplast Sifab AB (2)
Rasasen 157, 855 90, Sundsvall, Sweden
Tel.: (46) 60 67 27 70
Web Site: http://www.trioworld.com
Packaging Film Mfr
N.A.I.C.S.: 322220

Trioworld Bottnaryd AB (2)
Strakenvagen 3, 565 76, Bottnaryd, Sweden
Tel.: (46) 36 203 60
Web Site: http://www.trioworld.com
Packaging Film Mfr
N.A.I.C.S.: 322220

Subsidiary (Non-US):

Trioworld GmbH (2)
Dusseldorfer Str 38, 40721, Hilden, Germany
Tel.: (49) 2103 33 1920
Web Site: http://www.trioworld.com
Packaging Product Distr
N.A.I.C.S.: 423840

Trioworld Lundin AS (2)
Stalfjaera 1, 0975, Oslo, Norway
Tel.: (47) 22 420 290
Web Site: http://www.trioworld.com
Packaging Product Distr
N.A.I.C.S.: 423840

Trioworld OY (2)
Lakkisepankuja 4A, 02650, Espoo, Finland
Tel.: (358) 951 23 90 0
Web Site: http://www.trioworld.com
Packaging Product Distr
N.A.I.C.S.: 423840

Trioworld Ombree d'Anjou SAS (2)
24 Rue de la Pidale, 49420, Pouance,
France
Tel.: (33) 241810014
Web Site: http://www.trioworld.com
Packaging Product Distr
N.A.I.C.S.: 423840

Subsidiary (Domestic):

Trioworld Varberg AB (2)
Hammervagen 7, 432 32, Varberg, Sweden
Tel.: (46) 340 66 40 60
Web Site: http://www.trioworld.com
Packaging Film Mfr
N.A.I.C.S.: 322220

ALTPLUS INC.
Sunshine 60 45F 3-1-1 Higashi-
Ikebukuro, Toshima-ku, Tokyo,
1706045, Japan
Tel.: (81) 345776701
Web Site: https://www.altplus.co.jp
3672—(TKS)
Rev.: $31,103,830
Assets: $13,449,730
Liabilities: $6,685,870
Net Worth: $6,763,860
Earnings: ($2,977,800)
Emp.: 217
Fiscal Year-end: 09/30/23
Mobile Device Social Game Devel-
oper
N.A.I.C.S.: 513210
Takeshi Ishii (Pres & CEO)

Subsidiaries:

Shift Plus Inc. (1)
1-8 Ekimae-cho 7th Ekimae Tourist Build-
ing, Kochi, 780-0053, Japan
Tel.: (81) 88 802 5366
Web Site: https://shiftplus.inc
Software Publisher
N.A.I.C.S.: 513210

ALTRA D.D.
Fra Didaka Buntica 77, 88220, Siroki
Brijeg, Bosnia & Herzegovina
Tel.: (387) 63408176
ALSBR—(SARE)
Rev.: $25,748
Assets: $144,431
Liabilities: $26,583
Net Worth: $117,848
Earnings: $1,042
Emp.: 1
Fiscal Year-end: 12/31/20
Laboratory Testing Services
N.A.I.C.S.: 621511

**ALTRAD INVESTMENT AU-
THORITY SAS**
16 Avenue de la Gardie, 34510, Flo-
rensac, France
Tel.: (33) 467945252   FR
Web Site: https://www.altrad.com
Year Founded: 1985
Rev.: $4,088,276,920
Assets: $6,161,266,040
Liabilities: $4,903,760,520
Net Worth: $1,257,505,520
Earnings: $156,070,360
Emp.: 52,303
Fiscal Year-end: 08/31/22
Investment Holding Company; Con-
crete Mixers, Scaffolding & Construc-
tion Equipment Mfr
N.A.I.C.S.: 551112
Mohed Altrad (CEO)

Subsidiaries:

ALTRAD BALLIAUW Sp. Z o.o. (1)
ul Solec 22, 00-410, Warsaw, Poland

Tel.: (48) 668 594 275
Scaffolding Equipment Distr
N.A.I.C.S.: 423810

ALTRAD Baumann GmbH (1)
Ritter-Heinrich-Strasse 6-12, 88471, Lau-
pheim, Germany
Tel.: (49) 7392 7098 0
Web Site: http://www.altradbaumann.de
Scaffolding Equipment Distr
N.A.I.C.S.: 423810
Ralf Deitenberg (Co-Mng Dir)

**ALTRAD Betoniera si Esafodaje Ro-
mania s.r.l.** (1)
Hala 5 Baza Comcereal Sat Santu Floresti
Gruiu, 08116, Gruiu, Ilfov, Romania
Tel.: (40) 21 352 35 45
Construction Machinery & Equipment Distr
N.A.I.C.S.: 423810

ALTRAD CEDRIA (1)
57-59 Rue Jamel Abdenaceur Zone indus-
trielle Borj cedria, 2084, Tunis, Tunisia
Tel.: (216) 71 431 900
Scaffolding Equipment Distr
N.A.I.C.S.: 423810

ALTRAD Havico N.V. (1)
Wingepark 5B, 3110, Rotselaar, Belgium
Tel.: (32) 16 448 373
Mfr of Scaffolding
N.A.I.C.S.: 532490
Hugues Menager (Mng Dir)

ALTRAD NSG Limited (1)
Fourth Avenue Deeside Industrial Park,
Deeside, CH5 2NR, Flintshire, United King-
dom
Tel.: (44) 1244 833100
Web Site: http://www.altradnsg.com
Emp.: 100
Construction Machinery & Equipment Distr
N.A.I.C.S.: 423810
Michael Carr (Mng Dir)

ALTRAD plettac assco GmbH (1)
Plettac Platz 1, 58840, Plettenberg, Ger-
many
Tel.: (49) 239181501
Web Site: http://www.plettac-assco.de
Sales Range: $1-9.9 Million
Emp.: 3,800
Scaffolding & Scaffolding Services, Metal
Forming, Halls, Tents, Security Systems &
Services
N.A.I.C.S.: 333517
Ralf Deipenberg (Member-Mgmt Bd)

Subsidiary (Non-US):

ALTRAD plettac sarl. (2)
12 Avenue de la Sabliere, 94370, Sucy-en-
Brie, France
Tel.: (33) 149822700
Scaffolding Equipment Distr
N.A.I.C.S.: 423810

Altrad Alucon (2)
Szanto Kovacs Janos utja 162, 6800, Hod-
mezovasarhely, Hungary
Tel.: (36) 62 533 962
Web Site: http://www.altrad.com
Scaffolding Structures Mfr
N.A.I.C.S.: 331524

Subsidiary (Domestic):

Altrad plettac Production GmbH (2)
Woschkower Weg 11, 01983, Grossra-
schen, Germany
Tel.: (49) 35753 203 0
Web Site: http://www.plettac-production.de
Scaffolding Equipment Distr
N.A.I.C.S.: 423810

Subsidiary (Non-US):

Roth Geruste AG (2)
Bolacker 5, Gerlafingen, 4563, Switzerland
Tel.: (41) 326744360
Web Site: http://www.rothgerueste.ch
Scaffolding Services
N.A.I.C.S.: 423810
Martin Schweazer (CFO & Member-Exec
Bd)

ATIKA GmbH & Co. KG (1)
Josef-Drexler-Str 8, 89331, Burgau, Ger-
many
Tel.: (49) 82224147080

Web Site: http://www.atika.de
Construction Material Merchant Whslr
N.A.I.C.S.: 423390
Werner Mayer (Mgr-Production)

Altrad - Konskie Spolka z o.o. (1)
ul Warszawska 52, 26-200, Konskie, Poland
Tel.: (48) 41 375 12 48
Web Site: http://www.altrad-konskie.pl
Scaffolding Equipment Distr
N.A.I.C.S.: 423810

Altrad AnD B.V.B.A (1)
Aven Ackers 10, 9130, Verrebroek, Belgium
Tel.: (32) 3 735 08 20
Scaffolding Equipment Distr
N.A.I.C.S.: 423810

Altrad Asia Limited (1)
Jupiter Tower - Unit 603 6/F Block C Sea
View Estate 8 Watson Road, North point,
Hong Kong, China (Hong Kong)
Tel.: (852) 2503 1662
Web Site: http://www.altradasia.com
Logistics Consulting Services
N.A.I.C.S.: 541614

Altrad Babcock Limited (1)
Doosan House Crawely Busniess Quarter,
Crawley, RH10 9AD, W Sussex, United
Kingdom
Tel.: (44) 1293612888
Web Site: https://altradbabcock.com
Sales Range: $750-799.9 Million
Emp.: 4,000
Thermal Power, Nuclear, Petrochemical, Oil
& Gas & Pharmaceutical Industries Energy
Services
N.A.I.C.S.: 541690

**Altrad Balliauw Multiservices
N.V.** (1)
Aven Ackers 10, 9130, Verrebroek, Belgium
Tel.: (32) 37350330
Web Site: http://www.altradballiauw.com
Roofing & Insulation Material Merchant
Whslr
N.A.I.C.S.: 423330
Steven Beyers (Area Mgr)

Altrad Beaver 84 Ltd (1)
Churchill House Sopwith Crescent Hurri-
cane Way, Wickford, SS11 8YU, Essex,
United Kingdom
Tel.: (44) 1268 727 112
Web Site: http://www.beaver84.co.uk
Construction Machinery & Equipment Distr
N.A.I.C.S.: 423810
David Critchell (Dir-Comml)

Altrad Benelux NV (1)
Leuvensesteenweg 238, 3190, Boortmeer-
beek, Belgium
Tel.: (32) 15 50 94 10
Web Site: http://www.altradbenelux.be
Scaffolding Equipment Distr
N.A.I.C.S.: 423810

Altrad Bragagnolo Italia srl (1)
Via Ramon 26, 36028, Rossano Veneto,
Vicenza, Italy
Tel.: (39) 0424 540113
Construction Machinery & Equipment Distr
N.A.I.C.S.: 423810

Altrad Collectivites SA (1)
16 avenue de la Gardie, 34510, Florensac,
France
Tel.: (33) 467945244
Web Site:
     http://www.mefrancollectivites.com
Building Construction Services
N.A.I.C.S.: 236220

Altrad Famea Eca S.A.S. (1)
ZI Laville, 47240, Bon Encontre, France
Tel.: (33) 553664746
Building Construction Services
N.A.I.C.S.: 236220

Altrad Fort BV (1)
Simon Stevinstraat 6, 4004 JV, Tiel, Nether-
lands
Tel.: (31) 344 638 484
Web Site: http://www.altradfort.nl
Emp.: 50
Construction Machinery & Equipment Mfr &
Distr
N.A.I.C.S.: 333120
Herman Lindemann (Pres)

Altrad Hofmaninger GmbH (1)
Traun 8a, 4654, Bad Wimsbach-
Neydharting, Austria
Tel.: (43) 7245 25001 0
Web Site: http://www.altrad-hofmaninger.at
Construction Machinery & Equipment Distr
N.A.I.C.S.: 423810
Reinhold Mayr (Mgr)

Altrad Holding S.A. (1)
125 rue du Mas Carbonnier, 34000, Mont-
pellier, France
Tel.: (33) 4 67 94 52 52
Holding Company
N.A.I.C.S.: 551112

Altrad Italia srl (1)
Via Enrico Fermi 20, 20090, Assago, Italy
Tel.: (39) 0245712223
Web Site: http://www.altraditalia.it
Rev.: $10,816,242
Emp.: 15
Fiscal Year-end: 12/31/2004
Mfr of Scaffolding
N.A.I.C.S.: 561621

Altrad Lescha GmbH (1)
Josef-Drexler-Str 8, 89331, Burgau, Ger-
many
Tel.: (49) 8222 4130 0
Web Site: http://www.lescha.de
Construction Machinery & Equipment Mfr &
Distr
N.A.I.C.S.: 333120

Altrad Limex d.o.o. (1)
Vukovarska 77/a, 31540, Donji Miholjac,
Croatia
Tel.: (385) 31 496 870
Web Site: http://www.altrad-limex.com
Construction Machinery & Equipment Mfr
N.A.I.C.S.: 333120

Altrad Liv d.o.o. (1)
Sveti Jurij 18A, 9262, Rogasovci, Slovenia
Tel.: (386) 2 55 88 430
Web Site: http://www.altrad-liv.si
Construction Machinery & Equipment Mfr &
Distr
N.A.I.C.S.: 333120
Janez Golez (Mng Dir)

**Altrad Mostostal Montaz Sp. z
o.o.** (1)
ul Starzynskiego 1, 08-110, Siedlce, Poland
Tel.: (48) 25 640 24 00
Web Site: http://www.amm.siedlce.pl
Scaffolding Equipment Distr
N.A.I.C.S.: 423810

Altrad Plettac Iberica, S. L. (1)
Avda cadi 13 Pol Ind Sant Pere Molanta,
Olerdola, 08799, Spain
Tel.: (34) 93 00 24 070
Web Site: http://www.altrad.es
Scaffolding Equipment Distr
N.A.I.C.S.: 423810

Altrad Poland S.A. (1)
Ul Nowosielska 6, 15-617, Bialystok, Poland
Tel.: (48) 85 661 43 03
Web Site: http://www.altradpoland.pl
Construction Machinery & Equipment Mfr &
Distr
N.A.I.C.S.: 333120
Robert Jedynak (Mgr-Export)

Altrad Profix BVBA (1)
Jagersdreef 1, 2900, Schoten, Belgium
Tel.: (32) 36057639
Web Site: http://www.altradprofix.com
Insulation Painting & Wall Covering Ser-
vices
N.A.I.C.S.: 238310
Frank Verstraeten (Mng Dir)

Altrad Richard Fraisse SAS (1)
1 Virecourt, 33126, La Riviere, France
Tel.: (33) 5 57 55 56 85
Construction Machinery & Equipment Mfr
N.A.I.C.S.: 333120

Altrad Rodisola S.A. (1)
PG Ind Riu Clar C/Sofre 18, 43006, Tarra-
gona, Spain
Tel.: (34) 977 550 433
Scaffolding Equipment Distr
N.A.I.C.S.: 423810

Altrad Saint Denis S.A. (1)

Altrad Investment Authority SAS—(Continued)

ZA Stones Yellow, Saint-Denis-de-Cabanne,
France
Tel.: (33) 477442477
Web Site: http://www.altrad-saint-denis.fr
Building Construction Services
N.A.I.C.S.: 236220

Altrad Soframat Etem S.A. (1)
RN0, 13400, Toulon, Aubagne, France
Tel.: (33) 4 42 18 65 05
Web Site: http://www.altrad-soframat-
etem.com
Scaffolding Equipment Distr
N.A.I.C.S.: 423810

Altrad-Pomorze Spolka z o.o. (1)
ul Pomorska 36, 70-812, Szczecin, Poland
Tel.: (48) 91 469 37 25
Web Site: http://www.altrad-pomorze.pl
Scaffolding Equipment Distr
N.A.I.C.S.: 423810

Altrad-Prymat Sp. z o. o. (1)
ul Kosciuszki 1, 58-200, Dzierzoniow, Po-
land
Tel.: (48) 74 832 30 57
Web Site: http://www.prymat.net
Scaffolding Equipment Distr
N.A.I.C.S.: 423810

Beerenberg Corp. (1)
Kokstaddalen 33, 5257, Kokstad, Norway
Tel.: (47) 55526600
Web Site: http://www.beerenberg.com
Sales Range: $200-249.9 Million
Emp.: 2,000
Oil & Gas Production Facility Maintenance
Services
N.A.I.C.S.: 213112
Morten Walde (Pres & CEO)

Belle Engineering Ltd (1)
Sheen nr, Buxton, SK17 0EU, Derbyshire,
United Kingdom
Tel.: (44) 1298 84606
Web Site: http://www.belle-group.co.uk
Construction Machinery & Equipment Mfr
N.A.I.C.S.: 333120
Bob Williams (Mgr-Sls)

Belle Group inc. (1)
3959 Electric Rd - Ste 360, Roanoke, VA
24018
Tel.: (540) 345-5090
Construction Machinery & Equipment Mfr &
Distr
N.A.I.C.S.: 333120

Cape plc (1)
Office 1 First Floor 2 The Future Works
Brunel Way, Slough, SL1 1FQ, United King-
dom
Tel.: (44) 1895431705
Holding Company; Fire Protection & Insula-
tion Materials for the Construction Industry
Mfr
N.A.I.C.S.: 551112

Subsidiary (Non-US):

Cape East (Thailand) Limited (2)
155/1 Moo 6 Nikompattana District, Ray-
ong, 21180, Thailand
Tel.: (66) 33014800
Industrial Cleaning Services
N.A.I.C.S.: 561720

Cape East Philippines Inc (2)
6th Fl NOL Tower Commerce Avenue Mad-
rigal Business 6th Floor iHs Park, Alabang
Zapote Road, Muntinlupa, 1781, Philippines
Tel.: (63) 25010020
Industrial Cleaning Services
N.A.I.C.S.: 561720

Subsidiary (Domestic):

**Cape Industrial Services Group
Limited** (2)
Unit 2B Brindley Way 41 Business Park,
Paragon Business Village, Wakefield, WF2
0XQ, United Kingdom
Tel.: (44) 1924 877 860
Web Site: http://uk.altradservices.com
Industrial Services
N.A.I.C.S.: 238310

Subsidiary (Non-US):

Cape East LLC (3)

14 Al Mussafah, PO Box 347, Abu Dhabi,
United Arab Emirates
Tel.: (971) 2 6971300
Industrial Services
N.A.I.C.S.: 238310

Subsidiary (Domestic):

Cape East Limited (3)
Office 1 First Floor 2 The Future Works,
Brunel Way SL1 1FQ, Slough, SL1 1FQ,
United Kingdom
Tel.: (44) 1895 431 705
Coordination of International Industrial Ser-
vices Activities
N.A.I.C.S.: 238310

Subsidiary (Non-US):

Cape East Private Limited (3)
3 Internation Business Park Hex 02-22/ 23,
Nordice European Center, Singapore,
609927, Singapore (100%)
Tel.: (65) 62621822
Web Site: http://www.capeclc.com
Sales Range: $100-124.9 Million
Industrial Services
N.A.I.C.S.: 238310
Mohammad Iskandar Sulaiman (Mgr-Ops)

Subsidiary (Domestic):

Cape Industrial Services Limited (3)
Building 2 Fields End Business Park Davey
Road Thurnscoe, Goldthorpe, Rotherham,
S63 0JF, West Yorkshire, United Kingdom
Tel.: (44) 1924876200
Industrial Services
N.A.I.C.S.: 238310

Subsidiary (Non-US):

Cleton Insulation BV (3)
George Stephensonweg 15, 3133 KJ,
Vlaardingen, Netherlands
Tel.: (31) 4455444
Web Site: http://www.cleton.com
Insulation Services
N.A.I.C.S.: 238310

PCH Group Pty Ltd. (3)
Corner of Westcombe and Bellwood, PO
Box 2242, Brookside Centre, Darra, 4053,
QLD, Australia
Tel.: (61) 413 133 858
Web Site: http://www.pchgroup.com.au
Crane Hire, Franna Hire, Lifting, Pick &
Carry Services
N.A.I.C.S.: 541611
Nick Fraser (Dir)

Subsidiary (Domestic):

DBI Industrial Services Limited (2)
The Flarepath Elsham Wolds Industrial Es-
tate, Brigg, DN20 0SP, North Lincolnshire,
United Kingdom
Tel.: (44) 1652 688 108
Industrial Cleaning Services
N.A.I.C.S.: 561720

Subsidiary (Non-US):

R B Hilton Saudi Arabia Limited (2)
Royal Commission Support Industries Park
Lot 10 Block 17 Section 3, PO Box 2081, Al
Jubayl, 31951, Saudi Arabia
Tel.: (966) 3340 7910
Industrial Cleaning Services
N.A.I.C.S.: 561720

Total Corrosion Control Pty. Ltd. (2)
Lot 424 89 Office Rd Kwinana Beach,
Perth, 6167, WA, Australia
Tel.: (61) 894194455
Abrasive Blasting Services
N.A.I.C.S.: 561790

Generation UK Limited (1)
Trinity Street Off Tat Bank Road, Oldbury,
B69 4LA, West Midlands, United Kingdom
Tel.: (44) 121 544 3355
Web Site:
http://www.generationhireandsale.co.uk
Scaffolding Equipment Distr
N.A.I.C.S.: 423810

Irbal, S.A. (1)
Rua Direita 171, Nariz, 3810-568, Aveiro,
Portugal
Tel.: (351) 234 750 750

Web Site: http://www.irbal.com
Construction Machinery & Equipment Mfr
N.A.I.C.S.: 333120

**JALMAT ACTIVITES INTERNATION-
ALES, SA** (1)
ZA de la Verdiere 2, 13880, Velaux, France
Tel.: (33) 442108406
Web Site: http://www.jalmat.com
Building Construction Services
N.A.I.C.S.: 236220

**JALMAT OUEST ATLANTIQUE,
SA** (1)
36 rue de la Dutee, 44800, Saint Herblain,
France
Tel.: (33) 240929229
Web Site: http://www.jalmat.com
Building Construction Services
N.A.I.C.S.: 236220

JALMAT SUD OUEST, SA (1)
ZA Bordevieille, 31790, Saint Sauveur,
France
Tel.: (33) 562799240
Construction Material Merchant Whslr
N.A.I.C.S.: 423390

POUJAUD SAS (1)
Batiment A6 - Europarc de Pichaury,
13856, Aix-en-Provence, France
Tel.: (33) 4 88 78 38 00
Web Site: http://www.poujaud.fr
Scaffolding Equipment Mfr
N.A.I.C.S.: 333120

SARL COMI SERVICE (1)
Batiment A6 -Europarc de Pichaury, 13856,
Les Milles, France
Tel.: (33) 488783800
Building Construction Services
N.A.I.C.S.: 236220
Jean Louis Bonnet (Mgr-Site)

SPECTRA Scaffolding Ltd (1)
Warth Road Industrial Estate Warth Road,
Bury, BL9 9NB, Greater Manchester, United
Kingdom
Tel.: (44) 161 272 0200
Web Site:
http://www.spectrascaffolding.co.uk
Construction Engineering Services
N.A.I.C.S.: 541330
Kevin Jennings (Dir-Comml)

**Sparrows Offshore Group
Limited** (1)
Seton House Murcar Industrial Estate Den-
more Road Bridge of Don, Aberdeen, AB23
8JW, United Kingdom
Tel.: (44) 1224704868
Web Site: http://www.sparrowsgroup.com
Sales Range: $250-299.9 Million
Emp.: 2,000
Investment Management Service
N.A.I.C.S.: 523940
Matt Corbin (Dir-Ops-UK & Europe)

Subsidiary (US):

Sparrows Offshore LLC (2)
6758 Northwinds Dr, Houston, TX 77041
Tel.: (713) 896-0002
Industrial Machinery & Equipment Distr
N.A.I.C.S.: 423830
Lyle Schultz (Mgr-Fluid Power Products)

Star Events Limited (1)
Milton Road Thurleigh, Bedford, MK44 2DF,
United Kingdom
Tel.: (44) 1234771133
Web Site: http://www.stareventsltd.com
Construction Material Merchant Whslr
N.A.I.C.S.: 423390
Jo Xie (Project Mgr)

TRAD Scaffolding Company Ltd (1)
TRAD House Imperial Street Bromley-by-
Bow, London, E3 3ED, United Kingdom
Tel.: (44) 20 8980 1155
Web Site: http://www.trad.co.uk
Emp.: 100
Scaffolding Equipment Distr
N.A.I.C.S.: 485999
Hayden Smith (Chm)

Subsidiary (Domestic):

TRAD Hire & Sales Ltd. (2)
TRAD House Cromwell Road, Bredbury,
Stockport, SK6 2RF, United Kingdom
Tel.: (44) 161 494 2999

Web Site: http://www.tradhireandsales.co.uk
Scaffolding Equipment Distr
N.A.I.C.S.: 423810

Valmec Limited (1)
17 Ballantyne Road, Kewdale, 6105, WA,
Australia
Tel.: (61) 8 9266 8888
Web Site: http://www.valmec.com.au
Equipment Maintenance Services
N.A.I.C.S.: 811310
Steve Dropulich (Mng Dir)

ALTRI, SGPS, S.A.
Rua Manuel Pinto de Azevedo 818,
4100-320, Porto, Portugal
Tel.: (351) 228346502
Web Site: https://en.altri.pt
Year Founded: 2005
ALTR—(EUR)
Rev.: $1,127,726,594
Assets: $1,617,055,280
Liabilities: $958,872,642
Net Worth: $658,182,638
Earnings: $470,732,008
Emp.: 815
Fiscal Year-end: 12/31/22
Paper Pulp Mfr
N.A.I.C.S.: 322110
Paulo Jorge dos Santos Fernandes
(Vice Chm)

Subsidiaries:

Altri Florestal, S.A. (1)
Quinta do Furadouro s/n, Olho Marinho,
2510-582, Leiria, Portugal
Tel.: (351) 262965100
Emp.: 65
Paper Pulp Mfr
N.A.I.C.S.: 322120
Joaquim Ferreira Matos (Gen Mgr)

Altri Sales, S.A. (1)
Route de Clementy 62, 1260, Nyon, Switz-
erland
Tel.: (41) 22 365 51 60
Paper Pulp Whlsr
N.A.I.C.S.: 424490

**Altri, Participaciones Y Trading,
S.L.** (1)
Calle de Orense 25, 28020, Madrid, Spain
Tel.: (34) 914 17 44 84
Emp.: 1
Investment Management Service
N.A.I.C.S.: 523940
Alexandra Costa (Gen Mgr)

**Celulose Beira Industrial (Celbi),
S.A.** (1)
Leirosa, 3081-853, Figueira da Foz, Portu-
gal
Tel.: (351) 233955600
Web Site: http://www.celbi.pt
Paper Pulp Mfr
N.A.I.C.S.: 322120

**Viveiros do Furadouro Unipessoal,
Lda.** (1)
Quinta Furadouro, Olho Marinho, 2510-582,
Leiria, Portugal
Tel.: (351) 262240957
Web Site: http://viveirosdofuradouro.pt
Plant Cultivation Services
N.A.I.C.S.: 111421

ALTRON LIMITED.
Woodlands Campus 20 Woodlands
Drive Building F Woodlands Office
Park, Parktown, 2193, Gauteng,
South Africa
Tel.: (27) 116453600
Web Site: https://www.altron.com
Year Founded: 1965
AEL—(JSE)
Rev.: $740,159,040
Assets: $659,238,260
Liabilities: $365,849,260
Net Worth: $293,389,000
Earnings: $886,990
Emp.: 5,009
Fiscal Year-end: 02/28/23
Telecommunication Servicesb

N.A.I.C.S.: 517111
Mike J. Leeming *(Chm)*

Subsidiaries:

Altron Finance (Pty) Limited **(1)**
5 Winchester Rd, Parktown, Johannesburg, 2193, Gauteng, South Africa
Tel.: (27) 116453600
Financial Advisory Services
N.A.I.C.S.: 523940
Bill Venter *(Chm)*

Bytes Technology Group (Proprietary) Limited **(1)**
Bytes House Ave N 6 Mellis Rd, Rivonia, Johannesburg, 2128, Gauteng, South Africa
Tel.: (27) 112369500
Web Site: http://www.btgroup.co.za
Sales Range: $25-49.9 Million
Emp.: 18
Information Communications Technology Services
N.A.I.C.S.: 517810
Peter Riskowitz *(CFO-Altron TMT)*

Mediswitch Namibia Proprietary Limited **(1)**
Maerua Mall South East Block 3rd Floor Office 139 Centaurus Road, Windhoek, Namibia
Tel.: (264) 61250162
Web Site:
    http://www.mediswitchnamibia.com
Electronic Transmission Services
N.A.I.C.S.: 221121

Netstar Australia Pty Ltd **(1)**
Level 1 Unit 49 2 Slough Ave, Silverwater, 2128, NSW, Australia
Tel.: (61) 1800325052
Web Site:
    https://www.netstaraustralia.com.au
Tracking Device Distr
N.A.I.C.S.: 423690
Roger Buckeridge *(DIR)*

Netstar Proprietary Limited **(1)**
16th Road, Midrand, 1685, South Africa
Tel.: (27) 112075500
Web Site: https://www.netstar.co.za
Vehicle Tracking & Stolen Vehicle Recovery Services
N.A.I.C.S.: 561491
S. Graan *(Chm)*

Power Technologies (Proprietary) Limited **(1)**
House Hampton Park 20 Georgian Crescent, Bryanston, Johannesburg, 0011, Gauteng, South Africa
Tel.: (27) 117067184
Web Site: http://www.powertech.co.za
Sales Range: $50-74.9 Million
Emp.: 20
Electrical & Electronic Equipments Distr
N.A.I.C.S.: 423610
Bill Venter *(Chm)*

ALTRUIST TECHNOLOGIES PVT. LTD.
Plot No 2 Sector 22 HSIIDC IT Park, Panchkula, 134109, Haryana, India
Tel.: (91) 1722970008   In
Web Site:
    http://www.altruistindia.com
Year Founded: 2005
Emp.: 432
Holding Company; Mobile Social Networking Products & Services
N.A.I.C.S.: 551112
Dheeraj Aggarwal *(Co-Founder)*

Subsidiaries:

Info2cell.com **(1)**
Dubai Internet City Concord Tower Office 2301, PO Box 500067, Dubai, United Arab Emirates
Tel.: (971) 43912802
Web Site: http://www.info2cell.com
Wireless Mobile Application Service Provider
N.A.I.C.S.: 517810

ALTUR INVESTISSEMENT S.C.A.

9 rue de Tehran, 75008, Paris, France
Tel.: (33) 186640182   FR
Web Site: http://www.altur-investissement.com
Year Founded: 2006
ALTUR—(EUR)
Assets: $46,304,456
Liabilities: $8,768,923
Net Worth: $37,535,534
Earnings: $682,202
Fiscal Year-end: 12/31/19
Closed-End Investment Fund
N.A.I.C.S.: 525990
Francois Lombard *(Mng Dir)*

ALTUR S.A.
Strada Pitesti Nr 114, Judetul Olt, Slatina, Romania
Tel.: (40) 249432324
Web Site: https://www.altursa.ro
Year Founded: 1979
ALT—(BUC)
Rev.: $29,565,136
Assets: $24,838,898
Liabilities: $11,407,590
Net Worth: $13,431,307
Earnings: $1,808,319
Emp.: 499
Fiscal Year-end: 12/31/23
Motor Vehicle Parts Mfr
N.A.I.C.S.: 336390
Sergiu Burca *(CEO)*

ALTURAS MINERALS CORP.
1 Toronto Street Suite 201, Toronto, M5C 2V6, ON, Canada
Tel.: (416) 363-4900
Web Site:
    http://www.alturasminerals.com
ALT—(TSXV)
Assets: $277,734
Liabilities: $2,147,111
Net Worth: ($1,869,377)
Earnings: ($486,860)
Emp.: 2
Fiscal Year-end: 12/31/23
Mineral Exploration Services
N.A.I.C.S.: 213114
Mario A. Miranda *(CFO)*

ALTUS GROUP LIMITED
33 Yonge Street Suite 500, Toronto, M5E 1G4, ON, Canada
Tel.: (416) 641-9500   Ca
Web Site:
    https://www.altusgroup.com
Year Founded: 2005
AIF—(TSX)
Rev.: $438,981,116
Assets: $575,288,712
Liabilities: $275,324,228
Net Worth: $299,964,484
Earnings: $16,766,607
Emp.: 2,500
Fiscal Year-end: 12/31/20
Real Estate Development Services
N.A.I.C.S.: 531390
Alex Probyn *(Pres-Global)*

Subsidiaries:

ARGUS Software, Inc. **(1)**
10497 Town & Country Way Ste 600A, Houston, TX 77024
Tel.: (713) 621-4343
Web Site: http://www.argussoftware.com
Real Estate Software Developer
N.A.I.C.S.: 513210

Altus Geomatics L.P. **(1)**
900 840 7th Avenue SW, Calgary, T2P 3G2, AB, Canada
Tel.: (403) 234-7599
Web Site: http://www.altusgeomatics.com
Surveying & Mapping Services
N.A.I.C.S.: 541360

Subsidiary (Domestic):

Maltais Geomatics Inc. **(2)**
17011 105 Avenue, Edmonton, T5S 1M5, AB, Canada
Tel.: (780) 483-2015
Web Site: http://www.maltaisgeomatics.com
Sales Range: $1-9.9 Million
Emp.: 65
Geomatics Services
N.A.I.C.S.: 541360

Altus Group U.S. Inc. **(1)**
11700 Katy Fwy Energy Tower I Ste 260, Houston, TX 77079
Tel.: (713) 621-4343
Real Estate Consulting Service
N.A.I.C.S.: 531210
Stephanie Dubicki *(Exec VP)*

ALTUS HOLDINGS LIMITED
21 Wing Wo Street, Central, China (Hong Kong)
Tel.: (852) 25226122   Ky
Web Site: https://www.altus.com.hk
8149—(HKG)
Rev.: $7,205,726
Assets: $85,544,695
Liabilities: $28,714,817
Net Worth: $56,829,878
Earnings: $1,029,260
Emp.: 20
Fiscal Year-end: 03/31/22
Financial Advisory Services
N.A.I.C.S.: 523940
Arnold Tin Chee Ip *(Founder & Chm)*

ALTUS PROPERTY VENTURES, INC.
Brgy 1 San Francisco, San Nicolas, Laguna, Ilocos Norte, Philippines
Tel.: (63) 776001031   PH
Web Site:
    https://www.altusventures.com.ph
Year Founded: 2007
APVI—(PHI)
Rev.: $2,690,750
Assets: $16,477,129
Liabilities: $2,501,092
Net Worth: $13,976,037
Earnings: $1,348,768
Emp.: 15
Fiscal Year-end: 12/31/21
Real Estate Manangement Services
N.A.I.C.S.: 531311
Lance Y. Gokongwei *(Chm)*

ALTUS RENEWABLES LIMITED
Level 3 3926 Pacific Highway, PO Box 3216, Loganholme, 4129, QLD, Australia
Tel.: (61) 738013520   AU
Web Site:
    http://www.altusrenewables.com
Biomass-Based Fuel Production
N.A.I.C.S.: 211120
Denis P. Waddell *(Chm)*

Subsidiaries:

Proteq Pty Ltd. **(1)**
PO Box 4661, Loganholme, 4129, Australia
Tel.: (61) 7 3805 0280
Web Site: http://www.proteq.com.au
Wood Products Mfr
N.A.I.C.S.: 321113

ALTUS RESOURCE CAPITAL LIMITED
Anson Place Mill Court La Charrotie, Saint Peter Port, GY1 1EJ, Guernsey
Tel.: (44) 1481 722260
Web Site: http://www.altrescap.com
Year Founded: 2009
Investment Services
N.A.I.C.S.: 523999
Nicholas J. Falla *(Chm)*

ALTUS S.A.
ul Pankiewicza 3, 00-696, Warsaw, Poland
Tel.: (48) 223803285
Web Site: https://www.altustfi.pl
ALI—(WAR)
Sales Range: Less than $1 Million
Investment Services
N.A.I.C.S.: 523940
Piotr Goralewski *(Chm)*

ALTUS SISTEMAS DE AUTOMACAO S.A.
Av Theodomiro Porto Da Fonseca 3101 - Lote 1, 93022715, Sao Leopoldo, RS, Brazil
Tel.: (55) 5135899500   BR
Web Site: http://www.altus.com.br
Year Founded: 1982
Electric Equipment Mfr
N.A.I.C.S.: 335999
Fabiano Favaro *(CEO & Dir-IR)*

ALTUS TOWARZYSTWO FUNDUSZY INWESTYCYJNYCH S.A.
ul Pankiewicza 3, 00-696, Warsaw, Poland
Tel.: (48) 223803285
Web Site: http://www.altustfi.pl
ALI—(WAR)
Rev.: $13,768,547
Assets: $40,945,630
Liabilities: $6,504,065
Net Worth: $34,441,565
Earnings: $2,614,583
Fiscal Year-end: 12/31/23
Investment Fund Management Services
N.A.I.C.S.: 523940
Jakub Ryba *(Chm-Supervisory Bd)*

ALTWOOD GARAGE DOORS LTD.
140 Ashwarren Road, Downsview, M3J 2S6, ON, Canada
Tel.: (416) 635-5500
Web Site:
    http://www.altwooddoors.com
Year Founded: 1983
Rev.: $11,215,899
Emp.: 60
Garage Door Products Mfr
N.A.I.C.S.: 321911
Mario Urbano *(Owner & Pres)*

ALTYNEX COMPANY JSC
21 Astana st, Altyndy village Mulgazhar district, Aktobe, 030713, Kazakhstan
Tel.: (7) 132905082
Web Site: http://www.altynex.com
ATEC—(KAZ)
Rev.: $64,428,905
Assets: $101,219,138
Liabilities: $7,098,913
Net Worth: $94,120,225
Earnings: $34,429,315
Fiscal Year-end: 12/31/20
Metal Mining Services
N.A.I.C.S.: 213114

ALTYNGOLD PLC
28 Eccleston Square, London, SW1V 1NZ, United Kingdom
Tel.: (44) 2034323198   UK
Web Site: https://altyngold.uk
Year Founded: 2004
ALTN—(LSE)
Rev.: $64,434,000
Assets: $145,491,000
Liabilities: $74,809,000
Net Worth: $70,682,000
Earnings: $11,339,000
Emp.: 477
Fiscal Year-end: 12/31/23

AltynGold plc—(Continued)

Exploration & Development Company; Gold Ore Mining
N.A.I.C.S.: 212220
Kanat Assaubayev *(Chm)*

Subsidiaries:

Hambledon Mining Company Limited (1)
10 Novostroyevskaya, Glubokovsky Region, Sekisovka, Kazakhstan
Tel.: (7) 7233127927
Investment Holding Services
N.A.I.C.S.: 551112

ALUAR ALUMINIO ARGENTINO

Marcelo T de Alvear 590 piso 3, Buenos Aires, Argentina
Tel.: (54) 143137593
Web Site: https://www.aluar.com.ar
Year Founded: 1971
Electrical Component Mfr
N.A.I.C.S.: 335999
Daniel Friedenthal *(Vice Chm & Head-Audit Mgmt)*

ALUCON PUBLIC COMPANY LIMITED

500 Moo 1 Soi Sirikam Sukhumvit Road, Samrong Nua Sub-District Muang Samutprakarn District, Samut Prakan, 10270, Thailand
Tel.: (66) 23980147
Web Site: https://www.alucon.th.com
Year Founded: 1961
ALUCON—(THA)
Rev.: $184,981,419
Assets: $216,893,014
Liabilities: $24,738,018
Net Worth: $192,154,996
Earnings: $14,785,315
Emp.: 1,115
Fiscal Year-end: 12/31/23
Aluminium Container Mfr & Distr
N.A.I.C.S.: 332439
Takaaki Takeuchi *(Mng Dir)*

Subsidiaries:

Takeuchi Press Industries Company Limited (1)
1-10-1 Kamiakae-cho, Toyama, 930-0816, Japan
Tel.: (81) 764411856
Web Site: https://www.takeuchi-press.co.jp
Emp.: 806
Container Development Mfr
N.A.I.C.S.: 332439

ALUE CO., LTD.

2nd Floor Hulic Kudan Building 1-13-5 Kudankita, Chiyoda-Ku, Tokyo, 102-0073, Japan
Tel.: (81) 362689791
Web Site: https://www.alue.co.jp
Year Founded: 2003
7043—(TKS)
Rev.: $21,468,520
Assets: $12,208,980
Liabilities: $3,289,760
Net Worth: $8,919,220
Earnings: $397,040
Emp.: 196
Fiscal Year-end: 12/31/23
Vocational Rehabilitation Services
N.A.I.C.S.: 624310

ALUFLUORIDE LIMITED

Mulagada Mindi, Visakhapatnam, 530 012, AP, India
Tel.: (91) 8912548567
Web Site:
https://www.alufluoride.com
Year Founded: 1993
524634—(BOM)
Rev.: $18,756,137
Assets: $15,571,784

Liabilities: $6,284,706
Net Worth: $9,287,078
Earnings: $1,704,462
Emp.: 103
Fiscal Year-end: 03/31/23
Aluminium Fluoride Mfr
N.A.I.C.S.: 325180
Venkat Akkineni *(Mng Dir)*

ALUKO CO., LTD

31 Daehwa-ro 119beon-gil Daedeokgu, Daejeon, Korea (South)
Year Founded: 1956
001780—(KRS)
Rev.: $495,031,101
Assets: $626,587,585
Liabilities: $388,369,107
Net Worth: $238,218,478
Earnings: $12,059,510
Emp.: 202
Fiscal Year-end: 12/31/22
Aluminium Products Mfr
N.A.I.C.S.: 331315
Do Bong Park *(Chm)*

Subsidiaries:

Dongyang Gangchul Co., Ltd - 1st Factory (1)
131 32nd street Daehwa-ro, Daedeok-gu, Daejeon, Korea (South)
Tel.: (82) 426058200
Aluminium Products Mfr
N.A.I.C.S.: 331315

Dongyang Gangchul Co., Ltd - 2nd Factory (1)
100 Daehwa-ro, Daedeok-gu, Daejeon, Korea (South)
Tel.: (82) 426330990
Aluminium Products Mfr
N.A.I.C.S.: 331315

Dongyang Gangchul Co., Ltd - 5th Factory (1)
220 Daehwa-ro, Daedeok-gu, Daejeon, Korea (South)
Tel.: (82) 426058200
Aluminium Products Mfr
N.A.I.C.S.: 331315

ALULA WATER PTY LTD

260 Kent Avenue, Randburg, 2125, Gauteng, South Africa
Tel.: (27) 118860266 ZA
Web Site: http://www.alulawater.co.za
Water & Wastewater Treatment Equipment Mfr, Facilities Construction & Maintenance Services
N.A.I.C.S.: 221310
Dinao Lerutla *(CEO)*

ALUM S.A.

Str Isaccei nr 82, 2360405, Tulcea, Romania
Tel.: (40) 240535022
Web Site: https://www.alum.ro
BBGA—(BUC)
Rev.: $61,283,128
Assets: $51,600,250
Liabilities: $30,054,899
Net Worth: $21,545,351
Earnings: ($31,130,703)
Emp.: 1,310
Fiscal Year-end: 12/31/23
Aluminum Mfr
N.A.I.C.S.: 331313
Gheorghe Dobra *(Chm & CEO)*

ALUMEXX N.V.

Leerlooierstraat 30, 4871 EN, Etten-Leur, Netherlands
Tel.: (31) 763033596
Web Site: https://www.alumexx-nv.nl
ALX—(EUR)
Sales Range: $1-9.9 Million
Plastic Recycling Services
N.A.I.C.S.: 562920
Jeroen Van den Heuvel *(CEO)*

ALUMIL ALUMINIUM INDUSTRY S.A.

Kilkis Industrial Area, 61100, Kilkis, Greece
Tel.: (30) 2341079300 GR
Web Site: https://www.alumil.com
Year Founded: 1988
ALMY—(ATH)
Rev.: $434,269,329
Assets: $411,009,752
Liabilities: $298,999,797
Net Worth: $112,009,955
Earnings: $4,362,232
Emp.: 2,832
Fiscal Year-end: 12/31/23
Aluminium Extrusion Services
N.A.I.C.S.: 331318
George Alex Milonas *(Chm & CEO)*

Subsidiaries:

Alumil Albania Shpk. (1)
Kasar High Way Tirana, Durres, 1051, Albania
Tel.: (355) 48240230
Aluminum Material Mfr
N.A.I.C.S.: 331315

Alumil Bulgaria Ltd. (1)
2 Donka Ushlinova st, 1766, Sofia, Bulgaria
Tel.: (359) 893616016
Web Site: http://www.alumil.bg
Extruded Aluminum Products Mfr
N.A.I.C.S.: 331318

Subsidiary (Domestic):

Alumil Varna Ltd. (2)
West Industrial Zone 9009, Varna, Bulgaria
Tel.: (359) 5250 3636
Web Site: http://www.alumil.com
Emp.: 10
Extruded Aluminum Products Mfr
N.A.I.C.S.: 331318

Alumil Cy Ltd. (1)
19 Pentagias Str Viomichaniki Periochi Idaliou, Dali, Nicosia, Cyprus
Tel.: (357) 22461156
Aluminum Material Mfr
N.A.I.C.S.: 331315

Alumil Deutschland GmbH (1)
Dessauer Strasse 7, 71083, Herrenberg, Germany
Tel.: (49) 70329508280
Web Site: http://www.alumif.de
Extruded Aluminum Products Mfr
N.A.I.C.S.: 331318

Alumil France S.A.S. (1)
104 Rue d Aubagne, 13006, Marseille, France
Tel.: (33) 603995014
Aluminium Product Mfr & Distr
N.A.I.C.S.: 332999

Alumil Gulf fzc (1)
Technology Park, PO Box 54548, Ras al Khaimah, United Arab Emirates
Tel.: (971) 7 2444106
Extruded Aluminum Products Mfr
N.A.I.C.S.: 331318

Alumil Hungary K.T.F. (1)
Gyar utca 2, 2040, Budaors, Hungary
Tel.: (36) 2342 8498
Extruded Aluminum Products Mfr
N.A.I.C.S.: 331318

Alumil Italia S.R.L. (1)
Viale del lavoro 3, 37040, Arcola, Verona, Italy
Tel.: (39) 0456144411
Web Site: http://www.alumil-italia.com
Aluminum Window & Door Mfr
N.A.I.C.S.: 331315

Alumil Kosova shpk (1)
Rruga e Llapit, Kosovo Polje, Pristina, Serbia
Tel.: (381) 38 601 185
Extruded Aluminum Products Mfr
N.A.I.C.S.: 331318

Alumil LLC (1)
blvd Nezalezhnosti 18, 07400, Brovary, Ukraine
Tel.: (380) 443777357

Web Site: https://www.alumil.ua
Aluminum Extrusion Mfr & Distr
N.A.I.C.S.: 331318

Alumil Moldavia (1)
Bucuriei Street no 7, Chisinau, Moldova
Tel.: (373) 2259 5217
Extruded Aluminum Products Mfr
N.A.I.C.S.: 331318

Alumil Oceania Pty Ltd (1)
Unit 4 / 2-4 Picrite Close, Pemulwuy, Sydney, 2145, NSW, Australia
Tel.: (61) 298964060
Aluminum Material Mfr
N.A.I.C.S.: 331315

Alumil Polska sp. z o.o. (1)
Ul Sklodowskiej Curie 65, Torun, Poland
Tel.: (48) 56645 8801
Web Site: http://alumil.com.pl
Extruded Aluminum Products Mfr
N.A.I.C.S.: 331318

Alumil Rom Industry S.A. (1)
Soseaua Bucuresti-Ploiesti 42-44 Baneasa Business and Technology Park, Cladirea A, 52034, Bucharest, Romania
Tel.: (40) 214243456
Web Site: https://alumil.com
Rev.: $24,031,282
Assets: $15,987,162
Liabilities: $3,462,902
Net Worth: $12,524,259
Earnings: $1,411,607
Emp.: 156
Fiscal Year-end: 12/31/2022
Aluminum Processor
N.A.I.C.S.: 331318

Alumil S.A. (1)
Gogousi 8, 56429, Thessaloniki, Greece
Tel.: (30) 2313011000
Aluminum Material Mfr
N.A.I.C.S.: 331315

Alumil Skopje D.o.o. (1)
Boris Trajkovski 74A, 1000, Skopje, North Macedonia
Tel.: (389) 22460350
Extruded Aluminum Products Mfr
N.A.I.C.S.: 331318

Alumil Systems UK Limited (1)
First Floor 85 Great Portland Street, Hoxton, London, W1W 7LT, United Kingdom
Tel.: (44) 7399136343
Web Site: https://www.alumil.com
Aluminum Material Mfr
N.A.I.C.S.: 331315

Alumil Ukraine Ltd. (1)
77-a Vladimirskaya Str, 01033, Kiev, Ukraine
Tel.: (380) 44 377 7357
Extruded Aluminum Products Mfr
N.A.I.C.S.: 331318

Alumil Yu Industry A.D. (1)
Industrijska zona bb, Nova Pazova, 23330, Serbia
Tel.: (381) 22 321 302
Extruded Aluminum Products Mfr
N.A.I.C.S.: 331318

Subsidiary (Domestic):

Alumil SRB D.o.o. (2)
Dragoslava Bojovica 586, 32212, Cacak, Preljina, Serbia
Tel.: (381) 32 320 480
Extruded Aluminum Products Mfr
N.A.I.C.S.: 331318

Alumil Technic D.o.o. (2)
Autoput za Novi Sad 221, 11000, Belgrade, Serbia
Tel.: (381) 11 3774 822
Extruded Aluminum Products Mfr
N.A.I.C.S.: 331318

ALUMINA A.D.

Rajka Dukica Bb, 78230, Knezevo, Bosnia & Herzegovina
Tel.: (387) 51591685
Year Founded: 1977
ALUM-R-A—(BANJ)
Sales Range: Less than $1 Million
Emp.: 5
Aluminium Products Mfr

N.A.I.C.S.: 331315
Uros Vujic (Chm-Mgmt Bd)

ALUMINIJ D.D.
Bacevici bb, 88000, Mostar, Bosnia & Herzegovina
Tel.: (387) 36 375 555
Web Site: http://www.aluminij.ba
Year Founded: 1977
Aluminum Mfr
N.A.I.C.S.: 332312
Darko Juka (Head-Corp Comm)

ALUMINIUM BAHRAIN B.S.C.
Building 150 Road 94 Block 951 King Hamad Highway, 951, Askar, Bahrain
Tel.: (973) 17835100   BH
Web Site:
    https://www.albasmelter.com
Year Founded: 1971
ALBH—(LSE)
Rev.: $4,882,958,012
Assets: $6,941,948,489
Liabilities: $2,107,970,611
Net Worth: $4,833,977,879
Earnings: $1,103,861,967
Emp.: 3,146
Fiscal Year-end: 12/31/22
Aluminum Smelters
N.A.I.C.S.: 331314
Amin Sultan (Chief Power Officer)

ALUMINIUM COMPANY OF MALAYSIA BERHAD
No 3 Persiaran Waja Bukit Raja Industrial Estate, 41050, Klang, Selangor Darul Ehsan, Malaysia
Tel.: (60) 333466262
Web Site: https://www.alcom.com.my
Rev.: $71,525,951
Assets: $50,403,454
Liabilities: $10,651,803
Net Worth: $39,751,651
Earnings: $2,618,519
Fiscal Year-end: 03/31/17
Aluminum Sheet Mfr
N.A.I.C.S.: 331315

ALUMINIUM DU MAROC SA
Zone Industrielle-Route de Tetouan, BP 324, 90000, Tangiers, Morocco
Tel.: (212) 539329950
Web Site:
    https://www.aluminiumdumaroc.com
Year Founded: 1976
ALM—(CAS)
Sales Range: Less than $1 Million
Aluminum Alloy Trim Mfr
N.A.I.C.S.: 331313
Abdelouahed El Alami (Chm)

ALUMINIUM EXTRUSION INDUSTRIES PLC
Km4 Atta To Amaimo Road Inyishi Ikeduru L G A P M B, 1581, Owerri, Imo, Nigeria
Tel.: (234) 8155482071
Web Site:
    https://www.alexnigeria.com
ALEX—(NIGE)
Rev.: $7,141,928
Assets: $6,784,396
Liabilities: $1,702,326
Net Worth: $5,082,070
Earnings: $175,215
Fiscal Year-end: 12/31/19
Fabricated Structural Metal Mfr
N.A.I.C.S.: 332312

ALUMINUM CORPORATION OF CHINA LIMITED
No 62 North Xizhimen Street, Haidian District, Beijing, 100082, China
Tel.: (86) 1082298322   CN
Web Site: https://www.chalco.com.cn
Year Founded: 2001

ACHHY—(OTCIQ)
Rev.: $31,700,123,849
Assets: $29,824,761,742
Liabilities: $15,896,714,037
Net Worth: $13,928,047,705
Earnings: $1,772,363,516
Emp.: 64,504
Fiscal Year-end: 12/31/23
Aluminum Producer
N.A.I.C.S.: 331313
Zhu Runzhou (VP)

ALUMINUM PRODUCTS COMPANY LTD.
Alupco St 7 industrail Area, PO Box 2080, Dammam, 31451, Saudi Arabia
Tel.: (966) 38471300
Web Site: http://www.alupco.com
Year Founded: 1975
Sales Range: $150-199.9 Million
Emp.: 800
Extruded & Surface-Treated Aluminum Products Mfr
N.A.I.C.S.: 331318
Hashim S. Hashim (Chm)

ALUMTEK CORPORATION
P.O.B (14717-16883), Tehran, 15178, Iran
Tel.: (98) 21 44015118
Web Site:
    http://www.alumtekcorp.com
Year Founded: 1967
Emp.: 450
Overhead Conductor Mfr
N.A.I.C.S.: 339999
M. J. Safavian (Pres)

ALUPAR INVESTIMENTO S.A.
Rua Gomes de Carvalho 1 996 16 Andar - Vila Olimpia, Sao Paulo, 04547-006, SP, Brazil
Tel.: (55) 1145712400
Web Site: https://www.alupar.com.br
ALUP11—(BRAZ)
Rev.: $591,941,673
Assets: $5,083,227,015
Liabilities: $3,183,227,065
Net Worth: $1,899,999,949
Earnings: $205,749,981
Emp.: 848
Fiscal Year-end: 12/31/23
Eletric Power Generation Services
N.A.I.C.S.: 221118
Jose Luiz de Godoy Pereira (Chm, CFO, Chief Admin Officer & Exec VP-IR)

Subsidiaries:

Empresa Amazonense de Transmissao de Energia S.A.   (1)
No 66 Rua Olimpiadas 8th Floor, Sao Paulo, 04551-000, Brazil
Tel.: (55) 11 3382 8700
Electric Power Generation & Transmission Services
N.A.I.C.S.: 221118

Empresa Catarinense de Transmissao de Energia S.A.   (1)
Adolfo Melo 38 Sl 601, Florianopolis, 88015-090, Santa Catarina, Brazil
Tel.: (55) 48 3223 0225
Electric Power Generation & Transmission Services
N.A.I.C.S.: 221118

Ferreira Gomes Energia S.A.   (1)
Rua Gomes de Carvalho 1996 16 andar, Vila Olimpia, Sao Paulo, 04547-006, Brazil
Tel.: (55) 11 4571 2400
Web Site:
    http://ferreiragomesenergia.com.br
Hydroelectric Power Generation Services
N.A.I.C.S.: 221111
Marcelo Patricio Fernandes Costa (CFO, Chief Admin Officer & Dir-IR)

ALUPLAST GMBH

Auf der Breit 2, 76227, Karlsruhe, Germany
Tel.: (49) 721471710
Web Site: http://www.aluplast.net
Year Founded: 1982
Window & Door Systems
N.A.I.C.S.: 332321
Herr Bobay (CEO)

Subsidiaries:

Chelsea Building Products Inc.   (1)
565 Cedar Way, Oakmont, PA 15139-2049
Tel.: (412) 826-8077
Web Site:
    http://www.chelseabuildingproducts.com
Door & Window Frames Mfr
N.A.I.C.S.: 321911

ALUSSA ENERGY ACQUISITION CORP.
71 Fort Street, PO Box 500, Georgetown, KY1-1106, Cayman Islands
Tel.: (345) 9494900   Ky
Year Founded: 2019
ALUS—(NYSE)
Rev.: $2,003,660
Assets: $290,439,566
Liabilities: $285,439,560
Net Worth: $5,000,006
Earnings: ($3,186,865)
Emp.: 3
Fiscal Year-end: 12/31/20
Investment Services
N.A.I.C.S.: 523999
James Musselman (Chm)

ALUTEC CO., LTD.
564 Seongwang-Ro Gunseo-Myeon, Chungchongbuk-Do, Okcheon, 373841, Korea (South)
Tel.: (82) 437317141
Emp.: 75
Aluminum Mfr
N.A.I.C.S.: 331524

Subsidiaries:

Korea Plasma Technology U Co., Ltd.   (1)
1 Gwaerang 2-gil, Jeongnam-myeon, Hwaseong, 445-963, Gyeonggi, Korea (South)
Tel.: (82) 318313000
Web Site: https://www.kpt4u.com
Rev.: $28,279,335
Assets: $63,225,785
Liabilities: $32,543,498
Net Worth: $30,682,286
Earnings: $1,549,246
Emp.: 60
Fiscal Year-end: 12/31/2022
Metal Ceramic Coating Services
N.A.I.C.S.: 332812
Joon Young Park (CEO)

ALUWORKS LIMITED
Plot No 63/1 Heavy Industrial Area, PO Box 914, Greater Accra, Tema, Ghana
Tel.: (233) 302951206
Web Site: http://www.aluworks.com
ALW—(GHA)
Rev.: $11,726,440
Assets: $36,619,814
Liabilities: $39,116,071
Net Worth: ($2,496,257)
Earnings: ($5,745,318)
Emp.: 177
Fiscal Year-end: 12/31/20
Aluminum Fabricated Products Mfr
N.A.I.C.S.: 331318
Kwasi Okoh (Mng Dir)

ALV INFRASTRUCTURE DEVELOPMENT INVESTMENT JSC
Xa Hurong Phong huyen, A Luoi District, Hue, Thua Thien Hue, Vietnam
Tel.: (84) 2366514288

Web Site: http://alv.vn
ALV—(HNX)
Construction Services
N.A.I.C.S.: 236220
The Son Truong (Chm)

ALVAND TILE & CERAMIC COMPANY
23 Saeedi St Africa Ave, PO Box 19395-3111, Tehran, Iran
Tel.: (98) 21 22057811
Web Site:
    http://www.alvandtileco.com
ALVN—(THE)
Sales Range: Less than $1 Million
Ceramic Products Mfr
N.A.I.C.S.: 327110

ALVAND TILE & CERAMIC INDUSTRIES CO.
No 23 Saeedi ST Africa Blvd, Tehran, Iran
Tel.: (98) 2122039697
Web Site:
    http://www.alvandtileco.com
ALVN1—(THE)
Sales Range: Less than $1 Million
Ceramic Product Design & Mfr
N.A.I.C.S.: 327110

ALVARION LTD.
Givat Yeshayahu 26 D N, Migdal, 99825, Israel
Tel.: (972) 36456252   Il
ALVRQ—(OTCIQ)
Sales Range: Less than $1 Million
Telephone Apparatus Mfr
N.A.I.C.S.: 334210

ALVEEN SA
Les Jardins de la Duranne Batiment D 510 Rue Rene Descartes, FR-13857, Aix-en-Provence, Cedex 3, France
Tel.: (33) 442525354
Web Site: https://www.alveen.com
MLALV—(EUR)
Sales Range: $1-9.9 Million
Real Estate Manangement Services
N.A.I.C.S.: 531390
Michael Levy (Chm & CEO)

ALVIVA HOLDINGS LIMITED
International business Gateway Park Corner of New Road and 6th Street, PO Box 483, Halfway House, Midrand, 1685, Johannesburg, South Africa
Tel.: (27) 112377000   ZA
Web Site:
    http://www.alvivaholdings.com
Year Founded: 1993
AVV—(JSE)
Rev.: $1,016,158,601
Assets: $477,387,024
Liabilities: $307,531,169
Net Worth: $169,855,856
Earnings: $20,502,910
Emp.: 3,064
Fiscal Year-end: 06/30/21
Computer Hardware Mfr & Distr
N.A.I.C.S.: 423430
R. D. Lyon (CFO)

Subsidiaries:

Axiz Botswana Proprietary Limited   (1)
Plot 60 Unit 8 Gaborone International Commerce Park, Gaborone, Botswana
Tel.: (267) 3115777
Information Technology Services
N.A.I.C.S.: 541511

Boditse (Pty) Limited   (1)
Plot 60 Unit 2 International Commerce Park, Gaborone, Botswana
Tel.: (267) 3937477
Web Site: http://www.pinnacleafrica.com

Alviva Holdings Limited—(Continued)

Emp.: 20
Industrial Equipment Distr
N.A.I.C.S.: 423830
Rod Boyt *(Mng Dir)*

Centrafin Proprietary Limited **(1)**
2nd Floor 23 Magwa Crescent, Waterfall
City, Midrand, 2090, South Africa
Tel.: (27) 116546460
Web Site: http://www.centrafin.co.za
Asset Financial Services
N.A.I.C.S.: 523999
Jenny Gill *(Mng Dir)*

DataNet Infrastructure Group (Pty)
Limited **(1)**
269 16th street, Randjespark, Midrand,
1685, South Africa
Tel.: (27) 11 990 6000
Web Site: http://www.datanet.co.za
Emp.: 250
Electronic Enclosures Distr
N.A.I.C.S.: 423690

Datacentrix Holdings Limited **(1)**
Corporate Park North 238 Roan Crescent
Old Pretoria Road, Midrand, 1685, South
Africa **(100%)**
Tel.: (27) 877415000
Web Site: https://www.datacentrix.co.za
Technology Reseller & Solutions Provider
N.A.I.C.S.: 541512
Kenny Nkosi *(Mng Dir-Pub Sector Div)*

Subsidiary (Domestic):

Datacentrix (Proprietary) Limited **(2)**
379 Queens Crescent, Menlo Park, Preto-
ria, 0081, Gauteng, South Africa
Tel.: (27) 12 348 7555
Business Software Consulting Services
N.A.I.C.S.: 541511

Datacentrix Solutions (Proprietary)
Limited **(2)**
7 Wellington Rd, Johannesburg, 2193, Gau-
teng, South Africa
Tel.: (27) 123487555
Business Management Software Solutions
N.A.I.C.S.: 541511

Intdev Internet Technologies Propri-
etary Limited **(1)**
International Business Gateway Park Cnr
New and 6th Road, Midrand, 1685, South
Africa
Tel.: (27) 110822727
Web Site: http://web.intdev.co.za
Internet & Communication Services
N.A.I.C.S.: 517810
Pedro Maia *(Mng Dir)*

Obscure Technology Proprietary
Limited **(1)**
Block B Unit 2 Top Floor Southdowns Office
Park 21 Karee Street, Irene, Centurion,
0157, South Africa
Tel.: (27) 129412032
Web Site: http://www.obscuretech.net
Information Technology Services
N.A.I.C.S.: 541511
Justin Lee *(Mng Dir)*

Pinnacle Holdings Limited **(1)**
269 16th Road, Randjespark, Midrand,
1685, Gauteng, South Africa
Tel.: (27) 112653000
Web Site: http://www.pinnacle.co.za
Emp.: 591
Investment Management Service
N.A.I.C.S.: 523999

Pinnacle Micro (Pty) Limited **(1)**
128 15th Rd, Midrand, 1685, Gauteng,
South Africa
Tel.: (27) 112653000
Web Site:
　http://www.pinnacletechnologies.co.za
Emp.: 774
Information Technology Consulting Services
N.A.I.C.S.: 541512
Arnolt Fourie *(CEO)*

Pinnacle Micro Namibia (Pty)
Limited **(1)**
15 Edison Street Southern Industria, Windhoek, Namibia
Tel.: (264) 6124 9478

Industrial Equipment Distr
N.A.I.C.S.: 423830

SynergERP Limited - DWC LCC **(1)**
Business Tower -19th Floor Conrad
Sheikh Zayed Rd, PO Box 29923, Dubai,
United Arab Emirates
Tel.: (971) 547444528
Information Technology Services
N.A.I.C.S.: 541511

VH Fibre Optics Proprietary
Limited **(1)**
Unit 9 Commercial Park Aintree Road,
Northriding, Randburg, 2162, South Africa
Tel.: (27) 117914177
Web Site: http://www.vhfibre.co.za
Telecommunication Equipment Distr
N.A.I.C.S.: 423690
Johan Kleynhans *(Mng Dir)*

WorkGroup IT (Pty) Limited **(1)**
International Business Gateway Cnr New
Road and 6th Road, Midrand, 1685, South
Africa
Tel.: (27) 11 654 6000
Web Site: http://www.workgroup.co.za
Sales Range: $150-199.9 Million
Emp.: 50
Computer Software Distr
N.A.I.C.S.: 423430

ALVO MINERALS LIMITED
Units 8-9 88 Forrest Street,
Cottesloe, 6011, WA, Australia
Tel.: (61) 863141424　　　　　**AU**
Web Site: https://www.alvo.com.au
Year Founded: 2019
ALV—(ASX)
Rev.: $34,873
Assets: $1,724,168
Liabilities: $300,200
Net Worth: $1,423,969
Earnings: ($3,678,942)
Fiscal Year-end: 12/31/23
Mineral Exploration Services
N.A.I.C.S.: 212390
Carol Marinkovich *(Sec)*

ALVOPETRO ENERGY LTD.
Suite 1920 215 9th Avenue SW, Cal-
gary, T2P 1K3, AB, Canada
Tel.: (587) 794-4224　　　　　**AB**
Web Site: https://www.alvopetro.com
Year Founded: 2013
ALVOF—(OTCQX)
Rev.: $8,904,693
Assets: $80,388,000
Liabilities: $27,278,000
Net Worth: $53,110,000
Earnings: $5,706,000
Emp.: 27
Fiscal Year-end: 12/31/20
Oil & Gas Exploration
N.A.I.C.S.: 211120
John D. Wright *(Chm)*

Subsidiaries:

Alvopetro S. A. Extracao de Petroleo
Gas Natural **(1)**
Rua Ewerton Visco 290 Boulevard Side
Empresarial Sala 2004, Caminho Sas Ar-
vores, Salvador, Bahia, Brazil
Tel.: (55) 7134320917
Natural Gas Exploration Service
N.A.I.C.S.: 211130

ALX RESOURCES CORP.
Suite 408 - 1199 West Pender Street,
Vancouver, V6E 2R1, BC, Canada
Tel.: (604) 629-0293　　　　　**BC**
Web Site:
　https://www.alxresources.com
Year Founded: 2007
ALXEF—(OTCIQ)
Assets: $9,280,563
Liabilities: $194,813
Net Worth: $9,085,750
Earnings: ($1,401,679)
Fiscal Year-end: 12/31/22
Uranium Exploration Services

N.A.I.C.S.: 212290
Roger Leschuk *(Mgr-Corp Comm)*

ALZCHEM GROUP AG
Dr Albert-Frank Str 32, 83308, Trost-
berg, Germany
Tel.: (49) 8621860
Web Site: https://www.alzchem.com
Year Founded: 1908
ACT—(DEU)
Rev.: $596,808,699
Assets: $468,790,154
Liabilities: $288,241,528
Net Worth: $180,548,626
Earnings: $38,406,005
Emp.: 1,506
Fiscal Year-end: 12/31/23
Software Publishing Services
N.A.I.C.S.: 513210
Andreas Niedermaier *(CEO &*
Member-Mgmt Bd)

Subsidiaries:

AlzChem LLC **(1)**
11390 Old Roswell Rd Ste 124, Alpharetta,
GA 30009
Tel.: (770) 910-7719
Chemical Products Mfr
N.A.I.C.S.: 325998
Steve Krask *(CEO)*

AlzChem Shanghai Co., Ltd. **(1)**
No 700 Yishan Road, Xuhui District, Shang-
hai, 200233, China
Tel.: (86) 2154249788
Raw Material Distr
N.A.I.C.S.: 424590

Alzchem UK Ltd. **(1)**
Dafferns LLP One Eastwood BinleyBusi-
ness Park, Coventry, CV3 2UB, United
Kingdom
Tel.: (44) 78315784937
Chemical Products Mfr
N.A.I.C.S.: 325998

Suppliva GmbH **(1)**
Dr-Albert-Frank-Str 32, 83308, Trostberg,
Germany
Tel.: (49) 8621860
Agricultural Chemical Mfr
N.A.I.C.S.: 325320

ALZECURE PHARMA AB
Halsovagen 7, 141 57, Huddinge,
Sweden
Tel.: (46) 763162477
Web Site:
　https://www.alzecurepharma.se
Year Founded: 2012
ALZCUR—(OMX)
Rev.: $13,768
Assets: $2,997,274
Liabilities: $770,556
Net Worth: $2,226,718
Earnings: ($3,481,132)
Emp.: 11
Fiscal Year-end: 12/31/23
Pharmaceutical Product Mfr & Distr
N.A.I.C.S.: 325412
Marta Segerdahl *(Chief Medical*
Officer)

ALZINOVA AB
Alzinova AB Pepparedsleden 1, SE-
431 83, Molndal, Sweden
Tel.: (46) 708467975
Web Site: https://www.alzinova.com
Year Founded: 2011
ALZ—(OMX)
Rev.: $1,677
Assets: $10,454,642
Liabilities: $570,200
Net Worth: $9,884,442
Earnings: ($1,225,833)
Emp.: 4
Fiscal Year-end: 12/31/22
Biotechnology Research & Develop-
ment Services
N.A.I.C.S.: 541714

Per Wester *(CEO)*

AM GROUP HOLDINGS LIM-ITED
60 Paya Lebar Road 12-51/52 Paya
Lebar Square, Singapore, 409051,
Singapore
Tel.: (65) 62356678　　　　　**Ky**
Web Site:
　https://www.amgroupholdings.com
Year Founded: 2005
1849—(HKG)
Rev.: $36,403,143
Assets: $53,867,864
Liabilities: $21,897,905
Net Worth: $31,969,960
Earnings: $1,435,198
Emp.: 125
Fiscal Year-end: 06/30/22
Holding Company
N.A.I.C.S.: 551112
Li Lian Teo *(Chm & CEO)*

Subsidiaries:

Activa Media (S) Pte. Ltd. **(1)**
60 Paya Lebar Road 12-51/52 Paya Lebar
Square, Singapore, 409051, Singapore
Tel.: (65) 62356678
Web Site: https://www.activamedia.com.sg
Internet Marketing Services
N.A.I.C.S.: 541613

SG ActivaMedia (M) Sdn. Bhd. **(1)**
Unit 21-03 Level 21 Menara MBMR No 1
Jalan Syed Putra, 58000, Kuala Lumpur,
Malaysia
Tel.: (60) 391332398
Web Site: http://www.activamedia.com.my
Internet Marketing Services
N.A.I.C.S.: 541613

AM PM SYSTEMS
1110 - 2237 Hawkins Street, Port Co-
quitlam, V3B 0M2, BC, Canada
Web Site:
　http://www.ampmservice.com
Year Founded: 1987
Sales Range: $10-24.9 Million
Emp.: 200
Point of Sale System & Software
Support Services
N.A.I.C.S.: 541519
John Chan *(Owner)*

Subsidiaries:

AM PM USA SERVICE, LLC **(1)**
Unit 105 2105 S 48th St, Tempe, AZ 85282
Tel.: (480) 921-2608
Software Support & Management Services
N.A.I.C.S.: 541519

AM RESOURCES CORP.
410 St Nicolas Suite 236, Montreal,
H2Y 2P5, QC, Canada
Tel.: (514) 360-0576
Web Site: https://www.am-
　resources.com
Year Founded: 2007
AMR—(DEU)
Rev.: $358
Assets: $3,109,015
Liabilities: $1,959,175
Net Worth: $1,149,840
Earnings: ($437,883)
Fiscal Year-end: 12/31/20
Metal Exploration Services
N.A.I.C.S.: 213114
Martin Nicoletti *(CFO & Sec)*

AMA CORPORATION PLC
Flat 3-2, London, SW5 0BJ, United
Kingdom
Tel.: (44) 33255590921　　　　　**UK**
Year Founded: 2004
ALAMA—(EUR)
Rev.: $3,251,673
Assets: $13,763,220
Liabilities: $7,521,045

Net Worth: $6,242,176
Earnings: ($8,714,656)
Emp.: 80
Fiscal Year-end: 12/31/23
Software Development Services
N.A.I.C.S.: 541511
Christian Guillemot *(Chm & CEO)*

Subsidiaries:

Ama Xperteye GmbH **(1)**
At Mediapark 8, 50670, Cologne, Germany
Tel.: (49) 22155405070
Digital Transformation Services
N.A.I.C.S.: 518210

Ama Xperteye Inc. **(1)**
1 City Plz 421 Fayetteville St Ste 100, Raleigh, NC 27601
Tel.: (919) 754-4846
Emp.: 100
Software Technical Support Services
N.A.I.C.S.: 541990

AMA GROUP LIMITED
Level 4 130 Bundall Road, Bundall,
4217, QLD, Australia
Tel.: (61) 370665022 **AU**
Web Site:
https://www.amagroupltd.com
Year Founded: 2009
AMA—(ASX)
Rev.: $597,463,272
Assets: $563,822,113
Liabilities: $484,910,522
Net Worth: $78,911,592
Earnings: ($1,571,848)
Emp.: 3,400
Fiscal Year-end: 06/30/24
Automotive & Electrical Accessories
Whslr
N.A.I.C.S.: 423110
Andrew Hopkins *(CEO)*

Subsidiaries:

Accident Repair Management Pty
Ltd **(1)**
5-7 Stout Rd, Mount Druitt, 2770, NSW,
Australia
Tel.: (61) 24 722 5566
Web Site: https://www.accidentrm.com.au
Vehicle Repair Services
N.A.I.C.S.: 811111

Automotive Solutions Group
Limited **(1)**
Emirates House Level 9 167 Eagle Street,
Brisbane, 4000, QLD, Australia **(100%)**
Tel.: (61) 736073836
Automotive Parts Mfr & Distr
N.A.I.C.S.: 336390

Capital S.M.A.R.T. Repairs Australia
Pty Ltd **(1)**
960 Stud Road, Rowville, 3178, VIC, Australia
Tel.: (61) 39 717 1074
Web Site: https://www.capitalsmart.com.au
Vehicle Repair Services
N.A.I.C.S.: 811111

Capital S.M.A.R.T. Repairs New Zealand Pty Ltd **(1)**
6 Henry Rose Place, Albany, Auckland,
0632, New Zealand
Tel.: (64) 9 448 2470
Web Site: https://www.capitalsmart.co.nz
Vehicle Repair Services
N.A.I.C.S.: 811111

FluidDrive Holdings Pty Ltd **(1)**
70 Raglan Street, Preston, 3072, VIC, Australia
Tel.: (61) 39 485 9777
Web Site: https://fluiddrive.com.au
Automotive Transmission Repair Services
N.A.I.C.S.: 811114

MT Druitt Autobody Repairs Pty
Ltd **(1)**
7 Stout Road, Mount Druitt, 2770, NSW,
Australia
Tel.: (61) 29 625 3766
Vehicle Repair Services
N.A.I.C.S.: 811111

Matt George *(Mgr)*

Winter & Taylor Pty Ltd **(1)**
101 Mercer Street, Geelong, 3220, VIC,
Australia
Tel.: (61) 3 5216 0700
Web Site: http://www.wtholden.com.au
Car Dealership; Automotive Repair Services
N.A.I.C.S.: 441110

AMA INDUSTRIAL COMPANY
64th St 17th kilometer of Karaj Special Road, PO Box 37515-355,
13891-55113, Tehran, Iran
Tel.: (98) 2144983935
Web Site: http://www.ama-co.com
Year Founded: 1959
Welding Electrode Mfr
N.A.I.C.S.: 333992
Reza Bashartizadeh *(Chm)*

AMA MARINE PUBLIC COMPANY LIMITED
33/4 The 9th Towers Tower A 33rd
Floor Room TNA02 Rama 9 Rd,
Huaykwang, Bangkok, 10310, Thailand
Tel.: (66) 20012801 **TH**
Web Site:
https://www.amamarine.co.th
Year Founded: 1996
AMA—(THA)
Rev.: $89,051,980
Assets: $140,955,148
Liabilities: $54,578,263
Net Worth: $86,376,884
Earnings: $9,007,291
Fiscal Year-end: 12/31/23
Transportation Services
N.A.I.C.S.: 541614
Pisan Ratchakitprakarn *(Mng Dir)*

Subsidiaries:

Tssk Logistic Co., Ltd. **(1)**
36 Map Kha, Nikhom Phatthana District,
Rayong, 21180, Thailand
Tel.: (66) 38035290
Web Site: https://www.tssklogistics.co.th
Logistics Consulting Servies
N.A.I.C.S.: 541614

AMACON CONSTRUCTION LTD
Suite 300 911 Homer Street, Vancouver, V6B 2W6, BC, Canada
Tel.: (604) 602-7700
Web Site: http://www.amacon.com
Rev.: $12,780,908
Emp.: 50
Real Estate Development & Construction Services
N.A.I.C.S.: 531190
Don DeCotiis *(VP)*

AMAD INVESTMENT & REAL ESTATE DEVELOPMENT PLC
Queen Rania Al-Abullah St Building
Number 82, PO Box 926179, Amman, 11190, Jordan
Tel.: (962) 5156603
Year Founded: 1996
AMAD—(AMM)
Rev.: $1,574,174
Assets: $13,150,447
Liabilities: $178,302
Net Worth: $12,972,145
Earnings: ($208,325)
Emp.: 11
Fiscal Year-end: 12/31/20
Real Estate Investment Services
N.A.I.C.S.: 531390
Bshar Al- Tamimi *(Gen Mgr)*

AMADA HOLDINGS CO., LTD.
200 Ishida, Isehara, 259-1196, Kanagawa, Japan
Tel.: (81) 463961111 **JP**
Web Site: https://www.amada.co.jp

Year Founded: 1948
6113—(TKS)
Rev.: $2,667,135,000
Assets: $4,501,760,330
Liabilities: $969,402,770
Net Worth: $3,532,357,560
Earnings: $268,617,180
Emp.: 9,005
Fiscal Year-end: 03/31/24
Metalworking Machines & Bandsaws
Mfr
N.A.I.C.S.: 333517
Tsutomu Isobe *(Chm & Pres)*

Subsidiaries:

Amada Ailink Service Co., Ltd. **(1)**
2-15-14 Noge, Setagaya-ku, Tokyo, 158-0092, Japan
Tel.: (81) 357585622
Web Site: http://www.amada.co.jp
Electronic Device Information Services
N.A.I.C.S.: 519290

Amada Asia Pte. Ltd. **(1)**
12 Tannery Road 03-07 HB Centre 1, Singapore, 347722, Singapore
Tel.: (65) 6743 3244
Machine Tools Mfr
N.A.I.C.S.: 333517
Umada Sachiro *(Mng Dir)*

Subsidiary (Non-US):

Amada (India) Pvt. Ltd. **(2)**
C-Wing-412 Floral Deck Plaza MIDC Opp
Seepz, Andheri East, Mumbai, 400 093,
India
Tel.: (91) 22 28395592
Web Site: http://www.amadaindia.co.in
Sales Range: $50-74.9 Million
Emp.: 15
Metalworking Machines Mfr
N.A.I.C.S.: 333519
Niraj Seth *(Pres)*

Subsidiary (Domestic):

Amada Soft (India) Pvt. Ltd. **(3)**
Scendas IT Park chennai Unit No 6 1st
Floor Taramani Road, Opp CSIR Complex
Taramani, Chennai, 600 113, India
Tel.: (91) 4422542900
Web Site: http://www.amadasoft.co.in
Emp.: 10
Software Development Services
N.A.I.C.S.: 541511

Subsidiary (Non-US):

Amada (Malaysia) Sdn. Bhd. **(2)**
No 20 Jalan Pendaftar U1/54 Section U1,
Glenmarie Temasya Industrial Park, 40150,
Shah Alam, Selangor, Malaysia
Tel.: (60) 355696233
Cutting Machines Sales & Service
N.A.I.C.S.: 423830

Amada (Thailand) Co., Ltd. **(2)**
Asia Industrial Estate Suvarnabhumi AIES
88/41 Moo 4 Khongsuan, Bangbo, Bangkok, 10560, Samutprakam, Thailand
Tel.: (66) 21705900
Web Site: http://www.amada.co.th
Cutting Machines Sales & Service
N.A.I.C.S.: 423830
Koji Yamamoto *(Mng Dir)*

Amada Machine Tools (Thailand) Co.,
Ltd. **(2)**
700/146 Village No 1, Bankao Sub-District
Phan Thong, Chon Buri, 20160, Thailand
Tel.: (66) 3846 8920
Machine Tools Mfr
N.A.I.C.S.: 333517

Amada Oceania Pty. Ltd. **(2)**
Unit 7 16 Lexington Drive, Bella Vista,
2153, NSW, Australia **(100%)**
Tel.: (61) 288871100
Web Site: http://www.amada.com.au
Sales Range: $25-49.9 Million
Emp.: 6
Sales & After-Sales Service of Machines &
Tools
N.A.I.C.S.: 333243

Subsidiary (Domestic):

Amada Singapore (1989) Pte.
Ltd. **(2)**

100G Pasir Panjang Road 01-15/16 Interlocal Centre, Singapore, 118523, Singapore
Tel.: (65) 67436334
Web Site: http://www.amadabandsaw.com
Sales Range: $25-49.9 Million
Emp.: 12
Cutting Machines Sales & Service
N.A.I.C.S.: 423830

Subsidiary (Non-US):

Amada Vietnam Co., Ltd. **(2)**
469 Ha Huy Tap Yen Vien, Gia Lam, Hanoi,
Vietnam
Tel.: (84) 4 6261 4583
Web Site: http://www.amadavietnam.vn
Sales Range: $50-74.9 Million
Emp.: 10
Machine Tool Distr
N.A.I.C.S.: 423830

Amada Butsuryu Co., Ltd. **(1)**
200 Ishida, Isehara, 259-1196, Kanagawa,
Japan **(100%)**
Tel.: (81) 463963334
Web Site: http://www.amadabutsuryu.co.jp
Sales Range: $25-49.9 Million
Emp.: 50
Distribution Service & Agency for Importing
& Exporting Machines & Tools
N.A.I.C.S.: 423830

Amada Co., Ltd. **(1)**
200 Ishida, Isehara, 259-1196, Kanagawa,
Japan
Tel.: (81) 463961111
Web Site: http://www.amada.co.jp
Sales Range: $25-49.9 Million
Emp.: 16
Sales of Machines & Tools
N.A.I.C.S.: 423830

Amada Co., Ltd. - Ono Plant **(1)**
56 Hata-machi, Ono, Hyogo, Japan
Tel.: (81) 794 62 5931
Band Saw Blade Mfr
N.A.I.C.S.: 332216

Amada Documech Co., Ltd. **(1)**
200 Ishida, Isehara, 259-1196, Kanagawa,
Japan
Tel.: (81) 463 96 3171
Emp.: 15
Information Editing & Production Services
N.A.I.C.S.: 561410
Kiyoshi Serizawa *(Office Mgr)*

Amada Engineering Co., Ltd. **(1)**
Ishida, Isehara, 259-1196, Kanagawa, Japan
Tel.: (81) 463 91 8090
Web Site: http://www.amada.co.jp
Metalworking Machines Mfr
N.A.I.C.S.: 333248

Amada Europe S.A. **(1)**
ZI Paris Nord II 96 Avenue de la Pyramide,
93290, Tremblay, France
Tel.: (33) 149903000
Web Site: http://www.amada.fr
Sales Range: $50-74.9 Million
Emp.: 200
Development, Manufacture & Sales of Metalworking Machines & Tools
N.A.I.C.S.: 332216

Subsidiary (Non-US):

Amada Austria GmbH **(2)**
Wassergasse 1, 2630, Ternitz,
Austria **(100%)**
Tel.: (43) 263035170
Web Site: https://www.amada.at
Sales Range: $50-74.9 Million
Emp.: 120
Mfr & Sales of Bandsaw Blades & Punches
& Dies
N.A.I.C.S.: 332216
Katsuhiko Kawabata *(Mng Dir)*

Subsidiary (Domestic):

Amada Europe Software Center,
S.A.S **(2)**
Zi Paris Nord II - 96 Av De La Pyramide,
93290, Tremblay-les-Gonesse, France
Tel.: (33) 149903000
Emp.: 200
Software Development Services
N.A.I.C.S.: 541511

Amada Holdings Co., Ltd.—(Continued)

Subsidiary (Non-US):

Amada GmbH (2)
Amada Allee 1, 42781, Haan, Germany
Tel.: (49) 210421260
Web Site: http://www.amada.de
Sales Range: $75-99.9 Million
Emp.: 175
Cutting Machines Sales & Service
N.A.I.C.S.: 423830

Subsidiary (Domestic):

Amada Machine Tools Europe GmbH (3)
AMADA Allee 3, 42781, Haan, Germany
Tel.: (49) 210417770
Web Site: http://www.amada-mt.de
Sales Range: $50-74.9 Million
Emp.: 70
Sales of Cutting Machines & Machine Tools
N.A.I.C.S.: 423830

Subsidiary (Non-US):

Amada Italia S.r.l. (2)
Via Amada I 1/3, 29010, Pontenure, Piacenza, Italy
Tel.: (39) 0523 872111
Web Site: http://www.amada.it
Machine Tool Distr
N.A.I.C.S.: 423830

Subsidiary (Domestic):

Amada Engineering Europe S.p.A (3)
Via Amada I 1/3, 29010, Pontenure, Piacenza, Italy
Tel.: (39) 0523 952811
Web Site: http://www.computesweb.com
Machine Tool Software Development Services
N.A.I.C.S.: 541511

Crea S.r.l. (3)
Via Asti 43, 10026, Santena, Turin, Italy (100%)
Tel.: (39) 011 9496211
Web Site: http://www.crea-amada.it
Sales Range: $25-49.9 Million
Emp.: 40
Mfr of Metalworking Machines & Bandsaws
N.A.I.C.S.: 333243

Subsidiary (Non-US):

Amada Maquinaria S.l. (2)
Calle Marina N 12/14 Cornella De Llobregat, Barcelona, 08940, Spain
Tel.: (34) 93 4742725
Web Site: http://www.amada.co.jp
Sales Range: $25-49.9 Million
Emp.: 27
Machine Tool Distr
N.A.I.C.S.: 423830

Subsidiary (Domestic):

Amada S.A. (2)
ZI Paris Nord 2 96 Av de la Pyramide, 93290, Tremblay, France (100%)
Tel.: (33) 149903000
Web Site: http://www.amada.fr
Sales Range: $75-99.9 Million
Emp.: 100
Cutting Machines Sales & Service
N.A.I.C.S.: 423830

Subsidiary (Domestic):

Amada Machine Tools Europe GmbH France (3)
Zone industrielle Paris Nord II Ave De La Pyramide, 93290, Tremblay, France (100%)
Tel.: (33) 149903094
Web Site: http://www.amada-mt.de
Sales Range: $25-49.9 Million
Emp.: 19
Cutting Machines Sales & Service
N.A.I.C.S.: 423710

Amada Outillage S.A. (3)
Zone Industrielle, BP 35, 76720, Auffay, France
Tel.: (33) 2 3280 8100
Web Site: http://www.amada.co.jp
Machine Tools Mfr

N.A.I.C.S.: 333517

Subsidiary (Non-US):

Amada Sweden AB (2)
16 Borgens gata, 441 39, Alingsas, Sweden
Tel.: (46) 322 20 99 00
Web Site: http://www.amadasweden.se
Sales Range: $25-49.9 Million
Emp.: 23
Machine Tool Distr
N.A.I.C.S.: 423830

Amada Turkiye Makina Teknoloji Sanayi Ve Ticaret Ltd. (2)
Iktelli OSB Mh Aykosan Carsi B Blok VIP plaza Dis Kapi No 1, C Kapi No 27, 34490, Istanbul, Turkiye
Tel.: (90) 212 549 10 70
Web Site: http://www.amada.co.jp
Machine Tool Distr
N.A.I.C.S.: 423830

Amada United Kingdom Limited (2)
Spennells Valley Road, Kidderminster, DY10 1XS, Worcestershire, United Kingdom (100%)
Tel.: (44) 1562749500
Web Site: http://www.amada.co.uk
Sales Range: $75-99.9 Million
Emp.: 132
Cutting Machines Sales & Service
N.A.I.C.S.: 423830
Alan Parrott (Mng Dir)

Amada Franchise Center Co., Ltd. (1)
Ishida, Isehara, 259-1196, Kanagawa, Japan (100%)
Tel.: (81) 463963535
Web Site: http://amada.co.jp
Sales Range: $1-4.9 Billion
Emp.: 1,652
Agency for Sales Handling, Charge Accounting & Processing of Accounting Documents
N.A.I.C.S.: 561440

Amada Hong Kong Co., Ltd. (1)
Unit 1101 11/F Austin Tower 22-26 Austin Ave, Jordan, Kowloon, China (Hong Kong) (100%)
Tel.: (852) 28689186
Sales Range: $50-74.9 Million
Emp.: 6
Cutting Machines Sales & Service
N.A.I.C.S.: 423830

Amada International Industry & Trading (Shanghai) Co., Ltd. (1)
No 89 Zhuoqing Road, Shanghai, 200235, China (100%)
Tel.: (86) 2162121111
Web Site: http://www.amada.com.cn
Sales Range: $10-24.9 Million
Emp.: 70
Cutting Machines Sales & Service
N.A.I.C.S.: 423830

Amada International Trading (Shenzhen) Co., Ltd (1)
Rm 801-803 8/F Talfook Chong No 9 Shihua Rord Futian Free Trade Zone, Shenzhen, China
Tel.: (86) 755 8358 0011
Machine Tool Distr
N.A.I.C.S.: 423830

Amada Korea Co., Ltd. (1)
12 Harmony-ro 177beon-gil, Yeonsu-gu, Incheon, 22013, Korea (South)
Tel.: (82) 328216010
Web Site: http://www.amada.co.kr
Laser Cutting Machinery Mfr
N.A.I.C.S.: 332216

Amada Lianyungang Machine Tool Co., Ltd (1)
No 3-2 Songtiao Eco & Tech Development Zone, Lianyungang, Jiangsu, China
Tel.: (86) 518 8515 1111
Machine Tools Mfr
N.A.I.C.S.: 333517

Amada Lianyungang Machinery Co., Ltd. (1)
No 21 Zhenxing Road, Songtiao, Lianyungang, Jiangsu, China
Tel.: (86) 51885151111
Cutting Machines Sales & Service

N.A.I.C.S.: 333243

Amada Machine Tools Co., Ltd. (1)
200 Ishida, Isehara, 259-1196, Kanagawa, Japan
Tel.: (81) 463963351
Web Site: http://www.amada.co.jp
Sales & Services for Metal Cutting Machines & Machine Tools
N.A.I.C.S.: 423830
Masahiko Tadokoro (Pres)

Amada North America, Inc. (1)
7025 Firestone Blvd, Buena Park, CA 90621-1869
Tel.: (714) 739-2111
Web Site: http://www.amada.com
Sales Range: $150-199.9 Million
Emp.: 310
Holding Company; Regional Managing Office
N.A.I.C.S.: 551112

Subsidiary (Domestic):

Amada America, Inc. (2)
7025 Firestone Blvd, Buena Park, CA 90621-1869
Tel.: (714) 739-2111
Web Site: http://www.amada.com
Emp.: 20
Research & Development of Software for Machine Tools & Sheetmetal-Working Machines
N.A.I.C.S.: 423830

Subsidiary (Domestic):

Amada Cutting Technologies, Inc. (3)
4070 Winnetka Ave, Rolling Meadows, IL 60008-1374 (100%)
Tel.: (714) 670-1704
Web Site: http://www.amadabandsaw.com
Sales Range: $25-49.9 Million
Cutting Machines Sales & Service
N.A.I.C.S.: 423830

Amada Laser America Inc. (3)
11100 Alcovy Rd, Covington, GA 30014-6406 (80%)
Tel.: (770) 385-5114
Web Site: http://www.amadabandsaw.com
Sales Range: $25-49.9 Million
Emp.: 13
Cutting Machines Sales & Service
N.A.I.C.S.: 541820

Amada Machine Tools America, Inc. (3)
2324 Palmer Dr, Schaumburg, IL 60173
Tel.: (847) 285-4800
Web Site: http://amadamt.com
Sales Range: Less than $1 Million
Emp.: 18
Metalworking Machinery
N.A.I.C.S.: 423830

Amada Tool America, Inc. (3)
4A Treadeasy Ave, Batavia, NY 14020
Tel.: (585) 344-3900
Web Site: http://www.amada.com
Sales Range: $25-49.9 Million
Emp.: 70
Hand Tool Mfr
N.A.I.C.S.: 332216
Edward Dries (COO)

Subsidiary (Non-US):

Amada Canada Ltd. (2)
885 Ave Geroges Cros, Granby, J2J 1E8, QC, Canada (100%)
Tel.: (450) 378-0111
Web Site: http://www.amada.ca
Sales Range: $25-49.9 Million
Emp.: 30
Cutting Machines Sales & Service
N.A.I.C.S.: 333991

Amada De Mexico, S. de R.L. de C.V. (2)
Ave TLC 57-E Parque Industrial Stiva Aeropuerto, Apodaca, 66626, Nuevo Leon, Mexico
Tel.: (52) 81 1234 0700
Web Site: http://www.amada-mexico.com
Machine Tool Distr
N.A.I.C.S.: 423830

Amada Plantech Co., Ltd. (1)

200 Ishida, Isehara, 259-1196, Kanagawa, Japan
Tel.: (81) 463 96 3603
Commercial Building Landscaping Services
N.A.I.C.S.: 561730

Amada Shanghai Machine Tech Co., Ltd. (1)
No 89 Zhuoqing Road, Qingpu District, Shanghai, 201799, China
Tel.: (86) 21 6917 1352
Web Site: http://www.amada.co.jp
Machine Tools Mfr
N.A.I.C.S.: 333517

Amada Taiwan, Inc. (1)
333-82 No 21 Wenming Road, Gongsan District Linkou, Taoyuan, Hsien, Taiwan (100%)
Tel.: (886) 33283511
Web Site: http://www.amada.com.tw
Sales Range: $50-74.9 Million
Emp.: 80
Cutting Machines Sales & Service
N.A.I.C.S.: 423830

Amada Tool Precision Co., Ltd. (1)
200 Ishida, Isehara, 259-1196, Kanagawa, Japan
Tel.: (81) 463 91 8050
Machine Tool Mfr & Distr
N.A.I.C.S.: 333515

Amada Toyo Co., Ltd. (1)
3-73 Sameganji, Yatomi, 490-1415, Aichi, Japan
Tel.: (81) 567 52 2121
Sheet Metal Processing Machinery Mfr & Distr
N.A.I.C.S.: 333248

Amada do Brasil Ltda. (1)
Av Tambore 965/973, Tambore Barueri, 06460-000, Sao Paulo, SP, Brazil (100%)
Tel.: (55) 1141342324
Web Site: http://amada.com.br
Sales Range: $25-49.9 Million
Emp.: 7
Cutting Machines Sales & Service
N.A.I.C.S.: 333243

Beijing Amada Machine & Tooling Co., Ltd. (1)
No 3 705 Yong Chang Bei Lu, Beijing Economic Technological Development Area, Beijing, 100176, China (100%)
Tel.: (86) 1067869380
Web Site: http://www.amada.com
Cutting Machines Sales & Service
N.A.I.C.S.: 332216

Fujino Club Co., Ltd. (1)
350 Ishida, Isehara, 259-1116, Kanagawa, Japan
Tel.: (81) 463 96 3630
Web Site: http://www.oij.co.jp
Restaurant Management Services
N.A.I.C.S.: 722511
Hiroyuki Takeshita (Pres)

Miyachi Corporation (1)
2 6 6 Motoasakusa Taito, Tokyo, 111-0041, Japan (91.7%)
Tel.: (81) 352466700
Web Site: http://www.miyachi.com
Sales Range: $250-299.9 Million
Emp.: 965
Electronic Equipment Mfr; Lasers & Welding Equipment Mfr
N.A.I.C.S.: 334419

Nicotec Co., Ltd. (1)
1-15-12 Tamagawa Denenchofu, Setagaya-ku, Tokyo, 158-0085, Japan (100%)
Tel.: (81) 337225995
Web Site: http://www.nccgp.co.jp
Sales Range: $50-74.9 Million
Emp.: 150
Metal Working Machines & Tools Sales
N.A.I.C.S.: 332216

AMADEUS CAPITAL PARTNERS LTD.

4th Floor 130 Jermyn Street, London, SW1Y 4UR, United Kingdom
Tel.: (44) 3300240777
Web Site:
    http://www.amadeuscapital.com
Year Founded: 1997

Sales Range: $25-49.9 Million
Emp.: 30
Private Equity Firm Services
N.A.I.C.S.: 523999
Anne Glover *(Co-Founder & CEO)*

AMADEUS FIRE AG

Hanauer Landstrasse 160, D-60314,
Frankfurt, Germany
Tel.: (49) 69968760
Web Site: https://www.amadeus-
fire.de
AAD—(DEU)
Rev.: $488,306,656
Assets: $378,523,016
Liabilities: $211,280,495
Net Worth: $167,242,521
Earnings: $48,298,929
Emp.: 4,315
Fiscal Year-end: 12/31/23
Staffing Services
N.A.I.C.S.: 561320
Michael C. Wisser *(Vice Chm-
Supervisory Bd)*

Subsidiaries:

Akademie fur internationale Rech-
nungslegung (AkiR) GmbH   (1)
Lichtstrasse 45-49, 50825, Cologne, Ger-
many
Tel.: (49) 2219 364 4275
Web Site: https://www.ifrs-akademie.de
Accounting Seminar Services
N.A.I.C.S.: 541219

Amadeus FiRe Interim- und Projekt-
management GmbH   (1)
Darmstadter Landstrasse 116, 60598,
Frankfurt am Main, Hesse, Germany
Tel.: (49) 6996876150
Web Site: http://www.interim-
projektmanagement.de
Sales Range: $25-49.9 Million
Emp.: 100
Accounting Services
N.A.I.C.S.: 541219

Amadeus FiRe Services GmbH   (1)
Hanauer Landstrasse 160, 60314, Frankfurt
am Main, Germany
Tel.: (49) 6996876477
Web Site: http://www.amadeus-fire.de
Sales Range: $25-49.9 Million
Emp.: 9
Accounting & Auditing Services
N.A.I.C.S.: 541211

Endriss GmbH   (1)
Lichtstrasse 45-49, 50825, Cologne, Ger-
many
Tel.: (49) 221 936 4420
Web Site: https://www.endriss.de
Educational Program Services
N.A.I.C.S.: 923110

Greenwell Gleeson GmbH   (1)
Palazzo Michelangelo Gerbermuhlstrasse 9,
60594, Frankfurt am Main, Hesse, Germany
Tel.: (49) 6990027720
Web Site: http://www.greenwellgleeson.de
Professionals Recruiting Services
N.A.I.C.S.: 541612

Greenwell Gleeson Ltd.   (1)
Cathedral Place 42-44 Waterloo Street, Bir-
mingham, B2 5QB, United Kingdom
Tel.: (44) 121 233 9911
Web Site: https://www.greenwell-
gleeson.co.uk
Sales Range: $25-49.9 Million
Emp.: 20
Accounting Professionals Recruitment Ser-
vices
N.A.I.C.S.: 541612
Rob Lawton *(Mng Dir)*

Steuer-Fachschule Dr. Endriss GmbH
& Co. KG   (1)
Lichtstrasse 45-49, 50825, Cologne, Ger-
many
Tel.: (49) 221 936 4420
Web Site: https://www.endriss.de
Sales Range: $10-24.9 Million
Emp.: 50
Education Services

N.A.I.C.S.: 611691
Joerg Philippen *(Mng Dir)*

Subsidiary (Domestic):

Akademie fur Internationale Rech-
nungslegung Prof. Dr. Leibfried
GmbH   (2)
Lichtstrasse 45-49, 50825, Cologne, Ger-
many
Tel.: (49) 2219 364 4275
Web Site: https://www.ifrs-akademie.de
Sales Range: $10-24.9 Million
Emp.: 10
Education Services
N.A.I.C.S.: 611710

AMADEUS IT GROUP, S.A.

Salvador de Madariaga 1, 28027,
Madrid, Spain
Tel.: (34) 915820100   ES
Web Site: https://amadeus.com
Year Founded: 1987
AMS—(VAL)
Rev.: $6,237,732,186
Assets: $11,647,775,846
Liabilities: $7,395,555,440
Net Worth: $4,252,220,406
Earnings: $1,246,628,152
Emp.: 19,402
Fiscal Year-end: 12/31/19
Holding Company; Travel & Tourism
Information Solutions
N.A.I.C.S.: 551112
Jose Antonio Tazon Garcia *(Chm)*

Subsidiaries:

Amadeus (Beijing) Information Tech-
nology Co., Ltd.   (1)
Rm604-605 Raffles City Beijing Office
Tower, Dongcheng District, Beijing, 100007,
China
Tel.: (86) 1056516900
Software Development Services
N.A.I.C.S.: 541511

Amadeus Airport IT GmbH   (1)
Berghamer Strasse 6, Aufhausen, 85435,
Erding, Germany
Tel.: (49) 8122430
Information Technology Services
N.A.I.C.S.: 541511

Amadeus Albania sh.p.k.   (1)
Shyqyri Brari street near the Zoo, Tirana,
Albania
Tel.: (355) 42278191
Information Technology Services
N.A.I.C.S.: 541511

Amadeus Bilgi Teknolojisi Hizmetleri
A.S   (1)
Istanbul Havalimani Serbest Bolgesi Plaza
Ofis No 1401 Kat 14, Yesilkoy, 34830, Is-
tanbul, Turkiye
Tel.: (90) 2124650175
Information Technology Services
N.A.I.C.S.: 541511

Amadeus Bosna d.o.o. za marketing
Sarajevo   (1)
Mithata KariCa 1, 71000, Sarajevo, Bosnia
& Herzegovina
Tel.: (387) 33274910
Information Technology Services
N.A.I.C.S.: 541511

Amadeus Brasil Ltda.   (1)
Leopoldo Couto de Magalhaes Jr Street
758 16th Floor - Room 162, Itaim Bibi, Sao
Paulo, 04542-000, Brazil
Tel.: (55) 1121315275
Information Technology Services
N.A.I.C.S.: 541511

Amadeus Czech Republic & Slovakia
s.r.o.   (1)
Meteor Centre Office Park Sokolovsk 100
94 Praha 8, Karlin, 186 00, Prague, Czech
Republic
Tel.: (420) 234704321
Information Technology Services
N.A.I.C.S.: 541511

Amadeus Eesti AS   (1)

Rotermanni 18/1 3rd floor, 10111, Tallinn,
Estonia
Tel.: (372) 6408788
Information Technology Services
N.A.I.C.S.: 541511

Amadeus Egypt Computerized Reser-
vation Services S.A.E.   (1)
Star Capital 2 City Stars Complex 8th Floor
Omar Ibn El Khattab St, Heliopolis, 11771,
Cairo, Egypt
Tel.: (20) 24801126
Information Technology Services
N.A.I.C.S.: 541511

Amadeus GDS (Malaysia) Sdn.
Bhd.   (1)
Menara Dion 15-01 27 Jalan Sultan Ismail,
50250, Kuala Lumpur, Malaysia
Tel.: (60) 323022100
Information Technology Services
N.A.I.C.S.: 541511

Amadeus Global Travel Distribution
Ltd.   (1)
14 Riverside off Riverside Drive 4th Floor
Grosvenor Building Suite 4A, 6680-00100,
Nairobi, Kenya
Tel.: (254) 204282000
Information Technology Services
N.A.I.C.S.: 541511

Amadeus Hellas Electronic Travel
Information Services Single Member
Societe Anonyme   (1)
60 Poseidonos Avenue, Glyfada, 166 75,
Athens, Greece
Tel.: (30) 2109303000
Tourism & Transportation Services
N.A.I.C.S.: 561510

Amadeus Hospitality Americas,
Inc.   (1)
75 New Hampshire Ave, Portsmouth, NH
03801
Tel.: (603) 436-7500
Web Site: https://www.amadeus-
hospitality.com
Software Development Services
N.A.I.C.S.: 541511

Amadeus Hospitality Asia Pacific Pte.
Ltd.   (1)
10 Pasir Panjang Road 15-01/02, Mapletree
Business City, Singapore, 117438, Singa-
pore
Tel.: (65) 67355988
Information Technology Services
N.A.I.C.S.: 541511

Amadeus Hospitality Netherlands
B.V.   (1)
Chasseveld 15-G, 4811 DH, Breda, Nether-
lands
Tel.: (31) 765305353
Information Technology Services
N.A.I.C.S.: 541511

Amadeus Hospitality UK Limited   (1)
Heathrow Airport World Business Centre
Heathrow 4 Newall Road, London, TW6
2FL, United Kingdom
Tel.: (44) 2089900912
Home Management Services
N.A.I.C.S.: 541611

Amadeus IT Group Colombia
S.A.S.   (1)
Carrera 11 No 84-09 Piso 6, Edificio Torre
Amadeus, Bogota, Colombia
Tel.: (57) 15896600
Information Technology Services
N.A.I.C.S.: 541511

Amadeus IT Group S.A.   (1)
Salvador de Madariaga 1, Madrid, 28027,
Spain
Tel.: (34) 915820100
Web Site: http://www.amadeus.com
Sales Range: $1-4.9 Billion
Emp.: 650
Travel & Tourism Information Solutions
N.A.I.C.S.: 518210
Ana de Pro Gonzalo *(CFO)*

Subsidiary (Non-US):

AMADEUSGLOBAL Ecuador
S.A.   (2)
Av Republica de El Salvador No 35-126 y

Portugal Edificio Zante, Piso 2-Oficina 206,
Quito, Ecuador
Tel.: (593) 23333228
Web Site: https://www.amadeus.com
Tourism Software Consulting Services
N.A.I.C.S.: 541512

Amadeus Argentina S.A.   (2)
Ingeniero Butty 240 piso 4, 1001, Buenos
Aires, Argentina
Tel.: (54) 1150319250
Web Site: https://www.ar.amadeus.com
Emp.: 12
Information Technology Consulting Services
N.A.I.C.S.: 541512
Geoff Erby *(Country Mgr)*

Amadeus Asia Limited   (2)
Tel.: (66) 26961600
Travel & Tourism Information Solutions
N.A.I.C.S.: 518210
Eugene Chan *(Chief Comml Officer-Distr-
Asia Pacific)*

Amadeus Austria Marketing
GmbH   (2)
Alpenstrasse 108a, 5020, Salzburg, Austria
Tel.: (43) 662 639 660
Web Site: http://www.at.amadeus.com
Tourism Software Development Services
N.A.I.C.S.: 541511

Amadeus Benelux N.V.   (2)
Medialaan 30, 1800, Vilvoorde, Belgium
Tel.: (32) 2 257 99 11
Sales Range: $25-49.9 Million
Emp.: 4
Tourism Software Development Services
N.A.I.C.S.: 541511
Luc Pannecoeck *(Gen Mgr)*

Amadeus Bulgaria OOD   (2)
Vertigo Business Tower 4th - 6th floor 109
109 Bulgaria Blvd, 1404, Sofia, Bulgaria
Tel.: (359) 29532386
Emp.: 8
Tourism Software Consulting Services
N.A.I.C.S.: 541512
Milina Mileva *(Gen Mgr)*

Amadeus Central and West Africa
S.A.   (2)
7 Avenue Nogues 08, BPV 228, Abidjan,
Cote d'Ivoire
Tel.: (225) 20312240
Tourism Software Development Services
N.A.I.C.S.: 541511
Vasken Tokatlien *(Mgr)*

Amadeus Denmark A/S   (2)
Oldenburg Alle 3 1 tv, 2630, Taastrup, Den-
mark
Tel.: (45) 43592000
Web Site: http://www.amadeusdenmark.dk
Emp.: 15
Tourism Software Development Services
N.A.I.C.S.: 541511

Amadeus France SNC   (2)
Le Seine St Germain Batiment C 28 Ave Du
Bas Meudon, F 92445, Issy-les-Moulineaux,
France
Tel.: (33) 141338300
Sales Range: $25-49.9 Million
Emp.: 230
Travel Services
N.A.I.C.S.: 561510
George Rudas *(Mng Dir)*

Subsidiary (Domestic):

Amadeus France S.A.   (3)
Batiment C Le Seine Saint Germain 2/8 av-
enue du Bas, Issy-les-Moulineaux, 92445,
France
Tel.: (33) 141338100
Web Site: http://www.amadeus.com
Data Transaction Processing Services
N.A.I.C.S.: 518210
Geroge Rudas *(Dir Gen)*

Subsidiary (Non-US):

Amadeus GDS LLP   (2)
48 Auezov str 4th floor, 050008, Almaty,
Kazakhstan
Tel.: (7) 7273449405
Web Site: https://www.amadeus.ru
Software Consulting Services
N.A.I.C.S.: 541511

Amadeus IT Group, S.A.—(Continued)

Amadeus GDS Singapore Pte. Ltd.　(2)
10 Pasir Panjang Road 15-01/02, Mapletree Business City, Singapore, 117438, Singapore
Tel.: (65) 62206866
Emp.: 60
Information Technology Consulting Services
N.A.I.C.S.: 541512
Derek Seah (Gen Mgr)

Amadeus GTD (Malta) Limited　(2)
Birkirkara Road, San Gwann, SGN 4193, Malta
Tel.: (356) 21383873
Web Site: http://www.mt.amadeus.com
Emp.: 3
Tourism Software Consulting Services
N.A.I.C.S.: 541512
Simon Rossi (Gen Mgr)

Amadeus GTD Southern Africa Pty. Ltd.　(2)
Rentworks Place Turnberry Office Park 48 Grosvenor Road, Bryanston, 2021, South Africa
Tel.: (27) 11 548 7300
Web Site: http://www.amadeus.co.za
Emp.: 100
Software Consulting Services
N.A.I.C.S.: 541512
Peter Long (Gen Mgr)

Amadeus Germany GmbH　(2)
Siemensstrasse 1, 61352, Bad Homburg, Germany
Tel.: (49) 6172910
Web Site: https://www.de.amadeus.com
Sales Range: $200-249.9 Million
Travel & Tourism Information Solutions
N.A.I.C.S.: 541519
Bernd Schulz (Mng Dir)

Amadeus Global Travel Israel Ltd.　(2)
1 Ben YehudaTel Aviv, Tel Aviv, 6380101, Israel
Tel.: (972) 37950000
Tourism Software Consulting Services
N.A.I.C.S.: 541512

Amadeus Hellas S.A.　(2)
157 Sygrou Avenue N Smyrni, 171 21, Athens, Greece
Tel.: (30) 210 9303000
Web Site: http://www.amadeus.com
Emp.: 35
Tourism Software Consulting Services
N.A.I.C.S.: 541512
Eva Karamanou (Gen Mgr)

Amadeus Hong Kong Limited　(2)
Room 3701 37F ACE Tw Wicsor House 311 Tloudester Road, Central, China (Hong Kong)
Tel.: (852) 29130123
Information Technology Consulting Services
N.A.I.C.S.: 541512

Amadeus IT Pacific Pty. Ltd.　(2)
Level 7 180 Thomas Street, Locked Bag A5085, Haymarket, Sydney, 2000, NSW, Australia
Tel.: (61) 299033933
Travel & Tourism Software Development Services
N.A.I.C.S.: 541511
Andrew Gay (Gen Mgr-New Zealand & Pacific Islands)

Amadeus Italia S.P.A.　(2)
Via Pergolesi 25, 20124, Milan, Italy
Tel.: (39) 02725471
Web Site: https://www.amadeus.com
Software Consulting Services
N.A.I.C.S.: 541512

Amadeus Japan K.K.　(2)
Nihonbashi Takashimaya Mitsui Building 16F 2-5-1 Nihonbashi, Chuo-Ku, Tokyo, 103-6116, Japan
Tel.: (81) 345603700
Web Site: https://www.jp.amadeus.com
Travel Arrangement Software Development Services
N.A.I.C.S.: 541511

Amadeus Magyarszag Kft　(2)

Madach Trade Center building B 6th floor Madach Imre street 13-14, 1075, Budapest, Hungary
Tel.: (36) 18801100
Emp.: 14
Tourism Software Development Services
N.A.I.C.S.: 541511
Mathias Kamolz (Gen Mgr)

Amadeus Marketing (Schweiz) A.G.　(2)
Prime Tower Hardstrasse 201, 8005, Zurich, Switzerland
Tel.: (41) 442179797
Sales Range: $25-49.9 Million
Emp.: 23
Tourism Software Consulting Services
N.A.I.C.S.: 541512

Amadeus Marketing (UK) Ltd.　(2)
The Web House 106 High Street, Crawley, RH10 1BF, West Sussex, United Kingdom
Tel.: (44) 870 895 9199
Web Site: http://www.amadeus.com
Sales Range: $25-49.9 Million
Emp.: 100
Tourism Software Consulting Services
N.A.I.C.S.: 541512
Gavin Hambrey (Acct Mgr)

Amadeus Marketing Ireland Ltd.　(2)
65-66 Charlemont Street, Smithfield, Dublin, D02 E981, Ireland
Tel.: (353) 14255055
Web Site: https://www.ie.amadeus.com
Sales Range: $25-49.9 Million
Emp.: 10
Travel & Tourism Software Development Services
N.A.I.C.S.: 541511
Volker Lorenz (Gen Mgr)

Amadeus Marketing Phils Inc.　(2)
36 Floor Lkg Tower 6801 Ayala Ave, Makati, 1226, Philippines
Tel.: (63) 2 857 71 00
Web Site: http://www.amadeus.com.ph
Information Technology Consulting Services
N.A.I.C.S.: 541511

Amadeus Marketing Romania S.R.L.　(2)
11 - 11A George Enescu Street 8th floor Sector 1, 010301, Bucharest, Romania
Tel.: (40) 212230354
Web Site: https://www.amadeus.com
Emp.: 12
Automated Ticketing Software Development Services
N.A.I.C.S.: 541511
Georgeta Grigoroiu (Mgr-Customer Support)

Amadeus Maroc S.A.S.　(2)
7 Rue Naguib Mahfouz, Quartier Gauthier, 20000, Casablanca, Morocco
Tel.: (212) 22489800
Web Site: http://www.ma.amadeus.com
Sales Range: $10-24.9 Million
Emp.: 14
Travel Products Distr
N.A.I.C.S.: 561510

Subsidiary (US):

Amadeus North America, Inc.　(2)
3470 NW 82nd Ave Ste 1000, Miami, FL 33122
Tel.: (305) 499-6000
Web Site: https://www.amadeus.com
Holding Company; Travel & Tourism Information Solutions
N.A.I.C.S.: 551112
Scott Gutz (Pres & CEO)

Subsidiary (Domestic):

Air-Transport IT Services, Inc.　(3)
5950 Hazeltine National Dr Ste 210, Orlando, FL 32822　(100%)
Tel.: (407) 370-4664
Web Site: http://www.airit.com
IT Services
N.A.I.C.S.: 541519
Betros Wakim (CEO & CTO)

Unit (Domestic):

Amadeus North America, Inc. - E-Travel Business　(3)

---

307 Weaverly Oaks Rd Ste 401, Waltham, MA 02452
Tel.: (781) 522-8920
Web Site: http://www.amadeus.com
Sales Range: $1-9.9 Million
Emp.: 66
Computer Software Providers
N.A.I.C.S.: 561510
Tom Cates (VP)

Subsidiary (Domestic):

Amadeus Revenue Integrity Inc.　(3)
3530 E Campo Abierto Ste 200, Tucson, AZ 85718-5876
Tel.: (520) 577-6500
Web Site: http://www.amadeus.com
Emp.: 65
Tourism Software Development Services
N.A.I.C.S.: 541511
Sam Michel (Mgr-Software Dev)

Navitaire LLC　(3)
333 S 7th St Ste 1700, Minneapolis, MN 55402-2443
Tel.: (612) 317-7000
Web Site: https://www.navitaire.com
Emp.: 550
Accounting & Bookkeeping Services
N.A.I.C.S.: 541219

Subsidiary (Domestic):

Navitaire International Inc.　(4)
333 S 7th St Ste 500, Minneapolis, MN 55402-2443
Tel.: (612) 317-7000
Business Process Outsourcing Services
N.A.I.C.S.: 561499

Subsidiary (Domestic):

Newmarket International, Inc.　(3)
75 Newhampshire Ave, Portsmouth, NH 03801
Tel.: (603) 436-7500
Web Site: http://www.newmarketinc.com
Emp.: 300
Hospitality Industry Software Developer, Publisher, Whslr & Support Services
N.A.I.C.S.: 513210
Sean O'Neill (Strategic Advisor)

Subsidiary (Non-US):

Newmarket International Ltd.　(4)
Drapers Court Kingston Hall Road, Kingston upon Thames, KT1 2BQ, Surrey, United Kingdom
Tel.: (44) 208 481 6600
Hospitality Industry Software Whslr & Support Services
N.A.I.C.S.: 423430
Jo Stanford (Mng Dir & Head-Europe, Middle East, Africa & India)

Newmarket International Software (Shanghai) Co., Ltd.　(4)
Suite 1709 You You International Plaza No 76 Pujian Road, Pudong New Area, Shanghai, 200127, China
Tel.: (86) 21 2089 8333
Web Site: http://www.newmarketinc.com.cn
Hospitality Industry Software Developer, Publisher, Whslr & Support Services
N.A.I.C.S.: 513210
Tim Guo (Mng Dir & Head-Asia Pacific)

Newmarket International Software Pte. Ltd.　(4)
600 North Bridge Road #14-02 ParkView Square, Singapore, 188778, Singapore
Tel.: (65) 6735 5988
Hospitality Industry Software Whslr & Support Services
N.A.I.C.S.: 423430
Eries Ng (Dir-Sls-Asia)

Division (Domestic):

Newmarket International, Inc. - MTech Division　(4)
14000 SW 119th Ave Ste 201, Miami, FL 33186
Tel.: (305) 256-0429
Web Site: http://dl.m-tech.com
Hospitality Industry Service Optimization & Support Software Developer, Publisher, Whslr & Support Services
N.A.I.C.S.: 513210

Luis Segredo (Pres & Gen Mgr)

Subsidiary (Non-US):

Amadeus Norway AS　(2)
Epicenter Edvard Storms gate 2, 0166, Oslo, Norway
Tel.: (47) 21053100
Information Technology Consulting Services
N.A.I.C.S.: 541512
Jesper Soderstrom (Mng Dir)

Amadeus Paraguay S.R.L.　(2)
Edificio Inter Express 2do Piso Oficina 202, Asuncion, Paraguay
Tel.: (595) 21 450 707
Tourism Software Consulting Services
N.A.I.C.S.: 541512

Amadeus Peru S.A.　(2)
Victor Andres Belaunde 147 Edificio Real 5 Oficina 902, San Isidro, Lima, Peru
Tel.: (51) 80056103
Tourism Information Technology Consulting Services
N.A.I.C.S.: 541512

Amadeus Polska Sp. Z o.o.　(2)
Al Jerozolimskie 142B, 02-672, Warsaw, Poland
Tel.: (48) 225394200
Web Site: https://www.amadeus.com
Sales Range: $25-49.9 Million
Emp.: 60
Tourism Software Development Services
N.A.I.C.S.: 541511
Gawel Rek (Gen Mgr)

Subsidiary (Domestic):

Amadeus Purchase Debt, S.A.　(2)
Calle salvador De Madariaga 1, Madrid, 28027, Spain
Tel.: (34) 915820100
Web Site: http://www.es.amadeus.com
Financial Software Development Services
N.A.I.C.S.: 541511
Luis Maroto (Gen Mgr)

Subsidiary (Non-US):

Amadeus Rezervasyon Dagitim Sistemleri A.S.　(2)
Barbaros Plaza Is Merkezi Dikilitas Mah Emirhan Cad No 113 Kat 18, Ortakoy, 34349, Istanbul, Turkiye
Tel.: (90) 2123100700
Web Site: https://www.amadeus.com.tr
Travel Software Development Services
N.A.I.C.S.: 541511

Amadeus Scandinavia AB.　(2)
Halsingegatan 49, 6602, Stockholm, Sweden
Tel.: (46) 84580500
Sales Range: $25-49.9 Million
Emp.: 200
Tourism Software Consulting Services
N.A.I.C.S.: 541512
Jester Soderstrom (Gen Mgr)

Amadeus Services Ltd.　(2)
World Business Centre 3 1208 Newall Road, Heathrow, TW6 2RB, Middlesex, United Kingdom
Tel.: (44) 20 8990 0600
Sales Range: $75-99.9 Million
Emp.: 40
Tourism Software Consulting Services
N.A.I.C.S.: 541512

Subsidiary (Domestic):

Amadeus Soluciones Tecnologicas, S.A　(2)
Salvador de Madariaga 1, 28027, Madrid, Spain
Tel.: (34) 913298683
Travel Software Development Services
N.A.I.C.S.: 541511
Fernando Cuesta (Gen Mgr)

Subsidiary (Non-US):

Amadeus Sweden AB　(2)
Gavlegatan 22, Box 6602, 113 84, Stockholm, Sweden
Tel.: (46) 8 458 05 00
Web Site: http://www.amadeus.com
Tourism Software Development Services
N.A.I.C.S.: 541511

Amadeus Taiwan Company Limited (2)
Rm1304 13F No 168 Sec 3 Nan Jing E Rd,
Taipei, 104, Taiwan
Tel.: (886) 221831199
Web Site: https://www.tw.amadeus.com
Software Consulting Services
N.A.I.C.S.: 541511
Peiling Lu (Dir-IT)

Amadeus s.a.s. (2)
485 Route du Pin Montard, Sophia Antipolis, 06902, Nice, Cedex, France
Tel.: (33) 492946000
Travel System Software Development Services
N.A.I.C.S.: 541511

Onerail Global Holdings Pty. Ltd. (2)
L 12 300 Elizabeth St, Surry Hills, 2010,
NSW, Australia
Tel.: (61) 293215100
Sales Range: $25-49.9 Million
Emp.: 150
Online Reservation Software Development
Services
N.A.I.C.S.: 541511

Sistemas de Reservaciones CRS de Venezuela, C.A. (2)
Av Romulo Gallegos y 1era Av Sta Eduvigis
Torre KLM Piso 8 Ofc 8A y 8B, Urb Los Palos Grandes, Caracas, 1070, Venezuela
Tel.: (58) 212 283 1683
Information Technology Consulting Services
N.A.I.C.S.: 541512

Traveltainment AG (2)
Carlo-Schmid-Strasse 12 Aachen,
Wurselen, 52080, Germany
Tel.: (49) 2405 448 40
Web Site: http://www.traveltainment.de
Tourism Software Consulting Services
N.A.I.C.S.: 541512
Lothar Schmitz (VP-IT Core Dev)

Subsidiary (Non-US):

Traveltainment Polska Sp. z o.o. (3)
ul Domaniewska 49, 02-672, Warsaw, Poland
Tel.: (48) 22 377 17 50
Web Site: http://www.traveltainment.pl
Travel & Tour Operating Services
N.A.I.C.S.: 561520

Traveltainment UK Ltd. (3)
18-20 Tesla Court Innovation Way, Peterborough, PE2 6FL, United Kingdom
Tel.: (44) 1733 361 345
Web Site: http://www.traveltainment.co.uk
Sales Range: $25-49.9 Million
Emp.: 25
Online Ticket Booking & Tour Operating
Agencies
N.A.I.C.S.: 561599

Subsidiary (Non-US):

UAB Amadeus Lietuva (2)
Liepyno st 25A-2A, LT-08108, Vilnius, Lithuania
Tel.: (370) 52726869
Sales Range: $25-49.9 Million
Emp.: 7
Information Technology Consulting Services
N.A.I.C.S.: 541512

i:FAO AG (2)
Clemensstrasse 9, 60487, Frankfurt, Germany
Tel.: (49) 69768050
Web Site: http://www.ifao.net
Rev.: $1,089,842
Assets: $22,845,389
Liabilities: $2,818,237
Net Worth: $20,027,152
Earnings: $3,282,448
Fiscal Year-end: 12/31/2015
Software Publishing Services
N.A.I.C.S.: 513210
Karin Frauscher (Member-Mgmt Bd)

Amadeus IT Services UK Limited (1)
First Point Buckingham Gate Airport, Gatwick, RH6 0NT, West Sussex, United Kingdom
Tel.: (44) 8435090000
Information Technology Services
N.A.I.C.S.: 541511

Amadeus Information Technology LLC (1)
Tel.: (7) 8126050099
Information Technology Services
N.A.I.C.S.: 541511

Amadeus Integrated Solutions Pty Ltd (1)
Design Quarter 2nd Floor Building DQ2 Nicol Grove, William Nicol Drive and Leslie
Avenue, Johannesburg, 2191, Fourways,
South Africa
Tel.; (27) 115487300
Information Technology Services
N.A.I.C.S.: 541511

Amadeus Korea, Ltd. (1)
253-15 Gongdeok-dong, Mapo-gu, Seoul,
Korea (South)
Tel.: (82) 27102011
Information Technology Services
N.A.I.C.S.: 541511

Amadeus Lebanon S.A.R.L. (1)
Gefinor Centre Block B 12th Floor, PO Box
113, 113-5693, Beirut, Lebanon
Tel.: (961) 1734550
Information Technology Services
N.A.I.C.S.: 541511

Amadeus Leisure IT GmbH (1)
Carlo-Schmid-Strasse 12, Wurselen, 52146,
Aachen, Germany
Tel.: (49) 240544840
Information Technology Services
N.A.I.C.S.: 541511

Amadeus Macedonia DOOEL (1)
Ul Makedonija br 19, 1000, Skopje, North
Macedonia
Tel.: (389) 23090763
Information Technology Services
N.A.I.C.S.: 541511

Amadeus Marketing (Ghana) Ltd. (1)
No 14 Liberation Link Airport Commercial
Area, PO Box CT 4817, Cantonments, Accra, Ghana
Tel.: (233) 21765590
Information Technology Services
N.A.I.C.S.: 541511

Amadeus Marketing Nigeria Ltd. (1)
Swiss Spirit Hotel and Suits Annex Building
Eventive 4 79, Ken Sarowiwa Road, Port
Harcourt, Nigeria
Tel.: (234) 7033850853
Information Technology Services
N.A.I.C.S.: 541511

Amadeus Mexico, S.A. de C.V. (1)
Paseo de la Reforma 222 piso 9, Colonia
Juarez, 06600, Mexico, Mexico
Tel.: (52) 5552420860
Information Technology Services
N.A.I.C.S.: 541511

Amadeus Saudi Arabia Limited (1)
Tel.: (966) 122252333
Information Technology Services
N.A.I.C.S.: 541511

Amadeus Slovenija, d.o.o. (1)
Dunajska 122, 1000, Ljubljana, Slovenia
Tel.: (386) 16001133
Information Technology Services
N.A.I.C.S.: 541511

Amadeus Sofia Labs EOOD (1)
109 Bulgaria Blvd Vertigo Business Centre
Office 4 1, 1404, Sofia, Bulgaria
Tel.: (359) 70012343
Information Technology Services
N.A.I.C.S.: 541511

Amadeus Software Labs India Private Limited (1)
Plot No 7 Local Shopping Centre Pocket 6
7 Sector - C, Vasant Kunj, New Delhi,
110070, India
Tel.: (91) 1141336600
Information Technology Services
N.A.I.C.S.: 541511

Amadeus Software Technology (Shangai) Co., Ltd. (1)
Rm604-605 Raffles City Beijing Office
Tower, Beijing, 100007, China
Tel.: (86) 1056516900
Information Technology Services

N.A.I.C.S.: 541511

Amadeus Syria Limited Liability (1)
Atfeh Building Ibn Al Haitham Street, 10330,
Damascus, Syria
Tel.: (963) 113331003
Information Technology Services
N.A.I.C.S.: 541511

FAO Bulgaria EOOD (1)
109 Bulgaria Blvd Vertigo Business Centre
Offices 4 1 5 1, 1404, Sofia, Bulgaria
Tel.: (359) 24478900
Software Development Services
N.A.I.C.S.: 541511

FAO Group GmbH (1)
Clemensstrasse 9, 60487, Frankfurt am
Main, Germany
Tel.: (49) 6976805500
Web Site: http://www.cytric.net
Software Development Services
N.A.I.C.S.: 541511
Karin Frauscher (Gen Mgr)

ICM Airport Technics Australia Pty. Ltd. (1)
1/12 Lord Street Lakes Business Park,
Botany, 2019, NSW, Australia
Tel.: (61) 296957200
Web Site: https://www.autobagdrop.com.au
Airport Operation Services
N.A.I.C.S.: 488119

ICM Airport Technics LLC (1)
5950 Hazeltine Natl Dr Ste 210, Orlando,
FL 32822
Tel.: (678) 301-8369
Airport Operation Services
N.A.I.C.S.: 488119

ICM Airport Technics Singapore Pte. Ltd. (1)
80 Airport Boulevard 04-26 Terminal 1, Singapore, 819642, Singapore
Tel.: (65) 62066680
Airport Operation Services
N.A.I.C.S.: 488119

ICM Airport Technics UK Ltd. (1)
D'Albiac House Room 1045-1050 Cromer
Road, Hounslow, TW6 1SD, Middlesex,
United Kingdom
Tel.: (44) 7760358947
Airport Operation Services
N.A.I.C.S.: 488119

PT Amadeus Technology Indonesia (1)
Tel.: (62) 2139709921
Software Development Services
N.A.I.C.S.: 541511

Pyton Communication Services B.V. (1)
Strijp-S Videolab gebouw Torenallee 20,
5617 BC, Eindhoven, Netherlands
Tel.: (31) 881651390
Web Site: http://www.pyton.travel
Software Development Services
N.A.I.C.S.: 541511

Travel Audience, GmbH (1)
Elsenstrasse 106, 12435, Berlin, Germany
Tel.: (49) 30530230610
Web Site: https://www.travelaudience.com
Travel Advertising Services
N.A.I.C.S.: 561510
Arialdo Piatti (Mng Dir, Head-Product & Gen
Mgr)

TravelClick, Inc. (1)
7 Times Sq 38th Fl, New York, NY 10036
Tel.: (212) 817-4800
Web Site: http://www.travelclick.net
Hotel Ecommerce Solutions
N.A.I.C.S.: 513210
Jan Tissera (Pres-Intl)

Subsidiary (Domestic):

The Rubicon Group, LLC (2)
101 Marietta St NW Ste 3525, Atlanta, GA
30303
Tel.: (678) 553-1940
Sales Range: $25-49.9 Million
Emp.: 10
Market Analysis & Revenue Management
Software for Travel Industry
N.A.I.C.S.: 513210
Andrew Sawczyn (Sr Engr-Software)

Vedaleon Technologies Pty. Ltd. (1)
Level 8 313 Latrobe Street, Melbourne,
3000, VIC, Australia
Tel.: (61) 396069555
Web Site: http://www.vedaleon.com.au
Software Development Services
N.A.I.C.S.: 541511

Videopolis, S.A.S. (1)
57 rue Ganneron, 75018, Paris, France
Tel.: (33) 153063300
Web Site: http://www.videopolis.fr
Film Production Services
N.A.I.C.S.: 512110

AMAERO INTERNATIONAL LIMITED
13 Normanby Road, Notting Hill, Melbourne, 3168, VIC, Australia
Tel.: (61) 399059847   AU
Web Site:
https://www.amaero.com.au
Year Founded: 2013
3DA—(ASX)
Rev.: $515,429
Assets: $11,897,022
Liabilities: $2,143,739
Net Worth: $9,753,283
Earnings: ($8,168,335)
Fiscal Year-end: 06/30/23
Metalworking Machines Mfr
N.A.I.C.S.: 333519
Hank Holland (Chm & CEO)

AMAG AUSTRIA METALL AG
Lamprechthausenerstrasse 61, PO
Box 3, A-5282, Ranshofen, Austria
Tel.: (43) 77228010
Web Site: https://www.amag-al4u.com
AMAG—(VIE)
Rev.: $1,863,484,783
Assets: $1,934,907,188
Liabilities: $1,168,326,139
Net Worth: $766,581,049
Earnings: $117,936,542
Emp.: 2,214
Fiscal Year-end: 12/31/22
Aluminum Semis & Casthouse Products Mfr
N.A.I.C.S.: 331318
Heinrich Schaller (Deputy Chm-Supervisory Bd)

Subsidiaries:

AMAG Asia Pacific Ltd. (1)
2F No 46 Sec 2 Zhongcheng Rd, Shilin
Dist, 11147, Taipei, Taiwan
Tel.: (886) 228368906
Aluminium Product Distr
N.A.I.C.S.: 423510
Matthias Ramsl (Mng Dir)

AMAG Benelux B. V. (1)
Galgkade 3 b, 3133 KN, Vlaardingen,
Netherlands   (100%)
Tel.: (31) 104604499
Web Site: http://www.amag.com
Sales Range: $50-74.9 Million
Emp.: 3
Industrial Supplies Whslr
N.A.I.C.S.: 423840

AMAG China Ltd. (1)
Suite 8419 4th Floor Building 1 Wu-Hua Rd
No 73, HongKou District, Shanghai,
200086, China
Tel.: (86) 13331850376
Aluminium Product Distr
N.A.I.C.S.: 423510
Charles Chen (Gen Mgr)

AMAG Deutschland GmbH (1)
Lustheide 85 II, 51427, Bergisch Gladbach,
Germany
Tel.: (49) 2204586540
Aluminium Product Distr
N.A.I.C.S.: 423510

AMAG France S.A.R.L. (1)
65 Rue Jean Jacques Rousseau, 92150,
Suresnes, France
Tel.: (33) 141448481

AMAG Austria Metall AG—(Continued)

Aluminium Product Distr
N.A.I.C.S.: 423510

AMAG Italia S.R.L. (1)
Via Pantano 2, 20122, Mailand, Italy
Tel.: (39) 0272001663
Aluminium Product Distr
N.A.I.C.S.: 423510

AMAG Metal GmbH (1)
Lamprechtshausener Strasse 61, 5282, Ranshofen, Austria (100%)
Tel.: (43) 77228013846
Web Site: https://www.amag.at
Sales Range: $25-49.9 Million
Alumina Refining
N.A.I.C.S.: 331313

AMAG Rolling Eastern Europe, s.r.o. (1)
Business Centrum Ocelarska 35/1354, 190 00, Prague, Czech Republic
Tel.: (420) 725002993
Aluminium Product Distr
N.A.I.C.S.: 423510
David Bicovsky (Mng Dir)

AMAG Rolling GmbH (1)
Postfach 32, Ranshofen, 5282, Austria (100%)
Tel.: (43) 77228012686
Web Site: https://www.amag.at
Sales Range: $600-649.9 Million
Emp.: 900
Other Aluminum Rolling & Drawing
N.A.I.C.S.: 331318
Georg Weger (Mng Dir)

AMAG Rolling Iberia S.L. (1)
Travessera de Gracia 30 6 B, 08021, Barcelona, Spain
Tel.: (34) 934183906
Aluminium Product Distr
N.A.I.C.S.: 423510
Vicenc Llario (Mng Dir)

AMAG Service GmbH (1)
Lambrechts Hauser Strasse 36, PO Box 39, Ranshofen, 5282, Austria (100%)
Tel.: (43) 77228010
Web Site: https://www.amag.at
Sales Range: $150-199.9 Million
Real Estate Agents & Brokers Offices
N.A.I.C.S.: 531210

AMAG UK Ltd. (1)
Beckley Lodge Leatherhead Road, Bookham, KT23 4RN, Surrey, United Kingdom
Tel.: (44) 1372450661
Aluminium Product Distr
N.A.I.C.S.: 423510

AMAG USA Corp. (1)
600 E Crescent Ave Ste 207, Upper Saddle River, NJ 07458-1827
Tel.: (201) 962-7105
Aluminium Product Distr
N.A.I.C.S.: 423510
Wynn Werner (Mng Dir)

AMAG components Deutschland GmbH (1)
Gewerbestrasse 12-14, 83236, Ubersee, Germany
Tel.: (49) 864259590
Fabricated Metal Product Mfr & Distr
N.A.I.C.S.: 332999

AMAG components Karlsruhe GmbH (1)
Erzbergerstrasse 115, 76133, Karlsruhe, Germany
Tel.: (49) 72197390
Fabricated Metal Product Mfr & Distr
N.A.I.C.S.: 332999

Aluminium Austria Metall Quebec Inc, (1)
1010 Sherbrooke Ouest 2414, Montreal, H3A 2R7, QC, Canada
Tel.: (514) 844-1079
Aluminium Product Distr
N.A.I.C.S.: 423510

coilDNA GmbH (1)
Strasserau 6, 4020, Linz, Austria
Tel.: (43) 6648105400
Information Technology Services

N.A.I.C.S.: 541511

AMAGASA CO., LTD.
1-16-5 Ueno, Taito-ku, Tokyo, 110-0005, Japan
Tel.: (81) 338710111
Web Site: https://www.amagasa-co.com
Year Founded: 1990
3070—(TKS)
Rev.: $6,515,710
Assets: $4,225,640
Liabilities: $3,424,470
Net Worth: $801,170
Earnings: ($4,225,640)
Emp.: 39
Fiscal Year-end: 01/31/24
Women's Shoe Retailer & Whslr
N.A.I.C.S.: 458210
Ryoichi Hayakawa (Pres)

AMAIZEINGLY GREEN PRODUCTS, L.P.
201 MacDonald Rd, Collingwood, L9Y 4J1, ON, Canada
Tel.: (705) 445-1140
Web Site: http://www.amaizeinglygreen.com
Sales Range: $10-24.9 Million
Emp.: 50
Starch Mfr
N.A.I.C.S.: 311221
Daryl Dorchak (CEO)

Subsidiaries:

Amaizeingly Green Value Products ULC (1)
2680 14th Avenue Unit 5, Markham, L3R 5B2, ON, Canada
Tel.: (905) 947-9444
Web Site: http://www.amaizeinglygreen.com
Natural Fertilizer Mfr
N.A.I.C.S.: 325311

AMAL LIMITED
Atul House 310 B Veer Savarkar Marg, Mumbai, 400 028, Maharashtra, India
Tel.: (91) 2262559700
Web Site: https://www.amal.co.in
Year Founded: 1974
506597—(BOM)
Rev.: $5,978,004
Assets: $13,670,366
Liabilities: $8,845,719
Net Worth: $4,824,647
Earnings: $151,433
Emp.: 50
Fiscal Year-end: 03/31/22
Chemical Products Mfr
N.A.I.C.S.: 325199
Ankit T. Mankodi (Chief Compliance Officer & Sec)

AMAL SAMHA CO.
PO Box 25220, Damascus, Syria
Tel.: (963) 0116330890
Web Site: http://www.samha.com
Year Founded: 1980
Sales Range: $10-24.9 Million
Emp.: 550
Knitwear Mfr
N.A.I.C.S.: 315250
Ahmad Samha (Gen Mgr)

AMALGAMATED ELECTRICITY CO., LTD.
G-1 Ground Floor Nirmal Nest Chsl, Vayu Devta Mandir Complex Borivali W, Mumbai, 400103, India
Tel.: (91) 2267476080
Web Site: https://www.aecl.net.in
Year Founded: 1936
501622—(BOM)
Rev.: $1,970
Assets: $127,848
Liabilities: $118,130

Net Worth: $9,718
Earnings: ($14,015)
Fiscal Year-end: 03/31/21
Electric Power Distr
N.A.I.C.S.: 221122
Shreekant Kudtarkar (Sec)

AMALGAMATED METAL CORPORATION PLC
55 Bishopsgate, London, EC2N 3AH, United Kingdom
Tel.: (44) 2076264521 UK
Web Site: http://www.amcgroup.com
Year Founded: 1929
Sales Range: $750-799.9 Million
Emp.: 150
Trades, Distributes & Manufactures Metals, Metal Products & Chemicals
N.A.I.C.S.: 551112
V. H. Sher (Chm)

Subsidiaries:

AMC Physical Trading Ltd (1)
55 Bishopsgate, London, EC2N3AH, United Kingdom (100%)
Tel.: (44) 2076264521
Web Site: http://www.amcphysical-trading.co.uk
Sales Range: $100-124.9 Million
Emp.: 90
Commodity Contracts Brokerage
N.A.I.C.S.: 523160
Adam Sussmes (Gen Counsel)

AMC Treasury Services Ltd (1)
55 Bishopsgate, London, EC2N 3AH, United Kingdom (100%)
Tel.: (44) 2076264521
Web Site: http://www.amcgroup.co.uk
Sales Range: $100-124.9 Million
Emp.: 90
Commodity Contracts Brokerage
N.A.I.C.S.: 522110

AMT Futures Limited (1)
55 Bishopsgate, London, EC2N 3AH, United Kingdom (100%)
Tel.: (44) 2076264521
Web Site: http://www.amtfutures.co.uk
Sales Range: $100-124.9 Million
Emp.: 140
Commodity Contracts Brokerage Services
N.A.I.C.S.: 523160
Julian Rigby (Mng Dir)

Amalgamated Metal (Australia) Ltd (1)
32 Industrial Avenue, Thomastown, 3074, VIC, Australia
Tel.: (61) 393595811
Web Site: http://www.cagroup.com.au
Emp.: 60
Holding Company
N.A.I.C.S.: 551112
Nick Hardpastle (Gen Mgr)

Amalgamated Metal Trading Ltd (1)
55 Bishopsgate, London, EC2N 3AH, United Kingdom (100%)
Tel.: (44) 2076264521
Web Site: http://www.emcgroup.com
Sales Range: $100-124.9 Million
Emp.: 120
Commodity Contracts Brokerage
N.A.I.C.S.: 523160
J. W. Land (Mng Dir)

Amalgamet (South East Asia) Pte Ltd (1)
100 Beach Road Unit 22-07 Shaw Tower, 22-07 Shaw Towers, Singapore, 189702, Singapore (100%)
Tel.: (65) 62942058
Web Site: http://www.amcphysical-trading.co.uk
Sales Range: $50-74.9 Million
Emp.: 4
Metal Service Centers & Offices
N.A.I.C.S.: 423510
Antony Ho (Mgr)

BKS Surveys Ltd (1)
Killeague House Unit 17 Sandel Village Ctr Knocklynn Rd, Coleraine, Coleraine, BT52 1WW, United Kingdom (100%)
Tel.: (44) 2870352311

Sales Range: $25-49.9 Million
Emp.: 25
Geophysical Surveying & Mapping Services
N.A.I.C.S.: 541360
H. Afnoot (Gen Mgr)

British Metal Corporation (India) Pte Ltd (1)
Apeejay Ho 1st Floor, Dinsha Wachha Rd Backbay Recla, 400020, Mumbai, MH, India
Tel.: (91) 2222872344
Web Site: http://www.hindujagroup.com
Sales Range: $50-74.9 Million
Emp.: 8
Metal Service Centers & Metal Merchant Whslr
N.A.I.C.S.: 423510

Brookside Metal Company Ltd (1)
Bilston Lane, Willenhall, WV13 2QE, West Midlands, United Kingdom (100%)
Tel.: (44) 1902365500
Web Site: http://www.brooksidemetal.com
Sales Range: $25-49.9 Million
Emp.: 65
Powder Metallurgy Part Mfr
N.A.I.C.S.: 332117
Neil Jackson (Mng Dir)

Consolidated Alloys (NZ) Ltd (1)
Penrose, PO Box 12-387, Auckland, New Zealand (100%)
Tel.: (64) 6496229100
Web Site: http://www.consolidatedalloys.co.nz
Sales Range: $25-49.9 Million
Emp.: 30
Building Material Dealers
N.A.I.C.S.: 444180
B. Mudford (Gen Mgr)

Consolidated Alloys Pty Ltd (1)
32 Industrial Ave, 3074, Thomastown, VIC, Australia (100%)
Tel.: (61) 393595811
Web Site: http://www.cagroup.com.au
Sales Range: $25-49.9 Million
Emp.: 75
Plate Work Mfr
N.A.I.C.S.: 332313
Nick Hardpastle (Mng Dir)

Debro Steel Ltd. (1)
7 Blair Drive, Brampton, L6T 2H4, ON, Canada (100%)
Tel.: (905) 457-5235
Web Site: http://www.debrosteel.com
Sales Range: $25-49.9 Million
Emp.: 90
Plate Work Mfr
N.A.I.C.S.: 332313

Escoy Holdings Bhd. (1)
Suite 402 4th Floor Penang Plaza, 126 Jalan Burma, 10050, Penang, Malaysia
Tel.: (60) 4 226 1173
Holding Company
N.A.I.C.S.: 551112
Dato N. Ariff (Mng Dir)

Keeling & Walker Ltd (1)
Whieldon Rd, Stoke-on-Trent, ST4 4JA, United Kingdom (100%)
Tel.: (44) 1782744136
Web Site: http://www.keelingwalker.co.uk
Sales Range: $25-49.9 Million
Emp.: 32
Electroplating Plating Polishing Anodizing & Coloring
N.A.I.C.S.: 332813
Dieter Guhl (Mng Dir)

Subsidiary (Non-US):

Thermox Zinnoxide GmbH (2)
Bredeneyer Strasse 2B, Essen, 45133, Germany
Tel.: (49) 201125960
Web Site: http://www.thermox.eu
Sales Range: $25-49.9 Million
Emp.: 1
Primary Copper Smelting & Refining
N.A.I.C.S.: 331410
Dieter Guhl (Mng Dir)

Mil-Ver Metal Company Ltd (1)
Coronel Avenue, Rowleys Green Industrial Estate, Coventry, CV6 6AP, United Kingdom (100%)
Tel.: (44) 2476667098

Web Site: http://www.milver.com
Sales Range: $50-74.9 Million
Emp.: 107
Non Ferrous Metal Mfr
N.A.I.C.S.: 331492
Steve Miles *(Mng Dir)*

Premetalco Inc. **(1)**
110 Belfield Rd, Rexdale, M9W 1G1, ON,
Canada
Tel.: (416) 245-7386
Sales Range: $250-299.9 Million
Holding Company
N.A.I.C.S.: 551112

Division (Domestic):

Amalgamet Canada **(2)**
60 Yonge St Suite 1001, Toronto, M5E 1H5,
ON, Canada **(100%)**
Tel.: (416) 366-3954
Web Site: http://www.amalgamet.com
Sales Range: $25-49.9 Million
Emp.: 6
Minerals, Metals, Chemicals & High Purity
Materials Marketer & Whslr
N.A.I.C.S.: 238990
Manfred Naujoks *(VP)*

Thailand Smelting & Refining Co
Ltd **(1)**
800 Moo Sakdidej Road Tambon Vichit,
Amphur Muang, 83000, Phuket,
Thailand **(75%)**
Tel.: (66) 76371111
Web Site: http://www.thaisarco.com
Sales Range: $100-124.9 Million
Primary Copper Smelting & Refining
N.A.I.C.S.: 331410
D. M. Spratt *(Gen Mgr)*

Thermox Performance Materials
Ltd. **(1)**
Whieldon Rd, Stoke-on-Trent, ST4 4JA,
United Kingdom
Tel.: (44) 178 274 4136
Web Site: http://www.keelingwalker.uk
Emp.: 26
Tin Oxide Mfr
N.A.I.C.S.: 325180
Dieter Guhl *(Mng Dir)*

William Rowland Ltd **(1)**
9-13 Meadow St, Sheffield, S37BL, United
Kingdom **(100%)**
Tel.: (44) 1142769421
Web Site: http://www.william-rowland.com
Sales Range: $25-49.9 Million
Emp.: 30
Steel Investment Foundries
N.A.I.C.S.: 331512

AMALGAMATED REGIONAL TRADING (ART) HOLDINGS LTD.

202 Seke Road, PO Box 2777,
Graniteside, Harare, Zimbabwe
Tel.: (263) 4770097
Web Site: https://www.artcorp.co.zw
Year Founded: 1997
ARTD—(ZIM)
Rev.: $737,834
Assets: $1,727,340
Liabilities: $756,665
Net Worth: $970,675
Earnings: $276,682
Emp.: 802
Fiscal Year-end: 09/30/19
Holding Company
N.A.I.C.S.: 551112
Milton Macheka *(CEO-Grp)*

Subsidiaries:

Art Corporation Limited - Kadoma
Paper Mills Division **(1)**
Owl Mine Road Industrial Sites, Kadoma,
Zimbabwe
Tel.: (263) 6822311
Web Site:
   http://www.kadomapapermills.co.zw
Emp.: 70
Sanitary Paper Mfr
N.A.I.C.S.: 322291

Chloride Zimbabwe (Private)
Limited **(1)**

2 Newcastle Road Workington, Harare,
Zimbabwe
Tel.: (263) 4621470
Web Site: http://www.chloride.co.zw
Battery Mfr & Distr
N.A.I.C.S.: 335910

Eversharp Ltd **(1)**
4 Kelvin Close Graniteside, Harare, Zimba-
bwe
Web Site: http://www.eversharp.co.zw
Emp.: 85
Pen Mfr & Distr
N.A.I.C.S.: 339940

AMALGAMATED SECURITY SERVICES LIMITED

Building 1 RK Komplex Pine Indus-
trial, Saint Michael, Barbados
Tel.: (246) 5372775
Web Site: http://www.asslbdos.com
Year Founded: 1983
Security Services
N.A.I.C.S.: 561621
Michael Aboud *(Chm)*

Subsidiaries:

Massy Security (Guyana) Inc. **(1)**
Lot 0 Ruimveldt, Georgetown, 101191, Guy-
ana
Tel.: (592) 225 5773
Web Site: http://massysecuritygy.com
Security Patrol Services
N.A.I.C.S.: 561612

AMALGAME

580 Grand Allee Est, Bureau 250,
Quebec, G1R 2K2, QC, Canada
Tel.: (418) 529-1414 **QC**
Web Site: http://www.amalgame.ca
Year Founded: 1986
Sales Range: $25-49.9 Million
Emp.: 24
Advertising Agencies, Graphic Design
N.A.I.C.S.: 541810
Robin Brisson *(VP-Creative Strategy)*

AMAN BUILDERS INC.

244 2301 Premier Way, Sherwood
Park, T8H 2K8, AB, Canada
Tel.: (780) 449-5825
Web Site:
   https://www.amanbuilders.ca
Year Founded: 1985
Construction Services
N.A.I.C.S.: 236210

AMAN COTTON FIBROUS LIM-ITED

2 Ishakha Avenue Sector 6, Uttara,
Dhaka, 1230, Bangladesh
Tel.: (880) 279116913
Web Site:
   https://www.amancotton.com
ACFL—(CHT)
Rev.: $20,077,851
Assets: $49,048,935
Liabilities: $17,317,580
Net Worth: $31,731,355
Earnings: ($868,447)
Emp.: 552
Fiscal Year-end: 06/30/23
Financial Consulting Services
N.A.I.C.S.: 541611
Shofiqul Islam *(Chm)*

AMAN FEED LTD.

2 Ishakha Avenue Sector 6 Uttara,
Dhaka, 1230, Bangladesh
Tel.: (880) 79116913
Web Site: https://www.amanfeed.com
AMANFEED—(CHT)
Rev.: $113,172,331
Assets: $86,636,796
Liabilities: $52,238,414
Net Worth: $34,398,382
Earnings: $264,042
Emp.: 568
Fiscal Year-end: 06/30/23

Seafood Mfr & Distr
N.A.I.C.S.: 311119
Rafiqul Islam *(Chm)*

AMANA AGRICULTURAL & INDUSTRIAL INVESTMENT CO.

41 Yathreb Complex - Wasfi Al- Tal
Str, PO Box 2805, Amman, 11953,
Jordan
Tel.: (962) 553 9100
Year Founded: 1995
Sales Range: Less than $1 Million
Emp.: 29
Olive Tree Cultivating Services
N.A.I.C.S.: 115112

AMANA COOPERATIVE IN-SURANCE COMPANY

Al Malaz Salah Adeen ST, PO Box
27986, Riyadh, 11427, Saudi Arabia
Tel.: (966) 114757700
Web Site: http://www.amana.sa
Year Founded: 2010
8310—(SAU)
Rev.: $49,235,488
Assets: $120,239,729
Liabilities: $44,856,138
Net Worth: $75,383,591
Earnings: $6,783,553
Emp.: 112
Fiscal Year-end: 12/31/23
Insurance Agency Services
N.A.I.C.S.: 524210
Mahmoud M. Al-Toukhi *(Chm)*

AMANA INC.

2-2-43 Higashishinagawa,
Shinagawa-ku, Tokyo, Japan
Tel.: (81) 337404011
Web Site: http://www.amana.jp
Year Founded: 1979
2402—(TKS)
Rev.: $171,800,640
Assets: $101,678,720
Liabilities: $98,048,720
Net Worth: $3,630,000
Earnings: $793,760
Emp.: 820
Fiscal Year-end: 12/31/21
Visual Content Design Services
N.A.I.C.S.: 541430
Hironobu Shindo *(CEO)*

Subsidiaries:

Amanacliq Shanghai Limited **(1)**
2F Block 1 359 Xietu Road, Huang Pu Dis-
trict, Shanghai, 200023, China
Tel.: (86) 215 302 6306
Web Site: https://www.amanacliq.com
Visual Communication Services
N.A.I.C.S.: 541430

WORKS ZEBRA CO., LTD. **(1)**
Kagurazaka Technos Bldg 2F 4 Tsukiji-
machi, Shinjuku-ku, Tokyo, 162-0818, Ja-
pan
Tel.: (81) 3 5206 1230
Graphic Design Services
N.A.I.C.S.: 541430

needsplus Inc. **(1)**
2F Yoko Building 4-8-6 Akasaka, Minato-ku,
Tokyo, 107-0052, Japan
Tel.: (81) 35 786 0808
Web Site: https://www.needsplus.jp
Dispatching Business Services
N.A.I.C.S.: 492110

AMANA TAKAFUL PLC

Tel.: (94) 117501000
Web Site: https://www.takaful.lk
ATL—(COL)
Rev.: $27,465,663
Assets: $42,300,228
Liabilities: $28,219,664
Net Worth: $14,080,564
Earnings: $1,623,142
Emp.: 407

Fiscal Year-end: 12/31/22
Insurance Services
N.A.I.C.S.: 524113
M. Farhan Jabir *(Head-Human Re-sources)*

Subsidiaries:

Amana Takaful (Maldives) Plc **(1)**
H Palmayrah Sosun Magu, Male, 20069,
Maldives
Tel.: (960) 3315262
Web Site: https://www.takaful.mv
Fire Insurance Services
N.A.I.C.S.: 524113
Tyeab Akbarally *(Chm)*

AMANAH HARTA TANAH PNB

Tingkat 4 Balai PNB 201-A Jalan Tun
Razak, 50400, Kuala Lumpur, Malay-
sia
Tel.: (60) 320505100 **MY**
Web Site: http://www.ahp.com.my
Year Founded: 1989
Rev.: $9,380,843
Assets: $111,264,634
Liabilities: $42,655,862
Net Worth: $68,608,772
Earnings: $3,110,889
Fiscal Year-end: 12/31/19
Real Estate Investment Trust Ser-
vices
N.A.I.C.S.: 531120
Hafidz Atrash Kosai Mohd Zihim
(CEO)

AMANAH LEASING PUBLIC COMPANY LIMITED

16-16 /1 Soi Kasemsan 1 Phayathai
Road Wangmai, Patumwan, Bang-
kok, 10330, Thailand
Tel.: (66) 20916456
Web Site: https://www.amanah.co.th
Year Founded: 1992
AMANAH—(THA)
Rev.: $28,174,055
Assets: $136,662,341
Liabilities: $82,787,076
Net Worth: $53,875,265
Earnings: $5,517,426
Fiscal Year-end: 12/31/23
Finance Services
N.A.I.C.S.: 523999
Nantaphol Pongspaibool *(Mng Dir)*

AMANAHRAYA REAL ESTATE INVESTMENT TRUST

Level 46 Vista Tower The Intermark
384 Jalan Tun Razak, 50400, Kuala
Lumpur, Malaysia
Tel.: (60) 323800606 **MY**
Web Site:
   https://www.amanahrayareit.com.my
Year Founded: 2006
ARREIT—(KLS)
Rev.: $16,477,291
Assets: $298,898,081
Liabilities: $143,175,718
Net Worth: $155,722,363
Earnings: $2,603,291
Emp.: 7
Fiscal Year-end: 12/31/22
Trust Management Services
N.A.I.C.S.: 523940
Ishak Ishak *(Head-Fin)*

AMANAT HOLDINGS PJSC

One Central The Offices 5 Level 1
Office 108, PO Box 121012, Dubai,
United Arab Emirates
Tel.: (971) 43309999
Web Site: https://www.amanat.com
AMANAT—(DFM)
Rev.: $195,518,681
Assets: $1,037,340,463
Liabilities: $269,754,959
Net Worth: $767,585,504
Earnings: ($11,933,947)

AMANAT HOLDINGS PJSC

Amanat Holdings PJSC—(Continued)

Emp.: 21
Fiscal Year-end: 12/31/23
Investment Services
N.A.I.C.S.: 523940
Hamad Abdulla Alshamsi *(Chm)*

AMANAYA VENTURES LIMITED

69 70 First Floor Deep Complex Court Road, Amritsar, 143001, India
Tel.: (91) 9876330890
Web Site: https://www.amanaya.in
Year Founded: 2009
543804—(BOM)
Rev.: $1,331,467
Assets: $602,254
Liabilities: $11,450
Net Worth: $590,804
Earnings: $9,364
Emp.: 6
Fiscal Year-end: 03/31/23
Precious Metal Distr
N.A.I.C.S.: 423940
Manan Mahajan *(CFO)*

AMANET MANAGEMENT & SYSTEMS LTD.

Berzel 34 Ramat Hayil, Tel Aviv, 6971050, Israel
Tel.: (972) 37659559
Web Site: https://www.amanet.co.il
Year Founded: 1970
AMAN—(TAE)
Rev.: $91,906,063
Assets: $47,586,959
Liabilities: $20,255,560
Net Worth: $27,331,399
Earnings: $1,690,841
Emp.: 1,300
Fiscal Year-end: 12/31/23
Offices of Other Holding Companies
N.A.I.C.S.: 551112
Avraham Josipovitch Asaf *(Co-Founder & Chm)*

Subsidiaries:

Conkor Systems Ltd.   **(1)**
Hi-Tech Park Kibutz Saar, PO Box 3047, Nahariyya, Israel
Tel.: (972) 4 952 3139
Web Site: https://conkor.co.il
Software Project Developing Services
N.A.I.C.S.: 541511

Tesnet Software Testing, Ltd.   **(1)**
Habarzel 32 Building A Floor 3, Tel Aviv, Israel
Tel.: (972) 3 765 9580
Web Site: https://tesnet-group.com
Emp.: 300
Software Testing Services
N.A.I.C.S.: 541511
Alina Shmunis *(Mgr-QA)*

AMANGELDY GAS LLP

12 A Bokeikhan Street, Yessil district, Nur-Sultan, 010000, Kazakhstan
Tel.: (7) 172552315
Web Site:
    http://www.amangeldygas.kz
Year Founded: 1975
Rev.: $23,730,668
Assets: $143,069,768
Liabilities: $25,961,827
Net Worth: $117,107,941
Earnings: $15,529,578
Fiscal Year-end: 12/31/19
Natural Gas Extraction Services
N.A.I.C.S.: 211130
Yerken Z. Kasseyev *(Gen Dir)*

AMANI GOLD LIMITED

2/7 Havelock Street, Milton, West Perth, 6005, WA, Australia
Tel.: (61) 893898033   AU
Web Site:
    https://www.amanigold.com

Year Founded: 2005
ANL—(ASX)
Rev.: $104,688
Assets: $17,351,447
Liabilities: $251,162
Net Worth: $17,100,285
Earnings: ($2,695,432)
Fiscal Year-end: 06/30/24
Gold Ore Mining
N.A.I.C.S.: 212220
Qiuming Yu *(Exec Dir)*

AMANO CORPORATION

275 Ozutocho, Kohoku-ku, Yokohama, 2228558, Kanagawa, Japan
Tel.: (81) 454011441
Web Site: https://www.amano.co.jp
Year Founded: 1931
6436—(TKS)
Rev.: $1,010,431,040
Assets: $1,220,106,850
Liabilities: $373,346,020
Net Worth: $846,760,830
Earnings: $86,862,010
Emp.: 5,335
Fiscal Year-end: 03/31/24
Time Recorder & Time Information Systems; Parking Systems; Environmental Systems & Cleaning Systems
N.A.I.C.S.: 334512
Izumi Nakajima *(Chm)*

Subsidiaries:

AMANO UK LTD. - Parking Division   **(1)**
8 Newhouse Business Centre Old Crawley Road, Horsham, RH12 4RU, West Sussex, United Kingdom
Tel.: (44) 7708169135
Web Site: http://www.amano-parking.co.uk
Parking Software System Development Services
N.A.I.C.S.: 541511

Accu-Tech Systems, Ltd.   **(1)**
C1 Caerphilly Business Park, Caerphilly, CF83 3ED, Mid Glamorgan, United Kingdom
Tel.: (44) 2920 885599
Web Site: http://www.accu-tech.co.uk
Emp.: 2
Biometric & Data Collection Terminal Equipment Mfr
N.A.I.C.S.: 334118
Bert Peirsman *(Gen Mgr)*

Accu-Time Systems, Inc.   **(1)**
20B International Dr, Windsor, CT 06095
Tel.: (860) 870-5000
Web Site: https://www.accu-time.com
Emp.: 60
Biometric Device Mfr
N.A.I.C.S.: 334118

Amano Agency Corp.   **(1)**
275 Mamedo, Kohoku, Yokohama, 2220032, Kanagawa, Japan
Tel.: (81) 454391534
Web Site: http://www.amano.co.jp
Vacuum Cleaner Mfr
N.A.I.C.S.: 335210

Amano Business Solutions Corp.   **(1)**
Amano Galaxy Building 7-3-24 Kikuna, Kohoku-Ku, Yokohama, 222-0011, Kanagawa, Japan
Tel.: (81) 454301950
Web Site: http://www.i-abs.co.jp
Internet Payroll Services
N.A.I.C.S.: 541214

Amano Cincinnati Canada, Inc.   **(1)**
2740 Matheson Boulevard East Unit 4, Mississauga, L4W 4X3, ON, Canada
Tel.: (905) 624-4085
Web Site: http://www.amanomcgann.com
Emp.: 4
Time Recorder & Biometric Device Mfr
N.A.I.C.S.: 334118

Amano Cincinnati, Inc.   **(1)**
140 Harrison Ave, Roseland, NJ 07068
Tel.: (973) 403-1900
Web Site: http://timeweb.amano.com

Sales Range: $25-49.9 Million
Emp.: 50
Development, Mfr & Sales of Time Recording, Time Information & Parking Equipment
N.A.I.C.S.: 334519
Michael John Lee *(Pres & CEO)*

Branch (Domestic):

ACI Cincinnati   **(2)**
130 Commerce Blvd, Loveland, OH 45140-7726
Tel.: (513) 697-9000
Web Site: http://www.aci.com
Sales Range: $25-49.9 Million
Mfr, Developer & Distributor of Time Recording Equipment
N.A.I.C.S.: 333248

Amano Cleantech Malaysia Sdn. Bhd.   **(1)**
No 12 Jalan Pengacara U 1/48 Temasya Industrial Park, 40150, Shah Alam, Selangor Darul Ehsan, Malaysia
Tel.: (60) 3 5569 5003
Web Site: http://www.amano.com.my
Sales Range: $25-49.9 Million
Emp.: 22
Sales & Service of General Purpose Dust Collectors, Large Scale Dust Collectors, Pneumatic Conveyance Equipment, Industrial Vacuum Cleaners, Floor Cleaning Equipment & Air Cleaning Equipment
N.A.I.C.S.: 238290
Osamu Otani *(Mng Dir)*

Amano Corporation   **(1)**
236-3 Nagatake, Midori Ward, Sagamihara, 252-0154, Kanagawa, Japan   **(100%)**
Tel.: (81) 427847441
Web Site: http://www.amano.co.jp
Sales Range: $50-74.9 Million
Emp.: 130
Mfr of Electronic Time Recording & Time Information Equipment, P.C.B. & Plastic Components
N.A.I.C.S.: 334519
Takeshi Akagi *(Mng Operating Officer)*

Amano Corporation   **(1)**
8123 Hosoecho Kiga, Kita Ward, Hamamatsu, 431-1305, Shizuoka, Japan   **(100%)**
Tel.: (81) 535220951
Web Site: http://www.amano.co.jp
Sales Range: $100-124.9 Million
Emp.: 280
Mfr of General Purpose Dust Collectors, Large-Scale Dust Collection Equipment, Industrial Vacuum Cleaners, Floor Cleaning Equipment & Air Cleaning Equipment
N.A.I.C.S.: 333413
Izumi Nakajima *(Chm)*

Amano Corporation   **(1)**
275 Somatocho, Kohoku-ku, Yokohama, 222-8558, Kanagawa, Japan
Tel.: (81) 454391507
Web Site: https://www.amano.co.jp
Emp.: 5,083
E-Timing Services
N.A.I.C.S.: 513210

Amano Corporation - HOSOE FACILITY   **(1)**
8123 Kiga Hosoe-cho, Kita-ku, Hamamatsu, 431-1305, Shizuoka, Japan
Tel.: (81) 535220901
Web Site: http://www.amano.co.jp
Sales Range: $100-124.9 Million
Emp.: 280
Cleaning Equipment Mfr
N.A.I.C.S.: 333310

Amano Corporation - MIYAKODA FACILITY   **(1)**
1-6-2 Shinmiyakoda, Kita-ku, Hamamatsu, 431-2103, Shizuoka, Japan
Tel.: (81) 534841051
Web Site: http://www.amano.co.jp
Sales Range: $25-49.9 Million
Emp.: 59
Metal Die Mfr
N.A.I.C.S.: 331523

Amano Corporation - TSUKUI FACILITY   **(1)**
236-3 Nagatake, Midori-ku, Sagamihara, 252-0154, Kanagawa, Japan
Tel.: (81) 427847441

Web Site: http://www.amano.co.jp
Sales Range: $25-49.9 Million
Emp.: 130
Electronic Time Recorder Mfr
N.A.I.C.S.: 334513

Amano Corporation-YOKOHAMA FACILITY   **(1)**
275 Mamedo, Kohoku, Yokohama, 222-8558, Kanagawa, Japan
Tel.: (81) 454011441
Web Site: http://www.amano.co.jp
Sales Range: $150-199.9 Million
Emp.: 3,000
Software Development Services
N.A.I.C.S.: 541511

Amano Electronics Europe, N.V.   **(1)**
   (100%)
Tel.: (32) 89323920
Sales Range: $25-49.9 Million
Emp.: 25
Development, Manufacture & Sales of Time Recording, Time Information & Parking Equipment; Sales of Floor Cleaning Equipment & Chemicals
N.A.I.C.S.: 334519
Yamaga Hideharue *(Pres)*

Amano Europe Holdings N.V.   **(1)**
Westerring 2, 3600, Genk, Belgium
Tel.: (32) 89323920
Emp.: 3
Investment Management Service
N.A.I.C.S.: 523940
Bert Peirsman *(Gen Mgr)*

Amano International Trading (Shanghai) Co., Ltd.   **(1)**
Room No 901 Zhongdian Mansion No 1029 Nanquan Road N, Pudong, Shanghai, 200122, China   **(100%)**
Tel.: (86) 2158790030
Web Site: http://www.amano.com.cn
Sales Range: $25-49.9 Million
Emp.: 25
Sales of Time Recording, Time Information, Parking, Floor Cleaning, Environmental & Aqua Equipment
N.A.I.C.S.: 423420

Amano Korea Corporation   **(1)**
Rm 407 Woolim e-Biz Center 43 Yangsanro, Yeongdeungpo-gu, Seoul, 07270, Korea (South)   **(100%)**
Tel.: (82) 221649900
Web Site: https://www.amano.co.kr
Sales Range: $25-49.9 Million
Emp.: 25
Sales of Time Recording, Time Information, Parking, Floor Cleaning & Environmental Equipment
N.A.I.C.S.: 423420

Amano Maintenance Engineering Corp.   **(1)**
Amano 2nd Galaxy Building 4F 7-3-22 Kikuna, Kohoku-Ku, Yokohama, 222-8565, Kanagawa, Japan
Tel.: (81) 454301966
Web Site: https://www.amano-ame.co.jp
Sales Range: $25-49.9 Million
Emp.: 35
Environmental & Parking System Engineering Services
N.A.I.C.S.: 541330

Amano Malaysia Sdn.Bhd.   **(1)**
No 12 Jalan Pengacara U1/48 Temasya Industrial Park, 40150, Shah Alam, Selangor, Malaysia
Tel.: (60) 355695003
Web Site: https://www.amano.com.my
Sales Range: $25-49.9 Million
Emp.: 40
Time Management & Car Parking Control System Mfr
N.A.I.C.S.: 334513

Amano Management Service Corp.   **(1)**
Amano Daini Galaxy Building 7-3-22 Kikuna, Kohoku-Ku, Yokohama, 222-0011, Kanagawa, Japan
Tel.: (81) 454331945
Web Site: https://www.ams-amano.co.jp
Emp.: 400
Parking & Cleaning Business Management Services

N.A.I.C.S.: 541618

Amano McGann Canada Inc. (1)
4123 Belgreen Drive Unit 1, Ottawa, K1G
3N2, ON, Canada
Tel.: (613) 738-8047
Web Site: http://www.amanomcgann.ca
Emp.: 12
Parking Security Equipment Mfr
N.A.I.C.S.: 333310

Amano McGann, Inc. (1)
2699 Patton Rd, Roseville, MN 55113
Tel.: (612) 331-2020
Web Site: http://www.amanomcgann.com
Sales Range: $25-49.9 Million
Emp.: 70
Designer & Developer of Custom Application
Software for the Parking Industry
N.A.I.C.S.: 541512

Branch (Domestic):

Amano McGann (2)
8312 Page Ave, Saint Louis, MO
63130-1043 (100%)
Tel.: (314) 426-7727
Web Site: http://www.amanomcgann.com
Sales Range: $25-49.9 Million
Emp.: 9
Time Clocks & Parking Equipment Distr
N.A.I.C.S.: 459999

**Amano Musashi Electric
Corporation** (1)
4-10-3 Yahei, Kawaguchi, 332-0002, Sai-
tama, Japan
Tel.: (81) 482237722
Web Site: http://www.amano.co.jp
Electric Polisher Mfr
N.A.I.C.S.: 335210

Amano Parking Service Ltd. (1)
Unit 1 16/F Wealthy Plaza 138 Shau Kei
Wan Road, Hong Kong, China (Hong Kong)
Tel.: (852) 39967780
Parking Lot Management Services
N.A.I.C.S.: 812930

**Amano Secure Japan
Corporation** (1)
7-3-24 Kikuna, Kohoku-ku, Yokohama, 222-
0011, Kanagawa, Japan
Tel.: (81) 454301955
Web Site: http://www.e-timing.ne.jp
Time Stamp Services
N.A.I.C.S.: 561990

**Amano Software Engineering (Shang-
hai) Co., Ltd.** (1)
14F New Century Commercial Building 1111
Pudong South Road, Pudong New Area,
Shanghai, China (100%)
Tel.: (86) 2158365533
Web Site: http://www.ase.com.cn
Sales Range: $25-49.9 Million
Emp.: 60
Supplier of Computer Software
N.A.I.C.S.: 449210

**Amano Thai International Co.,
Ltd.** (1)
Room No 3A 3 rd Fl Chai-Ho Wong Wai Wit
Building 889 Moo 5, Srinakarin Road T
Samrong-Nua A Muang, Samut Prakan,
10270, Thailand
Tel.: (66) 274588123
Web Site: http://www.amanothai.co.th
Parking Lot Management Services
N.A.I.C.S.: 812930

**Amano Time & Air Singapore Pte.
Ltd.** (1)
Blk 213 Henderson Road 04-06/07 Hender-
son Industrial Park, Singapore, 159553,
Singapore (100%)
Tel.: (65) 62752885
Web Site: https://www.amano.com.sg
Sales Range: $25-49.9 Million
Emp.: 25
Sales of Time Recording, Time Information,
Parking, Floor Cleaning, Environmental &
Aqua Equipment
N.A.I.C.S.: 423420
Osamu Otami (Mng Dir)

**Amano Time & Ecology De Mexico
S.A.De C.V.** (1)
Av Guanajuato 115 Local 2 Jardines del
Moral, 37160, Leon, Guanajuato, Mexico

Tel.: (52) 4776882401
Web Site: https://www.amano-mx.com
Environmental Equipment Distr
N.A.I.C.S.: 423830

**Amano Time & Parking Spain,
S.A.** (1)
C/ Plomo n 5 - 7 Planta 2 - Oficina 2,
08038, Barcelona, Spain
Tel.: (34) 932237910
Parking Time Control Equipment Mfr
N.A.I.C.S.: 334513

Amano Vietnam Co., Ltd. (1)
20 Nguyen Dang Giai Street, Thao Dien
Ward Thu Duc City, Ho Chi Minh City, Viet-
nam
Tel.: (84) 2836366552
Web Site: http://www.amanovietnam.com.vn
Dust Collector & Vacuum Cleaner Product
Mfr & Distr
N.A.I.C.S.: 333413

**Environmental Technology
Company** (1)
1-6-2 Shintoda, Kita-Ku, Hamamatsu, 431-
2103, Shizuoka, Japan
Tel.: (81) 534841475
Web Site: https://www.eiseiken.co.jp
Emp.: 1
Environmental Consulting Services
N.A.I.C.S.: 541620

Horoquartz S.A. (1)
23 Avenue Carnot Immeuble Iliade - Bati-
ment A, 91300, Massy, France
Tel.: (33) 251531300
Web Site: http://www.horoquartz.fr
Sales Range: $75-99.9 Million
Emp.: 540
Electronic Temptation Software Develop-
ment Services
N.A.I.C.S.: 541511
Jean-Francois Bienvenu (Dir-Publication &
Gen Mgr)

P.T. Amano Indonesia (1)
Gedung Pusat Perfilman H Usmar Ismail
Lantai 3, Jl H R Rasuna Said Kav C-22,
Jakarta, 12940, Indonesia (100%)
Tel.: (62) 215278832
Web Site: https://www.amano.co.id
Sales Range: $25-49.9 Million
Emp.: 15
Sales & Service of Time Recording, Time
Information, Industrial Dust Collecting &
Pneumatic Conveyance Equipment
N.A.I.C.S.: 423420

Pioneer Eclipse Corporation (1)
1 Eclipse Rd, Sparta, NC 28675-0909
Tel.: (336) 372-8080
Web Site: https://pioneereclipse.com
Sales Range: $25-49.9 Million
Emp.: 136
Development, Manufacture & Sales of Floor
Cleaning Chemicals & Equipment for the
Industrial & Institutional Markets; Develops
High Speed, High Tech Floor Maintenance
Systems
N.A.I.C.S.: 325612
Jacqueline Van Delft (VP-Ops & Sls-Intl)

Subsidiary (Domestic):

Amano Business Credit (2)
1865 NE Dixie Hwy, Jensen Beach, FL
34957 (100%)
Tel.: (772) 283-9664
Web Site: http://www.amano-credit.com
Sales Range: $25-49.9 Million
Emp.: 10
Floor Cleaning Equipment Leasing
N.A.I.C.S.: 339940

Scopus-Omnibadges S.A.S. (1)
39 rue Louveau, Chatillon, 92320, France
Tel.: (33) 1 46 54 15 13
Web Site: http://www.omnibadges.com
Sales Range: $25-49.9 Million
Emp.: 40
Smartcard Mfr
N.A.I.C.S.: 326199
Alain Pomey (Pres)

AMANTA RESOURCES LTD.
1500 - 1040 West Georgia Street,
Vancouver, V6E 4H1, BC, Canada
Tel.: (604) 803-1769

AMH—(TSXV)
Sales Range: Less than $1 Million
Mineral Exploration Services
N.A.I.C.S.: 213114
Gerald D. Wright (Pres & CEO)

Subsidiaries:

Amanta Lao Co., Ltd. (1)
Unit 01/005 Luang Prabang Road Ban Si-
hom, PO box 5766, Chanthaboury District,
Vientiane, Lao People's Democratic Repub-
lic
Tel.: (856) 21 250 108
Mineral Exploration Services
N.A.I.C.S.: 212390

**AMAR FINANCE & LEASING
COMPANY (K.S.C.C.)**
Ahmed AlJaber Street AlBdour Tower,
PO Box 28776, Sharq Safat, 13148,
Kuwait, 13148, Kuwait
Tel.: (965) 1826050
Web Site:
https://www.amarfinance.com
Year Founded: 2004
AMAR—(KUW)
Rev.: $1,346,973
Assets: $71,967,906
Liabilities: $4,635,045
Net Worth: $67,332,861
Earnings: ($773,688)
Emp.: 20
Fiscal Year-end: 12/31/22
Real Estate Investment Services
N.A.I.C.S.: 523999
Hamad Mohamed Al-Saad (CEO)

AMARA HOLDINGS LTD.
100 Tras Street 06-01 100 AM, Sin-
gapore, 079027, Singapore
Tel.: (65) 68792515
Web Site:
https://www.amaraholdings.com
Year Founded: 1930
A34—(SES)
Rev.: $69,467,428
Assets: $583,841,529
Liabilities: $294,157,499
Net Worth: $289,684,030
Earnings: $4,784,158
Emp.: 441
Fiscal Year-end: 12/31/22
Investment Services
N.A.I.C.S.: 523999
Albert Hock Chuan Teo (CEO)

Subsidiaries:

**Amara Hospitality (Thailand) Co.,
Ltd.** (1)
180/1 Surawong Road Sipraya, Bangrak,
Bangkok, 10500, Thailand
Tel.: (66) 20218806
Hotel & Resort Services
N.A.I.C.S.: 721110

Amara Hotel Properties Pte Ltd (1)
100 Tras Street 06-01 100 AM, Singapore,
079027, Singapore
Tel.: (65) 68792515
Web Site: http://www.amarahotels.com
Home Management Services
N.A.I.C.S.: 721110

**Amara International Hotels & Resorts
Pte Ltd** (1)
100 Tras Street 100 AM 06-01, Singapore,
079027, Singapore
Tel.: (65) 68792515
Hotel & Resort Services
N.A.I.C.S.: 721110
Jim Khoo (VP-Ops)

**Amara Sentosa Investments Pte
Ltd** (1)
Amara Corporate Tower 06-01 100 Tras
Street, Singapore, 79027, Singapore
Tel.: (65) 62248866
Web Site: http://www.amaraholdings.com
Home Management Services
N.A.I.C.S.: 721110

Amarathai Restaurant Pte Ltd (1)
165 Tanjong Pagar Road Amara
Hotel/shopping Centre 01-06, Singapore,
088539, Singapore
Tel.: (65) 62224688
Emp.: 11
Restaurant Operators Services
N.A.I.C.S.: 722511
Lewis Chin (Mgr-Ops)

Creative Investments Pte Ltd (1)
Amara Hotel 05-03 165 Tanjong Pagar Rd,
Singapore, Singapore
Tel.: (65) 62248866
Property Development Services
N.A.I.C.S.: 531311

**Silk Road Restaurants International
Pte Ltd** (1)
100 Tras Street 06-01 Amara Corporate
Tower, Singapore, 79027, Singapore
Tel.: (65) 68792515
Web Site:
http://www.silkroadrestaurants.com
Emp.: 20
Hotel Investment & Management Services
N.A.I.C.S.: 721110

TTH Development Pte Ltd (1)
100 Tras Street L 06-01 100 AM, Singa-
pore, 79027, Singapore
Tel.: (65) 68792515
Emp.: 30
Property Development Services
N.A.I.C.S.: 531311

**Thanying Restaurant Singapore Pte.
Ltd.** (1)
165 Tanjong Pagar Road Amara Singapore
Level 2, Singapore, 088539, Singapore
Tel.: (65) 62224688
Web Site:
https://www.thanyingrestaurants.com
Hotel & Resort Services
N.A.I.C.S.: 721110
Erica Aurelio (Officer-Guest Rels)

**AMARA RAJA ENERGY & MO-
BILITY LIMITED**
Terminal A 1-18/1/AMR/NR Nana-
kramguda, Gachibowli, Hyderabad,
500032, India
Tel.: (91) 4023139000
Web Site: https://www.amaron.com
500008—(BOM)
Rev.: $1,197,805,245
Assets: $870,337,650
Liabilities: $248,924,130
Net Worth: $621,413,520
Earnings: $69,965,805
Emp.: 7,615
Fiscal Year-end: 03/31/22
Electronic Components Industry
N.A.I.C.S.: 335999
Jayadev Galla (Vice Chm & Mng Dir)

Subsidiaries:

**Amara Raja Power Systems
Limited** (1)
1-18/1/AMR/NR, Nanakramguda Gachi-
bowli, Hyderabad, 500032, India
Tel.: (91) 4023139000
Web Site: https://www.amararaja.com
Sales Range: $800-899,9 Million
Emp.: 3,000
Design & Development of Power Electronic
Products, Integration & Testing & Magnetics
Mfr
N.A.I.C.S.: 335313

Amaron Batteries (P) Ltd. (1)
Jail Rd, Gurgaon, 122001, Haryana, India
Tel.: (91) 1242311410
Sales Range: $25-49.9 Million
Emp.: 20
Batteries Mfr
N.A.I.C.S.: 335910
S.C Yadav (Branch Mgr)

Galla Foods Ltd. (1)
Riaz Garden-6th Floor 12 Kodambakkam
High Road, Chennai, 600 034, Tamil Nadu,
India
Tel.: (91) 4442910700
Web Site: https://gallafoods.com

Amara Raja Energy & Mobility
Limited—(Continued)

Sales Range: $25-49.9 Million
Emp.: 100
Food Processing & Export Services
N.A.I.C.S.: 311423

Mangal Precision Products Limited -
Works 1　　　　　　　　　　(1)
Karakambadi, 517520, Tirupati, Andhra
Pradesh, India
Tel.: (91) 877 2285561
Sales Range: $1-4.9 Billion
Automobile Components & Fasteners Mfr
N.A.I.C.S.: 332613

AMARIN CORPORATION PLC

88 Harcourt Street, Grand Canal
Docklands, Dublin, 2, Ireland
Tel.: (353) 16699020　　　　　UK
Web Site:
　　https://www.amarincorp.com
Year Founded: 1999
AMRN—(NASDAQ)
Rev.: $369,193,000
Assets: $886,179,000
Liabilities: $290,846,000
Net Worth: $595,333,000
Earnings: ($105,803,000)
Emp.: 365
Fiscal Year-end: 12/31/22
Pharmaceutical Researcher, Devel-
oper & Mfr
N.A.I.C.S.: 325412
Steven B. Ketchum (Chief Scientific
Officer, Pres-R&D & Sr VP)

Subsidiaries:

Amarin Pharma, Inc.　　　　　　(1)
1430 Route 206, Bedminster, NJ 07921
Tel.: (908) 719-1315
Pharmaceutical Products Distr
N.A.I.C.S.: 424210
Steve Ketchum (Pres-R&D & Sr VP)

AMARIN PRINTING & PUBLISHING PUBLIC COMPANY LIMITED

378 Chaiyaphruk Road Taling Chan,
Bangkok, 10170, Thailand
Tel.: (66) 24229999
Web Site: https://www.amarin.co.th
AMARIN—(THA)
Rev.: $125,199,282
Assets: $174,097,275
Liabilities: $36,433,862
Net Worth: $137,663,413
Earnings: $8,480,116
Emp.: 2,255
Fiscal Year-end: 12/31/23
Printing, Publishing & Television
Broadcasting Services
N.A.I.C.S.: 323111
Metta Utakapan (Chm & Pres)

Subsidiaries:

Amarin Book Center Company
Limited　　　　　　　　　　(1)
108 Village No 2 Bang Kruai-Chong Tanom
Road, Maha Sawat Subdistrict Bang Kruai
District, Nonthaburi, 11130, Thailand
Tel.: (66) 24229999
Web Site: https://amarinbooks.com
Television Broadcasting Services
N.A.I.C.S.: 516120
Nitima Luangaroonuthai (Mgr-Mktg &
Branding)

Amarin Television Company
Limited　　　　　　　　　　(1)
7/9-18 Arun Amarin Rd, Bangkok Noi,
Bangkok, 10700, Thailand
Tel.: (66) 24229191
Television Broadcasting Services
N.A.I.C.S.: 516120

AMARJOTHI SPINNING MILLS LTD

157 Kumaran Road, Tirupur, 641
601, Tamil Nadu, India

Tel.: (91) 4214311600
Web Site: https://www.amarjothi.net
521097—(BOM)
Rev.: $35,384,813
Assets: $40,443,872
Liabilities: $17,023,393
Net Worth: $23,420,479
Earnings: $3,028,143
Emp.: 341
Fiscal Year-end: 03/31/22
Cotton Yarn Mfr & Distr
N.A.I.C.S.: 313110
N. Rajan (Chm)

Subsidiaries:

Amarjothi Spinning Mills Ltd - Amar-
jothi Dyeing Division　　　　　(1)
Plot No E7-E9 & G11-G13 Sipcot Industrial
Growth Centre, Perundurai, Erode, 638
052, India
Tel.: (91) 4294 234114
Spinning Yarn Mfr
N.A.I.C.S.: 313110

AMARNATH SECURITIES LIMITED

1/104 Sarthak Nr Swastik Cross
Road Opp City Center, Navrangpura,
Ahmedabad, 380 009, India
Tel.: (91) 7768070196
Web Site:
　　https://www.amarnathsecurities.co.in
Year Founded: 1994
538465—(BOM)
Rev.: $33,329
Assets: $620,970
Liabilities: $79,062
Net Worth: $541,907
Earnings: $8,817
Fiscal Year-end: 03/31/22
Financial Services
N.A.I.C.S.: 523999
Aparna Akadkar (Compliance Officer
& Sec)

AMAROQ MINERALS LTD.

3400 1 First Canadian Place, PO Box
130, Toronto, M5X 1A4, ON, Canada
Tel.: (416) 587-9801
Web Site:
　　https://www.amaroqminerals.com
Year Founded: 2017
AMRQ—(LSE)
Rev.: $807,641
Assets: $80,762,050
Liabilities: $32,224,229
Net Worth: $48,537,821
Earnings: ($629,399)
Fiscal Year-end: 12/31/23
Gold Exploration & Mining Services
N.A.I.C.S.: 212220

AMARU, INC.

62 Ubi Road 1 06-14 Oxley Bizhub,
Singapore, 408730, Singapore
Tel.: (65) 63329287　　　　　NV
Web Site: https://www.amaruinc.com
AMRU—(OTCEM)
Sales Range: Less than $1 Million
Media Entertainment Services
N.A.I.C.S.: 541840
Sakae Torisawa (Chm)

Subsidiaries:

M2B World Asia Pacific Pte. Ltd. (1)
62 Cecil Street TPI Building 06-00, Singa-
pore, 049710, Singapore
Tel.: (65) 633 29123
Web Site: http://www.m2bworld.com
Broadband Entertainment Services
N.A.I.C.S.: 518210
Mike Ang Teck Hoe (Mgr-Fin)

M2B World Pte. Ltd.　　　　　(1)
35 Tai Seng Street 01-01 Tata Communications Exchange, Singapore, 534103, Singapore
Tel.: (65) 63093055
Broadband Media Entertainment Services

N.A.I.C.S.: 516120

AMASSE CAPITAL HOLDINGS LTD.

Room 1201 Prosperous Building
48-52 Des Voeux Road Central,
Hong Kong, China (Hong Kong)
Tel.: (852) 21109101　　　　　KY
Web Site: http://www.amasse.com.hk
8168—(HKG)
Rev.: $2,089,089
Assets: $6,419,593
Liabilities: $573,703
Net Worth: $5,845,890
Earnings: $725,255
Emp.: 16
Fiscal Year-end: 09/30/20
Financial Advisory Services
N.A.I.C.S.: 523940

AMASTEN FASTIGHETS AB

Master Samuelsgatan 42, SE-111 57,
Stockholm, Sweden
Tel.: (46) 20210575
Web Site: https://www.neobo.se
Year Founded: 1999
AMAST—(OMX)
Rev.: $71,957,614
Assets: $1,483,901,933
Liabilities: $850,006,416
Net Worth: $633,895,517
Earnings: $70,038,517
Emp.: 114
Fiscal Year-end: 12/31/20
Real Estate Services
N.A.I.C.S.: 531390
Jan-Erik Hojvall (Chm & CEO)

Subsidiaries:

Cell Impact AB　　　　　　　(1)
Platvagen 18, 691 50, Karlskoga, Sweden
Tel.: (46) 5 865 7450
Web Site: http://www.cellimpact.com
Rev.: $3,578,043
Assets: $29,650,180
Liabilities: $5,003,693
Net Worth: $24,646,487
Earnings: ($5,403,017)
Emp.: 36
Fiscal Year-end: 12/31/2020
Flow Field Plates Mfr
N.A.I.C.S.: 332999
Par Teike (CEO)

Exergy Fuel Cells S.r.l.　　　　(1)
Via Buozzi 53-55-57 I, Cadriano, 40057,
Bologna, Italy
Tel.: (39) 0516751129
Sales Range: $75-99.9 Million
Fuel Cell Research & Mfr
N.A.I.C.S.: 221118

Helbio S.A.　　　　　　　　(1)
10 Old National Rd Patron-Athinon, Rio,
26500, Patras, Greece　　　(100%)
Tel.: (30) 261 091 1538
Web Site: https://helbio.com
Sales Range: $75-99.9 Million
Hydrogen Fuel Production
N.A.I.C.S.: 221118
Xenophon E. Verykios (Mng Dir)

AMATA CORPORATION PUBLIC COMPANY LIMITED

2126 Kromadit Building New Petch-
buri Road Bangkapi, Huay Kwang,
Bangkok, 10310, Thailand
Tel.: (66) 27920000
Web Site: https://www.amata.com
Year Founded: 1989
AMATA—(THA)
Rev.: $283,127,449
Assets: $1,681,109,733
Liabilities: $930,085,095
Net Worth: $751,024,638
Earnings: $71,845,633
Emp.: 301
Fiscal Year-end: 12/31/23
Industrial Estate Developer & Man-
ager

N.A.I.C.S.: 236210
Viboon Kromadit (CMO & Member-
Exec Bd)

Subsidiaries:

Amata (Vietnam) Joint Stock
Company　　　　　　　　　(1)
Long Binh Ward, Bien Hoa, Dong Nai, Viet-
nam
Tel.: (84) 613991007
Industrial Park Development Services
N.A.I.C.S.: 236210

Amata Asia Limited　　　　　(1)
21st Floor Edinburgh Tower The Landmark
15 Queen's Road, Central, China (Hong
Kong)
Tel.: (852) 27920000
Industrial Estate Development Services
N.A.I.C.S.: 531390
Somhatai Panichewa (Chm)

Amata B. Grimm Power 1
Limited　　　　　　　　　　(1)
Amata Nakorn Industrial Estate, 700-371
Moo 6 Nongmaidaeng, Ampur Muang,
20000, Chon Buri, Thailand
Tel.: (66) 3821 3317
Web Site: http://www.amatapower.com
Sales Range: $50-74.9 Million
Emp.: 35
Electric Power Generation
N.A.I.C.S.: 221118

Amata City Co. Ltd.　　　　　(1)
700 Bangna-Trad Highway Km 57, A
Muang, Chon Buri, 20000,
Thailand　　　　　　　　(83.67%)
Tel.: (66) 38939007
Web Site: http://www.amata.com
Other Activities Related to Real Estate
N.A.I.C.S.: 531390
Aukkares Choochouy (Mgr)

Amata City Halong Joint Stock
Company　　　　　　　　　(1)
Song Khoai Industrial Park, Song Khoai
Commune, Quang Yen, Quang Ninh, Viet-
nam
Tel.: (84) 2033567007
Industrial Estate Development Services
N.A.I.C.S.: 531390
Nguyen Nhan (Gen Dir)

Amata City Rayong Co., Ltd.　　(1)
2126 Kromadit Building New Petchburi
Road, Huaykwang, Bangkok, 10310, Thai-
land
Tel.: (66) 27920000
Industrial Estate Development Services
N.A.I.C.S.: 531390
Chackchai Panichapat (Vice Chm)

Amata Facility Service Co. Ltd.　(1)
Amata Nakorn Industrial Estate, 700-2 Moo
1 Klongtamru Muang, 20000, Chon Buri,
Thailand　　　　　　　　　(91%)
Tel.: (66) 382150079
Web Site: http://www.amata.com
Sales Range: $25-49.9 Million
Emp.: 28
Other Management Consulting Services
N.A.I.C.S.: 541618
Aukkares Choochouy (Mng Dir)

Amata Global Pte. Ltd.　　　　(1)
25 Nort Bridge Road Level 7, Singapore,
179104, Singapore
Tel.: (65) 848830007
Industrial Estate Development Services
N.A.I.C.S.: 531390

Amata KWEG Education Co.,
Ltd.　　　　　　　　　　　(1)
Amata City Chonburi 700/4 Moo 1, Klong
Tam Ru Sub-district Muang District, Chon
Buri, 20000, Thailand
Tel.: (66) 38111007
Educational Support Services
N.A.I.C.S.: 611710
Stephen See (Gen Mgr)

Amata Natural Gas Distribution Co.
Ltd.　　　　　　　　　　　(1)
Amata Nakorn Industrial Estate 700/2 Moo
1 Bangna, Trad Rd Klong Tumru, 20000,
Chon Buri, Thailand　　　　(10%)
Tel.: (66) 38458601
Natural Gas Distribution

N.A.I.C.S.: 221210

Amata Summit Ready Built Co.
Ltd.   **(1)**
Amata City Chonburi 700 Bangna-Trad
Highway Km 57, A Muang, 20000, Chon
Buri, Thailand   **(49%)**
Tel.: (66) 38939007
Web Site: http://www.amatasummit.com
Sales Range: $50-74.9 Million
Emp.: 60
Other Construction Material Whslr
N.A.I.C.S.: 423390
Janjira Yamyim (Gen Mgr)

Amata VN PCL   **(1)**
2126 New Petchaburi road, Bangkapi Huay
Kwang, Bangkok, 10310, Thailand
Tel.: (66) 27920000
Web Site: https://amatavn.com
Rev.: $125,151,210
Assets: $386,401,297
Liabilities: $208,579,651
Net Worth: $177,821,646
Earnings: $12,403,709
Emp.: 166
Fiscal Year-end: 12/31/2023
Real Estate Manangement Services
N.A.I.C.S.: 531390
Yasuo Tsutsui (Head-Sales)

Amata Water Co. Ltd.   **(1)**
700/2 Moo 1 2nd Floor Amata Service Cen-
ter Building, Klong Tumru Amphur Muang,
20000, Chon Buri, Thailand   **(100%)**
Tel.: (66) 38939007
Web Site: http://www.amatawater.com
Production & Sale of Water Products for
Industrial Use
N.A.I.C.S.: 562219

Yangon Amata Smart & ECO City
Limited   **(1)**
708 7th Floor Hledan Center Corner of
Pyay and Hledan Road, Kamayut Township,
Yangon, Myanmar
Tel.: (95) 12305627
Industrial Estate Development Services
N.A.I.C.S.: 531390
Yasuo Tsutsui (Mng Dir)

AMATA SUMMIT GROWTH FREEHOLD & LEASEHOLD REAL ESTATE INVESTMENT TRUST

2126 Kromadit Building New Petch-
buri Road, Bangkapi Huay Kwang,
Bangkok, 10310, Thailand
Tel.: (66) 27920089
Web Site: https://www.amatareit.com
AMATAR—(THA)
Rev.: $10,891,438
Assets: $135,181,686
Liabilities: $32,335,977
Net Worth: $102,845,709
Earnings: $7,551,861
Fiscal Year-end: 12/31/23
Real Estate Investment Trust Ser-
vices
N.A.I.C.S.: 523991
Karntima Charoenchaiprasert (Mng
Dir)

AMATECH AG

Rossbergweg 2, Pfronten, 87459,
Germany
Tel.: (49) 836391050
Radio Frequency Identification Equip-
ment Mfr & Distr
N.A.I.C.S.: 334419

AMATEI INCORPORATED

9 Nishitakasu-cho, Amagasaki, 660-
0845, Hyogo, Japan
Tel.: (81) 664111236
Web Site: https://www.amatei.co.jp
Year Founded: 1949
5952—(TKS)
Rev.: $36,573,130
Assets: $35,409,770
Liabilities: $26,340,850
Net Worth: $9,068,920
Earnings: $879,130

Emp.: 159
Fiscal Year-end: 03/31/24
Nails Mfr & Distr
N.A.I.C.S.: 332618
Ryo Sato (Pres & CEO)

AMATHEON AGRI HOLDING N.V.

Friedrichstrasse 95, 10117, Berlin,
Germany
Tel.: (49) 30530009000
Web Site: https://www.amatheon-
agri.com
MLAAH—(EUR)
Rev.: $12,954,330
Assets: $89,716,465
Liabilities: $34,593,925
Net Worth: $55,122,540
Earnings: ($13,504,489)
Fiscal Year-end: 12/31/22
Holding Company; Farming
N.A.I.C.S.: 551112
Carl Heinrich Bruhn (Founder, CEO &
Member-Mgmt Bd)

Subsidiaries:

Real Meat Company Ltd.   **(1)**
Plot No 7193 Mwembeshi Road Light In-
dustrial Area, Lusaka, Zambia
Tel.: (260) 211287708
Web Site: https://realmeatafrica.com
Animal Meat Distr
N.A.I.C.S.: 424470

AMATHUS PUBLIC LIMITED

Amathus Building 2 Syntagmatos Str,
PO Box 53023, 3300, Limassol, Cy-
prus
Tel.: (357) 35725369122
Web Site: https://www.amathus.com
Year Founded: 1943
Home Management Services
N.A.I.C.S.: 721110

Subsidiaries:

ANC Worldchoice Holidays Ltd.   **(1)**
54 Kyprou Avenue and 45 Electroupoleos,
16452, Argyroupolis, Athens, Greece
Tel.: (30) 2109969711
Travel & Tourism Services
N.A.I.C.S.: 561510

Amathus (UK) Ltd.   **(1)**
7b High Street, Barnet, London, EN5 5UE,
Herts, United Kingdom
Tel.: (44) 2082753814
Travel & Tourism Services
N.A.I.C.S.: 561510

Amathus Corporation Ltd.   **(1)**
17 Homer Avenue, PO Box 21601, 1511,
Nicosia, Cyprus
Tel.: (357) 22362145
Logistics & Freight Forwarding Services
N.A.I.C.S.: 488510

Amathus Hotels Ltd.   **(1)**
Amathus Building 2 Syntagmatos Str, PO
Box 57499, 3316, Limassol, Cyprus
Tel.: (357) 25371808
Hotel Operator
N.A.I.C.S.: 721110

Amathus Maritime Ltd.   **(1)**
17 Homer Avenue, PO Box 21601, 1511,
Nicosia, Cyprus
Tel.: (357) 25716390
Shipping & Maritime Services
N.A.I.C.S.: 488390

Amathus Travel Ltd.   **(1)**
17 Homer Avenue, PO Box 21601, 1511,
Nicosia, Cyprus
Tel.: (357) 22456545
Travel Agency Services
N.A.I.C.S.: 561510

AMATI AIM VCT PLC

8 Coates Crescent, Edinburgh, EH3
7AL, United Kingdom
Tel.: (44) 1315039100

Web Site:
https://www.amatiglobal.com
AMAT—(LSE)
Rev.: $4,068,746
Assets: $183,362,190
Liabilities: $1,213,240
Net Worth: $182,148,950
Earnings: ($57,055,379)
Fiscal Year-end: 01/31/24
Other Financial Vehicles
N.A.I.C.S.: 525990
Paul Jourdan (CEO)

AMAZE CO., LTD.

1-7-17 Nishitsurusaki, Oita, 870-0105,
Japan
Tel.: (81) 975243301
Web Site: https://www.az-hotels.co.jp
Year Founded: 1911
6076—(FKA)
Sales Range: $75-99.9 Million
Emp.: 110
Food Service
N.A.I.C.S.: 722310
Kenichi Anami (Pres & CEO)

AMAZIA, INC.

1-2 Sakuragaokacho, Shibuya-ku,
Tokyo, 150-0031, Japan
Tel.: (81) 364153435
Web Site: https://www.amazia.co.jp
4424—(TKS)
Sales Range: Less than $1 Million
Software Development Services
N.A.I.C.S.: 541511
Ryosuke Sakuma (Pres & CEO)

AMAZING MICROELECTRONIC CORP.

18F No 2 Jian 8th Rd, Zhonghe Dist,
New Taipei City, 235, Taiwan
Tel.: (886) 282278989
Web Site: https://www.amazingic.com
Year Founded: 2006
6411—(TAI)
Microelectronic Product Mfr
N.A.I.C.S.: 333242
Li Chun-Chang (Chm)

AMAZONE H. DREYER GMBH & CO. KG

Am Amazonenwerk 9-13, D-49205,
Hasbergen, Germany
Tel.: (49) 54055010
Web Site: https://amazone.net
Year Founded: 1883
Agricultural Machinery Mfr
N.A.I.C.S.: 333111

AMAZONIA MINERACAO LTDA

Edificio Aquarius Center, Sala 704
Rua T 36, Goiania, Brazil
Tel.: (55) 62 2550211
Gold Mining
N.A.I.C.S.: 212220
Douglas Arantes (Pres & CEO)

AMBA ENTERPRISES LTD.

S No 132 H No 1/4/1 Premraj Indus-
trial Estate Shed No B-2 3 4, Dalvi-
wadi Nanded Phata, Pune, 411041,
India
Tel.: (91) 2228701692
Web Site: https://www.ambaltd.com
Year Founded: 1995
539196—(BOM)
Rev.: $15,230,146
Assets: $3,328,275
Liabilities: $712,688
Net Worth: $2,615,587
Earnings: $295,388
Emp.: 28
Fiscal Year-end: 03/31/21
Transformer Product Mfr
N.A.I.C.S.: 335311
Ketan H. Mehta (Mng Dir)

AMBALAL SARABHAI ENTER-PRISES LTD.

Shanti Sadan Mirzapur Road,
Ahmedabad, 380 001, Gujarat, India
Tel.: (91) 7925507671
Web Site: https://www.ase.life
500009—(BOM)
Rev.: $32,590,836
Assets: $31,463,359
Liabilities: $15,103,056
Net Worth: $16,360,303
Earnings: $6,445,312
Emp.: 104
Fiscal Year-end: 03/31/22
Pharmaceutical Preparation Mfr
N.A.I.C.S.: 325412
Kartikeya V. Sarabhai (Chm)

Subsidiaries:

Asence Pharma Pvt. Ltd.   **(1)**
Gorwa Road, Vadodara, 390 023, India
Tel.: (91) 2652283178
Web Site: https://www.asence.com
Pharmaceutical & Medicine Distr
N.A.I.C.S.: 424210
Mohal K. Sarabhai (Pres & CEO)

Sarabhai Chemicals (India) Pvt.
Ltd.   **(1)**
Shantisadan Mirzapur Rd, Ahmedabad, 380
001, Gujarat, India
Tel.: (91) 9720444999
Web Site:
https://www.sarabhaichemicals.com
Pharmaceutical & Medicine Mfr
N.A.I.C.S.: 325412
Kartikeya V. Sarabhai (Chm)

Synbiotics Ltd.   **(1)**
Plot No 570 571 576 A Maitry Marg ECP
Canal Road, Village - Luna Tal Padra Dist,
Vadodara, 391 440, India
Tel.: (91) 9099978530
Web Site: https://www.synbiotics.in
Medical Device Mfr
N.A.I.C.S.: 339112
Mohal Sarabhai (Mng Dir)

Systronics (India) Ltd.   **(1)**
B/116-129 1st floor Supath-II Complex, Nr
Juna Wadaj Bus Terminus Ashram Road,
Ahmedabad, 380 013, Gujarat, India
Tel.: (91) 7927556077
Web Site: https://www.systronicsindia.com
Electric Equipment Mfr
N.A.I.C.S.: 334419
Mohal K. Sarabhai (Chm)

AMBANI ORGOCHEM LIMITED

801 8th Floor 351-ICON Next to Na-
traj Rustomji Western Express High-
way, Andheri East, Mumbai, 400069,
Maharashtra, India
Tel.: (91) 2226827541
Web Site:
https://www.ambaniorganics.com
Year Founded: 1985
AMBANIORG—(NSE)
Rev.: $17,205,113
Assets: $15,305,993
Liabilities: $10,341,796
Net Worth: $4,964,197
Earnings: $274,438
Emp.: 95
Fiscal Year-end: 03/31/22
Paint & Coating Mfr
N.A.I.C.S.: 325510
Rakesh Shah (Mng Dir)

AMBAR PROTEIN INDUS-TRIES LIMITED

Sarkhej-Bavla Highway Opp Bhagyo-
day Hotel Changodar, Ahmedabad
District, Sanand, 382 210, India
Tel.: (91) 2717250220   In
Web Site:
https://www.ambarprotein.com
Year Founded: 1992
519471—(BOM)
Rev.: $46,458,144
Assets: $8,755,124

Ambar Protein Industries Limited—(Continued)

Liabilities: $6,148,465
Net Worth: $2,606,659
Earnings: $607,466
Emp.: 23
Fiscal Year-end: 03/31/22
Grocery Product Mfr & Distr
N.A.I.C.S.: 311225
Jayprakashbhai Jairambhai Vachhani (Chm)

AMBASSADOR INTRA HOLD-INGS LTD.

1093/1 305 Sur Mount Complex Behind Iscon Mandir SG Highway, Satellite Jodhpur, Ahmedabad, 380059, Gujarat, India
Tel.: (91) 7940030800
Web Site:
    https://www.ambassadorintra.in
Year Founded: 1982
542524—(BOM)
Clothes Mfr
N.A.I.C.S.: 313310
Siddharth Ajmera (Mng Dir)

AMBASSADOR THEATRE GROUP LIMITED

4th Floor Prince Consort House, London, SE1 7TJ, United Kingdom
Tel.: (44) 844 871 7627
Web Site: http://www.atgtickets.com
Year Founded: 1992
Sales Range: $25-49.9 Million
Emp.: 2,596
Theater Operator
N.A.I.C.S.: 512131
Peter Kavanagh (Dir-Bus Affairs)

Subsidiaries:

Sonia Friedman Productions Ltd   (1)
Duke of York's Theatre 104 St Martin's Lane, London, WC2N 4BG, United Kingdom
Tel.: (44) 2078458750
Web Site: http://www.soniafriedman.com
Film & Video Production Services
N.A.I.C.S.: 512120
Diane Benjamin (Gen Mgr & Exec Dir)

AMBEE PHARMACEUTICALS LIMITED

184/1 Tejgaon Industrial Area, Dhaka, 1208, Bangladesh
Tel.: (880) 28870777   BD
Web Site:
    https://www.ambeepharma.com
Year Founded: 1976
AMBEEPHA—(CHT)
Rev.: $1,833,972
Assets: $4,759,081
Liabilities: $4,542,989
Net Worth: $216,093
Earnings: $84,157
Emp.: 477
Fiscal Year-end: 06/30/23
Pharmaceuticals Product Mfr
N.A.I.C.S.: 325412
Naureen Aziz Mohammad Bhai (Mng Dir)

AMBEON HOLDINGS PLC

No 10 Gothami Road, 8, Colombo, Sri Lanka
Tel.: (94) 115700700
Web Site:
    https://www.ambeonholdings.com
Year Founded: 1910
GREG—(COL)
Rev.: $95,321,471
Assets: $116,097,520
Liabilities: $74,022,921
Net Worth: $42,074,599
Earnings: ($11,188,157)
Emp.: 2,734
Fiscal Year-end: 03/31/21
Investment Holding

N.A.I.C.S.: 551112
Ajith Devasurendra (Deputy Chm)

AMBER CAPITAL UK LLP

Kent House 14-17 Market Place, London, W1W 8AJ, United Kingdom
Tel.: (44) 2070794700
Web Site:
    http://www.amboroapital.com
Year Founded: 2005
Asset Management Firm
N.A.I.C.S.: 541618
Joseph Oughourlian (Founder, Mng Partner & Portfolio Mgr)

Subsidiaries:

Amber Capital, LP   (1)
900 3rd Ave, New York, NY 10022
Tel.: (212) 340-7340
Sales Range: $1-9.9 Million
Emp.: 50
Investment Advice
N.A.I.C.S.: 523940
Joseph Oughourlian (Principal)

AMBER ENTERPRISES INDIA LIMITED

Universal Trade Tower 1st Floor Sector 49 Sohna Road, Gurgaon, 122 018, Haryana, India
Tel.: (91) 1243923000   In
Web Site:
    https://www.ambergroupindia.com
Year Founded: 1990
540902—(BOM)
Rev.: $578,709,427
Assets: $670,550,776
Liabilities: $428,554,363
Net Worth: $241,996,414
Earnings: $1,519,559
Emp.: 1,095
Fiscal Year-end: 03/31/22
Electronic Equipment Mfr & Distr
N.A.I.C.S.: 333415
Jasbir Singh (Chm & CEO)

Subsidiaries:

IL JIN Electronics (India) Private Limited   (1)
Plot no 27&28 Ecotech-3 Extension-2 Udyog Kendra 2 Ecotech III, Noida, 201306, Uttar Pradesh, India   (90.2%)
Tel.: (91) 8005727756
Web Site: https://www.iljin.co.in
Home Appliance Product Mfr
N.A.I.C.S.: 335220
H. C. Sim (CEO)

AMBER HILL FINANCIAL HOLDINGS LTD.

Unit A 5/F Chunghing Commerical Building 62-63 Connaught Road, Central, China (Hong Kong)
Tel.: (852) 38450500   HK
Web Site: http://www.ahfh.com.hk
Year Founded: 1996
0033—(HKG)
Rev.: $38,121,458
Assets: $30,908,638
Liabilities: $6,715,086
Net Worth: $24,193,552
Earnings: $5,249,615
Emp.: 42
Fiscal Year-end: 06/30/22
Financial Planning Services
N.A.I.C.S.: 523999

AMBERTECH LIMITED

Unit 1 2 Daydream Street, Warriewood, 2102, NSW, Australia
Tel.: (61) 299987600
Web Site:
    http://www.ambertech.com.au
AMO—(ASX)
Rev.: $63,739,316
Assets: $33,890,224
Liabilities: $19,055,823
Net Worth: $14,834,402

Earnings: $909,455
Emp.: 144
Fiscal Year-end: 06/30/24
Professional Film Recording Equipment Mfr & Distr
N.A.I.C.S.: 333310
Peter Francis Wallace (Chm)

Subsidiaries:

Amber Technology (NZ) Limited   (1)
Unit 3 77 Porana Road, Hillcrest, Auckland, 0627, New Zealand
Tel.: (64) 94430753
Web Site: https://www.amber.co.nz
Electronic Equipment Distr
N.A.I.C.S.: 423690

AMBICA AGARBATHIES & AROMA INDUSTRIES LTD.

22b 8 26 Anasuya Building Chadalavadavari Street, Eluru, 534 002, Andhra Pradesh, India
Tel.: (91) 8812230216
Web Site:
    https://www.ambicaagarbathies.com
Year Founded: 1946
AMBICAAGAR—(NSE)
Rev.: $16,048,182
Assets: $29,913,456
Liabilities: $15,930,847
Net Worth: $13,982,610
Earnings: $327,737
Emp.: 190
Fiscal Year-end: 03/31/22
Incense Sticks Mfr
N.A.I.C.S.: 325998
Rohit Tibrewal (Sec)

AMBIENTA SGR S.P.A

Piazza Fontana 6, 20122, Milan, Italy
Tel.: (39) 027217461
Web Site: https://ambientasgr.com
Emp.: 100
Investment Services
N.A.I.C.S.: 523999

AMBIENTHESIS SPA

Via Cassanese 45, 20054, Segrate, MI, Italy
Tel.: (39) 02893801
Web Site: https://www.ambienthesis.it
GTH—(ITA)
Rev.: $191,426,206
Assets: $463,428,635
Liabilities: $420,423,888
Net Worth: $43,004,747
Earnings: $17,414,726
Emp.: 396
Fiscal Year-end: 12/31/23
Remediation Services
N.A.I.C.S.: 562910
Damiano Belli (CEO)

AMBIKA COTTON MILLS LIM-ITED

15 Valluvar Street Sivanandha Colony, Coimbatore, 641012, Tamil Nadu, India
Tel.: (91) 4222491501
Web Site: https://www.acmills.in
Year Founded: 1988
531978—(BOM)
Rev.: $126,327,993
Assets: $112,413,592
Liabilities: $13,469,206
Net Worth: $98,944,386
Earnings: $24,554,685
Emp.: 1,824
Fiscal Year-end: 03/31/22
Cotton Yarn Mfr
N.A.I.C.S.: 313110
P. V. Chandran (Chm & Mng Dir)

AMBIPAR EMERGENCY RE-SPONSE

Av Angelica 2330 ed New England

5th floor, Sao Paulo, 01228-200, SP, Brazil
Tel.: (55) 1134295022   Ky
Web Site: https://www.ambipar.com
Year Founded: 2023
AMBI—(NYSEAMEX)
Rev.: $516,494,167
Assets: $859,342,307
Liabilities: $588,767,574
Net Worth: $270,574,733
Earnings: $3,425,267
Emp.: 7,089
Fiscal Year-end: 12/31/23
Environmental Consulting Services
N.A.I.C.S.: 541620
Guilherme Patini Borlenghi (COO)

AMBIPAR PARTICIPACOES E EMPREENDIMENTOS SA

Av Angelica 2330 ed New England 5th floor, Sao Paulo, CEP 01234-000, Brazil
Tel.: (55) 1135263526
Web Site: https://ambipar.com
Year Founded: 1955
AMBP3—(BRAZ)
Rev.: $871,043,934
Assets: $2,081,245,721
Liabilities: $1,614,086,584
Net Worth: $467,159,137
Earnings: $10,126,562
Emp.: 14,576
Fiscal Year-end: 12/31/23
Losgistics & Response Services
N.A.I.C.S.: 541614
Guilherme Borlengh (CEO)

Subsidiaries:

Ambipar Response Limited   (1)
27-37 St George s Road, London, SW19 4EU, Pembrokeshire, United Kingdom   (100%)
Tel.: (44) 1646697041
Web Site: http://www.ambipar-response.com
Sales Range: $25-49.9 Million
Emp.: 10
Process Physical Distribution & Logistics Consulting Services
N.A.I.C.S.: 541614
Simon Rickaby (Mng Dir)

Subsidiary (US):

Allied International Emergency LLC   (2)
3024 Wichita Ct, Fort Worth, TX 76140
Tel.: (817) 595-0100
Web Site: http://www.aiemergency.com
Research & Development in the Social Sciences & Humanities
N.A.I.C.S.: 541720
Ty McKee (Pres)

Witt O'Brien's, LLC   (2)
818 Town & Country Blvd Ste 200, Houston, TX 77024
Tel.: (281) 320-9796
Web Site: https://www.wittobriens.com
Logistics Consulting Servies
N.A.I.C.S.: 541614
Tim Whipple (CEO)

Custom Environmental Services, Inc.   (1)
8041 N I 70 Frontage Rd # 5, Arvada, CO 80002
Tel.: (303) 423-9949
Web Site: http://www.customsvcs.com
Sales Range: $1-9.9 Million
Emp.: 90
Remediation Services
N.A.I.C.S.: 562910
Gerald Marks (Pres)

One Stop Environmental, LLC   (1)
4800 Division Ave, Birmingham, AL 35222-1620
Tel.: (205) 595-8188
Web Site: http://www.onestopenv.com
Sales Range: $1-9.9 Million
Emp.: 35
Hazardous Waste Remediation & Cleanup Services for Government, Military & Private Sector Clients

N.A.I.C.S.: 562211
Shannon Riley *(Pres)*

AMBITION DX HOLDINGS CO., LTD.
4-20-3 Ebisu, Shibuya-ku, Tokyo, 150-6012, Japan
Tel.: (81) 364398901
Web Site: https://www.am-bition.jp
3300—(TKS)
Rev.: $261,644,300
Assets: $167,268,240
Liabilities: $129,015,240
Net Worth: $38,253,000
Earnings: $10,188,360
Emp.: 30
Fiscal Year-end: 06/30/24
Residential Rental Property Services
N.A.I.C.S.: 531110
Masanori Fukushima *(CEO)*

AMBITION GROUP LIMITED
Level 5 55 Clarence Street, Sydney, 2000, NSW, Australia
Tel.: (61) 2 9249 5000
Web Site:
    http://www.ambition.com.au
Rev.: $77,096,557
Assets: $22,354,603
Liabilities: $15,418,752
Net Worth: $6,935,851
Earnings: ($785,415)
Emp.: 256
Fiscal Year-end: 12/31/19
Accounting & Financial Services
N.A.I.C.S.: 541211
Nick Waterworth *(Founder, Chm & CEO)*

Subsidiaries:

Ambition Group Limited - Ambition Technology Division **(1)**
Level 5 55 Clarence St, Sydney, 2000, NSW, Australia
Tel.: (61) 292486200
Web Site: http://www.ambition.com.au
Information Technology Recruiting Services
N.A.I.C.S.: 561311

Ambition Group Limited - Finance Division **(1)**
Level 5 55 Clarence St, Sydney, 2000, NSW, Australia
Tel.: (61) 292495000
Web Site: http://www.ambition.com.au
Sales Range: $10-24.9 Million
Emp.: 40
Accounting & Financial Professionals Recruitment Services
N.A.I.C.S.: 561311

Ambition Group Singapore PTE Limited **(1)**
One Raffles Place 14-62 Office Tower 2, Singapore, 048616, Singapore
Tel.: (65) 68545600
Web Site: http://www.ambition.com.sg
Sales Range: $25-49.9 Million
Emp.: 30
Recruitment Services
N.A.I.C.S.: 561311

Ambition Recruit Pty Limited **(1)**
Level 5 55 Clarence Street, Sydney, 2000, NSW, Australia
Tel.: (61) 292495000
Web Site: http://www.ambition.com.au
Sales Range: $25-49.9 Million
Emp.: 150
Employment Agencies
N.A.I.C.S.: 561311

The Ambition Group Limited (HK) **(1)**
Level 25 28 Hennessy Road, Hong Kong, China (Hong Kong)
Tel.: (852) 31013066
Web Site: http://www.ambition.com.hk
Sales Range: $25-49.9 Million
Emp.: 25
Recruitment Services
N.A.I.C.S.: 561311

The Ambition Group Limited (UK) **(1)**
13 Southampton Place, London, WC1A 2AL, United Kingdom
Tel.: (44) 2074044004
Web Site: http://www.ambition.co.uk
Emp.: 80
Recruitment Services
N.A.I.C.S.: 561311

Watermark Search International Pty Limited **(1)**
Level 10 83 Clarence Street, Sydney, 2000, NSW, Australia
Tel.: (61) 292331200
Web Site:
    http://www.watermarksearch.com.au
Sales Range: $25-49.9 Million
Emp.: 15
Employment Placement Agencies
N.A.I.C.S.: 561311

AMBITION MICA LIMITED
Shop No 28 1st Floor Vitthal Plaza Opp, Naroda GEB Off Dehgam Road Nava Naroda, Ahmedabad, 382330, Gujarat, India
Tel.: (91) 7929292629
Web Site:
    https://www.ambitionmica.com
539223—(BOM)
Rev.: $4,994,943
Assets: $10,826,632
Liabilities: $7,409,787
Net Worth: $3,416,845
Earnings: ($705,173)
Emp.: 41
Fiscal Year-end: 03/31/21
Laminated Product Mfr
N.A.I.C.S.: 326130
Rameshkumar Veljibhai Patel *(Exec Dir)*

AMBO AGRITEC LIMITED
3 Pretoria Street Chandrakunj Building, Kolkata, 700071, West Bengal, India
Tel.: (91) 3346020333
Web Site:
    https://www.amboagritec.com
Year Founded: 1994
543678—(BOM)
Rev.: $12,947,762
Assets: $3,485,869
Liabilities: $2,979,686
Net Worth: $506,183
Earnings: $162,612
Fiscal Year-end: 03/31/22
Snack Food Product Mfr
N.A.I.C.S.: 311919

AMBOW EDUCATION HOLDING LTD.
12th Floor Tower 1 Financial Street Changan Center, Shijingshan District, Beijing, 100043, China
Tel.: (86) 1062068000   Ky
Web Site: http://www.ambow.com
Year Founded: 2000
AMBO—(NYSEAMEX)
Rev.: $249,579
Assets: $26,963,581
Liabilities: $18,650,560
Net Worth: $8,313,021
Earnings: ($14,871,788)
Emp.: 65
Fiscal Year-end: 12/31/22
Educational & Career Enhancement Services
N.A.I.C.S.: 611710
Jin Huang *(Founder, Chm, Pres & CEO)*

Subsidiaries:

Bay State College **(1)**
31 St James Ave, Boston, MA 02116
Tel.: (617) 217-9000
Web Site: https://www.baystate.edu
Graduate & Undergraduate College

N.A.I.C.S.: 611310
Beijing Ambow Shida Education Technology Co., Ltd. **(1)**
2 F West Zone Block B Kelun Building, Chaoyang District, Beijing, 100020, China
Tel.: (86) 1065810099
Educational Support Services
N.A.I.C.S.: 611710

AMBRA S.A.
ul Pulawska 336, 02 819, Warsaw, Poland
Tel.: (48) 225663300
Web Site: https://www.ambra.com.pl
Year Founded: 1990
AMB—(WAR)
Rev.: $220,019,846
Assets: $193,950,409
Liabilities: $77,987,489
Net Worth: $115,962,920
Earnings: $19,064,463
Emp.: 400
Fiscal Year-end: 06/30/23
Wines & Non Alcoholic Beverages Mfr
N.A.I.C.S.: 312130
Piotr Kazmierczak *(Vice Chm-Mgmt Bd)*

Subsidiaries:

Euro Center Trade s.r.o. **(1)**
Nuselska 53, 140 00, Prague, Czech Republic
Tel.: (420) 242486890
Web Site: https://www.ectrade.cz
FMCG Distr
N.A.I.C.S.: 424490
Monika Vasiliadu *(Dir-Operation)*

Gurmetum s.r.o. **(1)**
Videnska 101/119, 619 00, Brno, Czech Republic
Tel.: (420) 242486890
Web Site: https://www.gurmetum.com
Wine Whslr
N.A.I.C.S.: 424490
Monika Vasiliadu *(Dir-Operation)*

Vinex Slaviantsi Poland Sp. Z.o.o. **(1)**
Ul Lelewela 33, 87-100, Torun, Poland
Tel.: (48) 566559016
Web Site: https://www.vinex.pl
Wine Mfr & Distr
N.A.I.C.S.: 312130

Vino-klub.cz, s. r. o. **(1)**
Opletalova 25, Nove Mesto, 110 00, Prague, Czech Republic
Tel.: (420) 724239045
Web Site: https://www.vino-klub.cz
Wine Whslr
N.A.I.C.S.: 424490
Radek Vychytil *(Owner)*

Zarea S.A. **(1)**
Bd Bucurestii Noi nr 176 sector 1, Bucharest, Romania
Tel.: (40) 216670020
Web Site: https://www.zarea.ro
Alcoholic Beverage Mfr & Distr
N.A.I.C.S.: 312140

karom Drinks S.R.L. **(1)**
Str Living Walls Nr 24, 77751, Bucharest, Romania
Tel.: (40) 21252920912
Web Site: http://www.karom.ro
Wine Whslr
N.A.I.C.S.: 424490

AMBRIAN PLC
41 Lothbury, London, EC2R 7HG, United Kingdom
Tel.: (44) 2076344700
Web Site: http://www.ambrian.com
Sales Range: $1-4.9 Billion
Emp.: 33
Investment Services; Metal Merchants
N.A.I.C.S.: 523999
John Coles *(Dir-Fin)*

Subsidiaries:

Ambrian Metals Limited **(1)**
6th Floor 62-64 Cornhill, London, EC3V 3NH, United Kingdom
Tel.: (44) 20 7634 4700
Web Site: http://www.ambrian.com
Emp.: 18
Metal Commodity Trading Services
N.A.I.C.S.: 523160
Mark Homer *(Mng Dir)*

AMBRILIA BIOPHARMA INC.
1010 Sherbrooke Street West Suite 1800, Montreal, H3A 2R7, QC, Canada
Tel.: (514) 751-2003   Ca
Year Founded: 1986
Sales Range: $1-9.9 Million
Emp.: 14
Oncology & Infectious Disease Pharmaceutical Products Mfr
N.A.I.C.S.: 325412
Brian L. Davies *(CFO)*

AMBROISE BOUVIER TRANSPORTS
Lieu Dit Megaudais Rn 12, 53500, Laval, France
Tel.: (33) 243087200
Rev.: $21,700,000
Emp.: 169
Trucking Service
N.A.I.C.S.: 484121
Anthony Ambroise *(Mgr)*

AMBROISIE CAPITAL HOLDING S.A.S.
21-25 rue Balzac, 75008, Paris, France
Tel.: (33) 1 4953 9038   FR
Web Site:
    http://www.olympiagroup.com
Year Founded: 2006
Holding Company; Investment Management Services
N.A.I.C.S.: 551112

Subsidiaries:

Kenmar Group Inc. **(1)**
680 5th Ave, New York, NY 10019
Tel.: (914) 307-7000
Web Site: http://www.kenmar.com
Sales Range: $50-74.9 Million
Emp.: 45
Alternative Investment Holding Company
N.A.I.C.S.: 551112
Marc S. Goodman *(Co-Founder, Pres, CEO & Co-Chief Investment Officer)*

Subsidiary (Domestic):

Kenmar Global Investment Management LLC **(2)**
900 King St Ste 100, Rye Brook, NY 10573
Tel.: (914) 307-7020
Web Site: http://www.kenmar.com
Investment Management Service
N.A.I.C.S.: 523940

Kenmar Securities Inc. **(2)**
680 5th Ave, New York, NY 10019
Tel.: (914) 307-7000
Web Site: http://www.kenmar.com
Sales Range: $25-49.9 Million
Emp.: 42
Securities Brokerage
N.A.I.C.S.: 523150
Kenneth A. Shewer *(Chm)*

Olympia Capital Management S.A. **(1)**
21-25 rue Balzac, 75008, Paris, France
Tel.: (33) 1 4953 9038
Web Site: http://www.olympiagroup.com
Emp.: 10
Investment Management Service
N.A.I.C.S.: 523940
Sergio Heuer *(Chm & Co-Chief Investment Officer)*

Ambroisie Capital Holding S.A.S.—(Continued)

Subsidiary (US):

Olympia Capital Management
Inc.   (2)
1211 Ave of the Americas Ste 2701, New
York, NY 10036
Tel.: (212) 403-9500
Web Site: http://www.olympiagroup.com
Investment Management Service
N.A.I.C.S.: 523940

AMBROMOBILIARE S.P.A.
Corso Venezia 16, 20121, Milan, Italy
Tel.: (39) 0287399069
Web Site:
    https://www.ambromobiliare.it
Financial Advisory Services
N.A.I.C.S.: 523940
Alberto Gustavo Franceschini (Chm)

AMBU A/S
Baltorpbakken 13, DK-2750, Ballerup,
Denmark
Tel.: (45) 72252000
Web Site: https://www.ambu.com
AMBU.B—(CSE)
Rev.: $479,952,540
Assets: $761,094,471
Liabilities: $101,141,642
Net Worth: $659,952,830
Earnings: $2,604,506
Emp.: 4,616
Fiscal Year-end: 09/30/23
Mfr & Developer of Medical Appara-
tus
N.A.I.C.S.: 334510
Britt Meelby Jensen (CEO)

Subsidiaries:

Ambu (Deutschland) GmbH   (1)
Steinkopfstrasse 4, 61231, Bad Nauheim,
Germany   (100%)
Tel.: (49) 60 329 2500
Web Site: https://www.ambu.de
Sales Range: $10-24.9 Million
Emp.: 20
Patient Monitoring Equipment, Airway Man-
agement & Emergency Products
N.A.I.C.S.: 621999

Ambu (Xiamen) Trading Ltd.   (1)
Room 1710 17th Floor No 450 Caoyang
Rd, Pu Tuo District, Shanghai, 200063, Fu-
jian, China
Tel.: (86) 5925676083
Web Site: https://ambuchina.com
Emp.: 2,250
Medical Diagnostic Equipment Distr
N.A.I.C.S.: 423450

Ambu Australia Pty. Ltd.   (1)
Unit 5 2 Daydream St, Warriewood, 2102,
NSW, Australia
Tel.: (61) 299981000
Emp.: 10
Medical Diagnostic Equipment Distr
N.A.I.C.S.: 423450
Anders Kolding (Mng Dir & Mgr-ST-Asia)

Ambu BV   (1)
Schiphol Boulevard 127, Schiphol Airport,
1118 BG, Schiphol, Netherlands
Tel.: (31) 182526060
Medical Equipment Distr
N.A.I.C.S.: 423450

Ambu France S.a.r.l.   (1)
Les Bureaux du Parc Avenue Jean-Gabriel
Domergue, CS3080, 33070, Bordeaux,
France   (100%)
Tel.: (33) 55 792 3150
Web Site: https://www.ambu.fr
Sales Range: $25-49.9 Million
Emp.: 30
Developer, Mfr & Marketer of Equipment &
Diagnostic Solutions & Vital Care for Hospi-
tals & Emergency Services
N.A.I.C.S.: 339112

Ambu Inc.   (1)
6721 Columbia Gateway Dr Ste 200, Columbia, MD 21046
Tel.: (410) 768-6464

Web Site: https://www.ambuusa.com
Sales Range: $25-49.9 Million
Emp.: 50
Sales of Medical Supplies
N.A.I.C.S.: 423450
Thomas Schmidt (CFO)

Subsidiary (Domestic):

King Systems Corporation   (2)
1401 6th Ave S, Clear Lake, IA
50428   (100%)
Tel.: (641) 355-1000
Sales Range: $25-49.9 Million
Emp.: 56
Software Reproducing
N.A.I.C.S.: 334610
David J. Kingland (Chm & Chief Innovation
Officer)

Ambu India Private Limited   (1)
DSM 201-202 DLF Towers Shivaji Marg,
New Delhi, 110015, India
Tel.: (91) 9818108964
Medical Device Mfr
N.A.I.C.S.: 339112
Amit Bhardwaj (Head-Country)

Ambu KK
MG Ichigaya Bldg 11th Floor 1-9, Gobancho
Chiyoda-ku, Tokyo, 102-0076, Japan
Tel.: (81) 362228723
Web Site: http://www.ambu.co.jp
Medical Device Mfr
N.A.I.C.S.: 339112

Ambu LLC   (1)
Tel.: (7) 4952218902
Web Site: https://www.ambu.com.ru
Medical Device Mfr
N.A.I.C.S.: 339112

Ambu Ltd.   (1)
Warehouse & Proces Complex Building No
C Xiang Yu F TZ, Hu Li District, Xiamen,
361006, China
Tel.: (86) 5926025212
N.A.I.C.S.: 541720

Ambu Ltd.   (1)
The Incubator 2 Alconbury Weald Enter-
prise Campus Alconbury Weald, Hunting-
don, PE28 4XA, Cambridgeshire, United
Kingdom
Tel.: (44) 1480498403
Sales Range: $25-49.9 Million
Emp.: 15
Medical Diagnostic Equipments Whslr
N.A.I.C.S.: 423450
Keith McCallum (Mng Dir)

Ambu Mexico Operations S. A. de C.
V.   (1)
Circuito Intermex Sur 4166, Industrial Park
Intermex, 32575, Ciudad Juarez, Mexico
Tel.: (52) 6566296730
Medical Equipment Mfr & Distr
N.A.I.C.S.: 339112

Ambu New Zealand Pty. Ltd.   (1)
PO Box 51, Waimauku, Auckland, 0812,
New Zealand
Tel.: (64) 21594053
Medical Equipment Mfr & Distr
N.A.I.C.S.: 339112

Ambu Nordic A/S   (1)
Baltorpbakken 13, 2750, Ballerup, Denmark
Tel.: (45) 72252250
Web Site: https://www.ambu.dk
Medical Device Mfr
N.A.I.C.S.: 339112

Ambu S.r.l.   (1)
Via Paracelso 20 Centro Direzionale Col-
leoni, 20864, Agrate Brianza, MB, Italy
Tel.: (39) 0396578100
Emp.: 9
Diagnostic Equipment Distr
N.A.I.C.S.: 423450

Ambu Sales & Services Sdn.
Bhd.   (1)
Mini-Circuits Building 3 Level 3 Plot 10,
Bayan Lepas Technoplex Phase IV, 11900,
Bayan Lepas, Penang, Malaysia
Tel.: (60) 42529100
Medical Device Mfr
N.A.I.C.S.: 339112

Firma Ambu, S.L.   (1)

Alcala 261-265 Edf 4 4 izq, 28027, Madrid,
Spain
Tel.: (34) 914116830
Web Site: https://www.ambu.es
Medical Device Mfr
N.A.I.C.S.: 339112

**AMCAD BIOMED CORPORA-
TION**
Fl 5-2 No 167 Fu Hsing N Rd, Taipei,
104, Taiwan
Tel.: (886) 227136227
Web Site: https://www.amcad.com.tw
Year Founded: 2008
4188—(TPE)
Rev.: $1,926,961
Assets: $17,317,387
Liabilities: $1,065,566
Net Worth: $16,251,821
Earnings: $1,699,121)
Fiscal Year-end: 12/31/22
Health Care Srvices
N.A.I.C.S.: 621999
C. C. Lee (Chm)

AMCIL LIMITED
Level 21 101 Collins Street, Mel-
bourne, 3000, VIC, Australia
Tel.: (61) 396509911
Web Site: https://www.amcil.com.au
AMH—(ASX)
Rev.: $6,362,847
Assets: $266,758,813
Liabilities: $29,558,627
Net Worth: $237,200,186
Earnings: $4,993,323
Fiscal Year-end: 06/30/24
Investment Services
N.A.I.C.S.: 523999
Robert Mark Freeman (Bd of Dirs &
Mng Dir)

AMCO INDIA LTD.
C53-54 Sector-57 Phase III, Noida,
201301, Uttar Pradesh, India
Tel.: (91) 1204601500
Web Site:
    https://www.amcoindialimited.com
530133—(BOM)
Rev.: $12,238,405
Assets: $7,239,605
Liabilities: $3,120,523
Net Worth: $4,119,082
Earnings: $200,927
Emp.: 59
Fiscal Year-end: 03/31/21
Leather Cloth Mfr
N.A.I.C.S.: 315250
Surender Kumar Gupta (Chm & Mng
Dir)

**AMCO UNITED HOLDING LIM-
ITED**
Unit 1104 Crawford House 70
Queens Road Central, Central, Hong
Kong, China (Hong Kong)
Tel.: (852) 29614871
Web Site: http://www.amco-
united.com
0630—(HKG)
Rev.: $8,823,893
Assets: $22,037,100
Liabilities: $19,667,003
Net Worth: $2,370,098
Earnings: ($13,292,003)
Emp.: 30
Fiscal Year-end: 12/31/22
Computer Printing & Imaging Prod-
ucts Mfr & Sales
N.A.I.C.S.: 423420
Minghui Jia (Exec Dir)

Subsidiaries:

Afex International (HK) Limited   (1)
5 F Kam Foo Indus Bldg 97-103 Ta Chuen
Ping St, Kwai Chung, New Territories,
China (Hong Kong)

Tel.: (852) 2427 1891
Web Site: http://www.afex.cc
Toner Cartridges Recycling Services
N.A.I.C.S.: 811210

Jackin Optical Marketing Company
Limited   (1)
Rm 1008 10th Fl Riley House 88 Lei Muk
Rd, Kwai Chung, New Territories, China
(Hong Kong)
Tel.: (852) 2 480 1398
Data Media Products Whslr
N.A.I.C.S.: 423430

Titron Industries Limited   (1)
Unit 3004 30/F Metroplaza II 223 Hing Fong
Road, Kwai Fong, New Territories, China
(Hong Kong)
Tel.: (852) 21551688
Emp.: 6,000
Plastic Moulding Product Mfr
N.A.I.C.S.: 333511
Agnes Lau (Asst Mgr-Ops)

AMCOR PLC
83 Tower Road North Warmley, Bris-
tol, BS30 8XP, United Kingdom
Tel.: (44) 1179753200
Web Site: https://www.amcor.com
Year Founded: 2018
AMCR—(NYSE)
Rev.: $13,640,000,000
Assets: $16,524,000,000
Liabilities: $12,571,000,000
Net Worth: $3,953,000,000
Earnings: $740,000,000
Emp.: 41,000
Fiscal Year-end: 06/30/24
Holding Company
N.A.I.C.S.: 551112
Graeme Richard Liebelt (Chm)

Subsidiaries:

Amcor Flexibles (Australia) Pty
Ltd   (1)
Level 11 60 City Road, Southbank, 3006,
VIC, Australia
Tel.: (61) 392269000
N.A.I.C.S.: 561910

Amcor Pty Ltd   (1)
Level 11 60 City Road, Southbank, Mel-
bourne, 3006, VIC, Australia
Tel.: (61) 392269000
Web Site: https://www.amcor.com
Rev.: $9,319,100,000
Assets: $9,046,700,000
Liabilities: $7,956,200,000
Net Worth: $1,090,500,000
Earnings: $735,400,000
Emp.: 33,344
Fiscal Year-end: 06/30/2018
Packaging & Containers Mfr
N.A.I.C.S.: 322220
Michael Schmitt (Exec VP)

Subsidiary (Domestic):

Amcor Flexibles Group Pty. Ltd.   (2)
109 Burwood Road, Hawthorn, 3122, VIC,
Australia
Tel.: (61) 3 9226 9000
Sales Range: $300-349.9 Million
Emp.: 1,150
Flexible Packaging Products Mfr
N.A.I.C.S.: 322220

Subsidiary (Non-US):

Amcor Flexibles (New Zealand)
Ltd.   (3)
26-38 Andrew Baxter Drive, Mangere, 2022,
Auckland, New Zealand
Tel.: (64) 92750169
Sales Range: $100-124.9 Million
Emp.: 350
Flexible Plastic Packaging
N.A.I.C.S.: 326113
Gavin Barris (Gen Mgr)

Amcor Flexibles A/S   (3)
Hattingvej 10 East Jutland, 8700, Horsens,
Denmark   (100%)
Tel.: (45) 70131400
Rev.: $350,966,016
Emp.: 300
N.A.I.C.S.: 311423

Amcor Flexibles Alzira S.L.U. **(3)**
Ctra CV50 Km 18 1 Apartado De Correos
15, Valencia, 46600, Alzira, Spain
Tel.: (34) 962458900
Packaging Material Whslr
N.A.I.C.S.: 423840

**Amcor Flexibles Bangkok Public
Company Limited** **(3)**
91 Moo 13 King Kaew Road, Tambon Ra-
cha Thewa Amphoe Bang Phli, Samut Pra-
kan, 10540, Thailand
Tel.: (66) 275022405
Flexible Packaging Services
N.A.I.C.S.: 561910

Amcor Flexibles Barcelona **(3)**
Avenida Sant Julia 222, 8400, Granollers,
Barcelona, Spain
Tel.: (34) 938602800
Emp.: 170
Packaging Material Whslr
N.A.I.C.S.: 423840
German Tijero *(Gen Mgr)*

Amcor Flexibles Burgdorf Gmbh **(3)**
Kirchbergstrasse 168170B Emmental, 3401,
Burgdorf, Switzerland
Tel.: (41) 344215111
Sales Range: $75-99.9 Million
Emp.: 220
Packaging Material Mfr & Whslr
N.A.I.C.S.: 322220

Amcor Flexibles Cramlington Ltd **(3)**
49 Colbourne Avenue, Nelson Park, Cram-
lington, NE23 1WD, Northumberland,
United Kingdom
Tel.: (44) 1670730684
Sales Range: $25-49.9 Million
Emp.: 50
Packaging Products Mfr
N.A.I.C.S.: 322220
John Roberts *(Mng Dir)*

Amcor Flexibles Denmark ApS **(3)**
Hattingvej 10, East Jutland, 8700, Horsens,
Denmark
Tel.: (45) 70131400
Sales Range: $125-149.9 Million
Emp.: 300
Plastic Plate & Sheet Mfr
N.A.I.C.S.: 326199

Amcor Flexibles Europa Sur S.L. **(3)**
Avenida Sant Julia 222, Granollers, 08403,
Barcelona, Spain
Tel.: (34) 938602828
Sales Range: $25-49.9 Million
Emp.: 250
Packaging Services
N.A.I.C.S.: 561910

Amcor Flexibles Europe **(3)**
Da Vinci Laan 2, B 1935, Zaventem,
Belgium   **(100%)**
Tel.: (32) 24162611
Web Site: http://www.amcor.com
Sales Range: $25-49.9 Million
Emp.: 45
Mfr of Flexible, Tobacco & Medical Packag-
ing
N.A.I.C.S.: 322220

Subsidiary (US):

Amcor Flexibles Inc. **(3)**
1919 S Butterfield Rd, Mundelein, IL 60060-
9735
Tel.: (847) 362-9000
Sales Range: $125-149.9 Million
Emp.: 300
Coating, Printing & Conversion of Paper &
Plastic Films For Flexible Medical Packag-
ing
N.A.I.C.S.: 561910

Subsidiary (Domestic):

Amcor Flexibles - Ashland Inc **(4)**
150 Homer Ave, Ashland, MA 01721-0227
Tel.: (508) 881-2440
Packaging Material Whslr
N.A.I.C.S.: 423840

Subsidiary (Non-US):

Amcor Flexibles Lugo **(3)**
2 Via Dalmastro, 36030, Lugo di Vicenza,
Italy
Tel.: (39) 0445329111

Flexible Packaging Mfr
N.A.I.C.S.: 322220

**Amcor Flexibles Phetchaburi Co.,
Ltd.** **(3)**
32 Moo 1 Petkasem Road, Khao Yoi,
76140, Phetchaburi, Thailand
Tel.: (66) 3256186065
Packaging Services
N.A.I.C.S.: 561910

Subsidiary (US):

Amcor Flexibles Puerto Rico Inc. **(3)**
50 Calle Baldorioty, Cidra, PR 00739-3436
Tel.: (787) 739-8667
Packaging Paper Products Mfr
N.A.I.C.S.: 322220

Subsidiary (Non-US):

Amcor Flexibles Rorschach AG **(3)**
Langrutistrasse 19, 9403, Goldach, Switzer-
land
Tel.: (41) 718443333
Sales Range: $75-99.9 Million
Emp.: 300
Packaging Services
N.A.I.C.S.: 561910

**Amcor Flexibles Sarrebourg
S.A.S.** **(3)**
48 Route de Sarreguemines, BP 50014,
57402, Sarrebourg, France
Tel.: (33) 387245300
Sales Range: $125-149.9 Million
Emp.: 300
Packaging Paper Products Mfr
N.A.I.C.S.: 322220

**Amcor Flexibles Singapore Pte
Ltd** **(3)**
98 Tuas Bay Drive, Singapore, 636833,
Singapore
Tel.: (65) 64505100
Sales Range: $25-49.9 Million
Emp.: 40
Packaging Materials Mfr & Distr
N.A.I.C.S.: 322220

Amcor Flexibles Singen GmbH **(3)**
AlusingenPlatz 1, 78224, Singen, Germany
Tel.: (49) 7731804
Sales Range: $400-449.9 Million
Emp.: 1,100
Aluminum Packaging Mfr
N.A.I.C.S.: 331315
Ludwig Wandinger *(Mng Dir)*

**Amcor Flexibles Transpac
B.V.B.A** **(3)**
Ottergemsesteenweg Zuid 801, Gent, 9000,
Belgium
Tel.: (32) 9 2408 211
Sales Range: $125-149.9 Million
Emp.: 400
Plastic Packaging Products Mfr
N.A.I.C.S.: 326199

Amcor Flexibles UK Ltd. **(3)**
83 Tower Road North, Warmley, Bristol,
BS30 8XP, United Kingdom   **(100%)**
Tel.: (44) 1179753200
Rev.: $1,000,000
Emp.: 40
Mfr of Flexible, Tobacco & Medical Packag-
ing
N.A.I.C.S.: 322220

Amcor Flexibles Zutphen B.V. **(3)**
Finsestraat 1, 7202 CE, Zutphen, Nether-
lands
Tel.: (31) 575599500
Sales Range: $150-199.9 Million
Emp.: 122
Flexible Packaging Mfr
N.A.I.C.S.: 322220

Subsidiary (Non-US):

Amcor Packaging UK Limited **(2)**
83 Tower Road North, Warmley, Bristol,
BS30 8XP, United Kingdom
Tel.: (44) 1179753000
Sales Range: $1-4.9 Billion
Emp.: 9,000
Tobacco Packaging & Flexible Packaging
Mfr
N.A.I.C.S.: 561910

Subsidiary (US):

Amcor Rigid Plastics USA, Inc. **(2)**
935 Technology Dr Ste 100, Ann Arbor, MI
48108   **(100%)**
Tel.: (734) 428-9741
Sales Range: $1-4.9 Billion
Emp.: 5,800
Plastic Packaging Products Mfr
N.A.I.C.S.: 322219

Plant (Domestic):

**Amcor Rigid Plastics USA, Inc. -
Tumwater Plant** **(3)**
3045 32nd Ave SE, Tumwater, WA 98512-
6161
Tel.: (360) 943-2527
Sales Range: $200-249.9 Million
Emp.: 570
Plastics Bottle Mfr
N.A.I.C.S.: 326160

Subsidiary (Non-US):

**Amcor Rigid Plastics de Mexico S.A.
de C.V.** **(3)**
Rogelio Gonzalez Caballero No 850 Parque
Ind Stiva, Apodaca, 66600, Nuevo Leon,
Mexico
Tel.: (52) 811 156 0200
Commercial Packaging Services
N.A.I.C.S.: 561910

**Amcor Rigid Plastics de Venezuela
S.A.** **(2)**
Calle Este-Oeste 4 Con Calle Norte-Sur 5,
Valencia, Carabobo, Venezuela
Tel.: (58) 2418391000
Sales Range: $200-249.9 Million
Emp.: 520
Plastic Foam Product Mfr
N.A.I.C.S.: 326140
Ernesto Molina *(Gen Mgr)*

**Amcor Tobacco Packaging Brabant
B.V.** **(2)**
Burgerhout 25, 4613 BZ, Bergen-op-Zoom,
Netherlands
Tel.: (31) 164212400
Sales Range: $100-124.9 Million
Emp.: 52
Tobacco Packaging Mfr
N.A.I.C.S.: 322220

**Amcor Tobacco Packaging
Novgorod** **(2)**
Rabochaya Street 15, Velikiy Novgorod,
173008, Russia
Tel.: (7) 8162643177
Web Site: http://www.amcor.com
Emp.: 400
Packaging Paper Products Whslr
N.A.I.C.S.: 424130

**Amcor Tobacco Packaging Polska
Spolka z.o.o** **(2)**
Ul Aleksandrowska 55, Lodz, 91-205, Po-
land
Tel.: (48) 426138138
Web Site: http://www.amcor.com
Packaging Container Mfr
N.A.I.C.S.: 332439

**Amcor Tobacco Packaging Switzer-
land GmbH** **(2)**
Industriestrasse W6, Rickenbach, 4613,
Switzerland
Tel.: (41) 622090111
Sales Range: $125-149.9 Million
Emp.: 300
Tobacco Packaging Products Mfr
N.A.I.C.S.: 322220
Frank Strube *(Gen Mgr)*

Joint Venture (Non-US):

BERICAP North America, Inc. **(2)**
835 Syscon Court, Burlington, L7L 6C5,
ON, Canada
Tel.: (905) 634-2248
Sales Range: $50-74.9 Million
Emp.: 40
Plastic Bottle Cap & Other Packaging En-
closure Products Mfr & Distr
N.A.I.C.S.: 326199

Subsidiary (US):

BERICAP, LLC **(3)**

1671 Champagne Ave Ste B, Ontario, CA
91761-3650
Tel.: (909) 390-5518
Web Site: http://www.bericap.com
Plastic Bottle Cap & Other Packaging En-
closure Products Mfr & Distr
N.A.I.C.S.: 326199

Subsidiary (Domestic):

BERICAP SC LLC **(4)**
1300 Mount Olive Rd, Cowpens, SC 29330
Tel.: (864) 463-1967
Emp.: 100
Plastic Cap & Closure Mfr
N.A.I.C.S.: 326199

Subsidiary (US):

Deluxe Packages **(2)**
800 N Walton Ave, Yuba City, CA 95993-
9352
Tel.: (530) 671-9000
Web Site: http://www.deluxepackages.com
Printing
N.A.I.C.S.: 323111

Subsidiary (Non-US):

Rio Tinto Alcan Packaging Group **(2)**
Immeuble Lesignac 1 Ave Ge Gaulbe,
92230, Gennevilliers, France
Tel.: (33) 157002000
Web Site:
    http://www.alcanpackagingfood.com
Flexible Pharmaceutical, Food & Tobacco
Packaging Mfr
N.A.I.C.S.: 322220

Plant (Non-US):

Alcan Packaging Baie D'urfe **(3)**
19701 Clark Graham Boulevard, Baie-
d'Urfe, H9X 3T1, QC, Canada
Tel.: (514) 457-4555
Sales Range: $125-149.9 Million
Emp.: 150
Pharmaceutical Packaging Mfr
N.A.I.C.S.: 322220

Subsidiary (Non-US):

**Alcan Packaging Izmir Gravur Baskili
Karton Sanayi Ve Ticaret AS** **(3)**
10006 1 Sk No 6 Staturk Organize Sanayi
Bolgesi Cigli, Izmir, 335620, Turkiye
Tel.: (90) 2323768758
Sales Range: $125-149.9 Million
Emp.: 170
Flexible Packaging Mfr
N.A.I.C.S.: 322220

Plant (Non-US):

Alcan Packaging Lainate **(3)**
Via Don L Sturzo 38, 20020, Lainate, Milan,
Italy
Tel.: (39) 02937501
Web Site: http://www.alcan.com
Sales Range: $150-199.9 Million
Emp.: 150
Flexible Food Packaging Mfr
N.A.I.C.S.: 322220

Subsidiary (Non-US):

Alcan Packaging Rorschach AG **(3)**
Langrutistrasse 19, 9403, Rorschach, Swit-
zerland
Tel.: (41) 718443333
Sales Range: $300-349.9 Million
Emp.: 275
Aluminum Food Packaging Mfr
N.A.I.C.S.: 331315
Laurent Mangnan *(Gen Mgr)*

**Alcan Technology & Management
AG** **(3)**
Badische Bahnofstrasse 16, 8212, Neu-
hausen, Switzerland
Tel.: (41) 526749201
Sales Range: $125-149.9 Million
Emp.: 140
Business Process Consulting, Engineering
& Research Services
N.A.I.C.S.: 541690

Subsidiary (Domestic):

Amcor Flexibles Saint Maur **(3)**
10 Avenue Raspail, 94103, Saint Maur-des-

Amcor plc—(Continued)

Fosses, Cedex, France
Tel.: (33) 145114000
Emp.: 100
Packaging Materials Mfr
N.A.I.C.S.: 322220

Subsidiary (Non-US):

Vinisa Fueguina S.R.L **(2)**
Perito Moreno 1793, Ushuaia, Tierra Del
Fuego, Argentina
Tel.: (54) 2901423444
Emp.: 80
Packaging Materials Mfr
N.A.I.C.S.: 322220

Zimmerlund & Co. **(2)**
Bernt Ankersgt 10B, 0183, Oslo, Norway
Tel.: (47) 22416226
N.A.I.C.S.: 322120

Bemis Company, Inc. **(1)**
2301 Industrial Dr, Neenah, WI 54956
Tel.: (920) 527-5000
Web Site: http://www.bemis.com
Rev.: $4,089,900,000
Assets: $3,571,000,000
Liabilities: $2,355,100,000
Net Worth: $1,215,900,000
Earnings: $225,700,000
Emp.: 15,700
Fiscal Year-end: 12/31/2018
Flexible Packaging & Pressure Sensitive
Products Mfr & Retailer
N.A.I.C.S.: 322220
Jorg Schneewind (Pres-Healthcare Packaging)

Subsidiary (Non-US):

American Plast S.A. **(2)**
Avenida Del Sesquicentenario 4055 Pablo
Nogues 1616, Buenos Aires,
Argentina **(100%)**
Tel.: (54) 1144896200
Plastics Product Mfr
N.A.I.C.S.: 326199
Luis Omar Oddone (Vice Chm)

Bemis (Shanghai) Trading Co.,
Ltd. **(2)**
Room 605 No 500 Fushan Road, Pudong,
Shanghai, 200122, China
Tel.: (86) 2150589370
Flexible Packaging Mfr
N.A.I.C.S.: 326199

Bemis Asia Pacific Sdn Bhd **(2)**
No 8 Jalan TP 5 Taman Perindustrian Sime
UEP, Subang Jaya, 47620, Selangor, Malaysia
Tel.: (60) 380266488
Web Site: http://www.bemis.com
Sales Range: $25-49.9 Million
Emp.: 145
Mfr of Laminates
N.A.I.C.S.: 322220

Bemis Brisbane Pty Ltd **(2)**
27 Union Circuit, Yatala, 4207, QLD, Australia
Tel.: (61) 733809111
Web Site: http://www.bemis.com
Emp.: 60
Paper Mfr
N.A.I.C.S.: 322299

Subsidiary (Domestic):

Bemis Clysar, Inc. **(2)**
2200 Badger Ave, Oshkosh, WI 54904
Tel.: (920) 527-7300
Web Site: http://www.bemis.com
Sales Range: $10-24.9 Million
Emp.: 5
Supplier Polyolefin Shrink Film
N.A.I.C.S.: 326113

Unit (Domestic):

Bemis Company **(2)**
1350 N Fruitridge Ave, Terre Haute, IN
47804-1716
Tel.: (812) 466-2213
Sales Range: $300-349.9 Million
Emp.: 1,000
Polyethylene Bags & Film Converter
N.A.I.C.S.: 326113

Bemis Custom Products **(2)**
720 Eagle Blvd, Shelbyville, TN 37160
Tel.: (931) 680-4000
Sales Range: $75-99.9 Million
Emp.: 220
Flexible Packaging Mfr
N.A.I.C.S.: 322220

Subsidiary (Non-US):

Bemis Deutschland Holdings
GmbH **(2)**
Muhlgrabenstr 7-9 North Rhine-Westphalia,
Meckenheim, 53340, Germany
Tel.: (49) 222592130
Web Site: http://www.bemis.com
Sales Range: $25-49.9 Million
Emp.: 30
Plastics Product Mfr
N.A.I.C.S.: 326199

Bemis Europe Flexible
Packaging **(2)**
176 Rue Des Piges, 6031, Charleroi, Belgium
Tel.: (32) 71277700
Web Site: http://www.bemis-europe.com
Sales Range: $25-49.9 Million
Emp.: 70
Flexible Packaging Mfr & Distr
N.A.I.C.S.: 322220

Bemis Flexible Packaging (Suzhou)
Co., Ltd. **(2)**
128 Xing Pu Road T Block Unit 02, Suzhou
Industrial Park, Suzhou, 215126, China
Tel.: (86) 512262797818
Web Site: http://www.bemis.com
Emp.: 71
Plastics Product Mfr
N.A.I.C.S.: 326199

Bemis Mayor Packaging Limited **(2)**
11F Kinsang Commercial Center 49 King
Yip St, Kwun Tong, Kowloon, China (Hong
Kong)
Tel.: (852) 23425194
Web Site: http://www.mayor.com.hk
Emp.: 30
Packaging Container Mfr
N.A.I.C.S.: 326199
Thomas Wong (Mng Dir)

Bemis Monceau S.A. **(2)**
Rue Piges 176, Monceau-Sur-Sambre,
Charleroi, 6031, Belgium
Tel.: (32) 71277700
Web Site: http://www.bemis.com
Emp.: 100
Packaging Film Mfr
N.A.I.C.S.: 322220

Bemis Packaging Deutschland
GmbH **(2)**
Egermannstrasse 1, 53359, Rheinbach,
Germany
Tel.: (49) 2226892880
Packaging Product Distr
N.A.I.C.S.: 424130

Bemis Packaging Mexico, S.A. de
C.V. **(2)**
Barroteran No 3047, Tlaquepaque, 45500,
Mexico
Tel.: (52) 3336681349
Gasket Packing & Sealing Mfr
N.A.I.C.S.: 339991

Bemis Packaging Polska Sp.
z.o.o. **(2)**
Centrum Biznesu Ozarow Ul Ozarowska
40/42, 05-850, Duchnice, Poland
Tel.: (48) 227217582
Web Site: http://www.bemis.com
Emp.: 10
Packaging Container Mfr
N.A.I.C.S.: 326199

Bemis Packaging Sverige A.B. **(2)**
Hemsogatan 10 A S, 211 24, Malmo, Sweden
Tel.: (46) 40285560
Web Site: http://www.bemis.com
Emp.: 2
Flexible Packaging Products Mfr
N.A.I.C.S.: 322220

Subsidiary (Domestic):

Bemis Performance Packaging,
Inc. **(2)**

2451 Badger Ave, Oshkosh, WI 54904
Tel.: (920) 303-8600
Web Site: http://www.bemispackaging.com
Rev.: $60,000,000
Emp.: 1,000
Flexible Packaging Materials
N.A.I.C.S.: 322220

Subsidiary (Non-US):

Bemis Elsham Limited **(3)**
The Flarepath Elsham Wold Industrial Estate, North Lincolnshire, Brigg, DN20 0SP,
United Kingdom
Tel.: (44) 1652680680
Web Site: http://www.bemis.com
Plastics Product Mfr
N.A.I.C.S.: 326199

Subsidiary (Non-US):

Bemis Piatra Neamt **(2)**
Strada Chimiei nr 1, 617410, Savinesti,
Romania
Tel.: (40) 233282828
Packaged Food Distr
N.A.I.C.S.: 424420

Bemis SAS **(2)**
Rue Des Hirondelles, Droue Dur Drouette,
F 28230, Epernon, Cedex, France **(100%)**
Tel.: (33) 237185550
Sales Range: $10-24.9 Million
Emp.: 40
Printing of Packaging Films
N.A.I.C.S.: 326112

Bemis Valkeakoski Oy **(2)**
Teollisuustie 1, PO Box 70, 37600,
Valkeakoski, Finland **(100%)**
Tel.: (358) 207513100
Web Site: http://www.nordicnet.net
Plastic Packaging Films & Pouches
N.A.I.C.S.: 322220

Curwood, Inc. **(2)**
Tel.: (920) 303-7300
Web Site: http://www.curwood.com
Sales Range: $700-749.9 Million
Emp.: 3,500
Laminated & Resealable Packaging & Printing Services
N.A.I.C.S.: 322220

Subsidiary (Non-US):

Bemis Flexible Packaging Canada
Limited **(3)**
Tel.: (416) 742-8910
Sales Range: $50-74.9 Million
Emp.: 153
Folding Paperboard Box Mfr
N.A.I.C.S.: 322212

Perfecseal, Inc. **(3)**
Tel.: (920) 303-7000
Web Site: http://www.perfecseal.com
Sales Range: $100-124.9 Million
Emp.: 800
Medical & Pharmaceutical Packaging Solutions
N.A.I.C.S.: 322220

Subsidiary (Non-US):

Dixie Toga SA **(2)**
Av Mario Haberfeld 555 - Parque Novo,
Mundo, 02145-000, Sao Paulo, SP, Brazil
Tel.: (55) 1129289200
Web Site: http://www.dixietoga.com.br
Sales Range: $600-649.9 Million
Packaging & Labeling Services
N.A.I.C.S.: 561910
Henry J. Theisen (Chm)

Subsidiary (Domestic):

Emplal Participacoes S.A. **(3)**
Alameda Araguaia 3327 Alphaville industrial, Barueri, 06455-000, Sao Paulo, Brazil
Tel.: (55) 1137955000
Extruded Plastic Molded Products Mfr
N.A.I.C.S.: 326199

Subsidiary (Domestic):

Emplal Nordeste Embalagens Plasticas Ltda. **(4)**
Estrada TDR Norte 7, 54590-000, Cabo de
Santo Agostinho, Pernambuco, Brazil
Tel.: (55) 8135276450

Emp.: 138
Packaging Supply Mfr
N.A.I.C.S.: 326199
Edilson Silva (Supvr-Quality)

Subsidiary (Non-US):

Dongguan Wonderful Packaging
Company Limited **(2)**
Xiangshan Industry City, Dalang, Dongguan, 523770, China
Tel.: (86) 76981114255
Plastic & Laminated Coated Bag Mfr
N.A.I.C.S.: 322220

Evadix Labels S.R.L. **(2)**
Strada Chimiei 1, Savinesti, 617410, Romania
Tel.: (40) 233281410
Packaging Products Mfr
N.A.I.C.S.: 326199

AMCORP GROUP BERHAD
2-01 Amcorp Tower 18 Persiaran Barat, Petaling Jaya, 46050, Malaysia
Tel.: (60) 37966 2300
Web Site: http://www.amcorp.com.my
Year Founded: 1911
Investment Holding Company
N.A.I.C.S.: 551112
Azman Hashim (Chm)

Subsidiaries:

Amcorp Properties Berhad **(1)**
2-01 PJ Tower 18 Persiaran Barat, 46050,
Petaling Jaya, Selangor, Malaysia **(71%)**
Tel.: (60) 379662628
Web Site: http://www.amcorpproperties.com
Rev.: $34,552,238
Assets: $453,852,135
Liabilities: $105,023,903
Net Worth: $348,828,233
Earnings: $3,626,618
Emp.: 158
Fiscal Year-end: 03/31/2021
Engineering & Construction Services
N.A.I.C.S.: 541330
Johnson Choon Seng Yap (Co-Sec)

Subsidiary (Domestic):

Blue Star M & E Engineering Sdn
Bhd **(2)**
13 Fl Manera Jalan Lumut, Jalan Lumut
Kompleks Damai, Kuala Lumpur, 50400,
Malaysia
Tel.: (60) 340418261
Web Site: http://www.mcorpproperties.com
Sales Range: $25-49.9 Million
Emp.: 31
Engineeering Services
N.A.I.C.S.: 541330

AMD INDUSTRIES LIMITED
18 Pusa Road Ist Floor, Karol Bagh,
New Delhi, 110 005, India
Tel.: (91) 1146830202
Web Site:
https://www.amdindustries.com
Year Founded: 1983
532828—(BOM)
Rev.: $28,751,213
Assets: $40,338,166
Liabilities: $21,211,295
Net Worth: $19,126,871
Earnings: $1,119,013
Emp.: 233
Fiscal Year-end: 03/31/22
Metal Packaging Services
N.A.I.C.S.: 561910
Ashok Gupta (Chm)

AMDOCS LIMITED
Hirzel House Smith Street, Saint Peter Port, GY1 2NG, Guernsey
Tel.: (44) 1481728444 **GY**
Web Site: https://www.amdocs.com
DOX—(NASDAQ)
Rev.: $5,004,989,000
Assets: $6,386,142,000
Liabilities: $2,886,965,000
Net Worth: $3,499,177,000

Earnings: $496,321,000
Emp.: 29,058
Fiscal Year-end: 09/30/24
Holding Company; Computer Services
N.A.I.C.S.: 551112
Tamar Rapaport-Dagim (CFO & COO)

Subsidiaries:

Amdocs Canadian Managed Services, Inc. **(1)**
1705 Tech Avenue Unit 2, Mississauga, L4W 0A2, ON, Canada
Tel.: (905) 614-4000
N.A.I.C.S.: 513210

Amdocs Inc. **(1)**
1390 Timberlake Manor Pkwy, Chesterfield, MO 63017-6041
Tel.: (314) 212-7000
Web Site: http://www.amdocs.com
Operations Support Software for Networks & Telecommunications Services
N.A.I.C.S.: 513210

Subsidiary (Non-US):

Actix Limited **(2)**
Building 4 Chiswick Park 3rd Floor 566 Chiswick Park Road, London, W4 5YE, United Kingdom
Tel.: (44) 208 727 2718
Web Site: http://www.actix.com
Software Development Services
N.A.I.C.S.: 541511
Vo Thanh (Dir-Global IT)

Amdocs (Finland) Oy **(2)**
Tehtaankatu 10, 00140, Helsinki, Finland
Tel.: (358) 50 388 8800
Computer System Design Services
N.A.I.C.S.: 541512

Amdocs (Italy) SRL **(2)**
Via di Tor Pagnotta 94, 00143, Rome, Italy
Tel.: (39) 06 0190 8401
Software Development Services
N.A.I.C.S.: 513210

Amdocs (Portugal) Software, Unipessoal Lda. **(2)**
Av das Forcas Armadas 125, Lisbon, 1600-079, Portugal
Tel.: (351) 21 799 7040
Software Developer
N.A.I.C.S.: 513210

Amdocs Australia Proprietary Limited **(2)**
Level 25 35 Collins Street, Melbourne, 3000, VIC, Australia
Tel.: (61) 3 9835 3200
Web Site: http://www.amdocs.com
Sales Range: $10-24.9 Million
Emp.: 40
Supplies Customer & Business Operations Management Software & Services to the Telecom Industry
N.A.I.C.S.: 541511

Amdocs B.V. **(2)**
Renier Nafzgerstraat 100-B, 6221, Maastricht, Netherlands
Tel.: (31) 43 351 5454
Software Development Services
N.A.I.C.S.: 513210

Amdocs Brazil Limitada **(2)**
Rua Bandeira Paulista, 702 8 Andar Itaim, CEP 04532 002, Sao Paulo, SP, Brazil
Tel.: (55) 1130404700
Web Site: http://www.amdocs.com.br
Sales Range: $10-24.9 Million
Emp.: 200
Supplies Customer & Business Operations Management Software & Services to the Telecom Industry
N.A.I.C.S.: 541511

Amdocs Canada, Inc. **(2)**
2 Bloor Street East Suite 400, Toronto, M4W 3Y7, ON, Canada
Tel.: (416) 355-4000
Web Site: http://www.amdocs.com
Sales Range: $50-74.9 Million
Emp.: 210
N.A.I.C.S.: 334418

Subsidiary (Domestic):

Amdocs Holdings ULC **(3)**
1705 Tech Avenue Unit 2, Mississauga, L4W 0A2, ON, Canada
Tel.: (416) 355-4001
Web Site: http://www.amdocs.com
Emp.: 88
Investment Management Service
N.A.I.C.S.: 523999

Subsidiary (Domestic):

Amdocs Champaign, Inc. **(2)**
2109 Fox Dr, Champaign, IL 61820
Tel.: (217) 353-7000
Software Publisher
N.A.I.C.S.: 513210

Subsidiary (Non-US):

Amdocs Chile SPA **(2)**
Av Del Condor 720 Huechuraba, Santiago, Chile
Tel.: (56) 2 2731 1000
Software Publisher
N.A.I.C.S.: 513210

Amdocs Development Centre India Private Limited **(2)**
Cybercity Tower 2, Magarpatta City Hadapsar, Pune, 411013, India
Tel.: (91) 20 40153000
Customer Relation Management Software Development Services
N.A.I.C.S.: 541511

Amdocs Hellas Ltd. **(2)**
Leof Kifisias, 151 24, Maroussi, Greece
Tel.: (30) 21 0727 9292
Computer System Design Services
N.A.I.C.S.: 541512

Branch (Domestic):

Amdocs Inc. - California **(2)**
1104 Investment Blvd, El Dorado Hills, CA 95762
Tel.: (916) 934-7000
Web Site: http://www.amdocs.com
Billing & Customer Management Software for Voice, Video & Data Services Markets
N.A.I.C.S.: 541511

Amdocs Inc. - San Jose **(2)**
2545 N 1st St, San Jose, CA 95131-1033
Tel.: (408) 965-7000
Web Site: http://www.amdocs.com
Sales Range: $100-124.9 Million
Emp.: 400
Supplier of Customer & Business Operations Management Software & Services to the Telecom Industry
N.A.I.C.S.: 517810

Amdocs Inc. - Seattle **(2)**
2211 Elliott Ave Ste 400, Seattle, WA 98121
Tel.: (206) 447-6000
Web Site: http://www.amdocs.com
Sales Range: $100-124.9 Million
Emp.: 300
Software Publisher
N.A.I.C.S.: 513210

Subsidiary (Non-US):

Amdocs Investments Switzerland Limited **(2)**
East Point Business Park 1st Floor Block S, Dublin, Ireland
Tel.: (353) 1 693 3669
Investment Services
N.A.I.C.S.: 523999

Amdocs Japan **(2)**
Tanbaya Bldg 3F 3 2 4 Kojimachi, Chiyoda Ku, Tokyo, 102 0083, Japan
Tel.: (81) 335141840
Web Site: http://www.amdocs.co.jp
Sales Range: $25-49.9 Million
Emp.: 12
Supplies Customer & Business Operations Management Software & Services to the Telecom Industry
N.A.I.C.S.: 541511

Amdocs Management Limited **(2)**
15 Fetter Lane, London, EC4A 1BW, United Kingdom
Tel.: (44) 2073432500
Web Site: http://www.amdocs.com

Sales Range: $25-49.9 Million
Emp.: 80
Customer & Business Operations, Management Software & Services to the Telecom Industry
N.A.I.C.S.: 541511

Subsidiary (Non-US):

Amdocs (CR) S.R.O. **(3)**
Amdocs PDC Delnicka 12, Rosmarin Business Centre, 170 00, Prague, 7, Czech Republic
Tel.: (420) 266773222
Web Site: http://www.amdocs.com
Sales Range: $10-24.9 Million
Emp.: 50
Supplier of Customer & Business Operations, Management Software & Services to the Telecom Industry
N.A.I.C.S.: 541511

Amdocs (Israel) Limited **(3)**
8 Hapnina St, Ra'anana, 43000, Israel
Tel.: (972) 97762222
Web Site: http://www.amdocs.com
Supplies Customer & Business Operations Management Software & Services to the Telecom Industry
N.A.I.C.S.: 541511

Subsidiary (Domestic):

Amdocs (UK) Limited **(3)**
15 Fetter Ln, 25 Farringdon St, London, EC4A 1BR, United Kingdom
Tel.: (44) 2073432500
Sales Range: $25-49.9 Million
Emp.: 100
Supplies Customer & Business Operations Management Software & Services to the Telecom Industry
N.A.I.C.S.: 541511
Kevin Picker (Mng Dir)

Subsidiary (Domestic):

Amdocs Systems Group Limited **(4)**
The Square, Lower Bristol Road, Bath, BA2 3BH, United Kingdom
Tel.: (44) 1225471300
Web Site: http://www.amdocs.com
Sales Range: $25-49.9 Million
Telecommunications Software Developer
N.A.I.C.S.: 513210

Subsidiary (Domestic):

Amdocs Systems Europe Limited **(5)**
Building 4 3rd Floor Chiswick Park Estate 566 Chiswick High Road, London, W4 5YE, United Kingdom
Tel.: (44) 208 727 2500
Software Publisher
N.A.I.C.S.: 513210

Amdocs Systems Limited **(5)**
Building 4 3rd Floor Chiswick Park Estate 566 Chiswick High Road, London, W4 5YE, United Kingdom
Tel.: (44) 208 727 2500
Software Publisher
N.A.I.C.S.: 513210

Cramer Systems International Limited **(5)**
Building 4 3rd Floor Chiswick Park Estate 566 Chiswick High Road, London, W4 5YE, United Kingdom
Tel.: (44) 208 727 2500
Software Publisher
N.A.I.C.S.: 513210

Subsidiary (Domestic):

European Support Limited **(4)**
15 Fetter ln, London, E4A A1BR, United Kingdom
Tel.: (44) 2073432500
Emp.: 153
Supplier of Customer & Business Operations, Management Software & Services to the Telecom Industry
N.A.I.C.S.: 541511

JacobsRimell **(4)**
Cutler Ct 4th Fl, 115 Houndsditch, London, EC3A 7BR, United Kingdom
Tel.: (44) 2070744100
Web Site: http://www.jacobsrimell.com

Sales Range: $10-24.9 Million
Emp.: 50
Fulfillment Solutions for Broadband Cable Industry
N.A.I.C.S.: 541519

Subsidiary (Non-US):

Amdocs Development Limited **(3)**
141 Omonia Ave The Maritime Ctr, PO Box 50483, Limassol, 3045, Cyprus
Tel.: (357) 25886000
Web Site: http://www.amdocs.com
Sales Range: $75-99.9 Million
Supplier of Customer & Business Operations, Management Software & Services to the Telecom Industry
N.A.I.C.S.: 541511

Division (Non-US):

Amdocs Digital Commerce Division **(3)**
Dammstrasse 4/2, 6923, Lauterach, Austria
Tel.: (43) 1532 64640
Web Site: http://www.amdocs.com
Software Development Services
N.A.I.C.S.: 541511

Subsidiary (Non-US):

Amdocs France **(3)**
10 Ave De Larche, 92419, Courbevoie, Cedex, France
Tel.: (33) 146911152
Sales Range: $25-49.9 Million
Emp.: 15
N.A.I.C.S.: 334418

Amdocs International GmbH **(3)**
Bahnhofstrasse 25, Zug, 6300, Switzerland
Tel.: (41) 417278696
Software Development Services
N.A.I.C.S.: 541511

Amdocs Software GmbH **(3)**
Forumstrasse 26, 41468, Neuss, Germany
Tel.: (49) 21313480
Web Site: http://www.amdocs.com
Sales Range: $25-49.9 Million
Emp.: 75
Supplies Customer & Business Operations Management Software & Services to the Telecom Industry
N.A.I.C.S.: 541511

Amdocs Software Systems Ltd. **(3)**
1st Fl Block S East Point Business Park, Dublin, 3, Ireland
Tel.: (353) 14393600
Web Site: http://www.amdocs.com
Sales Range: $25-49.9 Million
Emp.: 70
Supplier of Customer & Business Operations, Management Software & Services to the Telecom Industry
N.A.I.C.S.: 541511

Subsidiary (Non-US):

Amdocs Mexico S. De R.L. De C.V. **(2)**
Av Rafael Sanzio 150 Camichines Vallarta, Col Palmas Polanco, 45020, Zapopan, Mexico
Tel.: (52) 33 3777 0555
Software Publisher
N.A.I.C.S.: 513210

Amdocs Philippines Inc. **(2)**
12F Net One Center Bldg Bonifacio Global City, Taguig, 1634, Philippines
Tel.: (63) 2 479 5400
Software Development Services
N.A.I.C.S.: 513210

Subsidiary (Domestic):

Amdocs Qpass Inc. **(2)**
1390 Timberlake Manor Pkwy, Chesterfield, MO 63017
Tel.: (314) 212-7000
Software Publisher
N.A.I.C.S.: 513210

Subsidiary (Non-US):

Amdocs Singapore Pte. Ltd. **(2)**
9 Temasek Boulevard 16-04 Suntec Tower 2, Singapore, 038989, Singapore
Tel.: (65) 6602 7300

Amdocs Limited—(Continued)

Information Technology Consulting Services
N.A.I.C.S.: 541618

Amdocs Tethys Limited (2)
East Point Business Park 1st Floor Block S,
Dublin, Ireland
Tel.: (353) 1 693 3669
Computer System Design Services
N.A.I.C.S.: 541512

**Amdocs Vietnam Company
Limited** (2)
10th Floor Pacific Place Building Suite
1004, 83B Ly Thuong Kiet Str Hoan Kiem
Dist, Hanoi, Vietnam
Tel.: (84) 4 3946 1043
Software Publisher
N.A.I.C.S.: 513210

Subsidiary (Domestic):

**Celcite Management Solutions,
LLC** (2)
2553 Dulles View Dr 5th Fl, Herndon, VA
20171
Tel.: (703) 879-3879
Web Site: http://www.celcite.com
Emp.: 25
Other Scientific & Technical Consulting Services
N.A.I.C.S.: 541690
Anitha Sing (Mgr)

Projekt202 LLC (2)
1300 Guadalupe St Ste 300, Austin, TX
78701
Tel.: (512) 485-3070
Web Site: http://www.projekt202.com
Sales Range: $1-9.9 Million
Emp.: 55
Software
N.A.I.C.S.: 513210
Peter Eckert (Co-Founder & Chief Experience Officer)

Subsidiary (Domestic):

Big Nerd Ranch, LLC (3)
200 Arizona Ave NE, Atlanta, GA 30307
Tel.: (770) 817-6373
Web Site: http://www.bignerdranch.com
Sales Range: $1-9.9 Million
Emp.: 33
Educational Support Services
N.A.I.C.S.: 611710
Aaron Hillegass (Founder & Co-CEO)

Subsidiary (Domestic):

Vindicia, Inc. (2)
1800 Gateway Dr 100, Foster City, CA
94404
Tel.: (650) 522-4480
Web Site: http://www.vindicia.com
Sales Range: $1-9.9 Million
Emp.: 25
Security System Services
N.A.I.C.S.: 561621
Brett Thomas (CTO)

Vubiquity, Inc. (2)
3900 W Alemda Ste 1700, Burbank, CA
91505
Tel.: (818) 526-5000
Web Site: http://www.vubiquity.com
Multiplatform Video Services
N.A.I.C.S.: 516210
John Smith (Sr VP-Studio Sls-North
America)

Subsidiary (Non-US):

Vubiquity Group Limited (3)
3 More London Riverside, London, SE1
2AQ, United Kingdom
Tel.: (44) 208 727 2777
Video Content Services
N.A.I.C.S.: 516210

Subsidiary (Domestic):

Vubiquity Management Limited (4)
3 More London Riverside, London, SE1
2AQ, United Kingdom
Tel.: (44) 208 727 2777
Video Content Services
N.A.I.C.S.: 516210

Brite:Bill Group Limited (1)

7 Grand Canal Street Lower, Dublin, Ireland
Tel.: (353) 1 661 9426
Web Site: http://www.britebill.com
Billing Communications Services
N.A.I.C.S.: 522320
Gus Legge (Head-Product R&D)

Subsidiary (Domestic):

**Brite:Bill Employment Company
Limited** (2)
East Point Business Park 1st Floor Block S,
Dublin, Ireland
Tel.: (353) 1 693 3669
Financial Transaction Processing Services
N.A.I.C.S.: 522320

Brite:Bill Limited (2)
7 Grand Canal Street Lower, Dublin, Ireland
Tel.: (353) 1 661 9426
Mobile Billing Services
N.A.I.C.S.: 522320

Kenzan Media, LLC (1)
111 8th Ave 13th Fl, New York, NY 10011
Tel.: (212) 239-1010
Web Site: http://www.kenzan.com
Software Development Services
N.A.I.C.S.: 541511
Andy Pope (Head-Consulting)

Openet Telecom Ltd. (1)
6 Beckett Way Park West Business Park,
Dublin, 12, Ireland
Tel.: (353) 16204600
Web Site: http://www.openet.com
Software Development Services
N.A.I.C.S.: 541511
Niall Norton (CEO)

Subsidiary (Non-US):

Openet Japan (2)
Level 11 Aoyama Palacio Tower 3-6-7 Kita
Aoyama, Minato-ku, Tokyo, 107-0061, Japan
Tel.: (81) 3 5778 7825
Web Site: http://www.openet.com
Software Development Services
N.A.I.C.S.: 513210

**Openet Telecom Malaysia Sdn
Bhd.** (2)
Level 26 Centrepoint South The Boulevard
Mid Valley City, Lingkaran Syed Putra,
59200, Kuala Lumpur, Malaysia
Tel.: (60) 3 2 289 8500
Web Site: http://www.openet.com
Software Development Services
N.A.I.C.S.: 513210

Subsidiary (Domestic):

Openet Telecom Sales Limited (2)
6 Beckett Way, Park West Business Park,
VX26, Dublin, Ireland
Tel.: (353) 1 620 4600
Custom Computer Programming Services
N.A.I.C.S.: 541511

Subsidiary (US):

Openet Telecom, Inc. (2)
1886 Metro Center Dr Ste 310, Reston, VA
20190
Tel.: (703) 480-1820
Web Site: http://www.openet.com
Software Development Services
N.A.I.C.S.: 513210

Orbis Investment Ltd. (2)
3rd Floor Chiswick Park Estate 566 Chiswick High Road, London, W4 5YE, United
Kingdom
Tel.: (44) 208 727 2500
Investment Services
N.A.I.C.S.: 523999

**AME ELITE CONSORTIUM
BERHAD**
No 2 Jalan I-Park SAC 2 Taman Perindustrian I-Park SAC, Senai, 81400,
Johor, Malaysia
Tel.: (60) 75959666   MY
Web Site: https://www.ame-elite.com
Year Founded: 1995
AME—(KLS)
Rev.: $121,886,177
Assets: $386,831,559

Liabilities: $149,626,175
Net Worth: $237,205,384
Earnings: $30,055,927
Emp.: 576
Fiscal Year-end: 03/31/23
Construction Services
N.A.I.C.S.: 236220
Kelvin Lee Chai (Mng Dir)

Subsidiaries:

AME Construction Sdn. Bhd. (1)
Suite 6 03 Penthouse Wisma Academy No
4A Jalan 19/1, 46300, Petaling Jaya, Selangor, Malaysia
Tel.: (60) 379322911
Web Site:
  http://www.ameconstruction.com.my
Civil Engineering Services
N.A.I.C.S.: 541330
Kelvin Lee Chai (Mng Dir)

AME Development Sdn. Bhd. (1)
No 2 Jalan I-Park SAC 1/1 Taman Perindustrian I-Park SAC, 81400, Senai, Johor,
Malaysia
Tel.: (60) 75959999
Web Site: https://www.amedev.com.my
Property Development & Management Services
N.A.I.C.S.: 531390

**AME Engineering Industries Sdn.
Bhd.** (1)
PLO 3 Jalan Persiaran Teknologi Taman
Teknologi Johor, 81400, Senai, Johor Darul
Takzim, Malaysia
Tel.: (60) 75999998
Web Site: https://ame-engi.com.my
Emp.: 100
Steel Structure Products Mfr
N.A.I.C.S.: 332312
Lim Khai Wen (Mng Dir)

Asiamost Sdn. Bhd. (1)
No 2 Jalan i-Park SAC 1/1 Taman Perindustrian I-Park SAC, 81400, Senai, Johor,
Malaysia
Tel.: (60) 75959666
Web Site: https://www.aslamost.com.my
Mechanical & Electrical Contractor Services
N.A.I.C.S.: 238210

I Stay Management Sdn. Bhd. (1)
Fasa 1A Jalan Pekeliling Seroja 28 Kawasan Perindustrian i-Park, 81000, Kulai,
Johor, Malaysia
Tel.: (60) 76607571
Web Site: https://www.istay.com.my
Property Leasing Services
N.A.I.C.S.: 531110

Ipark Development Sdn. Bhd. (1)
No 1 Jalan I-Park SAC 1 Taman Perindustrian I-Park SAC, 81400, Senai, Johor, Malaysia
Tel.: (60) 75959999
Web Site: http://www.ipark.com.my
Property Development & Management Services
N.A.I.C.S.: 531390

**Quantum Renewable Energy Sdn.
Bhd.** (1)
PLO 3 Jalan Persiaran Teknologi Taman
Teknologi Johor, 81400, Senai, Johor, Malaysia
Tel.: (60) 167104421
Web Site: https://www.quantumre.com.my
Solar Panels Installation Services
N.A.I.C.S.: 238210

**AMEDEO AIR FOUR PLUS
LIMITED**
Ground Floor Dorey Court, Saint Peter Port, GY1 2HT, Guernsey
Tel.: (44) 1481702400
AA4—(LSE)
Rev.: $230,560,673
Assets: $1,580,766,736
Liabilities: $1,153,049,544
Net Worth: $427,717,192
Earnings: $24,670,583
Fiscal Year-end: 03/31/24
Financial Management Services
N.A.I.C.S.: 523999

Robin Hallam (Chm)

AMEDEO RESOURCES PLC
201 Temple Chambers 3-7 Temple
Avenue, London, EC4Y 0DT, United
Kingdom
Tel.: (44) 207 583 8304
Web Site:
  http://www.amedeoresources.com
Sales Range: Less than $1 Million
Emp.: 4
Investment Services
N.A.I.C.S.: 523999
Glen Lau (CEO)

AMEDIA AS
Akersgata 34, PO Box 1168, Sentrum, 0107, Oslo, Norway
Tel.: (47) 22 00 90 00   NO
Web Site: http://www.amedia.no
Print & Digital Media Services & Distr
N.A.I.C.S.: 323111
Thor Gjermund Eriksen (Mng Dir)

**AMENDOAS-HERDADE DA
PALHETA I. LTD.**
Avenida da Liberdade n 249 1, 1250-143, Lisbon, Portugal
Tel.: (351) 973501212   PT
Year Founded: 2016
Dry Fruit & Nut Distr
N.A.I.C.S.: 424490

AMER GROUP HOLDING
101, El Multaqa Al Araby St Off El
Moshir Ahmed Ismail St, Sheraton,
Cairo, Egypt
Tel.: (20) 224170463
Web Site: http://www.amergroup.com
AMER—(EGX)
Rev.: $87,926,666
Assets: $527,496,566
Liabilities: $416,419,219
Net Worth: $111,077,347
Earnings: ($513,149)
Fiscal Year-end: 12/31/20
Real Estate Developer, Manager &
Operator
N.A.I.C.S.: 531390
Mansour Amer (Founder)

**AMER INTERNATIONAL
GROUP CO., LTD.**
East Pacific International Center
7888th Shennan Boulevard, Shenzhen, 518040, China
Tel.: (86) 755 82785868
Web Site: http://en.amer.com.cn
Sales Range: $25-49.9 Million
Emp.: 15,000
Non Ferrous Metal Product Mfr
N.A.I.C.S.: 331110
Wang Wen Yin (Chm)

AMERGERIS WEALTH MANAGEMENT GROUP GMBH
Baarerstrasse 75, 6300, Zug, Switzerland
Tel.: (41) 41 560 0220   CH
Web Site: http://www.amergeris.com
Rev.: $6,000,000,000
Wealth Management, Private Equity
& Investment Services
N.A.I.C.S.: 523940
Remko van Ekelen (CEO)

Subsidiaries:

**Amergeris Wealth Management
AG** (1)
Muhlebachstrasse 54, 8008, Zurich, Switzerland
Tel.: (41) 5600220
Fund Management & Investment Banking
Services
N.A.I.C.S.: 523150
Hans Herrmann (Chm)

Orient Abrasives Limited (1)
GIDC Industrial Area, Porbandar, 360 577,
Gujarat, India **(23.73%)**
Tel.: (91) 2862221788
Web Site: http://www.orientabrasives.com
Rev.: $41,515,820
Assets: $46,387,136
Liabilities: $13,327,997
Net Worth: $33,059,140
Earnings: $1,551,991
Emp.: 259
Fiscal Year-end: 03/31/2021
Aluminium Products Mfr
N.A.I.C.S.: 331313
Pundarik Sanyal *(Chm)*

AMERICA MOVIL, S.A.B. DE C.V.
Lago Zurich 245 Edificio TELCEL
Piso 16 Col Ampliacion Granada,
Miguel Hidalgo, 11529, Mexico,
Mexico
Tel.: (52) 5525813700 **MX**
Web Site:
https://www.americamovil.com
Year Founded: 2000
AMX—(NYSE)
Rev.: $49,280,304,132
Assets: $94,463,659,971
Liabilities: $1,142,483,578,000
Net Worth: $25,467,272,716
Earnings: $4,879,014,047
Emp.: 176,083
Fiscal Year-end: 12/31/23
Wireless Telecommunication Services
N.A.I.C.S.: 517112
Carlos Jose Garcia Moreno Elizondo *(CFO)*

Subsidiaries:

AM Wireless Uruguay, S.A. (1)
Av San Martin 2460, Montevideo, 11800,
Uruguay
Tel.: (598) 22011500
Web Site: https://www.claro.com.uy
Telecommunication Servicesb
N.A.I.C.S.: 517810

AMX Paraguay, S.A. (1)
Avenida Mariscal Lopez 1730, Asuncion,
Paraguay
Tel.: (595) 2499000
Web Site: https://www.claro.com.py
Wireless Telecommunication Services
N.A.I.C.S.: 517112

AMX USA Holding, S.A. de C.V. (1)
Lago Alberto No 366 Anahuac, Miguel Hi-
dalgo, Mexico, 11320, Mexico
Tel.: (52) 5525813700
Investment Management Service
N.A.I.C.S.: 523940

Subsidiary (Domestic):

**Empresas y Controles en Comunica-
ciones, S.A. de C.V.** (2)
Insurgentes Sur No 3500 P B Penaa Pobre,
Tlalpan, Mexico, 14060, Mexico
Tel.: (52) 5552440260
Telecommunication Servicesb
N.A.I.C.S.: 517112

Grupo Telvista, S.A. de C.V. (2)
Blvd Agua Caliente No 11606, Tijuana,
22014, Mexico **(51.98%)**
Tel.: (52) 664 622 6800
Sales Range: $550-599.9 Million
Emp.: 3,000
Telemarketing Services
N.A.I.C.S.: 561422

**CTI Compania de Telefonos del Inte-
rior S.A.** (1)
Avda. Presidente Figueroa Alcorta, 3259,
Buenos Aires, Argentina
Tel.: (54) 1141098888
Web Site: http://www.cti.com.ar
Sales Range: $450-499.9 Million
Emp.: 1,300
Telecommunications
N.A.I.C.S.: 517111

**Compania de Telecomunicaciones de
El Salvador (CTE), S.A. de C.V.** (1)

Colonia Y Complejo Roma, San Salvador,
El Salvador
Tel.: (503) 2 2717010
Web Site: http://www.claro.com.sv
Sales Range: $400-449.9 Million
Emp.: 2,300
Telecommunication Servicesb
N.A.I.C.S.: 517810

Subsidiary (Non-US):

Cablenet, S.A. (2)
Ave Jean Paul Genie 500 Mts Abajo, Mana-
gua, Nicaragua
Tel.: (505) 22557300
Television Broadcasting Services
N.A.I.C.S.: 516120

Subsidiary (Domestic):

Telecomoda, S.A. de C.V. (2)
Km 10 1/2 Carretera A, Santa Tecla, El
Salvador
Tel.: (503) 22717020
Telecommunications Consulting Services
N.A.I.C.S.: 541618
Enrique Luna *(Mgr-Fin)*

Nextel Telecomunicacoes Ltda. (1)
Avenida das Nacoes Unidas 14171 27 an-
dar, Cond Rochavera Corporate Towers -
Crystal Tower Vila Gertrudes, Sao Paulo,
04794-000, Sao Paulo, Brazil **(100%)**
Tel.: (55) 11 4004 6611
Web Site: http://www.nextel.com.br
Sales Range: $200-249.9 Million
Digital Wireless Communication Services
N.A.I.C.S.: 517112

Sercotel, S.A. de C.V. (1)
Lago Zurich No. 245 Plaza Carso I Edificio
Telcel Piso 16, Mexico, 11529, Mexico
Tel.: (52) 55 2 581 4410
Web Site: http://www.americamovil.com
Wireless Telecommunication Services
N.A.I.C.S.: 517112

Subsidiary (Non-US):

America Movil Peru, S.A.C. (2)
Avda Carlos Villaran 140 Piso 12, Santa
Catalina La Victoria, Lima, Peru
Tel.: (51) 16131000
Web Site: http://www.claro.com.pe
Wireless Telecommunication Services
N.A.I.C.S.: 517112

Claro Chile S.A. (2)
Avenida El Salto 5450, Ciudad Empresarial,
Huechuraba, Santiago, Chile **(100%)**
Tel.: (56) 24445000
Web Site: https://www.clarochile.cl
Wireless Telecommunication Services
N.A.I.C.S.: 517112

**Claro Telecom Participacoes,
S.A.** (2)
Rua Mena Barreto 427, Rio de Janeiro,
22271-100, Brazil
Tel.: (55) 2125289090
Mobile Telecommunications Services
N.A.I.C.S.: 517112

Subsidiary (Domestic):

Claro S.A. (3)
Rua Florida 1970, Sao Paulo, 04565-001,
Brazil
Tel.: (55) 1155096144
Web Site: http://www.claro.com.br
Mobile Communication System Distr
N.A.I.C.S.: 423690

Subsidiary (Non-US):

Comunicacion Celular S.A. (2)
Calle 90 No 14-37 Piso 6, Bogota, Colom-
bia
Tel.: (57) 1 616 9797
Web Site: http://www.comcel.com.co
Wireless Telecommunication Services
N.A.I.C.S.: 517112

**Consorcio Ecuatoriano de Telecomu-
nicaciones, S.A.** (2)
Avenida Francisco de Orellana and Alberto
Borges, Guayaquil, Ecuador
Tel.: (593) 45004040
Web Site: https://www.claro.com.ec
Wireless Telecommunication Services
N.A.I.C.S.: 517112

Telmex Peru, S.A. (2)
Av Larco 1301 Torre Parque Mar, Miraflo-
res, Lima, Peru
Tel.: (51) 1 6105555
Web Site: http://www.telmex.com
Wireless Telecommunication Services
N.A.I.C.S.: 517112

Smart Systems Ltda. (1)
Los Dominicos 8630 Of 410, Santiago,
Chile
Tel.: (56) 225819336
Web Site: https://www.smart.cl
Wireless Communication Services
N.A.I.C.S.: 517112

**Telefonica Moviles Guatemala,
S.A.** (1)
Bulevar Los Proceres 20 09 Zona 10 Edifi-
cio Iberoplaza, Guatemala, Guatemala
Tel.: (502) 23797979
Web Site: http://www.movistar.com.gt
Telecommunication Servicesb
N.A.I.C.S.: 517810
Angel Vila *(CEO)*

**Telefonos de Mexico S.A.B. de
C.V.** (1)
Parque Via 190, Colonia Cuauhtemoc,
Mexico, 06599, Mexico **(100%)**
Tel.: (52) 5552221774
Web Site: http://www.telmex.com.mx
Emp.: 51,077
Telecommunication Servicesb
N.A.I.C.S.: 517112

Telekom Austria AG (1)
Lassallestrasse 9, 1020, Vienna,
Austria **(56.55%)**
Tel.: (43) 506640
Web Site: https://www.a1.group
Rev.: $5,349,339,725
Assets: $8,919,507,942
Liabilities: $5,079,709,274
Net Worth: $3,839,798,669
Earnings: $678,244,448
Emp.: 17,906
Fiscal Year-end: 12/31/2022
Telecommunication Servicesb
N.A.I.C.S.: 517810
Edith Hlawati *(Chm-Supervisory Bd)*

Subsidiary (Non-US):

A1 Bulgaria EAD (2)
Kukush street No 1 Ilinden municipality,
1309, Sofia, Bulgaria
Tel.: (359) 88123
Web Site: https://www.a1.bg
Telecommunication Servicesb
N.A.I.C.S.: 517112
Alexander Dimitrov *(Chm-Mgmt Bd & CEO)*

Subsidiary (Domestic):

GPS Bulgaria AD (3)
9 Vladimir Vazov blvd fl 3 Hadzhi Dimitar,
1510, Sofia, Bulgaria
Tel.: (359) 70020789
Web Site: https://www.gps.bg
Sales Range: $10-24.9 Million
Emp.: 20
Vehicle Telemetry & Tracking Services
N.A.I.C.S.: 561990

Subsidiary (Non-US):

A1 Hrvatska d.o.o. (2)
Vrtni put 1, 10000, Zagreb, Croatia
Tel.: (385) 146919091
Web Site: https://www.a1.hr
Wireless Telecommunication Services
N.A.I.C.S.: 517112
Ivan Gabric *(Sr Dir-Bus Customer)*

Subsidiary (Domestic):

A1 Telekom Austria AG (2)
Lassallestrasse 9, 1020, Vienna, Austria
Tel.: (43) 506640
Web Site:
http://internationalbusiness.a1.group
Telecommunication Servicesb
N.A.I.C.S.: 517810
Alejandro Douglass Plater *(Deputy Chm-
Supervisory Bd)*

Subsidiary (Domestic):

A1 Bank AG (3)
Berggasse 31, 1090, Vienna, Austria

Tel.: (43) 1 33161 4044
Web Site: http://www.a1bank.at
Mobile Banking Services
N.A.I.C.S.: 522320

**World-Direct eBusiness Solutions
GmbH** (3)
Lassallestrasse 9, 1020, Vienna, Austria
Tel.: (43) 512564464
Web Site: https://www.world-direct.at
Sales Range: $25-49.9 Million
Emp.: 75
Business Management Consulting Services
N.A.I.C.S.: 541611
Hans-Jurgen Klosch *(Mng Dir)*

Subsidiary (Domestic):

**Cable Runner Austria GmbH & Co.
KG** (2)
Kolbegasse 68, 1230, Vienna, Austria
Tel.: (43) 59099100
Web Site: https://www.cablerunner.com
Sales Range: $25-49.9 Million
Telecommunication Servicesb
N.A.I.C.S.: 517810
Anton Schwarz *(Co-CEO)*

Subsidiary (Non-US):

Cable Runner Iberica S.L. (2)
Travesia Colonia Estacion 6, 28231, Las
Rozas, Madrid, Spain
Tel.: (34) 916406040
Telecommunication Wiring Installation Ser-
vices
N.A.I.C.S.: 517810

FE VELCOM (2)
19 Masherov Avenue 8th Floor, Minsk,
220002, Belarus
Tel.: (375) 17 222 49 01
Web Site: http://www.velcom.by
Telecommunication Servicesb
N.A.I.C.S.: 517111

**Mass Response Deutschland
GmbH** (2)
Schanzenstrassee 38, 50829, Cologne,
Germany
Tel.: (49) 22159688800
Wireless Telecommunication Services
N.A.I.C.S.: 517112

Subsidiary (Domestic):

**Telekom Austria TA
Aktiengesellschaft** (2)
Lassallestrasse 9, 1020, Vienna, Austria
Tel.: (43) 5905910
Telecommunication Servicesb
N.A.I.C.S.: 517112

**Telekom Finanzmanagement
GmbH** (2)
Lassallestrasse 9, Vienna, 1020, Austria
Tel.: (43) 1515510
Telecommunication Servicesb
N.A.I.C.S.: 517111

**Telekom Projektentwicklungs
GmbH** (2)
Lassallestrasse 9, 1020, Vienna, Austria
Tel.: (43) 59059136206
Telecommunication Wiring Installation Ser-
vices
N.A.I.C.S.: 237130

Subsidiary (Non-US):

Vip mobile d.o.o. (2)
Omladinskih Brigada 21, Novi Beograd,
11070, Belgrade, Serbia
Tel.: (381) 112253333
Web Site: http://www.vipmobile.rs
Sales Range: $200-249.9 Million
Emp.: 700
Wireless Telecommunication Services
N.A.I.C.S.: 517112

Vip operator DOOEL (2)
Filip Vtori Makedonski 3, 1000, Skopje,
North Macedonia
Tel.: (389) 771234
Web Site: http://www.vip.mk
Telecommunication Servicesb
N.A.I.C.S.: 517112

Vipnet usluge d.o.o. (2)
1 Vrtni Put, Zagreb, 10000, Croatia
Tel.: (385) 14691091

America Movil, S.A.B. de C.V.—(Continued)

Web Site: http://www.vipnet.hr
Telecommunication Servicesb
N.A.I.C.S.: 517810

Telmex Colombia, S.A.   **(1)**
Carrera 7 No 71-52 Torre B Piso 18, Bogota, Colombia
Tel.: (57) 1 606 9606
Web Site: http://www.telmex.com.co
Telecommunication Servicesb
N.A.I.C.S.: 517810

Telmex Internacional, S.A.B. de C.V.
Avenida de los Insurgentes 3500, Colonia Pena Pobre, Delegacion Tlalpan, Mexico, 14060, DF, Mexico   **(97.5%)**
Tel.: (52) 55 5223 3200
Web Site:
  http://www.telmexinternacional.com
Sales Range: $5-14.9 Billion
Emp.: 24,769
Holding Company; International Telecommunications Services
N.A.I.C.S.: 551112
Carlos Slim Domit (Chm)

Subsidiary (Non-US):

Embratel Participacoes S.A.   **(2)**
Rua Regente Feijo 166 Sala 1687-B, Centro, Rio de Janeiro, 20060-060, RJ, Brazil
Tel.: (55) 2121216474
Web Site: http://www.embratel.com.br
Sales Range: $1-4.9 Billion
Emp.: 13,888
Telephone Communications
N.A.I.C.S.: 517111

Affiliate (Domestic):

Net Servicos de Comunicacao S.A.   **(3)**
Rua Verbo Divino 1356, Sao Paulo, 04719-002, Brazil   **(41.3%)**
Tel.: (55) 1121112785
Sales Range: $1-4.9 Billion
Emp.: 15,441
Cable & Broadband Internet Services
N.A.I.C.S.: 516210

AMERICAN AIRES, INC.
100 400 Applewood Crescent, Vaughan, L4K 0C3, ON, Canada
Tel.: (415) 707-0102
Web Site: https://www.airestech.com
Year Founded: 2012
WIFI—(CNSX)
Rev.: $4,152,903
Assets: $263,881
Liabilities: $1,846,193
Net Worth: ($1,582,311)
Earnings: ($3,584,172)
Emp.: 1
Fiscal Year-end: 12/31/23
Electromagnetic Device Mfr & Distr
N.A.I.C.S.: 334513
Dimitry Serov (Founder, Pres & CEO)

AMERICAN BIOFUELS INC.
STE 303 595 Howe St, PO Box 4, Vancouver, V6C 2T5, BC, Canada
Tel.: (604) 718-2800   Ca
Year Founded: 1980
ABS.H—(TSXV)
Rev.: $103,787
Assets: $10,770
Liabilities: $2,707,271
Net Worth: ($2,696,501)
Earnings: ($299,424)
Fiscal Year-end: 04/30/24
Oil & Gas Exploration Services
N.A.I.C.S.: 213112

AMERICAN COPPER DEVELOPMENT CORPORATION
Suite 710 1030 West Georgia Street, Vancouver, V6C 2Y3, BC, Canada
Tel.: (778) 372-9888   BC
Web Site: https://www.american-copper.com

Year Founded: 2020
ACDXF—(OTCIQ)
Rev.: $89,131
Assets: $16,492,496
Liabilities: $3,847,522
Net Worth: $12,644,975
Earnings: ($815,308)
Fiscal Year-end: 12/31/23
Mineral Mining Services
N.A.I.C.S.: 213115
Blaine Bailey (CFO)

AMERICAN CREEK RESOURCES LTD.
92 2nd Ave West, Box 70, Cardston, T0K 0K0, AB, Canada
Tel.: (403) 752-4040   BC
Web Site:
  https://www.americancreek.com
Year Founded: 2004
AMK—(TSXV)
Assets: $5,282,071
Liabilities: $45,546
Net Worth: $5,236,526
Earnings: ($816,461)
Fiscal Year-end: 12/31/23
Gold, Silver & Other Metals Mining Services
N.A.I.C.S.: 212220
Darren R. Blaney (Pres & CEO)

AMERICAN CRITICAL ELEMENTS INC.
Suite 1895 1066 West Hastings Street, Vancouver, V6E 3X1, BC, Canada
Tel.: (416) 865-6789
Year Founded: 1983
ACRE—(CNSX)
Assets: $235,257
Liabilities: $43,174
Net Worth: $192,083
Earnings: ($39,952)
Fiscal Year-end: 04/30/23
Metal Mining Services
N.A.I.C.S.: 212290
Wasserman Ramsay (Auditor-Chartered Accts)

AMERICAN HOTEL INCOME PROPERTIES REIT LP
810925 West Georgia Street, Vancouver, V6C 3L2, BC, Canada
Tel.: (604) 630-3134   ON
Web Site: https://www.ahipreit.com
Year Founded: 2012
AHOTF—(OTCQX)
Rev.: $281,367,000
Assets: $1,052,795,000
Liabilities: $730,689,000
Net Worth: $322,106,000
Earnings: ($35,582,000)
Emp.: 15
Fiscal Year-end: 12/31/22
Real Estate Investment Trust
N.A.I.C.S.: 525990
Robert Francis O'Neill (Founder)

Subsidiaries:

Lodging Enterprises, LLC   **(1)**
Tel.: (316) 630-6300
Emp.: 29
Specialty Hotel Management Services
N.A.I.C.S.: 721110
John O'Neill (Pres)

AMERICAN LITHIUM CORP.
Suite 710-1030 W Georgia St, Vancouver, V6E 2Y3, BC, Canada
Tel.: (604) 428-6128
Web Site:
  https://www.americanlithium.com
AMLI—(NASDAQ)
Rev.: $663,847
Assets: $144,932,985
Liabilities: $1,409,995

Net Worth: $143,522,990
Earnings: ($26,607,240)
Emp.: 55
Fiscal Year-end: 02/28/23
Mining Exploration Services
N.A.I.C.S.: 213114
Simon Clarke (CEO)

Subsidiaries:

Plateau Energy Metals Inc.   **(1)**
141 Adelaide Street West Suite 340, Toronto, M5H 3L5, ON, Canada
Tel.: (416) 360-3406
Web Site:
  http://www.plateauenergymetals.com
Rev.: $204
Assets: $1,115,879
Liabilities: $1,464,591
Net Worth: ($348,712)
Earnings: ($3,880,567)
Fiscal Year-end: 09/30/2020
Uranium Exploration & Mining Services
N.A.I.C.S.: 212290
Philip Gibbs (CFO)

AMERICAN METAL & TECHNOLOGY, INC.
No 11 Shi Xing Street Badachu Hi-Tech Zone, Shijingshan Dist, Beijing, 100041, China
Tel.: (86) 1088794106   DE
Year Founded: 1987
Sales Range: $1-9.9 Million
Emp.: 285
Precision Metal Casting, Metal Fabricated Products & Microprocessor Controlled Electronic Circuit Boards Mfr
N.A.I.C.S.: 331523
Chen Gao (Pres & CEO)

AMERICAN NANO SILICON TECHNOLOGIES, INC.
Nanchong Shili Industrial Street Economic & Technology Development, Xiaolong Chunfei Industrial Park, Nanchong, 637005, Sichuan, China
Tel.: (86) 8173634888
Year Founded: 1993
Sales Range: $1-9.9 Million
Emp.: 130
Chemicals Mfr
N.A.I.C.S.: 325180
Fachun Pu (Chm, Pres, CEO & CFO)

AMERICAN ORIENTAL BIOENGINEERING, INC.
1 Liangshuihe First Ave, Beijing E-Town Economic & Technology Development Area E-Town, Beijing, 100176, China
Tel.: (86) 10 5982 2039   NV
Year Founded: 1970
Sales Range: $125-149.9 Million
Nutraceutical & Pharmaceutical Products Developer & Distr
N.A.I.C.S.: 325412
Shujun Liu (Founder, Chm, Pres & CEO)

Subsidiaries:

Guangxi Boke Pharmaceutical Co., Ltd.   **(1)**
No 56 Keyuan Ave, Gaoxin Dist Xixiangtang, Nanning, 530003, Guangxi, China
Tel.: (86) 7713219100
Pharmaceutical Products Mfr & Distr
N.A.I.C.S.: 325412

AMERICAN OVERSEAS GROUP LIMITED
Seon Place 141 Front Street 3rd Floor, Hamilton, HM 19, Bermuda
Tel.: (441) 2921500   BM
Web Site: https://www.aoreltd.com
Year Founded: 1998

AORE.BH—(BERM)
Rev.: $49,615,788
Assets: $985,218,544
Liabilities: $948,919,462
Net Worth: $36,299,082
Earnings: $5,334,504
Emp.: 41
Fiscal Year-end: 12/31/23
Holding Company; Reinsurance Services
N.A.I.C.S.: 551112
Debra J. Roberts (Chm, Pres & CEO)

Subsidiaries:

RAM Reinsurance Company Ltd.   **(1)**
RAM Re House Penthouse Suite, 46 Reid Street, Hamilton, Bermuda
Tel.: (441) 2966501
Insurance Services
N.A.I.C.S.: 524130

AMERICAN PACIFIC MINING CORP.
Suite 910-510 Burrard Street, Vancouver, V6C 3A8, BC, Canada
Tel.: (604) 908-1695
Web Site:
  https://americanpacificmining.com
1QC—(CNSX)
Rev.: $123,226
Assets: $9,280,388
Liabilities: $116,793
Net Worth: $9,163,595
Earnings: ($2,022,486)
Fiscal Year-end: 12/31/20
Gold Mining Services
N.A.I.C.S.: 212220
Warwick Smith (CEO)

Subsidiaries:

Constantine Metal Resources Ltd.   **(1)**
Suite 320 - 800 West Pender St, Vancouver, V6C 2V6, BC, Canada
Tel.: (604) 629-2348
Web Site: http://www.constantinemetals.com
Rev.: $98
Assets: $18,083,907
Liabilities: $1,620,193
Net Worth: $16,463,714
Earnings: ($1,300,266)
Fiscal Year-end: 10/31/2021
Mineral Exploration Services
N.A.I.C.S.: 213114
Aris Morfopoulos (CFO)

Subsidiary (US):

Constantine North Inc.   **(2)**
120 2nd Ave N, Haines, AK 99827
Tel.: (907) 766-2057
Web Site:
  https://www.constantinemining.com
Metal Mining Services
N.A.I.C.S.: 213114

AMERICAN PATRIOT OIL & GAS LIMITED
Level 1 23 Oxford Street, Oakleigh, 3166, VIC, Australia
Tel.: (61) 3 9945 8739
Web Site: http://www.ap-oil.com
Rev.: $234,810
Assets: $3,974,080
Liabilities: $397,528
Net Worth: $3,576,552
Earnings: ($2,617,943)
Fiscal Year-end: 06/30/18
Oil & Gas Exploration & Development
N.A.I.C.S.: 211120
Richard Cooney (Chm)

AMERICAN POTASH CORP.
880 - 580 Hornby Street, Vancouver, V6C 3B6, BC, Canada
Tel.: (604) 803-5838   BC
Web Site:
  http://www.newtechminerals.ca
Year Founded: 2006

APCOF—(OTCIQ)
Rev.: $80,543
Assets: $697,121
Liabilities: $66,666
Net Worth: $630,456
Earnings: ($1,048,907)
Fiscal Year-end: 07/31/23
Potash Mining
N.A.I.C.S.: 212210
Jonathan George *(Pres & CEO)*

AMERICAN RARE EARTHS & MATERIALS, CORP.

200 Queens Quay E Unit 1, Toronto, M5A 4K9, ON, Canada
Tel.: (416) 362-2121   NV
Web Site:
http://www.americanrare.com
Year Founded: 2002
Emp.: 5
Metal Mining Services
N.A.I.C.S.: 212290
Philip Clark *(CFO)*

Subsidiaries:

Element 21 Golf Canada Inc   **(1)**
200 Queens Quay E Unit 1, Toronto, M5A 4K9, ON, Canada
Tel.: (416) 362-2121
Scandium Mining Services
N.A.I.C.S.: 212390

AMERICAN VIETNAMESE BIO-TECH INCORPORATION

1st Fl B10-79/3 Hoang Van Thai Phu My Hung Intl Financial Trading Ctr, Tan Phu Ward District 7, Ho Chi Minh City, Vietnam
Tel.: (84) 2866501148
Web Site:
https://www.amvibiotech.com
AMV—(HNX)
Rev.: $28,484,500
Assets: $200,191,300
Liabilities: $32,513,300
Net Worth: $167,678,000
Earnings: $5,464,000
Fiscal Year-end: 12/31/22
Diagnostic Test Kit Mfr
N.A.I.C.S.: 325413

AMERICAN WEST METALS LIMITED

Level 2 Suite 2 28 Ord Street, West Perth, 6005, WA, Australia
Tel.: (61) 861096653   AU
Web Site:
https://www.americanwest.com
Year Founded: 2020
AW1—(ASX)
Rev.: $194,463
Assets: $3,821,027
Liabilities: $3,033,346
Net Worth: $787,681
Earnings: ($8,180,723)
Fiscal Year-end: 06/30/23
Support Activities for Metal Mining
N.A.I.C.S.: 213114
Dave O'Neill *(Mng Dir)*

AMERICANA RESTAURANTS INTERNATIONAL PLC

17 floor Tower A Al Rayyan Complex Al Nahda, Sharjah, United Arab Emirates
Tel.: (971) 65092222
Web Site:
https://www.americana.com
6015—(SAU)
Rev.: $2,378,547
Assets: $1,340,547
Liabilities: $1,044,796
Net Worth: $295,751
Earnings: $262,955
Emp.: 40,546
Fiscal Year-end: 12/31/22

Restaurant Operators
N.A.I.C.S.: 722511

AMERICANAS S.A.

Rua Sacadura Cabral, Rio de Janeiro, 20081-902, Brazil
Tel.: (55) 2122066000
Web Site:
https://www.americanas.com.br
AMER3—(BRAZ)
Rev.: $4,613,593,842
Assets: $5,593,796,887
Liabilities: $10,360,715,657
Net Worth: ($4,766,918,770)
Earnings: ($2,308,063,434)
Fiscal Year-end: 12/31/22
Consumer Goods Retailer
N.A.I.C.S.: 459999
Leonardo Coelho *(CEO)*

Subsidiaries:

Lojas Americanas S.A.   **(1)**
Rua Sacadura Cabral 102, Rio de Janeiro, 20081-902, Brazil
Tel.: (55) 2122066708
Web Site: http://ri.lasa.com.br
Rev.: $4,093,273,957
Assets: $9,172,143,877
Liabilities: $6,805,274,728
Net Worth: $2,366,869,149
Earnings: $60,545,100
Emp.: 20,771
Fiscal Year-end: 12/31/2020
Holding Company; Discount Department & Specialty Retail Stores Owner & Operator
N.A.I.C.S.: 551112
Eduardo Saggioro Garcia *(Chm)*

AMERICAS GOLD AND SILVER CORPORATION

145 King Street West Suite 2870, Toronto, M5H 1J8, ON, Canada
Tel.: (416) 848-9503   Ca
Web Site: https://www.americas-gold.com
USAS—(NYSEAMEX)
Rev.: $85,016,000
Assets: $190,819,000
Liabilities: $92,230,000
Net Worth: $98,589,000
Earnings: ($45,187,000)
Emp.: 605
Fiscal Year-end: 12/31/22
Silver & Other Mineral Exploration & Mining
N.A.I.C.S.: 212220
Peter J. Hawley *(Founder)*

Subsidiaries:

Minera Cosala S.A. de C.V.   **(1)**
Carretera Federal Libre Mazatlan-Culiacan Km 1205 Nte Altos, No 718 Centro, Mazatlan, Sinaloa, Mexico
Tel.: (52) 6969650499
Sales Range: $100-124.9 Million
Emp.: 200
Metal Mining Services
N.A.I.C.S.: 213114

Minera Platte River Gold S.A. de RL de C.V.   **(1)**
Carr Federal Libre Mazatlan-Culiacan Km 1205 Norte Altos Fracc, Costa Brava III, CP 82157, Mazatlan, Mexico
Tel.: (52) 6699650957
Gold & Silver Metal Mfr
N.A.I.C.S.: 339910

U.S. Silver Idaho, Inc.   **(1)**
1041 Lake Gulch Rd, Wallace, ID 83873
Tel.: (208) 752-1116
Silver & Gold Mining Services
N.A.I.C.S.: 212220
Steve Long *(Sr VP-Mine Ops)*

AMERIGO RESOURCES LTD.

1021 West Hastings Street 9th floor, Vancouver, V6E 0C3, BC, Canada
Tel.: (604) 681-2802   BC
Web Site:
https://www.amerigoresources.com

Year Founded: 1992
RE8—(DEU)
Rev.: $157,460,000
Assets: $199,559,000
Liabilities: $94,706,000
Net Worth: $104,853,000
Earnings: $3,382,000
Emp.: 293
Fiscal Year-end: 12/31/23
Copper Mining Services
N.A.I.C.S.: 212230
Aurora G. Davidson *(Pres, CEO & CFO-Interim)*

Subsidiaries:

Minera Valle Central S.A   **(1)**
Colihues Km 13, Requinoa, Rancagua, Chile
Web Site: http://www.mineravallecentral.cl
Copper Mining Services
N.A.I.C.S.: 212230
Christian Caceres Meneses *(Gen Mgr)*

AMERIMARK GROUP AG

Steinhauserstrasse 74, 6301, Zug, Switzerland
Tel.: (41) 5080253
Web Site:
http://www.amerimarkag.com
Year Founded: 2015
CARS—(VIE)
Automotive Distr
N.A.I.C.S.: 423110
Nick Markosian *(Founder & CEO)*

AMERINST INSURANCE GROUP, LTD.

25 Church Street Continental Building, PO Box HM 1601, Hamilton, HMGX, Bermuda
Tel.: (441) 2952185   BM
Web Site: http://www.amerinst.bm
Year Founded: 1998
Rev.: $2,270,789
Assets: $4,082,455
Liabilities: $2,346,805
Net Worth: $1,735,650
Earnings: ($1,930,563)
Emp.: 15
Fiscal Year-end: 12/31/22
Insurance Holding Companies
N.A.I.C.S.: 551112
Thomas R. McMahon *(CFO, Treas & VP)*

AMERISE BIOSCIENCES LTD

24 Laxmi Chambers Navjeevan Press Road, Opp Old Gujarat High Court, Ahmedabad, 380014, Gujarat, India
Tel.: (91) 7926581329
Web Site:
http://www.amradeepindustries.club
531681—(BOM)
Assets: $768,205
Liabilities: $73,417
Net Worth: $694,788
Earnings: ($46,017)
Fiscal Year-end: 03/31/21
Laminate Sheet Mfr & Distr
N.A.I.C.S.: 326130
Sagar Gajera *(CFO)*

AMERIWEST LITHIUM INC.

306 1110 Hamilton Street, Vancouver, V6B 2S2, BC, Canada
Tel.: (604) 343-8661
Web Site:
https://ameriwestlithium.com
AWLI—(CNSX)
Assets: $1,238,019
Liabilities: $198,602
Net Worth: $1,039,417
Earnings: ($494,430)
Fiscal Year-end: 04/30/21
Mining Services
N.A.I.C.S.: 212290
Glenn Collick *(COO)*

AMEROPA AG

Rebgasse 108, Binningen, 4102, Switzerland
Tel.: (41) 613075011   CH
Web Site: https://www.ameropa.com
Year Founded: 1948
Sales Range: $800-899.9 Million
Emp.: 4,875
Grain & Fertilizer Trading
N.A.I.C.S.: 424910
Andreas Zivy *(CEO)*

Subsidiaries:

AMS Ameropa Marketing & Sales AG   **(1)**
Rebgasse 108, 4102, Binningen, Switzerland
Tel.: (41) 61 307 5011
Farming Services
N.A.I.C.S.: 115116

Agri Negoce S.A.   **(1)**
Impasse des Jasnieres, 72340, Paris, France
Tel.: (33) 2 43 44 41 83
Web Site: http://www.agrinegoce.fr
Fertilizer Distr
N.A.I.C.S.: 424910

Ameropa (Beijing) Trading Co. Ltd.   **(1)**
Room 802-803 Soho Nexus Center No 19A Dongsanhuan North Road, Chaoyang District, Beijing, 100020, China
Tel.: (86) 10 659 783 82
Web Site: http://www.ameropa.com
Fertilizer Distr
N.A.I.C.S.: 424910

Ameropa Asia Pte Ltd   **(1)**
One Temasek Avenue Suite 31-02 Millenia Tower, Singapore, 39192, Singapore
Tel.: (65) 64990800
Web Site: http://www.ameropa.com
Fertilizer Distr
N.A.I.C.S.: 424910
Alexander Chumakov *(Mng Dir)*

Ameropa Australia Pty Ltd   **(1)**
Level 8 5 Queens Road, Melbourne, 3004, VIC, Australia
Tel.: (61) 39 649 2800
Web Site: https://www.ameropa.com.au
Fertilizer Whslr
N.A.I.C.S.: 424910

Ameropa Chile - SAS   **(1)**
Orinoco 90 Floor 21 office 2119, Santiago, Las Condes, Chile
Tel.: (56) 2 2573 7745
Fertilizer Distr
N.A.I.C.S.: 424910

Ameropa Commodities (Pty) Ltd.   **(1)**
Unit 4 Rydal Vale Park 8 Rydal Vale Crescent, La Lucia, 4051, Durban, South Africa
Tel.: (27) 31 566 2258
Emp.: 13
Fertilizer Distr
N.A.I.C.S.: 424910
Grant Fincham *(Gen Mgr)*

Ameropa Conosur Srl.   **(1)**
Ortiz de Ocampo 3302 Module I 2 Floor Office 15, C1425DST, Buenos Aires, Argentina
Tel.: (54) 11 4808 5005
Fertilizer Distr
N.A.I.C.S.: 424910
Gustavo Vinuela *(Mng Dir)*

Ameropa Do Brasil Comercial Agricola Ltda.   **(1)**
Rua Joaquim Floriano No 1 052 Conj 32, Itaim Bibi, 04534-004, Sao Paulo, Brazil
Tel.: (55) 11 3089 5334
Web Site: http://www.ameropa.com.br
Fertilizer Distr
N.A.I.C.S.: 424910
Jens Stoier *(Gen Mgr)*

Ameropa Dungemittel GmbH   **(1)**
Kurze Muhren 3 /Spitalerhof, 20095, Hamburg, Germany
Tel.: (49) 40 309656 0
Fertilizer Distr
N.A.I.C.S.: 424910

Ameropa AG—(Continued)

Rafael Karczewski *(Mgr-NPK Product & Sulphuric Acid Sourcing-Europe)*

Ameropa Egypt (1)
25 Area 1 District 5 5th Settlement, Cairo, New Cairo, Egypt
Tel.: (20) 226162723
Fertilizer Distr
N.A.I.C.S.: 424910

Ameropa France S.a.r.l (1)
13 rue de la treille, 60300, Senlis, France
Tel.: (33) 344 533 010
Fertilizer Distr
N.A.I.C.S.: 424910

Ameropa Gesellschaft m.b.H. (1)
Graben 14, 1010, Vienna, Austria
Tel.: (43) 1 53 456 0
Fertilizer Distr
N.A.I.C.S.: 424910

Ameropa Iberia S.L. (1)
C/Joaquin Turina 2 Oficina 6B, 28224, Madrid, Spain
Tel.: (34) 91 351 8298
Fertilizer Distr
N.A.I.C.S.: 424910

Ameropa India Pvt Ltd (1)
C 620/621 215 Atrium Chakala Andheri Kurla Road, Andheri East, Mumbai, 400059, India
Tel.: (91) 22 617 131 70
Fertilizer Distr
N.A.I.C.S.: 424910
Reena Rupani *(Office Mgr)*

Ameropa Italia Srl (1)
Via Corrado Ricci 29 sc B, 48121, Ravenna, Italy
Tel.: (39) 0544 21 94 21
Fertilizer Distr
N.A.I.C.S.: 424910

Ameropa Ljubljana d.o.o. (1)
Celovska cesta 28A, 1000, Ljubljana, Slovenia
Tel.: (386) 1 234 85 70
Fertilizer Distr
N.A.I.C.S.: 424910

Ameropa Middle East - DMCC (1)
10th Floor Swiss Tower Cluster Y Jumeirah Lakes Towers, PO Box 643718, Dubai, United Arab Emirates
Tel.: (971) 4 278 9615
Fertilizer Distr
N.A.I.C.S.: 424910

Ameropa North America, Inc. (1)
2502 N Rocky Point Dr, Tampa, FL 33607
Tel.: (813) 282-8228
Sales Range: $25-49.9 Million
Emp.: 16
Grain & Fertilizer Trading
N.A.I.C.S.: 926140
Nicholas Adamchak *(Mng Dir)*

Ameropa Polska sp z o.o. (1)
Al Raclawickie 8/7, 20-037, Lublin, Poland
Tel.: (48) 81 528 45 61
Grain & Fertilizer Trading Services
N.A.I.C.S.: 424910

Ameropa Romania Services S.R.L. (1)
37-39 Jean Monnet Street Ground Floor Apartment 1 1st District, 11956, Bucharest, Romania
Tel.: (40) 21 410 05 51
Fertilizer Distr
N.A.I.C.S.: 424910
Elena Czarva *(Treas)*

Ameropa Turkey (1)
Dereboyu cad Akzambak sok Uphill Towers A blok Kat-28 D-155, Atasehir, Istanbul, Turkiye
Tel.: (90) 216 688 85 85
Web Site: http://www.ameropa.com
Fertilizer Distr
N.A.I.C.S.: 424910
Goker Pehlivanoglu *(Reg Mgr-Sls)*

Ameropa UK Ltd. (1)
2 Charlotte Mews Pavilion Place, Exeter, EX2 4HA, United Kingdom
Tel.: (44) 1392 214 455
Fertilizer Distr

N.A.I.C.S.: 424910
Dave Blackmore *(Mng Dir)*

Ameropa Vietnam (1)
70 Pham Ngoc Thach 4th Floor District 3, Ho Chi Minh City, Vietnam
Tel.: (84) 8 38 20 67 00
Fertilizer Distr
N.A.I.C.S.: 424910

Ameropa Zitni Terminal d.o.o. (1)
Vranjicki put 16, Vranjic, 21210, Solin, Croatia
Tel.: (385) 21 246 880
Web Site: http://www.ameropa-zitni-terminal.hr
Emp.: 50
Fertilizer Distr
N.A.I.C.S.: 424910

Azomures S.A. (1)
300 Gheorghe Doja Street, Mures, Tirgu Mures, 540237, Romania
Tel.: (40) 265 253700
Web Site: http://www.azomures.com
Sales Range: $550-599.9 Million
Emp.: 2,688
Fertilizer Mfr
N.A.I.C.S.: 325311
Andrew Henry Zivy *(Pres)*

Subsidiary (Domestic):

Chimpex S.A. (2)
54 Incinta Port Dana 54, 900900, Constanta, Romania
Tel.: (40) 241603536
Web Site: http://www.chimpex.ro
Sales Range: $10-24.9 Million
Cargo Handling Services
N.A.I.C.S.: 488320
Mihai Panait *(Gen Mgr)*

Impact Fertilisers Pty Ltd (1)
Suite 12 600 Lonsdale St, Melbourne, 3000, VIC, Australia
Tel.: (61) 3 8622 9920
Fertilizer Mfr
N.A.I.C.S.: 325312

Interbrau GmbH (1)
Kurze Muhren 1, 20095, Hamburg, Germany
Tel.: (49) 40 87 97 86 0
Web Site: http://www.interbrau.net
Food Products Distr
N.A.I.C.S.: 424490
Andrea Monien *(Head-Accts & Fin)*

Konzul d.o.o. (1)
Stevana Musica 1, Vojvodina, Novi Sad, Serbia
Tel.: (381) 21 489 8655
Web Site: https://www.konzul.rs
Animal Food Product Mfr
N.A.I.C.S.: 311119
Dragan Slijepcevic *(Gen Mgr)*

MG Produkt Kft (1)
Anna u 8, 7400, Kaposvar, Hungary
Tel.: (36) 8 251 1715
Web Site: https://www.mgprodukt.hu
Grain & Fertilizer Trading Services
N.A.I.C.S.: 424910
Imre Hanyecz *(Exec Dir)*

AMEROPA GRAINS SA
Theodor Burada Street 25, 900271, Constanta, Romania
Tel.: (40) 241625539
Web Site: http://www.ameropa.ro
Fertilizers Distr
N.A.I.C.S.: 325314
William Dujardin *(CEO)*

AMERRA CAPITAL MANAGEMENT LLC
Mamoura A Muroor 4th Road Bin Khalifa 15th Street, Abu Dhabi, United Arab Emirates
Web Site:
http://www.amerracapital.com
Privater Equity Firm
N.A.I.C.S.: 523999
Craig Tashjian *(Chief Investment Officer & Mng Partner)*

Subsidiaries:

Nireus S.A. (1)
1st Klm Koropiou, Koropi, 19400, Greece
Tel.: (30) 2106624280
Web Site: http://www.nireus.gr
Sales Range: $100-124.9 Million
Emp.: 1,000
Fish Farming Services
N.A.I.C.S.: 112511
Aristeidis Belles *(Co-Founder & Chm)*

Subsidiary (Non-US):

ILKNAK SU URUNLERI SAN Ve TIC A.S. (2)
Cahar Dudayev Bul 6518 Sok Urganclar Site No 44 A Block K 2 D 5, Karsiyaka, 35590, Izmir, Turkiye
Tel.: (90) 2323304086
Web Site: http://www.ilknak.com
Fish Farming Services
N.A.I.C.S.: 112511
Orhan Uncel *(Chm)*

Subsidiary (Domestic):

KEGO AGRI S.A (2)
10 klm Nea Artaki-Psahna Road, Evia, Nea Artaki, Greece
Tel.: (30) 2221042032
Web Site: http://www.kegoagri.gr
Fish Farming Services
N.A.I.C.S.: 112511
Aristides Belles *(Chm & CEO)*

AMERY CAPITAL LIMITED
25 Camperdown Street Level Three, London, E1 8DZ, United Kingdom
Tel.: (44) 20 7324 0615   UK
Web Site: http://www.amerycap.com
Year Founded: 2004
Privater Equity Firm
N.A.I.C.S.: 523999
Maurice Helfgott *(Founder, Chm & CEO)*

AMETHYSTUM STORAGE TECHNOLOGY CO., LTD.
Area B Guangzhou Meizhou Industrial, Transfer Industrial Park Shejiang Town Mei County, Meizhou, Guangdong, China
Tel.: (86) 400 998 9866
Web Site:
http://www.amethystum.com
Year Founded: 2010
688086—(SHG)
Rev.: $70,160,987
Assets: $404,313,530
Liabilities: $162,892,872
Net Worth: $241,420,658
Earnings: ($35,083,558)
Fiscal Year-end: 12/31/21
Optical Storage Devices Mfr
N.A.I.C.S.: 334112
Mu Zheng *(Chm)*

Subsidiaries:

Beijing Jingkai Information Storage Technology Co., Ltd. (1)
410 Floor 4 Shenzhou Building Zhongguancun South Street No 31, Haidian District, Beijing, China
Tel.: (86) 1068118978
Storage Product Mfr
N.A.I.C.S.: 334112

AMEX EXPLORATION INC.
410 St-Nicolas suite 236, Montreal, H2Y 2P5, QC, Canada
Tel.: (514) 866-8209
Web Site:
https://www.amexexploration.com
Year Founded: 1986
AMX—(OTCIQ)
Rev.: $204,368
Assets: $43,439,097
Liabilities: $8,805,796
Net Worth: $34,633,301
Earnings: ($1,413,253)

Fiscal Year-end: 12/31/20
Gold Exploration Services
N.A.I.C.S.: 212220
Jacques Trottier *(Chm)*

AMF GROUP JSC
25 Syganak St N P 7A, Esil District, Nur-Sultan, 010000, Kazakhstan
Tel.: (7) 717 279 6466
Web Site: http://www.amf.kz
AKFI—(KAZ)
Rev.: $28,367,528
Assets: $69,978,073
Liabilities: $14,052,157
Net Worth: $55,925,916
Earnings: $2,947,979
Emp.: 200
Fiscal Year-end: 12/31/20
Electric & Gas Distr
N.A.I.C.S.: 221122

AMF-BRUNS GMBH & CO. KG
Hauptstrasse 101, 26689, Apen, Germany
Tel.: (49) 4489727100
Web Site: https://www.amf-bruns.de
Year Founded: 1958
Emp.: 350
Safety Equipment Mfr
N.A.I.C.S.: 332911

AMFI CORP.
One Indiabulls Centre 701 Tower 2 B Wing 7th Floor 841, Senapati Bapat Marg Elphinstone Road, Mumbai, 400 013, India
Tel.: (91) 2243346700
Web Site: http://www.amfiindia.com
Insurance Services
N.A.I.C.S.: 524210
N. S. Venkatesh *(CEO)*

AMFIL TECHNOLOGIES INC.
600 Bloor St W, Toronto, M6G 1K4, ON, Canada
Tel.: (647) 880-5887   NY
Web Site:
https://www.snakesandlattes.com
AMFE—(OTCIQ)
Sales Range: $1-9.9 Million
Emp.: 1
Investment Services
N.A.I.C.S.: 523999
Roger Francis Mortimer *(Pres)*

AMFIRST REAL ESTATE INVESTMENT TRUST
Suite 101-2 Level 1 Tower 2 Wisma AmFIRST Jalan SS7/15, 47301, Petaling Jaya, Selangor, Malaysia
Tel.: (60) 379558780   MY
Web Site:
https://www.amfirstreit.com.my
Year Founded: 2006
5120—(KLS)
Rev.: $24,662,568
Assets: $411,165,593
Liabilities: $210,257,825
Net Worth: $200,907,768
Earnings: $1,322,925
Emp.: 21
Fiscal Year-end: 03/31/22
Trust Management Services
N.A.I.C.S.: 523940
Kim Wai Soo *(Chm)*

AMFORGE INDUSTRIES LTD.
1118 Dalamal Tower 11th Floor Free Press Journal Marg, Nariman Point, Mumbai, 400021, Maharashtra, India
Tel.: (91) 49637707   In
Web Site:
https://www.amforgeindia.in
Year Founded: 1971
513117—(BOM)
Rev.: $369,061

Assets: $2,540,641
Liabilities: $862,279
Net Worth: $1,678,362
Earnings: $221,334
Fiscal Year-end: 03/31/22
Steel Forging Mfr
N.A.I.C.S.: 332111
Jayesh Thakkar *(CFO)*

AMG BIOENERGY RE-SOURCES HOLDINGS LTD.
3791 Jalan Bukit Merah, E-Centre
Redhill #06-09, Singapore, 159471,
Singapore
Tel.: (65) 6223 1098   Ca
Web Site:
http://www.amgbioenergy.com
Year Founded: 2006
Sales Range: Less than $1 Million
Biodiesel Producer
N.A.I.C.S.: 221117
James Shoong Lim Lee *(Mng Dir)*

AMG CRITICAL MATERIALS N.V.
WTC Amsterdam Tower 7 13th Floor,
Strawinskylaan 1343, 1077 XX, Am-
sterdam, Netherlands
Tel.: (31) 207147140   NI
Web Site: https://www.amg-nv.com
AMG—(EUR)
Rev.: $1,642,774,000
Assets: $1,872,635,000
Liabilities: $1,354,786,000
Net Worth: $517,849,000
Earnings: $190,771,000
Emp.: 3,423
Fiscal Year-end: 12/31/22
Metal Processing & Engineering Ser-
vices
N.A.I.C.S.: 212290
Heinz C. Schimmelbusch *(Chm-Mgmt Bd & CEO)*

Subsidiaries:

AMG Advanced Metallurgical Group
N.V.   **(1)**
435 Devon Park Dr Ste 200, Wayne, PA
19087
Tel.: (610) 293-2501
Web Site: http://www.amg-nv.com
Specialty Metal Processing & Engineering
Services
N.A.I.C.S.: 551114
Heinz C. Schimmelbusch *(Chm-Mgmt Bd & CEO)*

Subsidiary (Non-US):

ALD Vacuum Technologies
GmbH   **(2)**
Otto-von-Guericke-Platz 1, 63457, Hanau,
Germany
Tel.: (49) 61813070
Web Site: http://www.ald-vt.com
Sales Range: $200-249.9 Million
Emp.: 500
Vacuum Furnace Systems Mfr & Marketer
N.A.I.C.S.: 333994
Michael Hohmann *(Chm-Mgmt Bd, CEO & Mng Dir)*

Subsidiary (US):

ALD Holcroft Vacuum Technologies
Co.   **(3)**
49630 Pontiac Trl, Wixom, MI 48393-2009
Tel.: (248) 668-4130
Web Site: http://www.ald-holcroft.com
Emp.: 5
Designs & Manufactures Vacuum Furnace
Systems Used for Heat Treating
N.A.I.C.S.: 333248

Subsidiary (Domestic):

ALD Industrie- und Montagepark
Staaken GmbH   **(3)**
Staakener Strasse 53-63, 13581, Berlin,
Germany   **(51%)**
Tel.: (49) 30 330 96 93 0
Web Site: http://www.ald-imp.de

Sales Range: $50-74.9 Million
Emp.: 130
Mfr of Heat Treating Furnace Systems
N.A.I.C.S.: 333994
Thomas Hess *(Mgr)*

ALD Own & Operate GmbH   **(3)**
Wilhelm-Rohn-Strasse 35, 63450, Hanau,
Germany   **(100%)**
Tel.: (49) 6181 307 3438
Web Site: http://www.ald-vt.com
Design & Manufacture of Vacuum Heat
Treating Systems
N.A.I.C.S.: 333248

Subsidiary (US):

ALD Thermal Treatment, Inc.   **(4)**
2656 24th St, Port Huron, MI
48060   **(100%)**
Tel.: (810) 357-0685
Web Site: http://www.aldtt.net
Vacuum Metal Heat Treating
N.A.I.C.S.: 332811

Subsidiary (Non-US):

ALD Tratamientos Termicos S.A. de
C.V.   **(4)**
Blvd Omega No 2270, Parque Industrial
Santa Maria, Ramos Arizpe, 25901,
Mexico   **(100%)**
Tel.: (52) 8448669775
Web Site: http://www.ald-vt.com
Design & Manufacture of Vacuum Heat
Treating Systems
N.A.I.C.S.: 333248

Subsidiary (Domestic):

VACUHEAT GmbH   **(4)**
Hohensteiner Strasse 11-13, 09212,
Limbach-Oberfrohna, Germany   **(100%)**
Tel.: (49) 3722402220
Web Site: http://www.vacuheat.net
Sales Range: $10-24.9 Million
Emp.: 50
Vacuum Heat Treating
N.A.I.C.S.: 332811

Subsidiary (Non-US):

ALD Thermo Technologies Far East
Co., Ltd.   **(3)**
10F Shinjuku Nomura Bldg 1-26-2 Nishi-
Shinjuku, Shinjuku-ku, Tokyo, 163 0558,
Japan   **(100%)**
Tel.: (81) 333403726
Web Site: http://www.ald-vt.com
Emp.: 3
Vacuum Heat Treating Furnace Systems
Mfr & Marketer
N.A.I.C.S.: 333994
Peter Lang *(Mng Dir)*

Subsidiary (US):

ALD Vacuum Technologies, Inc.   **(3)**
18 Thompson Rd, East Windsor, CT
06088   **(100%)**
Tel.: (860) 386-7227
Web Site: http://www.ald-vt.ve
Vacuum Heat Treating Furnace Systems
Marketer
N.A.I.C.S.: 333994
David Esser *(Pres)*

Subsidiary (Non-US):

ALD Vacuumyje Technologii
OOO   **(3)**
Daev per 20, 107045, Moscow,
Russia   **(100%)**
Tel.: (7) 4957876734
Web Site: http://www.ald-vt.com
Emp.: 5
Vacuum Heat Treating Furnace Systems
Mfr & Marketer
N.A.I.C.S.: 333994

Affiliate (Non-US):

Dynatech Furnaces Pvt. Ltd.   **(3)**
301/302 Jyoti Estate 14 Anand Nagar S N
Road, Andheri E, Mumbai, 400 069,
India   **(30%)**
Tel.: (91) 2226826781
Web Site: http://www.dynatechfurnaces.com
Sales Range: $25-49.9 Million
Emp.: 35
Vacuum Furnaces Mfr

N.A.I.C.S.: 333994

Subsidiary (Non-US):

Furnaces Nuclear Applications
Grenoble S.A.   **(3)**
4 avenue Charles de Gaulle, 38800, Le
Pont-de-Claix, France   **(100%)**
Tel.: (33) 4 76 33 64 40
Web Site: http://www.fnag.eu
Emp.: 45
Furnace Systems for Nuclear Applications
N.A.I.C.S.: 333994

Affiliate (Non-US):

Thermique Industrie Vide   **(3)**
ZI Les Iles Cordees RN 532, 38113, Veurey
Voroize, France   **(30%)**
Tel.: (33) 476539005
Web Site: http://www.tiv-fours.fr
Sales Range: $25-49.9 Million
Emp.: 27
Vacuum Heat Treating Furnace Systems
Mfr & Marketer
N.A.I.C.S.: 333994
Philippe Segovia *(Co-Founder)*

Subsidiary (Non-US):

AMG Advanced Metallurgical Group
Investment BV   **(2)**
WTC Amsterdam Toren C 13th Floor
Strawinskylaan 1343, 1077 XX, Amsterdam,
Netherlands
Tel.: (31) 207147140
Web Site: http://amg-nv.com
Emp.: 1
Investment Management Service
N.A.I.C.S.: 523999

AMG Alpoco UK Limited   **(2)**
Fullerton Road, Rotherham, S60 1DL,
United Kingdom
Tel.: (44) 1709787512
Web Site: http://www.amg-alpoco.com
Gas Atomized Aluminum & Alloy Powder
Mfr
N.A.I.C.S.: 331314

AMG Aluminum China Limited   **(2)**
No 289 Muyang Road, Jiaxing, 314033,
China
Tel.: (86) 18605739630
Aluminium Grain Refiner & Master Alloy Mfr
N.A.I.C.S.: 331314
Song Cheng *(Dir-Comml)*

Subsidiary (Domestic):

AMG Aluminum North America,
LLC   **(2)**
435 Devon Park Dr Bldg 200, Wayne, PA
19087
Aluminium Grain Refiner & Master Alloy Mfr
N.A.I.C.S.: 331314
Michael Wahl *(Pres)*

Plant (Domestic):

AMG Aluminum North America, LLC -
Henderson Plant   **(3)**
3293 McDonald Rd, Robards, KY 42452
Tel.: (270) 521-6681
Aluminium Grain Refiner & Master Alloy Mfr
N.A.I.C.S.: 331314

AMG Aluminum North America, LLC -
Wenatchee Plant   **(3)**
4400 Kawecki Rd, Malaga, WA 98828
Tel.: (509) 663-2165
Aluminium Grain Refiner & Master Alloy Mfr
N.A.I.C.S.: 331314

Subsidiary (Domestic):

KB Alloys, Inc.   **(3)**
2208 Quarry Dr Ste 201, Reading, PA
19609
Tel.: (610) 370-6585
Web Site: http://www.kballoys.com
Sales Range: $50-74.9 Million
Emp.: 150
Aluminum Master Alloys Mfr
N.A.I.C.S.: 325998

Subsidiary (Non-US):

AMG Aluminum UK Limited   **(2)**
Fullerton Road, Rotherham, S60 1DL,
South Yorkshire, United Kingdom

Tel.: (44) 1709833782
Aluminium Grain Refiner & Master Alloy Mfr
N.A.I.C.S.: 331314
Matthew Piper *(Mgr-Technical Support)*

AMG Analytical Services Limited   **(2)**
Fullerton Road, Rotherham, S60 1DL,
South Yorkshire, United Kingdom
Tel.: (44) 1709833763
Web Site: http://amg-s.com
Gas Atomized Aluminum & Alloy Powder
Mfr
N.A.I.C.S.: 331314

AMG Brazilian Holding BV   **(2)**
Strawinskylaan 1343, Amsterdam, 1077 XX,
Netherlands
Tel.: (31) 207147140
Investment Management Service
N.A.I.C.S.: 523999

AMG Coating Technologies
GmbH   **(2)**
Wilhelm-Rohn-Str 35, Hanau, 63450, Ger-
many
Tel.: (49) 61813070
Web Site: http://www.ald-vt.de
Sales Range: $75-99.9 Million
Emp.: 35
Metallurgical Products Coating Services
N.A.I.C.S.: 332812

AMG Euro Holdings CV   **(2)**
Strawinskylaan 1343, Amsterdam, 1077 XX,
Netherlands
Tel.: (31) 20 7147140
Investment Management Service
N.A.I.C.S.: 523999

Subsidiary (Domestic):

AMG Idealcast Solar Corporation   **(2)**
630 Solarex Ct, Frederick, MD 21703-8624
Tel.: (240) 439-6311
Sales Range: $25-49.9 Million
Emp.: 8
Solar Energy Equipment Distr
N.A.I.C.S.: 423720

Subsidiary (Non-US):

AMG Lithium GmbH   **(2)**
Industriepark Hochst Building B852, 65929,
Frankfurt am Main, Germany
Web Site: http://amg-lithium.com
Holding Company; Lithium Concentrate Mfr
N.A.I.C.S.: 551112

AMG Mineracao S.A.   **(2)**
Rodovia LMG 841 Zona Rural Nazareno,
Volta Grande, Belo Horizonte, 36370-000,
Minas Gerais, Brazil
Tel.: (55) 3233223012
Web Site: http://www.amgmineracao.com.br
Metal Mining Services
N.A.I.C.S.: 213114
Fabiano Jose de Oliveira Costa *(CEO)*

Subsidiary (Domestic):

AMG Vanadium, Inc.   **(2)**
60790 Southgate Rd, Cambridge, OH
43725   **(100%)**
Tel.: (740) 435-4600
Web Site: http://www.amg-v.com
Sales Range: $50-74.9 Million
Emp.: 120
Specialty Chemicals Mfr
N.A.I.C.S.: 325998

Subsidiary (Non-US):

Bogala Graphite Lanka PLC   **(2)**
Bogala Mines Aruggammana, 71041, Co-
lombo, Sri Lanka
Tel.: (94) 774401295
Web Site: http://www.gk-graphite.lk
Carbon & Graphite Product Mfr
N.A.I.C.S.: 335991
Amila Jayasinghe *(CEO)*

Branwell Graphite Ltd.   **(2)**
Crown House 3rd Floor 151 High Road,
Loughton, IG10 4LG, United Kingdom
Tel.: (44) 1992577334
Graphite Product Mfr
N.A.I.C.S.: 335991

Edelgraphit GmbH   **(2)**
Friesdorfer Str 242, 53175, Bonn, Germany
Tel.: (49) 2 28 31 02 36

AMG Critical Materials N.V.—(Continued)

Web Site: http://www.edelgraphit.de
Graphite Product Mfr
N.A.I.C.S.: 335991

GK Graphit Kropfmuhl GmbH (2)
Langheinrichstrasse 1, 94051, Hauzenberg,
Germany
Tel.: (49) 8586 6090
Web Site: http://www.gk-graphite.com
Emp.: 13
Nonmetallic Mineral Mining Services
N.A.I.C.S.: 212390
Thomas Junker (CEO & Mng Dir)

**GfE Gesellschaft fur Elektrometallur-
gie mbH** (2)
Hofener Str 45, 90431, Nuremberg, Ger-
many
Tel.: (49) 911931591
Web Site: http://www.gfe.com
Sales Range: $150-199.9 Million
Emp.: 400
Holding Company; Electrometallurgical
Products Mfr
N.A.I.C.S.: 551112

Subsidiary (Domestic):

GfE Fremat GmbH (3)
Gewerbegebiet Sud 20, 09618, Brand-
Erbisdorf, Germany
Tel.: (49) 373224720
Web Site: http://www.gfe.com
High Performance Metals & Materials Mfr
N.A.I.C.S.: 331110

Subsidiary (US):

GfE Materials Technology, Inc. (3)
435 Devon Park Rd Ste 200, Wayne, PA
19087
Tel.: (610) 293-5811
Web Site: http://www.gfe.com
Emp.: 2
Sales & Support Services
N.A.I.C.S.: 423510

Subsidiary (Domestic):

**GfE Metalle und Materialien
GmbH** (3)
Hofener Str 45, 90431, Nuremberg, Ger-
many
Tel.: (49) 911931592
Web Site: http://www.gfe.com
Emp.: 250
High Performance Metals & Materials Mfr
N.A.I.C.S.: 331110

Subsidiary (Non-US):

Graphit Kropfmuhl AG (2)
Langheinrichstrasse 1, Hauzenberg, 94051,
Germany
Tel.: (49) 85866090
Web Site: http://www.gk-graphite.com
Sales Range: $50-74.9 Million
Emp.: 699
Graphite Extraction & Processing
N.A.I.C.S.: 335991

Subsidiary (Domestic):

RW Silicium GmbH (3)
Wohlerstrasse 30, Postfach 1147, 94060,
Pocking, Germany
Tel.: (49) 85317020
Web Site: http://www.silicium.de
Sales Range: $75-99.9 Million
Emp.: 120
Silicon Extraction & Processing
N.A.I.C.S.: 212290
Stephan Bauer (Mng Dir)

Subsidiary (Non-US):

Graphite Tyn spol, s r.o. (2)
Pisecka 417, 375 01, Tyn nad Vltavou,
Czech Republic
Tel.: (420) 385 109 210
Web Site: http://www.graphite.cz
Sales Range: $25-49.9 Million
Emp.: 4
Graphite Mining Services
N.A.I.C.S.: 212390

Unit (Domestic):

**Kennametal, Inc. - International Spe-
cialty Alloys** (2)

599 Northgate Cir, New Castle, PA 16105
Tel.: (724) 657-1566
Custom Metal Alloys & Custom Metal Alloy
Powders Supplier
N.A.I.C.S.: 332117

Subsidiary (Non-US):

LSM Brasil S.A. (2)
Rodovia BR 383 km 94 - caixa postal 91 -
Colonia do Marcal, São João del Hei,
36302-812, Minas Gerais, Brazil
Tel.: (55) 33793500
Web Site: http://www.lsmbrasil.com.br
Emp.: 25
Aluminum Extruded Product Mfr
N.A.I.C.S.: 331318
Zdenek Fous (Mng Dir)

Subsidiary (Domestic):

Metallurg Holdings Corporation (2)
435 Devon Park Dr Bldg 200, Wayne, PA
19087-1945
Tel.: (610) 293-2501
Web Site: http://www.amg-nv.com
Emp.: 25
Investment Management Service
N.A.I.C.S.: 523999

Subsidiary (Non-US):

**Metallurg Servicios S.A. de R.L. de
C.V.** (2)
Eucken No 16 Int 502 Piso 5 Anzures,
Miguel Hidalgo, Mexico, 11590, Mexico
Tel.: (52) 5552500136
Metallurgical Services
N.A.I.C.S.: 327999

Subsidiary (Domestic):

Metallurg, Inc. (2)
435 Devon Park Dr Ste 200, Wayne, PA
19087-1937
Tel.: (610) 293-2501
Web Site: http://www.metallurg.com
Mfr of Ferrous Alloys, Ores & Minerals; Alu-
minum Master Alloys
N.A.I.C.S.: 331410

Holding (Non-US):

**AMG Aluminum Mexico, S.A. de
CV** (3)
Eucken No 16 Piso 5, Colonia Anzures,
Mexico, 11590, DF, Mexico
Tel.: (52) 5552546986
Sales Range: $1-9.9 Million
Emp.: 8
Aluminum Producer
N.A.I.C.S.: 331110
Jorge Gomez (Controller)

AMG Superalloys UK Limited (3)
Fullerton Road, Rotherham, S60 1DL,
South Yorkshire, United Kingdom
Tel.: (44) 1709828500
Web Site: http://www.amg-s.com
Emp.: 250
Metallurgical Product Mfr
N.A.I.C.S.: 331110
Kevin Lawson (Pres & Member-Mgmt Bd)

Subsidiary (Non-US):

**Companhia Industrial Fluminense
Mineracao S.A.** (4)
Brat Tqm 94 Colonie de Marca, Colonia do
Giarola, 36302-812, Sao Joao del Rei,
Brazil (100%)
Tel.: (55) 32 3379 3500
Web Site: http://www.amg-br.com
Emp.: 256
Mineral Mining
N.A.I.C.S.: 212390

LSM (Jiaxing) Co., Ltd. (4)
E Building 289 Muyang Road, Jiaxing,
314033, Zhejiang, China (100%)
Tel.: (86) 57382222125
Web Site: http://www.amgal.com
Emp.: 20
Metal
N.A.I.C.S.: 331110

Subsidiary (Domestic):

**The Aluminum Powder Company
Limited** (4)
41 Forge Lane, Minworth, Sutton Coldfield,

B76 1AH, West Midlands, United
Kingdom (100%)
Tel.: (44) 1213516119
Web Site: http://www.alpoco.co.uk
Sales Range: $25-49.9 Million
Emp.: 20
Mfr of Atomised Aluminum & Special Alloy
Powders
N.A.I.C.S.: 332117
Colin Deville (Mgr-Sls)

Subsidiary (Non-US):

**Societe Industrielle et Chimique de
l'Aisne S.A.S.** (2)
rue Geo Lufbery BP 70046, 02301, Chauny,
France
Tel.: (33) 3 23 40 35 30
Web Site: http://www.sica-chauny.com
Sales Range: $25-49.9 Million
Emp.: 70
Antimony Trioxide Mfr
N.A.I.C.S.: 325998

Sudamin Holding SPRL (2)
Lion Office Center, Chaussee de Nivelles
81, 1420, Braine-l'Alleud, Belgium (100%)
Tel.: (32) 23520960
Web Site: http://sudamin.lookchem.com
Sales Range: $50-74.9 Million
Emp.: 5
Metal Trader
N.A.I.C.S.: 425120

Subsidiary (Non-US):

**Produits Chimiques de Lucette
S.A.S.** (3)
ZI de la Vallee Verte, 53940, Le Genest-
Saint-Isle, France
Tel.: (33) 243012310
Web Site: http://www.pcdlucette.com
Antimony Oxide & Other Specialty Chemi-
cals Mfr
N.A.I.C.S.: 325998

Sudamin France S.A.S (3)
136 Bureaux De La Colline, 92210, Saint-
Cloud, France
Tel.: (33) 1 47 71 16 16
Web Site: http://www.sudamin.com
Sales Range: $25-49.9 Million
Nonferrous Metal Product Distr
N.A.I.C.S.: 423510

Subsidiary (Domestic):

Sudamin SPRL (3)
Chaussee de Nivelles 81, 1420, Braine-
l'Alleud, Belgium
Tel.: (32) 23520960
Web Site: http://www.sudamin.com
Sales Range: $50-74.9 Million
Emp.: 5
Metals & Ferro Alloy Distr
N.A.I.C.S.: 423510
Lukas Aleksandravicius (CEO)

Subsidiary (Non-US):

Sudamin Holdings SA (2)
Les Bureaux de la Colline de Saint-Cloud
136, 92213, Saint-Cloud, France
Tel.: (33) 1 47 71 16 16
Web Site: http://www.sudamin.com
Investment Management Service
N.A.I.C.S.: 523999

**The Aluminium Powder Company
Limited** (2)
Forge Lane Minworth, Sutton Coldfield,
B761AH, West Midlands, United Kingdom
Tel.: (44) 121 351 6119
Web Site: http://www.alpoco.com
Aluminium Powders Mfr
N.A.I.C.S.: 331318

VACUHEAT Verwaltungs GmbH (2)
Hohensteiner Strasse 11-13, Limbach-
Oberfrohna, 09212, Germany
Tel.: (49) 3722 40220
Nonferrous Metal Product Distr
N.A.I.C.S.: 423510

AMG Brazil S.A. (1)
Rodovia BR 383 Km 94 Colonia do Marcal,
PO Box 91, Sao Joao del Rei, 36302-812,
MG, Brazil
Tel.: (55) 3233793500
Web Site: https://amg-br.com

Aluminium Alloy Mfr & Distr
N.A.I.C.S.: 331314

AMG HOLDINGS CO., LTD.
5F Sakae VT Building 10-32 Nishiki
3-chome, Naka-ku, Nagoya,
4600003, Aichi, Japan
Tel.: (81) 522125190
Web Site: https://www.amg-hd.co.jp
Year Founded: 1986
8891—(TKS)
Rev.: $192,278,290
Assets: $219,101,670
Liabilities: $150,397,330
Net Worth: $68,704,340
Earnings: $7,204,900
Emp.: 252
Fiscal Year-end: 03/31/24
Real Estate Manangement Services
N.A.I.C.S.: 531390

**AMG PACKAGING & PAPER
COMPANY LTD.**
10 Retirement Crescent 5, Kingston,
Jamaica
Tel.: (876) 9686672
Web Site:
https://www.amgpackaging.com
Year Founded: 2005
AMG—(JAM)
Rev.: $6,619,394
Assets: $10,744,274
Liabilities: $2,421,228
Net Worth: $8,323,045
Earnings: $584,635
Emp.: 129
Fiscal Year-end: 08/31/23
Paperboard Box Product Mfr
N.A.I.C.S.: 322212
Sheldon Taylor (Mgr)

AMHULT 2 AB
Postflyget 7, 423 37, Torslanda, Swe-
den
Tel.: (46) 31923835
Web Site: https://www.amhult2.se
Construction Services
N.A.I.C.S.: 236220
Maria Nord Loft (CEO)

AMI ORGANICS LIMITED
Plot No 440/4 5 6 8206-B 478 479 &
494 495 Road No 82/A And 82/C, G I
D C Sachin, Surat, 394230, Gujarat,
India
Tel.: (91) 7573015366
Web Site:
https://www.amiorganics.com
Year Founded: 2007
AMIORG—(NSE)
Rev.: $71,375,481
Assets: $89,937,516
Liabilities: $18,647,129
Net Worth: $71,290,387
Earnings: $9,820,643
Emp.: 561
Fiscal Year-end: 03/31/22
Pharmaceutical Intermediate Mfr
N.A.I.C.S.: 325412
Ajit Choubey (Pres-Technical)

AMIA ENERGY GMBH
Magdalenenstraße 5, 20148, Ham-
burg, Germany
Tel.: (49) 3030809580
Web Site: https://amia-energy.de
Solar Panels Installation Services
N.A.I.C.S.: 221114

Subsidiaries:

Eigensonne GmbH (1)
Neue Grunstrasse 27, 10179, Berlin, Ger-
many
Tel.: (49) 3058949139
Web Site: http://www.eigensonne.de
Solar Panels Installation Services
N.A.I.C.S.: 221114

Josefine Schneider (Mgr-Sls & Ops)

AMIAD WATER SYSTEMS LTD.
D N Galil Elyon 1, Jerusalem,
1233500, Israel
Tel.: (972) 46909500
Web Site: https://www.amiad.com
Year Founded: 1962
Rev.: $115,585,000
Assets: $135,316,000
Liabilities: $77,727,000
Net Worth: $57,589,000
Earnings: ($895,000)
Emp.: 24
Fiscal Year-end: 12/31/19
Water Filtration Systems Mfr
N.A.I.C.S.: 333998
Avishay Afriat (CFO)

Subsidiaries:

Amiad Filtration Systems India Pvt
Ltd   (1)
Flat No 11 3rd Floor Dhiraj Galax Above
Asalkar Hospital, Chinchwad Gaon, Pune,
411033, India   (100%)
Tel.: (91) 8956339462
Web Site: http://www.amiadindia.com
Water Filtration Systems Sales & Installa-
tion Services
N.A.I.C.S.: 423720
Sudhir Mehta (CEO)

Amiad USA Inc.   (1)
120-J Talbert Rd, Mooresville, NC 28117
Tel.: (704) 662-3133
Web Site: http://us.amiad.com
Sales Range: $25-49.9 Million
Water Filtration Systems Sales & Installa-
tion Services
N.A.I.C.S.: 423720

Amiad Water Systems Europe
SAS   (1)
100 avenue de l Anguillon ZI des Iscles,
13160, Chateaurenard, France
Tel.: (33) 247 23 01 10
Web Site: http://www.amiadfrance.com
Sales Range: $25-49.9 Million
Emp.: 1
Water Filtration Systems Installation Ser-
vices
N.A.I.C.S.: 237110

Amiad Water Systems SAS   (1)
Zweigniederlassung Deutschland Prinz-
Regent-Str 68 a, 44795, Bochum, Germany
Tel.: (49) 234 588082 0
Web Site: http://www.amiad.com
Water Filtration Systems Mfr
N.A.I.C.S.: 221310

Filtration & Control Systems PTE
Ltd.   (1)
22 Sin Ming Lane Ste 07-71 Midview City,
Singapore, 573969, Singapore
Tel.: (65) 6 337 6698
Sales Range: $50-74.9 Million
Emp.: 3
Filtration Systems Sales & Installation Ser-
vices
N.A.I.C.S.: 423720
Lena Ng (Office Mgr)

Fitrasyon Aritim Sistemleri Sanayive
Ticaret FTS   (1)
Istanbul yolu 26 Km Yurt Orta Sanayii,
Saray, Ankara, Turkiye
Tel.: (90) 312 8155266
Water Filtration Systems Mfr
N.A.I.C.S.: 333998

PEP Filters, Inc.   (1)
120-J Talbert Rd, Mooresville, NC 28117-
7119
Tel.: (704) 662-3133
Web Site: http://pepfilters.com
Sales Range: $25-49.9 Million
Water Filtration Systems Mfr
N.A.I.C.S.: 333998

Yixing Taixing Environtaec Co.
Ltd.   (1)
70 Baihe Chang, Xingjie, Yixing, 214204,
Jiangsu, China
Tel.: (86) 5108 7134000
Water Filters & Filtration Systems Mfr

N.A.I.C.S.: 333998

AMICA S.A.
Mickiewicza Street 52, 64-510,
Wronki, Poland
Tel.: (48) 672546100
Web Site: https://www.amica.pl
Year Founded: 1945
AMC—(WAR)
Rev.: $721,011,177
Assets: $506,859,755
Liabilities: $236,204,268
Net Worth: $270,655,487
Earnings: ($1,016,260)
Emp.: 2,730
Fiscal Year-end: 12/31/23
Household Appliances Mfr
N.A.I.C.S.: 335220
Jacek Rutkowski (Chm-Mgmt Bd &
CEO)

Subsidiaries:

Amica International GmbH   (1)
Ul Mickiewicza 52, 64 510, Wronki, Poland
Tel.: (48) 672546100
Home Appliance Mfr
N.A.I.C.S.: 335220

Gram A/S   (1)
Aage Grams Vej 1, 6500, Vojens, Denmark
Tel.: (45) 73201000
Web Site: http://www.gram.dk
Home Appliance Mfr
N.A.I.C.S.: 335220

AMICCOM ELECTRONICS CORP.
10F No 18 Taiyuan St, Hsinchu
County, Zhubei, 30265, Taiwan
Tel.: (886) 35601717
Web Site: https://www.amiccom.com
5272—(TPE)
Rev.: $15,924,147
Assets: $40,137,823
Liabilities: $5,954,601
Net Worth: $34,183,222
Earnings: $1,508,426
Fiscal Year-end: 12/31/22
Semiconductor Devices Mfr
N.A.I.C.S.: 334413
San-Tien Tseng (Chm & Pres)

AMICOGEN, INC.
14-10 Worasan-ro 950beon-gil,
Munsan-eup, Jinju, 52840,
Gyeongsangnam-do, Korea (South)
Tel.: (82) 557596161
Web Site: https://www.amicogen.com
092040—(KRS)
Rev.: $110,674,823
Assets: $329,543,051
Liabilities: $199,323,372
Net Worth: $130,219,678
Earnings: ($35,121,422)
Emp.: 232
Fiscal Year-end: 12/31/22
Enzymes & Food Ingredients Mfr
N.A.I.C.S.: 325998
Yong-Chul Shin (Founder, Chm, Pres
& CEO)

Subsidiaries:

Amicogen, Inc. - 2nd Manufacturing
Facility   (1)
7-22 Worasan-ro 950beon-gil, Munsan-eup,
Jinju, 52840, Gyeongsangnam-do, Korea
(South)
Tel.: (82) 557596161
Enzymes & Food Ingredients Mfr
N.A.I.C.S.: 325998

AMICORP GROUP AG
Muhlebachstrasse 54, 8008, Zurich,
Switzerland
Tel.: (41) 44 252 0880   CH
Web Site: http://www.amicorp.com
Year Founded: 1992

Holding Company, Trust & Fund Administration & Other Financial Services
N.A.I.C.S.: 551112
Toine Knipping (CEO)

Subsidiaries:

Amicorp Netherlands B.V.   (1)
WTC Amsterdam Tower C-11 Strawinsky-
laan 1143, 1077 XX, Amsterdam, Nether-
lands
Tel.: (31) 205788388
Web Site: http://www.amicorp.com
Sales Range: $50-74.9 Million
Emp.: 15
Trust & Fund Administration & Other Finan-
cial Services
N.A.I.C.S.: 523991
Tony Izelaar (Mng Dir)

Amicorp Switzerland AG   (1)
Bellerivestrasse 17, 8008, Zurich, Switzer-
land
Tel.: (41) 44 252 0880
Web Site: http://www.amicorp.com
Emp.: 20
Trust & Fund Administration & Other Finan-
cial Services
N.A.I.C.S.: 523991
Peter Biggs (Dir-Ops)

AMIFA CO., LTD.
3F Aoyama Suncrest Bldg 2-13-5
Kita-Aoyama, Minato-ku, Tokyo,
1070061, Japan
Tel.: (81) 364329500
Web Site: https://www.amifa.co.jp
Year Founded: 1973
7800—(TKS)
Emp.: 62
Packaging Product Mfr & Distr
N.A.I.C.S.: 322220
Yuzo Fujii (Pres)

AMIGO HOLDINGS PLC
Unit 11A The Avenue Centre,
Bournemouth, BH2 5RP, Dorset,
United Kingdom
Tel.: (44) 8716640300   UK
Web Site: https://www.amigoplc.com
AMGO—(LSE)
Rev.: $24,362,535
Assets: $276,571,573
Liabilities: $260,666,498
Net Worth: $15,905,074
Earnings: ($43,928,301)
Emp.: 186
Fiscal Year-end: 03/31/23
Holding Company
N.A.I.C.S.: 551112
Roger Bennett (Sec)

Subsidiaries:

Amigo Loans Limited   (1)
Tel.: (44) 1202629161
Web Site: https://www.amigoloans.co.uk
Financial Services
N.A.I.C.S.: 522291

AMIGO LOANS INTERNA-TIONAL LIMITED
8 Mount Street Upper, Dublin, 2, Ire-
land
Tel.: (353) 12308340
Web Site: https://www.amigoloans.ie
Financial Services
N.A.I.C.S.: 522291

Subsidiaries:

Amigo Loans Ireland Limited   (1)
8 Mount Street Upper, Dublin, Ireland
Tel.: (353) 14819374
Web Site: https://www.amigoloans.ie
Financial Services
N.A.I.C.S.: 522291

AMIL PARTICIPACOES SA
Avenida das Americas 4200 Bloco 3
4 andar Barra da Tijuca, Rio de Janeiro, 22640-907, RJ, Brazil

---

Tel.: (55) 2138051155   BR
Web Site: http://www.amilpar.com.br
Year Founded: 1978
Emp.: 10,991
Health Care Assistance & Consulting
Services
N.A.I.C.S.: 524114

AMILOT CAPITAL INC.
1 First Canadian Place Suite 1600,
100 King St W, Toronto, M5X 1G5,
ON, Canada
Tel.: (416) 986-8660   ON
Web Site: http://www.tolimagold.com
Year Founded: 1935
ACI.H—(TSXV)
Assets: $1,019
Liabilities: $3,837,485
Net Worth: ($3,836,466)
Earnings: ($30,859)
Fiscal Year-end: 07/31/21
Gold Exploration Services
N.A.I.C.S.: 212220
Jaime A. Lopez (CEO)

Subsidiaries:

Tolima Gold S.A.S.   (1)
Carrera 25 3 -01, Medellin, Antioquia, Co-
lombia
Tel.: (57) 4 444 7479
Gold Exploration Services
N.A.I.C.S.: 212220

AMIMON, LTD.
2 Maskit St Building D 2nd Fl, PO
Box 12618, Herzliyya, 46733, Israel
Tel.: (972) 99629200   II
Web Site: http://www.amimon.com
Year Founded: 2004
Wireless Transmission Equipment
Development & Mfr
N.A.I.C.S.: 334220
Mor Arbiv (Coord-Ops)

AMIN PHARMACEUTICAL COMPANY
3rd Kilometers of Baharan Town
Zobe Ahan Highway, PO Box
81465/1588, Kelishad, Iran
Tel.: (98) 31 2318 0170
Web Site:
http://www.aminpharma.com
Year Founded: 1984
AMIN1—(THE)
Sales Range: Less than $1 Million
Pharmaceuticals Product Mfr
N.A.I.C.S.: 325412
Sh. Hashemi (Dir-QC)

AMIN TANNERY LIMITED
A-46/47 UPSIDC Leather Technology
Park, Banthar, Unnao, 209801, India
Tel.: (91) 7380794333
Web Site: https://www.amintannery.in
Year Founded: 1946
541771—(BOM)
Rev.: $3,703,709
Assets: $7,534,077
Liabilities: $5,966,128
Net Worth: $1,567,948
Earnings: $13,978
Fiscal Year-end: 03/31/21
Leather Product Mfr
N.A.I.C.S.: 316990
Veqarul Amin (Mng Dir)

AMINES & PLASTICIZERS LIMITED
D Building Shivsagar Estate 6th Floor
Dr Annie Besant Road, Worli, Mum-
bai, 400018, India
Tel.: (91) 2262211000
Web Site: https://www.amines.com
Year Founded: 1973
506248—(BOM)
Rev.: $77,582,341
Assets: $42,317,621

AMINES & PLASTICIZERS LIMITED—(Continued)
Liabilities: $20,168,394
Net Worth: $22,149,227
Earnings: $3,256,535
Emp.: 253
Fiscal Year-end: 03/31/22
Chemical Products Mfr
N.A.I.C.S.: 325998
Hemant Kumar Ruia *(Chm & Mng Dir)*

Subsidiaries:

AMINES & PLASTICIZERS LIMITED - UNIT-I (1)
D 21/21A TTC Industrial Area Turbhe Thane Belapur Road, Navi Mumbai, 400 075, India
Tel.: (91) 2262211200
Chemical Products Mfr
N.A.I.C.S.: 325998

AMINES & PLASTICIZERS LIMITED - UNIT-II (1)
Survey No 49 Khopoli-Pen Road, Village Vadval Taluka Khalapur Dist Raigad, Vadval, 410 203, Maharashtra, India
Tel.: (91) 2262211000
Chemical Products Mfr
N.A.I.C.S.: 325998

AMINEX PLC
Paramount Court Corrig Road Sandyford Business Park, Dublin, D18 R9C7, Ireland
Tel.: (353) 2031988415
Web Site: https://aminex-plc.com
AEX—(LSE)
Rev.: $112,000
Assets: $42,615,000
Liabilities: $10,006,000
Net Worth: $32,609,000
Earnings: ($1,119,000)
Emp.: 5
Fiscal Year-end: 12/31/23
Oil & Gas Exploration, Development & Production Services
N.A.I.C.S.: 211120
Thierry Murcia *(Mgr-Tanzania)*

Subsidiaries:

Aminex Petroleum Services Limited (1)
20-22 Wenlock Road, London, N1 7GU, United Kingdom
Tel.: (44) 2072913100
Sales Range: $50-74.9 Million
Emp.: 12
Oil & Gas Exploration Services
N.A.I.C.S.: 211120
Brian Hall *(Chm)*

Amossco Limited (1)
20-22 Wenlock Road, London, N1 7GU, United Kingdom
Tel.: (44) 2072913103
Web Site: http://www.amossco.com
Sales Range: $50-74.9 Million
Oil & Gas Exploration Services
N.A.I.C.S.: 211120

Korex Limited (1)
52 Stockwell Road, London, SW9 9ER, United Kingdom
Tel.: (44) 2077376864
Emp.: 5
Property Management Services
N.A.I.C.S.: 531311

Ndovu Resources Limited (1)
368 Msasani Road Oysterbay 2nd Floor Mikumi House, PO Box 105589, Msasani Peninsular, 14111, Dar es Salaam, Tanzania
Tel.: (255) 222600814
Web Site: http://www.aminex-plc.com
Sales Range: $50-74.9 Million
Emp.: 5
Oil & Gas Exploration Services
N.A.I.C.S.: 211120

Tanzoil NL (1)
6 Ling Court, Atwell, 6164, WA, Australia
Tel.: (61) 892210033

Sales Range: $50-74.9 Million
Petroleum Exploration Services
N.A.I.C.S.: 211120
Didier Murcia *(Mng Dir)*

AMINOLOGICS CO., LTD.
3F Samoh B/D 151 Yeoksam-ro, Gangnam-gu, Seoul, 135-925, Korea (South)
Tel.: (82) 27614570
Web Site: https://www.aminologics.co.kr
074430—(KRS)
Rev.: $20,967,424
Assets: $42,631,535
Liabilities: $3,204,595
Net Worth: $39,426,940
Earnings: ($5,585,030)
Emp.: 36
Fiscal Year-end: 12/31/22
Bio Technology Services
N.A.I.C.S.: 541714
J. S. Oh *(Co-CEO)*

AMIR MARKETING & INVESTMENTS IN AGRICULTURE LTD.
Zvi HaNahal 10 Emek Hefer Industries Park, Jerusalem, 38800, Israel
Tel.: (972) 46120200
Web Site: https://www.amir-agricul.co.il
AMRK—(TAE)
Rev.: $344,974,715
Assets: $243,226,961
Liabilities: $144,305,289
Net Worth: $98,921,673
Earnings: $5,751,070
Fiscal Year-end: 12/31/23
Farm Supplies Merchant Wholesalers
N.A.I.C.S.: 424910
Eli Chadges *(CFO)*

AMIRA NATURE FOODS LTD.
29E AU Tower Jumeirah Lake Towers, Dubai, United Arab Emirates
Tel.: (971) 4 4357303
Web Site: http://www.amira.net
Rev.: $413,901,480
Assets: $512,826,507
Liabilities: $271,217,631
Net Worth: $241,608,876
Earnings: ($93,595,764)
Emp.: 209
Fiscal Year-end: 03/31/18
Packaged Indian Specialty Rice Distr & Mfr
N.A.I.C.S.: 424490
Karan A. Chanana *(Chm & CEO)*

AMIT INTERNATIONAL LIMITED
403 A Dalamal Chambers 29 New marine lines, Mumbai, 400020, India
Tel.: (91) 202095533
Web Site: https://www.amitinternational.in
Year Founded: 1994
531300—(BOM)
Rev.: $61,011
Assets: $2,666,670
Liabilities: $21,676
Net Worth: $2,644,994
Earnings: $17,442
Emp.: 2
Fiscal Year-end: 03/31/21
Textile Products Mfr
N.A.I.C.S.: 314999
Kirti Jethalal Doshi *(Chm & Mng Dir)*

AMIT SECURITIES LIMITED
2 Shivaji Nagar, Indore, 452 003, India
Tel.: (91) 7313091700
Web Site: https://www.amitsecurities.com
Rev.: $116,116

Assets: $1,714,994
Liabilities: $1,021
Net Worth: $1,713,973
Earnings: ($10,664)
Emp.: 3
Fiscal Year-end: 03/31/19
Financial Investment Management Services
N.A.I.C.S.: 523940
Hemant Sharma *(Mng Dir)*

AMITA HOLDINGS CO., LTD.
324 Kudankita Chiyoda-Ku, Tokyo, 102-0073, Japan
Tel.: (81) 352158255
Web Site: http://www.amita-net.co.jp
Environmental Services Including Recycling & Waste Management
N.A.I.C.S.: 423930
Eisuke Kumano *(Pres & CEO)*

AMITEC OY
Garpintie 270, Laitila, 23800, Finland
Tel.: (358) 403002288
Web Site: http://www.amitec.fi
Year Founded: 1984
Stainless Materials Mfr
N.A.I.C.S.: 331513
Raine Kuusisto *(Owner)*

Subsidiaries:

Formeca Oy (1)
Vaakatie 9, 16300, Orimattila, Finland
Tel.: (358) 388411
Web Site: http://www.formeca.fi
Packaging Machinery Mfr
N.A.I.C.S.: 333993

AMIYA CORPORATION
11F Tornare Nihonbashi Hamacho 3-3-2 Nihonbashi Hamacho, Chuo-ku, Tokyo, 103-0007, Japan
Tel.: (81) 368229999
Web Site: https://www.amiya.co.jp
Year Founded: 1996
4258—(TKS)
Rev.: $25,233,310
Assets: $26,771,840
Liabilities: $14,109,100
Net Worth: $12,662,740
Earnings: $2,304,250
Fiscal Year-end: 12/31/23
Steel Products Mfr
N.A.I.C.S.: 331210

Subsidiaries:

JBS Shanghai, Inc. (1)
Room022 6F Hang Seng Bank Tower 1000 Lujiazui Ring Road, Pudong, Shanghai, 200120, China
Tel.: (86) 2150873773
Web Site: https://www.jbssh.com.cn
Computer Software Consulting Services
N.A.I.C.S.: 541512

Material Automation (Thailand) Co., Ltd. (1)
12th FL CTI Tower 191/78 Ratchadapisek Road, Klongtoey, Bangkok, 10110, Thailand
Tel.: (66) 22615100
Web Site: https://www.mat.co.th
Computer Software Consulting Services
N.A.I.C.S.: 541512

P.T. Awan Teknologi Global (1)
Gedung Tibyan Center Lantai 2 Jl H Nawi Raya No 191/17 RT7/RW 10, Gandaria Utara Kec Kby Baru Daerah Khusus Ibukota Jakarta, South Jakarta, 12140, Indonesia
Tel.: (62) 2127088802
Web Site: https://cloudtech.co.id
Information Technology Services
N.A.I.C.S.: 541519

Toontec Solutions Co., Ltd. (1)
2F No 58 Zhouzi St, Neihu Dist, Taipei, 114064, Taiwan
Tel.: (886) 277134176
Web Site: https://www.toontec-sol.com
Computer Software Consulting Services
N.A.I.C.S.: 541512

AMIYAKI TEI CO., LTD.
5128 Nyoishincho, Kasugai, 486-0918, Aichi, Japan
Tel.: (81) 568328800
Web Site: https://www.amiyakitei.co.jp
Year Founded: 1995
2753—(TKS)
Rev.: $210,804,870
Assets: $180,029,960
Liabilities: $41,920,620
Net Worth: $138,109,340
Earnings: $8,639,270
Fiscal Year-end: 03/31/24
Restaurant Services
N.A.I.C.S.: 722511
Keisuke Sato *(Chm & Pres)*

AMJ CAMPBELL, INC.
1445 Courtney Park Dr E, Mississauga, L5T 2E3, ON, Canada
Tel.: (905) 795-3785   ON
Web Site: http://www.amjcampbell.com
Year Founded: 1934
Sales Range: $50-74.9 Million
Emp.: 150
Moving Services for Household & Commercial Office Relocations
N.A.I.C.S.: 484210

AMJ LAND HOLDINGS LIMITED
60 Dr VB Gandhi Marg, Kalaghoda, Mumbai, 400001, Maharashtra, India
Tel.: (91) 2230213333
Web Site: https://www.amjland.com
Year Founded: 1964
500343—(BOM)
Rev.: $5,031,868
Assets: $24,187,718
Liabilities: $4,879,438
Net Worth: $19,308,280
Earnings: $1,229,619
Emp.: 3
Fiscal Year-end: 03/31/22
Paper Mfr
N.A.I.C.S.: 322299
S. K. Bansal *(Dir-Fin)*

AML FOODS LTD.
One Millars Court Shirley Street, PO Box N 7117, Nassau, Bahamas
Tel.: (242) 3222511
Web Site: http://www.amlfoods.com
AML—(BISX)
Rev.: $184,951,000
Assets: $111,910,000
Liabilities: $62,652,000
Net Worth: $49,258,000
Earnings: $2,803,000
Emp.: 857
Fiscal Year-end: 04/30/23
Stores & Fast Food Restaurant Franchise Owner & Operator
N.A.I.C.S.: 445110
Gavin Watchorn *(Pres & CEO)*

Subsidiaries:

Cost Right Nassau Limited (1)
Baillou Hill Rd Town Center Mall, Nassau, Bahamas
Tel.: (242) 6777266
Web Site: https://www.costrightnassau.com
Grocery Retailer
N.A.I.C.S.: 445110
Raymond Rolle *(Mgr-Store)*

Solomon's Fresh Market Limited (1)
Old Fort Town Center, Nassau, Bahamas
Tel.: (242) 6777280
Web Site: https://www.solomonsfreshmarkets.com
Grocery Retailer
N.A.I.C.S.: 445110
James Williams *(Mgr-Store)*

Solomon's Supercentre (Nassau) Limited (1)

East West Highway, PO Box SS-6322, Nassau, Bahamas
Tel.: (242) 3939775
Grocery Retailer
N.A.I.C.S.: 445110
Kevin George *(Gen Mgr)*

AML3D LIMITED
Unit 4 136 Mooringe Ave, Edinburgh, Plympton, 5037, SA, Australia
Tel.: (61) 882582658   AU
Web Site: https://www.aml3d.com
Year Founded: 2014
AL3—(ASX)
Rev.: $413,655
Assets: $5,761,808
Liabilities: $1,246,480
Net Worth: $4,515,328
Earnings: ($3,544,535)
Emp.: 19
Fiscal Year-end: 06/30/23
Metalworking Machines Mfr
N.A.I.C.S.: 333519
Andrew Sales *(Chief Technical Officer)*

AMLEX HOLDINGS BHD
No 799 Lorong Perindustrian Bukit Minyak 7 Taman Perindustrian, Bukit Minyak, 14100, Simpang Empat, Penang, Malaysia
Tel.: (60) 45013986
Web Site:
  https://www.amlextech.com
3011—(KLS)
Rev.: $11,698,725
Assets: $15,374,978
Liabilities: $5,357,343
Net Worth: $10,017,635
Earnings: $103,124
Fiscal Year-end: 03/31/24
Electric Equipment Mfr
N.A.I.C.S.: 334111

AMLOGIC SHANGHAI CO., LTD.
Building E5 Caohejing Kangqiao Business Oasis 2555 Xiupu Road, Pudong New District, Shanghai, 201315, China
Tel.: (86) 2150803377
Web Site: https://www.amlogic.cn
Year Founded: 2003
688099—(SHG)
Rev.: $778,505,982
Assets: $823,456,698
Liabilities: $131,060,929
Net Worth: $692,395,770
Earnings: $102,023,120
Fiscal Year-end: 12/31/22
Semiconductor Product Mfr
N.A.I.C.S.: 334413
Zhong John *(Chm & Gen Mgr)*

AMMAN STOCK EXCHANGE
PO Box 212466, Amman, 11121, Jordan
Tel.: (962) 6 5664081
Web Site: http://www.ase.com.jo
Year Founded: 1999
Stock Exchange Services
N.A.I.C.S.: 523210
Jalil Tarif *(CEO)*

AMMANN SWITZERLAND LTD
Eisenbahnstrasse 25, Langenthal, 4901, Switzerland
Tel.: (41) 629166161
Web Site: https://www.ammann.com
Year Founded: 1869
Construction Machinery Manufacturing
N.A.I.C.S.: 333120
Hans-Christian Schneider *(CEO)*

AMMB HOLDINGS BERHAD
Level 8 Bangunan AmBank Group No

55 Jalan Raja Chulan, 50200, Kuala Lumpur, Malaysia
Tel.: (60) 321673584   MY
Web Site:
  https://www.ambankgroup.com
Year Founded: 1975
AMBANK—(KLS)
Rev.: $1,321,460,174
Assets: $42,830,595,190
Liabilities: $38,598,589,720
Net Worth: $4,232,005,470
Earnings: $401,040,708
Emp.: 9,000
Fiscal Year-end: 03/31/24
Banking Services
N.A.I.C.S.: 522110
Azman Hashim *(Chm)*

Subsidiaries:

AM Nominees (Tempatan) Sdn Bhd   (1)
Level 9 Bangunan Ambank Group, Kuala Lumpur, Malaysia   (51%)
Tel.: (60) 320782788
Commericial Banking
N.A.I.C.S.: 522110

AMMerchant Bank Berhad   (1)
Ground Floor Bangunan AmBank Group, No 55 Jalan Raja Chulan, 50200, Kuala Lumpur, Malaysia
Tel.: (60) 320782100
Web Site: http://www.ambankgroup.com
Sales Range: $400-449.9 Million
Emp.: 747
Banking Services
N.A.I.C.S.: 522299

Am Ara Reit Managers Sdn Bhd   (1)
Level 16 Bangunan Group 55 Jalan Raja Chulan, 50200, Kuala Lumpur, Malaysia
Tel.: (60) 320269102
Web Site: http://www.amfirstreit.com.my
Sales Range: $50-74.9 Million
Emp.: 12
Commericial Banking
N.A.I.C.S.: 522110
Soo Kim Wai *(Chm)*

AmAssurance Berhad   (1)
9th Floor Bangunan AmAssurance, 1 Jalan Lumut, 50400, Kuala Lumpur, Malaysia   (70%)
Tel.: (60) 340478000
Sales Range: $350-399.9 Million
Emp.: 724
Direct Life Insurance Carriers
N.A.I.C.S.: 524113

AmBank (M) Berhad   (1)
Level 18 Menara AmBank No 8 Jalan Yap Kwan Seng, 50450, Kuala Lumpur, Malaysia
Tel.: (60) 321788888
Web Site: http://www.ambankgroup.com
Sales Range: $100-124.9 Million
Emp.: 250
Banking Services
N.A.I.C.S.: 522110

AmFunds Management Berhad   (1)
Level 9 & 10 Bangunan AmBank Group No 55 Jalan Raja Chulan, 50200, Kuala Lumpur, Malaysia
Tel.: (60) 320322888
Web Site: https://www.aminvest.com
Asset Management Services
N.A.I.C.S.: 531390

AmFutures Sdn Bhd   (1)
15th Floor Bangunan, AmBank Group 55 Jalan Raja Chu, 50200, Kuala Lumpur, Malaysia   (51%)
Tel.: (60) 392353223
Sales Range: $50-74.9 Million
Emp.: 7
Commodity Contracts Brokerage
N.A.I.C.S.: 523160
Stephen Kwong *(Dir-eBroking)*

AmG Insurance Berhad   (1)
9th Floor Bangunan AmAssurance No 1 Jln Lumut, 50400, Kuala Lumpur, Malaysia
Tel.: (60) 3 4047 8000
Web Site: http://www.amassurance.com.my
Insurance Management Services
N.A.I.C.S.: 524298

AmInternational (L) Ltd   (1)
Level 12 B Block 4 Office Tower, Financial Park Labuan Complex, 87000, Labuan, Malaysia   (51%)
Tel.: (60) 87413133
Web Site: http://www.ambankgroup.com
Sales Range: $50-74.9 Million
Emp.: 14
Commericial Banking
N.A.I.C.S.: 522110
Felix Leong *(VP)*

AmInvestment Bank Group   (1)
22nd Floor Bangunan Ambank Group, 55 Jalan Raja Chulan, Kuala Lumpur, 50200, Malaysia   (51%)
Tel.: (60) 320362633
Holding Company
N.A.I.C.S.: 551112

Subsidiary (Domestic):

AmInvestment Services Berhad   (2)
9th 10th Floor Bangunan AmBank Group, 55 Jalan Raja Chulan, 50200, Kuala Lumpur, Malaysia   (100%)
Tel.: (60) 20322888
Investment Advice
N.A.I.C.S.: 523940

AmIslamic Bank Berhad   (1)
Level 45 Menara AmBank, No 8 Jalan Yap Kwan Seng, 50450, Kuala Lumpur, Malaysia   (100%)
Tel.: (60) 321673000
Web Site: http://www.ambg.com.my
Commericial Banking
N.A.I.C.S.: 522110
Mokhzanee Muhammad Eqhwan *(Chm)*

AmProperty Trust Management Berhad   (1)
22nd Floor Bangunan Ambank Group, Kuala Lumpur, 50200, Malaysia   (51%)
Tel.: (60) 320782633
Real Estate Investment Trust
N.A.I.C.S.: 525990

AmREIT Managers Sdn Bhd   (1)
Suite 101-2 Level 1 Tower 2 Wisma Am-FIRST Jalan SS7/15, 47301, Petaling Jaya, Selangor, Malaysia
Tel.: (60) 379558780
Web Site: https://www.amfirstreit.com.my
Real Estate Investment Trust Services
N.A.I.C.S.: 531390
Soo Kim Wai *(Chm)*

Amsec Nominees (Asing) Sdn Bhd   (1)
Tingkat 22 Bangunanambank group, 55 Jalan Raja Chulan, 50200, Kuala Lumpur, Malaysia   (51%)
Tel.: (60) 320782788
Web Site: http://www.ambankgroup.com
Sales Range: $50-74.9 Million
Emp.: 100
Securities & Commodity Exchanges
N.A.I.C.S.: 523210

Amsec Nominees (Tempatan) Sdn Bhd   (1)
55 Jalan Raja Chulan 15th Floor, Kuala Lumpur, Malaysia   (51%)
Tel.: (60) 320782788
Securities & Commodity Exchanges
N.A.I.C.S.: 523210

Bonuskad Loyalty Sdn Bhd   (1)
Level 8 Blook C Menara Glomac Kelana Business Centre Jalan SS 7/2, Kelana Jaya, 47301, Petaling Jaya, Selangor Darul Ehsan, Malaysia
Tel.: (60) 376261000
Web Site: https://www.bonuslink.com.my
Consumer Reward Services
N.A.I.C.S.: 561990

MBf Cards (Msia) Sdn. Bhd.   (1)
Menara MBf Jalan Sultan Ismail, 50250, Kuala Lumpur, Malaysia
Tel.: (60) 321677600
Web Site: http://www.mbfcards.com
Credit & Charge Cards Issuing Services
N.A.I.C.S.: 522210
Kim Lee Mei *(Sr VP-Grp HR & Admin)*

Malaysian Ventures Management Incorporated Sdn Bhd
15th Fl Bangunan AmBank Group, No 55

Jalan Raja Chulan, Kuala Lumpur, 50200, Malaysia
Tel.: (60) 320782392
Web Site: http://www.ambankgroup.com
Sales Range: $25-49.9 Million
Emp.: 5
Management Consulting Services
N.A.I.C.S.: 541618
Francis Ng *(CEO)*

AMNIS THERAPEUTICS LTD.
Hailan St, PO Box 146, Or Akiva, 3060000, Israel
Tel.: (972) 72 2200333
Web Site: http://www.itgimedical.com
Sales Range: $1-9.9 Million
Biomedical Research & Development Services
N.A.I.C.S.: 541715

AMNODE AB
Sjorydsvagen 10-12, Box 17217, 335 32, Stockholm, Sweden
Tel.: (46) 705901822
Web Site: https://www.amnode.se
Year Founded: 2007
Fabricated Metal Mfr
N.A.I.C.S.: 332999
Peter Agren *(CFO)*

AMOEBA BIOCIDE SAS
38 Avenue de Freres Montgolfier, 69680, Chassieu, France
Tel.: (33) 426691600
Web Site: https://www.amoeba-nature.com
ALMIB—(EUR)
Sales Range: Less than $1 Million
Biological Product Mfr & Distr
N.A.I.C.S.: 325414
Fabrice Plasson *(Founder, Chm & CEO)*

AMOGREENTECH CO., LTD.
91 Gimpo-daero 1950beon-gil Tongjin-eup, Gimpo, Gyeonggi-do, Korea (South)
Tel.: (82) 319875398
Web Site:
  http://www.amogreentech.com
Year Founded: 2004
125210—(KRS)
Rev.: $112,281,466
Assets: $113,084,800
Liabilities: $68,928,206
Net Worth: $44,156,594
Earnings: $9,018,168
Emp.: 336
Fiscal Year-end: 12/31/22
Metal Products Mfr
N.A.I.C.S.: 332999
Seong Cheol Yang *(CEO)*

AMOREG
4th floor 53 Opebi Road Opebi, Ikeja, Lagos, Nigeria
Tel.: (234) 8023136648
Web Site: http://www.amoreg.org
Rev.: $5,404,459,451
Assets: $7,121,998,095
Liabilities: $1,549,071,821
Net Worth: $5,572,926,274
Earnings: $115,009,999
Emp.: 120
Fiscal Year-end: 12/31/19
Telecommunication Servicesb
N.A.I.C.S.: 517112
Funmi Nworie *(Gen Mgr)*

AMOREPACIFIC CORP.
100 Hangang-daero, Yongsan-gu, Seoul, Korea (South)
Tel.: (82) 260405114
Web Site: https://www.apgroup.com
Year Founded: 1945
090430—(KRS)
Rev.: $4,474,078,217
Assets: $5,627,376,818

Amorepacific Corp.—(Continued)

Liabilities: $1,262,620,931
Net Worth: $4,364,755,887
Earnings: $178,186,132
Emp.: 5,337
Fiscal Year-end: 12/31/21
Beauty & Health Care Products Mfr
N.A.I.C.S.: 325620
Kyung-Bae Suh *(Chm & CEO)*

Subsidiaries:

AMOREPACIFIC (Shanghai) R&I
Center Co., Ltd.　　　　　　　　　(1)
No 768 Boxue Road, Malu Town Jiading
District Chinese Mainland, Shanghai,
201801, China
Tel.: (86) 2139182624
Cosmetics Product Mfr & Distr
N.A.I.C.S.: 325620

AMOREPACIFIC Global Operations
Limited　　　　　　　　　　　　　(1)
Unit 1202 12/F Harbour East 218 Electric
Road, Hong Kong, China (Hong Kong)
Tel.: (852) 35838626
Cosmetic Product Distr
N.A.I.C.S.: 424590

AMOREPACIFIC Hong Kong Co.,
Limited　　　　　　　　　　　　　(1)
34th Floor World Trade Centre 280 Glouc-
ester Road, Causeway Bay, China (Hong
Kong)
Tel.: (852) 29703288
Cosmetics Product Mfr & Distr
N.A.I.C.S.: 325620

AMOREPACIFIC Japan Co., Ltd.　(1)
2nd Floor Ebisu East Building 1-13-7 Hiroo,
Shibuya-ku, Tokyo, 150-0012, Japan
Tel.: (81) 355616800
Makeup Product Distr
N.A.I.C.S.: 424210

AMOREPACIFIC SINGAPORE PTE
Co Ltd.　　　　　　　　　　　　　(1)
8 Cross Street Level 25 Manulife Tower,
Singapore, 048424, Singapore
Tel.: (65) 67374988
Web Site: https://sg.laneige.com
Makeup Product Distr
N.A.I.C.S.: 424210

AMOREPACIFIC Taiwan Co.,
Ltd.　　　　　　　　　　　　　　　(1)
22th Floor No 68 Section 5 Zhongxiao East
Road, Xinyi District, Taipei, 110, Taiwan
Tel.: (886) 227221199
Cosmetics Product Mfr & Distr
N.A.I.C.S.: 325620

AMOREPACIFIC Vietnam Ltd.　　(1)
4A Floor Vincom Center 72 Le Thanh Ton,
Dist 1, Ho Chi Minh City, Vietnam
Tel.: (84) 838246232
Cosmetics Product Mfr & Distr
N.A.I.C.S.: 325620

Amorepacific Australia Pty. Ltd.　(1)
Level 19 180 Lonsdale St, Melbourne,
3000, VIC, Australia
Tel.: (61) 396232360
Makeup Product Distr
N.A.I.C.S.: 424210

Amorepacific Canada Inc.　　　　(1)
1235 Bay Street 7th Floor, Toronto, M5R
3K4, ON, Canada
Tel.: (416) 921-5000
Cosmetics Product Mfr & Distr
N.A.I.C.S.: 325620

Amorepacific Europe S.A.S　　　(1)
6th Floor 49/53 Avenue des Champs Ely-
sees, 75008, Paris, France
Tel.: (33) 140712060
Cosmetics Product Mfr & Distr
N.A.I.C.S.: 325620

Amos Co., Ltd.　　　　　　　　　(1)
42 Dongtansandan 5-gil Dongtan-myeon,
Hwaseong, Gyeonggi, Korea (South)
Tel.: (82) 234520133
Web Site: http://www.amoskorea.co.kr
Stationary & Paint Item Mfr
N.A.I.C.S.: 325510

Annick Goutal S.A.S.　　　　　　(1)

14 Rue De Castiglione, 75001, Paris,
France
Tel.: (33) 142605282
Web Site: http://www.annickgoutal.com
Sales Range: $10-24.9 Million
Perfume & Cosmetics Retailer
N.A.I.C.S.: 456120

Cosvision Co., Ltd.　　　　　　　(1)
80 Daehwa-ro, Daedeok-gu, Daejeon, Ko-
rea (South)
Tel.: (82) 426055520
Web Site: https://www.cosvision.com
Emp.: 110
Makeup Product Mfr & Distr
N.A.I.C.S.: 325620

Innisfree Cosmetics India Private
Limited　　　　　　　　　　　　　(1)
15th Floor Tower B Vatika Tower Sector- 54
Golf Course Road, Gurugram, 122002,
Haryana, India
Tel.: (91) 1244035640
Web Site: https://in.innisfree.com
Makeup Product Distr
N.A.I.C.S.: 424210

Tata's Natural Alchemy, LLC　　(1)
1136 Wooster Rd, Whiting, VT 05778
Web Site:
　https://www.tataharperskincare.com
Cosmetics Product Mfr & Distr
N.A.I.C.S.: 325620

AMOREPACIFIC GROUP
100 Hangang-daero, Yongsan-gu,
Seoul, Korea (South)
Tel.: (82) 260405114
Web Site:
　https://us.amorepacific.com
Year Founded: 1949
002790—(KRS)
Rev.: $3,447,631,871
Assets: $5,868,319,916
Liabilities: $857,122,853
Net Worth: $5,011,197,063
Earnings: $47,735,801
Emp.: 88
Fiscal Year-end: 12/31/22
Holding Company
N.A.I.C.S.: 551112
Kyung-Bae Suh *(Chm & CEO)*

AMOS GROUP LIMITED
156 Gul Circle, Singapore, 629613,
Singapore
Tel.: (65) 62622323
Web Site:
　https://www.amosgroup.com
49B—(SES)
Rev.: $73,642,451
Assets: $105,278,519
Liabilities: $39,276,903
Net Worth: $66,001,616
Earnings: ($8,719,631)
Fiscal Year-end: 03/31/23
Holding Company; Offshore Oil &
Gas Rigging & Lifting Equipment Mfr
N.A.I.C.S.: 551112
Sharon Kar Choo Yeoh *(Sec)*

Subsidiaries:

AMOS Azerbaijan LLC　　　　　(1)
Binagadi distr Shamakhi Highway 7, Khoja-
hasan Settlement Sulutepe, AZ1153, Baku,
Azerbaijan
Tel.: (994) 124474748
Marine & Offshore Services
N.A.I.C.S.: 561110

AMOS Europe (UK) Limited　　(1)
Insch Business Park, Insch, AB52 6TA, Ab-
erdeenshire, United Kingdom
Tel.: (44) 1464670010
Marine & Offshore Services
N.A.I.C.S.: 488390

AMOS International (HK) Limited　(1)
A7-A9 Block A 2/F Merit Industrial Centre,
94 To Kwa Wan Road, Kowloon, China
(Hong Kong)
Tel.: (852) 28728832
Marine & Offshore Services
N.A.I.C.S.: 561110

AMOS International (S) Pte Ltd　(1)
Marine Supplies Solutions Centre 156 Gul
Circle, Singapore, 629613, Singapore
Tel.: (65) 62622323
Marine & Offshore Services
N.A.I.C.S.: 561110
Davy Wilson Suresh *(Mgr-IT)*

AMOS International (Shanghai) Co.,
Ltd　　　　　　　　　　　　　　　(1)
Building D 1525 Fengxiang Road, Shang-
hai, 200444, China
Tel.: (86) 2154101625
Marine & Offshore Services
N.A.I.C.S.: 561110

AMOS Kazakhstan LLP　　　　　(1)
Industrial Zone No 8 Site 12, 130097, Ak-
tau, Mangystau, Kazakhstan
Tel.: (7) 7292750458
Marine & Offshore Services
N.A.I.C.S.: 561110

AMOS Korea Co Ltd　　　　　　(1)
51 Saenggoksandan 1-Ro, Gangseo-gu,
Busan, 46729, Korea (South)
Tel.: (82) 517141844
Marine & Offshore Services
N.A.I.C.S.: 561110

AMOS Malaysia Sdn Bhd　　　　(1)
PLO 475-C Jalan Ipil, PO Box 91, Pasir Gu-
dang, 81707, Johor, Malaysia
Tel.: (60) 72518828
Marine & Offshore Services
N.A.I.C.S.: 561110

AMOS Middle East FZE　　　　　(1)
PO Box 51469, Hamriyah Free Zone,
Sharjah, United Arab Emirates
Tel.: (971) 67413003
Marine & Offshore Services
N.A.I.C.S.: 561110

AMOS Middle East Holdings
FZE　　　　　　　　　　　　　　　(1)
Hamriyah Free Zone, PO Box 51469,
Sharjah, United Arab Emirates
Tel.: (971) 67413003
Investment Services
N.A.I.C.S.: 551112

AMOS Supply Korea Co., Ltd.　(1)
51 Saenggoksandan 1-Ro, Gangseo-gu,
Busan, 46729, Korea (South)
Tel.: (82) 517146264
Marine & Offshore Services
N.A.I.C.S.: 561110

AMOS Supply Pte Ltd　　　　　　(1)
156 Gul Circle, Singapore, 629613, Singa-
pore
Tel.: (65) 62622323
Marine & Offshore Services
N.A.I.C.S.: 561110

AMOS Vietnam Pte Ltd　　　　　(1)
Road 12 Dong Xuyen Industrial Zone, Rach
Dua Ward, Vung Tau, Vietnam
Tel.: (84) 2543530988
Marine & Offshore Services
N.A.I.C.S.: 561110

Allseas Marine Services Pte Ltd　(1)
27B Benoi Road Pioneer Lot, Singapore,
629917, Singapore
Tel.: (65) 6265 2655
Web Site:
　http://www.allseasmarineservices.com
Logistics Consulting Servies
N.A.I.C.S.: 541614

Gaylin Vietnam Pte Ltd　　　　　(1)
Road No 12 Dong Xuyen Industrial Zone,
Rach Dua Ward, Vung Tau, Vietnam
Tel.: (84) 64 3 530988
Web Site: http://www.gaylin.com
Oil & Gas Rigging & Lifting Equipment Mfr
N.A.I.C.S.: 333132

Lv Yang Offshore Equipment Co.,
Ltd.　　　　　　　　　　　　　　　(1)
RM5401-9 No 5 Buiding No 19 Xinhuanxi
Road Teda, Tianjin, 300457, China
Tel.: (86) 2266230630
Marine & Offshore Services
N.A.I.C.S.: 561110

PT AMOS Utama Indonesia　　　(1)
Suite 3 6/F Union Space PIK Avenue Mall,
Jl Pantai Indah Barat No 1, Jakarta Utara,

14470, Indonesia
Tel.: (62) 2129492270
Marine & Offshore Services
N.A.I.C.S.: 561110
Ahmad Dukhaeri *(Mgr)*

PT. Gaylin　　　　　　　　　　　(1)
Equity Tower 49th Floor Suite 1208 Jl Jen-
dral Sudiman Kav, 52-53 SCBD, Jakarta,
12190, Indonesia
Tel.: (62) 21 2965 1150
Oil & Gas Rigging & Lifting Equipment Mfr
N.A.I.C.S.: 333132

Phoenix Offshore Co. Ltd　　　　(1)
Gomdoori Bldg 7 1324 Yeonsa-ri Yeoncho-
meon, Kyungsangnamdo, Geoje, Korea
(South)
Tel.: (82) 55 6386060
Oil & Gas Rigging & Lifting Equipment Mfr
N.A.I.C.S.: 333132

**AMOS LUZON DEVELOPMENT
AND ENERGY GROUP LTD.**
34 Yerushalayim St, Ra'anana,
4310801, Israel
Tel.: (972) 99705500　　　　Ⅱ
Web Site: https://www.romgeves.co.il
Year Founded: 1961
LUZN—(TAE)
Rev.: $247,921,532
Assets: $609,411,511
Liabilities: $426,230,964
Net Worth: $183,180,547
Earnings: $33,183,865
Emp.: 2,000
Fiscal Year-end: 12/31/23
Commercial & Institutional Building
Construction
N.A.I.C.S.: 236220

Subsidiaries:

U. Dori Construction Ltd.　　　　(1)
34 Jerusalem Street, PO Box 936,
Ra'anana, 4310801, Israel　　　(100%)
Tel.: (972) 9 970 5555
Web Site: http://www.dori.co.il
Building Construction Services
N.A.I.C.S.: 236116
Dana Chen *(Mgr-HR)*

AMOSENSE CO., LTD.
90 4Sandan 5-Gil Jiksan-eup,
Seobuk-gu, Cheonan,
Chungcheongnam-do, Korea (South)
Tel.: (82) 415905700
Web Site: http://www.amosense.com
Year Founded: 2008
357580—(KRS)
Emp.: 294
Electronic Components Mfr
N.A.I.C.S.: 334419
In-Eung Kim *(CEO)*

AMOTECH CO LTD
380 Namdongseo-ro, Namdong-gu,
Incheon, 21629, Korea (South)
Tel.: (82) 328210363
Web Site: https://www.amotech.co.kr
Year Founded: 1994
052710—(KRS)
Rev.: $165,452,935
Assets: $294,522,132
Liabilities: $158,952,486
Net Worth: $135,569,645
Earnings: ($7,063,713)
Emp.: 710
Fiscal Year-end: 12/31/22
Electronic Appliances
N.A.I.C.S.: 334416
Byunggyu Kim *(CEO)*

Subsidiaries:

AMOTECH KOREA Inc.　　　　　(1)
5BL-1Lot 617 Namchon-Dong, Namdong-
Gu, Incheon, 405-846, Korea (South)
Tel.: (82) 328210363
Web Site: https://global.amotech.co.kr
Electronic Products Mfr
N.A.I.C.S.: 333612

Amotech Co., Ltd. - Antenna Division (1)
5 Bl 1 Lot 617 Namchon-Dong, Namdong-Gu, 405-100, Incheon, Korea (South)
Tel.: (82) 328210363
Web Site: http://www.amotech.co.kr
Sales Range: $50-74.9 Million
Emp.: 120
Antenna Mfr
N.A.I.C.S.: 334220

Amotech Co., Ltd. - Motor Division (1)
Manho-ri Poseung-myun, Pyeongtaek, Gyeonggi-do, Korea (South)
Tel.: (82) 3180537000
Sales Range: $25-49.9 Million
Emp.: 50
Motor Mfr
N.A.I.C.S.: 336390

Amotech Co., Ltd. - Shandong Factory (1)
Room 609 West Tianan Hi-Tech Plaza, Phase II, Shenzhen, China
Tel.: (86) 75582507984
Web Site: http://www.amotech.co.kr
Sales Range: $100-124.9 Million
Emp.: 400
Electronic Products Mfr
N.A.I.C.S.: 334419

Amotech Co., Ltd. - Varistor Division (1)
5 Bl 1 Lot 617 Namchon-Dong, Namdong-Gu, 405-100, Incheon, Korea (South)
Tel.: (82) 5 9724578
Electronic Products Mfr
N.A.I.C.S.: 334416

AMOTIV LIMITED
144 Moray Street, South Melbourne, 3025, VIC, Australia
Tel.: (61) 392433311   AU
Web Site: https://amotiv.com
Year Founded: 1940
GUDDY—(OTCIQ)
Rev.: $659,170,670
Assets: $1,195,862,041
Liabilities: $572,419,869
Net Worth: $623,442,172
Earnings: $66,647,970
Fiscal Year-end: 06/30/24
Holding Company; Automotive Components & Fluid Pump Mfr
N.A.I.C.S.: 551112
Malcolm G. Tyler (Sec & Gen Counsel)

Subsidiaries:

AA Gaskets Pty Ltd (1)
29 Taras Avenue, Altona, 3025, VIC, Australia   (100%)
Tel.: (61) 393554400
Web Site: https://www.aagaskets.com.au
Automotive Gasket Mfr
N.A.I.C.S.: 339991

Subsidiary (Non-US):

NZ Gaskets Limited (2)
19 Bell Ave, Mt Wellington, Auckland, 1026, New Zealand   (100%)
Tel.: (64) 98290047
Web Site: https://www.nzgaskets.co.nz
Automotive Gasket Mfr
N.A.I.C.S.: 339991

Brown & Watson International Pty Ltd (1)
1500 Ferntree Gully Road, Knoxfield, 3180, VIC, Australia
Tel.: (61) 39 730 6000
Web Site: https://www.brownwatson.com.au
Automobile Parts Mfr
N.A.I.C.S.: 336390

Davey Products NZ Limited (1)
7 Rockridge Avenue, Penrose, Auckland, 1061, New Zealand   (100%)
Tel.: (64) 95709135
Web Site: http://www.daveynz.co.nz
Sales Range: $25-49.9 Million
Emp.: 30
Water Pumps & Pressure Systems Distr
N.A.I.C.S.: 333914

Peter Goodwin (Gen Mgr)

Davey Products Pty. Ltd. (1)
6 Lakeview Dr, Scoresby, 3179, VIC, Australia
Tel.: (61) 397309222
Sales Range: $50-74.9 Million
Emp.: 200
Mfr & Supplier of Pumps & Water Pressure Systems
N.A.I.C.S.: 333914

Dexion Asia Limited (1)
6/F Mtl Bldg Ph Ii Berth 1 Container Port Rd, Kwai Chung, New Territories, China (Hong Kong)
Tel.: (852) 24108383
Warehouse Construction Services
N.A.I.C.S.: 236220

Dexion Commercial (New Zealand) Limited (1)
39 Randwick Road, Moera, Lower Hutt, 5010, Wellington, New Zealand
Tel.: (64) 4 920 5400
Web Site: http://www.precisionworkspace.co.nz
Emp.: 30
Furniture Mfr & Whslr
N.A.I.C.S.: 337126
Ben King (Gen Mgr)

Disc Brakes Australia Pty Ltd (1)
Unit 33 Slough Business Park, Silverwater, Sydney, 2128, NSW, Australia
Tel.: (61) 29 748 0211
Web Site: https://dba.com.au
Brake Rotor Product Mfr & Distr
N.A.I.C.S.: 336340

Fully Equipped Limited (1)
2 Tasman Road, Te Rapa, Hamilton, New Zealand
Tel.: (64) 7 850 7000
Web Site: https://www.fullyequipped.co.nz
Motor Vehicles Mfr
N.A.I.C.S.: 336110

GUD (NZ) Limited (1)
626A Rosebank Rd, Avondale, Auckland, 1026, New Zealand   (100%)
Tel.: (64) 98287089
Web Site: http://www.ryco.co.nz
Sales Range: $25-49.9 Million
Emp.: 11
N.A.I.C.S.: 315990
Scott MacGuire (Mgr-Site)

Griffiths Equipment Limited (1)
19 Bell Avenue Mount Wellington, Auckland, 1060, New Zealand
Tel.: (64) 9 525 4575
Web Site: https://www.griffithsequipment.co.nz
Automobile Parts Distr
N.A.I.C.S.: 423120

Monarch Pool Systems Europe S.A.S. (1)
2 Rue Augustin Fresnel, 69680, Chassieu, Rhone, France
Tel.: (33) 472139507
Emp.: 6
Salt Water Pool System Distr
N.A.I.C.S.: 423910
Piron Sam (Gen Mgr)

RYCO Group Pty Limited (1)
29 Taras Avenue, Altona, 3025, VIC, Australia
Tel.: (61) 392433333
Web Site: http://www.rycofilters.com.au
Mfr & Distr of Automotive Filters
N.A.I.C.S.: 336390
Guy Nicholls (CEO)

Uneek 4x4 Australia Pty Ltd (1)
35 Gatwick Road, Bayswater, 3153, VIC, Australia
Tel.: (61) 39 729 3233
Automobile Parts Mfr
N.A.I.C.S.: 336390

Wesfil Australia Pty. Ltd. (1)
(100%)
Tel.: (61) 299392544
Web Site: http://www.wesfil.com.au
Sales Range: $25-49.9 Million
Emp.: 60
N.A.I.C.S.: 315990

XClutchUSA, Inc. (1)
3423 Southpark Pl Ste B, Grove City, OH 43123
Web Site: https://www.xclutchusa.com
Automobile Parts Mfr
N.A.I.C.S.: 336390

AMOUN INTERNATIONAL FOR INVESTMENT P.L.C
Al Sharif Nasser Bin Jameel Street Building No 85 First Floor, PO BOX 17523, Amman, 11195, Jordan
Tel.: (962) 65560511
Web Site: https://www.ammouninvest.com
Year Founded: 2008
AMON—(AMM)
Rev.: $1,128,174
Assets: $9,981,971
Liabilities: $155,542
Net Worth: $9,826,339
Earnings: ($60,193)
Emp.: 6
Fiscal Year-end: 12/31/23
Real Estate Development Services
N.A.I.C.S.: 531390
Emad Ghannam Al Saddi (CEO & Gen Dir)

AMOUN PHARMACEUTICAL COMPANY S.A.E.
1st industrial zone -block El Obour city, 13015, Cairo, Egypt
Tel.: (20) 246140100
Web Site: http://www.amoun.com
Year Founded: 1998
Pharmaceuticals Product Mfr
N.A.I.C.S.: 325412
Mohamed Roushdy (Pres)

AMOY DIAGNOSTICS CO., LTD.
39 Dingshan Road Haicang District, Xiamen, 361027, China
Tel.: (86) 5926806835
Web Site: http://www.amoydiagnostics.com
300685—(CHIN)
Rev.: $146,977,919
Assets: $272,528,073
Liabilities: $32,615,325
Net Worth: $239,912,749
Earnings: $36,830,078
Fiscal Year-end: 12/31/23
Pharmaceutical Product Mfr & Distr
N.A.I.C.S.: 325412

AMP GERMAN CANNABIS GROUP INC.
224 West 5th Avenue, Vancouver, V5Y 1J4, BC, Canada
Tel.: (236) 833-1602   AB
Web Site: http://www.amp-eu.com
Year Founded: 1997
XCX—(TSXV)
Assets: $613,598
Liabilities: $715,642
Net Worth: ($102,044)
Earnings: ($3,045,458)
Fiscal Year-end: 12/31/19
Railway Maintenance Equipment Supplier
N.A.I.C.S.: 488210

AMP LIMITED
Level 29 50 Bridge Street, Sydney, 2000, NSW, Australia
Tel.: (61) 280488162   AU
Web Site: https://www.amp.com.au
Year Founded: 1849
AMP—(ASX)
Rev.: $2,526,128,430
Assets: $24,777,818,410
Liabilities: $21,726,083,640
Net Worth: $3,051,734,770
Earnings: ($194,612,260)

Emp.: 5,900
Fiscal Year-end: 12/31/21
Financial Management & Capital Investment Services
N.A.I.C.S.: 523999
Debra Hazelton (Chm)

Subsidiaries:

AMP Australian Financial Services Holdings Limited (1)
Level 16 33 Alfred Street, Sydney, 2000, NSW, Australia   (100%)
Tel.: (61) 1300363267
Web Site: http://www.amp.com.au
Holding Company
N.A.I.C.S.: 551112

AMP Bank Limited (1)
33 Alfred Street, Sydney, 2000, NSW, Australia   (100%)
Tel.: (61) 280488162
Web Site: http://www.amp.com.au
Commercial Banking
N.A.I.C.S.: 522110
Rod Finch (Mng Dir)

AMP Capital Investors (US) Limited (1)
1114 Avenue of the Americas 16th Fl, New York, NY 10036
Tel.: (929) 481-7950
Web Site: https://www.ampcapital.com
Emp.: 10
Investment Management Service
N.A.I.C.S.: 523999
Brent Tasugi (Principal-New York)

AMP Capital Investors Limited (1)
PO Box 300, Parramatta, 2134, NSW, Australia
Tel.: (61) 292575000
Web Site: http://www.ampcapital.com
Sales Range: $100-124.9 Million
Emp.: 200
Investment Services
N.A.I.C.S.: 523940
Andrew Bird (Chief Investment Officer-Property)

Subsidiary (Domestic):

AMP Capital Holdings Limited (2)
L 24 33 Alfred St, 2000, Sydney, NSW, Australia   (85%)
Tel.: (61) 292575000
Web Site: http://www.amp.com.au
Sales Range: $1-4.9 Billion
Emp.: 3,500
Holding Company
N.A.I.C.S.: 551112
Andrew Jones (Global Head-infrastructure Debt)

Subsidiary (Non-US):

AMP Capital Investments Limited (2)
Level 14 HP Tower 171 Featherston Street, Wellington, New Zealand   (100%)
Tel.: (64) 44942299
Web Site: http://www.ampcapital.com.au
Investment Advice
N.A.I.C.S.: 523940

AMP Capital Investors (Luxembourg) S.a r.l. (2)
18-20 Rue Edward Steichen, 2540, Luxembourg, Luxembourg
Tel.: (352) 2784 8035
Emp.: 3
Investment Management Service
N.A.I.C.S.: 523999
Marc Lamberty (Mng Dir)

AMP Capital Investors (New Zealand) Limited (2)
Level 1 Meridian Building 55 Lady Elizabeth Lane, Queens Wharf, Wellington, 6011, New Zealand
Tel.: (64) 44942200
Web Site: http://www.ampcapital.com
Sales Range: $50-74.9 Million
Emp.: 55
Financial & Investment Services
N.A.I.C.S.: 523940
Rebekah Swan (Head-Product)

Subsidiary (Domestic):

AMP Capital Investors International Holdings Limited (2)

AMP Limited—(Continued)

L 12 50 Bridge St, Sydney, 2000, NSW,
Australia   **(100%)**
Tel.: (61) 292575000
Web Site: http://www.ampcapital.com.au
Holding Company
N.A.I.C.S.: 551112
Stephen Dunne *(Mng Dir)*

Subsidiary (Non-US):

AMP Capital Investors Property Japan KK   **(2)**
10th floor of Meiji Yasuda Life Building
2-1-1 Marunouchi, Chiyoda-Ku, Tokyo, 100-0005, Japan
Tel.: (81) 332127170
Web Site: http://www.ampcapital.com
Real Estate Management Services
N.A.I.C.S.: 531390

Subsidiary (Domestic):

AMP Capital Office and Industrial Pty Limited   **(2)**
Suite 19 45 Collins Street, Melbourne, Australia
Tel.: (61) 3 9655 3600
Financial Investment Services
N.A.I.C.S.: 523999

Joint Venture (Non-US):

Adven Oy   **(2)**
Karhumaenkuja 2, 01530, Vantaa, Finland
Tel.: (358) 10 344 5000
Web Site: https://adven.com
Sales Range: $125-149.9 Million
Emp.: 400
Heating & Cooling Services
N.A.I.C.S.: 221330
Esa Aarnio *(VP-Bus Dev)*

Subsidiary (Non-US):

Adven Eesti AS   **(3)**
Kassi 13, 12618, Tallinn, Estonia
Tel.: (372) 617 8600
Web Site: https://adven.com
Heating & Cooling Services
N.A.I.C.S.: 221330
Urmo Heinam *(Chm-Mgmt Bd & CEO)*

Joint Venture (Non-US):

Angel Trains Limited   **(2)**
123 Victoria Street, London, SW1E 6DE,
United Kingdom
Tel.: (44) 20 7592 0500
Web Site: http://www.angeltrains.co.uk
Emp.: 145
Rolling Stock Leasing Services
N.A.I.C.S.: 532411
Malcolm Brown *(CEO)*

Holding (US):

ITS Technologies & Logistics, LLC   **(2)**
8205 S Cass Ave Ste 115, Darien, IL 60561
Tel.: (708) 225-2400
Web Site: https://itsconglobal.com
Emp.: 3,100
Intermodal Rail Terminal Services, Auto
Loading & Unloading & Container Depot
Services
N.A.I.C.S.: 488510
Steven L. Rubin *(CEO)*

Subsidiary (Domestic):

ConGlobal Industries Inc.   **(3)**
8205 S Cass Ave Ste 115, Darien, IL 60561
Tel.: (708) 225-2400
Web Site: https://itsconglobal.com
Infrastructure Services Provider, Transportation, Stevedoring & Customs Bonded Warehousing, Container & Chassis Depot Services
N.A.I.C.S.: 488490
Rene Etcharren *(Pres & CEO)*

Holding (Non-US):

Magnet Networks Ltd.   **(2)**
International Exchange Centre, Clonshaugh
Industrial Estate, Dublin, 17, Ireland
Tel.: (353) 16810000
Web Site: http://www.magnet.ie

Sales Range: $25-49.9 Million
Television, Telephone & Broadband Internet
Services
N.A.I.C.S.: 517810
Mark Kellett *(CEO)*

AMP Custodian Services (NZ) Limited   **(1)**
86-90 Custom House Quay, Wellington,
6011, New Zealand
Tel.: (64) 44988000
Financial Investment Services
N.A.I.C.S.: 523999

AMP Finance Services Limited   **(1)**
L24 33 Alfred Street, Sydney, NSW,
Australia   **(100%)**
Tel.: (61) 292575000
Web Site: http://www.amp.com.au
Sales Range: $25-49.9 Million
Emp.: 100
Business Support Services
N.A.I.C.S.: 561499
Craig Duncan Meller *(Mng Dir)*

AMP Financial Planning Pty Limited   **(1)**
33 Alfred St Amp Building, Sydney, 2000,
NSW, Australia   **(100%)**
Tel.: (61) 292575000
Investment Advice
N.A.I.C.S.: 523940
Craig William Dunn *(Mng Dir)*

AMP Gbs Limited   **(1)**
L 22 Amp Building 33 Alfred St, Sydney,
NSW, Australia   **(100%)**
Tel.: (61) 292576273
Business Support Services
N.A.I.C.S.: 561499

AMP Group Finance Services Limited   **(1)**
L24 Amp Sydney Cove Bldg 33 Alfred St,
Sydney, 2000, NSW, Australia   **(100%)**
Tel.: (61) 292575453
Emp.: 3,005
Investment Advice
N.A.I.C.S.: 523940
Craig Duncan Meller *(Mng Dir)*

AMP Group Holdings Limited   **(1)**
L24 33 Alfred St, Sydney, NSW,
Australia   **(100%)**
Tel.: (61) 292575000
Web Site: http://www.amp.com.au
Business Support Services
N.A.I.C.S.: 561499

AMP Group Services Limited   **(1)**
L 24 33 Alfred St, 2000, Sydney, NSW,
Australia   **(100%)**
Tel.: (61) 292575000
Web Site: http://www.amp.com.au
Investment Advice
N.A.I.C.S.: 523940
Craig Denn *(CEO)*

AMP Holdings Limited   **(1)**
L 24 Amp Sydney Cove Bldg, Sydney,
2000, NSW, Australia   **(100%)**
Tel.: (61) 292575000
Web Site: http://www.ampcapital.com
Sales Range: $50-74.9 Million
Emp.: 10
Holding Company
N.A.I.C.S.: 551112
Craig William Dunn *(CEO & Mng Dir)*

AMP Insurance Investment Holdings Pty Limited   **(1)**
L 9 33 Alfred Street, Sydney, 2000, NSW, Australia
Tel.: (61) 292578444
Insurance Management Services
N.A.I.C.S.: 524298

AMP Investment Services Pty Limited   **(1)**
L 11 Amp Centre 50 Bridge St, Sydney,
NSW, Australia   **(100%)**
Tel.: (61) 292575000
Web Site: http://amp.com.au
Business Support Services
N.A.I.C.S.: 561499
Craig William Dunn *(Mng Dir)*

AMP Services (NZ) Limited   **(1)**
29 Custom St Auckland Central, PO Box

1290, Level 1 AMP Chambers, Auckland,
New Zealand   **(100%)**
Tel.: (64) 44988000
Web Site: http://www.amp.co.nz
Sales Range: $200-249.9 Million
Emp.: 500
Financial Transactions Processing Reserve
& Clearinghouse Activities
N.A.I.C.S.: 522320
Jack Regan *(Mng Dir)*

AMP Services Holdings Limited   **(1)**
AMP Bldg 33 Alfred Street, Sydney, 2000,
NSW, Australia   **(100%)**
Tel.: (61) 292575000
Web Site: http://www.amp.com.au
Sales Range: $350-399.9 Million
Emp.: 1,000
Nondepository Credit Intermediation
N.A.I.C.S.: 522299
Craig William Dunn *(Mng Dir)*

AMP Services Limited   **(1)**
Level 18 33 Alfred Street, 2000, Sydney,
NSW, Australia   **(100%)**
Tel.: (61) 92575190
Web Site: http://www.amp.com.au
Management Consulting Services
N.A.I.C.S.: 541618

AMP Superannuation (NZ) Limited   **(1)**
29 Customs Street, PO Box 55, Auckland,
1140, New Zealand   **(100%)**
Tel.: (64) 44988000
Web Site: http://www.amp.co.nz
Reinsurance Carriers
N.A.I.C.S.: 524130

AMP Superannuation Limited   **(1)**
L 14 Amp Sydney Cove Building 33 Alfred
St, Sydney, 2000, NSW, Australia
Tel.: (61) 292575000
Financial Management Services
N.A.I.C.S.: 523999
Rick Allert *(Chm)*

AMP Warringah Mall Pty Ltd   **(1)**
Cnr Condamine St Old Pittwater Road,
Brookvale, 2100, NSW, Australia
Tel.: (61) 29905 0633
Web Site: http://www.warringahmall.com.au
Shopping Mall Operation Services
N.A.I.C.S.: 445110

AXA Asia Pacific Holdings Limited   **(1)**
750 Collins Street, Docklands, Melbourne,
3008, VIC, Australia
Tel.: (61) 396163911
Sales Range: $5-14.9 Billion
Holding Company; Insurance Products &
Services
N.A.I.C.S.: 551112

Subsidiary (Non-US):

AMP Services (NZ) Limited   **(2)**
80 The Terrace, PO Box 1692, Wellington,
6140, New Zealand   **(100%)**
Tel.: (64) 4 439 5858
Web Site: http://www.amp.co.nz
Sales Range: $75-99.9 Million
Emp.: 200
Life Insurance
N.A.I.C.S.: 524113

Subsidiary (Domestic):

AXA Australia   **(2)**
Level 5 750 Collins St, Docklands, Melbourne, 3008, VIC, Australia
Tel.: (61) 386882204
Sales Range: $350-399.9 Million
Emp.: 1,000
Insurance & Financial Services
N.A.I.C.S.: 523999

National Mutual Funds Management Ltd.   **(2)**
750 Collins Street, Melbourne, 3000, VIC,
Australia
Tel.: (61) 396163911
Sales Range: $25-49.9 Million
Financial Management Services
N.A.I.C.S.: 541611

National Mutual Life Association of Australia Ltd.   **(2)**

---

750 Collins St, Melbourne, 3000, Victoria,
Australia   **(100%)**
Tel.: (61) 396163911
Sales Range: $600-649.9 Million
Emp.: 2,000
Life Insurance & Finance Services
N.A.I.C.S.: 524113
Richard Hugh Allert *(Chm)*

Arrive Wealth Management Limited   **(1)**
123 Eagle Street, Level 15 Riverside Centre, Brisbane, 4000, NSW,
Australia   **(100%)**
Tel.: (61) 730017000
Web Site: http://www.arrive.com.au
Emp.: 150
Investment Advice
N.A.I.C.S.: 523940

Collins Place No. 2 Pty Ltd   **(1)**
45 Collins St, Melbourne, 3000, VIC, Australia
Tel.: (61) 396553600
Emp.: 10
Real Estate Management Services
N.A.I.C.S.: 531390
Stave Dolan *(Gen Mgr)*

Collins Place Pty Limited   **(1)**
45 Collins Street, Melbourne, 3000, VIC,
Australia
Tel.: (61) 39 655 3618
Web Site: https://www.collinsplace.com.au
Emp.: 15
Real Estate Management Services
N.A.I.C.S.: 531390

Esvagt A/S   **(1)**
Dokvej 4, 6700, Esbjerg, Denmark
Tel.: (45) 78 730 730
Web Site: http://www.esvagt.com
Emp.: 1,000
Offshore Safety & Support Services
N.A.I.C.S.: 488390
Kristian Ole Jakobsen *(Deputy CEO)*

Glendenning Pty Limited   **(1)**
1132 Richmond Rd, Marsden Park, Sydney,
2765, NSW, Australia
Tel.: (61) 296271804
Business Support Services
N.A.I.C.S.: 561499

Hillross Alliances Limited   **(1)**
101 Peter Street Wagga, Sydney, 2650,
NSW, Australia
Tel.: (61) 2 5908 8700
Web Site: http://www.hillross.com.au
Business Management Consulting Services
N.A.I.C.S.: 541611

Hillross Financial Services Limited   **(1)**
Level 11 33 Alfred Street, Sydney, 2000,
NSW, Australia
Tel.: (61) 2 9257 4040
Web Site: http://www.hillross.com.au
Financial & Investment Services
N.A.I.C.S.: 523940

Hillross Innisfail Pty Limited   **(1)**
Shop 10 27 Owen St, Innisfail, 4860, QLD,
Australia
Tel.: (61) 740614588
Business Management Consulting Services
N.A.I.C.S.: 541611

Homemaker Megamall Auburn Pty Ltd   **(1)**
265 Parramatta Road Corner Parramatta
Rd & Duck St, Auburn, 2144, NSW, Australia
Tel.: (61) 29748 6900
Web Site:
http://www.auburnhomemegamall.com.au
Shopping Mall Operation Services
N.A.I.C.S.: 445110
Anna Le *(Mgr-Mktg-Casual Mall Leasing)*

Marrickville Metro Shopping Centre Pty Limited   **(1)**
34 Victoria Rd, Marrickville, 2204, NSW,
Australia
Tel.: (61) 295191066
Web Site:
http://www.marrickvillemetro.com.au
Emp.: 5
Shopping Mall Operation Services
N.A.I.C.S.: 445110

Mowla Pty. Ltd **(1)**
25 Collins St, Melbourne, 3000, VIC,
Australia **(100%)**
Tel.: (61) 396530000
Web Site:
http://www.sositelmelbourne.com.au
Sales Range: $150-199.9 Million
Emp.: 500
Amusement & Recreation Industries
N.A.I.C.S.: 713990
Clive Scott *(Gen Mgr)*

Priority One Financial Services
Limited **(1)**
Level 4 33 Alfred St, Sydney, NSW,
Australia **(100%)**
Tel.: (61) 296419641
Financial Services
N.A.I.C.S.: 522320

Roost 2007 Limited **(1)**
Level 21 AMP Centre 29 Customs St West,
Auckland, New Zealand
Tel.: (64) 9 337 7219
Web Site: http://www.roost.co.nz
Mortgage Loan Brokerage Services
N.A.I.C.S.: 522310

Sugarland Shopping Centre Pty
Limited **(1)**
115-119 Takalvan Street, West Bundaberg,
Bundaberg, 4670, QLD, Australia
Tel.: (61) 7 4152 5788
Sales Range: $250-299.9 Million
Emp.: 5
Stationery Product Distr
N.A.I.C.S.: 424120
Peter Cocking *(Mgr-Centre)*

AMPCO METAL SA

Route de Chesalles 48, PO Box 45,
Marly, 1723, Switzerland
Tel.: (41) 264399300
Web Site:
http://www.ampcometal.com
Year Founded: 1914
Sales Range: $25-49.9 Million
Emp.: 150
Producer of Copper Alloy Mfr
N.A.I.C.S.: 331529
Luis Bento *(Chm)*

Subsidiaries:

AMPCO METAL Deutschland
GmbH **(1)**
Wallensteinstrasse 10, PO Box 840, 82538,
Geretsried, Germany
Tel.: (49) 8171 93 660
Alloy Metal Distr
N.A.I.C.S.: 423510

AMPCO METAL INDIA PVT LTD **(1)**
A-8/4 At Village - Nighoje Chakan MIDC
Phase - IV, Tal Khed, Pune, 410 501, Ma-
harashtra, India
Tel.: (91) 2135 610810
Web Site: http://www.ampcometal.com
Emp.: 20
Alloy Metal Distr
N.A.I.C.S.: 423510
Tushar Tawar *(Dir)*

AMPCO METAL KOREA CO.,
LTD. **(1)**
39 Bucheon-ro 208beon-gil, Bucheon,
Gyeonggi-do, Korea (South)
Tel.: (82) 315481107
Alloy Metal Distr
N.A.I.C.S.: 423510

AMPCO METAL Srl **(1)**
Via F Crispi nr 4/A, 20871, Vimercate, Italy
Tel.: (39) 039 9711 749
Alloy Metal Distr
N.A.I.C.S.: 423510

AMPCO METAL s.r.o. **(1)**
Hviezdoslavovo namestie 13, 811 02, Brati-
slava, Slovakia
Tel.: (421) 2 54432337
Web Site: http://www.ampcometal.com
Alloy Metal Distr
N.A.I.C.S.: 423510

Ampco Metal (Foshan) Co. Ltd. **(1)**
No 9 Xinyue road Jinqiao Industrial City
Wusha Daliang town Shunde, Foshan,

528333, Guangdong, China
Tel.: (86) 757 2232 6571
Web Site: http://www.ampcometal.cn
Emp.: 30
Alloy Metal Distr
N.A.I.C.S.: 423510

Ampco Metal Ltd. **(1)**
17 Binns Cl Torrington Ave, Coventry, CV4
9TB, United Kingdom
Tel.: (44) 2476467011
Web Site: http://www.ampcometal.com
Rev.: $1,858,335
Emp.: 4
Mfr & Producer of Copper Alloys
N.A.I.C.S.: 331529

Ampco Metal Portugal Ltda. **(1)**
Vila Central 360, 4475 330, Porto, Mil-
heiros, Portugal
Tel.: (351) 229783080
Web Site: http://www.ampcometal.com
Sales Range: $25-49.9 Million
Emp.: 8
Mfr & Producer of Copper Alloys
N.A.I.C.S.: 331529

Ampco Metal SA - AREOSPACE
DIVISION **(1)**
27 rue JM Peters, 31840, Toulouse, France
Tel.: (33) 6 26 93 80 52
Alloy Metal Distr
N.A.I.C.S.: 423510

Ampco Metal SAS **(1)**
46 Avenue Des Freres Lumiere, Batiment A,
Trappes, 78190, France **(100%)**
Tel.: (33) 130492929
Web Site: http://www.ampcometal.com
Sales Range: $25-49.9 Million
Emp.: 4
Mfr & Producer of Copper Alloys
N.A.I.C.S.: 331529
Luis Bento *(CEO)*

Ampco Metal, Inc. **(1)**
1117 E Algonquin Rd, Arlington Heights, IL
60005-4756
Tel.: (847) 437-6000
Web Site: http://www.ampcometal.com
Sales Range: $25-49.9 Million
Emp.: 75
Mfr & Producer of Copper Alloys
N.A.I.C.S.: 331529
J. F. Dallin *(Pres)*

Division (Domestic):

Ampco Metal, Inc. - Welding Products
Division **(2)**
4475 N 124 St Ste F, Brookfield, WI 53005
Tel.: (262) 790-6940
Alloy Metal Distr
N.A.I.C.S.: 423510

AMPD VENTURES, INC.

210-577 Great Northern Way, Van-
couver, V5T 1E1, BC, Canada
Tel.: (604) 332-3329
Web Site: https://www.ampd.tech
AMPD—(CNSX)
Rev.: $1,212,331
Assets: $2,299,176
Liabilities: $933,129
Net Worth: $1,366,047
Earnings: ($2,570,147)
Fiscal Year-end: 05/31/21
Information Technology Management
Services
N.A.I.C.S.: 541512
Anthony Brown *(CEO)*

AMPER, S.A.

Cl virgilio 2, 28223, Pozuelo de Alar-
con, Spain
Tel.: (34) 917243000 **ES**
Year Founded: 1956
AMP—(MAD)
Sales Range: $450-499.9 Million
Emp.: 2,039
Civil & Military Communications Appli-
cations & Services
N.A.I.C.S.: 517112
Jaime Espinosa de los Monteros Pi-
tarque *(Chm)*

Subsidiaries:

Nucleo de Comunicaciones y Control,
S.L. **(1)**
C Virgilio 2, Pozuelo de Alarcon, 28223,
Madrid, Spain **(73.24%)**
Tel.: (34) 91 807 39 99
Web Site: http://www.nucleocc.com
Construction Engineering Services
N.A.I.C.S.: 541330

AMPERE LIMITED

15 Torbarrie Road, Toronto, M3L
1G5, ON, Canada
Tel.: (416) 661-3330
Web Site: http://www.ampere.ca
Year Founded: 1959
Rev.: $13,911,132
Emp.: 75
Electrical Contractor
N.A.I.C.S.: 238210
Jackie Li *(VP)*

AMPHION INNOVATIONS PLC

Fort Anne, Douglas, IM1 5PD, Isle of
Man
Tel.: (44) 2122106282 **IM**
Web Site:
http://www.amphionplc.com
Sales Range: Less than $1 Million
Emp.: 4
Operate Life Science & Technology
Companies
N.A.I.C.S.: 523940
Richard Cecil Eversfield Morgan
(Chm-Interim & CEO)

Subsidiaries:

Amphion Innovations US, Inc. **(1)**
330 Madison Ave, New York, NY 10017
Tel.: (212) 210-6282
Web Site: http://www.amphionplc.com
Sales Range: $50-74.9 Million
Emp.: 6
Operate Life Science & Technology Compa-
nies
N.A.I.C.S.: 523940
Richard Cecil Eversfield Morgan *(CEO)*

DataTern, Inc. **(1)**
330 Madison Ave 31st FL, New York, NY
10017
Tel.: (212) 210-6221
Web Site: http://www.datatern.com
Sales Range: $25-49.9 Million
Emp.: 1
Administrative Software Distr
N.A.I.C.S.: 541511

Polarean Imaging Plc **(1)**
2500 Meridian Pkwy Ste 175, Durham, NC
27713
Tel.: (919) 206-7900
Web Site: http://www.polarean.com
Sales Range: $1-9.9 Million
Medical Equipment Mfr
N.A.I.C.S.: 334510
Bastiaan Driehuys *(Founder & CTO)*

Subsidiary (Domestic):

Polarean, Inc. **(2)**
2500 Meridian Pkwy Ste 175, Durham, NC
27713
Tel.: (919) 206-7900
Web Site: http://www.polarean.com
Medical Equipment Mfr
N.A.I.C.S.: 334510
Bastiaan Driehuys *(Founder & CTO)*

AMPHITECH

1 R Robert et Sonia Delaunay,
75011, Paris, France
Tel.: (33) 143679377
Web Site: http://www.amphitech.fr
Rev.: $24,200,000
Emp.: 128
Telephone & Telegraph Apparatus
N.A.I.C.S.: 334210
Alain Wehrbach *(Mng Partner)*

AMPIRE CO., LTD.

4F No 116 Sec 1 Xintai 5th Rd, Xizhi

Dist, New Taipei City, 221, Taiwan
Tel.: (886) 226967269
Web Site: https://www.ampire.com.tw
Year Founded: 1998
8049—(TPE)
Rev.: $75,717,694
Assets: $80,621,361
Liabilities: $15,281,462
Net Worth: $65,339,899
Earnings: $14,122,628
Emp.: 159
Fiscal Year-end: 12/31/22
Electric Equipment Mfr
N.A.I.C.S.: 334111

AMPLE ELECTRONIC TECH-NOLOGY CO., LTD.

No 32 Dayou 3rd Street, Daliao Dis-
trict, Kaohsiung, 83163, Taiwan
Tel.: (886) 77873287
Web Site:
https://www.ampletec.com.tw
Year Founded: 2007
4760—(TPE)
Rev.: $29,018,228
Assets: $30,732,327
Liabilities: $7,890,473
Net Worth: $22,841,853
Earnings: $2,887,722
Fiscal Year-end: 12/31/22
Electronic Material Mfr & Distr
N.A.I.C.S.: 334419
Tseng Tsung *(Chm & CEO)*

AMPLEX AB

Fagerstagatan 3, PO Box 8064, 163
08, Spanga, Sweden
Tel.: (46) 8 546 802 20 **SE**
Web Site: http://www.amplexab.se
Sales Range: $350-399.9 Million
Emp.: 300
Holding Company
N.A.I.C.S.: 551112
Fredrik Celsing *(Pres & CEO)*

Subsidiaries:

BilPartner AB **(1)**
Bergavagen 6, Box 7074, Helsingborg,
Sweden
Tel.: (46) 42 38 11 00
Web Site: http://www.bilpartner.se
Automobile Rental Services
N.A.I.C.S.: 532111

Dosmar Oy **(1)**
Tormaniityntie 14, Espoo, 2710, Finland
Tel.: (358) 9 8870 230
Web Site: http://www.dosmar.fi
Sales Range: $10-24.9 Million
Emp.: 12,
Office Equipment Supplier
N.A.I.C.S.: 423420
Tuomo Vesala *(Mng Dir)*

Subsidiary (Non-US):

Postronic AB **(2)**
Stensatravagen 9, 127 39, Skarholmen,
Sweden
Tel.: (46) 8 50 10 84 00
Web Site: http://www.postronic.se
Office Equipment Supplier
N.A.I.C.S.: 423420

Frepart AB **(1)**
Mekanikervagen 10, 146 33, Tullinge, Swe-
den
Tel.: (46) 8 44 99 880
Web Site: http://www.frepart.se
Electronic Products Mfr
N.A.I.C.S.: 334513
Hjalmar Dverstorp *(Project Mgr)*

Iconex Sp. z o.o. **(1)**
ul Ogrodnicza 5, 05 082, Babice Nowe,
Poland
Tel.: (48) 22 722 9555
Web Site: http://www.iconex.pl
Emp.: 20
Electronic Equipment Distr
N.A.I.C.S.: 423440

Inteno BVBA **(1)**

Amplex AB—(Continued)

Heidestraat 257, 2070, Zwijdrecht, Belgium
Tel.: (32) 499 56 55 48
Telecommunications Equipment Mfr
N.A.I.C.S.: 334220
Horemans Erik (CEO)

**Inteno Broadband Technology
AS** (1)
Solheimveien 36, 1473, Lorenskog, Norway
Tel.: (47) 67911930
Web Site: http://www.inteno.no
Telecommunications Equipment Mfr
N.A.I.C.S.: 334220

Inteno Denmark A/S (1)
Hojbyvej 19, 4320, Lejre, Denmark
Tel.: (45) 4440 2500
Web Site: http://www.inteno.dk
Telecommunications Equipment Mfr
N.A.I.C.S.: 334220
Poul Walseth (CEO)

Inteno Netmedia Oy Ab (1)
Vaasanpuistikko 18, 65101, Vaasa, Finland
Tel.: (358) 7 144 50100
Web Site: http://www.inteno.fi
Emp.: 10
Telecommunications Equipment Mfr
N.A.I.C.S.: 334220
Martin Sten (CEO)

Kamic AB (1)
Grimstagatan 160, Box 39, 162 11, Val-
lingby, Sweden
Tel.: (46) 8 759 35 00
Web Site: http://www.kamicgroup.com
Electrical Components, Lighting & Electrical
Power Equipment Mfr
N.A.I.C.S.: 335999
Matthias Eriksson (COO & CFO)

Subsidiary (Domestic):

KAMIC Components AB (2)
Korkarlsvagen 4, 653 46, Karlstad, Sweden
Tel.: (46) 54 56 01 13
Web Site: http://www.kamiccomponents.com
Electrical Equipment Distr
N.A.I.C.S.: 327910

KAMIC Light & Safety AB (2)
Fagerstagatan 3, Box 8064, 163 08,
Spanga, Sweden
Tel.: (46) 8 759 35 00
Electrical Products Distr
N.A.I.C.S.: 423220

KAMIC Security AB (2)
Drivhjulsvagen 22, 126 30, Hagersten, Swe-
den
Tel.: (46) 8 603 38 00
Web Site: http://www.kamicsecurity.com
Electrical Equipment Distr
N.A.I.C.S.: 423610

Scanditron Sverige AB (2)
Grimstagatan 162, 162 58, Vallingby, Swe-
den
Tel.: (46) 8 795 24 00
Web Site: http://www.scanditron.se
Sales Range: $25-49.9 Million
Emp.: 20
Electronic Components Mfr
N.A.I.C.S.: 423690

Subsidiary (Non-US):

Scanditron Danmark A/S (3)
Lyshojen 12, 8520, Lystrup, Denmark
Tel.: (45) 86741233
Web Site: http://www.scanditron.dk
Sales Range: $25-49.9 Million
Emp.: 15
Electronic Components Supplier
N.A.I.C.S.: 423690

Scanditron Finland Oy (3)
Kylvopolku 6, 00680, Helsinki, Finland
Tel.: (358) 20 752 87 00
Web Site: http://www.scanditron.com
Sales Range: $25-49.9 Million
Emp.: 20
Electrical & Electronic Equipments Supplier
N.A.I.C.S.: 238210

Scanditron Finland Stencils (3)
PL 89 00381 Helsinki Hoylaamotie 3 b, 380,
Helsinki, Finland
Tel.: (358) 94393330

Web Site: http://www.scanditron.fi
Sales Range: $50-74.9 Million
Emp.: 5
Electronic Components Supplier
N.A.I.C.S.: 423690

Scanditron Sp. z.o.o. (3)
Ul Obywatelska 115, 94 104, Lodz, Poland
Tel.: (48) 426860246
Web Site: http://www.scanditron.pl
Sales Range: $25-49.9 Million
Emp.: 15
Electronic Components Supplier
N.A.I.C.S.: 423690
Martin S. Stromberg (Mng Dir)

Subsidiary (Domestic):

Scanditron Sweden Stencils (3)
Ullforsgatan 13, 752 28, Uppsala, Sweden
Tel.: (46) 18 56 11 61
Electrical Equipment Distr
N.A.I.C.S.: 423610

Kamic Installation Oy (1)
Kylvopolku 6, 680, Helsinki, Finland
Tel.: (358) 10 8328200
Web Site: http://www.kamicsecurity.fi
Telecommunication Equipment Distr
N.A.I.C.S.: 238210

LTG Display AB (1)
Vintervagen 2, 135 40, Tyreso, Sweden
Tel.: (46) 8 712 56 30
Web Site: http://www.ltg.se
Emp.: 22
Electronic Product Distr
N.A.I.C.S.: 423690
Andreas Pinto (Mgr-Mktg)

Microsec AB (1)
Box 6090, Hagersten, 129 07, Sweden
Tel.: (46) 8880170
Electrical Component Distr
N.A.I.C.S.: 423610

Optiscan Oy (1)
Karvaamokuja 2 A, 00380, Helsinki, Finland
Tel.: (358) 9 4766 766
Web Site: http://www.optiscangroup.com
Emp.: 40
Logistics Solution & Software Developer
N.A.I.C.S.: 541614
Mikko Mertjarvi (Mng Dir)

Subsidiary (Non-US):

Optiscan AB (2)
Fagerstagatan 3, SE 163 53, Spanga, Swe-
den
Tel.: (46) 8 632 66 50
Logistics Solutions & Software Developer
N.A.I.C.S.: 541614

Subsidiary (Non-US):

OOO Optiscan (3)
3-rd Golutvinski pereulok house 10 building
6, 119180, Moscow, Russia
Tel.: (7) 35894766766
Logistics Consulting Servies
N.A.I.C.S.: 541614

Optiscan Denmark (3)
Lundemarksvej 48, 4300, Holbaek, Den-
mark
Tel.: (45) 40 84 60 05
Logistics Consulting Servies
N.A.I.C.S.: 541614

Sunnex Equipment AB (1)
Grasdalsgatan 15, Box 2084, 650 02, Karl-
stad, Sweden
Tel.: (46) 54 555 160
Web Site: http://www.sunnex.se
Electric Equipment Mfr
N.A.I.C.S.: 335131
Bengt-Ake Rohr (Mgr-Production)

Subsidiary (Non-US):

Advanced Handling Ltd (2)
Northfields Industrial Estate Market Deep-
ing, Peterborough, PE6 8LD, United King-
dom
Tel.: (44) 1778 345 365
Web Site:
   http://www.advancedhandling.co.uk
Health Care Products Mfr
N.A.I.C.S.: 334510
Mike Prince (Mng Dir)

Subsidiary (Domestic):

BD Lift AB (2)
Karossvagen 4, Box 28, 264 31, Klippan,
Sweden
Tel.: (46) 435 15035
Web Site: http://www.bdlift.se
Emp.: 30
Construction Equipment Distr
N.A.I.C.S.: 423010
Kim Carlsen (Mgr-Mktg & Sls)

Colorlight AB (2)
Kassakallor Erikslund, 313 95, Stockholm,
Sweden
Tel.: (46) 35 38280
Web Site: http://www.colorlight.com
Electric Equipment Mfr
N.A.I.C.S.: 335139
Mattias Svensson (Mng Dir)

EG Electronics AB (2)
Fagerstagatan 3, Spanga, 16353, Sweden
Tel.: (46) 8 759 35 70
Web Site: http://www.egelectronics.com
Electrical & Electronic Equipments Supplier
N.A.I.C.S.: 238210
Kenneth Zaar (VP-Ops)

Subsidiary (Domestic):

Bromanco Bjorkgren AB (3)
Rallarvagen 37, 184 40, Akersberga, Swe-
den
Tel.: (46) 8 540 853 00
Web Site: http://www.bromancob.se
Electric Equipment Mfr
N.A.I.C.S.: 334416
Hans Linde (Mgr)

Subsidiary (Non-US):

**EG (Shanghai) Commercial Co.,
Ltd.** (3)
Room 1808 Shenshi Building, Number 511
Weihai Road, Shanghai, 200041, China
Tel.: (86) 2152130077
Web Site: http://www.etalgroup.com
Sales Range: $25-49.9 Million
Emp.: 12
Electronic Components Supplier
N.A.I.C.S.: 423690
Taylor Tang (Gen Mgr)

EG Componets Norway AS (3)
Drammensveien 211, 0281, Oslo, Norway
Tel.: (47) 23 25 46 00
Web Site: http://www.egelectronics.com
Sales Range: $25-49.9 Million
Emp.: 8
Electrical & Electronic Equipments Supplier
N.A.I.C.S.: 238210

**EG Power Electronics (India) Pvt.
Ltd.** (3)
No 406 4th Floor Barton Center MG Road,
560001, Bengaluru, Karnataka, India
Tel.: (91) 8041 7161 79
Electric Equipment Mfr
N.A.I.C.S.: 334416

Subsidiary (Domestic):

ETAL Group AB (3)
PO Box 39, 162 11, Vallingby, Sweden
Tel.: (46) 87593500
Web Site: http://www.etalgroup.com
Sales Range: $25-49.9 Million
Emp.: 4
Electronic Transformers Supplier
N.A.I.C.S.: 334416
Michael Nielsen (Mgr-Sls-Global)

Subsidiary (Non-US):

AS ETAL Group (4)
Narva Kadastiku 57, Narva, 21004, Estonia
Tel.: (372) 3576780
Web Site: http://www.etalgroup.com
Sales Range: $25-49.9 Million
Emp.: 100
Electronic Equipment Supplier
N.A.I.C.S.: 423690
Gordon Dunbar (Gen Mgr)

ETAL (UK) Ltd. (4)
Unit 2 Mid Sussex Business Park, Folders
Lane East, Ditchling, BN6 8SG, East Sus-
sex, United Kingdom
Tel.: (44) 1444 871186
Web Site: http://www.etalgroup.com

Sales Range: $50-74.9 Million
Emp.: 8
Electronic Components Supplier
N.A.I.C.S.: 423690
Gordon Dunbar (Mgr-Quality)

ETAL Group (Pvt.) Ltd. (4)
No 7 2nd Ln Maligawa Rd, Ratmalana, 10,
Sri Lanka
Tel.: (94) 112623754
Web Site: http://www.etalgroup.com
Emp.: 400
Electronic Components Supplier
N.A.I.C.S.: 423690
Scott Robinson (Gen Mgr)

Subsidiary (US):

ETAL, Inc. (4)
3250 Satellite Blvd, Duluth, GA 30096-4641
Tel.: (678) 957-1300
Electric Device Mfr
N.A.I.C.S.: 334419

Subsidiary (Domestic):

Osterlinds El-Agentur AB (3)
Gribbylundsvagen 11-13, Box 96, 183 21,
Taby, Sweden
Tel.: (46) 858708800
Web Site: http://osterlinds.verktyget.se
Sales Range: $25-49.9 Million
Emp.: 20
Electrical & Electronic Equipments Supplier
N.A.I.C.S.: 238210

Subsidiary (Non-US):

Electroline Ltd (2)
Unit 1106 Tower 3 Phase I Enterprise
Square 9 Sheung Yuet Road, Kowloon Bay,
Kowloon, China (Hong Kong)
Tel.: (852) 85583292
Web Site: http://www.heatlighting.com
Electric Equipment Mfr
N.A.I.C.S.: 335139

Finnlift Materiaalinkasittely OY. (2)
Rajatorpantie 41C, 1640, Vantaa, Finland
Tel.: (358) 207 341 680
Web Site: http://www.finnlift.fi
Electronic Equipment Distr
N.A.I.C.S.: 423440
Michael Hagman (Mng Dir)

Luxdesign AS (2)
Ovre Eiker Vei 177, PO Box 4026, 3048,
Drammen, Norway
Tel.: (47) 32216111
Web Site: http://www.luxdesign.no
Electrical Equipment Distr
N.A.I.C.S.: 423610
Morten Harstad (Co-Founder & Mgr-
Technical)

Subsidiary (Domestic):

Movomech AB (2)
Kabelvagen 9, Box 9083, 291 62, Kristian-
stad, Sweden
Tel.: (46) 44 28 29 00
Electric Equipment Mfr
N.A.I.C.S.: 335131
Kristian Paulsson (Mgr-Sls)

Subsidiary (Non-US):

Movomech Pronomic GmbH (2)
Halstenbachstrabe 3, 51645, Gummers-
bach, Germany
Tel.: (49) 2261 8188885
Electrical Component Distr
N.A.I.C.S.: 423610

Subsidiary (Domestic):

Pronomic AB (2)
Ellipsvagen 5, 141 75, Kungens Kurva,
Sweden
Tel.: (46) 8 50 10 84 00
Electronic Equipment Distr
N.A.I.C.S.: 423440

Subsidiary (US):

Roni, Inc. (2)
9319 Forsyth Park Dr, Charlotte, NC 28273
Tel.: (704) 714-4699
Web Site: http://www.roni.com
Electronic Equipment Distr
N.A.I.C.S.: 423440

Subsidiary (Non-US):

Sunnex Equipment Sarl   (2)
775 Rue Andre Ampere Z I Les Milles,
13851, Aix-en-Provence, France
Tel.: (33) 442 397 896
Web Site: http://www.sunnex.fr
Electronic Equipment Distr
N.A.I.C.S.: 423440

AMPLI SA
Przemyslowa 27, 33-100, Tarnow,
Poland
Tel.: (48) 146326626
Web Site: https://www.ampli.com.pl
APL—(WAR)
Rev.: $1,928,354
Assets: $2,610,772
Liabilities: $783,283
Net Worth: $1,827,490
Earnings: $89,431
Fiscal Year-end: 12/31/23
Electrical Equipment Distr
N.A.I.C.S.: 423610
Waldemar Madura (Chm-Mgmt Bd &
CEO)

**AMPLIA THERAPEUTICS LIM-
ITED**
Level 17 350 Queen Street, Mel-
bourne, 3000, VIC, Australia
Tel.: (61) 391231140   AU
Web Site: https://www.ampliatx.com
ATX—(ASX)
Rev.: $2,997,876
Assets: $9,679,278
Liabilities: $2,234,335
Net Worth: $7,444,943
Earnings: ($2,936,332)
Fiscal Year-end: 03/31/24
Pharmaceuticals Mfr
N.A.I.C.S.: 325412
Jeff Carter (CFO)

AMPLIFON S.P.A.
Via Giuseppe Ripamonti 133, 20141,
Milan, Italy
Tel.: (39) 025696554   IT
Web Site: https://www.amplifon.com
Year Founded: 1950
AMP—(ITA)
Rev.: $2,392,703,638
Assets: $4,317,621,018
Liabilities: $3,178,697,402
Net Worth: $1,138,923,615
Earnings: $193,797,848
Emp.: 715
Fiscal Year-end: 12/31/21
Hearing Aid Mfr & Distr
N.A.I.C.S.: 339112
Susan Carol Holland (Chm)

Subsidiaries:

Amplifon AG   (1)
Sihlbruggstrasse 109, 6340, Baar,
Switzerland   (100%)
Tel.: (41) 417267926
Web Site: https://www.amplifon.ch
Sales Range: $25-49.9 Million
Emp.: 25
Electronic Parts & Equipment Whslr
N.A.I.C.S.: 423620

Amplifon Beheer BV   (1)
Leigraafseweg 8, 6983 BP, Doesburg,
Netherlands   (100%)
Tel.: (31) 313485555
Sales Range: $50-74.9 Million
Emp.: 100
Hearing Aids & Equipment Whslr
N.A.I.C.S.: 423450

Amplifon Cote d'Azur SAS   (1)
40 Rue Leon Basso, 83700, Saint Raphael,
France   (100%)
Tel.: (33) 494830915
Web Site: http://www.amplifon.fr
Sales Range: $25-49.9 Million
Emp.: 4
Store Retailers
N.A.I.C.S.: 459999

Amplifon Deutschland GmbH   (1)
                                     (100%)
Tel.: (49) 4069454400
Sales Range: $25-49.9 Million
Emp.: 45
Electromedical & Electrotherapeutic Appara-
tus Mfr
N.A.I.C.S.: 334510

Amplifon France SA   (1)
Tel.: (33) 185746746
Web Site: https://www.amplifon.com
Hearing Aid Mfr & Distr
N.A.I.C.S.: 339112

Amplifon Groupe France SA   (1)
18 Rue Oberkampf, 75011, Paris,
France   (100%)
Tel.: (33) 156982222
Holding Company
N.A.I.C.S.: 551112

Amplifon Iberica SA   (1)
Paseo Zona Franca 83 95, 08038, Barce-
lona, Spain   (100%)
Tel.: (34) 0933945300
Web Site: http://www.amplifoniberica.es
Store Retailers
N.A.I.C.S.: 459999

Amplifon India Pvt Ltd.   (1)
2nd Floor Plot No 97 Sector 44, Gurgaon,
122003, India
Tel.: (91) 8001033800
Web Site: https://www.amplifon.com
Hearing Loss Diagnosis Services
N.A.I.C.S.: 621340

Amplifon Italia S.p.A.   (1)
via Vezza d'Oglio 7, 20139, Milan, Italy
Tel.: (39) 0800999968
Hearing Clinic Operator
N.A.I.C.S.: 621340

Amplifon Magyarorszag Ltd.   (1)
Konyves Kalman Krt 12-14 3rd floor, 1097,
Budapest, Hungary   (100%)
Tel.: (36) 613506070
Web Site: https://www.amplifon.com
Emp.: 23
Hearing Aids & Audiology Testing Laborato-
ries
N.A.I.C.S.: 621340

Amplifon Middle East SA   (1)
El Bardissi Street 2T Takseem Asmaa
Fahmy Ard El Golf Heliopolis, Cairo, Egypt
Tel.: (20) 19508
Web Site: http://www.amplifon.com.eg
Hearing Aid Mfr & Distr
N.A.I.C.S.: 339112

Amplifon Sietech Ltd.   (1)
273 Kensington Hogh Street, London, W8
6NA, United Kingdom   (100%)
Tel.: (44) 2077063051
Sales Range: $50-74.9 Million
Emp.: 3
Medical Dental & Hospital Equipment &
Supplies Whslr
N.A.I.C.S.: 423450

Amplifon Sud Ouest SAS   (1)
31 Allees Jean Jaures, Toulouse,
France   (100%)
Tel.: (33) 561993333
Store Retailers
N.A.I.C.S.: 459999

Amplifon USA   (1)
150 S 5th St Ste 2300, Minneapolis, MN
55402
Tel.: (763) 268-4103
Web Site: http://www.amplifonusa.com
Sales Range: $75-99.9 Million
Emp.: 200
Hearing Aids Retailer & Distr
N.A.I.C.S.: 339999
Heine Rouch (Pres)

Subsidiary (Domestic):

Miracle-Ear, Inc.   (2)
150 S 5th St Ste 2300, Minneapolis, MN
55402   (100%)
Tel.: (763) 268-4000
Web Site: https://www.miracle-ear.com
Sales Range: $25-49.9 Million
Emp.: 100
Mfr & Sales of Hearing Aids
N.A.I.C.S.: 334510

Sonus USA Inc.   (2)
1780 Barnes Blvd SW Bldg G, Tumwater,
WA 98512   (100%)
Tel.: (763) 268-4000
Web Site: http://www.sonusnetwork.com
Hearing Health Services; Testing Centers &
Hearing Aids
N.A.I.C.S.: 339112

Attune Hearing Pty. Ltd.   (1)
Level 3 135 Wickham Terrace, Spring Hill,
4000, QLD, Australia
Tel.: (61) 738370400
Web Site: https://www.attune.com.au
Hearing Clinic Operator
N.A.I.C.S.: 621340

Auckland Hearing Ltd.   (1)
66 Michaels Ave, Ellerslie, Auckland, 1051,
New Zealand
Tel.: (64) 95250522
Web Site: https://aucklandhearing.co.nz
Hearing Clinic Operator
N.A.I.C.S.: 621340

Auditech BV   (1)
Leigraafseweg 8, 6983BP, Doesburg,
Netherlands   (100%)
Tel.: (31) 313485522
Sales Range: $50-74.9 Million
Emp.: 10
Medical Dental & Hospital Equipment &
Supplies Whslr
N.A.I.C.S.: 423450

Bay Audio Pty. Ltd.   (1)
PO Box 415, Parramatta, 2124, NSW, Aus-
tralia
Tel.: (61) 1800054036
Web Site: https://www.bayaudio.com.au
Hearing Clinic Operator
N.A.I.C.S.: 621340

Bay Audiology Ltd.   (1)
PO Box 100260, North Shore, Auckland,
0745, New Zealand
Tel.: (64) 800700851
Web Site: https://www.bayaudiology.co.nz
Sales Range: $10-24.9 Million
Emp.: 40
Audiology Services
N.A.I.C.S.: 621340

Beter Horen BV   (1)
Misterstraat 14, 7101 EW, Winterswijk,
Netherlands   (100%)
Tel.: (31) 543519777
Web Site: https://www.beterhoren.nl
Sales Range: $50-74.9 Million
Emp.: 80
Medical Dental & Hospital Equipment &
Supplies Whslr
N.A.I.C.S.: 423450

Centre Auditiu Sant Boi SL   (1)
Ramadla Asael Casanova 12, Barcelona,
Spain   (100%)
Tel.: (34) 936543795
Drugs & Druggists Sundries Whslr
N.A.I.C.S.: 424210

Comfoor BV   (1)
Vlijtstraat 60-01, 7005 BN, Doetinchem,
Netherlands   (50%)
Tel.: (31) 314363588
Web Site: https://pluggerz.com
Sales Range: $25-49.9 Million
Emp.: 65
Surgical Appliance & Supplies Mfr
N.A.I.C.S.: 339113

Dilworth Hearing Ltd.   (1)
129 Beachlands Road, Beachlands, Auck-
land, 2018, New Zealand
Tel.: (64) 95380420
Web Site: https://dilworth.co.nz
Hearing Aid Mfr
N.A.I.C.S.: 339112

Electro Medical Instruments BV   (1)
Leigraafseweg 41B, 6983 BR, Doesburg,
Netherlands   (100%)
Tel.: (31) 313485588
Web Site: https://www.emid.nl
Emp.: 100
Surgical & Medical Instrument Mfr
N.A.I.C.S.: 339112

Elite Hearing LLC   (1)
150 S 5th St Ste 2300, Minneapolis, MN
55402

Tel.: (763) 268-4103
Audiology Practice Management Services
N.A.I.C.S.: 621999

GAES Colombia SAS   (1)
Tel.: (57) 8000413537
Web Site: https://www.gaes.co
Hearing Aid Mfr & Distr
N.A.I.C.S.: 339112

Hearing Supplies SA   (1)
Via Soave 2, Lugano, Switzerland   (100%)
Tel.: (41) 916409830
Electromedical & Electrotherapeutic Appara-
tus Mfr
N.A.I.C.S.: 334510
Bortesi Emrico (Gen Mgr)

Hometown Hearing Centre Inc.   (1)
255 Dundas St E, Waterdown, L8B 0E5,
ON, Canada
Tel.: (905) 769-0876
Web Site: https://hometownhearing.ca
Hearing Clinic Operator
N.A.I.C.S.: 621340

Horen Deventer BV   (1)
Graaf Florisstraat 1a, 7415 LK, Deventer,
Netherlands   (100%)
Tel.: (31) 570624880
Electromedical & Electrotherapeutic Appara-
tus Mfr
N.A.I.C.S.: 334510

Horen Nederland Beheer BV   (1)
Leigraafseweg 8, Doesburg, 6983 BB,
Netherlands   (100%)
Tel.: (31) 313485555
Sales Range: $50-74.9 Million
Emp.: 100
Holding Company
N.A.I.C.S.: 551112

Laboratoire d Audition de Arceaux
Sarl   (1)
Res Les Terrasses St Jean 74 Esplanade,
34430, Saint-Jean-de-Vedas,
France   (100%)
Tel.: (33) 467691275
Store Retailers
N.A.I.C.S.: 459999

Laide Auditive SA   (1)
Rue du Simplon 40, 1800, Vevey,
Switzerland   (100%)
Tel.: (41) 219222222
Web Site: http://www.amplifon.ca
Sales Range: $25-49.9 Million
Emp.: 100
Electromedical & Electrotherapeutic Appara-
tus Mfr
N.A.I.C.S.: 334510

Living Sounds Hearing Centre
Ltd.   (1)
12310 105 Ave, Edmonton, T5N 0Y4, AB,
Canada
Tel.: (825) 540-8383
Web Site: https://www.livingsounds.ca
Hearing Clinic Operator
N.A.I.C.S.: 621340

Microson S.A.   (1)
Pere street IV 160, 08005, Barcelona,
Spain
Tel.: (34) 933005800
Web Site: https://www.microson.es
Emp.: 130
Hearing Aid Mfr & Distr
N.A.I.C.S.: 339112

NHC Group Pty. Ltd.   (1)
Suite 401a 15 Orion Road, Lane Cove,
Sydney, 2066, NSW, Australia
Tel.: (61) 290918440
Web Site: http://www.nhc.com.au
Sales Range: $150-199.9 Million
Emp.: 4
Hearing Diagnostic & Rehabilitation Ser-
vices
N.A.I.C.S.: 621399

Nouvelle Audition SAS   (1)
37 route de Corbeil, 91390, Morsang-sur-
Orge, France
Tel.: (33) 169041258
Web Site: https://www.nouvelleaudition.fr
Hearing Clinic Operator
N.A.I.C.S.: 621340

Pilot Blankenfelde Medizinisch-
Elektronische Gerate GmbH   (1)

Amplifon S.p.A.—(Continued)

Wilhelm-Grünwald-Strasse 48-50, 15827,
Blankenfelde-Mahlow, Germany
Tel.: (49) 3379371865
Web Site: https://www.pilot-blankenfelde.de
Emp.: 8
Medical Equipment Mfr
N.A.I.C.S.: 334510

Raindrop Hearing Clinici Inc.   **(1)**
435 Stone Rd W Stone Road Mall Unit R6,
Guelph, N1G 2X6, ON, Canada
Tel.: (226) 780-3657
Hearing Clinic Operator
N.A.I.C.S.: 621340

**Societe de Construction et
d'Assemblages Metalliques SAS**   **(1)**
ZA de Kerbusson, 22600, Saint-Barnabe,
France   **(100%)**
Tel.: (33) 296282030
Web Site: http://www.scamsas.fr
Emp.: 67
Construction Metal Mfr
N.A.I.C.S.: 332999
Nicolas Couedic (Plant Mgr)

Terrace Hearing Clinic Ltd.   **(1)**
4550 Lakelse Ave, Terrace, V8G 1P8, BC,
Canada
Tel.: (778) 902-3410
Hearing Clinic Operator
N.A.I.C.S.: 621340

**The London Otological Centre
Ltd**   **(1)**
66 New Cavendish Street, London, W1U
2RW, United Kingdom   **(100%)**
Tel.: (44) 2076375111
Sales Range: $50-74.9 Million
Emp.: 4
Hearing Equipment Mfr
N.A.I.C.S.: 423450
Barrie Rogers (Mgr)

AMPLITUDE AUTOMOBILES

7-16 Rue Benjamin Franklin, ZAC de
la Vrillonnerie, 37170, Chambray les
Tours, Indre Et Loire, France
Tel.: (33) 247272121
Web Site: http://www.amplitude-
automobiles.fr
Rev.: $21,100,000
Emp.: 37
New & Used Car Dealers
N.A.I.C.S.: 441110
Dominique Frangolacci (Dir-Sls)

AMPLITUDE TECHNOLOGIES
SA

2-4 Rue du Bois Chaland, 91029,
Evry, France
Tel.: (33) 1 69 11 27 90
Web Site: http://www.amplitude-
technologies.com
Year Founded: 2001
Laser System Mfr
N.A.I.C.S.: 334510
Federico Canova (Dir-Publ)

Subsidiaries:

Amplitude Laser Inc.   **(1)**
1 Broadway, Cambridge, MA 02142
Tel.: (617) 401-2195
Web Site: http://www.amplitude-
systemes.com
Laser Product Mfr
N.A.I.C.S.: 334413
Eric Mottay (CEO)

Amplitude Systemes, S.A.   **(1)**
11 Avenue de Canteranne, Cite de la Pho-
tonique, 33600, Pessac, France
Tel.: (33) 556464060
Web Site: http://www.amplitude-
systemes.com
Laser Product Mfr
N.A.I.C.S.: 334413
Eric Mottay (CEO)

Continuum Electro-Optics, Inc.   **(1)**
140 Baytech Dr, San Jose, CA 95134
Tel.: (408) 727-3240
Web Site: http://www.continuumlasers.com

Sales Range: $25-49.9 Million
Emp.: 55
Laser Product Mfr
N.A.I.C.S.: 335999
Larry Cramer (Pres)

AMPLO S.A.

Bd Petrolului nr 10, 100521, Ploiesti,
Romania
Tel.: (40) 244573641
Web Site: http://www.amplo.ro
Year Founded: 1962
AMPL—(BUC)
Rev.: $409,022
Assets: $3,020,149
Liabilities: $1,612,436
Net Worth: $1,407,713
Earnings: ($731,679)
Emp.: 22
Fiscal Year-end: 12/31/20
Measuring Instruments Mfr
N.A.I.C.S.: 334515

AMPLYFI LTD

Pendyris Street, CF11 6BH, Cardiff,
United Kingdom - Wales
Tel.: (44) 02922676755
Web Site: http://www.amplyfi.com
Computer Software Development &
Publisher
N.A.I.C.S.: 513210
Chris Ganje (CEO)

Subsidiaries:

Deep Web Technologies   **(1)**
301 North Guadalupe St, Santa Fe, NM
87501
Tel.: (505) 820-0301
Web Site: http://www.deepwebtech.com
Software Reproducing
N.A.I.C.S.: 334610
Andy Alsop (VP-Bus Dev)

AMPOL FOOD PROCESSING
LTD.

392/56-57 Soi Preechapanich, Maha-
rat Rd. Praborommaharajwang,
Phranakorn District, Bangkok, 10200,
Thailand
Tel.: (66) 26223434
Web Site: http://www.ampolfood.com
Year Founded: 1988
Rev.: $21,390,940
Emp.: 600
Agricultural Products Mfr & Distr
N.A.I.C.S.: 424490
Jareeporn Theppadungporn (Chm)

AMPOL LIMITED

29 - 33 Bourke Road, Eora Country,
Alexandria, 2015, NSW, Australia
Tel.: (61) 292505000   **AU**
Web Site: http://www.ampol.com.au
Year Founded: 1941
ALD—(ASX)
Rev.: $16,572,613,081
Assets: $6,783,616,403
Liabilities: $4,219,331,711
Net Worth: $2,564,284,692
Earnings: $457,798,525
Emp.: 8,300
Fiscal Year-end: 12/31/21
Oil Refining & Marketing Services
N.A.I.C.S.: 324110
Viv Da Ros (CIO)

Subsidiaries:

Airport Fuel Services Pty Ltd   **(1)**
The Ulm Bldg 1 Link Road Sydney Interna-
tional, Terminal, Sydney, 2020, NSW,
Australia   **(40%)**
Tel.: (61) 296673626
Web Site: http://www.caltex.com.au
Emp.: 50
Petroleum Products Whslr & Distr
N.A.I.C.S.: 457210

Ampol Bendigo Pty Ltd   **(1)**
L 12 Mlc Ctr 19-29 Martin Pl, Sydney, 2000,

NSW, Australia   **(100%)**
Tel.: (61) 299250500
Petroleum Product Whslr
N.A.I.C.S.: 424710

Ampol Metro Fuels Pty Ltd   **(1)**
Allianz Center Level 28, Sydney, 2000,
NSW, Australia   **(100%)**
Tel.: (61) 292505000
Gasoline Stations & Convenience Stores
N.A.I.C.S.: 457110

**Australasian Lubricants Manufactur-
ing Company Pty Ltd**   **(1)**
1 Tanker St, Lytton, Brisbane, 4178, QLD,
Australia   **(50%)**
Tel.: (61) 733610900
Web Site: http://www.almc.com.au
Sales Range: $150-199.9 Million
Emp.: 400
Petroleum Product Whslr
N.A.I.C.S.: 424720

**Brisbane Airport Fuel Services Pty
Ltd**   **(1)**
PO Box 738, Hamilton, QLD,
Australia   **(100%)**
Tel.: (61) 738604647
Airport Operations
N.A.I.C.S.: 488119

Calstores Pty Ltd   **(1)**
Allianz Ctr L 24 2 Market St, Sydney, 2000,
NSW, Australia   **(100%)**
Tel.: (61) 292505000
Web Site: http://www.caltex.com.au
Sales Range: $200-249.9 Million
Emp.: 600
Gasoline Stations & Convenience Stores
N.A.I.C.S.: 457110

**Caltex Australia Custodians Pty
Ltd**   **(1)**
Allianz Center 2 Market St Level 24, Syd-
ney, 2000, NSW, Australia   **(100%)**
Tel.: (61) 292505000
Web Site: http://www.caltex.com.au
Sales Range: $200-249.9 Million
Emp.: 300
Oil Refining
N.A.I.C.S.: 324110

Caltex Australia Finance Pty Ltd   **(1)**
Level 24 2 Mark Street, Sydney, 2000,
NSW, Australia   **(100%)**
Tel.: (61) 292505000
Web Site: http://www.caltex.com.au
Sales Range: $150-199.9 Million
Emp.: 600
Business Service Centers
N.A.I.C.S.: 561439

**Caltex Australia Investments Pty
Ltd**   **(1)**
Allianz Center Level 25, 2000, Sydney,
NSW, Australia   **(100%)**
Tel.: (61) 292505000
Trusts Estates & Agency Accounts
N.A.I.C.S.: 525920

**Caltex Australia Management Pty
Ltd**   **(1)**
Level 24 2 Market Street, Sydney, 2000,
NSW, Australia   **(100%)**
Tel.: (61) 292505000
Web Site: http://www.caltex.com.au
Emp.: 600
Holding Company
N.A.I.C.S.: 551112

**Caltex Australia Petroleum Pty
Ltd**   **(1)**
Allianz Center Level 24 2 market, 2000,
Sydney, NSW, Australia   **(100%)**
Tel.: (61) 292505000
Web Site: http://www.caltex.com.au
Sales Range: $200-249.9 Million
Emp.: 600
Gasoline Stations & Convenience Stores
N.A.I.C.S.: 457110

**Caltex Lubricating Oil Refinery Pty
Ltd.**   **(1)**
Sir Joseph Banks Dr, Kurnell, 2231, Syd-
ney, NSW, Australia   **(100%)**
Tel.: (61) 296681111
Web Site: http://www.caltex.com.au
Sales Range: $750-799.9 Million
Emp.: 1,500
Oil & Gas Operations

N.A.I.C.S.: 213112

**Caltex Petroleum (Victoria) Pty
Ltd**   **(1)**
411 Douglas Parade, Melbourne, 3015,
VIC, Australia
Tel.: (61) 392879555
Petroleum Bulk Station Operating Services
N.A.I.C.S.: 424710
Paul Sharp (Mgr-Terminal)

**Caltex Petroleum Services Pty
Ltd**   **(1)**
L 24-2 Market St, Sydney, 2001, NSW,
Australia   **(100%)**
Tel.: (61) 292505000
Petroleum Products Whslr Not Bulk Stations
& Terminals
N.A.I.C.S.: 424720
Julian Segal (Mng Dir)

Geraldton Fuel Company Pty Ltd   **(1)**
120 Sloras Road, Geraldton, Geraldton,
6530, WA, Australia   **(50%)**
Tel.: (61) 899208000
Web Site: http://www.geraldtonfuel.com.au
Sales Range: $50-74.9 Million
Emp.: 10
Petroleum Product Whslr
N.A.I.C.S.: 424720

Gull New Zealand Ltd.   **(1)**
Level 4 507 Lake Road, Takapuna, Auck-
land, New Zealand
Tel.: (64) 94891452
Web Site: http://www.gull.nz
Fuel Product Distr
N.A.I.C.S.: 424720

**Hunter Pipe Line Company Pty
Ltd**   **(1)**
L24 2 Market Street, Sydney, 2000, NSW,
Australia   **(100%)**
Tel.: (61) 292505000
Web Site: http://www.Caltex.com
Sales Range: $150-199.9 Million
Emp.: 600
General Warehousing & Storage
N.A.I.C.S.: 493110

Jayvee Petroleum Pty Ltd   **(1)**
Level 24 2 Market St, Sydney, 2000, NSW,
Australia   **(100%)**
Tel.: (61) 292505000
Heating Oil Dealers
N.A.I.C.S.: 457210

Link Energy Pty Ltd   **(1)**
L 5 15 Ogilvie Rd, Mount Pleasant, WA,
Australia   **(50%)**
Tel.: (61) 893157888
Petroleum Product Whslr
N.A.I.C.S.: 424720

**Newcastle Pipe Line Company Pty
Ltd**   **(1)**
L 24 2 Market St, Sydney, 2000, NSW,
Australia   **(100%)**
Tel.: (61) 292505000
Sales Range: $350-399.9 Million
Emp.: 600
Oil & Gas Operations
N.A.I.C.S.: 213112
Julie Sejil (Mng Dir)

Real FF Pty Ltd   **(1)**
25-27 Down St, Collingwood, 3066, VIC,
Australia
Tel.: (61) 394160622
Web Site:
   http://www.nashicatering.foodstorm.com
Food Restaurant Services
N.A.I.C.S.: 722511

Solo Oil Australia Pty Ltd   **(1)**
Aooianz L 24 2 market Street, Sydney,
2000, NSW, Australia   **(100%)**
Tel.: (61) 292505000
Sales Range: $350-399.9 Million
Emp.: 600
Trusts Estates & Agency Accounts
N.A.I.C.S.: 525920

South Coast Oils Pty Ltd   **(1)**
19-29 Martin Pl, Sydney, NSW,
Australia   **(100%)**
Tel.: (61) 292505000
Petroleum Product Whslr
N.A.I.C.S.: 424720

**South East Queensland Fuels Pty
Ltd**   **(1)**

61 Ashover Rd, Rocklea, QLD,
Australia **(50%)**
Tel.: (61) 749766800
Fuel Dealers
N.A.I.C.S.: 457210

Sydney Metropolitan Pipeline Pty
Ltd **(1)**
L 24 No 2 Market street, Sydney, 2000,
NSW, Australia **(100%)**
Tel.: (61) 292505000
Web Site: http://www.caltex.com.au
Sales Range: $1-4.9 Billion
Emp.: 600
Crude Petroleum & Natural Gas Extraction
N.A.I.C.S.: 211120
Julian Segal *(Mng Dir)*

Terminals New Zealand Ltd. **(1)**
131 Hewletts Road Bay of Plenty, Mount
Maunganui, 3116, New Zealand
Tel.: (64) 94891452
Web Site: http://www.terminals.nz
Petroleum Terminal Services
N.A.I.C.S.: 424710

Tulloch Petroleum Services Pty
Ltd **(1)**
L24 Market St, Sydney, NSW,
Australia **(100%)**
Tel.: (61) 292505000
Web Site: http://www.tulloch.com.au
Sales Range: $200-249.9 Million
Emp.: 620
Gasoline Stations & Convenience Stores
N.A.I.C.S.: 457110

Z Energy Limited **(1)**
3 Queens Wharf, Wellington, 6011, New
Zealand
Tel.: (64) 800 474 355
Web Site: http://www.z.co.nz
Rev.: $2,530,880,000
Assets: $2,123,207,000
Liabilities: $1,396,298,000
Net Worth: $726,909,000
Earnings: $43,859,000
Emp.: 2,121
Fiscal Year-end: 03/31/2021
Fuel Distr, Importer & Sales
N.A.I.C.S.: 457210

AMPRION GMBH
Rheinlanddamm 24, 44139, Dort-
mund, Germany
Tel.: (49) 231 5849 0
Web Site: http://www.amprion.net
Sales Range: $300-349.9 Million
Emp.: 850
Electric Power Distribution Services
N.A.I.C.S.: 221122
Hans-Jurgen Brick *(Member-Mgmt
Bd)*

AMPVOLTS LIMITED
Cabin No 11 7th Floor Times Square
Andheri Workflo next to Sai Service,
Andheri East, Mumbai, 400069, India
Tel.: (91) 2241495895
Web Site: https://ampvolts.com
Year Founded: 2000
535719—(BOM)
Rev.: $127,334
Assets: $2,228,318
Liabilities: $162,417
Net Worth: $2,065,901
Earnings: ($251,994)
Emp.: 2
Fiscal Year-end: 03/31/24
Information Technology Services
N.A.I.C.S.: 541512
Dhiren Kothary *(Exec Dir)*

AMPYR GLOBAL ENERGY HOLDINGS PTE. LTD
61 Robinson Road No. 10-01, Singa-
pore, 068893, Singapore
Tel.: (65) 63719881
Web Site:
https://www.ampyrenergy.com
Renewable Energy
N.A.I.C.S.: 221114

AMRAPALI CAPITAL AND FINANCE SERVICES LIMITED
19-20-21 3rd Floor Narayan Cham-
bers, B/h Patang Hotel Asram Road,
Ahmedabad, 380009, India
Tel.: (91) 7926575105
Web Site: https://www.amrapali.com
536737—(BOM)
Rev.: $12,073,864
Assets: $24,062,769
Liabilities: $12,413,573
Net Worth: $11,649,197
Earnings: $77,476
Emp.: 23
Fiscal Year-end: 03/31/20
Securities Brokerage Services
N.A.I.C.S.: 523150

AMRAPALI FINCAP LIMITED
19-20-21 3rd Floor Narayan Cham-
bers Behind Patang Hotel Ashram
Road, Ahmedabad, 380009, Gujarat,
India
Tel.: (91) 7926575105
Web Site: https://www.amrapali.co.in
Year Founded: 2004
539265—(BOM)
Rev.: $11,767,740
Assets: $20,180,101
Liabilities: $40,954
Net Worth: $20,139,147
Earnings: $76,388
Emp.: 8
Fiscal Year-end: 03/31/21
Financial Lending Services
N.A.I.C.S.: 522310
Hasmukh A. Thakkar *(Mng Dir)*

AMRAPALI GROUP
C-56/40 Sector-62, Noida, 201301,
India
Tel.: (91) 1204055555
Web Site: http://www.amrapali.in
Emp.: 2,464
Real Estate Developers
N.A.I.C.S.: 236117
Anil Kumar Sharma *(Chm & Mng Dir)*

AMRAPALI INDUSTRIES LIMITED
19-20-21 3rd Floor Narayan Cham-
bers B/h Patang Hotel Ashram Road,
Ahmedabad, 380009, India
Tel.: (91) 7926575105
Web Site: https://www.amrapali.com
526241—(BOM)
Rev.: $26,271,831
Assets: $12,933,712
Liabilities: $1,698,320
Net Worth: $11,235,392
Earnings: ($122,575)
Emp.: 22
Fiscal Year-end: 03/31/21
Securities Brokerage Services
N.A.I.C.S.: 523150
Chirag Thakkar *(Mng Dir)*

AMRAWORLD AGRICO LTD.
24 Laxmi Chambers Navjeevan Press
Road, Opp Old Gujarat High Court,
Ahmedabad, 380014, Gujarat, India
Tel.: (91) 7926562165
Web Site:
https://www.amraworldagrico.shop
Year Founded: 1991
531991—(BOM)
Rev.: $4,095
Assets: $1,590,402
Liabilities: $13,066
Net Worth: $1,577,337
Earnings: $651
Fiscal Year-end: 03/31/21
Commodities Brokerage Services
N.A.I.C.S.: 523160
Nikunj Navinbhai Sanghani *(CFO)*

AMRELI STEELS LTD.
A/18 S I T E, Karachi, 75730, Paki-
stan
Tel.: (92) 21111267354
Web Site: https://amrelisteels.com
Year Founded: 1972
ASTL—(PSX)
Rev.: $163,660,259
Assets: $144,517,961
Liabilities: $92,130,240
Net Worth: $52,387,721
Earnings: ($2,440,701)
Emp.: 749
Fiscal Year-end: 06/30/23
Steel Products Mfr
N.A.I.C.S.: 331221
Abbas Akberali *(Chm)*

AMREST HOLDINGS SE
Paseo de la Castellana 163 10th
Floor, 28046, Madrid, Spain
Tel.: (34) 713861000
Web Site: https://www.amrest.eu
Year Founded: 1993
EAT—(BIL)
Rev.: $52,881,502
Assets: $839,197,065
Liabilities: $496,114,828
Net Worth: $343,082,236
Earnings: $37,017,052
Emp.: 45,000
Fiscal Year-end: 12/31/20
Fast Food Restaurant Owner & Op-
erator
N.A.I.C.S.: 722513
Jose Pares Gutierrez *(Chm)*

Subsidiaries:

AmRest Kft **(1)**
Becsi Ut 13, Budapest, 1023, Hungary
Tel.: (36) 14234000
Web Site: http://www.amrest.eu
Sales Range: $10-24.9 Million
Emp.: 30
Fast Food Restaurant Management Ser-
vices
N.A.I.C.S.: 722513

AmRest Pizza GmbH **(1)**
Dachauer Strasse 65, 80335, Munich, Ger-
many
Tel.: (49) 89551555900
Restaurant Operators
N.A.I.C.S.: 722511

AmRest Sp. z o.o. **(1)**
Ul Powstancow Slaskich 15-17, 53-332,
Wroclaw, Lower Silesian, Poland
Tel.: (48) 713861000
Sales Range: $25-49.9 Million
Emp.: 200
Restaurant Operating Services
N.A.I.C.S.: 722513
Henry Macgovern *(Gen Mgr)*

AmRest s.r.o. **(1)**
Walterovo namesti 329/3, 158 00, Prague,
5, Jinonice, Czech Republic
Tel.: (420) 235013311
Sales Range: $10-24.9 Million
Emp.: 60
Restaurant Operating Services
N.A.I.C.S.: 722513
Tomas Benda *(Mgr-IT)*

AmRest, LLC **(1)**
2120 Powers Ferry Rd Ste 350, Atlanta, GA
30339
Tel.: (770) 951-0586
Web Site: http://www.amrestapplebees.com
Sales Range: $250-299.9 Million
Emp.: 3,500
Franchise Bar-Restaurants Operator
N.A.I.C.S.: 722511

Amrest Coffee Deutschland Sp. z o.o.
& Co. KG **(1)**
Dachauer Strasse 65, 80335, Munich,
Germany **(100%)**
Tel.: (49) 8951265987
Web Site: http://www.starbucks.de
Coffee Shops; Coffee & Tea Retail
N.A.I.C.S.: 722515

CR Developpement SAS **(1)**
325 Chemin du Thym, 34670, Castelnau-le-
Lez, France
Tel.: (33) 686556691
Web Site: http://www.crdev.fr
Construction Services
N.A.I.C.S.: 236220

OOO AmRest **(1)**
Bolshoi Prospect VO 18, 199034, Saint Pe-
tersburg, Russia
Tel.: (7) 8123328310
Web Site: http://rabotavamrest.ru
Fast Food Restaurant Owner & Operator
N.A.I.C.S.: 722513
Jacek Tribuhovxki *(Pres-Div-Russia)*

RCP SARL **(1)**
200 Ch de Rouzies, Gaillac, 81600, Gaillac-
d'Aveyron, France
Tel.: (33) 563574914
Web Site: http://www.rcp-fr.com
Industrial Machinery Mfr
N.A.I.C.S.: 332710

SCM Sp. z o.o. **(1)**
Al Jana Pawla II 11, Warszawa, 00-828,
Chotomow, Poland
Tel.: (48) 225865400
Web Site: https://www.scmpoland.pl
Sales Range: $25-49.9 Million
Emp.: 25
Restaurant Meals Delivery Services
N.A.I.C.S.: 492210

Sushi Lyon 64 SAS **(1)**
64 Cours Vitton, Lyon, 69006, France
Tel.: (33) 826826628
Restaurant Operators
N.A.I.C.S.: 722511

Sushi Shop Amiens SARL **(1)**
9 Rue Des Corps Nuds Sans Teste,
Amiens, 80000, France
Tel.: (33) 826826628
Restaurant Operators
N.A.I.C.S.: 722511

Sushi Shop Angers SARL **(1)**
39 Rue Plantagenet, Angers, 49100, France
Tel.: (33) 826826628
Restaurant Operators
N.A.I.C.S.: 722511

Sushi Shop Caen SARL **(1)**
8 Rue Saint Pierre, Caen, 14000, France
Tel.: (33) 826826628
Restaurant Operators
N.A.I.C.S.: 722511

Sushi Shop Cauderan SAS **(1)**
7 Avenue De La Republique, Bordeaux,
33200, France
Tel.: (33) 826826628
Restaurant Operators
N.A.I.C.S.: 722511

Sushi Shop Courcelles SARL **(1)**
178 Rue de Courcelles, Paris, 75017,
France
Tel.: (33) 826826628
Restaurant Services
N.A.I.C.S.: 722511

Subsidiary (Domestic):

Sushi Shop Levallois SARL **(2)**
44 Rue Voltaire, Levallois-Perret, 92300,
France
Tel.: (33) 826826628
Restaurant Operators
N.A.I.C.S.: 722511

Sushi Shop Geneve SA **(1)**
Boulevard Georges Favon 6 Geneve, 1204,
Geneva, Switzerland
Tel.: (41) 900826826
Restaurant Operators
N.A.I.C.S.: 722511

Sushi Shop La Rochelle SARL **(1)**
36 Rue Chaudrier, La Rochelle, 17000,
France
Tel.: (33) 826826628
Restaurant Operators
N.A.I.C.S.: 722511

Sushi Shop Lausanne SARL **(1)**
Galerie Saint-Francois A, 1003, Lausanne,
Switzerland
Tel.: (41) 900826826

AmRest Holdings SE—(Continued)
Restaurant Operators
N.A.I.C.S.: 722511

Sushi Shop Le Mans SARL (1)
6 Boulevard Rene Levasseur, Le Mans,
72000, France
Tel.: (33) 826826628
Restaurant Operators
N.A.I.C.3.: 722511

Sushi Shop Lille Centre SAS (1)
15 Place de Bethune, Lille, 59800, France
Tel.: (33) 826826628
Restaurant Operators
N.A.I.C.S.: 722511

Sushi Shop Louise SA (1)
144 Avenue Louise, Ixelles, 1050, Brussels,
Belgium
Tel.: (32) 70757500
Restaurant Operators
N.A.I.C.S.: 722511

Sushi Shop Martyrs SARL (1)
32 Rue Des Martyrs, Paris, 75009, France
Tel.: (33) 826826628
Web Site: http://www.sushishop.fr
Restaurant Services
N.A.I.C.S.: 722511

Subsidiary (Domestic):

Sushi Shop Lepic SARL (2)
19 Rue Lepic, Paris, 75018, France
Tel.: (33) 826826628
Restaurant Operators
N.A.I.C.S.: 722511

Sushi Shop Nyon SARL (1)
1 Rue de La Morache, Nyon, 1260, Switzer-
land
Tel.: (41) 900826826
Restaurant Operators
N.A.I.C.S.: 722511

**Sushi Shop Rennes Nemours
SARL** (1)
8 Rue De Nemours, Rennes, 35000,
France
Tel.: (33) 826826628
Restaurant Operators
N.A.I.C.S.: 722511

Sushi Shop Rouen SAS (1)
6 Rue Guillaume Le Conquerant, Rouen,
76000, France
Tel.: (33) 826826628
Restaurant Operators
N.A.I.C.S.: 722511

Sushi Shop ST Dominique SARL (1)
86 Rue Saint Dominique, Paris, 75007,
France
Tel.: (33) 826826628
Restaurant Operators
N.A.I.C.S.: 722511

Sushi Shop Secretan SARL (1)
30 Avenue Secretan, Paris, 75019, France
Tel.: (33) 826826628
Restaurant Operators
N.A.I.C.S.: 722511

Sushi Shop Toulouse 3 SARL (1)
34-36 Rue Boulbonne, Toulouse, 31000,
France
Tel.: (33) 826826628
Restaurant Operators
N.A.I.C.S.: 722511

Sushi Shop Tours SARL (1)
5 Place Jean Jaures, Tours, 37000, France
Tel.: (33) 826826628
Restaurant Operators
N.A.I.C.S.: 722511

Sushi Shop Vincennes SARL (1)
36 Avenue de Paris, Vincennes, 94300,
France
Tel.: (33) 826826628
Restaurant Operators
N.A.I.C.S.: 722511

Sushi Shop Zurich GMBH (1)
Uraniastrasse 40, Zurich, 8001, Switzerland
Tel.: (41) 900826826
Restaurant Operators
N.A.I.C.S.: 722511

AMRIT CORP LTD

A-95 Sector-65, Noida, 201309, Uttar
Pradesh, India
Tel.: (91) 1204506900
Web Site: http://www.amritcorp.com
507525—(BOM)
Rev.: $15,873,025
Assets: $30,982,715
Liabilities: $3,546,980
Net Worth: $27,435,736
Earnings: ($71,362)
Emp.: 152
Fiscal Year-end: 03/31/23
Food Processing Services
N.A.I.C.S.: 311511
B. P. Maheshwari *(CFO & Exec
VP-F&A)*

AMRIT CORP. LIMITED

A-95 Sector-65, Noida, 201 309, UP,
India
Tel.: (91) 1204506900
Web Site: http://www.amritcorp.com
Year Founded: 1940
Rev.: $11,420,764
Assets: $33,280,297
Liabilities: $5,292,187
Net Worth: $27,988,110
Earnings: $1,791,986
Emp.: 163
Fiscal Year-end: 03/31/22
Holding Company
N.A.I.C.S.: 551112
Naresh Kumar Bajaj *(Chm & Mng
Dir)*

**AMRUTANJAN HEALTH CARE
LIMITED**
103 Old No 42-45 Luz Church Road,
Mylapore, Chennai, 600 004, India
Tel.: (91) 4424994465
Web Site:
https://www.amrutanjan.com
590006—(BOM)
Rev.: $14,351,105
Assets: $49,425,735
Liabilities: $9,735,371
Net Worth: $39,690,364
Earnings: $1,732,895
Emp.: 667
Fiscal Year-end: 03/31/23
Pain Balm Mfr
N.A.I.C.S.: 325412
Sivalenka Sambhu Prasad *(Chm,
Mng Dir & Exec Dir)*

**AMS ADVANCED MEDICAL
SERVICES GMBH**
Am Exerzierplatz 2, D-68167, Mann-
heim, Germany
Tel.: (49) 621 70095 100
Web Site: http://www.ams-
europe.com
Year Founded: 1997
Sales Range: Less than $1 Million
Emp.: 170
Clinical Research Services
N.A.I.C.S.: 622110
Christian Carls *(CEO)*

Subsidiaries:

**AMS Advanced Medical Services
GmbH** (1)
Schlossparkgasse 17, 1230, Vienna, Austria
Tel.: (43) 1801012650
Medical Research Services
N.A.I.C.S.: 541715

**AMS Advanced Medical Services
Ltd.** (1)
1 Lyric Square, London, W6 0NB, United
Kingdom
Tel.: (44) 2037511350
Medical Research Services
N.A.I.C.S.: 541715
Kathryn Hutchinson *(Mng Dir)*

AMS AG

Tobelbader Strasse 30, 8141, Unter-
premstatten, Austria
Tel.: (43) 31365000　　　　AT
Web Site: https://www.ams.com
Year Founded: 1981
AMS—(SWX)
Rev.: $3,853,585,231
Assets: $7,944,396,740
Liabilities: $5,899,527,697
Net Worth: $2,044,869,043
Earnings: ($1,731,429,799)
Emp.: 20,378
Fiscal Year-end: 12/31/23
Semiconductor Designer & Mfr
N.A.I.C.S.: 334413
Moritz M. Gmeiner *(Head-IR)*

Subsidiaries:

**OSRAM Continental Romania
S.R.L.** (1)
Strada Italiana nr 24 Cladirea Arion Green
Sector 2, 020976, Bucharest, Romania
Tel.: (40) 21 232 8561
Semiconductor Mfr
N.A.I.C.S.: 334413

OSRAM SL GmbH (1)
Marcel-Breuer-Strasse 6, 80807, Munich,
Germany
Tel.: (49) 896 2130
Web Site: https://www.osram.com
Semiconductor Mfr
N.A.I.C.S.: 334413

Osram Licht AG (1)
Marcel-Breuer-Strasse 6, 80807, Munich,
Germany (71.42%)
Tel.: (49) 8962130
Web Site: http://www.osram.com
Rev.: $6,187,873,120
Assets: $11,845,146,560
Liabilities: $7,976,190,560
Net Worth: $3,868,956,000
Earnings: ($39,303,680)
Emp.: 26,130
Fiscal Year-end: 12/31/2021
Lamp & Lighting System Mfr
N.A.I.C.S.: 335132

Subsidiary (Non-US):

Adb Stagelight S.A.S.U. (2)
45 Avenue Carnot, 94230, Cachan, France
Tel.: (33) 145361790
Electronic Lighting Product Mfr
N.A.I.C.S.: 335132
Joel Brieuc *(Sls Dir)*

Subsidiary (Domestic):

BAG Electronics GmbH (2)
Mohnestrasse 53, 59755, Arnsberg, Ger-
many
Tel.: (49) 293290009800
Web Site: http://www.bagelectronics.com
Electronic Parts Distr
N.A.I.C.S.: 423690
Michael Rademacher *(CEO & Mng Dir)*

Subsidiary (Non-US):

Clay Paky S.p.A. (2)
Via Pastrengo 3/b, Seriate, 24068, Ber-
gamo, Italy
Tel.: (39) 035654311
Web Site: https://www.claypaky.it
Lighting System Mfr
N.A.I.C.S.: 335132
Marcus Graser *(CEO)*

DP OSRAM Ukraine (2)
5 Dymytrova Str, Kiev, 3150, Ukraine
Tel.: (380) 44 583 59 00
Emp.: 25
Lighting Equipment Mfr
N.A.I.C.S.: 335139

Subsidiary (US):

LED Engin, Inc. (2)
651 River Oaks Pkwy, San Jose, CA 95134
Tel.: (408) 922-7200
Web Site: http://www.osram.us
Optic Component & Light Source Module
Mfr & Distr
N.A.I.C.S.: 335139

Novita Technologies, Inc. (2)

175 Old Shackle Is Rd, Hendersonville, TN
37075
Tel.: (615) 826-0372
Web Site: http://www.novitatech.com
Electrical Equipment & Component Mfr
N.A.I.C.S.: 335999
Mike Incorvaia *(CEO)*

Subsidiary (Non-US):

OAO OSRAM (2)
Ul Letnikovskaya 11/10 Building 1, Moscow,
115114, Russia
Tel.: (7) 495 935 70 70
Web Site: http://www.osram.ru
Sales Range: $25-49.9 Million
Emp.: 60
Lighting Equipment Mfr
N.A.I.C.S.: 335139

OSRAM (Malaysia) Sdn. Bhd. (2)
L8-02 8th Floor Tropicana City Office Tower
No 3 Jalan SS20/27, Pusat Dagang
Seksyen 16, 47400, Petaling Jaya, Selan-
gor, Malaysia
Tel.: (60) 3 7959 0000
Web Site: http://www.osram.com.my
Sales Range: $25-49.9 Million
Emp.: 2
Lighting Equipment Mfr
N.A.I.C.S.: 335139
Antonio Floris *(CEO)*

OSRAM (Pty.) Ltd. (2)
Block 2 Emerald Park 22 Reedbuck Cres-
cent Corporate Park South, Private Bag
x206, Randjespark, Midrand, 1685, Gau-
teng, South Africa
Tel.: (27) 102214000
Web Site: http://www.osram.co.za
Lighting Equipment Mfr
N.A.I.C.S.: 335139

OSRAM (Thailand) Co., Ltd. (2)
Charn Issara Tower II 19th Floor 2922/251
New Petchburi Road, Bangkapi Huayk-
wang, Bangkok, 10310, Thailand
Tel.: (66) 27635755
Lighting Installation Services
N.A.I.C.S.: 238210
Suphalak Onjean *(CFO)*

OSRAM A/S (2)
Dybendalsvaenget 3, 2630, Taastrup, Den-
mark
Tel.: (45) 43302040
Web Site: http://www.osram.dk
Lighting Equipment Mfr
N.A.I.C.S.: 335139

OSRAM AB (2)
Arenavagen 39, PO Box 5188, 121 18, Jo-
hanneshov, Sweden
Tel.: (46) 812870400
Web Site: http://www.osram.se
Lighting Equipment Mfr
N.A.I.C.S.: 335139

OSRAM AS (2)
Strandveien 50 Lysaker, Oslo, 1366, Nor-
way
Tel.: (47) 40 00 41 10
Lighting Equipment Mfr
N.A.I.C.S.: 335139

OSRAM Ampul Ticaret A.S. (2)
Barbaros Bulvari Morbasan Sok Koza Is
Merkezi B Blok Kat 8, Istanbul, 34349, Tur-
kiye
Tel.: (90) 212 306 90 00
Web Site: http://www.osram.com.tr
Lighting Equipment Mfr
N.A.I.C.S.: 335139

OSRAM Asia Pacific Ltd. (2)
208 Wireless Centre 3 Science Park East
Avenue Science Park, New Territories, Sha
Tin, China (Hong Kong)
Tel.: (852) 29433488
Lighting Installation Services
N.A.I.C.S.: 238210
Esther Tsui *(Mgr-HR)*

**OSRAM Asia Pacific Ltd.
(OAPAC)** (2)
208 Wireless Centre, 3 Science Park East
Avenue Science Park, Sha Tin, New Territo-
ries, China (Hong Kong)
Tel.: (852) 29433488
Web Site: http://www.osram.com.cn
Lighting Equipment Mfr

N.A.I.C.S.: 335139

OSRAM Asia Pacific Management Company Ltd. (2)
28/F Harbour Ring Plaza No 18 Xi Zang (M) Road, Shanghai, China
Tel.: (86) 2153852848
Lighting Installation Services
N.A.I.C.S.: 238210
Jackie Cheng (Sr Dir-Sls)

OSRAM Automotive Lamps Private Limited (2)
No 113 1st Floor Prestige Pinnacle Koramangala Industrial Estate, Bengaluru, 560095, Karnataka, India
Tel.: (91) 8042415000
Lighting Equipment Mfr
N.A.I.C.S.: 335139
Anurag Sharma (Mgr-Pur)

OSRAM Benelux B.V. (2)
Marten Meesweg 8-10, 3068 AV, Rotterdam, Netherlands
Tel.: (31) 887508800
Web Site: http://www.osram.nl
Sales Range: $25-49.9 Million
Emp.: 6
Lighting Equipment Mfr
N.A.I.C.S.: 335139
Jean-Marc Vogel (CEO)

OSRAM Ceska republika s.r.o. (2)
Zahradni 1442/46, 792 01, Bruntal, Czech Republic
Tel.: (420) 554 793 111
Web Site: http://www.osram.cz
Emp.: 50
Lighting Equipment Mfr
N.A.I.C.S.: 335139

OSRAM Chile Ltda. (2)
Av Providencia 1760 Oficina 2501 Piso 25, Santiago, 7500498, Chile
Tel.: (56) 2 6360500
Lighting Equipment Mfr
N.A.I.C.S.: 335139

OSRAM China Lighting Ltd. (2)
No 1 North Industrial Road, Foshan, 528000, Guangdong, China
Tel.: (86) 757 8648 2111
Lighting Equipment Mfr
N.A.I.C.S.: 335139

OSRAM Comercio de Solucoes de Iluminacao Ltda. (2)
Alameda Rio Negro 161 Conj 502 and 503 Alphaville, Barueri, 06454-000, Sao Paulo, Brazil
Tel.: (55) 8007767726
Lighting Installation Services
N.A.I.C.S.: 238210
Ricardo Leptich (CEO)

Subsidiary (Domestic):

OSRAM Continental GmbH (2)
Marcel-Breuer-Strasse 6, 80807, Munich, Germany
Tel.: (49) 8962130
Web Site: http://www.osram-continental.com
Emp.: 1,500
Automotive Lighting Component Mfr
N.A.I.C.S.: 336320
Dirk Linzmeier (CEO)

Subsidiary (Non-US):

OSRAM EOOD (2)
Area Koshovete 879, 4199, Trudovets, Bulgaria
Tel.: (359) 32348100
Web Site: http://www.osram.com
Lighting Equipment Mfr
N.A.I.C.S.: 335139

OSRAM Empresa de Aparelhagem Electrica Lda. (2)
Rua do Alto do Montijo No 15 - 4 Andar, Carnaxide, 2794-069, Portugal
Tel.: (351) 21 416 58 60
Web Site: http://www.osram.pt
Emp.: 40
Lighting Equipment Mfr
N.A.I.C.S.: 335139
Antonieta Loureiro (Gen Mgr)

Subsidiary (Domestic):

OSRAM GmbH (2)

Nonnendammallee 44, 13625, Berlin, Germany
Tel.: (49) 3033860
Lighting Mfr
N.A.I.C.S.: 335132

Subsidiary (US):

Vixar Inc. (3)
2355 Polaris Ave N Ste 100, Plymouth, MN 55447
Tel.: (763) 746-8045
Web Site: https://www.vixarinc.com
Semiconductor & Related Device Mfr
N.A.I.C.S.: 334413
Mary Hibbs-Brenner (Co-Founder & CEO)

Subsidiary (Non-US):

OSRAM Korea Co. Ltd. (2)
3f Floor Ye-Sung Bldg 554 Samsung-ro, Gangnam-Ku, Seoul, 06165, Korea (South)
Tel.: (82) 234903600
Web Site: http://www.osram.asia
Lighting Equipment Mfr
N.A.I.C.S.: 335139

OSRAM Kunshan Display Optic Co., Ltd. (2)
2/F No 6 Building No 199 Waihejing Road Free Trade Zone, Kunshan Development Zone, Kunshan, 215300, Jiangsu, China
Tel.: (86) 51283632600
Lighting Installation Services
N.A.I.C.S.: 238210
An Jing (Project Mgr & Engr-Electronic)

OSRAM Lighting Control Systems Ltd. (2)
Room 3006-10 China Resources Building No 26 Harbour Road, Wanchai, China (Hong Kong)
Tel.: (852) 36 52 56 78
Web Site: http://www.osram.com.hk
Lighting Equipment Mfr
N.A.I.C.S.: 335139

OSRAM Lighting Middle East FZE (2)
Office No 208 E-Wing Dubai Silicon Oasis HQ Building, PO Box 341112, Dubai, United Arab Emirates
Tel.: (971) 45231777
Lighting System Mfr
N.A.I.C.S.: 335132
John Balangue (Project Mgr)

OSRAM Lighting Private Limited (2)
1st Floor IFFCO Surinder Jhakhar Bhavan Plot-3 Sector-32, Gurgaon, 122001, Haryana, India
Tel.: (91) 1246261300
Lighting Installation Services
N.A.I.C.S.: 238210
Sanjay Narula (Sr Gen Mgr)

OSRAM Lighting Pte. Ltd. (2)
988 Toa Payoh North 03-01/07/08, Singapore, 319002, Singapore
Tel.: (65) 65520110
Lighting Installation Services
N.A.I.C.S.: 238210
Joseph Ng (Mgr-Comml)

OSRAM Lighting S.A.S.U. (2)
Immeuble Grand Sport 18 rue Gaston Romazzotti, 67120, Molsheim, France
Tel.: (33) 368418933
Electronic Lighting Product Mfr
N.A.I.C.S.: 335132
Steve Denni (Pres, CEO & Dir-BU Digital Sys)

OSRAM Lighting S.L. (2)
Avda Leonardo da Vinci 15, 28906, Getafe, Madrid, Spain
Tel.: (34) 914915217
Web Site: http://www.osram.es
Lighting System Mfr
N.A.I.C.S.: 335132

OSRAM Ltd. (2)
Tobu Yokohama Building No 3 8f 8-29 Kitasaiwai 2-chome, Nishi-ku, Yokohama, 220-0004, Kanagawa, Japan
Tel.: (81) 45 323 51 00
Web Site: http://www.osram.jp
Lighting Equipment Mfr
N.A.I.C.S.: 335139

OSRAM Middle East FZE (2)

Room 602 - 603 LOB 16, PO Box 17476, Jebel Ali Free Zone, Dubai, United Arab Emirates
Tel.: (971) 4 881 37 67
Lighting Equipment Mfr
N.A.I.C.S.: 335139

OSRAM Opto Semiconductors (China) Co., Ltd. (2)
No 57 Xi Qin Road, Xinwu District, Wuxi, 214000, Jiangsu, China
Tel.: (86) 51081908190
Lighting Installation Services
N.A.I.C.S.: 238210
S. L. Khoo (Gen Mgr)

OSRAM Opto Semiconductors (Japan) Ltd. (2)
1-7 Yokohama Diamond Building 19th Floor Golden Port-cho, Kanagawa-ku, Yokohama, 221-0056, Kanagawa, Japan
Tel.: (81) 455486473
Lighting Installation Services
N.A.I.C.S.: 238210
Jun Yoshimura (Mktg Mgr)

OSRAM Opto Semiconductors Asia Ltd. (2)
Room 3006 China Resources Building 26 Harbour Road, Wanchai, China (Hong Kong)
Tel.: (852) 3652 5522
Lighting Equipment Mfr
N.A.I.C.S.: 335139

Subsidiary (Domestic):

OSRAM Opto Semiconductors GmbH (2)
Leibnizstr 4, 93055, Regensburg, Germany
Tel.: (49) 941 85 05
Web Site: http://www.osram.com
Sales Range: $400-449.9 Million
Emp.: 150
Lighting Equipment Mfr
N.A.I.C.S.: 335139

Subsidiary (Non-US):

Osram Opto Semiconductors (Malaysia) Sdn Bhd (3)
Bayan Lepas Free Industrial Zone Phase 1, 11900, Bayan Lepas, Penang, Malaysia
Tel.: (60) 4 643 4404
Lighting Equipment Mfr
N.A.I.C.S.: 335139

Subsidiary (US):

Osram Opto Semiconductors, Inc. (3)
21800 Haggerty Road, Ste. 115, Northville, MI 48167
Tel.: (248) 596-0375
Web Site: http://www.osram-os.com
Sales Range: $25-49.9 Million
Emp.: 20
Semiconductor & Related Device Mfr
N.A.I.C.S.: 334413

Subsidiary (Non-US):

OSRAM Pte. Ltd. (2)
988 Toa Payoh North 03-01/ 07 / 08, Singapore, 319002, Singapore
Tel.: (65) 6552 0110
Web Site: http://www.osram.com
Lighting Equipment Mfr
N.A.I.C.S.: 335139

OSRAM Romania S.R.L. (2)
Italian Street no 24 Arion Green Building ground floor, 020976, Bucharest, Romania
Tel.: (40) 21 232 85 61
Web Site: http://www.osram.ro
Emp.: 1
Lighting Equipment Mfr
N.A.I.C.S.: 335139

OSRAM S.A. (2)
Ronda De Europa 5 Edificio D Planta 4, 28760, Madrid, Spain
Tel.: (34) 916555207
Web Site: http://www.osram.es
Lighting Equipment Mfr
N.A.I.C.S.: 335139

OSRAM S.A. (2)
Avenida Fondo de La Legua 1044,

B1640EDP, Martinez, Buenos Aires, Argentina
Tel.: (54) 1153687680
Lighting Installation Services
N.A.I.C.S.: 238210
Hernan Rodriguez (Head-Acctg & Controlling)

OSRAM S.A. de C.V. (2)
Camino a Tepalcapa No 8 Col San Martin, 54900, Tultitlan, Mexico
Tel.: (52) 55 58 99 18 00
Lighting Equipment Mfr & Whslr
N.A.I.C.S.: 335139

OSRAM S.p.A. (2)
Via Sant'Uguzzone 29, 20126, Milan, Italy
Tel.: (39) 0242491
Web Site: https://www.osram.it
Electronic Lighting Product Mfr
N.A.I.C.S.: 335132
Piero Lorenzetto (Mgr-Pur)

OSRAM Sales EOOD (2)
Blvd Shipchenski Prohod 9 FL 4, 1111, Sofia, Bulgaria
Tel.: (359) 32348248
Electric & Electronic Device Mfr
N.A.I.C.S.: 335999

OSRAM Sp. z o.o. (2)
Al Jerozolimskie 94, 00-807, Warsaw, Poland
Tel.: (48) 223765700
Web Site: http://www.osram.pl
Lighting Equipment Mfr
N.A.I.C.S.: 335139

OSRAM Taiwan Company Ltd. (2)
7th Floor No 87 Sung Chiang Road, Taipei, 10486, Taiwan
Tel.: (886) 2 25 13 17 99
Web Site: http://www.osram.com.tw
Emp.: 60
Lighting Equipment Mfr
N.A.I.C.S.: 335139

OSRAM Teknolojileri Ticaret Anonim Sirketi (2)
Buyukdere Caddesi Bahar Sokak No 13 River Plaza Kat-4 No 4, Levent, Istanbul, Turkiye
Tel.: (90) 2127034800
Lighting System Mfr
N.A.I.C.S.: 335132
Muzaffer Can Surucu (Country Mgr-Sls)

OSRAM d.o.o (2)
Djordja Stanojevica 14, 11070, Belgrade, Serbia
Tel.: (381) 11 228 17 17
Sales Range: $25-49.9 Million
Emp.: 1
Lighting Equipment Mfr
N.A.I.C.S.: 335139
Miroslav Lajesic (Gen Mgr)

OSRAM d.o.o. (2)
Kraljice Katarine 51, 88000, Mostar, Bosnia & Herzegovina
Tel.: (387) 36 449740
Web Site: http://www.osram.com
Lighting Equipment Mfr
N.A.I.C.S.: 335139

OSRAM d.o.o. (2)
Visnjevac 3, 10000, Zagreb, Croatia
Tel.: (385) 13032010
Web Site: http://www.osram.hr
Lighting Equipment Mfr
N.A.I.C.S.: 335139

OSRAM de Colombia Iluminaciones S.A. (2)
Cra 14 No 94 - 44 Torre A Oficina 301 y Oficina 303, Bogota, Colombia
Tel.: (57) 16445930
Web Site: http://www.osram.com.co
Sales Range: $25-49.9 Million
Emp.: 2
Lighting Equipment Mfr
N.A.I.C.S.: 335139
Patrick Kriegeskorte (CEO)

OSRAM de Peru S.A.C. (2)
Av Encalada 1257 Santiago de Surco, Lima, Peru
Tel.: (51) 1 6185800
Web Site: http://www.osram.com.pe
Lighting Equipment Mfr
N.A.I.C.S.: 335139

ams AG—(Continued)

OSRAM del Ecuador S.A. (2)
Av Francisco de Orellana y Alberto Borges
Edificio centrum 7mo, piso Oficina 4,
Guayaquil, Ecuador
Tel.: (593) 4 269 30 70
Web Site: http://www.osram.ec
Lighting Equipment Mfr
N.A.I.C.S.: 335139

OSRAM do Brasil Lampadas Eletricas Ltda. (2)
Av Dos Autonomistas 4229, 06090 901,
Osasco, Sao Paulo, Brazil
Tel.: (55) 11 36 84 74 08
Web Site: http://www.osram.com.br
Sales Range: $75-99.9 Million
Emp.: 200
Lighting Equipment Mfr
N.A.I.C.S.: 335139

OSRAM, Lda. (2)
Rua do Alto do Montijo n 15, 2790-012,
Carnaxide, Portugal
Tel.: (351) 210332210
Lighting System Mfr
N.A.I.C.S.: 335132
Antonieta Loureiro (CEO)

OSRAM-MELCO Toshiba Lighting Ltd. (2)
1-201-1 Funakoshi-cho, Yokosuka, 237-8510, Kanagawa, Japan
Tel.: (81) 468 62 22 92
Lighting Equipment Mfr
N.A.I.C.S.: 335139

OY OSRAM AB (2)
Vantaankoskentie 14, 01670, Vantaa, Finland
Tel.: (358) 984932200
Web Site: http://www.osram.com
Emp.: 40
Lighting Equipment Mfr
N.A.I.C.S.: 335139
ismo Korhonen (Gen Mgr)

Osram Argentina S.A.C.I. (2)
Ramos Mejia 2456, ADN Beccar, B 1643,
Buenos Aires, Argentina (100%)
Tel.: (54) 1163338000
Web Site: http://www.osram.com.ar
Sales Range: $50-74.9 Million
Emp.: 180
Mfr & Distribution of Electric Lamps
N.A.I.C.S.: 335139

Osram Australia Pty. Ltd. (2)
11 Fl Bldg 1 423 Pennant Hills Rd, Pennant
Hills, 2120, NSW, Australia (100%)
Tel.: (61) 294818399
Web Site: http://www.osram.com.au
Sales Range: $25-49.9 Million
Emp.: 50
Light Sources & Electronic Control Gear Mfr
N.A.I.C.S.: 335132

Osram Ltd. (2)
450 Brook Drive Reading, Manchester, RG2
6UU, Berkshire, United Kingdom (100%)
Tel.: (44) 1925649106
Web Site: http://www.osram.co.uk
Emp.: 742
Mfr & Distribution of Electric Lamps & Luminaries
N.A.I.C.S.: 335139

Osram S.A. (2)
1 Rue D Altorf, 67129, Molsheim,
France (100%)
Tel.: (33) 388497599
Web Site: http://www.osram.fr
Sales Range: $150-199.9 Million
Emp.: 541
Mfr & Distributor of Electric Lamps
N.A.I.C.S.: 335139
Pascal Rinckenberger (OOO)

Osram Societa Riunite Osram-Edison-Clerici S.p.A. (2)
Via SanUguzzone 29, 20126, Milan,
Italy (100%)
Tel.: (39) 0242491
Web Site: http://www.osram.it
Sales Range: $250-299.9 Million
Emp.: 919
Mfr & Distributor of Electric Lamps
N.A.I.C.S.: 335139

Osram Sylvania Ltd. (2)

55 Renfrew Drive - Suite 201, Markham,
L3R 8H3, ON, Canada (100%)
Tel.: (905) 754-5100
Web Site: http://www.sylvania.com
Sales Range: $25-49.9 Million
Emp.: 140
Sales & Distribution of Electric Lamps
N.A.I.C.S.: 335139

Subsidiary (US):

Osram Sylvania, Inc. (2)
200 Ballardvale St, Wilmington, MA
01887 (100%)
Tel.: (978) 753-5000
Web Site: http://www.sylvania.com
Sales Range: $1-4.9 Billion
Emp.: 11,200
Lighting Products & Precision Materials Mfr
& Distr
N.A.I.C.S.: 335139

Branch (Domestic):

Osram Sylvania Puerto Rico (3)
Bo Maney Rd 189 Km 9 0, Gurabo, PR
00778
Tel.: (787) 737-4701
Web Site: http://www.sylvania.com
Sales Range: $50-74.9 Million
Emp.: 146
Metal Plaster Bases
N.A.I.C.S.: 332323

Subsidiary (Non-US):

Osram de Mexico S.A. de C.V. (2)
Blvd TLC 50 Apodaca N L, 66600, Monterrey, Mexico (100%)
Tel.: (52) 8181964600
Web Site: http://www.osram-latam.com
Emp.: 500
Mfr & Distributor of Electric Lamps
N.A.I.C.S.: 335139

Osram do Brasil Companhia de Lampadas Eletricas S.A. (2)
Av Dos Autonomistas 4229, 06090 901,
Osasco, Brazil (100%)
Tel.: (55) 1136847408
Web Site: http://www.osram.com.br
Sales Range: $100-124.9 Million
Emp.: 560
Mfr & Distributor of Electric Lamps
N.A.I.C.S.: 335139

Osram, A.S. (2)
Komarnanska cesta 7, 94093, Nove Zamky,
Slovakia
Tel.: (421) 356464473
Lighting System Mfr
N.A.I.C.S.: 335132
Georgina Szellova (Mgr-HR)

P.T. OSRAM Indonesia (2)
Cowell Tower 8th Fl Jl Senen Raya No 135,
Jakarta, 10410, Indonesia
Tel.: (62) 2138901191
Web Site: http://www.osram.co.id
Sales Range: $75-99.9 Million
Emp.: 60
Lighting Equipment Mfr
N.A.I.C.S.: 335139

Siteco France S.A.S. (2)
201 rue Carnot, 94120, Fontenay-sous-Bois, France
Tel.: (33) 173434371
Lighting Installation Services
N.A.I.C.S.: 238210
Franck L'Hoste-Clos (Head-Sls)

Subsidiary (Domestic):

Siteco GmbH (2)
Georg-Simon-Ohm-Strasse 50, 83301,
Traunreut, Germany
Tel.: (49) 8669330
Web Site: https://www.siteco.com
Lighting Installation Services
N.A.I.C.S.: 238210
Susanne Pertl (Chm)

Subsidiary (Non-US):

Siteco Norway AS (2)
Lysaker Torg 8, 1366, Lysaker, Norway
Tel.: (47) 45377100
Technical Lighting Mfr & Distr
N.A.I.C.S.: 335139
Tom Egil Bergseng (CEO)

Siteco Poland Sp. z o.o. (2)
Al Jerozolimskie 94, 00-807, Warsaw, Poland
Tel.: (48) 223765766
Technical Lighting Mfr & Distr
N.A.I.C.S.: 335139
Kamila Trojanowska (Country Mgr-Sls)

Siteco UK Limited (2)
Hexagon Tower Crumpsall Vale, Blackley,
Manchester, M9 8GQ, United Kingdom
Tel.: (44) 3300555209
Technical Lighting Mfr & Distr
N.A.I.C.S.: 335139

Subsidiary (Domestic):

Traxon Technologies Europe GmbH (2)
Karl-Schurz-Str 38, 33100, Paderborn, Germany
Tel.: (49) 5251 54648 0
Web Site:
http://www.traxontechnologies.com
Lighting Equipment Mfr
N.A.I.C.S.: 335139

Subsidiary (US):

Traxon Technologies LLC (2)
200 Ballardvale St, Wilmington, MA 01887
Tel.: (978) 570-3000
Web Site:
http://www.traxontechnologies.com
Lighting Equipment Mfr
N.A.I.C.S.: 335139

Subsidiary (Non-US):

Traxon Technologies Ltd. (2)
208 Wireless Centre 3 Science Park East
Avenue, Hong Kong Science Park, Sha Tin,
China (Hong Kong)
Tel.: (852) 2943 3488
Web Site:
http://www.traxontechnologies.com
Lighting Equipment Mfr
N.A.I.C.S.: 335139

Texas Advanced Optoelectronic Solutions, Inc. (1)
1001 Klein Rd Ste 300, Plano, TX 75074
Tel.: (972) 673-0759
Web Site: http://www.taosinc.com
Sales Range: $75-99.9 Million
Emp.: 42
Optoelectronic Equipment Mfr
N.A.I.C.S.: 334413

ams International AG (1)
Rietstrasse 4, 8640, Rapperswil, Switzerland
Tel.: (41) 55 220 90 00
Web Site: http://www.ams.com
Sales Range: $25-49.9 Million
Emp.: 30
Electronic Components Distr
N.A.I.C.S.: 423690

ams Semiconductors India Pvt Ltd (1)
01-07 Cyber Pearl Block 2 HITEC City,
Madhapur, Hyderabad, 500081, Andhra
Pradesh, India
Tel.: (91) 40 4008 2350
Web Site: http://www.ams.com
Sales Range: $25-49.9 Million
Emp.: 30
Semiconductor Distr
N.A.I.C.S.: 423690

austriamicrosystems (Philippines) Inc. (1)
B2-1D Carmelray Industrial Park II Special
Economic Zone, Brgy Tulo, Calamba, 4027,
Laguna, Philippines
Tel.: (63) 49 508 01 62
Semiconductor Product Mfr
N.A.I.C.S.: 334413

austriamicrosystems France S.a.r.l. (1)
124 Avenue de Paris, 94300, Vincennes,
France (100%)
Tel.: (33) 143740090
Web Site:
http://www.austriamicrosystems.com
Sales Range: $50-74.9 Million
Emp.: 5
Other Electronic Parts & Equipment Whslr

N.A.I.C.S.: 423690

austriamicrosystems Germany GmbH (1)
Erdinger Strasse 14, 85609, Aschheim,
Germany (100%)
Tel.: (49) 896936430
Sales Range: $25-49.9 Million
Emp.: 7
Semiconductor & Related Device Mfr
N.A.I.C.S.: 334413

austriamicrosystems Italy S.r.l. (1)
Via A Volta 18, 20094, Corsico,
Italy (100%)
Tel.: (39) 0245864364
Web Site:
http://www.austriamicrosystems.com
Sales Range: $25-49.9 Million
Emp.: 35
Electrical Apparatus & Equipment Wiring
Supplies & Construction Material Whslr
N.A.I.C.S.: 423610

austriamicrosystems Japan Co. Ltd (1)
KF Building 5th Floor 4-13-8 Shiba, Minato-ku, 108-0014, Tokyo, Japan (100%)
Tel.: (81) 354846745
Sales Range: $25-49.9 Million
Emp.: 8
Prerecorded Tape Compact Disc & Record
Stores
N.A.I.C.S.: 449210

austriamicrosystems Spain S.L. (1)
austriamicrosystems Spain S.L., Lado Este,
46022, Valencia, Spain
Tel.: (34) 963726825
Web Site:
http://www.austriamicrosystems.com
Sales Range: $50-74.9 Million
Emp.: 10
Electronic Components Distr
N.A.I.C.S.: 423690

austriamicrosystems USA Inc (1)
8601 Six Forks Rd Ste 400, Raleigh, NC
27615 (100%)
Tel.: (919) 676-5292
Web Site:
http://www.austriamicrosystems.com
Sales Range: $25-49.9 Million
Emp.: 4
Semiconductor & Related Device Mfr
N.A.I.C.S.: 334413

AMS GMBH
Bruchstrasse 1-9, 57578, Elkenroth,
Germany
Tel.: (49) 274780080
Web Site:
http://amstechnologies.com
Year Founded: 1972
Sales Range: $10-24.9 Million
Emp.: 120
Metal Fitting Mfr
N.A.I.C.S.: 332999
Thomas Imhauser (Mng Dir)

AMS OSIGURANJE A.D.
Ruzveltova 16, PAK 145104, 11050,
Belgrade, Serbia
Tel.: (381) 113084900
Web Site: https://www.ams.co.rs
Year Founded: 1998
AMSO—(BEL)
Rev.: $54,078,615
Assets: $100,824,162
Liabilities: $69,222,688
Net Worth: $31,601,474
Earnings: $2,578,145
Emp.: 105
Fiscal Year-end: 12/31/23
Insurance Agency Services
N.A.I.C.S.: 524210
Vuceta Mandic (Exec Dir)

AMS POLYMERS LTD.
C-582 Saraswati Vihar Pitampura,
Delhi, 110 034, India
Tel.: (91) 9810035220
Web Site:
https://www.amspolymers.com

Year Founded: 1985
540066—(BOM)
Rev.: $7,178,891
Assets: $3,410,112
Liabilities: $2,958,351
Net Worth: $451,761
Earnings: $12,076
Emp.: 17
Fiscal Year-end: 03/31/22
Automobile Parts Mfr & Distr
N.A.I.C.S.: 336310
Anand Kumar *(Chm & Mng Dir)*

AMS PUBLIC TRANSPORT HOLDINGS LIMITED
11-12/F Abba Commercial Building
223 Aberdeen Main Road, Hong
Kong, China (Hong Kong)
Tel.: (852) 2 873 6808
Web Site: http://www.amspt.com
0077—(HKG)
Rev.: $43,749,758
Assets: $42,560,691
Liabilities: $36,648,377
Net Worth: $5,912,314
Earnings: ($2,371,297)
Emp.: 639
Fiscal Year-end: 03/31/22
Public Bus Transportation Services
N.A.I.C.S.: 485113
Ka Yan Wong *(Sec & Controller-Fin)*

AMSC ASA
Oksenoyveien 10 Building B, 1366,
Lysaker, Norway
Tel.: (47) 24130000
Web Site: https://www.amscasa.com
0JE5—(LSE)
Rev.: $93,654,000
Assets: $829,295,000
Liabilities: $654,275,000
Net Worth: $175,020,000
Earnings: $18,652,000
Emp.: 3
Fiscal Year-end: 12/31/22
Shipping Freight Services
N.A.I.C.S.: 483111
Pal Lothe Magnussen *(Pres & CEO)*

AMSC CO., LTD.
Yoyogi Community Bldg 1-11-2
Yoyogi Shibuya-ku, 151-0053, Tokyo,
Japan
Tel.: (81) 3 5302 1556
Web Site: http://www.amsc.co.jp
Year Founded: 1975
Sales Range: $200-249.9 Million
Wholesale Traders
N.A.I.C.S.: 425120
Shintaro Kurihara *(Pres)*

AMSECO EXPLORATION LTD.
620 rue Saint-Jacques bureau 110,
Montreal, H3C 1C7, QC, Canada
Tel.: (514) 284-5111
Web Site:
http://www.amsecoexploration.com
Year Founded: 1984
Sales Range: $1-9.9 Million
Metal Exploration Services
N.A.I.C.S.: 212290
Jean Desmarais *(Pres & CEO)*

AMSKY TECHNOLOGY CO., LTD.
No 3 Hongwei Road Sino-Singapore
Knowledge City, Jiulong Town
Huangpu District, Guangzhou,
510080, Guangdong, China
Tel.: (86) 15858125587
Web Site: https://www.amsky.com
Year Founded: 2006
300521—(CHIN)
Rev.: $22,440,969
Assets: $82,217,751
Liabilities: $10,961,933

Net Worth: $71,255,818
Earnings: ($850,142)
Fiscal Year-end: 12/31/23
Printing Equipment Mfr & Distr
N.A.I.C.S.: 323120
Li Mingzhi *(Chm)*

AMSONS APPARELS LTD
Flat No 116 1st Floor Hemkunt
Chamber 89 Nehru Place, New Delhi,
110019, India
Tel.: (91) 11 32317247
Web Site:
http://www.amsonsapparels.com
Year Founded: 2003
Emp.: 280
Silk, Polyester, Lace Fabrics, Netting
Fabrics, Coarse Cotton Fabric, Suit-
ing, Shirting, Linen, Jute & Other
Fabrics Distr
N.A.I.C.S.: 425120
Gaurav Bansal *(CFO)*

AMSONS GROUP
Plot No 62-64 Mbagala Industrial
Area Kilwa Rd, Dar es Salaam, Tan-
zania
Tel.: (255) 788026188   TZ
Web Site:
http://www.amsonsgroup.net
Year Founded: 2006
Diversified Holding Company
N.A.I.C.S.: 551112

Subsidiaries:

Bamburi Cement Plc   **(1)**
Kitui Road Off Kampala Rd Industrial Area,
PO Box 10921, 00100, Nairobi, Kenya
Tel.: (254) 722205471
Web Site: https://www.lafarge.co.ke
Rev.: $359,864,880
Assets: $480,051,300
Liabilities: $165,800,340
Net Worth: $314,250,960
Earnings: $3,511,020
Emp.: 729
Fiscal Year-end: 12/31/2019
Cement Mfr
N.A.I.C.S.: 327310
Seddiq Hassani *(Mng Dir-Grp)*

AMSPHERE LIMITED
1 Portsoken Street, London, E1 8BT,
United Kingdom
Tel.: (44) 8701208327
Web Site: http://www.amsphere.com
Sales Range: $10-24.9 Million
Emp.: 100
Software Testing Services
N.A.I.C.S.: 541690
Ricky Shankar *(CEO)*

**AMTD GROUP COMPANY LIM-
ITED**
23/F - 25/F Nexxus Building 41 Con-
naught Road Central, Hong Kong,
China (Hong Kong)
Tel.: (852) 31633288
Web Site:
https://www.amtdgroup.com
Year Founded: 2003
Emp.: 100
Financial Services
N.A.I.C.S.: 551112

Subsidiaries:

AMTD IDEA Group   **(1)**
23/F - 25/F Nexxus Building 41 Connaught
Road, Central, China (Hong Kong)
Tel.: (852) 31633389
Web Site: https://www.amtdinc.com
Rev.: $130,914,000
Assets: $1,486,590,000
Liabilities: $193,016,000
Net Worth: $1,293,574,000
Earnings: $153,383,000
Emp.: 232
Fiscal Year-end: 12/31/2023
Financial Investment Services

N.A.I.C.S.: 523940
Calvin Choi *(Chm & CEO)*

Subsidiary (Domestic):

AMTD Digital Inc.   **(2)**
25/F Nexxus Building 41 Connaught Road,
Central, China (Hong Kong)   **(97.1%)**
Tel.: (852) 31633298
Rev.: $33,066,000
Assets: $661,676,000
Liabilities: $140,574,000
Net Worth: $521,102,000
Earnings: $40,140,000
Emp.: 199
Fiscal Year-end: 04/30/2023
Digital Marketing Services
N.A.I.C.S.: 541870
Timothy Wai Cheung Tong *(Chm)*

**AMTECH ELECTRONICS INDIA
LIMITED**
E-6 GIDC Electronics Zone, Gandhi-
nagar, 382 028, Gujarat, India
Tel.: (91) 7923289101
Web Site:
http://www.amtechelectronics.com
Year Founded: 1987
Sales Range: $10-24.9 Million
Emp.: 80
Motion Control, Automation, Power
Quality & Industrial Electronics Equip-
ment Mfr
N.A.I.C.S.: 333248
Piyush Patel *(Mng Dir)*

Subsidiaries:

Amtech Drives, Inc.   **(1)**
745 Trabert Ave NW, Atlanta, GA 30318
Tel.: (770) 469-5240
Web Site: http://www.amtechdrives.com
Industrial Electronics Mfr
N.A.I.C.S.: 335311
Mark A. Johnson *(Mgr-Ops & Bus Dev-
Atlanta)*

Amtech Power Limited   **(1)**
B-9 GIDC Electronics Zone, Gandhinagar,
382 028, Gujarat, India
Tel.: (91) 7923289116
Web Site: http://www.amtechpower.in
Power Generation Control & Protection Sys-
tem Mfr & Installation Services
N.A.I.C.S.: 335311

AMTEK AUTO LIMITED
3 Local Shopping Centre, Pamposh
Enclave GK-1, New Delhi, 110048,
India
Tel.: (91) 11 4234 4444   In
Web Site: http://www.amtek.com
Sales Range: $1-4.9 Billion
Emp.: 1,415
Automotive & Non-Automotive Com-
ponents Mfr
N.A.I.C.S.: 336390

Subsidiaries:

Amtek Deutschland GmbH   **(1)**
Bonner Str 25 Hennef Sieg, Hennef, 53773,
Nordrhein-Westfalen, Germany
Tel.: (49) 224288040
Automotive Components Mfr
N.A.I.C.S.: 336390

Amtek Germany Holding GmbH &
Co. KG   **(1)**
Hauptsrasse 115, Offenburg, 77652, Baden-
Wurttemberg, Germany
Tel.: (49) 7831808181
Automotive Components Mfr
N.A.I.C.S.: 336390

Amtek Investments U.K. Limited   **(1)**
Chelmarsh Daimler Green, Coventry, CV6
3LT, United Kingdom
Tel.: (44) 24 7660 0300
Automotive Components Mfr
N.A.I.C.S.: 336390

Amtek Transportation Systems
Limited   **(1)**
Begampur Khataula P O Khandsa, 122 001,
Gurgaon, India

Tel.: (91) 9868601408
Web Site: http://www.amtek.com
Emp.: 50
Automotive Components Mfr
N.A.I.C.S.: 336390
V. K. Mittal *(VP-Ops)*

Castex Technologies Limited   **(1)**
3 LSC Pamposh Enclave Greater Kailash-I,
New Delhi, 110048, India   **(61.64%)**
Tel.: (91) 1142344444
Web Site: http://www.amtek.com
Rev.: $41,556,200
Assets: $1,005,885,272
Liabilities: $1,123,751,804
Net Worth: ($117,866,532)
Earnings: ($71,701,000)
Emp.: 870
Fiscal Year-end: 03/31/2020
Automotive Components Mfr
N.A.I.C.S.: 333612

JMT Auto Limited   **(1)**
C-19 And 20 D 8-12 NS 29-34, 7th Phase
Industrial Area Adityapur, Jamshedpur,
832109, Jharkhand, India
Tel.: (91) 6576626331
Web Site: http://www.jmtauto.com
Rev.: $51,476,566
Assets: $59,521,385
Liabilities: $41,486,363
Net Worth: $18,035,022
Earnings: ($7,964,406)
Emp.: 597
Fiscal Year-end: 03/31/2020
Automotive Components Mfr
N.A.I.C.S.: 336110
Mona K. Bahadur *(Officer-Compliance &
Sec)*

Metalyst Forgings Ltd.   **(1)**
Gat No 614 Village Kuruli, Tal Khed, Pune,
410501, Maharashtra, India   **(54.96%)**
Tel.: (91) 8087090023
Web Site: https://metalyst.co.in
Rev.: $25,829,799
Assets: $418,221,777
Liabilities: $594,301,426
Net Worth: ($176,079,649)
Earnings: ($41,418,441)
Emp.: 547
Fiscal Year-end: 03/31/2020
Steel Forging Mfr
N.A.I.C.S.: 332111

Neumayer Tekfor Automotive Brasil
Ltda.   **(1)**
Avenida Arquimedes 500 Jundiai, Sao
Paulo, 13211-840, Brazil
Tel.: (55) 11 2152 4800
Web Site: http://www.anmtekteksor.com
Emp.: 700
Automotive Components Mfr
N.A.I.C.S.: 336390
Jorge Jacomini *(Mng Dir)*

Neumayer Tekfor Schmolln
GmbH   **(1)**
Zum Wasserturm 79, Schmolln, 04626,
Thuringen, Germany
Tel.: (49) 34491 560
Emp.: 300
Automotive Components Mfr
N.A.I.C.S.: 336390
Kunal Sabharwal *(CEO)*

Tekfor Inc   **(1)**
3690 Long Rd, Wooster, OH 44691
Tel.: (330) 202-7667
Automotive Components Mfr
N.A.I.C.S.: 336390

Tekfor Services GmbH   **(1)**
Altenburger Strasse 21/2, 04626, Schmolln,
Germany
Tel.: (49) 34491 5574 0
Web Site: http://www.tekfor-services.de
Emp.: 300
Employee Placement Services
N.A.I.C.S.: 561311

Tekfor Services Inc.   **(1)**
2098 Portage Rd Ste 360, Wooster, OH
44691
Tel.: (330) 202-7284
Employee Placement Services
N.A.I.C.S.: 561311

AMTEK HOLDINGS BERHAD

AMTEK Holdings Berhad—(Continued)

No 12K Jalan Tandang, 46050, Petaling Jaya, Selangor Darul Ehsan, Malaysia
Tel.: (60) 377813633
Web Site: http://www.amtek.com.my
Rev.: $5,823,879
Assets: $8,217,838
Liabilities: $4,693,139
Net Worth: $3,524,699
Earnings: ($735,628)
Fiscal Year-end: 06/30/17
Garments & Shoes Mfr
N.A.I.C.S.: 315210
Azmin Mohd Nursin *(Chm)*

AMTEL HOLDINGS BERHAD
No 7 Jalan PJS 7/19 Bandar Sunway, 47500, Subang Jaya, Selangor Darul Ehsan, Malaysia
Tel.: (60) 356322449
Web Site: https://www.amtel.com.my
AMTEL—(KLS)
Rev.: $15,600,502
Assets: $19,430,968
Liabilities: $3,825,407
Net Worth: $15,605,561
Earnings: $1,223,217
Fiscal Year-end: 11/30/23
Electronic & Telecommunications Products Distr
N.A.I.C.S.: 238210
Yit Foong Hoh *(Co-Sec)*

Subsidiaries:

Amtel Cellular Sdn. Bhd. (1)
No 5 Jalan PJS 7/19, Subang Jaya, Bandar Sunway, 47500, Selangor, Malaysia
Tel.: (60) 356326788
Web Site: http://www.lokatoo.com
Sales Range: $25-49.9 Million
Emp.: 50
Global Positioning System Navigator Retailer
N.A.I.C.S.: 423690
Woon Huei Tan *(Mng Dir)*

Amtel Resources Sdn. Bhd. (1)
255 Lorong Perak 12 Mergong 2, 05150, Alor Setar, Kedah, Malaysia
Tel.: (60) 47339809
Web Site: http://www.amtel.com.my
Sales Range: $25-49.9 Million
Emp.: 7
Telecommunication Civil Works Contract Services
N.A.I.C.S.: 237130

AMTEX LIMITED
P-225 Tikka Gali 2 Montgomery Bazar, Faisalabad, Pakistan
Tel.: (92) 412428500
Web Site: https://www.amtextile.com
AMTEX—(PSX)
Rev.: $6,085,299
Assets: $11,907,811
Liabilities: $42,966,958
Net Worth: ($31,059,147)
Earnings: $496,135
Emp.: 78
Fiscal Year-end: 06/30/23
Home Textile & Garment Mfr
N.A.I.C.S.: 314120
Khurram Iftikhar *(CEO)*

AMTRADA HOLDING B.V.
Simon Carmiggeltstraat 6 50, Amsterdam, 1011 DJ, Netherlands
Tel.: (31) 205240520
Web Site: http://www.nedcoffee.com
Sales Range: $800-899.9 Million
Emp.: 7
Holding Company
N.A.I.C.S.: 551112
J.W.M. Hendriksen *(CEO)*

Subsidiaries:

Continaf B.V. (1)
Simon Carmiggeltstraat 6-50, 1011 DJ, Am-

sterdam, Netherlands
Tel.: (31) 20 524 0 524
Web Site: http://www.continaf.com
Cocoa Bean Whslr
N.A.I.C.S.: 424590

Daarnhouwer & Co. (1)
Korte Hogendijk 18, 1506 MA, Zaandam, Netherlands
Tel.: (31) 75 6126388
Web Site: http://www.daarnhouwer.com
Emp.: 18
Cocoa Bean Whslr
N.A.I.C.S.: 424590
Rene Strik *(CFO)*

Nedcoffee BV (1)
Simon Carmiggeltstraat 6-50, 1011 DJ, Amsterdam, Netherlands
Tel.: (31) 20 524 05 20
Web Site: http://www.nedcoffee.com
Sales Range: $25-49.9 Million
Coffee Bean Distr
N.A.I.C.S.: 424490

AMTRAN TECHNOLOGY
17F No 268 Lien Chen Rd, Jhonghe, Taipei, 235, Taiwan
Tel.: (886) 282280505
Web Site: https://www.amtran.com.tw
Year Founded: 1994
2489—(TAI)
Rev.: $542,325,595
Assets: $665,591,819
Liabilities: $224,895,672
Net Worth: $440,696,147
Earnings: $14,943,032
Emp.: 5,149
Fiscal Year-end: 12/31/23
Television Product Mfr
N.A.I.C.S.: 334419
Alpha Wu *(Chm, CEO & Gen Mgr)*

Subsidiaries:

Amtran Vietnam Technology Company Limited (1)
No 115 East-West Road VSIP Hai Phong Township, Industrial & Service Park Trung Ha Commune Thuy Nguyen District, Haiphong, Vietnam
Tel.: (84) 2258840505
Electronic Components Mfr
N.A.I.C.S.: 334220

Suzhou Raken Technology Ltd. (1)
No 278 Mayun Road, Suzhou New District, Suzhou, Jiangsu, China
Tel.: (86) 51268088500
Web Site: https://www.szraken.com
Emp.: 1,500
Electronic Components Mfr
N.A.I.C.S.: 334220

AMUR MINERALS CORPORATION
14 Gaidar Street Office 9, 680063, Khabarovsk, Russia
Tel.: (7) 4212755615
Web Site:
https://www.amurminerals.com
CRTX—(LSE)
Assets: $4,786,000
Liabilities: $662,000
Net Worth: $4,124,000
Earnings: ($9,647,000)
Emp.: 16
Fiscal Year-end: 12/31/23
Mineral Exploration Services
N.A.I.C.S.: 213115
Robin Young *(CEO)*

AMUSE GROUP HOLDING LTD.
Flat A-C 3A/F Metex House 24-32 Fui Yiu Kok Street, Tsuen Wan, China (Hong Kong)
Tel.: (852) 3 702 3276
Web Site:
http://www.amusegroupholding.com
Year Founded: 2004

8545—(HKG)
Rev.: $27,275,014
Assets: $28,552,303
Liabilities: $5,481,521
Net Worth: $23,070,782
Earnings: $1,119,159
Emp.: 39
Fiscal Year-end: 03/31/21
Toy Product Retailer
N.A.I.C.S.: 459120
Wai Keung Li *(Founder, Chm & CEO)*

Subsidiaries:

Lai Ga Toys Co. Limited (1)
Flat A-C 3A/F Metex House 24-32 Fui Yiu Kok Street, Tsuen Wan, China (Hong Kong)
Tel.: (852) 35950073
Web Site: https://www.flametoy.com
Toy Distr
N.A.I.C.S.: 423920

Sentinel International Co. Limited (1)
Tel.: (852) 35950073
Web Site: http://www.sentinel-toys.com
Toy Mfr & Whslr
N.A.I.C.S.: 339930

AMUSE INC.
20-1 Sakuragaoka-cho, Shibuya-ku, Tokyo, Japan
Tel.: (81) 354573333
Web Site: https://www.amuse.co.jp
Year Founded: 1978
4301—(TKS)
Rev.: $362,313,930
Assets: $389,355,440
Liabilities: $141,480,440
Net Worth: $247,875,000
Earnings: $2,584,510
Emp.: 346
Fiscal Year-end: 03/31/24
Media Visual & Artist Management Services
N.A.I.C.S.: 541430
Kuniko Osato *(Founder)*

Subsidiaries:

A-Sketch Inc. (1)
3F Ninomiya building 18-4 Sakuragaoka-cho, Shibuya-ku, Tokyo, 150-0031, Japan
Tel.: (81) 354575566
Web Site: http://www.a-sketch.com
Music Entertainment Services
N.A.I.C.S.: 711510

AZEAL Inc. (1)
Infosutawa 20-1 Sakuragaokacho, Shibuya-ku, Tokyo, 150-8570, Japan
Tel.: (81) 354573398
Web Site: http://www.techesko.com
Artist Management Services
N.A.I.C.S.: 711410

Amuse Edutainment Inc. (1)
2-34-4 Asakusa, Taito Ku, Tokyo, 111-0032, Japan
Tel.: (81) 358061181
Web Site: http://www.amusemuseum.com
Sales Range: $25-49.9 Million
Emp.: 10
Community Museums & Entertainment Services
N.A.I.C.S.: 712110
Kiyoshi Tatsumi *(Pres)*

Amuse Soft Entertainment, Inc. (1)
20-1 Shibuya Infos Tower 13 Floor Sakuragaoka, Shibuya-ku, Tokyo, 150-0031, Japan
Tel.: (81) 354573402
Web Site: http://www.amuse-s-e.co.jp
Sales Range: $25-49.9 Million
Emp.: 60
Audio & Video Production Services
N.A.I.C.S.: 512110
Tapsuro Hatanaka *(Pres)*

Brussels Co., Ltd. (1)
Mita Room 403 5-29-20 Shiba, Minato-ku, Tokyo, 108-0014, Japan
Tel.: (81) 362066550
Web Site: https://www.brussels.co.jp
Sales Range: $25-49.9 Million
Emp.: 30
Beverage Whslr

N.A.I.C.S.: 424820

J-Feel Inc. (1)
3-3-2 Shibuya Shibuya MK Building 6F, Shibuya-ku, Tokyo, 150-0002, Japan
Tel.: (81) 354688655
Web Site: http://www.j-feel.jp
Sales Range: $25-49.9 Million
Emp.: 10
Business Consulting Services
N.A.I.C.S.: 541611
Katsunori Takahashi *(Pres)*

Kirei Inc. (1)
8330 Arjons Dr, San Diego, CA 92126
Tel.: (619) 236-9924
Web Site: https://www.kireiusa.com
Architectural Design Services
N.A.I.C.S.: 541310

AMV CAPITAL CORPORATION
Suite 208 - 311 4th Avenue N, Saskatoon, S7K 2L8, SK, Canada
Tel.: (604) 683-8610
Web Site: https://abasca.ca
AMV—(TSXV)
Assets: $251,130
Liabilities: $4,273
Net Worth: $246,857
Earnings: ($42,015)
Fiscal Year-end: 04/30/22
Mineral Exploration Services
N.A.I.C.S.: 213115
Wang Sean Qiang *(Pres & CEO)*

AMVERTON BERHAD
9th Floor Menara Amverton Garden Business Center No 3 Jalan Istana, West Malaysia, 41000, Kelang, Selangor Darul Ehsan, Malaysia
Tel.: (60) 333732888
Web Site: http://www.amverton.com
Year Founded: 1978
Rev.: $29,433,255
Assets: $218,693,641
Liabilities: $40,846,339
Net Worth: $177,847,302
Earnings: $18,335,728
Fiscal Year-end: 12/31/18
Property Development & Construction Services
N.A.I.C.S.: 236115
Tau Chern Cheam *(Sec)*

Subsidiaries:

Epic Ventures Sdn. Bhd. (1)
Lot 20 Rawang Integrated Industrial Park W D T No 22, Pejabat Pos Rawang, 48000, Rawang, Selangor, Malaysia
Tel.: (60) 360922922
Web Site: http://www.epicventures.com
Automotive Spare Parts Distr
N.A.I.C.S.: 423120

AMVIG HOLDINGS LIMITED
Room 601-602 6th Floor Cofco Tower 262 Gloucester Road, Causeway Bay, China (Hong Kong)
Tel.: (852) 2970 7000
Web Site: http://www.amvig.com
Rev.: $309,151,184
Assets: $845,695,291
Liabilities: $326,699,438
Net Worth: $518,995,853
Earnings: $46,692,573
Emp.: 2,750
Fiscal Year-end: 12/31/19
Cigarette Packages Printing Services
N.A.I.C.S.: 316990
Su Ge *(Pres & CEO)*

Subsidiaries:

Leigh-Mardon Pacific Packaging Pte Ltd. (1)
25J Sungei Kadut St 1, Singapore, 729334, Singapore
Tel.: (65) 63650211
Cigarette Packages Printing Services
N.A.I.C.S.: 323111

World Grand Holdings Limited (1)

Rm 1311 Shun Tak Ctr W Tower 200 Connaught Rd, Central, China (Hong Kong)
Tel.: (852) 25451443
Hot Stamping Foils Whslr
N.A.I.C.S.: 332999

AMVIS HOLDINGS, INC.

7F Mitsui Sumitomo Insurance
TEPCO Building 1-6-1 Kyobashi,
Chuo-Ku, Tokyo, 104-0031, Japan
Tel.: (81) 362625105
Web Site: https://www.amvis.com
Year Founded: 2016
7071—(TKS)
Rev.: $226,773,650
Assets: $393,913,310
Liabilities: $205,865,240
Net Worth: $188,048,070
Earnings: $44,737,900
Emp.: 3,598
Fiscal Year-end: 09/30/23
Holding Company
N.A.I.C.S.: 551112
Keiichi Shibahara *(Founder, Chm, Pres & CEO)*

AMW CAPITAL LEASING & FINANCE PLC

No 185 Union Place, Colombo, 02,
Sri Lanka
Tel.: (94) 112446476
Web Site: http://www.capitalleasing.lk
Year Founded: 2006
AMCL.N0000—(COL)
Rev.: $4,298,858
Assets: $25,110,574
Liabilities: $15,406,116
Net Worth: $9,704,458
Earnings: $651,363
Emp.: 187
Fiscal Year-end: 12/31/22
Financial & Leasing Services
N.A.I.C.S.: 522220

AMWAL INVEST PLC

PO Box 940988, Amman, 11194, Jordan
Tel.: (962) 97451064341
Web Site:
    https://amwalinvestmentsllc.com
Year Founded: 2005
AMWL—(AMM)
Sales Range: $1-9.9 Million
Emp.: 17
Investment Management Service
N.A.I.C.S.: 523999
Qasem Newashi *(Chm)*

AN DUONG THAO DIEN REAL ESTATE TRADING INVESTMENT JOINT STOCK COMPANY

Room 1901 19th Floor Me Linh Point
Tower, 2 Ngo Duc Ke Ben Nghe
Ward District 1, Ho Chi Minh City,
Vietnam
Tel.: (84) 862754816
Web Site: http://www.adtdgroup.com
HAR—(HOSE)
Rev.: $752,806
Assets: $44,149,467
Liabilities: $194,258
Net Worth: $43,955,209
Earnings: $1,480,687
Fiscal Year-end: 12/31/23
Real Estate Development Services
N.A.I.C.S.: 531390
Nguyen Nhan Bao *(Chm & Gen Dir)*

AN GIANG IMPORT-EXPORT COMPANY

01 Ngo Gia Tu My Long, Long
Xuyen, An Giang, Vietnam
Tel.: (84) 2969999999
Web Site:
    https://www.angimex.com.vn

Year Founded: 1976
AGM—(HOSE)
Rev.: $32,464,117
Assets: $50,967,696
Liabilities: $50,068,424
Net Worth: $899,272
Earnings: ($9,099,679)
Fiscal Year-end: 12/31/23
Rice Farming Services
N.A.I.C.S.: 111160

AN HUI WENERGY CO., LTD.

25-27F Building B01 Yungu Financial
City No 2528 Chengdu Road, Baohe,
Hefei, 230041, Anhui, China
Tel.: (86) 5512225811
Web Site:
    http://www.wenergy.com.cn
Year Founded: 1993
000543—(SSE)
Rev.: $3,408,295,644
Assets: $6,344,778,492
Liabilities: $3,961,454,796
Net Worth: $2,383,323,696
Earnings: $59,689,656
Fiscal Year-end: 12/31/22
Electric Power Distribution Services
N.A.I.C.S.: 221122
Ming Li *(Chm)*

AN PHA PETROLEUM GROUP JOINT STOCK COMPANY

Room 805 8th Floor Paragon Building
No 3 Nguyen Luong Bang, Tan Phu
Ward District 7, Ho Chi Minh City,
Vietnam
Tel.: (84) 2854136338
Web Site:
    https://www.anphapetrol.com
Year Founded: 1999
ASP—(HOSE)
Rev.: $153,374,952
Assets: $93,600,467
Liabilities: $77,515,699
Net Worth: $16,084,768
Earnings: ($3,469,081)
Fiscal Year-end: 12/31/23
Liquefied Petroleum Gas Mfr
N.A.I.C.S.: 211130
Tran Minh Loan *(Exec Dir)*

AN PHAT BIOPLASTICS

Lot 11+ 12 An Dong Industrial Park,
Nam Sach, Hai Duong, Vietnam
Tel.: (84) 3203755997   VN
Web Site:
    http://www.anphatplastic.com
Year Founded: 2002
Sales Range: $150-199.9 Million
Plastic Products Including Plastic
Bags & Films Mfr
N.A.I.C.S.: 326199
Duong Anh Pham *(Chm)*

Subsidiaries:

An Phat Plastic & Green Environment
Joint Stock Company - Factory No
2   (1)
An Dong Industrial Zone, Hai Duong, Vietnam
Tel.: (84) 437555840
Plastics Product Mfr
N.A.I.C.S.: 326199

AN PHU IRRADIATION J.S.C.

119/A2 Group 4 Quarter 1B, An Phu
Ward, Thuan An, Binh Duong, Vietnam
Tel.: (84) 2743713116
Web Site: http://www.apic.com.vn
Year Founded: 2003
APC—(HOSE)
Rev.: $4,857,905
Assets: $36,687,548
Liabilities: $12,353,142
Net Worth: $24,334,406
Earnings: ($1,467,093)

Emp.: 227
Fiscal Year-end: 12/31/23
Food & Fruit Irradiation Services
N.A.I.C.S.: 561990

AN POST LLC

General Post Office O Connell Street,
Dublin, 1, Ireland
Tel.: (353) 1705 7494
Web Site: http://www.anpost.ie
Year Founded: 1984
Rev.: $1,025,927,016
Assets: $1,259,549,555
Liabilities: $1,026,208,388
Net Worth: $233,341,167
Earnings: $28,896,711
Emp.: 9,723
Fiscal Year-end: 12/31/18
Postal Service
N.A.I.C.S.: 491110
Patrick Knight *(Dir-HR)*

Subsidiaries:

Air Business Ltd   (1)
The Beacon Mosquito Way, Acrewood Way,
Hatfield, AL10 9WN, Hertfordshire, United
Kingdom   **(100%)**
Tel.: (44) 1727890600
Web Site: http://www.airbusiness.com
Sales Range: $25-49.9 Million
Emp.: 100
General Freight Trucking, Local
N.A.I.C.S.: 484110
Phil Ions *(Dir-Fin)*

An Post Billpost Processing Services
Limited   (1)
Enterprise House Cappa Road, Kilrush,
Clare, Ireland
Tel.: (353) 65 9080 212
Web Site: http://www.billpost.ie
Data Processing Services
N.A.I.C.S.: 541513

An Post Direct Limited   (1)
General Post Office, O'Connell Street, Dublin, 1, Ireland   **(100%)**
Tel.: (353) 17057000
Web Site: http://www.anpost.ie
Sales Range: $700-749.9 Million
Emp.: 2,000
Direct Title Insurance Carriers
N.A.I.C.S.: 524127

An Post National Lottery Co.   (1)
Lower Abbey St, Dublin, Ireland   **(80%)**
Tel.: (353) 18364444
Web Site: http://www.lottorey.ie
Sales Range: $50-74.9 Million
Emp.: 100
All Other Amusement & Recreation Industries
N.A.I.C.S.: 713990
Dermot Jgrissin *(Mng Dir)*

JMC Van Trans Limited   (1)
Newlands Naas Road, Dublin, 22,
Ireland   **(100%)**
Tel.: (353) 14602555
Web Site: http://www.jmcvantrans.ie
General Freight Trucking & Logistics Services
N.A.I.C.S.: 541614

Jordan & Co International
Limited   (1)
Unit 2 to 5 Parkside Avenue Two Station
Lane Industrial, Witney, OX28 4YX, United
Kingdom
Tel.: (44) 1993772644
Web Site: http://www.airbusonline.com
Emp.: 50
Courier Service
N.A.I.C.S.: 492110
Lindy Webb *(Dir-Production)*

One Direct (Ireland) Limited   (1)
An Post Insurance Athlone Business Park,
Athlone, Westmeath, Ireland
Tel.: (353) 1890 22 22 22
Web Site: http://www.onedirect.ie
Insurance Services
N.A.I.C.S.: 524113

Postpoint Services Limited   (1)

GPO O Connell Street, Dublin, D01 F5P2,
Ireland
Tel.: (353) 1890 20 42 20
Web Site: http://www.postpoint.ie
Electronic Bill Payment Services
N.A.I.C.S.: 561440

Precision Marketing Information
Limited   (1)
19-24 St Andrews Street, Dublin, D02
C966, Ireland   **(100%)**
Tel.: (353) 18584800
Web Site: http://www.dataireland.ie
Sales Range: $25-49.9 Million
Emp.: 25
Security System Services
N.A.I.C.S.: 561621

Printpost Limited   (1)
Unit 4 Broomhill Business Park, Tallaght,
Dublin, D24 HD43, Ireland   **(100%)**
Tel.: (353) 14513355
Web Site: http://www.printpost.ie
Sales Range: $10-24.9 Million
Emp.: 40
All Other Business Support Services
N.A.I.C.S.: 561499

AN TEXTILE MILLS LIMITED

35 KM Sheikhupura Road Tehsil,
Faisalabad, Jaranwala, Pakistan
Tel.: (92) 414713183
Web Site:
    https://www.antextile.com.pk
Year Founded: 1982
ANTM—(PSX)
Rev.: $6,031,859
Assets: $7,035,502
Liabilities: $3,710,293
Net Worth: $3,325,209
Earnings: ($704,157)
Emp.: 421
Fiscal Year-end: 06/30/23
Securities Brokerage Services
N.A.I.C.S.: 523150
Nazma Amer *(Chm)*

AN-SHIN FOOD SERVICES CO., LTD.

8F No 156-1 Songjiang Rd, Taipei,
104, Taiwan
Tel.: (886) 225675001   TW
Web Site: https://www.mos.com.tw
1259—(TPE)
Rev.: $179,015,414
Assets: $166,474,033
Liabilities: $103,767,408
Net Worth: $62,706,625
Earnings: $3,687,928
Emp.: 882
Fiscal Year-end: 12/31/22
Holding Company; Limited Service
Franchise Restaurants Operator
N.A.I.C.S.: 551112
Chien Yuan Lin *(Chm)*

ANA HOLDINGS INC.

Shiodome City Center 1-5-2 Higashi-
Shimbashi, Minato-ku, Tokyo, 105-
7140, Japan
Tel.: (81) 367351001   JP
Web Site: https://www.ana.co.jp
Year Founded: 1952
9202—(TKS)
Rev.: $13,589,684,080
Assets: $23,594,593,300
Liabilities: $16,636,728,830
Net Worth: $6,957,864,470
Earnings: $1,038,411,170
Emp.: 41,225
Fiscal Year-end: 03/31/24
Air Transportation, Hotel & Travel
Services
N.A.I.C.S.: 481111
Ichiro Fukuzawa *(CFO-Procurement & Exec VP)*

Subsidiaries:

ANA Aero Supply Systems Co.,
Ltd.   (1)

ANA Holdings Inc.—(Continued)

3-5-4 Haneda Airport, Ota-ku, Tokyo, 144-0041, Japan
Tel.: (81) 368314000
Web Site: https://www.aass.co.jp
Aircraft Maintenance & Repair Services
N.A.I.C.S.: 488190

ANA Air Service Fukushima Co., Ltd. (1)
21 Habakiden Kita-Sugama Oaza, Tamakawamura Ishikawa-gun, Fukushima, 963-6304, Japan
Tel.: (81) 247571222
Flight Support Business Services
N.A.I.C.S.: 488190

ANA Air Service Matsuyama Co., Ltd. (1)
2731 Minami-Yoshidamachi, Matsuyama, Ehime, Japan
Tel.: (81) 899725679
Airport Services
N.A.I.C.S.: 488119

ANA Air Service Saga Co., Ltd. (1)
9476-187 Inuido Oaza, Kawasoemachi, Saga, 840-2212, Japan
Tel.: (81) 952461115
Flight Support Business Services
N.A.I.C.S.: 488190

ANA Aircraft Maintenance Co., Ltd (1)
3-8-1 Minowa, Toyonaka, 560-0035, Japan
Tel.: (81) 668583833
Web Site: http://www.anam.co.jp
Sales Range: $125-149.9 Million
Emp.: 400
Aircraft Maintenance Services
N.A.I.C.S.: 488190

ANA Base Maintenance Technics Co., Ltd. (1)
ANA Airframe Maintenance Building 2F 3-5-4 Haneda Airport, Ota-ku, Tokyo, 144-0041, Japan
Tel.: (81) 367002310
Web Site: https://www.btc.ana-g.com
Emp.: 1,129
Aircraft Maintenance Services
N.A.I.C.S.: 488190

ANA Business Create Co., Ltd (1)
1-7-1 Hanedakuko Kukoshisetsu No 2 Sogo Building, Ota-ku, Tokyo, 144-0041, Japan
Tel.: (81) 337478211
Web Site: http://www.abc.co.jp
Sales Range: $50-74.9 Million
Emp.: 248
Aircraft Staff Recruitment Services
N.A.I.C.S.: 488190

ANA Business Jet Inc. (1)
Cross Office 1-18-6 Nishi-Shimbashi, Minato-ku, Tokyo, 105-0003, Japan
Tel.: (81) 335038110
Web Site: https://www.anabj.co.jp
Aviation Services
N.A.I.C.S.: 488190

ANA Cargo Inc. (1)
Shiodome City Center 1-5-2 Higashi-Shimbashi, Minato-Ku, Tokyo, 105-7140, Japan
Tel.: (81) 367351900
Web Site: http://www.anacargo.jp
Cargo & Logistics Services
N.A.I.C.S.: 541614

ANA Catering Service Co., Ltd. (1)
3-2-8 Haneda Airport, Ota-ku, Tokyo, 144-0041, Japan (100%)
Tel.: (81) 357575950
Web Site: https://www.anac.co.jp
Sales Range: $250-299.9 Million
Emp.: 700
In-Flight Meals Preparation
N.A.I.C.S.: 488190
Naoko Nishijima (CEO)

ANA Component Technics Co., Ltd. (1)
3-5-5 Haneda Airport, Ota-ku, Tokyo, 144-0041, Japan
Tel.: (81) 368314400
Web Site: https://www.ctc.ana-g.com
Emp.: 151
Aircraft Maintenance Services

ANA Engine Technics Co., Ltd. (1)
ANA Engine Maintenance Building 3F 3-6-7 Haneda Airport, Ota-ku, Tokyo, 144-0041, Japan
Tel.: (81) 364282300
Web Site: https://www.etc.ana-g.com
Emp.: 200
Aircraft Maintenance Services
N.A.I.C.S.: 488190

ANA Foods Co., Ltd. (1)
Shiodome City Center 1-5-2 Higashi-shimbashi, Minato-ku, Tokyo, 105-7140, Japan
Tel.: (81) 368520100
Aviation Services
N.A.I.C.S.: 488190

ANA Information Systems Planning Co., Ltd. (1)
7th Floor ANA Bijinesusenta Building 6-7-56 Higashi-Kojiya, Ota-ku, Tokyo, 144-0033, Japan (100%)
Tel.: (81) 3 3745 8111
Web Site: http://www.asp-kk.co.jp
System Consulting & System Integration Services
N.A.I.C.S.: 541690

ANA Line Maintenance Technics Co., Ltd. (1)
3-3-2 Haneda Airport, Ota-ku, Tokyo, 144-8515, Japan
Tel.: (81) 355399481
Web Site: https://www.ltc.ana-g.com
Emp.: 1,394
Aircraft Maintenance Services
N.A.I.C.S.: 488190

ANA Logistic Service Co., Ltd (1)
1-6-6 Hanedakuko No 1 Sogo Bldg 5 F, Ota-ku, Tokyo, 144-0041, Japan
Tel.: (81) 337479850
Web Site: http://www.als.ana-g.com
Sales Range: $150-199.9 Million
Emp.: 700
General Warehousing Storage Services
N.A.I.C.S.: 493110
Kahilo Koshikawa (Gen Mgr)

ANA Motor Service Co., Ltd. (1)
3-5-6 Haneda Airport, Ota-ku, Tokyo, 144-0041, Japan
Tel.: (81) 357567600
Web Site: https://www.anams.co.jp
Emp.: 116
Aircraft Parts Mfr & Distr
N.A.I.C.S.: 336413

ANA Sales Co., Ltd. (1)
2-14-1 Nihonbashi Kayabacho, Tokyo, 103-0027, Japan (100%)
Tel.: (81) 367353000
Web Site: http://www.anas.co.jp
Sales Range: $300-349.9 Million
Emp.: 1,700
Travel Services
N.A.I.C.S.: 561599
Masaharu Shirouzu (Pres)

ANA Sky Building Service Co., Ltd. (1)
3-5-10 Haneda Airport Utility Center Building 7F, Ota-ku, Tokyo, 144-0041, Japan
Tel.: (81) 367002805
Web Site: https://www.sbs.ana-g.com
Emp.: 1,758
Aircraft Maintenance & Repair Services
N.A.I.C.S.: 488190

ANA Telemart Co., Ltd. (1)
Gate City Osaki West Tower 17F 1-11-1 Osaki, Shinagawa-ku, Tokyo, 141-0032, Japan
Tel.: (81) 366260800
Web Site: https://www.ana-telemart.co.jp
Emp.: 1,102
Call Center Services
N.A.I.C.S.: 561422

ANA Trading Duty Free Co., Ltd. (1)
ANA Narita Sky Center 5C Narita International Airport, Narita, 282-0005, Japan
Tel.: (81) 476316510
Aviation Services
N.A.I.C.S.: 488190

ANA Wing Fellows VIE OJI Co., Ltd. (1)

Haneda Airport Terminal 1 3-3-2 Haneda Airport, Ota-ku, Tokyo, 144-8515, Japan
Tel.: (81) 357575757
Web Site: https://www.anawf.co.jp
Emp.: 297
Bread Mfr & Retailer
N.A.I.C.S.: 311812

ANA Wings (1)
3-3-2 Haneda Airport, Ota-ku, Tokyo, 144 8515, Japan (100%)
Tel.: (81) 367411120
Web Site: https://www.anawings.co.jp
Emp.: 1,992
Oil Transportation Services
N.A.I.C.S.: 481111

Air Japan Co., Ltd (1)
Narita Sky Ctr Narita International Airport, Minato-ku, Chiba, 282-0005, Japan
Tel.: (81) 367355900
Web Site: http://www.air-japan.co.jp
Sales Range: $125-149.9 Million
Emp.: 400
Oil Transportation Services
N.A.I.C.S.: 481111
Yuri Makasoto (Gen Mgr)

Air Next Co., Ltd. (1)
2-14-6 Minamisaiwai, Nishi-ku, Yokohama, 220-0005, Kanagawa, Japan
Tel.: (81) 453174501
Oil Transportation Services
N.A.I.C.S.: 488190

Air Nippon Co., Ltd. (1)
1-5-2 Higashi-Shimbashi, Minato-ku, Tokyo, 105 7133, Japan (100%)
Tel.: (81) 367355411
Web Site: http://www.air-nippon.co.jp
Sales Range: $125-149.9 Million
Emp.: 500
Domestic Air Transportation
N.A.I.C.S.: 481111

All Nippon Airways Trading Co., Ltd. (1)
Shiodome City Center 1-5-2 Higashi-shimbashi, Minato-ku, Tokyo, 105-7140, Japan
Tel.: (81) 367355011
Web Site: https://www.anatc.com
Rev.: $700,799,471
Assets: $444,962,009
Liabilities: $216,636,934
Net Worth: $228,325,074
Earnings: $16,775,685
Emp.: 1,785
Fiscal Year-end: 03/31/2023
Transportation Services
N.A.I.C.S.: 488510
Junichiro Miyagawa (Pres & CEO)

All Nippon Airways World Tours Co., Ltd. (1)
Shiodome City Ctr 1-5-2 Higashi-Shimbashi, Minato-ku, Tokyo, 105 7133, Japan
Tel.: (81) 367352000
Sales Range: $125-149.9 Million
Emp.: 260
N.A.I.C.S.: 481111

Chitose Airport Motor Service Co., Ltd. (1)
New Chitose Airport Bibi, Chitose, 066-0012, Hokkaido, Japan
Tel.: (81) 123452301
Web Site: https://www.ana.co.jp
Aircraft Maintenance Services
N.A.I.C.S.: 488190

Fujisey Co., Ltd. (1)
879 Kunitama-cho, Kofu, 400-0815, Yamanashi, Japan
Tel.: (81) 552326111
Web Site: https://www.fujisey.com
Emp.: 130
Souvenir Retailer
N.A.I.C.S.: 459420

International Airport Utility Co., Ltd (1)
3-3-2 Hanedakuko No 1 Ryokyaku Terminal Building 4f, Ota-ku, Tokyo, 144-0041, Japan
Tel.: (81) 357573300
Web Site: http://www.iau.co.jp
Airport Operation Services
N.A.I.C.S.: 488119

International Cargo Service Co., Ltd. (1)
ANA Component Maintenance Building CMB 3-5-5 Haneda Airport, Ota-ku, Tokyo, Japan
Tel.: (81) 357083301
Web Site: https://www.icslgs.co.jp
Cargo Transportation Services
N.A.I.C.S.: 541614

Musashi No Mori Country Club Co., Ltd. (1)
1028 Kamiyatsu Ogose-machi, Iruma-gun, Saitama, 350-0407, Japan
Tel.: (81) 492926311
Aviation Services
N.A.I.C.S.: 488190

Sky Building Service Co., Ltd (1)
Utility Center Building 7F 3-5-10 Haneda Airport, Ota-ku, Tokyo, 144-0041, Japan
Tel.: (81) 367002805
Web Site: http://www.sbs.ana-g.com
Sales Range: $200-249.9 Million
Emp.: 2,283
Building Maintenance Consulting Services
N.A.I.C.S.: 236220

ANAAM INTERNATIONAL HOLDING COMPANY GROUP
Anaam Building Prince Sultan Street, PO Box 6352, Jeddah, 21442, Saudi Arabia
Tel.: (966) 126623000
Web Site: https://www.anaamgroup.com
Year Founded: 1982
4061—(SAU)
Rev.: $8,083,774
Assets: $158,546,922
Liabilities: $83,501,060
Net Worth: $75,045,862
Earnings: ($8,389,680)
Emp.: 277
Fiscal Year-end: 12/31/22
Frozen Food Product Distr
N.A.I.C.S.: 424420
Mishaal Abdullah Turki Al Saud (Chm)

ANABELLE BITS PTY LTD.
8 Lord St, Botany, 2019, NSW, Australia
Tel.: (61) 293848000
Web Site: http://www.asi.com.au
Year Founded: 1995
Sales Range: $25-49.9 Million
Emp.: 100
Computer Products Distr
N.A.I.C.S.: 423430
Nathan Lowe (Mng Dir)

ANABOND LIMITED
No 36 Type II Dr VSI Estate, Thiruvanmiyur, Chennai, 600 041, Tamil Nadu, India
Tel.: (91) 44 23460041
Web Site: http://www.anabond.com
Year Founded: 1979
Developer, Mfr & Marketing of Engineering Adhesives & Sealants
N.A.I.C.S.: 325520
E. Srinivasan (Dir-Mktg)

ANABUKI KOSAN INC.
7-12 Kajiyacho, Takamatsu, 760-0028, Kagawa, Japan
Tel.: (81) 878223567
Web Site: https://www.anabuki.ne.jp
Year Founded: 1964
8928—(TKS)
Rev.: $836,583,780
Assets: $847,804,660
Liabilities: $596,093,700
Net Worth: $251,710,960
Earnings: $30,123,460
Emp.: 3,176
Fiscal Year-end: 06/30/24
Real Estate Manangement Services
N.A.I.C.S.: 531390

Tadashi Anabuki *(Pres & CEO)*

ANACACIA CAPITAL PTY LTD
Level 2 53 Cross Street, Double Bay,
Sydney, 2028, NSW, Australia
Tel.: (61) 2 8580 4600
Web Site:
http://www.anacacia.com.au
Privater Equity Firm
N.A.I.C.S.: 523999
Jeremy Samuel *(Founder & Mng Dir)*

Subsidiaries:

Big River Group Pty. Ltd. **(1)**
Trenayr Road, Junction Hill, Grafton, 2460,
NSW, Australia
Tel.: (61) 266440900
Web Site: http://www.bigrivergroup.com.au
Logging & Timber Services
N.A.I.C.S.: 113310
Jim Bindon *(CEO)*

ANACAP FINANCIAL PART-NERS LLP
1 Stephen Street, London, W1T 1AL,
United Kingdom
Tel.: (44) 2070705250 UK
Web Site: http://www.anacapfp.com
Year Founded: 2005
Emp.: 50
Privater Equity Firm
N.A.I.C.S.: 523999
Joe Giannamore *(Founder & Mng Partner)*

Subsidiaries:

Aldermore Bank PLC **(1)**
Apex Plaza Forbury Road, Reading, RG1
1AX, Lynch Wood, United Kingdom
Tel.: (44) 1182075045
Web Site: https://www.aldermore.co.uk
Sales Range: $200-249.9 Million
Emp.: 600
Banking Services
N.A.I.C.S.: 522110

Subsidiary (Domestic):

Aldermore Invoice Finance
Limited **(2)**
Saint James House, 7 Charlotte, Man-chester, M1 4DZ, United Kingdom
Tel.: (44) 16 1238 5000
Financial Investment Activities
N.A.I.C.S.: 523999
Clive Gould *(Dir-Risk)*

Brightside Group plc **(1)**
MMT Centre Severn Bridge, Aust, Bristol,
BS35 4BL, United Kingdom
Tel.: (44) 1454 635860
Web Site: http://www.brightsidegroup.co.uk
Emp.: 1,030
Financial Services
N.A.I.C.S.: 523940
James Jones *(CEO-Injury QED)*

Subsidiary (Domestic):

Injury QED Limited **(2)**
Ground Fl Helmont House Churchill Way,
Cardiff, CF10 2HE, Wales, United Kingdom
Tel.: (44) 8454819950
Web Site: http://www.injuryqed.co.uk
Sales Range: $10-24.9 Million
Emp.: 25
Medico Legal Reporting Services
N.A.I.C.S.: 621512

Cabot Financial Group Limited **(1)**
1 Kings Hill Avenue, Kings Hill, West Mall-ing, ME19 4UA, Kent, United Kingdom
Tel.: (44) 1732524600
Web Site: http://www.cabotcm.com
Sales Range: $100-124.9 Million
Consumer Debt Purchasing Services
N.A.I.C.S.: 522390
Glen Crawford *(Mng Dir)*

Subsidiary (Non-US):

Cabot Financial (Ireland) Limited **(2)**
Block D Cookstown Court Old Belgard
Road, Tallaght, Dublin, 24, Ireland
Tel.: (353) 1 6608011

Web Site: http://www.cabotfinancial.ie
Emp.: 1,500
Consumer Debt Purchasing Services
N.A.I.C.S.: 522390
Sean Webb *(CEO)*

Equa bank a.s. **(1)**
Lazarska 1718 3, 110 00, Prague, Czech
Republic
Tel.: (420) 222010510517
Web Site: http://www.equabank.cz
Sales Range: $50-74.9 Million
Emp.: 100
Banking Services
N.A.I.C.S.: 522110
Petr Rehak *(CEO)*

First Names (Isle of Man)
Limited **(1)**
International House Castle Hill Victoria
Road, Douglas, IM2 4RB, Isle of Man
Tel.: (44) 1624 630600
Web Site: http://www.firstnames.com
Sales Range: $10-24.9 Million
Emp.: 500
Financial Management Consulting Services
N.A.I.C.S.: 541611
Mark Lewin *(Dir-Client Svcs)*

Subsidiary (Non-US):

First Names (Cyprus) Limited **(2)**
Chapo Central 3rd Floor 20 Spyrou Kypri-anou Avenue, Nicosia, 1075, Cyprus
Tel.: (357) 22749000
Web Site: http://www.firstnames.com
Sales Range: $10-24.9 Million
Emp.: 44
Financial Management Services
N.A.I.C.S.: 541611
Christof Michael *(Gen Mgr)*

First Names (Jersey) Limited **(2)**
3 Rd Floor 37 Esplanade, Saint Helier, JE2
3QA, Jersey
Tel.: (44) 1534714500
Trustee & Corporate Services
N.A.I.C.S.: 541199
Mark Pesco *(CEO)*

First Names Corporate Services
Limited **(2)**
Universal House, Shannon, Ennis, Ireland
Tel.: (353) 61 364350
Web Site: http://www.ifgint.com
Financial Management Consulting Services
N.A.I.C.S.: 541611
Oonagh Hayes *(Mng Dir)*

Subsidiary (Domestic):

Moore Fund Administration (IOM)
Limited **(2)**
International House Castle Hill Victoria
Road, Douglas, IM2 4RB, Isle of Man
Tel.: (44) 1624 661020
Business Fund Administration Services
N.A.I.C.S.: 524292
Jonathan Trigg *(Mng Dir)*

Subsidiary (Non-US):

Moore Fund Administration (Jersey)
Limited **(2)**
IFG House 15 Union Street, Saint Helier,
JE1 1FG, Jersey
Tel.: (44) 1534 786260
Fund Administration Services
N.A.I.C.S.: 524292

Mediterranean Bank plc **(1)**
10 St Barbara Bastion, Valletta, VLT 1961,
Malta
Tel.: (356) 25574400
Web Site: http://www.medbank.com.mt
Sales Range: $50-74.9 Million
Emp.: 63
Banking Services
N.A.I.C.S.: 522110

Subsidiary (Domestic):

Mediterranean Corporate Bank
Limited **(2)**
121 The Promenade Tower Road, SLM
1605, Sliema, Malta
Tel.: (356) 2557 4400
Web Site: http://www.medirect.com.mt
Commercial Banking Services
N.A.I.C.S.: 522110

Mark Watson *(Exec Dir & CEO)*

ANACLE SYSTEMS LIMITED
3 Fusionopolis Way 14-21 Symbiosis,
Singapore, 138633, Singapore
Tel.: (65) 69142666 SG
Web Site: https://www.anacle.com
Year Founded: 2006
8353—(HKG)
Rev.: $19,785,302
Assets: $19,066,091
Liabilities: $5,799,647
Net Worth: $13,266,445
Earnings: $437,931
Emp.: 180
Fiscal Year-end: 05/31/24
Application Software Development
Services
N.A.I.C.S.: 541511
Sylvia Sundari Poerwaka *(CFO)*

Subsidiaries:

Anacle Systems Sdn Bhd **(1)**
3-12-6 Tower 3 UOA Business Park Jalan
Pengaturcara U1/51A Seksyen U1, 40150,
Shah Alam, Selangor, Malaysia
Tel.: (60) 355699012
Emp.: 6
Application Software Development Services
N.A.I.C.S.: 541511
Noor Sharazain Ahmad Noordin *(CEO)*

ANADOLU ANONIM TURK SIG-ORTA SIRKETI
Anadolu Sigorta Ruzgarl bahce Mah
Cam Pinari Sok No 6, 34805, Istan-bul, Turkiye
Tel.: (90) 08507240850 TR
Web Site:
https://www.anadolusigorta.com.tr
Year Founded: 1925
ANSGR—(IST)
Rev.: $1,202,867,936
Assets: $1,909,425,502
Liabilities: $1,495,678,035
Net Worth: $413,747,467
Earnings: $216,071,511
Fiscal Year-end: 12/31/23
Insurance Services
N.A.I.C.S.: 524298
Erdinc Gokalp *(Deputy CEO-Inward Reinsurance & Risk Engrg Dept)*

ANADOLU EFES BIRACILIK VE MALT SANAYII A.S.
Fatih Sultan Mehmet Mah Balkan
Cad No 58 Buyaka E Blok, Tepeustu
Umraniye, Tepeustu Umraniye,
34771, Istanbul, Turkiye
Tel.: (90) 2165868000
Web Site:
https://www.anadoluefes.com
Year Founded: 1969
AEBZY—(OTCIQ)
Rev.: $5,414,427,106
Assets: $8,982,175,518
Liabilities: $4,583,709,946
Net Worth: $4,398,465,573
Earnings: $1,403,846,514
Emp.: 20,653
Fiscal Year-end: 12/31/23
Beer & Soft Drink Bottler & Distr
N.A.I.C.S.: 312120
Tuncay Ozilhan *(Chm)*

Subsidiaries:

Anadolu Etap Penkon Gida ve Tarim
Urunleri San ve Tic. A.S. **(1)**
Fatih Sultan Mehmet Mah Balkan St No 58
Buyaka E Block Floor 4, Tepeustu Um-raniye, 34771, Istanbul, Turkiye
Tel.: (90) 2165788700
Web Site: http://www.anadoluetap.com
Fruit Juice Mfr & Distr
N.A.I.C.S.: 311411
Bahadir Acik *(Gen Mgr)*

Blue Hub Ventures B.V. **(1)**

Brightlands Campus Greenport Venlo Cam-pusgebouw Villa Flora, Villafloraweg 1,
5928 SZ, Venlo, Netherlands
Tel.: (31) 777820156
Web Site: https://bluehub.nl
Financial Investment Services
N.A.I.C.S.: 523999

Coca-Cola Beverages Pakistan
Ltd. **(1)**
26-Q College Road Gulberg 2, Lahore,
Pakistan
Tel.: (92) 42359843757
Web Site: http://www.coca-cola.pk
Bottle Mfr & Whslr
N.A.I.C.S.: 326160
Fahad Ashraf *(Gen Mgr)*

Efes Breweries International N.V. **(1)**
Strawinskylaan 1227, 1077 XX, Amsterdam,
Netherlands **(70.2%)**
Tel.: (31) 205752290
Web Site: http://www.efesinternational.com
Sales Range: $800-899.9 Million
Emp.: 4,704
Breweries
N.A.I.C.S.: 312120
Alejandro Jimenez *(CEO)*

Efes Deutschland GmbH **(1)**
Jan-Wellem-Strasse 1, 51065, Cologne,
Germany
Tel.: (49) 22197771747
Web Site: https://www.efes-deutschland.de
Bottle Mfr & Whslr
N.A.I.C.S.: 326160

Efes Pazarlama ve Dagitim Ticaret
A.S. **(1)**
Fatih Sultan Mehmet Mah Balkan Cad No
58/23 Buyaka E Blok Umraniye, 34771, Is-tanbul, Turkiye
Tel.: (90) 2165868000
Web Site: https://www.efespazarlama.com.tr
Alcoholic Beverages Mfr & Distr
N.A.I.C.S.: 424820

Efes Vitanta Moldova Brewery
S.A. **(1)**
167 Uzinelor Street, Chisinau, 2023, Mol-dova
Tel.: (373) 22885299
Web Site: https://efesmoldova.md
Beer & Soft Drinks Mfr
N.A.I.C.S.: 312120
Kamil Yazici *(Gen Mgr)*

JSC FE Efes Kazakhstan
Brewery **(1)**
Gogol str 75, 100014, Karaganda, 100014,
Kazakhstan
Tel.: (7) 7212516161
Web Site: https://www.efeskazakhstan.kz
Emp.: 750
Beer Mfr
N.A.I.C.S.: 311213
Omer Ogun *(Mng Dir)*

JSC Lomisi **(1)**
87a Tsereteli ave, 0119, Tbilisi, Georgia
Tel.: (995) 322357223
Web Site: https://www.lomisi.all.biz
Soft Drinks Mfr
N.A.I.C.S.: 312111

PJSC Efes Ukraine **(1)**
106 Illicha Ave, 83059, Donetsk, 83059,
Ukraine
Tel.: (380) 622028100
Web Site: https://www.efes-ukraine.com
Bottle Mfr & Whslr
N.A.I.C.S.: 326160

ZAO Moscow-Efes Brewery **(1)**
Ulitsa Podolskikh Kursantov 15B, Moscow,
117546, Russia
Tel.: (7) 4957979800
Beer Mfr
N.A.I.C.S.: 312120

Subsidiary (Domestic):

OOO Vostok Solod **(2)**
5 Ul Tikhoretskaya, Kazan, 420054, Russia
Tel.: (7) 8432789028
Beer Mfr
N.A.I.C.S.: 312120

ANADOLU GIRISIM SER-

MAYESI YATIRIM ORTAKLIGI A.S.

Asagi Ovecler Mah 1042 Cadde 1330 Sok 3/3 Cankaya, Ankara, Turkiye
Tel.: (90) 312 465 03 82
Web Site:
http://www.anadolugirisim.com
Venture Capital Investment Services
N.A.I.C.S.: 523999
Ozdemir Ucar *(Chm)*

ANAGENICS LIMITED

Suite 204 Level 2 55 Clarence Street, Sydney, 2000, NSW, Australia
Tel.: (61) 292216830
Web Site: https://anagenics.com
AN1—(ASX)
Rev.: $7,213,654
Assets: $4,134,681
Liabilities: $2,325,216
Net Worth: $1,809,464
Earnings: ($4,863,926)
Fiscal Year-end: 06/30/24
Research & Development in Biotechnology (except Nanobiotechnology)
N.A.I.C.S.: 541714
Maria Halasz *(CEO & Mng Dir)*

ANALABS RESOURCES BERHAD

Unit 621 6th Floor Block A Kelana Centre Point No 3 Jalan SS7/19, Kelana Jaya, 47301, Petaling Jaya, Selangor Darul Ehsan, Malaysia
Tel.: (60) 378809699
Web Site:
https://www.analabs.com.my
Year Founded: 1965
ANALABS—(KLS)
Rev.: $32,267,725
Assets: $139,591,745
Liabilities: $45,639,576
Net Worth: $93,952,169
Earnings: $6,410,794
Fiscal Year-end: 04/30/24
Paints & Lubricant Products Mfr
N.A.I.C.S.: 325510
Cynthia Gloria Louis *(Co-Sec)*

Subsidiaries:

Centralised Waste Treatment Plant Sdn. Bhd.   **(1)**
Unit 621 6th Floor Block A Kelana Centre Point No 3 Jalan SS7/19, Kelana Jaya, 47301, Petaling Jaya, 47301, Selangor Darul Ehsan, Malaysia   **(100%)**
Tel.: (60) 3 7880 9699
Web Site: http://www.analabs.com.my
Hazardous Waste Disposal Services
N.A.I.C.S.: 562211

Cleanway Disposal Services Pte. Ltd.   **(1)**
40 Penjuru Road, Singapore, 609145, Singapore
Tel.: (65) 62644411
Sales Range: $10-24.9 Million
Emp.: 40
Waste Collection & Disposal Services
N.A.I.C.S.: 562211

Inagro Sdn. Bhd.   **(1)**
Lot 6493 Batu 5 3/4 Jalan Kapar, 42100, Kelang, Selangor Darul Ehsan, Malaysia
Tel.: (60) 332918028
Sales Range: $25-49.9 Million
Emp.: 14
Agricultural Chemical Mfr
N.A.I.C.S.: 325320

ANALIZY ONLINE S.A

ul Skierniewicka 10A, 01-230, Warsaw, Poland
Tel.: (48) 224318297
Web Site:
https://www.analizyonline.com
Year Founded: 2000
Financial Consulting Services

N.A.I.C.S.: 541611
Michal Duniec *(Pres)*

ANALOG INTEGRATIONS CORP.

No 945 Boai St, Jubei City, Hsinchu, 302045, Taiwan
Tel.: (886) 35535565
Web Site: https://www.analog.com.tw
Year Founded: 1992
6291—(TPE)
Rev.: $44,299,347
Assets: $45,748,992
Liabilities: $12,574,243
Net Worth: $33,174,749
Earnings: $5,648,376
Fiscal Year-end: 12/31/22
Semiconductor Devices Mfr
N.A.I.C.S.: 334413
Ming-Ju Li *(Pres)*

ANALOGUE HOLDINGS LIMITED

13F Island Place Tower 510 Kings Road North Point, Hong Kong, China (Hong Kong)
Tel.: (852) 25618278   **BM**
Web Site: https://www.atal.com
Year Founded: 1977
1977—(HKG)
Rev.: $690,135,866
Assets: $573,852,399
Liabilities: $299,163,822
Net Worth: $274,688,577
Earnings: $40,538,285
Emp.: 2,559
Fiscal Year-end: 12/31/21
Investment Holding Company
N.A.I.C.S.: 523999
Lok To Otto Poon *(Chm)*

Subsidiaries:

Anlev (Uk) Holdings Limited   **(1)**
Milton Gate 60 Chiswell Street, London, EC1Y 4AG, United Kingdom
Tel.: (44) 1182066510
Web Site: https://www.anlev.com
Holding Company
N.A.I.C.S.: 551112

Subsidiary (Domestic):

Precision Lift Services Limited   **(2)**
Unit 1 Yardley Business Park Luckyn Lane, Basildon, SS14 3GL, Essex, United Kingdom
Tel.: (44) 1708250800
Elevator Maintenance & Repair Services
N.A.I.C.S.: 238290
Dean White *(Mng Dir)*

Transel Elevator & Electric Inc.   **(1)**
30-30 47th Ave Ste 610, Long Island City, NY 11101   **(51%)**
Tel.: (718) 609-2600
Web Site: https://www.teigroup.com
Emp.: 300
Construction Repair & Maintenance Services
N.A.I.C.S.: 811490
Mark Gregorio *(Pres & Mng Partner)*

ANALYST IMS INVESTMENT MANAGEMENT SERVICES LTD.

Alrov Tower 46 Rothschild Boulevard, Tel Aviv, 6688312, Israel
Tel.: (972) 37147147
Web Site: http://www.analyst.co.il
Year Founded: 1985
ANLT—(TAE)
Rev.: $54,702,582
Assets: $79,438,043
Liabilities: $28,243,956
Net Worth: $51,194,087
Earnings: $7,520,652
Emp.: 130
Fiscal Year-end: 12/31/23
Miscellaneous Financial Investment Activities

N.A.I.C.S.: 523999

ANALYTICA BIO-ENERGY CORP.

1896 Stoneybrook Court, Mississauga, L5L 3W2, ON, Canada
Tel.: (905) 824-6200   **DE**
Web Site:
http://www.analyticabioenergy.com
Year Founded: 2005
Sales Range: Less than $1 Million
Sewage Treatment Equipment Mfr
N.A.I.C.S.: 333310

ANALYTICA LIMITED

222 Bazaar Street, Maryborough, 4655, QLD, Australia
Tel.: (61) 732781950
Web Site:
http://www.analyticamedical.com
ALT—(ASX)
Rev.: $206,186
Assets: $601,006
Liabilities: $713,413
Net Worth: ($112,407)
Earnings: ($1,715,157)
Emp.: 2
Fiscal Year-end: 06/30/22
Medical Devices & Pharmaceutical Implants Development Services
N.A.I.C.S.: 334510
Ross Mangelsdorf *(CFO)*

ANALYTICAL TECHNOLOGY & CONTROL LIMITED

Broadway Market Lavington, Devizes, SN10 5RQ, Wiltshire, United Kingdom
Tel.: (44) 1380818411   **UK**
Web Site: http://atacgroup.com
Year Founded: 1993
Emp.: 100
Oil & Gas Equipment Mfr
N.A.I.C.S.: 333132
Stuart Smith *(Dir-Ops)*

ANALYTIXINSIGHT INC.

RPO Steeles West, North York, M5C 2B5, ON, Canada
Tel.: (647) 955-2933   **MB**
Web Site:
https://www.analytixinsight.com
Year Founded: 1999
ATIXF—(OTCIQ)
Rev.: $1,247,450
Assets: $5,508,169
Liabilities: $516,768
Net Worth: $4,991,401
Earnings: $3,110,570)
Fiscal Year-end: 12/31/22
Data Analytics Technology Services
N.A.I.C.S.: 541512
Prakash Hariharan *(Chm & CEO)*

ANAM ELECTRONICS CO., LTD.

Anam Building 27 Digital-ro 27ga-gil, Guro-gu, Seoul, 152-848, Korea (South)
Tel.: (82) 264244700
Web Site: https://www.aname.co.kr
Year Founded: 1973
008700—(KRS)
Rev.: $371,831,316
Assets: $213,647,673
Liabilities: $136,362,680
Net Worth: $77,284,993
Earnings: $10,753,237
Emp.: 139
Fiscal Year-end: 12/31/22
Consumer Electronics Product Mfr
N.A.I.C.S.: 334310
Taesu Kim *(CEO)*

Subsidiaries:

Anam Electronics Co., Ltd - Consumer A/V Division   **(1)**
645 Seonggok-dong Danwon-gu, Ansan, Gyeonggi-do, Korea (South)
Tel.: (82) 3149023519
Web Site: http://www.anam.co.kr
Audio Equipment Mfr
N.A.I.C.S.: 334310

ANAN INTERNATIONAL LIMITED

10 Anson Road 17-12 International Plaza, Singapore, 079903, Singapore
Tel.: (65) 62231471   **BM**
Web Site: http://www.cefci.com.sg
Y35—(SES)
Rev.: $2,565,928,000
Assets: $567,635,000
Liabilities: $413,950,000
Net Worth: $153,685,000
Earnings: $12,836,000
Emp.: 832
Fiscal Year-end: 12/31/23
Petroleum Product Distr
N.A.I.C.S.: 424720
Guang Ming Zhao *(CEO)*

Subsidiaries:

Dyneff SAS.   **(1)**
Millennium Park 1300 Albert Einstein Avenue, 34000, Montpellier, Cedex, France
Tel.: (33) 467123570
Web Site: https://www.dyneff.fr
Petroleum Product Distr
N.A.I.C.S.: 424720

Subsidiary (Non-US):

Dyneff Espagne SL   **(2)**
Avinguda Lluis Pericot 110, 17003, Girona, Spain
Tel.: (34) 972249283
Web Site: http://www.dyneff.es
Petroleum Product Distr
N.A.I.C.S.: 424720

ANAND PROJECTS LIMITED

SF 001 & 035 Second Floor Ansal Fortune Arcade Sector-18, Noida, 201301, UP, India
Tel.: (91) 1202511389
Web Site:
https://www.anandprojects.com
Year Founded: 1936
501630—(BOM)
Rev.: $718,652
Assets: $94,332,896
Liabilities: $89,526,893
Net Worth: $4,806,003
Earnings: ($8,218,288)
Emp.: 4
Fiscal Year-end: 03/31/22
Construction Engineering Services
N.A.I.C.S.: 541330
Alok Kumar Gupta *(CFO)*

ANAND RATHI WEALTH LIMITED

Floor No 2nd & 3rd Block B & C E Wing Trade Link Kamala Mills Compound, Senapati Bapat Marg Lower Parel, Mumbai, 400013, India
Tel.: (91) 2269815400
Web Site:
https://www.anandrathiwealth.in
Year Founded: 1994
543415—(BOM)
Financial Services
N.A.I.C.S.: 523150
Pradeep Gupta *(Co-Founder & VP)*

ANAND RAYONS LTD.

305-306 Jay Sagar Complex Behind Sub Jail Khatodara Ring Road, Surat, 395002, Gujarat, India
Tel.: (91) 2612635521

Web Site:
https://www.anandrayons.com
542721—(BOM)
Rev.: $45,608,260
Assets: $10,774,820
Liabilities: $6,683,721
Net Worth: $4,091,099
Earnings: $401,217
Emp.: 35
Fiscal Year-end: 03/31/22
Textile Products Mfr
N.A.I.C.S.: 314999
Anand Bakshi *(Chm & Mng Dir)*

ANANDA DEVELOPMENT PUBLIC COMPANY LIMITED
FYI Center 11th Floor 2525 Rama 4 Road, Klong Toei Klong Toei District, Bangkok, 10110, Thailand
Tel.: (66) 20562222
Web Site: https://www.ananda.co.th
Year Founded: 1999
ANAN—(THA)
Rev.: $111,486,557
Assets: $1,081,058,689
Liabilities: $735,511,367
Net Worth: $345,547,322
Earnings: ($25,870,636)
Emp.: 536
Fiscal Year-end: 12/31/23
Residential Housing Developer & Construction
N.A.I.C.S.: 236116
Santhad Natthakul *(Mng Dir-Housing Bus Unit)*

Subsidiaries:

Blue Deck Co., Ltd.   **(1)**
189 Moo 12 Rachedeva Sub-district, Bang Phli, 10540, Samut Prakan, Thailand
Tel.: (66) 27620330
Sport Club & Restaurant Operator
N.A.I.C.S.: 713940

Helix Co., Ltd.   **(1)**
193/47 12nd Floor Lake Rajada Office Complex, New Rajadapisek Road Khlong Toei, Bangkok, 10110, Thailand
Tel.: (66) 2697 3380 4
Building Construction Services
N.A.I.C.S.: 236220

The Agent (Property Expert) Co., Ltd.   **(1)**
Unit 1/1007-1008 2525 Fyi Center Building 1 10th Floor Rama 4 Road, Klongtoei, Bangkok, 10110, Thailand
Tel.: (66) 20562333
Web Site: https://www.theagent.co.th
Real Estate Brokerage & Consultancy Services
N.A.I.C.S.: 531210

The Works Community Management Co., Ltd.   **(1)**
2525 FYI Center Building 11th Floor Rama IV Rd, Khlong Toei, Bangkok, 10110, Thailand
Tel.: (66) 20562399
Web Site: https://www.theworks.co.th
Property Management Services
N.A.I.C.S.: 531311

ANANGEL-AMERICAN SHIPHOLDINGS LIMITED
354 Sygrou Ave, Kallithea, 17674, Greece
Tel.: (30) 2109467200   GR
Web Site:
http://www.anangelmar.com
Year Founded: 1987
Sales Range: $75-99.9 Million
Emp.: 300
Shipping Services
N.A.I.C.S.: 483111
Dimitri A. Stylianou *(CFO & Treas)*

ANANT RAJ LIMITED
H-65 Connaught Circus, New Delhi, 11001, India

Tel.: (91) 114034400
Web Site: https://www.anantraj.com
Year Founded: 1969
ANANTRAJ—(NSE)
Rev.: $68,419,547
Assets: $598,552,828
Liabilities: $233,493,842
Net Worth: $365,058,985
Earnings: $7,492,116
Emp.: 204
Fiscal Year-end: 03/31/22
Property Management Services
N.A.I.C.S.: 531311
Ashok Sarin *(Chm)*

ANANTI INC.
11 Nonhyeon-ro 136-gil, Gangnam-gu, Seoul, Korea (South)
Tel.: (82) 221904000
Web Site: https://www.ananti.kr
025980—(KRS)
Rev.: $249,540,718
Assets: $1,330,581,502
Liabilities: $938,924,757
Net Worth: $391,656,744
Earnings: $23,804,725
Emp.: 539
Fiscal Year-end: 12/31/22
Golf Club Management Services
N.A.I.C.S.: 713910
Lee Man Keu *(CEO)*

ANAP INC.
1-16-11 Jingumae, Shibuya-ku, Tokyo, 150-0001, Japan
Tel.: (81) 357722717
Web Site: https://www.anap.co.jp
Year Founded: 1992
3189—(TKS)
Rev.: $30,228,720
Assets: $11,902,200
Liabilities: $18,305,010
Net Worth: ($6,402,810)
Earnings: ($8,345,880)
Fiscal Year-end: 08/31/23
Women's & Girls' Clothing Retailer
N.A.I.C.S.: 458110
Toshiyasu Yataka *(Pres & CEO)*

ANAPASS, INC.
7th floor Dreammark One Data Center 61 Digitalro 31gil, Guro-gu, Seoul, 08375, Korea (South)
Tel.: (82) 269227400
Web Site: https://www.anapass.com
123860—(KRS)
Rev.: $34,200,619
Assets: $81,528,224
Liabilities: $51,640,686
Net Worth: $29,887,538
Earnings: ($10,362,810)
Emp.: 115
Fiscal Year-end: 12/31/22
Integrated Circuits Mfr
N.A.I.C.S.: 334413

ANARAFE SL
Calle Doctor Juan Dominguez Perez, 2 Las Palmas de Gran Canaria, Las Palmas, 35008, Spain
Tel.: (34) 92 832 73 83
Sales Range: Less than $1 Million
Marine Transportation Services
N.A.I.C.S.: 483212

Subsidiaries:

Compania Trasmediterranea, S.A.   **(1)**
Paseo de la Castellana 259D 19th Floor Torrespacio Building, 28046, Madrid, Spain
Tel.: (34) 91 736 99 57
Web Site: http://www.trasmediterranea.es
Maritime Passenger & Cargo Transportation Services
N.A.I.C.S.: 483114
Jorge Vega Penichet *(Pres)*

ANATARA LIFESCIENCES LTD
C-Perks Level 8 81 Flinders Street, Carlton South, Adelaide, 5000, SA, Australia
Tel.: (61) 733948202
Web Site:
https://www.anataralifesciences.com
ANR—(ASX)
Rev.: $430,039
Assets: $1,116,067
Liabilities: $204,894
Net Worth: $911,173
Earnings: ($969,045)
Fiscal Year-end: 06/30/24
Pharmaceuticals Mfr
N.A.I.C.S.: 325412
Stephen Denaro *(Sec)*

ANAX METALS LIMITED
Ground Floor West 20 Kings Park Road, West Perth, 6005, WA, Australia
Tel.: (61) 861431840   AU
Web Site: https://anaxmetals.com.au
Year Founded: 2003
ANX—(ASX)
Rev.: $161,311
Assets: $28,893,875
Liabilities: $14,010,017
Net Worth: $14,883,858
Earnings: ($1,861,583)
Emp.: 7
Fiscal Year-end: 06/30/24
Mineral Exploration Services
N.A.I.C.S.: 212290
Geoffrey Michael Huyshe Laing *(CEO & Mng Dir)*

ANBANG INSURANCE GROUP CO., LTD.
Anbang Tower No 6 Jianguomenwai Avenue, Chaoyang District, Beijing, 100022, China
Tel.: (86) 4001111111
Web Site:
http://www.anbanggroup.com
Emp.: 30,000
Insurance Services
N.A.I.C.S.: 524126

Subsidiaries:

Anbang Life Insurance Inc.   **(1)**
No 6 Anbang Building Jian Guo Meng Wai Street, Chaoyang District, Beijing, 100022, China
Tel.: (86) 1085257777
Web Site: http://www.anbanggroup.com
Fire Insurance Services
N.A.I.C.S.: 524113
Bin Ren *(Head-Pricing)*

Bank Nagelmackers NV   **(1)**
Sterrenkundelaan 23, 1210, Brussels, Belgium
Tel.: (32) 22297600
Web Site: http://www.nagelmackers.be
Sales Range: $100-124.9 Million
Emp.: 499
Commercial Banking & Lending Services
N.A.I.C.S.: 522110
Filip de Campenaere *(CFO)*

Chengdu Rural Commercial Bank Co., Ltd.   **(1)**
5 Kehua Middle Road, Wuhou, Chengdu, 610041, Sichuan, China
Tel.: (86) 4006028666
Commercial Banking Services
N.A.I.C.S.: 522110

TONGYANG Life Insurance Co., Ltd.   **(1)**
17/F Gran Seoul Bldg 33 Jong-ro, Jongno-gu, Seoul, 110-130, Korea (South)
Tel.: (82) 215771004
Web Site: http://www.myangel.co.kr
Insurance Services
N.A.I.C.S.: 524298
Luo Jian-rong *(CEO)*

ANBC, INC.

No 2 1200 Lane Xie-Chun Road Industrial, Shanghai, 201804, China
Tel.: (86) 2169584686   NV
Year Founded: 2006
SYUP—(OTCIQ)
Sales Range: $1-9.9 Million
Pharmaceuticals Product Mfr
N.A.I.C.S.: 325412

ANC CAPITAL VENTURES, INC.
6012 - 85 Avenue NW, Edmonton, T6B 0J5, AB, Canada
Tel.: (780) 466-6006
ANCV.P—(TSXV)
Assets: $230,888
Liabilities: $40,115
Net Worth: $190,772
Earnings: ($56,465)
Fiscal Year-end: 03/31/21
Business Consulting Services
N.A.I.C.S.: 522299
John Randolph Clifford *(CEO & CFO)*

ANCA PTY LTD
25 Gatwick Rd, Melbourne, 3153, VIC, Australia
Tel.: (61) 397518200
Web Site: http://www.anca.com
Year Founded: 1974
Sales Range: $50-74.9 Million
Emp.: 1,000
Tool Cutting & Grinding Equipment Mfr
N.A.I.C.S.: 333515
Patrick Gerard Boland *(Co-Founder & Mng Dir)*

Subsidiaries:

ANCA (Thailand) Ltd   **(1)**
Eastern Seaboard Industrial Estate No 109/20 Moo 4, Amphur Pluakdaeng, Rayong, 21140, Thailand
Tel.: (66) 3895 9252
Industrial Supplies Whslr
N.A.I.C.S.: 423840

ANCA (UK) Ltd   **(1)**
2 Eastwood Business Village, Harry Weston Road, Coventry, CV3 2UB, United Kingdom   **(100%)**
Tel.: (44) 2476447000
Web Site: http://www.anca.com
Sales Range: Less than $1 Million
Emp.: 9
Tool Cutting & Grinding Equipment Mfr
N.A.I.C.S.: 333515
Patrick John McCluskey *(Co-Founder & Mng Dir)*

ANCA (USA) Inc   **(1)**
31129 Century Dr, Wixom, MI 48393   **(100%)**
Tel.: (248) 926-4466
Web Site: http://www.anca.com
Sales Range: $10-24.9 Million
Emp.: 40
Tool Cutting & Grinding Equipment Mfr
N.A.I.C.S.: 333515
Russell Riddiford *(Gen Mgr)*

ANCA GmbH   **(1)**
Alois-Senefelder-Str 4, 68167, Mannheim, Germany   **(100%)**
Tel.: (49) 621338100
Web Site: http://www.ger.anca.com
Sales Range: $25-49.9 Million
Emp.: 25
Tool Cutting & Grinding Equipment Mfr
N.A.I.C.S.: 333515

ANCA Japan   **(1)**
3-60-1 Sakuragaoka-cho, Owariasahi, Aichi-ken, Japan
Tel.: (81) 561 53 8543
Industrial Supplies Whslr
N.A.I.C.S.: 423840

ANCA Machine Tool (Shanghai) Co. Ltd   **(1)**
West Wing 1/F Building 4 475 Fu Te No 1 Road Waigaoqiao FTZ, Shanghai, 200131, China

ANCA Pty Ltd—(Continued)

Tel.: (86) 21 5868 2940
Industrial Supplies Whslr
N.A.I.C.S.: 423840

ANCA Machine Tools Private Ltd (1)
64 Parimala Towers MES Road, Yesh-wantpur, Bengaluru, 560 022, India
Tel.: (91) 80 42198107
Industrial Supplies Whslr
N.A.I.C.S.: 423840

ANCA Motion Pty. Ltd. (1)
1 Bessemer Road, Bayswater, 3153, VIC, Australia
Tel.: (61) 3 9751 8900
Web Site: http://www.ancamotion.com
Electric Motor & Control System Mfr
N.A.I.C.S.: 333618
Paul Bocchi (Gen Mgr)

Subsidiary (Non-US):

ANCA Motion Taiwan Co., Ltd (2)
1F No 57 37 Rd Taichung Industrial Park, Taichung, 407, Taiwan
Tel.: (886) 4 2359 0082
Industrial Control Instrument Distr
N.A.I.C.S.: 423610

ANCA do Brasil (1)
Rua Francisco Ferreira Leao 377, Soro-caba, 18040-330, Sao Paulo, Brazil (100%)
Tel.: (55) 1532215512
Sales Range: $25-49.9 Million
Emp.: 4
Tool Cutting & Grinding Equipment Mfr
N.A.I.C.S.: 333517

ANCALA PARTNERS LLP
40 Gracechurch Street, London, EC3V 0BT, United Kingdom
Tel.: (44) 20 3440 3515
Web Site: http://www.ancala.com
Investment Holding Company
N.A.I.C.S.: 551112
Spence Clunie (Mng Partner)

Subsidiaries:

Augean PLC (1)
4 Rudgate Court Walton, Wetherby, LS23 7BF, Yorkshire, United Kingdom
Tel.: (44) 1937 844980
Web Site: http://www.augeanplc.com
Holding Company; Hazardous Waste Management Services
N.A.I.C.S.: 551112
Gene Wilson (Dir-Environmental Planning)

Subsidiary (Domestic):

Augean North Limited (2)
4 Rudgate Court, Walton, Wetherby, LS23 7BF, United Kingdom
Tel.: (44) 1937 846 681
Web Site: http://www.augeanplc.com
Hazardous Waste Landfill Operator
N.A.I.C.S.: 562212

Subsidiary (Domestic):

Augean North Sea Services Limited (2)
Yard B Blackdog Industrial Estate, Bridge Of Don, Aberdeen, AB23 8BT, United Kingdom
Tel.: (44) 122 471 9200
Web Site: http://www.augeanplc.com
Emp.: 100
Offshore Oil & Gas Waste Management Services
N.A.I.C.S.: 562112
Simon Gibb (Mng Dir)

Subsidiary (Domestic):

Augean South Limited (2)
4 Rudgate Court, Walton, Wetherby, LS23 7BF, W Yorkshire, United Kingdom
Tel.: (44) 1937 846 681
Web Site: http://www.augeanplc.com
Sales Range: $25-49.9 Million
Emp.: 200
Hazardous Waste Landfill Operator
N.A.I.C.S.: 562212

Augean Treatment Limited (2)

4 Rudgate Court, Walton, Wetherby, LS23 7BF, W Yorkshire, United Kingdom
Tel.: (44) 1937 844 980
Web Site: http://www.augeanplc.com
Sales Range: $25-49.9 Million
Hazardous Waste Treatment Services
N.A.I.C.S.: 562211

Future Industrial Services Ltd (2)
Image Business Park Acornfield Rd Knows-ley Ind Park, Liverpool, L33 7UF, United Kingdom
Tel.: (44) 1512033222
Web Site: http://www.futureindustrial.com
Waste Management Services
N.A.I.C.S.: 562219
David Lusher (CEO)

ANCHENG PROPERTY & CASUALTY INSURANCE CO., LTD.
1405-1406 Investment Mansion 128, Zhongshan 3 Road Yuzhong District, Chongqing, 400015, China
Tel.: (86) 2363855290
Web Site: http://www.e-acic.com
Property & Casualty Insurance Services
N.A.I.C.S.: 524126
Ke Xu (Gen Mgr)

ANCHOR CONSTRUCTION INDUSTRIAL PRODUCTS LTD
1810 Dublin Avenue, Winnipeg, R3H 0H3, MB, Canada
Tel.: (204) 633-0064
Web Site:
    https://www.anchorproducts.ca
Year Founded: 1967
Rev.: $13,857,093
Emp.: 65
Construction & Industrial Products Supplier
N.A.I.C.S.: 423840
Fil Fileccia (Pres)

ANCHOR GROUP LIMITED
25 Culross Road Bryanston, Sandton, 2191, South Africa
Tel.: (27) 115910677 ZA
Web Site:
    http://www.anchorgroup.co.za
ACG—(JSE)
Rev.: $34,192,236
Assets: $54,944,732
Liabilities: $9,611,628
Net Worth: $45,333,104
Earnings: ($16,808,188)
Emp.: 220
Fiscal Year-end: 12/31/20
Financial Services
N.A.I.C.S.: 523999
Peter Armitage (CEO)

Subsidiaries:

Anchor Capital Proprietary Limited (1)
25 Culross Road, Bryanston, Sandton, 2191, South Africa
Tel.: (27) 11 591 0677
Web Site: http://www.anchorcapital.co.za
Asset Management Services
N.A.I.C.S.: 523210
David Gibb (Mgr-Fund)

Anchor Securities Private Clients Proprietary Limited (1)
1st Floor 53 Richefond Circle, Ridgeside Office Park, Umhlanga, 4319, South Africa
Tel.: (27) 31 819 6400
Web Site: http://www.anchorspc.co.za
Financial Services
N.A.I.C.S.: 523210
Paul Patterson (Portfolio Mgr)

Portfolio Bureau Proprietary Limited (1)
Suite 1502 Portside 4 Bree Street, Cape Town, 8001, South Africa
Tel.: (27) 21 419 2277
Web Site: https://www.portfoliobureau.com

Financial Services
N.A.I.C.S.: 523210

Robert Cowen Investment Proprietary Limited (1)
25 Culross Road, Bryanston, Sandton, 2191, South Africa
Tel.: (27) 11 591 0585
Web Site: https://www.rcinv.co.za
Investment Services
N.A.I.C.S.: 523210
Andrew Lawson (Portfolio Mgr)

ANCHOR LAND HOLDINGS, INC.
16th Floor L V Locsin Building 6752 Ayala Avenue corner Makati Avenue, Makati, Philippines
Tel.: (63) 289887988
Web Site:
    https://www.anchorland.com.ph
Year Founded: 2004
ALHI—(PHI)
Rev.: $95,269,133
Assets: $712,800,851
Liabilities: $536,828,449
Net Worth: $175,972,402
Earnings: $11,210,338
Fiscal Year-end: 12/31/23
Residential & Commercial Real Estate Construction & Development Services
N.A.I.C.S.: 236117
Elizabeth Ventura (Pres)

Subsidiaries:

Posh Properties Development Corporation (1)
11th Floor Lv Locsin Building 6752 Ayala Avenue Corner Makati Ave, Makati, 1200, Philippines
Tel.: (63) 28517991
Property Management Services
N.A.I.C.S.: 531312

ANCHOR LAS AB
Kopmangatan 1, 633 56, Eskilstuna, Sweden
Tel.: (46) 16125280
Web Site: https://anchorlas.se
Year Founded: 1980
Padlock & Hasp Mfr
N.A.I.C.S.: 332510

ANCHOR RESOURCES LIMITED
Suite 506 Level 5 50 Clarence Street, Sydney, 2000, NSW, Australia
Tel.: (61) 290787668
Web Site:
    http://www.anchorresources.com.au
AHR—(ASX)
Rev.: $25,053
Assets: $8,978,774
Liabilities: $13,027,330
Net Worth: ($4,048,556)
Earnings: ($1,387,392)
Emp.: 3
Fiscal Year-end: 06/30/18
Mineral Exploration Services
N.A.I.C.S.: 213115
Jianguang Wang (Vice Chm)

ANCHORAGE CAPITAL PARTNERS PTY. LIMITED
Level 39 259 George Street, Sydney, 2000, NSW, Australia
Tel.: (61) 282597777 AU
Web Site:
    http://www.anchoragecapital.com.au
Sales Range: $25-49.9 Million
Emp.: 10
Privater Equity Firm
N.A.I.C.S.: 523999
Fiona Scarf (Office Mgr)

Subsidiaries:

Affinity Education Group Limited (1)

Level 14 100 Creek Steet, Brisbane, 4000, QLD, Australia
Tel.: (61) 7 3513 7700
Web Site:
    http://www.affinityeducation.com.au
Child Care Center
N.A.I.C.S.: 624410
Fiona Alston (Dir-Education & Pro Dev)

Brand Collective Pty Ltd. (1)
332 Lorimer Street, Port Melbourne, 3207, VIC, Australia
Tel.: (61) 3 9681 9681
Web Site: http://www.brandcollective.com.au
Emp.: 1,200
Footwear Distr
N.A.I.C.S.: 424340
Martin Matthews (CEO)

Dick Smith Holdings Limited (1)
2 Davidson Street, Chullora, 2190, NSW, Australia
Tel.: (61) 2 9642 9100
Web Site:
    http://www.dicksmithholdings.com.au
Holding Company; Consumer Electronics Retailer
N.A.I.C.S.: 551112
Michael Potts (CFO & Dir-Fin)

Subsidiary (Domestic):

Dick Smith Electronics Limited (2)
2 Davidson Street, Chullora, 2190, NSW, Australia (100%)
Tel.: (61) 2 9642 9100
Web Site: http://www.dicksmith.com.au
Sales Range: $1-4.9 Billion
Holding Company; Electronics Stores Owner, Operator & Franchisor
N.A.I.C.S.: 551112
Don Grover (Interim CEO)

Subsidiary (Domestic):

Dick Smith (Wholesale) Pty. Ltd. (3)
2 Davidson Street, Chullora, 2190, NSW, Australia
Tel.: (61) 2 9642 9100
Web Site: http://www.dicksmith.com.au
Electronic Product Distr
N.A.I.C.S.: 423690

Dick Smith Electronics Franchising Pty. Ltd. (3)
2 Davidson Street, Chullora, 2190, NSW, Australia
Tel.: (61) 2 9642 9213
Electronics-Store Franchisor
N.A.I.C.S.: 533110

Formwork & Scaffolding Pty Limited (1)
15 Sleigh Place, Hume, 2620, ACT, Australia
Tel.: (61) 2 6260 2558
Web Site: http://www.acrow.com.au
Construction Engineering Services
N.A.I.C.S.: 541330

Mark Group Australia Pty Ltd (1)
Level 1 6-10 Talavera Road, North Ryde, 2113, NSW, Australia
Tel.: (61) 2 8870 9800
Web Site: http://www.markaustralia.com.au
Solar Product Installation Services
N.A.I.C.S.: 238220
Robert Grant (CEO)

Shoes & Sox Pty Ltd (1)
Unit 1/21 Mars Road, Lane Cove, 2066, NSW, Australia
Tel.: (61) 2 9427 2607
Web Site: http://www.shoesandsox.com.au
Footwear Distr
N.A.I.C.S.: 424340
Usman Niazi (Mgr-Fin)

ANCHORSTONE HOLDINGS LTD.
Rm 2302 23/F Citicrop Centre 18 Whitfield Road, Causeway Bay, China (Hong Kong)
Tel.: (852) 25116668 Ky
Web Site:
    http://www.anchorstone.com.hk
Year Founded: 1991

1592—(HKG)
Rev.: $11,858,679
Assets: $35,422,551
Liabilities: $24,714,374
Net Worth: $10,708,178
Earnings: ($6,029,686)
Emp.: 30
Fiscal Year-end: 12/31/21
Marble & Granite Distr
N.A.I.C.S.: 423310
Gary Yue Yun Lui *(Chm & CEO)*

ANCHUN INTERNATIONAL HOLDINGS LTD.

No 539 Lusong Road, Changsha National Hi-tech Industrial Development Zone, Changsha, 410205, Hunan, China
Tel.: (86) 73188958633   SG
Web Site: https://www.anchun.com
Year Founded: 1993
BTX—(SES)
Rev.: $16,706,325
Assets: $61,790,512
Liabilities: $19,822,003
Net Worth: $41,968,509
Earnings: ($313,161)
Emp.: 273
Fiscal Year-end: 12/31/21
Holding Company
N.A.I.C.S.: 551112
Ding Zhong Xie *(Founder)*

ANCOM LOGISTICS BERHAD

No 2A Jalan 13/2 Sek 13, 46200, Petaling Jaya, Selangor, Malaysia
Tel.: (60) 374955000
Web Site: https://www.ancomlogistics.com.my
Year Founded: 1966
ANCOMLB—(KLS)
Rev.: $6,468,571
Assets: $9,348,783
Liabilities: $3,256,508
Net Worth: $6,092,275
Earnings: $106,243
Fiscal Year-end: 05/31/23
Switchgear Installation & Equipment Mfr
N.A.I.C.S.: 335313
Lim Chang Meng *(CFO)*

Subsidiaries:

Ancom Nylex Terminals Sdn. Bhd.   (1)
Jeti Petrokimia Pelabuhan Barat, Port Klang, 42920, Pulau Indah, Selangor, Malaysia
Tel.: (60) 331011372
Chemical Tank Farm & Warehouse Services
N.A.I.C.S.: 541330

Ancom-Chemquest Terminals Sdn. Bhd.   (1)
Jeti Petrokimia West Port Pulau Indah, 42920, Port Klang, Selangor, Malaysia
Tel.: (60) 331011372
Chemical Terminal Services
N.A.I.C.S.: 424710

Pengangkutan Cogent Sdn. Bhd. (1)
PTD 149227 Jalan Berjaya 7 Kempas Lama, Taman Perindustrian Berjaya, 81200, Johor Bahru, Johor Darul Takzim, Malaysia
Tel.: (60) 75583131
Chemical Transportation Services
N.A.I.C.S.: 488490

ANCOM NYLEX BERHAD

No 2A Jalan 13/2 Sek 13, 46200, Petaling Jaya, Selangor Darul Ehsan, Malaysia
Tel.: (60) 374955000
Web Site: https://www.ancomnylex.com
ANCOMNY—(KLS)
Rev.: $432,434,497
Assets: $254,967,619
Liabilities: $144,082,751

Net Worth: $110,884,868
Earnings: $16,259,683
Emp.: 949
Fiscal Year-end: 05/31/23
Agricultural Chemicals & Herbicides Mfr
N.A.I.C.S.: 115112
Wai Foong Wong *(Co-Sec)*

Subsidiaries:

Airefresh Industries (M) Sdn. Bhd.   (1)
No 28 Jalan USJ 1/3 Taman Perindustrian USJ 1, 47600, Subang Jaya, Selangor, Malaysia
Tel.: (60) 38 025 1887
Web Site: https://www.aire-fresh.com
Air Purifier Mfr
N.A.I.C.S.: 333413

Ancom Components Sdn. Bhd.   (1)
No 7 Jalan Empat Off Jalan Chan Sow Lin, 55200, Kuala Lumpur, Malaysia
Tel.: (60) 39 223 0288
Web Site: https://www.ancomcomponents.com.my
Residual Current Circuit Breaker Product Mfr
N.A.I.C.S.: 334419

Ancom Crop Care Sdn. Bhd.   (1)
No 31 Jalan Tukul P15/P Seksyen 15, 40200, Shah Alam, Selangor, Malaysia
Tel.: (60) 355194022
Web Site: http://www.ancomcropcare.com.my
Sales Range: $75-99.9 Million
Emp.: 120
Agrochemical Product Mfr
N.A.I.C.S.: 325311
Shamsuddin Basri *(Chm)*

Subsidiary (Domestic):

Ancom Bioscience Sdn. Bhd.   (2)
Lot 5 Persiaran Selangor, Seksyen 15, Shah Alam, 40000, Selangor, Malaysia
Tel.: (60) 355194022
Web Site: http://www.ancomcropcare.com.my
Sales Range: $50-74.9 Million
Emp.: 120
Agrochemical Products Distr
N.A.I.C.S.: 424910
Anthony Tan *(Gen Mgr)*

Dynamic Chemical Pte. Ltd.   (1)
3 International Business Park 03-04, Nordic European Centre, Singapore, 609927, Singapore
Tel.: (65) 6 224 4142
Web Site: https://www.dynamicchemical.com.sg
Petrochemical Mfr
N.A.I.C.S.: 325110

Entopest Environmental Services Sdn. Bhd.   (1)
2A Jalan 13/2 Section 13, 46200, Petaling Jaya, Selangor, Malaysia
Tel.: (60) 37 931 3232
Web Site: https://entopest.com.my
Pest Management Technology Services
N.A.I.C.S.: 561710
Lee Cheun Wei *(Mng Dir)*

Genovasi Malaysia Sdn. Bhd.   (1)
No 2A Gate C Jalan 13/2 Section 13, 46200, Petaling Jaya, Selangor, Malaysia
Tel.: (60) 37 954 0628
Web Site: https://www.dschoolmalaysia.com
Training Center Services
N.A.I.C.S.: 611430

Meru Utama Sdn. Bhd.   (1)
8th Floor Menara Manulife No 6 Jalan Gelanggang, Bukit Damansara, 50490, Kuala Lumpur, Selangor, Malaysia
Tel.: (60) 320112338
Web Site: http://www.meruutama.com
Emp.: 30
Airport Advertising Services
N.A.I.C.S.: 541810
Ong Pen Woon *(Gen Mgr)*

RedBerry Sdn. Bhd.   (1)
Lot 2A Jalan 13/2 Seksyen 13, 46200, Petaling Jaya, Selangor, Malaysia

Tel.: (60) 374951188
Web Site: http://www.redberry.com.my
Media Advertising Services
N.A.I.C.S.: 541840

Redberry Ambient Sdn. Bhd.   (1)
Redberry City Lot 2 Jalan 13/2 Seksyen 13, 46200, Petaling Jaya, Selangor, Malaysia
Tel.: (60) 37 495 1125
Web Site: https://redberryambient.com.my
Media Services
N.A.I.C.S.: 541840

Redberry Contact Center Sdn. Bhd.   (1)
No 2A Jalan 13/2 Seksyen 13, 46200, Petaling Jaya, Selangor, Malaysia
Tel.: (60) 32 718 4222
Web Site: https://www.redberrycc.com
Business Process Outsourcing Services
N.A.I.C.S.: 541611

Redberry Outdoors Sdn. Bhd.   (1)
Lot 2 Jalan 13/2 Seksyen 13, 46200, Petaling Jaya, Selangor, Malaysia
Tel.: (60) 37 495 1188
Web Site: https://redberry.com.my
Advertising Agency Services
N.A.I.C.S.: 541810

Wheel Sport Management Sdn. Bhd.   (1)
Lot 2A Jalan 13/2 Redberry City, 46200, Petaling Jaya, Selangor Darul Ehsan, Malaysia
Tel.: (60) 3 7495 1188
Web Site: http://www.malaysianrally.com
Sales Range: $50-74.9 Million
Emp.: 5
Motor Rally Promoter
N.A.I.C.S.: 711310
Raja Nor Mazli Mohar *(Mng Dir)*

iEnterprise Online Sdn. Bhd.   (1)
Unit 1003 & 1005 Block B Phileo Damansara II No 15 Jalan, 16/11 Off Jalan Damansara, 46350, Petaling Jaya, Selangor, Malaysia
Tel.: (60) 376651988
Web Site: http://www.ieol.com.my
Enterprise Resource Planning Applications Development Services
N.A.I.C.S.: 541511
Diana Quek *(Acct Dir)*

ANCORA CHUMBADORES LTDA.

Av da Saudade 690 JD Alves Nogueira, Vinhedo, 13289-010, Brazil
Tel.: (55) 1921364455
Web Site: http://www.ancora.com.br
Year Founded: 1992
Construction & Engineering Services
N.A.I.C.S.: 333120
Roberto Bernardi Anchor *(Dir)*

Subsidiaries:

Einhell Brasil Com. Distr. Ferr. E Equip. Ltda   (1)
Av Benedito Storani 1345, 13289-004, Vinhedo, SP, Brazil
Tel.: (55) 1921364477
Web Site: http://www.einhell.com.br
Power Tool, Garden Equipment & Heating & Air Conditioning Equipment Mfr
N.A.I.C.S.: 333991
Pedro Braga *(Dir-Comml)*

AND FACTORY, INC.

Sumitomo Fudosan Aobadai Tower 9F 3-6-28 Aobadai, Meguro-Ku, Tokyo, 153-0042, Japan
Tel.: (81) 367127646
Web Site: https://andfactory.co.jp
7035—(TKS)
Sales Range: Less than $1 Million
Software Development Services
N.A.I.C.S.: 541511
Takamasa Ohara *(Founder & Chm)*

ANDACOR S.A.

Neveria 4680 Las Condes, Las Condes, Santiago, Chile
Tel.: (56) 8899200

Web Site: http://www.elcolorado.cl
ANDACOR—(SGO)
Sales Range: Less than $1 Million
Recreational Services
N.A.I.C.S.: 713940

ANDALUSI BEVERAGES S.L.

Butchers Street 48 Poliviso, El Viso del Alcor, 41520, Seville, Spain
Tel.: (34) 955278883
Web Site: https://andalusidestilerias.com
Beverage Product Distr
N.A.I.C.S.: 424490

ANDATEE CHINA MARINE FUEL SERVICES CORPORATION

Unit C No 68 of West Binhai Road, Xigang District, Dalian, China
Tel.: (86) 411824089   DE
Web Site: http://www.andatee.com
AMCF—(OTCEM)
Sales Range: $250-299.9 Million
Blended Marine Fuel Oil Production, Storage, Distribution & Sales
N.A.I.C.S.: 424710

ANDEAN PRECIOUS METALS CORP.

181 Bay Street Suite 4400, Toronto, M5J 2T3, ON, Canada
Tel.: (437) 371-2820   Ca
Web Site: https://www.andeanpm.com
Year Founded: 2018
ANPMF—(OTCEM)
Rev.: $125,324,000
Assets: $269,890,000
Liabilities: $137,921,000
Net Worth: $131,969,000
Earnings: $38,540,000
Emp.: 250
Fiscal Year-end: 12/31/23
Business Consulting Services
N.A.I.C.S.: 522299
Alberto Morales *(Founder, Chm & Exec Chm)*

ANDEAN SILVER LIMITED

Level 2 8 Richardson Street, West Perth, 6005, WA, Australia
Tel.: (61) 862436542   AU
Web Site: https://www.andeansilver.com
Year Founded: 2020
MMC—(ASX)
Rev.: $6,686
Assets: $2,876,421
Liabilities: $132,073
Net Worth: $2,744,348
Earnings: ($1,085,311)
Emp.: 4
Fiscal Year-end: 06/30/23
Mining Services
N.A.I.C.S.: 212290

ANDERA PARTNERS SCA

374 rue Saint Honore, 75001, Paris, France
Tel.: (33) 1 85 73 64 00
Web Site: http://www.anderapartners.com
Year Founded: 2001
Privater Equity Firm
N.A.I.C.S.: 523999
Andrei Buzdugan *(CFO)*

Subsidiaries:

Abrisud SAS   (1)
15 Rue Louis ZI du Pont Peyrin, L'Isle-Jourdain, 32600, France
Tel.: (33) 5 82 95 49 49
Web Site: http://www.abrisud.com
Pool Enclosure Mfr
N.A.I.C.S.: 332322

Andera Partners SCA—(Continued)

Intescia Group SAS (1)
8 Rue Rouget de Lisle, Axe Seine Immeuble A, 92442, Issy-les-Moulineaux, Cedex, France
Tel.: (33) 1 71 16 31 31
Web Site: http://www.intescia-group.com
Trade Journals Publisher & Information Services
N.A.I.C.S.: 513120
Alexandre Sidomo (Pres & CEO)

Spherea Test & Services S.A.S. (1)
109 avenue Eisenhower, 31023, Toulouse, CEDEX 1, France
Tel.: (33) 5 34 55 40 00
Web Site: http://www.spherea.com
Sales Range: $100-124.9 Million
Emp.: 500
Electronic Equipment Repair & Maintenance Services in Aviation, Defense, Space, Energy & Transportation
N.A.I.C.S.: 811210
Patrick Freneuil (CTO & VP-Product Lines)

Subsidiary (Non-US):

Spherea Test & Services Ltd. (2)
23-25 Cobham Road, Ferndown Industrial Estate, Wimborne, BH21 7PE, Dorset, United Kingdom
Tel.: (44) 1202 872800
Web Site: http://www.spherea.com
Sales Range: $25-49.9 Million
Emp.: 35
Test Engineering Services
N.A.I.C.S.: 541330
Dave Aspin (Acct Mgr)

ANDERCO INVESTMENT PTE LTD
No 3 Tuas View Circuit LBG Building, Singapore, 637645, Singapore
Tel.: (965) 68620049
Emp.: 100
Investment Services
N.A.I.C.S.: 523999

Subsidiaries:

Aston Air Control Pte Ltd (1)
1 Jalan Berseh 03-02 New World Centre, Singapore, 209037, Singapore
Tel.: (65) 6 298 0682
Web Site: https://www.astonair.com
Air Conditioning Equipment Sales & Installation Services
N.A.I.C.S.: 423730
Yong Joo Joe Goh (CEO)

ANDERSELITE LTD.
Enterprise House Ocean Village, Southampton, SO14 3XB, United Kingdom
Tel.: (44) 2380219209
Web Site: http://www.anderselite.com
Year Founded: 1984
Emp.: 70
Construction, Engineering & Information Technology Market Staffing Solutions
N.A.I.C.S.: 561320

Subsidiaries:

AndersElite Ltd.- London (1)
1st Floor 100 Cannon Street, London, EC4N 6EU, United Kingdom
Tel.: (44) 2077437500
Web Site: http://www.anderselite.com
Construction, Engineering & Information Technology Market Staffing Solutions
N.A.I.C.S.: 561330

ANDERSEN & MARTINI HOLDING A/S
Agenavej 15, Greve, 2670, Denmark
Tel.: (45) 36931000
Web Site: http://www.am.dk
Rev.: $115,875,933
Assets: $50,773,018
Liabilities: $36,760,930
Net Worth: $14,012,088
Earnings: $248,851

Emp.: 246
Fiscal Year-end: 12/31/19
New & Used Car Dealer
Peter Hansen (CEO)

ANDERSON ANDERSON & BROWN LLP
Kingshill View Prime Four Business Park Kingswells, Aberdeen, AB15 8PU, United Kingdom
Tel.: (44) 1224625111
Web Site: https://aab.uk
Year Founded: 1990
Emp.: 300
Accounting Services
N.A.I.C.S.: 541219
Sheena Anderson (Owner)

Subsidiaries:

Dominion Systems, Inc. (1)
401 Hall St Ste 185, Grand Rapids, MI, 49504
Tel.: (616) 248-3835
Web Site: http://www.dominionsystems.com
Sales Range: $1-9.9 Million
Emp.: 43
Data Processing, Hosting & Related Services
N.A.I.C.S.: 518210
Jud Highhill (CEO)

ANDERSON GROUP LIMITED
Springfield Lodge Colchester Road, Chelmsford, CM2 5PW, Essex, United Kingdom
Tel.: (44) 1245399999
Web Site: http://www.andersongroup.co.uk
Year Founded: 1987
Sales Range: $75-99.9 Million
Emp.: 400
Construction & Architectural & Consulting Services
N.A.I.C.S.: 236220
Mark Anderson (Chm)

Subsidiaries:

3R Limited (1)
Springfield Lodge, Colchester Road, Chelmsford, CM2 5PW, Essex, United Kingdom
Tel.: (44) 1245399977
Web Site: http://www.threer.co.uk
Sales Range: $25-49.9 Million
Emp.: 10
Earthwork & Demolition Services
N.A.I.C.S.: 238910
Andrew Jay (Mng Dir)

Anderson Construction Ltd (1)
Springfield Lodge Colchester Rd, Chelmsford, CM2 5PW, Essex, United Kingdom
Tel.: (44) 1245399999
Web Site: http://www.andersongroup.co.uk
Sales Range: $25-49.9 Million
Emp.: 50
Groundworks & Civil Engineering Services
N.A.I.C.S.: 237990
Sean Emmett (Grp Comml Dir)

Anderson Design & Build (1)
Springfield Lodge, Colchester Road, Chelmsford, CM2 5PW, Essex, United Kingdom
Tel.: (44) 1245399940
Web Site: http://www.anderson-db.co.uk
Sales Range: $25-49.9 Million
Emp.: 10
Architectural & Building Design Services
N.A.I.C.S.: 541310
Mark Anderson (Gen Mgr)

Anderson Regenerate (1)
Springfield Lodge, Colchester Road, Chelmsford, CM2 5PW, United Kingdom
Tel.: (44) 1245399940
Web Site: http://www.andersongroup.co.uk
Sales Range: $25-49.9 Million
Emp.: 30
Land Acquisition Corporation
N.A.I.C.S.: 531312
Mark Anderson (Chm)

MAP Limited (1)
Brunswick House Ripple Road A13, Barking, IG11 OSL, Essex, United Kingdom
Tel.: (44) 2085927070
Web Site: http://www.mapplant.co.uk
Sales Range: $25-49.9 Million
Emp.: 20
Heavy Construction Equipment Services
N.A.I.C.S.: 423810
Darren Carter (Mng Dir)

ANDERSON INDUSTRIAL CORPORATION
5F No 88 Sec 6 Zhongshan N Rd, Shilin Dist, Taipei, 11155, Taiwan
Tel.: (886) 228376866
Web Site:
https://www.anderson.com.tw
1528—(TAI)
Rev.: $126,986,849
Assets: $181,705,346
Liabilities: $100,112,165
Net Worth: $81,593,182
Earnings: ($972,792)
Fiscal Year-end: 12/31/23
Industrial Machinery & Construction Plates Mfr
N.A.I.C.S.: 238910
Johnny Liao (Chm)

Subsidiaries:

Anderson America Corp. (1)
10620 Southern Loop Blvd, Pineville, NC 28134-8467
Tel.: (704) 522-1823
Web Site: http://www.andersonamerica.com
Sales Range: $25-49.9 Million
Emp.: 15
Woodworking & Printing Machinery Distr
N.A.I.C.S.: 423830

Anderson Europe GmbH (1)
Am Oberen Feld 5, 32758, Detmold, Germany
Tel.: (49) 52 319 6630
Web Site: https://www.andersoneurope.com
Emp.: 20
Precision Machinery Mfr
N.A.I.C.S.: 332721

Anderson Industrial Corporation - Houlung Factory (1)
No 1498 Zhonghua Rd, Hou-lung, 356003, Miaoli, Taiwan
Tel.: (886) 3 772 6876
Web Site: http://www.anderson.com.tw
Emp.: 200
Industrial Machinery Mfr
N.A.I.C.S.: 333248

Anderson Industrial Hong Kong Limited (1)
Mayor of Dongguan Changan Kam new 26th Street, Guangzhou, 530000, Guangdong, China
Tel.: (86) 769 82380598
Semiconductor & Electronic Components Distr
N.A.I.C.S.: 423690

Anderson Machinery (Singapore) Pte. Ltd. (1)
459 Pasir Ris Dr 4 10-257, Singapore, 510459, Singapore
Tel.: (65) 65840749
Web Site: http://www.anderson.tw
Emp.: 10
Woodworking Machinery Distr
N.A.I.C.S.: 423830

Anderson Taiwan (Central) (1)
No 33 Jing 2nd Rd Wuci Township, Taichung, 435, Taiwan
Tel.: (886) 4 2659 5866
Business Support Services
N.A.I.C.S.: 561499

Digital Photonics Corp. (1)
19F 5 No 81 Section 1 Sintai 5th Rd, Sijhih, Taipei, 221, Taiwan
Tel.: (886) 226984500
Web Site: http://www.thinkfly.com.tw
Sales Range: $25-49.9 Million
Emp.: 20
Digital Printers Mfr
N.A.I.C.S.: 334118

Sogotec Enterprise Co., Ltd. (1)
No 11 37th Road Taichung Industrial Area, Taichung, 407, Taiwan
Tel.: (886) 423591131
Web Site: http://www.anderson.com.tw
Emp.: 100
Numerical Control Machinery Mfr
N.A.I.C.S.: 333242

ANDERSON SPRATT GROUP
Anderson House Holywood Road, Belfast, BT4 2GU, Northern Ireland, United Kingdom
Tel.: (44) 28 9080 2000
Web Site:
http://www.asgandpartners.com
Year Founded: 1982
Emp.: 40
Advertising Agencies
N.A.I.C.S.: 541810
R. J. Colin Anderson (Chm & CEO)

Subsidiaries:

ASG Ltd (1)
Anderson House, Holywood Rd, Belfast, BT4 2GU, Northern Ireland, United Kingdom
Tel.: (44) 28 9080 2000
Web Site: http://www.asgireland.com
Emp.: 20
Advertising Agencies
N.A.I.C.S.: 541810
Colin Anderson (Chm)

Tibus (1)
Macken House, Mayer Street Upper, Dublin, 1, Ireland
Tel.: (353) 1 473 1650
Web Site: http://www.tibus.com
Emp.: 25
Advertising Agencies
N.A.I.C.S.: 541810
Rick McKee (Dir-Comml)

ANDERSSON & PARTNERS
Lille Strandstraede 18 P, 1254, Copenhagen, K, Denmark
Tel.: (45) 33144123
Year Founded: 1990
Sales Range: $10-24.9 Million
Emp.: 14
Advertising Agencies
N.A.I.C.S.: 541810
Peter Andersson (Owner)

ANDES TECHNOLOGY CORPORATION
10F No 1Sec 3 Gongdao 5th Rd, East Dist, Hsinchu, 300042, Taiwan
Tel.: (886) 35726533
Web Site:
https://www.andestech.com
Year Founded: 2005
6533—(TAI)
Rev.: $34,592,955
Assets: $174,498,178
Liabilities: $17,170,410
Net Worth: $157,327,768
Earnings: ($3,326,400)
Emp.: 503
Fiscal Year-end: 12/31/23
Central Processing Unit Mfr & Distr
N.A.I.C.S.: 334118
Ming-Kai Tsai (Co-Founder & Chm)

Subsidiaries:

Andes Technology USA Corporation (1)
2860 Zanker Rd Ste 104, San Jose, CA 95134
Tel.: (408) 809-2929
Electronic Processor Distr
N.A.I.C.S.: 423430

ANDFJORD SALMON AS
Kvalnesveien 69, Vesteralen, 8485, Myre, Norway
Web Site:
https://www.andfjordsalmon.com
Year Founded: 2014

ANDF—(OSL)
Agriculture Product Distr
N.A.I.C.S.: 424910
Bjarne Martinsen *(CFO)*

**ANDHRA PRADESH TANNER-
IES LTD.**
Leather Complex Area, Nellimarla,
Vizianagaram, 535 217, Andhra
Pradesh, India
Tel.: (91) 892226728
Web Site: https://www.aptl.net.in
Leather Mfr
N.A.I.C.S.: 316110
Uma Yelevarthy *(CFO)*

**ANDLAUER HEALTHCARE
GROUP, INC.**
100 Vaughan Valley Blvd, Vaughan,
L4H 3C5, ON, Canada
Tel.: (416) 744-4900   Ca
Web Site:
   https://www.andlauerhealthcare.com
AND—(TSX)
Rev.: $245,901,895
Assets: $197,758,037
Liabilities: $123,967,912
Net Worth: $73,790,126
Earnings: $29,502,908
Fiscal Year-end: 12/31/20
Holding Company
N.A.I.C.S.: 551112
Michael Andlauer *(CEO & Founder)*

Subsidiaries:

Accuristix Healthcare Logistics
Inc.   **(1)**
122 Stone Ridge Road, Vaughan, L4H 0A5,
ON, Canada
Tel.: (416) 637-3273
Web Site: http://www.accuristix.com
Logistic Services
N.A.I.C.S.: 488510
Andy McMullen *(Gen Mgr)*

Skelton Canada Inc.   **(1)**
2475 Aviation Lane, London, N5V 3Z9, ON,
Canada
Tel.: (519) 679-9180
Web Site: https://www.skelton-metals.com
Railroad Product Mfr & Distr
N.A.I.C.S.: 336510

Skelton Truck Lines, Inc.   **(1)**
2510 Davis Drive, Sharon, L0G 1V0, ON,
Canada
Tel.: (905) 895-6688
Web Site: https://www.skeltontruck.com
Shipping Services
N.A.I.C.S.: 488330

ANDO HOLDINGS LTD.
Room 1107 11F Lippon Sun Plaza 28
Canton Road, Tsim Sha Tsui, Kow-
loon, China (Hong Kong)
Tel.: (852) 23519122   NV
Year Founded: 2015
ADHG—(OTCBB)
Rev.: $39
Assets: $74,816
Liabilities: $195,485
Net Worth: ($120,669)
Earnings: ($78,750)
Fiscal Year-end: 09/30/19
Mobile Billboard Display Advertising
Services
N.A.I.C.S.: 541850
Leo Chi Kwong Lam *(Chm, Pres &
CEO)*

ANDON HEALTH CO., LTD.
No 3 Jinping Street Yaan Road, Nan-
kai District, Tianjin, 300190, China
Tel.: (86) 2287611660
Web Site: http://www.jiuan.com
Year Founded: 1995
002432—(SSE)
Rev.: $447,375,512
Assets: $3,131,800,620

Liabilities: $386,949,726
Net Worth: $2,744,850,894
Earnings: $173,295,331
Emp.: 1,500
Fiscal Year-end: 12/31/23
Medical Equipment & Product Mfr
N.A.I.C.S.: 334510

**ANDOVER CAPITAL CORPO-
RATION**
30 Saint Clair Avenue West Suite
1500, Toronto, M4V 3A1, ON,
Canada
Web Site:
   http://www.andovercapital.ca
Privater Equity Firm
N.A.I.C.S.: 523999

Subsidiaries:

NorthStar Scaffold Inc.   **(1)**
8 Penner Road Navin, Winnipeg, R5T 0H5,
MB, Canada
Tel.: (204) 806-6206
Web Site: https://www.scaffolding.ca
Emp.: 200
Scaffolding Services for Residential & Com-
mercial Construction
N.A.I.C.S.: 238290
Jonathan McCain *(Pres)*

Subsidiary (Domestic):

Sky-Hi Scaffolding Ltd.   **(2)**
3195 Production Way, Burnaby, V5A 3H2,
BC, Canada
Tel.: (604) 291-7245
Web Site: http://www.sky-hi.com
Rev.: $7,303,376
Emp.: 250
Scaffolding Services for Residential & Com-
merical Construction
N.A.I.C.S.: 236220
Kevin Lottis *(CEO)*

ANDRADA MINING LIMITED
Illovo Edge Office Park Bldg 3 2nd
Floor Corner, Harries and Fricker
Road, Illovo, South Africa
Tel.: (27) 112686555   GY
Web Site:
   https://www.afritinmining.com
Year Founded: 2017
ATMTF—(OTCQB)
Rev.: $12,405,294
Assets: $59,919,817
Liabilities: $14,894,446
Net Worth: $45,025,371
Earnings: ($10,229,543)
Emp.: 219
Fiscal Year-end: 02/28/23
Tin Mining
N.A.I.C.S.: 212290
Anthony Richard Viljoen *(CEO)*

**ANDRADE & CANELLAS EN-
ERGIA S.A.**
Rua Alexandre Dumas 2 100 13 an-
dar, Chac Santo Antonio, Sao Paulo,
04717-004, Brazil
Tel.: (55) 1121220400
Web Site:
   http://www.acenergia.com.br
Sales Range: $10-24.9 Million
Emp.: 80
Energy Consulting Services
N.A.I.C.S.: 541690
Andre Crisafulli *(Dir-Project Mgmt)*

**ANDRADE GUTIERREZ CON-
CESSOES S.A.**
Av Do Contorno 8123, 30110937,
Belo Horizonte, Minas Gerais, Brazil
Tel.: (55) 3132906797
Web Site: http://www.agcsa.com.br
Eletric Power Generation Services
N.A.I.C.S.: 221118
Renato Torres de Faria *(Dir-IR)*

Subsidiaries:

ANDRADE GUTIERREZ PARTICIPA-
COES S.A.   **(1)**
Av Do Contorno 8123, 30110062, Belo
Horizonte, MG, Brazil
Tel.: (55) 3132906645
Transportation Related Services
N.A.I.C.S.: 488999
Renato Torres De Faria *(CEO & Dir-IR)*

**ANDRE VOSS ERDBAU UND
TRANSPORT GMBH**
Am Liepengraben 6, Rostock, 18147,
Germany
Tel.: (49) 381128310
Web Site: http://www.andre-voss.de
Rev.: $12,309,871
Emp.: 60
Paving Materials Mfr
N.A.I.C.S.: 324121
Alexander Rau *(Mgr-Logistics)*

ANDREAS SIMONSEN GMBH
Am Lunedeich 138, 27572, Bremer-
haven, Germany
Tel.: (49) 408533450
Web Site:
   http://www.simonsengmbh.de
Year Founded: 1892
Sales Range: $25-49.9 Million
Emp.: 20
Fish & Seafood Distr
N.A.I.C.S.: 424460
Andreas Simonsen *(Mng Dir)*

Subsidiaries:

Andreas Simonsen GmbH Frozen
Fish Division   **(1)**
Stapelholmer Weg 15, 24963, Schleswig,
Germany
Tel.: (49) 463889510
Seafood Distr
N.A.I.C.S.: 424460

ANDREAS STIHL AG & CO.
Badstrasse 115, 71336, Waiblingen,
Germany
Tel.: (49) 7151260
Web Site: https://www.stihl.com
Year Founded: 1926
Rev.: $1,744,121,868
Assets: $9,551,415,169
Liabilities: $3,258,758,142
Net Worth: $6,292,657,027
Earnings: $4,948,117,894
Emp.: 6,003
Fiscal Year-end: 12/31/23
Outdoor Power Equipment Mfr
N.A.I.C.S.: 333991
Michael Traub *(Chm)*

Subsidiaries:

Stihl, Inc.   **(1)**
536 Viking Dr, Virginia Beach, VA
23452   **(100%)**
Tel.: (757) 486-9100
Web Site: http://www.stihlusa.com
Sales Range: $450-499.9 Million
Emp.: 2,100
Mfr of Chain Saws, Grass Trimmers, Leaf
Blowers, Grass Edgers & Augers
N.A.I.C.S.: 333991
Jackson D'Armond *(Mgr-Mktg Comm)*

Subsidiary (Non-US):

Stihl Ltd   **(2)**
1515 Sise Rd, PO Box 5666, London, N6A
4L6, ON, Canada   **(100%)**
Tel.: (519) 681-3000
Web Site: http://www.stihl.ca
Sales Range: $25-49.9 Million
Emp.: 90
Mfr of Chainsaws & Accessories
N.A.I.C.S.: 333991
Greg Quigt *(Pres)*

Subsidiary (Domestic):

Stihl Parts, Inc.   **(2)**

536 Viking Dr, Virginia Beach, VA
23452-7821   **(100%)**
Tel.: (757) 486-9100
Web Site: http://www.stihlusa.com
Sales Range: $400-449.9 Million
Emp.: 1,500
Distribution of Machinery
N.A.I.C.S.: 333991

USA Zama Inc.   **(1)**
114 Seaboard Ln, Franklin, TN 37067
Tel.: (615) 371-9493
Web Site: http://www.zamacarb.com
Sales Range: $25-49.9 Million
Emp.: 20
Carburetors Design & Whslr
N.A.I.C.S.: 336310
Mamoru Toda *(Pres)*

**ANDREW HENDRIKS & SONS
GREENHOUSES**
5095 N Service Road, Beamsville,
L3J 1V1, ON, Canada
Tel.: (905) 563-8132
Web Site:
   https://www.hendriksgreenhouses.com
Year Founded: 1953
Gardening Services
N.A.I.C.S.: 444240
Catherine Harrison *(Mgr-HR)*

ANDREW MACALLISTER SA
6 square de Opera Louis Jouvet,
75009, Paris, France
Tel.: (33) 178095960
Web Site: http://www.mac-
allister.com
Personnel Placement Services
N.A.I.C.S.: 561311
Martial Fabre *(Chm & CEO)*

ANDREW PELLER LIMITED
697 South Service Road, Grimsby,
L3M 4E8, ON, Canada
Tel.: (905) 643-4131   Ca
Web Site:
   https://www.andrewpeller.com
Year Founded: 1961
ADWPF—(OTCIQ)
Rev.: $285,039,544
Assets: $408,659,165
Liabilities: $230,304,825
Net Worth: $178,354,341
Earnings: ($2,106,829)
Emp.: 1,500
Fiscal Year-end: 03/31/24
Winery Owner & Wine Retailer
N.A.I.C.S.: 312130
John E. Peller *(Pres & CEO)*

Subsidiaries:

Black Hills Estate Winery Inc.   **(1)**
4190 Black Sage Road, Oliver, V0H 1T1,
BC, Canada
Tel.: (778) 400-7243
Web Site: http://www.blackhillswinery.com
Winery & Vineyard Mfr
N.A.I.C.S.: 312130

Gray Monk Cellars Ltd.   **(1)**
1055 Camp Road, Lake Country, Kelowna,
V4V 2H4, BC, Canada
Tel.: (236) 361-9287
Web Site: http://www.graymonk.com
Winery Product Distr
N.A.I.C.S.: 445320

Red Rooster Winery Ltd.   **(1)**
891 Naramata Road, Penticton, V2A 8T5,
BC, Canada
Tel.: (236) 239-1284
Web Site: http://www.redroosterwinery.com
Winery & Vineyard Mfr
N.A.I.C.S.: 312130

The Small Winemaker's Collection
Inc.   **(1)**
100 Broadview Ave Suite 318, Toronto,
M4M 3H3, ON, Canada
Tel.: (416) 463-7178
Web Site: http://www.smallwinemakers.ca
Emp.: 9
Winery Product Distr

Andrew Peller Limited—(Continued)
N.A.I.C.S.: 445320

Tinhorn Creek Vineyards Ltd. (1)
537 Tinhorn Creek Road, PO Box 2010,
Oliver, V0H 1T1, BC, Canada
Tel.: (250) 498-3743
Web Site: http://www.tinhorn.com
Winery Product Distr
N.A.I.C.S.: 445320

Wayne Gretzky Estates Limited (1)
1219 Niagara Stone Road, Niagara-on-the-
Lake, L0S 1J0, ON, Canada
Tel.: (289) 312-8556
Web Site:
http://www.gretzkyestateswines.com
Liquor Product Distr
N.A.I.C.S.: 445320

ANDREW SHERET LIMITED
721 Kings Road, Victoria, V8T 1W4,
BC, Canada
Tel.: (250) 287-9571
Web Site: http://www.sheret.com
Year Founded: 1989
Rev.: $55,123,098
Emp.: 250
Bathroom Accessories Mfr
N.A.I.C.S.: 327110
David Broad (VP)

ANDREW YULE & COMPANY LTD.
Yule House 8 Dr Rajendra Prasad
Sarani, Kolkata, 700 001, India
Tel.: (91) 3322428210
Web Site:
https://www.andrewyule.com
ANDREWYU—(NSE)
Rev.: $55,390,158
Assets: $101,234,897
Liabilities: $48,690,615
Net Worth: $52,544,283
Earnings: $1,726,002
Emp.: 14,621
Fiscal Year-end: 03/31/23
Industrial Machinery Mfr & Distr
N.A.I.C.S.: 333248
Ashit Midha (Gen Mgr-Sls & Liason-NR)

Subsidiaries:

Hooghly Printing Company Ltd. (1)
Yule House 8 Dr Rajendra Prasad Sarani,
Kolkata, 700 001, India
Tel.: (91) 33 22428210
Web Site: http://www.hooghlyprinting.com
Sales Range: $25-49.9 Million
Emp.: 55
Brochure & Pamphlet Printing Services
N.A.I.C.S.: 323113

ANDREWS REALTY LTD
410 650 W 41 Ave North Tower, Van-
couver, V5Z 1M9, BC, Canada
Tel.: (604) 263-2823
Web Site:
http://www.andrewsrealtyinc.com
Year Founded: 1986
Rev.: $10,694,229
Emp.: 115
Real Estate Services
N.A.I.C.S.: 531210
Stacey Pierce Andrews (VP)

ANDREWS SYKES GROUP PLC
St Davids Court Union Street,
Wolverhampton, WV1 4JJ, United
Kingdom
Tel.: (44) 800211611   UK
Web Site: http://www.andrews-
sykes.com
ASY—(AIM)
Rev.: $104,780,358
Assets: $121,459,227
Liabilities: $39,774,047
Net Worth: $81,685,181

Earnings: $21,484,474
Emp.: 551
Fiscal Year-end: 12/31/22
Warm Air Heating & Air-Conditioning
Equipment Mfr
N.A.I.C.S.: 333415

Subsidiaries:

Andrews Sykes B.V. (1)
Marconistraat 32, PO Box 33, 2665 JE,
Bleiswijk, Netherlands
Tel.: (31) 105214455
Web Site: https://www.andrewssykes.nl
Air Conditioning & Ventilation Rental Ser-
vices
N.A.I.C.S.: 238220

Andrews Sykes BVBA (1)
Boomsesteenweg 78 poort 11, 2630, Aart-
selaar, Belgium
Tel.: (32) 24649380
Web Site: https://www.andrewssykes.be
Air Conditioning & Ventilation Rental Ser-
vices
N.A.I.C.S.: 238220

Andrews Sykes Luxembourg SARL (1)
18 Route de Capellen, Holzem, L-8279,
Mamer, Luxembourg
Tel.: (352) 26103785
Web Site: https://www.andrewssykes.lu
Air Conditioning & Ventilation Rental Ser-
vices
N.A.I.C.S.: 238220

Climat Location SA (1)
Chemin de la Louve 15, 1196, Gland, Swit-
zerland
Tel.: (41) 800211611
Web Site: https://www.climatlocation.ch
HVAC Rental Services
N.A.I.C.S.: 238220

Climat Location SAS (1)
2 Rue des Meuniers, ZAC du Moulin Lamb-
lin Hallennes-lez-Haubourdin, 59320, Lille,
France
Tel.: (33) 800150100
Air Conditioning Equipment Distr
N.A.I.C.S.: 423730

Khansaheb Sykes LLC (1)
Khansaheb Building in Industrial Area 3, PO
Box 1848, Sharjah, United Arab Emirates
Tel.: (971) 80079537
Web Site: https://www.khansahebsykes.com
Pumping Equipment Distr
N.A.I.C.S.: 423830

Klimamieten AS GmbH (1)
Europa Allee 123, 50226, Frechen, Ger-
many
Tel.: (49) 8000060193
Web Site: https://www.klimamietenas.de
Emp.: 600
Air Conditioning Equipment Distr
N.A.I.C.S.: 423730

Nolo Climat S.R.L. (1)
Via Alessandro Giulini 29, 20015, Para-
biago, MI, Italy
Tel.: (39) 0331556021
Web Site: https://www.noloclimat.it
Air Conditioning & Ventilation Rental Ser-
vices
N.A.I.C.S.: 238220

ANDRITZ AG
Stattegger Strasse 18, 8045, Graz,
Austria
Tel.: (43) 31669020   AT
Web Site: https://www.andritz.com
Year Founded: 1852
ADRZY—(OTCIQ)
Rev.: $9,559,554,036
Assets: $9,379,953,639
Liabilities: $6,998,344,189
Net Worth: $2,381,609,450
Earnings: $556,683,961
Emp.: 29,717
Fiscal Year-end: 12/31/23
Holding Company; Customized Indus-
trial Equipment Mfr & Distr; Plant
Systems Designer & Construction
Services

N.A.I.C.S.: 551112
Wolfgang Leitner (Pres, CEO &
Member-Exec Bd)

Subsidiaries:

ANDRITZ (China) Ltd. (1)
18F/B Hanwei Plaza 7 Guanghua Road,
Chaoyang District, Beijing, 100004, China
Tel.: (86) 1065613388
Web Site: http://www.andritz.com
Industrial Machinery Distr
N.A.I.C.S.: 423830

ANDRITZ (Thailand) Ltd. (1)
Lake Rajada Office Complex Unit 22 E
193/96 Ratchadaphisek Road, Klongtoey,
Bangkok, 10110, Thailand
Tel.: (66) 2 264 0488
Web Site: http://www.andritz.com
Sales Range: $50-74.9 Million
Emp.: 5
Industrial Machinery & Equipment Distr
N.A.I.C.S.: 423830

ANDRITZ AB (1)
Gavlegatan 22, 11330, Stockholm,
Sweden   **(100%)**
Tel.: (46) 858602500
Web Site: http://www.andritz.com
Sales Range: $25-49.9 Million
Emp.: 10
Mfr of Equipment for the Pulp & Paper In-
dustry
N.A.I.C.S.: 333243
Ulf Lundstrom (VP)

Subsidiary (Domestic):

ANDRITZ Iggesund Tools AB (2)
Forsavagen 7, PO Box 6, 825 21, Igge-
sund, Sweden
Tel.: (46) 65029120
Web Site: http://www.iggesundtools.com
Sales Range: $25-49.9 Million
Emp.: 10
Industrial Tools Mfr
N.A.I.C.S.: 333515

NAF AB (2)
Gelbgjutaregatan 2, SE-581 87, Linkoping,
Sweden
Tel.: (46) 13316100
Web Site: https://www.naf.se
Sales Range: $25-49.9 Million
Emp.: 80
Flow Control Products
N.A.I.C.S.: 333914

**ANDRITZ AG - Russia Representa-
tive Office** (1)
Sadovaya-Samotechnaya 12 bid 1 off No
38-39, 127051, Moscow, Russia
Tel.: (7) 4959802327
Web Site: http://www.andritz.com
Industrial Machinery Distr
N.A.I.C.S.: 423830

**ANDRITZ AG - Taiwan Representa-
tive Office** (1)
3F No 77 Sec 2 Tun Hwa South Road, Tai-
pei, 106, Taiwan
Tel.: (886) 2 2722 7475
Web Site: http://www.andritz.com
Sales Range: $50-74.9 Million
Emp.: 1
Industrial Machinery Distr
N.A.I.C.S.: 423830

ANDRITZ Brasil Ltda. (1)
Av Vicente Machado 589 Centro, 80420
010, Curitiba, PR, Brazil   **(100%)**
Tel.: (55) 4121037611
Web Site: http://www.andritz.com
Sales Range: $50-74.9 Million
Emp.: 150
Mfr of Equipment & Machinery for the Pulp
& Paper Industry
N.A.I.C.S.: 333243
Diana Ho (Dir-Fin)

Subsidiary (Domestic):

**ANDRITZ FEED & BIOFUEL Brasil
Ltda.** (2)
Av Vicente Machado 589, Curitiba, 80420-
010, Parana, Brazil
Tel.: (55) 4733879146
Web Site: http://www.andritz.com
Industrial Machinery Mfr & Distr

N.A.I.C.S.: 333248

ANDRITZ SEPARATION Ltda. (2)
Rua Tabapua 627 - Conj 92, Itaim Bibi, Sao
Paulo, 04533-012, Brazil
Tel.: (55) 11 2168 0130
Web Site: http://www.andritz.com
Sales Range: $50-74.9 Million
Emp.: 5
Liquid Separation Machinery Distr
N.A.I.C.S.: 423830

Subsidiary (Domestic):

**ANDRITZ SEPARATION Industria e
Comercio de Equipamentos de Filtra-
cao Ltda.** (3)
Rua Progresso 450, Pomerode, 89107-000,
Brazil
Tel.: (55) 4733879100
Web Site: http://www.andritz.com
Sales Range: $75-99.9 Million
Emp.: 200
Liquid Separation Equipment Distr
N.A.I.C.S.: 423830

ANDRITZ Chile Ltda. (1)
Andres Bello 2777 Piso 11 Oficina 1101,
Las Condes, 7550053, Santiago, Chile
Tel.: (56) 2 462 4600
Web Site: http://www.andritz.com
Sales Range: $50-74.9 Million
Emp.: 500
Industrial Machinery Equipment Distr
N.A.I.C.S.: 423830

Plant (Domestic):

ANDRITZ Chile Ltda. (2)
Av Gran Bretana 4889, 4290319, Talca-
huano, Chile
Tel.: (56) 41 243 4740
Web Site: http://www.andritz.com
Pulp Machinery Equipment Whslr
N.A.I.C.S.: 423830

ANDRITZ Diatec S.R.L. (1)
Strada Statale 151, Collecorvino, Italy
Tel.: (39) 085820601
Disposable Hygiene Product Mfr & Distr
N.A.I.C.S.: 322291

ANDRITZ Dies & Rolls B.V. (1)
Spaarpot 112, 5667 KZ, Geldrop, Nether-
lands
Tel.: (31) 40 262 7777
Web Site: http://reports.andritz.com
Industrial Machinery Distr
N.A.I.C.S.: 423830

**ANDRITZ Energy & Environment
GmbH** (1)
Stattegger Strasse 18, Raaba, 8045, Graz,
Austria   **(100%)**
Tel.: (43) 31669020
Web Site: http://www.andritz.com
Sales Range: $250-299.9 Million
Emp.: 320
Energy Generation & Environmental Tech-
nology Plant System Mfr Engineering Ser-
vices
N.A.I.C.S.: 333611

ANDRITZ FEED & BIOFUEL A/S (1)
Tel.: (45) 72160300
Sales Range: $75-99.9 Million
Emp.: 200
Feed & Biofuel Processing Equipment Distr
N.A.I.C.S.: 423830

Unit (Non-US):

ANDRITZ FEED & BIOFUEL (2)
Industriestrasse 15A, 40822, Mettmann,
Germany
Tel.: (49) 2104 9197 0
Industrial Machinery Distr
N.A.I.C.S.: 423830

Representative Office (Non-US):

**ANDRITZ FEED & BIOFUEL A/S -
Venezuela Representative Office** (2)
Beverly Center Nivel 2 Of 2 Urb, El Vin,
Valencia, 2001, Venezuela
Tel.: (58) 241 842 2515
Web Site: http://www.andritz.com
Industrial Machinery Mfr & Distr
N.A.I.C.S.: 333248

ANDRITZ FEED & BIOFUEL A/S -
Vietnam Representative Office **(2)**
No 35 1A Street, Binh Tri Dong B Ward
Binh Tan District, Ho Chi Minh City, 10000,
Vietnam
Tel.: (84) 8 6253943 4
Web Site: http://www.andritz.com
Sales Range: $25-49.9 Million
Emp.: 10
Industrial Machinery Mfr & Distr
N.A.I.C.S.: 333248

Subsidiary (Non-US):

ANDRITZ FEED & BIOFUEL
B.V. **(2)**
Spaarpot 112, 5667 KZ, Geldrop, Nether-
lands
Tel.: (31) 40 262 7777
Web Site: http://www.andritz.com
Sales Range: $75-99.9 Million
Emp.: 120
Industrial Machinery Distr
N.A.I.C.S.: 423830

Unit (Non-US):

ANDRITZ FEED & BIOFUEL
Mexico **(2)**
Constitucion No 464 Entre Hidalgo y Bravo
Col Centro, 91700, Veracruz, Mexico
Tel.: (52) 229 178 3669
Farm Machinery Mfr & Whslr
N.A.I.C.S.: 333111

Subsidiary (Non-US):

ANDRITZ Feed & Biofuel Ltd. **(2)**
Unit 1 Stoneferry Park Foster Street, Hull,
HU8 8BT, United Kingdom **(100%)**
Tel.: (44) 1482825119
Sales Range: $25-49.9 Million
Emp.: 25
Feed Milling
N.A.I.C.S.: 311221

ANDRITZ Fabrics and Rolls
Limited **(1)**
Harumi Island Triton Square Office Tower Y
29F 1-8-11 Harumi, Chuo-ku, Tokyo, 104-
6129, Japan
Tel.: (81) 366309811
Data Processing Services
N.A.I.C.S.: 518210

ANDRITZ Fabrics and Rolls Oy **(1)**
Sementtitehtaankatu 10, PO Box 7, 04260,
Kerava, Finland
Tel.: (358) 204505555
Data Processing Services
N.A.I.C.S.: 518210

ANDRITZ Feed & Biofuel Canada
Inc. **(2)**
3 Allison Line, PO Box 249, Blenheim, N0P
1A0, ON, Canada
Tel.: (519) 676-7057
Animal Feed Mfr & Distr
N.A.I.C.S.: 311119

ANDRITZ Fiedler GmbH **(1)**
Weidener Strasse 9, 93057, Regensburg,
Germany
Tel.: (49) 94164010
Sales Range: $50-74.9 Million
Emp.: 27
Industrial Machinery Mfr
N.A.I.C.S.: 333248

ANDRITZ Fliessbett Systeme
GmbH **(1)**
Goethestrasse 36, 88214, Ravensburg,
Germany
Tel.: (49) 751560580
Sales Range: $25-49.9 Million
Emp.: 4
Fluid Bed System Mfr
N.A.I.C.S.: 332912

ANDRITZ Frautech S.r.l. **(1)**
Via Luigi Dalla Via 15, 36015, Schio, Italy
Tel.: (39) 0445575695
Web Site: http://www.andritz.com
Emp.: 5
Industrial Machinery & Equipment Mfr &
Distr
N.A.I.C.S.: 333248

ANDRITZ Hydro GmbH **(1)**
Penzinger Strasse 76, 1141, Vienna, Austria

Tel.: (43) 1891000
Sales Range: $1-4.9 Billion
Emp.: 200
Hydroelectric Power Plant Turbine & Other
Electromechanical Equipment Mfr & Ser-
vices
N.A.I.C.S.: 333611

Subsidiary (Non-US):

ANDRITZ HYDRO AB **(2)**
Vaplans Vag 29, PO Box 1, Nalden, 835 05,
Krokom, Sweden
Tel.: (46) 640 177 00
Sales Range: $50-74.9 Million
Emp.: 145
Industrial Machinery Mfr & Distr
N.A.I.C.S.: 333248

ANDRITZ HYDRO AS **(2)**
Tel.: (47) 61315200
Sales Range: $50-74.9 Million
Emp.: 150
Hydro Power Plant Machinery Mfr
N.A.I.C.S.: 333248

ANDRITZ HYDRO C.A. **(2)**
Avenida la Estancia Torre las Mercedes
Piso 6 Of 606, Chuao, 1060, Caracas, Ven-
ezuela
Tel.: (58) 212 9919159
Industrial Machinery Distr
N.A.I.C.S.: 423830

Subsidiary (US):

ANDRITZ HYDRO Corp. **(2)**
10735 David Taylor Dr Ste 500, Charlotte,
NC 28262
Tel.: (704) 943-4343
Web Site: http://reports.andritz.com
Electro Mechanical System Distr
N.A.I.C.S.: 423690
Jack Heaton *(Mgr-Sls)*

Subsidiary (Non-US):

ANDRITZ HYDRO GmbH **(2)**
Escher-Wyss-Weg 1, 88212, Ravensburg,
Germany
Tel.: (49) 751295110
Web Site: http://www.andritz-hydro.de
Sales Range: $125-149.9 Million
Emp.: 500
Electromechanical Equipment Mfr & Distr
N.A.I.C.S.: 333613
Gerhard Krriegler *(Gen Mgr)*

Representative Office (Non-US):

ANDRITZ HYDRO GmbH - Ukraine
Representative Office **(2)**
Uliza Artema 60 Office 306, 4053, Kiev,
Ukraine
Tel.: (380) 44 4843939
Electromechanical Equipment Distr
N.A.I.C.S.: 423690

ANDRITZ HYDRO GmbH - Vietnam
Representative Office **(2)**
108 Trieu Viet Vuong Street Hai Ba, Hanoi,
Vietnam
Tel.: (84) 4 394 54 765
Industrial Machinery Distr
N.A.I.C.S.: 423830

Subsidiary (Non-US):

ANDRITZ HYDRO Ltd. Sti. **(2)**
ITOB Organize Sanayi Bolgesi Sokak No
11, Tekeli - Menderes, Izmir, 10026, Turkiye
Tel.: (90) 2325703800
Web Site: http://www.andritz.com
Sales Range: $50-74.9 Million
Emp.: 60
Industrial Machinery Distr
N.A.I.C.S.: 423830

ANDRITZ HYDRO Ltda. **(2)**
Cra 67 No 100-20 Piso 9, 93228, Bogota,
Colombia
Tel.: (57) 1 7448200
Industrial Machinery Distr
N.A.I.C.S.: 423830

ANDRITZ HYDRO Ltee/Ltd. **(2)**
2260 32nd Avenue, Lachine, H3T 3H4, QC,
Canada
Tel.: (514) 631-7900
Web Site: http://www.andritz.com
Industrial Machinery Distr

N.A.I.C.S.: 423830

ANDRITZ HYDRO S.A. **(2)**
Centro Comercial y Empresarial El Polo II
Oficina C 304, Avenida El Polo 670, Lima,
Peru
Tel.: (51) 1 434 33 33
Industrial Machinery Distr
N.A.I.C.S.: 423830

ANDRITZ HYDRO S.A. de C.V. **(2)**
Av Ciudad Industrial No 977 Col Ciudad
Industrial, 58200, Morelia, Michoacan,
Mexico
Tel.: (52) 443 323 1530
Web Site: http://www.andritz.com
Industrial Machinery Mfr
N.A.I.C.S.: 333248

ANDRITZ HYDRO S.A.S. **(2)**
49-51 Boulevard Paul Langevin, 38601,
Fontaine, France
Tel.: (33) 476 859 523
Web Site: http://www.andritz.com
Sales Range: $50-74.9 Million
Emp.: 50
Hydroelectric Power Generation Services
N.A.I.C.S.: 221111

ANDRITZ HYDRO S.L. **(2)**
Poligono Industrial La Garza 2 Carretera de
Algete M-106 Km 2, 28110, Madrid, Spain
Tel.: (34) 914251000
Emp.: 10
Hydraulic Power Generation Equipment
Distr
N.A.I.C.S.: 423830

ANDRITZ HYDRO S.r.l.
Unipersonale **(2)**
Via Daniele Manin 16/18, 36015, Schio, Vi-
cenza, Italy
Tel.: (39) 0445678211
Web Site: http://www.andritz.com
Emp.: 158
Industrial Machinery Mfr
N.A.I.C.S.: 333248
Mario Aquila *(Mng Dir)*

ANDRITZ HYDRO s.r.o. **(2)**
Pocernicka 272/96, 10800, Prague, Czech
Republic
Tel.: (420) 234701811
Web Site: http://www.andritz.com
Sales Range: $25-49.9 Million
Emp.: 25
Electromechanical Equipment Distr
N.A.I.C.S.: 423830

ANDRITZ HYDRO, Inc. **(2)**
Unit 19 06 Corporate Center 141 Valero
Street Corner Sedeno St, Salcedo Village,
1227, Makati, Manila, Philippines
Tel.: (63) 2 50150 93
Emp.: 7
Hydraulic Power Generation Services
N.A.I.C.S.: 221111
Maricar Ranises *(Sec)*

ANDRITZ Hydro AG **(2)**
Obernaustrasse 4, 6010, Kriens, Switzer-
land
Tel.: (41) 413295111
Emp.: 26
Hydroelectric Power Plant Turbine & Other
Electromechanical Equipment Mfr & Ser-
vices
N.A.I.C.S.: 333611
Christian Dubois *(Mng Dir)*

Unit (Domestic):

ANDRITZ HYDRO AG ABMB
Bulach **(3)**
Feldstrasse 60, 8180, Bulach, Switzerland
Tel.: (41) 44 864 4700
Web Site: http://www.andritz.com
Coating & Drying Machinery Mfr
N.A.I.C.S.: 333248

Branch (Domestic):

ANDRITZ HYDRO SA **(3)**
Rue des Deux Gares 6, 1800, Vevey, Swit-
zerland
Tel.: (41) 21 925 7700
Web Site: http://www.andritz.com
Sales Range: $50-74.9 Million
Emp.: 90
Electromechanical Equipment Distr
N.A.I.C.S.: 423690

Subsidiary (Non-US):

Andritz HYDRO Private Limited **(2)**
D-17 MPAKVN Industrial Area, District
Raisen Mandideep, Bhopal, 462 046, India
Tel.: (91) 7480400400
Industrial Machinery & Equipment Distr
N.A.I.C.S.: 423830

Subsidiary (Non-US):

Andritz HYDRO Nepal Pvt. Ltd. **(3)**
Ward No 11 Maitighar Babarmahal, Kath-
mandu, Nepal
Tel.: (977) 14101652
Industrial Machinery & Equipment Distr
N.A.I.C.S.: 423830

Subsidiary (Non-US):

PT. ANDRITZ HYDRO **(2)**
Jl Talang No 3 Pegangsaan, Menteng, Ja-
karta, 10320, Indonesia
Tel.: (62) 213906929
Emp.: 100
Electromechanical Equipment Distr
N.A.I.C.S.: 423690

ANDRITZ Inc. **(1)**
1115 Northmeadow Pkwy, Roswell, GA
30076-3857
Tel.: (770) 640-2500
Web Site: http://www.andritz.com
Sales Range: $50-74.9 Million
Emp.: 250
Design & Engineering of Products for the
Pulp Industry
N.A.I.C.S.: 541330
Jay Miele *(VP & Gen Mgr)*

Branch (Domestic):

ANDRITZ Inc. - Glen Falls **(2)**
13 Pruyns Is Dr, Glens Falls, NY 12801
Tel.: (518) 798-7400
Web Site: http://www.andritz.com
Sales Range: $25-49.9 Million
Engineering Firm
N.A.I.C.S.: 811210

Division (Domestic):

ANDRITZ Inc. - Kusters Division **(2)**
201 Zima Park Dr, Spartanburg, SC 29301
Tel.: (864) 587-4848
Web Site: http://www.andritz.com
Emp.: 45
Non Woven & Paper Products Mfr
N.A.I.C.S.: 313230
Tammy Mittag *(Office Mgr)*

Branch (Domestic):

ANDRITZ Inc. - Pell City **(2)**
PO Box 767, Pell City, AL 35125-0767
Tel.: (205) 338-3331
Hydropower, Pulp & Paper Mfr
N.A.I.C.S.: 322110

Subsidiary (Domestic):

ANDRITZ KMPT Inc. **(2)**
8070 Production Dr, Florence, KY 41042
Tel.: (859) 547-1100
Web Site: http://www.andritz.com
Sales Range: $25-49.9 Million
Industrial Machinery Mfr & Distr
N.A.I.C.S.: 333248

ANDRITZ Paper Machinery Ltd. **(2)**
101 S Main St Ste 400, Janesville, WI
53545
Tel.: (608) 758-5920
Web Site: http://www.andritz.com
Paper Machinery Mfr
N.A.I.C.S.: 333243

ANDRITZ Separation Inc. **(2)**
1600 Boston Providence Hwy, Walpole, MA
02081 **(100%)**
Tel.: (508) 404-1400
Web Site: http://www.andritz.com
Sales Range: $25-49.9 Million
Emp.: 22
Mfr of Specialized Machinery for the Pro-
cess Industry
N.A.I.C.S.: 333998

Imagine That, Inc. **(2)**
6830 Via Del Oro Ste 230, San Jose, CA
95119-1390

ANDRITZ AG—(Continued)

Tel.: (408) 365-0305.
Web Site: http://www.extendsim.com
Software Publisher
N.A.I.C.S.: 513210
Kathi Hansen (Coord-Mktg)

ANDRITZ India Private Limited (1)
CB-14 Sector-1 Salt Lake Commercial
Complex Salt Lake, Salt Lake, Kulkata,
700064, India
Tel.: (91) 33 23212239
Sales Range: $75-99.9 Million
Emp.: 2
Hydroelectric Power Generation Services
N.A.I.C.S.: 221111
Mahadevan Anand (Mng Dir)

Subsidiary (Domestic):

ANDRITZ SEPARATION (India) Private Ltd. (2)
389 400/2a 400/2c Padur Road, Kuttampakkam Village Poonamallee Taluk Tiruvallur Dist, Chennai, 600 124, India
Tel.: (91) 44 4399 1111
Web Site: http://www.andritz.com
Sales Range: $25-49.9 Million
Industrial Machinery Mfr
N.A.I.C.S.: 333248

Subsidiary (Non-US):

ANDRITZ Technologies Pvt. Ltd. (2)
Tel.: (91) 8025444640
Sales Range: $50-74.9 Million
Emp.: 12
Industrial Machinery Mfr
N.A.I.C.S.: 333248
Suresh Chandra (Gen Mgr)

ANDRITZ Ingenieria S.A. (1)
PO Box 1017, Hospitalet de Llobregat,
08902, Barcelona, Spain
Tel.: (34) 932988598
Web Site: http://www.andritz.com
Emp.: 7
Mfr of Equipment for the Pulp & Paper Industry
N.A.I.C.S.: 333243

ANDRITZ Jochman s.r.o. (1)
Radlinskeho 19, 052 01, Spisska Nova Ves,
Slovakia
Tel.: (421) 53 4198 111
Sales Range: $25-49.9 Million
Emp.: 70
Industrial Steel Machinery Mfr
N.A.I.C.S.: 333248

ANDRITZ K.K. (1)
Harumi Triton Square Office Tower Y 29F
1-8-11, Harumi, Tokyo, 104-6229, Japan
Tel.: (81) 3 3536 9700
Web Site: http://www.andritz.com
Sales Range: $25-49.9 Million
Emp.: 50
Pulp & Paper Industry Machinery Distr
N.A.I.C.S.: 333243

ANDRITZ KMPT GmbH (1)
Industriestrasse 1-3, 85256, Vierkirchen,
Germany
Tel.: (49) 8139802990
Web Site: http://www.andritz.com
Solid & Liquid Separation Machinery Mfr
N.A.I.C.S.: 333248

ANDRITZ Kaiser GmbH (1)
Gewerbestrasse 30, Golshausen, 75015,
Bretten, Germany
Tel.: (49) 7252 910 01
Web Site: http://www.andritz.com
Punching & Metal Forming Presses Mfr
N.A.I.C.S.: 333517

ANDRITZ Kft. (1)
Dozsa telep 69, 6060, Tiszakecske, Hungary
Tel.: (36) 76542100
Sales Range: $100-124.9 Million
Emp.: 300
Electric Power Equipment Mfr
N.A.I.C.S.: 333611

ANDRITZ Kufferath GmbH (1)
Lommessemstrasse 32-36, 52353, Duren,
Germany
Tel.: (49) 24218010
Web Site: http://www.andritz.com

Forming Fabric Mfr & Distr
N.A.I.C.S.: 322291

ANDRITZ Kufferath s.r.o. (1)
Ku Bratke 5, 934 05, Levice, Slovakia
Tel.: (421) 36 6356 324
Web Site: http://www.andritz.com
Sales Range: $25-49.9 Million
Emp.: 79
Paper Industry Fabric Mfr & Distr
N.A.I.C.S.: 313320

ANDRITZ Kusters GmbH (1)
Eduard-Kusters-Str 1, 47805, Krefeld, Germany
Tel.: (49) 2151340
Web Site: http://www.kuesters.com
Sales Range: $125-149.9 Million
Emp.: 300
Nonwoven & Paper Finishing Machines Mfr
N.A.I.C.S.: 313230

ANDRITZ Ltd. (1)
Suite 5L Business Centre North Mill Bridgefoot, Belper, DE56 1YD, Derbyshire, United
Kingdom
Tel.: (44) 1773 599 540
Web Site: http://www.andritz.com
Solid & Liquid Separation Machinery Mfr
N.A.I.C.S.: 333248

ANDRITZ Ltd./Ltee. (1)
2260 32nd Avenue, Lachine, H3T 3H4, QC,
Canada
Tel.: (514) 631-7900
Web Site: http://www.andritz.com
Emp.: 300
Industrial Equipment Distr
N.A.I.C.S.: 423830

Subsidiary (Domestic):

ANDRITZ AUTOMATION Ltd. (2)
345 Wallace Street Suite 403, Nanaimo,
V9R 5B6, BC, Canada
Tel.: (250) 753-5307
Web Site: http://www.andritz.com
Sales Range: $50-74.9 Million
Emp.: 15
Industrial Machinery Distr
N.A.I.C.S.: 423830
Chris Bassett (Dir-Engrg)

ANDRITZ Fiber Drying Ltd. (2)
2260 32nd Ave, Lachine, H8T 3H4, QC,
Canada   (100%)
Tel.: (514) 631-7900
Web Site: http://www.andritz.com
Sales Range: $50-74.9 Million
Emp.: 60
Paper Treatment Systems
N.A.I.C.S.: 333310

**ANDRITZ Iggesund Tools Canada
Inc.** (2)
1405 Stevens Road 10, Kelowna, V1Z 3Y2,
BC, Canada
Tel.: (250) 769-1288
Industrial Machine Tool Mfr
N.A.I.C.S.: 333517

Division (Domestic):

ANDRITZ SEPARATION (2)
2600 Wentz Avenue, Saskatoon, S7K 2L1,
SK, Canada
Tel.: (306) 931-0801
Web Site: http://www.andritz.com
Emp.: 45
Industrial Machinery Equipment Distr
N.A.I.C.S.: 423830

ANDRITZ Maerz GmbH (1)
Corneliusstrasse 36, D-40215, Dusseldorf,
Germany   (100%)
Tel.: (49) 211384250
Web Site: http://www.andritz-maerz.com
Sales Range: $25-49.9 Million
Emp.: 40
Industrial Furnace Designer, Mfr & Installation
N.A.I.C.S.: 333994

ANDRITZ Metals France S.A.S. (1)
4 avenue Laurent Cely Hall A, 92600,
Asnieres-sur-Seine, France
Tel.: (33) 140803400
Industrial Steel Mfr & Distr
N.A.I.C.S.: 331110

**ANDRITZ Metals Germany
GmbH** (1)

Stephanopeler Str 22, 58675, Hemer, Germany
Tel.: (49) 2372540
Industrial Metal Mfr & Distr
N.A.I.C.S.: 331110

**ANDRITZ Metals Netherlands
B.V.** (1)
Willem Fenengastraat 10, 1096 BN, Amsterdam, Netherlands
Tel.: (31) 204602000
Industrial Metal Mfr & Distr
N.A.I.C.S.: 331110

ANDRITZ Metals USA Inc (1)
Southpointe Indus Park 500 Technology Dr,
Canonsburg, PA 15317-9584
Tel.: (724) 746-2300
Web Site: https://www.andritz.com
Design & Construction of Industrial Heat
Transfer & Automation Equipment
N.A.I.C.S.: 541330

ANDRITZ Oy (1)
Tammasaarenkatu 1, 00180, Helsinki, Finland
Tel.: (358) 204505555
Web Site: http://www.andritz.com
Sales Range: $25-49.9 Million
Emp.: 60
Design & Engineering of Heat Recovery for
the Pulp & Paper Industry
N.A.I.C.S.: 541330

Subsidiary (Domestic):

Savonlinna Works Oy (2)
Lypsyniemenkatu 5, PO Box 54, 57101,
Savonlinna, Finland   (100%)
Tel.: (358) 204506000
Supplier of Equipment Specializing in
Chemical & Heat Recovery for the Pulp &
Paper Industry
N.A.I.C.S.: 325998
Kaj Lindh (Mng Dir)

Subsidiary (Non-US):

ANDRITZ PULP & PAPER (1)
Stattegger Strasse 18, 8045, Graz, Austria
Tel.: (43) 316 69020
Web Site: http://www.andritz.com
Paper Idustry Machinery Mfr
N.A.I.C.S.: 333243

Subsidiary (US):

ANDRITZ Paperchine (2)
1155 Prairie Hill Rd, Rockton, IL 61072
Tel.: (815) 389-8200
Web Site: http://www.andritz.com
Paper Idustry Machinery Mfr
N.A.I.C.S.: 333243
Jean-Marc Boudreau (VP-Global Sls &
Mktg)

ANDRITZ Power Sdn. Bhd. (1)
A-9-2D Block A Plaza Mont Kiara 2 Jalan
Mont Kiara, Mont Kiara, 50480, Kuala Lumpur, Malaysia
Tel.: (60) 3 6201 1741
Sales Range: $75-99.9 Million
Emp.: 87
Eletric Power Generation Services
N.A.I.C.S.: 221118
Michael Kalum Moggie (Gen Mgr)

ANDRITZ Pty. Ltd. (1)
Suite 13 2nd Floor Granada Centre 22
Chartwell Drive, Umhlanga, 4319, Durban,
South Africa
Tel.: (27) 31 561 7271
Sales Range: $25-49.9 Million
Emp.: 50
Pulp & Paper Machinery Whslr
N.A.I.C.S.: 423830

Subsidiary (Domestic):

ANDRITZ DELKOR (Pty) Ltd. (2)
60 Kyalami Boulevard, Kyalami, 1684,
South Africa
Tel.: (27) 110127300
Sales Range: $50-74.9 Million
Emp.: 65
Mining Liquid Separation Equipment Distr
N.A.I.C.S.: 423810

**ANDRITZ Pumps Germany
GmbH** (1)
Marie-Curie-Strasse 19, 73529, Schwabisch
Gmund, Germany
Tel.: (49) 71716090

Industrial Pumps Mfr & Distr
N.A.I.C.S.: 333914

ANDRITZ Ritz GmbH (1)
Guglingstrasse 50, 73529, Schwabisch
Gmund, Germany
Tel.: (49) 7171 609 0
Sales Range: $50-74.9 Million
Emp.: 180
Centrifugal Pump & Motor Mfr
N.A.I.C.S.: 333914
Andreas Schulte (Mng Dir)

ANDRITZ S.R.L. (1)
Transilvaniei No 21, Sibiu, 555300, Cisnadie, Romania
Tel.: (40) 269206053
Web Site: http://www.lenser.ro
Sales Range: $25-49.9 Million
Emp.: 5
Filter Equipment Mfr
N.A.I.C.S.: 333413
Cristi Fodor (Dir Gen)

ANDRITZ SAS (1)
Allee de Garenne, ZI Le Buxerloux, 36000,
Chateauroux, France
Tel.: (33) 2 5461 3333
Web Site: http://www.andritz.com
Industrial Equipment Mfr
N.A.I.C.S.: 333248

Subsidiary (Domestic):

ANDRITZ Asselin-Thibeau (2)
41 Rue Camille Randoing, 76504, Elbeuf,
France
Tel.: (33) 232964242
Web Site: http://www.andritz.com
Emp.: 200
Textile Machinery Distr
N.A.I.C.S.: 423830

ANDRITZ Biax S.A.S. (2)
18 Rue du Lac Saint Andre Immeuble Le
Dauphin, Savoie Technolac, 73382, Le
Bourget du Lac, France
Tel.: (33) 479 268 560
Web Site: http://www.andritz.com
Industrial Machinery Mfr & Distr
N.A.I.C.S.: 333248

**ANDRITZ Boisfer Iggesund
S.A.S.** (2)
ZI de la Tuilliere, 01700, Miribel, France
Tel.: (33) 4 785 597 97
Web Site: http://www.andritz.com
Industrial Machine Tool Distr
N.A.I.C.S.: 423830

ANDRITZ Perfojet S.A.S. (2)
ZA Pre-Milliet 530 Rue Aristide Berges,
38330, Montbonnot-Saint-Martin, France
Tel.: (33) 4 7652 2311
Industrial Equipment Mfr
N.A.I.C.S.: 333248

ANDRITZ Selas S.A.S. (2)
4 Avenue Laurent Cely Hall A, 92600,
Asnieres-sur-Seine, France
Tel.: (33) 1 4080 3400
Sales Range: $25-49.9 Million
Emp.: 30
Industrial Furnace Distr
N.A.I.C.S.: 423830
Jurgan Ziemendorff (Pres)

ANDRITZ SEPARATION GmbH (1)
Edmund-Rumpler-Strasse 6A, 51149, Cologne, Germany
Tel.: (49) 220357520
Sales Range: $50-74.9 Million
Emp.: 15
Mechanical & Thermal Separation System
Mfr
N.A.I.C.S.: 333310

ANDRITZ Savonlinna Works Oy (1)
Lypsyniemenkatu 5, PO Box 54, 57101,
Savonlinna, Finland
Tel.: (358) 204505555
Industrial Equipment Mfr & Distr
N.A.I.C.S.: 334513

ANDRITZ Separation Italy S.R.L. (1)
Via Ravizza 58, 20149, Milan, Italy
Tel.: (39) 025743011
Industrial Equipment Mfr & Distr
N.A.I.C.S.: 334513

ANDRITZ Singapore Pte. Ltd. (1)

Tel.: (65) 65121800
Sales Range: $25-49.9 Million
Emp.: 5
Industrial Machinery Mfr
N.A.I.C.S.: 333248

Representative Office (Non-US):

ANDRITZ Singapore Pte. Ltd. (2)
Unit 4B MB Aguirre Building III F Reyes St
Balibago Santa Rosa, Laguna, 4026, Manila, Philippines
Tel.: (63) 2 420 8182
Industrial Machinery Distr
N.A.I.C.S.: 423830

ANDRITZ Sundwig GmbH (1)
Stephanopeler Strasse 22, 58675, Hemer, Germany
Tel.: (49) 2372 540
Emp.: 300
Industrial Machinery Mfr & Distr
N.A.I.C.S.: 333248

ANDRITZ THERMTEC B.V. (1)
Wijnhaven 76, 3011 WT, Rotterdam, Netherlands
Tel.: (31) 102801660
Sales Range: $25-49.9 Million
Emp.: 15
Industrial Furnace Distr
N.A.I.C.S.: 423830
Rodney Verkaart *(Gen Mgr)*

ASKO, Inc. (1)
501 W 7th Ave, Homestead, PA 15120
Tel.: (412) 461-4110
Web Site: https://www.askoinc.com
Cutting Tool & Machine Tool Accessory Mfr
N.A.I.C.S.: 333515
Al Zelt *(Dir-Sls & Mktg)*

AWEBA Werkzeugbau GmbH (1)
Damaschkestr 7, 08280, Aue, Germany
Tel.: (49) 37712730
Web Site: http://www.aweba.de
Machine Tools Mfr
N.A.I.C.S.: 333517

Andritz (Shanghai) Equipment & Engineering Co., Ltd. (1)
No 2288 Rongle East Road, Songjiang District, Shanghai, 201600, China
Tel.: (86) 2157745781
Industrial Machinery & Equipment Distr
N.A.I.C.S.: 423830

Andritz - Wolfensberger Special Alloy Foundry Co., Ltd. (1)
83 Zone B Sanshui, Central Technical Industry Park Sanshui District, Foshan, 528137, Guangdong, China
Tel.: (86) 75787393800
Emp.: 130
Industrial Machinery & Equipment Distr
N.A.I.C.S.: 423830

Andritz AG (1)
Warszawa 142, PO Box 46, 02-497, Warsaw, Poland
Tel.: (48) 607300808
Industrial Machinery & Equipment Distr
N.A.I.C.S.: 423830

Andritz AG (1)
Rm 6A2 and 6A3 Hanwei Plaza 7 Guanghua Road, Chaoyang District, Beijing, 100004, China
Tel.: (86) 1085262720
Industrial Machinery & Equipment Distr
N.A.I.C.S.: 423830

Andritz B.V. (1)
Nijverheidsweg 3c, Den Helder, 1785 AA, Hoorn, Netherlands
Tel.: (31) 223633474
Industrial Machinery & Equipment Distr
N.A.I.C.S.: 423830

Andritz Construcoes e Montagens Ltda. (1)
Alameda Tocantins 350 sala 1204, Industrial e Empresarial, Barueri, 06455-020, Sao Paulo, Brazil
Tel.: (55) 1141330000
Industrial Machinery & Equipment Distr
N.A.I.C.S.: 423830

Andritz Environmental Engineering (Shanghai) Co., Ltd. (1)
15F Tower B Baoland Plaza 588 Dalian

Road, Shanghai, 200082, China
Tel.: (86) 2131089399
Industrial Machinery & Equipment Distr
N.A.I.C.S.: 423830

Andritz Euroslot France SAS (1)
Usine du Relais des Priedons Sud, Scorbe Clairvaux, 86140, Vienne, France
Tel.: (33) 549939393
Industrial Machinery & Equipment Distr
N.A.I.C.S.: 423830

Andritz FBB GmbH (1)
Breite Strasse 194, 41238, Monchengladbach, Germany
Tel.: (49) 21669700400
Industrial Machinery & Equipment Distr
N.A.I.C.S.: 423830

Andritz FZCO (1)
Building No 6WB West Side Dafza, PO Box 66, Dubai, United Arab Emirates
Tel.: (971) 42146546
Industrial Machinery & Equipment Distr
N.A.I.C.S.: 423830

Andritz Fabrics & Rolls AG (1)
Am Langen Graben 22, 52353, Duren, Germany
Tel.: (49) 242184050
Industrial Machinery & Equipment Distr
N.A.I.C.S.: 423830

Andritz Fabrics & Rolls Inc. (1)
14101 Capital Blvd, Youngsville, NC 27596
Tel.: (919) 562-5867
Industrial Machinery & Equipment Distr
N.A.I.C.S.: 423830

Andritz Fabrics & Rolls S.A. de C.V. (1)
Circuito Balvanera No 2 Fracc Agro Ind Balvanera, Corregidora, 76920, Queretaro, Mexico
Tel.: (52) 4421929500
Industrial Machinery & Equipment Distr
N.A.I.C.S.: 423830

Andritz Gouda B.V. (1)
Coenecoop 88, 2741 PD, Waddinxveen, Netherlands
Tel.: (31) 182623723
Industrial Machinery & Equipment Distr
N.A.I.C.S.: 423830

Andritz HYDRO (Pty.) Ltd. (1)
76 Kyalami Boulevard Kyalami Business Park, 1684, Kyalami, Gauteng, South Africa
Tel.: (27) 110127357
Industrial Machinery & Equipment Distr
N.A.I.C.S.: 423830

Andritz HYDRO (SU), Lda. (1)
N 3 Rua s/n Municipio de Belas - Talatona, Condominio Talatona Village, Luanda, Angola
Tel.: (244) 928311182
Industrial Machinery & Equipment Distr
N.A.I.C.S.: 423830

Andritz HYDRO AG (1)
Avenue Felix Eboue 1er etage Immeuble SDV, 2345, Brazzaville, Congo, Republic of
Tel.: (242) 798575507
Industrial Machinery & Equipment Distr
N.A.I.C.S.: 423830

Andritz HYDRO Brasil Ltda. (1)
Via de Acesso Joao Gazerta 4 351 - A - Sala SR Filial AHB Chacaras, California, Aracatuba, 16026-680, Sao Paulo, Brazil
Tel.: (55) 1141330004
Industrial Machinery & Equipment Distr
N.A.I.C.S.: 423830

Andritz HYDRO Canada Inc. (1)
6100 Trans Canada Highway, Pointe-Claire, H9R 1B9, QC, Canada
Tel.: (514) 428-6700
Industrial Machinery & Equipment Distr
N.A.I.C.S.: 423830

Subsidiary (Domestic):

ANBO Inc. (2)
3 Allison Line, PO Box 249, Blenheim, N0P 1A0, ON, Canada
Tel.: (519) 676-7057
Industrial Machinery & Equipment Distr
N.A.I.C.S.: 423830
Roger Cossette *(Mgr-Reg Sls)*

HMI Construction Inc. (2)
1451 Graham Bell, Boucherville, J4B 6A1, QC, Canada
Tel.: (450) 449-3999
Web Site: https://www.hmiconstruction.ca
Engineering Construction Services
N.A.I.C.S.: 541330
Martin Chevalier *(Mgr-Proposal)*

Andritz HYDRO DRC SARL (1)
4239 de l Avenue Tombalbaye troisieme etage de l Immeuble le Prestige, Commune de la Gombe, Kinshasa, Congo, Democratic Republic of
Tel.: (243) 994547708
Industrial Machinery & Equipment Distr
N.A.I.C.S.: 423830

Andritz HYDRO Hammerfest (UK) Limited (1)
Tay House 2nd Floor Spaces Office 45 300 Bath Street, Glasgow, G2 4JR, Central Belt, United Kingdom
Tel.: (44) 2039586413
Industrial Machinery & Equipment Distr
N.A.I.C.S.: 423830

Andritz HYDRO Ltda. (1)
Alameda Tocantins 350 - Alphaville Industrial, Barueri, 06455-931, Sao Paulo, Brazil
Tel.: (55) 1141330000
Industrial Machinery & Equipment Distr
N.A.I.C.S.: 423830

Andritz HYDRO Oy (1)
Tel.: (358) 325643111
Industrial Machinery & Equipment Distr
N.A.I.C.S.: 423830

Andritz HYDRO, Unipessoal Lda. (1)
Edificio Peninsula Praca do Bom Sucesso n 127-131 Escritorio 508, 4150-146, Porto, Portugal
Tel.: (351) 309704970
Industrial Machinery & Equipment Distr
N.A.I.C.S.: 423830

Andritz MeWa GmbH (1)
Herdweg 4, Gechingen, 75391, Calw, Germany
Tel.: (49) 70569250
Industrial Machinery & Equipment Distr
N.A.I.C.S.: 423830

Subsidiary (Non-US):

Andritz MeWa Kft. (2)
Gesztenyefa utca 4, 9027, Gyor, Hungary
Tel.: (36) 96525764
Industrial Machinery & Equipment Distr
N.A.I.C.S.: 423830

Andritz Novimpianti S.r.l. (1)
Via del Fanucchi 17, Capannori, 55012, Marlia, Lucca, Italy
Tel.: (39) 058330219
Industrial Machinery & Equipment Distr
N.A.I.C.S.: 423830

Andritz O&M Private Limited (1)
D-17 MPAKVN Industrial Area, District Raisen Mandideep, Bhopal, 462 046, India
Tel.: (91) 7480403393
Industrial Machinery & Equipment Distr
N.A.I.C.S.: 423830

Andritz Ritz Immobilien GmbH (1)
Guglingstrasse 50, 73529, Schwabisch Gmünd, Germany
Tel.: (49) 71716090
Industrial Machinery & Equipment Distr
N.A.I.C.S.: 423830

Andritz Ritz Pte. Ltd. (1)
25 Tuas Ave 4, Singapore, 639375, Singapore
Tel.: (65) 65121800
Industrial Machinery & Equipment Distr
N.A.I.C.S.: 423830

Andritz Sdn. Bhd. (1)
A-30-7 Level 30 Block A Menara UOA Bangsar No 5 Jalan Bangsar Utama 1, 59000, Kuala Lumpur, Malaysia
Tel.: (60) 322012333
Industrial Machinery & Equipment Distr
N.A.I.C.S.: 423830

Andritz Separation & Pump Technologies India Private Limited (1)
S No 389 400/2A 400/2C Padur Road, Kut-

tampakkam Poonamallee Tiruvallur, Chennai, 600 124, India
Tel.: (91) 4443991111
Industrial Equipment Mfr & Distr
N.A.I.C.S.: 334513

Andritz Slovakia s.r.o. (1)
Chemlonska 1, 066 01, Humenne, Slovakia
Tel.: (421) 572909001
Emp.: 340
Industrial Machinery & Equipment Distr
N.A.I.C.S.: 423830

Andritz Soutec AG (1)
Rotfarb 4, Neftenbach, 8413, Winterthur, Switzerland
Tel.: (41) 523040707
Industrial Machinery & Equipment Distr
N.A.I.C.S.: 423830

Andritz Technologies AB (1)
Gavlegatan 22, PO Box 21154, 100 31, Stockholm, Sweden
Tel.: (46) 858602500
Industrial Machinery & Equipment Distr
N.A.I.C.S.: 423830

Andritz Technologies H.K. Ltd. (1)
Room 1905 19/F West Tower Shun Tak Centre 168-200 Connaught Road, Central, China (Hong Kong)
Tel.: (852) 39040988
Industrial Machinery & Equipment Distr
N.A.I.C.S.: 423830

Andritz Uruguay S.A. (1)
Ruta Vladimir Roslik Km 307 - Zona Franca UPM, 65000, Fray Bentos, Uruguay
Tel.: (598) 45620100
Industrial Machinery & Equipment Distr
N.A.I.C.S.: 423830

Andritz Vietnam Company Limited (1)
Suite 1410 Daeha Business Centre 360 Kim Ma Street, Ba Dinh, Hanoi, Vietnam
Tel.: (84) 2439454765
Electro Mechanical Equipment Mfr
N.A.I.C.S.: 335999

Anstalt für Stromungsmaschinen GmbH (1)
Andritzer Reichsstrasse 68B, 8045, Graz, Austria
Tel.: (43) 316692728
Industrial Machinery & Equipment Distr
N.A.I.C.S.: 423830

Bonetti Canada Inc. (1)
101 Place Jourdain, Trois Rivieres, G8W 2H3, QC, Canada
Tel.: (819) 694-2322
Industrial Machinery Equipment Mfr & Distr
N.A.I.C.S.: 333243

DIATEC s.r.l. (1)
Strada Statale 151 km 13, Collecorvino, 65013, Italy
Tel.: (39) 085 82060 1
Web Site: http://www.diatec.it
Industrial Machinery Mfr
N.A.I.C.S.: 333248

Subsidiary (US):

Arkwright Advanced Coating, Inc. (2)
538 Main St, Fiskeville, RI 02823
Tel.: (401) 821-1000
Web Site: http://www.sihlinc.com
Emp.: 65
Coated Paper Mfr
N.A.I.C.S.: 322220
Paul Jessey *(Dir-IT)*

SIHL LLC (2)
713 Fenway Ave Ste B, Chesapeake, VA 23323
Tel.: (757) 966-7180
Web Site: http://www.sihlinc.com
Printing Material Mfr
N.A.I.C.S.: 325910
Chris McInerney *(Mng Dir)*

Farina Presse S.r.l. (1)
Via Provinciale 31, 23867, Suello, LC, Italy
Tel.: (39) 031655881
Web Site: https://www.farinapresse.it
Machine Tools Mfr
N.A.I.C.S.: 333517

Huyck.Wangner Japan Limited - Asahi Plant (1)

ANDRITZ AG—(Continued)

881-1 Tsukuriya, Hokota, 311-1415, Ibaraki-Ken, Japan
Tel.: (81) 291371205
Industrial Machinery & Equipment Distr
N.A.I.C.S.: 423830

J. Parpala Oy (1)
Mannerheiminaukio 5, 67100, Kokkola, Finland
Tel.: (358) 204505555
Industrial Equipment Mfr & Distr
N.A.I.C.S.: 334513

Jaybee Eng. (Holdings) Pty. Ltd. (1)
3 Spring Street, Sydney, 2000, NSW, Australia
Tel.: (61) 282494336
Industrial Machinery & Equipment Distr
N.A.I.C.S.: 423830

Subsidiary (Non-US):

Andritz (NZ) Ltd. (2)
Young Read Woundberg Limited 13
McLean Street, Tauranga, 3110, New Zealand
Tel.: (64) 61282494336
Industrial Machinery & Equipment Distr
N.A.I.C.S.: 423830

LLC Andritz HYDRO
Boulevard Enthuziastov 2, 109544, Moscow, Russia
Tel.: (7) 9260791025
Industrial Machinery & Equipment Distr
N.A.I.C.S.: 423830

Lenser Filtration GmbH (1)
Breslauer Strasse 8, 89250, Senden, Germany
Tel.: (49) 73078010
Industrial Machinery & Equipment Distr,
N.A.I.C.S.: 423830

Subsidiary (Non-US):

Lenser Asia Sdn. Bhd. (2)
No 20 Jalan PJU 3/49 Sunway Damansara,
47810, Petaling Jaya, Selangor, Malaysia
Tel.: (60) 378037887
Web Site: http://www.lenser.de
Industrial Machinery & Equipment Distr
N.A.I.C.S.: 423830

Modul Systeme Engineering GmbH (1)
Bahnhofstrasse 28, 83410, Laufen, Germany
Industrial Machinery & Equipment Distr
N.A.I.C.S.: 423830
Michael Rupp (Mng Dir)

Otorio Ltd. (1)
Hamasger st 39, Tel Aviv, Israel
Tel.: (972) 545223813
Web Site: http://www.otorio.com
Petroleum Product Distr
N.A.I.C.S.: 424720
Yair Attar (Co-Founder & CTO)

PT. ANDRITZ (1)
VA Tech Building 3rd Floor Jl Talang No 3
Pegangsaan, Jakarta, 10320, Indonesia
Tel.: (62) 21 3905001
Web Site: http://www.andritz.com
Emp.: 20
Marketing & Sales of Equipment & Machinery for the Pulp & Paper Industry
N.A.I.C.S.: 322110
Sumarmo Hardiman (Gen Mgr)

Powerlase Technologies Limited (1)
3 & 4 Meadowbrook Industrial Estate Maxwell Way, Crawley, RH10 9SA, West Sussex, United Kingdom (50.1%)
Tel.: (44) 1293 456 222
Web Site: http://www.powerlase-photonics.com
Water Equipment Mfr
N.A.I.C.S.: 333992
Young Kwon (CTO)

Pressensysteme Schuler-Mexico, S.A. de C.V. (1)
Andador Norte N-2 Fraccionamiento Industrial Santa Elena Col, Parque Industrial
Chachapa Amozoc de Mota, 72990,
Puebla, Mexico
Tel.: (52) 2224310019

Industrial Machinery & Equipment Distr
N.A.I.C.S.: 423830

SOVEMA Global Services Inc. (1)
9787 Green Park Industrial Dr, Saint Louis,
MO 63123
Tel.: (636) 343-6112
Lithium Battery Mfr
N.A.I.C.S.: 335910

Schuler (China) Co., Ltd. (1)
Unit 01 5F No 699 Guangzhou West Road,
Jing An District, Shanghai, 200072, China
Tel.: (86) 2162632000
Metal Forming Machine Mfr
N.A.I.C.S.: 333519

Schuler AG (1)
Schuler-Platz 1, 73033, Goppingen,
Germany (96.62%)
Tel.: (49) 7161660
Web Site: http://www.schulergroup.com
Rev.: $1,272,496,918
Assets: $1,312,027,976
Liabilities: $847,286,076
Net Worth: $464,741,900
Earnings: ($138,750,654)
Emp.: 6,000
Fiscal Year-end: 12/31/2019
Metal Processing Services
N.A.I.C.S.: 423510
Ingrid Wolfframm (Deputy Chm-Supervisory Bd)

Subsidiary (Non-US):

Beutler Nova AG (2)
Hofmatt 4, 6142, Gettnau, Switzerland
Tel.: (41) 419727575
Web Site: https://www.beutler-nova.ch
Emp.: 115
Compact Press Solutions for Automotive &
Industrial Applications
N.A.I.C.S.: 336370
Adrian Achermann (CEO)

Subsidiary (Domestic):

Grabener Pressensysteme GmbH & Co. KG (2)
Wetzlarer Strasse 1, Werthenbach, 57250,
Netphen, Germany
Tel.: (49) 2737962239
Web Site: http://www.graebener-minting.com
Sales Range: $75-99.9 Million
Emp.: 150
Develops & Builds Press Systems &
ServicesKnuckle-Joint Presses for the Metalworking Industry
N.A.I.C.S.: 811310
Martin Stahlschmidt (Mng Dir)

Subsidiary (Non-US):

Prensas Schuler S.A. (2)
Av Fagundes de Oliveira, Sao Paulo,
09950-904, Diadema, Brazil (100%)
Tel.: (55) 1140758444
Sales Range: $150-199.9 Million
Emp.: 500
Development & Mfr of Oversized Presses
for the Metal Industry
N.A.I.C.S.: 423510
Paulo Tonicelli (Mng Dir)

Schuler (Dalian) Forming Technologies Co., Ltd. (2)
No 1 Weingarten Road, Ganjingzi, Dalian,
116113, China
Tel.: (86) 41187124002
Metal Forming Machinery Mfr
N.A.I.C.S.: 333517

Subsidiary (Domestic):

Schuler Automation GmbH & Co. KG (2)
Louis-Schuler Strasse 9, 75050, Gemmingen, Germany (100%)
Tel.: (49) 72678090
Web Site: http://www.schulergroup.com
Sales Range: $75-99.9 Million
Emp.: 200
Mfr & Sales of Special-Purpose Machine
Tools, Loaders & Transfers as well as Automation of Machine Tools
N.A.I.C.S.: 333517
Stephan Mergner (Mng Dir)

Schuler Cartec Engineering GmbH & Co. KG (2)
Heinrich-Hertz-Str 6, 88250, Weingarten,
Germany (100%)
Tel.: (49) 751 4006 0
Web Site: http://www.schulergroup.com
Sales Range: $50-74.9 Million
Emp.: 60
Automation & Production Systems of
Presses
N.A.I.C.S.: 423510

Subsidiary (Non-US):

Schuler France S.A. (2)
17 Rue Schertz, PO Box 26, 67023, Strasbourg, France
Tel.: (33) 388556100
Sales Range: $25-49.9 Million
Emp.: 40
Mfr of Mechanical Presses
N.A.I.C.S.: 332119

Schuler Iberica S.A.U. (2)
Edificio SCV Forum Planta 2a Puerta 4a
Ctra Sant Cugat-Rubi Km 01, No 40-50
Sant Cugat del Valles, 08174, Barcelona,
Spain (100%)
Tel.: (34) 935442300
Web Site: http://www.schulergroup.com
Sales Range: $50-74.9 Million
Emp.: 9
Automotive Metal Stamping
N.A.I.C.S.: 336370

Subsidiary (US):

Schuler Inc. (2)
7145 Commerce Blvd, Canton, MI
48187 (100%)
Tel.: (734) 207-7200
Web Site: http://www.schulergroup.com
Sales Range: $50-74.9 Million
Emp.: 100
Press Rebuilding & Modernization, Sales
Management & Project Coordination
N.A.I.C.S.: 423620
Paul Nicholson (Mng Dir)

Subsidiary (Domestic):

BCN Technical Services, Inc. (3)
1004 E State St, Hastings, MI 49058
Tel.: (269) 948-3300
Web Site: http://www.bcntechserv.com
Emp.: 80
Stamping Press Repair, Press Parts, Press
Rebuilds & Stamping Press Upgrades
N.A.I.C.S.: 332119
Ronald Fukui (CEO)

Graebener Press Systems Inc. (3)
175 Metro Ctr Blvd Ste 5, Warwick, RI
02886
Tel.: (401) 738-3307
Web Site: http://www.graebener-minting.com
Emp.: 120
Metal Forming Machinery & Assembly
Works Mfr
N.A.I.C.S.: 333517
Volker Wollschlager (Mgr-Svc & Tech Support)

Subsidiary (Non-US):

Schuler India Private Limited (2)
401-403 Keshava Bandra-Kurla Complex,
Bandra East, Mumbai, 400 051,
India (100%)
Tel.: (91) 2266800300
Web Site: http://www.schulerindia.com
Sales Range: $25-49.9 Million
Emp.: 29
Marketer of Press Technology & Press
Equipment
N.A.I.C.S.: 423830

Schuler Italia S.r.l. (2)
Via Erasmo da Rotterdam 4, 10134, Turin,
Italy
Tel.: (39) 0113166511
Emp.: 200
Mfr & Custom Services of Mechanical &
Hydraulic Presses & Presses for Forging
Hammers
N.A.I.C.S.: 332112
Cristiano Sarale (Mng Dir)

Schuler Poland Service Sp. z o.o. (2)

Strzelecka 5A, 47-206, Kedzierzyn-Kozle,
Poland
Tel.: (48) 774874234
Web Site: http://www.schulergroup.com
Sheet Metal Processing Services
N.A.I.C.S.: 332322

Subsidiary (Domestic):

Schuler Pressen GmbH (2)
Schuler-Platz 1, 73033, Goppingen,
Germany (100%)
Tel.: (49) 7161660
Web Site: https://www.schulergroup.com
Sales Range: $550-599.9 Million
Emp.: 1,200
Sheet Metal Forming Machine Tools &
Press Systems for Packaging & Can Making
N.A.I.C.S.: 332322

Plant (Domestic):

Schuler Pressen GmbH - Waghausel (3)
Louis-Schuler-Str 1, 68753, Waghausel,
Germany
Tel.: (49) 72549880
Web Site: http://www.schulergroup.com
Hydraulic Press Systems & Production
Lines for Automotive, Domestic Appliances
& Part Supplier Industries
N.A.I.C.S.: 333912
Norbert Broger (Mng Dir)

Subsidiary (Non-US):

Schuler Presses UK Limited (2)
Brineton St Quayside Dr, Amington Industrial Estate, Walsall, WS2 9LA, W Midlands,
United Kingdom
Web Site: http://www.schulergroup.com
Sales Range: $25-49.9 Million
Emp.: 22
Servicing of Mechanical & Hydraulic
Presses
N.A.I.C.S.: 333517
Andy Wright (Mgr-Sls)

Schuler Sales & Service (Shanghai) Co., Ltd. (2)
Room 721 Prime Tower No 22 Chaowai
Street, Chaoyang, Beijing, 100020, China
Tel.: (86) 1065882697
Web Site: http://www.schulergroup.com
Metal Processing Services
N.A.I.C.S.: 423510
Oemer Akyazici (CEO-China)

Schuler Slovakia Services s.r.o. (2)
L Stura 1, 01841, Dubnica nad Vahom,
Slovakia
Tel.: (421) 422861341
Web Site: http://www.schulergroup.com
Press & Metal Stamping Mfr
N.A.I.C.S.: 332119
Peter Leitmann (Mng Dir)

Schuler Thailand Co. Ltd. (2)
82/2 Moo 4 Highway 36 Rd, Nongplalai
Banglamung, Chon Buri, 20150, Thailand
Tel.: (66) 38493176
Web Site: http://www.schulergroup.com
Emp.: 15
Metal Processing & Stamping Services
N.A.I.C.S.: 423510
Vicky Green (Head-Svc)

Subsidiary (Domestic):

Vogtle Service GmbH & Co. KG (2)
Friedhofstrasse 115, 73054, Eislingen,
Germany (100%)
Tel.: (49) 716199730
Web Site: https://www.voegtle.de
Sales Range: $25-49.9 Million
Emp.: 30
Mfr of Hydroforming Press, Hydraulic &
Fine Blanking Presses
N.A.I.C.S.: 332322
Thomas Weber (Mng Dir)

Sindus Andritz Ltda. (1)
Tel.: (55) 5121214400
Industrial Machinery & Equipment Distr
N.A.I.C.S.: 423830

Sovema Group S.P.A. (1)
Via Spagna 13, 37069, Villafranca di Verona, Italy
Tel.: (39) 0456335711

Web Site: https://www.sovemagroup.com
Lead Acid Battery Mfr & Distr
N.A.I.C.S.: 325199

Warkaus Works Oy (1)
Relanderinkatu 2, PO Box 247, 78201,
Varkaus, Finland
Tel.: (358) 204505555
Industrial Machinery & Equipment Distr
N.A.I.C.S.: 423830

Xerium China Co., Ltd. (1)
No 681 West Yingbin Road, Bacheng Town,
Kunshan, Jiangsu, China
Tel.: (86) 51236696900
Industrial Machinery & Equipment Distr
N.A.I.C.S.: 423830

Xerium Technologies, Inc. (1)
14101 Capital Blvd, Youngsville, NC 27596
Tel.: (919) 556-7235
Web Site: http://www.xerium.com
Rev.: $481,048,000
Assets: $567,849,000
Liabilities: $704,315,000
Net Worth: ($136,466,000)
Earnings: ($14,646,000)
Emp.: 2,850
Fiscal Year-end: 12/31/2017
Paper Production
N.A.I.C.S.: 313210

Subsidiary (Non-US):

Huyck Argentina SA (2)
Calle 7 881, Berazategui, B1884BCQ, Bue-
nos Aires, Argentina
Tel.: (54) 1142756836
Sales Range: $25-49.9 Million
Emp.: 70
Paper Production Consumable Product Mfr
& Supplier
N.A.I.C.S.: 313210

Huyck.Wangner Australia Pty.
Limited (2)
36-40 Fellmongers Rd Breakwater, Gee-
long, 3219, VIC, Australia
Tel.: (61) 352237000
Emp.: 120
Paper Production Consumable Product Mfr
& Supplier
N.A.I.C.S.: 313210
Graham Futter *(Mgr-Svc)*

Huyck.Wangner Austria GmbH (2)
Huyckstrasse 1, Gloggnitz, 2640, Austria
Tel.: (43) 26624100
Emp.: 530
Paper Production Consumable Product Mfr
& Supplier
N.A.I.C.S.: 313210
Mario Schimanko *(Dir-IT)*

Huyck.Wangner Germany GmbH (2)
Mittnachtstrasse 22, 72760, Reutlingen,
Germany
Tel.: (49) 71213060
Web Site: http://www.xerium.com
Paper Production Consumable Product Mfr
& Supplier
N.A.I.C.S.: 333243

Huyck.Wangner Italia S.p.A (2)
Via Persicara 70, 04100, Latina, Italy
Tel.: (39) 077342711
Paper Production Consumable Product Mfr
& Supplier
N.A.I.C.S.: 333243
Alberto Sagripanti *(Mgr-Site)*

Huyck.Wangner Japan Limited (2)
Sumitomo Fudosan Ningyocho Bldg 2-2-1
Nihonbashi Horidome-cho, Chuo-Ku, Tokyo,
103-0012, Japan
Tel.: (81) 336643392
Sales Range: $25-49.9 Million
Emp.: 25
Paper Machine Clothing Mfr & Supplier
N.A.I.C.S.: 313210

Huyck.Wangner UK Ltd. (2)
The Links 2nd Floor Suite 6, Herne Bay,
CT6 7GQ, Kent, United Kingdom
Tel.: (44) 1227 744030
Web Site: http://www.xerium.com
Sales Range: $25-49.9 Million
Emp.: 4
Mfr Paper Forming Fabrics
N.A.I.C.S.: 313310
Russell Bird *(CEO)*

Subsidiary (Domestic):

J.J. Plank Corporation (2)
728 Watermark CT, Neenah, WI 54956
Tel.: (920) 733-4479
Web Site: http://www.jjplank.com
Spreader Rolls Mfr
N.A.I.C.S.: 333243

Subsidiary (Non-US):

Stowe Woodward Finland Oy (2)
Sementtitehtaankatu 10, Kerava, 4260,
Finland
Tel.: (358) 207299400
Sales Range: $25-49.9 Million
Emp.: 60
Paper Machine Clothing Mfr & Supplier
N.A.I.C.S.: 313210
Juha Niemi *(Plant Mgr)*

Subsidiary (Domestic):

Stowe Woodward LLC (2)
14101 Capital Blvd Ste 201, Youngsville,
NC 27596
Tel.: (919) 556-7235
Paper Production Consumable Product Mfr
& Supplier
N.A.I.C.S.: 313210

Weavexx Corporation (2)
14101 Capital Blvd, Youngsville, NC 27596
Tel.: (919) 556-7235
Web Site: http://www.xerium.com
Sales Range: $25-49.9 Million
Emp.: 60
Specialty Paper Machine Clothing Fabrics
Developer, Mfr & Distr
N.A.I.C.S.: 313210
David Pretty *(Pres)*

Weavexx, LLC (2)
14101 Capital Blvd, Youngsville, NC 27596
Tel.: (919) 556-7235
Web Site: http://www.xerium.com
Sales Range: $25-49.9 Million
Emp.: 100
Paper Machine Clothing Mfr & Supplier
N.A.I.C.S.: 333310

Subsidiary (Non-US):

Xerium Canada Inc. (2)
1 Boulevard Lee, Warwick, J0A 1M0, QC,
Canada
Tel.: (819) 358-7100
Sales Range: $25-49.9 Million
Emp.: 126
Paper Production Consumable Product Mfr
& Supplier
N.A.I.C.S.: 313210

Xerium Germany Holding GmbH (2)
Fohrstresse 39, Reutlingen, 72760, Ger-
many
Tel.: (49) 7121306301
Investment Management Service
N.A.I.C.S.: 551112

Xerium Technologies Brasil Industria
e Comercio S.A. (2)
Via Anhanguera Km 107 3-Parte-Bairro
Matao, Sumare, 13181-030, Sao Paulo,
Brazil
Tel.: (55) 1938548800
Paper Production Consumable Product Mfr
& Supplier
N.A.I.C.S.: 313210

Xerium Technologies Limited (2)
10 Bishops Square, Fleet Street, London,
E16EG, United Kingdom
Tel.: (44) 1227744030
Paper Production Consumable Product Mfr
& Distr
N.A.I.C.S.: 313210
Oliver Hakel *(Gen Mgr)*

ANDROMEDA METALS LIMITED

Level 10 431 King William Street, PO
Box 1210, Adelaide, 5000, SA, Aus-
tralia
Tel.: (61) 870899800   AU
Web Site:
   https://www.andromet.com.au
ADN—(ASX)
Rev.: $687,951

Assets: $105,547,552
Liabilities: $2,131,464
Net Worth: $103,416,088
Earnings: ($4,853,870)
Fiscal Year-end: 06/30/24
Mineral Exploration Services
N.A.I.C.S.: 213115
Nicholas J. Harding *(Sec)*

Subsidiaries:

Minotaur Exploration Ltd. (1)
Level 2 99 Frome St, Adelaide, 5000, SA,
Australia
Tel.: (61) 881114000
Web Site:
  http://www.minotaurexploration.com.au
Rev.: $85,693
Assets: $12,243,617
Liabilities: $2,867,404
Net Worth: $9,376,213
Earnings: ($2,130,234)
Emp.: 15
Fiscal Year-end: 06/30/2021
Metal & Mineral Exploration
N.A.I.C.S.: 213114
Andrew Woskett *(Mng Dir)*

ANDULELA INVESTMENT HOLDINGS LIMITED

108 4th Street, Parkmore, Sandton,
2196, South Africa
Tel.: (27) 11 888 8888   ZA
Web Site:
   http://www.andulelaholdings.com
Year Founded: 1950
AND—(JSE)
Sales Range: $75-99.9 Million
Investment Management Service
N.A.I.C.S.: 523940
Ashruf Kaka *(CEO)*

Subsidiaries:

Kilken Platinum Proprietary
Limited (1)
106 108 Fourth Street, Parkmore, Johan-
nesburg, 2196, Gauteng, South Africa
Tel.: (27) 147879900
Metal Products Mfr
N.A.I.C.S.: 332999
Arshuf Kaka *(CEO)*

Pro Roof Steel Merchants (PTA) Pro-
prietary Limited (1)
Willem Cruywagen Street, Akasia, Pretoria,
South Africa
Tel.: (27) 12 542 7554
Roofing Product Distr
N.A.I.C.S.: 423330

Pro Roof Steel Merchants Proprietary
Limited (1)
2 Nuffield Street, Duncanville, Vereeniging,
South Africa
Tel.: (27) 164505800
Web Site: http://www.proroof.co.za
Roofing Product Mfr
N.A.I.C.S.: 332322

ANE (CAYMAN) INC.

8th Floor Block B E Linke World
North District 999 Huaxu Road, Xu-
jing Town Qingpu District, Shanghai,
China   Ky
Web Site: https://www.ane56.com
Year Founded: 2010
9956—(HKG)
Rev.: $1,373,075,294
Assets: $799,880,095
Liabilities: $388,075,294
Net Worth: $411,804,802
Earnings: $56,386,381
Emp.: 3,142
Fiscal Year-end: 12/31/23
Transportation Services
N.A.I.C.S.: 484220
Disheng Lin Sam *(CFO)*

ANEKA JARINGAN HOLDINGS BERHAD

K-2-1 Pusat Perdagangan Bandar

Bukit Jalil, Persiaran Jalil 2, 57000,
Kuala Lumpur, Malaysia
Tel.: (60) 386575150   MY
Web Site:
   https://www.anekajaringan.com
ANEKA—(KLS)
Rev.: $41,253,138
Assets: $51,791,908
Liabilities: $31,832,228
Net Worth: $19,959,680
Earnings: ($2,699,574)
Emp.: 187
Fiscal Year-end: 08/31/23
Holding Company
N.A.I.C.S.: 551112
Ooi Chong Ping *(Gen Mgr)*

Subsidiaries:

PT Aneka Jaringan Indonesia (1)
Komplek Inkopal Blok G No 67 Jl Raya
Boulevard Barat, Kepala Gading Barat, Ja-
karta, 14240, Indonesia
Tel.: (62) 2145851741
Web Site: https://www.ptaji.co.id
Foundation & Basement Construction Ser-
vices
N.A.I.C.S.: 238110

ANEL ELECTRICAL PROJECT CONTRACTING TRADE INC.

Anel Business Center Saray Mah Site
Yolu Sokak No 5/4, Umraniye, 34768,
Istanbul, Turkiye
Tel.: (90) 2166362000
Web Site: https://anelgroup.com
Year Founded: 1986
ANELE—(IST)
Rev.: $76,440,319
Assets: $151,311,151
Liabilities: $119,019,974
Net Worth: $32,291,177
Earnings: $3,657,693
Emp.: 658
Fiscal Year-end: 12/31/22
Engineeering Services
N.A.I.C.S.: 541330
Ridvan Celikel *(Chm)*

Subsidiaries:

Anel Doga Entegre Geri Donusum
Endustri A.S (1)
Cepni Mah Space Impasse Administrative
Building Sit No 43 B, Kartepe, Kocaeli, Tur-
kiye
Tel.: (90) 2623522520
Web Site: http://www.aneldoga.com
Electronic Waste Recycling Material Ser-
vices
N.A.I.C.S.: 562920

Anel Elektrik Proje Taahhut Tic.
A.S (1)
Anel Business Center Saray Mah Site Yolu
Caddesi No 5/4, Umraniye, 34768, Istanbul,
Turkiye
Tel.: (90) 2166362000
Building Information Modeling Services
N.A.I.C.S.: 541310

Anel Elektrik Proje Taahhut ve Ticaret
A.S (1)
Timiryazevskaya Street 1 Business Centre-
Premier, 127422, Moscow, Russia
Tel.: (7) 4952873016
Building Information Modeling Services
N.A.I.C.S.: 541310

Anel Elektrik Proje Taahhut ve Ticaret
A.S (1)
BLDG 317 Office 3 and 5 St 250 Zone 43
Al-Hilal D-Ring Road, PO Box 21346, Doha,
Qatar
Tel.: (974) 44210201
Building Information Modeling Services
N.A.I.C.S.: 541310

Anel Elektrik Proje Taahhut ve Ticaret
A.S (1)
Transpolispark Siriusdreef 17-27, Hoofd-
dorp, 2132 WT, Amsterdam, Netherlands
Tel.: (31) 235689205
Building Information Modeling Services

Anel Electrical Project Contracting Trade
Inc.—(Continued)
N.A.I.C.S.: 541310

**Anel Engineering & Contracting
Limited** (1)
85 Tottenham Court Road, London, W1T
4TQ, United Kingdom
Tel.: (44) 2072683607
Building Information Modeling Services
N.A.I.C.S.: 541310

**AnelEmirates General Contracting
LLC** (1)
Zayed The First Street Pearl Plaza Building
Office No MZ-9W-10/C-69, PO Box 46373,
Khalidiya, Abu Dhabi, United Arab Emirates
Tel.: (971) 26664917
Building Information Modeling Services
N.A.I.C.S.: 541310

**AnelMarin Gemi Elk. Elkt. Sis. Tic. ve
San. A.S.** (1)
Metro Ofis Plaza Yesilbaglar Mah Kaptan
Sok No 19 Kat 9, Pendik, 34893, Istanbul,
Turkiye
Tel.: (90) 2166362000
Web Site: http://www.anelmarin.com
Cable Laying Services
N.A.I.C.S.: 238210

**AnelSis Muhendislik San. ve Tic. Ltd.
Sti.** (1)
Anel Business Center Saray Mah Site Yolu
Caddesi No 5/4, Umraniye, 34768, Istanbul,
Turkiye
Tel.: (90) 2166362000
Web Site: http://www.anelsis.com
Electrical Design Services
N.A.I.C.S.: 541330

ANEMOI INTERNATIONAL
Folio Chambers, PO Box 800, Road
Town, Tortola, Virgin Islands (British)
Web Site: http://www.anemoi-
international.com
Holding Company
N.A.I.C.S.: 551112
C Duncan Soukup (Chm)

Subsidiaries:

id4 AG (1)
Hirschengraben 31, 6003, Lucerne,
Switzerland (84%)
Tel.: (41) 445863748
Web Site: http://www.id4bank.ch
Software Development Services
N.A.I.C.S.: 541511

ANERI FINCAP LIMITED
B1/A Utkarsh Co-op Housing Society
M A Road, Andheri West, Mumbai,
400058, India
Tel.: (91) 2226204220
Web Site: http://www.anerifincap.com
Year Founded: 1990
531252—(BOM)
Rev.: $1,446,512
Assets: $43,631,101
Liabilities: $42,962,142
Net Worth: $668,958
Earnings: ($115,308)
Fiscal Year-end: 03/31/21
Financial Services
N.A.I.C.S.: 523999
Leena Kavassery (Mng Dir)

ANEST IWATA CORPORATION
3176 Shinyoshida-cho, Kohoku-ku,
Yokohama, 2238501, Japan
Tel.: 455911111
Web Site: https://www.anest-
iwata.co.jp
Year Founded: 1926
6381—(TKS)
Rev.: $353,139,250
Assets: $437,211,840
Liabilities: $106,222,700
Net Worth: $32,593,910
Earnings: $32,593,910
Emp.: 1,865
Fiscal Year-end: 03/31/24

Air Compressors, Air Pressure Equip-
ment, Air Driven Equipment, Vacuum
Equipment & Systems, Painting
Equipment, Liquid Application Equip-
ment & Systems Mfr & Sales
N.A.I.C.S.: 333912
Takahiro Tsubota (Pres & CEO)

Subsidiaries:

ANEST IWATA France S.A. (1)
25 Rue De Madrid, 38070, Saint-Quentin-
Fallavier, France
Tel.: (33) 474945969
Web Site: https://www.anest-iwata-
coating.com
Sales Range: $25-49.9 Million
Emp.: 17
Industrial Machinery & Equipment Whslr
N.A.I.C.S.: 423830

ANEST IWATA IBERICA S.L. (1)
Calle Torrassa 108 Passatge Dolors Ferrer
13 y Calle Gravina 16, 08930, Sant Adria
de Besos, Barcelona, Spain
Tel.: (34) 933 205 993
Web Site: http://www.anest-iwata.es
Spray Gun & Pump Mfr
N.A.I.C.S.: 333991
Santiago Garcia (Dir-Sls-Anest Iwata
Iberica)

**ANEST IWATA Motherson
Limited** (1)
B-123 124 Sector-63, Noida, 201301, India
Tel.: (91) 1204600500
Web Site: https://www.aimcompressors.com
Sales Range: $50-74.9 Million
Emp.: 150
Air & Gas Compressor Mfr
N.A.I.C.S.: 333912

ANEST IWATA SEGI Corporation (1)
148-6 Gajwa-dong Seo-gu, 404-250, In-
cheon, Korea (South)
Tel.: (82) 325780330
Web Site: http://www.ai-se.co.kr
Sales Range: $25-49.9 Million
Emp.: 15
Air & Gas Compressor Mfr
N.A.I.C.S.: 333912

**ANEST IWATA Scandinavia
Aktierbolag** (1)
Ogardesvagen 6C, 433 30, Partille, Sweden
Tel.: (46) 313402860
Web Site: http://www.anest-iwata.se
Sales Range: $25-49.9 Million
Emp.: 5
Engineeering Services
N.A.I.C.S.: 541330

**ANEST IWATA Shanghai Coating Ma-
chinery Co., Ltd.** (1)
2000 Wan Ping Nan Road, Shanghai,
China
Tel.: (86) 2164380190
Web Site: http://www.anest-iwata.co.jp
Air Compressor & Vacuum Pump Distr
N.A.I.C.S.: 423830

**ANEST IWATA Southeast Asia Co.,
Ltd.** (1)
91/1 5Ath Flr Chaiyo Building Room 5A10
Rama 9 Road, Huaykwang, Bangkok,
10310, Thailand
Tel.: (66) 26432870
Web Site:
https://www.anestiwatathailand.com
Sales Range: $25-49.9 Million
Emp.: 10
Air & Gas Compressor Mfr
N.A.I.C.S.: 333912

**ANEST IWATA Taiwan
Corporation** (1)
No 31 Guangfu North Road, Zhongxing Vil-
lage Hukou Township, Hsinchu, 30351, Tai-
wan
Tel.: (886) 35983206
Web Site: https://www.anestiwata.com.tw
Sales Range: $25-49.9 Million
Emp.: 45
Air & Gas Compressor Mfr
N.A.I.C.S.: 333912

Air Gunsa S.rl (1)
Via Degli Aceri 1, Cardano al Campo,
21010, Varese, Italy

Tel.: (39) 0331733120
Web Site: http://www.anest-iwataeu.com
Sales Range: $25-49.9 Million
Emp.: 25
Air Compressor & Vacuum Pump Mfr
N.A.I.C.S.: 333912
Vicentini Marco (Owner)

**Anest Iwata (Shanghai)
Corporation** (1)
Building 4 Honghui Lab 2354 Creative In-
dustry Park No 2354 Xietu Road, Xuhui
District, Shanghai, 200032, China
Tel.: (86) 2164079713
Web Site: https://www.anest-iwata-sh.com
Industrial Equipment Distr
N.A.I.C.S.: 423830

Anest Iwata (U.K.) Ltd. (1)
7 Chester Road Colmworth Business Park
Eaton Socon, Saint Neots, PE19 8YT, Cam-
bridgeshire, United Kingdom
Tel.: (44) 1480405419
Web Site: http://www.anest-iwata.co.uk
Sales Range: $50-74.9 Million
Emp.: 8
Printing Machinery Distr
N.A.I.C.S.: 423830
Tony Robson (Mng Dir)

Anest Iwata Air Engineering Inc. (1)
9525 Glades Dr, West Chester, OH 45011
Tel.: (513) 755-5130
Air Compressor Equipment Mfr & Distr
N.A.I.C.S.: 333912

Anest Iwata Australia Pty Ltd (1)
Unit 33 71 Kurrajong Ave, Mount Druitt,
2770, NSW, Australia
Tel.: (61) 298532000
Web Site: https://www.anest-iwata.com.au
Sales Range: $25-49.9 Million
Emp.: 15
Automotive Coating Distr
N.A.I.C.S.: 424950

Anest Iwata Deutschland GmbH (1)
Mommsenstrasse 5, 04329, Leipzig, Ger-
many
Tel.: (49) 3412414430
Web Site: https://www.anest-iwata-
coating.com
Emp.: 1,624
Air Compressor & Vacuum Pump Mfr
N.A.I.C.S.: 333912

Anest Iwata Europe GmbH (1)
Am Stahlbugel 2, 74206, Bad Wimpfen,
Germany
Tel.: (49) 7063 933 6714
Web Site: https://anest-iwata-air.com
Air Compressor Equipment Mfr & Distr
N.A.I.C.S.: 333912
Marcin Wojtecki (Mng Dir)

Anest Iwata Europe S.rl (1)
Corso Vigevano 46, 10155, Turin, Italy
Tel.: (39) 0112480868
Web Site: http://www.anest-iwataeu.com
Air Compressor Distr
N.A.I.C.S.: 423830

Anest Iwata Italia S.rl (1)
Via dell'Industria 21, 10023, Chieri, TO, Italy
Tel.: (39) 0112480868
Web Site: http://www.anest-iwata.it
Air Compressor Mfr
N.A.I.C.S.: 333912

Anest Iwata Korea Corporation (1)
9 MTV 4-ro 48beon-gil 516-1 Moknae-dong,
Danwon-gu, Ansan, Gyeonggi, Korea
(South)
Tel.: (82) 31 364 8120
Web Site: https://www.aikr.co.kr
Air Compressor Equipment Mfr & Distr
N.A.I.C.S.: 333912

**Anest Iwata Motherson Coating
Equipment Private Ltd.** (1)
B-123-124 Sector -63, Distt Gautam Buth
Nagar, Noida, 201301, Uttar Pradesh, India
Tel.: (91) 120 416 0111
Coating Equipment Mfr & Distr
N.A.I.C.S.: 325510

Anest Iwata Rus LLC (1)
Leninsky Pr-t 42 Bldg 5 Office 5835, Mos-
cow, Russia
Tel.: (7) 4959387728
Web Site: https://www.anestiwata.ru

Coating Equipment Mfr & Distr
N.A.I.C.S.: 325510

**Anest Iwata South Africa Pty.
Ltd.** (1)
1st Floor Building 1 152 Bryanston Dr, Bry-
anston, Johannesburg, 2091, Gauteng,
South Africa
Tel.: (27) 11 463 2169
Web Site: https://anest-iwata.store
Coating Equipment Distr
N.A.I.C.S.: 424950
Ayumi Nishiyama (Mng Dir)

Anest Iwata Sparmax Co., Ltd. (1)
4B-03 Taipei World Trade Center 4F No 5
Sec 5 HsinYi Rd, Taipei, 11011, Taiwan
Tel.: (886) 22 345 1868
Web Site: http://aispump.com
Air Compressor Equipment Mfr & Distr
N.A.I.C.S.: 333912

Anest Iwata USA Inc. (1)
10148 Commerce Park Dr, Cincinnati, OH
45246
Tel.: (513) 755-3100
Web Site: https://anestiwata.com
Emp.: 12
Air Compressor Mfr
N.A.I.C.S.: 333912

Anest Iwata Vietnam Co., Ltd. (1)
No 55 Hoa Lan Street, Ward 2 Phu Nhuan
District, Ho Chi Minh City, Vietnam
Tel.: (84) 28 395 0111
Web Site: https://anest-iwata.vn
Air Compressor Equipment Distr
N.A.I.C.S.: 423830
Kazunari Yamaguchi (Gen Dir)

Anest Iwata-Medea Inc (1)
1336 N Mason St, Portland, OR 97217
Tel.: (503) 253-7308
Web Site: https://www.iwata-airbrush.com
Emp.: 20
Airbrush Materials Distr
N.A.I.C.S.: 423840
Gary Glass (Pres)

Century Trading Co., Ltd (1)
1301 Daeryung Techno-Town 8 Gasan-
Dong, Geumcheon-ku, 481-11, Seoul, Ko-
rea (South)
Tel.: (82) 52 32 27 10
Air Compressor Mfr
N.A.I.C.S.: 333912

**Harder & Steenbeck GmbH & Co.
KG** (1)
Hans-Bockler-Ring 37, 22851, Norderstedt,
Germany
Tel.: (49) 4087 879 8930
Web Site: https://www.harder-airbrush.eu
Coating Equipment Mfr & Distr
N.A.I.C.S.: 325510
William Naemura (CEO)

**Iwata Service & Sales(M) Sdn.
Bhd.** (1)
8 Jalan Raja Arfah 1, Segambut, 51200,
Kuala Lumpur, Malaysia
Tel.: (60) 362428008
Web Site: https://iwatech.com
Sales Range: $25-49.9 Million
Emp.: 25
Air & Gas Compressor Mfr
N.A.I.C.S.: 333912

PT. Anest Iwata Indonesia (1)
Grand Slipi Tower 36th F Floor Jalan S Par-
man Kav 22-24 Slipi, Jakarta Barat, 11480,
Indonesia
Tel.: (62) 212 902 2453
Web Site: https://anest-iwata.co.id
Coating Equipment Distr
N.A.I.C.S.: 424950
Kenichi Ohgush (Mng Dir)

PT. INA Nusantara Abadi (1)
Jl Tomang Raya No 15, Jakarta Barat,
11440, Indonesia
Tel.: (62) 215601078
Web Site: https://www.iwata.co.id
Air Compressor Distr
N.A.I.C.S.: 423830

**Powerex Iwata Air Technology,
Inc.** (1)
150 Production Dr, Harrison, OH 45030
Web Site: https://www.powerexinc.com

Air Compressor Mfr & Distr
N.A.I.C.S.: 333912

Smooth Investment Co., Ltd.   **(1)**
G / F 14-16 Tai Nan Street, Mongkok, Kow-
loon, China (Hong Kong)
Tel.: (852) 23955297
Web Site: http://www.smooth.com.cn
Emp.: 40
Industrial Equipment Mfr & Distr
N.A.I.C.S.: 333248
Seelun Cheng *(Mng Dir)*

ANEXO GROUP PLC
5th Floor The Plaza 100 Old Hall
Street, Liverpool, L3 9QJ, United
Kingdom
Tel.: (44) 7971362020   UK
Web Site: https://www.anexo-
    group.com
Year Founded: 2018
ANX—(AIM)
Rev.: $171,776,952
Assets: $306,524,670
Liabilities: $124,790,966
Net Worth: $181,733,705
Earnings: $24,186,539
Emp.: 997
Fiscal Year-end: 12/31/22
Direct Property & Casualty Insurance
Carriers
N.A.I.C.S.: 524126
Alan Sellers *(Chm)*

Subsidiaries:

Bond Turner Limited   **(1)**
The Plaza 100 Old Hall Street, Liverpool,
L3 9QJ, United Kingdom
Tel.: (44) 1512363737
Web Site: http://www.bondturner.com
Law Practice Services
N.A.I.C.S.: 541110
Neil Ryder *(Mgr-Costs Dept)*

Direct Accident Management
Limited   **(1)**
139 New Court Way, Ormskirk, L39 2YT,
Lancashire, United Kingdom
Tel.: (44) 3450541000
Web Site: http://www.directaccident.co.uk
Car Lending Services
N.A.I.C.S.: 532112

ANFIELD ENERGY INC.
4390 Grange Street 2005, Burnaby,
V5H 1P6, BC, Canada
Tel.: (604) 669-5762   BC
Web Site:
    https://www.anfieldenergy.com
Year Founded: 1986
0ADN—(DEU)
Rev.: $481,622
Assets: $56,840,180
Liabilities: $19,388,846
Net Worth: $37,451,334
Earnings: $9,949,194
Emp.: 5
Fiscal Year-end: 12/31/23
Metal Mining Services
N.A.I.C.S.: 212290
Corey A. Dias *(CEO)*

ANFU CE LINK LIMITED
2F Bldg G Licheng Ind Park Shajing
Street, Baoan, Shenzhen, 518128,
China
Tel.: (86) 75527247356
Web Site: http://www.ce-link.com
Year Founded: 2009
300787—(SSE)
Rev.: $334,985,976
Assets: $380,342,196
Liabilities: $161,097,768
Net Worth: $219,244,428
Earnings: $45,768,996
Emp.: 10,000
Fiscal Year-end: 12/31/22
Wire Product Mfr
N.A.I.C.S.: 331491
Hongliang Zhou *(Chm & Gen Mgr)*

ANG INDUSTRIES LIMITED
101-106 Sharda Chamber IV Plot No
42 3 Local Shopping Complex Kal-
kaji, New Delhi, 110019, India
Tel.: (91) 11 26221237
Web Site:
    http://www.angindustries.com
Rev.: $13,537,158
Assets: $23,300,896
Liabilities: $28,839,129
Net Worth: ($5,538,233)
Earnings: ($16,215,145)
Fiscal Year-end: 03/31/17
Automotive Component Mfr & Distr
N.A.I.C.S.: 336340
Premjit Singh *(CEO & Mng Dir)*

ANG LIFESCIENCES INDIA LIMITED
SCO 113 1st Floor Darbara Complex
Ranjit Avenue B-Block, Amritsar, 143
001, India
Tel.: (91) 1835133455
Web Site:
    https://www.anglifesciences.com
Year Founded: 2006
540694—(BOM)
Rev.: $48,485,210
Assets: $39,725,650
Liabilities: $28,291,167
Net Worth: $11,434,482
Earnings: $5,503,202
Emp.: 682
Fiscal Year-end: 03/31/22
Pharmaceutical Preparation Mfr &
Distr
N.A.I.C.S.: 325412
Rajesh Gupta *(Mng Dir)*

ANGAS SECURITIES LIMITED
Level 14 26 Flinders Street, Adelaide,
5000, SA, Australia
Tel.: (61) 8 8410 4343   AU
Web Site:
    http://www.angassecurities.com
Year Founded: 2000
Sales Range: Less than $1 Million
Mortgage Services
N.A.I.C.S.: 522310
Matthew Hower *(Mng Dir)*

ANGEL FIBERS LIMITED
Survey No 100/1 Kalavad-Ranuja
Road, Haripar Taluka Kalavad Dis-
trict, Jamnagar, 361013, Gujarat,
India
Tel.: (91) 9998147801
Web Site:
    https://www.angelfibers.com
Year Founded: 2014
541006—(BOM)
Rev.: $34,595,379
Assets: $14,340,840
Liabilities: $10,094,421
Net Worth: $4,246,419
Earnings: $1,279,715
Emp.: 31
Fiscal Year-end: 03/31/22
Textile Products Mfr
N.A.I.C.S.: 313310
Rameshkumar J. Ranipa *(Chm)*

ANGEL GOLD CORP.
Suite 545 999 Canada Place, Van-
couver, V6C 3E1, BC, Canada
Tel.: (604) 684-6264
Web Site:
    http://www.angelgoldcorp.com
Year Founded: 1988
ANG—(TSXV)
Sales Range: Less than $1 Million
Gold Exploration Services
N.A.I.C.S.: 212220
Blanca Stella Frias *(Pres & CEO)*

ANGEL GROUP LTD.
The Angel House, 225 Marsh Wall,
London, E14 9FW, United Kingdom
Tel.: (44) 2075368688
Web Site:
    http://www.theangelgroup.com
Sales Range: $50-74.9 Million
Emp.: 220
Property Holding Company
N.A.I.C.S.: 531312
Julie A. Davey *(Owner)*

ANGEL HOLDINGS GODO KAI-SHA
8-1-5 Seikadai Seika-cho, Souraku,
Kyoto, 619-0238, Japan
Tel.: (81) 774986780
Playing Cards & Card Games Sup-
plier & Mfr
N.A.I.C.S.: 459120

Subsidiaries:

Gaming Partners International
Corporation   **(1)**
3945 W Cheyenne Ave Ste 208, North Las
Vegas, NV 89032
Tel.: (702) 384-2425
Web Site: http://www.gpigaming.com
Rev.: $87,009,000
Assets: $79,627,000
Liabilities: $15,837,000
Net Worth: $63,790,000
Earnings: $3,717,000
Emp.: 719
Fiscal Year-end: 12/31/2018
Table Game Equipment & Supplies for the
Casino Industry
N.A.I.C.S.: 339930
Alain M. Thieffry *(Chm, Pres, CEO, CFO,
Treas & Sec)*

Subsidiary (Non-US):

GPI   **(2)**
Tranformacion Y Dr Samuel Ocana G,
83455, San Luis Potosi, Sonora, Mexico
Tel.: (52) 6535341996
Web Site: http://www.gpigaming.com
Table Game Equipment & Supplies for the
Casino Industry Mfr
N.A.I.C.S.: 339930

Gaming Partners International   **(2)**
Z I Beaune-Savigny, Beaune, 21200, Bour-
gogne, France
Tel.: (33) 380262626
Web Site: http://www.gpigaming.com
Table Game Equipment & Supplies for the
Casino Industry Mfr
N.A.I.C.S.: 339930

Subsidiary (Domestic):

Gemgroup Inc.   **(2)**
2925 N 7 Hwy, Blue Springs, MO 64014
Tel.: (816) 220-1300
Web Site: http://www.gpigaming.com
Commercial Lithographic Printing
N.A.I.C.S.: 323111
Kaye Summers *(Pres & CEO)*

ANGEL HUMAN RESOURCES LTD
Angel House 4 Union Street London
Bridge, London, SE1 1SZ, United
Kingdom
Tel.: (44) 2079402000
Web Site: http://www.angelhr.org
Year Founded: 1965
Sales Range: $10-24.9 Million
Emp.: 58
Recruitment Services
N.A.I.C.S.: 561311
Russell Crawford *(Mng Dir)*

ANGEL ONE LIMITED
G-1 Ackruti Trade Centre Road No 7
Midc, Andheri East, Mumbai, 400093,
India
Tel.: (91) 8047480048
Web Site: http://www.angelone.in
Year Founded: 1996
ANGELBRKG—(NSE)

Brokerage Services
N.A.I.C.S.: 523150
Dinesh D. Thakkar *(Chm & Mng Dir)*

Subsidiaries:

Angel Fincap Private Limited   **(1)**
Ackruti Star AC397 5th Floor Central Road
MIDC, Andheri E, Mumbai, 400093, India
Tel.: (91) 2239413940
Financial Services
N.A.I.C.S.: 523999

ANGEL TELECOM CORP.
Blegistrasse 11a, 6340, Baar, CH-
6340, Switzerland
Tel.: (41) 1714956669   DE
Year Founded: 2004
AGLT—(OTCIQ)
Sales Range: Less than $1 Million
Telecommunication Servicesb
N.A.I.C.S.: 517112
Peter Michael Waneck *(Chm & CEO)*

ANGEL YEAST COMPANY LIMITED
No 168 Chengdong Avenue, Yichang,
443003, Hubei, China
Tel.: (86) 7176369520
Web Site:
    https://www.angelyeast.com
Year Founded: 1986
600298—(SHG)
Rev.: $1,803,198,969
Assets: $2,376,919,869
Liabilities: $1,027,838,312
Net Worth: $1,349,081,557
Earnings: $185,499,892
Emp.: 10,609
Fiscal Year-end: 12/31/22
Yeast Mfr
N.A.I.C.S.: 311999
Xiong Tao *(Chm)*

ANGELALIGN TECHNOLOGY INC.
6/F-7/F Building No 7 KIC Business
Center No 500 Zhengli Road, Yangpu
District, Shanghai, China   Ky
Web Site:
    https://www.angelalign.com
Year Founded: 2003
6699—(HKG)
Rev.: $204,359,077
Assets: $658,597,419
Liabilities: $186,786,110
Net Worth: $471,811,309
Earnings: $6,735,850
Emp.: 2,883
Fiscal Year-end: 12/31/23
Information Technology Services
N.A.I.C.S.: 541512
Huamin Li *(Founder)*

ANGELCARE HOLDING INC.
9975 avenue De Catania Local B,
Brossard, J4Z 3V6, QC, Canada
Web Site:
    http://www.angelcarebaby.com
Holding Company; Baby-Related
Products Mfr & Whslr
N.A.I.C.S.: 551112
Maurice Pinsonnault *(Founder, Pres
& CEO)*

Subsidiaries:

Angelcare Monitors Inc.   **(1)**
201 Boulevard de l'Industrie Local 104,
Candiac, J5R 6A6, QC, Canada
Web Site: http://www.angelcarebaby.com
Baby Monitors & Other Related Products
Mfr & Whslr
N.A.I.C.S.: 334290
Maurice Pinsonnault *(Founder, Pres &
CEO)*

Sassy, Inc.   **(1)**
3729 Patterson Ave SE, Kentwood, MI
49512

Angelcare Holding Inc.—(Continued)

Tel.: (616) 243-0767
Web Site: http://www.sassybaby.com
Sales Range: $10-24.9 Million
Emp.: 110
Toddler Toys & Products Mfr
N.A.I.C.S.: 339930
Dean F. Robinson (Pres)

ANGELINI ACRAF S.P.A.
Viale Amelia 70, 00181, Rome, Italy
Tel.: (39) 06780531
Web Site:
http://www.angelinipharma.com
Sales Range: $1-4.9 Billion
Emp.: 3,500
Pharmaceutical & Health Care Products Mfr
N.A.I.C.S.: 325412
Francesco Angelini (Chm & Pres)

Subsidiaries:

Angelini Farmaceutica Lda.   (1)
Rua Joao Chagas 53 - Piso 3 Cruz Quebrada Dafundo, 1499-040, Lisbon, Portugal
Tel.: (351) 214148300
Web Site: http://www.angelini.pt
Emp.: 127
Pharmaceutical Products Distr
N.A.I.C.S.: 424210

Angelini Farmaceutica S.A.   (1)
C/ Osi n 7, 08034, Barcelona, Spain
Tel.: (34) 932534500
Web Site: http://www.angelini.es
Emp.: 204
Pharmaceutical Products Distr
N.A.I.C.S.: 424210
Imma Valles de Ortado (Mgr-Quality Assurance)

Angelini Ilac San. ve Tic. A.S.   (1)
Mecidiyekoy Buyukdere Cad No 103/B Sarli Is Merkezi B Blok Daire 3, Sisli, 34394, Istanbul, Turkiye
Tel.: (90) 2122662423
Web Site: http://www.angelini.com.tr
Pharmaceutical Products Distr
N.A.I.C.S.: 424210
Mehmet Aydogan (Mgr-Regulatory Affairs)

Angelini Pharma Bulgaria Eood   (1)
10 Asen Yordanov Str, 1592, Sofia, Bulgaria
Tel.: (359) 29751395
Web Site: http://www.angelini.bg
Emp.: 65
Pharmaceutical Products Distr
N.A.I.C.S.: 424210

Angelini Pharma Ceska republika s.r.o.   (1)
Paterni 7, 635 00, Brno, Czech Republic
Tel.: (420) 546123111
Web Site: http://www.angelini.cz
Emp.: 100
Pharmaceutical Product Mfr & Distr
N.A.I.C.S.: 325412
Jozef Urban (Gen Mgr)

Angelini Pharma Hellas S.A.   (1)
Achaias Trizinias Street Nea Kifissia, 145 64, Athens, Greece
Tel.: (30) 2106269200
Web Site: http://www.angelini.gr
Emp.: 100
Pharmaceutical Products Distr
N.A.I.C.S.: 424210

Angelini Pharma Inc.   (1)
8322 Helgerman Ct, Gaithersburg, MD 20877
Tel.: (301) 330-7597
Web Site: http://www.angelini-us.com
Pharmaceutical Product Mfr & Distr
N.A.I.C.S.: 325412
Gary J. Mishkin (COO)

Angelini Pharma Magyarorszag Kft.   (1)
Dayka Gabor u 3 2nd Floor, 1118, Budapest, Hungary
Tel.: (36) 13361614
Emp.: 24
Pharmaceutical Products Distr
N.A.I.C.S.: 424210

Angelini Pharma Osterreich GmbH   (1)
Gewerbestrasse 18-20, 2102, Bisamberg, Austria
Tel.: (43) 22626060
Web Site: http://www.angelini.at
Emp.: 37
Pharmaceutical Products Distr
N.A.I.C.S.: 424210

Angelini Pharma Polska Sp.zo.o.   (1)
ui Podiesna 83, Zawiercie, Poland
Tel.: (48) 227028200
Web Site: http://www.angelini.pl
Emp.: 200
Pharmaceuticals Product Mfr
N.A.I.C.S.: 325412

Angelini Pharma RUS LLC   (1)
Trekhprudny lane 9 building 2 5th floor office 501-516, 123001, Moscow, Russia
Tel.: (7) 4959333950
Web Site: http://www.angelinipharma.ru
Pharmaceutical Products Distr
N.A.I.C.S.: 424210
Rita Bobro (Gen Mgr)

Angelini Pharma Slovenska republika s. r o.   (1)
Junova 33, 831 01, Bratislava, Slovakia
Tel.: (421) 259207320
Web Site: http://www.csc-pharma.sk
Emp.: 40
Pharmaceutical Products Distr
N.A.I.C.S.: 424210

Angelini Pharmaceuticals (PVT) LTD   (1)
221 - Block CCA Phase 4 DHA, Lahore, Pakistan
Tel.: (92) 4235743529
Emp.: 125
Pharmaceutical Products Distr
N.A.I.C.S.: 424210
Raza Masud (Dir-Mktg & Sls)

Angelini Pharmaceuticals Romania s.r.l.   (1)
Str Drumea Radulescu 52 sect 4, 040336, Bucharest, Romania
Tel.: (40) 318055912
Emp.: 87
Pharmaceutical Products Distr
N.A.I.C.S.: 424210
Corina Antipa (Gen Mgr)

Bertani Domains S.r.l.   (1)
Via Asiago 1, 37023, Grezzana, Verona, Italy
Tel.: (39) 045 8658444
Web Site: http://www.bertanidomains.it
Wine Distr
N.A.I.C.S.: 424810
Berardino Torrone (Area Mgr)

CSC Pharmaceuticals S.A.   (1)
17 Rue des Bains, 1212, Luxembourg, Luxembourg
Tel.: (352) 26478780
Pharmaceutical Products Distr
N.A.I.C.S.: 424210

Fameccanica Data S.p.A.   (1)
Via Aterno 136, Sambuceto di, 66020, San Giovanni Teatino, Chieti, Italy
Tel.: (39) 08545531
Web Site: https://www.fameccanica.com
Sales Range: $200-249.9 Million
Emp.: 670
Service Establishment Equipment & Supplies
N.A.I.C.S.: 423850

Fater S.p.A.   (1)
Via Mare Adriatico 122, Spoltore, 65010, Pescara, Italy
Tel.: (39) 0853551111
Web Site: http://www.fatergroup.com
Paper Products Mfr
N.A.I.C.S.: 322291

ITF Germany Gmbh   (1)
Neumarkter Str 80, 81673, Munich, Germany
Tel.: (49) 894366240
Web Site: http://www.itfcosmetics.de
Perfume Distr
N.A.I.C.S.: 456120

ITF S.p.A.   (1)

Strada Provinciale 25 Km 2 8, 26900, Lodi, Italy
Tel.: (39) 03714081
Web Site: http://www.itfcosmetics.com
Perfume Distr
N.A.I.C.S.: 456120
Paola Boselli (Mgr-Trade Mktg)

International Finaf 2000 S.A.   (1)
17 r des Bains, 1212, Luxembourg, Luxembourg
Tel.: (352) 26203671
Pharmaceutical Products Distr
N.A.I.C.S.: 424210

Rega Farma-Promocao de Produtos Farmaceuticos, S.A   (1)
Quinta Dos Palhas Rua Joao Chagas N 53 3, 1495-764, Lisbon, Portugal
Tel.: (351) 214148300
Pharmaceutical Products Distr
N.A.I.C.S.: 424210

Societa agricola Tenimenti Angelini S.r.l.   (1)
Localita Zuccole 4, Gorizia, 34076, Italy
Tel.: (39) 0577804253
Web Site: http://www.puiatti.com
Wine Distr
N.A.I.C.S.: 424820

ANGELO MORATTI S.A.PA.
SS 195 Sulcitana Km 19, Cagliari, 09018, Italy
Tel.: (39) 0706848465   IT
Holding Company
N.A.I.C.S.: 551112
Gian Marco Moratti (Chm)

Subsidiaries:

Saras S.p.A.   (1)
SS Sulcitana n 195 - Km 19, 09018, Sarroch, Cagliari, Italy   (50.02%)
Tel.: (39) 07090911
Web Site: http://www.saras.it
Rev.: $6,561,851,320
Assets: $4,139,399,709
Liabilities: $3,175,818,408
Net Worth: $963,581,301
Earnings: ($338,399,772)
Emp.: 1,687
Fiscal Year-end: 12/31/2020
Oil Refining & Production & Engineering Services
N.A.I.C.S.: 211120
Massimo Moratti (Chm)

Subsidiary (Domestic):

Akhela S.r.l.   (2)
Sesta Strada Ovest ZI Macchiareddu, Cagliari, 9010, Italy
Tel.: (39) 07024661000
Web Site: http://www.akhela.com
Corporate IT Consulting Services
N.A.I.C.S.: 541618
Piercarlo Ravasio (CEO)

Sarlux S.r.l.   (2)
S.S. Sulcitana No. 195 Km 19, 09018, Sarroch, Italy
Tel.: (39) 070 909241
Web Site: http://www.sarlux.it
Electric Power Generation
N.A.I.C.S.: 221118

ANGERMAYER, BRUMM & LANGE UNTERNEH-MENSGRUPPE GMBH
Grueneburgweg 18, 60322, Frankfurt am Main, Germany
Tel.: (49) 69 719 128 016 6
Investment Services
N.A.I.C.S.: 523999
Christian Angermayer (Co-CEO, Partner & Mng Dir)

ANGES, INC.
1F Saito Bio-Incubator 7-7-15 Saitoasagi, Ibaraki, Osaka, 5670085, Japan
Tel.: (81) 357302753   JP
Web Site: https://www.anges.co.jp
Year Founded: 1999

4563—(TKS)
Rev.: $1,077,680
Assets: $204,844,280
Liabilities: $19,774,010
Net Worth: $185,070,270
Earnings: ($52,728,330)
Emp.: 62
Fiscal Year-end: 12/31/23
Pharmaceutical Product Mfr & Distr
N.A.I.C.S.: 541715
Ei Yamada (Pres & CEO)

ANGIANG FISHERIES IMPORT & EXPORT JOINT STOCK COMPANY
1234 Tran Hung Dao, P Binh Khanh, Long Xuyen, An Giang, Vietnam
Tel.: (84) 2963852368
Web Site: https://www.agifish.com.vn
AGF—(HOSE)
Rev.: $18,618,321
Assets: $11,880,597
Liabilities: $19,242,707
Net Worth: ($7,362,110)
Earnings: ($248,148)
Fiscal Year-end: 12/31/23
Seafood Product Mfr
N.A.I.C.S.: 311710

ANGIOLAB, INC.
Hanshin S Mecca Suite 159 65 Techno 3ro Yuseong-gu, Daejeon, Korea (South)
Tel.: (82) 428675785
Web Site: http://www.angiolab.co.kr
Biotechnology Development Services
N.A.I.C.S.: 541714
Min-Young Kim (Pres & CEO)

ANGKOR RESOURCES CORP.
PO Box 153, Sexsmith, T0H 3C0, AB, Canada
Tel.: (780) 568-3801   BC
Web Site:
https://angkorresources.com
Year Founded: 2008
ANK—(TSXV)
Rev.: $166,518
Assets: $2,474,906
Liabilities: $2,070,080
Net Worth: $404,827
Earnings: ($740,808)
Emp.: 4
Fiscal Year-end: 07/31/23
Gold Mining Services
N.A.I.C.S.: 212220
Michael Weeks (Chm)

ANGLE PLC
10 Nugent Road Research Park, Guildford, GU2 7AF, Surrey, United Kingdom
Tel.: (44) 1483343434
Web Site: https://www.angleplc.com
Year Founded: 1994
ANPCF—(OTCIQ)
Rev.: $1,375,370
Assets: $64,240,522
Liabilities: $9,483,674
Net Worth: $54,756,848
Earnings: ($20,382,093)
Emp.: 128
Fiscal Year-end: 12/31/21
Administrative Management & General Management Consulting Services
N.A.I.C.S.: 541611
Andrew D. W. Newland (CEO & Founder)

Subsidiaries:

ANGLE Technology LLC   (1)
1000 Research Pk Blvd Ste 103, Charlottesville, VA 22911
Tel.: (434) 974-9700
Sales Range: $25-49.9 Million.
Emp.: 2

Consulting, Management & Venture Services
N.A.I.C.S.: 541611

ANGLE Technology Limited (1)
3 Frederick Sanger Rd Surrey Research Pk, Guildford, GU2 7YD, United Kingdom
Tel.: (44) 1522 668980
Web Site: http://www.angleplc.com
Sales Range: $25-49.9 Million
Emp.: 40
Business Management Services
N.A.I.C.S.: 541611

ANGLE Technology Ventures Limited (1)
3 Frederick Sanger Road, The Surrey Research Park, Guildford, GU27YD, United Kingdom (100%)
Tel.: (44) 1483295830
Web Site: http://www.angletechnologyventures.com
Sales Range: $25-49.9 Million
Emp.: 10
Management Consulting Services
N.A.I.C.S.: 541618

Novocellus Limited (1)
3 Frederick Sanger Rd Surrey Research Park, Guildford, GU2 7YD, Surrey, United Kingdom (62.67%)
Tel.: (44) 1483685830
Web Site: http://www.novocellus.com
Sales Range: $10-24.9 Million
Emp.: 10
Diagnostic Imaging Centers
N.A.I.C.S.: 621512
Andrew Newland (CEO)

Progeny BioVentures Limited (1)
20 Nugent Road, The Surrey Research Park, Guildford, GU27YG, United Kingdom (96.5%)
Tel.: (44) 1483295938
Sales Range: $25-49.9 Million
Emp.: 10
Business Support Services
N.A.I.C.S.: 561499

ANGLER GAMING PLC
Level G Office 1/3327 Quantum Hse 75 Abate Rigord Street, Ta' Xbiex, Malta
Tel.: (356) 99662000
Web Site: https://www.anglergaming.com
Year Founded: 2012
Rev.: $31,945,870
Assets: $13,987,588
Liabilities: $2,192,717
Net Worth: $11,794,871
Earnings: $7,241,823
Fiscal Year-end: 12/31/19
Gaming Concession Management Services
N.A.I.C.S.: 713290
S. Kalita (CEO)

ANGLESEY MINING PLC
Parys Mountain, Anglesey, Amlwch, LL68 9RE, United Kingdom
Tel.: (44) 1407831275   UK
Web Site: https://www.angleseymining.co.uk
Year Founded: 1984
AYM—(AIM)
Rev.: $1,599
Assets: $23,384,395
Liabilities: $5,531,858
Net Worth: $17,852,538
Earnings: ($1,193,727)
Emp.: 2
Fiscal Year-end: 03/31/23
Copper, Zinc & Lead Mining Services
N.A.I.C.S.: 212230
John F. Kearney (Chm)

ANGLING DIRECT PLC
2D Wendover Road Rackheath Industrial Estate, Norwich, NR13 6LH, Norfolk, United Kingdom
Tel.: (44) 1603400870   UK

Web Site: https://www.anglingdirect.co.uk
ANG—(AIM)
Rev.: $89,253,450
Assets: $69,933,270
Liabilities: $25,017,465
Net Worth: $44,915,805
Earnings: $1,469,490
Fiscal Year-end: 01/31/23
Fishing Equipment Retailer
N.A.I.C.S.: 423910
Martyn Page (Founder & Chm)

ANGLO AFRICAN OIL & GAS PLC
12 Berkeley Street, London, W1J 8DT, United Kingdom
Tel.: (44) 2039760030
Web Site: http://www.aaog.com
Year Founded: 2001
Oil & Gas Exploration Services
N.A.I.C.S.: 213112

ANGLO AMERICAN PLC
20 Carlton House Terrace, London, SW1Y 5AN, United Kingdom
Tel.: (44) 2079688888   UK
Web Site: http://www.angloamerican.com
Year Founded: 1975
AAM—(SWX)
Rev.: $30,652,000,000
Assets: $66,544,000,000
Liabilities: $34,927,000,000
Net Worth: $31,617,000,000
Earnings: $1,344,000,000
Emp.: 60,000
Fiscal Year-end: 12/31/23
Mineral Mining Services
N.A.I.C.S.: 551112
Richard Price (Gen Counsel & Sec)

Subsidiaries:

Anglo American Australia Limited (1)
Level 11 201 Charlotte Street, Brisbane, 4000, QLD, Australia
Tel.: (61) 738341333
Web Site: https://australia.angloamerican.com
N.A.I.C.S.: 541330
Dan van der Westhuizen (CEO)

Anglo American Brasil Limitada (1)
Paulista 2 300 10 Andar, Sao Paulo, 01310-300, Brazil
Tel.: (55) 1121257555
Web Site: http://www.angloamerican.com.br
Nickel Mining Services
N.A.I.C.S.: 212230
Wilfred Bruijn (CEO)

Subsidiary (Domestic):

Anglo Ferrous Brazil S.A. (2)
Praia Do Flamengo 154 Sala, 501 Parte Flamengo, 22210-030, Rio de Janeiro, Brazil
Tel.: (55) 21 2555 5557
Web Site: http://www.anglo-iron3.com.br
Iron Ore Mining Services
N.A.I.C.S.: 212210

Subsidiary (Domestic):

Anglo Ferrous Minas Rio Mineracao SA (3)
Da Americas 3 434 Bloco 03 - Sala 301, Rio de Janeiro, 22631-002, Brazil
Tel.: (55) 2130313434
Web Site: http://www.angloamerican.com
Metal Mining Services
N.A.I.C.S.: 212290
Paulo Castetari (Mgr)

Subsidiary (Domestic):

Copebras Limitada (2)
Rodovia Conego Domenico Rangoni - SP 055 Km 264 2 Oeste, 11573 904, Cubatao, Sao Paulo, Brazil
Tel.: (55) 13 3362 7069
Web Site: http://www.copebras.com.br

Sales Range: $550-599.9 Million
Emp.: 120
Phosphate Fertilizer Mfr & Distr
N.A.I.C.S.: 325312
Alan Green (Office Mgr)

Anglo American Chile (1)
Av Isidora Goyenechea 2800 Torre Titanium piso 47, Las Condes, Santiago, Chile
Tel.: (56) 22 230 6000
Web Site: https://chile.angloamerican.com
Sales Range: $200-249.9 Million
Emp.: 700
Copper Ore & Nickel Ore Mining
N.A.I.C.S.: 212230

Subsidiary (Domestic):

Anglo American Sur SA (2)
Isidora Goyenechea 2800 Titanium Tower 47th floor, Las Condes, Santiago, 7500524, Chile (50.1%)
Tel.: (56) 222306000
Web Site: http://chile.angloamerican.com
Holding Company; Copper Mining
N.A.I.C.S.: 551112

Joint Venture (Domestic):

Compania Minera Dona Ines de Collahuasi SCM (2)
Andres Bello 2687 Piso 11, Las Condes, Santiago, Chile (44%)
Tel.: (56) 223626500
Web Site: https://www.collahuasi.cl
Sales Range: $300-349.9 Million
Copper Mining
N.A.I.C.S.: 212230
Fernando Hernandez (VP-HR)

Anglo American Metallurgical Coal Holdings Limited (1)
201 Charlotte Street, Brisbane, 4000, QLD, Australia
Tel.: (61) 73 834 1333
Web Site: http://australia.angloamerican.com
Investment Management Service
N.A.I.C.S.: 523999

Anglo American Minerio de Ferro Brasil S.A (1)
Rua Maria Luiza Santiago 200, Santa Lucia, Belo Horizonte, MG, Brazil
Tel.: (55) 3135167100
Metal Mining Services
N.A.I.C.S.: 213114

Anglo American Niquel Brasil Ltda. (1)
Century Tower Building Rua Maria Luiza Santiago 200-8th floor, Santa Lucia, Belo Horizonte, 30360-740, MG, Brazil
Tel.: (55) 3135167100
Metal Mining Services
N.A.I.C.S.: 213114

Anglo American Peru S.A. (1)
Calle Esquilache 371 - piso 10, San Isidro, Lima, Peru
Tel.: (51) 16146000
Web Site: http://www.peru.angloamerican.com
Mining & Metal Services
N.A.I.C.S.: 213114

Anglo American Platinum Limited (1)
55 Marshall Street, 2001, Johannesburg, 2001, South Africa (79.83%)
Tel.: (27) 113736111
Web Site: https://www.angloplatinum.com
Rev.: $6,785,933,840
Assets: $9,215,448,900
Liabilities: $3,767,542,800
Net Worth: $5,447,906,100
Earnings: $732,269,160
Emp.: 22,334
Fiscal Year-end: 12/31/2023
Platinum Mining
N.A.I.C.S.: 212290
Gary A. Humphries (Head-Processing)

Anglo American Projects (UK) Ltd. (1)
20 Carlton House Terrace St James's, London, SW1Y 5AN, United Kingdom
Tel.: (44) 20 7968 8888
Web Site: http://www.angloamerican.com
Mining Company
N.A.I.C.S.: 213114

Subsidiary (Domestic):

Anglo American Woodsmith Limited (2)
20 Carlton House Terrace, London, SW1Y 5AN, United Kingdom
Tel.: (44) 1723470100
Web Site: http://uk.angloamerican.com
Mineral Exploration & Development Services
N.A.I.C.S.: 213115
Thomas Staley (CFO)

Subsidiary (Non-US):

Queensland Potash Pty Limited (3)
Se 7 3078 Surfers Paradise Bvd, Surfers Paradise, 4217, QLD, Australia
Tel.: (61) 412751051
Potash Mining Services
N.A.I.C.S.: 212390

Sirius Minerals (Australia) Pty Limited (3)
Level 12 48 Hunter Street, Sydney, 2000, NSW, Australia
Tel.: (61) 2 9917 8900
Sales Range: $50-74.9 Million
Emp.: 12
Mineral Mining Services
N.A.I.C.S.: 212390

Subsidiary (Domestic):

York Potash Limited (3)
7-10 Manor Court Manor Garth, Scarborough, YO11 9TU, United Kingdom
Tel.: (44) 845 543 8964
Web Site: http://www.yorkpotash.co.uk
Potash Mining Services
N.A.I.C.S.: 212390
Luke Jarvis (Dir-Comml)

Anglo American Resources Trading (China) Co. Ltd. (1)
No 1198 Century Avenue Pudong New Area Room 3201, Century Plaza Office Building 1, Shanghai, 200122, China
Tel.: (86) 2160336099
Web Site: https://china.angloamerican.com
N.A.I.C.S.: 541330
Stuart Chambers (Chm)

Anglo American South Africa Limited (1)
44 Main Street, Johannesburg, Gauteng, South Africa
Tel.: (27) 11 638 9111
Web Site: http://southafrica.angloamerican.com
Platinum, Thermal Coal, Diamonds & Iron Ore Mining Services
N.A.I.C.S.: 212210

Anglo Base Metals (Ireland) Ltd. (1)
Killoran Moyne, Thurles, Tipperary, Ireland
Tel.: (353) 50445600
Web Site: http://www.lisheenmine.ie
Sales Range: $150-199.9 Million
Emp.: 350
Holding Company; Metal Ore Mining
N.A.I.C.S.: 551112
Alan Buckley (Sec & Accountant)

Anglo Coal (German Creek) Pty Ltd (1)
Level 11 201 Charlotte Street, Brisbane, 4000, QLD, Australia
Tel.: (61) 738341333
N.A.I.C.S.: 541330

Anglo Operations (Pty) Ltd. (1)
44 Main Street, Johannesburg, South Africa
Tel.: (27) 116389111
Web Site: https://southafrica.angloamerican.com
N.A.I.C.S.: 541330
Duncan Wanblad (CEO)

Anglo Platinum Marketing Limited (1)
17 Charterhouse Street, London, EC1N 6RA, United Kingdom
Tel.: (44) 2079688888
N.A.I.C.S.: 541330

Colliery Training College (Pty) Limited (1)
Stevenson Street Crn O R Tambo Leraatsfontein, Private Bag X14, Klipfontein

Anglo American PLC—(Continued)

Emalahleni, Witbank, 1038, Mpumalanga, South Africa
Tel.: (27) 136923121
Web Site: http://www.ctctraining.co.za
Electronic Equipment Repair Training Services
N.A.I.C.S.: 611519

De Beers Group of Companies (1)
9 Rue St Vithe, 2763, Luxembourg, Luxembourg
Tel.: (352) 4025051
Web Site: http://www.debeersgroup.com
Sales Range: $1-4.9 Billion
Emp.: 11
Holding Company
N.A.I.C.S.: 551112
Bruce Cleaver (CEO)

Subsidiary (Non-US):

DE BEERS INDIA PVT. LTD (2)
83 Maker Chamber 6 Business Centre Nariman Point, 400 021, Mumbai, India
Tel.: (91) 22 2283 2971
Emp.: 8
Diamond Mining Services
N.A.I.C.S.: 212390

De Beers Auction Sales Belgium N.V. (2)
Schupstraat 21, 2018, Antwerp, Belgium
Tel.: (32) 32023311
Diamond Mining Services
N.A.I.C.S.: 212390

De Beers Auction Sales Hong Kong Limited (2)
Unit 1001 10F Unicorn Trade Centre 127-131 Des Voeux Road, Central, China (Hong Kong)
Tel.: (852) 25211722
Diamond Mining Services
N.A.I.C.S.: 212390

De Beers Auction Sales Israel Ltd (2)
11th Floor Yahalom Building 21 Tuval Street, Ramat Gan, Israel
Tel.: (972) 35752233
Diamond Mining Services
N.A.I.C.S.: 212390

De Beers Auction Sales Singapore Pte Ltd (2)
10 Collyer Quay Ocean Financial Centre 03-04, Singapore, 049315, Singapore
Tel.: (65) 64071734
Diamond Mining Services
N.A.I.C.S.: 212390

De Beers Canada (2)
900-250 Ferrand Drive, Toronto, M3C 3G8, ON, Canada
Tel.: (416) 645-1710
Web Site: http://www.debeerscanada.com
Diamond Mining
N.A.I.C.S.: 212390
Tony Guthrie (CEO)

De Beers Consolidated Mines Limited (2)
Cnr Crownwood Road and Diamond Drive Theta/Booysens Reserve, Private Bag X01, Southdale, Johannesburg, 2193, South Africa (100%)
Tel.: (27) 113747000
Web Site: http://www.debeersgroup.com
Sales Range: $5-14.9 Billion
Miner & Marketer of Gem & Industrial Diamonds; Mfr & Marketer of Synthetic Diamonds & Related Hard Materials for Use in Industry
N.A.I.C.S.: 212319

Subsidiary (US):

De Beers Diamond Jewellers Us, Inc. (2)
20 W 55th St Fl 7, New York, NY 10019
Tel.: (212) 751-2000
Sales Range: $1-9.9 Million
Emp.: 31
Jewelry Stores
N.A.I.C.S.: 458310

Subsidiary (Domestic):

De Beers Societe Anonyme (2)

48 Rue de Bragance, BP 185, 2011, Luxembourg, Luxembourg
Tel.: (352) 4041101
Diamond Mining Services
N.A.I.C.S.: 212390

Subsidiary (Non-US):

Debswana Diamond Company (Pty) Ltd (2)
Plot 64288 Airport Road Block 8, PO Box 329, Gaborone, Botswana
Tel.: (267) 361 4200
Web Site: http://www.debswana.com
Emp.: 4,000
Diamond Mining Services
N.A.I.C.S.: 212390
Bruce A. Cleaver (Chm)

Diamond Trading Company (2)
17 Charterhouse Street, London, EC1N 6RA, United Kingdom
Tel.: (44) 2074044444
Web Site: http://www.debeersgroup.com
Sales Range: $250-299.9 Million
Emp.: 900
Gem & Industrial Diamonds Marketing
N.A.I.C.S.: 423840

Subsidiary (Domestic):

Element Six S.A. (2)
rue Sainte Zithe, L 2763, Luxembourg, Luxembourg
Tel.: (352) 26 940 590
Diamond Supermaterial Mfr
N.A.I.C.S.: 423840

Subsidiary (US):

Element Six U.S. Corporation (3)
35 W 45th St, New York, NY 10036
Tel.: (212) 869-5155
Web Site: http://www.elementsix.com
Sales Range: $25-49.9 Million
Emp.: 8
Industrial Supplies Merchant Whslr
N.A.I.C.S.: 423830
Joseph Connolly (Gen Mgr)

De Beers Jewellers Japan K.K. (1)
New Otani Garden Court 7F 4-1 Kioicho, Chiyoda-ku, Tokyo, 102-0094, Japan
Tel.: (81) 362615084
N.A.I.C.S.: 339910

De Beers Namibia Holdings (Pty) Ltd. (1)
PO Box 23132, Windhoek, Namibia
Tel.: (264) 612043444
Metal & Mining Services
N.A.I.C.S.: 213114

De Beers Plc. (2)
44 Esplanade, Saint Helier, JE4 9WG, Jersey
Tel.: (44) 2074044444
Metal & Mining Services
N.A.I.C.S.: 213114

De Beers UK Limited (2)
17 Charterhouse Street, London, EC1N 6RA, United Kingdom
Tel.: (44) 2074044444
Diamond & Jewell Retailer
N.A.I.C.S.: 458310

Element Six (Production) Proprietary Limited (1)
1 Debid Road Nuffield Springs, Johannesburg, 1559, Gauteng, South Africa
Tel.: (27) 118129000
Machine Tools Mfr
N.A.I.C.S.: 333515

Element Six (UK) Limited (1)
Global Innovation Centre Fermi Avenue, Harwell Didcot, Oxford, OX11 0QR, Oxfordshire, United Kingdom
Tel.: (44) 1235441000
Web Site: http://www.e6.com
Synthetic Diamond Mfr
N.A.I.C.S.: 339910
Walter Huhn (CEO)

Element Six Abrasives Holdings Limited (1)
17 Charterhouse Street, London, EC1N 6RA, United Kingdom
Tel.: (44) 1235441000
Synthetic Diamond Mfr
N.A.I.C.S.: 339910

Element Six GmbH (1)
Stadeweg 18, Burghaun, 36151, Fulda, Germany
Tel.: (49) 6652820
Machine Tools Mfr
N.A.I.C.S.: 333515

Element Six Limited (1)
Shannon Airport, County Clare, Shannon, Ireland
Tel.: (353) 61471655
Synthetic Diamond Mfr
N.A.I.C.S.: 339910

Element Six Limited (1)
9F PMO Hatchobori 3-22-13 Hatchobori, Chuo-ku, Tokyo, 104-0032, Japan
Tel.: (81) 335239311
Synthetic Diamond Mfr
N.A.I.C.S.: 339910

Element Six Technologies (OR) Corp. (1)
23055 SE Stark St, Gresham, OR 97030
Tel.: (503) 573-2100
Synthetic Diamond Mfr
N.A.I.C.S.: 339910

Element Six Technologies Limited (1)
Global Innovation Centre Fermi Avenue, Harwell Didcot, Oxford, OX11 0QR, Oxfordshire, United Kingdom
Tel.: (44) 1344638200
Synthetic Diamond Mfr
N.A.I.C.S.: 339910

Element Six Technologies US Corporation (1)
3901 Burton Dr, Santa Clara, CA 95054
Tel.: (408) 986-2400
Web Site: http://www.e6cvd.com
Synthetic Diamond Mfr
N.A.I.C.S.: 339910

Element Six Trading (Shanghai) Co., Ltd. (1)
2802A Chong Hing Finance Center No 288 Nan Jing Road West, Huang Pu District, Shanghai, 200003, China
Tel.: (86) 2163595999
Synthetic Diamond Mfr
N.A.I.C.S.: 339910

First Mode Ipp Limited (1)
10 Bloomsbury Way, London, WC1A 2SL, United Kingdom
Tel.: (44) 2030592920
N.A.I.C.S.: 333611

IIDGR (UK) Limited (1)
20 Carlton House Terrace, London, SW1Y 5AN, United Kingdom
Tel.: (44) 2078587887
Web Site: http://www.iidgr.com
Synthetic Diamond Mfr
N.A.I.C.S.: 339910

Kumba Iron Ore Ltd. (1)
Centurion Gate124 Akkerboom Road, Centurion, 0157, South Africa (63.4%)
Tel.: (27) 126837000
Web Site: http://www.kumba.co.za
Rev.: $4,696,303,640
Assets: $5,376,509,040
Liabilities: $1,661,138,920
Net Worth: $3,715,370,120
Earnings: $1,623,180,300
Emp.: 5,878
Fiscal Year-end: 12/31/2023
Iron Ore Mining
N.A.I.C.S.: 212210
Timo S. Smit (Head-Mktg & Seaborne Logistics)

Kumba Singapore Pte. Ltd. (1)
10 Collyer Quay Level 38 Ocean Financial Centre, Singapore, 049315, Singapore
Tel.: (65) 64071600
Web Site:
    http://www.angloamericankumba.com
Mining & Metal Services
N.A.I.C.S.: 213114
Mandla Gantsho (Chm)

Kupfer Copper Germany GmbH (1)
Koenigsalle 2a, 40212, Dusseldorf, Germany
Tel.: (49) 15739337370
Electrical & Electronic Equipment Mfr

N.A.I.C.S.: 331420

Lightbox Jewelry Inc. (1)
3500 S DuPont Hwy, Dover, DE 19901
Web Site: http://www.lightboxjewelry.com
Jewelry Mfr
N.A.I.C.S.: 339910

Midland Quarry Products Ltd. (1)
Leicester Road, Whitwick, LE67 5GR, Leicestershire, United Kingdom
Tel.: (44) 3301232058
Web Site: https://www.mqp.co.uk
Sales Range: $50-74.9 Million
Emp.: 30
Aggregates & Crushed Stone Mining & Quarry Operations; Owned 50% by Anglo American plc & 50% by Hanson Limited
N.A.I.C.S.: 212319
Phil Bradshaw (Dir-Ops)

Minera Loma De Niquel, CA (1)
Autopista Regional Del Centro Km 54 Via Tiara, Tejerias, Venezuela (91%)
Tel.: (58) 2444000500
Web Site:
    http://www.mineralomadeniquel.com
Sales Range: $100-124.9 Million
Emp.: 150
Nickel Mining
N.A.I.C.S.: 212230

Minera Quellaveco S.A. (1)
Los Laureles 399, San Isidro, Lima, 27, Peru (80%)
Tel.: (51) 14224121
Copper Mining
N.A.I.C.S.: 212230

Spectrem Air Pty Ltd (1)
Lanseria Airport Hangar 111 Airport Road, Lanseria, South Africa
Tel.: (27) 116591518
Web Site: http://www.spectrem.co.za
Mineral Exploration Services
N.A.I.C.S.: 213114

Vergelegen Wines (Pty) Ltd. (1)
Lourensford Road Somerset West, Cape Town, South Africa
Tel.: (27) 218472100
Web Site: http://www.vergelegen.co.za
Wine Mfr
N.A.I.C.S.: 312130

ANGLO ASIAN MINING PLC
3rd Floor Tower 2 Hyatt Regency Business Centre 1033 Izmir St, 1065, Baku, 1065, Azerbaijan
Tel.: (994) 125963350
Web Site:
    https://www.angloasianmining.com
Year Founded: 2004
AAZ—(AIM)
Rev.: $45,855,000
Assets: $154,644,000
Liabilities: $69,836,000
Net Worth: $84,808,000
Earnings: ($24,242,000)
Emp.: 920
Fiscal Year-end: 12/31/23
Gold & Copper Mining
N.A.I.C.S.: 212220
William Roy Morgan (CFO)

Subsidiaries:

Azerbaijan International Mining Company Limited (1)
20/520 H Cavid Avenue, Baku, AZ1073, Azerbaijan
Tel.: (994) 125963350
Web Site: http://www.aimc.az
Gold & Metal Mining Services
N.A.I.C.S.: 212220
Reza Vaziri (Pres)

ANGLO EASTERN PLANTATIONS PLC
Quadrant House 6th Floor 4 Thomas More Square, London, E1W 1YW, United Kingdom
Tel.: (44) 2072164621
Web Site:
    https://www.angloeastern.co.uk

AEP—(LSE)
Rev.: $447,620,000
Assets: $630,210,000
Liabilities: $57,230,000
Net Worth: $572,980,000
Earnings: $101,480,000
Fiscal Year-end: 12/31/22
Oilseed Processing
N.A.I.C.S.: 111120
John Ewe Chuan Lim (Exec Dir-Corp Fin & Corp Affairs)

Subsidiaries:

Anglo-Eastern Plantations (M) Sdn. Bhd. (1)
Wisma Equity Level 7 150 Jalan Ampang, 50450, Kuala Lumpur, Malaysia
Tel.: (60) 321629808
Palm Oil Mfr
N.A.I.C.S.: 311225

PT Anglo-Eastern Plantations Management Indonesia (1)
Wisma HSBC Jalan Diponegoro Kav 11, Medan, 20152, North Sumatra, Indonesia
Tel.: (62) 614520107
Palm Oil Mfr
N.A.I.C.S.: 311225
Henry Tambunan (Head-HR & EA)

ANGLO EUROPEAN AVIATION AG
Quaderstrasse 7, 7000, Chur, Switzerland
Tel.: (41) 81 5330172
Web Site: http://www.angloeuropean.com
Year Founded: 1989
Sales Range: $10-24.9 Million
Air Charter Services
N.A.I.C.S.: 481111
Mark Everts (Mng Dir)

Subsidiaries:

Anglo-European (U.K.) Ltd (1)
Brewery Road, Crowle, DN17 4LT, North Lincs, United Kingdom
Tel.: (44) 1724711999
Aircraft Charter Services
N.A.I.C.S.: 481212

ANGLO PHILIPPINE HOLDINGS CORPORATION
6th Floor Quad Alpha Centrum 125 Pioneer Street, Mandaluyong, 1550, Metro Manila, Philippines
Tel.: (63) 286315139
Web Site: https://www.anglophil.com
Year Founded: 1958
APO—(PHI)
Rev.: $24,954,016
Assets: $218,531,494
Liabilities: $79,985,291
Net Worth: $138,546,202
Earnings: $22,858,310
Emp.: 13
Fiscal Year-end: 12/31/21
Oil & Mining Exploration Services
N.A.I.C.S.: 211120
Christopher M. Gotanco (Pres & COO)

ANGLO SCOTTISH ASSET FINANCE LIMITED
Unit 12-14 Lumley Court, Drum Industrial Estate Chester-le-Street, Durham, DH2 1AN, United Kingdom
Tel.: (44) 1914104776   UK
Web Site: https://www.angloscottish.co.uk
Year Founded: 2007
Financial Brokerage Services
N.A.I.C.S.: 523999

ANGLO-BOMARC MINES LTD.
701 West Georgia St, Suite 1500, Vancouver, V7Y 1G5, BC, Canada
Tel.: (604) 600-1386

Web Site: http://www.anglo-bomarcmines.com
Year Founded: 1967
ANB—(TSXV)
Sales Range: Less than $1 Million
Mineral Exploration Services
N.A.I.C.S.: 213114
Nizar Y. Bharmal (CFO)

ANGLO-EASTERN UNIVAN GROUP
17/F, Kingston International Centre, 19 Wang Chiu Road, Kowloon Bay, Kowloon, China (Hong Kong)
Tel.: (852) 39407000
Web Site: https://www.angloeastern.com
Year Founded: 1974
Emp.: 11,000
Ship Transportation Services
N.A.I.C.S.: 488999
Peter Cremers (Chm)

ANGLOGOLD ASHANTI PLC
112 Oxford Road Houghton Estate, Johannesburg, 2001, South Africa
Tel.: (27) 116376000   ZA
Web Site: https://www.anglogoldashanti.com
Year Founded: 1998
AU—(NYSE)
Rev.: $4,501,000,000
Assets: $8,072,000,000
Liabilities: $3,938,000,000
Net Worth: $4,134,000,000
Earnings: $316,000,000
Emp.: 13,144
Fiscal Year-end: 12/31/22
Gold Exploration, Mining & Processing
N.A.I.C.S.: 212220
Christine Ramon (CEO-Interim)

Subsidiaries:

AngloGold Ashanti North America Inc. (1)
4601 DTC Blvd Ste 550, Denver, CO 80237 (100%)
Tel.: (303) 889-0700
Rev.: $62,500,000
Emp.: 20
Holding Company; Gold Ore Exploration, Mining & Processing
N.A.I.C.S.: 551112
Ronald W. Largent (Exec VP)

Cerro Vanguardia S.A. (1)
Av San Martin 1032, Puerto San Julian, Santa Cruz, Argentina
Tel.: (54) 2962496260
Web Site: http://www.cerrovanguardia.com.ar
Gold & Silver Exploration Services
N.A.I.C.S.: 212290

Corvus Gold Inc. (1)
1750 -700 West Pender St, Vancouver, V6C 1G8, BC, Canada (100%)
Tel.: (604) 638-3246
Web Site: http://corvusgold.com
Rev.: $55,063
Assets: $8,655,317
Liabilities: $6,261,232
Net Worth: $2,394,085
Earnings: ($18,086,687)
Emp.: 1
Fiscal Year-end: 05/31/2021
Gold Mining Services
N.A.I.C.S.: 212220
Timothy Thompson (Pres)

ANGOSTURA HOLDINGS LIMITED
Corner Eastern Main Road and Trinity Avenue, Laventille, Trinidad & Tobago
Tel.: (868) 6231841
Web Site: http://www.angostura.com
Year Founded: 1824
Rev.: $123,047,328
Assets: $195,015,055

Liabilities: $29,223,450
Net Worth: $165,791,605
Earnings: $20,601,277
Emp.: 300
Fiscal Year-end: 12/31/19
Alcoholic Beverage Mfr & Distr
N.A.I.C.S.: 312130
Terrence Bharath (Chm)

Subsidiaries:

Angostura Limited (1)
Corner Eastern Main Road and Trinity Avenue, Laventille, Trinidad & Tobago (100%)
Tel.: (868) 6231841
Web Site: http://www.angostura.com
Sales Range: $75-99.9 Million
Emp.: 250
Wine & Distilled Alcoholic Beverage Merchant Whslr
N.A.I.C.S.: 424820

Servis Limited (1)
2774 Farrington St, Saint Paul, MN 55113-2450 (100%)
Tel.: (651) 486-0178
Sales Range: $25-49.9 Million
Emp.: 10
Carpet & Upholstery Cleaning Services
N.A.I.C.S.: 561740

Suriname Alcholic Beverages N.V. (1)
Cornelis Jongbawstraat 1828, Paramaribo, Suriname (75%)
Tel.: (597) 473344
Web Site: http://www.sabrum.com
Sales Range: $50-74.9 Million
Emp.: 90
Wine & Distilled Alcoholic Beverage Merchant Whslr
N.A.I.C.S.: 424820
Stephan Meegong (CEO & Mng Dir)

Trinidad Distillers Limited (1)
Eastern Main Rd & Angostura St, Laventille, Trinidad & Tobago (100%)
Tel.: (868) 623 2101
Sales Range: $25-49.9 Million
Emp.: 40
Wine & Distilled Alcoholic Beverage Merchant Whslr
N.A.I.C.S.: 424820

ANGROPREDUZECE D.D.
Cuprija bb, 77220, Cazin, Bosnia & Herzegovina
Tel.: (387) 37539100
ANPCRK1—(SARE)
Sales Range: Less than $1 Million
Emp.: 2
Shopping Center Management Services
N.A.I.C.S.: 531120

ANGROPROMET PREHRANA A.D.
Toplicina 18, Pozarevac, Serbia
Tel.: (381) 12 557 005
Year Founded: 1989
Sales Range: Less than $1 Million
Alcoholic Beverages Whslr
N.A.I.C.S.: 424820
Dragana Stokic (Exec Dir)

ANGROPROMET TIKVESANKA AD
15 Industriska Str, Kavadarci, North Macedonia
Tel.: (389) 70324797
Web Site: http://www.angro-promet.com
Year Founded: 1953
APTK—(MAC)
Rev.: $821,477
Assets: $3,227,178
Liabilities: $659,587
Net Worth: $2,567,590
Earnings: $13,419
Fiscal Year-end: 12/31/19
Warehouse Leasing Services
N.A.I.C.S.: 531130

ANGUS ENERGY PLC
Building 3 Chiswick Park 566 Chiswick High Road, London, W4 5YA, United Kingdom
Tel.: (44) 2088996380   UK
Web Site: https://www.angusenergy.co.uk
Year Founded: 2015
ANGS—(AIM)
Rev.: $3,555,108
Assets: $103,426,470
Liabilities: $210,374,082
Net Worth: ($106,947,612)
Earnings: ($126,749,790)
Fiscal Year-end: 09/30/22
Drilling Oil & Gas Wells
N.A.I.C.S.: 213111
George Lucan (Mng Dir)

ANGUS GOLD, INC.
18 King Street East Suite 902, Toronto, M5C 1C4, ON, Canada
Tel.: (416) 777-6772
Web Site: https://www.angusgold.com
ANGVF—(OTCQB)
Assets: $1,421,856
Liabilities: $439,073
Net Worth: $982,782
Earnings: ($3,106,903)
Fiscal Year-end: 01/31/22
Gold Mining Services
N.A.I.C.S.: 212220
Steve Burleton (Interim CEO)

ANGUS MONTGOMERY LTD.
9 Manchester Square, London, W1U 3PL, United Kingdom
Tel.: (44) 2078863000   UK
Web Site: http://www.montex.co.uk
Year Founded: 1895
Sales Range: $25-49.9 Million
Emp.: 30
Holding Company; Trade Show Organizer
N.A.I.C.S.: 551112
Sandy Angus (Chm)

Subsidiaries:

Montgomery Exhibitions Ltd. (1)
9 Manchester Square, London, W1U 3PL, United Kingdom
Tel.: (44) 2078863000
Web Site: http://www.montex.co.uk
Sales Range: $10-24.9 Million
Trade Show Organizer
N.A.I.C.S.: 561920
George Tsangari (CFO)

Division (Domestic):

Exhibition Consultants Ltd. (2)
9 Manchester Square, London, W1U 3PL, United Kingdom
Tel.: (44) 2078863000
Web Site: http://www.exhibitionconsultants.com
Emp.: 4
Exhibition Management Consultancy Services
N.A.I.C.S.: 541618
Rupert Owen (CEO)

Subsidiary (Non-US):

Specialised Exhibitions (Pty.) Limited (2)
Forum 3 Level 3 Braam Park 33 Hoofd Street, Ormonde Extension 5, Braamfontein, 2000, South Africa
Tel.: (27) 118351565
Web Site: http://www.specialised.com
Emp.: 65
Trade Show Organizer
N.A.I.C.S.: 561920
Gary Corin (Mng Dir)

ANGUS RESOURCES INC.
1836 West 5th Avenue Suite 205, Vancouver, V6J 1P3, BC, Canada
Tel.: (604) 318-4053   BC

Angus Resources Inc.—(Continued)

Year Founded: 2008
Investment Services
N.A.I.C.S.: 523999

ANGY (CHINA) MEDICAL LIMITED

Unit 2302 23/F New World Tower 1,
18 Queen's Road Central, Central,
China (Hong Kong)
Tel.: (852) 37560097　　　HK
Web Site: http://www.angy.hk
Year Founded: 2010
A01—(NSXA)
Rev.: $13,259,818
Assets: $4,860,056
Liabilities: $2,782,175
Net Worth: $2,077,881
Earnings: ($1,126,028)
Fiscal Year-end: 12/31/20
Medical Equipment Distr
N.A.I.C.S.: 423450

Subsidiaries:

Angy (Guangzhou) Medical Technology Co., Ltd.　　　(1)
Room 2713-2714 Metro Plaza No 183
Tianhe Road North, Guangzhou, China
Tel.: (86) 4008803337
Medical Equipment Whslr
N.A.I.C.S.: 423450

ANHEUSER-BUSCH INBEV SA/NV

Brouwerijplein 1, 3000, Leuven, Belgium
Tel.: (82) 16276111　　　BE
Web Site: https://www.ab-inbev.com
Year Founded: 2008
BUD—(NYSE)
Rev.: $50,746,000,000
Assets: $219,340,000,000
Liabilities: $126,664,000,000
Net Worth: $92,676,000,000
Earnings: $8,295,000,000
Emp.: 154,540
Fiscal Year-end: 12/31/23
Soft Drinks Mfr
N.A.I.C.S.: 551112

Subsidiaries:

AB - INBEV FRANCE S.A.S.　　(1)
Immeuble Crystal Zac Euralille 38 Allee
Vauban, 59110, La Madeleine, France
Tel.: (33) 320483030
Sales Range: $150-199.9 Million
Emp.: 30
Alcoholic Beverage Distr
N.A.I.C.S.: 424820

AB Inbev Africa B.V.　　　(1)
56 Grosvenor Bryanston, Sandton, 2191,
South Africa
Tel.: (27) 121414
N.A.I.C.S.: 312140

AB Inbev UK Limited　　　(1)
Bureau 90 Fetter Lane, EC4A 1EN, London, United Kingdom - England
Tel.: (44) 8706068008
Web Site:
　https://www.budweiserbrewinggroup.co.uk
Breweries Mfr
N.A.I.C.S.: 312120
Paula Lindenberg (Pres)

ABI SAB Group Holding Limited　(1)
Ab Inbev House Church Street West, Woking, GU21 6HT, United Kingdom
Tel.: (44) 1483264000
Web Site: http://www.ab-inbev.com
Holding Company; Beer Brewer & Other
Alcoholic & Non-Alcoholic Beverage Mfr &
Distr
N.A.I.C.S.: 551112

Subsidiary (Non-US):

Accra Brewery Limited　　　(2)
Graphic Road South Industrial Area, PO
Box GP 351, Accra, Ghana　　　(60%)
Tel.: (233) 800433433

Web Site: https://accrabrewery.com.gh
Beer, Soft Drinks & Non-Alcoholic Malt Beverages Mfr & Distr
N.A.I.C.S.: 312120
Adwoa Aaba Arthur (Dir-Legal & Corp Affairs)

Carlton & United Beverages Limited　　　(2)
77 Southbank Boulevard, Southbank, 3006,
VIC, Australia
Tel.: (61) 396332000
Web Site: http://cub.com.au
Beer & Wine
N.A.I.C.S.: 312120
Peter Filipovic (CEO)

Compania Cervecera de Canarias SA
Carretera Gral Cuesta Taco Km 0.5 La
Cuesta, Santa Cruz de Tenerife, 38320,
Spain
Tel.: (34) 34 901 50 00 05
Web Site:
　http://ww.cerveceradecanarias.com
Beer Mfr & Distr
N.A.I.C.S.: 312120

Heinrich's Syndicate Limited　(2)
Plot No 2744 2745 & 6249 Malambo Road,
PO Box 32740, Lusaka, 1010, Zambia
Tel.: (260) 211 244158
Beverages Mfr
N.A.I.C.S.: 312120

Queensland Breweries Pty Ltd　(2)
Ste 101 Level 1, Yatala, 4207, QLD, Australia
Tel.: (61) 738265830
Beverages Mfr
N.A.I.C.S.: 312120

SABMiller India Limited　　(2)
Green Heart Building Mfar Manyata Tech
Park Phase 4 Nagavara, Yeshwantpur,
Bengaluru, 560045, Karnataka, India
Tel.: (91) 80 3949 9999
Beer Mfr & Distr
N.A.I.C.S.: 312120

Division (Non-US):

SABMiller Latin America　　(2)
Carrera 9 76-49 4th Floor, Bogota, Colombia
Tel.: (57) 1 325 8600
Web Site: http://www.ab-inbev.com
Beer Brewer & Distr
N.A.I.C.S.: 312120

Subsidiary (Non-US):

Banks Holdings Limited　　(3)
Richard Cozier Drive Newton, Christ
Church, BB17047, Barbados
Tel.: (246) 2276700
Web Site: https://www.thebhlgroup.com
Food & Beverage Holding Company
N.A.I.C.S.: 551112
Lisa Ridley-Paul (Mgr-People-Grp)

Subsidiary (Domestic):

B&B Distribution Ltd.　　(4)
Newton, Christ Church, Barbados
Tel.: (246) 4182900
Web Site: http://www.thebhlgroup.com
Bottled Beverage Distribution
N.A.I.C.S.: 312111

Banks (Barbados) Breweries Limited　　　(4)
Newton, Christ Church, BB17047, Barbados
Tel.: (246) 2276700
Web Site: http://www.banksbeer.com
Bottled Beverage Mfr
N.A.I.C.S.: 424820

Barbados Bottling Co. Limited　(4)
Newton, Christ Church, Barbados
Tel.: (246) 4183300
Web Site: http://www.thebhlgroup.com
Soft Drink & Beverage Mfr & Bottler
N.A.I.C.S.: 312111

Barbados Dairy Industries Ltd.　(4)
The Pine, Saint Michael, BB14000, Barbados
Tel.: (246) 2276600
Web Site: https://www.thepinehilldairy.com

Dry, Condensed & Evaporated Dairy Products
N.A.I.C.S.: 311514
Gillian Marshall (Officer-HR)

Subsidiary (Domestic):

Bavaria SA　　　(3)
Carrera 53 A No 127-35, 110221, Bogota,
Colombia
Tel.: (57) 6017453333
Web Site: https://www.bavaria.co
Beer & Other Malt Beverages Mfr
N.A.I.C.S.: 312120

Plant (Domestic):

Bavaria SA - Barranquilla Brewery Plant　　　(4)
Calle 10 38 - 280, Barranquilla, Atlantico,
Colombia
Tel.: (57) 53504000
Beverages Mfr
N.A.I.C.S.: 312120

Bavaria SA - Tibito Malt Plant　(4)
Kilometro 6 Via Briceno Zipaquira Bavaria
Tibito Malt House, Zipaquira, Cundinamarca, Colombia
Tel.: (57) 15932140
Beverages Mfr
N.A.I.C.S.: 312120

Bavaria SA - Tocancipa Brewery Plant　　　(4)
Autopista Norte Km 30, Tocancipa, Cundinamarca, Colombia
Tel.: (57) 18786900
Beverages Mfr
N.A.I.C.S.: 312120

Bavaria SA - Tropical Malt Plant　(4)
Mamonal Km 14 Entrada a Pasacaballo,
Cartagena de Indias, Cartagena, Colombia
Tel.: (57) 56723100
Beverages Mfr
N.A.I.C.S.: 312120

Bavaria SA - Valle Brewery Plant　(4)
Calle 15 25A-37 Km 4 Autopista Cali -
Yumbo Costado Oriental, Yumbo, Valle del
Cauca, Colombia
Tel.: (57) 26919400
Beverages Mfr
N.A.I.C.S.: 312120

Subsidiary (Non-US):

Cerveceria Andina S.A.　　(3)
Av Francisco de Orellana s/n Cumbaya, PO
Box 17-01-4027, Quito, Ecuador (85.49%)
Tel.: (593) 2 2893 104
Web Site: http://www.cerveceriaandina.com
Beer Brewer & Distr
N.A.I.C.S.: 312120

Cerveceria Argentina S.A. Isenbeck　　　(3)
Esteban Echeverria 1980 Olivoss, Buenos
Aires, 1604, Argentina
Tel.: (54) 3487 428500
Beverage Product Mfr
N.A.I.C.S.: 312120

Cerveceria Hondurena, S.A de C.V　　　(3)
Boulevard del Norte Apartado Postal No 86,
San Pedro Sula, Honduras
Tel.: (504) 25451111
Web Site:
　https://www.cerveceriahondurena.com
Brewery Operator
N.A.I.C.S.: 312120

Cerveceria Nacional (CN) SA　(3)
Km 16 5 Via Daule Francisco de Orellana
Avenue, Cumbaya Parish, Guayaquil,
Ecuador　　　(95.58%)
Tel.: (593) 42162088
Web Site: https://www.cervecerianacional.ec
Beer Brewer & Distr
N.A.I.C.S.: 312120

Cerveceria Nacional, S.A.　(3)
Apartado 6-1393, El Dorado, Panama,
Panama　　　(97%)
Tel.: (507) 3056000
Web Site: http://www.cerveceria-nacional.com
Beer & Soft Drinks Mfr
N.A.I.C.S.: 312120

Cerveceria San Juan S.A.　(3)
Carretera Federico Basadre Km 13, Pucallpa, Peru
Tel.: (51) 61586000
Web Site: http://www.sanjuan.com.pe
Alcoholic Beverages Mfr
N.A.I.C.S.: 312120

Industrias La Constancia S.A.　(3)
Avenida Independencia 526, San Salvador,
El Salvador
Tel.: (503) 22228080
Web Site: https://www.laconstancia.com
Emp.: 3,000
Brewery Operator
N.A.I.C.S.: 312120

Union de Cervecerias Peruanas Backus y Johnston S.A.A.　(3)
3986 Av Nicolas Ayllon, Ate, Lima,
Peru　　　(93.65%)
Tel.: (51) 13113010
Web Site: http://www.backus.pe
Brewery Operator
N.A.I.C.S.: 312120

Subsidiary (Non-US):

SABMiller Vietnam Company Ltd　(2)
9th Floor No 58 Bovantan Street 3, Tan
Dinh Ward, 70000, Ho Chi Minh City, Vietnam
Tel.: (84) 835265505
Beverages Mfr
N.A.I.C.S.: 312120
Huong Ngo (Sec-Fin)

SABSA Holdings (Pty) Ltd.　(2)
65 Park Lane Sandown, Johannesburg,
2001, South Africa　　　(100%)
Tel.: (27) 114071700
Web Site: http://www.ab-inbev.co
Holding Company
N.A.I.C.S.: 551112

Subsidiary (Domestic):

The South African Breweries (Pty) Ltd.　　　(3)
56 Grosvenor road, PO Box 782178, Bryanston, Sandton, 2146, South Africa
Tel.: (27) 118818111
Web Site: https://www.sab.co.za
Emp.: 5,697
Alcoholic & Non-Alcoholic Beverage Producer & Distr
N.A.I.C.S.: 312120

Division (Domestic):

Amalgamated Beverage Industries　　　(4)
14 Pongola Crescent Eastgate Extension
17, PO Box 76202, Sandton, 2144, Wendywood, South Africa　　　(100%)
Tel.: (27) 117191400
Web Site: http://www.abi.co.za
Bottlers of Coca-Cola Products
N.A.I.C.S.: 312112

Subsidiary (Domestic):

Coleus Packaging (Pty) Limited　(4)
21 Potgieter Street, Alrode, 1457, Gauteng,
South Africa　　　(60%)
Tel.: (27) 100456841
Web Site: https://www.coleus.co.za
Bottle Caps Mfr
N.A.I.C.S.: 332999

Subsidiary (Non-US):

Coleus Crowns (Uganda) Ltd　(5)
KSW 1985 Oil Mill Complex, PO Box 54,
Kakira, Uganda
Tel.: (256) 75 322 4433
Bottle Caps Mfr
N.A.I.C.S.: 332999

Subsidiary (Domestic):

The South African Breweries Hop Farms (Pty) Ltd　　　(4)
Rob Roy Farm Montague St Blanco,
George, 6529, Western Cape, South Africa
Tel.: (27) 448028415
Web Site: http://www.sabmiller.com
Crop Farming Services
N.A.I.C.S.: 111998

The South African Breweries Maltings (Pty) Ltd (4)
Bredasdorp Road, Caledon, 7230, Gauteng, South Africa
Tel.: (27) 282143213
Web Site: http://www.sabmiller.com
Malt Mfr
N.A.I.C.S.: 311213

Subsidiary (Non-US):

Southern Sudan Beverages Ltd (2)
Plot 1 Kololomro Site, Juba, Sudan (South)
Tel.: (211) 477 186 036
Beverages Mfr
N.A.I.C.S.: 312120

Tanzania Breweries Limited (2)
Plot 79 Block AA Uhuru Street Mchichini, PO Box 9013, Ilala District, Dar es Salaam, Tanzania
Tel.: (255) 764702905
Web Site: https://tanzaniabreweries.co.tz
Rev.: $441,162,800
Assets: $403,911,040
Liabilities: $160,651,010
Net Worth: $243,260,030
Earnings: $64,591,160
Emp.: 1,515
Fiscal Year-end: 12/31/2019
Beer Production & Sales
N.A.I.C.S.: 312120
David Almeida (Chief Strategy & Tech Officer)

Ursus Breweries SA (2)
Pipera Road 43 Floreasca Park Corp A floor 2, 10072, Bucharest, Romania
Tel.: (40) 372858300
Web Site: https://ursus-breweries.ro
Beer Mfr
N.A.I.C.S.: 312120

Ambev S.A. (1)
Rua Dr Renato Paes de Barros 1017 3rd Floor, 04530-001, Sao Paulo, 04530-001, SP, Brazil (56%)
Tel.: (55) 1121221414
Web Site: https://www.ambev.com.br
Rev.: $15,324,016,800
Assets: $26,522,425,500
Liabilities: $10,502,655,950
Net Worth: $16,019,769,550
Earnings: $2,862,833,200
Emp.: 47,108
Fiscal Year-end: 12/31/2022
Beer & Ale Mfr
N.A.I.C.S.: 312120
Victorio Carlos De Marchi (Co-Chm)

Subsidiary (Non-US):

FNC S.A. (2)
Entre Rios 1060, Montevideo, 11800, Uruguay (97.89%)
Tel.: (598) 22001681
Web Site: http://www.fnc.com.uy
Sales Range: $25-49.9 Million
Emp.: 400
Beer & Soft Drink Mfr & Distr
N.A.I.C.S.: 312120

Anheuser Busch Inbev Italia SPA (1)
Piazza Gae Aulenti n 8, Milan, Italy
Tel.: (39) 0238595400
Web Site: https://www.ab-inbev.it
Breweries Distr
N.A.I.C.S.: 424490

Anheuser-Busch Americas Holdings LLC (1)
1 Busch Pl, Saint Louis, MO 63118
N.A.I.C.S.: 312140

Anheuser-Busch Companies, LLC (1)
1 Busch Pl, Saint Louis, MO 63118-1849
Tel.: (314) 577-2000
Web Site: http://www.anheuser-busch.com
Holding Company; Beer & Malt Beverage Mfr & Distr
N.A.I.C.S.: 551112
Ann Lawenstein (Corp Librarian)

Subsidiary (Domestic):

Anheuser-Busch Cos., Inc. (2)
1800 N Clybourn Ave, Chicago, IL 60614
Tel.: (773) 380-8080

Administrative Management & General Management Consulting Service
N.A.I.C.S.: 541611
Louis Cardinals (Mgr)

Anheuser-Busch International, Inc. (2)
1 Busch Pl, Saint Louis, MO 63118-1849
Tel.: (314) 577-2000
Web Site: http://www.abconference.com
Sales Range: $25-49.9 Million
Emp.: 37
International Beer Operations, Sales & Marketing & Equity Investments with International Brewers
N.A.I.C.S.: 424810
John H. Purnell (CEO)

Anheuser-Busch, Inc. (2)
1 Busch Pl, Saint Louis, MO 63118
Tel.: (314) 577-2000
Web Site: https://www.anheuser-busch.com
Beer & Malt Beverage Mfr & Distr
N.A.I.C.S.: 312120

Unit (Domestic):

Anheuser-Busch Sales Pomona (3)
2800 S Reservoir St, Pomona, CA 91766
Tel.: (800) 622-2667
Rev.: $60,300,000
Emp.: 180
Beer & Other Fermented Malt Liquors Mfr
N.A.I.C.S.: 424810

Anheuser-Busch Sales of Hawaii (3)
99-877 Iwaena St, Aiea, HI 96701-3220
Tel.: (808) 487-0055
Sales Range: $50-74.9 Million
Emp.: 225
Beer & Other Fermented Malt Liquors Mfr
N.A.I.C.S.: 424810

Anheuser-Busch Sales of Lima (3)
3535 Saint Johns Rd, Lima, OH 45804
Tel.: (419) 221-2337
Sales Range: $25-49.9 Million
Emp.: 100
Beer Distr
N.A.I.C.S.: 424810
Mark G. Guagenti (COO)

Subsidiary (Domestic):

August A. Busch & Company of Massachusetts, Inc. (3)
440 Riverside Ave, Medford, MA 02155-4948
Web Site: https://www.abwholesaler.com
Sales Range: $50-74.9 Million
Emp.: 250
Beer Wholesaler
N.A.I.C.S.: 424810
Mark Wahlgren (Gen Mgr)

Subsidiary (Non-US):

Busch Agricultural Resources, Inc. (3)
Tel.: (314) 984-4680
Sales Range: $25-49.9 Million
Emp.: 23
Agricultural Product Mfr
N.A.I.C.S.: 311212

Subsidiary (Non-US):

Pacific International Rice Mills (4)
Tel.: (530) 666-1691
Web Site: https://pirmirice.com
Sales Range: $10-24.9 Million
Rice Mfr
N.A.I.C.S.: 311212

Subsidiary (Domestic):

Busch Properties, Inc. (3)
1 Busch Pl, Saint Louis, MO 63118-1849
Tel.: (314) 577-2000
Sales Range: $5-14.9 Billion
Emp.: 30,000
Real Estate Holding Company
N.A.I.C.S.: 312120

Subsidiary (Domestic):

Kingsmill Realty Inc. (4)
100 Kingsmill Rd, Williamsburg, VA 23185-5579
Tel.: (757) 253-3933
Web Site: https://www.kingsmill.com

Sales Range: $25-49.9 Million
Emp.: 12
Real Estate Services
N.A.I.C.S.: 531210

Subsidiary (Domestic):

Elysian Brewing Company (3)
542 1st Ave S, Seattle, WA 98104
Tel.: (206) 382-4498
Web Site: https://www.elysianbrewing.com
Emp.: 263
Brewery & Restaurant Operator
N.A.I.C.S.: 312120

Subsidiary (Domestic):

Blue Point Brewing Company, Inc. (2)
225 W Main St, Patchogue, NY 11772-3304
Tel.: (631) 627-8292
Web Site: https://www.bluepointbrewing.com
Sales Range: $10-24.9 Million
Emp.: 25
Beer Brewery
N.A.I.C.S.: 312120

Craft Brew Alliance, Inc. (2)
929 N Russell St, Portland, OR 97227-1733 (100%)
Tel.: (503) 331-7270
Web Site: http://www.craftbrew.com
Rev.: $204,634,000
Assets: $249,385,000
Liabilities: $124,080,000
Net Worth: $125,305,000
Earnings: ($12,919,000)
Emp.: 655
Fiscal Year-end: 12/31/2019
Beer Brewer & Whslr
N.A.I.C.S.: 312120
Christine Perich (CFO, Chief Strategy Officer, Treas & Exec VP)

Subsidiary (Domestic):

Appalachian Mountain Brewery, Inc. (3)
163 Boone Creek Dr, Boone, NC 28607
Tel.: (828) 263-1111
Web Site: https://www.amb.beer
Beer Mfr
N.A.I.C.S.: 312120

Kona Brewery LLC (3)
74-5612 Pawai Pl, Brewery Block, HI 96740
Tel.: (808) 334-2739
N.A.I.C.S.: 312140
Cameron Healy (Co-Founder)

Wynwood Brewing Company, LLC (3)
565 NW 24th St, Miami, FL 33127
Tel.: (305) 982-8732
Web Site: https://www.wynwoodbrewing.com
Brewery Mfr
N.A.I.C.S.: 312120

Subsidiary (Domestic):

Cutwater Spirits, LLC (2)
9750 Distribution Ave, San Diego, CA 92121
Tel.: (858) 672-3848
Web Site: http://cutwaterspirits.com
Distilled Spirits Mfr & Whslr
N.A.I.C.S.: 312140
Jim Buechler (Pres & CEO)

Karbach Brewing Co. LLC (2)
2032 Karbach St, Houston, TX 77092-8406
Tel.: (713) 680-2739
Web Site: https://www.karbachbrewing.com
Craft Brewery & Restaurants
N.A.I.C.S.: 424810
Lauren Cernosek (Mgr-Supply Chain)

Manufacturers Railway Company (2)
1 Arsenal St, Saint Louis, MO 63118
Tel.: (314) 577-1749
Web Site: http://www.anheuser-busch.com
Sales Range: $1-9.9 Million
Emp.: 70
Switching Services
N.A.I.C.S.: 488210

Wicked Weed Brewing LLC (2)
91 Biltmore Ave, Asheville, NC 28801-3626
Tel.: (828) 575-9599

Web Site: http://www.wickedweedbrewing.com
Craft Breweries
N.A.I.C.S.: 312120
Joe Pawelek (Head-Brewing Ops)

Anheuser-Busch InBev Germany Holding GmbH (1)
Am Deich 18/19, 28199, Bremen, Germany
Tel.: (49) 42150940
Web Site: https://ab-inbev-media.de
Holding Company
N.A.I.C.S.: 551112

Anheuser-Busch Packaging Group, Inc. (1)
Tel.: (314) 821-0599
Packaging & Recycling Services
N.A.I.C.S.: 561910

Subsidiary (Non-US):

Anheuser-Busch Recycling Corporation (2)
Tel.: (314) 957-0787
Sales Range: $25-49.9 Million
Emp.: 25
Beer Can Recycling Services
N.A.I.C.S.: 423930

Eagle Packaging Inc. (2)
Tel.: (314) 298-6700
Sales Range: $10-24.9 Million
Emp.: 20
Food Products Assembling & Packaging Services
N.A.I.C.S.: 561990

Longhorn Glass Inc. (2)
Tel.: (512) 443-9000
Web Site: https://www.longhornglass.net
Sales Range: $50-74.9 Million
Emp.: 187
Packing Bottling & Canning Glass Mfr
N.A.I.C.S.: 327213

Metal Container Corporation (2)
Tel.: (314) 957-9500
Web Site: http://www.metal.com
Sales Range: $25-49.9 Million
Emp.: 60
Can Mfr
N.A.I.C.S.: 332431

BRASSERIE DE LUXEMBOURG MOUSEL - DIEKIRCH SA (1)
Grand Duchy of Luxembourg, PO Box 148, 9214, Diekirch, Luxembourg
Tel.: (352) 802131999
Sales Range: $25-49.9 Million
Emp.: 75
Alcoholic Beverages Mfr
N.A.I.C.S.: 312120
Benoit Bronckart (Mgr)

BRAUEREI BECK GmbH & CO. KG (1)
Am Deich 18/19, 28199, Bremen, Germany
Tel.: (49) 42150940
Web Site: https://www.becks.de
Alcoholic Beverage Mfr & Distr
N.A.I.C.S.: 312120

BRAUERGILDE HANNOVER AG (1)
Hildesheimer Str 132, Hannover, 30173, Germany
Tel.: (49) 51198080
Alcoholic Beverages Mfr
N.A.I.C.S.: 312120
Hans Josef Toussaint (Mng Dir)

BUDWEISER WUHAN INTERNATIONAL BREWING COMPANY LIMITED (1)
No 20 Youfang Street, Xiangfang District, Harbin, China
Tel.: (86) 451 55602920
Alcoholic Beverages Mfr
N.A.I.C.S.: 312120
Yan Chuang (Gen Mgr)

Brauerei Diebels GmbH & Co. KG (1)
Brauerei Diebels Strasse 1, 47661, Issum, Germany (80%)
Tel.: (49) 2835300
Sales Range: $25-49.9 Million
Emp.: 250
Malt Beverage Mfr
N.A.I.C.S.: 312120

Anheuser-Busch InBev SA/NV—(Continued)

Andre Castens *(Mgr-PR)*

Breckenridge Brewery (1)
2990 Brewery Ln, Littleton, CO 80120
Tel.: (303) 803-1380
Web Site: http://www.breckbrew.com
Breweries
N.A.I.C.S.: 312120

Brouwerij van Hoegaarden N.V. (1)
Stoopkensstraat 46, 3320, Hoegaarden, Belgium
Tel.: (32) 16769811
Web Site: http://www.hoegaarden.com
Sales Range: $50-74.9 Million
Emp.: 155
Beer Brewer & Whlsr
N.A.I.C.S.: 312120

**CERVECERIA BOLIVIANA NACIO-
NAL S.A.** (1)
Av Montes 400, PO Box 421, La Paz, Bolivia
Tel.: (591) 22454454
Web Site: https://www.cbn.bo
Beverage Products Mfr & Distr
N.A.I.C.S.: 312120

**CERVECERIA PARAGUAYA
S.A.** (1)
Ruta A Villeta Km 30, Ypane, 2660, Paraguay
Tel.: (595) 215886000
Alcoholic Beverages Mfr
N.A.I.C.S.: 312120

COBREW N.V. (1)
Brouwerijplein 1, 3000, Leuven, Belgium
Tel.: (32) 16276111
Web Site: http://www.inbev.com
Sales Range: $75-99.9 Million
Emp.: 40
Business Management Consulting Services
N.A.I.C.S.: 541611

**Cerveceria Cuauhtemoc Moctezuma
S.A. de C.V.** (1)
Avenida Alfonso Reyes 2202 Nte, Monterrey, 64442, Nuevo Leon, Mexico
Tel.: (52) 83285000
Beer Breweries
N.A.I.C.S.: 312120

**Cerveceria Y Malteria Quilmes Saica
Y G** (1)
Av 12 de Octubre and Gran Canaria, Quilmes, Buenos Aires, Argentina
Tel.: (54) 43491700
Web Site:
https://www.cerveceriaymalteriaquilmes.com
Brewery Product Mfr
N.A.I.C.S.: 312120

**Compania Cervecera AmBev
Dominicana** (1)
Av San Martin 279, Zona Industrial de Herrera, Santo Domingo, Dominican Republic
Tel.: (809) 540 7777
Web Site: http://www.ab-Inbev.com
Sales Range: $350-399.9 Million
Emp.: 1,600
Beer Breweries
N.A.I.C.S.: 312120

Crown Beers India Limited (1)
510/511 Minerva House Sarojini Devi Road, Banjara Hills, Secunderabad, 500003, Telangana, India (100%)
Tel.: (91) 4023324245
Sales Range: $25-49.9 Million
Emp.: 30
Beer Brewer & Distr
N.A.I.C.S.: 312120

**Four Peaks Brewing Company,
Inc.** (1)
1340 E 8th St Ste 104, Tempe, AZ 85281
Tel.: (480) 303-9967
Web Site: https://www.fourpeaks.com
Brewery & Restaurant Operator
N.A.I.C.S.: 312120

Grupo Modelo, S.A. de C.V. (1)
Calle Cerrada Palomas 22 6th floor, Reforma, 11650, Mexico, DF, Mexico
Tel.: (52) 8004663356
Web Site: https://www.grupomodelo.com
Beer Producer & Distr

N.A.I.C.S.: 312120
Cassiano De Stefano *(Pres)*

**HASSERODER BRAUEREI
GmbH** (1)
Auerhahnring 1, 38855, Wernigerode, Germany
Tel.: (49) 80052205205
Web Site: http://www.hasseroeder.de
Beverage Product Mfr
N.A.I.C.S.: 312120
Hannes Havliza *(Mng Dir)*

**INBEV SEDRIN BREWERY Co,
Ltd** (1)
No 1 West Xuejin Avenue, Hanjiang District, Putian, 351111, China
Tel.: (86) 5943587303
Beer Mfr
N.A.I.C.S.: 312120

**INTERBREW INTERNATIONAL
B.V.** (1)
Ceresstraat 1, Breda, 4811 CA, Netherlands
Tel.: (31) 765252398
Alcoholic Beverage Mfr & Distr
N.A.I.C.S.: 312120

InBev N.V. (1)
Ceresstraat 1, PO Box 3212, 4811 CA, Breda, Netherlands (100%)
Tel.: (31) 765252424
Web Site: http://www.inbev.com.nl
Sales Range: $25-49.9 Million
Emp.: 125
Beer Brewery
N.A.I.C.S.: 312120

InBev UK Ltd. (1)
Porter Tun House 500 Capability Green, Luton, LU1 3LS, Beds, United Kingdom (100%)
Tel.: (44) 1582391166
Sales Range: $750-799.9 Million
Emp.: 2,961
Brewing, Packaging, Beer Marketing & Distribution
N.A.I.C.S.: 312120

Kamenitza AD (1)
Northern Industrial Zone, 6300, Haskovo, Bulgaria (87%)
Tel.: (359) 32621560
Web Site: https://www.kamenitza.bg
Brewery
N.A.I.C.S.: 312120

Labatt Brewing Company Limited (1)
207 Queens Quay West Ste 299, Toronto, M5J 1A7, ON, Canada (100%)
Tel.: (416) 361-5050
Web Site: http://www.labatt.com
Sales Range: $750-799.9 Million
Emp.: 3,000
Brewing Company
N.A.I.C.S.: 312120

Plant (Domestic):

Columbia Brewing Company (2)
1220 Erikson St, PO Box 1950, Creston, V0B 1G0, BC, Canada (100%)
Tel.: (250) 428-9344
Web Site: http://www.labatt.com
Sales Range: $25-49.9 Million
Emp.: 125
Brewery Services
N.A.I.C.S.: 312120

La Brasserie Labatt (2)
50 Labatt Ave, Montreal, H8R 3E7, QC, Canada (100%)
Tel.: (514) 366-5050
Web Site: http://www.labatt.com
Sales Range: $300-349.9 Million
Emp.: 1,200
Beer Mfr
N.A.I.C.S.: 312120

Labatt Breweries Atlantic Region (2)
3055 Aricola St, Halifax, B3K 4G2, NS, Canada (100%)
Tel.: (902) 453-1867
Web Site: http://www.labatt.com
Sales Range: $125-149.9 Million
Emp.: 275
Beer Distr
N.A.I.C.S.: 424810

Labatt Breweries Ontario Ltd. (2)
445 Export Blvd, Mississauga, L5S 0A1,

ON, Canada (50%)
Tel.: (905) 696-3300
Web Site: http://www.labatts.com
Sales Range: $10-24.9 Million
Emp.: 50
Beer Mfr
N.A.I.C.S.: 312120

Labatt Breweries Prairie Region (2)
4344-99 St, Edmonton, T6E 6K8, AB, Canada
Tel.: (780) 436-6060
Web Site: http://www.labatt.com
Sales Range: $25-49.9 Million
Emp.: 200
Beer Mfr
N.A.I.C.S.: 312120

Labatt Breweries of London (2)
150 Simcoe St Ste A, London, N6A 4M3, ON, Canada (100%)
Tel.: (519) 663-5050
Web Site: http://www.labatt.com
Sales Range: $75-99.9 Million
Emp.: 450
Beer Mfr
N.A.I.C.S.: 312120

**Labatt Breweries of
Newfoundland** (2)
60 Leslie St, Saint John's, A1E 2V8, NL, Canada (100%)
Tel.: (709) 579-0121
Web Site: http://www.labatt.com
Sales Range: $25-49.9 Million
Emp.: 100
Beer Mfr
N.A.I.C.S.: 312120

Nile Breweries Ltd. (1)
Plot M90 Yusuf Lule Rd, Njeru, Jinja, Uganda
Tel.: (256) 332210009
Web Site: http://www.nilebreweries.com
Breweries Mfr
N.A.I.C.S.: 312120
Thomas Kamphuis *(Dir-Ops)*

Oriental Brewery Co., Ltd. (1)
8th floor ASEM Tower 517 Yeongdong-daero, Gangnam-gu, Seoul, 137-866, Korea (South)
Tel.: (82) 221495000
Web Site: https://www.ob.co.kr
Sales Range: $500-549.9 Million
Emp.: 1,582
Beer Brewery
N.A.I.C.S.: 312120

Pivovar Samson A.S. (1)
Lidicka tr 458/51, 370 01, Ceske Budejovice, Czech Republic
Tel.: (420) 386708120
Web Site: https://www.samson.cz
Brewery Product Mfr
N.A.I.C.S.: 312120

**SPATEN - FRANZISKANER - BRAU
GmbH** (1)
Marsstrasse 46-48, 80335, Munich, Germany
Tel.: (49) 8951220
Web Site: https://spatenbraeu.de
Alcoholic Beverages Mfr
N.A.I.C.S.: 312120

**ANHUI ANFU BATTERY TECH-
NOLOGY CO., LTD.**
1801 North Tower Baili Center No 888 Qianshan Road, Shushan District, Hefei, 238000, Anhui, China
Tel.: (86) 55162631389
Web Site: https://www.anfucorp.com
Year Founded: 1999
603031—(SHG)
Rev.: $474,992,407
Assets: $848,990,671
Liabilities: $451,796,024
Net Worth: $397,194,647
Earnings: $11,457,861
Fiscal Year-end: 12/31/22
Supermarket Operator
N.A.I.C.S.: 445110
Xia Zhubing *(Chm)*

ANHUI ANLI MATERIAL TECH-

NOLOGY CO., LTD.
Taohua Industrial Zone, Economic-Technological Development District, Hefei, 230093, Anhui, China
Tel.: (86) 55168992815
Web Site:
https://www.chinapuleather.com
Year Founded: 1994
300218 (CHIN)
Rev.: $274,164,696
Assets: $321,622,704
Liabilities: $121,599,036
Net Worth: $200,023,668
Earnings: $20,306,052
Emp.: 2,600
Fiscal Year-end: 12/31/22
Synthetic Leather Mfr
N.A.I.C.S.: 316990
Yao Heping *(Chm & Gen Mgr)*

**ANHUI ANNADA TITANIUM IN-
DUSTRY CO., LTD.**
No 1288 South Tongguan Road, Tongling, 244000, Anhui, China
Tel.: (86) 5623867940
Web Site: https://www.andty.com
Year Founded: 1994
002136—(SSE)
Rev.: $381,082,104
Assets: $268,399,872
Liabilities: $75,233,340
Net Worth: $193,166,532
Earnings: $37,656,684
Emp.: 790
Fiscal Year-end: 12/31/22
Chemical Products Mfr
N.A.I.C.S.: 325998
Liu Junchang *(Chm)*

**ANHUI CHAOYUE ENVIRON-
MENTAL TECHNOLOGY CO.,
LTD.**
Chaoyue Circular Economy Industrial Park, Nanqiao District, Chuzhou, 239060, Anhui, China
Tel.: (86) 5503512136
Web Site: https://www.ah-cy.cn
Year Founded: 2009
301049—(CHIN)
Rev.: $37,121,197
Assets: $175,779,845
Liabilities: $67,339,577
Net Worth: $108,440,267
Earnings: ($16,875,493)
Fiscal Year-end: 12/31/23
Waste Disposal Services
N.A.I.C.S.: 562211
Zhijiang Gao *(Chm)*

**ANHUI CONCH CEMENT COM-
PANY LIMITED**
NO 39 Wenhua Road, Wuhu, 241000, Anhui, China
Tel.: (86) 5533118688 CN
Web Site: https://www.conch.cn
Year Founded: 1997
AHCHF—(OTCIQ)
Rev.: $27,002,141,309
Assets: $30,791,036,253
Liabilities: $5,042,117,965
Net Worth: $25,748,918,288
Earnings: $5,577,754,527
Emp.: 47,539
Fiscal Year-end: 12/31/20
Cement Product Mfr
N.A.I.C.S.: 327310
Dengbang Gao *(Chm)*

Subsidiaries:

**Anhui Changfeng Conch Cement Co.,
Ltd.** (1)
Shuangdun Town, Changfeng, Hefei, China
Tel.: (86) 5516377090
Cement Mfr
N.A.I.C.S.: 327310

Conch Construction & Roofing
Inc. (1)
1075 Duval C-21 235, Key West, FL 33040
Tel.: (305) 304-4188
Web Site:
https://www.conchconstruction.com
Commercial Building Construction Services
N.A.I.C.S.: 541330

Guizhou New Shuanglong Cement
Co., Ltd. (1)
Mawo Villager Group Wujiang Community,
Wujiang Town Bozhou District, Zunyi,
563104, China
Tel.: (86) 85127393103
Cement Mfr
N.A.I.C.S.: 327310

PT Conch North Sulawesi
Cement (1)
JI Trans Sulawesi, Desa Solog Kec Lolak
Kab Bolaang Mongondow, Sulawesi, Indo-
nesia
Tel.: (62) 4342608222
Web Site: https://conch-nsc.com
N.A.I.C.S.: 327310

PT Conch South Kalimantan
Cement (1)
Seradang Village RT 02 Tabalong Regency,
Haruai District, Kalimantan, 71572, Indone-
sia
Tel.: (62) 8235 316 6668
Web Site: https://www.conch-skc.com
Cement Product Mfr & Distr
N.A.I.C.S.: 327310

Shanghai Conch Cement Co.,
Ltd. (1)
No 90 Punan Rd, Xidu Town Fengxia,
Shanghai, China
Tel.: (86) 2157159100
Cement Mfr
N.A.I.C.S.: 327310

Shanghai Conch Construction Mate-
rial International Trading Co.,
Ltd. (1)
Rm 1101-1102 Yu an Bldg No 738, Pudong
New Area, 200122, Shanghai, China
Tel.: (86) 2158209601
Emp.: 22
Cement Mfr
N.A.I.C.S.: 327310
Yuan Lin *(Gen Mgr)*

**ANHUI CONSTRUCTION ENGI-
NEERING GROUP CORPORA-
TION LIMITED**
Floors 26 - 29 Anjian Mansion Inter-
national 459 Huangshan Road, Hefei,
23001, Anhui, China
Tel.: (86) 55162865001
Web Site: https://www.aceg.com.cn
600502—(SHG)
Rev.: $11,248,781,872
Assets: $20,928,306,878
Liabilities: $17,701,593,853
Net Worth: $3,226,713,025
Earnings: $193,753,221
Fiscal Year-end: 12/31/22
Construction Engineering Services
N.A.I.C.S.: 541330
Shiyun Zhao *(Chm)*

**ANHUI COREACH TECHNOL-
OGY CO., LTD.**
Xinruida science and technology park
no 6988 fangxing avenue, jingkai dis-
trict, Hefei, 230000, Anhui, China
Tel.: (86) 55168103799
Web Site: https://coreach.com.cn
Year Founded: 2012
002983—(SSE)
Rev.: $133,976,700
Assets: $219,217,752
Liabilities: $59,494,500
Net Worth: $159,723,252
Earnings: $14,872,572
Fiscal Year-end: 12/31/22
Lighting Product Mfr & Distr
N.A.I.C.S.: 335131
You Peng *(Chm & Gen Mgr)*

**ANHUI DELI HOUSEHOLD
GLASS CO., LTD.**
Mentai Industrial Park, Fengyang,
Chuzhou, 233100, Anhui, China
Tel.: (86) 13921445950　　CN
Web Site:
https://www.deliglassware.com
Year Founded: 1996
002571—(SSE)
Rev.: $157,763,268
Assets: $392,545,764
Liabilities: $204,134,580
Net Worth: $188,411,184
Earnings: ($15,434,172)
Emp.: 2,000
Fiscal Year-end: 12/31/22
Household Glass Products Mfr &
Sales
N.A.I.C.S.: 327213
Shi Weidong *(Chm)*

Subsidiaries:

Shanghai Shige Industry Co.,
Ltd. (1)
269th DaPu Road ForeSight Plaza 28FL,
Shanghai, 200023, China
Tel.: (86) 2163263699
Web Site:
http://www.shanghaiindustriesgroup.com
Chemical Products Mfr
N.A.I.C.S.: 325998

**ANHUI EXPRESSWAY COM-
PANY LIMITED**
No 520 Wangjiang West Road, Hefei,
230088, Anhui, China
Tel.: (86) 5515338697　　CN
Web Site: http://www.anhui-
expressway.net
Year Founded: 1996
AUHEF—(OTCIQ)
Rev.: $617,356,018
Assets: $3,058,909,505
Liabilities: $1,223,480,824
Net Worth: $1,835,428,682
Earnings: $236,420,343
Emp.: 2,058
Fiscal Year-end: 12/31/21
Toll Expressway Construction & Man-
agement Services
N.A.I.C.S.: 237310
Xinyu Xie *(Sec & Deputy Gen Mgr)*

**ANHUI FENGYUAN PHARMA-
CEUTICAL CO., LTD.**
16 Dalian Road Baohe Industrial
Park, Hefei, 230051, Anhui, China
Tel.: (86) 55164846153
Web Site: http://www.bbcayy.com
Year Founded: 1960
000153—(SSE)
Rev.: $562,164,408
Assets: $627,481,296
Liabilities: $381,112,992
Net Worth: $246,368,304
Earnings: $21,681,972
Fiscal Year-end: 12/31/22
Pharmaceutical Product Mfr & Distr
N.A.I.C.S.: 325412
He Hongman *(Chm)*

**ANHUI FUHUANG STEEL
STRUCTURE CO., LTD.**
Fuhuang Industrial Park Huanglu
Town, Chaohu, 238076, Anhui, China
Web Site: http://www.fuhuang.cn
002743—(SSE)
Rev.: $667,995,120
Assets: $1,505,952,864
Liabilities: $1,055,150,928
Net Worth: $450,801,936
Earnings: $13,937,508
Emp.: 1,560
Fiscal Year-end: 12/31/22
Steel Structures Mfr & Installer
N.A.I.C.S.: 331110
Jing Cao *(Chm & Pres)*

**ANHUI GENUINE PAPER
PACKING CO., LTD.**
No 6888 Fangxing Avenue, Hefei
Economic and technological Develop-
ment Zone, Hefei, 230601, Anhui,
China
Tel.: (86) 55163844008
Web Site:
http://www.genuinepacking.com
Year Founded: 2004
603429—(SHG)
Rev.: $116,236,472
Assets: $263,774,282
Liabilities: $61,271,009
Net Worth: $202,503,272
Earnings: $23,435,161
Emp.: 300
Fiscal Year-end: 12/31/22
Cigarette Paper Mfr & Distr
N.A.I.C.S.: 322299
Shanshui Xu *(Chm)*

**ANHUI GOLDEN SEED WIN-
ERY CO., LTD.**
Golden Seed Cultural Park at the in-
tersection of Qinghe East Road, Xi-
angyang Road, Fuyang, 236000, An-
hui, China
Tel.: (86) 5582210568
Web Site: http://www.jzz.cn
Year Founded: 1998
600199—(SHG)
Rev.: $166,479,539
Assets: $476,588,081
Liabilities: $117,900,212
Net Worth: $358,687,869
Earnings: ($26,271,929)
Fiscal Year-end: 12/31/22
Liquor Product Mfr & Distr
N.A.I.C.S.: 312130
Xie Jinming *(Chm)*

**ANHUI GOURGEN TRAFFIC
CONSTRUCTION CO., LTD.**
Building A Xiangyuan Plaza No 310
Suixi Road, Luyang, Hefei, 230041,
Anhui, China
Tel.: (86) 55167119177
Web Site: https://www.gourgen.com
Year Founded: 1993
603815—(SHG)
Rev.: $912,479,396
Assets: $1,350,709,397
Liabilities: $1,031,656,336
Net Worth: $319,053,061
Earnings: $25,491,880
Emp.: 1,400
Fiscal Year-end: 12/31/22
Construction Services
N.A.I.C.S.: 236220
Xiankuan Hu *(Chm)*

**ANHUI GREAT WALL MILI-
TARY INDUSTRY CO., LTD.**
No 508 Shandong Road, Baohe Dis-
trict, Hefei, 230041, Anhui, China
Tel.: (86) 55162187330
Web Site: http://www.ahccjg.com.cn
Year Founded: 2000
601606—(SHG)
Rev.: $240,714,621
Assets: $586,418,915
Liabilities: $217,612,362
Net Worth: $368,806,553
Earnings: $11,229,669
Fiscal Year-end: 12/31/22
Engineering Product Distr
N.A.I.C.S.: 423860
Rong Tu *(Chm)*

**ANHUI GUANGXIN AGRO-
CHEMICAL CO., LTD.**
Fine Chemical Industrial Park, Xu-
ancheng, 242235, Anhui, China
Tel.: (86) 2150817211

Web Site:
https://www.chinaguangxin.com
Year Founded: 1993
603599—(SHG)
Rev.: $1,272,356,762
Assets: $1,944,752,608
Liabilities: $707,138,612
Net Worth: $1,237,613,996
Earnings: $325,119,759
Fiscal Year-end: 12/31/22
Pesticide & Agricultural Chemical Mfr
& Distr
N.A.I.C.S.: 325320

**ANHUI GUJING GROUP CO.,
LTD.**
Gujing Town, Bozhou, 23682, Anhui,
China
Tel.: (86) 5585710046
Web Site: http://www.gujing.com
Emp.: 6,000
Holding Company
N.A.I.C.S.: 551112

Subsidiaries:

Anhui Gujing Distillery Co., Ltd. (1)
Gujing Town, Bozhou, 236820, Anhui, China
Tel.: (86) 5585712231
Web Site: https://www.gujing.com
Rev.: $2,804,265,424
Assets: $4,904,312,597
Liabilities: $1,800,874,266
Net Worth: $3,103,438,331
Earnings: $635,407,081
Fiscal Year-end: 12/31/2023
Beverage Mfg
N.A.I.C.S.: 445320

**ANHUI GUOFENG NEW MATE-
RIALS CO., LTD.**
Intersection of Changning Avenue
and Mingchuan Road, Hefei, 230088,
Anhui, China
Tel.: (86) 55163367405
Web Site: https://www.guofeng.com
Year Founded: 1998
000859—(SSE)
Rev.: $345,437,352
Assets: $516,707,100
Liabilities: $108,470,232
Net Worth: $408,236,868
Earnings: $32,252,688
Emp.: 1,700
Fiscal Year-end: 12/31/22
Plastics Product Mfr
N.A.I.C.S.: 326199

ANHUI HELI CO., LTD.
No 668 Fang Xing Road, Hefei,
230601, Anhui, China
Tel.: (86) 55163648005
Web Site: https://www.helichina.com
Year Founded: 1958
600761—(SHG)
Rev.: $2,200,508,870
Assets: $2,074,218,649
Liabilities: $1,038,177,144
Net Worth: $1,036,041,505
Earnings: $126,941,593
Emp.: 8,000
Fiscal Year-end: 12/31/22
Industrial Vehicle & Construction Ma-
chinery Mfr
N.A.I.C.S.: 333924
Anguo Yang *(Chm & Vice Chm)*

Subsidiaries:

Heli America Inc. (1)
4025 Welcome All Rd Ste 150, Atlanta, GA
30349
Tel.: (404) 975-3143
Web Site:
https://www.heliforkliftamerica.com
Material Handling Equipment Mfr
N.A.I.C.S.: 333924

Heli Southeast Asia Co., Ltd. (1)
333/38-39 Tip 8 Project Moo 6 Bangpla,

Anhui Heli Co., Ltd.—(Continued)

Samut Prakan, 10540, Thailand
Tel.: (66) 21366331
Web Site: https://www.heliforkliftasia.ne
Industrial Truck Mfr & Distr
N.A.I.C.S.: 333924

ANHUI HENGYUAN COAL INDUSTRY & ELECTRICITY POWER CO., LTD.

No 157 Xichang Road, Suzhou, 234011, Anhui, China
Tel.: (86) 5573982147
Web Site: http://www.ahhymd.com.cn
Year Founded: 2000
600971—(SHG)
Rev.: $1,177,410,378
Assets: $2,924,978,340
Liabilities: $1,254,528,054
Net Worth: $1,670,450,334
Earnings: $352,792,473
Fiscal Year-end: 12/31/22
Coal Mining & Electric Power Generation Services
N.A.I.C.S.: 212115
Yang Lin (Chm)

ANHUI HONGLU STEEL CONSTRUCTION (GROUP) CO., LTD.

Shuangfeng Industrial Zone, Hefei, 231131, Anhui, China
Tel.: (86) 5516391405
Web Site: https://www.hong-lu.com
Year Founded: 2002
002541—(SSE)
Rev.: $2,786,614,272
Assets: $2,890,760,184
Liabilities: $1,731,081,456
Net Worth: $1,159,678,728
Earnings: $163,240,272
Fiscal Year-end: 12/31/22
Steel Structure Products Mfr
N.A.I.C.S.: 332312
Xiaobo Shang (Board of Directors & Chm)

ANHUI HONGYU WUZHOU MEDICAL MANUFACTURER CO., LTD.

No 2 Guanyin Road Economy Development Zone, Taihu, Anqing, 246400, Anhui, China
Tel.: (86) 5565129666
Web Site: https://www.hongyu-wuzhou.com
Year Founded: 2011
301234—(SSE)
Rev.: $76,814,244
Assets: $118,576,224
Liabilities: $17,009,460
Net Worth: $101,566,764
Earnings: $9,954,360
Fiscal Year-end: 12/31/22
Medical Device Mfr & Distr
N.A.I.C.S.: 339112
Huang Fan (Chm)

ANHUI HUAERTAI CHEMICAL CO., LTD.

Dongzhi Economic Development Zone, Xiangyu Dongzhi, Chizhou, 247260, Anhui, China
Tel.: (86) 5665299004
Web Site: https://www.ahhet.com
Year Founded: 2000
001217—(SSE)
Rev.: $246,575,063
Assets: $461,174,301
Liabilities: $158,174,512
Net Worth: $302,999,789
Earnings: $21,779,203
Fiscal Year-end: 12/31/23
Chemical Products Mfr
N.A.I.C.S.: 325311
Lijie Wu (Chm)

ANHUI HUAHENG BIOTECHNOLOGY CO., LTD.

No 32 Fengjin Road, ShuangFeng Development Zone, Hefei, 231031, Anhui, China
Tel.: (86) 55165689170
Web Site:
https://www.huahengbio.com
Year Founded: 2005
688639—(SHG)
Rev.: $199,178,727
Assets: $284,602,846
Liabilities: $76,579,832
Net Worth: $208,023,014
Earnings: $44,932,128
Fiscal Year-end: 12/31/22
Research & Development Biotechnology Services
N.A.I.C.S.: 541714
Henghua Guo (Chm & Gen Mgr)

ANHUI HUAMAO TEXTILE COMPANY LIMITED

No 80 South Fangzhi Road, Anqing, 246018, Anhui, China
Tel.: (86) 5565919788
Web Site: http://www.huamao.com.cn
Year Founded: 1998
000850—(SSE)
Rev.: $490,578,660
Assets: $1,025,122,176
Liabilities: $387,287,784
Net Worth: $637,834,392
Earnings: ($24,512,436)
Emp.: 6,000
Fiscal Year-end: 12/31/22
Textile Product Mfr & Distr
N.A.I.C.S.: 313310
Ni Junlong (Chm)

Subsidiaries:

Anhui Huamao Import & Export Co., Ltd. **(1)**
No 80 South Fangzhi Road, Anqing, 246018, Anhui, China
Tel.: (86) 5565919809
Textile Product Mfr & Distr
N.A.I.C.S.: 314999

ANHUI HUANGSHAN CAPSULE CO., LTD.

No 7 Huangjia Avenue Huangjia Park, Jingde County, Xuancheng, 242600, Anhui, China
Tel.: (86) 5638630268
Web Site: https://www.hsjn.com
Year Founded: 1989
002817—(SSE)
Rev.: $60,136,128
Assets: $145,691,676
Liabilities: $25,760,592
Net Worth: $119,931,084
Earnings: $8,543,340
Emp.: 700
Fiscal Year-end: 12/31/22
Medical Capsule Mfr & Distr
N.A.I.C.S.: 325998
Li Hejun (Chm)

ANHUI HUAQI ENVIRONMENTAL PROTECTION & TECHNOLOGY CO., LTD.

No 409 Meishan Road, Economic and Technological Development Zone, Ma'anshan, 243061, Anhui, China
Tel.: (86) 5552763187
Web Site: https://www.hqhb.com
Year Founded: 2002
300929—(SSE)
Rev.: $60,332,688
Assets: $251,057,664
Liabilities: $130,531,284
Net Worth: $120,526,380
Earnings: $6,159,348
Fiscal Year-end: 12/31/22

Engineeering Services
N.A.I.C.S.: 541330
Jian Wang (Chm)

ANHUI HUILONG AGRICULTURAL MEANS OF PRODUCTION CO., LTD.

No 1777 Qimen Road, Shushan District, Hefei, 230022, Anhui, China
Tel.: (86) 55162634360
Web Site: http://www.ahamp.com
Year Founded: 1990
002556—(SSE)
Rev.: $2,562,207,336
Assets: $1,628,046,108
Liabilities: $1,024,466,508
Net Worth: $603,579,600
Earnings: $71,669,988
Fiscal Year-end: 12/31/22
Fertilizer Product Whslr
N.A.I.C.S.: 424910
Cheng Cheng (Chm, Sec-Party Committee & Gen Mgr)

ANHUI HYEA AROMAS CO., LTD.

No 42 Shuzhou Avenue, Qianshan, Anqing, 246300, Anhui, China
Tel.: (86) 5568978283
Web Site:
https://www.anhuihuaye.com
Year Founded: 2002
300886—(SSE)
Rev.: $35,779,536
Assets: $86,510,268
Liabilities: $10,684,440
Net Worth: $75,825,828
Earnings: $2,917,512
Fiscal Year-end: 12/31/22
Chemical Product Mfr & Distr
N.A.I.C.S.: 325520
Wenliang Hua (Chm)

Subsidiaries:

Anhui Huaye Aromas Hefei Co., Ltd. **(1)**
North of Weisan Road, Hefei Circular Economy Demonstration Park, Anhui, China
Tel.: (86) 55167366939
Chemical Products Mfr
N.A.I.C.S.: 325998

ANHUI JIANGHUAI AUTOMOBILE GROUP CORP., LTD.

176 Dongliu Road, Hefei, 230022, Anhui, China
Tel.: (86) 55162296666
Web Site: https://jacen.jac.com.cn
Year Founded: 1964
600418—(SHG)
Rev.: $5,135,461,948
Assets: $6,610,409,157
Liabilities: $4,635,372,901
Net Worth: $1,975,036,256
Earnings: ($222,179,757)
Emp.: 5,000
Fiscal Year-end: 12/31/22
Automobile Mfr
N.A.I.C.S.: 336110
Xiang Xingchu (Chm)

Subsidiaries:

Anhui Ankai Automobile Co., Ltd. **(1)**
No 99 Huayuan Avenue, Hefei, Anhui, China
Tel.: (86) 55163732170
Web Site: https://www.ankaiglobal.com
Rev.: $208,913,796
Assets: $473,148,000
Liabilities: $462,257,172
Net Worth: $10,890,828
Earnings: ($33,653,880)
Emp.: 3,000
Fiscal Year-end: 12/31/2022
Automobile Mfr
N.A.I.C.S.: 336110
Huang Liping (Chm & Gen Mgr)

ANHUI JIANGNAN CHEMICAL INDUSTRY CO., LTD.

17th Floor Building J2 Phase II No 2800 Innovation Avenue, Shushan District, Hefei, 230088, Anhui, China
Tel.: (86) 55165862550
Web Site: https://www.ahjnhg.com
Year Founded: 1985
002226—(SSE)
Rev.: $988,842,816
Assets: $2,235,957,048
Liabilities: $864,417,528
Net Worth: $1,371,539,520
Earnings: $63,490,284
Fiscal Year-end: 12/31/22
Explosive Product Mfr & Whslr
N.A.I.C.S.: 325920
Yang Shize (Chm)

ANHUI JINCHUN NONWOVEN CO., LTD.

No 218 Nanjing North Road, Chuzhou, 239000, China
Tel.: (86) 5502201971
Web Site: http://www.czjinchun.com
Year Founded: 2011
300877—(SSE)
Rev.: $113,385,636
Assets: $264,479,904
Liabilities: $42,553,836
Net Worth: $221,926,068
Earnings: ($3,552,120)
Emp.: 700
Fiscal Year-end: 12/31/22
Textile Product Mfr & Distr
N.A.I.C.S.: 313310
Yang Ruxin (Chm)

ANHUI JINHE INDUSTRIAL CO., LTD.

No 127 East Street, Laian county, Chuzhou, 239200, Anhui, China
Tel.: (86) 5505612755
Web Site: https://www.jinheshiye.com
Year Founded: 1974
002597—(SSE)
Rev.: $1,017,970,200
Assets: $1,451,853,936
Liabilities: $464,069,736
Net Worth: $987,784,200
Earnings: $237,979,404
Fiscal Year-end: 12/31/22
Chemical Products Mfr
N.A.I.C.S.: 325998
Sun Caijun (Deputy Gen Mgr)

Subsidiaries:

Anhui Jinxuan Technological Co., Ltd. **(1)**
Jianhe Road Yanhua Industrial Park, Luqiao Town Dingyuan County, Chuzhou, Anhui, China
Tel.: (86) 5504351051
Chemical Product Research & Development Services
N.A.I.C.S.: 541715

Golden Wheat (Nanjing) International Trade Co., Ltd. **(1)**
Fl 9 Bldg E1 NJUT Technology Park No 15 Wanshou Road, Pukou District, Nanjing, China
Tel.: (86) 2585566055
Chemical Product Research & Development Services
N.A.I.C.S.: 541715

ANHUI JIUHUA MOUNTAIN TOURISM DEVELOPMENT CO., LTD

Qingyang County Wuxi Xincheng District, Chizhou, Anhui, China
Tel.: (86) 5665578899
Web Site: http://www.jiuhuashan.cc
603199—(SHG)
Rev.: $46,617,784
Assets: $207,470,681
Liabilities: $32,851,073

Net Worth: $174,619,608
Earnings: ($1,923,396)
Fiscal Year-end: 12/31/22
Tourism Services
N.A.I.C.S.: 561520
Chang Shu *(Chm)*

ANHUI JUAN KUANG ELECTRIC CO., LTD.
No 79 Shanmen South Road, Ningguo, 242300, Anhui, China
Tel.: (86) 5634180988
Web Site: http://www.jkdq.com
Sales Range: $75-99.9 Million
Emp.: 400
Capacitor Mfr
N.A.I.C.S.: 334416
Haito Wen *(Gen Mgr)*

ANHUI KORRUN CO., LTD.
No 1555 Tongle Road, Nanqiao District, Chuzhou, 201612, Anhui, China
Tel.: (86) 2157683170
Web Site: http://www.korrun.com
Year Founded: 2005
300577—(CHIN)
Rev.: $437,325,517
Assets: $505,364,363
Liabilities: $236,484,361
Net Worth: $268,880,002
Earnings: $16,285,345
Fiscal Year-end: 12/31/23
Bag Mfr & Distr
N.A.I.C.S.: 314999
Gao Xiaomin *(Deputy Gen Mgr)*

ANHUI KOUZI DISTILLERY CO., LTD.
No 9 Xiangshan South Road, Huaibei, 235199, Anhui, China
Tel.: (86) 5616898000
Web Site: https://www.kouzi.com
Year Founded: 2002
603589—(SHG)
Rev.: $720,968,461
Assets: $1,619,479,897
Liabilities: $369,320,824
Net Worth: $1,250,159,073
Earnings: $217,641,355
Emp.: 4,000
Fiscal Year-end: 12/31/22
Liquor Mfr & Distr
N.A.I.C.S.: 312130
Jin Xu *(Chm, Pres & Gen Mgr)*

ANHUI LANDUN PHOTOELECTRON CO., LTD.
Electronic Industrial Zone Shicheng Road, Tongling, 244000, Anhui, China
Tel.: (86) 5622291110
Web Site: http://www.ldchina.cn
Year Founded: 2001
300862—(CHIN)
Rev.: $90,565,620
Assets: $358,498,575
Liabilities: $72,079,480
Net Worth: $286,419,095
Earnings: $5,913,038
Fiscal Year-end: 12/31/23
Measuring Instruments Mfr
N.A.I.C.S.: 334513
Yonggang Yuan *(Chm)*

ANHUI LIUGUO CHEMICAL CO., LTD.
Tonggang Road, Tongling, 244000, Anhui, China
Tel.: (86) 5622170536
Web Site: https://www.liuguo.com
Year Founded: 1985
600470—(SHG)
Rev.: $1,059,910,432
Assets: $982,101,524
Liabilities: $712,888,287
Net Worth: $269,213,237
Earnings: $27,094,097

Emp.: 1,526
Fiscal Year-end: 12/31/22
Chemical Fertilizer Mfr & Distr
N.A.I.C.S.: 325314
Chen Shengqian *(Chm)*

ANHUI PROVINCIAL ARCHITECTURAL DESIGN & RESEARCH INSTITUTE CO., LTD.
No 7699 Fanhua Avenue, Hefei Economic & Technological Development Zone, Hefei, 230091, Anhui, China
Tel.: (86) 55162871307
Web Site: https://www.aadri.com
Year Founded: 1992
301167—(CHIN)
Rev.: $71,484,660
Assets: $184,920,840
Liabilities: $53,754,948
Net Worth: $131,165,892
Earnings: $11,559,132
Emp.: 1,000
Fiscal Year-end: 12/31/22
Architectural Services
N.A.I.C.S.: 541310
Wei Fahua *(Chm)*

ANHUI QUANCHAI ENGINE CO., LTD.
No 788 Wujingzi Road, Quanjiao County, Chuzhou, 239500, Anhui, China
Tel.: (86) 5505038198
Web Site: https://www.quanchai.com.cn
Year Founded: 1998
600218—(SHG)
Rev.: $693,052,069
Assets: $789,576,283
Liabilities: $348,248,258
Net Worth: $441,328,025
Earnings: $14,479,859
Emp.: 3,000
Fiscal Year-end: 12/31/22
Diesel Engine Mfr & Distr
N.A.I.C.S.: 333618
Xu Yuliang *(Gen Mgr)*

ANHUI SHENGYUN ENVIRONMENT PROTECTION GROUP CO., LTD.
New Donghuan Road Tongcheng City, Economic Development Zone, Anqing, 231400, Anhui, China
Tel.: (86) 5566207688
Sales Range: $150-199.9 Million
Conveying Machinery & Environmental Protection Mfr & Distr
N.A.I.C.S.: 333922
Yubin Liu *(Chm & Pres-Interim)*

ANHUI SHENJIAN NEW MATERIALS CO., LTD.
No 8 Baoshun Rd Qiaobei Industrial Park, Economic & Technological Development Zone, Wuhu, 241008, Anhui, China
Tel.: (86) 5535316333
Web Site: https://www.shen-jian.com
Year Founded: 1988
002361—(SSE)
Rev.: $353,280,096
Assets: $637,174,512
Liabilities: $298,126,764
Net Worth: $339,047,748
Earnings: $3,776,760
Emp.: 1,510
Fiscal Year-end: 12/31/22
Polyester Resins Mfr & Sales
N.A.I.C.S.: 325211
Liu Zhijian *(Pres)*

ANHUI SHINY ELECTRONIC TECHNOLOGY COMPANY LIMITED

Junction of Jingui Road and Tangwang Avenue, Hangbu Economic Development Zone Shucheng County, Lu'an, 231323, Anhui, China
Tel.: (86) 5648191989
Web Site: https://www.yinglidianzi.com
Year Founded: 2015
300956—(SSE)
Rev.: $192,679,344
Assets: $295,790,508
Liabilities: $132,749,604
Net Worth: $163,040,904
Earnings: ($3,922,776)
Fiscal Year-end: 12/31/22
Electronic Product Mfr & Distr
N.A.I.C.S.: 334419
Ming Dai *(Chm)*

ANHUI SIERTE FERTILIZER INDUSTRY CO., LTD.
Wangxi Park Ningguo Economic and Technologic Development Zone, Ningguo, 242300, Anhui, China
Tel.: (86) 5634181590
Web Site: http://www.sierte.com
Year Founded: 1997
002538—(SSE)
Rev.: $685,689,732
Assets: $974,867,400
Liabilities: $224,244,072
Net Worth: $750,623,328
Earnings: $74,492,028
Emp.: 1,500
Fiscal Year-end: 12/31/22
Fertilizer Mfr
N.A.I.C.S.: 325311
Yuan Qirong *(Chm & Gen Mgr)*

ANHUI SINONET & XINLONG SCIENCE & TECHNOLOGY CO., LTD.
No 118 Jiuhua North Road Wuhu Area China Anhui Pilot Free Trade Zone, Wuhu, 241008, Anhui, China
Tel.: (86) 5535772678
Web Site: https://www.ah-zdxl.com
Year Founded: 1998
002298—(SSE)
Rev.: $339,066,000
Assets: $1,043,869,788
Liabilities: $430,254,396
Net Worth: $613,615,392
Earnings: ($120,720,132)
Emp.: 840
Fiscal Year-end: 12/31/22
Voltage Switch Equipment, Components & Automatic Control Products Mfr
N.A.I.C.S.: 335313
Gan Hongliang *(Sec & Head-Investor Relations)*

ANHUI SUN-CREATE ELECTRONICS CO., LTD.
No 199 Xiangzhang Street High-tech Area, Hefei, 230088, Anhui, China
Tel.: (86) 55165391363
Web Site: http://www.sun-create.com
600990—(SHG)
Rev.: $381,983,977
Assets: $1,045,806,311
Liabilities: $658,973,564
Net Worth: $386,832,748
Earnings: $9,271,623
Fiscal Year-end: 12/31/22
Electronic Equipment Mfr & Distr
N.A.I.C.S.: 334511
Xinping Chen *(Chm)*

Subsidiaries:

ECU Electronic Industry Co., Ltd. (1)
No 88 Pihe Rd, Hefei, 230088, Anhui, China
Tel.: (86) 4006659997
Web Site: http://www.ecu.com.cn
Electrical Equipment Mfr & Distr

N.A.I.C.S.: 335999

ANHUI SUNHERE PHARMACEUTICAL EXCIPIENTS CO., LTD.
No 2 Hebin Road Economic and Technological Development Zone, Huainan, 232007, Anhui, China
Tel.: (86) 5542796125
Web Site: https://www.shanhe01.com
Year Founded: 2001
300452—(CHIN)
Rev.: $98,916,012
Assets: $165,749,220
Liabilities: $55,026,972
Net Worth: $110,722,248
Earnings: $18,351,684
Emp.: 600
Fiscal Year-end: 12/31/22
Pharmaceuticals Mfr
N.A.I.C.S.: 325412
Zhenglong Yin *(Chm)*

ANHUI TATFOOK TECHNOLOGY CO., LTD
3rd Industry Area Of Shajing Industry Company, Haoxiang Road Shajing Street Baoan District, Shenzhen, China
Tel.: (86) 75529816880
Web Site: https://www.tatfook.com
300134—(CHIN)
Rev.: $351,454,709
Assets: $915,394,545
Liabilities: $266,636,262
Net Worth: $648,758,283
Earnings: ($23,990,699)
Emp.: 6,683
Fiscal Year-end: 12/31/23
Wireless Radio Frequency Communication Products Mfr
N.A.I.C.S.: 334220

Subsidiaries:

Guangzhou Skytone Smart Technologies Co., Ltd. (1)
Room A216 No 13 No 232 Waihuan East Road Xiaoguwei Street, Panyu District, Guangzhou, 510006, Guangdong, China
Tel.: (86) 2038601746
Web Site: http://www.skytone.net.cn
Application Software Development Services
N.A.I.C.S.: 541511

Shenzhen Hyan Microelectronics Co., Ltd. (1)
Building 1-2 Tongfuyu Industrial Park Aiqun Road, Shiyan Town Baoan District, Shenzhen, China
Tel.: (86) 75528035313
Web Site: http://www.hyanlabel.com.cn
Antenna Mfr
N.A.I.C.S.: 334220

Ulanqab Darsen Graphite New Materials Co., Ltd. (1)
China Graphite Application Industrial Park, Xinghe, China
Tel.: (86) 4747581307
Web Site: http://www.darsen.cn
Graphite Product Mfr
N.A.I.C.S.: 335991

ANHUI TONGFENG ELECTRONICS CO., LTD.
Tongfeng Industrial Park 3rd Cuihu Road, Economic and Technological Development Zone, Tongling, 244000, Anhui, China
Tel.: (86) 5625885455
Web Site: https://en.tong-feng.com
Year Founded: 1952
600237—(SHG)
Rev.: $146,083,771
Assets: $270,203,914
Liabilities: $89,653,627
Net Worth: $180,550,286
Earnings: $10,382,355
Fiscal Year-end: 12/31/22

Anhui Tongfeng Electronics Co., Ltd.—(Continued)

Flim Capacitor Mfr & Distr
N.A.I.C.S.: 335999
Mingqiang Huang (Chm)

ANHUI TONGGUAN COPPER FOIL GROUP CO., LTD.
No 189 Qingxi Avenue, Economic & Technological Development Zone, Chizhou, 247100, Anhui, China
Tel.: (86) 5663206810
Year Founded: 2010
301217—(CHIN)
Rev.: $544,024,728
Assets: $870,574,068
Liabilities: $77,865,840
Net Worth: $792,708,228
Earnings: $37,221,444
Fiscal Year-end: 12/31/22
Copper Product Mfr & Distr
N.A.I.C.S.: 331420

ANHUI TONGYUAN ENVIRON-MENT ENERGY SAVING CO., LTD.
No 3966 Qimen Road, Baohe District, Hefei, 230009, Anhui, China
Tel.: (86) 55165583636
Web Site:
https://www.ahtongyuan.com
Year Founded: 1999
688679—(SHG)
Rev.: $179,244,693
Assets: $324,286,092
Liabilities: $167,493,325
Net Worth: $156,792,767
Earnings: $6,392,117
Fiscal Year-end: 12/31/22
Energy Distribution Services
N.A.I.C.S.: 221122
Ming Yang (Chm & Gen Mgr)

ANHUI TRANSPORT CON-SULTING & DESIGN INSTI-TUTE CO., LTD.
No 1008 Rainbow Road High-tech Zone, Hefei, 230088, Anhui, China
Tel.: (86) 55165371600
Web Site: https://www.atcdi.com.cn
Year Founded: 1960
603357—(SHG)
Rev.: $392,865,974
Assets: $789,733,952
Liabilities: $341,354,239
Net Worth: $448,379,713
Earnings: $62,174,876
Emp.: 1,000
Fiscal Year-end: 12/31/22
Civil Engineering Consulting Services
N.A.I.C.S.: 541330
Su Xinguo (Chm)

ANHUI TRUCHUM ADVANCED MATERIALS AND TECHNOL-OGY CO., LTD.
No 8 Jiuhua North Road, Wuhu, 241008, Anhui, China
Tel.: (86) 5535315978
Web Site: https://www.ahcjxc.com
002171—(SSE)
Rev.: $6,372,543,592
Assets: $2,301,813,987
Liabilities: $1,336,403,421
Net Worth: $965,410,566
Earnings: $72,821,862
Emp.: 6,000
Fiscal Year-end: 12/31/23
Non Ferrous Metal Mfr
N.A.I.C.S.: 331410
Chun Jiang (Chm)

ANHUI TUOSHAN HEAVY IN-DUSTRIES CO., LTD.
Tongli Avenue, Economic Develop-ment Zone Guangde County, Xu-ancheng, 242200, Anhui, China
Tel.: (86) 5636616555
Web Site:
https://www.tuoshangroup.com
001226—(SSE)
Rev.: $98,614,152
Assets: $155,011,428
Liabilities: $48,338,316
Net Worth: $106,673,112
Earnings: $8,259,732
Emp.: 800
Fiscal Year-end: 12/31/22
Construction Machinery Mfr & Distr
N.A.I.C.S.: 333120
Xu Yangshun (Chm & Gen Mgr)

Subsidiaries:

Zhejiang Tuoshan Machinery Co., Ltd. **(1)**
Puqing Industrial Area, Yuhuan, Zhejiang, China
Tel.: (86) 57687339966
Machinery Parts Mfr & Distr
N.A.I.C.S.: 333248

ANHUI WANTONG TECHNOL-OGY CO., LTD.
No 589 Wanshui Road High-tech Zone, Hefei, 230088, Anhui, China
Tel.: (86) 55162969206
Web Site: https://www.wantong-tech.net
Year Founded: 1999
002331—(SSE)
Rev.: $138,077,784
Assets: $374,679,864
Liabilities: $116,300,340
Net Worth: $258,379,524
Earnings: ($14,478,048)
Emp.: 200
Fiscal Year-end: 12/31/22
IT Services
N.A.I.C.S.: 541512
Chen Xiangwei (Chm)

ANHUI WANWEI UPDATED HI-TECH MATERIAL INDUSTRY COMPANY LIMITED
No 56 Wanwei Road, Chaohu, Hefei, 238002, Anhui, China
Tel.: (86) 55182189280
Web Site: http://www.wwgf.com.cn
Year Founded: 2010
600063—(SHG)
Rev.: $1,395,857,039
Assets: $1,859,661,433
Liabilities: $766,247,868
Net Worth: $1,093,413,564
Earnings: $192,247,123
Emp.: 3,200
Fiscal Year-end: 12/31/22
Chemical Products Mfr
N.A.I.C.S.: 325998
Fusheng Wu (Chm)

ANHUI WANYI SCIENCE & TECHNOLOGY CO., LTD.
No 8 Wenqu Road, High-tech Zone, Hefei, 230088, Anhui, China
Tel.: (86) 4001120066
Web Site: https://www.wayeal.com.cn
Year Founded: 2003
688600—(SHG)
Rev.: $94,826,286
Assets: $173,375,200
Liabilities: $49,062,597
Net Worth: $124,312,603
Earnings: $6,712,594
Emp.: 1,400
Fiscal Year-end: 12/31/22
Analytical Instrument Mfr & Distr
N.A.I.C.S.: 334516
Mu Zang (Chm & Gen Mgr)

Subsidiaries:

Anhui Bailu Electronic Technology Co., Ltd. **(1)**
No 8 Wenqu Road, High-tech Zone, Hefei, 230088, Anhui, China
Tel.: (86) 5516 810 7097
Web Site: https://www.baluelec.com
Industrial Machinery Mfr
N.A.I.C.S.: 333310

ANHUI XINBO ALUMINUM CO., LTD.
Yangcun Industrial Zone, Yangcun Town, Tianchang, 239304, Anhui, China
Tel.: (86) 5507867688
Web Site: https://www.xinbogf.com
Year Founded: 2013
003038—(SSE)
Rev.: $592,685,964
Assets: $622,805,976
Liabilities: $357,749,028
Net Worth: $265,056,948
Earnings: $26,399,412
Fiscal Year-end: 12/31/22
Aluminium Products Mfr
N.A.I.C.S.: 331313
Kaijian Tang (Chm)

ANHUI XINHUA MEDIA CO., LTD.
No 8 Biejing Road, Baohe District, Hefei, 230091, Anhui, China
Tel.: (86) 55162661323
Web Site: http://www.ahsxhsd.com
Year Founded: 2002
601801—(SHG)
Rev.: $1,640,796,366
Assets: $2,457,769,125
Liabilities: $866,061,640
Net Worth: $1,591,707,485
Earnings: $99,377,072
Fiscal Year-end: 12/31/22
Textbooks, Books, Video & Audio Products Publisher, Retailer & Whslr
N.A.I.C.S.: 513130
Zhang Kewen (Chm)

ANHUI XINLI FINANCE CO., LTD.
Haichang Avenue Yinping Town, Cha-ohu, 238001, Anhui, China
Tel.: (86) 55182389232
600318—(SHG)
Rev.: $43,948,499
Assets: $568,320,429
Liabilities: $280,709,751
Net Worth: $287,610,678
Earnings: ($19,447,955)
Fiscal Year-end: 12/31/22
Investment Services
N.A.I.C.S.: 523999
Jinhe Zhu (Chm)

ANHUI YINGJIA DISTILLERY CO., LTD.
Foziling Town, Huoshan County, Lu'an, 237271, Anhui, China
Tel.: (86) 5645231473
Web Site: http://www.yingjia.cn
Year Founded: 2003
603198—(SHG)
Rev.: $772,944,345
Assets: $1,412,456,811
Liabilities: $434,419,629
Net Worth: $978,037,183
Earnings: $239,399,733
Fiscal Year-end: 12/31/22
Liquor Mfr & Distr
N.A.I.C.S.: 312120
Yongpei Ni (Chm)

ANHUI YINGLIU ELECTROME-CHANICAL CO., LTD.
No 566 Fanhua Avenue Economic and Technological Development Zone, Hefei, 230601, Anhui, China
Tel.: (86) 55163737776
Web Site:
http://www.yingliugroup.com
Year Founded: 2006
603308—(SHG)
Rev.: $308,557,403
Assets: $1,389,882,583
Liabilities: $720,331,368
Net Worth: $669,551,215
Earnings: $56,397,065
Fiscal Year-end: 12/31/22
Industrial Machinery Equipment Mfr & Whslr
N.A.I.C.S.: 333998
Du Yingliu (Chm)

ANHUI YUANCHEN ENVIRON-MENTAL PROTECTION SCI-ENCE & TECHNOLOGY CO., LTD.
West Side of Hebai Road Zhanbei Community, Xinzhan District, Hefei, 230012, Anhui, China
Tel.: (86) 55166339782
Web Site: http://www.shychb.com
Year Founded: 2005
688659—(SHG)
Rev.: $81,296,149
Assets: $178,848,891
Liabilities: $88,587,542
Net Worth: $90,261,349
Earnings: $874,917
Emp.: 252
Fiscal Year-end: 12/31/22
Electrical Battery Mfr & Distr
N.A.I.C.S.: 335910
Hui Xu (Chm)

ANHUI ZHONGDING HOLDING (GROUP) CO., LTD.
Ningguo Economic & Tech Develop-ment Zone, Ningguo, 242300, Anhui, China
Tel.: (86) 563 418 1800 CN
Web Site: http://www.zdrpp.com
Year Founded: 1980
Holding Company; Automotive Parts Mfr
N.A.I.C.S.: 551112
Dinghui Xia (Chm)

Subsidiaries:

Anhui Zhongding Sealing Parts Co., Ltd. **(1)**
Zhongding Industrial Park Economic Tech-nology Development Zone, Ningguo, Xu-ancheng, 242300, Anhui, China
Tel.: (86) 5632290135
Web Site: http://www.zhongdinggroup.com
Rev.: $2,085,205,356
Assets: $2,965,853,124
Liabilities: $1,393,037,568
Net Worth: $1,572,815,556
Earnings: $135,380,700
Fiscal Year-end: 12/31/2022
Rubber Products Mfr
N.A.I.C.S.: 326299
Xia Yingsong (Chm & Gen Mgr)

Zhongding U.S.A., Inc. **(1)**
400 Detroit Ave, Monroe, MI 48162
Tel.: (734) 241-8870
Holding Company; Industrial Supplies Mfr & Distr
N.A.I.C.S.: 551112

Subsidiary (Domestic):

Zhongding Sealing Parts (USA), Inc. **(2)**
310 Railroad Ave Ext, Strasburg, OH 44680
Tel.: (330) 878-7800
Holding Company; Rubber Sealant Prod-ucts Mfr
N.A.I.C.S.: 551112

Subsidiary (Domestic):

Allied-Baltic Rubber, Inc. **(3)**
310 Railroad Ave Ext, Strasburg, OH 44680

Tel.: (330) 878-7800
Rubber Products
N.A.I.C.S.: 326299

BRP Hannibal, Inc. (3)
5151 Industrial Dr, Hannibal, MO
63401-0998 **(100%)**
Tel.: (573) 221-8933
Web Site: http://www.buckhornrubber.com
Rubber Products Mfr
N.A.I.C.S.: 326299
Freddy Urgeff *(Plant Mgr)*

**ANHUI ZHONGHUAN ENVI-
RONMENTAL PROTECTION
TECHNOLOGY CO., LTD.**
22nd Floor Block B1 Zhongchen Fu-
ture Port 1120 Dalian Road, Baohe
District, Hefei, 230051, Anhui, China
Tel.: (86) 55163868248
Web Site: https://www.ahzhhb.cn
Year Founded: 2011
300692—(CHIN)
Rev.: $114,671,436
Assets: $934,346,518
Liabilities: $587,258,525
Net Worth: $347,087,993
Earnings: $15,206,490
Fiscal Year-end: 12/31/23
Sewage Treatment Services
N.A.I.C.S.: 221320
Zhang Bozhong *(Chm)*

**ANHUI ZHONGYUAN NEW MA-
TERIALS CO., LTD.**
No 48 North Fengminghu Road,
Wuhu Economic & Technological De-
velopment Area, Wuhu, 241008, An-
hui, China
Tel.: (86) 5535316171
Web Site: https://www.zyxcl.cn
Year Founded: 2005
603527—(SHG)
Rev.: $1,000,970,877
Assets: $304,136,263
Liabilities: $137,984,783
Net Worth: $166,151,480
Earnings: $19,712,960
Fiscal Year-end: 12/31/22
Purple Copper Belt Mfr
N.A.I.C.S.: 331410

**ANI INTEGRATED SERVICES
LIMITED**
624-Lodha Supremus II A Wing North
Tower Road No 22 Wagle Estate,
Near New Passport Office, Thane,
400607, India
Tel.: (91) 912261560404
Web Site:
   https://www.aniintegrated.com
AISL—(NSE)
Rev.: $21,633,052
Assets: $11,262,178
Liabilities: $4,904,895
Net Worth: $6,357,283
Earnings: $356,497
Emp.: 5,000
Fiscal Year-end: 03/31/23
Engineeering Services
N.A.I.C.S.: 541330

ANI JOINT STOCK COMPANY
No 14B Ky Dong Street Ward 9, Dis-
trict 3, Ho Chi Minh City, Vietnam
Tel.: (84) 862905659
Web Site: http://www.ani.vn
Year Founded: 1993
SIC—(HNX)
Rev.: $43,061,038
Assets: $74,403,505
Liabilities: $53,827,323
Net Worth: $20,576,183
Earnings: $3,573,928
Emp.: 17
Fiscal Year-end: 12/31/22
Civil Construction Engineering Ser-
vices

N.A.I.C.S.: 237990
Dang Tat Thanh *(Gen Mgr)*

ANICOM HOLDINGS, INC.
Sumitomo Fudosan Shinjuku Grand
Tower 39F 8-17-1 Nishi-Shinjuku,
Shinjuku-ku, Tokyo, 160-0023, Japan
Tel.: (81) 353483911
Web Site: https://www.anicom.co.jp
Year Founded: 2000
8715—(TKS)
Rev.: $399,488,570
Assets: $438,619,770
Liabilities: $239,315,050
Net Worth: $199,304,720
Earnings: $36,355
Fiscal Year-end: 03/31/24
Insurance Services
N.A.I.C.S.: 524298
Nobuaki Komori *(Pres, Exec Officer &
Dir-Rep)*

Subsidiaries:

Anicom Insurance, Inc. (1)
Sumitomo Fudosan Shinjuku Grand Tower
39th Floor 8-17-1 Nishi-Shinjuku, Shinjuku-
ku, Tokyo, 160-8352, Japan
Tel.: (81) 8008888256
Web Site: https://www.anicom-sompo.co.jp
Emp.: 521
Insurance Services
N.A.I.C.S.: 524210

Anicom Pafe, Inc. (1)
Sumitomo Realty & Development Shinjuku
Grand Tower 39F 8-17-1, Nishi-Shinjuku
Shinjuku-ku, Tokyo, 160-0023, Japan
Tel.: (81) 353483795
Web Site: https://www.anicom-pafe.com
Veterinary Services
N.A.I.C.S.: 541940

Anicom Specialty Medical Institute,
Inc. (1)
Sumitomo Fudosan Shinjuku Grand Tower
39th Floor 8-17-1, Nishi-Shinjuku Shinjuku-
ku, Tokyo, 160-0023, Japan
Tel.: (81) 359256955
Web Site: https://www.anicom-med.co.jp
Veterinary Services
N.A.I.C.S.: 541940

ANIK INDUSTRIES LTD.
610 Tulsiani Chambers Nariman
Point, Mumbai, 400 021, India
Tel.: (91) 2222824851
Web Site: https://www.anikgroup.com
519383—(BOM)
Rev.: $16,688,708
Assets: $62,588,676
Liabilities: $7,706,299
Net Worth: $54,882,378
Earnings: $694,048
Emp.: 49
Fiscal Year-end: 03/31/23
Dairy Products Mfr
N.A.I.C.S.: 311514
Ashok K. Trivedi *(Exec Dir)*

Subsidiaries:

Anik Ferro-Alloys Pvt. Ltd (1)
2/1 South Tukoganj, Indore, 452 001, India
Tel.: (91) 7314018009
Web Site: http://www.anikgroup.com
Ferro Alloy Mfr
N.A.I.C.S.: 331110
Arvind Jain *(Gen Mgr)*

**ANIL SPECIAL STEEL INDUS-
TRIES LTD.**
Kanakpura PO Meenawala, Jaipur,
302012, India
Tel.: (91) 141 2470211
Web Site:
   http://www.anilspecialsteel.com
Year Founded: 1968
Hardened & Tempered Steel Strips
N.A.I.C.S.: 331210
Sudhir Khaitan *(Chm & Mng Dir)*

ANIMA HOLDING S.P.A.
Corso Garibaldi 99, 20121, Milan,
Italy
Tel.: (39) 002635361 IT
Web Site: https://www.animasgr.it
ANIM—(ITA)
Rev.: $1,504,695,944
Assets: $3,113,410,305
Liabilities: $3,104,453,979
Net Worth: $8,956,326
Earnings: $293,126,845
Emp.: 319
Fiscal Year-end: 12/31/20
Holding Company; Investment & As-
set Management Services
N.A.I.C.S.: 551112
Alessandro Melzi d'Eril *(CEO & Gen
Mgr)*

Subsidiaries:

ANIMA Sgr S.p.A. (1)
Corso Garibaldi 99, 20121, Milan,
Italy **(100%)**
Tel.: (39) 02806381
Web Site: http://www.animaholding.it
Investment & Asset Management Services
N.A.I.C.S.: 523940

Anima Alternative S.p.A. (1)
Corso Garibaldi 99, 20121, Milan, Italy
Tel.: (39) 02806381
Web Site: https://animaalternative.it
Asset Management Services
N.A.I.C.S.: 541611

Anima Alternative SGR S.p.A. (1)
Corso Garibaldi 99, 20121, Milan, Italy
Tel.: (39) 02806381
Web Site: https://animaalternative.it
Asset Management Services
N.A.I.C.S.: 523940

Castello SGR S.p.A. (1)
Via Giacomo Puccini 3, 20121, Milan, Italy
Tel.: (39) 02454361
Web Site: https://castellosgr.com
Asset Management Services
N.A.I.C.S.: 541611

Kairos Partners SGR, S.p.A. (1)
Via San Prospero 2, 20121, Milan, Italy
Tel.: (39) 02777181
Web Site: https://www.kairospartners.com
Wealth & Investment Fund Management
Services
N.A.I.C.S.: 523940

ANIMA HOLDING SA
Rua Natingui 862 1st andar Vila
Madalena, 05443-001, Sao Paulo,
05443-001, Brazil
Tel.: (55) 1143022611
Web Site:
   http://www.animaeducacao.com.br
Year Founded: 2003
ANIM—(ITA)
Rev.: $1,074,603,908
Assets: $2,565,932,805
Liabilities: $1,018,574,496
Net Worth: $1,547,358,309
Earnings: $160,249,034
Emp.: 376
Fiscal Year-end: 12/31/23
Educational Support Services
N.A.I.C.S.: 611710
Daniel Faccini Castanho *(CEO)*

Subsidiaries:

HSM do Brasil S.A. (1)
Alameda Tocantins 125 Alphaville Industrial,
Barueri, 06455-931, Sao Paulo, Brazil
Tel.: (55) 1146896666
Web Site: http://www.hsm.com.br
Educational Support Services
N.A.I.C.S.: 611710

ANIMALCARE GROUP PLC
Moorside Monks Cross, York, YO32
9LB, United Kingdom
Tel.: (44) 3308189717 UK
Web Site:
https://www.animalcaregroup.com

Year Founded: 1972
ANCR—(AIM)
Rev.: $88,932,749
Assets: $146,832,916
Liabilities: $48,748,101
Net Worth: $98,084,815
Earnings: $2,440,137
Emp.: 211
Fiscal Year-end: 12/31/22
Veterinary Products & Services De-
velopment, Marketing & Sales
N.A.I.C.S.: 459910
Chris J. Brewster *(CFO & Sec)*

Subsidiaries:

Animalcare Limited (1)
10 Great North Way York Business Park,
Nether Poppleton, York, YO26 6RB, United
Kingdom
Tel.: (44) 190 448 7687
Web Site: https://www.animalcare.co.uk
Sales Range: $25-49.9 Million
Emp.: 30
Veterinary Products Mfr & Supplier
N.A.I.C.S.: 459910

ECUPHAR NV/SA (1)
Legeweg 157-i, 8020, Oostkamp, Belgium
Tel.: (32) 5 031 4269
Web Site: https://www.ecuphar.be
Veterinary Healthcare Product Mfr
N.A.I.C.S.: 325412
Tom Almey *(Mgr-Regulatory Affairs-North
Europe & QP)*

Ecuphar BV (1)
Verlengde Poolseweg 16, 4818 CL, Breda,
Netherlands
Tel.: (31) 88 003 3800
Web Site: https://www.ecuphar.nl
Veterinary Services
N.A.I.C.S.: 541940

Ecuphar GmbH (1)
Brandteichstrasse 20, 17489, Greifswald,
Germany
Tel.: (49) 3834835840
Veterinary Pharmaceutical Mfr
N.A.I.C.S.: 325412

Ecuphar Veterinaria SL (1)
Slow Building C/ Cerdanya 10-12 pl 6, Sant
Cugat del Valles, 08173, Barcelona, Spain
Tel.: (34) 93 595 5000
Web Site: https://www.ecuphar.es
Veterinary Pharmaceutical Whslr
N.A.I.C.S.: 424690

Identicare Limited (1)
Moorside Monks Cross Drive, Huntington,
York, YO32 9LB, United Kingdom
Tel.: (44) 3309128059
Web Site: https://identichip.co.uk
Micro Chipping Product Mfr
N.A.I.C.S.: 334413

**ANIMOCA BRANDS CORPO-
RATION LIMITED**
Unit 417-421 Cyberport 1 100 Cyber-
port Road, Hong Kong, China (Hong
Kong)
Tel.: (852) 2534 0888
Web Site:
   http://www.animocabrands.com
Rev.: $5,064,255
Assets: $3,243,046
Liabilities: $2,879,388
Net Worth: $363,658
Earnings: ($6,281,259)
Emp.: 70
Fiscal Year-end: 12/31/17
Mobile Gaming Software
N.A.I.C.S.: 513210
David Kim *(Co-Founder)*

ANINO INTERNATIONAL PLC
21B Kofo Abayomi Street, Victoria
Island, Lagos, Nigeria
Tel.: (234) 1 2710578
Web Site:
   http://www.aninoplc.com.ng

Anino International Plc—(Continued)

Year Founded: 1981
Sales Range: $1-9.9 Million
Electric Power Generation & Distribution Services
N.A.I.C.S.: 221111

ANIPET ANIMAL SUPPLIES INC.

19038 24th Avenue, Surrey, V3S 3S9, BC, Canada
Tel.: (604) 536-3367
Web Site: http://www.anipet.com
Year Founded: 1977
Sales Range: $25-49.9 Million
Pet Supplies & Pet Food Distr
N.A.I.C.S.: 459910
Tammi Bell *(Mgr-Customer Svc & Acct Set Up)*

ANIPLUS INC.

28F Three lfc 10 Gukjeogeumyeung-Ro, Yeongdeungpo-Gu, Seoul, Korea (South)
Tel.: (82) 7071623715
Web Site: https://shop.aniplustv.com
Year Founded: 2018
310200—(KRS)
Rev.: $44,586,803
Assets: $108,554,901
Liabilities: $46,793,568
Net Worth: $61,761,334
Earnings: $4,177,113
Emp.: 41
Fiscal Year-end: 12/31/22
Television Broadcasting Services
N.A.I.C.S.: 516120
Seungtaek Jeon *(CEO)*

ANISERCO S.A.

Noordkustlaan 16A B3, 1702, Groot-Bijgaarden, Belgium
Tel.: (32) 24863900
Web Site: http://www.tomandco.be
Year Founded: 1991
Emp.: 58
Care Service Store & Pet Distr
N.A.I.C.S.: 459910
Lionel Desclee *(CEO)*

ANJAC SAS

15 rue de la Banque, 75002, Paris, France
Tel.: (33) 1 53 45 94 4
Web Site: https://www.anjac.com
Emp.: 100
Wellness & Beauty Products Mfr & Pharmaceutical Laboratories
N.A.I.C.S.: 456120
Aurelien Chaufou *(Pres)*

Subsidiaries:

Pillar 5 Pharma Inc.   (1)
365 Madawaska Blvd, Arnprior, K7S 0C9, ON, Canada
Tel.: (613) 623-1210
Web Site: http://www.pillar5pharma.com
Sales Range: $50-74.9 Million
Emp.: 120
Pharmaceuticals Mfr
N.A.I.C.S.: 325412
Jamie Moore *(COO)*

ANJANI FINANCE LIMITED

The Agarwal Corporate House, 1 Sanjana Park Adj Agarwal Public School, Bicholi Mardana Road, Indore, 452016, Madhya Pradesh, India
Tel.: (91) 7314949699
Web Site: https://anjanifin.com
Year Founded: 1989
531878—(BOM)
Rev.: $176,768
Assets: $2,810,426
Liabilities: $994,989
Net Worth: $1,815,436
Earnings: $57,712

Emp.: 6
Fiscal Year-end: 03/31/21
Non Banking Financial Services
N.A.I.C.S.: 523999
Sanjaykumar Agarwal *(Mng Dir)*

ANJANI FOODS LIMITED

Plot No 7 and 8 Anjani Vishnu Centre Nagarjuna Hills, Punjagutta, Hyderabad, 500082, Telangana, India
Tel.: (91) 4040334848
Web Site: https://www.anjanifoods.in
Year Founded: 1983
511153—(BOM)
Rev.: $4,827,937
Assets: $4,443,976
Liabilities: $2,840,429
Net Worth: $1,603,547
Earnings: $21,663
Emp.: 147
Fiscal Year-end: 03/31/22
Food Processing & Sales
N.A.I.C.S.: 311999
K. V. Vishnu Raju *(Chm)*

ANJANI PORTLAND CEMENT LTD.

6-3-553 Unit Nos E3 and E4 4th Floor Quena Square, Off Taj Deccan Road Erramanzil, Hyderabad, 500 082, Telangana, India
Tel.: (91) 4023353096
Web Site: https://www.anjanicement.com
APCL—(NSE)
Rev.: $90,659,205
Assets: $142,070,565
Liabilities: $96,115,110
Net Worth: $45,955,455
Earnings: ($7,985,250)
Emp.: 200
Fiscal Year-end: 03/31/23
Cement Mfr
N.A.I.C.S.: 327310
N. Venkata Raju *(Mng Dir)*

Subsidiaries:

Anjani Portland Cement Ltd. - Nalgonda Works   (1)
Anjani Puram Malkapuram Post Mellacheruvu Mandal, Chintalapalem Village, Nalgonda, 508 246, Andhra Pradesh, India
Tel.: (91) 8683230168
Cement Mfr
N.A.I.C.S.: 327310

Hitech Print Systems Ltd.   (1)
Anjani Vishnu Centre Plot No 7 8, Nagarjuna Hills, Hyderabad, 500 082, India
Tel.: (91) 4023351696
Web Site: https://www.hitechprint.com
Business Forms Printing Services
N.A.I.C.S.: 323111

ANJANI SYNTHETICS LTD.

221 Maliya New cloth Market O/s Raipur Gate, Ahmedabad, 380002, Gujarat, India
Tel.: (91) 7922173181
Web Site: https://www.anjanisynthetics.com
531223—(BOM)
Rev.: $36,723,977
Assets: $26,663,304
Liabilities: $17,157,382
Net Worth: $9,505,922
Earnings: $396,709
Emp.: 240
Fiscal Year-end: 03/31/21
Synthetic Textile Products Mfr
N.A.I.C.S.: 314999
Vasudev S. Agarwal *(Chm & Mng Dir)*

Subsidiaries:

Anjani Synthetics Ltd. - Ahmedabad Plant   (1)
140 Pirana Road, Piplej, Ahmedabad, 382 405, Gujarat, India

Tel.: (91) 79 22173181
Bed Sheet & Apparel Mfr
N.A.I.C.S.: 313240

ANJI FOODSTUFF CO., LTD.

Economic and Technological Development Zone 4-9A, Quanzhou, Fujian, China
Tel.: (86) 59522237566
Web Site: https://www.anjifood.com
Year Founded: 1995
603696—(SHG)
Rev.: $78,229,083
Assets: $88,068,694
Liabilities: $12,633,431
Net Worth: $75,435,263
Earnings: $1,943,010
Fiscal Year-end: 12/31/22
Seasoning Powder Mfr
N.A.I.C.S.: 311942

ANJI MICROELECTRONICS TECHNOLOGY SHANGHAI CO., LTD.

Building T6-5 South Zone Jinqiao Comprehensive Free Trade Zone, 5001 Huadong Road Pudong New Area, Shanghai, 201203, China
Tel.: (86) 2120693333
Web Site: https://www.anjimicro.com
Year Founded: 2006
688019—(SHG)
Rev.: $151,180,937
Assets: $287,483,223
Liabilities: $73,857,617
Net Worth: $213,625,606
Earnings: $42,321,755
Fiscal Year-end: 12/31/22
Electronic Product Mfr & Distr
N.A.I.C.S.: 334419
Wang Shumin *(Chm & Gen Mgr)*

Subsidiaries:

Ningbo Anji Microelectronics Technology Co., Ltd.   (1)
No 9 Yuntaishan Road Xiapu Street, Beilun District, Ningbo, Zhejiang, China
Tel.: (86) 57486066099
Semiconductor Material Mfr & Distr
N.A.I.C.S.: 334413

ANJI TECHNOLOGY CO., LTD.

No 19 Keji 5th Road Annan District, T'ainan, 709, Taiwan
Tel.: (886) 65105988
Web Site: https://www.anjitek.com
Year Founded: 2007
6477—(TAI)
Rev.: $49,112,592
Assets: $257,276,978
Liabilities: $142,770,752
Net Worth: $114,506,225
Earnings: $4,385,493
Fiscal Year-end: 12/31/23
Solar Module Mfr & Distr
N.A.I.C.S.: 333414
Kuo-Tueng Huang *(Chm)*

ANKA INDIA LIMITED

6 Legend Square Sector 33, Gurgaon, 122004, Haryana, India
Tel.: (91) 9355511187
Web Site: https://www.ankaindia.com
Year Founded: 1997
531673—(BOM)
Rev.: $6,825
Assets: $184,962
Liabilities: $26,797
Net Worth: $158,165
Earnings: ($8,822)
Fiscal Year-end: 03/31/21
Shoe Soles Mfr
N.A.I.C.S.: 316990
Manish Pandey *(CFO)*

ANKAMA SAS

5 Boulevard d'Armentieres, BP,

60403, 59057, Roubaix, Cedex 1, France
Tel.: (33) 3 20 36 36 09
Web Site: http://www.ankama.com
Year Founded: 2001
Animation & Online Games Developer
N.A.I.C.S.: 513210
Anthony Roux *(Dir-Publ)*

ANKER INNOVATIONS TECHNOLOGY CO., LTD.

Room 701 7th Floor Building 7 Changsha, Zhongdian Software Park, Changsha, 410205, Hunan, China
Tel.: (86) 73188706606
Web Site: http://www.anker-in.com
Year Founded: 2011
300866—(SSE)
Rev.: $2,000,773,008
Assets: $1,422,531,396
Liabilities: $447,581,160
Net Worth: $974,950,236
Earnings: $160,477,200
Emp.: 4,000
Fiscal Year-end: 12/31/22
Electronic Product Mfr & Distr
N.A.I.C.S.: 334419
Meng Yang *(Chm)*

ANKER-TEPPICHBODEN GEBRUDER SCHOELLER GMBH & CO. KG

Zollhausstrasse 112, 52353, Duren, Germany
Tel.: (49) 24218040
Web Site: http://www.anker.eu
Year Founded: 1854
Sales Range: $50-74.9 Million
Emp.: 330
Mfr of Carpets
N.A.I.C.S.: 314110
Christian Jordan *(Mgr-Acct-Banking & Insurances Industry)*

Subsidiaries:

ANKER-Teppichboden Gebruder Schoeller GmbH & Co. KG - Aviation Division   (1)
Zollhausstrasse 112, 52353, Duren, Germany
Tel.: (49) 24 21 804 0
Web Site: http://www.anker.eu
Sales Range: $100-124.9 Million
Emp.: 300
Aircraft Carpet Mfr
N.A.I.C.S.: 314110
Erwin Landherrr *(Mng Dir)*

ANKHU KHOLA HYDROPOWER COMPANY LTD

Anamnagar, Kathmandu, Nepal
Tel.: (977) 14102595
Web Site: https://www.aankhukholahydro.com.np
AKJCL—(NEP)
Rev.: $1,457,007
Assets: $14,467,157
Liabilities: $10,276,009
Net Worth: $4,191,148
Earnings: ($63,583)
Fiscal Year-end: 07/16/23
Hydropower Project Services
N.A.I.C.S.: 221111
Utsav Baral *(CEO)*

ANKIT METAL & POWER LTD.

35 Chittranjan Avenue, Kolkata, 700 012, India
Tel.: (91) 3322119805
Web Site: https://www.ankitmetal.com
532870—(BOM)
Rev.: $57,045,643
Assets: $166,049,438
Liabilities: $266,266,209
Net Worth: ($100,216,771)

Earnings: ($10,333,787)
Emp.: 1,019
Fiscal Year-end: 03/31/21
Steel Products Mfr & Distr
N.A.I.C.S.: 331110
Saurabh Jhunjhunwala *(CFO)*

ANKUSH FINSTOCK LIMITED
B/708 Fairdeal House Opp St xavier s Girls Hostel, Nr Swastik Char Rasta Off C G Road, Ahmedabad, 380009, Gujarat, India
Tel.: (91) 79 30182614
Web Site:
http://www.ankushfinstock.co.in
Year Founded: 1993
Rev.: $348,083
Assets: $941,769
Liabilities: $790,723
Net Worth: $151,046
Earnings: $43,602
Emp.: 6
Fiscal Year-end: 03/31/18
Securities Brokerage Services
N.A.I.C.S.: 523150
Samir P. Shah *(CFO)*

ANLI INTERNATIONAL CO., LTD.
8F No 215 Sec 4 New Taipei Blvd, Xinzhuang Dist, New Taipei City, 242, Taiwan
Tel.: (886) 285227056
Web Site: https://www.anli-group.com
Year Founded: 2010
5223—(TPE)
Rev.: $64,395,460
Assets: $111,800,988
Liabilities: $47,608,886
Net Worth: $64,192,102
Earnings: $6,127,255
Emp.: 628
Fiscal Year-end: 12/31/22
Metal Component Mfr & Distr
N.A.I.C.S.: 332215
Cheng-Kun Hsu *(Chm & CEO)*

ANLIMA YARN DYEING LIMITED
Suite 4/3 City Heart 67 Naya Paltan, Dhaka, 1000, Bangladesh
Tel.: (880) 249349881
Web Site: http://www.anlima.com
ANLIMAYARN—(CHT)
Rev.: $1,480,420
Assets: $3,863,618
Liabilities: $2,164,796
Net Worth: $1,698,821
Earnings: $13,200
Emp.: 209
Fiscal Year-end: 06/30/23
Yarn Dyeing Services
N.A.I.C.S.: 313110
Hubbun Nahar Hoque *(Chm)*

Subsidiaries:

Anlima Textile Limited   (1)
Suite 413 City Heart 67 Naya Paltan, Dhaka, 1000, Bangladesh
Tel.: (880) 2224441714
Knit & Fabrics Mfr
N.A.I.C.S.: 313240

ANMAR MECHANICAL AND ELECTRICAL CONTRACTORS LTD.
199 Mumford Rd, Lively, P3Y 1L2, ON, Canada
Tel.: (705) 692-0888
Web Site: https://www.anmar.ca
Year Founded: 1989
Rev.: $12,945,882
Emp.: 150
Heating Systems Repair & Maintenance Services
N.A.I.C.S.: 238220
Gianni Grossi *(Pres)*

Subsidiaries:

ANMAR Construction Africa (PTY) Ltd   (1)
8 Barratt Road Factoria, Krugersdorp, Gauteng, South Africa
Tel.: (27) 119556487
Web Site: http://www.anmarafrica.co.za
Furnace Repair & Maintenance Services
N.A.I.C.S.: 811310
Gideon Lubbe *(Mgr-Mtkg & Sls)*

ANMOL INDIA LIMITED
2/43 Block B Aggar Nagar Ludhiana, Guwahati, India
Tel.: (91) 9878076554
Web Site:
https://www.anmolindialtd.com
Year Founded: 1998
ANMOL—(NSE)
Rev.: $145,313,355
Assets: $40,490,128
Liabilities: $32,245,934
Net Worth: $8,244,194
Earnings: $2,123,245
Fiscal Year-end: 03/31/22
Coal Distr
N.A.I.C.S.: 423520
Vijay Kumar *(CEO & Mng Dir)*

ANN JOO RESOURCES BERHAD
Wisma Ann Joo Lot 19391 Batu 8 1/2 Jalan Klang Lama, 46000, Petaling Jaya, Selangor Darul Ehsan, Malaysia
Tel.: (60) 378770028
Web Site:
https://www.annjoo.com.my
ANNJOO—(KLS)
Rev.: $642,322,116
Assets: $576,967,407
Liabilities: $324,417,354
Net Worth: $252,550,053
Earnings: ($28,177,989)
Emp.: 2,030
Fiscal Year-end: 12/31/22
Steel & Steel Related Products Mfr
N.A.I.C.S.: 332431
Oi Wah Leong *(Co-Sec)*

Subsidiaries:

AJE Best-On Sdn. Bhd.   (1)
Jalan Gergaji 15/14, 40200, Shah Alam, Selangor Darul Ehsan, Malaysia
Tel.: (60) 355245883
Web Site: https://www.ajebest-on.com.my
Green Renewable Energy Consulting Services
N.A.I.C.S.: 541690

Ann Joo Green Energy Sdn. Bhd.   (1)
Jalan Gergaji 15/14, 40200, Shah Alam, Selangor Darul Ehsan, Malaysia
Tel.: (60) 355102888
Environmental Management Services
N.A.I.C.S.: 541620

Ann Joo Integrated Steel Sdn. Bhd.   (1)
Lot 1236 Prai Industrial Estate, 13600, Prai, Penang, Malaysia
Tel.: (60) 43888300
Steel Products Mfr
N.A.I.C.S.: 331210

Ann Joo Management Services Sdn. Bhd.   (1)
Wisma Ann Joo Lot 19391 Batu 8 1/2 Jalan Klang Lama, Pejabat Pos Kelana Jaya, 46000, Petaling Jaya, Selangor Darul Ehsan, Malaysia
Tel.: (60) 378770028
Steel Products Mfr
N.A.I.C.S.: 331210

Ann Joo Metal (Singapore) Pte. Ltd.   (1)
13 Jalan Terusan Blk 1 01-01, Singapore, 619293, Singapore
Tel.: (65) 65341539

Steel Product Distr
N.A.I.C.S.: 423510

Ann Joo Metal Sdn. Bhd.   (1)
Wisma Ann Joo Lot 19391 Batu 8 1/2 Jalan Klang Lama, Pejabat Pos Kelana Jaya, 46000, Petaling Jaya, Selangor Darul Ehsan, Malaysia
Tel.: (60) 378742233
Steel Products Mfr
N.A.I.C.S.: 331210

Anshin Steel Industries Sdn. Bhd.   (1)
Jalan Gergaji 15/14, 0200, Shah Alam, Selangor, Malaysia
Tel.: (60) 355102888
Steel Products Mfr
N.A.I.C.S.: 331210

Anshin Steel Processor Sdn. Bhd.   (1)
Jalan Gergaji 15/14, 40200, Shah Alam, Selangor Darul Ehsan, Malaysia
Tel.: (60) 355106911
Steel Products Mfr
N.A.I.C.S.: 331210

Bumi Segar Indah Sdn. Bhd.   (1)
Suite 619 Block B2 No 9 Jalan PJS 8/9, Leisure Commerce Square, 46150, Petaling Jaya, Selangor, Malaysia
Tel.: (60) 378655030
Web Site: https://bumisegarindah.com
Solid Waste Management Services
N.A.I.C.S.: 562111

Saga Makmur Industri Sdn. Bhd.   (1)
Lot 9 Persiaran Perusahaan Section 23, 40300, Shah Alam, Selangor Darul Ehsan, Malaysia
Tel.: (60) 355482088
Steel Products Mfr
N.A.I.C.S.: 331210

ANNA INFRASTRUCTURES LIMITED
Shop No 1 3 E-14/6 First Floor Shanta Tower Sanjay Place, Agra, 282002, Uttar Pradesh, India
Tel.: (91) 5622527004
Web Site: http://annainfra.com
Year Founded: 1993
530799—(BOM)
Rev.: $145,543
Assets: $1,188,574
Liabilities: $41,304
Net Worth: $1,147,269
Earnings: $27,432
Fiscal Year-end: 03/31/23
Real Estate Manangement Services
N.A.I.C.S.: 531390
Anil Kumar Agarwal *(Exec Dir)*

ANNAIK LIMITED
52 Tuas Avenue 9, Singapore, 639193, Singapore
Tel.: (65) 62102727
Web Site: https://www.annaik.com.sg
Year Founded: 1977
A52—(CAT)
Rev.: $36,097,099
Assets: $90,921,003
Liabilities: $31,153,526
Net Worth: $59,767,477
Earnings: $3,510,566
Emp.: 46
Fiscal Year-end: 12/31/23
Stainless Steel Piping Products Mfr & Distr
N.A.I.C.S.: 331210
Kim Keang Ng *(COO)*

Subsidiaries:

Ann Aik Pte Ltd   (1)
52 Tuas Ave 9, Singapore, 639193, Singapore
Tel.: (65) 62102727
Steel Products Whslr
N.A.I.C.S.: 331210
Ow Chin Seng *(Co-CEO)*

Ichinose Emico Valves (S) Pte Ltd.   (1)
52 Tuas Avenue 9, Singapore, 639193, Singapore
Tel.: (65) 62102725
Stainless Steel Pipe Mfr & Distr
N.A.I.C.S.: 331210

Metal Wang Pte Ltd   (1)
52 Tuas Avenue 9, Singapore, 639193, Singapore
Tel.: (65) 62102721
Web Site: https://www.metalwang.co
Steel Products Mfr
N.A.I.C.S.: 331110

Pioneer Environmental Technology Pte Ltd   (1)
135 Pioneer Road, 639589, Singapore, Singapore
Tel.: (65) 93690986
Water Treatment Equipment Mfr
N.A.I.C.S.: 333310

Shinsei Industry Sdn Bhd   (1)
1895 Lorong Industri 3 Kawasan Perindustrian Bukit Panchor, 14300, Nibong Tebal, Penang, Malaysia
Tel.: (60) 45269273
Web Site: https://www.ssflanges.com.my
Emp.: 130
Steel Products Mfr
N.A.I.C.S.: 331110

Shinsei Japan Industry Co Ltd   (1)
2nd floor Nakazato Daiichi Building 5-11-9 Nishinakajima, Yodogawa-Ku, Osaka, 532-0011, Japan
Tel.: (81) 66 100 5811
Web Site: https://www.shinseiindustry.co.jp
Sales Range: $50-74.9 Million
Emp.: 5
Machine Tools Import & Distr
N.A.I.C.S.: 423830

ANNAPURNA BHASKARI GROUP
D-41 Phase V IDA Jeedimetla, Hyderabad, 500 055, India
Tel.: (91) 40 23097637
Web Site:
http://www.annapurnabhaskari.com
Thermostat, Valve & Switch Mfr
N.A.I.C.S.: 332911
G. Krishna Prasad *(Mng Dir)*

Subsidiaries:

Annapurna Electronics & Services Pvt. Ltd.   (1)
D-41 Phase V I D A, Jeedimetla, Hyderabad, 500055, India
Tel.: (91) 40 2309 5371
Thermostat Mfr
N.A.I.C.S.: 334512

Joint Venture (Domestic):

Annapurna Kenmore Tube Products Pvt. Ltd.   (2)
Plot No 19/B Ida Balanagar, Hyderabad, 500037, Andhra Pradesh, India
Tel.: (91) 4023075683
Web Site:
http://www.annapurnakenmore.com
Emp.: 40
Fluid Power Pump & Motor Mfr
N.A.I.C.S.: 333996
G. Raghuram Sarma *(Mng Dir)*

Bhaskari Electrical Systems Pvt. Ltd.   (1)
Shed No F2 Gandhi Nagar IDA, Kukatpally, Hyderabad, 500072, India
Tel.: (91) 4023073032
Electrical Component Distr
N.A.I.C.S.: 423690

ANNEC GREEN REFRACTORIES CORPORATION
No 5 West Section Xidajie Street, Xinmi, 452370, Henan, China
Tel.: (86) 371 69938899
Web Site: http://www.annec.com.cn
Year Founded: 2010
Sales Range: $10-24.9 Million

Annec Green Refractories Corporation—(Continued)

Emp.: 734
Refractory Production & Sales
N.A.I.C.S.: 327120

ANNEX PUBLISHING & PRINTING INC.

105 Donly Drive South, PO Box 530,
Simcoe, N3Y 4N5, ON, Canada
Tel.: (519) 429-3966
Web Site: http://www.annexweb.com
Year Founded: 1997
Sales Range: $25-49.9 Million
Emp.: 100
Online Magazine Publishing & Distr
N.A.I.C.S.: 513120
Michael Fredericks (Pres & CEO)

ANNICA HOLDINGS LIMITED

100 Beach Road 17-01 Shaw Tower,
Singapore, 189702, Singapore
Tel.: (65) 62211123   **SG**
Web Site: https://www.annica.com.sg
Year Founded: 1983
5AL—(CAT)
Rev.: $11,105,595
Assets: $10,985,550
Liabilities: $10,554,279
Net Worth: $431,271
Earnings: ($1,242,682)
Emp.: 48
Fiscal Year-end: 12/31/22
Holding Company
N.A.I.C.S.: 551112
Sandra Liz Hon Ai Ling (CEO)

Subsidiaries:

Cahya Suria Energy Sdn. Bhd.   **(1)**
Unit 120 122 Lobby B Block A Kelana Centre Point, 3 Jln SS7/19 Kelana Jaya, 47301,
Petaling Jaya, Selangor, Malaysia
Tel.: (60) 333714725
Web Site: https://cahyasuria.com
Investment Services
N.A.I.C.S.: 523999

Subsidiary (Domestic):

Renosun International Sdn. Bhd.   **(2)**
45-G Jalan PJU 1A/41B, Pusat Dagangan
NZX, 47301, Petaling Jaya, Selangor,
Malaysia   **(100%)**
Tel.: (60) 376603399
Investment Services
N.A.I.C.S.: 523999

Industrial Engineering Systems Pte.
Ltd.   **(1)**
40 Ubi Crescent 01-01 Ubi Techpark, Singapore, 408567, Singapore
Tel.: (65) 61001080
Plant Engineering Services
N.A.I.C.S.: 541330

Subsidiary (Non-US):

IES Engineering Systems Sdn.
Bhd.   **(2)**
1st Floor Sublot 41 Block B Demak Laut
Commercial Centre, Phase 3 Jalan Bako,
93050, Kuching, Sarawak, Malaysia
Tel.: (60) 824233189
Investment Services
N.A.I.C.S.: 523999

P.J. Services Pte Ltd   **(1)**
40 Ubi Crescent 01-01 Ubi Techpark, Singapore, 408567, Singapore
Tel.: (65) 65453533
Web Site: https://pjservices.com.sg
Oil & Gas Exploration Services
N.A.I.C.S.: 211130
Musa Mohamad Sahir (Mng Dir)

Subsidiary (Non-US):

PT. Panah Jaya Sejahtera   **(2)**
Gedung Bangun Tijipta Lt 3B Jln Gatot Subroto No 54, Jakarta, 10260, Indonesia
Tel.: (62) 215708833
Oil & Gas Exploration Services
N.A.I.C.S.: 211130

Panah Jaya Services Sdn. Bhd.   **(1)**

Unit 120 122 Lobby B Block A Kelana Centre Point 3 Jln SS7/19, Kelana Jaya, 47301,
Petaling Jaya, Malaysia
Tel.: (60) 378064505
Web Site: https://www.panahjaya.com.my
Industrial Machinery & Spare Parts Whslr
N.A.I.C.S.: 423830
Azmi Nordin (Mng Dir)

ANNIDIS CORPORATION

100 Maple Grove Rd, Ottawa, K2V
1B8, ON, Canada
Tel.: (613) 596-1800   **ON**
Web Site: http://www.annidis.com
Year Founded: 2010
Rev.: $870,546
Assets: $1,670,109
Liabilities: $11,867,698
Net Worth: ($10,197,589)
Earnings: ($3,734,241)
Fiscal Year-end: 12/31/16
Healthcare Investment Services
N.A.I.C.S.: 523999

ANNIL CO., LTD.

13F-17F Tower A Block 3 1st Phase
of Tianan Yungu Industrial Park, No.
2018 Xuegang Road Bantian Subdistrict Longgang District, Shenzhen,
518129, Guangdong, China
Tel.: (86) 75522914860
Web Site: http://www.annil.com
Year Founded: 1996
002875—(SSE)
Rev.: $131,740,128
Assets: $185,058,432
Liabilities: $57,432,024
Net Worth: $127,626,408
Earnings: ($33,330,960)
Fiscal Year-end: 12/31/22
Children Apparel Distr
N.A.I.C.S.: 458110
Cao Zhang (Chm & Pres)

ANNONA ENERGY INC.

2316 A Willemar Avenue, Courtenay,
V9N 3M8, BC, Canada
Tel.: (250) 898-8882   **NV**
Year Founded: 2012
Oil & Gas Exploration
N.A.I.C.S.: 211120
Lawrence Jean (Pres, CEO, CFO,
Treas & Sec)

ANNOOR TEXTILE MILLS LIMITED

901 9th Floor Business Centre
Mumtaz Hassan Road, Karachi, Pakistan
Tel.: (92) 212400991
CLKTF—(OTCEM)
Yarn Product Mfr
N.A.I.C.S.: 313110

ANNUITY & LIFE RE (HOLDINGS), LTD.

16 Burnaby St, Hamilton, HM 11,
Bermuda
Tel.: (441) 278 7709   **BM**
Web Site: http://www.alre.bm
Year Founded: 1997
Sales Range: Less than $1 Million
Emp.: 10
Life & Annuity Reinsurance Services
N.A.I.C.S.: 524113
Martin A. Berkowitz (Chm)

Subsidiaries:

Annuity & Life Reassurance, Ltd.   **(1)**
Cumberland House, 1 Victoria Street, Hamilton, HM 11, Bermuda
Tel.: (441) 296 7667
Web Site: http://www.annuityandlifere.com
Reinsurance
N.A.I.C.S.: 524130

ANNUM BERHAD

Menara Exchange106 Lingkaran TRX
Tun Razak Exchange, 55188, Kuala
Lumpur, Sabah, Malaysia
Tel.: (60) 89767600
Web Site:
     https://www.annumberhad.com
ANNUM—(KLS)
Rev.: $78,292,391
Assets: $25,770,592
Liabilities: $6,695,318
Net Worth: $19,075,274
Earnings: ($14,927,391)
Fiscal Year-end: 06/30/23
Plywood Mfr
N.A.I.C.S.: 321211
Kai-Min Lin (Mng Dir)

Subsidiaries:

Cymao Plywood Sdn. Bhd.   **(1)**
Km 9 1 Jalan Batu Sapi, Locked Bag No
13, 90009, Sandakan, Sabah, Malaysia
Tel.: (60) 89612233
Web Site: http://www.cymao.com
Emp.: 1,000
Wood Products Mfr
N.A.I.C.S.: 321211

Poly-Ply Industries Sdn. Bhd.   **(1)**
Jalan Kapar Kampung Batu Empat, 42100,
Kelang, Selangor, Malaysia
Tel.: (60) 193815518
Sales Range: $25-49.9 Million
Emp.: 80
Decorative Panels Mfr
N.A.I.C.S.: 321918

ANOD BANK

Tourist Street 18, Ulaanbaatar, Mongolia
Tel.: (976) 11315315
Web Site: http://www.anodbank.com
Sales Range: $150-199.9 Million
Emp.: 450
Banking Services
N.A.I.C.S.: 522110
N. Davaa (Pres)

ANONYMOUS INTELLIGENCE COMPANY INC

610 700 West Pender Street, Vancouver, V6C 1G8, BC, Canada
Tel.: (778) 240-7724
Web Site:
     https://www.anonintelco.com
CNI—(CNSX)
Assets: $6,609,708
Liabilities: $592,867
Net Worth: $6,016,841
Earnings: ($3,113,922)
Emp.: 2
Fiscal Year-end: 09/30/21
Education Services
N.A.I.C.S.: 611710
Nilda Rivera (CFO)

ANOTO GROUP AB

Flaggan 1165, 11674, Stockholm,
Sweden
Tel.: (46) 7584301260
Web Site: https://www.anoto.com
ANOT—(OMX)
Rev.: $6,496,389
Assets: $22,359,905
Liabilities: $11,963,434
Net Worth: $10,396,471
Earnings: ($2,317,195)
Emp.: 40
Fiscal Year-end: 12/31/22
Text & Images Capturing & Processing Services
N.A.I.C.S.: 541519
Dennis Song (Chm)

Subsidiaries:

Anoto Inc.   **(1)**
200 Friberg Pkwy Ste 3003, Westborough,
MA 01581
Tel.: (508) 983-9550
Web Site: http://www.anoto.com

Text & Images Capturing & Processing Services
N.A.I.C.S.: 541519

Anoto K.K   **(1)**
3F Shiodome Building 1-2-20 Kaigan,
Minato-ku, Tokyo, 105-0002, Japan
Tel.: (81) 3 4570 3491
Web Site: http://www.anoto.co.jp
Sales Range: $25-49.9 Million
Emp.: 13
Text & Images Capturing & Processing Services
N.A.I.C.S.: 541519
Shinichi Yamashita (VP-Sls)

C Technologies   **(1)**
Emdalavagen 18, SE 223 69, Lund, Sweden
Tel.: (46) 465401000
Text & Images Capturing & Processing Services
N.A.I.C.S.: 541519

C Technologies AB   **(1)**
Traktorvagen 11, Box 4106, SE 227 22,
Lund, Sweden
Tel.: (46) 46 540 10 00
Web Site: http://www.cpen.com
Mfr & Developer of C-Pen Handheld Scanner & Solutions Software
N.A.I.C.S.: 513210

Livescribe, Inc.   **(1)**
7677 Oakport St 12th Fl, Oakland, CA
94621
Tel.: (510) 777-0071
Web Site: http://www.livescribe.com
Sales Range: $1-9.9 Million
Emp.: 50
Digital Writing & Drawing Solutions
N.A.I.C.S.: 334118

ANP HOLDING B.V.

Verrijn Stuartlaan 7, 2288 EK,
Rijswijk, Netherlands
Tel.: (31) 704141414
Web Site: http://www.anp.nl
Sales Range: $50-74.9 Million
Emp.: 200
News Agency
N.A.I.C.S.: 516210
Erik van Gruijthuijsen (Gen Dir)

ANPARIO PLC

Manton Wood Enterprise Park, Worksop, S80 2RS, Nottinghamshire,
United Kingdom
Tel.: (44) 1909537380
Web Site: https://www.anpario.com
ANP—(AIM)
Rev.: $39,868,950
Assets: $58,454,385
Liabilities: $8,696,490
Net Worth: $49,757,895
Earnings: $3,974,850
Fiscal Year-end: 12/31/22
High Performance Natural Feed Additives for Global Agriculture & Aquaculture Markets
N.A.I.C.S.: 325998
Richard P. Edwards (CEO)

Subsidiaries:

Anpario (Shanghai) Biotech Co.,
Ltd.   **(1)**
A8-217 No 808 Hong Qiao Rd, Shanghai,
200030, China
Tel.: (86) 2164483961
Animal Feed Product Distr
N.A.I.C.S.: 424910

Anpario (Thailand) Ltd.   **(1)**
65/152 18th Floor Chamnan Phenjati Bldg
Rama 9 Rd, Huay Kwang, Bangkok, 10310,
Thailand
Tel.: (66) 26438351
Animal Feed Product Distr
N.A.I.C.S.: 424910

Anpario Inc.   **(1)**
104 S Main St, Greenville, SC 29601
Tel.: (864) 641-6168
Animal Feed Product Distr
N.A.I.C.S.: 424910

Subsidiary (Domestic):

Bio-Vet, Inc.   (2)
10957 Blackhawk Dr, Blue Mounds, WI
53517
Tel.: (608) 437-8891
Web Site: http://www.bio-vet.com
Rev.: $4,100,000
Emp.: 13
Veterinary Services
N.A.I.C.S.: 541940
Gary Grimsman (Dir-Sls-Natl)

Anpario Malaysia Sdn. Bhd.   (1)
B-3A-2 Sunway Giza No 2 Jalan PJU 5/14
Kota Damansara, 47810, Petaling Jaya,
Selangor, Malaysia
Tel.: (60) 361516000
Animal Feed Product Distr
N.A.I.C.S.: 424910

Anpario Pty. Ltd.   (1)
PO Box 110, Hornsby, 2077, NSW, Austra-
lia
Tel.: (61) 294777944
Animal Feed Product Distr
N.A.I.C.S.: 424910

Anpario Saude e Nutricao Animal
Ltda.   (1)
Rua Brigadeiro Henrique Fontenelli 745
Sala 4 Parque, Sao Domingos, Sao Paulo,
05125-000, Brazil
Tel.: (55) 1139014267
Animal Feed Product Distr
N.A.I.C.S.: 424910

PT. Anpario Biotech Indonesia   (1)
18 Office Park Lt M Unit F2 Jl Tb Simatupang No 18, Jakarta Selatan, 12520, Indonesia
Tel.: (62) 2122708247
Animal Feed Product Distr
N.A.I.C.S.: 424910

ANPULO FOOD DEVELOP-
MENT, INC.
Hebaliang Industry Park Hangkong
Road, Laifeng Country Enshi Autono-
mous Prefecture, Wuhan, 445700,
Hubei, China
Tel.: (86) 718 6288576   NV
Year Founded: 2010
Investment Services
N.A.I.C.S.: 523999
Wenping Luo (CEO, CFO & Chief
Acctg Officer)

ANPULO FOOD, INC.
Hangkong Road Xiangfeng Town,
Laifeng County, Laifenghsien,
445700, Hubei, China
Tel.: (86) 7186288576   VG
Web Site: http://www.anpulo.cn
Year Founded: 2010
ANPFF—(OTCIQ)
Sales Range: $25-49.9 Million
Emp.: 338
Meat Processing & Distr
N.A.I.C.S.: 311612
Wenping Luo (Pres & CEO)

ANQUIRO VENTURES LTD.
595 Howe Street Suite 303, Vancou-
ver, V6C 2T5, BC, Canada
Tel.: (604) 718-2800
AQR.P—(TSXV)
Assets: $925
Liabilities: $152,898
Net Worth: ($151,973)
Earnings: ($34,719)
Fiscal Year-end: 06/30/24
Asset Management Services
N.A.I.C.S.: 523940

ANRAKUTEI CO., LTD.
4F Arusa B 2-3-5 Kami-Ochiai, Chuo-
ku, Saitama, 338-0001, Japan
Tel.: (81) 486126302
Web Site: https://www.anrakutei.co.jp
Year Founded: 1978

7562—(TKS)
Rev.: $200,018,600
Assets: $146,953,520
Liabilities: $101,767,560
Net Worth: $45,185,960
Earnings: $6,391,870
Emp.: 477
Fiscal Year-end: 03/31/24
Restaurant Operators
N.A.I.C.S.: 722511
Sen Yanagi (Chm, Pres & CEO)

ANRIKA GROUP SCANDINA-
VIA AB
Vastra Hamngatan 18, SE-411 17,
Gothenburg, Sweden
Tel.: (46) 3113 7110   SE
Web Site: http://www.anrika.se
Year Founded: 2010
Holding Company; Infrastructure &
Social Development Consulting Ser-
vices
N.A.I.C.S.: 551112
Lars Ake Junelind (CEO)

Subsidiaries:

Anrika Quality Services AB   (1)
Vastra Hamngatan 18, SE-411 17, Gothen-
burg, Sweden
Tel.: (46) 3113 7110
Web Site: http://www.anrika.se
Infrastructure Development Consultancy
Services
N.A.I.C.S.: 541690

ANRITSU CORPORATION
5-1-1 Onna, Atsugi, 243-8555, Kana-
gawa, Japan
Tel.: (81) 462231111   JP
Web Site: https://www.anritsu.com
Year Founded: 1931
6754—(TKS)
Rev.: $726,782,720
Assets: $1,064,771,850
Liabilities: $235,051,600
Net Worth: $829,720,250
Earnings: $50,731,750
Emp.: 4,083
Fiscal Year-end: 03/31/24
Optical & Electronic Measuring Instru-
ments, Communication Systems,
Computer Peripherals, Industrial Au-
tomation Systems, Devices & Inspec-
tion Systems Mfr
N.A.I.C.S.: 334519
Toshisumi Taniai (Sr Exec Officer-
Mgmt Audit Dept)

Subsidiaries:

AT Techmac Co., Ltd.   (1)
3461-4 Okami, Hiratsuka, 254-0012, Kana-
gawa, Japan
Tel.: (81) 463514111
Metal Detector Mfr
N.A.I.C.S.: 334519

Anritsu (China) Co., Ltd.   (1)
Room 2701-2705 Tower A New Caohejing
International Business Center, No 391 Gui
Ping Road, Shanghai, 200233, China
Tel.: (86) 2162370898
Metal Detector Mfr
N.A.I.C.S.: 334519

Anritsu A/S   (1)
Orestads Boulevard 73 4th floor, 2300, Co-
penhagen, Denmark
Tel.: (45) 72112200
Web Site: http://www.anritsu.com.tk
Sales Range: $25-49.9 Million
Emp.: 100
Electronic Measuring Instruments & Sys-
tems for Telecommunications
N.A.I.C.S.: 334515

Anritsu AB   (1)
Kistagangen 20 B 2 tr, Kista, 164 40, Stock-
holm, Sweden
Tel.: (46) 853470700
Emp.: 10

Measuring Equipment Sales & Maintenance
Services
N.A.I.C.S.: 423830

Anritsu AB   (1)
Technopolis Aviapolis Teknobulevardi 3-5
D208 5, 01530, Vantaa, Finland
Tel.: (358) 207418100
Metal Detector Mfr
N.A.I.C.S.: 334519

Anritsu Co. Ltd.   (1)
Unit 1006-7 10/F Greenfield Tower Concor-
dia Plaza, No 1 Science Museum Road
Tsim Sha Tsui East, Kowloon, China (Hong
Kong)
Tel.: (852) 23014980
Web Site: https://www.anritsu.com
Broadcast & Satellite Services & Sales
N.A.I.C.S.: 517410

Anritsu Company   (1)
490 Jarvis Dr, Morgan Hill, CA 95037-2809
Tel.: (408) 778-2000
Web Site: http://www.us.anritsu.com
Sales Range: $150-199.9 Million
Emp.: 450
Communication & Network Devices Mfr
N.A.I.C.S.: 423690
Wade Hulon (Pres)

Division (Domestic):

Microwave Measurement
Division   (2)
490 Jarvis Dr Bldg 12C, Morgan Hill, CA
95037-2809
Tel.: (408) 778-2000
Web Site: http://www.global.anritsu.com
Sales Range: $250-299.9 Million
Microwave Testing Equipment Mfr
N.A.I.C.S.: 423690
Alexander Chenakin (Dir-R&D)

Anritsu Company Limited   (1)
16th Floor Peakview Tower 36 Hoang Cau
Street, O Cho Dua Ward Dong Da District,
Hanoi, Vietnam
Tel.: (84) 2432012730
Metal Detector Mfr
N.A.I.C.S.: 334519

Anritsu Company, Inc.   (1)
7F No 316 Sec 1 NeiHu Rd, Taipei, 114,
Taiwan
Tel.: (886) 287511816
Metal Detector Mfr
N.A.I.C.S.: 334519

Anritsu Company, S.A. de C.V   (1)
Blvd Miguel de Cervantes Saavedra 169
Piso 1 Col, Granada, 11520, Mexico,
Mexico
Tel.: (52) 5541697104
Web Site: http://www.anritsu.com
Electronic Measuring Equipment Distr
N.A.I.C.S.: 423690

Anritsu Customer Support Co.,
Ltd.   (1)
5-1-1 Onna, Atsugi, 243-0032, Kanagawa,
Japan
Tel.: (81) 462966688
Electronic Measuring Instrument Mfr &
Whslr
N.A.I.C.S.: 334515

Anritsu Devices Co., Ltd.   (1)
5-1-1 Onna, Atsugi, 243-0032, Kanagawa,
Japan
Tel.: (81) 462966630
Optical & Electronic Device Mfr & Whslr
N.A.I.C.S.: 334419
Yasunobu Hashimoto (Pres)

Anritsu EMEA GmbH   (1)
Am Belvedere 10, 1100, Vienna, Austria
Tel.: (43) 171728710
Metal Detector Mfr
N.A.I.C.S.: 334519

Anritsu EMEA Ltd   (1)
200 Capability Green, Luton, LU1 3LU,
Bedfordshire, United Kingdom
Tel.: (44) 1582433200
Sales Range: $75-99.9 Million
Emp.: 100
Measuring Equipment Sales & Maintenance
Services
N.A.I.C.S.: 423830

Anritsu Electronica, Ltda.   (1)
Praca Amadeu Amaral 27 - 1 Andar, Bela
Vista, Sao Paulo, 01327-010, SP,
Brazil   **(100%)**
Tel.: (55) 1132832511
Web Site: http://www.anritsu.com
Sales Range: $25-49.9 Million
Emp.: 50
Sales & Marketing of Test Instruments for
Telecommunications
N.A.I.C.S.: 334515

Anritsu Electronics Ltd   (1)
700 Silver Seven Road Suite 120, Kanata,
K2V 1C3, ON, Canada
Tel.: (613) 591-2003
Web Site: http://www.anritsu.com
Sales Range: $25-49.9 Million
Emp.: 8
Electrical Measuring Instrument Mfr
N.A.I.C.S.: 334515
Tony Paredes (Gen Mgr)

Anritsu GmbH   (1)
Nemetschek Haus Konrad-Zuse-Platz 1,
81829, Munich, Germany   **(100%)**
Tel.: (49) 894423080
Web Site: http://www.anritsu.com
Sales Range: $25-49.9 Million
Emp.: 25
Sales & Marketing of Anritsu Products
N.A.I.C.S.: 449210

Anritsu India Private Limited   (1)
6th Floor Indiqube ETA No 38/4 Adjacent to
EMC2 Outer Ring Road, Doddanekundi,
Bengaluru, 560048, India
Tel.: (91) 8067281300
Metal Detector Mfr
N.A.I.C.S.: 334519

Anritsu Industrial Solutions (Shang-
hai) Co., Ltd.   (1)
Room 703-704 Sandhill Central No 505
Zhangjiang Road, Pudong New Area,
Shanghai, 201210, China
Tel.: (86) 2150463066
Metal Detector Mfr
N.A.I.C.S.: 334519

Anritsu Infivis (THAILAND) Co.,
Ltd.   (1)
700/678 Moo 1 Pangthong, Amata Nakorn
Industrial Estate, Phan Thong, 20160,
Chonburi, Thailand
Tel.: (66) 38447180
Metal Detector Mfr
N.A.I.C.S.: 334519

Anritsu Infivis B.V.   (1)
Grubbenvorsterweg 10, 5928 NX, Venlo,
Netherlands
Tel.: (31) 202254220
Metal Detector Mfr
N.A.I.C.S.: 334519

Anritsu Infivis Co., Ltd.   (1)
5-1-1 Onna, Atsugi, 243-0032, Kanagawa
Prefecture, Japan
Tel.: (81) 462966699
Industrial Machinery Product Distr
N.A.I.C.S.: 423830
Masumi Niimi (Pres)

Anritsu Infivis Inc.   (1)
1001 Cambridge Dr, Elk Grove Village, IL
60007
Tel.: (847) 419-9729
Metal Detector Mfr
N.A.I.C.S.: 334519

Anritsu Infivis Ltd.   (1)
Unit 3 Scott Road, Luton, LU3 3BF, United
Kingdom
Tel.: (44) 8455399729
Metal Detector Mfr
N.A.I.C.S.: 334519

Anritsu Kousan Co., Ltd.   (1)
5-1-1 Onna, Atsugi, 243-0032, Kanagawa,
Japan
Tel.: (81) 462966736
Metal Detector Mfr
N.A.I.C.S.: 334519

Anritsu Limited   (1)
200 Capability Green, Luton, LU1 3LU,
Bedfordshire, United Kingdom   **(100%)**
Tel.: (44) 1582433200
Web Site: http://www.anritsu.co.uk

Anritsu Corporation—(Continued)

Sales Range: $1-9.9 Million
Emp.: 100
Sales & Marketing of Wire & Wireless Communication Equipment
N.A.I.C.S.: 423610

Anritsu Philippines, Inc. (1)
Units 104-107 G/F Building A UP-Ayala Land Technohub Commonwealth Ave, Diliman Metro Manila, Quezon City, Philippines
Tel.: (63) 273699249
Metal Detector Mfr
N.A.I.C.S.: 334519

Anritsu Pte. Ltd (1)
Tel.: (65) 62822400
Web Site: http://www.anritsu.com
Sales Range: $25-49.9 Million
Emp.: 25
Electronic Testing & Measuring Instrument Mfr
N.A.I.C.S.: 334515

Anritsu Pty. Ltd (1)
Unit 20 21-35 Ricketts Road, Mount Waverley, 3149, VIC, Australia
Tel.: (61) 3 9558 8177
Web Site: http://www.anritsu.com
Sales Range: $25-49.9 Million
Emp.: 7
Electronic Measuring Equipment Mfr
N.A.I.C.S.: 334515

Anritsu Real Estate Co., Ltd. (1)
5-1-1 Onna, Atsugi, 243-0032, Kanagawa, Japan
Tel.: (81) 462966500
Real Estate Services
N.A.I.C.S.: 531390

Anritsu S.A (1)
12 avenue du Quebec Immeuble Goyave, 91140, Villebon-sur-Yvette, France
Tel.: (33) 160921550
Sales Range: $25-49.9 Million
Emp.: 13
Electronic Measuring Equipment Mfr
N.A.I.C.S.: 334515
Eric Fauxpoint (Gen Dir)

Anritsu S.r.l (1)
Spaces Eur Arte Viale dell'Arte 25, 00144, Rome, Italy
Tel.: (39) 065099711
Web Site: http://www.anritsu.com
Sales Range: $25-49.9 Million
Emp.: 15
Communication Equipment Mfr
N.A.I.C.S.: 334290

Anritsu Solutions S.r.l (1)
Via Sante Bargellini 4, 00157, Rome, Italy
Tel.: (39) 0643362400
Telecommunication Servicesb
N.A.I.C.S.: 517810

Anritsu Solutions SK, s.r.o. (1)
Karadzicova 14, 82108, Bratislava, Slovakia
Tel.: (421) 257780210
Metal Detector Mfr
N.A.I.C.S.: 334519

Azimuth Systems, Inc. (1)
43 Nagog Park Ste 205, Acton, MA 01720
Tel.: (978) 263-6610
Metal Detector Mfr
N.A.I.C.S.: 334519

Tohoku Anritsu Co., Ltd. (1)
301 Aza-Doba, Koriyama, 963-8824, Fukushima, Japan
Tel.: (81) 249562112
Electronic Measuring Instrument Mfr & Whslr
N.A.I.C.S.: 334515

ANS INDUSTRIES LIMITED
136 K M Vill & PO Shamgarh, Karnal, 132116, Haryana, India
Tel.: (91) 745244226
Web Site: https://www.ansfoods.com
Rev.: $66,143
Assets: $3,295,901
Liabilities: $1,507,332
Net Worth: $1,788,569
Earnings: ($133,699)
Emp.: 15

Fiscal Year-end: 03/31/19
Food Processing Services
N.A.I.C.S.: 311423
Mehinder Sharma (Mng Dir)

ANSA MCAL LIMITED
9th - 11th Floors TATIL Building 11 Maraval Road, Port of Spain, Trinidad & Tobago
Tel.: (868) 2355679   TT
Web Site: https://www.ansamcal.com
AMCL—(TRI)
Rev.: $1,041,550,298
Assets: $2,732,895,010
Liabilities: $1,354,747,802
Net Worth: $1,378,147,208
Earnings: $87,872,085
Emp.: 6,000
Fiscal Year-end: 12/31/23
Offices of Other Holding Companies
N.A.I.C.S.: 551112
A. Norman Sabga (Chm)

Subsidiaries:

4 Sweet Briar Limited (1)
Floors 9-11 TATIL Building 11 Maraval Road, Port of Spain, Trinidad & Tobago
Tel.: (868) 2256225
Real Estate Services
N.A.I.C.S.: 531390

6 Sweet Briar Road Limited (1)
Floors 9-11 TATIL Building 11 Maraval Road, Port of Spain, Trinidad & Tobago
Tel.: (868) 2256225
Beer Brewery Mfr
N.A.I.C.S.: 312120

ANSA Coatings Limited (1)
ANSA McAL Industrial Park 51-59 Tumpuna Road, South Guanapo, Arima, Trinidad & Tobago
Tel.: (868) 2772468
Web Site: https://www.ansacoatings.com
Paint & Coatings Mfr & Supplier
N.A.I.C.S.: 325510
Roger Roach (Mng Dir)

Subsidiary (Non-US):

Berger Paints Barbados Ltd. (2)
Exmouth Gap Brandons, Saint Michael, BB12069, Barbados   (100%)
Tel.: (246) 4259073
Web Site: https://www.bergerpaintscaribbean.com
Sales Range: $25-49.9 Million
Emp.: 50
Paint & Coating Mfr
N.A.I.C.S.: 325510
Ritesh Doshi (Mng Dir)

Berger Paints Jamaica Limited (2)
256 Spanish Town Road, Kingston, 11, Jamaica   (51%)
Tel.: (876) 6181096
Web Site: https://www.bergerpaintscaribbean.com
Paint Mfr & Distr
N.A.I.C.S.: 325510
Shashi Mahase (Gen Mgr)

Subsidiary (Domestic):

Penta Paints Caribbean Limited (2)
51-59 Tumpuna Rd S, Arima, Guanapo, Trinidad & Tobago   (100%)
Tel.: (868) 643 2425
Paint & Coating Mfr
N.A.I.C.S.: 325510
Claire Johnson (Mgr-Export)

Sissons Paints Limited (2)
ANSA McAL Industrial Park 51-59 Tumpuna Road, South Guanapo, Arima, Trinidad & Tobago
Tel.: (868) 2772468
Sales Range: $50-74.9 Million
Emp.: 100
Paint Product Mfr
N.A.I.C.S.: 325510
Roger Roach (Mng Dir)

Subsidiary (Non-US):

Sissons Paints (Grenada) Limited (3)

Frequente Industrial Park, Grand Anse, Saint George's, 473, Grenada
Tel.: (473) 4444157
Web Site: https://www.sissonspaints.com
Sales Range: $25-49.9 Million
Emp.: 30
Paint Products Mfr & Marketer
N.A.I.C.S.: 325510
Christopher De Allie (Mng Dir)

ANSA Financial Holdings (Barbados) Limited (1)
McEnearney Quality Complex, Wildey, Saint Michael, BB14007, Barbados
Tel.: (246) 4342900
Beer Brewery Mfr
N.A.I.C.S.: 312120

ANSA McAL (Barbados) Limited (1)
McEnearney Quality Complex, Wildey, BB14007, St Michael, Barbados   (70.9%)
Tel.: (246) 4342600
Holding Company
N.A.I.C.S.: 551112

Subsidiary (Domestic):

A.S. Bryden & Sons (Barbados) Ltd. (2)
Bryden Stokes Barbarees Hill, PO Box 403, Saint Michael, 12060, Barbados   (100%)
Tel.: (246) 4312600
Web Site: http://www.brydens.com
Wholesale Trade Distr
N.A.I.C.S.: 425120
Margaret A. Haynes (Gen Mgr-Food & Consumer Dept)

Subsidiary (Domestic):

Brydens Business Solutions Inc. (3)
Stokes & Bynoe Bldg Wildey Main Rd, Saint Michael, Barbados   (100%)
Tel.: (246) 430 7401
Office Equipment Sales
N.A.I.C.S.: 423420

Brydens Insurance Inc. (3)
Suite 400 3rd Floor Norman Centre, Bridgetown, BB 14012, Saint Michael, Barbados   (100%)
Tel.: (246) 431 3611
Web Site: http://www.brydensinsurance.com
Sales Range: $25-49.9 Million
Emp.: 33
Residential Property Managers
N.A.I.C.S.: 531311
Irvin Springer (Mgr-Claims)

Affiliate (Domestic):

Brydens Retail Inc. (3)
Norman Centre, Bridgetown, BB19188, Barbados   (100%)
Tel.: (246) 4312648
Stationery Whslr
N.A.I.C.S.: 424120

Brydens Xpress (Office Supplies) Inc. (3)
Lower Estate Factory Complex, BB19188, Saint Michael, BB19188, Barbados   (52%)
Tel.: (246) 4312646
Web Site: https://www.brydensxpress.com
Sales Range: $25-49.9 Million
Emp.: 20
Stationery Whslr
N.A.I.C.S.: 424120
Harry Lashley (Mng Dir)

Subsidiary (Domestic):

Consolidated Finance Company Limited (2)
Hasting Main Road Christ Church, BB15150, Bridgetown, W.I., Barbados   (100%)
Tel.: (246) 467 2350
Web Site: http://www.consolidated-finance.com
Financial Investment Activities
N.A.I.C.S.: 523999
Rolf Phillips (Pres & CEO)

McEnearney Quality, Inc. (2)
McEnearney Quality Complex, Wildey, BB14007, St Michael, Barbados
Tel.: (246) 4672400
Web Site: http://www.mqi.bb
Auto Dealership

N.A.I.C.S.: 441110
Celeste Spencer (Sec)

Trident Insurance Company Limited (2)
Trident Insurance Financial Centre Highway 7, Hastings, Christ Church, BB15154, Barbados
Tel.: (246) 2412347
Web Site: https://www.tridentins.com
Insurance Related Activities
N.A.I.C.S.: 524298
H.C. Algernon Leacock (Pres & CEO)

ANSA McAL (U.S.) Inc. (1)
11403 NW 39th St, Doral, FL 33178   (100%)
Tel.: (305) 599-8766
Web Site: https://www.ansamcal.com
Sales Range: $25-49.9 Million
Emp.: 21
Wholesale Trade Distr
N.A.I.C.S.: 425120
Wendell Beckles (Pres)

ANSA McAL Chemicals Ltd. (1)
North Sea Drive Pt Lisas Industrial estate, Savonetta, Trinidad & Tobago   (100%)
Tel.: (868) 2355560
Web Site: https://ansamcalchemicals.com
Sales Range: $25-49.9 Million
Emp.: 100
Basic Inorganic Chemical Mfr
N.A.I.C.S.: 325180
Sherrine Christopher (Mgr-Export)

ANSA McAL Enterprises Limited (1)
Lightpole 4 Depot Road, Longdenville, Chaguanas, Trinidad & Tobago
Tel.: (868) 2354227
Wine Mfr & Distr
N.A.I.C.S.: 312120
Adam Sabga (Head)

ANSA McAL Trading Inc. (1)
11403 NW 39th St, Miami, FL 33178
Tel.: (305) 599-8766
Logistic Services
N.A.I.C.S.: 541614
Mike Basanta (Sr Mgr-Operations)

ANSA McAL Trading Limited (1)
60 Beterverwagting East Coast, Demerara, Guyana   (100%)
Tel.: (592) 2200455
Web Site: https://www.ansamcalguyana.com
Sales Range: $25-49.9 Million
Emp.: 300
Wholesale Trading
N.A.I.C.S.: 425120
Troy Cadogan (Mng Dir)

ANSA Merchant Bank Limited (1)
4th Floor Tatil Building 11A Maraval Road, Port of Spain, Trinidad & Tobago   (82.48%)
Tel.: (868) 6238672
Web Site: https://www.ansabank.com
Rev.: $160,616,559
Assets: $1,173,820,385
Liabilities: $805,425,515
Net Worth: $368,394,869
Earnings: $40,327,193
Fiscal Year-end: 12/31/2019
Banking & Financial Services
N.A.I.C.S.: 522110
Anthony Norman Sabga (Chm)

ANSA Motors Limited (1)
25 Richmond Street, Port of Spain, Trinidad & Tobago
Tel.: (868) 2852277
Web Site: https://ansamotors.com
Automobile Product Distr
N.A.I.C.S.: 423110
Jerome Borde (Mng Dir)

ANSA Re Limited (1)
Meridian Place Choc Estate, Castries, Saint Lucia
Tel.: (758) 4507777
Wine Mfr & Distr
N.A.I.C.S.: 312120

ANSA Securities Limited (1)
ANSA Centre 11 Mareval Road, Port of Spain, Trinidad & Tobago
Tel.: (868) 6238672
Financial Services
N.A.I.C.S.: 523999
Gregory Hill (Mng Dir)

Alstons Building Enterprises Limited (1)
Building 2 Mingot Street, Mount Hope, Port of Spain, Trinidad & Tobago (100%)
Tel.: (868) 665 5221
Web Site: http://www.abelbestcrete.com
Sales Range: $50-74.9 Million
Emp.: 535
Steel Investment Foundries
N.A.I.C.S.: 331512

Division (Domestic):

ABEL Building Solutions (2)
Auchenskeoch Buccoo Bay Road, Scarborough, Carnbee, Trinidad & Tobago
Tel.: (868) 2355582
Web Site: https://buildwithabs.com
Air-Conditioning & Warm Air Heating Equipment & Commercial & Industrial Refrigeration Equipment Mfr
N.A.I.C.S.: 333415
Craig La Croix (Mng Dir)

Alstons Limited (1)
11th Floor Tatil Building 11 Maraval Road, Port of Spain, Trinidad & Tobago
Tel.: (868) 6253670
Wine Mfr & Distr
N.A.I.C.S.: 312120

Alstons Marketing Company Limited (1)
Uriah Butler Highway & Endeavour Road, Chaguanas, Trinidad & Tobago (100%)
Tel.: (868) 671271320
Web Site: https://www.amcott.info
Sales Range: $25-49.9 Million
Emp.: 300
Distribution & Marketing of a Wide Range of Food/Cold Chain Services, Pharmaceuticals, Wines & Spirits & Consumer Products
N.A.I.C.S.: 424410
Elizabeth Harford-Rooks (Dir-Cold Chain & Food Svc)

Alstons Shipping Limited (1)
Building 10 ANSA McAL Centre Uriah Butler Highway & Endeavour Road, PO Box 600, Chaguanas, Trinidad & Tobago (100%)
Tel.: (868) 2355643
Web Site: https://www.alstonsshippingtt.com
Navigational Services to Shipping
N.A.I.C.S.: 488330

Alstons Travel Limited (1)
67 Independence Square, Port of Spain, Trinidad & Tobago (100%)
Tel.: (868) 62522015
Sales Range: $10-24.9 Million
Emp.: 6
Traveler Accommodation
N.A.I.C.S.: 721199

Ansa Automotive Limited (1)
25 Richmond St, Port of Spain, Trinidad & Tobago (100%)
Tel.: (868) 6246632
Automotive Sales, Repair & Maintenance
N.A.I.C.S.: 811198

Ansa Coatings Jamaica Limited (1)
256 Spanish Town Road, Kingston, Jamaica
Tel.: (876) 923 6229
Chemical Products Distr
N.A.I.C.S.: 424690

Ansa Motors Guyana Inc. (1)
64 Beterverwagting Industrial Site, Demerara, Guyana
Tel.: (592) 2200930
Web Site: https://ansamotorsguyana.com
Automotive Products Mfr
N.A.I.C.S.: 336390
Adrian Singh (Mng Dir)

Ansa Polymer (1)
Ansa McAl Industrial Park Tumpuna Road South Guanapo, Arima, Trinidad & Tobago (100%)
Tel.: (868) 6433137
Web Site: https://www.ansapolymer.com
Unsupported Plastics Bag Mfr
N.A.I.C.S.: 326111
Ian Mitchell (Mng Dir)

Ansa Technologies Limited (1)
1st Floor GML Bld ANSA Center 4-10 Rodney Road, PO Box 10, Chaguanas, Trinidad & Tobago (100%)

Tel.: (868) 2828453
Web Site: https://www.ansatech.com
Sales Range: $25-49.9 Million
Emp.: 75
Oil & Gas Field Machinery & Equipment Mfr
N.A.I.C.S.: 333132
Lisa Ibrahim (CFO)

Bayside West Limited (1)
9th Floor Tatil Building 11 Maraval Road, Port of Spain, Trinidad & Tobago
Tel.: (868) 2232672
Real Estate Services
N.A.I.C.S.: 531390

Bestcrete Aggregates Limited (1)
LP 4 Depot Road, Longdenville, Chaguanas, Trinidad & Tobago
Tel.: (868) 2354227
Construction Materials Mfr
N.A.I.C.S.: 327120

Bryden Stokes Limited (1)
Barbarees Hill, Saint Michael, BB12060, Barbados
Tel.: (246) 4312600
Web Site: https://www.brydenstokes.com
Emp.: 330
Wine Distr
N.A.I.C.S.: 424820
Adrian Padmore (Mng Dir)

Burmac Machinery Ltd. (1)
25 Royal Rd, San Fernando, Trinidad & Tobago (100%)
Tel.: (868) 6572277
Web Site: http://www.ansamcal.com
Emp.: 25
Agricultural, Industrial & Construction Equipment Supplier
N.A.I.C.S.: 423440
Derek Innis (Gen Mgr)

Carib Brewery Limited (1)
Eastern Main Road, Champs Fleurs, Trinidad & Tobago (80%)
Tel.: (868) 6452337
Web Site: https://www.caribbrewery.com
Sales Range: $150-199.9 Million
Emp.: 900
Malt Mfr
N.A.I.C.S.: 311213
Gabriel Faria (Mng Dir)

Carib Glassworks Limited (1)
Eastern Main Rd, Champs Fleurs, Trinidad & Tobago (100%)
Tel.: (868) 6622231
Glass Packaging Producer
N.A.I.C.S.: 327213
Roger Mew (Mng Dir)

Caribbean Development Company (St.Kitts) Limited (1)
Buckley's Site, PO Box 1113, Basseterre, Saint Kitts & Nevis
Tel.: (869) 465 2309
Beer Brewery Mfr
N.A.I.C.S.: 312120

Caribbean Development Company Limited (1)
Eastern Main Rd, Champs Fleurs, Trinidad & Tobago (80%)
Tel.: (868) 6452337
Breweries
N.A.I.C.S.: 312120
Ian MacDonald (CEO)

Caribbean Roof Tile Company Limited (1)
C/o ABS ANSA Centre 1st Floor Guardian Media Ltd Building, Uriah Butler Highway & Endeavour Road, Chaguanas, Trinidad & Tobago (50%)
Tel.: (868) 2354227
Web Site: https://www.ansamcal.com
Piece Goods Notions & Dry Goods Whslr
N.A.I.C.S.: 424310

Carmax Limited (1)
Uriah Butler and Churchill Roosevelt Highway, Valsayn, Trinidad & Tobago (100%)
Tel.: (868) 6633635
Web Site: http://www.carmaxtt.com
Automobile Mfr
N.A.I.C.S.: 336110

Classic Motors Ltd (1)
Cor Richmond & Charles Streets, Port of

Spain, Trinidad & Tobago (100%)
Tel.: (868) 627 3714
Automobile Mfr
N.A.I.C.S.: 336110

Concretion Limited (1)
11th Floor TATIL Building 11 Maraval Road, Port of Spain, Trinidad & Tobago
Tel.: (868) 6253670
Real Estate Services
N.A.I.C.S.: 531390

DCI Miami, Inc. (1)
11403 NW 39th St, Doral, FL 33178 (100%)
Tel.: (305) 591-0885
Web Site: http://www.caribbeer.com
Sales Range: $50-74.9 Million
Emp.: 3
Beer & Ale Whslr
N.A.I.C.S.: 424810

Easi Industrial Supplies Limited (1)
North Sea Drive, Savonetta, Trinidad & Tobago
Tel.: (868) 636 3111
Liquid Sodium Hydroxide Distr
N.A.I.C.S.: 424690
Shivanand Maharaj (Mng Dir)

Grand Bazaar Ltd. (1)
The City of Grand Bazaar Churchill Roosevelt, Uriah Butler Highways, Port of Spain, Valsayn, Trinidad & Tobago (100%)
Tel.: (868) 662 2282
Sales Range: $50-74.9 Million
Emp.: 25
Real Estate Property Lessors
N.A.I.C.S.: 531190

Grenada Breweries Limited (1)
Grand Anse, PO Box 202, Saint George's, Grenada (55.54%)
Tel.: (473) 444 4248
Sales Range: $25-49.9 Million
Emp.: 140
Breweries
N.A.I.C.S.: 312120
Ron Antoine (Mng Dir)

Guardian Media Limited (1)
22-24 St Vincent Street, Port of Spain, Trinidad & Tobago
Tel.: (868) 2254465
Web Site: https://guardianmedia.co.tt
Television Broadcasting Services
N.A.I.C.S.: 516120
Brandon Khan (Mng Dir)

Indian River Beverage Corporation (1)
200 Imperial Blvd, Cape Canaveral, FL 32920
Tel.: (321) 728-4114
Web Site: https://www.floridabeer.com
Beer Brewery Mfr
N.A.I.C.S.: 312120
James Webb (Pres & CEO)

Iradio Inc. (1)
28 Garnett and Delph Avenue, Campbellville, Georgetown, Guyana
Tel.: (592) 2272826
Radio Broadcasting Services
N.A.I.C.S.: 334220

McEnearney Business Machines Limited (1)
34 Richmond Street, PO Box 1237, Port of Spain, Trinidad & Tobago (100%)
Tel.: (868) 625 1041
Web Site: https://www.ansamcal.com
Sales Range: $25-49.9 Million
Emp.: 90
Industrial Machinery Mfr
N.A.I.C.S.: 333248

McEnearney Motors Limited (1)
25 Richmond St, Port of Spain, Trinidad & Tobago (100%)
Tel.: (868) 627 367
Web Site: http://www.fordtrinidad.com
Automobile Mfr
N.A.I.C.S.: 336110
Jerome Borde (Mng Dir)

O'Meara Holdings Limited (1)
11th Floor Tatil Building 11 Maraval Road, Port of Spain, Trinidad & Tobago
Tel.: (868) 2232672
Real Estate Services

N.A.I.C.S.: 531390

Standard Distributors & Sales Barbados Limited (1)
Tudor Street, Bridgetown, Barbados
Tel.: (246) 430 7000
Furniture Equipment Retail Services
N.A.I.C.S.: 532420
Katrina Newton (CEO)

Standard Distributors Limited (1)
ANSA McAL Centre Endeavour Road, Chaguanas, Trinidad & Tobago
Tel.: (868) 2990219
Web Site: https://www.standardtt.com
Furniture Equipment Retail Services
N.A.I.C.S.: 532420
Ronald Milford (Mng Dir)

T/Wee Limited (1)
Golden Grove Rd, Piarco, Trinidad & Tobago
Tel.: (868) 369 5038
Wine Distr
N.A.I.C.S.: 424820
Abdel Ali (Mng Dir)

Tatil Life Assurance Limited (1)
11A Maraval Road, Port of Spain, Trinidad & Tobago
Tel.: (868) 6282845
Web Site: https://tatil.co.tt
Fire Insurance Services
N.A.I.C.S.: 524113
M. Musa Ibrahim (Mng Dir)

Tobago Marketing Company Limited (1)
Highmoor Plymouth Road, PO Box 182, Scarborough, 900313, Trinidad & Tobago
Tel.: (868) 6392455
Wine Distr
N.A.I.C.S.: 424820
David Lum Kong (Gen Mgr)

Trinidad & Tobago Insurance Limited (1)
Tatil Building 11A Maraval Road, Port of Spain, Trinidad & Tobago (100%)
Tel.: (868) 6282845
Insurance Related Activities
N.A.I.C.S.: 524298
Ray A. Sumairsingh (Chm)

Trinidad Match Limited (1)
Corner Gordon & Maingot St, Mt Hope, Port of Spain, Trinidad & Tobago (100%)
Tel.: (868) 6381974
Sales Range: $50-74.9 Million
Emp.: 30
Holding Company: Safety Matches
N.A.I.C.S.: 551112
Robert Mohammed (Mng Dir)

Trinidad Publishing Company Limited (1)
Guardian Building 22-24 St Vincent Street, Port of Spain, Trinidad & Tobago (100%)
Tel.: (868) 6238871
Newspaper Publishers
N.A.I.C.S.: 513110
Gabriel Faria (Mng Dir)

ANSAL BUILDWELL LTD
118 UFF Prakash Deep Building 7 Tolstoy Marg Connaught Place, New Delhi, 110 001, India
Tel.: (91) 1123353051
Web Site: https://ansalabl.com
523007—(BOM)
Rev.: $4,860,410
Assets: $64,804,331
Liabilities: $49,939,822
Net Worth: $14,864,509
Earnings: ($384,916)
Emp.: 2,000
Fiscal Year-end: 03/31/23
Real Estate Development Services
N.A.I.C.S.: 531210
Ashok Babu (Sec & Sr VP)

ANSAL HOUSING LTD
606 6th Floor Indra Prakash 21 Barakhamba Road, New Delhi, 110 001, India
Tel.: (91) 1123317466

Ansal Housing Ltd—(Continued)

Web Site: https://www.ansals.com
ANSALHSG—(NSE)
Rev.: $34,035,620
Assets: $324,377,863
Liabilities: $301,788,123
Net Worth: $22,589,740
Earnings: ($3,185,309)
Emp.: 207
Fiscal Year-end: 03/31/22
Property Development Services
N.A.I.C.S.: 236117
Sabu Thomas (*VP-HR & Admin*)

Subsidiaries:

ANSAL CLUBS PVT. LIMITED　　　(1)
Indra Prakash Building 606 6th Floor 21
Barakhamba Road, New Delhi, 110 001,
India
Tel.: (91) 1123317466
Web Site: http://www.ansals.com
Sales Range: $25-49.9 Million
Emp.: 30
Real Estate Agencies
N.A.I.C.S.: 531210

ANSAL PROPERTIES & IN-FRASTRUCTURE LIMITED
115 Ansal Bhawan 16 Kasturba Gandhi Marg, New Delhi, 110 001, India
Tel.: (91) 1123353550
Web Site: https://www.ansalapi.com
500013—(BOM)
Rev.: $110,212,680
Assets: $958,769,148
Liabilities: $993,054,494
Net Worth: ($34,285,347)
Earnings: ($14,405,882)
Emp.: 249
Fiscal Year-end: 03/31/22
Real Estate Services
N.A.I.C.S.: 237210
Sushil Ansal (*Chm*)

Subsidiaries:

Ansal IT City & Parks Ltd.　　　(1)
115 Ansal Bhawan 16 Kasturba Gandhi
Marg, New Delhi, 110 001, India
Tel.: (91) 1123353550
Commercial Building Construction Services
N.A.I.C.S.: 236220

ANSAR FINANCIAL AND DE-VELOPMENT CORPORATION
1825 Markham Road Suite 209,
Scarborough, M1B 4Z9, ON, Canada
Tel.: (416) 646-1271　　　　　　ON
Web Site:
　https://www.ansarfinancial.com
ACDX—(CNSX)
Rev.: $42,054
Assets: $12,051,788
Liabilities: $24,007
Net Worth: $12,027,782
Earnings: ($48,340)
Fiscal Year-end: 03/31/24
Real Estate Financial & Development
Services
N.A.I.C.S.: 525990
Pervez Nasim (*Chm & CEO*)

ANSARADA GROUP LIMITED
Level 2 80 George Street, The
Rocks, Sydney, 2000, NSW, Australia
Tel.: (61) 282410888　　　　　　AU
Web Site: https://www.ansarada.com
Year Founded: 2005
AND—(ASX)
Rev.: $33,754,320
Assets: $51,539,414
Liabilities: $21,572,015
Net Worth: $29,967,399
Earnings: ($3,290,083)
Emp.: 178
Fiscal Year-end: 06/30/23
Software Development Services
N.A.I.C.S.: 541511

Stuart Clout (*Chief Revenue Officer*)

Subsidiaries:

Ansarada Hong Kong Limited　　(1)
Lung Wo Rd, Central, Hong Kong, China
(Hong Kong)
Tel.: (852) 58080965
Software Development Services
N.A.I.C.S.: 541511

Ansarada Pte. Limited　　　　　(1)
168 Robinson Road12-01 Capital Tower,
Singapore, 068912, Singapore
Tel.: (65) 31636047
Software Development Services
N.A.I.C.S.: 541511

Ansarada UK Limited　　　　　(1)
34-37 Liverpool St, London, EC2M 7PP,
United Kingdom
Tel.: (44) 2030581060
Software Development Services
N.A.I.C.S.: 541511

ANSARI SUGAR MILLS LIM-ITED
1s floor Block-2 Hockey Club of Pakistan Stadium, Karachi, Pakistan
Tel.: (92) 297870011　　　　　PK
Web Site:
　https://www.ansarisugar.com.pk
Year Founded: 1989
ANSM—(PSX)
Rev.: $4,207,348
Assets: $40,196,837
Liabilities: $35,490,822
Net Worth: $4,706,015
Earnings: ($1,269,848)
Fiscal Year-end: 09/30/22
Sugar Mfr
N.A.I.C.S.: 311314
Aurangzeb Khan (*Chm*)

ANSELL LIMITED
678 Victoria St, Richmond, 3121,
VIC, Australia
Tel.: (61) 392707270　　　　　AU
Web Site: https://www.ansell.com
Year Founded: 1889
ANSLF—(OTCIQ)
Rev.: $1,952,100,000
Assets: $2,506,200,000
Liabilities: $949,600,000
Net Worth: $1,556,600,000
Earnings: $159,800,000
Emp.: 14,000
Fiscal Year-end: 06/30/22
Automotive & Industrial Products Mfr
N.A.I.C.S.: 313320
Magnus R. Nicolin (*CEO & Mng Dir*)

Subsidiaries:

Accufix Research Institute Inc.　(1)
17011 Lincoln Ave, Parker, CO 80134-8815
Tel.: (303) 754-0051
Web Site: http://www.accufix.com
Health Care Srvices
N.A.I.C.S.: 621610

Ansell (Hong Kong) Limited　　(1)
33 Wang Chiu Road Kowloon Bay, 2610B-12A 26/F Exchange Tower, Kowloon, 8523,
China (Hong Kong)　　　　　　(100%)
Tel.: (852) 2185 0600
Web Site: http://www.ansell.com
Rubber Products Mfr
N.A.I.C.S.: 326299

Ansell Canada Inc.　　　　　　(1)
105 Lauder, Cowansville, J2K 2K8, QC,
Canada
Industrial & Medical Gloves Mfr
N.A.I.C.S.: 339113

Ansell Commercial Mexico S.A. de
C.V.　　　　　　　　　　　　(1)
Blvd Bernardo Quintana 7001-C Q7001
Torre 2, Suites 1304-1306 Centro Sur,
76090, Queretaro, Mexico
Tel.: (52) 4422962050
Industrial & Medical Gloves Mfr
N.A.I.C.S.: 334519

Ansell Healthcare Europe N.V.　(1)
Riverside Business Park Block J, Boulevard
International 55, 1070, Brussels, Belgium
Tel.: (32) 25287400
Web Site: http://www.anselleu.com
Rubber Products Mfr
N.A.I.C.S.: 326299

Subsidiary (Non-US):

Ansell Protective Solutions AB　(2)
Arenagatan 8B, 215 33, Malmo,
Sweden　　　　　　　　　　　(100%)
Tel.: (46) 25287418
Web Site: http://protective.ansell.com
Sales Range: $25-49.9 Million
Emp.: 170
Protective Clothing & Related Products Mfr
& Whslr
N.A.I.C.S.: 339999
Magnus Andersson (*Mng Dir*)

Subsidiary (Non-US):

Ansell Norway AS　　　　　　(3)
Prof Birkelands vej 36 D, PO Box 58,
Leirdal, 1008, Oslo, Norway　　(100%)
Tel.: (47) 22904900
Web Site: http://protective.ansell.com
Sales Range: $1-9.9 Million
Emp.: 20
Protective Clothing & Related Products
Whslr
N.A.I.C.S.: 424350

Ansell Healthcare Japan Co. Ltd.　(1)
3-4-31 Roppongi, Minato-Ku, Tokyo, 106-0032, Japan
Tel.: (81) 355498171
Industrial & Medical Gloves Mfr
N.A.I.C.S.: 339113

Ansell Healthcare LLC　　　　(1)
111 Wood Ave S Ste 210, Iselin, NJ 08830
Tel.: (732) 345-5400
Web Site: http://www.ansellpro.com
Mfr of Healthcare Products
N.A.I.C.S.: 326299

Subsidiary (Domestic):

Ansell Sandel Medical Solutions
LLC　　　　　　　　　　　　(2)
9301 Oakdale Ave Ste 300, Chatsworth, CA
91311
Tel.: (818) 534-2500
Web Site: http://www.sandelmedical.com
Sales Range: $25-49.9 Million
Emp.: 32
Surgical Appliance & Supplies Mfr
N.A.I.C.S.: 339113
Wendell Franke (*Assoc Dir-Global Trng, Innovation & Surgical Supplies*)

Ansell International　　　　　(1)
678 Victoria St Level 3, Richmond, 3121,
VIC, Australia　　　　　　　　(100%)
Tel.: (61) 3 9270 7270
Web Site: http://www.ansell.com
Sales Range: $1-4.9 Billion
Emp.: 5,105
Mfr, Marketing & Distribution of Latex Products, Medical, Household & Industrial
Gloves & Condoms
N.A.I.C.S.: 315990

BarrierSafe Solutions International
Inc.　　　　　　　　　　　　(1)
540 Lake Cook Rd Ste 150, Deerfield, IL
60015
Tel.: (866) 931-3613
Web Site: http://www.barriersafe.com
Sales Range: $250-299.9 Million
Emp.: 25
Disposable Protective Glove Mfr
N.A.I.C.S.: 339113

Subsidiary (Domestic):

ONGUARD Industries LLC　　(2)
1850 Clark Rd, Havre De Grace, MD 21078
Tel.: (410) 272-2000
Web Site: http://www.onguardindustries.com
Sales Range: $50-74.9 Million
Emp.: 125
Protective Footwear & Apparel Mfr & Distr
N.A.I.C.S.: 316210

Careplus (M) Sdn Bhd　　　　(1)
Lot 120 And 121 Jalan Senawang 3,

Senawang Industrial Estate, 70450, Seremban, Negeri Sembilan, Malaysia　(100%)
Tel.: (60) 67292120
Web Site: http://www.careplus.com.my
Sales Range: $50-74.9 Million
Emp.: 20
Gloves Mfr & Whslr
N.A.I.C.S.: 339113

Comasec SAS　　　　　　　　(1)
5 Allee des Bas Tilliers, 92238, Gennevilliers, France
Tel.: (33) 1 47 92 92 92
Web Site: http://www.comasec.com
Sales Range: $25-49.9 Million
Emp.: 1,200
Industrial Gloves Mfr
N.A.I.C.S.: 315990

Subsidiary (Non-US):

Comasec Italia Srl　　　　　　(2)
Via Torricelli 2, 20090, Buccinasco, Milan,
Italy
Tel.: (39) 02 45707516
Web Site: http://www.comasec.com
Industrial Gloves Distr
N.A.I.C.S.: 423440

Marigold Industrial Gloves Iberia
S.L.　　　　　　　　　　　　(2)
Paseo de la Habana 4-1-1, 28036, Madrid,
Spain
Tel.: (34) 91 561 42 00
Web Site: http://www.comasec.com
Industrial Gloves Distr
N.A.I.C.S.: 423440

Marigold Industrial GmbH　　(2)
Samannstrasse 2-4, 66538, Neunkirchen,
Germany
Tel.: (49) 6821 8608 0
Web Site: http://www.comasec.com
Sales Range: $25-49.9 Million
Emp.: 27
Industrial Gloves Distr
N.A.I.C.S.: 423440

Marigold Industrial Sdn. Bhd.　(2)
Kulim Industrial Est, Kedah, 9000, Kulim,
Malaysia　　　　　　　　　　(100%)
Tel.: (60) 44891973
Web Site: http://www.ansell.com
Emp.: 900
Industrial & Household Gloves Mfr
N.A.I.C.S.: 315990

Subsidiary (US):

Marigold Industrial USA Inc.　(2)
141 Old Mill Rd, Greenville, SC 29607
Tel.: (866) 343-7025
Industrial Gloves Distr
N.A.I.C.S.: 423440

Cotac Corporation　　　　　　(1)
9938 Chemical Rd, Pasadena, TX 77507
Tel.: (281) 727-3720
Equipment Cleaning Services
N.A.I.C.S.: 561720

Hercules Equipamentos de Protecao
Ltda.　　　　　　　　　　　(1)
Av Robert Kennedy 675, Bairro Planalto,
Sao Bernardo do Campo, 09895-003, Brazil
Tel.: (55) 1133563100
Web Site: http://www.hercules.com.br
Technical Support & Maintenance Services
N.A.I.C.S.: 561990

Nitritex (M) Sdn. Bhd.　　　　(1)
2 Jalan Jurunilai U1/20 Seksyen U1, Hicom
Glenmarie Industrial Park, 40150, Shah
Alam, Selangor, Malaysia
Tel.: (60) 355693857
Clean Room Consumable & PPE Mfr
N.A.I.C.S.: 339113
Stephen Morgan (*Gen Mgr-Mfg & Sr Dir-Sls & Life Sciences Solutions-APAC*)

Nitritex Limited　　　　　　　(1)
Ground Floor 15 Kings Court Willie Snaith
Road, Newmarket, CB8 7SG, Suffolk,
United Kingdom
Tel.: (44) 1638663338
Web Site: http://www.nitritex.com
Clean Room Consumable & PPE Mfr
N.A.I.C.S.: 339113
Frank Tamburello (*Acct Mgr-Natl*)

Valeo Technologies LLC　　　(1)

8846 N Sam Houston Pkwy W Ste 110,
Houston, TX 77064
Web Site: http://www.valeosafety.com
Automobile Product Distr
N.A.I.C.S.: 423120

ANSHAN HIFICHEM CO., LTD.
No 8 1st Bao An Road TengAo Indus-
trial Park, Anshan, 114225, Liaoning,
China
Tel.: (86) 4128386888
Web Site: https://www.hifichem.com
Year Founded: 2006
300758—(CHIN)
Rev.: $171,530,299
Assets: $483,503,866
Liabilities: $235,556,793
Net Worth: $247,947,072
Earnings: $1,549,702
Fiscal Year-end: 12/31/23
Chemical Products Mfr
N.A.I.C.S.: 325998
Huixiang Xu *(Chm & Gen Mgr)*

**ANSHAN IRON & STEEL
GROUP CORPORATION**
396 Nan Zhong Hua Lu, Tie Dong
District, Anshan, China
Tel.: (86) 4126723090
Web Site:
  http://www.ansteelgroup.com
Sales Range: Less than $1 Million
Steel Producer
N.A.I.C.S.: 331110
Zhang Xiaogang *(Chm)*

Subsidiaries:

Angang Group Hong Kong Co.
Ltd.   **(1)**
Room 3412-13 Convention Plaza Office
Tower 1 Harbour Road, Wanchai, Hong
Kong, China (Hong Kong)
Tel.: (852) 28028318
Sales Range: $500-549.9 Million
Emp.: 55
Steel Distr & Retailer
N.A.I.C.S.: 213114

Subsidiary (Non-US):

Gindalbie Metals Ltd   **(2)**
6 Altona Street, West Perth, 6059, WA,
Australia   **(100%)**
Tel.: (61) 8 9480 8700
Web Site: http://www.gindalbie.com.au
Rev.: $696,978
Assets: $30,236,963
Liabilities: $1,395,516
Net Worth: $28,841,447
Earnings: ($1,066,149)
Emp.: 100
Fiscal Year-end: 06/30/2018
Iron Ore Developer
N.A.I.C.S.: 212210
Chris Stevens *(CEO)*

Subsidiary (Domestic):

Karara Mining Ltd.   **(3)**
Level 8 London House 216 St Georges Tce,
Perth, 6000, WA, Australia
Tel.: (61) 8 6298 1888
Web Site: http://www.kararamining.com.au
Sales Range: $50-74.9 Million
Emp.: 80
Iron Ore Mining Services
N.A.I.C.S.: 212210
Christopher Gerrard *(Gen Counsel & Sec)*

Angang Steel Company Ltd.   **(1)**
Production Area of Angang Steel, Tiexi Dis-
trict, Anshan, 114021, Liaoning, China
Tel.: (86) 4126734878
Web Site: http://www.ansteel.com.cn
Rev.: $15,459,348,630
Assets: $13,489,527,660
Liabilities: $5,237,943,480
Net Worth: $8,251,584,180
Emp.: 31,512
Fiscal Year-end: 12/31/2020
Steel Products Mfr & Distr
N.A.I.C.S.: 332111

Benxi Iron & Steel Group Co.
Ltd.   **(1)**
16 Renmin Road Pingshan Area, Benxi,
117000, Liaoning, China
Tel.: (86) 414 2843 889
Web Site: http://www.bxsteel.com
Steel Producer
N.A.I.C.S.: 331513
Tianchen Yu *(Chm)*

Sun Life Everbright Life Insurance
Company Limited   **(1)**
4th Floor Tianjin International Building 75
Nanjing Road, Heping District, Tianjin,
300050, China   **(12.5%)**
Tel.: (86) 22 2339 1188
Web Site: http://www.sunlife-everbright.com
Life Insurance Products & Services
N.A.I.C.S.: 524113

**ANSHAN SENYUAN ROAD &
BRIDGE CO., LTD.**
No 281 Anqian Road, Anshan,
114051, Liaoning, China
Tel.: (86) 4125223068
Web Site: http://www.assyrb.com
Year Founded: 2004
300210—(CHIN)
Rev.: $28,634,580
Assets: $167,119,524
Liabilities: $87,106,968
Net Worth: $80,012,556
Earnings: ($34,376,940)
Emp.: 118
Fiscal Year-end: 12/31/22
Road & Bridge Vehicle & Construc-
tion Machinery Mfr
N.A.I.C.S.: 336120
Li Gang *(Chm)*

**ANSHIN GUARANTOR SER-
VICE CO., LTD.**
9th Floor Shinagawa Seaside Park
Tower 4-12-4 Higashi Shinagawa,
Shinagawa-ku, Tokyo, 140-0002, Ja-
pan
Tel.: (81) 366270440
Web Site: https://anshin-gs.co.jp
Year Founded: 2002
7183—(TKS)
Sales Range: Less than $1 Million
Real Estate Lease Guarantee Service
N.A.I.C.S.: 531190
Masaru Amesaka *(Chm, Pres &
Dir-Rep)*

**ANSHUNI COMMERCIALS LIM-
ITED**
CC-5041-5042 Tower-C Bharat Dia-
mond Bourse, Bandra Kurla Complex
Bandra E, Mumbai, 400 051, India
Tel.: (91) 23631334
Web Site: http://www.anshuni.com
512091—(BOM)
Rev.: $170,469
Assets: $284,014
Liabilities: $607
Net Worth: $283,406
Earnings: $6,810
Emp.: 2
Fiscal Year-end: 03/31/21
Diamond Whslr
N.A.I.C.S.: 423940
Nitin Kalidas Mehta *(Mng Dir)*

ANSON ADVISORS INC
155 University Avenue Suite 207, To-
ronto, M5H 3B7, ON, Canada
Tel.: (416) 447-8874
Web Site: https://ansonfunds.com
Year Founded: 2003
Privately Held Alternative Asset Man-
agement
N.A.I.C.S.: 523999
Moez Kassam *(Chief Investment
Officer)*

ANSON RESOURCES LIMITED

Level 3 10 Eagle Street, Brisbane,
4000, QLD, Australia
Tel.: (61) 731327990
Web Site:
  https://www.ansonresources.com
Year Founded: 2009
ANSNF—(OTCQB)
Rev.: $465,373
Assets: $36,456,948
Liabilities: $3,297,579
Net Worth: $33,159,369
Earnings: ($6,568,488)
Emp.: 8
Fiscal Year-end: 06/30/24
Mineral Mining Services
N.A.I.C.S.: 212290
Bruce Andrew Richardson *(Chm &
CEO)*

ANSWEAR.COM SA
Aleja Pokoju 18, 31-564, Krakow,
Poland
Tel.: (48) 123800791
Web Site: https://www.answear.com
Year Founded: 2011
ANR—(WAR)
Rev.: $232,751,656
Assets: $138,189,280
Liabilities: $98,232,322
Net Worth: $39,956,957
Earnings: $6,186,234
Fiscal Year-end: 03/29/23
Online Shopping Services
N.A.I.C.S.: 425120
Krzysztof Bajolek *(Pres)*

**ANSWER TECHNOLOGY CO.,
LTD.**
21F No 75 Sec 1 Xintai 5th Rd, Xizhi
Dist, New Taipei City, 221, Taiwan
Tel.: (886) 226982526
Web Site: https://macnica.com
Year Founded: 2000
3528—(TAI)
Rev.: $205,904,633
Assets: $208,228,286
Liabilities: $149,063,535
Net Worth: $59,164,751
Earnings: $3,591,648
Emp.: 4,768
Fiscal Year-end: 12/31/23
Integrated Circuit Mfr & Distr
N.A.I.C.S.: 334413

ANT NEURO B.V.
Welbergweg 74, 7556 PE, Hengelo,
Netherlands
Tel.: (31) 850498175
Web Site: http://www.ant-neuro.com
Year Founded: 1997
Surgical & Medical Instrument Mfr
N.A.I.C.S.: 339112
Martijn Schreuder *(COO)*

Subsidiaries:

ANT Asia Co., Ltd.   **(1)**
Units 1605-06 Podium Plaza 5 Hanoi Road,
Tsim Sha Tsui, Kowloon, China (Hong
Kong)
Tel.: (852) 36763090
Web Site: http://www.ant-ap.com
Medical Equipment Distr
N.A.I.C.S.: 423450
Wilson Chan *(CEO)*

ANT North America, Inc.   **(1)**
1617 John F Kennedy Blvd Ste 821, Phila-
delphia, PA 19103
Tel.: (608) 204-0878
Web Site: http://www.ant-neuro.com
Emp.: 2
Medical, Dental & Hospital Equipment &
Supplies Merchant Whslr
N.A.I.C.S.: 423450
K. C. Chelette *(CEO)*

**ANT PRECISION INDUSTRY
CO., LTD.**
5F No 301 Sec 2 Tiding Blvd, Neihu

Dist, Taipei, 11493, Taiwan
Tel.: (886) 287510777
Web Site: https://www.ant-
  precision.com.tw
Year Founded: 1999
3646—(TPE)
Rev.: $25,955,195
Assets: $30,254,479
Liabilities: $12,811,619
Net Worth: $17,442,860
Earnings: $2,806,835
Fiscal Year-end: 12/31/22
Electronic Connector Mfr
N.A.I.C.S.: 334417
Ming-Jen Chen *(Chm & Pres)*

**ANTA SPORTS PRODUCTS
LIMITED**
16/F Manhattan Place 23 Wang Tai
Road, Kowloon Bay, Kowloon, China
(Hong Kong)
Tel.: (852) 21161660
Web Site: https://ir.anta.com
Year Founded: 1991
ANPDF—(OTCIQ)
Rev.: $7,428,417,147
Assets: $9,580,610,323
Liabilities: $4,341,493,132
Net Worth: $5,239,117,191
Earnings: $1,141,587,284
Emp.: 59,000
Fiscal Year-end: 12/31/22
Apparel Product Mfr
N.A.I.C.S.: 315990
Jie Zheng *(Exec Dir)*

Subsidiaries:

ANTA Netherlands B.V.   **(1)**
Chr Huygensstraat 30, 3281 ND, Nu-
mansdorp, Netherlands
Tel.: (31) 782046005
Web Site: https://antabv.com
Shipping Services
N.A.I.C.S.: 488330

Amer Sports Corporation   **(1)**
Konepajankuja 6, PO Box 1000, 00511,
Helsinki, Finland
Tel.: (358) 207122500
Web Site: http://www.amersports.com
Sporting Goods Mfr & Marketer
N.A.I.C.S.: 339920
Michael Schineis *(Pres-Winter Sports
Equipment & Member-Exec Bd)*

Subsidiary (Domestic):

Amer Sport Oy   **(2)**
Valimotie 7, 1510, Vantaa, Finland **(100%)**
Tel.: (358) 987587400
Web Site: http://www.amersport.fi
Sales Range: $25-49.9 Million
Emp.: 20
N.A.I.C.S.: 339920

Subsidiary (Non-US):

Amer Sports Asia Services
Limited   **(2)**
Rm 1115 11/F World Commerce Ctr 11
Canton Rd, Tsim Sha Tsui, Kowloon, China
(Hong Kong)
Tel.: (852) 21955100
Sporting Goods Distr
N.A.I.C.S.: 423910

Amer Sports Austria GMBH   **(2)**
Lackengasse 301, 5541, Altenmarkt, Austria
Tel.: (43) 6452 3900 0
Emp.: 50
Sporting Goods Distr
N.A.I.C.S.: 423910

Amer Sports Canada, Inc.   **(2)**
85 Davy Road, PO Box 909, Belleville, K8N
5B6, ON, Canada
Tel.: (613) 966-9220
Web Site: http://www.amercanada.com
Sales Range: $50-74.9 Million
Emp.: 80
Sporting Goods Distr
N.A.I.C.S.: 423910
Paul McKeown *(VP-Fin & Ops)*

Amer Sports China   **(2)**

ANTA Sports Products Limited—(Continued)

3Fl Bldg 2 759 Yang Gao Road, Pudong
New Area, 200127, Shanghai, China
Tel.: (86) 2151165288
Emp.: 250
Sporting Goods Distr
N.A.I.C.S.: 423910
Lucas Xie (Mgr-Mktg)

Subsidiary (US):

Amer Sports Company　　　　　(2)
1 Prudential Plz 130 E Randolph St Ste
600, Chicago, IL 60601
Tel.: (773) 714-6400
Web Site: http://www.wilson.com
Emp.: 200
Sporting Goods Mfr
N.A.I.C.S.: 339920
Andrew E. Page (CFO)

Subsidiary (Domestic):

Amer Sports Winter & Outdoor
Company　　　　　　　　　　(3)
2030 Lincoln Ave, Ogden, UT 84401
Tel.: (801) 624-7500
Web Site: http://www.amersports.com
Sales Range: $50-74.9 Million
Emp.: 120
Sporting Goods Mfr & Distr
N.A.I.C.S.: 339920

ClubCom Holding Company, Inc.　(3)
1209 N Orange St, Wilmington, DE 19801
Tel.: (302) 658-7581
Investment Management Service
N.A.I.C.S.: 523999

Subsidiary (Non-US):

Amer Sports Czech Republic
s.r.o.　　　　　　　　　　　　(2)
V Chotejne 7/700, Prague, 10200, Czech
Republic
Tel.: (420) 272 700 963
Web Site: http://www.amersports.cz
Sporting Goods Distr
N.A.I.C.S.: 423910
Maciej Kruczek (Country Mgr)

Amer Sports Deutschland GmbH　(2)
Parkring 15, 85748, Garching,
Germany　　　　　　　　　　(100%)
Tel.: (49) 898980102
Web Site: http://www.wilson.com
Sales Range: $50-74.9 Million
Emp.: 115
Sporting Goods Distr
N.A.I.C.S.: 339920

Amer Sports Estonia　　　　　(2)
Herne 28, 10135, Tallinn, Estonia
Tel.: (372) 64 59737
Web Site: http://www.amersports.com
Sporting Goods Distr
N.A.I.C.S.: 423910

Amer Sports Europe GmbH　　(2)
Parkring 15, 85748, Garching, Germany
Tel.: (49) 898980101
Sporting Goods Distr
N.A.I.C.S.: 423910

Subsidiary (Domestic):

Amer Sports Europe Services
GmbH　　　　　　　　　　　(3)
Im Hasfeld 2, Uberherrn, 66802, Germany
Tel.: (49) 68369190328
Web Site: http://www.amersports.com
Sales Range: $50-74.9 Million
Emp.: 110
Sporting Goods Distr
N.A.I.C.S.: 423910

Subsidiary (Non-US):

Amer Sports European Center
AG　　　　　　　　　　　　　(2)
Bachtalen 33, 6332, Cham, Switzerland
Tel.: (41) 417841212
Sales Range: $50-74.9 Million
Emp.: 80
Sporting Goods Distr
N.A.I.C.S.: 423910
Andreas Balz (Gen Mgr)

Subsidiary (Domestic):

Amer Sports Finance Oy　　　(2)

Makelankatu 91, 610, Helsinki, Finland
Tel.: (358) 9 875870
Financial Management Services
N.A.I.C.S.: 523999
Mikko Moilanen (Gen Mgr)

Subsidiary (Non-US):

Amer Sports France　　　　　(2)
80 Rue Condorcet, CS 80612, Villefontaine,
38096, Vaulx-Milleu, Cedex,
France　　　　　　　　　　(100%)
Tel.: (33) 474991515
Web Site: http://www.atomicsnow.com
Sales Range: $25-49.9 Million
Emp.: 25
N.A.I.C.S.: 339920

Amer Sports Holding GmbH　　(2)
Atomic Strasse 1, 5541, Altenmarkt, Austria
Tel.: (43) 645239000
Web Site: http://www.amersports.com
Investment Management Service
N.A.I.C.S.: 523999

Subsidiary (Non-US):

Amer Sports Denmark ApS　　　(3)
Kokkedal Industripark 14, 2980, Kokkedal,
Denmark
Tel.: (45) 22155133
Sales Range: $25-49.9 Million
Emp.: 1
Sporting Goods Distr
N.A.I.C.S.: 423910
Lars Stigmo (Mgr-Customer Svc)

Amer Sports Italia S.p.a.　　　(3)
Via Priula 78, 31040, Nervesa della Batta-
glia, Treviso, Italy
Tel.: (39) 0422 5291
Emp.: 7
Sporting Goods Distr
N.A.I.C.S.: 423910

Amer Sports Norge A/S　　　　(3)
Eyvind Lychesvei 9C, PO Box 293, 1338,
Sandvika, Norway
Tel.: (47) 67 531 330
Sporting Goods Distr
N.A.I.C.S.: 423910

Amer Sports Poland Sp. z.o.o.　(3)
ul Zablocie 43B, 30-701, Krakow, Poland
Tel.: (48) 123494700
Sporting Goods Distr
N.A.I.C.S.: 423910

Nikita ehf　　　　　　　　　　(3)
Skipholti 25, Reykjavik, Iceland
Tel.: (354) 5851000
Sales Range: $10-24.9 Million
Sporting Goods Distr
N.A.I.C.S.: 423910

ZAO Amer Sports　　　　　　(3)
Andropova av house 18 building 7 9th floor,
115432, Moscow, Russia
Tel.: (7) 49564126460
Web Site: http://www.amersports.com
Sales Range: $25-49.9 Million
Emp.: 100
Sports Equipment Mfr & Whslr
N.A.I.C.S.: 339920

Subsidiary (Non-US):

Amer Sports Holding S.A.S.　　(2)
63 Rue Condorcet, 38090, Villefontaine,
France
Tel.: (33) 474991515
Investment Management Service
N.A.I.C.S.: 523999

Subsidiary (Non-US):

Salomon S.A.　　　　　　　　(3)
Tel.: (33) 450654141
Sporting Goods Mfr
N.A.I.C.S.: 339920
Anthony Diana (Reg Mgr-Category-
Footwear-US)

Subsidiary (Non-US):

Salomon Canada Sports Ltd　　(4)
3545 Thimens Blvd, Saint Laurent,
H4R1V5, QC, Canada
Tel.: (514) 335-5948
Web Site: http://www.salomon.com
Sporting Goods Distr
N.A.I.C.S.: 423910

Arnold Tse (Mgr-Comml-Footwear)

Subsidiary (Non-US):

Amer Sports Latin America　　(2)
Av Santa Fe 495 Piso 15 Int 1501 Col Cruz
Manca, Cuajimalpa, 05349, Mexico, Mexico
Tel.: (52) 5591779100
Sporting Goods Mfr
N.A.I.C.S.: 339920

Amer Sports Netherlands　　　(2)
Plesmanstraat 1, 3833 LA, Leusden, Neth-
erlands
Tel.: (31) 33 432 0314
Sports Goods Retailer
N.A.I.C.S.: 459110
Arjan Buzzer (Gen Mgr)

Amer Sports Russia　　　　　(2)
Andropova av house 18 building 7 9th floor,
115432, Moscow, Russia
Tel.: (7) 4956412646
Web Site: http://www.amersports.com
Sporting Goods Distr
N.A.I.C.S.: 423910

Amer Sports SA　　　　　　(2)
Bachtalen 33, 6330, Cham, Switzerland
Tel.: (41) 583600606
Sales Range: $25-49.9 Million
Emp.: 30
Sporting Goods Distr
N.A.I.C.S.: 423910

Amer Sports Shanghai Trading
Ltd.　　　　　　　　　　　　(2)
2/F Bldg 3 Youyou Century Plaza No 428
Yanggao South Road, Pudong New Area,
Shanghai, 200127, China
Tel.: (86) 2151165288
Sales Range: $25-49.9 Million
Emp.: 50
Sporting Goods Distr
N.A.I.C.S.: 423910

Amer Sports Slovakia　　　　(2)
Hattalova 12/A, 83104, Bratislava, Slovakia
Tel.: (421) 244640011
Sales Range: $50-74.9 Million
Emp.: 3
Sporting Goods Distr
N.A.I.C.S.: 423910

Amer Sports Sourcing Ltd.　　(2)
Units 1102-5 11/F World Commerce Centre
11 Canton Road, Tsimshatsui, Kowloon,
China (Hong Kong)
Tel.: (852) 21955100
Sporting Goods Distr
N.A.I.C.S.: 423910

Amer Sports Suomi Oy　　　　(2)
Emp.: 20
Sporting Goods Mfr
N.A.I.C.S.: 339920
Heikki Takala (Mng Dir)

Amer Sports Sverige AB　　　(2)
Asboholmsgatan 16, Box 966, 504 51, Bo-
ras, Sweden
Tel.: (46) 33233700
Sporting Goods Mfr & Whslr
N.A.I.C.S.: 339920

Amer Sports UK & Ireland Ltd　(2)
Theta Lyon Way, Frimley, Camberley, GU16
7ER, United Kingdom
Tel.: (44) 1276 404 800
Web Site: http://www.wilson.com
Sales Range: $50-74.9 Million
Emp.: 100
Sporting Goods Distr
N.A.I.C.S.: 423910

Amer Sports UK Logistics Center　(2)
1-5 Crompton Way North Newmoor Indus-
trial Estate, Irvine, KA11 4HU, Ayrshire,
United Kingdom
Tel.: (44) 1294 219 117
Web Site: http://www.amersports.com
Sales Range: $25-49.9 Million
Emp.: 50
Logistics Consulting Servies
N.A.I.C.S.: 541614
Alistair Carey (Gen Mgr)

Subsidiary (Domestic):

Amer Tobacco Ltd.　　　　　(2)

Amerintie 1, 04300, Tuusula,
Finland　　　　　　　　　　(100%)
Tel.: (358) 9273011
Sales Range: $100-124.9 Million
Emp.: 320
Tobacco Products; Manufacturer & Marketer
of Philip Morris Cigarettes & Own Brands
N.A.I.C.S.: 312230

Subsidiary (Non-US):

Arc'teryx Equipment, Inc.　　(2)
110 - 2220 Dollarton Hwy, North Vancouver,
V7H 3B2, BC, Canada
Tel.: (604) 960-3001
Web Site: http://www.arcteryx.com
Sales Range: $25-49.9 Million
Emp.: 250
Outdoor Apparel & Gear Mfr
N.A.I.C.S.: 315990
Stuart Haselden (CEO)

Atomic Austria GmbH　　　　(2)
Atomic strasse 1, 5541, Altenmarkt,
Austria　　　　　　　　　　(100%)
Tel.: (43) 645239000
Web Site: http://www.atomicsnow.com
Sales Range: $200-249.9 Million
Emp.: 900
N.A.I.C.S.: 339920

Subsidiary (US):

Atomic Ski USA Inc.　　　　　(2)
2030 Lincoln Ave, Ogden, UT
84401　　　　　　　　　　(100%)
Tel.: (603) 880-6143
Sales Range: $25-49.9 Million
Emp.: 50
Ski Equipment Distr
N.A.I.C.S.: 423910
Michael Adams (Pres & Gen Mgr)

Subsidiary (Non-US):

Atomic Sports Canada　　　　(2)
2700 14th Ave Unit 1, Markham, L3R 0J1,
ON, Canada　　　　　　　(100%)
Tel.: (905) 470-9966
Web Site: http://www.atomicsnow.com
Sales Range: $25-49.9 Million
Emp.: 15
N.A.I.C.S.: 339920
Dave Deasley (Pres)

Subsidiary (US):

ENVE Composites LLC　　　　(2)
508 W Stockman Way, Ogden, UT 84401
Web Site: https://www.enve.com
Bicycle Components & Composite Wheels
Mfr
N.A.I.C.S.: 336991
Jeremy Venz (Mng Dir)

Subsidiary (Non-US):

Grupo Wilson, S.A. de C.V.　　(2)
Av Sante Fe No 495 P-18 Cruz Manca
Cuajimalpa De Morelos, Mexico, 05349,
Mexico
Tel.: (52) 5591779100
Sporting Goods Retailer
N.A.I.C.S.: 459110

Subsidiary (Domestic):

Asesoria Deportiva Especializada,
S.A. de C.V.　　　　　　　　(3)
Cruz Manca San Mateo Tlaltenango Cuaji-
malpa De Morelos, Mexico, Mexico
Tel.: (52) 55 9177 9127
Sporting Goods Mfr & Whslr
N.A.I.C.S.: 339920

Subsidiary (Non-US):

Mavic S.A.S.　　　　　　　　(2)
6 Rue de Bonlieu, Metz-Tessy, 74000,
Annecy, France
Tel.: (33) 456739771
Web Site: http://www.mavic.com
Sales Range: $125-149.9 Million
Emp.: 300
Motor Vehicle Parts Mfr & Distr
N.A.I.C.S.: 336390

Subsidiary (US):

Mavic, Inc.　　　　　　　　　(3)
17 Parkridge Rd, Haverhill, MA 01835

Tel.: (978) 469-8400
Web Site: http://www.amersports.com
Sporting Goods Distr
N.A.I.C.S.: 423910
Aaron Walker *(Mgr-Product Mdsg)*

Subsidiary (Non-US):

**Peak Performance Production
AB**   **(2)**
Magasin 1 Frihamnen, 102 53, Stockholm,
Sweden
Tel.: (46) 161 385 74 79
Web Site: http://www.peakperformance.com
Apparel Mfr & Distr
N.A.I.C.S.: 315990

Subsidiary (US):

**Salomon & Bonfire Snowboarding,
Inc.**   **(2)**
1111 NE Flanders Ste 205, Portland, OR
97232
Tel.: (503) 236-3473
Web Site: http://www.bonfiresnow.com
Snowboarding Apparels & Accessories Mfr
N.A.I.C.S.: 339920

Subsidiary (Domestic):

Suunto OY   **(2)**
Tammiston kauppatie 7 A, 01510, Vantaa,
Finland   **(100%)**
Tel.: (358) 9875870
Web Site: http://www.suunto.com
Sales Range: $50-74.9 Million
Emp.: 500
Diving Equipment, Compasses & Nautical
Equipment Mfr
N.A.I.C.S.: 339920
Heikki Norta *(CEO)*

Subsidiary (Domestic):

Amerc Oy   **(3)**
Makelankatu 91, 00610, Helsinki, Finland
Tel.: (358) 9 7257800
Communication Equipment Distr
N.A.I.C.S.: 423690

Subsidiary (US):

Wilson Sporting Goods Co.   **(2)**
1 Prudential Plaza 130 E Randolph St, Chicago, IL 60601   **(100%)**
Tel.: (773) 714-6400
Web Site: http://www.wilson.com
Sales Range: $125-149.9 Million
Emp.: 300
Sporting & Athletic Goods
N.A.I.C.S.: 339920

Subsidiary (Non-US):

Amer Sports Australia Pty. Ltd.   **(3)**
9 Chifley Drive Moorabbin Airport, Moorabbin, 3194, VIC, Australia   **(100%)**
Tel.: (61) 385866666
Sales Range: $10-24.9 Million
Emp.: 40
N.A.I.C.S.: 339920

Amer Sports Japan, Inc.   **(3)**
6F Shinjuku East Side Square 6-27-30
Shinjuku, Shinjuku -ku, Tokyo, 160-0022,
Japan   **(100%)**
Tel.: (81) 368252111
Web Site: https://www.amerjapan.com
Sales Range: $25-49.9 Million
Emp.: 100
Sales of Sporting Goods
N.A.I.C.S.: 459110

Amer Sports Korea Ltd.   **(3)**
                                                        (100%)
Tel.: (82) 25180781
Web Site: http://www.amersports.com
Sales Range: $25-49.9 Million
Emp.: 20
Sporting Equipment, Footwear, Apparel &
Accessories
N.A.I.C.S.: 339920

Amer Sports Malaysia Sdn Bhd   **(3)**
Suite 19 01 19th Floor Menara IGB No1
The Boulevard, Mid Valley City Lingkaran
Syed Putra, 59200, Kuala Lumpur, Malaysia
Tel.: (60) 3 2282 0009
Web Site: http://www.wilsonsports.com.my

Sales Range: $25-49.9 Million
Emp.: 40
Sporting Goods Distr
N.A.I.C.S.: 423910

Amer Sports Spain S.A.   **(3)**
Parque de Negocios Mas Blau II Calle
Conca de Barbera 4-6, El Prat del Llobregat, 08820, Barcelona, Spain   **(100%)**
Tel.: (34) 932625100
Web Site: http://www.amersports.net
Sales Range: $25-49.9 Million
Emp.: 25
N.A.I.C.S.: 339920

Amer Sports Taiwan   **(3)**
No 26-2 Gongyequ 18th Road, Nantun District, Taichung, 40850, Taiwan   **(100%)**
Tel.: (886) 423595363
Sales Range: $25-49.9 Million
Emp.: 50
Mfr of Athletic Apparel & Sporting Equipment
N.A.I.C.S.: 339920

Amer Sports UK Limited   **(3)**
1 Tanners Yard, London Road, Bagshot,
GU19 5HD, Surrey, United
Kingdom   **(100%)**
Tel.: (44) 1294316200
Sales Range: $25-49.9 Million
Emp.: 7
Sales of Sporting Goods
N.A.I.C.S.: 459110

**Amer Sports UK Ltd. - Logistics
Center**   **(3)**
1-5 Crompton Way, Irvine, KA11 4HU, Ayrshire, United Kingdom   **(100%)**
Tel.: (44) 1294 219 117
Web Site: http://www.amersports.net
Sales Range: $25-49.9 Million
Emp.: 100
Sporting & Athletic Goods Sales
N.A.I.C.S.: 459110

AmerSports Deutschland GmbH   **(3)**
                                                        (100%)
Sales Range: $50-74.9 Million
Emp.: 150
Sales of Sporting Goods
N.A.I.C.S.: 459110
Michael Apsmaier *(Mgr-Fin)*

Amersports Czech Republic   **(3)**
V Chotejne 700/7, 102 00, Prague, Czech
Republic   **(100%)**
Tel.: (420) 272700963
Sales Range: $25-49.9 Million
Emp.: 40
N.A.I.C.S.: 339920

Subsidiary (Domestic):

Athletic Training Equipment Company, Inc.   **(3)**
655 Spice Island Dr, Sparks, NV 89431
Tel.: (775) 352-2800
Web Site: http://www.atecsports.com
Sales Range: $25-49.9 Million
Emp.: 31
Mfr Small Track & Field
N.A.I.C.S.: 339920

Subsidiary (Non-US):

Wilson Brazil   **(3)**
Ave Brigadeiro Faria Lima 2391, 11 Andar
Conjunto 111 112, Sao Paulo, 01452 000,
SP, Brazil
Tel.: (55) 1130941900
Web Site: http://www.wilson.com
N.A.I.C.S.: 459110

Wilson France S.A.R.L.   **(3)**
ZI Petite Montagne Sud, F-91000, Evry,
Cedex, France
Tel.: (33) 160862222
Sales of Sporting Goods
N.A.I.C.S.: 459110

Plant (Domestic):

Wilson Sporting Goods Co.   **(3)**
217 Liberty St, Ada, OH 45810-1135
Tel.: (419) 634-9901
Web Site: http://www.wilson.com
Sales Range: $25-49.9 Million
Emp.: 150
Mfr of Sporting Goods
N.A.I.C.S.: 339920

Dan Riegle *(Mgr-Factory)*

Subsidiary (Non-US):

**Wilson Sporting Goods Co. de
Mexico**   **(3)**
No 495 Ave Sante Fe 18th Fl, Colonia Cruz
Manca, Mexico, 05349, DF,
Mexico   **(100%)**
Tel.: (52) 5591779100
Web Site: http://www.wilson.com
Sales Range: $25-49.9 Million
Emp.: 55
N.A.I.C.S.: 339920

Wilson Sporting Goods Company Kaohsiung Branch   **(3)**
14th Fl 2 6 Min Chuan 2nd Rd, Chien
Chen, Kaohsiung, 806, Taiwan   **(100%)**
Tel.: (886) 73365088
Web Site: http://www.wilsongolf.com
Sales Range: $25-49.9 Million
Emp.: 7
Sales of Sporting Goods
N.A.I.C.S.: 459110
Ann Huang *(Gen Mgr)*

**Wilson Sports Equipment Canada
Shields**   **(3)**
2700 14 Avenue Unit 1, Markham, L3R0J1,
ON, Canada   **(100%)**
Tel.: (905) 470-9966
Web Site: http://www.wilson.com
Sales Range: $25-49.9 Million
Emp.: 25
Sales of Sporting Goods
N.A.I.C.S.: 459110

SKC Group Limited   **(1)**
7-1-41/2 Kirlumpudi Layout, Visakhapatnam, 530003, India
Tel.: (91) 2564719
Web Site: https://skcgroup.co.in
N.A.I.C.S.: 518210
S. Chakravarty *(Chm)*

ANTALIS VENTURES CORP.
1700 - 666 Burrard Street, Vancouver, V6C 2V8, BC, Canada
Tel.: (604) 899-0584
Web Site: http://www.antalis.com
ANTV.P—(TSXV)
Sales Range: Less than $1 Million
Business Consulting Services
N.A.I.C.S.: 522299
John W. Greenslade *(CEO)*

ANTARCHILE S.A.
Av El Golf 150 piso 21, 7550107, Las
Condes, Santiago, Chile
Tel.: (56) 224617710   CL
Web Site: https://www.antarchile.cl
Year Founded: 1989
ANTARCHILE—(SGO)
Sales Range: $5-14.9 Billion
Emp.: 8,400
Diversified Financial Investment Services
N.A.I.C.S.: 523999
Jorge Andueza Fouque *(CEO & Gen
Mgr)*

Subsidiaries:

Empresas Copec S.A.   **(1)**
Avenida El Golf 150 Piso 17, 7550107, Las
Condes, Santiago, Chile   **(60.82%)**
Tel.: (56) 24617000
Web Site: http://www.empresascopec.cl
Sales Range: $900-999.9 Million
Emp.: 25
Gasoline & Petroleum By-Products Importer
& Distr
N.A.I.C.S.: 424720
Rodrigo Huidobro Alvarado *(CFO)*

Subsidiary (Domestic):

**Abastecedora de Combustibles
S.A.**   **(2)**
Avenida Vicuna Mackenna 55, Santiago,
Chile
Tel.: (56) 26939000
Web Site: http://www.abastible.cl
Gasoline & Petroleum
N.A.I.C.S.: 424720

Jose Odone *(CEO)*

Subsidiary (Non-US):

Arauco do Brasil SA   **(2)**
Avenida Iguacu n 2820 Agua Verde Curitiba, Parana, 80240-031, Brazil
Tel.: (55) 4132177171
Web Site: http://www.arauco.cl
Wood Paneling
N.A.I.C.S.: 321999

Subsidiary (Domestic):

Masisa do Brasil Ltda.   **(3)**
Rua Joao Gualberto 1259 23F andar, Curitiba, 80030-001, Parana, Brazil
Tel.: (55) 4132191850
Hardwood Veneer & Plywood Mfr
N.A.I.C.S.: 321211

Subsidiary (Domestic):

**Celulosa Arauco y Constitucion
S.A.**   **(2)**
Avenida El Golf 150 14th Floor, 7550107,
Las Condes, Santiago, Chile   **(99.98%)**
Tel.: (56) 224617200
Web Site: http://arauco.cl
Rev.: $7,102,070,000
Assets: $17,180,108,000
Liabilities: $8,920,124,000
Net Worth: $8,259,984,000
Earnings: $704,480,000
Emp.: 19,043
Fiscal Year-end: 12/31/2022
Holding Company; Forest Plantations,
Wood Pulp Mills, Sawmills & Wood Processing Plants Operator
N.A.I.C.S.: 551112
Matias Domeyko Cassel *(CEO)*

Joint Venture (Non-US):

Eufores, S.A.   **(3)**
Luis Alberto de Herrera 1248 Complejo
World Trade Center, Torre 3 Piso 9, Montevideo, Uruguay   **(50%)**
Tel.: (598) 2 623 6300
Web Site:
   https://www.montesdelplata.com.uy
Sales Range: $50-74.9 Million
Emp.: 250
Forest Nurseries & Wood Pulp Mills
N.A.I.C.S.: 113210

Subsidiary (Non-US):

Flakeboard Company Limited   **(3)**
80 Tiverton Court Suite 701, Markham, L3R
0G4, ON, Canada
Tel.: (905) 475-9686
Web Site: http://www.flakeboard.com
Sales Range: $25-49.9 Million
Emp.: 20
Composite Wood Products Mfr
N.A.I.C.S.: 321999
Kelly Shotbolt *(Pres & CEO)*

**Masisa Manufactura S.A. de
C.V.**   **(3)**
Carr Mexico - Toluca Km 525, Toluca,
52000, Mexico State, Mexico
Tel.: (52) 7282828850
Wood Product Distr
N.A.I.C.S.: 424990

Masnova Quimica S.A. de C.V.   **(3)**
Carretera Panamericana Km 959, 34304,
Durango, Mexico
Tel.: (52) 6188299650
Chemical Products Distr
N.A.I.C.S.: 424690

**Placacentro Masisa Mexico S.A. de
C.V.**   **(3)**
Jaime Balmes No 8 Piso 2 Despacho 202
Col Los Morales, Del Miguel Hidalgo,
11510, Mexico, Mexico
Tel.: (52) 5591382300
Reconstituted Wood Product Mfr
N.A.I.C.S.: 321219

Subsidiary (Domestic):

Compania de Petroleos de Chile Copec S.A.   **(2)**
Avenida El Golf 150 Piso 17, 7550107, Las
Condes, Santiago, Chile
Tel.: (56) 24617000
Web Site: http://www.ec.cl

AntarChile S.A.—(Continued)

Sales Range: $25-49.9 Million
Emp.: 20
Gasoline & Petroleum By-Products Importer & Distr
N.A.I.C.S.: 424720
Lorenzo Gazmuri Schleyer *(CEO)*

Corpesca S.A. (2)
Avenida El Golf 150 Piso 15, Las Condes, Santiago, Chile
Tel.: (56) 4764000
Web Site: http://www.corpesca.cl
Marine Product Mfr
N.A.I.C.S.: 311710

Orizon S.A. (2)
150 El Golf Ave 8th Floor, Las Condes, Santiago, Chile
Tel.: (56) 2 4764 100
Web Site: http://www.orizon.cl
Seafood Production & Canning
N.A.I.C.S.: 311710
Jorge Andueza Fouque *(Chm)*

PESQUERA IQUIQUE-GUANAYE S.A. (2)
Avda El Golf 150 Piso 15, PO Box 3781, Las Condes, Santiago, Chile
Tel.: (56) 4764100
Fishing Services
N.A.I.C.S.: 114119
Rodrigo Huidobro Alvarado *(Mgr-Fin & Admin)*

Joint Venture (Domestic):

Sociedad Minera Isla Riesco S.A. (2)
El Bosque Norte 500 Piso 23, Las Condes, Santiago, Chile
Tel.: (56) 2 429 6300
Web Site: http://www.minainvierno.cl
Coal Mining
N.A.I.C.S.: 212115

Subsidiary (Domestic):

Sociedad Nacional de Oleoductos S.A. (2)
Av Isabel La Catolica 4473 Casilla 243 Correo 34, 6761025, Las Condes, Santiago, Chile
Tel.: (56) 2 2081603
Web Site: http://www.sonacol.cl
Pipeline Engineering Services
N.A.I.C.S.: 541330
Fernando Prado Alvarez *(Chm)*

ANTARES VISION SPA
Via Del Ferro 16, 25039, Travagliato, Brescia, Italy
Tel.: (39) 00307283500
Web Site:
   https://antaresvisiongroup.com
Year Founded: 2007
AV—(ITA)
Rev.: $241,813,640
Assets: $628,093,584
Liabilities: $294,777,292
Net Worth: $333,316,292
Earnings: $19,643,179
Emp.: 1,186
Fiscal Year-end: 12/31/22
Safety Inspection Services
N.A.I.C.S.: 541380
Emidio Zorzella *(Co-Founder)*

Subsidiaries:

Antares Vision Asia Pacific Limited (1)
Tel.: (852) 97907580
Electrical & Electronic Product Mfr
N.A.I.C.S.: 335999

Antares Vision France SAS (1)
672 rue des Mercieres, 69140, Rillieux-la-Pape, France
Tel.: (33) 676433176
Electrical & Electronic Product Mfr
N.A.I.C.S.: 335999

Antares Vision India Private Limited (1)
Tel.: (91) 9136909250
Electrical & Electronic Product Mfr

Antares Vision North America LLC (1)
1 Whittendale Dr Ste A, Moorestown, NJ 08057
Tel.: (856) 780-3465
Electrical & Electronic Product Mfr
N.A.I.C.S.: 335999

Antares Vision Rus OOO (1)
Tel.: (7) 4952527471
Electrical & Electronic Product Mfr
N.A.I.C.S.: 335999

Antares Vision do Brasil (1)
Av das Nacoes Unidas 21476 - P1B Jardim Dom Bosco, Sao Paulo, 04795-002, SP, Brazil
Tel.: (55) 1123647512
Web Site: http://br.antaresvision.com
Electrical & Electronic Product Mfr
N.A.I.C.S.: 335999

Subsidiary (Domestic):

T 2 Software S.A. (2)
Avenida das Nacoes Unidas 21 476 - P1B, Santo Amaro, Sao Paulo, 04795-910, Brazil
Tel.: (55) 1150830815
Web Site: http://www.t2software.com.br
Software Development Services
N.A.I.C.S.: 541511

Convel S.R.L. (1)
Via dei Tigli 3, 20853, Biassono, Italy
Tel.: (39) 039492763
Web Site: https://convel.com
Power Generator Mfr
N.A.I.C.S.: 335312

FT System S.r.l. (1)
Via Leonardo Da Vinci 117, 29010, Alseno, PC, Italy
Tel.: (39) 0523945745
Web Site: http://www.ftsystem.com
Industrial Machinery Distr
N.A.I.C.S.: 423830

Tecnel S.R.L. (1)
Via Dorsale 13, 54100, Massa, Italy
Tel.: (39) 058525751
Web Site: https://www.tecnelsrl.com
Architectural Design Services
N.A.I.C.S.: 541310

Tradeticity Service d.o.o. (1)
Beogradskog Bataljona 4, 11040, Belgrade, Serbia
Tel.: (381) 117555929
Web Site: https://tradeticity.com
Software Provider
N.A.I.C.S.: 423430

Tradeticity d.o.o. (1)
Ulica grada Vukovara 284, 10 000, Zagreb, Croatia
Tel.: (385) 16264199
Web Site: https://tradeticity.com
Software Development Services
N.A.I.C.S.: 541511

rfXcel Corporation (1)
12657 Alcosta Blvd Ste 375, San Ramon, CA 94583
Tel.: (925) 824-0300
Web Site: http://www.rfxcel.com
Sales Range: $1-9.9 Million
Emp.: 41
Whol Computers/Peripherals
N.A.I.C.S.: 423430
Glenn Abood *(CEO)*

ANTARIKSH INDUSTRIES LIMITED
609 6th Floor Inizio Cardinal Gracious Road Opp PG Plaza, Chakala Andheri East, Mumbai, 400099, Maharashtra, India
Tel.: (91) 2225830011
Web Site:
   https://www.antarikshindustries.com
Year Founded: 1974
501270—(BOM)
Rev.: $3,105,566
Assets: $126,686
Liabilities: $29,443
Net Worth: $97,243

Earnings: $10,743
Emp.: 2
Fiscal Year-end: 03/31/22
Real Estate Manangement Services
N.A.I.C.S.: 531210
Bhagwanji Narsi Patel *(Mng Dir)*

ANTECO SA
Str Lamaitei Nr 2, 100105, Ploiesti, 100185, Prahova, Romania
Tel.: (40) 244543088
Web Site: http://www.anteco.ro
Year Founded: 1886
ANTE—(BUC)
Rev.: $226,469
Assets: $1,420,260
Liabilities: $89,683
Net Worth: $1,330,577
Earnings: $14,699
Emp.: 3
Fiscal Year-end: 12/31/23
Household Furniture Mfr
N.A.I.C.S.: 337126

ANTELOPE ENTERPRISE HOLDINGS LTD.
Junbing Industrial Zone, Anhai, Jingjiang, Fujian, China
Tel.: (86) 59585765053   VG
Web Site: http://www.aehltd.com
Year Founded: 2007
AEHL—(NASDAQ)
Rev.: $43,871,224
Assets: $16,854,019
Liabilities: $15,863,517
Net Worth: $990,503
Earnings: ($8,218,797)
Emp.: 63
Fiscal Year-end: 12/31/22
Holding Company; Ceramic Products Mfr
N.A.I.C.S.: 551112
Jiadong Huang *(Founder)*

ANTENGENE CORPORATION LIMITED
Suites 1206-1209 Block B Zhongshan SOHO Plaza 1065 West Zhongshan Road, Changning, Shanghai, China
Tel.: (86) 2123566665   Ky
Web Site: http://www.antengene.com
Year Founded: 2016
6996—(HKG)
Pharmaceutical Product Mfr & Distr
N.A.I.C.S.: 325412
Jay Mei *(Founder, Chm & CEO)*

ANTENNA GROUP
10-12 Kifisias Ave, Maroussi, 15125, Athens, Greece
Tel.: (30) 2106886100
Web Site: http://www.antenna-group.com
Year Founded: 1988
Emp.: 2,200
Media & Entertainment Organization Services
N.A.I.C.S.: 512250
Pete Smith *(Mng Dir)*

Subsidiaries:

Antenna TV S.A. (1)
Kifissias Ave 10 12, Maroussi, 151 25, Athens, Greece
Tel.: (30) 2106886100
Web Site: http://www.antenna.gr
Sales Range: $200-249.9 Million
Emp.: 750
Broadcast Television Network Services
N.A.I.C.S.: 516120
Jonathan Procter *(Mng Dir)*

ANTENNA HOUSE, INC.
1-6 chome-2 5th Floor Towa Building Tokyo East Bridge, Chuo-ku, Tokyo, Japan
Tel.: (81) 358299021

Web Site: http://www.antenna.co.jp
Year Founded: 1984
Emp.: 48
Document Formatting & Processing
N.A.I.C.S.: 561410

Subsidiaries:

Antenna House, Inc. (1)
3844 Kennett Pike Ste 200, Greenville, DE 19807
Tel.: (302) 427-2456
Software Development Services
N.A.I.C.S.: 541511

Beijing HYF software Co., Ltd (1)
604 Shijiabaoding Building B Dingcheng Avenue No 9, Chaoyang District, Beijing, 100101, China
Tel.: (86) 1084899242
Web Site: http://www.hyfsoft.com
Software Development Services
N.A.I.C.S.: 541511

ANTEOTECH LTD
Unit 4 26 Brandl Street Brisbane Technology Park, Eight Mile Plains, 4113, QLD, Australia
Tel.: (61) 732190085
Web Site: https://www.anteotech.com
ADO—(ASX)
Rev.: $2,902,100
Assets: $6,264,143
Liabilities: $2,721,192
Net Worth: $3,542,951
Earnings: ($5,929,832)
Emp.: 40
Fiscal Year-end: 06/30/24
Research & Development in Biotechnology (except Nanobiotechnology)
N.A.I.C.S.: 541714
Charlie Huang *(Head-Diagnostics & Life Science)*

ANTERIS TECHNOLOGIES LTD.
Toowong Tower Level 3 Suite 302 9 Sherwood Road, Toowong, 4066, QLD, Australia
Tel.: (61) 1300550310   AU
Web Site:
   https://www.anteristech.com
AMEUF—(OTCIQ)
Rev.: $7,099,667
Assets: $22,588,567
Liabilities: $11,595,372
Net Worth: $10,993,195
Earnings: ($17,551,135)
Emp.: 51
Fiscal Year-end: 12/31/21
Medical & Surgical Product Development Services
N.A.I.C.S.: 325412
John D. Seaberg *(Chm)*

Subsidiaries:

Admedus Sarl (1)
Rte de Pre-Bois 20, PO Box 1877, 1215, Geneva, Switzerland
Tel.: (41) 225756746
Medical Device Mfr
N.A.I.C.S.: 334510

ANTEVENIO SA
C/ Marques de Riscal 11 2, 28010, Madrid, Spain
Tel.: (34) 914149191
Web Site: https://www.antevenio.com
ALANT—(EUR)
Sales Range: $1-9.9 Million
Emp.: 187
Online Advertising Services
N.A.I.C.S.: 541890
Delia Perez *(Mgr-HR)*

ANTEX WESTERN LTD.
1340 Church Ave, Winnipeg, R2X 1G4, MB, Canada
Tel.: (204) 633-4815

Web Site:
  https://www.antexwestern.com
Year Founded: 1928
Sales Range: $10-24.9 Million
Emp.: 86
Flooring Contractors & Services
N.A.I.C.S.: 238330
Mike Kolas (Pres & CEO)

ANTHEM WORKS LTD.
550 Burrard St Ste 300, Vancouver,
V6C 2B5, BC, Canada
Tel.: (604) 689-3040
Web Site:
  http://www.anthemproperties.com
Year Founded: 1991
Sales Range: $10-24.9 Million
Emp.: 175
Retail, Industrial, Office & Residential
Real Estate Management
N.A.I.C.S.: 531390
Eric H. Carlson (Founder & CEO)

Subsidiaries:

Anthem Properties Group, Ltd.   **(1)**
Suite 1100 Bentall IV Box 49200 1055 Dun-
smuir Street, Vancouver, V7X 1K8, BC,
Canada
Tel.: (604) 689-3040
Web Site: http://www.anthemproperties.com
Emp.: 150
Real Estate Investment, Development &
Management Services
N.A.I.C.S.: 525990
Alexa Ulinder Baughen (VP-Investments &
Comm)

Subsidiary (Domestic):

United, Inc.   **(2)**
Suite 200 4820 Richard Road SW, Calgary,
T3E 6L1, AB, Canada
Tel.: (403) 265-6180
Web Site:
  http://www.unitedcommunities.com
Emp.: 40
Residential Real Estate Development &
Services
N.A.I.C.S.: 236117
Chris M. Kolozetti (Exec VP & COO)

**ANTI-AGING HOUSE HOLDING
LIMITED**
No 551Yucai Road Shamao Street,
Hannan District, Wuhan, China
Tel.: (86) 27 50755299
Web Site: http://www.a2hchina.com
Health & Beauty Products Mfr
N.A.I.C.S.: 325620
Jiwu Chen (Chm)

ANTIBE THERAPEUTICS INC.
15 Prince Arthur Avenue, Toronto,
M5R 1B2, ON, Canada
Tel.: (416) 922-3460   ON
Web Site:
  https://www.antibethera.com
Year Founded: 2009
ATE—(TSX)
Assets: $52,638,506
Liabilities: $22,674,670
Net Worth: $29,963,836
Earnings: ($14,528,350)
Emp.: 11
Fiscal Year-end: 03/31/23
Pharmaceuticals Mfr
N.A.I.C.S.: 325412
Walter M. Macnee (Chm)

ANTIBIOTICE S.A.
1 Valea Lupului Street, 707410, Iasi,
707410, Romania
Tel.: (40) 232209000
Web Site: https://www.antibiotice.ro
ATB—(BUC)
Rev.: $137,942,034
Assets: $244,500,991
Liabilities: $62,158,179
Net Worth: $182,342,812

Earnings: $17,457,555
Emp.: 1,352
Fiscal Year-end: 12/31/23
Anti-Infectives & Antibiotics Mfr
N.A.I.C.S.: 325411
Ioan Nani (Gen Mgr)

**ANTICA DITTA MARCHISIO
S.P.A.**
Via Cagliari 8, 10153, Turin, Italy
Tel.: (39) 0112481766
Web Site: http://www.mattioligioielli.it
Sales Range: $10-24.9 Million
Emp.: 100
Jewelry Mfr
N.A.I.C.S.: 339910
Luciano Mattioli (Owner)

**ANTIEN INDUSTRIES JOINT
STOCK COMPANY**
Southern Industrial Zone, Van Phu
Commune, Yen Bai, Vietnam
Tel.: (84) 2163856555
Web Site:
  https://www.antienindustries.com
Year Founded: 2009
HII—(HOSE)
Rev.: $324,721,755
Assets: $77,980,146
Liabilities: $38,287,325
Net Worth: $39,692,822
Earnings: $3,300,573
Emp.: 467
Fiscal Year-end: 12/31/23
Plastics Product Mfr
N.A.I.C.S.: 326199
Dinh Xuan Cuong (Pres)

ANTILIA GROUP, CORP.
Calle Duarte No 6, Sosua, Dominican
Republic
Tel.: (809) 829 217 2262   NV
Year Founded: 2016
Rev.: $576
Assets: $57,653
Liabilities: $40,575
Net Worth: $17,078
Earnings: ($30,265)
Emp.: 1
Fiscal Year-end: 01/31/19
Used Car Dealers
N.A.I.C.S.: 441120

ANTILLES GOLD LIMITED
55 Kirkham Road, PO Box 846, Bow-
ral, 2576, NSW, Australia
Tel.: (61) 248611740   AU
Web Site: https://antillesgold.net
ANTMF—(OTCIQ)
Rev.: $22,637
Assets: $29,125,550
Liabilities: $15,521,836
Net Worth: $13,603,714
Earnings: ($4,139,944)
Emp.: 10
Fiscal Year-end: 12/31/23
Holding Company; Gold Exploration
& Mining Development Services
N.A.I.C.S.: 551112
Brian Johnson (Chm)

Subsidiaries:

PanTerra Gold (Peru) S.A.   **(1)**
Av Republica Be Panama 3030 8th Fl, San
Isidro, Lima, 27, Peru   **(100%)**
Tel.: (51) 1 6179000
Gold Exploration & Mining Development
Services
N.A.I.C.S.: 213114

**ANTIN INFRASTRUCTURE
PARTNERS SAS**
374 rue Saint-Honore, 75001, Paris,
France
Tel.: (33) 170081300
Web Site: https://www.antin-ip.com
Year Founded: 2007

ANTIN—(EUR)
Independent Private Equity Firm
N.A.I.C.S.: 551112
Alain Rauscher (CEO & Mng Partner)

Subsidiaries:

CityFibre Infrastructure Holdings
Limited   **(1)**
15 Bedford Street, London, WC2E 9HE,
United Kingdom
Tel.: (44) 203 5100 602
Web Site: http://www.cityfibre.com
Rev.: $70,112,086
Assets: $450,829,507
Liabilities: $132,542,794
Net Worth: $318,286,713
Earnings: ($63,754,296)
Emp.: 462
Fiscal Year-end: 12/31/2018
Transformational Fibre Optic Infrastructure
Builder
N.A.I.C.S.: 335921
Greg Mesch (CEO)

Subsidiary (Domestic):

Entanet International Ltd.   **(2)**
Stafford Park 6, Telford, TF3 3AT, Shrop-
shire, United Kingdom
Tel.: (44) 330 100 0330
Web Site: http://www.enta.net
Voice & Data Telecommunications Services
N.A.I.C.S.: 517121
Elsa Chen (CEO)

FirstLight Fiber, Inc.   **(1)**
41 State St Fl 10, Albany, NY 12207
Tel.: (518) 598-0940
Web Site: http://www.firstlight.net
Telecommunications Resellers
N.A.I.C.S.: 517121
Patrick Coughlin (Chief Dev Officer)

Subsidiary (Domestic):

Bestweb Corporation   **(2)**
25 S Riverside Ave, Croton on Hudson, NY
10520
Tel.: (914) 271-4500
Web Site: http://www.bestweb.net
Sales Range: $1-9.9 Million
Emp.: 10
Internet Service Provider
N.A.I.C.S.: 517810

TruePath Technologies, Inc.   **(2)**
833 Phillips Rd Ste A, Victor, NY 14550
Tel.: (585) 672-5481
Web Site:
  http://www.truepathtechnologies.com
Computer Related Services
N.A.I.C.S.: 541519
Douglas Mauro (Pres)

Opdenergy Holding SA   **(1)**
Torre Spinola Planta 5 Cardenal Marcelo
Spinola 42, 28016, Madrid, Spain
Tel.: (34) 914559996
Web Site: https://www.opdenergy.com
Rev.: $123,406,854
Assets: $1,256,417,152
Liabilities: $1,137,665,990
Net Worth: $118,751,162
Earnings: $67,557,779
Emp.: 161
Fiscal Year-end: 12/31/2022
Holding Company
N.A.I.C.S.: 551112
Luis Cid (CEO)

ANTIOQUIA GOLD INC.
Suite 106 2 Toronto Street, Toronto,
M5C 2B5, ON, Canada
Tel.: (800) 348-9657   AB
Web Site:
  https://www.antioquiagoldinc.com
Year Founded: 2009
AGDXF—(OTCEM)
Rev.: $66,246,153
Assets: $95,333,872
Liabilities: $162,264,525
Net Worth: ($66,930,653)
Earnings: ($35,365,440)
Fiscal Year-end: 12/31/23
Gold Mining
N.A.I.C.S.: 212220

Gonzalo de Losada (Chm, Pres &
CEO)

ANTIPA MINERALS LTD.
Level 2 16 Ord Street, West Perth,
6005, WA, Australia
Tel.: (61) 894811103
Web Site:
  https://www.antipaminerals.com.au
AZY—(ASX)
Rev.: $421,307
Assets: $48,972,271
Liabilities: $3,233,254
Net Worth: $45,739,017
Earnings: ($4,486,955)
Fiscal Year-end: 06/30/22
Gold Ore & Silver Ore Mining
N.A.I.C.S.: 212220
Stephen Power (Chm)

ANTIPHON AB
Pappersvagen 1, S 670 40, Amotfors,
Sweden
Tel.: (46) 57131800
Web Site: http://www.antiphon.se
Sales Range: $10-24.9 Million
Emp.: 20
Sound Dampening Material Mfr
N.A.I.C.S.: 326299
Marianne Levin (Mgr-Fin & Acctg)

**ANTIPODES GLOBAL INVEST-
MENT COMPANY LIMITED**
Level 19 307 Queen Street, Brisbane,
4000, QLD, Australia
Tel.: (61) 730203710   AU
Web Site:
  http://www.antipodespartners.com
Rev.: $12,784,150
Assets: $459,111,069
Liabilities: $18,423,331
Net Worth: $440,687,737
Earnings: $5,390,898
Fiscal Year-end: 06/30/19
Mutual Fund Management Services
N.A.I.C.S.: 523940
Jonathan Trollip (Chm)

ANTIPODES VOYAGES SA
39 Rue Lhomond, Paris, 75005,
France
Tel.: (33) 143360918
Web Site: http://www.antipodes.travel
Travel Agency Operator
N.A.I.C.S.: 561510
Franck Manin (CEO)

**ANTISEPTICA CHEM.-PHARM
PRODUKTE GMBH**
Carl-Friedrich-Gauss-Strasse 7,
D-50259, Pulheim, Germany
Tel.: (49) 2234984660
Web Site: http://www.antiseptica.com
Year Founded: 1976
Rev.: $11,035,200
Emp.: 16
Medical Devices
N.A.I.C.S.: 621511
Hans-Joachim Molitor (Owner & Gen
Mgr)

ANTLER GOLD, INC.
Suite 2001 1969 Upper Water Street
Purdys Wharf Tower II, Halifax, B3J-
3R7, NS, Canada
Tel.: (902) 334-1670
Web Site: https://www.antlergold.com
ALRGF—(OTCIQ)
Assets: $3,040,543
Liabilities: $365,943
Net Worth: $2,674,600
Earnings: $602,819
Fiscal Year-end: 12/31/23
Gold Exploration & Mining Services
N.A.I.C.S.: 212220
Daniel Whittaker (Pres)

Antler Gold, Inc.—(Continued)

ANTLER HILL MINING LTD.
Suite 400 90 Adelaide Street West,
Toronto, M5H 3V9, ON, Canada
Tel.: (647) 951-6511   **AB**
Web Site:
http://www.antlerhillmining.com
Year Founded: 2009
AHM.H—(TSXV)
Rev.: $18,108
Assets: $402,338
Liabilities: $57,873
Net Worth: $344,465
Earnings: ($47,914)
Fiscal Year-end: 12/31/23
Capital Pool Company; Mining Services
N.A.I.C.S.: 212290
Matthew Wood *(Chm & CEO-Interim)*

ANTN CO., LTD.
151 Gasan digital 1-ro, Geumcheon-gu, Seoul, Korea (South)
Tel.: (82) 234435811
Web Site: http://www.antn.co.kr
Year Founded: 1995
050320—(KRS)
Rev.: $6,327,411
Assets: $12,796,693
Liabilities: $7,363,925
Net Worth: $5,432,768
Earnings: $229,028
Emp.: 38
Fiscal Year-end: 12/31/20
Software Development Services
N.A.I.C.S.: 541512
Choi Gi Yong *(CEO)*

ANTOFAGASTA PLC
103 Mount Street, London, W1K 2TJ,
United Kingdom
Tel.: (44) 2078080988   **UK**
Web Site:
https://www.antofagasta.co.uk
Year Founded: 1982
ANFGF—(OTCQX)
Rev.: $6,324,500,000
Assets: $19,647,200,000
Liabilities: $7,598,800,000
Net Worth: $12,048,400,000
Earnings: $1,299,400,000
Emp.: 7,753
Fiscal Year-end: 12/31/23
Mineral Mining Services
N.A.I.C.S.: 213115
Jean-Paul Luksic *(Chm)*

Subsidiaries:

Antofagasta Minerals S.A.   **(1)**
Av Apoquindo 4001 - piso 18, Santiago,
Chile
Tel.: (56) 22 798 7000
Web Site: https://www.aminerals.cl
Sales Range: $100-124.9 Million
Emp.: 150
Mining Operations
N.A.I.C.S.: 212230

Subsidiary (Domestic):

Minera Esperanza Ltda.   **(2)**
Apoquindo 4001 Piso 13, Las Condes, Santiago, Chile
Tel.: (56) 27987000
Web Site: http://www.mineraesperanza.cl
Copper & Gold Mining Services
N.A.I.C.S.: 212220

Subsidiary (Non-US):

Minera Los Pelambres Ltda.   **(2)**
Tel.: (56) 27987000
Copper Mining Services
N.A.I.C.S.: 212230

Compania Minera Zaldivar S.A.   **(1)**
Avenida Grecia 750, Antofagasta, 1271837,
Chile   **(50%)**
Tel.: (56) 55433400
Web Site: http://www.barrick.com
Gold Mining Services

N.A.I.C.S.: 212220

DMC (USA) Corporation   **(1)**
86 Northfield Ave, Edison, NJ 08837
Web Site: https://www.dmc.com
Emp.: 4,000
Thread Mfr
N.A.I.C.S.: 313110

FCAB Ingenieria y Servicios
Limitada   **(1)**
Bolivar 255 Antofagasta Casilla, Santiago,
Chile
Tel.: (56) 229257525
Web Site: https://www.fcab.cl
N.A.I.C.S.: 541330
Katharina Jenny *(Gen Mgr)*

Ferrocarril Antofagasta a Bolivia
SA   **(1)**
Bolivar 255, Antofagasta, Chile
Tel.: (56) 229257525
Railway Transportation Services
N.A.I.C.S.: 532411

Minera Antucoya SCM   **(1)**
Av Apoquindo 4001 Piso 18, Las Condes,
7550162, Santiago, Chile
Tel.: (56) 227987000
Web Site: https://web.antucoya.cl
N.A.I.C.S.: 541330

Minera Los Pelambres SCM   **(1)**
Av Apoquindo 4001 Piso 18, Las Condes,
7550162, Santiago, Chile
Tel.: (56) 227987000
Web Site: https://web.pelambres.cl
N.A.I.C.S.: 541330

Twin Metals Minnesota LLC   **(1)**
380 St Peter St Ste 705, Saint Paul, MN
55102
Tel.: (651) 842-6800
Web Site: https://www.twin-metals.com
Copper & Zinc Mining Services
N.A.I.C.S.: 212230
Derek Heinecke *(VP-Admin & Fin)*

ANTOLINI LUIGI & C. S.P.A.
Via Marconi 101, Sega di Cavaion,
37010, Verona, Italy
Tel.: (39) 045 6836611
Web Site: http://www.antolini.com
Sales Range: $100-124.9 Million
Emp.: 220
Dimensional Stone Distr
N.A.I.C.S.: 423940
Francesco Antolini *(Pres)*

ANTON BORER IMMOBILIEN AG
Wydenmattstrasse 10, Solothurn,
4228, Switzerland
Tel.: (41) 617899010
Engineering Services
N.A.I.C.S.: 541330

Subsidiaries:

Wirz Communications AG   **(1)**
Uetlibergstrasse 132, 8036, Zurich, Switzerland
Tel.: (41) 444575757
Web Site: http://www.wirz.ch
Emp.: 150
Advertising Services
N.A.I.C.S.: 541810
Geri Aebi *(CEO-WIRZ Services)*

Branch (Non-US):

Wirz & Hafner Werbeberatung
GmbH   **(2)**
Walter Kolb Str 14, 60594, Frankfurt am
Main, Germany
Tel.: (49) 69 61 09 00 0
Web Site: http://www.w-h.net
Advertising Services
N.A.I.C.S.: 541810
Alexander Kowalski *(Mng Partner)*

Wirz Werbeagentur GmbH   **(2)**
Gottfried-Keller-Gasse 2, 1030, Vienna,
Austria
Tel.: (43) 1 712 26 91 0
Web Site: http://www.wirz.at
Advertising Services
N.A.I.C.S.: 541810

ANTON DEBATIN GMBH
Vichystrasse 6, 76646, Bruchsal,
Germany
Tel.: (49) 72518009100
Web Site: http://www.debatin.com
Year Founded: 1923
Rev.: $58,803,251
Emp.: 230
Packaging Bags Mfr
N.A.I.C.S.: 322220

Subsidiaries:

Debatin UK Ltd   **(1)**
The Base Dartford Business Park Victoria
Road, Dartford, DA1 5FS, Kent, United
Kingdom
Tel.: (44) 8456038851
Web Site: http://www.debatin.co.uk
Packaging Bags Mfr
N.A.I.C.S.: 322220

ANTON OILFIELD SERVICES GROUP LIMITED
8 Pincui West Road, Chaoyang District, Beijing, 100102, China
Tel.: (86) 1057397788
Web Site: http://www.antonoil.com
3337—(OTCIQ)
Rev.: $432,609,578
Assets: $1,207,466,548
Liabilities: $784,036,854
Net Worth: $423,429,694
Earnings: ($12,832,870)
Emp.: 4,005
Fiscal Year-end: 12/31/20
Oil Field Services
N.A.I.C.S.: 213111
Lin Luo *(Founder & Chm)*

Subsidiaries:

Shandong Precede Petroleum Technology Co., Ltd.   **(1)**
Shengli Industrial Park, Dongying, 257000,
Shandong, China
Tel.: (86) 546 817 9866
Web Site: https://en.china-precede.com
Oilfield Technical Services
N.A.I.C.S.: 213112

ANTON PAAR GMBH
Anton Paar Strasse 20, 8054, Graz,
Austria
Tel.: (43) 3162570
Web Site: http://www.anton-paar.com
Year Founded: 1922
Emp.: 3,200
Laboratory Instruments & Process
Measuring Systems Developer, Mfr &
Distr
N.A.I.C.S.: 334516
Friedrich Santner *(CEO)*

Subsidiaries:

Anton Paar (Thailand) Ltd.   **(1)**
90 CW Tower 39th Floor Unit No A3902
Ratchadaphisek Road, Bangkok, 10310,
Thailand
Tel.: (66) 21539785
Laboratory Instrument Mfr & Distr
N.A.I.C.S.: 334516

Anton Paar Australia Pty Ltd   **(1)**
Level 2 2 Julius Avenue, North Ryde, 2113,
NSW, Australia
Tel.: (61) 283154400
Laboratory Instrument Mfr & Distr
N.A.I.C.S.: 334516

Anton Paar Austria GmbH   **(1)**
Anton Paar Strasse 20, 8054, Graz, Austria
Tel.: (43) 3162570
Laboratory Instrument Mfr & Distr
N.A.I.C.S.: 334516

Anton Paar Benelux BVBA   **(1)**
Everdenberg 7, 4902 TT, Oosterhout, Netherlands
Tel.: (31) 162319250
Laboratory Instrument Mfr & Distr
N.A.I.C.S.: 334516

Anton Paar Brasil Ltda.   **(1)**

Rua Jose de Magalhaes N 646, Vila Clementino, Sao Paulo, 04029-090, Brazil
Tel.: (55) 1159069000
Laboratory Instrument Mfr & Distr
N.A.I.C.S.: 334516

Anton Paar Canada Inc.   **(1)**
2920 Rue de Miniac, Montreal, H4S 1N5,
QC, Canada
Tel.: (514) 788-4862
Laboratory Instrument Mfr & Distr
N.A.I.C.S.: 334516

Anton Paar Colombia S.A.S.   **(1)**
Calle 26 No 69-76 Oficina, 1403, Bogota,
DC, Colombia
Tel.: (57) 6015084200
Laboratory Instrument Mfr & Distr
N.A.I.C.S.: 334516

Anton Paar Croatia d.o.o.   **(1)**
Ulica Velimira Skorpika 24/1, 10090, Zagreb, Croatia
Tel.: (385) 16609829
Laboratory Instrument Mfr & Distr
N.A.I.C.S.: 334516

Anton Paar Czech Republic
s.r.o.   **(1)**
Na Zahonech 809/6, 141 00, Prague,
Czech Republic
Tel.: (420) 233356634
Laboratory Instrument Mfr & Distr
N.A.I.C.S.: 334516

Anton Paar France S.A.S.   **(1)**
ZA Courtaboeuf 8 avenue de l'Atlantique,
91940, Les Ulis, France
Tel.: (33) 169181188
Laboratory Instrument Mfr & Distr
N.A.I.C.S.: 334516

Anton Paar Germany GmbH   **(1)**
Hellmuth-Hirth-Strasse 6, Scharnhausen,
73760, Ostfildern, Germany
Tel.: (49) 711720910
Laboratory Instrument Mfr & Distr
N.A.I.C.S.: 334516

Anton Paar Hungary Kft   **(1)**
Telepy u 24, 1096, Budapest, Hungary
Tel.: (36) 17943237
Laboratory Instrument Mfr & Distr
N.A.I.C.S.: 334516

Anton Paar India Pvt. Ltd.   **(1)**
760 Ground Floor, Phase 5 Udyog Vihar
Industrial Area, Gurgaon, 122 016, India
Tel.: (91) 1244932800
Laboratory Instrument Mfr & Distr
N.A.I.C.S.: 334516

Anton Paar Ireland Ltd.   **(1)**
Unit 21 Grattan Business Park Clonshaugh
Business and Technology Park, Dublin, D17
H526, Ireland
Tel.: (353) 12479820
Laboratory Instrument Mfr & Distr
N.A.I.C.S.: 334516

Anton Paar Italia S.R.L.   **(1)**
Via Albenga 78, 10098, Rivoli, Italy
Tel.: (39) 0119537560
Laboratory Instrument Mfr & Distr
N.A.I.C.S.: 334516

Anton Paar Japan K.K.   **(1)**
1st Fl Riverside Sumida 1-19-9 Tsutsumidori, Sumida-ku, Tokyo, 131-0034, Japan
Tel.: (81) 345632500
Laboratory Instrument Mfr & Distr
N.A.I.C.S.: 334516

Anton Paar Korea Ltd.   **(1)**
DaeDong Building 12F 109 Jungdae-Ro,
Songpa-Gu, 05718, Seoul, Korea (South)
Tel.: (82) 267475771
Laboratory Instrument Mfr & Distr
N.A.I.C.S.: 334516

Anton Paar Ltd.   **(1)**
Unit F The Courtyard Hatfield Rd, Saint Albans, AL4 0LA, Hertfordshire, United Kingdom
Tel.: (44) 1992514730
Laboratory Instrument Mfr & Distr
N.A.I.C.S.: 334516

Anton Paar Malaysia Sdn Bhd   **(1)**
Suite 12-04 Level 12 The Pinnacle, Persiaran Lagoon Bandar Sunway, 47500, Subang Jaya, Selangor, Malaysia

Tel.: (60) 376697888
Laboratory Instrument Mfr & Distr
N.A.I.C.S.: 334516

Anton Paar New Zealand Limited (1)
Unit 7 76 Paul Matthews Road, Rosedale,
Auckland, 0632, New Zealand
Tel.: (64) 94143190
Laboratory Instrument Mfr & Distr
N.A.I.C.S.: 334516

Anton Paar Nordic AB (1)
Lautruphoj 1, 2750, Ballerup, Denmark
Tel.: (45) 32422570
Laboratory Instrument Mfr & Distr
N.A.I.C.S.: 334516

**Anton Paar Olcum Aletleri Ticaret Ltd.
Sti.** (1)
Kucukbakkalkoy Mah Elvan Sk Pasific
Plaza B Blok, Atasehir, 34750, Istanbul,
Turkiye
Tel.: (90) 2165746665
Laboratory Instrument Mfr & Distr
N.A.I.C.S.: 334516

Anton Paar OptoTec GmbH (1)
Lise-Meitner-Str 6, 30926, Seelze, Germany
Tel.: (49) 511400950
Laboratory Instrument Mfr & Distr
N.A.I.C.S.: 334516

Anton Paar Poland Sp.z.o.o. (1)
ul Holubcowa 123, 02-854, Warsaw, Poland
Tel.: (48) 223955390
Laboratory Instrument Mfr & Distr
N.A.I.C.S.: 334516

Anton Paar ProveTec GmbH (1)
Ludwig-Erhard-Ring 13, 15827,
Blankenfelde-Mahlow, Germany
Tel.: (49) 3370856300
Laboratory Instrument Mfr & Distr
N.A.I.C.S.: 334516

Anton Paar QuantaTec Inc. (1)
1900 Corporate Dr, Boynton Beach, FL
33426
Tel.: (561) 731-4999
Laboratory Instrument Mfr & Distr
N.A.I.C.S.: 334516

**Anton Paar Shanghai Trading Co.,
Ltd.** (1)
11 Floor 2 Building High-Tec Oasis Park
2570 Hechuan Road, Shanghai, China
Tel.: (86) 4008202259
Laboratory Instrument Mfr & Distr
N.A.I.C.S.: 334516

Anton Paar ShapeTec BA d.o.o. (1)
Gornja Mocila bb, 74450, Brod, Bosnia &
Herzegovina
Tel.: (387) 66712271
Laboratory Instrument Mfr & Distr
N.A.I.C.S.: 334516

Anton Paar Singapore Pte Ltd. (1)
25 Bukit Batok Crescent 08-12 The Elitist,
Singapore, 658066, Singapore
Tel.: (65) 64604130
Laboratory Instrument Mfr & Distr
N.A.I.C.S.: 334516

Anton Paar Slovakia s.r.o. (1)
Hattalova 12/A, 83103, Bratislava, Slovakia
Tel.: (421) 232784530
Laboratory Instrument Mfr & Distr
N.A.I.C.S.: 334516

**Anton Paar Southern Africa (Pty)
Ltd** (1)
Gazelle Close Anton Paar Building Corpo-
rate Park South, Old Pretoria Road
Randjesfontein, Midrand, 1685, South Africa
Tel.: (27) 104430950
Laboratory Instrument Mfr & Distr
N.A.I.C.S.: 334516

Anton Paar Spain S.L.U. (1)
Camino de la Fuente de la Mora 9, 28050,
Madrid, Spain
Tel.: (34) 917520210
Laboratory Instrument Mfr & Distr
N.A.I.C.S.: 334516

Anton Paar Switzerland AG (1)
Pulverhausweg 13, 5033, Buchs, Switzer-
land
Tel.: (41) 627451680
Laboratory Instrument Mfr & Distr

Anton Paar Taiwan Co. Ltd. (1)
6F-3 No 32 Chenggong Road Section 1,
Taipei, 115, Taiwan
Tel.: (886) 289798228
Laboratory Instrument Mfr & Distr
N.A.I.C.S.: 334516

Anton Paar TriTec SA (1)
Vernets 6, 2035, Corcelles, Switzerland
Tel.: (41) 325521600
Laboratory Instrument Mfr & Distr
N.A.I.C.S.: 334516

Anton Paar USA, Inc. (1)
10215 Timber Ridge Dr, Ashland, VA 23005
Tel.: (804) 550-1051
Web Site: http://www.anton-paar.com
Sales Range: $1-9.9 Million
Emp.: 31
Laboratory Instruments & Process Measur-
ing Systems Distr
N.A.I.C.S.: 423490
Reinhard Eberl (Mng Dir)

MEP Instruments Pty Ltd (1)
Unit 11 56 Buffalo Road, Gladesville, 2111,
NSW, Australia
Tel.: (61) 2 8899 5200
Sales, Training & Service of Analytical Lab
Equipment
N.A.I.C.S.: 423490

ANTONG HOLDINGS CO., LTD.
Antong Holdings Building No 156
Tonggang West Street Donghai
Street, Fengze District, Quanzhou,
362000, Fujian, China
Tel.: (86) 4008665656
Web Site: https://www.antong56.com
Year Founded: 2002
600179—(SHG)
Rev.: $1,288,369,382
Assets: $1,811,836,124
Liabilities: $467,492,744
Net Worth: $1,344,343,380
Earnings: $328,826,698
Fiscal Year-end: 12/31/22
Chemical Product Mfr & Distr
N.A.I.C.S.: 325998

ANTONOV PLC
2 Hawkes Drive, Heathcote Industrial
Estate, Warwick, CV34 6LX, United
Kingdom
Tel.: (44) 1926455800
Web Site: http://www.antonovplc.com
Sales Range: Less than $1 Million
Emp.: 27
Automotive Transmission Products
Mfr
N.A.I.C.S.: 336390
Jan Eeuwe Haag (Chm & CEO)

Subsidiaries:

Antonov Automotive Technologies
B.V. (1)
Keystone Innovation Centre, Croxton Road,
Norfolk, IP24 1JD, United Kingdom
Tel.: (44) 1842768320
Web Site: http://www.antonovat.com
Automotive Components
N.A.I.C.S.: 336390

Antonov Automotive Technologies
Ltd (1)
2 Hawkes Drive Heathcote Industrial Estate,
Warwick, CV34 6LX, United Kingdom
Tel.: (44) 1926455800
Automotive Transmission Equipments Mfr
N.A.I.C.S.: 336390

ANTONY WASTE HANDLING
CELL LIMITED
A-59 Road No 10 Wagle Industrial
Estate, Wagale Industrial Estate
Thane West, Thane, 400604, Maha-
rashtra, India
Tel.: (91) 35449555
Web Site: https://www.antony-
waste.com
Year Founded: 2001

543254—(BOM)
Rev.: $91,016,193
Assets: $131,690,081
Liabilities: $58,977,432
Net Worth: $72,712,649
Earnings: $12,339,614
Emp.: 8,611
Fiscal Year-end: 03/31/22
Waste Management Services
N.A.I.C.S.: 562998
Jose Jacob Kallarakal (Chm & Mng
Dir)

Subsidiaries:

Antony Lara Enviro Solutions Private
Limited (1)
Integrated Solid Waste Management Facility
Project of MCGM Off, Eastern Express
Highway Near Kanamwar Nagar Kanjur-
marg East, Mumbai, 400 042, Maharashtra,
India
Tel.: (91) 8080032282
Web Site: https://www.antonylara.in
Solid Waste Management Services
N.A.I.C.S.: 562212

ANTRIM CONSTRUCTION
COMPANY LTD
130-134 High Street, Holywood,
BT18 9HW, Down, United Kingdom
Tel.: (44) 2890428661
Web Site:
http://www.antrimconstruction.net
Rev.: $24,104,817
Emp.: 55
Residential Home Construction Ser-
vices
N.A.I.C.S.: 236116
Jackie Scott (Mng Dir)

ANTRIM ENERGY INC.
Bankers Hall / Hollinsworth Bldg 610
301 - 8th Avenue SW, Calgary,
T2P1C5, AB, Canada
Tel.: (403) 264-5111   AB
Web Site:
http://www.antrimenergy.com
AEN—(OTCIQ)
Sales Range: Less than $1 Million
Emp.: 5
Oil & Gas Exploration, Production &
Sales
N.A.I.C.S.: 211120
Stephen E. Greer (Chm)

ANTWORKS PTE. LTD.
Level 39 10 Marina Boulevard Marina
Bay Financial Center Tower 2, Singa-
pore, 018983, Singapore
Tel.: (65) 6818 5724   SG
Web Site: http://ant.works
Cloud Platforms Developer & Ser-
vices
N.A.I.C.S.: 518210
Asheesh Mehra (Co-Founder)

Subsidiaries:

Benchmark Systems, Inc. (1)
1112 Church St, Lynchburg, VA 24504
Tel.: (434) 528-1038
Web Site: http://www.benchmark-
systems.com
Sales Range: $1-9.9 Million
Emp.: 50
Healthcare Industry Business Management
Software Developer
N.A.I.C.S.: 541511
Carolyn Fox (Dir-HR)

ANTZ CO., LTD.
53 Yangsan-ro, Yeongdeungpo-gu,
Seoul, 07271, Korea (South)
Tel.: (82) 226779960
Application Software Development
Services
N.A.I.C.S.: 541511
Park Chang-Jin (CEO)

ANUBHAV INFRASTRUCTURE
LIMITED
1A Fakir Dey Lane 1st Floor Bowba-
zar, 3rd Floor R NO 303, Howrah,
711 109, India
Tel.: (91) 8232013440
Web Site:
https://www.anubhavlimited.com
Year Founded: 2006
538833—(BOM)
Rev.: $51,953
Assets: $10,084,278
Liabilities: $581,233
Net Worth: $9,503,045
Earnings: ($2,987)
Emp.: 2
Fiscal Year-end: 03/31/21
Civil Engineering Services
N.A.I.C.S.: 541330
Dinesh Agarwal (Mng Dir & CFO)

ANUH PHARMA LTD.
3A Shiv Sagar Estate Dr A B Road,
Worli, Mumbai, 400018, India
Tel.: (91) 2266227575
Web Site:
https://www.anuhpharma.com
506260—(BOM)
Rev.: $67,136,610
Assets: $47,389,292
Liabilities: $18,209,305
Net Worth: $29,179,987
Earnings: $4,171,617
Emp.: 178
Fiscal Year-end: 03/31/22
Pharmaceuticals Product Mfr
N.A.I.C.S.: 325412
Ritesh Bipin Shah (Co-Mng Dir)

ANUKARAN COMMERCIAL
ENTERPRISES LIMITED
6/45 Old Anand Nagar near Reliance
Energy off Western Express Highway,
Santacruz East, Mumbai, 400 055,
India
Tel.: (91) 22 6158 8919
Web Site:
http://www.anukaranlimited.com
Sales Range: $1-9.9 Million
Fabric & Textile Product Whslr
N.A.I.C.S.: 424310
Kushal Shah (Mng Dir)

ANUP MALLEABLES LIMITED
G T Road NH2 Kandra PO Bhitia,
Govindpur, Dhanbad, 828109,
Jharkhand, India
Tel.: (91) 6540283002
Web Site:
http://www.anupmalleables.com
Year Founded: 1982
506087—(BOM)
Rev.: $613,655
Assets: $6,819,479
Liabilities: $4,235,339
Net Worth: $2,584,139
Earnings: $63,675
Fiscal Year-end: 03/31/20
Ferrous Casting Mfr
N.A.I.C.S.: 331523
Ashok Khaitan (Mng Dir)

ANUPAM FINSERV LTD.
501-502 Corporate Arena D P Pira-
mal Road, Mumbai, 400104, Gore-
gaon, India
Tel.: (91) 2246050267   In
Web Site:
https://www.anupamfinserv.com
Year Founded: 1991
530109—(BOM)
Rev.: $392,741
Assets: $2,650,003
Liabilities: $938,505
Net Worth: $1,711,498
Earnings: $172,865

Anupam Finserv Ltd—(Continued)

Emp.: 7
Fiscal Year-end: 03/31/21
Financial Management Services
N.A.I.C.S.: 523999
Nirmala Gala *(Mng Dir)*

Subsidiaries:

Vantage Knowledge Academy
Ltd. (1)
2nd Floor LN College H D Gaonkar Vidya
Sanku Plot No 89, Near General Kariappa
Bridge Rajendra Nagar, Mumbai, 400066,
India
Tel.: (91) 65656598
Web Site: http://www.vantagein.co.in
Rev.: $31,366
Assets: $566,687
Liabilities: $51,413
Net Worth: $515,274
Earnings: ($37,791)
Fiscal Year-end: 03/31/2018
Financial Management Consulting Services
N.A.I.C.S.: 541611
Neeta Rajesh Dedhia *(Mng Dir)*

ANUPAM RASAYAN INDIA LIMITED
8110 Sachin Gidc Estate, Sachin,
Surat, 394230, Gujarat, India
Tel.: (91) 2612398991
Web Site:
https://www.anupamrasayan.com
Year Founded: 1984
543275—(BOM)
Rev.: $147,571,106
Assets: $394,559,939
Liabilities: $158,844,914
Net Worth: $235,715,025
Earnings: $20,772,434
Emp.: 1,491
Fiscal Year-end: 03/31/22
Chemicals Mfr
N.A.I.C.S.: 325199
Kiran C. Patel *(Chm)*

ANUROOP PACKAGING LIMITED
607 Ijmima Interface Behind Infiniti
Mall-2, Malad West, Mumbai,
400064, India
Tel.: (91) 2249240182
Web Site:
https://www.anurooppackaging.com
Year Founded: 1995
542865—(BOM)
Rev.: $2,246,144
Assets: $4,873,225
Liabilities: $2,251,275
Net Worth: $2,621,949
Earnings: $402,117
Emp.: 12
Fiscal Year-end: 03/31/22
Corrugated Box Mfr
N.A.I.C.S.: 322211
Akash Sharma *(Chm & Mng Dir)*

ANV SECURITY GROUP, INC.
8th Floor Block B R&D Building Tsinghua Hi-Tech Park, Nanshan District,
Shenzhen, 518057, China
Tel.: (86) 75586656436 NV
Year Founded: 1981
Sales Range: Less than $1 Million
Emp.: 370
Network Video Surveillance & Video
Alarm Service Product Developer
N.A.I.C.S.: 561621
Weixing Wang *(Co-Founder, Chm & CEO)*

ANVA TUBES & COMPONENTS AB
Fraktgatan 6, 633 46, Eskilstuna,
Sweden
Tel.: (46) 016125050 SE

Web Site:
http://tubesandcomponents.anva.se
Sales Range: $10-24.9 Million
Steel, Pipe & Cast Iron Mfr & Whslr
N.A.I.C.S.: 331210
Markus Gunnerfjall *(CFO & Mng Dir)*

Subsidiaries:

AnVa Arion Sweden AB (1)
Gesallvagen 3, 544 50, Hjo, Sweden
Tel.: (46) 503 228 90
Web Site: http://arionsweden.anva.se
Emp.: 25
Machine Tools Mfr
N.A.I.C.S.: 333517
Patrick Stromberg *(CEO)*

AnVa GmbH (1)
Robert-Bosch-Strasse 33, D-73550, Waldstetten, Germany
Tel.: (49) 7171 495126
Web Site: http://www.anva.de
Industrial Machinery Mfr.
N.A.I.C.S.: 333998
Uwe Stutz *(Sls Mgr)*

AnVa KSG AB (1)
Gunnar W Anderssons Passage 27, 461
53, Trollhattan, Sweden
Tel.: (46) 520 21 18 20
Web Site: http://www.ksgab.se
Emp.: 25
Steel Products Mfr
N.A.I.C.S.: 331110
Anders Olausson *(Mng Dir)*

AnVa Rostfritt & Smide AB (1)
Stoerydsvagen 1, PO Box 91, SE-573 42,
Tranas, Sweden
Tel.: (46) 140 385160
Web Site: http://www.rostfrittosmide.se
Steel Products Mfr
N.A.I.C.S.: 331110
Hans-Peter Lindlof *(CEO & Mgr-Production)*

AnVa Titech System AB (1)
Vastra Ringvagen 4, 522 31, Tidaholm,
Sweden
Tel.: (46) 50219500
Web Site: http://titech.anva.se
Industrial Automation Mfr
N.A.I.C.S.: 333248
Mikael Helgevall *(Mng Dir)*

ANVIFISH JOINT-STOCK COMPANY
National Road 91 Thanh An Hamlet,
My Thoi Ward, Long Xuyen, An Giang, Vietnam
Tel.: (84) 76 923545
Web Site: http://www.anvifish.com
Year Founded: 2004
Fish Farming Services
N.A.I.C.S.: 112511
Minh Giau Truong *(Deputy CEO)*

ANWELL TECHNOLOGIES LTD.
8 Wilkie Road 03 01 Wilkie Edge,
Singapore, 228095, Singapore
Tel.: (65) 65337600
Web Site: http://www.anwell.com
Sales Range: $150-199.9 Million
Emp.: 2,375
Integrated Optical Disc Replication
Systems, Sub-Systems & Peripherals
Designer, Mfr & Sales
N.A.I.C.S.: 333310
Fan Kai Fan *(Founder, Chm & CEO)*

Subsidiaries:

Anwell Precision Technology (HK)
Limited (1)
Unit 10-15 9th Fl Metro Loft No 38 Kwai Hei
St, Kwai Chung, New Territories, China
(Hong Kong)
Tel.: (852) 24999178
Web Site: http://www.anwell.com
Sales Range: $25-49.9 Million
Emp.: 60
Optical Disc Mfr
N.A.I.C.S.: 334112

Anwell Solar Technologies
Limited (1)
Unit 10-15 9th Fl Metro Loft No 38 Kwai Hei
St, Kwai Chung, New Territories, China
(Hong Kong)
Tel.: (852) 24999178
Web Site: http://www.anwell.com
Emp.: 40
Optical Storage Media Disc Mfr
N.A.I.C.S.: 334112

Sungen International Limited (1)
Unit 1-7 6 F Metro Loft 38 Kwai Hei Street,
Kwai Chung, China (Hong Kong)
Tel.: (852) 35835286
Web Site: http://www.SUNGEN.com
Sales Range: $25-49.9 Million
Emp.: 20
Solar Cells Mfr & Mktg Services
N.A.I.C.S.: 334413

Umedisc Limited (1)
Rm 601 Metroloft 38 Kwai Hei St, Kwai
Chung, New Territories, China (Hong Kong)
Tel.: (852) 31062822
Web Site: http://www.umedisc.com
Sales Range: $25-49.9 Million
Emp.: 42
Optical Storage Media Disc Mfr
N.A.I.C.S.: 334112
Lawrence Luk *(Mgr)*

ANXIAN YUAN CHINA HOLDINGS LIMITED
Room 1215 Leighton Centre 77
Leighton Road, Causeway Bay, Hong
Kong, 999077, China (Hong Kong)
Tel.: (852) 3 115 2128 BM
Web Site:
http://www.anxianyuanchina.com
0922—(HKG)
Rev.: $40,105,944
Assets: $172,789,476
Liabilities: $43,304,003
Net Worth: $129,485,473
Earnings: $9,194,468
Emp.: 307
Fiscal Year-end: 03/31/22
Holding Company; Cemetery Services
N.A.I.C.S.: 551112
Fei Shing Law *(Deputy CEO & Sec)*

Subsidiaries:

Anxian Yuan (HK) Limited (1)
Room 1215 Leighton Centre 77 Leighton
Road, Causeway Bay, 999077, China
(Hong Kong)
Tel.: (852) 31152128
Holding Company
N.A.I.C.S.: 551112

Shanghai Liontown Hospital Logistics
Management Co., Ltd (1)
Block G 13th Floor Kelly Building No 432
West Huaihai Road, Shanghai, 200030,
China
Tel.: (86) 2152581051
Health Care Management Services
N.A.I.C.S.: 621610

Zhejiang Anxian Yuan Company
Limited (1)
2-1 Ban Shan Shui Hong Temple,
Hangzhou, 311108, Zhejiang, China
Tel.: (86) 4008840922
Cemetery Management Services
N.A.I.C.S.: 812220
Shi Hua *(Chm)*

ANXIN TRUST CO., LTD.
1F 2F and 29F Haitong Securities
Building No 689 Guangdong Road,
Huangpu District, Shanghai, 200001,
China
Tel.: (86) 2163410710
Web Site: http://www.anxintrust.com
Year Founded: 1995
600816—(SHG)
Sales Range: $25-49.9 Million
Portfolio Management Services
N.A.I.C.S.: 523940
Qin Yi *(Chm)*

ANXIN-CHINA HOLDINGS LIMITED
Rooms 3001-2 30th F Office Tower
Convention Plaza 1 Harbour Road,
Wanchai, China (Hong Kong)
Tel.: (852) 23428702 Ky
Web Site: http://www.anxin-china.com.hk
Sales Range: $75 00.0 Million
Emp.: 354
Emergency & Safety Products & Software
N.A.I.C.S.: 561621
Supeng Lin *(VP-Strategy Plng Dept)*

ANY SECURITY PRINTING COMPANY PLC
Halom utca 5, 1102, Budapest, Hungary
Tel.: (36) 14311200
Web Site: https://www.any.hu
Year Founded: 1851
ANY—(BUD)
Rev.: $118,327,113
Assets: $93,521,046
Liabilities: $64,486,090
Net Worth: $29,034,956
Earnings: $7,383,259
Emp.: 1,082
Fiscal Year-end: 12/31/22
Security Printing Services
N.A.I.C.S.: 561621
Gabor Peter *(CIO)*

Subsidiaries:

ATLAS Trade Distribution SRL (1)
Str Valea Cascadelor nr 21 cladirea 4 Sector 6, Bucharest, Romania
Tel.: (40) 728830305
Lithographic Printing Mfr
N.A.I.C.S.: 323111

Gyomai Kner Nyomda Zrt. (1)
10-12 Kossuth Street, Gyomaehdrod, 5500,
Bekes, Hungary
Tel.: (36) 66 887 400
Web Site: http://www.gyomaikner.hu
Printing Services
N.A.I.C.S.: 323111

Slovak Direct, spol. s.r.o. (1)
Nove Zahrady I/11, 821 05, Bratislava, Slovakia
Tel.: (421) 24823538283
Web Site: https://slovakdirect.sk
Plastic Card Mfr
N.A.I.C.S.: 326199

Specimen Papir es Nyomdaipari
Zrt. (1)
Kozma u 2, 1108, Budapest, Hungary
Tel.: (36) 14344720
Web Site: http://www.specimen.hu
Security Products Printing Services
N.A.I.C.S.: 323111

Tipo Direct Serv SRL (1)
2001 str Tighina 49/3 apartment 41C, Chisinau, Moldova
Tel.: (373) 22888285
Lithographic Printing Mfr
N.A.I.C.S.: 323111

Zipper Services SRL (1)
Bd 1 Decembrie 1918 No 1G Sect 3, Bucharest, Romania
Tel.: (40) 364101102
Lithographic Printing Mfr
N.A.I.C.S.: 323111

ANYANG IRON & STEEL GROUP CO., LTD.
Meiyuanzhuang, Yindu District, Anyang, 455004, Henan, China
Tel.: (86) 3723122587
Web Site: http://www.angang.com.cn
Year Founded: 1948
Sales Range: $1-4.9 Billion
Emp.: 35,000
Iron & Steel Products Mfr
N.A.I.C.S.: 332111

Subsidiaries:

AnYang Iron & Steel Inc. (1)
Meiyuan Zhuang, Yindu District, Anyang, 455004, Henan, China
Tel.: (86) 3723120175
Web Site: http://www.aysteel.com.cn
Rev.: $5,508,581,912
Assets: $5,984,947,697
Liabilities: $4,846,540,145
Net Worth: $1,138,407,552
Earnings: ($421,338,280)
Fiscal Year-end: 12/31/2022
Iron & Steel Product Mfr
N.A.I.C.S.: 331110
Cheng Guanjiang *(Chm)*

Xinyang Iron & Steel Co., Ltd. (1)
34 Xinming Road Minggang, Pingqiao District, Xinyang, Henan, China
Tel.: (86) 376 867 2022
Web Site: http://www.xyisco.com
Iron & Steel Products Mfr
N.A.I.C.S.: 332111
Dianzhou He *(Pres & Gen Mgr)*

ANYCOLOR INC.
Midtown East 11F 9-7-2 Akasaka, Minato-ku, Tokyo, 107-0052, Japan
Tel.: (81) 343354850
Web Site: https://www.anycolor.co.jp
Year Founded: 2017
5032—(TKS)
Entertainment Broadcasting Services
N.A.I.C.S.: 516120
Riku Tazumi *(CEO)*

ANYGEN CO LTD
206 Test Production Building
Gwangju Technopark 333 Cheomdan-gwa-ro, Buk-gu, Gwangju, 61008, Korea (South)
Tel.: (82) 627141166
Web Site: https://www.anygen.com
196300—(KRS)
Rev.: $6,643,954
Assets: $19,855,864
Liabilities: $9,581,083
Net Worth: $10,274,781
Earnings: ($4,759,045)
Emp.: 125
Fiscal Year-end: 12/31/22
Peptide Mfr & Distr
N.A.I.C.S.: 325199
Ji Yong Park *(Dir-R&D)*

ANYMEDI CO., LTD.
12th floor 4-ho 137 Olympic-ro 35-gil, Songpa-gu, 05510, Seoul, 05510, Korea (South)
Tel.: (82) 317961312
Web Site: https://www.anymedi.com
Year Founded: 2016
390110—(KRS)
Medical Device Mfr
N.A.I.C.S.: 339112
Guk Bae Kim *(CEO)*

ANYMIND GROUP, INC.
31/F Roppongi Hills Mori Tower
6-10-1 Roppongi, Minato-ku, Tokyo, 106-6131, Japan
Tel.: (81) 363845540
Web Site:
    https://www.anymindgroup.com
Year Founded: 2016
5027—(TKS)
Rev.: $237,231,400
Assets: $164,877,950
Liabilities: $68,425,590
Net Worth: $96,452,360
Earnings: $3,963,310
Emp.: 1,500
Fiscal Year-end: 12/31/23
Software Development Services
N.A.I.C.S.: 541511
Hitoshi Maruyama *(Mng Dir & Mng Dir-Publr Growth)*

ANYUAN COAL INDUSTRY

GROUP CO., LTD.
No 3 Dinggong Road, Xihu District, Nanchang, 330002, Jiangxi, China
Tel.: (86) 79187151886
600397—(SHG)
Rev.: $1,251,831,546
Assets: $1,247,882,374
Liabilities: $1,181,642,062
Net Worth: $66,240,313
Earnings: ($10,748,434)
Fiscal Year-end: 12/31/22
Coal Mining Services
N.A.I.C.S.: 212114
Hongxia Cao *(Deputy Gen Mgr)*

ANYWIRE CORPORATION
1 Babazusho, Nagaokakyo, 617-8550, Kyoto, Japan
Tel.: (81) 759561611
Web Site: https://www.anywire.jp
Year Founded: 2001
Telecommunication Servicesb
N.A.I.C.S.: 517810

ANZHENG FASHION GROUP CO., LTD.
Office Building 7 International Business Garden Lane 168 Linhong Road, Changning District, Shanghai, 200335, Zhejiang, China
Tel.: (86) 57387266066
Web Site:
    https://www.anzhenggroup.com
Year Founded: 2010
603839—(SHG)
Rev.: $317,750,093
Assets: $429,852,431
Liabilities: $105,934,173
Net Worth: $323,918,258
Earnings: ($49,823,551)
Emp.: 3,000
Fiscal Year-end: 12/31/22
Apparel Mfr & Distr
N.A.I.C.S.: 315250
Anzheng Zheng *(Chm, Pres & Gen Mgr)*

Subsidiaries:

Shanghai Fiona Chen Fashion Co., Ltd. (1)
Building7 No 168 LinHong Road, Changning District, Shanghai, 200335, China
Tel.: (86) 4008215899
Web Site: http://www.fionachen.cn
Fashion Apparels Retailer
N.A.I.C.S.: 458110

AO WORLD PLC
AO 5a The Parklands, Lostock, Bolton, BL6 4SD, United Kingdom
Tel.: (44) 1204672400
Web Site: https://www.ao-world.com
Year Founded: 2000
AO—(LSE)
Rev.: $1,311,916,185
Assets: $557,687,454
Liabilities: $383,741,480
Net Worth: $173,945,974
Earnings: $31,178,995
Emp.: 2,921
Fiscal Year-end: 03/31/24
Home Appliance Online Retailer
N.A.I.C.S.: 423620
John Roberts *(Founder & CEO)*

Subsidiaries:

AO Deutschland Limited (1)
Ben-Cammarata-Str 2, 50126, Bergheim, Germany
Tel.: (49) 22714869880
Web Site: http://www.ao.de
Electrical Product Retailer
N.A.I.C.S.: 449210

AO Recycling Limited (1)
Halesfield 15, Telford, TF7 4ER, United Kingdom
Tel.: (44) 1952583666

Web Site: http://www.ao-recycling.com
Electrical Product Retailer
N.A.I.C.S.: 449210

Electrical Appliance Outlet Limited (1)
Kemberton Rd, Hatesfield 16, Telford, TF7 4QS, United Kingdom
Tel.: (44) 1952947129
Web Site: http://www.ao-outlet.co.uk
Electrical Product Retailer
N.A.I.C.S.: 449210

Elekdirect Limited (1)
73 St Helens Rd, Bolton, BL3 3PR, United Kingdom
Tel.: (44) 1204531234
Web Site: http://www.elekdirect.co.uk
Electrical Product Retailer
N.A.I.C.S.: 449210

Expert Logistics Ltd. (1)
Weston Rd, Crewe, CW1 6BF, United Kingdom
Tel.: (44) 127 075 4830
Web Site: https://www.expertlogistics.co.uk
Sales Range: $25-49.9 Million
Emp.: 150
Distribution Company
N.A.I.C.S.: 541614

AOFRIO LIMITED
78 Apollo Drive Rosedale, Auckland, 632, New Zealand
Tel.: (64) 94774500
Web Site: https://aofrio.com
Year Founded: 1986
AOF—(NZX)
Rev.: $42,054,976
Assets: $37,030,016
Liabilities: $24,680,569
Net Worth: $12,349,447
Earnings: ($2,233,175)
Fiscal Year-end: 12/31/23
Other Electronic Parts & Equipment Merchant Wholesalers
N.A.I.C.S.: 423690
David Howell *(Chief Technical Officer)*

Subsidiaries:

AirMoVent Limited (1)
21 Arren Way Dr Rosedale, Auckland, 0632, New Zealand
Tel.: (64) 94146590
Web Site: http://www.wdtl.com
Sales Range: $25-49.9 Million
Emp.: 32
Induction Motor & Refrigeration Accessories Whslr
N.A.I.C.S.: 423610
Greg Allen *(Mng Dir)*

Wellington Drive Technologies Pte Ltd (1)
39 Tampines St 92 04-00, Singapore, Singapore
Tel.: (65) 81216015
Web Site: https://www.aofrio.com
Sales Range: $25-49.9 Million
Emp.: 32
Energy Saving Appliances Mfr
N.A.I.C.S.: 334512

Wellington Drive Technologies US, Inc. (1)
1407 Barclay Blvd, Buffalo Grove, IL 60089
Tel.: (847) 922-5098
Web Site: https://www.aofrio.com
Motor Vehicle Products Whslr
N.A.I.C.S.: 423120

Wellington Latin America Services SA de CV (1)
San Serafin No 4 Residencial, 76815, San Juan del Rio, Qro, Mexico
Tel.: (52) 14271129101
Refrigeration Controller Distr
N.A.I.C.S.: 423740

Wellington Motor Tecnolojileri San Tic Ltd Sti (1)
Fatih Sultan Mehmet Mah Poligon Cad No 8C Buyaka Kule 3 Floor, 11 Apartment 70 Tepeustu Umraniye, 34771, Istanbul, Turkiye
Tel.: (90) 2164201202

Web Site: https://www.aofrio.com
Sales Range: $25-49.9 Million
Emp.: 3
Energy Saving Appliances Mfr
N.A.I.C.S.: 334512

AOHATA CORPORATION
1-1-25 Tadanouminaka-Machi, Takehara, 729-2316, Hiroshima, Japan
Tel.: (81) 846260111   JP
Web Site: http://www.aohata.co.jp
Year Founded: 1932
Sales Range: $1-9.9 Million
Emp.: 378
Fruit Jellies, Jams & Preserves, Canned Fruits, Pasta Sauces, Cooking Sauces, Soups & Stews Mfr
N.A.I.C.S.: 311421
Eiichi Nozawa *(Chm)*

Subsidiaries:

AFC Co., Ltd. (1)
1-1-25 Tadanoumicyo, Takehara City, Hiroshima, 7292316, Japan
Tel.: (81) 846260777
Sales Range: $25-49.9 Million
Emp.: 3
Computer Controlled Warehousing of Processed Marine & Farm Produce
N.A.I.C.S.: 493130

Aohata Corporation, Jam Factory (1)
1-2-43 Tadanouminaka-machi, Takehara, 729-2316, Hiroshima, Japan
Tel.: (81) 846260586
Web Site: http://www.aohata.co.jp
Production & Sales of Processed Fruit Products, Jams & Jellies
N.A.I.C.S.: 333241

Geinan Shokuhin Co., Ltd. (1)
1678 Takeharacyo, Takehara City, Hiroshima, 725 0021, Japan
Tel.: (81) 846220232
Sales Range: $25-49.9 Million
Emp.: 180
Processed Fruit Products & Confectioneries Mfr & Sales
N.A.I.C.S.: 311999

Rainbow Shokuhin Co., Ltd. (1)
1-1-25 Tadanoumicyo, Takehara City, Hiroshima, 792 2316, Japan
Tel.: (81) 846262462
Web Site: http://www.aohata.co.jp
Local Food Specialties, Canned Goods, Oyster Extract & Other Health Foods Mfr
N.A.I.C.S.: 445298
Norio Yamamoto *(CEO)*

Techno-Aid Co., Ltd. (1)
1-1-25 Tadanouminaka-machi, Takehara, 729-2316, Hiroshima, Japan
Tel.: (81) 846262570
Web Site: http://www.aohata.co.jp
Introduction, Installation & Maintenance of Food Production Equipment; Sales of Food Production Equipment; Pest Extermination & Sanitizing
N.A.I.C.S.: 333241
Satoru Sakaguchi *(CEO)*

Tohoku Aohata Co., Ltd. (1)
484-1 Takanosu, Ooishidacyo
Kitamurayama-gun, Yamagata, 999 4101, Japan
Tel.: (81) 237353611
Web Site: http://www.aohata.co.jp
Processed Fruit Products, Processed Foods & Confectioneries Production & Sales
N.A.I.C.S.: 311999
Yukihiro Matsumoto *(CEO)*

AOI ELECTRONICS CO., LTD.
455-1 Kohzai Minamimachi, Takamatsu, 761-8014, Kagawa, Japan
Tel.: (81) 878821131
Web Site: https://www.aoi-
    electronics.co.jp
Year Founded: 1969
6832—(TKS)
Rev.: $224,350,010
Assets: $331,385,740
Liabilities: $46,091,530
Net Worth: $285,294,210

AOI Electronics Co., Ltd.—(Continued)

Earnings: ($34,768,600)
Emp.: 1,696
Fiscal Year-end: 03/31/24
Integrated Circuits, Modules, Thermal Print Heads, Chip Resistors & Resistor Networks Mfr
N.A.I.C.S.: 334412
Koji Nakayama (Pres)

Subsidiaries:

Hayama Industries Co., Ltd.   (1)
3-3-5 Asahimachi, Takamatsu, 760-0065, Kagawa, Japan
Tel.: (81) 878512001
Electronic Goods Mfr
N.A.I.C.S.: 334419

High Components Aomori Co., Ltd.   (1)
Aza Koizumi 275 Oaza Yamamichi, Tsuruta Town Kitatsugaru-gun, Aomori, 038-3515, Japan
Tel.: (81) 17 322 6340
Web Site: https://www.hc-aomori.co.jp
Semiconductor Mfr
N.A.I.C.S.: 334413
Akihiko Hiraishi (Pres)

Oume Electronics Co., Ltd.   (1)
3-3-2 Fujihashi Ome City, Tokyo, 198-0022, Japan
Tel.: (81) 42 832 1560
Web Site: https://www.oume-electronics.co.jp
Electronic Device Distr
N.A.I.C.S.: 423690
Yasuhiro Ueda (Pres)

AOI TYO HOLDINGS INC.

Osaki Center Bldg 5F 1-5-1 Osaki, Shinagawa-ku, Tokyo, 141-8580, Japan
Tel.: (81) 368935005
Web Site: http://www.aoityo.com
Year Founded: 2017
3975—(TKS)
Rev.: $598,149,930
Assets: $489,237,840
Liabilities: $274,999,130
Net Worth: $214,238,710
Earnings: ($11,737,600)
Fiscal Year-end: 12/31/19
Holding Company
N.A.I.C.S.: 551112
Yasuhito Nakae (CEO)

Subsidiaries:

AOI Pro. Inc.   (1)
Osaki Center Building 5F 1-5-1 Osaki, Shinagawa-ku, Tokyo, 141-8580, Japan
Tel.: (81) 337798000
Web Site: http://www.aoi-pro.com
Digital Content Business & Advertising Services
N.A.I.C.S.: 541810
Yoshio Sasuke (Sr Mng Officer)

Subsidiary (Domestic):

Digital Garden Inc.   (2)
2-36-13 Ebisu, Shibuya-ku, Tokyo, 150-0013, Japan
Tel.: (81) 3 5791 2215
Web Site: http://www.dgi.co.jp
Emp.: 11
Post Production Services
N.A.I.C.S.: 512191
Matsumoto Hirokazu (Pres)

Media Garden Inc.   (2)
2-1-56 Chigasaki-minami, Tsuduki-ku, Yokohama, 224 0037, Japan
Tel.: (81) 45 945 3800
Web Site: http://www.media-garden.co.jp
Emp.: 40
Commercial Film Studio
N.A.I.C.S.: 512110
Hitoshi Hara (Pres)

TYO Inc.   (2)
2-21-7 Kami Osaki, Shinagawa-ku, Tokyo, 141-0021, Japan
Tel.: (81) 3 5434 1580

Web Site: http://group.tyo.jp
Sales Range: $50-74.9 Million
Television Commercials Production Services
N.A.I.C.S.: 541890
Kazuyoshi Hayakawa (Pres & CEO)

Subsidiary (Domestic):

Camp KAZ Productions Inc.   (3)
3-1-35 Motoazabu, Minato-ku, Tokyo, 106-0046, Japan
Tel.: (81) 357721945
Web Site: http://www.campkaz.jp
Television Commercials Production Services
N.A.I.C.S.: 512110
Masaki Kuroda (Mgr-Production)

Ludens Co., Ltd.   (3)
Comfort Uehara Building 2F 2-43-7 Uehara, Shibuya-ku, Tokyo, 151-0064, Japan
Tel.: (81) 354520051
Web Site: http://www.ludens.co.jp
Computer Graphics & Visual Effects Production Services
N.A.I.C.S.: 512191

Mazri Inc.   (3)
3-2-5 Minami Aoyama, Minato-ku, Tokyo, 107-0062, Japan
Tel.: (81) 354142112
Web Site: http://www.mazri.com
Music Video Production Services
N.A.I.C.S.: 512110
Koji Chiba (CEO)

Monster Ultra Inc.   (3)
4-2-14 Roppongi, Minato-ku, Tokyo, 106-0032, Japan
Tel.: (81) 362291611
Web Site: http://www.monsterfilms.jp
Television Commercials & Music Video Production Services
N.A.I.C.S.: 512110

TYO Technical Ranch Inc.   (3)
Round Cross Minamiazabu Bldg 1F 4-11-21 Minami-Azabu, Minato-ku, Tokyo, 106-0047, Japan
Tel.: (81) 334732863
Web Site: http://www.ttr-inc.co.jp
Motion Picture Equipment Rental Services
N.A.I.C.S.: 532490
Jun Ebihara (Pres)

Theoria Communications Inc.   (3)
3-6-22 Shibakouen JC Bldg 4th Fl, Minato-ku, Tokyo, 105-0011, Japan
Tel.: (81) 368416007
Web Site: http://www.theoria.ne.jp
Website Planning & Production Services
N.A.I.C.S.: 513199
Joji Kojima (CEO)

ZEO Corporation   (3)
2-9-28 Hiroo, Shibuya-ku, Tokyo, 150-0012, Japan
Tel.: (81) 354678911
Web Site: http://www.zeo.co.jp
Marketing Communication Services
N.A.I.C.S.: 541613
Hiromasa Kuroi (Pres & CEO)

dwarf Inc.   (3)
4-14-18 Nukui, Nerima-ku, Tokyo, 176-0021, Japan
Tel.: (81) 359719888
Web Site: http://www.dwarf.co.jp
Animation Production Services
N.A.I.C.S.: 512191
Tsuneo Goda (Dir)

Rabbit Digital Group Co., Ltd.   (1)
1706/34 Rama VI Road, Rongmuang Pathumwan, Bangkok, 10330, Thailand
Tel.: (66) 2 219 2385
Web Site: https://www.rabbitstale.com
Emp.: 190
Advertising Services
N.A.I.C.S.: 541890

xpd Inc.   (1)
Cosmos Aoyama B1 5-53-67 Jingumae, Shibuya-ku, Tokyo, 150-0001, Japan
Tel.: (81) 35 468 5355
Web Site: https://xpd-inc.co.jp
Emp.: 360
Graphic Design Services
N.A.I.C.S.: 541430
Kazuyoshi Hayakawa (Pres & CEO)

AOKI HOLDINGS INC.

6-56 Kuzugaya, Tsuzuki-ku, Yokohama, 224-8588, Japan
Tel.: (81) 459411888
Web Site: http://www.aoki-hd.co.jp
8214—(TKS)
Rev.: $1,240,802,760
Assets: $1,562,121,470
Liabilities: $656,181,310
Net Worth: $905,940,160
Earnings: $50,064,140
Emp.: 3,014
Fiscal Year-end: 03/31/24
Fashion & Menswear Products Sales
N.A.I.C.S.: 541490
Akihiro Aoki (Pres)

Subsidiaries:

ANNIVERSAIRE Inc.   (1)
3-5-30 Kita-Aoyama, Minato-ku, Tokyo, 107-0061, Kanagawa, Japan
Tel.: (81) 357861088
Web Site: https://corp.anniversaire.co.jp
Emp.: 357
Bridal Services
N.A.I.C.S.: 812990

AOKI Inc.   (1)
6-56 Kuzugaya, Tsuzuki-ku, Yokohama, 224-8688, Kanagawa, Japan
Tel.: (81) 459411388
Web Site: http://www.aoki-style.com
Sales Range: Less than $1 Million
Emp.: 2,139
Clothes Distr & Fashion Designing Services
N.A.I.C.S.: 541490
Akihiro Aoki (Chm)

Kaikatsu Frontier Inc.   (1)
3-1-50 Kitayamada, Tsuzuki-ku, Yokohama, 224-0021, Kanagawa, Japan
Tel.: (81) 455904888
Web Site: https://www.kaikatsufrontier.co.jp
Emp.: 541
Women & Men Accessory Distr
N.A.I.C.S.: 458110

ORIHICA Inc.   (1)
6-56 Kuzugaya, Tsuzuki-ku, Yokohama, 224 8688, Kanagawa, Japan
Tel.: (81) 459455178
Web Site: http://www.orihica.com
Sales Range: $75-99.9 Million
Emp.: 500
Fashion Designing Services
N.A.I.C.S.: 541490
Kobaya Hi (Mgr)

VALIC Co., Ltd.   (1)
1-50 Kita-Yamata 3-Chome, Tsuzuki-ku, Yokohama, 224-0021, Kanagawa, Japan
Tel.: (81) 455904888
Web Site: http://www.valic.co.jp
Sales Range: $1-4.9 Billion
Emp.: 663
Entertainment Services
N.A.I.C.S.: 713990
Yusuke Nakabayashi (Pres & CEO)

AOKI SUPER CO., LTD.

1-1 Torii Nishi-tori, Nakamura-ku, Nagoya, 453-0054, Aichi, Japan
Tel.: (81) 52 4143600
Web Site: http://www.aokisuper.co.jp
Year Founded: 1974
99770—(JAS)
Sales Range: Less than $1 Million
Food Goods Retail Operator
N.A.I.C.S.: 459999
Toshiyuki Usami (Chm)

AON INC.

PO Box 296, Peterborough, K9J 7M4, ON, Canada
Tel.: (705) 742-5445
Web Site: http://www.aoninc.com
Sales Range: $150-199.9 Million
Emp.: 510
Retirement Community Development & Property Management Services
N.A.I.C.S.: 531311
Brad Smith (Pres & CEO)

AON PLC

122 Leadenhall Street, London, EC3V 4AN, United Kingdom
Tel.: (44) 2076235500   UK
Web Site: https://www.aon.com
Year Founded: 1979
AON—(NYSE)
Rev.: $13,376,000,000
Assets: $33,959,000,000
Liabilities: $34,701,000,000
Net Worth: ($742,000,000)
Earnings: $2,564,000,000
Emp.: 50,000
Fiscal Year-end: 12/31/23
Insurance Holding Company
N.A.I.C.S.: 551112
Gregory C. Case (CEO)

Subsidiaries:

Aon Corporation   (1)
200 E Randolph St, Chicago, IL 60601
Tel.: (312) 381-1000
Web Site: http://www.aon.com
Risk Solutions & Insurance Services
N.A.I.C.S.: 524298
Janet Osborn (Mng Dir-Washington)

Subsidiary (Domestic):

A&A Underwriting Services Inc.   (2)
7230 McGinnis Ferry Rd Ste 300, Suwanee, GA 30024-1289
Tel.: (678) 512-2400
Sales Range: Less than $1 Million
Emp.: 64
Insurance Brokers
N.A.I.C.S.: 524210

Subsidiary (Domestic):

Atlanta International Insurance Company   (3)
2 Central Sq, Cambridge, MA 02139-3311   (100%)
Tel.: (678) 512-2486
Rev.: $1,954,413
Assets: $83,885,188
Emp.: 14
Fire, Marine, And Casualty Insurance
N.A.I.C.S.: 524126

Subsidiary (Non-US):

AIM Gibraltar Ltd.   (2)
913 Europort, Gibraltar, Gibraltar
Tel.: (350) 20043882
Web Site: http://www.aon.com
Emp.: 19
Insurance Management Services
N.A.I.C.S.: 524298
Steven Lawler (Dir-Business Development)

AIM Sweden AB   (2)
Lagervagen 13 Byggnad 9, 832 56, Froson, Goteborg, Sweden
Tel.: (46) 635541035
Web Site: https://aimsweden.com
Risk Managemeng Srvices
N.A.I.C.S.: 524210

Accuracy SAS   (2)
16 Avenue Matignon, 75008, Paris, France
Tel.: (33) 158757000
Web Site: http://www.accuracy.com
Sales Range: $50-74.9 Million
Emp.: 100
Financial Advisory Services
N.A.I.C.S.: 523940
Christophe Leclerc (Partner)

Accuracy Srl   (2)
Piazza Cavour 2, 20121, Milan, Italy
Tel.: (39) 0236696201
Sales Range: $50-74.9 Million
Emp.: 15
Financial Advisory Services
N.A.I.C.S.: 523940
Giovanni Foti (Partner)

Subsidiary (Domestic):

Affinity Insurance Services, Inc.   (2)
159 E County Line Rd, Hatboro, PA 19040-1218
Tel.: (215) 773-4600
Web Site: http://www.affinityinsuranceservices.com

Sales Range: $250-299.9 Million
Emp.: 420
Insurance Services
N.A.I.C.S.: 524210
Bill Vit *(Pres)*

Subsidiary (Domestic):

Access Plans, Inc.   **(3)**
900 36th Ave NW Ste 105, Norman, OK
73072
Tel.: (405) 579-8525
Web Site: http://www.alliancehealthcard.com
Sales Range: $50-74.9 Million
Emp.: 78
Discount Medical Plan Services
N.A.I.C.S.: 524298

Subsidiary (Domestic):

Access Plans USA, Inc.   **(4)**
4929 W Royal Ln Ste 200, Irving, TX 75063
Tel.: (972) 915-3200
Web Site: http://www.accessplansusa.com
Sales Range: $25-49.9 Million
Emp.: 124
Healthcare Savings Membership Services
N.A.I.C.S.: 524298

Division (Domestic):

Care Entree   **(5)**
4929 W Royal Ln Ste 200, Irving, TX 75063
Tel.: (214) 259-0445
Web Site: https://www.careentree.com
Sales Range: $75-99.9 Million
Emp.: 60
Non-Insurance Health Care Services
N.A.I.C.S.: 561499

Subsidiary (Domestic):

America's Health Care Plan/Rx
Agency, Inc.   **(4)**
1100 NW Compton Dr 2nd Fl, Beaverton,
OR 97006
Tel.: (972) 915-3200
Web Site: https://www.ahcpsales.com
Insurance Marketing Consulting Services
N.A.I.C.S.: 524298

Subsidiary (Domestic):

JLT Services Corp.   **(3)**
13 Cornell Rd, Latham, NY 12110-1402
Tel.: (518) 782-3000
Web Site: http://www.jltservices.com
Sales Range: $25-49.9 Million
Emp.: 260
Insurance & Employee Benefits Services
N.A.I.C.S.: 524298

Subsidiary (Domestic):

Professional Dental Reviewers   **(4)**
13 Cornell Rd, Latham, NY 12110
Tel.: (518) 782-3000
Rev.: $2,700,000
Emp.: 16
Independent Dental Consultants
N.A.I.C.S.: 524291

Subsidiary (Domestic):

National Flood Services, Inc.   **(3)**
555 Corporate Dr, Kalispell, MT 59901
Tel.: (406) 756-8656
Web Site:
    https://www.nationalfloodservices.com
Flood Insurance
N.A.I.C.S.: 524126
Alan Blount *(CMO)*

Subsidiary (Non-US):

Agostini Insurance Brokers Grenada
Ltd   **(2)**
Scott Street, Saint George's, Grenada
Tel.: (473) 4734356861
Web Site: http://agostini.com
Insurance Management Services
N.A.I.C.S.: 524298

Agostini Insurance Brokers Ltd   **(2)**
119 Henry Street, Port of Spain, Trinidad &
Tobago
Tel.: (868) 6230576
Web Site: https://www.agostini.com
Emp.: 115
Insurance Management Services
N.A.I.C.S.: 524298

H. Alan Alcazar *(Chm)*

Agostini Insurance Brokers St. Lucia
Ltd   **(2)**
J E Bergasse Building 1st Floor Vide Bout-
ielle, West Indies, Castries, Saint Lucia
Tel.: (758) 4566500
Web Site: https://agostini.com
Insurance Management Services
N.A.I.C.S.: 524298
Mairi Low *(Sec & Controller-Fin)*

Subsidiary (Domestic):

Allen Insurance Associates, Inc.   **(2)**
520 N Harbor City Blvd, Melbourne, FL
32935-6555
Tel.: (321) 259-1998
Web Site: http://www.allenins.net
Emp.: 2
Advetising Agency
N.A.I.C.S.: 541810
Liz Allen *(Pres & CEO)*

Alliance HealthCard, Inc.   **(2)**
3500 Pkwy Ln Ste 720, Norcross, GA
30092
Tel.: (770) 734-9255
Web Site: http://www.alliancehealthcard.com
Emp.: 17
Health Insurance Services
N.A.I.C.S.: 524114

Subsidiary (Non-US):

Aon (Bermuda) Ltd.   **(2)**
Point House 6 Front Street, Hamilton,
HM11, Bermuda   **(70%)**
Tel.: (441) 2952220
Sales Range: $10-24.9 Million
Emp.: 127
N.A.I.C.S.: 524298

Aon (DIFC) Gulf LLC   **(2)**
DIFC Currency House Tower 2 Level 5, PO
Box 506746, Dubai, United Arab Emirates
Tel.: (971) 43896300
Insurance Brokerage Service Provider
N.A.I.C.S.: 524210
Mohamed M. Ismail Buhari *(Engr-IT Sup-
port)*

Aon (Thailand) Ltd.   **(2)**
989 Rama 1 Siam Tower Bldg 18th fl Unit A
C E, Bangkok, 10330, Thailand
Tel.: (66) 23054555
Risk Managemeng Srvices
N.A.I.C.S.: 524210

Aon Adjudication Services Ltd   **(2)**
Briarcliff House Kingsmead, Farnborough,
GU14 7TE, Hampshire, United Kingdom
Tel.: (44) 1252768000
Sales Range: $150-199.9 Million
Emp.: 950
Risk Managemeng Srvices
N.A.I.C.S.: 524210

Subsidiary (Domestic):

Aon Advisors, Inc.   **(2)**
Aon Center 200 E Randolph St, Chicago, IL
60601   **(100%)**
Tel.: (312) 381-3333
Sales Range: $300-349.9 Million
Emp.: 750
Insurance-Based Asset Management Pro-
grams
N.A.I.C.S.: 523940

Subsidiary (Non-US):

Aon Affinity Chile Ltda.   **(2)**
Av Apoquindo 5950 piso 10-11, Las Con-
des, 7560930, Santiago, Chile
Tel.: (56) 223365500
Web Site: http://www.aon.com
Sales Range: $75-99.9 Million
Emp.: 140
Risk Managemeng Srvices
N.A.I.C.S.: 524210

Aon Affinity sp zoo   **(2)**
00-12 Al Jana Pawla II, Warsaw, 00-124,
Poland
Tel.: (48) 228509700
Web Site: http://www.aon.com
Sales Range: $50-74.9 Million
Emp.: 70
Risk Managemeng Srvices
N.A.I.C.S.: 524210

Aon Asia Pacific Limited   **(2)**
34/F One Island East Taikoo Place 18
Westlands Road, Quarry Bay, Hong Kong,
999077, China (Hong Kong)
Tel.: (852) 28616666
Web Site: https://www.aon.com
Risk Managemeng Srvices
N.A.I.C.S.: 524210

Aon Austria Versicherungsmakler
GmbH   **(2)**
Schwarzenbergplatz 3, 1010, Vienna, Aus-
tria
Tel.: (43) 578000
Web Site: http://www.aon.com
Insurance Brokerage Services
N.A.I.C.S.: 524210

Subsidiary (Domestic):

Aon Benfield, Inc   **(2)**
200 E Randolph St Aon Ctr fl 3-15, Chi-
cago, IL 60601
Tel.: (312) 381-1000
Reinsurance Broker
N.A.I.C.S.: 524210
Richard Posgate *(CEO-EMEA)*

Subsidiary (Non-US):

Aon Bahrain W.L.L.   **(3)**
BMMI Tower Entrance 12th Floor Road
2813 Block 428, Al Seef Area, Manama,
1006, Bahrain
Tel.: (973) 17226066
Insurance Brokerage Service Provider
N.A.I.C.S.: 524210
Tony Meakin *(CEO)*

Aon Belgium NV   **(3)**
Telecomlaan 5-7, 1831, Diegem, Belgium
Tel.: (32) 27309511
Web Site: http://www.aon.be
Risk Managemeng Srvices
N.A.I.C.S.: 524210

Aon Benfield (Chile) Corredores de
Reaseguros Ltda.   **(3)**
Isidora Goyenechea 3477 Las Condes,
Santiago, 7550106, Chile
Tel.: (56) 222332116
Insurance Brokerage Service Provider
N.A.I.C.S.: 524210

Aon Benfield (New Zealand) Ltd.   **(3)**
Level 15 AMP Centre 29 Customs Street
West, PO Box 699, Auckland, 1010, New
Zealand
Tel.: (64) 93629580
Web Site: http://www.aon.co.nz
Sales Range: $150-199.9 Million
Emp.: 6
Reinsurance Services
N.A.I.C.S.: 524130
Jasmine Christie *(Gen Mgr)*

Aon Benfield (South Africa) Pty
Ltd.   **(3)**
The Galaxy Ste No 5 70-11 Eton Rd, Park-
down, Johannesburg, South Africa
Tel.: (27) 11 726 5755
Web Site: http://www.benfieldgroup.com
Sales Range: $1-4.9 Billion
Reinsurance Services
N.A.I.C.S.: 524130

Aon Benfield Bratislava s.r.o.   **(3)**
Karadzicova 16 City Business Centre V 5th
Floor, 821 08, Bratislava, Bratislavsky Kraj,
Slovakia
Tel.: (421) 232604222
Web Site: http://www.aon.com
Insurance Brokerage Service Provider
N.A.I.C.S.: 524291
Peter Stubbings *(CEO-ReSpecialty-Global
& Deputy)*

Aon Benfield Canada   **(3)**
225 King Street West Suite 1000, Toronto,
M5V 3M2, ON, Canada
Tel.: (416) 979-3300
Web Site: http://www.aon.com
Sales Range: $1-4.9 Billion
Emp.: 100
Reinsurance Services
N.A.I.C.S.: 524113

Aon Benfield China Limited   **(3)**
21/F Aon China Bldg 29 Queen S Rd C,

Central District, Hong Kong, China (Hong
Kong)
Tel.: (852) 28616694
Risk Managemeng Srvices
N.A.I.C.S.: 524210

Aon Benfield Colombia Ltda. Corre-
dores de Reaseguros   **(3)**
Av cr 9 113 52 of 505 Edif Torres Unidas 2,
Bogota, Colombia
Tel.: (57) 16222222
Emp.: 52
Risk Managemeng Srvices
N.A.I.C.S.: 524210

Subsidiary (Domestic):

Aon Benfield Fac Inc.   **(3)**
200 E Randolph St, Chicago, IL 60601-
6535
Tel.: (312) 381-1000
Risk Managemeng Srvices
N.A.I.C.S.: 524210
Paul Summers *(Global CEO)*

Subsidiary (Non-US):

Aon Benfield Greece SA   **(3)**
1-3 Tzavella & Ethnikis Antistaseos Str
Business Plaza Building 1, Halandri, 15231,
Greece
Tel.: (30) 2106386700
Web Site: http://www.aon.com
Risk Managemeng Srvices
N.A.I.C.S.: 524210

Aon Benfield Iberia, Correduria de
Reaseguros SA   **(3)**
Calle Rosario Pino 14 - 16, Madrid, 28020,
Spain
Tel.: (34) 902114611
Emp.: 700
Risk Managemeng Srvices
N.A.I.C.S.: 524210

Subsidiary (Domestic):

Aon Benfield Inc.   **(3)**
5600 W 83rd St 8200 Tower Ste 1100, Min-
neapolis, MN 55437
Tel.: (952) 886-8000
Web Site: http://www.aonbenfield.com
Sales Range: $400-449.9 Million
Emp.: 700
Reinsurance Brokerage & Related Risk
Management Services
N.A.I.C.S.: 524130

Subsidiary (Non-US):

Aon Benfield Israel Limited   **(3)**
4 Berkovitch Street Museum Building 18th
fl, 18th Floor, Tel Aviv, 64238, Israel
Tel.: (972) 36935100
Web Site: http://www.aon.com
Insurance Brokerage Service Provider
N.A.I.C.S.: 524210

Aon Benfield Italia Spa   **(3)**
Via Andrea Ponti 8/10, Milan, 20143, MI,
Italy
Tel.: (39) 02454341
Risk Managemeng Srvices
N.A.I.C.S.: 524210

Aon Benfield Limited   **(3)**
122 Leadenhall Street, London, EC3V 4PT,
United Kingdom
Tel.: (44) 2070880044
Web Site: http://www.aonbenfield.com
Sales Range: $650-699.9 Million
Reinsurance & Risk Intermediary Services
N.A.I.C.S.: 524130

Aon Benfield Malaysia Limited   **(3)**
Level 10 Tower 3 Avenue 7 the Horizon,
Bangsar South No 8 Jalan Kerinchi, 59200,
Kuala Lumpur, WP, Malaysia
Tel.: (60) 327736900
Risk Managemeng Srvices
N.A.I.C.S.: 524210

Aon Benfield Netherlands CV   **(3)**
Paalbergweg 2-4, Amsterdam, 1105 AG,
Netherlands
Tel.: (31) 204305200
Risk Managemeng Srvices
N.A.I.C.S.: 524210

Aon Benfield Peru Corredores
Reaseguros SA   **(3)**

Aon plc—(Continued)

Calle Andres Reyes 437 Piso 7, San Isidro, L27, Peru
Tel.: (51) 12124210
Web Site: http://www.aon.com
Sales Range: $50-74.9 Million
Emp.: 21
Risk Managemeng Services
N.A.I.C.S.: 524210
Luis Jose Pardo (CEO)

Aon Benfield Pte. Ltd. (3)
2 Shenton Way #26-01 SGX Centre 1, Singapore, 068804, Singapore
Tel.: (65) 65356511
Web Site: http://www.benfieldgroup.com
Sales Range: $150-199.9 Million
Emp.: 500
Reinsurance Services
N.A.I.C.S.: 524130

Aon Benfield Pty. Ltd. (3)
L 33 201 Kent St, Sydney, 2000, NSW, Australia
Tel.: (61) 292537000
Web Site: http://www.benfieldgroup.com
Sales Range: $25-49.9 Million
Emp.: 50
Reinsurance Services
N.A.I.C.S.: 524130

Aon Benfield Ruckversicherungsmak-ler Ges.mbH (3)
Geiselbergstrasse 17, Vienna, 1110, Austria
Tel.: (43) 57800231
Web Site: http://www.aon.com
Emp.: 10
Risk Managemeng Srvices
N.A.I.C.S.: 524210

Aon Benfield S.A. de C.V. (3)
Insurgentes 1457 Piso 8 Torre Manacar, Col Insurgentes Mixcoac, 03920, Mexico, DF, Mexico
Tel.: (52) 5555982398
Web Site: http://www.aonbenfield.com
Sales Range: $150-199.9 Million
Reinsurance Services
N.A.I.C.S.: 524130

Subsidiary (Domestic):

Aon Benfield Securities, Inc. (3)
Aon Ctr 200 E Randolph St, Chicago, IL 60601
Tel.: (312) 381-4488
Risk Managemeng Srvices
N.A.I.C.S.: 524210

Subsidiary (Non-US):

Aon Group Japan Ltd. (3)
Capitol Tower 11th Floor 2-10-3, Nagatacho Chiyoda-ku, Tokyo, 100-0014, Japan
Tel.: (81) 345894200
Insurance Brokerage Services
N.A.I.C.S.: 524210

Aon Reinsurance Solutions Asia Pte. Ltd. (3)
SGX Centre 1 2 Shenton Way 26-01, Singapore, 068804, Singapore
Tel.: (65) 65356511
Financial Services
N.A.I.C.S.: 551112
Vinod Krishnan (CEO)

Aon Reinsurance Solutions MENA Limited (3)
DIFC Al Fattan Currency House Tower 2 Level 5, PO Box 506746, Dubai, United Arab Emirates
Tel.: (971) 43896300
Insurance Management Services
N.A.I.C.S.: 524298
Ahmad Rajab (CEO)

Subsidiary (Domestic):

Paragon Strategic Solutions Inc. (3)
3600 American Blvd W Ste 700, Minneapolis, MN 55431
Tel.: (952) 886-8016
Sales Range: $600-649.9 Million
Emp.: 50
Reinsurance Risk Management Services
N.A.I.C.S.: 524130
Patrick Van Wert (Pres-Reinsurance Practice)

Subsidiary (Non-US):

Aon Beteiligungsmanagement Deutschland GmbH & Co. KG (2)
Caffamacherreihe 16, 20355, Hamburg, Germany
Tel.: (49) 4036050
Insurance Management Services
N.A.I.C.S.: 524298

Aon Bolivia SA Corredores de Seguros (2)
Aon Building St 14 N 8164, Calacoto, La Paz, Bolivia
Tel.: (591) 22790955
Web Site: https://www.aon.com
Risk Managemeng Srvices
N.A.I.C.S.: 524210

Aon Bulgaria EOOD (2)
Alexander Stamboliyski Blvd No 103 4th floor, Sofia, 1303, Bulgaria
Tel.: (359) 29337800
Web Site: http://www.aon.com
Sales Range: $50-74.9 Million
Emp.: 37
Risk Managemeng Srvices
N.A.I.C.S.: 524210

Aon Business Consulting Ltd. (2)
Ilica 216, 10000, Zagreb, Croatia
Tel.: (385) 14558780
Web Site: https://www.ano.hr
Insurance Brokerage Services
N.A.I.C.S.: 524210

Aon CR Srl (2)
Corso Andrea Podesta 1, Genoa, 16121, Italy
Tel.: (39) 01057141
Risk Managemeng Srvices
N.A.I.C.S.: 524210

Aon Canada Inc. (2)
20 Bay Street Suite 2300 Waterpark Place, Toronto, M5J 2N9, ON, Canada (100%)
Tel.: (416) 868-5500
Web Site: http://www.aon.ca
Sales Range: $100-124.9 Million
Emp.: 300
Insurance Agents Brokers & Service
N.A.I.C.S.: 524298

Subsidiary (Domestic):

Aon Tarizeau Inc. (3)
1801 Mcgill College Suite 550, Montreal, H3C 4M8, QC, Canada (100%)
Tel.: (514) 840-7810
Web Site: http://www.aon.com
Rev.: $1,133,900
Emp.: 200
Insurance Agents Brokers & Service
N.A.I.C.S.: 524298

Subsidiary (Non-US):

Aon Captive Services Group (2)
Aon House 30 Woodbourne Ave, Pembroke, HM 08, Bermuda (100%)
Tel.: (441) 2952220
Web Site: http://www.aon.com
Sales Range: $25-49.9 Million
Emp.: 100
Captive Management & Insurance Services
N.A.I.C.S.: 541611

Aon Cash Management B.V. (2)
Admiraliteitskade 62, 3063 ED, Rotterdam, Netherlands
Tel.: (31) 104488911
Financial Services
N.A.I.C.S.: 551112

Aon Central and Eastern Europe AS (2)
Vaclavske namesti 832/19, 110 00, Prague, Czech Republic
Tel.: (420) 234618357
Web Site: https://www.aon.com
Emp.: 2
Risk Managemeng Srvices
N.A.I.C.S.: 524210

Aon Centre for Innovation and Analytics Ltd (2)
Metropolitan Building James Joyce Street, Dublin, Ireland
Tel.: (353) 12666000
Web Site: http://www.aon.com

Insurance Management Services
N.A.I.C.S.: 524298
Todd Curry (CEO)

Subsidiary (Domestic):

Aon Consulting, Inc. (2)
1000 Rockey Ave, New York, NY 10038 (100%)
Tel.: (212) 441-1000
Web Site: http://www.aon.com
Sales Range: $150-199.9 Million
Insurance Brokerage & Financial Services
N.A.I.C.S.: 541612

Branch (Domestic):

Aon Consulting (3)
400 Atrium Dr, Somerset, NJ 08873
Tel.: (732) 302-2100
Web Site: http://www.aonconsulting.com
Rev.: $16,300,000
Emp.: 155
Administrative Management & General Management Consulting Services
N.A.I.C.S.: 541611
Daniel Hunger (CFO)

Aon Consulting (3)
555 E Lancaster Ave Ste 300, Radnor, PA 19087 (100%)
Tel.: (610) 834-2100
Web Site: http://www.aon.com
Rev.: $19,000,000
Emp.: 77
Employee Benefit Consulting Services
N.A.I.C.S.: 541612

Aon Consulting (3)
301 State Rt 17 Fl 4, Rutherford, NJ 07070-2599 (100%)
Tel.: (201) 460-6891
Web Site: http://www.aon.com
Sales Range: $10-24.9 Million
Emp.: 80
Insurance Brokers
N.A.I.C.S.: 541612

Subsidiary (Domestic):

Aon Consulting & Insurance Services (3)
199 Fremont St Fl 15, San Francisco, CA 94105-2253
Tel.: (415) 486-7500
Web Site: http://www.aon.com
Sales Range: $75-99.9 Million
Emp.: 250
Risk Managemeng Srvices
N.A.I.C.S.: 524210

Unit (Domestic):

Aon Consulting - San Francisco (4)
199 Fremont St Fl 14, San Francisco, CA 94105 (100%)
Tel.: (415) 486-7500
Web Site: http://www.aon.com
Sales Range: $75-99.9 Million
Emp.: 250
Provider of Human Resources Consulting Services
N.A.I.C.S.: 524210

Aon Insurance Services (4)
10880 Wilshire Blvd, Los Angeles, CA 90024-4101
Tel.: (310) 234-6800
Web Site: http://www.aon.com
Sales Range: $10-24.9 Million
Emp.: 90
Insurance Agents & Brokers
N.A.I.C.S.: 524210

Subsidiary (Non-US):

Aon Consulting (Benefits) Limited (3)
Lorica House, GU51 2RD, Fleet, United Kingdom - England
Tel.: (44) 8452184050
Insurance Management Services
N.A.I.C.S.: 524298

Aon Consulting (PNG) Ltd. (3)
Level 1 Aon Haus MacGregor Street, PO Box 479, Port Moresby, Papua New Guinea
Tel.: (675) 3224544
Risk Managemeng Srvices
N.A.I.C.S.: 524210
Chris Hagan (Gen Mgr)

Aon Consulting (Thailand) Ltd. (3)
989 Siam Tower Bldg 18Fl Rama I Rd Pathumwan, 10330, Bangkok, Thailand
Tel.: (66) 23054555
Insurance Brokerage Services
N.A.I.C.S.: 524210

Branch (Domestic):

Aon Consulting - Chicago (3)
200 E Randolph St, Chicago, IL 60601
Tel.: (312) 381-1000
Web Site: http://www.aon.com
Sales Range: $75-99.9 Million
Human Resource & Executive Search Consulting Services
N.A.I.C.S.: 541612

Subsidiary (Non-US):

Aon Consulting Argentina SA (3)
Emma de la Barra 353 Dique 4 Puerto Madero, Buenos Aires, C1107BXA, Argentina
Tel.: (54) 1148148000
Web Site: https://www.aon.com
Sales Range: $150-199.9 Million
Emp.: 50
Risk Managemeng Srvices
N.A.I.C.S.: 524210

Aon Consulting Lesotho (Pty) Ltd. (3)
4 Aon House Bowker Road, Old Europa, Maseru, 100, Lesotho
Tel.: (266) 22313540
Web Site: http://www.aon.com
Emp.: 30
Risk Managemeng Srvices
N.A.I.C.S.: 524210

Aon Consulting New Zealand Ltd. (3)
Level 16 AMP Centre 29 Customs Street West, Auckland, 1010, New Zealand (100%)
Tel.: (64) 93629000
Web Site: http://www.aon.co.nz
Sales Range: $10-24.9 Million
Emp.: 24
Provider of Human Capital Management Services
N.A.I.C.S.: 541611

Aon Consulting South Africa (Pty) Ltd. (3)
1 Sandton Drive 4th Floor, Sandton, Johannesburg, 2196, South Africa
Tel.: (27) 119447000
Web Site: http://www.aon.co.za
Risk Managemeng Srvices
N.A.I.C.S.: 524210

Aon Corporation Australia (3)
Level 33 201 Kent St, Sydney, 2000, NSW, Australia (100%)
Tel.: (61) 292537000
Web Site: https://www.aon.com.au
Sales Range: $25-49.9 Million
Emp.: 1,800
Human Capital Management, Insurance & Risk Services
N.A.I.C.S.: 541611

Branch (Domestic):

Aon Global Risk Consulting (3)
7650 W Courtney Campbell Causeway Ste 1000, Tampa, FL 33607-1481
Tel.: (813) 636-3550
Web Site: http://www.aon.com
Sales Range: $10-24.9 Million
Emp.: 90
Risk Solutions Consulting
N.A.I.C.S.: 541618
Brenda Cooper (Sr VP)

Subsidiary (Non-US):

Aon Hewitt - Montreal (3)
700 De La Gauchetiere Street West, Montreal, H3B 0A4, QC, Canada (100%)
Tel.: (514) 845-6231
Web Site: http://www.aon.com
Sales Range: $75-99.9 Million
Emp.: 500
Business Consulting Services
N.A.I.C.S.: 541611

Aon Hewitt Consulting Korea Inc. (3)
7th Floor Gwanghwamun Building 149

Sejong-daero, Jongro-gu, Seoul, 110-730, Korea (South)
Tel.: (82) 23993600
Insurance Brokerage Service Provider
N.A.I.C.S.: 524210

Subsidiary (Domestic):

Aon Management Consulting/Rath & Strong Inc. **(3)**
45 Hayden Ave Ste 2700, Lexington, MA 02421-7951
Tel.: (781) 861-1700
Sales Range: $1-9.9 Million
Emp.: 20
Consulting Services
N.A.I.C.S.: 541618
Daniel L. Quinn *(Pres & CEO)*

Subsidiary (Non-US):

Aon Reed Stenhouse, Inc. **(3)**
20 Bay Street, Toronto, M5J 2N9, ON, Canada **(100%)**
Tel.: (416) 868-5500
Web Site: http://www.aon.ca
Sales Range: $100-124.9 Million
Emp.: 400
International Insurance & Reinsurance Brokering & Risk Management
N.A.I.C.S.: 524298

Subsidiary (Domestic):

McLagan Partners Inc. **(3)**
1600 Summer St Ste 601, Stamford, CT 06905
Tel.: (203) 359-2878
Web Site: http://www.mclagan.aon.com
Sales Range: $25-49.9 Million
Emp.: 60
Consulting Services
N.A.I.C.S.: 541611

Radford **(3)**
2570 N 1st St Ste 500, San Jose, CA 95131
Tel.: (408) 321-2500
Web Site: http://www.radford.aon.com
Sales Range: $25-49.9 Million
Emp.: 65
Consulting Services
N.A.I.C.S.: 541618

Branch (Domestic):

Aon Corp. **(2)**
10461 Mill Run Cir, Owings Mills, MD 21117-5544
Tel.: (410) 363-5000
Web Site: http://www.aon.com
Rev.: $260,000
Emp.: 3
Insurance Brokers
N.A.I.C.S.: 524210
Frank G. Zarb *(Pres)*

Aon Corp. **(2)**
299 S Main St Ste 1700, Salt Lake City, UT 84111-2279
Tel.: (801) 488-2550
Web Site: http://www.ano.com
Sales Range: Less than $1 Million
Emp.: 10
Insurance Agents Brokers & Service
N.A.I.C.S.: 524298

Subsidiary (Non-US):

Aon Credit International Schweiz AG **(2)**
Vulkanstrasse 106, PO Box 1893, 8048, Zurich, Switzerland
Tel.: (41) 582661211
Emp.: 125
Insurance Management Services
N.A.I.C.S.: 524298
Felix Kenny *(Gen Mgr)*

Aon Denmark A/S **(2)**
Strandgade 4C, 1401, Copenhagen, Denmark
Tel.: (45) 32697000
Web Site: http://www.aon.com
Insurance Brokerage Services
N.A.I.C.S.: 524210

Aon Deutschland Beteiligungs GmbH **(2)**
Caffamacherreihe 16, Neustadt, 20355, Hamburg, Germany

Tel.: (49) 4036050
Insurance Management Services
N.A.I.C.S.: 524298

Aon Direct Group Espana SL **(2)**
Ayala 10 Fl 2, Madrid, 28001, Spain
Tel.: (34) 914320790
Sales Range: $50-74.9 Million
Emp.: 5
Direct Marketing Services
N.A.I.C.S.: 524210

Aon Direct Group Inc. **(2)**
2255 Sheppard Ave E Ste E400, Toronto, M2J 4Y1, ON, Canada **(100%)**
Tel.: (416) 756-1573
Web Site: http://www.aon.ca
Sales Range: Less than $1 Million
Emp.: 14
Insurance Agents Brokers & Service
N.A.I.C.S.: 524298

Aon Finland Oy **(2)**
Mannerheimintie 18, 00100, Helsinki, Finland
Tel.: (358) 201266200
Web Site: https://www.aon.com
Risk Managemeng Srvices
N.A.I.C.S.: 524210

Aon France Finance SA **(2)**
31-35 Rue de la Federation, 75717, Paris, France
Tel.: (33) 147831010
Web Site: http://www.aon.fr
Sales Range: $300-349.9 Million
Emp.: 800
Risk Managemeng Srvices
N.A.I.C.S.: 524210

Aon Gil y Carvajal Correduria de Seguros SA **(2)**
Toro 21 2 A, Salamanca, 37002, Spain
Tel.: (34) 923271224
Web Site: http://www.aon.es
Risk Managemeng Srvices
N.A.I.C.S.: 524210

Aon Global Risk Consulting AB **(2)**
Valhallavagen 117, 115 31, Stockholm, Sweden
Tel.: (46) 86141700
Management Consulting Services
N.A.I.C.S.: 541611
Martin Persson *(Mng Dir)*

Aon Global Risk Consulting Luxembourg Sarl **(2)**
534 Rue De Neudorf, 2220, Luxembourg, Luxembourg
Tel.: (352) 317171
Web Site: http://www.aon.lu
Sales Range: $50-74.9 Million
Emp.: 20
Risk Managemeng Srvices
N.A.I.C.S.: 524210
Fabrice Frere *(Mng Dir)*

Aon Global Services, Inc. **(2)**
25 Centurion Dr, Markham, L3R 5N8, ON, Canada **(100%)**
Tel.: (905) 477-8244
Web Site: http://www.globalsvr.com
Sales Range: $10-24.9 Million
Emp.: 20
Pension Mutual Insurance
N.A.I.C.S.: 524292

Aon Greece S.A. **(2)**
Athens Tower 24th Floor 2 Mesogion Street, Attiki, 11527, Athens, Greece
Tel.: (30) 2107472760
Web Site: http://www.aon.com
Insurance Management Services
N.A.I.C.S.: 524298
Panagiotis D. Galatis *(CFO, COO & Head-Compliance)*

Aon Group Holdings International 1 B.V. **(2)**
Admiraliteitskade 62, 3063 ED, Rotterdam, Netherlands
Tel.: (31) 104488911
Holding Company
N.A.I.C.S.: 551112

Subsidiary (Domestic):

Aon Group, Inc. **(2)**
200 E Randolph St, Chicago, IL 60601
Tel.: (312) 381-1000

Risk Managemeng Srvices
N.A.I.C.S.: 524210

Aon Healthcare **(2)**
199 Fremont St Fl 15, San Francisco, CA 94105-2253
Tel.: (415) 486-6200
Sales Range: $200-249.9 Million
Emp.: 250
N.A.I.C.S.: 524128
Matt Davis *(Pres)*

Aon Healthcare **(2)**
501 Corporate Centre Dr Ste 300, Franklin, TN 37067
Tel.: (615) 771-8100
Web Site: http://www.aon.com
Rev.: $2,900,000
Emp.: 35
Insurance Agents Brokers & Service
N.A.I.C.S.: 524210

Subsidiary (Non-US):

Aon Hewitt Financial Advice Ltd. **(2)**
Level 33 201 Kent Street, Sydney, 2000, NSW, Australia
Tel.: (61) 292537100
Web Site: http://www.aonhewitt.com.au
Insurance Management Services
N.A.I.C.S.: 524298
Jayson Walker *(Partner)*

Aon Hewitt Saudi Arabia LLC **(2)**
The Business Gate Building No 16 Zone B Airport Road, PO Box 61192, 11565, Riyadh, Saudi Arabia
Tel.: (966) 114422761
Web Site: http://www.aon.com
Human Resource Consulting Services
N.A.I.C.S.: 541612
Saleh Al-Harthi *(CEO)*

Aon Holding Deutschland GmbH **(2)**
Caffamacherreihe 16, 20355, Hamburg, Germany **(100%)**
Tel.: (49) 4036050
Web Site: http://www.aon-jh.com
Rev.: $118,154,428
Emp.: 750
Holding Company; Owner of Insurance Brokerage & Consulting Service Providers
N.A.I.C.S.: 524298
Jurgen Grupe *(Mng Dir)*

Subsidiary (Non-US):

Aon (Schweiz) AG **(3)**
Vulkanstrasse 106, PO Box 1893, 8048, Zurich, Switzerland **(100%)**
Tel.: (41) 582661211
Web Site: http://www.aon.com
Sales Range: $50-74.9 Million
Emp.: 100
Provider of Risk Management Services
N.A.I.C.S.: 524126

Subsidiary (Domestic):

Aon Jauch & Huebener GmbH **(3)**
Caffamacherreihe 16, 20355, Hamburg, Germany **(100%)**
Tel.: (49) 4036050
Web Site: http://www.aon.de
Sales Range: $125-149.9 Million
Provider of Insurance Brokerage & Consulting Services
N.A.I.C.S.: 524298

Subsidiary (Non-US):

Aon Jauch & Huebener GmbH **(3)**
Schwarzenbergplatz 3, 1010, Vienna, Austria **(100%)**
Tel.: (43) 578000
Web Site: http://www.aon.com
Sales Range: $25-49.9 Million
Emp.: 150
Insurance Brokerage & Consulting Services
N.A.I.C.S.: 524298

Subsidiary (Domestic):

Aon Jauch & Hubener Employee Benefit Consulting Ges.mbH **(4)**
Schwarzenbergplatz 3, 1010, Vienna, Austria
Tel.: (43) 578000
Risk Managemeng Srvices
N.A.I.C.S.: 524210

Subsidiary (Non-US):

Aon Slovakia **(3)**
Karadzicova 16 City Business Centre V 5th Floor, City Business Centre V, Bratislava, 821 08, Bratislavsky Kraj, Slovakia **(100%)**
Tel.: (421) 232604222
Web Site: http://www.aonstach.sk
Sales Range: Less than $1 Million
Emp.: 20
Provider of Insurance Brokerage & Consulting Services
N.A.I.C.S.: 524298
Radovan Skultety *(CEO)*

Jauch & Huebener spol. s.r.o. **(3)**
Sarikova 17, Prague, 120 00, Czech Republic **(100%)**
Tel.: (420) 222232288
Web Site: http://www.aon.cz
Sales Range: Less than $1 Million
Emp.: 70
Industrial & Personal Insurance Services
N.A.I.C.S.: 524113

Subsidiary (Non-US):

Aon Holdings Corretores de Seguros Ltda **(2)**
Rua Felix da Cunha 1009 Edificio Residencial Felix da Cunha 1009, 3rd floor Moinho de Ventos, Porto Alegre, 90570-001, Rio Grande Do Sul, Brazil
Tel.: (55) 5133231200
Web Site: http://www.aon.com
Emp.: 30
Risk Managemeng Srvices
N.A.I.C.S.: 524210

Aon Holdings Hong Kong Limited **(2)**
34/F One Island East Taikoo Place 18 Westlands Road, Quarry Bay, Hong Kong, 999077, China (Hong Kong)
Tel.: (852) 28616666
Insurance Management Services
N.A.I.C.S.: 524298

Aon Holdings Limited **(2)**
55 Bishopsgate, London, EC2N 3BD, United Kingdom
Tel.: (44) 2075787000
Insurance Management Services
N.A.I.C.S.: 524298

Aon Holdings Norway AS **(2)**
Stortingsgata 6, PO Box 1503, Vika, 0117, Oslo, Norway
Tel.: (47) 67112200
Web Site: http://www.aon.com
Sales Range: $75-99.9 Million
Emp.: 120
Risk Managemeng Srvices
N.A.I.C.S.: 524210

Aon Insurance Brokers (Malaysia) Sdn Bhd **(2)**
7th Floor Bangunan Malaysian Re No 17 Lorong Dungun Damansara Heights, Kuala Lumpur, 50490, Malaysia
Tel.: (60) 320956628
Web Site: http://www.aon.com
Sales Range: $50-74.9 Million
Emp.: 100
Insurance Brokerage Services
N.A.I.C.S.: 524210

Aon Insurance Brokers (Pvt) Ltd. **(2)**
Bahria Complex 3 2nd Floor MT Khan Road, Karachi, 74000, Pakistan
Tel.: (92) 21111266266
Web Site: http://www.aon.com
Sales Range: $25-49.9 Million
Emp.: 3
Risk Managemeng Srvices
N.A.I.C.S.: 524210
Farrukh Amlani *(CFO & Sec)*

Aon Insurance Managers (Barbados) Ltd. **(2)**
Sunrise House, PO Box 1304, Saint Michael, Barbados
Tel.: (246) 4364895
Web Site: https://www.aon.com
Sales Range: $50-74.9 Million
Emp.: 13
Risk Managemeng Srvices
N.A.I.C.S.: 524210
Hazira Chhiboo *(Mng Dir)*

Aon plc—(Continued)

Aon Insurance Managers (Dublin) Ltd. (2)
Metropolitan Building James Joyce Street, Dublin, Ireland
Tel.: (353) 12666000
Insurance Management Services
N.A.I.C.S.: 524298
Susan Crowley (Mgr-HR)

Aon Insurance Managers (Isle of Man) Ltd. (2)
Third Floor St Georges Court Upper Church Street, Douglas, IM1 1EE, Isle of Man
Tel.: (44) 1624692400
Web Site: http://www.aon.com
Emp.: 30
Insurance Management Services
N.A.I.C.S.: 524298
Gaynor Brough (Mng Dir)

Aon Insurance Managers (Liechtenstein) AG (2)
Industriering 14, 9491, Ruggell, Liechtenstein
Tel.: (423) 2350260
Web Site: http://www.aon.com
Emp.: 4
Insurance Management Services
N.A.I.C.S.: 524298
Denis Kallaert (Mng Dir)

Aon Insurance Managers (Luxembourg) SA (2)
534 Rue De Neudorf, 2220, Luxembourg, Luxembourg
Tel.: (352) 317171
Web Site: http://www.aon.lu
Sales Range: $25-49.9 Million
Emp.: 48
Risk Managemeng Srvices
N.A.I.C.S.: 524210
Lambert Schroeder (Mng Dir)

Aon Insurance Managers (Malta) Ltd. (2)
Vision Exchange Building Triq it-Territorjals Street Zone 1, Triq it-Territorjals Street Zone 1 Central Business District, Birkirkara, CBD 1070, Malta
Tel.: (356) 22471800
Web Site: https://www.aon.com
Insurance Management Services
N.A.I.C.S.: 524298
Mario Xuereb (Head-Insurance)

Aon Insurance Managers (Shannon) Limited (2)
Aon House Block K Shannon Free Zone, Shannon, Ireland
Tel.: (353) 61721000
Insurance Management Services
N.A.I.C.S.: 524298

Aon Insurance Managers (Singapore) Pte Ltd (2)
2 Shenton Way 26-01 SGX Centre 1, Singapore, 068804, Singapore
Tel.: (65) 62218222
Insurance Management Services
N.A.I.C.S.: 524298
George Ong (Gen Mgr)

Aon Insurance Managers (Switzerland) AG (2)
Bahnhofstrasse 28, Postfach 1128, 6300, Zug, Switzerland
Tel.: (41) 417272040
Insurance Management Services
N.A.I.C.S.: 524298

Aon Insurance Managers Gibraltar Ltd. (2)
Suite 913 Europort, Gibraltar, GX11, Gibraltar
Tel.: (350) 20043882
Insurance Brokerage Service Provider
N.A.I.C.S.: 524210
Isobel Randall (Mgr-HR)

Subsidiary (Domestic):

Aon International Holdings, Inc. (2)
200 E Randolph St Ll3, Chicago, IL 60601-6408
Tel.: (312) 381-1000
Risk Managemeng Srvices
N.A.I.C.S.: 524210

Aon Investments USA Inc. (2)
200 E Randolph St Ste 700, Chicago, IL 60601
Tel.: (312) 381-1200
Web Site: https://www.aon.com
Rev.: $9,700,000
Emp.: 88
Administrative Management & General Management Consulting Service
N.A.I.C.S.: 541611

Subsidiary (Non-US):

Aon Italia SpA (2)
Via Andrea Ponti 8/10 basement ground 1-2, 20143, Milan, MI, Italy
Tel.: (39) 02454341
Risk Managemeng Srvices
N.A.I.C.S.: 524210

Aon Kenya Insurance Brokers Ltd (2)
Aon Hse Building Mamlaka Road, 100, Nairobi, Kenya
Tel.: (254) 204974000
Web Site: http://www.aon.com
Insurance Management Services
N.A.I.C.S.: 524298
Joe Onsando (Chm)

Aon Korea Inc. (2)
29th Floor Center1 East Tower 26 Eulji-Ro 5-gil, Jung-gu, Seoul, 04539, Korea (South)
Tel.: (82) 222602600
Web Site: https://www.aon.com
Emp.: 130
Risk Managemeng Srvices
N.A.I.C.S.: 524210

Aon Latvia Sia (2)
Maskavas iela 257, Riga, LV-1019, Latvia
Tel.: (371) 67819900
Web Site: https://en.aon.lv
Sales Range: $50-74.9 Million
Emp.: 13
Risk Managemeng Srvices
N.A.I.C.S.: 524210
Aigars Milts (CEO)

Aon Lesotho (Pty) Ltd. (2)
4 Bowker Road, Old Europa, Maseru, 100, Lesotho
Tel.: (266) 22313540
Web Site: http://www.aon.com
Risk Managemeng Srvices
N.A.I.C.S.: 524210

Aon Limpopo (Pty) Ltd (2)
30 General Joubert Street 1st Floor, Polokwane, 0699, Limpopo, South Africa
Tel.: (27) 152994460
Insurance Management Services
N.A.I.C.S.: 524298
Landa van Wyk (Asst Branch Mgr)

Aon Luxembourg SA (2)
534 rue de Neudorf UTA Building, 2220, Luxembourg, Luxembourg
Tel.: (352) 317171
Web Site: http://www.aom.com
Emp.: 3
Risk Managemeng Srvices
N.A.I.C.S.: 524210

Aon MacDonagh Boland Group Ltd (2)
Metropolitan Building James Joyce Street, Dublin, Ireland
Tel.: (353) 12666000
Web Site: http://www.aon.ie
Sales Range: $150-199.9 Million
Emp.: 50
Risk Managemeng Srvices
N.A.I.C.S.: 524210

Aon Majan LLC (2)
Jawharat Al-Shatti Building Al Kharjiya Street Road 2817, 1st Floor Office 3 Shatti Al Qurm Area 67 Oman, Muscat, Oman
Tel.: (968) 24697451
Web Site: https://www.aon.com
Insurance Management Services
N.A.I.C.S.: 524298
Alex Logan (CEO)

Aon Management Solutions SAU (2)
C/ Rosario Pino 14-16, 28020, Madrid, Spain
Tel.: (34) 913405000
Insurance Management Services

N.A.I.C.S.: 524298

Aon Middle East Co LLC (2)
6th Floor Al Reem Tower Al Maktoum Street, Dubai, United Arab Emirates
Tel.: (971) 42026222
Emp.: 300
Insurance Management Services
N.A.I.C.S.: 524298

Aon Monia Oy (2)
Oulunkylan Tori 1, Helsinki, 640, Finland
Tel.: (358) 201266200
Web Site: http://www.aon.com
Sales Range: $25-49.9 Million
Emp.: 5
Risk Managemeng Srvices
N.A.I.C.S.: 524210

Aon Namibia (Pty) Ltd. (2)
5 Namlex Chmbrs, 333 Independence Avenue, Windhoek, Namibia
Tel.: (264) 61384000
Web Site: http://www.aon.com
Insurance Brokerage Service Provider
N.A.I.C.S.: 524210

Subsidiary (Domestic):

Aon National Flood Services, Inc. (2)
555 Corporate Dr, Kalispell, MT 59901
Tel.: (406) 756-8656
Web Site: http://www.nationalfloodservices.com
Emp.: 300
Insurance Management Services
N.A.I.C.S.: 524298
Megan Burke Roudebush (Mng Dir-Compliance)

Subsidiary (Non-US):

Aon Netherlands Operations BV (2)
Admiraliteitskade 62, 3063 ED, Rotterdam, Netherlands
Tel.: (31) 104487969
Risk Managemeng Srvices
N.A.I.C.S.: 524210

Aon New Zealand (2)
Level 21 Aon Centre 29 Customs Street West Shortland Street, Auckland, 1010, New Zealand
Tel.: (64) 93629000
Web Site: https://www.aon.co.nz
Emp.: 200
Risk Managemeng Srvices
N.A.I.C.S.: 524210
Geoff Blampied (CEO & Branch Mgr)

Aon Norway AS (2)
C Sundts - Gate 17/19 3rd fl, Bergen, 5804, Norway
Tel.: (47) 55576800
Web Site: https://www.aon.com
Risk Managemeng Srvices
N.A.I.C.S.: 524210

Aon PMI International Limited (2)
Lorica House 16a Cornet St, Saint Peter Port, GY1 1LF, Guernsey
Tel.: (44) 1481740313
Insurance Management Services
N.A.I.C.S.: 524298

Aon Parizeau Inc. (2)
700 Rue De La Gauchetiere O Bureau 1600, Montreal, H3B 0A4, QC, Canada
Tel.: (514) 842-5000
Web Site: http://www.aon.com
Sales Range: $75-99.9 Million
Emp.: 206
Risk Managemeng Srvices
N.A.I.C.S.: 524210

Aon Pensions Insurance Brokers GmbH (2)
Caffamacherreihe 16, 20355, Hamburg, Germany
Tel.: (49) 4036052580
Insurance Brokerage Services
N.A.I.C.S.: 524210

Aon Philippines, Inc. (2)
Exchange Tower One - 8th Floor Ayala North 6796, Ayala Avenue Legaspi Village, Makati, 1229, Philippines **(100%)**
Tel.: (63) 29081266
Web Site: http://www.aon.com

N.A.I.C.S.: 524298

Sales Range: $75-99.9 Million
Emp.: 106
Insurance Services
N.A.I.C.S.: 524126

Aon Polska Services Sp. z.o.o. (2)
Al Jerozolimskie 96, 00-807, Warsaw, Poland
Tel.: (48) 225518300
Web Site: http://www.aon.com
Insurance Management Services
N.A.I.C.S.: 524298
Jaroslaw Gniadek (CEO)

Aon Polska sp zoo (2)
ul Prosta 67, 00-838, Warsaw, Poland
Tel.: (48) 223788650
Web Site: http://www.aon.com
Sales Range: $75-99.9 Million
Emp.: 20
Risk Managemeng Srvices
N.A.I.C.S.: 524210

Subsidiary (Domestic):

Aon Premium Finance, LLC (2)
200 E Randolph St, Chicago, IL 60601
Tel.: (312) 381-4628
Insurance Finance Services
N.A.I.C.S.: 524298

Subsidiary (Non-US):

Aon Private Consulting A/S (2)
Strandgade 4C, 1401, Copenhagen, Denmark
Tel.: (45) 70257026
Web Site: http://www.aon.com
Sales Range: $50-74.9 Million
Emp.: 15
Pension Saving Services
N.A.I.C.S.: 524210

Aon Qatar LLC (2)
Office No 203-C 2nd Floor Al Jaidah Square Building, PO Box 16456, 63 Airport Road Umm Ghuwailina Zone 27, Doha, Qatar
Tel.: (974) 44083444
Web Site: https://www.aon.com
Sales Range: $50-74.9 Million
Emp.: 5
Insurance Brokerage Services
N.A.I.C.S.: 524210

Aon Re Middle East WLL (2)
BMMI Tower Entrance 12th Fl Road 2813 Block 428 Al Seef Area, Manama, 1006, Bahrain
Tel.: (973) 17226066
Web Site: http://www.aon.com
Risk Managemeng Srvices
N.A.I.C.S.: 524210

Aon Re Switzerland (2)
Elisabethenstrasse 15, 4010, Basel, Switzerland
Tel.: (41) 612060606
Web Site: http://www.aon.com
Sales Range: $50-74.9 Million
Emp.: 9
Risk Managemeng Srvices
N.A.I.C.S.: 524210

Aon Risk Services (NI) Limited (2)
15-17 Gloucester Street 8th Floor Victoria House, BT14LS, Belfast, Northern Ireland, United Kingdom
Tel.: (44) 2890242771
Emp.: 20
Insurance Management Services
N.A.I.C.S.: 524298
Karim Millar (Office Mgr)

Subsidiary (Domestic):

Aon Risk Services Inc. (2)
200 E Randolph St 14th Fl, Chicago, IL 60601 **(100%)**
Tel.: (312) 381-1000
Web Site: http://www.aon.com
Sales Range: $350-399.9 Million
Emp.: 2,000
Insurance Brokers
N.A.I.C.S.: 524210

Subsidiary (Domestic):

Aon Risk Services Companies, Inc. (3)
199 Waters St, New York, NY 10038-3526

Tel.: (212) 441-1000
Web Site: http://www.aon.com
Sales Range: $75-99.9 Million
Emp.: 1,000
Insurance Brokers
N.A.I.C.S.: 524210

Subsidiary (Domestic):

Aon Risk Insurance Services West, Inc.   (4)
425 Market St Ste 2800, San Francisco, CA 94105-2253
Tel.: (415) 486-7000
Emp.: 120
Risk Managemeng Srvices
N.A.I.C.S.: 524210

Aon Risk Service of Texas Inc.   (4)
301 Commerce St Ste 2370, Fort Worth, TX 76102
Tel.: (817) 810-4000
Web Site: http://www.aon.com
Rev.: $3,000,000
Emp.: 35
Insurance Agents Brokers & Service
N.A.I.C.S.: 524210

Aon Risk Services   (4)
390 N Broadway, Jericho, NY 11753-2125
Tel.: (516) 733-9200
Sales Range: $10-24.9 Million
Emp.: 105
Surety & Construction Insurance
N.A.I.C.S.: 524210
David Marino (Reg Exec VP)

Subsidiary (Non-US):

Aon Risk Services (Chile) SA   (4)
Hendaya 60 of 602, Las Condes, Santiago, Chile
Tel.: (56) 23365584
Web Site: http://www.aon.com
Sales Range: $75-99.9 Million
Emp.: 125
Risk Managemeng Srvices
N.A.I.C.S.: 524210
Carlos Bello (COO)

Aon Risk Services (Thailand) Ltd.   (4)
18th Floor Siam Tower Building 989 Rama I Road Patumwan, Bangkok, 10330, Thailand
Tel.: (66) 23054555
Risk Managemeng Srvices
N.A.I.C.S.: 524210

Aon Risk Services Australia Ltd.   (4)
Level 33 201 Kent Street, Sydney, 2000, NSW, Australia
Tel.: (61) 292537000
Web Site: http://www.aon.com.au
Emp.: 10
Risk Managemeng Srvices
N.A.I.C.S.: 524210

Subsidiary (Domestic):

Aon Risk Services Inc.   (4)
340 Pemberwick Rd, Greenwich, CT 06831-4240
Tel.: (203) 344-3300
Rev.: $10,900,000
Emp.: 95
Insurance Brokers Nec
N.A.I.C.S.: 541611

Aon Risk Services Inc.   (4)
1330 Post Oak Blvd Ste 900, Houston, TX 77056
Tel.: (832) 476-6000
Sales Range: Less than $1 Million
Emp.: 50
Insurance Brokers Nec
N.A.I.C.S.: 524298

Aon Risk Services Inc.   (4)
199 Fremont St Fl 15, San Francisco, CA 94105   (100%)
Tel.: (415) 486-6972
Web Site: http://www.aon.com
Rev.: $56,000,000
Emp.: 230
Insurance Brokers
N.A.I.C.S.: 524210

Aon Risk Services Inc.   (4)
315 W 3rd St, Little Rock, AR 72201
Tel.: (501) 374-9300
Web Site: http://www.aon.com

Sales Range: $1-9.9 Million
Emp.: 36
Insurance Agents Brokers & Service
N.A.I.C.S.: 524210

Aon Risk Services Inc.   (4)
1120 20th St NW Ste 600, Washington, DC 20036
Tel.: (202) 429-8506
Rev.: $14,000,000
Emp.: 70
Insurance Agents Brokers & Service
N.A.I.C.S.: 524210

Branch (Domestic):

Aon Huntington T Block Insurance Agency   (5)
1120 20th St NW Ste 600, Washington, DC 20036-3406
Tel.: (202) 223-0673
Insurance Brokers
N.A.I.C.S.: 524210
Debbie Romos (Office Mgr)

Subsidiary (Domestic):

Aon Risk Services Inc.   (4)
50 Kennedy Plz Fl 10, Providence, RI 02903-2393
Tel.: (401) 331-7700
Web Site: http://www.aon.com
Rev.: $7,000,000
Emp.: 30
Insurance Brokers
N.A.I.C.S.: 524210
David J Byrne (Sr VP)

Aon Risk Services Inc.   (4)
1650 Market St Ste 1000, Philadelphia, PA 19103-7301
Tel.: (215) 255-2000
Web Site: http://www.aon.com
Rev.: $17,700,000
Emp.: 180
Insurance Brokers
N.A.I.C.S.: 524210
Bruce Vassallo (CEO)

Aon Risk Services Inc.   (4)
1111 Metropolitan Ave Ste 400, Charlotte, NC 28204
Tel.: (704) 343-4106
Web Site: http://www.aon.com
Sales Range: $1-9.9 Million
Emp.: 50
Commercial Insurance Agents & Brokers
N.A.I.C.S.: 524210
Bruce Quintana (Mng Dir & Exec VP)

Aon Risk Services Inc.   (4)
1660 W 2nd St Skylight Office Tower Ste 650, Cleveland, OH 44113   (100%)
Tel.: (216) 621-8100
Sales Range: $1-9.9 Million
Emp.: 53
Insurance Agents
N.A.I.C.S.: 524210

Aon Risk Services Inc.   (4)
100 Bayview Cir 100, Newport Beach, CA 92660   (100%)
Tel.: (949) 608-6300
Web Site: http://www.armtech.com
Sales Range: $50-74.9 Million
Emp.: 120
Insurance Brokers
N.A.I.C.S.: 524298
Art Schuler (Mng Dir)

Aon Risk Services Inc.   (4)
707 Wilshire Blvd Ste 2600, Los Angeles, CA 90017   (100%)
Tel.: (213) 630-3200
Web Site: http://www.aon.com
Emp.: 200
Insurance Brokers
N.A.I.C.S.: 524210

Aon Risk Services Inc.   (4)
10700 Research Dr Ste 450, Milwaukee, WI 53226-3460   (100%)
Tel.: (414) 271-6420
Web Site: http://www.aon.com
Sales Range: $1-9.9 Million
Emp.: 25
Insurance Services
N.A.I.C.S.: 524210

Aon Risk Services Inc.   (4)
390 N Broadway, Jericho, NY 11753

Tel.: (516) 396-4290
Rev.: $2,600,000
Emp.: 10
Insurance Agents
N.A.I.C.S.: 524210

Aon Risk Services Inc. (LA)   (4)
639 Loyola Ave Ste 2560, New Orleans, LA 70113-7107
Tel.: (504) 522-5341
Web Site: http://www.aon.com
Sales Range: $10-24.9 Million
Emp.: 6
Insurance Agents, Nec
N.A.I.C.S.: 524210

Aon Risk Services Inc. Florida   (4)
1001 Brickell Bay Dr Ste 1100, Miami, FL 33131
Tel.: (305) 372-9950
Web Site: http://www.aon.com
Sales Range: $25-49.9 Million
Emp.: 180
Insurance Agents Brokers & Service
N.A.I.C.S.: 524210
Mike Parrish (Mng Dir)

Aon Risk Services Inc. of Colorado   (4)
1900 16th St Ste 1000, Denver, CO 80202   (100%)
Tel.: (303) 639-4100
Web Site: http://www.aon.com
Rev.: $6,000,000
Emp.: 120
Insurance Brokers Nec
N.A.I.C.S.: 524210

Aon Risk Services Inc. of Indiana   (4)
450 E 96th St Ste 275, Indianapolis, IN 46204   (100%)
Tel.: (317) 237-2400
Web Site: http://www.aon.com
Sales Range: $1-9.9 Million
Emp.: 36
Insurance
N.A.I.C.S.: 524210
Kevin Pastoor (Mng Dir)

Aon Risk Services Inc. of NJ   (4)
44 Whippany Rd, Morristown, NJ 07960   (100%)
Tel.: (973) 884-4000
Web Site: http://www.aon.com
Rev.: $5,900,000
Emp.: 125
Insurance Agents Brokers & Services
N.A.I.C.S.: 524210
Peter Hutton (Mng Dir)

Aon Risk Services Southwest, Inc.   (4)
5555 San Felipe Ste 1500, Houston, TX 77056
Tel.: (832) 476-6000
Web Site: http://www.aonriskservices.com
Risk Managemeng Srvices
N.A.I.C.S.: 524210

Subsidiary (Non-US):

Aon Risk Services Taiwan Ltd.   (4)
9/F No 136 Lotus Building Jen Ai Rd Sec 3, Taipei, Taiwan
Tel.: (886) 223252221
Web Site: http://www.aon.com
Sales Range: $75-99.9 Million
Emp.: 130
Risk Managemeng Srvices
N.A.I.C.S.: 524210

Subsidiary (Domestic):

Aon Risk Services of Oregon   (4)
851 SW 6th Ave, Portland, OR 97204   (100%)
Tel.: (503) 224-9700
Sales Range: $1-9.9 Million
Emp.: 35
Insurance Agents & Brokers
N.A.I.C.S.: 524210
Peter Johnson (Pres)

Aon Risk Services of Puerto Rico Inc   (4)
304 Ave Ponce de Leon Aon Ctr 1000 10th fl, San Juan, PR 00918   (100%)
Tel.: (787) 754-8787
Web Site: https://www.aon.com

Sales Range: $1-9.9 Million
Emp.: 77
Insurance Brokers Nec
N.A.I.C.S.: 524210

Aon Risk Services of Texas   (4)
5555 San Felipe Ste 1500, Houston, TX 77056
Tel.: (832) 476-6000
Web Site: http://www.aon.com
Rev.: $6,300,000
Emp.: 200
Insurance Brokers & Claim Adjusters
N.A.I.C.S.: 524210

Aon Risk Services, Inc. of Central California   (4)
1418 S Main St Ste 104, Salinas, CA 93908   (100%)
Tel.: (831) 422-9831
Sales Range: Less than $1 Million
Emp.: 15
Insurance Brokers
N.A.I.C.S.: 524210
Michael Mahoney (Mng Dir)

Aon Risk Services, Inc. of Massachusetts   (4)
53 State St Ste 2201, Boston, MA 02109   (100%)
Tel.: (617) 482-3100
Web Site: http://www.aonriskservices.com
Sales Range: $75-99.9 Million
Emp.: 250
Insurance Agents
N.A.I.C.S.: 524210

Subsidiary (Non-US):

Aon Risk Services, Japan, Ltd.   (4)
Bancho Kaikan Gobancho 12-1, Chiyoda-ku, Tokyo, 102-0076, Nagata, Japan   (100%)
Tel.: (81) 332375511
Web Site: http://www.aon.com
Sales Range: $50-74.9 Million
Emp.: 250
Risk Managemeng Srvices
N.A.I.C.S.: 541611

Aon Singapore Pte Ltd   (4)
2 Shenton Way 26 01 SGX Centre 1, Singapore, 068804, Singapore   (100%)
Tel.: (65) 62218222
Web Site: https://www.aon.com
Sales Range: $100-124.9 Million
Emp.: 400
Provider of Insurance
N.A.I.C.S.: 524298

Subsidiary (Domestic):

Stroz Friedberg, LLC   (4)
165 Broadway 28th Fl, New York, NY 10006
Tel.: (212) 981-6540
Web Site: http://www.strozfriedberg.com
Emp.: 200
Cybersecurity, Digital Forensics, Investigations & Risk Management Services
N.A.I.C.S.: 541519
Eric M. Friedberg (Founder & Pres)

Subsidiary (Domestic):

Elysium Digital LLC   (5)
53 State St Ste 2201, Boston, MA 02109
Tel.: (617) 848-5650
Web Site: https://www.elys.com
Cybersecurity, Digital Forensics, Investigations & Risk Management Services
N.A.I.C.S.: 541519

Gotham Digital Science, LLC   (5)
1 Liberty Plz, New York, NY 10006
Tel.: (212) 981-6540
Web Site: https://www.gdssecurity.com
International Security Services Specialists in Application & Network Infrastructure Security & Information Security Risk Management
N.A.I.C.S.: 928120
Joe Hemler (Founder)

Subsidiary (Non-US):

Aon Risk Solutions (Cayman) Ltd.   (2)
18 Forum Lane 2nd Floor, PO Box 69, Camana Bay, KY1-1102, Grand Cayman, Cayman Islands

Aon plc—(Continued)

Tel.: (345) 3459451266
Web Site: https://www.aon.com
Insurance Brokerage Service Provider
N.A.I.C.S.: 524210

Aon Riskminder A/S (2)
Voldbjergvej 12, 8240, Risskov, Denmark
Tel.: (45) 32697460
Web Site: http://www.optica.uk
Management Consulting Services
N.A.I.C.S.: 541618
Iver Moller (Project Mgr)

Aon Romania Broker de Asigurare - re asigurare SRL (2)
Victoria Center Calea Victoriei 145 7th Floor, Bucharest, 010072, Romania
Tel.: (40) 212125816
Web Site: http://www.aon.ro
Risk Managemeng Srvices
N.A.I.C.S.: 524210
Adrian Grecu (CEO)

Aon Rus Insurance Brokers LLC (2)
Moika river emb 42A of28N, 191186, Saint Petersburg, Russia
Tel.: (7) 8125711594
Emp.: 10
Risk Managemeng Srvices
N.A.I.C.S.: 524210

Subsidiary (Domestic):

Aon Securities Inc. (2)
200 E Randolph St, Chicago, IL 60601
Tel.: (312) 381-4514
Investment Consulting Services
N.A.I.C.S.: 523940

Subsidiary (Non-US):

Aon Singapore (Broking Centre) Pte. Ltd. (2)
2 Shenton Way 26-01 Sgx Centre 1, Singapore, 068804, Singapore
Tel.: (65) 62218222
General Insurance Service Provider
N.A.I.C.S.: 524298
Nick King (Assoc Dir-Marine-Asia)

Aon Specialist Seryices Private Limited (2)
No 13/14/15 SJR Ipark 2nd Tower Epip Industrial Area Whitefield, Bengaluru, 560066, Karnataka, India
Tel.: (91) 8030918000
Insurance Management Services
N.A.I.C.S.: 524298
Mahesh Shenoy (Mgr-HR)

Subsidiary (Domestic):

Aon Specialty Re, Inc. (2)
200 E Randolph St Aon Ctr fl 3-15, Chicago, IL 60601-6436 (100%)
Tel.: (312) 381-1000
Sales Range: $300-349.9 Million
Emp.: 500
Broker of Property & Casualty Facultative & Program Reinsurance
N.A.I.C.S.: 524298

Subsidiary (Non-US):

Aon Sweden AB (2)
Valhallavagen 117 H, PO Box 27093, 115 31, Stockholm, 102 51, Sweden
Tel.: (46) 86974000
Web Site: http://www.aon.com
Risk Managemeng Srvices
N.A.I.C.S.: 524210

Aon Taiwan Ltd. (2)
9/F No136 Lotus Building Jen Ai Rd Sec3, Taipei, 10657, Taiwan
Tel.: (886) 223252221
Web Site: https://www.aon.com
Risk Managemeng Srvices
N.A.I.C.S.: 524210

Aon Tanzania Ltd. (2)
488 Haile Selassie Rd Msasani Peninsula, PO Box 9232, Dar es Salaam, 9232, Tanzania
Tel.: (255) 222602441
Web Site: http://www.aon.com
Risk Managemeng Srvices
N.A.I.C.S.: 524210

Aon Tunisia So.car.gest S.A. (2)
Angle Avenue Habib Bourguiba 2 Imp de la Rose, Ariana, 2080, Tunisia
Tel.: (216) 71706967
Web Site: http://www.aon.com
Insurance Brokerage Service Provider
N.A.I.C.S.: 524291

Aon Tunisia S.A. (2)
Angle Avenue Habib Bourguiba 2 Imp de la Rose, Ariana, 2080, Tunisia
Tel.: (216) 71706967
Web Site: http://www.aon.com
Human Resource Consulting Services
N.A.I.C.S.: 541612

Aon UK Limited (2)
The Aon Centre The Leadenhall Building, 122 Leadenhall Street, London, EC3V 4AN, United Kingdom
Tel.: (44) 2076235500
Web Site: https://www.aon.com
Risk Management & Insurance Brokerage Services
N.A.I.C.S.: 524210
Simon Jeffreys (Chm)

Subsidiary (Non-US):

Aon Insurance Managers (Guernsey) Ltd. (3)
Maison Trinity Trinity Square Channel Islands, Saint Peter Port, GY1 4AT, Guernsey (100%)
Tel.: (44) 1481707909
Web Site: https://www.aon.com
Sales Range: $25-49.9 Million
Emp.: 65
Captive Management
N.A.I.C.S.: 562998

Subsidiary (Domestic):

Aon US Holdings, Inc. (2)
200 E Randolph St, Chicago, IL 60601
Tel.: (312) 381-1000
Emp.: 155
Insurance Management Services
N.A.I.C.S.: 524298

Subsidiary (Non-US):

Aon Versicherungsagentur Deutschland GmbH (2)
Caffamacherreihe 16 Neustadt, Hamburg, Germany
Tel.: (49) 4036050
Insurance Management Services
N.A.I.C.S.: 524298

Aon Versicherungsmakler Deutschland GmbH (2)
Caffamacherreihe 16, 20355, Hamburg, Germany
Tel.: (49) 4036053300
Web Site: http://www.aon.de
Sales Range: $300-349.9 Million
Emp.: 60
Risk Managemeng Srvices
N.A.I.C.S.: 524210

Aon Vietnam Limited (2)
44B Ly Thuong Kiet Street, Hoan Kiem District Suite 1201 12th Floor HCO Building, Hanoi, Vietnam
Tel.: (84) 2438260832
Risk Managemeng Srvices
N.A.I.C.S.: 524210

Aon Zambia Ltd (2)
No 8 11th Avenue Nkana West, Kitwe, Zambia
Tel.: (260) 212230355
Web Site: http://www.aon.com
Sales Range: $50-74.9 Million
Emp.: 10
Risk Managemeng Srvices
N.A.I.C.S.: 524210

Aon Zambia Pension Fund Administrators Limited (2)
Acacia Park Plot 22768 Thabo Mbeki Road, PO Box 35403, Arcades, Lusaka, Zambia
Tel.: (260) 211367288
Web Site: http://www.aonzambiaconsulting.co.zm
Pension Fund Consulting Services
N.A.I.C.S.: 525110

Subsidiary (Domestic):

Aon of Arizona Inc. (2)

2555 E Camelback, Phoenix, AZ 85016
Tel.: (602) 427-3200
Web Site: http://www.aon.com
Rev.: $5,800,000
Emp.: 40
Insurance Agents Brokers And Service
N.A.I.C.S.: 524210

Subsidiary (Non-US):

Aon-COFCO Insurance Brokers Co., Ltd. (2)
Room 4105 Jin Mao Tower 88 Century Boulevard, Pudong, Shanghai, 200121, China
Tel.: (86) 2138658000
Web Site: https://www.aon-cofco.com.cn
Risk Managemeng Srvices
N.A.I.C.S.: 524210

Subsidiary (Domestic):

Aon/Albert G. Ruben Insurance Services, Inc. (2)
15303 Ventura Blvd Ste 1200, Sherman Oaks, CA 91403-5817
Tel.: (818) 742-1400
Web Site: http://www.albertgruben.com
N.A.I.C.S.: 524210

Subsidiary (Non-US):

Asscom Insurance Brokers Srl (2)
Via Cristoforo Colombo 149, 00147, Rome, Italy
Tel.: (39) 0677729001
Web Site: http://www.asscombrokers.it
Insurance Brokerage Services
N.A.I.C.S.: 524210

Subsidiary (Domestic):

Bankers Insurance Service, Inc. (2)
200 E Randolph St 10th Fl, Chicago, IL 60601-6436
Web Site: https://www.bankersinsuranceservice.com
Sales Range: Less than $1 Million
Emp.: 10
Insurance Brokers
N.A.I.C.S.: 524298
Sam Ackerman (Chief Underwriting Officer)

Benefit Marketing Solutions, L.L.C. (2)
900 36th Ave NW Ste 105, Norman, OK 73072
Tel.: (405) 579-8525
Web Site: https://www.benefitmarketingsolutions.com
Insurance Agencies & Brokerage Services
N.A.I.C.S.: 524210
Brett Wimberley (Exec VP)

Subsidiary (Non-US):

Cardea Health Solutons Limited (2)
119 Henry Street, Port of Spain, Trinidad & Tobago
Tel.: (868) 6230576
Web Site: https://cardeabenefits.com
Health Insurance Services
N.A.I.C.S.: 524114
Edison Raphael (Mng Dir)

Carstens i Schues Poland Sp. z o.o. (2)
ul Krakowskie Przedmiescie 79 lok 313, 00-079, Warsaw, Poland
Tel.: (48) 228279693
Web Site: https://www.carstens.pol.pl
Insurance Brokerage Service Provider
N.A.I.C.S.: 524291
Johannes Josephus Jannsen (Member-Exec Bd)

Claims Fulfilment Company (Pty) Ltd. (2)
288 Kent Avenue, Johannesburg, 2194, Gauteng, South Africa
Tel.: (27) 315769258
Management Consulting Services
N.A.I.C.S.: 541611
Michelle Schoeman (Controller-Fin)

Cocubes Technologies Private Limited (2)
1205-1206 12th Floor Weldone Tech Park Sohna Road Sector 48, Gurgaon, 122002, Haryana, India
Tel.: (91) 1244919800

Web Site: http://www.cocubes.com
Human Resource Consulting Services
N.A.I.C.S.: 541612
Harpreet S. Grover (CEO & Founder)

Eswatini Insurance Brokers (Pty) Limited (2)
1st Floor Umkhiwa House Karl Grant Street, Mbabane, Eswatini
Tel.: (268) 4043226
Web Site: https://eib.co.sz
Human Resource Consulting Services
N.A.I.C.S.: 541612

Subsidiary (Domestic):

Financial Professional Risk Solutions, Inc. (2)
200 E Randolph St Ste 1100, Chicago, IL 60601
Tel.: (312) 381-3729
Sales Range: $1-9.9 Million
Emp.: 50
Insurance Brokers
N.A.I.C.S.: 524210

Subsidiary (Non-US):

Fundacion Aon Espana (2)
Calle Rosario Pino 14-16, 28020, Madrid, Spain
Tel.: (34) 913405137
Web Site: https://www.fundacionaon.es
Insurance Brokerage Service Provider
N.A.I.C.S.: 524291

GDS Risk Solution Correduria de Seguros S.L. (2)
C/ Via Augusta 252 - 260 6, 08017, Barcelona, Spain
Tel.: (34) 933662600
Web Site: http://www.gdsseguros.com
Insurance Management Services
N.A.I.C.S.: 524298

Grana y Asociados Corredores de Seguros SA (2)
Av Paseo de la Republica 3195 of 802, San Isidro, Lima, Peru
Tel.: (51) 16150800
Web Site: http://www.granaasociados.pe
Insurance Brokerage Services
N.A.I.C.S.: 524210

Groupe-Conseil Aon Inc. (2)
2600 Boul Laurier 750, Sainte-Foy, G1V 4W2, QC, Canada
Tel.: (418) 650-1119
Web Site: http://www.aon.ca
Emp.: 45
Risk Managemeng Srvices
N.A.I.C.S.: 524210

Subsidiary (Domestic):

Impact Forecasting, L.L.C. (2)
200 E Randolph St, Chicago, IL 60601
Tel.: (312) 381-5919
Web Site: http://www.aon.com
Sales Range: $50-74.9 Million
Emp.: 25
Risk Managemeng Srvices
N.A.I.C.S.: 524210

Subsidiary (Non-US):

Insurance Company of the Bahamas Limited (2)
33 Collins Avenue, PO Box N-8320, Nassau, Bahamas
Tel.: (242) 2423263100
Web Site: https://www.icbbahamas.com
Insurance Management Services
N.A.I.C.S.: 524298
Marvin V. Bethell (Chm)

Subsidiary (Domestic):

Johnsons Rooney Welch, Inc. (2)
MSC Ste 17203, Irvine, CA 92623
Tel.: (916) 784-6232
Web Site: https://www.jrwinc.com
Sales Range: Less than $1 Million
Emp.: 13
Crop Insurance
N.A.I.C.S.: 524210

K & K Insurance Group, Inc. (2)
1712 Magnavox Way, Fort Wayne, IN 46804
Tel.: (260) 459-5000

Web Site: https://www.kandkinsurance.com
Sales Range: $100-124.9 Million
Emp.: 300
Property & Casualty Insurance Agent
N.A.I.C.S.: 524210
Ron Norton *(Pres & CEO)*

Subsidiary (Non-US):

K&K Insurance Brokers, Inc. Canada **(2)**
5500 North Service Road Suite 404, Burlington, L7L 6W6, ON, Canada **(100%)**
Tel.: (905) 602-9339
Web Site: http://www.kandkcanada.com
Sales Range: Less than $1 Million
Emp.: 10
Insurance Agents & Brokers
N.A.I.C.S.: 524298

Minet Botswana **(2)**
Minet House Plot 50368 Showgrounds, PO Box 624, Gaborone Business Park, Gaborone, Botswana
Tel.: (267) 3617300
Web Site: https://www.minet.com
Sales Range: $50-74.9 Million
Emp.: 100
Risk Managemeng Srvices
N.A.I.C.S.: 524210
Bryn Williams *(Chief Comml Officer)*

Minet Inc. **(2)**
700 De La Gauchetiere Street West Suite 1800, Montreal, H3B 0A5, QC, Canada
Tel.: (514) 288-2273
Web Site: http://www.aon.com
Sales Range: $25-49.9 Million
Emp.: 30
Risk Managemeng Srvices
N.A.I.C.S.: 524298

Optika A/S **(2)**
Voldbjergvej 16, 8240, Risskov, Denmark
Tel.: (45) 88200000
Web Site: http://www.optica.dk
Insurance Management Services
N.A.I.C.S.: 524298
Poul Ronholt *(Dir-Admin)*

PT Aon Indonesia **(2)**
Menara Sudirman 3rd FloorJI Jend Sudirman Kav 60, Jakarta, Indonesia
Tel.: (62) 215220123
Risk Managemeng Srvices
N.A.I.C.S.: 524210

Subsidiary (Domestic):

Premier Auto Finance Inc. **(2)**
5050 N Broadway St, Chicago, IL 60640-3016
Tel.: (773) 765-1000
Sales Range: $25-49.9 Million
Emp.: 140
Investor
N.A.I.C.S.: 532112

Protective Marketing Enterprises **(2)**
1707 Market Pl Ste 300, Irving, TX 75063
Tel.: (205) 268-3317
Emp.: 3
Insurance Brokerage Service Provider
N.A.I.C.S.: 524291

Subsidiary (Non-US):

SIA "Aon Consulting" **(2)**
Biekensalas iela 21, Riga, 1004, Latvia
Tel.: (371) 67892554
Web Site: http://www.aon.com
Insurance Management Services
N.A.I.C.S.: 524298

Scorpio Partnership Limited **(2)**
The Leadenhall Building 122 Leadenhall Street, London, EC3V 4AN, United Kingdom
Tel.: (44) 2070865222
Web Site:
http://www.scorpiopartnership.com
Management Consulting Services
N.A.I.C.S.: 541611
David Lo *(Assoc Partner-North America)*

Tecsefin Guatemala **(2)**
6 Av 7-72 Z-10 Niv 3 Of 300, Guatemala, Guatemala
Tel.: (502) 23808800
Insurance Brokerage Service Provider
N.A.I.C.S.: 524210

Subsidiary (Domestic):

The Burchfield Group, Inc. **(2)**
1295 Northland Dr Ste 350, Saint Paul, MN 55120
Web Site: http://www.burchfieldgroup.com
Human Resources & Executive Search Consulting Services
N.A.I.C.S.: 541612
Brian Bullock *(Founder & CEO)*

Subsidiary (Non-US):

Townsend Group Asia Limited **(2)**
Two Exchange Square Suite 2903 29th Floor, Central, Hong Kong, 999077, China (Hong Kong)
Tel.: (852) 85234685900
Investment Management Service
N.A.I.C.S.: 523940

UADBB Aon Baltic **(2)**
A Gostauto 40B 1st floor, Vilnius, 01112, Lithuania
Tel.: (370) 52526000
Insurance Management Services
N.A.I.C.S.: 524298
Zilvinas Petrauskas *(CEO)*

USLP Underwriting Solutions LP **(2)**
1100-1st Street SE, Calgary, T2G 1B1, AB, Canada
Tel.: (403) 693-3760
Web Site: http://www.uslp.ca
Insurance Brokerage Service Provider
N.A.I.C.S.: 524210

Subsidiary (Domestic):

Underwriters Marine Services, Inc. **(2)**
3850 N Causeway Blvd Ste 1930, Metairie, LA 70002
Tel.: (504) 828-6311
Web Site: http://www.umsmarine.com
Sales Range: $50-74.9 Million
Emp.: 10
Insurance Agencies Brokerages
N.A.I.C.S.: 524210

Ward Financial Group, Inc. **(2)**
8040 Hosbrook Rd Ste 100, Cincinnati, OH 45236-2908
Tel.: (513) 791-0303
Web Site: http://www.wardinc.com
Emp.: 20
Insurance Brokerage Services
N.A.I.C.S.: 524210

Subsidiary (Non-US):

White Rock Insurance (Europe) PCC Limited **(2)**
2 Floor 53 Abate Rigord Street, Ta' Xbiex, XBX1122, Malta
Tel.: (356) 23433115
Insurance Management Services
N.A.I.C.S.: 524298

Subsidiary (Domestic):

Wrapid Specialty, Inc. **(2)**
707 Wilshire Blvd Ste 2600, Los Angeles, CA 90017
Tel.: (877) 616-4777
Web Site: http://www.wrapidspecialty.com
Wrap Administrator
N.A.I.C.S.: 524210

Aon Global Limited **(1)**
The Aon Centre The Leadenhall Building 122 Leadenhall Street, London, EC3V 4AN, United Kingdom
Tel.: (44) 2076235500
Web Site: http://www.aon.com
Professional Services
N.A.I.C.S.: 541990

Healthy Paws Pet Insurance LLC **(1)**
Tel.: (855) 898-8991
Web Site:
https://www.healthypawspetinsurance.com
Art Insurance Services
N.A.I.C.S.: 812910

NFP Corp. **(1)**
340 Madison Ave 20th Fl, New York, NY 10173
Tel.: (212) 301-4000
Web Site: http://www.nfp.com

Holding Company; Financial & Insurance Services
N.A.I.C.S.: 551112
Douglas W. Hammond *(CEO)*

Subsidiary (Domestic):

Achilles & Associates PC **(2)**
7756 Northcross Dr, Austin, TX 78757-1725
Tel.: (512) 451-2093
Web Site: http://www.achillesins.com
Emp.: 100
Insurance Agencies & Brokerages
N.A.I.C.S.: 524210

Alan Kaye Insurance Agency, Inc. **(2)**
301 N Canon DrÂ Ste 324, Beverly Hills, CA 90210
Tel.: (310) 277-9400
Web Site: http://www.alankayeins.com
Insurance Brokerage Services
N.A.I.C.S.: 524210
Alan L. Kaye *(Pres)*

Alexander Benefits Consulting, LLC **(2)**
1099 18th St Ste 2870, Denver, CO 80209
Tel.: (303) 296-2220
Web Site: http://www.alexanderbenefits.com
Emp.: 5
Employee Benefit Consulting Services
N.A.I.C.S.: 541612
Saul Locker *(Pres)*

American Benefits Group **(2)**
320 Riverside Dr, Florence, MA 01062
Tel.: (413) 584-9923
Web Site: http://www.amben.com
Emp.: 20
Insurance Brokerage Services
N.A.I.C.S.: 524210
Robert L. Cummings *(CEO & Mng Principal)*

Arnone Lowth Wilson & Leibowitz Inc. **(2)**
105 Broadhollow Rd, Melville, NY 11747
Tel.: (631) 423-7600
Insurance Brokerage Services
N.A.I.C.S.: 524210

Associated Agency Group, LLC **(2)**
8382 W Gage Blvd Ste A, Kennewick, WA 99336
Tel.: (509) 412-3521
Web Site: http://www.aag-services.com
Insurance Agencies & Brokerages
N.A.I.C.S.: 524210
Jeff Wolf *(Mktg Mgr)*

BMI Benefits, L.L.C. **(2)**
PO Box 511, Matawan, NJ 07747-2629
Tel.: (732) 583-1181
Web Site: http://www.bobmccloskey.com
Sales Range: $50-74.9 Million
Emp.: 40
Investment Management Service
N.A.I.C.S.: 523940
Derek Sawyer *(Mgr)*

Benefit Services Group **(2)**
7350 Campus Dr Ste 100, Colorado Springs, CO 80920
Tel.: (719) 520-3232
Web Site: http://www.benefitservices-co.com
Emp.: 14
Employee Benefit Consulting Services
N.A.I.C.S.: 524298
Tina Neuendorf *(Sr VP)*

Bernard R. Wolfe & Associates Inc. **(2)**
5550 Friendship Blvd Ste 570, Chevy Chase, MD 20815
Tel.: (301) 652-9677
Web Site: http://www.bernardwolfe.com
Investment Management Service
N.A.I.C.S.: 523940
Bernard R. Wolfe *(Chm & CEO)*

Brennan & Associates Risk Management & Insurance Services, Inc. **(2)**
2200 Powell St Ste 1225, Emeryville, CA 94608
Tel.: (510) 547-7400
Insurance Agencies & Brokerages
N.A.I.C.S.: 524210

Charon Planning Corporation **(2)**

2600 Kelly Rd Ste 300, Warrington, PA 18976
Tel.: (267) 482-8300
Web Site: http://www.charonplanning.com
Sales Range: $25-49.9 Million
Emp.: 60
Employee Benefit Consulting Services
N.A.I.C.S.: 541612
Christopher Gavigan *(Mng Dir & Principal)*

Clippinger Financial Group, L.L.C. **(2)**
415 Crosslake Dr, Evansville, IN 47715
Tel.: (812) 422-4000
Web Site: http://www.clippinger.us
Investment Advisory Services
N.A.I.C.S.: 523940
Scott W. Clippinger *(Principal)*

Compass Capital Management, LLC **(2)**
2 Pomperaug Office Park Ste 301, Southbury, CT 06488
Tel.: (203) 264-8282
Web Site: http://www.ccm-ria.com
Emp.: 7
Investment Management Service
N.A.I.C.S.: 523940
Thomas C. Paron *(Pres)*

Contemporary Benefits Design, Inc. **(2)**
1956 Wellness Blvd, Monroe, NC 28110
Tel.: (704) 296-0900
Web Site:
http://www.contemporarybenefits.com
Emp.: 20
Employee Benefit Consulting Services
N.A.I.C.S.: 541612
Ken Harbin *(Mng Partner)*

Corporate Benefit Advisors, Inc. **(2)**
1901 Roxborough Rd, Charlotte, NC 28211
Tel.: (704) 523-4222
Business Management Consulting Services
N.A.I.C.S.: 541611

Corporate Benefits, Inc. **(2)**
109 Laurens Rd Ste 1A, Greenville, SC 29607
Tel.: (864) 271-6430
Web Site:
http://www.corporatebenefitsinc.com
Sales Range: $25-49.9 Million
Emp.: 8
Employee Benefit Consulting Services
N.A.I.C.S.: 541612
Raymond P. Newsom *(Principal)*

Subsidiary (Non-US):

Dalton Timmis Insurance Group, Inc. **(2)**
35 Stone Church Road 3rd Floor, Ancaster, L8N 3S4, ON, Canada
Tel.: (905) 648-3922
Insurance Brokerage Services
N.A.I.C.S.: 524210
Domenic Tesone *(Co-Owner & Partner)*

Subsidiary (Domestic):

Delott & Associates, Inc. **(2)**
3701 Algonquin Rd Ste 240, Rolling Meadows, IL 60008-3116
Tel.: (847) 253-5922
Insurance Brokerage Services
N.A.I.C.S.: 524210

DiMeo Schneider & Associates LLC **(2)**
500 W Madison St Ste 1700, Chicago, IL 60661-4593
Tel.: (312) 853-1000
Web Site: http://www.dimeoschneider.com
Investment Consulting Services
N.A.I.C.S.: 523940
Michael S. Benoit *(Mng Dir-Wealth Office & Principal)*

Subsidiary (Domestic):

Fiduciary Investment Advisors LLC **(3)**
100 Northfield Dr, Windsor, CT 06095
Tel.: (860) 683-1187
Web Site: http://www.fiallc.com
Investment Advice
N.A.I.C.S.: 523940
Michael Goss *(Exec VP)*

Aon plc—(Continued)

Subsidiary (Domestic):

Dublin Insurance Services, Inc. (2)
6200 Village Pkwy Ste 201, Dublin, CA 94568
Tel.: (925) 803-1880
Web Site: http://www.dublininsurance.com
Insurance Brokerage Services
N.A.I.C.S.: 524210
Littleton Maydene (Mgr-Benefits)

EBS/Foran Insurance & Advisory Services, Inc. (2)
8 Taunton Ave, Dennis, MA 02638
Tel.: (508) 385-5135
Web Site: http://www.ebsforan.com
Emp.: 15
Employee Insurance Benefit Advisory & Administration Services
N.A.I.C.S.: 524298
John P. Foran (Founder & Pres)

ECA Marketing, Inc. (2)
7800 Equitable Dr Ste 200, Eden Prairie, MN 55344
Web Site:
   http://www.public.ecamarketing.com
Emp.: 50
Marketing Consulting Services
N.A.I.C.S.: 541613
Joe Spillman (Pres)

Educators Preferred Corporation (2)
26877 Northwestern Hwy Ste 305, Southfield, MI 48033
Tel.: (800) 747-1504
Web Site: http://www.epcinternet.com
Investment Management Service
N.A.I.C.S.: 523940
Merry Kelly (Pres)

Eilers Financial Services, Inc. (2)
Mad River Green Ste 2, Waitsfield, VT 05673-0626
Tel.: (802) 496-3192
Web Site: http://www.eilersfinancial.com
Investment Management Service
N.A.I.C.S.: 523940

Erisa Fiduciary Advisors, Inc. (2)
1160 Birchwood Rd, Weston, FL 33327
Tel.: (954) 385-5331
Web Site: http://www.efadvisor.com
Investment Advisory & Retirement Plan Consulting Services
N.A.I.C.S.: 523940
Bradley L. Larsen (Exec VP)

Excess Reinsurance Underwriters, Inc. (2)
48 N Broad St, Woodbury, NJ 08096
Tel.: (856) 251-2280
Web Site: http://www.excessre.com
Emp.: 35
Health Insurance Services
N.A.I.C.S.: 524114

Field Underwriters Agency, Inc. (2)
7777 Washington Village Dr, Dayton, OH 45459
Tel.: (937) 439-2900
Web Site: http://www.fieldunderwriters.net
Sales Range: $50-74.9 Million
Emp.: 3
Insurance Advisory Services
N.A.I.C.S.: 524298
Steven Braunschweiger (Owner)

Financial Concepts of the Twin Cities, Inc. (2)
9655 Schmidt Lake Rd, Plymouth, MN 55442
Tel.: (763) 450-1800
Web Site: http://www.fci-benefits.com
Emp.: 30
Employee Benefit Consulting Services
N.A.I.C.S.: 541612
Tom Miller (Pres)

Financial Concepts, Inc. (2)
9655 Schmidt Lake Rd, Plymouth, MN 55442
Tel.: (763) 450-1800
Web Site: http://www.fci-benefits.com
Emp.: 30
Financial Investment Consulting Services
N.A.I.C.S.: 525190
Tom Miller (Pres & CEO)

First Financial Resources Ltd. (2)
100 W Putnam Ave, Greenwich, CT 06830
Tel.: (203) 661-9191
Web Site:
   http://www.1financialresources.com
Financial Investment Advisory Services
N.A.I.C.S.: 523940

First Global Financial & Insurance Services Inc. (2)
11835 W Olympic Blvd Ste 600, Los Angeles, CA 90064
Tel.: (310) 477-7500
Web Site: http://www.totalfinancial.com
Emp.: 32
Insurance Brokerage Services
N.A.I.C.S.: 524210
Craig Brown (Controller)

First Person, Inc. (2)
9000 Keystone Crossing Ste 910, Indianapolis, IN 46240
Tel.: (317) 705-5900
Web Site:
   http://www.firstpersonadvisors.com
Employee Benefit Consulting Services
N.A.I.C.S.: 541612
Bryan Brenner (Founder & CEO)

Fleischer-Jacobs & Associates Inc. (2)
620 Hinesburg Rd, Burlington, VT 05407-2343
Tel.: (802) 865-5000
Web Site: http://www.fjgfinancial.com
Insurance Brokerage Services
N.A.I.C.S.: 524210

GCG Risk Management, Inc. (2)
100 Church St Ste 81, New York, NY 10007
Tel.: (212) 431-3000
Web Site:
   http://www.gcgriskmanagement.com
Insurance Agencies & Brokerages
N.A.I.C.S.: 524210
Joseph M. Gnesin (Pres)

Golden & Cohen LLC (2)
704 Quince Orchard Rd Ste 200, Gaithersburg, MD 20878
Tel.: (301) 330-5300
Web Site: http://www.golden-cohen.com
Emp.: 16
General Insurance Services
N.A.I.C.S.: 524113
Stephanie Cohen (CEO)

Hackett Valine & MacDonald, Inc. (2)
620 Hinesburg Rd, South Burlington, VT 05407
Tel.: (802) 658-1100
Web Site: http://www.hvm.com
Emp.: 45
Insurance Agencies & Brokerages
N.A.I.C.S.: 524210
Michael Walsh (Pres & CEO)

Hartfield Louisville, LLC (2)
12800 Town Pkwy Ste 201 Blvd 40243, Louisville, KY 40243
Tel.: (502) 499-1891
Web Site: http://www.nfp.com
Emp.: 6
Investment Management Service
N.A.I.C.S.: 523940
Mike Tolley (Pres)

Institutional Life Services, LLC (2)
340 Madison Ave 21st Fl, New York, NY 10173
Tel.: (212) 301-1051
Web Site: http://www.ilcompanies.com
Investment Management Service
N.A.I.C.S.: 523940
Marshall Abbott (Pres & CEO)

International Insurance Group, Inc. (2)
121 E Birch Ave Ste 207, Flagstaff, AZ 86001-4651
Tel.: (928) 214-9750
Web Site: http://www.mexpro.com
Insurance Agencies & Brokerages
N.A.I.C.S.: 524210

International Risk - IRC, Inc. (2)
1 Corporation Way Ste 230, Peabody, MA 01960
Tel.: (781) 581-9800

Web Site: http://www.irc-inc.org
Sales Range: $50-74.9 Million
Emp.: 10
Medical Insurance Services
N.A.I.C.S.: 524114
Michael S. McGrath (Pres & CEO)

Juno Search Partners, LLC (2)
1315 Walnut St Ste 522, Philadelphia, PA 19107
Tel.: (215) 545-5866
Web Site:
   http://www.junosearchpartners.com
Human Resource Consulting Services
N.A.I.C.S.: 541612
Vicki Sack (Co-Founder)

KGS Insurance Services, LLC (2)
505 Main St Middletown, Middletown, CT 06457
Tel.: (860) 704-8020
Insurance Agencies
N.A.I.C.S.: 524210

Kempkey Insurance Services, Inc. (2)
1500 3rd St Ste B, Napa, CA 94559-2809
Tel.: (888) 536-7539
Insurance Agencies & Brokerages
N.A.I.C.S.: 524210

LTCI Partners, LLC (2)
2924 Marketplace Dr Ste 102, Madison, WI 53719
Tel.: (800) 245-8108
Web Site: http://www.ltcipartners.com
Insurance Brokerage Services
N.A.I.C.S.: 524210
Sandra Latham (Principal & Project Mgr)

Lincoln Benefits Group, Inc. (2)
550 Pinetown Rd Ste 270, Fort Washington, PA 19034
Tel.: (215) 887-8330
Web Site: http://www.lbg1.com
Sales Range: $25-49.9 Million
Emp.: 20
Employee Benefit Consulting Services
N.A.I.C.S.: 541612
Debbie Britt (Mgr)

Longnecker & Associates Inc. (2)
11011 Jones Rd Ste 200, Houston, TX 77070
Tel.: (281) 378-1350
Web Site: http://www.longnecker.com
Emp.: 15
Compensation Consulting Services
N.A.I.C.S.: 541612
Chris Crawford (Pres)

M & M Brokerage Services, Inc. (2)
75 Rockefeller Plz Fl 21, New York, NY 10019
Tel.: (212) 767-7444
Web Site: http://www.bsiinsurance.com
Insurance Brokerage Services
N.A.I.C.S.: 524210
Marvin Meyer (Founder & Pres)

M.T.D. Associates, L.L.C. (2)
290 Lafayette Ave Ste 203, Hawthorne, NJ 07506
Tel.: (973) 423-1120
Insurance Brokerage Services
N.A.I.C.S.: 524210

Maguire Financial Advisors, LLC (2)
2111 E Highland Ave Ste 170, Phoenix, AZ 85016-9209
Tel.: (602) 808-5595
Web Site:
   http://www.maguirefinancialgroup.com
Emp.: 3
Insurance Brokerage Services
N.A.I.C.S.: 524210
Tom Maguire (Gen Mgr)

Managed Care Consultants LLC (2)
237 W Lancaster Ave Ste 251, Devon, PA 19333-1580
Tel.: (610) 254-8099
Web Site: http://www.mcc-usa.net
Insurance Agencies & Brokerages
N.A.I.C.S.: 524210

Management Brokers, Inc. (2)
9301 Wilshire Blvd Ste 613, Beverly Hills, CA 90210
Tel.: (310) 278-5943

Web Site:
   http://www.managementbrokers.com
Insurance Brokerage Services
N.A.I.C.S.: 524210
Richard M. Horowitz (Pres)

Maschino Hudelson & Associates LLC (2)
4811 Gaillardia Pkwy Ste 300, Oklahoma City, OK 73142
Tel.: (405) 235-0036
Web Site: http://www.nfp.com
Emp.: 35
Investment Management Service
N.A.I.C.S.: 523940
David A. Maschino (Partner)

Michael G. Rudelson and Company (2)
414 Avondale St, Houston, TX 77006
Tel.: (713) 942-7117
Web Site:
   http://www.rudelsoninvestments.com
Investment Management Service
N.A.I.C.S.: 523940
Michael G. Rudelson (Pres)

Michelsen Benefits Group, Inc. (2)
307 East Blvd, Charlotte, NC 28203
Tel.: (704) 644-6423
Scientific & Technical Consulting Services
N.A.I.C.S.: 541690
Kanku Michelsen (Dir-HR)

Mitchell & Moroneso Insurance Services Inc. (2)
306 W 7th St Ste 888, Fort Worth, TX 76102
Tel.: (817) 338-0888
Investment Management Service
N.A.I.C.S.: 523940

Monaghan, Tilghman & Hoyle, Inc. (2)
1104 Kenilworth Dr Ste 301, Baltimore, MD 21204
Tel.: (443) 632-0230
Sales Range: $50-74.9 Million
Emp.: 6
General Insurance Services
N.A.I.C.S.: 524210

NFP Benefit Planning Services, Inc. (2)
929 S Alpine Rd Ste 402, Rockford, IL 61108
Tel.: (815) 397-3737
Insurance Brokerage Services
N.A.I.C.S.: 524210

NFP Brokerage Insurance Services, Inc. (2)
1250 S Capital of Texas Hwy Bldg 2 125, West Lake Hills, TX 78746-6395
Tel.: (512) 697-6869
Insurance Brokerage Services
N.A.I.C.S.: 524210

NFP Clippinger Financial Group, LLC (2)
415 Cross Lake Dr Ste A, Evansville, IN 47715
Tel.: (812) 422-4000
Insurance Brokerage Services
N.A.I.C.S.: 524210

NFP Corporate Services (2)
1405 Davis Ave, Endwell, NY 13760
Tel.: (607) 754-7222
Sales Range: $50-74.9 Million
Emp.: 30
Insurance Brokerage Services
N.A.I.C.S.: 524210
Robert Sedor (CEO)

NFP Corporate Services (NY), LLC. (2)
340 Madison Ave 21st Fl, New York, NY 10173
Tel.: (866) 903-9162
Web Site: http://www.nfp.com
Management Consulting Services
N.A.I.C.S.: 541611

NFP FDR Financial Group, Inc. (2)
4000 Hollywood Blvd Ste 495 S, Hollywood, FL 33021
Tel.: (800) 330-5332
Web Site: http://www.nfp-fdr.com

Financial Management Services
N.A.I.C.S.: 523940
Jamie Johnson (Dir-Employee Benefits)

NFP Mid-Atlantic SG, LLC (2)
4740 Corridor Pl Ste B, Beltsville, MD 20705
Tel.: (800) 311-1031
Insurance Brokerage Services
N.A.I.C.S.: 524298
Scott Golden (Principal)

NFP Mitchell & Moroneso Insurance Services, Inc. (2)
306 W 7th St Ste 888, Fort Worth, TX 76102
Tel.: (817) 338-0888
Sales Range: $50-74.9 Million
Emp.: 4
Insurance Brokerage Services
N.A.I.C.S.: 524210

NFP Mosse & Mosse Associates, Inc. (2)
50 Salem St Bldg B, Lynnfield, MA 01940
Tel.: (781) 224-1709
Web Site: http://www.mosseandmosse.com
Management Consulting Services
N.A.I.C.S.: 541611
Jonathan R. Mosse (Pres-Health & Welfare)

NFP National Madison Group, Inc. (2)
340 Madison Ave Fl 21, New York, NY 10173
Tel.: (800) 774-2995
Web Site: http://www.nationalmadison.com
Wealth Preservation Services
N.A.I.C.S.: 525190

NFP Property & Casualty Services, Inc. (2)
8201 N Hayden Rd, Scottsdale, AZ 85258
Tel.: (480) 947-3556
Web Site: http://www.nfp.com
Sales Range: $10-24.9 Million
Insurance Brokerage Services
N.A.I.C.S.: 524210
Frank Maglalang (VP)

Subsidiary (Domestic):

SDN Insurance Agency, LLC (3)
300 Spindrift Dr, Amherst, NY 14221
Tel.: (716) 633-3400
Web Site: http://sdnins.com
Insurance Brokerage Services
N.A.I.C.S.: 524210
William Gallagher (Pres)

Subsidiary (Domestic):

Landmark Group of Brighton, Inc. (4)
1956 W Henrietta Rd, Rochester, NY 14623
Tel.: (585) 272-1956
Web Site: http://www.landmarkinsurance.net
Sales Range: $1-9.9 Million
Emp.: 20
Insurance Agencies & Brokerages
N.A.I.C.S.: 524210
Christopher K. Shea (Pres)

Subsidiary (Domestic):

NFP Structured Settlements, Inc. (2)
1579 F Monroe Dr Ste 194, Atlanta, GA 30324
Tel.: (800) 229-2228
Web Site: http://www.nfpstructures.com
Financial Planning & Settlement Services
N.A.I.C.S.: 524291
Claire B. Blajsczak (Office Mgr-Cleveland)

NFP The Benefits Solution Group, Inc. (2)
8702 Jefferson Hwy Ste A, Baton Rouge, LA 70809-2233
Tel.: (225) 922-4394
Web Site: http://www.nfp.com
Financial Brokerage Services
N.A.I.C.S.: 524210
Chris Ciesielski (Pres)

NFP The Hartfield Company, Inc. (2)
3620 Blackiston Blvd Ste 100, New Albany, IN 47150
Tel.: (812) 948-9201
Web Site: http://www.nfp.com

Sales Range: $50-74.9 Million
Emp.: 9
General Insurance Services
N.A.I.C.S.: 524210
Douglas A. Sidebottom (VP-Grp Benefits)

NFP-AIS Insurance Services, Inc. (2)
905 Military Cutoff Rd uNIT 100, Wilmington, NC 28405
Tel.: (910) 794-6100
Insurance Related Activities
N.A.I.C.S.: 524298
Ken McGee (Pres)

NFP-National Account Services, Inc. (2)
7272 E Indian School Rd Ste 415, Scottsdale, AZ 85251
Tel.: (480) 946-5600
Web Site: http://www.nfp.com
Insurance Brokerage Services
N.A.I.C.S.: 524210

National Enrollment Services, Inc. (2)
450 Skokie Blvd Ste 702, Northbrook, IL 60062-7915
Tel.: (800) 966-6637
Web Site: http://www.nesbenefits.com
Insurance Brokerage Services
N.A.I.C.S.: 524210
Tish Johnson (Coord-Voluntary Benefits)

National Insurance Brokerage, LLC (2)
2101 Park Ctr Dr Ste 210, Orlando, FL 32835
Tel.: (800) 291-7985
Web Site: http://www.niblife.com
Insurance Brokerage Services
N.A.I.C.S.: 524210

National Madison Group, Inc. (2)
340 Madison Ave 21st Fl, New York, NY 10173
Tel.: (800) 774-2995
Web Site: http://www.nationalmadison.com
Insurance Brokerage Services
N.A.I.C.S.: 524210
Alex Kim (Dir-Case Design)

Nemco Brokerage, Inc. (2)
340 Madison Ave 21st Fl, New York, NY 10173
Tel.: (212) 421-5700
Insurance Brokerage Services
N.A.I.C.S.: 524210

NuVision Financial Corporation, Inc. (2)
2435 Wall St Ste 101, Conyers, GA 30013-8580
Tel.: (770) 483-4818
Emp.: 4
Insurance Brokerage Services
N.A.I.C.S.: 524210
Samauel Wishon (Pres)

Oklahoma Financial Center, Inc. (2)
12436 St Andrews Dr, Oklahoma City, OK 73120
Tel.: (405) 302-2900
Web Site: http://www.okfin.com
Investment Management Service
N.A.I.C.S.: 523940
Karen Cunningham (Founder & Pres)

P&A Capital Advisors, Inc. (2)
500 5th Ave Ste 2700, New York, NY 10110
Tel.: (212) 764-6455
Web Site: http://www.pacapadvisors.com
Emp.: 30
Investment Management Service
N.A.I.C.S.: 523940
David Alexander (Co-Founder & Pres)

PRW Associates Insurance Agency, Inc. (2)
2 Batterymarch Park, Quincy, MA 02169-7448
Tel.: (617) 745-0900
Insurance Brokerage Services
N.A.I.C.S.: 524210
Gary Wentling (Gen Mgr)

Portell Financial Services, Inc. (2)
1210 Washington St, Highland, IL 62249
Tel.: (618) 654-4426
Web Site: http://www.portellfs.com

Investment Management Service
N.A.I.C.S.: 523940
Donald J. Portell (CEO)

Potomac Basin Group Associates, LLC (2)
4740 Corridor Pl, Beltsville, MD 20705
Tel.: (301) 937-0422
Web Site: http://www.potomacbasin.com
Emp.: 50
Insurance Agencies & Brokerage Services
N.A.I.C.S.: 524210
Brian E. Crockett (COO)

Poulos Insurance, Inc. (2)
723 Concord Ave, Saint Johnsbury, VT 05819
Tel.: (802) 748-1200
Web Site: http://www.poulosinsurance.com
Sales Range: $1-9.9 Million
Emp.: 23
Property & Casualty Insurance Services
N.A.I.C.S.: 524210
David Spaulding (Exec VP)

Preferred Benefits Group, Inc. (2)
39-40 Broadway, Fair Lawn, NJ 07410
Tel.: (201) 796-0660
Web Site: http://www.pbgroup.com
Emp.: 10
Employee Benefit Consulting Services
N.A.I.C.S.: 541612
Jeffrey D. Benedict (VP & Partner)

Pro Financial Services, LLC (2)
500 W Madison St Ste 2660, Chicago, IL 60661
Tel.: (312) 376-4640
Web Site: http://www.pfsins.com
Disability Insurance Services
N.A.I.C.S.: 524113
Daniel Burns (Pres)

ProVise Management Group, LLC (2)
611 Druid Rd E Ste 105, Clearwater, FL 33756
Tel.: (727) 441-9022
Web Site: http://www.provise.com
Rev.: $706,000,000
Emp.: 30
Financial Planning & Wealth Management Services
N.A.I.C.S.: 523940
Nancy Croy (Exec VP)

Professional Benefits Solutions, Inc. (2)
8945 Guilford Rd Ste 145, Columbia, MD 21046
Tel.: (301) 369-2379
Web Site: http://www.probeninc.com
Employee Benefit Consulting Services
N.A.I.C.S.: 541612
Joe Duckett (Principal)

RealCare Insurance Marketing, Inc. (2)
19310 Sonoma Hwy Ste A, Sonoma, CA 95476
Tel.: (707) 939-8088
Web Site: http://www.realcarecar.com
Insurance Brokerage Services
N.A.I.C.S.: 524210
Thomas Henry (Pres)

Renaissance Benefit Advisors, Inc. (2)
2500 York Rd Ste 210, Jamison, PA 18929
Tel.: (267) 482-8300
Investment Management Service
N.A.I.C.S.: 523940

Retirement Investment Advisors, Inc. (2)
3001 United Founders Blvd Ste A, Oklahoma City, OK 73112
Tel.: (405) 842-3443
Web Site: http://www.theretirementpath.com
Emp.: 8
Investment Advisory Services
N.A.I.C.S.: 523940
Joseph W. Bowie (Founder)

Rose & Kiernan Inc. (2)
99 Troy Rd Ste 3, East Greenbush, NY 12061
Tel.: (518) 244-4245
Web Site: http://www.rkinsurance.com

Sales Range: $10-24.9 Million
Emp.: 200
Insurance Services
N.A.I.C.S.: 524210
John F. Murray (Chm, Pres & CEO)

Roux Agency, Inc. (2)
85 Webster St, Lewiston, ME 04240-6110
Tel.: (207) 784-9358
Insurance Related Activities
N.A.I.C.S.: 524298

SST Benefits Consulting & Insurance Services Inc. (2)
4364 Town Ctr Blvd Ste 315, El Dorado Hills, CA 95762
Tel.: (916) 270-2020
Web Site: http://www.sstbenefits.com
Business Consulting & Insurance Services
N.A.I.C.S.: 541611
Bill Tugaw (Pres & CEO)

STA Benefits, Ltd. (2)
6010 Hwy 191 E Ste 210, Odessa, TX 79762
Tel.: (432) 337-1131
Web Site: http://www.stabenefits.com
Emp.: 10
Business Management Consulting Services
N.A.I.C.S.: 541611
Steven P. Thompson (Pres, CEO & Principal)

Schmidt Financial Group, Inc. (2)
620 Kirkland Way Ste 205, Kirkland, WA 98033
Tel.: (425) 893-9195
Web Site:
http://www.schmidtfinancialgroup.com
Investment Advisory Services
N.A.I.C.S.: 523940
Glenda S. Schmidt (Pres)

Schwartz Benefit Services, Inc. (2)
500 W Madison St Ste 2700, Chicago, IL 60661
Tel.: (312) 630-0800
Web Site: http://www.schwartzbrothers.com
Insurance Services
N.A.I.C.S.: 524210
Lydia Bates (Acct Exec)

Sontag Advisory, LLC (2)
295 Madison Ave 5th Fl, New York, NY 10017
Tel.: (212) 973-1200
Web Site: http://www.sontagadvisory.com
Sales Range: $50-74.9 Million
Emp.: 35
Investment Management Service
N.A.I.C.S.: 523940
Howard Sontag (Founder & Chm)

Stallard Financial Strategies, Inc. (2)
8080 N Central Expy Ste 1500, Dallas, TX 75206-3785
Tel.: (214) 443-2400
Insurance Brokerage Services
N.A.I.C.S.: 524210

The Benefits Solution Group Inc. (2)
8702 Jefferson Hwy Ste A, Baton Rouge, LA 70809
Tel.: (225) 922-4394
Web Site:
http://www.benefitssolutiongroup.net
Investment Management Service
N.A.I.C.S.: 523940

The Hebets Company (2)
2575 E Camelback Rd Ste 700, Phoenix, AZ 85016
Tel.: (602) 840-7505
Web Site: http://www.hebetsco.com
Sales Range: $25-49.9 Million
Emp.: 12
Business Consulting Services
N.A.I.C.S.: 541611
Jamie Hebets (VP)

Thorbahn and Associates Insurance Agency, Inc. (2)
141 Longwater Dr Ste 101, Norwell, MA 02061
Tel.: (617) 847-3900
Emp.: 50
Employee Benefit Consulting Services
N.A.I.C.S.: 541612
John Thorbahn (Pres)

Udell Associates, Inc. (2)

Aon plc—(Continued)

1605 Main St Ste 1110, Sarasota, FL 34236
Tel.: (941) 951-0443
Web Site: http://www.wealthenjoyment.com
Investment Management Service
N.A.I.C.S.: 523940
Bruce S. Udell (CEO)

United Advisors, LLC (2)
40 Wall St 17th Fl, New York, NY 10005
Tel.: (212) 444-2362
Web Site: http://www.unitedadvisorsllc.com
Insurance Brokerage Services
N.A.I.C.S.: 524210
Kevin Hughes (Mng Partner-Private Client Grp)

Van den Heuvel & Fountain Inc. (2)
PO Box 962, Branchville, NJ 07826
Tel.: (973) 948-3200
Web Site: http://www.atpinsurance.com
Emp.: 7
Insurance Brokerage Services
N.A.I.C.S.: 524210
Steve Tague (Pres)

Wealthspire Advisors, L.P. (2)
521 5th Ave 15th Fl, Rockville, NY 10175
Tel.: (212) 973-1200
Web Site: http://www.wealthspire.com
Wealth Management Advisory Services
N.A.I.C.S.: 523940
Kelly L. Baumbach (Mng Dir & Principal-Wealth Advisory)

Subsidiary (Domestic):

Judith Heft Associates, LLC (3)
34 5th St, Stamford, CT 06905-5012
Tel.: (203) 978-1858
Web Site: http://www.judithheft.com
All Other Support Services
N.A.I.C.S.: 561990
Judith Heft (Mgr)

Private Ocean LLC (3)
100 Smith Ranch Rd Ste 300, San Rafael, CA 94903
Tel.: (415) 788-1952
Financial Planning Services
N.A.I.C.S.: 523940
Susan Dickson (COO)

Subsidiary (Domestic):

Weber's Insurance Services, Inc. (2)
3626 Crossings Dr, Prescott, AZ 86305
Tel.: (928) 445-8720
Web Site: http://www.weber-insurance.com
Sales Range: $1-9.9 Million
Emp.: 15
Insurance Services
N.A.I.C.S.: 524210
William Weber (Pres)

AORERE RESOURCES LIMITED
Level 1 93 The Terrace, PO Box 231, Takaka, Wellington, 7142, New Zealand
Tel.: (64) 3 525 9170   NZ
Web Site:
  http://www.aorereresources.co.nz
Rev.: $196,965
Assets: $146,049
Liabilities: $211,034
Net Worth: ($64,985)
Earnings: ($181,556)
Fiscal Year-end: 03/31/19
Financial Investment Services
N.A.I.C.S.: 523999
Chris D. Castle (Mng Dir)

AOSHIKANG TECHNOLOGY CO., LTD.
Aoshikang PCB Industrial Park Changchun Economic Development Zone, Yiyang, Hunan, China
Tel.: (86) 7372223303
Web Site: https://www.askpcb.com
Year Founded: 2005
002913—(SSE)
Rev.: $641,274,192
Assets: $1,081,387,476
Liabilities: $549,695,484

Net Worth: $531,691,992
Earnings: $43,074,720
Fiscal Year-end: 12/31/22
Electronic Parts Mfr & Distr
N.A.I.C.S.: 334412

AOTECAR NEW ENERGY TECHNOLOGY CO., LTD.
No 8 Mozhou E Road, Jiangning District, Nanjing, 211111, Jiangsu, China
Tel.: (86) 2552602600
Web Site: https://www.aotecar.com
Year Founded: 2000
002239—(SSE)
Rev.: $874,717,272
Assets: $1,705,826,304
Liabilities: $914,128,956
Net Worth: $791,697,348
Earnings: $12,499,812
Emp.: 8,000
Fiscal Year-end: 12/31/22
Investment Services
N.A.I.C.S.: 523999
Yongming Zhang (Board of Directors & Chm)

AOVO TOURISTIK AG
Esperantostrasse 4, DE-30519, Hannover, Germany
Tel.: (49) 51133644000
Web Site: https://www.aovo.de
A8N—(DEU)
Travel Tour Operator
N.A.I.C.S.: 561520
Gerhard M. Griebler (Chm)

AOWEI HOLDING LIMITED
18/F Tesbury Centre 28 Queens Road East, Wanchai, China (Hong Kong)
Tel.: (852) 8567 0808   Ky
Web Site:
  http://www.aoweiholding.com
Year Founded: 2004
Rev.: $116,705,062
Assets: $334,043,339
Liabilities: $144,969,602
Net Worth: $189,073,737
Earnings: ($14,162,750)
Emp.: 849
Fiscal Year-end: 12/31/19
Iron Ore Mining Services
N.A.I.C.S.: 212210
Yanjun Li (Chm)

AOXIN Q & M DENTAL GROUP LIMITED
9 Raffles Place 26-01 Republic Plaza, Singapore, 68898, Singapore
Tel.: (65) 62351188   SG
Web Site:
  https://www.aoxinqm.com.sg
Year Founded: 2011
1D4—(CAT)
Rev.: $24,965,493
Assets: $44,587,324
Liabilities: $6,978,169
Net Worth: $37,609,155
Earnings: ($6,661,972)
Emp.: 416
Fiscal Year-end: 12/31/23
Dental Care Services
N.A.I.C.S.: 621399
Yongxin Shao (CEO)

Subsidiaries:

Anshan Lishan District Aoxin Q & M Stomatology Polyclinic Co., Ltd. (1)
No 149 Shengli North Road, Lishan District, Anshan, Liaoning, China
Tel.: (86) 4126431666
Dental Equipment Whslr
N.A.I.C.S.: 423450

Dalian Aoxin Quanmin Stomatology Hospital Co., Ltd. (1)
No 172 Jinma Road, Development District,

Dalian, Liaoning, China
Tel.: (86) 41187617777
Dental Equipment Whslr
N.A.I.C.S.: 423450

Gaizhou City Aoxin Q & M Stomatology Hospital Co., Ltd. (1)
Room 107-207 1-2/F Building 8 Huayang Garden Office, Xicheng, Kaiping, Liaoning, China
Tel.: (86) 4177673688
Dental Equipment Whslr
N.A.I.C.S.: 423450

Huludao Aoxin Q & M Stomatology Hospital Co., Ltd. (1)
No.81A Longwan Street, Longgang District, Huludao, Liaoning, China
Tel.: (86) 4298210555
Dental Equipment Whslr
N.A.I.C.S.: 423450

Huludao City Aoxin Stomatology Polyclinic Co., Ltd. (1)
No 17-19 Lida Development Xinhua Street Bohai Street, Lianshan District, Huludao, Liaoning, China
Tel.: (86) 4292186003
Dental Equipment Whslr
N.A.I.C.S.: 423450

Huludao Longgang District Aoxin Stomatology Polyclinic Co., Ltd. (1)
No D Building 55-3 Long Wan Street, Longgang District, Huludao, Liaoning, China
Tel.: (86) 4292033777
Dental Equipment Whslr
N.A.I.C.S.: 423450

Jinzhou Aoxin Youxin Dental Clinic Co., Ltd. (1)
No 14-77 Anheli, Linghe District, Jinzhou, Liaoning, China
Tel.: (86) 4163317777
Dental Equipment Whslr
N.A.I.C.S.: 423450

Panjin Aoxin Quanmin Stomatology Hospital Co., Ltd. (1)
Block 0A04-0A05 LeYuan Community, Xinglongtai District, Panjin, Liaoning, China
Tel.: (86) 4276517777
Dental Equipment Whslr
N.A.I.C.S.: 423450

Panjin Jingcheng Q & M Stomatology Co., Ltd. (1)
No 92-1 Shiyou Street, Xinglongtai District, Panjin, Liaoning, China
Tel.: (86) 4277804899
Dental Equipment Whslr
N.A.I.C.S.: 423450

Panjin Jinsai Q & M Stomatology Co., Ltd. (1)
No 169 Shengli Street, Shuangtaizi District, Panjin, Liaoning, China
Tel.: (86) 4273811118
Dental Equipment Whslr
N.A.I.C.S.: 423450

Shenyang Aoxin Q & M Stomatology Hospital Co., Ltd. (1)
No 196 DaNan Street, Shenhe District, Shenyang, Liaoning, China
Tel.: (86) 2424818888
Dental Equipment Whslr
N.A.I.C.S.: 423450
Zhang Dong Wei (Deputy Gen Mgr-Fin)

Shenyang Heping Q & M Aoxin Stomatology Polyclinic Co., Ltd. (1)
No 31 Xita Street, Heping District, Shenyang, Liaoning, China
Tel.: (86) 2424815555
Dental Equipment Whslr
N.A.I.C.S.: 423450

Shenyang Huanggu Aoxin Dental Clinic Co., Ltd. (1)
No 11 Kunshan Middle Road, Huanggu District, Shenyang, Liaoning, China
Tel.: (86) 2486261199
Dental Equipment Whslr
N.A.I.C.S.: 423450

Shenyang Maotai Q & M Medical Equipment Co., Ltd. (1)
Room 2101 No 107 Nanjing North Street,

Heping District, Shenyang, Liaoning, China
Tel.: (86) 2422874848
Dental Equipment Whslr
N.A.I.C.S.: 423450
Cui Guo An (Gen Mgr)

Shenyang Qingaomei Oral Restorative Technology Co., Ltd. (1)
Room 601 Block C No 113 Nanjing North Street, Heping District, Shenyang, Liaoning, China
Tel.: (86) 2486737370
Dental Equipment Whslr
N.A.I.C.S.: 423450

Shenyang Shenhe Aoxin Stomatology Polyclinic Co., Ltd. (1)
Lot F623 No 173 QingNian Main Street, Shenhe District, Shenyang, Liaoning, China
Tel.: (86) 2484111333
Dental Equipment Whslr
N.A.I.C.S.: 423450

Zhuanghe City Aoxin Dawei Dental Co., Ltd. (1)
No 10 Xiangyang Road 2nd Section Chengguan Street, Zhuanghe, Dalian, Liaoning, China
Tel.: (86) 41189856668
Dental Equipment Whslr
N.A.I.C.S.: 423450

AOYAMA TRADING CO. LTD.
1-3-5 Oji-cho, Fukuyama, 721-8556, Hiroshima, Japan
Tel.: (81) 849753939
Web Site: https://www.aoyama-syouji.co.jp
8219—(TKS)
Rev.: $1,280,271,070
Assets: $2,218,296,170
Liabilities: $1,022,699,200
Net Worth: $1,195,596,970
Earnings: $66,688,290
Emp.: 10,889
Fiscal Year-end: 03/31/24
Men Apparel Sales
N.A.I.C.S.: 315210
Osamu Aoyama (Pres)

Subsidiaries:

Aoyama Capital Co., Ltd. (1)
Aoyama Funamachi Building 8-14 Funamachi, Fukuyama, 720-0043, Hiroshima, Japan
Tel.: (81) 849207000
Web Site: https://www.aoyama-card.co.jp
Emp.: 80
Fashion Accessory Whslr
N.A.I.C.S.: 424350

Ascon Co., Ltd. (1)
1-15-27 Minato-cho, Fukuyama, 721-0964, Hiroshima, Japan
Tel.: (81) 849200111
Web Site: https://www.ascon.co.jp
Emp.: 492
Retail Support Services
N.A.I.C.S.: 541611

Fukuryo Co. Ltd. (1)
1-chome-74 Issha, Meito, Nagoya, 465-0093, Aichi, Japan
Tel.: (81) 527021231
Web Site: https://www.fukuryo.com
Suit Mfr & Whslr
N.A.I.C.S.: 315210

Minit Asia Pacific Co., Ltd. (1)
2-19-6 Yanagibashi First Building 2F, Taito-ku, Tokyo, Japan
Tel.: (81) 358392230
Web Site: https://www.minit.co.jp
Emp.: 735
Shoe Repair Services
N.A.I.C.S.: 811430
Kenichi Sasaki (Fin Dir)

Minit Australia Pty Limited (1)
Unit 2 Riverwood Business Park 92-100 Belmore Rd North, Riverwood, 2210, NSW, Australia
Tel.: (61) 295219100
Web Site: http://dev.mistermint.co
Shoe Repair Services
N.A.I.C.S.: 811430

Robyn Thomas *(Mgr-IT)*

SYG Inc. (1)
2-15-9 Uchikanda The Kanda 282 6F / 7F, Chiyoda-ku, Tokyo, 101-0047, Japan
Tel.: (81) 335262300
Web Site: http://www.syginc.jp
System Development Services
N.A.I.C.S.: 541511

Seigo Co., Ltd. (1)
1F Aoyama Oji Building 2-14-38 Oji-cho, Fukuyama, 721-0965, Hiroshima, Japan
Tel.: (81) 849207077
Web Site: https://www.100yenplaza.com
Emp.: 84
Stationery Accessory Whslr
N.A.I.C.S.: 424350

AOYAMA ZAISAN NETWORKS CO., LTD.
3F Aoyama Tower Place 8-4-14 Akasaka, Minato-ku, Tokyo, 107-0052, Japan
Tel.: (81) 64395800
Web Site: https://www.azn.co.jp
8929—(TKS)
Rev.: $255,934,820
Assets: $166,551,190
Liabilities: $98,600,630
Net Worth: $67,950,560
Earnings: $14,619,580
Emp.: 318
Fiscal Year-end: 12/31/23
Asset Consulting & Management Services
N.A.I.C.S.: 541611
Masazumi Hasumi *(Pres)*

AOYUAN BEAUTY VALLEY TECHNOLOGY CO., LTD.
No 108 Huangpu Avenue West, Panyu, Guangzhou, 441133, Guangdong, China
Tel.: (86) 20845067524
Web Site:
http://www.aoyuanbeauty.com
Year Founded: 1993
000615—(SSE)
Rev.: $190,399,515
Assets: $524,919,644
Liabilities: $492,626,352
Net Worth: $32,293,292
Earnings: ($222,318,528)
Fiscal Year-end: 12/31/22
Real Estate Investment Services
N.A.I.C.S.: 531190
Guo Shiguo *(Chm)*

AOYUAN HEALTHY LIFE GROUP COMPANY LIMITED
Floor 26 The Cameron No 33 Cameron Road, Tsim Sha Tsui, Kowloon, 999077, China (Hong Kong)
Tel.: (852) 39162688 Ky
Web Site:
http://www.aoyuanjksh.com
Year Founded: 2000
3662—(HKG)
Rev.: $228,817,040
Assets: $311,832,050
Liabilities: $172,504,987
Net Worth: $139,327,063
Earnings: $22,908,226
Emp.: 3,091
Fiscal Year-end: 12/31/22
Property Management Services
N.A.I.C.S.: 531311
Zheng Wei *(Pres)*

AOYUAN MEIGU TECHNOLOGY CO., LTD.
F 13A Auyuan Tower 48 Wanhui No 1 Road, Panyu District, Guangzhou, China
Tel.: (86) 2081938999
Web Site:
http://www.aoyuanbeauty.com

Year Founded: 1993
000615—(SSE)
Rev.: $192,167,050
Assets: $465,247,607
Liabilities: $411,069,852
Net Worth: $54,177,755
Earnings: ($52,975,727)
Fiscal Year-end: 12/31/23
Chemical Fiber Mfr
N.A.I.C.S.: 327999

AP (THAILAND) PUBLIC COMPANY LIMITED
170/57 18th Floor Ocean Tower 1 New Ratchadapisek Road, Klongtoey, Bangkok, 10110, Thailand
Tel.: (66) 22612518
Web Site: https://www.apthai.com
Year Founded: 1991
AP—(THA)
Rev.: $1,120,949,218
Assets: $2,450,481,295
Liabilities: $1,261,282,579
Net Worth: $1,189,198,716
Earnings: $176,730,952
Emp.: 3,171
Fiscal Year-end: 12/31/23
Property Development Services
N.A.I.C.S.: 236220
Somchai Wattanasaowapak *(Chief IT Officer)*

Subsidiaries:

Bangkok CitiSmart Co., Ltd. (1)
170/48 15th Floor Ocean Tower1 Ratchadapisek Rd, Khwaeng Khlong Toei Khet Khlong Toei, Bangkok, 10110, Thailand
Tel.: (66) 26618999
Web Site: https://www.bkkcitismart.com
Property Brokerage Services
N.A.I.C.S.: 531390
Kayong Stantichwat *(COO)*

Clay More Innovation Lab Co., Ltd. (1)
No 170/43 Ocean Tower 1 Building 14th Floor Soi Sukhumvit 16 Sammitr, Ratchadaphisek Tat Mai Road KlongToei Sub-district KlongToei District, Bangkok, Thailand
Tel.: (66) 24085276
Web Site: http://www.claymorelab.com
Product Development Services
N.A.I.C.S.: 541613

Smart Service & Management Co., Ltd. (1)
170/39 13th Fl Ocean Tower 1 Ratchadapisek Rd, Klongtoey, Bangkok, 10110, Thailand
Tel.: (66) 20797777
Web Site: https://www.smartservice.co.th
Real Estate Services
N.A.I.C.S.: 531390

Trillion Development Co Ltd (1)
Flat 5C 5th Floor Lee Ko Industrial Building, 324 Kwun Tong Road Kwun Tong, Kowloon, China (Hong Kong) (100%)
Tel.: (852) 36111848
Web Site: http://www.trillionhk.com
Sales Range: $50-74.9 Million
Emp.: 5
Other Real Estate Property Lessors
N.A.I.C.S.: 531190

Vaari Digital Co., Ltd. (1)
FYI Center Building 2 3rd Floor 2/301-2/310 Rama 4 Road, Klongtoey, Bangkok, 10110, Thailand
Tel.: (66) 891941914
Web Site: http://www.vaari.co
Computer Programming Services
N.A.I.C.S.: 541511
Phata Techatewon *(Co-Founder)*

AP ACQUISITION CORP.
Unit 2710 27/F The Center 99 Queen's Road, Central, China (Hong Kong)
Tel.: (852) 29180050 Ky
Web Site:
https://www.apacquisitioncorp.com
Year Founded: 2021

APCA—(NYSE)
Rev.: $2,562,680
Assets: $180,695,192
Liabilities: $186,689,976
Net Worth: ($5,994,784)
Earnings: $1,226,432
Emp.: 1
Fiscal Year-end: 12/31/22
Investment Services
N.A.I.C.S.: 523999
Richard Lee Folsom *(Chm)*

AP HOLDINGS CO., LTD
1-10-1 Nishi-Ikebukuro, Toshima-Ku, Tokyo, 171-0021, Japan
Tel.: (81) 364358440
Web Site: https://www.apcompany.jp
Year Founded: 2001
3175—(TKS)
Rev.: $136,152,780
Assets: $54,704,360
Liabilities: $53,600,490
Net Worth: $1,103,870
Earnings: ($2,987,720)
Emp.: 690
Fiscal Year-end: 03/31/24
Chicken & Fish Production & Distribution
N.A.I.C.S.: 424460
Hisashi Yoneyama *(Chm, Pres & Sr Exec Officer)*

Subsidiaries:

AP Company USA, Inc. (1)
1600 Kapiolani Blvd Ste 1328, Honolulu, HI 96814
Tel.: (808) 202-2557
Hotel Services
N.A.I.C.S.: 721110

AP MEMORY TECHNOLOGY CORPORATION
10F-1 No 1 Taiyuan 1st St, Zhubei, 30288, Hsinchu, Taiwan
Tel.: (886) 35601558
Web Site:
https://www.apmemory.com
6531—(TAI)
Rev.: $138,229,074
Assets: $409,221,705
Liabilities: $38,974,360
Net Worth: $370,247,345
Earnings: $47,253,669
Emp.: 205
Fiscal Year-end: 12/31/23
Integrated Circuit Mfr & Distr
N.A.I.C.S.: 334413
Michael Kuo-Chih Tsai *(Chm)*

Subsidiaries:

CascadeTeq Inc. (1)
8F-5 No 1 Taiyuan 1st Street, Hsinchu County, Zhubei, Taiwan
Tel.: (886) 227935340
Web Site: https://cascadeteq.com
Micro Chipping Product Mfr
N.A.I.C.S.: 334413

AP OIL INTERNATIONAL LTD.
18 Pioneer Sector 1 Jurong, Singapore, 628428, Singapore
Tel.: (65) 68615503
Web Site: https://www.apoil.com.sg
Year Founded: 1975
5AU—(SES)
Rev.: $35,004,923
Assets: $52,447,171
Liabilities: $9,513,747
Net Worth: $42,933,424
Earnings: $396,122
Emp.: 104
Fiscal Year-end: 12/31/23
Lubricating Oils & Specialty Chemicals Mfr
N.A.I.C.S.: 324191
Leng Woon Ho *(Chm)*

Subsidiaries:

A.I.M. Chemical Industries Pte Ltd (1)
No 19 Tractor Road, Jurong, Singapore, 627977, Singapore (100%)
Tel.: (65) 62654700
Web Site: http://www.aimchem.com.sg
Sales Range: $25-49.9 Million
Emp.: 45
Chemicals Manufacturing
N.A.I.C.S.: 325998

AP Oil Pte Ltd (1)
30 Gul Crescent, Jurong, Singapore, 629535, Singapore
Tel.: (65) 68615503
Petroleum Lubricating Oil Mfr & Whslr
N.A.I.C.S.: 324191

AP Oil Singapore (Chongqing) Ltd. (1)
Room C1 16F Langgao Kaiyue Business Building No 2 West Nanping Road, Nanan District, Chongqing, 400060, China
Tel.: (86) 2362826687
Petroleum Lubricating Oil Mfr & Whslr
N.A.I.C.S.: 324191

AP Oil Singapore (Shanghai) Limited (1)
Room 2102 East Tower BHC Business Center 2218 Hunan Road, Shanghai, 201204, China
Tel.: (86) 2168922202
Petroleum Lubricating Oil Mfr & Whslr
N.A.I.C.S.: 324191

Alpha Pacific Petroleum (S) Pte Ltd (1)
18 Pioneer Sector 1, Jurong, Singapore, 628428, Singapore (100%)
Tel.: (65) 68622765
Web Site: https://www.apoil.com.sg
Sales Range: $25-49.9 Million
Emp.: 10
Lubricating Oils & Greases Mfg
N.A.I.C.S.: 324191

GB Chemicals Pte Ltd (1)
51 Benoi Road Blk 6 01-01, Liang Huat Industrial Complex, Singapore, 629908, Singapore
Tel.: (65) 68630220
Web Site: https://www.gbchemicals.com.sg
Emp.: 30
Cleaning Chemicals Mfr & Distr
N.A.I.C.S.: 325411

AP RENTALS HOLDINGS LTD.
Unit 806A 8/F Tower 2 South Seas Centre 75 Mody Road, Tsim Sha Tsui East, Kowloon, China (Hong Kong)
Tel.: (852) 2 751 7555 Ky
Web Site:
http://www.aprentalshk.com
1496—(HKG)
Rev.: $17,386,246
Assets: $41,102,057
Liabilities: $13,724,891
Net Worth: $27,377,166
Earnings: ($574,606)
Emp.: 130
Fiscal Year-end: 03/31/22
Holding Company
N.A.I.C.S.: 551112
Pong Sing Lau *(Co-Founder, Chm & CEO)*

Subsidiaries:

AP Equipment Rentals (Singapore) Pte. Ltd. (1)
1 Gul Street 5, Singapore, 629215, Singapore
Tel.: (65) 97239777
Web Site:
https://www.apequipmentrentals.com.sg
Construction Machinery Rental Services
N.A.I.C.S.: 532412

APA GROUP
Level 25 580 George Street, Sydney, 2000, NSW, Australia
Tel.: (61) 296930000 AU

APA Group—(Continued)

Web Site: http://www.apa.com.au
Natural Gas Infrastructure Services
N.A.I.C.S.: 211130
Adam Watson (CFO)

Subsidiaries:

APA GasNet Australia Pty
Limited   (1)
180 Greens Rd, Dandenong, 3175, VIC,
Australia
Tel.: (61) 397975222
Web Site: http://www.apa.com.au
Gas Transmission Services
N.A.I.C.S.: 486210
Ed Deprince (Mgr)

Subsidiary (Domestic):

APA GasNet Australia (Operations)
Pty. Ltd.   (2)
180 Greens Rd, 3175, Dandenong, Victoria,
Australia
Tel.: (61) 397975277
Web Site: http://www.apa.com.au
Sales Range: $50-74.9 Million
Emp.: 150
Gas Transmission Services
N.A.I.C.S.: 486210

APT Facility Management Pty.
Ltd.   (1)
Level 19 HSBC Bldg 580 George St, Syd-
ney, 2000, NSW, Australia
Tel.: (61) 296930000
Web Site: http://www.apa.com.au
Sales Range: $25-49.9 Million
Emp.: 100
Gas Transmission Services
N.A.I.C.S.: 486210
Michael McCormack (Mng Dir)

APT Goldfields Pty. Ltd.   (1)
Level 8 Australia Pl 15-17 William St, 6000,
Perth, Western Australia, Australia
Tel.: (61) 894224100
Sales Range: $50-74.9 Million
Emp.: 70
Gold Mining Services
N.A.I.C.S.: 212220

APT O&M Services Pty Ltd.   (1)
Level 19 HSBC Bldg 580 George St, Syd-
ney, 2000, NSW, Australia
Tel.: (61) 296930000
Natural Gas Transportation Services
N.A.I.C.S.: 486210

APT Parmelia Pty. Ltd.   (1)
Level 5 233 Adelaide Ter, Perth, 6000, WA,
Australia
Tel.: (61) 893205600
Web Site: http://www.apa.com.au
Gas Transmission Services
N.A.I.C.S.: 486210

APT Pipelines (Qld) Pty Limited   (1)
Level 5 Airport Central Tower, 241 O Rior-
dan St, Mascot, 2020, NSW, Australia
Tel.: (61) 296930000
Web Site: http://www.apa.com.au
Natural Gas Transportation Services
N.A.I.C.S.: 486210
Micheale McCormack (CEO)

Central Ranges Pipeline Pty. Ltd.   (1)
5 Phoenix St, Westdale, Tamworth, 2340,
NSW, Australia
Tel.: (61) 267615522
Sales Range: $25-49.9 Million
Emp.: 4
Gas Transmission Services
N.A.I.C.S.: 486210
Garry Green (Mgr)

Goldfields Gas Transmission Pty.
Ltd.   (1)
Level 8 Australia Pl 15 17 William St, Perth,
6000, Western Australia, Australia
Tel.: (61) 894224100
Web Site: http://www.ggt.com.au
Gas Transmission Services
N.A.I.C.S.: 486210
David A. King (Gen Mgr)

N.T. Gas Pty. Ltd.   (1)
16 Georgina Crescent, Palmerston, Darwin,
0830, NT, Australia   (100%)

Tel.: (61) 889248100
Sales Range: $75-99.9 Million
Emp.: 25
Natural Gas Distribution Pipeline System
N.A.I.C.S.: 221210

South East Australia Gas Pty Ltd   (1)
Level 4 70 Hindmarsh Square, Adelaide,
5000, SA, Australia   (50%)
Tel.: (61) 8 8236 6800
Web Site: http://www.seagas.com.au
Natural Gas Pipeline Transportation Ser-
vices
N.A.I.C.S.: 486210
Jeff Cooke (Sec & Mgr-Fin & Comml)

APA HOLDINGS CO., LTD.
Akasaka Mitsuke Honsha Building
3-2-3 Akasaka 1-7 Floor, Tokyo, 107-
0052, Japan
Tel.: (81) 3 5570 2111   JP
Web Site: http://www.apa.co.jp
Year Founded: 1971
Holding Company; Hotels & Resorts
Management, Urban Development &
Construction
N.A.I.C.S.: 551112
Toshio Motoya (Pres & CEO)

Subsidiaries:

Okabe North America, Inc.   (1)
1090 Georgia St, Vancouver, V6E 3V7, BC,
Canada
Tel.: (604) 688-0050
Home Leasing Services
N.A.I.C.S.: 531110

Subsidiary (Domestic):

Coast Hotels Ltd.   (2)
535 Thurlow Street Suite 700, Vancouver,
V6E3L2, BC, Canada
Tel.: (604) 682-7982
Web Site: http://www.coasthotels.com
Hotel & Resort Operator
N.A.I.C.S.: 721110
Linda Hagen (Dir-Brand Engagement)

APA-AUSTRIA PRESSE AGEN-
TUR EG
Laimgrubengasse 10, Vienna, 1060,
Austria
Tel.: (43) 1 360 60 0
Web Site: http://www.apa.at
Sales Range: $125-149.9 Million
Emp.: 511
News Agency
N.A.I.C.S.: 516210
Peter Kropsch (Mng Dir)

Subsidiaries:

Gentics Software GmbH   (1)
Gonzagagasse 11/25, Vienna, 1010, Austria
Tel.: (43) 1 7109904 0
Web Site: http://www.gentics.com
Emp.: 25
Content Management Software Services
N.A.I.C.S.: 513210
Alexander Szlezak (Co-CEO & Chief Sls
Officer)

APAC OPTO ELECTRONICS,
INC.
3 Tzu Chiang Road Hsinchu Indus-
trial Park, Hukow, Hsinchu, 303, Tai-
wan
Tel.: (886) 35986799
Web Site:
https://www.apacoe.com.tw
Year Founded: 1998
4908—(TPE)
Rev.: $27,664,322
Assets: $58,896,883
Liabilities: $5,788,044
Net Worth: $53,108,839
Earnings: $8,157,709
Fiscal Year-end: 12/31/22
Electronic Products Mfr
N.A.I.C.S.: 334419
Chen-Yen Yeh (Chm & Pres)

APAC RESOURCES LIMITED
Room 2304 23rd Floor Allied Kajima
Building, 138 Gloucester Road, Wan-
chai, China (Hong Kong)
Tel.: (852) 25410338   BM
Web Site:
https://www.apacresources.com
1104—(HKG)
Rev.: $56,054,432
Assets: $452,854,687
Liabilities: $11,662,581
Net Worth: $441,192,105
Earnings: ($55,139,382)
Emp.: 14
Fiscal Year-end: 06/30/20
Investment Management Service
N.A.I.C.S.: 523940
Andrew Ferguson (CEO)

Subsidiaries:

APAC Resources Asia Limited   (1)
Room 2304 23rd Floor Allied Kajima Build-
ing 138 Gloucester Road, Wanchai, China
(Hong Kong)
Tel.: (852) 25410338
Web Site: https://www.apacresources.com
Investment Fund Management Services
N.A.I.C.S.: 525110

APACER TECHNOLOGY INC.
No 32 Zhongcheng Rd, Tucheng Dist,
New Taipei City, 236, Taiwan
Tel.: (886) 222678000
Web Site: https://www.apacer.com
Year Founded: 1997
8271—(TAI)
Rev.: $249,564,921
Assets: $208,362,332
Liabilities: $62,442,883
Net Worth: $145,919,449
Earnings: $19,775,401
Emp.: 163
Fiscal Year-end: 12/31/23
Memory Modules, Flash Memory Re-
lated Application Products, Dynamic
Random Access Memory (DRAMs)
Products & Flash Memory Products
Mfr
N.A.I.C.S.: 334112
I-Shih Chen (Co-Chm)

Subsidiaries:

Apacer Electronic (Shanghai) Co.,
Ltd.   (1)
501b Building 2 No 299 Youle Road,
Changning District, Shanghai, 200051,
China
Tel.: (86) 2162289939
Sales Range: $25-49.9 Million
Emp.: 10
Storage Devices Mfr
N.A.I.C.S.: 334112

Apacer Memory America, Inc.   (1)
386 Fairview Way Ste 102, Milpitas, CA
95035
Tel.: (408) 518-8699
Storage Devices Mfr
N.A.I.C.S.: 334112
Pei-Fen Chen (Mgr-Sls)

Apacer Technologies Pvt Ltd.   (1)
1874 South End C Cross 9th Block Jayana-
gar, Bengaluru, 560069, Karnataka, India
Tel.: (91) 8041529061
Sales Range: $25-49.9 Million
Emp.: 8
Storage Devices Mfr
N.A.I.C.S.: 334112

Apacer Technology Corp.   (1)
6F Daiyontamachi Bldg 2-17-12, Shibaura
Minato-Ku, Tokyo, 108-0023, Japan
Tel.: (81) 35 419 2668
Web Site: http://eu.apacer.com
Storage Devices Mfr
N.A.I.C.S.: 334112

UD INFO Corp.   (1)
3F-4 No 8 Ln 609 Sec 5 Chongxin Rd, Sanchong District, New Taipei City, Taiwan
Tel.: (886) 277136050

Web Site: https://www.udinfo.com.tw
Flash Product Mfr
N.A.I.C.S.: 334112

APACS
Mercury House Triton Ct 14 Finsbury
Sq, London, EC2A 1LQ, United King-
dom
Tel.: (44) 2077116200
Sales Range: $50-74.9 Million
Emp.: 150
Market Research & Payment Delivery
Services
N.A.I.C.S.: 541910
Paul Smee (CEO)

APACT CO., LTD.
7280-26 Seodong-daero Iljuk-myeon,
Anseong, 17530, Gyeonggi-do, Korea
(South)
Tel.: (82) 3180461700
Web Site: https://www.apact.co.kr
Year Founded: 2007
200470—(KRS)
Rev.: $56,486,777
Assets: $164,249,573
Liabilities: $76,218,615
Net Worth: $88,030,957
Earnings: $2,370,006
Emp.: 647
Fiscal Year-end: 12/31/22
Semiconductor Devices Mfr
N.A.I.C.S.: 334413
Seong Dong Lee (CEO)

APAMAN CO., LTD.
1-8-1 Marunouchi, Chiyoda-ku, To-
kyo, 100-0005, Japan
Tel.: (81) 332318020
Web Site: https://www.apamanshop-
hd.co.jp
Year Founded: 1999
8889—(TKS)
Rev.: $429,975,920
Assets: $321,772,880
Liabilities: $277,457,840
Net Worth: $44,315,040
Earnings: $5,827,360
Fiscal Year-end: 09/30/21
Holding Company
N.A.I.C.S.: 551111
Koji Omura (Pres & CEO)

Subsidiaries:

3L Entrance, Inc.   (1)
TKP Ichigaya Building 2F 8 Ichigaya
Yahata-cho, Shinjuku-ku, Tokyo, 162-0844,
Japan
Tel.: (81) 352277321
Room Rental Management Services
N.A.I.C.S.: 531120

Apaman Energy Co., Ltd.   (1)
2-6-1 Otemachi Asahi Seimei Otemachi
Building 3rd Floor, Chiyoda-ku, Tokyo, 100-
0004, Japan
Tel.: (81) 36 848 7800
Web Site: https://www.apaman-energy.co.jp
Electric Power Services
N.A.I.C.S.: 221122

Fabbit Philippines Inc.   (1)
26F Twenty-Four Seven McKinley 24th
Street corner 7th Avenue, Bonifacio Global
City, Taguig, 1634, Metro Manila, Philip-
pines
Tel.: (63) 28 864 4100
Web Site: https://www.fabbit.com.ph
Packaging Services
N.A.I.C.S.: 561910

Myhouse Co., Ltd.   (1)
1-22-17 Tsuruma, Yamato, 242-0004, Kana-
gawa, Japan
Tel.: (81) 46 244 6508
Web Site: https://myhousejapan.jp
Real Estate Breakage Services
N.A.I.C.S.: 531390

APAQ TECHNOLOGY CO.,
LTD.

4F No 2&6 Kedong 3rd Road Chunan Science Park, Chunan, 35053, Miaoli, Taiwan
Tel.: (886) 37777588
Web Site: https://www.apaq.com.tw
6449—(TAI)
Rev.: $77,813,026
Assets: $153,780,164
Liabilities: $68,711,847
Net Worth: $85,068,318
Earnings: $10,581,621
Emp.: 1,080
Fiscal Year-end: 12/31/22
Capacitor Mfr
N.A.I.C.S.: 334416

Subsidiaries:

Apaq Technology Co., Ltd. - Wuxi
Factory   (1)
No 1201 Lianfu Road Xishan Economic Development District, Wuxi, Jiangsu, China
Tel.: (86) 51081025298
Capacitor Mfr
N.A.I.C.S.: 334416

APAR INDUSTRIES LTD.

APAR house Bldg no 4 & 5 Corporate Park V N Purav marg, Chembur, Mumbai, 400 071, Maharashtra, India
Tel.: (91) 2225263400
Web Site: https://www.apar.com
Year Founded: 1958
APARINDS—(NSE)
Rev.: $1,964,183,130
Assets: $1,121,709,225
Liabilities: $816,441,990
Net Worth: $305,267,235
Earnings: $87,048,780
Emp.: 1,500
Fiscal Year-end: 03/31/23
Power Transmission Equipment Mfr
N.A.I.C.S.: 333613
Kushal N. Desai *(Chm & Mng Dir)*

APARTAMENTUL SA

Str Depozitelor 39Bis, Arges, Pitesti, Romania
Tel.: (40) 248 632677
Sales Range: $1-9.9 Million
Emp.: 102
Building Construction Services
N.A.I.C.S.: 236116
Ion Cantu *(Pres & Gen Mgr)*

APATOR S.A.

ul Gdanska 4a Lok C4, 87-100, To-run, Poland
Tel.: (48) 566191111
Web Site: https://www.apator.com
APT—(WAR)
Rev.: $230,692,872
Assets: $233,385,449
Liabilities: $103,819,718
Net Worth: $129,565,731
Earnings: $14,533,294
Emp.: 2,151
Fiscal Year-end: 12/31/19
Switchgear & Metering Equipment
Mfr
N.A.I.C.S.: 335313
Krzysztof Malec *(COO & Member-Exec Bd)*

Subsidiaries:

APATOR CONTROL Sp. z o.o.   (1)
ul Zolkiewskiego 21/29, 87 100, Torun, Kuyavian-Pomeranian, Poland
Tel.: (48) 566191601
Web Site: http://www.acontrol.com.pl
Sales Range: $25-49.9 Million
Emp.: 100
Electrical Equipment Mfr & Distr
N.A.I.C.S.: 334515

APATOR GmbH   (1)
Internationales Handelszentrum Friedrichstrasse 95, 10117, Berlin, Germany
Tel.: (49) 3081799740
Web Site: http://www.apator.de

Sales Range: $50-74.9 Million
Office Equipment Whslr
N.A.I.C.S.: 423420

APATOR KFAP Sp. z o.o.   (1)
ul Zigmonta Srtago 150, 30 011, Krakow, Lesser Poland, Poland
Tel.: (48) 126374222
Web Site: http://www.kfap.pl
Sales Range: $25-49.9 Million
Emp.: 40
Metering Equipments Mfr
N.A.I.C.S.: 334514
Adam Kulwik *(Mgr-Sls)*

APATOR METRIX S.A.   (1)
ul Grunwaldzka 14, 83-110, Tczew, Poland
Tel.: (48) 585309200
Web Site: http://www.metrix.com.pl
Sales Range: $25-49.9 Million
Metering Instruments Mfr
N.A.I.C.S.: 335313

APATOR MINING Sp. z o.o.   (1)
Al Rozdzienskiego 188, 40-203, Katowice, Silesian, Poland
Tel.: (48) 508140984
Web Site: http://www.apator-mining.com.pl
Mechanical Equipment Mfr & Distr
N.A.I.C.S.: 333912

APATOR RECTOR Sp. z o.o.   (1)
ul Wroclawska 17B, 65-427, Zielona Gora, Lubusz, Poland
Tel.: (48) 566191364
Web Site: http://www.rector.com.pl
Computing Equipment Services & Mfr
N.A.I.C.S.: 561990

Apator Elkomtech S.A.   (1)
Ul Wolowa 2c, Lodz, Poland
Tel.: (48) 426387500
Electronic Device Distr
N.A.I.C.S.: 423690

Apator Powogaz S.A.   (1)
Jaryszki 1c, Zerniki, 62-023, Poznan, Wielkopolska, Poland
Tel.: (48) 618418101
Web Site: http://www.powogaz.com.pl
Metering Instruments Mfr
N.A.I.C.S.: 334513

Subsidiary (Domestic):

APATOR TELEMETRIA Sp. z
o.o.   (2)
ul Portowa 13A, 76 200, Slupsk, Pomeranian, Poland
Tel.: (48) 509599499
Web Site: https://www.telemetria.eu
Sales Range: $25-49.9 Million
Telemetric Products Mfr & Support Services
N.A.I.C.S.: 334514

WODPOL Sp. z o.o.   (2)
ul Ks Pr St Slonki 24, 34 300, Zywiec, Silesian, Poland
Tel.: (48) 338618527
Web Site: http://www.wodpol.zywiec.pl
Sales Range: $25-49.9 Million
Building Architectural Design Services
N.A.I.C.S.: 541310

FAP Pafal S.A.   (1)
street Lukasinskiego 26, 58-100, Swidnica, Poland
Tel.: (48) 748527100
Electronic Device Distr
N.A.I.C.S.: 423690

APAVE SA

Canopy Building 6 rue du General Audran, CS 60123, Courbevoie, Cedex, France
Tel.: (33) 55677 27 36
Web Site: http://www.apave-international.com
Inspection & Technical Support Services
N.A.I.C.S.: 541990

APAX GLOBAL ALPHA LTD.

East Wing Trafalgar Court Les Banques, PO Box 656, Saint Peter Port, GY1 3PP, Guernsey
Tel.: (44) 2076666526

Web Site:
https://www.apaxglobalalpha.com
APAX—(LSE)
Rev.: $77,240,314
Assets: $1,442,897,671
Liabilities: $14,302,903
Net Worth: $1,428,594,768
Earnings: $59,033,006
Fiscal Year-end: 12/31/23
Financial Investment Services
N.A.I.C.S.: 523999
Sarah Wojcik *(Mgr-Fund)*

APAX PARTNERS LLP

33 Jermyn Street, London, SW1Y 6DN, United Kingdom
Tel.: (44) 2078726300   UK
Web Site: http://www.apax.com
Year Founded: 1981
Private Equity & Investment Advisory Firm
N.A.I.C.S.: 523999
Tom Hall *(Partner)*

Subsidiaries:

Altus Fire & Life Safety   (1)
1756 86th St., Brooklyn, NY 11214
Tel.: (718) 234-8600
Web Site: https://www.altusfire.com
Facilities Services
N.A.I.C.S.: 561210

Subsidiary (Domestic):

Crime Intervention Alarm Co Inc (2)
320 Loucks Rd Unit 5, York, PA 17404
Tel.: (717) 846-4004
Web Site: http://www.cialarm.com
Rev.: $1,600,000
Emp.: 17
Security Systems Services, except Locksmiths
N.A.I.C.S.: 561621
John Lakatosh *(Pres)*

Answers Corporation   (1)
6665 Delmar Blvd Ste 3000, Saint Louis, MO 63130
Tel.: (314) 664-2010
Web Site: http://www.answers.com
Sales Range: $10-24.9 Million
Search Engine Portals
N.A.I.C.S.: 519290
Jeff Schneiderman *(CTO)*

Subsidiary (Domestic):

Webcollage, Inc.   (2)
462 7th Ave, New York, NY 10018
Tel.: (212) 563-2112
Web Site: http://www.webcollage.com
Sales Range: $10-24.9 Million
Emp.: 55
Web Services
N.A.I.C.S.: 541519
John Federman *(CEO)*

Apax Investment (Shanghai) Company Ltd   (1)
65th Floor Shanghai World Financial Center 100 Century Avenue, Pudong New District, Shanghai, 200120, China
Tel.: (86) 21 5198 5600
Investment Management Service
N.A.I.C.S.: 523999

Apax Partners (Israel) Ltd.   (1)
Museum Tower 4 Berkowitz Street, Tel Aviv, 64238, Israel
Tel.: (972) 37774400
Web Site: http://www.apax.com
Sales Range: $50-74.9 Million
Emp.: 60
Private Equity Advisory Firm
N.A.I.C.S.: 523999
Zehavit Cohen *(Mng Partner & Head-Office)*

Apax Partners (UK) Ltd   (1)
33 Jermyn Street, London, SW1Y 6DN, United Kingdom
Tel.: (44) 20 7872 6300
Web Site: http://www.apax.com
Financial Services
N.A.I.C.S.: 523999

Subsidiary (Non-US):

Lutech SpA   (2)

Via Milano 150, 20093, Cologno Monzese, MI, Italy
Tel.: (39) 0225427011
Web Site: http://www.lutech.it
Information Technology Consulting, System Integration & Outsourcing Services
N.A.I.C.S.: 541512
Giuseppe Di Franco *(Mng Dir)*

Subsidiary (Domestic):

Lutech Advanced Solutions
S.p.A.   (3)
Caldera Business Park Via Caldera 21, 20153, Milan, Italy
Tel.: (39) 02454061
Web Site: http://atos.net
Emp.: 750
Information Technology Solutions & Consulting Services
N.A.I.C.S.: 541690
Giuseppe Di Franco *(CEO)*

Sisge Medical srl   (3)
Terza Strada 8 Interporto SiTO, 10040, Rivalta di Torino, TO, Italy
Tel.: (39) 011 3981420
Web Site: http://www.sisge-med.it
Sales Range: $1-9.9 Million
Emp.: 20
Intergrated System Design Services
N.A.I.C.S.: 541512

Apax Partners Beteiligungsberatung GmbH   (1)
Theatinerstr 3, Munich, 80333, Germany   (100%)
Tel.: (49) 899989090
Private Equity Advisory Firm
N.A.I.C.S.: 523999
Isabelle Probstel *(Head-Holdcos-Global)*

Apax Partners Brazil Consultoria Ltda.   (1)
Av Brigadeiro Faria Lima 2277 Cj 1704, Sao Paulo, 01452-000, Brazil
Tel.: (55) 11 4949 3700
Investment Management Service
N.A.I.C.S.: 523999
Denis Pedreira *(Principal)*

Apax Partners Espana, S.L.   (1)
Diagonal 640 5 andar, 08017, Barcelona, Spain   (100%)
Tel.: (34) 93 545 6500
Web Site: http://www.apax.com
Sales Range: $50-74.9 Million
Emp.: 5
Private Equity Advisory Firm
N.A.I.C.S.: 523999

Apax Partners Hong Kong Ltd   (1)
16/F Nexxus Building 41 Connaught Road, Central, Hong Kong, China (Hong Kong)
Tel.: (852) 2200 5813
Investment Management Service
N.A.I.C.S.: 523999
Irene Liu *(Principal-Retail & Consumer)*

Apax Partners India Advisers Private Limited   (1)
2nd Floor Devchand House Shivsagar Estate Dr Annie Besant Road, Worli, Mumbai, 400 018, India
Tel.: (91) 22 4050 8400
Web Site: http://www.apax.us.com
Emp.: 13
Investment Management Service
N.A.I.C.S.: 523999
Gautam Narayan *(Partner-Svcs)*

Apax Partners SAS   (1)
1 Rue Paul Cezanne, 75008, Paris, Cedex 16, France
Tel.: (33) 153650100
Web Site: http://www.apax.fr
Privater Equity Firm
N.A.I.C.S.: 523999
Eddie Misrahi *(Pres)*

Joint Venture (Domestic):

Infopro Digital SAS   (2)
Antony Parc 2-10 place du General de Gaulle, BP 20156, La Croix de Berny, 92 186, Antony, Cedex, France
Tel.: (33) 1 77 92 92 92
Web Site: http://www.infopro-digital.com
Sales Range: $500-549.9 Million
Emp.: 3,200

Apax Partners LLP—(Continued)

Professional Information, Multimedia Software & Print Publication Services
N.A.I.C.S.: 513210
Christophe Czajka *(Founder & Exec Chm)*

Subsidiary (Non-US):

Docu Group Deutsche Holding GmbH (3)
Arnulfstr 124, 80636, Munich, Germany
Tel.: (49) 892351937 50
Web Site: http://www.docugroup.info
Construction Industry Business to Business Publishing Services
N.A.I.C.S.: 513199
Christophe Czajka *(Mng Dir)*

Subsidiary (Domestic):

Bauverlag BV GmbH (4)
Avenwedderstr 55, 33311, Gutersloh, Germany
Tel.: (49) 5241802791
Web Site: http://www.bauverlag.de
Architecture & Construction Industry Information Publisher
N.A.I.C.S.: 519290
Michael Voss *(CEO)*

Subsidiary (Non-US):

Haynes Publishing Group PLC (3)
Sparkford, Yeovil, BA22 7JJ, Somerset, United Kingdom
Tel.: (44) 1963440635
Web Site: http://www.haynes.co.uk
Instructional Book, Manual & Video Publisher
N.A.I.C.S.: 513130
Eddie Bell *(Chm)*

Subsidiary (US):

Haynes North America, Inc (4)
859 Lawrence Dr, Newbury Park, CA 91320
Tel.: (805) 498-6703
Web Site: http://www.haynes.com
Books Publishing Services
N.A.I.C.S.: 513130
Dan Benhardus *(CFO & Sr VP)*

Subsidiary (Domestic):

J H Haynes & Co Ltd (4)
Yeovil, Somerset, BA22 7JJ, United Kingdom
Tel.: (44) 1963440635
Web Site: http://www.haynes.co.uk
Sales Range: $25-49.9 Million
Emp.: 75
Book Publisher & Distr
N.A.I.C.S.: 513130
Jeremy Haynes-Round *(Mng Dir)*

Subsidiary (US):

Odcombe Press LP (4)
1299 Bridgestone Pkwy, La Vergne, TN 37086
Tel.: (615) 793-5414
Web Site: http://www.haynes.com
Sales Range: $25-49.9 Million
Emp.: 60
Printing Services
N.A.I.C.S.: 323117
Nigel Clenns *(VP-Ops)*

Subsidiary (Domestic):

Vivid Automotive Data (UK) Ltd (4)
Ground Fl N Barn, Broughton Hall Business Park, Skipton, BD23 3AE, Yorkshire, United Kingdom
Tel.: (44) 1756794393
Sales Range: $25-49.9 Million
Emp.: 4
Database Management Services
N.A.I.C.S.: 541513

Subsidiary (Non-US):

Vivid Italia srl (4)
Strada San Luigi 27, I 10043, Orbassano, Italy
Tel.: (39) 0119040768
Database Management Services
N.A.I.C.S.: 541513

Apax Partners, L.P. (1)
601 Lexington Ave, New York, NY 10022

Tel.: (212) 753-6300
Web Site: http://www.apax.com
Sales Range: $50-74.9 Million
Emp.: 65
Private Equity Advisory Firm
N.A.I.C.S.: 523999
Seth A. Brody *(Partner & Global Head-Operational Excellence)*

Attenti Ltd. (1)
2 Habarzel St, Tel Aviv, 69710, Israel
Tel.: (972) 37671700
Web Site: http://www.attentigroup.com
Electronic People Monitoring Technology & Services
N.A.I.C.S.: 334419
Eyal Sharoni *(CFO)*

Subsidiary (US):

Attenti US, Inc. (2)
1838 Gunn Hwy, Odessa, FL 33556
Tel.: (813) 749-5454
Web Site: http://www.attentigroup.com
Electronic People Monitoring Technology & Services
N.A.I.C.S.: 334419
David Segal *(Chief Product Officer)*

Authority Brands, LLC (1)
7120 Samuel Morse Dr Ste 300, Columbia, MD 21046
Web Site: http://www.theauthoritybrands.com
Marketing, Technology & Operational Support Services
N.A.I.C.S.: 561499
Ashish Karandikar *(Partner)*

Subsidiary (Domestic):

Clockwork, Inc. (2)
12 Greenway Plaza Ste 250, Houston, TX 77046
Tel.: (941) 366-9692
Web Site: http://www.clockworkhomeservices.com
Home Services Franchisor for Plumbing, HVAC & Electrical Industries
N.A.I.C.S.: 533110
Rebecca Cassel *(Pres-CSG)*

Subsidiary (Domestic):

Authority Brands US Home Services, Inc. (3)
7120 Samuel Morse Dr Ste 300, Columbia, MD 21046
Holding Company; Residential Heating, Ventilation, Air Conditioning & Plumbing Contractor Services
N.A.I.C.S.: 551112

Subsidiary (Domestic):

Color World Housepainting, Inc. (2)
94 Village Pointe Dr, Powell, OH 43065
Tel.: (614) 861-6618
Web Site: http://www.colorworldhousepainting.com
Painting & Wall Covering Contractors
N.A.I.C.S.: 238320
Tom Hodgson *(Founder & CEO)*

Doodycalls Franchising, LLC (2)
114 4th St SE Ste A, Charlottesville, VA 22902
Tel.: (703) 255-1143
Web Site: http://www.doodycalls.com
Rev.: $1,085,000
Emp.: 5
Hazardous Waste Treatment & Disposal
N.A.I.C.S.: 562211
Jacob D'Aniello *(Founder & Pres)*

Homewatch International, Inc. (2)
6251 Greenwood Plz Blvd Ste 250, Greenwood Village, CO 80111
Tel.: (303) 758-5111
Web Site: http://www.homewatchcaregivers.com
Women Healthcare Services
N.A.I.C.S.: 621610
Jennifer Tucker *(COO)*

Junkluggers, LLC (2)
11 Eliot St, Fairfield, CT 06824-5125
Web Site: http://www.junkluggers.com
General Freight Trucking
N.A.I.C.S.: 484121
Joshua E. Cohen *(CEO)*

Screenmobile Corp. (2)
72050 Corporate Way Ste A, Thousand Palms, CA 92276-3333
Tel.: (760) 343-3500
Web Site: http://www.screenmobile.com
Other Building Material Dealers
N.A.I.C.S.: 444180
Dale Dennis *(Pres)*

The Cleaning Authority LLC (2)
7230 Lee Deforest Dr, Columbia, MD 21046
Tel.: (443) 602-9154
Web Site: http://www.thecleaningauthority.com
Emp.: 25
Home Cleaning Services
N.A.I.C.S.: 561790
Rob Webble *(CFO)*

Auto Trader Group Plc (1)
1 Tony Wilson Place, Manchester, M15 4FN, United Kingdom (100%)
Tel.: (44) 3451110006
Web Site: http://www.autotrader.co.uk
Rev.: $621,148,360
Assets: $822,940,860
Liabilities: $168,139,720
Net Worth: $654,801,140
Earnings: $290,457,020
Emp.: 1,160
Fiscal Year-end: 03/31/2023
Online Automotive Marketplace Operator
N.A.I.C.S.: 441330
Ed Williams *(Chm)*

Azentio Software Pte. Ltd. (1)
38 Beech Road #29-11 South Beach Tower, Singapore, 189767, Singapore
Web Site: http://www.azentio.com
Computer Software Services
N.A.I.C.S.: 541512
Sanjay Singh *(CEO)*

Capio AB (1)
Lilla Bommen 5, PO Box 1064, SE-405 22, Gothenburg, Sweden
Tel.: (46) 317324000
Web Site: http://www.capio.com
Rev.: $1,864,989,360
Assets: $1,709,238,960
Liabilities: $1,008,848,880
Net Worth: $700,390,080
Earnings: $45,264,960
Emp.: 13,314
Fiscal Year-end: 12/31/2017
Hospital & Healthcare Facilities Owner & Operator
N.A.I.C.S.: 622110
Pascal Roche *(CEO)*

Division (Domestic):

Actica Omsorg AB (2)
Gardatorget 1, Gothenburg, 41250, Sweden
Tel.: (46) 317737500
Web Site: http://www.actica.se
Sales Range: $10-24.9 Million
Emp.: 15
Elder Care Services
N.A.I.C.S.: 621610

Capio Proximity Care (2)
Lilla Bommen 5, PO Box 1064, SE-405 22, Gothenburg, Sweden
Tel.: (46) 317324000
Web Site: http://www.capio.com
Healtcare Services
N.A.I.C.S.: 621999

Subsidiary (Non-US):

Clinique La Metaire (2)
Av De Bois Bougy, CH 1260, Nyon, Switzerland
Tel.: (41) 223632020
Web Site: http://www.lametaire.ch
Mental Health Care Services
N.A.I.C.S.: 621330
Catherine Colin *(Mng Dir)*

Subsidiary (Domestic):

GHP Specialty Care AB (2)
Sodra Hamngatan 45, SE-411 06, Gothenburg, Sweden
Tel.: (46) 317125300
Web Site: http://www.ghp.se
Rev.: $167,481,552
Assets: $141,918,000
Liabilities: $82,965,568
Net Worth: $58,952,432

Earnings: $8,301,440
Emp.: 764
Fiscal Year-end: 12/31/2020
Health Care Clinic Operator
N.A.I.C.S.: 621498
Daniel Ohman *(CEO)*

Subsidiary (Domestic):

Global Health Partner Swe AB (3)
Sodra Hamngatan 45, 411 09, Gothenburg, Sweden
Tel.: (46) 317125300
Web Site: http://www.ghp.com
Sales Range: $10-24.9 Million
Emp.: 14
Health Care Management Services
N.A.I.C.S.: 621491
Daniel Ohman *(CEO)*

Subsidiaries:

Orthocenter Goteborg AB (3)
Gruvgatan 8, 421 30, Vastra Frolunda, Sweden
Tel.: (46) 31450200
Health Care Srvices
N.A.I.C.S.: 621999

Specialistkliniken for Dentala Implantat KB (3)
Varmdovagen 121, 131 57, Nacka, Sweden
Tel.: (46) 87183050
Web Site: http://www.nacka.specialisttandlakarna.se
Sales Range: $25-49.9 Million
Emp.: 45
Dental Implant Services
N.A.I.C.S.: 339116

Stockholm Arrhythmia Center AB (3)
Sjukhusbacken 10 Sodersjukhuset, 118 83, Stockholm, Sweden
Tel.: (46) 86165200
Web Site: http://www.arytmicenter.se
Sales Range: $10-24.9 Million
Emp.: 5
Health Care Srvices
N.A.I.C.S.: 621999

Vita Bariatric Clinics Stockholm AB (3)
Valhallavagen 91, 114 27, Stockholm, Sweden
Tel.: (46) 84062841
Health Care Srvices
N.A.I.C.S.: 621999

Subsidiary (Non-US):

Vita Clinics UK Ltd (3)
38 Highfield Rd Edgbaston, Birmingham, B15 3ED, United Kingdom
Tel.: (44) 8008494050
Bariatric Surgery & Medical Weight Management
N.A.I.C.S.: 621999

Cengage Learning Holdings II, Inc. (1)
3 Ctr Plz Ste 700, Boston, MA 02108
Tel.: (513) 229-1000
Web Site: https://www.cengagegroup.com
Rev.: $1,502,700,000
Assets: $2,600,400,000
Liabilities: $2,485,700,000
Net Worth: ($389,400,000)
Earnings: ($80,900,000)
Emp.: 4,400
Fiscal Year-end: 03/31/2024
Holding Company; Library Reference & Educational Materials Publishing & Learning Solutions
N.A.I.C.S.: 551112
Michael E. Hansen *(CEO)*

Subsidiary (Domestic):

Cengage Learning, Inc. (2)
3 Ctr Plz Ste 700, Boston, MA 2108
Tel.: (513) 229-1000
Web Site: http://www.cengage.com
Library Reference & Educational Materials Publishing & Learning Solutions
N.A.I.C.S.: 513130
Michael E. Hansen *(CEO)*

Subsidiary (Domestic):

Advanced Instructional Systems, Inc. (3)

1791 Varsity Dr Ste 200, Raleigh, NC
27606
Tel.: (919) 829-8181
Web Site: https://www.webassign.com
Sales Range: $1-9.9 Million
Emp.: 25
Online Software Solutions Services
N.A.I.C.S.: 513210
Rob Simora *(CTO)*

Division (Domestic):

Cengage Higher Education **(3)**
20 Davis Dr, Belmont, CA 94002
Tel.: (650) 595-2350
Web Site:
    http://www.academic.cengage.com
Educational Book Publishing
N.A.I.C.S.: 513130

Unit (Domestic):

South-Western Cengage
Learning **(4)**
5191 Natorp Blvd, Mason, OH 45040
Tel.: (513) 229-1000
Web Site: http://www.cengagelearning.com
Sales Range: $200-249.9 Million
Accounting, Marketing & Management Edu-
cation Book Publisher
N.A.I.C.S.: 513130

Wadsworth Cengage Learning **(4)**
10 Davis Dr, Belmont, CA 94002-3002
Tel.: (650) 595-2350
Web Site:
    http://www.academic.cengage.com
Educational Software & Textbook Publisher
N.A.I.C.S.: 513130

Subsidiary (Non-US):

Cengage Learning Asia **(3)**
30A Kallang Place 12-06, UIC Bldg, Singa-
pore, 339213, Singapore
Tel.: (65) 64101200
Web Site: https://www.cengageasia.com
Sales Range: $50-74.9 Million
Emp.: 70
Educational & Reference Book Publisher
N.A.I.C.S.: 513130

Cengage Learning Australia Pty.
Limited **(3)**
80 Dorcas St Level 7, Victoria, 3205, VIC,
Australia
Tel.: (61) 396854111
Web Site: http://www.cengage.com.au
Sales Range: $50-74.9 Million
Emp.: 200
Educational & Reference Book Publishing
N.A.I.C.S.: 513130
Tamara Silver *(Mgr-HR)*

Subsidiary (Domestic):

Delmar Cengage Learning **(3)**
5 Maxwell Dr Executive Woods, Clifton
Park, NY 12065-2919
Tel.: (518) 348-2300
Web Site: http://www.cengage.com
Sales Range: $100-124.9 Million
Emp.: 294
Educational, Technical & Vocational Pub-
lishers
N.A.I.C.S.: 513130

Subsidiary (Non-US):

Gale Group Inc. **(3)**
Tel.: (248) 699-4253
Web Site: http://www.gale.com
Sales Range: $300-349.9 Million
Reference Book & Electronic Reference
Materials Publisher
N.A.I.C.S.: 513140
Paul Gazzolo *(Sr VP & Gen Mgr)*

Division (Domestic):

Macmillan Reference USA **(4)**
12 Lunar Dr, Woodbridge, CT 06525-2322
Tel.: (203) 397-2600
Web Site: http://gale.cengage.com
Sales Range: $25-49.9 Million
Emp.: 55
Publisher of Academic & Professional Ref-
erence Materials, Newspapers & U.S. &
Foreign Patents
N.A.I.C.S.: 513130

Subsidiary (Domestic):

Learning Objects, Inc. **(3)**
1528 Connecticut Ave NW, Washington, DC
20036
Tel.: (202) 265-3276
Web Site: https://www.learningobjects.com
Education Technology Software Publisher
N.A.I.C.S.: 513210

Subsidiary (Non-US):

Nelson Education Ltd. **(3)**
1120 Birchmount Rd, Scarborough, M1K
5G4, ON, Canada
Tel.: (416) 752-9448
Web Site: http://www.nelson.com
Sales Range: $100-124.9 Million
Education & Reference Book Publisher
N.A.I.C.S.: 513130
Steve Brown *(Pres & CEO)*

Coalfire Systems, Inc. **(1)**
11000 Westmoor Cir Ste 450, Westminster,
CO 80021
Tel.: (303) 554-6333
Web Site: http://www.coalfire.com
Audit, Security & Compliance Management
Solutions
N.A.I.C.S.: 541512
Adam Shnider *(Exec VP-Comml Svcs)*

Subsidiary (Domestic):

Denim Group, Ltd. **(2)**
1354 N Loop 1604 E Ste 110, San Antonio,
TX 78232
Tel.: (210) 572-4400
Web Site: http://www.denimgroup.com
Rev.: $5,300,000
Emp.: 51
Custom Computer Programming Services
N.A.I.C.S.: 541511
Sheridan Chambers *(Principal)*

Veris Group, LLC **(2)**
22630 Davis Dr Ste 225, Sterling, VA 20164
Tel.: (703) 760-9163
Applications Software Mfr
N.A.I.C.S.: 513210
William E. Malone *(VP)*

Cole Haan, Inc. **(1)**
150 Ocean Rd, Greenland, NH
03840 **(100%)**
Tel.: (603) 430-7800
Web Site: http://www.colehaan.com
Rev.: $686,576,000
Assets: $587,858,000
Liabilities: $423,069,000
Net Worth: $164,789,000
Earnings: $33,137,000
Emp.: 1,000
Fiscal Year-end: 06/01/2019
Footwear, Accessories & Outerwear Retailer
N.A.I.C.S.: 424340
Jack A. Boys *(CEO)*

Subsidiary (Domestic):

Cole Haan Company Store **(2)**
109 Newbury St, Boston, MA 02116-2902
Tel.: (617) 536-7826
Web Site: http://www.colehaan.com
Emp.: 13
Rubber & Plastics Footwear Mfr
N.A.I.C.S.: 316210
Gina Nieves *(Gen Mgr)*

Subsidiary (Non-US):

Cole Haan Japan, Inc. **(2)**
Rene Aoyama Bldg 3F 3-3-11 Kita, Minato-
Ku, Tokyo, 107-0061, Japan
Tel.: (81) 3 3470 7700
Web Site: http://www.colehaan.co.jp
Sales Range: $50-74.9 Million
Emp.: 240
Footwear Retailer
N.A.I.C.S.: 424340

Contech Construction Products
Inc. **(1)**
9025 Ctr Pointe Dr Ste 400, West Chester,
OH 45069
Tel.: (513) 645-7000
Web Site: http://www.contech-cpi.com
Sales Range: $700-749.9 Million
Civil Engineering Services
N.A.I.C.S.: 237990

Subsidiary (Domestic):

ConTech **(2)**
6523 188th St NE, Arlington, WA 98223-
8707
Tel.: (360) 435-2181
Web Site: http://www.contech-cpi.com
Sales Range: $25-49.9 Million
Emp.: 15
Mfr of Metal Culvert Pipe
N.A.I.C.S.: 423510

Contech Inc. **(2)**
710 SW Armco Ave, Hillsboro, OR 97123
Tel.: (503) 640-2783
Web Site: http://www.conteches.com
Sales Range: $25-49.9 Million
Emp.: 7
Metal Culvert Pipe Mfr & Distr
N.A.I.C.S.: 332996
Mike Roche *(Gen Mgr)*

Deposition Solutions, LLC **(1)**
13101 NW Fwy Ste 210, Houston, TX
77040
Tel.: (800) 676-2401
Web Site: http://www.lexitaslegal.com
Court Reporting & Deposition Services
N.A.I.C.S.: 561492
Gary Buckland *(CEO)*

Subsidiary (Domestic):

Barrister Reporting Service, Inc. **(2)**
1325 Franklin Avenue Suite 520, Garden
City, NY 11530
Tel.: (212) 732-8066
Document Preparation Services
N.A.I.C.S.: 561410

Benchmark Reporting Agency,
Inc. **(2)**
222 S 9th St Ste 450, Minneapolis, MN
55402-3373
Tel.: (612) 338-3376
Web Site: http://www.benchmark-
reporting.com
Court Reporting & Stenotype Services
N.A.I.C.S.: 561492
Eric Goldberg *(Principal)*

Division (Domestic):

Deposition Solutions, LLC - Records
Retrieval Division **(2)**
325 N Saint Paul St Ste 1900, Dallas, TX
75201
Tel.: (972) 247-3800
Web Site: http://www.lexitaslegal.com
Records Retrieval Litigation Support Ser-
vices
N.A.I.C.S.: 541199
Brandy Patrick *(Pres-Defense Records)*

Subsidiary (Domestic):

Imber Court Reporters Inc. **(2)**
27959 Smyth Dr, Valencia, CA 91355
Tel.: (661) 295-4678
Web Site:
    http://www.imbercourtreporters.com
Sales Range: $1-9.9 Million
Emp.: 8
Litigation Support & Court Reporting Ser-
vices
N.A.I.C.S.: 561492
Heather Imber Pemble *(Pres & CEO)*

Oasis Reporting Services LLC **(2)**
400 S 7th St Ste 400, Las Vegas, NV
89101
Tel.: (702) 476-4500
Web Site: http://www.oasisreporting.com
Court Reporting & Stenotype Services
N.A.I.C.S.: 561492

Registered Agent Solutions, Inc. **(2)**
1701 Directors Blvd Ste 300, Austin, TX
78744
Web Site: http://www.rasi.com
Planning Services
N.A.I.C.S.: 541611
Sean Prewitt *(Founder & Pres)*

Subsidiary (Domestic):

Allstate Corporate Services
Corp. **(3)**
1222 Ave M 301, Brooklyn, NY 11230
Tel.: (718) 382-9990

Web Site:
    https://allstatecorporateservices.com
Sales Range: $1-9.9 Million
Emp.: 43
Corporate Filing & Research Services
N.A.I.C.S.: 541611

Corp2000, Inc. **(3)**
720 14th St, Sacramento, CA 95814
Web Site: http://www.corp2000.com
Sales Range: $1-9.9 Million
Emp.: 14
Business-To-Business Services
N.A.I.C.S.: 561499
Lee Scott *(Pres)*

Esquire Assist Ltd. **(3)**
125 Locust St, Harrisburg, PA 17101-1411
Tel.: (717) 232-9398
Web Site: http://www.esquireassist.com
Law firm
N.A.I.C.S.: 541199

HIQ Corporate Services, Inc. **(3)**
516 N Charles St Ste 501, Baltimore, MD
21201-5052
Tel.: (410) 752-8030
Web Site: http://www.hiq-agents.com
Corporate Document Filing, Retrieval &
Search Services
N.A.I.C.S.: 561499
James Strott *(CEO)*

Subsidiary (Domestic):

Team Legal **(2)**
13100 Wortham Ctr Dr Ste 140, Houston,
TX 77065-5619
Tel.: (713) 937-4242
Web Site: http://www.teamlegal.net
Investigation Services
N.A.I.C.S.: 561611
James Gates *(Co-Founder & Pres)*

The Axiom Group, Inc. **(2)**
2869 Jolly Rd, Okemos, MI 48864
Tel.: (877) 886-5090
Web Site: http://www.axiomcopy.com
Office Administrative Services
N.A.I.C.S.: 561110
Matthew Garza *(Supvr-Records Admin)*

V.A. Anderson Enterprises, Inc. **(2)**
570 W Lambert Rd Ste C, Brea, CA 92821
Tel.: (714) 990-6100
Sales Range: $1-9.9 Million
Emp.: 140
Support Services
N.A.I.C.S.: 561990
Bob Flynn *(Sec & VP)*

Yorkson Legal Inc. **(2)**
800 2nd Ave Rm 804, New York, NY
10017-9221
Tel.: (212) 265-1400
Web Site: http://www.yorkson.com
Temporary Help Service
N.A.I.C.S.: 561320
Michael Reichwald *(Pres)*

ECI Software Solutions, Inc. **(1)**
4400 Alliance Gateway Fwy Ste 154, Fort
Worth, TX 76177
Tel.: (682) 831-0827
Web Site: http://www.ecisolutions.com
Business Software Technology Solutions
N.A.I.C.S.: 513210
Ron Books *(Chm)*

Subsidiary (Non-US):

PJLM Software Inc. **(2)**
5760-9 Street SE Suite 109, Calgary, T2H
1Z9, AB, Canada
Tel.: (403) 685-4932
Managed Print & Computer Software Services
N.A.I.C.S.: 513210

Subsidiary (Domestic):

ProfitKey International, Inc. **(2)**
50 Stiles Rd, Salem, NH 03079-2412
Tel.: (603) 898-9800
Web Site: http://www.profitkey.com
Sales Range: $1-9.9 Million
Emp.: 25
Develops & Markets Integrated Manufactur-
ing Software & Information Control Systems
N.A.I.C.S.: 513210
Joseph J. Di Zazzo *(COO)*

Apax Partners LLP—(Continued)

**Engineering Ingegneria Informatica
S.p.A.** **(1)**
Via San Martino della Battaglia 56, 00185,
Rome, Italy
Tel.: (39) 0649201
Web Site: http://www.eng.it
Rev.: $1,350,017,666
Assets: $1,916,630,513
Liabilities: $1,212,256,939
Net Worth: $704,373,574
Earnings: $65,988,631
Emp.: 10,730
Fiscal Year-end: 12/31/2018
Engineeering Services
N.A.I.C.S.: 541330
Michele Cinaglia (Founder & Chm)

Subsidiary (Domestic):

**Engineering Ingegneria Informatica
S.p.A - Osimo** **(2)**
Via Edison 2, Osimo, 60027, Ancona, Italy
Tel.: (39) 07171021
Web Site: http://www.eng.it
Utilities IT Solutions & Services
N.A.I.C.S.: 541519

Subsidiary (Non-US):

**Engineering International Belgium
SA** **(2)**
Rue de la Loi 82, 1040, Brussels,
Belgium **(100%)**
Tel.: (32) 2 2305707
Web Site: http://www.eng.it
Information Technology Consulting Services
N.A.I.C.S.: 541512

Subsidiary (Domestic):

Engineering.mo S.p.A **(2)**
Viale Carlo Viola 76, 11026, Pont San Mar-
tin, Aosta, Italy **(100%)**
Tel.: (39) 0125810201
Web Site: http://www.eng.it
Information Technology Services
N.A.I.C.S.: 541512

Engiweb Security S.R.L. **(2)**
Via San Martino della Battaglia, 00185,
Rome, Italy **(100%)**
Tel.: (39) 0649201
Web Site: http://www.eng.it
Business Security Software Applications
Services
N.A.I.C.S.: 561621

Municipia S.p.A. **(2)**
Via San Martino Della Battaglia 56, Rome,
00185, Italy **(100%)**
Tel.: (39) 06 49201
Web Site: http://www.eng.it
Software Solutions Services
N.A.I.C.S.: 541512

Nexen S.p.A **(2)**
Corso Stati Uniti 23/C, Padua, 35127,
Italy **(100%)**
Tel.: (39) 0498283411
Web Site: http://www.nexen.it
Business Consulting Services
N.A.I.C.S.: 541611
Maria Cristina Barbero (Dir & Mgr-IT Strat-
egy & Area Mgmt)

**GNB - Companhia de Seguros de
Vida, S.A.** **(2)**
Av Columbano Bordalo Pinheiro 75 11, An-
dar, 1070-061, Lisbon, Portugal
Tel.: (351) 213167100
Commercial Banking Services
N.A.I.C.S.: 522110

Groupe Royer **(1)**
1 Rue Eugene Freyssinet - ZI de I Aumail-
lerie, 35133, Fougeres, France
Tel.: (33) 2 99 94 82 82
Web Site: http://www.grouperoyer.com
Footwear Distr
N.A.I.C.S.: 424340
Jacques Royer (Chm-Exec Bd)

Incisive Media Limited **(1)**
Haymarket House, 28-29 Haymarket, Lon-
don, SW1Y 4RX, United Kingdom
Tel.: (44) 2074849700
Web Site: http://www.incisivemedia.com

Sales Range: $75-99.9 Million
Business Information Publishing through
Magazines, Web Sites, Newsletters & Data-
bases
N.A.I.C.S.: 513120
Jamie Campbell-Harris (CFO)

Subsidiary (US):

American Lawyer Media, Inc. **(2)**
120 Broadway 5th Fl, New York, NY 10271
Tel.: (212) 457-9400
Web Site: http://www.alm.com
Legal & Business Publishing
N.A.I.C.S.: 513120
Larry Selby (VP-E-Products-Substantive
Law Grp)

Subsidiary (Domestic);

Law.com **(3)**
1035 Market St Ste 500, San Francisco, CA
94103-1650
Tel.: (415) 633-2500
Web Site: http://www.law.com
Sales Range: $25-49.9 Million
Emp.: 42
Online Legal News, Information, Related
Products & Services
N.A.I.C.S.: 517810
Larry W. Sonsini (Chm)

**The New York Law Publishing
Company** **(3)**
120 Broadway 5th Fl, New York, NY 10271
Tel.: (212) 457-9545
Web Site:
　　http://www.newyorklawjournal.com
Sales Range: $100-124.9 Million
Emp.: 250
Publishing Newspapers for Lawyers
N.A.I.C.S.: 513110
William L. Pollak (Pres & CEO)

Subsidiary (Non-US):

**Global Professional Media
Limited** **(2)**
Haymarket House 28-29 Haymarket, SW1Y
4RX, London, United Kingdom - England
Tel.: (44) 870 240 8859
Web Site: http://www.incisivemedia.com
Sales Range: $25-49.9 Million
Emp.: 82
B2B Information, Business Technology &
Professional Services
N.A.I.C.S.: 561499
Tim Weller (CEO & Chm)

**Incisive Financial Publishing
Limited** **(2)**
Tower 2 20th Floor Admiralty Centre, 18
Harcourt Road Admiralty, Wanchai, China
(Hong Kong)
Tel.: (852) 25452710
Sales Range: $25-49.9 Million
Emp.: 70
All Other Publishers
N.A.I.C.S.: 513199

Incisive Media **(2)**
20/F Tower 2 Admiralty Centre, 18 Harcourt
Road, Hong Kong, China (Hong Kong)
Tel.: (852) 3411 4983
Web Site: http://www.incisivemedia.com
Media Marketing
N.A.I.C.S.: 541613

Subsidiary (Domestic):

**Incisive Media Investment
Limited** **(2)**
28/29 Haymarket House, London,
SW1Y4RX, United Kingdom
Tel.: (44) 2074849700
Web Site: http://www.incisivemedia.com
Emp.: 400
Book Publishers
N.A.I.C.S.: 513130
Tim Weller (CEO)

Incisive RWG Limited **(2)**
28/29 Haymarket House, SW1Y4RX, Lon-
don, United Kingdom
Tel.: (44) 2074849700
Web Site: http://www.incisivemedia.com
Book Publishers
N.A.I.C.S.: 513130
Tim Weller (CEO)

**VNU Business Publications
Limited** **(2)**
32-34 Broadwick St, London, W1A 2HG,
United Kingdom
Tel.: (44) 2073169000
Sales Range: $100-124.9 Million
Publisher of Finance & Technology Trade
Magazines
N.A.I.C.S.: 513120

InfoVista S.A.S. **(1)**
23 Avenue Carnot, 91300, Massy, France
Tel.: (33) 164867900
Web Site: http://www.infovista.com
Monitor Information Technology Perfor-
mance Software Services
N.A.I.C.S.: 541511
Yann Le Helloco (CTO)

Subsidiary (US):

Empirix Inc. **(2)**
600 Park Dr Ste 100, Billerica, MA 01821
Tel.: (978) 313-7000
Web Site: http://www.empirix.com
Voice Testing & Monitoring Products & Ser-
vices
N.A.I.C.S.: 541512
Marcel Bernard (Co-Chm)

InfoVista Corporation **(2)**
20405 Exchange St Ste 301, Herndon, VA
20147
Tel.: (855) 323-5757
Web Site: http://www.infovista.com
Monitor Information Technology Perfor-
mance Software Services
N.A.I.C.S.: 541511
Jose Duarte (CEO)

Subsidiary (Non-US):

InfoVista GmbH **(2)**
Theodor-Heuss-Allee 112, 60486, Frankfurt
am Main, Germany
Tel.: (49) 69667741322
Web Site: http://www.infovista.com
Monitor Information Technology Perfor-
mance Software Services
N.A.I.C.S.: 541511

InfoVista IBE SA **(2)**
C/Lopez de Hoyos 35-1, Office No 5,
28002, Madrid, Spain
Tel.: (34) 917459965
Web Site: http://www.infovista.com
Monitor Information Technology Perfor-
mance Software Services
N.A.I.C.S.: 541511

InfoVista Pte Ltd **(2)**
300 Tampines Avenue 5 Level 09-02, Sin-
gapore, 529653, Singapore
Tel.: (65) 64497641
Web Site: http://www.infovista.com
Monitor Information Technology Perfor-
mance Software Services
N.A.I.C.S.: 541511

InfoVista UK Limited **(2)**
16 St Martins Le Grand St Pauls, London,
EC1A 4EN, United Kingdom
Tel.: (44) 2073978616
Web Site: http://www.infovista.com
Monitor Information Technology Perfor-
mance Software Services
N.A.I.C.S.: 541511

Itefin Participations SAS **(1)**
45 Avenue Kleber, Paris, 75016, France
Tel.: (33) 1 44 04 50 00
Holding Company
N.A.I.C.S.: 551112

**Keystone Peer Review Organization,
Inc.** **(1)**
777 E Park Dr, Harrisburg, PA 17111
Tel.: (717) 564-8288
Web Site: http://www.kepro.com
Managed Health Care Services
N.A.I.C.S.: 621999
Gayle Smith (VP-Pub Programs-Federal)

Subsidiary (Domestic):

**Independent Medical Expert Consult-
ing Services, Inc.** **(2)**
100 W Main St Ste 310, Lansdale, PA
19446
Web Site: http://www.imedecs.com

Insurance Related Activities
N.A.I.C.S.: 524298
Joyce Muller (Pres & CEO)

eQHealth Solutions, LLC **(2)**
8440 Jefferson Hwy Ste 101, Baton Rouge,
LA 70809
Tel.: (225) 926-6353
Web Site: http://www.eqhs.com
Sales Range: $25-49.9 Million
Emp.: 475
Community Health Care Services
N.A.I.C.S.: 621498
Ron Ritchey (Chief Medical Officer)

Marlink AS **(1)**
Lysaker Torg 45, 1366, Lysaker, Norway
Tel.: (47) 2258 2000
Web Site: http://marlink.com
Maritime Satellite Communications Services
N.A.I.C.S.: 517410

Subsidiary (Non-US):

Marlink Communications S.A. **(2)**
Megaro Makedonia 367 Syngrou Avenue
3rd Floor, 175 64, Palaion Faliron, Greece
Tel.: (30) 210 94 00 377
Sales Range: $25-49.9 Million
Emp.: 3
Maritime Satellite Communications Services
N.A.I.C.S.: 517410
Yiannis Serafim (Gen Mgr)

Marlink K.K. **(2)**
9th Fl HAKUWA Bldg 3-2-1 Kojimachi,
Chiyoda-ku, Tokyo, 102-0083,
Japan **(100%)**
Tel.: (81) 3 3288 0370
Sales Range: $25-49.9 Million
Emp.: 3
Maritime Satellite Communications Services
N.A.I.C.S.: 517410
Shinogu Suzuki (Country Mgr)

Marlink Ltd. **(2)**
Northside House Mount Pleasant Barnet,
London, EN4 9EE, United Kingdom
Tel.: (44) 171 638 9588
Maritime Satellite Communications Services
N.A.I.C.S.: 517410
Kate Callaghan (Mgr-Mktg)

Marlink Pte. Ltd. **(2)**
16 Collyer Quay 08-00, Singapore, 049318,
Singapore **(100%)**
Tel.: (65) 6597 0254
Sales Range: $1-9.9 Million
Emp.: 4
Maritime Satellite Communications Services
N.A.I.C.S.: 517410

Marlink S.A. **(2)**
Rue de Stalle 140, 1180, Brussels, Belgium
Tel.: (32) 23717111
Web Site: http://marlink.com
Sales Range: $25-49.9 Million
Emp.: 20
Maritime Satellite Communications Services
N.A.I.C.S.: 517410

Marlink SAS **(2)**
137 rue du Faubourg St Denis, Paris,
75010, France
Tel.: (33) 1 53 35 95 00
Maritime Satellite Communications
N.A.I.C.S.: 517410
Erik Ceuppens (CEO)

Subsidiary (US):

ITC Global Inc. **(3)**
3430 S Sam Houston Pkwy E Ste #500,
Houston, TX 77047
Tel.: (727) 898-3835
Web Site: http://www.itcglobal.com
Satellite Communication Services
N.A.I.C.S.: 517410
Joe Spytek (Founder & CEO)

Subsidiary (Non-US):

ITC Global Australia **(4)**
48 Mordaunt Circuit, Canning Vale, 6155,
WA, Australia
Tel.: (61) 8 6263 0444
Web Site: http://www.itcglobal.com
Satellite Communication Services
N.A.I.C.S.: 517410

ITC Global Guinea **(4)**

1ere Etage Immeuble Zein Suite 1-1
Quartier Almamya Commune de Kaloum,
BP 6532, Conakry, Guinea
Tel.: (224) 657 414100
Web Site: http://www.itcglobal.com
Satellite Communication Services
N.A.I.C.S.: 517410

ITC Global UK (4)
60 Carden Place, Aberdeen, AB10 1UP,
United Kingdom
Tel.: (44) 1224 536502
Web Site: http://www.itcglobal.com
Satellite Communications
N.A.I.C.S.: 517410

One Call Care Management, Inc. (1)
20 Waterview Blvd PO Box 614, Parsippany, NJ 07054
Tel.: (973) 394-8461
Web Site: http://www.onecallcm.com
Sales Range: $500-549.9 Million
Diagnostic Imaging & Electrodiagnostic
Scheduling Services Network Operator
N.A.I.C.S.: 621399
Robert Zeccardi (CMO & Chief Sls Officer)

Subsidiary (Domestic):

One Call Care Management, Inc. (2)
841 Prudential Dr Ste 900, Jacksonville, FL
32207
Tel.: (800) 848-1989
Web Site: http://www.onecallcm.com
Diagnostic Imaging & Electrodiagnostic
Scheduling Services Network Operator
N.A.I.C.S.: 621399
Jessica Taft (VP-Mktg & Branding)

**One Call Care Transport + Translate
Enterprises, LLC** (2)
8855 Grissom Pkwy, Titusville, FL 32780
Tel.: (321) 383-4111
Sales Range: $25-49.9 Million
Emp.: 75
Transportation & Interpretation Services for
Patients
N.A.I.C.S.: 621999
Dave Olson (COO)

TechHealth, Inc. (2)
14025 Riveredge Dr Ste 400, Tampa, FL
33637-2003
Tel.: (813) 490-1900
Web Site: http://www.techhealth.com
Sales Range: $10-24.9 Million
Emp.: 200
Web-Based Solutions for the Delivery &
Payment of Ancillary Healthcare Services
N.A.I.C.S.: 541511
Thomas R. Sweet (CEO)

PIB Group Limited (1)
70 Gracechurch Street, London, EC3V
0HR, United Kingdom
Tel.: (44) 3300589700
Web Site: http://www.pibgroup.co.uk
Insurance Brokerage Services
N.A.I.C.S.: 524210

Subsidiary (Domestic):

COBRA Holdings Ltd (2)
1 Minster Court, Mincing Lane, London,
EC3R 7AA, United Kingdom
Tel.: (44) 2072040014
Web Site: http://www.cobraholdings.co.uk
Insurance Brokerage Services
N.A.I.C.S.: 524298
Stephen Mark Burrows (CEO)

Subsidiary (Domestic):

**COBRA Financial Services
Limited** (3)
Canterbury House 2-6 Sydenham Road,
Croydon, CR0 9XE, Surrey, United Kingdom
Tel.: (44) 20 8256 1910
Web Site: http://www.cobrafs.co.uk
Financial Advisory Services
N.A.I.C.S.: 523940
Lee Wallis (Mng Dir)

COBRA Network Limited (3)
1 Minster Court Mincing Lane, London,
EC3R 7AA, United Kingdom
Tel.: (44) 20 7204 0014
Web Site: http://www.cobranetwork.co.uk
Emp.: 10

Insurance Brokerage Services
N.A.I.C.S.: 524210
Steve Burrows (CEO)

COBRA UK & Ireland Limited (3)
Old Lloyd's Chambers 139 Manchester
Road, Broadheath, Altrincham, WA14 5HY,
Cheshire, United Kingdom
Tel.: (44) 161 928 4444
Web Site: http://www.cobrauki.co.uk
Emp.: 21
Insurance Brokerage Services
N.A.I.C.S.: 524210
Kevin McNeill (Dir-Construction)

**COBRA Underwriting Agencies
Limited** (3)
1st Floor Canterbury House 2-6 Sydenham
Road, Croydon, CR0 9XE, Surrey, United
Kingdom
Tel.: (44) 20 8256 1910
Web Site:
    http://www.cobraunderwriting.co.uk
Insurance Underwriting Services
N.A.I.C.S.: 524127
Michael Bowler (Mng Dir)

Subsidiary (Domestic):

**Thistle Insurance Services
Limited** (2)
Rossington's Business Park, West Carr
Road, Retford, Nottinghamshire, England,
DN22 7SW, United Kingdom
Tel.: (44) 8006524990
Web Site: https://www.thistleinsurance.co.uk
General Insurance Services
N.A.I.C.S.: 524113

Paradigm B.V. (1)
WTC A Tower 7th Floor Strawinskylaan 717,
1077 XX, Amsterdam, Netherlands
Tel.: (31) 203337570
Web Site: http://www.pdgm.com
Sales Range: $125-149.9 Million
Emp.: 7
Software Solutions for Oil & Gas Exploration
N.A.I.C.S.: 541511

Subsidiary (Non-US):

Paradigm FZ-LLC (2)
Building 2 Office 101, PO Box 500148,
Dubai Internet City, Dubai, United Arab
Emirates
Tel.: (971) 43910673
Web Site: http://www.pdgm.com
Sales Range: $10-24.9 Million
Software Services for Oil & Gas Production
Industry
N.A.I.C.S.: 513210

**Paradigm Geophysical (UK)
Limited** (2)
Dukes Court Bldg C 3rd Flr, Dukes Street,
Woking, GU21 5BH, Surrey, United Kingdom
Tel.: (44) 1483758000
Web Site: http://www.pdgm.com
Sales Range: $10-24.9 Million
Software Services for Oil & Gas Production
Industry
N.A.I.C.S.: 513210

**Paradigm Geophysical Canada
Limited** (2)
125 9th Avenue SE Suite 2110, Calgary,
T2G 0P6, AB, Canada
Tel.: (403) 571-1555
Web Site: http://www.pdgm.com
Sales Range: $10-24.9 Million
Software Services for Oil & Gas Production
Industry
N.A.I.C.S.: 513210

Subsidiary (US):

Paradigm Geophysical Corp. (2)
2 Memorial Plz 820 Gessner Rd Ste 400,
Houston, TX 77024
Tel.: (713) 393-4800
Web Site: http://www.pdgm.com
Sales Range: $25-49.9 Million
Oil & Natural Gas Software Systems
N.A.I.C.S.: 513210
Samhita Shah (Dir-Mktg Comm)

Subsidiary (Non-US):

Paradigm Geophysical LLC (2)

Dubininskaya Street 53 Building 5, Moscow,
Russia
Tel.: (7) 4959334440
Web Site: http://www.pdgm.com
Sales Range: $10-24.9 Million
Software Services for Oil & Gas Production
Industry
N.A.I.C.S.: 513210
Mikhail Porechenkov (Gen Dir)

Paradigm Geophysical S.A. (2)
Carlos Pellegrini 713 Piso 9, Buenos Aires,
C1009ABO, Argentina
Tel.: (54) 1143225735
Web Site: http://www.pdgm.com
Sales Range: $10-24.9 Million
Software Services for Oil & Gas Production
Industry
N.A.I.C.S.: 513210

Paradigm Geophysical Sdn Bhd (2)
Level 12 Tower 1 Etiqa Twins 11 Jalan
Pinang, 11 Jalan Pinang, Kuala Lumpur,
50450, Malaysia
Tel.: (60) 321638111
Web Site: http://www.pdgm.com
Sales Range: $10-24.9 Million
Emp.: 25
Software Services for Oil & Gas Production
Industry
N.A.I.C.S.: 513210
Jonathan Ling (Reg VP-Asia Pacific)

**Paradigm Technology (Beijing) Co.,
Ltd.** (2)
1803 Capital Mansion No 6 Xin Yan South
Road, Chao Yang District, Beijing, 100004,
China
Tel.: (86) 1064654870
Web Site: http://www.pdgm.com
Sales Range: $10-24.9 Million
Software Services for Oil & Gas Production
Industry
N.A.I.C.S.: 513210

**Psagot Ofek Investment House
Ltd.** (1)
4 Ahad Ha am Street, Tel Aviv, 65142, Israel
Tel.: (972) 3 796 8888
Web Site: http://www.psagot.co.il
Sales Range: $50-74.9 Million
Emp.: 50
Investment Management Service
N.A.I.C.S.: 523150
Ronen Tov (CEO)

Quality Distribution, Inc. (1)
4041 Park Oaks Blvd Ste 200, Tampa, FL
33610
Tel.: (813) 630-5826
Web Site: http://www.qualitydistribution.com
Sales Range: $900-999.9 Million
Holding Company; Bulk Freight Transportation Services
N.A.I.C.S.: 551112
Gary R. Enzor (Chm & CEO)

Subsidiary (Domestic):

QC Energy Resources, LLC (2)
102 Pickering Way Ste 105, Exton, PA
19341
Tel.: (855) 426-4285
Web Site: http://www.qc-energy.com
Transportation & Logistic Services
N.A.I.C.S.: 488999
Rocky Gunter (CFO)

Quality Carriers, Inc. (2)
4041 Park Oaks Blvd Ste 200, Tampa, FL
33610
Tel.: (800) 282-2031
Web Site: http://www.qualitycarriersinc.com
Bulk Freight Transportation Services
N.A.I.C.S.: 488510
Randy Strutz (Pres)

Subsidiary (Domestic):

Boasso America Corporation (3)
100 Intermodal Dr, Chalmette, LA 70043
Tel.: (504) 279-8544
Web Site: http://www.boassoamerica.com
Tank Repair & Cleaning Services
N.A.I.C.S.: 811310
Chuck Carey (Reg Dir)

Subsidiary (Domestic):

Boasso America - Channelview (4)

16230 DeZavala Rd, Channelview, TX
77530
Tel.: (888) 858-3251
Web Site: http://www.boassoamerica.com
Tank Repair & Cleaning Services
N.A.I.C.S.: 811310
Joe Acevedo (Mgr-Tank Dept)

Boasso America - Charleston (4)
2001 Sewanee Rd, Charleston, SC 29405
Tel.: (877) 534-2327
Tank Repair & Cleaning Services
N.A.I.C.S.: 811310
Jack Patterson (Mgr-Transportation)

Boasso America - Chesapeake (4)
4209 S Military Hwy, Chesapeake, VA
23321
Tel.: (800) 562-4714
Web Site: http://www.boassoamerica.com
Tank Repair & Cleaning Services
N.A.I.C.S.: 811310
Carl DeSonia (Mgr-Terminal)

Boasso America - Chicago (4)
900 E 120th St, Chicago, IL 60628
Tel.: (800) 226-8265
Web Site: http://www.boassoamerica.com
Tank Repair & Cleaning Services
N.A.I.C.S.: 811310
Lance White (Mgr-Terminal)

Boasso America - Detroit (4)
7650 Melville Ave, Detroit, MI 48209
Tel.: (888) 232-0933
Web Site: http://www.boassoamerica.com
Tank Repair & Cleaning Services
N.A.I.C.S.: 811310
Stephen Huesgen (Mgr-Terminal)

Boasso America - Garden City (4)
6061 Commerce Ct, Garden City, GA
31408
Tel.: (866) 292-4043
Web Site: http://www.boassoamerica.com
Tank Repair & Cleaning Services
N.A.I.C.S.: 811310
Eric Walker (Mgr-Terminal)

Boasso America - Jacksonville (4)
1827 E 30th St, Jacksonville, FL 32206
Tel.: (888) 475-0336
Web Site: http://www.boassoamerica.com
Tank Repair & Cleaning Services
N.A.I.C.S.: 811310
Eric Dunn (Mgr-Terminal)

**Boasso America - West
Memphis** (4)
5050 Commerce St, West Memphis, AR
72301
Tel.: (870) 400-0402
Web Site: http://www.boassoamerica.com
Tank Repair & Cleaning Services
N.A.I.C.S.: 811310
Tommy Dickerson (Mgr-Terminal)

Branch (Domestic):

**Quality Carriers, Inc. - River
Falls** (3)
10375 Us 84, River Falls, AL 36476
Tel.: (800) 223-2880
Web Site: http://www.qualitycarriersinc.com
Bulk Freight Transportation Services
N.A.I.C.S.: 484121
Chris Weaver (Mgr-Facility)

SavATree, LLC (1)
550 Bedford Rd, Bedford Hills, NY 10507
Tel.: (800) 341-8733
Web Site: https://www.savatree.com
Full-service Tree, Shrub & Lawn Care Company
N.A.I.C.S.: 561730
Carmine Schiavone (CEO)

Subsidiary (Domestic):

1611 Summit, Inc. (2)
4207 Country Ln, Charlotte, NC 28270-0203
Tel.: (704) 525-7148
Web Site: http://www.arborscapes.net
Landscaping Services
N.A.I.C.S.: 561730
Jason Tebben (Founder)

**Abundant Tree Care Services
LLC** (2)

Apax Partners LLP—(Continued)

10002 Park Lk Dr, Louisville, KY 40229-1774
Tel.: (502) 297-1578
Web Site: http://www.abundant-treecare.com
Landscaping Services
N.A.I.C.S.: 561730
Kevin Bold (Owner)

Arbor Art Tree Care Inc. (2)
808 Heathcote Ave, Nashville, TN 37210-2910
Tel.: (615) 299-9999
Web Site: http://www.arborart.net
Landscaping Services
N.A.I.C.S.: 561730

Arborwell, Inc. (2)
2337 American Ave, Hayward, CA 94545
Tel.: (510) 881-4260
Web Site: http://www.arborwell.com
Rev.: $11,800,000
Emp.: 110
Landscaping Services
N.A.I.C.S.: 561730
Andy Lavelle (Pres)

Bozeman Tree Service, Inc. (2)
5061 Love Ln, Bozeman, MT 59718
Tel.: (406) 522-8733
Web Site: http://www.bozemantreeservice.com
Professional, Scientific & Technical Services
N.A.I.C.S.: 541990

Greenhaven, Inc. (2)
1901 Williamson Ct, Louisville, KY 40223
Tel.: (502) 244-8770
Web Site: http://www.greenhaventreecare.com
Landscaping & Tree Care Services
N.A.I.C.S.: 561730
Robert Rollins (Founder)

Kens Tree Care Inc. (2)
401 Paulding Ave, Northvale, NJ 07647
Tel.: (201) 768-0694
Web Site: http://www.kenstreecare.com
Landscaping Services
N.A.I.C.S.: 561730
Kenneth Barber (Pres)

Lou Giroud Tree Service, Inc. (2)
1955 Pioneer Rd, Huntingdon Valley, PA 19006
Tel.: (215) 682-7704
Web Site: http://www.giroudtree.com
Landscaping Services
N.A.I.C.S.: 561730
Andrew Slousky (VP)

Mountain High Tree Service, Inc. (2)
5717 W 11th Ave, Lakewood, CO 80214
Tel.: (303) 232-0666
Web Site: http://www.mountainhightree.com
Sales Range: $10-24.9 Million
Landscaping Services
N.A.I.C.S.: 561730
Ralph Bronk (Owner)

Mr. Amoto Lawn & Tree Service, LLC (2)
13611 Energy Way, Waverly, NE 68462-1451
Tel.: (402) 476-8873
Web Site: http://www.mramotollc.com
Landscaping Services
N.A.I.C.S.: 561730

Red Cedar Arborists & Landscapers, Inc. (2)
185 New Hackensack Rd, Wappingers Falls, NY 12590
Tel.: (845) 475-8284
Web Site: http://www.redcedarinc.com
Landscaping Services
N.A.I.C.S.: 561730
Steve Relyea (Owner)

Swingle, Inc. (2)
8585 E Warren Ave, Denver, CO 80231
Tel.: (303) 337-6200
Web Site: http://www.myswingle.com
Landscaping & Lawn Services
N.A.I.C.S.: 561730
Thomas R. Tolkacz (Owner & CEO)

Taddiken Tree Company (2)

5717 Arapahoe Ave, Boulder, CO 80303-0303
Tel.: (303) 554-7035
Web Site: http://www.taddikentree.com
Landscaping Services
N.A.I.C.S.: 561730
Kyle Cutshall (Supvr-Production)

Thrive, Inc. (2)
1590 Stowe Rd, Reston, VA 20194-1601
Tel.: (703) 709-0007
Web Site: http://www.thrivinglandscapes.com
Landscaping Services
N.A.I.C.S.: 561730

Tree-Tech, Inc. (2)
1248 Sussex Tpke, Mount Freedom, NJ 07970
Tel.: (973) 895-8930
Web Site: http://www.treetechinc.com
Sales Range: $1-9.9 Million
Emp.: 85
Landscaping Services
N.A.I.C.S.: 561730
James Bellis (Co-Founder)

Vine & Branch, Inc. (2)
4721 E 146th St, Carmel, IN 46033
Tel.: (317) 846-3778
Web Site: http://www.vineandbranch.net
Landscaping Services
N.A.I.C.S.: 561730
Judson Scott (Pres)

Yellowstone Tree Surgeons, Inc. (2)
3120 1st Ave S, Billings, MT 59101
Tel.: (406) 656-5810
Web Site: http://www.yvts.com
Emp.: 100
Landscaping Services
N.A.I.C.S.: 561730
Tom Yelvington (Pres)

Sophos Group plc (1)
The Pentagon Abingdon Science Park, Abingdon, OX14 3YP, United Kingdom
Tel.: (44) 1235 559 933
Web Site: http://www.sophos.com
Holding Company
N.A.I.C.S.: 551112
Kris Hagerman (CEO)

Subsidiary (US):

Rook Security, LLC (2)
11350 N Meridian St Ste 600, Carmel, IN 46032
Cyber Detection & Response Services
N.A.I.C.S.: 541511
J. J. Thompson (Founder & CEO)

Subsidiary (Domestic):

Sophos Ltd. (2)
The Pentagon, Abingdon Science Park, Abingdon, OX14 3YP, United Kingdom
Tel.: (44) 1235559933
Web Site: http://www.sophos.com
Sales Range: $250-299.9 Million
Emp.: 1,000
Computer Security & Data Protection Software Publisher
N.A.I.C.S.: 513210
Jan Hruska (Co-Founder)

Subsidiary (Non-US):

Astaro GmbH & Co. KG (3)
Amalienbadstr 41/Bau 52, 76227, Karlsruhe, Germany
Tel.: (49) 721 25516 0
Web Site: http://www.astaro.com
Sales Range: $25-49.9 Million
Emp.: 220
Computer Security Services
N.A.I.C.S.: 541512
Jan Hichert (CEO)

Subsidiary (US):

Invincea, Inc. (3)
3975 University Dr Ste 330, Fairfax, VA 22030
Tel.: (703) 352-7680
Computer Software Product Mfr
N.A.I.C.S.: 513210

Reflexion Networks, Inc. (3)
18 Commerce Way, Woburn, MA 01801
Tel.: (781) 569-6666

Web Site: http://www.reflexion.net
Emp.: 25
Cloud-based Email Security, Archiving, Encryption & Continuity Services
N.A.I.C.S.: 513210
David Hughes (Pres)

Subsidiary (Non-US):

Sophos AB (3)
Farogatan 33, 164 51, Kista, Sweden
Tel.: (46) 8 584 00 600
Web Site: http://www.sophos.com
Security Software Publisher
N.A.I.C.S.: 513210

Sophos Anti-Virus Asia Pte Ltd. (3)
2 Shenton Way SGX Centre 1 17 01, Singapore, 068804, Singapore
Tel.: (65) 68009500
Web Site: http://www.sophos.com
Security Software Publisher
N.A.I.C.S.: 513210

Sophos B.V. (3)
Hoevestein 11B, 4903 SE, Oosterhout, Netherlands
Tel.: (31) 162 480 240
Web Site: http://www.sophos.com
Emp.: 15
Security Software Publisher
N.A.I.C.S.: 513210

Sophos GmbH (3)
Gustav Stresemann Ring 1, 65189, Wiesbaden, Germany
Tel.: (49) 611 5858 0
Web Site: http://www.sophos.com
Security Software Publisher
N.A.I.C.S.: 513210

Subsidiary (US):

Sophos Inc. (3)
3 Van de Graaff Dr 2nd Fl, Burlington, MA 01803
Tel.: (781) 494-5800
Web Site: http://www.sophos.com
Computer Security & Data Protection Software Publisher
N.A.I.C.S.: 513210
Matt Fairbanks (CMO)

Subsidiary (Non-US):

Sophos Italy S.r.l. (3)
Via Tonale 26, 20125, Milan, Italy
Tel.: (39) 02 91 18 08
Web Site: http://www.sophos.it
Security Software Publisher
N.A.I.C.S.: 513210

Sophos K.K. (3)
Nisseki Yokohama Building 15F, 1 1 8 Sakuragicho Naka ku, Yokohama, 231 0062, Kanagawa, Japan
Tel.: (81) 45 227 1800
Web Site: http://www.sophos.co.jp
Security Software Publisher
N.A.I.C.S.: 513210

Sophos Pty Ltd. (3)
One Elizabeth Plaza, North Sydney, 2060, NSW, Australia
Tel.: (61) 2 9409 9100
Web Site: http://www.sophos.com
Emp.: 5
Security Software Publisher
N.A.I.C.S.: 513210
Ashley Wearne (Gen Mgr-Australia & New Zealand)

Sophos Sarl (3)
80 Quai Voltaire, 95870, Bezons, France
Tel.: (33) 1 34 34 80 00
Web Site: http://www.sophos.fr
Security Software Publisher
N.A.I.C.S.: 513210

Syneron Medical Ltd. (1)
Industrial Zone Tavor Building, PO Box 550, Yoqne'am Illit, 20692, Israel
Tel.: (972) 732442200
Web Site: http://candelamedical.com
Sales Range: $250-299.9 Million
Aesthetic Medical Products Designer, Mfr & Distr
N.A.I.C.S.: 334510
Robert Fielitz (Pres & Mng Dir-Internal Ops)

Subsidiary (US):

Candela Corporation (2)

530 Boston Post Rd, Wayland, MA 01778-1833 (100%)
Tel.: (508) 358-7400
Web Site: http://www.candelamedical.com
Aesthetic Laser Therapy Technologies Developer, Mfr & Distr
N.A.I.C.S.: 334510
Ellen Bonnell (COO)

Subsidiary (Non-US):

Candela France SARL (3)
Parc Victoria Bat Toronto 12 Avenue de Scandinavie, Les Ulis, 91940, France
Tel.: (33) 160129370
Web Site: http://www.syneron-candela.com
Aesthetic Laser Therapy Technologies Distr
N.A.I.C.S.: 423450

Candela Italia S.r.l. (3)
Via Santa Cornelia 5/A, Formello, Rome, 00060, Italy
Tel.: (39) 0690405212
Web Site: http://www.syneron-candela.com
Aesthetic Laser Therapy Technologies Distr
N.A.I.C.S.: 423450
Raffaele Riccardi (Country Mgr)

Candela Laser (Deutschland) GmbH (3)
Schleussnerstrasse 42, Neu-Isenburg, 63263, Germany
Tel.: (49) 6102599850
Web Site: http://www.syneron-candela.com
Aesthetic Laser Therapy Technologies Distr
N.A.I.C.S.: 423450
Michael Leonard Johnson (Mng Dir)

Syneron Candela (UK) Limited (3)
The Charter Building, Uxbridge, UB8 1JG, Mddx, United Kingdom
Tel.: (44) 8455210698
Web Site: http://www.syneron-candela.com
Aesthetic Laser Therapy Technologies Distr
N.A.I.C.S.: 423450

Syneron Candela Co., Ltd. (3)
Toso Building 8F 6-8-7 Ginza, Chuo-ku, Tokyo, 104-0061, Japan
Tel.: (81) 3 3289 2077
Web Site: http://www.candelakk.co.jp
Aesthetic Laser Therapy Technologies Distr
N.A.I.C.S.: 423450

Syneron Candela Corporation Australia Pty Ltd (3)
Unit 14/8 Campbell Street, Artarmon, Sydney, 2064, NSW, Australia
Tel.: (61) 300 226 335
Web Site: http://www.syneron-candela.com
Aesthetic Laser Therapy Technologies Distr
N.A.I.C.S.: 423450

Syneron Candela S.A. (3)
Avenida De Castilla 2 Parque Empresarial San Fernando, Edificio Europa PB Esq B 28830 San Fernando de Henares, Madrid, 28022, Spain
Tel.: (34) 91 656 85 63
Web Site: http://www.syneron-candela.com
Aesthetic Laser Therapy Technologies Distr
N.A.I.C.S.: 423450

Subsidiary (US):

Cooltouch, Inc. (2)
9085 Foothills Blvd, Roseville, CA 95747
Tel.: (877) 858-2665
Web Site: http://www.cooltouch.com
Medical Laser Mfr
N.A.I.C.S.: 334510
Sunnie Thornton (Coord-Mktg & Event)

Subsidiary (Non-US):

Syneron Candela Canada (2)
6150 Kennedy Road Unit 10, Mississauga, L5T 2J4, ON, Canada
Tel.: (905) 670-9449
Web Site: http://www.syneron-candela.com
Aesthetic Medical Products Mfr & Distr
N.A.I.C.S.: 334510

Syneron Medical (HK) Ltd. (2)
Room 2502-03 Hopewell Centre, 183 Queens Road East, Wanchai, China (Hong Kong)
Tel.: (852) 25434326
Web Site: http://www.syneron-candela.com
Aesthetic Medical Products Distr
N.A.I.C.S.: 423450

TIVIT Terceirizacao de Processos, Servicos e Tecnologia S.A. **(1)**
Av Brigadeiro Faria Lima 1355 22nd Floor
Pinheiros, Sao Paulo, 01452 002, Brazil
Tel.: (55) 1137572222
Web Site: http://www.tivit.com.br
Sales Range: $550-599.9 Million
Business Process & IT Outsourcing Services
N.A.I.C.S.: 541512
Alexandre Sande *(Mgr-IR)*

Takko ModeMarkt GmbH & Co KG **(1)**
Alfred Krupp Str 21, 48291, Berlin, Germany
Web Site: http://www.takko-fashion.com
Rev.: $1,585,696,000
Emp.: 7,235
Clothing Retailer
N.A.I.C.S.: 458110
Alexander Mattschull *(Mng Dir-Product Mgmt & Logistics)*

ThoughtWorks, Inc. **(1)**
200 E Randolph St Ste 25, Chicago, IL 60601-6501
Tel.: (312) 373-1000
Web Site: http://www.thoughtworks.com
Computer System Design Services
N.A.I.C.S.: 541512
Guo Xiao *(Pres & CEO)*

Thoughtworks Holding, Inc. **(1)**
200 E Randolph St 25th Fl, Chicago, IL 60601 **(100%)**
Tel.: (312) 373-1000
Rev.: $1,296,238,000
Assets: $1,461,850,000
Liabilities: $683,628,000
Net Worth: $778,222,000
Earnings: ($105,393,000)
Emp.: 12,500
Fiscal Year-end: 12/31/2022
Holding Company
N.A.I.C.S.: 551112
Ian Davis *(Chm)*

Top Right Group Limited **(1)**
Greater London House, Hampstead Road, London, NW1 7EJ, United Kingdom
Tel.: (44) 207 728 5000
Web Site: http://www.topright-group.com
Sales Range: $1-4.9 Billion
Emp.: 600
Holding Company; Magazine Publisher & Trade Exhibition Organizer
N.A.I.C.S.: 551112
Tracey Gray *(Dir-People)*

Subsidiary (Non-US):

AME Info FZ LLC **(2)**
Dubai Media City Phase II Building 4 Office 204-205, PO Box 502100, Dubai, United Arab Emirates
Tel.: (971) 43902700
Business & Financial Information Services
N.A.I.C.S.: 516210
Phil Blizzard *(Head-Brdcst)*

Bounty Services Pty Ltd. **(2)**
54-58 Park St, Sydney, 2000, NSW, Australia
Tel.: (61) 292828000
Web Site: http://www.bountybags.com.au
Emp.: 2
Magazine Publisher
N.A.I.C.S.: 513120
Jo Runciman *(Publr)*

Subsidiary (Domestic):

EMAP Limited **(2)**
Telephone House 69-77 Paul Street, London, EC2A 4NQ, United Kingdom
Tel.: (44) 20 3033 2600
Web Site: http://www.emap.com
Sales Range: $25-49.9 Million
Emp.: 350
Magazine Publisher
N.A.I.C.S.: 513120
Natasha Christie-Miller *(CEO)*

Subsidiary (Non-US):

EMAP Communications BV **(3)**
Zonnebaan 27, 3606 CH, Maarssen, Netherlands

Tel.: (31) 302411088
Web Site: http://www.emap.nl
Sales Range: $25-49.9 Million
Magazine Publisher
N.A.I.C.S.: 513120

Subsidiary (US):

EMAP Communications USA **(3)**
420 Lexington Ave Ste 244, New York, NY 10170-0299
Tel.: (212) 599-5209
Provider of Business Services
N.A.I.C.S.: 513199

Subsidiary (Domestic):

EMAP Construction Networks Ltd. **(3)**
Greater London House Hampstead Road, London, NW1 7EJ, United Kingdom
Tel.: (44) 2077285000
Sales Range: $50-74.9 Million
Magazine Publisher
N.A.I.C.S.: 513120

Subsidiary (Domestic):

Construction Research Communications Ltd. **(4)**
151 Rosebery Ave, London, EC1R 4GB, United Kingdom
Tel.: (44) 2075056600
Sales Range: $25-49.9 Million
Publishers for the UK Building Research Establishment
N.A.I.C.S.: 513120

EMAP Construct Ltd. **(4)**
151 Roseberry Ave, London, EC1R 4QX, United Kingdom
Tel.: (44) 2074056600
Sales Range: $25-49.9 Million
Magazine & Directory Publisher
N.A.I.C.S.: 513120

EMAP Maclaren **(4)**
19th And 20th Floor Leon House, Croydon, CR0 9XT, Surrey, United Kingdom
Tel.: (44) 2082775000
Sales Range: $25-49.9 Million
Emp.: 150
Magazine & Directory Publisher
N.A.I.C.S.: 513120

Subsidiary (Domestic):

EMAP Public Sector Management Ltd. **(3)**
Greater London House Hampstead Road, London, NW1 7EJ, United Kingdom
Tel.: (44) 2078740200
Magazine & Directory Publisher & Online Information Service
N.A.I.C.S.: 513120

Subsidiary (Non-US):

Media Corporation Publishing (M) **(2)**
137 Jalan SS 25 2 311 Pont 01 11th Fl, Jaya Mewah, Petaling Jaya, 46500, Malaysia
Tel.: (60) 379579698
Sales Range: $25-49.9 Million
Emp.: 30
Magazine Publisher
N.A.I.C.S.: 513120

Tosca Limited **(1)**
1175 Peachtree St Ste 1900, Atlanta, GA 30361
Tel.: (920) 617-4000
Web Site: http://www.toscaltd.com
Reusable Container Leasing Services
N.A.I.C.S.: 321920
Susan Heil *(CMO)*

Trade Me Group Limited **(1)**
Level 5 2 Market Lane, Wellington, 6011, New Zealand
Tel.: (64) 9 375 5998
Web Site: http://www.trademe.co.nz
Rev.: $177,775,255
Assets: $655,920,062
Liabilities: $125,511,973
Net Worth: $530,408,089
Earnings: $68,569,330
Emp.: 600
Fiscal Year-end: 06/30/2018
Electronic Shopping Services

N.A.I.C.S.: 518210
Jon MacDonald *(CEO)*

Truvo NV/SA **(1)**
Uitbreidingstraat 80 bus 3, 2600, Berchem, Belgium
Tel.: (32) 32856411
Web Site: http://www.truvo.com
Sales Range: $500-549.9 Million
Online & Print Directory Publisher
N.A.I.C.S.: 513140
Wim van Neutegem *(VP-Tax & Treasury)*

Subsidiary (Non-US):

Gouden Gids B.V. **(2)**
Harkerbergweg 88, 1101 CM, Amsterdam, Zuidoost, Netherlands
Tel.: (31) 205676767
Web Site: http://www.truvo.nl
Sales Range: $100-124.9 Million
Business & Services Contact Information Directory
N.A.I.C.S.: 513140

Paginas Amarelas S.A. **(2)**
Ave D Joao II No 1 17 01 74 Piso, 1990 083, Lisbon, Portugal
Tel.: (351) 218989500
Web Site: http://www.paginasamarelas.pt
Sales Range: $50-74.9 Million
Emp.: 200
Yellow Pages for Telephone Directories
N.A.I.C.S.: 517810

Publitec B.V. **(2)**
Herikerberweg 88, 1101 CM, Amsterdam, Netherlands
Tel.: (31) 205676869
Web Site: http://www.publitec.nl
Sales Range: $25-49.9 Million
Emp.: 100
Marketing, Media Measurement, Business & Directory Information
N.A.I.C.S.: 513140

Unilabs S.A. **(1)**
Place Cornavin 12, 1201, Geneva, Switzerland
Tel.: (41) 229097777
Web Site: http://www.unilabs.com
Sales Range: $450-499.9 Million
Laboratory & Radiology Services
N.A.I.C.S.: 621512
Paul Hokfelt *(Chm)*

Subsidiary (Non-US):

Alpha Medical, s.r.o. **(2)**
Zaborskeho 2, 036 01, Martin, Slovakia
Tel.: (421) 850 150 000
Web Site: http://www.alphamedical.sk
Medical Laboratory Services
N.A.I.C.S.: 621511
Jozef Karlik *(CFO)*

Unilabs AB **(2)**
Ekonomi V3, PO Box 1061, 40522, Gothenburg, Sweden
Tel.: (46) 317253000
Web Site: http://www.unilabs.se
Sales Range: $10-24.9 Million
Emp.: 35
Laboratory & Radiology Services
N.A.I.C.S.: 621512
Martin Swegmark *(Regional Head)*

Vyaire Medical, Inc. **(1)**
26125 N Riverwoods Blvd, Mettawa, IL 60045 **(50.1%)**
Tel.: (833) 327-3284
Web Site: http://www.vyaire.com
Respiratory Products Mfr & Distr
N.A.I.C.S.: 339112
Steven Dyson *(Chm)*

Branch (Domestic):

Vyaire Medical **(2)**
22745 Savi Ranch Pkwy, Yorba Linda, CA 92887
Tel.: (714) 283-2228
Web Site: http://www.vyaire.com
Respiratory Diagnostics, Ventilation & Anesthesia Delivery & Patient Monitoring Services
N.A.I.C.S.: 339112

Plant (Non-US):

Vyaire Medical **(2)**

Cda Via De La Produccion No 85, Mexicali, B C 21397, Mexico
Tel.: (52) 6865615500
Surgical & Medical Instrument Mfr
N.A.I.C.S.: 339112

rue21, inc. **(1)**
800 Commonwealth Dr Ste 100, Warrendale, PA 15086-7527
Tel.: (724) 776-9780
Web Site: http://www.rue21.com
Sales Range: $900-999.9 Million
Emp.: 2,807
Apparel & Fragrance Retailer & Mfr
N.A.I.C.S.: 458110
John P. Bugnar *(Sr VP & Dir-Stores)*

APB RESOURCES BERHAD
No 47 Lot 540 Jalan TUDM Kg Baru Subang Seksyen U6, 40150, Shah Alam, Selangor Darul Ehsan, Malaysia
Tel.: (60) 378461389
Web Site: https://www.apb-resources.com
APB—(KLS)
Rev.: $16,511,684
Assets: $36,245,898
Liabilities: $3,884,607
Net Worth: $32,361,290
Earnings: $1,816,034
Fiscal Year-end: 09/30/22
Fabrication & Non Destructive Testing Services
N.A.I.C.S.: 238390
Kim Chee Cheok *(Sec)*

APC GROUP, INC.
G/F MyTown New York Bldg, General E Jacinto St corner Capas St Brgy Guadalupe Nuevo, Makati, 1212, Philippines
Tel.: (63) 286628888
Web Site:
https://www.apcaragorn.net
APC—(PHI)
Rev.: $246,698
Assets: $4,856,728
Liabilities: $2,087,397
Net Worth: $2,769,331
Earnings: $90,895
Emp.: 2
Fiscal Year-end: 12/31/23
Oil & Gas Exploration Services
N.A.I.C.S.: 211120
Edmundo L. Tan *(Compliance Officer & Sec)*

Subsidiaries:

Environment and General Services, Inc. **(1)**
042 Justice Ramon Jabson St, Brgy Malinao, Pasig, 1552, Philippines
Tel.: (63) 28 638 3474
Web Site: https://www.egsi.ph
Sales Range: $300-349.9 Million
Building Cleaning & Janitorial Services
N.A.I.C.S.: 561720
Paul Magaziner *(Principal)*

APC TECHNOLOGY GROUP PLC
6 Stirling Park Laker Road Rochester Airport Estate, Rochester, ME1 3QR, Kent, United Kingdom
Tel.: (44) 330 313 3220
Web Site: http://www.apc-plc.co.uk
Rev.: $23,136,059
Assets: $21,589,967
Liabilities: $11,204,442
Net Worth: $10,385,526
Earnings: $853,993
Emp.: 89
Fiscal Year-end: 08/31/18
Electronic Components Mfr
N.A.I.C.S.: 334419
Phil Lancaster *(Dir-Bus Dev)*

APC Technology Group plc—(Continued)

Subsidiaries:

Aspen Electronics Limited **(1)**
1-3 Kildare Close Eastcote, Ruislip, HA4
9UR, United Kingdom
Tel.: (44) 2088681311
Web Site: http://www.aspen-electronics.com
Electronic Parts Distr
N.A.I.C.S.: 449210
Jennie Holmes (Mgr-Acct)

EEVS Insight Limited **(1)**
22 Long Acre, London, WC2E 9LY, United
Kingdom
Tel.: (44) 3303138484
Web Site: http://www.eevs.co.uk
Ecological Restoration Consulting Services
N.A.I.C.S.: 541620
Hilary Wood (Dir-Ops)

Wavelength Electronics Limited **(1)**
Kent Innovation Centre Thanet Reach Busi-
ness Park, Broadstairs, CT10 2QQ, Kent,
United Kingdom
Tel.: (44) 1843609380
Web Site:
   http://www.wavelengthelectronics.co.uk
Electronic Component Mfr & Distr
N.A.I.C.S.: 334419
Paul Glover (Mng Dir)

APCB INC.
No 6 Lane 84 Chun-Ying St, Shu-Lin
Dist, New Taipei City, 23863, Taiwan
Tel.: (886) 226832626
Web Site: http://www.apcb.com.tw
Year Founded: 1981
6108—(TAI)
Rev.: $194,609,430
Assets: $291,015,326
Liabilities: $174,493,273
Net Worth: $116,522,053
Earnings: $1,775,957
Emp.: 3,150
Fiscal Year-end: 12/31/23
Printed Circuit Board Mfr
N.A.I.C.S.: 334412
Yuexia Cao (Chm)

**APCO INDUSTRIES CO. LIM-
ITED**
10 Industrial Street, Toronto, M4G
1Z1, ON, Canada
Tel.: (416) 421-6161
Web Site:
   http://www.apcoindustries.com
Year Founded: 1935
Rev.: $12,292,321
Emp.: 33
Metals & Chemical Products Mfr
N.A.I.C.S.: 332812
James Grierson (Pres)

**APCO SERVICE STATIONS
PTY. LTD.**
343 Thompson Road, Geelong, 3215,
VIC, Australia
Tel.: (61) 352779379
Web Site: http://www.apco.com.au
Sales Range: $75-99.9 Million
Emp.: 11
Petroleum Whslr, Convenience Store
Retailing
N.A.I.C.S.: 424720

**APCOTEX INDUSTRIES LIM-
ITED**
NKM International House 178 Back-
bay Reclamation, Babubhai M Chinai
Marg, Mumbai, 400020, Maharashtra,
India
Tel.: (91) 222 283 8302
Web Site: http://www.apcotex.com
523694—(NSE)
Rev.: $131,692,702
Assets: $82,562,748
Liabilities: $28,486,431
Net Worth: $54,076,318
Earnings: $13,487,033

Emp.: 483
Fiscal Year-end: 03/31/22
Synthetic Rubber Mfr
N.A.I.C.S.: 325212
Anand V. Kumashi (Officer-
Compliance & Sec)

**APE ANGEWANDTE PHYSIK &
ELEKTRONIK GMBH**
Plauener Strasse 163-165 Haus N,
13053, Berlin, Germany
Tel.: (49) 30986011
Web Site: https://www.ape-berlin.de
Year Founded: 1992
Emp.: 70
Water Equipment Mfr
N.A.I.C.S.: 334510

**APE PTACEK ENGINEERING
GMBH**
Bayerwaldstrasse 9, 81737, Munich,
Germany
Tel.: (49) 896302090
Web Site: http://www.ape.de
Year Founded: 1989
Sales Range: $10-24.9 Million
Programming & Hardware Integration
Service
N.A.I.C.S.: 541511
Helmut Ptacek (Founder)

**APEEJAY SURRENDRA
GROUP LTD.**
Apeejay House 15 Park Street, Kol-
kata, 700 016, India
Tel.: (91) 33 4403 5455
Web Site:
   http://www.apeejaygroup.com
Tea Plantations, Real Estate, Ware-
housing & Other Retail Services
N.A.I.C.S.: 311920
Karan Paul (Chm)

**APELOA PHARMACEUTICAL
CO., LTD.**
No 399 Jiangnan Road, Dongyang,
Jinhua, 322118, Zhejiang, China
Tel.: (86) 57986557527
Web Site: http://www.apeloa.com
Year Founded: 1997
000739—(SSE)
Rev.: $1,480,505,364
Assets: $1,687,130,640
Liabilities: $912,230,748
Net Worth: $774,899,892
Earnings: $138,879,468
Fiscal Year-end: 12/31/22
Pharmaceuticals Mfr
N.A.I.C.S.: 325412
Fangmeng Zhu (Chm & Gen Mgr)

APERAM SA
24-26 Boulevard d Avranches, 1160,
Luxembourg, Luxembourg
Tel.: (352) 27362700
Web Site: https://www.aperam.com
APAM—(OTCIQ)
Rev.: $4,451,141,760
Assets: $4,874,884,560
Liabilities: $2,167,843,600
Net Worth: $2,707,040,960
Earnings: $214,942,000
Emp.: 9,500
Fiscal Year-end: 12/31/20
Steel Products Mfr
N.A.I.C.S.: 331110
Timoteo Di Maulo (Co-CEO)

Subsidiaries:

Aperam BioEnergia Ltda **(1)**
Praca Primeiro de Maio 09 - Centro, Timo-
teo, MG, Brazil
Tel.: (55) 3138497000
Charcoal & Wood Mfr & Distr
N.A.I.C.S.: 325194
Jaime Gasparini (Chm-Exec Bd)

Aperam Istanbul Paslanmaz Celik
Sanayi ve Ticaret A.S. **(1)**
G O S B Ihsan Dede Cad caddesi 700 Sok
No 120, 41480, Gebze, Kocaeli, Turkiye
Tel.: (90) 262 751 2914
Web Site: https://www.aperam.com.tr
Stainless Steel Mfr & Distr
N.A.I.C.S.: 331110

Aperam SA - Montevideo Unit **(1)**
Cno Casavalle 5146 esq Fortet, Montevi-
deo, 12400, Uruguay
Tel.: (598) 2 320 1443
Stainless Steel Mfr
N.A.I.C.S.: 331110

Aperam SA - Ribeirao Pires Unit **(1)**
Rodovia Indio Tibirica - KM 50 Barro
Branco, Ribeirao Pires, 09431-600, Sao
Paulo, Brazil
Tel.: (55) 11 4822 7001
Stainless Steel Mfr
N.A.I.C.S.: 331110

Aperam SA - Sumare Unit **(1)**
Av Parque Industrial 530, Monte Alegre,
Sumare, 13175-575, Sao Paulo, Brazil
Tel.: (55) 19 3578 0150
Stainless Steel Mfr
N.A.I.C.S.: 331110

Aperam Stainless Belgium N.V. **(1)**
Swinnenwijerweg 5 Industriegebied Genk
Zuid - Zone 6A, 3600, Genk, Belgium
Tel.: (32) 89302111
Web Site: http://www.aperam.com
Emp.: 1,000
Stainless Steel Mfr & Distr
N.A.I.C.S.: 331110

Aperam Stainless Europe S.A. **(1)**
6 rue Andre Campra, 93210, La Plaine
Saint-Denis, Cedex, France
Tel.: (33) 1 71 92 06 52
Sales Range: $5-14.9 Billion
Emp.: 5,500
Stainless Steel Sheet Mfr; Special Strip
Products; Leaded Steels
N.A.I.C.S.: 331221

Subsidiary (Domestic):

Aperam Alloys Imphy **(2)**
Innovatis 5 Rue Luigi Cherubini, F-93212,
Saint Denis, Cedex, France
Tel.: (33) 171920000
Web Site: http://www.imphyalloys.com
Sales Range: $650-699.9 Million
Emp.: 1,030
Nickel & Cobalt Alloys Mfr
N.A.I.C.S.: 331492

Aperam Alloys Rescal SAS **(2)**
200 rue de la Couronne des Pres, 78680,
Epone, France
Tel.: (33) 13 090 0400
Web Site: https://www.aperam.com
Electric Housewares & Fans
N.A.I.C.S.: 335210

Aperam Stainless Precision
Europe **(2)**
2 Place du General de Gaulle, BP 9,
25150, Pont-de-Roide, France
Tel.: (33) 38 199 6300
Web Site: http://www.aperam.com
Sales Range: $125-149.9 Million
Emp.: 247
Stainless Steel Precision Strips Mfr
N.A.I.C.S.: 331221

Aperam Stainless Services & Solu-
tions Argentina S.A **(1)**
Avenida Descartes 4200 Parque Industrial,
Buenos Aires, B1667AYN, Argentina
Tel.: (54) 2320555555
Stainless Steel Mfr & Distr
N.A.I.C.S.: 331110

Aperam Stainless Services & Solu-
tions Brazil **(1)**
Av Mercedez Bens 1420 Distrito Industrial,
Campinas, 13054-750, Sao Paulo, Brazil
Tel.: (55) 19 3211 4000
Stainless Steel Mfr & Distr
N.A.I.C.S.: 331110

Aperam Stainless Services & Solutions France S.A. **(1)**

Rue Pierre Loti, BP 53, 62330, Isbergues,
France
Tel.: (33) 321635800
Stainless Steel Distr
N.A.I.C.S.: 423510

Aperam Stainless Services & Solu-
tions Germany GmbH **(1)**
Hildener Str 28, 40699, Erkrath, Germany
Tel.: (49) 2104 309 0
Stainless Steel Mfr & Distr
N.A.I.C.S.: 331110

Aperam Stainless Services & Solu-
tions Iberica SI **(1)**
Carrer del Torrent Fondo 7 Poligono Indus-
trial Can Calderon Viladecans, Viladecans,
08840, Barcelona, Spain
Tel.: (34) 934259700
Stainless Steel Distr
N.A.I.C.S.: 423510

Aperam Stainless Services & Solu-
tions International S.A. **(1)**
Business Center Greenwood bld 9 Floor 5
office 172, Krasnogorsk, Moscow, 143441,
Russia
Tel.: (7) 495 2133023
Stainless Steel Distr
N.A.I.C.S.: 423510

Aperam Stainless Services & Solu-
tions Italy Srl **(1)**
Viale Brenta 27/29, 20139, Milan, Italy
Tel.: (39) 0371490410
Stainless Steel Distr
N.A.I.C.S.: 423510

Aperam Stainless Services & Solu-
tions Luxembourg SA **(1)**
Site du PED 15 Avenue de l'Europe, BP 55,
4801, Rodange, Luxembourg
Tel.: (352) 505 4811
Web Site: https://www.aperam.com
Emp.: 50
Stainless Steel Mfr & Distr
N.A.I.C.S.: 331110

Aperam Stainless Services & Solu-
tions Poland Sp. z o.o **(1)**
Ul Henryka Krupanka 97, 41103, Siemiano-
wice, Slaskie, Poland
Tel.: (48) 32 763 6100
Web Site: https://www.aperam.com
Steel Polishing & Finishing Services
N.A.I.C.S.: 423510

Aperam Stainless Services & Solu-
tions Tubes Brazil **(1)**
Av Brig Faria Lima 1355-20 andar-Jd Pau-
listano, 01452-909, Sao Paulo, Brazil
Tel.: (55) 11 3818 1945
Stainless Steel Mfr
N.A.I.C.S.: 331110

Aperam Stainless Services & Solu-
tions Tubes Czech Republic **(1)**
Predlicka 453/26, 400 01, Usti nad Labem,
Czech Republic
Tel.: (420) 477757101
Stainless Steel Mfr
N.A.I.C.S.: 331110
Jiri Vais (CFO)

Aperam Stainless Services & Solu-
tions UK Ltd **(1)**
9 Midland Way Barlborough Links, Barlbor-
ough, S43 4XA, Derby, United Kingdom
Tel.: (44) 1246571660
Stainless Steel Mfr & Distr
N.A.I.C.S.: 331110
Bryn Kinsey (Mng Dir)

Aperam Stainless Services & Solutions USA, LLC **(1)**
7077 18-1/2 Mile Rd, Sterling Heights, MI
48314
Tel.: (586) 480-1277
Steel Polishing & Finishing Services
N.A.I.C.S.: 332813

Stainless Service Andino S/A **(1)**
Manzana B-Lote 7-Calle 1 F-N 3 364 Bo-
dega 21, Zona Franca de Barranquilla, Bar-
ranquilla, Colombia
Tel.: (57) 5372 3333
Stainless Steel Mfr
N.A.I.C.S.: 331110

**APERTURE DEBT SOLUTIONS
LLP**

Water's Edge, Clarendon Dock, Belfast, BT1 3BH, United Kingdom
Tel.: (44) 333 939 7919   UK
Web Site: http://www.apertureiva.com
Year Founded: 2015
Financial Intermediation Services
N.A.I.C.S.: 522390
Karen Bridson *(Assoc Dir-Client Svc-North West & North Wales)*

APETIT PLC

Sornaistenkatu 1 A, 00580, Helsinki, Finland
Tel.: (358) 1040200
Web Site: https://www.apetitgroup.fi
APETI—(HEL)
Rev.: $196,093,244
Assets: $126,591,841
Liabilities: $22,987,265
Net Worth: $103,604,576
Earnings: $5,611,915
Emp.: 324
Fiscal Year-end: 12/31/22
Frozen Foods, Jams, Marmalades & Fish Product Developer, Producer & Marketer
N.A.I.C.S.: 311412
Harri Eela *(Chm-Supervisory Bd)*

Subsidiaries:

Apetit Kala Oy   **(1)**
Mastotie 7, 70460, Kuopio, Finland
Tel.: (358) 104024500
Web Site: http://www.apetit.fi
Sales Range: $50-74.9 Million
Emp.: 300
Fish & Seafood Markets
N.A.I.C.S.: 445250

Apetit Kasvioljy Oy   **(1)**
Satamatie 64, PL 21, 02401, Kirkkonummi, Finland
Tel.: (358) 104022300
Frozen Food Product Mfr & Distr
N.A.I.C.S.: 311412

Apetit Pakaste Oy   **(1)**
Maakunnantie 4, PO Box 130, 27801, Sakyla, Finland
Tel.: (358) 104024300
Web Site: http://apetit.fi
Sales Range: $25-49.9 Million
Emp.: 100
Food Mfr
N.A.I.C.S.: 311999

Apetit Suomi Oy   **(1)**
Upseerinkatu 1, PO Box 403, 02601, Espoo, Finland
Tel.: (358) 104024300
Frozen Food Product Mfr
N.A.I.C.S.: 311412

Avena Nordic Grain Oy   **(1)**
Sornaistenkatu 1, 00580, Helsinki, Finland
Tel.: (358) 1040202
Web Site: http://www.avena.fi
Sales Range: $25-49.9 Million
Emp.: 20
Oilseed & Grain Combination Farming
N.A.I.C.S.: 111191

Subsidiary (Non-US):

OU Avena Nordic Grain   **(2)**
Tehnika 3, Jarvamaa, 72213, Turi, Estonia
Tel.: (372) 5038151
Web Site: http://www.ang.ee
Grains & Oilseeds Distr
N.A.I.C.S.: 424590

Too Avena Astana   **(2)**
Business Center Raion Almaty Baraeva str 16, Nur-Sultan, Kazakhstan
Tel.: (7) 7172592679
Grains & Oilseeds Distr
N.A.I.C.S.: 424590

Mildola Oy   **(1)**
Satamatie 64, Kantvik, 2640, Finland
Tel.: (358) 104022300
Web Site: http://www.mildola.fi
Sales Range: $25-49.9 Million
Emp.: 100
Oilseed & Grain Combination Farming
N.A.I.C.S.: 111191

SIA Baltic Feed   **(1)**
PO Box 34, 3101, Tukums, Latvia
Tel.: (371) 3181127
Food Mfr
N.A.I.C.S.: 311999

Sandanger AS   **(1)**
Industritomta Sor, 6083, Gjerdsvika, Norway
Tel.: (47) 70026440
Web Site: http://www.sunnmoere.com
Sales Range: $25-49.9 Million
Emp.: 50
Processed Seafood Distr
N.A.I.C.S.: 424460

UAB Avena Nordic Grain   **(1)**
Asanavicictes G 13B - 56, 01122, Vilnius, Lithuania
Tel.: (370) 52430290
Web Site: http://www.avena.si
Sales Range: $25-49.9 Million
Emp.: 5
Oilseed & Grain Combination Farming
N.A.I.C.S.: 111191

Zao Avena St.Petersburg   **(1)**
1 Artilerijskaja Str Europa House, 191104, Saint Petersburg, Russia
Tel.: (7) 8127188090
Sales Range: $50-74.9 Million
Emp.: 4
Grains & Oilseeds Distr
N.A.I.C.S.: 424590

APEX ACE HOLDING LIMITED

Units 2-3 1/F Sun Cheong Industrial Building 1 Cheung Shun Street, Kowloon, China (Hong Kong)
Tel.: (852) 24280008   Ky
Web Site: http://www.apexace.com
6036—(HKG)
Rev.: $340,520,098
Assets: $141,119,211
Liabilities: $97,221,384
Net Worth: $43,897,827
Earnings: $2,143,648
Emp.: 140
Fiscal Year-end: 12/31/21
Electronic Component Mfr & Distr
N.A.I.C.S.: 334419
Kwong Bing Lee *(Founder, Chm & CEO)*

Subsidiaries:

AVT International Limited   **(1)**
Unit 2-3 1/F 1 Cheung Shun Street, Sun Cheong Industrial Building, Kowloon, China (Hong Kong)
Tel.: (852) 24280008
Web Site: http://www.avt.com.hk
Electronic Components Distr
N.A.I.C.S.: 423690
Danny Chan *(Mgr)*

APEX BIOTECHNOLOGY CORP.

No 7 Li-Hsin 5th Rd Hsinchu Science Park, Hsin-chu, 30078, Taiwan
Tel.: (886) 35641952
Web Site: https://www.apexbio.com
1733—(TAI)
Rev.: $54,826,415
Assets: $75,117,038
Liabilities: $16,353,379
Net Worth: $58,763,659
Earnings: $3,784,100
Emp.: 710
Fiscal Year-end: 12/31/23
Testing Strips & Monitoring System Mfr & Distr
N.A.I.C.S.: 334510
Thomas Y. S. Shen *(Chm & CEO)*

Subsidiaries:

Apex Biotechnology Suzhou Corporation   **(1)**
Room 403 Building 1 Weixin Road SIP, Suzhou, China
Tel.: (86) 13913517313
Diagnostic Equipment Distr
N.A.I.C.S.: 423450

APEX CAPITAL & FINANCE LIMITED

L-3 Green Park Extension, New Delhi, 110016, India
Tel.: (91) 1140348775
Web Site:
   https://www.apexfinancials.in
Year Founded: 1985
541133—(BOM)
Rev.: $68,918,967
Assets: $870,605,238
Liabilities: $525,466,805
Net Worth: $345,138,433
Earnings: $8,442,064
Emp.: 7
Fiscal Year-end: 03/31/21
Financial & Investment Services
N.A.I.C.S.: 523150
Shekhar Singh *(Mng Dir)*

APEX DEVELOPMENT PUBLIC COMPANY LIMITED

900 Tonson Tower 18th Floor Zone A, Ploenchit Road Lumpini Pathumwan, Bangkok, 10110, Thailand
Tel.: (66) 26362465
Web Site: https://www.apexpcl.com
Year Founded: 1988
APEX—(THA)
Rev.: $3,376,420
Assets: $70,097,679
Liabilities: $97,110,199
Net Worth: ($27,012,520)
Earnings: ($10,170,342)
Fiscal Year-end: 12/31/22
Real Estate Development Services
N.A.I.C.S.: 531390
Pongphan Sampawakoop *(Chm)*

APEX EQUITY HOLDINGS BERHAD

Lot 9 01 Level 9 Kompleks Ostia Kajang Jalan Cheras Batu 14 1/2, 43000, Kajang, Selangor, Malaysia
Tel.: (60) 378908877
Web Site:
   https://www.apexequity.com.my
Year Founded: 1990
APEX—(KLS)
Rev.: $9,930,997
Assets: $81,413,148
Liabilities: $9,860,470
Net Worth: $71,552,678
Earnings: $1,592,947
Fiscal Year-end: 12/31/23
Holding Company; Securities Brokerage & Dealing, Investment Advisory & Asset Management Services
N.A.I.C.S.: 551112
Cheng Han Tan *(Co-Sec)*

Subsidiaries:

Apex Equity Capital Sdn. Bhd.   **(1)**
Level 6 Menara Apex Off Jalan Semenyih Bukit Mewah, Bukit Mewah, 43000, Kajang, Selangor Darul Ehsan, Malaysia
Tel.: (60) 38 736 1118
Web Site: https://www.apexequity.com.my
Sales Range: $150-199.9 Million
Emp.: 300
Property Development Services
N.A.I.C.S.: 531311
Chan Guan Seng *(Mng Dir)*

JF Apex Nominees (Asing) Sdn. Bhd.   **(1)**
6F Menara Apex Jalan Semenyir Bukit Mewas, Kajang, 43000, Selangor, Malaysia
Tel.: (60) 387361118
Web Site: http://www.apexequity.com.my
Sales Range: $25-49.9 Million
Emp.: 200
Business Support Services
N.A.I.C.S.: 541611

JF Apex Securities Berhad   **(1)**
Level 6 Menara Apex Off Jalan Semenyih Bukit Mewah, 43000, Kajang, Selagor Darul Ehsan, Malaysia

Tel.: (60) 38 739 1118
Web Site: https://www.apexequity.com.my
Sales Range: $100-124,9 Million
Emp.: 120
Securities Brokerage Services
N.A.I.C.S.: 523150
Tan Cheng Han *(Sec & Head-Fin Grp)*

APEX FOOTWEAR LIMITED

House No 06 Road No 137 Block No SE D Gulshan-1, Dhaka, 1212, Bangladesh
Tel.: (880) 255044841
Web Site:
   https://www.apexfootwearltd.com
APEXFOOT—(CHT)
Rev.: $150,833,410
Assets: $223,739,305
Liabilities: $195,336,731
Net Worth: $28,402,574
Earnings: $1,524,552
Emp.: 10,538
Fiscal Year-end: 06/30/23
Leather Footwear Mfr
N.A.I.C.S.: 316210
Atiqul Islam *(Head-Tanning Unit-Global)*

Subsidiaries:

Apex Enterprises Limited   **(1)**
Opp Nanavati Hundai Workshop B/H Taluka Sangh N H No 08, Sisodra, Navsari, 396424, India
Tel.: (91) 2637265345
Web Site: https://www.apex-enterprise.com
Polyester Fabric Mfr
N.A.I.C.S.: 325220
Umar Khan *(Dir-Technical)*

Apex Pharma Limited   **(1)**
House 06 Road 137 Block SE D, Gulshan, Dhaka, 1212, Bangladesh
Tel.: (880) 9863026
Web Site: https://www.apexpharmabd.com
Pharmaceuticals Product Mfr
N.A.I.C.S.: 325412
Manzur Elahi *(Chm & Mng Dir)*

APEX FROZEN FOODS LIMITED

3-160 Panasapadu, East Godavari District, Kakinada, 533 005, Andhra Pradesh, India
Tel.: (91) 8842383902   In
Web Site:
   https://www.apexfrozenfoods.in
Year Founded: 1995
APEX—(NSE)
Rev.: $112,750,706
Assets: $89,651,043
Liabilities: $29,615,695
Net Worth: $60,035,348
Earnings: $6,044,930
Emp.: 3,282
Fiscal Year-end: 03/31/21
Aquaculture Product Mfr & Distr
N.A.I.C.S.: 112512
Karuturi Satyanarayana Murthy *(Chm & Mng Dir)*

APEX FUND SERVICES HOLDINGS LTD.

20 Reid Street 3rd Floor Williams House, PO Box 2460, Hamilton, HM 11, Bermuda
Tel.: (441) 2922739   BM
Web Site:
   http://www.apexfundservices.com
Year Founded: 2003
Rev.: $80,000,000,000
Emp.: 3,000
Holding Company; Fund Administration Services
N.A.I.C.S.: 551112
Peter Hughes *(Founder & CEO)*

Subsidiaries:

Apex Corporate Services (Netherlands) B.V.   **(1)**

Apex Fund Services Holdings Ltd.—(Continued)

Van Heuven Goedhartlaan 935A, 1181 LD,
Amstelveen, Netherlands
Tel.: (31) 20 564 6160
Fund Services
N.A.I.C.S.: 523940
Ingrid Mulder *(Mng Dir)*

Apex Financial Services, Inc. **(1)**
12 Castle Street, Saint Helier, JE2 3RT,
Jersey
Tel.: (44) 153 484 7000
Fund Services
N.A.I.C.S.: 523940

**Apex Fund & Corporate Services
(Guernsey) Limited** **(1)**
1 Royal Plaza Royal Avenue, Saint Peter
Port, GY1 2HL, Guernsey
Tel.: (44) 148 171 3843
Fund Management Services
N.A.I.C.S.: 523940

**Apex Fund & Corporate Services
(Jersey) Limited** **(1)**
12 Castle Street, Saint Helier, JE2 3RT,
Jersey
Tel.: (44) 153 471 2500
Fund Services
N.A.I.C.S.: 523940
Antoinette Kyriacou *(Head)*

**Apex Fund & Corporate Services
(UK) Limited** **(1)**
6th Floor 140 London Wall, London, EC2Y
5DN, United Kingdom
Tel.: (44) 203 697 5353
Fund Management Services
N.A.I.C.S.: 523940
Adam Hewitson *(Head)*

**Apex Fund Services (Abu Dhabi)
Ltd.** **(1)**
801 Al Maqam Tower Abu Dhabi Global
Market Square Al Maryah Island, Abu
Dhabi, United Arab Emirates
Tel.: (971) 2 672 6327
Fund Management Services
N.A.I.C.S.: 523940

**Apex Fund Services (Bulgaria)
EOOD** **(1)**
Macedonia Square1 Alabin Street 11th
Floor, 1000, Sofia, Bulgaria
Tel.: (359) 2 907 7500
Fund Management Services
N.A.I.C.S.: 523940
Karl Salemangi *(Head)*

**Apex Fund Services (Canada)
Ltd.** **(1)**
350 Bay Street Suite 1200, Toronto, M5H
2S6, ON, Canada
Tel.: (416) 361-5049
Fund Management Services
N.A.I.C.S.: 523940

**Apex Fund Services (Charlotte)
LLC** **(1)**
15720 Brixham Hill Ave Ste 206, Charlotte,
NC 28277
Tel.: (704) 752-8996
Fund Services
N.A.I.C.S.: 523940
Jonathan Schmitz *(Mng Dir & Head)*

**Apex Fund Services (Chicago)
LLC** **(1)**
1 N Franklin St, Chicago, IL 60606
Tel.: (312) 280-0330
Fund Management Services
N.A.I.C.S.: 523940
Chris Albright *(Mng Dir)*

**Apex Fund Services (HK)
Limited** **(1)**
17th Floor Beautiful Group Tower 77 Con-
naught Road, Central, China (Hong Kong)
Tel.: (852) 3 749 6500
Fund Management Services
N.A.I.C.S.: 523940

Apex Fund Services (IOM) Ltd. **(1)**
Second Floor Exchange House 54-58 Athol
Street, Douglas, IM1 1JD, Isle of Man
Tel.: (44) 1624 630 400
Web Site: http://www.apexfundservices.com
Fund Administration Services
N.A.I.C.S.: 523940

**Apex Fund Services (Ireland)
Ltd.** **(1)**
2nd Floor Block 5 Irish Life Centre Abbey
Street Lower, Dublin, D01 P767, Ireland
Tel.: (353) 1 411 2949
Fund Management Services
N.A.I.C.S.: 523940
Barry Hindmarch *(Head-Real Estate)*

Apex Fund Services (Malta) Ltd **(1)**
Quad Central Q3 Level 9 Triq L-Esportaturi,
Zone 1 Central Business District, Birkirkara,
CBD 1040, Malta
Tel.: (356) 2 792 2220
Fund Management Services
N.A.I.C.S.: 523940

**Apex Fund Services (Mauritius)
Ltd.** **(1)**
4th Floor 19 Bank Street Cybercity, Ebene,
72201, Mauritius
Tel.: (230) 404 8800
Fund Services
N.A.I.C.S.: 523940
Santosh K. Gujadhur *(Mng Dir)*

**Apex Fund Services (Singapore) Pte.
Ltd.** **(1)**
9 Temasek Boulevard Suntec Tower 2 12-
01/02, Singapore, 038989, Singapore
Tel.: (65) 6 295 2335
Fund Management Services
N.A.I.C.S.: 523940
Ashmita Chhabra *(Head-Business Develop-
ment)*

**Apex Fund Services (Sydney) Pty
Limited** **(1)**
Level 10 12 Shelley St, Sydney, 2000,
NSW, Australia
Tel.: (61) 27 201 9000
Fund Management Services
N.A.I.C.S.: 523940
David Potter *(Head-Business Development)*

Apex Fund Services (UK) Ltd. **(1)**
Veritas House 125 Finsbury Pavement,
London, EC2A 1NQ, United Kingdom
Tel.: (44) 203 697 5353
Web Site: http://www.apexfundservices.com
Fund Administration Services
N.A.I.C.S.: 523940
Paul Spendiff *(Mng Dir)*

**Apex Fund Services (Uruguay)
S.A.** **(1)**
WTC Free Zone Dr Luis Bonavita 1294
Suite 1412, Montevideo, 11300, Uruguay
Tel.: (598) 2 626 2423
Fund Services
N.A.I.C.S.: 523940
Eugenia Bilat Suchov *(Ops Mgr)*

**Apex Fund Services Bahrain
WLL** **(1)**
Office 82 Wind Tower Road 1705 Block
317, Diplomatic Area, Manama, Bahrain
Tel.: (973) 1 753 0217
Fund Management Services
N.A.I.C.S.: 523940

Apex Fund Services LLP **(1)**
1st Floor NOB Building, Blueridge Hinjewadi
Phase I, Pune, 411045, Maharashtra, India
Tel.: (91) 206 740 0212
Fund Management Services
N.A.I.C.S.: 523940

Apex Fund Services Limited **(1)**
15 Floor Block C Yintai Center 2 Jian-
guomen Wai Street, Chaoyang District, Bei-
jing, China
Tel.: (86) 1381 045 7655
Fund Services
N.A.I.C.S.: 523940
Debbie Lee *(Mng Dir)*

Apex Fund Services Ltd. **(1)**
20 Reid Street 3rd Floor Williams House,
PO Box 2460, Hamilton, HM11, Bermuda
Tel.: (441) 292 2739
Web Site: http://www.apexfundservices.com
Fund Administration Services
N.A.I.C.S.: 523940
Peter Hughes *(Founder)*

Apex Fund Services US Inc. **(1)**
150 E 52nd St Ste 8003, New York, NY
10022
Tel.: (646) 517-1490

Fund Administration Services
N.A.I.C.S.: 523940
Dennis Westley *(Mng Dir & Head-North
America)*

Apex Group Ltd. **(1)**
1st Floor Block 2 Harcourt Centre Harcourt
Street, Dublin, Ireland
Tel.: (353) 19601468
Web Site: https://www.apexgroup.com
Fund Services
N.A.I.C.S.: 523940
Peter Hughes *(Founder & CEO)*

Subsidiary (Non-US):

Efficient Group Limited **(2)**
81 Dely Road, Hazelwood, Pretoria, 0081,
South Africa
Tel.: (27) 879447999
Web Site: http://www.efgroup.co.za
Financial & Asset Management Services
N.A.I.C.S.: 523999

Subsidiary (Domestic):

**Boutique Collective Investments (RF)
(Pty) Ltd** **(3)**
Catnia Building Bella Rosa Village Bella
Rosa Street, Bellville, 7530, South Africa
Tel.: (27) 21 007 1500
Web Site: http://www.bcis.co.za
Financial Management Services
N.A.I.C.S.: 523999
Robert Walton *(CEO)*

Efficient Select (Pty) Ltd **(3)**
81 Dely Road, Hazelwood, Pretoria, 0081,
South Africa
Tel.: (27) 879447999
Emp.: 9
Asset Management Services
N.A.I.C.S.: 531390

Subsidiary (Non-US):

European Depositary Bank SA **(2)**
3 Rue Gabriel Lippmann, 5365, Munsbach,
Luxembourg
Tel.: (352) 4245451
Web Site:
https://www.europeandepositarybank.com
Banking & Related Financial Investment
Services
N.A.I.C.S.: 522110
David Claus *(CEO)*

**Apex Investment Consulting (Shang-
hai) Co., Ltd.** **(1)**
Room 1210 - 1213 818 West Nanjing Road,
Shanghai, China
Tel.: (86) 215 289 5005
Fund Services
N.A.I.C.S.: 523940

**BRL Trust Servicos Fiduciarios e Par-
ticipacoes Ltda.** **(1)**
Rua Iguatemi 151 19 andar, Itaim, 01451-
011, Sao Paulo, Brazil
Tel.: (55) 11 3133 0350
Web Site: http://www.brltrust.com.br
Emp.: 60
Trust Services & Fund Management
N.A.I.C.S.: 523991
Rodrigo Boccanera Gomes *(Partner)*

**Mainstream Group Holdings
Limited** **(1)**
Level 1 51-57 Pitt Street, Sydney, 2000,
NSW, Australia
Tel.: (61) 2 9247 3326
Web Site: http://www.mainstreamgroup.com
Holding Company; Investment Fund Man-
agement Services
N.A.I.C.S.: 551112
Byram Johnston *(Chm & Co-Founder)*

Subsidiary (US):

Fundadministration, Inc. **(2)**
4175 Veterans Memorial Hwy Ste 202,
Ronkonkoma, NY 11779
Tel.: (212) 802-7980
Financial Management Services
N.A.I.C.S.: 541611

Subsidiary (Non-US):

**Mainstream Fund Services (Cayman)
Limited** **(2)**

3rd Floor Citrus Grove Goring Avenue,
Grand Cayman, Georgetown, Cayman Is-
lands
Tel.: (345) 7436620
Financial Management Services
N.A.I.C.S.: 541611
Angela Nightingale *(CEO)*

**Mainstream Fund Services (HK)
Limited** **(2)**
17/F Winsome House 73 Wyndham Street,
Central, China (Hong Kong)
Tel.: (852) 35806551
Financial Management Services
N.A.I.C.S.: 541611
Amber Lo *(Head-Fund Svcs & Country Mgr)*

**Mainstream Fund Services (IOM)
Limited** **(2)**
Millennium House 46 Athol Street, IM1 1JB,
Douglas, Isle of Man
Tel.: (44) 1624692600
Fund Administrative Services
N.A.I.C.S.: 541611

**Mainstream Fund Services (Ireland)
Limited** **(2)**
Oyster Point Temple Road, Co Dublin,
Blackrock, A94 K2P4, Ireland
Tel.: (353) 12799660
Financial Management Services
N.A.I.C.S.: 541611
Barbara Purcell *(CEO)*

**Mainstream Fund Services (Malta)
Limited** **(2)**
Office 14 1st Floor II-Piazzetta Block B
Tower Road, Sliema, SLM 1605, Malta
Tel.: (356) 20939001
Financial Management Services
N.A.I.C.S.: 541611
Natalya Pace *(Country Mgr)*

**Mainstream Fund Services Pte
Ltd** **(2)**
138 Robinson Road 27-01 and 02 Oxley
Tower, Singapore, 068906, Singapore
Tel.: (65) 69507600
Financial Management Services
N.A.I.C.S.: 541611
John Davis *(Country Mgr)*

Subsidiary (US):

Mainstream PE Services, Inc. **(2)**
420 Lexington Ave Ste 2260, New York, NY
10170
Tel.: (212) 802-7980
Financial Management Services
N.A.I.C.S.: 541611

Branch (Domestic):

Mainstream PE Services, Inc. **(3)**
4266 Bell Rd, Newburgh, IN 47630
Tel.: (212) 802-7980
Financial Management Services
N.A.I.C.S.: 541611

Subsidiary (Domestic):

ShareBPO Pty Ltd **(2)**
Level 1 51-57 Pitt Street, Sydney, 2000,
NSW, Australia
Tel.: (61) 282598885
Financial Management Services
N.A.I.C.S.: 541611

Mola Administration GmbH **(1)**
Am Weiher 19, 20255, Hamburg, Germany
Tel.: (49) 4055 502 9870
Web Site: https://www.mola-
administration.de
Financial Vehicle Services
N.A.I.C.S.: 525990

Throgmorton UK Ltd. **(1)**
6th Floor 140 London Wall, London, EC2Y
5DN, United Kingdom
Tel.: (44) 118 939 3200
Web Site: https://throgmorton.co.uk
Fund Services
N.A.I.C.S.: 523940
Kerry Kelly *(Head)*

APEX HEALTHCARE BERHAD
1-5 Jalan TTC 1 Cheng Industrial Estate, 75250, Melaka, Malaysia
Tel.: (60) 63370980   MY

Web Site:
https://apexhealthcare.com.my
7090—(KLS)
Rev.: $203,781,011
Assets: $244,365,987
Liabilities: $44,480,397
Net Worth: $199,885,591
Earnings: $86,632,319
Emp.: 917
Fiscal Year-end: 12/31/23
Pharmaceutical & Consumer Health-care Products Mfr
N.A.I.C.S.: 325412
Kirk Chin Kee *(Chm & CEO)*

Subsidiaries:

ABio Marketing Sdn. Bhd.　(1)
No 2 Jalan SS 13/5, 47500, Subang Jaya, Selangor Darul Ehsan, Malaysia
Tel.: (60) 356293688
Web Site: http://www.apexpharmacy.com
Sales Range: $50-74.9 Million
Emp.: 100
Pharmaceutical Products Distr
N.A.I.C.S.: 424210

Apex Pharmacy Corporate Sdn. Bhd.　(1)
No 2 Jalan SS 13/5, 47500, Subang Jaya, Selangor, Malaysia
Tel.: (60) 356376888
Emp.: 1,800
Pharmaceutical Products Distr
N.A.I.C.S.: 424210

Apex Pharmacy Marketing Sdn. Bhd.　(1)
2 Jalan SS 13/5, 47500, Subang Jaya, Selangor Darul Ehsan, Malaysia
Tel.: (60) 356293688
Web Site: https://www.apexpharma.com.my
Emp.: 120
Pharmaceutical Products Distr
N.A.I.C.S.: 424210

Subsidiary (Non-US):

Apex Pharma Marketing Pte. Ltd.　(2)
4 Loyang Way 1, Singapore, 508708, Singapore
Tel.: (65) 67413803
Web Site:
https://www.apexpharmacy.com.sg
Emp.: 40
Pharmaceuticals & Personal Care Products Distr
N.A.I.C.S.: 424210

Apex Retail Sdn Bhd　(1)
83A Jalan Munshi Abdullah, 75100, Melaka, Malaysia
Tel.: (60) 6 282 5296
Web Site:
https://www.apexpharmacy.com.my
Pharmaceutical & Healthcare Product Mfr & Distr
N.A.I.C.S.: 325412

Subsidiary (Domestic):

CS Health Store Sdn Bhd　(2)
J1-098 Level 1 Floor City Square Shopping Centre 106 & 108, Jalan Wong Ah Fook, 80000, Johor Bahru, Johor, Malaysia
Tel.: (60) 72211398
Pharmaceutical & Healthcare Product Distr
N.A.I.C.S.: 424210

Avex Pharmaceuticals Pte. Ltd.　(1)
4 Loyang Way 1, Singapore, 507708, Singapore
Tel.: (65) 67413803
Pharmaceutical & Healthcare Product Distr
N.A.I.C.S.: 424210

Xepa-Soul Pattinson (Malaysia) Sdn. Bhd.　(1)
1-5 Jalan TTC 1, Cheng Industrial Estate, 75250, Melaka, Malaysia
Tel.: (60) 63351515
Web Site: https://xepasp.com
Emp.: 450
Pharmaceuticals Product Mfr
N.A.I.C.S.: 325412
Tah Peng Kee *(Co-Founder)*

Subsidiary (Non-US):

Xepa-Soul Pattinson (S) Pte. Ltd.　(2)
No 4 Loyang Way 1, Singapore, 508708, Singapore
Tel.: (65) 6 743 8648
Web Site: https://xepasp.com
Sales Range: $25-49.9 Million
Emp.: 12
Pharmaceuticals Distr
N.A.I.C.S.: 424210

APEX HOLDING LIMITED
Rupayan Golden Age 5th and 6th Floor 99 Gulshan Avenue, Gulshan, Dhaka, 1212, Bangladesh
Tel.: (880) 2 9883358
Web Site:
http://www.apexholdings.com
Year Founded: 1998
Holding Company Services
N.A.I.C.S.: 551112
Zafar Ahmed *(Chm & Mng Dir)*

Subsidiaries:

Apex Foods Limited　(1)
Rupayan Golden Age 5th & 6th Floor 99 Gulshan Avenue, Gulshan, Dhaka, 1212, Bangladesh
Tel.: (880) 222283358
Web Site: https://www.apexfoods.com
Rev.: $22,072,150
Assets: $10,626,457
Liabilities: $3,541,819
Net Worth: $7,084,638
Earnings: $463,668
Emp.: 465
Fiscal Year-end: 06/30/2023
Seafood Processing Services
N.A.I.C.S.: 311710
Zafar Ahmed *(Chm)*

Apex Lingerie Limited　(1)
Rupayan Golden Age 5th & 6th Floor, 99 Gulshan Avenue Gulshan, Dhaka, 1212, Bangladesh
Tel.: (880) 2 9883358
Lingerie Mfr
N.A.I.C.S.: 315250

Apex Spinning & Knitting Mills Limited　(1)
18 Gulshan Avenue Shanta Skymark, Gulshan, Dhaka, 1212, Bangladesh
Tel.: (880) 29883358
Web Site: https://www.apexknitting.com
Rev.: $52,899,825
Assets: $17,937,339
Liabilities: $12,248,672
Net Worth: $5,688,667
Earnings: $336,096
Emp.: 5,435
Fiscal Year-end: 06/30/2022
Knitted Garment Mfr
N.A.I.C.S.: 314999
Zahur Ahmed *(Mng Dir)*

Apex Textile Printing Mills Limited　(1)
Rupayan Golden Age 5th & 6th Floors 99 Gulshan Avenue, 99 Gulshan Avenue gulshan, Dhaka, 1212, Bangladesh
Tel.: (880) 2 9883358
Web Site: http://www.apextextileprinting.com
Knit Garments & Lingerie Mfr
N.A.I.C.S.: 315120
Zahur Ahmed *(Mng Dir)*

Apex Yarn Dyeing Limited　(1)
Rupayan Golden Age 5th & 6th Floor, 99 Gulshan Avenue Gulshan, Dhaka, 1212, Bangladesh
Tel.: (880) 2 9883358
Web Site: http://www.apexthreads.com
Yarn & Thread Producer
N.A.I.C.S.: 313110
Zahur Ahmed *(Mng Dir)*

Matex Bangladesh Limited　(1)
Rupayan Golden Age 5th & 6th Floors, 99 Gulshan Avenue Gulshan, Dhaka, 1212, Bangladesh
Tel.: (880) 2 9883358
Web Site: http://www.matexbd.com
Chemicals & Dyes Mfr
N.A.I.C.S.: 325130

APEX INTEC CO., LTD.
619-9 Indonggasan-ro, Gasan-Myeon, Chilgok, Gyeongsangbuk-do, Korea (South)
Tel.: (82) 549767667
Web Site: https://www.apexint.co.kr
Year Founded: 1997
207490—(KRS)
Light Mfr
N.A.I.C.S.: 335139
Kwon Jin Kim *(CEO)*

APEX INTERNATIONAL CO., LTD.
Room 503 5th Floor No 205 Dunhua North Road, Songshan District, Taipei, 10595, Taiwan
Tel.: (886) 227170032
Web Site: https://www.apex-intl.com.tw
Year Founded: 2009
4927—(TAI)
Rev.: $412,971,337
Assets: $591,617,428
Liabilities: $364,830,622
Net Worth: $226,786,806
Earnings: ($26,160,174)
Emp.: 7,962
Fiscal Year-end: 12/31/23
Printed Circuit Board Mfr & Distr
N.A.I.C.S.: 334412
Shu-Mu Wang *(Founder & Chm)*

Subsidiaries:

Apex Asia Pacific Private Limited　(1)
Plot No E-19/B E-19/C Sinnar Malegaon MIDC, Nashik, 422113, Maharashtra, India
Tel.: (91) 2551661111
Printing Rolls Mfr & Distr
N.A.I.C.S.: 333248

Apex Circuit (Thailand) Co., Ltd.　(1)
39/234-236 Moo 2 Rama 2 Rd Bangkrachao, Amphur Muang, 74000, Samutsakhon, Thailand
Tel.: (66) 34 490537
Printed Circuit Board Mfr & Distr
N.A.I.C.S.: 334412

Subsidiary (Non-US):

Apex Electronics (Shen Zhen) Co., Ltd.　(2)
No 8 KF Avenue Hi-Tech Industrial Park, Shenzhen, Guangdong, China
Tel.: (86) 75583015568
Web Site: http://www.hkinventory.com
Printed Circuit Board Distr
N.A.I.C.S.: 423690

Apex Europe B.V.　(1)
Metaalweg 8, 5527, Hapert, Netherlands
Tel.: (31) 497361111
Printing Rolls Mfr & Distr
N.A.I.C.S.: 333248

Apex Italy S.r.l.　(1)
Via Pietro Nenni snc, 21057, Olgiate Olona, VA, Italy
Tel.: (39) 0331379063
Printing Rolls Mfr & Distr
N.A.I.C.S.: 333248

Approach Excellence Trading Ltd.　(1)
Palm Grove House Rd Town, PO Box 438, Tortola, Virgin Islands (British)
Tel.: (284) 227170032
Supply Chain Integration Services
N.A.I.C.S.: 541614

Panhuizen Graveerindustrie B.V.　(1)
De Hoefkens 5, 5707 AZ, Helmond, Netherlands
Tel.: (31) 492538534
Printing Rolls Mfr & Distr
N.A.I.C.S.: 333248

Shye Feng Enterprise (Thailand) Co., Ltd.　(1)
88/1 Moo 2 Sethakij Rd, Nadee, Amphur Muang, 74000, Samutsakhorn, Thailand
Tel.: (66) 348310102
Web Site: https://www.sfnthai.com
Printed Circuit Board Mfr & Distr

N.A.I.C.S.: 334418

APEX INTERNATIONAL FINANCIAL ENGINEERING RESEARCH & TECHNOLOGY CO., LIMITED
1145th Floor No 329 Xinhu 2nd Road, Neihu District, Taipei, Taiwan
Tel.: (886) 287919799
Web Site: https://www.apex.com.tw
Year Founded: 1988
5210—(TPE)
Rev.: $9,678,736
Assets: $27,708,220
Liabilities: $11,468,812
Net Worth: $16,239,408
Earnings: ($384,329)
Emp.: 180
Fiscal Year-end: 12/31/22
Information Technology Consulting Services
N.A.I.C.S.: 541512

Subsidiaries:

APEX KINGWIN International Co., Ltd.　(1)
9F-2 No 490 Sec 2 Renai Rd, Linkou Dist, Taipei, Taiwan
Tel.: (886) 226012722
Web Site: https://www.akwfintech.com
Asset Management Services
N.A.I.C.S.: 531390

APEX-Power Green Technology Co., Ltd.　(1)
5th Floor No 329 Xinhu 2nd Road, Neihu District, Taipei, 114, Taiwan
Tel.: (886) 287919799
Financial Information Services
N.A.I.C.S.: 522320

Youying (Shanghai) Information Tech. Co., Ltd.　(1)
Room 409 Building 28 Lane 879 Zhongjiang Road, Putuo District, Shanghai, China
Tel.: (86) 2160402266
Financial Information Services
N.A.I.C.S.: 522320

APEX INVESTMENT SERVICES BERHAD
3rd Floor Menara MBSB 46 Jalan Dungun, Damansara Heights, 50490, Kuala Lumpur, Malaysia
Tel.: (60) 320959999
Web Site: http://www.apexis.com.my
Year Founded: 1997
Emp.: 25
Investment Management & Advisory Services
N.A.I.C.S.: 523940

APEX LIMITED PARTNERSHIP
1710 14th Ave NW Ste 300 &200, Calgary, T2N 1M5, AB, Canada
Tel.: (403) 264-3232
Web Site: http://www.apexland.com
Year Founded: 1991
Sales Range: $25-49.9 Million
Emp.: 150
Commercial Real Estate Acquirer, Developer & Retailer
N.A.I.C.S.: 531210
Frank Boyd *(Chm)*

Subsidiaries:

Centrex Homes　(1)
1710-14th Avenue Northwest Suite 200, Calgary, T2N 1M5, AB, Canada
Tel.: (403) 282-4446
Web Site: http://www.centrexhomes.ca
Emp.: 80
Residential Home Building
N.A.I.C.S.: 236115

Excel Homes LP　(1)
Suite 200 1710 - 14th Ave NW, Calgary, T2N 4Y6, AB, Canada
Tel.: (403) 253-1433
Web Site: http://www.excelhomes.net

Apex Limited Partnership—(Continued)

Sales Range: $50-74.9 Million
Emp.: 120
Residential Builders
N.A.I.C.S.: 236115

APEX MINING CO., INC.
3304B West Tower PSE Centre Exchange Road, Ortigas Center, Pasig, Philippines
Tel.: (63) 287062805
Web Site:
  https://www.apexmines.com
APX—(PHI)
Rev.: $131,407,693
Assets: $324,766,786
Liabilities: $167,864,314
Net Worth: $156,902,472
Earnings: $31,877,056
Emp.: 1,728
Fiscal Year-end: 12/31/20
Gold Mining Services
N.A.I.C.S.: 212220
Ramon Y. Sy *(Chm)*

APEX PARTNERS PROPRIETARY LIMITED
Commerce Square 39 Rivonia Road, Sandton, Johannesburg, 2196, South Africa
Tel.: (27) 10 900 2150
Web Site:
  http://www.apexpartners.co.za
Holding Company
N.A.I.C.S.: 551112
Charles Petit *(Founder)*

Subsidiaries:

Torre Industries Limited   **(1)**
11 Avalon Road West Lake View Ext 11, Modderfontein, 1609, South Africa
Tel.: (27) 119237000
Web Site: http://www.torreindustries.com
Investment Holding Company
N.A.I.C.S.: 551112
Shivan Mansingh *(CFO)*

Subsidiary (Non-US):

Kanu Equipment Congo Limited **(2)**
Rue de Kinsoundi Quartier Wharf, Pointe Noire, Congo, Republic of
Tel.: (242) 6 438 7619
Web Site: http://www.kanuequipment.com
Construction Equipment Distr
N.A.I.C.S.: 423810

Kanu Equipment Cote'Ivoire
Limited   **(2)**
Yopougon Zone Industrielle 30, BP 115, Abidjan, 30, Cote d'Ivoire
Tel.: (225) 57923797
Web Site: http://www.kanuequipment.com
Construction Equipment Distr
N.A.I.C.S.: 423810

Kanu Equipment Ghana Limited **(2)**
House no 38/24 George Walker Bush Highway, Dzorwulu, Accra, Ghana
Tel.: (233) 207 252 598
Web Site: http://www.kanuequipment.com
Construction Equipment Distr
N.A.I.C.S.: 423810

Kanu Equipment Liberia Ltd.   **(2)**
Sinkor Old Road, PO Box 1858, Monrovia, 1000, Liberia
Tel.: (231) 777 55 56 77
Web Site: http://www.kanuequipment.com
Construction Equipment Distr
N.A.I.C.S.: 423810

Kanu Equipment Sierra Leone **(2)**
117 Wilkinson Road, Freetown, Sierra Leone
Tel.: (232) 99 00 18 00
Web Site: http://www.kanuequipment.com
Construction Equipment Distr
N.A.I.C.S.: 423810

Subsidiary (Domestic):

Torre Holdings (Pty) Ltd.   **(2)**
461 Flower Close Greenhills Industrial Estate, Tunney Extension 9, Germiston, South Africa
Tel.: (27) 11 822 8782
Web Site: http://www.safrench.co.za
Holding Company; Industrial & Automotive Equipment & Components Mfr & Distr
N.A.I.C.S.: 551112

Subsidiary (Domestic):

Torre Parts and Components   **(3)**
59 Merino Avenue, City Deep, Johannesburg, 2049, South Africa
Tel.: (27) 116272500
Web Site: http://www.torreparts.com
Holding Company; Automotive & Industrial Components Mfr
N.A.I.C.S.: 551112

Subsidiary (Domestic):

Torre Automotive (Pty) Limited **(4)**
76 White Road, Retreat, Cape Town, 7945, South Africa
Tel.: (27) 217106800
Web Site: http://www.torreparts.com
Aftermarket Automotive Components Mfr
N.A.I.C.S.: 336390

Subsidiary (Domestic):

Tractor and Grader Supplies (Pty)
Ltd   **(2)**
11 Avalon Road Westlake View Ext 11, Modderfontein, 1609, Gauteng, South Africa
Tel.: (27) 11 392 7533
Web Site: http://www.tags.co.za
Industrial Machinery & Equipment Distr
N.A.I.C.S.: 423830

APEX PARTNERS PTY LTD
133 Alexander Street, Crows Nest, 2065, NSW, Australia
Tel.: (61) 300856338
Web Site:
  http://www.apexpartners.com.au
Financial Services Company
N.A.I.C.S.: 523999
Ryan Love *(Dir)*

APEX REFORESTATION LTD
PO Box 34156, Vancouver, V6J 4N1, BC, Canada
Tel.: (604) 736-0063
Web Site: http://apex-reforestation-ltd.bc.bcolumbia.com
Rev.: $21,253,210
Emp.: 2
Forestry Services
N.A.I.C.S.: 115310
Marc Hobday *(Pres)*

APEX RESOURCES INC.
Suite 615- 625 Howe Street, Vancouver, V6C 2T6, BC, Canada
Tel.: (604) 628-0519
Web Site:
  https://www.apxresources.com
SLMLF—(OTCIQ)
Rev.: $412
Assets: $2,334,142
Liabilities: $427,000
Net Worth: $1,907,142
Earnings: ($247,322)
Fiscal Year-end: 12/31/23
Mineral Exploration Services
N.A.I.C.S.: 213114
Marc Lee *(CFO)*

APEX SCIENCE & ENGINEERING CORP.
4F No 112 Shin-Min St, Chungho Dist, Taipei, 235, Taiwan
Tel.: (886) 222287331
Web Site:
  https://www.apexgrp.com.tw
Year Founded: 1976
3052—(TAI)
Rev.: $113,936,553
Assets: $249,525,155
Liabilities: $140,070,468
Net Worth: $109,454,687

Earnings: $6,775,107
Fiscal Year-end: 12/31/23
Optoelectronics Mfr
N.A.I.C.S.: 334419

APEX TANNERY LIMITED
Plot XA1 XA2 XA3 and XS8 BSCIC Chamra Shilpa Nagari Harindhara, Hemayetpur Savar, Dhaka, 1340, Bangladesh
Tel.: (880) 1711686592   **BD**
Web Site:
  https://www.apextannery.com
Year Founded: 1976
APEXTANRY—(DHA)
Rev.: $14,882,274
Assets: $37,210,720
Liabilities: $26,004,552
Net Worth: $11,206,168
Earnings: $145,082
Emp.: 806
Fiscal Year-end: 06/30/22
Leather Goods Mfr
N.A.I.C.S.: 316990
Manzur Elahi *(Chm)*

APFT BERHAD
Suite 9B 03 Level 10 Wisma E and CÂ 2 Lorong Dungun Kiri, Damansara Heights, 50490, Kuala Lumpur, Malaysia
Tel.: (60) 320923177
Web Site: http://www.apft.com.my
Rev.: $14,895,700
Assets: $1,631,791
Liabilities: $2,527,729
Net Worth: ($895,938)
Earnings: $3,738,823
Emp.: 9
Fiscal Year-end: 04/30/19
Flight Training & Education Services
N.A.I.C.S.: 611512
Y. M. Shamsulbhari Azman Shah *(Exec Dir)*

Subsidiaries:

PT Technic Engineering Sdn.
Bhd.   **(1)**
46 Jalan TPP 1/10 Taman Industri Puchong Batu 12, Puchong, 47100, Selangor, Malaysia
Tel.: (60) 380626818
Web Site: http://www.pttechnic.com
Sales Range: $10-24.9 Million
Civil Engineering Services
N.A.I.C.S.: 541330
Choo Thin Chee *(Mng Dir)*

APG & CO., PTY. LTD.
Level 3 11 Bowden Street, Alexandria, 2015, NSW, Australia
Tel.: (61) 283063700
Web Site: http://www.apgandco.com
Fashion Apparel Distr
N.A.I.C.S.: 458110
Elisha Hopkinson *(Creative Dir)*

APG ASSET MANAGEMENT NV
Oude Lindestraat 70, 6411 EJ, Heerlen, Netherlands
Tel.: (31) 455799222
Web Site: http://www.apg.nl
Investment Management Service
N.A.I.C.S.: 523999
Gerard van Olphen *(Chm)*

Subsidiaries:

Astoria Energy LLC   **(1)**
1710 Steinway St, Astoria, NY 11105
Tel.: (718) 274-7700
Web Site: http://www.astoriaenergy.com
Fossil Fuel Power Generation
N.A.I.C.S.: 221112
Chuck McCall *(CEO)*

Brisa Auto-Estradas de Portugal, S.A.   **(1)**
Quinta da Torre da Aguilha - Edificio Brisa, 2785-599, Sao Domingos de Rana, Portugal
Tel.: (351) 214448500
Web Site: http://www.brisa.pt
Rev.: $853,839,235
Earnings: $180,718,820
Emp.: 2,344
Fiscal Year-end: 12/31/2018
Highway & Street Construction Services
N.A.I.C.S.: 237310
Vasco De Mello *(Chm)*

Subsidiary (US):

BRISA NORTH AMERICA, INC **(2)**
1420 Peachtree St N E 220, Atlanta, GA 30309-3049
Tel.: (404) 835-8400
Road & Building Construction Services
N.A.I.C.S.: 237310

Subsidiary (Domestic):

BRISA O&M, S.A.   **(2)**
Quinta Da Torre Da Agulha Edificio Brisa, Sao Domingos de Rana, 2785-599, Portugal
Tel.: (351) 214448500
Civil Engineering Construction Services
N.A.I.C.S.: 237310

Subsidiary (US):

BRISA UNITED STATES, LLC **(2)**
2755 Nothwoods Pkwy, Norcross, GA 30071
Tel.: (404) 835-8400
Sales Range: $25-49.9 Million
Emp.: 7
Highway & Street Construction Services
N.A.I.C.S.: 237310

Subsidiary (Domestic):

Brisa - Servicos Viarios, SGPS,
S.A.   **(2)**
Quinta da Torre Da Aguilha, Edificio Brisa Domingos De Ran, Cascais, 2785-599, Portugal
Tel.: (351) 214448500
Web Site: http://www.brisa.pt
Other Holding Companies Offices
N.A.I.C.S.: 551112

Brisa Assistencia Rodoviaria,
S.A.   **(2)**
Quinta Da Aguilha, Quinta Da Torre Da Aguilha, Cascais, 2785599S AO, Portugal
Tel.: (351) 214448500
Web Site: http://www.brisa.com
All Other Support Activities for Transportation
N.A.I.C.S.: 488999
Vasco Mello *(Pres)*

Brisa Internacional, SGPS, S.A. **(2)**
Edificio Brisa, Quinta Da Torre Da Aguilha, Cascais, Portugal
Tel.: (351) 214449100
Other Holding Companies Offices
N.A.I.C.S.: 551112

CONTROLAUTO - CONTROLO TECNICO AUTOMOVEL, S.A. **(2)**
Rua Alfredo Lopes Vilaverde 15-B Room 7, 2770-009, Paco d'Arcos, Portugal
Tel.: (351) 21 441 8376
Web Site: https://www.controlauto.pt
Emp.: 40
Automotive Control & Maintenance Services
N.A.I.C.S.: 811121
Zosa Enjra *(Gen Mgr)*

M. CALL, S.A.   **(2)**
Taguspark Edificio Mcall Tecnologia III Corpo 5, 2740-257, Porto Salvo, Portugal
Tel.: (351) 707 50 30 40
Web Site: http://www.mcall.pt
Emp.: 80
Business Process Outsourcing Services
N.A.I.C.S.: 561499
Joel Pereira *(Mng Dir)*

APG SECURITIES JOINT STOCK COMPANY
5th Floor Grand Building 32 Hoa Ma, Hai Ba Trung District, Hanoi, Vietnam
Tel.: (84) 439410277

Web Site: https://www.apsi.com.vn
APG—(HOSE)
Rev.: $10,904,486
Assets: $75,280,928
Liabilities: $2,652,209
Net Worth: $72,628,720
Earnings: $5,777,847
Emp.: 35
Fiscal Year-end: 12/31/23
Investment Banking & Securities Brokerage Services
N.A.I.C.S.: 523150
Nguyen Ho Hung *(Chm)*

APG/SGA SA
Carrefour de Rive 1, CH -1207, Geneva, Switzerland
Tel.: (41) 582207000
Web Site: https://www.apgsga.ch
Year Founded: 1900
APGN—(SWX)
Rev.: $348,262,749
Assets: $209,984,479
Liabilities: $108,849,224
Net Worth: $101,135,255
Earnings: $25,933,481
Emp.: 481
Fiscal Year-end: 12/31/22
Holding Company; Outdoor Advertising Services
N.A.I.C.S.: 551112
Beat Holenstein *(Member-Exec Bd-Mktg & Innovation)*

Subsidiaries:

APG, Allgemeine Plakatgesellschaft APG **(1)**
Giesshubelstrasse 4, Postfach 1501, 8027, Zurich, Switzerland
Tel.: (41) 582207000
Web Site: http://www.apgsga.ch
Sales Range: $150-199.9 Million
Advertising Agency Services
N.A.I.C.S.: 541810

APG-SGA Traffic SA **(1)**
Muhlemattstr 50, Postfach 2222, Aarau, 5001, Switzerland **(100%)**
Tel.: (41) 628341073
Web Site: http://www.traffic.ch
Sales Range: $25-49.9 Million
Emp.: 10
Advertising Agencies
N.A.I.C.S.: 541810
Daniel Sluopk *(Gen Mgr)*

Allgemeine Plakatgesellschaft APG **(1)**
23 rue des Vollandes, Postfach 6195, 1211, Geneva, Switzerland **(100%)**
Tel.: (41) 227370200
Web Site: http://www.apg.ch
Sales Range: $150-199.9 Million
Display Advertising
N.A.I.C.S.: 541850

Alma Quattro d.o.o. **(1)**
Dositejeva 20, 11000, Belgrade, Serbia **(100%)**
Tel.: (381) 11 202 8900
Web Site: https://www.almaquattro.rs
Other Services Related to Advertising
N.A.I.C.S.: 541890

Alpenplakat AG **(1)**
Bosch 80A, 6331, Hunenberg, Switzerland
Tel.: (41) 783 1144
Web Site: https://alpenplakat.ch
Offset Printing Paper Mfr
N.A.I.C.S.: 323111

Amco Srl **(1)**
Careat 100, Brasov, 500002, Romania
Tel.: (40) 268415591
Web Site: http://www.amcosrl.com
Sales Range: $25-49.9 Million
Emp.: 17
Advertising Agency Services
N.A.I.C.S.: 541810
Reno Ortolani *(CEO)*

Bercher SA Publicite Generale **(1)**
Rte de Pre-boise 20, Postfach 1895, 1215, Geneva, Switzerland **(100%)**
Tel.: (41) 223473388

Web Site: http://www.bercher.ch
Sales Range: $25-49.9 Million
Emp.: 6
Advertising Agencies
N.A.I.C.S.: 541810

Europlakat d.o.o. **(1)**
Zagorska 2, 10000, Zagreb, Croatia **(51%)**
Tel.: (385) 13031000
Web Site: https://www.europlakat.hr
Sales Range: $25-49.9 Million
Emp.: 50
Display Advertising
N.A.I.C.S.: 541850
Hrvoje Prtacin *(CEO)*

Subsidiary (Non-US):

Europlakat Bulgaria OOD **(2)**
Schiptschenski prochod 42 Block 248, BG-1113, Sofia, Bulgaria **(65%)**
Tel.: (359) 28707280
Web Site: http://www.europlakat.com
Display Advertising
N.A.I.C.S.: 541850

Europlakat Kft **(2)**
Alkotas u 1719, 1123, Budapest, Hungary **(67.57%)**
Tel.: (36) 14888440
Display Advertising
N.A.I.C.S.: 541850

Europlakat Yugoslavia d.o.o. **(2)**
Dositejeva 20-3, 11000, Belgrade, Serbia **(100%)**
Tel.: (381) 113285093
Web Site: http://www.aqyu.com
Sales Range: $10-24.9 Million
Emp.: 50
Other Services Related to Advertising
N.A.I.C.S.: 541890

Proreklam-Europlakat d.o.o. **(2)**
Koprska ul 98, 1000, Ljubljana, Slovenia **(33%)**
Tel.: (386) 12001550
Web Site: http://www.europlakat.si
Sales Range: $10-24.9 Million
Emp.: 50
Advertising Agencies
N.A.I.C.S.: 541810
Marko Kolbl *(Mng Dir)*

Interflash d.o.o. **(1)**
Gubceva cesta 28, 8210, Trebnje, Slovenia **(100%)**
Tel.: (386) 73482222
Web Site: http://www.interflash.si
Sales Range: $25-49.9 Million
Emp.: 1
All Other Business Support Services
N.A.I.C.S.: 561491
Dejan Smuk *(Mng Dir)*

International Metropolis Media d.o.o. **(1)**
Dositejeva 20/3, 11000, Belgrade, Serbia
Tel.: (381) 11 202 89 20
Web Site: http://www.aqyu.com
Emp.: 5
Outdoor Advertising Services
N.A.I.C.S.: 541850

Neonlight Kft **(1)**
Szepvolgyi ut 43, 1037, Budapest, Hungary
Tel.: (36) 1 244 8080
Web Site: http://www.neonlight.hu
Outdoor Display Advertising Services
N.A.I.C.S.: 541850

Paron AG **(1)**
Giesshubelstrasse 4, 8045, Zurich, Switzerland **(100%)**
Tel.: (41) 443875300
Web Site: http://www.paron.ch
Sales Range: $25-49.9 Million
Emp.: 7
Outdoor Power Equipment Stores
N.A.I.C.S.: 561491

Publifutura Affichage Italia Srl **(1)**
Via 1 Maggio 17, Tavernerio, 22038, Como, Italy **(100%)**
Tel.: (39) 031 337 1661
Web Site: https://publifutura.it
Sales Range: $25-49.9 Million
Emp.: 4
Advertising Agencies
N.A.I.C.S.: 541810

RBN Romanian Billboard Network Srl **(1)**
Str Bucium 17, Iasi, Romania
Tel.: (40) 232 276000
Outdoor Advertising Services
N.A.I.C.S.: 541850

Swiss Poster Research Plus AG **(1)**
Giesshubelstrasse 4, 8045, Zurich, Switzerland **(100%)**
Tel.: (41) 44 385 8060
Web Site: https://spr-plus.ch
Sales Range: $25-49.9 Million
Emp.: 3
Marketing Research & Public Opinion Polling
N.A.I.C.S.: 541910

Swissplakat AG **(1)**
Bosch 80A, 6331, Hunenberg, Switzerland
Tel.: (41) 7831144
Web Site: https://www.swissplakat.ch
Billboard Mfr
N.A.I.C.S.: 339950

Visiorama AG **(1)**
Messinastrasse 30, FL-9495, Triesen, Liechtenstein **(100%)**
Tel.: (423) 3880588
Web Site: http://www.visiorama.ch
Sales Range: $25-49.9 Million
Emp.: 7
Advertising Agencies
N.A.I.C.S.: 541810

API GROUP CORPORATION
Ritter House Wickhams Cay II Road Town, Tortola, VG1 110, Virgin Islands (British)　　　　VG
Web Site:
　http://www.j2acquisitionlimited.com
Year Founded: 2017
APG—(NYSE)
Rev.: $6,558,000,000
Assets: $8,091,000,000
Liabilities: $5,964,000,000
Net Worth: $2,127,000,000
Earnings: $29,000,000
Emp.: 26,000
Fiscal Year-end: 12/31/22
Holding Company
N.A.I.C.S.: 551112
Paul Myners *(Chm)*

Subsidiaries:

APi Group, Inc. **(1)**
1100 Old Hwy 8 NW, New Brighton, MN 55112
Tel.: (651) 636-4320
Web Site: http://www.apigroupinc.com
Sales Range: $900-999.9 Million
Emp.: 200
Specialty Contractor Services
N.A.I.C.S.: 238990
Russell Becker *(Pres & CEO)*

Subsidiary (Domestic):

3S Incorporated **(2)**
8686 SW Pkwy, Harrison, OH 45030
Tel.: (513) 202-5070
Web Site: http://www.3s-incorporated.com
Emp.: 30
Fire & Security System Installation Services
N.A.I.C.S.: 561621
Matt Euson *(Pres)*

APi Construction Company **(2)**
1100 Old Hwy 8 NW, New Brighton, MN 55112
Tel.: (651) 636-4320
Web Site: https://www.apiconst.com
Insulation Contractor
N.A.I.C.S.: 238310
Huck Finn *(Pres)*

APi National Service Group **(2)**
1200 Old Hwy 8 NW, New Brighton, MN 55112
Tel.: (651) 925-8525
Web Site: https://www.api-nsg.com
Emp.: 43
Fire Safety System Installation Services
N.A.I.C.S.: 238210
Colleen Mosselle *(Pres)*

APi Supply, Inc. **(2)**

624 Arthur St NE, Minneapolis, MN 55413
Tel.: (612) 379-8000
Web Site: https://www.apisupplyinc.com
Sales Range: $10-24.9 Million
Emp.: 18
Aerial Work Platform Rental, Retail & Maintenance Services
N.A.I.C.S.: 532412
Joel Groethe *(Pres)*

APi Systems Group, Inc. **(2)**
10575 Vista Park Rd, Dallas, TX 75238
Tel.: (214) 349-2221
Web Site: http://www.afpgusa.com
Fire & Security System Installation Services
N.A.I.C.S.: 238201

APi Systems Integrators **(2)**
7306 W Yellowstone Hwy, Casper, WY 82604
Tel.: (307) 266-5222
Web Site:
　http://www.apisystemsintegrators.com
Sales Range: $10-24.9 Million
Emp.: 24
Low Voltage Systems Integrator
N.A.I.C.S.: 423690

American Fire Protection Group, Inc. **(2)**
8000 W 78th St Ste 111, Edina, MN 55439
Tel.: (952) 641-7650
Web Site: http://www.afpgusa.com
Emp.: 16
Fire Safety System Installation Services
N.A.I.C.S.: 238210

Subsidiary (Domestic):

Standard Automatic Fire Enterprises Inc. **(3)**
500 Graham Rd, College Station, TX 77845
Tel.: (979) 690-0301
Web Site: http://www.safesprinklers.com
Sales Range: $10-24.9 Million
Emp.: 150
Fire Sprinkler System Installation
N.A.I.C.S.: 922160
Jeff Sosebee *(Div Mgr)*

Subsidiary (Domestic):

Anco Products, Inc. **(2)**
2500 S 17th St, Elkhart, IN 46517-1412 **(100%)**
Tel.: (574) 293-5574
Web Site: https://www.ancoproducts.com
Sales Range: $10-24.9 Million
Emp.: 65
Flexible Air Ducts & Connectors Mfr; Insulation for Metal & Post Frame Buildings & Other Commercial Insulation Mfr
N.A.I.C.S.: 326199

Classic Industrial Services, Inc. **(2)**
456 Highlandia Dr, Baton Rouge, LA 70810
Tel.: (225) 756-4450
Web Site: https://www.classicindustrial.com
Industrial Engineering Services
N.A.I.C.S.: 541330
Michael Landes *(Pres)*

Davis-Ulmer Sprinkler Co. **(2)**
1 Commerce Dr, Amherst, NY 14228-2395
Tel.: (716) 691-3200
Web Site: https://www.davisulmer.com
Sales Range: $25-49.9 Million
Fire Sprinkler System Installation
N.A.I.C.S.: 238220

Subsidiary (Domestic):

W & M Sprinkler Company, Inc. **(3)**
50 Broadway, Hawthorne, NY 10532
Tel.: (914) 741-2222
Web Site: https://www.wmfireprotection.com
Sales Range: $25-49.9 Million
Emp.: 10
Fire Safety System Installation Services
N.A.I.C.S.: 238210
Hank Munier *(Pres)*

Subsidiary (Domestic):

W & M Sprinkler NYC LLC **(4)**
1433 Bassett Ave Ste 2B, Bronx, NY 10461
Tel.: (718) 409-5616
Web Site: http://www.wmsprinkler.com
Fire Safety System Installation Services
N.A.I.C.S.: 238210
Emile Hank Munier III *(Pres)*

APi Group Corporation—(Continued)

Subsidiary (Domestic):

Delta Fire Systems Inc. (2)
1507 S Pioneer Rd, Salt Lake City, UT
84104-4113
Tel.: (801) 972-4500
Web Site: https://www.deltafiresystems.com
Sales Range: $10-24.9 Million
Emp.: 100
Fire Sprinkler System Installation
N.A.I.C.S.: 238220
Dan Schindler (Pres)

Doody Mechanical, Inc. (2)
1301 L'orient St, Saint Paul, MN 55117
Tel.: (651) 487-1061
Sales Range: $10-24.9 Million
Emp.: 50
Provider of Sheet Metal Fabrication
N.A.I.C.S.: 238220

Garage Door Store (2)
900 W Division St, Waite Park, MN 56387-
1338
Tel.: (320) 251-7000
Web Site:
    https://www.twincitygaragedoor.com
Sales Range: $10-24.9 Million
Emp.: 5
Door Installation Services
N.A.I.C.S.: 238190

Grunau Company, Inc. (2)
1100 W Anderson Ct, Oak Creek, WI 53154
Tel.: (414) 216-6900
Web Site: https://www.grunau.com
Sales Range: $25-49.9 Million
Emp.: 400
Installs & Services Mechanical Systems,
Including HVAC, Plumbing, Fire Protection
& Specialized Electrical Systems
N.A.I.C.S.: 238220
Ted Angelo (Exec VP)

Subsidiary (Non-US):

Habtech Communications (2)
15-2430 Lucknow Drive, Mississauga, L5S-
1V3, ON, Canada
Tel.: (905) 612-8259
Web Site: http://www.habtech.ca
Security Management System Mfr
N.A.I.C.S.: 334290

Halon Banking Systems (2)
2430 Lucknow Dr Ste 15, Mississauga, L4S
1V3, ON, Canada
Tel.: (905) 567-1607
Web Site:
    http://www.halonbankingsystems.com
Halon Retailer
N.A.I.C.S.: 457210

Subsidiary (Domestic):

Industrial Contractors, Inc. (2)
701 Channel Dr, Bismarck, ND 58501-7706
Tel.: (701) 258-9908
Web Site: https://www.icinorthdakota.com
Sales Range: $25-49.9 Million
Emp.: 45
Power Plants Maintenance & Contracting
N.A.I.C.S.: 238220
Jeff Hammes (Pres & CEO)

Industrial Fabricators, Inc. (2)
PO Box 370, Thorp, WI
54771-0370 **(100%)**
Tel.: (715) 669-5512
Web Site: http://www.industrialfabinc.com
Sales Range: $10-24.9 Million
Emp.: 10
Industrial Silencer Mfr
N.A.I.C.S.: 333248
Peter Kaz (Plant Mgr)

International Fire Protection, Inc. (2)
243 Royal Dr, Madison, AL 35758-1788
Tel.: (256) 562-1311
Web Site: https://www.candoifp.com
Rev.: $33,758,363
Emp.: 250
Fire Sprinkler System Installation
N.A.I.C.S.: 238220

Island Fire Sprinkler, Inc. (2)
630 Broadway Ave Unit 1, Holbrook, NY
11741
Tel.: (631) 472-4500

Web Site: http://www.islandfirespk.com
Sales Range: $1-9.9 Million
Emp.: 26
Designs & Installs Fire Suppression Piping
Systems
N.A.I.C.S.: 238990
Brian McMahon (Pres)

J. Koski Company (2)
310 Belknap St, Superior, WI 54880
Tel.: (715) 399-0531
Web Site: http://www.jkoskicompany.com
Construction Engineering Services
N.A.I.C.S.: 541330

LeJeune Steel Company (2)
118 W 60th St, Minneapolis, MN
55419-2316 **(100%)**
Tel.: (612) 861-3321
Web Site: https://www.lejeunesteel.com
Sales Range: $10-24.9 Million
Emp.: 100
Mfr of Structural Steel for Construction of
Industrial, Commercial & Large-Scale Resi-
dential Facilities
N.A.I.C.S.: 332312
Kris Arthur (VP)

M. Lukas Company (2)
1301 Badger Rd, Kaukauna, WI 54130
Tel.: (920) 766-7820
Web Site: http://www.mlukascompany.com
Refractory Product Whslr
N.A.I.C.S.: 423840

**Metropolitan Mechanical Contractors,
Inc.** (2)
7450 Flying Cloud Dr, Eden Prairie, MN
55344
Tel.: (952) 941-7010
Web Site: https://www.metromech.com
Emp.: 300
Mechanical Contractor
N.A.I.C.S.: 541330
Bill Ball (Pres)

NYCO, Inc. (2)
10730 Briggs Dr Ste B, Inver Grove
Heights, MN 55077
Tel.: (651) 457-4069
Web Site: https://www.nycoinc.com
Sales Range: $10-24.9 Million
Emp.: 60
Mechanical Insulation Contractor
N.A.I.C.S.: 238310
Gregory Fredlund (Pres)

Reliance Fire Protection, Inc. (2)
709 E Ordnance Rd Ste 510, Baltimore, MD
21226
Tel.: (443) 989-3000
Web Site:
    https://www.reliancefireprotection.com
Fire Suppression Systems Design & Instal-
lation
N.A.I.C.S.: 238990
David W. Shilling (Pres)

**Rich Fire Protection Company,
Inc.** (2)
34 Somerset Ave, Pleasantville, NJ 08232
Tel.: (609) 641-7776
Web Site: https://www.richfire.com
Emp.: 30
Fire Protection Services, Including Design,
Project Management, Fabrication, Installa-
tion, Inspection, Repair & Maintenance
N.A.I.C.S.: 922160
Frank Rich (Pres)

**Security Fire Protection Company,
Inc.** (2)
4495 S Mendenhall Rd, Memphis, TN
38141-6702
Tel.: (901) 362-6250
Web Site: https://www.securityfire.com
Sales Range: $25-49.9 Million
Contractors for Fire Protection Services
N.A.I.C.S.: 238220
David Dixon (Pres)

**Signal One Fire and Communication,
LLC** (2)
4346 E Elwood St Ste 100, Phoenix, AZ
85040
Tel.: (480) 752-1777
Web Site: http://www.signalonefire.com
Sales Range: $10-24.9 Million
Emp.: 40
Fire & Security System Installation Services

N.A.I.C.S.: 561621

Tessier's, Inc. (2)
218 E 1st Ave, Mitchell, SD 57301-3426
Tel.: (605) 996-7548
Web Site: https://www.tessiersinc.com
Sales Range: $25-49.9 Million
Warm Air Heating & Air Conditioning Con-
tractor
N.A.I.C.S.: 238220
Mike Wagner (VP)

The Jamar Company (2)
4701 Mike Colalillo Dr, Duluth, MN
55807-2762 **(100%)**
Tel.: (218) 628-1027
Web Site: https://www.jamarcompany.com
Sales Range: $25-49.9 Million
Emp.: 70
Industrial & Commercial Mechanical & Spe-
cialty Contracting
N.A.I.C.S.: 238220
Craig Fellman (Pres)

Division (Domestic):

ASDCO (3)
4631 Mike Colalillo Dr, Duluth, MN 55807-
2762
Tel.: (218) 628-4444
Web Site: http://www.asdcosupply.com
Sales Range: $25-49.9 Million
Emp.: 65
Construction Materials Distr
N.A.I.C.S.: 423390
Kevin Osterling (Mgr-Industrial Dept)

Subsidiary (Domestic):

Twin City Garage Door Company (2)
5601 Boone Ave N, New Hope, MN 55428-
3048
Tel.: (763) 533-3838
Web Site:
    http://www.twincitygaragedoor.com
Sales Range: $25-49.9 Million
Emp.: 35
Provider of Installation & Service for Com-
mercial & Residential Overhead Doors
N.A.I.C.S.: 444110
Lisa Donabauer (Pres)

United Piping, Inc. (2)
4510 Airport Rd, Duluth, MN 55811
Tel.: (218) 727-7676
Web Site: https://www.unitedpiping.us
Sales Range: $1-9.9 Million
Emp.: 50
General & Mechanical Contractor Specializ-
ing in Pipeline Facility Construction & Main-
tenance for Oil & Gas Industry
N.A.I.C.S.: 332996
Rick Hansen (Pres)

**United States Alliance Fire Protection,
Inc.** (2)
28427 N Ballard Unit H, Lake Forest, IL
60045-4542
Tel.: (847) 816-0050
Web Site:
    https://www.usafireprotectioninc.com
Sales Range: $25-49.9 Million
Full Service Industrial Fire Protection, Resi-
dential Fire Sprinklers & Commercial Fire
Sprinkler Systems
N.A.I.C.S.: 922160
Chad Huennekens (Pres)

Branch (Domestic):

**United States Alliance Fire Protection,
Inc.** (3)
15775 W Schaefer Ct, New Berlin, WI
53151
Tel.: (262) 782-3311
Web Site:
    http://www.unitedstatesfireprotection.com
Sales Range: $50-74.9 Million
Emp.: 50
Full Service Industrial Fire Protection, Resi-
dential Fire Sprinklers & Commercial Fire
Sprinkler Systems
N.A.I.C.S.: 922160

Subsidiary (Domestic):

VFP Fire Systems, Inc. (2)
301 York Ave, Saint Paul, MN 55130
Tel.: (651) 558-3300
Web Site: https://www.vfpfire.com

Sales Range: $10-24.9 Million
Emp.: 50
Fire Protection Systems Installer
N.A.I.C.S.: 922160

**Viking Automatic Sprinkler
Company** (2)
301 York Ave, Saint Paul, MN
55130 **(100%)**
Tel.: (651) 558-3300
Web Site: https://www.vikingsprinkler.com
Sales Range: $10-24.9 Million
Emp.: 50
Fire Protection Systems Contracting Ser-
vices
N.A.I.C.S.: 238220

Subsidiary (Non-US):

Vipond Fire Protection, Inc. (2)
6380 Vipond Drive, Mississauga, L5T 1A1,
ON, Canada **(100%)**
Tel.: (905) 564-7060
Web Site: http://www.vipond.ca
Sales Range: $10-24.9 Million
Emp.: 100
Provider of Fire Protection Systems Con-
tracting Services
N.A.I.C.S.: 922160
Mike Farren (Pres)

Vipond, Inc. (2)
6380 Vipond Drive, Mississauga, L5T 1A1,
ON, Canada
Tel.: (905) 564-7060
Web Site: http://www.vipond.ca
Sales Range: $50-74.9 Million
Emp.: 650
Fire Safety System Installation Services
N.A.I.C.S.: 238210
Mike Farren (Pres)

Subsidiary (Non-US):

Vipond Fire Protection, LTD (3)
10 - 12 Glenfield Road Kelvin Industrial Es-
tate, East Kilbride, G75 0RA, Glasgow,
United Kingdom
Tel.: (44) 1355237525
Web Site: http://www.vipondfire.co.uk
Fire Safety System Installation Services
N.A.I.C.S.: 238210

Subsidiary (Domestic):

Western States Fire Protection (2)
7026 S Tucson Way, Centennial, CO
80112-3921
Tel.: (303) 792-0022
Web Site: http://www.wsfp.com
Sales Range: $10-24.9 Million
Emp.: 30
Provider of Fire Protection Systems Con-
tracting Services
N.A.I.C.S.: 238220
Gene Postma (Pres)

**Wisconsin Structural Steel
Company** (2)
Hwy 63 N, Barronett, WI 54813-0038
Tel.: (715) 822-2647
Web Site: http://www.api.com
Sales Range: $10-24.9 Million
Emp.: 100
Mfr Structural Steel Products
N.A.I.C.S.: 332312
Lee R. Anderson Sr. (CEO)

**Northland Constructors of Duluth,
Inc.** (1)
4843 Rice Lk Rd, Duluth, MN 55803
Tel.: (218) 722-8170
Web Site:
    https://www.northlandconstructors.com
Civil Engineering Services
N.A.I.C.S.: 541330

Train Oilfield Services Ltd. (1)
3001 23 St, Didsbury, T0M 0W0, AB,
Canada
Tel.: (403) 335-0031
Web Site: https://www.trainoil.ca
Pipeline Construction Services
N.A.I.C.S.: 237120

**API POWER COMPANY LIM-
ITED**
4th Floor Trade Tower Nepal
Thapathali, Kathmandu, Nepal

Tel.: (977) 15111093
Web Site:
    https://www.apipower.com.np
Year Founded: 2003
API—(NEP)
Rev.: $3,356,351
Assets: $89,264,561
Liabilities: $57,805,646
Net Worth: $31,458,915
Earnings: $332,456
Fiscal Year-end: 12/31/23
Hydroelectric Power Services
N.A.I.C.S.: 221111
Satish Neupane *(Chm)*

APIAM ANIMAL HEALTH LIMITED

27-33 Piper Lane East, Bendigo,
3550, VIC, Australia
Web Site: http://www.apiam.com.au
AHX—(ASX)
Rev.: $128,016,973
Assets: $164,254,301
Liabilities: $85,546,932
Net Worth: $78,707,370
Earnings: $1,449,360
Emp.: 1,219
Fiscal Year-end: 06/30/23
Animal Health Products & Services
N.A.I.C.S.: 115210
Andrew Vizard *(Chm)*

Subsidiaries:

Agnes Banks Equine Clinic Pty.
Limited   **(1)**
5 Price Lane, Agnes Banks, 2753, NSW,
Australia
Tel.: (61) 245885200
Web Site: https://www.abec.net.au
Equine Veterinary Services
N.A.I.C.S.: 541940

Country Vet Wholesaling Pty.
Ltd.   **(1)**
27-33 Piper Lane, East Bendigo, 3550, VIC,
Australia
Tel.: (61) 1800426142
Web Site: https://countryvet.com.au
Horse Rug & Dog Collar Distr
N.A.I.C.S.: 424590

Gympie & District Veterinary Services
Pty. Ltd.   **(1)**
109 River Road, Gympie, 4570, QLD, Australia
Tel.: (61) 754822488
Web Site:
    https://www.gympievetservice.com.au
Veterinary Services
N.A.I.C.S.: 541940

North Hill Veterinary Clinic Pty.
Ltd.   **(1)**
133 Marsh Street, Armidale, 2350, NSW,
Australia
Tel.: (61) 267721686
Web Site: https://www.northhillvet.com.au
Horse & Veterinary Care Services
N.A.I.C.S.: 541690

Portec Veterinary Services Pty.
Ltd.   **(1)**
1/8 Tomlinson Rd, Welshpool, 6106, WA,
Australia
Tel.: (61) 893615550
Animal Veterinary Services
N.A.I.C.S.: 541940

Quirindi Feedlot Services Pty.
Ltd.   **(1)**
81 Pryor Street, Quirindi, 2343, NSW, Australia
Tel.: (61) 267412004
Web Site: https://quirindifeedlot.com.au
Veterinary Consulting Services
N.A.I.C.S.: 541690

Quirindi Veterinary Clinic Pty.
Ltd.   **(1)**
81 Pryor Street, Quirindi, 2343, NSW, Australia
Tel.: (61) 267466300
Web Site:
    https://www.quirindivetclinic.com.au

Veterinary Care Services
N.A.I.C.S.: 541690

Scottsdale Veterinary Services Pty.
Ltd.   **(1)**
8 Charles Street, Scottsdale, 7260, TAS,
Australia
Tel.: (61) 363522996
Web Site:
    https://www.scottsdalevets.com.au
Veterinary Medicine & Surgery Services
N.A.I.C.S.: 541940

Smithton Veterinary Service Pty.
Ltd.   **(1)**
3 Rubicon Street, Smithton, TAS, Australia
Tel.: (61) 364526333
Web Site: https://www.smithtonvet.com.au
Veterinary Medicine & Surgery Services
N.A.I.C.S.: 541940

South Yarra Pharma Pty. Ltd.   **(1)**
81-83 Toorak Rd, South Yarra, 3141, VIC,
Australia
Tel.: (61) 398204101
Web Site:
    https://southyarrapharmacy.com.au
Pharmaceutical Products Distr
N.A.I.C.S.: 424210

Warrnambool Veterinary Clinic Pty.
Ltd.   **(1)**
514 Raglan Parade, Warrnambool, 3280,
VIC, Australia
Tel.: (61) 355590222
Web Site: https://wvc.com.au
Veterinary Medicine & Surgery Services
N.A.I.C.S.: 541940

Westvet Wholesale Pty. Ltd.   **(1)**
Unit 1 8 Tomlinson Rd, Welshpool, 6106,
WA, Australia
Tel.: (61) 800791270
Web Site: https://www.westvet.com.au
Dog Collars & Cat Cages Distr
N.A.I.C.S.: 423820

APIARY CAPITAL LLP

6 Warwick Street, London, W1B 5LX,
United Kingdom
Tel.: (44) 2030347600
Web Site:
    https://www.apiarycapital.com
Emp.: 100
Financial Services
N.A.I.C.S.: 523999

APIO (AFRICA) LTD

P.O Box 57121, Tel Aviv, 61570, Israel
Tel.: (972) 35445233
Web Site: http://www.apio.net
Year Founded: 1966
AILN—(TAE)
Rev.: $528,802
Assets: $9,738,638
Liabilities: $1,669,568
Net Worth: $8,069,070
Earnings: ($6,697,057)
Emp.: 35
Fiscal Year-end: 12/31/23
Telecommunication Servicesb
N.A.I.C.S.: 517112
Stan Bharti *(Co-Chm)*

APIS INDIA LIMITED

18/32 East Patel Nagar, New Delhi,
110 008, India
Tel.: (91) 1143206666
Web Site: https://www.apisindia.com
Year Founded: 1924
506166—(BOM)
Rev.: $40,400,164
Assets: $34,828,944
Liabilities: $22,206,584
Net Worth: $12,622,360
Earnings: $1,048,088
Emp.: 184
Fiscal Year-end: 03/31/22
Honey Mfr & Distr
N.A.I.C.S.: 311999
Vikas Aggarwal *(Compliance Officer & Sec)*

APIS PARTNERS, LLP

8 Lancelot Place, London, SW7 1DR,
United Kingdom
Tel.: (44) 2036530500
Web Site: http://apis.pe
Privater Equity Firm
N.A.I.C.S.: 523999
Matteo Stefanel *(Co-Founder & Mng Partner)*

APL APOLLO TUBES LTD.

37 Hargobind Enclave Vikas Marg,
New Delhi, 110092, India
Tel.: (91) 1122373437
Web Site: https://www.aplapollo.com
Year Founded: 1986
APLAPOLLO—(NSE)
Rev.: $178,867,143
Assets: $60,775,397
Liabilities: $27,141,660
Net Worth: $33,633,737
Earnings: $8,449,077
Emp.: 1,195
Fiscal Year-end: 03/31/22
Steel Pipe & Tube Mfr
N.A.I.C.S.: 331110
Sanjay Gupta *(Chm)*

Subsidiaries:

Shri Lakshmi Metal Udyog
Limited   **(1)**
Plot No 16 - F1 2nd Main Road, KIADB Industrial Area Attibele Anekal Taluk, Bengaluru, 562107, Karnataka, India
Tel.: (91) 8553323
Structural Steel Tube Mfr
N.A.I.C.S.: 331210
Arjun Thakur *(Sr Mgr-F&A)*

Subsidiary (Domestic):

Apollo TriCoat Tubes Limited   **(2)**
37 Hargobind Enclave Vikas Marg, New
Delhi, 110092, India   **(55.82%)**
Tel.: (91) 112 237 3437
Web Site: http://www.apollotricoat.com
Rev.: $201,283,842
Assets: $62,301,890
Liabilities: $20,770,959
Net Worth: $41,530,930
Earnings: $14,334,002
Emp.: 237
Fiscal Year-end: 03/31/2021
Steel Product Mfr & Whslr
N.A.I.C.S.: 331110
Surbhi Arora *(Compliance Officer & Sec)*

APLAB LIMITED

Plot No B/92 Road No 27, Thane,
400 604, Mumbai, India
Tel.: (91) 2262612008   In
Web Site: https://www.aplab.com
Year Founded: 1962
517096—(BOM)
Rev.: $7,417,506
Assets: $12,219,737
Liabilities: $15,779,873
Net Worth: ($3,560,136)
Earnings: ($52,850)
Emp.: 350
Fiscal Year-end: 03/31/21
Electronic Products Mfr
N.A.I.C.S.: 335999
Rajesh K. Deherkar *(Sec & Controller-Fin)*

Subsidiaries:

Aplab Limited-Mumbai   **(1)**
Deodhar Centre 424 Marol Maroshi Road,
Mumbai, 400 083, Andheri East, India
Tel.: (91) 22 678 95300
Web Site: http://www.aplab.com
Sales Range: $25-49.9 Million
Emp.: 100
Oscilloscopes Mfr
N.A.I.C.S.: 333310
Kavin Valia *(Dir)*

Sprylogic Technologies Ltd   **(1)**
Aplab Unit no 2 Plot No B-92 Road No 27,

Wagle Estate, Thane, 400 604, Maharastra,
India
Tel.: (91) 2225835515
Web Site: http://sprylogic.com
Sales Range: $25-49.9 Million
Emp.: 42
Software Services
N.A.I.C.S.: 513210

APLAYA CREATIONS LIMITED

DPT-208 2nd Floor DLF Prime Towers F-79-80, Okhla Industrial Area
Phase-1, New Delhi, 110020, India
Tel.: (91) 11 41049222   In
Web Site:
    http://www.aplayacreations.com
Rev.: $21,098,474
Assets: $17,107,988
Liabilities: $13,824,721
Net Worth: $3,283,266
Earnings: $42,456
Emp.: 7
Fiscal Year-end: 03/31/19
Online Training Services
N.A.I.C.S.: 611710
Shaswat Sinha *(CFO & Exec Dir)*

APLEX TECHNOLOGY, INC.

15F-1 No 186 Jian Yi Road, Zhonghe
Dist, New Taipei City, 235, Taiwan
Tel.: (886) 282262881
Web Site: https://www.aplex.com
Year Founded: 2004
6570—(TPE)
Rev.: $35,547,791
Assets: $42,748,304
Liabilities: $15,611,731
Net Worth: $27,136,573
Earnings: $5,366,507
Fiscal Year-end: 12/31/22
Electronic Products Mfr
N.A.I.C.S.: 334111
Chuan-Te Li *(Chm & Pres)*

APLICACIONES Y TRATAMIENTOS DE SISTEMAS S.A.

Jacinto Benavente Street 2 Building
B 2nd Floor, Tripark Business Park,
28232, Madrid, Spain
Tel.: (34) 634888000
Web Site:
    https://www.knowmadmood.com
Year Founded: 1994
ATSI—(MAD)
Emp.: 2,400
Software Development Services
N.A.I.C.S.: 541511
Jose Manuel Rufino *(Pres)*

APLISENS S.A.

Morelowa 7, 03-192, Warsaw, Poland
Tel.: (48) 228140777
Web Site: https://www.aplisens.com
Year Founded: 1992
APN—(WAR)
Rev.: $41,463,669
Assets: $58,979,421
Liabilities: $4,464,685
Net Worth: $54,514,736
Earnings: $8,387,449
Fiscal Year-end: 12/31/23
Measuring Instruments Mfr
N.A.I.C.S.: 334511
Edmund Kozak *(Chm-Supervisory Bd)*

Subsidiaries:

CZAH Pomiar Sp. z o.o.   **(1)**
Ul Porcelanowa 25, 40-241, Katowice, Poland
Tel.: (48) 326073150
Web Site: https://www.czah.pl
Measurement Equipment Mfr
N.A.I.C.S.: 334519

APLITT S.A.

Ul Arkonska 11, 80-387, Gdansk,
Poland

Aplitt S.A.—(Continued)

Tel.: (48) 58 511 20 00
Web Site: http://www.tfskok.pl
Financial Services
N.A.I.C.S.: 523999

APLIX CORPORATION

2-20-9 Nishiwaseda, Shinjuku-ku, Tokyo, 169-0051, Japan
Tel.: (81) 5037861715
Web Site: https://www.aplix.co.jp
Year Founded: 1986
3727—(TKS)
Rev.: $26,665,490
Assets: $23,205,570
Liabilities: $5,097,710
Net Worth: $18,107,860
Earnings: $2,382,240
Emp.: 49
Fiscal Year-end: 12/31/23
Software Developer & Sales
N.A.I.C.S.: 513210

Subsidiaries:

iaSolution Inc. **(1)**
7F No 100 Sec 4 Civic Blvd, Daan Dist, Taipei, Taiwan
Tel.: (886) 227761680
Web Site: http://www.iasolution.net
Sales Range: $50-74.9 Million
Emp.: 200
Software Development Services
N.A.I.C.S.: 513210

Subsidiary (Non-US):

Aplix Korea Corporation **(2)**
2302 Trade Tower 159-1 Samsung-dong, Gangnam-ku, Seoul, 135-090, Korea (South)
Tel.: (82) 220510884
Web Site: http://www.aplix.co.jp
Sales Range: $25-49.9 Million
Emp.: 9
Software Development Services
N.A.I.C.S.: 513210

APM AUTOMOTIVE HOLDINGS BERHAD

Lot 600 Pandamaran Industrial Estate Locked Bag No 218, 42009, Port Klang, Selangor Darul Ehsan, Malaysia
Tel.: (60) 331618888
Web Site: https://www.apm.com.my
APM—(KLS)
Rev.: $419,334,352
Assets: $467,024,818
Liabilities: $139,703,092
Net Worth: $327,321,726
Earnings: $18,808,446
Emp.: 3,800
Fiscal Year-end: 12/31/23
Automobile Parts Mfr
N.A.I.C.S.: 441330
Soon Hock Sow (Exec VP)

Subsidiaries:

APM Aluminium Castings Sdn. Bhd. **(1)**
Lot 1 Jalan 6/3 Kawasan Perusahaan Seri Kembangan, 43300, Seri Kembangan, Selangor, Malaysia
Tel.: (60) 389456880
Aluminium Die Casting & Component Mfr
N.A.I.C.S.: 331524

APM Auto Components (Thailand) Ltd. **(1)**
59 M001 Rangsit-Pathumthani Road, Banklang Sub-District Muang Pathumthani District, Pathumthani, 12000, Thailand
Tel.: (66) 25672882
Extrusion & Injection Part Mfr
N.A.I.C.S.: 326199

APM Auto Components (USA) Inc. **(1)**
708 Fellowship Rd, Mount Laurel, NJ 08054
Tel.: (856) 273-3616
Web Site: https://apm-autocomponents.com

Automobile Component Distr
N.A.I.C.S.: 423120

APM Auto Components (Vietnam) Co. Ltd. **(1)**
25A Dai Lo Tu Do, Vietnam Singapore Industrial Park, Thuan An, VS AT, Binh Duong, Vietnam
Tel.: (84) 650 3767 227
Automobile Parts Mfr
N.A.I.C.S.: 336390

APM Auto Electrics Sdn. Bhd. **(1)**
No 6 Jalan Jasmine 3 Kawasan Perindustrian Bukit Beruntung, Seksyen BB10 Bandar Bukit Beruntung, 48300, Rawang, Selangor Darul Ehsan, Malaysia
Tel.: (60) 560997700
Web Site: http://www.apm-automotive.com
Electronic Components Mfr
N.A.I.C.S.: 334419

APM Auto Parts Marketing (Malaysia) Sdn. Bhd. **(1)**
Lot 1 Jalan Raja Lumu Pandamaran Industrial Estate, PO Box 144, 42008, Port Klang, Selangor, Malaysia
Tel.: (60) 331618888
Automotive Part & Accessory Mfr
N.A.I.C.S.: 336390

APM Auto Parts Marketing Sdn. Bhd. **(1)**
Lot 1 Jalan Raja Lumu, PO Box 144, Pandamaran Industrial Estate, 42008, Port Klang, Selangor, Malaysia
Tel.: (60) 331618888
Web Site: http://www.apm-automotive.com
Automotive Parts & Accessories Distr
N.A.I.C.S.: 423120

APM Auto Safety Systems Sdn. Bhd. **(1)**
No 4 Jalan Jasmine 3 Seksyen BB10 Bandar Bukit Beruntung, 48300, Rawang, Selangor, Malaysia
Tel.: (60) 360997700
Air Bag & Steering Wheel Mfr
N.A.I.C.S.: 336390

APM Climate Control Sdn. Bhd. **(1)**
Lot 600 Pandamaran Industrial Estate, Locked Bag No 218, 42009, Port Klang, Selangor Darul Ehsan, Malaysia
Tel.: (60) 331618888
Web Site: http://www.apm-automotive.com
Sales Range: $50-74.9 Million
Emp.: 220
Air Conditioners & Radiators Mfr
N.A.I.C.S.: 333414

APM Coil Springs Sdn. Bhd. **(1)**
Lot 1 Jalan Raja Lumu, PO Box 144, Pandamaran Industrial Estate, 42008, Port Klang, Selangor Darul Ehsan, Malaysia
Tel.: (60) 331618888
Sales Range: $50-74.9 Million
Emp.: 111
Coil Spring Mfr
N.A.I.C.S.: 332613
Kam Sim Kwang (Gen Mgr)

APM Delta Seating Systems Sdn. Bhd. **(1)**
No 1 Kawasan Perusahaan Padang Meha Padang Serai, 09400, Kedah, Darul Aman, Malaysia
Tel.: (60) 44850845
Automotive Seat Mfr
N.A.I.C.S.: 336360

APM Engineering & Research Sdn. Bhd. **(1)**
C-1-05 Block C Oasis Square No 2 Jalan Pju 1a/7a Ara Damansara, Saujana Resort Seksyen U2, 47301, Petaling Jaya, Selangor Darul Ehsan, Malaysia
Tel.: (60) 378316688
Automotive Components Research Services
N.A.I.C.S.: 541715

APM Plastics Sdn. Bhd. **(1)**
No 8 Jalan Jasmine 3 Kawasan Perindustrian Bukit Beruntung, Seksyen BB10 Bandar Bukit Beruntung, 48300, Rawang, Selangor Darul Ehsan, Malaysia
Tel.: (60) 360997700
Sales Range: $450-499.9 Million
Emp.: 1,200
Injection Molded Plastic Products Mfr

N.A.I.C.S.: 326121

APM Seatings Sdn. Bhd. **(1)**
Lot 600 Pandamaran Industrial Estate Locked Bag No 218, 42009, Port Klang, Selangor Darul Ehsan, Malaysia
Tel.: (60) 331685336
Automobile Parts Mfr
N.A.I.C.S.: 336390

APM Shock Absorbers Sdn. Bhd. **(1)**
Lot 600 Pandamaran Industrial Estate, Locked Bag No 242, 42009, Port Klang, Selangor Darul Ehsan, Malaysia
Tel.: (60) 331618888
Automobile Parts Mfr
N.A.I.C.S.: 336390

APM Springs (Vietnam) Co. Ltd. **(1)**
25 Dai Lo Tu Do, Vietnam Singapore Industrial Park Thuan An District, Thuan An, Binh Duong, Vietnam
Tel.: (84) 650 376 7078
Web Site: http://www.apm.com.my
Leaf Spring Mfr
N.A.I.C.S.: 332613

APM Springs Sdn. Bhd. **(1)**
Lot 601 Pandamaran Industrial Estate, PO Box 144, 42008, Port Klang, Selangor Darul Ehsan, Malaysia
Tel.: (60) 331618888
Automobile Parts Mfr
N.A.I.C.S.: 336390

APM TACHI-S Seating Systems Sdn. Bhd. **(1)**
No 2 Jalan Jasmine 3 Kawasan Perindustrian Bukit Beruntung, Seksyen BB10 Bandar Bukit Beruntung, 48300, Rawang, Selangor, Malaysia
Tel.: (60) 360997700
Car Seat Mfr
N.A.I.C.S.: 336360

APM-Coachair Sdn. Bhd. **(1)**
Lot 600 Pandamaran Industrial Estate Jalan Raja Lumu, Locked Bag 218, 42009, Port Klang, Selangor Darul Ehsan, Malaysia
Tel.: (60) 331618888
Automobile Parts Mfr
N.A.I.C.S.: 336390

APM-TS B.V. **(1)**
Binnenhaven 127, 7547 BG, Enschede, Netherlands
Tel.: (31) 541358245
Web Site: https://www.ts-automotive.nl
Spring & Propeller Set Mfr
N.A.I.C.S.: 336330

Auto Parts Manufacturers Co. Sdn. Bhd. **(1)**
No 4 Jalan Jasmine 3 Kawasan Perindustrian Bukit Beruntung, Seksyen BB10 Bandar Bukit Beruntung, 48300, Rawang, Selangor Darul Ehsan, Malaysia
Tel.: (60) 360997700
Web Site: http://www.apm-automotive.com.my
Automobile Seats Mfr
N.A.I.C.S.: 336360

Fuji Seats (Malaysia) Sdn. Bhd. **(1)**
No 6 Jalan Jasmine 3 Kawasan Perindustrian Bukit Beruntung, Seksyen BB10 Bandar Bukit Beruntung, 48300, Rawang, Selangor Darul Ehsan, Malaysia
Tel.: (60) 3 6099 7700
Web Site: http://www.apm.com.my
Emp.: 1,000
Automobile Parts Mfr
N.A.I.C.S.: 336390

McConnell Seats Australia Pty. Ltd. **(1)**
130 Northcorp Boulevard, Broadmeadows, 3047, VIC, Australia
Tel.: (61) 393507277
Web Site: https://mcconnellseats.com.au
Transportation Seating Mfr
N.A.I.C.S.: 336360

Omnimatics Sdn. Bhd. **(1)**
First Floor Lot 1 Jalan 6/3 Kawasan Perindustrian, 43300, Seri Kembangan, Selangor, Malaysia
Tel.: (60) 162991506
Web Site: http://www.omnimatics.io
Auto Parts Mfr

N.A.I.C.S.: 336390

P.T. APM Armada Suspension **(1)**
Suryacipta City of Industry Jl Surya Utama kav I-15 A Ciampel, Karawang, 41361, Jawa Barat, Indonesia
Tel.: (62) 2678610174
Sales Range: $25-49.9 Million
Emp.: 70
Automotive Coil Springs Mfr & Distr
N.A.I.C.S.: 332613

PT APM Auto Components Indonesia **(1)**
Suryacipta City of Industry Jl Surya Utama kav 1-MIJK Ciample, Karawang, 41361, Jawa Barat, Indonesia
Tel.: (62) 2678610174
Radiator & Air Conditioning Cooling System Component Mfr
N.A.I.C.S.: 333415

Radiators Australia (2000) Pty. Ltd. **(1)**
11-13 Redwood Drive, Notting Hill, VIC, Australia
Tel.: (61) 395433788
Web Site: http://www.ra2000.com.au
Sales Range: $25-49.9 Million
Emp.: 35
Radiators Mfr & Distr
N.A.I.C.S.: 336390

TC Aluminium Castings Sdn. Bhd. **(1)**
Lot 1 Jalan 6/3 Kawasan Perusahaan Seri Kembangan, 51200, Seri Kembangan, Malaysia
Tel.: (60) 362568888
Aluminum Casting Mfr
N.A.I.C.S.: 331524

APM GROUP LTD.

Sword House Totteridge Road, High Wycombe, HP13 6DG, Buckinghamshire, United Kingdom
Tel.: (44) 1494 452450
Web Site: http://www.apmg-international.com
Year Founded: 1993
Sales Range: $25-49.9 Million
Emp.: 131
Management Consulting Services
N.A.I.C.S.: 541614
Richard Pharro (CEO)

APM INDUSTRIES LIMITED

SP-147 RIICO Industrial Area, Bhiwadi Dist, Alwar, 301 019, Rajasthan, India
Tel.: (91) 1493265400
Web Site: https://www.apmindustries.co.in
Year Founded: 1973
523537—(BOM)
Rev.: $43,441,125
Assets: $32,749,080
Liabilities: $12,153,960
Net Worth: $20,595,120
Earnings: $2,013,375
Emp.: 2,156
Fiscal Year-end: 03/31/22
Yarn Mfr & Distr
N.A.I.C.S.: 313110
Rajendra Kumar Rajgarhia (Chm)

APN EUROPEAN RETAIL PROPERTY GROUP

Level 30 101 Collins St, Melbourne, 3000, VIC, Australia
Tel.: (61) 386561000
Web Site: http://www.apngroup.com.au
Sales Range: $50-74.9 Million
Emp.: 60
Retail Properties Management
N.A.I.C.S.: 531390
Howard Brenchley (Chief Investment Officer)

APNA MICROFINANCE BANK LIMITED

23 A Sunderdas Road, Zaman Park,
Lahore, Pakistan
Tel.: (92) 4236305314
Web Site:
https://www.apnabank.com.pk
AMBL—(KAR)
Rev.: $21,825,417
Assets: $132,298,553
Liabilities: $120,227,887
Net Worth: $12,070,666
Earnings: $344,701
Emp.: 1,146
Fiscal Year-end: 12/31/19
Financial Services
N.A.I.C.S.: 523999
Mian Muhammad Akram Shahid
(Chm)

APODACA INVERSIONES IN-MOBILIARIAS SOCIMI, S.A.
Piso 2 A Calle Ponzano 76, 28003,
Madrid, Spain
Tel.: (34) 590873518
Web Site:
https://www.apodacasocimi.com
Year Founded: 2019
MLASO—(EUR)
Rev.: $2,415,528
Assets: $38,946,182
Liabilities: $2,336,118
Net Worth: $36,610,064
Earnings: $758,623
Emp.: 10
Fiscal Year-end: 12/31/23
Real Estate Investment Services
N.A.I.C.S.: 531190

APOGEE MINERALS LTD.
505 Burrard Street Suite 1030, Van-
couver, V7X 1M5, BC, Canada
Tel.: (604) 639-3856   Ca
Web Site:
https://www.apogeemineralsltd.com
Year Founded: 2018
APMI—(TSXV)
Rev.: $13,327
Assets: $668,584
Liabilities: $15,904
Net Worth: $652,680
Earnings: ($123,824)
Fiscal Year-end: 07/31/23
Business Consulting Services
N.A.I.C.S.: 522299
Jordan Trimble *(Dir)*

APOGEE OPTOCOM CO., LTD.
1F No 5 Nan-Ke 3rd Rd, Tainan Sci-
ence Industrial Park Hsin-shi, Tainan
City, Taiwan
Tel.: (886) 65053700
Web Site:
https://www.nextapogee.com.tw
Year Founded: 2003
6426—(TAI)
Rev.: $19,510,146
Assets: $45,498,702
Liabilities: $4,900,385
Net Worth: $40,598,318
Earnings: $2,800,550
Fiscal Year-end: 12/31/22
Optical Component Mfr
N.A.I.C.S.: 333310

APOLLO 8 MAINTENANCE SERVICES LTD.
40 Wynford Dr Ste 108, North York,
M3C 1J5, ON, Canada
Tel.: (416) 461-8748
Web Site: http://www.apolloeight.com
Year Founded: 1972
Rev.: $16,954,265
Emp.: 900
Building Cleaning & Maintenance
Services
N.A.I.C.S.: 561720

APOLLO BELL INTERNA-TIONAL PLC
Schadowstrasse 11e, 40212, Dussel-
dorf, Germany
Tel.: (49) 211 36 116 0
Web Site: http://www.apollobell.com
GPS Software
N.A.I.C.S.: 513210
Norbert Wollnik *(CEO)*

APOLLO CONSOLIDATED LIM-ITED
1202 Hay Street West, Perth, 6005,
WA, Australia
Tel.: (61) 8 9320 4700   AU
Web Site:
http://www.apolloconsolidated.com
Year Founded: 2002
AOP—(ASX)
Sales Range: Less than $1 Million
Gold Exploration Services
N.A.I.C.S.: 212220
Nick Castleden *(Mng Dir)*

Subsidiaries:

Aspire Minerals Pty Ltd.   (1)
99a Goddard Street, Lathlain, Perth, 6100,
WA, Australia
Tel.: (61) 8 6102 5755
Gold Exploration Services
N.A.I.C.S.: 212220

APOLLO FINVEST (INDIA) LIM-ITED
301 Plot No B-27 Commerce Centre
Off, New Link Road Near Morya
House Andheri West Andheri, Mum-
bai, 400 053, Maharashtra, India
Tel.: (91) 2262231667
Web Site:
https://www.apollofinvest.com
512437—(BOM)
Rev.: $6,300,021
Assets: $10,041,158
Liabilities: $2,943,445
Net Worth: $7,097,713
Earnings: $1,375,429
Emp.: 20
Fiscal Year-end: 03/31/23
Investment Management Service
N.A.I.C.S.: 523999
Mikhil R. Innani *(Mng Dir)*

APOLLO FOOD HOLDINGS BERHAD
No 70 Jalan Langkasuka Larkin In-
dustrial Area, 80350, Johor Bahru,
Johor, Malaysia
Tel.: (60) 72365096
Web Site:
http://www.apollofood.com.my
APOLLO—(KLS)
Rev.: $54,025,463
Assets: $52,138,156
Liabilities: $4,595,890
Net Worth: $47,542,266
Earnings: $11,455,542
Emp.: 774
Fiscal Year-end: 04/30/24
Confectionary Product Mfr
N.A.I.C.S.: 311351
Chiang Heng Liang *(Chm)*

APOLLO FOREST PRODUCTS LTD
1515 Nicholson St, PO Box 129,
Prince George, V2N 1V7, BC,
Canada
Tel.: (250) 996-8297
Web Site: http://www.sinclar.com
Year Founded: 1969
Rev.: $33,560,751
Emp.: 140
Lumber Products Supplier & Mfr
N.A.I.C.S.: 423310
Greg Stewart *(Pres)*

APOLLO FUTURE MOBILITY GROUP LIMITED
Units 301 and 302 3F Building 22E
Phase Three, Hong Kong Science
Park Pak Shek Kok, Hong Kong,
China (Hong Kong)
Tel.: (852) 28106683   Ky
Web Site: http://apollofmg.com
Year Founded: 1989
0860—(HKG)
Rev.: $68,173,540
Assets: $655,432,894
Liabilities: $185,999,607
Net Worth: $469,433,286
Earnings: ($46,349,350)
Emp.: 193
Fiscal Year-end: 09/30/21
Diamond Jewelry Mfr & Whslr
N.A.I.C.S.: 339910
Eric King Fung Ho *(Chm)*

Subsidiaries:

Ideenion Automobil AG   (1)
Lilienthalstr 17, 85080, Gaimersheim, Ger-
many
Tel.: (49) 8458333500
Web Site: https://www.ideenion.de
Software Development Services
N.A.I.C.S.: 541511

Omas SRL   (1)
Via del Fonditore 10, 40138, Bologna, Italy
Tel.: (39) 051 6027911
Web Site: http://www.omas.com
Stationery Product Mfr & Distr
N.A.I.C.S.: 339940

APOLLO GLOBAL CAPITAL, INC.
Unit 504 Galleria Corporate Center
EDSA corner Ortigas Ave, Brgy
Ugong Norte, Quezon City, Philip-
pines
Tel.: (63) 285328654
Web Site:
https://www.apolloglobalcapital.com
Year Founded: 1998
APL—(PHI)
Assets: $80,095,812
Liabilities: $7,510,412
Net Worth: $72,585,400
Earnings: ($2,149,435)
Fiscal Year-end: 12/31/23
Holding Company
N.A.I.C.S.: 551112
Salvador Santos-Ocampo *(Chm)*

Subsidiaries:

JDVC Resources Corporation   (1)
Unit 504 Galleria Corporate Center EDSA
corner Ortigas Ave, Brgy Ugong Norte,
Quezon City, Philippines
Tel.: (63) 24168960
Web Site: http://www.jdvcresources.com
Magnetite Mining Services
N.A.I.C.S.: 212210
Alfonso Yap Go *(Chm)*

APOLLO HOSPITALS ENTER-PRISE LIMITED
No 19 Bishop Gardens Raja Annam-
alaipuram, Chennai, 600028, India
Tel.: (91) 4428290956   In
Web Site:
https://www.apollohospitals.com
508869—(BOM)
Rev.: $2,012,119,200
Assets: $1,800,762,600
Liabilities: $998,456,550
Net Worth: $802,306,050
Earnings: $151,296,600
Emp.: 71,113
Fiscal Year-end: 03/31/22
Hospital Owner & Operator
N.A.I.C.S.: 622110
P. Preetha Reddy *(Vice Chm)*

Subsidiaries:

Apollo CVHF Limited   (1)

Opp GNFC Tower Pakwan Cross Road S G
Highway, Bodakdev, Ahmedabad, Gujarat,
India
Tel.: (91) 7096400400
Web Site: http://www.apollocvhf.com
Healtcare Services
N.A.I.C.S.: 621999
Sameer I. Dani *(CEO)*

Apollo Cosmetic Surgical Centre Pvt
Limited   (1)
No 14 Jayammal Street Teynampet, Chen-
nai, 600 018, India
Tel.: (91) 44 66321565
Emp.: 30
Plastic Surgery Services
N.A.I.C.S.: 621111
S. Arumugam *(Gen Mgr)*

Apollo Gleneagles PET-CT
Limited   (1)
Apollo Hospital Campus, Jubilee Hills,
Hyderabad, 5000096, India
Tel.: (91) 4023607777
Web Site: http://www.apollohealthcity.com
Sales Range: $450-499.9 Million
Health & Allied Services
N.A.I.C.S.: 621610
Prathap Chandra Reddy *(Chm)*

Apollo Health and Lifestyle
Limited   (1)
7-1-617/A 615 and 616 Imperial Towers 7th
Floor, Ameerpet, Hyderabad, 500 038, Te-
langana, India
Tel.: (91) 4049047777
Web Site: https://www.apolloclinic.com
Health Care Srvices
N.A.I.C.S.: 621999
Neeraj Garg *(CEO)*

Subsidiary (Domestic):

Apollo Koramangala Cradle
Limited   (2)
58 5th Cross 18th Main 6th Block Near
Anand Sweets, Koramangala, Bengaluru,
560 095, India
Tel.: (91) 860 500 4424
Web Site: http://www.thecradle.in
Maternity Clinic Operator
N.A.I.C.S.: 621111
Neeraj Garg *(CEO)*

ISIS Health Care India Private
Limited   (2)
65 The Apollo Clinic M M Road, Fraser
Town, 560 005, Bengaluru, Karnataka, India
Tel.: (91) 80 25489030
Emp.: 20
Hospital Operator
N.A.I.C.S.: 622110
Sanjeev Pubbichetty *(Gen Mgr)*

Apollo Lavasa Health Corporation
Limited   (1)
Plot 13 Parsik Hill Road Off Uran Road
Sector-23, CBD Belapur, Navi Mumbai, 400
614, India
Tel.: (91) 2233503350
Web Site:
http://www.mumbai.apollohospitals.com
Hospital Services
N.A.I.C.S.: 622110

Apollo Nellore Hospital Limited   (1)
16/ 111/ 1133 Muttukur Road Pinakini Na-
gar, Nellore, 524004, Andhra Pradesh, India
Tel.: (91) 8616667333
Hospital Services
N.A.I.C.S.: 622110

Apollo Rajshree Hospitals Private
Limited   (1)
Scheme No 74 C Sector D Vijay Nagar,
Indore, 452 010, Madhya Pradesh, India
Tel.: (91) 7312445566
Hospital Services
N.A.I.C.S.: 622110

Apollo Sugar Clinics Limited   (1)
7th Floor Imperial Towers Ameerpet Above
South India Shopping Mall, Hyderabad,
500016, Telangana, India
Tel.: (91) 18001031010
Web Site: https://www.apollosugar.com
Healtcare Services
N.A.I.C.S.: 621999
Anand Wasker *(CEO)*

Apollo Hospitals Enterprise Limited—(Continued)

Imperial Hospital & Research Centre Limited (1)
Near Main Circle Shastri Nagar, Jaipur, 302016, Rajasthan, India
Tel.: (91) 1412300111
Web Site: http://www.imperialhospital.in
Hospital Services
N.A.I.C.S.: 622110
N. B. Rajoria (Founder)

Samudra Healthcare Enterprises Limited (1)
13-1-3 Main Road, Kakinada, 533001, India
Tel.: (91) 8842302600
Web Site: https://www.apollokakinada.com
Health Care Srvices
N.A.I.C.S.: 621999
Venkataramana I. (CEO)

Sapien Biosciences Private Limited (1)
1st Floor AIMSR Building Apollo Health City, Jubilee Hills, Hyderabad, 500 096, India
Tel.: (91) 9985925652
Web Site: https://www.sapienbio.co.in
Healtcare Services
N.A.I.C.S.: 621999
Sreevatsa G. Natarajan (Co-Founder)

Unique Home Health Care Limited (1)
No 55 Greams Road 1st Floor Ali Towers Thousand Lights, Chennai, 600 006, India
Tel.: (91) 2829 1750
Web Site: http://www.uhhc.co.in
Women Healthcare Services
N.A.I.C.S.: 621610

APOLLO MACHINE & WELDING LTD.
4141-93 St, Edmonton, T6E 5Y3, AB, Canada
Tel.: (780) 463-3060
Web Site: https://www.apollomachine.com
Year Founded: 1971
Rev.: $11,164,130
Emp.: 200
Machine Equipment Supplier
N.A.I.C.S.: 333515
Robert Norton (Founder)

APOLLO MICRO SYSTEMS LIMITED
Plot No 128/A Road No 12 BEL Road IDA Mallapur Uppal Mandal, Hyderabad, 500 076, Telangana, India
Tel.: (91) 914027167000   In
Web Site: https://www.apollo-micro.com
Year Founded: 1985
APOLLO—(NSE)
Rev.: $40,724,748
Assets: $94,544,159
Liabilities: $42,100,695
Net Worth: $52,443,464
Earnings: $2,557,669
Emp.: 280
Fiscal Year-end: 03/31/23
Electromechanical Component Mfr & Distr
N.A.I.C.S.: 334511
Chandrapati Venkata Siva Prasad (Dir-Technical)

APOLLO MINERALS LIMITED
Level 9 28 The Esplanade, Perth, 6000, WA, Australia
Tel.: (61) 893226322
Web Site: https://www.apollominerals.com
AON—(ASX)
Rev.: $19,180
Assets: $9,058,851
Liabilities: $876,603
Net Worth: $8,182,248
Earnings: ($1,398,653)
Fiscal Year-end: 06/30/22

Support Activities for Nonmetallic Minerals (except Fuels) Mining
N.A.I.C.S.: 213115
Ian Middlemas (Chm)

Subsidiaries:

Southern Exploration Pty Limited (1)
262-266 Pirie St, Adelaide, 5001, SA, Australia
Tel.: (61) 883424914
Iron Ore Exploration Services
N.A.I.C.S.: 212210

APOLLO PIPES LIMITED
37 Hargobind Enclave, Vikas Marg, New Delhi, 110092, India
Tel.: (91) 1206587777   In
Web Site: https://www.apollopipes.com
Year Founded: 1985
APOLLOPIPE—(NSE)
Rev.: $107,544,119
Assets: $74,237,027
Liabilities: $18,909,495
Net Worth: $55,327,531
Earnings: $6,792,909
Emp.: 620
Fiscal Year-end: 03/31/22
Holding Company
N.A.I.C.S.: 551112
Sameer Gupta (Mng Dir)

APOLLO SIGN & MILLWORK LTD.
Unit A1 4242 Phillips Avenue, Burnaby, V5A 2X2, BC, Canada
Tel.: (604) 437-3000
Web Site: http://www.apolloshop.com
Year Founded: 1997
Millwork & Sign Design & Mfr
N.A.I.C.S.: 339950
Gordon Sagoo (Gen Mgr)

APOLLO SILVER CORP.
710-1030 W Georgia St, Vancouver, V6E 2Y3, BC, Canada
Tel.: (604) 428-6128
Web Site: https://apollosilver.com
Year Founded: 1999
APGOF—(OTCQB)
Rev.: $150,123
Assets: $72,672,921
Liabilities: $1,943,424
Net Worth: $70,729,497
Earnings: ($8,299,052)
Emp.: 4
Fiscal Year-end: 11/30/22
Mineral Exploration Services
N.A.I.C.S.: 213114
Tom Peregoodoff (Pres & CEO)

APOLLO SINDOORI HOTELS LIMITED
No 43/5 Hussain Mansion Ground Floor Greams Road Thousand Lights, Chennai, 600 006, India
Tel.: (91) 49045002
Web Site: https://www.apollosindoori.com
APOLSINHOT—(NSE)
Rev.: $51,352,296
Assets: $46,333,929
Liabilities: $29,950,543
Net Worth: $16,383,385
Earnings: $2,308,898
Emp.: 1,300
Fiscal Year-end: 03/31/23
Catering Services
N.A.I.C.S.: 722320
G. Venkatraman (Chm)

APOLLO SOLAR ENERGY, INC.
485 Tengfei 3rd Shuangliu Southwest Airport Economic Development Zone, Shuangliu, Chengdu, 610207, China

Tel.: (86) 2885623888   NV
Web Site: http://www.apollosolarenergy.com.cn
Sales Range: Less than $1 Million
Emp.: 76
Tellurium-Based Metals Processing & Refining Services
N.A.I.C.S.: 331420
Huakang David Zhou (Sec)

APOLLO TYRES LTD.
Apollo House 7 Institutional Area Sector 32, Gurgaon, 122001, Haryana, India
Tel.: (91) 1242383002
Web Site: https://corporate.apollotyres.com
500877—(NSE)
Rev.: $2,876,199,554
Assets: $3,645,226,904
Liabilities: $2,041,060,886
Net Worth: $1,604,166,018
Earnings: $87,168,900
Emp.: 8,014
Fiscal Year-end: 03/31/22
Tiles Mfr
N.A.I.C.S.: 326211
Onkar S. Kanwar (Chm & Mng Dir)

Subsidiaries:

Apollo (South Africa) Holdings (Pty) Ltd. (1)
150 Denne Road Hughes, Boksburg, 1459, Gauteng, South Africa
Tel.: (27) 312421111
Automotive Tire Whslr
N.A.I.C.S.: 423130

Apollo Tires (US) Inc. (1)
6 Concourse Pkwy Bldg 6 Ste 2920, Atlanta, GA 30328
Rubber Tyre Mfr & Distr
N.A.I.C.S.: 326211

Apollo Tyres (Austria) Gesellschaft m.b.H. (1)
Seybelgasse 10-12, 1230, Vienna, Austria
Tel.: (43) 18693325
Vehicle Tyre Mfr & Distr
N.A.I.C.S.: 326211

Apollo Tyres (Belux) S.A. (1)
Buro & Design Center Heizel Esplanade Bus 6, 1020, Brussels, Belgium
Tel.: (32) 22164575
Tyre Mfr & Distr
N.A.I.C.S.: 326211

Apollo Tyres (Germany) GmbH (1)
Am Prime Park 17, 65479, Raunheim, Germany
Tel.: (49) 61429523005
Automotive Tire Whslr
N.A.I.C.S.: 423130

Apollo Tyres (Hungary) Kft. (1)
Apollo ut 106, 3212, Gyongyoshalasz, Hungary
Tel.: (36) 37886501
Automotive Tire Whslr
N.A.I.C.S.: 423130

Apollo Tyres (Hungary) Sales Kft. (1)
Alkotas u 39/c Alkotas Irodahaz, 1123, Budapest, Hungary
Tel.: (36) 13795433
Rubber Tyre Mfr & Distr
N.A.I.C.S.: 326211

Apollo Tyres (Malaysia) Sdn Bhd (1)
Unit 1504 Level-15 Uptown-1 1 Jalan SS21/58, Damansara Uptown, 47400, Petaling Jaya, Selangor, Malaysia
Tel.: (60) 377355555
Automotive Tire Whslr
N.A.I.C.S.: 423130

Apollo Tyres (Middle East) FZE. (1)
JAFZA One Tower A Office 1907, Jebel Ali, Dubai, United Arab Emirates
Tel.: (971) 48841603
Automotive Tire Whslr
N.A.I.C.S.: 423130

Apollo Tyres (R&D) GmbH (1)

Rheinstrasse 103, 56179, Vallendar, Germany
Tel.: (49) 2618076600
Vehicle Tyre Mfr & Distr
N.A.I.C.S.: 326211

Apollo Tyres (Thailand) Limited (1)
719 23rd Floor KPN Tower Rama 9 Road, Bang Kapi Huay Kwang, Bangkok, 10310, Thailand
Tel.: (66) 27706714
Automotive Tire Whslr
N.A.I.C.S.: 423130

Apollo Tyres (UK) Holdings Ltd. (1)
8 Waterloo Place, St James s, London, SW1Y 4BE, United Kingdom
Tel.: (44) 2070251680
Rubber Tyre Mfr & Distr
N.A.I.C.S.: 326211

Apollo Tyres (UK) Pvt. Ltd. (1)
8 Waterloo Place St James's, London, SW1Y 4BE, United Kingdom
Tel.: (44) 2070251680
Automotive Tire Whslr
N.A.I.C.S.: 423130

Apollo Tyres (UK) Sales Ltd. (1)
1 Beechwood - Cherry Hall Road Kettering Business Park, Kettering, NN14 1UE, United Kingdom
Tel.: (44) 3303331294
Rubber Tyre Mfr & Distr
N.A.I.C.S.: 326211

Apollo Tyres AG (1)
Mellingerstrasse 2A, Postfach 2112, 5402, Baden, Switzerland
Tel.: (41) 562033030
Tyre Mfr & Distr
N.A.I.C.S.: 326211

Apollo Tyres B.V. (1)
Ir Schiffstraat 370, 7547 RD, Enschede, Netherlands
Tel.: (31) 534888888
Automotive Tire Whslr
N.A.I.C.S.: 423130

Apollo Tyres Global R & D B.V (1)
Colosseum 2, 7521 PT, Enschede, Netherlands
Tel.: (31) 534888777
Automotive Tire Whslr
N.A.I.C.S.: 423130

Apollo Tyres Holdings (Singapore) Pte. Ltd. (1)
9 Temasek Boulevard 42-01 Suntec Tower Two, Singapore, 038989, Singapore
Tel.: (65) 68046262
Automotive Tire Whslr
N.A.I.C.S.: 423130

Apollo Tyres Iberica S.A.U. (1)
Cityparc Edificio Bruselas Ctra De Hospitalet 147-149, Cornella de Llobregat, 08940, Barcelona, Spain
Tel.: (34) 934745141
Tyre Mfr & Distr
N.A.I.C.S.: 326211

Apollo Vredestein (UK) Ltd. (1)
1 Beechwood Cherry Hall Road Kettering Business Park, Kettering, NN14 1UE, Northamptonshire, United Kingdom
Tel.: (44) 3303331294
Web Site: http://www.vredestein.co.uk
Tiles Mfr
N.A.I.C.S.: 326211

Apollo Vredestein B.V. (1)
Ir Schiffstraat 370, 7547 RD, Enschede, Netherlands
Tel.: (31) 534888888
Web Site: http://www.apollovredestein.com
Sales Range: $400-449.9 Million
Motor Vehicle Tire Mfr
N.A.I.C.S.: 326211
Karl Naylor (Mgr-UK)

Subsidiary (Non-US):

Apollo Vredestein Schweiz AG (2)
Mellingerstrasse 2A, Postfach 2112, 5402, Baden, Switzerland
Tel.: (41) 562033030
Web Site: http://www.vredestein.ch
Motor Vehicle Tire Distr
N.A.I.C.S.: 423130

NV Vredestein SA   **(2)**
Esplanade Heysel boite 6, 1020, Brussels, Belgium
Tel.: (32) 22168100
Web Site: http://www.vredestein.be
Sales Range: $25-49.9 Million
Emp.: 8
Motor Vehicle Tire Distr
N.A.I.C.S.: 423130

Subsidiary (Domestic):

Vredestein Consulting B.V.   **(2)**
Ir Schiffstraat 370, 7547 RD, Enschede, Netherlands
Tel.: (31) 534888888
Web Site: https://www.apollovredestein.com
Sales Range: $25-49.9 Million
Technological Consulting Services
N.A.I.C.S.: 541690
Kornelis Tetman Hettema *(Mng Dir)*

Subsidiary (Non-US):

Vredestein France S.A.   **(2)**
59 Avenue Victor Hugo, F-75116, Paris, France
Tel.: (33) 820838281
Sales Range: $25-49.9 Million
Emp.: 10
Motor Vehicle Tire Distr
N.A.I.C.S.: 423130

Vredestein GmbH   **(2)**
Rheinstrasse 103, PO Box 1370, 56173, Vallendar, Germany
Tel.: (49) 26180760
Web Site: http://www.vredestein.com
Sales Range: $25-49.9 Million
Emp.: 30
Motor Vehicle Tire Distr
N.A.I.C.S.: 423130
Michael Lutz *(Gen Mgr)*

Vredestein GmbH   **(2)**
Seybellgasse 10-12, 1230, Vienna, Austria
Tel.: (43) 186933250
Web Site: http://www.vredestein.at
Motor Vehicle Tire Distr
N.A.I.C.S.: 423130

Vredestein Iberica S.A.   **(2)**
Cityparc Building Brussels Ctra De Hospitalet 147-149, Cornella De Llobregat, 08940, Barcelona, Spain
Tel.: (34) 934745141
Web Site: http://www.vredestein.es
Sales Range: $25-49.9 Million
Emp.: 10
Motor Vehicle Tire Distr
N.A.I.C.S.: 423130

Vredestein Nordic AB   **(2)**
Flojelbergsgatan 18, 431 37, Molndal, Sweden
Tel.: (46) 31580010
Web Site: http://www.vredestein.se
Sales Range: $25-49.9 Million
Emp.: 10
Motor Vehicle Tire Distr
N.A.I.C.S.: 423130
Bo Christer Manssom *(CEO)*

Apollo Vredestein Kft.   **(1)**
Alkotas ut 39/c, 1123, Budapest, Hungary
Tel.: (36) 3795433
Automotive Tire Whslr
N.A.I.C.S.: 423130

Apollo Vredestein Opony Polska Sp. Zo.o.   **(1)**
Ul Prosta 32, 00-838, Warsaw, Poland
Tel.: (48) 228868100
Web Site: http://www.vredestein.pl
Tiles Mfr
N.A.I.C.S.: 326211

Apollo Vredestein Tires Inc.   **(1)**
1175 Peachtree St NE 10th Fl, Atlanta, GA 30361
Tel.: (770) 302-2163
Web Site: http://www.vredestein.com
Tiles Mfr
N.A.I.C.S.: 326211

Reifencom GmbH   **(1)**
Datenschutz Sudfeldstr 16, 30453, Hannover, Germany
Tel.: (49) 51112321010
Web Site: https://www.reifen.com
Automotive Tire Whslr

N.A.I.C.S.: 423130
Michael Harle *(Mng Dir)*

APOORVA LEASING FINANCE & INVESTMENT COMPANY LTD.
C-1/9 First Floor Sector-31 Gautam Budh Nagar, Noida, 201301, Uttar Pradesh, India
Tel.: (91) 01204372849   In
Year Founded: 1983
539545—(BOM)
Rev.: $1,376,125
Assets: $20,417,083
Liabilities: $420,161
Net Worth: $19,996,922
Earnings: $918,195
Emp.: 13
Fiscal Year-end: 03/31/22
Financial Investment Services
N.A.I.C.S.: 523999
Atul Singh Tyagi *(Mng Dir & CFO)*

APOS A.D.
Somborska 28, Apatin, Serbia
Tel.: (381) 25773611
Web Site: https://www.aposad.com
Year Founded: 1989
APOS—(BEL)
Rev.: $713,437
Assets: $670,868
Liabilities: $36,172
Net Worth: $634,696
Earnings: $58,349
Emp.: 13
Fiscal Year-end: 12/31/22
Material Recycling Services
N.A.I.C.S.: 562920
Milan Sasic *(Exec Dir)*

APOSENSE LTD.
5-7 Odem St, PO Box 7119, 49170, Petah Tiqwa, Israel
Tel.: (972) 39247211
Web Site: http://www.aposense.com
Sales Range: $10-24.9 Million
Emp.: 30
Molecular Imaging & Drug Development
N.A.I.C.S.: 541715
Alon Dumanis *(Chm)*

APP ANNIE LTD.
35/F Central Plaza, 18 Harbour Road, Hong Kong, Wan Chai, China (Hong Kong)
Tel.: (852) 2824 8593
Web Site: http://www.appannie.com
Business Intelligence Services
N.A.I.C.S.: 561499
Bertrand Schmitt *(Founder & CEO)*

Subsidiaries:

Distimo Holding B.V.   **(1)**
Plompetorengracht 17, 3512 CB, Utrecht, Netherlands
Tel.: (31) 30 82 00 567
Web Site: http://www.distimo.com
Sales Range: $1-9.9 Million
Emp.: 35
Mobile Analytics Software
N.A.I.C.S.: 513210
Tom Jansen *(Co-Founder & CTO)*

APP SYSTEMS SERVICES PTE. LTD.
11 Toh Guan Road East 03-01 APP Enterprise Building, Singapore, 608603, Singapore
Tel.: (65) 64256611
Web Site:
   http://www.appsystems.com.sg
Year Founded: 1982
Sales Range: $10-24.9 Million
Emp.: 80
Distr of Individual Components & Vacuum Systems

N.A.I.C.S.: 423830
Song Lin Lee *(Mng Dir)*

Subsidiaries:

APP Engineering Sdn Bhd   **(1)**
No 18 & 18-1 Block 1A Jalan Kuchai Maju 1, Dynasty 3 Kuchai Entrepreneurs Park, Kuala Lumpur, 58200, Malaysia
Tel.: (60) 379846611
Web Site: http://www.app-msia.com
Mfr of Individual Components & Vacuum Systems
N.A.I.C.S.: 335210

APP Systems Services (India) Pvt Ltd   **(1)**
SS-58 Second Floor Aditya Mega Mall Plot No 9D CBD, Ground East Karkardooma, Delhi, 110092, India
Tel.: (91) 11 2238 5355
Semiconductor Device Whslr
N.A.I.C.S.: 423690
Vivek Sheel *(Engr-Sls)*

APP Systems Services (Thailand) Co. Ltd.   **(1)**
29/4 Moo 9 Taladkwan, Muang Nontaburi, 11000, Nonthaburi, Thailand
Tel.: (66) 25269700
Web Site: http://www.appsystems.com.sg
Sales Range: Less than $1 Million
Emp.: 10
Mfr of Individual Components & Vacuum Systems
N.A.I.C.S.: 335210
Surachart Kittikwangthong *(Country Mgr)*

APP Systems Services Pte. Ltd.   **(1)**
Bintaro Trade Center Blok D2 No 7, Bintaro Jaya Sektor 7, Jakarta, 15224, Tangerang, Indonesia
Tel.: (62) 21 745 1687
Web Site: http://www.appsystems.com.sg
Mfr of High Technology Products; Plasma, Thin Films, Vacuum Technology, Cryogenics, Thermal & Bioscience Related Technologies Delivering Solutions
N.A.I.C.S.: 541715

APPAREL GROUP PTY. LTD.
830 Elizabeth St, Waterloo, 2017, NSW, Australia
Tel.: (61) 2 8306 3700   AU
Web Site:
   http://www.apgandco.com.au
Emp.: 1,400
Holding Company; Clothing Mfr & Retailer
N.A.I.C.S.: 551112
Adrian Jones *(CEO)*

Subsidiaries:

JAG Apparel   **(1)**
11 Bowden Street, Alexandria, 2015, NSW, Australia
Tel.: (61) 2 8306 3700
Web Site: http://www.jag.com.au
Sales Range: $25-49.9 Million
Casual & Denim Clothing Designer & Mfr
N.A.I.C.S.: 315250
Cathy Johnson *(Head-Mdse)*

APPASIA BERHAD
1-40-1 Menara Bangkok Bank Berjaya Central Park No 105 Jalan Ampang, 50450, Kuala Lumpur, Malaysia
Tel.: (60) 321813666   MY
Web Site: https://www.appasia.com
Year Founded: 1984
APPASIA—(KLS)
Rev.: $12,682,109
Assets: $5,920,476
Liabilities: $820,402
Net Worth: $5,100,074
Earnings: $121,358
Fiscal Year-end: 12/31/22
Mobile Application Development Services
N.A.I.C.S.: 541511
Hong Chye Toh *(Exec Dir)*

Subsidiaries:

AppAsia Stream Sdn. Bhd.   **(1)**
Unit 2-3A Level 2 Oval Damansara 685, Jalan Damansara Taman Tun Dr Ismail, 60000, Kuala Lumpur, Malaysia
Tel.: (60) 1155019096
Web Site:
   https://www.appasiastream.com.my
Video Production Services
N.A.I.C.S.: 512110

Extol Corporation Sdn Bhd.   **(1)**
1-40-1 Menara Bangkok Bank Berjaya Central Park No 105 Jalan Ampang, 50450, Kuala Lumpur, Malaysia
Tel.: (60) 321813666
Web Site: https://www.extolcorp.com
Antivirus Software Development Services
N.A.I.C.S.: 541511
Justin Tan *(CEO)*

APPBANK INC.
1-12-1 Nishi-Shinjuku, Shinjuku-ku, Tokyo, 160-0023, Japan
Tel.: (81) 363020561
Web Site: http://www.appbank.co.jp
Year Founded: 2012
6177—(TKS)
Rev.: $3,474,100
Assets: $1,985,200
Liabilities: $1,786,680
Net Worth: $198,520
Earnings: ($2,984,890)
Fiscal Year-end: 12/31/23
Technology Media Site Operation
N.A.I.C.S.: 516210
Shiraishi Mitsuzou *(Pres & CEO)*

APPEN LIMITED
Level 6/9 Help St, Chatswood, 2067, NSW, Australia
Tel.: (61) 294686300   AU
Web Site: https://www.appen.com
Year Founded: 1996
APX—(ASX)
Rev.: $388,133,000
Assets: $254,941,000
Liabilities: $106,955,000
Net Worth: $147,986,000
Earnings: ($239,068,000)
Emp.: 1,386
Fiscal Year-end: 12/31/22
Data Processing Services
N.A.I.C.S.: 518210
Kerri Reynolds *(Sr VP-Human Resources)*

Subsidiaries:

Appen Japan Pty Ltd.   **(1)**
Shin-Marunouchi Building 9F 1-5-1, Marunouchi Chiyoda-ku, Tokyo, Japan
Tel.: (81) 368222971
Web Site: https://appen.co.jp
Software Development Services
N.A.I.C.S.: 541511

Leapforce, Inc.   **(1)**
5050 Hopyard Rd Ste 425, Pleasanton, CA 94588
Tel.: (925) 730-0073
Web Site: http://www.leapforceathome.com
Data Processing Services
N.A.I.C.S.: 518210

Mendip Media Group Limited   **(1)**
Rockeagle House Pynes Hill, Exeter, EX2 5AZ, Devon, United Kingdom
Tel.: (44) 1392213958
Transcription Services
N.A.I.C.S.: 561410

APPENINN NYRT.
Kelenhegyi ut 43 B ep 5 em 1, HU-1118, Budapest, Hungary
Tel.: (36) 13468869
Web Site:
   http://www.appeninnholding.com
0AP—(DEU)
Rev.: $21,514,426
Assets: $232,574,370
Liabilities: $109,978,568

Appeninn Nyrt.—(Continued)

Net Worth: $122,595,802
Earnings: $22,011,168
Emp.: 8
Fiscal Year-end: 12/31/23
Property Development
N.A.I.C.S.: 237210
Gyorgy Adamosi (Pres)

APPIA RARE EARTHS & URANIUM CORP.

Suite 500-2 Toronto St, Toronto, M5C 2B6, ON, Canada
Tel.: (416) 546-2707   Ca
Web Site: https://www.appiareu.com
Year Founded: 2007
API—(CNSX)
Rev.: $94,704
Assets: $21,060,168
Liabilities: $2,358,979
Net Worth: $18,701,189
Earnings: ($1,619,916)
Emp.: 5
Fiscal Year-end: 09/30/23
Uranium Mining
N.A.I.C.S.: 212290
Anastasios Drivas (Pres & CEO)

APPIAN CAPITAL ADVISORY LLP

33 Saint James's Street 5th Floor, London, SW1A 1HD, United Kingdom
Tel.: (44) 207 004 0952   UK
Web Site:
  http://www.appiancapital.com
Year Founded: 2011
Emp.: 12
Private Equity Investment Advisory & Portfolio Management Services
N.A.I.C.S.: 523940
Michael W. Scherb (Founder & CEO)

APPIER GROUP, INC.

40F 2-5-1 Atago Mori Tower Atago Green Hills, Minato-ku, Tokyo, 105-6240, Japan
Tel.: (81) 364356617
Web Site: https://www.appier.com
Year Founded: 2012
4180—(TKS)
Rev.: $187,303,620
Assets: $268,370,680
Liabilities: $62,115,490
Net Worth: $206,255,190
Earnings: $7,104,180
Emp.: 574
Fiscal Year-end: 12/31/23
Software Development Services
N.A.I.C.S.: 541511
Joe Su (Co-Founder & CTO)

Subsidiaries:

Appier Pte Ltd.   (1)
8 Marina View #13-01A Asia Square Tower 1, Singapore, 018960, Singapore
Tel.: (65) 6320 9760
Web Site: https://www.appier.com
IT Services & IT Consulting
N.A.I.C.S.: 561499

Subsidiary (US):

Woopra Inc.   (2)
1112 Bryant St, San Francisco, CA 94103
Tel.: (415) 618-0622
Web Site: http://www.woopra.com
Web Data Analytical Software
N.A.I.C.S.: 513210
Elie Khoury (Co-Founder & CEO)

APPILI THERAPEUTICS, INC.

21-1344 Summer Street, Halifax, B3H 0A8, NS, Canada
Tel.: (902) 442-4655
Web Site:
  https://www.appilitherapeutics.com
Year Founded: 2015

APLIF—(OTCQB)
Rev.: $271,588
Assets: $2,336,752
Liabilities: $7,854,898
Net Worth: ($5,518,146)
Earnings: ($6,895,288)
Emp.: 8
Fiscal Year-end: 03/31/23
Pharmaceuticals Product Mfr
N.A.I.C.S.: 325412
Don Cilia (Pres & CEO)

APPIRITS, INC.

6-27-8 Jingumae, Shibuya-Ku, Tokyo, 150-0001, Japan
Tel.: (81) 366909870
Web Site: https://www.appirits.com
Year Founded: 2000
4174—(TKS)
Rev.: $59,747,430
Assets: $32,507,650
Liabilities: $15,009,530
Net Worth: $17,498,120
Earnings: $2,736,740
Emp.: 544
Fiscal Year-end: 01/31/24
Software Development Services
N.A.I.C.S.: 541511
Junji Wada (Chm, Pres & CEO)

APPLE FLAVOR & FRAGRANCE GROUP CO., LTD.

No 33 Cao Xin Road, Jiading District, Shanghai, 201809, China
Tel.: (86) 2159940388
Web Site: https://www.cnaff.com
Year Founded: 1995
603020—(SHG)
Rev.: $449,594,707
Assets: $543,412,682
Liabilities: $77,779,452
Net Worth: $465,633,230
Earnings: $15,447,229
Fiscal Year-end: 12/31/22
Chemical Product Mfr & Distr
N.A.I.C.S.: 325998
Wei Zhonghao (Chm & Gen Mgr)

Subsidiaries:

Apple Flavor & Fragrance USA Corp.   (1)
55 Carter Dr Ste 103, Edison, NJ 08817
Tel.: (732) 393-0600
Chemical Product & Preparation Distr
N.A.I.C.S.: 424690

Beijing Apple Kaixin Foods Tech Co., Ltd.   (1)
Room 2006 Anfu Buliding No 1 Nanfang Village Zuoanmen Outer, Fengtai District, Beijing, 100078, China
Tel.: (86) 1067657321
Chemical Product Mfr & Distr
N.A.I.C.S.: 325998

Biou (zhejiang) Food Industry Co., Ltd.   (1)
No 2 Workshop No 56 Zhenyiqun Road Yao Zhuang, Jiashan, 314117, Zhejiang, China
Tel.: (86) 57384772300
Chemical Product Mfr & Distr
N.A.I.C.S.: 325998

Dalian Apple Foods Ingredients Co., Ltd.   (1)
Room 1123 Zhongnan Building A No 18 West Zhonghua Rd, Ganjingzi District, Dalian, 116033, China
Tel.: (86) 41183787638
Chemical Product Mfr & Distr
N.A.I.C.S.: 325998

Guangzhou Apple Foods Tech Co., Ltd.   (1)
Room 8081 8088 Dongpengdebao Business Center No 109 Huanhua Rd, Liwan District, Guangzhou, 510370, China
Tel.: (86) 2084352600
Chemical Product Mfr & Distr
N.A.I.C.S.: 325998

Hangzhou Tianshun Food Co., Ltd.   (1)
Zhejiang Industrial Zone, Hangzhou, 310013, China
Tel.: (86) 57186019332
Chemical Product & Preparation Mfr
N.A.I.C.S.: 325998

Henan HuaLong Aroma Chemicals Co., Ltd.   (1)
Development Zone, Puyang, 457000, Henan, China
Tel.: (86) 3938910886
Chemical Product Mfr & Distr
N.A.I.C.S.: 325998

Kunming Apple Kaixin Foods Ingredients Co., Ltd.   (1)
Room 1503 Building 2 Run Cheng No 1 Street Xinzhong Rd, Xishan District, Kunming, 650228, Yunnan, China
Tel.: (86) 87164586206
Chemical Product Mfr & Distr
N.A.I.C.S.: 325998

PT Apple Flavor & Fragrance Indonesia   (1)
Kawasan Industri Jababeka II Blok II No 11 Kel Pasir Sari, Kec Cikarang Selatan, Bekasi, Indonesia
Tel.: (62) 2189321709
Chemical Product & Preparation Mfr
N.A.I.C.S.: 325998
Alex Yap (VP)

Qingdao Apple Foods Tech Co., Ltd.   (1)
Room 2030-2032 B Building Wanda Plaza No 33 Lianyungang Rd, Shibei District, Qingdao, 266000, China
Tel.: (86) 53255662905
Chemical Product Mfr & Distr
N.A.I.C.S.: 325998

Shanghai Apple Aromatech Flavors Technology Co., Ltd.   (1)
No 33 Cao Xin Road, Shanghai, 201809, China
Tel.: (86) 2159940388
Chemical Product & Preparation Mfr
N.A.I.C.S.: 325998
Fabian Humbert (Mgr-R&D)

Shanghai Apple Aromatic Plantation Co., Ltd.   (1)
No 1277 Baoqian Road, Shanghai, 201808, China
Tel.: (86) 59908736
Chemical Product & Preparation Mfr
N.A.I.C.S.: 325998

Shanghai Apple Botanic-Tech Co., Ltd.   (1)
No 680 Bei He Road, Shanghai, 201807, China
Tel.: (86) 2169021588
Chemical Product & Preparation Mfr
N.A.I.C.S.: 325998

Shanghai Apple Foods Ingredients Co., Ltd.   (1)
Rm1301B No 17 Lane1377 Jiangchang Road, Jingan District, Shanghai, 200072, China
Tel.: (86) 2161079389
Chemical Product Mfr & Distr
N.A.I.C.S.: 325998

Shanghai Apple Foods Tech (Group) Co., Ltd.   (1)
No 733 Gaoping Road Apple Building, Shanghai, 200436, China
Tel.: (86) 2166523100
Chemical Product Mfr & Distr
N.A.I.C.S.: 325998

Shanghai Kaixin Biotech Co., Ltd.   (1)
No 1133 Zhang Heng Road, Shanghai, 201807, China
Tel.: (86) 69021588
Chemical Product Mfr & Distr
N.A.I.C.S.: 325998

Shanghai Mengze Trading Co., Ltd.   (1)
Rm616 No 733 Gao Ping Road, Shanghai, 200436, China
Tel.: (86) 2150496639

Chemical Product Mfr & Distr
N.A.I.C.S.: 325998
Jimi Xu G. Y. (COO)

Shanghai PuYang Biotech Co., Ltd.   (1)
Rm901 No 133 tiantong Road, Hongkou District, Shanghai, China
Tel.: (86) 2162500058
Chemical Product Mfr & Distr
N.A.I.C.S.: 325998

Shanghai Pujia Food Technology Co., Ltd.   (1)
Rm 803 No 99 Lane 777 Guang Zhong W Road, Zha Bei District, Shanghai, China
Tel.: (86) 2126015678
Chemical Product & Preparation Mfr
N.A.I.C.S.: 325998

Sichuan Apple Foods Co., Ltd.   (1)
No 1341 13 Floor Unit 1 7 Floor No 1700 Tianfu North High Tech Zone, Chengdu, 610041, Sichuan, China
Tel.: (86) 2884127892
Chemical Product Mfr & Distr
N.A.I.C.S.: 325998

Tianjin Apple Northern Tech Co., Ltd.   (1)
Room 1112 C Building Haitai Information Plaza No 8 Huatian Street, Huayuan Industiral Zone Gaoxin District, Tianjin, 300384, China
Tel.: (86) 2223708385
Chemical Product Mfr & Distr
N.A.I.C.S.: 325998

Zhengzhou Apple Foods Tech Co., Ltd.   (1)
Room 2713 Building 8 No 68 Courtyard Zhengtong Rd, Erqi District, Zhengzhou, China
Tel.: (86) 37163265663
Chemical Product Mfr & Distr
N.A.I.C.S.: 325998

APPLE GREEN HOLDING, INC.

207 South Tower 5811 Cooney Road, Richmond, V6X 3M1, BC, Canada
Tel.: (604) 332-9800   NV
Web Site:
  https://www.applegreenholding.com
Year Founded: 2010
AGPL—(OTCIQ)
Sales Range: Less than $1 Million
Software Services
N.A.I.C.S.: 541511
Ghee Yaw Loy (CEO)

APPLE INTERNATIONAL CO., LTD.

2-3-3 Hinaga, Yokkaichi, 510-0885, Mie, Japan
Tel.: (81) 593473515
Web Site: https://www.apple-international.com
Year Founded: 1996
2788—(TKS)
Rev.: $219,158,990
Assets: $119,615,390
Liabilities: $56,032,270
Net Worth: $63,583,120
Earnings: $7,139,630
Emp.: 21
Fiscal Year-end: 12/31/23
Automotive Distr
N.A.I.C.S.: 441120
Kazuki Kubo (Chm & CEO)

APPLEGREEN PLC

17 Joyce Way Parkwest Business Park, Dublin, D12 F2V3, Ireland
Tel.: (353) 1 512 4800
Web Site:
  http://www.applegreenstores.com
Year Founded: 1992
Gas Stations & Convenience Stores
N.A.I.C.S.: 424720
Daniel Kitchen (Chm)

Subsidiaries:

Bob Brandi Stations, Inc. (1)
279 Cedarcrest Dr, Lexington, SC 29072
Tel.: (803) 957-7367
Convenience Store & Fuel Station Operator
N.A.I.C.S.: 445131

APPLEONE SERVICES LTD
170 University Ave Ste 401, Toronto, M5H 3B3, ON, Canada
Tel.: (416) 363-1663
Web Site: http://www.appleone.ca
Sales Range: $75-99.9 Million
Emp.: 175
Employment Services
N.A.I.C.S.: 561311
Gary Gregg (Pres & CEO)

APPLICAD PUBLIC COMPANY LIMITED
69 Soi Sukhumvit 68 Sukhumvit Rd, Bangna, Bangkok, 10260, Thailand
Tel.: (66) 27449045   TH
Web Site:
https://www.applicadthai.com
Year Founded: 1994
APP—(THA)
Rev.: $26,450,889
Assets: $23,124,460
Liabilities: $12,707,796
Net Worth: $10,416,664
Earnings: $1,485,796
Emp.: 371
Fiscal Year-end: 12/31/23
Software Development Services
N.A.I.C.S.: 541511
Prapas Tangadulrat (CEO)

Subsidiaries:

Deti Co., Ltd. (1)
324/36 Room No 307-309 3rd Floor
Bangna Residence Building, Sanphawut
Road Bang Na Nuea Sub-district Bang Na
District, Bangkok, 10260, Thailand
Tel.: (66) 2744782728
Web Site: https://www.deti.co.th
Architectural Design Services
N.A.I.C.S.: 541310

PT Indonesia Applicad Co., Ltd. (1)
Kirana Boutique Office Blok F1/5 Jl Raya
Boulevard, kelapa Gading Timur, Jakarta
Utara, 14240, Indonesia
Tel.: (62) 2129365222
Web Site:
https://www.applicadindonesia.com
Software Design Services
N.A.I.C.S.: 541511

Rabbit Prototype Co., Ltd. (1)
326/2 Soi Kusolsilp, Bangna Subdistrict
Bangna District, Bangkok, 10260, Thailand
Tel.: (66) 27449874
Web Site: https://rabbit-service.com
Rapid Prototyping Services
N.A.I.C.S.: 541420

APPLIDE CORPORATION
3-3-1 Higashi-Hie, Hakata-ku, Fukuoka, 812-0007, Japan
Tel.: (81) 92 4817801
Web Site: http://www.applied-net.co.jp
Year Founded: 1982
Rev.: $273,477,360
Assets: $133,350,960
Liabilities: $89,093,040
Net Worth: $44,257,920
Earnings: $7,370,400
Fiscal Year-end: 03/31/18
Computer Mfr & Distr
N.A.I.C.S.: 334111

APPLIED CO., LTD.
3-3-1 Higashihie, Hakata-Ku, Fukuoka, 812-0007, Japan
Tel.: (81) 120313767
Web Site: https://www.applied-g.jp
Year Founded: 1977

3020—(TKS)
Rev.: $283,033,590
Assets: $119,442,700
Liabilities: $50,592,940
Net Worth: $68,849,760
Earnings: $7,998,100
Emp.: 425
Fiscal Year-end: 03/31/24
Computer Peripheral Equipment Mfr & Distr
N.A.I.C.S.: 334118
Yoshiharu Oka (Founder, Chm, Pres & CEO)

APPLIED DB PUBLIC COMPANY LIMITED
252 Moo 4 Bangpoo Industrial Estate
Soi 3C Sukhumvit Road, Prakasa
Muang Samutprakarn, Samut Prakan, 10280, Thailand
Tel.: (66) 27094040
Web Site: https://www.adb.co.th
Year Founded: 2005
ADB—(THA)
Rev.: $47,873,232
Assets: $41,180,828
Liabilities: $23,648,088
Net Worth: $17,532,740
Earnings: ($1,363,452)
Emp.: 256
Fiscal Year-end: 12/31/23
Adhesive & Plastic Compound Mfr
N.A.I.C.S.: 325211
Wang Wanapaison (Chm & CEO)

APPLIED DEVELOPMENT HOLDINGS LIMITED
Suite 803 8th Floor Harcourt House
39 Gloucester Road, Wanchai, China
(Hong Kong)
Tel.: (852) 37039680
Web Site: http://www.applieddev.com
0519—(HKG)
Rev.: $1,435,676
Assets: $185,261,584
Liabilities: $72,663,721
Net Worth: $112,597,863
Earnings: ($21,007,875)
Emp.: 38
Fiscal Year-end: 06/30/22
Resort & Property Development Services
N.A.I.C.S.: 721110
Zhanming Wu (Chm & CEO-Acting)

Subsidiaries:

Applied Investment (Asia)
Limited (1)
Rm 3402-3 34 F China Merchants Tower
Shun Tak Ctr 168-200 Connaught Rd,
Sheung Wan, China (Hong Kong)
Tel.: (852) 25538267
Investment Holding Services
N.A.I.C.S.: 523999

Applied Toys Limited (1)
Rm 4103-4105 Far E Fin Ctr 16 Harcourt
Rd, Admiralty, Central, China (Hong Kong)
Tel.: (852) 25538267
Investment Management Service
N.A.I.C.S.: 523940

APPLIED ENGINEERING PTE. LTD.
46 Tuas Road, Singapore, 638499, Singapore
Tel.: (65) 6862 1726   SG
Web Site:
http://www.appliedengineering.com.sg
Year Founded: 1969
Sales Range: $1-9.9 Million
Processing Equipment Designer, Fabricator & Distr
N.A.I.C.S.: 332999
Chin Nam Chua (Owner & Mng Dir)

APPLIED GRAPHENE MATERIALS PLC

The Wilton Centre, Redcar, TS10
4RF, Cleveland, United Kingdom
Tel.: (44) 1642438214
Web Site:
https://www.appliedgraphene.com
Year Founded: 2010
AGM—(OTCIQ)
Rev.: $167,000
Assets: $11,937,074
Liabilities: $1,489,419
Net Worth: $10,447,655
Earnings: ($4,309,403)
Emp.: 30
Fiscal Year-end: 07/31/21
Carbon & Graphite Product Manufacturing
N.A.I.C.S.: 335991
Bryan Dobson (Chm)

APPLIED TECHNOLOGIES INTERNET SAS
85 avenue President JF Kennedy, 8
Impasse Rudolph Diesel, 33700,
Merignac, France
Tel.: (33) 156541430
Web Site: http://www.atinternet.com
Year Founded: 1996
Sales Range: $10-24.9 Million
Emp.: 130
Web Analytics Software Development Services
N.A.I.C.S.: 513210
Alain Llorens (Founder & Pres)

Subsidiaries:

AT Internet Brazil (1)
Funchal 411, Itaim Bibi, Sao Paulo, 04551-060, Brazil
Tel.: (55) 11 3192 3991
Web Site: http://www.atinternet.com
Emp.: 6
Web Analytics Software
N.A.I.C.S.: 513210
Edward Hieux (Mgr)

AT Internet GmbH (1)
Leonrodstrasse 52-58, 80636, Munich, Germany
Tel.: (49) 8923028421
Web Site: http://www.atinternet.com
Emp.: 10
Web Analytics Software
N.A.I.C.S.: 513210
Mathieu Llores (CEO)

AT Internet Inc. (1)
33 rue Prince, Montreal, H3C 2M7, QC, Canada
Tel.: (514) 658-3571
Web Analytics Software
N.A.I.C.S.: 513210

AT Internet Ltd (1)
Gilmoora House 57-61 Mortimer Street,
London, W1W 8HS, United Kingdom
Tel.: (44) 20 3178 5356
Web Analytics Software
N.A.I.C.S.: 513210

AT Internet Pte. Ltd (1)
75 High Street, Singapore, 179435, Singapore
Tel.: (65) 6295 6053
Web Site: http://www.atinternet.com
Web Analytics Software
N.A.I.C.S.: 513210

AT Internet SL (1)
Avenida de Concha Espina 8 1a izq, 28036, Madrid, Spain
Tel.: (34) 91 1105829
Web Analytics Software
N.A.I.C.S.: 513210

APPLIED TECHNOLOGY CO., LTD.
Umeda Center Building 2-4-12 Nakazakinishi, Kita-ku, Osaka, 530-0015, Japan
Tel.: (81) 663730440
Web Site: https://www.apptec.co.jp
Year Founded: 1984
43560—(TKS)

Sales Range: Less than $1 Million
Computer Aided Design Services
N.A.I.C.S.: 541512
Toshiro Funahashi (Pres & CEO)

APPLITEK NV/SA
Industrial Zone De Prijkels Venecoweg 19, B-9810, Nazareth, Belgium
Tel.: (32) 9 386 34 02
Web Site: http://www.applitek.com
Year Founded: 1985
Sales Range: $10-24.9 Million
Emp.: 40
Industrial Monitoring Equipment Mfr
N.A.I.C.S.: 334513
Jo Laurier (Founder & Chm)

APPLY ADVANCED MOBILE TECHNOLOGIES LTD.
4 HaNehoshet St, Tel Aviv, Israel
Tel.: (972) 73 2015520
Web Site: http://www.applyltd.com
Year Founded: 2013
Rev.: $4,061,743
Assets: $3,256,823
Liabilities: $1,926,343
Net Worth: $1,330,480
Earnings: ($1,526,536)
Emp.: 7
Fiscal Year-end: 12/31/18
Financial Investment Services
N.A.I.C.S.: 523999

APPLY ASA
Moseidsletta 122, 4033, Stavanger, Norway
Tel.: (47) 51639000
Web Site: http://www.apply.no
Year Founded: 1979
Sales Range: $500-549.9 Million
Emp.: 1,200
Oil & Gas Industry Services
N.A.I.C.S.: 213112
Karsten Gudmundset (CEO)

Subsidiaries:

Aluminium Technologies Sdn
Bhd (1)
Unit 9 1st Floor Bangunan Halimatul Sa
adiah, Gadong, BE 3519, Negara, Brunei
Darussalam
Tel.: (673) 2 452416
Fabricated Steel Product Distr
N.A.I.C.S.: 332312

Apply Capnor Poland Sp. z o.o. (1)
Al gen Bora-Komorowskiego 25b, 31-476,
Krakow, Poland
Tel.: (48) 12 395 12 44
Web Site: http://www.applycapnor.pl
Surveying Services
N.A.I.C.S.: 541370
Barbara Gastol (Mgr-Mktg)

Apply Capnor US, Inc. (1)
1120 NASA Pkwy Ste 470, Houston, TX
77058
Tel.: (281) 549-6108
Surveying Services
N.A.I.C.S.: 541370
Charles Huff (Mgr-Ops)

Apply Emtunga AB (1)
Ekvagen 26, PO Box 175, 534 23, Vara,
Sweden
Tel.: (46) 512 103 50
Web Site: http://www.emtunga.com
Fabricated Steel Product Mfr
N.A.I.C.S.: 332312
Anders Palmgren (VP-Engrg, Procurement & IT)

Apply LQ Partner AS (1)
Haugesund Offshore Base, Killingoy, 5501,
Haugesund, Norway
Tel.: (47) 52708700
Web Site: http://www.reanco.no
Sales Range: $25-49.9 Million
Emp.: 15
Offshore Living Quarters Refurbishment
Products & Services

Apply ASA—(Continued)

N.A.I.C.S.: 332311

Apply Leirvik AS (1)
Storhaugvegen 130, Stord, 5416, Norway
Tel.: (47) 53 49 62 00
Web Site: http://www.applyleirvik.no
Sales Range: $100-124.9 Million
Emp.: 350
Offshore Living Quarters Mfr
N.A.I.C.S.: 332311
Leif Stale Lidal (Sr VP-Bus Dev)

Apply Leirvik International Pte Ltd (1)
2 International Business Park 02-25, The Strategy Tower 2, Singapore, 609930, Singapore
Tel.: (65) 6664 8666
Web Site: http://www.applyleirvik-int.com
Engineering Services
N.A.I.C.S.: 541330
Nandkishore Karade (Mgr-Technical)

Apply Rig & Modules AS (1)
Moseidveien 17, 4033, Stavanger, Norway
Tel.: (47) 815 30 600
Web Site: http://www.applyrm.no
Emp.: 200
Engineering Services
N.A.I.C.S.: 541330
Morten Solland (Dir-Divisional)

Apply Sorco AS (1)
Moseidfletta 122, Forus, Stavanger, 4033, Norway
Tel.: (47) 51639000
Web Site: http://www.applysorco.no
Sales Range: $100-124.9 Million
Emp.: 300
Offshore Oil & Gas Facility Engineering Construction & Support Services
N.A.I.C.S.: 541330
Agnar Kongshaug (VP-Ops & Engrg Svcs)

Subsidiary (Non-US):

APPLY Poland Sp. z o.o. (2)
Ul Dekerta 24, 30 703, Krakow, Poland
Tel.: (48) 12 442 09 00
Web Site: http://www.applypoland.com
Emp.: 50
Engineering Services
N.A.I.C.S.: 541330
Magdalena Litwa (Mgr-Admin)

APPOLLO ISPAT COMPLEX LIMITED
407 Tejgaon Industrial Area, Dhaka, 1208, Bangladesh
Tel.: (880) 9137533
Web Site: http://www.appollo-ispat.com
Year Founded: 1995
APOLOISPAT—(DHA)
Sales Range: Less than $1 Million
Steel Products Mfr
N.A.I.C.S.: 331221

APPOSITE CAPITAL LLP
Genesis House 17 Godliman Street, London, EC4V 5BD, United Kingdom
Tel.: (44) 20 3475 1710   UK
Web Site:
    http://www.appositecapital.com
Healthcare-Focused Private Equity Firm
N.A.I.C.S.: 523999
David Porter (Founding Partner)

Subsidiaries:

Summit Medical Group Limited (1)
Industrial Park, Bourton-on-the-Water, GL54 2HQ, Glos, United Kingdom
Tel.: (44) 1451 821 311
Web Site: http://www.summit-medical.co.uk
Medical & Dental Instruments & Supplies Mfr & Whslr
N.A.I.C.S.: 551112
Daniel Bee (CEO)

Subsidiary (Non-US):

ORTHOMED S.A.S (2)
360 avenue Saint Esteve ZAC de St Es-

teve, 06640, Saint-Jeannet, France
Tel.: (33) 4 92 12 33 7
Web Site: http://www.orthomed.fr
Medical Equipment Distr
N.A.I.C.S.: 423450

Subsidiary (Domestic):

Summit Medical Limited (2)
Bourton On The Water Industrial Park, Bourton-on-the-Water, GL54 2HQ, Glos, United Kingdom
Tel.: (44) 1451 821311
Web Site: http://www.summit-medical.co.uk
Surgical Appliance Mfr & Distr
N.A.I.C.S.: 339113

Subsidiary (US):

Westmed Medical Group, P.C. (2)
2700 Westchester Ave, Purchase, NY 10577
Tel.: (914) 681-5282
Web Site: http://www.westmedgroup.com
Health Practitioners
N.A.I.C.S.: 621399
Kristy Chipley (Sr Mgr-HR)

APPOTRONICS CORP., LTD.
20-22F Joint Headquarters Building High-tech Zone, Shenzhen, China
Web Site:
    https://www.appotronics.com
Year Founded: 2006
688007—(SHG)
Rev.: $356,776,702
Assets: $608,402,382
Liabilities: $223,493,171
Net Worth: $384,909,211
Earnings: $16,769,488
Fiscal Year-end: 12/31/22
Projector Equipment Mfr & Distr
N.A.I.C.S.: 333310
Yi Li (Pres)

APPSCATTER GROUP PLC
9 Appold St, London, EC2A 2AP, United Kingdom
Tel.: (44) 2080047212   UK
Web Site: http://www.appscatter.com
Year Founded: 2017
Rev.: $1,207,276
Assets: $18,284,889
Liabilities: $3,044,206
Net Worth: $15,240,683
Earnings: ($13,312,673)
Emp.: 39
Fiscal Year-end: 12/31/18
Software Development Services
N.A.I.C.S.: 541511
Philip Marcella (Founder & CEO)

APPSENSE LTD.
3300 Daresbury Business Park, Daresbury, Warrington, WA4 4BU, United Kingdom
Tel.: (44) 8452232100
Web Site: http://www.appsense.com
Sales Range: $50-74.9 Million
Emp.: 285
User Virtualization Technology & Services
N.A.I.C.S.: 513210
Darron Antill (CEO)

APPULSE CORPORATION
3504-64 Avenue SE, Calgary, T2C 1P4, AB, Canada
Tel.: (403) 236-2883
Web Site:
    https://www.appulsecorp.net
Year Founded: 2001
APL—(TSXV)
Rev.: $53,468
Assets: $6,796,582
Liabilities: $482,727
Net Worth: $6,313,854
Earnings: $1,274,951
Fiscal Year-end: 12/31/23

Industries Equipment Sales & Maintenance
N.A.I.C.S.: 811310
Dennis R. Schmidt (CFO)

Subsidiaries:

Design Machining Unlimited Inc. (1)
3504 - 64 Avenue SE, Calgary, T2C 1P4, AB, Canada
Tel.: (403) 236-4020
Web Site: http://www.designmachining.com
Industrial Equipment Distr
N.A.I.C.S.: 423830

APQ GLOBAL LIMITED
2nd Floor Lefebvre Place Lefebvre Place, PO Box 142, Saint Peter Port, GY12JP, Guernsey
Tel.: (44) 2034789707
Web Site: https://www.apqglobal.com
APQ—(TISE)
Rev.: $7,198,826
Assets: $41,914,424
Liabilities: $34,678,902
Net Worth: $7,235,522
Earnings: ($16,364,752)
Fiscal Year-end: 12/31/22
Diversified Financial Services
N.A.I.C.S.: 523999
Philip Soulsby (Fin Dir)

Subsidiaries:

Delphos International, Ltd. (1)
2121 K St NW Ste 1020, Washington, DC 20037
Tel.: (202) 337-6300
Web Site:
    http://www.delphosinternational.com
Rev.: $1,200,000
Emp.: 15
Administrative Management & General Management Consulting Services
N.A.I.C.S.: 541611
William A. Delphos (Partner)

New Markets Media & Intelligence Ltd. (1)
22a St James s Square, London, SW1Y 4JH, United Kingdom
Tel.: (44) 2034789710
Web Site: https://www.newmarkets.media
Media Broadcasting Services
N.A.I.C.S.: 516120

Parish Group Limited (1)
Suite 2 Block C Hirzel Court, PO Box 142, Saint Peter Port, Guernsey
Tel.: (44) 1481729002
Web Site: https://parish-group.com
Accounting Services
N.A.I.C.S.: 525920

APRENDERE SKOLOR AB
Triewaldsgrand 2 2 tr, 111 29, Stockholm, Sweden
Tel.: (46) 840028900
Web Site:
    https://www.aprendereskolor.se
Year Founded: 1992
APRNDR—(NASDAQ)
Emp.: 400
Educational Support Services
N.A.I.C.S.: 611310

APROGEN BIOLOGICS, INC.
545 Dunchon-daero Jungwon-gu, Seongnam, Gyeonggi-do, Korea (South)
Tel.: (82) 3180220537
Web Site: http://www.en.aprogen-pharm.com
Year Founded: 1960
003060—(KRS)
Rev.: $51,500,384
Assets: $540,470,929
Liabilities: $137,246,457
Net Worth: $403,224,473
Earnings: $10,760,342
Emp.: 427
Fiscal Year-end: 12/31/22
Pharmaceutical Product Mfr & Whslr

N.A.I.C.S.: 325412
Jeong Chul Kim (Pres & CEO)

APROGEN HEALTHCARE & GAMES INC.
545 Dunchon-daero, Jungwon-gu, Seongnam, Gyeonggi-do, Korea (South)
Tel.: (82) 3180220513
Web Site: http://www.aprogen-hng.com
Year Founded: 2000
109960—(KRS)
Rev.: $7,361,662
Assets: $163,672,375
Liabilities: $10,704,098
Net Worth: $152,968,277
Earnings: ($4,300,229)
Emp.: 18
Fiscal Year-end: 12/31/22
Biologics & Pharmaceutical Mfr
N.A.I.C.S.: 325412
Jae Seop Kim (CEO)

APROGEN KIC INC.
B1 Floor 545 Dunchon-daero Jungwon-gu, Seongnam, Gyeonggi-do, Korea (South)
Tel.: (82) 317823433
Web Site: http://www.aprogen-kic.com
Year Founded: 1971
007460—(KRS)
Rev.: $60,093,919
Assets: $460,087,467
Liabilities: $106,498,644
Net Worth: $353,588,823
Earnings: ($75,669,698)
Emp.: 353
Fiscal Year-end: 12/31/22
Plant Equipment Mfr & Maintenance
N.A.I.C.S.: 333994

APS ENERGIA SA
ul Struzanska 14 05126, Stanislawow Pierwszy, 05-126, Warsaw, Poland
Tel.: (48) 227620000
Web Site: https://www.apsenergia.pl
APE—(WAR)
Rev.: $34,430,554
Assets: $24,918,784
Liabilities: $12,118,497
Net Worth: $12,800,288
Earnings: $115,875
Fiscal Year-end: 12/31/22
Power Supply Equipment Mfr
N.A.I.C.S.: 335999
Piotr Szewczyk (Chm-Mgmt Bd)

Subsidiaries:

APS Energia Caucasus Ltd. (1)
3/5 Adil Iskenderov Str 2, AZ1000, Baku, Azerbaijan
Tel.: (994) 124373040
Power Supply Equipment Mfr
N.A.I.C.S.: 335999

APS Energia Czech s.r.o. (1)
Kubanske namesti 1391/11, 100 00, Prague, 10, Czech Republic
Tel.: (420) 326210761
Power Supply Equipment Mfr
N.A.I.C.S.: 335999

APS Energia Turk Elektrik Sanayi ve Ticaret Ltd. (1)
Armada Is Merkezi Bestepe Mah Dumlupinar Blv A/22 Blok No 6 Kat 14, No 1429 Yenimahalle, 06560, Ankara, Turkiye
Tel.: (90) 3122956370
Power Supply Equipment Mfr
N.A.I.C.S.: 335999

ENAP SA (1)
Wilczkowice Gorne 41, 26-900, Kozienice, Poland
Tel.: (48) 3320684
Web Site: https://enap.pl
Automation Cabinet Services
N.A.I.C.S.: 238210

OOO APS Energia RUS (1)
st Blagodatskaya building 76 D, 620087,
Yekaterinburg, Russia
Tel.: (7) 3433449990
Web Site: http://www.apsenergia.ru
Power Supply Equipment Mfr
N.A.I.C.S.: 335999

TOO APS Energia Kazakhstan (1)
Nursultan Nazarbayev Avenue House
117/62 Office 3, 050000, Almaty, Kazakh-
stan
Tel.: (7) 7272722278
Power Supply Equipment Mfr
N.A.I.C.S.: 335999

APS HOLDINGS CORPORA-
TION
23-12 Dongtansandan 9-gil, Dongtan-
myeon, Hwaseong, 445-811,
Gyeonggi-do, Korea (South)
Tel.: (82) 317761800
Web Site: https://apsinc.co.kr
Year Founded: 1994
054620—(KRS)
Rev.: $32,249,328
Assets: $290,433,703
Liabilities: $122,474,054
Net Worth: $167,959,648
Earnings: $5,050,122
Emp.: 80
Fiscal Year-end: 12/31/22
Semiconductor Equipment Mfr
N.A.I.C.S.: 333242
Young-Joo Kim *(CEO)*

Subsidiaries:

APS China Corporation (1)
Rm305 Ouyin Center Bld 1369 Wuzhong
Road, Minhang District, Shanghai, China
Tel.: (86) 2154322613
Semiconductor Equipment Mfr & Distr
N.A.I.C.S.: 334413

APS Vietanm Co. Ltd. (1)
Lot No 6 N2 Nguyen Cao Street, Vo Cuong
ward, Bac Ninh, Vietnam
Tel.: (84) 2416504703
Semiconductor Equipment Mfr & Distr
N.A.I.C.S.: 334413

APSE CAPITAL LTD.
21 Gloucester Place, London, W1U
8HR, United Kingdom
Tel.: (44) 20 7292 9333   UK
Web Site: http://apsecapital.com
Investment Services
N.A.I.C.S.: 523999
Tim Green *(Co-Founder & Mng Part-
ner)*

Subsidiaries:

Terraquest Solutions Limited (1)
Quayside Tower 252-260 Broad Street, Bir-
mingham, B1 2HF, United Kingdom
Tel.: (44) 1212341300
Web Site: http://www.terraquest.co.uk
Land Referencing Services
N.A.I.C.S.: 531190
Geoff Keal *(Mng Dir)*

APT MEDICAL, INC.
Room 601 Building B Tongfang Infor-
mation Port No 11 Langshan Road,
Nanshan, Shenzhen, 518057, China
Tel.: (86) 75583591013
Web Site: https://www.aptmed.com
Year Founded: 2002
688617—(SHG)
Rev.: $170,728,927
Assets: $312,527,353
Liabilities: $61,061,757
Net Worth: $251,465,596
Earnings: $50,265,966
Fiscal Year-end: 12/31/22
Medical Product Mfr & Distr
N.A.I.C.S.: 339112
Cheng Zhenghui *(Pres)*

Subsidiaries:

Hunan APT Medical Inc. (1)
No 009 Xiangxiang Road Xiangxiang Eco-
nomic Development Zone, Xiangxi, 411400,
Hunan, China
Tel.: (86) 73156841398
Medical Equipment Mfr & Distr
N.A.I.C.S.: 339112

P.T. APT Medical Indonesia (1)
APL Tower Lantai 17 Unit T8 Central Park
Jl Letjen S Parman, Tanjung Duren Grogol
Petamburan, Jakarta Barat, 11470, Indone-
sia
Tel.: (62) 2138789011
Vascular Intervention Medical Device Mfr
N.A.I.C.S.: 339112

**Shanghai Hongtong Industrial Co.,
Ltd.** (1)
West area 19th floor building 20 No 487
Tianlin Road, Xuhui District, Shanghai,
China
Tel.: (86) 2164954001
Medical Equipment Mfr & Distr
N.A.I.C.S.: 339112

APT PACKAGING LTD.
J-18 MIDC Chikalthana, Aurangabad,
431 210, Maharashtra, India
Tel.: (91) 2402485895
Web Site: http://www.aptpackaging.in
Plastic Tank Mfr
N.A.I.C.S.: 326122
Arvind Machhar *(Chm & Mng Dir)*

APT RESOURCES & SER-
VICES SRL
82/B2 Clucerului, Sect 1, 011368,
Bucharest, Romania
Tel.: (40) 212221303
Web Site: http://www.apt.ro
Year Founded: 1994
Emp.: 32
Public Relations Agency
N.A.I.C.S.: 541820
Andrew Littauer *(Pres)*

APT SATELLITE INTERNA-
TIONAL COMPANY LIMITED
22 Dai Kwai St, Tai Po, New Territo-
ries, China (Hong Kong)
Tel.: (852) 26002100
Web Site: http://www.apstar.com
Holding Company
N.A.I.C.S.: 551112
Xiaowu Rui *(Chm)*

Subsidiaries:

APT Satellite Holdings Limited (1)
No 22 Dai Kwai Street Tai Po Industrial Es-
tate, Tai Po, New Territories, China (Hong
Kong)   **(51.83%)**
Tel.: (852) 26002100
Web Site: http://www.apstar.com
Rev.: $114,693,014
Assets: $928,126,021
Liabilities: $161,919,428
Net Worth: $766,206,593
Earnings: $29,853,969
Emp.: 110
Fiscal Year-end: 12/31/2020
Satellite Telecommunication Services
N.A.I.C.S.: 517410
Xun Chen *(Exec VP-Technical Ops & En-
grg)*

APTABIO THERAPEUTICS INC.
13 Heungdeok 1-ro Heungdeok IT
Valley, Giheung-Gu, Yongin, 16954,
Gyeonggi-do, Korea (South)
Tel.: (82) 313653693
Web Site: https://www.aptabio.com
Year Founded: 2009
293780—(KRS)
Rev.: $37,087
Assets: $43,039,233
Liabilities: $2,871,825
Net Worth: $40,167,407
Earnings: ($8,103,153)

Emp.: 30
Fiscal Year-end: 12/31/22
Pharmaceutical Preparation Mfr
N.A.I.C.S.: 325412
Soo Jin Lee *(CEO)*

APTAMER GROUP PLC
Windmill House Innovation Way,
York, YO10 5BR, United Kingdom
Tel.: (44) 1904217404   UK
Web Site:
https://www.aptamergroup.com
Year Founded: 2008
APTA—(AIM)
Rev.: $2,211,563
Assets: $3,475,133
Liabilities: $3,091,391
Net Worth: $383,741
Earnings: ($9,891,442)
Emp.: 46
Fiscal Year-end: 06/30/23
Biotechnology Research & Develop-
ment Services
N.A.I.C.S.: 541714

APTAMER SCIENCES INC.
282-ho POSTECH Biotech Center 77
Cheongam-ro, Nam-Gu, Pohang,
37673, Gyeongsangbuk-do, Korea
(South)
Tel.: (82) 317860317
Web Site: https://www.aptsci.com
Year Founded: 2011
291650—(KRS)
Rev.: $274,780
Assets: $35,009,981
Liabilities: $12,596,065
Net Worth: $22,413,916
Earnings: ($5,457,646)
Emp.: 36
Fiscal Year-end: 12/31/22
Biotechnology Research & Develop-
ment Services
N.A.I.C.S.: 541714
Sung Key Jang *(Chief Strategy Offi-
cer)*

APTECH LIMITED
Aptech House A-65 MIDC Marol,
Andheri E, Mumbai, 400 093, Maha-
rashtra, India
Tel.: (91) 2268282300
Web Site: https://www.aptech-
worldwide.com
532475—(BOM)
Rev.: $56,361,873
Assets: $57,714,394
Liabilities: $26,978,407
Net Worth: $30,735,987
Earnings: $8,115,473
Emp.: 505
Fiscal Year-end: 03/31/23
Education Services
N.A.I.C.S.: 611420
Ketan H. Shah *(Officer-Compliance &
Sec)*

Subsidiaries:

AGLSM Sdn. Bhd. (1)
E-8-6 Suite 11 11 Megan Avenue 1 189
Jalan Tun Razak, 50400, Kuala Lumpur,
Malaysia
Tel.: (60) 374935909
Sales Range: $10-24.9 Million
Emp.: 5
Information Technology Training & Educa-
tional Services
N.A.I.C.S.: 611420

**Avalon Aviation Academy Private
Limited** (1)
Aptech House A-65 M I D C Marol, Andheri
E, Mumbai, 400093, Maharashtra, India
Tel.: (91) 2228272300
Web Site: http://www.avalonacademy.in
Emp.: 300
Aviation & Hospitality Training School Man-
agement Services
N.A.I.C.S.: 611310

Ravi Dighe *(VP)*

**First English Education Institutes
Limited** (1)
No 79 100 Feet Rd Banashankari 3rd
Stage, Bengaluru, 560 065, Karnataka,
India
Tel.: (91) 80 6530 4231
Sales Range: $10-24.9 Million
Emp.: 7
English Training & Exam Preparation Ser-
vices
N.A.I.C.S.: 611630

APTITUDE SOFTWARE
GROUP PLC
138 Cheapside 8th Floor, London,
EC2V 6BJ, United Kingdom
Tel.: (44) 20336873200   UK
Web Site:
https://www.aptitudesoftware.com
Year Founded: 1974
APTD—(LSE)
Rev.: $94,275,435
Assets: $150,735,925
Liabilities: $74,601,111
Net Worth: $76,134,814
Earnings: $5,207,018
Emp.: 482
Fiscal Year-end: 12/31/23
Holding Company; Business Process
Management, Billing & Financial Sys-
tems Software Products & Services
N.A.I.C.S.: 551112
Philip B. Wood *(Deputy CEO & CFO)*

Subsidiaries:

**Aptitude Software (Canada)
Limited** (1)
2 Bloor Street West Suite 700, Toronto,
M4W 3R1, ON, Canada
Tel.: (416) 642-6508
Financial Management Services
N.A.I.C.S.: 541611

MPP Global Solutions Limited (1)
401 Faraday Street Birchwood Park, War-
rington, WA3 6GA, United Kingdom
Tel.: (44) 8448731418
Software Development Services
N.A.I.C.S.: 541511

Microgen (South Africa) Limited (1)
5th Fl Sunclare Bldg 21 Dreyer St, Clare-
mont, Cape Town, 7708, Western Cape,
South Africa
Tel.: (27) 216572840
Web Site: http://www.microgen.com
Sales Range: $25-49.9 Million
Emp.: 8
Software Development Consulting Services
N.A.I.C.S.: 541618

Microgen Aptitude Limited (1)
Fleet House 3 Fleetwood Park, Barley Way,
Fleet, GU51 2QJ, Hants, United
Kingdom   **(100%)**
Tel.: (44) 1252772300
Sales Range: $10-24.9 Million
Business Process Management Software
Publisher
N.A.I.C.S.: 513210

**Microgen Banking Systems
Limited** (1)
Unit 1 Fleetwood Pk Barley Way, Fleet,
GU51 2QJ, Hampshire, United Kingdom
Tel.: (44) 1252772300
Sales Range: $25-49.9 Million
Banking Software Development Services
N.A.I.C.S.: 541511

Microgen Limited (1)
Fleet House 3 Fleetwood Park, Barley Way,
Fleet, GU51 2QJ, Hampshire, United King-
dom
Tel.: (44) 1252772300
Web Site: http://www.microgen.com
Sales Range: $25-49.9 Million
Emp.: 250
Financial Systems Software Publisher &
Services
N.A.I.C.S.: 513210

**Microgen Management Services
Limited** (1)

Aptitude Software Group Plc—(Continued)

Fleet House 3 Fleetwood Business Park
Barley Way, Fleet, GU51 2QJ, Hampshire,
United Kingdom
Tel.: (44) 1252772300
Staff Recruitment Services
N.A.I.C.S.: 561311

Microgen Poland Sp. Z.o.o. **(1)**
Ul Muchoborska 0, 54-424, Wroclaw, Lower
Silesian, Poland
Tel.: (48) 713583010
Sales Range: $25-49.9 Million
Emp.: 82
Business Management Software Development Services
N.A.I.C.S.: 541511
Neil Thomson (Gen Mgr)

Microgen Solutions Inc **(1)**
470 Atlantic Ave 4th Fl, Boston, MA 02210
Tel.: (617) 273-8289
Web Site: http://www.microgen.com
Sales Range: $25-49.9 Million
Emp.: 8
Business Management Consulting Services
N.A.I.C.S.: 541611

Microgen UK Limited **(1)**
Fleet House 3 Fleetwood Park, Barley Way,
Fleet, GU51 2QJ, Hants, United
Kingdom **(100%)**
Tel.: (44) 1252772300
Web Site: http://www.microgen.com
Sales Range: $1-9.9 Million
Emp.: 60
Billing & Document Management Services
N.A.I.C.S.: 561499

APTIV PLC

5 Hanover Quay Grand Canal Dock,
Dublin, D02 VY79, Ireland
Tel.: (353) 12597013   JE
Web Site: https://www.aptiv.com
Year Founded: 2011
APTV—(NYSE)
Rev.: $20,051,000,000
Assets: $24,427,000,000
Liabilities: $12,682,000,000
Net Worth: $11,745,000,000
Earnings: $2,938,000,000
Emp.: 154,000
Fiscal Year-end: 12/31/23
Holding Company
N.A.I.C.S.: 551112
Kevin P. Clark (Chm, Pres & CEO)

Subsidiaries:

Auburn Enterprises LLC **(1)**
57 Labrie Ln, Greene, ME 04236
Tel.: (207) 946-3420
Management Consulting Services
N.A.I.C.S.: 541618

Control-Tec, LLC **(1)**
999 Republic Dr, Allen Park, MI 48101
Tel.: (313) 228-0401
Web Site: http://www.control-tec.com
Automobile Parts Mfr
N.A.I.C.S.: 336390
Dave Ploucha (Founder & Pres)

Delphi Automotive LLP **(1)**
Courtney Road, Gillingham, ME8 ORU,
United Kingdom
Tel.: (44) 1634234422
Automobile Parts Mfr
N.A.I.C.S.: 336390

Subsidiary (Non-US):

Aptiv Safety & Mobility Services Singapore Pte. Ltd **(2)**
501 Ang Mo Kio Industrial Park I, Singapore, 569621, Singapore
Tel.: (65) 64538544
Automobile Parts Mfr
N.A.I.C.S.: 336390

Subsidiary (Domestic):

BorgWarner Automotive Systems Singapore Investments Pte. Ltd. **(3)**
501 Ang Mo Kio Industrial Park 1 Ang Mo
Kio, Singapore, 569621; Singapore
Tel.: (65) 64538544

Motor Vehicle Electrical & Electronic Equipment Mfr
N.A.I.C.S.: 336320

Subsidiary (Non-US):

Delphi Automotive Systems (Thailand) Ltd. **(3)**
64/26 Moo 4 Eastern Seaboard Industrial
Estate, Pluakdaeng, Rayong, 21140, Thailand
Tel.: (66) 3865 6100
Automobile Parts Mfr
N.A.I.C.S.: 336390

Subsidiary (US):

Delphi China LLC **(3)**
5725 Delphi Dr, Troy, MI 48098-2815
Tel.: (248) 813-2000
Web Site: http://www.delphi.com
Motor Vehicle Parts Mfr
N.A.I.C.S.: 336390

Subsidiary (Non-US):

Delphi Electrical Centers (Shanghai)
Co., Ltd. **(4)**
No 88 Yuan Guo Road Anting, Jiading,
Shanghai, 201814, China
Tel.: (86) 2159562200
Electronic Components Mfr
N.A.I.C.S.: 334419

Delphi Electronics (Suzhou) Co.
Ltd. **(4)**
No 123 Changyang Street Industrial Park
Zone, Suzhou, 215126, Jiangsu, China
Tel.: (86) 512 6283 1888
Motor Vehicle Electrical Equipment Mfr
N.A.I.C.S.: 336320

Delphi Packard Tanger SA **(4)**
Ilot 53 Lot 1 Tfz, Tangiers, 90000, Morocco
Tel.: (212) 539329801
Motor Vehicle Parts & Accessories Supplier
& Mfr
N.A.I.C.S.: 336390

Subsidiary (Non-US):

Centro Tecnico Herramental, S.A. de
C.V. **(2)**
Km 8 54 Carr Saltillo - Piedras Negras No
8540, Saltillo, 25900, Mexico
Tel.: (52) 8444115500
Motor Vehicle Parts Mfr
N.A.I.C.S.: 336390

Subsidiary (US):

DPH Holdings Corporation **(2)**
5725 Delphi Dr, Troy, MI 48098-2815
Tel.: (248) 813-2000
Web Site: http://www.delphi.com
Sales Range: $5-14.9 Billion
Emp.: 12,700
Automotive Parts Distr & Mfr
N.A.I.C.S.: 336211
Sidney Johnson (Sr VP-Global Supply
Mgmt)

Subsidiary (Domestic):

Antaya Technologies Corporation **(3)**
72 Fenner St, Cranston, RI 02910
Tel.: (401) 941-7050
Web Site: http://www.antaya.com
Automotive Electrical Parts Mfr & Distr
N.A.I.C.S.: 336320

Subsidiary (Non-US):

Antaya Technologies Corporation
(Zhuhai) Ltd. **(4)**
9 Pingdong Sixth Rd, Nanping Hi-Tech Industrial Park, Zhuhai, Guangdong, China
Tel.: (86) 7568919920
Motor Vehicle Parts Mfr
N.A.I.C.S.: 336390
Ning Wang (Office Mgr)

Division (Domestic):

Delphi Electronics & Safety **(3)**
2151 E Lincoln Rd, Kokomo, IN
46902-9005 **(100%)**
Tel.: (765) 451-5011
Web Site: http://www.delphi.com
Sales Range: $1-4.9 Billion
Emp.: 7,000

Automotive Control Electronics & Hybrid
Circuits Mfr
N.A.I.C.S.: 336320
David Paja (Pres)

Subsidiary (Non-US):

Delphi Delco Electronics Operations
Delnosa, S.A. de C.V. **(4)**
Carretera A Matamoros Km 109, 88500,
Reynosa, Mexico
Tel.: (52) 8999215000
Sales Range: $150-199.9 Million
Emp.: 700
Electronic Air Controls & Engine Control
Computer Assembler
N.A.I.C.S.: 334519

Delphi Delco Electronics de Mexico
S.A. de C.V. **(4)**
Avenida Uniones Y Avenida Michigan,
Parke Industrial Del Norte, 87310, Matamoros, Tamaulipas, Mexico **(100%)**
Tel.: (52) 8688111600
Sales Range: $100-124.9 Million
Assembly of Radio Circuit Boards & Automobile Radios
N.A.I.C.S.: 334310

Division (Domestic):

Delphi Energy Chassis Systems **(3)**
5725 Delphi Dr, Troy, MI 48098-2815
Tel.: (765) 451-5011
Web Site: http://www.delphi.com
Sales Range: $5-14.9 Billion
Mfr of Automotive Parts
N.A.I.C.S.: 423120

Subsidiary (Non-US):

Delphi Energy Chassis Systems, Asia
Headquarters **(4)**
1 1 110 Tsutsujigaoka, Akishima, 196-8668,
Tokyo, Japan **(100%)**
Tel.: (81) 425497200
Sales Range: $150-199.9 Million
N.A.I.C.S.: 441330
K. Yoshida (Mgr-Mktg)

Delphi Energy Chassis Systems, European Regional Headquarters **(4)**
64 Ave de la Plaine de France, 93290,
Charles de Gaulle, Cedex, France
Tel.: (33) 149904990
Sales Range: $150-199.9 Million
N.A.I.C.S.: 441330

Delphi Energy Chassis Systems,
South American Regional
Headquarters **(4)**
Avenida Goias 1860, Sao Caetano do Sul,
09550 050, SP, Brazil **(100%)**
Tel.: (55) 1142349500
Sales Range: $125-149.9 Million
Emp.: 300
N.A.I.C.S.: 441330

Subsidiary (Domestic):

Delphi Medical Systems
Corporation **(3)**
5725 Delphi Dr, Troy, MI 48098
Tel.: (888) 526-1426
Web Site: http://www.delphimedical.com
Sales Range: $100-124.9 Million
Medical Monitoring Device Mfr
N.A.I.C.S.: 334510

Division (Domestic):

Delphi Product & Service
Solutions **(3)**
5820 Delphi Dr, Troy, MI 48098-2819
Tel.: (248) 267-8800
Web Site: http://www.delphi-pss.com
Sales Range: $150-199.9 Million
Aftermarket Automotive Electronics, Replacement Parts & Services
N.A.I.C.S.: 423120

Subsidiary (Domestic):

Monarch Antenna, Inc. **(3)**
3055 Plymouth Rd Ste 200, Ann Arbor, MI
48105
Tel.: (734) 213-4944
Web Site: http://www.monarchantenna.com
Antenna Mfr
N.A.I.C.S.: 334220

Tayfun Oezdemir (Founder, Pres & CTO)

PUREDEPTH, INC. **(3)**
303 Twin Dolphin Dr Ste 600, Redwood
City, CA 94065
Tel.: (649) 524-5211
Web Site: http://www.puredepth.com
Multi-Layer Display Technology & Related
Products Developer, Marketer, Licensor &
Supporter
N.A.I.C.S.: 334419
Darryl S. K. Singh (CEO)

Subsidiary (Non-US):

Delphi **(2)**
64 Ave de la Plaine de France, PO Box
65059, 95972, Charles de Gaulle, Cedex,
France **(100%)**
Tel.: (33) 149904990
Mfr of Brake Systems, Spark Plugs, Fuel
Pumps & Other Automotive Components
N.A.I.C.S.: 336340

Delphi **(2)**
Avenida Goias 1860, Sao Caetano do Sul,
9550050, SP, Brazil **(100%)**
Tel.: (55) 1142349500
Web Site: http://www.delphi.com.br
Batteries, Ignition Coils & Distributors Mfr
N.A.I.C.S.: 336320

Delphi Aftermarket America do
Sul **(2)**
Av Goeas 1860, 09550 050, Sao Caetano
do Sul, SP, Brazil **(50%)**
Tel.: (55) 1142349500
Mfr of Automotive Components
N.A.I.C.S.: 336330

Delphi Alambrados Automotrices,
S.A. de C.V. **(2)**
Av De Las Fabricas No 5838, Nuevo Laredo, 88275, Tamaulipas, Mexico
Tel.: (52) 8677114900
Motor Vehicle Parts Distr
N.A.I.C.S.: 423120

Delphi Automotive Customer Technology Center **(2)**
Avenue de Luxembourg, 4940, Bascharage,
Luxembourg **(100%)**
Tel.: (352) 50181
Web Site: http://www.delphi.com
Automotive Systems Engineering Support
N.A.I.C.S.: 541330

Delphi Automotive Systems - Portugal
S.A. **(2)**
Estrada Paco Thurs Lumiar Polo Tec De
Lisboa Lote 4 Edif Delphi, Lisbon, 1600545,
Portugal
Tel.: (351) 217 10 14 00
Automotive Electrical Equipment Mfr
N.A.I.C.S.: 336320

Delphi Automotive Systems Limited
Sirketi **(2)**
Organize Sanayi Bolgesi 1 Cad No15Â Yukari Dudullu, Yusufpasa Umraniye, Istanbul,
Turkiye
Tel.: (90) 2165283000
Motor Vehicle Electrical & Electronic Equipment Mfr
N.A.I.C.S.: 336320

Delphi Automotive Systems Sweden
AB **(2)**
Gustaf Larsons vag 18, Gothenburg, 41878,
Sweden
Tel.: (46) 31 750 96 00
Emp.: 90
Motor Vehicle Electrical & Electronic Equipment Mfr
N.A.I.C.S.: 336320

Subsidiary (Domestic):

Delphi Automotive Systems UK
Limited **(2)**
Spartan Close, Warwick, CV34 6AG, Warwickshire, United Kingdom
Tel.: (44) 1926472400
Automotive Electric Parts Distr
N.A.I.C.S.: 423690

Subsidiary (Non-US):

Delphi Automotive Systems do Brasil
Ltda. **(2)**

Av Goias 1820/1860 Santa Paula, Sao
Caetano do Sul, 13422-210, Sao Paulo,
Brazil
Tel.: (55) 11 4234 9500
Automotive Parts Mfr & Distr
N.A.I.C.S.: 336390

Delphi Cableados, S.A. de C.V. (2)
Calle Apozol 101 Col Solidaridad, Fresnillo,
Zacatecas, Mexico
Tel.: (52) 493 983 9310
Motor Vehicle Parts Mfr
N.A.I.C.S.: 336390

Delphi Deutschland GmbH (2)
Delphiplatz 1, 42119, Wuppertal, 42119,
North Rhine-Westphal, Germany
Tel.: (49) 2022910
Emp.: 900
Motor Vehicle Electrical & Electronic Equip-
ment Mfr
N.A.I.C.S.: 336320
Thomas Aurich (Head-Corp Comm)

**Delphi Energy & Engine Management
Systems** (2)
Av Goias 1860, Sao Caetano do Sul, Sao
Paulo, 09550-050, Brazil
Tel.: (55) 1142349500
Web Site: http://www.delphi.com
Mfr of Throttle Body Fuel Injection
N.A.I.C.S.: 336310

Delphi Holding GmbH (2)
Industriestrasse 1, Grosspetersdorf, 7503,
Austria
Tel.: (43) 3362 4100
Sales Range: $75-99.9 Million
Emp.: 200
Investment Management Service
N.A.I.C.S.: 523940
Wolfgang Proell (Mgr-HR)

Subsidiary (Non-US):

Delphi Thermal Hungary KFT (3)
Deli Iparterulet Szugyi Ut, 2660, Balassag-
yarmat, Hungary
Tel.: (36) 35 50 21 00
Automotive Heating & Cooling Equipment
Distr
N.A.I.C.S.: 423120

Subsidiary (Non-US):

**Delphi Holdings Luxembourg S.a
r.l.** (2)
1 route de Luxembourg, Bascharage, 4940,
Luxembourg
Tel.: (352) 501810
Web Site: http://www.delphi.com
Emp.: 700
Investment Management Service
N.A.I.C.S.: 551112

Subsidiary (Non-US):

Ondas Media, S.A. (3)
Velazquez 157 - 1a Planta, 28002, Madrid,
Spain
Tel.: (34) 915245725
Web Site: http://www.ondasmedia.com
Communication Service
N.A.I.C.S.: 517810

Subsidiary (Non-US):

Delphi Insurance Limited (2)
4th Floor 25-28 Adelaide Rd, Dublin, 2,
Ireland
Tel.: (353) 16053000
General Insurance Services
N.A.I.C.S.: 524210

**Delphi Italia Automotive Systems
S.r.l.** (2)
Via Nobili Efrem 2, Molinella, 40062, Bolo-
gna, Italy
Tel.: (39) 0516906310
Motor Vehicle Electrical & Electronic Equip-
ment Mfr
N.A.I.C.S.: 336320

**Delphi Packard Austria
Ges.m.b.H.** (2)
Industriestr 1, Grosspetersdorf, 7503, Aus-
tria
Tel.: (43) 336241000
Automotive Wiring Systems Mfr
N.A.I.C.S.: 441330
Wolfgang Baller (Mng Dir)

Delphi Packard Electric Systems (2)
Poligono Ind De Landaben Calle A, Pam-
plona, 31012, Spain (100%)
Tel.: (34) 948179100
Web Site: http://www.delphi.com
Mfr of Automotive Power & Signal Distribu-
tion Systems
N.A.I.C.S.: 336350

Delphi Packard Espana, SL (2)
Calle A Pg Ind Landaben S/N, Pamplona,
31012, Navarre, Spain
Tel.: (34) 948179100
Automobile Component Distr
N.A.I.C.S.: 423120
Javier Carlos Tainta Esquiroz (Mng Dir)

Delphi Poland S.A. (2)
Ul Podgorki Tynieckie 2, Krakow, 30-399,
Poland
Tel.: (48) 12 252 1100
Web Site: http://www.delphikrakow.pl
Automotive Components Mfr
N.A.I.C.S.: 336390

Delphi Rimir S.A. de CV (2)
Ave Michigan Y Ohio S/N 87316, Matam-
oros, Tamaulipas, Mexico (100%)
Tel.: (52) 52503777
Assembly of Plastic Bumpers; Supported by
Fisher Guide Division
N.A.I.C.S.: 326199

**Delphi Sistemas de Energia, S.A. de
C.V.** (2)
Calle Alamedas No 750 Fracc Arboledas,
Torreon, 27077, Coahuila, Mexico
Tel.: (52) 871 747 6000
Motor Vehicle Brake System Mfr
N.A.I.C.S.: 336340

Delphi Slovensko s.r.o. (2)
Cacovska cesta 1447/1, 905 01, Senica,
Slovakia
Tel.: (421) 34 6957 111
Automotive Electronic Component Mfr &
Distr
N.A.I.C.S.: 336320

**Delphi Technical Centre
Luxembourg** (2)
Ave de Luxembourg Bascharage, Luxem-
bourg, 4940, Luxembourg (100%)
Tel.: (352) 50181
Web Site: http://www.delphi.com
Mfr of Electric Fuel Pumps
N.A.I.C.S.: 336320

**Korea Delphi Automotive Systems
Corporation** (2)
580-1 Buk-Ri Nongong-Eup, Dalseong-Gun,
Daegu, 711-712, Korea (South)
Tel.: (82) 53 610 1500
Web Site: http://www.kdac.co.kr
Emp.: 2,500
Automotive Components Mfr
N.A.I.C.S.: 336390
Park Young-Chul (Mgr-Sls Plng)

Subsidiary (Non-US):

Changshu KDAC Co., Ltd. (3)
No 66 Xiangjiang Road Dongnan Develop-
ment Zone, Changshu, 215500, Jiangsu,
China
Tel.: (86) 51252309222
Sales Range: $50-74.9 Million
Emp.: 120
Automotive Brake System Mfr
N.A.I.C.S.: 336340

Subsidiary (Non-US):

**Sistemas Electricos y Conmutadores,
S.A. de C.V.** (2)
Ave Antonio J Bermudez 1230, Ciudad
Juarez, 32470, Chihuahua, Mexico
Tel.: (52) 656 649 2800
Motor Vehicle Parts Mfr
N.A.I.C.S.: 336390

TecAlliance GmbH (2)
Steinheilstrasse 10, 85737, Ismaning, Ger-
many
Tel.: (49) 893212160
Web Site: http://www.teccom.de
Software Development Services
N.A.I.C.S.: 541511

**Delphi Connection Systems Belgium
NV** (1)

Zwartzustersvest 21, 2800, Mechelen, Bel-
gium
Tel.: (32) 15445600
Motor Vehicle Parts Mfr
N.A.I.C.S.: 336390

**Delphi Connection Systems Japan
Ltd.** (1)
31F Shinjukunomura Building 1-26-2, Nishi-
Shinjuku, Shinjuku, 163-0569, Japan
Tel.: (81) 353811840
Web Site: http://www.delphi.jp
Automobile Parts Mfr
N.A.I.C.S.: 336390

**Delphi Connection Systems Mexico
S. de R.L. de C.V.** (1)
Av Valle Del Cedro No 1230, Chihuahua,
Ciudad Juarez, 32574, Mexico
Tel.: (52) 6566925833
Emp.: 300
Motor Vehicle Parts Mfr
N.A.I.C.S.: 336390

**Delphi Connection Systems Nantong
Ltd.** (1)
No 9 Hebin Rd Tongzhou Economic & De-
velopment Zone, Nantong, 226300, Ji-
angsu, China
Tel.: (86) 51385363869
Automobile Parts Mfr
N.A.I.C.S.: 336390

Harwich Holding GmbH (1)
Groser Moorweg 45, 25436, Tornesch, Ger-
many
Tel.: (49) 4122701500
Holding Company
N.A.I.C.S.: 551112

HellermannTyton Group PLC (1)
Griffin House 135 High Street, Crawley,
RH10 1DQ, W Sussex, United Kingdom
Tel.: (44) 1293 537272
Sales Range: $600-649.9 Million
Holding Company; Cable Tie, Fitting & Insu-
lation Products Mfr
N.A.I.C.S.: 551112
Tim Jones (Dir)

Subsidiary (Non-US):

**HellermannTyton (Mexico) S. de R.L.
de C.V.** (2)
Anillo Periferico Sur 7980 Edificio 2-D
Parque Industrial Tecnologico, Santa Maria
Tequepexpan, 45601, Tlaquepaque, Jalisco,
Mexico
Tel.: (52) 33 3133 9880
Web Site: http://www.hellermanntyton.us
Cable Distr
N.A.I.C.S.: 423510

HellermannTyton (Pty.) Ltd. (2)
34 Milky Way Avenue, Linbro Business Park
2065, Rivonia, 2128, Johannesburg, South
Africa
Tel.: (27) 118796680
Web Site: http://www.hellermanntyton.co.za
Cable Accessories Mfr & Electrical Products
Reseller
N.A.I.C.S.: 334290

**HellermannTyton (Wuxi) Electrical
Accessories Co., Ltd.** (2)
No 231 Xing Chuang Ba Lu, Wuxi Singa-
pore Industrial Park, Wuxi, 214028, Ji-
angsu, China
Tel.: (86) 51085282536
Web Site:
http://www.hellermanntyton.com.cn
Cable Products Mfr
N.A.I.C.S.: 332618

HellermannTyton AB (2)
Isafjordsgatan 5, 16407, Jarfalla, Sweden
Tel.: (46) 858089000
Web Site: http://www.hellermanntyton.se
Cable Care Products Mfr
N.A.I.C.S.: 335929
Bjorn Rilegard (CEO)

Branch (Non-US):

HellermannTyton AB Danmark (3)
Industrivej 44A, 4000, Roskilde, Denmark
Tel.: (45) 70237120
Web Site: http://www.hellermanntyton.dk
Cable Products Mfr
N.A.I.C.S.: 332618

Subsidiary (Non-US):

HellermannTyton AS (2)
Stromsveien 177 Alnabru, N 0614, Oslo,
Norway
Tel.: (47) 23174700
Web Site: http://www.hellermanntyton.no
Cable Products Mfr
N.A.I.C.S.: 335929
Knut Bodding (Gen Mgr)

**HellermannTyton Australia Pty
Ltd** (2)
U 2 12-14 Mangrove Lane, Taren Point,
2229, NSW, Australia
Tel.: (61) 295252133
Electric Equipment Mfr
N.A.I.C.S.: 336320

HellermannTyton B.V. (2)
Vanadiumweg 11-C, 3812 PX, Amersfoort,
Netherlands
Tel.: (31) 334600690
Web Site: http://www.hellermanntyton.nl
Cable Products Distr
N.A.I.C.S.: 335929
Rik Vroege (Mng Dir-Mktg & Ops)

HellermannTyton Co., Ltd. (2)
Sasazuka Sun Building 6 F 1-48-3 S, To-
kyo, 151-0073, Yubinbango, Japan (49%)
Tel.: (81) 3 5790 3113
Web Site: http://www.hellermanntyton.co.jp
Emp.: 291
Electronic & Information Communication
Wiring Mfr
N.A.I.C.S.: 335931
Toshiki Kimura (Sr Mng Dir)

Subsidiary (US):

HellermannTyton Corporation (2)
7930 N Faulkner Rd, Milwaukee, WI 53224-
3423
Tel.: (414) 355-1130
Web Site: http://www.hellermanntyton.us
Cable Care Products Mfr
N.A.I.C.S.: 335929
Jim Campion (Mng Dir)

Subsidiary (Domestic):

HellermannTyton Data Ltd. (2)
Cornwell Business Park Salthouse Road,
Brackmills, NN4 7EX, Northampton, United
Kingdom
Tel.: (44) 1604 707 420
Web Site: http://www.htdata.co.uk
Network Infrastructure Designer, Developer
& Mfr
N.A.I.C.S.: 335929
Matthew Hunter (Gen Mgr)

Subsidiary (Non-US):

HellermannTyton Espana SL (2)
Avda de la Industria 37 2 2, Alcobendas,
28108, Madrid, Spain
Tel.: (34) 916612835
Web Site: http://www.hellermanntyton.es
Automobile Parts Mfr
N.A.I.C.S.: 336390

HellermannTyton GmbH (2)
Grosser Moorweg 45, 25436, Tornesch,
Germany
Tel.: (49) 41227010
Web Site: http://www.hellermanntyton.de
Cable Care Products Mfr
N.A.I.C.S.: 335929
Britta Etzen (Controller)

HellermannTyton GmbH - Austria (2)
Rennbahnweg 65, 1220, Vienna, Austria
Tel.: (43) 125999550
Web Site: http://www.hellermanntyton.at
Cable Products Mfr
N.A.I.C.S.: 332618
Hans-Christian Niemann (Mng Dir)

Subsidiary (Domestic):

**HellermannTyton Ltd. -
Manchester** (2)
Sharston Green Bus Park 1 Robeson Way,
Altrincham Rd Wythenshawe, Manchester,
M22 4TY, United Kingdom
Tel.: (44) 161 945 4181
Web Site: http://www.hellermanntyton.co.uk
Cable Mfr & Communications Products
Supplier

Aptiv PLC—(Continued)

N.A.I.C.S.: 334290

Plant (Domestic):

HellermannTyton Ltd. - Plymouth (3)
William Prance Rd, Plymouth, PL6 5WR,
United Kingdom
Tel.: (44) 1752701261
Web Site: http://www.hellermanntyton.co.uk
Cable Accessories Mfr
N.A.I.C.S.: 335929

Subsidiary (Non-US):

HellermannTyton Ltda. (2)
Av Jose Benassi 100 Parque Industrial,
CEP 13213 085, Jundiai, Sao Paulo, Brazil
Tel.: (55) 1121369090
Web Site:
http://www.hellermanntyton.com.br
Cable Accessories Mfr
N.A.I.C.S.: 331420
Alexandro Zavarizi (Pres-South America)

HellermannTyton Oy (2)
Sahkotie 8, Vantaa, 1510, Finland
Tel.: (358) 98700450
Web Site: http://www.hellermanntyton.fi
Cable Products Mfr
N.A.I.C.S.: 332618

HellermannTyton Pte Ltd. (2)
545 Indus Park A, Yishun Ave 7, Singapore,
768741, Singapore
Tel.: (65) 65861919
Web Site:
http://www.hellermanntyton.com.sg
Cable Products Mfr
N.A.I.C.S.: 335929
Heng Guan Lee (Gen Mgr)

HellermannTyton S.A.S. (2)
2 Rue Des Hetres CS 80543, 78196,
Trappes, France
Tel.: (33) 0130138000
Web Site: http://www.hellermanntyton.fr
Cable Accessories & Insulation Tubings Mfr
N.A.I.C.S.: 335929

HellermannTyton S.L. (2)
Avenida Belaindustriale 37/39 2F no.2,
28100, Alcobendas, Spain
Tel.: (34) 916612835
Web Site: http://www.hellermanntyton.es
Cable Products Mfr
N.A.I.C.S.: 332618
Jordi Torres (Mng Dir)

HellermannTyton SRL-Argentina (2)
Martin de Gainza 801 Pque Ind Buen Ayre,
Trujui-Moreno, Buenos Aires, Argentina
Tel.: (54) 2374056680
Web Site:
http://www.hellermanntyton.com.ar
Cable Products Mfr
N.A.I.C.S.: 332618

HellermannTyton Srl (2)
Via Visco 3/5, 35010, Limena, Italy
Tel.: (39) 049767870
Web Site: http://www.hellermanntyton.it
Cable Products Mfr
N.A.I.C.S.: 332618

HellermannTyton sp. z.o.o. (2)
ul Berdychow 57A, 62-410, Slupca, Poland
Tel.: (48) 632401849
Web Site: http://www.hellermanntyton.pl
Automobile Parts Mfr
N.A.I.C.S.: 336390

Hellermanntyton India Pvt. Ltd. (1)
Office No- 131 3rd floor Tower - A The
Corenthum A-41 Sector 62, Noida, 201309,
Uttar Pradesh, India
Tel.: (91) 1204133384
Web Site: https://www.hellermanntyton.com
Electrical Cable Connecting Product Mfr &
Distr
N.A.I.C.S.: 335929

Winchester Interconnect
Corporation (1)
68 Water St, Norwalk, CT 06854
Tel.: (203) 741-5400
Web Site: https://www.winconn.com
Electronic Connector Products Mfr
N.A.I.C.S.: 423690
Andy Robinson (Dir-Sls)

Subsidiary (Domestic):

Clements National Company (2)
2150 Parkes Dr, Broadview, IL 60155
Tel.: (708) 594-5890
Web Site: http://www.clementsnational.com
Power & Signal Connectors Mfr
N.A.I.C.S.: 334417

Division (Domestic):

SRC Haverhill (2)
5590 Skylane Blvd, Santa Rosa, CA 95403
Tel.: (707) 573-1900
Web Site: http://www.src-cables.com
Cable Connectors Mfr
N.A.I.C.S.: 335929
Dan Hirschnitz (Gen Mgr)

Subsidiary (Domestic):

Tekna Seal LLC (2)
5301 E River Rd, Minneapolis, MN 55421
Tel.: (800) 419-1613
Web Site: http://www.teknaseal.com
Hermetically Sealed Connectors, Glass-to-
Metal Feedthroughs, Hermetic seals,
Lithium Battery Seals & Ceramic-to-Metal
Seals Mfr
N.A.I.C.S.: 339991

Winchester Interconnect RF
Corporation (2)
135 Ward Hill Ave, Haverhill, MA 01835
Tel.: (978) 469-0555
Web Site: https://www.winconn.com
Electronic Components Mfr
N.A.I.C.S.: 334419

APTORUM GROUP LIMITED
17 Hanover Square, London, W1S
1BN, United Kingdom
Tel.: (44) 21176611 Ky
Web Site:
https://www.aptorumgroup.com
Year Founded: 2010
APM—(NASDAQ)
Rev.: $1,295,889
Assets: $20,867,371
Liabilities: $13,034,066
Net Worth: $7,833,305
Earnings: ($9,799,560)
Emp.: 18
Fiscal Year-end: 12/31/22
Pharmaceutical Product Mfr & Distr
N.A.I.C.S.: 325412
Ian Huen (Founder, Chm & CEO)

APTOSE BIOSCIENCES INC.
251 Consumers Road Suite 1105,
Toronto, M2J 4R3, ON, Canada
Tel.: (647) 479-9828 Ca
Web Site: https://www.aptose.com
Year Founded: 1986
APTO—(NASDAQ)
Rev.: $779,000
Assets: $51,027,000
Liabilities: $13,286,000
Net Worth: $37,741,000
Earnings: ($41,823,000)
Emp.: 35
Fiscal Year-end: 12/31/22
Antisense, Immunotherapy & Chemo-
therapy Technologies for Cancer
Treatment
N.A.I.C.S.: 325412
Fletcher Payne (CFO & Sr VP)

APTUS VALUE HOUSING FI-
NANCE INDIA LIMITED
No 8B Doshi Towers 8th Floor No
205 Poonamallee High Road, Kil-
pauk, Chennai, 600010, Tamil Nadu,
India
Tel.: (91) 4445650000
Web Site:
https://www.aptusindia.com
APTUS—(NSE)
Rev.: $114,689,621
Assets: $775,871,788
Liabilities: $377,815,606
Net Worth: $398,056,181

Earnings: $50,524,124
Emp.: 2,271
Fiscal Year-end: 03/31/22
Loan Services
N.A.I.C.S.: 522291
M. Anandan (Chm & Mng Dir)

Subsidiaries:

Aptus Finance India Private
Limited (1)
No 8B Doshi Towers 8th Floor No 205 Poo-
namallee High Road Kilpauk, Kilpauk,
Chennai, 600 010, Tamil Nadu, India
Tel.: (91) 4445650000
Financial Services
N.A.I.C.S.: 523999
Balaji P. (Exec Dir & CFO)

APURES CO LTD.
44 Hansan-Gil Cheongbuk-Eup,
Pyeongtaek, 17792, Gyeonggi-do,
Korea (South)
Tel.: (82) 316830643
Web Site: http://www.apures.com
149300—(KRS)
Biotechnology Research & Develop-
ment Services
N.A.I.C.S.: 541714
Hyeonsu Kim (Asst Mgr)

AQ GROUP AB
Regattagatan 29, SE 723 48, Vast-
eras, Sweden
Tel.: (46) 21404700
Web Site: https://www.aqgroup.com
AQ—(OMX)
Rev.: $677,362,856
Assets: $534,247,473
Liabilities: $236,402,634
Net Worth: $297,844,840
Earnings: $38,682,364
Emp.: 7,222
Fiscal Year-end: 12/31/22
Industrial Components & Systems
N.A.I.C.S.: 333248
Patrik Nolaker (Chm)

Subsidiaries:

AQ Anton Kft (1)
Sport u 16, 8900, Zalaegerszeg, Hungary
Tel.: (36) 92550010
Web Site: https://www.anton.hu
Construction Machinery Mfr
N.A.I.C.S.: 333120

AQ Components Mjallom AB (1)
Kustvagen 8, SE-873 97, Mjallom, Sweden
Tel.: (46) 613722200
Emp.: 45
Industrial Electric Components Mfr & Distr
N.A.I.C.S.: 334413

AQ Components Suzhou Co.,
Ltd, (1)
No 7 Standard Workshop No 98 Hengshan
Road, New Hi-Tech Industry Park Suzhou
New District, Suzhou, 215009, China
Tel.: (86) 51268081216
Emp.: 200
Sheet Metal Parts Mfr
N.A.I.C.S.: 332322
James Wang (Project Mgr-Sls)

AQ Components Vasteras AB (1)
Kretskortsvagen 6, 721 36, Vasteras, Swe-
den
Tel.: (46) 21186230
Emp.: 55
Sheet Metal Parts Mfr
N.A.I.C.S.: 332322
Emma Ostling (Deputy Mng Dir & Mgr-Site)

AQ Electric & Enclosures Suzhou
Co., Ltd. (1)
No 226 Huajin Road, Suzhou New District,
Suzhou, 215153, China
Tel.: (86) 51266620315
Sheet Metal Mfr & Distr
N.A.I.C.S.: 332322

AQ Electric AD (1)
R Daskalov str 68, 2400, Radomir, Bulgaria
Tel.: (359) 77782220

Emp.: 1,050
Sheet Metal Parts Mfr
N.A.I.C.S.: 332322
Emil Nikolov (Mng Dir)

AQ Electric Suzhou Co., Ltd. (1)
No 66 Yinyan Road Yangshan Science
Technology Park, Suzhou New District, Su-
zhou, 215151, China
Tel.: (86) 51266163996
Emp.: 200
Transformer Component Mfr
N.A.I.C.S.: 335311

AQ Enclosure Solleftea AB (1)
Overgardsvagen 4, 881 41, Solleftea, Swe-
den
Tel.: (46) 62025600
Sheet Metal Parts Mfr
N.A.I.C.S.: 332322
Joakim Falk (Mng Dir)

AQ Inductives Hungary Kft (1)
4 Trafo str, 6000, Kecskemet, Hungary
Tel.: (36) 76500000
Electronic Component Mfr & Distr
N.A.I.C.S.: 334419

AQ Lasertool OU (1)
Lagre tee 2, Lemmetsa Kula Parnu Linn,
88311, Parnu, Estonia
Tel.: (372) 4459580
Emp.: 320
Aluminum & Steel Product Mfr
N.A.I.C.S.: 332431
Rein Volt (Mng Dir)

AQ Magnetica Italy S.r.l. (1)
Via Marcora 20, 60022, Castelfidardo, AN,
Italy
Tel.: (39) 0717823855
Electromagnetic Component Mfr
N.A.I.C.S.: 335999

AQ Magnit AD (1)
21 Hristo Smirnenski Str, Godech, 2240,
Sofia, Bulgaria
Tel.: (359) 7238006
Emp.: 400
Insulated Inductive Component Mfr
N.A.I.C.S.: 335999
Rumen Rusinov (Mgr-Comml)

AQ ParkoPrint AB (1)
Marielundsvagen 1, 803 22, Gavle, Sweden
Tel.: (46) 26663400
Emp.: 45
Vending Machine Mfr
N.A.I.C.S.: 333310
Hans Stromberg (Mgr-Purchase & Quality)

AQ Plastronic AD (1)
32 San Stefano Str, 5004, Veliko Tarnovo,
Bulgaria
Tel.: (359) 62612320
Emp.: 121
Electronic Products Mfr
N.A.I.C.S.: 334419
Peter Fartsov (Sls Mgr)

AQ Special Sheet Metal AB (1)
Industrigatan 4, Lyrestad, 548 73, Vastra
Gotaland, Sweden
Tel.: (46) 50164580
Emp.: 150
Metal Products Mfr
N.A.I.C.S.: 332999
Lars Gafvert (Mng Dir)

AQ Trafo AB (1)
Gesallgatan 15, 745 39, Enkoping, Sweden
Tel.: (46) 17123600
Insulated Inductive Component Mfr
N.A.I.C.S.: 335999
Niklas Ericsson (Mng Dir)

AQ Trafotek AS (1)
Gaasi tee 14 Rae vald, 75306, Harjumaa,
Estonia
Tel.: (372) 6510160
Emp.: 300
Power Transformer Mfr
N.A.I.C.S.: 335311

AQ Trafotek OY (1)
Kaarinantie 700, 20540, Turku, Finland
Tel.: (358) 22759200
Web Site: https://trafotek.fi
Transformer Mfr & Distr
N.A.I.C.S.: 335311

AQ Transformer Solutions Inc. (1)
823 Fairview Rd, Wytheville, VA 24382
Tel.: (276) 228-7943
Transformer Distr
N.A.I.C.S.: 423690

AQ Wiring Systems Canada Inc. (1)
400 rue du Condor, Sainte-Eustache, J7R
0M7, QC, Canada
Tel.: (450) 491-4040
Electrical Wire Mfr
N.A.I.C.S.: 332618

AQ Wiring Systems NY, Inc. (1)
18 Northern Ave Ste 100, Plattsburgh, NY
12903
Tel.: (518) 324-4800
Web Site: https://aqwiringny.com
Electrical Wire Mfr
N.A.I.C.S.: 332618

AQ Wiring Systems S.A. de C.V. (1)
Avenida Recursos Hidraulicos No 80 Colo-
nia Lazaro Cardenas, 54916, Tultitlan, Es-
tado de Mexico, Mexico
Tel.: (52) 5558941174
Wiring Device Mfr
N.A.I.C.S.: 335931

AQ Wiring Systems Sp.z.o.o. (1)
ul Zakladowa 97, 92-402, Lodz, Poland
Tel.: (48) 426760662
Emp.: 2,600
Cable Harness Mfr
N.A.I.C.S.: 335931
Mariusz Kopec (Mng Dir)

AQ Wiring Systems UAB (1)
Pazalvaiciu st 1, 35289, Panevezys, Lithu-
ania
Tel.: (370) 64031201
Emp.: 2,600
Cable Harness Mfr
N.A.I.C.S.: 335931
Nerijus Olsauskas (Mng Dir)

**AQAR REAL ESTATE INVEST-
MENTS COMPANY - K.S.C.**
Al Qibla Block 13 Street 23 Building
19 Al Sahraa Tower 30th Floor, PO
Box 20017, Safat, 13061, Kuwait,
13061, Kuwait
Tel.: (965) 22213967   KW
Web Site: https://www.aqar.com.kw
Year Founded: 1997
AQAR—(KUW)
Rev.: $3,161,633
Assets: $115,913,104
Liabilities: $24,360,775
Net Worth: $91,552,329
Earnings: $3,105,090
Emp.: 11
Fiscal Year-end: 12/31/22
Real Estate Manangement Services
N.A.I.C.S.: 531390
Dhari AbdulAziz AlNassar (Chm)

AQUA BIO TECHNOLOGY ASA
Bygdoy Alle, 257, Oslo, Norway
Tel.: (47) 33484610
Web Site:
https://www.aquabiotechnology.com
3FZ—(DEU)
Rev.: $648,439
Assets: $6,207,279
Liabilities: $6,035,470
Net Worth: $171,809
Earnings: ($1,731,018)
Emp.: 2
Fiscal Year-end: 12/31/22
Cosmetic Product & Ingredient Mfr
N.A.I.C.S.: 325620
Arvid Lindberg (Head-Sls & Mktg)

AQUA CAPITAL
Av Cidade Jardim 803 6th floor, CEP
01453-000, Sao Paulo, Brazil
Tel.: (55) 1120391600
Web Site: http://aqua.capital
Year Founded: 2009
Privater Equity Firm
N.A.I.C.S.: 523940
Sebastia Popik (Founder & CEO)

Subsidiaries:

Agro100 (1)
Avenida Dez de Dezembro, Londrina,
86064, Brazil
Tel.: (55) 4333731100
Agricultural Farming
N.A.I.C.S.: 111998

**AQUA CORPORATION PUBLIC
COMPANY LIMITED**
121/68-69 21st Floor R S Tower
Building Ratchadaphisek Rd, Din-
Daeng, Bangkok, 10400, Thailand
Tel.: (66) 26948888
Web Site: https://www.aquacorp.co.th
Year Founded: 1994
AQUA—(THA)
Rev.: $26,978,635
Assets: $263,992,910
Liabilities: $92,473,447
Net Worth: $171,519,463
Earnings: $934,435
Fiscal Year-end: 12/31/23
Investment Management Service
N.A.I.C.S.: 523940
Yuth Chinsupakul (Chm)

**AQUA GUARDIAN GROUP
LIMITED**
Level 9 175 Collins St, Melbourne,
3000, VIC, Australia
Tel.: (61) 3 8530 2000
Web Site:
http://www.aquaguardiangroup.com
Water Conservation Technology &
Related Services
N.A.I.C.S.: 541620
Alan Cornell (Deputy Chm)

AQUA LOGISTICS LIMITED
5th Floor B Wing Trade Star Building,
Andheri Kurla Road Andheri East,
Mumbai, 400 059, Maharashtra, India
Tel.: (91) 226 777 0200
Web Site:
http://www.aqualogistics.com
Year Founded: 1999
Sales Range: $25-49.9 Million
Emp.: 154
Logistics & Supply Chain Services
N.A.I.C.S.: 541614
Rajesh G. Uchil (Chm)

AQUA ONLINE
2nd St Hutton Ct, 1 Summit Rd,
Parklands, 2121, South Africa
Tel.: (27) 117507300
Year Founded: 1998
Emp.: 250
Advertising, Content,
Digital/Interactive, Graphic Design,
Internet/Web Design
N.A.I.C.S.: 541810
Brent Shahim (Mng Dir)

AQUA POWER SYSTEMS INC.
2-7-17 Omori Honcho, Ota-ku, Tokyo,
143-0011, Japan
Tel.: (81) 357643380   NV
Web Site: https://www.aps-j.jp
Year Founded: 2010
APSI—(OTCIQ)
Rev.: $654,133
Assets: $155,733
Liabilities: $63,045
Net Worth: $92,688
Earnings: $554,911
Fiscal Year-end: 03/31/22
Magnesium Air Fuel Cell Products
Mfr
N.A.I.C.S.: 221118
Tadashi Ishikawa (Founder, CEO,
CFO, Treas & Sec)

AQUA SIGNAL GMBH

Von Thunen Strasse 12, 28307,
Bremen, Germany
Tel.: (49) 42148930
Web Site: http://glamox.com
Rev.: $56,000,000
Emp.: 230
Light Mfr
N.A.I.C.S.: 335139
Markus Barner (Mng Dir)

AQUA-PURE VENTURES INC.
135 Commercial Drive Unit 1, Cal-
gary, T3Z 2A7, AB, Canada
Tel.: (403) 301-4123   Ca
Web Site:
http://www.fountainquail.com
Year Founded: 1992
Sales Range: $1-9.9 Million
Waste Water Management Services
N.A.I.C.S.: 562998

Subsidiaries:

Salsnes North America Inc (1)
Unit 1 135 Commercial Drive, Calgary, T3Z
2A7, AB, Canada
Tel.: (403) 301-4125
Web Site: http://www.salsnes.ca
Sales Range: $25-49.9 Million
Emp.: 1
Water Treatment Equipment Mfr
N.A.I.C.S.: 333310

AQUAFIN HOLDING S.P.A.
Viale dell Industria 5, 37036, San
Martino Buon Albergo, Italy
Tel.: (39) 0458871488   IT
Year Founded: 1956
Investment Holding Company
N.A.I.C.S.: 551112
Giulio Bonazzi (CEO)

Subsidiaries:

Aquafil S.p.A. (1)
Via Linfano 9, 38062, Arco, TN,
Italy   (68.87%)
Tel.: (39) 00464581111
Web Site: https://www.aquafil.com
Rev.: $752,325,707
Assets: $782,381,826
Liabilities: $593,085,474
Net Worth: $189,296,352
Earnings: $31,460,177
Emp.: 2,744
Fiscal Year-end: 12/31/2022
Nylon Mfr
N.A.I.C.S.: 313110
Giulio Bonazzi (Chm & CEO)

Subsidiary (US):

Aquafil U.S.A., Inc. (2)
1 Aquafil Dr, Cartersville, GA 30120
Tel.: (678) 605-8100
Web Site: http://www.aquafilusa.com
Nylon Products Mfr & Whslr
N.A.I.C.S.: 313110

Subsidiary (Domestic):

O'Mara, Inc. (3)
160 Fashion Ave, Rutherford College, NC
28671
Tel.: (828) 874-2100
Web Site: http://www.omarainc.com
Throwing & Winding Mills
N.A.I.C.S.: 313110

**AQUAGOLD INTERNATIONAL,
INC.**
2500 1100 Boulevard Rene-Levesque
West, Montreal, H3B 5C9, QC,
Canada
Tel.: (450) 973-1042
AQUI—(OTCIQ)
Sales Range: Less than $1 Million
Spring Water
N.A.I.C.S.: 312112

AQUALINE LTD.
6th Floor Daiichi Uenoya Bldg 8-8
Kamihacchobori, Naka-ku, Hiroshima,
730-0012, Japan

Tel.: (81) 825026644
Web Site: https://www.aqualine.jp
Year Founded: 1996
6173—(TKS)
Rev.: $34,351,050
Assets: $10,677,540
Liabilities: $10,301,770
Net Worth: $375,770
Earnings: ($2,665,840)
Emp.: 67
Fiscal Year-end: 02/29/24
Pipeline Repair Services
N.A.I.C.S.: 486990
Takeshi Ohkochi (Pres)

**AQUALISA PRODUCTS LIM-
ITED**
The Flyers Way, Westerham, TN16
1DE, Kent, United Kingdom
Tel.: (44) 1959560000   UK
Web Site: http://www.aqualisa.co.uk
Year Founded: 1977
Shower Mfr & Distr
N.A.I.C.S.: 326191
David Hollander (CEO)

**AQUANEX, SERVICIO DOMI-
CILIARIO DEL AGUA DE EX-
TREMADURA SA**
Baldomero Díaz de Entresotos 3,
Bajo Merida, 06800, Extremadura,
Spain
Tel.: (34) 924330612
Web Site: https://www.aquanex.es
Environmental Services
N.A.I.C.S.: 541620
Ivan Jose Vicente Garcia (Dir)

Subsidiaries:

ABS Materials, Inc. (1)
1909 Old Mansfield Rd, Wooster, OH
44691
Tel.: (330) 234-7999
Web Site: http://www.absmaterials.com
Sales Range: $1-9.9 Million
Emp.: 25
Basic Organic Chemical Mfr
N.A.I.C.S.: 325199
Paul Edmiston (Chief Science Officer)

Unit (Non-US):

PWA-ProSep Malaysia (2)
Letter Box 73 32rd Floor UBN Tower No 10
Jalan P Ramlee, 50250, Kuala Lumpur,
Malaysia
Tel.: (60) 3 2715 6680
Web Site: http://www.pwasystems.com
Water Purification Equipment Whslr
N.A.I.C.S.: 423440

Subsidiary (Domestic):

Produced Water Absorbents, Inc. (2)
5353 W Sam Houston Pkwy N Ste 150,
Houston, TX 77041
Tel.: (281) 504-2040
Web Site: http://www.pwasystems.com
Waste Treatment Services
N.A.I.C.S.: 488390
Michael Smith (Mng Dir-Europe)

AQUAPORIN A/S
Nymollevej 78, 2800, Kongens Lyn-
gby, Denmark
Tel.: (45) 82303082
Web Site: https://www.aquaporin.com
Year Founded: 1992
AQP—(CSE)
Rev.: $8,613,824
Assets: $37,991,347
Liabilities: $17,564,932
Net Worth: $20,426,415
Earnings: ($13,079,828)
Emp.: 82
Fiscal Year-end: 12/31/23
Waste Treatment Services
N.A.I.C.S.: 221310
Klaus Juhl Wulff (CFO)

Aquaporin A/S—(Continued)

Subsidiaries:

Aquaporin Asia Pte. Ltd.   **(1)**
1 Cleantech Loop 02-14 CleanTech One,
Singapore, 637141, Singapore
Tel.: (65) 62686343
Waste Treatment Services
N.A.I.C.S.: 221310

Aquaporin US Inc.   **(1)**
14241 E Firestone Blvd Ste 422, La Mirada,
CA 90638
Tel.: (714) 512-0593
Water Purifiers Mfr
N.A.I.C.S.: 333310

AQUARIUS AI, INC.
499 Broughton Street Suite 202, Van-
couver, V6G 3K1, BC, Canada
Tel.: (604) 265-7511
Web Site: http://www.aquariusai.ca
WH4—(DEU)
Rev.: $193,600
Assets: $182,279
Liabilities: $1,106,268
Net Worth: ($923,989)
Earnings: ($5,654,903)
Fiscal Year-end: 12/31/23
Digital Marketing Services
N.A.I.C.S.: 541613
Chris Bradley *(CEO)*

Subsidiaries:

Lighthouse Digital Inc.   **(1)**
2802 Flintrock Trce Ste 360, Austin, TX
78738
Web Site: http://www.lighthousedigital.com
Marketing Services
N.A.I.C.S.: 541613

AQUARIUS SURGICAL TECH-NOLOGIES INC.
89 Scollard Street, Toronto, M5R
1G4, ON, Canada
Tel.: (902) 496-7594   ON
Web Site:
https://aquariussurgical.com
Year Founded: 1986
AQQRF—(OTCIQ)
Rev.: $151,985
Assets: $507,387
Liabilities: $3,377,918
Net Worth: ($2,870,530)
Earnings: ($539,686)
Fiscal Year-end: 03/31/23
Medical Laser Systems
N.A.I.C.S.: 334510
David J. Hennigar *(Chm)*

AQUASIUM TECHNOLOGY LIMITED
Denny Industrial Ctr, Waterbeach,
CB25 9QX, Cambs, United Kingdom
Tel.: (44) 1223863481
Web Site: http://www.aquasium.com
Year Founded: 1995
Sales Range: $10-24.9 Million
Emp.: 50
Technology Investment Firm
N.A.I.C.S.: 523999
Gavin Crick *(Dir-Fin)*

Subsidiaries:

Cambridge Vacuum Engineering
Limited   **(1)**
Denny Industrial Center, Pembroke Avenue,
Waterbeach, CB25 9QX, Cambs, United
Kingdom
Tel.: (44) 1223863481
Web Site: http://www.camvaceng.co.uk
Sales Range: $100-124.9 Million
Vacuum Furnaces & Electron Beam Weld-
ing Systems Mfr
N.A.I.C.S.: 333994
Robert Nicholson *(Mng Dir)*

Subsidiary (US):

Cambridge Vacuum Engineering
Inc.   **(2)**

630 Silver St Unit 7A PO Box 867,
Agawam, MA 01001-0867
Tel.: (413) 789-4600
Web Site: http://www.camvaceng.com
Sales Range: $25-49.9 Million
Emp.: 4
Vacuum Furnaces & Electron Beam Weld-
ing Systems Mfr
N.A.I.C.S.: 333994

EBTEC Corporation   **(1)**
120 Shoemaker Ln, Agawam, MA 01001
Tel.: (413) 786-0393
Web Site: http://www.ebteccorp.com
Sales Range: $25-49.9 Million
Laser Processing, Electron Beam Welding,
Heat-Treating, Abrasive Waterjet Process-
ing, Manual Welding & General Machining
Services
N.A.I.C.S.: 332811
Rita Ducharme *(Mgr-HR)*

AQUATUS A.D.
Ulica Bulevar Oslobodenja 162 b,
Belgrade, Serbia
Tel.: (381) 11 66 44 214
Web Site: http://www.aquatus.ls.rs
Year Founded: 1998
AQUA—(BEL)
Sales Range: Less than $1 Million
Fruit & Vegetable Mfr
N.A.I.C.S.: 311411
Milorad Relic *(CEO)*

AQUILA ACQUISITION COR-PORATION
46/F ChampionTower 3 Garden
Road, Central, China (Hong Kong)
Tel.: (852) 39000888   Ky
Web Site: https://www.aquilaacq.com
Year Founded: 2021
7836—(HKG)
Rev.: $1,206,737
Assets: $131,209,677
Liabilities: $134,656,410
Net Worth: ($3,446,733)
Earnings: ($17,310,535)
Fiscal Year-end: 12/31/22
Investment Management Service
N.A.I.C.S.: 523999
Rongfeng Jiang *(Chm)*

AQUILA SA
ZI de Courtine BP 90949, 84092, Avi-
gnon, Cedex 9, France
Tel.: (33) 825800887
Web Site: https://www.reseau-
aquila.fr
Year Founded: 1993
ALAQU—(EUR)
Sales Range: $10-24.9 Million
Surveillance Service Provider
N.A.I.C.S.: 561621

AQUILA SERVICES GROUP PLC
29a Bermondsey Wall West, Tempus
Wharf, London, SE16 4SA, United
Kingdom
Tel.: (44) 207 934 0175
Web Site:
http://www.aquilaservicegroup.com
AQSG—(LSE)
Rev.: $13,738,769
Assets: $11,522,970
Liabilities: $3,183,853
Net Worth: $8,339,116
Earnings: $786,120
Emp.: 86
Fiscal Year-end: 03/31/22
Management Consulting Services
N.A.I.C.S.: 541611
Derek Joseph *(Chm)*

Subsidiaries:

3C Consultants Ltd.   **(1)**
Minerva Mill Innovation Centre Station
Road, Alcester, B49 5ET, Warwickshire,
United Kingdom

Tel.: (44) 333 900 3003
Web Site: https://www.3cconsultants.co.uk
Organization Management Services
N.A.I.C.S.: 541611
Colin Sales *(CEO & Mng Dir)*

Aquila Treasury & Finance Solutions
Limited   **(1)**
Tempus Wharf 29a Bermondsey Wall West,
London, SE16 4SA, United Kingdom
Tel.: (44) 203 195 2800
Web Site: https://www.atfsltd.co.uk
Consulting Services
N.A.I.C.S.: 541618
David Mairs *(Grp Dir)*

Assetcore Ltd.   **(1)**
7 Garrett Street, London, EC1Y 0TY, United
Kingdom
Tel.: (44) 203 637 8951
Web Site: https://assetcore.org
Information Technology Services
N.A.I.C.S.: 541519
Janyne Latimer *(Sr Mgr)*

Oaks Consultancy Ltd.   **(1)**
10 Sovereign Court Graham Street, Bir-
mingham, B1 3JR, United Kingdom
Tel.: (44) 121 709 5577
Web Site:
https://www.oaksconsultancy.co.uk
Consulting Services
N.A.I.C.S.: 541618

AQUILINI INVESTMENT GROUP
Gate 16 in Rogers Arena 700 Pat
Quinn Way, Vancouver, V6B 1L8,
BC, Canada
Tel.: (604) 899-5398
Web Site: http://www.aquilini.com
Sales Range: $25-49.9 Million
Emp.: 50
Equity Investment Firm
N.A.I.C.S.: 523999

Subsidiaries:

Canucks Sports & Entertainment   **(1)**
800 Griffiths Way, Vancouver, V6B 6G1,
BC, Canada   **(100%)**
Tel.: (604) 899-7400
Web Site: http://canucks.nhl.com
Sales Range: $10-24.9 Million
Holding Company; Professional Hockey
Franchise & Sports Arena Owner & Opera-
tor
N.A.I.C.S.: 551112
Francesco Aquilini *(Chm & Governor)*

Unit (Domestic):

Vancouver Canucks   **(2)**
800 Griffiths Way, Vancouver, V6B 6G1,
BC, Canada
Tel.: (604) 899-4600
Web Site: http://www.canucks.nhl.com
Professional Hockey Franchise
N.A.I.C.S.: 711211
Francesco Aquilini *(Chm-NHL)*

AQUIRIAN LIMITED
Level 5 190 St Georges Terrace,
Perth, 6000, WA, Australia
Tel.: (61) 863705400   AU
Web Site: https://www.aquirian.com
Year Founded: 2017
AQN—(ASX)
Rev.: $17,162,034
Assets: $16,766,771
Liabilities: $8,952,199
Net Worth: $7,814,573
Earnings: $356,534
Fiscal Year-end: 06/30/23
Mining Services
N.A.I.C.S.: 212290
David Kelly *(Mng Dir)*

Subsidiaries:

Aquirian Technology Pty Ltd.   **(1)**
19 Overlord Place, Acacia Ridge, 4110,
QLD, Australia
Tel.: (61) 732744750
Web Site: https://www.aquariustech.com.au
Water Treatment Equipment Mfr & Distr

N.A.I.C.S.: 333310

Cybem Services Pty Ltd.   **(1)**
29 Finance Pl, Malaga, 6090, WA, Australia
Tel.: (61) 892485001
Web Site: https://www.cybem.com.au
Mining Machinery Maintenance Services
N.A.I.C.S.: 811310

Modular Training Pty Ltd.   **(1)**
Level 3/190 St Georges Terrace, Perth,
6000, WA, Australia
Tel.: (61) 863705400
Web Site:
https://www.modulartraining.com.au
Mining Equipment Mfr & Distr
N.A.I.C.S.: 333131

TBS Mining Solutions Pty Ltd.   **(1)**
Level 5 190 St Georges Terrace, Perth,
6000, WA, Australia
Tel.: (61) 863705400
Web Site:
https://www.tbsminingsolutions.com
Mining Equipment Mfr & Distr
N.A.I.C.S.: 333131

TBS Workforce Pty Ltd.   **(1)**
Level 5 190 St Georges Terrace, Perth,
6000, WA, Australia
Tel.: (61) 863705400
Web Site: https://www.tbsworkforce.com
Workforce Management Services
N.A.I.C.S.: 926110

AQUIS ENTERTAINMENT LIM-ITED
21 Binara Street, Canberra, 2601,
ACT, Australia
Tel.: (61) 262577074   AU
Web Site:
http://www.aquisentertainment.com
Year Founded: 2010
AQS—(ASX)
Rev.: $21,195
Assets: $20,015,425
Liabilities: $29,853,630
Net Worth: ($9,838,205)
Earnings: $5,404,549
Emp.: 199
Fiscal Year-end: 12/31/22
Tourism Development Services
N.A.I.C.S.: 721110
Tony Fung *(Chm)*

Subsidiaries:

Casino Canberra Limited   **(1)**
21 Binara St, PO Box 262, Canberra, 2601,
ACT, Australia
Tel.: (61) 262433700
Casino Hotel Operator
N.A.I.C.S.: 721120

AQUIS EXCHANGE PLC
Floor 2 63 Queen Victoria St, Lon-
don, EC4N 4UA, United Kingdom
Tel.: (44) 2035976311   UK
Web Site: https://www.aquis.eu
Year Founded: 2018
Privater Equity Firm
N.A.I.C.S.: 523999
Niki Beattie *(Chm)*

ARA GROUP LIMITED
83 Alexander St, Crows Nest, 2065,
NSW, Australia
Tel.: (61) 300233305
Web Site: https://aragroup.com
Emp.: 100
Industrial Facilities Services
N.A.I.C.S.: 561210

ARA LOGOS LOGISTICS TRUST
5 Temasek Boulevard 12-01 Suntec
Tower Five, Singapore, 038985, Sin-
gapore
Tel.: (65) 68359232   SG
Web Site: http://www.cache-reit.com
Year Founded: 2010

K2LU—(SES)
Rev.: $88,657,637
Assets: $1,066,369,456
Liabilities: $477,423,399
Net Worth: $588,946,057
Earnings: $33,695,066
Fiscal Year-end: 12/31/20
Investment Management Service
N.A.I.C.S.: 523940
Daniel Cerf (Co-CEO)

ARA US HOSPITALITY TRUST
5 Temasek Boulevard 12-01 Suntec
Tower Five, Singapore, 038985, Sin-
gapore
Tel.: (65) 68359232   SG
Web Site:
    https://investor.araushotels.com
Year Founded: 2018
XZL—(SES)
Rev.: $55,203,000
Assets: $762,525,000
Liabilities: $657,225,000
Net Worth: $105,300,000
Earnings: ($23,287,000)
Fiscal Year-end: 12/31/23
Real Estate Investment Trust Ser-
vices
N.A.I.C.S.: 531190
Jin Yong Lee (CEO)

ARAB AFRICAN INTERNA-
TIONAL BANK
5 Midan Al Saray Al Koubra, Garden
City, Cairo, Egypt
Tel.: (20) 2 2794 5094   EG
Web Site: http://www.aaib.com
Year Founded: 1964
Sales Range: $600-649.9 Million
Emp.: 1,522
Personal, Commercial & Investment
Banking Services
N.A.I.C.S.: 522110
Omar Mohamed Abdelaziz Khattab
(Head-Treasury & Fin Institutions
Grp)

Subsidiaries:

Arab African Investment
Management   (1)
5 Midan Al Saray Al Koubra, Garden City,
Cairo, Egypt
Tel.: (20) 2 2792 6825
Web Site: http://www.aaim.com.eg
Investment Management Service
N.A.I.C.S.: 523940
Hassan E. Abdalla (Mng Dir)

ARAB ALUMINIUM INDUSTRY
CO. LTD.
Ain El-Basha, PO Box 35042, Am-
man, 11180, Jordan
Tel.: (962) 65343965
Web Site:
    https://www.aralaluminum.com
Year Founded: 1976
AALU—(AMM)
Rev.: $13,195,098
Assets: $20,075,227
Liabilities: $3,813,281
Net Worth: $16,261,946
Earnings: $269,510
Emp.: 209
Fiscal Year-end: 12/31/20
Aluminium Products Mfr
N.A.I.C.S.: 331315
Osamah Hussein Aggad (Gen Mgr)

ARAB BANK PLC
PO Box 950545, Amman, 11195, Jor-
dan
Tel.: (962) 65600000
Web Site: https://www.arabbank.com
Year Founded: 1982
ARBK—(AMM)
Rev.: $3,659,678,000
Assets: $68,273,971,000

Liabilities: $56,917,120,000
Net Worth: $11,356,851,000
Earnings: $829,636,000
Emp.: 7,382
Fiscal Year-end: 12/31/23
Banking Services
N.A.I.C.S.: 522110
Sabih Taher Masri (Chm)

Subsidiaries:

AL-NISR AL-ARABI
INSURANCE   (1)
Shmeisani - Esam Ajlouni St - Building no
21, PO Box 9194, Amman, 11191, Jordan
Tel.: (962) 65685171
Web Site: https://www.al-nisr.com
Rev.: $61,872,729
Assets: $160,760,838
Liabilities: $128,725,922
Net Worth: $32,034,916
Earnings: $4,318,968
Emp.: 276
Fiscal Year-end: 12/31/2020
Insurance Services
N.A.I.C.S.: 524298
Yacoub Manawil Sabella (Vice Chm & Gen
Mgr)

Al Arabi Investment Group Co.   (1)
Tel.: (962) 6 552 2239
Web Site: https://www.ab-invest.net
Emp.: 59
Commercial Banking Services
N.A.I.C.S.: 522110
Qutaiba Al-Hawamdeh (CEO)

Arab Bank (Switzerland) Ltd.   (1)
Nuschelerstrasse 1, PO Box 1065, 8001,
Zurich, Switzerland
Tel.: (41) 44 265 7111
Web Site: https://www.arabbank.ch
Sales Range: $50-74.9 Million
Emp.: 60
Banking & Financial Services
N.A.I.C.S.: 522110
Serge Robin (CEO)

Arab Bank Australia Ltd   (1)
Exchange Centre Level 7 20 Bridge Street,
Sydney, 2000, NSW, Australia
Tel.: (61) 29 377 8900
Web Site: https://www.arabbank.com.au
Sales Range: $50-74.9 Million
Emp.: 50
Banking Services
N.A.I.C.S.: 522110

Arab Bank-Syria   (1)
Al Mhdi Bn Barakeh Street - Building Num-
ber 21, PO Box 38, Damascus, Syria
Tel.: (963) 11 9421
Web Site: http://www.arabbank-syria.com
Sales Range: Less than $1 Million
Commercial Banking Services
N.A.I.C.S.: 522110

Arab Investment Bank S.A.L.   (1)
Riad El Solh Squar Banks Street BCD, PO
Box 11-1015, Beirut, 1107 2070,
Lebanon   (66.65%)
Tel.: (961) 1985111
Sales Range: $50-74.9 Million
Emp.: 6
Banking Services
N.A.I.C.S.: 522110
Ahmed Bekhit (CIO)

Arab National Leasing Company
Ltd   (1)
Al-Madina Al-Monawara St, PO Box 720,
Tla Al-Ali, Amman, Jordan
Tel.: (962) 6 553 1640
Financial Lending Services
N.A.I.C.S.: 523999

Arab Sudanese Bank Limited   (1)
Alsouq Alarabi-Block no 1 Alwaha Offices-
Floor 11, PO Box 955, Khartoum, Sudan
Tel.: (249) 1565 50001
Web Site:
    http://www.arabsudanesebank.com
Commercial Banking Services
N.A.I.C.S.: 522110

Arab Tunisian Bank   (1)
9 Rue Hedi Nouira, 1001, Tunis,
Tunisia   (64.24%)
Tel.: (216) 7 135 1155

Web Site: https://www.atb.tn
Banking Services
N.A.I.C.S.: 522110

Europe Arab Bank PLC   (1)
13 - 15 Moorgate, London, EC2R 6AD,
United Kingdom
Tel.: (44) 2073158500
Web Site: http://www.eabplc.com
Commercial Banking Services
N.A.I.C.S.: 522110
Nemeh Sabbagh (Chm)

Finance Accountancy Mohassaba
SA   (1)
24 Rue Neuve -Vu-Molard, PO Box 3155,
1211, Geneva, Switzerland   (100%)
Tel.: (41) 229083000
Web Site: http://www.arabbank.ch
Sales Range: $50-74.9 Million
Emp.: 8
Banking Services
N.A.I.C.S.: 522110

Islamic International Arab Bank
plc   (1)
PO Box 925802, Amman, 11190,
Jordan   (100%)
Tel.: (962) 65694901
Sales Range: $100-124.9 Million
Emp.: 150
Banking Services
N.A.I.C.S.: 522110
Mohsen Abu Awad (Chief Bus & Investment
Officer)

Oman Arab Bank S.A.O.C.   (1)
Sultan Qaboos Street, PO Box 2010, Ghu-
brah, 112, Ruwi, Oman   (49%)
Tel.: (968) 24754444
Web Site: http://www.oman-arabbank.com
Sales Range: $50-74.9 Million
Emp.: 100
Banking Services; Owned 51% by Oman
International Development & Investment
Co. SAOG & 49% by Arab Bank plc
N.A.I.C.S.: 522110
Rashad Al Musafir (CEO)

Subsidiary (Domestic):

alizz islamic bank SAOG   (2)
Alizz Tower, PO Box 753, CBD Area, 112,
Ruwi, Oman
Tel.: (968) 80072265
Web Site: https://www.alizzislamic.com
Rev.: $106,593,986
Assets: $2,243,075,665
Liabilities: $1,982,332,795
Net Worth: $260,742,870
Earnings: ($19,669,395)
Emp.: 236
Fiscal Year-end: 12/31/2020
Commercial Banking Services
N.A.I.C.S.: 522110
Mohammed Shukri Ghanem (Vice Chm)

ARAB BANKING CORPORA-
TION B.S.C.
ABC Tower Building 152 Road 1703
Block 317 Diplomatic Area, PO Box
5698, Manama, Bahrain
Tel.: (973) 17543000   BH
Web Site: https://www.bank-abc.com
Year Founded: 1980
ABC—(BAH)
Rev.: $1,460,000,000
Assets: $30,068,000,000
Liabilities: $25,579,000,000
Net Worth: $4,489,000,000
Earnings: $194,000,000
Emp.: 436
Fiscal Year-end: 12/31/19
Banking & Investment Services
N.A.I.C.S.: 522110
Ismail Mokhtar (COO)

Subsidiaries:

ABC International Bank plc   (1)
Arab Banking Corporation House 1-5 Moor-
gate, London, EC2R 6AB, United Kingdom
Tel.: (44) 2037654000
Web Site: http://www.arabbanking.com
Sales Range: $150-199.9 Million
Trade Finance & Investment Services
N.A.I.C.S.: 522299

James Boucher (COO)

Subsidiary (Non-US):

ABC S.A.   (2)
8 rue Halevy, 75009, Paris, France
Tel.: (33) 149525400
Commercial Banking Services
N.A.I.C.S.: 522110
Frederic Le Serre (CEO)

ABC Islamic Bank EC   (1)
ABC Tower Diplomatic Area, PO Box 2808,
Manama, 2808, Bahrain
Tel.: (973) 17543342
Banking Services
N.A.I.C.S.: 523150
Hammad Hassan (Mng Dir)

Arab Banking Corporation
(Jordan)   (1)
Shmeisani Abdul Rahim Al-Waked Street
Bank ABC Jordan Building, PO Box
926691, Amman, 11190, Jordan (86.98%)
Tel.: (962) 65633500
Web Site: https://www.bank-abc.com
Rev.: $99,013,433
Assets: $1,903,606,594
Liabilities: $1,672,811,764
Net Worth: $230,794,829
Earnings: $9,399,425
Emp.: 533
Fiscal Year-end: 12/31/2022
Financial & Banking Services
N.A.I.C.S.: 523150
George Farah Sofia (CEO & Gen Mgr)

Arab Banking Corporation - Egypt
S.A.E.   (1)
90th Street North-N 39 B Fifth Settlement,
PO Box 46, New Cairo, Egypt
Tel.: (20) 225861199
Financial & Banking Services
N.A.I.C.S.: 523150
Ayman Tawfik (Head-Compliance)

Arab Banking Corporation Algeria
SpA   (1)
38 Avenue Des Trois Freres Bouaddou, PO
Box 367, Bir Mourad Rais, Algiers, Algeria
Tel.: (213) 23569523
Web Site: https://www.bank-abc.com
Financial & Banking Services
N.A.I.C.S.: 523150
Nadir Idir (CEO)

Arab Banking Corporation Tunisia,
S.A.   (1)
ABC Building Rue du Lac d Annecy Les
Berges du La, 1053, Tunis, Tunisia
Tel.: (216) 71861861
Web Site: https://www.bank-abc.com
Financial & Banking Services
N.A.I.C.S.: 523150

Arab Financial Services Company
B.S.C.   (1)
Office 1201 12th Floor Bahrain Financial
Harbour East Tower, PO Box 2152, Building
No 1398 Road 4626 Block 346, Manama,
Bahrain
Tel.: (973) 17299444
Web Site: https://www.afs.com.bh
Financial Services
N.A.I.C.S.: 523999

Banco ABC Brasil S.A.   (1)
Av Cidade Jardim 803-2nd floor, Itaim Bibi,
Sao Paulo, 01453-0000, Brazil (60.11%)
Tel.: (55) 1131702000
Web Site: https://www.abcbrasil.com.br
Rev.: $1,067,560,080
Assets: $10,816,880,533
Liabilities: $9,764,003,244
Net Worth: $1,052,877,289
Earnings: $145,575,692
Fiscal Year-end: 12/31/2023
Banking Services
N.A.I.C.S.: 522299
Sergio Ricardo Borejo (Officer-IR, Member-
Exec Bd & Exec VP-Admin)

ARAB CENTER FOR PHARMA-
CEUTICAL & CHEMICAL IN-
DUSTRIES CO.
King Abdullah II Industrial City, PO
Box 22, Sahab, 11512, Jordan
Tel.: (962) 4022470

Arab Center for Pharmaceutical & Chemical Industries Co.—(Continued)

Year Founded: 1983
APHC—(AMM)
Sales Range: Less than $1 Million
Emp.: 55
Pharmaceuticals Product Mfr
N.A.I.C.S.: 325412
Husam AL-Deen AL-Rifa'e (Gen Mgr)

ARAB COMPANY FOR LAND RECLAMATION S.A.E.
First Street El-Sayd Club, Dokki, Giza, Egypt
Tel.: (20) 33377610
Web Site: https://www.arclam.com
Year Founded: 1964
Land Reclamation Services
N.A.I.C.S.: 237210

ARAB COMPANY FOR PAINT PRODUCTS
Industrial Zone, PO Box 469, Nablus, Palestine
Tel.: (970) 92311303
Web Site: https://www.apcpaints.ps
Year Founded: 1990
APC—(PAL)
Rev.: $6,669,140
Assets: $9,318,451
Liabilities: $2,605,581
Net Worth: $6,712,871
Earnings: $244,197
Emp.: 48
Fiscal Year-end: 12/31/23
Paint Product Mfr & Whslr
N.A.I.C.S.: 325510
Faeq Sayegh (VP)

ARAB COTTON GINNING COMPANY
28 Talat-Harb Street, Cairo, Egypt
Tel.: (20) 225756012
Web Site: https://www.arabcot.com
Year Founded: 1963
ACGC.CA—(EGX)
Sales Range: Less than $1 Million
Cotton Ginning Services
N.A.I.C.S.: 115111
Ahmed Mohamed Abdelfatah (Mgr-Investor Relations)

ARAB DEVELOPMENT INVESTMENT COMPANY
8 Mohammed Khader Hussein St Ard Elgolf, Heliopolis, Cairo, Egypt
Tel.: (20) 24193052
Web Site:
http://www.arabianrealestate-aleco.com
Year Founded: 1991
Real Estate Management Services
N.A.I.C.S.: 531390

ARAB EAST INVESTMENT COMPANY
Shat Al-Arab St Om Othainah Villa No 11, PO Box 851322, Amman, 11185, Jordan
Tel.: (962) 65511227
Web Site: https://www.aeivco.com
Year Founded: 1996
AEIV—(AMM)
Rev.: $22,040
Assets: $90,673,358
Liabilities: $17,354,245
Net Worth: $73,319,112
Earnings: $1,021,422
Emp.: 6
Fiscal Year-end: 12/31/21
Real Estate Investment Services
N.A.I.C.S.: 531390

ARAB ELECTRICAL INDUSTRIES

Industrial, PO Box 3, Sahab, 11512, Jordan
Tel.: (962) 5859124   JO
Web Site: http://www.aei-jo.com
Year Founded: 1983
AEIN—(AMM)
Rev.: $44,927
Assets: $4,733,590
Liabilities: $1,311,904
Net Worth: $3,421,687
Earnings: ($75,971)
Emp.: 108
Fiscal Year-end: 12/31/20
Electric Equipment Mfr
N.A.I.C.S.: 335999
Mohammed El Kaysi (Mng Dir)

Subsidiaries:

ITALCLEM S.p.A.   (1)
Via Cefalonia 70, 25124, Brescia, Italy
Tel.: (39) 03 022 4572
Web Site: https://www.italclem.com
Emp.: 23
Electrical Component Mfr
N.A.I.C.S.: 335999

ARAB FINANCIAL SERVICES B.S.C.
PO Box 2152, Manama, Bahrain
Tel.: (973) 17290333
Web Site: http://www.afs.com.bh
Year Founded: 1984
Sales Range: $25-49.9 Million
All Other Nondepository Credit Intermediation
N.A.I.C.S.: 522299
Balasubramanian Chandrasekhar (CEO)

ARAB HEAVY INDUSTRIES P.J.S.C
PO Box 529, Ajman, United Arab Emirates
Tel.: (971) 65263232
Web Site: http://www.ahi-uae.com
Sales Range: $25-49.9 Million
Ship Repair Services
N.A.I.C.S.: 336611

ARAB INFORMATION MANAGEMENT SERVICES
PO Box 23906, Kuwait, 13100, Kuwait
Tel.: (965) 2444070
Web Site: http://www.aims-kw.com
Year Founded: 1980
Sales Range: $25-49.9 Million
Emp.: 430
Information Technology Consulting Services
N.A.I.C.S.: 541512

ARAB INSURANCE GROUP B.S.C.
Arig House Building 131 Road 1702 Diplomatic Area 317, PO Box 26992, Manama, Bahrain
Tel.: (973) 17544444   BH
Web Site: https://www.arig.net
Year Founded: 1980
ARIG—(BAH)
Rev.: $1,299,000
Assets: $452,353,000
Liabilities: $174,989,000
Net Worth: $277,364,000
Earnings: $19,914,000
Fiscal Year-end: 12/31/22
Insurance Services
N.A.I.C.S.: 524126
Mohamed Saif Al Hameli (Vice Chm)

Subsidiaries:

Arig Capital Limited   (1)
4th Floor Mitre House 12-14 Mitre Street, London, EC3A 5BU, United Kingdom
Tel.: (44) 2032070081
Reinsurance Services

N.A.I.C.S.: 524130
Arima Insurance Software W.L.L.   (1)
Arig House Building 131 Road 1702 Diplomatic Area 317, PO Box 15642, Manama, 15642, Bahrain   (100%)
Tel.: (973) 17544111
Web Site: https://www.arima.com.bh
Sales Range: $50-74.9 Million
Emp.: 30
Investment Advice
N.A.I.C.S.: 523940
Adel Al-Mudaifa (Gen Mgr)

Gulf Warranties W.L.L.   (1)
Office 03 3rd Floor Oasis Center, PO Box 123090, Sheikh Zayed Road, Dubai, United Arab Emirates   (100%)
Tel.: (971) 43355347
Web Site: https://www.gulfwarranties.com
Sales Range: $50-74.9 Million
Emp.: 13
Investment Advice
N.A.I.C.S.: 523940
Wael Al-Saafin (Gen Mgr)

Takaful Re Limited   (1)
Daman Tower 401, Level 4 Tenancy 3, Daman, 211181, United Arab Emirates   (100%)
Tel.: (971) 43600535
Web Site: http://www.takaful-re.ae
Investment Advice
N.A.I.C.S.: 523940
Firas El Azem (Gen Mgr)

ARAB INTERNATIONAL CO. FOR EDUCATION & INVESTMENT PLC
Al Arab st 21Amman Jordan, PO Box 541350, Amman, 11931, Jordan
Tel.: (962) 65609999
Web Site: https://www.asu.edu.jo
Year Founded: 1989
AIEI—(AMM)
Rev.: $28,185,660
Assets: $134,791,979
Liabilities: $26,871,721
Net Worth: $107,920,258
Earnings: $6,649,000
Emp.: 920
Fiscal Year-end: 12/31/20
Education Services
N.A.I.C.S.: 611710
Haitham Abdullah Abdulhalim Abu Khadijah (Vice Chm)

ARAB INTERNATIONAL FOOD FACTORIES & INVESTMENT COMPANY
Al- Madina Al-Monawara St, 926065, Al-Haitham Complex- Building num 156- 2nd floor, Amman, 11190, Jordan
Tel.: (962) 65522581
Year Founded: 1994
AIFF—(AMM)
Sales Range: $1-9.9 Million
Emp.: 2
Baby Food Mfr
N.A.I.C.S.: 311422
Razan Al-Zo'ubi (Gen Mgr-Acting)

ARAB INTERNATIONAL HOTELS PLC.
Al-Shmeisani Alal Al-Fasi St, PO Box 941676, Amman, 11194, Jordan
Tel.: (962) 65674852
Web Site: http://www.aiho-group.com
Year Founded: 1975
AIHO—(AMM)
Rev.: $4,471,518
Assets: $96,427,360
Liabilities: $31,238,892
Net Worth: $65,188,468
Earnings: ($8,694,848)
Emp.: 376
Fiscal Year-end: 12/31/20
Tourism & Hotel Management Services
N.A.I.C.S.: 721110

Bassam Farah Maayeh (Mng Dir)

ARAB INVESTORS UNION CO. FOR REAL ESTATES DEVELOPING P.L.C
Airport Street beside International School, PO Box 850906, Amman, 11185, Jordan
Tel.: (962) 5736407
Year Founded: 2006
UNAI—(AMM)
Assets: $3,574,140
Liabilities: $211,924
Net Worth: $3,362,215
Earnings: ($36,714)
Emp.: 2
Fiscal Year-end: 12/31/20
Real Estate Investment Services
N.A.I.C.S.: 531390
Fayyad Al-Nabulsi (Gen Mgr)

ARAB ISLAMIC BANK
Nablus St, PO Box 631, Al-Bireh, Palestine
Tel.: (970) 22941800
Web Site: http://www.aibnk.com
Year Founded: 1995
AIB—(PAL)
Rev.: $75,836,085
Assets: $1,738,370,083
Liabilities: $1,597,366,185
Net Worth: $141,003,898
Earnings: $5,519,706
Emp.: 411
Fiscal Year-end: 12/31/23
Commercial Banking Services
N.A.I.C.S.: 522110

ARAB JORDAN INVESTMENT BANK
AJIB Tower 200 Zahran Street, PO Box 8797, Amman, 11121, Jordan
Tel.: (962) 65607138
Web Site: https://www.ajib.com
Year Founded: 1978
AJIB—(AMM)
Rev.: $127,611,607
Assets: $3,103,255,845
Liabilities: $2,786,508,126
Net Worth: $316,747,720
Earnings: $16,271,827
Emp.: 774
Fiscal Year-end: 12/31/20
Commercial & Investment Banking Services
N.A.I.C.S.: 522110
Hani Al-Qadi (Chm)

Subsidiaries:

Arab Jordan Investment Bank (Qatar) L.L.C.   (1)
Qatar Financial Center Tower No 1 17th Floor, Doha, Qatar
Tel.: (974) 44967338
Financial Services
N.A.I.C.S.: 541611

United Arab Jordan Company for Investment & Financial Brokerage   (1)
Housing Bank Complex Fifth Floor, PO Box 8789, Amman, 11121, Jordan
Tel.: (962) 65652441
Investment & Financial Services
N.A.I.C.S.: 523999

ARAB JORDANIAN INSURANCE GROUP
Al-Shareef Nasser bin Jameel st, PO Box 840657, Amman, 11184, Jordan
Tel.: (962) 62223666
Web Site: https://www.ajig.com
Year Founded: 1996
ARGR—(AMM)
Rev.: $29,426,014
Assets: $37,059,635
Liabilities: $24,618,081
Net Worth: $12,441,555

Earnings: $1,765,247
Emp.: 74
Fiscal Year-end: 12/31/20
Insurance Services
N.A.I.C.S.: 524298

ARAB LIFE & ACCIDENT IN-SURANCE COMPANY P.S.C.

Abd Al-Hamid Sharaf St Shmeisani,
PO Box 925250, Amman, 11190, Jordan
Tel.: (962) 65693180
Web Site:
   http://www.arabinsurance.jo
Year Founded: 1981
ARIN—(AMM)
Rev.: $20,178,119
Assets: $19,472,065
Liabilities: $14,026,125
Net Worth: $5,445,940
Earnings: ($496,207)
Emp.: 139
Fiscal Year-end: 12/31/19
General Insurance Services
N.A.I.C.S.: 524298
Diraar Y. Alghanim *(Chm)*

ARAB MOLTAQA INVEST-MENTS COMPANY

7A Cornich El-Nil Dallah Tower,
Maadi, Cairo, Egypt
Tel.: (20) 225256050
Web Site: https://www.amic-eg.com
Year Founded: 1990
AMIA.CA—(EGX)
Sales Range: Less than $1 Million
Financial Investment Services
N.A.I.C.S.: 523999
Abdulaziz Mohammed Abdo Yamani
(Chm)

ARAB NATIONAL BANK

PO Box 56921, Riyadh, 11564, Saudi
Arabia
Tel.: (966) 114029000
Web Site: https://www.anb.com.sa
Year Founded: 1979
1080—(SAU)
Rev.: $2,041,506,466
Assets: $56,693,265,698
Liabilities: $48,065,707,506
Net Worth: $8,627,558,192
Earnings: $817,772,297
Emp.: 4,029
Fiscal Year-end: 12/31/22
Banking Services
N.A.I.C.S.: 522110
Obaid A. Alrasheed *(CEO & Mng Dir)*

Subsidiaries:

ANB Invest   **(1)**
PO Box 220009, 11311, Riyadh, Saudi Arabia
Tel.: (966) 114062500
Web Site: http://www.anbinvest.com.sa
Investment Banking Services
N.A.I.C.S.: 523150
Bassam Al-Mubarak *(CEO)*

ARAB PALESTINIAN INVEST-MENT COMPANY

Al-Ayyam st Palestine Automobile Co
Building 3rd fl, POBox 2190, Ramallah, Palestine
Tel.: (970) 22977040
Web Site: https://www.apic.ps
Year Founded: 1994
APIC—(PAL)
Rev.: $1,190,013,402
Assets: $797,870,595
Liabilities: $584,701,876
Net Worth: $213,168,719
Earnings: $18,587,895
Emp.: 3,150
Fiscal Year-end: 12/31/23
Holding Company
N.A.I.C.S.: 551112

Tarek Omar Aggad *(Chm & CEO)*

Subsidiaries:

Arab Leasing Company PSC   **(1)**
Al-Ayyam Street Beitunia, Industrial Zone,
Ramallah, Palestine
Tel.: (970) 2 298 0026
Financial Lending Services
N.A.I.C.S.: 522220
Sufian Deriah *(Gen Mgr)*

Arab Palestinian Shopping
Centers   **(1)**
Plaza Mall, PO Box 4185, Al-Bireh, Palestine
Tel.: (970) 22428581
Web Site: http://www.plaza.ps
Grocery Store Operator
N.A.I.C.S.: 445110

National Aluminum & Profiles Company PLC   **(1)**
Qusin Junction, BO Box 178, Beit Iba, Nablus, Palestine
Tel.: (970) 9 234 7222
Web Site: https://www.napco.ps
Aluminum Profile Mfr & Whslr
N.A.I.C.S.: 331315
Ali Aqqad *(Chm)*

Unipal General Trading Company
PSC   **(1)**
Abd el-Hamid Shuman St 23, PO Box 2190,
Industrial Zone, Ramallah, Palestine
Tel.: (970) 2 298 1060
Web Site: https://www.unipalgt.com
Emp.: 300
Consumer Products Distr
N.A.I.C.S.: 424990
Imad Khoury *(CEO)*

ARAB PETROLEUM INVEST-MENTS CORPORATION

7201 King Faysal Road - Al Bahar
Unit No 1, 34218, Al Khobar, Saudi
Arabia
Tel.: (966) 13 847 0444
Web Site: http://www.apicorp.org
Year Founded: 1975
Petroleum Investment Services
N.A.I.C.S.: 523999
Ali Hassan Fadel *(Officer-Compliance, Gen Counsel & Sec)*

Subsidiaries:

APICORP Petroleum Shipping Fund
Limited   **(1)**
Head Office Building Dammam Coastal
Road, PO Box 9599, Al Rakkah, Dammam,
31423, Saudi Arabia
Tel.: (966) 138470444
Fund Managing Services
N.A.I.C.S.: 523940

Saudi Mechanical Industries Co. **(1)**
Second Industrial City Street No 234, Riyadh, Saudi Arabia
Tel.: (966) 112651979
Web Site: http://www.smi.com.sa
Steel Works & Rolling Mills, Pumps &
Pumping Equipment Mfr
N.A.I.C.S.: 333914
Ahmad A. Khraishi *(COO)*

ARAB PHOENIX HOLDINGS

PO Box 140626, Amman, 11814,
Jordan
Tel.: (962) 65885558   JO
Web Site: https://phoenix.jo
Year Founded: 2005
PHNX—(AMM)
Rev.: $4,876,222
Assets: $88,108,054
Liabilities: $27,844,639
Net Worth: $60,263,415
Earnings: ($1,224,369)
Emp.: 23
Fiscal Year-end: 12/31/23
Holding Company; Real Estate Development Services
N.A.I.C.S.: 531390
Omar Khalifeh *(Chm)*

ARAB POLVARA COMPANY FOR SPINNING & WEAVING COMPANY

Swords Mail Bag, PO Box 21533, El
Seyouf, Alexandria, Egypt
Tel.: (20) 33300543
Web Site:
   https://www.arabpolvara.com.eg
Year Founded: 2014
APSW.CA—(EGX)
Sales Range: Less than $1 Million
Yarn Mfr
N.A.I.C.S.: 313110
Raafat Tawfiq Ahmed Qabil *(Chm & Mng Dir)*

ARAB POTASH COMPANY PLC

Al Shmeisani Al Jaheth St, PO Box
1470, Amman, 11118, Jordan
Tel.: (962) 65200520
Web Site:
   https://www.arabpotash.com
Year Founded: 1956
APOT—(AMM)
Rev.: $643,399,004
Assets: $1,578,337,367
Liabilities: $262,711,375
Net Worth: $1,315,625,992
Earnings: $178,970,732
Emp.: 1,688
Fiscal Year-end: 12/31/20
Potassium Chloride Fertilizer Producer
N.A.I.C.S.: 325312
Adnan Al Ma'aitah *(VP-HR & Corp Affairs)*

Subsidiaries:

Arab Fertilizers and Chemicals Industries Ltd.   **(1)**
PO Box 2564, Durra Southern Industrial
Area, Al Aqabah, 77110, Jordan
Tel.: (962) 3 201 7174
Web Site: https://kemapco.com
Sales Range: $75-99.9 Million
Emp.: 255
Fertilizers & Chemicals Mfr
N.A.I.C.S.: 325180
Bassam Al Zoumot *(Gen Mgr)*

Arab Potash Company PLC - Potash
Plant   **(1)**
PO Box 1470, Amman, 11118, Jordan
Tel.: (962) 32397100
Potash Mfr
N.A.I.C.S.: 325998

Jordan Magnesia Company   **(1)**
Extrema Al Quraishi Building No 7 Behind
Ministry Of Industry & Trade, PO Box
941701, Amman, 11194, Jordan
Tel.: (962) 65691201
Emp.: 4
Magnesium Oxide Mfr
N.A.I.C.S.: 325180
Jamal Sarayrah *(Chm)*

Numeira Mixed Salts & Mud Co. **(1)**
Zahran St Alhusaini Complex Building No
33, PO Box 941681, Amman, 11118,
Jordan   **(52.7%)**
Tel.: (962) 65826889
Web Site: https://numeira.com
Sales Range: $25-49.9 Million
Emp.: 60
Cosmetics & Skin Care Products
N.A.I.C.S.: 325620
Firas Thalji *(Mgr-Fin)*

ARAB REAL ESTATE COM-PANY K.S.C.C.

7th Floor Emad Commercial Complex
Ahmed Al Jaber Street, Po Box
26980, Sharq, Kuwait, 13130, Kuwait
Tel.: (965) 840004
Web Site: http://www.arec-kwt.com
Year Founded: 1976
ARABREC—(KUW)
Rev.: $42,968,426
Assets: $450,203,715

Liabilities: $329,255,715
Net Worth: $120,948,000
Earnings: $6,696,919
Emp.: 15
Fiscal Year-end: 12/31/22
Real Estate Services
N.A.I.C.S.: 531390
Emad Jawad Bukhamseen *(Chm)*

ARAB REAL ESTATE DEVEL-OPMENT COMPANY PSC

Al-madina Al-Monawara St Al-Haitham Building No 156, PO Box
941554, Amman, 11194, Jordan
Tel.: (962) 6 5563002
Year Founded: 1995
ARED—(AMM)
Sales Range: Less than $1 Million
Emp.: 23
Real Estate Investment Services
N.A.I.C.S.: 523999
Bashar Al-Zubi *(Gen Mgr)*

ARAB SATELLITE COMMUNI-CATIONS ORGANIZATION

Diplomatic Quarter Alfazari Square
Abdulla bin Huthafa Al Sahmy Street,
PO Box 1038, Pub Pension Agcy
Complex C-6, Riyadh, 11431, Saudi
Arabia
Tel.: (966) 1 482 0000
Web Site: http://www.arabsat.com
Year Founded: 1976
Satellite Telecommunication Services
N.A.I.C.S.: 517410
Khalid A. Balkheyour *(Pres & CEO)*

Subsidiaries:

Hellas Sat Consortium Limited   **(1)**
Hellas Sat Space Centre Panagias Galaktotrofousas 1, Kofinou, Larnaca, 7735,
Cyprus   **(99.05%)**
Tel.: (357) 22 861400
Web Site: http://www.hellas-sat.net
Sales Range: $25-49.9 Million
Emp.: 15
Satellite Communication Services
N.A.I.C.S.: 517410

Subsidiary (Non-US):

Hellas Sat S.A.   **(2)**
99 Kifissias Avenue, GR 151 24, Maroussi,
Athens, Greece
Tel.: (30) 210 6100600
Web Site: http://www.hellas-sat.net
Sales Range: $25-49.9 Million
Emp.: 50
Satellite Telecommunication Services
N.A.I.C.S.: 517410

ARAB SEA INFORMATION SYSTEM CO

Eastern Ring Road between exit 13-14, Riyadh, Saudi Arabia
Tel.: (966) 14964444
Web Site: https://www.arabsea.com
Year Founded: 1980
7201—(SAU)
Rev.: $10,978,488
Assets: $39,762,834
Liabilities: $5,885,232
Net Worth: $33,877,602
Earnings: ($2,605,356)
Emp.: 157
Fiscal Year-end: 12/31/23
Software Development Services
N.A.I.C.S.: 513210
Muhammad Saleh Al Suhibani *(Chm)*

ARAB SHIPBUILDING & RE-PAIR YARD CO.

PO Box 50110, Hidd, Bahrain
Tel.: (973) 17671111
Web Site: http://www.asry.net
Year Founded: 1977
Sales Range: $100-124.9 Million
Emp.: 1,700

Arab Shipbuilding & Repair Yard Co.—(Continued)

Ship Building & Repairing Services
N.A.I.C.S.: 336611
Nils Kristian Berge *(CEO)*

Subsidiaries:

ASRY Marketing Services Ltd. **(1)**
28 Bolton Street, Mayfair, London, W1J
8BP, United Kingdom
Tel.: (44) 2073189800
Sales Range: $25-49.9 Million
Emp.: 3
Marketing Services for Arab Shipbuilding &
Repair Yard
N.A.I.C.S.: 561499

ARAB SUPPLY & TRADING CO.

Prince Sultan Bin Abdul Aziz St, PO
Box 245, Tabuk, Saudi Arabia
Tel.: (966) 144220400
Web Site: http://www.astra.com.sa
Year Founded: 1976
Sales Range: $500-549.9 Million
Emp.: 5,500
Diversified Holding Company; Trad-
ing, Agriculture, Manufacturing, Con-
tracting, Medical & Healthcare & Real
Estate Services
N.A.I.C.S.: 551112
Sabih Taher Masri *(Chm)*

Subsidiaries:

ASTRA Agricultural Co. Ltd. **(1)**
PO Box 54061, Riyadh, 11514, Saudi Ara-
bia
Tel.: (966) 114772346
Web Site: https://www.astra-agri.com.sa
Sales Range: $75-99.9 Million
Emp.: 180
Farm Supplies Whslr
N.A.I.C.S.: 424910

ASTRA Food Processing Co. **(1)**
Jordan Road, PO Box 1485, Tabuk, Saudi
Arabia
Tel.: (966) 44226661
Web Site: http://www.astra.com.sa
Sales Range: $25-49.9 Million
Emp.: 100
Food Processing Services
N.A.I.C.S.: 311999

ASTRA Grain Trade Division **(1)**
PO Box 42412, 21541, Jeddah, Saudi Ara-
bia
Tel.: (966) 2 637 4027
Commodity Trading Services
N.A.I.C.S.: 523160

ASTRA Industrial Complex for Fertil-
izers & Agrochemicals Co. Ltd. **(1)**
PO Box 30447, 31952, Al Khobar, Saudi
Arabia
Tel.: (966) 381 21406
Fertilizer Mfr
N.A.I.C.S.: 325311
Jehad Atiyat *(CEO)*

ASTRA Supermarket and Commercial
Division **(1)**
PO Box 1483, Tabuk, Saudi Arabia
Tel.: (966) 44 33775
Grocery Whslr
N.A.I.C.S.: 424410

Agricultural Plastic Industrial Com-
pany (APICO) **(1)**
King Abdallah II Industrial City Al Azraq St
250, PO Box 9, Amman, 512, Jordan
Tel.: (962) 64022555
Agricultural Plastic Products Mfr
N.A.I.C.S.: 326199

Arab Supply & Trading Co. - Food
Supply Division **(1)**
PO Box 254, Tabuk, Saudi Arabia
Tel.: (966) 442 20400
Food Products Distr
N.A.I.C.S.: 424490

Ayla Oasis Development
Company **(1)**
Astra Plaza Al Hussein Bin Ali St, PO Box
83, Amman, 11118, Jordan

Tel.: (962) 6 461 2324
Web Site: http://www.aylaoasis.com
Travel Tour Operator
N.A.I.C.S.: 561520
Hussein Elshare *(Project Mgr)*

Golden Wheat Mills Company **(1)**
PO Box 641, Burnham Village, Ramallah,
Palestine
Tel.: (970) 22818013
Web Site: http://www.gwmc.ps
Sales Range: $25-49.9 Million
Emp.: 55
Wheat Product Production & Marketing Ser-
vices
N.A.I.C.S.: 311211

Jordan Vegetable Oil Industries
Company **(1)**
PO Box 128, PO Box 128, Amman, 11512,
Jordan
Tel.: (962) 64023601
Web Site: http://www.vegoils.net
Emp.: 69
Vegetable Oil Producer & Exporter
N.A.I.C.S.: 311224
Azzam Alahmad *(Gen Mgr)*

Nour Communication Company **(1)**
PO Box 21557, 11485, Riyadh, Saudi Ara-
bia
Tel.: (966) 14776555
Web Site: http://www.nour.com.sa
Sales Range: $200-249.9 Million
Emp.: 900
Telecommunication System Contractor
N.A.I.C.S.: 517111

Palestine Development & Investment
Ltd. **(1)**
6th Floor office Building Q Center, PO Box
666, Ramallah, Palestine
Tel.: (970) 22948222
Web Site: http://www.padico.com
Rev: $109,314,000
Assets: $730,709,000
Liabilities: $334,783,000
Net Worth: $395,926,000
Earnings: ($19,620,000)
Emp.: 100
Fiscal Year-end: 12/31/2023
Economic Development & Investment Ser-
vices
N.A.I.C.S.: 523999
Munib R. Masri *(Chm)*

Subsidiary (Domestic):

Palestine Industrial Investment Co.
Ltd. **(2)**
Abu-Ra ed Building - University St, PO Box
1769, Nablus, Palestine
Tel.: (970) 92386180
Web Site: https://www.piico.ps
Sales Range: $25-49.9 Million
Emp.: 7
Holding Company
N.A.I.C.S.: 551112
Abdul Al-Hakim Fuqaha *(Gen Mgr)*

Subsidiary (Domestic):

Palestine Plastic Industries Co.
Ltd. **(3)**
Palestine west bank Nablus deersharf Ind
zone, PO Box 1949, Nablus, Palestine
Tel.: (970) 92398716
Web Site: http://www.ppic-pal.com
Sales Range: $25-49.9 Million
Plastics Product Mfr
N.A.I.C.S.: 326199

Palestine Poultry Co. Ltd. **(3)**
Rafidia Main Street, PO Box 1835, Nablus,
Palestine
Tel.: (970) 92389409
Web Site: https://aziza.ps
Sales Range: $50-74.9 Million
Poultry Feed & Hatchery
N.A.I.C.S.: 112340
Abdul-Hakim Foqaha *(Chm)*

The National Carton Industry
Company **(3)**
East Industrial Zone, PO Box 803, Nablus,
Palestine
Tel.: (970) 92311290
Web Site: https://www.nci.ps
Rev: $4,876,184
Assets: $9,254,777

Liabilities: $2,352,080
Net Worth: $6,902,697
Earnings: $804,308
Fiscal Year-end: 12/31/2020
Carton Mfr & Whslr
N.A.I.C.S.: 322212
Mahdi Hayaty Al Masri *(Chm)*

Subsidiary (Domestic):

The Palestine Securities Exchange,
Ltd. **(2)**
Seventh Floor-ASAL building-Rafedya St,
PO Box 128, Nablus, Palestine
Tel.: (970) 92390999
Web Site: http://www.p-s-e.com
Stock Exchange Services
N.A.I.C.S.: 523210
Khaled Jian *(Deputy CEO & Head-Admin &
Fin Affairs Dept)*

Saudi Mais Company for Medical
Products **(1)**
PO Box 3900, 14335-55599, Riyadh, Saudi
Arabia
Tel.: (966) 12650184
Web Site: http://www.mais.com.sa
Sales Range: $100-124.9 Million
Emp.: 300
Medical Products Mfr & Distr
N.A.I.C.S.: 339112

ARAB UNION INTERNATIONAL INSURANCE CO. LTD.

Al Abdali King Hussein St Building No
264, PO Box 7241, Amman, 11118,
Jordan
Tel.: (962) 65684459
Web Site: https://ruminsurance.com
AIUI—(AMM)
Rev.: $14,877,307
Assets: $24,211,301
Liabilities: $15,947,539
Net Worth: $8,263,762
Earnings: ($297,309)
Emp.: 54
Fiscal Year-end: 12/31/20
Insurance Services
N.A.I.C.S.: 524298
Salem Alkhazaleh *(Chm)*

ARAB WEAVERS UNION COMPANY P.L.C.

King Abullah Second Industerial Area,
PO Box 116, Sahab, Amman, 11512,
Jordan
Tel.: (962) 64022792
Web Site:
http://www.kaloutigroup.com
Rev.: $7,468,636
Assets: $20,193,430
Liabilities: $2,661,668
Net Worth: $17,531,762
Earnings: ($1,177,510)
Emp.: 158
Fiscal Year-end: 12/31/17
Carpet & Industrial Yarn Product Mfr
N.A.I.C.S.: 314110

ARABI HOLDING GROUP COMPANY K.S.C.C.

Safat, PO Box 4090, Kuwait, 13041,
Kuwait
Tel.: (965) 24724057
Web Site:
https://www.arabigroup.com
Year Founded: 1981
Rev: $393,424,308
Assets: $799,645,273
Liabilities: $691,376,391
Net Worth: $108,268,882
Earnings: $5,228,986
Emp.: 5,000
Fiscal Year-end: 12/31/18
Holding Company
N.A.I.C.S.: 551112
Salah Mohammad Saqer Al Maoush-
erji *(Exec Dir)*

Subsidiaries:

Arabi Agriculture Co. **(1)**
Shuwaikh Industrial Area Block 174/175 4th
Ring Road, PO Box 4090, Safat, Kuwait,
13041, Kuwait **(100%)**
Tel.: (965) 4817878
Web Site: http://www.arabigroup.com
Sales Range: $25-49.9 Million
Emp.: 20
Landscaping & Irrigation Services
N.A.I.C.S.: 541320

Arabi Company W.L.L. **(1)**
Ghazally Street Opposite Centrepoint Al
Rai, PO Box 4090, Safat, Kuwait, 13041,
Kuwait **(100%)**
Tel.: (965) 24724057
Web Site: http://www.arabicompany.net
Sales Range: $125-149.9 Million
Emp.: 175
Distr of Oil, Petrochemicals, Water Equip-
ment, Irrigation Equipment, Agricultural Ma-
terials, Power Tools, Garage Equipment,
Building Systems & Safety Equipment
N.A.I.C.S.: 221210

Arabi Enertech Company K.S.C. **(1)**
PO Box 9831, Ahmadi, Kuwait
Tel.: (965) 23986083
Web Site: http://www.arabienertech.net
Emp.: 6,000
Engineering Construction Services
N.A.I.C.S.: 541330

Arabi Engineering Co. **(1)**
PO Box 9831, Ahmadi, 61009,
Kuwait **(100%)**
Tel.: (965) 3986083
Web Site: http://www.arabienertech.com
Sales Range: $150-199.9 Million
Emp.: 734
Engineeering Services
N.A.I.C.S.: 541330

Arabi Gulf Services & Industrial Sup-
plies Co. **(1)**
PO Box 2250, Ruwi, 112, Oman
Tel.: (968) 24811238
Web Site: http://www.arabigsis.com
Sales Range: $50-74.9 Million
Emp.: 150
Provider of Industrial Products
N.A.I.C.S.: 334513

Arabi Industrial Services & Supplies
Co. **(1)**
PO Box 4090, Safat, 13041, Kuwait,
Kuwait **(100%)**
Tel.: (965) 4817878
Web Site: http://www.arabigroup.com
Sales Range: $25-49.9 Million
Emp.: 25
Construction & Maintenance Services Spe-
cializing in Heating, Ventilation & Air Condi-
tioning
N.A.I.C.S.: 333414

Arabi Medical & Scientific Equipment
Co. W.L.L. **(1)**
E Ahmadi, PO Box 3562, Safat, Kuwait,
13036, Kuwait **(100%)**
Tel.: (965) 4817878
Web Site: http://www.arabigroup.com
Sales Range: $25-49.9 Million
Emp.: 100
Sales & Service of Medical & Scientific
Equipment
N.A.I.C.S.: 456199

Hasibat Information Technologist
Company **(1)**
Beirut Street Al Safat Tower 3rd & 4th
Floors, PO Box 27728, Hawalli, 13138, Ku-
wait
Tel.: (965) 22675401
Web Site: http://www.hasibat.com
Emp.: 70
Information Technology Solutions & Ser-
vices
N.A.I.C.S.: 541512
Fawaz Yousef Sultan Al-Salem *(Chm)*

Key BS JLT W.L.L. **(1)**
1902 JLT-Cluster Y Swiss Tower, Dubai,
United Arab Emirates
Tel.: (971) 44585212
Web Site: http://www.keybs.net
Payment Solution Banking Services

N.A.I.C.S.: 522320
Salah Al Maousherji *(Chm)*

Warba MEchanical Equipments L.L.C. **(1)**
PO Box 34152, Abu Dhabi, United Arab Emirates
Tel.: (971) 25547887
Electronic Parts Distr
N.A.I.C.S.: 423690

ARABIA INSURANCE CO.
FL5-6-7 Bldg Arabia House Phoenicia St, PO Box 11-2172, Beirut, Lebanon
Tel.: (961) 1363610
Web Site:
   http://www.arabiainsurance.com
Sales Range: $50-74.9 Million
Emp.: 120
Provider of Insurance Services
N.A.I.C.S.: 524298
Wahbe A. Tamari *(Chm)*

Subsidiaries:

AL MASHRIQ FINANCIAL INVESTMENT CO. s.a.l. **(1)**
PO Box 11-961, Beirut, Lebanon
Tel.: (961) 1 364700
Fire Insurance Services
N.A.I.C.S.: 524298

ARABIA INSURANCE COMPANY - SYRIA S.A. **(1)**
PO Box 34801, Damascus, Syria
Tel.: (963) 11 6627745
Web Site: http://www.arabiasyria.com
Fire Insurance Services
N.A.I.C.S.: 524298
Farouk Joud *(Chm)*

ARABIA s.a.l. Holding Company **(1)**
Arabia House Building Phoenicia Street, PO Box 11-2172, Beirut, Lebanon
Tel.: (961) 1 363610
Investment Management Service
N.A.I.C.S.: 523940
Hani Atallah Freij *(Chm)*

ARABIA INSURANCE COMPANY
Al Shareef Abd Al Hameed Sharaf St Building 3, PO Box 20031, Amman, 11118, Jordan
Tel.: (962) 65630530
Web Site: https://www.aicj.jo
Year Founded: 1975
AICJ—(AMM)
Rev.: $29,861,647
Assets: $39,816,515
Liabilities: $24,738,453
Net Worth: $15,078,062
Earnings: $877,971
Emp.: 82
Fiscal Year-end: 12/31/20
Insurance Related Services
N.A.I.C.S.: 524298
Muneer Butros Ibrahimq Mouasher *(Chm)*

Subsidiaries:

Arabia Insurance Company S.A.L. **(1)**
Green Tower Baniyas Street, Deira, Dubai, United Arab Emirates
Tel.: (971) 42280022
Medical Insurance Services
N.A.I.C.S.: 524114

ARABIA INSURANCE COOPERATIVE COMPANY
6984 King Abdul Aziz Branch Road Bin Tami Center, Riyadh, 12252-4483, Saudi Arabia
Tel.: (966) 336021511
Web Site: https://www.aicc.com.sa
Year Founded: 2007
8160—(SAU)
Rev.: $195,492,128
Assets: $411,769,935
Liabilities: $352,526,440

Net Worth: $59,243,494
Earnings: $2,207,064
Emp.: 200
Fiscal Year-end: 12/31/22
Insurance Agency Services
N.A.I.C.S.: 524210
Abdulaziz Abdulhadi Alqahtani *(Chm)*

ARABIAN AGRICULTURAL SERVICES CO.
Prince Sultan Ibn Abdul Aziz St, PO Box 53845, Riyadh, 11593, Saudi Arabia
Tel.: (966) 112612222
Web Site: http://www.arasco.com
Year Founded: 1983
Sales Range: $150-199.9 Million
Emp.: 1,800
Animal Feed Mfr
N.A.I.C.S.: 311119
Abdullah S. Al Rubaian *(Chm)*

Subsidiaries:

Arasco Chemical Co. **(1)**
Industrial City, PO Box 6977, 31452, Dammam, Saudi Arabia
Tel.: (966) 38123456
Sales Range: $25-49.9 Million
Emp.: 30
Organic Chemical Mfr
N.A.I.C.S.: 325199

Arasco Cold Store Co. **(1)**
Second Industrial City Alkharj Hwy, PO Box 53845, 11593, Riyadh, Saudi Arabia
Tel.: (966) 14982039
Sales Range: $25-49.9 Million
Emp.: 25
Refrigerated Warehousing & Storage
N.A.I.C.S.: 493120

Arasco Feed Mill Co. **(1)**
Alkhobar Costal Road Near King Abdulaziz Port, PO Box 6977, 31452, Dammam, Saudi Arabia
Tel.: (966) 38591171
Sales Range: $250-299.9 Million
Emp.: 700
Farm Product Raw Material Whslr
N.A.I.C.S.: 424590

Arasco Transport, Handling and Shipping Co. **(1)**
Alkhobar Costal Road Near King Abdulaziz Port, PO Box 6977, 31452, Dammam, Saudi Arabia
Tel.: (966) 38591171
Sales Range: $50-74.9 Million
Emp.: 200
Freight Transportation Arrangement
N.A.I.C.S.: 488510

ARABIAN CEMENT COMPANY
Gamal Abdel Naser square Fifth Settlement Arabella Plaza, Office Building A 5th floor, New Cairo, Egypt
Tel.: (20) 225316277
Web Site:
   https://www.arabiancement.com
Year Founded: 1997
ARCC.CA—(EGX)
Rev.: $127,438,037
Assets: $81,984,559
Liabilities: $44,988,544
Net Worth: $36,996,016
Earnings: $14,709,637
Fiscal Year-end: 12/31/23
Cement Mfr
N.A.I.C.S.: 327310
Generoso Bertolin Agustin *(Chm)*

Subsidiaries:

Cementos La union-Spain SA **(1)**
Avenida dels Gremis 41, Poligono Industrial Sector 13 Ribarroja del Turia, 46394, Valencia, Spain
Tel.: (34) 961668330
Web Site: http://www.launion.es
Building Materials Distr
N.A.I.C.S.: 444180
Vicente Aliaga Garcia *(CIO)*

ARABIAN CEMENT COMPANY LTD.
Fifth Settlement Arabella Plaza Office Building 5th Floor, Gamal Abdel Naser Square, 11835, New Cairo, Egypt
Tel.: (20) 216277
Web Site:
   https://www.arabiancement.com
Year Founded: 1956
3010—(SAU)
Rev.: $98,591,728
Assets: $80,302,457
Liabilities: $55,774,440
Net Worth: $24,528,017
Earnings: $7,570,700
Emp.: 457
Fiscal Year-end: 12/31/22
Cement Mfr
N.A.I.C.S.: 327310
Ibrahim Sulaiman Al Rajhi *(Chm)*

Subsidiaries:

Arabian Cement Co. **(1)**
8605 King Abdul Aziz Rd, Jeddah, 23523, Saudi Arabia
Tel.: (966) 126949700
Web Site:
   https://www.arabiancement.com.sa
Cement Mfr
N.A.I.C.S.: 327310
Abdullah Mohammed Rahimi *(Chm)*

ARABIAN FOOD INDUSTRIES COMPANY
32C Murad Street, PO Box 245, Giza, Egypt
Tel.: (20) 235724924
Web Site: http://www.domty.org
Year Founded: 1990
DOMT.CA—(EGX)
Rev.: $158,262,295
Assets: $76,127,753
Liabilities: $48,689,813
Net Worth: $27,437,940
Earnings: $9,583,713
Emp.: 2,600
Fiscal Year-end: 12/31/23
Food Mfr
N.A.I.C.S.: 311513
Omar El Damaty *(CEO)*

ARABIAN INTERNATIONAL HEALTHCARE HOLDING COMPANY
Qortubah Al Marhoma Street Business Gate, PB 1646, Riyadh, 11464, Saudi Arabia
Tel.: (966) 112439494
Web Site: https://www.tibbiyah.com
Year Founded: 2013
9530—(SAU)
Rev.: $171,356,540
Assets: $381,567,298
Liabilities: $292,079,976
Net Worth: $89,487,323
Earnings: $8,385,484
Emp.: 60
Fiscal Year-end: 12/31/22
Holding Company
N.A.I.C.S.: 551112
Alaa Ameen *(CEO)*

ARABIAN OUD COMPANY
Salahuddin Street, Malaz District, Riyadh, 61193, Saudi Arabia
Tel.: (966) 14742222   SA
Web Site: http://www.arabianoud.com
Year Founded: 1982
Perfume Mfr & Retailer
N.A.I.C.S.: 325620

ARABIAN PETROLEUM LIMITED
Office no 629/630 Avior corporate park LBS road Opp Johnson & John-

son, Mulund west, Mumbai, 400080, India
Tel.: (91) 9167944480
Web Site:
   https://arabianpetroleum.co
Year Founded: 2006
ARABIAN—(NSE)
Lubricating Oil Product Mfr
N.A.I.C.S.: 324191

ARABIAN PIPES COMPANY
Kingdom of Saudi Arabia, PO Box 42734, Riyadh, 11551, Saudi Arabia
Tel.: (966) 112650123
Web Site: https://www.arabian-pipes.com
Year Founded: 1991
2200—(SAU)
Rev.: $98,341,661
Assets: $250,879,898
Liabilities: $195,931,290
Net Worth: $54,948,608
Earnings: ($52,019,042)
Emp.: 340
Fiscal Year-end: 12/31/20
Steel Pole Mfr
N.A.I.C.S.: 331110
Khalid Abdullah Rashid Abunayyan *(Deputy Chm)*

ARABIAN PLASTIC INDUSTRIAL CO. LTD.
Industrial City 1 Street 45 Phase 3, Jeddah, Saudi Arabia
Tel.: (966) 126380101
Web Site: https://www.apico.com.sa
Year Founded: 1996
9548—(SAU)
Rev.: $31,072,683
Assets: $39,343,162
Liabilities: $19,826,834
Net Worth: $19,516,328
Earnings: $2,079,004
Fiscal Year-end: 12/31/21
Plastic Fabrication Product Mfr
N.A.I.C.S.: 315990

ARABIAN SHIELD COOPERATIVE INSURANCE COMPANY
5th Floor Cercon Building No 15 Olaya Street, PO Box 61352, Riyadh, 11565, Saudi Arabia
Tel.: (966) 112505400
Web Site: https://www.der3.com
8070—(SAU)
Rev.: $198,206,906
Assets: $714,207,439
Liabilities: $417,477,403
Net Worth: $296,730,036
Earnings: $7,444,341
Fiscal Year-end: 12/31/22
General Insurance Services
N.A.I.C.S.: 524126
Sultan Mohammed Saud Al Kabeer *(Chm)*

Subsidiaries:

AL AHLI TAKAFUL COMPANY **(1)**
Khaldiyah Business Center, PO Box 48510, Jeddah, 21582, Saudi Arabia
Tel.: (966) 126901199
Rev.: $66,104,714
Assets: $289,949,304
Liabilities: $223,355,663
Net Worth: $66,593,641
Earnings: $3,743,113
Emp.: 65
Fiscal Year-end: 12/31/2020
Insurance & Financial Services
N.A.I.C.S.: 523940

ARABIAN STEEL PIPES MFG CO. LTD
Amman Industrial Estate, PO Box 13, Sahab, 11512, Amman, 11512, Jordan
Tel.: (962) 64022136

Arabian Steel Pipes MFG Co. LTD—(Continued)

Web Site: https://www.asp-jo.com
ASPMM—(AMM)
Rev.: $8,418,462
Assets: $22,590,902
Liabilities: $5,205,060
Net Worth: $17,385,842
Earnings: ($1,185,763)
Emp.: 130
Fiscal Year-end: 12/31/20
Steel Pipes & Tubes Mfr
N.A.I.C.S.: 331110

ARABIAN STORES COMPANY LTD.

Madina Road, PO Box 53868, Jeddah, 21593, Saudi Arabia
Tel.: (966) 126687851
Web Site: http://www.sarawat.com.sa
Year Founded: 1981
Sales Range: $75-99.9 Million
Emp.: 400
Grocery Retailer
N.A.I.C.S.: 445110

ARABTEC HOLDING PJSC

1st Floor Low Rise IPIC Building Sultan Bin Zayed the First Street, PO Box 7340, Abu Dhabi, United Arab Emirates
Tel.: (971) 23337777
ARTC—(DFM)
Rev.: $2,119,445,298
Assets: $2,790,591,303
Liabilities: $2,669,752,384
Net Worth: $120,838,919
Earnings: ($231,032,521)
Emp.: 45,000
Fiscal Year-end: 12/31/19
Holding Company; Construction Services
N.A.I.C.S.: 551112
Waleed Al Mokarrab Al Muhairi *(Chm)*

Subsidiaries:

Arabtec Engineering Services L.L.C. **(1)**
Unit No 338 3rd Floor & Unit No 244 2nd Floor European Business Center, PO Box 27566, Dubai Investment Park, Dubai, United Arab Emirates
Tel.: (971) 4 347 1968
Web Site: http://www.aesuae.com
Emp.: 600
Engineering Services
N.A.I.C.S.: 541330
Amin Shahin *(CEO)*

Target Engineering Construction Company LLC **(1)**
Al Badie Commercial Tower 10th Floor Al Khaleej Al Arabi Street, PO Box 960, Capital Center, Abu Dhabi, United Arab Emirates
Tel.: (971) 2 2052222
Web Site: http://www.target.ae
Emp.: 9,000
Engineering Services
N.A.I.C.S.: 541330

ARAD INVESTMENT & INDUSTRIAL DEVELOPMENT LTD.

Beyit Isras Har Sinayi 3 TD 1058, Tel Aviv, 65816, Israel
Tel.: (972) 37130200
Year Founded: 1963
ARAD—(TAE)
Rev.: $836,841,263
Assets: $3,225,703,500
Liabilities: $1,734,284,819
Net Worth: $1,491,418,681
Earnings: $152,537,917
Fiscal Year-end: 12/31/23
Offices of Other Holding Companies
N.A.I.C.S.: 551112

ARAD LTD.

Kibbutz, Dalia, 1923900, Israel
Tel.: (972) 49897911
Web Site: https://www.arad.co.il
Valve Mfr
N.A.I.C.S.: 332911
Ziv Hilleli *(CEO)*

ARAD-OPHIR LTD.

87 Sokolov St, Ramat HaSharon, 4723811, Israel
Tel.: (972) 35409111
Web Site: https://www.arad-ophir.co.il
Year Founded: 1994
Information Technology Services
N.A.I.C.S.: 541512

ARAFA HOLDING

15 St Near North Area Nasr City Public Free Zone, Cairo, Egypt
Tel.: (20) 222731093
Web Site:
https://www.concretefashion.com
Year Founded: 1907
Rev.: $239,936,989
Assets: $440,479,301
Liabilities: $272,669,888
Net Worth: $167,809,413
Earnings: $7,037,482
Fiscal Year-end: 01/31/18
Holding Company
N.A.I.C.S.: 551112
Mohamed T. Khalifa *(Mng Dir-Investments)*

ARAFURA RARE EARTHS LIMITED

Level 6 432 Murray St, Perth, 6000, WA, Australia
Tel.: (61) 863702800
Web Site: https://www.arultd.com
ARU—(ASX)
Rev.: $3,561,309
Assets: $113,575,247
Liabilities: $17,345,077
Net Worth: $96,230,170
Earnings: ($67,424,166)
Emp.: 950
Fiscal Year-end: 06/30/24
Support Activities for Nonmetallic Minerals (except Fuels) Mining
N.A.I.C.S.: 213115
Gavin John Lockyer *(CEO & Mng Dir)*

ARAG SE

ARAG Platz 1, 40472, Dusseldorf, Germany
Tel.: (49) 2119633535
Web Site: http://www.arag.com
Insurance Company
N.A.I.C.S.: 523999
Paul-Otto Fassbender *(Chm-Mgmt Bd)*

Subsidiaries:

DAS Legal Expenses Insurance Company Limited **(1)**
Europa House Harcourt St, Dublin, 2, Ireland **(100%)**
Tel.: (353) 16707470
Web Site: http://www.das.ie
Sales Range: $50-74.9 Million
Emp.: 12
Insurance Services
N.A.I.C.S.: 524298
Adrienne O'Sullivan *(CEO)*

DAS UK Holdings Limited **(1)**
Das House Quay Side Temple Back, Bristol, BS1 6NH, United Kingdom
Tel.: (44) 11 7934 2000
Web Site: http://www.das.aom.uk
Legal Advisory Services
N.A.I.C.S.: 541199

Subsidiary (Non-US):

DAS Legal Protection Insurance Company Limited **(2)**
390 Bay Street Suite 1610, Toronto, M5H 2Y2, ON, Canada

Tel.: (416) 342-5400
Web Site: http://www.das.ca
Sales Range: $25-49.9 Million
Emp.: 28
Fire Insurance Services
N.A.I.C.S.: 524113

Subsidiary (Domestic):

Everything Legal Ltd. **(2)**
South Quay Temple Back, Bristol, BS1 6BE, United Kingdom
Tel.: (44) 84 5833 9792
Web Site: http://www.everythinglegal.co.uk
Legal Advisory Services
N.A.I.C.S.: 541199
Paul Asplin *(Mng Dir)*

ARAI & CO., LTD.

4-33-1 Kambei-cho, Otsu-ku, Himeji, Hyogo, Japan
Tel.: (81) 792396786
Web Site: https://www.arai-co-ltd.com
Logistic Services
N.A.I.C.S.: 541614

ARAKAWA CHEMICAL INDUSTRIES, LTD.

1-3-7 Hiranomachi, Chuo-ku, Osaka, 541-0046, Japan
Tel.: (81) 662098500
Web Site:
https://www.arakawachem.co.jp
Year Founded: 1976
4968—(TKS)
Rev.: $477,387,420
Assets: $829,012,980
Liabilities: $452,785,000
Net Worth: $376,227,980
Earnings: ($6,887,620)
Emp.: 1,668
Fiscal Year-end: 03/31/24
Chemicals Mfr
N.A.I.C.S.: 325998
Takashi Une *(Bd of Dirs & Pres)*

Subsidiaries:

ARAKAWA CHEMICAL (CHINA) INC. **(1)**
Room2111-2112 Tower B No 100 Zunyi Road, Changning District, Shanghai, 200051, China
Tel.: (86) 21 62375326
Web Site: http://www.arakawachem.com.cn
Sales Range: $50-74.9 Million
Emp.: 200
Industrial Chemicals Mfr
N.A.I.C.S.: 325180

Arakawa Chemical (Taipei), Ltd. **(1)**
Room 701 7th Floor No 152 Section 1 Zhongshan North Road, Zhongshan District, Taipei, Taiwan
Tel.: (886) 22 531 5178
Web Site: https://www.taipei-arakawa.com.tw
Electronic Material Distr
N.A.I.C.S.: 423690

Arakawa Chemical (USA) Inc. **(1)**
625 N Michigan Ave Ste 1700, Chicago, IL 60611
Tel.: (312) 642-1750
Web Site: https://www.arakawa-usa.com
Sales Range: $25-49.9 Million
Emp.: 5
Chemical Product & Preparation Mfr
N.A.I.C.S.: 325998

Arakawa Chemical Industries, Ltd - Fuji Plant **(1)**
366-1 Atsuhara, Fuji, 419-0201, Shizuoka, Japan
Tel.: (81) 545 71 1201
Web Site: http://www.arakawachem.co.jp
Industrial Chemicals Mfr
N.A.I.C.S.: 325180

Arakawa Chemical Industries, Ltd - Kushiro Plant **(1)**
1-2-68 Otanoshike, Minami, Kushiro, 084-0915, Hokkaido, Japan
Tel.: (81) 154578236
Web Site: http://www.arakawachem.co.jp
Papermaking Chemical Mfr

N.A.I.C.S.: 325180

Arakawa Chemical Industries, Ltd - Osaka Plant **(1)**
1-1-9 Tsurumi, Tsurumi-ku, Osaka, 538-0053, Japan
Tel.: (81) 669115881
Web Site: http://www.arakawachem.co.jp
Sales Range: $25-49.9 Million
Emp.: 100
Industrial Chemicals Mfr
N.A.I.C.S.: 325180

Arakawa Chemical Industries, Ltd - Tsurusaki Plant **(1)**
1120-3 Aza Higashi Matsuura Oaza, Iejima, Oita, 870-0113, Japan
Tel.: (81) 975273682
Papermaking Chemical Mfr
N.A.I.C.S.: 325180

Arakawa Chemical Industries, Ltd - Mizushima Plant **(1)**
4-1-1 Matsue, Kurashiki, 712-8052, Okayama, Japan
Tel.: (81) 864557611
Web Site: http://www.arakawachem.co.jp
Papermaking Chemical Mfr
N.A.I.C.S.: 322299

Arakawa Chemical Industries, Ltd - Onahama Plant **(1)**
399-5 Aza Otsurugi Shimokawa Izumimachi, Iwaki, 971-8183, Fukushima, Japan
Tel.: (81) 246567731
Web Site: http://www.arakawachem.co.jp
Sales Range: $25-49.9 Million
Emp.: 100
Papermaking Chemical Mfr
N.A.I.C.S.: 325180

Arakawa Chemical Industries, Ltd - Tokushima Plant **(1)**
1577 Nakashima Nakagawa-Cho, Anan, 779-1245, Tokushima, Japan
Tel.: (81) 884420573
Web Site: http://www.arakawachem.co.jp
Papermaking Chemical Mfr
N.A.I.C.S.: 325180
Hirohiko Morioka *(Gen Mgr)*

Arakawa Europe GmbH **(1)**
Hafenstr 2, 04442, Zwenkau, Germany
Tel.: (49) 34206799010
Web Site: https://www.arakawaeurope.com
Sales Range: $25-49.9 Million
Emp.: 6
Resins Mfr & Distr
N.A.I.C.S.: 325211
Katsuhiko Tahara *(Mng Dir)*

Guangxi Arakawa Chemical Industries, Ltd. **(1)**
No 1 5th Road Wuzhou Export Oriented Industrial Zone, Wuzhou, 543100, Guangxi, China
Tel.: (86) 774 5819611
Web Site: http://www.gxwzarakawa.com.cn
Emp.: 250
Papermaking Chemical Distr
N.A.I.C.S.: 424690

Guangxi Wuzhou Arakawa Chemical Industries, Ltd. **(1)**
No 1 5th Road Wuzhou Export Oriented Industrial Zone, Wuzhou, 543100, Guangxi, China
Tel.: (86) 7743830388
Web Site: http://www.gxwzarakawa.com
Sales Range: $125-149.9 Million
Emp.: 277
Industrial Chemicals Mfr
N.A.I.C.S.: 325180
Akihiro Higashi *(Mng Dir)*

KAKUTAMA SERVICE CO., LTD. **(1)**
1-3-7 Hiranomachi, Chuo-ku, Osaka, 541-0046, Japan
Tel.: (81) 662098605
Web Site: http://www.arakawachem.co.jp
Sales of Non-Life Insurance & Real-Estate Brokerage Services
N.A.I.C.S.: 524298

KOATSU CHEMICAL INDUSTRIES, Ltd. **(1)**
5-1-12 Tsurumachi, Taisho-ku, Osaka, 551-0023, Japan
Tel.: (81) 665520151

Web Site: http://www.koatsuchem.co.jp
Emp.: 73
Industrial Chemicals Mfr
N.A.I.C.S.: 325180

**Nantong Arakawa Chemical Indus-
tries, Ltd.** (1)
No 18 Jianghe Road, Nantong Economic
Technological Development Area, Nantong,
226017, Jiangsu, China
Tel.: (86) 51385996390
Web Site: http://www.arakawachem.co.jp
Emp.: 77
Industrial Chemical Distr
N.A.I.C.S.: 424690

Pelnox, Ltd. (1)
8-7 Bodai, Hadano, 259-1302, Kanagawa,
Japan
Tel.: (81) 463868000
Web Site: https://www.pelnox.co.jp
Emp.: 160
Resin Compounds Mfr
N.A.I.C.S.: 325211

**Taiwan Arakawa Chemical Industries,
Ltd.** (1)
No 4 Gongjian South Road, Liudu Industrial
Zone, Keelung, 206007, Taiwan
Tel.: (886) 224515236
Web Site: https://www.arakawachem.com.tw
Chemicals Mfr
N.A.I.C.S.: 325180

**Wuzhou Arakawa Chemical Indus-
tries, Ltd.** (1)
1 Xidi Road 3, Wuzhou, 543002, Guangxi,
China
Tel.: (86) 7743830388
Web Site: http://www.wzarakawa.com.cn
Rosin Derivatives Mfr
N.A.I.C.S.: 325211

**Yamaguchi Seiken Kogyo Co.,
Ltd.** (1)
2-1631 Shimizuyama, Midori-ku, Nagoya,
459-8009, Japan
Tel.: (81) 52 625 2333
Web Site: https://www.neopolish-ysk.co.jp
Abrasive Product Mfr & Distr
N.A.I.C.S.: 327910

ARALIA SYSTEMS LTD.
Milnwood 13 North Parade, Horsham,
RH12 2BT, West Sussex, United
Kingdom
Tel.: (44) 1403 240303   UK
Web Site:
    http://www.araliasystems.com
Year Founded: 1996
Emp.: 12
Surveillance Software Mfr
N.A.I.C.S.: 513210
Glynn C. Wright *(Founder & CEO)*

Subsidiaries:

Aralia Systems, Inc. (1)
1 N Charles St Ste 302, Baltimore, MD
21201
Tel.: (443) 692-3597
Web Site: http://www.araliasystems.com
Sales Range: $1-9.9 Million
Emp.: 14
Surveillance Software Mfr
N.A.I.C.S.: 513210
Robert Norrington *(CFO)*

ARAM GROUP P.J.S.C
Al Khan Street, PO Box 5440,
Sharjah, United Arab Emirates
Tel.: (971) 65565570   AE
Web Site:
    https://www.sharjahgroup.ae
Year Founded: 1976
ARAM—(ABU)
Rev.: $2,460,552
Assets: $42,138,603
Liabilities: $8,642,991
Net Worth: $33,495,612
Earnings: $1,196,431
Fiscal Year-end: 12/31/23
Property Investment Services
N.A.I.C.S.: 531110

Ziyad Mahmoud Khairullah Al Haji
(Chm)

ARAMBHAN GROUP
17 Bahubali Building Cawasji Patel
Street, Horniman Circle, Mumbai, 400
001, Fort, India
Tel.: (91) 2222044204
Web Site:
    http://www.arambhangroup.com
Maritime Logistics of Oil & Gas
N.A.I.C.S.: 488320
Alfred Arambhan *(Founder & Mng
Dir)*

Subsidiaries:

**Arambhan Hospitality Services
Limited** (1)
Floor-1 17A Patel Building Cawasji Patel
Road Horniman Circle, Fort, Mumbai,
400001, Maharashtra, India
Tel.: (91) 2265650232
Web Site: http://www.arambhangroup.com
Rev.: $604,024
Assets: $1,969,890
Liabilities: $5,941,803
Net Worth: ($3,971,913)
Earnings: ($463,252)
Emp.: 19
Fiscal Year-end: 03/31/2020
Hospitality Services
N.A.I.C.S.: 561990
Alfred Micheal Arambhan *(Chm & Mng Dir)*

ARAMEX PJSC
Alquds Street Bldg No 401 Opposite
to Ranteesi Building, Amman, Jordan
Tel.: (962) 65358855
Web Site: https://www.aramex.com
Year Founded: 1982
ARMX—(DFM)
Rev.: $3,302,724
Assets: $1,563,248,677
Liabilities: $846,644,419
Net Worth: $716,604,258
Earnings: $136,398,987
Emp.: 15,929
Fiscal Year-end: 12/31/19
Transportation Services & Solutions
N.A.I.C.S.: 492110
Fadi Ghandour *(Founder & Vice
Chm)*

Subsidiaries:

Access USA Shipping, LLC (1)
4299 Express Ln, Sarasota, FL 34238
Tel.: (941) 227-4444
Web Site: http://www.myus.com
Sales Range: $75-99.9 Million
International Freight & Shipping Services
N.A.I.C.S.: 481112
Robin Roach *(Mgr-Customer Svc)*

**Arab American International Express
Company** (1)
Courier Ground - 1st - 4th - 6th Fl Auto-
strade Chalouhi Sin El-Fil, PO Box 55606,
Beirut, Lebanon
Tel.: (961) 1517012
Freight Forwarding Services
N.A.I.C.S.: 488510

Aramex (UK) Limited (1)
Suite 11C Styal Road, Manchester, M22
5WB, United Kingdom
Tel.: (44) 1753210500
Courier Service
N.A.I.C.S.: 492110

Aramex Amman (1)
18 Khalil Al Salem St, PO Box 3371,
Khalda, Amman, 11181, Jordan
Tel.: (962) 65358855
Logistics & Distribution Services
N.A.I.C.S.: 541614

Aramex Emirates LLC (1)
Building No DIC 14 Office No S11, PO Box
3841, Dubai, United Arab Emirates
Tel.: (971) 43900365
Freight Transportation Arrangement
N.A.I.C.S.: 488510

Aramex Hong Kong Limited (1)

1/F Mapletree Logistics Hub, Tsing Yi,
China (Hong Kong)
Tel.: (852) 35567000
Courier Service
N.A.I.C.S.: 492110

Aramex India Private Limited (1)
F 08 Ground Fl marol nand dham ind Est
marol maroshi rd, Andheri East, Mumbai,
400059, Maharashtra, India
Tel.: (91) 2233003300
Logistics & Transportation Services
N.A.I.C.S.: 541614

Aramex International Egypt (1)
31 Musadak Str, PO Box 12311, Dokki,
Giza, Egypt
Tel.: (20) 2 33388466
Transportation Services
N.A.I.C.S.: 481112

**Aramex International Egypt for Air &
Local services (S.A.E)** (1)
Engineering Square4th, Industrial Zone, 6th
of October City, Egypt
Tel.: (20) 16996
Courier Service
N.A.I.C.S.: 492110

**Aramex International Hava Kargo Ve
Kerye Anonim Sirketi** (1)
15 Temmuz Mah Gulbahar Cad No 19/3
B-C-D Blok, Gunesli, Istanbul, Turkiye
Tel.: (90) 2129991222
Courier Service
N.A.I.C.S.: 492110

Aramex International Limited (1)
18 Khalil Al Salem St, PO Box 3371, Am-
man, Jordan
Tel.: (962) 65358855
Web Site: http://www.aramex.com
Sales Range: $1-4.9 Billion
Emp.: 3,000
Transportation & Logistics Services
N.A.I.C.S.: 488999
Emad Shishawi *(VP-Fin)*

**Aramex International Logistics Private
Ltd.** (1)
9 Airline Road Cargo Agent Bldg D Unit
01-18 and 01-19, Singapore, 819827, Sin-
gapore
Tel.: (65) 65460113
Courier Service
N.A.I.C.S.: 492110

Aramex Ireland (1)
Ballyboughal Bellinstown, Ballyboughal,
Dublin, Ireland
Tel.: (353) 1 8078000
Web Site: http://www.aramex.com
Emp.: 50
Logistics & Freight Forwarding Services
N.A.I.C.S.: 541614
Frank Kilbride *(Country Mgr)*

Aramex Jordan Ltd. (1)
King Hussein Business Park, Amman, Jor-
dan
Tel.: (962) 65515111
Courier Service
N.A.I.C.S.: 492110

Aramex Kuwait KSE (1)
PO Box 22751, Kuwait, Kuwait
Tel.: (965) 8200110
Web Site: http://www.aramex.com
Freight Transportation Arrangement
N.A.I.C.S.: 488510

Aramex Nederland BV (1)
Fokkerweg 300, 1438 AN, Oude Meer,
Netherlands
Tel.: (31) 206558020
Web Site: http://www.aramex.com
Air Freight Transportation Services
N.A.I.C.S.: 481112

Aramex Saudi Limited Company (1)
king Fahed Road to the north which leads
to Qaseem Road, at intersection of King
Salman Road, Riyadh, Saudi Arabia
Tel.: (966) 8001000880
Courier Service
N.A.I.C.S.: 492110

Aramex South Africa Pty Ltd (1)
Cnr Alpha and Kraal Streets Old East End,
Bloemfontein, South Africa
Tel.: (27) 514114999

Courier Service
N.A.I.C.S.: 492110

Memo Express Services LLC (1)
PO Box 13001, Dubai, United Arab Emir-
ates
Tel.: (971) 42118111
Freight Transportation Arrangement
N.A.I.C.S.: 488510

ARAMIS GROUP SAS
23 Avenue Aristide Briand, 94110,
Arcueil, France
Tel.: (33) 14913662
Web Site: https://www.aramis.group
Year Founded: 2001
ARAMI—(EUR)
Rev.: $2,146,826,361
Assets: $677,466,608
Liabilities: $477,776,797
Net Worth: $199,689,811
Earnings: ($35,691,577)
Emp.: 2,339
Fiscal Year-end: 09/30/23
Used Car Dealer Services
N.A.I.C.S.: 441120
Alejandro Garcia-Mella *(Chief Market-
place Officer)*

ARAMIT CEMENT LTD.
53 Kalurghat Heavy Industrial Estate,
Chittagong, 4208, Bangladesh
Tel.: (880) 31670473
Web Site:
    https://www.aramitcement.com
ARAMITCEM—(DHA)
Rev.: $8,447,911
Assets: $76,617,959
Liabilities: $71,672,196
Net Worth: $4,945,763
Earnings: ($6,635,766)
Fiscal Year-end: 06/30/22
Building Materials Mfr
N.A.I.C.S.: 327120
Rukhmila Zaman *(CEO & Mng Dir)*

ARAMIT GROUP
53 Kalurghat Heavy Industrial Estate
PO Mohara, Chittagong, 4208, Ban-
gladesh
Tel.: (880) 31670473
Web Site: https://aramitgroup.net
Year Founded: 1963
ARAMIT—(DHA)
Sales Range: Less than $1 Million
Building Materials Mfr
N.A.I.C.S.: 327390
Bisweswar Gupta *(Sec)*

Subsidiaries:

Aramit Limited (1)
53 Kalurghat Heavy Industrial Estate PO
Mohara, Chittagong, 4208, Bangladesh
Tel.: (880) 31670473
Web Site: http://www.aramitlimited.com
Cement Coated Roofing Material Mfr
N.A.I.C.S.: 324122
S. M. Alamgir Chy *(Chm)*

Aramit Thai Aluminium Limited (1)
53 Kalurghat Heavy Industrial Estate PO
Mohara, Chittagong, 4208, Bangladesh
Tel.: (880) 31670473
Web Site: http://www.aramitthai.com
Aluminum Extruded Product Mfr
N.A.I.C.S.: 331313
Syed Kamruzzaman *(COO)*

ARAN RESEARCH & DEVEL-
OPMENT (1982) LTD.
43 Haeshel Street Caesarea Buis-
ness Park, PO Box 3067, Caesarea,
3088900, Israel
Tel.: (972) 46239000
Web Site: https://www.aran-rd.com
Year Founded: 1982
ARAN—(TAE)
Rev.: $47,506,008
Assets: $62,749,274
Liabilities: $34,593,728

Aran Research & Development (1982)
Ltd.—(Continued)

Net Worth: $28,155,546
Earnings: $4,905,926
Emp.: 170
Fiscal Year-end: 12/31/23
Research & Development in the
Physical, Engineering & Life Sciences
(except Nanotechnology & Biotech-
nology)
N.A.I.C.S.: 541715

ARANETA PROPERTIES, INC.
21st Floor BDO Valero Towers Valero
Street, Salcedo Village, Makati, 1700,
Philippines
Tel.: (63) 28481501
Web Site:
    https://www.aranetaproperties.com
ARA—(PHI)
Rev.: $764,782
Assets: $35,103,107
Liabilities: $4,290,467
Net Worth: $30,812,640
Earnings: ($50,443)
Emp.: 31
Fiscal Year-end: 12/31/22
Property Development Services
N.A.I.C.S.: 531311
Christine P. Base (Sec)

ARANJIN RESOURCES LIM-
ITED
Shangri-La Hotel Olympic Street 19A,
Sukhbaatar District 1, Ulaanbaatar,
14241, Mongolia
Tel.: (976) 99990754
Web Site:
    https://www.aranjinresources.com
Year Founded: 2014
ARJNF—(OTCIQ)
Rev.: $48,292
Assets: $898,935
Liabilities: $856,292
Net Worth: $42,643
Earnings: ($694,216)
Fiscal Year-end: 12/31/23
Support Activities for Nonmetallic
Minerals (except Fuels) Mining
N.A.I.C.S.: 213115
Matthew Wood (Chm)

ARARA, INC.
Aoyama Tower Building Annex
2-24-15 Minami-Aoyama, Minato-ku,
Tokyo, 107-0062, Japan
Tel.: (81) 354143611
Web Site: https://www.arara.com
Year Founded: 2006
4015—(TKS)
Rev.: $42,625,660
Assets: $51,389,640
Liabilities: $25,172,340
Net Worth: $26,217,300
Earnings: $460,280
Fiscal Year-end: 08/31/24
Software Development Services
N.A.I.C.S.: 541511
Hiroki Inoue (COO & Exec VP)

Subsidiaries:

valuedesign, Inc.   (1)
Sumitomofudousanhattyoubori Bld 6F 3-3-5
Hatchobori Chuo-ku, Tokyo, 104-0032, Ja-
pan
Tel.: (81) 355420088
Web Site: http://www.valuedesign.jp
Rev.: $21,518,640
Assets: $19,543,920
Liabilities: $6,417,840
Net Worth: $13,126,080
Earnings: ($542,080)
Fiscal Year-end: 06/30/2021
Electronic Card Processing Services
N.A.I.C.S.: 522320

Subsidiary (Non-US):

Valuedesign Singapore Pte. Ltd.   (2)

30 Raffles Place 17 Chevron House, Singa-
pore, 048622, Singapore
Tel.: (65) 68096200
Card Issuing Services
N.A.I.C.S.: 522210
Amos Wong (Mgr)

ARARATBANK OJSC
Buzand St Bldg 87 Prem 85, 0002,
Yerevan, Armenia
Tel.: (374) 10592323
Web Site: http://www.araratbank.am
ARBK—(ARM)
Rev.: $59,248,699
Assets: $909,117,200
Liabilities: $775,667,285
Net Worth: $133,449,915
Earnings: $33,494,060
Emp.: 1,012
Fiscal Year-end: 12/31/22
Commercial Banking Services
N.A.I.C.S.: 522110
Grigor Hovhannisyan (Chm)

ARATA CORPORATION
East 21 Tower 6-3-2 Toyo, Koto-ku,
Tokyo, 135-0016, Japan
Tel.: (81) 356352800
Web Site: https://www.arata-gr.jp
Year Founded: 2002
2733—(TKS)
Rev.: $6,240,824,890
Assets: $2,095,211,360
Liabilities: $1,369,968,770
Net Worth: $725,242,590
Earnings: $68,228,420
Emp.: 2,893
Fiscal Year-end: 03/31/24
Pet Supplies, Household Products &
Cosmetics Distr
N.A.I.C.S.: 424990
Nobuyuki Hatanaka (Chm)

Subsidiaries:

Arata (Thailand) Co., Ltd.   (1)
54 B B Building 8th Floor Room No 3823
Sukumvit21 Asoke Rd, Klongtoey Nue Wat-
tana, Bangkok, 10110, Thailand
Tel.: (66) 22620671
Web Site: http://www.arata.co.th
Cosmetic Product Whslr
N.A.I.C.S.: 456120
Hiroshi Nakaya (Mng Dir)

Arata Vietnam Company Limited   (1)
2nd Floor The Landmark Building 5B Ton
Duc Thang, Ben Nghe Ward District 1, Ho
Chi Minh City, Vietnam
Tel.: (84) 283357100
Web Site: https://aratavietnam.com
Cosmetic Product Distr
N.A.I.C.S.: 424210

D-Nee Cosmetics Co., Ltd.   (1)
Shin-Yokohama 3-6-12th Sodai 12 Building
303, Kohoku Ward, Yokohama, 222-0033,
Kanagawa, Japan
Tel.: (81) 120872248
Web Site: https://jsmbeauty.jp
Cosmetic Product Mfr & Distr
N.A.I.C.S.: 325620

Japell (Hong Kong) Co., Limited   (1)
Shop Nos 2110-2111 Level 2 Lok Fu Plaza
Lok Fu Estate, No 198 Junction Road, Kow-
loon, China (Hong Kong)
Tel.: (852) 23394010
Pet Related Product Whslr
N.A.I.C.S.: 424990

Japell Co., Ltd.   (1)
3-105 Momoyama-cho, Kasugai, 486-0802,
Aichi, Japan
Tel.: (81) 568854111
Web Site: https://www.japell.com
Emp.: 831
Pet Food Whslr
N.A.I.C.S.: 424490
Kunihiro Tsuge (Founder & Co-Chm)

Japell Partnership Service Co.,
Ltd.   (1)
3-105 Momoyama-cho, Kasugai, 486-0802,
Aichi Prefecture, Japan

Tel.: (81) 568858822
Pet Styling Services
N.A.I.C.S.: 812910

Living Arata Co., Ltd.   (1)
435-1 Tanjo, Mihara-ku, Sakai, 587-0011,
Osaka Prefecture, Japan
Tel.: (81) 723693000
Home Goods Whslr
N.A.I.C.S.: 423220

Mobby Co., Ltd.   (1)
4-3-18 Nishiyawata, Hiratsuka, 254-0073,
Kanagawa Prefecture, Japan
Tel.: (81) 463735666
Pet Related Product Distr
N.A.I.C.S.: 459910

Siam Arata Co., Ltd.   (1)
54 B B Building 8th Floor Room No 3823
Sukhumvit 21 Asoke Road, Klongtoey Nue
Wattana, Bangkok, 10110, Thailand
Tel.: (66) 22582223
Cosmetic Product Whslr
N.A.I.C.S.: 456120

Vet's Choice Japan Corporation   (1)
3-105 Momoyamacho, Kasugai, 486-0802,
Aichi, Japan
Tel.: (81) 120091067
Web Site: https://www.vetschoice.co.jp
Animal Feed Mfr & Distr
N.A.I.C.S.: 311111

ARAVALI SECURITIES & FI-
NANCE LIMITED
Plot No 136 Ground Floor Rider
House Sector - 44, Gurgaon, 122
003, Haryana, India
Tel.: (91) 1244284578
Web Site:
    https://www.aravalisecurities.com
512344—(BOM)
Rev.: $486,403
Assets: $963,560
Liabilities: $942,525
Net Worth: $21,034
Earnings: $225,286
Fiscal Year-end: 03/31/22
Investment Management Service
N.A.I.C.S.: 523999
Ranjan Kumar Poddar (Chm & Mng
Dir)

ARAYA INDUSTRIAL CO., LTD.
2-12-12 Minamisenba, Chuo-ku,
Osaka, 5420081, Japan
Tel.: (81) 662530221
Web Site: https://www.araya-kk.co.jp
Year Founded: 1919
7305—(TKS)
Rev.: $294,515,160
Assets: $384,616,070
Liabilities: $146,589,970
Net Worth: $238,026,100
Earnings: $11,177,510
Emp.: 291
Fiscal Year-end: 03/31/24
Steel Product Mfr & Distr
N.A.I.C.S.: 332999
Tomoji Inoue (Pres)

ARAZU INCORPORATED
The Office 23 Barton Road Market
Bosworth, Nuneaton, CV13 0LQ,
Warwickshire, United Kingdom
Tel.: (44) 1455 290363   FL
Web Site: http://www.arazuinc.com
Year Founded: 2014
Rev.: $7,824
Assets: $137
Liabilities: $836,483
Net Worth: ($836,346)
Earnings: ($538,084)
Emp.: 1
Fiscal Year-end: 04/30/18
Motorcycle Aftermarket Products Distr
N.A.I.C.S.: 423120
Paul Clewlow (Chm, CEO, CFO &
Chief Acctg Officer)

ARB BERHAD
22-08 Level, 106 Lingkaran TRX,
55188, Kuala Lumpur, Malaysia
Tel.: (60) 327150238
Web Site:
    https://www.arbberhad.com
ARBB—(KLS)
Rev.: $125,715,132
Assets: $87,088,360
Liabilities: $8,017,989
Net Worth: $79,970,370
Earnings: $16,829,630
Fiscal Year-end: 06/30/22
Plywood & Wooden Flooring Board
Mfr
N.A.I.C.S.: 321211
Yun Nyen Lim (Exec Dir)

ARB CORPORATION LIMITED
42-44 Garden Street, PO Box 105,
Kilsyth, 3137, VIC, Australia
Tel.: (61) 397616622   AU
Web Site: https://www.arb.com.au
Year Founded: 1975
ARB—(ASX)
Rev.: $466,581,862
Assets: $529,025,772
Liabilities: $88,710,603
Net Worth: $440,315,169
Earnings: $68,565,037
Emp.: 120
Fiscal Year-end: 06/30/24
Motor Vehicle Parts Mfr & Distr
N.A.I.C.S.: 336390
Roger G. Brown (Bd of Dirs & Chm)

Subsidiaries:

Auto Styling Truckman Group
Limited   (1)
Truckman 14 Narrowboat Way, Dudley,
DY2 0EZ, United Kingdom
Tel.: (44) 1384485405
Web Site: https://www.truckman.co.uk
Emp.: 150
Vehicle Accessories Mfr
N.A.I.C.S.: 332119

ARB HOLDINGS LIMITED
10 Mack Road Prospecton, Durban,
4133, KwaZulu-Natal, South Africa
Tel.: (27) 319100150
Web Site: http://www.arbhold.co.za
ARH—(JSE)
Rev.: $199,430,763
Assets: $140,071,414
Liabilities: $46,975,946
Net Worth: $93,095,468
Earnings: $14,424,163
Emp.: 886
Fiscal Year-end: 06/30/21
Electrical Product Whslr
N.A.I.C.S.: 423610
William R. Neasham (CEO & Mng
Dir)

Subsidiaries:

Consolidated Electrical Distributor
(Pty) Ltd   (1)
79 5th Street, Wynberg, Sandton, 2090,
South Africa
Tel.: (27) 11 314 8869
Web Site: https://www.cedsa.co.za
Circuit Breaker Distr
N.A.I.C.S.: 423610
Jeffry Nala (Mgr-Store)

CraigCor Distribution Co (Pty)
Ltd   (1)
15-17 Poplar Crescent, Lords View Indus-
trial Park Chloorkop, Midrand, 1685, Gau-
teng, South Africa
Tel.: (27) 11 574 5300
Web Site: https://www.craigcor.co.za
Automation Equipment Distr
N.A.I.C.S.: 423830
Timothy Mountjoy (Natl Sls Mgr)

Eurolux (Pty) Ltd   (1)
72 5th Street, Wynberg, Sandton, 2090,
South Africa

Tel.: (27) 11 608 2970
Web Site: https://www.eurolux.co.za
Light Mfr
N.A.I.C.S.: 335139
Joey du Preez *(Project Mgr)*

GMC Powerlines (Pty) Ltd **(1)**
15 Poplar Crescent, Lords View Industrial
Business Park Chloorkop, Midrand, South
Africa
Tel.: (27) 11 472 0820
Web Site: https://www.gmcpowerlines.co.za
Electrical Equipment Mfr & Distr
N.A.I.C.S.: 335139

Xact ERP Solutions (Pty) Ltd **(1)**
35 Island Circle Unit 408 Island Office Park,
Riverhorse Valley, Durban, 4017, South
Africa
Tel.: (27) 31 569 1814
Web Site: https://www.xacterp.com
Accounting Software Services
N.A.I.C.S.: 541219
Gavin Ian Carter *(Sr Mgr-Dev)*

ARB IOT GROUP LIMITED
2F 09 Pusat Perdagangan IOI No 1
Persiaran Puchong Jaya Selatan,
Bandar Puchong Jaya, 47100, Pu-
chong, Selangor, Malaysia
Tel.: (65) 88567206   Ky
Web Site:
    https://www.arbiotgroup.com
Year Founded: 2022
ARBB—(NASDAQ)
Rev.: $12,322,458
Assets: $57,795,357
Liabilities: $1,870,524
Net Worth: $55,924,833
Earnings: ($11,581,711)
Emp.: 13
Fiscal Year-end: 06/30/24
Information Technology Services
N.A.I.C.S.: 541512
Kok Leong Liew *(Chm)*

ARBEIT-TIMES CO., LTD.
7F/8F Kanda Business Cube 5-1
Kanda Tomiyama-cho, Chiyoda-Ku,
Tokyo, 101-0043, Japan
Tel.: (81) 332542501
Web Site: http://www.atimes.co.jp
Year Founded: 1973
23410—(TKS)
Rev.: $30,614,620
Assets: $28,246,560
Liabilities: $4,636,860
Net Worth: $23,609,700
Earnings: ($226,880)
Fiscal Year-end: 02/29/24
Magazine Publishing Services
N.A.I.C.S.: 513120

ARBEJDERNES LANDSBANK A/S
Vesterbrogade 5, Copenhagen, 1502,
Denmark
Tel.: (45) 38484848
Web Site: http://www.al-bank.dk
Banking Services
N.A.I.C.S.: 522110
Brian Skjrbk Rasmussen *(Head-Intl Dept)*

Subsidiaries:

Vestjysk Bank A/S **(1)**
Torvet 4-5, 7620, Lemvig,
Denmark   **(60.7%)**
Tel.: (45) 96632000
Web Site: https://www.vestjyskbank.dk
Rev.: $206,425,895
Assets: $6,070,422,943
Liabilities: $5,214,110,634
Net Worth: $856,312,309
Earnings: $78,579,387
Emp.: 619
Fiscal Year-end: 12/31/2022
Commercial Banking Services
N.A.I.C.S.: 522110
Lars Holst *(Vice Chm)*

Subsidiary (Domestic):

Den Jyske Sparekasse AS **(2)**
Borgergade 3, 7200, Grindsted, Denmark
Tel.: (45) 76720999
Web Site: http://www.djs.dk
Rev.: $114,123,485
Assets: $2,391,950,468
Liabilities: $2,128,537,611
Net Worth: $263,412,857
Earnings: $22,140,208
Emp.: 355
Fiscal Year-end: 12/31/2019
Commercial Banking Services
N.A.I.C.S.: 522110
Claus E. Petersen *(CEO)*

ARBEJDSMARKEDETS TIL-LAEGSPENSION
Kongens Vaenge 8, 3400, Hillerod,
Denmark
Tel.: (45) 70111213   DK
Web Site: http://www.atp.dk
Year Founded: 1964
Emp.: 3,376
Pension Fund Administrative Services
N.A.I.C.S.: 524292
Torben M. Andersen *(Chm-Supervisory Bd)*

Subsidiaries:

ATP Ejendomme A/S **(1)**
Gothersgade 49, 1123, Copenhagen, Den-
mark
Tel.: (45) 3336 6161
Web Site: http://www.atp-ejendomme.dk
Emp.: 60
Real Estate Investment Services
N.A.I.C.S.: 531390
Michael Nielsen *(Mng Dir)*

ATP Private Equity Advisors ApS **(1)**
Sjaeleboderne 2 1st Floor, 1122, Copenha-
gen, Denmark
Tel.: (45) 3319 3070
Web Site: http://www.atp-pep.com
Privater Equity Firm
N.A.I.C.S.: 523999
Torben Vangstrup *(Mng Partner)*

TDC Holding A/S **(1)**
Teglholmsgade 1, 0900, Copenhagen, C,
Denmark   **(16.66%)**
Tel.: (45) 70110330
Web Site: http://www.tdcgroup.com
Rev.: $2,302,027,000
Assets: $9,226,189,000
Liabilities: $6,451,042,500
Net Worth: $2,775,146,500
Earnings: $246,246,000
Emp.: 6,433
Fiscal Year-end: 12/31/2022
Holding Company; Telecommunications
Services
N.A.I.C.S.: 551112
Mike Parton *(Chm)*

Subsidiary (Domestic):

Nuuday A/S **(2)**
Teglholmsgade 1, 2450, Copenhagen, Den-
mark
Tel.: (45) 70110330
Web Site: https://nuuday.com
Emp.: 3,075
Digital Media Streaming & Telecommunica-
tions Services
N.A.I.C.S.: 517121

Punktum dk A/S **(2)**
Ørestads Boulevard 108 11, 2300, Copen-
hagen, Denmark
Tel.: (45) 33646000
Web Site: https://www.punktum.dk
Sales Range: $10-24.9 Million
Emp.: 43
Internet Domain Name Registration & Host-
ing Services
N.A.I.C.S.: 518210
Jakob Bring Truelsen *(CEO)*

TDC Solutions A/S **(2)**
Teglholmsgade 1 G 455, 0900, Copenha-
gen, C, Denmark
Tel.: (45) 70110330
Telecommunications, Internet & Business
Management Services

N.A.I.C.S.: 517111

YouSee A/S **(2)**
Teglholmsgade 1, DK-0900, Copenhagen,
Denmark
Tel.: (45) 70704040
Web Site: http://yousee.dk
Cable Television & Internet Services
N.A.I.C.S.: 516210

Subsidiary (Domestic):

DKTV A/S **(3)**
Teglholmsgade 1,, 2450, Copenhagen,
Denmark
Tel.: (45) 43324700
Web Site: https://www.dktv.dk
Emp.: 422
Cable Television & Internet Services
N.A.I.C.S.: 516210

Branch (Domestic):

Dansk Kabel TV A/S - Esbjerg **(4)**
Skjoltsgate 49, 6700, Esbjerg, Denmark
Tel.: (45) 43324700
Web Site: https://www.dktv.dk
Cable Television & Internet Services
N.A.I.C.S.: 516210

ARBICO PLC.
Plot D Block 7 Industrial Crescent
Ilupeju, Lagos, Nigeria
Tel.: (234) 12950547
Web Site: http://www.arbicong.com
Year Founded: 1958
ARBICO—(NIGE)
Rev.: $14,516,509
Assets: $21,510,889
Liabilities: $21,918,540
Net Worth: ($407,651)
Earnings: $1,080,036
Emp.: 232
Fiscal Year-end: 12/31/20
Construction & Civil Engineering Ser-
vices
N.A.I.C.S.: 237990
Alkimos Makaronidis *(Mng Dir)*

ARBONA AB
Biblioteksgatan 29 2nd tr, 114 35,
Stockholm, Sweden
Tel.: (46) 733141406
Web Site: http://www.arbona.se
Asset Management Services
N.A.I.C.S.: 523940
Martin Zetterstrom *(CEO)*

Subsidiaries:

Mertiva AB **(1)**
Upplandsgatan 67, SE-113 28, Stockholm,
Sweden
Tel.: (46) 86610026
Web Site: http://www.mertiva.se
Sales Range: $200-249.9 Million
Emp.: 7
Diabetes Vaccine Mfr
N.A.I.C.S.: 325412
Erik Nerpin *(Chm)*

ARBONIA AG
Amriswilerstrasse 50, 9320, Arbon,
Switzerland
Tel.: (41) 714474141   CH
Web Site: https://www.arbonia.com
Year Founded: 1874
ARBN—(SWX)
Rev.: $599,720,706
Assets: $1,762,037,089
Liabilities: $667,467,319
Net Worth: $1,094,569,769
Earnings: ($16,899,216)
Emp.: 5,893
Fiscal Year-end: 12/31/23
Offices of Other Holding Companies
N.A.I.C.S.: 551112
Knut Bartsch *(Head-Sanitary Equip-
ment Div)*

Subsidiaries:

AFG Immobilien AG **(1)**
Aargauerstrasse 3, Postfach 134, 8048,

Zurich, Thurgau, Switzerland
Tel.: (41) 433333995
Sales Range: $100-124.9 Million
Emp.: 500
Kitchen Furnitures Mfr
N.A.I.C.S.: 337121
Christoph Schoenenberger *(Mng Dir)*

AFG Immobilien AG **(1)**
Aargauerstrasse 3, 8048, Zurich, Switzer-
land
Tel.: (41) 433333995
Web Site: http://www.agf-immobilien.ch
Apartment Rental Services
N.A.I.C.S.: 531110

AFG International AG **(1)**
Amriswilerstrasse 50, Postfach 134, 9320,
Arbon, Thurgau, Switzerland
Tel.: (41) 714474141
Modular Kitchen Design & Installation Ser-
vices
N.A.I.C.S.: 541490
Felix Bodmer *(CFO)*

AFG Management AG **(1)**
Amriswilerstrasse 50, Postfach 134, 9320,
Arbon, Thurgau, Switzerland
Tel.: (41) 714474141
Business Support Services
N.A.I.C.S.: 561499
Felix Bodmer *(CFO)*

AFG RUS **(1)**
Altufevskoe shosse 1 room XII BC Beta-
Center, Moscow, 127106, Russia
Tel.: (7) 4956462719
Heating Equipment Mfr
N.A.I.C.S.: 333414

AFG Schweiz AG **(1)**
Amriswilerstrasse 50, 9320, Arbon, Thur-
gau, Switzerland
Tel.: (41) 714474141
Web Site: http://www.afg.ch
Kitchen Cabinet Mfr
N.A.I.C.S.: 337110

AFG Services AG **(1)**
Amriswilerstrasse 50, Postfach 550, 9320,
Arbon, Thurgau, Switzerland
Tel.: (41) 714474545
Kitchen & Sanitary Equipments Distr
N.A.I.C.S.: 423220

**AFG Warendorfer Immobilien
GmbH.** **(1)**
Mielestrasse 1, 48231, Warendorf,
Nordrhein-Westfalen, Germany
Tel.: (49) 2581590
Web Site: http://www.warendorf.eu
Sales Range: $50-74.9 Million
Emp.: 180
Kitchenware Mfr
N.A.I.C.S.: 327110

Arbonia France S.a.r.l. **(1)**
17A Rue d'Altkirch, Hagenbach, 68210,
Fontaine, France
Tel.: (33) 389400253
Web Site: https://www.arbonia.fr
Sales Range: $25-49.9 Million
Interior Designing Services
N.A.I.C.S.: 541410

Arbonia Management AG **(1)**
Amriswilerstrasse 50, 9320, Arbon, Switzer-
land
Tel.: (41) 714474554
Heating Equipment Mfr
N.A.I.C.S.: 333414

Subsidiary (Non-US):

Single Temperiertechnik GmbH **(2)**
Ostring 17-19, 73269, Hochdorf, Germany
Tel.: (49) 715330090
Web Site: http://www.single-temp.de
Emp.: 140
Temperature Control Systems Mfr
N.A.I.C.S.: 334512
Karsten Sauer *(Mng Dir)*

Teknos Deutschland GmbH **(2)**
Edelzeller Strasse 62, 36043, Fulda, Ger-
many
Tel.: (49) 661 1080
Web Site: https://www.teknos.com
Wood Paints & Coatings Mfr
N.A.I.C.S.: 325510
Andre Brunotte *(Mng Dir)*

Arbonia AG—(Continued)

Subsidiary (Domestic):

Teknos Feyco AG (2)
Rte de Prilly 23, CH-1023, Crissier, Switzerland
Tel.: (41) 216360309
Web Site: http://feycotreffert.com
Paints & Varnishes Mfr
N.A.I.C.S.: 325510

Subsidiary (US):

Teknos US, Inc. (3)
2205 Beltway Blvd Ste 500, Charlotte, NC 28214
Tel.: (704) 588-5812
Web Site: http://www.teknos.com
Wood Surface Paints & Coatings Mfr
N.A.I.C.S.: 325510
Cynthia Stewart (Mng Dir)

Arbonia Riesa GmbH (1)
Industriestrasse A 11, 01612, Glaubitz, Germany
Tel.: (49) 3526568960
Web Site: https://www.arbonia-solutions.com
Household Radiators Mfr
N.A.I.C.S.: 333414

Arbonia Services AG (1)
Amriswilerstrasse 50, 9320, Arbon, Switzerland
Tel.: (41) 714405122
Heating Equipment Mfr
N.A.I.C.S.: 333414

Arbonia Solutions AG (1)
Amriswilerstrasse 50, 9320, Arbon, Switzerland
Tel.: (41) 714474747
Web Site: https://www.arbonia-solutions.com
Heating Equipment Mfr
N.A.I.C.S.: 333414

Asta AG (1)
Industriestrasse 12, PO Box 650, 9320, Arbon, Thurgau, Switzerland
Tel.: (41) 714474949
Web Site: http://www.asta.ch
General Freight Trucking Services
N.A.I.C.S.: 484110
Roger Z'Brun (Mgr)

Bekon-Koralle AG (1)
Baselstrasse 61, 6252, Dagmersellen, Switzerland
Tel.: (41) 627486060
Web Site: https://www.koralle.ch
Shower Door Mfr
N.A.I.C.S.: 332321

CICSA Industriales del Calor S.L. (1)
Paseo de Las Flores, No 21-27 - Nave 2
Pol Ind Logipark, 28823, Coslada, Madrid, Spain
Tel.: (34) 914850867
Web Site: https://www.
Bathroom Radiator Distr
N.A.I.C.S.: 423720

Chromage Pyreneen SA. (1)
Route de Pau ZA du Gabarn, Escout, 64870, Oloron Sainte Marie, Pyrenees-Atlantiques, France
Tel.: (33) 559397101
Web Site: http://www.hartchrom.com
Sales Range: $25-49.9 Million
Emp.: 72
Industrial Engineering Services
N.A.I.C.S.: 541330

Dobroplast Fabryka Okien sp. z o.o. (1)
Stary Laskowiec 4, 18-300, Zambrow, Poland
Tel.: (48) 862763500
Web Site: http://www.dobroplast.pl
Aluminium Window Mfr & Distr
N.A.I.C.S.: 332321

EgoKiefer AG (1)
Hohenemserstrasse 32, 9444, Diepoldsau, Sankt Gallen, Switzerland
Tel.: (41) 717573333
Web Site: http://www.egokiefer.ch
Windows, Doors Mfr & Distr
N.A.I.C.S.: 321911

EgoKiefer SA (1)
Route du Pre-du-Bruit 1/ZIA11, 1844, Villeneuve, Vaud, Switzerland
Tel.: (41) 219670800
Web Site: http://www.egokiefer.ch
Windows & Doors Mfr
N.A.I.C.S.: 321911

Garant Turen-und Zargen GmbH (1)
Garantstrasse 1 Gewerbepark Thorey, OT Ichtershausen Amt Wachsenburg, 99334, Wachtersbach, Germany
Tel.: (49) 36202910
Web Site: https://www.garant.de
Wood Window & Door Mfr
N.A.I.C.S.: 321911

Glasverarbeitungsgesellschaft Deggendorf mbH (1)
Auwiesenstrasse 6, 94469, Deggendorf, Germany
Tel.: (49) 99125080
Web Site: https://www.arbonia-glassysteme.de
Bathroom Radiator Distr
N.A.I.C.S.: 423720

Hartchrom Schoch GmbH. (1)
Muhlackerstr 10, Diefenbach, Sternenfels, 75447, Baden-Wurttemberg, Germany
Tel.: (49) 704395320
Web Site: http://www.sti-surface.com
Sales Range: $50-74.9 Million
Emp.: 100
Surface Treatment & Coating Services
N.A.I.C.S.: 212114

Hartchrom Teikuro Automotive GmbH. (1)
Muhlackerstrasse 10, Diefenbach, 75447, Sternenfels, Germany
Tel.: (49) 70439532500
Web Site: http://www.sti-surface.com
Sales Range: $25-49.9 Million
Surface Treatment & Industrial Engineering Services
N.A.I.C.S.: 541330

Heizkorper Prolux AG (1)
Amriswilerstrasse 50, 9320, Arbon, Thurgau, Switzerland
Tel.: (41) 714474848
Web Site: http://www.prolux-ag.ch
Sales Range: $25-49.9 Million
Emp.: 20
Household Radiators Mfr & Distr
N.A.I.C.S.: 333414

Invado Sp. z.o.o. (1)
Dzielna ul Lesna 2, Ciasna, 42-793, Lubliniec, Poland
Tel.: (48) 343510540
Web Site: https://www.invado.pl
Wood Window & Door Mfr
N.A.I.C.S.: 321911
Marta Rzeszut (Chm & Mng Dir)

Kermi GmbH (1)
Pankofen-Bahnhof 1, 94447, Plattling, Germany
Tel.: (49) 99315010
Web Site: https://www.kermi.com
Sales Range: $200-249.9 Million
Plumbing Products
N.A.I.C.S.: 332913
Alexander Kaiss (Mng Dir)

Subsidiary (Non-US):

Kermi Sp.z.o.o. (2)
Ul Graniczna 8b, 54-610, Wroclaw, Lower Silesian, Poland
Tel.: (48) 713540370
Web Site: https://www.kermi.com
Household Radiators & Shower Enclosures Mfr
N.A.I.C.S.: 333414
Knut Bartsch (Mng Dir & Pres-Germany)

Kermi s.r.o. (2)
Dukelska 1427, 349 01, Stribro, Plzen, Czech Republic
Tel.: (420) 374611111
Web Site: https://www.kermi.com
Household Radiators & Shower Enclosures Mfr
N.A.I.C.S.: 333415

Koralle Sanitarprodukte GmbH (1)
Wilhelmstrasse 8, 32602, Vlotho, Germany

Tel.: (49) 5733140
Web Site: http://www.koralle.de
Shower Door Mfr
N.A.I.C.S.: 332321

PZP Heating a.s. (1)
Podzamci 786, 517 73, Opocno, Czech Republic
Tel.: (420) 494664203
Web Site: https://www.pzpheating.cz
Heat Pump Mfr & Distr
N.A.I.C.S.: 333415

Prolux Solutions AG (1)
Amriswilerstrasse 50, 9320, Arbon, Switzerland
Tel.: (41) 714474848
Web Site: https://www.prolux-solutions.com
Plumbing & Heating Equipment Distr
N.A.I.C.S.: 423720

RWD Schlatter AG (1)
St Gallerstrasse 21, 9325, Roggwil, Thurgau, Switzerland
Tel.: (41) 714546300
Web Site: https://www.rwdschlatter.ch
Sales Range: $50-74.9 Million
Emp.: 200
Doors & Frames Mfr
N.A.I.C.S.: 332321

STI France SAS (1)
Route de Pau ZA du Gabarn, Escout, 64870, Oloron Sainte Marie, France
Tel.: (33) 559 39 71 01
Web Site: http://www.sti-surface.com
Sales Range: $25-49.9 Million
Aircraft Components Mfr
N.A.I.C.S.: 336413
Pierre Aubert (Gen Mgr)

STI Hartchrom AG (1)
Schulstrasse 70, 9323, Steinach, Sankt Gallen, Switzerland
Tel.: (41) 714479797
Web Site: http://www.hartchrom.com
Emp.: 187
Surface Treatment & Coating Services
N.A.I.C.S.: 332812

STI Hartchrom Inc. (1)
25 Gibson St, Watervliet, NY 12189-3342
Tel.: (518) 880-0411
Sales Range: $25-49.9 Million
Emp.: 20
Metal Surface Coating Services
N.A.I.C.S.: 332812

STI Immobilien (Deutschland) GmbH (1)
Muhlackerstrasse 10, Diefenbach, 75447, Sternenfels, Germany
Tel.: (49) 704395320
Web Site: http://www.hartchrom.com
Sales Range: $75-99.9 Million
Real Estate Property Development Services
N.A.I.C.S.: 531210

STI Surface Technologies International Holding AG (1)
Schulstrasse 70, 9323, Steinach, Sankt Gallen, Switzerland
Tel.: (41) 714479797
Web Site: http://www.sti-surface.com
Surface Treatment & Coating Services
N.A.I.C.S.: 332812

Sabiana S.p.A. (1)
Via Piave 53, 20011, Corbetta, MI, Italy
Tel.: (39) 0297203
Web Site: https://www.sabiana.it
Heating Equipment Mfr
N.A.I.C.S.: 333414

Skyfens Sp. z o.o. (1)
Zaklad Produkcji Okien Dachowych Ul Vetterow 7, 20-277, Lublin, Poland
Tel.: (48) 795527710
Web Site: https://skyfens.pl
Skylight Mfr
N.A.I.C.S.: 332321

Slovaktual s.r.o. (1)
Pravenec 272, 972 16, Pravenec, Trencin, Slovakia
Tel.: (421) 46 544 79 16
Web Site: http://www.slovaktual.sk
Sales Range: $125-149.9 Million
Windows & Doors Mfr
N.A.I.C.S.: 321911

TPO Holz-Systeme GmbH (1)
Farbereistrasse 8, Leutershausen, 91578, Ansbach, Germany
Tel.: (49) 9823924400
Web Site: https://www.tpo-holz.de
Wood Window & Door Mfr
N.A.I.C.S.: 321911

Termovent Komerc d.o.o. (1)
Kneza Milosa 88a Skyline 1 Floor, Belgrade, Serbia
Tel.: (381) 606601068
Web Site: https://termovent.com
Air Handling Equipment Mfr
N.A.I.C.S.: 333413

Wertbau GmbH (1)
Am Dasslitzer Kreuz 3, Langenwetzendorf, 07957, Greiz, Germany
Tel.: (49) 366256110
Web Site: http://www.wertbau.de
Shower Door Mfr
N.A.I.C.S.: 332321

ARBOR METALS CORP.
Suite 2200 885 West Georgia Street, Vancouver, V6C3G1, BC, Canada
Tel.: (403) 852-4869   BC
Web Site:
   https://www.arbormetalscorp.com
Year Founded: 2011
ABRMF—(OTCIQ)
Assets: $130,468
Liabilities: $507,875
Net Worth: ($377,407)
Earnings: ($994,222)
Fiscal Year-end: 10/31/22
Metal Mining
N.A.I.C.S.: 212290
Mark L. P. Ferguson (CEO)

ARBOR TECHNOLOGY CORP.
10F No 700 Zhongzheng Rd, Zhonghe Dist, New Taipei City, 235, Taiwan
Tel.: (886) 282269396
Web Site: https://www.arbor-technology.com
Year Founded: 1993
3594—(TPE)
Rev.: $54,659,307
Assets: $118,731,641
Liabilities: $48,521,434
Net Worth: $70,210,207
Earnings: $4,066,124
Fiscal Year-end: 12/31/23
Computer Peripheral Equipment Mfr
N.A.I.C.S.: 334118
Eric Lee (Founder, Chm & CEO)

Subsidiaries:

Arbor Italia S.R.L. (1)
C so Orbassano 336, 10137, Turin, Italy
Tel.: (39) 01119700011
Iota Computing & Mobility Solutions Services
N.A.I.C.S.: 518210

ARBORGEN HOLDINGS LIMITED
Suite 107 100 Parnell Road, Auckland, 1052, New Zealand
Tel.: (64) 93569800   NZ
Web Site: http://www.rubicon-nz.com
Year Founded: 2001
ARB—(NZX)
Rev.: $56,100,000
Assets: $199,800,000
Liabilities: $50,500,000
Net Worth: $149,300,000
Earnings: ($2,500,000)
Fiscal Year-end: 03/31/23
Forestry, Horticulture, Agriculture Research & Development Services
N.A.I.C.S.: 541715
David Mabon Knott (Co-Chm)

Subsidiaries:

ArborGen Inc. (1)
2011 Broadbank Ct, Ridgeville, SC 29472

Tel.: (843) 851-4129
Web Site: http://www.arborgen.com
Biotechnology Tree Seedling Products
N.A.I.C.S.: 113210
John Pait *(VP-Mktg, Sls & Product Dev)*

ARBORITE
385 Lafleur, Quebec, H8R 3H7, QC,
Canada
Web Site: http://www.arborite.com
Year Founded: 1942
Laminate Mfr
N.A.I.C.S.: 326130

Subsidiaries:

Lamin-Art, Inc. **(1)**
1670 Basswood Rd, Schaumburg, IL 60173
Tel.: (800) 323-7624
Web Site: http://www.laminart.com
Decorative Laminates, Wood Veneer & Metallic Surfaces Mfr & Distr
N.A.I.C.S.: 423840
Diane Borges *(Mgr-Customer Svc)*

ARBURG GMBH & CO.
Arthur Hehl Strasse, 72290, Lossburg, Germany
Tel.: (49) 7446330
Web Site: http://www.arburg.com
Year Founded: 1923
Sales Range: $250-299.9 Million
Emp.: 2,400
Mfr of Injection Molding Machinery &
Equipment
N.A.I.C.S.: 333248
Michael Hehl *(Mng Dir)*

Subsidiaries:

ARBURG (HK) Ltd. **(1)**
Level 23 One Island East 18 Westlands
Road, Quarry Bay, Hong Kong, China
(Hong Kong)
Tel.: (852) 28863007
Industry Machinery Distr
N.A.I.C.S.: 423830
Zhao Tong *(Pres)*

ARBURG (Thailand) Co., Ltd. **(1)**
59/4 Moo 16 Srinakarin Road Tambol Bangkaew, Amphur, Bang Phli, 10540, Samut
Prakan, Thailand
Tel.: (66) 23494062
Industry Machinery Distr
N.A.I.C.S.: 423830
Ratree Boonsay *(Pres)*

ARBURG A/S **(1)**
Korskildeeng 4, 2670, Greve, Denmark
Tel.: (45) 36776399
Industry Machinery Distr
N.A.I.C.S.: 423830
Steffen Eppler *(Mgr-Admin)*

ARBURG AG **(1)**
Sudstrasse 15, 3110, Munsingen, Switzerland
Tel.: (41) 317242323
Industry Machinery Distr
N.A.I.C.S.: 423830
Marcel Spadini *(Branch Mgr)*

ARBURG BV **(1)**
Krommewetering 81, 3543 AM, Utrecht,
Netherlands
Tel.: (31) 302426060
Industry Machinery Distr
N.A.I.C.S.: 423830
Wilfred van Muilekom *(Engr-Sls & Application)*

ARBURG GesmbH **(1)**
Hegelgasse 8, 1010, Vienna, Austria
Tel.: (43) 17102302
Industry Machinery Distr
N.A.I.C.S.: 423830
Eberhard Lutz *(Branch Mgr)*

ARBURG Hungaria Kft. **(1)**
Del-Pesti Uzleti Park II Illatos ut 38, 1097,
Budapest, Hungary
Tel.: (36) 13998010
Industry Machinery Distr
N.A.I.C.S.: 423830
Gabriella Hollen *(Mgr-Agency)*

ARBURG Ltda. **(1)**

Rua Missionaros 292-Sto Amaro, 04729-
000, Sao Paulo, SP, Brazil
Tel.: (55) 1120391919
Industry Machinery Distr
N.A.I.C.S.: 423830
Santos Ronie *(Controller-Fin)*

ARBURG N.V. **(1)**
Ambachtelijke Zone De Vunt 13 bus 11,
3220, Holsbeek, Belgium
Tel.: (32) 16441290
Industry Machinery Distr
N.A.I.C.S.: 423830
Simon Bemong *(Mng Dir)*

ARBURG Polska Sp. z o o. **(1)**
ul Polna 33, Opacz k, 05-816, Warsaw,
Poland
Tel.: (48) 227238650
Industry Machinery Distr
N.A.I.C.S.: 423830

ARBURG Sdn Bhd **(1)**
No 35 Jalan PJS 11/24 Bandar Sunway Industrial Park, 46150, Petaling Jaya, Selangor, Malaysia
Tel.: (60) 356366213
Industry Machinery Distr
N.A.I.C.S.: 423830
Visvesvaran Nagappa *(Branch Mgr)*

ARBURG spol. s r o. **(1)**
Cernovicka 40, 618 00, Brno, Czech Republic
Tel.: (420) 548422471
Industry Machinery Distr
N.A.I.C.S.: 423830

ARBURG, S.A. de C.V. **(1)**
Calle Acceso III No 42 Int 4 Zona Industrial
Benito Juarez, 76120, Queretaro, Mexico
Tel.: (52) 4422095326
Industry Machinery Distr
N.A.I.C.S.: 423830
Guillermo Fasterling *(Branch Mgr)*

Arburg, Inc. **(1)**
644 W St Rocky hill, Rocky Hill, CT
06067 **(100%)**
Tel.: (860) 667-6500
Web Site: http://www.arburg.us
Sales Range: $50-74.9 Million
Emp.: 57
Plastic Processing Equipment; Injection
Molding Machines Mfr
N.A.I.C.S.: 423830
Friedrich Kanz *(Pres)*

Nomis d.o.o. **(1)**
Havidiceva 27, 10020, Zagreb, Croatia
Tel.: (385) 16535130
Web Site: http://www.nomis.hr
Industry Machinery Mfr
N.A.I.C.S.: 333248

PT ARBURG **(1)**
Puri Niaga III Jl Puri Kencana Blok M8 No
2G, Jakarta, 11610, Indonesia
Tel.: (62) 2158303455
Industry Machinery Distr
N.A.I.C.S.: 423830
David Chan *(Pres)*

ARBUTHNOT BANKING GROUP PLC
Arbuthnot House 20 Finsbury Circus,
London, EC2M 7EA, United Kingdom
Tel.: (44) 2070122500
Web Site:
  https://www.arbuthnotlatham.co.uk
Year Founded: 1833
ARBB—(AIM)
Rev.: $149,032,143
Assets: $4,487,923,565
Liabilities: $4,224,689,284
Net Worth: $263,234,280
Earnings: $20,437,544
Emp.: 718
Fiscal Year-end: 12/31/22
Commericial Banking
N.A.I.C.S.: 522110
Henry Angest *(Chm & CEO)*

Subsidiaries:

Arbuthnot Latham & Co. Limited **(1)**
Arbuthnot House 7 Wilson Street, London,
EC2M 2SN, United Kingdom

Tel.: (44) 207 012 2500
Web Site:
  https://www.arbuthnotlatham.co.uk
Sales Range: $50-74.9 Million
Emp.: 50
Private Banking & Wealth Management
Services
N.A.I.C.S.: 523999
James W. Fleming *(Vice Chm)*

Renaissance Asset Finance
Limited **(1)**
3rd Floor Phoenix Place Christopher Martin
Road, Basildon, SS14 3GQ, Essex, United
Kingdom
Tel.: (44) 126 826 9500
Web Site: https://www.renaissanceaf.com
Asset Finance Services
N.A.I.C.S.: 523999
Mark Lester *(Mng Dir)*

ARC FINANCE LIMITED
18 Rabindra Sarani Poddar Court
Gate No-4 4th Floor Room No 3, Kolkata, 700 001, West Bengal, India
Tel.: (91) 9830286229 In
Web Site: https://www.arcfinance.in
Year Founded: 1982
540135—(BOM)
Rev.: $4,449,049
Assets: $10,820,872
Liabilities: $3,822,295
Net Worth: $6,998,577
Earnings: $38,725
Emp.: 7
Fiscal Year-end: 03/31/22
Consumer Lending Services
N.A.I.C.S.: 522291
Sapna Agarwal *(Co-CFO)*

ARC FINANCIAL CORP.
4300 400 - 3 Avenue SW, Calgary,
T2P 4H2, AB, Canada
Tel.: (403) 292-0680
Web Site:
  https://www.arcfinancial.com
Year Founded: 1989
Sales Range: $1-4.9 Billion
Emp.: 55
Investment Management Service
N.A.I.C.S.: 523940
Kevin J. Brown *(Chm)*

Subsidiaries:

Ember Resources Inc. **(1)**
Devon Tower 800 400 3rd Ave S W, Calgary, T2P 4H2, AB, Canada
Tel.: (403) 270-0803
Web Site: https://www.emberresources.com
Sales Range: $25-49.9 Million
Gas Production
N.A.I.C.S.: 221210

Kiwetinohk Resources Corp. **(1)**
Suite 1700 250 - 2 St. S.W, Calgary, T2P
0C1, AB, Canada **(55.64%)**
Tel.: (587) 392-4424
Web Site: https://kiwetinohk.com
Oil & Gas & Electric Energy Mfr
N.A.I.C.S.: 213112
Patrick Carlson *(CEO)*

ARC FUNDS LIMITED
Level 7 330 Collins Street, Melbourne, 3000, VIC, Australia
Tel.: (61) 386899997 AU
Web Site:
  https://www.arcfunds.com.au
ARC—(ASX)
Rev.: $61,363
Assets: $1,460,358
Liabilities: $74,932
Net Worth: $1,385,426
Earnings: ($554,179)
Fiscal Year-end: 06/30/24
Financial Services
N.A.I.C.S.: 523999
James Jackson *(Chm)*

ARC MINERALS LTD

2nd Floor 180 Piccadilly, London,
W1J 9HF, United Kingdom
Tel.: (44) 2079172942
Web Site:
  http://www.arcminerals.com
ARCM—(AIM)
Assets: $10,797,451
Liabilities: $3,539,130
Net Worth: $7,258,321
Earnings: ($7,235,969)
Emp.: 64
Fiscal Year-end: 12/31/22
Gold & Other Precious Metals Mining
& Exploration Services
N.A.I.C.S.: 212220
Vassilios Carellas *(COO)*

ARC RESOURCES LTD.
1200 308 4th Ave SW, Calgary, T2P
0H7, AB, Canada
Tel.: (403) 503-8600 AB
Web Site:
  http://www.arcresources.com
ARX—(TSX)
Rev.: $4,177,513,482
Assets: $9,147,447,736
Liabilities: $3,660,412,204
Net Worth: $5,487,035,532
Earnings: $1,179,360,272
Emp.: 622
Fiscal Year-end: 12/31/23
Oil & Gas Exploration & Production
Services
N.A.I.C.S.: 211120
Sean Calder *(VP)*

Subsidiaries:

Seven Generations Energy Ltd **(1)**
525-8th Avenue SW Eighth Avenue Place
East Suite 4400, Calgary, T2P 1G1, AB,
Canada
Tel.: (403) 718-0700
Web Site: http://www.7genergy.com
Rev.: $2,259,065,004
Assets: $6,456,635,976
Liabilities: $2,478,076,692
Net Worth: $3,978,559,284
Earnings: $362,570,712
Emp.: 255
Fiscal Year-end: 12/31/2019
Oil & Gas Exploration
N.A.I.C.S.: 211120
Kevin Johnston *(VP-Fin & Controller)*

ARCA CAPITAL SLOVAKIA, A.S.
Bratislava Business Center V Plynarenska 7/A, 821 09, Bratislava,
Slovakia
Tel.: (421) 258253510
Web Site: http://www.arcacapital.com
Year Founded: 1999
Investment Management Service
N.A.I.C.S.: 523940
Rastislav Velic *(Chm)*

Subsidiaries:

ACS Plyn, s.r.o. **(1)**
Druzstevna 1090/86, Solcany, 956 17, Topolcany, Slovakia
Tel.: (421) 907842591
Web Site: http://www.acsplyn.sk
Gas Distr
N.A.I.C.S.: 424720

Subsidiary (Domestic):

Nitrianska Teplarenska Spolocnost,
A.S. **(2)**
Janka Krala 122, 949 01, Nitra, Slovakia
Tel.: (421) 376923427
Web Site: http://www.ntsas.sk
Heating Product Distr
N.A.I.C.S.: 423730
Andrea Sekova *(Chm)*

Arca Capital Bohemia, a.s. **(1)**
Polygon House Doudlebska 1699/5, 140
00, Prague, Czech Republic
Tel.: (420) 224231813
Private Equity Services

Arca Capital Slovakia, A.S.—(Continued)

N.A.I.C.S.: 523940
Juraj Krupa *(Portfolio Mgr)*

Arca Capital Finance Group, a.s. **(1)**
V Celnici 1031/4, 110 00, Prague, Czech
Republic
Tel.: (420) 226224751
Fund & Asset Management Services
N.A.I.C.S.. **523940**

Wiener Privatbank Immobilienmakler
GmbH **(1)**
Parkring 12, 1010, Vienna, Austria
Tel.: (43) 13771550
Web Site: http://www.wpb-makler.com
Commercial Banking Services
N.A.I.C.S.: 522110
Elisabeth Rist *(CEO)*

ARCA CONTINENTAL, S.A.B.
DE C.V.
Av San Jeronimo 813 Pte, CP. 64640,
Monterrey, NL, Mexico
Tel.: (52) 8181511400 MX
Web Site:
https://www.arcacontal.com
AC—(MEX)
Rev.: $8,627,835,538
Assets: $12,642,450,290
Liabilities: $5,146,128,676
Net Worth: $7,496,321,615
Earnings: $622,691,216
Emp.: 61,000
Fiscal Year-end: 12/31/19
Soft Drink Bottling Services
N.A.I.C.S.: 312111
Jorge Humberto Santos Reyna *(Chm)*

Subsidiaries:

Corporacion Lindley S.A. **(1)**
Jr Cajamarca N 371, Rimac, Lima, Peru
Tel.: (51) 481 2070
Web Site: http://www.lindley.pe
Softdrink & Beverage Mfr
N.A.I.C.S.: 312111

Great Plains Coca-Cola Bottling
Company **(1)**
600 N May Ave, Oklahoma City, OK 73107-
6324
Tel.: (405) 280-2000
Web Site:
http://www.greatplainscocacola.com
Soft Drinks Mfr
N.A.I.C.S.: 312111
Chris Sheehan *(Acct Exec)*

Grupo Continental, S.A. **(1)**
Avenida Hidalgo 2303 Col Smith, 89140,
Tampico, Tamaulipas, Mexico
Tel.: (52) 8332412500
Web Site: http://www.contal.com
Sales Range: $1-4.9 Billion
Carbonated & Non-Carbonated Soft Drinks
Production & Distribution Services
N.A.I.C.S.: 312111

Subsidiary (Domestic):

Concentrados Industriales, S.A. de
C.V. **(2)**
Eje 118 y Av Producto Terminado S/N,
Zona Indust, 78320, San Luis Potosi,
Mexico
Tel.: (52) 14448245055
Web Site: http://www.e-coinsa.com.mx
Sales Range: $25-49.9 Million
Emp.: 55
Chemical Development Services
N.A.I.C.S.: 325199

Embotelladora Lagunera, S.A. de
C.V. **(2)**
Mexico 222 Col Ex-Ejido Cuba, Gomez
Palacio, 35140, Mexico
Tel.: (52) 8717492500
Web Site: http://www.emblagunera.com
Soft Drinks Mfr
N.A.I.C.S.: 312111

Embotelladora San Luis, S.A. de
C.V. **(2)**
Lado Oriente Glorieta Juarez s/n, Col Hoga-
res Ferrocarrileros, San Luis Potosi, 78070,
Mexico
Tel.: (52) 4448348700
Soft Drinks Mfr
N.A.I.C.S.: 312111

Grossman y Asociados, S.A. de
C.V. **(2)**
Ave Hidalgo 2303, Smith, 89140, Tampico,
Tamaulipas, Mexico
Tel.: (52) 8332412500
Business Consulting Services
N.A.I.C.S.: 561499

Petstar, S.A. de C.V. **(1)**
Rio Papaloapan 153 Sta Cruz Atzcapotzal-
tongo, Toluca, 07850, Mexico
Tel.: (52) 722 272 6617
Waste Collection Services
N.A.I.C.S.: 562111
Leo Nava *(Mgr-Natl Accounts)*

Wise Foods, Inc. **(1)**
228 Raseley St, Berwick, PA 18603-4533
Tel.: (570) 759-4000
Web Site: http://www.wisesnacks.com
Sales Range: $350-399.9 Million
Mfr & Retailer of Snack Foods
N.A.I.C.S.: 311919

ARCA IMPRESA GESTIONI
SGR S.P.A.
Via Borrome 5, Milan, 20123, Italy
Tel.: (39) 02 29 02 29 85 IT
Privater Equity Firm
N.A.I.C.S.: 523999
Gianluca Banfi *(Mng Dir)*

ARCA INVESTMENTS, A.S.
Plynarenska 7/A, Bratislava Business
Center V, Bratislava, 2, Slovakia
Tel.: (421) 421 2 58 25 35 10 Sk
Year Founded: 1999
Rev.: $2,630,717,000
Private Equity, Real Estate Invest-
ment & Financial Services Firm
N.A.I.C.S.: 523999
Pavol Krupa *(Founder & Chm)*

ARCA REGLER GMBH
Kempener Str 18, 47918, Tonisvorst,
Germany
Tel.: (49) 215677090 De
Web Site: http://www.arca-valve.com
Year Founded: 1949
Sales Range: $75-99.9 Million
Emp.: 300
Control Valve Mfr
N.A.I.C.S.: 332911
Joachim Lukoschek *(Co-CEO & Mng
Dir)*

Subsidiaries:

ARCA Valvulas S.A. de C.V. **(1)**
Edif 42C Depto 305, 11200, Mexico, Mexico
Tel.: (52) 5553959836
Web Site: http://www.arca-Valvulas.com
Sales Range: $25-49.9 Million
Emp.: 7
Control Valve Mfr
N.A.I.C.S.: 332911

ARTES Valve & Service GmbH **(1)**
Lessingstrasse 79, 13158, Berlin, Germany
Tel.: (49) 30 912 047 10
Web Site: http://www.artes-valve.com
Valve Mfr
N.A.I.C.S.: 332911
Horst Jakel *(Exec Dir)*

FELUWA Pumpen GmbH **(1)**
Beulertweg 10, Murlenbach, 54570, Eifel,
Germany
Tel.: (49) 6594 10 0
Web Site: http://www.feluwa.de
Sales Range: $50-74.9 Million
Emp.: 140
Control Valve, Pumps & Level Indicator Mfr
N.A.I.C.S.: 332911
Rudiger Kaspers *(Chm)*

Guangzhou ARCA Valve Ltd. **(1)**
Room 807 Building 2 Industrial Plaza, No
730 Ying Bin Road, 511400, Guangzhou,
Panyu, China
Tel.: (86) 203921186
Web Site: http://www.arca-valve.com.cn
Control Valve Mfr
N.A.I.C.S.: 332911

Von Rohr ARCA BV **(1)**
Stuyvenburchstraat 56A, 6961 CW, Ee-
rbeek, Netherlands
Tel.: (31) 313 654000
Web Site: http://www.vonrohr-arca.nl
Valve Mfr
N.A.I.C.S.: 332911

WEKA AG **(1)**
Schuerlistrasse 8, CH-8344, Hinwil, Switzer-
land
Tel.: (41) 43 8334343
Web Site: http://www.weka-ag.ch
Emp.: 60
Valves & Actuators Mfr
N.A.I.C.S.: 332911
Marcel Fuerst *(Mng Dir-Sls)*

von Rohr Armaturen AG **(1)**
Fichtenhagstr 4, CH-4132, Muttenz, Swit-
zerland
Tel.: (41) 61 4614848
Web Site: http://www.von-rohr.ch
Pneumatic & Electrical Control Valves
N.A.I.C.S.: 332911

ARCADIA GROUP LIMITED
Colegrave House 70 Berners Street,
London, W1T 3NL, United Kingdom
Tel.: (44) 844 243 0000 UK
Web Site:
http://www.arcadiagroup.co.uk
Year Founded: 1900
Sales Range: $1-4.9 Billion
Emp.: 24,000
Men's & Women's Clothing Retailer
N.A.I.C.S.: 458110
Ian Grabiner *(CEO)*

ARCADIA MINERALS LIMITED
Tel.: (61) 861589990 AU
Web Site:
https://www.arcadiaminerals.global
Year Founded: 2020
AM7—(ASX)
Rev.: $29,602
Assets: $8,040,722
Liabilities: $120,765
Net Worth: $7,919,958
Earnings: ($1,778,974)
Emp.: 2
Fiscal Year-end: 06/30/23
Mineral Exploration Services
N.A.I.C.S.: 212390
Kyla Garic *(Sec)*

ARCADIS N.V.
Gustav Mahlerplein 97-103, 1082
MS, Amsterdam, Netherlands Nl
Web Site: http://www.arcadis.com
Year Founded: 1888
ARCAD—(EUR)
Rev.: $5,523,040,071
Assets: $4,171,686,721
Liabilities: $3,000,220,775
Net Worth: $1,171,465,946
Earnings: $176,136,439
Emp.: 32,324
Fiscal Year-end: 12/31/23
Holding Company; Architectural &
Environmental Engineering & Con-
sulting Services
N.A.I.C.S.: 551112
Mark Fenner *(Chief Sls & Mktg Offi-
cer)*

Subsidiaries:

ARCADIS Asia **(1)**
Zhongrong Plaza Unit 1203 1088 South
Pudong Rd, Pudong New Area, Shanghai,
200122, China
Tel.: (86) 21587 61 451
Web Site: http://www.arcadis.com
Construction Engineering Services
N.A.I.C.S.: 541330

ARCADIS Belgium Holding NV **(1)**
Posthofbrug 12 City Link, Antwerp, 2600,
Belgium
Tel.: (32) 495044146
Investment Management Service
N.A.I.C.S.: 523999

ARCADIS Belgium N.V. **(1)**
Borsbeeksebrug 22, 2600, Berchem,
Belgium **(100%)**
Tel.: (32) 25057500
Sales Range: $25-49.9 Million
Emp.: 150
Engineering Services
N.A.I.C.S.: 541330
Luc Hellemans *(Mng Dir)*

ARCADIS CZ a.s. **(1)**
Na Strzi 1702/65, 140 62, Prague, Czech
Republic
Tel.: (420) 296 330 111
Sales Range: $25-49.9 Million
Emp.: 4
Construction Engineering Services
N.A.I.C.S.: 541330

ARCADIS Chile SA **(1)**
Antonio Bellet 292 Office 706, Providencia,
Santiago, 7500966, Chile
Tel.: (56) 223816000
Web Site: http://www.arcadis.com
Sales Range: $150-199.9 Million
Engineeering Services
N.A.I.C.S.: 541330

Subsidiary (Non-US):

ARCADIS Peru **(2)**
240 Monte Rosa Jr of 603, Urb Chacarilla
Pond, Lima, 33, Peru
Tel.: (51) 1 652 2465
Web Site: http://www.arcadis.pe
Sales Range: $25-49.9 Million
Emp.: 40
Engineeering Services
N.A.I.C.S.: 541330

ARCADIS Deutschland Gmbh **(1)**
Europaplatz 3, 64293, Darmstadt, Germany
Tel.: (49) 61513880
Web Site: http://www.arcadis.com
Sales Range: $1-4.9 Billion
Emp.: 200
Engineeering Services
N.A.I.C.S.: 541330

ARCADIS ESG **(1)**
200-216 rue Raymond Losserand, 75014,
Paris, France
Tel.: (33) 14 623 7777
Web Site: https://www.arcadis.com
Sales Range: $150-199.9 Million
Engineeering Services
N.A.I.C.S.: 541330

ARCADIS Eurometudes S.A. **(1)**
Calea Grivitei Nr 136 Corp A floor 1 room
e02-e06, Bucharest, 33697, Romania
Tel.: (40) 21 31 22699
Sales Range: $25-49.9 Million
Emp.: 2
Infrastructure Construction Engineering
Services
N.A.I.C.S.: 541330
Alexandrina Odelea *(Mgr)*

ARCADIS Holding France S.A.S. **(1)**
9 Avenue Reaumur, 92350, Le Plessis-
Robinson, France
Tel.: (33) 1 46 23 77 77
Investment Management Service
N.A.I.C.S.: 523999
Paul Souai *(Pres)*

ARCADIS ITALIA Srl **(1)**
Via Monte Rosa 93, 20149, Milan, Italy
Tel.: (39) 0200624665
Web Site: http://www.arcadis.com
Sales Range: $25-49.9 Million
Construction Engineering Services
N.A.I.C.S.: 541330
Domenico Santi *(Mng Dir)*

ARCADIS Logos Ltda. **(1)**
Edificio Plaza Centenario Avenida das Na-
coes Unidas 12 995, 14 Andar-conjunto 141
Brooklin Paulista, Sao Paulo, 04578-911,
Brazil
Tel.: (55) 1131173171
Web Site: http://www.logoseng.com.br

Power Plant Construction Engineering Services
N.A.I.C.S.: 237130

ARCADIS Nederland BV (1)
Amsterdamseweg 13, 6814 CM, Arnhem, Netherlands (100%)
Tel.: (31) 884261261
Sales Range: $75-99.9 Million
Emp.: 800
Engineeering Services
N.A.I.C.S.: 541330

Subsidiary (Domestic):

ARCADIS Bouw BV (2)
Piet Mondriaanlaan 26, PO Box 220, 3812 GV, Amersfoort, Netherlands (100%)
Tel.: (31) 88 426 1261
Web Site: https://www.arcadis.com
Engineering Services
N.A.I.C.S.: 541330

Subsidiary (Domestic):

VOF Stationseiland (3)
Piatmondreaan 26, PO Box 220, 3800 AE, Amersfoort, Netherlands (100%)
Tel.: (31) 334771200
Sales Range: $150-199.9 Million
Emp.: 800
Engineering Services
N.A.I.C.S.: 541330

Subsidiary (Domestic):

ARCADIS Infra B.V. (2)
Piet Mondriaanlaan 26, 3812 GV, Amersfoort, Netherlands (100%)
Tel.: (31) 884261261
Web Site: http://www.arcadis.nl
Emp.: 800
Engineeering Services
N.A.I.C.S.: 541330
Rob Mooren (Mng Dir)

ARCADIS Ruiwitelijke Ohtwilleling BV (2)
2130 Hoosdvorp Jupitarstraat 122, PO Box 410, Arnhem, 6800 AG, Netherlands (100%)
Tel.: (31) 235668411
Web Site: http://www.arcadis.com
Sales Range: $25-49.9 Million
Emp.: 200
N.A.I.C.S.: 813920
Don C. A. M. Hardy (Reg Dir-South)

ARCADIS Spatial Information (2)
Hetrietveld 59 A, PO Box 882, 7301 BC, Apeldoorn, Netherlands (100%)
Tel.: (31) 555815900
Engineeering Services
N.A.I.C.S.: 541330

Subsidiary (Domestic):

Kafi BV (3)
Bontemolanlaan 19A, PO Box 114, 3448 AC, Woerden, Netherlands (100%)
Tel.: (31) 348485400
Sales Range: $10-24.9 Million
Emp.: 30
Engineeering Services
N.A.I.C.S.: 541330

Subsidiary (Domestic):

Cannock Chase B.V. (4)
Van Heemstraweg 58, 6651 KH, Druten, Netherlands (100%)
Tel.: (31) 88 116 8222
Web Site: https://www.cannockchasepublic.nl
Engineeering Services
N.A.I.C.S.: 541330

ARCADIS Sp. z.o.o. (1)
Woloska 22A, 02-670, Warsaw, Poland
Tel.: (48) 222032000
Construction Engineering Services
N.A.I.C.S.: 541330
Marcin Klammar (Gen Mgr)

ARCADIS U.S., Inc. (1)
630 Plz Dr Ste 100, Highlands Ranch, CO 80129 (100%)
Tel.: (720) 344-3500
Web Site: http://www.arcadis-us.com
Sales Range: $50-74.9 Million
Emp.: 157

Environmental Engineering & Design Services
N.A.I.C.S.: 541690
Donnell Duncan (Engr-Structural-Atlanta)

Subsidiary (Domestic):

ARCADIS G&M, Inc. (2)
10205 Westheimer Rd Ste 800, Houston, TX 77042-3709 (100%)
Tel.: (713) 953-4800
Web Site: http://www.arcadis.com
Sales Range: $10-24.9 Million
Emp.: 40
Buildings & Infrastructure Projects
N.A.I.C.S.: 541330

Branch (Domestic):

ARCADIS U.S., Inc. - Austin (2)
1717 W 6th St Ste 210, Austin, TX 78703
Tel.: (512) 451-1188
Web Site: http://www.arcadis.com
Sales Range: $25-49.9 Million
Emp.: 15
Environmental Engineering Consulting & Construction
N.A.I.C.S.: 541690

ARCADIS U.S., Inc. - Tampa (2)
3109 W Dr Martin Luther King Jr Blvd Ste 350, Tampa, FL 33607
Tel.: (813) 903-3100
Web Site: http://www.arcadis-us.com
Engineeering Services
N.A.I.C.S.: 541330

Subsidiary (Domestic):

CallisonRTKL, Inc. (2)
200 E Pratt St Ste 4100, Baltimore, MD 21202
Tel.: (410) 537-6000
Web Site: http://www.callisonrtkl.com
Architectural, Engineering & Planning Services
N.A.I.C.S.: 541310
Robyn Miller (Principal & Gen Counsel)

Subsidiary (Domestic):

CallisonRTKL, Inc. (3)
1420 Fifth Ave Ste 2400, Seattle, WA 98101
Tel.: (206) 623-4646
Web Site: http://www.callisonrtkl.com
Architectural Design & Engineering Services
N.A.I.C.S.: 541310
Lucy Baraquio (Principal)

Subsidiary (Non-US):

CallisonRTKL-UK Ltd. (3)
Black Bull Yard 18 - 22 Hatton Wall, London, EC1N 8JH, United Kingdom
Tel.: (44) 2073060404
Web Site: http://www.rtkl.com
Sales Range: $25-49.9 Million
Emp.: 6
Architectural Design Services
N.A.I.C.S.: 541310

Branch (Domestic):

RTKL Associates Inc. (3)
1717 Pacific Ave Ste 100, Dallas, TX 75201-4655
Tel.: (214) 871-8877
Web Site: http://www.rtkl.com
Sales Range: $25-49.9 Million
Emp.: 237
Engineeering Services
N.A.I.C.S.: 561110

Subsidiary (Non-US):

RTKL International Ltd. (3)
Suite 2106 Platinum 233 Taicang Road, Shanghai, 200020, China
Tel.: (86) 21 6122 7922
Web Site: http://www.arcadis.com
Emp.: 140
Architectural Design Services
N.A.I.C.S.: 541310

Subsidiary (Domestic):

Rise International L.L.C. (2)
790 Frontage Rd, Northfield, IL 60093
Tel.: (847) 441-4262
Web Site: http://www.riseinternational.org

Sales Range: $10-24.9 Million
Technical Management Consulting Services
N.A.I.C.S.: 541690

Arcadis (UK) Limited (1)
80 Fenchurch Street, London, EC3M 4BY, United Kingdom
Tel.: (44) 2078122000
Web Site: http://www.arcadis.com
Engineering, Surveying & Environmental Consulting Services
N.A.I.C.S.: 541330

Subsidiary (Domestic):

Arcadis LLP (2)
80 Fenchurch Street, London, EC3M 4BY, United Kingdom
Tel.: (44) 2078122000
Property & Infrastructure Consulting Services
N.A.I.C.S.: 541690

Arcadis Australia Pacific Holdings Pty. Ltd. (1)
Level 16 580 George Street, Sydney, 2000, NSW, Australia
Tel.: (61) 289079000
Business Consulting Services
N.A.I.C.S.: 541618

Arcadis France S.A.S. (1)
200-216 rue Raymond Losserand, 75014, Paris, France
Tel.: (33) 146237777
Web Site: https://www.arcadis.com
Business Consulting Services
N.A.I.C.S.: 541618

Arcadis, Ltd. (1)
80 Fenchurch Street, London, EC3M 4BY, United Kingdom
Tel.: (44) 2078122000
Web Site: http://www.arcadis.com
Engineeering Services
N.A.I.C.S.: 541330
Mark Cowlard (CEO-UK & Ireland)

Subsidiary (Non-US):

ACLA Ltd. (2)
17/F Two Harbour Square 180 Wai Yip Street, Kwun Tong, Kowloon, China (Hong Kong)
Tel.: (852) 28933933
Web Site: http://www.acla.com.hk
Architectural Services
N.A.I.C.S.: 541310
Phyllis Cheung (Bus Dir-Landscape)

Arcadis - Middle East (2)
Building 53 6th Floor Dubai Healthcare City, Dubai, United Arab Emirates
Tel.: (971) 4 3193 333
Web Site: http://www.arcadis.com
Consulting & Engineering Services
N.A.I.C.S.: 541330
Jeroen Ijntema (CFO)

Arcadis - Philippines (2)
12F 8 Rockwell Hidalgo Drive Rockwell Center, Barangay Poblacion, Makati, 1210, Metro Manila, Philippines
Tel.: (63) 27 908 2888
Web Site: http://www.arcadis.com
Engineering & Consulting Services
N.A.I.C.S.: 541330
Matt Bennion (COO-Asia)

Arcadis - Sydney (2)
Level 16 580 George Street, Sydney, 2000, NSW, Australia
Tel.: (61) 289079000
Web Site: http://www.arcadis.com
Design & Engineering Consultants
N.A.I.C.S.: 237990
Greg Steele (CEO)

CallisonRTKL (2)
27 Dongsanhuan Beilu 9th Floor Tower B Jiaming Center, Chaoyang District, Beijing, 100020, China
Tel.: (86) 10 5775 6800
Web Site: http://www.callisonrtkl.com
Advisory & Design Consulting Services
N.A.I.C.S.: 541420

Hyder Consulting GmbH Deutschland (2)
Grunewaldstrasse 61-62, 10825, Berlin, Germany

Tel.: (49) 306705210
Web Site: http://www.arcadis.com
Advisory & Design Consulting Services
N.A.I.C.S.: 541490

Hyder Consulting India Pvt Ltd (2)
135 4th RMZ Titanium Old Airport Road Kodihalli, Bengaluru, 560017, India
Tel.: (91) 80 3059 1400
Web Site: http://www.arcadis.com
Advisory & Design Consulting Services
N.A.I.C.S.: 541490

Darwish Consulting Engineers (1)
27 Nazih Khalifa St, Heliopolis, 11341, Cairo, Egypt (26%)
Tel.: (20) 22581559
Web Site: http://www.dce-ltd.com
Emp.: 120
Engineeering Services
N.A.I.C.S.: 541330

Eptisa Servicios De Ingenieria S.A. (1)
35-37 Emilio Munoz St, 28037, Madrid, Spain (100%)
Tel.: (34) 915949500
Web Site: http://www.eptisa.es
Sales Range: $75-99.9 Million
Emp.: 1,000
Engineeering Services
N.A.I.C.S.: 541330

EurAsia Consult (1)
c/o Centre of Economic Conjuncture & Analysis, Dzhandosov 59 3rd Fl, 480035, Almaty, Kazakhstan
Tel.: (7) 3272551319
Web Site: http://www.euroconsult.nl
Engineeering Services
N.A.I.C.S.: 541330

IBI Group Inc. (1)
55 St Clair Avenue West 7th Floor, Toronto, M4V 2Y7, ON, Canada
Tel.: (416) 596-1930
Web Site: http://www.ibigroup.com
Rev.: $415,156,460
Assets: $254,686,638
Liabilities: $184,749,138
Net Worth: $69,937,500
Earnings: $18,834,262
Emp.: 3,200
Fiscal Year-end: 12/31/2021
Software Development & Consulting Services
N.A.I.C.S.: 541511
David M. Thom (Pres)

Subsidiary (US):

Bearsch Compeau Knudson, Architects & Engineers, PC (2)
41 Chenango St, Binghamton, NY 13901-1956
Tel.: (607) 772-0007
Web Site: http://www.bckpc.com
Sales Range: $1-9.9 Million
Emp.: 80
Architectural Design & Engineering Services
N.A.I.C.S.: 541310

Subsidiary (Domestic):

CHBA-IBI Inc. (2)
100 rue Peel 4e etage, Montreal, H3C 0L8, QC, Canada
Tel.: (514) 316-1010
Web Site: http://www.cardinal-hardy.ca
Emp.: 275
Architectural Design & Engineering Services
N.A.I.C.S.: 541310
Louis Lemay (Pres)

Subsidiary (US):

CRJA-IBI Group (2)
115 Broad St, Boston, MA 02110
Tel.: (617) 896-2500
Architectural Design & Engineering Services
N.A.I.C.S.: 541310

Subsidiary (Domestic):

CSM Engineering Ltd. (2)
9908 Franklin Avenue Suite 102, Fort McMurray, T9H 2K5, AB, Canada
Tel.: (780) 790-1034
Architectural Design & Engineering Services
N.A.I.C.S.: 541310
Bruce Piggott (Project Mgr)

ARCADIS N.V.—(Continued)

Subsidiary (US):

Dull Olson Weekes Architects, Inc. (2)
319 SW Washington St Ste 200, Portland, OR 97205
Tel.: (503) 226-6950
Web Site: http://www.dowa.com
Rev.: $5,000,000
Emp.: 50
Architectural Services
N.A.I.C.S.: 541310
Steve Olson (Co-Owner)

IBI Group Architects (USA) Inc. (2)
907 SW Harvey Milk St, Portland, OR 97205-2809
Tel.: (503) 222-2045
Professional Consulting Services
N.A.I.C.S.: 541990

Subsidiary (Non-US):

IBI Group Consultants (Ireland) Limited (2)
19-21 Denzille Lane, Dublin, Ireland
Tel.: (353) 1 634 4020
Professional Consulting Services
N.A.I.C.S.: 541990

Subsidiary (Domestic):

IBI Group Geomatics (Canada) Inc. (2)
227 11 Avenue SW Suite 300, Calgary, T2R 1R9, AB, Canada
Tel.: (403) 270-5600
Professional Consulting Services
N.A.I.C.S.: 541990

Subsidiary (Non-US):

IBI Group Greece Business Consultants Single Member Societe Anonyme IBI Hellas S.A. (2)
17 Andrea Papandreou Street, 151 24, Maroussi, Greece
Tel.: (30) 210 683 6660
Professional Consulting Services
N.A.I.C.S.: 541990

IBI Group India Private Limited (2)
415 Vipul Plaza Sector-54 Suncity, Gurgaon, 122003, Haryana, India
Tel.: (91) 1244840700
Professional Consulting Services
N.A.I.C.S.: 541990

Subsidiary (US):

IBI Group Professional Services (USA) Inc. (2)
1100 Park Central Blvd S Ste 3500, Pompano Beach, FL 33064
Tel.: (954) 974-2200
Professional Consulting Services
N.A.I.C.S.: 541990

Subsidiary (Non-US):

IBI Group Saudi Limited Company (2)
Office 410-411 Sada Business Center 1 Wadi Awal Street, Al Olaya, Riyadh, Saudi Arabia
Tel.: (966) 553080577
Professional Consulting Services
N.A.I.C.S.: 541990

IBI Taylor Young Ltd. (2)
Chadsworth House Wilmslow Road, Handforth, SK9 3HP, Cheshire, United Kingdom
Tel.: (44) 1625542200
Architectural Design & Engineering Services
N.A.I.C.S.: 541310
Neil Lewin (Dir-Studio)

Subsidiary (Domestic):

IBI-MAAK Caribbean Limited (2)
9133 Leslie Street Suite 201, Richmond Hill, L4B 4N1, ON, Canada
Tel.: (905) 763-2322
Professional Consulting Services
N.A.I.C.S.: 541990

IBI-MAAK Inc. (2)
9133 Leslie Street Suite 201, Richmond Hill, L4B 4N1, ON, Canada

Tel.: (905) 326-9833
Web Site: http://www.maakgroup.com
Engineeering Services
N.A.I.C.S.: 541330

Subsidiary (Non-US):

IBIB Group Consultants (Israel) Ltd. (2)
13 Yehuda and Noach Moses St North Wing 1st Floor, Agish Ravad Building, Tel Aviv, Israel
Tel.: (972) 723160900
Professional Consulting Services
N.A.I.C.S.: 541990

Subsidiary (US):

M.E /IBI Group (2)
635 Brooksedge Blvd, Westerville, OH 43081
Tel.: (614) 818-4900
Web Site: http://www.mecompanies.com
Emp.: 85
Architectural Design & Engineering Services
N.A.I.C.S.: 541310

Subsidiary (Non-US):

Nightingale Architects Limited (2)
Princes Manor Barn Reading Road, Harwell, OX11 0LU, Oxfordshire, United Kingdom
Tel.: (44) 1235 820222
Web Site: http://www.ibi-nightingale.com
Architectural Design & Engineering Services
N.A.I.C.S.: 541310
Richard Harrington (Chm)

Subsidiary (Domestic):

Page + Steele / IBI Group Architects (2)
95 St Clair Avenue West Suite 200, Toronto, M4V 1N6, ON, Canada
Tel.: (416) 924-9966
Web Site: http://www.pagesteele.com
Emp.: 125
Architectural Design & Engineering Services
N.A.I.C.S.: 541310
Sol Wassermuhl (Pres)

SGA-IBI Group Architects (2)
103 Church Street Suite 201, Toronto, M5C 2G3, ON, Canada
Tel.: (416) 466-3920
Emp.: 50
Architectural Design & Engineering Services
N.A.I.C.S.: 541310

Subsidiary (US):

TETRA - IBI Group Architecture Planning (2)
75 E Santa Clara St Ste 100, San Jose, CA 95113
Tel.: (408) 924-0811
Web Site: http://www.ibigroup.com
Architectural Design & Engineering Services
N.A.I.C.S.: 541310

Texas - IBI Group, Inc. (2)
455 E Medical Ctr Blvd Ste 500, Webster, TX 77598
Tel.: (281) 286-6605
Web Site: https://www.ibigrouptexas.com
Architectural Design & Engineering Services
N.A.I.C.S.: 541310
Mark R. French (Sr Principal)

Logos Engenharia S.A. (1)
Rua Voluntarios da Patria, Santana 2820 - 7th floor - Room 76, Sao Paulo, 02402-100, SP, Brazil (100%)
Tel.: (55) 1129508226
Web Site: http://www.logosengenharia.com
Sales Range: $75-99.9 Million
Emp.: 400
Engineeering Services
N.A.I.C.S.: 541330

Ukron (1)
Serpova st 3, 252115, Kiev, Ukraine
Tel.: (380) 444441014
Engineeering Services
N.A.I.C.S.: 541330

ARCAPITA GROUP HOLDINGS LIMITED
Building 551 Road 4612 Block 346

Bahrain Bay, PO Box 1357, Manama, Bahrain
Tel.: (973) 17218333   **BH**
Web Site: http://www.arcapita.com
Year Founded: 1997
Rev.: $54,091,000
Assets: $291,130,000
Liabilities: $66,228,000
Net Worth: $224,902,000
Earnings: $21,879,000
Fiscal Year-end: 06/30/19
Privater Equity Firm
N.A.I.C.S.: 523940
Mohammed Chowdhury (CFO)

Subsidiaries:

Arcapita Bank B.S.C. (c) (1)
PO Box 1406, Manama, Bahrain
Tel.: (973) 017218333
Web Site: http://www.arcapita.com
Sales Range: $125-149.9 Million
Emp.: 268
Real Estate, Private Equity & Venture Capital Investment Services
N.A.I.C.S.: 523150
Atif Ahmed Abdulmalik (CEO)

Subsidiary (Non-US):

Arcapita Investment Advisors UK Limited (2)
15th Floor The Shard, London, SE1 9SG, United Kingdom
Tel.: (44) 20 7824 5600
Investment Management Service
N.A.I.C.S.: 523940

Arcapita Investment Management Singapore Pte. Ltd. (2)
152 Beach Road 10-01/02 Gateway East, Singapore, 189721, Singapore
Tel.: (65) 6248 0720
Investment Management Service
N.A.I.C.S.: 523940

Subsidiary (US):

Arcapita, Inc. (2)
75 14th St 24th Fl, Atlanta, GA 30309
Tel.: (404) 920-9000
Web Site: http://www.arcapita.com
Sales Range: $50-74.9 Million
Emp.: 30
Financial Management & Investment Services
N.A.I.C.S.: 523999

Holding (Domestic):

Church's Chicken, Inc. (3)
980 Hammond Dr NE Ste 1100, Atlanta, GA 30328-8187
Tel.: (770) 350-3800
Web Site: http://www.churchs.com
Sales Range: $1-4.9 Billion
Fast Food Restaurant Operator
N.A.I.C.S.: 722513
Edward Williams (VP-Ops)

Subsidiary (US):

MC Sign Company (2)
8959 Tyler Blvd, Mentor, OH 44060
Tel.: (440) 953-2280
Web Site: http://www.themcgroup.com
Sign Mfr
N.A.I.C.S.: 339950
Tim Eippert (Owner)

Holding (Non-US):

profine GmbH (2)
Muelheimer Strasse 26 Tor 3, Troisdorf, 53840, Germany
Tel.: (49) 224199530
Web Site: http://www.profine-group.com
Sales Range: $800-899.9 Million
Plastic Floor Coverings, Wall Panels, Windows, Doors & Motor Vehicle Parts
N.A.I.C.S.: 326199
Achim Judt (COO & Member-Mgmt Bd)

Subsidiary (Non-US):

Koemmerling Tianjin Kunststoff Co. Ltd. (3)
No 2 Zhonghong Road Jinnan Economic Development Area, Tianjin, 300350, China

Tel.: (86) 2288515188
Web Site: http://www.koemmerling.com.cn
Plastics Product Mfr
N.A.I.C.S.: 326199
Yves Baracco (Gen Mgr)

Subsidiary (US):

Kommerling USA, Inc. (3)
3402 Stanwood Blvd, Huntsville, AL 35811
Tel.: (256) 851-4099
Web Site: http://www.kommerlingusa.com
Sales Range: $25-49.9 Million
Emp.: 100
Plastics Mfr; PVC Sheets Mfr
N.A.I.C.S.: 326199
Teresa Heckaman (Office Mgr)

Subsidiary (Non-US):

SAO profine RUS (3)
2 Roschinski pr 8, 115419, Moscow, Russia
Tel.: (7) 4952329330
Web Site: http://www.profine-group.ru
Emp.: 100
Mfr of Plastic Profiles for Windows & Doors; Supplier of Shutter Solutions & PVC Sheets
N.A.I.C.S.: 326199
Jangerd Fos (Gen Dir)

profine Austria GmbH (3)
Kaerntnerstrasse 155, Graz, 8053, Austria
Tel.: (43) 31626167014
Web Site: http://www.profine-group.de
Sales Range: $25-49.9 Million
Emp.: 50
Mfr of Plastic Profiles for Windows & Doors; Supplier of Shutter Solutions & PVC Sheets
N.A.I.C.S.: 326199
Heinz Doppler (Mgr)

profine BH d.o.o. (3)
Magistralni put-A br 33, Tuzla, 75270, Zivinice, Bosnia & Herzegovina
Tel.: (387) 35304600
Web Site: http://www.profine.ba
Mfr of Plastic Profiles for Windows & Doors; Supplier of Shutter Solutions & PVC Sheets
N.A.I.C.S.: 326199

profine Belux BVBA (3)
Zone 3 Doornveld 110, Zellik, 1731, Belgium
Tel.: (32) 24669960
Web Site: http://www.kommerling.be
Emp.: 9
Plastic Profiles for Windows & Doors; Supplier of Shutter Solutions & PVC Sheets
N.A.I.C.S.: 424610
Frederik Declercq (Gen Mgr)

profine Croatia doo (3)
Vukomericka bb, 10410, Velika Gorica, Croatia
Tel.: (385) 16253100
Web Site: http://www.profine-croatia.hr
Sales Range: $25-49.9 Million
Emp.: 15
Mfr of Plastic Profiles for Windows & Doors; Supplier of Shutter Solutions & PVC Sheets
N.A.I.C.S.: 326199

profine France SAS (3)
ZI rue Gutleutfeld, BP 50, 67441, Marmoutier, Alsace, France
Tel.: (33) 388715050
Web Site: http://www.profine-group.fr
Sales Range: $25-49.9 Million
Emp.: 100
Mfr of Plastic Profiles for Windows & Doors; Supplier of Shutter Solutions & PVC Sheets
N.A.I.C.S.: 326199

profine Iberia S.A. (3)
Poligono Industrial Alcamar S/N, Camarma de Esteruelas, 28816, Madrid, Spain
Tel.: (34) 918866045
Web Site: http://www.profine-group.es
Mfr of Plastic Profiles for Windows & Doors; Supplier of Shutter Solutions & PVC Sheets
N.A.I.C.S.: 326199
Jose-Ramon Navarro (Gen Mgr)

profine Italia SRL (3)
Via Casilini 65 loc, 03018, Paliano, FR, Italy
Tel.: (39) 0775538149
Web Site: http://www.kbaitalia.it
Mfr of Plastic Profiles for Windows & Doors; Supplier of Shutter Solutions & PVC Sheets
N.A.I.C.S.: 326199

profine Nederland b.v. (3)
Regterweistraat 13, Waardenburg, 4181,
Netherlands
Tel.: (31) 418651717
Web Site: http://www.kbe-online.nl
Sales Range: $25-49.9 Million
Emp.: 8
Plastic Profiles for Windows & Doors; Sup-
plier of Shutter Solutions & PVC Sheets
N.A.I.C.S.: 424610
Bart de Weger (Gen Mgr)

profine Polska Sp. z o.o. (3)
ul Strachowicka 40, 54512, Wroclaw, Po-
land
Tel.: (48) 713471160
Web Site: http://www.profine.pl
Plastic Profiles for Windows & Doors; Sup-
plier of Shutter Solutions & PVC Sheets
N.A.I.C.S.: 424610

profine Romania SRL (3)
Soseaua de Centura, Alexandriei 152-156,
077025, Bragadiru, Romania
Tel.: (40) 214932145
Web Site: http://www.profine-group.com
Mfr of Plastic Profiles for Windows & Doors;
Supplier of Shutter Solutions & PVC Sheets
N.A.I.C.S.: 326199

profine Schweiz AG (3)
Herblingerstrasse 119, 8207, Schaffhausen,
Switzerland
Tel.: (41) 526440544
Web Site: http://www.koemmerling.ch
Plastic Profiles for Windows & Doors Mfr &
Distr
N.A.I.C.S.: 424610

profine UK Ltd. (3)
Lancaster Road Fradley Park, Fradley,
Lichfield, WS13 8RY, Staffs, United King-
dom
Tel.: (44) 1543444900
Web Site: http://www.kbe-online.com
Sales Range: $25-49.9 Million
Emp.: 18
Mfr of Plastic Profiles for Windows & Doors;
Supplier of Shutter Solutions & PVC Sheets
N.A.I.C.S.: 326199

profine Ukraine (3)
Jaroslawiw Wal 5-a, 01034, Kiev, Ukraine
Tel.: (380) 442341184
Web Site: http://www.profine.ua
Sales Range: $25-49.9 Million
Emp.: 25
Mfr of Plastic Profiles for Windows & Doors;
Supplier of Shutter Solutions & PVC Sheets
N.A.I.C.S.: 326199

**Arcapita Investment Management
B.S.C.(c)** (1)
Building 551 Road 4612 Block 346 Bahrain
Bay, PO Box 1357, Manama, Bahrain
Tel.: (973) 97317216333
Rev.: $17,456,000
Assets: $15,227,000
Liabilities: $2,203,000
Net Worth: $13,024,000
Earnings: ($60,000)
Fiscal Year-end: 06/30/2019
Privater Equity Firm
N.A.I.C.S.: 523999
Ahmed Al Shirawa (Mng Dir)

ARCEE INDUSTRIES LIMITED
7th K M Barwala Road Talwandi
Rana, Hisar, 125 001, Haryana, India
Tel.: (91) 1662276178
Year Founded: 1992
520121—(BOM)
Rev.: $4,675,603
Assets: $1,674,691
Liabilities: $911,929
Net Worth: $762,762
Earnings: $63,445
Emp.: 37
Fiscal Year-end: 03/31/22
Plastic Tank Mfr
N.A.I.C.S.: 326122
Shruti Gupta (Exec Dir)

ARCELORMITTAL S.A.
24-26 Boulevard d'Avranches,
L-1160, Luxembourg, Luxembourg

Tel.: (352) 47921 LU
Web Site:
https://luxembourg.arcelormittal.com
Year Founded: 2007
MT—(NYSE)
Rev.: $68,275,000,000
Assets: $93,917,000,000
Liabilities: $37,849,000,000
Net Worth: $56,068,000,000
Earnings: $1,022,000,000
Emp.: 126,756
Fiscal Year-end: 12/31/23
Steel Products Mfr
N.A.I.C.S.: 551112
Lakshmi Niwas Mittal (Exec Chm)

Subsidiaries:

AM/NS Calvert (1)
1 Thyssenkrupp Dr, Calvert, AL
36513 **(50%)**
Tel.: (251) 289-3000
Web Site: http://usa.arcelormittal.com
Sales Range: $900-999.9 Million
Emp.: 4,000
Coiled Carbon Steel Mfr & Distr
N.A.I.C.S.: 332111

ARCELORMITTAL GENK N.V. (1)
Kanaaloever 3, 3600, Genk, Belgium
Tel.: (32) 89 30 18 05
Sales Range: $50-74.9 Million
Emp.: 135
Cold Rolled Steel Mfr
N.A.I.C.S.: 331221
Johan Aelter (Gen Mgr)

**ARCELORMITTAL HAMILTON
INC.** (1)
1330 Burlington St E, Po Box 2460, Hamil-
ton, L8N 3J5, ON, Canada
Tel.: (905) 548-6411
Rolled Steel Product Mfr & Distr
N.A.I.C.S.: 331221

ARCELORMITTAL LESAKA S.A. (1)
Barrio Arratzubi N 5, 31770, Lesaka, Na-
varra, Spain
Tel.: (34) 948628300
Steel Products Mfr
N.A.I.C.S.: 331110

**ARCELORMITTAL SAGUNTO
SL** (1)
Carretera de Acceso IV Planta KM 3 9,
46520, Sagunto, Spain
Tel.: (34) 962658100
Web Site: http://www.arcelormittal.com
Cold Rolled Coil Mfr
N.A.I.C.S.: 334416

**ARCELORMITTAL SESTAO
S.L.U** (1)
Chavarri 6, 48910, Sestao, Spain
Tel.: (34) 944894403
Emp.: 350
Rolled Steel Products Mfr
N.A.I.C.S.: 331221

Arcelor International Export S.A. (1)
19 Ave de la Liberte, Luxembourg, 2930,
Luxembourg
Tel.: (352) 47921
Sales Range: $250-299.9 Million
Emp.: 900
Sales & Distr of Steel Products; Beams,
Sections, Bars, Rods, Plates, Sheets,
Tubes & Other Products
N.A.I.C.S.: 425120
Lakshmi Niwas Mittal (CEO)

Subsidiary (Non-US):

**ArcelorMittal International Antwerp
SA** (2)
Noordlaan 147, 2030, Antwerp, Belgium
Tel.: (32) 32440800
Sales Range: $25-49.9 Million
Emp.: 20
Steel Mfrs
N.A.I.C.S.: 331513

Arcelor RPS (1)
66 Rue De Luxembourg, L 4221, Esch-sur-
Alzette, Luxembourg
Tel.: (352) 53133105
Web Site: http://www.rps.arcelor.com

Sales Range: $25-49.9 Million
Emp.: 100
Rails & Special Sections Sheet Piling
N.A.I.C.S.: 332322

**ArcelorMittal - ArcelorMittal Avellino
Mill** (1)
Stabilimento di Avellino Zona Industriale,
San Mango sul Calore, 83040, Luogosano,
Avellino, Italy
Tel.: (39) 082779210
Web Site: http://www.arcelormittal.com
Steel Building Construction Services
N.A.I.C.S.: 238120

**ArcelorMittal - ArcelorMittal Canossa
Mill** (1)
Stabilimento di Canossa, Via De Gasperi
43, 42026, Canossa, Reggio Emilia, Italy
Tel.: (39) 0522872711
Web Site: http://www.arcelormittal.com
Metal Products Mfr
N.A.I.C.S.: 322220

**ArcelorMittal - ArcelorMittal Desvres
Mill** (1)
Rue Bidet 65, 62240, Desvres, France
Tel.: (33) 321992800
Web Site: http://www.arcelormittal.com
Steel Mfrs
N.A.I.C.S.: 331110

**ArcelorMittal - ArcelorMittal Dunker-
que Mill** (1)
Rue du Comte Jean Grande Synthe 2508,
59381, Dunkerque, France
Tel.: (33) 328293000
Rolled Steel Products Mfr
N.A.I.C.S.: 331221

**ArcelorMittal - ArcelorMittal Etxebarri
Mill** (1)
Egetiaga Uribarri 34 Apto 20, 48450, Etxe-
barri, Biscay, Spain
Tel.: (34) 944894000
Web Site: http://www.arcelormittal.com
Rolled Steel Products Mfr
N.A.I.C.S.: 331221

**ArcelorMittal - ArcelorMittal Mardyck
Mill** (1)
Route de Spycker 1, 59792, Grande-
Synthe, France
Tel.: (33) 328295200
Cold Rolled Steel Mfr
N.A.I.C.S.: 331221

**ArcelorMittal - ArcelorMittal Mon-
tataire Mill** (1)
Route de Saint Leu, 60160, Montataire,
France
Tel.: (33) 344557501
Web Site: http://www.arcelormittal.com
Steel Galvanizing & Sheet Mfr
N.A.I.C.S.: 331110

**ArcelorMittal - ArcelorMittal Mouzon
Mill** (1)
7 Rue Albert Ollivet, 08210, Mouzon,
08210, France
Tel.: (33) 324298700
Sales Range: $50-74.9 Million
Emp.: 130
Steel Products Mfr
N.A.I.C.S.: 331221

ArcelorMittal - Coteau du Lac (1)
25 Rue De L'Acier, Coteau du Lac, J0P
1B0, QC, Canada
Tel.: (450) 763-0915
Sales Range: $25-49.9 Million
Emp.: 65
Hot-Dip Galvanized Steel Mfr
N.A.I.C.S.: 331221
Gilles Lahaie (Gen Mgr)

**ArcelorMittal Ambalaj Celigi Sanayi
ve Ticaret A.S.** (1)
Nispetiye Cad Ozden Is Merkezi No 22-Kat
3, Levent, Istanbul, 34330, Turkiye
Tel.: (90) 212 325 27 18
Steel Sheet & Slitted Coil Mfr
N.A.I.C.S.: 331221

ArcelorMittal Ancenis (1)
Zac de l'Aeropole, Ancenis, 44150, France
Tel.: (33) 4 78 97 62 30
Metal Sheet Mfr
N.A.I.C.S.: 332999

ArcelorMittal Annaba Spa (1)
Sidi Amar El-Hadjar Complex, B P 2055,
Annaba, 23000, Algeria
Tel.: (213) 38871525
Web Site: http://www.mittalsteel.com
Iron & Steel Mills
N.A.I.C.S.: 331110

**ArcelorMittal Atlantique et Lorraine
S.A.S.** (1)
2 Rue Bidet, 62240, Desvres, France
Tel.: (33) 321992800
Steel Products Mfr
N.A.I.C.S.: 331221
Bernard Maille (Mgr)

**ArcelorMittal Belval & Differdange
S.A.** (1)
66 Rue De Luxembourg, L 4221, Esch-sur-
Alzette, Luxembourg
Tel.: (352) 53131
Web Site: http://www.arcelor.com
Sales Range: $200-249.9 Million
Emp.: 600
Long Carbon Steel Sheet & Bearing Piles
Mfr
N.A.I.C.S.: 331221

ArcelorMittal Beryslav (1)
Kirova Str 52, Beryslav, 74300, Ukraine
Tel.: (380) 564993129
Limestone Mfr
N.A.I.C.S.: 212312

ArcelorMittal Bissen S.A. (1)
Route de Finsterthal, 7769, Bissen, Luxem-
bourg
Tel.: (352) 8357721
Web Site:
http://www.luxembourg.arcelormittal.com
Emp.: 350
Sales of Steel Products; Beams, Sections,
Bars, Rods, Sheet, Plates, Tubes & other
Products
N.A.I.C.S.: 238120

ArcelorMittal Brasil S.A. (1)
Avenida Carandai 1115 Funcionarios, Belo
Horizonte, 30130-915, MG, Brazil
Tel.: (55) 3184532235
Web Site: https://brasil.arcelormittal.com
Holding Company; Steel Mfr
N.A.I.C.S.: 332111
Benjamin Baptista Filho (Pres)

Subsidiary (Non-US):

**Acindar Industria Argentina de Aceros
S.A.** (2)
Estanislao Zeballos 2739, 1643, Buenos
Aires, Argentina
Tel.: (54) 1147198500
Web Site: http://www.acindar.com.ar
Sales Range: $700-749.9 Million
Emp.: 6
Steel Products Mfr
N.A.I.C.S.: 332111

Subsidiary (Domestic):

ArcelorMittal Tubarao (2)
Av Brigadeiro Eduardo Gomes 930 - Jardim
Limoeiro, 29163-970, Serra, Espirito Santo,
Brazil
Tel.: (55) 27 3348 1333
Web Site: http://www.cst.com.br
Steel Products Mfr
N.A.I.C.S.: 331221

Votorantim Siderurgia S.A. (2)
Av Professor Darcy Ribeiro 4 300 Casa da
Lua, Brasilia, 27523 300, Rio de Janeiro,
Brazil
Tel.: (55) 24 2108 6352
Fabricated Steel Mfr
N.A.I.C.S.: 332312

ArcelorMittal Bremen GmbH (1)
Carl-Benz-Strasse 30, 28237, Bremen, Ger-
many
Tel.: (49) 4216480
Web Site: https://bremen.arcelormittal.com
Sales Range: $800-899.9 Million
Emp.: 3,700
Hot & Cold Rolled Sheet in Coils & Plates
Mfr
N.A.I.C.S.: 331221

Subsidiary (Domestic):

Bremer Galvanisierungs GmbH (2)

ArcelorMittal S.A.—(Continued)

Carl Den Str 30, D 28237, Bremen, Germany
Tel.: (49) 4216481500
Web Site: http://www.bregal.de
Sales Range: $75-99.9 Million
Emp.: 131
Hot Dip Galvanizing Line
N.A.I.C.S.: 212210

ArcelorMittal Cariacica (1)
Leopoldina Avenue 900 - Vasco da Gama, Cariacica, 29140-080, Espirito Santo, Brazil
Tel.: (55) 27 3246 6000
Web Site: http://www.arcelormittal.com
Rolled Steel Products Mfr
N.A.I.C.S.: 331221

ArcelorMittal Commercial RPS Deutschland GmbH (1)
Subbelrather Strasse 13, D-50672, Cologne, Germany
Tel.: (49) 35253133213
Sales Range: $200-249.9 Million
Emp.: 1,000
Mfr of Sheet Piles, Rails & Special Sections
N.A.I.C.S.: 332312

ArcelorMittal Distribution S.A.S. (1)
16 Avenue de la Malle, Saint Brice Courcelles, F-51076, Reims, Cedex, France
Tel.: (33) 326846565
Steel Product Distr
N.A.I.C.S.: 541614

Unit (Non-US):

ArcelorMittal Distribution Solutions (2)
19 Ave Be La liberpe, L-1160, Luxembourg, Luxembourg
Tel.: (352) 4792 2859
Web Site: http://www.arcelormittal.com
Sales Range: $150-199.9 Million
Emp.: 800
Steel Product Distr
N.A.I.C.S.: 423510
Lakshmi Niwas Mittal (Chm)

ArcelorMittal Dofasco Inc. (1)
1330 Burlington St E, PO Box 2460, Hamilton, L8N 3J5, ON, Canada
Tel.: (905) 544-3761
Web Site: http://www.dofasco.ca
Sales Range: $5-14.9 Billion
Emp.: 7,400
Galvanized, Tinplate & Chromium-Coated Flat Rolled Steels & Tubular Products Mfr
N.A.I.C.S.: 331111
Monique Biancucci (VP-People & Culture)

Subsidiary (Domestic):

ArcelorMittal Mines Canada Inc. (2)
1801 Mcgill College Suite 1400, Montreal, H3A 2N4, QC, Canada
Tel.: (514) 285-1464
Iron Ore Product Distr
N.A.I.C.S.: 423510

Subsidiary (Domestic):

ArcelorMittal Woodstock (2)
193 Givins Street, PO Box 1589, Woodstock, N4S 0A7, ON, Canada
Tel.: (519) 537-6671
Web Site: http://www.tubular.arcelormittal.com
Sales Range: $100-124.9 Million
Emp.: 400
Steel Tubing Mfr
N.A.I.C.S.: 331210
Tim Abbott (Gen Mgr)

Plant (Domestic):

ArcelorMittal Brampton (3)
14 Holtby Ave, Brampton, L6X 2M3, ON, Canada
Tel.: (905) 451-2400
Web Site: http://www.dofascotube.com
Sales Range: $125-149.9 Million
Mfr of Automotive Steel Tubing
N.A.I.C.S.: 331210

Subsidiary (US):

Dofasco Tubular Products (3)
2105 Four Gateway Center, Pittsburgh, PA 15222-1211
Tel.: (412) 263-3200
Web Site: http://www.dofascotube.com

Retailer of Tubular Steel Products
N.A.I.C.S.: 331210

Affiliate (Domestic):

Baycoat Ltd. (2)
244 Lanark Street, Hamilton, L8N 3K7, ON, Canada
Tel.: (905) 561-0965
Web Site: http://www.dofasco.ca
Sales Range: $75-99.9 Million
Emp.: 250
Paint Services to Rolled Steel Coils; Owned 50% by Dofasco, Inc. & 50% by Stelco Incorporated
N.A.I.C.S.: 238320

Joint Venture (Domestic):

DJ Galvanizing (2)
300 Sprucewood Avenue, Windsor, N9C 3Y6, ON, Canada
Tel.: (519) 250-2100
Sales Range: $25-49.9 Million
Emp.: 100
Hot-Dip Galvanizing Services; Owned 50% by Dofasco, Inc. & 50% by JFE Steel Corporation
N.A.I.C.S.: 331221
Paul Dunmore (Pres)

Subsidiary (US):

Dofasco USA Inc. (2)
26899 Northwestern Hwy, Southfield, MI 48034-2195
Tel.: (248) 357-3090
Web Site: http://www.dofasco.ca
Sales Range: $25-49.9 Million
Emp.: 10
Steel Whslr
N.A.I.C.S.: 423510

Subsidiary (Domestic):

Quebec Cartier Mining Co. (2)
24 Des Iles Blvd Ste 201, Port-Cartier, G5B 2H3, QC, Canada
Tel.: (418) 766-2000
Web Site: http://www.qcmines.com
Sales Range: $650-699.9 Million
Emp.: 1,800
Iron Ore Products Mfr
N.A.I.C.S.: 212210

ArcelorMittal Duisburg GmbH (1)
Vohwinkelstrasse 107, 47137, Duisburg, Germany
Tel.: (49) 20360667353
Web Site: http://www.arcelormittalduisburg.de
Rolled Steel Products Mfr
N.A.I.C.S.: 331221

ArcelorMittal Eisenhuttenstadt GmbH (1)
Werkstrasse 1, 15890, Eisenhuttenstadt, Germany
Tel.: (49) 3364370
Web Site: https://eisenhuettenstadt.arcelormittal.com
Rev.: $1,637,202,210
Emp.: 3,000
Rolled Steel Products Mfr
N.A.I.C.S.: 331221
Hedwig Vergote (Chm-Supervisory Bd)

ArcelorMittal Escazu SA (1)
2-1251 San Rafael de Escazu, San Rafael, San Jose, Costa Rica
Tel.: (506) 22058900
Web Site: http://www.arcelormittal.com
Business Process Support Services
N.A.I.C.S.: 561110

ArcelorMittal Espana S.A. (1)
La Granda, 33418, Gozon, Asturias, Spain
Tel.: (34) 985126000
Sales Range: $50-74.9 Million
Emp.: 200
Flat Carbon Steel Products Mfr & Distr
N.A.I.C.S.: 331221

Subsidiary (Domestic):

Europerfil S.A. (2)
Avenida de la Granvia 179, 08908, L'Hospitalet de Llobregat, Spain
Tel.: (34) 932616333
Web Site: https://www.europerfil.com

Building Exterior Metal Cladding Products Mfr & Whslr
N.A.I.C.S.: 332311

ArcelorMittal Flat Carbon Europe S.A. (1)
19 Avenue de la Liberte, Luxembourg, 2930, Luxembourg
Tel.: (352) 47922629
Web Site: http://www.arcelormittal.com
Rolled Steel Products Mfr
N.A.I.C.S.: 331221

ArcelorMittal France S.A. (1)
1 Rue Luigi Cherubini, 93200, Saint Denis, France
Tel.: (33) 141256010
Sales Range: $600-649.9 Million
Emp.: 577
Steel Mfrs
N.A.I.C.S.: 331513

ArcelorMittal Gandrange S.A (1)
Site Industriel, 57175, Amenville, France
Tel.: (33) 387706000
Web Site: http://www.ispat.com
Sales Range: $200-249.9 Million
Emp.: 1,000
Mfr of Wire Rods, Rails, Light Girders, Steel Piling & Rolled Steel
N.A.I.C.S.: 331221

ArcelorMittal Geel (1)
Lammerdries 10 Industriezone Geel-West Zone 4, 2440, Geel, Belgium
Tel.: (32) 14563050
Web Site: https://flateurope.arcelormittal.com
Sales Range: $125-149.9 Million
Emp.: 70
Coil Coating Services
N.A.I.C.S.: 324199

ArcelorMittal Genk Stainless Service Belgium N.V. (1)
Kanaaloever 3, Genk, 3600, Belgium
Tel.: (32) 89 30 18 05
Rev.: $929,000,000
Emp.: 100
Stainless Steel Flat Products Mfr
N.A.I.C.S.: 331221
Serge Vranken (Controller)

ArcelorMittal Gent (1)
John Kennedylaan 51, 9042, Gent, Belgium
Tel.: (32) 93473111
Sales Range: $1-4.9 Billion
Emp.: 5,500
Steel Electro-Galvanizing
N.A.I.C.S.: 332813

ArcelorMittal Gent N.V. (1)
John Kennedylaan 51, 9042, Gent, Belgium
Tel.: (32) 93473111
Web Site: https://belgium.arcelormittal.com
Sales Range: $1-4.9 Billion
Emp.: 5,500
Flat Steel Products & Wide High Quality Cold Rolled Sheet Steel Mfr
N.A.I.C.S.: 331221

ArcelorMittal Gipuzkoa S.L. (1)
Ctra Madrid - Irun Km 417, 20212, Olaberria, Gipuzkoa, Spain
Tel.: (34) 943805000
Rolled Steel Products Mfr
N.A.I.C.S.: 331221

ArcelorMittal Hamburg GmbH (1)
Dradenaustrasse 33, 21129, Hamburg, Germany
Tel.: (49) 4074080
Sales Range: $500-549.9 Million
Emp.: 700
N.A.I.C.S.: 212210

ArcelorMittal Hautmont (1)
12 Rue des Usines, 59330, Hautmont, France
Tel.: (33) 171921811
Precision Tube Mfr
N.A.I.C.S.: 331110

ArcelorMittal Hunedoara S.A. (1)
DJ 687-No 4 Hunedoara, 331111, Hunedoara, Romania
Tel.: (40) 254716121
Web Site: https://www.arcelormittalhunedoara.ro
Sales Range: $400-449.9 Million
Emp.: 2,200
Iron & Steel Mills

N.A.I.C.S.: 331110

ArcelorMittal Infrastructure G.P (1)
1010 de Swrigny Suite 200, Longueuil, J4K 5G7, QC, Canada
Tel.: (514) 285-1464
N.A.I.C.S.: 333131

ArcelorMittal International Luxembourg S.A. (1)
24-26 Boulevard D Abranches, 2930, Luxembourg, Luxembourg
Tel.: (352) 4792 1
Web Site: http://luxembourg.arcelormittal.com
Steel Slab & Bar Distr
N.A.I.C.S.: 423510

ArcelorMittal Itauna (1)
Clara Chaves Street 150 Sao Judas, Tadeu, Itauna, 35681-168, Minas Gerais, Brazil
Tel.: (55) 37 3249 4400
Steel Bar & Beam Mfr
N.A.I.C.S.: 331221

ArcelorMittal Jubail (1)
Crossroads 305 308, PO Box 10090, Jubail 2 Industrial City, 31961, Al Jubayl, Saudi Arabia
Tel.: (966) 48873815
Precision Tube Mfr
N.A.I.C.S.: 331110

ArcelorMittal Juiz de Fora. (1)
Br-040 km 769 Dias Tavares, Juiz de Fora, 36105-000, Minas Gerias, Brazil
Tel.: (55) 32 3229 1000
Rolled & Drawn Steel Product Mfr
N.A.I.C.S.: 331221

ArcelorMittal Kryviy Rih (1)
Dnipropetrovsk region, Krivorozhstali street, Krivoy Rog, 50095, Ukraine
Tel.: (380) 564992695
Iron & Steel Mills
N.A.I.C.S.: 331110

ArcelorMittal Lazaro Cardenas S.A. de C.V. (1)
Francisco J Mujica 1-B Colonia Centro, 60950, Michoacan, Lazaro Cardenas, Mexico
Tel.: (52) 5552490773
Web Site: http://pc.arcelormittal.com
Sales Range: $450-499.9 Million
Emp.: 1,100
Produces, Sells & Exports Steel & Slab Products
N.A.I.C.S.: 332618
P. S. Venkataramanan (CEO)

ArcelorMittal Logistics Belgium (1)
Atlantic House Noordelaan 147, 2030, Antwerp, Belgium
Tel.: (32) 33030600
Sales Range: $50-74.9 Million
Emp.: 60
Steel Producer
N.A.I.C.S.: 212210
Frank De Fyn (VP-Ops)

ArcelorMittal London (1)
2440 Scanlan Street, London, NSW 6H7, ON, Canada
Tel.: (519) 451-7701
Sales Range: $25-49.9 Million
Emp.: 50
Steel Products Mfr
N.A.I.C.S.: 331221

ArcelorMittal Long Products Canada G.P. (1)
4000 route des Acieries, Contrecoeur, J0L 1C0, QC, Canada
Tel.: (450) 587-8600
Web Site: http://long-canada.arcelormittal.com
Emp.: 1,900
Steel Products Mfr
N.A.I.C.S.: 331110
Francois Perras (CEO)

ArcelorMittal Madrid S.L. (1)
Carretera da Toledo Km 9 2, Villaverde, 28021, Madrid, Spain
Tel.: (34) 917972300
Rolled Steel Products Mfr
N.A.I.C.S.: 331221

ArcelorMittal Mediterranee S.A.S. (1)

6 oue jangoe campoa 93212 seine cegex,
Saint Denis, 93212, France
Tel.: (33) 171920000
Rolled Steel Products Mfr
N.A.I.C.S.: 331221

ArcelorMittal Mexico S.A. de C.V. (1)
Torre Trebol Park 18th Floor Av Lazaro
Cardenas No 2424, Col Residencial San
Agustin, Monterrey, Nuevo Leon, Mexico
Tel.: (52) 8112236700
Web Site: http://mexico.arcelormittal.com
Steel Slab Mfr
N.A.I.C.S.: 331110

ArcelorMittal Monlevade S.A. (1)
Getulio Vargas Avenue 100, Joao Monl-
evade, 35930-900, Minas Gerais, Brazil
Tel.: (55) 31 38591212
Web Site: http://www.arcelormittal.com
Rolled Steel Products Mfr & Distr
N.A.I.C.S.: 331221

ArcelorMittal Monterrey (1)
Saltilo km 28 2 Col Arco Vial, 66050, Mon-
terrey, 66050, Mexico
Tel.: (52) 8182208042
Steel Tube & Pipe Mfr
N.A.I.C.S.: 331210
Servando Martinez *(Mgr-Mktg)*

ArcelorMittal Montreal Inc. (1)
4000 Rte Des Acieries, Contrecoeur, J0L
1C0, QC, Canada
Tel.: (450) 587-8600
Sales Range: $400-449.9 Million
Emp.: 2,300
Producer of Semi-Finished Products, Slabs,
Billets & Other Steel Products
N.A.I.C.S.: 331221

Subsidiary (US):

Walker Wire & Steel Company (2)
660 East 10 Mile Rd, Ferndale, MI 48220-
1036
Tel.: (248) 399-4800
Web Site: http://www.mittalsteel.com
Sales Range: $50-74.9 Million
Emp.: 150
Mfr of Steel Wiredrawing
N.A.I.C.S.: 331222

ArcelorMittal Point Lisas Ltd (1)
Mediterranean Drive, Point Lisas, Couva,
Trinidad & Tobago
Tel.: (868) 636 2211
Emp.: 750
N.A.I.C.S.: 212210

ArcelorMittal Poland S.A. (1)
Al Jozefa Pilsudskiego 92, 41-308, Dab-
rowa Gornicza, Poland
Tel.: (48) 327766666
Web Site: https://poland.arcelormittal.com
Iron & Steel Mills
N.A.I.C.S.: 331110
Czeslaw Sikorski *(Mng Dir-Health & Safety,
Coke Production & Special Projects & VP)*

ArcelorMittal Projects Belgium NV (1)
Industrielaan 2 Nolimpark 1323, 3900,
Overpelt, Belgium
Tel.: (32) 11 800 890
Web Site: http://www.arcelormittal.com
Sales Range: $25-49.9 Million
Emp.: 3
Rolled Steel Products Mfr
N.A.I.C.S.: 331221

ArcelorMittal Projects Netherlands BV (1)
Mannesmannweg 5, 4794 SL, Heijningen,
Netherlands
Tel.: (31) 880083700
Web Site: http://www.damwand.nl
Sales Range: $50-74.9 Million
Emp.: 150
Rolled Steel Products Mfr
N.A.I.C.S.: 331221

ArcelorMittal Rodange & Schifflange S.A. (1)
2 rue de l'Industrie, L 4823, Rodange, Luxembourg
Tel.: (352) 50191
Web Site:
https://luxembourg.arcelormittal.com

Sales Range: $100-124.9 Million
Emp.: 318
Industrial Products Mfr
N.A.I.C.S.: 334513

ArcelorMittal Rongcheng (1)
No 36 Chengshan Dadao W, Rongcheng,
264300, Shandong, China
Tel.: (86) 6317523619
Web Site: http://www.arcelormittal.com
Steel Cord & Bead Wire Mfr
N.A.I.C.S.: 331221

ArcelorMittal Ruhrort GmbH (1)
Vohwinkelstrasse 107, 47137, Duisburg,
Germany
Tel.: (49) 20360667353
Web Site:
https://www.duisburg.arcelormittal.com
Sales Range: $350-399.9 Million
Emp.: 950
N.A.I.C.S.: 212210

ArcelorMittal SSC UK Ltd (1)
Strawberry Ln, Willenhall, WV13 3SE,
Wolverhampton, United Kingdom
Tel.: (44) 1902365243
Sales Range: $125-149.9 Million
Emp.: 130
N.A.I.C.S.: 212210

ArcelorMittal Shipping Ltd. (1)
7th Fl Berkeley Square House, London,
W1J 6DA, United Kingdom
Tel.: (44) 2073980720
Sales Range: $10-24.9 Million
Emp.: 20
Management of Cargo Vessels; Chartering
Services; Freight Forwarding
N.A.I.C.S.: 488320

ArcelorMittal South Africa Ltd. (1)
Delfos Boulevard, Vanderbijlpark, 1900,
Gauteng, South Africa
Tel.: (27) 168899111
Web Site: http://www.arcelormittal.co.za
Sales Range: $1-4.9 Billion
Emp.: 9,000
Steel & Steel Products
N.A.I.C.S.: 331513
Lakshmi Niwas Mittal *(Chm)*

Unit (Domestic):

ArcelorMittal South Africa Ltd. - Newcastle Works (2)
Iscor Road, Newcastle, 2940, South Africa
Tel.: (27) 343147911
Web Site: http://www.arcelormittalsa.com
Sales Range: $350-399.9 Million
Emp.: 1,850
Rolled Steel Products Mfr
N.A.I.C.S.: 331221

ArcelorMittal South Africa Ltd. - Pretoria Works (2)
Frikkie Meyer Road, Pretoria West, 0001,
Pretoria, 0001, South Africa
Tel.: (27) 123802510
Web Site: http://www.arcelormittalsa.com
Rolled Steel Products Mfr
N.A.I.C.S.: 331221

ArcelorMittal South Africa Ltd. - Saldanha Works (2)
Ystervarkensrug, 7395, Saldanha, 7395,
South Africa
Tel.: (27) 227094000
Web Site: http://www.arcelormittalsa.com
Rolled Steel Products Mfr
N.A.I.C.S.: 331221

ArcelorMittal South Africa Ltd. - Vanderbijlpark Works (2)
Delfos Boulevard, Vanderbijlpark, 1900,
South Africa
Tel.: (27) 168899111
Web Site: http://www.arcelormittalsa.com
Sales Range: $700-749.9 Million
Emp.: 4,500
Rolled Steel Products Mfr
N.A.I.C.S.: 331221

ArcelorMittal South Africa Ltd. - Vereeniging Works (2)
273 General Hertzog Road Peacehaven,
Leeuwkuil, Vereeniging, 1930, South Africa
Tel.: (27) 164504125
Web Site: http://www.arcelormittalsa.com

Sales Range: $150-199.9 Million
Emp.: 908
Rolled Steel Products Mfr
N.A.I.C.S.: 331221

ArcelorMittal St. Chely d'Apcher Mill (1)
Rue des Martyrs du Maquis, 48200, Saint-
Chely-d'Apcher, 48200, France
Tel.: (33) 466495700
Sales Range: $50-74.9 Million
Emp.: 190
Steel Products Mfr
N.A.I.C.S.: 331110

ArcelorMittal Steel North America (1)
1 S Dearborn, Chicago, IL 60603
Tel.: (312) 899-3991
Sales Range: $125-149.9 Million
Emp.: 2
Steel Distrubution
N.A.I.C.S.: 423510

ArcelorMittal Tallinn OU (1)
Koorma 5 Muuga Harbor, Viimsi, 74004,
Estonia
Tel.: (372) 6056 600
Steel Sheet Mfr
N.A.I.C.S.: 332322

ArcelorMittal Tubular Products Iasi SA (1)
Calea Chisinaului Street 132, 700180, Iasi,
Romania
Tel.: (40) 232203103
Web Site: https://tubular.arcelormittal.com
Iron & Steel Mills; Welded Carbon Steel
Tubes Mfr
N.A.I.C.S.: 331110

ArcelorMittal Tubular Products Karvina a.s. (1)
Rude armady 471, 733 23, Karvina, Czech
Republic
Tel.: (420) 596391111
Web Site: https://www.jakl.cz
Sales Range: $100-124.9 Million
Emp.: 421
Steel Products Mfr
N.A.I.C.S.: 331221
Daniel Stolarz *(Mgr-Bus)*

ArcelorMittal Tubular Products Roman S.A. (1)
Seamless Stefan cel Mare 15A/1, 611038,
Roman, Neamt, Romania
Tel.: (40) 372688160
Sales Range: $800-899.9 Million
Emp.: 3,100
Iron & Steel Mills
N.A.I.C.S.: 331110

ArcelorMittal Warszawa Sp. z.o.o. (1)
ul Kasprowicza 132, 01-949, Warsaw, Po-
land
Tel.: (48) 228358000
Web Site: https://www.arcelormittal-
warszawa.com
Steel Products Mfr
N.A.I.C.S.: 331110
Dariusz Marchewka *(CFO & Member-Mgmt Bd)*

Arcelormittal Asturias S.A. (1)
Lugar Trasona 90, 33400, Aviles, Spain
Tel.: (34) 985126000
Web Site: http://www.arcelormittal.com
Heavy Plate Steel Rod & Rail Mfr
N.A.I.C.S.: 331110

Arcelormittal Celaya S.a. De C.v. (1)
Carr Celaya-Salamanca KM 7 5 Rancho El
Chinaco, 38110, Villagran, Mexico
Tel.: (52) 4616188985
Steel Products Mfr
N.A.I.C.S.: 331221
Victor M. Cairo *(CEO)*

Arcelormittal guapiles (1)
70201 Pococi, Guapiles, Limon, Costa Rica
Tel.: (506) 22058901
Rolled Steel Product Mfr & Distr
N.A.I.C.S.: 331221

Baffinland Iron Mines Corporation (1)
2275 Upper Middle Road East Suite 300,
Oakville, L6H 0C3, ON, Canada   **(70%)**
Tel.: (416) 364-8820

Web Site: http://www.baffinland.com
Sales Range: $1-9.9 Million
Emp.: 20
Iron Ore Mining
N.A.I.C.S.: 212210
Fernando Ragone *(CFO)*

Circuit Foil Luxembourg S.a.r.l. (1)
Rue Salzbach, PO Box 9, 9501, Wiltz,
Luxembourg   **(90%)**
Tel.: (352) 9575511
Web Site: http://www.circuitfoil.com
Sales Range: $125-149.9 Million
Emp.: 350
Electro-Deposited Copper Foils Mfr
N.A.I.C.S.: 331420
Luc Helsen *(CEO)*

Subsidiary (Domestic):

Circuit Foil Service S.A. (2)
Rue Salzbach, PO Box 19, L-9501, Wiltz,
Luxembourg
Tel.: (352) 957907
Web Site: http://www.circuitfoil.com
Sales Range: $25-49.9 Million
Emp.: 12
Copper Foil Mfr
N.A.I.C.S.: 331420

Cockerill Sambre S.A. (1)
Quai du Halage 10, Flemalle, 4400, Bel-
gium
Tel.: (32) 42361111
Sales Range: $800-899.9 Million
Emp.: 3,000
Iron & Steel Industry
N.A.I.C.S.: 331110
Dehut Bernard *(CEO)*

Subsidiary (Domestic):

Cockerill Mecanique Prestations (2)
14 Quai d'Ougnee, 4102, Seraing, Belgium
Tel.: (32) 43302793
Sales Range: $10-24.9 Million
Emp.: 105
Steel Producer
N.A.I.C.S.: 331110

Etilam S.A. (1)
52 Avenue du General Sarrail, 52115, Saint
Dizier, Cedex, France
Tel.: (33) 325556800
Web Site: http://www.etilam.fr
Rev.: $37,587,000
Emp.: 150
Cold Rolling & Coating of Steel; Fastening
Devices for the Building Industry
N.A.I.C.S.: 331221

Ferrometalli Safem S.p.A. (1)
Distribuzione Italia Sede di Monza, Viale
Monza 97, 20900, Monza, MB, Italy
Tel.: (39) 03928121
Sales Range: $75-99.9 Million
Emp.: 150
Steel Service Center
N.A.I.C.S.: 423510

Galtec N.V. (1)
51 John Kennedylaan, Gent, B 9042, Bel-
gium
Tel.: (32) 93473111
Sales Range: $1-4.9 Billion
Emp.: 10,000
Iron Ore Mining
N.A.I.C.S.: 212210

Industeel Belgium S.A. (1)
266 Rue de Chatelet, 6030, Charleroi,
6030, Belgium
Tel.: (32) 71441699
Sales Range: $200-249.9 Million
Emp.: 950
Steel Products Mfr
N.A.I.C.S.: 331110

Kiswire ArcelorMittal Ltd. (1)
134 Yoosan-dong, Yangsan, 626 230,
Kyungnam, Korea (South)
Tel.: (82) 55 380 3404
Sales Range: $10-24.9 Million
Emp.: 500
Steel Cord Producer
N.A.I.C.S.: 331221

Branch (US):

ArcelorMittal-Kiswire LLC (2)

ArcelorMittal S.A.—(Continued)

7901 Cleveland Ave Nw Ste A, North Canton, OH 44720-8386
Tel.: (330) 670-8310
Steel & Wire Products Mfr
N.A.I.C.S.: 541613

Laserflash S.A. (1)
Industriestrasse 34, 4700, Eupen, Belgium
Tel.: (32) 87596800
Web Site: https://www.laserflash.be
Sales Range: $25-49.9 Million
Emp.: 40
Steel
N.A.I.C.S.: 331513

Mid-Vol Coal Sales, Inc. (1)
640 Clover Dew Dairy Rd, Princeton, WV 24740
Tel.: (304) 325-5719
Sales Range: $50-74.9 Million
Emp.: 14
Coal Mining & Merchant Whslr
N.A.I.C.S.: 423520
Dave Lambert (Acct Mgr)

PJSC ArcelorMittal Kryvyi Rih (1)
Kryvorizhstal st Ordzhonikidze 1, 50095, Krivoy Rog, Dnepropetrovsk, Ukraine
Tel.: (380) 564991888
Web Site: http://ukraine.arcelormittal.com
Steel Products Mfr
N.A.I.C.S.: 331110
Mauro Longobardo (CEO)

Segal S.C. (1)
50 Chaussee De Ramioul, B 4400, Ivoz-Ramet, Belgium
Tel.: (32) 42737373
Sales Range: $50-74.9 Million
Emp.: 140
Hot Dip Galvanized Steel Corrosion Protection for Automobiles
N.A.I.C.S.: 331110
Betrand Legaune (CEO)

Societe Nationale de Siderurgie S.A. (1)
Twin Center corner Bd Zerktouni and Massira Al Khadra, Tower A 18th floor, Casablanca, 20000, Morocco
Tel.: (212) 522954100
Web Site: https://www.sonasid.ma
Rolled Steel Product Mfr & Distr
N.A.I.C.S.: 331221

ARCH BIOPARTNERS INC.
27 St Clair Avenue East, PO Box 305, Toronto, M4T 2M5, ON, Canada
Tel.: (647) 428-7031   Ca
Web Site:
https://www.archbiopartners.com
ACHFF—(OTCQB)
Pharmaceuticals Mfr
N.A.I.C.S.: 325412
Richard Muruve (Co-Founder & CEO)

ARCH CAPITAL GROUP LTD.
100 Pitts Bay Road, Pembroke, HM 08, Bermuda
Tel.: (441) 2789250   BM
Web Site: https://www.archgroup.com
Year Founded: 2000
ACGL—(NASDAQ)
Rev.: $13,634,000,000
Assets: $58,906,000,000
Liabilities: $40,553,000,000
Net Worth: $18,353,000,000
Earnings: $4,403,000,000
Emp.: 6,400
Fiscal Year-end: 12/31/23
Asset Management Services
N.A.I.C.S.: 523999
Janice Englesbe (Chief Risk Officer & Sr VP)

Subsidiaries:

Alternative Re Limited (1)
waterloo house ground floor 10 pitts rd, PO Box 929, Pembroke, HM 08, Bermuda
Tel.: (441) 2789245
Web Site: http://www.alternativegroup.bm

Sales Range: $50-74.9 Million
Emp.: 10
Financial Management Services
N.A.I.C.S.: 523999

Alternative Underwriting Services, Ltd. (1)
Wessex House 45 Reid Street, Hamilton, HM 12, Bermuda
Tel.: (441) 441 278 9245
Financial Management Services
N.A.I.C.S.: 523999
Arthur Cronin (Pres)

Arch Capital Group (U.S.) Inc. (1)
223 S W St 18th Fl, Raleigh, NC 27603
Tel.: (212) 651-6500
Reinsurance Services
N.A.I.C.S.: 524130

Subsidiary (Domestic):

Arch Capital Services Inc. (2)
360 Hamilton Ave Ste 600, White Plains, NY 10601
Tel.: (914) 872-3600
Emp.: 35
Insurance Agencies Services
N.A.I.C.S.: 524210
Debra Connor (CFO)

Arch Insurance Company (2)
3100 Broadway Ste 511, Kansas City, MO 64111
Tel.: (816) 410-3020
Web Site:
http://www.archinsurancegroup.com
Sales Range: $50-74.9 Million
Emp.: 24
General Insurance Services
N.A.I.C.S.: 524210
Glenn Ballew (Exec VP)

Arch Insurance Group, Inc. (2)
1 Liberty Plz 53rd Fl, New York, NY 10006
Tel.: (212) 651-6500
Web Site: http://www.archinsurance.com
Insurance Related Activities
N.A.I.C.S.: 524298
John A. Rafferty (Chief Underwriting Officer-Fin & Professional Lines)

Subsidiary (Domestic):

Arch Excess & Surplus Insurance Company (3)
300 Plaza Three, Jersey City, NJ 07311
Tel.: (201) 743-4013
Sales Range: $350-399.9 Million
Emp.: 1,000
Direct Property Insurance Services
N.A.I.C.S.: 524126

Arch Indemnity Insurance Company (3)
300 Plaza Three, Jersey City, NJ 07311
Tel.: (201) 743-4013
Sales Range: $350-399.9 Million
Emp.: 1,000
Direct Property Insurance Services
N.A.I.C.S.: 524126

Arch Specialty Insurance Agency Inc. (3)
2345 Grand Blvd Ste 900, Kansas City, MO 64108-2685
Tel.: (816) 531-7668
Emp.: 35
Insurance Brokerage Services
N.A.I.C.S.: 524210

Arch Specialty Insurance Company (3)
300 Plaza Three Fl 3, Jersey City, NJ 07311
Tel.: (201) 743-4013
Web Site: http://www.archinsurance.com
Direct Property Insurance Services
N.A.I.C.S.: 524126

Subsidiary (Domestic):

Arch Reinsurance Company Inc. (2)
445 South St Ste 220, Morristown, NJ 07962-1988
Tel.: (973) 898-9575
Web Site: http://www.archreco.com
Sales Range: $50-74.9 Million
Emp.: 50
Insurance Related Activities

N.A.I.C.S.: 524298
Barry Golub (CFO)

Subsidiary (Domestic):

Arch Re Facultative Underwriters Inc. (3)
74 Batterson Park Rd, Farmington, CT 06032
Tel.: (860) 255-5400
Web Site: http://www.archrefac.com
Sales Range: $50-74.9 Million
Reinsurance Services
N.A.I.C.S.: 524130
Kenneth Vivian (Co-Pres & CEO)

Subsidiary (Domestic):

First American Services Corporation (2)
1000 NW 57th Ct Ste 170, Miami, FL 33126
Tel.: (305) 442-8420
Financial Management Services
N.A.I.C.S.: 523999

United Guaranty Corporation (2)
230 N Elm St, Greensboro, NC 27401-2429
Web Site: http://www.ugcorp.com
Mortgage Insurance Products & Services
N.A.I.C.S.: 524126
Donna DeMaio (CEO)

Subsidiary (Domestic):

United Guaranty Commercial Insurance Company of North Carolina (3)
230 N Elm St, Greensboro, NC 27401
Tel.: (336) 373-0232
Insurance Services
N.A.I.C.S.: 524126

United Guaranty Credit Insurance Company (3)
230 N Elm St, Greensboro, NC 27401
Tel.: (877) 642-4642
Mortgage & Reinsurance Services
N.A.I.C.S.: 524126

Arch Financial Holdings Australia Pty Ltd (1)
Level 38 120 Collins Street, Melbourne, 3000, VIC, Australia
Tel.: (61) 1300770547
N.A.I.C.S.: 531390

Arch Insurance (EU) Designated Activity Company (1)
Level 2 Block 3 The Oval 160 Shelbourne Road, Ballsbridge, Dublin, D04 E7K5, Ireland
Tel.: (353) 16699700
Underwriting & Claim Insurance Services
N.A.I.C.S.: 524128
Soren Scheuer (Pres & CEO)

Arch Insurance (UK) Limited (1)
60 Great Tower Street 5th Floor, London, EC3R 5AZ, United Kingdom
Tel.: (44) 2076214500
Reinsurance Services
N.A.I.C.S.: 524130

Arch Insurance Canada Ltd. (1)
200 Bay Street South Tower Suite 3100, PO Box 119, Toronto, M5J 2J2, ON, Canada
Tel.: (416) 309-8100
N.A.I.C.S.: 524210

Arch Insurance Company (Europe) Ltd. (1)
60 Great Tower Street 5th Floor, London, EC3R 5AZ, United Kingdom
Tel.: (44) 2076214500
Web Site: http://www.archinsurance.co.uk
Sales Range: $100-124.9 Million
Emp.: 120
Insurance Related Activities
N.A.I.C.S.: 524298
Rene Dubois (Sr VP & Head-Legal, Regulatory & Compliance)

Arch Investment Management Ltd. (1)
Waterloo House 100 Pitts Bay Road, Pembroke, HM 08, Bermuda
Tel.: (441) 2789180
N.A.I.C.S.: 524210

Arch LMI Pty Ltd (1)

153-155 Clarence Street Level 10, Sydney, 2000, NSW, Australia
Tel.: (61) 280584900
N.A.I.C.S.: 524210

Arch MI Asia Limited (1)
16th Floor The Hennessy 256 Hennessy Road, Wanchai, China (Hong Kong)
Tel.: (852) 34056628
Web Site: http://www.archcapgroup.com
Mortgage & Reinsurance Services
N.A.I.C.S.: 524126

Arch Mortgage Assurance Company (1)
230 N Elm St, Greensboro, NC 27401
Tel.: (336) 373-0232
N.A.I.C.S.: 524210

Arch Mortgage Insurance Limited (1)
230 N Elm St, Greensboro, NC 27401
N.A.I.C.S.: 524210

Arch Re Accident & Health ApS (1)
Frederiksgade 19, 1265, Copenhagen, Denmark
Tel.: (45) 88887660
Web Site: http://www.archre.dk
Sales Range: $50-74.9 Million
Emp.: 4
Accident & Health Insurance Services
N.A.I.C.S.: 524130

Arch Reinsurance Europe Underwriting Limited (1)
Level 2 Block 3 The Oval 160 Shelbourne Road Ballsbridge, Dublin, 4, Ireland
Tel.: (353) 16699700
Web Site: http://www.archre.eu
Emp.: 50
Reinsurance Services
N.A.I.C.S.: 524130
Richard Lange (Head-Credit & Surety)

Arch Reinsurance Ltd. (1)
Waterloo House 100 Pitts Bay Road, Pembroke, Hamilton, HM 08, Bermuda
Tel.: (441) 2789200
Web Site: http://www.archreinsurance.bm
Business Support Services
N.A.I.C.S.: 561499
Jerome Halgan (CEO)

Arch U.S. MI Holdings Inc. (1)
230 N. Elm St., Greensboro, NC 27401
Tel.: (800) 909-4264
Web Site: http://mi.archcapgroup.com
Mortgage Guaranty Insurance
N.A.I.C.S.: 524126

Subsidiary (Domestic):

Arch Mortgage Insurance Company (2)
PMI Plz 3003 Oak Rd, Walnut Creek, CA 94597
Tel.: (415) 284-2500
Web Site: http://mi.archcapgroup.com
Mortgage Guaranty Insurance
N.A.I.C.S.: 524126

RMIC Companies, Inc. (2)
101 N Cherry Street, Ste. 101, Winston-Salem, NC 27101
Tel.: (800) 386-4007
Web Site: https://www.rmic.com
Mortgage Insurance Products & Services
N.A.I.C.S.: 524130

Subsidiary (Domestic):

Republic Mortgage Insurance Company (3)
101 N Cherry St Ste 101, Winston Salem, NC 27101
Web Site: https://www.rmic.com
Sales Range: $125-149.9 Million
Emp.: 300
Mortgage Insurance Products & Services
N.A.I.C.S.: 524128

Arch Underwriters Inc. (1)
210 Hudson St Ste 300, Jersey City, NJ 07311-1107
Tel.: (201) 743-4000
N.A.I.C.S.: 524126
Mark Lange (Chief Middle Market Exec Officer)

Arch Underwriting Agency (Australia) Pty. Ltd. (1)

Level 8 22 William Street, Melbourne, 3000, VIC, Australia
Tel.: (61) 396295444
Insurance Carrier Services
N.A.I.C.S.: 524130

Arch Underwriting at Lloyd's (Austra-lia) Pty Ltd (1)
Level 10 155 Clarence Street, Sydney, 2000, NSW, Australia
Tel.: (61) 282848400
Web Site: http://www.archinsurance.com.au
Sales Range: $50-74.9 Million
Emp.: 8
Reinsurance Services
N.A.I.C.S.: 524130
Dominic Brannigan *(Reg Mgr-Melbourne)*

Barbican Group Holdings Ltd. (1)
North Suite 4 Town Mills Rue du Pre, Saint Peter Port, Guernsey
Tel.: (44) 1481 750400
Web Site:
http://www.barbicaninsurance.com
Insurance Holding Company
N.A.I.C.S.: 551112

Subsidiary (Non-US):

Barbican Corporate Member Limited (2)
33 Gracechurch Street, London, EC3V 0BT, United Kingdom
Tel.: (44) 2070821955
Insurance Services
N.A.I.C.S.: 524298

Subsidiary (Domestic):

Barbican Reinsurance Company Limited (2)
Suite 4 North Town Mills, Rue du Pre, Saint Peter Port, GY1 1LT, Guernsey
Tel.: (44) 1481 750400
Web Site: http://www.barbicanre.gg
Reinsurance
N.A.I.C.S.: 524130

Subsidiary (Non-US):

Burns & Wilcox Limited (2)
Upper Ground Floor 1 Minster Court Mincing Lane, London, EC3R 7AA, United Kingdom
Tel.: (44) 2073980440
Web Site: https://www.burnsandwilcox.co.uk
Insurance Services
N.A.I.C.S.: 524298

Seacurus Limited (2)
Suite 3 Level 3 Baltic Place West Baltic Place South Shore Road, Gateshead, NE8 3BA, England, United Kingdom
Tel.: (44) 1914690859
Web Site: http://www.seacurus.com
Insurance Services
N.A.I.C.S.: 524298

Gulf Reinsurance Limited (1)
Emirates Financial Towers N 416 4th Floor North Tower, Dubai, United Arab Emirates
Tel.: (971) 43825700
N.A.I.C.S.: 524210

McNeil & Company, Inc. (1)
67 Main St, Cortland, NY 13045
Tel.: (607) 756-4970
Web Site:
http://www.mcneilandcompany.com
Rev.: $7,500,000
Emp.: 50
Fiscal Year-end: 12/31/2006
Insurance Agent/Broker
N.A.I.C.S.: 524210
Daniel F. McNeil *(Chm & CEO)*

Subsidiary (Domestic):

Wilson Gregory Agency Inc. (2)
2309 Market St, Camp Hill, PA 17011
Tel.: (717) 730-9777
Web Site: http://www.wilsongregory.com
Insurance Agencies & Brokerages
N.A.I.C.S.: 524210
Mark Gregory *(VP-Ops)*

Resource Underwriting Pacific Pty Ltd (1)
Level 8 22 William Street, Melbourne, 3000, VIC, Australia
Tel.: (61) 396295444

General Insurance Services
N.A.I.C.S.: 524210

United Guaranty Services, Inc. (1)
230 N Elm St, Greensboro, NC 27401
N.A.I.C.S.: 524210

Watford Holdings Ltd. (1)
Waterloo House 1st Floor 100 Pitts Bay Road, Pembroke, HM 08, Bermuda (11%)
Tel.: (441) 278 3455
Web Site: http://www.watfordre.com
Rev.: $728,546,000
Assets: $3,532,060,000
Liabilities: $2,590,716,000
Net Worth: $941,344,000
Earnings: $60,512,000
Emp.: 11
Fiscal Year-end: 12/31/2020
Holding Company
N.A.I.C.S.: 551112
Robert L. Hawley *(CFO)*

Subsidiary (Non-US):

Axeria IARD S.A. (2)
27 rue Maurice Flandin CS 53713, Tower Credit Lyonnais, 69444, Lyon, Cedex 03, France
Tel.: (33) 427461400
Web Site: http://www.axeria-iard.fr
Indemnity Insurance Services
N.A.I.C.S.: 524128

ARCH PHARMALABS LIMITED
541-A Arch House Marol Maroshi Road, Andheri E, Mumbai, 400 059, India
Tel.: (91) 22 33089200 In
Web Site:
http://www.archpharmalabs.com
Year Founded: 1999
Emp.: 2,355
Pharmaceutical Product Mfr & Whslr
N.A.I.C.S.: 325412
Ajit A. Kamath *(Chm & Mng Dir)*

ARCHANA SOFTWARE LIMITED
Land Marvel Nest F1 3rd Floor, Adyar, Chennai, 600 020, Tamil Nadu, India
Tel.: (91) 4464555955
Web Site:
https://www.archanasoftware.com
Year Founded: 1994
530565—(BOM)
Rev.: $20,030
Assets: $388,004
Liabilities: $49,253
Net Worth: $338,751
Earnings: ($13,722)
Fiscal Year-end: 03/31/21
Software Development Services
N.A.I.C.S.: 541511
Raj Mohan C. *(CFO)*

ARCHEAN CHEMICAL INDUSTRIES LIMITED
No 2 Ground Floor North Crescent Road, T Nagar, Chennai, 600017, Tamil Nadu, India
Tel.: (91) 4461099999
Web Site:
https://www.archeanchemicals.com
Year Founded: 2003
543657—(BOM)
Rev.: $156,030,420
Assets: $209,075,767
Liabilities: $173,218,541
Net Worth: $35,857,226
Earnings: $25,745,797
Emp.: 247
Fiscal Year-end: 03/31/22
Chemical Products Mfr
N.A.I.C.S.: 325199

ARCHEAN STAR RESOURCES INC.

410 744 West Hastings Street, Vancouver, V6C 1A5, BC, Canada
Tel.: (604) 684-3394 BC
Web Site:
http://www.archeanstar.com
Gold Mining Services
N.A.I.C.S.: 212220
Graeme O'Neill *(Pres & CEO)*

ARCHER CAPITAL PTY. LTD.
Suite 7 Pier 2/3 13 Hickson Road, Dawes Point, Sydney, 2000, NSW, Australia
Tel.: (61) 282433333 AU
Web Site:
http://www.archercapital.com.au
Year Founded: 1997
Rev.: $2,464,350,000
Emp.: 25
Investment Management Service
N.A.I.C.S.: 523940
Peter Wiggs *(CEO)*

Subsidiaries:

Aero-Care Pty Ltd. (1)
Office 3 No 5 The Circuit, Brisbane, 4007, QLD, Australia
Tel.: (61) 7 3107 1920
Web Site: http://www.aerocare.com.au
Flight Support Services
N.A.I.C.S.: 488190
Stephen Payne *(Mgr-Airport Svcs)*

Allity Pty Ltd (1)
678 Victoria Street, Richmond, 3121, VIC, Australia
Tel.: (61) 3 9291 1200
Web Site: http://www.allity.com.au
Emp.: 40
Elder Care Services
N.A.I.C.S.: 623312
David Armstrong *(CEO)*

CarShare Australia Pty. Ltd. (1)
Suite 402 Level 4 59 Goulburn St, Sydney, 2000, NSW, Australia
Tel.: (61) 2 8039 3700
Web Site: http://www.goget.com.au
Car Rental Services
N.A.I.C.S.: 532111
Bruce Jeffreys *(Co-Founder)*

D&B Australasia Pty. Ltd. (1)
479 St Kilda Road, Melbourne, 3004, VIC, Australia
Tel.: (61) 132333
Web Site: http://dnb.com.au
Consumer Credit Reporting Services
N.A.I.C.S.: 561450

Subsidiary (Domestic):

CLI Lawyers Pty. Ltd. (2)
Ground Floor 479 St Kilda Road, Melbourne, VIC, Australia
Tel.: (61) 395735100
Web Site: http://www.mglawyers.com.au
Legal Support Services
N.A.I.C.S.: 541110

Subsidiary (Domestic):

CLI Lawyers SA Pty. Ltd. (3)
Ground Floor 479 St Kilda Road, PO Box 7267, Melbourne, 3004, VIC, Australia
Tel.: (61) 395735100
Web Site: http://www.mglawyers.com.au
Internet Service Provider
N.A.I.C.S.: 517121

Subsidiary (Domestic):

Decision Intellect Pty. Ltd. (2)
Level 4 990 Whitehouse Road, Boxhill, Melbourne, 3128, VIC, Australia
Tel.: (61) 398485503
Web Site: http://www.decisionintellect.com
Credit Risk Consulting Services
N.A.I.C.S.: 541611
Vaughan Dixon *(Dir)*

Dun & Bradstreet (Australia) Pty. Ltd. (2)
Ground Floor 479 St Kilda Rd 4th Fl, Melbourne, 3004, VIC, Australia
Tel.: (61) 132333
Web Site: http://www.dnb.com.au

Business Information Publishing
N.A.I.C.S.: 513140
Jesse Dumoff *(CIO)*

Subsidiary (Non-US):

Dun & Bradstreet (New Zealand) Ltd. (2)
Level 3 1 Queen St, Auckland, New Zealand
Tel.: (64) 93598000
Business Information Publishing
N.A.I.C.S.: 513140

Fuelfix Pty Ltd (1)
14 Allen Street, Geraldton, 6530, WA, Australia
Tel.: (61) 8 9921 0404
Web Site: http://www.fuelfix.com.au
Emp.: 20
Fuel Distr
N.A.I.C.S.: 424710
Mark Westbrook *(Mng Dir)*

Team Moto Pty. Ltd. (1)
59 Moss St, Springwood, 4127, QLD, Australia
Tel.: (61) 7 3442 1380
Web Site: http://www.teammoto.com.au
Motor Vehicle Parts Distr
N.A.I.C.S.: 423110

V8 Supercars Australia Pty Ltd (1)
45 Nerang Street, Southport, 4215, QLD, Australia
Tel.: (61) 7 5630 0364
Web Site: http://www.v8supercars.com.au
Event Management Services
N.A.I.C.S.: 711310

ARCHER EXPLORATION CORP.
353 Water Street Suite 401, Vancouver, V6B 1B8, BC, Canada BC
Web Site:
https://www.archerexploration.com
Year Founded: 2018
RCHRD—(OTCQB)
Rev.: $169,092
Assets: $29,985,202
Liabilities: $2,486,953
Net Worth: $27,498,249
Earnings: ($2,465,491)
Fiscal Year-end: 12/31/23
Mineral Exploration Services
N.A.I.C.S.: 213115
Jacquelin Gauthier *(VP)*

ARCHER LIMITED
Sandnesveien 358, 4312, Sandnes, Norway
Tel.: (47) 51308000
Web Site:
https://www.archerwell.com
ARHVF—(OTCIQ)
Rev.: $114,948,294
Assets: $89,035,038
Liabilities: $69,747,554
Net Worth: $19,287,484
Earnings: $2,762,377
Emp.: 4,856
Fiscal Year-end: 12/31/23
Offshore Drilling Services
N.A.I.C.S.: 213112
Dag Skindlo *(CEO)*

Subsidiaries:

Archer (UK) Limited (1)
Archer House Main Road, Blackburn, Aberdeen, AB21 0BP, United Kingdom
Tel.: (44) 1224767500
Oil & Gas Well Drilling Services
N.A.I.C.S.: 213111
Kenny Dey *(Gen Mgr)*

Archer Oil Tools AS (1)
Lagerveien 24, 4033, Stavanger, Norway
Tel.: (47) 51308800
Oil Tool Distr
N.A.I.C.S.: 213112

Archer Pressure Pumping LLC (1)
2105 E Murphy St, Odessa, TX 79761
Tel.: (432) 363-3900

Archer Limited—(Continued)

Oil & Gas Pumping Services
N.A.I.C.S.: 213112

Archer Well Company (Australia) Pty Ltd. **(1)**
17 Truganina Rd, Malaga, 6090, WA, Australia
Tel.: (61) 861601200
Oil & Gas Well Drilling Services
N.A.I.C.S.: 213111

DLS Argentina Limited **(1)**
Bouchard 551 Piso 22 Ciudad Autonoma, Buenos Aires, C1106ABG, Argentina
Tel.: (54) 1151292900
Web Site: http://www.dls-argentina.com.ar
Oil & Gas Well Drilling Services
N.A.I.C.S.: 213111

Great White Energy Services, Inc. **(1)**
14201 Caliber Dr Ste 300, Oklahoma City, OK 73134
Tel.: (405) 285-5812
Sales Range: $75-99.9 Million
Emp.: 569
Drilling Oil & Gas Wells
N.A.I.C.S.: 213111

Great White Pressure Control LLC **(1)**
4500 SE 59th St, Oklahoma City, OK 73135
Tel.: (405) 605-2700
Web Site:
http://www.greatwhitepressurecontrol.com
Oil Field Services
N.A.I.C.S.: 213111
Jim Morton *(Controller)*

ARCHER MATERIALS LIMITED
Lot Fourteen Frome Road, Adelaide, 5000, SA, Australia
Tel.: (61) 882723288
Web Site: https://archerx.com.au
AXE—(ASX)
Rev.: $2,054,676
Assets: $15,284,615
Liabilities: $727,871
Net Worth: $14,556,744
Earnings: ($3,207,232)
Emp.: 8
Fiscal Year-end: 06/30/24
Graphite, Magnesite, Manganese, Copper, Gold & Uranium Exploration Services
N.A.I.C.S.: 212230
Gregory English *(Chm)*

ARCHERMIND TECHNOLOGY (NANJING) CO., LTD.
Building B Cloud Security City No 19 Ningshuang Road, Yuhuatai District, Nanjing, 210012, Jiangsu, China
Tel.: (86) 2551887700
Web Site:
https://www.archermind.com
Year Founded: 2006
300598—(CHIN)
Rev.: $264,446,438
Assets: $338,668,050
Liabilities: $118,969,474
Net Worth: $219,698,577
Earnings: $26,485,547
Emp.: 500
Fiscal Year-end: 12/31/23
Mobile Software Solution Services
N.A.I.C.S.: 541511

ARCHIBALD INGALL STRETTON
Berners House 47-48 Berners St, London, W1T 3NF, United Kingdom
Tel.: (44) 207 467 6100
Web Site: http://www.aislondon.com
Emp.: 110
Advertising Agencies
N.A.I.C.S.: 541810
Stuart Archibald *(Partner)*

ARCHIDPLY DECOR LIMITED
No-50 Millenium Towers Queens Road Swamy Shivanandapuram Shivaji Nagar, Residency Road, Bengaluru, 560025, India
Tel.: (91) 8043714281
Web Site:
https://www.archidplydecor.com
513231—(BOM)
Rev.: $5,878,536
Assets: $9,696,127
Liabilities: $2,885,105
Net Worth: $6,811,022
Earnings: $26,904
Emp.: 43
Fiscal Year-end: 03/31/22
Interior Design Services
N.A.I.C.S.: 541410
Shyam Daga *(Chm & Mng Dir)*

ARCHIDPLY INDUSTRIES LTD
Plot No 7 Sector-9 Integrated Industrial Estate SIDCUL Pantnagar, Udham Singh Nagar, Rudrapur, 263153, Uttarakhand, India
Tel.: (91) 5944250270
Web Site: https://www.archidply.com
Year Founded: 1976
ARCHIDPLY—(NSE)
Rev.: $57,886,606
Assets: $33,862,811
Liabilities: $19,692,650
Net Worth: $14,170,161
Earnings: $1,672,302
Emp.: 1,500
Fiscal Year-end: 03/31/23
Plywood Mfr
N.A.I.C.S.: 321211
Deen Dayal Daga *(Chm)*

ARCHIES LIMITED
191 F sector 4 IMT Manesar, Gurgaon, 122050, Haryana, India
Tel.: (91) 1141410000
Web Site:
http://www.archiesonline.com
532212—(BOM)
Rev.: $12,711,330
Assets: $24,018,909
Liabilities: $9,372,404
Net Worth: $14,646,505
Earnings: $328,624
Emp.: 609
Fiscal Year-end: 03/31/23
Greeting Cards, Stationery & Gift Products Retailer
N.A.I.C.S.: 459420
Anil Moolchandani *(Chm & Exec Dir)*

ARCHIMED SAS
Terra Mundi 2 place de Francfort, 69003, Lyon, France
Tel.: (33) 481113533
Web Site: http://www.archimed-group.eu
Investment Firm
N.A.I.C.S.: 523999
Benoit Adelus *(Partner)*

Subsidiaries:

Actigraph, LLC **(1)**
49 E Chase St, Pensacola, FL 32502
Tel.: (850) 332-7900
Web Site: http://www.actitrainer.com
Sales Range: $1-9.9 Million
Emp.: 15
Electromedical & Electrotherapeutic Apparatus Mfr
N.A.I.C.S.: 334510
Jeff Arnett *(Sr VP-Corp Dev & Strategy)*

Instem plc **(1)**
Diamond Way Stone Business Park, Stone, ST15 0SD, Staffordshire, United Kingdom
Tel.: (44) 1785825600
Web Site: http://www.instem.com
Rev.: $62,478,201
Assets: $123,791,479
Liabilities: $59,569,965

Net Worth: $64,221,514
Earnings: $2,278,254
Emp.: 436
Fiscal Year-end: 12/31/2021
Laboratory Data & Information Management Solutions
N.A.I.C.S.: 513210
Nigel J. Goldsmith *(CFO & Sec)*

Subsidiary (Domestic):

BioWisdom Ltd. **(2)**
Harston Mill, Harston, Cambridge, CB22 7GG, United Kingdom
Tel.: (44) 1223874800
Web Site: http://www.instem.com
Sales Range: $25-49.9 Million
Emp.: 15
Pharmaceutical Industry Healthcare Intelligence & Consultation Services
N.A.I.C.S.: 541690

Subsidiary (Non-US):

Instem Information Systems (Shanghai) Limited **(2)**
Room 205 Building 16 88 Darwin Road, Zhangjiang High-Tech Park Pudong District, Shanghai, 201203, China
Tel.: (86) 215 131 2080
Web Site: https://www.instem-china.cn
Data Management Services
N.A.I.C.S.: 518210
Phil Reason *(CEO)*

Subsidiary (US):

Instem Life Science Systems, Ltd. **(2)**
161 Washington St, Conshohocken, PA 19428
Tel.: (610) 941-0990
Web Site: http://www.instem-lss.com
Sales Range: $25-49.9 Million
Emp.: 15
Laboratory Data & Information Management Solutions
N.A.I.C.S.: 513210

Leadscope, Inc. **(2)**
1393 Dublin Rd, Columbus, OH 43215
Tel.: (614) 209-2426
Web Site: http://www.leadscope.com
Sales Range: $1-9.9 Million
Emp.: 13
Custom Computer Programming Services
N.A.I.C.S.: 541511
Michael Conley *(CFO)*

Subsidiary (Domestic):

Perceptive Instruments Limited **(2)**
St Francis House Olding Road, Bury Saint Edmunds, IP33 3TA, United Kingdom
Tel.: (44) 1284 765566
Web Site: http://www.perceptive.co.uk
Emp.: 5
Data Processing Services
N.A.I.C.S.: 518210

Jeisys Medical Inc. **(1)**
307 308 401 808 1015 96 Gamasanro, Geumcheon-gu, Seoul, Korea (South) **(91.35%)**
Tel.: (82) 226036417
Web Site: https://www.jeisys.com
Rev.: $89,393,512
Assets: $90,596,169
Liabilities: $29,270,774
Net Worth: $61,325,395
Earnings: $20,808,524
Emp.: 200
Fiscal Year-end: 12/31/2022
Medical Device Mfr
N.A.I.C.S.: 339112

Natus Medical Incorporated **(1)**
3150 Pleasant View Rd, Middleton, WI 53562
Tel.: (608) 829-8500
Web Site: http://www.natus.com
Rev.: $473,438,000
Assets: $564,288,000
Liabilities: $139,538,000
Net Worth: $424,750,000
Earnings: $13,177,000
Emp.: 1,400
Fiscal Year-end: 12/31/2021
Hearing Screening & Diagnostic Systems, Jaundice Management Products, Newborn Care Products, Neurology Diagnostic Systems & Sleep Diagnostic Systems Developer & Mfr

N.A.I.C.S.: 334516
Thomas J. Sullivan *(CEO)*

Subsidiary (Non-US):

Alpine ApS **(2)**
Tonsbakken 16-18, Skovlunde, 2740, Denmark **(100%)**
Tel.: (45) 44579000
Web Site: http://www.natus.com
Sales Range: $25-49.9 Million
Emp.: 40
Gastroenterology Diagnostic Medical Device Whslr
N.A.I.C.S.: 423450

Deltamed S.A. **(2)**
22 rue Charcot, 75013, Paris, France **(100%)**
Tel.: (33) 1 42 46 57 19
Web Site: http://www.natus.com
Emp.: 3
Mfr of Medical Devices Used in Neurophysiology
N.A.I.C.S.: 339112

Subsidiary (Domestic):

Embla Systems LLC **(2)**
11001 W 10th Ave Ste 200, Broomfield, CO 80021 **(100%)**
Tel.: (716) 691-0718
Web Site: http://www.embla.com
Sales Range: $25-49.9 Million
Emp.: 34
Sleep Disorder Diagnostic Device Mfr
N.A.I.C.S.: 339112

Subsidiary (Non-US):

Excel Tech Corp. **(2)**
2568 Bristol Circle, Oakville, L6H 5S1, ON, Canada
Tel.: (905) 829-5300
Surgical & Medical Instrument Mfr
N.A.I.C.S.: 339112

Excel Tech Ltd. **(2)**
2568 Bristol Circle, Oakville, L6H 5S1, ON, Canada
Tel.: (905) 829-5300
Web Site: http://www.xltek.com
Sales Range: $10-24.9 Million
Emp.: 140
Nervous System Monitoring & Diagnosing Product Developer, Mfr & Marketer
N.A.I.C.S.: 339112

Subsidiary (Domestic):

Global Neuro-Diagnostics, LP **(2)**
2670 Firewheel Dr Ste B, Flower Mound, TX 75028
Web Site: http://www.globalneuro.natus.com
Professional, Scientific & Technical Services
N.A.I.C.S.: 541990
Donna Bray *(Chief Clinical Officer)*

Subsidiary (Non-US):

Medix I.C.S.A. **(2)**
Marcos Sastre 1675 El Talar Tigre, B1618EWC, Buenos Aires, Argentina **(100%)**
Tel.: (54) 11 5354 3700
Web Site: http://www.medix.com.ar
Developer, Mfr & Marketer of Newborn Care Products, Including Incubators, Infant Radiant Warmers & Phototherapy Lamps
N.A.I.C.S.: 423450

Natus Europe GmbH **(2)**
Robert-Koch-Str 1, 82152, Planegg, Germany
Tel.: (49) 89 839 42 0
Web Site: http://www.natus.com
Emp.: 7
Develops & Manufactures Products for Detection & Diagnosis of Hearing Disorders
N.A.I.C.S.: 339112

Natus Manufacturing Ireland, Ltd. **(2)**
IDA Business Park, Gort, Galway, Ireland
Tel.: (353) 91647400
Medical Instrument Mfr
N.A.I.C.S.: 339113

Natus Medical Denmark ApS **(2)**
Hoerskaetten 9, 2630, Taastrup, Denmark
Tel.: (45) 45755555

Medical Equipment Mfr
N.A.I.C.S.: 339112

Division (Domestic):

Natus Medical Inc.   (2)
1 Bio Logic Plz, Mundelein, IL 60060-3708
Tel.: (847) 949-5200
Web Site: http://www.blsc.com
Sales Range: $25-49.9 Million
Emp.: 124
Developer & Mfr of Hearing Screening &
Diagnostic Products, Brain Activity Analysis
Instruments & Sleep Diagnostic Products
N.A.I.C.S.: 334510

Subsidiary (Domestic):

Natus Neurology Incorporated   (2)
3150 Pleasant View Rd, Middleton, WI
53562
Tel.: (608) 829-8500
Web Site: http://www.natus.com
Sales Range: $75-99.9 Million
Emp.: 400
Electromedical & Electrotherapeutic Appara-
tus Mfr
N.A.I.C.S.: 334510

Division (Domestic):

Natus Neurology Inc. - Grass
Products   (3)
200 Metro Center Blvd Unit 8, Warwick, RI
02886
Tel.: (401) 773-2600
Web Site: http://www.neuro.natus.com
Sales Range: $10-24.9 Million
Emp.: 250
Designs & Develops Research Instruments,
Software & Supplies for Neurology & Life
Science Markets
N.A.I.C.S.: 334516

Subsidiary (Non-US):

Otometrics A/S   (2)
Hoerskaetten 9, 2630, Taastrup, Denmark
Tel.: (45) 45755555
Web Site: http://www.otometrics.natus.com
Emp.: 1,000
Hearing & Balance Instrumentation Mfr
N.A.I.C.S.: 334516

Subsidiary (Non-US):

Otometrics France   (3)
Parc Du Moulin De Massy 37 Rue Du
Saule Trapu, 91300, Massy, France
Tel.: (33) 1 60 13 76 66
Web Site: http://www.otometrics.natus.com
Hearing Aid Mfr
N.A.I.C.S.: 334510

Otometrics GmbH   (3)
An Der Kleimannbrucke 75, Munster,
48157, Germany
Tel.: (49) 251 203 983 0
Web Site: http://www.otometrics.com
Hearing Instruments Mfr
N.A.I.C.S.: 334510

North American Science Associates,
Inc.   (1)
6750 Wales Rd, Northwood, OH 43619-
1012
Tel.: (419) 666-9455
Web Site: http://www.namsa.com
Research & Development in the Physical,
Engineering & Life Sciences
N.A.I.C.S.: 541715
John Gorski (Vice Chm)

Subsidiary (Domestic):

American Preclinical Services
LLC   (2)
8945 Evergreen Blvd NW, Minneapolis, MN
55433
Tel.: (763) 717-2042
Web Site:
   http://www.americanpreclinical.com
Research & Development in Biotechnology
N.A.I.C.S.: 541714
Pam Conforti (Owner)

Clinlogix, LLC   (2)
321 Norristown Rd Ste 100, Ambler, PA
19002-2793
Tel.: (215) 855-9054

Web Site: http://www.clinlogix.com
Rev.: $1,300,000
Emp.: 14
Administrative Management & General
Management Consulting Service
N.A.I.C.S.: 541611
Andrew Brailsford (Dir-Project Mgmt)

Syntactx, LLC   (2)
4 World Trade Ctr 150 Greenwich St 44th
Fl, New York, NY 10006
Tel.: (212) 228-9000
Web Site: http://www.syntactx.com
Clinical Research Services
N.A.I.C.S.: 541910
Heather Andrews (Dir-Bus Dev)

ARCHIT ORGANOSYS LTD.

9th Floor Venus Benecia Nr Pakwan
Restaurant Bodakdev S G Highway,
Ahmedabad, 380 054, India
Tel.: (91) 22822007
Web Site: https://www.architorg.com
Year Founded: 1989
524640—(BOM)
Rev.: $12,974,898
Assets: $11,942,085
Liabilities: $6,408,607
Net Worth: $5,533,478
Earnings: $683,387
Emp.: 85
Fiscal Year-end: 03/31/21
Chemical Products Mfr
N.A.I.C.S.: 325199
Archana Kandarp Amin (Exec Dir)

ARCHITECTS STUDIO JAPAN INC.

4-2 Marunouchi 3-chome Shin-
Nisseki Bldg 1F, Chiyoda-ku, Tokyo,
100-0005, Japan
Tel.: (81) 362063159
Web Site: https://www.asj-net.com
Year Founded: 2002
6085—(TKS)
Rev.: $3,913,120
Assets: $3,595,840
Liabilities: $3,179,410
Net Worth: $416,430
Earnings: ($2,386,210)
Emp.: 60
Fiscal Year-end: 03/31/24
Architectural Services
N.A.I.C.S.: 541310
Yuhei Maruyama (Chm & Pres)

ARCHON MINERALS LIMITED

Suite 2801 323 Jervis Street, Van-
couver, V6P 3P8, BC, Canada
Tel.: (604) 682-3303
Year Founded: 1985
ACS—(TSXV)
Assets: $48,282,959
Liabilities: $49,811,064
Net Worth: ($1,528,105)
Earnings: ($872,241)
Fiscal Year-end: 05/31/24
Mineral Exploration Services
N.A.I.C.S.: 212390
Stewart Blusson (CEO & CFO)

ARCHON TECHNOLOGIES LTD

9 Hamenofim Street Ackerstein Tow-
ers Bldg A 8th Floor, PO Box 2148,
Herzliya Pituach, 46120, Israel
Tel.: (972) 99716026
Web Site: http://www.archon-
   technologies.com
Year Founded: 2006
Patent Trading Services
N.A.I.C.S.: 926150
Leedor Agam (CEO)

ARCHOS S.A.

3 Rue Ampere, 91430, Igney, France
Tel.: (33) 169331690
Web Site: https://www.archos.com

JXR—(EUR)
Sales Range: $25-49.9 Million
Emp.: 172
Multimedia Devices Mfr
N.A.I.C.S.: 334310
Henri Crohas (Chm)

Subsidiaries:

Archos GmbH   (1)
Business Park Vierwinden, Konrad Zuse
Strasse 22, 41516, Grevenbroich, Germany
Tel.: (49) 2182570410
Web Site: http://www.archos.com
Consumer Electronics Mfr
N.A.I.C.S.: 334419

Archos Inc.   (1)
7951 E Maplewood Ave #260, Greenwood
Village, CO 80111
Tel.: (303) 962-3350
Web Site: http://www.archos.com
Sales Range: $25-49.9 Million
Emp.: 50
Consumer Electronics Mfr
N.A.I.C.S.: 334419

Archos UK Ltd.   (1)
PO Box 1420, Southampton, SO15 1WF,
United Kingdom
Tel.: (44) 2380711778
Web Site: http://www.archos.com
Sales Range: $25-49.9 Million
Emp.: 15
Consumer Electronics Mfr
N.A.I.C.S.: 334419

ARCHOSAUR GAMES INC.

No 8 Hangxing Science Park No 11
HePingLi East Street, Dongcheng
District, Beijing, China
Web Site: https://www.zloong.com
Year Founded: 1997
9990—(HKG)
Rev.: $125,787,688
Assets: $379,876,911
Liabilities: $56,724,911
Net Worth: $323,151,999
Earnings: ($43,691,986)
Emp.: 1,087
Fiscal Year-end: 12/31/23
Software Development Services
N.A.I.C.S.: 541511
Qing Li (Chm)

ARCHTIS LIMITED

10 National Circuit Level 3, Barton,
2600, ACT, Australia
Tel.: (61) 261622792   AU
Web Site: https://www.archtis.com
Year Founded: 2006
ARHLF—(OTCQB)
Rev.: $6,543,481
Assets: $11,094,766
Liabilities: $4,789,793
Net Worth: $6,304,973
Earnings: ($2,841,864)
Fiscal Year-end: 06/30/24
Data Management Technology Ser-
vices
N.A.I.C.S.: 518210
Daniel Lai (CEO)

Subsidiaries:

archTIS EU GmbH   (1)
Heiner-Fleischmann-Str 7, 74172, Neckar-
sulm, Germany
Tel.: (49) 15236257821
Software Development Services
N.A.I.C.S.: 541511

archTIS UK Limited   (1)
15 Westferry Circus, Canary Wharf, Lon-
don, E14 4HD, United Kingdom
Tel.: (44) 2081452582
Software Development Services
N.A.I.C.S.: 541511

archTIS US, Inc.   (1)
177 Huntington Ave Ste 1703 73999, Boston, MA 02115
Tel.: (617) 302-9305
Software Development Services

N.A.I.C.S.: 541511

ARCLAND RESOURCES, INC.

801-560 Cardero St, Vancouver, V6G
3G1, BC, Canada
Tel.: (604) 669-6168
ADR.H—(TSX)
Assets: $189,459
Liabilities: $20,353
Net Worth: $169,105
Earnings: ($42,758)
Fiscal Year-end: 11/30/22
Mineral Exploration & Mining Ser-
vices
N.A.I.C.S.: 212390
George Lian (CFO)

ARCLANDS CORP

445 Kamisukoro, Sanjo, 955-8501,
Niigata, Japan
Tel.: (81) 256336000
Web Site: https://www.arclands.co.jp
Year Founded: 1970
9842—(TKS)
Rev.: $2,202,841,730
Assets: $2,486,611,890
Liabilities: $1,658,428,990
Net Worth: $828,182,900
Earnings: $64,696,250
Emp.: 13,094
Fiscal Year-end: 02/29/24
Household Goods Store Operator
N.A.I.C.S.: 459999

Subsidiaries:

Arcland Service Holdings Co.,
Ltd.   (1)
New-Chiyoda Building 5F 1-8-4
Kandasakuma-cho, Chiyoda-ku, Tokyo, 101-
0025, Japan   (55.03%)
Tel.: (81) 352985281
Rev.: $427,923,760
Assets: $324,144,480
Liabilities: $100,952,720
Net Worth: $223,191,760
Earnings: $25,332,560
Emp.: 503
Fiscal Year-end: 12/31/2021
Restaurant Chain Operator
N.A.I.C.S.: 722511
Kenichiro Usui (Pres)

Subsidiary (Domestic):

Meal Works Co., Ltd.   (2)
Shin Ochanomizu Bldg 14F 4-3 Kanda Su-
rugadai, Chiyoda-ku, Tokyo, Japan
Tel.: (81) 352171539
Web Site: http://www.mealworks.co.jp
Restaurant Operators
N.A.I.C.S.: 722511
Issei Kojima (Pres)

ARCO TOWERS REIT

4 Konstantin Petkanov Str, Lozenets
Vitosha, 1700, Sofia, 1700, Bulgaria
Tel.: (359) 29398888
Web Site:
   https://www.arcotowers.com
ARCT—(BUL)
Sales Range: Less than $1 Million
Real Estate Investment Services
N.A.I.C.S.: 525990
Peyo Nikolov (Exec Dir)

ARCO VARA AS

Maakri 30, 10145, Tallinn, Estonia
Tel.: (372) 6144630   EE
Web Site: https://www.arcovara.com
Year Founded: 1992
ARC1T—(TAL)
Rev.: $20,243,956
Assets: $38,845,347
Liabilities: $15,645,215
Net Worth: $23,200,132
Earnings: $3,918,755
Emp.: 18
Fiscal Year-end: 12/31/23
Real Estate Development Services
N.A.I.C.S.: 531390

Arco Vara AS—(Continued)

Tarmo Sild *(Chm-Supervisory Bd)*

Subsidiaries:

Arco Development SIA (1)
Lacplesa 20a, Riga, 1011, Latvia
Tel.: (371) 67365555
Real Estate Development Services
N.A.I.C.S.: 531390

Iztok Parkside Eood (1)
58A Kosta Lulchev str, 1574, Sofia, Bulgaria
Tel.: (359) 878999555
Web Site: https://www.iztokparkside.bg
Building Real Estate Services
N.A.I.C.S.: 531110

ARCO-IRIS GOLD CORPORATION
Suite 22 Postnet, PO Box 1006,
6600, Plettenberg Bay, South Africa
Tel.: (27) 764965865 NV
Web Site: http://www.arco-iris.co.za
Year Founded: 2012
Gold Mining
N.A.I.C.S.: 212220
Stacey Aaron *(Pres & Sec)*

ARCOMA AB
Annavagen 1, 352 46, Vaxjo, Sweden
Tel.: (46) 470706900
Web Site: https://www.arcoma.se
Year Founded: 2010
ARCOMA—(OMX)
Rev.: $11,712,421
Assets: $9,397,098
Liabilities: $5,099,890
Net Worth: $4,297,208
Earnings: $177,958
Emp.: 32
Fiscal Year-end: 12/31/22
Digital Radiographic Systems
N.A.I.C.S.: 334510
Johan Henningsson *(Mgr-R&D)*

ARCOMET & CO.
Industrieweg 139, Paal, 3583, Beringen, Belgium
Tel.: (32) 11450950
Web Site: http://www.arcomet.com
Sales Range: $75-99.9 Million
Emp.: 200
Crane Mfr
N.A.I.C.S.: 333923
Philippe Cohet *(CEO)*

Subsidiaries:

Arcomet (Hong Kong) Ltd (1)
Lot 2943 DD111 Wing Ling lane, Want Toi
Shan, Wang Toi Shan, New Territories,
China (Hong Kong)
Tel.: (852) 23 96 88 73
N.A.I.C.S.: 532412
Leung Ping Wah *(Country Mgr)*

Arcomet Asia Pte Ltd (1)
41 Sungei Kadut Street 6, Singapore,
728871, Singapore
Tel.: (65) 6562 3313
Crane Rental & Leasing Services
N.A.I.C.S.: 532412
Scott Story *(CEO)*

Arcomet Deutschland GmbH & Co.
KG
Am Meilenstein 12, 53909, Zulpich, Germany
Tel.: (49) 2252 83 81 0
Crane Rental & Leasing Services
N.A.I.C.S.: 532412
Egon Vonken *(CFO)*

Arcomet Italia SPA (1)
Via Piccinelli 11, 22076, Mozzate, Italy
Tel.: (39) 0 331 83 49 81
Crane Rental & Leasing Services
N.A.I.C.S.: 532412

Arcomet Torenkranen Nederland
BV (1)
Postbus 53, 5460 AB, Veghel, Netherlands

Tel.: (31) 4 13 31 19 77
Crane Rental & Leasing Services
N.A.I.C.S.: 532412
Marcel Pruysers *(Country Mgr)*

Mobile Tower Cranes (MTC) B.V. (1)
De Amert 210, 5462 GH, Veghel,
Netherlands (100%)
Tel.: (31) 413311977
Web Site: http://www.mtc-cranes.com
Rev.: $9,985,072
Emp.: 20
Construction Machinery Mfr
N.A.I.C.S.: 333120
Marshall Prysers *(Mgr-Comml)*

P & J Arcomet LLC (1)
9031 Euclid Ave, Manassas, VA 20110
Tel.: (703) 365-7888
Crane Rental & Leasing Services
N.A.I.C.S.: 532412
Peter Jehle *(Mng Dir)*

ARCONTECH GROUP PLC
1st Floor 11-21 Paul Street, London,
EC2A 4JU, United Kingdom
Tel.: (44) 2072562300
Web Site: https://www.arcontech.com
ARC—(AIM)
Rev.: $3,744,313
Assets: $11,915,428
Liabilities: $2,450,322
Net Worth: $9,465,106
Earnings: $828,978
Emp.: 14
Fiscal Year-end: 06/30/22
Stock Market Data Services
N.A.I.C.S.: 541512
Richard Last *(Chm)*

Subsidiaries:

Arcontech Ltd. (1)
8th Fl Finsbury Tower, 103-105 Bunhill
Row, London, EC1Y 8LZ, United Kingdom
Tel.: (44) 2072562300
Web Site: http://www.arcontech.com
Real-Time Market Data Distribution & Trading Systems
N.A.I.C.S.: 518210

**ARCOR SOCIEDAD ANONIMA,
INDUSTRIAL Y COMERCIAL**
Maipu 1210 2nd, 3rd & 6th Floor,
Buenos Aires, 1006, Argentina
Tel.: (54) 11 4310 9500
Web Site: http://www.arcor.com.ar
Year Founded: 1951
Sales Range: $1-4.9 Billion
Emp.: 13,000
Food Product Mfr & Sales
N.A.I.C.S.: 311999
Luis Alejandro Pagani *(Chm)*

Subsidiaries:

Arcopar S.A. (1)
Ruta Mariscal Estigarribia Km 10 1/2 Nro
740, San Lorenzo, Paraguay
Tel.: (595) 21 509943
Food Products Mfr
N.A.I.C.S.: 311999

Arcor A.G. (1)
Tarragona 107-109 18th Floor, Barcelona,
08014, Spain
Tel.: (34) 93 2294 560
Web Site: http://www.arcor.com
Emp.: 20
Food Products Sales
N.A.I.C.S.: 424410

Arcor Canada Inc. (1)
5659 McAdam Road Unit A3, Mississauga,
L4Z 1N9, ON, Canada
Tel.: (905) 502-0012
Food Products Mfr
N.A.I.C.S.: 311999

Arcor Ecuador (1)
Av de las Americas & Eugenio Almazan,
Las Americas Building Mecanos 1st Fl Of
101-104, Guayaquil, Ecuador
Tel.: (593) 4229 0014
Food Products Mfr & Distr
N.A.I.C.S.: 311999

Arcor Trading (Shanghai) Co.
Ltd. (1)
Unit 909 No 1101 Pudong Nan Lu, Shanghai, 200120, China
Tel.: (86) 21 5835 1716
Food Products Sales
N.A.I.C.S.: 424490

Arcor U.S.A. Inc. (1)
6205 Blue Lagoon Dr Ste 350, Miami, FL
33126
Food Products Mfr & Sales
N.A.I.C.S.: 311999

Arcor de Peru S.A. (1)
Av Guillermo Prescott 325, San Isidro, 027,
Lima, Peru
Tel.: (51) 1 422 8088
Confectionary Product Mfr
N.A.I.C.S.: 311340

Arcor do Brasil Limitada (1)
Edificio Continental Square 16 andar Rua
Olimpiadas, 205 Vila Olimpia, 04551-000,
Sao Paulo, Brazil
Tel.: (55) 11 3046 6800
Food Products Mfr & Sales
N.A.I.C.S.: 311999

Bagley Latinoamerica S.A. (1)
Edificio International Plaza, Moreno 877
Piso 12, 1091, Buenos Aires, Argentina
Tel.: (54) 114 341 09500
Web Site: http://www.arcor.com.ar
Sales Range: $250-299.9 Million
Emp.: 4,900
Cookies, Snacks, Cereal Bars & Cereals
Mfr
N.A.I.C.S.: 311230

Cartocor S.A. (1)
Calle Hernan Darias S/N Parque Industrial
Gral, Belgrano, Parana, E3100AJB, Entre
Rios, Argentina
Tel.: (54) 343 420 6000
Web Site: http://www.cartocor.com
Emp.: 654
Corrugated Cardboard Mfr
N.A.I.C.S.: 322211

Converflex S.A. (1)
Maipu 1300 Piso 4, Buenos Aires, 1006,
Argentina
Tel.: (54) 11 4310 9859
Web Site: http://www.converflex.net
Flexible Packaging Mfr
N.A.I.C.S.: 326112

Industria Dos en Uno de Colombia
Ltda (1)
Calle 109 #18B 31 Oficina 401, Bogota,
Colombia
Tel.: (57) 1619 6492
Food Products Mfr & Sales
N.A.I.C.S.: 311999

La Campagnola S.A.C.I. (1)
Av Fulvio Salvador Pagani 493, Arroyito,
2434, Argentina
Tel.: (54) 11 4310 9500
Web Site: http://www.lacampagnola.com
Fresh & Frozen Seafood Producer
N.A.I.C.S.: 311710

La Serrana S.A. (1)
Av Dole Via a La Guardia 5055 y 5to anillo,
Santa Cruz, Bolivia (100%)
Tel.: (591) 3 354 0047
Food Products Mfr & Sales
N.A.I.C.S.: 311999

Mundo Dulce S.A. de C.V. (1)
Juan Salvador Agraz N 50 Piso 3, Santa
Fe, Mexico, DF, Mexico
Tel.: (52) 1 5552 926231
Confectionary Product Mfr
N.A.I.C.S.: 311351

Unidal Venezuela S.A. (1)
Calle Guaicaipuro y Calle Mohedano Torre
Hener Piso 6, El Rosal, Caracas, Venezuela
Tel.: (58) 212 740 581074
Food Products Sales
N.A.I.C.S.: 311999

Van Dam S.A. (1)
Br Batile y Ordonez 6791, Montevideo, Uruguay
Tel.: (598) 2359 7013
Food Products Mfr & Sales

N.A.I.C.S.: 311999

**ARCOS DORADOS HOLDINGS
INC.**
Dr Luis Bonavita 1294 Office 501,
WTC Free Zone, 11300, Montevideo,
Uruguay
Tel.: (598) 26263000 VG
Web Site:
http://www.arcosdorados.com
ARCO—(NYSE)
Rev.: $3,618,902,000
Assets: $2,636,630,000
Liabilities: $2,312,203,000
Net Worth: $324,427,000
Earnings: $140,343,000
Emp.: 93,647
Fiscal Year-end: 12/31/22
Fast Food Restaurant Owner & Operator
N.A.I.C.S.: 722513
Woods Staton *(Chm)*

Subsidiaries:

Alimentos Latinoamericanos Venezuela ALV, C.A. (1)
Ave Casanova C C Elrecreo, Caracas, Venezuela
Tel.: (58) 2128220000
Restaurant Operators
N.A.I.C.S.: 722511

Arcos Dorados Aruba N.V. (1)
J E J E Irausquin Boulevard, Oranjestad,
Aruba
Tel.: (297) 2975861728
Restaurant Operators
N.A.I.C.S.: 722511

Arcos Dorados Colombia S.A.S (1)
Calle 116 No 7-15 Oficina 1401, Bogota,
Colombia
Tel.: (57) 16538000
Restaurant Operators
N.A.I.C.S.: 722511

Arcos Dorados Costa Rica ADCR,
S.A. (1)
150 S De Auto Mercado Los Yoses, San
Jose, Costa Rica
Tel.: (506) 25230200
Restaurant Operators
N.A.I.C.S.: 722511

Arcos Dorados Puerto Rico, LLC (1)
300 Felisa Rincon De Gautier Ste 10, San
Juan, PR 00926
Tel.: (787) 748-8200
Restaurant Operators
N.A.I.C.S.: 722511

Arcos Dourados Comercio de Alimentos Ltda. (1)
Alameda Amazonas 253, Alphaville Barueri,
Sao Paulo, 06454-070, Brazil
Tel.: (55) 1141969800
Web Site: http://www.mcdonalds.com.br
Restaurant Services
N.A.I.C.S.: 722511

Arcos Mendocinos S.A. (1)
Calle Godoy Cruz 2650, Mendoza, Argentina
Tel.: (54) 2614396950
Restaurant Operators
N.A.I.C.S.: 722511

Arcos SerCal Inmobiliaria, S. de R.L.
de C.V. (1)
Antonio Dovali Jaime No 75 3rd floor, Colonia Lomas de Santa Faith Alvaro Obregon,
01219, Mexico, Mexico
Tel.: (52) 5530033422
Web Site: http://www.mcdonalds.com.mx
Restaurant Services
N.A.I.C.S.: 722511

Operaciones Arcos Dorados de Peru,
(1)
Ave LaFloresta 97 Office 302, San Borja,
Peru
Tel.: (51) 13726300
Restaurant Operators
N.A.I.C.S.: 722511

Sistemas Central America, S.A. (1)

Calle 78, San Francisco, Panama
Tel.: (507) 2706700
Restaurant Operators
N.A.I.C.S.: 722511

ARCOTECH LTD.
F-701 A Lado Sarai, New Delhi,
110030, India
Tel.: (91) 1129523251
Web Site: http://www.arcotech.in
Rev.: $65,159,383
Assets: $102,721,536
Liabilities: $79,635,942
Net Worth: $23,085,593
Earnings: ($13,213,923)
Emp.: 95
Fiscal Year-end: 03/31/19
Non Ferrous Metal Mfr
N.A.I.C.S.: 331410
Arvind Kumar Saraf *(Chm)*

ARCS COMPANY LIMITED
2-32 Minami 13-jo Nishi 11-chome,
Chuo-ku, Sapporo, 064-8610, Hok-
kaido, Japan
Tel.: (81) 115301000
Web Site: https://www.arcs-g.co.jp
Year Founded: 1961
9948—(TKS)
Rev.: $4,194,139,130
Assets: $1,949,551,480
Liabilities: $688,885,670
Net Worth: $1,260,665,810
Earnings: $83,420,940
Emp.: 5,720
Fiscal Year-end: 02/29/24
Supermarket Store Operator
N.A.I.C.S.: 445110
Koichi Miura *(Chm)*

ARCSOFT CORP., LTD.
No 392 Binxing Road, Binjiang Dis-
trict, Hangzhou, 310052, Zhejiang,
China
Tel.: (86) 57188210600
Web Site: https://www.arcsoft.com.cn
Year Founded: 2003
688088—(SHG)
Rev.: $74,643,449
Assets: $418,767,444
Liabilities: $56,604,675
Net Worth: $362,162,769
Earnings: $8,114,741
Fiscal Year-end: 12/31/22
Software Development Services
N.A.I.C.S.: 541511
Hui Deng *(Chm & Gen Mgr)*

**ARCTECH SOLAR HOLDING
CO., LTD.**
No 190 Huayang Road, Lujia Town,
Kunshan, 215300, Jiangsu, China
Tel.: (86) 51257353472
Web Site: http://www.arctechsolar.us
Year Founded: 2009
688408—(SHG)
Rev.: $519,843,762
Assets: $785,167,190
Liabilities: $434,263,925
Net Worth: $350,903,264
Earnings: $6,238,098
Emp.: 1,300
Fiscal Year-end: 12/31/22
Holding Company
N.A.I.C.S.: 551112
Hao Cai *(Chm & Gen Mgr)*

Subsidiaries:

Arctech Solar (Changzhou) Co.,
Ltd. **(1)**
19 Xingye Rd, Zhixi Town Jintan District,
Changzhou, 213251, Jiangsu, China
Tel.: (86) 51982901280
Solar Tracking Equipment Mfr
N.A.I.C.S.: 334413

Arctech Solar (Japan) Co., Ltd. **(1)**
Sakura Bld 2-6-B 2-5-5 Toranomon, Minato-

ku, Tokyo, 105-0001, Japan
Tel.: (81) 362573955
Solar Tracking Equipment Mfr
N.A.I.C.S.: 334413

Arctech Solar (Shanghai)
Company **(1)**
Unit A 9/F Tower 6 Kingboard Square 269
Tongxie Rd, Shanghai, 200335, China
Tel.: (86) 2160256830
Solar Tracking Equipment Mfr
N.A.I.C.S.: 334413

Arctech Solar India Pvt. Ltd. **(1)**
Unit Nos 533-536 Tower-A2 5th Floor,
Spaze i-Techpark Sector 49 Sohna Road,
Gurgaon, 122018, Haryana, India
Tel.: (91) 1244047882
Solar Tracking Equipment Mfr
N.A.I.C.S.: 334413

Arctech Solar, Inc. **(1)**
2233 Watt Ave Ste 255, Sacramento, CA
95825
Tel.: (916) 899-7890
Solar Tracking Equipment Mfr
N.A.I.C.S.: 334413

ARCTIC BIOSCIENCE AS
Industrivegen 42, 6155, Orsta, Nor-
way
Tel.: (47) 94875469   NO
Web Site: https://www.arctic-
   bioscience.com
Year Founded: 2011
ABS—(OSL)
Rev.: $3,118,026
Assets: $27,734,304
Liabilities: $3,851,315
Net Worth: $23,882,989
Earnings: ($4,204,200)
Emp.: 20
Fiscal Year-end: 12/31/23
Biotechnology Research & Develop-
ment Services
N.A.I.C.S.: 541714
Christer Valderhaug *(CEO)*

**ARCTIC BLUE BEVERAGES
AB**
Aleksanterinkatu 19, 00100, Helsinki,
Finland
Tel.: (358) 456567323
Web Site:
   https://www.arcticbluebeverage.com
Year Founded: 2017
ARCTIC—(OMX)
Rev.: $637,322
Assets: $1,276,630
Liabilities: $1,051,284
Net Worth: $225,346
Earnings: ($1,822,622)
Emp.: 5
Fiscal Year-end: 12/31/23
Alcoholic Beverages Mfr
N.A.I.C.S.: 312140
Antti Villanen *(Chm)*

**ARCTIC CO-OPERATIVES LIM-
ITED**
1645 Inkster Blvd, Winnipeg, R2X
2W7, MB, Canada
Tel.: (204) 697-2243
Web Site: http://www.arcticco-op.com
Year Founded: 1972
Sales Range: $75-99.9 Million
Emp.: 1,000
General Merchandise Retailer
N.A.I.C.S.: 455219
Mary Nirlungayuk *(VP-Corp Svcs)*

Subsidiaries:

ARDICOM Digital Communications
Inc. **(1)**
2nd Floor NWT Communications Bldg 5120
- 49th Street, PO Box 356, Yellowknife, X1A
2N3, NT, Canada
Tel.: (867) 669-0035
Telecommunication Servicesb
N.A.I.C.S.: 517112

Nunavut Sealink & Supply
Incorporated **(1)**
Tel.: (867) 979-3799
Web Site: http://www.arcticsealift.com
Sales Range: $25-49.9 Million
Emp.: 3
Domestic Sea Freight Transportation Ser-
vices
N.A.I.C.S.: 488510
Stephane Daigle *(Gen Mgr)*

ARCTIC FISH HOLDING AS
Sindragata 10, 400, Isafjorour, Ice-
land
Tel.: (354) 4567100
Web Site: https://www.arcticfish.is
Year Founded: 2011
AFISH—(OSL)
Rev.: $98,134,452
Assets: $249,067,226
Liabilities: $154,422,122
Net Worth: $94,645,104
Earnings: ($14,213,489)
Emp.: 131
Fiscal Year-end: 12/31/23
Holding Company
N.A.I.C.S.: 551112
Neil Shiran Thorisson *(CFO)*

ARCTIC FOX LITHIUM CORP.
905-1030 Georgia Street West, Van-
couver, V6E 2Y3, BC, Canada
Tel.: (604) 689-2646   BC
Web Site:
   https://www.arcticfoxlithium.com
Year Founded: 2013
AFX—(CNSX)
Assets: $150,593
Liabilities: $7,074
Net Worth: $143,518
Earnings: ($108,752)
Fiscal Year-end: 06/30/22
Mineral Exploration Services
N.A.I.C.S.: 213115
Gerald George Carlson *(VP)*

ARCTIC MINERALS AB
Kopmangatan 22, 831 30, Ostersund,
Sweden
Tel.: (46) 703608130
Web Site: https://arcticminerals.se
Year Founded: 1999
ARCT—(OMX)
Rev.: $656
Assets: $5,688,087
Liabilities: $806,335
Net Worth: $4,881,752
Earnings: ($1,766,744)
Emp.: 1
Fiscal Year-end: 12/31/22
Gold Mining Services
N.A.I.C.S.: 212220
Martin Johansson *(Auditor)*

ARCTIC PAPER S.A.
Ul Fabryczna 1, 66-470, Kostrzyn,
nad Odra, Poland
Tel.: (48) 957210550
Web Site:
   https://www.arcticpaper.com
ATC—(WAR)
Rev.: $920,064,615
Assets: $644,170,006
Liabilities: $309,045,855
Net Worth: $335,124,152
Earnings: $47,426,286
Emp.: 1,503
Fiscal Year-end: 12/31/21
Paper Mfr
N.A.I.C.S.: 322120
Michal Jarczynski *(Chm-Mgmt Bd &
CEO)*

Subsidiaries:

Arctic Paper Baltic States SIA **(1)**
K Vardemara iela 33-20, Riga, LV-1010,
Latvia
Tel.: (371) 67332323

Emp.: 4
Paper Product Distr
N.A.I.C.S.: 424130
Savicka Mara *(Mgr-Customer Svc)*

Arctic Paper Benelux S.A. **(1)**
Ophemstraat 24, 3050, Oud-Heverlee, Bel-
gium
Tel.: (32) 16470746
Web Site: http://www.arcticpaper.com
Emp.: 10
Paper Product Distr
N.A.I.C.S.: 424130

Arctic Paper Danmark A/S **(1)**
At The Cave 50, 5610, Assens, Denmark
Tel.: (45) 43664366
Paper Product Distr
N.A.I.C.S.: 424130
Leif-Arne Karlsen *(Mgr-Admin)*

Arctic Paper Deutschland GmbH **(1)**
Am Sandtorkai 71, 20457, Hamburg, Ger-
many
Tel.: (49) 405148530
Emp.: 16
Paper Product Distr
N.A.I.C.S.: 424130

Arctic Paper Espana SL **(1)**
Avenida Diagonal 472-474 ES-9-1, 08006,
Barcelona, Spain
Tel.: (34) 933684927
Emp.: 2
Paper Product Distr
N.A.I.C.S.: 424130

Arctic Paper France SAS **(1)**
30 rue du Chateau des Rentiers, Olympia-
des, 75013, Paris, France
Tel.: (33) 143449206
Emp.: 9
Paper Product Distr
N.A.I.C.S.: 424130

Arctic Paper Grycksbo AB **(1)**
Kungsvagen 1, Box 1, 790 20, Grycksbo,
Sweden
Tel.: (46) 2368000
Emp.: 430
Paper Products Mfr
N.A.I.C.S.: 322299
Michael Fejer *(Mng Dir)*

Arctic Paper Italia srl **(1)**
Piazzale Biancamano 8, 20121, Milan, Italy
Tel.: (39) 03483058625
Emp.: 6
Paper Product Distr
N.A.I.C.S.: 424130

Arctic Paper Kostrzyn S.A. **(1)**
Ul Fabryczna 1, Kostrzyn nad Odra, 66-
470, Kostrzyn, Poland
Tel.: (48) 957210600
Web Site:
   https://en.arcticpaperkostrzyn.com
Emp.: 460
Paper Products Mfr
N.A.I.C.S.: 322299
Henryk Derejczyk *(Mng Dir)*

Arctic Paper Mochenwangen
GmbH **(1)**
Fabrikstrasse 62, 88284, Wolpertswende,
Germany
Tel.: (49) 7502 401
Emp.: 190
Paper Products Mfr
N.A.I.C.S.: 322299

Arctic Paper Munkedals AB **(1)**
Bruksvagen, SE-455 81, Munkedal, Swe-
den
Tel.: (46) 104518000
Paper Products Mfr
N.A.I.C.S.: 322299
Goran Lindqvist *(Mng Dir)*

Arctic Paper Norge AS **(1)**
Rosenholmveien 25 No 1414, 1414, Trolla-
sen, Norway
Tel.: (47) 66 82 35 50
Paper Product Distr
N.A.I.C.S.: 424130

Arctic Paper Papierhandels
GmbH **(1)**
Hainburgerstrasse 34a, A-1030, Vienna,
Austria
Tel.: (43) 17127090

Arctic Paper S.A.—(Continued)

Emp.: 70
Paper Product Distr
N.A.I.C.S.: 424130

Arctic Paper Polska Sp. z o.o. (1)
ul Okrezna 9, 02-916, Warsaw, Poland
Tel.: (48) 222030500
Paper Product Distr
N.A.I.C.S.: 424130

Arctic Paper Schweiz AG (1)
Technoparkstrasse 1, 8005, Zurich, Switzerland
Tel.: (41) 44 274 80 80
Paper Product Distr
N.A.I.C.S.: 424130
Heinz Schaer (Mng Dir)

Arctic Paper Sverige AB (1)
Kurodsvagen 9, 451 55, Uddevalla, Sweden
Tel.: (46) 522266326
Paper Product Distr
N.A.I.C.S.: 424130

Arctic Paper UK Limited (1)
8 St Thomas Street, London, SE1 9RR,
Surrey, United Kingdom
Tel.: (44) 2039172450
Emp.: 9
Paper Product Distr
N.A.I.C.S.: 424130
Rob Slowe (Mng Dir)

Rottneros AB (1)
Vallviks Bruk, 826 79, Soderhamn, Sweden
Tel.: (46) 27062000
Web Site: https://www.rottneros.com
Rev.: $273,492,569
Assets: $279,647,393
Liabilities: $95,201,225
Net Worth: $184,446,168
Earnings: $12,011,833
Emp.: 287
Fiscal Year-end: 12/31/2023
Pulp & Paper Producer
N.A.I.C.S.: 322110
Ingemar Eliasson (Dir-Pur)

Subsidiary (Domestic):

Rottneros Bruk AB (2)
Box 70370, 68694, Stockholm,
Sweden (100%)
Tel.: (46) 56517600
Sales Range: $50-74.9 Million
Emp.: 130
Pulp Mill
N.A.I.C.S.: 322110
Kristin Israelsson (Mng Dir)

Subsidiary (Non-US):

Rottneros Miranda SA (2)
Carretera de Logrono S-N, PO Box 6, Miranda de Ebro, 09200, Vitoria,
Spain (100%)
Tel.: (34) 947310245
Pulp Mill
N.A.I.C.S.: 322110

Subsidiary (Domestic):

Rottneros Packaging AB (2)
Box 70 370, 107 24, Stockholm, Sweden
Tel.: (46) 859001000
Food Packaging Products Mfr
N.A.I.C.S.: 322220
Kasper Skuthalla (Mng Dir)

Subsidiary (Non-US):

SIA Rottneros Baltic AB (2)
Locu street 1, Ventspils, LV3601, Tukums,
Latvia (100%)
Tel.: (371) 3629273
Sales Range: $25-49.9 Million
Emp.: 13
Pulp Mill
N.A.I.C.S.: 322110

Subsidiary (Domestic):

Vallviks Bruk AB (2)
Ronnvagen 17, Vallvik, 82021, Soderhamn,
Sweden (100%)
Tel.: (46) 859001033
Web Site: http://www.rottneros.com
Sales Range: $50-74.9 Million
Emp.: 200
Pulp Mill

N.A.I.C.S.: 322110

ARCTIC STAR EXPLORATION CORP.
Suite 1100 1111 Melville Street, Vancouver, V6E 3V6, BC, Canada
Tel.: (604) 218-8772
Web Site: https://www.arcticstar.ca
Year Founded: 2001
ADD—(TSXV)
Assets: $3,690,429
Liabilities: $512,691
Net Worth: $3,177,738
Earnings: ($1,114,826)
Fiscal Year-end: 12/31/20
Diamond Exploration & Development
Services
N.A.I.C.S.: 212390
Patrick Power (Pres & CEO)

ARCTICZYMES TECHNOLOGIES ASA
Sykehusveien 23, 9019, Tromso,
Norway
Tel.: (47) 77648900
Web Site:
　　https://www.arcticzymes.com
AZT—(OSL)
Rev.: $12,716,054
Assets: $29,469,518
Liabilities: $3,168,391
Net Worth: $26,301,127
Earnings: $3,035,285
Emp.: 61
Fiscal Year-end: 12/31/22
Pharmaceuticals Product Mfr
N.A.I.C.S.: 325412
Borge Sorvoll (CFO)

ARCURE
14 rue Scandicci Tour Essor, 93500,
Pantin, France
Tel.: (33) 144068190
Web Site: https://www.arcure.net
ALCUR—(EUR)
Rev.: $23,252,108
Assets: $20,789,465
Liabilities: $13,256,217
Net Worth: $7,533,248
Earnings: $1,987,960
Emp.: 53
Fiscal Year-end: 12/31/23
Industrial Machinery Mfr
N.A.I.C.S.: 333248
Patrick Mansuy (Co-Founder)

Subsidiaries:

Blaxtair Inc. (1)
541 N Fairbanks CT 2200, Chicago, IL
60611
Tel.: (312) 999-5590
Civil Work Services
N.A.I.C.S.: 237990

Durstmuller GmbH (1)
Salzburger Str 59, Lambach, 4650, Wels,
Austria
Tel.: (43) 7245282500
Web Site: http://www.dula.at
Personal Protective Equipment Mfr
N.A.I.C.S.: 339113

**Magna Makine San. Ve Tic.
Ltd.Sti.** (1)
Turgut Ozal Cad No 17, Sekerpinar Mah,
Cayirova, Kocaeli, Turkiye
Tel.: (90) 2626552427
Web Site: http://magnamakine.com
Excavator Safety System Services
N.A.I.C.S.: 561621

ARCUS ASA
Destilleriveien 11, 1481, Hagan, Norway
Tel.: (47) 6706 5000
Web Site: http://www.arcus.no
Year Founded: 1996
ARCUS—(OSL)
Rev.: $313,713,328

Assets: $634,732,804
Liabilities: $445,987,383
Net Worth: $188,745,422
Earnings: $15,134,739
Emp.: 435
Fiscal Year-end: 12/31/19
Holding Company; Wine & Distilled
Spirits Mfr & Whslr
N.A.I.C.S.: 551112
Kenneth Hamnes (CEO)

Subsidiaries:

Arcus-Gruppen AS (1)
Destilleriveien 11, 1481, Hagan,
Norway (100%)
Tel.: (47) 67065000
Web Site: http://www.arcus.no
Distilled Spirits & Wine Mfr & Whslr
N.A.I.C.S.: 312140
Kenneth Hamnes (CEO)

Subsidiary (Domestic):

Arcus AS (2)
Destilleriveien 11, 1481, Hagan, Norway
Tel.: (47) 6706 5000
Web Site: http://www.arcus.no
Wine & Distilled Spirits Mfr & Whslr
N.A.I.C.S.: 424820
Holger Gramstad (Country Mgr)

Subsidiary (Non-US):

Arcus Finland OY (2)
Kalevankatu 30 A 6 krs, 00100, Helsinki,
Finland
Tel.: (358) 40 560 0617
Web Site: http://www.arcusfinland.com
Alcoholic Beverage Distr
N.A.I.C.S.: 424820
Hanne Lindroos-Koski (Mgr-Sls & Mktg)

Arcus Sweden AB (2)
Box 7471, SE-103 92, Stockholm,
Sweden (100%)
Tel.: (46) 8 545 534 30
Web Site: http://www.arcussweden.se
Alcoholic Beverage Mfr & Distr
N.A.I.C.S.: 312120
Petter Berglund (Country Mgr)

Subsidiary (Domestic):

Arcus Wine Brands AS (2)
Destilleriveien 11, 1481, Hagan,
Norway (100%)
Tel.: (47) 67065000
Web Site: http://www.vingruppen.no
Wine & Alcoholic Beverage Distr
N.A.I.C.S.: 424820
Janne Holm (Portfolio Mgr)

Subsidiary (Non-US):

Vingruppen i Norden AB (2)
Regeringsgatan 109, Stockholm, 10392,
Sweden
Tel.: (46) 8 660 84 15
Web Site: http://www.vingruppen.se
Alcoholic Beverage Distr
N.A.I.C.S.: 424820
Svante Selling (CEO)

Subsidiary (Domestic):

Vinordia AS (2)
Destilleriveien 11, Gjellerasen, Norway
Tel.: (47) 6706 5000
Web Site: http://www.arcus.no
Beverage Distr
N.A.I.C.S.: 424820

Vectura AS (1)
Destilleriveien 11, 1481, Hagan,
Norway (100%)
Tel.: (47) 67 06 50 00
Web Site: http://www.vectura.no
Beverage Logistics Services
N.A.I.C.S.: 541614
Jon Simen Rustad (Dir-Fin)

ARCUS DEVELOPMENT GROUP INC.
Suite 403 - 905 West Pender Street,
Vancouver, V6C 1L6, BC, Canada
Tel.: (778) 893-9325　　　　　　Ca

Web Site:
　　https://www.arcusdevelopment.com
Year Founded: 2006
ARCUF—(OTCEM)
Assets: $60,777
Liabilities: $6,656
Net Worth: $54,121
Earnings: ($32,086)
Fiscal Year-end: 07/31/23
Mineral Exploration Services
N.A.I.C.S.: 213114
Ian J. Talbot (Pres & CEO)

ARCUS INFRASTRUCTURE PARTNERS LLP
2nd Floor 6 St Andrew Street, London, EC4A 3AE, United Kingdom
Tel.: (44) 2078323400
Web Site: http://www.arcusip.com
Year Founded: 2009
Fund Management Services
N.A.I.C.S.: 523999
Simon Gray (Co-Mng Partner)

Subsidiaries:

Alpha Trains (1)
22 rue Alfred de Musset, 2175, Luxembourg, Luxembourg
Tel.: (352) 2620 3113
Web Site: http://www.alpha-trains.eu
Railway Transportation Services
N.A.I.C.S.: 482112
Fernando Perez (Mng Dir-Locomotives Div)

Brisa (1)
Quinta da Torre da Aguilha-Edificio Brisa,
2785-599, Sao Domingos de Rana, Portugal
Tel.: (351) 21 444 95 69
Web Site: http://www.brisa.pt
Railway Transportation Services
N.A.I.C.S.: 482112
Bruno Tavares (Mgr-Project Fin)

Forth Ports PLC (1)
1 Prince Of Wales Dock, Edinburgh, EH6
7DX, United Kingdom
Tel.: (44) 1315558700
Web Site: http://www.forthports.co.uk
Sales Range: $250-299.9 Million
Commercial Port Operator
N.A.I.C.S.: 488310
Charles G. Hammond (CEO)

Subsidiary (Domestic):

FP Newhaven Two Limited (2)
1 Prince Of Wales Dock, Edinburgh, United
Kingdom
Tel.: (44) 1313431000
Sales Range: $50-74.9 Million
Real Estate Agents & Managers
N.A.I.C.S.: 531210

Forth Estuary Towage Limited (2)
1 Prince of Wales Dock, Edinburgh, VEX
67DX, United Kingdom (100%)
Tel.: (44) 1315558700
Web Site: http://www.forthports.co.uk
Sales Range: $50-74.9 Million
Real Estate Agents & Managers
N.A.I.C.S.: 531210
Charles Hammond (Mng Dir)

Forth Properties Limited (2)
1 Prince of Wales Dock, Edinburgh, EH6
7DX, United Kingdom
Tel.: (44) 1315558700
Web Site: http://www.forthports.co.uk
Real Estate Agents & Managers
N.A.I.C.S.: 531210
Stuart Paterson (Head-Fin)

Forth Property Developments Ltd (2)
1 Prince Of Wales Dock, Edinburgh, EH6
7DX, United Kingdom
Tel.: (44) 1315558700
Web Site: http://www.forthports.co.uk
Sales Range: $50-74.9 Million
Emp.: 100
Real Estate Agents & Managers
N.A.I.C.S.: 531210
Charles Hammond (CEO)

Ocean Terminal Limited (2)

98 Ocean Dr Leith, Edinburgh, EH6 6JJ,
United Kingdom
Tel.: (44) 1315558888
Web Site: http://www.oceanterminal.com
Sales Range: $25-49.9 Million
Emp.: 6
Business Service Centers
N.A.I.C.S.: 561439
Dennis Jones *(Mgr-Centre)*

Port of Dundee Ltd (2)
Port Office Spanner Gate Rd, Dundee, D1
3LU, United Kingdom (100%)
Tel.: (44) 1382224121
Web Site:
   http://www.dundeerenewables.com
Freight Transportation Arrangement
N.A.I.C.S.: 488510

Port of Tilbury London Limited (2)
Neptune House, Tilbury, RM18 7EH, Essex,
United Kingdom
Tel.: (44) 1375852424
Web Site: http://www.forthport.co.uk
Sales Range: $100-124.9 Million
Emp.: 600
Freight Transportation Arrangement
N.A.I.C.S.: 488510
Pary Jliding *(COO)*

TDF S.A.S. (1)
Tel.: (33) 155951000
Web Site: http://www.tdf.fr
Television, Radio, Telecommunications &
Satellite Communications Infrastructure
Operator
N.A.I.C.S.: 517810
Olivier Huart *(Chm & CEO)*

Workdry International Limited (1)
Bournemouth Road Chandler's Ford, East-
leigh, SO53 3ZL, Hants, United Kingdom
Tel.: (44) 1600772256
Web Site: https://www.workdry.com
Pump Rental & Wastewater Treatment Ser-
vices
N.A.I.C.S.: 333914
Dan Lee *(CEO)*

Subsidiary (US):

Holland Pump Mfg., Inc. (2)
7321 Westport Pl, West Palm Beach, FL
33413
Tel.: (561) 697-3333
Web Site: http://www.hollandpump.com
Pumping System Rentals & Services
N.A.I.C.S.: 333914
Win Blodgett *(Pres)*

Subsidiary (Domestic):

Holland Pump of Louisiana, Inc (3)
17353 Opportunity Ave, Baton Rouge, LA
70817-3442
Tel.: (225) 756-1380
Web Site: https://hollandpump.com
Transportation Equipment & Supplies Mer-
chant Whslr
N.A.I.C.S.: 423860

ARCUS S.A.
5/7 Kolejowa Street, Warsaw, 01-217,
Poland
Tel.: (48) 22 536 08 00
Web Site: http://www.arcus.pl
Rev.: $36,744,307
Assets: $27,499,083
Liabilities: $15,842,847
Net Worth: $11,656,236
Earnings: ($9,825)
Emp.: 219
Fiscal Year-end: 12/31/18
Information Technology Consulting
Services
N.A.I.C.S.: 541512
Michal Czeredys *(Chm-Mgmt Bd)*

Subsidiaries:

Arcus Systemy Informatyczne Sp. z
o.o. (1)
ul Wojciechowska 9a, 20-704, Lublin, Po-
land
Tel.: (48) 814521600
Web Site: http://www.arcussi.pl
Information & Technology Services
N.A.I.C.S.: 541519

Lukasz Sztyber *(Pres)*

DocuSoft Sp. z o.o. (1)
Al Armii Krajowej 220, 43-300, Bielsko-
Biala, Poland
Tel.: (48) 338105775
Web Site: http://www.docusoft.pl
Document Circulation System Mfr
N.A.I.C.S.: 334510
Andrzej Nycz *(CEO)*

GEOTIK Sp. z o.o. (1)
ul Kolejowa 5/7, 01-217, Warsaw, Poland
Tel.: (48) 228860050
Web Site: http://www.geotik.pl
Telemetry Station Mfr
N.A.I.C.S.: 334519
Piotr Majewski *(CEO)*

ARCVIA MINERVA SA
Bd Revolutiei No 55 Floor I Apart-
ment 4, Arad, Romania
Tel.: (40) 357100900
Web Site:
   http://www.arcviaminerva.ro
Sales Range: $1-9.9 Million
Emp.: 6
Real Estate Development Services
N.A.I.C.S.: 531390

ARCWEST EXPLORATION INC.
1100-1199 West Hastings Street,
Vancouver, V6E 3T5, BC, Canada
Tel.: (604) 638-3695   BC
Web Site:
   https://arcwestexploration.com
Year Founded: 2010
AWX—(TSXV)
Rev.: $40,574
Assets: $4,244,294
Liabilities: $140,882
Net Worth: $4,103,412
Earnings: ($258,353)
Fiscal Year-end: 12/31/23
Investment Services
N.A.I.C.S.: 523999
William John Meekison *(CFO)*

ARD FINANCE S.A.
56 rue Charles Martel, Luxembourg,
L-2134, Luxembourg
Tel.: (352) 26 25 85 55   LU
Year Founded: 2011
Rev.: $6,660,000,000
Assets: $9,069,000,000
Liabilities: $11,156,000,000
Net Worth: ($2,087,000,000)
Earnings: $1,256,000,000
Emp.: 16,341
Fiscal Year-end: 12/31/19
Holding Company
N.A.I.C.S.: 551112

ARD GRUP BILISIM
TEKNOLOJILERI A.S.
Koc Towers Sogutozu Street No 2 A
Block Floor 20-21 No 60, Cankaya,
06510, Ankara, Turkiye
Tel.: (90) 3122992595
Web Site:
   https://www.ardinformatics.com.tr
ARDYZ—(IST)
Rev.: $38,627,824
Assets: $78,964,832
Liabilities: $19,469,573
Net Worth: $59,495,259
Earnings: $15,018,853
Fiscal Year-end: 12/31/23
Information Technology Consulting
Services
N.A.I.C.S.: 541512

ARDAGH GROUP S.A.
56 rue Charles Martel, L-2134, Luxembourg, Luxembourg
Tel.: (352) 26258555   LU
Web Site:
   http://www.ardaghgroup.com
Year Founded: 2011

ARD—(NYSE)
Rev.: $9,402,000,000
Assets: $11,514,000,000
Liabilities: $13,747,000,000
Net Worth: ($2,233,000,000)
Earnings: ($495,000,000)
Emp.: 20,000
Fiscal Year-end: 12/31/23
Holding Company; Glass & Metal
Packaging Mfr & Distr
N.A.I.C.S.: 551112
Paul R. Coulson *(Chm & CEO)*

Subsidiaries:

Ardagh Glass Holmegaard A/S (1)
Glasvaerksvej 52, Fensmark, 4684, Hol-
megaard, Denmark
Tel.: (45) 55546200
Metal Packaging & Container Distr
N.A.I.C.S.: 424130

Ardagh Glass Italy S.r.l. (1)
SS Trinita, Montorio al Vomano, 64046,
Teramo, Italy
Tel.: (39) 086159511
Metal Packaging & Container Distr
N.A.I.C.S.: 424130

Ardagh Glass Limmared AB (1)
Storgarten 22, Limmared, 514 83, Tranemo,
Sweden
Tel.: (46) 325618300
Metal Packaging & Container Distr
N.A.I.C.S.: 424130

Ardagh Glass Sales Limited (1)
Ardagh House South County Business
Park, Leopardstown, Dublin, Ireland
Tel.: (353) 15682000
Metal Packaging & Container Distr
N.A.I.C.S.: 424130

Ardagh Metal Beverage Europe
GmbH (1)
Grafenauweg 4, 6300, Zug, Switzerland
Tel.: (41) 445597101
Metal Packaging & Container Distr
N.A.I.C.S.: 424130

Ardagh Packaging Group Limited (1)
4 Richview Office Park, Clonskeagh, Dublin,
14, Ireland
Tel.: (353) 16052400
Web Site: http://www.ardaghgroup.com
Sales Range: $400-449.9 Million
Emp.: 17,700
Glass & Metal Packaging Mfr
N.A.I.C.S.: 327213

Subsidiary (US):

Ardagh Glass Inc. (2)
1509 Macedonia Ave, Muncie, IN
47302-3664 (100%)
Tel.: (765) 741-7000
Web Site: http://www.ardaghgroup.com
Glass Bottle & Jar Mfr
N.A.I.C.S.: 327213

Plant (Domestic):

Ardagh Glass Inc. - Bridgeton (3)
443 S East Ave, Bridgeton, NJ 08302-3461
Tel.: (856) 455-2000
Web Site: http://www.ardaghgroup.com
Sales Range: $125-149.9 Million
Emp.: 350
Glass Container Mfr
N.A.I.C.S.: 327213

Ardagh Glass Inc. - Dunkirk (3)
524 E Ctr St, Dunkirk, IN 47336
Tel.: (765) 768-7891
Glass Container Mfr
N.A.I.C.S.: 327213

Ardagh Glass Inc. - Madera (3)
2441 Ave 12, Madera, CA 93637-9384
Tel.: (559) 675-4700
Glass Container Mfr
N.A.I.C.S.: 327213
Mirko Muller *(Gen Mgr)*

Subsidiary (Domestic):

Marion Glass Equipment & Technol-
ogy Company (3)
123 E McKinley St, Marion, IN 46952
Tel.: (765) 662-1172

Web Site: http://www.gps-america.biz
Sales Range: $25-49.9 Million
Emp.: 95
Glass Manufacturing Equipment Parts &
Services
N.A.I.C.S.: 333248

Subsidiary (Non-US):

Ardagh Glass Limited (2)
Headlands Lane, Knottingley, WF11 0HP, W
Yorkshire, United Kingdom
Tel.: (44) 1977674111
Web Site: http://www.ardaghgroup.com
Sales Range: $125-149.9 Million
Emp.: 300
Glass Container Mfr
N.A.I.C.S.: 327213

Ardagh Metal Packaging Netherlands
B.V. (2)
Zutphenseweg 51, 7418 AH, Deventer,
Netherlands
Tel.: (31) 570682000
Web Site: http://www.ardaghgroup.com
Aluminium Cans Mfr
N.A.I.C.S.: 332431

Ardagh Metal Packaging UK
Limited (2)
Salhouse Road, Norwich, NR7 9AT, Norfolk,
United Kingdom
Tel.: (44) 1603 427 313
Sales Range: $25-49.9 Million
Emp.: 45
Mfrs. Cans
N.A.I.C.S.: 332431

Plant (Domestic):

Ardagh Metal Packaging UK Ltd. -
Sutton-in-Ashfield Plant (3)
Coxmoor Road, Sutton in Ashfield, NG17
5LA, Notts, United Kingdom
Tel.: (44) 1623518030
Sales Range: $50-74.9 Million
Metal Food Packaging Product Mfr
N.A.I.C.S.: 332431
David Horton *(Plant Mgr)*

Subsidiary (US):

Ardagh Metal Packaging USA,
Inc. (2)
Carnegie Office Park 600 N Bell Ave Bldg 1
Ste 200, Carnegie, PA 15106
Tel.: (412) 429-5290
Web Site: http://www.ardaghgroup.com
Sales Range: $10-24.9 Million
Emp.: 30
Metal Packaging
N.A.I.C.S.: 561910

Heye International GmbH (1)
Lohplatz 1, 31683, Obernkirchen, Germany
Tel.: (49) 5724260
Web Site: http://www.heye-international.com
Laboratory Equipment Distr
N.A.I.C.S.: 423490
Michael Husken *(Mng Dir)*

ARDAGH METAL PACKAGING
S.A.
56 rue Charles Martel, 2134, Luxem-
bourg, Luxembourg
Tel.: (352) 26258555   LU
Web Site:
   https://www.ardaghmetalpackaging.com
Year Founded: 2021
AMBP—(NYSE)
Rev.: $4,812,000,000
Assets: $5,669,000,000
Liabilities: $5,563,000,000
Net Worth: $106,000,000
Earnings: ($50,000,000)
Emp.: 6,400
Fiscal Year-end: 12/31/23
Metal & Glass Packaging Product Mfr
N.A.I.C.S.: 327213
Oliver Graham *(CEO)*

ARDAKAN INDUSTRIAL CE-
RAMICS CO.
No 21 8th floor Fereshte St Agha Bo-
zorgi St above Agha Bozorgi, Shirin

Ardakan Industrial Ceramics Co.—(Continued)

Building, Isfahan, Iran
Tel.: (98) 21263725774
Web Site: http://www.aic.ir
Year Founded: 1996
ARDK1—(THE)
Sales Range: Less than $1 Million
Emp.: 177
Ceramic Products Mfr
N.A.I.C.S.: 327110

ARDEA RESOURCES LIMITED

Suite 2 45 Ord St, West Perth, 6005,
WA, Australia
Tel.: (61) 862445136　　　　　　　**AU**
Web Site:
　https://www.ardearesources.com.au
ARL—(ASX)
Rev.: $623,415
Assets: $39,918,824
Liabilities: $3,078,864
Net Worth: $36,839,960
Earnings: ($5,145,120)
Fiscal Year-end: 06/30/24
Gold Ore & Silver Ore Mining
N.A.I.C.S.: 212220
Matthew Painter (Gen Mgr-
Exploration)

ARDEL STEEL

455 Longman Crescent, Regina, S4N
6G3, SK, Canada
Tel.: (306) 721-2995
Web Site: http://www.ardelsteel.com
Year Founded: 1980
Rev.: $11,553,274
Emp.: 35
Reinforcing Steel & Fabricator Distr
N.A.I.C.S.: 423440
Arnie Matt (Founder)

ARDEN SOFTWARE LTD.

Arden House Shepley Lane Marple,
Stockport, SK6 7JW, Greater Man-
chester, United Kingdom
Tel.: (44) 161 449 6600
Web Site:
　http://www.ardensoftware.com
Year Founded: 1988
Packaging & Printing Software Ser-
vices
N.A.I.C.S.: 513210
Martin Poynter (Mng Dir)

Subsidiaries:

Cimex Corp.　　　　　　　　　　　　　**(1)**
30 Front St Ste 2, Belchertown, MA 01007
Tel.: (413) 323-1090
Web Site: http://www.cimexcorp.com
Rev.: $1,989,000
Emp.: 9
Computer System Design Services
N.A.I.C.S.: 541512
Andrew Carey (Pres)

ARDENTEC CORPORATION

No 3 Gongye 3rd Rd, Shengli Vil Hu-
Kou Township, Hsin-chu, 303036,
Taiwan
Tel.: (886) 35976688　　　　　　　**CN**
Web Site: https://www.ardentec.com
Year Founded: 1999
Emp.: 1,500
IT Testing Services
N.A.I.C.S.: 519290
Chih-Yuan Lu (Chm & CEO)

Subsidiaries:

Giga Solution Tech. Co., Ltd.　　　　**(1)**
7F No 6 Technology Road 5 Hsinchu Sci-
ence Park, Hsin-chu, 30078,
Taiwan
Tel.: (886) 36116168　　　　**(88.63%)**
Web Site: http://www.giga-solution.com
Integrated Circuit Testing Services
N.A.I.C.S.: 334515
Liang-Po Chen (Pres)

ARDEPRO CO. LTD.

2F Keio Shinjuku 3 Chome Bldg 1-24
Shinjuku 3-Chome, Shinjuku-ku, To-
kyo, Japan
Tel.: (81) 353672001
Web Site: http://www.ardepro.co.jp
8925—(TKS)
Rev.: $136,081,929
Assets: $126,580,773
Liabilities: $68,787,578
Net Worth: $57,793,195
Earnings: $12,685,828
Emp.: 24
Fiscal Year-end: 07/31/23
Leasing Building & Real Estate
N.A.I.C.S.: 531110
Yuichi Shiitsuka (Pres)

ARDI INVESTMENTS & TRAD-ING COMPANY LIMITED

Shop No 3 Hemu Castle Dadabhai
Road Near Gokhilbai School Vile
Parle W, Mumbai, 400 056, Maha-
rashtra, India
Tel.: (91) 2226248888
Web Site: https://www.ardi.co.in
Year Founded: 1981
504370—(BOM)
Rev.: $22
Assets: $655,709
Liabilities: $721,809
Net Worth: ($66,100)
Earnings: ($4,467)
Fiscal Year-end: 03/31/20
Financial Services
N.A.I.C.S.: 523999
Atulkumar Balchandbhai Shah (CFO)

ARDIAN SAS

20 Place Vendome, 75001, Paris,
France
Tel.: (33) 141719200　　　　　　　**FR**
Web Site: http://www.ardian.com
Year Founded: 1996
Privater Equity Firm
N.A.I.C.S.: 523999
Dominique Senequier (Pres)

Subsidiaries:

Ardian Germany GmbH　　　　　　　**(1)**
An der Welle 4, 60322, Frankfurt, Germany
Tel.: (49) 69 50 50 41 500
Web Site: http://www.ardian-investment.com
Privater Equity Firm
N.A.I.C.S.: 523999
Caspar von Meibom (Mng Dir-Mid Market
Enterprise Capital)

Ardian Investment Singapore Pte.
Ltd.　　　　　　　　　　　　　　　　**(1)**
1 Temasek Avenue Unit 20-02A Millenia
Tower, Singapore, 039192, Singapore
Tel.: (65) 65133410
Web Site: http://www.ardian-investment.com
Emp.: 11
Privater Equity Firm
N.A.I.C.S.: 523999
Jenhoo Han (Mng Dir)

Ardian Investment Switzerland
AG　　　　　　　　　　　　　　　　**(1)**
Bahnhofstrasse 20, 8001, Zurich, Switzer-
land
Tel.: (41) 442132727
Web Site: http://www.ardian.com
Emp.: 10
Privater Equity Firm
N.A.I.C.S.: 523999
Martin Kessi (Mng Dir-Zurich)

Ardian Investment UK Limited　　　**(1)**
1 Grafton Street, London, W1S 4FE, United
Kingdom
Tel.: (44) 2071544300
Web Site: http://www.ardian.com
Emp.: 15
Private Equity Services
N.A.I.C.S.: 523999
Stefano Mion (Sr Mng Dir-New York)

Ardian Italy S.r.l.　　　　　　　　　**(1)**
Piazza S Fedele 2, 20121, Milan, Italy

Tel.: (39) 02 5844 2401
Web Site: http://www.ardian-investment.com
Privater Equity Firm
N.A.I.C.S.: 523999
Paolo Bergonzini (Mng Dir-Small Market
Enterprise Capital)

Ardian US LLC　　　　　　　　　　　**(1)**
1370 Avenue of the Americas, New York,
NY 10019
Tel.: (212) 641-8604
Web Site: http://www.ardian.com
Privater Equity Firm
N.A.I.C.S.: 523999
Benoit Verbrugghe (Head-USA)

Subsidiary (Domestic):

Acousti Engineering Co. of
Florida　　　　　　　　　　　　　　　**(2)**
4656 SW 34th St, Orlando, FL
32811-6450　　　　　　　　　　　**(60%)**
Tel.: (407) 425-3467
Web Site: http://www.acousti.com
Acoustical Interior Contracting & Noise Con-
trol
N.A.I.C.S.: 238310
James R. Verner (Pres & CEO)

Subsidiary (Domestic):

Acousti Engineering Co.　　　　　　**(3)**
4656 34th St S W, Orlando, FL 32811
Tel.: (407) 425-3467
Web Site: http://www.acousti.com
Sales Range: $125-149.9 Million
Emp.: 1,500
Engineeering Services
N.A.I.C.S.: 541330
George Estes (VP, Gen Mgr & Reg Mgr)

Subsidiary (Domestic):

Colonial Bag Corporation　　　　　　**(2)**
25721 Network Pl, Chicago, IL 60673-1257
Tel.: (630) 690-3999
Web Site: http://www.colonialbag.com
Can Liner Mfr
N.A.I.C.S.: 325211

Subsidiary (Domestic):

Redi-Bag, Inc.　　　　　　　　　　　**(3)**
17100 W Valley Hwy, Tukwila, WA 98188
Tel.: (425) 251-9841
Sales Range: $1-9.9 Million
Emp.: 45
Unsupported Plastics Film & Sheet (except
Packaging) Mfr
N.A.I.C.S.: 326113
Dan Ulrich (VP)

Subsidiary (Domestic):

Revere Plastics Systems, LLC.　　　**(2)**
39555 Orchard Hill Pl, Novi, MI 48375
Tel.: (419) 547-6918
Web Site:
　http://www.revereplasticssystems.com
Injection Molded Plastic Products Mfr
N.A.I.C.S.: 326199

Subsidiary (Domestic):

Ferguson Production, Inc.　　　　　　**(3)**
2130 Industrial Dr, McPherson, KS 67460
Tel.: (620) 241-2400
Web Site:
　http://www.fergusonproduction.com
Sales Range: $10-24.9 Million
Emp.: 140
Plastic Pipe & Pipe Fitting Mfr
N.A.I.C.S.: 326122
Scott Ferguson (Pres)

Plant (Domestic):

Revere Plastics Systems, LLC - Pop-
lar Bluff　　　　　　　　　　　　　　**(3)**
1452 Rowe Pkwy, Poplar Bluff, MO 63901-
7012
Tel.: (573) 785-0871
Web Site: http://www.revereindustries.com
Injection Molded Plastic Products Mfr
N.A.I.C.S.: 326199

Holding (Domestic):

Tom Barrow Company　　　　　　　　**(2)**
2800 Plant Atkinson Rd, Atlanta, GA 30080-
7240

Tel.: (404) 351-1010
Web Site: http://www.tombarrow.com
Warm Air Heating & Air Conditioning
N.A.I.C.S.: 423730
Jane Jones (VP-HR)

Subsidiary (Domestic):

CMH Solutions LLC　　　　　　　　　**(3)**
6400 Ctr St Ste 72, Mentor, OH 44060-
4137
Tel.: (440) 299-8111
Web Site: http://www.cmhsol.com
Computer Related Services
N.A.I.C.S.: 541519
Chris Varholick (Pres)

R.F. Peck Co., Inc.　　　　　　　　　**(3)**
22 Computer Dr W, Albany, NY 12205
Tel.: (518) 869-3541
Web Site: http://www.rfpeck.com
Rev.: $11,900,000
Emp.: 40
Warm Air Heating & Air-Conditioning Equip-
ment & Supplies Merchant Whslr
N.A.I.C.S.: 423730
Terrence Seery (Principal)

Artefact S.A.　　　　　　　　　　　　**(1)**
19 rue Richer, 75009, Paris,
France　　　　　　　　　　　　**(50.36%)**
Tel.: (33) 1 79724545
Web Site: http://www.artefact.com
Sales Range: $75-99.9 Million
Emp.: 800
Internet Search Marketing Services
N.A.I.C.S.: 541613
Lennert de Rijk (Mng Dir-Digital & Data
Mktg-Netherlands)

Subsidiary (Non-US):

GUAVA Ltd.　　　　　　　　　　　　　**(2)**
Pool Innovation Centre Trevenson Road,
Pool, Redruth, TR15 3PL, Cornwall, United
Kingdom　　　　　　　　　　　**(90.49%)**
Tel.: (44) 207 802 9500
Internet Marketing Services
N.A.I.C.S.: 541810
Liz Chandler (CFO)

Metapeople GmbH　　　　　　　　　　**(2)**
21 Philosophenweg, 47 051, Duisburg, Ger-
many
Tel.: (49) 203 4105 0400
Internet Marketing Services
N.A.I.C.S.: 541810
Julius Ewig (Country Mgr)

Subsidiary (Domestic):

Metaapes GmbH　　　　　　　　　　　**(3)**
Philosophenweb 21, 47051, Duisburg, Ger-
many
Tel.: (49) 203 4105 0400
Internet Marketing Services
N.A.I.C.S.: 541810
Julius Ewig (Country Mgr)

Subsidiary (Non-US):

NetBooster Agency Italy srl　　　　　**(2)**
Largo Francesco Richini 2/A, 20123, Milan,
Italy　　　　　　　　　　　　　　**(100%)**
Tel.: (39) 0 258 437 725
Internet Marketing Services
N.A.I.C.S.: 541810
Deborah Casalaspro (Country Mgr)

NetBooster GmbH　　　　　　　　　　**(2)**
Eschenheimer Aniage 31a, 60318, Frank-
furt, Germany　　　　　　　　　**(100%)**
Tel.: (49) 697 071 9149
Internet Marketing Services
N.A.I.C.S.: 541810
Gilles Bourdin (Dir-Bus Dev)

NetBooster Holding A/S　　　　　　　**(2)**
Pilestraede 52A 3 sal, 1112, Copenhagen,
Denmark
Tel.: (45) 702 780 89
Emp.: 60
Internet Services
N.A.I.C.S.: 551112
Hans-Jorgen Albertsen (Country Mgr)

NetBooster Mena Middle East &
North Africa FZ-LLC　　　　　　　　　**(2)**
Office 304 Floor 03 Building EIB No 01,
Dubai Internet City, Dubai, United Arab
Emirates　　　　　　　　　　　　**(100%)**

Tel.: (971) 144 343 249
Internet Marketing Services
N.A.I.C.S.: 541810

NetBooster Spain SL (2)
Plaza de Manuel Becerra 15, 28028, Madrid, Spain (100%)
Tel.: (34) 915 815 434
Internet Marketing Services
N.A.I.C.S.: 541810
Raul Alcazar (Country Mgr)

NetBooster Sweden AB (2)
Sankt Eriksgatan 63, 112 34, Stockholm, Sweden (90.49%)
Tel.: (46) 823 2470
Internet Marketing Services
N.A.I.C.S.: 541810
Monica Bolin (Country Mgr)

NetBooster UK Limited (2)
9th Floor 50 Broadway Westminster, London, SW1H 0RG, United Kingdom
Tel.: (44) 207 802 9500
Web Site: http://www.netbooster.co.uk
Emp.: 30
Internet Marketing Services
N.A.I.C.S.: 541810
Emmanuel Arendarczyk (Country Mgr)

Subsidiary (Domestic):

Pixidis Sarl (2)
4-6 passage Louis-Philippe, 75011, Paris, France (100%)
Tel.: (33) 140 402 700
Internet Marketing Services
N.A.I.C.S.: 541810

Assist Digital S.p.A. (1)
Via Melchiorre Gioia, 70, 20125, Milan, Italy
Tel.: (39) 0248000000
Web Site: https://assistdigital.com
IT Services
N.A.I.C.S.: 513210

Subsidiary (Domestic):

Inspearit S.r.l. (2)
Via Cassia 1081, 189, Rome, Italy
Tel.: (39) 0630260607
Software Development Services
N.A.I.C.S.: 541511

Biofarma Srl (1)
in Via Castelliere 2, Mereto di Tomba, 33036, Udine, Italy
Tel.: (39) 0432868711
Web Site: https://www.biofarmagroup.it
Pharmaceuticals Mfr
N.A.I.C.S.: 325412

CELLI S.p.A. (1)
Via Casino Albini 605, 47842, Rimini, Italy
Tel.: (39) 0541 755211
Web Site: http://www.celli.com
Celli Beer, Water & Soft Drink Dispensing Systems
N.A.I.C.S.: 333310
Mauro Gallavotti (Pres & CEO)

Subsidiary (Non-US):

ADS2 Brands Limited (2)
Unit 5 Montgomery Way, Stratton Business Park, Biggleswade, SG18 8UB, United Kingdom
Tel.: (44) 1767342500
Web Site: http://www.ads2brands.com
Beverage Dispensing Equipment Mfr
N.A.I.C.S.: 333241
Sean Fortune (Dir-Creative & Technical)

Dedalus S.p.A. (1)
Via di Collodi 6/C, 50141, Florence, Italy (60%)
Tel.: (39) 035996711
Web Site: http://www.dedalus.eu
Healthcare Software Developer
N.A.I.C.S.: 513210
Giorgio Moretti (Pres)

Subsidiary (Domestic):

NoemaLife S.p.A. (2)
Via Gobetti 52, 40129, Bologna, Italy
Tel.: (39) 051 4193911
Web Site: http://www.noemalife.com
Sales Range: $50-74.9 Million
Emp.: 400
Software Development Services

N.A.I.C.S.: 541511
Cristina Signifredi (Co-Founder)

Subsidiary (Non-US):

AGFA HEALTHCARE - KNIGHTS-BRIDGE GMBH (3)
Diefenbachgasse 35, 1150, Vienna, Austria
Tel.: (43) 189966
Emp.: 180
Healthcare Software Development Services
N.A.I.C.S.: 541511

AGFA HEALTHCARE GMBH (3)
Konrad-Zuse-Platz 1-3, 53227, Bonn, Germany
Tel.: (49) 228 26 68 000
Web Site: http://www.agfahealthcare.com
Healthcare Software Development Services
N.A.I.C.S.: 541511

Subsidiary (Domestic):

AGFA HEALTHCARE GERMANY GMBH (4)
Johanniterstrasse 30, 53113, Bonn, Germany
Tel.: (49) 2282668000
Healthcare Information Technology Consulting Services
N.A.I.C.S.: 541512

Subsidiary (Domestic):

Codices S.R.L. (3)
Via Gaetano Malasoma 24, 56121, Pisa, Italy
Tel.: (39) 050 31 60 136
Web Site: http://www.codices.com
Software Development Services
N.A.I.C.S.: 541511
Marcello Roselli (Mgr-Quality)

ConnexxaLife S.R.L. (3)
Viale Magna Grecia 197/O, 88100, Catanzaro, Italy
Tel.: (39) 0961 789472
Web Site: http://www.connexxa.it
Software Development Services
N.A.I.C.S.: 541511
Fabio Tinello (Project Mgr)

KerLife S.R.L. (3)
Via Giovanni Grillo 61 Scala A, Messina, Italy
Tel.: (39) 090 9412220
Software Development Services
N.A.I.C.S.: 541511
Nicola D'Angelo (Head-Admin & Reporting)

Mtt-Pro S.R.L. (3)
via Abetone 26, 38068, Rovereto, Italy
Tel.: (39) 0464 480750
Web Site: http://www.mttpro.it
Software Development Services
N.A.I.C.S.: 541511
Jonni Santi (CEO)

Subsidiary (Non-US):

NoemaLife Argentina Srl (3)
Avenida Corrientes 545 Piso 8vo frente, Buenos Aires, Argentina
Tel.: (54) 11 4706 2061
Software Development Services
N.A.I.C.S.: 541511

NoemaLife Chile (3)
La Dehesa 181 Of 713 Region Metropolitana, Lo Barnechea, Chile
Tel.: (56) 2 25 85 84 49
Software Development Services
N.A.I.C.S.: 541511

NoemaLife GmbH (3)
Alt-Moabit 94, Berlin, Germany
Tel.: (49) 30 3973830
Software Development Services
N.A.I.C.S.: 541511
K. D. Claudio Gast (Mng Dir)

NoemaLife MENA FZ-LLC (3)
Office No 124 Building No 05 First Floor Dubai Internet City, Dubai, United Arab Emirates
Tel.: (971) 4 368 8412
Software Development Services
N.A.I.C.S.: 541511

NoemaLife Mexico De RL De CV (3)
Av Gabriel Mancera No 1041 Colonia del

Valle Centro Delegacio, Benito Juarez, Mexico, 03100, Mexico
Tel.: (52) 33 3002 4155
Software Development Services
N.A.I.C.S.: 541511

NoemaLife UK Ltd (3)
2-3 St Johns Street, Stamford, Lincolnshire, United Kingdom
Tel.: (44) 787 524 3704
Software Development Services
N.A.I.C.S.: 541511
Robyn Tolley (Mng Dir)

Subsidiary (Domestic):

Praezision Life S.R.L. (3)
Via Brusa 6 Bodio Lomnago, Varese, 21020, Italy
Tel.: (39) 0332 948424
Web Site: http://www.praezision.it
Software Development Services
N.A.I.C.S.: 541511
Laura Radaelli (Project Mgr)

Service Life S.R.L. (3)
Via dellArtigianato 14, Cagliari, Italy
Tel.: (39) 070 2110083
Web Site: http://www.servicelife.net
Software Development Services
N.A.I.C.S.: 541511

Solinfo S.R.L. (3)
Via dell'Edilizia 59, 36100, Vicenza, Italy
Tel.: (39) 0444 962 966
Web Site: http://www.solinfo.it
Software Development Services
N.A.I.C.S.: 541511
Luca Andreacchio (Project Mgr-IT)

Diam International SAS (1)
40 Rue Pierre Curie, 78130, Les Mureaux, France
Tel.: (33) 1 3492 8360
Web Site: http://www.diaminternational.com
Mfr of Rubber
N.A.I.C.S.: 326299
Michel Vaissaire (Chm & CEO)

Subsidiary (US):

D3, LLC (2)
75 Marcus Dr, Melville, NY 11747
Tel.: (631) 454-6600
Web Site: http://www.diam-int.com
Sales Range: $150-199.9 Million
Point-of-Purchase Showcases & Shelving Systems Designer, Mfr & Distr
N.A.I.C.S.: 337215
Claire-Marie Schoenig (VP-Fin & Gen Mgr-Open Sell Div)

Subsidiary (Non-US):

DIAM AUSTRALIA PTY. LTD (2)
45 Merola Way, Campbellfield, 3061, VIC, Australia
Tel.: (61) 3 9357 5725
Emp.: 12
Cosmetics Distr
N.A.I.C.S.: 424210
David Watts (Mng Dir)

DIAM Deutschland GmbH (2)
Hanauer Landstrasse 182/Aufgang E, 60314, Frankfurt, Germany
Tel.: (49) 69 3487938 10
Web Site: http://www.diaminter.com
Emp.: 15
Cosmetics Distr
N.A.I.C.S.: 424210
Davide Russo (Mng Dir)

DIAM JAPAN K.K. (2)
Consolare 420 3-2-10 Honmachi, Shibuya-Ku, Tokyo, 151-0071, Japan
Tel.: (81) 3 6383 4067
Cosmetics Distr
N.A.I.C.S.: 424210

DIAM TUNISIA SARL (2)
ZI Sidi Abdelhamid, 4000, Sousse, Tunisia
Tel.: (216) 73 322 906
Cosmetics Distr
N.A.I.C.S.: 424210

DIAM TURKIYE (2)
Aydinli Mah 1 Nolu Cad No 27, Tuzla, Istanbul, 34953, Turkiye
Tel.: (90) 216 593 06 54
Cosmetics Distr

N.A.I.C.S.: 424210
Ibrahim Alagui Imlahi (Project Mgr)

DIAM UK LTD (2)
Jubilee Drive, Loughborough, LE11 5XS, Leicestershire, United Kingdom
Tel.: (44) 1509 211 111
Cosmetics Distr
N.A.I.C.S.: 424210
Clive Bagley (Dir-Technical)

Diam Display (China) Co., Ltd. (2)
299 Qinhe Road, Zhangpu, Kunshan, 215321, Nanjing, China
Tel.: (86) 512 5788 7299
Web Site: http://www.diaminternational.com
Sales Range: $75-99.9 Million
Point-of-Purchase Showcases & Shelving Systems Designer, Mfr & Distr
N.A.I.C.S.: 337215

Subsidiary (Domestic):

FieldFlex Europe SAS (2)
4 Rue Bernard Palissy, 78440, Gargenville, France
Tel.: (33) 892976384
Web Site: http://www.fieldflexservices.com
Sign & Point-of-Purchase Display Designer & Mfr
N.A.I.C.S.: 339950

Unit (Non-US):

FieldFlex Benelux (3)
Delften 23 Hal 85, Westmalle, 2390, Belgium
Tel.: (32) 3309 2550
Web Site: http://www.fieldflexbenelux.com
Sign & Point-of-Purchase Display Designer & Mfr
N.A.I.C.S.: 339950
Birgitte Oeyen (Gen Mgr)

Entreprise Boyer (1)
16 Rue De La Mairie, 77167, Poligny, France
Tel.: (33) 164785700
Web Site: http://www.entrepriseboyer.com
Nonresidential Construction Services
N.A.I.C.S.: 236220
Gilles Boyer (Pres & Dir-Publication)

Envision Pharma Inc. (1)
75 Kings Highway Cutoff, Fairfield, CT 06824
Tel.: (203) 480-0080
Web Site: http://www.envisionpharmagroup.com
Emp.: 1,000
Scientific Communications & Technology Services
N.A.I.C.S.: 541990
Loubna Bouarfa (Chm)

Subsidiary (Non-US):

Envision Pharma Limited (2)
Ground Floor 26-28 Hammersmith Grove, London, W6 7HA, United Kingdom
Tel.: (44) 208 834 3930
Web Site: http://www.envisionpharmagroup.com
Scientific Communications & Technology Services
N.A.I.C.S.: 541990

Florida Food Products, LLC (1)
2231 W CR 44, Eustis, FL 32726
Tel.: (352) 357-4141
Web Site: http://www.floridafood.com
Flavoring Syrup & Concentrate Mfr
N.A.I.C.S.: 311930
Pavan Soma (Dir-Res)

Holding Solina SA (1)
PA du Hindre III Rue des Ecotais 201, BP 29, 35310, Breal-sous-Monfort, Brittany, France
Tel.: (33) 2 99 60 07 60
Web Site: http://www.solina-group.com
Sales Range: $300-349.9 Million
Holding Company; Food Industry Ingredient Solutions Developer & Mfr
N.A.I.C.S.: 551112
Fanny Legave (Mgr-Mktg & Comm)

Subsidiary (Non-US):

SFK Food A/S (2)
Niels Bohrs Vej 55, Stilling, DK 8660, Skan-

Ardian SAS—(Continued)

derborg, Denmark
Tel.: (45) 86 29 11 00
Web Site: http://www.sfkfood.dk
Sales Range: $50-74.9 Million
Emp.: 120
Seasonings & Other Food Ingredients Mfr
N.A.I.C.S.: 311999
Inge Fabrin *(Mgr-Pur)*

Subsidiary (Domestic):

Solina France SASU   **(2)**
Parc d'Activite du Hindre III 201 rue des
Ecotais, 35310, Breal-sous-Monfort, France
Tel.: (33) 2 9960 0760
Web Site: http://www.solina-group.com
Food Industry Ingredient Solutions Devel-
oper & Mfr
N.A.I.C.S.: 311999
Laurent Weber *(CEO)*

London Luton Airport Group
Limited   **(1)**
Airport Way, Luton, LU2 9LY, Beds, United
Kingdom   **(49%)**
Tel.: (44) 1582405100
Web Site: http://www.london-luton.co.uk
Sales Range: $200-249.9 Million
Emp.: 600
Air Transportation Management Services
N.A.I.C.S.: 488190
Elliot Renton *(CFO)*

Subsidiary (Domestic):

London Luton Airport Operations
Limited   **(2)**
Airport Way, Luton, LU2 9LY, Bedfordshire,
United Kingdom
Tel.: (44) 1582405100
Web Site: http://www.london-luton.co.uk
Airport Operation Services
N.A.I.C.S.: 488119
Glyn Jones *(Mng Dir)*

Opodo Limited   **(1)**
26-28 Hammersmith Grove, Hammersmith
Emban, London, W6 7BA, United Kingdom
Tel.: (44) 8703525000
Web Site: http://www.opodo.com
Internet Travel Agency Services
N.A.I.C.S.: 561599
Caroline Noble *(Mng Dir)*

PHOTONIS Technologies S.A.S. **(1)**
Domaine de PELUS Axis Business Park Bat
5E, 18 Avenue de Pythagore, 33700, Meri-
gnac, France
Tel.: (33) 556164050
Web Site: http://www.photonis.com
Sales Range: $200-249.9 Million
Electro-Optic Components Mfr
N.A.I.C.S.: 333310
Goossen Boers *(CEO)*

Subsidiary (Domestic):

PHOTONIS France S.A.S.   **(2)**
Avenue Roger Roncier-Industrial Zone
Beauregard, PO Box 520, Avenue Ariane
Parc Cabera Sgd, 19100, Brive-la-Gaillarde,
Cedex, France
Tel.: (33) 555863700
Web Site: http://www.photonis.com
Electro-Optic High Precision Sensor Mfr
N.A.I.C.S.: 333310
Kees Brouwer *(COO)*

Subsidiary (Non-US):

PHOTONIS Netherlands B.V.   **(2)**
Dwazziewegen 2, 9301 ZR, Roden, Nether-
lands
Tel.: (31) 505018808
Web Site: http://www.photonis.com
Sales Range: $75-99.9 Million
Emp.: 370
Image Intensifiers Mfr & Distr
N.A.I.C.S.: 334513

Subsidiary (US):

PHOTONIS USA, Inc.   **(2)**
Sturbridge Business Pk, Sturbridge, MA
01566
Tel.: (508) 347-4000
Web Site: http://www.photonis.com
Electro-Optical Products Mfr
N.A.I.C.S.: 334511

Margaret Cooley *(Mgr-Intl Mktg)*

Subsidiary (Domestic):

PHOTONIS USA Pennsylvania,
Inc.   **(3)**
1000 New Holland Ave, Lancaster, PA
17601-5606
Tel.: (717) 295-6000
Web Site: http://www.photonisusa.com
Sales Range: $75-99.9 Million
Emp.: 50
Electron Tubes & Electro-Optical Devices
Mfr
N.A.I.C.S.: 334419
Robert Rutherford *(VP-Sls & Mktg)*

RIEMSER Pharma GmbH   **(1)**
An der Wiek 7, Greifswald, 17493, Ger-
many
Tel.: (49) 38351 76 0
Web Site: http://www.riemser.com
Sales Range: $125-149.9 Million
Emp.: 300
Pharmaceuticals Mfr
N.A.I.C.S.: 325412
Beatrice von Buchwaldt *(CFO)*

Revima Group SAS   **(1)**
1 Avenue du Latham 47, BP 1, Caudebec-
en-Caux, 76490, Rives-en-Seine, France
Tel.: (33) 2 3595 7000
Web Site: http://www.revima-group.com
Holding Company; Aircraft Maintenance,
Repair & Overhaul Services
N.A.I.C.S.: 551112
Olivier Legrand *(Pres)*

Subsidiary (Domestic):

Revima SASU   **(2)**
1 Avenue du Latham 47, BP 1, Caudebec-
en-Caux, 76490, Rives-en-Seine, France
Tel.: (33) 2 3595 7000
Web Site: http://www.revima-group.com
Aircraft Maintenance, Repair & Overhaul
Services
N.A.I.C.S.: 488190
Olivier Legrand *(Pres)*

STACI SAS   **(1)**
ZAC des Bethunes 36 av du Fond de Vaux,
F-95310, Paris, France   **(75%)**
Tel.: (33) 134402900
Web Site: http://www.staci.com
Sales Range: $200-249.9 Million
Advertising & Promotional Logistics Ser-
vices
N.A.I.C.S.: 541870
Thomas Mortier *(CEO)*

Saur SA   **(1)**
1 Ave Eugene Freyssinet, 78064, Saint-
Quentin-en-Yvelines, France   **(20%)**
Tel.: (33) 130602260
Web Site: http://www.saur.com
Sales Range: $1-4.9 Billion
Water Treatment & Sanitation Services
N.A.I.C.S.: 562219
Olivier Brousse *(Mng Dir & Pres)*

Subsidiary (Domestic):

Coved   **(2)**
1 rue Antoine Lavoisier, 78064, Guyancourt,
France
Tel.: (33) 130602260
Sales Range: $550-599.9 Million
Sanitation Management Services
N.A.I.C.S.: 562998
Brousse Olivier *(Mng Dir)*

Stereau SAS   **(2)**
1 rue Antoine Lavoisier, 78064, Saint-
Quentin-en-Yvelines, France
Tel.: (33) 130606491
Web Site: http://www.stereau.fr
Sales Range: $10-24.9 Million
Emp.: 50
Waste Treatment Services
N.A.I.C.S.: 562219
Caroline Catoire *(CFO)*

Study Group UK Limited   **(1)**
1 Billinton Way, Brighton, BN1 4LF, E Sus-
sex, United Kingdom
Tel.: (44) 1273339339
Web Site: http://www.studygroup.com
Sales Range: $25-49.9 Million
Emp.: 200

University Preparation & Traditional Sec-
ondary Education Programs
N.A.I.C.S.: 611710
James Pitman *(Mng Dir)*

Syclef Holding SAS   **(1)**
1 av Claude Rey, 13790, Rousset, France
Tel.: (33) 484492614
Web Site: http://www.syclef.fr
Emp.: 230
Refrigeration Systems Installation & Mainte-
nance Services
N.A.I.C.S.: 238220
Herve Loheac *(Chm)*

Subsidiary (Domestic):

GEA Refrigeration France SAS **(2)**
Geneglace Ice Technology Centre 9 Rue
des Orfevres, Les Sorinieres, 44840,
France
Tel.: (33) 2 51 19 10 51
Web Site: http://www.matal.fr
Air Conditioning Machinery Mfr
N.A.I.C.S.: 333415
Bellaudelle Pascal *(Mgr-Pur)*

The RDI Group   **(1)**
1025 W Thorndale Ave, Itasca, IL 60143
Tel.: (630) 773-2500
Web Site: http://www.therdigroup.com
Liquid Automation Machinery & Equipment
Mfr
N.A.I.C.S.: 333998
Curtis Maas *(Chm & CEO)*

Trigo SAS   **(1)**
4 Avenue Pablo Picasso CS 70134, 92024,
Nanterre, Cedex, France
Tel.: (33) 141440585
Web Site: http://www.trigo-group.com
Emp.: 8,000
Quality Control Outsourcing Services
N.A.I.C.S.: 561499
Matthieu Rambaud *(CEO)*

Subsidiary (US):

Supplier Management Solutions,
Inc.   **(2)**
27476 Via Industria, Temecula, CA 92590
Tel.: (951) 676-1100
Web Site: http://www.smssolutionsinc.com
Professional, Scientific & Technical Services
N.A.I.C.S.: 541990

Supply Chain Services International,
Inc   **(2)**
8515 N University St, Peoria, IL
61615   **(100%)**
Tel.: (877) 345-5651
Web Site: https://campaign.trigo-group.com
Logistics, Quality Assurance & Technical
Services to Suppliers & OEMs Worldwide
N.A.I.C.S.: 541614

Weber Automotive GmbH   **(1)**
Otto Lilienthal Strasse 5, 88677, Markdorf,
Germany
Tel.: (49) 7544 9630
Web Site: http://www.weber-automotive.com
Motor Vehicle Parts Mfr
N.A.I.C.S.: 336390
Udo Hahnel *(Head-Sls-Europe)*

d&b audiotechnik GmbH   **(1)**
Eugen-Adolff-Str 134, 71522, Backnang,
Germany
Tel.: (49) 719196690
Web Site: http://www.dbaudio.com
Audio Equipment Mfr
N.A.I.C.S.: 334310
Gerhard Mayr *(Co-Mng Dir)*

ARDIDEN LIMITED

Level 1 45 Ventnor Avenue, West
Perth, 6005, WA, Australia
Tel.: (61) 861845938   **AU**
Web Site:
   https://www.ardiden.com.au
ADV—(ASX)
Rev.: $394,382
Assets: $21,236,812
Liabilities: $77,642
Net Worth: $21,159,171
Earnings: ($6,806,932)
Fiscal Year-end: 06/30/24
Other Metal Ore Mining

N.A.I.C.S.: 212290
Tara Robson *(CFO & Sec)*

ARDMORE CONSTRUCTION LIMITED

Byrne House Jeffreys Road Brims-
down, Enfield, EN3 7UB, Middlesex,
United Kingdom
Tel.: (44) 20 8344 0300
Web Site:
   http://www.ardmoregroup.co.uk
Year Founded: 1974
Sales Range: $450-499.9 Million
Emp.: 280
Construction Engineering Services
N.A.I.C.S.: 541330
Alan Edgar *(Dir-Construction)*

ARDMORE SHIPPING CORPO-RATION

69 Pitts Bay Road Ground Floor,
Pembroke, HM08, Bermuda
Tel.: (441) 4057800   **MH**
Web Site:
   https://www.ardmoreshipping.com
Year Founded: 2010
ASC—(NYSE)
Rev.: $395,978,000
Assets: $690,951,000
Liabilities: $153,550,000
Net Worth: $537,401,000
Earnings: $116,808,000
Emp.: 834
Fiscal Year-end: 12/31/23
Petroleum Products & Chemical
Transportation Services
N.A.I.C.S.: 483111
Anthony Gurnee *(Pres & CEO)*

Subsidiaries:

Anglo Ardmore Ship Management
Limited   **(1)**
17/F Kingston International Centre 19 Wang
Chiu Road Kowloon Bay, Kowloon, China
(Hong Kong)
Tel.: (852) 39407000
Shipping Transportation Services
N.A.I.C.S.: 926120

Ardmore Shipping (Asia) Pte
Limited   **(1)**
3 Anson Road 10-01 - Springleaf Tower,
Singapore, 079900, Singapore
Tel.: (65) 63299400
Shipping Transportation Services
N.A.I.C.S.: 926120

Ardmore Shipping Services (Ireland)
Limited   **(1)**
Unit 1102 One Albert Quay, Cork, T12
X8N6, Ireland
Tel.: (353) 212409500
Engineering Consulting Services
N.A.I.C.S.: 541330

ARDO N.V.

Wezestraat 61, 8850, Ardooie, Bel-
gium
Tel.: (32) 51310621
Web Site: http://www.ardo.com
Year Founded: 1973
Sales Range: $800-899.9 Million
Emp.: 3,000
Frozen Vegetables Producer & Whslr
N.A.I.C.S.: 445230
Gan Haspeslagh *(CEO)*

Subsidiaries:

ARDO Mochov s.r.o.   **(1)**
Sezemicka 2757/2, Horni Pocemice, 193
00, Prague, Czech Republic
Tel.: (420) 326 597 045
Frozen Vegetable & Fruit Whslr
N.A.I.C.S.: 424420

Ardo A/B   **(1)**
Enhagsvagen 7, 187 40, Taby, Sweden
Tel.: (46) 8 768 1550
Frozen Vegetable & Fruit Mfr & Distr
N.A.I.C.S.: 311411

Ardo A/S (1)
Slipshavnsvej 2, 5800, Nyborg, Denmark
Tel.: (45) 65310310
Sales Range: $25-49.9 Million
Emp.: 50
Frozen Vegetable & Fruit Whslr
N.A.I.C.S.: 424420
AnneMette Thomsen (Sec)

Ardo Austria Frost GmbH (1)
Marchfelder Strasse 2, Gross-Enzersdorf,
2301, Austria
Tel.: (43) 2249 3535 0
Web Site: http://www.ardo.com
Sales Range: $50-74.9 Million
Emp.: 200
Frozen Vegetable & Fruit Mfr & Distr
N.A.I.C.S.: 311411
Roman Gabriel (Dir-Sls-Retail)

Ardo B.V. (1)
Industrieweg 9-11, Zundert, 4880, Nether-
lands
Tel.: (31) 765 999999
Web Site: http://www.ardo.com
Emp.: 150
Frozen Vegetable & Fruit Mfr & Distr
N.A.I.C.S.: 311411
Paul Wortel (Mgr-Investments)

Ardo GmbH (1)
Gothaer Strasse 2, Ratingen, 40880, Ger-
many
Tel.: (49) 2102 20280
Sales Range: $25-49.9 Million
Emp.: 20
Frozen Vegetable & Fruit Whslr
N.A.I.C.S.: 424420
Jan Haspeslagh (Mgr)

Ardo Italia SRL (1)
Via PO 134 A, 43100, Parma, Italy
Tel.: (39) 0521 929 912
Sales Range: $25-49.9 Million
Emp.: 50
Frozen Vegetable & Fruit Mfr & Distr
N.A.I.C.S.: 311411

Ardo SA (1)
Route de Carhaix, 56110, Gourin, France
Tel.: (33) 297 234876
Web Site: http://www.ardo.com.pl
Frozen Vegetable & Fruit Mfr & Distr
N.A.I.C.S.: 311411

Ardo Shangai Marketing Co. Ltd (1)
Zhao Jia Bang Lu 680 Room 906, 200031,
Shanghai, China
Tel.: (86) 21 6473 8068
Frozen Vegetable & Fruit Mfr & Distr
N.A.I.C.S.: 311411

Ardo Sp.Z.o.o. (1)
Ul Chlopickiego 17/19, 04-314, Warsaw,
Poland
Tel.: (48) 510 080 311
Web Site: http://www.ardo.com
Sales Range: $50-74.9 Million
Emp.: 1
Frozen Vegetable & Fruit Whslr
N.A.I.C.S.: 424420
Krzysztof Stanksiewicz (Mgr)

Ardo UK Ltd. (1)
Ashford Road, Charing, TN27 0DF, United
Kingdom
Tel.: (44) 1233 714714
Web Site: http://www.ardouk.com
Sales Range: $75-99.9 Million
Emp.: 130
Frozen Vegetable & Fruit Whslr
N.A.I.C.S.: 424420
Amanda Waugh (Bus Mgr-Foodservice Sec-
tor)

Ardofoods Ireland Ltd. (1)
Leopardstown Business Centre Ballyogan
Avenue 5, Dublin, Ireland
Tel.: (353) 12 957355
Emp.: 3
Frozen Vegetable & Fruit Whslr
N.A.I.C.S.: 424420
Billy Noctor (Gen Mgr)

Ardovries Espana S.A. (1)
Avenida Ramon Y Cajal 4, Dos Hermanas,
41700, Seville, Spain
Tel.: (34) 955 66 06 48
Frozen Vegetable & Fruit Mfr & Distr
N.A.I.C.S.: 311411

ARDOUR WORLD LIMITED
York House 8th Floor Empire Way,
Wembley, HA9 0PA, Middlesex,
United Kingdom
Tel.: (44) 2087828744
Web Site:
   http://www.ardourworld.com
Year Founded: 2003
Sales Range: $100-124.9 Million
Emp.: 10
Metal Product Whslr
N.A.I.C.S.: 423510

Subsidiaries:

Global Ardour Recycling Limited (1)
Longridge Rd,, Preston, PR2 5BX, United
Kingdom
Tel.: (44) 1772654321
Web Site: https://globalardour.co.uk
Waste Management Services
N.A.I.C.S.: 562998

ARDOVA PLC.
Plot 89A Ajose Adeogun Street, Victo-
ria Island, Lagos, Nigeria
Tel.: (234) 012784168
Web Site: http://www.ardovaplc.com
Year Founded: 1964
ARDOVA—(NIGE)
Rev.: $525,758,690
Assets: $331,156,051
Liabilities: $286,514,922
Net Worth: $44,641,129
Earnings: ($10,044,144)
Emp.: 169
Fiscal Year-end: 12/31/21
Petroleum Product Mfr
N.A.I.C.S.: 324199
Samuel Eze (Head-PMS & Retail
Transformation)

Subsidiaries:

Ap Renewables Ltd. (1)
175 Longwood Road South Suite B21,
Hamilton, L8P 0A1, ON, Canada
Web Site: https://aprenewables.com
Renewable Energy Generation Services
N.A.I.C.S.: 221118

ARDSHINBANK CJSC
13 and 13 Grigor Lusavorich, 0015,
Yerevan, Armenia
Tel.: (374) 10 59 0404   AM
Web Site: http://www.ardshinbank.am
Year Founded: 2003
Rev.: $117,939,388
Assets: $1,485,544,259
Liabilities: $1,325,805,451
Net Worth: $159,738,809
Earnings: $19,778,383
Fiscal Year-end: 12/31/19
Commericial Banking
N.A.I.C.S.: 522110
Artak K. Ananyan (Chm-Mgmt Bd)

ARE HOLDINGS, INC.
Nissay Sannomiya Building 16F
4-4-17 Kano-cho, Chuo-ku, Kobe,
650-0001, Hyogo, Japan
Tel.: (81) 783335633
Web Site:
   https://www.asahiholdings.com
5857—(TKS)
Rev.: $2,130,092,330
Assets: $2,101,966,780
Liabilities: $1,265,960,420
Net Worth: $836,006,360
Earnings: $161,878,900
Fiscal Year-end: 03/31/24
Metal Recycle & Environmental Con-
servation
N.A.I.C.S.: 331410
Tomoya Higashiura (Pres & CEO)

Subsidiaries:

Asahi G&S Sdn. Bhd. (1)
Plot 65 Lintang Bayan Lepas 6 Phase IV
Non FTZ, Bayan Lepas, 11900, Penang,

Pulau Pinang, Malaysia
Tel.: (60) 46461292
Web Site: http://www.asahiholdings.com
Sales Range: $50-74.9 Million
Emp.: 5
Metal Refining Services
N.A.I.C.S.: 423810

Asahi Pretec Corporation (1)
11F Sapir Tower 1-7-12 Marunouchi,
Chiyoda-ku, Tokyo, 100-0005, Hyogo, Ja-
pan
Tel.: (81) 362701820
Web Site: https://www.asahipretec.com
Metal Refining Services
N.A.I.C.S.: 423810

Asahi Pretec Korea Co., Ltd. (1)
710 186 Gonghang-daero, Gangnam-Gu,
Seoul, 135-973, Korea (South)
Tel.: (82) 16612845
Sales Range: $50-74.9 Million
Emp.: 8
Metal Refining Services
N.A.I.C.S.: 423810

Asahi Refining Canada Ltd. (1)
130 Glidden Road, Brampton, L6W 3M8,
ON, Canada
Tel.: (905) 453-6120
Gold Mining Services
N.A.I.C.S.: 212220

Asahi Refining Florida, LLC (1)
Tel.: (305) 685-8505
Gold & Silver Refining & Production Fabri-
cation
N.A.I.C.S.: 331410

Subsidiary (Domestic):

Republic Metals Corp. (2)
12900 NW 38th Ave, Miami, FL 33054
Tel.: (305) 685-8505
Web Site:
   http://www.republicmetalscorp.com
Sales Range: $1-9.9 Million
Emp.: 146
Primary Smelting & Refining of Nonferrous
Metal (except Copper & Aluminum)
N.A.I.C.S.: 331410
David Comite (CFO)

Asahi Refining USA Inc. (1)
4601 W 2100 S, Salt Lake City, UT 84120
Tel.: (801) 972-6466
Gold Mining Services
N.A.I.C.S.: 212220

Fuji Rozai Co., Ltd. (1)
8th Floor Nishi-Kamata NS Bldg 6-36-11
Nishi-Kamata, Ota-ku, Tokyo, 144-0051,
Japan
Tel.: (81) 337358111
Machine Tools Mfr
N.A.I.C.S.: 333515

INTER CENTRAL, INC. (1)
MFPR Nihonbashi Honcho Building 1F
3-7-2 Nihonbashi Honcho, Chuo-ku, Tokyo,
103-0023, Japan
Tel.: (81) 366616381
Web Site: https://www.i-central.co.jp
Information Technology Services
N.A.I.C.S.: 541511

JW Glass Recycling Co., Ltd. (1)
4-3-2 Shin-kiba, Koto-ku, Tokyo, 136-0082,
Japan
Tel.: (81) 335216303
Machine Tools Mfr
N.A.I.C.S.: 333515

AREA QUEST INC.
7F Shinjuku Island Tower 6-5-1 Nishi
Shinjuku, Shinjuku-ku, Tokyo, 163-
1307, Japan
Tel.: (81) 359083301
Web Site: https://www.area-
quest.com
Year Founded: 2000
8912—(TKS)
Rev.: $14,486,380
Assets: $27,032,120
Liabilities: $16,937,060
Net Worth: $10,095,060
Earnings: $833,480
Emp.: 38

Fiscal Year-end: 06/30/24
Real Estate Manangement Services
N.A.I.C.S.: 531390
Kiyohara Masato (Pres)

AREALINK CO. LTD.
Floor 20 North Wing Akihabara UDX
Bldg14 1 Sotokanda 4 chome,
Chiyoda-ku, Tokyo, 101-0021, Japan
Tel.: (81) 355779222
Web Site: https://www.arealink.co.jp
8914—(TKS)
Sales Range: $100-124.9 Million
Emp.: 107
Real Estate Services
N.A.I.C.S.: 531110
Kazuki Kurino (Gen Mgr-Mktg Dept &
Dir-Mktg Div)

ARECOR THERAPEUTICS PLC
Chesterford Research Park, Little
Chesterford, Saffron Walden, CB10
1XL, United Kingdom
Tel.: (44) 1223426060   UK
Web Site: https://www.arecor.com
Year Founded: 2021
AREC—(AIM)
Rev.: $2,984,045
Assets: $27,027,777
Liabilities: $5,352,158
Net Worth: $21,675,619
Earnings: ($11,499,068)
Emp.: 37
Fiscal Year-end: 12/31/22
Biotechnology Research & Develop-
ment Services
N.A.I.C.S.: 541714

Subsidiaries:

Tetris Pharma Ltd. (1)
2nd Floor 79 - 81 High Street, Marlow, SL7
1AB, Buckinghamshire, United Kingdom
Tel.: (44) 1628337579
Web Site: https://tetrispharma.com
Pharmaceutical Mfr & Distr
N.A.I.C.S.: 325412

**AREEYA PROPERTY PUBLIC
COMPANY LIMITED**
999 Praditmanutham Road Saphan-
song, Wangthonglang, Bangkok,
10310, Thailand
Tel.: (66) 27989999
Web Site:
   https://investor.areeya.co.th
Year Founded: 2000
A—(THA)
Rev.: $77,040,840
Assets: $399,620,023
Liabilities: $315,367,698
Net Worth: $84,252,325
Earnings: ($10,926,206)
Emp.: 398
Fiscal Year-end: 12/31/23
Residential Building Construction
Services
N.A.I.C.S.: 236117
Wisit Laohapoonrungsee (Chm &
CEO)

Subsidiaries:

One Up Co., Ltd. (1)
999 Praditmanutham Rd Saphansong,
Wangthonglang, Bangkok, Thailand
Tel.: (66) 27989999
Web Site: http://www.oneup.co.th
Construction Management Services
N.A.I.C.S.: 236116
Dennis Ong Boon Seong (CEO)

**AREF THALASSA SOCIMI,
S.A.U.**
Paseo de la Castellana 93 6th floor,
28046, Madrid, Spain   ES
Web Site:
   https://www.arefthalassasocimi.com
Year Founded: 2022

AREF THALASSA SOCIMI, S.A.U.

Aref Thalassa SOCIMI, S.A.U.—(Continued)

MLARE—(EUR)
Rev.: $7,596,865
Assets: $174,838,282
Liabilities: $133,830,445
Net Worth: $41,007,838
Earnings: ($11,365,493)
Fiscal Year-end: 12/31/23
Real Estate Investment Services
N.A.I.C.S.: 531190
German Fernandez *(Co-Chm)*

AREIT, INC.

28F Tower One and Exchange Plaza
Ayala Triangle Ayala Avenue, Makati,
1226, Philippines
Tel.: (63) 79083296 PH
Web Site: https://www.areit.com.ph
Year Founded: 2006
AREIT—(PHI)
Rev.: $68,982,447
Assets: $1,175,273,367
Liabilities: $158,411,495
Net Worth: $1,016,861,872
Earnings: $50,611,954
Emp.: 13
Fiscal Year-end: 12/31/21
Real Estate Investment Services
N.A.I.C.S.: 531190
Jose Emmanuel H. Jalandoni *(Chm)*

ARELIS SAS

ZI de Marville, 55600, Marville,
France
Tel.: (33) 3 29 88 10 55
Web Site: http://www.arelis.com
Year Founded: 1979
Sales Range: $75-99.9 Million
Emp.: 500
Radio & Television Transmitters Mfr
N.A.I.C.S.: 334220

Subsidiaries:

Thomson Broadcast SAS **(1)**
1 Rue de l'Hautil, BP 150, 78702, Conflans-
Sainte-Honorine, Cedex, France **(100%)**
Tel.: (33) 134903100
Web Site: http://www.thomson-
broadcast.com
Sales Range: $150-199.9 Million
Emp.: 80
Radio & Television Transmission Equipment
Mfr
N.A.I.C.S.: 334220
Maud Vazquez *(Mgr-Comm)*

AREM PACIFIC CORP.

271 Blackburn Road, Mount Waver-
ley, 3149, VIC, Australia
Tel.: (61) 393955324 DE
Web Site: http://www.arempac.com
Year Founded: 1998
ARPC—(OTCIQ)
Rev.: $343,479
Assets: $259,811
Liabilities: $304,903
Net Worth: ($45,092)
Earnings: ($53,666)
Emp.: 1
Fiscal Year-end: 06/30/23
Asset Management Services
N.A.I.C.S.: 523940
Thomas Tang *(Pres)*

ARENA BILGISAYAR SANAYI VE TICARET A.S.

Merkez Mahallesi Gokturk Caddesi
No 4 Gokturk Eyup, 34077, Istanbul,
Turkiye
Tel.: (90) 2123646464
Web Site: http://www.arena.com.tr
Year Founded: 1991
ARENA—(IST)
Rev.: $1,051,126,000
Assets: $382,839,000
Liabilities: $324,774,000
Net Worth: $58,065,000
Earnings: $8,682,000
Emp.: 409
Fiscal Year-end: 12/31/22
Computer Peripheral Whslr
N.A.I.C.S.: 423430
Raj Shankar *(Chm)*

Subsidiaries:

Adeo Bilisim Danismanlik I lizmetleri
San. Ve Tic, A.S. **(1)**
Fetih Mah Tahrali Sk Tahrali Sitesi Ka-
vakyeli Plaza C Blok D16/17, Istanbul, Tur-
kiye
Tel.: (90) 216 472 35 35
Web Site: http://adeo.com.tr
Information Technology Consulting Services
N.A.I.C.S.: 541512

ARENA FAKTORING A.S.

Eski Buyukdere Caddesi Iz Plaza Giz
No 9 Kat 11, Maslak, 34398, Istanbul,
Turkiye
Tel.: (90) 2129600505
Web Site:
http://www.arenafaktoring.com.tr
ARNFK—(IST)
Sales Range: Less than $1 Million
Financial Management Services
N.A.I.C.S.: 551112

ARENA HOLDING S.P.A.

Piazza Marconi 25, 00144, Rome,
Italy
Tel.: (39) 065919341
Web Site: http://www.arenaholding.it
Holding Company; Food Products
N.A.I.C.S.: 551112
Dante Di Dario *(Chm)*

Subsidiaries:

Arena Agroindustrie Alimentari
SpA **(1)**
Localita Monteverde, 86021, Bojano, Cam-
pobasso, Italy
Tel.: (39) 08747501
Frozen Food Mfr
N.A.I.C.S.: 311710

Arena Holding S.p.A. - Cremeria del
Lattaito Plant **(1)**
Via Orazio 51, San Paolo di Civitate,
71016, Foggia, Italy
Tel.: (39) 0882551281
Ice Cream Mfr
N.A.I.C.S.: 311520

Arena Holding S.p.A. - Garbini
Plant **(1)**
Via Carrozze Vaccili 13, Castelplanio,
60032, Ancona, Italy
Tel.: (39) 07318101
Livestock Breeding Services
N.A.I.C.S.: 115210

Arena Holding S.p.A. - La Faraona
Plant **(1)**
Via Rotta Vecchia 4, Montagnana, 35044,
Padua, Italy
Tel.: (39) 0429806211
Meat Mfr
N.A.I.C.S.: 311615

Arena Holding S.p.A. - Mare Pronto
Plant **(1)**
Contrada S Leonardo 25, Grottammare,
63013, Ascoli Piceno, Italy
Tel.: (39) 0735735798
Frozen Food Mfr
N.A.I.C.S.: 311710

Arena Holding S.p.A. - Marsili
Plant **(1)**
Via Santissima Trinita 17 Porte di Tram-
bileno, 38068, Rovereto, Trentino, Italy
Tel.: (39) 0464484700
Salted Meat Mfr
N.A.I.C.S.: 311612

Arena Holding S.p.A. - Naturicchi
Plant **(1)**
Via P Neruda 87, Gatteo, 47030, Forli, Italy
Tel.: (39) 0541816811
Livestock Breeding Services
N.A.I.C.S.: 115210

Arena Holding S.p.A. - Tu in Cucina
Plant **(1)**
Localita rivolta del Re Z Ind Ie A, 86039,
Termoli, Campobasso, Italy
Tel.: (39) 0875755003
Pasta Mfr
N.A.I.C.S.: 311991

Avicola Molisana Srl **(1)**
Localita Montevordo, Bojano, 3000, Naploo,
Italy
Tel.: (39) 08747501
Broilers & Meat Type Chicken Production
N.A.I.C.S.: 112320

ARENA HOSPITALITY GROUP D.D.

Smareglina Ulica 3, 52100, Pula,
Croatia
Tel.: (385) 52223811
Web Site:
https://www.arenahospitality.com
ARNT—(ZAG)
Rev.: $139,637,929
Assets: $519,144,497
Liabilities: $283,536,814
Net Worth: $235,607,683
Earnings: $4,033,558
Emp.: 1,100
Fiscal Year-end: 12/31/23
Portfolio Management & Investment
Advice
N.A.I.C.S.: 523940
Reuel Slonim *(Pres)*

ARENA INVESTMENT MANAGEMENT LIMITED

71 Flinders Lane, Melbourne, 3000,
VIC, Australia
Tel.: (61) 3 9093 9000 AU
Web Site:
http://www.arenainvest.com.au
Investment Fund Management Ser-
vices
N.A.I.C.S.: 523940
Robert de Vos *(Gen Mgr-Property)*

Subsidiaries:

Arena REIT **(1)**
Level 5 41 Exhibition Street, Melbourne,
3000, VIC, Australia
Tel.: (61) 390939000
Web Site: http://www.arena.com.au
Rev.: $65,555,555
Assets: $1,083,776,705
Liabilities: $273,138,354
Net Worth: $810,638,351
Earnings: $38,400,107
Fiscal Year-end: 06/30/2024
Real Estate Investment Trust
N.A.I.C.S.: 525990
Gareth Winter *(CFO & Sec)*

ARENA.PL SA

Ul Marszalkowska 111, 00-102, War-
saw, Poland
Tel.: (48) 616285162
Web Site:
https://www.hipower.energy
Year Founded: 2007
8G6—(DEU)
Online Shopping Services
N.A.I.C.S.: 425120
Bartosz Berlinski *(VP)*

ARENDALS FOSSEKOMPANI ASA

Langbryggen 9, 4841, Arendal, Nor-
way
Tel.: (47) 37234400
0DHA—(LSE)
Rev.: $423,659,339
Assets: $724,225,199
Liabilities: $374,664,234
Net Worth: $349,560,964
Earnings: ($3,003,787)
Emp.: 2,301
Fiscal Year-end: 12/31/22
Electricity Generation & Distr

N.A.I.C.S.: 221122
Gunnar Line *(Mgr-Fin)*

Subsidiaries:

Arendal Lufthavn Gullknapp AS **(1)**
Arendal lufthavn Gullknapp Gullknappveien
410, PO Box 280, Froland, 4820, Arendal,
Norway
Tel.: (47) 91169727
Web Site: https://www.gullknapp.no
Airport Operator
N.A.I.C.S.: 488119

Cogen Energia Espana S.L **(1)**
Colquide 6 Ed Prisma Portal 11 A, Las Ro-
zas, 28230, Madrid, Spain
Tel.: (34) 916347584
Web Site: https://cogen-energia.com
Power Plant Construction Services
N.A.I.C.S.: 237990
Antonio Quilez *(Dir Gen)*

EFD Inducao Brasil Ltd. **(1)**
Rua Eng Carlos Alberto Calandrino 400 Jd
Panamericano Cond Empresarial, Soro-
caba, 18087-161, SP, Brazil
Tel.: (55) 1534124561
Induction Heating Product Mfr
N.A.I.C.S.: 333994

EFD Induction AS **(1)**
Bolevegen 10, N-3724, Skien, Norway
Tel.: (47) 35506000
Web Site: https://www.efd-induction.com
Heating Equipment Mfr
N.A.I.C.S.: 333414
Truls Larsen *(Founder)*

Subsidiary (Non-US):

EFD Induction (Shanghai) Co.
Ltd. **(2)**
Bldg H No 1688 Zhuan Xing Road Xin
Zhuang Industrial Park, Shanghai, 201 108,
China
Tel.: (86) 2154420227
Heating Equipment Mfr333414
N.A.I.C.S.: 333414
Qin Song *(Mgr)*

EFD Induction AB **(2)**
Kokillgatan 3, Box 200 47, 720 20, Vast-
eras, Sweden
Tel.: (46) 21 300010
Heating Equipment Mfr
N.A.I.C.S.: 333414

EFD Induction Co. Ltd. **(2)**
3792/1-2 Soi Wat Dansamrong Moo 3, Am-
phur Muangsamutprakarn, Samut Prakan,
10270, Thailand
Tel.: (66) 2757 4128
Heating Equipment Mfr
N.A.I.C.S.: 333414
Wasawat Nuntipattanawong *(Mgr)*

EFD Induction Ges.m.b.H **(2)**
Perfektastrasse 87 Top 3, A-1230, Vienna,
Austria
Tel.: (43) 6641617345
Heating Equipment Mfr
N.A.I.C.S.: 333414
Matthias Gruber *(Mgr)*

EFD Induction GmbH **(2)**
Lehener Strasse 91, Postfach 426,
D-79106, Freiburg, Germany
Tel.: (49) 76188510
Heating Equipment Mfr
N.A.I.C.S.: 333414
Henk de Lange *(Mgr)*

Subsidiary (US):

EFD Induction Inc. **(2)**
31511 Dequindre Rd, Madison Heights, MI
48071
Tel.: (248) 658-0700
Heating Equipment Mfr
N.A.I.C.S.: 333414
Randy Borden *(Mgr)*

Subsidiary (Non-US):

EFD Induction K.K. **(2)**
ERVIC Yokohama 11th floor Yoshidamachi,
Naka-ku, Yokohama, 231-0041, Kanagawa,
Japan
Tel.: (81) 452315011
Heating Equipment Mfr

N.A.I.C.S.: 333414
Tetsuro Yanagawa *(Mgr)*

EFD Induction Ltd. (2)
Well Lane Rear Door Unit 1 units 1 2
Wednesfield Way Ind, Estate Well Lane
Wednesfield, Wolverhampton, WV11 1XP,
United Kingdom
Tel.: (44) 1902308800
Web Site: https://www.efdinduction.co.uk
Heating Equipment Mfr
N.A.I.C.S.: 333414
Andy Hall *(Mgr)*

EFD Induction Ltda. (2)
Evandro Nishimuni Rua Antonio Carlos de
Barros Bruni 136, 18052-017, Sorocaba,
Brazil
Tel.: (55) 15 3031 4562
Heating Equipment Mfr
N.A.I.C.S.: 333414
Evandro Nishimuni *(Mgr)*

EFD Induction Pvt. Ltd. (2)
Plot 16 C&D KIADB Ind Area Attibele, Bengaluru, 562 107, India
Tel.: (91) 80 2 7820 404
Heating Equipment Mfr
N.A.I.C.S.: 333414
Hubert Reilard *(Mgr)*

EFD Induction S.A (2)
20 avenue de Grenoble, BP 30, F-38171,
Seyssinet-Pariset, Cedex, France
Tel.: (33) 476493250
Heating Equipment Mfr
N.A.I.C.S.: 333414

EFD Induction SL (2)
Avenida Penota 7 Entrada por Ortuno de
Alango 15, 48920, Portugalete, Spain
Tel.: (34) 944720936
Heating Equipment Mfr
N.A.I.C.S.: 333414
Johan I. Larsen *(Mgr)*

EFD Induction Sp. z o.o (2)
Gen J Sowinskiego 3, 44-101, Gliwice, Poland
Tel.: (48) 322376226
Heating Equipment Mfr
N.A.I.C.S.: 333414

EFD Induction Srl (2)
Via Della Birona 30/32, I-20900, Monza,
MB, Italy
Tel.: (39) 039323320
Heating Equipment Mfr
N.A.I.C.S.: 333414
Johan I. Larsen *(Mgr)*

EFD Induction Group AS (1)
Bolevegen 4B, 3724, Skien, Norway
Tel.: (47) 35506000
Hydroelectric Power Generation Services
N.A.I.C.S.: 221111

EFD Induction Marcoussis S.A. (1)
11 ZI du Fond des Pres, 91460, Paris,
France
Tel.: (33) 169014664
Induction Heating Product Mfr
N.A.I.C.S.: 333994

Factlines AS (1)
Fred Olsens Gate 1, 0152, Oslo, Norway
Tel.: (47) 48203000
Web Site: https://factlines.com
Software Development Services
N.A.I.C.S.: 541511

Glamox Far East Pte Ltd. (1)
53 Ubi Avenue 3 02-01, Singapore, 408863,
Singapore
Tel.: (65) 6748 1977
Emp.: 14
Lighting Product Distr
N.A.I.C.S.: 423610
Lim Gek Yong *(Mgr-Fin & Admin)*

Kelin Kraft AS (1)
Stokkamyrv 18A, 4313, Sandnes, Norway
Tel.: (47) 51936591
Web Site: http://www.kelinkraft.com
Emp.: 8
Accounting & Invoicing Services
N.A.I.C.S.: 541219

Kontali Analyse AS (1)
Nordmorsveien 54, 6517, Kristiansund, Norway

Tel.: (47) 71683300
Web Site: https://www.kontali.no
Seafood Distr
N.A.I.C.S.: 424460
Thomas Aas *(Mng Dir)*

Markedskraft ASA (1)
Langbryggen 9, PO Box 62, Arendal, 4801,
Norway
Tel.: (47) 37 00 97 00
Web Site: http://www.markedskraft.com
Electric Power Distribution Services
N.A.I.C.S.: 221122
Anne Fredriksen *(Portfolio Mgr)*

Subsidiary (Non-US):

Powel AG (2)
Peter Merian-Strasse 90, 4052, Basel, Switzerland
Tel.: (41) 61 270 84 40
Web Site: http://www.powel.ch
Software Development Services
N.A.I.C.S.: 541511
Alfred Hofmann *(Bus Mgr-Projects & Svcs)*

NSSL Global Ltd (1)
6 Wells Place Gatton Park Business Centre, Redhill, RH1 3DR, Surrey, United Kingdom
Tel.: (44) 1737648800
Web Site: https://www.nsslglobal.com
Satellite Communication Services
N.A.I.C.S.: 517410
Sally-Anne Ray *(CEO-Grp)*

NSSLGlobal APS. (1)
Vestre Gade 6, 2605, Brondby, Denmark
Tel.: (45) 36703603
Satellite Telecommunication Services
N.A.I.C.S.: 517410

NSSLGlobal GmbH (1)
Hanskampring 4, 22885, Barsbuttel, Germany
Tel.: (49) 40682770
Information Technology Services
N.A.I.C.S.: 541519

NSSLGlobal LLC (1)
1000 Riverbend Dr Ste A, Saint Rose, LA
70087
Tel.: (504) 800-6290
Satellite Telecommunication Services
N.A.I.C.S.: 517410

NSSLGlobal PTE Ltd. (1)
11 Lorong 3 Toa Payoh Block B 03-25
Jackson Square, Singapore, 319579, Singapore
Tel.: (65) 63583991
Satellite Telecommunication Services
N.A.I.C.S.: 517410

NSSLGlobal Polska SP. Z.o.o. (1)
ul Klaudyny 21/9, 901-684, Warsaw, Poland
Tel.: (48) 224047864
Satellite Telecommunication Services
N.A.I.C.S.: 517410

NSSLGlobal Technologies AS (1)
Rolfsbuktveien 4B, 1364, Fornebu, Norway
Tel.: (47) 67535337
Satellite Telecommunication Services
N.A.I.C.S.: 517410

Powel ASA (1)
Klaebuveien 197, 7037, Trondheim, Norway
Tel.: (47) 73804500
Emp.: 280
Software Development Services
N.A.I.C.S.: 541511
Bard Mikkelsen *(Chm)*

Scanmatic AS (1)
Kilsundveien 126, 4920, Staubo, Norway
Tel.: (47) 370 59500
Web Site: http://www.scanmatic.no
Emp.: 42
Control Equipment Mfr & Distr
N.A.I.C.S.: 334511
Johannes Skar *(CMO & Mgr-Sls)*

Subsidiary (Non-US):

**Scanmatic Environmental Technology
AB** (2)
Smedbyvagen 8, 184 32, Akersberga, Sweden
Tel.: (46) 702390145
Web Site: http://www.smetab.se

Environmental Engineering Services
N.A.I.C.S.: 541330

Seafood TIP. (1)
Goylaan 15, 3525 AA, Utrecht, Netherlands
Tel.: (31) 302720313
Web Site: https://www.seafood-tip.com
Seafood Distr
N.A.I.C.S.: 424460
Sander Visch *(Mng Dir)*

Tekna Inc. (1)
3400 Tech Cir, Kalamazoo, MI 49008
Tel.: (269) 978-3500
Web Site: https://teknateam.com
Medical Device Mfr & Distr
N.A.I.C.S.: 339112

Tekna Systemes Plasma Inc (1)
2935 Boul Industriel, Sherbrooke, J1L 2T9,
QC, Canada
Tel.: (819) 820-2204
Web Site: https://www.tekna.com
Chemical Product Mfr & Distr
N.A.I.C.S.: 325199
Luc Dionne *(CEO)*

Subsidiary (Non-US):

Tekna Plasma Europe SAS (2)
200 Boulevard de la Resistance, 71000,
Macon, France
Tel.: (33) 385231045
Chemical Product Mfr & Distr
N.A.I.C.S.: 325199
Remy Pontone *(Dir Gen)*

Volue AG (1)
Peter Merian-Strasse 90, 4052, Basel, Switzerland
Tel.: (41) 612708440
Hydroelectric Power Generation Services
N.A.I.C.S.: 221111

Volue Germany GmbH (1)
Richard-Strauss-Strasse 82, 81679, Munich,
Germany
Tel.: (49) 89437777977
Software Development Services
N.A.I.C.S.: 541511

Volue Gmbh (1)
Kaistrasse 5, 40221, Dusseldorf, Germany
Tel.: (49) 21188231581
Software Development Services
N.A.I.C.S.: 541511

ARENT, INC.
KDX Hamamatsucho Bldg 3F 2-7-19
Hamamatsucho, Minato-ku, Tokyo,
105-0013, Japan
Tel.: (81) 362283393
Web Site: https://www.arent.co.jp
Year Founded: 2012
5254—(TKS)
Rev.: $18,280,580
Assets: $31,473,200
Liabilities: $5,815,700
Net Worth: $25,657,500
Earnings: $4,092,760
Fiscal Year-end: 06/30/24
Construction Services
N.A.I.C.S.: 236210
Kamobayashi Broad Track *(Pres)*

ARES ASIA LIMITED
96/F International Commerce Centre
1 Austin Road West, Hong Kong,
China (Hong Kong)
Tel.: (852) 2273 3888   BM
Web Site: http://www.aresasialtd.com
Rev.: $198,348,000
Assets: $26,127,000
Liabilities: $18,823,000
Net Worth: $7,304,000
Earnings: ($1,476,000)
Emp.: 9
Fiscal Year-end: 03/31/19
Footwear Mfr
N.A.I.C.S.: 316210
Pui Ki Leung *(Sec)*

ARES INTERNATIONAL CORPORATION

3F No111 Sec 2 Zhongshan N Rd,
Taipei, 104, Taiwan
Tel.: (886) 225221351
Web Site: https://www.ares.com.tw
2471—(TAI)
Rev.: $27,529,807
Assets: $47,728,047
Liabilities: $17,838,908
Net Worth: $29,889,138
Earnings: $5,657,935
Emp.: 400
Fiscal Year-end: 12/31/23
Information Technology Services
N.A.I.C.S.: 513210
Frank Lin *(Pres)*

**ARES STRATEGIC MINING
INC.**
Unit 1001- 409 Granville Street, Vancouver, V6C 1T2, BC, Canada
Tel.: (604) 345-1576   ON
Web Site:
https://www.aresmining.com
Year Founded: 2009
ARS—(CNSX)
Rev.: $24,574
Assets: $13,195,992
Liabilities: $5,480,044
Net Worth: $7,715,948
Earnings: ($3,351,139)
Emp.: 8
Fiscal Year-end: 09/30/23
Investment Services
N.A.I.C.S.: 523999
Basil Roy Botha *(Chm & Pres)*

ARETTO WELLNESS INC.
151 West Hastings Street, Vancouver, V6B 1H4, BC, Canada   BC
Web Site: https://www.rritual.com
Year Founded: 2019
RRSFF—(OTCIQ)
Rev.: $70,377
Assets: $27,882
Liabilities: $1,210,242
Net Worth: ($1,182,360)
Earnings: ($9,014,186)
Fiscal Year-end: 06/30/22
Food Product Mfr & Distr
N.A.I.C.S.: 311412
Nathan Nowak *(CEO)*

**AREV LIFE SCIENCES
GLOBAL CORP.**
18- 91 Golden Drive, Coquitlam, V3K
6R2, BC, Canada
Tel.: (778) 379-8551
Web Site:
https://www.arevlifesciences.com
AREVF—(OTCIQ)
Rev.: $36,281
Assets: $186,621
Liabilities: $890,329
Net Worth: ($703,708)
Earnings: ($1,066,784)
Fiscal Year-end: 12/31/22
Natural Product Mfr
N.A.I.C.S.: 325411
Mike Withrow *(CEO)*

AREX INDUSTRIES LIMITED
612 G I D C Chhatral, Kalol, Gandhinagar, 382 729, Gujarat, India
Tel.: (91) 2764233635
Web Site: https://www.arex.co.in
Year Founded: 1989
526851—(BOM)
Rev.: $7,345,911
Assets: $7,978,998
Liabilities: $4,106,944
Net Worth: $3,872,055
Earnings: $504,763
Emp.: 299
Fiscal Year-end: 03/31/22
Woven Fabrics Mfr
N.A.I.C.S.: 313210
Dinesh A. Bilgi *(Mng Dir & CFO)*

AREX INDUSTRIES LIMITED—(Continued)

AREZZO INDUSTRIA E COM-ERCIO S.A.
Rua Fernandes Tourinho 147 room 402, Bairro Savassi, Belo Horizonte, 30112-000, Minas Gerais, Brazil
Tel.: (55) 3121211000   BR
Web Site:
https://www.arezzoco.com.br
Year Founded: 1972
ARZZ3—(BRAZ)
Rev.: $866,407,084
Assets: $1,068,251,165
Liabilities: $544,646,131
Net Worth: $523,605,034
Earnings: $71,266,690
Fiscal Year-end: 12/31/23
Women's Footwear & Accessories Mfr & Sls
N.A.I.C.S.: 458110
Alexandre Cafe Birman *(Co-CEO)*

ARFIN INDIA LIMITED
Plot No 117 Ravi Industrial Estate Behind Prestige Hotel, Billeshwarpura Chhatral, Gandhinagar, 382729, Gujarat, India
Tel.: (91) 2764232620
Web Site: https://www.arfin.co.in
Year Founded: 1992
539151—(BOM)
Rev.: $72,019,748
Assets: $33,702,915
Liabilities: $23,104,427
Net Worth: $10,598,488
Earnings: $1,254,066
Emp.: 286
Fiscal Year-end: 03/31/22
Aluminium Products Mfr
N.A.I.C.S.: 331315
Mahendra R. Shah *(Chm)*

ARG MBH & CO. KG
Essener Strasse 33, D-46047, Oberhausen, Germany
Tel.: (49) 2088995690
Web Site: https://argkg.com/
Natural Gas Transportation Services
N.A.I.C.S.: 486210

ARGAMAN INDUSTRIES LTD.
Hasadna 6 Ta Do'ar 2465, Kfar Saba, Israel
Tel.: (972) 97643305
Year Founded: 1934
Rev.: $19,507,103
Assets: $28,856,109
Liabilities: $33,272,860
Net Worth: ($4,416,751)
Earnings: ($2,551,901)
Emp.: 537
Fiscal Year-end: 12/31/17
Apparel Product Mfr & Whslr
N.A.I.C.S.: 314999
Yair Rotlevy *(CEO)*

ARGAN SA
21 rue Beffroy, 92200, Neuilly-sur-Seine, France
Tel.: (33) 147470546
Web Site: https://www.argan.fr
ARG—(EUR)
Rev.: $202,724,363
Assets: $4,494,023,624
Liabilities: $2,371,910,807
Net Worth: $2,122,112,816
Earnings: ($294,126,283)
Emp.: 29
Fiscal Year-end: 12/31/23
Warehouse Construction & Rental Services
N.A.I.C.S.: 236210
Ronan Le Lan *(Chm-Mgmt Bd)*

ARGENICA THERAPEUTICS LIMITED
4/117 Broadway, Nedlands, 6009, WA, Australia
Tel.: (61) 893293396   AU
Web Site:
https://www.argenica.com.au
Year Founded: 2019
AGN—(ASX)
Rev.: $1,180,737
Assets: $6,220,815
Liabilities: $1,222,158
Net Worth: $4,998,657
Earnings: ($3,139,495)
Fiscal Year-end: 06/30/23
Pharmaceutical Preparation Manufacturing
N.A.I.C.S.: 325412
Bruno Meloni *(Chief Scientific Officer)*

ARGENT GROUP EUROPE LIMITED
Level 5 9 Hatton Street, London, NW8 8PL, United Kingdom
Tel.: (44) 20 7723 5458
Web Site:
http://www.argentgroup.com
Year Founded: 1997
Sales Range: $750-799.9 Million
Emp.: 854
Investment Management Service
N.A.I.C.S.: 523940
David Gray *(Founder & Mng Dir)*

Subsidiaries:

Belwood Foods Limited   (1)
42 Brookhill Leys Road, New Eastwood, Nottingham, NG16 3HZ, Nottinghamshire, United Kingdom
Tel.: (44) 1773716321
Web Site: http://www.belwoodfoods.com
Meat Product Distr
N.A.I.C.S.: 424470

Fairfax Meadow Europe Limited (1)
6 Newmarket Drive, Osmaston Park Industrial Estate, Derby, DE24 8SW, United Kingdom
Tel.: (44) 3444937051
Web Site: http://www.fairfaxmeadow.co.uk
Meat Product Distr
N.A.I.C.S.: 424470
Penny Tomlinson *(Mng Dir)*

New Zealand Light Leathers Ltd (1)
Meadows Road, PO Box 2051, Washdyke, Timaru, New Zealand
Tel.: (64) 36874000
Web Site: http://www.nzll.co.nz
Leather Product Mfr
N.A.I.C.S.: 316990
Hans-Peter Mathis *(Accountant)*

Norton Folgate Marketing Ltd   (1)
Nickle Farm Ashford Road, Chartham, Canterbury, CT4 7PF, Kent, United Kingdom
Tel.: (44) 1227204900
Web Site: http://www.nortonfolgate.com
Fruit Distr
N.A.I.C.S.: 424480
Matt Hancock *(Mng Dir)*

Orchard World Ltd   (1)
790 The Crescent Colchester Business Park, Colchester, CO4 9YQ, Essex, United Kingdom
Tel.: (44) 1206843465
Web Site: http://www.orchardworld.co.uk
Fruit Distr
N.A.I.C.S.: 424480
Mark Culley *(Mng Dir)*

Poupart Ltd   (1)
Turnford Place Great Cambridge Road, Turnford, Broxbourne, EN10 6NH, Herts, United Kingdom
Tel.: (44) 1992473024
Web Site: http://www.poupart.co.uk
Fresh Fruit Distr
N.A.I.C.S.: 424480
Adam Olins *(Mng Dir)*

PrepWorld Ltd   (1)
Court Lodge Farm Dale Road, Southfleet, Kent, DA13 9NQ, United Kingdom
Tel.: (44) 1474832569
Web Site: http://www.prepworld.com

Fruit Distr
N.A.I.C.S.: 424480

Tendercut Meats Ltd   (1)
Tendercut House Brickfield Lane, Chandlers Ford, Eastleigh, SO53 4DP, Hants, United Kingdom
Tel.: (44) 2380252444
Web Site: http://www.tendercutmeats.co.uk
Emp.: 900
Veal Product Mfr
N.A.I.C.S.: 311612
Mike Roberts *(Mng Dir)*

VitalBerry BV   (1)
Schanseind 16, 4921 PM, Made, Netherlands
Tel.: (31) 162690422
Web Site: http://www.vitalberry.eu
Fruit Distr
N.A.I.C.S.: 424480
Rob Vissers *(Controller-Fin)*

ARGENT INDUSTRIAL LIMITED
First Floor Ridge 63 8 Sinembe Crescent Sinembe Park, PO Box 5108, La Lucia Ridge Office Estate, Durban, 4019, South Africa
Tel.: (27) 317910061
Web Site: https://www.argent.co.za
ART—(JSE)
Rev.: $129,878,801
Assets: $114,047,941
Liabilities: $34,146,748
Net Worth: $79,901,192
Earnings: $12,477,160
Fiscal Year-end: 03/31/23
Steel Trading Services
N.A.I.C.S.: 331110
Teunis Scharrighuisen *(Chm)*

Subsidiaries:

Allan Maskew (Pty) Ltd   (1)
11 Barnsley Avenue, PO Box 653, Benoni South, Benoni, 1500, Gauteng, South Africa
Tel.: (27) 119742941
Web Site: https://www.allanmaskew.co.za
Sales Range: $25-49.9 Million
Emp.: 52
Rubber Mouldings Mfr
N.A.I.C.S.: 326291

Argent Steel Group (Pty) Ltd   (1)
Montague Gardens, Cape Town, 7460, South Africa
Tel.: (27) 215077100
Web Site: http://www.gammid.co.za
Sales Range: $25-49.9 Million
Emp.: 50
Steel Products Whslr
N.A.I.C.S.: 423510

Burbage Iron Craft Ltd.   (1)
Unit 16 Mill Park Hawks Green Ind Estate, Cannock, WS11 7XT, United Kingdom
Tel.: (44) 1543438217
Web Site:
https://www.burbageironcraft.co.uk
Timber Gate Mfr
N.A.I.C.S.: 332323

Burbage Iron Craft Services Limited   (1)
Unit 16 Mill Park Hawks Green Ind Estate, Cannock, WS11 7XT, Staffordshire, United Kingdom
Tel.: (44) 1543438217
Web Site: http://www.burbageironcraft.co.uk
Sales Range: $25-49.9 Million
Emp.: 10
Gates & Fencing Distr
N.A.I.C.S.: 444180

Cannock Gates Ltd.   (1)
Martindale Hawks Green Ind Estate, Cannock, WS11 7XT, United Kingdom
Tel.: (44) 1543462500
Web Site: https://www.cannockgates.co.uk
Wooden Gate Mfr & Distr
N.A.I.C.S.: 332323

Castor & Ladder Proprietary Limited   (1)
10 Aberdein St Roodekop, Germiston, 1401, South Africa

Tel.: (27) 861523337
Web Site: https://castorandladder.co.za
Aluminium Ladder Mfr & Whslr
N.A.I.C.S.: 332999

Excalibur Vehicle Accessories (Pty) Ltd   (1)
7 Borax St, Alrode, Alberton, 1451, South Africa
Tel.: (27) 118647610
Web Site: http://www.excaliburacc.co.za
Sales Range: $25-49.9 Million
Emp.: 100
Vehicle Parts Mfr
N.A.I.C.S.: 332510

Fencing and Gates   (1)
Unit 16 Sketchley Ln Indus Estate, Hinckley, LE9 3ER, Leicestershire, United Kingdom
Tel.: (44) 844 8920130
Sales Range: $25-49.9 Million
Emp.: 20
Iron & Steel Gates & Fence Mfr
N.A.I.C.S.: 332323

Fuel Proof Limited   (1)
Middleton Business Park Middleton Road, Morecambe, LA3 3FH, Lancashire, United Kingdom
Tel.: (44) 1524850685
Web Site: https://www.fuelproof.co.uk
Fuel Storage Tank Mfr
N.A.I.C.S.: 332420

Gammid Group Proprietary Limited   (1)
77 Goodwood Rd, Durban, 3610, South Africa
Tel.: (27) 317008594
Web Site: https://www.gammid.co.za
Stainless Steel Products Distr
N.A.I.C.S.: 423390

Gammid Trading (Pty) Ltd   (1)
7 Borax St, Alrode, Johannesburg, 1451, Gauteng, South Africa
Tel.: (27) 118647610
Web Site: http://www.gammid.co.za
Emp.: 25
Aluminum & Steel Products Whslr
N.A.I.C.S.: 331318
Quintin Jenkings *(Gen Mgr)*

Giflo Engineering (Pty) Ltd   (1)
Stand 245 4th St, Ga-Rankuwa, 0208, North-West, South Africa
Tel.: (27) 127033346
Web Site: http://www.giflo.co.za
Automobile Parts Mfr
N.A.I.C.S.: 332510
Neels Potgieter *(Mgr-Logistics)*

Hendor Mining Supplies (Pty) Ltd (1)
56 Mullet Rd, Wadeville, 1422, Gauteng, South Africa
Tel.: (27) 118241148
Sales Range: $50-74.9 Million
Emp.: 150
Metal Scrapers Mfr
N.A.I.C.S.: 332216
Mike Daniel *(Mng Dir)*

Jetmaster (Pty) Ltd   (1)
7 Borax Street, Alrode, Alberton, 1451, Gauteng, South Africa
Web Site: http://www.jetmaster.co.za
Sales Range: $25-49.9 Million
Emp.: 13
Fireplaces & Barbecues Mfr
N.A.I.C.S.: 332999

Koch's Cut & Supply Steel Centre (Pty) Ltd   (1)
22 Kyalami Road, Westmead, Pinetown, 3608, Kwazulu-Natal, South Africa
Tel.: (27) 317004422
Web Site: https://www.kochscutsupply.co.za
Sales Range: $50-74.9 Million
Emp.: 70
Steel Processing Services
N.A.I.C.S.: 423510
Roy Meaker *(Co-Founder)*

Megamix (Proprietary) Limited   (1)
11 Prima Drive, Helderberg Industrial Park Strand, Cape Town, 7140, South Africa
Tel.: (27) 218458189
Web Site: https://megamixconcrete.co.za
Sales Range: $25-49.9 Million
Emp.: 60
Readymix Concrete Mfr

N.A.I.C.S.: 327320
Michael Maree *(Mgr)*

New Joules Engineering North America Inc. (1)
4401 Clary Blvd, Kansas City, MO 64130
Tel.: (816) 921-7441
Sales Range: $25-49.9 Million
Emp.: 14
Industrial Engineering Services
N.A.I.C.S.: 541330

OSA Door Parts Limited (1)
Ashville Industrial Estate, Runcorn, WA7 3EZ, Cheshire, United Kingdom
Tel.: (44) 1928703580
Web Site: https://www.osadoorparts.co.uk
Industrial Doors Mfr & Distr
N.A.I.C.S.: 332321

Partington Engineering Limited (1)
Hollyhill Road Forest Vale Industrial Estate, Cinderford, GL14 2YA, Gloucestershire, United Kingdom
Tel.: (44) 1594824676
Web Site: https://www.partington-engineering.com
Material Handling Machinery Mfr & Distr
N.A.I.C.S.: 333924

Pro Crane Services Proprietary Limited (1)
9 Sprite Place Surprise Farm, Pinetown, 3610, KwaZulu-Natal, South Africa
Tel.: (27) 317001334
Web Site: https://www.procrane.co.za
Lifting Equipment Mfr
N.A.I.C.S.: 333992

Tricks Wrought Iron Services Proprietary Limited (1)
No 9 Sprite Pl Westmead, Pinetown, 3610, Kwazulu Natal, South Africa
Tel.: (27) 317006588
Web Site: https://www.trickswroughtiron.co.za
Steel Product Mfr & Distr
N.A.I.C.S.: 331511

Xpanda Security Proprietary Limited (1)
10 Aberdein Rd Roodekop, Germiston, 1400, South Africa
Tel.: (27) 861972632
Web Site: https://www.xpanda.co.za
Wooden Gate Mfr & Distr
N.A.I.C.S.: 332323

ARGENT MINERALS LIMITED
Tel.: (61) 863112818
Web Site: https://www.argentminerals.com.au
ARD—(ASX)
Rev.: $19,752
Assets: $2,613,511
Liabilities: $108,205
Net Worth: $2,505,306
Earnings: ($1,322,935)
Emp.: 3
Fiscal Year-end: 06/30/24
Minerals Exploration
N.A.I.C.S.: 213115
Emmanuel Correia *(Co-Sec)*

ARGENTEX GROUP PLC
25 Argyll Street, London, W1F 7TU, United Kingdom
Tel.: (44) 2037720300   UK
Web Site: https://www.argentex.com
Year Founded: 2011
AGFX—(AIM)
Rev.: $43,549,609
Assets: $122,822,520
Liabilities: $80,913,911
Net Worth: $41,908,609
Earnings: $9,341,075
Emp.: 86
Fiscal Year-end: 03/31/22
Financial Brokerage Services
N.A.I.C.S.: 523160
Carl Jani *(Co-Founder & Co-CEO)*

ARGENTIL CAPITAL PARTNERS LIMITED

8th Floor The Octagon, 13A AJ Marinho Drive, Victoria Island, Lagos, Nigeria
Tel.: (234) 1 2710710 3
Web Site: http://www.argentilcp.com
Investment Services
N.A.I.C.S.: 523999
Adekunle Adedeji *(Chm)*

ARGENTINA LITHIUM & ENERGY CORP.
Suite 411 - 837 West Hastings Street, Vancouver, V6C 3N6, BC, Canada
Tel.: (604) 687-1828   Ca
Web Site: https://argentinalithium.com
Year Founded: 2000
LIT—(OTCIQ)
Assets: $68,840
Liabilities: $239,908
Net Worth: ($171,068)
Earnings: ($156,512)
Fiscal Year-end: 12/31/20
Exploration & Mining Services
N.A.I.C.S.: 212210
Nikolaos Cacos *(Pres & CEO)*

ARGENTUM 47, INC.
Tyttenhanger House Coursers Rd Colney Heath, Saint Albans, AL4 0PG, United Kingdom
Tel.: (44) 1216154720   NV
Web Site: https://www.argq.io
Year Founded: 2010
ARGQ—(OTCIQ)
Rev.: $404,000
Assets: $180,000
Liabilities: $1,256,000
Net Worth: ($1,076,000)
Earnings: ($15,288,000)
Fiscal Year-end: 12/31/22
Business Consulting Services
N.A.I.C.S.: 541611
Enzo Taddei *(CFO & Sec)*

ARGENTUM SILVER CORP.
Suite 401 217 Queen Street West, Toronto, M5V 0R2, ON, Canada
Tel.: (416) 855-9304   Ca
Web Site: https://www.argentumsilvercorp.com
Year Founded: 2007
ASL—(TSXV)
Rev.: $13,781
Assets: $865,018
Liabilities: $153,516
Net Worth: $711,502
Earnings: ($240,079)
Fiscal Year-end: 06/30/21
Mineral Exploration Services
N.A.I.C.S.: 213114
James Fairbairn *(CFO)*

ARGENX SE
Laarderhoogtweg 25, 1101 EB, Amsterdam, Netherlands
Tel.: (31) 3293103400
Web Site: http://www.argenx.com
ARGX—(NASDAQ)
Rev.: $1,268,594,000
Assets: $4,542,458,000
Liabilities: $444,951,000
Net Worth: $4,097,507,000
Earnings: ($295,053,000)
Emp.: 1,148
Fiscal Year-end: 12/31/23
Human Monoclonal Antibodies Researcher & Developer
N.A.I.C.S.: 541715
Tim Van Hauwermeiren *(Co-Founder & CEO)*

Subsidiaries:

Argenx Japan KK (1)
Hulic Jp Akasaka Building 2-5-8, Akasaka Minato-ku, Tokyo, 107-0052, Japan
Tel.: (81) 345789752

Pharmaceutical Mfr & Distr
N.A.I.C.S.: 325412

ARGEO AS
Nye Vakas v 14, 1395, Hvalstad, Norway
Tel.: (47) 66859099   NO
Web Site: https://www.argeo.no
Year Founded: 2014
ARGEO—(OSL)
Rev.: $10,126,000
Assets: $71,601,000
Liabilities: $36,591,000
Net Worth: $35,010,000
Earnings: ($16,935,000)
Emp.: 49
Fiscal Year-end: 12/31/23
Engineeering Services
N.A.I.C.S.: 541330
Odd Erik Rudshaug *(CFO)*

ARGEX TITANIUM INC.
3080 Le Carrefour Boulevard Suite 530, Laval, H7T 2R5, QC, Canada
Tel.: (450) 681-6868   Ca
Web Site: http://www.argex.ca
Year Founded: 2005
Mineral Exploration Services
N.A.I.C.S.: 212290
Mazen Alnaimi *(Chm & CEO)*

ARGHA KARYA PRIMA INDUSTRY TBK
Jalan Pahlawan Karang Asem Ba Citeureup, Bogor, 16810, Indonesia
Tel.: (62) 218752707
Web Site: https://arghakarya.com
AKPI—(INDO)
Rev.: $176,872,629
Assets: $217,650,915
Liabilities: $110,374,628
Net Worth: $107,276,287
Earnings: ($1,925,952)
Emp.: 1,079
Fiscal Year-end: 12/31/23
Polypropylene Mfr
N.A.I.C.S.: 325211

ARGILETUM MERCHANT S.P.A.
Piazzale delle Belle Arti 8, 00196, Rome, Italy
Tel.: (39) 06 879 30000
Web Site: http://www.methorios.it
Year Founded: 2004
Rev.: $2,736,456
Assets: $38,581,525
Liabilities: $12,707,696
Net Worth: $25,873,828
Earnings: ($67,664,400)
Emp.: 11
Fiscal Year-end: 12/31/15
Financial Advisory & Investment Services
N.A.I.C.S.: 523940
Giuseppe Spaziani *(CEO)*

Subsidiaries:

Mediocredito Europeo SPA (1)
Via Vincenzo Lamaro 13, 00173, Rome, Italy
Tel.: (39) 06684451
Web Site: http://www.mediocreditoeuropeo.com
Sales Range: $1-9.9 Million
Financial Support Services
N.A.I.C.S.: 523940
Alessandro Maione *(CEO)*

ARGIS-GALAC SEA
15 Rue Florian Laporte, 56100, Lorient, Morbihan, France
Tel.: (33) 297831000
Web Site: http://www.argisgalacsea.com
Sales Range: $25-49.9 Million
Emp.: 15

Groceries, General Line
N.A.I.C.S.: 424410
Regis Prive *(Owner)*

ARGO BLOCKCHAIN PLC
Eastcastle House 27/28 Eastcastle Street, London, W1W 8DH, United Kingdom
Tel.: (44) 2078877633   UK
Web Site: https://www.argomining.co
Year Founded: 2017
ARBK—(NASDAQ)
Rev.: $64,305,692
Assets: $124,120,047
Liabilities: $108,639,324
Net Worth: $15,480,723
Earnings: ($263,711,313)
Emp.: 48
Fiscal Year-end: 12/31/22
Gold Exploration & Mining Services
N.A.I.C.S.: 212220
Perry Hothi *(CTO)*

ARGO EXPLORATION LIMITED
Level 4 100 Albert Road, Melbourne, 3205, VIC, Australia
Tel.: (61) 396927222
Web Site: http://www.argoexploration.com.au
Sales Range: Less than $1 Million
Emp.: 5
Mineral Exploration & Development
N.A.I.C.S.: 213115
Melanie Jaye Leydin *(Sec)*

Subsidiaries:

Athena Mines Limited (1)
Ste 304 22 St Kilda Rd, Saint Kilda, 3182, VIC, Australia
Tel.: (61) 396927222
Web Site: http://www.argoexploration.com.au
Sales Range: $50-74.9 Million
Emp.: 3
Mineral Exploration & Mining Services
N.A.I.C.S.: 213115

ARGO FINANZIARIA S.P.A.
Str Provinciale 211 della Lomellina, Localita San Guglielmo 3/13, 15057, Tortona, Alessandria, Italy
Tel.: (39) 01318791   IT
Web Site: http://www.gruppogavio.it
Sales Range: $1-4.9 Billion
Emp.: 5,600
Investment Holding Company; Construction, Technology, Energy, Transportation & Logistics Services
N.A.I.C.S.: 551112

Subsidiaries:

ASTM S.p.A. (1)
Corso Regina Margherita 165, 10144, Turin, Italy **(59%)**
Tel.: (39) 0114392111
Web Site: https://www.astm.it
Rev.: $3,048,885,945
Assets: $9,106,332,259
Liabilities: $5,503,505,161
Net Worth: $3,602,827,098
Earnings: $176,525,109
Emp.: 6,075
Fiscal Year-end: 12/31/2020
Highway & Road Construction
N.A.I.C.S.: 237310

Subsidiary (Domestic):

Ativa S.p.A. (2)
Strada della Cebrosa 86, 10156, Turin, Torino, Italy **(100%)**
Tel.: (39) 0113814100
Web Site: http://www.ativa.it
Other Motor Vehicle Electrical & Electronic Equipment Mfr
N.A.I.C.S.: 336320

Finsina S.p.A. (2)
Via lineages F 0001, 20124, Milan, Italy
Tel.: (39) 022771191
All Other Business Support Services

Argo Finanziaria S.p.A.—(Continued)

N.A.I.C.S.: 561499

SINA S.p.A. **(2)**
Via Ponte Roitero 1, Splimbergo, 33097,
Pordenone, Italy **(100%)**
Tel.: (39) 0427598111
Web Site: http://www.sinaauto.com
Sales Range: $25-49.9 Million
Emp.: 00
Used Car Dealers
N.A.I.C.S.: 441120

Satap S.p.A. **(2)**
Via Bonzanigo 22, 10144, Turin, Torino,
Italy **(100%)**
Tel.: (39) 0114392111
Web Site: http://www.a4torinomilano.it
Highway Street & Bridge Construction
N.A.I.C.S.: 237310

Sineco S.p.A. **(2)**
19020 Ceparana di Follo 5, 19020, Trieste,
Italy **(100%)**
Tel.: (39) 0187931400
Web Site: http://www.sineco.ws
Sales Range: $25-49.9 Million
Emp.: 20
Iron & Steel Mills
N.A.I.C.S.: 331110

**Societa Iniziative Autostradali e
Servizi S.p.A.** **(2)**
Via Bonzanigo 22, 10144, Turin,
Italy **(75.91%)**
Tel.: (39) 0114392102
Web Site: http://www.grupposias.it
Sales Range: $1-4.9 Billion
Technology & Motor Sector Investment Services
N.A.I.C.S.: 541611
Umberto Tosoni (CEO)

Subsidiary (Domestic):

ABC Costruzioni srl **(3)**
Edilizia Industrializzata Sede e Stabilimento,
Zona Industriale Artigianale 13, 33010,
Udine, Italy
Tel.: (39) 0432 986016
Web Site: http://www.abccostruzioni.it
Construction Engineering Services
N.A.I.C.S.: 541330

Autocamionale della Cisa S.p.A. **(3)**
Via Camboara 26/A, Ponte Taro, Parma,
43010, Italy
Tel.: (39) 0521 613711
Web Site: http://www.autocisa.com
Highway Construction Services
N.A.I.C.S.: 237310

Autostrada Asti-Cuneo S.p.A. **(3)**
Via XX Settembre n 98/E, 00187, Rome,
Italy
Tel.: (39) 0131 879 222
Web Site: http://www.asticuneo.it
Highway Construction Services
N.A.I.C.S.: 237310

**Autostrada Ligure Toscana
S.p.A.** **(3)**
Via Don Tazzoli 9, 55041, Camaiore, Italy
Tel.: (39) 0584 9091
Web Site: http://www.salt.it
Highway Construction Services
N.A.I.C.S.: 237310

Holding (Non-US):

**EcoRodovias Infraestructura e Logis-
tica S.A.** **(3)**
Rua Gomes de Carvalho 1510 3 Andar,
0454 7005, Sao Paulo, 0454 7005, SP,
Brazil **(41%)**
Tel.: (55) 1137872667
Web Site: http://www.ecorodovias.com.br
Rev.: $1,581,162,075
Assets: $4,640,585,672
Liabilities: $4,106,762,551
Net Worth: $533,823,121
Earnings: $106,653,793
Emp.: 5,450
Fiscal Year-end: 12/31/2023
Intermodal Logistics & Infrastructure Construction Services
N.A.I.C.S.: 541614
Marco Antonio Cassou (Chm)

Subsidiary (Domestic):

Euroimpianti Electronic S.p.A. **(3)**

Strada Statale Per Alessandria n 6/A,
15057, Tortona, Italy
Tel.: (39) 0131 8691
Web Site: http://www.euroimpiantiel.it
Electronic Component Mfr & Installation
Services
N.A.I.C.S.: 334419

SAV S.p.A. **(3)**
Strada Barat 13, 11024, Chatillon, Italy
Tel.: (39) 0166 56 04 11
Web Site: http://www.sav-a5.it
Highway Construction Services
N.A.I.C.S.: 237310

SINELEC S.p.A. **(3)**
SP 211 della Lomellina 3/13, 15057, Tortona, Italy
Tel.: (39) 0131 8791
Web Site: http://www.sinelec.it
Highway Construction Services
N.A.I.C.S.: 237310
Paolo Patri (Project Mgr)

ARGO GLOBAL LISTED IN-
FRASTRUCTURE LIMITED
Level 25 91 King William Street, Adelaide, 5000, SA, Australia
Tel.: (61) 882109555   AU
Web Site:
    https://www.argoinfrastructure.com
Year Founded: 2015
ALI—(ASX)
Rev.: $37,543,310
Assets: $323,225,680
Liabilities: $16,403,491
Net Worth: $306,816,188
Earnings: $22,883,797
Fiscal Year-end: 06/30/22
Investment & Portfolio Management
Services
N.A.I.C.S.: 523999
Jason Beddow (Mng Dir)

ARGO GOLD INC.
350 Bay Street Suite 700, Toronto,
M5H 2S6, ON, Canada
Tel.: (416) 786-7860
Web Site: https://www.argogold.ca
P3U—(BER)
Assets: $806,799
Liabilities: $353,427
Net Worth: $453,372
Earnings: ($1,069,083)
Fiscal Year-end: 12/31/22
Mining & Exploration Services
N.A.I.C.S.: 212290
David McDonald (Controller)

ARGO GRAPHICS INC.
ARGO Nihonbashi Building 5-14
Nihonbashi-hakozaki-cho, Chuo-ku,
Tokyo, 103-0015, Japan
Tel.: (81) 356412020
Web Site: https://www.argo-
    graph.co.jp
Year Founded: 1985
7595—(TKS)
Rev.: $393,367,710
Assets: $496,100,330
Liabilities: $149,465,320
Net Worth: $346,635,010
Earnings: $43,097,200
Emp.: 1,135
Fiscal Year-end: 03/31/24
Advanced Graphics Systems for
CAD/CAM Applications
N.A.I.C.S.: 541430
Yoshimaro Fujisawa (Chm & CEO)

Subsidiaries:

Argo Business Services Inc. **(1)**
2-6-32 Takashima Yokohama East Exit
Wisport Building 15F, Nishi-ku, Yokohama,
220-0011, Kanagawa, Japan
Tel.: (81) 45 451 2955
Web Site: https://www.argo-bs.co.jp
Emp.: 87
Computer System Operation Services
N.A.I.C.S.: 541512

**D&A Technology (Shanghai) Co.,
Ltd.** **(1)**
Room 2406 Meiluo Building No 30 Tianyaoqiao Road, Xuhui District, Shanghai,
200030, China
Tel.: (86) 1360 171 4702
Web Site: https://www.danda.com.cn
Information Technology Services
N.A.I.C.S.: 541511

HPC Solutions Co., Ltd. **(1)**
1st Floor of Daiwa Kodenmacho Building
3-2 Nihonbashi Odenmacho, Chuo-ku, Tokyo, 103-0011, Japan
Tel.: (81) 35 640 7858
Web Site: https://www.hpc-sol.co.jp
Emp.: 22
Computer Cluster System Distr
N.A.I.C.S.: 423430

Hulinks Inc. **(1)**
5-14 Nihonbashi Hakozaki-cho, Chuo-ku,
Tokyo, 103-0015, Japan
Tel.: (81) 35 642 8380
Web Site: https://www.hulinks.co.jp
Information Technology Services
N.A.I.C.S.: 541511
Yoshimaro Fujisawa (Pres & CEO)

Jedat Inc. **(1)**
HSB Teppozu 1-1-12 Minato, Chuo-ku, Tokyo, 104-0043, Japan **(51%)**
Tel.: (81) 362628401
Web Site: https://www.jedat.co.jp
Sales Range: Less than $1 Million
Emp.: 120
Computer Systems Design & Related Services
N.A.I.C.S.: 541512
Kazutoshi Matsuo (Pres, Pres & CEO)

Subsidiary (Non-US):

**AJM Technology (Shanghai) Co.,
Ltd.** **(2)**
Block G 14th Floor 99 Huaihai East Road,
Huangpu District, Shanghai, 200021, China
Tel.: (86) 2162190626
Web Site: http://www.ajm-tech.com
Information Technology Consulting Services
N.A.I.C.S.: 541512

MDCGroup, Inc. **(1)**
Unit 907 Coherco Finacial Tower Trade St
Cor Investment Drive, Madrigral Business
Park, Muntinlupa, 1770, Metro Manila, Philippines
Tel.: (63) 917 521 2857
Web Site: https://www.mdcgroup.org.ph
Mechanical Product Mfr
N.A.I.C.S.: 333613

Techspire Co., Ltd. **(1)**
Marumasu Kojimachi Building 6F 3-3-8 Kojimachi, Chiyoda-ku, Tokyo, 102-0083, Japan
Tel.: (81) 33 525 8951
Web Site: https://www.techspire.co.jp
Software Development Services
N.A.I.C.S.: 541511
Shigeo Kosaka (CEO)

ARGO GROUP LIMITED
33-37 Athol Street, Douglas, IM1
1LB, Isle of Man
Tel.: (44) 2075354000   IM
Web Site:
    https://www.argogrouplimited.com
ARGO—(AIM)
Rev.: $3,048,000
Assets: $6,068,000
Liabilities: $950,000
Net Worth: $5,118,000
Earnings: ($14,430,000)
Emp.: 22
Fiscal Year-end: 12/31/23
Investment Management Service
N.A.I.C.S.: 523150
Kyriakos Rialas (CEO)

Subsidiaries:

**ARGO Real Estate Opportunities
Fund** **(1)**
51-53 Clucerului St, Bucharest, Romania
Tel.: (40) 212232160
Web Site:
    http://www.argocapitalproperty.com

Sales Range: $50-74.9 Million
Emp.: 25
Investment Advisory Services
N.A.I.C.S.: 523940

**Argo Capital Management (Cyprus)
Limited** **(1)**
Jackie Court Suite 401 10 Vasilissis Frederikis Street, 1066, Nicosia, 1066, Cyprus
Tel.: (357) 22668900
Sales Range: $25-49.9 Million
Emp.: 4
Investment Management Service
N.A.I.C.S.: 541618

**Argo Capital Management
Limited** **(1)**
2nd Floor 24-25 New Bond Street, London,
W1S 2RR, United Kingdom
Tel.: (44) 2070167660
Sales Range: $25-49.9 Million
Emp.: 15
Investment Management Service
N.A.I.C.S.: 541618

ARGO INVESTMENTS LIMITED
Level 25 91 King William Street, Adelaide, 5000, SA, Australia
Tel.: (61) 882109500   AU
Web Site:
    https://www.argoinvestments.com.au
Year Founded: 1946
ARG—(ASX)
Rev.: $190,651,041
Assets: $4,936,588,521
Liabilities: $689,005,740
Net Worth: $4,247,582,782
Earnings: $168,911,591
Fiscal Year-end: 06/30/24
Investment Management Service
N.A.I.C.S.: 523940
Jason Beddow (Mng Dir)

ARGO LIVING SOILS CORP.
1130 W Pender St 820, Vancouver,
V6E 4A4, BC, Canada
Tel.: (604) 351-2742   BC
Web Site:
    https://www.argolivingsoils.com
Year Founded: 2018
ARLSF—(OTCIQ)
Rev.: $2,665
Assets: $101,986
Liabilities: $22,496
Net Worth: $79,490
Earnings: ($429,756)
Fiscal Year-end: 11/30/23
Agriculture Product Mfr & Distr
N.A.I.C.S.: 325199
Peter Hoyle (CEO)

ARGO PANTES TBK
Wisma Argo manunggal 2nd Floor Jl
Jend Gatot Subroto Kav 22, Jakarta,
12930, Indonesia
Tel.: (62) 212520068
Web Site:
    https://www.argopantes.com
Year Founded: 1977
ARGO—(INDO)
Rev.: $6,697,726
Assets: $70,884,330
Liabilities: $62,405,768
Net Worth: $8,478,562
Earnings: ($2,282,215)
Emp.: 10
Fiscal Year-end: 12/31/23
Textile Products Mfr
N.A.I.C.S.: 314999
Surjanto Purnadi (Chm)

ARGON DENIMS LIMITED
Plot-33 section 7, Mirpur, Dhaka,
1216, Bangladesh
Tel.: (880) 29020491
Web Site:
    https://www.argondenims.com
Year Founded: 2006

ARGONDENIM—(CHT)
Rev.: $35,177,327
Assets: $70,738,160
Liabilities: $30,607,437
Net Worth: $40,130,724
Earnings: $1,090,089
Emp.: 550
Fiscal Year-end: 06/30/21
Textile Fabric Mfr
N.A.I.C.S.: 313210
Shabnam Shehnaz Chowdhury
(Chm)

ARGONAUT EXPLORATION INC.

268 McKinnon Place NE, Calgary,
T2E 7B9, AB, Canada
Tel.: (403) 969-7903
Web Site:
http://www.argonautexploration.com
Year Founded: 2005
Sales Range: Less than $1 Million
Mineral Exploration Services
N.A.I.C.S.: 213114
Raymond A. Cook (Founder, Pres,
CEO & Acting CFO)

ARGOS CARPETS & FLOOR-ING

1914 Merivale Road, Ottawa, K2G
1E8, ON, Canada
Tel.: (613) 226-6573
Web Site: http://www.argoscarpets.ca
Year Founded: 1978
Rev.: $14,320,800
Emp.: 30
Carpet & Rug Dealers
N.A.I.C.S.: 314110

ARGOS WITYU S.A.

Rue du Rhone 118, 1204, Geneva,
Switzerland
Tel.: (41) 228496633   CH
Web Site:
http://www.argos.wityu.fund
Year Founded: 1989
Privater Equity Firm
N.A.I.C.S.: 523999
Anna-Karin Portunato (Compliance &
Risk Officer)

Subsidiaries:

Argos Wityu France SAS   (1)
112 avenue de Wagram, 75017, Paris,
France
Tel.: (33) 153672050
Web Site: http://www.argos.wityu.fund
Privater Equity Firm
N.A.I.C.S.: 523999
Louis Godron (Partner)

Holding (Domestic):

Axyntis SAS   (2)
45 rue de Pommard, 75012, Paris, France
Tel.: (33) 1 44 06 77 00
Web Site: http://www.axyntis.com
Sales Range: $75-99.9 Million
Emp.: 460
Specialty Chemicals Mfr
N.A.I.C.S.: 325199
David Simonnet (CEO)

Subsidiary (Domestic):

Synthexim SAS   (3)
Rue des Mouettes, ZI des Dunes, Calais,
61 200, France
Tel.: (33) 3 21 96 85 00
Web Site: http://www.axyntis.com
Emp.: 39
Pharmaceutical & Specialty Chemical Mfr
N.A.I.C.S.: 325199

Argos Wityu Italia S.p.A.   (1)
Piazza Diaz 5, 20122, Milan, Italy
Tel.: (39) 0200660700
Web Site: http://www.argos.wityu.fund
Privater Equity Firm
N.A.I.C.S.: 523999
Jean-Pierre de Benedetto (Partner)

Henri Selmer Paris   (1)
59 rue Marcadet, 75011, Paris, France
Tel.: (33) 149238740
Web Site: http://www.selmer.fr
Saxophone Designer, Mfr, Whslr, Retailer &
Repairer
N.A.I.C.S.: 339992

ARGOSY MINERALS LIMITED

Level 2 22 Mount Street, Perth, 6000,
WA, Australia
Tel.: (61) 861888181   AU
Web Site:
https://www.argosyminerals.com.au
AGY—(ASX)
Rev.: $618,226
Assets: $45,400,426
Liabilities: $299,061
Net Worth: $45,101,365
Earnings: ($7,233,305)
Fiscal Year-end: 12/31/23
Metal Exploration Services
N.A.I.C.S.: 212210
Jerko Zuvela (Mng Dir)

ARGOSY PROPERTY LIMITED

39 Market Place, Auckland, 1010,
New Zealand
Tel.: (64) 93043400   NZ
Web Site: https://www.argosy.co.nz
ARG—(NZX)
Rev.: $78,358,253
Assets: $1,237,432,407
Liabilities: $505,151,312
Net Worth: $732,281,095
Earnings: ($33,059,210)
Emp.: 36
Fiscal Year-end: 03/31/24
Investment Management Service
N.A.I.C.S.: 523940
Philip Michael Smith (Chm)

ARGOSY RESEARCH, INC.

No 15-3 Niupu S Rd, Xiangshan, Hs-
inchu, 300, Taiwan
Tel.: (886) 35302747
Web Site: https://www.argosy.com.tw
Year Founded: 1987
3217—(TPE)
Rev.: $81,555,139
Assets: $150,698,183
Liabilities: $29,795,798
Net Worth: $120,902,386
Earnings: $19,093,612
Emp.: 18
Fiscal Year-end: 12/31/22
Optical Product Mfr
N.A.I.C.S.: 333310
Chao-Liang Wang (Chm)

ARGUS (SHANGHAI) TEXTILE CHEMICALS CO., LTD.

198 Heyou Road, Jiading District,
Shanghai, 201803, China
Tel.: (86) 2169136448
Web Site: https://www.argus.net.cn
Year Founded: 1999
603790—(SHG)
Rev.: $107,858,228
Assets: $227,686,076
Liabilities: $51,120,623
Net Worth: $176,565,453
Earnings: $5,796,161
Fiscal Year-end: 12/31/22
Textile Chemical Product Mfr & Distr
N.A.I.C.S.: 325199
Bing Xie (Chm & Gen Mgr)

Subsidiaries:

Argus (Shanghai) Textile Auxiliary
Co., Ltd.   (1)
No 388 Jinyu Liu Rd, Jiangqiao, Jiading,
Shanghai, China
Tel.: (86) 2169136448
Textile Chemical Product Mfr
N.A.I.C.S.: 325998
Andy Gu (Deputy Gen Mgr)

ARGUS GROUP HOLDINGS LIMITED

The Argus Building 14 Wesley Street,
Hamilton, HM 11, Bermuda
Tel.: (441) 2980888   BM
Web Site: http://www.argus.bm
Year Founded: 1962
AGH—(BERM)
Rev.: $202,436,000
Assets: $1,802,314,000
Liabilities: $1,661,051,000
Net Worth: $141,263,000
Earnings: $27,651,000
Emp.: 379
Fiscal Year-end: 03/31/22
Insurance Services
N.A.I.C.S.: 524298
Andrew H. Bickham (Exec VP-
Broking)

Subsidiaries:

Data Communications Ltd   (1)
1st Floor Cnr Mgr Gonin Lislet Geoffroy
Streets, Port Louis, Mauritius
Tel.: (230) 2101327
Web Site: http://www.dcl.mu
Sales Range: $25-49.9 Million
Emp.: 50
All Other Information Services
N.A.I.C.S.: 519290
Ganesh Ramlingun (Chm)

ARGUS S.A.

Str Industriala nr 1, Constanta, Ro-
mania
Tel.: (40) 241676840
Web Site: https://www.argus-oil.ro
UARG—(BUC)
Rev.: $118,752,120
Assets: $54,865,982
Liabilities: $25,576,309
Net Worth: $29,289,673
Earnings: $386,362
Emp.: 217
Fiscal Year-end: 12/31/20
Vegetable Oils Producer
N.A.I.C.S.: 311225
Robu Sabin (Mgr-Technical)

ARGYLE STREET MANAGE-MENT LIMITED

Unit 601-2 6th Floor St George's
Building 2 Ice House Street, Central,
China (Hong Kong)
Tel.: (852) 2106 0888   VG
Web Site: http://www.asmhk.com
Year Founded: 2002
Rev.: $1,000,000,000
Emp.: 53
Equity Investment Firm
N.A.I.C.S.: 523999
V-Nee Yeh (Co-Founder & Chm)

ARGYLL PARTNERS LTD.

15 South Molton Street, London,
W1K 5QR, United Kingdom
Tel.: (44) 2074093508
Web Site:
http://www.argyllpartners.co.uk
Year Founded: 2004
Sales Range: $25-49.9 Million
Emp.: 5
Privater Equity Firm
N.A.I.C.S.: 523999
Christopher Steed (Founder & Part-
ner)

Subsidiaries:

DWW Woolworth Deutschland GmbH
& Co. KG   (1)
Lyoner Strasse 52, 60528, Frankfurt am
Main, Germany
Tel.: (49) 6966010
Web Site: http://www.woolworth.de
Sales Range: $125-149.9 Million
Variety Stores
N.A.I.C.S.: 455219

ARHT MEDIA INC.

195 Bentworth Ave Unit 2, Toronto,
M6A 1P9, ON, Canada
Tel.: (416) 782-8042
Web Site: https://arht.tech
ART.H—(TSXV)
Rev.: $3,715,412
Assets: $2,611,882
Liabilities: $4,577,865
Net Worth: ($1,965,983)
Earnings: ($8,503,195)
Emp.: 26
Fiscal Year-end: 12/31/23
Investment Services
N.A.I.C.S.: 523999
Larry O'Reilly (CEO)

ARIADNE AUSTRALIA LIM-ITED

Tel.: (61) 282275500
Web Site:
https://www.ariadne.com.au
ARA—(ASX)
Rev.: $1,815,585
Assets: $137,440,924
Liabilities: $19,321,725
Net Worth: $118,119,200
Earnings: $761,891
Fiscal Year-end: 06/30/24
Investment Company; Car Park Infra-
structure Operations, Property Devel-
opment, Resorts & Apartments Man-
agement, Asset & Financial Services
Management, Maritime Infrastructure
Ownership & Operation
N.A.I.C.S.: 523999
Gary Weiss (Exec Dir)

Subsidiaries:

FinClear Pty. Ltd.   (1)
Level 5 53 Walker St, North Sydney, 2060,
NSW, Australia
Tel.: (61) 280396000
Web Site: http://www.finclear.com.au
Emp.: 60
Financial Investment Services
N.A.I.C.S.: 523999
Andrea Marani (COO)

ARIAKE JAPAN CO., LTD.

3-2-17 Ebisu-Minami, Shibuya-ku,
Tokyo, 150-0022, Japan
Tel.: (81) 337913301
Web Site:
https://www.ariakejapan.com
2815—(TKS)
Rev.: $396,474,410
Assets: $902,906,170
Liabilities: $107,861,980
Net Worth: $795,044,190
Earnings: $48,603,330
Emp.: 549
Fiscal Year-end: 03/31/24
Natural Seasonings, Agricultural &
Livestock Products & Marine Prod-
ucts Mfr & Marketer; Restaurants
Management
N.A.I.C.S.: 311999
Naoki Shirakawa (Mng Dir & Gen
Mgr-Production Dept)

Subsidiaries:

ARIAKE JAPAN Co Ltd - Kyushu
Plant   (1)
1572-21 Aza Kourahama Kouramen, Saza-
cho Kita-Matsuura-gun, Nagasaki, 857-
0361, Japan
Tel.: (81) 956635500
Web Site: http://www.ariakejapan.com
Sales Range: $150-199.9 Million
Food Products Mfr & Supplier
N.A.I.C.S.: 424460

Ariake Farm Co., Ltd.   (1)
512 Chuo Reclamation, Isahaya, 854-0038,
Nagasaki, Japan
Tel.: (81) 957355155
Web Site: https://www.ariake-farm.co.jp
Vegetable Farming Services

ARIAKE JAPAN Co., Ltd.—(Continued)

N.A.I.C.S.: 111219

F. P. Natural Ingredients S.A.S (1)
Rue Marie Harel, Monitaouge, 61000, Ce-rise, France
Tel.: (33) 233282800
Web Site: https://www.ariake-europe.com
Sales Range: $50-74.9 Million
Emp.. 29
Net Worth: The Mfr
N.A.I.C.S.: 424420
Food Products Mfr & Supplier
N.A.I.C.S.: 424420

F.P.N.I. BELGIUM N.V. (1)
Leemkuilstraat 5, 3630, Maasmechelen, Limburg, Belgium
Tel.: (32) 89460150
Web Site: http://www.ariake-europe.com
Sales Range: $25-49.9 Million
Emp.: 37
Food Products Mfr & Supplier
N.A.I.C.S.: 424460
Tomoki Tagawa (Pres)

Henningsen Nederland B.V. (1)
Schouwslootweg 3-5, 5145 PG, Waalwijk, Netherlands
Tel.: (31) 416 650333
Web Site: http://www.henningsen.nl
Sales Range: $1-9.9 Million
Emp.: 45
Dehydrated Meat Products Mfr
N.A.I.C.S.: 311999
Henri van Boxtel (Dir-Operational)

Qingdao Ariake Foodstuff Co., (1)
Ltd.
138 Xining Road Jiaonan, Qingdao, 266423, Shandong, China
Tel.: (86) 53288163152
Web Site: http://www.ariakejapan.com
Sales Range: $25-49.9 Million
Emp.: 208
Natural Seasonings Mfr & Whslr
N.A.I.C.S.: 311942

Taiwan Ariake Foods Co., Ltd. (1)
No 188 Ln 53 Sec 2 Hur Sheng Rd, Ping-tung, Taiwan
Tel.: (886) 87550525
Web Site: http://www.ariake.com.tw
Emp.: 59
Food Products Mfr
N.A.I.C.S.: 424420
Kuramoto Kanya (Pres)

ARIAN RESOURCES CORP.
800 - 1199 West Hastings St, Van-couver, V6E 3T5, BC, Canada
Tel.: (778) 786-8856   BC
Year Founded: 2007
ARC—(TSXV)
Holding Company; Gold Ore Mining
N.A.I.C.S.: 551112
Zahir Dhanani (Pres & CEO)

ARIANA RESOURCES PLC
2nd Floor Regis House 45 King Wil-liam Street, London, EC4R 9AN, United Kingdom
Tel.: (44) 2034762080   UK
Web Site:
    https://www.arianaresources.com
AAU—(AIM)
Assets: $27,918,425
Liabilities: $712,919
Net Worth: $27,205,506
Earnings: ($2,928,061)
Emp.: 17
Fiscal Year-end: 12/31/23
Gold Ore & Silver Ore Mining
N.A.I.C.S.: 212220
William Payne (CFO)

Subsidiaries:

Galata Madencilik San. ve Tic. (1)
Ltd.
Farabi Sokak No 7 5, Cankaya, Ankara, 6520, Turkiye
Tel.: (90) 3124681365
Web Site: http://www.arianaresources.com
Sales Range: $50-74.9 Million
Emp.: 10
Gold Mining Services

N.A.I.C.S.: 212220
Erhan Sener (Mng Dir)

Galata Mineral Madencilik San. ve (1)
Tic. A.S.
Beytepe Mahallesi1815 Sokak No 36 Can-kaya, Ankara, Turkiye
Tel.: (90) 3124681365
Gold Exploration Resource Services
N.A.I.C.S.: 541612

ARIANNE PHOSPHATE INC.
901 boulevard Talbot suite 302, Chi-coutimi, G7H 6N7, QC, Canada
Tel.: (418) 549-7316
Web Site: https://www.arianne-inc.com
Year Founded: 1997
DAN—(TSXV)
Assets: $50,438,990
Liabilities: $21,314,356
Net Worth: $29,124,635
Earnings: ($527,507)
Fiscal Year-end: 12/31/23
Phosphate Mining
N.A.I.C.S.: 212390
Dominique Bouchard (Chm)

ARICH ENTERPRISE CO., LTD.
14F-5 No 880 Zhongzheng Road, Zhonghe Dist, New Taipei City, 23586, Taiwan
Tel.: (886) 282277999
Web Site: https://www.arich.com.tw
Year Founded: 1960
4173—(TPE)
Rev.: $35,142,763
Assets: $154,554,138
Liabilities: $95,715,224
Net Worth: $58,838,914
Earnings: $1,957,821
Fiscal Year-end: 12/31/22
Pharmaceutical Products Distr
N.A.I.C.S.: 424210
Hsien-Cheng Chang (Pres)

ARIES AGRO LIMITED
Aries House Plot No 24, Deonar Go-vandi East, Mumbai, 400 043, India
Tel.: (91) 912225564052
Web Site: https://www.ariesagro.com
532935—(BOM)
Rev.: $65,666,792
Assets: $70,958,733
Liabilities: $37,809,312
Net Worth: $33,149,421
Earnings: $2,174,377
Emp.: 958
Fiscal Year-end: 03/31/23
Fertilizer Mfr & Distr
N.A.I.C.S.: 325312
Rahul Mirchandani (Chm & Mng Dir)

Subsidiaries:

Golden Harvest Middle East FZC (1)
Golden Harvest Middle East Fzc, PO Box 9267, SAIF Zone, Sharjah, United Arab Emirates
Tel.: (971) 65578812
Web Site: http://www.ghmefzc.com
Sales Range: $25-49.9 Million
Emp.: 15
Chelated Chemical Mfr
N.A.I.C.S.: 325998

Subsidiary (Domestic):

Amarak Chemicals FZC (2)
Al Hayl Fujairah Free Zone, PO Box 5283, Fujairah, United Arab Emirates
Tel.: (971) 9 277 4831
Web Site: https://www.amarakfzc.com
Sales Range: $25-49.9 Million
Emp.: 12
Sulphur Bentonite Mfr
N.A.I.C.S.: 325998

ARIF HABIB CORPORATION LIMITED

Arif Habib Centre 23 MT Khan Road, Karachi, 74000, Pakistan
Tel.: (92) 21324607179   PK
Web Site:
    https://www.arifhabibcorp.com
Year Founded: 1994
AHCL—(PSX)
Rev.: $28,599,527
Assets: $207,863,670
Liabilities: $74,084,923
Net Worth: $133,778,746
Earnings: $13,720,270
Fiscal Year-end: 06/30/23
Financial Holding Company; Com-mercial & Investment Banking, Secu-rities Brokerage, Private Equity & As-set Management Services
N.A.I.C.S.: 551111
Asadullah Khawaja (Chm)

Subsidiaries:

Arif Habib DMCC (1)
Unit AG-15E AG Tower Silver Plot 11 Jumeirah Lake Towers, Dubai, United Arab Emirates
Tel.: (971) 92212415213
Web Site: http://www.arifhabibdmcc.com
Commodity Brokerage Services
N.A.I.C.S.: 523160
Arif Habib (Mng Dir)

Bank Makramah Limited (1)
Plot No G-2 Block 2 Scheme 5, Clifton, Ka-rachi, Pakistan
Tel.: (92) 21111124365
Web Site: https://www.bankmakramah.com
Rev.: $4,554,063
Assets: $1,024,774,453
Liabilities: $1,070,684,514
Net Worth: ($45,910,061)
Earnings: ($18,918,446)
Emp.: 1,713
Fiscal Year-end: 12/31/2023
Banking Services
N.A.I.C.S.: 522110
Nasser Abdullah Hussain Lootah (Chm)

Sachal Energy Development (Private) (1)
Limited
2nd Floor Plot No 576 Business District South Phase - 8, Bahria Town, Rawalpindi, Pakistan
Tel.: (92) 512153350
Web Site: https://www.sedlpk.com
Emp.: 50
Wind Power Generation Services
N.A.I.C.S.: 221115

ARIGATOU SERVICES CO., LTD.
3-6-30 Hachicho Nishi, Imabari, 794-0832, Ehime, Japan
Tel.: (81) 898232243
Web Site: https://www.arigatou-s.com
Year Founded: 2000
3177—(TKS)
Rev.: $68,985,700
Assets: $38,420,710
Liabilities: $18,965,750
Net Worth: $19,454,960
Earnings: $2,538,220
Emp.: 183
Fiscal Year-end: 02/29/24
Used Good Recycling Stores; Res-taurants; DVD Rental Stores; Real Estate Rentals
N.A.I.C.S.: 455219
Masayuki Imoto (Pres & CEO)

ARIHANT CAPITAL MARKETS LTD.
1011 Solitaire Corporate Park Andher, Ghatkopar Link Road Chakala And-heri East, Mumbai, 400093, India
Tel.: (91) 2242254800
Web Site:
    https://www.arihantcapital.com
511605—(BOM)
Rev.: $16,517,031
Assets: $62,590,588
Liabilities: $31,828,787

Net Worth: $30,761,801
Earnings: $3,491,110
Emp.: 292
Fiscal Year-end: 03/31/23
Financial Services
N.A.I.C.S.: 523999
Ashok Kumar Jain (Founder, Chm & Co-Mng Dir)

Subsidiaries:

Arihant Capital (IFSC) Limited (1)
1011 Solitaire Corporate Park Andheri Ghatkopar Link Road Chakala, Andheri E, Mumbai, 4000093, India
Tel.: (91) 7314217003
Investment Banking Services
N.A.I.C.S.: 523150

ARIHANT FOUNDATIONS & HOUSING LIMITED
New No 3 Old No 25 Ganapathy Colony 3rd Lane Off Cenotaph Road, Teynampet, Chennai, 600 018, India
Tel.: (91) 4442244444
Web Site:
    https://www.arihantspaces.com
531381—(BOM)
Rev.: $12,903,343
Assets: $82,904,721
Liabilities: $71,022,101
Net Worth: $11,882,621
Earnings: ($647,251)
Emp.: 28
Fiscal Year-end: 03/31/22
Property Development Services
N.A.I.C.S.: 531390
Kamal Lunawath (Chm & Mng Dir)

Subsidiaries:

North Town Estates Private (1)
Limited
New 3 Old 25 3rd Street Off Cenotaph Road Ganapaty Colony, Chennai, 600018, Tamil Nadu, India
Tel.: (91) 7601000555
Web Site: http://www.perambur2.com
Civil Engineering Services
N.A.I.C.S.: 541330

ARIHANT INSTITUTE LIMITED
Binali Complex Office number 221 Backside 2nd Floor, Naranpura, Ahmedabad, 380013, India
Tel.: (91) 9714112277
Web Site: https://arihantinstitute.com
Year Founded: 1998
Rev.: $244,645
Assets: $2,075,800
Liabilities: $165,888
Net Worth: $1,909,911
Earnings: $23,243
Fiscal Year-end: 03/31/19
Educational Support Services
N.A.I.C.S.: 611710
Vinodbhai Chimanlal Shah (Chm)

ARIHANT MULTI COMMER-CIAL LIMITED
F/3 1st Floor Shah Arcade 1 C Wing, Rani Sati Marg Malad E, Mum-bai, 400 097, India
Tel.: (91) 22 28822184   In
Web Site:
    http://www.arihantmulticom.com
Year Founded: 1982
Sales Range: $1-9.9 Million
Textile Product Whslr
N.A.I.C.S.: 424310

ARIHANT SUPERSTRUC-TURES LIMITED
Arihant Aura Floor No 25 Plot No 13/1-TTC Industrial Area, Thane Be-lapur Road Turbhe MIDC Turbhe, Navi Mumbai, 400 705, India
Tel.: (91) 2262493333
Web Site: https://www.asl.net.in

506194—(BOM)
Rev.: $53,471,200
Assets: $140,979,179
Liabilities: $107,451,749
Net Worth: $33,527,430
Earnings: $5,825,178
Emp.: 291
Fiscal Year-end: 03/31/23
Real Estate Development Services
N.A.I.C.S.: 531390
Ashok B. Chhajer *(Chm & Mng Dir)*

Subsidiaries:

Arihant Vatika Realty Private
Limited   (1)
302 Persipolis Building Plot No 74 Sector
17, Vashi, Mumbai, 400 703, India
Tel.: (91) 2241113333
Web Site: http://www.asl.net.in
Sales Range: $75-99.9 Million
Real Estate Development Services
N.A.I.C.S.: 531390
Tushar Khatri *(Gen Mgr-Sls)*

ARIHANT TOURNESOL LTD.

217 Inspire BKC Bandra Kurla Com-
plex, Mumbai, 400060, Maharashtra,
India
Tel.: (91) 2269123200
Web Site: https://www.bn-
holdings.com
Year Founded: 1991
526125—(BOM)
Rev.: $7
Assets: $22,062
Liabilities: $20,678
Net Worth: $1,384
Earnings: ($21,112)
Fiscal Year-end: 03/31/21
Edible Oil Whslr
N.A.I.C.S.: 424490
Anand Thole *(Exec Dir)*

ARIHANT'S SECURITIES LIM-
ITED

138 Dr Radhakrishnan Salai, My-
lapore, Chennai, 600 004, India
Tel.: (91) 4428444555
Web Site:
https://www.arihantssecurities.com
Year Founded: 1994
531017—(BOM)
Rev.: $64,155
Assets: $803,002
Liabilities: $75,908
Net Worth: $727,095
Earnings: $27,013
Fiscal Year-end: 03/31/21
Financial Services
N.A.I.C.S.: 523999
Nishikanth Mohanlal Choudhary *(Mng
Dir)*

ARIMA PHOTOVOLTAIC & OP-
TICAL CORP.

12F No 58 Rueihu St, Neihu, Taipei,
11494, Taiwan
Tel.: (886) 226587718
Web Site: http://www.arima.com.tw
Year Founded: 1987
Sales Range: $800-899.9 Million
Emp.: 10,126
Optoelectronic Product Mfr
N.A.I.C.S.: 334419
David Su *(CEO)*

Subsidiaries:

Arima Communications
Corporation   (1)
No 16 Lane 658 Yingtao Rd, Yingge Town,
Taipei, 23943, Taiwan
Tel.: (886) 226705577
Web Site: http://www.arimacomm.com.tw
Sales Range: $900-999.9 Million
Emp.: 3,500
Mobile Communications Products Mfr
N.A.I.C.S.: 334290
Chih-Cher Chiou *(Chm)*

Arima Display Corporation   (1)
No 248-47 Shin-Sheng Rd, L.E.P.Z., Kaoh-
siung, Taiwan
Tel.: (886) 78115388
Web Site: http://www.arimadisp.com
Sales Range: $400-449.9 Million
Emp.: 2,050
Flat Panel Displays Mfr
N.A.I.C.S.: 334513
Stephen Lee *(Chm, Pres & CEO)*

Arima Optoelectronics
Corporation   (1)
7F No 349 Sec 2 Renhe Rd, Dashi,
Taoyuan, 335, Taiwan
Tel.: (886) 35985999
Web Site: http://www.aocepi.com.tw
Rev.: $6,289,772
Assets: $7,118,268
Liabilities: $7,016,929
Net Worth: $101,339
Earnings: ($2,604,933)
Fiscal Year-end: 12/31/2020
Electronic Components Mfr
N.A.I.C.S.: 334419

ARIMA REAL ESTATE SOCIMI
SA

Edif Torre Serrano c/ Serrano 47,
28001, Madrid, Spain
Tel.: (34) 910532803
Web Site:
https://www.arimainmo.com
Year Founded: 2002
ARM—(MAD)
Real Estate Investment Services
N.A.I.C.S.: 531390
Chony Martin Vicente-Mazariegos
(Board of Directors & CFO)

ARIMELIA ITG SOCIMI, S.A.

Calle Velazquez 150, Bajo, 28002,
Madrid, Spain
Tel.: (34) 604231831
Web Site: https://www.arimelia.com
Year Founded: 2019
MLARI—(EUR)
Real Estate Investment Services
N.A.I.C.S.: 531190
Ryan Craig Howsam *(Chm)*

ARINSIRI LAND PUBLIC COM-
PANY LIMITED

No 49/82 Bangsaen Road Line 4
North, Saensuk Subdistrict Mueang
District, Chon Buri, 20130, Thailand
Tel.: (66) 38191581
Web Site: https://www.arinsiri.com
Year Founded: 2014
ARIN—(THA)
Rev.: $3,479,391
Assets: $23,568,137
Liabilities: $14,114,609
Net Worth: $9,453,528
Earnings: ($1,104,332)
Fiscal Year-end: 12/31/23
Real Estate Development Services
N.A.I.C.S.: 531390
Werapong Chuenpagdee *(Chm)*

ARION BANK HF.

Borgartuni 19 105, 581008-0150,
Reykjavik, Iceland
Tel.: (354) 4447000
Web Site: http://www.arionbanki.is
Year Founded: 2008
Rev.: $479,866,610
Assets: $8,903,666,650
Liabilities: $7,341,406,900
Net Worth: $1,562,259,750
Earnings: $9,053,000
Emp.: 801
Fiscal Year-end: 12/31/19
Banking Services
N.A.I.C.S.: 522110
Stefan Petursson *(CFO)*

Subsidiaries:

Eignabjarg ehf.   (1)

Alfheimum 74, 104, Reykjavik, Iceland
Tel.: (354) 422 1400
Web Site: http://www.iak.is
Emp.: 25
Portfolio Management Services
N.A.I.C.S.: 523940
Vardar Fridjonsson *(Gen Mgr)*

Eignarhaldsfelagio Landey ehf.   (1)
Borgartuni 19, 105, Reykjavik, Iceland
Tel.: (354) 5944200
Web Site: https://www.landey.is
Real Estate Manangement Services
N.A.I.C.S.: 531390

Okkar liftryggingar hf.   (1)
Laugavegur 182, 105, Reykjavik, Iceland
Tel.: (354) 540 1400
Web Site: http://www.okkar.is
Fire Insurance Services
N.A.I.C.S.: 524113

Valitor Holding hf.   (1)
Dalshraun 3, 220, Hafnarfjordur, Iceland
Tel.: (354) 500683 0589
Web Site: http://www.valitor.is
Electronic Payment Services
N.A.I.C.S.: 522320
Vidar Thorkelsson *(CEO)*

ARION BANKI HF

Borgartuni 19, 105, Reykjavik, Ice-
land
Tel.: (354) 4447000
Web Site: https://www.arionbanki.is
ARION—(NASDAQ)
Rev.: $906,133,760
Assets: $11,228,945,920
Liabilities: $9,762,090,560
Net Worth: $1,466,855,360
Earnings: $189,453,760
Emp.: 822
Fiscal Year-end: 12/31/23
Financial Banking Services
N.A.I.C.S.: 522110
Brynjolfur Bjarnason *(Chm)*

ARION TECHNOLOGY INC.

ARION Bldg 24 Simin-daero 327,
Dongan-gu, Anyang, 14055,
Gyeonggi-Do, Korea (South)
Tel.: (82) 313613000
Web Site: http://www.arion.co.kr
Year Founded: 1999
058220—(KRS)
Rev.: $7,539,493
Assets: $23,973,549
Liabilities: $31,837,289
Net Worth: ($7,863,740)
Earnings: ($26,783,460)
Emp.: 45
Fiscal Year-end: 12/31/20
Broadcasting Equipment Mfr
N.A.I.C.S.: 334220
JeongPil Lee *(CEO)*

ARIP PUBLIC COMPANY LIM-
ITED

99/16-20 Ratchadapisek Road, Din-
Daeng, Bangkok, 10400, Thailand
Tel.: (66) 26423400
Web Site: https://www.aripplc.com
ARIP—(THA)
Rev.: $5,638,450
Assets: $8,589,511
Liabilities: $1,478,901
Net Worth: $7,110,610
Earnings: $173,319
Emp.: 69
Fiscal Year-end: 12/31/21
Magazine & Internet Publishing Ser-
vices
N.A.I.C.S.: 513120
Manu Leopairote *(Co-Chm)*

ARISAWA MANUFACTURING
CO., LTD.

Minami Honcho 1-5-5, Joetsu, 943
8610, Niigata, Japan
Tel.: (81) 255245121

Web Site: https://www.arisawa.co.jp
Year Founded: 1949
5208—(TKS)
Rev.: $278,373,540
Assets: $454,873,760
Liabilities: $149,187,700
Net Worth: $305,686,060
Earnings: $10,833,790
Emp.: 1,468
Fiscal Year-end: 03/31/24
Plastics & Resins Mfr
N.A.I.C.S.: 325211
Yoshihiko Toda *(Sr Mng Operating
Officer & Exec Gen Mgr-Performance
Materials Bus)*

Subsidiaries:

Arisawa Fiber Glass Co., Ltd.   (1)
1-5-5 Minamihoncho, Joetsu, 943-0841,
Niigata, Japan
Tel.: (81) 25 524 7551
Web Site: https://www.arisawa-
fiberglass.co.jp
Glass Cloth Product Mfr
N.A.I.C.S.: 327212

Arisawa Jushi Kogyo Co., Ltd.   (1)
Saitama Prefecture Higashi-ryoke 1-18-2,
Kawaguchi, 332-0003, Niigata, Japan
Tel.: (81) 482224981
Web Site: http://www.arisawa.co.jp
Sales Range: $200-249.9 Million
Emp.: 700
Plastics Product Mfr
N.A.I.C.S.: 326199
Toda Yoshihiko *(Pres)*

Arisawa Kenpan Co., Ltd.   (1)
Minami-senba 4-12-12, Chuo-ku, Osaka,
542-0081, Japan
Tel.: (81) 6 6244 4134
Electronic Materials Mfr
N.A.I.C.S.: 334419

Arisawa Manufacturing Co., Ltd. - 3D
Material Division   (1)
Yanagibashi 2-12-5, Taito-ku, Tokyo, 111-
0052, Japan
Tel.: (81) 338613625
Web Site: http://www.arisawa.co.jp
Sales Range: $25-49.9 Million
Emp.: 50
Electronic Materials Mfr
N.A.I.C.S.: 334513
Sanji Prisawa *(Pres)*

Arisawa Manufacturing Co., Ltd. -
Circuit Material Division   (1)
Yanagibashi 2-12-5, Taito-ku, Tokyo, 111-
0052, Japan
Tel.: (81) 338613509
Web Site: http://www.arisawa.co.jp
Sales Range: $25-49.9 Million
Emp.: 35
Electronic Materials Mfr
N.A.I.C.S.: 334513
Sanji Arisawa *(Pres)*

Arisawa Manufacturing Co., Ltd. -
Electrical Insulating & Composite Ma-
terial Division   (1)
2-12-5 Yanagibashi, Taito-ku, Tokyo, 111-
0052, Japan
Tel.: (81) 338612141
Sales Range: $25-49.9 Million
Emp.: 60
Electronic Materials Mfr
N.A.I.C.S.: 334513
Sanji Arisawa *(Pres)*

Arisawa Manufacturing Co., Ltd. -
Electronic Material Division   (1)
Yanagibashi 2-12-5, Taito-ku, Tokyo, 111-
0052, Japan
Tel.: (81) 338613562
Web Site: http://www.arisawa.co.jp
Sales Range: $25-49.9 Million
Emp.: 40
Electronic Materials Mfr
N.A.I.C.S.: 334513

Arisawa Manufacturing Co., Ltd. -
Nakadahara Factory   (1)
Oaza-Nakadahara 1, Joetsu, 943-8610, Nii-
gata, Japan
Tel.: (81) 255247487

Arisawa Manufacturing Co., Ltd.—(Continued)

Sales Range: $200-249.9 Million
Electronic Materials Mfr
N.A.I.C.S.: 334513

**Arisawa Manufacturing Co., Ltd. -
Nakadahara-Nishi Factory**   **(1)**
Oaza-Nakadahara 55, Joetsu, 943-8610,
Niigata, Japan
Tel.: (81) 25241723
Web Site: http://www.arisawa.co.jp
Electronic Materials Mfr
N.A.I.C.S.: 334513

Arisawa Sogyo Co., Ltd.   **(1)**
1-5-5 Minamihoncho, Joetsu, 943-0841,
Niigata, Japan
Tel.: (81) 255242313
Web Site: http://www.arisawa-sogyo.co.jp
Sales Range: $50-74.9 Million
Emp.: 150
Plastics Product Mfr
N.A.I.C.S.: 326199
Yutaka Hayakawa *(Pres)*

Asuna Co., Ltd.   **(1)**
Nana Bldg 6f Taito-Ku, Tokyo, 111-0052,
Japan
Tel.: (81) 338616415
Web Site: http://www.asuna-3d.com
Sales Range: $25-49.9 Million
Emp.: 5
Electronic Materials Mfr
N.A.I.C.S.: 334419
Kenji Matsuhiro *(Pres)*

Colorlink Japan Co., Ltd.   **(1)**
PMO Nihonbashi-Odenmacho 3F 6-8
Nihonbashi-Odenmacho, Chuo-ku, Tokyo,
103-0011, Japan
Tel.: (81) 362311311
Web Site: http://www.colorlink.co.jp
Precision Optics Mfr
N.A.I.C.S.: 333310

Protec Arisawa America, Inc.   **(1)**
2455 Ash St, Vista, CA 92081
Tel.: (760) 599-4800
Fibber Reinforced Pressure Vessel Mfr
N.A.I.C.S.: 332420
Luis Avina *(Pres)*

**Quality Experience Design Co.,
Ltd.**   **(1)**
Waseda Incubation Ctr 09 1-22-3 Nishi-
waseda, Shinjuku, 169-0051, Tokyo, Japan
Tel.: (81) 363803092
Web Site: http://www.qxd.co.jp
Sales Range: $25-49.9 Million
Emp.: 12
Media Technology Services
N.A.I.C.S.: 518210
Keiji Ohta *(CEO)*

Satosen Co., Ltd.   **(1)**
3-7-27 Tsumori, Nishinari-ku, Osaka, 557-
0062, Japan
Tel.: (81) 66 657 0777
Web Site: https://www.satosen.co.jp
Emp.: 170
Printed Circuit Board Mfr
N.A.I.C.S.: 334412
Keita Miyahara *(Pres)*

ThinFlex Corp.   **(1)**
No 8 Luke 2nd Rd, Luzhu Dist, Kaohsiung,
821, Taiwan   **(84.5%)**
Tel.: (886) 76955236
Web Site: http://www.thinflex.com.tw
Rev.: $96,738,016
Assets: $122,695,792
Liabilities: $72,593,761
Net Worth: $50,102,031
Earnings: $4,678,541
Fiscal Year-end: 12/31/2019
Flexible Printed Circuit Board Mfr
N.A.I.C.S.: 334412
Chieh-Hung Wu *(Pres)*

ARISE AB
Linjegatan 7, 301 18, Halmstad, Swe-
den
Tel.: (46) 104507100
Web Site: https://www.arise.se
Year Founded: 2007
ARISE—(OMX)
Rev.: $47,982,739
Assets: $360,296,422

Liabilities: $151,519,457
Net Worth: $208,776,965
Earnings: $18,928,102
Emp.: 71
Fiscal Year-end: 12/31/23
Wind Power Generation & Turbine
Mfr
N.A.I.C.S.: 221118
Joachim Gahm *(Chm)*

Subsidiaries:

Arise Service & Projektering AB   **(1)**
Industrigatan 18, Laholm, 312 34, Halland,
Sweden
Tel.: (46) 430685000
Eletric Power Generation Services
N.A.I.C.S.: 221118

Arise Wind Farm 3 AB   **(1)**
PO Box 808, 301 18, Halmstad, Halland,
Sweden
Tel.: (46) 430685008
Sales Range: $50-74.9 Million
Emp.: 30
Eletric Power Generation Services
N.A.I.C.S.: 221118

Arise Wind Farm 4 AB   **(1)**
Kristian IV S Vag 3, 302 50, Halmstad, Hal-
land, Sweden
Tel.: (46) 352020900
Eletric Power Generation Services
N.A.I.C.S.: 221118

**ARISON HOLDINGS (1998)
LTD.**
Goulda Center 23 Shaul Hamelech
Boulevard, Tel Aviv, 64367, Israel
Tel.: (972) 36073100
Web Site: http://www.arison.co.il
Holding Company
N.A.I.C.S.: 551112
Shari Arison *(Owner)*

Subsidiaries:

Arison Investments Ltd.   **(1)**
Goulda Ctr 23 Shaul Hamelech Blvd, Tel
Aviv, 63467, Israel
Tel.: (972) 37180200
Web Site: http://www.arison.co.il
Investment Holding Company
N.A.I.C.S.: 551112
Efrat Peled *(Chm & CEO)*

**The Ted Arison Family Foundation
(Israel) A Public Benefit Company
Ltd.**   **(1)**
Goulda Center 23 Shaul Hamelech Boule-
vard, Tel Aviv, 64367, Israel
Tel.: (972) 36073100
Grantmaking & Giving Services
N.A.I.C.S.: 813219
Jason Arison *(Chm)*

**ARISTOCRAT LEISURE LIM-
ITED**
Building A Pinnacle Office Park 85
Epping Rd, North Ryde, 2113, NSW,
Australia
Tel.: (61) 290136000   **AU**
Web Site: https://www.aristocrat.com
Year Founded: 1953
ALL—(ASX)
Rev.: $4,104,909,696
Assets: $7,121,536,154
Liabilities: $2,735,997,914
Net Worth: $4,385,538,241
Earnings: $948,099,368
Emp.: 7,800
Fiscal Year-end: 09/30/23
Gambling Machine Operators
N.A.I.C.S.: 551112
Christie Roser *(Chief People & Cul-
ture Officer)*

Subsidiaries:

Aristocrat (Macau) Pty Limited   **(1)**
35-341 Alameda Dr Carlos Assumpcao 17th
Floor Hotline Centre, Macau, China (Macau)
Tel.: (853) 28722777

Web Site: http://www.aristocratgaming.com
Emp.: 30
Electronic Game Machine Mfr
N.A.I.C.S.: 334419
Chris Rowe *(Gen Mgr)*

Aristocrat Argentina S.A.   **(1)**
San Vladimiro 3056 1 Piso of 7 San Isidro,
Buenos Aires, 1107, Argentina
Tel.: (54) 1147085400
Web Site: http://www.aristocratgaming.com
Emp.: 1
Electronic Gaming Machines Mfr
N.A.I.C.S.: 333998

Aristocrat International Pty Ltd   **(1)**
Bldg A Pinnacle Off Park 85 Epping Rd,
North Ryde, 2113, NSW, Australia
Tel.: (61) 290136000
Electronic Gaming Machines Mfr
N.A.I.C.S.: 334419

Subsidiary (Non-US):

Aristocrat Leisure Cyprus Limited   **(2)**
Eagle Star House 5th Floor 35 Theklas Ly-
sioti Street, Limassol, 3030, Cyprus
Tel.: (357) 25817411
Electronic Gaming Machines Mfr
N.A.I.C.S.: 334419

**Aristocrat Service Mexico, S.A. DE
C.V.**   **(2)**
Av de las Palmas 425 of 1401 Col, Lomas
de Chapultepec, Mexico, 11000, Mexico
Tel.: (52) 5552824800
Emp.: 8
Electronic Gaming Machines Mfr
N.A.I.C.S.: 334419
Carlos Carrion *(Gen Mgr)*

**Aristocrat Technologies Europe
Limited**   **(2)**
25 Riverside Way, Uxbridge, UB8 2YF,
Middlesex, United Kingdom
Tel.: (44) 1895618500
Web Site: http://www.aristocrat.com.au
Sales Range: $25-49.9 Million
Emp.: 35
N.A.I.C.S.: 459110

Subsidiary (Domestic):

**Aristocrat Technologies Europe (Hold-
ings) Limited**   **(3)**
25 Riverside Way, Uxbridge, UB8 2YF,
Middlesex, United Kingdom
Tel.: (44) 1895618500
Web Site: http://www.aristocratgaming.com
Sales Range: $25-49.9 Million
Emp.: 25
Electronic Gaming Machines Mfr
N.A.I.C.S.: 334419
James Boja *(Mng Dir)*

Subsidiary (Non-US):

**Aristocrat Technologies Spain
S.L**   **(3)**
Centre D Empreses de Noves Tecnologies,
Avinguda del Parc Tecnologic 3, Cer-
danyola del Valles, 08290, Spain
Tel.: (34) 935824444
Web Site: http://www.aristocratgaming.co.uk
Sales Range: $25-49.9 Million
Emp.: 3
Electronic Gaming Machines Mfr
N.A.I.C.S.: 334419
Jaime Riera *(Gen Mgr)*

Subsidiary (Non-US):

**Aristocrat Technologies India Private
Ltd**   **(2)**
7th Floor ETT Building Film City 24 Sector
16A Gautam Budh Nagar, Noida, Uttar
Pradesh, India
Tel.: (91) 1204677400
Electronic Game Machine Mfr
N.A.I.C.S.: 334419

Aristocrat Properties Pty Ltd   **(1)**
Building A Pinnacle Office Park 85 Epping
Rd, North Ryde, 2113, NSW, Australia
Tel.: (61) 290136000
Web Site: http://www.aristocrattaming.com
Casino Operator
N.A.I.C.S.: 713210
Jamie R. Odell *(Gen Mgr)*

**Aristocrat Technical Services Pty
Ltd**   **(1)**
Building A Pinnacle Office Park 85 Epping
Rd, North Ryde, 2113, NSW, Australia
Tel.: (61) 290136000
Web Site:
    http://www.aristocratgaming.com.au
Electronic Gaming Equipment Mfr
N.A.I.C.S.: 334419

**Aristocrat Technologies Australia Pty.
Ltd.**   **(1)**
Building A Pinnacle Office Park 85 Epping
Road, Shailer Park, North Ryde, 2113,
NSW, Australia   **(100%)**
Tel.: (61) 29 013 6000
Web Site: https://www.aristocrat.com
Sales Range: $25-49.9 Million
Emp.: 22
Sporting Goods
N.A.I.C.S.: 459110

Subsidiary (Domestic):

**Aristocrat Technology Gaming Sys-
tems Pty Limited**   **(2)**
85 Epping Rd, North Ryde, 2113, NSW,
Australia
Tel.: (61) 290136000
Electronic Gaming Machines Mfr
N.A.I.C.S.: 334419

**Aristocrat Technologies Macau
Limited**   **(1)**
335-341 Alameda Dr Carlos Assumpcao
Hotline Center 17th Floor Unit A, Macau,
China (Macau)
Tel.: (853) 28722777
Game Publishing Services
N.A.I.C.S.: 513210

**Aristocrat Technologies NZ
Limited**   **(1)**
Unit E 7 Echelon Place Highbrook, Auck-
land, 2013, New Zealand   **(100%)**
Tel.: (64) 92592000
Web Site: http://www.aristocratgaming.com
Sales Range: $25-49.9 Million
Emp.: 80
Gaming Technologies, Systems & Solutions
N.A.I.C.S.: 334118

Aristocrat Technologies, Inc.   **(1)**
10220 Aristocrat Way, Las Vegas, NV
89135
Tel.: (702) 270-1000
Web Site: http://www.aristocrat-us.com
Sales Range: $25-49.9 Million
Emp.: 100
Hobby, Toy & Game Shops
N.A.I.C.S.: 459120

Big Fish Games, Inc.   **(1)**
906 Alaskan Way Ste 700, Seattle, WA
98104
Tel.: (206) 213-5753
Web Site: http://www.bigfishgames.com
Online & Mobile Interactive Games Creator
& Distr
N.A.I.C.S.: 339930
Carey DiJulio *(Sr VP-Product & Mktg & Gen
Mgr-Self Aware Games Studio)*

K.K. Aristocrat Technologies   **(1)**
7th Floor Ryukakusan Building 2-5-12
Higashi-kanda, Chiyoda-ku, Tokyo, 101
0031, Japan
Tel.: (81) 358350521
Web Site: http://www.aristocrat.co.jp
Sales Range: $75-99.9 Million
Emp.: 79
Slot Machines, Gaming Development, Pro-
duction & Sales
N.A.I.C.S.: 334118

Plarium Global Limited   **(1)**
2 Abba Eban Blvd, Herzliya, Israel
Tel.: (972) 99540211
Game Publishing Services
N.A.I.C.S.: 513210

Video Gaming Technologies, Inc.   **(1)**
308 Mallory Station Rd, Franklin, TN 37067
Tel.: (615) 372-1000
Web Site: https://www.vgt.net
Emp.: 630
Coin-Operated Gambling Machines Devel-
oper, Mfr & Whslr
N.A.I.C.S.: 339999

Plant (Domestic):

Video Gaming Technologies, Inc. - Tulsa   (2)
12000 E Skelly Dr, Tulsa, OK 74128
Tel.: (918) 384-7000
Web Site: https://www.vgt.net
Coin-Operated Gambling Machines Mfr
N.A.I.C.S.: 339999

ARISTON HOLDING N.V.
Via Broletto 44, 20121, Milan, Italy
Web Site:
    https://www.aristongroup.com
Year Founded: 1930
ARIS—(EUR)
Rev.: $2,921,737,312
Assets: $3,535,488,840
Liabilities: $2,292,264,312
Net Worth: $1,243,224,528
Earnings: $172,322,072
Emp.: 7,975
Fiscal Year-end: 12/31/22
Holding Company
N.A.I.C.S.: 551112
Laurent Jacquemin *(CEO)*

Subsidiaries:

Ariston Deutschland GmbH   (1)
Hohenzollernstrasse 31, D-72379, Hechingen, Germany
Tel.: (49) 7471187650
Gas Cylinder & Electric Water Heater Mfr
N.A.I.C.S.: 332410

Ariston Thermo CZ s.r.o.   (1)
Podebradska 88/55, Hloubetin, 198 00, Prague, Czech Republic
Tel.: (420) 222713455
Gas Cylinder & Electric Water Heater Mfr
N.A.I.C.S.: 332410

Ariston Thermo Maroc S.A.   (1)
Casablanca Logistics 1 lot No 12 Etage 1 Appt No 3 Z I de, Ouled Saleh Casablanca, Bouskoura, Morocco
Tel.: (212) 522352283
Gas Cylinder & Electric Water Heater Mfr
N.A.I.C.S.: 332410

Ariston Thermo Romania S.r.l.   (1)
Str Polona 68-72 Polona Business Center - Etaj 11 Sector 1, Bucharest, Romania
Tel.: (40) 212319523
Gas Cylinder & Electric Water Heater Mfr
N.A.I.C.S.: 332410

Ariston Thermo UK Ltd.   (1)
3 Juniper West Fenton Way, Basildon, SS15 6SJ, United Kingdom
Tel.: (44) 3332408777
Gas Cylinder & Electric Water Heater Mfr
N.A.I.C.S.: 332410

Ariston Thermo USA LLC   (1)
272 Duchaine Blvd, New Bedford, MA 02745
Tel.: (508) 763-8071
Web Site: https://www.htproducts.com
Water Heating Services
N.A.I.C.S.: 532411

Ariston Thermo Vietnam Ltd.   (1)
8th Floor Hanoi Tourist Building 18 Ly Thuong Kiet, Hoan Kiem, Hanoi, Vietnam
Tel.: (84) 837108245
Heat Pump Water Heater Services
N.A.I.C.S.: 532411

Atag Heating B.V.   (1)
PO Box 105, 7130 AC, Lichtenvoorde, Netherlands
Tel.: (31) 544391777
Web Site: https://www.atagverwarming.nl
Water Heating Services
N.A.I.C.S.: 532210

Atag Heizungstechnik GmbH   (1)
Dinxperloer Str 18, 46399, Bocholt, Germany
Tel.: (49) 28712380886
Web Site:
    https://www.atagheizungstechnik.de
Air Water Heat Pump Services
N.A.I.C.S.: 532411

Atag Verwarming Belgie B.V.B.A.   (1)

Leo Baekelandstraat 3, 2950, Kapellen, Belgium
Tel.: (32) 36416440
Web Site: https://www.atagverwarming.be
Heating Equipment Mfr
N.A.I.C.S.: 332410

Atmor Industries Ltd.   (1)
6 Hasadna st St, Kefar Sava, 4442405, Israel
Tel.: (972) 99612700
Web Site: https://atmor.net
Electric Instant Water Heater Mfr & Distr
N.A.I.C.S.: 333414

Cuenod S.A.S.   (1)
2 rue Josue Heilmann, 68800, Vieux-Thann, France
Tel.: (33) 369155130
Web Site: https://www.cuenod.com
Hardware & Plumbing Whslr
N.A.I.C.S.: 423720

Ecoflam Bruciatori S.p.A.   (1)
Via Roma 64, 31023, Resana, Italy
Tel.: (39) 0423719500
Burner & Boiler Mfr
N.A.I.C.S.: 332410

Elco Austria GmbH   (1)
Aredstrasse 16-18, A-2544, Leobersdorf, Austria
Tel.: (43) 2256639990
Web Site: https://www.elco.at
Emp.: 45
Oil Burner Mfr & Distr
N.A.I.C.S.: 332410

Elco Burners B.V.   (1)
Meerpaalweg 1, 1332 BB, Almere, Netherlands
Tel.: (31) 886957311
Burner & Boiler Mfr
N.A.I.C.S.: 332410

Elco Burners GmbH   (1)
Dreieichstrasse 10, 64546, Morfelden-Walldorf, Germany
Tel.: (49) 6105287287
Burner & Boiler Mfr
N.A.I.C.S.: 332410

Elco Heating Solutions Limited   (1)
3 Juniper West Fenton Way Southfields Business Park, Basildon, SS15 6SJ, Essex, United Kingdom
Tel.: (44) 3456460442
Web Site: https://www.elco.co.uk
Burner & Boiler Mfr
N.A.I.C.S.: 332410

Gastech-Energi A/S   (1)
Sindalsvej 8, 8240, Risskov, Denmark
Tel.: (45) 70101540
Web Site: https://www.gastech.dk
Heat Pumps & Gas Boiler Services
N.A.I.C.S.: 532210

Ingrado S.R.L.   (1)
Via Innocenzo Malvasia 6, 40131, Bologna, Italy
Tel.: (39) 0282180016
Web Site: https://www.ingrado.com
Water Heating Services
N.A.I.C.S.: 532210

NTI Boilers Inc.   (1)
30 Stonegate Drive, Saint John, E2H 0A4, NB, Canada
Tel.: (506) 657-6000
Web Site: https://www.ntiboilers.com
Boiler & Water Heater Mfr
N.A.I.C.S.: 332410

P.T. Ariston Thermo Indonesia   (1)
Dipo Business Center Lantai 15 Jl Jendral Gatot Subroto Kav 51-52, Jakarta, 10260, Indonesia
Tel.: (62) 2129865999
Gas Cylinder & Electric Water Heater Mfr
N.A.I.C.S.: 332410

Thermowatt Professional S.R.L.   (1)
Via S Giovanni Battista 21, Arcevia, 60011, Ancona, Italy
Tel.: (39) 03907319881
Web Site: https://www.thermowatt.com
Emp.: 770
Electric Heating System Mfr
N.A.I.C.S.: 333414

ARISTON THERMO S.P.A.
Viale Aristide Merloni 45, Fabriano, 60044, Ancona, Italy
Tel.: (39) 07326011
Web Site: http://www.ariston.com
Sales Range: $1-4.9 Billion
Emp.: 6,800
Air Conditioners, Boilers & Water Heaters
N.A.I.C.S.: 333415
Paolo Merloni *(Chm)*

Subsidiaries:

Domotec SA   (1)
Lindengutstrasse 16, 4663, Aarburg, Switzerland
Tel.: (41) 62 787 87 87
Web Site: http://www.domotec.ch
Emp.: 52
Heater Mfr & Distr
N.A.I.C.S.: 333414
Ueli Ehrbar *(Mng Dir)*

Elcotherm AG   (1)
Sarganserstrasse 100, CH 7324, Vilters, Switzerland
Tel.: (41) 817252525
Web Site: http://www.elco.ch
Emp.: 160
Electronic Services
N.A.I.C.S.: 221122
Rene Schuermann *(Mng Dir)*

Subsidiary (Domestic):

Cipag SA   (2)
Rte de la Z I du Verney 4, 1070, Puidoux, Switzerland
Tel.: (41) 21 926 66 66
Web Site: http://www.cipag.ch
Water Heating System Mfr & Distr
N.A.I.C.S.: 333310

ARITZIA, INC.
118-611 Alexander Street, Vancouver, V6A 1E1, BC, Canada
Tel.: (604) 251-3132
Web Site: https://www.aritzia.com
Year Founded: 1984
ATZ—(TSX)
Rev.: $1,169,219,156
Assets: $1,114,425,136
Liabilities: $699,182,307
Net Worth: $415,242,829
Earnings: $122,753,031
Emp.: 6,569
Fiscal Year-end: 02/27/22
Clothing & Accessory Distr
N.A.I.C.S.: 424350
Jennifer Wong *(Pres, CEO, COO & Sec)*

Subsidiaries:

Aritzia LP   (1)
118 - 611 Alexander Street, Vancouver, V6A 1E1, BC, Canada
Web Site: https://www.aritzia.com
Apparel Distr
N.A.I.C.S.: 458110

CYC Design Corporation   (1)
2772 Natal Street, Vancouver, V5M 2H1, BC, Canada
Tel.: (604) 877-0062
Web Site: https://cycdesigncorp.com
Apparel Accessories & Apparel Mfr
N.A.I.C.S.: 339999

ARIUS TECHNOLOGY INC.
999 West Hastings Street Suite 1260, Vancouver, V6C 2W2, BC, Canada
Tel.: (905) 264-8559
Web Site:
    http://www.ariustechnology.com
Sales Range: $1-9.9 Million
Direct Color Scanning Systems Developer & Mfr
N.A.I.C.S.: 333310
Patrick Robinson *(Co-Founder & Chm)*

Subsidiaries:

Arius Technology Inc. - Vaughan   (1)
Unit 19 115 Woodstream Boulevard, Vaughan, L4L 8K5, ON, Canada
Tel.: (905) 264-8559
Web Site: http://www.ariustechnology.com
Emp.: 18
Direct Color Scanning Systems Developer & Mfr
N.A.I.C.S.: 333310
John Bell *(Chief Scientist)*

ARIX BIOSCIENCE PLC
20 Berkeley Square, London, W1J 6EQ, United Kingdom
Tel.: (44) 2072901050   UK
Web Site:
    http://www.arixbioscience.com
Year Founded: 2015
ARIX—(LSE)
Sales Range: $1-9.9 Million
Emp.: 16
Investment Brokerage Services
N.A.I.C.S.: 523150
Mark Chin *(Mng Dir)*

ARIZONA SILVER EXPLORATION INC.
Suite 970 -777 Hornby Street, Vancouver, V6Z 1S4, BC, Canada
Tel.: (604) 559-3511   BC
Web Site:
    https://arizonasilverexploration.com
Year Founded: 2011
AZS—(TSXV)
Assets: $6,218,887
Liabilities: $139,647
Net Worth: $6,079,239
Earnings: ($1,201,648)
Fiscal Year-end: 08/31/23
Investment Services
N.A.I.C.S.: 523999
Dong H. Shim *(CFO & Sec)*

ARIZONA SONORAN COPPER COMPANY INC.
Simpson Tower 401 Bay Street Suite 2704, Box 4, Toronto, M5H 2Y4, ON, Canada
Tel.: (775) 340-2719   BC
Web Site:
    https://www.arizonasonoran.com
Year Founded: 2019
ASCUF—(OTCQX)
Assets: $69,578,000
Liabilities: $3,596,000
Net Worth: $65,982,000
Earnings: $7,121,000
Emp.: 17
Fiscal Year-end: 12/31/22
Mineral Mining Services
N.A.I.C.S.: 213115
Bernie Loyer *(Sr VP)*

ARJOWIGGINS SECURITY SAS
32 avenue Pierre Grenier, 92517, Boulogne-Billancourt, Cedex, France
Tel.: (33) 157759300   FR
Web Site:
    http://www.security.arjowiggins.com
Year Founded: 1770
Security Paper Products Mfr
N.A.I.C.S.: 322120
Michel Jacques Giordani *(VP)*

ARJUN INFRASTRUCTURE PARTNERS LIMITED
33 St James's Square, London, SW1Y 4JS, United Kingdom
Tel.: (44) 20 3709 5330   UK
Web Site: http://www.aip-am.co.uk
Year Founded: 2015
Sales Range: Less than $1 Million
Investment Advisory Services
N.A.I.C.S.: 523940

Arjun Infrastructure Partners
Limited—(Continued)

Surinder Toor *(Mng Partner)*

Subsidiaries:

South Staffordshire Plc **(1)**
Green Lane, Walsall, WS2 7PD, West Midlands, United Kingdom **(75%)**
Tel.: (44) 1922638282
Web Site:
http://www.south-staffordshire.com
Rev.: $367,439,764
Assets: $1,208,311,060
Liabilities: $1,079,077,840
Net Worth: $129,233,220
Earnings: $3,709,291
Emp.: 2,714
Fiscal Year-end: 03/31/2020
Holding Company
N.A.I.C.S.: 551112
Phil C. Newland *(CEO-Grp)*

Subsidiary (Domestic):

Cambridge Water Plc **(2)**
90 Fulbourn Road, Cambridge, CB1 9JN, United Kingdom
Tel.: (44) 1223706050
Web Site: http://www.cambridge-water.co.uk
Sales Range: $25-49.9 Million
Emp.: 90
Drinking Water Services
N.A.I.C.S.: 221310
Tim Orange *(Dir-Fin & Head-Customer Ops)*

Echo Managed Services Ltd. **(2)**
Green Lane, Walsall, WS2 7PD, W Midlands, United Kingdom **(100%)**
Tel.: (44) 8451212122
Web Site:
http://www.echomanagedservices.com
Sales Range: $200-249.9 Million
Emp.: 600
Water Utility Customer Management, Billing & Cash Collection Services
N.A.I.C.S.: 926130
Noigel Biker *(Gen Mgr)*

Subsidiary (Domestic):

Rapid Systems Ltd. **(3)**
Green Lane, Walsall, WS2 7PD, W Midlands, United Kingdom
Tel.: (44) 8451212122
Web Site: http://www.echo-ms.com
Utility Customer Management Software Services
N.A.I.C.S.: 518210
Nigel Baker *(Mng Dir)*

Subsidiary (Domestic):

Integrated Water Services Ltd. **(2)**
Green Lane, Walsall, WS2 7PD, United Kingdom
Tel.: (44) 345 6006028
Web Site: http://www.integrated-water.co.uk
Water Systems Mfr & Distr
N.A.I.C.S.: 221310

Subsidiary (Domestic):

Green Compliance Water Division Ltd. **(3)**
Unit 2 Derwent Close, Warndon, WR4 9TY, Worcs, United Kingdom
Tel.: (44) 33 022 31313
Web Site: http://www.greencompliance.com
Water Management, Air Hygiene Technologies & Services
N.A.I.C.S.: 924110

Division (Domestic):

Integrated Water Services Ltd. - Pipeline Services Div **(3)**
Park Lane West, Tipton, Dudley, DY4 8LH, United Kingdom **(100%)**
Tel.: (44) 1215201006
Web Site: http://www.upls.co.uk
Underground Water Main Assessment, Repair & Replacement Services
N.A.I.C.S.: 237120

Subsidiary (Domestic):

OnSite Central Limited **(2)**
89 Blackpole West, Blackpole, Worcester,

WR3 8TJ, Worchestershire, United Kingdom **(100%)**
Tel.: (44) 1905 340054
Web Site: http://www.onsite.co.uk
Sales Range: $25-49.9 Million
Emp.: 100
Waste Water Management & Sewer Inspection Services
N.A.I.C.S.: 562098
Alan Plante *(Mng Dir)*

South Staffordshire Water PLC **(2)**
Green Lane, Walsall, WS2 7PD, W Midlands, United Kingdom
Tel.: (44) 192263828
Web Site: http://www.south-Staffordshire.com
Sales Range: $500-549.9 Million
Emp.: 700
Water Distr
N.A.I.C.S.: 221310

Subsidiary (Domestic):

Aqua Direct Ltd. **(3)**
Elmhurst Spring Lichfield Road, Elmhurst, Lichfield, WS13 8HQ, Staffs, United Kingdom
Tel.: (44) 1543493613
Web Site: http://www.aqua-direct.co.uk
Emp.: 19
Spring & Mineral Water Bottler & Distr
N.A.I.C.S.: 312112
Helene James *(Dir-Sls & Mktg)*

ARK MINES LTD
Tel.: (61) 292332688
Web Site:
https://www.arkmines.com.au
Year Founded: 2007
Rev.: $2,892
Assets: $2,737,790
Liabilities: $5,698,726
Net Worth: ($2,960,936)
Earnings: ($504,982)
Fiscal Year-end: 06/30/18
Gold & Base Metal Mining Services
N.A.I.C.S.: 212220
Ian Burnham Mitchell *(Sec)*

ARK RESOURCES HOLDINGS SDN BHD
1019 1Sky Tingkat Mahsuri 2, Bayan Lepas Pulau, 11950, Penang, Malaysia
Tel.: (60) 46118808
Web Site: https://www.ark-resources.com.my
Year Founded: 1983
ARK—(KLS)
Rev.: $1,543,106
Assets: $3,912,434
Liabilities: $1,194,582
Net Worth: $2,717,852
Earnings: ($173,402)
Emp.: 9
Fiscal Year-end: 03/31/23
Engineering & Construction Services
N.A.I.C.S.: 541330
Mohamad Zekri Ibrahim *(Chm)*

ARKADIA CAPITAL CORP.
c/o 1400 350 7th Av SW, Calgary, T2P 3N9, AB, Canada
Tel.: (403) 299-9600   AB
Year Founded: 2011
AKC—(TSXV)
Sales Range: Less than $1 Million
Investment Holding Company
N.A.I.C.S.: 551112
Dennis L. Nerland *(Pres & CEO)*

ARKAN AL-KUWAIT REAL ESTATE COMPANY KSCC
66th floor Al Hamra Tower, Sharq, Kuwait, Kuwait
Tel.: (965) 22050666
Web Site:
https://www.arkanalkuwait.com
ARKAN—(KUW)
Rev.: $22,516,016

Assets: $478,740,295
Liabilities: $332,717,878
Net Worth: $146,022,417
Earnings: $2,923,426
Emp.: 280
Fiscal Year-end: 10/31/23
Real Estate Services
N.A.I.C.S.: 531390
Fahad Almukhaizim *(Chm)*

ARKCORE, INC.
3rd Floor Sky Building Ikebukuro West Exit 2-14-4 Ikebukuro, Toshima-ku, Tokyo, 123-0871, Japan
Tel.: (81) 359281537
Web Site: https://arkcore.co.jp
Year Founded: 2002
3384—(NGO)
Sales Range: Less than $1 Million
Motor Vehicle Distr
N.A.I.C.S.: 423110
Yasuhiro Masato *(CEO)*

ARKEMA S.A.
420 rue d'Estienne d'Orves, 92705, Colombes, Cedex, France
Tel.: (33) 149008080   FR
Web Site: https://www.arkema.com
Year Founded: 1953
AKE—(OTCIQ)
Rev.: $9,683,444,160
Assets: $13,155,678,640
Liabilities: $6,725,842,240
Net Worth: $6,429,836,400
Earnings: $407,775,680
Emp.: 20,600
Fiscal Year-end: 12/31/20
Vinyl Products, Industrial Chemicals & Performance Chemicals Mfr
N.A.I.C.S.: 325211
Bernard Boyer *(Exec VP-Strategy)*

Subsidiaries:

ARKEMA CHINA INVESTMENT Co. Ltd **(1)**
Investment Management Service
N.A.I.C.S.: 523999

Subsidiary (Domestic):

ARKEMA (Changshu) Fluorochemical Co. Ltd **(2)**
No 18 Haining Road, Advanced Materials Industrial Park, Changshu, 215522, China
Tel.: (86) 51252322538
Chemical Products Mfr
N.A.I.C.S.: 325180

Afinitica Technologies S.L. **(1)**
Edifici Eureka Campus UAB, Bellaterra, 08193, Barcelona, Spain
Tel.: (34) 93 143 1952
Web Site: https://www2.afinitica.com
Adhesive Mfr
N.A.I.C.S.: 325520

Altuglas International Denmark A/S **(1)**
Industrivej 16, 9700, Brønderslev, Denmark
Tel.: (45) 96464646
Sales Range: $50-74.9 Million
Emp.: 81
Acrylic Sheet Mfr & Distr
N.A.I.C.S.: 326113
Flemming Saaby *(Mgr-Production)*

Altuglas International S.A.S. **(1)**
420 rue d Estienne d Orves, 92705, Colombes, Cedex, France
Tel.: (33) 1 7866 2300
Web Site: http://www.altuglasint.com
Sales Range: $700-749.9 Million
Acrylic Resin & Sheet Products
N.A.I.C.S.: 326130

Subsidiary (US):

Altuglas International **(2)**
100 PA Route 413, Bristol, PA 19007
Tel.: (215) 826-2600
Mfr of Acrylic Resin & Sheet Products
N.A.I.C.S.: 326130

Unit (Domestic):

Altuglas International **(3)**
4350 Camp Ground Rd, Louisville, KY 40216
Tel.: (502) 449-6100
Sales Range: $25-49.9 Million
Emp.: 76
Mfr of Acrylic Resin Sheet Products
N.A.I.C.S.: 326130

Subsidiary (Non-US):

Maquiladora General de Matamoros S.A. de C.V **(3)**
Poniente 2 No 17, Matamoros, 87470, Mexico
Tel.: (52) 8688128065
Web Site: http://www.altuglasint.com
Sales Range: $50-74.9 Million
Emp.: 175
Mfr of Acrylic Sheets & Plastic Modifiers
N.A.I.C.S.: 326130

Subsidiary (Non-US):

Altuglas International **(2)**
7FL DongSung Building 17-8 Yoipo Dong Young Teung To Gu, Seoul, 07236, Korea (South)
Tel.: (82) 237036700
Web Site: http://www.altuglas.com
Sales Range: $25-49.9 Million
Emp.: 10
Mfr of Acrylic Resin & Sheet Products
N.A.I.C.S.: 326130

Arkema (Changshu) Polyamides Co., Ltd. **(1)**
No 18 Haining Road, Advanced Materials Industrial Park, Changshu, 215522, Jiangsu, China
Tel.: (86) 51252322688
Emp.: 800
Chemicals Mfr
N.A.I.C.S.: 325998

Arkema (Suzhou) Polyamides Co., Ltd. **(1)**
No 1 Feng Nan Road, Fenghuang Town, Zhangjiagang, 215613, Jiangsu, China
Emp.: 165
Chemicals Mfr
N.A.I.C.S.: 325998

Arkema B.V. **(1)**
Tankhoofd 10 - Harbor no 3255, Vondelingenplaat, 3196 KE, Rotterdam, Netherlands
Tel.: (31) 10 472 5100
Web Site: https://www.arkema.com
Sales Range: $25-49.9 Million
Emp.: 20
Distr & Retailer of Chemical Products
N.A.I.C.S.: 424690

Subsidiary (Domestic):

Arkema Rotterdam BV **(2)**
Tankhoofd 10, Vondelingenplaat, 3196 KE, Rotterdam, Netherlands
Tel.: (31) 104725100
Web Site: http://www.arkema.com
Sales Range: $25-49.9 Million
Chemicals & Fungicides Mfr
N.A.I.C.S.: 325998

Arkema Vlissingen B.V. **(2)**
Europaweg Zuid 2 Harbor no 9850, 4389 PD, Vlissingen, Netherlands **(100%)**
Tel.: (31) 113617000
Sales Range: $75-99.9 Million
Mfr of Plastic Heat Stabilizers, Glass Coatings & Fertilizers
N.A.I.C.S.: 325211

Arkema Changshu Chemicals Co. Ltd. **(1)**
Tel.: (86) 51252322538
Chemical Products Mfr
N.A.I.C.S.: 325180

Arkema Chemicals India Private Ltd. **(1)**
D-43 Trans Thane Creek, MIDC Industrial Area, Mumbai, 400706, India
Tel.: (91) 2267377122
Chemicals Mfr
N.A.I.C.S.: 325998

Arkema Chemicals Saudi Arabia **(1)**

Tel.: (966) 138469110
Chemicals Mfr
N.A.I.C.S.: 325998

Arkema Co. Ltd (1)
Suite 3212 32/F Tower 1 The Gateway 25
Canton Road, Tsim Sha Tsui, Kowloon,
China (Hong Kong)
Tel.: (852) 2629 1826
Chemical Products Distr
N.A.I.C.S.: 424690

Arkema Coatex Brasil Industria e Comercio Ltda. (1)
Rua Beta S/N - Polo Petroquimico, Cama-
cari, 42810-300, BA, Brazil
Tel.: (55) 7136345083
Coated Resin & Additive Distr
N.A.I.C.S.: 424690

Arkema Coating Resins Ltd. (1)
Laporte Rd North East, Stallingborough,
Grimsby, DN41 8FG, Lincolnshire, United
Kingdom
Tel.: (44) 1469572464
Chemicals Mfr
N.A.I.C.S.: 325998

Arkema Coating Resins Malaysia Sdn. Bhd. (1)
PLO 491 Jalan Keluli, Pasir Gudang Indus-
trial Estate, 81700, Pasir Gudang, Johor,
Malaysia
Tel.: (60) 72536688
Chemicals Mfr
N.A.I.C.S.: 325998

Arkema Coatings Resins, S.A.U. (1)
Carretera de Olzinelles S/N, Sant Celoni,
08470, Barcelona, Spain
Tel.: (34) 938674000
Emp.: 11
Chemical Products Distr
N.A.I.C.S.: 424690
Peter Heerwegh (Mng Dir)

Arkema Company Ltd. (1)
Unit 4112 - 4116 41/F Tower 1 Metroplaza
223 Hing Fong Road, Kwai Fong, China
(Hong Kong)
Tel.: (852) 26291047
Chemicals Mfr
N.A.I.C.S.: 325998

Arkema Deutschland GmbH (1)
Tersteegenstr 28, 40474, Dusseldorf, Ger-
many
Tel.: (49) 2 114 5520
Web Site: https://www.arkema.com
Sales Range: $50-74.9 Million
Emp.: 60
Chemical Distr
N.A.I.C.S.: 424690

Arkema Europe SA (1)
420 rue d Estienne d Orves, 92705, Co-
lombes, Cedex, France
Tel.: (33) 14 900 8080
Web Site: https://www.arkema.com
Emp.: 800
Chemical Products Mfr
N.A.I.C.S.: 325199

Subsidiary (Non-US):

Arkema GmbH (2)
Tel.: (49) 21145520
Sales Range: $25-49.9 Million
Emp.: 4
Chemical Products Mfr
N.A.I.C.S.: 325998
Heike Laustroer (Mgr-Sls)

Arkema Hydrogen Peroxide Co., Ltd. (1)
No 555 Shuangbai Road, Minhang District,
Shanghai, 201108, China
Tel.: (86) 2164341928
Emp.: 110
Hydrogen Peroxide Mfr
N.A.I.C.S.: 325180

Arkema Inc. (1)
2000 Market St, Philadelphia, PA 19103-
3231
Tel.: (215) 419-7000
Web Site: http://www.arkema-inc.com
Sales Range: $1-4.9 Billion
Emp.: 800
Chemicals Mfr
N.A.I.C.S.: 325998

Chris Giangrasso (Sr VP-HR, Comm & Site
Svcs)

Joint Venture (Domestic):

American Acryl LP (2)
4631 Old Hwy 146 Ste B, Pasadena, TX
77507
Tel.: (281) 909-2600
Web Site: https://www.americanacryl.com
Sales Range: $10-24.9 Million
Mfr of Amines, Acids, Salts & Esters. Joint
Venture of Arkema S.A. (50%) & NA Indus-
tries, Inc. (50%).
N.A.I.C.S.: 325199

Subsidiary (Non-US):

Arkema Canada Inc. (2)
1100 Burloak Drive Suite 107, Burlington,
L7L 6B2, ON, Canada
Tel.: (905) 331-5000
Web Site: http://www.arkema.ca
Sales Range: $50-74.9 Million
Emp.: 7
Distr of Hydrogen Peroxide
N.A.I.C.S.: 325180

Division (Domestic):

Arkema Canada Inc. (3)
1100 Burloak Drive Suite 107, Becancour,
L7L 6B2, ON, Canada
Tel.: (905) 331-5000
Web Site: https://www.arkema.com
Sales Range: $25-49.9 Million
Emp.: 62
Mfr of Hydrogen Peroxide
N.A.I.C.S.: 325180

Unit (Domestic):

Arkema Coating Resins (2)
410 Gregson Dr, Cary, NC 27511-6445
Tel.: (919) 469-6700
Web Site:
   http://www.arkemacoatingresins.com
Sales Range: $450-499.9 Million
Emp.: 1,650
Specialty Coating Resins Developer & Mfr
N.A.I.C.S.: 325991

Plant (Domestic):

Arkema Coating Resins - Alsip (3)
12840 S Pulaski Rd, Alsip, IL 60803-1917
Tel.: (708) 396-3000
Sales Range: $10-24.9 Million
Emp.: 40
Specialty Coating Resins Developer & Mfr
N.A.I.C.S.: 325991

Arkema Coating Resins - Torrance Plant (3)
19206 Hawthorne Blvd, Torrance, CA
90503-1505
Tel.: (310) 214-5300
Sales Range: $25-49.9 Million
Emp.: 60
Specialty Coating Resins Developer & Mfr
N.A.I.C.S.: 325991

Unit (Domestic):

Arkema Research Center (2)
900 1st Ave, King of Prussia, PA 19406
Tel.: (610) 878-6500
Web Site: http://www.arkema-americas.com
Sales Range: $150-199.9 Million
Emp.: 600
Chemical Research & Development Ser-
vices
N.A.I.C.S.: 541715
Ryan Dirkx (VP-R&D)

Subsidiary (Domestic):

Coatex Inc. (2)
547 Ecology Ln, Chester, SC 29706-4722
Tel.: (803) 377-6200
Web Site: http://www.coatex.com
Sales Range: $25-49.9 Million
Emp.: 56
Chemical Products Mfr
N.A.I.C.S.: 325199

Delaware Chemicals Corporation (2)
1105 N Market St Ste 1300, Wilmington, DE
19801-1241
Tel.: (302) 427-0263
Chemical Products Mfr

N.A.I.C.S.: 325998

ODOR-TECH LLC (2)
7591 Esler Field Rd, Pineville, LA 71360
Tel.: (318) 767-0821
Web Site: http://www.odor-tech.com
Emp.: 17
Natural Gas Distribution Services
N.A.I.C.S.: 221210

Sartomer USA, LLC (2)
502 Thomas Jones Way, Exton, PA 19341-
2530
Tel.: (610) 363-4100
Sales Range: $50-74.9 Million
Emp.: 150
Specialty Chemicals Mfr & Supplier
N.A.I.C.S.: 325998

Subsidiary (Non-US):

Sartomer Asia Limited (3)
Unit 4112 - 4116 Level 41 Tower 1 Metro-
plaza, Kwai Fong, Hong Kong, China (Hong
Kong)
Tel.: (852) 26291826
Web Site: https://asia.sartomer.arkema.com
Inorganic Chemical Mfr
N.A.I.C.S.: 325998

Plant (Domestic):

Sartomer USA, LLC (3)
601 Tightsqueeze Industrial Rd, Chatham,
VA 24531-3678
Tel.: (434) 432-3705
Web Site: http://americas.sartomer.com
Sales Range: $25-49.9 Million
Emp.: 100
Mfr of Industrial Inorganic Chemicals
N.A.I.C.S.: 325998
Marcel Dewols (CEO)

Sartomer USA, LLC (3)
610 S Bolmar St, West Chester, PA 19382-
3805
Tel.: (610) 692-8401
Web Site: http://americas.sartomer.com
Sales Range: $25-49.9 Million
Emp.: 90
Mfr Inorganic Chemicals, Plastic Materials &
Resins
N.A.I.C.S.: 325998

Subsidiary (Domestic):

Viking chemical company (2)
157 Hwy Ave N, Blooming Prairie, MN
55917
Tel.: (507) 583-6641
Web Site: http://www.arkema.com
Emp.: 46
Chemical Products Mfr
N.A.I.C.S.: 325199

Arkema Iniciadores SA de CV (1)
Via Gustavo Baz 2160 Edificio 3 Fracc In-
dustrial La Loma, 54070, Tlalnepantla,
Mexico
Tel.: (52) 55 5002 7101
Chemical Products Mfr
N.A.I.C.S.: 325998

Arkema K.K. (1)
Fukoku-Seimei Bldg 15F 2-2-2 Uchisaiwa-
icho, Chiyoda-ku, Tokyo, 100-0011, Japan
Tel.: (81) 352519900
Web Site: https://www.arkema.com
Specialty Chemicals Distr
N.A.I.C.S.: 424690
Atsushi Miyabo (VP)

Arkema Kimya Sanayi ve Ticaret AS (1)
Mecidiyekoy Nahallesi Oguz Sokak No 4
KAT Z - A/7, Sisli, 34387, Istanbul, Turkiye
Tel.: (90) 2129429800
Chemicals Mfr
N.A.I.C.S.: 325998

Arkema Korea Holding Co., Ltd. (1)
7F 21 Gukhoe-daero 62 gil, Yeongdeungpo-
gu, Seoul, 07236, Korea (South)
Tel.: (82) 237036700
Web Site: https://www.arkema.com
Product Management & Marketing Services
N.A.I.C.S.: 541613

Subsidiary (Domestic):

PI Advanced Materials Co., Ltd (2)

Grand Central B16F 14 Sejong-daero 5-ga,
Jung-gu, Seoul, 04527, Gyeonggi-do, Korea
(South) **(54.07%)**
Tel.: (82) 221818600
Web Site: https://pimaterials.com
Rev.: $212,029,810
Assets: $382,730,404
Liabilities: $120,835,787
Net Worth: $261,894,617
Earnings: $35,059,942
Emp.: 217
Fiscal Year-end: 12/31/2022
Plastics Films Mfr
N.A.I.C.S.: 326112
Jin Hong Lee (CFO)

Plant (Domestic):

SKC KOLON PI, Inc. - Gumi Plant (3)
214-8 Gongdan-dong, Gumi,
Gyeongsangbuk-do, Korea (South)
Tel.: (82) 544693786
Plastic Film Mfr & Distr
N.A.I.C.S.: 326112

SKC KOLON PI, Inc. - Jincheon Plant (3)
27 Godeung 1-gil Iwol-myeon, Jincheon,
Chungcheongbuk-do, Korea (South)
Tel.: (82) 435394545
Plastic Film Mfr & Distr
N.A.I.C.S.: 326112

Arkema Ltd (1)
Whitewall Way, Strood, ME2 4ES, Kent,
United Kingdom
Tel.: (44) 1634718588
Sales Range: $25-49.9 Million
Emp.: 12
Chemical Products Distr
N.A.I.C.S.: 424690

Arkema Mexico S.A de C.V (1)
Km 6 5 Carr Nanchital Las Choapas, Esta-
cion Municipio de Ixhuatlan del Sureste,
96360, Veracruz, Mexico
Tel.: (52) 9212160739
Industrial Chemical Distr
N.A.I.C.S.: 424690

Arkema North Europe B.V. (1)
Tankhoofd 10, Vondelingenplaat, 3196 KE,
Rotterdam, Netherlands
Tel.: (31) 10 472 51 00
Web Site: http://www.arkema.com
Emp.: 100
Chemical Products Distr
N.A.I.C.S.: 424690

Arkema Pte Ltd (1)
1 Science Park Road 04-01/05, Singapore
Science Park II The Capricorn, Singapore,
117528, Singapore
Tel.: (65) 6419 9199
Web Site: http://www.arkema.com
Sales Range: $25-49.9 Million
Emp.: 4
Chemical Products Mfr
N.A.I.C.S.: 325199

Arkema Pty. Ltd. (1)
Level1 6 English Street Essendon Fields,
Melbourne, 3041, VIC, Australia
Tel.: (61) 392115000
Sales Range: $25-49.9 Million
Emp.: 15
Chemical Distr
N.A.I.C.S.: 424690

Arkema Quimica Ltda (1)
Av Ibirapuera 2033 - 4th floor, Sao Paulo,
04029-901, Brazil
Tel.: (55) 112 148 8522
Web Site: https://www.arkema.com
Emp.: 44
Mfr of Organic Peroxides & Distr of Chemi-
cals
N.A.I.C.S.: 325199

Arkema Quimica S.A (1)
Carretera de Olzinelles S/N, Sant Celoni,
08470, Barcelona, Spain
Tel.: (34) 93 867 4000
Web Site: https://www.arkema.com
Sales Range: $25-49.9 Million
Emp.: 30
Chemical Distr
N.A.I.C.S.: 424690

Arkema Shanghai Distribution Co. Ltd (1)

Arkema S.A.—(Continued)

D Part No. 28 Warehouse No 500 Fu Te Road No 2 East, Shanghai, 200131, China
Tel.: (86) 2150461605
Chemical Products Distr
N.A.I.C.S.: 424690

Arkema Srl (1)
Via Caldera 21, 20153, Milan, Italy
Tel.: (39) 0293 5131
Web Site: http://www.arkema.com
Emp.: 265
Chemical Products Mfr
N.A.I.C.S.: 325199

Arkema sp Z.o.o (1)
ul Przemyslowa, 88-100, Inowroclaw, Poland
Tel.: (48) 523555710
Chemical Products Distr
N.A.I.C.S.: 424690

Arr-maz Do Brasil Ltda. (1)
Estrada Sao Lourenco 525 Chacaras Rio-Petropolis, Duque de Caxias, 25243-150, RJ, Brazil
Tel.: (55) 2126777800
Chemicals Mfr
N.A.I.C.S.: 325998

ArrMaz Chemicals (Yunnan) Co., Ltd. (1)
Room 2802 CD Building Beichen Fortune Centre, Panlong District, Kunming, 650224, Yunnan, China
Tel.: (86) 87163538442
Chemicals Mfr
N.A.I.C.S.: 325998

ArrMaz Gulf Chemical Company Ltd. (1)
Al-Munirah Tower 4th Floor Office 11 King Faizal Bin Fahd Street, PO Box 2739, Al Khobar, 31952, Saudi Arabia
Tel.: (966) 13 887 9494
Web Site: http://www.amgc.com.sa
Chemicals Mfr
N.A.I.C.S.: 325998

Arrmaz Morocco Sarlau (1)
N 4 Route de Taddart Lotissement Chah 1 Californie, Casablanca, 20100, Morocco
Tel.: (212) 522214604
Chemicals Mfr
N.A.I.C.S.: 325998

Blueridge Films Inc. (1)
10921 Lamore Dr, Disputanta, VA 23842
Tel.: (804) 862-8700
Web Site: http://www.blueridgefilms.com
Polyethylene Film Mfr
N.A.I.C.S.: 326113
Kirit Mehta (Pres)

Bostik (Shanghai) Management Co., Ltd. (1)
Building 1 No 968 Guanghua Road, Minhang District, Shanghai, 201108, China
Tel.: (86) 2160763101
Adhesive Mfr
N.A.I.C.S.: 325520

Bostik (Thailand) Co., Ltd. (1)
No 24 Blessing Will Building 6th Floor Room 601 Srinagarindra Rd, Nongbon, Bangkok, 10250, Thailand
Tel.: (66) 23616460
Adhesive Mfr
N.A.I.C.S.: 325520

Bostik A/S (1)
Naverland 2, Box 1480, 2600, Glostrup, Denmark
Tel.: (45) 44841500
Web Site: https://www.bostik.com
Adhesive Mfr
N.A.I.C.S.: 325520

Bostik AB (1)
Strandbadsv 22, Box 903, 251 09, Helsingborg, Sweden
Tel.: (46) 42195000
Adhesive Mfr
N.A.I.C.S.: 325520
Robert Massey (CEO-Northern Europe)

Bostik Aerosols GmbH (1)
Giebelstadter Weg 16, Albertshausen, 97234, Bad Kissingen, Germany
Tel.: (49) 936690710

Adhesive Mfr
N.A.I.C.S.: 325520

Bostik Argentina, S.A. (1)
3 de Febrero 2750 3er piso, 1428, Buenos Aires, Argentina
Tel.: (54) 1147846464
Adhesive Mfr
N.A.I.C.S.: 325520

Bostik Belux S.A. - N.V. (1)
Antwerpsesteenweg 19, 9080, Lochristi, Belgium
Tel.: (32) 92551717
Adhesive Mfr
N.A.I.C.S.: 325520

Bostik Egypt For Production of Adhesives S.A.E (1)
Industrial Development Group - E2 6th of October City, Giza, Egypt
Tel.: (20) 238289100
Emp.: 27
Adhesive Mfr
N.A.I.C.S.: 325520

Bostik Findley (Malaysia) Sdn. Bhd. (1)
Lot 112 113, Kawasan Perindustrian Senawang, 70450, Seremban, Negeri Sembilan, Malaysia
Tel.: (60) 66789788
Adhesive Mfr
N.A.I.C.S.: 325520

Bostik Findley China Co., Ltd. (1)
75 Xinzhuang 2 Road GETD, Yonghe District, Guangzhou, 511156, China
Tel.: (86) 32226169
Chemicals Mfr
N.A.I.C.S.: 325998

Bostik GmbH (1)
An der Bundesstr Nr 16, Borgholzhausen, 33829, Gutersloh, Germany
Tel.: (49) 54258010
Adhesive Mfr
N.A.I.C.S.: 325520

Bostik Hellas S.A. (1)
Metsovou 3, Moschato, 18346, Piraeus, Greece
Tel.: (30) 2104831140
Adhesive Mfr
N.A.I.C.S.: 325520

Bostik India Private Ltd. (1)
124/1 124/2A Kachanayakanahalli Off Hosur Road, Bommasandra Post, Bengaluru, 560099, Karnataka, India
Tel.: (91) 8027833520
Adhesive Mfr
N.A.I.C.S.: 325520

Bostik Kimya Sanayi Ve Ticaret A.S. (1)
Mecidiyekoy Mh Oguz St Biz Plaza No 4A/7 Zemin Floor, Sisli, 34381, Istanbul, Turkiye
Tel.: (90) 2129429800
Adhesive Mfr
N.A.I.C.S.: 325520

Bostik L.L.C. (1)
Dvintsev 12 St Building 1, Moscow, Russia
Tel.: (7) 4957873171
Chemicals Mfr
N.A.I.C.S.: 325998

Bostik Mexicana S.A. de C.V. (1)
Esfuerzo Nacional No 2, Naucalpan, Mexico
Tel.: (52) 5521227250
Adhesive Mfr
N.A.I.C.S.: 325520

Bostik New Zealand Ltd. (1)
19 Eastern Hutt Road, Wingate, Lower Hutt, 5019, New Zealand
Tel.: (64) 508222777
Adhesive Mfr
N.A.I.C.S.: 325520

Bostik OY (1)
PL 46, 33311, Tampere, Finland
Tel.: (358) 108438800
Adhesive Mfr
N.A.I.C.S.: 325520

Bostik Philippines Inc. (1)
35th Floor Raffles Corporate Center F Ortigas Jr Road Ortigas Center, Pasig, 1600, Philippines

Tel.: (63) 279005656
Adhesive Mfr
N.A.I.C.S.: 325520

Bostik Romania S.r.l (1)
Str Rasaritului DN7 no 51, Buftea, Ilfov, Romania
Tel.: (40) 372833300
Adhesive Mfr
N.A.I.C.S.: 325520

Bostik SA (1)
420 rue d'Estienne d'Orves, CS 90067, 92705, Colombes, Cedex, France
Tel.: (33) 14 900 9000
Web Site: https://www.bostik.com
Emp.: 6,000
Adhesives, Sealants & Lubricants Mfr & Distr
N.A.I.C.S.: 325520

Subsidiary (Non-US):

Bostik Canada Ltd. (2)
655 Alphonse-Deshaies Blvd, Becancour, G9H 2Y8, QC, Canada
Tel.: (514) 593-0418
Web Site: https://www.bostik.com
Emp.: 3
Adhesives, Sealants & Lubricants Distr
N.A.I.C.S.: 424690
Marie-France Joannette (Mgr-Ops)

Bostik Industries Limited (2)
Newtown, Swords, Dublin, K69 YD23, Ireland
Tel.: (353) 1 862 4900
Web Site: https://www.bostik.com
Sales Range: $25-49.9 Million
Emp.: 60
Adhesives, Sealants & Lubricants Mfr
N.A.I.C.S.: 325520

Bostik Ltd (2)
Ulverscroft Road, Leicester, LE4 6BW, United Kingdom
Tel.: (44) 178 527 2625
Web Site: https://www.bostik.com
Emp.: 800
Adhesives, Sealants & Lubricants Mfr & Distr
N.A.I.C.S.: 325520

Bostik Netherland B.V. (2)
Zeggeveld 10, PO Box 180, 4705 RP, Roosendaal, Netherlands
Tel.: (31) 165590590
Sales Range: $25-49.9 Million
Emp.: 65
Mfr & Distribution of Adhesives, Sealants & Lubricants
N.A.I.C.S.: 325520

Subsidiary (Domestic):

Bostik B.V. Construction Division (3)
De Voerman 8, 5215 MH, 's-Hertogenbosch, Netherlands
Tel.: (31) 736244244
Web Site: http://www.bostik.com
Sales Range: $25-49.9 Million
Emp.: 75
Adhesives, Sealants & Lubricants Mfr & Distr
N.A.I.C.S.: 325520

Bostik B.V. Industrial Division (3)
De Voerman 8, 5215 MH, 's-Hertogenbosch, Netherlands
Tel.: (31) 736244244
Web Site: http://www.bostik.com
Sales Range: $25-49.9 Million
Emp.: 80
Mfr of Adhesives, Sealants & Coatings for Construction & Industry
N.A.I.C.S.: 325520

Subsidiary (US):

Bostik, Inc. (2)
11320 W Watertown Plank Rd, Wauwatosa, WI 53226
Tel.: (414) 774-2250
Web Site: https://www.bostik.com
Emp.: 250
Adhesives, Sealants & Lubricants Mfr & Distr
N.A.I.C.S.: 325520
Scott Banda (Dir-Mktg & Bus Dev)

Branch (Domestic):

Bostik, Inc. - Boston (3)
211 Boston St, Middleton, MA 01949
Tel.: (978) 777-0100
Web Site: https://www.bostik.com
Adhesives, Sealants & Lubricants & Distr
N.A.I.C.S.: 325520

Plant (Domestic):

Bostik, Inc. - Conyers (3)
1500 Parker Rd, Conyers, GA 30094
Tel.: (770) 922-4545
Web Site: www.bostik.com
Adhesives, Sealants & Lubricants Mfr
N.A.I.C.S.: 325520

Bostik, Inc. - Greenville (3)
6997 Pelham Rd, Greenville, SC 29615
Tel.: (864) 288-5369
Web Site: http://www.bostik.com
Emp.: 55
Adhesives, Sealants & Lubricants Mfr
N.A.I.C.S.: 325520
Jeff Mills (Plant Mgr)

Bostik, Inc. - Louisville (3)
7401 Intermodal Dr, Louisville, KY 40258
Tel.: (502) 933-4694
Web Site: http://www.bostik.com
Emp.: 50
Adhesives, Sealants & Lubricants Mfr
N.A.I.C.S.: 325520
Nicole Collins (Plant Mgr)

Bostik, Inc. - Temecula (3)
27460 Bostik Ct, Temecula, CA 92590
Tel.: (951) 296-6425
Web Site: http://www.bostik.com
Adhesives, Sealants & Lubricants Mfr
N.A.I.C.S.: 325520

Subsidiary (Non-US):

Mydrin Findley Srl (2)
via Pregnana 63, 20017, Rho, MI, Italy
Tel.: (39) 0293513599
Web Site: www.bostik-findley.com
Sales Range: $25-49.9 Million
Emp.: 100
Mfr & Distribution of Adhesives, Sealants & Lubricants
N.A.I.C.S.: 325520

Bostik Sp z.o.o. (1)
ul Poznanska 11b, Sady, 62-080, Tarnowo Podgorne, Poland
Tel.: (48) 618961740
Adhesive Mfr
N.A.I.C.S.: 325520

Bostik Technology GmbH (1)
Industriestrasse 1-7, Schwepnitz, 01936, Bautzen, Germany
Tel.: (49) 357976460
Adhesive Mfr
N.A.I.C.S.: 325520

Bostik UAB (1)
Minties 48-68, 09220, Vilnius, Lithuania
Tel.: (370) 65210059
Adhesive Mfr
N.A.I.C.S.: 325520

Bostik-Nitta Co., Ltd. (1)
2-22 Futamata, Yao, 581-0024, Osaka, Japan
Tel.: (81) 729488286
Chemicals Mfr
N.A.I.C.S.: 325998

COATEX SAS (1)
35 Rue Ampere ZI Lyon Nord, BP 8, 69730, Genay, France
Tel.: (33) 47 208 2000
Web Site: https://www.coatex.com
Emp.: 400
Rheological Additives Mfr
N.A.I.C.S.: 325998

Casda Biomaterials Co., Ltd. (1)
No 86 Dongfeng Road, North Industry Zone Taocheng District, Hengshui, 053000, Hebei, China
Tel.: (86) 3186109000
Emp.: 200
Seasick Acid Mfr
N.A.I.C.S.: 325199

Ceca S.A. (1)
89 Boulevard National, 92250, La Garenne-Colombes, France
Tel.: (33) 149003800
Web Site: http://www.cecachemicals.com
Sales Range: $250-299.9 Million
Emp.: 832
Mfr of Absorbents, Additives, Filter Aids & Surfactants
N.A.I.C.S.: 325998

Subsidiary (Non-US):

Ceca Italiana S.p.A (2)
Via Galileo Galilei 51 53, 20096, Pioltello, MI, Italy
Tel.: (39) 02929191
Web Site: http://www.cecachemicals.com
Sales Range: $25-49.9 Million
Emp.: 60
Chemical Products
N.A.I.C.S.: 325180

Febex S.A. (2)
Rte des Placettes, CP 189, 1880, Bex, Switzerland
Tel.: (41) 24 463 0550
Web Site: https://www.febex.ch
Emp.: 50
Mfr of Chemicals
N.A.I.C.S.: 325998

Changshu Coatex Additives Co. Ltd (1)
No 18 Haining Rd Fushan Haiyu Town, Changshu, 215522, Jiangsu, China
Tel.: (86) 51252325580
Sales Range: $25-49.9 Million
Emp.: 4
Chemical Products Mfr
N.A.I.C.S.: 325180
Sophia Xing *(Mgr)*

Coatex Asia Pacific Inc. (1)
7F Dongsung Building 17-8, Yeouido-Dong - Yeongdeungpo-gu, 07236, Seoul, Korea (South)
Tel.: (82) 2237036753
Chemicals Mfr
N.A.I.C.S.: 325998

Coatex Central Eastern Europe s.r.o. (1)
Tomasikova 30, 821 01, Bratislava, Slovakia
Tel.: (421) 24 825 0870
Web Site: http://www.coatex.com
Chemical Products Mfr
N.A.I.C.S.: 325199

Coatex Netherlands BV (1)
Middenweg 47a Haven M312, Moerdijk, 4782 PM, Netherlands
Tel.: (31) 168409020
Sales Range: $25-49.9 Million
Emp.: 2
Chemical Products Distr
N.A.I.C.S.: 424690

Den Braven France S.a.r.l. (1)
Rue du Buisson du Roi Z I Le Meux, BP 20114, 60881, Le Meux, Cedex, France
Tel.: (33) 344916868
Adhesive Mfr
N.A.I.C.S.: 325520

Den Braven SA (Proprietary) Ltd. (1)
2 Highview Boulevard Ferndale Extension 26, Randburg, Gauteng, South Africa
Tel.: (27) 117923830
Web Site: https://www.denbraven.com
Adhesive Mfr
N.A.I.C.S.: 325520

Den Braven Sealants GmbH (1)
Steinabruckler Str 48, Wollersdorf, 2752, Wiener Neustadt, Austria
Tel.: (43) 2633413990
Adhesive Mfr
N.A.I.C.S.: 325520

Dorlyl SNC (1)
297 Rue Des Chantiers, BP 1152, 76063, Le Havre, France
Tel.: (33) 235536850
Web Site: http://www.dorlyl.com
Sales Range: $50-74.9 Million
Emp.: 70
Mfr of Vinyl Compounds
N.A.I.C.S.: 325211

Subsidiary (Non-US):

Rionil Compostos Vinilcos Ltda (2)
Rodovia Washington Luiz 14 235, Duque de Caxias, 25240-000, Rio de Janeiro, Brazil
Tel.: (55) 2126761731
Web Site: http://www.rionil.com.br
Mfr of Vinyl Compounds
N.A.I.C.S.: 325211

Jiangsu Bostik Adhesive Co., Ltd. (1)
No 15-9 Xing Gang Road Changshu Economic Development Zone, Changshu, 215537, Jiangsu, China
Tel.: (86) 51252266004
Chemicals Mfr
N.A.I.C.S.: 325998

Lambson Limited (1)
Clifford House York Road, Wetherby, LS22 7NS, West Yorkshire, United Kingdom
Tel.: (44) 193 784 0150
Web Site: https://www.lambson.com
Chemicals Mfr
N.A.I.C.S.: 325998

MEM Bauchemie GmbH (1)
Am Emsdeich 52, Ostfriesland, 26789, Leer, Germany
Tel.: (49) 192 5800
Web Site: https://www.mem.de
Adhesive Mfr
N.A.I.C.S.: 325520

MLPC International SA (1)
209 avenue Charles Despiau, 40370, Rion-des-Landes, France
Tel.: (33) 558570200
Sales Range: $50-74.9 Million
Emp.: 200
Synthetic Products Mfr
N.A.I.C.S.: 325130
Jean-Marc Espinosa *(Gen Mgr)*

PT Bostik Indonesia (1)
Setiabudi Atrium Building 2nd Floor Suite 203 A Jl HR Rasuna Said, Kav 62, Jakarta Selatan, 12920, Indonesia
Tel.: (62) 215210404
Adhesive Mfr
N.A.I.C.S.: 325520

Prochimir Inc. (1)
2791 Research Dr, Rochester Hills, MI 48309
Tel.: (248) 564-2003
Plastic Packaging Film Mfr
N.A.I.C.S.: 326112

Prochimir SAS (1)
34 rue Rene Truhaut ZI de Montifaut, 85700, Pouzauges, France
Tel.: (33) 25 157 0551
Web Site: https://www.prochimir.com
Emp.: 65
Plastic Packaging Film Mfr
N.A.I.C.S.: 326112

SEKI Arkema Co Ltd (1)
10 Gongdandong-gil Chilseo-myeon 79 Gyenae-ri, Haman-gun, Haman, 52002, Gyeongsangnam-do, Korea (South)
Tel.: (82) 55 587 8055
Web Site: https://www.seki-arkema.co.kr
Chemical Products Mfr
N.A.I.C.S.: 325199

Sartomer (Guangzhou) Chemicals Co., Ltd. (1)
26 Southern 4th Road Xiaohu Island, Nansha, Guangzhou, 511455, China
Tel.: (86) 2034973951
Emp.: 130
Coating & Adhesive Mfr
N.A.I.C.S.: 325998

Shanghai Arkema Gaoyuan Chemicals Co. Ltd (1)
No 3 Workshop No 8999 Hunan Highway Xuanqiao Town, Pudong New, Shanghai, 201314, China
Tel.: (86) 2158188821
Web Site: http://www.arkema.com.cn
Sales Range: $25-49.9 Million
Emp.: 60
Chemical Products Mfr
N.A.I.C.S.: 325199

Siroflex Ltd. (1)
Dodworth Business Park, Barnsley, S75 3SP, South Yorkshire, United Kingdom
Tel.: (44) 122 677 1600
Web Site: https://www.siroflex.co.uk
Emp.: 1,200
Sealant Adhesive & Foam Distr
N.A.I.C.S.: 424690

Societe Marocaine des Colles (1)
8 Rue EL Haouza Oukacha, 20580, Casablanca, Morocco
Tel.: (212) 52 234 1538
Web Site: https://www.sader.co.ma
Adhesive Mfr
N.A.I.C.S.: 325520

Sunclear Srl (1)
Via Villapia 27, 20010, Casorezzo, MI, Italy
Tel.: (39) 029035661
Plastic Sheet Distr
N.A.I.C.S.: 424610

Taixing Sunke Chemicals Co., Ltd. (1)
No 58 Tongyuan Road, Economic Development Zone, Taixing, 225400, China
Tel.: (86) 52380370800
N.A.I.C.S.: 325199

Vetek SAU (1)
3 Febrero 2750 3 Piso, C1428AHT, Buenos Aires, Argentina
Tel.: (54) 1147884117
Web Site: http://www.veteksa.com.ar
Adhesive Mfr
N.A.I.C.S.: 325520

ARKIL HOLDING A/S
Sondergard Alle 4, 6500, Vojens, Denmark
Tel.: (45) 73225050
Web Site: http://www.arkil.dk
Year Founded: 1941
Rev.: $505,140,417
Assets: $324,552,996
Liabilities: $184,942,917
Net Worth: $139,610,079
Earnings: $17,942,496
Emp.: 1,823
Fiscal Year-end: 12/31/17
Abutment Construction Services
N.A.I.C.S.: 237310
Agnete Raaschou-Nielsen *(Chm)*

ARKLE PRINT LTD
17 Gatelodge Close, Round Spinney, Northampton, NN3 8RJ, United Kingdom
Tel.: (44) 1604499506
Web Site: http://www.arkleprint.co.uk
Rev.: $11,448,096
Emp.: 72
Printing Services
N.A.I.C.S.: 323111
Tony Lawson *(Mng Dir)*

ARKLE RESOURCES PLC
162 Clontarf Road, Dublin, 3, Ireland
Tel.: (353) 18332833 IE
Web Site:
https://www.arkleresources.com
Year Founded: 2006
ARK—(AIM)
Assets: $4,608,341
Liabilities: $562,023
Net Worth: $4,046,317
Earnings: $(327,874)
Fiscal Year-end: 12/31/23
Zinc & Lead Mining Services
N.A.I.C.S.: 212230
John Teeling *(Chm)*

ARKRAY, INC.
Yousuien-nai 59 Gansuin-cho, Kamigyo-ku, Kyoto, 602-0008, Japan
Tel.: (81) 756628979
Web Site: http://www.arkray.co.jp
Year Founded: 1960
Emp.: 2,148
Medical Laboratory Instrument Mfr
N.A.I.C.S.: 334516

Takeshi Matsuda *(Pres & CEO)*

Subsidiaries:

ARKRAY Factory, Inc. (1)
1480 Koji Konan-cho, Koka, 520-3306, Shiga, Japan
Tel.: (81) 748 86 6833
Diagnostic Device Distr
N.A.I.C.S.: 423450

Plant (Domestic):

ARKRAY Factory, Inc. - Kusatsu Factory (2)
7-5-6 Ogaki, Ritto, 520-3024, Shiga, Japan
Tel.: (81) 77 553 6773
Diagnostic Device Distr
N.A.I.C.S.: 423450

ARKRAY Global Business, Inc. (1)
Kyoto Miyuki Bldg 10F 689 Takanna-cho, Nakagyo-ku, Kyoto, 604-8153, Japan (100%)
Tel.: (81) 75 662 8967
Web Site: http://www.arkray.co.jp
Holding Company
N.A.I.C.S.: 551112
Takeshi Matsuda *(Pres & CEO)*

Subsidiary (Non-US):

ARKRAY & PARTNERS Pte. Ltd. (2)
101 Thomson Road 13-04 United Square, Singapore, 307591, Singapore
Tel.: (65) 6258 3400
Diagnostic Device Distr
N.A.I.C.S.: 423450

ARKRAY Co. Ltd., Inc. (2)
Unit 1912 Entrata Tower Civic Drive Filinvest Corporate Center, Muntinlupa, 1781, Batangas, Philippines
Tel.: (63) 2 843 4731
Diagnostic Device Distr
N.A.I.C.S.: 423450

ARKRAY Europe, B.V. (2)
Prof J H Bavincklaan 5, 1183 AT, Amstelveen, Netherlands
Tel.: (31) 88 2757100
Web Site: http://www.arkray-diabetes.nl
Diagnostic Device Distr
N.A.I.C.S.: 423450

ARKRAY Factory Ltd. (2)
Dock Lane Melton, Woodbridge, IP12 1PE, Suffolk, United Kingdom
Tel.: (44) 1394 446700
Diagnostic Device Mfr
N.A.I.C.S.: 334510

ARKRAY Factory Pinghu, Inc. (2)
2F/L Building 5 No 988 Xinxing No 2 Road of PETDZ, Pinghu, 314200, Zheijiang, China
Tel.: (86) 573 8563 7577
Diagnostic Device Mfr
N.A.I.C.S.: 334510

ARKRAY Factory Shanghai, Inc. (2)
No 72-1 887 Zuchongzhi Rd Zhangjiang High-tech Park, Pudong, Shanghai, 201203, China
Tel.: (86) 21 5131 7071
Diagnostic Device Mfr
N.A.I.C.S.: 334510
Oikoshi Minoru *(Mgr-Quality Engrg)*

ARKRAY Healthcare Pvt. Ltd. (2)
7th Floor Opulence 6th Road TPS III, Santacruz, Mumbai, 400055, India
Tel.: (91) 22 6155 9355
Web Site: http://www.arkray.co.in
Diagnostic Device Distr
N.A.I.C.S.: 423450

ARKRAY Industry, Inc. (2)
Lot 22 in Phase 1A First Philippines Industrial Park, Barangay Sta Anastacia, Santo Tomas, Philippines
Tel.: (63) 43 405 6450
Diagnostic Device Mfr
N.A.I.C.S.: 334510

ARKRAY Ltd. (2)
4 Programmistov St, Dubna, 141983, Moscow, Russia
Tel.: (7) 4997033492
Diagnostic Device Mfr
N.A.I.C.S.: 334510

ARKRAY, Inc.—(Continued)

ARKRAY Marketing Shanghai, Inc. (2)
Tomson Commercial Building 318 710
DongFang Road, Pudong, Shanghai,
200122, China
Tel.: (86) 21 5081 2554
Web Site: http://www.arkray.cn
Diagnostic Device Distr
N.A.I.C.S.: 423450

ARKRAY Tech Xi'an, Inc. (2)
Tai Bai Ge 205 No 72 Keji 2nd Rd, Xi'an,
710075, Shaanxi, China
Tel.: (86) 29 8766 9939
Diagnostic Device Mfr
N.A.I.C.S.: 334510

Subsidiary (US):

ARKRAY USA, Inc. (2)
5198 W 76th St, Edina, MN 55439
Tel.: (952) 646-3200
Web Site: http://www.arkrayusa.com
Rev.: $22,000,000
Create Acquire Market & Support Diagnostic & Medical Testing Equipment Distr
N.A.I.C.S.: 423450
Daniel J. Sobiech (Gen Mgr)

Subsidiary (Non-US):

Color Trading Sp. z o. o. (2)
ul Zolny 40, 02-815, Warsaw, Poland
Tel.: (48) 22 643 04 45
Web Site: http://www.colortrading.pl
Diagnostic Device Distr
N.A.I.C.S.: 423450
Marcin Burdyn (Jr Mgr-Sls)

PT. ARKRAY (2)
Mega Plaza 12th Floor Jl HR Rasuna Said
Kav C-3, Jakarta, 12920, Indonesia
Tel.: (62) 21 5212120
Web Site: http://www.arkray.id
Emp.: 6
Diagnostic Device Distr
N.A.I.C.S.: 423450

Karada Lab, Inc. (1)
Yousuien-nai 59 Gansuin-cho, Kamigyo-ku,
Kyoto, 602-0008, Japan
Tel.: (81) 50 5830 1040
Research & Development Services
N.A.I.C.S.: 541715

ARKU MASCHINENBAU GMBH
Siemensstrasse 11, 76532, Baden-
Baden, Germany
Tel.: (49) 722150090
Web Site: http://www.arku.de
Year Founded: 1928
Sales Range: $10-24.9 Million
Emp.: 192
Sheet Metal Mfr & Contract Leveling
Services
N.A.I.C.S.: 332322
Marcus Bartle (Mng Dir)

Subsidiaries:

ARKU Coil Systems Inc. (1)
11405 Grooms Rd, Cincinnati, OH 45242
Tel.: (513) 985-0500
Web Site: http://www.us.arku.com
Sheet Metal Product Distr
N.A.I.C.S.: 423510
Franck Hirschmann (Exec VP-Sls)

Arku Leveling Systems (Kunshan) Co., Ltd. (1)
No 329 Jujin Rd Zhangpu Township, Kunshan, 215321, China
Tel.: (86) 51236853910
Web Site: http://www.arku.com
Sheet Metal Product Distr
N.A.I.C.S.: 423510

ARLA FOODS AMBA
Sonderhoj 14, 8260, Viby, Denmark
Tel.: (45) 89381000   **DK**
Web Site: http://www.arla.com
Year Founded: 1881
Rev.: $11,924,010,750
Assets: $7,589,046,650
Liabilities: $4,707,839,640

Net Worth: $2,881,207,010
Earnings: $344,280,790
Emp.: 19,190
Fiscal Year-end: 12/31/18
Holding Company Dairy Products Mfr
& Distr
N.A.I.C.S.: 551112
Peder Tuborgh (CEO)

Subsidiaries:

Arla DP Holding A/S (1)
Sonderhoj 14, 8260, Viby,
Denmark   (100%)
Tel.: (45) 89381000
Sales Range: $150-199.9 Million
Emp.: 300
Holding Company
N.A.I.C.S.: 551112

Arla Foods AB (1)
Gardsvagen 7D, 169 70, Solna,
Sweden   (100%)
Tel.: (46) 87895000
Web Site: http://www.arlafoods.com
Sales Range: $1-4.9 Billion
Emp.: 3,800
Milk Production; Dairy Products Mfr & Distr
N.A.I.C.S.: 112120

Subsidiary (Non-US):

Arla Ingman Oy Ab (2)
Kotkatie 34 Soderkulla, 01151, Sipoo, Finland
Tel.: (358) 9 272 001
Web Site: http://www.arla.fi
Dairy Product Mfr & Distr
N.A.I.C.S.: 311514

Subsidiary (Domestic):

Ranuan Meijeri Oy (3)
Repotie 2, 97700, Ranua, Finland
Tel.: (358) 16 332 0600
Web Site: http://www.ranuanmeijeri.fi
Dairy Products Mfr
N.A.I.C.S.: 311514
Sami Kilpelainen (CEO)

Subsidiary (Domestic):

Boxholm Mejeri AB (2)
Alvkullevagen 7, 590 12, Boxholm, Sweden
Tel.: (46) 142 29 33 30
Web Site: http://www.boxholmsost.se
Emp.: 33
Cheese Mfr
N.A.I.C.S.: 311513

Milko Sverige AB (2)
Box 31, 182 11, Danderyd, Sweden
Tel.: (46) 8 568 966 00
Dairy Product Mfr & Distr
N.A.I.C.S.: 311514

Silvadden AB (2)
Nedre vattugatan 3, Ostersund, 831 45,
Jamtland, Sweden
Tel.: (46) 63 14 50 00
Dairy Products Mfr
N.A.I.C.S.: 311514

Arla Foods AS (1)
Jerikoveien 10c 2 Etasje, 1067, Oslo,
Norway   (100%)
Tel.: (47) 23141860
Web Site: http://www.arla.no
Sales Range: $25-49.9 Million
Emp.: 22
Cheese & Other Dairy Products Whslr
N.A.I.C.S.: 424430

Arla Foods Artis Ltd (1)
Barochnaya st 10 bldg 1 BC Vorontsov,
197110, Saint Petersburg, Russia
Tel.: (7) 8123 466006
Web Site: http://www.arla.ru
Dairy Products Distr
N.A.I.C.S.: 424490

Arla Foods B.V. (1)
Gildenstraat 30, 3861 RJ, Nijkerk, Netherlands
Tel.: (31) 3324 76222
Web Site: http://www.arla.nl
Emp.: 350
Dairy Products Distr
N.A.I.C.S.: 424990

Arla Foods Bangladesh Ltd. (1)
Cotton House 5th Floor House 2 Road
113/A Gulshan 2, Dhaka, 1212, Bangladesh
Tel.: (880) 29857436
Web Site: http://www.arlafoods.com
Emp.: 40
Dairy Product Mfr & Distr
N.A.I.C.S.: 311514

Arla Foods Deutschland GmbH (1)
Im Scheid 1, 54597, Pronsfeld, Germany
Tel.: (49) 6556 79 0
Web Site: http://www.arlafoods.de
Emp.: 1,000
Dairy Products Distr
N.A.I.C.S.: 424490

Subsidiary (Domestic):

Arla Foods Kasereinen GmbH (2)
Ahegg 22, 88239, Wangen im Allgau, Germany
Tel.: (49) 7522 7990
Dairy Product Mfr & Distr
N.A.I.C.S.: 311514

Arla Foods Financial Services Centre Sp. z o.o. (1)
Centrum Biurowe Neptun Al Grunwaldzka
103A, ul Heweliusza 9, 80-244, Gdansk,
Poland   (100%)
Tel.: (48) 587638400
Web Site: http://www.arla.pl
Sales Range: $50-74.9 Million
Emp.: 120
Internal Corporate Finance & Accounting
Services
N.A.I.C.S.: 541219

Arla Foods GmbH (1)
Wahler Street 2, 40472, Dusseldorf,
Germany   (100%)
Tel.: (49) 211472310
Web Site: http://www.arlafoods.de
Sales Range: $25-49.9 Million
Emp.: 75
Dairy Products Mfr
N.A.I.C.S.: 311511

Arla Foods Hellas S.A. (1)
Leoforos Kifisias Avenue 6-8 Caracas Center, 151 25, Maroussi, Greece   (100%)
Tel.: (30) 2108196100
Web Site: http://www.arlafoods.gr
Sales Range: $25-49.9 Million
Emp.: 35
Cheese & Other Dairy Products Whslr
N.A.I.C.S.: 424430

Arla Foods Inc. (1)
675 Rivermede Road, Concord, L4K 2G9,
ON, Canada   (100%)
Tel.: (905) 669-9393
Web Site: http://www.arlafoods.ca
Sales Range: $50-74.9 Million
Emp.: 200
Cheese & Other Dairy Products Mfr & Distr
N.A.I.C.S.: 311513

Arla Foods Inc. (1)
645 Martinsville Rd, Basking Ridge, NJ
07920
Tel.: (908) 604-6551
Web Site: http://www.arlafoodsusa.com
Cheese & Butter Mfr & Dairy Product Distr
N.A.I.C.S.: 424430

Subsidiary (Domestic):

Arla Foods Production LLC (2)
489 Holland Ct, Kaukauna, WI 54130-8953
Tel.: (920) 766-5765
Web Site: http://www.arlafoodsusa.com
Emp.: 200
Dairy Product Mfr & Distr
N.A.I.C.S.: 311514
Sue Roberts (Mgr-HR)

Arla Foods Ingredients amba (1)
Sonderhoj 14, 8260, Viby,
Denmark   (100%)
Tel.: (45) 89381000
Web Site:
    http://www.arlafoodsingredients.com
Sales Range: $900-999.9 Million
Emp.: 600
Lactose-Based Proteins & Other Basic Organic Food Ingredient Chemicals Developer, Mfr & Whslr
N.A.I.C.S.: 325199

Henrik Andersen (CEO)

Subsidiary (Non-US):

Arla Foods Ingredients GmbH (2)
Am Bahnhof 1, 31097, Harbarnsen,
Germany   (100%)
Tel.: (49) 5060 6090
Web Site:
    http://www.arlafoodsingredients.com
Sales Range: $50-74.9 Million
Emp.: 90
Holding Company; Lactose-Based Proteins
& Other Basic Organic Food Ingredient
Chemicals Mfr & Whslr
N.A.I.C.S.: 551112
Luis Cubel (Comml Dir)

Affiliate (Domestic):

Biolac GmbH & Co. KG (3)
Am Bahnhof 1, Harbarnsen, 31097,
Germany   (50%)
Tel.: (49) 50606090
Web Site: http://www.biolac.com
Sales Range: $25-49.9 Million
Emp.: 70
Lactose-Based Proteins & Other Basic Organic Food Ingredient Chemicals Mfr &
Whslr
N.A.I.C.S.: 325199

Subsidiary (Non-US):

Arla Foods Ingredients K.K. (2)
Shibadaimon Makita Bldg 4fl5-8Shiba-
Daimon2-chome, Minato-ku, Tokyo, 105-
0012, Japan   (100%)
Tel.: (81) 334350295
Web Site:
    http://www.arlafoodsingredients.com
Sales Range: $25-49.9 Million
Emp.: 10
Lactose-Based Proteins & Other Basic Organic Food Ingredient Chemicals Whslr
N.A.I.C.S.: 424690

Arla Foods Ingredients Korea Co., Ltd. (2)
308 Gangnam-daero, Gangnam-gu, Seoul,
135-080, Korea (South)   (100%)
Tel.: (82) 234529488
Web Site:
    http://www.arlafoodsingredients.com
Sales Range: $25-49.9 Million
Emp.: 2
Lactose-Based Proteins & Other Basic Organic Food Ingredient Chemicals Whslr
N.A.I.C.S.: 424690
Seung Joo Lee (Dir-Sls)

Affiliate (Non-US):

Arla Foods Ingredients S.A. (2)
Avenida Fondo de la Legua 1380, Martinez,
B1640FTX, Buenos Aires,
Argentina   (50%)
Tel.: (54) 1153684100
Sales Range: $25-49.9 Million
Emp.: 100
Lactose-Based Proteins & Other Basic Organic Food Ingredient Chemicals Mfr
N.A.I.C.S.: 325199
Bjarne S. Pedesen (Gen Mgr)

Subsidiary (Non-US):

Arla Foods Ingredients S.A. de C.V. (2)
Av Insurgentes Sur 949 702Colonia Ciudad
de los, Delegacion Benito Juarez Federal
District, CP 03710, Mexico, Guanajuato,
Mexico   (100%)
Tel.: (52) 5557503171
Web Site:
    http://www.arlafoodsingredients.com
Lactose-Based Proteins & Other Basic Organic Food Ingredient Chemicals Whslr
N.A.I.C.S.: 424690

Subsidiary (US):

Arla Foods Ingredients, Inc. (2)
645 Martinsville Rd, Basking Ridge, NJ
07920   (100%)
Tel.: (908) 604-8551
Web Site:
    http://www.arlafoodsingredients.com
Lactose-Based Proteins & Other Basic Organic Food Ingredient Chemicals Whslr

N.A.I.C.S.: 424690

Subsidiary (Domestic):

Danmark Protein A/S (2)
Norre Vium Sonderupvej 26, 6920, Videbaek, Denmark **(100%)**
Tel.: (45) 72 17 77 77
Sales Range: $25-49.9 Million
Emp.: 200
Mfr of Whey Protein Concentrates, Permeate/Lactose & Functional Milk Proteins
N.A.I.C.S.: 311514
Erik Veslov (Plant Mgr)

Arla Foods Ltda (1)
Av Selma Parada 201 CJTO 132, 13091-010, Campinas, Sao Paulo, Brazil
Tel.: (55) 19 32071069
Dairy Product Mfr & Distr
N.A.I.C.S.: 311514

Arla Foods S.A. (1)
Calle Jose Echegaray 8 Bldg 3, Centro Empresarial El Plantio, Madrid, 28232, Spain **(100%)**
Tel.: (34) 91 710 2112
Web Site: http://www.arlafoods.es
Sales Range: $25-49.9 Million
Emp.: 16
Dairy Product Whslr
N.A.I.C.S.: 424430
Ignacio Cuadrado (Gen Mgr)

Arla Foods S.A.R.L. (1)
97 Cours Gambetta, 69481, Lyon, Cedex 03, France **(100%)**
Tel.: (33) 472 848 810
Sales Range: $50-74.9 Million
Emp.: 7
Dairy Product Whslr
N.A.I.C.S.: 424430

Arla Foods S.r.l. (1)
Via Cavour 2, Cirimido, 22074, Lomazzo, CO, Italy **(100%)**
Tel.: (39) 0313525011
Web Site: http://www.arlafoods.com
Sales Range: $50-74.9 Million
Emp.: 5
Dairy Product Whslr
N.A.I.C.S.: 424430

Arla Foods SA (1)
ul Klobucka 25, 02-699, Warsaw, Poland **(100%)**
Tel.: (48) 2273 75 473
Web Site: http://www.arla.pl
Sales Range: $75-99.9 Million
Emp.: 130
Holding Company; Regional Managing Office
N.A.I.C.S.: 551112

Subsidiary (Domestic):

Arla Foods Sp. z o.o. (2)
ul Lipowa 15, 78-120, Goscino, Poland **(100%)**
Tel.: (48) 943549100
Web Site: http://www.arla.pl
Sales Range: $100-124.9 Million
Cheese & Other Dairy Products Mfr & Distr
N.A.I.C.S.: 311513

Arla Foods Trading A/S (1)
Romersgade 18, Copenhagen, 1362, Denmark
Tel.: (45) 89381083
Dairy Product Mfr & Distr
N.A.I.C.S.: 311514

Arla Foods UK plc (1)
Arla House 4 Savannah Way Leeds Valley Park, Leeds, LS10 1AB, United Kingdom **(93.7%)**
Tel.: (44) 1133827000
Web Site: http://www.arlafoods.co.uk
Sales Range: $1-4.9 Billion
Emp.: 2,900
Holding Company; Dairy Products Mfr & Distr
N.A.I.C.S.: 551112
Ash Amirahmadi (Mng Dir)

Subsidiary (Domestic):

Arla Foods Limited (2)
Arla House 4 Savannah Way Leeds Valley

Park, Leeds, LS10 1AB, United Kingdom **(100%)**
Tel.: (44) 113 382 7000
Web Site: http://www.arlafoods.co.uk
Sales Range: $100-124.9 Million
Emp.: 400
Butter, Milk & Other Dairy Products Mfr & Distr
N.A.I.C.S.: 311512
Jessica Hardcastle (Sr Brand Mgr-Lurpak)

Branch (Domestic):

Arla Foods (3)
Plym House, 3 Longbridge Road, Plymouth, PL6 8LT, Devon, United Kingdom
Tel.: (44) 1752 331871
Co-Operative Milk Processor, Marketer, Purchaser & Distr
N.A.I.C.S.: 424430

Subsidiary (Domestic):

Arla Foods (Westbury) Ltd (3)
The Butter Prod Fac Stephenson Road, Westbury, BA13 4WD, Wiltshire, United Kingdom
Tel.: (44) 1373 306000
Dairy Product Mfr & Distr
N.A.I.C.S.: 311514

Subsidiary (Domestic):

Arla Foods UK Plc-Oswestry Packing Facility (2)
Maesbury Road, Oswestry, SY10.8NL, Shropshire, United Kingdom **(100%)**
Tel.: (44) 1691 654564
Web Site: http://www.arlafoods.co.uk
Sales Range: $75-99.9 Million
Emp.: 400
Dairy Packing Facilities
N.A.I.C.S.: 488991
Paula Jones (Dir-Factory)

Subsidiary (Domestic):

Cornish Country Larder Ltd. (3)
The Creamery Trevarrian, Newquay, TR8 4AH, Cornwall, United Kingdom
Tel.: (44) 1637 860331
Web Site: http://www.ccl-ltd.co.uk
Cheese Mfr
N.A.I.C.S.: 311513
Chris Seamarks (Mgr-Fin)

Cocio Chokolademaelk A/S (1)
Oresundsvej 15, 6715, Esbjerg, Denmark **(50%)**
Tel.: (45) 76140888
Web Site: http://www.cocio.dk
Sales Range: $25-49.9 Million
Emp.: 55
Flavored Milk Mfr
N.A.I.C.S.: 311511

Danya Foods Ltd. (1)
PO Box 3164, Riyadh, 11583, Saudi Arabia **(75%)**
Tel.: (966) 14981414
Sales Range: $25-49.9 Million
Emp.: 200
Provider of Dairy Products
N.A.I.C.S.: 311511

Falbygdens Ost AB (1)
Falbygdens Goteborgsvagen 19, 521 30, Falkoping, Sweden
Tel.: (46) 515 29 32 00
Web Site: http://www.falbygdensost.se
Cheese Mfr
N.A.I.C.S.: 311513

Hansa Logistik eG (1)
Industriegebiet, 23936, Upahl, Germany
Tel.: (49) 38822 50 331
Web Site: http://www.hansa-logistik-eg.de
Emp.: 700
Logistics Consulting Servies
N.A.I.C.S.: 541614

Kingdom Food Products ApS (1)
Bernstorffsgade 33, 1577, Copenhagen, Denmark
Tel.: (45) 33969200
Dairy Product Mfr & Distr
N.A.I.C.S.: 311514

Mejeriforeningen (1)
Danish Dairy Board 1 Sonderhoj, 8260, Viby, Denmark

Tel.: (45) 8731 2000
Web Site: http://www.danishdairyboard.dk
Farmer Association
N.A.I.C.S.: 813910

Rynkeby Foods A/S (1)
Vestergade 30, Ringe, 5750, Denmark **(100%)**
Tel.: (45) 63623200
Web Site: http://www.rynke.dk
Sales Range: $100-124.9 Million
Emp.: 200
Fruit Juice & Fruit Product Mfr
N.A.I.C.S.: 311411
Jorgen Dirksen (Mng Dir)

Subsidiary (Non-US):

Krogab Sverige AB (2)
Tryffelslingan 8, 181 57, Lidingo, Sweden
Tel.: (46) 8 731 60 60
Web Site: http://www.rynkebykrogab.se
Canned Fruit & Vegetable Juice Mfr & Distr
N.A.I.C.S.: 311421

Team-Pack GmbH (1)
Keplerstrasse 45, 76185, Karlsruhe, Germany
Tel.: (49) 7 21 59 86 210
Web Site: http://www.team-pack.de
Packaging Product Distr
N.A.I.C.S.: 423840

ARLA PLAST AB
Vastanavagen 2, Borensberg, 591 75, Motala, Sweden
Tel.: (46) 141203800
Web Site: https://www.arlaplast.com
Year Founded: 1969
ARPL—(OMX)
Rev.: $95,076,194
Assets: $73,543,323
Liabilities: $20,305,900
Net Worth: $53,237,424
Earnings: $6,265,981
Emp.: 250
Fiscal Year-end: 12/31/23
Plastics Product Mfr
N.A.I.C.S.: 326112
Christian Krichau (CEO)

ARLAN WAGONS LLP
Office 105 17 Nauryzbai Batyr St, Almaty, 050016, Kazakhstan
Tel.: (7) 272446425
Web Site: http://www.arlanwagons.kz
ARWA—(KAZ)
Rev.: $188,622
Assets: $367,916
Liabilities: $1,150,269
Net Worth: ($782,353)
Earnings: ($1,479,567)
Fiscal Year-end: 12/31/19
Freight Forwarding Services
N.A.I.C.S.: 488510
Dmitriy Anchutkin (Gen Dir)

ARLANDASTAD GROUP AB
Pionjärvägen 77 entré A ingång 1 Arlandstad, Stockholm 195 61, 195 61, Stockholm , Sweden
Tel.: (46) 8 440 42 40
Web Site:
https://arlandastadgroup.se
Emp.: 100
Real Estate Services & Property Management
N.A.I.C.S.: 531190

ARLITECH ELECTRONIC CORP.
14f No 646 Sec 5 Chung Hsing Rd, Sanchung Dist, New Taipei City, Taiwan
Tel.: (886) 229998313
Web Site: https://www.arlitech.com
Year Founded: 2001
6432—(TPE)
Rev.: $34,824,532
Assets: $38,635,212
Liabilities: $13,780,977

Net Worth: $24,854,235
Earnings: $1,434,668
Fiscal Year-end: 12/31/22
Electronic Product Distr
N.A.I.C.S.: 423690
Qin-Xian Wang (Chm & Gen Mgr)

Subsidiaries:

Beckmann Elektronik GmbH (1)
Dieselstrasse 7, 85232, Bergkirchen, Germany
Tel.: (49) 813131180
Web Site: https://beckmann-elektronik.de
Emp.: 30
Electronic Components Distr
N.A.I.C.S.: 423610

Moduli Elettronici e Componenti S.p.A. (1)
Via della Salute 24, 40132, Bologna, Italy
Tel.: (39) 0516418156
Industrial Equipment Distr
N.A.I.C.S.: 423690

Nippon Mik Corp. (1)
7-1 Sumiyoshi-cho, Shinjuku-ku, Tokyo, Japan
Tel.: (81) 333555061
Web Site: https://www.nippon-mik.co.jp
Electrical Component Distr
N.A.I.C.S.: 423610

TaeKyong Electronics Corp. (1)
RM3410 Ma-Dong Chungang Circulation Complex 1258 Kurobon, Dong Kuro-Ku, Seoul, Korea (South)
Tel.: (82) 26813332
Electrical Component Distr
N.A.I.C.S.: 423610

ARM CEMENT LIMITED
The Westwood 9th Floor Ring Road, PO Box 41908, Westlands, 00100, Nairobi, Kenya
Tel.: (254) 733636456
Web Site: http://www.armafrica.com
Rev.: $83,494,397
Assets: $409,911,043
Liabilities: $210,082,013
Net Worth: $199,829,030
Earnings: ($62,878,195)
Emp.: 1,963
Fiscal Year-end: 12/31/17
Cement Mfr
N.A.I.C.S.: 327310
Surendra L. Bhatia (Deputy Mng Dir)

ARMADA DATA CORPORATION
1230 Crestlawn Drive, Mississauga, L4W 1A6, ON, Canada
Tel.: (905) 624-4913
Web Site:
https://www.armadadata.com
ARD—(TSXV)
Rev.: $2,463,813
Assets: $1,147,176
Liabilities: $531,778
Net Worth: $615,398
Earnings: $12,850
Emp.: 20
Fiscal Year-end: 05/31/21
Business Information Services
N.A.I.C.S.: 561499
R. James Matthews (Pres & CEO)

ARMADA METALS LIMITED
Level 10 Kyle House 27 Macquarie Place, Sydney, 2000, NSW, Australia
Tel.: (61) 7788581890   AU
Web Site:
https://www.armadametals.com.au
Year Founded: 2021
AMM—(ASX)
Rev.: $8,632
Assets: $10,400,771
Liabilities: $6,545,286
Net Worth: $3,855,485
Earnings: ($2,965,682)
Fiscal Year-end: 12/31/23

Armada Metals Limited—(Continued)

Metal Exploration Services
N.A.I.C.S.: 213114
Ross McGowan *(CEO)*

ARMADA TOOLWORKS LIM-ITED

4S5 6 L O F Dr, Lindsay, K9V 6K8, ON, Canada
Tel.: (705) 328-9599   ON
Web Site:
  http://www.armadatoolworks.com
Year Founded: 2000
Sales Range: $25-49.9 Million
Emp.: 120
Special Die Tool Jig & Fixture Mfr
N.A.I.C.S.: 333514
Ross Chandler *(CEO)*

ARMADALE CAPITALL PLC

I Arbrook Lane, Esher, KT10 9EG, Surrey, United Kingdom
Tel.: (44) 2072361177
Web Site:
  https://www.armadalecapitalplc.com
ACP—(AIM)
Assets: $8,991,874
Liabilities: $95,619
Net Worth: $8,896,255
Earnings: ($255,811)
Emp.: 5
Fiscal Year-end: 12/31/22
Investment Services
N.A.I.C.S.: 523999
Nicholas Johansen *(Chm)*

ARMADILLO RESOURCES LTD.

Unit 12-7621 Vantage Way, Delta, V4G 1A6, BC, Canada
Tel.: (604) 952-6676   BC
Web Site:
  http://www.armadilloresources.com
Year Founded: 2007
Sales Range: Less than $1 Million
Investment Services
N.A.I.C.S.: 523999
Leslie Einar Kjosness *(Pres & CEO)*

ARMAEC ENERGY GROUP PLC

51 Hertford Street Mayfair, London, W1J 7ST, United Kingdom
Tel.: (44) 8700 34 0008
Web Site:
  http://www.armaecenergy.com
Year Founded: 2007
Wind Farms Developer
N.A.I.C.S.: 221118
Peter Hughes *(Chm)*

ARMAN FINANCIAL SERVICES LTD.

502-3-4 Sakar III Opp Old High Court Off Ashram Road, Ahmedabad, 380 014, Gujarat, India
Tel.: (91) 7940507000
Web Site:
  https://www.armanindia.com
ARMANFIN—(NSE)
Rev.: $57,862,992
Assets: $278,209,400
Liabilities: $228,292,646
Net Worth: $49,916,753
Earnings: $12,805,242
Emp.: 370
Fiscal Year-end: 03/31/23
Financial Services
N.A.I.C.S.: 523999
Jayendrabhai B. Patel *(Vice Chm, CEO & Co-Mng Dir)*

Subsidiaries:

Namra Finance Limited   (1)
502-3-4 Sakar III Opp Old High Court Off

Ashram Road, Ahmedabad, 380014, Gujarat, India
Tel.: (91) 18001027626
Web Site: https://www.namrafinance.com
Financial Management Services
N.A.I.C.S.: 541611
Jayendra B. Patel *(Vice Chm & Mng Dir)*

ARMAN HOLDINGS LIMITED

Office No 106 Sanskruti AC Market Parvat Godadara BRTS Road, Parvat Patia, Surat, 391050, Gujarat, India
Tel.: (91) 9586006569   In
Web Site:
  https://www.armanholdings.in
Year Founded: 1982
538556—(BOM)
Rev.: $214,599
Assets: $901,762
Liabilities: $3,878
Net Worth: $897,884
Earnings: $176
Emp.: 5
Fiscal Year-end: 03/31/21
Holding Company
N.A.I.C.S.: 551112
Deepak Kumar Babel *(Chm & Mng Dir)*

ARMANDO TESTA S.P.A.

Via Luisa del Carretto 58, 10131, Turin, Italy
Tel.: (39) 011 88 10111   IT
Web Site: http://www.armandotesta.it
Year Founded: 1946
Rev.: $791,310,000
Emp.: 150
Advertising Services
N.A.I.C.S.: 541810
Marco Testa *(Chm & CEO)*

Subsidiaries:

Armando Testa   (1)
12 Rue Rougemont, 75009, Paris, France
Tel.: (33) 1 53302 880
Web Site: http://www.armandotesta.fr
Advertising Services
N.A.I.C.S.: 541810

Armando Testa Brussels NV   (1)
Dreve de Willerieken 20, Brussels, 1160, Belgium
Tel.: (32) 2 678 0606
Web Site: http://www.armandotesta.com
Emp.: 15
Advertising Services
N.A.I.C.S.: 541810
Philippe Gelder *(CEO & Founding Partner)*

Armando Testa GmbH   (1)
Lindleystr 12, 60314, Frankfurt, Germany
Tel.: (49) 69 13 38 860
Web Site: http://www.armandotesta.com
Emp.: 4
Advertising Services
N.A.I.C.S.: 541810

Armando Testa Ltd.   (1)
81 Oxford Street, Gainsborough House, London, W1D 2EU, United Kingdom
Tel.: (44) 207 851 4800
Emp.: 20
Advertising Services
N.A.I.C.S.: 541810

Armando Testa S.p.A.   (1)
Via Washington 17, Milan, 20146, Italy
Tel.: (39) 02 48 08 21
Web Site: http://www.armandotesta.com
Advertising Services
N.A.I.C.S.: 541810

Armando Testa S.p.A.   (1)
Via Giovanni da Castells Bolognese 81, 00153, Rome, Italy
Tel.: (39) 06 58 31 71
Web Site: http://www.armandotesta.com
Advertising Services
N.A.I.C.S.: 541810

Armando Testa SL   (1)
Avda de Brasil 30 Posterior, 28020, Madrid, Spain
Tel.: (34) 91 4183300
Web Site: http://www.armandotesta.es

Emp.: 10
Advertising Services
N.A.I.C.S.: 541810

Bitmama S.r.l.   (1)
Via Luisa del Carretto 58, 10131, Turin, Italy
Tel.: (39) 0118810711
Web Site: http://www.bitmama.it
Advertising Services
N.A.I.C.S.: 541810
Claudio Papetti *(CEO)*

In Testa HQ   (1)
Washington Street 17, 20146, Milan, Italy
Tel.: (39) 02 480 12776
Advertising Services
N.A.I.C.S.: 541810

Little Bull   (1)
Via Giovanni De Castle Bolognese 81, 00153, Rome, Italy
Tel.: (39) 06 58317700
Advertising Services
N.A.I.C.S.: 541810

Max Information   (1)
Via Della Zecca 1, Galleria Aquaderni 5, Bologna, 40121, Italy
Tel.: (39) 051 235 001
Web Site: http://www.maxinformation.com
Emp.: 20
Advertising Services
N.A.I.C.S.: 541810
Ezio Campellone *(Pres)*

Media Italia HQ   (1)
Via Luisa del Carretto 58, 10131, Turin, Italy
Tel.: (39) 011 8109 311
Web Site: http://www.mediaitalia.it
Emp.: 115
Advertising Services
N.A.I.C.S.: 541870
Eugenio Bona *(Pres)*

ARMATURE AD

Krusevacka 30, 37230, Aleksandrovac, Serbia
Tel.: (381) 373552350
Web Site: https://www.armature.rs
PPTA—(BEL)
Rev.: $15,151,411
Assets: $12,606,540
Liabilities: $3,526,629
Net Worth: $9,079,911
Earnings: $288,320
Emp.: 511
Fiscal Year-end: 12/31/22
Metal Products Mfr
N.A.I.C.S.: 332722

ARMATURE DNS 2000 INC.

11001 Jean Meunier, Montreal, H1G 4S7, QC, Canada
Tel.: (514) 324-1141
Web Site: http://www.dns-2000.com
Year Founded: 1977
Alternators, Starters, Water Pumps & Calipers Mfr
N.A.I.C.S.: 334515
Roberto Bagorda *(VP-Sls)*

ARMATURES BOIS-FRANCS INC.

249 Bonaventure Blvd, Victoriaville, G6T 1V5, QC, Canada
Tel.: (819) 758-7501
Web Site: http://www.abf-inc.com
Year Founded: 1976
Rev.: $66,044,000
Emp.: 500
Reinforcing Steel & Wire-Mesh Mfr
N.A.I.C.S.: 238120
Luis Monte *(VP-Construction)*

ARMBUSINESSBANK CJSC

48 Nalbandyan Str, 0010, Yerevan, Armenia
Tel.: (374) 60372500
Web Site:
  http://www.armbusinessbank.am
Year Founded: 1991

Sales Range: $75-99.9 Million
Emp.: 949
Commercial Banking Services
N.A.I.C.S.: 522110
Arsen Mikayelyan *(Chm)*

ARMCO CAPITAL INC.

84 Chain Lake Dr Ste 500, Halifax, B3S IA2, NS, Canada
Tel.: (902) 423-4000
Web Site:
  http://www.armcocapital.com
Year Founded: 1982
Rev.: $33,802,335
Emp.: 60
Residential & Industrial Building Construction & Services
N.A.I.C.S.: 623990
Robert MacPherson *(Pres)*

ARMECONOMBANK OJSC

Amiryan Str 23/1, 0002, Yerevan, Armenia
Tel.: (374) 10538835
Web Site: http://www.aeb.am
Year Founded: 1988
HEZB—(ARM)
Rev.: $83,127,817
Assets: $1,040,914,731
Liabilities: $916,031,586
Net Worth: $124,883,146
Earnings: $18,084,722
Emp.: 939
Fiscal Year-end: 12/31/22
Commercial Banking Services
N.A.I.C.S.: 522110
Saribek Sukiasyan *(Chm)*

ARMEYSKI HOLDING AD

Tsar Osvoboditel 33, Sofia, 1000, Bulgaria
Tel.: (359) 29863583
Web Site: http://www.arm-hold.com
ARMH—(BUL)
Sales Range: Less than $1 Million
Holding Company
N.A.I.C.S.: 551112

ARMOIRES FABRITEC LTEE.

80 Boulevard de l'Aeroport, Bromont, J2L 1S9, QC, Canada
Tel.: (450) 534-1659
Web Site: http://fabritec.ca
Year Founded: 1983
Sales Range: $25-49.9 Million
Emp.: 703
Kitchen & Bathroom Cabinet Mfr
N.A.I.C.S.: 337110
Clovis Bourgeois *(Pres)*

Subsidiaries:

Armoires Fabritec Ltee.-Cookshire   (1)
705 Rue Pope, Cookshire, J0B1M0, QC, Canada
Tel.: (819) 875-5421
Sales Range: $25-49.9 Million
Emp.: 100
Kitchen Cabinet Components Mfr
N.A.I.C.S.: 337110

ARMOR MINERALS INC.

Suite 555 - 999 Canada Place, Vancouver, V6C 3E1, BC, Canada
Tel.: (604) 687-1717   BC
Web Site:
  https://www.armorminerals.com
Year Founded: 2006
RCZRF—(OTCEM)
Rev.: $92,275
Assets: $2,027,621
Liabilities: $17,791
Net Worth: $2,009,829
Earnings: ($6,172)
Fiscal Year-end: 03/31/24
Zinc & Copper Exploration Services
N.A.I.C.S.: 212230

Linda Chang *(CFO)*

Subsidiaries:

Cerro La Mina S.A.   (1)
Calle Los Antares 320 Tower B 806, Santiago De Surco, Lima, Peru
Tel.: (51) 1 628 5124
Sales Range: $50-74.9 Million
Emp.: 15
Metal Mining Services
N.A.I.C.S.: 212290
Thomas Findley *(Gen Mgr)*

ARMOUR ENERGY LIMITED
Level 27 111 Eagle Street, Brisbane, 4000, QLD, Australia
Tel.: (61) 733030620
Web Site:
http://www.armourenergy.com.au
AJQ—(ASX)
Rev.: $13,779,927
Assets: $82,776,869
Liabilities: $43,072,903
Net Worth: $39,703,966
Earnings: ($8,432,687)
Emp.: 37
Fiscal Year-end: 06/30/22
Gas Exploration
N.A.I.C.S.: 211120
Nicholas Mather *(Chm)*

ARMOUR PLASTICS LIMITED
Pennywell Industrial Estate, Sunderland, SR4 9EN, Tyne & Wear, United Kingdom
Tel.: (44) 1915346061   UK
Web Site: http://www.armour-plastics.com
Year Founded: 1971
Sales Range: $25-49.9 Million
Emp.: 50
Mfr of Sanitary Ware in Vacuum-Formable Materials; Thermoformed Products & Machinery
N.A.I.C.S.: 326199
Sean Mulloy *(Mng Dir)*

Subsidiaries:

Armour Plastics Limited - Engineering Division   (1)
Alston Road Pattinson Ind Est, Washington, NE38 8QH, Tyne & Wear, United Kingdom
Tel.: (44) 191 416 7786
Web Site: http://www.armour-engineering.com
Plastic Thermoforming Machinery Mfr
N.A.I.C.S.: 333248
Sean Mulloy *(Mng Dir)*

Armour Plastics Limited - Renaissance Baths Division   (1)
Pennywell Industrial Estate, Sunderland, SR4 9EN, Tyne & Wear, United Kingdom
Tel.: (44) 191 534 6061
Web Site: http://www.renaissance-baths.co.uk
Sanitary Ware Mfr
N.A.I.C.S.: 332999

ARMOUR TRANSPORTATION SYSTEMS
689 Edinburgh Dr, Moncton, E1E 2L4, NB, Canada
Tel.: (506) 857-0205
Web Site: http://www.armour.ca
Sales Range: $150-199.9 Million
Emp.: 1,300
Transportation & Logistics Management Services
N.A.I.C.S.: 532411
Wesley Armour *(Pres & CEO)*

Subsidiaries:

Armour Courier Services Inc.   (1)
244 Edinburgh Dr, Moncton, E1E 4C7, NB, Canada
Tel.: (506) 857-3919
Courier Delivery Services
N.A.I.C.S.: 492110

Armour Logistics Services Inc.   (1)
350 English Dr, Moncton, E1E 3Y9, NB, Canada
Tel.: (506) 861-0270
Logistics Consulting Servies
N.A.I.C.S.: 541614

Armour Transport Inc   (1)
160 Stewart Ave, Sussex, E4E 2G2, NB, Canada
Tel.: (506) 432-4120
Logistics Consulting Servies
N.A.I.C.S.: 541614

Diamond's Transfer Ltd   (1)
-, PO Box 70, Winsloe, C0A 2H0, PE, Canada
Tel.: (902) 368-1400
Sea Freight Transportation Services
N.A.I.C.S.: 483211

Hillman's Transfer Limited   (1)
410 Gateway Avenue Sydport Industrial Park, Sydney, B2A 4V1, NS, Canada
Tel.: (902) 564-8113
Web Site: http://www.hillmanstransfer.com
Emp.: 60
Freight Transportation Services
N.A.I.C.S.: 484121
Eddie Hillman *(Pres)*

Pole Star Transport Inc   (1)
40 Lawrence St, Amherst, B4H 3G6, NS, Canada
Tel.: (506) 406-5054
Web Site:
https://www.polestartransportation.com
Emp.: 2,000
Freight Transportation Services
N.A.I.C.S.: 484110

Way's Transport Ltd.   (1)
Watsons Pond Industrial Park, PO Box 355, Corner Brook, A2H 6E3, NL, Canada
Tel.: (709) 634-4763
Web Site: http://www.waystransport.ca
Freight Transportation Services
N.A.I.C.S.: 484121

ARMSTRONG CRAVEN LIMITED
Westgate House 44 Hale Road, Hale, WA14 2EX, Cheshire, United Kingdom
Tel.: (44) 2037012020   UK
Web Site:
http://www.armstrongcraven.com
Year Founded: 1990
Sales Range: $10-24.9 Million
Emp.: 51
Executive Search Service
N.A.I.C.S.: 561312
Matthew Mellor *(Mng Dir)*

ARMSTRONG ENERGY GLOBAL LIMITED
Trendz Venkat Sai Gateway 1st Floor Green Land Colony, Gachibowli, Hyderabad, 5000032, India
Tel.: (91) 40 2300 1230   In
Web Site:
http://www.armstongenergy.com
Holding Company; Solar Farm Owner & Operator
N.A.I.C.S.: 551112
Ramnath Nandakumar *(Mng Dir)*

Subsidiaries:

AEG Solar India Pvt. Ltd.   (1)
Trendz Venkat Sai Gateway 1st Floor Green Land Colony, Gachibowli, Hyderabad, 5000032, India
Tel.: (91) 40 2300 1230
Web Site:
http://www.armstrongenergyglobal.com
Solar Farm Operator
N.A.I.C.S.: 221114
Ramnath Nandakumar *(Mng Dir)*

ARMSTRONG INDUSTRIAL CORPORATION LTD.
988 Toa Payoh North 06-03, Singapore, 319002, Singapore

Tel.: (65) 6804 9623
Web Site:
http://www.armstrong.com.sg
Year Founded: 1974
Sales Range: $150-199.9 Million
Emp.: 100
Dampening, Insulation, Sealing & Cushion Products Designer, Marketer & Mfr
N.A.I.C.S.: 333248
Gilbert Peng Koon Ong *(Founder, Chm & CEO)*

Subsidiaries:

Armstrong Mechanical Components Company Limited   (1)
Rojana Industrial Park Estate 2 42 9 Moo 4 Tambol Baanchang, Amphur U-Thai, Ayutthaya, 13210, Thailand
Tel.: (66) 3595034043
Web Site: http://www.armstrong.co.th
Sales Range: $75-99.9 Million
Emp.: 300
Industrial Engineering Services
N.A.I.C.S.: 541330

Armstrong Odenwald Changchun (AOC) Technology Co Ltd   (1)
No 48 Hongmian St Huadu Zone, 510800, Guangzhou, Guangdong, China
Tel.: (86) 2036872881
Industrial Engineering Services
N.A.I.C.S.: 541330

Armstrong Odenwald Technology (Tianjin) Co Ltd   (1)
No B3-3 Aida International Industry Area, Xiqing Eco Techno Develop Zone, 300385, Tianjin, China
Tel.: (86) 2223870777
Industrial Engineering Services
N.A.I.C.S.: 541330

Armstrong Odenwald Technology (Wuhan) Co Ltd   (1)
No 101 Dazhuan Rd Dajijie Industrial Area, Caidian, Wuhan, 430113, Hubei, China
Tel.: (86) 2769160770
Web Site: http://www.armstrong.com.sg
Industrial Engineering Services
N.A.I.C.S.: 541330

Armstrong Rubber & Chemical Products Company Limited   (1)
591 Moo 17 Soi Bangplee-Phattana Theparuk Rd, Amphur, Bang Sao Thong, 10540, Samutprakarn, Thailand
Tel.: (66) 7052021 30
Web Site: http://www.armstrong.co.th
Rubber & Chemicals Mfr
N.A.I.C.S.: 325212

Armstrong Rubber Manufacturing Pte Ltd   (1)
988 Toa Payoh North 06-03, Singapore, 319002, Singapore
Tel.: (65) 66658588
Web Site: http://www.armstrongasia.com
Sales Range: $125-149.9 Million
Rubber Products Mfr
N.A.I.C.S.: 326291
Gilbert Ong *(Gen Mgr)*

Armstrong Rubber Technology (Thailand) Company Limited   (1)
42 10 Moo 4 Rojana Industrial Park Tambol Baanchang, Amphur U-Thai, Ayutthaya, Thailand
Tel.: (66) 35 950160 3
Sales Range: $25-49.9 Million
Emp.: 40
Industrial Engineering Services
N.A.I.C.S.: 541330

Armstrong Technology (Suzhou) Co Ltd   (1)
No 2 Bao Da Rd Suzhou Industrial Park, KuaTang Sub-District, 215122, Suzhou, JiangSu, China
Tel.: (86) 51262750285
Sales Range: $25-49.9 Million
Emp.: 150
Industrial Engineering Services
N.A.I.C.S.: 541330
Liew Chieton *(Gen Mgr)*

Armstrong Technology (Wuxi) Co Ltd   (1)

No 5 XingChuan 1Road Wuxi Singapore Industrial Park, Wuxi, 214028, Jiangsu, China
Tel.: (86) 51085282400
Web Site: http://www.armstrongasia.com
Industrial Engineering Services
N.A.I.C.S.: 541330

Hardyflex Industries Sdn Bhd   (1)
No 70 Jalan TSB 9 Taman Industry, Sungai Buloh, 47000, Sclangor Darul Ehsan, Malaysia
Tel.: (60) 3 6157 0318
Web Site: http://www.armstrong.net.my
Rubber Products Mfr
N.A.I.C.S.: 326291

ARMY & NAVY DEPARTMENT STORES LIMITED
74 W Cordova St, Vancouver, V6B 1C9, BC, Canada
Tel.: (604) 683-9660
Web Site:
http://www.armyandnavy.ca
Sales Range: $125-149.9 Million
Emp.: 1,000
Clothing Retailer
N.A.I.C.S.: 458110
Jacqui Cohen *(Pres & CEO)*

ARMY WELFARE TRUST LLC
AWT Plaza The Mall, Rawalpindi, 46000, Pakistan
Tel.: (92) 5192724004
Web Site: http://www.awt.com.pk
Year Founded: 1971
Sales Range: $800-899.9 Million
Emp.: 3,375
Military Pension Trust Management & Financial Investment Services
N.A.I.C.S.: 524292
Akhtar Mehmood *(CEO)*

Subsidiaries:

Askari Aviation Services Pvt Ltd.   (1)
Near Old Benazir Bhutto International Airport, Chaklala, Rawalpindi, 46210, Pakistan
Tel.: (92) 515505760
Web Site: https://askariaviation.com
Aviation Services
N.A.I.C.S.: 488190
Irfan Hassan *(CEO)*

Askari Development Holdings Pvt Ltd   (1)
Army Welfare Trusr AWT Plaza The Mall, Rawalpindi, Pakistan
Tel.: (92) 5192724004
Welfare Trust Services
N.A.I.C.S.: 523991

Askari Enterprises Pvt Ltd   (1)
4th Floor AWT Plaza The Mall, Rawalpindi, Pakistan
Tel.: (92) 519271745
Web Site:
https://www.askarienterprises.com.pk
Military Equipment Distr
N.A.I.C.S.: 423860
Muhammad Latif *(CEO)*

Askari Guards (Pvt) Limited   (1)
283-C Raja Akram Road Near Race Course Ground, Rawalpindi, Pakistan
Tel.: (92) 515793451
Web Site: https://www.askariguards.com
Security Guards & Patrol Services
N.A.I.C.S.: 561612

Askari Life Assurance Company Limited   (1)
Office No 1104 11th Floor Emerald Tower Plot No G-19 Block 5, KDA Improvement Scheme No 5 Clifton, Karachi, Pakistan
Tel.: (92) 21111225275
Web Site: https://www.askarilife.com
Rev.: $1,944,629
Assets: $4,958,208
Liabilities: $3,128,945
Net Worth: $1,829,263
Earnings: ($1,692,947)
Fiscal Year-end: 12/31/2019
Real Estate Investment Management Services
N.A.I.C.S.: 531390

Army Welfare Trust LLC—(Continued)

Jehanzeb Zafar (CEO)

Askari Real Estate Ltd. (1)
6 th Floor AWT Plaza 5-A The Mall, Rawalpindi, Pakistan
Tel.: (92) 5192724004
Web Site: https://awtrealestate.com.pk
Real Estate Services
N.A.I.O.O.: 501210

MAL Pakistan Ltd. (1)
D-46 Block 5 KDA Scheme 5, Clifton, Karachi, Pakistan
Tel.: (92) 21111840840
Welfare Trust Services
N.A.I.C.S.: 523991

ARN MEDIA LIMITED
LG Floor 40 Mount Street, North Sydney, 2060, NSW, Australia
Tel.: (61) 288999999   AU
Web Site: https://arn.com.au
A1N—(ASX)
Rev: $257,612,560
Assets: $433,436,414
Liabilities: $217,942,238
Net Worth: $215,494,176
Earnings: ($4,712,213)
Fiscal Year-end: 12/31/23
Producer of Media & News Publications: Owned 39.1% by Independent News & Media PLC
N.A.I.C.S.: 513110
Ciaran Davis (CEO & Mng Dir)

Subsidiaries:

APN Digital Pty. Ltd. (1)
Level 1 Elizabeth Plz, Sydney, 2060, NSW, Australia
(100%)
Tel.: (61) 299284900
Custom Internal Software Programming Services
N.A.I.C.S.: 541511

APN Educational Media (1)
Level 19 233 Castlereagh Street, Sydney, 2000, NSW, Australia
(100%)
Tel.: (61) 299368666
Web Site: http://www.apned.com.au
Sales Range: $25-49.9 Million
Emp.: 20
Publishing Services
N.A.I.C.S.: 561410
David Williams (Gen Mgr)

APN New Zealand Limited (1)
46 Albert Street, Auckland, 1010, New Zealand
Tel.: (64) 9 379 5050
Web Site: http://www.apn.com
Emp.: 70
Multimedia Holding Company; Newspaper & Online Publishing, Radio Broadcasting & Outdoor Advertising Services
N.A.I.C.S.: 551112
Kursten Shalfoon (CMO)

Subsidiary (Non-US):

APN Media (NZ) Limited (2)
Tel.: (64) 9 373 6400
Web Site: http://www.nzherald.co.nz
Sales Range: $200-249.9 Million
Emp.: 200
Newspaper Publishers
N.A.I.C.S.: 513110

Subsidiary (Non-US):

APN Educational Media (NZ) Limited (3)
Tel.: (64) 4 471 1080
Web Site: http://www.apn-ed.co.nz
Sales Range: $25-49.9 Million
Emp.: 18
Education & Health Materials Publisher
N.A.I.C.S.: 513130

APN Specialist Publications NZ Limited (3)
Tel.: (64) 9 373 6400
Business Directories Publisher
N.A.I.C.S.: 513140

NZME Online Limited (3)

Tel.: (64) 9 379 5050
Web Site: http://advertising.nzme.co.nz
Online Publishing & Advertising Services
N.A.I.C.S.: 541890

APN Online (Australia) Pty Limited (1)
L 4 100 Willian St, Sydney, 2011, NSW, Australia
Tel.: (61) 282898450
Online Publishing Services
N.A.I.C.S.: 513199

APN Superannuation Pty Ltd (1)
L 3 33 Park Rd, Milton, 4064, QLD, Australia
Tel.: (61) 733070333
Newspaper Publishing Services
N.A.I.C.S.: 513110

Australian Provincial Newspapers Ltd (1)
Level 4 100 William Street, Sydney, 2011, NSW, Australia
Tel.: (61) 293334999
Web Site: http://www.apn.com.au
Emp.: 15
Newspaper Publishing Services
N.A.I.C.S.: 513110
Ciaran Davis (Gen Mgr)

Subsidiary (Domestic):

Australian Provincial Newspapers International Pty Limited
L-4 100 William Street, Sydney, 2011, NSW, Australia
Tel.: (61) 293334999
Newspaper Publishing Services
N.A.I.C.S.: 513110

Australian Radio Network Pty. Limited (1)
3 Byfield Street, North Ryde, 2113, NSW, Australia
Tel.: (61) 288999888
Web Site: http://www.arn.com.au
Sales Range: $50-74.9 Million
Emp.: 500
Radio Network Operator
N.A.I.C.S.: 516210
Ciaran Davis (CEO)

Subsidiary (Domestic):

Grant Broadcasters Pty. Ltd. (2)
Suite 303 10-12 Clarke Street, Crows Nest, 2065, NSW, Australia
Tel.: (61) 294378888
Web Site:
http://www.grantbroadcasters.com.au
Radio Broadcasting Services
N.A.I.C.S.: 516210
Janet Cameron (Mng Dir)

Radio 96FM Perth Pty. Limited (2)
Level 1 169 Hay Street, Perth, 6004, WA, Australia
Tel.: (61) 89 323 9600
Web Site: https://www.96fm.com.au
Radio Broadcasting Services
N.A.I.C.S.: 516110

Biffin Pty Limited (1)
L 4 100 William St, Woolloomooloo, 2011, Australia
Tel.: (61) 293334999
Web Site: http://www.apn.com.au
Newspaper Publishing Services
N.A.I.C.S.: 513110
Brett Chenoweth (CEO)

GSP Print Pty Ltd (1)
19 Ash Road, Prestons, Sydney, 2170, NSW, Australia
Tel.: (61) 28 784 5120
Web Site: https://www.gspprint.com.au
Outdoor Banner Printing Services
N.A.I.C.S.: 323111

Gatton Star Pty Ltd (1)
45 North Street, Gatton, 4343, QLD, Australia
Tel.: (61) 754622266
Web Site: http://www.gattonstar.com.au
Newspaper Publishing Services
N.A.I.C.S.: 513110
Bruce Horrocks (Mgr-Sls)

Gladstone Newspaper Company Pty Ltd (1)

130 Open Dr, Gladstone, QLD, Australia
Tel.: (61) 749703030
Web Site:
http://www.gladstonepacific.com.au
Sales Range: $25-49.9 Million
Emp.: 30
Newspaper Publishing Services
N.A.I.C.S.: 513110
Carl Carter (Gen Mgr)

Gulgong Pty Limited (1)
L 4 100 William St, Woolloomooloo, 2011, NSW, Australia
Tel.: (61) 293334999
Sales Range: $25-49.9 Million
Emp.: 20
Newspaper Publishing Services
N.A.I.C.S.: 513110

Haswell Pty Limited (1)
L 10 300 Ann St, Brisbane, 4000, QLD, Australia
Tel.: (61) 733070300
Sales Range: $25-49.9 Million
Emp.: 60
Newspaper Publishing Services
N.A.I.C.S.: 513110

Melbourne Independent Newspapers Pty Ltd (1)
L 4 100 William St, North Sydney, 2055, NSW, Australia
Tel.: (61) 293334999
Web Site: http://www.apn.com.au
Emp.: 30
Newspaper Publishing Services
N.A.I.C.S.: 513110
Justin Nelson (CEO)

NZME Limited (1)
2 Graham Street, Auckland, 1010, New Zealand
Tel.: (64) 93795050
Web Site: https://www.nzme.co.nz
Rev.: $212,118,492
Assets: $177,191,407
Liabilities: $96,376,837
Net Worth: $80,814,570
Earnings: $7,444,017
Emp.: 565
Fiscal Year-end: 12/31/2023
Media Broadcasting Services
N.A.I.C.S.: 516210
Michael Boggs (CEO)

The Gold Coast Press Pty Limited (1)
333 Park Rd, Milton, 4064, QLD, Australia
Tel.: (61) 733273300
Newspaper Publishing Services
N.A.I.C.S.: 513110

ARNAV CORPORATION LIMITED
Unit 704 Jay Antariksh Near Marol Metro Station Andheri E, Mumbai, 400 099, Maharashtra, India
Tel.: (91) 22 64501225
Web Site: http://www.arnavcorp.co.in
Rev.: $955,784
Assets: $14,009,605
Liabilities: $66,854
Net Worth: $13,942,751
Earnings: $1,873
Fiscal Year-end: 03/31/18
Book Whslr
N.A.I.C.S.: 424920
Dhiren Vitthaldas Negandhi (Chm & Mng Dir)

ARNECKE SIEBOLD RECHT-SANWALTE PARTNER-SCHAFTSGESELLSCHAFT
Hamburger Allee 4 WestendGate, Frankfurt am Main, Germany
Tel.: (49) 69 97 98 85 0
Web Site:
http://www.arneckesiebold.de
Emp.: 34
Law firm
N.A.I.C.S.: 541110
Georg Arnecke (Co-Partner)

Subsidiaries:

SIBETH Partnerschaft (1)

Oberanger 34-36, Munich, Germany
Tel.: (49) 89 3 88 08 0
Web Site: http://www.sibeth.com
Emp.: 18
Law firm
N.A.I.C.S.: 541110

ARNES WELDING LTD.
835 Mission Street, Winnipeg, R2J 0A4, MB, Canada
Tel.: (204) 233-7111
Web Site: https://www.arnes.com
Year Founded: 1954
Sales Range: $10-24.9 Million
Emp.: 80
Truck Trailer Mfr
N.A.I.C.S.: 336212
Gerald Bouchard (Pres)

ARNOLD BROS. TRANSPORT LTD
739 Lagimodiere Blvd, Winnipeg, R2J 0T8, MB, Canada
Tel.: (204) 257-6666
Web Site:
https://www.arnoldbros.com
Year Founded: 1958
Sales Range: $75-99.9 Million
Emp.: 750
Transportation & Delivery Services
N.A.I.C.S.: 484121
Gary Arnold (Exec VP)

ARNOLD CLARK AUTOMO-BILES LIMITED
454 Hillington Road, Glasgow, G52 4FH, United Kingdom
Tel.: (44) 1414222700
Web Site: http://www.arnoldclark.com
Year Founded: 1954
Sales Range: $1-4.9 Billion
Emp.: 7,500
Automobile Dealership Operator
N.A.I.C.S.: 441110
Eddie Hawthorne (Grp Mng Dir)

Subsidiaries:

Arnold Clark Finance Limited (1)
St Georges House 163 St Georges Road, Glasgow, G3 6LB, United Kingdom
Tel.: (44) 141 332 2626
Web Site: http://www.acvm.co.uk
Vehicle Fleet Leasing Services
N.A.I.C.S.: 532112

Arnold Clark Insurance Services Limited (1)
64 Craigentinny Avenue North Seafield, Midlothian, Edinburgh, EH6 7LJ, United Kingdom
Tel.: (44) 131 5555999
Vehicle Insurance Services
N.A.I.C.S.: 524126

GTG Training Limited (1)
1330 South Street, Glasgow, G14 0BJ, United Kingdom
Tel.: (44) 1419505600
Web Site: http://www.gtg.co.uk
Educational Support Services
N.A.I.C.S.: 611710
Pauline Marshall (Bus Mgr)

Harry Fairbairn Limited (1)
167 Fenwick Road, Giffnock, Glasgow, G46 6JB, United Kingdom
Tel.: (44) 1412787899
Web Site: http://www.harryfairbairn.co.uk
New Car Dealers
N.A.I.C.S.: 441110
Cameron Smith (Mgr-Sls)

ARNOLD HOLDINGS LIMITED
B-208 Ramji House 30 Jambulwadi J S S Road, Mumbai, 400002, India
Tel.: (91) 2222016640
Web Site:
https://www.arnoldholdings.in
Year Founded: 1981
537069—(BOM)
Rev.: $5,115,784

Assets: $7,538,652
Liabilities: $155,221
Net Worth: $7,383,431
Earnings: $94,313
Emp.: 6
Fiscal Year-end: 03/31/21
Holding Company
N.A.I.C.S.: 551112
Soniya Agarwal *(Officer-Compliance & Sec)*

ARNON CORPORATION
1801 Woodward Drive, Ottawa, K2C 0R3, ON, Canada
Tel.: (613) 226-2000
Web Site: http://www.arnon.ca
Year Founded: 1960
Rev.: $71,303,750
Emp.: 250
Commercial & Residential Building Construction & Services
N.A.I.C.S.: 623990

ARNOTTS LTD.
12 Henry Street, Dublin, Ireland
Tel.: (353) 18050400   IE
Web Site: http://www.arnotts.ie
Year Founded: 1843
Sales Range: $200-249.9 Million
Emp.: 1,200
Department Store Owner & Operator
N.A.I.C.S.: 455110
Sarah Williams *(Head-PR)*

Subsidiaries:

Asgard Financial Services Ltd   (1)
104 Middle Abbey St, Dublin, 1, Ireland   **(100%)**
Tel.: (353) 18732410
Sales Range: $25-49.9 Million
Emp.: 5
Financial Brokerages
N.A.I.C.S.: 523150

Boyers & Co. Limited   (1)
19-22 North Earl Street, Dublin, 1, Ireland   **(100%)**
Tel.: (353) 18050403
Sales Range: $25-49.9 Million
Emp.: 100
Department Store & Boutiques
N.A.I.C.S.: 455110

ARO GRANITE INDUSTRIES LTD.
1001 l0th Floor DLF Tower A Jasola, New Delhi, 110 025, India
Tel.: (91) 1141686169
Web Site: https://www.arotile.com
AROGRANITE—(NSE)
Rev.: $24,570,887
Assets: $55,212,789
Liabilities: $29,599,793
Net Worth: $25,612,997
Earnings: $825,566
Emp.: 296
Fiscal Year-end: 03/31/21
Granite Tiles & Slabs Mfr & Distr
N.A.I.C.S.: 326199
Sunil K. Arora *(Mng Dir, Mng Dir & Head/Head-Mktg)*

Subsidiaries:

Aro Granite Industries Ltd. - Unit I   (1)
103 SIPCOT Industrial Complex, Hosur, 635 126, Tamilnadu, India
Tel.: (91) 4344276860
Sales Range: $200-249.9 Million
Emp.: 950
Granite Tile & Slab Mfr
N.A.I.C.S.: 327991

Aro Granite Industries Ltd. - Unit II   (1)
Koneripalli Village, Shoolagiri, Hosur, 635 117, Tamilnadu, India
Tel.: (91) 4344252100

Sales Range: $200-249.9 Million
Emp.: 800
Granite Tile & Slab Mfr
N.A.I.C.S.: 327991
Sunil Kumar Arora *(Mng Dir & Head-Mktg)*

ARO PALACE S.A.
B-dul Eroilor nr 27, 500030, Brasov, Romania
Tel.: (40) 268478800
Web Site: https://www.aro-palace.ro
Year Founded: 1991
ARO—(BUC)
Rev.: $17,329,858
Assets: $32,153,777
Liabilities: $1,102,929
Net Worth: $31,050,848
Earnings: $7,551,751
Emp.: 123
Fiscal Year-end: 12/31/23
Hotel Operator
N.A.I.C.S.: 721110
Daniela Anghelus *(Gen Mgr)*

AROA BIOSURGERY LIMITED
64 Richard Pearse Drive, Mangere, Auckland, 2022, New Zealand
Tel.: (64) 98693035
Web Site: https://aroa.com
Year Founded: 2008
ARX—(ASX)
Rev.: $37,894,737
Assets: $69,689,593
Liabilities: $8,750,000
Net Worth: $60,939,593
Earnings: ($236,842)
Emp.: 270
Fiscal Year-end: 03/31/23
Biotechnology Research & Development Services
N.A.I.C.S.: 541714
Brian Ward *(Founder)*

AROBS TRANSILVANIA SOFT-WARE S.A.
44 46 Henri Barbusse Street, 400616, Cluj-Napoca, Romania
Tel.: (40) 264202116
Web Site: https://arobs.com
Year Founded: 1998
AROBS—(BUC)
Rev.: $91,992,108
Assets: $103,418,037
Liabilities: $44,495,958
Net Worth: $58,922,078
Earnings: $6,871,168
Emp.: 1,254
Fiscal Year-end: 12/31/23
Software Development Services
N.A.I.C.S.: 513210
Voicu Oprean *(Founder & CEO)*

Subsidiaries:

Enea Services Romania SRL   (1)
319 Splaiul Independentei OB403A District 6, Bucharest, 60044, Romania
Tel.: (40) 21 311 43 00
Web Site: http://www.enea.com
Computer System Design Services
N.A.I.C.S.: 541512

AROCA DEL PINAR SOCIMI, S.A.
C/Nanclares de Oca 1B, 28022, Madrid, Spain
Tel.: (34) 917456859   ES
Web Site: https://www.arocadelpinarsocimi.es
Year Founded: 2018
MLARO—(EUR)
Rev.: $236,579,257
Assets: $9,047,451,813
Liabilities: $9,082,023
Net Worth: $9,038,369,790
Earnings: $229,844,841
Fiscal Year-end: 12/31/21
Investment Management Service

N.A.I.C.S.: 523999

AROCELL AB
Tel.: (46) 87996750
Web Site: https://www.arocell.com
Year Founded: 2000
80R—(DEU)
Diagnostic Product Mfr & Distr
N.A.I.C.S.: 334510
Gustav Sten *(COO)*

AROMA AD
12 Kiril Blagoev Str, 1271, Sofia, 1271, Bulgaria
Tel.: (359) 29350304
Web Site: https://www.aroma.bg
Year Founded: 1924
AROM—(BUL)
Sales Range: Less than $1 Million
Cosmetics Products Mfr
N.A.I.C.S.: 456120
Dimitar Lukanov Lukanov *(CEO)*

AROMA CELTE SA
ZA Kerhollo, 22200, Saint Agathe, France
Tel.: (33) 296924370
Web Site: http://www.aroma-celte.com
Chemical Product Mfr & Distr
N.A.I.C.S.: 325998

AROMA COSMETICS AD
12 Kiril Blagoev Str, Sofia, 1271, Bulgaria
Tel.: (359) 2 9350304   BG
Web Site: http://aroma.bg
Cosmetics Products Mfr
N.A.I.C.S.: 456120
Dimitar Lukanov Lukanov *(Vice Chm, CEO & VP)*

AROMA ENTERPRISES (INDIA) LIMITED
88 Ajanta Commercial Center Nr Income Tax Circle Ashram Road, Ahmedabad, 380 009, Gujarat, India
Tel.: (91) 7927540175
Web Site: https://www.aromaenterprises.in
Year Founded: 1994
531560—(BOM)
Assets: $3,544,604
Liabilities: $3,756,516
Net Worth: ($211,912)
Earnings: ($35,495)
Emp.: 4
Fiscal Year-end: 03/31/23
Financial & Leasing Services
N.A.I.C.S.: 523999
Ankit Shukla *(CFO)*

AROOT CO., LTD.
28-6 Gajangsaneopdong-ro, Osan, Gyeonggi-do, Korea (South)
Tel.: (82) 3180775000
Web Site: https://www.aroot.co.kr
Year Founded: 2002
096690—(KRS)
Rev.: $49,768,847
Assets: $150,446,479
Liabilities: $37,913,277
Net Worth: $112,533,202
Earnings: $4,689,248
Emp.: 68
Fiscal Year-end: 12/31/22
Printer Mfr
N.A.I.C.S.: 333248
Jun Min Lee *(CEO)*

Subsidiaries:

Xeonics Co., Ltd.   (1)
195-66 Saneop-ro, Gwonseon-gu, Suwon, 16648, Gyeonggi-do, Korea (South)
Tel.: (82) 316860300
Web Site: https://en.xeonics.co.kr
Electrical Equipment Mfr & Distr

N.A.I.C.S.: 335999

ARORA HOTELS LIMITED
Southgate Avenue, Crawley, RH10 6LW, United Kingdom
Tel.: (44) 1293 530 000
Web Site: http://www.arorahotels.com
Year Founded: 1999
Sales Range: $10-24.9 Million
Emp.: 995
Home Management Services
N.A.I.C.S.: 721110
Bruno Delrieux *(Gen Mgr)*

Subsidiaries:

Buckinghamshire Golf Company, Ltd.   (1)
Denham Court Drive, Denham, UB9 5PG, Buckinghamshire, United Kingdom **(100%)**
Tel.: (44) 1895835777
Web Site: http://www.buckinghamshiregc.com
Sales Range: $75-99.9 Million
Emp.: 200
Golf Course & Clubhouse
N.A.I.C.S.: 713910

ARORA-MATTHEY LIMITED
166 Netaji Subhash Chandra Bose Road, Regent Park, Kolkata, 700 040, India
Tel.: (91) 33 2471 1207
Web Site: http://www.aroramatthey.com
Year Founded: 1964
Sales Range: $25-49.9 Million
Emp.: 100
Precious Metal Products, Alloys, Compounds & Catalysts Mfr
N.A.I.C.S.: 331314
Sarva Arora *(Mng Dir)*

Subsidiaries:

Arora-Matthey Limited Visakhapatnam Unit   (1)
58B JNPC, Parawada, Visakhapatnam, 531 019, Andra Pradesh, India
Tel.: (91) 8924236103
Metal Products Mfr
N.A.I.C.S.: 331420

AROUND NOON FOODS LIMITED
Cooper Parry Sky View Argosy Road, East Midlands Airport Castle Donington, Derby, DE74 2SA, United Kingdom
Tel.: (44) 2830262333
Web Site: http://www.aroundnoon.com
Year Founded: 2016
Food-to-Go Specialists
N.A.I.C.S.: 311999
Gareth Chambers *(Dir)*

Subsidiaries:

Chef in a Box Limited   (1)
81 Haunch Lane, Birmingham, B13 0NX, United Kingdom
Tel.: (44) 1753686844
Packaged Food Distr
N.A.I.C.S.: 424420

AROUNDTOWN SA
Tel.: (352) 288313
Web Site: https://www.aroundtown.de
AT1—(DEU)
Rev.: $1,729,764,731
Assets: $36,217,677,531
Liabilities: $19,867,904,166
Net Worth: $16,349,773,365
Earnings: ($2,618,605,655)
Emp.: 1,347
Fiscal Year-end: 12/31/23
Real Estate Investment
N.A.I.C.S.: 531190
Eyal Ben David *(CFO)*

Aroundtown SA—(Continued)

Subsidiaries:

TLG Immobilien AG **(1)**
TLG IMMOBILIEN AGAlexanderstrasse 1,
10178, Berlin, Germany **(79.89%)**
Tel.: (49) 30247050
Web Site: https://www.tlg.eu
Commercial Real Estate Developer & Manager
N.A.I.C.S.: 236220
Peter Finkbeiner *(Member-Mgmt Bd)*

Subsidiary (Domestic):

Triangel Frankfurt Immobilien GmbH
& Co. KG **(2)**
Taunusanlage 16, 60325, Frankfurt, Germany
Tel.: (49) 69743038829
Web Site: https://www.main-triangel.de
N.A.I.C.S.: 541330

WCM Beteiligungs- und
Grundbesitz-Aktiengesellschaft **(2)**
Alexanderstrasse 1, 10178, Berlin, Germany
Tel.: (49) 30247050
Web Site: https://ir.wcm.de
Rev.: $313,178,156
Assets: $5,232,012,212
Liabilities: $3,627,376,624
Net Worth: $1,604,635,588
Earnings: $122,064,740
Emp.: 28
Fiscal Year-end: 12/31/2019
Investment Company
N.A.I.C.S.: 523150
Peter Finkbeiner *(Exec Bd)*

Subsidiary (Domestic):

Allboden AG Allgemeine
Grundstucks-Aktiengesellschaft **(3)**
Am Borsigturm 11, Podbielskistr 166B,
13507, Berlin, Germany
Tel.: (49) 30 43657700
Web Site: http://www.allboden.de
Equity Holding
N.A.I.C.S.: 525990

AROVELLA THERAPEUTICS LIMITED

Corporate One 84 Hotham Street,
Preston, 3072, VIC, Australia
Tel.: (61) 398636472 **AU**
Web Site: https://www.arovella.com
ALA—(ASX)
Rev.: $896,871
Assets: $8,188,495
Liabilities: $1,306,819
Net Worth: $6,881,676
Earnings: ($3,867,317)
Fiscal Year-end: 06/30/21
Pharmaceuticals Product Mfr
N.A.I.C.S.: 325412
Michael Baker *(CEO & Mng Dir)*

Subsidiaries:

Malaria Research Company Pty
Ltd **(1)**
Level 1 Unit 12 55 Howe Street, Osborne
Park, 6017, WA, Australia
Tel.: (61) 861425555
Web Site: http://www.mrc-malaria.com
Healtcare Services
N.A.I.C.S.: 621999
Steve Carter *(CEO)*

AROWANA INC.

Level 11 153 Walker Street, North
Sydney, 2060, NSW, Australia
Tel.: (61) 2 8083 9800 **Ky**
Web Site: http://www.arowanaco.com
Year Founded: 2014
Investment Services
N.A.I.C.S.: 523999
Kevin T. Chin *(Chm & CEO)*

AROWAY ENERGY INC.

Suite 340 1414 - 8th Street SW, Calgary, T2R 1J6, AB, Canada

Web Site:
http://www.arowayenergy.com
Year Founded: 1980
Sales Range: $1-9.9 Million
Emp.: 1
Oil & Gas Exploration Services
N.A.I.C.S.: 213112
Christopher R. Cooper *(Pres & CEO)*

ARPA-SEVAN OJSC

V Vagharshyan Str 20, Yerevan,
0012, Armenia
Tel.: (374) 12211111
Web Site: http://www.arpa-sevan.am
Year Founded: 1969
ASEV—(ARM)
Construction Services
N.A.I.C.S.: 236220

ARPADIS GROUP

Hertogenpark Desguinlei 88A, 2018,
Antwerp, Belgium
Tel.: (32) 3 206 9375
Web Site: http://www.arpadis.com
Sales Range: $75-99.9 Million
Investment Management Service
N.A.I.C.S.: 523940
Eric Goldschneider *(Mng Dir)*

ARPAK INTERNATIONAL INVESTMENTS LTD.

King's Arcade 20-A Markaz F-7, Islamabad, Pakistan
Tel.: (92) 5126508057
Year Founded: 1977
ARPAK—(PSX)
Rev.: $56,702
Assets: $1,440,400
Liabilities: $42,977
Net Worth: $1,397,423
Earnings: ($274,505)
Emp.: 4
Fiscal Year-end: 06/30/23
Financial Services
N.A.I.C.S.: 523999
Rizwan Ullah Khan *(CFO)*

ARPICO INSURANCE PLC

Tel.: (94) 112200910
Web Site:
https://www.arpicoinsurance.com
Year Founded: 2011
AINS.N0000—(COL)
Rev.: $7,718,047
Assets: $15,379,171
Liabilities: $8,996,835
Net Worth: $6,382,336
Earnings: $120,623
Emp.: 422
Fiscal Year-end: 12/31/22
Insurance Services
N.A.I.C.S.: 524210
L. A. C. Priyanthi *(Mgr-Actuarial)*

ARPLAMA N.V.

Industriezone De Heze, Hagelberg 8,
B 2250, Olen, Belgium
Tel.: (32) 14 23 73 92
Web Site:
http://www.arplamagroup.com
Sales Range: $10-24.9 Million
Emp.: 120
Thermosets Mfr & Distr
N.A.I.C.S.: 334513

Subsidiaries:

Pla-Ma Belgium NV **(1)**
Industriezone De Heze, Hagelberg 8, B
2550, Olen, Belgium
Tel.: (32) 14 23 73 92
Web Site: http://www.arplamagroup.com
Polyurethane Processing
N.A.I.C.S.: 326199

S.C. Arplama Romania S.R.L. **(1)**
86 Tudor Vladimirescu, 505200, Fagaras,
Romania
Tel.: (40) 268280322

Web Site: http://www.arplama.ro
Emp.: 200
Polyester Processing
N.A.I.C.S.: 326199
Bcabirlat Micolas *(Mgr)*

ARQIT QUANTUM INC.

3 Orchard Place, London, SW1H
0BF, United Kingdom
Tel.: (44) 2039170155 **Ky**
Web Site: https://www.arqit.uk
Year Founded: 2021
ARQQ—(NASDAQ)
Rev.: $293,000
Assets: $26,719,000
Liabilities: $14,901,000
Net Worth: $11,818,000
Earnings: ($23,977,000)
Emp.: 82
Fiscal Year-end: 09/30/24
Software Development Services
N.A.I.C.S.: 541511
David Williams *(CEO)*

ARQUATI S.P.A.

Via San Vitale 3, 43038, Sala
Baganza, Italy
Tel.: (39) 05218321 **IT**
Web Site: http://www.arquati.it
Rev.: $18,174,000
Emp.: 200
Fabrics & Furnishings
N.A.I.C.S.: 423220
Stefano Talza *(Pres)*

ARQUEONAUTAS WORLD-WIDE - ARQUEOLOGIA SUBAQUATICA S.A.

Rua das Murcas 88 3rd Fl, 9000-058,
Funchal, Portugal
Tel.: (351) 214663040
Year Founded: 1995
Sales Range: Less than $1 Million
Emp.: 30
Marine Archeological Services
N.A.I.C.S.: 541715
Nikolaus Graf Sandizel *(CEO)*

ARR PLANNER CO., LTD.

10th floor 1-13-3 Higashisakura, NHK
Nagoya Broadcasting Center Building
Higashi-Ku, Nagoya, 461-0005, Japan
Tel.: (81) 529575820
Web Site:
https://www.arrplanner.co.jp
Year Founded: 2003
2983—(TKS)
Rev.: $227,376,300
Assets: $180,114,360
Liabilities: $149,237,410
Net Worth: $30,876,950
Earnings: $1,566,890
Emp.: 368
Fiscal Year-end: 01/31/24
Real Estate Development Services
N.A.I.C.S.: 531311
Yusuke Koga *(Founder & Chm)*

ARRAIL G ROUP LIMITED

F6 Building 11 Yard 18 Ziyue Road
Chaolai High-Tech Industrial Park,
Chaoyang, Beijing, 100012, China
Tel.: (86) 1051078008 **Ky**
Web Site:
https://www.arrailgroup.com
Year Founded: 1999
6639—(HKG)
Rev.: $204,051,423
Assets: $423,908,396
Liabilities: $189,098,638
Net Worth: $234,809,759
Earnings: ($30,924,346)
Emp.: 3,409
Fiscal Year-end: 03/31/23
Dental Care Services
N.A.I.C.S.: 424210

Bo Qu *(COO)*

ARRAS GROUP S.P.A

Largo Domodossola 7, 20145, Milan,
MI, Italy
Tel.: (39) 079582881
Web Site:
https://www.arrasgrouppa.com
Year Founded: 2020
AGU—(EUR)
Emp.: 12
Real Estate Development Services
N.A.I.C.S.: 531190

ARRAY MARKETING GROUP INC.

45 Progress Ave, Toronto, M1P 2Y6,
ON, Canada
Tel.: (416) 299-4865
Web Site:
http://www.arraymarketing.com
Sales Range: $25-49.9 Million
Emp.: 600
Store & Office Display Cases & Fixtures
N.A.I.C.S.: 337212
Thomas Hendren *(Chm & Head-Bus Dev-Global)*

Subsidiaries:

Array Asia Ltd. **(1)**
Suite 1409 14/F XinHua Insurance Building
MinTian Road, FuTian Center, Shenzhen,
518026, China
Tel.: (86) 755 3333 6835
Web Site: http://www.arraymarketing.com
Emp.: 22
Marketing Services
N.A.I.C.S.: 541613
Chung Ng *(Gen Mgr)*

Array Marketing Group Inc. - Array
Bradford Fixture Division **(1)**
35 Reagens Industrial Parkway, Bradford,
L3Z 2A4, ON, Canada
Tel.: (416) 213-5740
Sales Range: $25-49.9 Million
Emp.: 75
Fixture & Floor Stand Mfr
N.A.I.C.S.: 337215
Ken Simpson *(Pres)*

Array New York **(1)**
200 Madison Ave Ste 2121, New York, NY
10016
Tel.: (212) 750-3367
Marketing Services
N.A.I.C.S.: 541613

Summit Manufacturing LLC **(1)**
59 Spence St, Bay Shore, NY 11706
Tel.: (631) 952-1570
Web Site: http://www.summitmfg.net
Graphic Design Services
N.A.I.C.S.: 541430
Louis Marinello *(Pres)*

ARRHYTHMIA NETWORK TECHNOLOGY SL

Europa Avenue 34D Second floor
module C, Pozuelo de Alarcon, CP
28224, Madrid, Spain
Tel.: (34) 915135418
Web Site: https://www.arrhytnet.com
Medical Equipment Distr
N.A.I.C.S.: 423450

ARRIBATEC GROUP ASA

Lorenfaret 1D, 0585, Oslo, Norway
Tel.: (47) 40003355 **NO**
Web Site: https://www.arribatec.com
Year Founded: 1998
ARR—(OSL)
Rev.: $52,926,381
Assets: $46,327,822
Liabilities: $22,084,057
Net Worth: $24,243,765
Earnings: ($2,129,411)
Emp.: 329
Fiscal Year-end: 12/31/23
Information Technology Services

N.A.I.C.S.: 541512
Geir Johansen *(CEO)*

Subsidiaries:

Arribatec Hospitality AS   (1)
Lorenfaret 1D, 0585, Oslo, Norway
Tel.: (47) 913787803
Web Site: https://hospitality.arribatec.com
Software Development Services
N.A.I.C.S.: 541511

ARRIBATEC SOLUTIONS ASA
Nedre Vollgate 4, 0158, Oslo, Norway
Tel.: (47) 22120012   NO
Web Site: http://hiddn.no
Year Founded: 2016
HIDDN—(OSL)
Rev.: $983,343
Assets: $694,245
Liabilities: $924,411
Net Worth: ($230,166)
Earnings: ($3,790,980)
Emp.: 3
Fiscal Year-end: 12/31/19
Investment Holding Company
N.A.I.C.S.: 551112
Oystein Tvenge *(Chm)*

ARRICANO REAL ESTATE PLC
13th Floor 33 T Schevchenko Boulevard, 01032, Kiev, Ukraine
Tel.: (380) 445949470
Web Site: http://www.arricano.com
ARO—(AIM)
Rev.: $32,303,000
Assets: $296,501,000
Liabilities: $177,107,000
Net Worth: $119,394,000
Earnings: $20,180,000
Emp.: 78
Fiscal Year-end: 12/31/20
Commercial Real Estate Development & Management
N.A.I.C.S.: 237210
Anna Chubotina *(CEO & Dir-Retail Leasing Dept)*

ARRIYADH DEVELOPMENT COMPANY
Third floor Al Tameer Development Center for Wholesale, PO Box 7442, Qasr Al Hakam District Riyadh, Riyadh, 11462, Saudi Arabia
Tel.: (966) 114110333
Web Site: https://www.ardco.com.sa
Year Founded: 1994
4150—(SAU)
Rev.: $90,447,031
Assets: $744,542,524
Liabilities: $109,670,859
Net Worth: $634,871,666
Earnings: $72,408,612
Fiscal Year-end: 12/31/23
Building Construction Services
N.A.I.C.S.: 236220
Ali Abdullah Al-Hassoun *(CEO)*

ARROW CAPITAL CORP.
Tova Group Building Ground Floor Calle 50 y Aquilino de la Guardia, PO Box 0816-07844, Panama, Panama
Tel.: (507) 228 2222
Year Founded: 2012
AROW—(PAN)
Sales Range: Less than $1 Million
Holding Company
N.A.I.C.S.: 551112

ARROW CAPITAL MANAGEMENT, INC.
36 Toronto St Ste 750, Toronto, M5C 2C5, ON, Canada
Tel.: (416) 323-0477
Web Site: http://www.arrow-capital.com
Year Founded: 1999

Portfolio Management Services
N.A.I.C.S.: 523940
James McGovern *(CEO & Mng Dir)*

ARROW CARS INTERNATIONAL, INC.
Carretera Guadalmar 48, Malaga, Spain
Tel.: (34) 952623297
Emp.: 8
Automobile Sales
N.A.I.C.S.: 441110
Jeremy Dean Harris *(CEO)*

ARROW CONSTRUCTION PRODUCTS LIMITED
50 Gervais Court, PO Box 760, Fredericton, E3B 5B4, NB, Canada
Tel.: (506) 458-9610
Web Site: http://www.arrowco.ca
Year Founded: 1979
Rev.: $15,302,311
Emp.: 45
Construction Materials Supplier
N.A.I.C.S.: 333120

ARROW EC INCOME ADVANTAGE ALTERNATIVE FUND
36 Toronto Street Suite 750, Toronto, M5C 2C5, ON, Canada
Tel.: (416) 323-0477   ON
Web Site: http://www.arrow-capital.com
Year Founded: 2012
Rev.: $10,546,880
Assets: $405,592,839
Liabilities: $314,142,186
Net Worth: $91,450,653
Earnings: $2,791,513
Fiscal Year-end: 12/31/18
Investment Services
N.A.I.C.S.: 523999
James McGovern *(Founder, CEO, Mng Dir & Portfolio Mgr)*

ARROW EXPLORATION CORP.
203 2303 4 Street SW, Calgary, T2S 2S7, AB, Canada
Tel.: (403) 237-5700   AB
Web Site: https://www.arrowexploration.ca
AXL—(TSXV)
Rev.: $50,596,786
Assets: $62,275,023
Liabilities: $20,765,500
Net Worth: $41,509,523
Earnings: ($1,106,613)
Fiscal Year-end: 12/31/23
Investment Services
N.A.I.C.S.: 211120
P. Gage Jull *(Chm)*

ARROW GLOBAL GROUP PLC
12 Booth Street, Manchester, M2 4AW, United Kingdom
Tel.: (44) 333 003 0303   UK
Web Site: http://www.arrowglobalir.net
Year Founded: 2013
Rev.: $445,311,809
Assets: $2,188,564,615
Liabilities: $1,923,808,974
Net Worth: $264,755,641
Earnings: $48,905,629
Emp.: 2,441
Fiscal Year-end: 12/31/19
Holding Company; Debt Collection & Receivables Management Services
N.A.I.C.S.: 551112
Jonathan Bloomer *(Chm)*

Subsidiaries:

Arrow Global Limited   (1)
Belvedere 12 Booth Street, Manchester, M2 4AW, United Kingdom
Tel.: (44) 161 242 1724
Web Site: http://www.arrowglobal.net

Emp.: 500
Debt Collection & Receivables Management Services
N.A.I.C.S.: 561440
Zachary Lewy *(Founder & Chief Investment Officer)*

Europa Investimenti S.p.A.   (1)
Via Lanzone 31, 20123, Milan, Italy
Tel.: (39) 02 894 58850
Web Site: http://www.europainvestimenti.com
Emp.: 35
Privater Equity Firm
N.A.I.C.S.: 523999
Stefano Bennati *(CEO)*

Holding (Domestic):

Cose Belle d'Italia S.p.A.   (2)
Corso Cristoforo Colombo 9, 20144, Milan, Italy   (78.89%)
Tel.: (39) 0287371
Web Site: http://www.cosebelleditalia.com
Television Content Development & Media Management Services
N.A.I.C.S.: 516120
Stefano Corti *(Chm & CEO)*

Focum Belgium BVBA   (1)
Bellevue 3, 9050, Gent, Belgium
Tel.: (32) 92982691
Web Site: http://www.focum.be
Finance Services
N.A.I.C.S.: 541611

Focum Groep B.V.   (1)
Van Asch van Wijckstraat 55-F, PO Box 2178, 3811 LP, Amersfoort, Netherlands
Tel.: (31) 887306500
Web Site: http://www.focum.nl
Finance Services
N.A.I.C.S.: 541611

Mars Capital Finance Ireland DAC   (1)
One Warrington Place, PO Box 12546, Dublin, Ireland
Tel.: (353) 1890303702
Web Site: http://www.marscapital.ie
Finance Services
N.A.I.C.S.: 541611

Mars Capital Finance Limited   (1)
Belvedere 12 Booth Street, Manchester, M2 4AW, United Kingdom
Tel.: (44) 330 33 55 111
Web Site: http://www.marscapital.co.uk
Mortgage Administration Services
N.A.I.C.S.: 522299
Toby Morrell *(Head-Investment)*

PARR Credit S.R.L.   (1)
Via Pieve Torina 44-46/a, 00156, Rome, Italy
Tel.: (39) 0696705200
Web Site: http://www.parrcredit.it
Finance Services
N.A.I.C.S.: 541611

Vegagest SGR Spa   (1)
Via Lanzone n 31, 20123, Milan, Italy
Tel.: (39) 0230468301
Web Site: http://www.vegagest.it
Finance Services
N.A.I.C.S.: 541611

Zenith Service S.p.A.   (1)
Via Vittorio Betteloni 2, 20131, Milan, Italy
Tel.: (39) 027788051
Web Site: http://www.zenithservice.it
Finance Services
N.A.I.C.S.: 541611
Umberto Rasori *(CEO)*

ARROW GREENTECH LIMITED
1/F Laxmi Industrial Estate New Link Road, Andheri West, Mumbai, 400 053, India
Tel.: (91) 2249743758
Web Site: https://www.arrowgreentech.com
Year Founded: 1960
ARROWGREEN—(NSE)
Rev.: $15,167,880
Assets: $16,579,290
Liabilities: $2,891,070
Net Worth: $13,688,220

Earnings: $1,673,490
Fiscal Year-end: 03/31/23
Coated Packaging Product Mfr
N.A.I.C.S.: 326112
Shilpan P. Patel *(Chm & Co-Mng Dir)*

Subsidiaries:

Arrow Coated Products (UK) Limited   (1)
14 Burman Road, Liverpool, L19 6PN, United Kingdom
Tel.: (44) 2071010740
Coated Packaging Product Mfr
N.A.I.C.S.: 326112

ARROW HOME GROUP CO., LTD.
Arrow Headquarter Building Chuangxing 1st Road, Lecong Town Shunde Dist, Foshan, 528145, Guangdong, China
Tel.: (86) 75729964169
Web Site: https://en.arrowgroup.com.cn
Year Founded: 2013
001322—(SSE)
Rev.: $1,054,889,784
Assets: $1,415,038,248
Liabilities: $749,144,916
Net Worth: $665,893,332
Earnings: $83,261,412
Fiscal Year-end: 12/31/22
Household Appliance Mfr & Distr
N.A.I.C.S.: 335220
Yuerong Xie *(Chm & Gen Mgr)*

ARROW MINERALS LTD
Unit 4 38 Colin Street, West Perth, 6005, WA, Australia
Tel.: (61) 893833330   AU
Web Site: https://arrowminerals.com.au
Year Founded: 2005
AMD—(ASX)
Rev.: $592,604
Assets: $3,932,080
Liabilities: $837,154
Net Worth: $3,094,926
Earnings: ($507,715)
Fiscal Year-end: 12/31/23
Mineral Exploration Services
N.A.I.C.S.: 213114
Frazer Tabeart *(Chm)*

ARROW SYNDICATE PUBLIC COMPANY LIMITED
31 Mu 1 Phanthong, Chon Buri, 20160, Thailand
Tel.: (66) 38740371
Web Site: https://www.arrowpipe.com
Year Founded: 1988
ARROW—(THA)
Rev.: $39,858,716
Assets: $44,680,062
Liabilities: $7,975,538
Net Worth: $36,704,523
Earnings: $2,967,072
Fiscal Year-end: 12/31/23
Electrical Conduits & Fittings Mfr
N.A.I.C.S.: 332996
Vichai Thosuwanchinda *(Chm)*

ARROWCREST GROUP PTY. LTD.
34 Burleigh Avenue, Woodville, 5012, SA, Australia
Tel.: (61) 884684000   AU
Web Site: http://www.roh.au
Year Founded: 1946
Sales Range: $100-124.9 Million
Emp.: 300
Holding Company; Automotive Operations & Industrial & Farm Equipment
N.A.I.C.S.: 551112
Andrew Gwinnett *(Chm)*

Arrowcrest Group Pty. Ltd.—(Continued)

Subsidiaries:

Flocast Australia Pty Ltd   **(1)**
Factory 2 105 Newlands Road, PO Box 650, Reservoir, 3058, VIC, Australia
Tel.: (61) 393506333
Web Site: http://www.flocast.com.au
Sales Range: $25-49.9 Million
Emp.: 32
Iron & Steel Forgings
N.A.I.C.S.: 332111
Jawahar Mahri *(Mng Dir)*

John Shearer (Holdings) Limited   **(1)**
Share Street, Kilkenny, 5009, SA, Australia
Tel.: (61) 882689555
Web Site: http://www.johnshearer.com.au
Sales Range: $10-24.9 Million
Emp.: 30
Holding Company; Farming Machinery Mfr
N.A.I.C.S.: 551112
Andrew William Grinnett *(Chm)*

Subsidiary (Domestic):

Brownbuilt Pty Limited   **(2)**
Lot 1 Boc Rd, Caringbah, 2229, NSW, Australia
Tel.: (61) 295260555
Web Site: http://www.brownbuilt.com.au
Sales Range: $25-49.9 Million
Emp.: 70
Steel Office Shelving & Storage System Mfr
N.A.I.C.S.: 337214
Amit Misra *(Gen Mgr)*

John Shearer Limited   **(2)**
Share Street, Kilkenny, SA, Australia
Tel.: (61) 882689555
Web Site: http://www.johnshearer.com.au
Sales Range: $25-49.9 Million
Emp.: 30
Farming Machinery Mfr
N.A.I.C.S.: 333111
Franco Perrotta *(Mgr-Ops)*

Kockums Industries (Australia) Pty Ltd   **(2)**
188 Northbourne Road, Campbellfield, 3061, VIC, Australia
Tel.: (61) 393054001
Web Site: http://www.kockumsindustries.com
Sales Range: $25-49.9 Million
Emp.: 20
Transport Equipment Mfr
N.A.I.C.S.: 336120

ROH Wheels Australia   **(1)**
28 Sheffield Street, Woodville, 5012, SA, Australia
Tel.: (61) 884684140
Web Site: http://www.roh.com.au
Sales Range: $50-74.9 Million
Emp.: 250
Alloy & Steel Wheel Mfr for Aftermarket
N.A.I.C.S.: 336390
Andrew Gwinnett *(CEO)*

Subsidiary (Non-US):

R.O.H. AUTO PRODUCTS PHILIP-PINES, INC.   **(2)**
Marcos Alvarez Avenue Talon 5, Las Pinas, 1747, Manila, Philippines
Tel.: (63) 2 801 11 16
Automobile Parts Distr
N.A.I.C.S.: 441330

ARROWEDGE LTD.
Unit 7/8 The Concept Centre Innovation Close, Poole, BH12 4QT, Dorset, United Kingdom
Tel.: (44) 1202 763539
Web Site:
http://www.arrowedge.co.uk
Year Founded: 1982
Pharmaceutical Product Whslr
N.A.I.C.S.: 424210
Ullas Patel *(Founder & Mng Dir)*

ARSAN TEKSTIL TICARET VE SANAYI AS
Karacasu Karaziyaret Mah Fatih Sultan Mehmet Caddesi No 7/A, Dulkad-iroglu, 46100, Kahramanmaras, Turkiye
Tel.: (90) 3442512801
Web Site:
https://www.arsantextile.com
ARSAN—(IST)
Rev.: $32,961,683
Assets: $55,156,735
Liabilities: $11,367,361
Net Worth: $43,789,374
Earnings: $15,080,190
Fiscal Year-end: 12/31/22
Textile Products Mfr
N.A.I.C.S.: 339999
Alisan Arikan *(Chm)*

ARSEUS MEDICAL NV
Rijksweg 10, 2880, Bornem, Belgium
Tel.: (32) 3830 7300   **BE**
Web Site: http://www.arseus-medical.be
Sales Range: $25-49.9 Million
Surgical & Clinical Care Equipment & Supplies Mfr & Distr
N.A.I.C.S.: 339113
Cedric De Quinnemar *(Co-Owner)*

Subsidiaries:

Arseus Hospital NV   **(1)**
Rijksweg 10, 2880, Bornem, Belgium
Tel.: (32) 38307300
Sales Range: $10-24.9 Million
Emp.: 30
Hospital Equipment & Supplies Mfr & Distr
N.A.I.C.S.: 423450
Cedric Dequenne *(CEO)*

ARSHIYA LIMITED
CO-1 Survey Nos 178/3 & 178/4, Sai Village Taluka Raigad District, Panvel, 410 221, India
Tel.: (91) 2242305500
Web Site:
https://www.arshiyalimited.com
Year Founded: 1981
506074—(BOM)
Rev.: $22,136,997
Assets: $246,956,701
Liabilities: $225,424,413
Net Worth: $21,532,288
Earnings: ($21,409,602)
Emp.: 55
Fiscal Year-end: 03/31/23
Logistics Consulting Servies
N.A.I.C.S.: 541614
Ajay S. Mittal *(Chm-Grp & Co-Mng Dir)*

ARSS INFRASTRUCTURE PROJECTS LIMITED
Plot-no-38 Sector-A Zone-D Mancheswar Industrial Estate, Bhubaneswar, 751 010, Odisha, India
Tel.: (91) 6742602763
Web Site: https://arssgroup.in
Year Founded: 2000
533163—(BOM)
Rev.: $41,718,713
Assets: $216,785,355
Liabilities: $234,909,156
Net Worth: ($18,123,801)
Earnings: ($15,071,047)
Emp.: 774
Fiscal Year-end: 03/31/22
Railway Infrastructure, Roads, Highways, Bridges & Irrigation Construction Services
N.A.I.C.S.: 237310
Subash Agarwal *(Chm)*

ART ADVANCED RESEARCH TECHNOLOGIES INC.
2300 Alfred Nobel Boulevard, Saint Laurent, H4S 2A4, QC, Canada
Tel.: (514) 832-0777
Web Site: http://www.art.ca
Year Founded: 1993

Sales Range: $1-9.9 Million
Emp.: 58
Optical Imaging Products Developer, Mfr & Marketer
N.A.I.C.S.: 333310
Kira Wampler *(CEO)*

ART DESIGN & COMMUNICA-TION JOINT STOCK COMPANY
187B Giang Vo Cat Linh, Dong Da, Hanoi, Vietnam
Tel.: (84) 435121569
Web Site: http://adc.net.vn
Year Founded: 2007
ADC—(HNX)
Rev.: $39,041,500
Assets: $16,195,600
Liabilities: $8,955,700
Net Worth: $7,239,900
Earnings: $1,315,200
Fiscal Year-end: 12/31/22
Books Publishing Services
N.A.I.C.S.: 513130
Le Hoang Hai *(Chm-Mgmt Bd)*

ART FORCE JAPAN CO., LTD.
1299 Kawana, Ito, Shizuoka, 414-0044, Japan
Tel.: (81) 120844128
Web Site:
https://www.artforcejapan.co.jp
Year Founded: 1990
5072—(TKS)
Rev.: $29,551,120
Assets: $21,539,420
Liabilities: $15,491,650
Net Worth: $6,047,770
Earnings: ($170,160)
Emp.: 164
Fiscal Year-end: 12/31/23
Building Construction Services
N.A.I.C.S.: 236220
Yoshihiro Yamaguchi *(Pres & CEO)*

ART GROUP HOLDINGS LIM-ITED
Unit 1407 14th Floor China Merchants Tower Shun Tak Centre, 168-200 Connaught Road, Central, China (Hong Kong)
Tel.: (852) 31065606   **Ky**
0565—(HKG)
Rev.: $23,809,837
Assets: $296,326,133
Liabilities: $165,743,685
Net Worth: $130,582,448
Earnings: $11,370,748
Emp.: 141
Fiscal Year-end: 06/30/22
Holding Company; Fabric Mfr & Sales
N.A.I.C.S.: 551112
Jinyan Chen *(Chm)*

ART NIRMAN LTD.
410 4th Floor JBR Arcade Science City Road Sola, Ahmedabad, 380060, Gujarat, India
Tel.: (91) 8866404499
Web Site: https://www.artnirman.com
Year Founded: 2011
ARTNIRMAN—(NSE)
Rev.: $8,712,172
Assets: $19,335,890
Liabilities: $13,038,746
Net Worth: $6,297,144
Earnings: $114,324
Emp.: 39
Fiscal Year-end: 03/31/20
Construction Services
N.A.I.C.S.: 236220
Ashokkumar Raghuram Thakker *(Chm & Mng Dir)*

ART VIVANT CO., LTD.
Glass Cube Shinagawa 13th floor
41314 HigashiShinagawa,

Shinagawa-Ku, Tokyo, 140-0002, Japan
Tel.: (81) 357837171
Web Site: https://www.artvivant.co.jp
Year Founded: 1971
7523—(TKS)
Rev.: $72,749,660
Assets: $226,286,740
Liabilitioc: $121,267,060
Net Worth: $105,019,680
Earnings: $11,673,260
Emp.: 328
Fiscal Year-end: 03/31/24
Art Dealing & Financial Services
N.A.I.C.S.: 459920
Katsumi Nozawa *(Founder, Chm & Pres)*

ART-INVEST REAL ESTATE MANAGEMENT GMBH & CO. KG
Tunisstrasse 29 Enggasse 3, 50667, Cologne, Germany
Tel.: (49) 221 270579 00
Web Site: http://www.art-invest.de
Real Estate Developers
N.A.I.C.S.: 531210
Markus Wiedenmann *(Mng Dir & CEO)*

Subsidiaries:

GHOTEL GmbH   **(1)**
Graurheindorfer Str 92, 53117, Bonn, Germany
Tel.: (49) 2289610980
Web Site: http://www.ghotel.de
Sales Range: $50-74.9 Million
Emp.: 83
Hotel & Apartment Building Operator
N.A.I.C.S.: 713210

Subsidiary (Domestic):

GHOTEL Deutschland GmbH   **(2)**
Graurheindorfer Str 92, Bonn, 53117, Germany
Tel.: (49) 2289610980
Web Site: http://www.ghotel.de
Emp.: 13
Home Management Services
N.A.I.C.S.: 721110

GHOTEL Germany GmbH   **(2)**
Graurheindorfer Str 92, Bonn, 53117, Germany
Tel.: (49) 2289610980
Web Site: http://www.ghotel.de
Emp.: 12
Home Management Services
N.A.I.C.S.: 721110

GHOTEL Hotel und Boardinghaus Deutschland GmbH   **(2)**
Graurheindorfer Str 92, Bonn, 53117, Germany
Tel.: (49) 2289610980
Sales Range: $10-24.9 Million
Emp.: 10
Home Management Services
N.A.I.C.S.: 721110

ARTA CAPITAL SGEIC SA
Plaza Marques de Salamanca 10 4 D, 28006, Madrid, Spain
Tel.: (34) 917817882
Web Site: http://www.artacapital.com
Privater Equity Firm
N.A.I.C.S.: 523999
Ramon Carne *(Mng Partner)*

Subsidiaries:

Nuadi   **(1)**
Poligono Arazuri Orcoyen C/D Pamplona, Navarra, 31170, Spain
Tel.: (34) 948281090
Automobile Component Distr
N.A.I.C.S.: 423120

ARTA TECHFIN CORPORA-TION LIMITED
13/F Fortis Tower 77-79 Gloucester

Road, Wanchai, Hong Kong, China
(Hong Kong)
Tel.: (852) 3928 6999
Web Site: http://www.artatechfin.com
0279—(HKG)
Rev.: $3,375,794
Assets: $182,932,721
Liabilities: $566,625,391
Net Worth: ($383,692,671)
Earnings: ($90,504,234)
Emp.: 67
Fiscal Year-end: 03/31/21
Investment Services
N.A.I.C.S.: 523999
Mun Yee Chow *(Sec)*

Subsidiaries:

Freeman Insurance Services
Limited **(1)**
8F China United Ctr, 28 Marble Rd, North
Point, China (Hong Kong)
Tel.: (852) 25111045
Insurance Provider
N.A.I.C.S.: 524210

Freeman Investment Holdings
Limited **(1)**
31st Fl China United Ctr, 28 Marble Rd,
North Point, China (Hong Kong)
Tel.: (852) 31980279
Web Site: http://www.freeman279.com
Financial Investment Services
N.A.I.C.S.: 523999

Wins Finance Holdings Inc. **(1)**
1F Building 1B No 58 Jianguo Road, Cha-
oyang District, Beijing, 100024,
China **(67%)**
Tel.: (86) 1082255118
Web Site: http://www.winsholdings.com
Rev.: $527,992
Assets: $2,058,955
Liabilities: $7,182,862
Net Worth: ($5,123,907)
Earnings: ($409,254)
Emp.: 15
Fiscal Year-end: 06/30/2023
Holding Company; Corporate Financial
Leasing, Guarantee & Advisory Services
N.A.I.C.S.: 551112
Renhui Mu *(Chm, CEO, COO & Dir)*

Subsidiary (Domestic):

Wins Finance Group Ltd. **(2)**
1F Building 7 No 58 Jianguo Rd, Chaoy-
ang District, Beijing, 100024, China
Tel.: (86) 10 8225 5118
Web Site: http://www.winsfinance.com
Holding Company
N.A.I.C.S.: 551112

Subsidiary (Domestic):

Jinshang International Financial Leasing Co., Ltd. **(3)**
1F Building 7 No 58 Jianguo Road, Chaoyang District, Beijing, 100024, China
Tel.: (86) 10 8225 5118
Corporate Financial Leasing Services
N.A.I.C.S.: 522220

ARTAFLEX INC.
174 W Beaver Creek Rd, Richmond
Hill, L4B 1B4, ON, Canada
Tel.: (905) 470-0109 ON
Web Site: http://www.artaflex.com
Year Founded: 1985
Sales Range: $50-74.9 Million
Emp.: 385
Electronic Equipment Instrument &
Component Mfr
N.A.I.C.S.: 334290
Paul Walker *(Chm, Pres & CEO)*

ARTAL GROUP S.A.
10-12 Avenue Pasteur, 2310, Luxem-
bourg, Luxembourg
Tel.: (352) 2242591 LU
Investment Holding Company
N.A.I.C.S.: 551112
Anne Goffard *(Mng Dir)*

Subsidiaries:

Artal Luxembourg S.A. **(1)**
10-12 Avenue Pasteur, 2310, Luxembourg,
Luxembourg
Tel.: (352) 224259
Emp.: 50
Investment Management Service
N.A.I.C.S.: 523940
Anne Goffard *(Mng Dir)*

ARTANES MINING GROUP AD
Kosta Lulchev 20, Sofia, 1113, Bul-
garia
Tel.: (359) 28054864
AMG—(BUL)
Sales Range: Less than $1 Million
Mining Services
N.A.I.C.S.: 212290

ARTE SALON HOLDINGS, INC.
VORT Yokohama Kannai III 2F
1-2-12 Bandai-cho, Naka-ku, Yoko-
hama, 231-0031, Japan
Tel.: (81) 45 6636123
Web Site: http://www.arte-hd.com
Year Founded: 1988
2406—(JAS)
Rev.: $76,152,560
Assets: $80,798,960
Liabilities: $54,924,320
Net Worth: $25,874,640
Earnings: ($1,897,280)
Fiscal Year-end: 12/31/20
Holding Company
N.A.I.C.S.: 551112
Naoki Yoshihara *(Chm)*

Subsidiaries:

Arte Straits Holdings Pte. Ltd. **(1)**
177 River Valley Road 02-15 / 16 Liang
Court Shopping Center, Singapore, 179030,
Singapore
Tel.: (65) 63335662
Web Site: http://www.ashsg.com
Beauty Salon Operator
N.A.I.C.S.: 812112
Ning Lim *(Mgr-Admin)*

Ash Co., Ltd. **(1)**
1-2-12 Bandaicho Naka-ku Yokohama
VORT Yokohama Kannai III 8F, Tokyo, 170-
0002, Japan
Tel.: (81) 456636120
Web Site: http://ash-hair.com
Emp.: 1,400
Beauty Salon Operator
N.A.I.C.S.: 812112

ARTEA SA
55 avenue Marceau, 75116, Paris,
France
Tel.: (33) 176607240
Web Site: http://www.fonciere-
artea.com
Real Estate Support Services
N.A.I.C.S.: 531390
Philippe Baudry *(Chm & CEO)*

ARTEC CONSTRUCTION LTD.
#103 816 Willow Park Drive South-
east, Calgary, T2J 5S1, AB, Canada
Tel.: (403) 242-1861
Web Site: http://www.artecgroup.net
Year Founded: 2000
Sales Range: $10-24.9 Million
Emp.: 35
Building Construction Services
N.A.I.C.S.: 236220
Marvin Boyko *(Owner)*

ARTEC TECHNOLOGIES AG
Muhlenstrasse 1518, 49356, Die-
pholz, Germany
Tel.: (49) 544159950
Web Site: https://www.artec.de
A6T—(DEU)
Rev.: $3,194,474
Assets: $3,582,992
Liabilities: $669,113

Net Worth: $2,913,879
Earnings: $10,792
Emp.: 22
Fiscal Year-end: 12/31/23
Software Publishing Services
N.A.I.C.S.: 513210
Thomas A. Hoffmann *(CEO &
Member-Mgmt Bd)*

ARTECH POWER & TRADING LTD.
101 - 104 1st Floor Tower A Penin-
sula Corporate Park GK Road, Lower
Parel West, Mumbai, 400013, India
Tel.: (91) 2261171101
Web Site:
http://www.artechpower.com
Year Founded: 1989
Electrical Component Mfr
N.A.I.C.S.: 335999
Ankit Mehta *(CFO)*

ARTEFACT PROJECTS LTD.
106 54/3 Chhatrapati Square,
Wardha Road, Nagpur, 440 015, In-
dia
Tel.: (91) 917127197100
Web Site:
https://www.artefactprojects.com
531297—(BOM)
Rev.: $4,723,096
Assets: $11,247,088
Liabilities: $4,831,993
Net Worth: $6,415,095
Earnings: $535,641
Emp.: 391
Fiscal Year-end: 03/31/21
Engineering & Architectural Services
N.A.I.C.S.: 541330
Siddharth P. Shah *(Exec Dir)*

Subsidiaries:

Artefact Infrastructure Ltd. **(1)**
3rd Floor 54/3 Artefact Tower Chhatrapati
Square Wardha Road, Nagpur, 440015,
Maharashtra, India
Tel.: (91) 7127197100
Web Site: http://www.ailexportngp.com
Sales Range: $25-49.9 Million
Bridge & Building Construction Services
N.A.I.C.S.: 237310

ARTELCOM S.A.
Europarc 3 allee des Cerisiers,
94000, Creteil, France
Tel.: (33) 1 56 71 51 51
Web Site: http://www.artelcom.fr
Year Founded: 1991
Sales Range: $1-9.9 Million
Emp.: 50
Information Technology Integration
Services
N.A.I.C.S.: 541512

Subsidiaries:

Artelcom Grand Sud SAS **(1)**
290 rue Ferdinand Perrier Parc Ariane 1,
69800, Saint Priest, France
Tel.: (33) 472794242
Web Site: http://www.artelcom.fr
Information Technology Integration Services
N.A.I.C.S.: 541512
Lionel Smeers *(Chm & CEO)*

ARTELIA HOLDING SA
First Part Dieu 2 avenue Lacassagne,
69003, Lyon, France
Tel.: (33) 476334000
Web Site:
http://www.arteliagroup.com
Engineeering Services
N.A.I.C.S.: 541330
Benoit Clocheret *(CEO)*

Subsidiaries:

ADP Ingenierie **(1)**
Airport Orly Cent Pk Bldg 641, 91200,
Athis-Mons, Essonne, France

Tel.: (33) 149751100
Sales Range: $25-49.9 Million
Emp.: 25
Airport Fields & Terminal Services
N.A.I.C.S.: 488119

Subsidiary (Non-US):

ADPI Libya **(2)**
El Nasser St, Tripoli, Libya
Tel.: (218) 21 333 8430
Airport Fields & Terminal Services
N.A.I.C.S.: 488119

Auxitec Batiment SAS **(1)**
171 boulevard Amiral Mouchez, 76086, Le
Havre, France
Tel.: (33) 235537272
Web Site:
http://www.auxitec.arteliagroup.com
Rev.: $12,700,000
Emp.: 125
Engineeering Services
N.A.I.C.S.: 541330
Pierre Michel *(Exec Dir)*

ARTEMIS ALPHA TRUST PLC
Cassini House 57 St James s Street,
London, SW1A 1LD, United Kingdom
Tel.: (44) 2073996000
Web Site:
https://www.artemisfunds.com
ATS—(LSE)
Rev.: $93,032,332
Assets: $253,497,186
Liabilities: $6,625,674
Net Worth: $246,871,512
Earnings: $90,789,379
Fiscal Year-end: 04/30/21
Asset Management Services
N.A.I.C.S.: 523940
John Dodd *(Mgr-Fund)*

ARTEMIS ELECTRICALS & PROJECTS LTD.
Artemis Complex Gala No 105 & 108
National Express Highway, Vasai
East, Thane, 401208, Maharashtra,
India
Tel.: (91) 2279635174
Web Site:
https://www.artemiselectricals.com
Year Founded: 2009
542670—(BOM)
Rev.: $4,686,059
Assets: $17,400,570
Liabilities: $7,936,888
Net Worth: $9,463,682
Earnings: ($1,640,839)
Emp.: 16
Fiscal Year-end: 03/31/22
Light Emitting Diode Mfr
N.A.I.C.S.: 334413
Krishnakumar Laxman Bangera
(Chm)

ARTEMIS GLOBAL LIFE SCI-ENCES LIMITED
SF-202 Peach Tree C-Block Sushant
Lok-I, Gurgaon, 122 002, India
Tel.: (91) 1244262305 In
Web Site: http://www.aglsl.in
Year Founded: 2011
AGLSL—(NSE)
Rev.: $78,944,281
Assets: $79,492,170
Liabilities: $37,419,241
Net Worth: $42,072,929
Earnings: $2,923,725
Emp.: 2
Fiscal Year-end: 03/31/19
Health Care Management Services
N.A.I.C.S.: 813920
Onkar S. Kanwar *(Chm)*

ARTEMIS GOLD, INC.
Suite 3083-595 Burrard St, Vancou-
ver, V7X 1L3, BC, Canada
Tel.: (604) 558-1107 Ca

Artemis Gold, Inc.—(Continued)

Web Site:
  https://www.artemisgoldinc.com
ARGTF—(OTCIQ)
Rev.: $565,045
Assets: $367,508,441
Liabilities: $39,477,131
Net Worth: $328,031,309
Earnings: ($10,725,647)
Emp.: 29
Fiscal Year-end: 12/31/21
Mineral Exploration & Mining Services
N.A.I.C.S.: 213115
Chris Batalha *(CFO & Sec)*

ARTEMIS HOLDING AG

Bahnhofstrasse 4, 6052, Hergiswil, Switzerland
Tel.: (41) 62 787 31 31   CH
Web Site: http://www.artemis-holding.com
Sales Range: $1-4.9 Billion
Emp.: 11,938
Holding Company
N.A.I.C.S.: 551112
Thomas A. Erb *(Chm)*

Subsidiaries:

Artemis Immobilien AG   **(1)**
Gishalde 1 Postfach 234, 4663, Aarburg, Switzerland
Tel.: (41) 62 787 3245
Web Site: https://www.artemis-immobilien.com
Real Estate Services
N.A.I.C.S.: 531390

Artemis Real Estate SRL   **(1)**
Str Splaiul Nistrului Nr 1, Timisoara, Romania
Tel.: (40) 74 333 2290
Web Site: https://www.artemisrealestate.ro
Real Estate Services
N.A.I.C.S.: 531390

Feintool International Holding AG **(1)**
Industriering 8, 3250, Lyss, Switzerland
Tel.: (41) 323875111
Web Site: https://feintool.com
Rev.: $954,515,521
Assets: $1,014,374,723
Liabilities: $415,138,581
Net Worth: $599,236,142
Earnings: $18,276,053
Emp.: 3,390
Fiscal Year-end: 12/31/2022
Holding Company
N.A.I.C.S.: 551112
Alexander von Witzleben *(Chm)*

Subsidiary (Non-US):

Feintool Automotive System Parts (Tianjin) Co., Ltd.   **(2)**
No 216 Jingsi Road, 300308, Tianjin, China
Tel.: (86) 22 5926 58 38
Web Site: http://www.feintool.com
Automotive Components Mfr
N.A.I.C.S.: 441330

Feintool Beijing Swisstec   **(2)**
Hua Qiao Gong Yu 2-43 Hiadian District Chegongzhuang W Rd, Beijing, 100044, China   **(100%)**
Tel.: (86) 1068418447
Web Site: http://www.feintool.com
Sales Range: $25-49.9 Million
Emp.: 6
N.A.I.C.S.: 333517

Subsidiary (US):

Feintool Equipment Corp.   **(2)**
6833 Creek Rd, Cincinnati, OH 45242   **(100%)**
Tel.: (513) 791-0066
Web Site: http://www.feintool.com
Sales Range: $25-49.9 Million
Emp.: 6
Sales & Consulting Services for Peripheral Systems & Presses
N.A.I.C.S.: 541330
Beat Andres *(Dir-Mktg & Sls)*

Subsidiary (Domestic):

Feintool Cincinnati, Inc.   **(3)**
11280 Cornell Park Dr, Cincinnati, OH 45242-1812   **(100%)**
Tel.: (513) 247-0110
Mfr of Fineblanking Presses, Fineblanking Tools & Fineblanking Parts
N.A.I.C.S.: 333514

Feintool Tennessee, Inc.   **(3)**
2930 Old Franklin Rd, Antioch, TN 37013-3114   **(100%)**
Tel.: (615) 641-7770
Sales Range: $25-49.9 Million
Emp.: 11
Mfr of Automotive Parts
N.A.I.C.S.: 332812

Subsidiary (Domestic):

Feintool France S.a.r.l.   **(2)**
Industriering 3, 3250, Lyss, Switzerland   **(100%)**
Web Site: http://www.feintool.com
Sales Range: $100-124.9 Million
Emp.: 360
N.A.I.C.S.: 333517

Feintool International Management Ltd.   **(2)**
Industriering 8, Lyss, 3250, Terne, Switzerland   **(100%)**
Tel.: (41) 323875111
Web Site: http://www.feintool.com
Sales Range: $50-74.9 Million
Emp.: 200
N.A.I.C.S.: 333517
Stefan Etzold *(Mgr-Sls)*

Subsidiary (Non-US):

Feintool Italia S.r.L.   **(2)**
Corso Galileo Ferraris no 26, IT-10121, Turin, Italy   **(100%)**
Tel.: (39) 011 539 809
Web Site: http://www.feintool.com
Seller of Fineblanking & Automation Systems
N.A.I.C.S.: 333517

Feintool Japan Co., Ltd.   **(2)**
260-53 Aza Yanagi Machi Hase, Atsugi, 243-0036, Kanagawa, Japan   **(100%)**
Tel.: (81) 462477452
Web Site: http://www.feintool.com
Sales Range: $25-49.9 Million
Emp.: 48
Mfr of Fineblanking Presses, Fineblanking Tools & Fineblanking Parts
N.A.I.C.S.: 333517
Yuji Mori *(Pres)*

Subsidiary (Domestic):

Feintool Parts & Components Ltd.   **(2)**
Industriering 8, Lyss, 3250, Terne, Switzerland   **(100%)**
Tel.: (41) 323875111
Web Site: http://www.feintool.com
Sales Range: $100-124.9 Million
Emp.: 350
N.A.I.C.S.: 333517
Daniel Fluri *(Mgr-Sls)*

Feintool Research & Development AG   **(2)**
Industriering 8, Lyss, 3250, Terne, Switzerland   **(100%)**
Tel.: (41) 323875111
Web Site: http://www.feintool.com
Sales Range: $25-49.9 Million
Emp.: 10
N.A.I.C.S.: 333517

Feintool System Parts AG   **(2)**
Industriering 8, 3250, Lyss, Switzerland   **(100%)**
Tel.: (41) 323875111
Web Site: http://www.feintool.com
Sales Range: $100-124.9 Million
Emp.: 350
Mfr of Machine Tools
N.A.I.C.S.: 333517
Heinz Loosli *(CEO)*

Subsidiary (Non-US):

Feintool System Parts Ettlingen GmbH   **(2)**

Englerstrasse 18, 76275, Ettlingen, Germany
Tel.: (49) 724332020
Web Site: http://www.feintool.com
Tool Mfr
N.A.I.C.S.: 333517

Feintool System Parts Jena GmbH   **(2)**
Lobstedter Strasse 85, 07749, Jena, Germany
Tel.: (49) 3641506100
Web Site: http://www.feintool.com
Machine Tools & Parts Mfr & Distr
N.A.I.C.S.: 333517

Subsidiary (Domestic):

Feintool Teile & Komponenten AG   **(2)**
Industriering 8, Lyss, 3250, Terne, Switzerland   **(100%)**
Tel.: (41) 323875111
Web Site: http://www.feintool.com
Sales Range: $100-124.9 Million
Emp.: 100
Mfr of Machine Tools
N.A.I.C.S.: 333517
Fruteieger Ernst *(Gen Mgr)*

Heinrich Schmid Maschinen-und Werkzeugbau AG   **(2)**
Grunfeldstrasse 25, CH 8645, Jona, Switzerland   **(100%)**
Tel.: (41) 552252111
Web Site: http://www.schmidpress.com
Sales Range: $25-49.9 Million
Emp.: 64
N.A.I.C.S.: 333517

Franke Holding AG   **(1)**
Franke-Strasse 2, PO Box 230, 4663, Aarburg, Switzerland
Tel.: (41) 62 787 3443
Web Site: http://www.franke.com
Sales Range: $1-4.9 Billion
Emp.: 8,431
Holding Company; Kitchen Systems; Industrial Engineering; Beverage Containers; Metal Construction; Commercial Kitchens; Coffee Machines; Bathroom Furniture & Sanitary Equipment Mfr
N.A.I.C.S.: 551112
Michael Pieper *(Vice Chm)*

Subsidiary (Non-US):

Franke AquaRotter GmbH   **(2)**
Parkstrasse 1-5, PO Box 1335, 14974, Ludwigsfelde, Germany
Tel.: (49) 33788180
Web Site: http://www.franke-aquarotter.de
Sales Range: $100-124.9 Million
Emp.: 270
Faucets, Shower Heads & Fittings Mfr
N.A.I.C.S.: 332913
Verina Koepser *(Mgr-PR)*

Subsidiary (US):

Franke Consumer Products, Inc.   **(2)**
800 Aviation Pkwy, Smyrna, TN 37167
Tel.: (615) 462-4000
Web Site: http://www.frankeksd.com
Consumer Kitchen Sink, Faucet & Other Related Products Mfr & Whslr
N.A.I.C.S.: 332913
Heather Berry *(Mktg Mgr)*

Plant (Domestic):

Franke Consumer Products, Inc.   **(3)**
600 Franke Dr, Ruston, LA 71270-7440
Tel.: (318) 255-5600
Web Site: http://www.frankeksd.com
Sales Range: $75-99.9 Million
Mfr of Stainless Steel Sinks
N.A.I.C.S.: 332999

Subsidiary (Domestic):

Franke Foodservice Systems AG **(2)**
Franke-Strasse 2, PO Box 233, 4663, Aarburg, Switzerland
Tel.: (41) 62 787 3131
Web Site: http://www.franke.com
Foodservice Equipment Distr
N.A.I.C.S.: 333310
Thomas R. Campion *(Pres & CEO)*

Subsidiary (US):

Franke Foodservice Systems, Inc.   **(2)**
800 Aviation Pkwy, Smyrna, TN 37167
Tel.: (615) 462-4000
Web Site: http://www.franke.com
Sales Range: $25-49.9 Million
Emp.: 80
Foodservice Equipment Mfr & Whslr
N.A.I.C.S.: 333310

Subsidiary (Domestic):

Franke Industrie AG   **(2)**
Franke-Strasse 2, PO Box 227, 4663, Aarburg, Switzerland
Tel.: (41) 62 787 3697
Aircraft Engine Parts Mfr
N.A.I.C.S.: 336412
Markus Hodel *(Mng Dir)*

Franke Kaffeemaschinen AG   **(2)**
Franke Strasse 9, PO Box 235, 4663, Aarburg, Switzerland
Tel.: (41) 62 787 38 87
Web Site: http://www.franke.com
Coffee Machine Mfr
N.A.I.C.S.: 333310
Yvo Locher *(Pres & CEO)*

Subsidiary (Non-US):

Franke Kindred Canada Limited   **(2)**
1000 Kindred Rd, PO Box 190, Midland, L4R 4K9, ON, Canada
Tel.: (705) 526-5427
Web Site: http://www.frankekindred.com
Sales Range: $25-49.9 Million
Stainless Steel Sinks
N.A.I.C.S.: 332999
Howard Spaulding *(VP-Ops)*

Subsidiary (Domestic):

Franke Kuchentechnik AG   **(2)**
Franke-Strasse 2, PO Box 236, 4663, Aarburg, Switzerland
Tel.: (41) 62 787 3131
Web Site: http://www.franke.com
Residential Kitchen Systems Services
N.A.I.C.S.: 333310
Lars Volkel *(Pres & CEO)*

Franke Management AG   **(2)**
Franke-Strasse 2, PO Box 229, 4663, Aarburg, Switzerland
Tel.: (41) 62 787 3443
Web Site: http://www.franke.com
Residential Kitchens & Bathroom Systems; Industrial Engineering; Beverage Containers; Coffee Machines Mfr
N.A.I.C.S.: 336412
Alexander Zschokke *(Pres, CEO & Member-Mgmt Bd)*

Franke Water Systems AG   **(2)**
Hauptstrasse 57, PO Box 179, 5726, Unterkulm, Switzerland
Tel.: (41) 62 768 6868
Web Site: http://www.kwc.ch
Water System Services
N.A.I.C.S.: 221310
Roger Basler *(Pres & CEO)*

ARTEMIS INVESTMENT MANAGEMENT LIMITED

1325 Lawrence Ave E Suite 200, Toronto, M3A 1C6, ON, Canada
Tel.: (416) 934-7455
Web Site: http://www.artemisfunds.ca
Investment Fund Management Services
N.A.I.C.S.: 523940
Sean Lawless *(Chief Compliance Officer & Portfolio Mgr)*

ARTEMIS MEDICARE SERVICES LIMITED

Sector 51, Gurgaon, 122001, Haryana, India
Tel.: (91) 9711209940
Web Site:
  https://www.artemishospitals.com
Year Founded: 2007

542919—(BOM)
Rev.: $76,262,632
Assets: $96,869,232
Liabilities: $47,556,832
Net Worth: $49,312,400
Earnings: $4,286,305
Emp.: 1,789
Fiscal Year-end: 03/31/22
Health Care Srvices
N.A.I.C.S.: 621610
Onkar Kanwar *(Chm)*

ARTEMIS RESOURCES LTD
Level 2 10 Ord Street, West Perth,
6005, WA, Australia
Tel.: (61) 894864036
Web Site:
   https://www.artemisresources.com
ARV—(ASX)
Rev.: $53,408
Assets: $35,242,604
Liabilities: $4,953,592
Net Worth: $30,289,012
Earnings: ($11,295,792)
Fiscal Year-end: 06/30/23
Mining Industry
N.A.I.C.S.: 541330
Edward Mead *(Gen Mgr-Exploration)*

ARTEMIS VCT PLC
6th Floor Exchange Plaza 50 Lothian
Road, Edinburgh, EH3 9BY, United
Kingdom
Tel.: (44) 1312257300
Web Site:
   http://www.artemisfunds.com
Rev.: $346,262
Assets: $28,776,504
Liabilities: $219,037
Net Worth: $28,557,467
Earnings: ($7,645,316)
Fiscal Year-end: 09/30/19
Asset Management Services
N.A.I.C.S.: 523940
Andy Gray *(Mgr-Fund)*

ARTERIA NETWORKS CORP.
Sumitomo Fudosan Shimbashi Build-
ing 6-9-8 Shimbashi, Minato-ku, To-
kyo, 105-0004, Japan
Tel.: (81) 36 821 1881
Web Site: http://www.arteria-net.com
4423—(TKS)
Rev.: $536,291,360
Assets: $959,104,080
Liabilities: $688,741,680
Net Worth: $270,362,400
Earnings: $62,029,440
Emp.: 858
Fiscal Year-end: 03/31/22
Telecommunication Servicesb
N.A.I.C.S.: 517112
Koji Kabumoto *(Pres & CEO)*

Subsidiaries:

Tsunagu Network Communications,
Inc.   **(1)**
Tel.: (81) 344772000
Web Site: http://www.tsunagunet.com
Telecommunication Servicesb
N.A.I.C.S.: 517810

ARTERIA S.A.
Stawki 2A, 00-193, Warsaw, Poland
Tel.: (48) 224820200
Web Site: http://arteria.pl
ARR—(WAR)
Rev.: $52,448
Assets: $27,826
Liabilities: $16,068
Net Worth: $11,759
Earnings: ($1,534)
Fiscal Year-end: 12/31/20
Marketing Services
N.A.I.C.S.: 561422
Marcin Marzec *(Chm-Mgmt Bd)*

ARTERRA BIOSCIENCE SRL
Via Benedetto Brin 69, 80142,
Naples, Italy
Tel.: (39) 0816584411
Web Site: https://www.arterrabio.it
Year Founded: 2004
ABS—(ITA)
Sales Range: Less than $1 Million
Biotechnology Research & Develop-
ment Services
N.A.I.C.S.: 541714
Gabriella Colucci *(Founder)*

ARTGEN BIOTECH PJSC
Tel.: (7) 4956468076
Web Site: https://artgen.ru
Year Founded: 2003
ISKJ—(MOEX)
Sales Range: $1-9.9 Million
Biotechnology Research & Develop-
ment Services
N.A.I.C.S.: 541714
Igor Chernykh *(Mng Dir)*

ARTGO HOLDINGS LIMITED
13/F and 23/F Tower B Haifu Center
No 599 Sishui Road, Huli District,
Xiamen, China
Tel.: (86) 5922103888
Web Site: http://www.artgo.cn
3313—(HKG)
Rev.: $12,505,288
Assets: $233,224,056
Liabilities: $74,607,718
Net Worth: $158,616,338
Earnings: ($20,825,251)
Emp.: 209
Fiscal Year-end: 12/31/22
Marble Mining, Production & Supply
N.A.I.C.S.: 212312
Weiwen Gu *(Vice Chm)*

ARTGREEN CO., LTD.
1-8-8 Fukuzumi, Koto-Ku, Tokyo,
135-0032, Japan
Tel.: (81) 368235874
Web Site: https://www.artgreen.co.jp
34190—(NGO)
Rev.: $20,066,640
Assets: $11,093,280
Liabilities: $6,621,120
Net Worth: $4,472,160
Earnings: $145,200
Fiscal Year-end: 10/31/21
Flower Distr
N.A.I.C.S.: 424930
Yutaka Tanaka *(Founder & Pres)*

ARTHALAND CORPORATION
ArthaLand Century Pacific Tower 5th
Avenue corner 30th Street, Bonifacio
Global City, Taguig, 1634, Metro Ma-
nila, Philippines
Tel.: (63) 284036910
Web Site: https://www.arthaland.com
ALCO—(PHI)
Rev.: $61,821,745
Assets: $721,162,766
Liabilities: $491,278,319
Net Worth: $229,884,448
Earnings: $23,193,729
Emp.: 135
Fiscal Year-end: 12/31/21
Property Development Services
N.A.I.C.S.: 531312
K. Cuyegkeng *(Chm)*

ARTHUR D. LITTLE SAS
7 Place d'lena, 75116, Paris, France
Tel.: (33) 155742900   FR
Web Site: http://www.adlittle.com
Year Founded: 1968
Sales Range: $25-49.9 Million
Emp.: 60
Management Consulting Services
N.A.I.C.S.: 541611
Ignacio Garcia Alves *(CEO)*

Subsidiaries:

Arthur D. Little (Schweiz) AG   **(1)**
Sempacherstrasse 15, Wollishsen, CH
8038, Zurich, Switzerland   **(100%)**
Tel.: (41) 447228989
Web Site: http://www.adlittle.ch
Sales Range: $25-49.9 Million
Emp.: 20
Management Consulting Services
N.A.I.C.S.: 541611
Caraten Vollrath *(Mng Dir)*

Arthur D. Little AB   **(1)**
Kungsgatan 12-14, PO Box 70434, Stock-
holm, 107 25, Sweden   **(100%)**
Tel.: (46) 850306500
Web Site: http://www.adlittle.com
Emp.: 55
Management Consulting Services
N.A.I.C.S.: 541611
Bo Lenerius *(Mng Partner)*

Branch (Domestic):

Arthur D. Little AB   **(2)**
Vasagatan 43A, 411 37, Gothenburg,
Sweden   **(100%)**
Tel.: (46) 317581000
Web Site: http://www.adlittle.se
Sales Range: $10-24.9 Million
Emp.: 40
Management Consulting Services
N.A.I.C.S.: 541611
Bo Lenerius *(Mng Partner)*

Arthur D. Little Asia Pacific Ltd. **(1)**
66F The Center 99 Queen's Road, Central,
China (Hong Kong)   **(100%)**
Tel.: (852) 28248489
Web Site: http://www.adlittle.cn
Management Consulting Services
N.A.I.C.S.: 541611
Mijin Lee *(Controller)*

Subsidiary (Non-US):

Arthur D. Little (M) Sdn Bhd   **(2)**
Office Suite 19-13-2 Level 13 UOA Centre
19 Jalan Pinang, 50450, Kuala Lumpur,
Malaysia   **(100%)**
Tel.: (60) 321646063
Web Site: http://www.adlittle.com.my
Sales Range: $25-49.9 Million
Emp.: 10
Management Consulting Services
N.A.I.C.S.: 541611
Thomas Kuruvilla *(Mng Partner)*

Arthur D. Little Asia Ptd. Ltd.   **(2)**
Level 21 Centennial Tower 3 Temasek Av-
enue, Singapore, 039190, Singapore
Tel.: (65) 62972300
Web Site: http://www.adlittle.com.sg
Management Consulting Services
N.A.I.C.S.: 541611
Thomas Kuruvilla *(Mng Partner)*

Arthur D. Little China Limited   **(2)**
Lippo Plaza 222 Middle Huaihai Road,
Shanghai, China
Tel.: (86) 21 6447 8866
Web Site: http://www.adlittle.cn
Management Consulting Services
N.A.I.C.S.: 541618
Jian Xu *(Mng Partner)*

Unit (Domestic):

Arthur D. Little Hong Kong   **(2)**
21/F Icbc Twr 3 Garden Rd, Central, China
(Hong Kong)
Tel.: (852) 28456221
Management Consulting Services
N.A.I.C.S.: 541618

Subsidiary (Non-US):

Arthur D. Little Japan, Inc.   **(2)**
Toranomon 37 Mori Building 13F 3-5-1
Toranomon, Minato-ku, Tokyo, 105 0001,
Japan   **(100%)**
Tel.: (81) 334362196
Web Site: http://www.adl.co.jp
Sales Range: $10-24.9 Million
Management Consulting Services
N.A.I.C.S.: 541611
Yusuke Harada *(Mng Dir)*

Arthur D. Little Korea   **(2)**
9th Floor Leema Building 146-1 Susong-

dong, Chongro-ku, Seoul, 110 755, Korea
(South)   **(100%)**
Tel.: (82) 27202040
Web Site: http://www.adl.co.kr
Sales Range: $10-24.9 Million
Management Consulting Services
N.A.I.C.S.: 541611
Kevin Lee *(Mng Dir)*

Arthur D. Little Austria GmbH   **(1)**
Schottengasse 1, Vienna, 1010,
Austria   **(100%)**
Tel.: (43) 1 515 41 0
Web Site: http://www.adlittle.at
Sales Range: $25-49.9 Million
Emp.: 40
Management Consulting Services
N.A.I.C.S.: 541611
Karim Taga *(Mng Partner)*

Arthur D. Little Benelux N.V.   **(1)**
Strawinskylaan 10, 1077 XZ, Amsterdam,
Netherlands   **(100%)**
Tel.: (31) 20 301 6500
Web Site: http://www.adlittle.nl
Sales Range: $25-49.9 Million
Emp.: 7
Management Consulting Services
N.A.I.C.S.: 541618
Ignacio Garcia Alves *(CEO)*

Arthur D. Little Benelux S.A.   **(1)**
Avenue de Bourgetlaan 42, Brussels, 1130,
Belgium   **(100%)**
Tel.: (32) 27617200
Web Site: http://www.adlittle.be
Sales Range: $25-49.9 Million
Emp.: 50
Management Consulting Services
N.A.I.C.S.: 541611
Kurt Baes *(Partner-Belgium)*

Arthur D. Little GmbH   **(1)**
The Squaire, 60600, Frankfurt am Main,
Germany   **(100%)**
Tel.: (49) 69 450098 0
Web Site: http://www.adlittle.de
Management Consulting Services
N.A.I.C.S.: 541611
Matthias von Bechtolsheim *(Dir-Central Eu-
rope)*

Branch (Domestic):

Arthur D. Little GmbH   **(2)**
Nymphenburger Hofe Nymphenburger Str
4, Munich, 80335, Germany   **(100%)**
Tel.: (49) 8938088700
Web Site: http://www.adlittle.com
Sales Range: $10-24.9 Million
Emp.: 40
Management Consulting Services
N.A.I.C.S.: 541611
Dr. Fabian Doemer *(Pres)*

Arthur D. Little Limited   **(1)**
Unit 300 Science Park, Milton Road, Cam-
bridge, CB4 0XL, United Kingdom   **(100%)**
Tel.: (44) 1223 427 100
Web Site: http://www.adlittle.co.uk
Management Consulting Services
N.A.I.C.S.: 541611
Richard Eagar *(Partner-Tech & Innovation
Mgmt)*

Branch (Domestic):

Arthur D. Little   **(2)**
Suite 5 Sicilian House Sicilian Avenue, Lon-
don, WC1A 2QS, United Kingdom   **(100%)**
Tel.: (44) 207 7660 200
Web Site: http://www.adlittle.com
Emp.: 30
Management Consulting Services
N.A.I.C.S.: 541611
Nick White *(Mng Partner)*

Arthur D. Little Middle East FZ
LLC   **(1)**
Office 606 6th Floor Arjaan Tower Al Sufouh
Road, PO Box 112687, Dubai Media City,
Dubai, United Arab Emirates
Tel.: (971) 4 4335401
Web Site: http://www.adlittle.ae
Emp.: 5
Management Consulting Services
N.A.I.C.S.: 541611
Thomas Kuruvilla *(Mng Partner)*

Branch (Non-US):

Arthur D. Little Saudi Arabia   **(2)**

Arthur D. Little SAS—(Continued)

Suite 502 5th Floor Entrance D The Plaza,
PO Box 305005, Akaria Complex Olaya
Road, Riyadh, 11361, Saudi Arabia
Tel.: (966) 112930023
Web Site: http://www.adl.com.sa
Management Consulting Services
N.A.I.C.S.: 541611

Arthur D. Little S.L.   **(1)**
C/Ortega y Gasset 20 Planta 3a, 28006,
Madrid, Spain   **(100%)**
Tel.: (34) 91 702 7400
Web Site: http://www.adlittle.es
Sales Range: $25-49.9 Million
Emp.: 30
Management Consulting Services
N.A.I.C.S.: 541611
Jesus Porpal (Partner)

Branch (Non-US):

Arthur D. Little   **(2)**
Edificio Mira Lisboa Av Fontes Pereira de
Melo no 21 8, 1050-116, Lisbon, Portugal
Tel.: (351) 210091500
Web Site: http://www.adlittle.pt
Management Consulting Services
N.A.I.C.S.: 541611
Grant Greatrex (Mng Dir)

Arthur D. Little S.p.A.   **(1)**
Corso Monforte 54, 20122, Milan,
Italy   **(100%)**
Tel.: (39) 02 67 37 61
Web Site: http://www.adlittle.it
Sales Range: $25-49.9 Million
Management Consulting Services
N.A.I.C.S.: 541611
Saverio Caldani (Mng Partner)

Arthur D. Little, Inc.   **(1)**
1 Federal St Ste 2810, Boston, MA
02110   **(100%)**
Tel.: (617) 532-9550
Web Site: http://www.adlittle-us.com
Sales Range: $150-199.9 Million
Management Consulting Services
N.A.I.C.S.: 541611

Cutter Information, LLC   **(1)**
37 Broadway Ste 1, Arlington, MA 02474-
5552
Tel.: (781) 648-8700
Web Site: http://www.cutter.com
Scientific & Technical Consulting Services
N.A.I.C.S.: 541690
Michael Harris (Sr VP)

ARTI YATIRIM HOLDING A.S.

Evazim Mah Koru Sokak Zorlu Cen-
ter Teras Evler No 2 Kat T0 D 11,
34340, Besiktas, Turkiye
Tel.: (90) 2124016942
Web Site:
   http://www.artiyatirimholding.com.tr
Year Founded: 2006
ARTI—(IST)
Rev.: $875,981
Assets: $2,151,857
Liabilities: $2,083,414
Net Worth: $68,443
Earnings: ($4,778,456)
Fiscal Year-end: 12/31/19
Portfolio Management Services
N.A.I.C.S.: 523940
Miryam Mastaoglu (Gen Mgr)

ARTIFEX MUNDI S.A.

ul Zelazna 2, 40-851, Katowice, Po-
land
Tel.: (48) 327470447
Web Site:
   https://www.artifexmundi.com
Year Founded: 2006
ART—(WAR)
Rev.: $20,958,435
Assets: $251,213,160
Liabilities: $46,278,201
Net Worth: $204,934,959
Earnings: $6,331,047
Fiscal Year-end: 12/31/23
Computer Game Development Ser-
vices

N.A.I.C.S.: 541511
Przemyslaw Blaszczyk (Pres, CEO &
CFO)

ARTIFICIAL ELECTRONICS INTELLIGENT MATERIAL LIMITED

42 Commercial Complex Hiranandani
Parks Vadakapattu, Chengalpattu
District, Chennai, 603204, India
Tel.: (91) 9342961663   In
Web Site: https://www.software13.in
Year Founded: 1992
526443—(BOM)
Rev.: $15,684
Assets: $109,036
Liabilities: $6,443
Net Worth: $102,593
Earnings: ($10,115)
Fiscal Year-end: 03/31/21
Software Development Services
N.A.I.C.S.: 541511
Chandan M. Parmar (CEO & Mng
Dir)

ARTIFICIAL LIFE, INC.

15 F Somptueux Central 52-54 Wel-
lington Street, Central, China (Hong
Kong)
Tel.: (852) 31022800   DE
Web Site: http://www.artificial-life.com
Year Founded: 1999
ALIF—(OTCEM)
Intelligent Robot Developer for the
Internet
N.A.I.C.S.: 513210
Eberhard Schoneburg (Chm, CEO &
CFO)

Subsidiaries:

Artificial Life Asia Limited   **(1)**
26F 88 Hing Fat St, Causeway Bay, Hong
Kong, China (Hong Kong)
Tel.: (852) 31022800
Web Site: http://www.artifical-life.com
Sales Range: $25-49.9 Million
Mobile Phone Applications Mktg & Distr
N.A.I.C.S.: 517112

Artificial Life Source Holding
PLC   **(1)**
Kurfurstendamm 30, 10719, Berlin, Ger-
many
Tel.: (49) 30 886200 117
Web Site: http://www.alife-source.com
Mobile Phone Applications Mktg & Distr
N.A.I.C.S.: 517112
Devan Nair (Chm & CEO)

ARTIFICIAL MIND & MOVEMENT

416 Maisonneuve Ouest Bureau 600,
Montreal, H3A 1L2, QC, Canada
Tel.: (514) 843-4484
Web Site: http://www.a2m.com
Year Founded: 1992
Sales Range: $25-49.9 Million
Emp.: 450
Software Developer
N.A.I.C.S.: 513210
David Lightbown (Dir-Tech)

ARTINI HOLDINGS LIMITED

Unit D 16/F Eton Building 288 Des
Voeux Road Central, Sheung Wan,
China (Hong Kong)
Tel.: (852) 34685554   BM
Web Site: http://www.artini.com.hk
Year Founded: 1992
0789—(HKG)
Rev.: $8,120,730
Assets: $19,676,055
Liabilities: $3,050,565
Net Worth: $16,625,490
Earnings: ($182,963)
Emp.: 24
Fiscal Year-end: 03/31/23

Holding Company; Retail Chain Op-
erator & Fashion Accessories Mfr,
Marketer, Distr & Sales
N.A.I.C.S.: 551112
Shao Hua Lin (Exec Dir)

ARTINOVA AB

Hokedalen 40, 668 92, Vastra Gota-
land, Sweden
Tel.: (46) 313393390
Web Site: http://www.artinova.se
Year Founded: 1923
Sales Range: $1-9.9 Million
Emp.: 9
Paper Coating & Converting Services
N.A.I.C.S.: 322220

Subsidiaries:

Artin Papiervertriebs GmbH   **(1)**
Wilhelm Strasse 42, 47807, Krefeld,
Germany   **(100%)**
Tel.: (49) 151301961
Paper Products Mfr
N.A.I.C.S.: 322220

Artinova Poland Sp. z o.o.   **(1)**
T Dzialynskiego 1d/13, 62 020, Swarzedz,
Poland
Tel.: (48) 618159170
Web Site: http://www.artinova.se
Paper Coating & Converting Services
N.A.I.C.S.: 322299

CPA GmbH   **(1)**
Geringer Winkel 8, 75057, Kurnbach, Ger-
many
Tel.: (49) 7258 910 30
Paper Products Mfr
N.A.I.C.S.: 322299

Frank Crossley & Son Ltd   **(1)**
Pilgrims Court 15-17 West Street, Surrey,
Reigate, RH2 9BL, United Kingdom
Tel.: (44) 1737 242 592
Web Site: http://www.crossleys.net
Paper Products Mfr
N.A.I.C.S.: 322299

Paper One s.r.l   **(1)**
Via Borgazzi 183-185, 20900, Monza, Italy
Tel.: (39) 0210 34 56
Web Site: http://www.paper-one.it
Paper Products Mfr
N.A.I.C.S.: 322299

Secopa S.L.   **(1)**
C/ Jacint Verdaguer 105 2-2, Molins de Rei,
Barcelona, Spain
Tel.: (34) 93 680 00 54
Paper Products Mfr
N.A.I.C.S.: 322299
Marc Sabate Rius (CEO)

ARTIS REAL ESTATE INVESTMENT TRUST

Suite 600-220 Portage Avenue, Win-
nipeg, R3C 0A5, MB, Canada
Tel.: (204) 947-1250
Web Site: https://www.artisreit.com
Year Founded: 2004
AX.UN—(TSX)
Rev.: $359,001,591
Assets: $3,801,756,417
Liabilities: $1,975,995,472
Net Worth: $1,825,760,945
Earnings: $16,852,658
Emp.: 206
Fiscal Year-end: 12/31/20
Real Estate Investment Services
N.A.I.C.S.: 523999
Armin Martens (Pres & CEO)

ARTISAN (UK) PLC

2B Vantage Park Washingley Road,
Huntingdon, PE29 6SR, Cam-
bridgeshire, United Kingdom
Tel.: (44) 1480436666   UK
Web Site: http://www.artisan-
plc.co.uk
Year Founded: 1998
Rev.: $30,091,632
Assets: $17,499,161

Liabilities: $7,217,410
Net Worth: $10,281,751
Earnings: $2,429,484
Emp.: 53
Fiscal Year-end: 06/30/19
Holding Company; Real Estate De-
velopment Services
N.A.I.C.S.: 551112
Michael Eyres (Exec Dir)

Subsidiaries:

Artisan (UK) Developments
Limited   **(1)**
Vantage House Vantage Park, Washingley
Road, Huntingdon, PE29 6SR, Cambs,
United Kingdom
Tel.: (44) 1480436777
Web Site: http://www.artisan-plc.co.uk
Sales Range: $50-74.9 Million
Emp.: 6
Residential House Building Services
N.A.I.C.S.: 531110
Michael Eyres (Mng Dir)

Artisan (UK) Projects Limited   **(1)**
Vantage Park Washingley Rd, Huntingdon,
PE29 6SR, Cambridgeshire, United King-
dom
Tel.: (44) 1480436666
Web Site: http://www.artisan-plc.co.uk
Sales Range: $50-74.9 Million
Emp.: 6
Residential House Building Services
N.A.I.C.S.: 531110
Chris Musselle (Gen Mgr)

Artisan (UK) Properties Limited   **(1)**
Vantage Park, Washingley Rd, Huntingdon,
PE29 6SR, United Kingdom
Tel.: (44) 1480436777
Web Site:
   http://www.artisandevelopment.co.uk
Sales Range: $50-74.9 Million
Emp.: 6
Residential House Building Services
N.A.I.C.S.: 531110

Rippon Homes Limited   **(1)**
The Willows Ransom Wood Business Park
Southwell Road West, Mansfield, NG21
0HJ, Nottinghamshire, United Kingdom
Tel.: (44) 1623659000
Web Site: http://www.ripponhomes.co.uk
Emp.: 10
Residential House Building Services
N.A.I.C.S.: 531110

ARTISAN ACQUISITION CORP.

71 Fort Street, PO Box 500, George-
town, KY1-1106, Grand Cayman,
Cayman Islands
Tel.: (345) 852 2523 1056   Ky
Year Founded: 2021
ARTAU—(NASDAQ)
Investment Services
N.A.I.C.S.: 523999
Yin Pan Cheng (CEO)

ARTISAN ENERGY CORPORATION

Suite 1350 734 - 7th Avenue SW,
Calgary, T2P 3P8, AB, Canada
Tel.: (403) 984-9275   AB
Web Site:
   http://www.artisanenergy.ca
Year Founded: 2010
Sales Range: Less than $1 Million
Investment Services
N.A.I.C.S.: 523999
John Bell (CFO)

ARTISTIC DENIM MILLS LIMITED

Plot No 59 2326 Sector16 Korangi
Industrial Area, Karachi, 74900, Paki-
stan
Tel.: (92) 21111236236
Web Site:
   https://www.admdenim.com
ADMM—(KAR)
Rev.: $55,768,352
Assets: $93,325,360

Liabilities: $44,830,498
Net Worth: $48,494,862
Earnings: $6,223,768
Emp.: 504
Fiscal Year-end: 06/30/19
Cotton Fabric Garments Mfr
N.A.I.C.S.: 313210
Faisal Ahmed *(CEO)*

ARTITALIA GROUP INC.
11755 Rodolphe Forget, Montreal,
H1E 7J8, QC, Canada
Tel.: (514) 643-0114
Web Site: http://www.artitalia.ca
Year Founded: 1984
Emp.: 500
Display Fixtures Mfr
N.A.I.C.S.: 335132
Jeff Kastner *(Acct Exec)*

ARTIVISION TECHNOLOGIES PTE. LTD.
10 Ubi Crescent 05-05 Ubi Tech
Park, Singapore, 408564, Singapore
Tel.: (65) 6749 7290
5NK—(SES)
Assets: $801,172
Liabilities: $7,792,346
Net Worth: ($6,991,174)
Earnings: ($1,231,034)
Emp.: 27
Fiscal Year-end: 03/31/20
Video Management Products & Solutions
N.A.I.C.S.: 334310
Kenneth Tzu Seoh Goh *(CEO)*

ARTIZA NETWORKS, INC.
Faret Tachikawa Center Square
2-36-2 Akebono-cho, Tachikawa, 190-0012, Tokyo, Japan
Tel.: (81) 425293494
Web Site:
https://www.artizanetworks.com
Year Founded: 1990
6778—(TKS)
Rev.: $17,534,180
Assets: $55,507,280
Liabilities: $12,035,700
Net Worth: $43,471,580
Earnings: ($889,460)
Emp.: 173
Fiscal Year-end: 07/31/24
Communication Test Equipment Developer & Sales
N.A.I.C.S.: 334290
Takashi Tokonami *(Founder, Chm & CEO)*

Subsidiaries:

Artiza (Shanghai) Software Development Co., Ltd. (1)
Room 303 Building B No 1308 Lianhua
Road, Minhang District, Shanghai, 201102, China
Tel.: (86) 215 212 3100
Web Site: http://www.artiza.co.jp
Network Equipment Mfr
N.A.I.C.S.: 334515

Artiza Networks, Inc. - Rancho Palos
Verdes Branch (1)
27034 Springcreek Rd, Rancho Palos
Verdes, CA 90275
Tel.: (310) 702-4608
Network Equipment Distr
N.A.I.C.S.: 423690

ARTMARKET.COM
Domaine de la Source, 69270, Saint-Romain, France
Tel.: (33) 478220000
Web Site: https://www.artprice.com
PRC—(EUR)
Sales Range: $1-9.9 Million
Online Auction Services
N.A.I.C.S.: 459420

Thierry Ehrmann *(Co-Founder & Dir-Publication)*

ARTNATURE INC.
3-40-7 Yoyogi, Shibuya-ku, Tokyo,
151-0053, Japan
Tel.: (81) 333793334
Web Site: https://www.artnature.co.jp
Year Founded: 1967
7823—(TKS)
Rev.: $283,238,500
Assets: $329,515,110
Liabilities: $151,904,410
Net Worth: $177,610,700
Earnings: $9,663,820
Emp.: 3,780
Fiscal Year-end: 03/31/24
Wigs & Hairpieces Mfr
N.A.I.C.S.: 339999
Yoshikata Igarashi *(Chm & Pres)*

Subsidiaries:

Artnature (Shanghai) Inc. (1)
Room 1005b Financial Plaza No 333 Jiuji-ang Road, Huangpu District, Shanghai,
China
Tel.: (86) 2133183501
Web Site: https://www.artnature.com.cn
Wig Mfr & Distr
N.A.I.C.S.: 339999

Artnature Malaysia Sdn. Bhd. (1)
The Gardens Mid Valley City Isetan Gardens GF, 59200, Kuala Lumpur, Malaysia
Tel.: (60) 1126332306
Wig Mfr & Distr
N.A.I.C.S.: 339999

Artnature Singapore Pte. Ltd. (1)
1 Scotts Road 24-05 Shaw Centre, Singapore, 228208, Singapore
Tel.: (65) 91506423
Web Site: https://www.artnature.asia
Wig Mfr & Distr
N.A.I.C.S.: 339999

ARTNER CO., LTD.
Sumitomo Nakanoshima Building 2F
Nakanoshima 3-2-18, Kita Ward,
Osaka, 530-0005, Japan
Tel.: (81) 664457551
Web Site: https://www.artner.co.jp
Year Founded: 1962
2163—(TKS)
Rev.: $69,444,320
Assets: $42,901,760
Liabilities: $12,671,120
Net Worth: $30,230,640
Earnings: $6,079,040
Emp.: 1,079
Fiscal Year-end: 01/31/21
Employment Services
N.A.I.C.S.: 561311
Sozo Sekiguchi *(Pres)*

ARTNET AG
Oranienstrasse 164, 10969, Berlin,
Germany
Tel.: (49) 302091780
Web Site: https://www.artnet.com
Year Founded: 1990
ART—(DEU)
Rev.: $25,775,364
Assets: $13,930,839
Liabilities: $9,151,082
Net Worth: $4,779,757
Earnings: ($1,103,870)
Emp.: 129
Fiscal Year-end: 12/31/23
Online Art Sales
N.A.I.C.S.: 459920
Hans Neuendorf *(Chm-Supervisory Bd)*

Subsidiaries:

artnet UK Ltd. (1)
4 Cromwell Place Offices L & M, London,
SW7 2JE, United Kingdom
Tel.: (44) 2077290824
Online Art Sales

N.A.I.C.S.: 459920
artnet Worldwide Corporation (1)
1 World Trade Ctr 85th Fl, New York, NY
10007
Tel.: (212) 497-9700
Sales Range: $50-74.9 Million
Emp.: 100
Research Services for Fine & Decorative
Arts
N.A.I.C.S.: 327910

ARTQUEST INTERNATIONAL ALLIANCES, INC.
2525 Daniel Johnson Blvd Suite 290,
Laval, H7T 1S9, QC, Canada
Tel.: (450) 681-1150
Computer Programming, Data Processing & Printing Services
N.A.I.C.S.: 541511
Guy Le Henaff *(Chm & CTO)*

ARTRA GROUP CORPORATION
No 4-6-9 Tatsubori, Nishi-ku, Osaka,
550-0012, Japan
Tel.: (81) 665337622
Web Site: https://www.artra-group.co.jp
Year Founded: 2005
6029—(TKS)
Rev.: $31,883,730
Assets: $32,415,480
Liabilities: $22,156,250
Net Worth: $10,259,230
Earnings: $375,770
Emp.: 70
Fiscal Year-end: 12/31/23
Orthopedic Clinic Management Services
N.A.I.C.S.: 541611
Hiroyuki Kuze *(Chm & Pres)*

ARTRONIQ BERHAD
No 12 Jalan Pelukis U1/46B Temasya
Industrial Park, 40150, Shah Alam,
Selangor, Malaysia
Tel.: (60) 355697728
Web Site: https://www.artroniq.com
Year Founded: 2002
ARTRONIQ—(KLS)
Rev.: $31,533,863
Assets: $19,940,459
Liabilities: $10,947,357
Net Worth: $8,993,102
Earnings: ($2,476,574)
Emp.: 19
Fiscal Year-end: 06/30/23
Investment Holding Services
N.A.I.C.S.: 551112
Steven Chin Fung Wong *(Chm)*

Subsidiaries:

Artroniq Innovation Sdn Bhd (1)
No 12 Jalan Pelukis U1/46B, Temasya Industrial Park, 40150, Shah Alam, Selangor,
Malaysia
Tel.: (60) 355697728
Web Site: https://www.artroniq.my
Information Technology Services
N.A.I.C.S.: 541511

Artronix Sdn. Bhd. (1)
No 12 Jalan Pelukis U1/46B Temasya Industrial Park, 40150, Shah Alam, Selangor,
Malaysia
Tel.: (60) 355697728
Web Site: https://artronix.my
Computer Products Distr
N.A.I.C.S.: 423430

Fujim Digital Sdn. Bhd. (1)
15 Lintang Bayan Lepas 6 Taman Perindustrian Bayan Lepas Fasa 4, 11900, Bayan
Lepas, Penang, Malaysia
Tel.: (60) 46459821
Web Site: https://www.fujim.com.my
Metal Fabrication Mfr
N.A.I.C.S.: 332312

ARTRYA LIMITED

1257 Hay Street, West Perth, 6005,
WA, Australia
Tel.: (61) 864787816   AU
Web Site: https://www.artrya.com
Year Founded: 2018
AYA—(ASX)
Rev.: $649,410
Assets: $21,573,971
Liabilities: $1,650,910
Net Worth: $19,923,062
Earnings: ($7,260,872)
Emp.: 1,200
Fiscal Year-end: 06/30/23
Custom Computer Programming Services
N.A.I.C.S.: 541511
Bernie Ridgeway *(Chm)*

ARTS ALLIANCE VENTURES
Pulawska Str 2, 02-566, Warsaw,
Poland
Tel.: (48) 9522105435
Web Site: http://www.artsalliance.pl
Software Development Services
N.A.I.C.S.: 541511
Andrzej Zajac *(CEO)*

ARTS GROUP CO., LTD.
No 111 Bada Street Suzhou Industrial
Park, Suzhou, 215123, Jiangsu,
China
Tel.: (86) 51262586258
Web Site: https://www.artsgroup.cn
Year Founded: 1995
603017—(SHG)
Rev.: $247,097,373
Assets: $476,534,294
Liabilities: $274,688,486
Net Worth: $201,845,807
Earnings: $12,181,736
Fiscal Year-end: 12/31/22
Construction Engineering Services
N.A.I.C.S.: 541330
Feng Zhenggong *(Chm)*

ARTS OPTICAL INTERNATIONAL HOLDINGS LTD
Unit 308 3rd Floor Sunbeam Centre
27 Shing Yip Street, Kwun Tong,
Kowloon, China (Hong Kong)
Tel.: (852) 23435223
Web Site: http://www.artsgroup.com
1120—(HKG)
Rev.: $145,873,133
Assets: $139,122,518
Liabilities: $61,864,020
Net Worth: $77,258,498
Earnings: $15,302,678
Emp.: 3,500
Fiscal Year-end: 12/31/22
Optical Products Design, Sales & Mfr
N.A.I.C.S.: 334112
Kim Ying Ng *(Exec Dir)*

Subsidiaries:

Argent Optical Manufactory
Limited (1)
Rm 308 3 F Sunbeam Center 27 Shing Yip
St, Kwun Tong, Kowloon, China (Hong
Kong)
Tel.: (852) 23435223
Web Site: http://www.arksgroup.com
Sales Range: $25-49.9 Million
Emp.: 80
Optical Frames Mfr
N.A.I.C.S.: 339115
Hoi Ying Ng *(Mng Dir)*

Arts Optical Company Limited (1)
Unit 308 3 F Sunbeam Ctr 27 Shing Yip St,
Kwun Tong, Kowloon, China (Hong Kong)
Tel.: (852) 23435223
Sales Range: $25-49.9 Million
Emp.: 100
Optical Frames Mfr
N.A.I.C.S.: 339115
Hoi Ying Ng *(Chm)*

Arts Studio Limited (1)
Room 308 3/F Sunbeam Centre 27 Shing

Arts Optical International Holdings Ltd—(Continued)

Yip Street, Kwun Tong, Kowloon, China
(Hong Kong)
Tel.: (852) 23435223
Web Site: http://www.artstudiohk.com
Frame & Sunglass Mfr
N.A.I.C.S.: 339115

Eyeconcept Limited (1)
Rm 308 3 F Sunbeam Ctr 27 Shing Yip St,
Kwun Tong, Kowloon, China (Hong Kong)
Tel.: (852) 23435223
Web Site: http://www.eyeconcept.com.hk
Sales Range: $25-49.9 Million
Emp.: 10
Optical Frames Mfr
N.A.I.C.S.: 339115
Hans Stetter (Gen Mgr)

Stepper France (1)
9 Rue Charles Coulomb, CS 66423, Zone
Arago, 28000, Chartres, Cedex, France
Tel.: (33) 130598650
Web Site: http://www.stepperfrance.com
Frame & Sunglass Mfr
N.A.I.C.S.: 339115

**Stepper South Africa (Proprietary)
Limited** (1)
PO Box 53544, Troyeville, Johannesburg,
2139, Gauteng, South Africa
Tel.: (27) 114022020
Frame & Sunglass Distr
N.A.I.C.S.: 456130

ARTSAKHHEK OJSC
Vazgen Sargsyan 25A, Stepanakert,
Azerbaijan
Web Site: http://www.artsakhhek.am
Year Founded: 2007
Electricity Generation Services
N.A.I.C.S.: 237130
Vahram Beglaryan (Gen Dir)

ARTSON ENGINEERING LTD
2nd Floor One Boulevard Lake Bou-
levard Road, Hiranandani Business
Park Powai, Mumbai, 400 076, India
Tel.: (91) 9100510001
Web Site: https://www.artson.net
522134—(BOM)
Rev.: $23,684,647
Assets: $19,182,714
Liabilities: $19,115,091
Net Worth: $67,622
Earnings: ($686,445)
Emp.: 184
Fiscal Year-end: 03/31/22
Tankage Construction & Services
N.A.I.C.S.: 541330
Deepak Tibrewal (Sec)

Subsidiaries:

Tata Projects Limited (1)
Mithona Towers-1 1-7-80 to 87 Pren-
derghast Road, 500003, Secunderabad,
India
Tel.: (91) 4066238801
Web Site: http://www.tataprojects.com
Construction Services
N.A.I.C.S.: 236220
Banmali Agrawala (Chm)

ARUJ INDUSTRIES LTD.
2-Km Off Raiwind-Manga Rd, Lahore,
Pakistan
Tel.: (92) 4235393125
Web Site: https://www.aruj.com
ARUJ—(LAH)
Rev.: $9,228,625
Assets: $8,557,936
Liabilities: $6,104,328
Net Worth: $2,453,608
Earnings: $84,525
Emp.: 317
Fiscal Year-end: 06/30/19
Woven Fusible Interlining Mfr
N.A.I.C.S.: 313210

ARUMA RESOURCES LIMITED

Level 1 2 Richardson Street, West
Perth, 6005, WA, Australia
Tel.: (61) 893210177
Web Site:
https://www.arumaresources.com
AAJ—(ASX)
Rev.: $765,467
Assets: $1,607,523
Liabilities: $105,064
Net Worth: $1,502,459
Earnings: ($761,848)
Emp.: 4
Fiscal Year-end: 06/30/24
Gold Ore & Silver Ore Mining
N.A.I.C.S.: 212220
Peter Schwann (Mng Dir)

**ARUN VALLEY HYDROPOWER
DEVELOPMENT CO. LTD.**
2nd Floor Trade Tower Nepal,
Thapathali, Kathmandu, Nepal
Tel.: (977) 15111086
Web Site:
https://www.arunhydro.com.np
Year Founded: 1997
AHPC—(NEP)
Rev.: $1,042,382
Assets: $23,786,750
Liabilities: $9,676,171
Net Worth: $14,110,579
Earnings: $637,270
Fiscal Year-end: 07/16/22
Hydroelectric Power Generation Ser-
vices
N.A.I.C.S.: 221111
Ramesh Prasad Neupane (Mng Dir)

ARUNA HOTELS LTD.
145 Aruna Centre Sterling Road Nun-
gumbakam, Chennai, 600034, Tamil
Nadu, India
Tel.: (91) 4425303404
Year Founded: 1960
500016—(BOM)
Rev.: $506,238
Assets: $22,616,985
Liabilities: $19,975,492
Net Worth: $2,641,493
Earnings: ($340,240)
Emp.: 15
Fiscal Year-end: 03/31/22
Hotel Operator
N.A.I.C.S.: 721110
Nagaraj P. (CFO)

ARUNDEL AG
Gotthardstrasse 21, CH 8002, Zurich,
Switzerland
Tel.: (41) 445127880
Web Site: https://www.arundel-
ag.com
ARON—(SWX)
Rev.: $8,593,429
Assets: $195,431,297
Liabilities: $182,235,060
Net Worth: $13,196,237
Earnings: ($3,254,042)
Emp.: 11
Fiscal Year-end: 12/31/22
Financial Services
N.A.I.C.S.: 523940
Ralph Beney (Exec Dir)

Subsidiaries:

Arundel (Mauritius) Limited (1)
33 Ecith Cavell Street, Port Louis, Mauritius
Tel.: (230) 405 2000
Investment Services
N.A.I.C.S.: 523999

Arundel Group Limited (1)
Arundel House 31A St James's Square,
London, SW1Y 4JR, United Kingdom
Tel.: (44) 2077667000
Investment Services
N.A.I.C.S.: 523999

ARUNIS ABODE LTD.

501 FP No 765 TPS 111 JN Off SV
Road, Kora Kendra Road Borivali
West, Mumbai, 400092, India
Tel.: (91) 67869000
Web Site: http://www.arunis.co
Year Founded: 1995
526935—(BOM)
Rev.: $246,819
Assets: $1,408,598
Liabilities: $602,238
Net Worth: $806,360
Earnings: $23,369
Emp.: 6
Fiscal Year-end: 03/31/22
Securities Brokerage Services
N.A.I.C.S.: 523150
Monalisa Digant Parikh (Chm & Mng
Dir)

**ARUNJYOTI BIO VENTURES
LIMITED**
1-98/1/JSIC/6F/604-B6th Floor Jain
Sadhguru Capital Park, Beside Image
Gardens Madhapur Shaikpet,
Hyderabad, 500081, Telangana, India
Tel.: (91) 7799040405
Web Site: https://abvl.co.in
Year Founded: 1986
530881—(BOM)
Rev.: $752,758
Assets: $642,001
Liabilities: $376,491
Net Worth: $265,510
Earnings: $9,318
Emp.: 6
Fiscal Year-end: 03/31/21
Securities Investment Services
N.A.I.C.S.: 523999

ARUP GROUP LTD.
13 Fitzroy Street, London, W1T 4BQ,
United Kingdom
Tel.: (44) 2076361531
Web Site: http://www.arup.com
Year Founded: 1946
Sales Range: $800-899.9 Million
Emp.: 2,500
Engineeering Services
N.A.I.C.S.: 541330
Alan Belfield (Chm)

Subsidiaries:

Arup (Pty) Limited (1)
10 High Street Melrose Arch, Johannes-
burg, 2076, South Africa
Tel.: (27) 11 218 7600
Engineeering Services
N.A.I.C.S.: 541330

Arup - S.I.G.M.A. Ltd (1)
Bagatelle Office Park, Moka, Mauritius
Tel.: (230) 601 9800
Web Site: http://www.arup.com
Engineeering Services
N.A.I.C.S.: 541330
Derick Steinhobel (Dir)

Arup Advisory Inc. (1)
35 E Wacker Dr Ste 1800, Chicago, IL
60601
Tel.: (312) 849-5610
Emp.: 1,000
Engineeering Services
N.A.I.C.S.: 541330

Arup Americas, Inc. (1)
77 Water St 4th Fl, New York, NY 10005
Tel.: (212) 229-2669
Sales Range: $150-199.9 Million
Emp.: 300
Engineeering Services
N.A.I.C.S.: 541330
Joseph Dennis (Gen Counsel)

Arup Associates Limited (1)
8 Fitzroy St, London, W1T 4BJ, United
Kingdom
Tel.: (44) 20 775 55555
Web Site: http://www.arupassociates.com
Engineeering Services
N.A.I.C.S.: 541330

Arup B.V. (1)
Beta Building Naritaweg 118, 1043 CA, Am-
sterdam, Netherlands
Tel.: (31) 20 305 8500
Web Site: http://www.arup.com
Emp.: 180
Engineeering Services
N.A.I.C.S.: 541330
Zonder Blenken (Gen Mgr)

Arup Botswana Limited (1)
Marula ground floor Prime Plaza Plot 54358
CBD, Gaborone, Botswana
Tel.: (267) 395 3494
Engineeering Services
N.A.I.C.S.: 541330

Arup Brasil Consultoria Ltda (1)
Av Rio Branco 1, Centro, Rio de Janeiro,
20090-003, Brazil
Tel.: (55) 21 3554 7740
Engineeering Consulting Services
N.A.I.C.S.: 541330
Ricardo Pittella (Principal-Civil Engrg)

Arup Canada Inc. (1)
600 Boulevard de Maisonneuve West Office
750, Montreal, H3A 3J2, QC, Canada
Tel.: (514) 448-6694
Emp.: 100
Engineeering Services
N.A.I.C.S.: 541330
Andrew McAlpine (Principal)

Arup China Limited (1)
Room 3008 30/F Jing Guang Centre, Hu
Jia Lou Chaoyang District, Beijing, 100020,
China
Tel.: (86) 10 5960 1188
Engineeering Services
N.A.I.C.S.: 541330

Arup Colombia S.A.S. (1)
Calle 100 8a-49 Torre B PH, Bogota, Co-
lombia
Tel.: (57) 1 6467357
Engineeering Services
N.A.I.C.S.: 541330
Federico Torres (Gen Mgr)

Arup Deutschland GmbH (1)
Joachimstaler Strasse 41, 10623, Berlin,
Germany
Tel.: (49) 30 885 9100
Emp.: 150
Engineeering Services
N.A.I.C.S.: 541330
Nicos Peonides (Assoc Dir-Architecture &
Plng)

Arup Government Projects Inc. (1)
1120 Connecticut Ave NW, Washington, DC
20036
Tel.: (212) 897-1360
Engineeering Services
N.A.I.C.S.: 541330

Arup Ireland Limited (1)
50 Ringsend Road, Dublin, D04 T6X0, Ire-
land
Tel.: (353) 1 233 4455
Web Site: http://www.arup.com
Emp.: 550
Engineeering Services
N.A.I.C.S.: 541330
Eoghan Lynch (Chm)

Arup Italia S.r.l. (1)
Corso Italia 13, 20122, Milan, Italy
Tel.: (39) 02 8597 9301
Engineeering Services
N.A.I.C.S.: 541330

Arup Latin America S.A.U. (1)
Alcala 54, 28014, Madrid, Spain
Tel.: (34) 91 523 9276
Emp.: 120
Engineeering Services
N.A.I.C.S.: 541330

**Arup Muhendislik ve Musavirlik Lim-
ited Sirketi** (1)
Cinnah Cad Nihat Erim Is Merkezi 37/13 &
18, Cankaya, Ankara, 06550, Turkiye
Tel.: (90) 212 318 63 00
Emp.: 300
Engineeering Services
N.A.I.C.S.: 541330

Arup New Zealand Limited (1)
Suite 305 Level 5 87-93 Queen Street,

Auckland, New Zealand
Tel.: (64) 27 428 8428
Engineeering Services
N.A.I.C.S.: 541330

Arup Partner Pty Limited (1)
L 10 201 Kent St, Sydney, 2000, NSW,
Australia
Tel.: (61) 293209320
Engineeering Services
N.A.I.C.S.: 541330

Arup Pty Limited (1)
Level 7 182 Victoria Square, Adelaide,
5000, SA, Australia
Tel.: (61) 8 8413 6500
Engineeering Services
N.A.I.C.S.: 541330

Arup Singapore Private Limited (1)
10 Hoe Chiang Road 26-01 Keppel Towers,
Singapore, 089315, Singapore
Tel.: (65) 6411 2500
Emp.: 400
Engineeering Services
N.A.I.C.S.: 541330

Arup Texas Inc. (1)
10370 Richmond Ave Ste 475, Houston, TX
77042
Tel.: (713) 783-2787
Web Site: http://www.arup.com
Emp.: 35
Engineeering Services
N.A.I.C.S.: 541330
Brian Raine (Principal)

Arup Vietnam Limited (1)
8/F Star Building 33 Ter - 33 Bis Mac Dinh
Chi Street, District 1, Ho Chi Minh City,
Vietnam
Tel.: (84) 8 6291 4062
Engineeering Services
N.A.I.C.S.: 541330
Neil Harvey (Gen Dir)

Arup d.o.o. (1)
Kneginje Zorke 77, 11000, Belgrade, Serbia
Tel.: (381) 1 1209 9850
Engineeering Services
N.A.I.C.S.: 541330

OASYS Limited (1)
Central Square Forth Street, Newcastle
upon Tyne, NE1 3PL, United Kingdom
Tel.: (44) 191 238 7559
Web Site: http://www.oasys-software.com
Information Technology Consulting Services
N.A.I.C.S.: 541511

Subsidiary (Non-US):

Oasys Australia Pty Ltd (2)
Level 4 108 Wickham Street, Fortitude Val-
ley, 4006, QLD, Australia
Tel.: (61) 7 3023 6221
Information Technology Consulting Services
N.A.I.C.S.: 541511

**Ove Arup & Partners Danmark
A/S** (1)
Frederiksborggade 15, 1360, Copenhagen,
Denmark
Tel.: (45) 30 50 30 02
Engineeering Services
N.A.I.C.S.: 541330

**Ove Arup & Partners Hong Kong
Limited** (1)
80 Tat Chee Avenue, Kowloon, China
(Hong Kong)
Tel.: (852) 2528 3031
Engineeering Services
N.A.I.C.S.: 541330

**Ove Arup & Partners International
Limited** (1)
Parkin House 8 St Thomas Street, Win-
chester, SO23 9HE, United Kingdom
Tel.: (44) 191 2616080
Engineeering Services
N.A.I.C.S.: 541330

**Ove Arup & Partners Ireland
Limited** (1)
1 Albert Quay, Cork, T12X8N6, Ireland
Tel.: (353) 21 427 7670
Web Site: http://www.arup.com
Emp.: 130
Engineeering Services
N.A.I.C.S.: 541330

Eoghan Lynch (Gen Mgr)

**Ove Arup & Partners Poland Sp.
zo.o** (1)
Krolewska 16, 00-103, Warsaw, Poland
Tel.: (48) 22 455 45 00
Engineeering Services
N.A.I.C.S.: 541330

**Ove Arup & Partners Scotland
Limited** (1)
1 West Regent Str, Glasgow, G2 1RW,
United Kingdom
Tel.: (44) 1413328534
Web Site: http://www.arup.com
Engineeering Services
N.A.I.C.S.: 541330

Ove Arup (Thailand) Limited (1)
2034/134 New Petchburi Rd, Bangkok,
Thailand
Tel.: (66) 2 716 1561
Engineeering Services
N.A.I.C.S.: 541330

ARVEE LABORATORIES (IN-
DIA) LIMITED
403 Entice Building Opposite Jayanti-
lal Park BRTS Bus Stop, Iskcon-
Bopal Road Ambli, Ahmedabad, 380
058, Gujarat, India
Tel.: (91) 2717430479
Web Site: https://www.arveelabs.com
ARVEE—(NSE)
Rev.: $7,517,375
Assets: $4,638,246
Liabilities: $1,273,680
Net Worth: $3,364,566
Earnings: $493,856
Emp.: 67
Fiscal Year-end: 03/31/23
Chemical Products Mfr
N.A.I.C.S.: 325199
Shalin Sudhakarbhai Patel (Mng Dir)

ARVESTA BV
Aarschotsesteenweg 84, 3012, Leu-
ven, Sweden
Tel.: (32) 16242626
Web Site: https://arvesta.eu
Emp.: 100
Agricultural & Horticultural Supplies
Distr
N.A.I.C.S.: 424910

ARVIDA GROUP LIMITED
39 Market Place, Auckland, 1010,
New Zealand
Tel.: (64) 99721180   NZ
Web Site: https://www.arvida.co.nz
ARV—(NZX)
Rev.: $192,973,684
Assets: $2,249,974,282
Liabilities: $1,416,254,187
Net Worth: $833,720,096
Earnings: $49,321,172
Emp.: 2,900
Fiscal Year-end: 03/31/23
Rest Home Operator
N.A.I.C.S.: 623311
Peter Wilson (Chm)

Subsidiaries:

**Aria Bay Retirement Village
Limited** (1)
3-7 Woodlands Crescent, Browns Bay,
Auckland, 0630, New Zealand
Tel.: (64) 94791871
Personal Care Services
N.A.I.C.S.: 812199

Aria Gardens Limited (1)
11 Bass Road, Albany, Auckland, 0632,
New Zealand
Tel.: (64) 94157934
Personal Care Services
N.A.I.C.S.: 812199

**Aria Park Retirement Village
Limited** (1)
1-3 Claude Road, Epsom, Auckland, 1023,
New Zealand

Tel.: (64) 96308430
Personal Care Services
N.A.I.C.S.: 812199

**Ashwood Park Retirement Village
Limited** (1)
118-130 Middle Renwick Road, Spring-
lands, Blenheim, 7241, New Zealand
Tel.: (64) 35779990
Personal Care Services
N.A.I.C.S.: 812199

Bainlea House (2013) Limited (1)
29 Wiltshire Court, Rangiora, 7400, New
Zealand
Tel.: (64) 33136055
Personal Care Services
N.A.I.C.S.: 812199

**Bainswood House Rest Home
Limited** (1)
191 King Street Street, Rangiora, 7400,
New Zealand
Tel.: (64) 33135905
Personal Care Services
N.A.I.C.S.: 812199

**Bethlehem Country Club Village
Limited** (1)
111 Carmichael Road, Bethlehem, Tau-
ranga, New Zealand
Tel.: (64) 75792030
Personal Care Services
N.A.I.C.S.: 812199

**Copper Crest Retirement Village
Limited** (1)
52 Condor Dr, Pyes Pa, Tauranga, 3112,
New Zealand
Tel.: (64) 75786245
Personal Care Services
N.A.I.C.S.: 812199

**Glenbrae Rest Home & Hospital
Limited** (1)
22 Hilda Street, Fenton Park, Rotorua,
3010, New Zealand
Tel.: (64) 73490014
Personal Care Services
N.A.I.C.S.: 812199

Lansdowne Park Village Limited (1)
100 Titoki Street Wairarapa, Lansdowne,
Masterton, 5810, New Zealand
Tel.: (64) 63770123
Personal Care Services
N.A.I.C.S.: 812199

**Lauriston Park Retirement Village
Limited** (1)
91 Coleridge Street, Leamington, Cam-
bridge, 3432, New Zealand
Tel.: (64) 78270793
Personal Care Services
N.A.I.C.S.: 812199

**Park Lane Retirement Village
Limited** (1)
35 Whiteleigh Avenue, Addington,
Christchurch, New Zealand
Tel.: (64) 33384495
Personal Care Services
N.A.I.C.S.: 812199

**The Cascades Retirement Resort
Limited** (1)
55 Pembroke Street, Hamilton Lake, Hamil-
ton, 3204, New Zealand
Tel.: (64) 78392348
Personal Care Services
N.A.I.C.S.: 812199

ARVIND & COMPANY SHIP-
PING AGENCIES LIMITED
5th Floor City Point Opp Town Hall,
Jamnagar, 361001, Gujarat, India
Tel.: (91) 2882551901
Web Site:
https://www.arvindshipping.com
Year Founded: 1987
ACSAL—(NSE)
Rev.: $1,019,413
Assets: $4,105,165
Liabilities: $2,995,713
Net Worth: $1,109,453
Earnings: $453,652
Emp.: 15

Fiscal Year-end: 03/31/23
Navigational Shipping Services
N.A.I.C.S.: 488330

ARVIND FASHIONS LTD.
Naroda Road, Ahmedabad, 380 025,
Gujarat, India
Tel.: (91) 7968268000
Web Site: https://www.arvind.com
542484—(BOM)
Rev.: $426,278,580
Assets: $445,381,755
Liabilities: $329,300,790
Net Worth: $116,080,965
Earnings: ($32,309,550)
Emp.: 2,187
Fiscal Year-end: 03/31/22
Textile Products Mfr
N.A.I.C.S.: 314999
Sanjay S. Lalbhai (Chm & Mng Dir)

Subsidiaries:

Arvind Envisol Limited (1)
Arvind Mill Premises Naroda road, Ahmeda-
bad, 380025, Gujarat, India
Tel.:(91) 18008439988
Web Site: https://www.arvindenvisol.com
Emp.: 400
Waste Water Treatment Services
N.A.I.C.S.: 221320

**Arya Omnitalk Wireless Solutions Pri-
vate Limited** (1)
Office No 202 2nd Floor Summer Court
Magarpatta City, Hadapsar, Pune, 411013,
India
Tel.: (91) 2067470100
Web Site: https://www.aryaomnitalk.com
Vehicle Tracking Services
N.A.I.C.S.: 517810
Vipen Malhotra (Pres)

ARVIND INTERNATIONAL LTD.
15 Ganesh Chandra Avenue 2nd
Floor, Kolkata, 700013, West Bengal,
India
Tel.: (91) 33 22368504
Web Site:
http://www.arvindinternational.com
Sales Range: $1-9.9 Million
Emp.: 7
Polystyrene Foam Mfr
N.A.I.C.S.: 326140
Arvind Bajoria (Mng Dir & CFO)

ARVIND MAFATLAL GROUP
Mafatlal House 4th Floor H T Parekh
Marg, Backbay Reclamation, Mum-
bai, 400 020, India
Tel.: (91) 2266173636
Web Site:
http://www.arvindmafatlalgroup.com
Holding Company: Textiles
N.A.I.C.S.: 551112
Hrishikesh A. Mafatlal (Chm)

Subsidiaries:

Mafatlal Industries Limited (1)
Mafatlal House 5th Floor HT Parekh Marg,
Backbay Reclamation, Mumbai, 400 020,
India
Tel.: (91) 2267713800
Web Site: https://www.mafatlals.com
Rev.: $144,028,931
Assets: $166,993,458
Liabilities: $73,313,195
Net Worth: $93,680,264
Earnings: $3,911,503
Emp.: 948
Fiscal Year-end: 03/31/2022
Textile Products Mfr
N.A.I.C.S.: 313310
Hrishikesh A. Mafatlal (Chm)

NOCIL Limited (1)
Mafatlal House H T Parekh Marg Backbay
Reclamation, Churchgate, Mumbai, 400020,
India
Tel.: (91) 2266364062
Web Site: http://www.nocil.com
Rev.: $215,013,435
Assets: $249,863,250

Arvind Mafatlal Group—(Continued)

Liabilities: $52,592,085
Net Worth: $197,271,165
Earnings: $24,039,015
Emp.: 675
Fiscal Year-end: 03/31/2022
Rubber Chemicals Mfr
N.A.I.C.S.: 325212
Hrishikesh A. Mafatlal (Chm)

ARVIND REMEDIES LTD

190 Poonamalle High Road, Chennai, 600 084, Tamil Nadu, India
Tel.: (91) 4443439595
Web Site:
   http://www.arvindremedies.com
Year Founded: 1988
Sales Range: $150-199.9 Million
Ayurvedic Pharmaceutical Products
Mfr & Distr
N.A.I.C.S.: 325412
B. Arvind Shah (CEO & Mng Dir)

ARVOG

D Wing 202 2nd floor Trade World,
Opp Bombay Canteen Kamala Mills
Lower Parel, Mumbai, 400013, India
Tel.: (91) 2243470278
Web Site: https://www.arvog.com
Year Founded: 1984
508954—(BOM)
Rev.: $6,070,116
Assets: $28,129,249
Liabilities: $7,447,203
Net Worth: $20,682,045
Earnings: $1,717,307
Emp.: 23
Fiscal Year-end: 03/31/23
Financial Services
N.A.I.C.S.: 523999
Sachin B. Kothari (Exec Dir)

Subsidiaries:

Supama Forex Private Limited (1)
A/7 Grant Road, Mumbai, 400007, Maharashtra, India
Tel.: (91) 2223016111
Web Site:
   http://supamaforexprivatelimited.site
Money Exchange Services
N.A.I.C.S.: 523160

ARWAY CORPORATION

Toronto Rpo Royal Bank Plaza, PO
Box 64039, Toronto, M5J 2T6, ON,
Canada
Tel.: (631) 655-6733   ON
Web Site: https://www.arway.ai
Year Founded: 2022
ARWYF—(OTCQB)
Software Development Services
N.A.I.C.S.: 541511
Evan Gappelberg (CEO)

ARX EQUITY PARTNERS S.R.O.

Ehlenuv dum 28 rijna 12, 110 00,
Prague, 1, Czech Republic
Tel.: (420) 22 423 5399   CZ
Web Site: http://www.arxequity.com
Privater Equity Firm
N.A.I.C.S.: 523999
Brian Wardrop (Mng Partner)

Subsidiaries:

Nutricia Deva a.s. (1)
Generala Klapalka 519, CZ-549 01, Nove
Mesto nad Metuji, Czech Republic
Tel.: (420) 491439111
Web Site: http://www.deva.cz
Baby Food Mfr
N.A.I.C.S.: 311999
Pavel Kvasinsky (Sls Mgr-EMEA)

ARX GOLD CORPORATION

Level 13 40 Creek Street, Brisbane,
4000, QLD, Australia   NV
Web Site: http://arxgold.net

Year Founded: 2008
Emp.: 1
Gold Exploration Services
N.A.I.C.S.: 212220
Brian Smith (CEO)

ARYA ELECTRONICS IRAN CO.

Djashrivareh Crossing Damavand Rd,
PO Box 17445-499, Tehran, Iran
Tel.: (98) 21 7733 2182
Emp.: 150
Electronic Products Mfr
N.A.I.C.S.: 334220
M. T. Salehi (Chm & Mng Dir)

ARYA RESOURCES LTD.

3200-650 West Georgia Street, Vancouver, V6B 4P7, BC, Canada
Tel.: (403) 701-7299
RBZ—(TSXV)
Assets: $86,796
Liabilities: $142,025
Net Worth: ($55,229)
Earnings: ($483,541)
Fiscal Year-end: 04/30/24
Business Consulting Services
N.A.I.C.S.: 541611

ARYAMAN FINANCIAL SERVICES LTD

60 Khataou Building Alkesh Dinesh
Marg, Fort, Mumbai, 400 001, India
Tel.: (91) 2262166999
Web Site: https://www.afsl.co.in
Year Founded: 1994
530245—(BOM)
Rev.: $11,570,614
Assets: $13,480,699
Liabilities: $4,825,507
Net Worth: $8,655,192
Earnings: $1,027,135
Emp.: 23
Fiscal Year-end: 03/31/22
Merchant Banking Services
N.A.I.C.S.: 523150
Shripal Shah (CFO)

Subsidiaries:

Aryaman Capital Markets Ltd (1)
718 A P J Towers Dalal Street, Fort, Mumbai, 400001, India
Tel.: (91) 2222721104
Web Site: https://www.afsl.co.in
Rev.: $18,440,727
Assets: $6,354,444
Liabilities: $3,950,515
Net Worth: $2,403,929
Earnings: $34,685
Fiscal Year-end: 03/31/2021
Investment Banking & Financial Services
N.A.I.C.S.: 523150
Shripal Shah (VP-Merchant Banking Div & Exec Dir)

ARYAN SHARES & STOCK BROKERS LTD.

No-7 7th Cross Street Second Floor
Shenoy Nagar, Chennai, 600030,
Tamil Nadu, India
Tel.: (91) 4442021600
Web Site: http://www.assbl.com
542176—(BOM)
Rev.: $259,810
Assets: $2,117,220
Liabilities: $237,674
Net Worth: $1,879,547
Earnings: $39,060
Emp.: 7
Fiscal Year-end: 03/31/21
Financial Consulting Services
N.A.I.C.S.: 523940
Shanmukh N. Shah (Mng Dir)

ARYAVAN ENTERPRISE LIMITED

308 Shital Varsha Arcade Opp Girish

Cold Drinks C G Road Navrangpura,
Ahmedabad, 380 009, Gujarat, India
Tel.: (91) 9824136618
Web Site: https://aryavanenterprise.in
539455—(BOM)
Rev.: $30,966
Assets: $364,941
Liabilities: $3,123
Net Worth: $361,817
Earnings: ($31,456)
Emp.: 3
Fiscal Year-end: 03/31/23
Recyclable Material Distr
N.A.I.C.S.: 423930
Jitendra Kumar (Mng Dir)

ARYT INDUSTRIES LTD.

7 Naplada Street, Or Yehuda, 60218,
Israel
Tel.: (972) 119723538
Holding Company
N.A.I.C.S.: 551112

ARVEE LABORATORIES (INDIA) LIMITED

ARYZTA AG

Ifangstrasse 9, 8952, Schlieren, Switzerland
Tel.: (41) 445834200   CH
Web Site: https://www.aryzta.com
Year Founded: 2008
ARYN—(SWX)
Rev.: $3,287,286,855
Assets: $2,074,789,553
Liabilities: $1,320,850,421
Net Worth: $753,939,132
Earnings: $173,213,900
Emp.: 7,771
Fiscal Year-end: 12/31/23
Bakery Products Mfr & Distr
N.A.I.C.S.: 311812
Kevin Toland (CEO)

Subsidiaries:

ARYZTA Bakeries Deutschland
GmbH (1)
Gewerbegebiet Strohugel Industriestrasse
4, Lutherstadt, 06295, Eisleben, Germany
Tel.: (49) 34757290
Web Site: http://www.aryzta.de
Frozen Baked Product Mfr & Whslr
N.A.I.C.S.: 311813
Nigel Scully (Mng Dir)

ARYZTA Food Solutions GmbH (1)
Konrad-Goldmann-Strasse 5b, D - 79100,
Freiburg, Germany
Tel.: (49) 761704910
Web Site: https://aryzta.de
Frozen Baked Product Mfr & Whslr
N.A.I.C.S.: 311813
Nigel Scully (Mng Dir)

ARYZTA Holdings Asia Pacific
BV (1)
Paasheuvelweg, Amsterdam, 1105 BH,
Netherlands
Tel.: (31) 205646160
Investment Management Service
N.A.I.C.S.: 523999

ARYZTA Ltd. (1)
Grange Castle Business Park, Clondalkin,
Dublin, 22, Ireland
Tel.: (353) 14647200
Web Site: https://aryzta.ie
Sales Range: $1-4.9 Billion
Emp.: 4,973
Bakery Products Mfr & Distr
N.A.I.C.S.: 311812
Pat Morrissey (Chief Admin Officer, Gen Counsel & Sec)

Subsidiary (Domestic):

Cuisine de France Limited (2)
Grange Castle Business Park, Clondalkin,
Dublin, 22, Ireland
Tel.: (353) 14057200
Web Site: http://www.cuisinedefrance.ie
Sales Range: $200-249.9 Million
Emp.: 600
Specialty Breads, Pastries & Baked Confectionery Mfr & Whslr
N.A.I.C.S.: 311812

Subsidiary (Domestic):

Cuisine de France (UK) Limited (3)
Grange Castle Business Park Clondalkin,
Dublin, 22, Ireland
Tel.: (353) 2892603222
Web Site: http://www.cuisinedefrance.com
Sales Range: $150-199.9 Million
Specialty Breads, Pastries & Baked Confectionery Mfr & Whslr
N.A.I.C.S.: 311812
David O'Donoghue (CEO)

Subsidiary (US):

Cuisine de France Inc. (3)
350 S NW Hwy Ste 302, Park Ridge, IL
60068
Tel.: (847) 692-1916
Specialty Breads, Pastries & Baked Confectionery Mfr & Whslr
N.A.I.C.S.: 311812

Subsidiary (US):

La Brea Bakery, Inc. (2)
6080 Ctr Dr Ste 900, Los Angeles, CA
90045
Web Site: http://www.labreabakery.com
Emp.: 45
Bread Mfr & Retailer
N.A.I.C.S.: 311812
John Yamin (CEO)

ARYZTA Polska Sp.z o.o. (1)
street Zachodnia 10, 05-825, Grodzisk Mazowiecki, Poland
Tel.: (48) 227347486
Web Site: https://aryzta.pl
Frozen Baked Product Mfr & Whslr
N.A.I.C.S.: 311813

Dalgety Agra Polska Sp. z.o.o. (1)
Obornicka 233, 60-650, Poznan, Poland
Tel.: (48) 61 842 94 66
Seeds & Fertilizer Distr
N.A.I.C.S.: 424910

Fornetti Kft (1)
Varosfold 92, 6000, Kecskemet, Hungary
Tel.: (36) 76502070
Web Site: https://www.fornetti.hu
Frozen Baked Product Mfr & Whslr
N.A.I.C.S.: 311813
Istvan Herczeg (COO)

France Distribution SAS (1)
Zac De Bel Air N 14 16 14 Avenue Joseph
Paxton, Ferrieres en Brie, 77164, France
Tel.: (33) 164116401
Sales Range: $75-99.9 Million
Emp.: 200
Bakery Food Products Distr
N.A.I.C.S.: 424420

Fresca SAS (1)
29 rue Helene Boucher ZA de la Butte Au
Berger, Chilly Mazarin, Paris, 91380,
France
Tel.: (33) 1 64 54 54 00
Food Products Distr
N.A.I.C.S.: 424420

Fresh Start Bakeries Industrial
LTDA (1)
Avenida das Comunicacoes 333 - Industrial
Anhanguera, Osasco, 06278-080, Brazil
Tel.: (55) 1136872744
Bakery Food Products Mfr
N.A.I.C.S.: 311813

Hiestand & Suhr Handels und Logistik GmbH (1)
Konrad-Goldmann-Strabe 5b, Achkarren,
79235, Freiburg, Germany
Tel.: (49) 7662930316
Emp.: 50
Frozen Bakery Products Mfr
N.A.I.C.S.: 311813
Pedro Rodriguez (Gen Mgr)

Hiestand Holdings (Switzerland)
AG (1)
Talacker 41, Zurich, 8001, Switzerland
Tel.: (41) 447552525
Investment Management Service
N.A.I.C.S.: 523999

Subsidiary (Domestic):

ARYZTA Food Solutions Schweiz
AG (2)

Ifangstrasse 9, CH-8952, Schlieren,
Switzerland　　　　　　　　　**(100%)**
Tel.: (41) 447384343
Web Site: http://www.aryzta.ch
Frozen Bakery Products Mfr
N.A.I.C.S.: 311813

Subsidiary (Non-US):

Fricopan GmbH　　　　　　　　　　**(3)**
Strohugel Industrial Estate Industriestrasse
4, Lutherstadt, 06295, Eisleben, Germany
Tel.: (49) 34757290
Web Site: https://aryzta.de
Sales Range: $75-99.9 Million
Emp.: 2
Frozen Bakery Products Mfr
N.A.I.C.S.: 311813
Ralph Koschek *(Mng Dir)*

Hiestand Beteiligungsholding GmbH
& Co. KG　　　　　　　　　　　　**(3)**
Albert Einstein Strasse 1, 97447, Gerol-
zhofen, Germany
Tel.: (49) 938297110
Emp.: 357
Frozen Food Product Mfr
N.A.I.C.S.: 311412
Gerhard Seufert *(Plant Mgr)*

Subsidiary (Non-US):

ARYZTA Food Solutions Japan Co.,
Ltd.　　　　　　　　　　　　　　**(4)**
CIRCLES nishishinjuku 1F 3-6-4 nishishin-
juku, Shinjuku-ku, Tokyo, 160-0023, Japan
Tel.: (81) 359093551
Web Site: https://aryzta.co.jp
Emp.: 60
Baked Goods Mfr
N.A.I.C.S.: 311813
Oliver Ryf *(Mng Dir)*

HIESTAND AUSTRIA GMBH　　**(4)**
Industriezentrum No Sud Str 3 Obj 74,
2351, Wiener Neudorf, Austria
Tel.: (43) 2236 677 277 0
Sales Range: $25-49.9 Million
Emp.: 17
Frozen Food Product Distr
N.A.I.C.S.: 424420
Dettrech Alexander *(Gen Mgr)*

Subsidiary (Domestic):

**HIESTAND DEUTSCHLAND
GMBH**　　　　　　　　　　　　**(4)**
Albert-Einstein-Strasse 1, 97447, Gerol-
zhofen, Germany
Tel.: (49) 938297120
Web Site: https://aryzta.de
Emp.: 35
Bakery Food Products Mfr & Distr
N.A.I.C.S.: 311813

Subsidiary (Non-US):

**HIESTAND MALAYSIA SDN
BHD**　　　　　　　　　　　　　**(4)**
Lot 2 Jalan P 10/14 Seksyen 10, 43650,
Bandar Baru Bangi, Selangor Darul Ehsan,
Malaysia
Tel.: (60) 3 8925 7771
Web Site: http://www.hiestand.com.my
Frozen Bakery Food Mfr
N.A.I.C.S.: 311813

Masstock Arable (UK) Ltd　　　**(1)**
Andoversford, Cheltenham, GL54 4LZ,
Gloucestershire, United Kingdom
Tel.: (44) 8456073322
Agronomy Consulting Services
N.A.I.C.S.: 541690

Mette Munk A/S　　　　　　　　**(1)**
Goteborggade 3-5, 5000, Odense, Denmark
Tel.: (45) 7 020 2371
Web Site: https://mettemunk.dk
Emp.: 75
Commercial Bakery
N.A.I.C.S.: 311812

Origin Enterprises plc　　　　　**(1)**
4-6 Riverwalk Citywest Business Campus,
Dublin, D24 DCW0, Ireland　**(68.8%)**
Web Site: https://www.originenterprises.com
Rev.: $2,650,731,707
Assets: $1,484,568,314
Liabilities: $1,041,450,464

Net Worth: $443,117,850
Earnings: $55,074,466
Emp.: 2,796
Fiscal Year-end: 07/31/2023
Agricultural Products, Cereal & Food Mfr
N.A.I.C.S.: 325311
Declan Giblin *(CEO-Latin American)*

Subsidiary (Domestic):

Goulding Chemicals Limited　　**(2)**
Centre Park Road Marina, Cork, Ireland
Tel.: (353) 214911611
Sales Range: $25-49.9 Million
Emp.: 30
Nitrogenous Fertilizer Mfr
N.A.I.C.S.: 325311
Tim O'Mahony *(Mng Dir)*

Subsidiary (Non-US):

Origin Fertilisers (UK) Limited　**(2)**
Tel.: (44) 1763255500
Sales Range: $25-49.9 Million
Emp.: 15
Fertilizer Mfr
N.A.I.C.S.: 325314

Subsidiary (Domestic):

R. & H. Hall Limited　　　　　　**(2)**
Level 5 Number 4 Custom House Plaza
Harbourmaster Place, Dublin, D01 R3K6,
Ireland
Tel.: (353) 17900200
Animal Feed Raw Material Supplier
N.A.I.C.S.: 311119

Pre Pain B.V.　　　　　　　　　**(1)**
Kleibultweg 94, 7575 BX, Oldenzaal, Neth-
erlands
Tel.: (31) 541531030
Web Site: https://www.prepain.com
Frozen Baked Product Mfr & Whslr
N.A.I.C.S.: 311813
Gerben Vollenbroek *(Comml Dir)*

R & H Hall Trading Limited　　　**(1)**
Clarendon Ho 23 Clarendon Rd, Belfast,
BT1 3BG, United Kingdom
Tel.: (44) 2890313360
Web Site: http://www.wrbarnett.com
Bakery Food Products Distr
N.A.I.C.S.: 424420

**ARZAN FINANCIAL GROUP
FOR FINANCING & INVEST-
MENT K.S.P.C.**
Arzan Tower Ahmed Al Jaber Street,
PO Box 26442, Safat, Kuwait, 13125,
Kuwait
Tel.: (965) 1820200　　　　　　**KW**
Web Site: https://www.arzan.com.kw
Year Founded: 1980
ARZAN—(KUW)
Rev.: $54,639,007
Assets: $629,163,892
Liabilities: $120,202,993
Net Worth: $508,960,899
Earnings: $32,500,036
Emp.: 50
Fiscal Year-end: 12/31/22
Financial Services
N.A.I.C.S.: 523999
Jassem Hassan Zainal *(Vice Chm &
CEO)*

Subsidiaries:

Arzan Securities Brokerage Co.
SAE　　　　　　　　　　　　　**(1)**
13 Ahmed Orabi st, Elmohandessen,
3755201, Giza, Egypt
Tel.: (20) 33450345
Web Site: https://www.arzanegypt.com
Financial Brokerage Services
N.A.I.C.S.: 523999

Arzan Wealth (DIFC) Co. Limited　**(1)**
Office No 206 Level 2 Gate Village 7 DIFC,
PO Box 506686, Dubai, United Arab Emir-
ates
Tel.: (971) 44214024
Web Site: https://www.arzanwealth.com
Financial Investment Services
N.A.I.C.S.: 523999
Nitin Kumar Modi *(Sr Mgr-Investment)*

International Finance Company -
SAL　　　　　　　　　　　　　**(1)**
Hamra main street Estral Building-3rd Floor,
Beirut, Lebanon
Tel.: (961) 1350390
Web Site: https://www.icflebanon.com
Financial Services
N.A.I.C.S.: 541611

ARZNEIWERK AG VIDA
Ordensmeisterstr 15-16, 12099, Ber-
lin, Germany
Tel.: (49) 30399280900
Web Site: https://www.arzneiwerk.ag
Year Founded: 1983
TLIK—(DEU)
Rev.: $5,131,425
Assets: $1,445,162
Liabilities: $16,338
Net Worth: $1,428,824
Earnings: $1,014,360
Emp.: 18
Fiscal Year-end: 12/31/20
Telecommunications Technology Ser-
vices
N.A.I.C.S.: 517111
Oliver Olbrich *(Chm-Mgmt Bd &
CEO)*

Subsidiaries:

Euro rx Arzneimittel GmbH　　　**(1)**
Auf Dem Farnkamp 11, 30900, Wedemark,
Germany
Tel.: (49) 5130583850
Web Site: https://eurorx.de
Pharmaceutical Product Whslr
N.A.I.C.S.: 424210

GVL Rechenzentrum GmbH　　　**(1)**
Ordensmeisterstr 15 -16, 12099, Berlin,
Germany
Tel.: (49) 3062932053
Web Site: https://www.gvlrz.de
Information Technology & Software Devel-
opment Services
N.A.I.C.S.: 541511

ARZON LIMITED
4485 Mainway, Burlington, L7L 7P3,
ON, Canada
Tel.: (905) 561-2424
Web Site:
　http://www.arzonlimited.com
Rev.: $16,814,700
Emp.: 45
Welded Tube Mfr
N.A.I.C.S.: 331210
Jeff Carubba *(Pres)*

**ARZUM ELEKTRIKLI EV
ALETLERI SANAYI VE TI-
CARET A.S.**
Otakcilar Caddesi No 78 Kat 1 Blok
No B1B, Eyup, 34050, Istanbul, Tur-
kiye
Tel.: (90) 2124678080
Web Site: https://www.arzum.com.tr
ARZUM—(IST)
Rev.: $47,502,150
Assets: $40,953,123
Liabilities: $34,714,028
Net Worth: $6,239,095
Earnings: $1,254,635
Emp.: 175
Fiscal Year-end: 12/31/22
Household Appliance Mfr & Distr
N.A.I.C.S.: 335220
Talip Murat Kolbasi *(Chm)*

AS COMPANY S.A.
Ionias Street, Oreokastro, 570 13,
Thessaloniki, Greece
Tel.: (30) 2310572000
Web Site: https://www.ascompany.gr
Year Founded: 1990
ASCO—(ATH)
Rev.: $30,928,557
Assets: $44,325,652
Liabilities: $6,872,436

Net Worth: $37,453,216
Earnings: $2,785,561
Emp.: 72
Fiscal Year-end: 12/31/22
Toy & Electronic Games Mfr
N.A.I.C.S.: 339930

Subsidiaries:

AS Kids Toys S.r.l.　　　　　　**(1)**
Calea Bucurestilor Ground Floor Room P1,
Ilfov, 075100, Otopeni, Romania
Tel.: (40) 217969271
Web Site: http://www.askids.ro
Toy Mfr & Distr
N.A.I.C.S.: 339930

**AS DITTON PIEVADKEZU
RUPNICA**
Visku St 17, 5410, Daugavpils, Latvia
Tel.: (371) 65402333
Web Site: http://www.dpr.lv
Year Founded: 1949
DPK1R—(RSE)
Rev.: $5,502,628
Assets: $9,384,126
Liabilities: $8,058,744
Net Worth: $1,325,381
Earnings: ($19,604)
Emp.: 150
Fiscal Year-end: 12/31/19
Mechanical Equipment Mfr
N.A.I.C.S.: 333613
Rolands Zarans *(Chm)*

AS EKSPRESS GRUPP
Parda 6, 10151, Tallinn, Estonia
Tel.: (372) 6698381
Web Site: https://www.egrupp.ee
Year Founded: 1989
EEG1T—(TAL)
Rev.: $80,677,779
Assets: $116,752,401
Liabilities: $54,338,227
Net Worth: $62,414,174
Earnings: $3,699,084
Emp.: 1,102
Fiscal Year-end: 12/31/23
Newspaper Publishers
N.A.I.C.S.: 513110
Mari-Liis Ruutsalu *(Chm-Mgmt Bd)*

Subsidiaries:

AS Printall　　　　　　　　　　**(1)**
Tala 4, 11415, Tallinn, Harju, Estonia
Tel.: (372) 6698400
Web Site: https://www.printall.ee
Sales Range: $450-499.9 Million
Newspaper Printing Services
N.A.I.C.S.: 323111
Andres Ottas *(Mgr-Sls)*

Bilesu Paradize SIA　　　　　　**(1)**
3 Duntes Street, Riga, 1013, Latvia
Tel.: (371) 90002000
Web Site: https://www.bilesuparadize.lv
Electronic Ticket Operator
N.A.I.C.S.: 561599

D Screens SIA　　　　　　　　　**(1)**
Delu iela 4c, Riga, 1004, Latvia
Tel.: (371) 27755077
Web Site: https://www.dscreens.lv
Outdoor Advertising Services
N.A.I.C.S.: 541850

Delfi AS　　　　　　　　　　　　**(1)**
Delu Street 4-8 C entrance 3rd floor, Riga,
1004, Latvia
Tel.: (371) 6 778 4050
Web Site: https://www.delfi.lv
Sales Range: $25-49.9 Million
Emp.: 50
Newspaper Publishing Services
N.A.I.C.S.: 513110

Subsidiary (Domestic):

Mango.lv SIA　　　　　　　　　**(2)**
Mukusalas 41, Riga, 1004, Latvia
Tel.: (371) 67784070
Sales Range: $25-49.9 Million
Emp.: 50

AS Ekspress Grupp—(Continued)

Internet Entertainment Site Publishing Services
N.A.I.C.S.: 516210

Delfi UAB　　　　　　　　　　　　(1)
Gyneju st 16, 01109, Vilnius, Lithuania
Tel.: (370) 52045400
Web Site: https://www.delfi.lt
Sales Range: 325-49.9 Million
Emp.: 60
Newspaper Publishing Services
N.A.I.C.S.: 513110

Eesti Ajalehed AS　　　　　　　　　(1)
Narva mnt 11E, 10151, Tallinn, Harju, Estonia
Tel.: (372) 6698080
Web Site: https://ekspress.delfi.ee
Newspaper Publishing Services
N.A.I.C.S.: 513110

Ekspress Meedia AS　　　　　　　　(1)
Narva Mnt 13, 10151, Tallinn, Estonia
Tel.: (372) 669 8040
Web Site: https://www.ekspressmeedia.ee
Media Services
N.A.I.C.S.: 541840

Hea Lugu OU　　　　　　　　　　　(1)
Parda 6, 10151, Tallinn, Estonia
Tel.: (372) 6613399
Web Site: https://www.healugu.ee
Book Publishers
N.A.I.C.S.: 513110
Tiina Kaalep (CEO)

Printall AS　　　　　　　　　　　　(1)
Tala 4, 11415, Tallinn, Estonia
Tel.: (372) 669 8400
Web Site: https://www.printall.ee
Printing Plate Mfr
N.A.I.C.S.: 323120

TOV Delfi　　　　　　　　　　　　　(1)
Bud 28/2 N P N 43 Vul Mikhaila, Grushevskogo, Kiev, 01021, Ukraine
Tel.: (380) 442211950
Online Advertising Agencies
N.A.I.C.S.: 541810

AS ENERGOFIRMA JAUDA
Krustpils iela 119, Riga, LV 1057, Latvia
Tel.: (371) 67725789
Web Site: http://www.jauda.com
Year Founded: 1961
Sales Range: $25-49.9 Million
Electrical Equipment Mfr & Distr
N.A.I.C.S.: 335999
Janis Simins (Chm)

AS INFORTAR
Sadama 5, 10111, Tallinn, Estonia
Tel.: (372) 6409978　　　　　　　EE
Web Site: http://www.infortar.ee
Investment Holding Company
N.A.I.C.S.: 551112
Ain Hanschmidt (CEO)

Subsidiaries:

AS Eesti Gaas　　　　　　　　　　(1)
Sadama 7, Tallinn, 10111, Estonia　(67%)
Tel.: (372) 6 303 003
Web Site: http://www.gaas.ee
Rev.: $179,791,283
Assets: $215,358,037
Liabilities: $180,679,332
Net Worth: $34,678,705
Earnings: $11,602,869
Emp.: 230
Fiscal Year-end: 12/31/2019
Natural Gas Distr; Electric Power Distr
N.A.I.C.S.: 221210
Raul Kotov (Member-Mgmt Bd)

Subsidiary (Non-US):

JSC Gaso　　　　　　　　　　　　(2)
Vagonu Street 20, Riga, LV-1009, Latvia
Tel.: (371) 67041818
Web Site: http://www.gaso.lv
Gas Distribution Services
N.A.I.C.S.: 221210

AS Tallink Grupp　　　　　　　　　(1)

Sadama 5, 10111, Tallinn, Estonia　　(68.47%)
Tel.: (372) 6409800
Web Site: https://en.tallink.com
Rev.: $922,094,050
Assets: $1,716,768,959
Liabilities: $849,395,077
Net Worth: $867,373,882
Earnings: $87,064,797
Emp.: 4,912
Fiscal Year-end: 12/31/2023
Coastal & Great Lakes Passenger Transportation
N.A.I.C.S.: 483114
Enn Pant (Chm-Supervisory Bd)

Subsidiary (Domestic):

AS Tallink Baltic　　　　　　　　　(2)
Sadama 5, 10111, Tallinn, Harju, Estonia
Tel.: (372) 6409800
Web Site: http://www.tallink.ee
Sales Range: $125-149.9 Million
Emp.: 500
Marine Passenger Transport Services
N.A.I.C.S.: 483112

AS Tallink Duty Free　　　　　　　(2)
Sadama 5/7, 10111, Tallinn, Harju, Estonia
Tel.: (372) 6409813
Web Site: http://www.shopping.tallink.com
Sales Range: $25-49.9 Million
Emp.: 300
Shipping Goods Supplier
N.A.I.C.S.: 424990

Subsidiary (Non-US):

HTG Stevedoring OY　　　　　　　(2)
Tyynenmerenkatu 9, PO Box 100, 00181, Helsinki, Finland
Tel.: (358) 918041
Stevedoring Services
N.A.I.C.S.: 488320

OOO Tallink-Ru　　　　　　　　　(2)
Nevsky 114-116 8th floor, 191025, Saint Petersburg, Russia
Tel.: (7) 8124496754
Web Site: http://www.tallinksilja.ru
Cargo Shipping & Passenger Transportation Services
N.A.I.C.S.: 483112

Subsidiary (Domestic):

OU HT Laevateenindus　　　　　　(2)
Sadama 5/7, 10111, Tallinn, Harju, Estonia
Tel.: (372) 6 40 9945
Crewing & Ship Management Services
N.A.I.C.S.: 483112

OU HT Meelelahutus　　　　　　　(2)
Sadama 5/7, 10111, Tallinn, Estonia
Tel.: (372) 6409800
Web Site: http://www.tallink.ee
Sales Range: $25-49.9 Million
Emp.: 10
Cruise Ship Entertainment Services
N.A.I.C.S.: 487210

OU Hansatee Kinnisvara　　　　　(2)
Sadama 5/7, 10111, Tallinn, Estonia
Tel.: (372) 6 409 800
Web Site: http://www.tallink.com
Vehicle Leasing Services
N.A.I.C.S.: 532112

OU Hera Salongid　　　　　　　　(2)
Sadama 5/7, 10111, Tallinn, Harju, Estonia
Tel.: (372) 6409800
Web Site: http://www.herasalongid.ee
Sales Range: $25-49.9 Million
Emp.: 15
Body Massaging Services
N.A.I.C.S.: 812199

OU TLG Hotell　　　　　　　　　　(2)
Sadama 5/7, 10111, Tallinn, Harju, Estonia
Tel.: (372) 6409800
Web Site: http://www.tallinkhotels.com
Sales Range: $25-49.9 Million
Emp.: 110
Home Management Services
N.A.I.C.S.: 721110

OU Tallink Travel Club　　　　　　(2)
Sadama 5, 10111, Tallinn, Harju, Estonia
Tel.: (372) 6409854
Web Site: https://www.travelclub.tallink.com
Emp.: 4

Travel & Tour Operating Agencies
N.A.I.C.S.: 561510

SIA HT Shipmanagement　　　　　(2)
Tartu Maantee 13, 10145, Tallinn, Harju, Estonia
Tel.: (372) 6 40 9948
Web Site: http://www.tallink.com
Crewing & Ship Management Services
N.A.I.C.S.: 483112

Subsidiary (Non-US):

SIA TLG Hotell Lalvija　　　　　　(2)
Elizabetes 24, Riga, 1050, Latvia
Tel.: (371) 67099760
Web Site: http://www.hotels.tallink.com
Emp.: 100
Home Management Services
N.A.I.C.S.: 721110

Sally AB　　　　　　　　　　　　　(2)
Norrgatan 2, 22100, Mariehamn, Finland
Tel.: (358) 918041
Freight Transportation Services
N.A.I.C.S.: 488510

Tallink Latvija AS　　　　　　　　(2)
Eksporta iela 3a, Riga, LV-1010, Latvia
Tel.: (371) 67099705
Web Site: https://www.tallink.com
Passenger & Cargo Transportation Services
N.A.I.C.S.: 481112

Tallink Silja Oy　　　　　　　　　(2)
Itamerenkatu 11-13, PO Box 100, 00181, Helsinki, Finland
Tel.: (358) 918041
Web Site: https://www.tallink.com
Marine Passenger Transportation Services
N.A.I.C.S.: 483112

Subsidiary (Non-US):

Tallink Silja AB　　　　　　　　　(3)
Hamnpirsvagen 10, 11541, Stockholm, Sweden
Tel.: (46) 86663300
Web Site: https://www.tallink.com
Marine Cargo Containers Leasing
N.A.I.C.S.: 488320

Tallink Silja GmbH　　　　　　　　(3)
Mattentwiete 6, 20457, Hamburg, Germany
Tel.: (49) 40547541222
Web Site: https://www.tallink.com
Passenger Transportation & Cargo Shipping Services
N.A.I.C.S.: 483112

AS LATVIJAS BALZAMS
A Caka 160, 1012, Riga, 1012, Latvia
Tel.: (371) 67081213
Web Site: https://www.lb.lv
Year Founded: 1900
UM9—(STU)
Rev.: $95,866,671
Assets: $215,215,606
Liabilities: $44,763,779
Net Worth: $170,451,827
Earnings: $10,724,091
Emp.: 562
Fiscal Year-end: 12/31/21
Alcohol Beverage Product Mfr
N.A.I.C.S.: 312140
Intars Geidans (Chm & Mng Dir)

AS MERKO EHITUS
Jarvevana tee 9G, 11314, Tallinn, Estonia
Tel.: (372) 6805105
Web Site: https://www.merko.ee
Year Founded: 1990
Sales Range: $300-349.9 Million
Emp.: 757
Construction Engineering Services
N.A.I.C.S.: 541330
Toomas Annus (Chm-Supervisory Bd)

Subsidiaries:

AS Merko Ehitus Eesti　　　　　　(1)
Jarvevana tee 9g, Tallinn, 11314, Estonia　　　　　　　　　　　　(100%)
Tel.: (372) 680 5105
Web Site: http://www.merko.ee
Construction Engineering Services

N.A.I.C.S.: 237990

Subsidiary (Domestic):

AS Gustaf　　　　　　　　　　　　(2)
Ringi 10, 80010, Parnu, Estonia　(92.5%)
Tel.: (372) 443 1300
Web Site: http://www.gustaf.ee
Construction Engineering Services
N.A.I.C.S.: 237990

AS Merko Infra　　　　　　　　　　(2)
Jarvevana tee 9g, 11314, Tallinn, Estonia　　　　　　　　　　　　(100%)
Tel.: (372) 680 5015
Web Site: http://www.merko.ee
Construction Engineering Services
N.A.I.C.S.: 237990

AS Merko Tartu　　　　　　　　　　(2)
Raekoja plats 20, Tartu, 51004, Estonia　　　　　　　　　　　　　(66%)
Tel.: (372) 730 2890
Web Site: http://www.merkotartu.ee
Construction Engineering Services
N.A.I.C.S.: 237990

AS Tallinna Teed　　　　　　　　　(2)
Betooni 24, 11415, Tallinn, Estonia (100%)
Tel.: (372) 606 1901
Web Site: http://www.talteede.ee
Construction Engineering Services
N.A.I.C.S.: 541330
Tonu Toomik (Chm)

OU Fort Ehitus　　　　　　　　　　(2)
Tare tee 2-5, 74001, Viimsi, Estonia　　　　　　　　　　　　　　(75%)
Tel.: (372) 50 27165
Emp.: 8
Construction Engineering Services
N.A.I.C.S.: 237990

OU Gustaf Tallinn　　　　　　　　(2)
Sopruse pst 145, Tallinn, 13417, Estonia　　　　　　　　　　　　(80%)
Tel.: (372) 656 3523
Web Site: http://www.gustaf-tallinn.ee
Emp.: 30
Construction Engineering Services
N.A.I.C.S.: 237990
Tiit Ponerants (Gen Mgr)

SIA Merks　　　　　　　　　　　　(1)
Skanstes iela 50, LV-1013, Riga, Latvia　　　　　　　　　　　　(100%)
Tel.: (371) 6737 3380
Web Site: http://www.merks.lv
Emp.: 80
Construction Engineering Services
N.A.I.C.S.: 541330
Oskars Ozolins (Chm-Mgmt Bd)

UAB Merko Statyba　　　　　　　　(1)
Laisves pr 3, Vilnius, 4215, Lithuania　　　　　　　　　　　　　(100%)
Tel.: (370) 5210 5330
Web Site: http://www.merko.lt
Emp.: 100
Construction Engineering Services
N.A.I.C.S.: 237990
Saulius Putrimas (Gen Dir)

AS OLAINFARM
5 Rupnicu Street, Olaine, LV-2114, Latvia
Tel.: (371) 67013705
Web Site: http://lv.olainfarm.com
Year Founded: 1972
OLF1R—(OMX)
Rev.: $153,667,189
Assets: $188,886,786
Liabilities: $46,093,438
Net Worth: $142,793,349
Earnings: $26,462,292
Emp.: 2,166
Fiscal Year-end: 12/31/19
Pharmaceuticals Product Mfr
N.A.I.C.S.: 325412
Genadijs Melnis (Dir-Admin Dept)

Subsidiaries:

Joint-Stock Company Olainfarm Kazakhstan　　　　　　　　　　　(1)
151/115 Abai Avenue office 807, Almaly district, 050009, Almaty, Kazakhstan
Tel.: (7) 273334652

Chemical Pharmaceutical Product Mfr &
Distr
N.A.I.C.S.: 325412

Limited Liability Company Olainfarm
Azerbaijan　　　　　　　　　　(1)
55 Khojaly Avenue AGA Business Center,
Khatai district, AZ1025, Baku, Azerbaijan
Tel.: (994) 556115500
Chemical Pharmaceutical Product Mfr &
Distr
N.A.I.C.S.: 325412

Limited liability company Olainfarm
Asia　　　　　　　　　　　　　(1)
Frunze street 340 office 421, Sverdlovsk
district, Bishkek, Kyrgyzstan
Tel.: (996) 7010570235
Chemical Pharmaceutical Product Mfr &
Distr
N.A.I.C.S.: 325412

Limited liability company Olainfarm
Ozbaxt　　　　　　　　　　　　(1)
Oybek Avenue 24, 100000, Tashkent, Uz-
bekistan
Tel.: (998) 712814640
Chemical Pharmaceutical Product Mfr &
Distr
N.A.I.C.S.: 325412

Limited liability company Olainfarm
pharmaceutical & medical products
industry & trade　　　　　　　(1)
Kibris Sehitleri Caddesi No 134/1 D 204
Alsancak, Izmir, Turkiye
Tel.: (90) 5078406767
Chemical Pharmaceutical Product Mfr &
Distr
N.A.I.C.S.: 325412

AS ONE CORPORATION
Takuji Iuchi 2-1-27 Edobori, Nishi-ku,
Osaka, 550-8527, Japan
Tel.: (81) 664471210
Web Site: https://www.as-1.co.jp
Year Founded: 1962
7476—(TKS)
Rev.: $631,492,960
Assets: $633,449,520
Liabilities: $206,033,700
Net Worth: $427,415,820
Earnings: $49,575,000
Emp.: 711
Fiscal Year-end: 03/31/24
Scientific Equipment Whslr
N.A.I.C.S.: 423490
Takuji Iuchi (Pres)

Subsidiaries:

AS ONE SHANGHAI
Corporation　　　　　　　　　(1)
E13F No 918 Middle Huai Hai Rd, Shang-
hai, China
Tel.: (86) 2154033266
Web Site: http://www.as-1.cn
Scientific Instrument Distr
N.A.I.C.S.: 423490
Masato Sato (Mgr-Medical)

Nikko Hansen & Co., Ltd.　　　(1)
4-15-5 Temma, Kita-ku, Osaka, 530-0043,
Japan
Tel.: (81) 648017727
Web Site: https://www.nikko-hansen.com
Emp.: 22
Plastic Product Mfr & Distr
N.A.I.C.S.: 326199

AS PRICEWATERHOUSECOO-
PERS
Parnu mnt 15, 10141, Tallinn, Estonia
Tel.: (372) 6141858　　　　　EE
Web Site: http://www.pwc.ee
Emp.: 150
Accounting, Tax & Business Consult-
ing Services
N.A.I.C.S.: 541211
Ago Vilu (Pres)

AS REVERTA
Kr Valdemara iela 31, Riga, LV-1887,
Latvia

Tel.: (371) 6 777 9100　　　　　LV
Web Site: http://www.reverta.lv
Year Founded: 1992
Sales Range: Less than $1 Million
Emp.: 20
Banking Services
N.A.I.C.S.: 522110
Uldis Dzenitis (Head-Security Depart-
ment)

Subsidiaries:

AB Parex Bankas　　　　　　　(1)
K Kalinausko Street 13, 03107, Vilnius,
Lithuania
Tel.: (370) 852664600
Web Site: http://www.parex.lt
Sales Range: $1-9.9 Million
Emp.: 186
Banking Services
N.A.I.C.S.: 522110

Parex Asset Management　　　(1)
ZAMeierovica Blvd 14, 1010, Riga, Latvia
Tel.: (371) 7010810
Web Site: http://www.parex.lv
Sales Range: $50-74.9 Million
Asset Management Services
N.A.I.C.S.: 523999

Subsidiary (Non-US):

Parex Asset Management
Russia　　　　　　　　　　　(2)
40/4 B Ordinka Street, Moscow, Russia
Tel.: (7) 4959336226
Web Site: http://www.parexam.ru
Sales Range: $50-74.9 Million
Emp.: 10
Asset Management Services
N.A.I.C.S.: 523999
Popemko Aleksey (Mng Dir)

Parex Asset Management
Ukraine　　　　　　　　　　　(2)
172 Gorkogo Street, 03150, Kiev, Ukraine
Tel.: (380) 445691088
Web Site: http://www.parex.ua
Sales Range: $50-74.9 Million
Asset Management Services
N.A.I.C.S.: 523999

UAB Parex Investiciju Valdymas　(2)
K Kalinausko Street 13, 03107, Vilnius,
Lithuania
Tel.: (370) 52649730
Web Site: http://www.parexinvest.lt
Sales Range: $50-74.9 Million
Emp.: 16
Investment Banking
N.A.I.C.S.: 523150

Parex Bank Sweigniederlassung
Berlin　　　　　　　　　　　　(1)
Franzosische Strasse 15, 10117, Berlin,
Germany
Tel.: (49) 3030345870
Banking Services
N.A.I.C.S.: 522110

Parex Brokerage System　　　(1)
Citadeles Street 2, 1010, Riga, Latvia
Tel.: (371) 7323835
Web Site: http://www.dtc.lv
Sales Range: $50-74.9 Million
Emp.: 40
Securities Brokerage Services
N.A.I.C.S.: 523150

Parex Leasing & Factoring　　(1)
Brivibas Street 224, 1039, Riga, Latvia
Tel.: (371) 7001100
Web Site: http://www.parexgroup.com
Leasing & Factoring Services
N.A.I.C.S.: 525990

Parex Open Pension Fund　　　(1)
K Barona Street 20 22 Republikas lautuns
2A, 1010, Riga, Latvia
Tel.: (371) 7064717
Web Site: http://www.parex.lv
Sales Range: $50-74.9 Million
Emp.: 6
Pension Fund Management Services
N.A.I.C.S.: 525110

UAB NIF Lietuva　　　　　　　(1)
18a Gelezinio vilko, 08104, Vilnius, Lithuania

Tel.: (370) 52194360
Real Estate Manangement Services
N.A.I.C.S.: 531210

AS RIGAS AUTO-
ELEKTROAPARATU RUPNICA
Klijanu iela 18, Riga, 1013, Latvia
Tel.: (371) 67371459
Web Site: http://www.rarlv.carrd.co
RAR1R—(RSE)
Sales Range: Less than $1 Million
Automobile Equipment Mfr
N.A.I.C.S.: 336110
Eriks Kazha (Chm-Mgmt Bd)

AS SANGAR
Sopruse Pst 2, 50050, Tartu, Estonia
Tel.: (372) 7307300
Web Site: http://www.sangar.ee
Year Founded: 1956
Sales Range: $10-24.9 Million
Emp.: 300
Shirts & Other Apparel Mfr
N.A.I.C.S.: 315990
Inno Kalberg (CFO)

Subsidiaries:

SIA Sangar Trading　　　　　　(1)
Krasta 46, 1003, Riga, Latvia　(100%)
Tel.: (371) 7030382
Clothing & Furnishings Merchant Whslr
N.A.I.C.S.: 424350

Sangar Valga Vabrik AS　　　　(1)
7 Sepa, 68203, Valga, Estonia
Tel.: (372) 7666500
Men's & Boys' Suits & Coats Mfr
N.A.I.C.S.: 315250

AS TALLINNA VESI
Adala 10, 10614, Tallinn, Estonia
Tel.: (372) 6262200　　　　　EE
Web Site: https://www.tallinnavesi.ee
Year Founded: 1967
TVE1T—(BX)
Rev.: $67,491,997
Assets: $311,162,380
Liabilities: $181,931,781
Net Worth: $129,230,599
Earnings: $14,178,165
Emp.: 351
Fiscal Year-end: 12/31/23
Waste Treatment Services
N.A.I.C.S.: 221310
Simon Roger Gardiner (Chm-
Supervisory Bd)

AS TRIGON CAPITAL GROUP
Parnu Mnt 18 4th Floor, 10141, Tal-
linn, Estonia
Tel.: (372) 6679200
Web Site:
　http://www.trigoncapital.com
Year Founded: 1994
Sales Range: $1-9.9 Million
Emp.: 30
Investment Services
N.A.I.C.S.: 523999
Joakim Helenius (Founder & Exec
Chm)

ASA BANKA D.D.
Trg medunarodnog prijateljstva 25,
71 000, Sarajevo, Bosnia & Herze-
govina
Tel.: (387) 33586870
Web Site: http://www.asabanka.ba
IKBZRK2—(SARE)
Rev.: $48,762,840
Assets: $1,703,471,618
Liabilities: $1,496,692,635
Net Worth: $206,778,983
Earnings: $25,965,120
Emp.: 678
Fiscal Year-end: 12/31/23
Banking Services
N.A.I.C.S.: 522110

ASA BANKA D.D. SARAJEVO
Trg Medunarodnog Prijateljstva 25,
71000, Sarajevo, Bosnia & Herze-
govina
Tel.: (387) 33586870
Web Site: http://www.asabanka.ba
IKBZRK2—(SARE)
Rev.: $9,274,774
Assets: $614,422,700
Liabilities: $562,838,210
Net Worth: $51,584,489
Earnings: $3,705,100
Emp.: 678
Fiscal Year-end: 12/31/21
Commercial Banking Services
N.A.I.C.S.: 522110

ASA HOLDING D.O.O.
Bulevar Mese Selimovica 16, 71 000,
Sarajevo, Bosnia & Herzegovina
Tel.: (387) 33770900　　　　　BA
Web Site: http://www.asa.ba
Sales Range: $125-149.9 Million
Emp.: 470
Holding Company; New Automobile &
Motor Vehicle Parts Distr
N.A.I.C.S.: 551112
Nihad Imamovic (Chm & Pres)

Subsidiaries:

ASA Aleasing d.o.o.　　　　　(1)
Stupine B2 prostor A6, 75000, Tuzla, Bos-
nia & Herzegovina
Tel.: (387) 35 252 102
Web Site: http://www.asa-aleasing.ba
Motor Vehicle Financial Leasing Services
N.A.I.C.S.: 525990
Mirsad Sarajlic (Mgr)

ASA PSS d.o.o　　　　　　　(1)
Trg medunarodnog prijateljstva bb, 71000,
Sarajevo, Bosnia & Herzegovina
Tel.: (387) 33 77 53 00
Web Site: http://www.asa-pss.ba
Car Maintenance Services
N.A.I.C.S.: 811111
Sead Basic (Gen Mgr)

ASA INTERNATIONAL GROUP
PLC
Rembrandt Tower 35th Floor Am-
stelplein 1, 1096 HA, Amsterdam,
Netherlands
Tel.: (31) 208463554　　　　　UK
Web Site: https://www.asa-
　international.com
Year Founded: 2007
ASAI—(LSE)
Rev.: $176,610,000
Assets: $490,027,000
Liabilities: $413,417,000
Net Worth: $76,610,000
Earnings: $8,757,000
Emp.: 13,432
Fiscal Year-end: 12/31/23
Business Loan Services
N.A.I.C.S.: 522291
Dirk Brouwer (Founder & CEO)

Subsidiaries:

ASA International India Microfinance
Limited　　　　　　　　　　　(1)
Block GN-37/2 Victoria Park 4th Floor Sec-
tor V, Salt Lake City, Kolkata, 700 091,
West Bengal, India
Tel.: (91) 3323578508
Web Site: http://india.asa-international.com
Financial Banking Services
N.A.I.C.S.: 522110
Saibal Mitra (Head-Fin & Treasury)

ASA Microfinance (Tanzania)
Ltd.　　　　　　　　　　　　(1)
Plot-12 Block-33H Malongwe Street Kasaba
St Mwananyamala Area, PO Box 61627,
Mwinyi Juma Road Kinondoni, Dar es Sa-
laam, Tanzania
Tel.: (255) 222760722
Web Site: http://tanzania.asa-
international.com

ASA International Group plc—(Continued)

Financial Banking Services
N.A.I.C.S.: 522110
M. D. Abu Sayed (Deputy Mng Dir)

ASA Microfinance (Uganda) Limited (1)
Plot 228 Buye-Kigoowa Ntinda, PO Box 245, Kampala, Uganda
Tel.: (256) 200906777
Web Site: https://uganda.asa-international.com
Microfinance Loans Services
N.A.I.C.S.: 522291

ASA Pakistan Limited (1)
Office No 601 & 602 Lakson Square Building No3, Karachi, Pakistan
Tel.: (92) 2135211431
Web Site: http://pakistan.asa-international.com
Financial Banking Services
N.A.I.C.S.: 522110
Saeed Uddin Khan (CEO)

ASA Savings & Loans Limited (1)
No 612 South Odorkor Busia Junction Odorkor - Mallam Road, Accra, Ghana
Tel.: (233) 302328405
Web Site: https://ghana.asa-international.com
Asset Financing Loan Services
N.A.I.C.S.: 522390

Pagasa Philippines Finance Corporation, Inc. (1)
7th Floor Jenkinsen Tower 80 Timog Ave, Metro Manila, Quezon City, 1103, Philippines
Tel.: (63) 287091761
Web Site: https://philippines.asa-international.com
Microfinance Services
N.A.I.C.S.: 522291

ASA JOINT STOCK COMPANY
5th Floor Nam Long Building 66A Tran Hung Dao, Hoan Kiem District, Hanoi, Vietnam
Tel.: (84) 02463275775
Web Site:
https://www.asacorp.com.vn
Personal Care Product Mfr & Distr
N.A.I.C.S.: 325620
Jane Cooper (CEO)

ASA RESOURCE GROUP PLC.
One Fleet Place, London, EC4M 7WS, United Kingdom
Tel.: (44) 203 696 5470
Web Site:
http://asaresourcegroup.com
Year Founded: 1987
Multi-Commodity Mining & Exploration Company
N.A.I.C.S.: 212290
Ian B. Dearing (Exec Dir)

ASA SAN MARINO S.P.A.
Strada dei Censiti 18-20, 47890, Falciano, San Marino
Tel.: (378) 0549 90 5275   SM
Web Site: http://www.gruppoasa.com
Year Founded: 1961
Metal Can & Container Mfr & Whslr
N.A.I.C.S.: 332431
Emilio Amati (Chm)

Subsidiaries:

ASA Italia SARL (1)
Via Montegrappa 59, 25038, Rovato, Brescia, Italy
Tel.: (39) 030 770 3258
Web Site: http://www.gruppoasa.com
Metal Can & Container Mfr & Whslr
N.A.I.C.S.: 332431

ASAGAMI CORPORATION
Kokusai Bldg 6F 3-1-1 Marunouchi, Chiyoda-ku, Tokyo, 100-0005, Japan
Tel.: (81) 368802200
Web Site: https://www.asagami.co.jp

9311—(TKS)
Rev.: $261,980,740
Assets: $301,078,890
Liabilities: $167,279,270
Net Worth: $133,799,620
Earnings: $5,671,380
Fiscal Year-end: 03/31/24
Logistic Services
N.A.I.C.S.: 484110
Kenichi Kimura (COO)

ASAHI BROADCASTING GROUP HOLDINGS CORPORATION
1-1-30 Fukushima, Fukushima-ku, Osaka, 553-8503, Japan
Tel.: (81) 664585321
Web Site: https://asahi.co.jp
Year Founded: 1951
9405—(TKS)
Rev.: $597,887,720
Assets: $814,517,250
Liabilities: $311,145,920
Net Worth: $503,371,330
Earnings: ($5,843,240)
Fiscal Year-end: 03/31/24
Television Broadcasting Services
N.A.I.C.S.: 512110
Susumu Okinaka (Pres & Dir-Rep, Overall Mgmt, Investor Relations, and Internal Auditing)

Subsidiaries:

ABC Development Corporation (1)
6-20-12 Fukushima, Fukushima-ku, Osaka, 553-0003, Japan
Tel.: (81) 664511111
Web Site: https://www.abcd.ne.jp
Emp.: 89
Real Estate Management Services
N.A.I.C.S.: 531210

ABC FRONTIER HOLDINGS, INC. (1)
18F 2-3-1 Hamamatsucho, Minato-ku, Tokyo, 104-0045, Japan
Tel.: (81) 351484161
Web Site: https://www.abc-frontier.co.jp
Business Management Services
N.A.I.C.S.: 561110

ABC HORIZON PTE. LTD. (1)
152 Beach Road 18-05 Gateway East, Singapore, 189731, Singapore
Tel.: (65) 62915457
Web Site: https://abc-horizon.sg
Emp.: 6
Television Broadcasting Services
N.A.I.C.S.: 516120

ABC Libra Co., Ltd. (1)
ABC Annex 5F 2-4-3 Fukushima, Fukushima-ku, Osaka, 553-0003, Japan
Tel.: (81) 664523666
Web Site: https://www.abclibra.co.jp
Program Production Services
N.A.I.C.S.: 512110

ABC Media Communications (1)
2-4-3 Fukushima, Osaka, 553-0003, Japan
Tel.: (81) 664588811
Web Site: http://www.abcmc.co.jp
Radio Broadcasting Services
N.A.I.C.S.: 516210

HOUSING SUPPORT Corporation (1)
1-1-1 Imamiya, ABC Housing Wellbe Minouchi, Minoh, 562-0033, Osaka, Japan
Tel.: (81) 727377400
Web Site: https://www.housing-support.com
Emp.: 22
Real Estate Management Services
N.A.I.C.S.: 531210

ASAHI CO., LTD.
707 Tomori, Kawajima-machi Hiki-gun, Saitama, 350-0166, Japan
Tel.: (81) 492975577
Web Site:
https://www.asahicorporation.com
Year Founded: 1975
3333—(TKS)

Sales Range: $450-499.9 Million
Emp.: 52
Bicycle Store Operator
N.A.I.C.S.: 423110
Yuji Okada (Pres)

ASAHI CONCRETE WORKS CO., LTD.
1-8-2 Tsukiji, Chuo-ku, Tokyo, 104-0045, Japan
Tel.: (81) 335421201
Web Site: https://www.asahi-concrete.co.jp
Year Founded: 1923
5268—(TKS)
Sales Range: $100-124.9 Million
Concrete Product Mfr & Distr
N.A.I.C.S.: 327332
Hisayoshi Nakanishi (Chm)

ASAHI DIAMOND INDUSTRIAL CO. LTD.
4-1 Kioi-cho New Otani Garden Court 11F, Chiyoda-ku, Tokyo, 102-0094, Japan
Tel.: (81) 332226311
Web Site: https://www.asahidia.co.jp
6140—(TKS)
Rev.: $255,496,330
Assets: $488,485,610
Liabilities: $65,491,880
Net Worth: $422,993,730
Earnings: $13,940,490
Emp.: 2,059
Fiscal Year-end: 03/31/24
Diamond & Jewelry Tool Mfr
N.A.I.C.S.: 339910
Kazuki Kataoka (Pres)

Subsidiaries:

Asahi Diamond (Thailand) Co., Ltd. (1)
909 Ample Tower 5th Floor Unit 5/3 Debaratna Road, Bangna-Nuea Bangna, Bangkok, 10260, Thailand
Tel.: (66) 23483861
Machine Tools Mfr
N.A.I.C.S.: 333515

Asahi Diamond America, Inc. (1)
9872 Windisch Rd, West Chester, OH 45069
Tel.: (513) 759-5222
Web Site:
https://www.asahidiamondamerica.com
Sales Range: $25-49.9 Million
Emp.: 12
Diamond Tool Mfr
N.A.I.C.S.: 333514

Asahi Diamond Industrial Australia Pty., Ltd. (1)
1B/81 Bassett Street, Mona Vale, 2103, NSW, Australia
Tel.: (61) 299977033
Web Site: https://www.asahi-diamond.com.au
Sales Range: $50-74.9 Million
Emp.: 10
Diamond Tool Suppliers
N.A.I.C.S.: 423840

Asahi Diamond Industrial Co. Ltd. - Chiba No.2 Factory (1)
1-35 Miharadai Chonan-machi, Chosei-gun, Chiba, 297-0143, Japan
Tel.: (81) 475463101
Web Site: http://www.asahidia.co.jp
Sales Range: $25-49.9 Million
Emp.: 100
Diamond Tool Mfr
N.A.I.C.S.: 333514

Asahi Diamond Industrial Co. Ltd. - Chiba Tsurumai Factory (1)
787 Tabi, Ichihara, 290-0515, Chiba, Japan
Tel.: (81) 436883221
Diamond Jewelry Mfr
N.A.I.C.S.: 339910

Asahi Diamond Industrial Co. Ltd. - Mie Factory (1)

7-8-1 Yumegaoka, Iga, 518-0131, Mie, Japan
Tel.: (81) 595267321
Web Site: http://www.asahidia.co.jp
Diamond Jewelry Mfr
N.A.I.C.S.: 339910

Asahi Diamond Industrial Co. Ltd. - Tamagawa Factory (1)
3-4-35 Kuji, Takatsu-ku, Kawasaki 213-0032, Kanagawa, Japan
Tel.: (81) 448336221
Web Site: http://www.asahidia.co.jp
Diamond Jewelry Mfr
N.A.I.C.S.: 339910

Asahi Diamond Industrial Europe SAS (1)
47 Avenue d'Orleans, CS70841, 28008, Chartres, France
Tel.: (33) 237244040
Web Site: http://www.asahidia.eu
Sales Range: $50-74.9 Million
Emp.: 130
Diamond & Cutting Tools Mfr
N.A.I.C.S.: 333515
Dominique Bourges (Pres)

Asahi Diamond Industrial Germany GmbH (1)
Westfaliche Strasse 169 D, 44309, Dortmund, Germany
Tel.: (49) 23190620060
Machine Tools Mfr
N.A.I.C.S.: 333515

Asahi Diamond Industrial Malaysia SDN. BHD. (1)
K-6-11 No2 Jalan Solaris Mon't Kiara, 50480, Kuala Lumpur, Malaysia
Tel.: (60) 362010390
Machine Tools Mfr
N.A.I.C.S.: 333515

Asahi Diamond Industrial Scandinavia AB (1)
Bostallsvagen 1, 702 27, Orebro, Sweden
Tel.: (46) 19100050
Web Site: https://www.asahidia.se
Machine Tools Mfr
N.A.I.C.S.: 333515

Asahi Diamond de Mexico, S.A. de C.V. (1)
Pro Blvd Campestre No 2502 Torre San Mateo I Piso 2 Int 203, Fraccionamiento El Refugio Campestre, Leon, Gto, Mexico
Tel.: (52) 773909466
Web Site:
http://www.asahidiamonddemexico.com
Machine Tools Mfr
N.A.I.C.S.: 333515

Koremura Asahi Diamond Industrial Co., Ltd. (1)
365 Tokiwa, Kamakura, 248-0022, Kanagawa, Japan
Tel.: (81) 467310721
Web Site: https://www.koremura.co.jp
Machine Tools Mfr
N.A.I.C.S.: 333515

P.T. Asahi Diamond Industrial Indonesia (1)
Jln Jababeka Blok F No 35, Cikarang Industrial Estate, Bekasi, 17530, West Java, Indonesia
Tel.: (62) 218936217
Web Site: http://www.asahi-indonesia.com
Sales Range: $25-49.9 Million
Emp.: 100
Diamond Tools Mfr & Sales
N.A.I.C.S.: 333514

Shanghai Xu Hui Diamond Industrial Co., Ltd. (1)
Building No 7 No 1280 Lian Xi Road, Pu-Dong New District, Shanghai, 201204, China
Tel.: (86) 2150426478
Web Site: http://www.adishanghai.com
Diamond Cutting Tool Mfr
N.A.I.C.S.: 333514
Kazuo Kogawa (Mng Dir)

Shinhan Diamond Industrial Co., Ltd. (1)
375 Namdongdong-ro, Namdong-gu Namdong Industries Park 36B - 10L, In-

cheon, Korea (South)
Tel.: (82) 328103310
Web Site: http://www.en.shinhandia.co.kr
Diamond Cutting Tool Mfr
N.A.I.C.S.: 333514

Taiwan Asahi Diamond Industrial Co., Ltd. (1)
No 248 Hwa-kong St, Pa-Deh Dist, Taoyuan, 33464, Taiwan
Tel.: (886) 33636971
Web Site: https://www.taiwandiamond.com
Sales Range: $150-199.9 Million
Emp.: 350
Diamond Tools & Cutting Tools Mfr & Sales
N.A.I.C.S.: 327910

Yamanashi Asahi Diamond Industrial Co., Ltd. (1)
800 Wakao Shinden, Tatsuoka-machi, Nirasaki, 407-0031, Yamanashi, Japan
Tel.: (81) 551227501
Web Site: http://www.yamanashiasahi.co.jp
Emp.: 140
Diamond Mfr
N.A.I.C.S.: 212390

ASAHI EITO CO., LTD.
10F 1 - 3 - 8 Tokiwamachi, Chuo-ku, Osaka, 540-0028, Japan
Tel.: (81) 677772073
Web Site: https://www.asahieito.co.jp
Year Founded: 1950
5341—(TKS)
Rev.: $24,935,530
Assets: $19,759,830
Liabilities: $11,436,170
Net Worth: $8,323,660
Earnings: ($4,417,070)
Emp.: 69
Fiscal Year-end: 11/30/23
Sanitary Ware Mfr & Distr
N.A.I.C.S.: 332999
Koji Machimoto *(Pres)*

Subsidiaries:

Vina Asahi Co., Ltd. (1)
1F May Plaza 63D Vo Van Tan Street Ward 6 Dist 3, Ho Chi Minh City, Vietnam
Tel.: (84) 2839302300
Web Site: http://www.asahieito.com.vn
Sanitaryware Distr
N.A.I.C.S.: 423720

ASAHI GROUP HOLDINGS LTD.
1-23-1 Azumabashi, Sumida-Ku, Tokyo, 130-8602, Japan
Tel.: (81) 356085126   JP
Web Site: https://www.asahigroup-holdings.com
Year Founded: 1949
ASBRF—(OTCIQ)
Rev.: $21,645,215,680
Assets: $44,022,200,640
Liabilities: $26,993,648,000
Net Worth: $17,028,552,640
Earnings: $1,485,880,000
Emp.: 30,020
Fiscal Year-end: 12/31/21
Holding Company
N.A.I.C.S.: 551112
Ryoichi Kitagawa *(Mng Exec Officer)*

Subsidiaries:

Asahi Beer (China) Investment Co., Ltd. (1)
Room 903-905 CITIC Pacific Plaza No 1168 Nanjing West Road, Jing'an District, Shanghai, 200041, China
Tel.: (86) 215 292 9952
Web Site: https://www.asahibeer.com.cn
Financial Investment Services
N.A.I.C.S.: 523999

Asahi Beer Taiwan Co., Ltd. (1)
13F-3 No 318 Songjiang Road, Zhongshan District, Taipei, 10468, Taiwan
Tel.: (886) 800020898
Web Site: https://www.asahibeer.tw
Brewery Distr
N.A.I.C.S.: 424810

Asahi Beer U.S.A., Inc. (1)
3625 Del Amo Blvd Ste 250, Torrance, CA 90503-1670   **(92.2%)**
Tel.: (310) 214-9051
Web Site: https://www.asahisuperdry.com
Sales Range: $25-49.9 Million
Emp.: 15
Import & Distribution of Beer
N.A.I.C.S.: 424810

Asahi Beverages (NZ) Ltd. (1)
Level 1 96 St Georges Bay Road, Parnell, Auckland, 1052, New Zealand
Tel.: (64) 800420001
Web Site: https://www.asahibeverages.co.nz
Brewery Distr
N.A.I.C.S.: 424810

Asahi Beverages Pty Ltd (1)
58 Queens Bridge Street, Southbank, 3006, VIC, Australia
Tel.: (61) 800244054
Web Site: https://www.asahi.com.au
N.A.I.C.S.: 312120

Asahi Biocycle Co. Ltd. (1)
2-4-1 Ebisuminami, Shibuya-ku, Tokyo, 150-0022, Japan
Tel.: (81) 364123277
Web Site: https://www.asahibiocycle.com
Emp.: 108
Agriculture Biocycle Services
N.A.I.C.S.: 115112

Asahi Breweries, Ltd. (1)
1-23-1 Azumabashi, Sumida, Tokyo, 130-8602, Japan
Tel.: (81) 570005112
Web Site: https://www.asahibeer.co.jp
N.A.I.C.S.: 312120
Kazuo Matsuyama *(Pres)*

Asahi Calpis Wellness Co., Ltd. (1)
2-4-1 Ebisu Minami, Shibuya-ku, Tokyo, 150-0022, Japan
Tel.: (81) 364123252
Web Site: http://www.asahicalpis-w.co.jp
Food Service
N.A.I.C.S.: 722310

Asahi Food & Healthcare Co., Ltd. (1)
2-4-1 Ebisu Minami, Shibuya-ku, Tokyo, 150-0022, Japan   **(100%)**
Tel.: (81) 363033250
Web Site: http://www.asahi-gf.co.jp
Emp.: 1,200
Quasi-Pharmaceutical Products & Yeast Extract Mfr
N.A.I.C.S.: 325412
Noriyuki Karasawa *(Pres)*

Asahi Group Foods, Ltd. (1)
Asahi Group Calpis Ebisu Building 2-4-1 Ebisu Minami, Shibuya-ku, Tokyo, 150-0022, Japan
Tel.: (81) 363032794
Web Site: http://www.asahi-gf.co.jp
Restaurant Services
N.A.I.C.S.: 722511

Asahi International, Ltd. (1)
Griffin Brewery Chiswick Lane South, London, W4 2QB, United Kingdom
Tel.: (44) 2089962400
Brewery Mfr
N.A.I.C.S.: 312120

Asahi Soft Drinks Co., Ltd. (1)
1-23-1 Azumabashi, Sumida-ku, Tokyo, 130-8602, Japan
Tel.: (81) 570005112
Web Site: https://www.asahiinryo.co.jp
Sales Range: $1-4.9 Billion
Emp.: 3,300
Soft Drinks, Coffee & Tea Mfr
N.A.I.C.S.: 312111
Yonejo Taichi *(Pres)*

Subsidiary (Domestic):

Asahi Calpis Beverages Co., Ltd. (2)
5-8-20 Mukojima, Sumida-ku, Tokyo, 131-0033, Japan   **(80%)**
Tel.: (81) 356085555
Distribution of Soft Drinks Through Vending Machines
N.A.I.C.S.: 445132

Subsidiary (Domestic):

Calpis Beverages Co., Ltd. (3)

1F Daikanyama CA Building, 2-20-3 Ebisu-nishi, Shibuya Ku, Tokyo, 150 0021, Japan
Tel.: (81) 337802240
Importer of Soft Drinks
N.A.I.C.S.: 312111

Asahi UK Ltd. (1)
Griffin Brewery Chiswick Lane South, London, W4 2QB, United Kingdom
Tel.: (44) 1483718100
Web Site: https://uk.asahibeer.co.uk
Alcoholic Beverage Whslr & Distr
N.A.I.C.S.: 424810
Shoma Amin *(Mgr-PR)*

Beijing Beer Asahi Co., Ltd. (1)
No 1 N Yanqi Roa Yanqi Industrial Economic Development Zone, Beijing, 101407, China
Tel.: (86) 1065677001
Alcoholic Beverage Distr
N.A.I.C.S.: 424820

Birra Peroni s.r.l. (1)
Via Renato Birolli 8, 00155, Rome, Italy
Tel.: (39) 06225441
Web Site: https://www.birraperoni.it
Beer Mfr & Distr
N.A.I.C.S.: 312120

Boon Rawd Brewery Co, Ltd (1)
999 Samsen Road, Dusit, Bangkok, 10300, Thailand
Tel.: (66) 2 242 4000
Web Site: https://www.boonrawd.co.th
Alcoholic Beverage Distr
N.A.I.C.S.: 424820

Calpis Co., Ltd. (1)
4-1 2-chome Ebisu-minami, Shibuya-ku, Tokyo, 150-0022, Japan   **(100%)**
Tel.: (81) 364123130
Web Site: https://www.calpis.co.jp
Sales Range: $50-74.9 Million
Emp.: 844
Mfr & Distr of Fruit Beverages, Health Functioning Beverages, Dairy Products, Liquors & Feedstuff Additives
N.A.I.C.S.: 311511

Subsidiary (Domestic):

Calpis Foods Service Co., Ltd. (2)
3F Calpis Building 2-4-1 Ebisu-minami, Shibuya-ku, Tokyo, 150-0022, Japan
Tel.: (81) 3 5768 7481
Web Site: http://www.calpis-cfs.co.jp
Milk & Dairy Products Mfr & Distr
N.A.I.C.S.: 311511
Megumi Nakayama Tsukasa *(Pres)*

Subsidiary (US):

Calpis U.S.A. Inc. (2)
3625 Del Amo Blvd Ste 255, Torrance, CA 90503
Tel.: (310) 324-5900
Web Site: https://asahibev.com
Sales Range: $25-49.9 Million
Emp.: 6
Milk Beverages, Soft Drinks & Animal Feed Products Distr
N.A.I.C.S.: 424490

Subsidiary (Non-US):

PT Calpis Indonesia (2)
EJIP Industrial Park Plot 7C, Cikarang Selatan, Bekasi, 17550, Indonesia
Tel.: (62) 218970240
Web Site: http://www.calpico.co.id
Soft Drinks Mfr & Distr
N.A.I.C.S.: 312111

Carlton & United Breweries Pty Ltd (1)
131 Cascade Rd, Hobart, 7004, TAS, Australia
Tel.: (61) 800007282
Web Site: https://cub.com.au
N.A.I.C.S.: 312120
Danny Celoni *(CEO)*

Cornish Orchards Ltd. (1)
Westnorth Manor Farm, Duloe, Liskeard, PL14 4PW, Cornwall, United Kingdom
Tel.: (44) 1503269007
Brewery Distr
N.A.I.C.S.: 424810

Enoteca Co., Ltd. (1)

5-14-15 Minami-Azabu, Minato-ku, Tokyo, 106-0047, Japan
Tel.: (81) 33 280 6388
Web Site: https://www.enoteca.jp
Wine Retailer, Importer, E-Commerce & Mail Order Sales
N.A.I.C.S.: 445320

Etika Dairies Sdn. Bhd. (1)
Lot LS-1 Persiaran Satu Meru Industrial Park, Off Persiaran Hamzah Alang, Kelang, 42000, Selangor, Malaysia
Tel.: (60) 333922988
Web Site: http://www.dairychamp.com
Sales Range: $150-199.9 Million
Emp.: 440
Milk & Dairy Products Mfr
N.A.I.C.S.: 311511
Alex Tee *(Mgr-Export Sls)*

Subsidiary (Non-US):

PT Sentraboga Intiselera (2)
Jl Raya Gn Gangsir Km 4 5, Malang, 67155in, East Java, Indonesia
Tel.: (62) 343656986
Land Leasing Services
N.A.I.C.S.: 531190

Subsidiary (Domestic):

Susu Lembu Asli (Johore) Sdn. Bhd. (2)
Plot 169 Jalan Angkasa Mas 3 Kawasan Perindustrian Tebrau II, Johor Bahru, 81100, Johor, Malaysia
Tel.: (60) 73525584
Web Site: http://www.goodday.com.my
Sales Range: $25-49.9 Million
Emp.: 50
Milk Processing & Distr
N.A.I.C.S.: 424430

Susu Lembu Asli Marketing Sdn. Bhd. (2)
Lot 31 Jalan 213 Section 51, Petaling Jaya, 46050, Selangor, Malaysia
Tel.: (60) 377858811
Web Site: http://www.goodday.com.my
Sales Range: $25-49.9 Million
Emp.: 50
Dairy Products Marketer & Distr
N.A.I.C.S.: 424430
Lee Song Yong *(Founder)*

Independent Liquor (NZ) Ltd. (1)
35 Hunua Road, PO Box 72148, Auckland, 2110, Papakura, New Zealand
Tel.: (64) 92983000
Web Site: http://www.independentliquor.co.nz
Sales Range: $650-699.9 Million
Emp.: 218
Alcoholic Beverages Distr & Mfr
N.A.I.C.S.: 424820

Kompania Piwowarska S.A. (1)
street Szwajcarska 11, 61-285, Poznan, Poland
Tel.: (48) 616677794
Brewery Operator
N.A.I.C.S.: 312120
Wojciech Molinski *(VP-Personnel)*

Koninklijke Grolsch N.V. (1)
Brouwerslaan 1, 7548 XA, Enschede, Netherlands
Tel.: (31) 53 483 3333
Web Site: https://www.royalgrolsch.com
Emp.: 600
Brewery
N.A.I.C.S.: 312120
Ard Bossema *(Dir-Mktg)*

Subsidiary (Domestic):

De Klok Dranken B.V. (2)
Bolwerk 5, 7141 JM, Groenlo, Netherlands
Tel.: (31) 85 760 2216
Web Site: https://www.deklokdranken.nl
Emp.: 200
Breweries
N.A.I.C.S.: 312120

Grolsch International B.V. (2)
Brouwerslaan 1, 7548 XA, Enschede, Netherlands
Tel.: (31) 534833333
Web Site: https://www.grolsch.nl
Holding Company

Asahi Group Holdings Ltd.—(Continued)

N.A.I.C.S.: 551112

Subsidiary (Non-US):

The Swaen B.V.   (2)
Tel.: (31) 11 468 1930
Web Site: https://theswaen.com
Emp.: 50
Malt Mfr
N.A.I.C.S.: 311213

LB Co., Ltd.   (1)
3469-1 Kurohama, Hasuda, 349-0101, Saitama, Japan
Tel.: (81) 487691133
Web Site: http://www.elbee.jp
Sales Range: $150-199.9 Million
Emp.: 355
Health Drinks & Other Long Shelf-Life Beverage Products Mfr & Distr
N.A.I.C.S.: 311999

Lotte Asahi Co., Ltd.   (1)
Alcoholic Beverages Whslr
N.A.I.C.S.: 445298
Jeong Jae-Hark (CEO)

Meantime Brewing Company Ltd.   (1)
Brewery Shop Unit 1 Meantime Brewing Company Blackwall Lane, London, SE10 0AR, United Kingdom
Tel.: (44) 2082931111
Web Site:
   https://www.meantimebrewing.com
Craft Beer Brewery
N.A.I.C.S.: 312140
Alastair Hook (Founder)

Nectar Imports Limited   (1)
Cold Berwick Hill, Berwick, Saint Leonards, SP3 5GN, Wiltshire, United Kingdom
Tel.: (44) 1747827030
Brewery Distr
N.A.I.C.S.: 424810

Nippon Freeze Drying Co., Ltd.   (1)
2095-1 Toyoshina, Azumino, 399-8205, Nagano, Japan
Tel.: (81) 263725568
Emp.: 70
Dried Food Mfr
N.A.I.C.S.: 311423

Plzensky Prazdroj Slovensko, A.S.   (1)
Pivovarska 9, Velky Saris, 082 21, Presov, Slovakia
Tel.: (421) 517772111
Web Site: https://www.prazdroj.sk
Food & Beverage Distr
N.A.I.C.S.: 445298

Plzensky Prazdroj a.s.   (1)
U Prazdroje 64/7, 301 00, Plzen, Czech Republic   (100%)
Tel.: (420) 377062111
Web Site: https://www.prazdroj.cz
Sales Range: $350-399.9 Million
Emp.: 2,204
Brewery
N.A.I.C.S.: 312120

Qingdao Tsingtao Beer & Asahi Beverage Co., Ltd.   (1)
Wusi Square Hong Kong Middle Road, Qingdao Brewery Building, Qingdao, 266071, Shandong, China
Tel.: (86) 8008600899
Beer Whslr
N.A.I.C.S.: 424810

Schweppes Australia Pty Ltd   (1)
2 Beverage Drive, Tullamarine, 3043, VIC, Australia
Tel.: (61) 80 024 4054
Web Site: https://schweppes.com.au
Sales Range: $400-449.9 Million
Emp.: 1,500
Carbonated Soft Drinks Mfr & Distr
N.A.I.C.S.: 312111

The Dark Star Brewing Company Limited   (1)
Star Road, Partridge Green, Horsham, RH13 8RA, West Sussex, United Kingdom
Tel.: (44) 1403713085
Web Site: http://www.darkstarbrewing.co.uk
Food & Beverage Distr

N.A.I.C.S.: 445298

The Nikka Whisky Distilling Co., Ltd.   (1)
5-4-31 Minami-Aoyama, Minato-ku, Tokyo, 107-8616, Japan
Tel.: (81) 334980331
Web Site: http://www.nikka.com
Sales Range: $100-124.9 Million
Emp.: 440
Distilled & Blended Liquors Mfr
N.A.I.C.S.: 312140

Wakodo Co., Ltd.   (1)
2-4-1 Ebisu-Minami, Shibuya-ku, Tokyo, 150 0022, Japan
Tel.: (81) 3 6303 1251
Web Site: http://www.wakodo.co.jp
Sales Range: $150-199.9 Million
Emp.: 480
Baby Food & Powdered Milk Mfr
N.A.I.C.S.: 311999

Yantai Beer Asahi Co., Ltd.   (1)
100 Huanshan Road, Zhifu District, Yantai, 264001, Shandong, China
Tel.: (86) 5356082283
Sales Range: $400-449.9 Million
Emp.: 1,327
Brewery
N.A.I.C.S.: 312120

ASAHI INDUSTRIES LIMITED
Ecomax Musrane Taluka Wada, Thane, 421312, Maharashtra, India
Tel.: (91) 2224984896
Year Founded: 1993
514482—(BOM)
Rev.: $150
Assets: $7,607,732
Liabilities: $10,523,427
Net Worth: ($2,915,695)
Earnings: ($370,516)
Emp.: 35
Fiscal Year-end: 03/31/21
Textile Product Mfr & Whslr
N.A.I.C.S.: 314999
Swaroop Singh Bhati (Compliance Officer & Sec)

ASAHI INFRASTRUCTURE & PROJECTS LIMITED
302 3rd Floor Yashwant Shopping Center Carter Road No 7, Opp Railway Station Borivali E, Mumbai, 400066, Maharashtra, India
Tel.: (91) 07242441444
Year Founded: 1988
Housing Construction Services
N.A.I.C.S.: 236118

ASAHI INTECC CO., LTD.
3-100 Akatsukicho, Nagoya, 489-0071, Aichi, Japan
Tel.: (81) 561485551
Web Site: https://www.asahi-intecc.co.jp
Year Founded: 1976
7747—(NGO)
Rev.: $669,032,679
Assets: $1,192,000,036
Liabilities: $246,674,969
Net Worth: $945,325,067
Earnings: $98,339,039
Emp.: 9,371
Fiscal Year-end: 06/30/24
Medical Devices, Ultra-Thin Stainless Steel Wire Ropes & Terminal Processing Products Mfr
N.A.I.C.S.: 339112
Masahiko Miyata (Pres & CEO)

Subsidiaries:

Asahi Intecc Europe B.V.   (1)
Strawinskylaan 527 WTC Tower B-5th floor, 1077 XX, Amsterdam, Netherlands
Tel.: (31) 207940640
Medical Device Mfr & Distr
N.A.I.C.S.: 339112

Asahi Intecc GMA Co., Ltd.   (1)

3898-1 Asaba, Fukuroi, 437-1101, Shizuoka, Japan
Tel.: (81) 537 48 0151
Medical Device Mfr
N.A.I.C.S.: 339112

Asahi Intecc Hanoi Co., Ltd.   (1)
G03 Thang Long Industrial Park, Dong Anh District, Hanoi, Vietnam
Tel.: (84) 439550038
Medical Device Mfr
N.A.I.C.S.: 339112

Asahi Intecc J-sales, Inc.   (1)
13/F Shinjuku-Sanei Building 1-22-2 Nishi-Shinjuku, Shinjuku-ku, Tokyo, 160-0023, Japan
Tel.: (81) 3 5339 6290
Medical Device Sales
N.A.I.C.S.: 339112

Asahi Intecc Latin Promacao De Vendas LTDA   (1)
Avenida Bem Te Vi 77 Sala 42, Moema, Sao Paulo, 04524-030, Brazil
Tel.: (55) 1126155020
Medical Device Mfr & Distr
N.A.I.C.S.: 339112

Asahi Intecc Latin Promocao De Vendas E Comercio De Produtos Cirurgicos Ltda.   (1)
Avenida Bem Te Vi 77 Sala 42, Moema, Sao Paulo, 04524-030, Brazil
Tel.: (55) 1126155020
Medical Device Mfr & Distr
N.A.I.C.S.: 334510

Asahi Intecc Scientific (Beijing) Co., Ltd.   (1)
Unit1007 East Ocean Center 24A Jianguomenwai Avenue, Chaoyang District, Beijing, 100022, China
Tel.: (86) 1065155788
Medical Device Mfr & Distr
N.A.I.C.S.: 339112

Asahi Intecc Thailand Co., Ltd.   (1)
142-1 Moo 5 Bangkadi Industrial Park Tiwanon Road, Tambol Bangkadi Amphur Muang, Pathumthani, 12000, Thailand
Tel.: (66) 25011302
Medical Device Mfr
N.A.I.C.S.: 339112

Asahi Intecc USA, Inc.   (1)
22 Executive Park Ste 110, Irvine, CA 92614
Tel.: (949) 756-8636
Medical Device Mfr & Distr
N.A.I.C.S.: 339112

Asahi Surgical Robotics Co., Ltd.   (1)
Lab 1 NEXT Medical Device Innovation Center, National Cancer Center Hospital East 6-5-1 Kashiwanoha, Kashiwa, 277-8577, Japan
Tel.: (81) 471361496
Web Site: https://asahi-surgrob.com
Surgical Product Mfr
N.A.I.C.S.: 339112

Filmecc Co., Ltd.   (1)
1703 Wakita-cho, Moriyama-ku, Nagoya, 463-0024, Aichi, Japan
Tel.: (81) 527681212
Web Site: http://www.asahi-intecc.co.jp
Medical Device Mfr & Distr
N.A.I.C.S.: 339112

Filmecc USA, Inc.   (1)
3002 Dow Ave Ste 216, Tustin, CA 92780
Tel.: (949) 756-8252
Web Site: https://filmecc-us.com
Medical Equipment Mfr & Distr
N.A.I.C.S.: 334510

Kardia S.R.L.   (1)
Via Cormons 18, 20151, Milan, Italy
Tel.: (39) 0233402708
Web Site: https://www.kardia.it
Emp.: 16
Medical Device Distr
N.A.I.C.S.: 423450

Nihon Chemical Coat Co., Ltd.   (1)
8-17-25 Seishin, Chuo-ku, Sagamihara, 252-0216, Kanagawa, Japan
Tel.: (81) 427700531
Chemical Products Mfr
N.A.I.C.S.: 325998

Rev.1 Engineering, Inc.   (1)
41823 Enterprise Cir N Ste 200, Temecula, CA 92590
Tel.: (951) 696-3933
Web Site: https://rev1engineering.com
Medical Device Development Process Services
N.A.I.C.S.: 541715

Toyoflex Cebu Corporation   (1)
5th St 3rd Ave Peza, Lapu-Lapu, Cebu, Philippines
Tel.: (63) 323405880
Automobile Equipment Mfr
N.A.I.C.S.: 336110

Toyoflex Corporation   (1)
9F S-tec Information Building 24-1 Nishishinjuku1-chome, Shinjuku-ku, Tokyo, 160-0023, Japan
Tel.: (81) 35 909 4801
Web Site: https://www.toyoflex.com
Automobile Equipment Mfr
N.A.I.C.S.: 336110
Kenji Miyata (Pres)

ASAHI INTELLIGENCE SERVICE CO.,LTD.
11F SAPIA Tower 1712 Marunouchi, Chiyoda-Ku, Tokyo, 100-0005, Japan
Tel.: (81) 352248281
Web Site: https://www.aiskk.co.jp
97990—(TKS)
Sales Range: Less than $1 Million
Information Technology Related Services
N.A.I.C.S.: 519290
Hiroshi Tanaka (Pres)

ASAHI KASEI CORPORATION
Hibiya Mitsui Tower 1-1-2 Yurakucho, Chiyoda-ku, Tokyo, 100-0006, Japan
Tel.: (81) 366993000   JP
Web Site: https://www.asahi-kasei.com
Year Founded: 1931
3407—(TKS)
Rev.: $18,408,043,580
Assets: $24,210,645,300
Liabilities: $11,991,234,050
Net Worth: $12,219,411,250
Earnings: $289,557,660
Emp.: 49,295
Fiscal Year-end: 03/31/24
Chemical Products Mfr
N.A.I.C.S.: 551112
Hideki Kobori (Pres & Exec Officer)

Subsidiaries:

Asahi Chemical (H.K.) Ltd.   (1)
Prudential Tower The Gtwy, Tsim Sha Tsui, Kowloon, China (Hong Kong)   (100%)
Tel.: (852) 25227875
Web Site: http://www.asahi-kasei.co.jp
Sales Range: $25-49.9 Million
Emp.: 30
Mfr & Marketer of Chemicals, Plastics, Fibers & Textiles, Housing & Construction Materials & Special Products & Services
N.A.I.C.S.: 325211

Asahi Glass Fine Techno Korea Co., Ltd.   (1)
5 Block Gumi 4th National Industrial Complex Sandong-Myeon, Bonsan-Ri, Gumi, Kyung-Buk, Korea (South)
Tel.: (82) 57874000
Web Site: http://www.afk.co.kr
Display Glass Mfr
N.A.I.C.S.: 327215

Asahi Kasei (China) Co., Ltd.   (1)
8/F One ICC Shanghai International Commerce Centre, No 999 Huai Hai Zhong Road, Shanghai, 200031, China
Tel.: (86) 2163916111
N.A.I.C.S.: 325998

Asahi Kasei Advance (Shanghai) Co., Ltd.   (1)
8/F One ICC Shanghai International Commerce Centre, No 999 Huai Hai Zhong Road, Shanghai, 200031, China
Tel.: (86) 2162955353

Textile Products Mfr
N.A.I.C.S.: 314999

Asahi Kasei Advance Corp. (1)
6th-8th 11th Floors Sumitomo Fudosan
Onarimon-ekimae Bldg 6-17-21, Shimbashi
Minato-ku, Tokyo, 105-0004, Japan
Tel.: (81) 354045030
Web Site: https://www.asahi-kasei.co.jp
Textile Products Mfr
N.A.I.C.S.: 314999

**Asahi Kasei Advance Thailand Co.,
Ltd.** (1)
62 Moo 11 Soi Wilalai Bangna-Trad
Bangchauluong, Bangplee, Samut Prakan,
10540, Thailand
Tel.: (66) 23372840
Textile Products Mfr
N.A.I.C.S.: 314999

Asahi Kasei America, Inc. (1)
800 3rd Ave 30th Fl, New York, NY
10022-4212 **(100%)**
Tel.: (212) 371-9900
Web Site: https://www.ak-america.com
Sales Range: $50-74.9 Million
Mfr & Research of Chemicals
N.A.I.C.S.: 424690

Asahi Kasei Amidas Co., Ltd. (1)
3-22 Kanda Nishikicho, Chiyoda-ku, Tokyo,
101-8480, Japan
Tel.: (81) 367771100
Web Site: http://www.amidas.co.jp
Emp.: 671
Human Resource Consulting Services
N.A.I.C.S.: 541612

**Asahi Kasei Bioprocess Europe
SA/NV** (1)
Silver Building Boulevard Auguste Reyers
70, Schaerbeek, 1030, Brussels, Belgium
Tel.: (32) 25260500
Sales Range: $50-74.9 Million
Emp.: 15
Bio Process Virus Removal Products Whslr
N.A.I.C.S.: 423450

Asahi Kasei Bioprocess, Inc. (1)
1855 Elmdale Ave, Glenview, IL 60026
Tel.: (847) 556-9700
Web Site: http://www.ak-bio.com
Sales Range: $25-49.9 Million
Emp.: 30
Laboratory Equipment Mfr
N.A.I.C.S.: 334516
Andrea Zuckert (Office Mgr)

**Asahi Kasei Business Management
(Shanghai) Co., Ltd.** (1)
8/F One ICC Shanghai International Com-
merce Centre No 999, Huai Hai Zhong
Road, Shanghai, 200031, China
Tel.: (86) 21 6391 6111
Business Management Consulting Services
N.A.I.C.S.: 541618

**Asahi Kasei Chemicals
Corporation** (1)
1-105 Kanda Jinbocho Chiyoda-ku, Tokyo,
101-8101, Japan **(100%)**
Tel.: (81) 332963200
Web Site: http://www.asahi-kasei.co.jp
Sales Range: $1-4.9 Billion
Emp.: 6,851
Organic & Inorganic Industrial Chemicals,
Synthetic Resins, Synthetic Rubber, Fertil-
izer, Coating Materials, Food Additives &
Plastic Film, Sheet & Foam Mfr
N.A.I.C.S.: 325180
Yuji Kobayashi (Pres)

Subsidiary (Domestic):

Asahi Kasei Finechem Co., Ltd. (2)
1-8-7 Fukumachi, Nishiyodogawa-ku,
Osaka, 555-0034, Japan
Tel.: (81) 664723156
Web Site: http://www.asahikasei-fc.jp
Sales Range: $50-74.9 Million
Emp.: 140
Chemical Products Mfr & Marketer
N.A.I.C.S.: 325998
Masaaki Nasu (Pres)

Subsidiary (Non-US):

Asahi Kasei Plastics Ltd. (2)
1 HarbourFront Place 16-03, Singapore,

098633, Singapore **(100%)**
Tel.: (65) 63243001
Web Site: https://www.asahi-kasei.com.sg
Sales Range: $25-49.9 Million
Mfr & Marketer of Chemicals, Plastics, Fi-
bers & Textiles, Housing & Construction
Materials & Special Products & Services
N.A.I.C.S.: 325211

Subsidiary (US):

**Asahi Kasei Plastics North America,
Inc.** (2)
900 E Van Riper Rd, Fowlerville, MI
48836 **(100%)**
Tel.: (517) 223-2000
Web Site: http://www.akplastics.com
Sales Range: $50-74.9 Million
Emp.: 180
Resin Mfr
N.A.I.C.S.: 325211
John W. Moyer (Chm & CEO)

Subsidiary (Non-US):

**Asahi Photoproducts Europe
n.v./s.a.** (2)
Paepsem Business Park Boulevard Pae-
psem 22, 1070, Brussels, Belgium **(100%)**
Tel.: (32) 25260530
Web Site: http://www.asahi-
photoproducts.com
Sales Range: $25-49.9 Million
Liquid & Solid Photopolymers & Printing
Plate Making Systems Mfr
N.A.I.C.S.: 325998

**Tongsuh Petrochemical Corp.,
Ltd.** (2)
One IFC 19F 10 Gukjegeumyung-ro,
Yeongdeungpo-gu, Seoul, 150-742, Korea
(South) **(100%)**
Tel.: (82) 232150700
Web Site: https://www.tspc.co.kr
Sales Range: $50-74.9 Million
Emp.: 191
Chemicals Mfr
N.A.I.C.S.: 325998
Jong Kyung Chae (Pres & CEO)

**Asahi Kasei Chemicals Korea Co.,
Ltd.** (1)
27 - 2 Youido-Dong, Yongdungpo-Gu,
Seoul, 150880, Korea (South)
Tel.: (82) 32782599
Web Site: http://www.asahi-kasei.co.jp
Chemical Product Whslr
N.A.I.C.S.: 424690

**Asahi Kasei Construction
Materials** (1)
1-105 Kanda Jinbocho, Chiyoda-ku, Tokyo,
101-8101, Japan **(100%)**
Tel.: (81) 332963500
Web Site: http://www.asahi-kasei.co.jp
Sales Range: $1-4.9 Billion
Construction Materials Mfr
N.A.I.C.S.: 326140
Masateru Sakai (Pres & Exec Officer)

Asahi Kasei E-materials Corp. (1)
Jinbocho-Mitsui Building 1-105 Kanda Jin-
bocho, Chiyoda-ku, Tokyo, 101-8101, Japan
Tel.: (81) 3 3296 3235
Web Site: http://www.asahi-kasei.co.jp
Electric Device Mfr
N.A.I.C.S.: 334419

Asahi Kasei EMD Corporation (1)
Hibiya Mitsui Tower 1-1-2 Yurakucho,
Chiyoda-ku, Tokyo, 100-0006,
Japan **(100%)**
Tel.: (81) 366993943
Web Site: http://www.akm.com
Sales Range: $900-999.9 Million
Electronics Materials & Products Mfr
N.A.I.C.S.: 334419

Subsidiary (US):

AKM Semiconductor, Inc. (2)
226 Airport Pwy Ste 470, San Jose, CA
95110
Tel.: (408) 436-8580
Web Site: http://www.akm.com
Sales Range: $25-49.9 Million
Emp.: 50
Electronic Devices Sales
N.A.I.C.S.: 423690

Asahi Kasei Epoxy Co., Ltd. (1)
1-2 Yuraku-cho 1-chome, Chiyoda-ku, To-
kyo, Japan
Tel.: (81) 332963354
Epoxy Resin Chemical Mfr
N.A.I.C.S.: 325998

Asahi Kasei Europe GmbH (1)
Fringsstrasse 17, 40221, Dusseldorf, Ger-
many
Tel.: (49) 21133992000
Web Site: http://www.asahi-kasei.eu
Textile Products Mfr
N.A.I.C.S.: 314999

Asahi Kasei Fibers (H.K.) Ltd. (1)
Suite 508 South Tower World Finance Cen-
tre Harbour City 17 Canton Road, Tsim Sha
Tsui, Kowloon, China (Hong Kong)
Tel.: (852) 25227875
Textile Products Mfr
N.A.I.C.S.: 314999

Asahi Kasei Fibers Italy SRL (1)
Via E Cantoni 1, 21013, Gallarate, VA, Italy
Tel.: (39) 0331213716
Web Site:
http://www.asahikaseifibersitalia.com
Yarn Fiber Mfr
N.A.I.C.S.: 314999

**Asahi Kasei Geotechnologies Co.,
Ltd.** (1)
Nihonbashi Kakigaracho, Tokyo, 103-0014,
Japan
Tel.: (81) 356376711
Web Site: http://www.asahi-kasei.co.jp
Civil Engineering Construction Material
Whslr
N.A.I.C.S.: 423390

**Asahi Kasei Home Products
Corp.** (1)
1-1-2 Yurakucho Hibiya Mitsui Tower,
Chiyoda-ku, Tokyo, 100-0006, Japan
Tel.: (81) 366993430
Web Site: https://www.asahi-kasei.co.jp
Household Product Distr
N.A.I.C.S.: 423220

Asahi Kasei Homes Corp. (1)
1-105 Kanda Jinbocho, Chiyoda-ku, Tokyo,
101-8101, Japan
Tel.: (81) 368993000
Web Site: http://www.asahi-kasei.co.jp
Real Estate Manangement Services
N.A.I.C.S.: 531390
Takuya Magara (Exec Officer)

Subsidiary (Domestic):

Chuo Build Industry Co., Ltd. (2)
6F Sunrise Bldg 11-12 Tomizawa-cho Ni-
hombashi, Chuo-ku, Tokyo, 103-0006, Ja-
pan
Tel.: (81) 336619631
Web Site: http://www.chuo-build.co.jp
Sales Range: $75-99.9 Million
Construction Equipment Distr
N.A.I.C.S.: 423810
Yukata Shono (Dir-Equipment Sls Div)

Subsidiary (US):

Erickson Framing AZ LLC (2)
250 N Beck Ave, Chandler, AZ 85226
Tel.: (480) 627-1100
Web Site:
http://www.ericksoncompanies.com
Construction Services
N.A.I.C.S.: 423390
Jeff Carlstrom (Mgr-Ops)

ODC Construction, LLC (2)
1911 Traylor Blvd, Orlando, FL 32804
Tel.: (407) 447-5999
Web Site: http://www.odcbuilds.com
Sales Range: $25-49.9 Million
Emp.: 20
New Single-Family Housing Construction
N.A.I.C.S.: 236115
Isaac Lidsky (CEO & Partner)

Asahi Kasei India Pvt. Ltd. (1)
The Capital 1502-B Plot No C-70 G-Block
Bandra Kurla Complex, Bandra East, Mum-
bai, 400051, India
Tel.: (91) 2267103962
Web Site: http://www.asahi-kasei.in
Textile Products Mfr

N.A.I.C.S.: 314999

**Asahi Kasei Medical (Hangzhou) Co.,
Ltd.** (1)
No 10 No 19 Street, Hangzhou Economic
and Technological Development Zone,
Hangzhou, 310018, Zhejiang, China
Tel.: (86) 57186737228
Web Site: https://amc.net.cn
Medical & Surgical Equipment Distr
N.A.I.C.S.: 423450

Asahi Kasei Medical Co., Ltd. (1)
1-1-2 Yurakucho, Chiyoda-ku, Tokyo, 100-
0006, Japan **(100%)**
Tel.: (81) 366993750
Web Site: https://www.asahi-kasei.co.jp
Sales Range: $100-124.9 Million
Emp.: 3,000
Leukocyte Reduction Filters & Virus Re-
moval Filters Mfr
N.A.I.C.S.: 339112
Yutaka Shibata (Pres)

**Asahi Kasei Medical Europe
GmbH** (1)
Herriotstrasse 1, 60528, Frankfurt am Main,
Germany
Tel.: (49) 6966371500
Sales Range: $25-49.9 Million
Emp.: 20
Medical Device Whslr
N.A.I.C.S.: 423450

**Asahi Kasei Medical Europe
GmbH** (1)
Via Torino 151/C, Mestre, 30172, Venice,
Italy
Tel.: (39) 0415319686
Medical Device Distr
N.A.I.C.S.: 423450

**Asahi Kasei Medical Trading (Korea)
Co., Ltd.** (1)
7F Sanhakfund Building 329, Gangnam-
daero Seocho-gu, Seoul, 6627, Korea
(South)
Tel.: (82) 25857661
Web Site: http://www.asahi-kasei.co.jp
Medical Device Whslr
N.A.I.C.S.: 423450

**Asahi Kasei Microdevices (Shanghai)
Co., Ltd.** (1)
Room103 BLK6 REEB1987 center No 91
Yimei Road, Minhang, Shanghai, 200031,
China
Tel.: (86) 2163915500
Semiconductor Devices Mfr
N.A.I.C.S.: 334413

Asahi Kasei Microdevices Corp. (1)
Hibiya Mitsui Tower 1-1-2 Yurakucho,
Chiyoda-ku, Tokyo, 100-0006, Japan
Tel.: (81) 366993943
Web Site: https://www.akm.com
Electric Equipment Mfr
N.A.I.C.S.: 334419
Eiji Honda (Pres, CEO & Exec Officer)

**Asahi Kasei Microdevices Europe
GmbH** (1)
Am Seestern 4, 40547, Dusseldorf, Ger-
many
Tel.: (49) 2112806610
Semiconductor Devices Mfr
N.A.I.C.S.: 334413

**Asahi Kasei Microdevices Europe
SAS** (1)
Bureaux de la Colline Batime 1 Rue
Royale, 92210, Saint-Cloud, Hauts De
Seine, France
Tel.: (33) 141128040
Sales Range: $50-74.9 Million
Emp.: 8
Electronic Components Distr
N.A.I.C.S.: 423690

**Asahi Kasei Microdevices Korea
Corp.** (1)
19F One IFC 10 Gookjegeumyoong-Ro
Yeouido-Dong, Yeongdeungpo-Gu, Seoul,
07326, Korea (South)
Tel.: (82) 237750990
Electronic Components Distr
N.A.I.C.S.: 423690

**Asahi Kasei Microdevices Taiwan
Corp.** (1)

Asahi Kasei Corporation—(Continued)

Rm B 3F No 39 Sec 2 Dunhua S Rd, Da an
Dist, Taipei, 10681, Taiwan
Tel.: (886) 227062558
Semiconductor Devices Mfr
N.A.I.C.S.: 334413

**Asahi Kasei Microsystems Co.,
Ltd.** (1)
1-24-1 Nishi-shinjuku, Shinjuku, 160-8345,
Japan
Tel.: (81) 366993933
Information Technology Consulting Services
N.A.I.C.S.: 541512

**Asahi Kasei Microza (Hangzhou) Co.,
Ltd.** (1)
No 435 Avenue 23 Hangzhou Economic &
Technological Development Zone,
Hangzhou, 310018, China
Web Site: http://www.asahi-kasei.co.jp
Industrial Filtration Membranes & System
Mfr
N.A.I.C.S.: 333248

**Asahi Kasei Mortgage
Corporation** (1)
2-3-1 Nishi Shinjuku Shinjuku Monoris 17f,
Shinjuku-ku, Tokyo, 160-0023,
Japan (100%)
Tel.: (81) 333447052
Web Site: http://www.asahi-kasei.co.jp
Mortgage Business Management Services
N.A.I.C.S.: 522299
Naoji Ogura (Pres)

Asahi Kasei Pharma (1)
1-1-2 Yurakucho, Chiyoda-ku, Tokyo, 100-
0006, Japan (100%)
Tel.: (81) 366993600
Web Site: https://www.asahikasei-
pharma.co.jp
Sales Range: $1-4.9 Billion
Pharmaceuticals, Pharmaceutical Intermedi-
ates, Diagnostic Reagents, Nutritional Prod-
ucts & Animal Health Products
N.A.I.C.S.: 325412
Yoshikazu Aoki (Pres & Exec Officer)

**Asahi Kasei Pharma (Beijing) Co.,
Ltd.** (1)
Suite 2009 2010 Gemdale Plaza 91 Jian-
guo Road, Chaoyang District, Beijing,
100022, China
Tel.: (86) 1065693939
Pharmaceuticals Product Mfr
N.A.I.C.S.: 325412

**Asahi Kasei Plastics (Guangzhou)
Co., Ltd.** (1)
Room 3702 Floor 37 TaiKoo Hui Office
Building 1 No 385 Tianhe Road, Tianhe Dis-
trict, Guangzhou, 510620, China
Tel.: (86) 2085271616
Plastics Product Mfr
N.A.I.C.S.: 326199

**Asahi Kasei Plastics (Hong Kong)
Co., Ltd.** (1)
Room 2604 26th Floor Miramar Building
132 Nathan Road, Tsim Tsa Tsui, Kowloon,
China (Hong Kong)
Tel.: (852) 21514000
Web Site: https://www.apsh.com.cn
Plastic Resin Whslr
N.A.I.C.S.: 424610
Hatae Masahiro (Gen Mgr)

**Asahi Kasei Plastics Singapore Pte.
Ltd.** (1)
20 Sakra Road Jurong Island, Singapore,
627889, Singapore
Tel.: (65) 63161777
Web Site: https://www.asahi-kasei.com.sg
Sales Range: $50-74.9 Million
Plastic Resin Whslr
N.A.I.C.S.: 424610
Kawashima Hiroshi (Mng Dir)

**Asahi Kasei Plastics Vietnam Co.,
Ltd.** (1)
703-704 7th Floor Saigon Tower Building 29
D Le Duan Street, Quan 1, Ho Chi Minh
City, Vietnam
Tel.: (84) 2838220012
Web Site: https://www.asahi-kasei-
plastics.com
N.A.I.C.S.: 326199

Asahi Kasei Reform Co., Ltd. (1)
2-3-10 5th Floor, Shinjuku-ku, Tokyo,
1600022, Japan
Tel.: (81) 333566110
Home Maintenance & Remodeling Services
N.A.I.C.S.: 236118

**Asahi Kasei Spandex America,
Inc.** (1)
1566 Bushy Park Rd, Goose Creek, SC
29445-6336
Tel.: (843) 820-6513
Textile Machinery Mfr
N.A.I.C.S.: 333248

**Asahi Kasei Spandex Europe
GmbH** (1)
Chempark / Bldg E4, 41538, Dormagen,
Germany
Tel.: (49) 2133 4798 201
Web Site: http://www.dorlastan.com
Sales Range: $50-74.9 Million
Spandex Fiber Mfr
N.A.I.C.S.: 322219

**Asahi Kasei Synthetic Rubber Singa-
pore Pte. Ltd.** (1)
1 Angsana Drive, Jurong, 627586, Singapore
Tel.: (65) 69332555
Web Site: https://www.asahi-kasei.com.sg
N.A.I.C.S.: 325212

Asahi Kasei Technoplus Co., Ltd. (1)
Plastic & Fiber Products Mfr & Distr
N.A.I.C.S.: 326199

Asahi Kasei Technosystem Corp. (1)
Hibiya Mitsui Tower 24F 1-1-2 Yurakucho,
Chiyoda-ku, Tokyo, 100-0006, Japan
Tel.: (81) 366993927
Web Site: https://www.asahi-kasei.co.jp
Emp.: 138
Electronic Device Mfr & Distr
N.A.I.C.S.: 334419
Yasumi Takahashi (Pres)

Asahi Kasei Trading Co., Ltd. (1)
3-23 Nakanoshima 3-chome, Kita-ku,
Osaka, 530-8205, Japan
Tel.: (81) 676363600
Web Site: http://www.asahi-kasei.co.jp
Sales Range: $500-549.9 Million
Emp.: 132
Textile Fabric Distr
N.A.I.C.S.: 424310

Asahi Kasei Zoll Medical Corp. (1)
13th Floor Kowa Nishi-Shinbashi Building
2-1-1 Nishi-Shinbashi, Minato-ku, Tokyo,
105-0003, Japan
Tel.: (81) 362054920
Web Site: https://www.ak-zoll.com
N.A.I.C.S.: 423450
Takayuki Tanaka (Pres)

Asahi Kasei-Beijing (1)
Room 1407 New China Insurance Tower No
12, Jian Guo Men Wai Ave, Beijing,
100022, China (100%)
Tel.: (86) 1065693939
Sales Range: $25-49.9 Million
Emp.: 30
Mfr & Marketer of Chemicals, Plastics, Fi-
bers & Textiles, Housing & Construction
Materials & Special Products & Services
N.A.I.C.S.: 325211

Asahi Kasei-Shanghai (1)
Rm 1811 Shanghai International Trade Ctr,
2200 Yan An Rd W, Shanghai, 200335,
China (100%)
Tel.: (86) 2162780408
Web Site: http://www.asahi-kasei.co.jp
Sales Range: $25-49.9 Million
Emp.: 9
Mfr & Marketer of Chemicals, Plastics, Fi-
bers & Textiles, Housing & Construction
Materials & Special Products & Services
N.A.I.C.S.: 325211

Asahi Photoproducts (UK) Ltd. (1)
1 Prospect Way Hutton Industrial Estate,
Shenfield, CM13 1XA, United Kingdom
Tel.: (44) 1277232877
Web Site: http://www.asahi-
photoproducts.com
Sales Range: $50-74.9 Million
Emp.: 10
Specialty Chemicals Distr

N.A.I.C.S.: 424690

Asahi Research Center Co., Ltd. (1)
Hibiya Mitsui Tower 1-1-2 Yurakucho,
Chiyoda-ku, Tokyo, 100-0006, Japan
Tel.: (81) 366993095
Web Site: https://arc.asahi-kasei.co.jp
Sales Range: $25-49.9 Million
Emp.: 30
Biotechnology Research & Development
Services
N.A.I.C.S.: 541714

Asahi SKB Co., Ltd. (1)
2511-5 Kamiichihara, Kasama, 309-1731,
Ibaraki, Japan
Tel.: (81) 296721515
Web Site: http://www.asahiskb.com
Shotgun Cartridges Mfr
N.A.I.C.S.: 332992

**Asahi-Schwebel (Taiwan) Co.,
Ltd.** (1)
330 Min Tsu Rd Sec 6, Chung-li, 32050,
Taoyuan, Taiwan
Tel.: (886) 34901121
Textile Fabric Product Mfr
N.A.I.C.S.: 314999

**Asahikasei Plastics (America)
Inc.** (1)
900 E Van Riper Rd, Fowlerville, MI 48836
Tel.: (517) 223-2000
Web Site: http://www.akplastics.com
Emp.: 256
Plastics Materials & Resin Mfr
N.A.I.C.S.: 325211

**Asahikasei Plastics (Shanghai) Co.,
Ltd.** (1)
8/F One ICC Shanghai International Com-
merce Centre, No 999 Huai Hai Zhong
Road, Shanghai, 200031, China
Tel.: (86) 2163915252
Web Site: http://www.asahikasei.com.cn
Plastic Resin Whslr
N.A.I.C.S.: 424610

**Asahikasei Plastics (Thailand) Co.,
Ltd.** (1)
77 Moo 2 Hi-Tech Industrial Estate Banlain,
Bangpa-in, 13160, Thailand
Tel.: (66) 35350720
Web Site: http://www.asahi-kasei.co.th
Emp.: 230
Chemical Products Mfr
N.A.I.C.S.: 325998
Tetsuya Hoshino (Mng Dir)

Calliditas Therapeutics AB (1)
D5 Kungsbron 1, SE-111 22, Stockholm,
Sweden (98.38%)
Tel.: (46) 84113005
Web Site: https://www.calliditas.se
Rev.: $98,015,468
Assets: $238,418,944
Liabilities: $144,873,435
Net Worth: $93,545,509
Earnings: ($50,329,677)
Emp.: 178
Fiscal Year-end: 12/31/2022
Pharmaceuticals Product Mfr
N.A.I.C.S.: 325412
Renee Aguiar-Lucander (CEO)

Subsidiary (Non-US):

Genkyotex S.A. (2)
218 avenue Marie Curie Forum 2 Archparc,
Saint-Julien- en-Genevois, 74160, Ar-
champs, France (100%)
Tel.: (33) 561287060
Web Site: http://www.genkyotex.com
Therapeutic Product Developer & Mfr
N.A.I.C.S.: 325412

Celgard, LLC (1)
13800 S Lakes Dr, Charlotte, NC
28273 (100%)
Tel.: (704) 588-5310
Web Site: http://www.celgard.com
Emp.: 250
Lithium Battery Separator Developer, Mfr,
Distr & Services
N.A.I.C.S.: 335910
Lie Shi (Pres)

Subsidiary (Non-US):

Celgard Korea, Ltd. (2)

806-3 Yangcheong-Ri, Ochang-Eup, Cheon-
gwon, 363-883, Chungbuk, Korea (South)
Tel.: (82) 432192940
Web Site: http://www.celgard.com
Storage Battery Distr & Services
N.A.I.C.S.: 335910

Polypore K.K. (2)
Hibiya Mitsui Tower 1-1-2 Yurakucho,
Chiyoda-ku, Tokyo, 100-0006, Japan
Tel.: (81) 368913750
Web Site: http://www.celgard.com
Storage Battery Mfr
N.A.I.C.S.: 335910

Crystal Is, Inc. (1)
70 Cohoes Ave, Green Island, NY 12183
Tel.: (518) 271-7375
Web Site: https://cisuvc.com
Sales Range: $1-9.9 Million
Emp.: 22
Semiconductor & Related Device Mfr
N.A.I.C.S.: 334413
Leo J. Schowalter (CTO)

**Dupont-Asahi Flash Spun Products
Co., Ltd.** (1)
Sanno Park Tower 2-11-1 Nagata-cho,
Chiyoda-ku, Tokyo, 100-6111, Japan
Tel.: (81) 355212600
Textile Products Mfr
N.A.I.C.S.: 314999

**Erickson Framing Operations
LLC** (1)
250 N Beck Ave, Chandler, AZ 85226
Tel.: (480) 627-1100
Web Site:
https://www.ericksoncompanies.com
N.A.I.C.S.: 326220
Larry Butts (Pres)

**Formosa Asahi Spandex Co.,
Ltd.** (1)
Rm 386 12F Tun Hwa N road, Taipei, Tai-
wan
Tel.: (886) 227122211
Web Site: http://www.formosa.com
Sales Range: $25-49.9 Million
Emp.: 12
Elastic Products Mfr; Owned 50% by For-
mosa Plastics Corporation & 50% by Asahi
Kasei Corporation
N.A.I.C.S.: 326199

**Hangzhou Asahikasei Spandex Co.,
Ltd.** (1)
M18-5-7 Hangzhou Economic & Technologi-
cal Development Zone, Hangzhou, 310018,
China
Tel.: (86) 57186721888
Textile Products Mfr
N.A.I.C.S.: 314999

**Hangzhou Asahikasei Textiles Co.,
Ltd.** (1)
M10-5-2 Hangzhou Economic Technological
Development Zone, Hangzhou, 310018,
Zhejiang, China
Tel.: (86) 57186912193
Broadwoven Fabric Products Mfr
N.A.I.C.S.: 313210

Japan Elastomer Co., Ltd. (1)
1-105 Kandajimbocho Mitsui Bldg, Chiyoda-
Ku, Tokyo, 101-0051, Japan
Tel.: (81) 332963250
Synthetic Rubber Mfr
N.A.I.C.S.: 325212

Jcam Agri Co., Ltd. (1)
6-6 Kandasudacho 2-Chome, Chiyoda-ku,
Tokyo, 101-0041, Japan
Tel.: (81) 352978900
Web Site: https://www.jcam-agri.co.jp
N.A.I.C.S.: 325314

PS Japan Corp. (1)
18F Sumitomo Fudosan Korakuen Bldg
1-4-1 Koishikawa, Bunkyo-ku, Tokyo, 112-
0002, Japan
Tel.: (81) 356896543
Web Site: http://www.psjp.com
Polystyrene Mfr & Distr
N.A.I.C.S.: 326140
Takeshi Uchida (Mng Dir)

PTT Asahi Chemical Co., Ltd. (1)
8 Phangmuang Chapoh 3-1 Road, Huaypong Sub-district Muang District, Rayong,

21150, Thailand
Tel.: (66) 38974800
Web Site: https://www.pttac.com
Petrochemical Products Mfr
N.A.I.C.S.: 324110

Pllypore K.K. **(1)**
B-506 10 Baekseokgongdan 1-Ro, Seobuk-gu, Cheonan, 31094, Chungcheongnam-do, Korea (South)
Tel.: (82) 419056000
N.A.I.C.S.: 561990

Polypore (Shanghai) Membrane Products Co., Ltd. **(1)**
L1 3rd Floor No 207 Tai Gu Road
WaiGaoQiao Free Trade Zone, Shanghai, 200131, China
Tel.: (86) 2158666200
N.A.I.C.S.: 335910

Polypore International, LP **(1)**
11430 N Community House Rd Ste 350, Charlotte, NC 28277-1591
Tel.: (704) 587-8409
Web Site: https://polypore.com
Sales Range: $650-699.9 Million
Holding Company; Plastic Electronics Components Mfr
N.A.I.C.S.: 551112
Detlef Dohmen *(CIO)*

Subsidiary (Domestic):

Daramic, LLC **(2)**
11430 N Community House Rd Ste 350, Charlotte, NC 28277
Tel.: (704) 587-8599
Web Site: https://www.daramic.com
Automotive & Specialty Battery Separator Mfr
N.A.I.C.S.: 335910

Subsidiary (Non-US):

Daramic Holding S.A.S. **(3)**
25 Rue de Westrich, BP 90149, 67603, Selestat, Cedex, France
Tel.: (33) 388824108
N.A.I.C.S.: 561990

Daramic S.A.S. **(3)**
25 Rue De Westrich, 67603, Selestat, France
Tel.: (33) 388824000
Specialty & Automotive Battery Separator Mfr
N.A.I.C.S.: 335910
Jean-Francois Gsell *(Dir-Fin)*

Daramic Separadores de Baterias Ltda. **(3)**
Avenida das Nacoes Unidas N 18801 Sala 107, Condominio NovAmerica Office Park Jardim Dom Bosco, Sao Paulo, 04757-025, SP, Brazil
Tel.: (55) 1138198794
N.A.I.C.S.: 335910

Daramic Tianjin PE Separator Co., Ltd. **(3)**
No 11 Sijing Road, Tianjin, 300300, China
Tel.: (86) 75586608688
N.A.I.C.S.: 335910

Daramic Xiangyang Battery Separator Co., Ltd. **(3)**
No 6 Shenzhen Road, Shenzhen Industrial Park, Xiangyang, 441000, Hubei, China
Tel.: (86) 7102869794
N.A.I.C.S.: 335910

Polyxylenol Singapore Pte. Ltd. **(1)**
20 Sakra Road, Singapore, 627889, Singapore
Tel.: (65) 63161777
Emp.: 110
Specialty Chemicals Mfr
N.A.I.C.S.: 325998
Kawashima Hiroshi *(Mng Dir)*

Sage Automotive Interiors, Inc. **(1)**
3 Research Dr Ste 300, Greenville, SC 29607
Tel.: (864) 987-7778
Web Site: https://www.sageautomotiveinteriors.com
Automotive Interior Fabric Product Mfr
N.A.I.C.S.: 336390
Dave Gable *(CFO)*

Subsidiary (Domestic):

Sage Automotive Interiors, Inc. - Abbeville Plant **(2)**
601 Brooks St, Abbeville, SC 29620
Tel.: (864) 459-2121
Automotive Interiors Mfr
N.A.I.C.S.: 336390

Sage Automotive Interiors, Inc. - Gayley Plant **(2)**
518 Pumpkintown Rd, Marietta, SC 29661
Tel.: (864) 250-6100
Sales Range: $50-74.9 Million
Emp.: 300
Motor Vehicle Parts Mfr
N.A.I.C.S.: 336390
Matthew Barre *(Plant Mgr)*

Sage Automotive Interiors, Inc. - Sharon Plant **(2)**
1395 Hwy 72 W, Abbeville, SC 29620
Tel.: (864) 302-8854
Sales Range: $25-49.9 Million
Emp.: 110
Automotive Fabric Interior Mfr
N.A.I.C.S.: 336390

Subsidiary (Non-US):

Sage Automotive Interiors, Ltd. **(2)**
Saisho Bldg 5/F 8-1-14 Nishigotanda, Shinagawa-ku, Tokyo, 141-0031, Japan
Tel.: (81) 354228640
Automotive Interior Product Mfr
N.A.I.C.S.: 336360

Sage Automotive Interiors, Ltd. **(2)**
Unit 1 Phoenix Park Blekewater Rd, Blackburn, BB1 5SJ, United Kingdom
Tel.: (44) 161 762 3686
Web Site: http://www.sageautomotiveinteriors.com
Emp.: 16
Automotive Interior Design Services
N.A.I.C.S.: 541410
Daniel Russian *(Gen Mgr)*

Sage Brasil Interiors Automotivos Industria e Comercio, Ltda. **(3)**
Rodovia Presidente Dutra KM 201, Aruja, Sao Paulo, 07400-000, Brazil
Tel.: (55) 11 4653 8161
Motor Vehicle Parts Mfr
N.A.I.C.S.: 336390

Sanyo Petrochemical Co., Ltd. **(1)**
Jimbochomitsui Bldg, Chiyoda-Ku, Tokyo, 101-0051, Japan
Tel.: (81) 332963221
Web Site: http://www.asahikasei.co.jp
Sales Range: $25-49.9 Million
Emp.: 10
Petrochemical Mfr
N.A.I.C.S.: 325110
Tetsuya Shibari *(Gen Mgr)*

Senseair AB **(1)**
Stationsgatan 12, Box 96, 824 08, Delsbo, Sweden
Tel.: (46) 653717770
Web Site: http://www.senseair.com
Air & Gas Sensing Mfr
N.A.I.C.S.: 333912

Sun Plastech Inc. **(1)**
1055 Parsippany Blvd Ste 405, Parsippany, NJ 07054
Tel.: (973) 257-1999
Web Site: http://www.asaclean.com
Emp.: 22
Asaclean Purging Compound Mfr & Distr
N.A.I.C.S.: 325211

Sun Trading Co., Ltd. **(1)**
4-10-1 Shiba Hanfa Bldg 7f, Minato-Ku, Tokyo, 108-0014, Japan
Tel.: (81) 3 5476 9941
Chemical Product Whslr
N.A.I.C.S.: 424690

Thai Asahi Kasei Spandex Co., Ltd. **(1)**
1788 Singha Complex Building 17th Floor Room No 1705-1706, New Petchaburi Road Bang Kapi Huai Khwang, Bangkok, 10310, Thailand
Tel.: (66) 2643285860
Web Site: http://www.taspandex.co.th
Spandex Bare Yarn Mfr & Distr

N.A.I.C.S.: 424310

Thai Asahi Kasei Spandex Co., Ltd. - Amphur Sriracha Factory **(2)**
919 moo 11 Tambol Nongkhaam, Amphur Sriracha, Chon Buri, Thailand
Tel.: (66) 38 483 005
Web Site: http://www.taspandex.co.th
Spandex Bare Yarn Mfr
N.A.I.C.S.: 313110

Tong Suh Petrochemical Corp., Ltd. **(1)**
One IFC B/D 19F 10 Gookjegeumyoong-Ro, Yeongdeungpo-Gu, Seoul, 150742, Korea (South)
Tel.: (82) 232150700
Web Site: http://www.tspc.co.kr
Sales Range: $750-799.9 Million
Emp.: 210
Chemical Products Mfr & Distr
N.A.I.C.S.: 325998
Jong Kyung Chae *(Pres & CEO)*

Veloxis Pharmaceuticals A/S **(1)**
Amerika Plads 37, 2100, Kabnhavn, Denmark
Tel.: (45) 70333300
Web Site: http://www.veloxis.com
Pharmaceutical Development Services
N.A.I.C.S.: 325412
Brett Fleshman *(VP-Strategy & Corp Dev)*

Veloxis Pharmaceuticals, Inc. **(1)**
1001 Winstead Dr Ste 310, Cary, NC 27513
Tel.: (919) 591-3090
Web Site: http://www.veloxis.com
Pharmaceuticals Product Mfr
N.A.I.C.S.: 325412
Masaya Etoh *(Chm)*

Zoll Medical Corporation **(1)**
269 Mill Rd, Chelmsford, MA 01824-4105
Tel.: (978) 421-9655
Web Site: http://www.zoll.com
Cardiac Resuscitation Devices Mfr
N.A.I.C.S.: 334510
Alex N. Moghadam *(Pres-Data Mgmt Products)*

Subsidiary (Domestic):

Bio-Detek, Inc. **(2)**
525 Narragansett Park Dr, Pawtucket, RI 02861-4323 **(100%)**
Tel.: (401) 729-1400
Web Site: http://www.bio-detek.com
Sales Range: $100-124.9 Million
Emp.: 160
Medical Equipment
N.A.I.C.S.: 339112

Cardiac Science Corporation **(2)**
N7 W22025 Johnson Dr Ste 100, Waukesha, WI 53186
Tel.: (262) 953-3500
Web Site: http://www.cardiacscience.com
Diagnostic & Therapeutic Cardiological Products Developer, Mfr & Marketer
N.A.I.C.S.: 334510

Subsidiary (Non-US):

Cardiac Science Holdings UK Ltd. **(3)**
Unit 2 Rugby Park Heaton Mersey Industrial Estate Battersea Road, Stockport, SK4 3EB, Cheshire, United Kingdom
Tel.: (44) 1619260000
Web Site: http://www.cardiacscience.co.uk
Diagnostic & Therapeutic Cardiological Products Developer, Mfr & Marketer
N.A.I.C.S.: 339112
Shawn Ingram *(Mng Dir)*

Cardiac Science International A/S **(3)**
Willemoesgade 8 kld th, 2100, Copenhagen, Denmark
Tel.: (45) 44380500
Web Site: http://www.cardiacscience.com
Emp.: 4
Diagnostic & Therapeutic Cardiological Products Developer, Mfr & Marketer
N.A.I.C.S.: 339112
Carsten Roth *(Mng Dir)*

Subsidiary (Domestic):

Golden Hour Data Systems, Inc. **(2)**

10052 Mesa Rdg Ct Ste 200, San Diego, CA 92121
Tel.: (858) 768-2500
Web Site: http://www.goldenhour.com
Freight Transportation Arrangement
N.A.I.C.S.: 488510
Alex N. Moghadam *(Pres)*

Subsidiary (Non-US):

Itamar Medical Ltd. **(2)**
9 Halamish Street, Caesarea, 3079883, Israel
Tel.: (972) 46177000
Web Site: http://www.itamar-medical.com
Rev.: $41,034,000
Assets: $64,140,000
Liabilities: $21,068,000
Net Worth: $43,072,000
Earnings: ($10,939,000)
Emp.: 257
Fiscal Year-end: 12/31/2020
Medical Device Mfr & Distr
N.A.I.C.S.: 334510
Giora Yaron *(Co-Founder & Chm)*

Subsidiary (Non-US):

I.M.E. 2016 B.V **(3)**
Taconiskade 430, 1087 HW, Amsterdam, Netherlands
Tel.: (31) 203690583
Clinical Services
N.A.I.C.S.: 621610

Subsidiary (US):

Itamar Medical, Inc. **(3)**
3290 Cumberland Club Dr Ste 100, Atlanta, GA 30339
Web Site: https://www.itamar-medical.com
Clinical Services
N.A.I.C.S.: 621610

Subsidiary (Domestic):

Respicardia, Inc. **(2)**
12400 Whitewater Dr Ste 150, Minnetonka, MN 55343
Tel.: (952) 540-4470
Web Site: http://www.cardiacconcepts.com
Miscellaneous Ambulatory Health Care Services
N.A.I.C.S.: 621999
Peter Sommerness *(CEO)*

TherOx, Inc. **(2)**
17500 Cartwright Rd Ste 100, Irvine, CA 92614
Tel.: (949) 757-1999
Web Site: http://www.therox.com
Medical Device Mfr & Research Services
N.A.I.C.S.: 339112
Kevin T. Larkin *(Pres & CEO)*

Zoll Data Systems **(2)**
11802 Ridge Pkwy Ste 400, Broomfield, CO 80021 **(100%)**
Tel.: (303) 801-0000
Web Site: https://www.zolldata.com
Sales Range: $50-74.9 Million
Emp.: 160
Cardiac Resuscitation Equipment
N.A.I.C.S.: 531210

Subsidiary (Non-US):

Zoll International Holding BV **(2)**
Einsteinweg 8A, 6662 PW, Elst, Netherlands **(100%)**
Tel.: (31) 481366410
Web Site: https://www.zoll.com
Sales Range: $1-9.9 Million
Emp.: 15
Medical Equipment
N.A.I.C.S.: 339112
Jurgen Kappers *(Mng Dir & Gen Mgr-Benelux)*

Zoll Medical Australia Pty. Ltd. **(2)**
14/39 Herbert St, Saint Leonards, 2065, NSW, Australia **(100%)**
Tel.: (61) 284248700
Web Site: https://www.zoll.com
Sales Range: $10-24.9 Million
Emp.: 21
Medical Equipment
N.A.I.C.S.: 339112

Zoll Medical Canada, Inc. **(2)**
405 Britannia Road East Units 17-19, Mis-

Asahi Kasei Corporation—(Continued)

sissauga, L4Z 3E6, ON, Canada **(100%)**
Tel.: (905) 629-5005
Web Site: http://www.zoll.com
Sales Range: $1-9.9 Million
Emp.: 6
Medical Equipment
N.A.I.C.S.: 339112
Richard A. Packer (CEO)

Zoll Medical Deutschland
(GmbH) **(2)**
Emil-Hoffmann Strasse 13, 50996, Cologne,
Germany **(100%)**
Tel.: (49) 223687870
Web Site: http://www.zoll.com
Sales Range: $10-24.9 Million
Emp.: 20
Medical Equipment
N.A.I.C.S.: 339112
Alexander Aigner (Mng Dir)

Zoll Medical France S.A. **(2)**
2 rue Rene Caudron PA le Val St Quentin
Bat D, 78960, Voisins-le-Bretonneux,
France **(100%)**
Tel.: (33) 130577040
Sales Range: $1-9.9 Million
Emp.: 9
Medical Equipment
N.A.I.C.S.: 339112

Zoll Medical New Zealand Pty.
Ltd. **(2)**
Unit G 65 Brisbane Street, Sydenham,
Christchurch, 8023, New Zealand **(100%)**
Tel.: (64) 33415016
Web Site: http://www.zoll.com
Sales Range: $1-9.9 Million
Emp.: 2
Medical Equipment
N.A.I.C.S.: 339112
Scott Rogers (Mng Dir)

Zoll Medical U.K. Ltd. **(2)**
9 Seymour Court Tudor Road Manor Park,
Tunor Road Manor Park, Runcom, WA7
1SY, Cheshire, United Kingdom **(100%)**
Tel.: (44) 1928241700
Web Site: https://www.zoll.com
Sales Range: $10-24.9 Million
Emp.: 25
Medical Equipment
N.A.I.C.S.: 339112
Richard Knell-Millre (Gen Mgr)

Zoll Medical Italia Srl **(1)**
Via Francesco Corselli 11, 29122,
Piacenza, Italy
Tel.: (39) 05231901052
Web Site: https://www.zoll.com
Semiconductor Devices Mfr
N.A.I.C.S.: 334413

ASAHI KOGYOSHA CO., LTD.
1-25-7 Hamamatsu-cho, Minato-ku,
Tokyo, 105-8543, Japan
Tel.: (81) 364528181
Web Site:
   https://www.asahikogyosha.co.jp
Year Founded: 1925
1975—(TKS)
Rev.: $605,978,360
Assets: $555,319,320
Liabilities: $299,142,160
Net Worth: $256,177,160
Earnings: $24,536,320
Emp.: 987
Fiscal Year-end: 03/31/24
Air Conditioning System Installation
Services
N.A.I.C.S.: 238220
Yasutomo Takasu (Pres)

Subsidiaries:

Asahi Engineering (Malaysia) Sdn.
Bhd. **(1)**
E-28-01 Menara Suezcap 2 KL Gateway No
2 Jalan Kerinchi, Gerbang Kerinchi Lestari,
59200, Kuala Lumpur, Malaysia
Tel.: (60) 37 932 3722
Web Site: https://asahiengineering.com.my
Air Conditioning Installation Services
N.A.I.C.S.: 238220

Asahi Kogyosha Co., Ltd. - Equip-
ment Division **(1)**
616-8 Toyotomi-cho, Funabashi, 274-0053,
Chiba-ken, Japan
Tel.: (81) 474076101
Air Conditioning Equipment Mfr
N.A.I.C.S.: 333415

ASAHI NET, INC.
21st floor Kabukiza Tower 4-12-15
Ginza, Chuo-ku, Tokyo, 104-0061,
Japan
Tel.: (81) 335413892   JP
Web Site: https://www.asahi-net.co.jp
Year Founded: 1990
3834—(TKS)
Sales Range: $75-99.9 Million
Emp.: 126
Internet Connection Services
N.A.I.C.S.: 513199
Jiro Hijikata (Pres)

ASAHI PRINTING CO., LTD.
Ichibammachi Square Bldg 1-1
Ichiban-machi, Toyama, 930-0061,
Toyama-ken, Japan
Tel.: (81) 764211177
Web Site: https://www.asahi-pp.co.jp
Year Founded: 1946
3951—(TKS)
Rev.: $276,767,310
Assets: $454,093,780
Liabilities: $228,223,470
Net Worth: $225,870,310
Earnings: $10,754,470
Emp.: 1,149
Fiscal Year-end: 03/31/24
Printed Packaging Material Mfr &
Distr
N.A.I.C.S.: 326112
Jugo Asahi (Chm)

Subsidiaries:

Asahi Jinzai Service Co., Ltd. **(1)**
1F Ages Building 3-9, Otemachi, Toyama,
930-0084, Japan
Tel.: (81) 764215515
Web Site: https://www.asahi-js.jp
Employment Placement Services
N.A.I.C.S.: 561311

Asahi Printing Business Support Co.,
Ltd. **(1)**
492-2 Itakura, Fuchu, Toyama, 939-2721,
Japan
Tel.: (81) 764615377
Web Site: https://www.asahi-abs.co.jp
Emp.: 29
Printing Business Support Services
N.A.I.C.S.: 561499

Kyowa Carton Co., Ltd. **(1)**
277-5 Mizuhashi Kaihatsu, Toyama, 939-
3542, Japan
Tel.: (81) 764791188
Web Site: https://www.kyowa-carton.co.jp
Emp.: 126
Packaging Materials Mfr
N.A.I.C.S.: 326199

Sakamoto Printing Co., Ltd. **(1)**
6-3-11 Nakatsu, Kita-ku, Osaka, 531-0071,
Japan
Tel.: (81) 664576767
Web Site: http://www.sakamoto.co.jp
Packaging Materials Mfr
N.A.I.C.S.: 326199

Shin-Nippon Industries Sdn.
Bhd. **(1)**
No 4 Jalan Tahana, Tampoi Industrial Es-
tate, 80350, Johor, Darul Takzim, Malaysia
Tel.: (60) 72361263
Web Site: https://www.shin-nippon.com.my
Paperboard & Plastic Material Mfr
N.A.I.C.S.: 322219

ASAHI SEIREN CO., LTD.
9-37 Ota, Yao, 581 0037, Japan
Tel.: (81) 72 953 2212   JP
Web Site:
   http://www.asahiseiren.com

Year Founded: 1935
Aluminum Alloy Mfr
N.A.I.C.S.: 331313
Keizo Taniyama (Chm)

Subsidiaries:

Summit Showa Aluminum Ltd. **(1)**
1-11-16 Nishinakajima, Yodogawa-Ku,
Osaka, 532 0011, Japan
Tel.: (81) 668853310
Aluminum Die-Castings Mfr
N.A.I.C.S.: 331523

ASAHI SONGWON COLORS LTD.
Asahi House 20 Times Corporate
Park, Thaltej-Shilaj road Thaltej,
Ahmedabad, 380059, India
Tel.: (91) 7968325000
Web Site:
   https://www.asahisongwon.com
532853—(BOM)
Rev.: $69,671,061
Assets: $74,625,000
Liabilities: $39,127,943
Net Worth: $35,497,057
Earnings: ($2,520,991)
Emp.: 139
Fiscal Year-end: 03/31/23
Color Pigments Mfr
N.A.I.C.S.: 325130
Paru M. Jaykrishna (Founder, Chm &
Co-Mng Dir)

Subsidiaries:

Asahi Tennants Color Private
Limited **(1)**
Dahej 2, Village Vadadla, Gujarat, 392130,
India
Tel.: (91) 9925246370
Web Site:
   http://asahitennantscolorprivatelimited.site
Chemical Products Mfr
N.A.I.C.S.: 325199

ASAHI YUKIZAI CORPORA-TION
21st Floor Ueno Frontier Tower
3-24-6 Ueno, Taito-ku, Tokyo, 110-
0005, Japan
Tel.: (81) 358268829
Web Site: https://www.asahi-
   yukizai.co.jp
Year Founded: 1945
4216—(TKS)
Rev.: $577,885,860
Assets: $670,062,310
Liabilities: $196,303,780
Net Worth: $473,758,530
Earnings: $75,235,020
Emp.: 1,652
Fiscal Year-end: 03/31/24
Industrial Resins & Plastic Piping Ma-
terials Mfr
N.A.I.C.S.: 325211
Kazuya Nakano (Pres & Exec Officer-
Bus Gen)

Subsidiaries:

AOC Techno Co., Ltd. **(1)**
15-9-2 Uchikanda Furukawa Chiyoda Bldg
3rd Floor, Chiyoda-Ku, Tokyo,
Japan **(100%)**
Tel.: (81) 332562451
Web Site: http://www.aoc-techno.co.jp
Industrial Supplies Whslr
N.A.I.C.S.: 423840

ASAHI AV VALVE (SHANGHAI) CO.,
LTD. **(1)**
No 18 Shanghai Malu Fengdeng Industry
City 615 Fengdeng Road, Malu Town Jiad-
ing District, Shanghai, 201818, China
Tel.: (86) 2161392600
Industrial Valve Mfr
N.A.I.C.S.: 332911

Asahi AV Trading Co ,Ltd **(1)**
No 2-12 Kandatsukasamachi 2-Chome

Chiyoda-Ku, Chiyoda-Ku, Tokyo, 101-0048,
Japan **(36%)**
Tel.: (81) 332547958
Web Site: http://www.asahi-avt.com
Sales Range: $50-74.9 Million
Emp.: 30
Industrial Machinery & Equipment Whslr
N.A.I.C.S.: 423830
Nobuhiro Suzuki (Gen Mgr)

Asahi Asia Pacific Pte. Ltd. **(1)**
209 Woodlands Avenue 9 05-57/58 Wood-
lands Spectrum II, Singapore, 738959, Sin-
gapore
Tel.: (65) 6 755 8033
Web Site: https://asahi-asiapac.com.sg
Plastic Material Distr
N.A.I.C.S.: 424610
Go Nakagawara (Mng Dir)

Asahi Av Europe GmbH **(1)**
Westendstrasse 16-22, 60325, Frankfurt am
Main, Germany
Tel.: (49) 697 137 3030
Web Site: https://www.asahiav-europe.com
Plastic Valve Product Mfr
N.A.I.C.S.: 326122

Asahi Modi Materials Pvt., Ltd. **(1)**
Plot No 913, Jhagadia GIDC District,
Bharuch, 393110, Gujarat, India
Tel.: (91) 991 010 7325
Web Site: https://ammpl.in
Resin-Coated Sand Product Mfr & Distr
N.A.I.C.S.: 327999
Alok Modi (Chm)

Asahi Organic Chemicals (Nantong)
Co., Ltd. **(1)**
No 21 Tong Wang Road Nantong ETDZ,
Nantong, 226017, Jiangsu, China
Tel.: (86) 51383592400
Web Site: http://www.asahi-yukizai.co.jp
Phenolic Resins Mfr
N.A.I.C.S.: 325211

Asahi Organic Chemicals Industry
Co., Ltd. - Aichi Plant **(1)**
1-4-16 Nishiki, Naka-ku, Nagoya, 460-0003,
Aichi, Japan
Tel.: (81) 522228533
Phenolic Resins Mfr
N.A.I.C.S.: 325211

Asahi Organic Chemicals Industry
Co., Ltd. - Hirosima Plant **(1)**
5088-61 Shinjomachi Oji, Shobara, 727-
0004, Hiroshima, Japan
Tel.: (81) 824728011
Phenolic Resins Mfr
N.A.I.C.S.: 325211

Asahi Organic Chemicals Trading
(Shanghai) Co., Ltd. **(1)**
2007-2008 2299 Yan An Road West,
Changning District, Shanghai, 200336,
China
Tel.: (86) 2162787862
Web Site: http://www.asahi-yukizai.co.jp
Sales Range: $50-74.9 Million
Emp.: 10
Organic Chemical Distr
N.A.I.C.S.: 424690

Asahi Yuki Hanbai Nishi-Nihon
K.K. **(1)**
2-11-29 Shiohama, Koto-Ku, Japan
Tel.: (81) 336998621
Sales Range: $25-49.9 Million
Emp.: 20
Chemical & Allied Products Merchant Whslr
N.A.I.C.S.: 424690

Asahi Yukizai Mexico S.A. De
C.V. **(1)**
Calle Carretera Panamericana Sur KM 114
354, 20393, Aguascalientes, Mexico
Tel.: (52) 449 129 3252
Web Site: https://asahi-yukizai.com.mx
Plastic Valve Product Mfr
N.A.I.C.S.: 326122
Kenta Akamine (Dir)

Asahi/America, Inc. **(1)**
655 Andover St, Lawrence, MA 01843
Tel.: (781) 321-5409
Web Site: https://www.asahi-america.com
Sales Range: $25-49.9 Million
Emp.: 100

Mfr & Distributor of Thermoplastic Valves, Actuation & Piping Systems & Flow Meter Devices
N.A.I.C.S.: 326122
Leo Lester *(Sr VP-Engrg & Ops)*

ASAHI-SEIKI MANUFACTUR-ING CO., LTD.

Asahimae-cho Owariasahi, Aichi, Nagoya, 488-8655, Japan
Tel.: (81) 561533119
Web Site: http://www.asahiseiki-mfg.co.jp
Year Founded: 1953
Sales Range: $100-124.9 Million
Emp.: 482
Precision Metal Components, Automatic Presses, Spring-Forming Machines, Automatic Assembly Machines, Machine Tools, Airplane Parts & Small Arms Ammunition Mfr
N.A.I.C.S.: 332999
Hiroshi Yamaguchi *(Pres)*

Subsidiaries:

Asahi-Seiki Manufacturing Co., Ltd Machinery Division **(1)**
Asahimae-cho, Owariasahi, Aichi, Japan
Tel.: (81) 561533119
Web Site: http://www.asahiseiki-mfg.co.jp
Sales Range: $100-124.9 Million
Emp.: 480
Spring & Metal Mfr
N.A.I.C.S.: 332613
Hiroshi Yamaguchi *(Pres)*

Asahi-Seiki Manufacturing Co., Ltd. Precision Engineering Division **(1)**
Asahimae cho, Owariasahi, 4888655, Aichi, Japan
Tel.: (81) 561533118
Web Site: http://www.asahiseiki-mfg.co.jp
Sales Range: $100-124.9 Million
Spring & Metal Mfr
N.A.I.C.S.: 332613
Hiroshi Yamaguchi *(Pres)*

ASAHIMATSU FOODS CO., LTD.

3-7-3 Tagawa, Yodogawa-Ku, Osaka, 532-0027, Japan
Tel.: (81) 663064121
Web Site: https://www.asahimatsu.co.jp
Year Founded: 1950
2911—(TKS)
Rev.: $53,527,780
Assets: $65,696,790
Liabilities: $13,001,870
Net Worth: $52,694,920
Earnings: $1,533,520
Emp.: 313
Fiscal Year-end: 03/31/24
Perishable Food Product Mfr & Whslr
N.A.I.C.S.: 311991
Hirotaka Kinoshita *(Pres)*

ASAHIOZU CORPORATION

3294-1 Kushitsumachi, Nobeoka, 889-0514, Miyazaki, Japan
Tel.: (81) 982372906
Year Founded: 1973
Nonwoven Product Mfr
N.A.I.C.S.: 313230

ASAHIPEN CORPORATION

4-1-12 Tsurumi, Tsurumi-Ku, Osaka, 538-8666, Japan
Tel.: (81) 69305001
Web Site: https://www.asahipen.jp
Year Founded: 1940
4623—(TKS)
Rev.: $113,070,660
Assets: $142,597,530
Liabilities: $52,014,090
Net Worth: $90,583,440
Earnings: $2,511,800
Emp.: 259
Fiscal Year-end: 03/31/24

Paint & Coating Mfr & Distr
N.A.I.C.S.: 325510

ASAKA INDUSTRIAL CO., LTD.

117 2-cho Kaisan-cho, Sakai-ku, Sakai, 590-0982, Osaka, Japan
Tel.: (81) 72 2295221
Web Site: http://www.asaka-ind.co.jp
Year Founded: 1931
5962—(TKS)
Sales Range: $50-74.9 Million
Emp.: 150
Hand Tool Mfr & Distr
N.A.I.C.S.: 332216
Shuichiro Koga *(Pres)*

ASAKA RIKEN CO., LTD.

47 Aza Maseguchi Kanaya Tamura-machi, Koriyama, 963-0725, Fukushima, Japan
Tel.: (81) 249444744
Web Site: https://www.asaka.co.jp
Year Founded: 1969
5724—(TKS)
Rev.: $55,450,320
Assets: $59,459,280
Liabilities: $27,102,240
Net Worth: $32,357,040
Earnings: $2,582,160
Emp.: 220
Fiscal Year-end: 09/30/24
Metal Products Collection, Recycling & Sales
N.A.I.C.S.: 423510
Keita Yamada *(Chm)*

Subsidiaries:

Asaka Kouun Co., Ltd. **(1)**
1-2 Aza Shinya Kanaya Tamura-machi, Koriyama, 963-0725, Fukushima, Japan
Tel.: (81) 24 944 9427
Nonferrous Metal Products Mfr
N.A.I.C.S.: 331491

Asaka Riken Co., Ltd. - Fukuyama Plant **(1)**
22-1 Aza Okabura Fukuhara Fukuyama-machi, Koriyama, 963-8061, Fukushima, Japan
Tel.: (81) 249447913
Precious Metal Product Mfr
N.A.I.C.S.: 331410

Asaka Riken Co., Ltd. - Iwaki Plant **(1)**
246-23 Aza Egoshi Kurosuno Izumi-machi, Iwaki, 971-8184, Fukushima, Japan
Tel.: (81) 24 684 6295
Web Site: http://www.asaka.co.jp
Precious Metal Product Mfr
N.A.I.C.S.: 331410

ASAKUMA CO., LTD.

1410 Ueda Nishi 2-chome, Tenpa-ku, Nagoya, 4680058, Japan
Tel.: (81) 528007781
Web Site: https://www.asakuma.co.jp
Year Founded: 1948
7678—(TKS)
Rev.: $43,256,090
Assets: $26,559,140
Liabilities: $8,819,960
Net Worth: $17,739,180
Earnings: $921,700
Fiscal Year-end: 01/31/24
Restaurant Operators
N.A.I.C.S.: 722511

ASAMA

., Ho Chi Minh City, Vietnam
Tel.: (84) 8 6818 3157
Web Site: http://www.asamafarm.com
Cryptocurrency Mining
N.A.I.C.S.: 523160

Subsidiaries:

Groovy Company, Inc. **(1)**
1000 Brickell Ave Ste 715, Miami, FL 33131
Tel.: (404) 734-3277
Web Site: www.sanp.us

Gold Exploration Company
N.A.I.C.S.: 212220

ASAMER BAUSTOFFE AG

Unterthalham Strasse 2, Ohlsdorf, 4694, Gmunden, Austria
Tel.: (43) 507991721
Web Site: http://www.abag.at
ASAM—(VIE)
Sales Range: Less than $1 Million
Concrete & Cement Mfr
N.A.I.C.S.: 327310

ASANTE GOLD CORPORATION

Suite 615-800 West Pender Street, Vancouver, V6C 2V6, BC, Canada
Tel.: (604) 558-1134
Web Site: https://www.asantegold.com
Year Founded: 2011
1A9—(DEU)
Rev.: $434,329,834
Assets: $691,413,577
Liabilities: $648,395,378
Net Worth: $43,018,198
Earnings: ($105,905,006)
Fiscal Year-end: 01/31/24
Gold Mining
N.A.I.C.S.: 212220
Douglas R. MacQuarrie *(Founder)*

ASANTE INCORPORATED

1-33-15 Shinjuku, Shinjuku-ku, Tokyo, 160-0022, Japan
Tel.: (81) 332265511
Web Site: https://www.asante.co.jp
Year Founded: 1970
6073—(TKS)
Rev.: $90,510,730
Assets: $106,592,860
Liabilities: $28,971,630
Net Worth: $77,621,230
Earnings: $3,576,010
Emp.: 998
Fiscal Year-end: 03/31/24
Construction, Home Improvement & Repair Services
N.A.I.C.S.: 236118
Makoto Munemasa *(Pres)*

ASANUMA CORPORATION

1-2-3 Minatomachi, Naniwa-ku, Osaka, 5560017, Japan
Tel.: (81) 665855500
Web Site: https://www.asanuma.co.jp
1852—(TKS)
Rev.: $1,009,188,360
Assets: $669,269,110
Liabilities: $347,329,060
Net Worth: $321,940,050
Earnings: $30,868,700
Emp.: 1,281
Fiscal Year-end: 03/31/24
Construction Services
N.A.I.C.S.: 236220
Sho Asanuma *(Exec Officer)*

Subsidiaries:

Asanuma Construction Ltd. **(1)**
230 C Harmon Industrial Park, Tamuning, GU 96921
Tel.: (671) 646-4243
Sales Range: $25-49.9 Million
Emp.: 18
Construction Engineering Services
N.A.I.C.S.: 541330

Asanuma Corporation - Precast Concrete Plant **(1)**
Shiraoka-cho, Minami-ku, Saitama, Japan
Tel.: (81) 480 92 1881
Web Site: http://www.asanuma.co.jp
Precast Concrete Products Mfr
N.A.I.C.S.: 327331

ASARFI HOSPITAL LIMITED

Baramuri Bishunpur Polytechnic, Dhanbad, 828130, Jharkhand, India
Tel.: (91) 9608833708
Web Site: https://www.asarfi.in
Year Founded: 2005
543943—(BOM)
Software Development Services
N.A.I.C.S.: 541511

ASARINA PHARMA AB

Karolinska Institutet Science Park Fogdevreten 2, 171 65, Solna, Sweden
Tel.: (46) 852484482
Web Site: https://www.asarinapharma.com
ASAP—(OMX)
Rev.: $16,777
Assets: $603,272
Liabilities: $439,574
Net Worth: $163,698
Earnings: ($1,273,453)
Emp.: 5
Fiscal Year-end: 12/31/23
Pharmaceuticals Product Mfr
N.A.I.C.S.: 325412
Paul De Potocki *(Chm)*

ASAS CAPITAL LTD

702 South Tower PO BOX 506806 Emirates Financial Towers, United Arab Emirates
Tel.: (971) 4346470
Web Site: https://asascapital.com
Year Founded: 2009
Private Equity
N.A.I.C.S.: 523940
Himanshu Khandelwal *(CEO)*

Subsidiaries:

Udacity, Inc. **(1)**
2465 Latham St 1st Fl, Mountain View, CA 94040
Tel.: (650) 938-9090
Web Site: http://in.udacity.com
Sales Range: $50-74.9 Million
Emp.: 400
Data Science Services
N.A.I.C.S.: 541513
Sebastian Thrun *(Founder, Chm & Pres)*

ASAS DUNIA BERHAD

Wisma Asas No 228 Lebuh Chulia, Pulau Penang, 10200, Malaysia
Tel.: (60) 42559999
Web Site: http://www.asasdunia.com.my
Year Founded: 1982
Sales Range: $25-49.9 Million
Building Construction & Property Investment Services
N.A.I.C.S.: 236118
Sook Fun Thum *(Co-Sec)*

Subsidiaries:

Asas Mutiara Sdn. Bhd. **(1)**
Wisma Asas No 228-B Chulia Street, Pulau Penang, 10200, Malaysia
Tel.: (60) 45881999
Web Site: http://www.asasdunia.com
Real Estate Property Development Services
N.A.I.C.S.: 531210

Fung Yik Sdn. Bhd. **(1)**
Wisma Asas 228B Lebuh Chulia, 10200, Pulau Penang, Malaysia
Tel.: (60) 42559999
Web Site: http://www.asasdunia.com
Sales Range: $25-49.9 Million
Emp.: 30
Real Estate Property Development Services
N.A.I.C.S.: 531210
Jerry Fook Sing Chan *(Mng Dir)*

ASAX CO., LTD.

1-3-14 Hiroo, Shibuya-ku, Tokyo, 150-0012, Japan
Tel.: (81) 120665555
Web Site: https://www.asax.co.jp

Asax Co., Ltd.—(Continued)

Year Founded: 1969
8772—(TKS)
Sales Range: $25-49.9 Million
Real Estate Loan Services
N.A.I.C.S.: 522292
Tsunefumi Kusama (Pres)

ASBI JOINT STOCK COMPANY

5th Khoroo, Bayangol District, Ulaan-
baatar, Mongolia
Tel.: (976) 11 687390
CND—(MONG)
Sales Range: Less than $1 Million
Building Construction Services
N.A.I.C.S.: 236220

ASBISC ENTERPRISES PLC

1 Iapetou Agios Athanasios, 4101,
Limassol, Cyprus
Tel.: (357) 25857097
Web Site: https://www.asbis.com
Year Founded: 1990
ASB—(WAR)
Rev.: $3,252,794
Assets: $1,012,221
Liabilities: $731,080
Net Worth: $281,140
Earnings: $56,270
Emp.: 2,673
Fiscal Year-end: 12/31/23
Computer Peripheral Equipment Distr
N.A.I.C.S.: 423430
Marios Christou (CFO)

Subsidiaries:

ASBIS CZ, spol. s r.o. **(1)**
Obchodni 103, Cestlice, Prague, Czech
Republic
Tel.: (420) 2 72 117 111
Web Site: http://www.asbis.cz
Computer Peripheral & Software Distr
N.A.I.C.S.: 423430
Peter Jandek (Gen Mgr)

ASBIS D.O.O. **(1)**
Cara Dusana 205a, Zemun, 11080, Bel-
grade, Serbia
Tel.: (381) 113107700
Web Site: http://www.asbis.rs
Sales Range: $25-49.9 Million
Computer Peripheral Equipments & Soft-
ware Distr
N.A.I.C.S.: 423430

ASBIS Europe BV **(1)**
Haarstraat 27, 4201 JA, Gorinchem, South
Holland, Netherlands
Tel.: (31) 183610190
Web Site: http://www.canyon-ch.com
Sales Range: $50-74.9 Million
Emp.: 10
Computer Peripheral & Software Distr
N.A.I.C.S.: 423430

ASBIS HUNGARY COMMERCIAL
LTD **(1)**
Vaci Boulevard 81-85, 1139, Budapest,
Hungary
Tel.: (36) 12361000
Web Site: http://www.asbis.hu
Sales Range: $25-49.9 Million
Emp.: 30
Computer Peripheral & Software Distr
N.A.I.C.S.: 423430
Andrez Velsko (Gen Mgr)

ASBIS Hellas Single Member
S.A. **(1)**
132 Eleftheriou Venizelou Ave, 14231, Nea
Ionia, Greece
Tel.: (30) 2102719100
Web Site: https://www.asbis.gr
Information Technology Products Distr
N.A.I.C.S.: 423430

ASBIS IT Solutions Hungary Kft. **(1)**
Reitter Ferenc utca 46-48, 1135, Budapest,
Hungary
Tel.: (36) 12361000
Web Site: https://www.asbis.hu
Computer Component Services
N.A.I.C.S.: 423690

ASBIS KYPROS LTD **(1)**

26 Spyrou Kyprianou Street, Germasogeia,
4040, Limassol, Cyprus
Tel.: (357) 25257350
Web Site: http://www.asbis.com.cy
Sales Range: $25-49.9 Million
Computer Peripheral Equipments & Soft-
ware Distr
N.A.I.C.S.: 423430

ASBIS Kazakhstan LLP **(1)**
st Tulkubasskaya house 2/4, Zhetysu dis-
trict, Almaty, 050018, Kazakhstan
Tel.: (7) 7273904606
Web Site: http://www.asbis.kz
Sales Range: $25-49.9 Million
Computer Peripheral Equipments & Soft-
ware Distr
N.A.I.C.S.: 423430

ASBIS LV SIA **(1)**
Bauskas iela 58 A, Riga, LV-1004, Latvia
Tel.: (371) 67892570
Web Site: http://www.asbis.lv
Sales Range: $25-49.9 Million
Computer Peripheral Equipments & Soft-
ware Distr
N.A.I.C.S.: 423420

ASBIS Ltd. **(1)**
Dmitrovskoe shosse 85 BC RTS, PO Box
18, 127238, Moscow, Russia
Tel.: (7) 4957750641
Web Site: http://www.asbis.ru
Computer Peripheral & Software Distr
N.A.I.C.S.: 423430

ASBIS ME FZE **(1)**
PO Box 17706, Jebel Ali South S10715,
Dubai, United Arab Emirates
Tel.: (971) 48863850
Web Site: http://www.asbisme.ae
Sales Range: $50-74.9 Million
Computer Peripheral Equipments & Soft-
ware Distr
N.A.I.C.S.: 423430

Subsidiary (Non-US):

ASBIS TR BILGISAYAR LIMITED
SIRKETI **(2)**
Barbaros Mah Evren Caddesi No 56 Kat 1,
Yenisahra, 34746, Istanbul, Turkiye
Tel.: (90) 2164707440
Web Site: http://www.asbis.com.tr
Sales Range: $25-49.9 Million
Emp.: 20
Computer Peripheral Equipments & Soft-
ware Distr
N.A.I.C.S.: 423430

ASBIS PL SP.Z O.O. **(1)**
Ul M Slowikowskiego 81c Ideal Idea City
Park - Budynek H4, 05-090, Raszyn, Po-
land
Tel.: (48) 501867434
Web Site: http://solutions.asbis.pl
Sales Range: $25-49.9 Million
Computer Peripheral & Software Distr
N.A.I.C.S.: 423430

ASBIS UKRAINE LTD. **(1)**
street Gazova 30, Kiev, 03061, Ukraine
Tel.: (380) 444554411
Web Site: http://www.asbis.ua
Sales Range: $25-49.9 Million
Computer Peripheral Equipments & Soft-
ware Distr
N.A.I.C.S.: 423430

ASBIS VILNIUS UAB **(1)**
Atelties g 25 B, 06326, Vilnius, Lithuania
Tel.: (370) 5 259 5610
Web Site: http://www.asbis.lt
Computer Peripheral Equipment & Software
Distr
N.A.I.C.S.: 423430

ASBIS-Baltik AS **(1)**
Turi 10c, 11313, Tallinn, Harju, Estonia
Tel.: (372) 6407130
Web Site: http://www.asbis.ee
Sales Range: $50-74.9 Million
Computer Peripheral Equipments & Soft-
ware Distr
N.A.I.C.S.: 423430

ASBISc-CR d.o.o. **(1)**
Slavonska avenija 24/6 -1 kat, 10000, Zagreb, Croatia

Tel.: (385) 16009900
Web Site: http://www.asbis.hr
Sales Range: $25-49.9 Million
Computer Peripheral & Software Distr
N.A.I.C.S.: 423430

Advanced Systems Company
LLC **(1)**
7764 Ishaq Ibn Abdul Rahman, AR Rabwah
District, Jeddah, 23416, Saudi Arabia
Tel.: (966) 122752821
Web Site: http://www.ascomed.com
Medical Equipment Mfr
N.A.I.C.S.: 339112

Asbis Baltics SIA **(1)**
Bauskas iela 58a, Riga, 1004, Latvia
Tel.: (371) 60003602
Web Site: https://www.asbis.lv
Computer Component Mfr
N.A.I.C.S.: 334419

Asbis Bulgaria Limited **(1)**
Europe Shopping Center Building N 3 7
Iskarsko Shosse Blvd, 1528, Sofia, Bulgaria
Tel.: (359) 24284112
Web Site: http://www.asbis.bg
Software Equipment Mfr & Distr
N.A.I.C.S.: 334111

Asbis Ca LLC **(1)**
St Kozitarnov 50 Business center 2nd Floor,
Yunusabad District, Tashkent, Uzbekistan
Tel.: (998) 971440197
Web Site: https://www.asbis.uz
Computer Equipment Supplier
N.A.I.C.S.: 423430

Asbis Cr d.o.o. **(1)**
Slavonska avenija 24/6 -1 kat, 10000, Za-
greb, Croatia
Tel.: (385) 16009900
Web Site: https://www.asbis.hr
Computer Component Services
N.A.I.C.S.: 423690

Asbis Middle East FZE **(1)**
Jebel Ali South S10715, PO Box 17706,
Dubai, United Arab Emirates
Tel.: (971) 48863850
Web Site: https://www.asbisme.ae
Computer Component Mfr
N.A.I.C.S.: 334419

Asbis Poland Sp. z o.o. **(1)**
Ul M Slowikowskiego 81c Ideal Idea City
Park-Budynek H4, 05-090, Raszyn, Poland
Tel.: (48) 501867434
Web Site: http://www.solutions.asbis.pl
Software Equipment Mfr & Distr
N.A.I.C.S.: 334111

Asbis Romania S.R.L. **(1)**
Splaiul Independentei 319 incinta Sema
Parc Sector 6, Bucharest, 060044, Roma-
nia
Tel.: (40) 213371097
Web Site: http://www.asbis.ro
Software Equipment Mfr & Distr
N.A.I.C.S.: 334111

Asbis SK sp.l s.r.o **(1)**
Tuhovska 33, 831 06, Bratislava, Slovakia
Tel.: (421) 232165111,
Web Site: http://www.online.asbis.sk
Software Equipment Mfr & Distr
N.A.I.C.S.: 334111

Asbis Slovenia d.o.o. **(1)**
Brodisce 15, 1236, Trzin, Slovenia
Tel.: (386) 59079927
Web Site: http://www.asbis.si
Software Equipment Mfr & Distr
N.A.I.C.S.: 334111

Asbis d.o.o. **(1)**
Dzemala Bijedica 162, 71 000, Sarajevo,
Bosnia & Herzegovina
Tel.: (387) 33770200
Web Site: http://www.asbis.ba
Software Equipment Mfr & Distr
N.A.I.C.S.: 334111

Breezy Poland Sp. Z.o.o. **(1)**
ul Obozowa 30a/41, 30-383, Krakow, Po-
land
Tel.: (48) 883033883
Web Site: https://www.breezy.pl
Protective Masks Supplier
N.A.I.C.S.: 423450

Megatrend d.o.o. Sarajevo **(1)**
Dzemala Bijedica 162, Sarajevo, 71000,
Bosnia & Herzegovina
Tel.: (387) 33770200
Web Site: http://www.asbis.ba
Sales Range: $25-49.9 Million
Emp.: 20
Computer Peripheral Equipments & Soft-
ware Distr
N.A.I.C.S.: 423430
Adnan Bajramovic (Gen Mgr)

Prestigio Plaza Ltd. **(1)**
26 Spyrou Kyprianou Str Prestigio Plaza,
4040, Limassol, Cyprus
Tel.: (357) 25257399
Web Site: http://www.prestigioplaza.com
Sales Range: $25-49.9 Million
Emp.: 482
Online Trading Services
N.A.I.C.S.: 425120

Subsidiary (Non-US):

Prestigio Europe spol. s.r.o. **(2)**
Na Dlouhem 79, Jazlovice, Ricany, 25101,
Czech Republic
Tel.: (420) 227186003
Web Site: http://www.prestigio.cz
Sales Range: $25-49.9 Million
Emp.: 20
Computer Peripheral Equipments & Soft-
ware Distr
N.A.I.C.S.: 423430
Martin Zeman (Gen Mgr)

ASC PTY. LTD.

694 Mersey Road North, Osborne,
5017, SA, Australia
Tel.: (61) 8 8348 7000 **AU**
Web Site: http://www.asc.com.au
Year Founded: 1985
Rev.: $522,499,492
Assets: $304,051,231
Liabilities: $209,617,224
Net Worth: $94,434,007
Earnings: $21,287,876
Emp.: 1,300
Fiscal Year-end: 06/30/19
Naval Ships & Submarine Building
N.A.I.C.S.: 336611
Stuart Whiley (CEO & Mng Dir)

ASC TELECOM AG

Seibelstrasse 2 4, 63768, Hosbach,
Germany
Tel.: (49) 602150010
Web Site:
http://www.asctelecom.com
Year Founded: 1964
Rev.: $35,048,970
Emp.: 131
Software Solutions Services
N.A.I.C.S.: 541511
Marco Mueller (COO)

Subsidiaries:

ASC Americas L.P. **(1)**
69 Charlton St, New York, NY 10014
Tel.: (917) 475-9200
Web Site: http://www.ascamericas.com
Software Development Services
N.A.I.C.S.: 541511
Eric Franzen (VP-Sls & Ops)

ASC Japan Inc. **(1)**
NCC Ningyocho Bldg 3-7-3 Nihonbashi
Ningyocho, Chuo, 103-0013, Tokyo, Japan
Tel.: (81) 356437220
Web Site: http://www.ascjpn.com
Software Development Services
N.A.I.C.S.: 541511
Yoshio Ota (Mgr-Sls)

ASC Schweiz AG **(1)**
Gewerbestrasse 6, 6330, Cham, Switzer-
land
Tel.: (41) 417980040
Web Site: http://www.asc-ch.ch
Software Development Services
N.A.I.C.S.: 541511
Stefan A. Butler (Mgr-Bus Dev)

ASC Technologies AG **(1)**
Sheikh Mohammed Bin Zayed Road, PO
Box Number 341325, Wing F Office 107/2,

Dubai, United Arab Emirates
Tel.: (971) 43712763
Software Development Services
N.A.I.C.S.: 541511

ASC Technologies GmbH (1)
Nell-Breuning-Allee 6, 66115, Saarbrucken,
Germany
Tel.: (49) 6818449680
Web Site: http://www.asc-sb.de
Software Development Services
N.A.I.C.S.: 541511

ASC Technologies S.A.S. (1)
15 rue Tronchet 1er etage Immeuble B,
75008, Paris, France
Tel.: (33) 175436530
Web Site: http://www.asctechnologies.fr
Software Development Services
N.A.I.C.S.: 541511

ASC Telecom Singapore Pte. Ltd. (1)
54 Serangoon North Avenue 4 03-03T Cyberhub North, Singapore, 555854, Singapore
Tel.: (65) 68765890
Software Development Services
N.A.I.C.S.: 541511

ASC UK Technologies Ltd (1)
1 Stanhope Gate Stanhope Road, Camberley, GU15 3DW, Surrey, United Kingdom
Tel.: (44) 1276676070
Web Site: http://www.asctechnologies.co.uk
Software Development Services
N.A.I.C.S.: 541511

ASC WFO Solutions do Brasil Ltda. (1)
Av Brig Faria Lima 1912 11 andar - Conj 11-G Edificio Cal Center II, Jardim Paulistano, Sao Paulo, 01451-907, Brazil
Tel.: (55) 1140404500
Web Site:
    http://www.asctechnologies.com.br
Software Development Services
N.A.I.C.S.: 541511

ASCELIA PHARMA AB
Hyllie Stationstorg 31, 215 32,
Malmo, Sweden
Tel.: (46) 735179118
Web Site: https://www.ascelia.com
Year Founded: 2000
ACE—(OMX)
Rev.: $1,668,680
Assets: $20,471,588
Liabilities: $3,531,990
Net Worth: $16,939,597
Earnings: ($12,290,595)
Emp.: 24
Fiscal Year-end: 12/31/22
Pharmaceuticals Product Mfr
N.A.I.C.S.: 325412
Magnus Corfitzen (CEO)

Subsidiaries:

Ascelia Pharma Inc. (1)
485C US Hwy 1 S Ste 350, Iselin, NJ 08830
Tel.: (848) 212-8554
Orphan Oncology Treatment Services
N.A.I.C.S.: 622310

Oncoral Pharma ApS (1)
Energivej 42, Ballerup, 2750, Copenhagen, Denmark
Tel.: (45) 23207302
Medical Equipment Mfr
N.A.I.C.S.: 339112

ASCENCIA LIMITED
1st floor Bagatelle Office Park, Moka,
Mauritius
Tel.: (230) 4600707   MU
Web Site:
    http://www.ascenciamalls.com
Year Founded: 2007
ASCE—(MAU)
Rev.: $27,073,006
Assets: $416,968,195
Liabilities: $187,197,539
Net Worth: $229,770,657

Earnings: $24,816,638
Emp.: 64
Fiscal Year-end: 06/30/22
Real Estate Development Services
N.A.I.C.S.: 531390
Frederic Tyack (CEO)

ASCENCIO S.A.
Avenue Jean-Mermoz 1/4, Box 4,
6041, Gosselies, Belgium
Tel.: (32) 71919500
Web Site: https://www.ascencio.be
Year Founded: 2006
ASCE—(EUR)
Rev.: $55,387,438
Assets: $848,768,616
Liabilities: $368,774,013
Net Worth: $479,994,604
Earnings: $36,483,920
Emp.: 21
Fiscal Year-end: 09/30/23
Real Estate Investment Services
N.A.I.C.S.: 525990
Stephanie Vanden Broecke (Dir-Legal)

Subsidiaries:

Etudibel S.A. (1)
Ave Jean Mermoz 1b4, 6041, Gosselies,
Belgium
Tel.: (32) 71919500
Sales Range: $25-49.9 Million
Real Estate Investment Services
N.A.I.C.S.: 531390

ASCEND GENE AND CELL THERAPIES GMBH
Fraunhoferstrasse 9b, 82152,
Planegg, Germany
Tel.: (49) 89217036500   De
Emp.: 100
Healthcare Therapy Services
N.A.I.C.S.: 621610

ASCENDANT RESOURCES INC.
3205-200 Bay Street, Toronto, M5J
2T1, ON, Canada
Tel.: (647) 796-0066   ON
Web Site:
    https://www.ascendantresource.com
Year Founded: 2006
ASDRF—(OTCQB)
Assets: $7,910,000
Liabilities: $4,051,000
Net Worth: $3,859,000
Earnings: ($4,722,000)
Emp.: 9
Fiscal Year-end: 12/31/21
Mineral Mining Services
N.A.I.C.S.: 212230
Mark Brennan (Co-Founder, Chm & CEO)

ASCENDAS HOSPITALITY TRUST
1 Fusionopolis Place 10-10 Galaxis,
Singapore, 138522, Singapore
Tel.: (65) 65088670
Web Site: http://www.a-htrust.com
Q1P—(SES)
Rev.: $201,609,229
Assets: $1,417,603,859
Liabilities: $572,427,131
Net Worth: $845,176,728
Earnings: $171,268,858
Emp.: 23
Fiscal Year-end: 03/31/19
Real Estate Investment Trust
N.A.I.C.S.: 525990
Juay Hiang Tan (CEO)

ASCENDENT CAPITAL PARTNERS (ASIA) LIMITED
Suite 1609 16/F Jardine House 1

Connaught Place, Central, Hong
Kong, China (Hong Kong)
Tel.: (852) 2165 9000   HK
Web Site:
    http://www.ascendentcp.com
Year Founded: 2011
Privater Equity Firm
N.A.I.C.S.: 523999
Liang Meng (Co-Founder & Mng Partner)

ASCENDIA S.A.
Dacia 99 Floor 4, 20053, Bucharest,
Romania
Tel.: (40) 371089200
Web Site: https://www.ascendia.ro
ASC—(BUC)
Rev.: $2,693,130
Assets: $5,022,356
Liabilities: $2,670,464
Net Worth: $2,351,892
Earnings: $281,711
Emp.: 47
Fiscal Year-end: 12/31/23
Software Development Services
N.A.I.C.S.: 541511
Cosmin Malureanu (Gen Mgr)

ASCENDIO CO., LTD.
5th Floor Ilheung Bldg 1490-25 Seochodong, Seochogu, Seoul, 137-070,
Korea (South)
Tel.: (82) 215440332
Web Site:
    http://www.kiwimediagroup.com
Year Founded: 1977
012170—(KRS)
Rev.: $14,252,743
Assets: $56,112,589
Liabilities: $31,361,745
Net Worth: $24,750,844
Earnings: ($12,980,231)
Emp.: 41
Fiscal Year-end: 12/31/22
Investment Services
N.A.I.C.S.: 523999
Han Seung-Il (Pres)

Subsidiaries:

Imagine Asia Co., Ltd. (1)
113 Apgujeong-ro Apgujeong-dong,
Gangnam-gu, Seoul, 135-899, Korea
(South)
Tel.: (82) 2 3443 1960
Web Site: http://www.imagineasia.com
Movie & Performance Events Production
Services
N.A.I.C.S.: 512110
Jae-Hyun Shim (CEO)

ASCENDIS HEALTH LIMITED
31 Georgian Crescent East, PO Box
X21, Bryanston, Johannesburg, Gauteng, South Africa
Tel.: (27) 110369600
Web Site:
    http://www.ascendishealth.com
Year Founded: 2008
ASC—(JSE)
Rev.: $81,086,461
Assets: $51,263,269
Liabilities: $21,536,666
Net Worth: $29,726,603
Earnings: ($15,116,446)
Fiscal Year-end: 06/30/23
Health Care Srvices
N.A.I.C.S.: 621999
Kieron Futter (CFO)

Subsidiaries:

Ascendis Animal Health (Pty) Ltd (1)
The Matrix unit 3A Bridgeway Precinct,
Century City, Cape Town, South Africa
Tel.: (27) 10 880 0778
Web Site: https://www.ascendisvet.com
Animal Health Products Mfr
N.A.I.C.S.: 311119

Ascendis Health Direct (Pty) Ltd (1)

Tuscany Office Park 6 Coombe Place,
Sandton, Johannesburg, 2128, South Africa
Tel.: (27) 113178300
Web Site: http://www.ascendisdirect.com
Pharmaceuticals Product Mfr
N.A.I.C.S.: 325412

Avima (Pty) Ltd (1)
18 Aschenberg Street Chamdor, Krugersdorp, South Africa
Tel.: (27) 11 769 1300
Web Site: https://www.avima.co.za
Pest Control Product Mfr
N.A.I.C.S.: 325320

Efekto Care (Pty) Ltd (1)
15 Diesel Road, Isando, 1601, South Africa
Tel.: (27) 112875700
Web Site: http://www.efekto.co.za
Pest Control Product Mfr
N.A.I.C.S.: 325320

Enia Lipotech SL (1)
C/ Granja N 1 3, Alcobendas, 28108, Madrid, Spain
Tel.: (34) 91 661 2335
Web Site: https://www.enialipotech.com
Pharmaceuticals Product Mfr
N.A.I.C.S.: 325412

Heritage Resources Ltd. (1)
Room 902 9/F Valley Centre 80-82 Morrison Hill Road, Wanchai, China (Hong Kong)
Tel.: (852) 6 730 1118
Web Site:
    https://www.heritageresourcesltd.com
Financial Services
N.A.I.C.S.: 523210
Gordon Lee (Gen Mgr)

Innovative Pest Management (Pty)
Ltd (1)
192 Pandan Loop 05-24 Pantech Business
Hub, Singapore, 128381, Singapore
Tel.: (65) 6 100 5266
Web Site: https://www.innovativepest.sg
Pest Control Product Mfr
N.A.I.C.S.: 325320

Klub M5 (Pty) Ltd (1)
85 Swart Street Chamdor Eldoraigne X3,
Centurion, Johannesburg, 0157, South Africa
Tel.: (27) 126531782
Pest Control Product Mfr
N.A.I.C.S.: 325320

Kyron Laboratories (Pty) Ltd (1)
29 Barney Road, Benrose, Johannesburg,
2094, South Africa
Tel.: (27) 11 618 1544
Web Site: https://www.kyronlabs.co.za
Veterinary Pharmaceutical Product Mfr
N.A.I.C.S.: 325412

Nutra Essential Otc SL (1)
C de los Aragoneses 11, Alcobendas,
28108, Madrid, Spain
Tel.: (34) 91 661 2335
Web Site: https://www.nutraessential.com
Medical Product Distr
N.A.I.C.S.: 423450

Remedica Ltd. (1)
Aharnon Street, Limassol Industrial Estate,
3056, Limassol, Cyprus
Tel.: (357) 2 555 3000
Web Site: https://www.remedica.eu
Pharmaceuticals Product Mfr
N.A.I.C.S.: 325412

Respiratory Care Africa (Pty) Ltd (1)
Stand 208 Padlock Lane Boundary Park
Cnr Malibongwe and Epsom Ave, Northriding, Johannesburg, 2169, South Africa
Tel.: (27) 11 568 9047
Web Site: https://rca.co.za
Women Healthcare Services
N.A.I.C.S.: 621610

The Compounding Pharmacy of
South Africa (Pty) Ltd (1)
2 Eaton Ave Cnr Bryanston Dr, Bryanston,
South Africa
Tel.: (27) 114630310
Web Site: https://www.compounding.co.za
Pharmaceuticals Product Mfr
N.A.I.C.S.: 325412

The Integrative Medical Centre (Pty)
Ltd (1)

Ascendis Health Limited—(Continued)

460 Brunswick Street, Fitzroy, 3068, VIC, Australia
Tel.: (61) 39 485 8000
Web Site:
https://www.integratedmedical.com.au
Women Healthcare Services
N.A.I.C.S.: 621610

ASCENDIS PHARMA A/S
Tuborg Boulevard 12, DK-2900, Hellerup, Denmark
Tel.: (45) 70222244   **DK**
Web Site:
https://www.ascendispharma.com
ASND—(NASDAQ)
Rev.: $246,074,027
Assets: $761,686,566
Liabilities: $896,106,618
Net Worth: ($134,420,052)
Earnings: ($444,183,002)
Emp.: 879
Fiscal Year-end: 12/31/23
Pharmaceutical Research & Development Services
N.A.I.C.S.: 325412
Jan Moller Mikkelsen *(Founder, Pres & CEO)*

Subsidiaries:

Ascendis Pharma Endocrinology, Inc.   (1)
902 Carnegie Ctr Blvd Ste 301, Princeton, NJ 08540
Tel.: (609) 651-8600
Biotechnology Research Services
N.A.I.C.S.: 541714

Ascendis Pharma GmbH   (1)
Im Neuenheimer Feld 584, 69120, Heidelberg, Germany
Tel.: (49) 6221998900
Biopharmaceutical Product Mfr
N.A.I.C.S.: 325412

Ascendis Pharma, Inc.   (1)
1000 Page Mill Rd, Palo Alto, CA 94304
Tel.: (650) 352-8389
Web Site: https://www.ascendispharma.us
Biopharmaceutical Product Mfr
N.A.I.C.S.: 325412

ASCENDO INTERNATIONAL HOLDINGS PTE. LTD.
9 Little Road 02-01,, Singapore, 536985, Singapore
Tel.: (65) 66103737   **SG**
Year Founded: 2017
Holding Companies
N.A.I.C.S.: 551112

Subsidiaries:

Ascendo Academy Pte. Ltd.   (1)
9 Little Road 02-01, Singapore, 536985, Singapore
Tel.: (65) 66103737
Web Site: https://www.ascendo.edu.sg
Consulting & Training Services
N.A.I.C.S.: 541618
Richard Lament *(Mgr-Bus Dev)*

Ascer Pte. Ltd.   (1)
9 Little Road 05-01, Singapore, 536985, Singapore
Tel.: (65) 63980067
Web Site: https://www.ascerhr.com
Consulting & Training Services
N.A.I.C.S.: 541618

Educare Global Academy Pte. Ltd.   (1)
62 Cecil Street TPI Building 03-00, Singapore, 49710, Singapore
Tel.: (65) 69085994
Web Site: https://ega.edu.sg
Education Training Services
N.A.I.C.S.: 611710

Educare Human Capital Private Limited   (1)
9 Little Road 02-01, Singapore, 536985, Singapore
Web Site: https://www.ehc.sg

Consulting & Training Services
N.A.I.C.S.: 541618

ASCENT BRIDGE LIMITED
15 Tuas South Street 13, Singapore, 636936, Singapore
Tel.: (65) 62612244
Web Site: https://www.aei.com.sg
AWG—(SES)
Rev.: $2,974,423
Assets: $32,323,120
Liabilities: $6,049,802
Net Worth: $26,273,318
Earnings: ($6,597,524)
Fiscal Year-end: 03/31/23
Precision Aluminium Extrusion Products
N.A.I.C.S.: 331318
Sun Quan *(Exec Dir)*

Subsidiaries:

AEI Engineering Pte Ltd   (1)
12 Penjuru Ln, Block C, Singapore, 609192, Singapore
Tel.: (65) 62652646
Web Site: http://www.aei.com.sg
Sales Range: $25-49.9 Million
Emp.: 30
Engineeering Services
N.A.I.C.S.: 541330

ASCENT DEVELOPMENT CO., LTD
19th Floor No 557-1 Sec 4 Zhongxiao East Rd, Xinyi Dist, Taipei, 11072, Taiwan
Tel.: (886) 227566777
Web Site:
https://www.ascentglobal.com.tw
Year Founded: 1964
1439—(TAI)
Rev.: $6,513,980
Assets: $173,548,638
Liabilities: $71,688,607
Net Worth: $101,860,031
Earnings: $6,381,471
Fiscal Year-end: 12/31/23
Wool Product Mfr
N.A.I.C.S.: 327993
Jiaqi Hou *(Chm)*

ASCENT RESOURCES PLC
5 New Street Square, London, EC4A 3TW, United Kingdom
Tel.: (44) 2072514905
Web Site:
https://www.ascentresources.co.uk
AST—(AIM)
Rev.: $733,401
Assets: $807,877
Liabilities: $2,726,584
Net Worth: ($1,918,707)
Earnings: ($52,879,323)
Emp.: 7
Fiscal Year-end: 12/31/22
Crude Petroleum Extraction Services
N.A.I.C.S.: 211120
James Parsons *(Chm)*

ASCENTAGE PHARMA GROUP INTERNATIONAL
218 Xinghu Street Building B7 7th Floor, Suzhou Industrial Park, Suzhou, 215000, Jiangsu, China
Tel.: (86) 51285557777   **Ky**
Web Site:
http://www.ascentagepharma.com
Year Founded: 2009
6855—(HKG)
Rev.: $29,443,424
Assets: $397,368,644
Liabilities: $339,993,061
Net Worth: $57,375,583
Earnings: ($123,962,530)
Emp.: 580
Fiscal Year-end: 12/31/22
Pharmaceutical Product Mfr & Distr

N.A.I.C.S.: 325412
Dajun Yang *(Co-Founder, Chm & CEO)*

Subsidiaries:

Ascentage Pharma Group Inc.   (1)
700 King Farm Blvd Ste 510, Rockville, MD 20850
Tel.: (301) 520-1026
Pharmaceuticals Product Mfr
N.A.I.C.S.: 325412

ASCENTECH, K.K.
9F Daito Bldg 3 Kanda-Neribeicho Chiyoda-ku, Tokyo, 101-0022, Japan
Tel.: (81) 352969331
Web Site: http://www.ascentech.co.jp
Year Founded: 2009
3565—(TKS)
Rev.: $44,142,340
Assets: $32,762,890
Liabilities: $10,642,090
Net Worth: $22,120,800
Earnings: $3,403,200
Emp.: 88
Fiscal Year-end: 01/31/24
Information Technology Consulting Services
N.A.I.C.S.: 541512
Naohiro Sato *(Chm & CEO)*

ASCLETIS PHARMA, INC.
12/F Building 3 No 371 Mingxing Road, Hipark Xiaoshan, Hangzhou, Zhejiang, China
Tel.: (86) 57185389730   **Ky**
Web Site: http://www.ascletis.com
Year Founded: 2013
1672—(HKG)
Rev.: $11,778,172
Assets: $433,578,018
Liabilities: $15,456,897
Net Worth: $418,121,121
Earnings: ($30,491,395)
Emp.: 266
Fiscal Year-end: 12/31/21
Pharmaceutical Product Mfr & Distr
N.A.I.C.S.: 325412
Jinzi J. Wu *(Founder, Chm & CEO)*

ASCO CONSTRUCTION LTD.
381 County Rd 17, Hawkesbury, K6A 2R2, ON, Canada
Tel.: (613) 632-0121
Web Site:
http://www.ascoconstruction.com
Year Founded: 1988
Rev.: $22,833,381
Emp.: 23
Architectural & Construction Services
N.A.I.C.S.: 541330

ASCO INDUSTRIES NV/SA
Weiveldlaan 2, 1930, Zaventem, Belgium
Tel.: (32) 27160611   **BE**
Web Site: http://www.asco.be
Year Founded: 1995
Sales Range: $125-149.9 Million
Emp.: 705
Slat Actuation Systems Mfr
N.A.I.C.S.: 336413
Emile Boas *(Founder)*

Subsidiaries:

ASCO Aerospace Canada Ltd.   (1)
8510 River Road, Delta, V4G 1B5, BC, Canada
Tel.: (604) 946-4900
Aerospace Equipment Mfr
N.A.I.C.S.: 336413

ASCO Aerospace USA, LLC   (1)
3003 N Perkins Rd, Stillwater, OK 74075
Tel.: (405) 533-5800
Sales Range: $25-49.9 Million
Emp.: 13
Aerospace Equipment Mfr
N.A.I.C.S.: 336413

Randy Stokes *(Engr-Mfg)*

ASCO Aerospace do Brasil   (1)
Avenida Dr Nelson D Avila 389-Sala 71B Centro, Sao Jose dos Campos, 12 3204 6632, Brazil
Tel.: (55) 12 3204 6632
Aerospace Equipment Mfr
N.A.I.C.S.: 336413

ASCO Deutschland GmbH   (1)
Otto-Mueller Strasse 55, 63688, Gedern, Oberhessen, Germany
Tel.: (49) 6045 9612 0
Sales Range: $50-74.9 Million
Emp.: 200
Aerospace Equipment Mfr
N.A.I.C.S.: 336413
Kissel Holger *(Sr Program Mgr)*

ASCOM HOLDING AG
Zugerstrasse 32, CH-6340, Baar, Switzerland
Tel.: (41) 415447800   **CH**
Web Site: https://www.ascom.com
Year Founded: 1987
ASCN—(SWX)
Rev.: $318,224,070
Assets: $230,004,657
Liabilities: $149,486,040
Net Worth: $80,518,617
Earnings: $7,361,055
Emp.: 1,282
Fiscal Year-end: 12/31/20
Holding Company; Healthcare Telecommunication Services
N.A.I.C.S.: 551112
Daniel Lack *(Member-Exec Bd, Sec & Sr VP-Legal, Comm & IR)*

Subsidiaries:

Ascom (Finland) OY   (1)
Lemminkaisenkatu 46, 20520, Turku, Finland   **(100%)**
Tel.: (358) 2 415 1200
Web Site: https://www.ascom.com
Sales Range: $25-49.9 Million
Emp.: 25
Wireless Solutions, Security Communications & Network Testing
N.A.I.C.S.: 334290

Ascom (France) SA   (1)
48 rue Carnot, CS 30061, 92156, Suresnes, Cedex, France
Tel.: (33) 147696464
Web Site: https://www.ascom.com
General Management Consulting Services
N.A.I.C.S.: 541611

Ascom (Malaysia) Sdn Bhd   (1)
V Shop Office and Retail 2 V02-05-01 Lingkaran SV Sunway Velocity, 55100, Kuala Lumpur, Malaysia
Tel.: (60) 397707000
Information Technology Services
N.A.I.C.S.: 541519

Ascom (Schweiz) AG   (1)
Stettbachstrasse 6, 8600, Dubendorf, Switzerland   **(100%)**
Tel.: (41) 319991111
Web Site: http://www.ascom.ch
Sales Range: $25-49.9 Million
Emp.: 100
Communications Equipment
N.A.I.C.S.: 334290

Subsidiary (Domestic):

Ascom Immobilien AG   (2)
Belpstrasse 37, 3000, Bern, Switzerland   **(100%)**
Tel.: (41) 319991111
Web Site: http://www.ascom.ch
Sales Range: $25-49.9 Million
Emp.: 30
Communications Equipment
N.A.I.C.S.: 334290

Ascom Network Testing AG   (2)
Glutz Blotzheim Strasse 1 3, CH 4503, Solothurn, Switzerland   **(100%)**
Tel.: (41) 326242121
Web Site: http://www.ascom.ch

Sales Range: $25-49.9 Million
Communications Network Testing Services
N.A.I.C.S.: 541990
Rikard Lundqvist *(Gen Mgr)*

Ascom Security Solutions AG (2)
Gewerbepark, Postfach 500, 5506, Magenwil, Switzerland **(100%)**
Tel.: (41) 628895000
Web Site: http://www.ascom.ch
Sales Range: $25-49.9 Million
Emp.: 50
Telephone Handsets & Military Radio Equipment Development & Mfr
N.A.I.C.S.: 334220

Ascom Systec AG (2)
Gewerbepark, Hintermaettlistrasse, 5506, Magenwil, Switzerland **(100%)**
Tel.: (41) 628895281
Web Site: http://www.ascom.ch
N.A.I.C.S.: 334290

Ascom (Sweden) AB (1)
Grimbodalen 2, PO Box 8783, 417 05, Gothenburg, Sweden
Tel.: (46) 31559400
Web Site: https://www.ascom.com
Emp.: 250
Wireless Telecommunication Services
N.A.I.C.S.: 517112
Aage Rask Andersen *(Mng Dir)*

Subsidiary (Domestic):

Ascom Tateco AB (2)
Grimbodalen 2, PO Box 8783, 402 76, Gothenburg, Sweden **(100%)**
Tel.: (46) 31559400
Web Site: http://www.ascom.com
Sales Range: $25-49.9 Million
Emp.: 200
Wireless Alarms & Security Software
N.A.I.C.S.: 517112

Ascom (US) Inc. (1)
300 Perimeter Park Dr, Morrisville, NC 27560
Tel.: (919) 234-2500
Web Site: https://www.ascom.com
Sales Range: $50-74.9 Million
Emp.: 130
Wireless Communications for Hospitals, Manufacturing Industry, Retail & Hotels
N.A.I.C.S.: 517112
Tom McKearney *(Sr VP-Bus Dev & Mktg)*

Ascom B.V. (1)
Orteliuslaan 982, 3528 BD, Utrecht, Netherlands **(100%)**
Tel.: (31) 302409100
Web Site: https://www.ascom.com
Sales Range: $100-124.9 Million
Emp.: 350
Other Communications Equipment Manufacturing
N.A.I.C.S.: 334290

Subsidiary (Non-US):

Ascom (Belgium) NV (2)
Belgicastraat 11, 1930, Zaventem, Belgium **(100%)**
Tel.: (32) 27271311
Web Site: https://www.ascom.com
Sales Range: $25-49.9 Million
Emp.: 160
Mission-Critical Communications Solutions
N.A.I.C.S.: 334290

Subsidiary (Domestic):

Ascom (Nederland) BV (2)
Orteliuslaan 982, 3528 BD, Utrecht, Netherlands
Tel.: (31) 302409100
Web Site: https://www.ascom.com
Emp.: 33
Telecommunications Peripherals Distr
N.A.I.C.S.: 517810

Subsidiary (Domestic):

Mocsa Real Estate BV (3)
Savannahweg 31, Postbus 40242, Utrecht, 3542 AW, Netherlands
Tel.: (31) 30 2409100
Web Site: http://www.ascom.com
Emp.: 150
Real Estate Development Services
N.A.I.C.S.: 531390

Joe Hoonhout *(Mng Dir)*

TPA Traffic & Parking Automation Systems (3)
Blankenweg 22, 6827 BW, Arnhem, Netherlands **(100%)**
Tel.: (31) 263553535
Web Site: http://www.tpa.nl
Sales Range: $25-49.9 Million
N.A.I.C.S.: 334290

Ascom Colombia S.A. (1)
Apartado Aereo 8539 Calle 37 No 20 51, Bogota, Colombia **(100%)**
Tel.: (57) 3239390
Sales Range: $25-49.9 Million
Emp.: 50
N.A.I.C.S.: 334290

Ascom Danmark A/S (1)
Delta Park 46 3, 2665, Vallensbaek, Denmark
Tel.: (45) 70203883
Web Site: https://www.ascom.com
Information Technology Services
N.A.I.C.S.: 541519

Ascom Denmark A/S (1)
Delta Park 46, 2665, Vallensbaek, Denmark
Tel.: (45) 7 020 3883
Web Site: https://www.ascom.com
Sales Range: $25-49.9 Million
Emp.: 50
N.A.I.C.S.: 334290

Ascom Deutschland GmbH (1)
Kruppstrasse 105, 60388, Frankfurt, Germany **(100%)**
Tel.: (49) 695800570
Web Site: https://www.ascom.com
Emp.: 30
N.A.I.C.S.: 334290

Subsidiary (Domestic):

Technologiepark Teningen GmbH (2)
Tscheulinstr 21, Teningen, 79331, Germany
Tel.: (49) 76414550
Sales Range: $50-74.9 Million
Electric Transformers Converters & Rectifier Mfr
N.A.I.C.S.: 334419

Ascom HPF SA (1)
BP 29, F 74130, Bonneville, France **(100%)**
Tel.: (33) 450970010
Web Site: http://www.ascom.fr
Sales Range: $25-49.9 Million
Emp.: 300
Mfr & Marketer of Telephones
N.A.I.C.S.: 334210

Ascom India Pvt Ltd (1)
34 Udyog Vihar Phase IV, Gurgaon, 122016, Haryana, India **(100%)**
Tel.: (91) 1246342083
Web Site: http://www.ascom.co.in
N.A.I.C.S.: 334290

Ascom Integrated Wireless Pty Ltd (1)
Suite 7 03 L7 185 O'Riordan St, Mascot, 2020, NSW, Australia **(100%)**
Tel.: (61) 29 698 9000
Web Site: https://www.ascom.com
Sales Range: $1-9.9 Million
Emp.: 100
Mobile, Emergency Communications, Asset Tracking & Duress Alarm Solutions
N.A.I.C.S.: 334290

Ascom Network Testing AB (1)
Laboratorgrand 3, 931 62, Skelleftea, Sweden
Tel.: (46) 10 492 5000
Web Site: http://www.ascom.com
Network Testing Services
N.A.I.C.S.: 541380

Ascom Norway (1)
Alf Bjerckes vei 8, 0582, Oslo, Norway
Tel.: (47) 2 324 7700
Web Site: http://www.ascom.com
Sales Range: $25-49.9 Million
Emp.: 36
N.A.I.C.S.: 334290

Ascom Poland Sp. Z.o.o. (1)
UL Fabryczna 16/22 office 24, 00-446, War-

saw, Poland **(100%)**
Tel.: (48) 226226255
Web Site: http://www.ascom.com.pl
Sales Range: $25-49.9 Million
Emp.: 15
Communications Holding Company
N.A.I.C.S.: 334290

Ascom Solutions (Singapore) Pte Ltd (1)
2 Gambas Crescent 06-08 Nordcom II, Singapore, 757044, Singapore
Tel.: (65) 63727666
Web Site: https://www.ascom.com
Information Technology Services
N.A.I.C.S.: 541519

Ascom UK Group Ltd. (1)
Enterprise Drive Aldridge Road Streetly, Birmingham, B74 2DY, West Midlands, United Kingdom
Tel.: (44) 121 353 6151
Web Site: http://www.ascom.com
Emp.: 65
Wireless Telecommunication Services
N.A.I.C.S.: 517112
Paul Lawrence *(Mng Dir)*

Subsidiary (Domestic):

Ascom (UK) Ltd. (2)
Wall Island Birmingham Road, Lichfield, WS14 0QP, United Kingdom **(100%)**
Tel.: (44) 1213536151
Web Site: https://www.ascom.com
Sales Range: $25-49.9 Million
Emp.: 40
N.A.I.C.S.: 334290

Ascom UMS S.r.l. (1)
Via Amilcare Ponchielli 29, 50018, Scandicci, Florence, Italy
Tel.: (39) 0550512161
Web Site: https://www.ascom.com
Information Technology Services
N.A.I.C.S.: 541519

Maticmind SpA (1)
Via Benedetto Croce 1, 20090, Vimodrone, Milan, Italy **(100%)**
Tel.: (39) 0227 4261
Web Site: https://www.ascom.com
Sales Range: $25-49.9 Million
Emp.: 737
Communications Holding Company
N.A.I.C.S.: 334290

Subsidiary (Domestic):

Tecnonet S.p.A. (2)
Via Appia Pignatelli 235, 00178, Rome, Italy
Tel.: (39) 06716781
Telecommunication Servicesb
N.A.I.C.S.: 541618

ASCOM LEASING & INVESTMENTS LTD.
Aditya Group 331 Four Point Complex Vip Road, Vesu, Surat, 395007, India
Tel.: (91) 8758580040
Web Site:
   https://www.ascomfinance.com
Year Founded: 1986
ASCOM—(NSE)
Rev.: $1,460,009
Assets: $5,355,273
Liabilities: $1,278,657
Net Worth: $4,076,616
Earnings: $653,690
Emp.: 3
Fiscal Year-end: 03/12/21
Financial Services
N.A.I.C.S.: 541611
Pradeep Champaklal Wadiwalal *(Chm)*

ASCOPIAVE S.P.A.
Via Verizzo 1030, 31053, Pieve di Soligo, Treviso, Italy
Tel.: (39) 00438980098
Web Site:
   https://www.gruppoascopiave.it
ASC—(ITA)
Rev.: $201,303,623

Assets: $1,674,221,313
Liabilities: $625,423,493
Net Worth: $1,048,797,821
Earnings: $72,098,916
Emp.: 463
Fiscal Year-end: 12/31/20
Natural Gas Distr
N.A.I.C.S.: 221210
Nicola Cecconato *(Chm & CEO)*

Subsidiaries:

AP Reti Gas Nord Est S.R.L. (1)
Via Jacopo Corrado 1, 35128, Padua, PD, Italy
Tel.: (39) 0497802411
Web Site: https://www.apretigasnordest.it
Natural Gas Distribution Services
N.A.I.C.S.: 221210

AP Reti Gas Rovigo S.r.l. (1)
Viale del Lavoro 24, 45100, Rovigo, RO, Italy
Tel.: (39) 0425987511
Web Site: https://www.apretigasrovigo.it
Natural Gas Distr
N.A.I.C.S.: 221210

AP Reti Gas S.p.A. (1)
Via Verizzo 1030, 31053, Pieve di Soligo, TV, Italy
Tel.: (39) 0438980098
Web Site: https://www.apretigas.it
Natural Gas Distr
N.A.I.C.S.: 221210

Amgas Blu S.r.l. (1)
Viale Manfredi s n, 71121, Foggia, Italy
Tel.: (39) 0800126465
Web Site: https://www.amgasblu.it
Natural Gas Distr
N.A.I.C.S.: 221210

Asco EG S.p.A. (1)
Via Verizzo 1030, 31053, Pieve di Soligo, Italy
Tel.: (39) 0445780914
Web Site: https://www.ascoeg.it
Eletric Power Generation Services
N.A.I.C.S.: 221118

Asco Renewables S.p.A. (1)
Via Verizzo 1030, 31053, Pieve di Soligo, TV, Italy
Tel.: (39) 0438980098
Web Site: https://www.ascorenewables.it
Holding Company
N.A.I.C.S.: 551112

Ascopiave Energie S.p.A. (1)
Via Verizzo 1030, 31053, Pieve di Soligo, TV, Italy
Tel.: (39) 0800366466
Web Site: http://www.ascopiavenergie.it
Natural Gas Distr
N.A.I.C.S.: 221210

Blue Meta S.p.A. (1)
Via Galimberti No 6/A, 24124, Bergamo, BG, Italy
Tel.: (39) 0354526811
Web Site: http://www.bluemeta.it
Natural Gas Distr
N.A.I.C.S.: 221210

Cart Acqua S.R.L. (1)
Via Verizzo 1030, 31053, Pieve di Soligo, TV, Italy
Tel.: (39) 0438980098
Web Site: https://www.cartacqua.it
Water Supply Management Services
N.A.I.C.S.: 221310

Etra Energia S.r.l. (1)
Via del Telarolo No 9, 35013, Cittadella, PD, Italy
Tel.: (39) 0800766858
Web Site: https://www.etraenergia.it
Natural Gas Distr
N.A.I.C.S.: 221210

Romeo Gas S.p.A. (1)
Via Verizzo 1030, 31053, Pieve di Soligo, TV, Italy
Tel.: (39) 0438980098
Web Site: https://www.romeogas.it
Natural Gas Distribution Services
N.A.I.C.S.: 221210

ASCOT CORP.

Ascot Corp.—(Continued)

3-1-30 Jingumae, Shibuya-ku, Tokyo,
150-0001, Japan
Tel.: (81) 367210248
Web Site:
https://www.ascotcorp.co.jp
Year Founded: 1999
3264—(TKS)
Rev.: $256,037,520
Assets: $537,527,760
Liabilities: $341,596,800
Net Worth: $195,930,960
Earnings: $20,998,320
Fiscal Year-end: 09/30/24
Condominium Units & Houses Developer; Real Estate Investment & Property Management Services
N.A.I.C.S.: 236116
Takumi Hamasaki *(Pres & CEO)*

Subsidiaries:

Ascot Asset Consulting Corp. **(1)**
Daiwa Aoyama Building 5F 3-1-30 Jingumae, Shibuya-ku, Tokyo, 150-0001, Japan
Tel.: (81) 367210148
Web Site: https://www.ascotac.co.jp
Real Estate & Asset Management Consulting Services
N.A.I.C.S.: 541618

ASCOT RESOURCES LTD.

1050-1095 West Pender Street, Vancouver, V6E 2M6, BC, Canada
Tel.: (778) 725-1060   BC
Web Site: https://www.ascotgold.com
Year Founded: 1986
AOTVF—(OTCQX)
Assets: $265,228,905
Liabilities: $64,022,577
Net Worth: $201,206,327
Earnings: ($2,306,161)
Emp.: 12
Fiscal Year-end: 12/31/21
Gold Exploration & Mining Development Services
N.A.I.C.S.: 213114
Richard N. Zimmer *(Chm)*

ASDION BERHAD.

Level 5 Tower 8 Avenue 5 Bangsar
South City, Taman Tun Dr Ismail,
59200, Kuala Lumpur, Malaysia
Tel.: (60) 377331399   MY
Web Site:
https://www.asdiongroup.com
Year Founded: 2002
ASDION—(KLS)
Rev.: $812,240
Assets: $8,392,859
Liabilities: $6,010,509
Net Worth: $2,382,350
Earnings: ($856,863)
Fiscal Year-end: 09/30/22
Investment Holding Services
N.A.I.C.S.: 551112
Razmi Alias *(Exec Dir-Bus Dev)*

Subsidiaries:

Transeaways Shipping Sdn.
Bhd. **(1)**
A-155 2nd Floor Jalan Air Putih, 25300,
Kuantan, Pahang Darul Makmur,
Malaysia **(51%)**
Tel.: (60) 95660811
Web Site: http://www.transeaways.com
Shipping Services
N.A.I.C.S.: 488510

ASE S.P.A.

Via Verdi 33, 20010, San Giorgio,
Legnano, Italy
Tel.: (39) 0331402216
Web Site: http://www.ase-spa.com
Year Founded: 1919
Sales Range: $10-24.9 Million
Emp.: 80
Industrial Component Mfr

N.A.I.C.S.: 333310
Paolo Fantini *(CEO)*

ASE TECHNOLOGY HOLDING CO., LTD.

26 Chin 3rd Rd, Nanzih, Kaohsiung,
811, Taiwan
Tel.; (886) 73617131   TW
Web Site: https://www.aseglobal.com
Year Founded: 1984
ASX—(NYSE)
Rev.: $20,547,842,000
Assets: $24,270,582,000
Liabilities: $14,603,276,000
Net Worth: $9,667,306,000
Earnings: $2,244,050,000
Emp.: 95,727
Fiscal Year-end: 12/31/21
Holding Company
N.A.I.C.S.: 551112
Jason C. S. Chang *(Chm)*

Subsidiaries:

ASE (Kunshan) Inc. **(1)**
No 373 Songnan Road, Qiandeng, Kunshan, 215341, Jiangsu, China
Tel.: (86) 51255288888
Web Site: http://www.aseks.aseglobal.com
Integrated Device Mfr
N.A.I.C.S.: 334413

ASE Singapore Pte. Ltd. **(1)**
2 Woodlands Loop, Singapore, 738074,
Singapore
Tel.: (65) 66314256
Web Site: https://www.aseglobal.com.sg
Integrated Device Mfr
N.A.I.C.S.: 334413
Lee Kwai Mun *(Pres)*

Advanced Semiconductor Engineering, Inc. **(1)**
26 Chin 3rd Rd, Nantzih, Kaohsiung, 811,
Taiwan
Tel.: (886) 73617131
Web Site: http://www.aseglobal.com
Rev.: $9,773,346,649
Assets: $12,245,984,453
Liabilities: $5,471,896,660
Net Worth: $6,774,087,793
Earnings: $824,326,069
Emp.: 68,753
Fiscal Year-end: 12/31/2017
Semiconductor Packaging Services
N.A.I.C.S.: 334413

Subsidiary (Domestic):

ASE (Chung Li), Inc. **(2)**
550 Chung-Hwa Road Section 1, Chung-li,
320, Taiwan **(100%)**
Tel.: (886) 34527121
Web Site: https://www.asecl.com.tw
Semiconductor Mfr
N.A.I.C.S.: 334413

Subsidiary (Non-US):

ASE Assembly & Test (Shanghai)
Limited **(2)**
No 669 Guoshoujing Road Zhangjiang Hi-
Tech Park, Pudong New Area, Shanghai,
201203, China
Tel.: (86) 2150801060
Web Site: https://www.asesh.com.cn
Semiconductor Device Packaging & Testing
Services
N.A.I.C.S.: 561910

ASE Electronics (M) Sdn. Bhd. **(2)**
Plot 20 Phase IV Free Industrial Zone,
Bayan Lepas, 11900, Penang,
Malaysia **(100%)**
Tel.: (60) 46328888
Web Site: https://www.asemal.com.my
Sales Range: $75-99.9 Million
Emp.: 4,000
N.A.I.C.S.: 334413
Lee Kwai Mun *(Chm)*

ASE Japan Co., Ltd. **(2)**
1863 Iriuda Takahata-machi,
Higashiokitama-gun, Yamagata, 992-0324,
Japan
Tel.: (81) 238572211
Web Site: https://www.asejp.aseglobal.com

Emp.: 430
Electronic Component Mfr & Distr
N.A.I.C.S.: 334419

Subsidiary (Domestic):

ASE Kaohsiung **(2)**
No 26 Chin 3rd Road Nantze Export Processing Zone, Kaohsiung, 811, Taiwan
Tel.: (886) 73617131
Web Site: https://asekhsite.aseglobal.com
Semiconductor Devices Mfr
N.A.I.C.S.: 334413

Subsidiary (Non-US):

ASE Korea Inc. **(2)**
76 Saneopdanji-gil Paju-si, Gyeonggi-do,
Seoul, 413 830, Korea (South) **(100%)**
Tel.: (82) 319400114
Web Site: https://www.asekr.com
Semiconductor Assemblies & Test Solution
Services
N.A.I.C.S.: 334413

Subsidiary (Domestic):

ASE Test Limited **(2)**
26 Chin 3rd Road NEPZ, Nantze District,
Kaohsiung, Taiwan
Tel.: (886) 73617131
Semiconductor Chip Testing Services
N.A.I.C.S.: 334413

ASE Test, Inc. **(2)**
26 Chin 3rd Rd, Nanzih Dist, Kaohsiung,
811, Taiwan
Tel.: (886) 73617131
Integrated Circuit Testing Services
N.A.I.C.S.: 541380

Subsidiary (US):

ISE Labs, Inc. **(2)**
46800 Bayside Pkwy, Fremont, CA 94538
Tel.: (510) 687-2500
Web Site: https://www.iselabs.com
Semiconductor Engineering & Testing Services
N.A.I.C.S.: 334413
Tien Wu *(CEO)*

Subsidiary (Domestic):

J&R Industrial Inc. **(2)**
107 Neihuan North Road Nanzih Export
Processing Zone, Kaohsiung, 811, Taiwan
Tel.: (886) 73617131
Semiconductor Device Distr
N.A.I.C.S.: 423690

StarChips Technology Inc. **(2)**
2F No 5 R D 1st Rd Hsinchu Science Park,
Hsinchu, 30076, Taiwan **(33.3%)**
Tel.: (886) 35775767
Web Site: http://www.starchips.com.tw
Semiconductor Devices Mfr
N.A.I.C.S.: 334413

Subsidiary (Non-US):

Universal Scientific Industrial (Shanghai) Co., Ltd. **(2)**
No 1558 Zhang Dong Rd Pudong New
Area, Shanghai, 201203, China
Tel.: (86) 2158966996
Web Site: https://www.usiglobal.com
Rev.: $9,619,657,070
Assets: $5,415,854,844
Liabilities: $3,204,577,434
Net Worth: $2,211,277,410
Earnings: $429,619,381
Emp.: 23,000
Fiscal Year-end: 12/31/2022
Electrical Equipment Mfr & Whslr
N.A.I.C.S.: 334419
Jeffrey Chen *(Chm)*

Subsidiary (Non-US):

Universal Global Scientific Industrial
Co., Ltd. **(3)**
No 141 Lane 351 Sec 1 Taiping Road, Nantou County, Tsao Tuen, 542007, Taiwan
Tel.: (886) 492350876
Electronic Parts & Equipment Distr
N.A.I.C.S.: 423690

Subsidiary (Domestic):

Universal Scientific Industrial Co.,
Ltd. **(2)**

Rm 6 3F No 66 Sanchong Road, Nangang
District, Taipei, 115602, Taiwan
Tel.: (886) 227820366
Web Site: http://www.usi.com.tw
Emp.: 10,787
Electronics Mfr for Computing, Communications, Consumer Electronics & Car Electronics Industries
N.A.I.C.S.: 334419
Jeffrey Chen *(Chm)*

Subsidiary (Non-US):

USI Japan Co., Ltd. **(3)**
Sumitomo Fudosan Shin-yokohama Bldg
10F 2-5-5, Shin-yokohama Kouhoku-ku,
Yokohama, 222-0033, Japan
Tel.: (81) 454787317
Circuit Board Assembly Services
N.A.I.C.S.: 334418

USI Scientific Industrial (Shanghai)
Co., Ltd. **(3)**
200 JinQiu Road PuDong New Area,
Shanghai, 2012 03, China
Tel.: (86) 2158966996
Emp.: 7
Circuit Board Assembly Services
N.A.I.C.S.: 334418
Jessie Wei *(Mgr-Bus Dept)*

Subsidiary (Non-US):

AsteelFlash Group **(4)**
6 rue Van Gogh, 93360, Neuilly-Plaisance,
France
Tel.: (33) 149445300
Web Site: http://www.asteelflash.com
Industrial Electronic Mfr
N.A.I.C.S.: 334419
Gilles Benhamou *(Founder & CEO)*

Subsidiary (Non-US):

Asteelflash Bedford Limited **(5)**
Unit 1 and 2 - St Martins Way, St Martins
Business Centre, Bedford, MK42 0LF,
United Kingdom
Tel.: (44) 1234216222
Web Site: https://www.asteelflash.com
Electronic System Distr
N.A.I.C.S.: 423690

Asteelflash Bonn GmbH **(5)**
Allerstrasse 31, Hersel, 53332, Bornheim,
Germany
Tel.: (49) 22229964101
Web Site: https://www.asteelflash.com
Electronic System Distr
N.A.I.C.S.: 423690

Asteelflash Design Solutions Hamburg GmbH **(5)**
Meiendorfer Strasse 205 c, 22145, Hamburg, Germany
Tel.: (49) 402022997363
Web Site: https://www.asteelflash.com
Electronic Components Mfr
N.A.I.C.S.: 334220
Albert Buckers *(Sls Dir)*

Subsidiary (Domestic):

Asteelflash Developpement **(5)**
43 Chemin du Vieux Chene, 38240, Meylan, France
Tel.: (33) 476633350
Electronic Components Mfr
N.A.I.C.S.: 334220

Subsidiary (Non-US):

Asteelflash Eberbach GmbH **(5)**
Neuer Weg-Nord 49, 69412, Eberbach,
Germany
Tel.: (49) 627181200
Web Site: https://www.asteelflash.com
Electronic System Distr
N.A.I.C.S.: 423690

Subsidiary (Domestic):

Asteelflash Est **(5)**
9 rue Ampere, 67120, Duttlenheim, France
Tel.: (33) 388046450
Electronic Components Mfr
N.A.I.C.S.: 334220

Subsidiary (US):

Asteelflash Fremont **(5)**

4211 Starboard Dr, Fremont, CA 94538
Tel.: (510) 440-2840
Web Site: https://www.asteelflash.com
Electronic Equipment Distr
N.A.I.C.S.: 423690

Subsidiary (Non-US):

Asteelflash Hersfeld GmbH **(5)**
Konrad-Zuse-Strasse 19, 36251, Bad Hers-
feld, Germany
Tel.: (49) 662184201
Electronic System Distr
N.A.I.C.S.: 423690
Daniel Heinemann *(Mgr-Bus Admin)*

Asteelflash Hersfeld GmbH **(5)**
Konrad-Zuse-Strasse 19, 36251, Bad Hers-
feld, Germany
Tel.: (49) 662184201
Web Site: https://www.asteelflash.com
Electronic Components Mfr
N.A.I.C.S.: 334220
Felix Timmermann *(Exec VP)*

Subsidiary (Domestic):

Asteelflash Normandie **(5)**
49 Rue de la République, 76250, Déville-
lès-Rouen, France
Tel.: (33) 232107000
Electronic Components Mfr
N.A.I.C.S.: 334220

Subsidiary (Non-US):

Asteelflash Plzen s.r.o. **(5)**
Podnikatelska 1227/24, 301 00, Plzen,
Czech Republic
Tel.: (420) 373740905
Web Site: https://www.asteelflash.com
Electronic System Distr
N.A.I.C.S.: 423690

Asteelflash Suzhou **(5)**
No 8 Gutang Road Wetdz, Wujiang District,
Suzhou, 215200, Jiangsu, China
Tel.: (86) 51263436156
Web Site: https://www.asteelflash.com
Electronic System Distr
N.A.I.C.S.: 423690

Asteelflash Tijuana **(5)**
Av. Producción 5-A Parque Industrial Finsa
Otay Universidad cp, 22427, Tijuana, Baja
California, Mexico
Tel.: (52) 6194989174
Electronic System Distr
N.A.I.C.S.: 423690

Subsidiary (US):

USI@Work, Inc. **(3)**
2000 Regency Pkwy, Ste 420, Cary, 27518-
8509, North Carolina
Tel.: (919) 771-2788
Electronic Circuit Board Assembly & Repair
Services
N.A.I.C.S.: 334418

Subsidiary (Domestic):

Yang Ting Tech Co., Ltd. **(2)**
No 5-2 S 2nd Rd, Tanzi Shiang, Taichung,
42760, Taiwan
Tel.: (886) 4 25343141
Web Site: http://www.yangting.com.tw
Semiconductor Devices Mfr
N.A.I.C.S.: 334413

Asteelflash Germany Gmbh **(1)**
Konrad-Zuse-Strasse 19, 36251, Bad Hers-
feld, Germany
Tel.: (49) 662184201
Electronic Components Mfr
N.A.I.C.S.: 334419

Asteelflash Mexico S.A. de C.V. **(1)**
Avenida Produccion No 5-B Parque Indus-
trial Finsa, 22435, Tijuana, Baja California,
Mexico
Tel.: (52) 6194989174
Electronic Components Mfr
N.A.I.C.S.: 334419

Asteelflash Schwandorf Gmbh **(1)**
Allerstrasse 31, 53332, Bornheim, Germany
Tel.: (49) 22229964101
Electronic Components Mfr
N.A.I.C.S.: 334419

Asteelflash Tunisie S.A. **(1)**

104 Avenue De luma, 2036, La Soukra,
Tunisia
Tel.: (216) 36066015
Electronic Components Mfr
N.A.I.C.S.: 334419

Asteelflash Usa Corp. **(1)**
4211 Starboard Dr, Fremont, CA 94538
Tel.: (510) 440-2840
N.A.I.C.S.: 334419

ISE Labs,China, Inc. **(1)**
No 169 Shengxia Road, Pudong New Area,
Shanghai, 201203, China
Tel.: (86) 150877568
N.A.I.C.S.: 333242

Siliconware Precision Industries Co.,
Ltd. **(1)**
No 123 Sec 3 Da Fong Road, Tantzi Dist,
Taichung, Taiwan
Tel.: (886) 425341525
Web Site: http://www.spil.com.tw
Rev.: $2,958,844,284
Assets: $4,308,591,957
Liabilities: $1,814,475,975
Net Worth: $2,494,115,983
Earnings: $249,737,259
Emp.: 23,746
Fiscal Year-end: 12/31/2019
Semiconductor Chip Packaging & Testing
Services
N.A.I.C.S.: 334413
Chi-Wen Tsai *(Chm & Pres)*

Plant (Domestic):

Siliconware Precision Industries Co.,
Ltd. - Changhua Facility **(2)**
No 8 Sec 2 Zhangxin Rd, Hemei, 50854,
Changhua, Taiwan
Tel.: (886) 47218888
Semiconductor Devices Mfr
N.A.I.C.S.: 334413

Siliconware Precision Industries Co.,
Ltd. - Hsinchu IG Facility **(2)**
No 4 Yanxin 4th Rd Hsinchu Science Park,
Hsinchu, 30077, Taiwan
Tel.: (886) 35773151
Web Site: https://www.spil.com.tw
Semiconductor Devices Mfr
N.A.I.C.S.: 334413

Siliconware Precision Industries Co.,
Ltd. - Hsinchu IIIG Facility **(2)**
No 1-1 Yanfa 2nd Rd Baoshan Township,
Hsinchu, 300092, Taiwan
Tel.: (886) 35787799
Web Site: https://www.spil.com.tw
Semiconductor Devices Mfr
N.A.I.C.S.: 334413

Subsidiary (Non-US):

Siliconware Technology (SuZhou)
Limited **(2)**
No 288 Feng Li St, SuZhou Industrial Park,
Suzhou, China **(100%)**
Tel.: (86) 51262535288
Semiconductor & Related Device Mfr
N.A.I.C.S.: 334413

Subsidiary (US):

Siliconware USA, Inc. **(2)**
1735 Technology Dr Ste 300, San Jose, CA
95110 **(100%)**
Tel.: (408) 573-5500
Electronic Parts & Equipment Whslr
N.A.I.C.S.: 423690

Usi America Inc. **(1)**
4211 Starboard Dr, Fremont, CA 94538
Tel.: (510) 440-2840
N.A.I.C.S.: 333242

ASEANA PROPERTIES LTD.
Osprey House Old Street, Saint He-
lier, JE2 3RG, Channel Islands, Jer-
sey
Tel.: (44) 1534487106
Web Site:
  https://www.aseanaproperties.com
ASPL—(LSE)
Rev.: $1,205,000
Assets: $137,358,000
Liabilities: $80,906,000

Net Worth: $56,452,000
Earnings: ($10,473,000)
Emp.: 235
Fiscal Year-end: 12/31/23
Real Estate
N.A.I.C.S.: 525990

Subsidiaries:

Hoa Lam-Shangri-La Healthcare Ltd.
Liability Co **(1)**
532A Kinh Duong Vuong Binh Tri Dong B
Ward, Binh Tan District, Ho Chi Minh City,
Vietnam
Tel.: (84) 862661188
Web Site: http://www.hoalam-shangrila.com
Healthcare Parking Services
N.A.I.C.S.: 621999

ASEC COMPANY FOR MINING
26 Street 265 New Maadi, Cairo,
Egypt
Tel.: (20) 225203371
Web Site: https://www.ascom.com.eg
Year Founded: 1975
Metal Ore Mining Services
N.A.I.C.S.: 212290
Fayez Habib Gress *(Chm & Chm)*

Subsidiaries:

Ascom Carbonate & Chemical Manu-
facturing Company **(1)**
48 El-Nasr Street, PO Box 120, New Maadi,
Cairo, Egypt
Tel.: (20) 225177980
Web Site: http://www.accm.com.eg
Calcium Carbonate Mining Services
N.A.I.C.S.: 212312

Ascom Precious Metals Mining
SAE **(1)**
26 Street 265, New Maadi, Cairo, Egypt
Tel.: (20) 225203371
Gold Exploration Services
N.A.I.C.S.: 213114
Amir Naguib *(Mng Dir)*

Glassrock Insulation Company **(1)**
28 265 St from Lasilky St, New Maadi,
Cairo, Egypt
Tel.: (20) 1150077221
Web Site: http://www.glassrock.com.eg
Mineral Wool Mfr
N.A.I.C.S.: 327993
Amir Naguib *(Chm & Mng Dir)*

Nebta For Geology & Mining Ltd. **(1)**
Block 4 House 4, Khartoum, Sudan
Tel.: (249) 153967709
Gold Exploration Services
N.A.I.C.S.: 213114
Ahmed Hammad *(Gen Mgr)*

**ASECO INTEGRATED SYS-
TEMS LTD.**
635 Fourth Line Unit 16, Oakville,
L6L 5B3, ON, Canada
Tel.: (905) 339-0059
Web Site: http://www.aseco.net
Year Founded: 1988
Rev.: $16,245,544
Emp.: 90
Mfr Consulting & Systems Integration
Services Provider
N.A.I.C.S.: 541500
Brad Walker *(Pres)*

ASEED HOLDINGS CO., LTD.
723 Funamachi, Fukuyama, 720-
0043, Hiroshima, Japan
Tel.: (81) 849235552
Web Site: https://www.aseed-hd.co.jp
Year Founded: 1972
9959—(TKS)
Rev.: $153,748,600
Assets: $125,114,080
Liabilities: $81,289,780
Net Worth: $43,824,300
Earnings: $5,076,480
Emp.: 638
Fiscal Year-end: 03/31/24
Holding Company

N.A.I.C.S.: 551112

Subsidiaries:

HOSHAKU INRYO CO., LTD. **(1)**
2061-3 Beppu Shiwa cho, Higashi-
hiroshima, 739-0267, Hiroshima, Japan
Tel.: (81) 824334959
Emp.: 67
Beverages Mfr
N.A.I.C.S.: 312111

SHANGHAI ASEED CO., LTD. **(1)**
Room 8013 Huasheng Building 601 Zhang
Yang Road Pu Dong, Shanghai, China
Tel.: (86) 2158399787
Beverage Distr
N.A.I.C.S.: 424810

ASEEM GLOBAL LTD.
5476 South Basti Harphool Singh Sa-
dar Thana Road Sadar Bazar, Delhi,
110006, India
Tel.: (91) 1123528157 In
Web Site:
  http://www.aseemglobal.com
Year Founded: 1983
Rev.: $27,845,600
Assets: $23,741,076
Liabilities: $23,370,571
Net Worth: $370,505
Earnings: ($1,882,008)
Fiscal Year-end: 03/31/16
Metal Product Whslr
N.A.I.C.S.: 423510

**ASEFA PUBLIC COMPANY
LIMITED**
5 Moo1 Rama II Road Khok-krabue,
Mueang Samutsakhon, Samut Sak-
hon, 74000, Thailand
Tel.: (66) 26867777
Web Site: https://www.asefa.co.th
Year Founded: 1997
ASEFA—(THA)
Rev.: $100,226,012
Assets: $97,252,836
Liabilities: $51,169,428
Net Worth: $46,083,408
Earnings: $4,909,200
Emp.: 1,304
Fiscal Year-end: 12/31/23
Electric Power Distribution
N.A.I.C.S.: 221122
Soracit Phungsuk *(Chm)*

**ASEGURADORA GENERAL
S.A.**
10A Calle 3 17, Zona 10, Guatemala,
00110, Guatemala
Tel.: (502) 2285 7200
Web Site:
  http://www.aseguresemejor.com
Insurance Services
N.A.I.C.S.: 524128

**ASELSAN ELEKTRONIK
SANAYI VE TICARET AS**
Mehmet Akif Ersoy Mah Istiklal Marsi
Caddesi No 16, Yenimahalle, 06200,
Ankara, Türkiye
Tel.: (90) 3125921000
Web Site: https://www.aselsan.com
Year Founded: 1975
ASELS—(IST)
Rev.: $1,089,764,699
Assets: $2,348,808,235
Liabilities: $1,117,600,408
Net Worth: $1,231,207,827
Earnings: $366,576,856
Emp.: 9,935
Fiscal Year-end: 12/31/22
Telecommunications Equipment Mfr
N.A.I.C.S.: 334290
Nuh Yilmaz *(CFO-Financial Mgmt)*

Subsidiaries:

Mikroelektronik Ar-Ge Tasarim ve Ticaret Ltd. Co. **(1)**

Aselsan Elektronik Sanayi Ve Ticaret AS—(Continued)

ITU Ayazaga Kampusu Resitpasa Mah Katar Cad 4 ARI-3 Teknokent B203, Sariyer, 34467, Istanbul, Turkiye
Tel.: (90) 2122867892
Web Site: https://mkr-ic.com
Modems Mfr
N.A.I.C.S.: 334118

TUYAR Mikroelektronik Sanayi ve Ticaret Anonim Sirketi (1)
Teknopark Istanbul Sanayi Mah Teknopark Bulvari No 1 9A Blok, 1 Kat No 207, 34906, Istanbul, Turkiye
Tel.: (90) 2165155162
Web Site: https://tuyar.com.tr
Microchip Mfr
N.A.I.C.S.: 334413

ASENOVA KREPOST AD
Ivan Vazov N 2, 4230, Asenovgrad, Bulgaria
Tel.: (359) 33160450
Web Site: https://www.asenova-krepost.com
ASKR—(BUL)
Sales Range: Less than $1 Million
Plastic Packaging Materials Mfr
N.A.I.C.S.: 326112
Bogdan Atanasov Bibov (CEO)

ASEP MEDICAL HOLDINGS INC.
420-730 View Street, Vancouver, V8W 3Y7, BC, Canada
Tel.: (778) 600-0509   BC
Web Site:
  https://www.asepmedical.com
Year Founded: 2021
SEPSF—(OTCQB)
Assets: $20,200,627
Liabilities: $394,009
Net Worth: $19,806,619
Earnings: ($4,294,935)
Fiscal Year-end: 12/31/22
Holding Company
N.A.I.C.S.: 551112
Evan Haney (Chief Scientific Officer)

ASETEK A/S
Assensvej 2, DK-9220, Aalborg, Denmark
Tel.: (45) 96450047
Web Site: https://www.asetek.com
Year Founded: 2000
ASTK—(CSE)
Rev.: $50,650,000
Assets: $78,615,000
Liabilities: $35,867,000
Net Worth: $42,748,000
Earnings: ($4,325,000)
Emp.: 140
Fiscal Year-end: 12/31/22
Data Centers, Servers, Work Stations, Gaming & High Performance PCs Energy Efficient Liquid Cooling Systems
N.A.I.C.S.: 334111
Andre Eriksen (Founder & CEO)

Subsidiaries:

Asetek Danmark A/S (1)
Assensvej 2, 9220, Aalborg, Denmark
Tel.: (45) 96450047
Computer Hardware Mfr & Distr
N.A.I.C.S.: 332510

ASETRONICS AG
Freiburgstrasse 251, 3018, Bern, Switzerland
Tel.: (41) 313293111   CH
Web Site: http://www.asetronics.ch
Year Founded: 1852
Sales Range: $75-99.9 Million
Emp.: 180
Electronic Components Mfr
N.A.I.C.S.: 334419

Andre Maurer (Chm & CEO)

ASF GROUP LIMITED
3B Macquarie Street, Sydney, 2000, NSW, Australia
Tel.: (61) 292519088   AU
Web Site:
  https://www.asfgroupltd.com
AFA—(A3X)
Rev.: $1,795,540
Assets: $5,833,333
Liabilities: $24,021,100
Net Worth: ($18,187,767)
Earnings: ($6,629,941)
Fiscal Year-end: 06/30/24
Mineral Resources
N.A.I.C.S.: 423520
Min Yang (Chm)

Subsidiaries:

ASF (Hong Kong) Ltd. (1)
11/F Times Tower 391-407 Jaffe Road, Causeway Bay, China (Hong Kong)
Tel.: (852) 21511206
Real Estate Development Services
N.A.I.C.S.: 531390

ASFLOW CO LTD.
38 Jeongnam Sandan-Ro Jeongnam-Myeon, Hwaseong, Gyeonggi-do, Korea (South)
Tel.: (82) 313522301
Web Site: https://www.asflow.com
Year Founded: 2000
159010—(KRS)
Semiconductor Equipment Mfr
N.A.I.C.S.: 334413
Kang Du-Hong (CEO)

ASGARD INVESTMENT HOTELS SOCIMI SA
Calle Nuestra Senora de Gracia, Marbella, 29604, Malaga, Spain
Tel.: (34) 567544738
Real Estate Investment Services
N.A.I.C.S.: 531190
Audun Lekve (CEO & Sec)

ASGENT, INC.
6-4 Akashicho, Chuo-ku, Tokyo, 104-0044, Japan
Tel.: (81) 368537401
Web Site: https://www.asgent.com
Year Founded: 1997
4288—(TKS)
Sales Range: $25-49.9 Million
Network Security Services
N.A.I.C.S.: 561621
Takahiro Sugimoto (Pres & CEO)

ASH & LACY BUILDING SYSTEMS LTD
Bromford Lane, West Bromwich, B70 7JJ, West Midlands, United Kingdom
Tel.: (44) 1215251444
Web Site: http://www.ashandlacy.com
Sales Range: $25-49.9 Million
Emp.: 350
Commercial & Institutional Building Construction
N.A.I.C.S.: 236220
David Wright (Mng Dir)

ASH-SHARQIYAH DEVELOPMENT COMPANY
King Khaled Street Unit 8 Al Nakheel, Dammam, 32244 7849, Saudi Arabia
Tel.: (966) 138099439
Web Site:
  https://www.asharqiyah.com.sa
Year Founded: 1986
6060—(SAU)
Rev.: $71,606
Assets: $49,213,360
Liabilities: $12,101,348
Net Worth: $37,112,012

Earnings: ($852,429)
Emp.: 10
Fiscal Year-end: 12/31/22
Agricultural Product Mfr
N.A.I.C.S.: 111199
Mohammed Ahmed Alrahmah (Mng Dir)

ASHANTI SANKOFA INC.
908 - 938 Howe Street, Vancouver, V6Z 1N9, BC, Canada
Tel.: (604) 314-9293   BC
Web Site:
  http://www.ashantisankofa.com
Year Founded: 1980
ASI—(TSXV)
Assets: $196,500
Liabilities: $302,222
Net Worth: ($105,722)
Earnings: ($512,396)
Fiscal Year-end: 02/29/20
Gold Exploration & Development Services
N.A.I.C.S.: 212220
Nancy Zhao (CFO)

ASHAPURA MINECHEM LIMITED
278 Jeeven Udyog Building Dr D N Road Fort, Mumbai, 400 001, India
Tel.: (91) 2266651700   In
Web Site: https://www.ashapura.com
ASHAPURMIN—(NSE)
Emp.: 625
Mineral Mining Services
N.A.I.C.S.: 212390
Sachin Polke (Officer-Compliance, Sec & VP)

Subsidiaries:

Ashapura International Limited (1)
Jeevan Udyog Bldg D N Road Fort, Mumbai, 400 001, India
Tel.: (91) 2266651700
Web Site: http://www.ashapura.com
Sales Range: $75-99.9 Million
Emp.: 25
Foundry Grade Bentonite Supplier
N.A.I.C.S.: 423520

Subsidiary (Domestic):

Aeon Procare Private Limited (2)
3rd Floor Lawrence Mayo Gldg Dr D N Road Fort, Mumbai, 400 001, India
Tel.: (91) 2266149565
Web Site: https://www.aeonprocare.com
Pharmaceuticals Mfr
N.A.I.C.S.: 325412

Ashapura Midgulf NV (1)
Industrieweg 32 Ware house - No 8, 2280, Grobbendonk, Herentals, Belgium
Tel.: (32) 35411981
Web Site: https://www.ashapuramidgulf.com
Building Materials Whslr
N.A.I.C.S.: 423390

Ashapura Perfoclay Limited (1)
Jeevan Udyog Building 3rd Floor 278 D N Road, Fort, Mumbai, 400 001, India
Tel.: (91) 226 665 1700
Web Site: https://www.aplgalleon.com
Emp.: 4,700
Clay & Ceramic Mining Services
N.A.I.C.S.: 327110

Orient Abrasives Limited (1)
GIDC Industrial Area, Porbandar, 360 577, Gujarat, India   (39.1%)
Tel.: (91) 2862221788
Web Site: https://www.orientabrasives.com
Rev.: $41,515,820
Assets: $46,387,136
Liabilities: $13,327,997
Net Worth: $33,059,140
Earnings: $1,551,991
Emp.: 259
Fiscal Year-end: 03/31/2021
Aluminium Products Mfr
N.A.I.C.S.: 331313
Pundarik Sanyal (Chm)

PT Ashapura Resources (1)

Apt Mediterania Palace Ruko Tower C / OR, Kemayoran, Jakarta Pusat, 10630, Indonesia
Tel.: (62) 213 983 4522
Mineral Mining Services
N.A.I.C.S.: 213114

Sohar Ashapura Chemicals LLC (1)
PO Box 1160, 112, Ruwi, Oman
Tel.: (968) 2 200 4600
Web Site: https://www.sacoman.net
Chemical & Fertilizer Mining Services
N.A.I.C.S.: 212390

ASHAPURI GOLD ORNAMENT LTD.
109 to 112-A Super Mall Nr LalBunglow C G Road, Ahmedabad, 380 009, Gujarat, India
Tel.: (91) 7926462170
Web Site:
  https://www.ashapurigold.com
542579—(BOM)
Rev.: $16,057,466
Assets: $10,958,046
Liabilities: $355,259
Net Worth: $10,602,787
Earnings: $348,098
Fiscal Year-end: 03/31/21
Gold Jewellery Mfr & Distr
N.A.I.C.S.: 339910
Dinesh Soni (Mng Dir)

ASHARI AGENCIES LTD.
601 Disco Compound G T Road, Ghaziabad, 201001, Uttar Pradesh, India
Tel.: (91) 1204122041
Web Site:
  http://www.ashariagencies.in
Year Founded: 1985
Rev.: $117,012
Assets: $1,117,298
Liabilities: $10,464
Net Worth: $1,106,833
Earnings: ($616,658)
Fiscal Year-end: 03/31/19
Financial Banking Services
N.A.I.C.S.: 522110

ASHBURTON
17 Hilary Street, PO Box 239, Saint Helier, JE4 8SJ, Jersey
Tel.: (44) 1534512000
Web Site:
  http://www.ashburtoninvestments.com
Sales Range: $25-49.9 Million
Emp.: 90
Investment Advice & Management
N.A.I.C.S.: 523940
Nick Taylor (CFO)

Subsidiaries:

RMB CIS MANCO (Proprietary) Limited (1)
1 Merchant Place Corner Fredman Drive & Rivonia Road, 2196, Sandton, South Africa
Tel.: (27) 112828271
Web Site: http://www.rmb.co.za
Currency Exchange Services
N.A.I.C.S.: 523160

ASHFAQ TEXTILE MILLS LIMITED
8-A Officers Colony No 1 Susan Road, Faisalabad, Pakistan
Tel.: (92) 418740101
Web Site:
  https://www.ashfaqtextile.com
Year Founded: 1988
ASHT—(PSX)
Rev.: $1,208,702
Assets: $4,148,498
Liabilities: $808,165
Net Worth: $3,340,333
Earnings: ($287,362)
Fiscal Year-end: 06/30/23
Woven Fabrics Mfr

N.A.I.C.S.: 313210
Ashfaq Ahmed *(CEO & Mng Dir)*

ASHIANA AGRO INDUSTRIES LIMITED
No 34 Andal Nagar Baluchetty Chatram, Kancheepuram Taluk, Kanchipuram, 631551, Tamil Nadu, India
Tel.: (91) 4428344820
Web Site: https://www.aail.in
Year Founded: 1990
519174—(BOM)
Rev.: $124,939
Assets: $336,869
Liabilities: $6,642
Net Worth: $330,226
Earnings: $5,603
Emp.: 3
Fiscal Year-end: 03/31/22
Edible Oil Mfr
N.A.I.C.S.: 311224
Pavan Kumar Matli *(Exec Dir)*

ASHIANA HOUSING LTD
5F Everest 46/C Chowringhee Road, Kolkata, 700 071, West Bengal, India
Tel.: (91) 334037860
Web Site:
  https://www.ashianahousing.com
523716—(BOM)
Rev.: $31,885,035
Assets: $254,427,810
Liabilities: $153,958,350
Net Worth: $100,469,460
Earnings: ($960,960)
Emp.: 526
Fiscal Year-end: 03/31/22
Real Estate Development Services
N.A.I.C.S.: 531210
Vishal Gupta *(Co-Mng Dir)*

ASHIANA ISPAT LTD.
A-1116 RIICO Industrial Area Phase III Bhiwadi, Alwar, 301019, Rajasthan, India
Tel.: (91) 1493220777
Web Site: http://www.ashianaispat.in
513401—(BOM)
Rev.: $59,922,545
Assets: $21,104,483
Liabilities: $16,443,841
Net Worth: $4,660,642
Earnings: $138,288
Emp.: 159
Fiscal Year-end: 03/31/22
Construction Engineering Services
N.A.I.C.S.: 237990
Naresh Chand Jain *(Chm)*

ASHIKA CAPITAL LIMITED
1008 Raheja Ctr 214 Nariman Point, Mumbai, 400021, India
Tel.: (91) 2266111700
Web Site:
  http://www.ashikagroup.com
Sales Range: $25-49.9 Million
Emp.: 30
Merchant Banking Services
N.A.I.C.S.: 523150
Rajendra Kanoongo *(Pres)*

ASHIMA LTD.
Texcellence Complex Nr Anupam Cinema Khokhra, Ahmedabad, 380 021, India
Tel.: (91) 7967777000
Web Site: https://www.ashima.in
ASHIMASYN—(NSE)
Rev.: $28,663,635
Assets: $43,353,765
Liabilities: $12,477,465
Net Worth: $30,876,300
Earnings: $2,446,080
Emp.: 213
Fiscal Year-end: 03/31/22

Cotton Fabric Mfr
N.A.I.C.S.: 313210
Chintan Navnitlal Parikh *(Chm & Mng Dir)*

ASHIMORI INDUSTRY CO., LTD.
7-11-61 Senrioka, Settsu, 566-0001, Osaka, Japan
Tel.: (81) 663881212
Web Site: https://www.ashimori.co.jp
Year Founded: 1878
3526—(TKS)
Rev.: $452,051,290
Assets: $356,021,210
Liabilities: $206,859,950
Net Worth: $149,161,260
Earnings: $21,264,370
Emp.: 2,400
Fiscal Year-end: 03/31/24
Automotive Safety Parts Mfr
N.A.I.C.S.: 336390
Shigeyuki Washine *(Pres & CEO)*

Subsidiaries:

Allsafe Japan Ltd. (1)
1-1-8 Sakuragicho 9F Nisseki Yokohama Building, Naka-ku, Yokohama, 231-0062, Kanagawa, Japan
Tel.: (81) 45 681 8171
Web Site: http://www.allsafejapan.com
Logistics Equipment Mfr & Distr
N.A.I.C.S.: 336390

Subsidiary (Domestic):

Allsafe Japan Ltd. - Tohoku Plant (2)
37-1 Aza Ishinazaka Furukawa Tsukanome, Osaki, Miyagi, Japan
Tel.: (81) 229238500
Motor Vehicle Parts Mfr
N.A.I.C.S.: 336390

Ashimori (Thailand) Co., Ltd. (1)
89 Moo 9 Wellgrow Industrial Estate Bangna-Trad Rd K m 36, Tambol Bangwua Bangpakong District, Chachoengsao, 24180, Thailand
Tel.: (66) 385717519
Web Site: http://www.ashimori.co.th
Emp.: 961
Automobile Interior Parts Mfr & Distr
N.A.I.C.S.: 336360

Ashimori Engineering Co., Ltd. (1)
4-8 1-chome Tosabori, Nishi-ku, Osaka, 550-0001, Japan
Tel.: (81) 664596063
Motor Vehicle Parts Mfr
N.A.I.C.S.: 336390

Ashimori India Private Limited (1)
Plot No SP2-11 New Industrial Complex Majrakath, Alwar District, 301705, Neemrana, Rajasthan, India
Tel.: (91) 14946706338
Automobile Interior Parts Mfr & Distr
N.A.I.C.S.: 336360

Ashimori Industria de Mexico, S.A. de C.V (1)
Circuito San Roque Norte 345 Parque Industrial Santa Fe Ampliacion, Silao, Guanajuato, Mexico
Tel.: (52) 4727489148
Automobile Interior Parts Mfr & Distr
N.A.I.C.S.: 336360

Ashimori Industry Co., Ltd. - Fukui Plant (1)
8-5 Ungetsu 2-go Tada, Obama, 917-0026, Fukui, Japan
Tel.: (81) 770561212
Motor Vehicle Parts Mfr
N.A.I.C.S.: 336390

Ashimori Industry Co., Ltd. - Hamamatsu Plant (1)
26 Kozawatari-cho, Minami-ku, Hamamatsu, 432-8063, Shizuoka, Japan
Tel.: (81) 534451522
Motor Vehicle Parts Mfr
N.A.I.C.S.: 336390

Ashimori Industry Co., Ltd. - Sasayama Plant (1)

40-2 Nishimachi, Tamba, Sasayama, 669-2342, Hyogo, Japan
Tel.: (81) 795521177
Motor Vehicle Parts Mfr
N.A.I.C.S.: 336390

Ashimori Industry Yamaguchi Co., Ltd. (1)
3-96 Sayama, Yamaguchi, Japan
Tel.: (81) 839883260
Automotive Exterior Parts Mfr
N.A.I.C.S.: 336360

Ashimori Korea Co., Ltd. (1)
Sinpyeong-ri 134 Dowon-ro Jijeong-myeon, Wonju, 26351, Gangwon-do, Korea (South)
Tel.: (82) 337426623
Automobile Interior Parts Mfr & Distr
N.A.I.C.S.: 336360

Ashimori Technology (Wuxi) Co., Ltd. (1)
Lot B-18-F Xin Chang Road S No 12, Wuxi National High & New Technology Industrial Development Zone, Wuxi, Jiangsu, China
Tel.: (86) 51085331155
Automobile Interior Parts Mfr & Distr
N.A.I.C.S.: 336360

Ashimori Textile Manufacturing Co., Ltd. (1)
Ri-59 4-chome Tsurugi-honmachi, Hakusan, Ishikawa, Japan
Tel.: (81) 762720213
Narrow Woven Fabric Mfr
N.A.I.C.S.: 313220

Jet Trading Co., Ltd. (1)
4-8 1-chome Tosabori, Nishi-ku, Osaka, 550-0001, Japan
Tel.: (81) 664596066
Firefighting Product Distr
N.A.I.C.S.: 423850

Shibata Industry Co., Ltd. (1)
3-6 1-chome Kamisun cho, Tachikawa, Tokyo, Japan
Tel.: (81) 425347792
Civil Engineering Services
N.A.I.C.S.: 541330

ASHINCKIY METZAVOD PAO
Asha she is Mira d 9, Chelyabinsk, 456010, Russia
Tel.: (7) 3515931462   RU
Web Site: https://www.amet.ru
AMEZ—(MOEX)
Sales Range: Less than $1 Million
Steel Products Mfr
N.A.I.C.S.: 331221
Shepelev Oleg Igorevich *(Deputy Chm)*

ASHIRWAD CAPITAL LIMITED
303 Tantia Jogani Industrial Estate Opp Lodha Bellissimo, J R Boricha Marg Lower Parel, Mumbai, 400 011, India
Tel.: (91) 2243443555
Web Site:
  https://www.ashirwadcapital.in
512247—(BOM)
Rev.: $166,873
Assets: $1,755,834
Liabilities: $31,037
Net Worth: $1,724,797
Earnings: $135,262
Emp.: 3
Fiscal Year-end: 03/31/22
Securities Brokerage Services
N.A.I.C.S.: 523150

ASHIRWAD STEELS & INDUSTRIES LIMITED
6 Waterloo Street Room No 506, Kolkata, 700069, West Bengal, India
Tel.: (91) 3322430372   In
Web Site:
  https://www.ashirwadsteels.com
Year Founded: 1986
526847—(BOM)
Rev.: $606,497
Assets: $10,699,634

Liabilities: $601
Net Worth: $10,699,034
Earnings: $2,288,532
Emp.: 6
Fiscal Year-end: 03/31/23
Sponge Iron Mfr
N.A.I.C.S.: 331110
Dalbir Chhibbar *(Mng Dir)*

ASHISH POLYPLAST LTD.
A/305 Samudra Near Hotel Klassic Gold Off C G Road, Ahmedabad, 380 006, Gujarat, India
Tel.: (91) 7926445090
Web Site:
  https://www.ashishpolyplast.com
530429—(BOM)
Rev.: $2,245,302
Assets: $1,024,173
Liabilities: $279,061
Net Worth: $745,113
Earnings: $43,898
Fiscal Year-end: 03/31/22
Pneumatic Hose Mfr
N.A.I.C.S.: 332912
Aayushi P. Soni *(Compliance Officer & Sec)*

ASHLEY HOUSE PLC
Unit 1 Barnes Wallis Court Wellington Road, Cressex Business Park, High Wycombe, HP12 3PS, United Kingdom
Tel.: (44) 1628 600 340
Web Site:
  http://www.ashleyhouseplc.com
Year Founded: 1991
Rev.: $24,923,643
Assets: $16,695,360
Liabilities: $9,277,898
Net Worth: $7,417,462
Earnings: $2,363,658
Emp.: 82
Fiscal Year-end: 04/30/18
Health Care Srvices
N.A.I.C.S.: 621111
Antony J. Walters *(CEO)*

ASHLEY SERVICES GROUP LIMITED
Level 10 92 Pitt Street, Sydney, 2000, NSW, Australia
Tel.: (61) 2 9216 4747
Web Site:
  http://www.ashleyservicesgroup.com
Sales Range: $200-249.9 Million
Emp.: 350
Employment & Training Services
N.A.I.C.S.: 561311
Ross Shrimpton *(Mng Dir)*

ASHMORE EMERGING MARKETS INCOME FUND
61 Aldwych, London, WC2B 4AE, United Kingdom
Tel.: (44) 20 3077 6000
Investment Services
N.A.I.C.S.: 523999
George Grunebaum *(Pres & CEO)*

ASHMORE GLOBAL OPPORTUNITIES LTD.
Trafalgar Court Les Banques, Saint Peter Port, GY1 3QL, Guernsey
Tel.: (44) 1481745001
Web Site: http://www.agol.com
AGOL—(AIM)
Sales Range: $1-9.9 Million
Financial Services
N.A.I.C.S.: 525910
Richard Hotchkis *(Chm)*

ASHMORE GROUP PLC
61 Aldwych, London, WC2B 4AE, United Kingdom
Tel.: (44) 2030776000   UK

Ashmore Group plc—(Continued)

Web Site:
https://www.ashmoregroup.com
Year Founded: 1992
ASHM—(LSE)
Rev.: $239,256,825
Assets: $1,238,245,701
Liabilities: $112,360,970
Net Worth: $1,125,884,730
Earnings: $124,115,268
Emp.: 283
Fiscal Year-end: 06/30/24
Emerging Market Debt & Equity Portfolio Management
N.A.I.C.S.: 523999
John Taylor (Sec)

Subsidiaries:

Ashmore Investment Management India LLP　　　　　(1)
507A Kakad Chambers Dr Annie Besant Road Worli, Mumbai, 400 018, India
Tel.: (91) 2262690000
Market Research Services
N.A.I.C.S.: 541613

Ashmore Investment Management Limited　　　　　(1)
61 Aldwych, London, WC2B 4AE, United Kingdom
Tel.: (44) 2030776000
Web Site: http://www.ashmoregroup.com
Sales Range: $125-149.9 Million
Emp.: 150
Emerging Market Debt & Equity Portfolio Management
N.A.I.C.S.: 523999

Holding (Non-US):

AEI　　　　　(2)
Clifton House 75 Fort Street, PO Box 190GT, Georgetown, Cayman Islands
Tel.: (345) 9494900
Sales Range: $5-14.9 Billion
Emp.: 15,430
Energy Infrastructure Owner & Operator
N.A.I.C.S.: 335311
Ronald W. Haddock (Chm)

Subsidiary (US):

AEI Services LLC　　　　　(3)
1600 Smith St Ste 4900, Houston, TX 77002
Tel.: (713) 345-5200
Earnings: $158,000,000
Emp.: 120
Holding Company; Energy Services
N.A.I.C.S.: 551112
Ronald W. Haddock (Chm)

Subsidiary (Non-US):

Gas Natural de Lima y Callao S.A.　　　　　(3)
Calle Morelli 150 C C La Rambla - Torre 2, San Borja, Lima, 27, Peru
Tel.: (51) 16117500
Web Site: http://www.calidda.com.pe
Sales Range: $125-149.9 Million
Emp.: 186
Natural Gas Supplier
N.A.I.C.S.: 221210

Avenida Partners LLC　　　　　(1)
130 Newport Center Dr Ste 220, Newport Beach, CA 92660
Tel.: (949) 734-7810
Web Site: https://www.avenidapartners.com
Real Estate Services
N.A.I.C.S.: 531210
Robert D. May (Mng Partner)

Stracon GyM S.A.　　　　　(1)
Av Santo Toribio 143 Oficina 401 San Isidro, Lima, 15046, Peru　　　　(63%)
Tel.: (51) 12080230
Web Site: http://www.stracon.com
Construction & Mining Services
N.A.I.C.S.: 423810
Jose Luis del Corral (VP-Intl & Country Mgr)

ASHNISHA INDUSTRIES LTD.

23 3rd Floor Sarthik Complex Nr Fun Republic Iscon Cross Road, Mithakhali, Ahmedabad, 380015, Gujarat, India
Tel.: (91) 7926463227
Web Site: https://www.ashnisha.in
541702—(BOM)
Rev.: $68,658
Assets: $2,040,742
Liabilities: $419,178
Net Worth: $1,621,564
Earnings: ($18,484)
Emp.: 1
Fiscal Year-end: 03/31/22
Steel & Steel Alloy Product Mfr
N.A.I.C.S.: 331110
Dimpal J. Solanki (Compliance Officer & Sec)

ASHNOOR TEXTILE MILLS LIMITED

Behrampur Road Village Khandsa, Gurgaon, 122 001, Haryana, India
Tel.: (91) 1244940550
Web Site:
https://www.ashnoortex.com
Year Founded: 1984
507872—(BOM)
Rev.: $16,209,880
Assets: $16,768,353
Liabilities: $11,098,138
Net Worth: $5,670,215
Earnings: $740,033
Emp.: 435
Fiscal Year-end: 03/31/21
Textile Mill Operator
N.A.I.C.S.: 314999
Suneel Gupta (Chm & Mng Dir)

ASHOK ALCO CHEM LIMITED

12/13 Jeevan Udyog Building 278 Dr DN Road Fort, Mumbai, 400 001, India
Tel.: (91) 2266106338
Web Site:
http://www.ashokalcochem.com
Year Founded: 1992
524594—(BOM)
Rev.: $2,808,474
Assets: $8,235,823
Liabilities: $2,595,684
Net Worth: $5,640,139
Earnings: $149,904
Emp.: 5
Fiscal Year-end: 03/31/22
Specialty Chemical Mfr & Whslr
N.A.I.C.S.: 325199
Deepak Bhardwaj (CEO)

Subsidiaries:

Aeonx Digital Solutions Private Limited　　　　　(1)
278 Jeevan Udyog Building DN Road Fort, Mumbai, 400 001, India
Tel.: (91) 2266221640
Web Site: https://www.aeonx.digital
Business Consulting Services
N.A.I.C.S.: 541611

ASHOK PIRAMAL GROUP

2 Peninsual Spenta Mathuradas Mills Senapati Bapat Marg Lower Parel, Mumbai, 400013, India
Tel.: (91) 22 6615 4651
Web Site:
http://www.ashokpiramalgroup.com
Year Founded: 1934
Holding Company; Textiles, Engineering, Real Estate & Entertainment
N.A.I.C.S.: 551112
Urvi Piramal (Chm)

Subsidiaries:

Integra Apparels and Textiles Pvt Ltd　　　　　(1)
Krishna Reddy Industrial Area 7th Mile Kudlu Gate, Bengaluru, 560 068, Karna-

taka, India
Tel.: (91) 8040523000
Web Site: http://www.integraapparels.com
Textile Products Distr
N.A.I.C.S.: 424310
C. Anil (Mgr-Mktg)

Morarjee Textiles Ltd　　　　　(1)
503 5th Floor Peninsula Tower-1 Peninsula Corporate Park, Ganpatrao Kadam Marg Lower Parel, Mumbai, 400 013, India
Tel.: (91) 2266154651
Web Site: https://www.morarjee.com
Rev.: $26,623,997
Assets: $89,629,886
Liabilities: $90,321,204
Net Worth: ($691,318)
Earnings: ($8,416,959)
Fiscal Year-end: 03/31/2021
Fabrics Mfr
N.A.I.C.S.: 313210
Urvi A. Piramal (Chm)

Subsidiary (Non-US):

Morarjee International SRL　　　　　(2)
Corso Europa 209, 20017, Milan, Italy
Tel.: (39) 02 9316 9580
Textile Products Sales
N.A.I.C.S.: 314999

PMP Auto Components Pvt. Ltd.　　　(1)
3rd Floor Bhagat House Shyam Nagar, Off Jogeshwari Vikhroli Link Road Jogeshwari East, Mumbai, 400060, India
Tel.: (91) 22 2838 1670
Web Site: http://www.pmpauto.com
Auto Components Mfr & Sales
N.A.I.C.S.: 334419
S. N. Somani (CEO)

Peninsula Land Limited　　　　　(1)
503 5th Floor Peninsula Tower-1 Peninsula Corporate Park, Ganpatrao Kadam Marg Lower Parel, Mumbai, 400013, India
Tel.: (91) 2266229300
Web Site: https://www.peninsula.co.in
Rev.: $37,533,405
Assets: $309,197,070
Liabilities: $309,351,315
Net Worth: ($154,245)
Earnings: ($4,423,965)
Emp.: 160
Fiscal Year-end: 03/31/2021
Real Estate Management Services
N.A.I.C.S.: 531390
Rajeev A. Piramal (Vice Chm & Mng Dir)

Pune Football Club Limited　　　　　(1)
Peninsula Centre Plot No 4, Galaxy Co operative Society Off Dhole Patil Road, Pune, 411 001, India
Tel.: (91) 9764002228
Web Site: http://www.punefc.com
Sports Club Operator
N.A.I.C.S.: 713940
Abhishek Mehta (Mgr-Mktg)

ASHOKA BUILDCON LTD.

S No 861 Ashoka House Ashoka Marg, Vadala, Nasik, 422 011, India
Tel.: (91) 2536633705
Web Site:
https://www.ashokabuildcon.com
533271—(BOM)
Rev.: $1,124,094,180
Assets: $2,340,321,643
Liabilities: $2,070,759,245
Net Worth: $269,562,398
Earnings: $50,902,038
Emp.: 4,000
Fiscal Year-end: 03/31/23
Roads, Bridges, Commercial Buildings Operators & Mfr
N.A.I.C.S.: 237310
Ashok M. Katariya (Chm)

Subsidiaries:

Ashoka Concessions Limited　　　　　(1)
S No 861 Ashoka House Ashoka Marg, Vadala, Nashik, 422 011, Maharashtra, India
Tel.: (91) 2536633705
Web Site:
http://www.ashokaconcessions.com
Infrastrcuture Management Services
N.A.I.C.S.: 237310

Ashoka Technologies Private Limited　　　　　(1)
Ashoka House Ashoka Marg, Nashik, 422 011, Maharashtra, India
Tel.: (91) 2533011705
Web Site: http://www.ashokatech.com
Automation Product Mfr
N.A.I.C.S.: 334418
Mathivanan Natarajan (Asst Mgr-Pur)

ASHOKA INDIA EQUITY INVESTMENT TRUST PLC

6th Floor 125 London Wall, London, EC2Y 5AS, United Kingdom
Tel.: (44) 7767102572
Web Site:
https://www.ashokaindiaequity.com
AIE—(LSE)
Rev.: $143,819,514
Assets: $577,813,447
Liabilities: $27,460,819
Net Worth: $550,352,628
Earnings: $122,160,010
Fiscal Year-end: 06/30/24
Investment Advisory Services
N.A.I.C.S.: 523940
Andrew Watkins (Chm)

ASHOKA METCAST LIMITED

7th Floor Ashoka Chambers Opp HCG Hospital Mithkhali Six Roads, Mithakhali, Ahmedabad, 380 006, Gujarat, India
Tel.: (91) 7926463226
Web Site:
https://www.ashokametcast.in
540923—(BOM)
Rev.: $9,191,948
Assets: $10,125,179
Liabilities: $4,224,749
Net Worth: $5,900,430
Earnings: $285,431
Emp.: 2
Fiscal Year-end: 03/31/22
Steel Product Mfr & Distr
N.A.I.C.S.: 332312
Shalin A. Shah (Mng Dir)

Subsidiaries:

Rhetan Rolling Mills Private Limited　　　　　(1)
7th Floor Ashoka Chambers Mithakhali Six Roads, Mithakhali, Ahmedabad, 380006, Gujarat, India
Tel.: (91) 7926463227
Web Site: http://www.rhetan.com
Steel Bar Mfr
N.A.I.C.S.: 331110

ASHOKA REFINERIES LIMITED

408 Wallfort Ozone Fafadih, Raipur, 492001, CG, India
Tel.: (91) 7714030947
Web Site:
https://www.ashokarefineries.com
Year Founded: 1991
526983—(BOM)
Rev.: $104,847
Assets: $321,607
Liabilities: $54,234
Net Worth: $267,372
Earnings: $1,117
Fiscal Year-end: 03/31/21
Cargo Handling Services
N.A.I.C.S.: 488490
Punit Mittal (Gen Mgr)

ASHRAM ONLINE.COM LIMITED

New No 29 Old No 2 Mookathal Street Purasawalkam, Ambattur Industrial Estate, Chennai, 600 007, India
Tel.: (91) 4445891221
Web Site:
https://www.ashramonline.in

526187—(BOM)
Rev.: $101,885
Assets: $1,354,583
Liabilities: $34,661
Net Worth: $1,319,923
Earnings: ($90,306)
Emp.: 4
Fiscal Year-end: 03/31/21
Infrastructure Development Services
N.A.I.C.S.: 237990
Sangita Tatia (Exec Dir)

ASHS LTD.
The Stable Block Plough Brewery
516 Wandsworth Road, London, SW8
3JX, United Kingdom
Tel.: (44) 2075010168
Web Site:
http://www.anyahindmarch.com
Year Founded: 1987
Sales Range: $50-74.9 Million
Emp.: 250
Handbag, Shoe & Accessory Designer & Mfr
N.A.I.C.S.: 316990
Anya Hindmarch (Founder)

Subsidiaries:

Anya Hindmarch Japan
Corporation (1)
8 Chome Nishigotanda Dist., Shinagawa
Ward, Tokyo, 141-8520, Japan
Tel.: (81) 354968619
Web Site: http://www.anyahindmarch.jp
Sales Range: $25-49.9 Million
Emp.: 12
Handbag, Shoe & Accessory Designer &
Mfr
N.A.I.C.S.: 316990

ASHTEAD GROUP PLC
100 Cheapside, London, EC2V 6DT,
United Kingdom
Tel.: (44) 2077269700   UK
Web Site: https://www.ashtead-group.com
Year Founded: 1984
AHT—(LSE)
Rev.: $9,667,300,000
Assets: $18,729,300,000
Liabilities: $12,721,300,000
Net Worth: $6,008,000,000
Earnings: $1,617,700,000
Emp.: 25,347
Fiscal Year-end: 04/30/23
Equipment Rental Services
N.A.I.C.S.: 532490
Michael Pratt (CFO)

Subsidiaries:

Ashtead Financing Limited (1)
Kings House 36-37 King Street, London,
EC2V 8BB, United Kingdom
Tel.: (44) 2077269700
Sales Range: $25-49.9 Million
Emp.: 11
Financial Consulting Services
N.A.I.C.S.: 541611
Geoff Crabble (CEO)

Ashtead Plant Hire Co. Ltd. (1)
102 Dalton Ave, Birchwood Park Birchwood,
Warrington, WA3 6YE, Cheshire, United
Kingdom (100%)
Tel.: (44) 1925281000
Web Site: http://www.aplant.com
Sales Range: $75-99.9 Million
Emp.: 120
Equipment Rental
N.A.I.C.S.: 532490

Sunbelt Rentals, Inc. (1)
2341 Deerfield Dr, Fort Mill, SC
29715 (100%)
Tel.: (704) 348-2676
Web Site: https://www.sunbeltrentals.com
Industrial Equipment & Tool Rental Services
N.A.I.C.S.: 532490
Brendan Horgan (CEO)

Subsidiary (Domestic):

ComRent International, LLC (2)
7640 Investment Ct, Owings, MD 20736
Tel.: (410) 257-3000
Web Site: http://www.comrent.net
Electrical Apparatus & Equipment Wiring
Supplies & Related Equipment Merchant
Whslr
N.A.I.C.S.: 423610
David Smidlein (VP-Sls)

MSP Equipment Rentals, Inc. (2)
3120 New Castle Ave, New Castle, DE
19720-3901
Tel.: (302) 669-0595
Web Site: http://www.msprentals.com
Consumer Electronics & Appliances Rental
N.A.I.C.S.: 532210
John Desmond (Mgr-Svc)

Division (Domestic):

Sunbelt Rentals Climate Control
Services (2)
900 C Tryens Rd, Aston, PA 19014-1522
Tel.: (610) 295-0156
Web Site: http://www.sunbeltrentals.com
Warm Air Heating, Air-Conditioning Equip-
ment & Supplies Merchant Whslr
N.A.I.C.S.: 423730
Kevin Kelly (Gen Mgr)

Whites Location Equipment Supply
Inc. (1)
3975 Kitchener Street, Burnaby, Vancouver,
V5C 3L9, BC, Canada
Tel.: (604) 436-1418
Web Site: https://whitesles.com
N.A.I.C.S.: 512110
Jason Bilodeau (Dir-Operations)

William F. White International
Inc. (1)
800 Islington Avenue, Toronto, M8Z 6A1,
ON, Canada
Tel.: (416) 239-5050
Fire Equipment Mfr
N.A.I.C.S.: 333310

ASHTEAD TECHNOLOGY
HOLDINGS PLC
Ashtead House Discovery Drive
Westhill, Aberdeenshire, AB32 6FG,
United Kingdom
Tel.: (44) 1224771888   UK
Web Site: https://www.ashtead-technology.com
AT—(LSE)
Equipment Rental Solutions Services
N.A.I.C.S.: 532490
Allan Pirie (CEO)

Subsidiaries:

Alfred Cheyne Engineering
Limited (1)
Cheyne House Towie Barclay Works, Turriff,
AB53 8EN, Aberdeenshire, United Kingdom
Tel.: (44) 1888511600
Web Site: http://www.ace-winches.com
Sales Range: $25-49.9 Million
Emp.: 253
Winch Mfr
N.A.I.C.S.: 333923

Subsidiary (Non-US):

ACE Winches Norge AS (2)
Kanalarmen 10, 4033, Stavanger, Norway
Tel.: (47) 51839520
Web Site: http://www.ace-winches.no
Winch Mfr
N.A.I.C.S.: 333923
Rune Midtun (Country Mgr)

Ashtead Technology Ltd. (1)
Ashtead House Discovery Drive Arnhall
Business Park, Westhill, AB32 6FG, United
Kingdom
Tel.: (44) 1224771888
Web Site: http://www.ashtead-technology.com
Environmental Monitoring, Underwater Posi-
tioning & Surveying, Remote Visual Inspec-
tion & Non-Destructive Testing Equipment
Rental Services

N.A.I.C.S.: 532490
Graham Clark (CTO)

ASHTROM GROUP LTD.
Yarkon 3 Bnei Brak LYFE Towers
Building A 33rd floor, Tel Aviv,
6789910, Israel
Tel.: (972) 36231212
Web Site: https://www.ashtrom.co.il
Year Founded: 1963
Construction Services
N.A.I.C.S.: 236220
Gil Gueron (Mng Dir)

ASHTROM PROPERTIES LTD.
Yona Kremnitzky 10, Tel Aviv,
6789910, Israel
Tel.: (972) 36231330
Web Site: http://www.ashtrom.co.il
ASPR—(TAE)
Rev.: $79,648,016
Assets: $2,010,063,513
Liabilities: $1,296,059,104
Net Worth: $714,004,409
Earnings: ($20,863,931)
Fiscal Year-end: 12/31/23
Building Construction Services
N.A.I.C.S.: 236220
Yaron Rokman (CEO)

ASHUR INTERNATIONAL
BANK FOR INVESTMENT
87 Building 99 Str 903, PO Box 3636,
Oqba Ibn Naffi Square, Baghdad,
Iraq
Tel.: (964) 7809156080
Web Site: https://ashurbank.iq
Year Founded: 2005
BASH—(IRAQ)
Sales Range: $10-24.9 Million
Emp.: 192
Investment Banking Services
N.A.I.C.S.: 523150
Safwan Kusay (Co-Chm)

ASI INDUSTRIES LIMITED
Marathon Innova A Wing 7th Floor
Off Ganpatrao Kadam Marg, Lower
Parel, Mumbai, 400 013, India
Tel.: (91) 2240896100
Web Site: https://www.asigroup.co.in
Year Founded: 1945
502015—(BOM)
Rev.: $33,240,234
Assets: $62,047,099
Liabilities: $22,173,265
Net Worth: $39,873,834
Earnings: ($7,630,923)
Emp.: 730
Fiscal Year-end: 03/31/22
Stone Quarrying & Shaping Services
N.A.I.C.S.: 212311
Deepak Jatia (Chm & Mng Dir)

ASI INNOVATION SAS
14 Allee Rene Fonck, 51100, Reims,
France
Tel.: (33) 3 26 06 05 25
Web Site: http://www.asi-innovation.fr
Aircraft Design & Aviation Engineer-
ing Services
N.A.I.C.S.: 336411
Jean-Pierre Kohn (Co-Founder &
CEO)

ASIA - PACIFIC INVESTMENT
JOINT STOCK COMPANY
3th Floor Grand Plaza Building No
117 Tran Duy Hung, Trung Hoa Ward
Cau Giay District, Hanoi, Vietnam
Tel.: (84) 435771983
Web Site: http://apeci.com.vn
Year Founded: 2006
API—(HNX)
Rev.: $78,260,400
Assets: $253,435,700

Liabilities: $154,920,000
Net Worth: $98,515,700
Earnings: $12,113,100
Fiscal Year-end: 12/31/22
Real Estate Investment Services
N.A.I.C.S.: 531390
Nguyen Do Lang (Chm)

ASIA AGRICULTURAL MA-
CHINERY CO., LTD.
168 Geum-dong Yuga-myeon,
Dalseong-gun, Daegu, Korea (South)
Tel.: (82) 535807777
Web Site: http://www.asiakor.com
Year Founded: 1945
Rev.: $92,489,209
Assets: $109,470,863
Liabilities: $20,882,811
Net Worth: $88,588,052
Earnings: $446,731
Fiscal Year-end: 12/31/18
Agricultural Machinery Mfr
N.A.I.C.S.: 333111

Subsidiaries:

Asia Agricultural Machinery Co., Ltd. -
First Factory (1)
168 Geum-dong Yuga-myeon, Dalseong-
gun, Daegu, Korea (South)
Tel.: (82) 12311594
Agricultural Machinery Mfr
N.A.I.C.S.: 333111

ASIA AIR SURVEY CO., LTD.
Shinyuri 21 Building 3F 1-2-2 Manpu-
kuji, Asao-ku, Kawasaki, 215-0004,
Kanagawa, Japan
Tel.: (81) 449697510
Web Site: https://www.ajiko.co.jp
Year Founded: 1954
9233—(TKS)
Rev.: $264,485,360
Assets: $238,840,830
Liabilities: $96,891,940
Net Worth: $141,948,890
Earnings: $13,102,320
Emp.: 1,762
Fiscal Year-end: 09/30/23
Aerial Surveying Services
N.A.I.C.S.: 541370
Kiichiro Ogawa (Pres & CEO)

Subsidiaries:

Asia Air Survey Myanmar Co.,
Ltd (1)
Room207 2nd Floor Tower E Diamond Con-
dminium Pyay Road, Kamaryut Township,
Yangon, Myanmar
Tel.: (95) 1501380
Web Site: https://www.aasmyanmar.com
Surveying Services
N.A.I.C.S.: 541360

ASIA ALLIED INFRASTRUC-
TURE HOLDINGS LIMITED
C1 5/F Hong Kong Spinners Indus-
trial Building Phase 1, 601-603 Tai
Nan West Street Cheung Sha Wan,
Kowloon, China (Hong Kong)
Tel.: (852) 37985711   BM
Web Site:
http://www.asiaalliedgroup.com
Year Founded: 1968
0711—(HKG)
Rev.: $971,768,597
Assets: $1,105,943,653
Liabilities: $803,448,794
Net Worth: $302,494,859
Earnings: ($24,388,183)
Emp.: 6,500
Fiscal Year-end: 03/31/21
Holding Company; Construction Ser-
vices
N.A.I.C.S.: 551112
Christina Wai Hang Li (Exec Dir)

Asia Allied Infrastructure Holdings
Limited—(Continued)

Subsidiaries:

Chun Wo (China) Limited (1)
Rm C2 5 F Hong Kong Spinners Indus
Bldg, 601-603 Tai Nan W St, Cheung Sha
Wan, Kowloon, China (Hong Kong)
Tel.: (852) 27458389
Web Site: http://www.chunwo.com
Sales Range: $400-449.9 Million
Emp.: 3,000
Building Construction Services
N.A.I.C.S.: 236220
Dominic Pang Yat Ting (Chm)

**Chun Wo Building Construction
Limited** (1)
Rm C2 5 Fl Hong Kong Spinners Indus
Bldg Block 1 & 2, 601-603 Tai Nan W St,
Cheung Sha Wan, Kowloon, China (Hong
Kong)
Web Site: http://www.chunwo.com
Sales Range: $500-549.9 Million
Emp.: 3,000
Building Construction & Design Services
N.A.I.C.S.: 236220

**Chun Wo Civil Engineering
Limited** (1)
5C Hong Kong Spinners Industrial Building
Phase 1 Tai Nan West Street, Cheung Sha
Wan, 601-603, Kowloon, China (Hong
Kong)
Tel.: (852) 37588711
Emp.: 300
Civil Engineering Services
N.A.I.C.S.: 541330

**Chun Wo Construction and Engineer-
ing Company Limited** (1)
Rm C2 5 F Hong Kong Spinners Indus Bldg
Block 1 & 2, Cheung Sha Wan, Kowloon,
China (Hong Kong)
Tel.: (852) 27458389
Web Site: http://www.chunwo.com
Emp.: 2,000
Commercial Building Construction Services
N.A.I.C.S.: 236220
Clement Kwok (Mng Dir)

Chun Wo Contractors Limited (1)
Rm C2 5 F Hong Kong Spinners Indus Bldg
Block 1 & 2, Cheung Sha Wan, Kowloon,
China (Hong Kong)
Tel.: (852) 27458389
Web Site: http://www.chunwo.com
Emp.: 2,000
Commercial Building Construction Services
N.A.I.C.S.: 236220
Clement Kwok (Mng Dir)

**Chun Wo E & M Engineering
Limited** (1)
Room C2 5 Floor Hong Kong Spinners In-
dus Bldg Block 1 & 2, Cheung Sha Wan,
Kowloon, China (Hong Kong)
Emp.: 40
Electrical & Mechanical Engineering Ser-
vices
N.A.I.C.S.: 541330

**Chun Wo Elegant Decoration Engi-
neering Company Limited** (1)
Rm C2 5 F Hong Kong Spinners Indus Bldg
Block 1 & 2, Cheung Sha Wan, Kowloon,
China (Hong Kong)
Tel.: (852) 27458389
Sales Range: $75-99.9 Million
Emp.: 3,000
Interior Design & Decorating Services
N.A.I.C.S.: 541410
Clement Kwok (Mng Dir)

Chun Wo Foundations Limited (1)
Rm C2 5 F Hong Kong Spinners Indus Bldg
Block 1 & 2, 601-603 Tai Nan W St, Ch-
eung Sha Wan, Kowloon, China (Hong
Kong)
Tel.: (852) 27458389
Web Site: http://www.chunwo.com
Emp.: 3,000
Foundation & Underground Construction
Services
N.A.I.C.S.: 237990
Clement Kwok (Mng Dir)

**City Professional Management
Limited** (1)

9B-9C 9/F & the whole floor of 10/F No 9
Po Lun Street, Lai Chi kok, Kowloon, China
(Hong Kong)
Tel.: (852) 37588988
Web Site: http://www.csgcitypro.com
Sales Range: $750-799.9 Million
Emp.: 2,000
Property & Facility Management Services
N.A.I.C.S.: 531312
Michael W T Wong (Mng Dir)

City Security Company Limited (1)
9B-9C 9/F and the whole floor of 10/F No 9
Po Lun Street, Lai Chi Kok, Kowloon, China
(Hong Kong)
Tel.: (852) 37588988
Web Site: https://www.citysecurity.com.hk
Security System Installation & Guarding
Services
N.A.I.C.S.: 238210
Michael W. T. Wong (Mng Dir)

**Modern Living Investments Holdings
Limited** (1)
Units 1102-03 11/F Delta House No 3 On
Yiu Street, New Territories, Sha Tin, China
(Hong Kong) (85.96%)
Tel.: (852) 25722388
Web Site: http://www.modernliving.com.hk
Rev.: $51,763,343
Assets: $25,752,833
Liabilities: $6,590,730
Net Worth: $19,162,103
Earnings: $2,700,450
Emp.: 1,339
Fiscal Year-end: 12/31/2022
Real Estate Management Services
N.A.I.C.S.: 531311
Alfred Lee Ming Sung (CFO)

ASIA ALUMINIUM HOLDINGS LIMITED
12th Floor Railway Plaza, 39
Chatham Road South, Kowloon,
China (Hong Kong)
Tel.: (852) 21568688
Web Site:
http://www.asiaalumgroup.com
Sales Range: $400-449.9 Million
Aluminium Extrusion Services
N.A.I.C.S.: 331318
Kwong Wui Chun (Chm)

ASIA AMALGAMATED HOLD-INGS CORPORATION
Uniwide Dr A Santos Ave San Isidro
Sucat, Paranaque, Philippines
Tel.: (63) 8748565
Year Founded: 1970
Holding Company
N.A.I.C.S.: 551112
Jimmy N. Gow (Chm & Pres)

ASIA AVIATION PUBLIC COM-PANY LIMITED
Don Mueang International Airport 3rd
Floor Central Office Building, Room
No 3200 Vibhavadee Rangsit Rd Don
Mueang, Bangkok, 10210, Thailand
Tel.: (66) 25625700
Web Site: https://www.aavplc.com
AAV—(THA)
Rev.: $1,253,799,082
Assets: $1,979,036,940
Liabilities: $1,733,464,251
Net Worth: $245,572,689
Earnings: $13,598,174
Emp.: 4,962
Fiscal Year-end: 12/31/23
Oil Transportation Services
N.A.I.C.S.: 481111
Tassapon Bijleveld (Co-Chm)

ASIA BIOMASS PUBLIC COM-PANY LIMITED
99/9 Rama II Road, Samae Dam
Subdist Bang Khun Thian, Bangkok,
10150, Thailand
Tel.: (66) 24150054
Web Site:
https://www.asiabiomass.com

Year Founded: 1984
ABM—(THA)
Rev.: $69,574,286
Assets: $40,648,057
Liabilities: $25,896,829
Net Worth: $14,751,228
Earnings: ($2,243,040)
Fiscal Year-end: 12/31/23
Biomaca Fuel Mfr & Distr
N.A.I.C.S.: 324199

ASIA BRANDS BERHAD
Lot 10449 Jalan Nenas Batu 4 1/2
Kampung Jawa, 41000, Klang, Selan-
gor, Malaysia
Tel.: (60) 351618822 MY
Web Site:
https://www.asiabrands.com.my
Year Founded: 1970
ASIABRN—(KLS)
Rev.: $41,261,464
Assets: $69,196,578
Liabilities: $18,644,687
Net Worth: $50,551,891
Earnings: $1,801,541
Fiscal Year-end: 03/31/24
Textile & Apparel Mfr & Distr
N.A.I.C.S.: 313310
Chin Huat Ng (Mng Dir-Grp)

Subsidiaries:

Bumcity Sdn. Bhd. (1)
Lot 59 60 Lorong Kuang Bulan, Taman Ke-
pong, Kuala Lumpur, Malaysia
Tel.: (60) 3 6272 4360
Specialty Clothing Stores Operator
N.A.I.C.S.: 458110

Diesel Marketing Sdn. Bhd. (1)
Lot 10449 Batu 4 1/2 Kampung Jawa,
41000, Klang, Selangor, Malaysia (100%)
Tel.: (60) 16 666 0316
Web Site: http://www.asiabrands.com.my
Ready-Made Sports & Casual Clothing Re-
tail & Distribution
N.A.I.C.S.: 458110
Karen Ho (Mgr-Comm)

VFUSA Marketing Sdn. Bhd. (1)
Lot 46 Lorong Kuang Bulan, Taman Ke-
pong, Kuala Lumpur, Malaysia
Tel.: (60) 362726573
Ready-Made Women's Lingerie Retail &
Distribution
N.A.I.C.S.: 458110

ASIA CAPITAL GROUP PUB-LIC COMPANY LIMITED
349 SJ Infinite I Business Complex
24th Floor Unit 2401-2405 Vibhavadi,
Rangsit Road Chompol Chatuchak,
Bangkok, 10900, Thailand
Web Site: http://www.acap.co.th
Year Founded: 1998
Investment Advice Services
N.A.I.C.S.: 523940
Yiem Chundprasit (Chm)

ASIA CAPITAL LTD.
203 Aziz Avenue CTS-1381 Near
Railway Crossing Vallabhbhai Patel
Road, Vile Parle West, Mumbai, 400
056, India
Tel.: (91) 2226100787
Web Site: https://www.asiacapital.in
538777—(BOM)
Rev.: $58,585
Assets: $680,144
Liabilities: $124,130
Net Worth: $556,014
Earnings: $23,453
Emp.: 3
Fiscal Year-end: 03/31/23
Financial Support Services
N.A.I.C.S.: 523999
Kaveri Ghosh (Officer-Compliance &
Sec)

ASIA CAPITAL PLC

Level 6 4747 Green Lanka Towers
Nawam Mawatha, 02, Colombo, Sri
Lanka
Tel.: (94) 115320000
Web Site: https://www.asiacapital.lk
ACAP—(COL)
Rev.: $1,531,261
Assets: $15,653,953
Liabilities: $16,116,451
Net Worth: ($479,498)
Earnings: ($2,527,090)
Emp.: 180
Fiscal Year-end: 03/31/23
Investment Banking Services
N.A.I.C.S.: 523150
Stefan Abeyesinhe (Exec Dir)

Subsidiaries:

Asia Asset Finance PLC (1)
No 76 Park Street, 02, Colombo, Western
Province, Sri Lanka
Tel.: (94) 117699000
Web Site: https://www.asiaassetfinance.com
Financial Investment Management Services
N.A.I.C.S.: 523940
Roshan De Silva Gunasekera (COO)

ASIA CAPITAL PUBLIC COM-PANY LIMITED
349 SJ Infinite I Business Complex
24th Floor, Unit 2401-2405 Vibhavadi
Rangsit Road Chompol Chatuchak,
Bangkok, 10900, Thailand
Tel.: (66) 27933888
Web Site: http://www.acap.co.th
Year Founded: 1998
ACAP—(THA)
Rev.: $6,912,658
Assets: $81,902,451
Liabilities: $70,118,528
Net Worth: $11,783,923
Earnings: $10,393,509
Fiscal Year-end: 12/31/23
Investment Banking Services
N.A.I.C.S.: 523150
Sugunya Sukjaroenkraisri (CEO)

Subsidiaries:

ACAP (Malaysia) Sdn. Bhd. (1)
Lot 24 AB 24th Floor UBN Tower No 10
Jalan P Ramlee, 50250, Kuala Lumpur,
Malaysia
Tel.: (60) 3 2026 4099
Mortgage Loan Brokerage Services
N.A.I.C.S.: 522310

**ACAP Asset Management Company
Limited** (1)
195 Empire Tower 2-3 22nd Floor, Yan-
Nawa Sathorn, Bangkok, 10120, Thailand
Tel.: (66) 2 694 4999
Asset Management Services
N.A.I.C.S.: 531390

ASIA CARBON INDUSTRIES, INC.
Xi Gu Nan Street, Qing Xu County,
Taiyuan, 030407, Shanxi, China
Tel.: (86) 3515966868 MD
Web Site:
http://www.asiacarbonindustries.com
Year Founded: 2008
ACRB—(OTCEM)
Sales Range: $25-49.9 Million
Emp.: 202
Holding Company; Carbon Black Mfr
N.A.I.C.S.: 551112
Guoyun Yao (Chm, Pres, CEO &
Sec)

ASIA CASSAVA RESOURCES HOLDINGS LIMITED
Units 612-613 617 6/F Houston Cen-
tre 63 Mody Road Tsim Sha Tsui
East, Kowloon, China (Hong Kong)
Tel.: (852) 2 369 9908 Ky
Web Site:
http://www.asiacassava.com

0841—(HKG)
Rev.: $462,395,751
Assets: $376,722,333
Liabilities: $269,293,602
Net Worth: $107,428,732
Earnings: $4,448,520
Emp.: 250
Fiscal Year-end: 03/31/22
Dried Cassava Chips
N.A.I.C.S.: 111998
Ming Chuan Chu (Chm & Chm)

Subsidiaries:

Alush (Thailand) Co., Ltd. (1)
59 Moo 1 Pranakorngserayutaya, 13190,
Ayutthaya, Thailand (100%)
Tel.: (66) 35366135
Procurement & Sales of Dried Cassava
Chips
N.A.I.C.S.: 311423
Yuk Ming Liu (Exec Dir)

Artwell Enterprises Limited (1)
Units 612 3 6/F Houston Ctr 63 Mody Rd,
Kowloon, China (Hong Kong)
Tel.: (852) 23699908
Web Site: http://www.asiacassava.com.hk
Sales Range: $50-74.9 Million
Emp.: 20
Real Estate Investment Services
N.A.I.C.S.: 531390
Ming-Chuan Chu (Mgr)

Rizhao Yushun Cassava. Co.,
Ltd. (1)
Unit 3203 32nd Floor Block 1 No 37 Dong-
hai Xi Road, Qingdao, Shangdong,
China (100%)
Tel.: (86) 6333288028
Dried Cassava Chips Mfr
N.A.I.C.S.: 311423

ASIA CEMENT CORPORATION
30th and 31st Floor No 207 Section 2
Dunhua South Road, Da'an District,
Taipei, 106, Taiwan
Tel.: (886) 227338000
Web Site: https://www.acc.com.tw
1102—(TAI)
Rev.: $2,622,152,326
Assets: $11,011,702,092
Liabilities: $4,737,345,189
Net Worth: $6,274,356,903
Earnings: $362,474,560
Emp.: 468
Fiscal Year-end: 12/31/23
Cement & Concrete Mfr
N.A.I.C.S.: 327320
Douglas Tong Hsu (Co-Pres)

Subsidiaries:

Asia Cement (China) Holdings
Corporation (1)
No 6 Yadong Road Ma-Tou Town,
Ruichang, 332207, Jiangxi, China (67.7%)
Tel.: (86) 7924888999
Web Site: https://www.achc.com.cn
Rev.: $1,801,122,665
Assets: $3,281,276,355
Liabilities: $573,467,328
Net Worth: $2,707,809,026
Earnings: $279,041,833
Emp.: 3,774
Fiscal Year-end: 12/31/2021
Holding Company; Cement, Concrete & Re-
lated Products Mfr & Sales
N.A.I.C.S.: 551112
Peter Hsu (Vice Chm)

Asia Cement (Singapore) Pte.
Ltd. (1)
5 Little Road 09-01 Cemtex Industrial Build-
ing, Singapore, 536983, Singapore
Tel.: (65) 62828733
Web Site: http://www.asiacement.com.sg
Sales Range: $25-49.9 Million
Emp.: 20
Cement Whslr
N.A.I.C.S.: 327310
J. H. Lin (Deputy Mng Dir)

Asia Cement Corporation - Hsinchu
Plant (1)
No 109 Sec 2 Zhongfeng Rd, Hengshan

Township, Hsinchu, 312, Taiwan
Tel.: (886) 35931011
Web Site: http://www.acc.com.tw
Cement & Clinker Mfr
N.A.I.C.S.: 327310

Asia Cement Corporation - Hualien
Plant (1)
No 125 Xinxing Rd, Xincheng Township,
Hua-lien, 971, Taiwan
Tel.: (886) 38612101
Cement & Clinker Mfr
N.A.I.C.S.: 327310

Asia Continent Investment Holdings
Pte. Ltd. (1)
5 Little Road 09-01 Cemtex IndustrialBuild-
ing, Singapore, 536983, Singapore
Tel.: (65) 62828733
Sales Range: $50-74.9 Million
Emp.: 10
Investment Management Service
N.A.I.C.S.: 523940

Subsidiary (Non-US):

Jiangxi Yadong Cement Co., Ltd. (2)
Changjiang Road, Jiujiang EconomicDevel-
opment Zone, Jiujiang, 332207, Jiangxi,
China
Tel.: (86) 7924888999
Cement Product Mfr & Distr
N.A.I.C.S.: 327310
Z. L. Wu (Chm)

Chiahui Power Corp. (1)
No 688 Songzijiao, Minxiong Township,
Chiayi, 621, Taiwan
Tel.: (886) 52721129
Eletric Power Generation Services
N.A.I.C.S.: 221112

Fu Da Transportation Co., Ltd. (1)
No 139 Sec 1 Datong Rd, Xizhi, New Taipei
City, 221, Taiwan
Tel.: (886) 223770788
Freight Trucking Services
N.A.I.C.S.: 484110

Fu-Ming Transportation Co. Ltd. (1)
No 139 Sec 1 Datong Rd, Xizhi, New Taipei
City, 221, Taiwan
Tel.: (886) 223770788
Web Site: http://www.fu-ming.com.tw
Freight Trucking Services
N.A.I.C.S.: 484110

Jiangxi Yali Transport Co., Ltd. (1)
No 8 Yadong, Ma-Tou Town, Ruichang,
332207, Jiangxi, China
Tel.: (86) 792488810
Land Transportation Services
N.A.I.C.S.: 485310

Nan Hwa Cement Corp. (1)
No 90 Sec 2 Linkong Rd, LongchinDist, Tai-
chung, 411, Taiwan
Tel.: (886) 426392688
Web Site: http://www.asiacement.com.tw
Furnace Slag Powder Mfr
N.A.I.C.S.: 327992

Nanchang Yali Concrete Produce
Ltd. (1)
Melin AVE Bashuihu Industries Zone ETDZ,
Nanchang, 330012, Jiangxi, China
Tel.: (86) 7918352214
Web Site: http://www.acc.com.tw
Cement Mfr
N.A.I.C.S.: 327310

Sichuan Yadong Cement Co.,
Ltd. (1)
No 66 AnPeng Road, Tianpeng Town
Pengzhou, Chengdu, 611930, Sichuan,
China
Tel.: (86) 2883731000
Web Site: http://www.yadong-sc.com
Cement Mfr
N.A.I.C.S.: 327310

Sichuan Yali Transport Co., Ltd. (1)
No 68 Anpeng Road, Pengzhou, Chengdu,
610000, Sichuan, China
Tel.: (86) 2883731222
General Freight Trucking Services
N.A.I.C.S.: 484110

Ya Li Precast & Prestressed Concrete Industries Corp. (1)
No 3 Section 2 Jiayuan Road, Shulin Dis-

trict, New Taipei City, Taiwan
Tel.: (886) 226803123
Web Site: https://www.yalipc.tw
Cement & Concrete Mfr
N.A.I.C.S.: 327310

Ya Tung Ready-Mixed Concrete
Corp. (1)
No 139 Section 1 Datong Rd, Xizhi District,
New Taipei City, 22145, Taiwan
Tel.: (886) 286923315
Web Site: https://www.yatung.com.tw
Readymix Concrete Mfr
N.A.I.C.S.: 327320

Yuan Long Stainless Steel Corp. (1)
No 28 Da-Ye S Rd, Lin Hai Industrial Park
Hsiao-Kang, Kaohsiung, 812, Taiwan
Tel.: (886) 79757988
Web Site: https://en.ylss.com.tw
Emp.: 251
Metal Products Mfr
N.A.I.C.S.: 332313

ASIA COAL LIMITED
Unit A 60/F Bank of China Tower 1
Garden Road, Central, Hong Kong,
China (Hong Kong)
Tel.: (852) 21520098 BM
Web Site:
http://www.asiacoallimited.com
Rev.: $606,995
Assets: $1,215,525
Liabilities: $14,427,130
Net Worth: ($13,211,605)
Earnings: ($4,720,715)
Emp.: 27
Fiscal Year-end: 03/31/18
Investment Services; Coal Mining &
Personal Care Products
N.A.I.C.S.: 523999
Xinjiang Zhu (Chm)

ASIA COMMERCIAL BANK
442 Nguyen Thi Minh Khai Street,
Ward 5 District 3, Ho Chi Minh City,
Vietnam
Tel.: (84) 2838247247 VN
Web Site: https://www.acb.com.vn
Year Founded: 1993
ACB—(HOSE)
Rev.: $2,228,403,106
Assets: $30,599,085,654
Liabilities: $27,578,490,394
Earnings: $683,024,284
Emp.: 13,655
Fiscal Year-end: 12/31/23
Commercial Banking Services
N.A.I.C.S.: 522110
Hung Huy Tran (Chm)

Subsidiaries:

ACB Capital Management Company
Limited (1)
12th Floor ACB Building 480 Nguyen Thi
Minh Khai, Ward 2 District 3, Ho Chi Minh
City, Vietnam
Tel.: (84) 838301099
Web Site: http://www.acbcapital.com.vn
Investment Fund Management Services
N.A.I.C.S.: 523940
Luong Van Tu (Chm)

ASIA COMMERCIAL HOLD-
INGS LIMITED
3901 39th Floor The Hopewell Centre
183 Queen's Road East, Wanchai,
China (Hong Kong)
Tel.: (852) 2 819 6192
Web Site:
http://www.asiacommercial.com
0104—(HKG)
Rev.: $101,225,439
Assets: $112,196,864
Liabilities: $51,773,346
Net Worth: $60,423,519
Earnings: $10,745,969
Emp.: 116
Fiscal Year-end: 03/31/22
Watch Whslr

N.A.I.C.S.: 423940
Ka Chung Cheng (Sec & Dir-Fin)

Subsidiaries:

Accord Watch & Jewellery (Interna-
tional) Limited (1)
19th Floor 9 Des Voeux Road West, Hong
Kong, China (Hong Kong)
Tel.: (852) 25173008
Web Site:
http://www.accordinternational.com
Watches & Luxury Products Whslr
N.A.I.C.S.: 423940

Juvenia (Hong Kong) Company
Limited (1)
19th Fl 9 Des Voeux Rd West, Western
District, Hong Kong, China (Hong Kong)
Tel.: (852) 28196192
Watches & Luxury Products Whslr
N.A.I.C.S.: 423940

Juvenia Montres S.A. (1)
Rue du Chatelot 21, 2300, La Chaux-de-
Fonds, Switzerland
Tel.: (41) 329257000
Web Site: https://www.juvenia.ch
Sales Range: $25-49.9 Million
Emp.: 12
Jewelry & Watches Whslr
N.A.I.C.S.: 423940

Time City (Hong Kong) Limited (1)
19 F 9 Des Voeux Road West, Western
District, Hong Kong, China (Hong Kong)
Tel.: (852) 28196192
Watches & Luxury Products Sales
N.A.I.C.S.: 423940

Wakmann Watch (International) Com-
pany Limited (1)
19 Floor 9 Des Voeux Road West, Hong
Kong, China (Hong Kong)
Tel.: (852) 28552227
Watch Distr
N.A.I.C.S.: 423940

ASIA CUANON TECHNOLOGY
(SHANGHAI) CO., LTD.
No 28 xintao Road Qingpu Industrial
Zone, Shanghai, 201707, China
Tel.: (86) 2159705888
Web Site: http://www.cuanon.com
Year Founded: 2009
603378—(SHG)
Rev.: $436,320,869
Assets: $924,290,013
Liabilities: $682,021,136
Net Worth: $242,268,877
Earnings: $14,844,576
Fiscal Year-end: 12/31/22
Insulation Board Mfr
N.A.I.C.S.: 321219
Jinzhong Li (Founder, Chm, Pres &
Gen Mgr)

ASIA DEVELOPMENT CAPI-
TAL CO., LTD.
9F Strong Akasaka Bldg 3-5-5 Aka-
saka, Minato-ku, Tokyo, 107-0052,
Japan
Tel.: (81) 3 5561 6040
Web Site:
http://www.asiadevelop.com
Sales Range: $10-24.9 Million
Emp.: 48
Investment Services
N.A.I.C.S.: 523999
Shinsuke Amiya (Pres)

Subsidiaries:

Kosugi Sangyo Co., Ltd. (1)
8-5 Nihonbashi Horidome 2-Chome, Chuo-
Ku, Tokyo, 103 8550, Japan
Tel.: (81) 336623111
Web Site: http://www.kosugi.jp
Wearing Apparel Mfr & Sales
N.A.I.C.S.: 458110

ASIA ENERGY LOGISTICS
GROUP LIMITED
Suite 802-803 8/F One Pacific Place

Asia Energy Logistics Group Limited—(Continued)

88 Queensway, Hong Kong, China
(Hong Kong)
Tel.: (852) 31270600
Web Site: https://www.aelg.com.hk
0351—(HKG)
Rev.: $6,178,658
Assets: $36,142,389
Liabilities: $4,399,895
Net Worth: $31,742,494
Earnings: $14,345,414
Emp.: 20
Fiscal Year-end: 12/31/20
Construction Management Services
N.A.I.C.S.: 115116
Yongyuan Fu *(Exec Dir)*

ASIA ENTERPRISES HOLDING LIMITED

3 Pioneer Sector Walk, Singapore,
627897, Singapore
Tel.: (65) 62236377
Web Site:
    https://www.asiaenterprises.com.sg
Year Founded: 1961
A55—(SES)
Rev.: $72,294,176
Assets: $87,421,041
Liabilities: $11,301,219
Net Worth: $76,119,821
Earnings: $4,592,896
Fiscal Year-end: 12/31/23
Steel Mfrs
N.A.I.C.S.: 331110
Choon Bok Lee *(Chm)*

Subsidiaries:

Asia-Beni Steel Industries (Pte)
Ltd   (1)
3 Pioneer Sector Walk, Singapore, 627897,
Singapore   **(100%)**
Tel.: (65) 68613677
Web Site:
    http://www.asiaenterprises.com.sg
Emp.: 50
Steel Processing Services
N.A.I.C.S.: 331110
Yvonne Lee *(Mng Dir)*

ASIA EQUITY EXCHANGE GROUP INC.

Suite 2501A 25/F Skyline Tower 39
Wang Kwong Road, Kowloon Bay,
China (Hong Kong)
Tel.: (852) 28182998   NV
Year Founded: 2013
AEEX—(OTCBB)
Sales Range: $25-49.9 Million
Emp.: 39
Investment Services
N.A.I.C.S.: 523999
Zaixian Yu *(Sec)*

ASIA EURO OIL PLC

77 Gracechurch Street, London,
EC3V 0AS, United Kingdom
Tel.: (44) 20 343 28179
Web Site: http://www.asiaeurooil.com
Sales Range: Less than $1 Million
Oil & Gas Exploration & Production
N.A.I.C.S.: 211120
Mehmet Gulec *(CEO)*

ASIA FASHION HOLDINGS LIMITED

Jimei Textile Park Fuxia Road,
Fuqing, 350301, Fujian, China
Tel.: (86) 59185361757   BM
Year Founded: 2007
Investment Holding Services
N.A.I.C.S.: 551112
Han Yuegao *(CEO)*

ASIA FIBER PUBLIC COMPANY LIMITED

33/133-136 Surawongse Road Suri-
yawongse, Bangrak, Bangkok, 10500,
Thailand
Tel.: (66) 26327071
Web Site: https://www.asiafiber.com
Year Founded: 1970
AFC—(THA)
Rev.: $20,219,974
Assets: $41,157,014
Liabilities: $9,071,771
Net Worth: $32,085,242
Earnings: ($2,127,658)
Emp.: 469
Fiscal Year-end: 06/30/23
Nylon Product Mfr & Distr
N.A.I.C.S.: 339999
Chen Namchaisiri *(Pres)*

ASIA FILE CORPORATION BHD.

Tel.: (60) 46426601
Web Site: https://www.asia-file.com
ASIAFLE—(KLS)
Rev.: $63,879,798
Assets: $189,999,563
Liabilities: $21,649,781
Net Worth: $168,349,782
Earnings: $11,536,470
Emp.: 700
Fiscal Year-end: 03/31/21
Stationery Product Mfr
N.A.I.C.S.: 327110
Soon Huat Lim *(Chm)*

Subsidiaries:

ABBA Marketing Sdn. Bhd.   (1)
Plot 16 Kawasan Perindustrian Bayan
Lepas Phase 4 Mk12, 11900, Bayan Lepas,
Penang, Malaysia
Tel.: (60) 46425199
Web Site: https://www.abbaware.com
Sales Range: $50-74.9 Million
Emp.: 6
Stationery Product Distr
N.A.I.C.S.: 424120
Lim Soon Huat *(Mng Dir)*

Plastoreg Smidt GmbH (Office Sup-
plies Division)   (1)
Heiligenstadter Strasse 32, Kirchgandern,
37318, Thuringia, Germany
Tel.: (49) 36081640
Dividers Mfr
N.A.I.C.S.: 322230
Diana Lindemann *(Sec)*

Plastoreg Smidt GmbH (Specials
Division)   (1)
Kasseler Landstrasse 12, 37213, Witzen-
hausen, Germany
Tel.: (49) 55426060
Web Site: http://www.plastoreg.de
Sales Range: $25-49.9 Million
Emp.: 150
Dividers Mfr
N.A.I.C.S.: 322230

Premier Stationery Limited   (1)
Unit A Hamilton Close, Basingstoke, RG21
6YT, Hampshire, United Kingdom
Tel.: (44) 1256335551
Web Site:
    https://www.premierstationery.co.uk
Sales Range: $25-49.9 Million
Emp.: 20
Stationery Products Import & Distr
N.A.I.C.S.: 424120
Rod Martin *(Mng Dir)*

Sin Chuan Marketing Sdn. Bhd.   (1)
No 3 Jln Bp 4/8 Bandar Bukit Puchong,
47100, Puchong, Selangor, Malaysia
Tel.: (60) 380685324
Web Site: http://www.asia-file.com
Stationery Product Distr
N.A.I.C.S.: 424120

ASIA GLOBAL CROSSING LTD.

Mintflower Place 2nd Floor, Hamilton,
HM 08, Bermuda
Tel.: (441) 2966485
Telecommunication Servicesb
N.A.I.C.S.: 517810

Bill Barney *(Pres & COO)*

ASIA GREEN AGRICULTURE CORPORATION

Shuinan Industrial Area, Songxi
County, Nanping, 353500, Fujian,
China
Tel.: (86) 599 2335520   NV
Web Site: http://www.fjyada.com.cn
Year Founded: 2008
Sales Range: $125-149.9 Million
Emp.: 390
Green & Organic Food Mfr & Distr
N.A.I.C.S.: 311421
Youdai Zhan *(Chm, Pres & CEO)*

ASIA GREEN BIOTECHNOL-OGY CORP.

Suite 1150 707 - 7 Avenue SW, Cal-
gary, T2P 3H6, AB, Canada
Tel.: (403) 863-6034
Web Site:
    https://asiagreenbiotechnology.com
ASIA—(CNSX)
Assets: $345,280
Liabilities: $22,161
Net Worth: $323,119
Earnings: ($432,470)
Fiscal Year-end: 12/31/20
Biotechnology Research & Develop-
ment Services
N.A.I.C.S.: 541714
Vincent E. Ghazar *(CFO)*

ASIA GREEN ENERGY PUBLIC COMPANY LIMITED

273/1 Rama 2 Road, Samaedam
Bangkhunthian, Bangkok, 10150,
Thailand
Tel.: (66) 28940088
Web Site: https://www.age.co.th
Year Founded: 2004
AGE—(THA)
Rev.: $387,776,496
Assets: $220,229,476
Liabilities: $122,661,447
Net Worth: $97,568,029
Earnings: $8,322,631
Fiscal Year-end: 12/31/23
Coal & Palm Shell Distr
N.A.I.C.S.: 423520
Panom Kuansataporn *(Mng Dir)*

Subsidiaries:

Grand Power (2019) Co., Ltd.   (1)
56/290 56/291 56/292 Village No 7 Phan-
thainorasing, Subdistrict Mueang Samut
Sakhon District, Samut Sakhon, 74000,
Thailand
Tel.: (66) 34440742
Web Site: https://www.gpw-power.com
Fuel Distr
N.A.I.C.S.: 424720

Vina Age Co., Ltd.   (1)
Floor 8th PAX Sky Building No 159C De
Tham street, Co Giang Ward Dist 1, Ho Chi
Minh City, Vietnam
Tel.: (84) 2838376887
Web Site: https://www.vinaage.com
Coal Product Distr
N.A.I.C.S.: 423520

ASIA GROCERY DISTRIBU-TION LIMITED

UG Mai Tong Industrial Building 22
Sze Shan Street, Yau Tong, Hong
Kong, China (Hong Kong)
Tel.: (852) 2 345 4491   Ky
Web Site: http://www.agdl.com.hk
Year Founded: 1970
8413—(HKG)
Rev.: $31,132,161
Assets: $15,885,564
Liabilities: $2,805,057
Net Worth: $13,080,507
Earnings: ($275,630)
Emp.: 59

Fiscal Year-end: 03/31/22
Grocery Product Distr
N.A.I.C.S.: 424490
Kenny Siu Man Wong *(Chm)*

ASIA HOLDINGS CO., LTD.

430 Asia Tower Nonhyeon-ro,
Gangnam Gu, Seoul, Korea (South)
Tel.: (82) 25276700
Web Site:
    https://www.asiaholdings.co.kr
Year Founded: 1957
002030—(KRS)
Rev.: $1,589,454,552
Assets: $2,440,882,352
Liabilities: $1,010,598,336
Net Worth: $1,430,284,016
Earnings: $64,441,590
Emp.: 11
Fiscal Year-end: 12/31/22
Holding Company
N.A.I.C.S.: 551112
Hoonbeom Lee *(Pres & CEO)*

Subsidiaries:

Asia Cement Co., Ltd.   (1)
430 Nonhyeon-ro, Gangnam-gu, Seoul, Ko-
rea (South)
Tel.: (82) 25276500
Web Site: https://www.asiacement.co.kr
Rev.: $797,791,910
Assets: $1,564,687,465
Liabilities: $814,038,151
Net Worth: $750,649,314
Earnings: $48,722,795
Emp.: 464
Fiscal Year-end: 12/31/2022
Cement Mfr & Distr
N.A.I.C.S.: 327310
Yun-Moo Lee *(Vice Chm)*

Asia Holdings Co., Ltd. - Daejeon
Plant   (1)
25 Bangdumal 1-gil, Daedeok-gu, Daejeon,
Korea (South)
Tel.: (82) 429324646
Readymix Concrete Mfr
N.A.I.C.S.: 327320

Asia Holdings Co., Ltd. - Hongseong
Plant   (1)
48 Chungseo-ro 966beon-gil Guhang-
myeon, Hongseong, Chungcheongnam, Ko-
rea (South)
Tel.: (82) 416345003
Readymix Concrete Mfr
N.A.I.C.S.: 327320

Asia Holdings Co., Ltd. - Jecheon
Plant   (1)
14 Songhaksan-ro Songhak-myeon, Je-
cheon, Chungcheongbuk-do, Korea (South)
Tel.: (82) 436495000
Readymix Concrete Mfr
N.A.I.C.S.: 327320

Asia Holdings Co., Ltd. - Jungbu
Plant   (1)
60 Arirang-ro 55beon-gil, Daedeok-gu, Dae-
jeon, Korea (South)
Tel.: (82) 426263524
Readymix Concrete Mfr
N.A.I.C.S.: 327320

Asia Holdings Co., Ltd. - Seoul Remi-
con Plant   (1)
108 Anyangcheondong-ro, Dongan-gu, Anyang, Gyeonggi-do, Korea (South)
Tel.: (82) 314523450
Ready Mix Concrete Distr
N.A.I.C.S.: 423320

Asia Holdings Co., Ltd. - Suwon
Plant   (1)
1006 Deogyeong-daero, Gwonseon-gu, Su-
won, Gyeonggi-do, Korea (South)
Tel.: (82) 312320070
Ready Mix Concrete Distr
N.A.I.C.S.: 423320

Asia Holdings Co., Ltd. - Yongin
Plant   (1)
15 Hyeongje-ro 17beon-gil Namsa-myeon,
Cheoin, Yongin, Gyeonggi-do, Korea
(South)

Tel.: (82) 313230761
Ready Mix Concrete Distr
N.A.I.C.S.: 423320

Asia Industry Development Co., Ltd. (1)
San 32-9 Bangheung-ri, Useong-myeon, Gongju, 32532, Chungcheongnam-do, Korea (South)
Tel.: (82) 418557983
Web Site: https://www.asiasan.co.kr
Emp.: 13
Electronic Components Mfr
N.A.I.C.S.: 334419
Seo Hyo-Won *(Pres & CEO)*

Gyeongju World Resort Co., Ltd. (1)
544 Bomun-ro, Gyeongju, 38117, Gyeongsangbuk-do, Korea (South)
Tel.: (82) 15448765
Providing Guide Services
N.A.I.C.S.: 561510

Wooshin Venture Investment Co., Ltd. (1)
1st floor Asia Tower 430 Nonhyeon-ro, Gangnam-gu, Seoul, Korea (South)
Tel.: (82) 25385906
Financial & Investment Services
N.A.I.C.S.: 523999

ASIA HOTEL PUBLIC COMPANY LIMITED
296 Phayathai Road, Ratchathewi, Bangkok, 10400, Thailand
Tel.: (66) 22170808
Web Site: https://www.asiahotel.co.th
Year Founded: 1964
ASIA—(THA)
Rev.: $34,694,122
Assets: $298,117,020
Liabilities: $121,510,225
Net Worth: $176,606,794
Earnings: ($1,768,158)
Emp.: 1,059
Fiscal Year-end: 12/31/23
Home Management Services
N.A.I.C.S.: 721110
Ganlayanee Roungrayubchai *(Dir-Sls-F&B)*

Subsidiaries:

Asia Airport Hotel Co., Ltd. (1)
99/2 Moo 8 Phaholyothin Road, Lamlukka, Pathumthani, 12130, Thailand
Tel.: (66) 29926999
Web Site: https://www.asiahotel.co.th
Hotel Operator
N.A.I.C.S.: 721110

Asia Pattaya Hotel Co., Ltd. (1)
352 Moo 12 Pratamnak Road, Nongprue Pattaya City, Chon Buri, 20150, Thailand
Tel.: (66) 38250577
Web Site: https://www.asiahotel.co.th
Hotel Operator
N.A.I.C.S.: 721110

ASIA INSURANCE CO.
No 299 Taleghani St, POB 15815-1885, 1599836511, Tehran, Iran
Tel.: (98) 21 88800950
Web Site: http://www.bimehasia.com
Year Founded: 1959
Insurance Services
N.A.I.C.S.: 524298
F. M. F. Moazami *(Chm)*

ASIA INSURANCE LIMITED
Rupayan Trade Centre 14th Floor 114-115 Kazi Nazrul Islam Avenue, Banglamotor, Dhaka, 1000, Bangladesh
Tel.: (880) 255138581
Web Site:
https://www.asiainsurancebd.com
Year Founded: 2000
ASIAINS—(CHT)
Rev.: $1,608,857
Assets: $23,458,204
Liabilities: $13,148,030
Net Worth: $10,310,174

Earnings: $871,169
Emp.: 258
Fiscal Year-end: 12/31/23
Insurance Services
N.A.I.C.S.: 524298
Yussuf Abdullah Harun *(Chm)*

ASIA INTERACTIVE MEDIA INC.
Level 30 Bank of China Tower 1 Garden Road, Central, China (Hong Kong)
Tel.: (852) 9836 2643   NV
Year Founded: 2000
Rev.: $35,000
Assets: $13,774
Liabilities: $15,162
Net Worth: ($1,388)
Earnings: $6,504
Fiscal Year-end: 12/31/19
Investment Services
N.A.I.C.S.: 523999
Ken Ng *(Pres, CEO, CFO, Chief Acctg Officer, Treas & Sec)*

ASIA LOGISTICS (CHINA) LIMITED
Unit C 5F Block 1 Wah Fung Industrial Centre 33-39 Kwai Fung Crescent, Kwai Chung, China (Hong Kong)
Tel.: (852) 2545 4500   HK
Web Site:
http://www.asialogistics.com.hk
Year Founded: 2000
Freight & Cargo Shipping Services
N.A.I.C.S.: 488510
Stephan Lam *(Mgr)*

ASIA MEDIA CO., LTD.
C607 Shiji Kemao Building 66 Zhongguancun East Road, Haidian District, Beijing, 100190, China
Tel.: (86) 1062670066
Web Site: http://www.asiamedia.jp
Sales Range: $25-49.9 Million
Emp.: 150
Television Program Guide Services
N.A.I.C.S.: 516120
Zhang Kianwei *(CEO)*

ASIA MEDIA GROUP BERHAD
Level 15 Unit 15-2 Menara Choy Fook On 1B Jalan Yong Shook Lin, 46050, Petaling Jaya, Selangor, Malaysia
Tel.: (60) 1155555582
Web Site: https://mmmgroup.com.my
Year Founded: 2007
MMM—(KLS)
Rev.: $1,569,079
Assets: $3,783,581
Liabilities: $1,036,501
Net Worth: $2,747,080
Earnings: $44,300
Emp.: 100
Fiscal Year-end: 03/31/24
Digital Transit Media Services
N.A.I.C.S.: 541890
Munir Shah Mustapha *(Chm)*

ASIA METAL PUBLIC COMPANY LIMITED
55 55/1 moo 2 Soi Watnamdaeng Srinakarin Rd T Bangkaew, A Bangplee, Samut Prakan, 10540, Thailand
Tel.: (66) 23387222   TH
Web Site:
https://www.asiametal.co.th
Year Founded: 1993
AMC—(THA)
Rev.: $232,845,694
Assets: $150,104,343
Liabilities: $52,833,128
Net Worth: $97,271,215
Earnings: $12,173,921

Emp.: 423
Fiscal Year-end: 12/31/23
Steel Products Mfr
N.A.I.C.S.: 339999
Chusak Yongvongphaiboon *(Mng Dir)*

ASIA MINERAL JOINT STOCK COMPANY
Lot 32 C Nam Cam Industrial Zone, Nghi Loc, Nghe An, Vietnam
Tel.: (84) 2383791777
Web Site: https://www.amcvina.vn
AMC—(HNX)
Rev.: $16,517,100
Assets: $7,487,500
Liabilities: $2,490,400
Net Worth: $4,997,100
Earnings: $631,900
Emp.: 100
Fiscal Year-end: 12/31/22
Stone Powder Mining, Exploration & Processing
N.A.I.C.S.: 212312
Le Van Chien *(Sls Dir)*

ASIA NEO TECH INDUSTRIAL CO., LTD.
No 308 Mingxing St, Guishan Dist, Taoyuan, 333, Taiwan
Tel.: (886) 33591777
Web Site:
https://www.asianeotech.com
Year Founded: 2000
4542—(TPE)
Rev.: $24,187,193
Assets: $44,369,634
Liabilities: $24,279,117
Net Worth: $20,090,517
Earnings: $250
Fiscal Year-end: 12/31/22
Automatic Drying Equipment Mfr
N.A.I.C.S.: 334512
Ming-Chih Wu *(Pres)*

ASIA OPTICAL CO., INC.
No 22-3 South 2nd Rd, Tanzi Dist, Taichung, 427058, Taiwan
Tel.: (886) 425342550
Web Site: https://www.asia-optical.com
Year Founded: 1980
3019—(TAI)
Rev.: $583,086,148
Assets: $684,871,226
Liabilities: $199,976,251
Net Worth: $484,894,975
Earnings: $35,566,368
Emp.: 10,363
Fiscal Year-end: 12/31/23
Optical Component Mfr
N.A.I.C.S.: 339115

Subsidiaries:

AOF Imaging Technology Limited (1)
2F Continental Electric Bldg 17 Wang Chiu Road, Kowloon Bay, Kowloon, China (Hong Kong)
Tel.: (852) 27508662
Web Site: http://www.aof-imaging.com
Sales Range: $25-49.9 Million
Emp.: 40
Optoelectronic Device Mfr
N.A.I.C.S.: 334419

Subsidiary (Non-US):

AOF Imaging Technology, Japan Ltd. (2)
2F & 3F Benex S-3 Bldg 3-20-8 Shin-Yokohama, Kohoku-ku, Yokohama, 222-0033, Kanagawa, Japan
Tel.: (81) 454759228
Digital Camera & Optical Disk Drives Mfr
N.A.I.C.S.: 334112

Asia Optical International Ltd. (1)
C/o Shellbourne Trust Company (bvi) Limited Palm Grove House, Wickhams Cay 1, Road Town, VG1110, Tortola, Virgin Islands (British)

Tel.: (284) 494 2616
Investment Management Service
N.A.I.C.S.: 523940

Scopro Optical Co., Inc. (1)
Boncraft Building Mayon Corner Pinatubo Street, 1550, Mandaluyong, Philippines
Tel.: (63) 25347230
Web Site: http://www.scopro.net
Emp.: 600
Optical Component Mfr
N.A.I.C.S.: 327215
Sean Huang *(Gen Mgr)*

ASIA ORIENT HOLDINGS LIMITED
30th Floor YF Life Tower 33 Lockhart Road, Wanchai, China (Hong Kong)
Tel.: (852) 2 866 3336
Web Site:
http://www.asiaorient.com.hk
0214—(HKG)
Rev.: $359,683,044
Assets: $5,097,215,050
Liabilities: $2,511,090,854
Net Worth: $2,586,124,195
Earnings: ($189,704,042)
Emp.: 360
Fiscal Year-end: 03/31/22
Property Management Services
N.A.I.C.S.: 531311
Phileas Po Lam Kwan *(Exec Dir)*

Subsidiaries:

Asia Orient Company Limited (1)
29-31 F Asia Orient Tower Town Pl 33 Lockhart Rd, Wanchai, China (Hong Kong)
Tel.: (852) 28663336
Web Site: http://www.asiastandard.com
Sales Range: $25-49.9 Million
Emp.: 50
Property Management Services
N.A.I.C.S.: 531311
Samuel Fung *(Mgr)*

Prosperity Land Cleaning Service Limited (1)
30 F Asia Orient Tower Town Pl 33 Lockhard Rd, Wanchai, China (Hong Kong)
Tel.: (852) 29729831
Web Site: http://www.asia-standard.com.hk
Sales Range: $10-24.9 Million
Emp.: 50
Buildings & Residential Cleaning Services
N.A.I.C.S.: 561720
Alec Wong *(Gen Mgr)*

Prosperity Land Estate Management Limited (1)
30/F YF Life Tower 33 Lockhart Road, Wanchai, China (Hong Kong)
Tel.: (852) 28663336
Web Site:
https://www.prosperityland.com.hk
Sales Range: $50-74.9 Million
Emp.: 10
Property Management Services
N.A.I.C.S.: 531311

ASIA PACIFIC GENERAL INSURANCE CO. LIMITED
Homestead Gulshan Link Tower 6th Floor Ta-99 Gulshan-Badda Link Road, Middle Badda, Dhaka, 1212, Bangladesh
Tel.: (880) 9666771771
Web Site: https://www.apgicl.com
Year Founded: 1999
ASIAPACINS—(CHT)
Rev.: $1,206,357
Assets: $14,205,300
Liabilities: $5,262,866
Net Worth: $8,942,434
Earnings: $800,609
Fiscal Year-end: 12/31/23
Insurance Services
N.A.I.C.S.: 524298
Kashimiri Kamal *(Vice Chm)*

ASIA PACIFIC RESOURCES

INTERNATIONAL HOLDINGS LTD.
80 Raffles Pl Ste 50-01 UOB Plz 1,
Singapore, 048624, Singapore
Tel.: (65) 62169318   BM
Web Site: http://www.aprilasia.com
Year Founded: 1994
Sales Range: $1-4.9 Billion
Emp.: 7,000
Paper & Pulp Manufacturing
N.A.I.C.S.: 322110
Alagaratnam Joseph Devanesan
(Vice Chm)

ASIA PACIFIC SATELLITE LNC.
Flr 9 Unit 2 98 Gasan digital 2-ro,
Geumcheon-gu, Seoul, Korea (South)
Tel.: (82) 220267777
Web Site: https://www.apsi.co.kr
Year Founded: 2000
211270—(KRS)
Rev.: $41,114,365
Assets: $83,832,628
Liabilities: $18,368,381
Net Worth: $65,464,246
Earnings: $3,127,421
Fiscal Year-end: 12/31/22
Modem Mfr & Distr
N.A.I.C.S.: 334418
Ryoo Jang-Soo *(CEO)*

ASIA PACIFIC TELECOM CO., LTD.
8F No 32 Jihu Rd, Neihu Dist, Taipei,
114, Taiwan
Tel.: (886) 255558888
Web Site: http://www.aptg.com.tw
3682—(TAI)
Rev.: $420,658,605
Assets: $1,294,791,915
Liabilities: $535,151,193
Net Worth: $759,640,723
Earnings: ($174,287,217)
Emp.: 1,532
Fiscal Year-end: 12/31/22
Telecommunication Servicesb
N.A.I.C.S.: 517810
Fang-Ming Lu *(Chm)*

ASIA PACIFIC WIRE & CABLE CORPORATION LIMITED
15Fl B No 77 Sec 2 Dunhua South
Road, Taipei, 106, Taiwan
Tel.: (886) 227122558   BM
Web Site: https://www.apwcc.com
APWC—(NASDAQ)
Rev.: $433,893,000
Assets: $371,019,000
Liabilities: $159,591,000
Net Worth: $211,428,000
Earnings: $4,757,000
Emp.: 1,207
Fiscal Year-end: 12/31/22
Mfr & Distributor of Power Cable,
Telecommunications Cable & Enameled Wire
N.A.I.C.S.: 331318
Daphne Hsu *(Controller-Financial)*

Subsidiaries:

Australia Pacific Electric Cables Pty.,
Ltd.   **(1)**
89 Platinum St, Crestmead, 4132, QLD,
Australia
Tel.: (61) 738023688
Web Site: https://www.apeccables.com.au
Emp.: 50
Electrical Cables Mfr
N.A.I.C.S.: 335921

Charoung Thai Wire & Cable Public
Co. Ltd.   **(1)**
589/71 Central City Tower Floor 12A Debaratana Road, North Bangna Sub-district
Bangna District, Bangkok, 10260, Thailand

Tel.: (66) 27456118
Web Site: https://ctw.co.th
Wire & Cable Product Mfr & Distr
N.A.I.C.S.: 335929

Shandong Pacific Fiber Optics Cable
Co., Ltd.   **(1)**
No 1 Optoelectronics Industrial Park,
Yanggu, Liaocheng, Shandong, China
Tel.: (86) 6356515999
Web Site: https://en.spfosd.com
Electronic Cable Mfr
N.A.I.C.S.: 335921

Shandong Pacific Rubber Cable Co.,
Ltd.   **(1)**
14 Xihu Yanggu, Liaocheng, Shandong,
China
Tel.: (86) 6356512568
Web Site: http://www.apwcc.com
Electronic Cable Mfr
N.A.I.C.S.: 335921

Shanghai Yayang Electric Co.,
Ltd.   **(1)**
2525 Daye Road Wuqiao Zhuang Hang
Town, Feng Xian District, Shanghai,
201402, China
Tel.: (86) 2157403196
Web Site: http://www.yayang.com.cn
Sales Range: $50-74.9 Million
Emp.: 200
Copper Wires Mfr
N.A.I.C.S.: 331420

Sigma Cable Co. (Pte) Ltd.   **(1)**
19 Benoi Road, Jurong Town, Singapore,
629909, Singapore
Tel.: (65) 62650877
Web Site: https://www.sigmacable.com
Emp.: 100
Power Cable Mfr
N.A.I.C.S.: 335921

Sigma-Epan International Pte.,
Ltd.   **(1)**
Tel.: (65) 65699100
Web Site: http://www.epanwire.com.sg
Sales Range: $25-49.9 Million
Emp.: 10
Electrical Cables Mfr
N.A.I.C.S.: 335921

Subsidiary (Non-US):

Epan Industries Pte Ltd   **(2)**
Tel.: (65) 65699100
Web Site: https://www.epanwire.com.sg
Sales Range: $25-49.9 Million
Emp.: 8
Electronic Cable Mfr
N.A.I.C.S.: 335921

ASIA PACK LIMITED
3rd Floor Miraj Campus Uper Ki
Oden Nathdwara, Rajsamand,
313301, Rajasthan, India
Tel.: (91) 2942528435
Web Site:
    https://www.asiapackltd.com
Year Founded: 1985
530899—(BOM)
Rev.: $86,057
Assets: $2,630,061
Liabilities: $43,111
Net Worth: $2,586,950
Earnings: $25,805
Emp.: 4
Fiscal Year-end: 03/31/22
Business Management Consulting
Services
N.A.I.C.S.: 541611
Jitendra Purohit *(CEO)*

ASIA PAPER MANUFACTURING CO., LTD.
231 Seohaean-ro, Siheung, 06223,
Gyeonggi-do, Korea (South)
Tel.: (82) 25276882
Web Site:
    https://www.asiapaper.co.kr
Year Founded: 1958
002310—(KRS)
Rev.: $784,942,335
Assets: $793,805,317

Liabilities: $176,917,938
Net Worth: $616,887,379
Earnings: $72,404,932
Emp.: 271
Fiscal Year-end: 12/31/22
Linerboards & Corrugated Boxes Mfr
N.A.I.C.S.: 322211
Byungmoo Lee *(Chm)*

ASIA PILE HOLDINGS CORPORATION
Daiwa River Gate 36-2 Nihonbashi
Hakozakicho, Chuo-ku, Tokyo, 103-
0015, Japan
Tel.: (81) 358434173
Web Site: https://www.asiapile-
hd.com
Year Founded: 2005
5288—(TKS)
Rev.: $681,828,110
Assets: $629,470,300
Liabilities: $304,773,880
Net Worth: $324,696,420
Earnings: $25,256,810
Emp.: 2,667
Fiscal Year-end: 03/31/24
Concrete Pile Mfr
N.A.I.C.S.: 327331
Akira Kurose *(Chm & Pres)*

Subsidiaries:

FECON Mining Joint Stock
Company   **(1)**
ThiSon Industrial Cluster, Kim Bang,
Hanam, Vietnam   **(51%)**
Tel.: (84) 2263533038
Web Site: https://www.feconmining.com.vn
Rev.: $18,909,646
Assets: $33,271,513
Liabilities: $9,185,499
Net Worth: $24,086,014
Earnings: $644,862
Emp.: 266
Fiscal Year-end: 12/31/2023
Concrete Products Mfr
N.A.I.C.S.: 327390

Japan Pile Corporation   **(1)**
Daiwa River Gate 36-2 Nihonbashi-
Hakozakicho, Chuo-ku, Tokyo, 103-0015,
Japan
Tel.: (81) 358434192
Building Construction Services
N.A.I.C.S.: 236220

Phan Vu Investment Corporation   **(1)**
A2 Truong Son Street Ward 2, Tan Binh
District, Ho Chi Minh City, Vietnam
Tel.: (84) 8222008846
Web Site: https://www.phanvu.vn
Concrete Pipe Mfr
N.A.I.C.S.: 327332
Phan Khac Long *(Chm)*

VJP Co., Ltd.   **(1)**
Lot No C-4 Thilawa SEZ Zone A, Yangon,
Myanmar
Tel.: (95) 1250911
Web Site: https://www.vjpspunpile.com
Eletric Power Generation Services
N.A.I.C.S.: 221118

ASIA PIONEER ENTERTAINMENT HOLDINGS LIMITED
Industrial Lee Cheung F10 Estrada
Marginal do Hipodromo 56-66 Em,
Macau, China (Macau)
Tel.: (853) 28306196   Ky
Web Site: http://www.apemacau.com
Year Founded: 2005
8400—(HKG)
Rev.: $3,801,224
Assets: $4,612,768
Liabilities: $2,521,561
Net Worth: $2,091,207
Earnings: ($247,498)
Emp.: 38
Fiscal Year-end: 12/31/23
Electronic Equipment Mfr & Distr
N.A.I.C.S.: 339999

Allen Tat Yan Huie *(Co-Founder &
Chm)*

Subsidiaries:

Asia Pioneer Entertainment
Limited   **(1)**
Industrial Lee Cheung F10 Estrada Marginal do Hipodromo NS 56-66, Macau,
China (Macau)
Tel.: (853) 28306196
Electronic Gaming Equipment Distr
N.A.I.C.S.: 423920
Herman Ng Man Ho *(Mng Dir)*

ASIA PLASTIC RECYCLING HOLDING LIMITED
12F 2 No 190 Siwei 4th Rd, Lingya
Dist, Kaohsiung, 802, Taiwan
Tel.: (886) 72696099
Web Site: http://www.asia-
recycle.com
1337—(TAI)
Rev.: $25,247,195
Assets: $149,808,458
Liabilities: $5,949,671
Net Worth: $143,858,787
Earnings: ($13,456,685)
Emp.: 670
Fiscal Year-end: 12/31/23
Plastic Materials
N.A.I.C.S.: 326199
Jin Zao Ding *(Chm & CEO)*

ASIA PLUS GROUP HOLDINGS PUBLIC COMPANY LIMITED
11 Floor Sathorn City Tower 175
South Sathorn Road, Sathorn, Bangkok, 10120, Thailand
Tel.: (66) 26801111   TH
Web Site:
    https://www.asiaplusgroup.co.th
Year Founded: 1974
ASP—(THA)
Rev.: $68,471,985
Assets: $410,379,241
Liabilities: $267,546,098
Net Worth: $142,833,143
Earnings: $11,908,657
Emp.: 715
Fiscal Year-end: 12/31/23
Security Brokerage Services
N.A.I.C.S.: 523150
Chali Sophonpanich *(Chm)*

Subsidiaries:

Asia Plus Advisory Company
Limited   **(1)**
11th Floor Sathorn City Tower 175 South
Sathorn Road, Sathorn, Bangkok, 10120,
Thailand   **(99.99%)**
Tel.: (66) 26804002
Financial Services
N.A.I.C.S.: 523940

Asia Plus Securities Company
Limited   **(1)**
3/1 Fl Sathorn City Tower 175 South
Sathorn Road, Sathorn, Bangkok, 10120,
Thailand   **(99.99%)**
Tel.: (66) 26801111
Web Site: https://www.asiaplus.co.th
Investment Services
N.A.I.C.S.: 523999

Asset Plus Fund Management Company Limited   **(1)**
17th Floor Sathorn City Tower Building No
175 South Sathorn, Thung Maha Mek Subdistrict Sathorn District, Bangkok, 10120,
Thailand   **(99.99%)**
Tel.: (66) 26721000
Web Site: https://www.assetfund.co.th
Fund Management Services
N.A.I.C.S.: 525910

ASIA POLY HOLDINGS BERHAD
308 Block A 3rd Floor Kelana Business Centre, 97 Jalan SS 7/2 Kelana

Jaya, 47301, Petaling Jaya, Selangor Darul Ehsan, Malaysia
Tel.: (60) 374921818　　MY
Web Site: http://asiapoly.com.my
ASIAPLY—(KLS)
Rev.: $19,488,538
Assets: $49,942,410
Liabilities: $19,660,310
Net Worth: $30,202,100
Earnings: ($2,118,244)
Emp.: 189
Fiscal Year-end: 12/31/22
Investment Holding Services
N.A.I.C.S.: 551112
Boon Leong Yeo *(Chm)*

Subsidiaries:

Asia Poly Industrial Sdn. Bhd.　(1)
Lot 758 Jalan Haji Sirat, Mukim Kapar, 42100, Klang, Selangor, Malaysia
Tel.: (60) 33 342 2567
Web Site: https://asiapoly.com.my
Cast Acrylic Product Mfr & Whslr
N.A.I.C.S.: 325211

Dolphin International Berhad　(1)
EG-2 Block E Oasis Square No 2 Jalan PJU 1A/7A, 47301, Petaling Jaya, Selangor Darul Ehsan, Malaysia
Tel.: (60) 78327563
Web Site: https://dolphinint.com.my
Rev.: $3,747,353
Assets: $11,661,155
Liabilities: $4,722,917
Net Worth: $6,938,238
Earnings: ($1,861,817)
Fiscal Year-end: 06/30/2023
Electro-Automation, Pneumatic & Hydraulic Systems & Products Mfr
N.A.I.C.S.: 333248
Teck Yin Low *(Co-Founder & Mng Dir-Grp)*

ASIA POLYMER CORPORATION

12th Floor No 37 Ji-Hu Road, Nei-Hu District, Taipei, 114, Taiwan
Tel.: (886) 287516888
Web Site: https://www.apc.com.tw
Year Founded: 1977
1308—(TAI)
Rev.: $219,664,729
Assets: $490,914,956
Liabilities: $54,697,830
Net Worth: $436,217,126
Earnings: $3,802,740
Emp.: 242
Fiscal Year-end: 12/31/23
Plastic Tablets & Resins Mfr
N.A.I.C.S.: 325211
Quintin Wu *(Chm)*

Subsidiaries:

Asia Polymer Corporation - Lin Yuan Plant　(1)
No 3 Industrial 1st Rd Lin Yuan, Kaohsiung, Taiwan
Tel.: (886) 77040988
Polyethylene Resin Mfr & Distr
N.A.I.C.S.: 325199

ASIA POWER CORPORATION LIMITED

10 Anson Ave 14-10, Singapore, 48621, Singapore
Tel.: (65) 63245788　　SG
Web Site:
　http://www.asiapower.com.sg
Year Founded: 1997
Sales Range: $10-24.9 Million
Emp.: 2,000
Power Generation Plants Management & Operation Services
N.A.I.C.S.: 335311
Liang Xue *(Chm & CEO)*

Subsidiaries:

JAZ Technology Development (Shenzhen) Co., Ltd　(1)
4/F 5/F 201 Jinzhong Section OCT Eastern Industrial Park, Nanshan District, Shenzhen,

518053, Guangdong, China
Tel.: (86) 75586095518
Eletric Power Generation Services
N.A.I.C.S.: 221118

ASIA PRECISION PUBLIC COMPANY LIMITED

223/53 13th Floor Country Complex Tower A Sunphawut Road, Bangna District, Bangkok, 10260, Thailand
Tel.: (66) 23615494
Web Site:
　http://www.asiaprecision.com
Year Founded: 1995
APCS—(THA)
Rev.: $49,264,555
Assets: $110,473,723
Liabilities: $58,188,883
Net Worth: $52,284,840
Earnings: $2,898,294
Emp.: 153
Fiscal Year-end: 12/31/23
Precision Machined Parts
N.A.I.C.S.: 332999
Apichart Karoonkornsakul *(Pres)*

ASIA RESOURCES HOLDINGS LIMITED

Unit 2601 26/F West Tower Shun Tak Centre Nos 168-200 Connaught Road, Central, China (Hong Kong)
Tel.: (852) 31010899　　BM
Web Site:
　http://www.asiaresources899.com
899—(HKG)
Rev.: $4,183,124
Assets: $347,376,304
Liabilities: $49,565,172
Net Worth: $297,811,132
Earnings: ($20,352,892)
Emp.: 25
Fiscal Year-end: 03/31/19
Pharmaceutical Product Mfr & Distr
N.A.I.C.S.: 325412
Yuguo Li *(Chm)*

Subsidiaries:

Century Strong Limited　(1)
Flat 4 3/F 27 Lee Chung Street, Tak King Industrial Building, Chai Wan, China (Hong Kong)
Tel.: (852) 2 896 5272
Web Site: https://www.centurystrong.com.hk
Pest Management Services
N.A.I.C.S.: 561710

ASIA SEED CO., LTD.

515 B 167 Songpa-daero, Songpa-gu, Seoul, 138-16, Korea (South)
Tel.: (82) 24434303
Web Site: https://asiaseed.net
Year Founded: 2004
154030—(KRS)
Rev.: $22,427,864
Assets: $39,230,119
Liabilities: $19,040,567
Net Worth: $20,189,552
Earnings: $15,333
Emp.: 209
Fiscal Year-end: 09/30/21
Seed Producer
N.A.I.C.S.: 311224
Kyoung-Ou Ryu *(Pres & CEO)*

ASIA SERMKIJ LEASING PUBLIC COMPANY LIMITED

24th Fl Sathorn City Tower 175 South Sathorn Rd Tungmahamek, Sathorn, 10120, Bangkok, Thailand
Tel.: (66) 26796226
Web Site: https://ask-th.listedcompany.com
Year Founded: 1984
ASK—(THA)
Rev.: $189,710,110
Assets: $2,263,221,937
Liabilities: $1,952,077,920

Net Worth: $311,144,017
Earnings: $35,578,260
Emp.: 884
Fiscal Year-end: 12/31/23
Automobile Leasing Services
N.A.I.C.S.: 532112
Tze-Ting Yang *(Chm)*

ASIA SIYAKA COMMODITIES PLC

Deutsche House Building 320 T B Jayah Mawatha, 010, Colombo, Sri Lanka
Tel.: (94) 114600700
Web Site: https://asiasiyaka.lk
Year Founded: 1998
ASIY.N0000—(COL)
Rev.: $3,442,891
Assets: $13,299,881
Liabilities: $8,626,604
Net Worth: $4,673,276
Earnings: ($22,518)
Emp.: 109
Fiscal Year-end: 03/31/21
Broking & Packaging Services
N.A.I.C.S.: 561910
Shashike Silva *(Sr VP-Mktg Low Grown)*

ASIA STANDARD INTERNATIONAL GROUP LIMITED

30th Floor YF Life Tower, 33 Lockhart Road, Wanchai, China (Hong Kong)
Tel.: (852) 2 866 3336
Web Site:
　http://www.asiastandard.com
0129—(HKG)
Rev.: $323,705,620
Assets: $4,517,186,701
Liabilities: $2,400,610,843
Net Worth: $2,116,575,859
Earnings: ($130,566,841)
Emp.: 253
Fiscal Year-end: 03/31/22
Commercial, Retail & Residential Property Investment & Development Services
N.A.I.C.S.: 531390
Phileas Po Lam Kwan *(Exec Dir)*

Subsidiaries:

Asia Standard Hotel Group Limited　(1)
30th Floor YF Life Tower, 33 Lockhart Road, Wanchai, China (Hong Kong)　　(66.7%)
Tel.: (852) 28663336
Web Site:
　http://www.asiastandardhotelgroup.com
Rev.: $153,148,705
Assets: $1,469,919,396
Liabilities: $934,491,987
Net Worth: $535,427,410
Earnings: $43,448,566
Emp.: 300
Fiscal Year-end: 03/31/2019
Hotel Operator
N.A.I.C.S.: 721110
Jing Poon *(Chm)*

ASIA STRATEGIC HOLDINGS LIMITED

80 Raffles Place 32-01 UOB Plaza 1, Singapore, 048624, Singapore
Tel.: (65) 86223877　　SG
Web Site: https://asia-strategic.com
Year Founded: 2013
ASIA—(LSE)
Rev.: $24,054,547
Assets: $27,007,244
Liabilities: $32,639,564
Net Worth: ($5,632,320)
Earnings: ($5,319,684)
Emp.: 2,231
Fiscal Year-end: 09/30/23
Investment Management Service
N.A.I.C.S.: 523940
Enrico Cesenni *(CEO)*

Subsidiaries:

EXERA Myanmar Limited　(1)
Building No 3A Min Ye Kyaw Swar Business Building, Min Ye Kyaw Swar Street Lanmadaw Township, Yangon, Myanmar
Tel.: (95) 9775111551
Web Site: https://www.exera.asia
Emp.: 1,000
Security & Investigation Services
N.A.I.C.S.: 561611
Mark Wakeford *(CEO)*

Wall Street English Limited Liability Company　(1)
21 Le Quy Don, Phuong Vo Thi Sau Quan 3, Ho Chi Minh City, Vietnam
Tel.: (84) 1800646448
Web Site: https://wallstreetenglish.edu.vn
English Language Education Learning Services
N.A.I.C.S.: 611630

ASIA TECH IMAGE, INC.

2F No 880 Zhongzheng Rd, Zhonghe Dist, New Taipei City, Taiwan
Tel.: (886) 282286401
Web Site: https://www.atii.com.tw
4974—(TPE)
Rev.: $134,235,375
Assets: $129,150,830
Liabilities: $33,698,246
Net Worth: $95,452,584
Earnings: $18,094,800
Emp.: 594
Fiscal Year-end: 12/31/22
Printer Mfr
N.A.I.C.S.: 333248
I-Jen Lai *(Chm & Pres)*

ASIA TELE-NET & TECHNOLOGY CORPORATION LIMITED

Tai Po Industrial Estate 11 Dai Hei Street, Tai Po, New Territories, China (Hong Kong)
Tel.: (852) 26662288
Web Site: http://www.atnt.biz
0679—(HKG)
Rev.: $40,758,308
Assets: $230,881,463
Liabilities: $79,890,225
Net Worth: $150,991,238
Earnings: ($4,184,040)
Emp.: 431
Fiscal Year-end: 12/31/22
Investment Services
N.A.I.C.S.: 551112
Kwok Lun Nam *(Deputy Chm)*

Subsidiaries:

PAL Sales LLC　(1)
3 Flanders Rd, Bethlehem, CT 06751-2208
Tel.: (203) 266-7616
Web Site: http://www.palsales.com
Plating Equipment Mfr & Distr
N.A.I.C.S.: 333248
Don Monfort *(Pres)*

Process Automation (China) Limited　(1)
Block 1 Sino Master Industrial Park Datianyang Industrial Zone, Songgang Street Committee Baoan District, Shenzhen, 518105, Guangdong, China
Tel.: (86) 75527042766
Web Site: http://www.palchina.com.cn
Electroplating Machine Mfr & Distr
N.A.I.C.S.: 333248

Process Automation (Europe) Limited　(1)
Unit 7 The Farriers, Annscroft, Shrewsbury, SY5 8AN, United Kingdom
Tel.: (44) 1743860086
Web Site: http://www.paleurope.com
Electroplating Machine Distr
N.A.I.C.S.: 423830

Process Automation (Shenzhen) Limited　(1)
Block 1 Sino Master Industrial Park Datianyang Industrial Zone, Songgang Street Committee Baoan District, Shenzhen,

Asia Tele-Net & Technology Corporation
Limited—(Continued)

518105, Guangdong, China
Tel.: (86) 75527042766
Web Site: http://www.pal-szx.com.cn
Electroplating Machine Mfr & Distr
N.A.I.C.S.: 333248

Process Automation Taiwan Co.
Ltd   **(1)**
No 172 Changchun 2nd Rd, Zhongli,
Taoyuan, 320, Taiwan
Tel.: (886) 34332006
Web Site: http://www.paltw.com
Electroplating Machine Distr
N.A.I.C.S.: 423830

ASIA TIME CORPORATION
Room 1601-1604 16/F CRE Centre,
889 Cheung Sha Wan Road, Kow-
loon, China (Hong Kong)
Tel.: (852) 2310 0101   **DE**
Year Founded: 2006
Sales Range: $75-99.9 Million
Emp.: 35
Watches & Watch Movements Com-
ponents Distr
N.A.I.C.S.: 423940
Kai Shun Kwong (Chm & CEO)

ASIA UNITED BANK CORPO-
RATION
Joy Nostalg Center No 17 ADB Av-
enue, Ortigas Center, Pasig, 1600,
Philippines
Tel.: (63) 286313333
Web Site: https://www.aub.com.ph
Year Founded: 1997
AUB—(PHI)
Rev.: $357,258,749
Assets: $6,413,108,940
Liabilities: $5,530,740,834
Net Worth: $882,368,106
Earnings: $149,148,486
Emp.: 2,027
Fiscal Year-end: 12/31/23
Banking Services
N.A.I.C.S.: 522110
Abraham T. Co (Chm)

Subsidiaries:

Cavite United Rural Bank
Corporation   **(1)**
636 Aguinaldo Highway Tanzang Luma 3,
Imus, Cavite, Philippines
Tel.: (63) 464351701
Web Site: https://www.curb.com.ph
Rural Banking Services
N.A.I.C.S.: 522110
Abraham T. Co (Chm)

Rural Bank of Angeles, Inc.   **(1)**
Corner Miranda Street Sto Entierro Street
Barangay Sto, Rosario, Angeles, Pam-
panga, Philippines
Tel.: (63) 9338680493
Web Site: http://rba.com.ph
Commercial Banking Services
N.A.I.C.S.: 522110
Jenny Arcilla (Officer-Svc)

ASIA VETS HOLDINGS LTD.
21 Bukit Batok Crescent 29-84
Wcega Tower, Singapore, 658065,
Singapore
Tel.: (65) 62533540
Web Site: https://www.asiavets.com
5RE—(CAT)
Rev.: $1,794,246
Assets: $14,378,002
Liabilities: $601,059
Net Worth: $13,776,943
Earnings: ($568,323)
Emp.: 17
Fiscal Year-end: 12/31/22
Integrated Circuits Mfr
N.A.I.C.S.: 334412

ASIA VITAL COMPONENTS
CO., LTD.

Rm 3 7F No 24 Wuquan 2nd Rd,
Xinzhuang District, New Taipei City,
242, Taiwan
Tel.: (886) 222996930
Web Site: https://www.avc.co
Year Founded: 1991
3017—(TAI)
Rev.: $1,935,784,485
Assets: $2,343,674,230
Liabilities: $1,498,418,433
Net Worth: $845,255,797
Earnings: $190,145,648
Emp.: 12,026
Fiscal Year-end: 12/31/23
Fans & Blowers Mfr
N.A.I.C.S.: 238220
Ching-Hang Shen (Chm & Pres)

Subsidiaries:

Asia Vital Components Co., Ltd. -
AVC Taipei Factory   **(1)**
7F-3 No 24 Wucyuan 2 Road, Sinjhuang
District, Taipei, 24892, Taiwan
Tel.: (886) 222996930
Emp.: 300
Thermal Conductivity Instruments Mfr
N.A.I.C.S.: 334516

Furukawa Avc Electronics (Suzhou)
Co., Ltd.   **(1)**
No 169 PuTian Road, WeiTing Town Su-
Zhou Industry Park, Suzhou, 215121, China
Tel.: (86) 51262713192
Micro Heat Pipe Mfr
N.A.I.C.S.: 332410

ASIA-EXPRESS LOGISTICS
HOLDINGS LIMITED
Unit 1613-1615 Level 16 Tower 1
Metroplaza 223 Hing Fong Road,
Kwai Fong, China (Hong Kong)   **Ky**
Web Site: https://www.asia-
expresslogs.com
Year Founded: 1995
8620—(HKG)
Holding Company
N.A.I.C.S.: 551112
Le Bon Chan (Chm)

ASIA-PAC FINANCIAL INVEST-
MENT COMPANY LIMITED
Room 2703 27/F Shui On Centre 6-8
Harbour Road, Wanchai, China
(Hong Kong)
Tel.: (852) 2 511 6868
Web Site: http://www.gca.com.hk
8193—(HKG)
Rev.: $6,677,166
Assets: $25,461,942
Liabilities: $10,043,415
Net Worth: $15,418,527
Earnings: ($6,060,383)
Emp.: 21
Fiscal Year-end: 03/31/22
Asset Advisory, Asset Appraisal, Cor-
porate & Consulting Services
N.A.I.C.S.: 523940
Kwok Kwong Ip (Founder, Mng Dir &
Officer-Compliance)

Subsidiaries:

Greater China Appraisal Limited **(1)**
Room 2703 Shui On Centre 6-8 Harbour
Road, Wanchai, China (Hong Kong)
Tel.: (852) 25116868
Web Site: http://www.gca-valuation.com
Business Management Consulting Services
N.A.I.C.S.: 541611

Greater China Asset Services
Limited   **(1)**
Room 304 Shui On Centre 6-8 Harbour
Road, Wanchai, China (Hong Kong)
Tel.: (852) 31053538
Web Site: https://gca-capital.com
Financial Advisory Services
N.A.I.C.S.: 523940

Greater China Corporate Consultancy
& Services Limited   **(1)**

Room 2703 27/F Shui On Centre 6-8 Har-
bour Road, Wanchai, China (Hong Kong)
Tel.: (852) 25116868
Web Site: http://www.gca-corpserv.com
Financial Consulting Services
N.A.I.C.S.: 523940

ASIA-PACIFIC SECURITIES
JOINT STOCK COMPANY
03 Floors Grand Plaza Building No
117 Tran Duy Hung Trung Hoa, Cau
Giay District, Hanoi, Vietnam
Tel.: (84) 435730200
Web Site: http://www.apec.com.vn
Year Founded: 2006
APS—(HNX)
Rev.: $1,033,725
Assets: $14,316,493
Liabilities: $583,058
Net Worth: $13,733,435
Earnings: ($1,375,307)
Emp.: 200
Fiscal Year-end: 12/31/19
Investment Banking & Securities Bro-
kerage Services
N.A.I.C.S.: 523150

ASIA-PACIFIC STRATEGIC IN-
VESTMENTS LIMITED
1 Scotts Road 20-07 Shaw Centre,
Singapore, 228208, Singapore
Tel.: (65) 67354118
Web Site:
https://www.asiastrategic.com.sg
5RA—(CAT)
Assets: $24,054,094
Liabilities: $9,402,001
Net Worth: $14,652,093
Earnings: ($4,686,180)
Fiscal Year-end: 06/30/23
Real Estate Agency
N.A.I.C.S.: 531390
Yeow Ming Choo (Chm & CEO)

Subsidiaries:

Huzhou Dixi Gengdu Ecological Agri-
culture Development Co., Ltd.   **(1)**
Industry Area Yang Dong Mining Area, Hefu
Town, Huzhou, 313017, Zhejiang, China
Tel.: (86) 5723966901
Real Estate Development Services
N.A.I.C.S.: 531390

ASIA-POTASH INTERNA-
TIONAL INVESTMENT
(GUANGZHOU) CO., LTD.
51/F CTF Finance Centre No 6 Zhuji-
ang East Road, Tianhe District,
Guangzhou, 510623, Guangdong,
China
Tel.: (86) 2085506280
Web Site: https://www.asia-
potash.com
Year Founded: 1999
000893—(SSE)
Rev.: $486,643,248
Assets: $1,803,630,348
Liabilities: $171,160,236
Net Worth: $1,632,470,112
Earnings: $284,825,268
Emp.: 575
Fiscal Year-end: 12/31/22
Edible Oil Mfr
N.A.I.C.S.: 311225
Liu Binyan (Sec)

ASIABASEMETALS INC.
1111 West Hastings Street 15th Floor,
Vancouver, V6E 2J3, BC, Canada
Tel.: (604) 765-2030   **BC**
Web Site:
https://www.asiabasemetals.com
Year Founded: 2009
ABZ—(TSXV)
Assets: $15,714
Liabilities: $313,767
Net Worth: ($298,053)

Earnings: ($500,720)
Fiscal Year-end: 09/30/23
Zinc & Base Metals Mining Services
N.A.I.C.S.: 212230
Rajinder Chowdhry (Founder, Chm,
Pres & CEO)

ASIACREDIT BANK JSC
5b block Nurly Tau business center,
17/1 Al-Farabi ave, Almaty, 050059,
Kazakhstan
Tel.: (7) 273308811
Web Site:
http://www.asiacreditbank.kz
Commercial Banking Services
N.A.I.C.S.: 522110
Orifdzhan Kabulovich Shadiev (Chm)

ASIAFIN HOLDINGS CORP.
Suite 30 02 30th Floor Menara KH
Jalan Sultan Ismail, 50250, Kuala
Lumpur, Malaysia
Tel.: (60) 321487170   **NV**
Web Site:
http://www.asiafingroup.com
Year Founded: 2019
Assets: $877,690
Liabilities: $21,162
Net Worth: $856,528
Earnings: ($112,202)
Emp.: 3
Fiscal Year-end: 12/31/22
Holding Company
N.A.I.C.S.: 551112
Kai Cheong Wong (Founder, Pres,
CEO, Treas & Sec)

ASIAMEDIC LTD.
350 Orchard Road No 08-00 Shaw
House, Singapore, 238868, Singa-
pore
Tel.: (65) 67898888
Web Site:
https://www.asiamedic.com.sg
Year Founded: 1974
505—(CAT)
Rev.: $17,875,306
Assets: $21,929,374
Liabilities: $11,888,828
Net Worth: $10,040,545
Earnings: $1,454,888
Emp.: 138
Fiscal Year-end: 12/31/23
Medical Facilities Owner & Operator
N.A.I.C.S.: 622310
Soon Soo Foo (Sec)

Subsidiaries:

Aesthetic Medical Centre Pte Ltd   **(1)**
350 Orchard Road 08 00, Shaw House,
Singapore, 238868, Singapore   **(100%)**
Tel.: (65) 67323801
Web Site: http://www.astiqueclinic.com.sg
Plastic Surgical Medical Facility
N.A.I.C.S.: 622310

AsiaMedic Astique The Aesthetic
Clinic Pte Ltd   **(1)**
1 Grange Road Orchard Building 12-02,
Singapore, 239693, Singapore
Tel.: (65) 67323801
Web Site: https://www.astiqueclinic.com.sg
Aesthetic Treatment Services
N.A.I.C.S.: 621311
Anjum Shabeena (Mgr-Clinic)

AsiaMedic Eye Centre Pte. Ltd.   **(1)**
350 Orchard Road 08-00, Shaw House,
Singapore, 238868, Singapore   **(100%)**
Tel.: (65) 67898888
Web Site: http://www.asiamedic.com.sg
Eye Treatment & Surgery Center
N.A.I.C.S.: 621320
Andi Solaiman (Acting CEO)

AsiaMedic PET/CT Centre Pte
Ltd   **(1)**
350 Orchard Road 08-00, Shaw House,
Singapore, 238868, Singapore   **(100%)**
Tel.: (65) 68387900

Web Site: http://www.asiamedic.com.sg
Diagnostic Imaging Centers
N.A.I.C.S.: 621512

Complete Healthcare International
Pte Ltd   (1)
350 Orchard Road 10-01 Shaw House, Sin-
gapore, 238868, Singapore
Tel.: (65) 67762288
Web Site: https://www.ohi health.oom.cg
Health Care Srvices
N.A.I.C.S.: 621999

The Orchard Imaging Centre Pte
Ltd   (1)
350 Orchard Road 08-00, Shaw House,
Singapore, 238868, Singapore   **(100%)**
Tel.: (65) 65056092
Web Site: http://www.asiamedic.com.sg
Diagnostic Imaging Centers
N.A.I.C.S.: 621512

Wellness Assessment Centre Pte
Ltd   (1)
350 Orchard Road 08-00, Shaw House,
Singapore, 238868, Singapore   **(100%)**
Tel.: (65) 68387933
Web Site: http://www.asiamedic.com.sg
Wellness Center
N.A.I.C.S.: 622310

ASIAMET RESOURCES LIM-ITED
Level 22 303 Collins Street, Mel-
bourne, 3000, VIC, Australia
Tel.: (61) 6045362711   BM
Web Site:
    http://www.asiametresources.com
ARS—(AIM)
Rev.: $2,670
Assets: $3,592,356
Liabilities: $1,037,450
Net Worth: $2,554,905
Earnings: ($4,696,566)
Fiscal Year-end: 12/31/22
Copper, Gold & Coal Mining Services
N.A.I.C.S.: 212230
Antony Manini *(Chm)*

ASIAN AMERICAN MEDICAL GROUP LIMITED
6A Napier Road Gleneagles Hospital
Annexe Block 02-36A 36 B 37, Sin-
gapore, 258500, Singapore
Tel.: (65) 6 476 2088   SG
Web Site: http://www.aamg.co
Year Founded: 1994
AJJ—(ASX)
Rev.: $1,179,266
Assets: $6,518,921
Liabilities: $2,462,301
Net Worth: $4,056,619
Earnings: ($4,385,076)
Fiscal Year-end: 08/31/21
Medical Devices
N.A.I.C.S.: 622110
Kai Chah Tan *(Chm)*

ASIAN BAMBOO AG
Stadthausbrucke 1-3, 20355, Ham-
burg, Germany
Tel.: (49) 4037644798
Web Site: http://www.asian-
    bamboo.com
Year Founded: 1992
5AB—(DEU)
Sales Range: $25-49.9 Million
Emp.: 812
Bamboo Producer
N.A.I.C.S.: 111421
Qiu Hai *(Controller-Fin)*

ASIAN BEARING LTD.
14 Peters Road Royapettah, Chen-
nai, 600 014, India
Tel.: (91) 442865155
Automotive Bearing Mfr
N.A.I.C.S.: 332991
Rajesh Bharwani *(COO)*

ASIAN CAPITAL RESOURCES (HOLDINGS) LIMITED
Room 2102 21/F Fu Fai Commercial
Centre 27 Hillier Street, Sheung Wan,
China (Hong Kong)
Tel.: (852) 31811688   Ky
Web Site: http://www.airnet.com.hk
8025—(HKG)
Rev.: $4,041,113
Assets: $5,730,488
Liabilities: $6,410,318
Net Worth: ($679,830)
Earnings: ($2,066,775)
Emp.: 33
Fiscal Year-end: 12/31/22
Investment Management Service
N.A.I.C.S.: 523940
Xuan Xie *(Chm & Compliance Offi-
cer)*

ASIAN CITRUS HOLDINGS LIMITED
1/F Ching Cheong Industrial Building
1-7 Kwai Cheong Road, Kwai Chung
New Territories, Wanchai, China
(Hong Kong)
Tel.: (852) 39510000   BM
Web Site: http://www.asian-
    citrus.com
0073—(HKG)
Rev.: $21,996,666
Assets: $35,328,847
Liabilities: $4,453,968
Net Worth: $30,874,879
Earnings: ($3,170,834)
Emp.: 47
Fiscal Year-end: 06/30/22
Orange Plantation Owner & Operator
N.A.I.C.S.: 111310
Hoi Yue Ng *(Deputy CEO)*

Subsidiaries:

Asian Citrus (H.K.) Company
Limited   (1)
Rm 1109 1111 Wayson Comml Bldg 28
Connaught Rd W, Sheung Wan, China
(Hong Kong)
Tel.: (852) 25590323
Web Site: http://www.asian-citrus.com
Orange Cultivation & Sales
N.A.I.C.S.: 111310

Lucky Team Biotech Development
(Hepu) Limited   (1)
No 51 Mingyuan Rd Wujia, Hepu, Beihai,
536100, Guangxi, China
Tel.: (86) 7797198851
Orange Cultivation
N.A.I.C.S.: 111310
Pang Yi *(Mng Dir)*

ASIAN DEVELOPMENT BANK
6 ADB Avenue, Metro Manila, Man-
daluyong, 1550, Philippines
Tel.: (63) 26324444
Web Site: http://www.adb.org
Year Founded: 1966
Sales Range: $1-4.9 Billion
Emp.: 2,000
Economic Development Services
N.A.I.C.S.: 523999
Bindu N. Lohani *(VP-Knowledge
Mgmt & Sustainable Dev)*

ASIAN EUROPEAN FOOT-WEAR
Zi De La Croix Rouge, Malville,
44260, Nantes, France
Tel.: (33) 240570300
Rev.: $21,600,000
Emp.: 20
Womens, Childrens & Infants Cloth-
ing
N.A.I.C.S.: 424350
Stephane Rohel *(Pres)*

ASIAN FLORA LIMITED
H No 1-8-364 Soap Factory Lane

Chikkadapally, Hyderabad, 500 020,
Telangana, India
Tel.: (91) 4023355044
Web Site: http://www.asianflora.in
Year Founded: 1994
531392—(BOM)
Assets: $152,568
Liabilities: $2,043,232
Net Worth: ($1,800,664)
Earnings: ($21,374)
Emp.: 5
Fiscal Year-end: 03/31/22
Agricultural Product Whslr
N.A.I.C.S.: 424930
Setty Sangameshwar *(Mng Dir)*

ASIAN GRANITO INDIA LIM-ITED
202 Dev Arc Opp Iskcon Temple S G
Highway, Ahmedabad, 380 015, Gu-
jarat, India
Tel.: (91) 7966125500
Web Site:
    https://www.aglasiangranito.com
532888—(BOM)
Rev.: $215,599,266
Assets: $263,670,252
Liabilities: $89,312,005
Net Worth: $174,358,248
Earnings: ($11,862,628)
Emp.: 1,503
Fiscal Year-end: 03/31/23
Building Products Industry
N.A.I.C.S.: 327120
Mukeshbhai Patel *(Mng Dir)*

Subsidiaries:

Amazoone Ceramics Limited   (1)
305 Dev Arc Opp Iskcon Temple S G High-
way, Ahmedabad, 380015, Gujarat, India
Tel.: (91) 9909986521
Web Site: https://www.amazoone.co.in
Ceramic Tile Mfr
N.A.I.C.S.: 327110

Asian Granito India Limited - Gujarat
Unit   (1)
Ceramic Zone Dalpur, Sabarkantha Dist,
Parantij, 383 120, Gujarat, India
Tel.: (91) 2770 240931
Ceramic Wall Tiles Mfr
N.A.I.C.S.: 327120

Crystal Ceramic Industries Private
Limited   (1)
101 102 103 Elanza Vertex Sindhu Bhavan
Road B/h Armieda Bodakdev, Ahmedabad,
380 054, Gujarat, India
Tel.: (91) 7434850411
Web Site: https://www.crystalceramic.com
Ceramic Tile Mfr
N.A.I.C.S.: 327110

Powergrace Industries Limited   (1)
305 Dev Arc Opp Iscon Temple S G High-
way, Ahmedabad, India
Tel.: (91) 18001210141
Web Site:
    https://www.powergraceindustries.com
Tile & Stone Product Mfr
N.A.I.C.S.: 327991

ASIAN GROWTH PROPERTIES LIMITED
Portcullis TrustNet Chambers, PO
Box 3444, Road Town, Tortola, Virgin
Islands (British)
Tel.: (284) 4945296   VG
Web Site:
    http://www.asiangrowth.com
Year Founded: 2004
Sales Range: $75-99.9 Million
Property Investment, Development &
Management Services
N.A.I.C.S.: 531390
Lincoln Lu *(CEO)*

ASIAN HOTELS & PROPER-TIES PLC

No 77 Galle Road, 3, Colombo, 03,
Sri Lanka
Tel.: (94) 115540404   LK
Year Founded: 1993
AHPL—(COL)
Rev.: $28,016,904
Assets: $152,829,956
Liabilities: $45,516,990
Not Worth: $107,312,966
Earnings: ($1,107,696)
Emp.: 1,390
Fiscal Year-end: 03/31/23
Property Development Services
N.A.I.C.S.: 237210
Krishan Niraj Jayasekara Balendra
(Chm & Mng Dir)

ASIAN HOTELS (EAST) LIM-ITED
Hyatt Regency Kolkata JA-1 Sector
III, Salt Lake City, Kolkata, 700 106,
India
Tel.: (91) 3368201344
Web Site: https://www.ahleast.com
AHLEAST—(NSE)
Rev.: $13,427,218
Assets: $125,008,870
Liabilities: $31,273,611
Net Worth: $93,735,260
Earnings: ($4,709,059)
Emp.: 212
Fiscal Year-end: 03/31/22
Restaurant Operating Services
N.A.I.C.S.: 722511
Radhe Shyam Saraf *(Chm)*

Subsidiaries:

Robust Hotels Private Limited   (1)
No 365 Anna Salai Teynampet, Chennai,
600018, Tamil Nadu, India
Tel.: (91) 4461001250
Web Site: https://www.robusthotels.in
Hotel Operator
N.A.I.C.S.: 721110

ASIAN HOTELS (NORTH) LIM-ITED
Bhikaiji Cama Place M G Marg, New
Delhi, 110066, India
Tel.: (91) 1126791234
Web Site:
    https://www.asianhotelsnorth.com
ASIANHOTNR—(NSE)
Rev.: $18,396,282
Assets: $212,387,175
Liabilities: $180,226,437
Net Worth: $32,160,738
Earnings: ($61,948,218)
Emp.: 620
Fiscal Year-end: 03/31/22
Hotel Services
N.A.I.C.S.: 721120
Shiv Kumar Jatia *(Chm & Mng Dir)*

ASIAN HOTELS (WEST) LIM-ITED
6th Floor Aria Towers JW Marriott
New Delhi Aerocity Asset Area 4,
Hospitality District Near IGI Airport,
New Delhi, 110 037, India
Tel.: (91) 1146101210
Web Site:
    https://www.asianhotelswest.com
AHLWEST—(BOM)
Rev.: $60,251,496
Assets: $160,131,740
Liabilities: $145,000,319
Net Worth: $15,131,421
Earnings: $135,067
Emp.: 422
Fiscal Year-end: 03/31/20
Home Management Services
N.A.I.C.S.: 721110
Sushil Kumar Gupta *(Chm & Mng
Dir)*

Asian Hotels (West) Limited—(Continued)

Subsidiaries:

Aria Hotels and Consultancy Services
Pvt. Ltd.　　　　　　　　　　(1)
Arya Tower 6th Floor, New Delhi, 110037,
India
Tel.: (91) 1141200000
Home Management Services
N.A.I.C.S.: 721110

ASIAN INSULATORS PUBLIC COMPANY LIMITED

254 Seri Thai Road, Kannayaow,
Bangkok, 10230, Thailand
Tel.: (66) 25171451
Web Site:
　https://www.asianinsulators.com
Year Founded: 1981
AI—(THA)
Rev.: $255,372,436
Assets: $107,087,557
Liabilities: $17,056,957
Net Worth: $90,030,600
Earnings: $3,985,697
Fiscal Year-end: 12/31/23
Electrical Equipment Mfr & Distr
N.A.I.C.S.: 335999
Narong Thareratanavibool (Chm)

ASIAN LIFE INSURANCE COMPANY

Maitidevi-30, Kathmandu, Nepal
Tel.: (977) 14510115
Web Site:
　https://www.asianlife.com.np
Year Founded: 2008
ALICL—(NEP)
Rev.: $82,653,660
Assets: $323,925,952
Liabilities: $296,269,033
Net Worth: $27,656,920
Earnings: $2,577,166
Emp.: 434
Fiscal Year-end: 07/16/23
Insurance Services
N.A.I.C.S.: 524298
Dinesh Lal Shrestha (CEO)

ASIAN MARINE SERVICES PUBLIC COMPANY LIMITED

128 Moo 3 Suksawad Rd Laemfapa
Prasamutjedee, Samut Prakan,
10290, Thailand
Tel.: (66) 281520607
Web Site: https://www.asimar.com
Year Founded: 1981
ASIMAR—(THA)
Rev.: $16,744,626
Assets: $24,248,332
Liabilities: $11,661,946
Net Worth: $12,586,386
Earnings: $517,138
Emp.: 481
Fiscal Year-end: 12/31/23
Marine & Cargo Handling Services
N.A.I.C.S.: 488320
Prakit Pradipasen (Co/Co-Chm)

Subsidiaries:

General Marine Company
Limited　　　　　　　　　　(1)
128 Moo 3 Suksawad Rd Prasamutjedee
Laemfapa, Samut Prakan, 10290, Thailand
Tel.: (66) 281520607
Marine & Cargo Handling Services
N.A.I.C.S.: 488320

ASIAN MICRO HOLDINGS LTD.

63 Hillview Avenue 08-01 Lam Soon
Industrial Building, Singapore,
669569, Singapore
Tel.: (65) 68627777
Web Site:
　https://asianmicro.listed.com
Year Founded: 1966

585—(CAT)
Rev.: $2,375,857
Assets: $2,269,398
Liabilities: $1,035,247
Net Worth: $1,234,150
Earnings: ($602,005)
Emp.: 11
Fiscal Year-end: 06/30/23
Holding Company
N.A.I.C.S.: 551112
Kee Liew Lim (Chm, CEO & Mng Dir)

Subsidiaries:

ACI Industries Pte Ltd　　　　(1)
63 Hillview Avenue Unit No 0801 Lam Soon
Industrial Building, Singapore, 669569, Sin-
gapore
Tel.: (65) 68627777
Adhesives, Cleanroom, Industrial & Static
Control Products Mfr
N.A.I.C.S.: 325520
Victor Lim (Gen Mgr)

AM NGV (S) Pte. Ltd.　　　　(1)
3 Tech Park Crescent, Singapore, 638129,
Singapore
Tel.: (65) 8627777
Natural Gas Distr
N.A.I.C.S.: 221210
Hla Myo Aung (Mgr-Operation)

AM NGV (T) Co., Ltd.　　　　(1)
140 Moo 16 Bangpa-in T Bangkrasan, Industrial Estate A Bangpa-in, Ayutthaya,
13160, Thailand
Tel.: (66) 35258998
Natural Gas Distr
N.A.I.C.S.: 221210

Asian Micro (Thailand) Co., Ltd.　(1)
130/171 130/172 Moo 3 Wang Chula Sub-
District, Wang Noi District, Ayutthaya,
13170, Thailand
Tel.: (66) 35 722022
Web Site: http://www.asianmicro.sg
Electronic Hardware Mfr
N.A.I.C.S.: 332510

Asian Micro Co. Ltd.　　　　(1)
140 Moo 16 Bangpa-in Industrial Estate T
Bangkrasan, A Bangpa-in, Ayutthaya,
13160, Thailand
Tel.: (66) 3 525 8998
Web Site:
　http://asianmicro.listedcompany.com
Contract Engineering Assemblies & Other
Support Services
N.A.I.C.S.: 541330

Asian Micro Technology Co. Ltd.　(1)
Building 1A, Export Processing Zone,
No.200 Suhong Middle Road, Suzhou,
215021, China
Tel.: (86) 51262586877
Web Site:
　http://asianmicro.listedcompany.com
Contract Engineering Assemblies & Other
Support Services
N.A.I.C.S.: 541330

Suzhou Asian Micro Recovery Tech-
nology Co Ltd　　　　　　　(1)
No 288 Lian Yi Road, Lu Zhi, Suzhou,
China
Tel.: (86) 51 2660 10238
Web Site: http://www.szasianmicro.com
Polyethylene Bags Mfr
N.A.I.C.S.: 326199

ASIAN PAC HOLDINGS BER-HAD

12th Floor Menara SMI, No 6 Lorong
P Ramlee, 50250, Kuala Lumpur,
Malaysia
Tel.: (60) 327863388
Web Site:
　https://www.asianpac.com.my
ASIAPAC—(KLS)
Rev.: $34,320,083
Assets: $499,634,190
Liabilities: $236,981,250
Net Worth: $262,652,940
Earnings: ($1,181,318)
Emp.: 377
Fiscal Year-end: 03/31/22

Property Investment & Development
N.A.I.C.S.: 531311
Yee Kean Wong (Controller-Fin)

ASIAN PACIFIC TIMBER MAR-KETING PTY LTD

25 Vallance St, Saint Marys, 2760,
NSW, Australia
Tel.: (61) 0298334777
Year Founded: 1986
Sales Range: $50-74.9 Million
New Home Renovation & Commer-
cial Project Timber Whslr
N.A.I.C.S.: 337212
Gerry Gardiner (Chm & Co-Owner)

Subsidiaries:

Asian Pacific Timber Marketing Pty
Ltd　　　　　　　　　　　(1)
100 Potassium St, Narangba, 4504, QLD,
Australia
Tel.: (61) 738179999
Sales Range: $25-49.9 Million
Emp.: 27
New Home Renovation & Commercial Proj-
ect Timber Whslr
N.A.I.C.S.: 321999
Dave Alcock (Mng Dir)

ASIAN PAINTS LIMITED

Asian Paints House 6A Shantinagar,
Santacruz E, Mumbai, 400055, India
Tel.: (91) 2262181000　　　　In
Web Site:
　https://www.asianpaints.com
Year Founded: 1942
ASIANPAINT—(NSE)
Rev.: $4,181,412,385
Assets: $3,093,099,934
Liabilities: $1,121,288,892
Net Worth: $1,971,811,043
Earnings: $503,007,014
Emp.: 8,056
Fiscal Year-end: 03/31/23
Paints Mfr
N.A.I.C.S.: 325510
Manish Choksi (Vice Chm)

Subsidiaries:

Apco Coatings　　　　　　　(1)
7-9-11 Ruve Place Tavakubu, Tavakubu,
Lautoka, Fiji
Tel.: (679) 6662799
Web Site: http://www.apcocoatings.com
Sales Range: $25-49.9 Million
Emp.: 65
Paint & Coatings Mfr
N.A.I.C.S.: 325510

Asian Paints (Bangladesh)
Limited　　　　　　　　　　(1)
The Pearl Trade Center PTC Cha-90/3
Progoti Sarani, North Badda, Dhaka, 1212,
Bangladesh
Tel.: (880) 2222286920
Web Site: https://www.asianpaints.com.bd
Paints Mfr
N.A.I.C.S.: 325510

Asian Paints (Lanka) Limited　　(1)
No 81 Koralawella Road, Moratuwa, Sri
Lanka
Tel.: (94) 117770730
Web Site: http://www.asianpaints.com
Paints & Coating Mfr
N.A.I.C.S.: 325510
Channa Hewage (Mgr-Mktg)

Asian Paints (Nepal) Pvt. Limited　(1)
Balkumari-08, PO Box 4805, Lalitpur, Nepal
Tel.: (977) 15203045
Web Site: https://www.asianpaintsnepal.com
Sales Range: $50-74.9 Million
Emp.: 200
Paints & Coatings Mfr
N.A.I.C.S.: 325510

Asian Paints (S.I.) Limited　　　(1)
1898-1900 Industrial Estate, Ranadi, Honiara, Solomon Islands
Tel.: (677) 30485

Sales Range: $50-74.9 Million
Emp.: 10
Paints Mfr & Distr
N.A.I.C.S.: 325510

Asian Paints (Vanuatu) Limited　(1)
PO Box 253, Port-Vila, Vanuatu
Tel.: (678) 25963
Sales Range: $50-74.9 Million
Emp.: 6
Paint Mfr & Distr
N.A.I.C.S.: 325510

Asian Paints Industrial Coatings
Ltd.　　　　　　　　　　　(1)
Asian Paints House 6A Shantinagar, Santa-
cruz (E), Mumbai, 400 055, India
Tel.: (91) 2239818000
Web Site: http://www.asianpaints.com
Emp.: 200
Industrial Coating Mfr
N.A.I.C.S.: 325510

Asian Paints International Private
Limited　　　　　　　　　　(1)
140 Robinson Road Crown at Robinson
11-05, Singapore, 068907, Singapore
Tel.: (65) 62615224
Web Site: http://www.asianpaints.com.sg
Paints Mfr
N.A.I.C.S.: 325510
Chaitanya Dabholkar (Head-Fin)

Berger International Ltd.　　　　(1)
40 Robinson Road Crown at Robinson 11-
05, Singapore, 068907, Singapore (96.7%)
Tel.: (65) 62615224
Sales Range: $75-99.9 Million
Emp.: 3,500
Specialty Paints & Coatings Mfr
N.A.I.C.S.: 325510

Subsidiary (Non-US):

Apco Coatings Ltd.　　　　　(2)
444 Newman Road, Geebung, Brisbane,
4034, QLD, Australia
Tel.: (61) 732657890
Web Site: http://auspaint.com.au
Sales Range: $25-49.9 Million
Emp.: 40
Paint & Coating Mfr
N.A.I.C.S.: 325510

Berger Paints (Hong Kong) Ltd.　(2)
Room 601 Shiu Fung Hong Building, 239-
241 Wing Lok Street, Sheung Wan, China
(Hong Kong)　　　　　　　(100%)
Tel.: (852) 25443768
Web Site: http://www.bergeronline.com
Sales Range: $25-49.9 Million
Emp.: 5
Paint Varnish & Supplies Whslr
N.A.I.C.S.: 424950
Ken Yen (Gen Mgr)

Berger Paints (Thailand) Ltd　　(2)
83 Moo 4 Poochaosamingprad Road Sam-
rong, Klang Prapradaeng, 10130, Samut
Prakan, Thailand　　　　　(100%)
Tel.: (66) 275420048
Web Site: http://www.bergeronline.com
Sales Range: $25-49.9 Million
Emp.: 70
Paint & Coating Mfr
N.A.I.C.S.: 325510

Berger Paints Bahrain W.L.L.　　(2)
Sitra Indl Area - 3rd Gate, PO Box 26688,
Sitra, Bahrain
Tel.: (973) 17123700
Web Site:
　https://www.asianpaintsarabia.com
Sales Range: $25-49.9 Million
Emp.: 75
Paint & Coating Mfr
N.A.I.C.S.: 325510

Berger Paints Emirates Limited　(2)
Al Qouz Indl Area-1 Opp TCTI factory, PO
Box 27524, Dubai, 27524, United Arab
Emirates
Tel.: (971) 43391000
Web Site:
　https://www.asianpaintsarabia.com
Sales Range: $25-49.9 Million
Emp.: 200
Paints Mfr & Distr
N.A.I.C.S.: 325510
A. K. Paranthaman (Mgr-Mktg)

Berger Paints Ningbo Co. Ltd. **(2)**
No 17 Jinqi Road Beilun Shiqiao, Economic & Tech Development Zone, 315821, Ningbo, Zhejiang, China
Tel.: (86) 57486178116
Sales Range: $25-49.9 Million
Emp.: 40
Paint & Coating Mfr
N.A.I.C.S.: 325510

Causeway Paints Lanka (Private) Limited **(1)**
15 Noel Mendis Mawatha Moderawila Industrial Estate, Panadura, Sri Lanka
Tel.: (94) 777272272
N.A.I.C.S.: 325510

Kadisco Paint & Adhesive Industry S.C. **(1)**
PO Box 120919, Addis Ababa, Ethiopia
Tel.: (251) 114391038
Web Site:
    https://www.kadiscoasianpaints.com
Paints Mfr
N.A.I.C.S.: 325510

PT Asian Paints Indonesia **(1)**
Gedung Palma Tower LT 16 UnitC D E JL RA Kartini 11-5 Kav, 6 Sektor II-Kota Adm, Jakarta Selatan, Indonesia
Tel.: (62) 81511518888
N.A.I.C.S.: 325510

Samoa Paints Limited **(1)**
PO Box 3219, Apia, Samoa (Western)
Tel.: (685) 22504
Web Site: http://www.same.org.ws
Paints Mfr
N.A.I.C.S.: 325510

Sleek International Private Limited **(1)**
Lotus Corporate Park 3rd Floor of D&G Wings Near Graham Firth Compound, Off WE Highway Goregaon, Mumbai, 400063, India
Tel.: (91) 18002120500
Web Site: https://www.sleekworld.com
N.A.I.C.S.: 337110

ASIAN PAY TELEVISION TRUST

50 Raffles Place No 32-01 Singapore Land Tower, Singapore, 048623, Singapore
Tel.: (65) 67278370
Web Site: https://www.aptt.sg
APTTF—(OTCIQ)
Rev.: $201,768,537
Assets: $1,637,667,196
Liabilities: $1,110,746,799
Net Worth: $526,920,397
Earnings: ($307,811,103)
Emp.: 898
Fiscal Year-end: 12/31/23
Pay TV & Broadband Investment Services
N.A.I.C.S.: 523999
Lum Sung Yong *(Chm)*

ASIAN PETROPRODUCTS & EXPORTS LIMITED

24 Suwernapuri Soceity Chikuwadi, Near Jetalpur Road Alkapuri, Vadodara, 390007, Gujarat, India
Tel.: (91) 9879504335
Web Site: https://asianpetro.in
Year Founded: 1991
524434—(BOM)
Rev.: $75,225
Assets: $331,204
Liabilities: $607,630
Net Worth: ($276,426)
Earnings: ($40,281)
Emp.: 4
Fiscal Year-end: 03/31/22
Petro Chemical Mfr & Distr
N.A.I.C.S.: 325180
Jaykishor Chaturvedi *(Chm & Mng Dir)*

ASIAN PHYTOCEUTICALS

PUBLIC COMPANY LIMITED

84/3 M4 Northern Region Industrial Estate West T Banklang, A Muang, Lamphun, 51000, Thailand
Tel.: (66) 53581374
Web Site: https://www.apco.co.th
Year Founded: 1988
APCO—(THA)
Rev.: $9,036,149
Assets: $20,572,296
Liabilities: $2,695,452
Net Worth: $17,876,843
Earnings: $3,174,195
Emp.: 102
Fiscal Year-end: 12/31/23
Botanical Extracts Used for Dietary Supplements, Cosmetics & Personal Care Products
N.A.I.C.S.: 325411
Maleeratna Plumchitchom *(Chm)*

Subsidiaries:

Asian Life Co., Ltd. **(1)**
8/F RS Tower 121/33-34 Ratchadapisek Rd Dindaeng, Bangkok, 10400, Thailand
Tel.: (66) 2646 4800
Dietary Supplements & Natural Cosmetics Whslr
N.A.I.C.S.: 424210

Green Gold Co., Ltd. **(1)**
84/3 Moo 4, Muang, Lamphun, 51000, Thailand
Tel.: (66) 53581374
Web Site: http://www.apco.co.th
Emp.: 150
Dietary Supplements Mfr
N.A.I.C.S.: 325412

ASIAN SEA CORPORATION PUBLIC COMPANY LIMITED

55/2 Moo 2 Rama 2 Road Bangkrajao Muang, Samut Sakhon, 7400, Thailand
Tel.: (66) 3484557591
Web Site: https://www.asiansea.co.th
Year Founded: 1982
ASIAN—(THA)
Rev.: $282,670,516
Assets: $263,282,377
Liabilities: $80,900,582
Net Worth: $182,381,795
Earnings: $8,830,863
Emp.: 5,000
Fiscal Year-end: 12/31/23
Frozen Seafood Processing
N.A.I.C.S.: 311710
Somsak Amornrattanachaikul *(Chm & CEO)*

Subsidiaries:

Asian Alliance International Co., Ltd. **(1)**
8/8 Moo 3 Rama 2 Road, Banbor, Amphur Muang, 74000, Samutsakorn, Thailand
Tel.: (66) 34845575
Web Site: http://www.asianalliance.co.th
Frozen Seafood Distr
N.A.I.C.S.: 424460
Ajara Mhordee *(Sr Mgr-Comml)*

Asian Group SCS Europe GmbH **(1)**
Toebele 1, Rechberghausen, 73098, Goppingen, Germany
Tel.: (49) 71619650203
Frozen Seafood Distr
N.A.I.C.S.: 424460
Heiko Weissinger *(Mng Partner)*

Asian Group Services Co., Ltd. **(1)**
3388/22 Pharam4 Road Klongton, Klongtoey, Bangkok, Thailand
Tel.: (66) 21179328
Frozen Seafood Distr
N.A.I.C.S.: 424460

Asian Pets Care Corporation Co., Ltd. **(1)**
742 Sukhumvit42 Road Khlong Toei, Khlong Toei, Bangkok, 10110, Thailand
Tel.: (66) 23675021
Web Site: https://asianpetcare.com

Veterinary Food Mfr & Distr
N.A.I.C.S.: 311111

ASIAN STAR ANCHOR CHAIN CO., LTD. JIANGSU

NO 88 Meirengang Road Dongxing, Jingjiang, 214533, Jiangsu, China
Tel.: (86) 52384681282
Web Site: https://www.anchor-chain.com
Year Founded: 1981
601890—(SHG)
Rev.: $212,913,273
Assets: $647,936,340
Liabilities: $177,018,538
Net Worth: $470,917,802
Earnings: $20,922,633
Emp.: 1,500
Fiscal Year-end: 12/31/22
Anchor Chain Mfr
N.A.I.C.S.: 332999
An Xiang Tao *(Chm)*

ASIAN STAR CO.

8F Nissan Yokohama Bldg 2-6-32 Takashima, Nishi-ku, Yokohama, 220-0011, Kanagawa, Japan
Tel.: (81) 453242444
Web Site: http://www.yoko.co.jp
Year Founded: 1988
8946—(TKS)
Rev.: $15,066,250
Assets: $25,630,350
Liabilities: $10,301,770
Net Worth: $15,328,580
Earnings: $283,600
Fiscal Year-end: 12/31/23
Real Estate Development Services
N.A.I.C.S.: 531390

Subsidiaries:

Griffin Partners Co. **(1)**
2-6-32 Takashima Yokohama East Exit Wisport Building 8F, Nishi-ku, Yokohama, 220-0011, Kanagawa, Japan
Tel.: (81) 452732240
Web Site: http://www.griffin-p.co.jp
Real Estate Lending Services
N.A.I.C.S.: 531110

ASIAN STAR COMPANY LTD

114 Mittal Court -C Nariman Point, Mumbai, 400021, India
Tel.: (91) 2222811371
Web Site:
    https://www.asianstargroup.com
Year Founded: 1971
531847—(BOM)
Rev.: $604,749,641
Assets: $332,111,612
Liabilities: $152,832,293
Net Worth: $179,279,318
Earnings: $12,807,467
Emp.: 715
Fiscal Year-end: 03/31/22
Diamond & Jewellery Mfr & Retailer
N.A.I.C.S.: 339910
Arvind Tarachand Shah *(Exec Dir)*

Subsidiaries:

Asian Star Company Limited (USA) **(1)**
551 5th Ave Ste 3502, New York, NY 10176
Tel.: (212) 354-0666
Sales Range: $25-49.9 Million
Emp.: 5
Diamond Jewelry Mfr
N.A.I.C.S.: 339910
Mehul Shroff *(VP)*

Asian Star Jewels Private Limited **(1)**
114 Mittal Court - C Nariman Point, Andheri, Mumbai, 400 021, Maharashtra, India
Tel.: (91) 2262444111
Web Site: https://www.asianstargroup.com
Sales Range: $25-49.9 Million
Emp.: 30
Diamond Jewelry Designer

N.A.I.C.S.: 458310

ASIAN TEA & EXPORTS LIMITED

Sikkim Commerce House 4/1 Middleton Street, Kolkata, 700 071, India
Tel.: (91) 3340063601
Web Site:
    https://www.asianteaexports.com
011053—(KOL)
Rev.: $11,562,014
Assets: $15,831,366
Liabilities: $7,770,495
Net Worth: $8,060,871
Earnings: $391,127
Emp.: 6
Fiscal Year-end: 03/31/22
Tea Mfr & Whslr
N.A.I.C.S.: 311920
Hariram Garg *(Founder & Mng Dir)*

ASIAN TELEVISION NETWORK INTERNATIONAL LTD.

330 Cochrane Drive, Markham, L3R 8E4, ON, Canada
Tel.: (905) 948-8199
Web Site:
    https://www.asiantelevision.com
AITVF—(OTCIQ)
Rev.: $5,490,172
Assets: $5,123,899
Liabilities: $5,103,713
Net Worth: $20,186
Earnings: ($1,079,417)
Fiscal Year-end: 12/31/23
Television Broadcasting Services
N.A.I.C.S.: 516120

Subsidiaries:

Asian Television Network Inc. **(1)**
330 Cochrane Drive, Markham, L3R 8E4, ON, Canada
Tel.: (905) 948-8199
Web Site: http://www.asiantelevision.com
Television Broadcasting Services
N.A.I.C.S.: 516120

ASIAN TERMINALS, INC.

ATI Bldg A Bonifacio Drive Port Area, 1018, Manila, 1018, Philippines
Tel.: (63) 25286000
Web Site:
    https://www.asianterminals.com.ph
Year Founded: 1986
ATI—(PHI)
Rev.: $232,185,075
Assets: $659,585,888
Liabilities: $228,222,883
Net Worth: $431,363,005
Earnings: $46,544,763
Fiscal Year-end: 12/31/21
Harbor Port Operator
N.A.I.C.S.: 488310
Patrick Chan *(VP-Ops-Manila & Cavite)*

ASIANLOGIC LIMITED

3/F Oriental Crystal Commercial Building 46 Lyndhurst Terrace, Central, China (Hong Kong)
Tel.: (852) 25810100
Web Site: http://www.asianlogic.com
Year Founded: 2002
Sales Range: $10-24.9 Million
Emp.: 2,000
Online Gambling Services
N.A.I.C.S.: 713290
Thomas Alexej Hall *(Vice Chm)*

Subsidiaries:

Bayview Technologies, Inc **(1)**
43rd Fl Yuchengco Tower Gil Puyat Ave, RCBC Plz 6819 Ayala Ave cor, Makati, 1200, Philippines
Tel.: (63) 28872525
Web Site:
    http://www.bayviewtechnology.com
Emp.: 125

AsianLogic Limited—(Continued)

Online Gambling Services
N.A.I.C.S.: 541511

**Cantonvalley Macau Company
Limited**　(1)
Ed AIA Tower, Macau, China (Macau)
Tel.: (853) 28286632
Administrative Management Service Providers
N.A.I.C.S.: 541611

Emphasis Services Limited　(1)
43 F Yuchengco Tower RCBC Plz 6819
Ayala Ave cor Gil Puyat Ave, Makati, Philippines
Tel.: (63) 28872525
Web Site: http://www.esl-asia.com
Online Gambling Services
N.A.I.C.S.: 713210

Internet Sports Marketing Limited　(1)
3/F Oriental Crystal Building 46 Lyndhurst
Terrace, Central, China (Hong Kong)
Tel.: (852) 25810100
Web Site: http://www.ismhongkong.com
Online Sports & Leisure Marketing Services
N.A.I.C.S.: 541910
Nick Chappell (Mgr)

Orient Capital Ventures Limited　(1)
300-1055 W Hastings St, Vancouver, V6E
2E9, BC, Canada
Tel.: (604) 689-0618
Web Site: http://www.orientvc.com
Emp.: 1
Investment Holding Services
N.A.I.C.S.: 551112
Mian Kuang (Gen Mgr)

ASIAPHARMA HOLDINGS LTD.
137 Telok Ayer Street Unit 05-05,
Singapore, 68602, Singapore
Tel.: (65) 6220 0119
Web Site: http://www.luye.com
Emp.: 20
Investment Holding Company
N.A.I.C.S.: 551112
Dian Bo Liu (Chm)

Subsidiaries:

Luye Pharma Group Ltd.　(1)
No 9 Baoyuan Road, Laishan District, Yantai, 264003, Shandong, China
Tel.: (86) 5356717618
Web Site: http://www.luye.cn
Rev.: $839,824,502
Assets: $3,404,647,350
Liabilities: $1,854,389,581
Net Worth: $1,550,257,769
Earnings: $81,894,758
Emp.: 5,005
Fiscal Year-end: 12/31/2022
Orthopaedics, Neurology, Gastroenterology
& Hepatology Drugs Mfr
N.A.I.C.S.: 325412
Dian Bo Liu (Chm & CEO)

Subsidiary (Non-US):

Luye Pharma AG　(2)
Am Windfeld 35, 83714, Miesbach, Germany
Tel.: (49) 8025 2867 0
Web Site: http://www.luyepharma.eu
Pharmaceuticals Product Mfr
N.A.I.C.S.: 325412
Jorg Scheidle (Chm)

ASIAPHOS LIMITED
22 Kallang Avenue 03-02 Hong Aik
Industrial Building, Singapore,
339413, Singapore
Tel.: (65) 62923119
Web Site: https://www.asiaphos.com
5WV—(CAT)
Rev.: $638,705
Assets: $82,446,499
Liabilities: $23,345,937
Net Worth: $59,100,562
Earnings: ($2,087,492)
Fiscal Year-end: 12/31/20
Phosphate Mining
N.A.I.C.S.: 212390
Hian Eng Ong (CEO & Chm)

Subsidiaries:

Sichuan Mianzhu Norwest Phosphate
Chemical Co., Ltd.　(1)
Gongxing Industrial Zone, Mianzhu, Sichuan, China
Tel.: (86) 2886615096
Chemicals Mfr
N.A.I.C.S.: 325998

ASIARAY MEDIA GROUP LIMITED
16/F Kornhill Plaza-Office Tower 1
Kornhill Road, Quarry Bay, China
(Hong Kong)
Tel.: (852) 21511222
Web Site: http://www.asiaray.com
1993—(HKG)
Rev.: $232,112,930
Assets: $442,682,323
Liabilities: $404,472,744
Net Worth: $38,209,579
Earnings: ($12,600,760)
Emp.: 932
Fiscal Year-end: 12/31/22
Out-of-Home Advertising
N.A.I.C.S.: 541850
Vincent Tak Hing Lam (Chm & CEO)

Subsidiaries:

Beijing Asiaray Advertising　(1)
31/F Block C Huaxi International Center 6
Jia Jianguomenwai Avenue, Chaoyang District, Beijing, 100022, China
Tel.: (86) 1065179999
Out-of-Home Advertising
N.A.I.C.S.: 541810

Chengdu Asiaray Advertising　(1)
Room 5 14/F International Financial Square
No 3 1 Hongxing Road, 3rd Section Jinjiang
District, Chengdu, 610021, Sichuan, China
Tel.: (86) 2886736536
Web Site: http://www.asiaray.com
Emp.: 12
Advertising Agencies
N.A.I.C.S.: 541810

Shanghai Asiaray Advertising　(1)
Room 2102 21/F ZhaofengPlaza 1027
Chang Ning Road, Chang Ning District,
Shanghai, 200050, China
Tel.: (86) 2164031999
Advertising Agencies
N.A.I.C.S.: 541810

ASIATIC CARPETS LTD
Oriental Carpet Centre 105 Eade
Road, London, N4 1TJ, United Kingdom
Tel.: (44) 2088002000
Web Site: http://www.asiatic.co.uk
Year Founded: 1960
Carpets & Rugs Mfr & Distr
N.A.I.C.S.: 541740
Stephen Crook (Mgr-Natl Sls)

**ASIATIC GROUP (HOLDINGS)
LIMITED**
65 Joo Koon Circle, Singapore,
629078, Singapore
Tel.: (65) 68630188　　　　SG
Web Site: https://www.asiatic.com.sg
Year Founded: 2002
5CR—(SES)
Rev.: $33,308,633
Assets: $40,265,283
Liabilities: $22,456,465
Net Worth: $17,808,818
Earnings: $1,030,011
Emp.: 142
Fiscal Year-end: 03/31/24
Fire Safety Equipment Installation
Services
N.A.I.C.S.: 238220
Kah Chye Tay (Chm)

**ASIATRAVEL.COM HOLDINGS
LIMITED**
No11 Lorong 3 Toa Payoh 04-16 Blk

B Jackson Square, Singapore,
319579, Singapore
Tel.: (65) 67326773　　　　SG
Year Founded: 1995
Holding Company; Travel & Tour Services
N.A.I.C.S.: 551112
Tuang Poh Boh (Chm & CEO)

Subsidiaries:

AT Express Pte. Ltd.　(1)
22 Cavenagh Orchard Road 01-15A Hotel
Grand Central, Singapore, 229617, Singapore
Tel.: (65) 67343933
Emp.: 3
Hotel Reservation Services
N.A.I.C.S.: 561599

AT Reservation Pte Ltd　(1)
111 North Bridge Road 01-33 Peninsula
Plaza, Singapore, 179098, Singapore
Tel.: (65) 63383025
Hotel & Travel Reservation Services
N.A.I.C.S.: 561599

Subsidiary (Non-US):

AT Phil., Inc.　(2)
Ground Floor Edgardo Angara Wing IBP
Building Jade Street, Ortigas Center, Pasig,
1605, Metro Manila, Philippines
Tel.: (63) 2 634 4220
Web Site: http://www.asiatravel.com
Travel & Tour Operating Agencies
N.A.I.C.S.: 561510

Asia Travel Network Ltd　(2)
Room A 4/F Milton Mansion 96 Nathan
Road, Tsim Tsa Tsui, Kowloon, China (Hong
Kong)
Tel.: (852) 27360922
Web Site: http://www.asiatravel.com
Travel & Tour Operating Services
N.A.I.C.S.: 561599
Magdalene Yeo Wee Tiang (Exec VP-Ops)

Asiatravel Online Sdn Bhd　(2)
148-03 3rd Floor Jalan Bukit Bintang, Kuala
Lumpur, 55100, Malaysia
Tel.: (60) 321436555
Sales Range: $25-49.9 Million
Emp.: 9
Online Air Ticketing Services
N.A.I.C.S.: 561599

Asia Middle East Tours (L.L.C.)　(1)
Shop Numbers WB21 WB22 WB23, PO
Box 112758, Bur Dubai, Dubai, United Arab
Emirates
Tel.: (971) 4 396 8787
Web Site: http://www.asiatravel.com
Sales Range: $25-49.9 Million
Emp.: 17
Travel & Tour Operating Agencies
N.A.I.C.S.: 561510

Asia Travel Network Ltd.　(1)
Room 4F Milton Mansion 96 Nathan Road,
Tsim Tsa Tsui, Kowloon, China (Hong Kong)
Tel.: (852) 27360922
Web Site: http://www.asiatravel.com
Sales Range: $50-74.9 Million
Emp.: 20
Travel & Tour Operating Agencies
N.A.I.C.S.: 561510
Sam Tsui (Mgr)

OV International Pte Ltd　(1)
22 Cavenagh Road Orchard Road 02-05
Hotel Grand Central, Singapore, Singapore
Tel.: (65) 62519688
Web Site: http://www.asiatravel.com
Travel & Tour Operating Agencies
N.A.I.C.S.: 561510

SH Tours Pte Ltd　(1)
615 Lorong 4 Poa Payoh Unit No X01-01,
Singapore, 319516, Singapore
Tel.: (65) 67349923
Web Site: http://www.asiatours.com.sg
Sales Range: $25-49.9 Million
Emp.: 100
Travel & Tour Operating Agencies
N.A.I.C.S.: 561510

ASICS CORPORATION
1-1 Minatojima-Nakamachi 7-Chome,

Chuo-ku, Kobe, 650-8555, Hyogo,
Japan
Tel.: (81) 783032231
Web Site: https://corp.asics.com
Year Founded: 1949
ASCCF—(OTCIQ)
Rev.: $3,911,513,760
Assets: $3,347,082,640
Liabilities: $1,028,604,480
Net Worth: $1,418,478,160
Earnings: $90,798,400
Emp.: 8,904
Fiscal Year-end: 12/31/21
Sports Goods Mfr & Whslr
N.A.I.C.S.: 339920
Yasuhito Hirota (Chm, Pres, CEO &
COO)

Subsidiaries:

ASICS America Corporation　(1)
7755 Irvine Center Dr Ste 400, Irvine, CA
92618
Tel.: (949) 453-8888
Web Site: https://corp.asics.com
Emp.: 170
Sporting Apparel Mfr
N.A.I.C.S.: 424340
Richard Sullivan (Exec VP-Sls, Categories
& Mktg)

ASICS Apparel Industry Corp.　(1)
57-3-1 Iehisacho, Echizen, 915-0801, Fukui, Japan
Tel.: (81) 778223330
Sports Product Mfr & Distr
N.A.I.C.S.: 339920

ASICS Asia Pte. Ltd.　(1)
Raffles Place 24-00, Singapore, 048616,
Singapore
Tel.: (65) 62026700
Sports Product Mfr & Distr
N.A.I.C.S.: 339920

ASICS Austria GmbH　(1)
Moosfeldstrasse 1 2 OG/Raum B34 B34,
5101, Bergheim, Austria
Tel.: (43) 64582000700
Sports Product Mfr & Distr
N.A.I.C.S.: 339920

ASICS Canada Corporation　(1)
5015 Spectrum Way unit 401 4th floor, Mississauga, L4W 0E4, ON, Canada
Tel.: (819) 566-8866
Sports Product Mfr & Distr
N.A.I.C.S.: 339920

ASICS China Trading Co., Ltd.　(1)
Room 2108 Building 2 No 533 Loushanguan Road, Changning District, Shanghai, 20005, China
Tel.: (86) 2162363000
Sports Product Mfr & Distr
N.A.I.C.S.: 339920

ASICS Denmark A/S　(1)
Robert Jacobsens vej 66 2, 2300, Copenhagen, Denmark
Tel.: (45) 20354060
Sports Product Mfr & Distr
N.A.I.C.S.: 339920

ASICS Deutschland GmbH　(1)
Hansemannstrasse 67, 41468, Neuss, Germany
Tel.: (49) 213138020
Sports Product Mfr & Distr
N.A.I.C.S.: 339920

ASICS Europe B.V.　(1)
Taurusavenue 165, 2132 LS, Hoofddorp,
Netherlands
Tel.: (31) 882742600
Sports Product Mfr & Distr
N.A.I.C.S.: 339920

ASICS France S.A.S.　(1)
1310 avenue des Platanes, CS 55000,
34974, Lattes, Cedex, France
Tel.: (33) 467154000
Sports Product Mfr & Distr
N.A.I.C.S.: 339920

ASICS Hong Kong Limited　(1)
Units 706-7 7/F Tower A Manulife Financial
Centre No 223-231, Wai Yip Street, Kwun
Tong, China (Hong Kong)

Tel.: (852) 35982022
Sports Product Mfr & Distr
N.A.I.C.S.: 339920

ASICS Iberia S.L. (1)
Carrer del Doctor Ferran 25, 08034, Barcelona, Spain
Tel.: (34) 934921879
Sports Product Mfr & Distr
N.A.I.C.S.: 339920

ASICS India Private Limited (1)
6th Floor Two Horizon Centre Golf Course road, Gurgaon, 122002, Haryana, India
Tel.: (91) 1244339120
Sports Product Mfr & Distr
N.A.I.C.S.: 339920

ASICS Italia S.r.L. (1)
Via Fratelli Ceirano 3/A 12100, Madonna Dell'Olmo, Cuneo, Italy
Tel.: (39) 0171416111
Sports Product Mfr & Distr
N.A.I.C.S.: 339920

ASICS Korea Corporation (1)
15F Samhwa Tower 16 Euljl-ro 5-gll, Jung-gu, Seoul, 04539, Korea (South)
Tel.: (82) 236603637
Sports Product Mfr & Distr
N.A.I.C.S.: 339920

ASICS Malaysia Sdn. Bhd. (1)
Level 23B Axiata Tower 9 Jalan Stesen Sentral 5, Kuala Lumpur Sentral, 50470, Kuala Lumpur, Malaysia
Tel.: (60) 322601100
Sports Product Mfr & Distr
N.A.I.C.S.: 339920

ASICS Middle East Trading LLC (1)
Building 05 Third Floor Unit B307, PO Box 49744, Dubai Design District, Dubai, United Arab Emirates
Tel.: (971) 45543845
Sports Product Mfr & Distr
N.A.I.C.S.: 339920

ASICS Norge AS (1)
Luhrtoppen 2, PO Box 204, 1471, Lorenskog, Norway
Tel.: (47) 67921950
Sports Product Mfr & Distr
N.A.I.C.S.: 339920

ASICS Oceania Pty. Ltd. (1)
10 Interchange Drive, Eastern Creek, 2766, NSW, Australia
Tel.: (61) 298532300
Sports Product Mfr & Distr
N.A.I.C.S.: 339920

ASICS Polska Sp.zo.o. (1)
Ul Bitwy Warszawskiej 1920r 7b, 02-366, Warsaw, Poland
Tel.: (48) 226091523
Sports Product Mfr & Distr
N.A.I.C.S.: 339920

ASICS Sourcing (Vietnam) Co., Ltd. (1)
Room 1206-08 37 Ton Duc Thang Street, District 1, Ho Chi Minh City, Vietnam
Tel.: (84) 739117230
Sports Product Mfr & Distr
N.A.I.C.S.: 339920

ASICS South Africa Pty. Ltd. (1)
3rd Floor Old Warehouse Building Black River Park Fir Street, Observatory, Cape Town, South Africa
Tel.: (27) 213007711
Sports Product Mfr & Distr
N.A.I.C.S.: 339920

ASICS Sports Complex Corp. (1)
D Tower Toyosu 2F 3F 4-20 Toyosu 6-chome, Koto-ku, Tokyo, 135-0061, Japan
Tel.: (81) 363698872
Sports Product Mfr & Distr
N.A.I.C.S.: 339920

ASICS Sports Mexico, S.A. de C.V. (1)
Av Prolongacion Paseo de la Reforma No 1236, Colonia Santa Fe, 05348, Mexico, Mexico
Tel.: (52) 5547375099
Sports Product Mfr & Distr
N.A.I.C.S.: 339920

ASICS Sverige AB (1)
Hamngatan 15, 111 47, Stockholm, Sweden
Tel.: (46) 854440960
Sports Product Mfr & Distr
N.A.I.C.S.: 339920

ASICS Taiwan Corporation (1)
4F No 88 Sec 2 Jhongsiao E Rd, Jhongjheng Dist, Taipei, 10050, Taiwan
Tel.: (886) 223412118
Sports Product Mfr & Distr
N.A.I.C.S.: 339920

ASICS Thailand Co., Ltd. (1)
11/1 A/A Sathorn Tower 14th Floor Unit 01 South Sathorn Road, Yannawa Sathorn, Bangkok, 10120, Thailand
Tel.: (66) 228510114
Sports Product Mfr & Distr
N.A.I.C.S.: 339920

ASICS Trading Co., Ltd. (1)
5-2 Yasakadai 3-chome, Suma-ku, Kobe, 654-0161, Hyogo, Japan
Web Site: http://www.asics-trading.co.jp
Sports Product Retailer
N.A.I.C.S.: 459110

ASICS Tryus Service Corp. (1)
3-28 Shioe 1-chome, Amagasaki, 661-8577, Hyogo, Japan
Tel.: (81) 664965166
Sports Product Mfr & Distr
N.A.I.C.S.: 339920

ASICS UK Limited (1)
Clearwater 3 Lingley Mere Business Park Lingley Green Avenue, Warrington, WA5 3UZ, United Kingdom
Tel.: (44) 1925241041
Sports Product Mfr & Distr
N.A.I.C.S.: 339920

Jiang Su ASICS Co., Ltd. (1)
No 377 PuBei Rd, FoHo New and Hi-Tech Industrial Development Zone, Jiangsu, 215211, China
Tel.: (86) 51263272765
Sports Product Mfr & Distr
N.A.I.C.S.: 339920

NISHI Athletic Goods Co., Ltd. (1)
1-18 Shinsuna 3-chome, Koto-ku, Tokyo, 136-0075, Japan
Tel.: (81) 363699000
Sports Product Mfr & Distr
N.A.I.C.S.: 339920

SANIN ASICS Industry Corp. (1)
2900 Wataricho Sakaiminato, Tottori, 684-0072, Japan
Tel.: (81) 859450871
Textile Products Mfr
N.A.I.C.S.: 314999

ASIL CELIK SANAYI VE TICARET A.S.
Gemic Koyu Mevkii, Orhangazi, 16800, Bursa, Turkiye
Tel.: (90) 224 280 61 00
Web Site: http://www.asilcelik.com.tr
Year Founded: 1974
Steel Product Mfr & Distr
N.A.I.C.S.: 331110

ASIMILAR GROUP PLC
4 More London Riverside, London, SE1 2AU, United Kingdom
Tel.: (44) 1923221910   UK
Web Site:
    https://www.asimilargroup.com
Year Founded: 2002
ASLR—(AQSE)
Rev.: $17,475
Assets: $8,397,058
Liabilities: $343,442
Net Worth: $8,053,616
Earnings: ($44,026,176)
Fiscal Year-end: 09/30/22
Protective Window Films & Glass Containment Anchoring System Mfr & Supplier
N.A.I.C.S.: 326113
Mohammed Sohail Bhatti *(Dir-Fin)*

ASIRO INC.
Shinjuku I-Land Wing 4F Nishi-Shinjuku 6-3-1, Shinjuku-ku, Tokyo, 1600023, Japan
Tel.: (81) 362794581
Web Site: https://www.asiro.co.jp
Year Founded: 2009
7378—(TKS)
Rev.: $21,311,352
Assets: $38,729,390
Liabilities: $13,102,935
Net Worth: $25,626,454
Earnings: $3,326,280
Emp.: 50
Fiscal Year-end: 10/31/22
Recruitment Services
N.A.I.C.S.: 561311

ASIT C.MEHTA FINANCIAL SERVICES LTD.
Nucleus House Saki-Vihar Road Andheri East, Mumbai, 400072, Maharashtra, India
Tel.: (91) 2228583333
Web Site: https://www.acmfsl.com
530723—(BOM)
Rev.: $5,670,319
Assets: $23,250,904
Liabilities: $21,878,477
Net Worth: $1,372,428
Earnings: $199,735
Emp.: 1
Fiscal Year-end: 03/31/22
Financial Software Development Services
N.A.I.C.S.: 541511
Asit Chimanlal Mehta *(Chm)*

ASITE SOLUTIONS LTD.
1 Mark Square, London, EC2A 4EG, United Kingdom
Tel.: (44) 2077497880
Web Site: http://www.asite.com
Sales Range: $1-9.9 Million
Emp.: 120
Data Logistics Technology
N.A.I.C.S.: 561499
Tony Ryan *(CEO)*

Subsidiaries:

Asite Solutions Private Limited (1)
A4 Shivalik Business Ctr, Ahmedabad, 380054, Gujarat, India
Tel.: (91) 7940211900
Information Technology Services
N.A.I.C.S.: 541512
Ritesh Narain *(CEO)*

ASIX ELECTRONICS CO. LTD.
4F No 8 Hsin Ann Rd, Hsinchu Science Park, Hsinchu, 300, Taiwan
Tel.: (886) 3 5799500
Web Site: http://www.asix.com.tw
Year Founded: 1995
Semiconductor Mfr
N.A.I.C.S.: 333242
Jui Jeng Chen *(Chm)*

ASJ INC.
3-2-16 Sakae-cho, Kawaguchi, 332-0017, Saitama, Japan
Tel.: (81) 482595111
Web Site: https://www.asj.ad.jp
Year Founded: 1984
2351—(TKS)
Rev.: $18,812,060
Assets: $28,006,570
Liabilities: $10,457,020
Net Worth: $17,549,550
Earnings: $740,320
Emp.: 156
Fiscal Year-end: 03/31/24
Internet Services
N.A.I.C.S.: 518210
Haruaki Maruyama *(Chm & CEO)*

Subsidiaries:

ASJ Commerce Inc. (1)
2-20-23 Totsukahigashi, Kawaguchi, 333-0802, Japan
Tel.: (81) 484209831
Web Site: https://www.asj-commerce.co.jp
Logistics Management Services
N.A.I.C.S.: 541614

eFUSION Co., Ltd. (1)
3-2-16 Sakae-cho, Kawaguchi, 332-0017, Japan
Tel.: (81) 5055333616
Web Site: https://www.efusion.co.jp
Software Development Services
N.A.I.C.S.: 541511

ASKA PHARMACEUTICAL CO., LTD.
5-1 Shibaura 2-chome, Minato-ku, Tokyo, 108-8532, Japan
Tel.: (81) 3 5484 8366
Web Site: http://www.aska-pharma.co.jp
Rev.: $423,156,360
Assets: $744,677,640
Liabilities: $350,966,280
Net Worth: $393,711,360
Earnings: $15,800,640
Emp.: 842
Fiscal Year-end: 03/31/19
Pharmaceuticals Mfr
N.A.I.C.S.: 325412
Takashi Yamaguchi *(Pres)*

Subsidiaries:

ASKA Animal Health Co., Ltd. (1)
Oase Shibaura MJ Building 4F 2-15-6 Shibaura, Minato-ku, Tokyo, 108-0023, Japan
Tel.: (81) 354394188
Web Site: http://www.aska-animal.co.jp
Veterinary Drug Mfr & Distr
N.A.I.C.S.: 325412

ASKARI GENERAL INSURANCE COMPANY LIMITED
3rd Floor AWT Plaza The Mall, Rawalpindi, Pakistan
Tel.: (92) 111444687   PK
Web Site: https://www.agico.com.pk
Year Founded: 1995
AGIC—(PSX)
Rev.: $8,620
Assets: $24,967,501
Liabilities: $16,192,128
Net Worth: $8,775,373
Earnings: $1,261
Emp.: 377
Fiscal Year-end: 12/31/22
Insurance Services
N.A.I.C.S.: 524298
Abdul Waheed *(Pres & CEO)*

ASKARI METALS LIMITED
17 Lacey Street, Perth, 6000, WA, Australia
Tel.: (61) 400408878   AU
Web Site:
    https://www.askarimetals.com
Year Founded: 2020
AS2—(ASX)
Rev.: $13,482
Assets: $8,011,450
Liabilities: $839,950
Net Worth: $7,171,500
Earnings: ($4,047,029)
Fiscal Year-end: 06/30/23
Metal Exploration Services
N.A.I.C.S.: 213114
Robert Downey *(Chm)*

ASKER MUNAI EXPLORATION JSC
Republic Square 15, Bostandycsky district, 050013, Almaty, Kazakhstan
Tel.: (7) 273442832
AMXP—(KAZ)

Asker Munai Exploration JSC—(Continued)

Assets: $69,861,093
Liabilities: $95,902,936
Net Worth: ($26,041,843)
Earnings: ($9,350,772)
Fiscal Year-end: 12/31/23
Hydrocarbon Raw Material Exploration Services
N.A.I.C.S.: 213112
Kenchimova Aynur *(CEO & Gen Dir)*

ASKLEPIOS KLINIKEN GMBH & CO. KGAA

Rubenkamp 226, 22307, Hamburg, Germany
Tel.: (49) 40 18 18 82 66 96   De
Web Site: http://www.asklepios.com
Year Founded: 1984
Rev.: $4,251,461,141
Assets: $5,265,616,436
Liabilities: $3,499,313,891
Net Worth: $1,766,302,545
Earnings: $157,263,060
Emp.: 36,265
Fiscal Year-end: 12/31/19
Hospital Operator
N.A.I.C.S.: 622110
Kai Hankeln *(CEO & Member-Mgmt Bd)*

Subsidiaries:

AKG Klinik Hohwald GmbH   **(1)**
Hohwaldstrasse 40, Neustadt, 1844, Sachsen, Germany
Tel.: (49) 35965670
Healtcare Services
N.A.I.C.S.: 622110

AKG Klinik Parchim GmbH   **(1)**
John-Brinckman-Strasse 8-10, 19370, Parchim, Germany
Tel.: (49) 3871 37 0
Healtcare Services
N.A.I.C.S.: 622110

Angiologikum GmbH   **(1)**
Wordemanns Weg 25-27, 22527, Hamburg, Germany
Tel.: (49) 408890090
Health Care Srvices
N.A.I.C.S.: 621999

Asklepios - ASB Krankenhaus Radeberg GmbH   **(1)**
Pulsnitzer Str 60, 01454, Radeberg, Germany
Tel.: (49) 3528 459 0
Healtcare Services
N.A.I.C.S.: 622110

Asklepios Fachkliniken Brandenburg GmbH   **(1)**
Anton-Saefkow-Allee 2, Brandenburg an der Havel, 14772, Brandenburg, Germany
Tel.: (49) 33 81 78 0
Healtcare Services
N.A.I.C.S.: 622310

Asklepios Fachklinikum Stadtroda GmbH   **(1)**
Bahnhofstrasse 1a, 07646, Stadtroda, Germany
Tel.: (49) 36 428 56 10
Healtcare Services
N.A.I.C.S.: 622210

Asklepios Gesundheitszentrum Bad Tolz GmbH   **(1)**
Schutzenstr 17, 83646, Bad Tolz, Germany
Tel.: (49) 8041 507 20 21
Healtcare Services
N.A.I.C.S.: 622310

Asklepios Harzkliniken GmbH   **(1)**
Kosliner Strasse 12, 38642, Goslar, Germany
Tel.: (49) 53 21 44 0
Healtcare Services
N.A.I.C.S.: 622110

Asklepios Klinik Alsbach GmbH   **(1)**
Asklepiosweg 15, Falkenstein, 61462, Konigstein, Germany
Tel.: (49) 61 74 90 60 00

Healtcare Services
N.A.I.C.S.: 622310

Asklepios Klinik Altona   **(1)**
Paul-Ehrlich-Strasse 1, 22763, Hamburg, Germany
Tel.: (49) 40 18 18 81 0
Healtcare Services
N.A.I.C.S.: 622110

Asklepios Klinik Am Kurpark Bad Schwartau   **(1)**
Am Kurpark 6-12, 23611, Bad Schwartau, Germany
Tel.: (49) 4 51 20 04 0
Healtcare Services
N.A.I.C.S.: 622310

Asklepios Klinik Bad Griesbach GmbH & Cie OHG   **(1)**
Ludwig Promenade 6, 94086, Bad Griesbach, Germany
Tel.: (49) 85 32 980 0
Healtcare Services
N.A.I.C.S.: 622310
Andrea Iretzberger *(Mgr-Front Office)*

Asklepios Klinik Bad Salzungen GmbH   **(1)**
Am See, 36433, Bad Salzungen, Germany
Tel.: (49) 36 95 65 0
Healtcare Services
N.A.I.C.S.: 622110

Asklepios Klinik Bad Wildungen GmbH   **(1)**
Laustrasse 35, 34537, Bad Wildungen, Germany
Tel.: (49) 5621 85 0
Healtcare Services
N.A.I.C.S.: 622310

Asklepios Klinik Barmbek GmbH   **(1)**
Rubenkamp 220, 22291, Hamburg, Germany
Tel.: (49) 40 18 18 82 0
Healtcare Services
N.A.I.C.S.: 622110

Asklepios Klinik Dr. Walb Homberg/Ohm   **(1)**
Am Hohen Tor 16, 35315, Homberg (Ohm), Germany
Tel.: (49) 6633 919 170
Healtcare Services
N.A.I.C.S.: 622110

Asklepios Klinik Gauting GmbH   **(1)**
Robert-Koch-Allee 2, 82131, Gauting, Germany
Tel.: (49) 89 8 57 91 0
Web Site: http://www.asklepios.com
Emp.: 500
Healtcare Services
N.A.I.C.S.: 622110
Rainer Pfrommer *(Mng Dir)*

Asklepios Klinik Lenggries GmbH   **(1)**
Bergweg 21, 83661, Lenggries, Germany
Tel.: (49) 8042 504 0
Web Site: http://www.fachklinik.de
Healtcare Services
N.A.I.C.S.: 622310

Asklepios Klinik Lich GmbH   **(1)**
Goethestr 4, 35423, Lich, Germany
Tel.: (49) 64 04 81 0
Healtcare Services
N.A.I.C.S.: 622110

Asklepios Klinik Lindau GmbH   **(1)**
Friedrichshafen Str 82, 88131, Lindau, Germany
Tel.: (49) 83 82 276 0
Healtcare Services
N.A.I.C.S.: 622310

Asklepios Klinik Lindenlohe GmbH   **(1)**
Lindenlohe 18, 92421, Schwandorf, Germany
Tel.: (49) 94 31 888 0
Healtcare Services
N.A.I.C.S.: 622310

Asklepios Klinik Nord GmbH   **(1)**
Tangstedter Landstrasse 400, 22417, Hamburg, Germany
Tel.: (49) 40 18 18 87 0

Healtcare Services
N.A.I.C.S.: 622310

Asklepios Klinik Pasewalk GmbH   **(1)**
Prenzlauer Chaussee 30, 17309, Pasewalk, Germany
Tel.: (49) 39 73 23 0
Healtcare Services
N.A.I.C.S.: 622110

Asklepios Klinik Sankt Augustin GmbH   **(1)**
Arnold-Janssen Strasse 29, 53757, Saint Augustin, Germany
Tel.: (49) 22 41 249 0
Healtcare Services
N.A.I.C.S.: 622110

Asklepios Klinik Schaufling GmbH   **(1)**
Hausstein 2, 94571, Schaufling, Germany
Tel.: (49) 9904 77 1110
Healtcare Services
N.A.I.C.S.: 622310

Asklepios Klinik Sobernheim GmbH   **(1)**
Korczakstr 2, 55566, Sobernheim, Germany
Tel.: (49) 6751 874 0
Healtcare Services
N.A.I.C.S.: 622310

Asklepios Klinik St. Georg   **(1)**
Lohmuhlenstr 5, 20099, Hamburg, Germany
Tel.: (49) 40 18 18 85 0
Healtcare Services
N.A.I.C.S.: 622310

Asklepios Klinik Wandsbek   **(1)**
Alphonsstr 14, 22043, Hamburg, Germany
Tel.: (49) 40 18 18 83 0
Healtcare Services
N.A.I.C.S.: 622310

Asklepios Klinik Wiesbaden GmbH   **(1)**
Geisenheimer Strasse 10, 65197, Wiesbaden, Germany
Tel.: (49) 611 847 2003
Healtcare Services
N.A.I.C.S.: 622310

Asklepios Kliniken Langen-Seligenstadt GmbH   **(1)**
Rontgenstrasse 20, 63225, Langen, Germany
Tel.: (49) 6103 9 12 0
Healtcare Services
N.A.I.C.S.: 622110

Asklepios Kliniken Verwaltungs - gesellschaft mbH - Medicine & Science Division   **(1)**
Lohmuhlenstrasse 5 Haus P, 20099, Hamburg, Germany
Tel.: (49) 40 18 18 85 25 41
Healtcare Services
N.A.I.C.S.: 622110

Asklepios Kliniken Verwaltungs - gesellschaft mbH - labor & collective bargaining law Division   **(1)**
Debusweg 3, 61462, Konigstein, Germany
Tel.: (49) 61 74 90 10 00
Labor Management Services
N.A.I.C.S.: 813930

Asklepios Kliniken Weissenfels - Hohenmolsen GmbH   **(1)**
Naumburger Strasse 76, 06667, Weissenfels, Germany
Tel.: (49) 34 43 40 0
Healtcare Services
N.A.I.C.S.: 622310

Asklepios Klinikum Bad Abbach GmbH   **(1)**
Kaiser-Karl V -Allee 3, 93077, Bad Abbach, Germany
Tel.: (49) 94 05 18 0
Healtcare Services
N.A.I.C.S.: 622310

Asklepios Klinikum Harburg   **(1)**
Eissendorfer Pferdeweg 52, 21075, Hamburg, Germany
Tel.: (49) 40 18 18 86 0
Healtcare Services
N.A.I.C.S.: 622110

Asklepios Klinikum Uckermark GmbH   **(1)**
Auguststr 23, 16303, Schwedt an der Oder, Germany
Tel.: (49) 33 32 53 0
Healtcare Services
N.A.I.C.S.: 622310

Asklepios MVZ Bayern GmbH   **(1)**
Bahnhofplatz 2, 00000, Landsberg am Lech, Germany
Tel.: (49) 819191680
Web Site: http://www.dr-steffen.de
Health Care Srvices
N.A.I.C.S.: 621999

Asklepios MVZ Brandenburg GmbH   **(1)**
Am Klinikum 1, Schwedt, 16303, Brandenburg, Germany
Tel.: (49) 3332533100
Health Care Hospital Services
N.A.I.C.S.: 622110

Asklepios MVZ Hessen GmbH   **(1)**
Dudenhofer Strasse 9, 63500, Seligenstadt, Germany
Tel.: (49) 610391261023
Health Care Hospital Services
N.A.I.C.S.: 622110

Asklepios MVZ Mitteldeutschland GmbH   **(1)**
Johannes-R-Becher-Str 1, 7546, Berlin, Germany
Tel.: (49) 365 486270
Healtcare Services
N.A.I.C.S.: 622110

Asklepios MVZ Niedersachsen GmbH   **(1)**
Kosliner Strasse 12, 38642, Goslar, Germany
Tel.: (49) 5321440
Health Care Hospital Services
N.A.I.C.S.: 622110

Asklepios MVZ Nord Schleswig Holstein GmbH   **(1)**
Herzog-Carl-Friedrich-Platz 1, 21031, Hamburg, Germany
Tel.: (49) 40 7211504
Healtcare Services
N.A.I.C.S.: 622110

Asklepios MVZ Sachsen-Anhalt GmbH   **(1)**
Naumburger Strasse 76, 06667, Weissenfels, Germany
Tel.: (49) 3443401540
Health Care Hospital Services
N.A.I.C.S.: 622110

Asklepios Nordseeklinik Westerland GmbH   **(1)**
Norderstrasse 81, Sylt, 25980, Westerland, Germany
Tel.: (49) 46 51 84 0
Healtcare Services
N.A.I.C.S.: 622110

Asklepios Poland sp. z o.o.   **(1)**
B Krzywoustego 9-10, 70-250, Szczecin, Poland
Tel.: (48) 798 380 380
Healtcare Services
N.A.I.C.S.: 622110

Asklepios Psychiatrie Niedersachsen GmbH   **(1)**
Rosdorfer Weg 70, 37081, Gottingen, Germany
Tel.: (49) 551 402 0
Healtcare Services
N.A.I.C.S.: 622310

Asklepios Rehaklinik Bad Oldesloe GmbH   **(1)**
Schutzenstrasse 55 Haus D, 23843, Bad Oldesloe, Germany
Tel.: (49) 4531681011
Health Care Hospital Services
N.A.I.C.S.: 622110

Asklepios Schwalm-Eder-Kliniken GmbH   **(1)**
Krankenhausstr 27, 34613, Schwalmstadt, Germany
Tel.: (49) 66 91 7 99 0
Healtcare Services

N.A.I.C.S.: 622110

Asklepios Stadtklinik Bad Tolz GmbH (1)
Schutzenstrasse 15, 83646, Bad Tolz, Germany
Tel.: (49) 80 41 507 01
Web Site: http://www.asklepios.com
Healtcare Services
N.A.I.C.S.: 622110

Asklepios Sudpfalzkliniken GmbH (1)
Luitpoldstrasse 14, 76870, Kandel, Germany
Tel.: (49) 7275 71 0
Healtcare Services
N.A.I.C.S.: 622110

Asklepios Therapie GmbH (1)
Kurhausstrasse 16, 36433, Bad Salzungen, Germany
Tel.: (49) 3695 65 1193
Healtcare Services
N.A.I.C.S.: 622110

Asklepios Weserbergland-Klinik GmbH (1)
Grune Muhle 90, 37671, Hoxter, Germany
Tel.: (49) 52 71 98 0
Healtcare Services
N.A.I.C.S.: 622310

Asklepios Westklinikum Hamburg GmbH (1)
Suurheid 20, 22559, Hamburg, Germany
Tel.: (49) 40 81 91 20 00
Healtcare Services
N.A.I.C.S.: 622310

Asklepios medi top Pflegedienst & Service GmbH (1)
Sulldorfer Landstrasse 39, 22589, Hamburg, Germany
Tel.: (49) 40 866 270 0
Healtcare Services
N.A.I.C.S.: 621610

Blomenburg Holding GmbH (1)
Burgstrasse 1, Selent, 24238, Kiel, Germany
Tel.: (49) 43843370100
Web Site: http://www.blomenburg.com
Health Care Srvices
N.A.I.C.S.: 621999

Digital Infusion GmbH (1)
Rigaer Str 44, 10247, Berlin, Germany
Tel.: (49) 3021230707888
Web Site: http://www.digital-infusion.de
Digital Health Care Services
N.A.I.C.S.: 621999
Georg Dorner (Chief Sls Officer)

Fachklinik Rhein/Ruhr fur Herz/Kreislauf- und Bewegungssystem GmbH & Co. KG (1)
Auf der Rotsch 2, Essen, 45219, Germany
Tel.: (49) 2054 880
Healtcare Services
N.A.I.C.S.: 622110

Fachklinik Zwieselberg GmbH (1)
Alte Wolterdinger Strasse 68, 78166, Donaueschingen, Germany
Tel.: (49) 771851200
Web Site: http://www.fachklinik-zwieselberg.de
Clinic Care Services
N.A.I.C.S.: 621498

Fachklinikum Wiesen GmbH (1)
Kirchberger Strasse 2, 08134, Wildenfels, Germany
Tel.: (49) 37603 54 0
Healtcare Services
N.A.I.C.S.: 622110

Furstenberg Institut GmbH (1)
Gorch-Fock-Wall 3, 20354, Hamburg, Germany
Tel.: (49) 403808200
Web Site: http://www.fuerstenberg-institut.de
Wealth Management Services
N.A.I.C.S.: 923120
Reinhild Furstenberg (Mng Dir)

GKB Klinikbetriebe GmbH (1)
Frankfurter Strasse 33, 64732, Bad Konig, Germany

Tel.: (49) 60 63 501 0
Healtcare Services
N.A.I.C.S.: 622110

Health Care Concept GmbH (1)
Neuer Wall 10, 20354, Hamburg, Germany
Tel.: (49) 40822153086
Web Site: http://www.healthcare-concept.de
Health Care Srvices
N.A.I.C.S.: 621610

INSITE-Interventions GmbH (1)
Clemensstrasse 10-12, 60487, Frankfurt am Main, Germany
Tel.: (49) 6990555290
Health Care Srvices
N.A.I.C.S.: 621999

Lungenpraxis am Wordemannsweg GmbH (1)
Wordemanns Weg 25-27, 22527, Hamburg, Germany
Tel.: (49) 40889009680
Health Screening Services
N.A.I.C.S.: 621111

MEDICLIN Aktiengesellschaft (1)
Okenstr 27, 77652, Offenburg, Germany (52.73%)
Tel.: (49) 7814880
Web Site: https://www.mediclin.de
Rev.: $753,766,467
Assets: $1,005,357,743
Liabilities: $791,748,410
Net Worth: $213,609,333
Earnings: $10,843,489
Emp.: 7,431
Fiscal Year-end: 12/31/2019
Health Care Srvices
N.A.I.C.S.: 622110
Volker Hippler (Chm-Mgmt Bd & CEO)

Subsidiary (Domestic):

Cortex Software GmbH (2)
Okenstrasse 27, 77652, Offenburg, Germany
Tel.: (49) 781488500
Web Site: http://www.cortex-software.de
Sales Range: $25-49.9 Million
Emp.: 70
Software Development Services
N.A.I.C.S.: 541511
Hermann Steppe (Pres)

Herzzentrum Lahr/Baden GmbH & Co. KG (2)
Hohbergweg 2, 77933, Lahr, Germany
Tel.: (49) 78219250
Web Site: http://www.herzzentrum-lahr.de
Sales Range: $50-74.9 Million
Hospital Management Services
N.A.I.C.S.: 622110

KB Krankenhausbeteiligungsgesellschaft mbH & Co. KG (2)
Auf der Rotsch 2, 45219, Essen, Nordrhein-Westfalen, Germany
Tel.: (49) 2054880
Web Site: http://www.fachklinik-rheinruhr.de
Sales Range: $50-74.9 Million
Emp.: 300
Hospital Management Services
N.A.I.C.S.: 622110

Kraichgau-Klinik Aktiengesellschaft (2)
Fritz-Hagner-Promenade 15, 74906, Bad Rappenau, Germany
Tel.: (49) 72648020
Web Site: http://www.kraichgau-klinik.de
Sales Range: $25-49.9 Million
Hospital Management Services
N.A.I.C.S.: 622110

Kraichgau-Klinik Bad Rappenau GmbH & Co. KG (2)
Fritz-Hagner-Promenade 15, 74906, Bad Rappenau, Germany
Tel.: (49) 72648020
Web Site: http://www.kraichgau-klinik.de
Sales Range: $25-49.9 Million
Emp.: 120
Hospital Management Services
N.A.I.C.S.: 622310
Laupenthal Christian (Gen Mgr)

MC Service GmbH (2)
Okenstrasse 27, 77652, Offenburg, Baden-Wurttemberg, Germany

Tel.: (49) 7814880
Cleaning & Building Support Services
N.A.I.C.S.: 561720
Frank Abele (Mng Dir)

MEDUSPLUS GMBH (2)
Auf der Rotsch 2, 45219, Essen, Germany
Tel.: (49) 2054880
Web Site: http://www.fachklinik-rheinruhr.de
Sales Range: $50-74.9 Million
Emp.: 400
Catering Services
N.A.I.C.S.: 722310
Dirk Schmitz (Mng Dir)

MPS Medizinische Personal- und Servicegesellschaft mbH Kettwig (2)
Auf der Rotsch 2, 45219, Essen, Nordrhein-Westfalen, Germany
Tel.: (49) 2054880
Web Site: http://www.mediclin.ge
Medical Personnel Recruitment & Placement Services
N.A.I.C.S.: 561311

MVZ MediClin Bonn GmbH (2)
Villenstr 4-8, 53129, Bonn, Germany
Tel.: (49) 22853060
Sales Range: $10-24.9 Million
Emp.: 76
Hospital Management Services
N.A.I.C.S.: 622110

MediClin Catering GmbH (2)
Okenstrasse 27, 77652, Offenburg, Baden-Wurttemberg, Germany
Tel.: (49) 7814880
Web Site: http://www.mediclin.de
Sales Range: $25-49.9 Million
Emp.: 180
Catering Services
N.A.I.C.S.: 722320

MediClin Geschaftsfuhrungs-GmbH (2)
Okenstrasse 27, 77652, Offenburg, Germany
Tel.: (49) 7814880
Sales Range: $25-49.9 Million
Emp.: 130
Hospital Management Services
N.A.I.C.S.: 622110

MediClin GmbH & Co. KG (2)
Okenstrasse 27, 77652, Offenburg, Germany
Tel.: (49) 7814880
Sales Range: $25-49.9 Million
Emp.: 200
Hospital Management Services
N.A.I.C.S.: 622310

MediClin Immobilien Verwaltung GmbH (2)
Okenstrasse 27, 77652, Offenburg, Germany
Tel.: (49) 7814880
Sales Range: $75-99.9 Million
Emp.: 130
Real Estate Property Management Services
N.A.I.C.S.: 531312

MediClin Krakenhaus am Crivitzer See (2)
Amtsstrasse 1, 19089, Crivitz, Germany
Tel.: (49) 3863 5200
Web Site: http://www.krankenhaus-am-crivitzer-see.de
Hospital Surgical & Management Services
N.A.I.C.S.: 622110
Anja Trilk (Mgr-Nursing)

MediClin Krankenhaus am Crivitzer See GmbH (2)
Amtsstrasse 1, 19087, Crivitz, Mecklenburg-Western, Germany
Tel.: (49) 38635200
Hospital Management Services
N.A.I.C.S.: 622310
Hans-Heinrich Uhlmann (Mng Dir)

MediClin Muritz-Klinikum GmbH & Co. KG (2)
Weinbergstrasse 19, Muritz, 17192, Waren, Germany
Tel.: (49) 3991770
Web Site: http://www.mueritz-klinikum.de
Hospital Management Services
N.A.I.C.S.: 622110

MediClin Pflege GmbH (2)
Okenstrasse 27, Offenburg, 77652, Baden-Wurttemberg, Germany
Tel.: (49) 781488239
Web Site: http://www.mediclin.de
Hospital Management Services
N.A.I.C.S.: 622110

MediClin Therapie GmbH (2)
Okenstrasse 27, 77652, Offenburg, Germany
Tel.: (49) 7814880
Web Site: http://www.mediclin-therapie.de
Sales Range: $25-49.9 Million
Emp.: 130
Therapy Services
N.A.I.C.S.: 621498

MediClin a la Carte GmbH (2)
Mainzer Strasse 82, Homburg, Homburg, Germany
Tel.: (49) 6841 959 78 93
Catering & Cafeteria Services
N.A.I.C.S.: 722514

MediServ GmbH (2)
Auf der Rotsch 2, 45219, Essen, Germany
Tel.: (49) 2054880
Medical Equipment Whslr
N.A.I.C.S.: 423450

Reha-Klinik GmbH & Co. KG (2)
Oeninger Weg 59, Soltau, 29614, Lower Saxony, Germany
Tel.: (49) 51918000
Hospital Management Services
N.A.I.C.S.: 622110

Rehabilitationszentrum Gernsbach/Schwarzwald GmbH & Co. KG (2)
Langer Weg 3, 76593, Gernsbach, Germany
Tel.: (49) 7224 9920
Web Site: http://www.reha-zentrum-gernsbach.de
Sales Range: $10-24.9 Million
Hospital Management & Rehabilitation Services
N.A.I.C.S.: 622310

Vitalisklinik Verwaltungs-GmbH (2)
Am Weinberg 3, 36251, Bad Hersfeld, Hessen, Germany
Tel.: (49) 66212050
Web Site: http://www.vitalisklinik.de
Sales Range: $25-49.9 Million
Emp.: 130
Hospital Management Services
N.A.I.C.S.: 622110

Yvonne Mobilien-Leasing GmbH (2)
Okenstr 27, Offenburg, 77652, Germany
Tel.: (49) 781 488 189
Web Site: http://www.mediclin.de
Machinery & Equipment Leasing Services
N.A.I.C.S.: 532412
Volker Seldkamp (Gen Mgr)

MEDILYS Laborgesellschaft mbH (1)
Paul-Ehrlich-Str 1, 22763, Hamburg, Germany
Tel.: (49) 40 1818 81 5900
Medical Laboratory Services
N.A.I.C.S.: 621511

MVZ Asklepios Klinik Seligenstadt GmbH (1)
Dudenhofer Str 9, 63500, Seligenstadt, Germany
Tel.: (49) 61 82 83 0
Healtcare Services
N.A.I.C.S.: 622110

MVZ Hanse Histologikum GmbH (1)
Fangdieckstr 75a, 22547, Hamburg, Germany
Tel.: (49) 40 70 70 85 100
Web Site: http://www.pathologie-hh.de
Medical Laboratory Services
N.A.I.C.S.: 621511

MVZ Sobernheim GmbH (1)
Staudernheimer Strasse 57, 55566, Bad Sobernheim, Germany
Tel.: (49) 67518560440
Web Site: http://www.mvz-sobernheim.de
Medical Care Services
N.A.I.C.S.: 621610

Asklepios Kliniken GmbH & Co. KGaA—(Continued)

MediClin MVZ Achern GmbH (1)
Berliner Strasse 1, 77855, Achern, Germany
Tel.: (49) 784122020
Web Site: http://www.mediclin-fachaerzte-achern.de
Health Care Facility Services
N.A.I.C.S.: 621999

MediClin Medizinisches Versorgungszentrum GmbH (1)
Richard-Wagner-Str 1, 4109, Leipzig, Germany
Tel.: (49) 341 308990
Healtcare Services
N.A.I.C.S.: 622110

Minddistrict B.V. (1)
Jan Evertsenstraat 723, 1061 XZ, Amsterdam, Netherlands
Tel.: (31) 857440860
Mental Health Care Services
N.A.I.C.S.: 621330
Nathalie Faber (Mgr-HR)

Minddistrict GmbH (1)
Friedrichstrasse 68, 10117, Berlin, Germany
Tel.: (49) 30767598219
Mental Health Care Services
N.A.I.C.S.: 621330
Theresa Meier (Mgr-Implementation & Bus Dev)

Minddistrict Ltd. (1)
38 Chancery Lane, London, WC2A 1EN, United Kingdom
Tel.: (44) 2035148689
Web Site: http://www.minddistrict.com
Mental Health Care Services
N.A.I.C.S.: 621330
Mark Willems (CEO)

OT-Rhein-Main GmbH (1)
Europa-Allee 1c, Fohren, 54343, Trier, Germany
Tel.: (49) 650291580
Web Site: http://www.ottomueller.de
Medical Device Distr
N.A.I.C.S.: 423450

ProFuss GmbH (1)
Stauffacherstrasse 28, 8004, Zurich, Switzerland
Tel.: (41) 442117222
Web Site: http://www.profuss.ch
Foot Care Pedicure Services
N.A.I.C.S.: 812113

Provivere GmbH (1)
Friedrichsberger Strasse 56, 22081, Hamburg, Germany
Tel.: (49) 40 251 745 0
Healtcare Services
N.A.I.C.S.: 622110

Pulso Europe BV (1)
Diestsesteenweg 52 Bus 0201, 3010, Leuven, Belgium
Tel.: (32) 16208596
Web Site: http://www.pulso-europe.eu
Health Management Consulting Services
N.A.I.C.S.: 541618
Antje Ketelers (Sr Project Mgr)

Pulso Europe Lda (1)
Rua Sacadura Cabral 41A, 1495-702, Alges, Portugal
Tel.: (351) 214195551
Health Management Consulting Services
N.A.I.C.S.: 541618

Pulso South East Europe P.C. (1)
Apollo Tower 64 Louise Riencourt St, 115 23, Athens, Greece
Tel.: (30) 2106905100
Health Management Consulting Services
N.A.I.C.S.: 541618

RHON-KLINIKUM Aktiengesellschaft (1)
Schlossplatz 1, D-97616, Bad Neustadt an der Saale, Germany (92.58%)
Tel.: (49) 9771650
Web Site: https://en.rhoen-klinikum-ag.com
Rev.: $1,924,826,490
Assets: $2,001,625,881
Liabilities: $539,748,840
Net Worth: $1,461,877,041
Earnings: $3,025,155

Emp.: 18,449
Fiscal Year-end: 12/31/2020
Holding Company; Hospital & Health Care Service Centers Operator
N.A.I.C.S.: 551112
Frank Steibli (Head-Comm)

Subsidiary (Domestic):

ESB-Gemeinnützige Gesellschaft fur berufliche Bildung mbH (2)
Schlossplatz 6, 97616, Bad Neustadt an der Saale, Germany
Tel.: (49) 97716526700
Web Site: http://www.esb-bildung.de
Healthcare Training Services
N.A.I.C.S.: 611430

Haus Saaletal GmbH (2)
Salzburgweg 7, 97616, Neustadt, Saale, Germany
Tel.: (49) 9771 905 0
Sales Range: $10-24.9 Million
Emp.: 100
Specialty Hospitals
N.A.I.C.S.: 622310

Heilbad Bad Neustadt GmbH (2)
Salzburger Leite 1, 97616, Bad Neustadt an der Saale, Germany
Tel.: (49) 9719088774
Real Estate Manangement Services
N.A.I.C.S.: 531390

Herz-und Gefass-Klinik GmbH (2)
Salzburger Leite 1, Schweinfurt, 97616, Germany
Tel.: (49) 9771660
Specialty Outpatient Facilities
N.A.I.C.S.: 622310

IGB Integratives Gesundheitszentrum Boizenburg GmbH (2)
Vor Dem Muhlentor 3, Boizenburg, 19258, Germany
Tel.: (49) 388476370
Health Care Srvices
N.A.I.C.S.: 621999

Kinderhort Salzburger Leite gGmbH (2)
An Der Wandelhalle 20, Bad Neustadt an der Saale, 97616, Germany
Tel.: (49) 9771 652113
Nursing Home Operating Services
N.A.I.C.S.: 621610

Klinik Feuerberg GmbH (2)
Salzburger Leite 1, Bad Neustadt an der Saale, 97616, Germany
Tel.: (49) 9771 670 2
Clinical Healthcare Services
N.A.I.C.S.: 622110

Klinik Haus Franken GmbH (2)
Salzburger Leite 1, 97616, Bad Neustadt an der Saale, Germany
Tel.: (49) 97716704
Sales Range: $200-249.9 Million
Emp.: 2,000
General Medical & Surgical Hospitals
N.A.I.C.S.: 622110

Klinik fur Herzchirurgie der Herz- und Gefass-Klinik GmbH (2)
Salzburger Leite 1, 97616, Bad Neustadt an der Saale, Germany
Tel.: (49) 9771660
Web Site: http://www.handchirurgie.de
General Medical & Surgical Hospitals
N.A.I.C.S.: 622110
Martin Siebert (CEO)

Klinikum Frankfurt (Oder) GmbH (2)
Mullroser Chaussee 7, 15236, Frankfurt, Germany
Tel.: (49) 3355480
Web Site: http://www.klinikumffo.de
General Medical & Surgical Hospitals
N.A.I.C.S.: 622110

Krankenhaus Cuxhaven GmbH (2)
Altenwalder Chaussee 10, 27474, Cuxhaven, Germany
Tel.: (49) 4721 78 0
Health Care & Hospital Services
N.A.I.C.S.: 622110

Kreiskrankenhaus Gifhorn GmbH (2)
Campus 6, 38518, Gifhorn, Germany
Tel.: (49) 5371870

Sales Range: $100-124.9 Million
Emp.: 800
General Medical & Surgical Hospitals
N.A.I.C.S.: 622110

MVZ Augenarztliches Diagnostik- und Therapiezentrum Dusseldorf GmbH (2)
Banner Str 7, 40589, Dusseldorf, Germany
Tel.: (49) 211 0866810
General Hospitality Services
N.A.I.C.S.: 622110

MVZ Bad Neustadt/ Saale GmbH (2)
Von-Guttenberg-Str 10, 97616, Bad Neustadt an der Saale, Germany
Tel.: (49) 97716626010
Web Site: http://mvz.campus-nes.de
Health & Medical Care Services
N.A.I.C.S.: 621999

MVZ Universitatsklinikum Marburg GmbH (2)
Baldingerstrasse, 35043, Marburg, Germany
Tel.: (49) 6421 2820
Health Care Hospital Services
N.A.I.C.S.: 622110

Marburger Ionenstrahl-Therapie BetriebsGesellschaft mbH (2)
Albrecht Kossel Str 1, 35043, Marburg, Germany
Tel.: (49) 64215866008
Web Site: http://www.mit-marburg.de
Therapy Center Services
N.A.I.C.S.: 621340

Medgate Deutschland GmbH (2)
Schlossplatz 1, 97616, Bad Neustadt an der Saale, Germany
Tel.: (49) 97716512710
Web Site: http://www.medgate.de
Healtcare Services
N.A.I.C.S.: 621999
Verena Weissenseel (CEO)

Mittelweser Kliniken GmbH Krankenhaus Hoya (2)
Ziegelkampstrasse 39, 31582, Nienburg, Germany
Tel.: (49) 502192100
General Medical & Surgical Hospitals
N.A.I.C.S.: 622110

Mittelweser Kliniken GmbH Nienburg Hoya Stolzenau (2)
Krankenhaus Nienburg Ziegelkampstrasse 39, 31582, Nienburg, Germany
Tel.: (49) 502192100
General Hospitality Services
N.A.I.C.S.: 622110
Ronald Gudath (Mng Dir)

Neurologische Klinik GmbH (2)
Von-Guttenberg-Strasse 10, Schweinfurt, 97616, Germany
Tel.: (49) 97719080
Web Site: http://www.rhoenklinik.de
Specialty Hospitals
N.A.I.C.S.: 622310
Kreaven Berd (Mng Dir)

Park-Krankenhaus Leipzig-Sudost Gmbh (2)
Strumpellstr 41, Leipzig, Leipzig, 04289, Germany
Tel.: (49) 3418640
Web Site: http://www.rhoen-klinikum-ag.com
General Medical & Surgical Hospitals
N.A.I.C.S.: 622110

Psychosomatische Klinik (2)
Salzburger Leite 1, 97616, Schweinfurt, Germany
Tel.: (49) 97716701
General Medical & Surgical Hospitals
N.A.I.C.S.: 622110

RHON-Cateringgesellschaft mbH (2)
Schlossplatz 1, 97616, Bad Neustadt an der Saale, Germany
Tel.: (49) 97716516110
Health & Medical Care Services
N.A.I.C.S.: 621999

RHON-Innovations GmbH (2)
Schlossplatz 1, 97616, Bad Neustadt an der Saale, Germany

Tel.: (49) 97716512250
Web Site: http://www.rhoen-innovations.com
Financial Investment Services
N.A.I.C.S.: 523999
Julian Schmitt (Mng Dir)

RK Klinik Betriebs GmbH Nr. 31 (2)
Schlossplatz 1, 97616, Bad Neustadt an der Saale, Germany
Tel.: (49) 9771 650
Health Care Hospital Services
N.A.I.C.S.: 622110
Stephan Holzinger (CEO)

Soteria Klinik Leipzig GmbH (2)
Morawitzstrasse 4, 4289, Leipzig, Germany
Tel.: (49) 341 870 0
General Hospitality Services
N.A.I.C.S.: 622110

Universitatsklinikum Gieben und Marburg GmbH (2)
Baldingerstrasse, Marburg, 35033, Germany
Tel.: (49) 642158660300
Sales Range: $450-499.9 Million
Emp.: 4,500
General Medical & Surgical Hospitals
N.A.I.C.S.: 622110

Universitatsklinikum Giessen und Marburg GmbH (2)
Rudolf-Buchheim-Strasse 8, 35392, Giessen, Germany
Tel.: (49) 64198560
Web Site: http://www.ukgm.de
Hospital Care Services
N.A.I.C.S.: 622110

Zentralklinik Bad Berka GmbH (2)
Robert-Koch-Allee 9, 99437, Bad Berka, Germany
Tel.: (49) 3645850
Web Site: http://www.zentralklinik.de
General Medical & Surgical Hospitals
N.A.I.C.S.: 622110
Kerstin Haase (Mng Dir)

Sachsische Schweiz Kliniken GmbH (1)
Dr - Steudner- Strasse 75b, 1855, Berlin, Germany
Tel.: (49) 35 971 6 0
Healtcare Services
N.A.I.C.S.: 622310

Samedi GmbH (1)
Rigaer Str 44, 10247, Berlin, Germany
Tel.: (49) 30212307070
Web Site: http://www.samedi.de
Software Services
N.A.I.C.S.: 541511
Katrin Keller (Mng Dir)

Sanomed Sanitatshaus fur Orthopadie und Rehabilitationstechnik GmbH (1)
Staudernheimer Strasse 57, 55566, Bad Sobernheim, Germany
Tel.: (49) 67518560430
Web Site: http://www.sanomed.de
Medical Equipment Retailer
N.A.I.C.S.: 456199

ZIT Zentralinstitut fur Transfusionsmedizin GmbH (1)
Eilbektal 111, 22089, Hamburg, Germany
Tel.: (49) 40 1818842551
Healtcare Services
N.A.I.C.S.: 622110

medicum Hamburg MVZ GmbH (1)
Beim Strohhause 2, 20097, Hamburg, Germany
Tel.: (49) 408079790
Web Site: http://www.medicum-hamburg.de
Diabetes Centre Services
N.A.I.C.S.: 621111

ASKO HOLDING A.S.
OSB Mahallesi 83426 Cad no 1, Sehitkamil, 27600, Gaziantep, Turkiye
Tel.: (90) 3422115900
Web Site: https://asko.com.tr
Industrial Machinery Manufacturer
N.A.I.C.S.: 333924
Sami KonuKoglu (Chm)

Subsidiaries:

Basak Traktor Tarim Ziraat Ve Is
Makinalari Sanayi Ticaret A.S.   **(1)**
Hanli Sakarya Mah Basak St No 62/1, Sa-
karya, Turkiye
Tel.: (90) 2642958300
Web Site: https://basaktraktor.com.tr
Agricultural Equipment & Machinery Manu-
facturing
N.A.I.C.S.: 333111

Subsidiary (Non-US):

Buhler Industries Inc.   **(2)**
1260 Clarence Avenue, Winnipeg, R3T 1T2,
MB, Canada   **(96.7%)**
Tel.: (204) 661-8711
Web Site: https://www.buhlerindustries.com
Rev.: $180,115,753
Assets: $175,829,692
Liabilities: $103,380,459
Net Worth: $72,449,233
Earnings: $5,356,066
Fiscal Year-end: 12/31/2023
Farm Equipment Mfr
N.A.I.C.S.: 333112
Grant Adolph *(COO)*

Subsidiary (US):

ISCO Inc.   **(3)**
6360 Fiesta Dr, Columbus, OH 43235-5205
Tel.: (614) 792-2206
Web Site: https://www.iscoinc.com
Sales Range: $1-9.9 Million
Emp.: 10
Hardware Product Whslr
N.A.I.C.S.: 423710
Brian Amerine *(Pres)*

Progressive Manufacturing Ltd.   **(3)**
452 Sunapee St, Newport, NH 03773
Tel.: (603) 298-5778
Web Site: https://www.progressive-mfg.com
Emp.: 25
Precision Sheet Metal Mfr
N.A.I.C.S.: 332322

ASKO-STRAKHOVANIE PJSC

Ul Red D 4, Chelyabinsk, 454091,
Russia
Tel.: (7) 3512652735
Web Site: http://www.acko.ru
Emp.: 100
Fire Insurance Services
N.A.I.C.S.: 524113
Arkadiy Markovich Lyubavin *(CEO)*

ASKOLL EVA SPA

Via Industria 30, 36031, Dueville,
Italy
Tel.: (39) 0444920260
Web Site:
  https://www.askollelectric.com
Year Founded: 1978
EVA—(ITA)
Sales Range: Less than $1 Million
Electric Motor Mfr
N.A.I.C.S.: 336390
Elio Marioni *(Founder & Chm)*

ASKUL CORPORATION

Toyosu Cubic Garden 3-2-3 Toyosu
Koto-ku, Tokyo, 135-0061, Japan
Tel.: (81) 343305001
Web Site: http://www.askul.co.jp
Year Founded: 1997
2678—(TKS)
Rev.: $3,117,818,020
Assets: $1,606,639,820
Liabilities: $1,069,008,860
Net Worth: $537,630,960
Earnings: $126,508,790
Emp.: 3,687
Fiscal Year-end: 05/31/24
Office Supply Mail Order Services
N.A.I.C.S.: 424120
Hitoshi Yoshida *(VP & VP)*

Subsidiaries:

ASKUL (Shanghai) Trading Co.,
Ltd.   **(1)**

A502 Building 4 Mingyuan Business Center
No 118 Jiashan Road, Xuhui District,
Shanghai, 200031, China
Tel.: (86) 21 5466 8787
Office Equipment & Supplies Distr
N.A.I.C.S.: 423420

ASKUL LOGIST Corporation   **(1)**
Toyosu Cubic Garden 3-2-3 Toyosu, Koto-
ku, Tokyo
Tel.: (81) 343305575
Emp.: 3,607
Freight Forwarding Services
N.A.I.C.S.: 484110

ASMARU Corporation   **(1)**
1-1-3 Jingu-mae, Shibuya-ku, Tokyo, Japan
Tel.: (81) 35 772 6422
Web Site: http://www.askul.co.jp
Office Equipment & Supplies Distr
N.A.I.C.S.: 423420

AlphaPurchase Co., Ltd   **(1)**
Mita International Building 15th floor 1-4-28
Mita, Minato-ku, Tokyo, 108-0073, Japan
Tel.: (81) 36 635 5140
Web Site: https://www.alphapurchase.co.jp
Emp.: 249
Business Support Services
N.A.I.C.S.: 561499
Masayuki Tada *(Pres & CEO)*

Bizex Corporation   **(1)**
3-8-10 Tatsumi, Koto-ku, 135-0053,
Japan
Tel.: (81) 3 5569 2055
Office Equipment & Supplies Distr
N.A.I.C.S.: 423420

Businessmart Corporation   **(1)**
3-8-10 Tatsumi, Koto-ku, Tokyo, 135-0053,
Japan
Tel.: (81) 33 522 3234
Web Site: http://www.askul.co.jp
Office Equipment & Supplies Distr
N.A.I.C.S.: 423420

Charm Co., Ltd.   **(1)**
1810-3 Shinozuka, Oura-cho, Oura, Gunma
Prefecture, Japan
Tel.: (81) 120894828
Web Site: https://www.charm.co.jp
Emp.: 546
Pet Supplies Retailer
N.A.I.C.S.: 424720

SOLOEL Corporation   **(1)**
Uni-works Shinjuku Gyoen 4F 1-12-5 Shin-
juku, Shinjuku-ku, Tokyo, 160-0022, Japan
Tel.: (81) 12 040 1662
Web Site: https://www.soloel.com
Office Equipment & Supplies Distr
N.A.I.C.S.: 423420

ASL INDUSTRIES LIMITED

C-54 55 & 56 Phase Iv Ns -7 & 8
Phase Vi B-13 B-14P B-27P & B-28,
Adityapur Industrial Area Gamharia,
Jamshedpur, 832108, India
Tel.: (91) 8986809898
Web Site: https://www.aslindustries.in
ASLIND—(NSE)
Rev.: $14,662,423
Assets: $4,525,871
Liabilities: $8,878
Net Worth: $4,516,992
Earnings: $206,792
Emp.: 2
Fiscal Year-end: 03/31/22
Sheet Metal Products Mfr
N.A.I.C.S.: 332322
Ankit Goyal *(Mng Dir)*

ASL MARINE HOLDINGS LTD

19 Pandan Road, Singapore, 609271,
Singapore
Tel.: (65) 62643833   SG
Web Site: https://www.aslmarine.com
Year Founded: 1974
A04—(SES)
Rev.: $248,843,275
Assets: $414,806,225
Liabilities: $360,805,484
Net Worth: $54,000,741
Earnings: $2,658,021

Emp.: 752
Fiscal Year-end: 06/30/23
Ship Building Services
N.A.I.C.S.: 336611
Kok Tian Ang *(Chm, CEO & Mng Dir)*

Subsidiaries:

PT. ASL Shipyard Indonesia   **(1)**
Jl Brigadir Jenderal Katamso Km 08 Tan-
jung Uncang Tj Uncang, Kota Batam,
Batam, 29422, Kepulauan Riau, Indonesia
Tel.: (62) 778391935
Ship Building Services
N.A.I.C.S.: 336611
Steven Yen *(Chief Compliance Officer)*

VOSTA LMG (Zhuhai) Ltd.   **(1)**
Room 405 B 4/f Shihang Building No 171
Jingshan Road Jida, Zhuhai, Guangdong,
China
Tel.: (86) 7563321886
Dredging Equipment Mfr & Distr
N.A.I.C.S.: 333120

VOSTA LMG Design GmbH   **(1)**
Vierhorn 2, 23556, Lubeck, Germany
Tel.: (49) 4518085100
Dredging Equipment Mfr
N.A.I.C.S.: 333120

VOSTA LMG IP & Software B.V.   **(1)**
Siriusdreef 1-15, 2132 WT, Hoofddorp,
Netherlands
Tel.: (31) 883240700
Intellectual Property Leasing Services
N.A.I.C.S.: 533110

VOSTA LMG India Pvt. Ltd.   **(1)**
415 World Trade Centre Babar Road Con-
naught Circus, New Delhi, 110001, India
Tel.: (91) 1143504545
Dredging Equipment Mfr & Distr
N.A.I.C.S.: 333120

ASLAN CEMENT A.S.

Cami Mahallesi Kaplan Caddesi No
149, Darica, 41700, Kocaeli, Turkiye
Tel.: (90) 2627454747
Web Site:
  http://www.aslancimento.com.tr
Year Founded: 1910
ASLAN—(IST)
Rev.: $14,329,834,211
Assets: $152,140,501,375
Liabilities: $105,138,946,058
Net Worth: $47,001,555,317
Earnings: ($4,159,814,398)
Fiscal Year-end: 03/31/20
Construction Materials Mfr
N.A.I.C.S.: 327215
Murat Idris Sela *(Gen Mgr)*

ASLAN PHARMACEUTICALS LIMITED

3 Temasek Avenue Level 18, Singa-
pore, 39190, Singapore
Tel.: (65) 62224235   Ky
Web Site: https://ir.aslanpharma.com
Year Founded: 2014
ASLN—(NASDAQ)
Rev.: $12,000,000
Assets: $24,626,525
Liabilities: $37,913,456
Net Worth: ($13,286,931)
Earnings: ($44,219,604)
Emp.: 35
Fiscal Year-end: 12/31/23
Pharmaceuticals Product Mfr
N.A.I.C.S.: 325412
Carl Firth *(Founder & CEO)*

Subsidiaries:

ASLAN Pharmaceuticals (Shanghai)
Co. Ltd.   **(1)**
Room 1902 Jin Hang Tower No 83 Wan
Hang Du Road, Jing An District, Shanghai,
200040, China
Tel.: (86) 13817077567
Pharmaceuticals Product Mfr
N.A.I.C.S.: 325412

ASLAN Pharmaceuticals Taiwan
Ltd.   **(1)**
Room 3711-15 37F Taipei Nanshan Plaza
No 100 Songren Rd, Xinyi District, Taipei,
110, Taiwan
Tel.: (886) 237257770
Pharmaceuticals Product Mfr
N.A.I.C.S.: 325412

ASM GROUP S.A.

pl Malachowskiego 2, 00-066, War-
saw, Poland
Tel.: (48) 507812750
Web Site: https://www.asmgroup.pl
ASM—(WAR)
Rev.: $58,117,599
Assets: $36,211,331
Liabilities: $26,540,804
Net Worth: $9,670,528
Earnings: ($812,720)
Fiscal Year-end: 12/31/22
Holding Company
N.A.I.C.S.: 551112
Dorota Kenny *(Pres & Member-Mgmt
Bd)*

Subsidiaries:

ASM Sales Force Agency Sp. z
o.o.   **(1)**
Swietokrzyska 18, 00-052, Warsaw, Poland
Tel.: (48) 224169696
Web Site: http://www.asmsalesforce.pl
Emp.: 15,000
General Marketing Services
N.A.I.C.S.: 541613
Zbigniew Sierocki *(Dir-Operational Div)*

Gruppo Trade Service Polska Sp. z
o.o.   **(1)**
ul Swietokrzyska 18, 00-052, Warsaw, Po-
land
Tel.: (48) 228299480
Web Site: http://gruppotradeservice.pl
Merchandising Services
N.A.I.C.S.: 455219

Vertikom GmbH   **(1)**
Schleifweg 37, 90409, Nuremberg, Ger-
many
Tel.: (49) 9116605800
Web Site: http://www.vertikom.com
Emp.: 850
Holding Company
N.A.I.C.S.: 551112
Gert Pieplow-Scholl *(CEO)*

Subsidiary (Non-US):

Vertikom Austria GmbH   **(2)**
Billrothstrasse 58/2, 1190, Vienna, Austria
Tel.: (43) 136941110
General Marketing Services
N.A.I.C.S.: 541613

Subsidiary (Domestic):

Vertikom Sales Berlin GmbH   **(2)**
Oranienburger Strasse 3, 10178, Berlin,
Germany
Tel.: (49) 3060272300
General Marketing Services
N.A.I.C.S.: 541613

Vertikom Sales GmbH   **(2)**
Helfmann Park 7, 65760, Eschborn, Ger-
many
Tel.: (49) 619664050
Web Site: http://www.vertikom-sales.com
General Marketing Services
N.A.I.C.S.: 541613
Niels Schiff *(Mng Dir)*

Subsidiary (Non-US):

Vertikom Switzerland GmbH   **(2)**
Nordstrasse 145, 8037, Zurich, Switzerland
Tel.: (41) 445753700
Web Site: http://www.vertikom.ch
General Marketing Services
N.A.I.C.S.: 541613
Caroline Duetsch Kubik *(Mng Dir)*

Wunderknaben Kommunikation
GmbH   **(1)**
Alte Giesserei 12, 40699, Erkrath, Germany
Tel.: (49) 2117306030
Web Site: http://www.wunderknaben.com

ASM Group S.A.—(Continued)

General Marketing Services
N.A.I.C.S.: 541613

ASM INTERNATIONAL N.V.
Versterkerstraat 8, 1322 AP, Almere,
Netherlands
Tel.: (31) 881008810   NI
Web Site: https://www.asm.com
Year Founded: 1968
ASM—(OTCIQ)
Rev.: $1,631,252,565
Assets: $2,738,900,277
Liabilities: $460,854,072
Net Worth: $2,278,046,206
Earnings: $350,534,783
Emp.: 2,583
Fiscal Year-end: 12/31/20
Front-End Chip Making Equipment
Mfr
N.A.I.C.S.: 333242
Martin C. J. Van Pernis (Executives)

Subsidiaries:

ASM America Inc.   **(1)**
3440 E University Dr, Phoenix, AZ
85034-7200   **(100%)**
Tel.: (602) 470-5700
Sales Range: $150-199.9 Million
Emp.: 300
Industrial Machinery & Equipment Whslr
N.A.I.C.S.: 423830

ASM China Ltd   **(1)**
Room 201A Building D Changtai Plaza
2889 Alley Jinke road, Pudong, Shanghai,
201203, China   **(100%)**
Tel.: (86) 215 036 8588
Web Site: https://www.asm.com
Sales Range: $25-49.9 Million
Emp.: 30
Other Electronic Parts & Equipment Whslr
N.A.I.C.S.: 423690

ASM Europe B.V.   **(1)**
Versterkerstraat 8, 1322 AP, Almere,
Netherlands   **(100%)**
Tel.: (31) 88 100 8711
Web Site: https://www.asm.com
Sales Range: $75-99.9 Million
Emp.: 300
All Other Business Support Services
N.A.I.C.S.: 561499

Subsidiary (Non-US):

ASM Belgium N.V.   **(2)**
Kapeldreef 75, 3001, Leuven, Belgium
Web Site: http://www.asm.com
Electronic Components Mfr
N.A.I.C.S.: 334419

ASM Far East Marketing Ltd.   **(1)**
2F No 1 Jinshan 8th St East Dist, Front
End Sales and Service, Hsin-chu, 300,
Taiwan   **(100%)**
Tel.: (886) 3 666 7722
Web Site: http://www.asm.com
Emp.: 70
Power Boiler & Heat Exchanger Mfr
N.A.I.C.S.: 332410

ASM France S.A.R.L.   **(1)**
223 Rue des Becasses, 38920, Crolles,
France   **(100%)**
Tel.: (33) 47 692 2824
Sales Range: $25-49.9 Million
Emp.: 11
Relay & Industrial Control Mfr
N.A.I.C.S.: 335314

ASM Front-End Manufacturing Singa-
pore Pte Ltd   **(1)**
4 Woodlands Height, Singapore, 737860,
Singapore   **(100%)**
Tel.: (65) 65122922
Sales Range: $100-124.9 Million
Emp.: 450
Wafer & Semiconductor Process Manufac-
turing
N.A.I.C.S.: 333310

ASM Front-End Sales And Services
Taiwan Co. Ltd   **(1)**
2F-5 No1 Jinshan 8th St, East Dist, Hsinchu, 300, Taiwan   **(100%)**

Tel.: (886) 3 666 7722
Sales Range: $25-49.9 Million
Emp.: 54
Other Electronic Component Mfr
N.A.I.C.S.: 334419

ASM Genitech Korea Ltd.   **(1)**
SungKong-Kwan 1 dong Cheonan Valley
514 Sameun-ri Jiksan-eup, Cheonan, Korea
(South)   **(100%)**
Tel.: (82) 429352255
Web Site: http://www.asm.com
Sales Range: $25-49.9 Million
Emp.: 85
Semiconductor Machinery Mfr
N.A.I.C.S.: 333242

ASM Germany Sales B.V   **(1)**
Peter-Henlein-Strasse 28, 85540, Haar,
Germany   **(100%)**
Tel.: (49) 894623650
Web Site: http://www.asm.com
Sales Range: $25-49.9 Million
Emp.: 37
Space Research & Technology
N.A.I.C.S.: 927110

ASM IP Holding B.V.   **(1)**
Tel.: (31) 881008810
Investment Management Service
N.A.I.C.S.: 523999

ASM Japan K.K.   **(1)**
23-1 6-chome Nagayama, Tama, 206-0025,
Tokyo, Japan   **(100%)**
Tel.: (81) 42 337 6311
Web Site: http://www.ism.com
Sales Range: $100-124.9 Million
Emp.: 300
Other Commercial & Service Industry Ma-
chinery Mfr
N.A.I.C.S.: 333310

Plant (Domestic):

ASM Japan K.K. - Nagaoka
Factory   **(2)**
392-1 Mishimashimbo, Nagaoka, 940-2311,
Niigata, Japan
Tel.: (81) 258 42 2400
Web Site: http://www.asm.com
Semiconductor Devices Mfr
N.A.I.C.S.: 334413

ASM NuTool, Inc.   **(1)**
3440 E University Dr, Phoenix, AZ 85034-
7200
Tel.: (602) 470-5700
Web Site: http://www.asm.com
Sales Range: $100-124.9 Million
Emp.: 500
Wafer Transfer Device Mfr
N.A.I.C.S.: 334413

ASM Pacific Holding B.V.   **(1)**
Versterkerstraat 8, 1322 AP, Almere, Neth-
erlands
Tel.: (31) 881008810
Emp.: 100
Investment Management Service
N.A.I.C.S.: 523999

ASM Pacific Technology Ltd.   **(1)**
19/F Gateway ts 8 Cheung Fai Road, Tsing
Yi, New Territories, China (Hong
Kong)   **(52.8%)**
Tel.: (852) 26192000
Web Site: http://www.asmpacific.com
Rev.: $2,468,845,613
Assets: $3,159,007,703
Liabilities: $1,137,172,500
Net Worth: $2,021,835,203
Earnings: $333,803,543
Emp.: 12,000
Fiscal Year-end: 12/31/2022
Semiconductor & Related Device Mfr
N.A.I.C.S.: 334413
Orasa Livasiri (Chm)

Subsidiary (Domestic):

ASM Assembly Automation Ltd.   **(2)**
4/F Watson Center 16-22 Kung Yip Street,
Kwai Chung, New Territories, China (Hong
Kong)
Tel.: (852) 26192000
Semiconductor Machinery Mfr
N.A.I.C.S.: 333242

Subsidiary (Non-US):

ASM Assembly Equipment (M) Sdn.
Bhd.   **(2)**

No 22 24 26 Ground Floor Jalan PS 3
Plaza Semabok, 75050, Melaka, Malaysia
Tel.: (60) 62644636
Web Site: https://www.asmpacific.com
Sales Range: $25-49.9 Million
Emp.: 30
All Other Industrial Machinery Mfr
N.A.I.C.S.: 333248

ASM Assembly Equipment Bangkok
Limited   **(2)**
46/175 Suriphon Grand Place Nuanchan
Rd Nuanchan, Bueng Kum, Bangkok,
10230, Thailand
Tel.: (66) 207308615
Web Site: https://www.asmpacific.com
Sales Range: $25-49.9 Million
Emp.: 55
Other Electronic Component Mfr
N.A.I.C.S.: 334419

Subsidiary (US):

ASM Assembly Systems LLC   **(2)**
3975 Lakefield Ct Ste 106, Suwanee, GA
30024
Tel.: (770) 797-3000
Web Site: http://www.asm-smt.com
Industrial Machinery Mfr
N.A.I.C.S.: 333998
Brian Smith (Dir-Sls & Mgr-Channel)

Subsidiary (Non-US):

ASM Assembly Technology Co.
Limited   **(2)**
5/F Tachikawa F-Building 1-7-18 Nishiki-
Cho, Tachikawa, 190-0022, Tokyo, Japan
Tel.: (81) 42 521 7751
Web Site: https://www.asmat.co.jp
Semiconductor Device Distr
N.A.I.C.S.: 423690

ASM Laser Separation International
(ALSI) B.V.   **(2)**
Platinawerf 20, 6641 TL, Beuningen, Neth-
erlands
Tel.: (31) 246782888
Semiconductor Machinery & Equipment Mfr
N.A.I.C.S.: 334413

Subsidiary (US):

ASM Pacific Assembly Products,
Inc.   **(2)**
3440 E University Dr, Phoenix, AZ
85034-7200   **(54%)**
Tel.: (602) 437-4760
Sales Range: $25-49.9 Million
Emp.: 10
Semiconductor Equipment Mfr
N.A.I.C.S.: 333242
Joann Colletti (Office Mgr)

Subsidiary (Non-US):

ASM Semiconductor Materials (Shen-
zhen) Co. Ltd.   **(2)**
12-15 Fuqiao Industry Zone 2 Bao'an,
Shenzhen, 518103, Guangdong, China
Tel.: (86) 755 29618000
Semiconductor Devices Mfr
N.A.I.C.S.: 334413

ASM Technology (Huizhou) Co.
Limited   **(2)**
198 Jinshi 7th Road, Jiulong Hi-tech Indus-
trial Park Xiaojinkou Huicheng, Huizhou,
516023, Guangdong, China
Tel.: (86) 7528213000
Sales Range: $350-399.9 Million
Emp.: 210
Semiconductor Equipment Mfr
N.A.I.C.S.: 333242

ASM Technology (M) Sdn. Bhd.   **(2)**
Plo 534 Jalan Keluli 8 Kawasan Perindus-
trian Pasir Gudang, 81700, Pasir Gudang,
Johor, Malaysia
Tel.: (60) 72533500
Semiconductor Equipment Mfr
N.A.I.C.S.: 334413

ASM Technology Singapore Pte
Ltd   **(2)**
2 Yishun Avenue 7, Singapore, 768924,
Singapore   **(53.35%)**
Tel.: (65) 6 752 6311
Web Site: https://www.asmpacific.com

Sales Range: $150-199.9 Million
Emp.: 700
Semiconductor & Related Device Mfr
N.A.I.C.S.: 334310

Subsidiary (US):

TEL NEXX, Inc.   **(2)**
900 Middlesex Tpke Bldg 6, Billerica, MA
01821
Tel.: (978) 932-2000
Web Site: https://www.nexxsystems.com
Sales Range: $25-49.9 Million
Emp.: 139
Semiconductors & Related Products Mfr
N.A.I.C.S.: 334413
Kenji Washino (Co-Chm)

ASM Services and Support Ireland
Ltd.   **(1)**
Unit 23 Hills Industrial Estate, Lucan, Dub-
lin, Ireland   **(100%)**
Tel.: (353) 1 621 9100
Web Site: https://www.asm.com
Sales Range: $25-49.9 Million
Emp.: 40
Semiconductor & Related Device Mfr
N.A.I.C.S.: 334310

ASM Services and Support Israel
Ltd   **(1)**
Edwards Building 5 Habarzel St Gat 2000
Industrial Zone, Kiryat Gat, 82107, Israel
Tel.: (972) 8 860 9181
Sales Range: $25-49.9 Million
Emp.: 3
Semiconductor Equipment Repair Services
N.A.I.C.S.: 811310

ASM United Kingdom Sales B.V   **(1)**
Versterkerstraat 9, 1323 AP, Almere,
Netherlands   **(100%)**
Tel.: (31) 881008711
Web Site: http://www.asn.com
Sales Range: $75-99.9 Million
Emp.: 150
Other Commercial Equipment Whslr
N.A.I.C.S.: 423440

ASM Wafer Process Equipment Sin-
gapore Pte Ltd   **(1)**
543 Yishun Industrial Park A, Singapore,
768765, Singapore   **(100%)**
Tel.: (65) 6 512 2962
Web Site: http://www.asm.com
Sales Range: $25-49.9 Million
Emp.: 15
Engineeering Services
N.A.I.C.S.: 541330

ASM MESSEPROFIS AG
Im Dreispitz 1, Erlen, 8586, Switzer-
land
Tel.: (41) 581000600
Web Site: http://www.messeprofis.ch
Promotional Service
N.A.I.C.S.: 541890

Subsidiaries:

Impact Unlimited GmbH   **(1)**
Hubstrasse 104, Ch-9500, Wil, Switzerland
Tel.: (41) 71 790 0055
Events, Exhibits & Meetings Solutions
N.A.I.C.S.: 541890

ASM TECHNOLOGIES LIM-
ITED
80/2 Lusanne Court Richmond Road,
Bengaluru, 560 025, Karnataka, India
Tel.: (91) 8066962301
Web Site: https://www.asmltd.com
526433—(BOM)
Rev.: $27,109,446
Assets: $19,944,015
Liabilities: $11,007,906
Net Worth: $8,936,109
Earnings: $1,897,487
Emp.: 1,191
Fiscal Year-end: 03/31/22
Business Consulting & Software De-
velopment Services
N.A.I.C.S.: 561499
Narsingh Rathod (CFO)

Subsidiaries:

ASM Digital Technologies Inc. **(1)**
2020 Calamos Ct Ste 200, Naperville, IL
60563-2793
Tel.: (630) 799-1563
Software Digital Technology Services
N.A.I.C.S.: 541512

ASM Digital Technologies Pte
Ltd. **(1)**
24-01 Vision Exchange 2 Venture Drive,
Singapore, 608526, Singapore
Tel.: (65) 62705737
Software Digital Technology Services
N.A.I.C.S.: 541512

Advanced Synergic Pte. Ltd. **(1)**
24-01 Vision Exchange 2 Venture Drive, 30
Tohguan Rd, Singapore, 608526, Singapore
Tel.: (65) 62705737
Web Site: http://www.asmltd.com
Sales Range: $10-24.9 Million
Emp.: 50
Business Consulting & Software Services
N.A.I.C.S.: 561499

ESR Associates Inc **(1)**
1715 Indian Wood Cir Ste 200, Maumee,
OH 43537
Tel.: (419) 897-7902
Web Site: http://www.esr-associates.com
Software System Consulting Services
N.A.I.C.S.: 541512

Pinnacle Talent Inc. **(1)**
2020 Calamos Ct Ste 200, Naperville, IL
60563-2793
Tel.: (630) 799-1563
Business Consulting & Software Services
N.A.I.C.S.: 561499
Sundar Ramanathan *(Office Mgr)*

Semcon Engineering UK Ltd **(1)**
19 St Catherines Rd, NG316TT, Grantham,
United Kingdom
Tel.: (44) 7850612561
Web Site: http://www.semcon.com
Sales Range: $25-49.9 Million
Emp.: 150
Engineeering Services
N.A.I.C.S.: 541330

ASMALLWORLD AG

Seidengasse 20, 8001, Zurich, Swit-
zerland
Tel.: (41) 442155025   **CH**
Web Site:
   https://www.asmallworldag.com
Year Founded: 2004
ASWN—(SWX)
Rev.: $20,182,594
Assets: $13,638,692
Liabilities: $16,082,373
Net Worth: ($2,443,681)
Earnings: $1,611,419
Fiscal Year-end: 12/31/22
Online Information Services
N.A.I.C.S.: 513199
Jan Luescher *(CEO)*

Subsidiaries:

First Class & More FZE **(1)**
PO Box 16318, Ras al Khaimah, United
Arab Emirates
Tel.: (971) 72042744
Web Site: https://www.first-class-and-
     more.de
Luxury Travel Web Portal Services
N.A.I.C.S.: 561599

First Class & More International
AG **(1)**
Lowenstrasse 40, 8001, Zurich, Switzerland
Tel.: (41) 1701501152
Web Site: https://www.first-class-and-
     more.com
Luxury Travel Web Portal Services
N.A.I.C.S.: 561599
Alexander Koenig *(Founder & CEO)*

ASMAR

Edificio Rapa Nui Building Prat 856,
Piso 13, Valparaiso, Chile
Tel.: (56) 322260000

Web Site: http://www.asmar.cl
Year Founded: 1895
Sales Range: $550-599.9 Million
Emp.: 4,000
Ship Building & Repair Services
N.A.I.C.S.: 336611

ASMARQ CO., LTD.

4F Shibuya Property Tower 1-32-12
Higashi, Shibuya-ku, Tokyo, 150-
0011, Japan
Tel.: (81) 354685101
Web Site: https://www.asmarq.co.jp
Year Founded: 1998
4197—(TKS)
Emp.: 264
Recruitment Services
N.A.I.C.S.: 561311
Masakazu Machida *(CEO)*

ASMECO (THAILAND) LTD.

60/2 Krungtep-Nont 7 Road, Non-
thaburi, 11000, Thailand
Tel.: (66) 25252128   **TH**
Pharmaceuticals Product Mfr
N.A.I.C.S.: 325412

ASMEDIA TECHNOLOGY INC.

6F No 115 Minquan Rd, Xindian Dis-
trict, New Taipei City, 231, Taiwan
Tel.: (886) 222196088
Web Site:
   https://www.asmedia.com.tw
Year Founded: 2004
5269—(TAI)
Rev.: $164,097,458
Assets: $556,378,858
Liabilities: $77,643,217
Net Worth: $478,735,641
Earnings: $81,836,007
Fiscal Year-end: 12/31/22
Integrated Circuits Mfr
N.A.I.C.S.: 334413
Che-Wei Lin *(Pres)*

ASML HOLDING N.V.

De Run 6501, 5504 DR, Veldhoven,
Netherlands
Tel.: (31) 402683000   **NI**
Web Site: https://www.asml.com
Year Founded: 1983
ASML—(NASDAQ)
Rev.: $25,425,472,100
Assets: $36,864,789,500
Liabilities: $24,453,605,260
Net Worth: $12,411,184,240
Earnings: $7,232,261,400
Emp.: 38,656
Fiscal Year-end: 12/31/23
Holding Company; Lithography
Equipment Mfr
N.A.I.C.S.: 551112
Marcel Kemp *(Head-IR-Europe)*

Subsidiaries:

ASML (Shanghai) International Trad-
ing Co., Ltd **(1)**
Jinke Road 2889 No1 Block A / No2 Block
B Chantime Square, Pudong, Shanghai,
China
Tel.: (86) 2120366330
Sales Range: $50-74.9 Million
Emp.: 70
Lithography Equipment Distr
N.A.I.C.S.: 423690

ASML (Tianjin) Co. Ltd. **(1)**
Race Course Road 59 25F Units 09 10 11
Ping An Building, He Xi District, Tianjin,
300204, China   **(100%)**
Tel.: (86) 2283865464
Sales Range: $25-49.9 Million
Emp.: 10
Lithography Equipment Mfr & Distr
N.A.I.C.S.: 323120

ASML Belgium BVBA **(1)**
Kapeldreef 75, 3001, Leuven, Belgium
Tel.: (32) 402683000
Lithography Equipment Mfr & Distr

N.A.I.C.S.: 333242

ASML Equipment Malaysia Sdn.
Bhd. **(1)**
Khtp Business Centre 2F Suite 2 02 Kulim
Hi-Tech Park, 09000, Kulim, Kedah Darul
Aman, Malaysia
Tel.: (60) 44031008
Lithography Equipment Mfr & Distr
N.A.I.C.S.: 333242

ASML France S.a.r.l. **(1)**
127 Rue Marcel Reynaud, 38920, Crolles,
France
Tel.: (33) 476044040
Sales Range: $25-49.9 Million
Emp.: 30
Lithography Equipment Mfr
N.A.I.C.S.: 333242
Brige Leonel *(Dir-Customer Svcs)*

ASML Germany GmbH **(1)**
Hermann-Reichelt-Strasse 3a, 01109, Dres-
den, Germany
Tel.: (49) 35179600
Lithography Equipment Mfr
N.A.I.C.S.: 333242

ASML Hong Kong Ltd. **(1)**
Matheson Street 1 Suites 3704-6 Times
Square Tower Two, Hong Kong, China
(Hong Kong)
Tel.: (852) 22951168
Semiconductor Equipment Mfr
N.A.I.C.S.: 333242

ASML Ireland Ltd. **(1)**
Maynooth Business Park Block C Office
Ground Floor, Maynooth, Kildare, Ireland
Tel.: (353) 16066635
Industrial Furnace Mfr
N.A.I.C.S.: 333994

ASML Japan Co. Ltd. **(1)**
Kita Shinagawa 4-7-35 4F Gotenyama Trust
Tower Building, Shinagawa-ku, Tokyo, 140-
0001, Japan
Tel.: (81) 357931800
Web Site: http://www.asml.com
Emp.: 100
Lithography Equipment Mfr & Distr
N.A.I.C.S.: 333242
Ihirohs Ishiwata *(Mng Dir)*

ASML Korea Co., Ltd. **(1)**
25 Samsung 1-ro 5-gil, Gyunggi-Do, Hwa-
sun, 18449, Gyeonggi-do, Korea
(South)   **(100%)**
Tel.: (82) 313791500
Sales Range: $50-74.9 Million
Emp.: 200
Lithography Equipment Mfr & Distr
N.A.I.C.S.: 323120

ASML Netherlands B.V. **(1)**
De Run 6501, 5504 DR, Veldhoven, Nether-
lands
Tel.: (31) 402683000
Lithography Equipment Mfr & Distr
N.A.I.C.S.: 333242

ASML Singapore Pte. Ltd. **(1)**
151 Lorong Chuan New Tech Park 06-08,
Singapore, 556741, Singapore
Tel.: (65) 64840123
Sales Range: $50-74.9 Million
Emp.: 150
Lithography Equipment Mfr & Distr
N.A.I.C.S.: 333242

ASML Taiwan Ltd. **(1)**
11F No 1 Sec 3 Gongdao 5th Road Taifei
ONE, Hsin-chu, 30069, Taiwan
Tel.: (886) 35166266
Lithography Equipment Mfr & Distr
N.A.I.C.S.: 333242

ASML US, Inc. **(1)**
8555 S River Pkwy, Tempe, AZ 85284-2601
Tel.: (480) 383-4422
Web Site: http://www.asml.com
Sales Range: $50-74.9 Million
Emp.: 150
N.A.I.C.S.: 323120

Branch (Domestic):

ASML Austin **(2)**
2324 Ridgepoint Dr Ste G1, Austin, TX
78744-1060   **(100%)**
Tel.: (512) 443-4244

Web Site: http://www.asml.com
Sales Range: $25-49.9 Million
Emp.: 50
Distr of Semicondutor Devices
N.A.I.C.S.: 423690

Subsidiary (Domestic):

ASML Capital US, Inc. **(2)**
2650 W Geronimo Pl, Chandler, AZ 85224-
2601
Tel.: (480) 696-2888
Web Site: http://www.asml.com
Emp.: 100
Investment Management Service
N.A.I.C.S.: 523999

ASML Participation US Inc. **(2)**
8555 S River Pkwy, Tempe, AZ 85284-2601
Tel.: (480) 383-4422
Lithography Equipment Mfr
N.A.I.C.S.: 333242

ASML Ventures 1 Inc. **(2)**
8555 S River Pkwy, Tempe, AZ 85284-2601
Tel.: (480) 383-4422
Investment Management Service
N.A.I.C.S.: 523940

Brion Technologies, Inc **(2)**
4211 Burton Dr, Santa Clara, CA 95054
Tel.: (408) 653-1500
Web Site: http://www.brion.com
Emp.: 500
Semiconductor Design & Mfr
N.A.I.C.S.: 333242
Shauh-Teh Juang *(Sr VP-Mktg & Bus Dev)*

Division (Non-US):

Brion Technologies (Shenzhen) Co.,
Ltd. **(3)**
2A-3 Bldg B1 Shenzhen Cyber-Tech Zone
High-Tech Industrial Pk, Shenzhen, 518057,
China
Tel.: (86) 075526037380
Web Site: http://www.brion.com
Sales Range: $25-49.9 Million
Emp.: 100
Semiconductor Design & Wafer Mfg Optimi-
zation Solutions
N.A.I.C.S.: 333242

Brion Technologies KK **(3)**
Prime Kanda Bldg 10F, 8-2 2-chome
Kandasuda-cho, Chiyoda-ku, 101-0041, To-
kyo, Japan
Tel.: (81) 352981561
Semiconductor Design & Wafer Mfg Optimi-
zation Solutions
N.A.I.C.S.: 333242

Subsidiary (Domestic):

Cymer, Inc. **(2)**
17075 Thornmint Ct, San Diego, CA 92127-
1712
Tel.: (858) 385-7300
Web Site: https://www.cymer.com
Rev.: $538,625,000
Assets: $1,023,230,000
Liabilities: $273,450,000
Net Worth: $749,780,000
Earnings: ($36,365,000)
Emp.: 1,100
Fiscal Year-end: 12/31/2012
Excimer Lasers Mfr for Semiconductor Fab-
rication
N.A.I.C.S.: 333242

Subsidiary (Non-US):

Cymer B.V. **(3)**
De Run 4312B, 5503 LN, Veldhoven,
Netherlands   **(100%)**
Tel.: (31) 402513684
Web Site: http://www.cymer.com
Sales Range: $10-24.9 Million
Emp.: 20
Lasers for Semiconductor Fabrication
N.A.I.C.S.: 333242

Cymer Japan, Inc. **(3)**
18F Gate City Osaki East Tower 1-11-2
Osaki, Shinagawa-ku, Tokyo, 141-0032,
Chiba, Japan   **(100%)**
Tel.: (81) 357453100
Sales Range: $25-49.9 Million
Emp.: 50
Lasers for Semiconductor Fabrication
N.A.I.C.S.: 333242

ASML Holding N.V.—(Continued)

Cymer Korea, Inc.   **(3)**
Suite 404 4FL Ssangyong Platinum Bldg 2
Dongtan Jiseong-ro, CheongBook-Myeon
Pyungtaek, Hwaseong, 45-160, Gyeonggi-do, Korea (South)
Tel.: (82) 316801500
Sales Range: $25-49.9 Million
Emp.: 50
Lasers for Semiconductor Fabrication
N.A.I.C.S.: 333242

Cymer Semiconductor Equipment
(Shanghai) Co., Ltd.   **(3)**
King Tower 806 No 28 Xinjinqiao Road, Pu-dong, Shanghai, 201206, China
Tel.: (86) 2150326300
Sales Range: $125-149.9 Million
Emp.: 15
Lasers Mfr
N.A.I.C.S.: 333242
G. Kaiaiji (CEO)

Cymer Singapore Pte. Ltd.   **(3)**
151 Lorong Chuan 06-08 New Tech Park,
Singapore, 556741, Singapore   **(100%)**
Tel.: (65) 63958599
Sales Range: $10-24.9 Million
Emp.: 10
Lasers for Semiconductor Fabrication
N.A.I.C.S.: 333242

Cymer Southeast Asia Ltd.   **(3)**
11F No 1 Sec 3 Gongdao 5th Rd,
Kuang-Fu Road Sec 2, Hsin-chu, 300 69,
Taiwan   **(100%)**
Tel.: (886) 36596900
Sales Range: $125-149.9 Million
Emp.: 40
Lasers Mfr
N.A.I.C.S.: 333242

Hermes Microvision, Inc.   **(1)**
7F No 18 Puding Road, East District, Hsin-chu, 300, Taiwan
Tel.: (886) 3666 9229
Web Site: http://www.hermes-microvision.com
Wafer Inspection Tool Developer, Mfr & Whslr
N.A.I.C.S.: 333242

Subsidiary (Non-US):

Hermes-Microvision, Inc.   **(2)**
Tel.: (408) 597-8600
Wafer Inspection Tool Research & Development
N.A.I.C.S.: 541715

ASMO CORPORATION
Shinjuku NS Building 25th floor 2-4-1
Nishi-Shinjuku, Shinjuku-ku, Tokyo,
163-0825, Shizuoka, Japan
Tel.: (81) 369110550
Web Site: https://www.asmo1.co.jp
Year Founded: 1975
2654—(TKS)
Rev.: $135,723,130
Assets: $64,295,470
Liabilities: $20,319,140
Net Worth: $43,976,330
Earnings: $3,100,090
Emp.: 1,554
Fiscal Year-end: 03/31/24
Meat Product Whslr
N.A.I.C.S.: 424470
Kazuhiro Ueda (Pres)

Subsidiaries:

ASMO Catering Malaysia SDN.
BHD.   **(1)**
Lot 8 06 88 Jalan Raja Chulan, 50450,
Kuala Lumpur, Malaysia
Tel.: (60) 321101479
Web Site: https://www.malaysia.asmo-catering.com
Emp.: 13
Restaurant Management Services
N.A.I.C.S.: 561110

ASMPT GMBH & CO. KG
Rupert-Mayer-Str 48, 81379, Munich,
Germany

Tel.: (49) 892080022000
Web Site: https://smt.asmpt.com
Electronic Products Mfr
N.A.I.C.S.: 334417

ASN BROKER PCL
388 IBM Tower 16 Floor Zone B Pha-holyothin Rd, Samsennai Phayathai,
Bangkok, 10400, Thailand
Tel.: (66) 24948388
Web Site:
       https://www.asnbroker.co.th
Year Founded: 2005
ASN—(THA)
Rev.: $4,705,746
Assets: $16,280,362
Liabilities: $7,702,885
Net Worth: $8,577,477
Earnings: $57,800
Fiscal Year-end: 12/31/23
Insurance Brokerage Services
N.A.I.C.S.: 524210
Thawatchai Loetrungroeng (Chm,
Vice Chm & CEO)

ASO CO., LTD.
7-18 Yoshiomachi, Iizuka, 820-0018,
Fukuoka, Japan
Tel.: (81) 48 22 3604   **JP**
Web Site: http://www.aso-group.jp
Year Founded: 1872
Emp.: 14,029
Medical, Construction & Environmental Consulting Services
N.A.I.C.S.: 541690
Iwao Aso (Pres & CEO)

Subsidiaries:

Nittoc Construction Co., Ltd.   **(1)**
4th 5th and 6th floors Daiwa Higashi Nihon-bashi Building 3-10-6, Higashi-nihonbashi
Chuo-ku, Tokyo, 103-0004, Japan
Tel.: (81) 356455050
Web Site: https://www.nittoc.co.jp
Rev.: $475,126,800
Assets: $359,749,250
Liabilities: $134,764,680
Net Worth: $224,984,570
Earnings: $20,266,260
Emp.: 1,198
Fiscal Year-end: 03/31/2024
Civil Engineering Services
N.A.I.C.S.: 541330
Norihisa Nagai (Pres)

Subsidiary (Domestic):

Midori Industries Co., Ltd.   **(2)**
13-18 Akashi-Cho, Chuo-ku, Tokyo, 104-0044, Japan
Tel.: (81) 335410792
Civil Engineering Services
N.A.I.C.S.: 541330

ASO FOAM CRETE CO., LTD.
36-1 Kariyado, Nakahara-ku, Kawa-saki, 211-0022, Kanagawa, Japan
Tel.: (81) 444222061
Web Site: https://www.asofoam.co.jp
Year Founded: 1961
1730—(TKS)
Sales Range: $25-49.9 Million
Emp.: 102
Construction Services
N.A.I.C.S.: 333120
Koichi Hanaoka (Pres)

ASO SAVINGS & LOANS PLC.
Plot 266 FMBN Building Cadastral
Zone A0, Central Business District,
Abuja, Nigeria
Tel.: (234) 7003300000   **NG**
Web Site: https://www.asoplc.com
Year Founded: 1995
Mortgage Banking Services
N.A.I.C.S.: 522310
Ali Mohammed Magashi (Chm)

ASOCIACION DE COOPERATI-

VAS ARGENTINAS C.L.
Avda Eduardo Madero 942, 1106,
Buenos Aires, Argentina
Tel.: (54) 11 4310 1300
Web Site: http://www.acacoop.com.ar
Year Founded: 1922
Sales Range: $150-199.9 Million
Emp.: 2,680
Grain & Agriculture Production Services
N.A.I.C.S.: 112111
Hector Zorzon (Pres)

Subsidiaries:

Aca Salud   **(1)**
Ayacucho 1262, Buenos Aires, Argentina
Tel.: (54) 1148279400
Web Site: http://www.acasalud.com.ar
Health Care Srvices
N.A.I.C.S.: 621999

La Segunda S.A.   **(1)**
Brig Gral Juan Manuel de Rosas 957
S2000CCE Rosario, S2000 CCE, Rosario,
Argentina
Tel.: (54) 3414201000
Web Site: https://www.lasegunda.com.ar
General Insurance Services
N.A.I.C.S.: 524210

ASOLID TECHNOLOGY CO.,
LTD.
7F 1 No 83 Sec 2 Gongdao 5th Rd,
Hsinchu, 300, Taiwan
Tel.: (886) 35736032
Web Site: https://www.asolid-tek.com
Year Founded: 2008
6485—(TPE)
Rev.: $60,080,386
Assets: $75,577,588
Liabilities: $13,236,563
Net Worth: $62,341,025
Earnings: $13,339,587
Fiscal Year-end: 12/31/22
Electric Equipment Mfr
N.A.I.C.S.: 334419

ASOLO S.P.A.
Via Delle Industrie 2, Nervesa della
Battaglia, 31040, Italy
Tel.: (39) 04228866
Web Site: http://www.asolo.com
Year Founded: 1975
Outdoor Equipment Mfr
N.A.I.C.S.: 339920
Marco Zanatta (Chm)

Subsidiaries:

Asolo North America Inc.   **(1)**
190 Hanover St, Lebanon, NH 03766
Tel.: (603) 448-8827
Sales Range: $25-49.9 Million
Emp.: 7
Outdoor Equipment Distr
N.A.I.C.S.: 339920

ASOS PLC
Greater London House Hampstead
Road, London, NW1 7FB, United
Kingdom
Tel.: (44) 2077561000
Web Site: https://www.asosplc.com
ASOMF—(OTCIQ)
Rev.: $5,309,364,060
Assets: $3,916,343,340
Liabilities: $2,512,460,860
Net Worth: $1,403,882,480
Earnings: $174,331,248
Emp.: 3,017
Fiscal Year-end: 08/31/21
Offices of Other Holding Companies
N.A.I.C.S.: 551112
Jo Butler (Chief People Officer)

ASPACOIL LTD
43 Hwasan 1-gil Onsan-eup Ulju-gun,
Ulsan, Korea (South)
Tel.: (82) 522392161

Web Site: http://www.aspacoil.co.kr
Lubricant & Grease Mfr
N.A.I.C.S.: 333914
Kim Jong-Chun (CEO)

ASPEED TECHNOLOGY INC.
4F No 1 Sec 3 Gongdao 5th Rd, East
Dist, Hsinchu, 300, Taiwan
Tel.: (880) 35751185
Web Site:
       https://www.aspeedtech.com
Year Founded: 2004
5274—(TPE)
Rev.: $162,872,589
Assets: $185,315,761
Liabilities: $44,998,999
Net Worth: $140,316,762
Earnings: $65,835,413
Emp.: 111
Fiscal Year-end: 12/31/22
Semiconductor Device Mfr & Distr
N.A.I.C.S.: 334413
Hung-Ju Huang (VP-Hardware R&D)

Subsidiaries:

ASPEED Technology (U.S.A.)
Inc.   **(1)**
2107 N 1st St Ste 530, San Jose, CA
95131
Tel.: (408) 650-6682
Technical Services
N.A.I.C.S.: 541990

ASPEN (GROUP) HOLDINGS
LIMITED
Aspen House 300 Jalan Macalister,
10450, George Town, Penang, Ma-laysia
Tel.: (60) 42275000   **SG**
Web Site:
       https://investor.aspen.com.my
Year Founded: 2013
1F3—(SES)
Rev.: $52,037,731
Assets: $208,547,745
Liabilities: $147,641,970
Net Worth: $60,905,776
Earnings: ($12,804,663)
Emp.: 135
Fiscal Year-end: 06/30/24
Real Estate Development Services
N.A.I.C.S.: 531210
M. Murly (Co-Founder, Pres & CEO)

Subsidiaries:

Aspen Vision City Sdn. Bhd.   **(1)**
Aspen House 300 Jalan Macalister, 10450,
George Town, Penang, Malaysia
Tel.: (60) 4 227 5000
Web Site: https://aspenvisioncity.com.my
Grocery Product Services
N.A.I.C.S.: 445110

ASPEN GROUP LIMITED
285A Crown Street, Surry Hills, 2010,
NSW, Australia
Tel.: (61) 291517500
Web Site:
       https://www.aspengroup.com.au
APZ—(ASX)
Rev.: $61,231,971
Assets: $446,682,690
Liabilities: $157,114,716
Net Worth: $289,567,974
Earnings: $32,345,085
Fiscal Year-end: 06/30/24
Commercial, Industrial & Retail Property Management
N.A.I.C.S.: 236210
John Carter (Co-CEO)

Subsidiaries:

Aspen Equity Investments Pty.
Limited   **(1)**
PO Box 509, Wheaton, IL 60187
Tel.: (630) 681-8810
Web Site: https://aspenequity.com
Investment & Financial Services

N.A.I.C.S.: 523999

Aspen Funds Management Ltd. **(1)**
Level 3 129 St Georges Tce, 256 Adelaide
Ter, Perth, 6000, WA, Australia
Tel.: (61) 892208400
Web Site: http://www.aspengroup.com.au
Sales Range: $100-124.9 Million
Emp.: 120
Fund Management Services
N.A.I.C.S.: 523940

Aspen Property Trust **(1)**
21 Oxford Street Bondi Junction, Sydney,
2022, NSW, Australia
Tel.: (61) 291517500
Web Site: http://www.aspengroup.com.au
Rev.: $5,796,544
Assets: $92,761,494
Liabilities: $18,301,638
Net Worth: $74,459,857
Earnings: $3,823,565
Fiscal Year-end: 06/30/2020
Trust Management Services
N.A.I.C.S.: 523940

ASPEN GROUP LTD.
Hashlosha 2, Tel Aviv, 6106054, Is-
rael
Tel.: (972) 35652222
Web Site: https://www.aspen.co.il
Year Founded: 1978
ASGR—(TAE)
Rev.: $69,552,423
Assets: $1,457,347,401
Liabilities: $1,027,155,668
Net Worth: $430,191,732
Earnings: ($36,138,140)
Emp.: 32
Fiscal Year-end: 12/31/23
New Multifamily Housing Construction
(except For-Sale Builders)
N.A.I.C.S.: 236116

ASPEN GROUP RESOURCES CORP.
1000 910 7th Avenue SW, Calgary,
T2P 3N8, AB, Canada
Tel.: (805) 693-5800   YT
Sales Range: $1-9.9 Million
Emp.: 9
Oil & Gas Services
N.A.I.C.S.: 213112
Robert L. Calentine *(CEO)*

ASPEN PHARMACARE HOLD-INGS LIMITED
Aspen Place 9 Rydall Vale Park
Douglas Saunders Drive, PO Box
1587, La Lucia Ridge, Durban, 2052,
South Africa
Tel.: (27) 315808600
Web Site:
https://www.aspenpharma.com
APNHF—(OTCIQ)
Rev.: $2,149,843,154
Assets: $7,091,540,891
Liabilities: $2,537,415,900
Net Worth: $4,554,124,991
Earnings: $276,090,791
Emp.: 8,612
Fiscal Year-end: 06/30/23
Holding Company; Pharmaceutical
Products Developer, Mfr & Distr
N.A.I.C.S.: 551112
Michael Gus Attridge *(Founder,
Deputy CEO-Grp & Fin Dir)*

Subsidiaries:

Aspen API Inc. **(1)**
5500 Bradley St, Sioux City, IA 51111
Tel.: (712) 233-2304
Sales Range: $350-399.9 Million
Pharmaceuticals Product Mfr
N.A.I.C.S.: 325412
Timothy Hadden *(Gen Mgr)*

Aspen Asia Company Limited **(1)**
Suite 3001 30th Floor Oxford House 979
Kings Road, Hong Kong, China (Hong
Kong)

Tel.: (852) 39026600
Pharmaceuticals Mfr
N.A.I.C.S.: 325414

Aspen Colombiana S.A.S. **(1)**
Carrera 69 No 19 A -51 Bodega 1 3 Piso,
Bogota, Colombia
Tel.: (57) 17567759
Pharmaceuticals Mfr
N.A.I.C.S.: 325412

Aspen France SAS **(1)**
21 avenue Edouard Belin, 92500, Rueil-
Malmaison, France
Tel.: (33) 139177000
Web Site: https://www.aspenpharma.fr
Healtcare Services
N.A.I.C.S.: 621610

Aspen Germany GmbH **(1)**
Balanstrasse 73 Building No 24 2nd floor,
81541, Munich, Germany
Tel.: (49) 8993083800
Web Site: https://www.aspenpharma.de
Emp.: 500
Pharmaceutical Product Mfr & Distr
N.A.I.C.S.: 325414

Aspen Global Incorporated **(1)**
GBS Plaza Cnr La Salette et Royal Roads,
Grand Baie, Mauritius
Tel.: (230) 2691111
Web Site: https://www.aspngl.com
Emp.: 200
Pharmaceuticals Distr
N.A.I.C.S.: 424210

Aspen Healthcare FZ LLC **(1)**
1404 14th Floor Tower A Business Central
Towers, PO Box 503049, Dubai Internet
City, Dubai, United Arab Emirates
Tel.: (971) 44393455
Web Site: https://www.aspenpharma.ae
Healtcare Services
N.A.I.C.S.: 621610
Daniel Vella Friggieri *(CEO)*

Aspen Healthcare Malta Ltd. **(1)**
The Corner Level 0 Triq Santa Margerita,
Siggiewi, Malta
Tel.: (356) 79849838
Pharmaceuticals Mfr
N.A.I.C.S.: 325412

**Aspen Healthcare Taiwan
Limited** **(1)**
Suite A 20F No 207 Section 2 Dun Hua
South Road, Taipei, 10602, Taiwan
Tel.: (886) 227303088
Pharmaceuticals Mfr
N.A.I.C.S.: 325412

**Aspen Medical Products Malaysia
Sdn. Bhd.** **(1)**
Unit 1302A Level 13A Uptown 1 1 Jalan
SS21/58 Damansara Uptown, 47400, Petal-
ing Jaya, Selangor, Malaysia
Tel.: (60) 377339795
Pharmaceutical Products Distr
N.A.I.C.S.: 424210

**Aspen Notre Dame de Bondeville
SAS** **(1)**
1 rue de l'abbaye, 76960, Notre-Dame-de-
Bondeville, France
Tel.: (33) 235143400
Web Site: https://www.aspenndb.com
Emp.: 720
Pharmaceuticals Product Mfr
N.A.I.C.S.: 325412

Aspen Pharma (Pty) Limited **(1)**
Ground Floor 34-36 Chandos Street, St
Leonards, Sydney, 2065, NSW, Australia
Tel.: (61) 284368300
Pharmaceuticals Product Mfr
N.A.I.C.S.: 325412

**Aspen Pharma - Industria Farmaceu-
tica Ltda** **(1)**
Av das Americas 3434 bloco 01 7 andar,
Barra da Tijuca, Rio de Janeiro, 29161-376,
Brazil
Tel.: (55) 2135446900
Web Site: https://www.aspenpharma.com.br
Pharmaceutical Preparation Mfr
N.A.I.C.S.: 325412

Aspen Pharma Ireland Limited **(1)**
3016 Lake Drive Citywest Business Campus, Dublin, 24, Ireland

Tel.: (353) 16308400
Pharmaceuticals Mfr
N.A.I.C.S.: 325412

Aspen Pharma Trading Limited **(1)**
3016 Lake Drive Citywest Business Cam-
pus, Dublin, Ireland
Tel.: (353) 1 630 8400
Web Site: https://www.aspenpharma.com
Sales, Marketing & Distribution of Branded
& Generic Pharmaceuticals
N.A.I.C.S.: 325412

**Aspen Pharmacare Australia Pty.
Ltd.** **(1)**
34-36 Chandos Street, Saint Leonards,
2065, NSW, Australia
Tel.: (61) 284368300
Web Site: https://www.aspenpharma.com.au
Pharmaceutical Products Mfr & Distr
N.A.I.C.S.: 325412

Aspen Pharmacare Canada Inc. **(1)**
8 - 1155 North Service Road West, Oak-
ville, L6M 3E3, ON, Canada
Web Site: https://www.aspenpharma.ca
Pharmaceutical Products Distr
N.A.I.C.S.: 424210

Aspen Pharmacare Espana S.L. **(1)**
Av Diagonal 512 Planta 1 interior oficina 4,
08006, Barcelona, Spain
Tel.: (34) 933658585
Web Site: https://www.aspenpharma.es
Pharmaceuticals Product Mfr
N.A.I.C.S.: 325414

**Aspen Pharmacare Nigeria
Limited** **(1)**
Plot 28 Ilupeju Bye-pass Ilupeju, Lagos,
Nigeria
Tel.: (234) 1295995
Web Site: https://www.aspennigeria.com
Pharmaceutical Product Mfr & Distr
N.A.I.C.S.: 325414

Aspen Pharmacare UK Limited **(1)**
One Kingdom Street 4th Floor Office 419-
420 Paddington Central, London, W2 6BD,
United Kingdom
Tel.: (44) 1628678130
Pharmaceuticals Mfr
N.A.I.C.S.: 325412

Aspen Philippines Incorporated **(1)**
Units 1001-1002 Trade and Financial Tower
Corner 7th and 32nd Streets, Bonifacio
Global City Metro Manila, Taguig, Philip-
pines
Tel.: (63) 277928000
Web Site: https://www.aspen.ph
Emp.: 100
Pharmaceutical Product Mfr & Distr
N.A.I.C.S.: 325414

**Beta Healthcare (Uganda)
Limited** **(1)**
Plot 12/14 3rd Street Industrial Area, PO
Box 7511, Kampala, Uganda
Tel.: (256) 414347754
Web Site: https://www.betacare.co.ug
Pharmaceuticals Mfr
N.A.I.C.S.: 325412

Beta Healthcare International Ltd **(1)**
Mogadishu Road off Lunga Lunga Road
Industrial Area, PO Box 42569, 00100, Nai-
robi, 00100, Kenya
Tel.: (254) 735992699
Web Site: https://www.betacare.co.ke
Pharmaceuticals, Nutraceuticals & Herbal
Products Preparations Mfr
N.A.I.C.S.: 325412
Sanjay Mohan Advani *(CEO)*

**Fine Chemicals Corporation (Pty)
Ltd** **(1)**
15 Hawkins Avenue Epping Industria, Ep-
ping, Cape Town, 7460, Western Cape,
South Africa
Tel.: (27) 215308100
Web Site: https://www.fcc.co.za
Sales Range: $125-149.9 Million
Emp.: 400
Pharmaceutical Preparation Mfr
N.A.I.C.S.: 325412

Kama Industries Limited **(1)**
Labone Nyaniba Estate Junction Ring Road
East, PO Box 5437, Labone, Accra, Ghana

Tel.: (233) 302782705
Web Site: https://www.aspenghana.com
Pharmaceutical Product Mfr & Distr
N.A.I.C.S.: 325414

Krok Brothers Holdings (Pty) Ltd **(1)**
69 Mellville Rd, Hyde Park, Johannesburg,
2196, Gauteng, South Africa
Tel.: (27) 114474785
Pharmaceutical Preparation Mfr
N.A.I.C.S.: 325412

Pharmacare Ltd **(1)**
Tel.: (27) 112393000
Web Site:
https://www.aspenpharmasa.co.za
Emp.: 500
Pharmaceutical Preparation Mfr
N.A.I.C.S.: 325412
Stephen Saad *(CEO)*

ASPENLEAF ENERGY LIM-ITED
Suite 2150 500 4th Avenue SW, Cal-
gary, T2P 2V6, AB, Canada
Tel.: (587) 390-6444   AB
Web Site:
http://www.aspenleafenergy.com
Oil & Gas Exploration & Production
N.A.I.C.S.: 211120
Bryan Gould *(CEO)*

ASPERMONT LIMITED
613-619 Wellington Street, Perth,
6000, WA, Australia
Tel.: (61) 862639100
Web Site:
https://www.aspermont.com
00W—(DEU)
Rev.: $12,299,648
Assets: $14,750,690
Liabilities: $9,751,300
Net Worth: $4,999,390
Earnings: $88,112
Emp.: 76
Fiscal Year-end: 09/30/21
Computing Infrastructure Providers,
Data Processing, Web Hosting & Re-
lated Services
N.A.I.C.S.: 518210
Ajit Patel *(Grp COO)*

Subsidiaries:

Aspermont Media **(1)**
1 Poultry, London, EC2R 8EJ, United King-
dom
Tel.: (44) 208 187 2330
Web Site: http://www.aspermontmedia.com
Sales Range: $25-49.9 Million
Emp.: 55
Subscription Based B2B Information Con-
tent Through Digital, Print, Conferencing &
Events Channels
N.A.I.C.S.: 561499

ASPHERE INNOVATIONS PUB-LIC COMPANY LIMITED
51 Major Tower Rama 9 - Ramkham-
haeng 18th Floor, Room 3-8 Rama 9
Road Hua Mak Bangkapi, Bangkok,
10240, Thailand
Tel.: (66) 27698888
Web Site: https://asphere.co
Year Founded: 2001
AS—(THA)
Rev.: $42,305,966
Assets: $49,063,421
Liabilities: $21,529,288
Net Worth: $27,534,133
Earnings: $5,828,656
Emp.: 246
Fiscal Year-end: 12/31/23
Software Games Development &
Publisher
N.A.I.C.S.: 334610
Kittipong Wallin *(Deputy Mng Dir-
Mobile Games)*

Subsidiaries:

AS Online Sdn. Bhd. **(1)**

Asphere Innovations Public Company Limited—(Continued)

Suite 21 01 Level 21 Menara IGB Mid Valley City Lingkaran Syed Putra, 59200, Kuala Lumpur, Malaysia
Tel.: (60) 3 2287 1503
Online Games Publishing Services
N.A.I.C.S.: 513210
Sylvia Kheng (Mgr-HR)

Asiasoft Online Pte. Ltd (1)
5 Tampines Central 1 04-01 Tampines Plaza, Singapore, 529541, Singapore
Tel.: (65) 6825 8500
Web Site: http://www.asiasoftsea.com
Online Games Publishing Services
N.A.I.C.S.: 513210

CIB Development Sdn. Bhd. (1)
Suite 6 05-6 07 6th Floor Menara Summit Persiaran Kewajipan USJ I, 47600, Subang Jaya, Malaysia
Tel.: (60) 3 8023 8315
Online Games Publishing Services
N.A.I.C.S.: 513210
Ku Foo Keong (CEO)

Funbox Company Limited (1)
No 1168/15 17 Lumpini Tower Rama 4 Road Tungmahamek, Sathorn, Bangkok, 10120, Thailand
Tel.: (66) 2343 1000
Web Site: http://www.funbox.co.th
Online Games Publishing Services
N.A.I.C.S.: 513210

Level Up! (Philippines), Inc. (1)
11/F Pacific Star Building Makati Avenue, Legaspi Village, Makati, 1200, Philippines
Tel.: (63) 27519611
Web Site: http://www.levelupgames.ph
Online Game Publisher
N.A.I.C.S.: 513210

PT. Asiasoft (1)
Grand Slipi Tower 9th Floor Unit G No 105 RT/RW 001/004, District Palmerah Sub District Palmerah, Jakarta, 11480, DKI Jakarta, Indonesia
Tel.: (62) 180660900
Online Games Publishing Services
N.A.I.C.S.: 513210
Suyudi Koeswanto (Mng Dir)

Playcybergames Company Limited (1)
No 9 UM Tower Room 9/244 24th Floor Ramkhamhaeng Road, Suanluang, Bangkok, 10250, Thailand
Tel.: (66) 2717 3515
Web Site: http://www.playcybergames.com
Online Games Publishing Services
N.A.I.C.S.: 513210

ASPIAL CORPORATION LIMITED
Aspial One 55 Ubi Avenue 3, Singapore, 408864, Singapore
Tel.: (65) 62814218
Web Site: https://www.aspial.com
Year Founded: 1970
A30—(SES)
Rev.: $454,440,657
Assets: $1,210,813,451
Liabilities: $829,728,849
Net Worth: $381,084,602
Earnings: ($12,951,602)
Emp.: 68
Fiscal Year-end: 12/31/23
Jewelry Retail, Property Development & Financial Services
N.A.I.C.S.: 458310

Subsidiaries:

AF Global Limited (1)
Aspial One 55 Ubi Avenue 3 04-01, Singapore, 408864, Singapore
Tel.: (65) 62662222
Web Site: http://www.afgl.com.sg
Rev.: $12,041,960
Assets: $236,016,484
Liabilities: $41,485,442
Net Worth: $194,531,042
Earnings: ($467,887)
Fiscal Year-end: 12/31/2022

Holding Company; Hospitality & Investment Services
N.A.I.C.S.: 551112
Yue Kai Chay (CEO)

Subsidiary (Non-US):

Cityview Apartments and Commercial Centre Limited (2)
12 Mac Dinh Chi Street, Da Kao Ward District 1, Ho Chi Minh City, Vietnam
Tel.: (84) 838221111
Web Site: http://www.cityview.com.vn
Apartment Building Rental Services
N.A.I.C.S.: 531110

Gateway Enterprise Company Limited (2)
Souphanouvang Avenue, PO Box 4793, Sikottabong District, Vientiane, Lao People's Democratic Republic
Tel.: (856) 21 250 888
Property Management Services
N.A.I.C.S.: 531312

L.C. (London) Ltd (2)
100 Cromewell Road, London, SW7 4ER, United Kingdom
Tel.: (44) 2073732222
Web Site: http://www.lcdgi.com
Home Management Services
N.A.I.C.S.: 561110

Subsidiary (Domestic):

L.C. Logistics Pte Ltd (2)
55 Ubi Avenue 1 #06-11 Ubi 55 Building, Singapore, 408935, Singapore
Tel.: (65) 62662222
Web Site: http://www.lcdgi.com
Real Estate Property Development Services
N.A.I.C.S.: 531210

LCD (Indochina) Pte Ltd (2)
55 Ubi Avenue 1 #06-11 Ubi 55 Building, Singapore, 408935, Singapore
Tel.: (65) 62662222
Web Site: http://www.lcdgi.com
Property Management Services
N.A.I.C.S.: 531311

LCD (Vietnam) Pte Ltd (2)
55 Ubi Avenue 1 #06-11 Ubi 55 Building, Singapore, 408935, Singapore
Tel.: (65) 62662222
Web Site: http://www.lcdgi.com
Investment Management Service
N.A.I.C.S.: 523940

LCD Property Management Pte Ltd (2)
55 Ubi Avenue 1 #06-11 Ubi 55 Building, Singapore, 408935, Singapore
Tel.: (65) 6266 2222
Web Site: http://www.lcdgi.com
Property Management Services
N.A.I.C.S.: 531311

ZONE X Leisure Pte Ltd (2)
Terminal 3 65 Airport Boulevard B2-23, Singapore, 819663, Singapore
Tel.: (65) 69081013
Web Site: http://www.zonex.com.sg
Gaming Centers Operation Services
N.A.I.C.S.: 713120

Aspial Lifestyle Limited (1)
Aspial One 55 Ubi Ave 3, Singapore, 408864, Singapore
Tel.: (65) 62814218
Web Site: https://www.aspiallifestyle.com
Investment Services
N.A.I.C.S.: 523999

Aspial-Lee Hwa Jewellery Pte. Ltd. (1)
55 Ubi Avenue 3 04-08 AspialOne Building, Singapore, 408864, Singapore
Tel.: (65) 6 382 1111
Web Site: https://www.leehwajewellery.com
Jewelry Retailer
N.A.I.C.S.: 458310
Mavis Toh (Bus Dir)

Goldheart Bullion Pte. Ltd. (1)
68 Orchard Road 01-59, Singapore, 238839, Singapore
Tel.: (65) 96617123
Web Site: http://www.goldheartbullion.com
Gold Retailer
N.A.I.C.S.: 458310

Sam Chua (Asst Mgr)

Lee Hwa Jewellery Pte. Ltd. (1)
55 Ubi Avenue 3 04-08 AspialOne Building, Singapore, 408864, Singapore
Tel.: (65) 31298168
Web Site: https://shop.leehwajewellery.com
Jewelry Retailer
N.A.I.C.S.: 458310

Niessing (Australia) Pty. Ltd. (1)
Shop G19 Strand Arcade 412-414 George St, Sydney, 2000, NSW, Australia
Tel.: (61) 280670683
Jewelry Mfr
N.A.I.C.S.: 339910

Niessing (Hong Kong) Limited (1)
1 Austin Rd W, Tsim Sha Tsui, Hong Kong, China (Hong Kong)
Tel.: (852) 26983588
Jewelry Mfr
N.A.I.C.S.: 339910

Niessing Manufaktur GmbH & Co. KG (1)
Butenwall 117, 48691, Vreden, Germany
Tel.: (49) 25643000
Web Site: https://www.niessing.com
Jewelry Mfr
N.A.I.C.S.: 339910
Matthias Erning (Acct Mgr-Mktg)

PHC Hotels Sdn. Bhd. (1)
No 171 Lebuh Noordin, 10300, Penang, Malaysia
Tel.: (60) 43758888
Web Site: http://www.phchotels.com.my
Hotel Services
N.A.I.C.S.: 721110

World Class Global Limited (1)
Aspial One 55 Ubi Avenue 3, Singapore, 408864, Singapore (100%)
Tel.: (65) 68500188
Web Site: http://www.wcg.com.sg
Rev.: $127,997,614
Assets: $490,528,923
Liabilities: $390,059,025
Net Worth: $100,469,898
Earnings: ($4,277,660)
Fiscal Year-end: 12/31/2020
Real Estate Brokerage Services
N.A.I.C.S.: 531210
Sheng Tiong Ng (CEO)

ASPIAL LIFESTYLE LIMITED
80 Raffles Place 32-01 UOB Plaza 1, Singapore, 048624, Singapore
Tel.: (65) 62252626
Web Site: https://www.aspiallifestyle.com
5UF—(CAT)
Rev.: $198,421,970
Assets: $389,973,714
Liabilities: $274,758,497
Net Worth: $115,215,217
Earnings: $22,187,813
Fiscal Year-end: 12/31/20
Pawnbroker & Jewelry Retailer
N.A.I.C.S.: 522291
Leok Cheng Ng (CEO)

Subsidiaries:

Maxi-Cash (Clementi) Pte. Ltd. (1)
442 Clementi Avenue 3 01-97, Singapore, 120442, Singapore
Tel.: (65) 67767387
Pawnshop Services
N.A.I.C.S.: 522299

Pit-Stop Credit (SG) Pte. Ltd. (1)
200 Jln Sultan 01-18E Textile Centre, Singapore, 199018, Singapore
Tel.: (65) 62971909
Web Site: https://pitstopcredit.com.sg
Loan Agency Services
N.A.I.C.S.: 522310

ASPINWALL & CO. LTD.,
P B No 560 Subramanian Road Willingdon Island, Kochi, 682003, India
Tel.: (91) 4842745400
Web Site: https://www.aspinwall.in
Year Founded: 1867

ASPINWALL—(NSE)
Rev.: $35,880,390
Assets: $32,725,875
Liabilities: $11,721,255
Net Worth: $21,004,620
Earnings: $2,084,355
Emp.: 747
Fiscal Year-end: 03/30/22
Logistics Consulting Services
N.A.I.C.S.: 541614
T. R. Radhakrishnan (CFO)

Subsidiaries:

Aspinwall & Co. Ltd., - Coffee Division (1)
P B No 901, Kulshekar, Mangalore, 575 005, India
Tel.: (91) 8242881300
Web Site: https://www.aspinwallcoffee.com
Coffee Mfr
N.A.I.C.S.: 311920

Aspinwall & Co. Ltd., - Logistics Division (1)
B Wing 403/404 Mahavir Icon Plot No 89/90 Sector 15, CBD Belapur East, Navi Mumbai, 400 614, India
Tel.: (91) 2265222761
Web Site: http://www.aspinwall.in
Freight Forwarding Services
N.A.I.C.S.: 488510

Aspinwall & Co. Ltd., - Natural Fibre Division (1)
181/7 A1 A2 Narasingapuram Mannur PO, Pollachi, 642 005, India
Tel.: (91) 4259277001
Web Site: https://www.aspinwall-coir.com
Timber Product Mfr
N.A.I.C.S.: 313110

Aspinwall & Co. Ltd., - Sandy Springs Branch (1)
8525 Dunwoody Pl, Sandy Springs, GA 30350
Tel.: (678) 832-6034
Timber Product Mfr
N.A.I.C.S.: 313110

ASPIRA PATHLAB & DIAGNOSTICS LIMITED
Flat No 2 R D Shah Bldg Shraddhanand Road Opp Ghatkopar, Railway Station Ghatkopar W, Mumbai, 400 086, Maharashtra, India
Tel.: (91) 2271975756
Web Site:
https://www.aspiradiagnostics.com
Year Founded: 1973
540788—(BOM)
Rev.: $2,680,396
Assets: $2,475,468
Liabilities: $729,702
Net Worth: $1,745,767
Earnings: $608,708
Emp.: 108
Fiscal Year-end: 03/31/22
Health Care Srvices
N.A.I.C.S.: 621511
Pankaj Shah (Mng Dir)

ASPIRANT GROUP, INC.
1001 ARK Hills Front Tower 2-23-1 Akasaka, Minato-ku, Tokyo, 107-0052, Japan
Tel.: (81) 3 3568 2572   JP
Web Site: http://www.aspirantgroup.jp
Year Founded: 2012
Equity Investment Firm
N.A.I.C.S.: 523999
Akitoshi Nakamura (CEO)

Subsidiaries:

FCM CO., LTD. (1)
3-8-36 Kamiji, Higashinari-ku, Osaka, 537-0003, Japan (100%)
Tel.: (81) 6 69751324
Web Site: http://www.fc-m.co.jp
Emp.: 319
Metal Plating Services
N.A.I.C.S.: 213114

Parking Management Organization, Ltd.　(1)
2F Shibuya Park Bldg 3-6-6 Shibuya, Shibuya-ku, Tokyo, 150-0002, Japan
Tel.: (81) 334062477
Web Site: http://www.pmo.co.jp
Parking Lot Management Services
N.A.I.C.S.: 812930
Masato Hiraishi (Pres)

Takara Chouun Co., Ltd　(1)
22-38 Maedomaricho, Nagasaki, 850-0075, Japan
Tel.: (81) 95 894 8701
Transportation Services
N.A.I.C.S.: 488999

ASPIRE GLOBAL INC.
14 Jianan Road Tangwei Fuyong Town, Baoan District, Shenzhen, Guangdong, China
Tel.: (86) 3027386680　　　Ky
Web Site:
　http://www.aspireglobal.com
Year Founded: 2020
ASPG—(NASDAQ)
Rev.: $79,025,838
Assets: $183,988,253
Liabilities: $122,901,928
Net Worth: $61,086,325
Earnings: $19,145,140
Emp.: 1,333
Fiscal Year-end: 06/30/20
Digital Marketing Services
N.A.I.C.S.: 541870
Tsachi Maimon (CEO)

ASPIRE MINING LIMITED
190 St Georges Tce Mezzanine Floor, Perth, 6000, WA, Australia
Tel.: (61) 733030827
Web Site:
　https://www.aspiremininglimited.com
AKM—(ASX)
Rev.: $1,364,366
Assets: $45,834,746
Liabilities: $137,555
Net Worth: $45,697,191
Earnings: ($373,831)
Emp.: 100
Fiscal Year-end: 06/30/23
Coal Mining & Exploration
N.A.I.C.S.: 212114
David Paull (Chm)

ASPO OYJ
Mikonkatu 13 A 7 Floor, Po Box 499, FI-00101, Helsinki, Finland
Tel.: (358) 95211
Web Site: https://www.aspo.com
Year Founded: 1929
ASPO—(HEL)
Rev.: $694,364,343
Assets: $448,856,033
Liabilities: $293,789,122
Net Worth: $155,066,911
Earnings: $22,325,707
Emp.: 945
Fiscal Year-end: 12/31/22
Holding Company
N.A.I.C.S.: 551112
Gustav Nyberg (Chm)

Subsidiaries:

AtoBatC Shipping AB　(1)
Hamntorget 2A, 27 139, Ystad, Sweden
Tel.: (46) 411558866
Web Site: https://www.atobatc.se
Fleet Logistics Services
N.A.I.C.S.: 488510
Frida Rowland (Dir)

AtoBatC Shipping Cyprus Ltd.　(1)
Lampousas 1, 1095, Nicosia, Cyprus
Tel.: (357) 95219933
Marine Transportation Services
N.A.I.C.S.: 561910

ESL Shipping Ltd　(1)
Lintulahdenkuja 10, 00500, Helsinki, Finland

Tel.: (358) 95211
Web Site: https://www.eslshipping.com
Marine Cargo Handling Services
N.A.I.C.S.: 488320
Taina Muona (Coord-Crewing)

FLLC Leipurin　(1)
Dzerzhinsky Avenue 104 room 1302, 220116, Minsk, Belarus
Tel.: (375) 173859780
Bread Mfr & Distr
N.A.I.C.S.: 311812

ILS Nordic AB　(1)
Kanalvagen 3A, 194 61, Upplands Vasby, Sweden
Tel.: (46) 839 1005
Web Site: https://www.ilsnordic.se
Lubricant Distr
N.A.I.C.S.: 424720

Kauko GmbH　(1)
Februaary-59, 22335, Hamburg, Germany
Tel.: (49) 16094618374
Web Site: https://www.kauko-shop.de
Monitor Mfr & Distr
N.A.I.C.S.: 334519

Kaukomarkkinat Oy　(1)
Lintulahdenkuja 10, FI 00500, Helsinki, Finland
Tel.: (358) 95211
Web Site: http://www.kaukomarkkinat.fi
Sales Range: $25-49.9 Million
Emp.: 779
Industrial Machinery Supplier
N.A.I.C.S.: 423830

Subsidiary (Non-US):

Kaukomarkkinat Shanghai Ltd.　(2)
Rm 2806-2807 Tower B City Center 100 Zun Yi Road, Shanghai, 200051, China
Tel.: (86) 21 62700640
Paper Idustry Machinery Mfr
N.A.I.C.S.: 333243

OOO Kauko Rus　(2)
5 of 4008 Torzhkovskaya Ul, Saint Petersburg, 197342, Russia
Tel.: (7) 8123244062
Business Support Services
N.A.I.C.S.: 561499

LLC Leipurin　(1)
Street Stetsenka 19 Building 68, Kiev, 04128, Ukraine
Bread Mfr & Distr
N.A.I.C.S.: 311812

LLC Telko Central Asia　(1)
st Dostyk Avenue 38 Business Center Ken Dala 7th floor Block B, 050010, Almaty, Kazakhstan
Tel.: (7) 7273131066
Plastic Raw Material Mfr & Distr
N.A.I.C.S.: 325211
Rianna Zuyeva (Sls Mgr)

Leipurin Oy　(1)
Tahkotie 1 E 2, 01530, Vantaa, Finland
Tel.: (358) 9 521 70
Web Site: http://www.leipurin.com
Sales Range: $125-149.9 Million
Emp.: 160
Food Products Machinery Distr
N.A.I.C.S.: 423440

Subsidiary (Non-US):

Leipurin Estonia AS　(2)
Aasa 1 Loo, Joelahtme, 74201, Harju, Estonia
Tel.: (372) 6 201 485
Web Site: http://www.leipurin.com
Food Packaging Machinery Distr
N.A.I.C.S.: 423830

OOO Leipurien Tukku　(2)
5 office 351, St Voronezh, 191119, Saint Petersburg, Russia
Tel.: (7) 8123252013
Web Site: http://www.leipurin.com
Food Packaging Machinery Distr
N.A.I.C.S.: 423830

SIA Leipurin　(2)
Noliktavu iela 5, Dreilini pagasts Ropazu novads, Stopini, 2130, Latvia
Tel.: (371) 67808080
Web Site: https://www.leipurin.com

Sales Range: $25-49.9 Million
Emp.: 27
Food Products Machinery Distr
N.A.I.C.S.: 423830

UAB Leipurin　(2)
Sandraugos g 9, 52102, Kaunas, Lithuania
Tel.: (370) 37409887
Web Site: http://www.leipurin.com
Food Processing Machinery Distr
N.A.I.C.S.: 423440

Leipurin PLC　(1)
Tahkotie 1 E 2, 01530, Vantaa, Finland
Tel.: (358) 952170
Web Site: https://www.leipurin.com
Bakery Product Mfr & Distr
N.A.I.C.S.: 311812

Norra Skeppnings Gruppen AB　(1)
Skeppgatan 28, 61330, Oxelosund, Sweden
Tel.: (46) 41 163 4383
Web Site: https://www.nordicshipping.com
Port Agency Services
N.A.I.C.S.: 488510
Emelie Johansson (Mgr)

TOO Leipurin　(1)
unit Baitursynov 85 office 323, 050012, Almaty, Kazakhstan
Tel.: (7) 7272935905
Bread Mfr & Distr
N.A.I.C.S.: 311812

Telko Ltd.　(1)
Keilaranta 17, 02150, Espoo, Finland
Tel.: (358) 95211
Web Site: https://www.telko.com
Plastic Product Distr
N.A.I.C.S.: 424610

Telko Oy　(1)
Keilaranta 17, 02150, Espoo, Finland
Tel.: (358) 9 5211
Web Site: http://www.telko.com
Sales Range: $250-299.9 Million
Emp.: 220
Industrial Chemicals & Plastics Distr
N.A.I.C.S.: 424690
Aki Ojanen (Chm)

Subsidiary (Non-US):

Aspokem International B.V.　(2)
Fred Roeskestraat 123, Amsterdam, 1076 EE, Noord-Holland, Netherlands
Tel.: (31) 205771177
Chemical Products Distr
N.A.I.C.S.: 424690

FLLC Telko　(2)
Dzerzhinskogo Pr 104 Office 1302, 220116, Minsk, Belarus
Tel.: (375) 172713347
Sales Range: $50-74.9 Million
Emp.: 1
Industrial Chemical & Plastic Products Distr
N.A.I.C.S.: 424690
Juris Avotins (Gen Mgr)

LLC Telko　(2)
Grygoriia Andriushchenko Srt 4-G, 01135, Kiev, Ukraine
Tel.: (380) 443775550
Sales Range: $25-49.9 Million
Emp.: 25
Chemical Products Distr
N.A.I.C.S.: 424690

Molub-Alloy AB　(2)
E A Rosengrens Gata 19, Vastra Frolunda, 421 31, Sweden
Tel.: (46) 31815990
Web Site: http://www.moluballoy.se
Emp.: 15
Industrial Lubricants Distr
N.A.I.C.S.: 811191

Subsidiary (Domestic):

Rauma Terminal Services Oy　(2)
Iso-Hakunintie, 26100, Rauma, Finland
Web Site: http://www.raumastevedoring.fi
Sales Range: $25-49.9 Million
Emp.: 7
Liquid Products Storage Services
N.A.I.C.S.: 493110

Subsidiary (Non-US):

Telko Denmark A/S　(2)

Frederiksgade 2 3 sal, 3400, Hillerod, Denmark
Tel.: (45) 48251266
Emp.: 5
Chemical & Plastic Products Distr
N.A.I.C.S.: 424690

Telko Estonia OU　(2)
Moisa 4, 13522, Tallinn, Estonia
Tel.: (372) 6548835
Web Site: http://www.aspokem.ee
Industrial Chemical Distr
N.A.I.C.S.: 424690

Telko Latvia SIA　(2)
Ciekurkalna 2 linija 75, Riga, 1026, Latvia
Tel.: (371) 67840530
Sales Range: $25-49.9 Million
Emp.: 9
Specialty Chemicals Distr
N.A.I.C.S.: 424690

Telko Lietuva UAB　(2)
Taikos pr 88A 606, Kaunas, 51183, Lithuania
Tel.: (370) 37 742673
Emp.: 10
Chemical & Plastio Products Distr
N.A.I.C.S.: 424690

Telko Norway AS　(2)
C J Hambrosplass 2C, 0164, Oslo, Norway
Tel.: (47) 2299 6293
Web Site: http://www.telko.com
Industrial Lubricant Distr
N.A.I.C.S.: 424720

Telko Shanghai Ltd.　(2)
Room 2804-05 Tower B City Center No 100 ZunYi Road, Shanghai, 200051, China
Tel.: (86) 2152660630
Web Site: http://www.telko.com
Emp.: 6
Chemical Products Distr
N.A.I.C.S.: 424690

Telko-Poland Sp. z o.o.　(2)
Taneczna 18, 02-829, Warsaw, Poland
Tel.: (48) 223301200
Web Site: https://www.telko.com
Emp.: 12
Food Products Mfr & Distr
N.A.I.C.S.: 311999

Wilfert Chemical Denmark A/S　(2)
Frederiksgade 2a, 3400, Hillerod, Frederiksborg, Denmark
Tel.: (45) 48251266
Chemical Products Mfr
N.A.I.C.S.: 325998

Wilfert Chemical Nordic A/S　(2)
Frederiksgade 2, 3400, Hillerod, Denmark
Tel.: (45) 48 25 12 66
Web Site: http://www.wilfert.dk
Plastic Material Distr
N.A.I.C.S.: 424610

Wilfert Chemical Sweden AB　(2)
Sorgardsvagen 29, 19144, Sollentuna, Sweden
Tel.: (46) 8 594 956 70
Chemical Products Distr
N.A.I.C.S.: 424690

Telko Romania SRL　(1)
Bd General Gheorghe Magheru 32-36 sc C et 2 ap 9 sector 1, 010337, Bucharest, Romania
Tel.: (40) 771432423
Plastic Raw Material Mfr & Distr
N.A.I.C.S.: 325211

Telko Solution LLC　(1)
str Shota Rustaveli 12 6th floor, Yakkasaray district, 100070, Tashkent, Uzbekistan
Tel.: (998) 781133585
Plastic Raw Material Mfr & Distr
N.A.I.C.S.: 325211
Kamola Bakieva (Accountant)

Telko Sweden AB　(1)
E A Rosengrensgata 19, 421 31, Vastra Frolunda, Sweden
Tel.: (46) 31815990
Plastic Raw Material Mfr & Distr
N.A.I.C.S.: 325211
Christina Hamsten (Sls Mgr)

Telko UAB　(1)

Aspo Oyj—(Continued)

Taikos pr 88A-606, 51183, Kaunas, Lithuania
Tel.: (370) 37742673
Plastic Raw Material Mfr & Distr
N.A.I.C.S.: 325211

Vulganus Oy (1)
Varikontie 2, 15550, Nastola, Finland
Tel.: (358) 387 3750
Web Site: https://www.vulganus.com
Cooling Equipment Mfr & Distr
N.A.I.C.S.: 333415
Jyri Johansson (Mng Dir)

ASPOCOMP GROUP OYJ
Keilaranta 1, FI-02150, Espoo, Finland
Tel.: (358) 207756860
Web Site:
https://www.aspocomp.com
ACG1V—(HEL)
Rev.: $42,212,389
Assets: $33,922,944
Liabilities: $10,392,834
Net Worth: $23,530,110
Earnings: $3,825,815
Emp.: 156
Fiscal Year-end: 12/31/22
Holding Company; Electronic Component Mfr
N.A.I.C.S.: 551112
Jari Isoaho (COO)

Subsidiaries:

Aspocomp (Thailand) Co., Ltd. (1)
684-685 Moo 11 Sukhapibal 8 Road, Si Racha, 20280, Bangkok, Chonburi, Thailand
Tel.: (66) 384805914
Electronic Components Mfr
N.A.I.C.S.: 334419

Aspocomp AB (1)
Veddestavagen 3, 175 62, Jarfalla, Sweden (100%)
Tel.: (46) 708974269
Web Site: http://www.aspocomp.com
Electronic Components Mfr
N.A.I.C.S.: 334419

Aspocomp Oy (1)
Tukijantie 11, Oulu, 90590, Finland (100%)
Tel.: (358) 959181
Sales Range: $25-49.9 Million
Emp.: 100
Electronic Components Mfr
N.A.I.C.S.: 334419
Mikko Montonen (CEO)

P.C.B. Center (Thailand) Co., Ltd. (1)
600 Sukhapibal 8 Road, Nongkham Sriracha, Chon Buri, Thailand (75%)
Tel.: (66) 38480591
Sales Range: $200-249.9 Million
Printed Circuit Board Mfr
N.A.I.C.S.: 334412

ASPREY
167 New Bond St, London, W1S 4AY, United Kingdom
Tel.: (44) 2074936767
Web Site: http://www.asprey.com
Sales Range: $25-49.9 Million
Emp.: 100
Jewelry, Leather Goods, Clothing & Accessories Mfr
N.A.I.C.S.: 339910

ASR NEDERLAND N.V.
Archimedeslaan 10, 3584 BA, Utrecht, Netherlands
Tel.: (31) 302579111   NI
Web Site: https://www.asrnl.com
Year Founded: 1720
ASRNL—(OTCIQ)
Rev.: $6,519,533,779
Assets: $70,730,628,103
Liabilities: $63,442,693,719
Net Worth: $7,287,934,384
Earnings: $782,430,391
Emp.: 2,188

Fiscal Year-end: 12/31/22
Holding Company; Insurance Products & Services
N.A.I.C.S.: 551112
Kick van der Pol (Chm-Supervisory Bd)

Subsidiaries:

AEGON Nederland N.V. (1)
AEGONplein 50, PO Box 202, Hague, 2591 TV, Netherlands
Tel.: (31) 703443210
Sales Range: $700-749.9 Million
Emp.: 2,000
Provider of Interest-Sharing Life Insurance & Other Insurance Products
N.A.I.C.S.: 524128

Subsidiary (Non-US):

AEGON Belgium (2)
Avenue du Port 86c b113, 1000, Brussels, Belgium
Tel.: (32) 80099123
Web Site: http://www.moneymaxx.be
Sales Range: $50-74.9 Million
Emp.: 10
Life Insurance Savings Products
N.A.I.C.S.: 524128

AEGON Levensverzekering N.V. (2)
Tel.: (31) 703443210
Sales Range: $75-99.9 Million
Emp.: 200
Provider of Life Insurance Products
N.A.I.C.S.: 524113

Subsidiary (Domestic):

AEGON Schadeverzekering N.V. (2)
Aegonplein 50, 2591 TV, Hague, Netherlands
Tel.: (31) 0703443210
Property & Casualty Insurance Products & Services
N.A.I.C.S.: 524126

ASR Real Estate B.V. (1)
Archimedeslaan 10, 3584 BA, Utrecht, Netherlands
Tel.: (31) 302572380
Web Site: http://www.en.asrrealestate.nl
Real Estate Services
N.A.I.C.S.: 531390
Dick Gort (CEO)

ASR Vermogensbeheer N.V. (1)
Archimedeslaan 10, 3584 BA, Utrecht, Netherlands
Tel.: (31) 625258257
Web Site:
http://www.asrvermogensbeheer.nl
Investment Banking Services
N.A.I.C.S.: 523150

ASR Verzekeringen N.V. (1)
Archimedeslaan 10, 3584 BA, Utrecht, Netherlands
Tel.: (31) 302579111
Web Site: http://www.asr.nl
Sales Range: $1-4.9 Billion
Emp.: 4,000
Life Insurance & Pension Product & Services
N.A.I.C.S.: 524113

Ardanta N.V. (1)
De Ruyterlaan 8, 7511 JH, Enschede, 7511JH, Netherlands
Tel.: (31) 534881122
Web Site: https://www.ardanta.nl
Sales Range: $75-99.9 Million
Emp.: 60
Funeral Insurance Products & Services
N.A.I.C.S.: 524128

Bedrijfsartsengroep Holding B.V. (1)
Abe Lenstra Boulevard 44, 8448 JB, Heerenveen, Netherlands
Tel.: (31) 882332330
Web Site: https://www.bedrijfsartsengroep.nl
Health Care Srvices
N.A.I.C.S.: 621610

Corins B.V. (1)
19 Gatwick Street, 1043 GL, Amsterdam, Netherlands
Tel.: (31) 203017770

Web Site:
https://www.corinsamsterdam.com
Insurance Services
N.A.I.C.S.: 524210

De Amersfoortse Verzekeringen N.V. (1)
Stadsring 15, 3811 HM, Amersfoort, Netherlands
Tel.: (31) 334642911
Web Site: http://www.amersfoortse.nl
Sales Range: $500-549.9 Million
Emp.: 700
Income & Disability Insurance; Pension Products & Services
N.A.I.C.S.: 524128

Dutch ID B.V. (1)
Beveland 2, 1948 RA, Beverwijk, Netherlands
Tel.: (31) 251261222
Web Site: https://dutch-id.nl
E-bike Mfr
N.A.I.C.S.: 336991

Falcon Leven N.V. (1)
Capellalaan 115, 2132 JM, Hoofddorp, Netherlands (100%)
Tel.: (31) 235648300
Web Site: http://www.falconleven.nl
Sales Range: $100-124.9 Million
Emp.: 125
Flexible & Term Life Insurance Products & Services
N.A.I.C.S.: 524113

Felison Assuradeuren B.V. (1)
Zadelmakerstraat 140, 1991 JE, Velserbroek, Netherlands
Tel.: (31) 235201500
Web Site: https://www.felison.nl
Insurance Services
N.A.I.C.S.: 524210

PoliService B.V. (1)
PO Box 369, 3700AJ, Zeist, Netherlands
Tel.: (31) 306981818
Web Site: https://poliservice.nl
Emp.: 45
Financial Services
N.A.I.C.S.: 523999

Supergarant Verzekeringen B.V. (1)
Veursestraatweg 98, 2265 CG, Leidschendam, Netherlands
Tel.: (31) 703204680
Web Site: https://www.supergarant.nl
Insurance Services
N.A.I.C.S.: 524210

Van Kampen Geld B.V. (1)
Boedijnhof 153, 1628 SH, Hoorn, Netherlands
Tel.: (31) 229287888
Web Site: https://vkg.nl
Financial Advisory Services
N.A.I.C.S.: 523940

Van Kampen Groep Holding B.V. (1)
Boedijnhof 153, 1628 SH, Hoorn, Netherlands
Tel.: (31) 229287888
Web Site: https://vkg.nl
Financial Investment Advice Services
N.A.I.C.S.: 523940

ASRA MINERALS LIMITED
104 Colin Street, West Perth, 6005, WA, Australia
Tel.: (61) 894208208   AU
Web Site:
https://asraminerals.com.au
ASR—(ASX)
Rev.: $201,700
Assets: $12,352,774
Liabilities: $2,187,630
Net Worth: $10,165,144
Earnings: ($14,522,157)
Fiscal Year-end: 12/31/23
Tin & Precious Minerals Exploration & Mining Services
N.A.I.C.S.: 212290
Paul Summers (Chm)

ASROCK INC.
2F No 37 Sec 2 Jhongyang S Rd, Beitou District, Taipei, 112, Taiwan

Tel.: (886) 228965588
Web Site: https://www.asrock.com.tw
Year Founded: 2002
3515—(TAI)
Rev.: $621,074,734
Assets: $470,104,433
Liabilities: $179,606,913
Net Worth: $290,497,520
Earnings: $31,968,147
Emp.: 15
Fiscal Year-end: 12/31/23
Motherboard Mfr
N.A.I.C.S.: 334118
Hsu-Tien Tung (Chm)

Subsidiaries:

ASJade Technology Inc. (1)
21F No 185 Sec 2 Xinhai Rd, Da'an Dist, Taipei, Taiwan
Tel.: (886) 227303888
Web Site: https://www.asjadetech.com
Software Development Services
N.A.I.C.S.: 541511

ASRock America, Inc. (1)
13848 Magnolia Ave, Chino, CA 91710
Tel.: (909) 590-8308
Computer Parts Distr
N.A.I.C.S.: 423430

ASRock Europe B.V. (1)
Bijsterhuizen 11-11, 6546 AR, Nijmegen, Netherlands
Tel.: (31) 243454433
Computer Parts Distr
N.A.I.C.S.: 423430

ASRR CAPITAL LTD.
Sonol Tower 9th Floor 52 Menahem Begin Rd, Tel Aviv, 6713701, Israel
Tel.: (972) 37763555
Web Site: http://www.asrr.co.il
Year Founded: 1984
Sales Range: Less than $1 Million
Real Estate Investment Services
N.A.I.C.S.: 523999

ASSA ABLOY AB
Klarabergsviadukten 90, PO Box 70340, SE-107 23, Stockholm, Sweden
Tel.: (46) 850648500   SE
Web Site: https://www.assaabloy.com
Year Founded: 1994
ASSA—(OMX)
Rev.: $13,969,067,287
Assets: $19,492,028,844
Liabilities: $10,394,405,244
Net Worth: $9,097,623,599
Earnings: $1,353,961,943
Emp.: 61,000
Fiscal Year-end: 12/31/23
Door Opening Solution Products Mfr
N.A.I.C.S.: 561621
Lucas Boselli (Exec VP & Head-Americas Div)

Subsidiaries:

A/S Ruko (1)
Marielundvej 20, PO Box 505, 2730, Herlev, Denmark
Tel.: (45) 44544454
Web Site: http://www.ruko.dk
Sales Range: $75-99.9 Million
Emp.: 150
Locks & Security Products & Services
N.A.I.C.S.: 332510
Kim Hansen (Mgr-Fin)

ASSA ABLOY (SA) (Pty) Ltd (1)
176 Progress Road Technikon, Roodepoort, Johannesburg, 1724, South Africa
Tel.: (27) 11 76 15 000
Web Site: http://www.assaabloy.com
Sales Range: $100-124.9 Million
Emp.: 300
Electronic Door Lock Mfr
N.A.I.C.S.: 334419

ASSA ABLOY (Switzerland) Ltd. (1)
Untere Schwandenstrasse 22, 8805, Richterswil, Switzerland

Tel.: (41) 44 787 3434
Web Site:
   http://www.assaabloyopeningsolutions.ch
Hardware Mfr
N.A.I.C.S.: 332510
Christian Kaelin *(CFO & Dir-HR & IT)*

ASSA ABLOY (Zhongshan) Security Technology Company Limited (1)
33-35 Chrysanthemum Road East, Zhongshan, 528415, Guangdong, China
Tel.: (86) 760 2210 2326
Web Site: http://www.assaabloy.com
Electric Equipment Mfr
N.A.I.C.S.: 335999

ASSA ABLOY Asia Holding AB (1)
Klarabergsviadukten 90, PO Box 70340, 111 64, Stockholm, Sweden
Tel.: (46) 850648500
Emp.: 90
Investment Management Service
N.A.I.C.S.: 523940
Johan Molin *(Pres & CEO)*

ASSA ABLOY Asia Pacific Ltd (1)
1901 19 Floor Tower 3 China Hong Kong City 33 Canton Road, Kowloon, China (Hong Kong)
Tel.: (852) 22607234
Web Site:
   http://www.assaabloyasiapacific.com
Electro Mechanical Product Mfr
N.A.I.C.S.: 334419
Magnus Kagevik *(Gen Mgr)*

ASSA ABLOY Australia Pacific Pty Ltd (1)
235 Huntingdale Road, Oakleigh, 3166, VIC, Australia
Tel.: (61) 385743888
Sales Range: $100-124.9 Million
Emp.: 320
Hardware Mfr
N.A.I.C.S.: 332510
David Oliver *(Gen Mgr)*

ASSA ABLOY Australia Pty Ltd (1)
235 Huntingdale Road, Oakleigh, 3166, VIC, Australia
Tel.: (61) 3 8574 3888
Web Site:
   http://www.assaabloyopenings.com.au
Emp.: 400
Electronic Safety System Mfr
N.A.I.C.S.: 334290

ASSA ABLOY Austria GmbH (1)
Hutteldorferstrasse 216 c, 1140, Vienna, Austria
Tel.: (43) 12125111
Web Site:
   http://www.assaabloyopeningsolutions.at
Sales Range: $25-49.9 Million
Door Locks Mfr
N.A.I.C.S.: 332510

ASSA ABLOY Baltic AS (1)
Priisle 10, 13914, Tallinn, Estonia
Tel.: (372) 6 559 101
Sales Range: $25-49.9 Million
Emp.: 15
Safety Equipment Mfr
N.A.I.C.S.: 332510

ASSA ABLOY Chile Ltda (1)
Los Vientos 19930 Module F Pudahuel, Santiago, Chile
Tel.: (56) 2 560 9200
Web Site: http://assaabloy.cl
Door Handle & Lock Mfr
N.A.I.C.S.: 332510

ASSA ABLOY Colombia S.A.S. (1)
Calle 12 No 32 39, Bogota, Colombia
Tel.: (57) 3183659422
Web Site: https://www.assaabloy.com.co
Security System Services
N.A.I.C.S.: 561621

ASSA ABLOY Danmark A/S (1)
Marielundvej 20, 2730, Herlev, Denmark
Tel.: (45) 44537080
Web Site: http://www.assaabloy.dk
Hardware Mfr
N.A.I.C.S.: 332510

ASSA ABLOY Deutschland GmbH (1)
Attilastrasse 61-67, 12105, Berlin, Germany

Tel.: (49) 3081062648
Web Site: http://www.assaabloy.com
Emp.: 480
Lock Mfr
N.A.I.C.S.: 332510

ASSA ABLOY ES Production s.r.o (1)
D5 Logistics Park, 349 01, Ostrov u Stribra, Czech Republic
Tel.: (420) 374 634 111
Web Site: http://www.assaabloy.com
Sales Range: $50-74.9 Million
Emp.: 150
Hardware Mfr
N.A.I.C.S.: 332510

ASSA ABLOY East Africa Ltd. (1)
Dunga Close Off Dunga Road-Industrial Area, PO Box 42837, Off Dunga Road-Industrial Area, 00100, Nairobi, Kenya
Tel.: (254) 206531569
Web Site: https://www.assaabloy.com
Security Locks Distr
N.A.I.C.S.: 423710

ASSA ABLOY Entrance Systems AB (1)
Lodjursgatan 10, PO Box 353, 26123, Landskrona, Sweden (100%)
Tel.: (46) 10 47 47 000
Web Site: http://www.assaabloyentrance.se
Automated Door Systems Mfr & Distr
N.A.I.C.S.: 561621
Tzachi Wiesenfeld *(Exec VP & Head-EMEA)*

Subsidiary (US):

4Front Engineered Solutions, Inc. (2)
1612 Hutton Dr Ste 140, Carrollton, TX 75006
Tel.: (972) 466-0707
Web Site: http://www.4frontes.com
Sales Range: $150-199.9 Million
Warehouse & Loading Dock Equipment Mfr
N.A.I.C.S.: 333248
Keith Moore *(Pres)*

Branch (Domestic):

4Front Engineered Solutions - Muskego (3)
W 183 S 8253 Racine Ave, Muskego, WI 53150-8125
Tel.: (262) 679-6200
Sales Range: $25-49.9 Million
Emp.: 65
Seals & Shelters Mfr for Shipping & Receiving Docks
N.A.I.C.S.: 332311

Subsidiary (Domestic):

APS Resources (3)
6219 W Eastwood Ct, Mequon, WI 53092-4479 (100%)
Tel.: (262) 518-1000
Web Site: http://apsresource.com
Sales Range: $25-49.9 Million
Emp.: 15
Material Handling Industry Aftermarket Solutions & Services
N.A.I.C.S.: 811310

Branch (Non-US):

Dock Products Canada (3)
600 Orwell Street Unit 6, Mississauga, L5A 3R9, ON, Canada (100%)
Tel.: (905) 276-0565
Web Site: http://www.dockproducts.com
Sales Range: $25-49.9 Million
Emp.: 25
Loading Dock Equipment Mfr
N.A.I.C.S.: 333248
Melissa Garcia *(Mgr-HR)*

Subsidiary (Domestic):

TKO Doors (3)
N56 W24701 Corporate Cir, Sussex, WI 53089-9907 (100%)
Tel.: (262) 820-1217
Web Site: http://www.tkodoors.com
Sales Range: $25-49.9 Million
Emp.: 25
Mfr of Doors for Loading Docks
N.A.I.C.S.: 332321

Subsidiary (Non-US):

ASSA ABLOY Entrance Systems (Suzhou) Co., Ltd. (2)
Unit 1 No 29 Huahong Street, Suzhou Industrial Park, Suzhou, 215126, Jiangsu, China
Tel.: (86) 51288180120
Web Site: http://www.bessam.com
Sales Range: $25-49.9 Million
Emp.: 80
Furniture Mfr
N.A.I.C.S.: 332510

ASSA ABLOY Entrance Systems Denmark A/S (2)
Lupinvej 12, 9500, Hobro, Denmark (100%)
Tel.: (45) 70228280
Web Site: http://www.assaabloyentrance.dk
Sales Range: $25-49.9 Million
Emp.: 30
Garage Doors, Wall Systems, Dock Loading Systems, Storage Cabinets & Lockers Mfr & Whlsr
N.A.I.C.S.: 321911

ASSA ABLOY Entrance Systems Finland Oy (2)
Bullfinches 9, 01730, Vantaa, Finland
Tel.: (358) 10 386 9000
Web Site: http://www.assaabloyentrance.fi
Emp.: 50
Door Mfr
N.A.I.C.S.: 332321

ASSA ABLOY Entrance Systems France SAS (2)
1 Rue Des Violettes, FR-94864, Bonneuil-sur-Marne, France
Tel.: (33) 1 43 77 55 66
Door Locks Mfr
N.A.I.C.S.: 332510

ASSA ABLOY Entrance Systems GmbH (2)
Concorde Business Park 2 / F / 1-4, 2320, Vienna, Austria
Tel.: (43) 19145537
Web Site: http://www.besam.at
Sales Range: $25-49.9 Million
Emp.: 50
Security Lock Mfr
N.A.I.C.S.: 332722

ASSA ABLOY Entrance Systems Italy S.p.A. (2)
Via Monzoro 142, 20010, Milan, Italy
Tel.: (39) 02 936 11 311
Door Locks Mfr
N.A.I.C.S.: 332510

ASSA ABLOY Entrance Systems Italy Srl (2)
via Guido Rossa 5, 24048, Carugate, MI, Italy
Tel.: (39) 029215681
Web Site: http://www.assaabloyentrance.it
Industrial & Garage Doors, Wall Systems, Dock Loading Systems, Storage Cabinets & Lockers Mfr
N.A.I.C.S.: 321911

ASSA ABLOY Entrance Systems Kft. (2)
Nagytetenyi ut 112, 1222, Budapest, Hungary
Tel.: (36) 14247274
Web Site: http://www.assaabloyentrance.hu
Door Automation Systems Mfr
N.A.I.C.S.: 332321

ASSA ABLOY Entrance Systems NV (2)
Gontrode Heirweg 192, 9090, Melle, Belgium (100%)
Tel.: (32) 28000303
Web Site: http://www.assaabloyentrance.be
Sales Range: $25-49.9 Million
Emp.: 150
Industrial & Garage Doors, Wall Systems, Dock Loading Systems, Storage Cabinets & Lockers Mfr & Whslr
N.A.I.C.S.: 321911

ASSA ABLOY Entrance Systems Norway AS (2)
Stromsveien 179, PO Box 96, Alnabru, 0614, Oslo, Norway

Tel.: (47) 22655450
Web Site: http://www.assaabloyentrance.no
Emp.: 20
Marketing & Sales of Industrial & Garage Doors
N.A.I.C.S.: 444180
Preben Hoegh *(CFO)*

Subsidiary (Domestic):

ASSA ABLOY Entrance Systems Sweden AB (2)
Redegatan 7, Box 5087, Vastra Frolunda, 426 05, Gothenburg, Sweden (100%)
Tel.: (46) 10 47 47 120
Web Site: http://www.crawfordsolution.com
Sales Range: $25-49.9 Million
Emp.: 75
Industrial & Garage Doors, Wall Systems, Dock Loading Systems, Storage Cabinets & Lockers Mfr & Whslr
N.A.I.C.S.: 332321

Subsidiary (Non-US):

ASSA ABLOY Entrance Systems, spol. s r.o. (2)
U Blazenky 2155/18, 150 00, Prague, Czech Republic
Tel.: (420) 286 001 560
Web Site: http://www.assaabloyentrance.cz
Door Locks Mfr
N.A.I.C.S.: 332510

ASSA ABLOY Mercor Doors sp. z o.o. (2)
ul Arkonska 6 building A2, 80 387, Gdansk, Poland
Tel.: (48) 601692914
Web Site: http://www.mercordoors.com.pl
Fire Prevention Doors Mfr
N.A.I.C.S.: 332321

Subsidiary (Domestic):

BEM Sp. z o.o. (3)
Miroslaw 26A K Plocka, 09 472, Slupno, Plock, Poland
Tel.: (48) 242622738
Web Site: http://www.bem.plo.pl
Sales Range: $75-99.9 Million
Emp.: 450
Fire Prevention Door & Window Mfr
N.A.I.C.S.: 332321

Subsidiary (Non-US):

Hasil A.S. (3)
Gen Sochora Street 6176 6a, 708 00, Ostrava, Czech Republic
Tel.: (420) 5969491112
Web Site: http://www.hasil.cz
Sales Range: $25-49.9 Million
Emp.: 150
Fire Resistant Doors & Shutters Mfr
N.A.I.C.S.: 332321
Jan Koci *(Mng Dir)*

Subsidiary (Non-US):

Hasil s.r.o. (4)
Tomasikova 19, Bratislava, 821 02, Slovakia
Tel.: (421) 248269401
Web Site: http://www.hasil.sk
Emp.: 18
Fire Resistant Doors & Shutters Mfr
N.A.I.C.S.: 332321
Roziar Pavol *(Dir-Sls)*

Subsidiary (US):

Adams Rite Manufacturing Co. (2)
260 Santa Fe St, Pomona, CA 91767
Tel.: (909) 632-2300
Web Site: http://www.adamsrite.com
Sales Range: $25-49.9 Million
Emp.: 187
Mfr of Doors & Door Hardware including Maximum Security Locks
N.A.I.C.S.: 332510

Holding (Non-US):

Adams Rite Europe Limited (3)
School Street, Willenhall, WV13 3PW, West Midlands, United Kingdom (100%)
Tel.: (44) 8452232124
Web Site: http://www.adamsrite.co.uk
Sales Range: $25-49.9 Million
Emp.: 40
Distr of Security Door & Window Hardware

ASSA ABLOY AB—(Continued)
N.A.I.C.S.: 332510

Subsidiary (US):

Albany Door Systems, Inc. (2)
975 A Old Norcross Rd, Lawrenceville, GA 30045
Tel.: (770) 338-5000
Web Site: http://www.albanydoors.com
Sales Range: $25-49.9 Million
Emp.: 80
Mfr of Fast-Acting Roll Up Doors
N.A.I.C.S.: 332321
Norm Sugate *(Mgr-Ops)*

Amarr Company (2)
165 Carriage Ct, Winston Salem, NC 27015
Tel.: (336) 744-5100
Web Site: http://www.amarr.com
Sales Range: $50-74.9 Million
Garage Door Mfr
N.A.I.C.S.: 321911
Richard A. Brenner *(Vice Chm)*

Subsidiary (Domestic):

Fimbel Door Company (3)
PO Box 96, Whitehouse Station, NJ 08888
Tel.: (908) 534-1732
Web Site: http://www.fimbelads.com
Sales Range: $10-24.9 Million
Emp.: 100
Commercial & Residential Garage Doors Mfr
N.A.I.C.S.: 332321

Subsidiary (Non-US):

Assa Abloy Entrance Systems Australia Pty Ltd (2)
Unit 4 18-22 Winterton Road, Clayton, 3168, VIC, Australia
Tel.: (61) 385404300
Automatic Door Mfr
N.A.I.C.S.: 332321

Assa Abloy Entrance Systems UK & Ireland
Ground Floor 14 Herbert St, Dublin, 2, Ireland
Tel.: (353) 4690 76747
Web Site:
http://www.assaabloyentrance.co.uk
Automatic Entrances, Overhead Sectional Doors Mfr & Maintenance
N.A.I.C.S.: 321911

Besam (Manufacturing) Pte. Ltd. (2)
33 Ubi Ave 3 No 03-52 Vertex, Singapore, 408868, Singapore
Tel.: (65) 67456228
Web Site: http://www.besam.com
Sales Range: $25-49.9 Million
Emp.: 26
Mfr of Door Automation Systems
N.A.I.C.S.: 332321
Kenneth Ng *(Gen Mgr)*

Besam Automatic Door Systems Trading Co. Ltd. (2)
Suite 1903 Modern Comm Commercial Tower 218 Hengfeng Road, Shanghai, 200070, China
Tel.: (86) 21 5128 8909
Web Site: http://www.besam.com
Mfr of Door Automation Systems
N.A.I.C.S.: 335999

Besam Belgie N.V. (2)
Centrum Zuid 3042, Houthalen, 3530, Limburg, Belgium
Tel.: (32) 11609500
Web Site: http://www.besam.be
Sales Range: $75-99.9 Million
Emp.: 80
Mfr of Door Automation Systems
N.A.I.C.S.: 332321

Subsidiary (US):

Besam Entrance Solutions Inc (2)
92 N Main St Bldg 19 Unit A, Windsor, NJ 08561
Tel.: (609) 443-5800
Web Site: http://www.besam.com
Sales Range: $50-74.9 Million
Emp.: 150
Mfr of Door Automation Systems
N.A.I.C.S.: 335999

Karen Maslow *(Mgr-Mktg)*

Subsidiary (Non-US):

Besam GmbH (2)
Lagerstrasse 45, Dieburg, 64807, Germany (100%)
Tel.: (49) 60712080
Web Site: http://www.besam.de
Sales Range: $25-49.9 Million
Emp.: 50
Mfr of Door Automation Systems
N.A.I.C.S.: 332321
Peter M. Fprick *(Gen Mgr)*

Besam Iberica SA (2)
Sepulveda 7A, 28108, Madrid, Spain (100%)
Tel.: (34) 916574860
Web Site: http://www.besam.es
Sales Range: $10-24.9 Million
Emp.: 100
Mfr of Door Automation Systems
N.A.I.C.S.: 332321

Besam Limited (2)
Washington House Brooklands Close, Sunbury-on-Thames, TW16 7EQ, Middlesex, United Kingdom (100%)
Tel.: (44) 1932765888
Web Site: http://www.besam.com
Sales Range: $25-49.9 Million
Emp.: 155
Mfr of Door Automation Systems
N.A.I.C.S.: 332321

Besam Maschinenhandels GmbH (2)
2320 Sschwrzht, 1140, Vienna, Austria (100%)
Tel.: (43) 019145537
Web Site: http://www.besam.at
Sales Range: $25-49.9 Million
Emp.: 100
Mfr of Door Automation Systems
N.A.I.C.S.: 332321
Clamia Elizabeth *(Gen Mgr)*

Besam Nederland BV (2)
Horapark 6, Postbus 8155, NL-6710, Ede, Netherlands
Tel.: (31) 318698969
Web Site: http://www.besam.com
Sales Range: $75-99.9 Million
Emp.: 200
Door Mfr
N.A.I.C.S.: 332321

Besam Oy (2)
Agrnonitti 2, 00790, Helsinki, Finland (100%)
Tel.: (358) 972885400
Web Site: http://www.besam.fi
Sales Range: $1-9.9 Million
Emp.: 5
Mfr of Door Automation Systems
N.A.I.C.S.: 332321

Besam Polska Sp. z.o.o. (2)
ul J Olbrachta 94, Warsaw, 01 102, Poland (100%)
Tel.: (48) 223318680
Web Site: http://www.besam.pl
Sales Range: $1-9.9 Million
Emp.: 26
Mfr of Door Automation Systems
N.A.I.C.S.: 332321

Besam S.p.A. (2)
Via Monzoro 142, IT 20010, Milan, Italy (100%)
Tel.: (39) 0293611311
Web Site: http://www.besam.com
Sales Range: $1-9.9 Million
Emp.: 24
Mfr of Door Automation Systems
N.A.I.C.S.: 332321

Besam SA (2)
10 Rond Pt Du General De Gaulle, 94864, Bonneuil, France (100%)
Tel.: (33) 143775566
Web Site: http://www.besam.fr
Sales Range: $25-49.9 Million
Emp.: 70
Mfr of Door Automation Systems
N.A.I.C.S.: 332321
Juan Vargues *(Pres & CEO)*

Besam Spol.s.r.o. (2)

U Blazenky 2155/18, 197.00, Prague, Czech Republic (100%)
Tel.: (420) 286001560
Web Site: http://www.besam.cz
Sales Range: $25-49.9 Million
Emp.: 16
Mfr of Door Automation Systems
N.A.I.C.S.: 332321

Subsidiary (US):

Besam US Inc. (2)
1900 Airport Rd, Monroe, NC 28110
Tel.: (704) 290-5520
Web Site: http://www.besam-usa.com
Sales Range: $350-399.9 Million
Automatic Door Mfr
N.A.I.C.S.: 332321
Keren Maslow *(VP-Mktg)*

Subsidiary (Domestic):

Cardo AB (2)
Roskildevegen 1, PO Box 486, SE 201 24, Malmo, Sweden
Tel.: (46) 40350400
Web Site: http://www.cardo.se
Sales Range: $1-4.9 Billion
Industrial Doors, Loading Dock Equipment & Braking Systems Mfr
N.A.I.C.S.: 332321

Subsidiary (Non-US):

Cardo Door International AG (3)
Industriestrasse 11, CH 6343, Rotkreuz, Switzerland
Tel.: (41) 417905901
Marketer & Retailer of Industrial & Garage Doors
N.A.I.C.S.: 444180

Cardo Door Production B.V. (3)
Postbus 22, 3925 ZG, Scherpenzeel, Netherlands
Tel.: (31) 725750700
Sales Range: $125-149.9 Million
Emp.: 300
Automatic Door Mfr
N.A.I.C.S.: 321911
Safet Radoncic *(Plant Mgr)*

Cardo Door Production GmbH (3)
Normstahlstrasse 1-3, 85366, Moosburg, Germany
Tel.: (49) 8761 6830
Door Locks Mfr
N.A.I.C.S.: 332510

Subsidiary (Domestic):

Crawford International AB (3)
Roskildevegen 1, PO Box 171, SE 201 21, Malmo, Sweden (100%)
Tel.: (46) 10 47 47 06
Web Site: http://www.cardo.se
Sales Range: $400-449.9 Million
Emp.: 100
Industrial & Garage Doors, Dock Loading Systems, Rapid Action Rolling Doors, Door-Operating Equipment with Attendant Automation Mfr
N.A.I.C.S.: 321911

Subsidiary (Non-US):

ASSA ABLOY Entrance Systems (Porto) (4)
Rua do Xisto 670 - Fraction D and E, Maia, 4470-389, Portugal
Tel.: (351) 229871260
Web Site: http://www.assaabloyentrance.pt
Industrial & Garage Doors, Wall Systems, Dock Loading Systems, Storage Cabinets & Lockers Mfr & Whslr
N.A.I.C.S.: 332321

Alsta Nassau BV (4)
Bredaseweg 51, 4844 CK, Drimmelen, Netherlands (100%)
Tel.: (31) 332776100
Web Site: http://www.alsta-nassau.nl
Industrial Door Mfr
N.A.I.C.S.: 321911

Subsidiary (Domestic):

Cardo Door Production AB (4)
Gamla Flygplatsvagen 2 4, SE 423 21, Torslanda, Sweden (100%)
Tel.: (46) 31566000

Web Site: http://www.assaabloy.com
Sales Range: $25-49.9 Million
Mfr of Industrial & Garage Doors, Wall Systems, Dock Loading Systems, Storage Cabinets & Lockers
N.A.I.C.S.: 321911

Subsidiary (Non-US):

Clever-Crawford SA (4)
1/5 Rue Des Cevennes, I Ge la, 91090, Lisses, Petite Montangne, France
Tel.: (33) 160868900
Web Site: http://www.crawfordsolutions.fr
Sales Range: $25-49.9 Million
Emp.: 60
N.A.I.C.S.: 321911
Michon Yammick *(Pres)*

Crawford Combursa S.L.U. (4)
Marie Curie 17-19 Edificio Autocampo II Oficinas B5-B7, 28529, Rivas-Vaciamadrid, Madrid, Spain
Tel.: (34) 91 660 10 70
Door Locks Mfr
N.A.I.C.S.: 332510

Crawford Deur B.V. (4)
kelvinstraat 9 1704RS, PO Box 159, 1700 AD, Heerhugowaard, Netherlands
Tel.: (31) 725752125
Web Site: http://www.crawford.nl
Sales Range: $75-99.9 Million
Industrial & Garage Doors, Wall Systems, Dock Loading Systems, Storage Cabinets & Lockers Mfr
N.A.I.C.S.: 321911

Crawford Door (Kunshan) Co., Ltd. (4)
Block L 5th Floor East Hope Plaza No 1777 Shiji Avenue, Pu Dong New District, Shanghai, 200 122, China
Tel.: (86) 21 2025 1196
Web Site: http://www.crawfordsolutions.cn
Sales Range: $25-49.9 Million
Emp.: 100
Industrial & Garage Doors, Wall Systems, Dock Loading Systems, Storage Cabinets & Lockers Mfr & Whslr
N.A.I.C.S.: 332321
Glen Chen *(Project Coord)*

Subsidiary (Domestic):

Crawford Door Forsaljnings AB (4)
Redegatan 7, PO Box 5087, 426 05, Vastra Frolunda, Sweden
Tel.: (46) 317691200
Web Site: http://www.crawfordsolutions.com
Sales Range: $25-49.9 Million
Mfr of Industrial & Garage Doors, Wall Systems, Dock Loading Systems, Storage Cabinets & Lockers
N.A.I.C.S.: 321911

Subsidiary (Non-US):

Crawford Door M.E. AB (4)
Dubai Investment Park, PO Box 80983, Dubai, 80983, United Arab Emirates
Tel.: (971) 4 885 2888
Web Site: http://www.crawfordsolutions.ae
Sales Range: $25-49.9 Million
Emp.: 52
Door Mfr, Installer & Distr
N.A.I.C.S.: 321911
Derek Salmons *(Mgr-Sls)*

Crawford Normstahl N.V. (4)
Oezerstaat 19, 9820, Lokeren, Belgium (100%)
Tel.: (32) 92727100
Web Site: http://www.normstahl.be
Sales Range: $25-49.9 Million
Emp.: 10
Industrial & Garage Doors, Wall Systems, Dock Loading Systems, Storage Cabinets & Lockers Mfr & Whslr
N.A.I.C.S.: 321911

Crawford Poland Sp. zo.o. (4)
ul Marecka 49, PL 05 220, Zielonka, Poland
Tel.: (48) 22 750 6245
Web Site: http://www.crawfordsolutions.pl
Sales Range: $25-49.9 Million
Emp.: 17
Industrial & Garage Doors, Wall Systems, Dock Loading Systems, Storage Cabinets & Lockers Mfr & Whslr

N.A.I.C.S.: 321911

Crawford Production Romania
Srl　　　　　　　　　　　　　　　　　(4)
Parcul Industrial D J 687/2, 331170, Hune-
doara, Romania
Tel.: (40) 354808380
Sales Range: $25-49.9 Million
Electronic Safety Equipment Mfr
N.A.I.C.S.: 334419

Crawford Tor GmbH　　　　　　　(4)
IZ No-Sud Strasse 2 Objekt M27, Wiener
Neudorf, 2320, Austria　　　　　　(100%)
Tel.: (43) 22 36 61 66 50
Sales Range: $25-49.9 Million
Emp.: 30
Mfr & Wholesaler of Industrial & Garage
Doors, Wall Systems, Dock Loading Sys-
tems, Storage Cabinets & Lockers
N.A.I.C.S.: 321911
Hermann Niessler (Gen Mgr)

Crawford UK Ltd.　　　　　　　　(4)
7 Churchill Way 35 A Business Park, Cha-
pel Town, Sheffield, S35 2PY, United King-
dom
Tel.: (44) 1142574330
Web Site: http://www.assaabloy.com
Sales Range: $25-49.9 Million
Emp.: 50
Industrial & Garage Doors, Wall Systems,
Dock Loading Systems, Storage Cabinets &
Lockers Mfr
N.A.I.C.S.: 321911
Leo David (Gen Mgr)

Crawford hafa GmbH　　　　　(4)
Gottlieb-Daimler-Str 12, Wennigsen, 30974,
Germany
Tel.: (49) 5103 7014945
Web Site: http://www.assaabloyentrance.de
Sales Range: $25-49.9 Million
Door Mfr
N.A.I.C.S.: 332510
Henning Adams (Mng Dir)

Subsidiary (Non-US):

Crawford Hafa AG　　　　　　　(5)
Vorstadt 20, PO Box 208, CH 3380, Wan-
gen, Switzerland
Tel.: (41) 326316363
Web Site: http://www.crawfordhafa.ch
Sales Range: $75-99.9 Million
Emp.: 13
Industrial Door Mfr
N.A.I.C.S.: 321911

Crawford-hafa SRL　　　　　　(5)
Via Maccani 108/21, 38100, Trento, Italy
Tel.: (39) 0461432511
Web Site: http://www.crawford.it
Door Locks Mfr
N.A.I.C.S.: 332510

Subsidiary (Non-US):

Crawford hafa
GmbH-Wenningsen　　　　　　(4)
Fangdieckstrasse 64, 22547, Hamburg,
Germany　　　　　　　　　　　　　(100%)
Tel.: (49) 405470060
Web Site: http://www.crawford.de
Sales Range: $10-24.9 Million
Emp.: 30
Garage Doors, Wall Systems, Dock Loading
Systems, Storage Cabinets & Lockers Mfr
N.A.I.C.S.: 321911

Subsidiary (Domestic):

Megadoor AB　　　　　　　　　(4)
Servicegatan 6, 931 24, Skelleftea,
Sweden　　　　　　　　　　　　　(100%)
Tel.: (46) 10 47 47 190
Web Site: http://www.megadoor.se
Sales Range: $25-49.9 Million
Emp.: 35
Mfr of Industrial & Garage Doors, Wall Sys-
tems, Dock Loading Systems, Storage
Cabinets & Lockers
N.A.I.C.S.: 321911

Subsidiary (US):

Megadoor Inc.　　　　　　　　(4)
350 Dividend Dr, Peachtree City, GA
30269-0957
Tel.: (770) 631-2400
Web Site: http://www.megadoor.com

Sales Range: $25-49.9 Million
Emp.: 50
Industrial & Garage Doors, Wall Systems,
Dock Loading Systems, Storage Cabinets &
Lockers Mfr
N.A.I.C.S.: 423390

Subsidiary (Non-US):

Normstahl Crawford Tor GmbH　(4)
Drautendorf 58, Niederwaldkirchen, Steyr,
4400, Austria　　　　　　　　　　(100%)
Tel.: (43) 723131280
Web Site: http://www.normstahl.at
Sales Range: $25-49.9 Million
Emp.: 30
N.A.I.C.S.: 321911
Juergen Hertramps (Gen Mgr)

Normstahl Schweiz AG　　　　(4)
Industriestrasse 1, CH 9462, Montlingen,
Switzerland　　　　　　　　　　　(100%)
Tel.: (41) 717639797
Web Site: http://www.normstahl.com
Sales Range: $25-49.9 Million
Emp.: 20
Industrial Door Mfr
N.A.I.C.S.: 321911

P C Henderson Ltd.　　　　　　(4)
Durham Road, Bowburn, DH6 5NG, Dur-
ham, United Kingdom
Tel.: (44) 1913777345
Web Site: http://www.pchenderson.com
Sales Range: $75-99.9 Million
Metal Doors, Sash, Trim, Sliding Door Gear
& Garage Doors Mfr
N.A.I.C.S.: 332321

Subsidiary (Non-US):

Henderson Nederland BV　　　(5)
Rootven 14, 5531 MB, Bladel,
Netherlands　　　　　　　　　　(100%)
Tel.: (31) 497332020
Web Site: http://www.henderson.nl
Sales Range: $75-99.9 Million
Emp.: 8
Door Gear Mfr
N.A.I.C.S.: 332321

P.C. Henderson (Ireland) Ltd.　(5)
Westlink Industrial Estate Kylemore Road,
Dublin, 10, Ireland　　　　　　　(100%)
Tel.: (353) 16434816
Web Site: http://www.pchenderson.ie
Sales Range: $1-9.9 Million
Emp.: 21
Industrial & Garage Doors, Wall Systems,
Dock Loading Systems, Storage Cabinets &
Lockers Mfr & Whslr
N.A.I.C.S.: 327120

Subsidiary (Non-US):

Saudi Crawford Doors Factory
Ltd.　　　　　　　　　　　　　　(4)
Satan Industrial City, PO Box 25960, Ri-
yadh, 11476, Saudi Arabia　　　(60%)
Tel.: (966) 112652225
Web Site:
　http://www.crawfordsolutions.com.sa
Sales Range: $25-49.9 Million
Emp.: 55
Mfr of Industrial & Garage Doors, Wall Sys-
tems, Dock Loading Systems, Storage
Cabinets & Lockers
N.A.I.C.S.: 321911

ASSA ABLOY Entrance Systems
Austria GmbH　　　　　　　　(1)
Concorde Business Park 2 / F / 1-4, 2320,
Schwechat, Austria
Tel.: (43) 191455370
Web Site:
　https://www.assaabloyentrance.com
N.A.I.C.S.: 332321

ASSA ABLOY Entrance Systems
IDDS AB　　　　　　　　　　　(1)
Box 5087, 426 05, Vastra Frolunda, Swe-
den
Tel.: (46) 104747000
Web Site:
　https://www.assaabloyentrance.com
Metal Door Product Mfr
N.A.I.C.S.: 332321

ASSA ABLOY Forsakrings AB　(1)
Tel.: (46) 850648500

Emp.: 85
Safety Equipment Mfr
N.A.I.C.S.: 332510
Johan Molin (Gen Mgr)

ASSA ABLOY Gecis Sistemleri
A.S.　　　　　　　　　　　　　　(1)
Aydinli Mah Boya Vernik Organize Sanayi
Bolgesi 1 No Iu Cadde No 17, Tuzla,
34959, Istanbul, Turkiye
Tel.: (90) 2165931280
Security System Services
N.A.I.C.S.: 561621

ASSA ABLOY Global Solutions
AB　　　　　　　　　　　　　　(1)
Formansvagen 11, 117 43, Stockholm,
Sweden
Tel.: (46) 87751600
Electronic Security System Product Mfr
N.A.I.C.S.: 334290

ASSA ABLOY Guoqiang (Shandong)
Hardware Technology CO., Ltd　(1)
No 518 Tingjin West Road, Laoling,
253600, Shandong, China
Tel.: (86) 5342119510
Web Site: http://www.guoqiang.cn
Emp.: 1,300
Hardware Mfr
N.A.I.C.S.: 332510

ASSA ABLOY Holding Italia
S.p.A.　　　　　　　　　　　　(1)
Via Modena 68, 40017, San Giovanni in
Persiceto, Bologna, Italy
Tel.: (39) 0516812411
Investment Management Service
N.A.I.C.S.: 523999

ASSA ABLOY Holdings (SA) Ltd　(1)
176 Progress Rd Technikon, 1725, Roode-
poort, Gauteng, South Africa
Tel.: (27) 117615000
Sales Range: $200-249.9 Million
Emp.: 400
Investment Management Service
N.A.I.C.S.: 523940
Thomas Gumede (Mgr-Fin)

ASSA ABLOY Hong Kong
Limited　　　　　　　　　　　　(1)
16th Floor Excel Centre 483A Castle Peak
Road Cheung Sha Wan, Kowloon, China
(Hong Kong)
Tel.: (852) 22607288
Web Site:
　http://www.assaabloyopenings.com.hk
Lock Mfr
N.A.I.C.S.: 332722

ASSA ABLOY Hospitality (Canada)
Ltd.　　　　　　　　　　　　　　(1)
160 Four Valley Drive, Vaughan, L4K 4T9,
ON, Canada
Tel.: (800) 898-2857
Door Locks Mfr
N.A.I.C.S.: 332510

ASSA ABLOY Hospitality GmbH　(1)
Ostring 13, Nordenstadt, 65205, Wies-
baden, 65205, Germany
Tel.: (49) 6122 7033 0
Web Site: http://www.assaabloy.com
Emp.: 15
Hardware Mfr
N.A.I.C.S.: 332510
Marcus Nettelbeck (Mng Dir)

ASSA ABLOY Hospitality Iberica,
S.L.　　　　　　　　　　　　　　(1)
Rua Duarte Leite N 43 Palhais, Charneca
da Caparica, Almada, Portugal
Tel.: (351) 212 978 790
Web Site:
　http://www.assaabloyhospitality.com
Emp.: 13
Safety Equipment Mfr
N.A.I.C.S.: 332510
Luis Alves (Mng Dir)

ASSA ABLOY Hospitality Ltd　(1)
21 Stadium Way Portman Road, Reading,
RG30 6BX, Berkshire, United Kingdom
Tel.: (44) 118 945 2200
Sales Range: $25-49.9 Million
Emp.: 40
Hardware Mfr
N.A.I.C.S.: 332510

ASSA ABLOY Hospitality Ltd　(1)
19 Floor Benson Tower 74 Hung To Road,
Kwun Tong, Kowloon, China (Hong Kong)
Tel.: (852) 2316 2200
Web Site: http://www.assaabloy.com
Hardware Mfr
N.A.I.C.S.: 332510
Kelvin Kwok (Mgr-Sls)

ASSA ABLOY Hospitality Ltd　(1)
1035/22 Soi KhunVijit Klongton Nua, 10110,
Bangkok, Thailand
Tel.: (66) 2381 5621 7
Web Site: http://www.assaabloy.com
Hardware Mfr
N.A.I.C.S.: 332510

ASSA ABLOY Hospitality Pte Ltd　(1)
8 Chang Charn Road Link THM Building
06-01, Singapore, 159637, Singapore
Tel.: (65) 6305 7670
Web Site: http://www.vingcardelsafe.com
Sales Range: $25-49.9 Million
Emp.: 15
Lock Mfr
N.A.I.C.S.: 332510
Vegard Prypz (Mng Dir)

ASSA ABLOY Hospitality Shanghai
Ltd　　　　　　　　　　　　　　(1)
Building 19-20 No 99 Huajia Road Songji-
ang Industrial Zone, Songjiang District,
Shanghai, 201613, China
Tel.: (86) 21 37746161
Web Site: http://www.assaabloy.com
Sales Range: $50-74.9 Million
Emp.: 200
Electronic Safety System Mfr
N.A.I.C.S.: 334290
Dai Grace (Dir-Fin)

ASSA ABLOY Hospitality sas　(1)
37 rue Adam Ledoux, 92404, Courbevoie,
France
Tel.: (33) 1 41 88 03 03
Web Site: http://www.vingcardelsafe.com
Sales Range: $25-49.9 Million
Emp.: 30
Safety Equipment Mfr
N.A.I.C.S.: 332510

ASSA ABLOY Hungary Kereskedelmi
Kft.　　　　　　　　　　　　　　(1)
Zahony u 7 Graphisoft park C epulet, Buda-
pest, Hungary
Tel.: (36) 1 226 1616
Web Site: http://www.assaabloy.hu
Door Locks Mfr
N.A.I.C.S.: 332510

ASSA ABLOY IP AB　　　　　　(1)
Klaradergsviadukten 90, PO Box 70340,
107 23, Stockholm, Sweden
Tel.: (46) 850648500
Sales Range: $25-49.9 Million
Emp.: 70
Security System Services
N.A.I.C.S.: 561621

ASSA ABLOY Identification Technol-
ogy Group AB　　　　　　　　(1)
Klarabergsviadukten 90, PO Box 70340,
11164, Stockholm, Sweden
Tel.: (46) 850648500
Web Site: http://www.assaabloy.com
Sales Range: $25-49.9 Million
Emp.: 70
Safety Equipment Mfr
N.A.I.C.S.: 332510

ASSA ABLOY India Private Ltd.　(1)
16th Floor Tower B Building No 5, DLF Cy-
ber Terraces DLF Phase III, Gurgaon, 122
002, Haryana, India
Tel.: (91) 124 4407060
Web Site: http://www.assaabloy.com
Sales Range: $25-49.9 Million
Emp.: 40
Hardware Mfr
N.A.I.C.S.: 332510

ASSA ABLOY Industrietore
GmbH　　　　　　　　　　　　(1)
Concorde Business Park 2 / F / 1-4, 2320,
Schwechat, Austria
Tel.: (43) 13900570900
Automatic Sliding Door Mfr
N.A.I.C.S.: 332321

ASSA ABLOY Italia S.p.A.　　(1)

ASSA ABLOY AB—(Continued)

Via Bovaresa 13, 40017, San Giovanni in
Persiceto, Bologna, Italy
Tel.: (39) 051 6812411
Web Site:
 http://www.assaabloyopeningsolutions.it
Emp.: 80
Hardware Mfr
N.A.I.C.S.: 332510

ASSA ABLOY Japan Co Ltd   **(1)**
3F Shiba Bldg 1-16-5 Hamamatsucho,
Minato-ku, Tokyo, 105-0013, Japan
Tel.: (81) 368091607
Web Site:
 http://www.assaabloyopeningsolutions.jp
Hardware Mfr
N.A.I.C.S.: 332510

ASSA ABLOY Korea Co., Ltd.   **(1)**
10th floor of Jplatz Building 186 Gasan
Digital 1-ro, Geumcheon-gu, Seoul, Korea
(South)
Tel.: (82) 221075700
Web Site:
 http://www.assaabloyopeningsolutions.kr
Sales Range: $50-74.9 Million
Emp.: 150
Door Locks Mfr
N.A.I.C.S.: 332722

ASSA ABLOY Kredit AB   **(1)**
Klarabergsviadukten 90, PO Box 7034, 117
43, Stockholm, Sweden
Tel.: (46) 850648500
Sales Range: $25-49.9 Million
Emp.: 70
Safety Equipment Mfr
N.A.I.C.S.: 332510
Johan Molin *(CEO)*

ASSA ABLOY Limited   **(1)**
School Street, Willenhall, WV13 3PW, West
Midland, United Kingdom
Tel.: (44) 8452232124
Web Site:
 http://www.assaabloyopenings.co.uk
Holding Company; Locks & Other Door
Products Mfr
N.A.I.C.S.: 551112

Subsidiary (Domestic):

Abloy UK Ltd   **(2)**
Portobello Works School Street, Willenhall,
WV13 3PW, West Midlands, United King-
dom
Tel.: (44) 1902 364500
Web Site: http://www.abloy.co.uk
Door Locks Mfr
N.A.I.C.S.: 332510
Steve Walsh *(Mgr-Customer Liaison)*

Division (Domestic):

Abloy UK Ltd   **(3)**
2 3 Hatters Lane Croxley Business Pk,
Watford, WD18 8QY, Herts, United
Kingdom   **(100%)**
Tel.: (44) 1923255066
Web Site: http://www.abloy.co.uk
Sales Range: $10-24.9 Million
Emp.: 50
Electric Locking, Cylinder, Padlocks & Door
Operators
N.A.I.C.S.: 332510

Subsidiary (Domestic):

Exidor Limited   **(2)**
Progress Drive, Cannock, WS11 0JE,
Staffs, United Kingdom   **(100%)**
Tel.: (44) 1543 578 661
Web Site: http://www.exidor.co.uk
Emergency Exit Hardware Mfr & Distr
N.A.I.C.S.: 332510
Kevin Nolan *(CEO)*

Yale UK Ltd.   **(2)**
School Street, Willenhall, WV13 3PW, W
Midlands, United Kingdom   **(100%)**
Tel.: (44) 1902364606
Web Site: http://yalehome.co.uk
Sales Range: $75-99.9 Million
Emp.: 500
Locks & Security Products Mfr
N.A.I.C.S.: 332510

Subsidiary (Non-US):

**Yale Security Products (Hong Kong)
Limited**   **(3)**

16th Floor Excel Centre 483A Castle Peak
Road, Cheung Sha Wan, Kowloon, China
(Hong Kong)   **(100%)**
Tel.: (852) 22600888
Web Site: http://www.yalehome.com.hk
Sales Range: $25-49.9 Million
Emp.: 50
Holding Company
N.A.I.C.S.: 551112

**Yale Security Products S.p.A.
(Italy)**   **(3)**
Via Ardeatina 2491 - Km 22,500, 40, Santa
Palomba, RM, Italy   **(100%)**
Tel.: (39) 0692894250
Web Site: http://www.yalelock.com
Sales Range: $50-74.9 Million
Emp.: 200
Mfr of Locksets & Padlocks
N.A.I.C.S.: 332510

ASSA ABLOY Malaysia Sdn Bhd   **(1)**
Level 1 East Wing Wisma Consplant 1 No 2
Jalan SS16/4, 47500, Subang Jaya, Sel-
agor Darul Ehsan, Malaysia
Tel.: (60) 356517800
Web Site:
 http://www.assaabloyopenings.com.my
Sales Range: $25-49.9 Million
Emp.: 15
Door Locks Mfr
N.A.I.C.S.: 332510

**ASSA ABLOY Mexico, S.A de
CV.**   **(1)**
Pelicano 242 Col Granjas Modernas,
07460, Mexico, Mexico
Web Site: https://www.assaabloy.com.mx
Industrial Control Product Mfr & Distr
N.A.I.C.S.: 335314

**ASSA ABLOY Mobile Services
AB**   **(1)**
Formansvagen 11, 117 43, Stockholm,
Sweden
Tel.: (46) 87751600
Security System Services
N.A.I.C.S.: 561621

ASSA ABLOY NV   **(1)**
Canadalaan 73, 8620, Nieuwpoort, Belgium
Tel.: (32) 58 234 101
Web Site: http://www.assaabloy.be
Hardware Mfr
N.A.I.C.S.: 332510

ASSA ABLOY Nederland B.V.   **(1)**
Meerval 5, 4941 SK, Raamsdonksveer,
Netherlands
Tel.: (31) 88 639 46 00
Web Site:
 http://www.assaabloyopeningsolutions.nl
Hardware Mfr
N.A.I.C.S.: 332510

Subsidiary (Domestic):

IAI industrial systems B.V.   **(2)**
De Run 5406, 5504 DE, Veldhoven, Nether-
lands
Tel.: (31) 402542445
Web Site: http://www.iai.nl
Engineering Services
N.A.I.C.S.: 541330
Henk Roelofs *(Mng Dir)*

**ASSA ABLOY New Zealand
Limited**   **(1)**
6 Armstrong Road, Albany, Auckland, 0632,
New Zealand
Tel.: (64) 94489188
Web Site:
 http://www.assaabloyopeningsolutions.nz
Emp.: 200
Door & Window Mfr
N.A.I.C.S.: 332510

**ASSA ABLOY Occidente, SA de
CV**   **(1)**
Av Periferico Sur No 7980 Edif 2B Col
Santa Maria Tequepexpan, Tlaquepaqu,
45601, Guadalajara, Jalisco, Mexico
Tel.: (52) 33 3540 5400
Web Site: http://www.tesa.com.mx
Sales Range: $25-49.9 Million
Emp.: 200
Lock Mfr
N.A.I.C.S.: 332510

ASSA ABLOY Poland Sp. z o.o.   **(1)**

Jana Olbrachta 94, Warsaw, 01102, Poland
Tel.: (48) 22 751 53 54
Web Site: http://www.assaabloy.com.pl
Sales Range: $25-49.9 Million
Emp.: 35
Door Locks Mfr
N.A.I.C.S.: 332722

ASSA ABLOY Portugal, Lda.   **(1)**
Rua Cidade de Cordova 3A Zona Industrial
de Alfragide Sul, Alfragide, 2610-038, Ama-
dora, Portugal
Tel.: (351) 21 471 96 23
Web Site:
 http://www.assaabloyopeningsolutions.pt
Emp.: 7
Safety Equipment Mfr
N.A.I.C.S.: 332510
Joao Reis do Carmo *(Gen Mgr)*

**ASSA ABLOY Portugal, Unipessoal,
Lda**   **(1)**
Praceta Do Comercio 13b, Alfragide, 2610-
042, Amadora, Portugal
Tel.: (351) 214719623
Web Site: http://www.assaport.com
Safety Equipment Mfr
N.A.I.C.S.: 332510

**ASSA ABLOY Sicherheitstechnik
GmbH**   **(1)**
Bildstockstrasse 20, 72458, Albstadt, Ger-
many
Tel.: (49) 7431 123 0
Web Site:
 http://www.assaabloyopeningsolutions.de
Emp.: 400
Electromechanical Lock Mfr
N.A.I.C.S.: 334514
Andreas Wagener *(Mng Dir)*

Plant (Domestic):

**ASSA ABLOY Sicherheitstechnik
GmbH - Berlin plant**   **(2)**
Goerzallee 299, 14167, Berlin, Germany
Tel.: (49) 30 8106 0
Door Locks Mfr
N.A.I.C.S.: 332510

ASSA ABLOY Singapore Pte Ltd   **(1)**
10 Arumugam Road 06-00 Lion Building A,
Singapore, 409957, Singapore
Tel.: (65) 6880 0000
Web Site: http://www.assaabloy.com.sg
Emp.: 25
Door Locks Mfr
N.A.I.C.S.: 332722
Patrick Ng *(Gen Mgr)*

**ASSA ABLOY South Asia Pte
Ltd**   **(1)**
60 Macpherson Road Block 1 08-08 Sie-
mens Center, Singapore, 348615, Singa-
pore
Tel.: (65) 68800000
Web Site:
 http://www.assaabloysouthasia.com
Door Locks Mfr
N.A.I.C.S.: 332510

**ASSA ABLOY Svensk Fastighets
AB**   **(1)**
PO Box 70340, 107 23, Stockholm, Swe-
den
Tel.: (46) 8 506 485 00
Door Locks Mfr
N.A.I.C.S.: 332510

ASSA ABLOY Thailand Ltd   **(1)**
1919 Preecha Group Building 5th Floor Pat-
tanakarn Road, Suanluang, 10250, Bang-
kok, Thailand
Tel.: (66) 2 722 7371
Web Site: http://www.assaabloy.co.th
Door Locks Mfr
N.A.I.C.S.: 332722

ASSA ABLOY, Inc.   **(1)**
110 Sargent Dr, New Haven, CT 06511
Tel.: (203) 624-5225
Sales Range: $1-4.9 Billion
Emp.: 7,000
Holding Company; Regional Managing Of-
fice
N.A.I.C.S.: 551112

Subsidiary (Domestic):

AADG, Inc.   **(2)**

1502 12th St NW, Mason City, IA
50401-5809   **(100%)**
Tel.: (641) 423-1334
Web Site: http://www.curries.com
Mfr of Steel Doors & Frames
N.A.I.C.S.: 332321
Dean Peterson *(VP-Hollow Metal Sls Ad-
min)*

Unit (Domestic):

Ceco Door Products   **(3)**
9159 Telecom Dr, Milan, TN 38358
Tel.: (731) 686-8345
Web Site: http://www.cecodoor.com
Sales Range: $75-99.9 Million
Emp.: 32,000
Side-Hinged Door Systems Mfr
N.A.I.C.S.: 332321

Graham Wood Doors   **(3)**
525 9th St SE, Mason City, IA 50401
Tel.: (641) 423-2444
Web Site: http://www.grahamdoors.com
Wood Door Mfr
N.A.I.C.S.: 321911

Group (Domestic):

**ASSA ABLOY Door Security
Solutions**   **(2)**
110 Sargent Dr, New Haven, CT 06511
Tel.: (203) 624-5225
Web Site: http://www.assaabloydss.com
Sales Range: $300-349.9 Million
Emp.: 600
Holding Company; Door Lock & Other Se-
curity Hardware Mfr
N.A.I.C.S.: 551112

Subsidiary (Domestic):

Abloy Security Inc.   **(3)**
6005 Commerce Dr Ste 330, Irving, TX
75063-2664
Tel.: (972) 753-1127
Web Site: http://www.abloyusa.com
Sales Range: $1-9.9 Million
Emp.: 17
Assembling of Locks
N.A.I.C.S.: 423990
Jerry Burhans *(Mng Dir)*

Corbin Russwin, Inc.   **(3)**
225 Episcopal Rd, Berlin, CT 06037-4004
Tel.: (860) 225-7411
Web Site: http://www.corbin-russwin.com
Sales Range: $100-124.9 Million
Emp.: 400
Mfr of Residential Commercial & Industrial
Locksets & Builders Hardware
N.A.I.C.S.: 332510

McKinney Products Company   **(3)**
225 Episcopal Rd, Berlin, CT 06037-1524
Tel.: (570) 346-7551
Web Site:
 http://www.assaabloydooraccessories.us
Sales Range: $25-49.9 Million
Emp.: 14
Mfr of Door Hinges
N.A.I.C.S.: 332510

**Medeco High Security Locks,
Inc.**   **(3)**
3625 Alleghany Dr, Salem, VA
24153   **(100%)**
Tel.: (540) 380-1603
Web Site: http://www.medeco.com
Sales Range: $50-74.9 Million
Emp.: 250
High Security Mechanical & Electronic
Locks Mfr
N.A.I.C.S.: 332510

Sargent Manufacturing Company   **(3)**
100 Sargent Dr, New Haven, CT 06536-
0915
Tel.: (203) 562-2151
Web Site: http://www.sargentlock.com
Sales Range: $150-199.9 Million
Mfr of High Quality Architectural Hardware,
Locks, Door Closers & Exit Devices
N.A.I.C.S.: 332510

Security Metal Products Corp   **(3)**
5678 Concours St, Ontario, CA 91764
Tel.: (909) 593-2100
Web Site: http://www.secmet.com

Sales Range: $25-49.9 Million
Emp.: 14
Metal Doors, Sash & Trim Mfr
N.A.I.C.S.: 332321

Group (Domestic):

ASSA ABLOY Sales & Marketing
Group, Inc.   (2)
110 Sargent Dr, New Haven, CT
06511-5918   (100%)
Tel.: (203) 624-5225
Web Site: http://www.assaabloyiss.com
Emp.: 3,400
Locking Systems, Industrial & Technical
Products Distr
N.A.I.C.S.: 423990

Subsidiary (Domestic):

Dominion Building Products   (2)
6949 Fairbanks N Houston Rd, Houston,
TX 77040
Tel.: (713) 466-6790
Web Site: http://www.dominionproducts.com
Sales Range: $25-49.9 Million
Emp.: 50
Mfr of Steel Doors, Frames & Aluminum
Windows
N.A.I.C.S.: 332999
Daryl Lahodny (Mgr-Svcs Center)

Subsidiary (Non-US):

Fleming Door Products Ltd   (2)
101 Ashbridge Circle, Woodbridge, L4L
3R5, ON, Canada   (100%)
Tel.: (416) 749-2111
Web Site: http://www.flemingdoor.com
Sales Range: $25-49.9 Million
Emp.: 200
Mfr of Commercial Side-Hinged Steel Doors
& Frames
N.A.I.C.S.: 332321

Subsidiary (Domestic):

HID Global Corporation   (2)
611 Center Ridge Dr, Austin, TX 78753
Tel.: (512) 776-9000
Web Site: http://www.hidglobal.com
Sales Range: $25-49.9 Million
Emp.: 100
Access Control Cards & Readers Mfr
N.A.I.C.S.: 334515
Bjorn Lidefelt (Exec VP & Head)

Subsidiary (Domestic):

ActivIdentity Corporation   (3)
6623 Dumbarton Cir, Fremont, CA 94555
Tel.: (510) 574-0100
Web Site: http://www.actividentity.com
Sales Range: $50-74.9 Million
Corporate Security Services
N.A.I.C.S.: 513210

Subsidiary (Non-US):

ActivIdentity Australia Pty. Ltd.   (4)
Unit 3 6 Kennedy Street, Kingston, 2604,
ACT, Australia
Tel.: (61) 262084888
Web Site: http://www.actividentity.com
Sales Range: $100-124.9 Million
Digital Identity Assurance Services
N.A.I.C.S.: 513210

ActivIdentity Europe S.A.   (4)
24-28 avenue du General de Gaulle,
92156, Suresnes, France
Tel.: (33) 142048400
Sales Range: $10-24.9 Million
Emp.: 50
Digital Identity Assurance Services
N.A.I.C.S.: 513210
Sandrine Paulin (Mgr-Logistics)

ActivIdentity Japan K.K.   (4)
Marunouchi Trust Tower Main Bldg 20th Fl
1 8 3 Marunouchi, Chiyoda-ku, Tokyo, 100-
0005, Japan
Tel.: (81) 352885222
Sales Range: $100-124.9 Million
Digital Identity Assurance Services
N.A.I.C.S.: 513210

ActivIdentity UK Ltd.   (4)
Waterloo Business Centre, 117 Waterloo
Rd, London, SE1 8UL, United Kingdom
Tel.: (44) 2079600220

Web Site: http://www.actividentity.com
Sales Range: $100-124.9 Million
Digital Identity Assurance Services
N.A.I.C.S.: 513210

Subsidiary (Domestic):

Cross Match Technologies, Inc.   (3)
3950 RCA Blvd Ste 5001, Palm Beach Gar-
dens, FL 33410
Tel.: (561) 622-1650
Web Site: http://www.crossmatch.com
Sales Range: $125-149.9 Million
Biometric Identity Management Systems,
Applications & Technologies Mfr
N.A.I.C.S.: 541512
Kathryn Hutton (Gen Counsel & Sr VP)

Subsidiary (Non-US):

Cross Match Technologies
GmbH   (4)
Unstrutweg 4, 07743, Jena, Germany
Tel.: (49) 3641 4297 0
Web Site: http://www.crossmatch.com
Biometric Identity Management Systems,
Applications & Technologies Mfr
N.A.I.C.S.: 541512
Kathryn Hutton (Mng Dir)

Branch (Domestic):

Cross Match Technologies, Inc. -
Redwood City   (4)
720 Bay Rd, Redwood City, CA 94063
Tel.: (650) 261-6070
Sales Range: $10-24.9 Million
Biometric Identity Management Systems,
Applications & Technologies Mfr
N.A.I.C.S.: 541512
Vance Bjorn (CTO)

Subsidiary (Domestic):

Demoteller Systems, Inc.   (3)
1212 Royal Pkwy, Euless, TX
76040   (100%)
Tel.: (817) 494-9300
Web Site: http://www.demoteller.com
Sales Range: $1-9.9 Million
Emp.: 32
Supplier of Instant Issuance Solutions for
Financial Markets
N.A.I.C.S.: 525990
Charlie East (Pres)

Subsidiary (Non-US):

HID Asia Pacific Ltd.   (3)
19/F 625 Kings Road Island East, North
Point, China (Hong Kong)   (100%)
Tel.: (852) 31609800
Web Site: http://www.hidgroval.com
Sales Range: $25-49.9 Million
Emp.: 40
Access Control Products Mfr
N.A.I.C.S.: 335314
Craig Sandness (Mng Dir)

HID China Ltd.   (3)
Unit 1503 15/F Phase 2 Tower East Ch-
uangxin Science & Technology Plaza, Tian
An Cyber Park Futian Disctrict, Shenzhen,
518040, China
Tel.: (86) 755 8835 3190
Web Site: http://www.hidglobal.com
Sales Range: $25-49.9 Million
Emp.: 10
Electronic Safety Equipment Mfr
N.A.I.C.S.: 334419

HID Corporation Ltd.   (3)
3 Cae Gwyrdd Green Meadow Springs
Business Park, Cardiff, CF15 7AB, United
Kingdom
Tel.: (44) 2920528500
Web Site: http://www.hidglobal.com
Sales Range: $25-49.9 Million
Emp.: 60
Mfr of Access Control Products
N.A.I.C.S.: 335314

HID Corporation Ltd.   (3)
35 Boulevard de la Victoire, 67000, Stras-
bourg, France
Tel.: (33) 3 90 22 10 66
Safety Equipment Mfr
N.A.I.C.S.: 332510

HID Global GmbH   (3)
Ferihumerstrasse 13, 4040, Linz, Austria

Tel.: (43) 732 602220
Sales Range: $25-49.9 Million
Emp.: 20
Identification Component Mfr
N.A.I.C.S.: 326199
Andrew Lintell (Dir-Sls-Identity Assurance-
EMEA)

HID Global GmbH   (3)
Am Klingenweg 6a, 65396, Walluf, Ger-
many
Tel.: (49) 6995421276
Web Site: http://www.hidglobal.com
Electric Device Mfr
N.A.I.C.S.: 334419

Subsidiary (Domestic):

HID Global Rastede GmbH   (4)
Klein Feldhus 23, 26180, Rastede, Ger-
many
Tel.: (49) 440291190
Web Site: http://www.hidglobal.de
Sales Range: $25-49.9 Million
Emp.: 60
Smartcard Mfr
N.A.I.C.S.: 326199

Subsidiary (Non-US):

HID Global Ireland Teoranta Ltd.   (3)
Sales Range: $50-74.9 Million
Radio Frequency Identity Card Mfr
N.A.I.C.S.: 326199
Gearoid Mitchell (Head-Ops)

HID Global Sdn. Bhd.   (3)
Kawansan Perindustrian Tampoi No 5 Jalan
Dewani 1/1, 81100, Johor Bahru, Malaysia
Tel.: (60) 7 3342008
Electric Equipment Mfr
N.A.I.C.S.: 334419
Wei Jin Lee (Head-Secure Issuance-Asia
Pacific)

HID Global Switzerland S.A.   (3)
Rte Pra-Charbon 27, 1614, Granges-
Paccot, Veveyse, Switzerland
Tel.: (41) 219080100
Sales Range: $25-49.9 Million
Emp.: 30
Electronic Components Mfr
N.A.I.C.S.: 334419

HID India Private Ltd   (3)
No.1 2 Murphy Road Tower D Annexe Mil-
lenia Towers, Ulsoor, Bengaluru, 560 008,
India
Tel.: (91) 80 255 435 66
Sales Range: $25-49.9 Million
Emp.: 25
Electronic Components Mfr
N.A.I.C.S.: 334419
Ranjith Nambiar (Dir-Sls)

Subsidiary (Domestic):

IdenTrust, Inc.   (3)
5225 Wiley Post Way Ste 450, Salt Lake
City, UT 84116
Tel.: (801) 384-3500
Web Site: http://www.identrust.com
Sales Range: $10-24.9 Million
Emp.: 63
Identity Authentication Solutions
N.A.I.C.S.: 513210

InvoTech Systems, Inc.   (3)
20951 Burbank Blvd Ste B, Encino, CA
91367
Tel.: (818) 461-9800
Web Site: http://www.invotech.com
Prepackaged Software
N.A.I.C.S.: 513210
Oswald Lares (Dir-Sls & Mktg)

Janam Technologies LLC   (3)
100 Crossways Park W Ste 105, Woodbury,
NY 11797
Tel.: (516) 677-9500
Web Site: http://www.janam.com
Electrical Equipment & Component Mfr
N.A.I.C.S.: 335999
Dwight Ogletree (VP-Sls)

LaserCard Corporation   (3)
1875 N Shoreline Blvd, Mountain View, CA
94043
Tel.: (650) 969-4428
Web Site: http://www.lasercard.com

Sales Range: $50-74.9 Million
Holding Company; Optical Memory Cards &
Drives Mfr
N.A.I.C.S.: 551112

Omni-ID USA, Inc.   (3)
1200 Ridgeway Ave Ste 106, Rochester,
NY 14615
Tel.: (585) 713-1000
Web Site: http://www.omni-id.com
Emp.: 170
Radio Frequency Identification Tags Mfr
N.A.I.C.S.: 334413
Charles Burton (Dir-Ops)

Quantum Secure, Inc.   (3)
100 Century Ctr Ct Ste 800, San Jose, CA
95112
Tel.: (408) 453-1008
Web Site: http://www.quantumsecure.com
Security Software Development Services
N.A.I.C.S.: 541512
Ajay Jain (Pres & CEO)

Unit (Domestic):

YSG Door Security Consultants   (2)
1902 Airport Rd, Monroe, NC
28110-7396   (100%)
Tel.: (704) 283-2101
Web Site: http://www.ysgsecurity.com
Sales Range: $25-49.9 Million
Emp.: 100
Door Hardware Mfr
N.A.I.C.S.: 332510
John Davenport (VP-Fin)

Subsidiary (Non-US):

Yale-Corbin Canada Limited   (2)
160 4th Valley Drive, Vaughan, L4K 4T9,
ON, Canada   (100%)
Tel.: (905) 564-5854
Sales Range: $25-49.9 Million
Emp.: 50
Distribution of Hardware
N.A.I.C.S.: 423710

ASSA OEM AB   (1)
Akarevagen 1, 43533, Molnlycke,
Sweden   (100%)
Tel.: (46) 317044000
Door Opening Solution Products Mfr
N.A.I.C.S.: 332510

ASSA, INC   (1)
110 Sargent Dr, New Haven, CT 06511
Tel.: (203) 603-5959
Lock Mfr
N.A.I.C.S.: 332510

Abloy Canada Inc.   (1)
9630 Trans Canada, Montreal, H4S 1V9,
QC, Canada
Tel.: (514) 335-9500
Web Site: http://www.abloy.com
Sales Range: $25-49.9 Million
Emp.: 14
Door Automation Software Development
Services
N.A.I.C.S.: 541511

Abloy High Security Locks Private
Ltd   (1)
2105 & 06 Cyber One Plot No 4 & 6, Sector
- 30A Vashi, Navi Mumbai, 400703, Maha-
rashtra, India
Tel.: (91) 2243427100
Web Site: http://www.abloy.in
Sales Range: $25-49.9 Million
Emp.: 6
Lock Mfr
N.A.I.C.S.: 332510

Abloy Mul-T-Lock Mexico S.A. de
C.V.   (1)
Av De los Arcos 36-H Industrial Naucalpan
2 Seccion, 53370, Mexico, Mexico
Tel.: (52) 55 5312 2220
Web Site: http://www.mul-t-lock.mx
Door Locks Mfr
N.A.I.C.S.: 332722
Enrique Margolin (Pres)

Abloy Oy   (1)
Wahlforssinkatu 20, P.O.B. 108, 80100, Jo-
ensuu, Finland
Tel.: (358) 20 599 2501
Web Site: http://www.abloy.com
Emp.: 750

ASSA ABLOY AB—(Continued)

Mfr of Architectural Hardware, Locks, Door Closers & Door Automatics
N.A.I.C.S.: 332510

Agta Record AG (1)
Allmendstrasse 24, CH-8320, Fehraltorf, Switzerland (98.04%)
Tel.: (41) 449549191
Web Site: http://www.record.group
Rev: $431,905,398
Assets: $418,157,042
Liabilities: $123,866,738
Net Worth: $294,290,304
Earnings: $29,595,566
Emp.: 2,588
Fiscal Year-end: 12/31/2018
Automatic Door System Mfr
N.A.I.C.S.: 332321
Stefan Riva (CEO)

Subsidiary (Non-US):

Automatismes Batiment SA (2)
ZAE LA BUTTE AUX BERGERS 4-6 Rue Nungesser et Coli, 91380, Chilly-Mazarin, France
Tel.: (33) 169331260
Web Site: http://www.bornes-escamotables-ab.fr
Automatic Doors & Gates Distr
N.A.I.C.S.: 423310

BLASI GmbH (2)
Carl-Benz-Str 5-15, 77972, Mahlberg, Germany
Tel.: (49) 7822 893 0
Web Site: http://www.blasi.info
Sales Range: $25-49.9 Million
Emp.: 100
Automatic Door Mfr
N.A.I.C.S.: 332321
Peter Dorner (Mgr-Fin)

CORDVER S.A. (2)
37 Portes du Grand Lyon ZAC du Champ Perier, 01700, Neyron, France
Tel.: (33) 437497520
Sales Range: $25-49.9 Million
Emp.: 10
Flexible Doors Mfr
N.A.I.C.S.: 332321
Stefan Riva (Gen Mgr)

Doorways Pty. Ltd. (2)
119 Metrolink Circuit, Campbellfield, 3061, VIC, Australia
Tel.: (61) 383392888
Automatic Door Mfr
N.A.I.C.S.: 332321

KOS Spezialturen GmbH (2)
Landwehr 152-156, 46514, Schermbeck, Germany
Tel.: (49) 2853448990
Web Site: http://www.kos-tueren.de
Door System Mfr
N.A.I.C.S.: 332321

Metro Doors Ltd. (2)
5220 General Rd, Mississauga, L4W 1G8, ON, Canada
Tel.: (905) 602-6002
N.A.I.C.S.: 337110

PACA Ascenseurs Services SAS (2)
4 Avenue Lamartine, 13170, Les Pennes-Mirabeau, France
Tel.: (33) 442341370
Web Site: https://www.paca-ascenseurs.fr
N.A.I.C.S.: 238290

Paxter Security & Automation Sdn Bhd (2)
No 30 and 32 Jalan PJU 1A/13 Taman Perindustrian Jaya, Ara Damansara, 46050, Petaling Jaya, Malaysia
Tel.: (60) 378459868
Web Site: http://www.paxter.com.my
Automatic Door Mfr
N.A.I.C.S.: 332321

Subsidiary (US):

Record - USA Inc (2)
4324 Phil Hargett Ct, Monroe, NC 28111
Tel.: (704) 289-9212
Web Site: http://www.recorddoors.com
Sales Range: $25-49.9 Million
Emp.: 60
Automatic Door Mfr

N.A.I.C.S.: 332321
Marty Licciardello (Pres)

Subsidiary (Non-US):

Record Ajto kft (2)
Gyari ut 56, 2310, Szigetszentmiklos, Hungary
Tel.: (36) 304448887
Web Site: http://www.record.hu
Sales Range: $25-49.9 Million
Emp.: 14
Automatic Door Mfr
N.A.I.C.S.: 332321
Arpad Jambor (Mng Dir)

Record Automatic Door (Shanghai) Co., Ltd. (2)
No 1969 No 5 Rd sinks plant, Qingpu Industrial Park, Shanghai, China
Tel.: (86) 2169213237
Web Site: http://www.record.net.cn
Automatic Door Mfr
N.A.I.C.S.: 332321

Record Automatic Doors (Australia) Pty. Ltd. (2)
30 Prince William Drive, Seven Hills, 2147, NSW, Australia
Tel.: (61) 288114000
Web Site: http://www.recorddoors.com.au
Automatic Door Mfr
N.A.I.C.S.: 332321
Graeme McDougall (Project Mgr)

Record Automatic Doors (M) Sdn Bhd (2)
No 30 32 and 34 Jalan Pju 1A/13, Ara Damansara, 46050, Petaling Jaya, Selangor, Malaysia
Tel.: (60) 378459868
Web Site: http://www.recorddoors.my
Automatic Door Mfr
N.A.I.C.S.: 332321

Record BMT as (2)
Hovedstensvej 33, 2650, Hvidovre, Denmark
Tel.: (45) 36782300
Web Site: http://www.record-danmark.dk
Sales Range: $25-49.9 Million
Emp.: 25
Automatic Door Mfr
N.A.I.C.S.: 332321
Martin Statler (CEO)

Record Industry (2)
les Tribouilleres, 38460, Cremieu, France
Tel.: (33) 474905290
Emp.: 25
Automatic Door Mfr
N.A.I.C.S.: 332321

Subsidiary (US):

Record North America Inc. (2)
4324 Phil Hargett Ct, Monroe, NC 28110
Web Site: https://www.recorddoors.com
N.A.I.C.S.: 321911

Subsidiary (Non-US):

Record Portes Automatiques S.A (2)
6 rue de l Orme, 91165, Saint-Germain, France
Tel.: (33) 169793110
Web Site: http://www.record-portes-automatiques.fr
Flexible Doors Mfr
N.A.I.C.S.: 332321

Record Puertas Automaticas SA (2)
Francesc Vila 20, Sant Cugat, 08173, Barcelona, Spain
Tel.: (34) 936742650
Web Site: http://www.record.es
Security & Sliding Door Mfr
N.A.I.C.S.: 332321

Record Sverige AB (2)
Spinnerivagen 1 2tr, 448 50, Tollered, Sweden
Tel.: (46) 855064630
Web Site: http://www.record.se
Automatic Door Mfr
N.A.I.C.S.: 332321

Record Turautomation GmbH (2)
Otto-Wels-Str 9, 42111, Wuppertal, Germany
Tel.: (49) 202 60 90 10

Web Site: http://www.record.de
Automatic Door Mfr
N.A.I.C.S.: 332321

Record automatic doors (Canada), Inc. (2)
4120 Ridgeway Dr Unit 26, Mississauga, L5L 5S9, ON, Canada
Tel.: (905) 632-2235
Web Site: http://www.mactechsystems.ca
Automatic Door Mfr
N.A.I.C.S.: 332321
Nancy McCorquodale (Office Mgr)

Svaton SA (2)
60 rue Marcel Dassault, 93147, Bondy, France
Tel.: (33) 148473112
Automatic Door Mfr
N.A.I.C.S.: 332321
Maarkus Kaast (CEO)

VERCOR S.A (2)
2110 Avenue St-Jean, 38360, Noyarey, France
Tel.: (33) 476539999
Web Site: http://www.vercor.fr
Sales Range: $250-299.9 Million
Emp.: 50
Automatic Door Distr
N.A.I.C.S.: 423310

Van Nelfen Deurtechniek B.V. (2)
Houtduifstraat 6, 4901 BP, Oosterhout, Netherlands
Tel.: (31) 162447720
Web Site: http://www.vannelfen.com
Automatic Door Mfr
N.A.I.C.S.: 332321

Subsidiary (Domestic):

agtatec ag (2)
Allmendstrasse 24, 8320, Fehraltorf, Switzerland
Tel.: (41) 449549316
Automatic Door Mfr
N.A.I.C.S.: 332321
Franz Eigl (Mgr)

Subsidiary (Non-US):

record Austria GmbH (2)
Zwingenstrasse 17, 2380, Perchtoldsdorf, Austria
Tel.: (43) 18658875
Web Site: http://www.record.co.at
Automatic Door Mfr
N.A.I.C.S.: 332321

record Elemat, S.A. (2)
C Torrent Vila 20 Pol Ind Can Magi-Apdo 185, 08173, Sant Cugat del Valles, Barcelona, Spain
Tel.: (34) 936742650
Web Site: http://www.record.elemat.es
Emp.: 42
Automatic Door Mfr
N.A.I.C.S.: 332321
Paulo Gomes (Gen Mgr)

record Holding Nederland B.V. (2)
Cardanuslaan 30, 6865 HK, Doorwerth, Netherlands
Tel.: (31) 263399777
Sales Range: $25-49.9 Million
Emp.: 90
Automatic Door Mfr
N.A.I.C.S.: 332321
Hans Wijnstekers (Mgr)

Subsidiary (Domestic):

record automatische deuren B.V. (3)
Cardanuslaan 30, 6865 HK, Doorwerth, Netherlands
Tel.: (31) 26 33 99 777
Web Site: http://www.recordbv.nl
Sales Range: $25-49.9 Million
Emp.: 100
Automatic Door Mfr
N.A.I.C.S.: 332321

Subsidiary (US):

record Indiana (2)
756 International Dr, Franklin, IN 46131
Tel.: (317) 535-3667
Web Site: http://www.agta-record.com
Emp.: 200
Automatic Door Mfr

N.A.I.C.S.: 332321

Subsidiary (Domestic):

record Turautomation AG (2)
Allmendstrasse 24, Fehraltorf, 8320, Zurich, Switzerland
Tel.: (41) 449549191
Web Site: http://www.record.ch
Emp.: 100
Automatic Door Mfr
N.A.I.C.S.: 332321

Subsidiary (Non-US):

record UK ltd (2)
Unit D 9 Watt Place Hamilton International Park, Blantyre, G72 0AH, United Kingdom
Tel.: (44) 1698376411
Web Site: http://www.recorduk.co.uk
Sales Range: $50-74.9 Million
Emp.: 180
Automatic Door Mfr
N.A.I.C.S.: 332321

record avtomatska vrata d.o.o. (2)
Poslovna cona A 26, 4208, Sencur, Slovenia
Tel.: (386) 59074100
Web Site: http://www.record.si
Sales Range: $25-49.9 Million
Emp.: 10
Automatic Door Mfr
N.A.I.C.S.: 332321

record dorrautomatik sweden AB (2)
Fagelviksvagen 9, Stockholm, 145 84, Sweden
Tel.: (46) 855064630
Web Site: http://www.rdarecord.se
Automatic Door Mfr
N.A.I.C.S.: 332321

record drzwi automatyczne Sp.zo.o (2)
Stara Iwiczna ul Nowa 23, 05-500, Piaseczno, Poland
Tel.: (48) 227377100
Web Site: http://pl.record.global
Sales Range: $25-49.9 Million
Emp.: 20
Automatic Door Mfr
N.A.I.C.S.: 332321

Subsidiary (Domestic):

record international ltd (2)
Allmendstrasse 24, 8320, Fehraltorf, Switzerland
Tel.: (41) 449549191
Web Site: http://www.agta-record.com
Emp.: 250
Automatic Door Mfr
N.A.I.C.S.: 332321
Franz Heigl (Gen Mgr)

Ameristar Perimeter Security USA, Inc. (1)
1555 N Mingo Rd, Tulsa, OK 74116
Tel.: (918) 835-0898
Web Site: http://www.ameristarfence.com
Metal Fence Mfr
N.A.I.C.S.: 332999

Angel Metal Co., Ltd. (1)
1099 Wolam-dong, Dalseo-gu, Daegu, 704-833, Korea (South)
Tel.: (82) 5 3581 0049
Web Site: http://www.angellock.co.kr
Lock Mfr
N.A.I.C.S.: 332510

Arran Isle Ltd. (1)
4 Coop Place, Bradford, BD5 8JX, West Yorkshire, United Kingdom
Tel.: (44) 1422 328850
Web Site: http://www.arranisle.com
Sales Range: $150-199.9 Million
Emp.: 1,000
Building Product Distr
N.A.I.C.S.: 444180
Mark Wild (Dir-Corp Svcs)

Subsidiary (Domestic):

Carlisle Brass Limited (2)
Parkhouse Road, Carlisle, CA3 0JU, United Kingdom
Tel.: (44) 1228511770
Web Site: http://www.carlislebrass.com

Sales Range: $25-49.9 Million
Emp.: 60
Metals Service Center
N.A.I.C.S.: 423510

Heywood Williams Components Limited (2)
1 Brunel Close Drayton Fields Industrial Estate, Daventry, NN11 8RB, Northants, United Kingdom
Tel.: (44) 1327312400
Web Site: http://www.mila.co.uk
Sales Range: $50-74.9 Million
Emp.: 150
PVC Window & Door Hardware Mfr
N.A.I.C.S.: 332510

Unit (Domestic):

Heywood Williams Components Limited (3)
Telford Way, Bedford, B67 6RG, United Kingdom
Tel.: (44) 1234242724
Construction Materials Whslr
N.A.I.C.S.: 423390

Subsidiary (US):

LaSalle Bristol Corp. (2)
601 County Rd 17, Elkhart, IN 46516
Tel.: (574) 295-4400
Web Site: http://www.lasallebristol.com
Emp.: 650
Building Material Mfr & Distr
N.A.I.C.S.: 444180
Larry Campbell (Pres-Distr)

Assa Industrie AB (1)
Kungsgatan 71, PO Box 371, 631 05, Eskilstuna, Sweden (100%)
Tel.: (46) 16177000
Web Site:
http://www.assaabloyopeningsolutions.se
Sales Range: $200-249.9 Million
Emp.: 300
Access and Door Opening Solution Products Mfr
N.A.I.C.S.: 332510

B.C Lasepartner A/S (1)
Ostbirkvej 7 Seden, Odense, 5240, Denmark
Tel.: (45) 66108219
Web Site: http://laasepartner.dk
Hardware Mfr
N.A.I.C.S.: 332510

BAB IKON GmbH Schliesstechnik (1)
Bahlerstrasse 29, Postfach 60 04 19, 14469, Potsdam, Germany
Tel.: (49) 33128880
Web Site: http://www.babikon.com
Sales Range: $50-74.9 Million
Emp.: 100
N.A.I.C.S.: 332510

Baodean Security Products Co. Ltd (1)
273 Wenchang Road West, Taizhou, 318058, Zhejiang, China
Tel.: (86) 576 82881688
Web Site: http://www.baodean.com
Rev.: $79,195,000
Emp.: 2,300
Door Lock Mfr & Distr
N.A.I.C.S.: 332510

Baron Metal Industries Inc. (1)
101 Ashbridge Circle, Woodbridge, L4L 3R5, ON, Canada
Tel.: (416) 749-2111
Web Site: http://www.baronmetal.com
Sales Range: $50-74.9 Million
Emp.: 200
Steel Metal Door Mfr & Distr
N.A.I.C.S.: 332321

CERRADURAS DE COLOMBIA - CERRACOL S.A.S. (1)
Calle 11A Bis No 32A - 17, Bogota, Colombia
Tel.: (57) 1 5962000
Web Site: http://www.yalehome.com.co
Lock Mfr
N.A.I.C.S.: 332510

CERTEGO Oy (1)

Rajatorpantie 8 Virtatalo, 01600, Vantaa, Finland
Tel.: (358) 1070 0700
Web Site: http://www.certego.fi
Security Systems Distr & Services
N.A.I.C.S.: 561621

Caldwell Manufacturing Company North America, LLC (1)
2605 Manitou Rd, Rochester, NY 14624-1109
Tel.: (585) 352-2800
Web Site: http://www.caldwellmfgco.com
Sales Range: $75-99.9 Million
Emp.: 160
Mfr of Balances & PVC Weatherstrip Products, Sash Balance Systems & Vertical Window Sliding Systems
N.A.I.C.S.: 332613
Eric Mertz (Pres & CEO)

Subsidiary (Domestic):

Advantage Manufacturing Corp. (2)
788 Old Dutch Rd, Victor, NY 14564
Tel.: (585) 742-1570
Web Site:
http://www.advantagemanufacturing.com
Hinge Mfr
N.A.I.C.S.: 332510

Subsidiary (Non-US):

Caldwell Hardware, Ltd (2)
Herald Way Binley Industrial Estate, Coventry, CV3 2RQ, United Kingdom
Tel.: (44) 24 7643 7900
Web Site: http://www.caldwell.co.uk
Window Frame Whslr
N.A.I.C.S.: 423310

Capitol Door Services (1)
5860 Alder Ave, Sacramento, CA 95828-1147
Tel.: (916) 266-8000
Web Site: http://www.capitoldoors.com
Automatic Doors & Security Solutions
N.A.I.C.S.: 561621
Roger Lopez (Mgr)

Cheil Industry Co. Ltd (1)
301-1201 Bucheon Techno Park 365 Samjung-Dong, Ohjung-Gu, 421-741, Bucheon, Korea (South)
Tel.: (82) 32 720 6000
Web Site: http://www.cheilauto.com
Door Locks Mfr
N.A.I.C.S.: 332510
Kui Hwan Lee (CEO)

Chubb Union Zimbabwe (Pvt) Ltd (1)
4 Conald Road, Graniteside, Harare, Zimbabwe
Tel.: (263) 4 759 196
Web Site: http://www.assaabloy.com
Emp.: 40
Hardware Mfr
N.A.I.C.S.: 332510
Devon Govendor (Mgr)

City Lasepartner A/S (1)
Kirkevaenget 7, 2500, Valby, Denmark
Tel.: (45) 33 12 12 12
Hardware Mfr
N.A.I.C.S.: 332510

DYNACO Europe NV (1)
Waverstraat 21, Moorsel, 9310, Belgium
Tel.: (32) 53 72 98 98
Web Site: http://www.dynacodoor.com
Emp.: 130
Industrial Door Mfr
N.A.I.C.S.: 332321
Dirk Wouters (Mng Dir)

Ditec Entrematic US Inc (1)
1405 Pkwy View Dr, Pittsburgh, PA 15205
Tel.: (412) 200-5750
Web Site: http://www.hunterautomatics.ca
Sales Range: $25-49.9 Million
Emp.: 4
Metal Door Mfr
N.A.I.C.S.: 332321

Ditec S.p.A. (1)
Via V Pisani 20, 20124, Milan, Italy
Tel.: (39) 02 96 39 11
Web Site: http://www.ditec.it

Sales Range: $100-124.9 Million
Emp.: 550
Automatic Door Distr
N.A.I.C.S.: 423310

Subsidiary (Non-US):

DITEC ESPANA S.L.U. (2)
Pol Ind Valldegata Calle Draper 14, 08350, Barcelona, Spain
Tel.: (34) 93 795 83 99
Hardware Mfr
N.A.I.C.S.: 332510

DITEC Entrematic Canada Inc. (2)
221A Racco Pkwy, Vaughan, L4J 8X9, ON, Canada
Tel.: (416) 674-8880
Web Site: http://www.hunterautomatics.ca
Sales Range: $25-49.9 Million
Emp.: 34
Automatic Swinging Door Mfr
N.A.I.C.S.: 335999

Subsidiary (Domestic):

Ditec D.D. Lazio S.r.l. (2)
Via Casilina 1746/R, 00133, Rome, Italy
Tel.: (39) 0620744853
Door Locks Mfr
N.A.I.C.S.: 332510

Ditec D.D. Lombardia S.r.l. (2)
Via Piersanti Mattarella 10, 20093, Cologno Monzese, Italy
Tel.: (39) 02 27321141
Web Site: http://www.assaabloy.com
Hardware Mfr
N.A.I.C.S.: 332510

Subsidiary (Non-US):

Ditec Swiss S.A. (2)
via Passeggiata 24, 6828, Balerna, Switzerland
Tel.: (41) 848558855
Web Site: http://www.ditec.it
Door Mfr
N.A.I.C.S.: 321911

Ditec Tur GmbH (2)
Erich-Ollenhauer-Str 29, 61440, Oberursel, Germany
Tel.: (49) 9321 2307 0
Web Site: http://www.assaabloy.com
Door Mfr
N.A.I.C.S.: 332510

Door Systems Inc. (1)
751 Expy Dr, Itasca, IL 60143-1321
Tel.: (630) 250-0101
Web Site: http://www.doorsystems.com
Assembly, Installation & Servicing of Overhead Doors & Dock Equipment
N.A.I.C.S.: 238130

EMTEK Products, Inc. (1)
13285 Temple Ave, City of Industry, CA 91746
Tel.: (626) 961-0413
Web Site: http://emtek.com
Sales Range: $25-49.9 Million
Emp.: 50
Door Locks Mfr
N.A.I.C.S.: 332510
Greg Gainer (Pres)

Electronic Security Devices, Inc. (1)
10027 S 51st St Ste 102, Phoenix, AZ 85044
Tel.: (623) 582-4626
Web Site: http://www.securitypower.com
Sales Range: $100-124.9 Million
Emp.: 300
Electronic Security Device Mfr
N.A.I.C.S.: 334419

Flexi Force B.V. (1)
Hanzeweg 19, 3771 NG, Barneveld, Netherlands
Tel.: (31) 342 427777
Web Site: http://www.flexiforce.com
Sales Range: $25-49.9 Million
Emp.: 100
Hardware Mfr
N.A.I.C.S.: 332510

Subsidiary (Non-US):

Flexi Force Iberica, S.L. (2)
Apartado Correos 403 Ctra Nacional 332

Km 211, 46780, Valencia, Spain
Tel.: (34) 96 285 82 50
Web Site: http://www.flexiforce.com
Emp.: 6
Hardware Mfr
N.A.I.C.S.: 332510

Flexi Force Italia S.r.l. (2)
Via Caduti di Nassiriya SNC, Offlaga, Brescia, 25020, Italy
Tel.: (39) 0309936510
Web Site: http://www.flexiforce.com
Sales Range: $25-49.9 Million
Emp.: 6
Hardware Mfr
N.A.I.C.S.: 332510
Julio Gonzalez Boyle (Mng Dir)

Flexi Force Poland Sp. Z.o.o. (2)
Ludwika Norblina 17/19, 95-015, Glowno, Poland
Tel.: (48) 42 650 04 91
Web Site: http://www.flexiforce.com
Hardware Mfr
N.A.I.C.S.: 332510
Jan Moszczynski (Mng Dir)

FlexiForce Hungary Kft. (2)
Kulso-Hadhazi utca 18, Hajduboszormeny, 4220, Hungary
Tel.: (36) 52561260
Hardware Mfr
N.A.I.C.S.: 332510
Imre Olah (Mng Dir)

Frameworks Manufacturing Inc. (1)
1910 Cypress Station Dr Ste 100, Houston, TX 77090
Tel.: (713) 692-5222
Web Site: http://frameworks.com
Sales Range: $25-49.9 Million
Emp.: 50
Interior Aluminum Door Mfr & Distr
N.A.I.C.S.: 332321
Dale Waite (Pres)

HID Global SAS (1)
Le Green Walk Batiment D 33 Rue de Verdun, 92150, Suresnes, France
Tel.: (33) 142048400
Security System Services
N.A.I.C.S.: 561621

Hanchett Entry Systems Inc. (1)
10027 S 51st St Ste 102, Phoenix, AZ 85044
Tel.: (623) 582-4626
Web Site: http://www.hesinnovations.com
Sales Range: $100-124.9 Million
Emp.: 300
Electrical Safety Equipment Mfr
N.A.I.C.S.: 335999
Laurie Springer (Dir-HR)

Helton Industries Ltd. (1)
30840 Peardonville Rd, Abbotsford, BC, Canada
Tel.: (604) 854-3660
Web Site: http://www.heltonindustries.com
Sales Range: $10-24.9 Million
Emp.: 180
Commercial Hardware Mfr
N.A.I.C.S.: 332510
Gerhard Rauch (Co-Founder)

Henderson Nederlands BV (1)
Rootven 14, 5531 MB, Bladel, Netherlands
Tel.: (31) 497 33 20 20
Web Site: http://www.henderson.nl
Sales Range: $25-49.9 Million
Emp.: 7
Door Mfr & Distr
N.A.I.C.S.: 332510

IDD Parts B.V. (1)
Marchandweg 23, 3771 ML, Barneveld, Netherlands
Tel.: (31) 342 490990
Web Site: http://www.iddparts.net
Door Locks Mfr
N.A.I.C.S.: 332510

JPM S.A. (1)
40 route de Paris Avermes, 03021, Moulins, France
Tel.: (33) 4 70 48 40 00
Lock Mfr
N.A.I.C.S.: 332510

Jerith Manufacturing LLC (1)
14400 McNulty Rd, Philadelphia, PA 19154

ASSA ABLOY AB—(Continued)

Tel.: (215) 676-4068
Web Site: http://www.jerith.com
Ornamental Fences & Architectural Metal
Work Mfr
N.A.I.C.S.: 332323

KESO GmbH (1)
Maurerstrasse 6, 21244, Buchholz, Germany
Tel.: (49) 4181 924 0
Web Site: http://www.keso.de
Door Locks Mfr
N.A.I.C.S.: 332722

Lasepartner A/S (1)
Vesterlundvej 20, 2730, Herlev, Denmark
Tel.: (45) 70112211
Web Site: http://www.laasepartner.dk
Sales Range: $25-49.9 Million
Emp.: 50
Door Locks Mfr
N.A.I.C.S.: 332722

Medeco Security Locks Inc (1)
3625 Alleghany Dr, Salem, VA 24153
Tel.: (540) 380-5000
Security Lock Mfr
N.A.I.C.S.: 561622

Mul-T-Lock Ltd. (1)
1 Hirot St, Yavne, 8110601, Israel (100%)
Tel.: (972) 800800108
Web Site: https://www.mul-t-lock.co.il
Sales Range: $75-99.9 Million
Emp.: 350
Develops, Manufactures, Markets & Installs
High Security Cylinders & Locks
N.A.I.C.S.: 561621
Tzachi Wisenfeld (Chm)

Subsidiary (Domestic):

Alba Locking Products, Ltd (2)
Izhak Ben-Tzvi 42 St Ramat-Elyahou Industrial Area, POB 4594, 75633, Rishon le Zion, Israel
Tel.: (972) 3 9615955
Web Site: http://www.alba.co.il
Sales Range: $25-49.9 Million
Emp.: 40
Hardware Mfr & Distr
N.A.I.C.S.: 332510
Oren Avigdoo (CEO)

Subsidiary (Non-US):

Mul-T-Lock Czech, s.r.o. (2)
Dolnomecholupska 1418/12, Prague, 102 00, Czech Republic
Tel.: (420) 226 806 260
Web Site: http://www.multlock.cz
Sales Range: $25-49.9 Million
Emp.: 10
Lock Mfr
N.A.I.C.S.: 332510
Jan Pospichal (Dir-Czech Republic)

Subsidiary (US):

Mul-T-Lock Machinery Ltd. (2)
300 1 State Route 17 S Ste 7, Lodi, NJ 07644-3821
Tel.: (973) 778-3220
Sales Range: $25-49.9 Million
Emp.: 18
Mfr of Lock Industry Specialized Machines
N.A.I.C.S.: 332510

Subsidiary (Domestic):

Mul-T-Lock Machinery Ltd. (2)
Mul-T-Lock Park, 81104, Yavne, Israel
Tel.: (972) 8 942 4660
Web Site: http://www.mul-t-lock.com
Cutting Tool Mfr & Distr
N.A.I.C.S.: 333515

Subsidiary (Non-US):

Mul-T-Lock Technologies Italy SRL (2)
Strada Del Mescolin 62, 31016, Cordignano, Treviso, Italy
Tel.: (39) 0438 912275
Web Site: http://www.mul-t-lock.it
Sales Range: $25-49.9 Million
Emp.: 20
Hardware Mfr
N.A.I.C.S.: 332510

Bruno Azzalini (Gen Mgr)

Subsidiary (US):

Mul-T-Lock USA, Inc. (2)
100 Commerce Way Ste 2, Hackensack, NJ 07601
Tel.: (973) 778-3320
Web Site: http://www.mul-t-lock.com
Emp.: 15
Door Lock & Master Key Mfr
N.A.I.C.S.: 332510
Roy Miller (Pres)

Nemef B.V. (1)
Papegaaiweg 35, 7345 DK, Apeldoorn, Wenum-Wiesel, Netherlands
Tel.: (31) 553128400
Web Site: http://www.nemef.nl
Sales Range: $75-99.9 Million
Emp.: 130
Marketing of Industrial Products
N.A.I.C.S.: 424130

Normstahl GmbH (1)
Drautendorf 58, 4174, Niederwaldkirchen, Austria
Tel.: (43) 72 31 31 28 0
Web Site: http://normstahl.com
Emp.: 50
Safety Equipment Distr
N.A.I.C.S.: 423850

P C Henderson (Ireland) Limited (1)
Westlink Industrial Estate Kylemore Road 10, Dublin, Ireland
Tel.: (353) 1 643 6816
Web Site: http://www.pchenderson.ie
Sales Range: $25-49.9 Million
Emp.: 6
Sliding Gear System Mfr
N.A.I.C.S.: 332510

PORTAFEU SAS (1)
24 Rue des Hautes-Rives, BP 8206, Romilly-sur-Andelle, 27108, Val-de-Reuil, Cedex, France
Tel.: (33) 2 32 68 37 37
Web Site: http://www.portafeu.fr
Door Mfr
N.A.I.C.S.: 332510

Pan Pan DOOR Co LTD (1)
Shuiyuan Town, Yingkou, 115116, Liaoning, China
Tel.: (86) 417 5179389
Metal Door Mfr
N.A.I.C.S.: 332321

Premier Steel Doors & Frames (1)
PO Box 7269, Monroe, LA 71211
Tel.: (318) 361-0796
Web Site: http://www.trustpremier.com
Security Locks Mfr
N.A.I.C.S.: 561621

Subsidiary (Domestic):

Megamet Industries, Inc. (2)
3228 6th Ave N, Birmingham, AL 35222-1222
Tel.: (205) 322-7700
Web Site: http://www.megametusa.com
Rev.: $1,500,000
Emp.: 9
Metal Window & Door Mfr
N.A.I.C.S.: 332321
Edward Wall (Pres)

Productos Metalicos de Seguridad, S.A. de C.V. (1)
Pelicano 242 Del Gustavo A Madero, 07460, Mexico, Mexico
Tel.: (52) 55 51 18 06 00
Metal Door Mfr
N.A.I.C.S.: 332321

Pyropanel Developments Pty Ltd (1)
235 Huntingdale Road, Oakleigh, 3166, VIC, Australia
Tel.: (61) 3 9837 8500
Web Site: http://www.pyropanel.com.au
Sales Range: $25-49.9 Million
Emp.: 10
Fire Protection Door Mfr
N.A.I.C.S.: 332321

Ruko A/S (1)
Marielundvej 20, Herlev, 2730, Denmark
Tel.: (45) 44 54 44 54
Web Site: http://www.ruko.com

Lock Mfr
N.A.I.C.S.: 332510

SECURITY MERCHANTS AUSTRALIA PTY LTD. (1)
Axxess Business Park Unit 144 & 145 / 45 Gilby Road, Mount Waverley, 3149, VIC, Australia
Tel.: (61) 3 9558 8455
Web Site: http://www.security-merchants.com
Emp.: 12
Electronic Security Equipment Distr
N.A.I.C.S.: 423690

Safemark Systems, LP (1)
2101 Park Center Dr, Orlando, FL 32835
Tel.: (407) 299-0044
Web Site: http://www.safemark.com
Commercial Safe & Other Secure Storage Product Designer & Mfr
N.A.I.C.S.: 332999
John Foley (VP-Sls)

Subsidiary (Domestic):

Best Lockers, LLC (2)
9104 Guilford Rd Ste K, Columbia, MD 21045
Web Site: http://www.bestlockers.com
Electronically Secured Commercial Storage Locker Mfr & Whslr
N.A.I.C.S.: 337215
Daryle Bobb (Pres)

Safeplace Ltd. (1)
POB 637, Yavne, 81104, Israel
Tel.: (972) 8 9424279
Web Site: http://www.safeplace-israel.com
Industrial Safety Equipment Mfr & Distr
N.A.I.C.S.: 334419
Ravid Brosh (Pres)

Samhwa Precision Co., Ltd. (1)
2 Na-601 Shiwha Industrial Complex 1262 Jeongwang-dong, Siheung, 429-450, Gyeonggi-do, Korea (South)
Tel.: (82) 31 497 8822
Web Site: http://www.kingdoorcloser.com
Sales Range: $100-124.9 Million
Emp.: 300
Door Closer & Floor Spring Mfr
N.A.I.C.S.: 332321
Tim Jin (Mgr-Quality Control)

Securistyle Group Holdings Limited (1)
Unit A-F Kingsmead Industrial Estate, Cheltenham, GL51 7RE, Gloucestershire, United Kingdom
Tel.: (44) 1242 221 200
Sales Range: $100-124.9 Million
Emp.: 205
Investment Management Service
N.A.I.C.S.: 523999

Securitech Group, Inc. (1)
54-45 44th St, Maspeth, NY 11378
Tel.: (718) 392-9000
Web Site: http://www.securitech.com
Emp.: 50
Hardware Mfr
N.A.I.C.S.: 332510
William Nelson (VP-Sls & Mktg)

Shenzhen Longdian Science Technology Industrial Co., Ltd. (1)
No 7 Shenzhen Komeito Zhendong Hang Road East community, Shenzhen, 518106, China
Tel.: (86) 755 3395 3606
Web Site: http://www.longdiandoor.com
Door Mfr
N.A.I.C.S.: 332321

Sistemas y Technicas de Seguridad, S.A. (1)
Sierra de Segura 15, 28830, San Fernando de Henares, Madrid, Spain
Tel.: (34) 916785500
Web Site: http://www.stslocks.com
Sales Range: $50-74.9 Million
Emp.: 60
Marketing of Industrial Products
N.A.I.C.S.: 424130

Skidata AG (1)
Untersbergstrasse 40, Grodig, 5083, Salzburg, Austria
Tel.: (43) 6 246 8880

Web Site: https://www.skidata.com
Sales Range: $200-249.9 Million
Emp.: 600
Computer & Software Stores
N.A.I.C.S.: 449210

Subsidiary (Non-US):

Cytel (Shanghai) Ltd. (2)
6/F Building 5 No 258 Jinzang Road, Jinqiao Export Processing Zone, Shanghai, China
Tel.: (86) 215 899 0712
Web Site: https://www.subin.cn
Parking Equipment Mfr
N.A.I.C.S.: 334514

SkiData (Schweiz) AG (2)
Schutzenwiese 8, Kriessern, 9451, Saint Gallen, Switzerland
Tel.: (41) 71 737 9393
Web Site: https://www.skidata.com
Sales Range: $25-49.9 Million
Emp.: 50
Computer & Software Stores
N.A.I.C.S.: 449210

Subsidiary (US):

Skidata Inc. (2)
400 Raritan Ctr Pkwy Ste C, Edison, NJ 08817 (100%)
Tel.: (908) 243-0000
Web Site: https://www.skidata.com
Sales Range: $25-49.9 Million
Emp.: 100
Management Consulting Services
N.A.I.C.S.: 541618

Slagelse Laseservice A/S (1)
Bredegade 14, 4200, Slagelse, Denmark
Tel.: (45) 58524148
Metal Door Mfr
N.A.I.C.S.: 332321

Solid AB (1)
Landskronavagen 23, 250 22, Helsingborg, Sweden (100%)
Tel.: (46) 771113113
Web Site: https://www.solidab.se
Sales Range: $50-74.9 Million
Emp.: 25
Door Opening Solution Products Mfr
N.A.I.C.S.: 332510

Stiles Custom Metal, Inc. (1)
1885 Kinser Rd, Ceres, CA 95307
Tel.: (209) 538-3667
Web Site: https://stilesdoors.com
Metal Window & Door Mfr
N.A.I.C.S.: 332321

Sure - Loc Hardware, Inc. (1)
2855 S 1030 W, Salt Lake City, UT 84119
Tel.: (801) 261-9362
Web Site: http://www.surelochardware.com
Emp.: 45
Hardware Merchant Whslr
N.A.I.C.S.: 423710
Bruce Cummings (Pres)

Swesafe AB (1)
Agatan 6, PO Box 503, 749 35, Enkoping, Sweden
Tel.: (46) 771254545
Web Site: http://www.certego.se
Security Equipment Supplier
N.A.I.C.S.: 423710

TESA Talleres de Escoriaza S.A.U. (1)
Barrio de Ventas n 35, 20305, Irun, Guipuzcoa, Spain
Tel.: (34) 943669100
Web Site: http://www.tesa.es
Sales Range: $200-249.9 Million
Emp.: 600
Lock Mfr
N.A.I.C.S.: 332510

Timelox AB (1)
Lodjursgatan 2, SE 261 44, Landskrona, Sweden (100%)
Tel.: (46) 41851300
Web Site: http://www.timelox.com
Sales Range: $1-9.9 Million
Emp.: 40
Mfr of Electronic Locking Systems
N.A.I.C.S.: 561621

Traka Plc (1)

30 Stilebrook Road, Olney, MK46 5EA,
Buckinghamshire, United Kingdom
Tel.: (44) 1234 712345
Web Site: http://www.traka.com
Sales Range: $25-49.9 Million
Emp.: 100
Electronic Key Mfr
N.A.I.C.S.: 334419

TrioVing a.s.   **(1)**
Amoanolitveien 1, PO Box 510, N 1523,
Ski, Moss, Norway   **(100%)**
Tel.: (47) 69245200
Web Site: http://www.trioving.no
Sales Range: $75-99.9 Million
Emp.: 180
N.A.I.C.S.: 332510
Indeborj Veftad *(Mgr-Fin)*

Vigil Health Solutions Inc.   **(1)**
2102-4464 Markham Street, Victoria, V8Z
7X8, BC, Canada
Tel.: (250) 383-6900
Web Site: http://www.vigil.com
Rev.: $4,709,689
Assets: $6,088,960
Liabilities: $2,220,323
Net Worth: $3,868,637
Earnings: $552,660
Fiscal Year-end: 03/31/2021
Health Care Srvices
N.A.I.C.S.: 621999
Troy Griffiths *(Pres & CEO)*

VingCard Elsafe AS   **(1)**
Vanrikinkuja 2, 2600, Espoo, Finland
Tel.: (358) 20 599 4200
Web Site: http://www.vingcardelsafe.com
Electronic Safety System Mfr
N.A.I.C.S.: 334419
Kim Lindstrom *(Mgr-Sls)*

**VingCard Elsafe Japan
Corporation**   **(1)**
Kitanomaru Residence 2F 2-3-9 Kudankita
Chiyodaku, Kudankita Chiyoda-Ku, Tokyo,
1020073, Japan
Tel.: (81) 335561717
Web Site: http://www.vce.co.jp
Electronic Door Lock Distr
N.A.I.C.S.: 423690
Yoshini Tsutaki *(Gen.mgr)*

**VingCard Elsafe Pacific
Corporation**   **(1)**
816 N Marine Corps Dr EVA II Bldg Ste
118, Tumon, GU 96913-4493
Tel.: (671) 649-0163
Web Site: http://www.vcepacific.com
Emp.: 8
Electronic Door Lock Sales & Installation
Services
N.A.I.C.S.: 423690
Yoshimi Tsutaki *(Pres)*

**Yale La Fonte Sistemas de Segur-
anca LTDA**   **(1)**
Rua Augusto Ferreira de Moraes 618, So-
corro, 04763-001, Sao Paulo, Brazil
Tel.: (55) 11 5693 4700
Web Site: http://www.yalelafonte.com.br
Sales Range: $50-74.9 Million
Emp.: 200
Electronic Security System Mfr
N.A.I.C.S.: 334419

**Yale Residential Security Products,
Inc.**   **(1)**
225 Episcopal Rd, Berlin, CT 06037
Tel.: (678) 728-7400
Web Site: http://us.yalehome.com
Door Locks Mfr
N.A.I.C.S.: 332510

Yale Security (SA) (Pty) Ltd   **(1)**
176 Progress Road, Techikon, Roodepoort,
1724, South Africa
Tel.: (27) 11 781 9110
Sales Range: $100-124.9 Million
Emp.: 354
Hardware Mfr
N.A.I.C.S.: 332510

Yalelock Spain   **(1)**
C/Aramburuzabala 23, Escoriaza, 20540,
Guipuzcoa, Spain
Tel.: (34) 943 71 29 29
Web Site: http://www.yalelock.es
Sales Range: $25-49.9 Million
Emp.: 6
Security Lock Mfr

N.A.I.C.S.: 561622

**Zhejiang FACEA Vehicle Locks Co
Ltd.**   **(1)**
No 80 Xinze Road Suzhou Industrial Park,
Suzhou, 215006, Jiangsu, China
Tel.: (86) 512 87182968
Door Locks Mfr
N.A.I.C.S.: 332510

effeff France S.A.S.   **(1)**
5A rue des Carrieres CS 30052, 67172,
Brumath, Cedex, France
Tel.: (33) 3 88 59 31 59
Web Site: http://www.effeff.de
Safety Equipment Mfr
N.A.I.C.S.: 332510

ASSAM ENTRADE LIMITED
26/49 Birhana Road, Kanpur,
208001, India
Tel.: (91) 5123500151
Web Site:
   https://www.assamentrade.com
Year Founded: 1985
542911—(BOM)
Rev.: $984,438
Assets: $7,899,187
Liabilities: $456,538
Net Worth: $7,442,649
Earnings: $305,856
Emp.: 7
Fiscal Year-end: 03/31/22
Financial Services
N.A.I.C.S.: 523150
Nishant Gupta *(Mng Dir)*

ASSAM PETRO-CHEMICALS
LTD.
4th Floor Orion Place Bhangagarh
GS Road, Guwahati, 781005, India
Tel.: (91) 361 246 1470
Web Site:
   http://www.assampetrochemical.com
Rev.: $12,452,599
Assets: $133,758,244
Liabilities: $64,510,223
Net Worth: $69,248,021
Earnings: ($1,380,042)
Emp.: 313
Fiscal Year-end: 03/31/20
Petrochemical Products Mfr
N.A.I.C.S.: 325110
Bikul Ch. Deka *(Chm)*

ASSAS FOR CONCRETE
PRODUCTS CO. LTD.
Al Jeeza, PO Box 248, Amman,
16010, Jordan
Tel.: (962) 64711609
Web Site: https://www.assas.jo
Year Founded: 1997
ASAS—(AMM)
Rev.: $7,024,087
Assets: $15,980,484
Liabilities: $6,799,108
Net Worth: $9,181,376
Earnings: ($642,149)
Emp.: 132
Fiscal Year-end: 12/31/20
Construction Materials Supplier
N.A.I.C.S.: 423320

ASSECO POLAND S.A.
Olchowa 14, 35-322, Rzeszow, Po-
land
Tel.: (48) 178885555   **PL**
Web Site: https://www.asseco.com
Year Founded: 1991
ASOZF—(OTCIQ)
Sales Range: $1-4.9 Billion
Holding Company; Software Pub-
lisher & Distr
N.A.I.C.S.: 551112
Torben Falholt *(CEO-Asseco Den-
mark)*

Subsidiaries:

ADH Soft Sp. z.o.o.   **(1)**
Ul 17 Stycznia 74, Warsaw, 02142, Poland
Tel.: (48) 22 646 62 02
Web Site: http://www.adh.com.pl
Financial Software Development Services
N.A.I.C.S.: 541511
Pawel Barchwic *(Chm)*

Asseco Austria GmbH   **(1)**
Pummerinfeld 1b, 4490, Sankt Florian, Aus-
tria
Tel.: (43) 72242005130
Web Site: http://www.asseco.com
Sales Range: $25-49.9 Million
Emp.: 40
IT Development Services
N.A.I.C.S.: 541512
Markus Haller *(Pres)*

Asseco Business Solutions S.A.   **(1)**
4c Konrada Wallenroda Str, 20-607, Lublin,
Poland
Tel.: (48) 815353000
Web Site: http://www.assecobs.pl
Rev.: $85,041,200
Assets: $119,819,625
Liabilities: $28,966,990
Net Worth: $90,852,635
Earnings: $21,425,413
Emp.: 1,069
Fiscal Year-end: 12/31/2022
Business Management Software Publisher
N.A.I.C.S.: 513210
Wojciech Barczentewicz *(Chm-Mgmt Bd)*

Subsidiary (Domestic):

Macrologic S.A.   **(2)**
Klopotowskiego 22, 03-717, Warsaw,
Poland   **(96.73%)**
Tel.: (48) 222 566 222
Web Site: http://www.assecobs.pl
Information Technology Consulting Services
N.A.I.C.S.: 541511

Asseco Central Europe, a.s.   **(1)**
Trencianska 56/A, 821 09, Bratislava,
Slovakia   **(98.68%)**
Tel.: (421) 2 20 838 400
Web Site: http://www.asseco.com
Rev.: $65,621,520
Assets: $163,475,042
Liabilities: $50,187,218
Net Worth: $113,287,824
Earnings: $9,226,954
Emp.: 3,000
Fiscal Year-end: 12/31/2018
Information Technology Consulting Services
N.A.I.C.S.: 541512
Jozef Klein *(Chm, CEO & Dir-Pub SK BU)*

Asseco Denmark A/S   **(1)**
Kronprinsessegade 54, 1306, Copenhagen,
Denmark
Tel.: (45) 33 36 46 60
Web Site: http://www.asseco.dk
Sales Range: $25-49.9 Million
Emp.: 3
Information Technology Consulting Services
N.A.I.C.S.: 541512
Torben Falholt *(CEO)*

Asseco Germany AG   **(1)**
Amalienbadstrabe 41 Bau 54, 76227,
Karlsruhe, Germany
Tel.: (49) 721 91432 0
Software Development & Management Ser-
vices
N.A.I.C.S.: 541511
Markus Haller *(CEO)*

**Asseco South Eastern Europe
S.A.**   **(1)**
Branickiego 13, 02-972, Warsaw, Poland
Tel.: (48) 225748630
Web Site: https://see.asseco.com
Rev.: $393,280,661
Assets: $469,510,627
Liabilities: $188,367,834
Net Worth: $281,142,793
Earnings: $49,235,291
Emp.: 3,806
Fiscal Year-end: 12/31/2022
Software & Computer Applicatons
N.A.I.C.S.: 541512
Piotr Jelenski *(Chm-Mgmt Bd)*

Subsidiary (Non-US):

Asseco SEE Sh.p.k.   **(2)**

Veternik Zona Industriale Nn, 10000, Pris-
tina, Kosovo, Serbia
Tel.: (381) 38 55 77 99
Web Site: http://www.asseco.com
Software Development Services
N.A.I.C.S.: 541511

Asseco SEE Teknoloji A.S.   **(2)**
Spine Tower Buyukdere Cad 243 Kat 24,
34485, Istanbul, Turkiye
Tel.: (90) 212 385 05 05
Web Site: http://tr.asseco.com
Banking Software Development Services
N.A.I.C.S.: 541511
Hatice Ayas *(Chm-Mgmt Bd)*

Asseco SEE d.o.o.   **(2)**
Litostrojska Cesta 44c, 1000, Ljubljana,
Slovenia
Tel.: (386) 1 620 52 80
Web Site: http://www.asseco.com
Emp.: 35
Software Development Services
N.A.I.C.S.: 541511
Tamas Pletser *(Gen Mgr)*

Asseco SEE d.o.o.   **(2)**
Fra Andela Zvizdovica 1, 71000, Sarajevo,
Bosnia & Herzegovina
Tel.: (387) 33 726 230
Financial Software Development Services
N.A.I.C.S.: 541511
Darko Glamocanin *(Chm-Mgmt Bd)*

Asseco SEE d.o.o.   **(2)**
Ulica Grada Vukovara 269d, 10000, Za-
greb, Croatia
Tel.: (385) 1 30 30 000
Financial Software Development Services
N.A.I.C.S.: 541511
Ljiljana Ivanek *(Member-Mgmt Bd)*

Asseco SEE d.o.o.   **(2)**
Bulevar Milutina Milankovica 19g, 11070,
Belgrade, Serbia
Tel.: (381) 11 2013 111
Software Development & Management Ser-
vices
N.A.I.C.S.: 541511
Milos Matovic *(Dir-Fin)*

Asseco SEE d.o.o.   **(2)**
Admirala Zmajevica Br 11, 81000,
Podgorica, Montenegro
Tel.: (382) 20 651 951
Web Site: http://www.asseco.com
Sales Range: $25-49.9 Million
Emp.: 9
Software Development Services
N.A.I.C.S.: 541511
Marko Simonovic *(CEO)*

Asseco SEE d.o.o.e.l.   **(2)**
Naroden front 17, 1000, Skopje, North
Macedonia
Tel.: (389) 2 32 48 000
Software Development & Management Ser-
vices
N.A.I.C.S.: 541511
Aleksandar Kormushoski *(Member-Mgmt
Bd)*

Asseco SEE sh.p.k.   **(2)**
EGT Tower no 6/1, Tirana, Albania
Tel.: (355) 4 226 9320
Web Site: http://www.asseco.com
Sales Range: $25-49.9 Million
Emp.: 9
Software Developer
N.A.I.C.S.: 513210
Fedrico Montilla *(Mgr-Bus Dev)*

EST A.S.   **(2)**
Podoli 1237, 584 01, Ledec nad Sazavou,
Czech Republic
Tel.: (420) 569 726 097
Web Site: http://www.estplus.cz
Printing Equipment Distr
N.A.I.C.S.: 424950
Ivana Drahokoupilova *(Dir-Sls & Fin)*

Asseco Spain SA   **(1)**
Julian Camarillo 26 3 A-1, 28037, Madrid,
Spain
Tel.: (34) 913 756 000
Web Site: http://es.asseco.com
Emp.: 150
Information Technology Consulting Services
N.A.I.C.S.: 541512
Jose Antonio Pinilla *(CEO)*

Asseco Poland S.A.—(Continued)

Combidata Poland Sp. z.o.o. **(1)**
ul Zwirki i Wigury 15, 81-387, Gdynia, Poland
Tel.: (48) 58 550 95 50
Educational Software Development Services
N.A.I.C.S.: 541511

Formula Systems (1985) Ltd. **(1)**
Yahadut Canada 1 st. Or Yehuda, 6037501, Israel **(50.7%)**
Tel.: (972) 35389292
Web Site: https://www.formulasystems.com
Rev.: $2,620,903,000
Assets: $2,812,601,000
Liabilities: $1,504,416,000
Net Worth: $1,308,185,000
Earnings: $165,732,000
Emp.: 21,900
Fiscal Year-end: 12/31/2023
Holding Company; Software Developer
N.A.I.C.S.: 551112
Asaf Berenstin (CFO)

Subsidiary (Domestic):

Magic Software Enterprises Ltd. **(2)**
5 HaPlada St, Or Yehuda, 6037501, Israel **(47.12%)**
Tel.: (972) 35389292
Web Site: https://www.magicsoftware.com
Rev.: $535,052,000
Assets: $522,406,000
Liabilities: $231,462,000
Net Worth: $290,944,000
Earnings: $42,502,000
Emp.: 3,628
Fiscal Year-end: 12/31/2023
Computer Network & Internet Software Developer
N.A.I.C.S.: 513210
Guy Bernstein (CEO)

Subsidiary (US):

CoreTech Consulting Group LLC **(3)**
500 W. Office Center Dr, Ste 150, Washington, PA 19034
Tel.: (215) 706-4500
Web Site: http://www.coretech.com
Information Technology Services
N.A.I.C.S.: 519290

Subsidiary (Domestic):

Theoris Inc. **(4)**
8888 Keystone Crossing Ste 1550, Indianapolis, IN 46240
Tel.: (317) 849-4444
Web Site: http://www.theoris.com
Rev.: $23,500,000
Emp.: 500
Provider of Technology Solutions: Computer Software Systems Analysis & Design
N.A.I.C.S.: 541511

Subsidiary (Non-US):

Magic Software Enterprises France **(3)**
9 bis rue Henri Martin, 92415, Boulogne, Cedex, France **(100%)**
Tel.: (33) 149105858
Web Site: http://www.magicsoftware.com
Developer of Computer Network & Internet Software
N.A.I.C.S.: 541512
Eric Choppe (Mng Dir)

Magic Software Enterprises GmbH **(3)**
Lise Meitner Strasse 3, 85737, Ismaning, Germany **(100%)**
Tel.: (49) 89962730
Web Site: http://www.magicsoftware.com
Developer of Computer Network & Internet Software
N.A.I.C.S.: 513210
Stephan Romeder (VP-Bus Dev)

Magic Software Enterprises Hungary Ltd. **(3)**
Pava Str 8/III, Budapest, H-1094, Hungary
Tel.: (36) 12169910
Web Site: http://www.magicsoftware.com
Developer of Computer Network & Internet Software
N.A.I.C.S.: 541512

Marton Szluha (Gen Mgr)

Subsidiary (US):

Magic Software Enterprises Inc. **(3)**
24422 Avenida de Carlota Ste 365, Laguna Hills, CA 92653 **(100%)**
Tel.: (949) 250-1718
Web Site: http://www.magicsoftware.com
Developer of Computer Network & Internet Software
N.A.I.C.S.: 513210

Subsidiary (Non-US):

Magic Software Enterprises India Pvt. Ltd. **(3)**
9-12 Tara Icon Mumbai Pune Road, Pune, 411 003, India **(100%)**
Tel.: (91) 2041022022
Developer of Computer Network & Internet Software
N.A.I.C.S.: 541512
Srinivas Reddy (Reg Mgr)

Magic Software Enterprises Nederland B.V. **(3)**
Wiltonstraat 40, 3905 KW, Veenendaal, Netherlands **(100%)**
Tel.: (31) 306566266
Web Site: http://www.magicsoftware.com
Developer of Computer Network & Internet Software
N.A.I.C.S.: 541512

Magic Software Enterprises UK Ltd. **(3)**
Lily Hill House Lily Hill Rd, Bracknell, RG12 2SJ, Berks, United Kingdom **(100%)**
Tel.: (44) 1344667000
Web Site: http://www.magicsoftware.com
Developer of Computer Network & Internet Software
N.A.I.C.S.: 541512

Magic Software Japan KK **(3)**
Shinjyuku Front Tower 24F 2-21-1 Kitashinjyuku, Shinjyuku-ku, Tokyo, 169-0074, Japan **(100%)**
Tel.: (81) 359373300
Web Site: http://www.magicsoftware.com
Developer of Computer Network & Internet Software
N.A.I.C.S.: 541512

Subsidiary (Domestic):

Matrix IT Ltd. **(2)**
3 Atir Yeda Kfar Saba, Herzliya Pituach, 46120, Israel **(50.1%)**
Tel.: (972) 99598840
Web Site: https://www.matrix-globalservices.com
Rev.: $1,445,532,510
Assets: $1,128,382,356
Liabilities: $822,408,607
Net Worth: $305,973,748
Earnings: $68,201,408
Emp.: 11,200
Fiscal Year-end: 12/31/2023
Computer System Design Services
N.A.I.C.S.: 541512
Nic Cronin (Mng Dir)

Subsidiary (US):

Exzac, Inc. **(3)**
Harborside Financial Ctr Plz 5 Ste 2720, Jersey City, NJ 07311
Tel.: (201) 204-5300
Web Site: http://www.exzac.com
Sales Range: $10-24.9 Million
Emp.: 300
Management Consulting Services
N.A.I.C.S.: 541611
Ruth Ben-Hur (Controller)

Network Infrastructure Technologies, Inc. **(3)**
90 John St 7th Fl, New York, NY 10038
Tel.: (212) 404-7340
Web Site: http://www.nitconnect.com
Information Technology Services Solutions
N.A.I.C.S.: 519290
Lior Blik (Pres & CEO)

Xtivia, Inc. **(3)**
304 S 8th St Ste 201, Colorado Springs, CO 80905
Tel.: (719) 623-5870

Web Site: http://www.xtivia.com
Sales Range: $10-24.9 Million
Emp.: 250
IT Solutions
N.A.I.C.S.: 541512
Dennis Robinson (Pres & CEO)

Subsidiary (Domestic):

Connect The Knowledge Network Corp. **(4)**
5602 S Nevada St, Littleton, CO 80120-1116
Tel.: (303) 730-7171
Web Site: http://www.connectknowledge.com
Sales Range: $10-24.9 Million
Emp.: 15
Computer System Design Services
N.A.I.C.S.: 541512
Maureen Clarry (Mng Dir)

Subsidiary (US):

nextSource Inc. **(2)**
1040 Ave of the Americas 24th Fl, New York, NY 10018 **(100%)**
Tel.: (212) 736-5870
Web Site: http://www.nextsource.com
Workforce Management Software & Services
N.A.I.C.S.: 513210
Catherine Candland (CEO)

ZUI Novum Sp. z.o.o. **(1)**
Ul Spokojna 9a, 18-400, Lomza, Poland
Tel.: (48) 86 216 98 00
Sales Range: $25-49.9 Million
Emp.: 5
Banking Software Development Services
N.A.I.C.S.: 541511

ZUI OTAGO Sp, z o.o. **(1)**
Ul Heweliusza 11, Gdansk, 80-890, Poland
Tel.: (48) 58 740 4000
Software Development Management Services
N.A.I.C.S.: 541511

ASSEMBLIN AB
Vastberge Alle 1, Hagersten, 126 30, Sweden
Tel.: (46) 10 472 60 00
Web Site: http://www.assemblin.com
Engineeering Services
N.A.I.C.S.: 541330
Fredrik Allthin (Pres)

ASSEMS INC.
31 Eulsukdo-daero 873 beon-gil, Saha-gu, Busan, Korea (South)
Tel.: (82) 517133900
Web Site: https://assems1.itrocks.kr
Year Founded: 2003
136410—(KRS)
Rev.: $40,691,478
Assets: $76,161,452
Liabilities: $30,989,964
Net Worth: $45,171,488
Earnings: $5,562,297
Emp.: 90
Fiscal Year-end: 12/31/22
Adhesive Mfr
N.A.I.C.S.: 325520

ASSET FIVE GROUP PUBLIC COMPANY LIMITED
199 S Oasis Building 12th Floor Unit 1210 1211 1212, Vibhavadi Rangsit Road Chom Phon Subdistrict Chatuchak District, Bangkok, 10900, Thailand
Tel.: (66) 20263512
Web Site: https://www.assetfive.co.th
Year Founded: 2013
A5—(THA)
Rev.: $43,662,603
Assets: $99,988,523
Liabilities: $59,066,731
Net Worth: $40,921,791
Earnings: $14,783,806
Emp.: 60
Fiscal Year-end: 12/31/23

Real Estate Development Services
N.A.I.C.S.: 531390
Kriangkrai Siravanichkan (Chm)

ASSET PLUS LIMITED
Level 2 Bayleys House 30 Gaunt Street, Wynyard Quarter, Auckland, 1010, New Zealand
Tel.: (64) 90000101   NZ
Web Site:
   https://www.assetplusnz.co.nz
Year Founded: 1994
APL—(NZX)
Sales Range: $10-24.9 Million
Diversified Property Trust
N.A.I.C.S.: 523940

ASSET RESOLUTION LIMITED
Unit 3B Level 3 60 Hindmarsh Square, Adelaide, 5000, SA, Australia
Tel.: (61) 884230170   AU
Web Site:
   http://www.arlimited.com.au
Year Founded: 2012
ASS—(NSXA)
Rev.: $114,833
Assets: $6,531,765
Liabilities: $101,558
Net Worth: $6,430,208
Earnings: ($138,523)
Fiscal Year-end: 06/30/20
Financial Services
N.A.I.C.S.: 522299
Victoria Marie Allinson (Sec)

ASSET VANTAGE SYSTEMS PVT. LTD.
167 Atlanta Building Nariman Point, Mumbai, 400021, Maharashtra, India
Tel.: (91) 2222873546   In
Web Site:
   http://www.assetvantage.com
Year Founded: 2011
Financial Management Software Developer, Publisher & Whslr
N.A.I.C.S.: 513210
Sunil K. Dalal (Chm & Mng Dir)

Subsidiaries:

Asset Vantage Inc. **(1)**
396 Pacific St Ste 201, Stamford, CT 06902
Web Site: http://www.assetvantage.com
Financial Management Software Whslr
N.A.I.C.S.: 423430
Mark Rogozinski (Global CEO)

Subsidiary (Domestic):

Financial Navigator, Inc. **(2)**
275 Saratoga Ave Ste 260, Santa Clara, CA 95050
Tel.: (650) 962-0300
Web Site: http://www.finnav.com
Sales Range: $1-9.9 Million
Custom Computer Programming Services
N.A.I.C.S.: 541511
C. Edward Van Deman (Co-Founder & CEO)

ASSET WORLD CORP PUBLIC COMPANY LIMITED
54th FL Empire Tower 1 South Sathorn Rd, Yannawa Sathorn, Bangkok, 10120, Thailand
Tel.: (66) 21809999   TH
Web Site:
   https://www.assetworldcorp-th.com
Year Founded: 2009
AWC—(THA)
Rev.: $554,960,910
Assets: $5,033,784,308
Liabilities: $2,480,186,356
Net Worth: $2,553,597,952
Earnings: $149,011,772
Emp.: 6,810
Fiscal Year-end: 12/31/23
Real Estate Development Services
N.A.I.C.S.: 531390
Karn Prativedwannakij (CFO)

Subsidiaries:

Asiatique Riverfront Co., Ltd. (1)
2194 Charoenkrung Road, Wat Phrayakrai
District Bangkor Laem, Bangkok, 10120,
Thailand
Tel.: (66) 922460812
Web Site: http://www.asiatiquethailand.com
Ship Restaurant Operator
N.A.I.C.S.: 722511

**T.C.C. Commercial Property Manage-
ment Co., Ltd.** (1)
Empire Tower South Sathorn Rd, Yannawa
Sathorn, Bangkok, 10120, Thailand
Tel.: (66) 26702000
Web Site: http://www.tcccpm.com
Property Management Services
N.A.I.C.S.: 531311

ASSETCO PLC
Singleton Court Business Park, Wo-
nastow Road, Monmouth, NP25 5JA,
United Kingdom
Tel.: (44) 2085153999   UK
Web Site: http://www.assetco.com
Year Founded: 2003
ASTO—(AIM)
Rev.: $9,261,396
Assets: $115,586,298
Liabilities: $17,605,710
Net Worth: $97,980,588
Earnings: ($10,484,172)
Fiscal Year-end: 09/30/22
Fire & Rescue Services
N.A.I.C.S.: 922160
Tudor Davies *(Chm)*

Subsidiaries:

AssetCo Technical Rescue (1)
Meldon Quarry Training Centre Meldon
Quarry, Okehampton, Devon, EX20 4LT,
Cornwall, United Kingdom
Tel.: (44) 1208814538
Web Site: https://www.rigsystems.co.uk
Sales Range: $10-24.9 Million
Emp.: 6
Rescue Training & Consulting Services
N.A.I.C.S.: 611699
Matt Bray *(Mng Dir)*

AssetCo UAE (1)
PO Box 62104, Abu Dhabi, United Arab
Emirates
Tel.: (971) 25587707
Sales Range: $25-49.9 Million
Emergency Planning & Support Services
N.A.I.C.S.: 624230

Nene Whitewater Centre Ltd. (1)
Bedford Road, Northampton, NN4 7AA,
United Kingdom
Tel.: (44) 1604634040
Web Site:
  https://www.northamptonactive.com
Sales Range: $50-74.9 Million
Emp.: 4
Sporting Facilities & Training Services
N.A.I.C.S.: 713940

River & Mercantile Group PLC (1)
30 Coleman Street, London, EC2R 5AL,
United Kingdom
Tel.: (44) 203 327 5100
Web Site:
  http://www.riverandmercantile.com
Holding Company; Advisory & Asset Man-
agement Services
N.A.I.C.S.: 551112
James Barham *(CEO)*

SVM Asset Management Limited (1)
7 Castle Street, Edinburgh, EH2 3AH,
United Kingdom
Tel.: (44) 1312266699
Web Site: http://www.svmonline.co.uk
Asset Management Services
N.A.I.C.S.: 523940
Giles Robinson *(Head-Sls & Mktg)*

Saracen Fund Managers Limited (1)
6th Floor 7 Castle Street, Edinburgh, EH2
3AH, United Kingdom
Tel.: (44) 1312029100
Web Site:
  https://www.saracenfundmanagers.com

Fund Management Services
N.A.I.C.S.: 525190

ASSETOWL LIMITED
Tel.: (61) 894249320   AU
Web Site: https://www.assetowl.com
Year Founded: 2014
AO1—(ASX)
Assets: $19,304
Liabilities: $1,208,761
Net Worth: ($1,189,457)
Earnings: ($347,517)
Emp.: 20
Fiscal Year-end: 06/30/24
Investment Services
N.A.I.C.S.: 523999
Sean Meakin *(Sec)*

**ASSETWISE PUBLIC COM-
PANY LIMITED**
9 Soi Ram Intra 5 Intersection 23,
Anusawari Subdistrict Bang Khen
District, Bangkok, 10220, Thailand
Tel.: (66) 21680000
Web Site: https://assetwise.co.th
Year Founded: 2005
ASW—(THA)
Rev.: $197,633,336
Assets: $711,225,230
Liabilities: $492,757,303
Net Worth: $218,467,927
Earnings: $35,405,032
Emp.: 574
Fiscal Year-end: 12/31/23
Holding Company
N.A.I.C.S.: 551112
Sarawut Charuchinda *(Chm)*

**ASSICURAZIONI GENERALI
S.P.A.**
Piazza Duca degli Abruzzi 2, 34132,
Trieste, Italy
Tel.: (39) 040671111   IT
Web Site: https://www.generali.com
Year Founded: 1831
G—(EUR)
Rev.: $104,697,634,080
Assets: $669,034,610,400
Liabilities: $629,983,947,840
Net Worth: $39,050,662,560
Earnings: $2,495,783,680
Emp.: 72,644
Fiscal Year-end: 12/31/20
Real Estate Management Services
N.A.I.C.S.: 551112
Sandro Panizza *(Chief Insurance &
Investments Officer-Grp)*

Subsidiaries:

AXA Insurance S.A. (1)
48 Michalakopoulou Str, 115 28, Athens,
Greece
Tel.: (30) 210 72 68 000
Web Site: http://www.axa-insurance.gr
General Insurance Services
N.A.I.C.S.: 524210

**Akcionarsko drustvo za reosiguranje
Generali Reosiguranje Srbija** (1)
Vladimira Popovica 8, 11070, Novi Beograd,
Serbia
Tel.: (381) 112220555
Property & Casualty Insurance Services
N.A.I.C.S.: 524126

**Akcionarsko drustvo za upravljanje
dobrovoljnim penzijskim fondom
Generali** (1)
Vladimira Popovica 8, 11070, Novi Beograd,
Serbia
Tel.: (381) 112011764
Web Site: https://www.penzijskifond.rs
Pension Fund Management Services
N.A.I.C.S.: 523940
Natasa Marjanovic *(Pres)*

Alfuturo Servizi Assicurativi s.r.l. (1)
Piazza Tre Torri 1, 20145, Milan, Italy
Tel.: (39) 0240824100

Web Site:
  https://www.alfuturoserviziassicurativi.it
N.A.I.C.S.: 531390

Alleanza Assicurazioni S.p.A. (1)
Piazza Tre Torri 1, 20145, Milan,
Italy   **(50.4%)**
Tel.: (39) 0240824111
Web Site: https://www.alleanza.it
Sales Range: $5-14.9 Billion
Emp.: 3,600
Fire Insurance Services
N.A.I.C.S.: 524113

Subsidiary (Domestic):

Agricola San Giorgio S.p.A. (2)
Via Zovatto 71 Loncon, Annone, 30020,
Venice, Italy   **(100%)**
Tel.: (39) 0422864411
Web Site: http://www.genagricola.it
Sales Range: $1-9.9 Million
Emp.: 15
Grower of Bread Wheat, Durum Wheat,
Sweet Corn, Rice, Sugar Beets, Wine
Grapes, Pears & Actinide
N.A.I.C.S.: 111140

Fondi Alleanza S.G.R.p.A. (2)
Via Luigi Sturzo 35, 20154, Milan,
Italy   **(100%)**
Tel.: (39) 0248248111
Web Site: http://www.fondialleanza.it
Manager of Mutual Funds
N.A.I.C.S.: 525910

La Venezia Assicurazioni S.p.A. (2)
Via Ferretto 1, 31021, Mogliano Veneto,
Treviso, Italy   **(100%)**
Tel.: (39) 0415939701
Web Site: http://www.genertellife.it
Life Insurance
N.A.I.C.S.: 524113

Subsidiary (Domestic):

Semgimenenea S.p.A. (3)
Via Ferretto 1, 31021, Mogliano Veneto, TV,
Italy   **(100%)**
Tel.: (39) 0415939801
Sales Range: $50-74.9 Million
Emp.: 50
Securities Brokerage
N.A.I.C.S.: 523150

Alleanza Toro S.p.A. (1)
Via Mazzini 53, 10123, Turin, Italy
Tel.: (39) 0110029111
Web Site: http://www.toroassicurazioni.it
Sales Range: $1-4.9 Billion
Emp.: 3,213
Life, Property & Casualty Insurance Ser-
vices
N.A.I.C.S.: 524126
Luigi De Puppi *(Chm & CEO)*

Subsidiary (Domestic):

**Alleanza Toro Servizi Assicurativi
S.r.l** (2)
Piazza Duca degli Abruzzi 1, 34132, Tri-
este, Italy
Tel.: (39) 02 62961
General Insurance Services
N.A.I.C.S.: 524210

ISIM S.p.A. (2)
Louis Pasteur Street 6/D, 10146, Turin, Italy
Tel.: (39) 011798194
Marketing Consulting Services
N.A.I.C.S.: 541613

**Ambulanta ZDRAVJE, zdravstvene
storitve, d.o.o.** (1)
Path to the Spring 6, Polje, 1260, Ljubljana,
Slovenia
Tel.: (386) 30704429
Web Site: http://www.ambulanta-zdravje.si
Ambulatory Health Care Services
N.A.I.C.S.: 621999

Assicurazioni Generali (1)
28 Liberty St Ste 3040, New York, NY
10005
Tel.: (212) 602-7600
Web Site: https://www.generaliusa.com
Insurance Services
N.A.I.C.S.: 524298
John Martini *(CEO)*

**Assicurazioni Generali S.p.A. - Gen-
erali Global London Unit** (1)
55 Mark Lane, London, EC3R 7NE, United
Kingdom
Tel.: (44) 2072656200
Web Site: https://www.generali.co.uk
General Insurance Services
N.A.I.C.S.: 524298

Banca Generali S.p.A. (1)
Via Machiavelli 4, 34132, Trieste,
Italy   **(50.6%)**
Tel.: (39) 0407777111
Web Site: https://www.bancagenerali.com
Rev.: $1,252,772,866
Assets: $16,184,504,969
Liabilities: $16,040,982,669
Net Worth: $143,522,300
Earnings: $337,635,807
Emp.: 962
Fiscal Year-end: 12/31/2020
Asset Management, Financial Planning &
Investment Banking & Advisory Services
N.A.I.C.S.: 523150
Giancarlo Fancel *(Chm)*

Subsidiary (Domestic):

BG Fiduciaria Sim S.p.A. (2)
Via Ugo Bassi 6, 20159, Milan, Italy
Tel.: (39) 0268826511
Web Site: http://www.bgfiduciaria.it
Emp.: 8
Asset Management Services
N.A.I.C.S.: 523940
Piero Mastrorosa *(Mgr)*

GenerFid S.p.A. (2)
Via dei Piatti 11, 20123, Milan, Italy
Tel.: (39) 0243827917
Web Site: https://generfid.it
Asset Management Services
N.A.I.C.S.: 523940

Subsidiary (Non-US):

Generali Fund Management S.A. (2)
14 Allee Marconi, 2120, Luxembourg, Lux-
embourg
Tel.: (352) 28126500
Web Site: https://www.bgfml.lu
Sales Range: $25-49.9 Million
Emp.: 20
Investment Management Service
N.A.I.C.S.: 523999
Marylene Alix *(Gen Mgr)*

Cafel Inversiones 2008, S.L. (1)
Calle Orense 2 - 7, Madrid, 28020,
Spain   **(100%)**
Tel.: (34) 981619353
Real Estate Management Services
N.A.I.C.S.: 531390

Caja de Seguros S.A. (1)
Fitz Roy 957 RA-1414, Buenos Aires, Ar-
gentina
Tel.: (54) 1148578118
Insurance Services
N.A.I.C.S.: 524210

Care Management Network Inc. (1)
Erin Court Suite 1 Upper Bishop's Court
Hill, Saint Michael, Barbados
Tel.: (246) 246 467 7120
Elder & Disability Care Services
N.A.I.C.S.: 624120

Casaletto S.r.l (1)
Via Di Monteverde 244, Rome, 00151, Italy
Tel.: (39) 065344087
Real Estate Development Services
N.A.I.C.S.: 531390

City Empiria a.s. (1)
Hvezdova 1716/2b Praha 4 Nusle, Prague,
14078, Czech Republic
Tel.: (420) 26 1141112
Property Leasing Services
N.A.I.C.S.: 531110

D.A.S. Legal Services S.r.l. (1)
9/b v Fermi, 37135, Verona, Italy
Tel.: (39) 0458372611
Legal Management Services
N.A.I.C.S.: 541199

Donatello Intermediazione Srl (1)
Via Giosue Carducci 4, 00187, Rome, Italy
Tel.: (39) 0647221
Insurance Management Services

Assicurazioni Generali S.p.A.—(Continued)

N.A.I.C.S.: 524298

Europ Assistance (Thailand) Company Limited (1)
17th Floor Thanapoom Tower 1550 New Petchaburi Rd Makkasan Ratthawi, Bangkok, 10400, Thailand
Tel.: (66) 21805589
Web Site: https://newstore.europ-assistance.co.th
Travel Insurance Services
N.A.I.C.S.: 561510

Europ Assistance Malaysia Sdn. Bhd.
Office Suite 01-13 13th Floor Menara Symphony No 5 alan Prof, Khoo Kay Kim Seksyen 13, 46200, Petaling Jaya, Malaysia
Tel.: (60) 376283888
Travel Insurance Services
N.A.I.C.S.: 561510

Europ Assistance VAI S.p.A. (1)
Via del Mulino 4, 20057, Assago, Italy
Tel.: (39) 0258163803
Web Site: https://www.europassistance.it
Fire Insurance Services
N.A.I.C.S.: 524113

GP Consulting Penzugyi Tanacsado Kft. (1)
Vaci ut 36-38, 1132, Budapest, Hungary
Tel.: (36) 617806619
Web Site: http://www.gpconsulting.hu
Property & Casualty Insurance Services
N.A.I.C.S.: 524126

Genagricola 1851 S.p.A. (1)
Via Trento 8, 34132, Trieste, Italy
Tel.: (39) 0422864511
Web Site: https://genagricola1851.net
Emp.: 350
Agricultural Services
N.A.I.C.S.: 541690

Genagricola S.p.A. (1)
Via Mons P L Zovatto 71, Annone Veneto, 30020, Venice, Italy
Tel.: (39) 0422864511
Web Site: https://www.genagricola.it
Wine Mfr & Distr
N.A.I.C.S.: 312130

General Securities Corp. (1)
2007 Fayette st, Kansas City, MO 64116
Tel.: (816) 472-7170
Securities Brokerage Services
N.A.I.C.S.: 523150
Gailen Stockwell (VP-Investments & Retirement Plans)

Generali (Schweiz) Holding AG (1)
Soodmattenstrasse 10, 8134, Adliswil, Switzerland (57%)
Tel.: (41) 584724040
Web Site: https://www.generali.ch
Sales Range: $350-399.9 Million
Emp.: 1,800
Holding Company; Insurance & Investment Services
N.A.I.C.S.: 524128

Subsidiary (Non-US):

Fortuna Investment AG (2)
Stadtle 35, 9490, Vaduz, Liechtenstein
Tel.: (423) 2320592
Web Site: http://www.generali.com
Investment Management Service
N.A.I.C.S.: 523999

Subsidiary (Domestic):

Fortuna Rechtsschutz-Versicherung-Gesellschaft AG (2)
Soodmattenstrasse 2, 8134, Adliswil, Switzerland (100%)
Tel.: (41) 584727200
Web Site: http://www.generali.ch
Sales Range: $25-49.9 Million
Emp.: 30
Provider of Legal Insurance Products
N.A.I.C.S.: 524128

Generali Assurances Generales (2)
Ep 3000, 1260, Nyon, Switzerland (98.98%)
Tel.: (41) 223170232

Web Site: http://www.generali.ch
Sales Range: $150-199.9 Million
Emp.: 400
Provider of Insurance
N.A.I.C.S.: 524128

Generali Investments Schweiz AG (2)
Soodmattenstr 10, 8134, Adliswil, Switzerland
Tel.: (41) 584725306
Web Site: http://www.generali.ch
Sales Range: $25-49.9 Million
Emp.: 33
Investment Management Service
N.A.I.C.S.: 523999

Generali Personenversicherungen AG (2)
Soodmattenstrasse 10, 8134, Adliswil, Switzerland (80%)
Tel.: (41) 800881882
Web Site: http://www.generali.ch
Sales Range: $300-349.9 Million
Emp.: 900
Life Insurance Products
N.A.I.C.S.: 524113

House of InsurTech Switzerland AG (2)
Soodmattenstrasse 10, 8134, Adliswil, Switzerland
Tel.: (41) 447124400
General Insurance Services
N.A.I.C.S.: 524210

Generali Akademie GmbH i.L. (1)
Am Schloss 1-3, 51429, Bergisch Gladbach, Germany
Tel.: (49) 2204424200
Web Site: http://www.akademie-generali.de
Conference & Meeting Planning Services
N.A.I.C.S.: 561920

Generali Alapkezelo Zartkoruen Mukodo Reszvenytarsasag (1)
Terez krt 42-44, 1066, Budapest, Hungary
Tel.: (36) 3017345
Web Site: https://www.alapkezelo.hu
Investment Services
N.A.I.C.S.: 523150

Generali Allgemeine Versicherungen AG (1)
Avenue Perdtemps 23, Case Postale 3000, 1260, Nyon, Switzerland
Tel.: (41) 584710101
Web Site: http://www.generali.ch
General Insurance Services
N.A.I.C.S.: 524298

Generali Argentina S.A. (1)
Reconquista 458 - 3er Piso, C1003ABJ, Buenos Aires, Argentina
Tel.: (54) 11 48577942
Web Site: http://www.generali.com.ar
Insurance Management Services
N.A.I.C.S.: 524298

Generali Asset Management S.p.A. (1)
Via Ugo Bassi 6, 20159, Milan, Italy (100%)
Tel.: (39) 0260765711
Web Site: http://www.generali.com
Sales Range: $100-124.9 Million
Emp.: 200
Investment Fund Management
N.A.I.C.S.: 525910

Generali Brasil Seguros S.A. (1)
RJ Av Barao de, Rio de Janeiro, 20220-460, RJ, Brazil (100%)
Tel.: (55) 2125080100
Web Site: http://www.generali.com.br
Sales Range: $150-199.9 Million
Emp.: 340
Holding Company
N.A.I.C.S.: 551112

Generali Bulgaria Holding AD (1)
68 Knyaz Al Dondukov blvd, Sofia, 1504, Bulgaria
Tel.: (359) 29267111
Web Site: http://www.generali.bg
Sales Range: $25-49.9 Million
Emp.: 250
Holding Company; Insurance Services
N.A.I.C.S.: 551112

Subsidiary (Domestic):

Generali Insurance AD (2)
68 Knyaz Al Dondukov Blvd, Dianabad District, 1504, Sofia, Bulgaria
Tel.: (359) 29267222
Web Site: http://www.generali.bg
Insurance Agents
N.A.I.C.S.: 524210

Generali Zakrila Health Insurance AD (2)
68 Knyaz Al Dondukov blvd, 1504, Sofia, Bulgaria
Tel.: (359) 29267222
Web Site: http://www.generali.bg
Health Care Management Services
N.A.I.C.S.: 621999

Generali Business Solutions S.c.p.A. (1)
Via Machiavelli 4, 34132, Trieste, Italy
Tel.: (39) 040671111
Fire Insurance Services
N.A.I.C.S.: 524113
Philippe Donnet (CEO)

Generali CEE Holding B.V. (1)
Na Pankraci 1658/121, PO Box 39, 140 21, Prague, Czech Republic
Tel.: (420) 224559160
Web Site: http://www.generalicee.com
Emp.: 126
Insurance Services
N.A.I.C.S.: 524210
Gregor Pilgram (Chief Distr Officer)

Generali Ceska Pojistovna A.S. (1)
PO Box 305, 659 05, Brno, Czech Republic
Tel.: (420) 241114114
Web Site: http://en.generaliceska.cz
Property & Casualty Insurance Services
N.A.I.C.S.: 524126
Roman Juras (Co-Chm & CEO)

Generali Consulting Solutions LLC (1)
7 World Trade Ctr 250 Greenwich St 33rd Fl, New York, NY 10007-0010
Tel.: (212) 602-7600
Software Management Consulting Services
N.A.I.C.S.: 541618

Subsidiary (Domestic):

Generali Warranty Services, LLC (2)
7 World Trade Ctr 250 Greenwich St 33rd Fl, New York, NY 10007
Tel.: (212) 602-7600
Web Site: http://www.generaliwarranty.com
Insurance Services
N.A.I.C.S.: 524210

Generali Deutschland Gesellschaft fur bAV mbH (1)
Aachenmunchener-Platz 1, 52064, Aachen, Germany
Tel.: (49) 2414563501
N.A.I.C.S.: 531390

Generali Deutschland Krankenversicherung AG (1)
Adenauerring 7, 81737, Munich, Germany
Tel.: (49) 22116360
Health Insurance Services
N.A.I.C.S.: 524210

Generali Deutschland Lebensversicherung AG (1)
Adenauerring 7, 81737, Munich, Germany
Tel.: (49) 8951210
Health Insurance Services
N.A.I.C.S.: 524210

Generali Ecuador Compania de Seguros S.A. (1)
Edificio World Trade Center-Torre B piso 15 Avenida, Francisco de Orellana, Guayaquil, 1085, Ecuador (51.37%)
Tel.: (593) 42630170
Web Site: http://www.generali.com.ec
Sales Range: $100-124.9 Million
Emp.: 120
Insurance Services
N.A.I.C.S.: 524128
Miguel Babra Lyon (Pres)

Generali Employee Benefits Bruxelles (1)

149 Avenue Louise, 1050, Brussels, Belgium
Tel.: (32) 2 5372760
Web Site: http://www.geb.com
Sales Range: $25-49.9 Million
Emp.: 80
Employee Benefit Consulting Services
N.A.I.C.S.: 541612
Fabiano Rossetto (CFO)

Generali Engagement Solutions GmbH (1)
Adenauerring 9, 81737, Munich, Germany
Tel.: (49) 8007879700
Web Site: https://www.generalivitality.com
Health Insurance Services
N.A.I.C.S.: 524210

Generali Espana, Holding de Entidades de Seguros, S.A. (1)
Calle Orense 2, 28020, Madrid, Spain (81%)
Tel.: (34) 913301400
Web Site: http://www.generali.es
Sales Range: $25-49.9 Million
Emp.: 50
Holding Company; Insurance Services
N.A.I.C.S.: 551112

Subsidiary (Domestic):

Generali Espana, S.A. de Seguros y Reaseguros (2)
Calle Orense 2, 28020, Madrid, Spain
Tel.: (34) 918373707
Web Site: https://www.generali.es
Insurance Services
N.A.I.C.S.: 524210

Hermes S.L. (2)
C/ Colquide 6-2 3, Madrid, Spain
Tel.: (34) 916407640
Business Management Consulting Services
N.A.I.C.S.: 541618

Vitalicio Torre Cerda S.l. (2)
C/ Orense 2, Madrid, 28020, Spain
Tel.: (34) 915244007
Sales Range: $25-49.9 Million
Emp.: 15
Real Estate Lending Services
N.A.I.C.S.: 531190

Generali Finance Spolka z ograniczona odpowiedzialnoscia (1)
Ul Postepu 15B, 02-676, Warsaw, Poland
Tel.: (48) 225430500
Insurance Services
N.A.I.C.S.: 524210

Generali France Holding S.A. (1)
7 Et 9 Blvd Haussmann, 75009, Paris, France (75.58%)
Tel.: (33) 0158384000
Web Site: http://www.generali.fr
Sales Range: $50-74.9 Million
Emp.: 100
Holding Company
N.A.I.C.S.: 551112

Subsidiary (Domestic):

Europeenne de Protection Juridique S.A. (2)
7 boulevard Haussmann, 75442, Paris, Cedex 09, France (99.98%)
Tel.: (33) 158386560
Web Site: http://www.epj-assurances.com
Sales Range: $25-49.9 Million
Emp.: 50
Provider of Legal Insurance Services
N.A.I.C.S.: 524128

GPA-IARD S.A. (2)
7 boulevard Haussmann, 75447, Paris, Cedex 09, France (100%)
Tel.: (33) 158341515
Web Site: http://www.gpa.fr
Provider of Insurance Products
N.A.I.C.S.: 524298

Generali France Assurances S.A. (2)
7 9 Blvd Haussmann, 75009, Paris, Cedex 09, France (68.96%)
Tel.: (33) 0158384000
Web Site: http://www.generali.fr
Provider of Insurance Products
N.A.I.C.S.: 524128

Subsidiary (Domestic):

E-Cie Vie S.A. **(3)**
7/9 Boulevard Haussmann, 75009, Paris, France
Tel.: (33) 1 58 38 81 00
Web Site: http://www.e-cie-vie.fr
Insurance Management Services
N.A.I.C.S.: 524298

Expert & Finance S.A. **(3)**
Grand Hotel-Dieu - 9 place Amedee Bonnet, 69288, Lyon, Cedex 02, France
Tel.: (33) 437245200
Web Site: https://expertetfinance.fr
Sales Range: $50-74.9 Million
Emp.: 90
Financial Management Services
N.A.I.C.S.: 523999

Generali France Immobilier SAS **(3)**
7 Boulevard Haussmann, Paris, 75009, France
Tel.: (33) 1 58 38 23 00
Web Site: http://www.generali-immobilier.fr
Real Estate Manangement Services
N.A.I.C.S.: 531390
Philippe Depoux *(Pres)*

Generali IARD S.A. **(3)**
2 Rue Pillet-Will, 75009, Paris, France
Tel.: (33) 158384000
Web Site: https://www.generali.fr
Emp.: 5,000
General Insurance Services
N.A.I.C.S.: 524210

Subsidiary (Non-US):

GFA Caraibes SA **(4)**
Imm La Levee 106 bd General de Gaulle, 97200, Fort-de-France, Martinique
Tel.: (596) 590426
Web Site: https://www.gfacaraibes.fr
Insurance Services
N.A.I.C.S.: 524210

Subsidiary (Domestic):

L'Equite S.A. **(4)**
7 Boulevard Haussmann, 75442, Paris, Cedex, France
Tel.: (33) 158381010
Insurance Services
N.A.I.C.S.: 524210

Affiliate (Domestic):

Generali Informatique S.A. **(3)**
7 Blvd Haussmann, 75009, Paris, France **(41.1%)**
Tel.: (33) 158384000
Web Site: http://www.generali.fr
Sales Range: $25-49.9 Million
Emp.: 47
Provider of Data Processing Services
N.A.I.C.S.: 518210

Subsidiary (Domestic):

Generali Vie S.A. **(3)**
11 Boulevard Haussmann 09, Paris, 75311, France
Tel.: (33) 1 58 38 74 00
Web Site: http://www.generali-patrimoine.fr
Fire Insurance Services
N.A.I.C.S.: 524113

Subsidiary (Domestic):

COSEV@D SAS **(4)**
7 Boulevard Haussmann, Paris, 75009, France
Tel.: (33) 158388000
Web Site: http://www.generalifr.com
Emp.: 3,000
Insurance Management Services
N.A.I.C.S.: 524298

Generali Gerance S.A. **(4)**
11 Boulevard Haussmann, 75009, Paris, France
Tel.: (33) 158387400
General Insurance Services
N.A.I.C.S.: 524210

Subsidiary (Non-US):

Generali Luxembourg S.A. **(4)**
1 rue Peternelchen, Hesperange, 2370, Luxembourg, Luxembourg

Tel.: (352) 27862620
Web Site: https://www.generali.lu
Insurance Services
N.A.I.C.S.: 524210

Subsidiary (Domestic):

Risque et Serenite S.A. **(4)**
41-43 Rue Saint Dominique, 75007, Paris, France
Tel.: (33) 1 53 70 77 77
Web Site: http://www.risqueetserenite.fr
Venture Capital Management Services
N.A.I.C.S.: 523910
Arnaug Pomel *(Mgr-HR)*

Subsidiary (Domestic):

L'Equite Compagnie d'Assurances et de Reassurances Contre les risques de toute nature S.A. **(3)**
7 Boulevard Haussmann, 75442, Paris, Cedex, France **(50.11%)**
Tel.: (33) 1 58 38 10 10
Sales Range: $75-99.9 Million
Emp.: 134
Non-Life Insurance Products
N.A.I.C.S.: 524128

L'Equite IARD S.A. **(3)**
2 rue Pillet-Will, 75009, Paris, France
Tel.: (33) 158381010
Web Site: https://www.equite.com
Sales Range: $1-4.9 Billion
Emp.: 5,000
Insurance Management Services
N.A.I.C.S.: 524298

Subsidiary (Non-US):

PRUDENCE CREOLE S.A. **(3)**
32 Rue Alexis de Villeneuve, 97400, Saint-Denis, Reunion
Tel.: (262) 262709500
Web Site: https://www.prudencecreole.com
Insurance Management Services
N.A.I.C.S.: 524298

Subsidiary (Domestic):

Suresnes Immobilier S.A. **(3)**
39 Bis Boulevard Mar de Lattre de Tassigny, 92150, Suresnes, France
Tel.: (33) 1 47 72 74 93
Sales Range: $50-74.9 Million
Emp.: 2
Real Estate Manangement Services
N.A.I.C.S.: 531390

Subsidiary (Domestic):

Generali Patrimoine **(2)**
2 Rue Pillet-will, La Plaine, 75009, Paris, Cedex, France **(60%)**
Tel.: (33) 58388100
Web Site: https://www.generali-patrimoine.fr
Sales Range: $25-49.9 Million
Emp.: 40
Life Insurance Products
N.A.I.C.S.: 524113

Affiliate (Domestic):

La Federation Continentale Compagnie d'Assurances Sur la Vie S.A. **(2)**
2-8 RueLuigi Cherubini, 93200, Paris, cedex 9, France **(95%)**
Tel.: (33) 158387400
Web Site: http://www.federation-continentale.fr
Life Insurance
N.A.I.C.S.: 524113

Generali France S.A. **(1)**
7 and 9 bld Haussmann, 75309, Paris, Cedex, France
Tel.: (33) 158388000
Insurance Services
N.A.I.C.S.: 524210
Jean-Laurent Granier *(Country Mgr)*

Generali Health Solutions GmbH **(1)**
Hansaring 40-50, 50670, Cologne, Germany
Tel.: (49) 22116365000
Web Site: https://www.generalihealthsolutions.de
Health Care Management Services
N.A.I.C.S.: 524114

Generali Hellas A.E.A.Z. Property & Casualty Insurance Co. **(1)**
Megalou Alexandrou Ave and 1 vas Sofias, Marousi, 15124, Athens, Greece **(99.22%)**
Tel.: (30) 2106142034
Web Site: http://www.generaliusb.com
Property & Casualty Insurance
N.A.I.C.S.: 524128

Generali Hellas Insurance Company S.A. **(1)**
Syggrou Ave 40 Lagoumitzi St, 11745, Athens, Greece **(99.97%)**
Tel.: (30) 2108096100
Web Site: http://www.generali.gr
Sales Range: $100-124.9 Million
Emp.: 250
Fire Insurance Services
N.A.I.C.S.: 524113

Generali Hellas Insurance Company S.A. **(1)**
Syggrou Ave 40 Lagoumitzi St, 11745, Athens, Greece
Tel.: (30) 2108096100
Web Site: https://www.generali.gr
Emp.: 484
Insurance Management Services
N.A.I.C.S.: 524298

Generali Holding Vienna AG **(1)**
Landskrongasse 1-3, Vienna, 1010, Austria
Tel.: (43) 1534010
Web Site: http://www.generali-holding.at
Sales Range: $1-4.9 Billion
Emp.: 4,000
Financial Holding Company; Insurance Products, Banking & Other Financial Services
N.A.I.C.S.: 551111

Subsidiary (Non-US):

B.V. Algemene Holding en Financierings Maatschappij **(2)**
Diemerhof 42, 1112 XN, Diemen, Netherlands **(100%)**
Tel.: (31) 206604461
Sales Range: $125-149.9 Million
Emp.: 500
Holding Company
N.A.I.C.S.: 551112

Subsidiary (Domestic):

BAWAG PSK Versicherung AG **(2)**
Kratochwjlestrasse 4, 1220, Vienna, Austria
Tel.: (43) 15461674000
Web Site: https://www.bawag-versicherung.at
Insurance Management Services
N.A.I.C.S.: 524298

CA Global Property Internationale Immobilien AG **(2)**
Herrengasse 17, 1010, Vienna, Austria
Tel.: (43) 1 534 73 322
Investment Management Service
N.A.I.C.S.: 523999

Subsidiary (Non-US):

Europai Utazasi Biztosito Rt. **(2)**
Vaci ut 36-38, 1132, Budapest, Hungary **(70%)**
Tel.: (36) 4523580
Web Site: http://eub.hu
Sales Range: $1-9.9 Million
Emp.: 30
Provider of Insurance Products
N.A.I.C.S.: 524128

Subsidiary (Domestic):

Europaische Reiseversicherungs AG **(2)**
Kratochwjlestr 4, 1220, Vienna, Austria **(75%)**
Tel.: (43) 13172500
Web Site: https://www.europaeische.at
Sales Range: $10-24.9 Million
Emp.: 60
Provider of Travel Insurance
N.A.I.C.S.: 524128
Andreas Sturmlechner *(Member-Mgmt Bd)*

Subsidiary (Domestic):

Care Consult Versicherungsmakler GmbH **(3)**

Kratochwjlestrasse 4, 1220, Vienna, Austria **(100%)**
Tel.: (43) 13172500
Web Site: http://www.careconsult.at
Sales Range: $50-74.9 Million
Emp.: 5
Provider of Travel & Legal Insurance Products
N.A.I.C.S.: 524128

TTC Training Center Unternehmensberatung GmbH **(3)**
Kratochwjlestrasse 4, 1220, Vienna, Austria
Tel.: (43) 1317250073980
Web Site: https://ttc.at
Sales Range: $10-24.9 Million
Emp.: 2
Professional Training Services
N.A.I.C.S.: 611430
Christian Widerna *(Mgr)*

Subsidiary (Non-US):

Generali Asigurari S.A. **(2)**
Strasse Gheorghe Manu 5 Sector 1, 010442, Bucharest, Romania **(83%)**
Tel.: (40) 212122920
Web Site: http://www.generali.ro
Sales Range: $10-24.9 Million
Emp.: 130
Provider of Insurance Products
N.A.I.C.S.: 524128

Subsidiary (Domestic):

Generali Bank AG **(2)**
Landskrongasse 1-3, 1010, Vienna, Austria
Tel.: (43) 1260670
Web Site: https://www.generalibank.at
Financial Advisory Services
N.A.I.C.S.: 523940
Michael Scherhammer *(Member-Mgmt Bd)*

Subsidiary (Domestic):

Generali FinanzService GmbH **(3)**
Landskrongasse 1-3, Vienna, 1010, Austria
Tel.: (43) 153219190
Web Site: http://www.generali-finanzservice.at
Emp.: 8
Financial Services
N.A.I.C.S.: 523999
Claus Friqz *(Gen Mgr)*

Generali Telefon- + Auftragsservice GmbH **(3)**
Landskrongasse 1-3, 1010, Vienna, Austria
Tel.: (43) 1 53401 0
General Insurance Services
N.A.I.C.S.: 524210

Subsidiary (Domestic):

Generali Group Insurance AG **(2)**
Landskrongasse 1-3, Postfach 173, 1010, Vienna, Austria **(92.19%)**
Tel.: (43) 1534010
Web Site: https://www.generali.at
Sales Range: $250-299.9 Million
Emp.: 500
Life, Health, Property & Casualty Insurance Products & Services
N.A.I.C.S.: 524298

Generali IT-Solutions GmbH **(2)**
Kratochwjlestrasse 4, 1220, Vienna, Austria
Tel.: (43) 1 53401 0
Information Technology Consulting Services
N.A.I.C.S.: 541512

Generali Immobilien AG **(2)**
Bauernmarkt 12, Vienna, 1010, Austria
Tel.: (43) 1 53401 0
Real Estate Development Services
N.A.I.C.S.: 531390

Subsidiary (Non-US):

Generali Velky Spalicek S.r.o. **(3)**
Vaclavske namesti 823/33, 110 00, Prague, 1, Czech Republic
Tel.: (420) 5 43 23 73 85
Web Site: http://www.velkyspalicek.cz
Sales Range: $25-49.9 Million
Emp.: 5
Shopping Mall Operator
N.A.I.C.S.: 531120
Dagmar Spackova *(CEO)*

Vaci utca Center Kft **(3)**

Assicurazioni Generali S.p.A.—(Continued)

1056 Budapest Vaci utca 81, 1056, Budapest, Hungary
Tel.: (36) 14110442
Web Site: https://www.vaciutcacenter.hu
Sales Range: $25-49.9 Million
Emp.: 500
Real Estate Management Services
N.A.I.C.S.: 531390

Subsidiary (Domestic):

Generali Leasing GmbH　　　　　　(2)
Landskrong 1-3, 1010, Vienna, Austria
Tel.: (43) 1 51403 4229
Car Lending Services
N.A.I.C.S.: 532112

Generali Pensionskasse AG　　　　(2)
Landskrongasse 1-3, 1010, Vienna, Austria
Tel.: (43) 1 53401 0
Pension Fund Management Services
N.A.I.C.S.: 525110

Subsidiary (Non-US):

Generali Pojistovna a.s.　　　　　　(2)
Belehradska 299/132, 120 84, Prague, 2,
Czech Republic　　　　　　　　　　(100%)
Tel.: (420) 244188188
Web Site: http://www.generali.cz
Sales Range: $300-349.9 Million
Emp.: 700
Insurance Products
N.A.I.C.S.: 524128

Subsidiary (Domestic):

Generali Car Care s.r.o.　　　　　　(3)
Belehradska 132, Prague, 120 84, Czech
Republic
Tel.: (420) 221 091 391
General Insurance Services
N.A.I.C.S.: 524210

Generali Development spol sro　　(3)
Belehradska 132, Prague, 120 84, Czech
Republic
Tel.: (420) 221 091 199
Web Site:
　　http://www.generalidevelopment.com
Information Technology Consulting Services
N.A.I.C.S.: 541512

Generali Penzijni Fond a.s.　　　　(3)
Belehradska 132, 120 84, Prague, Czech
Republic
Tel.: (420) 221 091 367
Web Site: http://www.generalipf.cz
Pension Fund Management Services
N.A.I.C.S.: 525110

Subsidiary (Non-US):

Generali Providencia Biztosito
Rt.　　　　　　　　　　　　　　　　　(2)
Terez Krt 42-44, 1066, Budapest,
Hungary　　　　　　　　　　　　　　(100%)
Tel.: (36) 013017100
Web Site: http://www.generali.hu
Sales Range: $1-4.9 Billion
Provider of Insurance Products
N.A.I.C.S.: 524128

Subsidiary (Domestic):

Autotal Biztositasi Szolgaltato
Kft.　　　　　　　　　　　　　　　　　(3)
Hizlalo Ter 1, Budapest, 1107, Hungary
Tel.: (36) 1 277 0514
Insurance Management Services
N.A.I.C.S.: 524298

Genertel Biztosito Zrt　　　　　　　(3)
Vaci ut 36-38, 1132, Budapest, Hungary
Tel.: (36) 612880000
Web Site: https://www.genertel.hu
Insurance Management Services
N.A.I.C.S.: 524298

Subsidiary (Domestic):

Generali Sales Promotion GmbH　(2)
Kratochwjlestrasse 4 1220, 1100, Vienna,
Austria
Tel.: (43) 1879545071015
Web Site: http://www.generali.at
Marketing Consulting Services
N.A.I.C.S.: 541613

Subsidiary (Domestic):

Car Care Consult Versicherungsmakler GmbH
Kratochwjlestrasse 4, 1100, Vienna, Austria
Tel.: (43) 16419977
Web Site: http://www.carcc.at
General Insurance Services
N.A.I.C.S.: 524210

Generali TVG Vorsorgemanagement
GmbH　　　　　　　　　　　　　　　(3)
Alpenstrasse 102, 5020, Salzburg, Austria
Tel.: (43) 662 876636 0
Web Site: http://www.tvg-vorsorge.com
Pension Fund Management Services
N.A.I.C.S.: 525110

Subsidiary (Domestic):

Generali VIS Informatik GmbH　　(2)
Kratochwjlestr 4, 1220, Vienna, Austria
Tel.: (43) 1534 01 33 83
General Insurance Services
N.A.I.C.S.: 524210

Subsidiary (Non-US):

Generali Zavarovalnica d.d.　　　　(2)
Krziceva 3, 1000, Ljubljana,
Slovenia　　　　　　　　　　　　　(67.06%)
Tel.: (386) 14757100
Web Site: http://www.generali.si
Sales Range: $150-199.9 Million
Emp.: 350
Provider of Personal Life & Property Insurance Products; Joint Venture of Generali
Holding Vienna AG (67.06%) & Interunfall
Versicherung AG (32.94%)
N.A.I.C.S.: 524113

Holdux Beteiligungsgesellschaft　(2)
St Alban-Vorstadt 17, 4052, Basel,
Switzerland　　　　　　　　　　　　(100%)
Holding Company
N.A.I.C.S.: 551112

Subsidiary (Domestic):

RISK-AKTIV Versicherungsservice
GmbH　　　　　　　　　　　　　　　(2)
Landskrongasse 1-3, 1010, Vienna, Austria
Tel.: (43) 1 534 01 1461 0
Web Site: http://www.riskaktiv.at
Sales Range: $25-49.9 Million
Emp.: 120.
Automotive Inspection Services
N.A.I.C.S.: 811198

Generali Immobiliare Italia Sgr
S.p.A.　　　　　　　　　　　　　　　(1)
Via Machiavelli 4, 34132, Milan, Italy
Tel.: (39) 0243531102
Web Site: http://www.generali-immobiliare.it
Asset Management Services
N.A.I.C.S.: 523940

Generali Insurance (Thailand) Co.,
Ltd.　　　　　　　　　　　　　　　　(1)
87/2 CRC Tower All Seasons Place 16th
Floor, Unit 1601 and 1607 Wireless Road
Lumpini Patumwan, Bangkok, 10330, Thailand
Tel.: (66) 26853828
Web Site: https://generali.co.th
General Insurance Services
N.A.I.C.S.: 524210

Generali Insurance Agency Company
Limited　　　　　　　　　　　　　　(1)
Room 501 Tower 1 Qianhai Kerry Center
Qianhai Blvd, Nanshan District, Shenzhen,
China
Tel.: (86) 75526922917
Web Site: https://www.generaliagency.cn
N.A.I.C.S.: 531390

Generali Investments CEE, Investicni
Spolecnost, A.S.　　　　　　　　　(1)
Na Pankraci 1720/123, 140 21, Prague,
Czech Republic
Tel.: (420) 281044198
Web Site: https://www.generali-investments.cz
Asset Management Services
N.A.I.C.S.: 523940
Josef Benes (Co-Chm & CEO)

Generali Investments Europe
S.p.A.　　　　　　　　　　　　　　　(1)

Via Trento 8, 34132, Trieste, Italy
Tel.: (39) 040 671 111
Web Site: http://www.generali-investments-europe.com
Insurance Management Services
N.A.I.C.S.: 524298
Vincent Chaigneau (Head-Res-Paris)

Subsidiary (Non-US):

Generali Investments Asia
Limited　　　　　　　　　　　　　　(2)
21/F CityPlaza One 1111 Kings Road Taikoo Shing, Hong Kong, China (Hong Kong)
Tel.: (852) 225210707
Web Site: https://www.generaliasia.com
Sales Range: $50-74.9 Million
Emp.: 100
Asset Management & Investment Advisory
Services
N.A.I.C.S.: 523940

Generali Investments Partners S.p.A.
Societa di Gestione Risparmio　　(1)
Via Silvio D'Amico 40, 00145, Rome, Italy
Tel.: (39) 06505731
Investment Management Service
N.A.I.C.S.: 523940
Gabriele Alberici (Head-Sls)

Generali Investments, druzba za upravljanje, d.o.o.　　　　　　　　　(2)
Dunajska Cesta 63, 1000, Ljubljana, Slovenia
Tel.: (386) 15826780
Web Site: http://www.generali-investments.si
Asset Management Services
N.A.I.C.S.: 523940
Luka Podlogar (Pres)

Generali Italia S.p.A.　　　　　　　(1)
Via Don Giovanni Bosco 31, 31021, Mogliano Veneto, TV, Italy
Tel.: (39) 0415901664
Web Site: https://www.generali.it
Property & Casualty Insurance Services
N.A.I.C.S.: 524126
Alberto Santoro (Chief Risk Officer)

Generali PPF Holding BV　　　　　(1)
Strawinskylaan 933, 1077 XX, Amsterdam,
Netherlands　　　　　　　　　　　　(76%)
Tel.: (31) 208813120
Web Site: http://www.generalippf.eu
Sales Range: $25-49.9 Million
Emp.: 8
Holding Company
N.A.I.C.S.: 551112
Sergio Balbinot (Chm)

Subsidiary (Non-US):

Classic Life Insurance　　　　　　(2)
Business Center Syretska 5 Bldg 3, Kiev,
04073, Ukraine
Tel.: (380) 44 200 0 216
Web Site: http://www.classiclife.com.ua
Emp.: 15
Fire Insurance Service
N.A.I.C.S.: 524113
Prokofiev Alexander (CEO)

Generali Osiguranje Srbija a.d.o.　(2)
Vladimira Popovica 8, 11070, Belgrade,
Serbia
Tel.: (381) 112220555
Web Site: https://www.generali.rs
Sales Range: $150-199.9 Million
Emp.: 1,668
Insurance Management Services
N.A.I.C.S.: 524113
Gorana Rasic (CFO & Member-Exec Bd)

Subsidiary (Non-US):

Delta Generali Holding d.o.o.　　(3)
Kralja Nikole 27a, 81000, Podgorica, Montenegro
Tel.: (382) 11 222 3785
Web Site: http://www.generali.com
Sales Range: $25-49.9 Million
Emp.: 30
Investment Management Service
N.A.I.C.S.: 523999

Subsidiary (Domestic):

Delta Generali Osiguranje ad　　(4)
Kralja Nikole 27/VI VI Sprat, Podgorica,
Montenegro

Tel.: (382) 20 444 800
Web Site: http://www.deltagenerali.me
Sales Range: $100-124.9 Million
Emp.: 30
General Insurance Services
N.A.I.C.S.: 524210

Subsidiary (Domestic):

Delta Generali RE a.d.　　　　　　(3)
Milentija Popovica 7 b, 11000, Belgrade,
Serbia
Tel.: (381) 11 2220 555
Web Site: http://www.deltagenerali.rs
Reinsurance Services
N.A.I.C.S.: 524130

Voluntary Pension Fund M.Delta　(3)
Vladimira Popovica 8, 11000, Belgrade,
Serbia
Tel.: (381) 11 20 11 764
Web Site: http://www.penzijskifond.rs
Sales Range: $25-49.9 Million
Emp.: 20
Pension Fund Management Services
N.A.I.C.S.: 525110
Darko Radovanovic (Chm)

Subsidiary (Non-US):

Generali Osiguranje d.d.　　　　　(2)
Slavonska avenija 1b, 10000, Zagreb,
Croatia
Tel.: (385) 14600400
Web Site: https://www.generali.hr
General Insurance Services
N.A.I.C.S.: 524210

Generali Slovensko Poist'ovna
a.s.　　　　　　　　　　　　　　　　(2)
Plynarenska 7/C, 824 79, Bratislava, Slovakia
Tel.: (421) 258276666
Web Site: http://www.gsl.sk
Insurance Provider
N.A.I.C.S.: 524128

Iszao PPF Insurance　　　　　　　(2)
Pobediteley Avenue 59 Office 202, Minsk,
220035, Belarus
Tel.: (375) 17 200 45 56
Web Site: http://www.ppfinsurance.by
Sales Range: $50-74.9 Million
Insurance Services
N.A.I.C.S.: 524298
Sergei Slizovskiy (Mng Dir)

Generali Pensions- und Sicherungs-
Management GmbH　　　　　　　　(1)
Oeder Weg 151, 60318, Frankfurt, Germany
Tel.: (49) 6915022540
Health Insurance Services
N.A.I.C.S.: 524210

Generali Pensionsfonds AG　　　(1)
Oeder Weg 151, 60318, Frankfurt, Germany
Tel.: (49) 6915022626
Health Insurance Services
N.A.I.C.S.: 524210

Generali Powszechne Towarzystwo
Emerytalne S.A.　　　　　　　　　(1)
Ul Postepu 15, 02-676, Warsaw, Poland
Tel.: (48) 22 5430 500
Life Insurance Management Services
N.A.I.C.S.: 524113

Generali Properties S.p.A.　　　　(1)
Piazza Duca Degli Abruzzi 1, Trieste,
34132, Italy
Tel.: (39) 0406 79 91 11
Web Site: http://www.generaliproperties.com
Real Estate Management Services
N.A.I.C.S.: 531390

Generali Real Estate S.p.A.　　　(1)
Via Machiavelli 4, 34132, Trieste, Italy
Tel.: (39) 0243531102
Web Site:
　　https://www.generalirealestate.com
Emp.: 400
Real Estate Manangement Services
N.A.I.C.S.: 531390

Generali Realties Ltd　　　　　　　(1)
16 Levontin, Tel Aviv, Israel
Tel.: (972) 3 5665333
Property Management Services
N.A.I.C.S.: 531311

Generali Ruckversicherung AG (1)
Landskrongasse 1-3, Postfach 173, 1010,
Vienna, Austria
Tel.: (43) 1534010
Web Site: http://www.generali.com
Reinsurance Services
N.A.I.C.S.: 524130

**Generali Saxon Land Development
Company Limited** (1)
100 Leman Street, London, E1 8AJ, United
Kingdom
Tel.: (44) 207 265 6200
Emp.: 6
Real Estate Investment & Development
N.A.I.C.S.: 531390

Generali Seguros, S.A. (1)
Avenida da Liberdade 242, 1250-149, Lis-
bon, Portugal
Tel.: (351) 213112800
Web Site: http://www.generali.pt
Emp.: 350
Insurance Services
N.A.I.C.S.: 524210
Pedro Luis Francisco Carvalho (CEO)

**Generali SicherungsTreuhand
GmbH** (1)
Oeder Weg 151, 60318, Frankfurt am Main,
Germany
Tel.: (49) 6915022644
General Insurance Services
N.A.I.C.S.: 524210

**Generali Societate de Administrare a
Fondurilor de Pensii Private S.A.** (1)
Piata Charles de Gaulle nr 15 Etaj 1 Sector
1, 011857, Bucharest, Romania
Tel.: (40) 213135150
Web Site: https://pensii.generali.ro
Pension Fund Management Services
N.A.I.C.S.: 525110

**Generali Vietnam Life Insurance
Ltd** (1)
Generali Plaza - 43 - 45 Tu Xuong, Ward
07 District 03, Ho Chi Minh City, Vietnam
Tel.: (84) 2862886888
Web Site: http://generali.vn
Sales Range: $50-74.9 Million
Emp.: 80
Insurance Management Services
N.A.I.C.S.: 524298
Nguyen Thi Hong Thanh (CEO & Member-
Mgmt Bd)

**Generali Zakrila Medical & Dental
Centre EOOD** (1)
79-81 Knyaz Al Dondukov Blvd, 1504, So-
fia, Bulgaria
Tel.: (359) 29420700
Web Site: https://www.generali.bg
Healtcare Services
N.A.I.C.S.: 621999

**Generali Zycie Towarzystwo Ubez-
pieczen S.A.** (1)
przy ul Postepu 15B, 02-676, Warsaw, Po-
land
Tel.: (48) 913913913
Web Site: http://www.generali.pl
Insurance Management Services
N.A.I.C.S.: 524298

**Generali do Brasil Partipacoes
S.A.** (1)
Avenida Rio Branco 128, 20040 002, Rio
de Janeiro, Brazil (79%)
Tel.: (55) 2125080100
Web Site: http://www.generali.com.br
Sales Range: $150-199.9 Million
Emp.: 265
Holding Company
N.A.I.C.S.: 551112
Claudio Mele (Pres)

**Generali penzijni spolecnost,
A.S.** (1)
Na Pankraci 1720/123, Nusle, 140 21,
Prague, Czech Republic
Tel.: (420) 261149111
Web Site: https://www.generalipenze.cz
Insurance Services
N.A.I.C.S.: 524210

**Generali-Ingatlan Vagyonkezelo es
Szolgaltato Kft.** (1)
Vaci ut 36-38, 1132, Budapest, Hungary

Tel.: (36) 205271812
Web Site: http://www.generali.ingatlan.com
Office Space Rental Services
N.A.I.C.S.: 531120

Genertel S.p.A. (1)
Via Machiavelli 4, 34132, Trieste,
Italy (100%)
Tel.: (39) 0406768666
Web Site: https://www.genertel.it
Sales Range: $150-199.9 Million
Provider of Insurance Services
N.A.I.C.S.: 524128

Genertellife S.p.A. (1)
Via Ferretto n 1, 31021, Mogliano Veneto,
TV, Italy
Tel.: (39) 0415932199
Web Site: https://www.genertellife.it
Sales Range: $100-124.9 Million
Emp.: 150
General Insurance Services
N.A.I.C.S.: 524210

Subsidiary (Domestic):

Genertel Servizi Assicurativi S.r.l. (2)
Via Erminio Ferretto 1, Mogliano Veneto,
31021, Treviso, Italy
Tel.: (39) 0415939701
Insurance Management Services
N.A.I.C.S.: 524298

Gruppo Generali Servizi S.r.l. (1)
Piazza Buca Degli Abruzzi 2, Trieste,
34132, Italy (67%)
Tel.: (39) 0040671111
Sales Range: $350-399.9 Million
Emp.: 1,000
Insurance Services
N.A.I.C.S.: 524128

Il Tiglio - Societa' Agricola S.r.l. (1)
Via Monsignor Paolo Lino Zovatto 71,
30020, Venice, Italy
Tel.: (39) 0422864 511
Wine Mfr
N.A.I.C.S.: 312130

Inf - Societa' Agricola S.p.A. (1)
Contrada Colle Cavalieri, 00040, Lanuvio,
Italy
Tel.: (39) 069374049
Food Products Mfr
N.A.I.C.S.: 311999

Subsidiary (Non-US):

S.C. La Quercia S.r.l. (2)
Str Drumul Morii 7A, 305600, Sannicolau
Mare, Romania
Tel.: (40) 256370458
Insurance Management Services
N.A.I.C.S.: 524298

Landy Courtage S.A.S. (1)
7 Boulevard Haussmann, 75009, Paris,
France
Tel.: (33) 8 99 54 41 43
Insurance Agency Services
N.A.I.C.S.: 524210

MPI Generali Insurans Berhad (1)
8th Floor Menara Multi-Purpose Capital
Square 8 Jalan Munshi Abdullah, 50100,
Kuala Lumpur, Malaysia
Tel.: (60) 32 034 9888
Web Site: https://www.mpigenerali.com
General Insurance Services
N.A.I.C.S.: 524114
K. G. Krishnamoorthy Rao (CEO)

**Makefet Financial Services - Insur-
ance Agency Ltd.** (1)
PO Box 50445, Tel Aviv, 61500, Israel
Tel.: (972) 3 511 1777
Insurance Agency Services
N.A.I.C.S.: 524210

**Migdal Stock Exchange Services
(N.E.) Ltd.** (1)
26 Saadia Gaon Street 2nd Floor, Tel Aviv,
65141, Israel
Tel.: (972) 3 519 4111
Securities Brokerage Services
N.A.I.C.S.: 523150

Migdal Underwriting Business (1)
26 Saadia Gaon, Tel Aviv, 67135, Israel
Tel.: (972) 3 5190441
Financial Management Services

N.A.I.C.S.: 523999

**Mivtach-Simon Insurance Agencies
Ltd.** (1)
14 Achad Ha Am Street Migdal Africa Israel,
Tel Aviv, 65142, Israel
Tel.: (972) 3 796 6666
Web Site: http://www.mvs.co.il
Insurance Agency Services
N.A.I.C.S.: 524210

Montcalm Wine Importers Ltd. (1)
7 World Trade Ctr 250 Greenwich St 33rd
Fl, New York, NY 10007
Tel.: (212) 602-7700
Web Site: http://www.montcalmwines.com
Wine Distr
N.A.I.C.S.: 424820
Michele Ricci (Exec Mng Dir)

**NKFE Insurance Agency Company
Limited** (1)
Rm 713B Tower B Hung Hom Commercial
Centre 37 Ma Tau Wai Road, Hunghom,
Kowloon, China (Hong Kong)
Tel.: (852) 27108399
Web Site: http://www.nkfe.com.hk
Property & Casualty Insurance Services
N.A.I.C.S.: 524126

**Participatie Maatschappij Graafschap
Holland N.V.** (1)
Diemerhof 42, 1112 XN, Diemen,
Netherlands (100%)
Tel.: (31) 0206604444
Sales Range: $150-199.9 Million
Emp.: 450
Holding Company
N.A.I.C.S.: 551112
Sergio Balbinot (Vice Chm)

Subsidiary (Non-US):

Belgica Insurance Holding S.A. (2)
149 Avenue Louise, 1050, Brussels,
Belgium (100%)
Holding Company
N.A.I.C.S.: 551112

Subsidiary (Domestic):

Generali Asia N.V. (2)
Diemerhof 42, 1112 XN, Diemen, Nether-
lands
Tel.: (31) 206604444
Insurance Management Services
N.A.I.C.S.: 524298
Anete Mosman (Gen Mgr)

Subsidiary (Non-US):

**Generali Life (Hong Kong)
Limited** (3)
21/F 1111 King's Road, Taikoo Shing, China
(Hong Kong)
Tel.: (852) 25210707
Web Site: https://www.generali.com.hk
Insurance Services
N.A.I.C.S.: 524210
Tim Vandecasteele (Head-Employee Ben-
efits)

**Generali Life Assurance Philippines,
Inc.** (3)
10th Floor Petron Mega Plaza 358 Sen Gil
Puyat Avenue, Makati, 1227, Philippines
Tel.: (63) 288880808
Web Site: http://www.generali.com.ph
Health Insurance Services
N.A.I.C.S.: 524114
Robert Hector John Spence (Chm)

**PT Asuransi Jiwa Generali
Indonesia** (3)
Generali Tower Lantai 7 Gran Rubina Bus-
siness Park Kawasan, Rasuna Epicentrum
JI HR Rasuna Said Kavling C-22, Jakarta,
12940, Indonesia
Tel.: (62) 2129963700
Web Site: https://www.generali.co.id
Financial Management Services
N.A.I.C.S.: 523999
Edy Tuhirman (CEO)

Subsidiary (Domestic):

Generali Finance B.V. (2)
Diemerhof 42, PO Box 1888, 1112 XN, Die-
men, Netherlands (60%)
Tel.: (31) 206604444

Sales Range: $50-74.9 Million
Emp.: 1
Insurance Services
N.A.I.C.S.: 524298

Subsidiary (Domestic):

Generali Capital Finance B.V. (3)
Diemerhof 42, 1112 XN, Diemen, Nether-
lands
Tel.: (31) 206604444
Emp.: 450
Financial Management Services
N.A.I.C.S.: 523999

Subsidiary (Domestic):

Generali Kent B.V. (2)
Diemerhof 42, Diemen, 1112XN, North Hol-
land, Netherlands (80%)
Tel.: (31) 206601655
Holding Company
N.A.I.C.S.: 551112
F. Von Senk (Gen Mgr)

Subsidiary (Non-US):

Generali Sigorta A.S. (3)
Altunizade Mah Ord Prof Dr Fahrettin Kerim
Gokay Cad Altinyurt Plaza, No 38 Ic Kapi
No 5 Uskudar, 34662, Istanbul, 34662,
Turkiye (97.36%)
Tel.: (90) 8505555555
Web Site: https://www.generali.com.tr
Sales Range: $75-99.9 Million
Emp.: 170
Provider of Insurance Products
N.A.I.C.S.: 524128

Subsidiary (Domestic):

Generali Turkey Holding B.V. (2)
Diemerhof 42, 1112 XN, Diemen, Nether-
lands
Tel.: (31) 20 6604444
Emp.: 300
General Insurance Services
N.A.I.C.S.: 524298
Annette Mosman (CEO)

Affiliate (Domestic):

Redoze Holding N.V. (2)
Diemerhof 42, 1112 XN, Diemen,
Netherlands (43.97%)
Holding Company
N.A.I.C.S.: 551112

Peltours Insurance Agencies Ltd. (1)
Aurec Building 16 Abba Hillel Road, Ramat
Gan, 52506, Israel
Tel.: (972) 3 753 7111
Insurance Management Services
N.A.I.C.S.: 524298

REFICOR s.r.o. (1)
Na Pankraci 1658, Prague, 140 21, Czech
Republic
Tel.: (420) 234689111
Business Management Consulting Services
N.A.I.C.S.: 541611

S.C. Genagricola Romania (1)
Str Drumul Moril 9, 305600, Sannicolau
Mare, Romania
Tel.: (40) 256370458
Investment Management Service
N.A.I.C.S.: 523999

SCI Parcolog Isle D'Abeau 3 (1)
7 Boulevard Haussmann, 75009, Paris,
France
Tel.: (33) 8 99 96 77 59
Financial Management Services
N.A.I.C.S.: 523999

Sementi Dom Dotto S.p.A. (1)
Via lavariano 41, 33050, Mortegliano,
Udine, Italy
Tel.: (39) 0432760442
Web Site: https://www.sddspa.it
Vegetable Seed & Animal Food Distr
N.A.I.C.S.: 424910

Subsidiary (Domestic):

Agenzia la Torre S.r.l. (2)
Pratovarino Region 14, Moasca, Asti, Italy
Tel.: (39) 0141832070
Real Estate Development Services
N.A.I.C.S.: 531390

Assicurazioni Generali S.p.A.—(Continued)

Subsidiary (Non-US):

CPM Internacional d.o.o. (2)
Zitnjak Bb, 10000, Zagreb, Croatia
Tel.: (385) 12 49 97 00
Vegetable Farming Services
N.A.I.C.S.: 111219

Subsidiary (Domestic):

Sementi Ross S.r.l. (2)
Str Delle Saline 5, 34015, Muggia, Italy
Tel.: (39) 040 232481
Financial Management Services
N.A.I.C.S.: 523999

Sycomore Asset Management
S.A. (1)
14 avenue Hoche, 75008, Paris, France
Tel.: (33) 144401600
Web Site: http://en.sycomore-am.com
Asset Management Services
N.A.I.C.S.: 523940
Jean-Pierre Grignon (Head-French Bus
Dev)

Transocean Holding Corporation (1)
1 Liberty Plz Fl 37, New York, NY 10006-1414
Tel.: (212) 602-7600
Investment Management Service
N.A.I.C.S.: 523999

Subsidiary (Non-US):

Participatie Maatschappij Transhol
B.V. (2)
Diemerhof 42, Diemen, 1112 XN, Noord-Holland, Netherlands
Tel.: (31) 206604444
Financial Investment Management Services
N.A.I.C.S.: 523999

UMS-Generali Marine S.p.A. (1)
Via 12 October 1, 16100, Genoa,
Italy (97.09%)
Tel.: (39) 01084071
Web Site: http://www.umsgeneralimarine.it
Sales Range: $50-74.9 Million
Emp.: 30
Marine Transport Insurance
N.A.I.C.S.: 524128

Univerzalni sprava majetku as (1)
Na Pankraci 1658, 140 21, Prague, Czech
Republic
Tel.: (420) 556 422 111
Real Estate Management Services
N.A.I.C.S.: 531390

Vera Assicurazioni S.p.A. (1)
Corso di Porta Vigentina 9, 20122, Milan,
Italy
Tel.: (39) 0800550323
Web Site: https://www.veraassicurazioni.it
Vehicle Insurance Services
N.A.I.C.S.: 524126

Vera Financial Designated Activity
Company (1)
Beaux Lane House Mercer Street Lower,
Dublin, D02 DH60, Ireland
Tel.: (353) 16319555
Web Site: https://www.verafinancial.com
Fire Insurance Services
N.A.I.C.S.: 524113

Vera Protezione S.p.A. (1)
Corso di Porta Vigentina 9, 20122, Milan,
Italy
Tel.: (39) 0800549330
Vehicle Insurance Services
N.A.I.C.S.: 524126

Vera Vita S.p.A. (1)
Via Massaua 6, 20146, Milan, Italy
Tel.: (39) 0458392777
Web Site:
   https://www.veravitaassicurazioni.it
Fire Insurance Services
N.A.I.C.S.: 524113

Vignadoro S.r.l. (1)
B-Dul Stefan Augustin Doinas 20, Arad,
315600, Romania
Tel.: (40) 257256955
Grape Farming Services
N.A.I.C.S.: 312130

ZAD Victoria AD (1)
69-71 Iskar Str, Sofia, Bulgaria (67%)
Tel.: (359) 700 19 577
Web Site: http://www.victoria-insbg.com
Sales Range: $10-24.9 Million
General Insurance Products & Services
N.A.I.C.S.: 524126
Dancho Danchev (Chm & Co-CEO)

ASSIETTA PRIVATE EQUITY SGR S.P.A.
Via Cesare Cantu 1, 20123, Milan,
Italy
Tel.: (39) 0289096595 IT
Web Site: http://www.apesgr.it
Year Founded: 2000
Privater Equity Firm
N.A.I.C.S.: 523999
Marco Cornaglia (CEO)

ASSITECA SPA
Palazzo Assiteca Via G Sigieri 14,
20135, Milan, Italy
Tel.: (39) 0254 6791
Web Site: http://www.assiteca.it
ASSI—(ITA)
Rev.: $98,896,657
Assets: $180,196,319
Liabilities: $114,171,049
Net Worth: $66,025,269
Earnings: $6,703,734
Emp.: 616
Fiscal Year-end: 06/30/20
Insurance Agent & Broker Services
N.A.I.C.S.: 524210
Luciano Lucca (Chm)

Subsidiaries:

A & B Insurance & Reinsurance
S.r.l. (1)
Palazzo Assiteca Via G Sigieri 14, 20135,
Milan, Italy
Tel.: (39) 02550541
Insurance Services
N.A.I.C.S.: 524210

Assiteca Agricoltura S.r.l. (1)
Via Francia 4, 37135, Verona, Italy
Tel.: (39) 0458094711
Insurance Services
N.A.I.C.S.: 524210

Assiteca BSA S.r.l. (1)
Via Calcinaro 2085/10, 47521, Cesena, FC,
Italy
Tel.: (39) 0547632622
Insurance Services
N.A.I.C.S.: 524210

Assiteca Consulting S.r.l. (1)
Via G Sigieri 14, 20135, Milan, Italy
Tel.: (39) 02546791
Insurance Services
N.A.I.C.S.: 524210

ASSIUT ISLAMIC TRADING
Al Wataniyah Office Building 2nd fl Al
Jomhouriya St, Asyut, Egypt
Tel.: (20) 10 02885966
Year Founded: 1987
AITG.CA—(EGX)
Sales Range: Less than $1 Million
Construction Materials Whslr
N.A.I.C.S.: 423320

ASSMANN BERATEN + PLA-NEN GMBH
Nordstrasse 23, D-38106, Braun-schweig, Germany
Tel.: (49) 53139010
Web Site: http://www.assmann.info
Year Founded: 1959
Rev.: $31,859,925
Emp.: 315
Design & Project Management Services
N.A.I.C.S.: 541618
Peter Warnecke (Member-Mgmt Bd)

ASSOCIATE GLOBAL PART-NERS LIMITED
Level 12 2 Chifley Square, Sydney,
2000, NSW, Australia
Tel.: (61) 1300001750 AU
Web Site:
   https://www.associateglobal.com
Year Founded: 1997
APL—(ASX)
Rev.: $4,150,641
Assets: $8,486,912
Liabilities: $3,328,659
Net Worth: $5,158,253
Earnings: ($532,853)
Fiscal Year-end: 06/30/24
Miscellaneous Financial Investment
Activities
N.A.I.C.S.: 523999
Martin Switzer (CEO & Mng Dir)

Subsidiaries:

Contango Funds Management
Limited (1)
Level 12 2 Chifley Square, Sydney, 2000,
NSW, Australia
Tel.: (61) 1300052054
Web Site: https://www.associateglobal.com
Asset Management Services
N.A.I.C.S.: 523940

ASSOCIATED ALCOHOLS & BREWERIES LTD.
4th Floor BPK Star Tower A B Road,
Indore, 452008, India
Tel.: (91) 7314780400
Web Site:
   https://www.associatedalcohols.com
Year Founded: 1989
ASALCBR—(NSE)
Rev.: $72,124,484
Assets: $54,629,211
Liabilities: $11,926,374
Net Worth: $42,702,837
Earnings: $8,299,964
Emp.: 547
Fiscal Year-end: 03/31/22
Alcoholic Distilleries Mfr
N.A.I.C.S.: 325193
Sumit Jaitely (Compliance Officer &
Sec)

ASSOCIATED BRANDS INDUS-TRIES LIMITED
Bhagowtie Trace, El Socorro, Trinidad
& Tobago
Tel.: (868) 638 4006
Web Site: http://www.abil-tt.com
Year Founded: 1974
Sales Range: $150-199.9 Million
Emp.: 650
Snack Foods, Chocolate Confection-ery, Biscuits & Breakfast Cereals Mfr
& Distr
N.A.I.C.S.: 311919

Subsidiaries:

Associated Brands Industries Limited
- Biscuit Division (1)
Churchill Roosevelt Highway, Arima, Trini-dad & Tobago
Tel.: (868) 6421971
Web Site: http://www.abil-tt.com
Sales Range: $25-49.9 Million
Emp.: 150
Biscuit Mfr & Distr
N.A.I.C.S.: 311919
Gregory Lok Jack (Gen Mgr)

Confectionery & Snacks (Barbados)
Ltd (1)
Greenhill, Saint Michael, Barbados
Tel.: (246) 424 6870
Confectionery Mfr & Distr
N.A.I.C.S.: 311351

Confectionery & Snacks (Jamaica)
Ltd (1)
Lots 21-22 Cookson Avenue Cookson &

Bushy Park Pen Naggo Head, Old Harbour,
Jamaica
Tel.: (876) 939 7461
Confectionery Mfr & Distr
N.A.I.C.S.: 311351
Latoya Smith (Brand Mgr)

Sunshine Industries Ltd (1)
Corinth Estate Marisule, Gros Islet, Saint
Lucia
Tel.: (758) 450 2014
Confectionery Mfr & Distr
N.A.I.C.S.: 311351

Universal Foods Limited (1)
Point Lisas Industrial Estate, Point Lisas,
Trinidad & Tobago
Tel.: (868) 636 7965
Web Site: http://www.abil-tt.com
Sales Range: $25-49.9 Million
Emp.: 120
Breakfast Cereal Mfr & Distr
N.A.I.C.S.: 311230
Neil Poon Tip (Mng Dir)

ASSOCIATED BRITISH ENGI-NEERING PLC
61-65 Church Street, Harston, Cam-bridge, CB22 7NP, United Kingdom
Tel.: (44) 1223260022 UK
Web Site: https://www.abeplc.co.uk
Year Founded: 2006
Rev.: $1,439,069
Assets: $2,472,051
Liabilities: $7,177,577
Net Worth: ($4,705,526)
Earnings: ($2,196,674)
Emp.: 20
Fiscal Year-end: 03/31/19
Diesel & Related Engineering Ser-vices
N.A.I.C.S.: 541330
Colin Weinburg (Co-Chm)

Subsidiaries:

British Polar Engines Limited (1)
133 Helen Street, Glasgow, G51 3HD,
Scotland, United Kingdom
Tel.: (44) 1414452455
Web Site:
   http://www.britishpolarengines.co.uk
Engine Parts Mfr & Distr & Engines Mainte-nace Services
N.A.I.C.S.: 336412

ASSOCIATED CERAMICS LIM-ITED
17 Ganesh Chandra Avenue 4th
Floor, Kolkata, 700013, India
Tel.: (91) 3322367358
Web Site:
   https://www.associatedceramics.com
Year Founded: 1970
11067—(CSE)
Sales Range: $1-9.9 Million
Emp.: 97
Refractory Products Mfr
N.A.I.C.S.: 327120
Arun Agarwal (Mng Dir)

ASSOCIATED ENGINEERS, LTD.
23/F Stelux House 698 Prince Ed-ward Road East, San Po Kong, Kow-loon, China (Hong Kong)
Tel.: (852) 27671000 HK
Web Site: http://www.ael.hk
Year Founded: 1961
Sales Range: $150-199.9 Million
Emp.: 500
Airport, Logistic, Construction, Envi-ronmental & Material Handling Engi-neering Services
N.A.I.C.S.: 541330
G.T. Chow (Mng Dir)

Subsidiaries:

Associated Engineers Zhuhai S.E.Z.
Ltd. (1)
Zaobei Industrial Zone Qianshan, Zhuhai,

519070, Guangdong, China
Tel.: (86) 7568615663
Web Site: http://www.zael.cn
Industrial Engineering Services
N.A.I.C.S.: 541330
Eric Chan *(Asst Mgr)*

ASSOCIATED INDUSTRIES CHINA, INC.

5F-1 No 3-1 Park Street, Nangang District, Taipei, 11503, Taiwan
Tel.: (886) 226558080
Web Site: https://www.agneovo.com
Year Founded: 1978
9912—(TAI)
Rev.: $16,697,308
Assets: $23,562,673
Liabilities: $10,200,595
Net Worth: $13,362,078
Earnings: ($1,856,601)
Emp.: 73
Fiscal Year-end: 12/31/23
LCD Monitor Whslr
N.A.I.C.S.: 334419
Jackson Yun Yu *(Chm)*

Subsidiaries:

AG Neovo Technology B.V.   **(1)**
Molenbaan 9, 2908 LL, Capelle aan den IJssel, Netherlands
Tel.: (31) 104425737
Computer Parts Distr
N.A.I.C.S.: 423430

AG Neovo Technology
Corporation   **(1)**
2362 Qume Dr Ste A, San Jose, CA 95131
Tel.: (408) 321-8210
Computer Parts Distr
N.A.I.C.S.: 423430

ASSOCIATED INTERNA-TIONAL HOTELS LTD.

9/F iSQUARE 63 Nathan Road, Tsim Sha Tsui, Kowloon, China (Hong Kong)
Tel.: (852) 28100993   HK
Web Site: https://aihl.etnet.com.hk
0105—(HKG)
Rev.: $38,863,738
Assets: $1,264,360,501
Liabilities: $62,287,924
Net Worth: $1,202,072,576
Earnings: ($144,555,883)
Emp.: 33
Fiscal Year-end: 03/31/22
Holding Company
N.A.I.C.S.: 551112
Hooi Hong Cheong *(Chm & CEO)*

ASSOCIATED MOTOR FI-NANCE COMPANY PLC

146 Havelock Road, 5, Colombo, Sri Lanka
Tel.: (94) 112687158
Web Site: https://www.amf.lk
Year Founded: 1962
AMF.N0000—(COL)
Rev.: $13,270,193
Assets: $53,337,891
Liabilities: $43,568,637
Net Worth: $9,769,254
Earnings: $667,298
Emp.: 322
Fiscal Year-end: 03/31/23
Financing & Leasing Services
N.A.I.C.S.: 522220
Rohan Karunaratne *(Chm)*

Subsidiaries:

Arpico Finance Company PLC   **(1)**
No 146 Havelock Road, Colombo, 00500, Sri Lanka
Tel.: (94) 115553663
Web Site: https://amf.lk
Rev.: $22,906,922
Assets: $87,071,020
Liabilities: $78,733,042
Net Worth: $8,337,978

Earnings: $2,034,372
Emp.: 403
Fiscal Year-end: 03/31/2019
Leasing & Financial Services
N.A.I.C.S.: 551112
Chandrin Fernando *(CEO)*

ASSOCIATED RETAILERS LIM-ITED

169 Burnley Street, Richmond, 3121, VIC, Australia
Tel.: (61) 394298266
Web Site: http://www.arl.com.au
Sales Range: $125-149.9 Million
Emp.: 75
Independent Retail Stores
N.A.I.C.S.: 459999
John Symons *(CEO)*

ASSOCIATED SERVICES LIM-ITED

Room 101 1st Floor Marium Heights Plot C/11 Block 7&8 Commercial Area, Off Shahrah-e-Faisal, Karachi, Pakistan
Tel.: (92) 21 34325565
Textile Mill Operator
N.A.I.C.S.: 313110

ASSOCIATION DES CENTRES DISTRIBUTEURS E. LECLERC

52 Rue Camille Des Moulins, 92451, Issy-les-Moulineaux, France
Tel.: (33) 146625100   FR
Web Site: http://www.e-leclerc.com
Year Founded: 1949
Sales Range: $5-14.9 Billion
Emp.: 72,000
Central Supermarket & Hypermarket
N.A.I.C.S.: 445110
Edouard Leclerc *(Co-Chm & Pres)*

ASSOCIAZIONE DEI FONOGRAFICI ITALIANI

Via Vittor Pissani 6, 20124, Milan, Italy
Tel.: (39) 026696263
Web Site: http://www.afi.mi.it
Year Founded: 1948
Sales Range: $10-24.9 Million
Emp.: 5
Sound & Video Media
N.A.I.C.S.: 524292
Leopoldo Lombardi *(Pres)*

ASSORE LIMITED

Assore House 15 Fricker Road Illovo Boulevard, Johannesburg, 2196, South Africa
Tel.: (27) 11 770 6800
Web Site: http://www.assore.com
Rev.: $578,950,155
Assets: $2,425,637,994
Liabilities: $306,092,586
Net Worth: $2,119,545,408
Earnings: $424,154,844
Emp.: 1,204
Fiscal Year-end: 06/30/19
Minerals & Metals Mining Services
N.A.I.C.S.: 212390
Edward M. Southey *(Deputy Chm)*

Subsidiaries:

Minerais U.S. LLC   **(1)**
105 Raider Blvd Ste 104, Hillsborough, NJ 08844
Tel.: (908) 874-7666
Web Site: http://www.mineraisus.com
Sales Range: $1-9.9 Million
Emp.: 10
Alloy Product Distr
N.A.I.C.S.: 423520
Hal Kohn *(Principal)*

Wonderstone Limited   **(1)**
Assore House 15 Fricker Road Illovo Boulevard, Johannesburg, 2196, South Africa
Tel.: (27) 117706845

Web Site: http://www.wonderstone.co.za
Mineral Mining Services
N.A.I.C.S.: 213114

ASSUMPTION MUTUAL LIFE INSURANCE COMPANY

770 Main St, PO Box 160, Moncton, E1C 8L1, NB, Canada
Tel.: (506) 853-6040   Ca
Web Site: http://www.assumption.ca
Year Founded: 1903
Rev.: $115,674,394
Assets: $1,245,933,924
Liabilities: $1,147,715,211
Net Worth: $98,218,713
Earnings: $5,566,907
Fiscal Year-end: 12/31/18
Life Insurance & Portfolio Management Products & Services
N.A.I.C.S.: 524113
Rejean Boudreau *(VP)*

Subsidiaries:

Louisbourg Investments Inc.   **(1)**
1000-770 Main Street, Moncton, E1C 1E7, NB, Canada
Tel.: (506) 853-5410
Web Site:
    https://www.louisbourginvestments.com
Rev.: $876,319,710
Emp.: 12
Pension Fund Endowment & Private Wealth Portfolio Management Services
N.A.I.C.S.: 523940
Luc Gaudet *(CEO)*

ASSURA PLC

3 Barrington Road, Altrincham, WA14 1GY, United Kingdom
Tel.: (44) 1615524506
Web Site: https://www.assuraplc.com
AGR—(LSE)
Rev.: $199,192,124
Assets: $3,549,861,152
Liabilities: $1,690,355,973
Net Worth: $1,859,505,178
Earnings: ($36,354,456)
Emp.: 76
Fiscal Year-end: 03/31/24
Healthcare REIT
N.A.I.C.S.: 531390
Jonathan Murphy *(CEO)*

Subsidiaries:

Assura Investments Limited   **(1)**
3300 Daresbury Business Park, Warrington, WA4 4HS, Cheshire, United Kingdom
Tel.: (44) 1625529191
Investment Services
N.A.I.C.S.: 523940

Assura Pharmacy Limited   **(1)**
Wbw Greenhall Ave, Lostock, Warrington, WA66HL, United Kingdom
Tel.: (44) 1925420660
Web Site: http://www.cohenschaminst.co.uk
Sales Range: $50-74.9 Million
Emp.: 200
Pharmaceutical Supplies & Services
N.A.I.C.S.: 456110
Graham Roberts *(Mng Dir)*

Assura Properties Limited   **(1)**
3300 Daresbury Business Park, Warrington, WA4 4HS, Cheshire, United Kingdom
Tel.: (44) 1928737000
Sales Range: $25-49.9 Million
Property Investment Services
N.A.I.C.S.: 531312

Subsidiary (Domestic):

Assura Properties UK Limited   **(2)**
The Brew House, Greenalls Avenue, Warrington, WA4 6HL, Cheshire, United Kingdom
Tel.: (44) 1928737000
Sales Range: $50-74.9 Million
Emp.: 25
Property Investment Services
N.A.I.C.S.: 531312

Assura Property Management
Limited   **(1)**
The Brew House Greenalls Ave, Warrington, WA4 6HI, Cheshire, United Kingdom
Tel.: (44) 1925420660
Web Site: http://www.assuragroup.co.uk
Sales Range: $25-49.9 Million
Emp.: 35
Property Management Services
N.A.I.C.S.: 531311

ASSURED GUARANTY LTD.

30 Woodbourne Avenue, Hamilton, HM 08, Bermuda
Tel.: (441) 2795700   BM
Web Site:
    http://www.assuredguaranty.com
Year Founded: 2003
AGO—(NYSE)
Rev.: $1,373,000,000
Assets: $12,539,000,000
Liabilities: $6,774,000,000
Net Worth: $5,765,000,000
Earnings: $739,000,000
Emp.: 350
Fiscal Year-end: 12/31/23
Holding Company
N.A.I.C.S.: 551112
Dominic John Frederico *(Pres & CEO)*

Subsidiaries:

Assured Guaranty (Europe) Plc   **(1)**
11th Floor 6 Bevis Marks, London, EC3A 7BA, United Kingdom
Tel.: (44) 2075621900
Web Site: http://www.assuredguaranty.com
Insurance Brokerage Services
N.A.I.C.S.: 524210

Subsidiary (Domestic):

Assured Guaranty (London) Plc   **(2)**
11th Floor 6 Bevis Marks, London, EC3A 7BA, United Kingdom
Tel.: (44) 2075621900
Bond Insurance Services
N.A.I.C.S.: 524126
Sandali Harvey *(Sec)*

Assured Guaranty (Europe) SA.   **(1)**
71 rue du Faubourg Saint-Honore, 75008, Paris, France
Tel.: (33) 142933016
Financial Investment Services
N.A.I.C.S.: 523999

Assured Guaranty Corp.   **(1)**
Level 46 Governor Phillip Tower 1 Farrer Place, Sydney, 2000, NSW,
Australia   **(100%)**
Tel.: (61) 299479738
Web Site: http://www.assuredguaranty.com
Sales Range: $50-74.9 Million
Emp.: 3
Insurance Services
N.A.I.C.S.: 524113

Assured Guaranty Re Ltd.   **(1)**
30 Woodbourne Ave, Hamilton, HM 08,
Bermuda   **(100%)**
Tel.: (441) 2795700
Web Site: http://www.assuredguaranty.com
Sales Range: $50-74.9 Million
Emp.: 75
Reinsurance Carriers
N.A.I.C.S.: 524130

Subsidiary (Domestic):

Assured Guaranty Re Overseas
Ltd   **(2)**
30 Woodbourne Ave, Hamilton, HM 08,
Bermuda   **(100%)**
Tel.: (441) 2795700
Web Site: http://www.assuredguaranty.com
Sales Range: $25-49.9 Million
Emp.: 20
Other Holding Companies Offices
N.A.I.C.S.: 551112
Gary Burnet *(Pres)*

Assured Guaranty US Holdings
Inc   **(1)**
    (100%)

Assured Guaranty Ltd.—(Continued)
Tel.: (212) 974-0100
Web Site: http://www.assuredguaranty.com
Direct Life Insurance Carriers
N.A.I.C.S.: 524113

Subsidiary (Domestic):

Assured Guaranty Mortgage Insurance Company (2)
31 W 52nd St, New York, NY 10019
Tel.: (212) 974-0100
Direct Property & Casualty Insurance Services
N.A.I.C.S.: 524126

Subsidiary (Domestic):

AG Financial Products Inc. (3)
1325 Ave of the Flr 18, New York, NY 10019 (100%)
Tel.: (212) 974-0100
Web Site: http://www.assuredguaranty.com
Sales Range: $10-24.9 Million
Emp.: 15
Financial Services
N.A.I.C.S.: 561499
Robert A. Bailenson (CFO)

Assured Guaranty Corp. (3)
1633 Broadway 23rd 24th Fl, New York, NY 10019
Tel.: (212) 974-0100
Sales Range: $150-199.9 Million
Other Direct Insurance
N.A.I.C.S.: 524128
William B. O'Keefe (Sr Mng Dir-Bus Dev)

Assured Guaranty Municipal Holdings Inc. (3)
1633 Broadway, New York, NY 10019
Tel.: (212) 974-0100
Investment Management Service
N.A.I.C.S.: 523940

Subsidiary (Domestic):

BlueMountain CLO Management, LLC (2)
280 Park Ave 12th Fl, New York, NY 10017
Tel.: (212) 905-3900
Asset Management Services
N.A.I.C.S.: 523940

Municipal Assurance Corp. (2)
1633 Broadway, New York, NY 10019
Tel.: (212) 974-0100
Web Site: http://www.macmunibonds.com
General Insurance Services
N.A.I.C.S.: 524210
William J. Hogan (Sr Mng Dir-Pub Fin)

Assured Healthcare Partners LLC (1)
717 5th Ave Ste 1202, New York, NY 10022
Tel.: (212) 905-2100
Web Site: https://www.ahpartners.com
Healtcare Services
N.A.I.C.S.: 621610
Ameya Agge (Co-Mng Dir)

Subsidiary (Domestic):

National Partners in Healthcare, LLC (2)
2221 Lakeside Blvd Ste 600, Richardson, TX 75082
Tel.: (866) 535-5001
Web Site: https://nphllc.com
Anesthesiology Services
N.A.I.C.S.: 621399
Mike Saunders (CEO)

Subsidiary (Domestic):

MedStream Anesthesia PLLC (3)
82 Patton Ave Ste 510, Asheville, NC 28801
Tel.: (828) 210-9386
Web Site: http://www.medstream.biz
Sales Range: $50-74.9 Million
Emp.: 72
Health Care Consulting Services
N.A.I.C.S.: 621610
Kenneth R. Ellington (Founder & Pres)

Assured Investment Management (London) LLP (1)
6 Bevis Marks 12th Floor, London, EC3A 7BA, United Kingdom

Tel.: (44) 2076470700
Financial Investment Services
N.A.I.C.S.: 523999

ASSURIA N.V.
Grote Combeweg 37, PO Box 1030, Paramaribo, Suriname
Tel.: (597) 473400　　　　　　SR
Web Site: http://www.assuria.sr
Sales Range: $25-49.9 Million
Emp.: 153
Holding Company; Life, Medical, Property & Casualty Insurance Products & Services
N.A.I.C.S.: 551112
A.K. Achaibersing (Mng Dir-Non-Life Insurance)

Subsidiaries:

Assuria Beleggingsmaatschappij N.V. (1)
Grote Combeweg 37, PO Box 1030, Paramaribo, Suriname (99.67%)
Tel.: (597) 473400
Web Site: http://www.assuria.sr
Investment Services
N.A.I.C.S.: 523999
S. Smit (Grp CEO & Mng Dir)

Assuria Levensverzekering N.V. (1)
Grote Combeweg 37, PO Box 1030, Paramaribo, Suriname (99.3%)
Tel.: (597) 473400
Web Site: http://www.assuria.sr
Life Insurance Products & Services
N.A.I.C.S.: 524113
Smidt Stephen (Mng Dir)

Assuria Life (GY) Inc. (1)
Lot 178 Church Street South Cummingsburg, Georgetown, Guyana
Tel.: (592) 226 7052
Insurance Management Services
N.A.I.C.S.: 524298

Assuria Medische Verzekering N.V. (1)
Henck Arronstraat 5-7, PO Box 1501, Paramaribo, Suriname (99.48%)
Tel.: (597) 477955
Sales Range: $75-99.9 Million
Emp.: 80
Medical Insurance Products & Services
N.A.I.C.S.: 524114

Assuria Schadeverzekering N.V. (1)
Henck Arronstraat 5-7, PO Box 1501, Paramaribo, Suriname (100%)
Tel.: (597) 477955
Web Site: http://www.assuria.sr
Property & Casualty Insurance Products & Services
N.A.I.C.S.: 524126

De Surinaamsche Bank N.V. (1)
Henck Arronstraat 26-30, PO Box 1806, Paramaribo, Suriname (49%)
Tel.: (597) 471100
Sales Range: $300-349.9 Million
Emp.: 350
Retail & Commercial Banking, Asset Management, Loans, Transfer & Treasury Services
N.A.I.C.S.: 522110

Gulf Insurance Limited (1)
1 Gray Street & Tragarete Road St Clair, Port of Spain, Trinidad & Tobago
Tel.: (868) 622 5878
Web Site: http://www.gulfinsuranceltd.com
Insurance Management Services
N.A.I.C.S.: 524298
Jason Clarke (Chm)

ASSYSTEM S.A.
9-11 Allee de L'arche Tour Egee, La Defense, 92400, Courbevoie, France
Tel.: (33) 141252900　　　　　　FR
Web Site: https://www.assystem.com
Year Founded: 1966
ASY—(EUR)
Rev.: $480,682,063
Assets: $781,998,705
Liabilities: $395,100,367
Net Worth: $386,898,338

Earnings: $37,448,737
Emp.: 7,041
Fiscal Year-end: 12/31/21
Engineering & Innovation Consultancy Services
N.A.I.C.S.: 541330
Dominique Louis (Chm & CEO)

Subsidiaries:

ANAFI Plus (1)
Za Le Pont Rouge, Tremuson, 22440, France
Tel.: (33) 296948888
Engineering Services
N.A.I.C.S.: 541330

Assystem (IOM) Ltd (1)
11 Spring Valley Estate Cooil Rd, Braddan, Isle of Man
Tel.: (44) 1624638400
Sales Range: $25-49.9 Million
Emp.: 45
Engineering Services
N.A.I.C.S.: 541330
Brian Maddrell (Mgr-Ops)

Assystem Deutschland Holding GmbH (1)
Sportallee 77, Hamburg, 22335, Germany
Tel.: (49) 405079610
Engineering Services
N.A.I.C.S.: 541330

Subsidiary (Domestic):

Assystem Services Deutschland GmbH (2)
Erwin-von-Kreibig-Strasse 3, 80807, Munich, Germany
Tel.: (49) 89 608090 0
Web Site: http://www.assystem-germany.com
Engineering Services
N.A.I.C.S.: 541330
Alexander Graf (CEO)

Subsidiary (Domestic):

Expleo Germany Holding GmbH (3)
Stollwerckstrasse 11, 51149, Cologne, Germany
Tel.: (49) 220391540
Web Site: http://www.de.expleogroup.com
Information Technology Independent Quality Services
N.A.I.C.S.: 541690
Gerard Brescon (Chief People Officer)

Subsidiary (Domestic):

Expleo Germany GmbH - Munich (4)
Wilhelm Wagenfeld Str 1 3, 80807, Munich, Germany
Tel.: (49) 896080900
Web Site: http://www.de.expleogroup.com
Management Consulting Services
N.A.I.C.S.: 541611

Subsidiary (Non-US):

Expleo Group Limited (4)
7-11 Moorgate, London, EC2R 6AF, United Kingdom
Tel.: (44) 2074484620
Web Site: http://www.uk.expleogroup.com
Software Testing & Quality Management Services
N.A.I.C.S.: 541511

Expleo Netherlands BV (4)
Van Deventerlaan 31 51, 3528 AG, Utrecht, Netherlands
Tel.: (31) 886558880
Web Site: http://www.nl.expleogroup.com
Software Testing & Quality Management Services
N.A.I.C.S.: 541511

Expleo Nordic AB (4)
Narvavagen 12, 115 22, Stockholm, Sweden
Tel.: (46) 820 706 0
Software Testing Services
N.A.I.C.S.: 541511

Expleo Solutions Limited (4)
6A Sixth Floor Prince Infocity II No 283/3 & 283/4 Rajiv Gandhi Salai, OMR Kandancha-

vadi, Chennai, 600096, India (53.13%)
Tel.: (91) 4443923200
Web Site: https://www.in.expleogroup.com
Financial Software Applications Developer
N.A.I.C.S.: 513210

Expleo Technology Ireland Limited (4)
30 North Wall Quay, Dublin, Co Dublin, Ireland
Tel.: (353) 16709916
Web Site: http://www.ie.expleogroup.com
Software Testing & Quality Management Services
N.A.I.C.S.: 541511

SQS Software Quality Systems (Schweiz) AG, Zurich (4)
Richtistrasse 7, 8304, Zurich, Wallisellen, Switzerland
Tel.: (41) 445 627 333
Web Site: http://www.ch.expleogroup.com
Software Testing Solutions
N.A.I.C.S.: 541512

Subsidiary (US):

Trissential, LLC (4)
1905 East Wayzata Blvd, Minneapolis, MN 55391
Tel.: (952) 595-7970
Web Site: http://www.trissential.com
Administrative Management & General Management Consulting Services
N.A.I.C.S.: 541611
Keith Korsi (Founder & CEO)

Assystem Developpement (1)
70 Blvd De Courcelles, Paris, 75017, France
Tel.: (33) 134525000
Web Site: http://www.assystem.com
Engineering Services
N.A.I.C.S.: 541330

Assystem ENVY A.S. (1)
Cetin Emec Bulvari 1314 Cadde No 7 Ovecler, Ankara, Turkiye
Tel.: (90) 3125838800
Web Site: http://www.envy.com.tr
Emp.: 140
Engineering & Consulting Services
N.A.I.C.S.: 541330
Onur Oztuncer (Mgr)

Assystem Engineering & Consulting (Shanghai) Co , Ltd (1)
Tangchen Xongxin, Office A1405, 188 Zhangyang Road, Shanghai, Pudong, China (100%)
Tel.: (86) 2158368110
Web Site: http://www.assystem.com
Engineering Services
N.A.I.C.S.: 541330

Assystem Environnement (1)
70 Boulevard De Courcelles, 75017, Paris, France
Tel.: (33) 155650300
Sales Range: $25-49.9 Million
Emp.: 20
Engineering Services
N.A.I.C.S.: 541330

Assystem Facilities (1)
70 Boulevard De Courcelles, Paris, 75017, France (100%)
Tel.: (33) 155650300
Sales Range: $25-49.9 Million
Emp.: 5
Engineering Services
N.A.I.C.S.: 541330
Dominique Louis (Gen Dir)

Assystem France (1)
70 Boulevard De Courcelles, Paris, 75017, France (100%)
Tel.: (33) 155650300
Web Site: http://www.assytems.com
Sales Range: $25-49.9 Million
Emp.: 55
Engineering Services
N.A.I.C.S.: 541330
Dominique Louis (CEO)

Assystem GmbH (1)
Sportallee 77, Hamburg, Germany
Tel.: (49) 405079610
Web Site: http://www.assystem-germany.com

Sales Range: $150-199.9 Million
Emp.: 600
Engineering Services
N.A.I.C.S.: 541330

Assystem Group Uk Ltd (1)
5B Tower House St Catherine's Court, Sunderland Enterprise Park, SR53XJ, Sunderland, United Kingdom
Tel.: (44) 1915160222
Web Site: http://www.inbis.com
Sales Range: $350-399.9 Million
Emp.: 1,500
Engineering Services
N.A.I.C.S.: 541330

Assystem Iberia (1)
Avenida De Espana 23 Planta 3, Alcobendas, 28100, Madrid, Spain
Tel.: (34) 944393550
Web Site: http://www.assystem.es
Sales Range: $25-49.9 Million
Emp.: 200
Engineering Services
N.A.I.C.S.: 541330

Assystem India Pvt Ltd (1)
Prestige Blue Chip Software Park 4th Floor 2nd Block No 9 Hosur Road, Bengaluru, 560 029, India
Tel.: (91) 80 4112 3660
Web Site: http://www.assystem-india.com
Sales Range: $25-49.9 Million
Emp.: 30
Engineering Services
N.A.I.C.S.: 541330

Assystem Innovation (1)
23 place de Wicklow, 75017, Paris, France (100%)
Tel.: (33) 134525000
Management Consulting Services
N.A.I.C.S.: 541618
Dominique Louis (Gen Mgr)

Assystem Italia Srl (1)
Viale Risorgimento 5, Beinasco, Italy (100%)
Tel.: (39) 0238093582
Engineering Services
N.A.I.C.S.: 541330

Assystem Portugal (1)
Travessa Da Telheira 305 Sala 10, Perafita, Matosinhos, 4455-563, Portugal
Tel.: (351) 229997130
Sales Range: $25-49.9 Million
Emp.: 20
Engineering Services
N.A.I.C.S.: 541330
George Garcia (Gen Mgr)

Assystem Romania Srl (1)
Sector 5 48 Mitropolit Dosoftei Street, Bucharest, Romania (100%)
Tel.: (40) 742100219
Web Site: http://www.assystemromania.ro
Sales Range: $25-49.9 Million
Emp.: 80
Testing Laboratories
N.A.I.C.S.: 541380

Assystem Technologies & Services SA (1)
70 Boulevard De Courcelles, Paris, 75017, France (100%)
Tel.: (33) 155650300
Web Site: http://www.assystem.com
Sales Range: $25-49.9 Million
Emp.: 50
Engineering Services
N.A.I.C.S.: 541330
Dominic Louis (CEO)

AssystemBrime Portugal (1)
Sala 10 Travessa Da Telheira 305, Perafita, 4455-563, Porto, Portugal (100%)
Tel.: (351) 229997130
Sales Range: $25-49.9 Million
Emp.: 23
Engineering Services
N.A.I.C.S.: 541330
Clara Siguairedo (Asst Mgr)

Athos Aeronautique (1)
Immeuble Neos Aeroparc D Entzh 1 Rue Icare, 67960, Entzheim, France
Tel.: (33) 534396404
Aircraft Mfr
N.A.I.C.S.: 336411

Eurosyn Developpement SAS (1)
16 Ave Du Quebec, 91140, Villebon-sur-Yvette, France
Tel.: (33) 160926400
Web Site: http://www.eurosyn.fr
Emp.: 30
Engineering Services
N.A.I.C.S.: 541330
Herve Dessi (Pres)

Expleo Engineering UK Ltd (1)
Club Street Bamber Bridge, Preston, PR5 6FN, Lancashire, United Kingdom
Tel.: (44) 1772645000
Web Site: http://expleogroup.com
Engineering Services
N.A.I.C.S.: 541330

AST GROUPE SA
78 rue Elisee Reclus, 69150, Decines-Charpieu, Cedex, France
Tel.: (33) 472816464
Web Site: https://www.ast-groupe.fr
Year Founded: 1993
ASP—(EUR)
Sales Range: $200-249.9 Million
Real Estate Development Services
N.A.I.C.S.: 531390

Subsidiaries:

Perform'Habitat SAS (1)
5 rue Eugene Faure CS 30623, 38026, Grenoble, Cedex, France
Tel.: (33) 456523200
Web Site: http://www.perform-habitat.com
Construction Services
N.A.I.C.S.: 236220

ASTA CO LTD
11th Fl AICT Bldg A 145 Gwanggyo-ro, Yeongtong-gu, Suwon, 16229, Gyeonggi-do, Korea (South)
Tel.: (82) 318930375
Web Site: https://www.astams.com
Year Founded: 2006
246720—(KRS)
Rev.: $2,565,925
Assets: $8,387,639
Liabilities: $2,836,794
Net Worth: $5,550,846
Earnings: ($2,147,172)
Emp.: 31
Fiscal Year-end: 12/31/22
Analytical Instrument Mfr & Distr
N.A.I.C.S.: 334516
EungJoon Jo (Chm)

ASTAIRE GROUP PLC
46 Worship Street, London, EC2A 2EA, United Kingdom
Tel.: (44) 2074924750 UK
Web Site:
http://www.astairegroup.co.uk
Investment Banking Services
N.A.I.C.S.: 523150
Chris Roberts (Dir-Fin)

ASTAKA HOLDINGS LIMITED
No 22 Jalan Padi Emas 1/4 Uda Business Centre, 81200, Johor Bahru, Johor, Malaysia
Tel.: (60) 72315457 SG
Web Site:
https://www.astaka.com.my
Year Founded: 1993
Rev.: $49,824,409
Assets: $126,639,180
Liabilities: $103,911,026
Net Worth: $22,728,154
Earnings: ($4,475,682)
Emp.: 97
Fiscal Year-end: 06/30/20
Travel Agency Services
N.A.I.C.S.: 561510
Zamani Kasim (Exec Dir)

ASTANA FINANCE, JSC
12 Begelidinov Street, Nur-Sultan, 010000, Kazakhstan

Tel.: (7) 7172592938 KZ
Web Site: http://www.af.kz
Year Founded: 2006
Sales Range: $200-249.9 Million
Financial Services
N.A.I.C.S.: 522299
Erlan Shakibayev (Chm-Mgmt Bd & CEO)

Subsidiaries:

Bank of Astana JSC (1)
Building 22 microdistrict Koktem-2, Almaty, 050040, Kazakhstan
Tel.: (7) 27 259 60 60
Web Site: http://www.bankastana.kz
Banking Services
N.A.I.C.S.: 522110

ASTANA INTERNATIONAL EXCHANGE LIMITED
55/19 Mangilik El St Block C 3 4, Nur-Sultan, 010000, Kazakhstan
Tel.: (7) 717 223 5366 KZ
Web Site: http://www.aix.kz
Year Founded: 2017
Securities Exchange Operator
N.A.I.C.S.: 523210
Timothy Bennett (CEO & Chm-Mgmt Bd)

ASTANAGAS KMG JSC
8 Dinmuhamed Konaev str, Esil county, Nur-Sultan, 010000, Kazakhstan
Tel.: (7) 172907760
Web Site: http://www.astanagas.kz
AKMG—(KAZ)
Rev.: $73,686,739
Assets: $546,235,014
Liabilities: $433,498,398
Net Worth: $112,736,616
Earnings: $5,347,646
Fiscal Year-end: 12/31/23
Oil & Gas Field Engineering Services
N.A.I.C.S.: 213112

ASTARTA HOLDING N.V.
38/44 Pochayninska Str, 04070, Kiev, Ukraine
Tel.: (380) 445859494
Web Site:
http://www.astartaholding.com
AST—(WAR)
Rev.: $641,077,308
Assets: $786,170,670
Liabilities: $234,057,345
Net Worth: $552,113,326
Earnings: $64,322,237
Emp.: 4,714
Fiscal Year-end: 12/31/23
Sugar Mfr
N.A.I.C.S.: 111991
Marc Van Campen (Chief Corp Officer)

ASTEC LIFESCIENCES LTD
Godrej One 3rd Floor Pirojshanagar Eastern Express Highway, Vikhroli East, Mumbai, 400 079, Maharashtra, India
Tel.: (91) 2269218000
Web Site:
https://www.godrejastec.com
Year Founded: 1994
533138—(BOM)
Rev.: $55,612,570
Assets: $116,893,903
Liabilities: $72,588,731
Net Worth: $44,305,172
Earnings: ($5,622,231)
Emp.: 551
Fiscal Year-end: 03/31/24
Chemicals Mfr
N.A.I.C.S.: 325998
Ashok V. Hiremath (Mng Dir)

ASTEK GROUP PLC

Astek House Atlantic St, Altrincham, WA15 5DL, Cheshire, United Kingdom
Tel.: (44) 1619423900
Web Site:
http://www.astekgroup.co.uk
Sales Range: $1-9.9 Million
Emp.: 11
Medical Devices & Diagnostics
N.A.I.C.S.: 339113
Mark Shupac (Dir-Tech)

ASTEL JSC
67 B Mametova Str 3rd Floor, 050004, Almaty, Kazakhstan
Tel.: (7) 7273120000
Web Site: https://www.astel.kz
Year Founded: 1993
ASTL—(KAZ)
Rev.: $54,201,706
Assets: $30,389,000
Liabilities: $8,394,094
Net Worth: $21,994,906
Earnings: $4,979,090
Emp.: 315
Fiscal Year-end: 12/31/20
Telecommunication Servicesb
N.A.I.C.S.: 517112
Vladimir Breusov (Pres)

ASTELLAS PHARMA INC.
2-5-1 Nihonbashi-Honcho, Chuo-ku, Tokyo, 103-8411, Japan
Tel.: (81) 332443000 JP
Web Site: https://www.astellas.com
Year Founded: 1923
ALPMF—(OTCIQ)
Rev.: $12,546,857,840
Assets: $22,577,583,600
Liabilities: $8,441,802,160
Net Worth: $14,135,781,440
Earnings: $1,201,152,480
Emp.: 14,522
Fiscal Year-end: 03/31/22
Pharmaceutical Product Developer & Mfr
N.A.I.C.S.: 325412
Yoshihiko Hatanaka (Chm)

Subsidiaries:

Astellas Analytical Science Laboratories, Inc. (1)
2-1-6 Kashima Astellas Seiyaku Kk Kashima Jigyojo, Yodogawa-Ku, Osaka, 532-0031, Japan (100%)
Tel.: (81) 663901231
Web Site: http://www.astellas.com
Emp.: 130
Pharmaceutical Products Research & Development Services
N.A.I.C.S.: 541715
Ryoichi Uematsu (Pres)

Astellas Business Service Co., Ltd. (1)
3-17-1 Hasune, Itabashi-Ku, Tokyo, 174-0046, Japan
Tel.: (81) 359165115
Pharmaceuticals Product Mfr
N.A.I.C.S.: 325412

Astellas Farma Colombia SAS (1)
Calle 113 No 7 -80 Oficina 1502, 110111, Bogota, Colombia
Tel.: (57) 18000180462
N.A.I.C.S.: 325412

Astellas Farma Limitada (1)
Lagoas Park Edificio 5 Torre C Piso 6, 2740-245, Porto Salvo, Portugal
Tel.: (351) 21 440 1300
Web Site: https://www.astellas.com
Emp.: 20
Pharmaceuticals Product Mfr
N.A.I.C.S.: 325412
Luiz Claudio Dutra (Mng Dir-Brasil)

Astellas Learning Institute Co., Ltd. (1)
2-5-1 Nihombashihoncho, Chuo-Ku, Tokyo, 103-0023, Japan
Tel.: (81) 332443481

Astellas Pharma Inc.→(Continued)

Pharmaceuticals Product Mfr
N.A.I.C.S.: 325412

Astellas Pharma (Pty) Limited (1)
Mirage, Bedfordview, 2007, Johannesburg,
South Africa
Tel.: (27) 11 615 9433
Sales Range: $25-49.9 Million
Emp.: 43
Pharmaceuticals Product Mfr
N.A.I.C.S.: 325412
Derek Haynes *(Gen Mgr)*

**Astellas Pharma (Thailand) Co.,
Ltd.** (1)
No 1788 Singha Complex Building 19th
Floor Room No 1908-1914, New Petchaburi
Road Khwaeng Bangkapi Khet Huai
Kwang, Bangkok, 10310, Thailand
Tel.: (66) 209696005
Web Site: http://www.astellas.com
Drug Distr
N.A.I.C.S.: 424210

Astellas Pharma A.G. (1)
Grindelstrasse 6, 8304, Wallisellen, Switzer-
land
Tel.: (41) 43 233 60 20
Pharmaceuticals Product Mfr
N.A.I.C.S.: 325412

Astellas Pharma AE (1)
6-8 Agisilaou Str, Marousi, 15123, Athens,
Greece
Tel.: (30) 2108199900
Web Site: http://www.astellas.com
Sales Range: $25-49.9 Million
Emp.: 60
Pharmaceuticals Product Mfr
N.A.I.C.S.: 325412

**Astellas Pharma Australia Pty
Ltd** (1)
Suite 2 01 2 Banfield Road, Macquarie
Park, 2113, NSW, Australia
Tel.: (61) 298141100
Web Site: http://www.astellas.com
Drug Distr
N.A.I.C.S.: 424210

Astellas Pharma B.V. (1)
Sylviusweg 62, Leiden, 2333 BE, Nether-
lands
Tel.: (31) 71 5455 854
Pharmaceuticals Product Mfr
N.A.I.C.S.: 325412

Astellas Pharma B.V. (1)
Medialaan 50, 1800, Vilvoorde, Belgium
Tel.: (32) 25580710
Web Site: http://www.astellas.com
Drug Distr
N.A.I.C.S.: 424210

Astellas Pharma Co., Limited (1)
5 Water Side Citywest Business Campus
Nass Road, Dublin, 24, Ireland
Tel.: (353) 1 467 1555
Web Site: http://www.astellas.ie
Pharmaceuticals Product Mfr
N.A.I.C.S.: 325412

Astellas Pharma DMCC (1)
Platinum Tower 26th Floor Jumeirah Lakes
Towers Cluster I, PO Box 282872, Dubai,
United Arab Emirates
Tel.: (971) 44475952
Web Site: https://www.astellas.com
N.A.I.C.S.: 325412

Astellas Pharma Europe Ltd. (1)
Lovett House Lovett Road, Staines-upon-
Thames, TW18 3AZ, Surrey, United
Kingdom (100%)
Tel.: (44) 01784419400
Web Site: http://www.inchcape.co
Sales Range: $1-4.9 Billion
Emp.: 3,200
Pharmaceutical Manufacturing
N.A.I.C.S.: 325412
Eugene Van Rensburg *(CFO-EMEA)*

Subsidiary (Non-US):

Astellas Pharma Sp (2)
ul Osmanska 14, 02-823, Warsaw,
Poland (100%)
Tel.: (48) 225451111
Web Site: http://www.astellas.com

Sales Range: $50-74.9 Million
Emp.: 120
Provider of Pharmaceuticals
N.A.I.C.S.: 325412

Astellas Ireland (2)
Waterside Citywest Business Campus Naas
Road, Dublin, D24 X7FT, Ireland (100%)
Tel.: (353) 14671555
Web Site: http://www.astellas.ie
Sales Range: $25-49.9 Million
Emp.: 400
Pharmaceutical Ingredient Mfr
N.A.I.C.S.: 325412

Subsidiary (Domestic):

Astellas Ltd. (2)
Lovett House Lovett Rd, Staines-upon-
Thames, TW1 83AZ, Surrey, United
Kingdom (100%)
Tel.: (44) 1784419400
Sales Range: $50-74.9 Million
Emp.: 250
Provider of Pharmaceuticals
N.A.I.C.S.: 325412

Subsidiary (Non-US):

Astellas Pharma A/S (2)
Arne Jacobsens Alle 15, 2300, Copenha-
gen, Denmark (100%)
Tel.: (45) 43430355
Web Site: http://www.astellas.com
Sales Range: $25-49.9 Million
Emp.: 40
Provider of Pharmaceuticals
N.A.I.C.S.: 325412

Astellas Pharma AB (2)
Box 21046, 200 21, Malmo,
Sweden (100%)
Tel.: (46) 406501500
Web Site: http://www.astellas.com
Sales Range: $10-24.9 Million
Emp.: 6
Pharmaceuticals Manufacturer
N.A.I.C.S.: 325412

Astellas Pharma Europe B.V. (2)
Hogemaat 2, 7942 JG, Meppel, Nether-
lands
Tel.: (31) 522235300
Web Site: http://www.astellas.com
Sales Range: $100-124.9 Million
Emp.: 500
Pharmaceutical Mfr & Developer
N.A.I.C.S.: 325412

Subsidiary (Domestic):

Astellas B.V. (3)
Sylviusweg 62, 2333 BE, Leiden,
Netherlands (100%)
Tel.: (31) 715455050
Web Site: http://www.astellas.com
Provider of Pharmaceutical Research & De-
velopment Services
N.A.I.C.S.: 325412

Astellas Pharma Europe (3)
Manufacturing Meppel Hogemaat 2, 7942
JG, Meppel, Netherlands
Tel.: (31) 52 223 5300
Web Site: http://www.astellas.eu
Sales Range: $125-149.9 Million
Emp.: 300
Mfr of Pharmaceuticals
N.A.I.C.S.: 325412

Subsidiary (Non-US):

Astellas Pharma GmbH (2)
Donau-City-Strasse 7, 1220, Vienna, Austria
Tel.: (43) 18772668
Web Site: http://www.astellas.com
Sales Range: $25-49.9 Million
Emp.: 40
Pharmaceuticals Whslr
N.A.I.C.S.: 424210

Astellas Pharma GmbH (2)
Ridlerstrasse 57, 80339, Munich, Germany
Tel.: (49) 89454401
Web Site: http://www.astellas.com
Sales Range: $200-249.9 Million
Emp.: 900
Pharmaceuticals Marketer
N.A.I.C.S.: 424210

Astellas Pharma Ltda (2)

Lagoas Park Edificio 5 Torre C Piso 6, Edi-
fico Cinema No 1, 2740-245, Porto Salvo,
Portugal (100%)
Tel.: (351) 214401300
Web Site: http://www.yamanouchi-eu.com
Sales Range: $25-49.9 Million
Emp.: 64
Provider of Pharmaceuticals
N.A.I.C.S.: 325412

Astellas Pharma Sarl (2)
26 quai Charles Pasqua, 92309, Levallois-
Perret, Cedex, France
Tel.: (33) 155917500
Web Site: http://www.astellas.com
Sales Range: $25-49.9 Million
Emp.: 50
Provider of Pharmaceuticals
N.A.I.C.S.: 325412
Patrick Errard *(Mng Dir)*

Astellas Pharma, S.A. (2)
Torre Espacio Paseo de la Castellana no
259 D, Planta 31, 28046, Madrid, Pozuelo
de Alarcon, Spain (30%)
Tel.: (34) 914952700
Web Site: http://www.astellas.com
Sales Range: $25-49.9 Million
Emp.: 100
Pharmaceuticals
N.A.I.C.S.: 325412

Subsidiaries:

Fujisawa SA (2)
Avenida Bruselas 20 Planta 1, Edificio Gor-
bea IV, E-28108, Alcobendas, Madrid,
Spain
Tel.: (34) 914902810
Provider of Pharmaceuticals
N.A.I.C.S.: 325412

Yabrofarma LDA (2)
Edificio Cinema, Rua Jose Fontana N 1-1,
2770-101, Paco d'Arcos, Portugal
Provider of Pharmaceuticals
N.A.I.C.S.: 325412

Astellas Pharma Ges.mbH (1)
Donau-City-Strasse 7, 1220, Vienna, Austria
Tel.: (43) 1 877 26 68
Sales Range: $25-49.9 Million
Emp.: 57
Pharmaceuticals Product Mfr
N.A.I.C.S.: 325412
Berthold Cvach *(Gen Mgr)*

**Astellas Pharma Hong Kong Co.,
Ltd.** (1)
Unit 1103-08 11/F Tower 1 Grand Century
Place 193 Prince Edward Road, West Mon-
gkok, Kowloon, China (Hong Kong)
Tel.: (852) 3377 9801
Web Site: http://www.astellas.com
Sales Range: $25-49.9 Million
Emp.: 18
Pharmaceuticals Product Mfr
N.A.I.C.S.: 325412

**Astellas Pharma India Private
Limited** (1)
301 3rd Floor C and B Square 127 Andheri
Kurla Road, Chakala Andheri East, Mumbai,
400 069, India
Tel.: (91) 2261557600
Web Site: http://www.astellas.com
Drug Distr
N.A.I.C.S.: 424210

**Astellas Pharma International
B.V.** (1)
Sylviusweg 62, 2353 EW, Leiden, Nether-
lands
Tel.: (31) 715455854
Web Site: http://www.astellas.com
Pharmaceutical Products Distr
N.A.I.C.S.: 424210

Astellas Pharma Kft. (1)
Csorsz u 49-51, Budapest, 1124, Hungary
Tel.: (36) 1 577 8200
Pharmaceuticals Product Mfr
N.A.I.C.S.: 325412

Astellas Pharma Korea, Inc. (1)
7th floor Parnas Tower 521 Teheran-ro,
Gangnam-gu, Seoul, 135766, Korea
(South)
Tel.: (82) 23 448 0504
Web Site: https://www.astellas.com
Emp.: 200
Pharmaceutical Mfr & Sales

N.A.I.C.S.: 424210
Hae-Doh Jung *(CEO)*

Astellas Pharma Ltd. (1)
Space 68 Chertsey Road, Woking, GU21
5BJ, Surrey, United Kingdom
Tel.: (44) 2033798700
Web Site: http://www.astellas.com
Pharmaceuticals Product Mfr
N.A.I.C.S.: 325412

**Astellas Pharma Malaysia Sdn.
Bhd.** (1)
Suite 18 05 Level 18 Centrepoint North
Tower, Mid Valley City Lingkaran Syed Pu-
tra, 59200, Kuala Lumpur, Malaysia
Tel.: (60) 322026999
Web Site: http://www.astellas.com
Drug Distr
N.A.I.C.S.: 424210

Astellas Pharma Philippines Inc. (1)
Units A & B 20th Floor 6811 BPI-Philam Life
Makati Ayala Avenue, Salcedo Village Bel-
Air, Makati, 6811, Philippines
Tel.: (63) 88451558
Web Site: http://www.astellas.com
Pharmaceuticals Mfr
N.A.I.C.S.: 325412

Astellas Pharma S.A.S (1)
26 quai Charles Pasqua, 92309, Levallois-
Perret, Cedex, France
Tel.: (33) 1 55 91 75 00
Web Site: http://www.astellas.com
Sales Range: $75-99.9 Million
Emp.: 200
Pharmaceutical Product Mfr & Whslr
N.A.I.C.S.: 325412

Astellas Pharma S.p.A. (1)
Via del Bosco Rinnovato 6 - Edificio U7,
20090, Assago, MI, Italy
Tel.: (39) 02 92 138 1
Web Site: http://www.astellas.eu
Sales Range: $50-74.9 Million
Emp.: 180
Pharmaceuticals Product Mfr
N.A.I.C.S.: 325412

**Astellas Pharma Singapore Pte.
Ltd.** (1)
6 Temasek Boulevard 26-03/05 Suntec
Tower Four, Singapore, 038986, Singapore
Tel.: (65) 65009330
Web Site: http://www.astellas.com
Drug Distr
N.A.I.C.S.: 424210

Astellas Pharma Sp.zo.o. (1)
Poleczki 21 Str, 02-822, Warsaw, Poland
Tel.: (48) 22 545 11 11
Pharmaceutical Products Distr
N.A.I.C.S.: 424210

Astellas Pharma Taiwan, Inc. (1)
5F No 10 Sec 3 Min-Sheng E Rd, Taipei,
104, Taiwan
Tel.: (886) 2 2507 5799
Pharmaceutical Product Mfr & Whslr
N.A.I.C.S.: 325412

Astellas Pharma Tech Co., Ltd. (1)
2-5-1 Nihonbashihoncho, Chuo-Ku, Tokyo,
103-8411, Japan
Tel.: (81) 332446320
Web Site: http://atec.astellas.com
Sales Range: $50-74.9 Million
Emp.: 1,270
Pharmaceutical Product Mfr & Whslr
N.A.I.C.S.: 424210

**Astellas Pharma ilac Ticaret ve
Sanayi A.s.** (1)
Maslak Link Plaza Eski Buyukdere Caddesi
No 3-5 Kat 14, Maslak Sariyer, 34398, Is-
tanbul, Turkiye
Tel.: (90) 212 440 08 00
Web Site: http://www.astellas.com
Sales Range: $25-49.9 Million
Emp.: 29
Pharmaceuticals Product Mfr
N.A.I.C.S.: 325412

Astellas Pharma s.r.o (1)
Rohanske nabrezi 678/29, Karlin, 186 00,
Prague, Czech Republic
Tel.: (420) 221401500
Web Site: http://www.astellas.cz
Sales Range: $25-49.9 Million
Emp.: 50
Pharmaceuticals Product Mfr

N.A.I.C.S.: 325412

Astellas Research Technologies Co., Ltd. (1)
Miyukigaoka 21, Tsukuba, 305-8585, Ibaraki, Japan
Tel.: (81) 29 854 1590
Pharmaceuticals Product Mfr
N.A.I.C.S.: 325412

Astellas Tokai Co., Ltd. (1)
180 Ozumi, Yaizu, 425-0072, Shizuoka, Japan
Tel.: (81) 546275111
Sales Range: $125-149.9 Million
Emp.: 50
Pharmaceuticals Product Mfr
N.A.I.C.S.: 325412

Astellas US Holding, Inc. (1)
1 Astellas Way, Northbrook, IL 60062
Tel.: (224) 205-8800
Pharmaceuticals Product Mfr
N.A.I.C.S.: 325412

Subsidiary (Domestic):

Iveric bio, Inc. (2)
8 Sylvan Way, Parsippany, NJ 07054
Tel.: (609) 474-6455
Web Site: https://www.iverícbio.com
Rev.: $2,264,000
Assets: $666,823,000
Liabilities: $132,166,000
Net Worth: $534,657,000
Earnings: ($185,211,000)
Emp.: 163
Fiscal Year-end: 12/31/2022
Biopharmaceutical Mfr Focusing on Eye Diseases
N.A.I.C.S.: 325412
Snehal Shah *(Chief Regulatory Officer)*

Astellas US LLC (1)
1 Astellas Way, Northbrook, IL 60062
Tel.: (847) 317-8800
Web Site: http://www.astellas.us
Emp.: 3,000
Holding Company; Pharmaceutical Products Mfr & Whslr
N.A.I.C.S.: 551112
Masao Yoshida *(Pres & CEO)*

Subsidiary (Domestic):

Agensys, Inc. (2)
2225 Colorado Ave, Santa Monica, CA 90404
Tel.: (310) 820-8029
Web Site: http://www.agensys.com
Sales Range: $25-49.9 Million
Emp.: 100
Cancer Treatment Developer
N.A.I.C.S.: 541715
Sef Kurstjens *(Pres & CEO)*

Subsidiary (Non-US):

Astellas Pharma Canada, Inc. (2)
675 Cochrane Drive Suite 500 West Tower, Markham, L3R 0B8, ON, Canada
Tel.: (905) 470-7990
Web Site: http://www.astellas.com
Sales Range: $50-74.9 Million
Emp.: 110
Proprietary Pharmaceuticals Marketer
N.A.I.C.S.: 424210

Subsidiary (Domestic):

Astellas Pharma US, Inc. (2)
1 Astellas Way, Northbrook, IL 60062-6111 **(100%)**
Tel.: (847) 317-8800
Web Site: http://www.astellas.com
Sales Range: $200-249.9 Million
Emp.: 3,000
Pharmaceutical Product Developer & Mfr
N.A.I.C.S.: 325412
Walt Johnston *(Sr VP-Sls & Mktg-Urology & Hospital Markets)*

Astellas Research Institute of America LLC (2)
8045 Lamon Ave, Skokie, IL 60077
Tel.: (847) 933-7400
Pharmaceutical Laboratory Operating Services
N.A.I.C.S.: 621511

Astellas US Technologies, Inc. (2)

330 Marshall Ave, Norman, OK 73072 **(100%)**
Tel.: (405) 217-6400
Web Site: http://www.us.astellas.com
Sales Range: $25-49.9 Million
Emp.: 86
Developer of Drug Delivery Technologies
N.A.I.C.S.: 541715
John DeMay *(Pres)*

Astellas Venture Management LLC (2)
2882 Sand Hill Rd Ste 121, Menlo Park, CA 94026
Tel.: (650) 926-0731
Web Site: http://www.astellasventure.com
Investment Fund Management Services
N.A.I.C.S.: 523940
Kenichiro Shimokawa *(Sr Dir-Investment)*

OSI Pharmaceuticals, Inc. (2)
41 Pinelawn Rd, Melville, NY 11747-3149
Tel.: (631) 962-2000
Web Site: http://www.osip.com
Sales Range: $400-449.9 Million
Emp.: 512
Pharmaceutical Research & Development Services
N.A.I.C.S.: 325413

Unit (Domestic):

OSI Oncology Development (3)
2860 Wilderness Pl, Boulder, CO 80301-5467
Tel.: (303) 546-7600
Web Site: http://www.osip.com
Sales Range: $50-74.9 Million
Emp.: 150
Pharmaceutical Research & Development Services
N.A.I.C.S.: 325412

Subsidiary (Domestic):

Perseid Therapeutics LLC (2)
515 Galveston Dr, Redwood City, CA 94063
Tel.: (650) 298-5800
Pharmaceutical Research & Development Services
N.A.I.C.S.: 541715

Audentes Therapeutics, Inc. (1)
600 California St 17th Fl, San Francisco, CA 94108
Tel.: (415) 818-1001
Web Site: http://www.audentestx.com
Sales Range: $1-9.9 Million
Biotechnology Developer & Mfr
N.A.I.C.S.: 325414
Thomas M. Soloway *(COO & Exec VP)*

Fujisawa Synthelabo Pharmaceuticals Co., Ltd. (1)
2nd Fl No 325 Sec 1 Tun Hwa South Rd, Taipei, 106, Taiwan
Tel.: (886) 227091980
Provider of Pharmaceuticals; Joint Venture of Fujisawa Pharmaceutical Co., Ltd. (49%) & Sanofi-Synthelabo S.A. (51%)
N.A.I.C.S.: 325412

Fujisawa Taiwan Co., Ltd. (1)
3rd Floor, No. 325, Sec. 1 Tun Hwa South Road, Taipei, 106, Taiwan
Tel.: (886) 2 2709 1980
Provider of Pharmaceuticals
N.A.I.C.S.: 325412

JSC Astellas Pharma (1)
St Marksistskaya 16, 109147, Moscow, Russia
Tel.: (7) 4957370756
Web Site: http://www.astellas.com
Drug Distr
N.A.I.C.S.: 424210

Lotus Estate Co., Ltd. (1)
2-5-1 Nihombashihoncho, Chuo-Ku, Tokyo, 103-0023, Japan
Tel.: (81) 332443400
Web Site: http://www.astellas.com
Emp.: 6
Real Estate Manangement Services
N.A.I.C.S.: 531390

P.T. Astellas Pharma Indonesia (1)
Plaza Oleos 5th Floor Jl TB Simatupang No 53A, Jakarta Selatan, 12520, Jakarta, Indonesia
Tel.: (62) 22780171

Web Site: http://www.astellas.com
Pharmaceuticals Product Mfr
N.A.I.C.S.: 325412

Yamanouchi (Thailand) Co., Ltd. (1)
10th Fl Wave Pl 55 Wireless Rd, Lumpini, Patumwan, Bangkok, 10330, Thailand
Provider of Pharmaceuticals
N.A.I.C.S.: 325412

ZAO Astellas Pharma (1)
Marksistskaya Ulitsa 16, 109147, Moscow, Russia
Tel.: (7) 4957370756
Web Site: https://aebrus.ru
Sales Range: $125-149.9 Million
Emp.: 400
Pharmaceuticals Product Mfr
N.A.I.C.S.: 325412

ASTENA HOLDINGS CO., LTD.
8-2 Nihonbashi Honcho 4-Chome, Chuo-ku, Tokyo, 1038403, Japan
Tel.: (81) 332790481
Web Site: https://astena-hd.com
Year Founded: 1941
8095—(TKS)
Rev.: $368,566,560
Assets: $476,830,860
Liabilities: $274,049,770
Net Worth: $202,781,090
Earnings: $8,238,580
Emp.: 160
Fiscal Year-end: 11/30/23
Pharmaceutical Product Mfr & Whslr
N.A.I.C.S.: 325412
Keitaro Iwaki *(Pres & CEO)*

Subsidiaries:

AMI Co., Ltd. (1)
Matsuo, Sanbu, Chiba, Sarutou, Japan
Tel.: (81) 153724209
Web Site: http://www.e-ami.jp
Pharmaceutical Products Distr
N.A.I.C.S.: 424210
Akira Katsumata *(Representative Dir)*

APROS Co., Ltd. (1)
Touka Bldg 6F 1-16-1 Ginza, Chuo-ku, Tokyo, 104-0061, Japan
Tel.: (81) 120996996
Web Site: https://www.iwaki-kk.co.jp
Cosmetic Product Mfr & Distr
N.A.I.C.S.: 325620

Bohen-Kasei Co., Ltd. (1)
9-32 Nikura 7-Chome, Wako, 351-0115, Saitama, Japan
Tel.: (81) 332790546
Seasoning Product Mfr & Distr
N.A.I.C.S.: 311942

Iwaki Seiyaku Co., Ltd. (1)
8-2 Nihonbashi-honcho 4-Chome, Chuo-ku, Tokyo, 103-0023, Japan
Tel.: (81) 366266250
Pharmaceuticals Mfr
N.A.I.C.S.: 325412

Plant (Domestic):

Torii Pharmaceutical Co., Ltd.-Sakura Plant (2)
8-2 Nihonbashi-honcho 4-Chome, Chuo-ku, Tokyo, 103-0023, Chiba, Japan
Tel.: (81) 366266250
Pharmaceuticals Product Mfr
N.A.I.C.S.: 325412

Meltex Inc. (1)
4-8-2 Nihonbashi Honcho, Chuo-ku, Tokyo, 103-0023, Japan
Tel.: (81) 332790671
Emp.: 355
Chemical Product Mfr & Distr
N.A.I.C.S.: 325199
Keitaro Iwaki *(Chm)*

Subsidiary (Non-US):

Meltex (HK) Ltd. (2)
Unit 1 11/F Millenium Trade Centre 56 Kwai Cheong Rd, Kwai Chung, Hong Kong, New Territories, China (Hong Kong)
Tel.: (852) 24208938
Chemical Products Distr
N.A.I.C.S.: 424690

Meltex (Tianjin) Ltd. (2)
Unit 2407 The Exchange Tower 2 189 Nanjing Road, Tianjin, 300051, China
Tel.: (86) 2223471617
Emp.: 7
Chemical Products Distr
N.A.I.C.S.: 325199
Takita Kunio *(CEO)*

Meltex Asia (Thailand) Co., Ltd. (2)
700/831 Moo 6, Tambol Nongtumlueng Amphur Phanthong, Chon Buri, 20160, Thailand
Tel.: (66) 38185545
Chemical Products Mfr
N.A.I.C.S.: 325199
Yoshiro Katsuta *(Mng Dir)*

Meltex Asia Pacific Co., Ltd. (2)
938 Soi Sukhumvit 101 Punnawithi 28 Sukhumvit Road Bangchak, Prakanong, Bangkok, 10260, Thailand
Tel.: (66) 23319905
Chemical Products Distr
N.A.I.C.S.: 424690

Subsidiary (Domestic):

Meltex Inc. - Kumagaya Factory (2)
823-5 Miizugahara, Kumagaya, 360-0844, Saitama, Japan
Tel.: (81) 485334600
Chemical Products Mfr
N.A.I.C.S.: 325199

Subsidiary (Non-US):

Meltex Korea Co., Ltd. (2)
Gunpo IT VALLEY B-1905-6 Gosan-ro 148beon-gil 17, Gunpo, Gyeonggi-do, Korea (South)
Tel.: (82) 3180867170
Chemical Products Distr
N.A.I.C.S.: 424690

Meltex Taiwan Inc. (2)
8F No 65 Sec 1 Qingfeng Rd, Zhongli Dist, Taoyuan, 32056, Taiwan
Tel.: (886) 32873590
Chemical Products Distr
N.A.I.C.S.: 424690
Mikio Shimada *(Gen Mgr)*

Subsidiary (Domestic):

Tokai Meltex Inc. (2)
3-4-45 Obata, Yokkaichi, 510-0875, Mie, Japan
Tel.: (81) 593454468
Chemical Product Mfr & Distr
N.A.I.C.S.: 325199

Tokyo Kakoki Co., Ltd. (2)
Minamihara Industrial Estate 14017-50 Nakaminowa, Minowa Kami-ina, Nagano, 399-4601, Japan
Tel.: (81) 265798041
Web Site: http://www.tokyo-kakoki-n.jp
Emp.: 57
Printed Circuit Board Mfr & Distr
N.A.I.C.S.: 334412
Naoyuki Kobayashi *(Pres)*

Subsidiary (Non-US):

Tcm Trading & Service Company Limited (3)
No 18 Jalan Emas SD 5/1A, Bandar Sri Damansara, 52200, Kuala Lumpur, Malaysia
Tel.: (60) 162300022
Web Site: http://www.tokyokakoki.com
Emp.: 2
Printed Circuit Board Distr
N.A.I.C.S.: 423690
Eric Chha *(Gen Mgr)*

Tokyo Kakoki (Shanghai) Co., Ltd. (3)
No 353 Xin Yu Road, Song Jiang qu, Shanghai, 201600, China
Tel.: (86) 2157796308
Printed Circuit Board Mfr & Distr
N.A.I.C.S.: 334412

ASTER DM HEALTHCARE LTD.
33rd Floor Tower D-Aspect Tower Executive Tower at Bay Avenue, PO

Aster DM Healthcare Ltd.—(Continued)

Box 8703, Business Bay, Dubai,
United Arab Emirates
Tel.: (971) 44546001
Web Site:
　　https://www.asterdmhealthcare.com
540975—(BOM)
Rev.: $1,440,097,116
Assets: $1,784,209,580
Liabilities: $1,201,455,548
Net Worth: $582,754,032
Earnings: $57,009,772
Emp.: 30,330
Fiscal Year-end: 03/31/23
Healtcare Services
N.A.I.C.S.: 621111
Azad Moopen *(Chm & Mng Dir)*

Subsidiaries:

Aster Pharmacies Group LLC　　**(1)**
3rd Floor A Block Al Hudaiba Awards Build-
ing Jumeirah Road, PO Box 50585, Dubai,
United Arab Emirates
Tel.: (971) 800700600
Web Site: https://www.asterpharmacy.ae
Health Care Equipment Mfr
N.A.I.C.S.: 339112
Azaad Moopen *(Chm & Mng Dir)*

Emed Human Resources India Pri-
vate Limited　　**(1)**
Second Floor PDR Bhavan Palliyil Lane
Foreshore Road, Cochin, India
Tel.: (91) 9656900735
Web Site: https://www.emedhr.com
Healtcare Services
N.A.I.C.S.: 621999

Eurohealth Systems FZ LLC　　**(1)**
Ibn Sina Building 27 Block B Office 301
Dubai Healthcare City, PO Box 8703,
Dubai, United Arab Emirates
Tel.: (971) 44281483
Web Site:
　　https://www.eurohealthsystems.com
Healtcare Services
N.A.I.C.S.: 621999

Harley Street Medical Centre
LLC　　**(1)**
Villa No A17 A18 A19 A20 A21 A22 and
A23 Marina Ring Road, Abu Dhabi, United
Arab Emirates
Tel.: (971) 26133999
Web Site: https://www.hsmc.ae
Healtcare Services
N.A.I.C.S.: 621999

Komali Fertility Centre LLP　　**(1)**
6th Floor Ramesh Hospitals Collector Office
Road, Guntur, India
Tel.: (91) 8340864999
Web Site:
　　http://www.komalifertilitycentre.com
Fertility Center Services
N.A.I.C.S.: 621410

Medshop Garden Pharmacy LLC **(1)**
Zen Cluster Discovery Gardens, Dubai,
United Arab Emirates
Tel.: (971) 44329596
Healtcare Services
N.A.I.C.S.: 621999

Metro Medical Center L.L.C.　　**(1)**
Tel.: (971) 67469694
Web Site:
　　http://www.metromedicalcentre.com
Healtcare Services
N.A.I.C.S.: 621999

Modern Dar Al Shifa Pharmacy
LLC　　**(1)**
Plot No 26 Mussafah Industrial Area 9, Abu
Dhabi, United Arab Emirates
Tel.: (971) 25538408
Healtcare Services
N.A.I.C.S.: 621999

Noor Al Shefa Clinic LLC　　**(1)**
99 Al Waha St-Al QuozAl Quoz 4, PO Box
45491, Jebel Ali Industrial Area 1, Dubai,
United Arab Emirates
Tel.: (971) 48878155
Web Site: http://www.nooralshefa.com
Medical Clinic Services

N.A.I.C.S.: 622110

Sanghamitra Hospitals Private
Limited　　**(1)**
Bus Stand NH 5 Near Nellore Ambedkar
Colony Ramnagar, Ongole, 523001, Andhra
Pradesh, India
Tel.: (91) 8592234599
Web Site:
　　http://www.sanghamitrahospitals.com
Hospital Equipments Mfr
N.A.I.C.S.: 339112

Shindagha Pharmacy LLC　　**(1)**
Shindagha City Centre Near Carrefour Hy-
per Market, Dubai, United Arab Emirates
Tel.: (971) 43933889
Healtcare Services
N.A.I.C.S.: 621999

ASTERIA CORPORATION

19F Ebisu Prime Square Tower
1-1-39 Hiroo, Shibuya-ku, Tokyo,
150-0012, Japan
Tel.: (81) 357181250
Web Site: https://www.asteria.com
Year Founded: 1998
3853—(TKS)
Rev.: $19,228,490
Assets: $50,150,070
Liabilities: $12,096,300
Net Worth: $38,053,770
Earnings: ($11,970,710)
Fiscal Year-end: 03/31/24
Software Developer; Technical Sup-
port & Consulting Services
N.A.I.C.S.: 513210
Yoichiro Hirano *(Founder, Chm &
CEO)*

ASTERION INDUSTRIAL PART-
NERS SGEIC SA

Jose Ortega Gasset 30 bajo, 28006,
Madrid, Spain
Tel.: (34) 910887404
Web Site:
　　http://www.asterionindustrial.com
Investment Services
N.A.I.C.S.: 523999
Jesus Olmos Clavijo *(Founder, CEO
& Partner)*

Subsidiaries:

STEAG GmbH　　**(1)**
Ruttenscheider Strasse 1-3, 45128, Essen,
Germany
Tel.: (49) 20180100
Web Site: http://www.steag.com
Sales Range: $1-4.9 Billion
Emp.: 6,378
Electric Power Production & Distribution
Services
N.A.I.C.S.: 221112
Wolfgang Cieslik *(Member-Mgmt Bd)*

Subsidiary (Domestic):

Felix Holtken GmbH　　**(2)**
Kalscheurener Strasse 30, 50997, Cologne,
Germany
Tel.: (49) 22332778
Web Site: http://www.hoeltken-koeln.de
Building Maintenance Services
N.A.I.C.S.: 561790

MINERALplus GmbH　　**(2)**
Stollenstrasse 12-16, 45966, Gladbeck,
Germany
Tel.: (49) 204340010
Web Site: http://www.mineralplus.de
Waste Recycling Services
N.A.I.C.S.: 562920

STEAG Energy Services GmbH　**(2)**
Ruttenscheider Strasse 1-3, 45128, Essen,
Germany　　**(100%)**
Tel.: (49) 20180100
Web Site: http://www.steag-
　energyservices.com
Sales Range: $1-4.9 Billion
Emp.: 2,500
Power Plant Engineering, Consulting, Op-
eration & Maintenance Services
N.A.I.C.S.: 541330

Joachim Rumstadt *(Mng Dir)*

Subsidiary (Non-US):

STEAG Energy Services (India) Pvt.
Ltd.　　**(3)**
A29 Sector 16, Noida, 201301, India
Tel.: (91) 1204625000
Web Site: http://www.steag.in
Emp.: 1,000
Power Plant Engineering Consulting Opera-
tion & Maintenance Services
N.A.I.C.S.: 541330
Jacob T. Verghese *(Member-Mgmt Bd)*

STEAG Energy Services do Brasil
Ltda.　　**(3)**
Av Rio Branco 109 - Centro, Rio de Ja-
neiro, RJ, Brazil
Tel.: (55) 2135468601
Web Site: http://www.steag.com.br
Power Plant Engineering, Consulting, Op-
eration & Maintenance Services
N.A.I.C.S.: 541330
Juracy Moteiro *(Mng Dir)*

Subsidiary (Domestic):

STEAG KETEK IT GmbH　　**(3)**
Centroallee 261, D-46047, Oberhausen,
Germany
Tel.: (49) 208 29980 0
Power Plant Supplying System Technology
N.A.I.C.S.: 221113

STEAG Solar Energy Solutions
GmbH　　**(3)**
Carl-Zeiss-Strasse 4, 97076, Wurzburg,
Germany
Tel.: (49) 931250640
Web Site:
　　http://www.energy.gildemeister.com
Sales Range: $25-49.9 Million
Emp.: 145
Energy Management Solutions
N.A.I.C.S.: 221114
Andre Kremer *(Mng Dir)*

Subsidiary (Domestic):

STEAG Fernwarme GmbH　　**(2)**
Huyssenallee 100, 45128, Essen, Germany
Tel.: (49) 2018014900
Web Site: http://www.steag-fernwaerme.de
Sales Range: $150-199.9 Million
Emp.: 175
Steam Heat Supply Services
N.A.I.C.S.: 221330
Udo Wichert *(Comml Dir & Chm-Mgmt Bd)*

STEAG New Energies GmbH　　**(2)**
St Johanner Str 101-105, 66115, Saar-
brucken, Germany
Tel.: (49) 681949400
Web Site: http://www.steag-
　newenergies.com
Emp.: 50
Energy Consulting Services
N.A.I.C.S.: 541690
Markus Laukamp *(Dir-Sls & Mktg)*

STEAG Power Saar GmbH　　**(2)**
Trierer Strasse 4, 66111, Saarbrucken, Ger-
many
Tel.: (49) 681949405
Web Site: http://www.power-saar.steag-
　saarenergie.de
Coal-Fired Power Plants Operator
N.A.I.C.S.: 221112
Wolfgang Cieslik *(Chm-Supervisory Bd)*

Holding (Domestic):

GbR Gemeinschaftskraftwerk
West　　**(3)**
Frankfurter Strasse 430, 46562, Voerde,
Germany　　**(78.6%)**
Tel.: (49) 2855120
Electric Power Generation Plant
N.A.I.C.S.: 221112

Subsidiary (Domestic):

STEAG Technischer Service
GmbH　　**(2)**
Trierer Str 4, 66111, Saarbrucken, Germany
Tel.: (49) 681949405
Web Site: http://www.steag-
　technischerservice.com
Construction Engineering Services

N.A.I.C.S.: 541330
Sorgenia S.p.A　　**(1)**
Via V Viviani 12, Milan, 20124, Italy
Tel.: (39) 02671941
Web Site: http://www.sorgenia.it
Natural Gas Production Services
N.A.I.C.S.: 213112
Simone Lonostro *(Gen Mgr)*

ASTI CORPORATION

2804 Yonezu-cho, Minami-ku, Ha-
mamatsu, 432-8056, Shizuoka, Japan
Tel.: (81) 534445111
Web Site: https://www.asti.co.jp
Year Founded: 1963
6899—(TKS)
Rev.: $420,442,270
Assets: $317,346,100
Liabilities: $156,604,120
Net Worth: $160,741,980
Earnings: $17,813,950
Emp.: 4,346
Fiscal Year-end: 03/31/24
Telecommunications Equipment Mfr
N.A.I.C.S.: 334290
Mikio Uehira *(Chm)*

Subsidiaries:

ASTI Corporation - Fukuroi
Factory　　**(1)**
2754 Ohno, Fukuroi, 437-1112, Shizuoka-
ken, Japan
Tel.: (81) 538237411
Telecommunications Equipment Mfr
N.A.I.C.S.: 334290

ASTI Corporation - Hamamatsu
Factory　　**(1)**
4-1 Oohara-cho, Kita-ku, Hamamatsu, 433-
8102, Shizuoka-ken, Japan
Tel.: (81) 534386010
Telecommunications Equipment Mfr
N.A.I.C.S.: 334290

ASTI Corporation - Iwata Factory **(1)**
1401 Hirama, Iwata, 438-0203, Shizuoka-
ken, Japan
Tel.: (81) 538665575
Telecommunications Equipment Mfr
N.A.I.C.S.: 334290

ASTI Corporation - Kakegawa
Factory　　**(1)**
180 Hatsuma, Kakegawa, 436-0081,
Shizuoka-ken, Japan
Tel.: (81) 537213481
Telecommunications Equipment Mfr
N.A.I.C.S.: 334290

ASTI Corporation - Miyakoda
Factory　　**(1)**
1-5-1 Shin-miyakoda, Kita-ku, Hamamatsu,
431-2103, Shizuoka-ken, Japan
Tel.: (81) 534285181
Web Site: https://www.asti.co.jp
Telecommunications Equipment Mfr
N.A.I.C.S.: 334290

ASTI Electronics Corporation　　**(1)**
Dong An Tan Dong Hiep Hamlet, Ben Cat,
Binh Duong, Vietnam
Tel.: (84) 6503742464
Emp.: 200
Telecommunication Equipment Distr
N.A.I.C.S.: 423690

ASTI Electronics India Private
Limited　　**(1)**
Plot No 399 Sector-8 IMT Manesar, Gur-
gaon, 122 050, Haryana, India
Tel.: (91) 1242291925
Electric Equipment Mfr
N.A.I.C.S.: 334419
Susumu Watanabe *(Mng Dir)*

ASTI Research & Development Viet-
nam Corporation　　**(1)**
3rd floor 24 Hai Ho, Thanh Binh Hai Chau
District, Da Nang, Vietnam
Tel.: (84) 2363555059
Web Site: https://asti-dn.com
Electronic Circuit Board Distr
N.A.I.C.S.: 423690

ASTI HOLDINGS LIMITED

33 Ubi Ave 3 06-72 Vertex, Singapore, 408868, Singapore
Tel.: (65) 86871566   SG
Web Site: https://www.astigp.com
Year Founded: 1990
575—(SES)
Rev.: $40,249,362
Assets: $65,845,942
Liabilities: $20,832,443
Net Worth: $45,013,499
Earnings: ($8,716,333)
Emp.: 2,525
Fiscal Year-end: 12/31/21
Semiconductor Mfr & Distr
N.A.I.C.S.: 334413
Michael Soon Gnee Loh (Chm & CEO)

Subsidiaries:

ASTI (USA), Inc.   (1)
1321 Ridder Park Dr Ste 10, San Jose, CA 95131
Tel.: (408) 638-5100
Semiconductor Mfr
N.A.I.C.S.: 334413

Dragon Group International
Limited   (1)
33 Ubi Ave 3 06-72 Vertex, Singapore, 408868, Singapore   **(61.61%)**
Tel.: (65) 86871566
Web Site: https://www.dragongp.com
Rev.: $1,944,000
Assets: $6,189,000
Liabilities: $8,313,000
Net Worth: ($2,124,000)
Earnings: ($8,209,000)
Fiscal Year-end: 12/31/2017
Electronics Distr
N.A.I.C.S.: 423690
Michael Soon Gnee Loh (Exec Chm, Chm & CEO)

EoPlex Limited   (1)
Room2 9/F 148 Electric Road North Point, Central, China (Hong Kong)
Tel.: (852) 23946586
Semiconductor Mfr
N.A.I.C.S.: 334413

Nanjing Dragon Treasure Boat Development Co., Ltd.   (1)
No 1 Binjiang Dadao Ave, Gulou District, Nanjing, 210029, China
Tel.: (86) 2583241996
Semiconductor Mfr
N.A.I.C.S.: 334413

Reel Service (Philippines), Inc.   (1)
No 5 Circuit Street Light Industry & Science Park, Cabuyao, 4025, Laguna, Philippines
Tel.: (63) 495430480
Plastic Tape Mfr & Distr
N.A.I.C.S.: 326112

Reel Service Limited   (1)
55 Nasmyth Road Fife, Southfield Industrial Estate, Glenrothes, KY6 2SD, United Kingdom
Tel.: (44) 1592773208
Plastic Tape Mfr & Distr
N.A.I.C.S.: 326112
Gary Smith (Mng Dir)

Spire Technologies (Taiwan) Ltd.   (1)
1F No 227 Sheng Li Road, Hsinchu, 30045, Taiwan
Tel.: (886) 35250345
Semiconductor Mfr
N.A.I.C.S.: 334413

Spire Technologies Pte Ltd   (1)
Blk 25 Kallang Avenue 06-01, Kallang Basin Industrial Estate, Singapore, 339416, Singapore
Tel.: (65) 63915310
Semiconductor Mfr
N.A.I.C.S.: 334413

Telford Industries Pte Ltd   (1)
Blk 25 Kallang Avenue 03-01, Kallang Basin Industrial Estate, Singapore, 339416, Singapore
Tel.: (65) 63922112
Semiconductor Mfr
N.A.I.C.S.: 334413
Don Berino (Mgr-Team)

Subsidiary (Non-US):

Telford Service (Melaka) Sdn.
Bhd.   (2)
No 169 Jalan Usaha 12 Kawasan Perindustrian Ayer Keroh, 75450, Melaka, Malaysia
Tel.: (60) 62328331
Semiconductor Mfr
N.A.I.C.S.: 334413

Telford Service Sdn. Bhd.   (2)
Bayan Lepas Free Industrial Zone Phase III, 11900, Bayan Lepas, Penang, Malaysia
Tel.: (60) 46428125
Semiconductor Mfr
N.A.I.C.S.: 334413

Telford SVC. Phils., Inc.   (1)
Linares St Gateway Business Park Special Export Processing Zone, Brgy Javalera Gen Trias, Cavite, 4107, Philippines
Tel.: (63) 464330524
Semiconductor Mfr
N.A.I.C.S.: 334413

Telford Technologies (Shanghai) Pte Ltd   (1)
No 25 Sui De Road Lane 2 Level 3, Shanghai, 200331, China
Tel.: (86) 13788965121
Semiconductor Mfr
N.A.I.C.S.: 334413

ASTIKA HOLDINGS, INC.

Level 1 703 Rosebank Road Avondale, Auckland, 1348, New Zealand
Tel.: (64) 98209421   FL
Year Founded: 2011
ASKH—(OTCIQ)
Sales Range: Less than $1 Million
Holding Company
N.A.I.C.S.: 551112
Ralph Willmott (Sec)

ASTINO BERHAD

1499 and 1500 Lot Baru 10030 MK 11 Jalan Changkat, Nibong Tebal, 14300, Penang, Malaysia
Tel.: (60) 45856666
Web Site: https://www.astino.com.my
ASTINO—(KLS)
Rev.: $130,942,222
Assets: $123,380,741
Liabilities: $12,352,804
Net Worth: $111,027,937
Earnings: $5,996,614
Emp.: 580
Fiscal Year-end: 07/31/23
Industrial Metal Roofing Systems Mfr
N.A.I.C.S.: 332311
Lay Hoon Ch'ng (Sec)

Subsidiaries:

Astino (Malaysia) Colour Steel Sheet Sdn. Bhd.   (1)
Lot 3 Jalan Jasmine 6 Bukit Beruntung Industrial Park, Mukim Serendah, 48300, Rawang, 48300, Selangor Darul Ehsan, Malaysia
Tel.: (60) 360283882
Web Site: http://www.astino.com.my
Sales Range: $25-49.9 Million
Emp.: 60
Metal Roofing Sheets Mfr & Distr
N.A.I.C.S.: 332322

Astino Southern Sdn. Bhd.   (1)
Lot 719 Jalan Seri Emas 28, Taman Seri Telok Mas, 75460, Melaka, Melaka, Malaysia
Tel.: (60) 62617923
Roofing Sheets & Building Materials Whslr
N.A.I.C.S.: 423330
Mr. Ng (CEO)

Ooi Joo Kee & Brothers Sdn. Bhd.   (1)
Lot 1218 Jalan Serunai Kawasan Perusahaan Valdor, Seberang Perai Selantan, 14200, Sungai Bakap, Penang, Malaysia
Tel.: (60) 45829988
Roofing Sheets Whslr
N.A.I.C.S.: 423330
Back Teng Ng (Co-Mng Dir)

ASTIVITA LIMITED

1821 Ipswich Road, Rocklea, 4106, QLD, Australia
Tel.: (61) 737262000
Web Site: http://www.astivita.com
Year Founded: 2004
AIR—(ASX)
Rev.: $3,117,881
Assets: $4,070,450
Liabilities: $2,829,732
Net Worth: $1,240,718
Earnings: ($5,104,148)
Fiscal Year-end: 06/30/20
Bathroom, Kitchen & Solar Products Importer & Distr
N.A.I.C.S.: 423720

ASTMAX TRADING, INC.

2-10-2 Higashigotanda, Shinagawa-ku, Tokyo, 141-0022, Japan
Tel.: (81) 354478400   JP
Web Site: https://www.astmax.co.jp
Year Founded: 2012
7162—(TKS)
Rev.: $98,191,550
Assets: $94,476,730
Liabilities: $55,028,250
Net Worth: $39,448,480
Earnings: $2,941,450
Emp.: 61
Fiscal Year-end: 03/31/24
Asset Management Services
N.A.I.C.S.: 541618
Hideaki Ushijima (Chm & Co-CEO)

Subsidiaries:

Astmax Energy, Inc.   (1)
5F Higashi Gotanda Square 2-10-2, Higashi Gotanda Shinagawa-ku, Tokyo, 141-0022, Japan
Tel.: (81) 8001236070
Web Site: https://astmaxenergy.co.jp
Electricity Distribution Services
N.A.I.C.S.: 221122

Astmax Investments Management, Inc.   (1)
2-10-2 Higashigotanda 5th Fl, Shinagawa-ku, Tokyo, Japan   **(100%)**
Tel.: (81) 3 5447 8411
Web Site: http://www.astmaxim.com
Investment Advisory & Management Services
N.A.I.C.S.: 523940
Shinichiro Shiraki (Co-CEO & Chief Investment Officer)

ITC Investment Partners Corporation   (1)
11-3 Kita-Aoyama 2-chome, Minato-ku, Tokyo, 107-0061, Japan
Tel.: (81) 3 5770 2710
Web Site: http://www.itc-ip.com
Sales Range: $10-24.9 Million
Asset Management Services
N.A.I.C.S.: 523940

Oshamanbe Agri Co., Ltd.   (1)
92 Tomino, Oshamanbe-cho Yamakoshi-gun, Hokkaido, 049-3514, Japan
Tel.: (81) 7048006833
Web Site: https://www.oshamanbe-agri.co.jp
Tomato Mfr
N.A.I.C.S.: 311411

ASTON BAY HOLDINGS LTD.

80 Richmond St W Ste 204, Toronto, M5H 2A4, ON, Canada
Tel.: (416) 456-3516   BC
Web Site:
   https://astonbayholdings.com
Year Founded: 2011
Copper & Zinc Exploration
N.A.I.C.S.: 212230

ASTON MARTIN LAGONDA GLOBAL HOLDINGS PLC

Banbury Road, Gaydon, Warwick, CV35 0DB, United Kingdom
Tel.: (44) 1926644644

Web Site:
   https://www.astonmartinlagonda.com
Year Founded: 1913
AML—(LSE)
Rev.: $1,715,546,700
Assets: $3,854,919,740
Liabilities: $2,895,629,240
Net Worth: $959,290,500
Earnings: ($655,297,860)
Emp.: 2,473
Fiscal Year-end: 12/31/22
Offices of Other Holding Companies
N.A.I.C.S.: 551101
Amedeo Felisa (CEO)

Subsidiaries:

Aston Martin Japan GK   (1)
1-2-3 Kita Aoyama, Minato-ku, Tokyo, 107-0061, Japan
Tel.: (81) 354100070
Car Mfr & Distr
N.A.I.C.S.: 336999

ASTON MINERALS LIMITED

Suite 23 Level 1 513 Hay Street, Subiaco, 6008, WA, Australia
Tel.: (61) 861436740
Web Site: https://astonminerals.com
ASO—(ASX)
Rev.: $105,402
Assets: $3,556,911
Liabilities: $131,390
Net Worth: $3,425,521
Earnings: ($3,929,872)
Fiscal Year-end: 06/30/24
Manganese Exploration Services
N.A.I.C.S.: 212290
Robert Jewson (Mng Dir)

ASTON VILLA LIMITED

Villa Park, Birmingham, B6 6HE, United Kingdom
Tel.: (44) 1213275353   UK
Web Site: http://www.avfc.co.uk
Year Founded: 1874
Sales Range: $1-9.9 Million
Emp.: 114
Professional Football Team
N.A.I.C.S.: 711211
Tony Xia (Co-Chm)

Subsidiaries:

Aston Villa Football Club Limited   (1)
Villa Park, Birmingham, B6 6HE, United Kingdom
Tel.: (44) 1213272299
Web Site: http://www.avfc.co.uk
Football Club
N.A.I.C.S.: 711211
Paul Faulkner (Gen Mgr)

ASTORG PARTNERS S.A.S.

68 rue du Faubourg Saint-Honore, 75008, Paris, France
Tel.: (33) 153054000   FR
Web Site: http://www.astorg.com
Year Founded: 1998
Privater Equity Firm
N.A.I.C.S.: 523999
Thierry Timsit (Co-Founder & Mng Partner)

Subsidiaries:

Astorg Partners UK   (1)
3 Hill Street, London, W1J 5LA, United Kingdom
Tel.: (44) 207 409 5066
Financial Investment Services
N.A.I.C.S.: 523999

CitizenHawk, Inc.   (1)
220 W 42nd St 11th Fl, New York, NY 10036
Web Site: http://www.citizenhawk.com
All Other Support Services
N.A.I.C.S.: 561900
Stephen Stolfi (Chief Comml Officer)

Corden Pharma International GmbH   (1)

Astorg Partners S.A.S.—(Continued)

Otto-Hahn-Strasse, 68723, Plankstadt, Germany
Tel.: (49) 6202 99 2299
Web Site: http://www.cordenpharma.com
Pharmaceutical Preparation Mfr
N.A.I.C.S.: 325412
Riku Rautsola (Pres & CEO)

Subsidiary (US):

Corden Pharma Colorado Inc. (2)
2075 N 55th St, Boulder, CO 80301-2803
Tel.: (303) 442-1926
Web Site: http://www.cordenpharma.com
Active Pharmaceutical Ingredients Mfr
N.A.I.C.S.: 325412
Brian McCudden (Mng Dir)

Subsidiary (Domestic):

Corden Pharma Boulder, Inc. (3)
4876 Sterling Dr, Boulder, CO 80301-2350
Tel.: (303) 442-1926
Web Site: http://www.cordenpharma.com
Specialty Pharmaceuticals & Patient Care Products Mfr
N.A.I.C.S.: 325412
Brian McCudden (Mng Dir)

Subsidiary (Non-US):

Corden Pharma S.p.A. (2)
Viale dell'Industria 3, 20867, Caponago, MB, Italy
Tel.: (39) 02 95452 1
Web Site: http://www.cordenpharma.com
Pharmaceutical Prepations Mfr; Clinical Trials Management Services
N.A.I.C.S.: 325412
Karsten Benzing (COO)

Subsidiary (Domestic):

Corden Pharma Bergamo S.p.A. (3)
Via Bergamo 121, 24047, Treviglio, Bergamo, Italy
Tel.: (39) 0363 31401
Web Site: http://www.cordenpharma.com
Emp.: 1,500
Active Pharmaceutical Ingredients Mfr
N.A.I.C.S.: 325412
Laura Coppi (Mng Dir)

Corden Pharma Latina S.p.A. (2)
Via del Murillo KM 2 800, 04013, Sermoneta, Italy
Tel.: (39) 07 733101
Web Site: http://www.cordenpharma.com
Pharmaceutical Preparation Mfr
N.A.I.C.S.: 325412
Alessandro Zucconi (Mng Dir)

Subsidiary (Non-US):

Corden Pharma Switzerland LLC (2)
Eichenweg 1, 4410, Liestal, Switzerland
Tel.: (41) 61 906 5959
Web Site: http://www.cordenpharma.com
Emp.: 100
Chemically Synthesized Materials Mfr for Pharmaceutical Industry
N.A.I.C.S.: 325412
Christian Ewers (COO & Gen Mgr)

Unit (US):

Corden Pharma Switzerland LLC (3)
500 Kendall St, Cambridge, MA 02139 (100%)
Tel.: (617) 401-2828
Sales Range: $250-299.9 Million
Pharmaceuticals Producut Sales
N.A.I.C.S.: 424210

Subsidiary (Non-US):

Corden PharmaChem Ireland Ltd. (2)
Unit 4 OC Commercial Park, Little Island, Cork, Ireland
Tel.: (353) 212427383
Web Site:
    http://www.cordenpharmachem.com
Sales Range: $25-49.9 Million
Emp.: 12
Pharmaceuticals
N.A.I.C.S.: 325412

Peptisyntha S.A. (2)

310 rue de Ransbeek, 1120, Brussels, Belgium (100%)
Tel.: (32) 2 263 1411
Web Site: http://www.peptisyntha.com
Sales Range: $25-49.9 Million
Emp.: 40
Producer of Therapeutic Peptides
N.A.I.C.S.: 325412
Georges Blondeel (Mgr-Purification)

Delinian Limited (1)
8 Bouverie Street, London, EC4Y 8AX, United Kingdom
Tel.: (44) 2077798888
Web Site: http://www.delinian.com
Rev.: $432,841,136
Assets: $1,325,542,036
Liabilities: $527,609,992
Net Worth: $797,932,044
Earnings: $48,063,288
Emp.: 2,748
Fiscal Year-end: 09/30/2022
Holding Company; Trade Magazine, Newsletter, Journal & Book Publisher; Conference, Seminar & Training Course Organizer
N.A.I.C.S.: 551112
Tim Bratton (Sec)

Subsidiary (US):

Euromoney Training, Inc. (2)
225 Park Ave S 8th Fl, New York, NY 10003 (100%)
Tel.: (212) 361-3299
Web Site:
    http://www.euromoneytraining.com
Legal, Information Technology Audit, Information Security, Banking & Financial Training Services
N.A.I.C.S.: 611430

MIS Training Institute, LLC (2)
153 Cordaville Rd, Southborough, MA 01772-1834
Tel.: (508) 879-7999
Web Site: http://www.misti.com
Audit & Information Security Training Courses & Services; Conference & Trade Show Organizer
N.A.I.C.S.: 611430
Fred Roth (VP-IT Audit Div)

Subsidiary (Domestic):

Metal Bulletin Limited (2)
Nestor House PlayHouse Yard, London, EC4V 5EX, United Kingdom
Tel.: (44) 2078279977
Web Site: http://www.metalbulletin.com
Sales Range: $100-124.9 Million
Emp.: 460
Data Management & Publishing Services
N.A.I.C.S.: 513140

Subsidiary (US):

American Metal Market (3)
707 Grant St Ste 1340, Pittsburgh, PA 15219
Tel.: (412) 765-2580
Web Site: http://www.amm.com
Sales Range: $25-49.9 Million
Emp.: 15
Journal Publisher
N.A.I.C.S.: 513120
Raju Daswani (Mng Dir)

Subsidiary (Non-US):

Metal Bulletin Japan (3)
Rm 701 Oak Mansions, Negishi 5 16 5, Taito Ku, Tokyo, 1100003, Japan
Tel.: (81) 338765760
Web Site: http://www.metalbulletin.com
Data Management & Publishing
N.A.I.C.S.: 513140

Metal Bulletin Singapore (3)
3 Raffles Pl 08-01, Singapore, 048617, Singapore
Tel.: (65) 63335523
Web Site: http://www.metalbulletin.com
Sales Range: $25-49.9 Million
Emp.: 10
Data Management & Publishing
N.A.I.C.S.: 513140

Subsidiary (US):

Ned Davis Research Inc. (2)
600 Bird Bay Dr W, Venice, FL 34285

Tel.: (941) 412-2300
Web Site: http://www.ndr.com
Sales Range: $10-24.9 Million
Emp.: 90
Investment Research & Advisory Services
N.A.I.C.S.: 541910
Brian Frohn (Mng Dir)

RISI, Inc (2)
4 Alfred Cir, Bedford, MA 01730
Tel.: (322) 536-0748
Web Site: http://www.risiinfo.com
Price Reporting, Analytics & Events Organization & Services
N.A.I.C.S.: 519290
Matt Graves (Sr VP-Fastmarkets Indices)

Random Lengths Publications, Inc. (2)
450 Country Club Road Ste 315, Eugene, OR 97401
Tel.: (541) 686-9925
Web Site: https://www.rlmyprint.com
Periodical Publishers
N.A.I.C.S.: 513120

The Deal, LLC (2)
Hippodrome Bldg 1120 Ave of the Americas, New York, NY 10036
Tel.: (212) 224-3069
Web Site: http://www.thedeal.com
Internet Advertising Services
N.A.I.C.S.: 541810
Robert Kondracki (Chief Acctg Officer)

Fastmarkets Limited (1)
8 Bouverie Street, London, EC4Y 8AX,, United Kingdom
Tel.: (44) 2077798260
Web Site: https://www.fastmarkets.com
Price Reporting Agency
N.A.I.C.S.: 561499
Raju Daswani (CEO)

Subsidiary (US):

Hardwood Market Report L.P. (2)
845 Crossover Ln 103, Memphis, TN 38117
Tel.: (901) 767-9126
Web Site: http://www.hmr.com
Rev.: $2,264,000
Emp.: 8
Periodical Publishers
N.A.I.C.S.: 513120
David Caldwell (Partner)

Financiere Ofic (1)
35 rue Baudin, 92593, Levallois-Perret, Cedex, France
Tel.: (33) 1 5563 8010
Web Site: http://www.onduline.com
Sales Range: $450-499.9 Million
Holding Company; Lightweight Building Materials Mfr & Distr
N.A.I.C.S.: 551112

HRA Pharma, SA (1)
15 rue Beranger, 75 003, Paris, France
Tel.: (33) 1 40 33 11 30
Web Site: http://www.hra-pharma.com
Pharmaceutical Product Mfr & Distr
N.A.I.C.S.: 325412
Geoff Allan (CFO)

Subsidiary (Non-US):

HRA Pharma Deutschland, GmbH (2)
Massenbergstrasse 9-13, 44787, Bochum, Germany
Tel.: (49) 234 51 65 92 0
Web Site: http://www.hra-pharma.com
Pharmaceutical Products Distr
N.A.I.C.S.: 424210

HRA Pharma Iberia S.L. (2)
Paseo de la Castellana 1436B, 28046, Madrid, Spain
Tel.: (34) 902107428
Web Site: http://www.hra-pharma.com
Pharmaceutical Products Distr
N.A.I.C.S.: 424210

HRA Pharma Italia S.r.l. (2)
Via Cristoforo Colombo 436, 00145, Rome, Italy
Tel.: (39) 06 59600987
Web Site: http://www.hra-pharma.com
Pharmaceutical Products Distr
N.A.I.C.S.: 424210

HRA Pharma UK & Ireland Ltd (2)
Haines House 21 John Street, London, WC1N 2BF, Bloomsbury, United Kingdom
Tel.: (44) 2037501720
Web Site: http://www.hra-pharma.com
Pharmaceutical Products Distr
N.A.I.C.S.: 424210
Tony Fraser (Dir-European Affiliates)

Hamilton Thorne Ltd. (1)
100 Cummings Ctr Ste 465E, Beverly, MA 01915
Tel.: (978) 921-2050
Web Site: https://www.hamiltonthorne.com
Rev.: $39,777,886
Assets: $69,808,718
Liabilities: $18,742,793
Net Worth: $51,065,925
Earnings: $971,235
Fiscal Year-end: 12/31/2020
Investment Services
N.A.I.C.S.: 523999
Meg Spencer (Co-Founder)

Subsidiary (Domestic):

Embryotech Labs Inc. (2)
323 Andover St, Wilmington, MA 01887
Tel.: (978) 658-4600
Web Site: http://www.embryotech.com
Rev.: $2,240,000
Emp.: 10
Surgical & Medical Instrument Mfr
N.A.I.C.S.: 339112

IGM Resins B.V. (1)
Gompenstraat 49, 5145 RM, Waalwijk, Netherlands
Tel.: (31) 416286073
Web Site: http://www.igmresins.com
Specialty Chemical Mfr & Whslr
N.A.I.C.S.: 325998
Edward Frindt (CEO)

Subsidiary (US):

IGM Resins USA Inc. (2)
3300 Westinghouse Blvd, Charlotte, NC 28273
Tel.: (704) 588-2500
Web Site: http://www.igmresins.com
Specialty Chemical Whslr
N.A.I.C.S.: 424690

Linxens (1)
6 rue Helene Boucher, 78280, Guyancourt, France (70%)
Tel.: (33) 1 34 98 09 50
Web Site: http://www.linxens.com
Sales Range: $250-299.9 Million
Emp.: 700
Smart Card Flexible Tape Material Mfr
N.A.I.C.S.: 334417
Christophe Duverne (CEO)

Parkeon S.A.S. (1)
100 Avenue de Suffren, F-75015, Paris, France
Tel.: (33) 158098110
Web Site: http://www.parkeon.com
Electronic Parking & Transport Management System Developer Mfr
N.A.I.C.S.: 334118
Bertrand Barthelemy (CEO)

Subsidiary (Non-US):

Flowbird Sverige AB (2)
Borgarfjordsgatan 7, 164 40, Kista, Sweden
Tel.: (46) 8 799 37 00
Web Site: http://www.caleaccess.com
Parking Meter Mfr
N.A.I.C.S.: 333310
Anton Kaya (Mng Dir)

Subsidiary (Non-US):

Cale Australia Pty. Ltd. (3)
Unit 3 4 Bookham Street, Morley, 6062, WA, Australia
Tel.: (61) 8 6102 2842
Web Site: http://www.caleaccess.com.au
Electronic Equipment Distr
N.A.I.C.S.: 423850

Cale Parking Iberica SL (3)
Calle Jazmin 66 3 planta, Izquierda, 28033, Madrid, Spain
Tel.: (34) 91 599 03 52
Web Site: http://www.caleaccess.com
Electronic Equipment Distr

N.A.I.C.S.: 423850

Stadtraum Systems Sp.z o.o **(3)**
ul Druzbickiego 11, 61-693, Poznan, Poland
Tel.: (48) 061 657 64 64
Web Site: http://www.parkomat.pl
Electronic Equipment Distr
N.A.I.C.S.: 423850

Subsidiary (Non-US):

Parkeon GmbH **(2)**
Schreberweg 1, D-24119, Kiel, Germany
Tel.: (49) 431 3059 0
Web Site: http://www.parkeon.de
Emp.: 40
Parking & Transportation Management Terminal Mfr
N.A.I.C.S.: 334118

Parkeon Pty Ltd. **(2)**
Unit 6 51-53 Bourke Road, Alexandria, Sydney, 2015, NSW, Australia
Tel.: (61) 2 9275 8849
Web Site: http://www.parkeon.com
Parking & Transportation Management Terminal Mfr
N.A.I.C.S.: 334118
Scott Leary (Mgr-Svc)

Parkeon S.A.S. **(2)**
Lambroekstraat 5 A, 1831, Diegem, Belgium
Tel.: (32) 28928015
Web Site: http://www.parkeon.be
Parking & Transportation Management Terminal Mfr
N.A.I.C.S.: 334118
Bart Steegmans (Gen Mgr-Benelux)

Parkeon S.L.U. **(2)**
C/ Maria de Molina 374A Planta, 28006, Madrid, Spain
Tel.: (34) 917829300
Web Site: http://www.parkeon.es
Parking & Transportation Management Terminal Mfr
N.A.I.C.S.: 334118
Jose Luis Sanz Mejias (Project Mgr & Sls Mgr)

Parkeon S.p.A **(2)**
Via Ripmonti 89, 20141, Milan, Italy
Tel.: (39) 0102525014
Web Site: http://www.parkeon.it
Parking & Transportation Management Terminal Mfr
N.A.I.C.S.: 334118

Subsidiary (US):

Parkeon, Inc. **(2)**
40 Twosome Dr Ste Unit 7, Moorestown, NJ 08057
Tel.: (856) 234-8000
Web Site: http://www.parkeon.com
Electronic Parking & Transport Management Systems Mfr & Distr
N.A.I.C.S.: 334514
Lisa Monte Carlo (Mgr-HR)

SCT Telecom S.A.S. **(1)**
ZAC de Nozal Chaudron, 17/19 Avenue de la Metallurgie, F-93210, La Plaine Saint-Denis, France **(52%)**
Tel.: (33) 892 020 220
Sales Range: $75-99.9 Million
Integrated Commercial Telecommunications Services
N.A.I.C.S.: 517121

Services Generaux de Gestion S.A. **(1)**
412F route d'Esch, L 2086, Luxembourg, Luxembourg
Tel.: (352) 46 6111 1
Web Site: http://www.sgggroup.com
Emp.: 550
Accounting, Tax & Financial Services to Private Equity Industry
N.A.I.C.S.: 541219
Serge Krancenblum (CEO & Member-Mgmt Bd)

Subsidiary (Non-US):

SGG Belgium S.A. **(2)**
Avenue Louise 209 A, B-1050, Brussels, Belgium
Tel.: (32) 26275570
Web Site: http://www.sgggroup.com

Corporate Administration Services
N.A.I.C.S.: 561499
Joannes van de Kimmenade (Dir)

SGG Netherlands N.V. **(2)**
Hoogoorddreef 15, 1101 BA, Amsterdam, Netherlands
Tel.: (31) 205222555
Web Site: http://www.sgggroup.com
Corporate Administration Services
N.A.I.C.S.: 561499
Luc Hollman (Mng Dir)

SGG Suisse S.A. **(2)**
3 Place Isaac Mercier, CH-1211, Geneva, Switzerland
Tel.: (41) 228070380
Web Site: http://www.sgggroup.com
Commercial Banking Services
N.A.I.C.S.: 522110

eResearchTechnology, Inc. **(1)**
1818 Market St Ste 1000, Philadelphia, PA 19103-3638
Tel.: (215) 972-0420
Web Site: http://www.ert.com
Medical Diagnostic & Testing Web-Based Software & Consulting Services
N.A.I.C.S.: 513210
Steve Nuckols (Chief Comml Officer & Exec VP)

Subsidiary (Domestic):

APDM, Inc. **(2)**
2828 SW Corbett Ave Ste 130, Portland, OR 97201-4811
Tel.: (503) 445-7757
Web Site: http://www.apdm.com
Electromedical & Electrotherapeutic Apparatus Mfr
N.A.I.C.S.: 334510
Thomas Rolke (CEO)

BioClinica, Inc. **(2)**
211 Carnegie Ct Dr, Princeton, NJ 08540
Tel.: (877) 632-9432
Web Site: http://www.bioclinica.com
Medical Imaging Solutions & Cardiac Safety Services for Clinical Trial Sponsors
N.A.I.C.S.: 621511
David S. Herron (Pres & CEO)

Subsidiary (Non-US):

eResearchTechnology GmbH **(2)**
Sieboldstrasse 3, Estenfeld, 97230, Wurzburg, Germany
Tel.: (49) 9305 720 60
Web Site: http://www.ert.com
Medical Diagnostic & Testing Web-Based Software & Consulting Services
N.A.I.C.S.: 513210

Subsidiary (US):

Biomedical Systems Corp. **(3)**
77 Progress Pkwy, Maryland Heights, MO 63043
Tel.: (314) 576-6800
Web Site: http://www.biomedsys.com
Sales Range: $1-9.9 Million
Health/Allied Services
N.A.I.C.S.: 621999
Timothy Barrett (Pres)

Subsidiary (Non-US):

eResearchTechnology Limited **(2)**
Peterborough Business Park, Lynch Wood, Peterborough, PE2 6FZ, Cambs, United Kingdom
Tel.: (44) 1733 374800
Web Site: http://www.ert.com
Medical Diagnostic & Testing Web-Based Software & Consulting Services
N.A.I.C.S.: 513210

Branch (Domestic):

eResearchTechnology, Inc. - Bridgewater **(2)**
685 US Hwy 202 206 2nd Fl, Bridgewater, NJ 08807-1774
Tel.: (908) 704-8010
Web Site: http://www.ert.com
Medical Diagnostic & Testing Web-Based Software
N.A.I.C.S.: 513210
Tom Devine (CIO, Chief Dev Officer Exec VP)

ASTORIA A.D.
Milovana Milovanovica 1, 11000, Belgrade, Serbia
Tel.: (381) 11 360 51 00
Web Site: http://www.astoria.rs
Year Founded: 1993
Sales Range: $1-9.9 Million
Emp.: 2
Home Management Services
N.A.I.C.S.: 721110

ASTORY CO LTD.
401 14F R&D Tower Nurikkum Sqare Square Building 396 World Cup Bukro, Mapo-Gu, Seoul, Korea (South)
Tel.: (82) 220882585
Web Site: https://www.astory.co.kr
Year Founded: 2004
241840—(KRS)
Rev.: $54,978,773
Assets: $77,683,551
Liabilities: $32,810,258
Net Worth: $44,873,293
Earnings: $3,133,965
Emp.: 48
Fiscal Year-end: 12/31/22
Television Broadcasting Services
N.A.I.C.S.: 516120
Sang-Baek Lee (CEO)

ASTRA EXPLORATION INC.
595 Burrard Street Suite 1723, Vancouver, V6E 3V7, BC, Canada BC
Tel.: (604) 428-0939
Web Site: https://www.astra-exploration.com
Year Founded: 2020
ATEPF—(OTCQB)
Assets: $914,774
Liabilities: $93,851
Net Worth: $820,922
Earnings: ($2,126,700)
Fiscal Year-end: 03/31/23
Mineral Mining Services
N.A.I.C.S.: 213115
Brian Miller (CEO)

ASTRA INDUSTRIAL GROUP COMPANY
PO Box 1560, Riyadh, 11441, Saudi Arabia
Tel.: (966) 114752002
Web Site: https://www.aig.sa
Year Founded: 1988
1212—(SAU)
Rev.: $691,680,708
Assets: $939,861,919
Liabilities: $429,747,163
Net Worth: $510,114,755
Earnings: $129,494,424
Emp.: 4,500
Fiscal Year-end: 12/31/22
Pharmaceutical Products, Fertilizers & Agricultural Pesticides Mfr
N.A.I.C.S.: 325311
Khaled Sabih Al Masri (Pres)

Subsidiaries:

ASTRA Industrial Complex Co. for Fertilizers & Agrochemicals **(1)**
PO Box 30447, 31952, Al Khobar, Saudi Arabia
Tel.: (966) 38121406
Web Site: http://www.astra-agri.com.sa
Sales Range: $25-49.9 Million
Emp.: 80
Fertilizer & Agrochemical Producer
N.A.I.C.S.: 325311

ASTRA Polymer Compounding Co. Ltd. **(1)**
PO Box 3863, 11481, Al Khobar, Saudi Arabia
Tel.: (966) 38123459
Web Site: http://www.astra-polymer.com
Polymers & Thermoplastic Compound Mfr
N.A.I.C.S.: 326199

ASTRACHEM Morocco Co. **(1)**

Zone Industrielle Lot No15 - B P 1303, 80152, Ait Melloul, Morocco
Tel.: (212) 528308778
Fertilizer Mfr & Distr
N.A.I.C.S.: 325311

ASTRACHEM Saudi Arabia Co. **(1)**
Villa no 07 Rue Aissat Idir Cooperative Immobiliere Dar El Bahdja, Cheraga, Algeria
Tel.: (213) 23363278
Fertilizer Mfr & Distr
N.A.I.C.S.: 325311

Agrostulln GmbH **(1)**
Werksweg 2, 92551, Stulln, Germany
Tel.: (49) 943530690
Web Site: https://www.agrostulln.com
Chemical Product Mfr & Distr
N.A.I.C.S.: 325998

Astra Industrial Complex Co. For fertilizers and pesticides Ltd. **(1)**
Second Industrial Area, Dammam, Saudi Arabia
Tel.: (966) 114772346
Web Site: https://astrachem.net
Agrochemical Mfr & Distr
N.A.I.C.S.: 325320

Astra Industrial Complex Co. Ltd. **(1)**
2nd Floor Office 15 Al Bayt Building No 2 Salaheddin St Malaz, PO Box 54061, Riyadh, 11514, Saudi Arabia
Tel.: (966) 114772346
Agrochemical Fertilizer & Veterinary Pesticide Distr
N.A.I.C.S.: 424910

Subsidiary (Non-US):

AstraChem Ukraine Ltd. **(2)**
1 Chornovola Str, 08133, Vyshneve, Kiev, Ukraine
Tel.: (380) 443790177
Agrochemical Fertilizer & Veterinary Pesticide Distr
N.A.I.C.S.: 424910

Astra Nova Co. **(1)**
Caglayan Mah Eski Lara Yolu 2049 Sok Kaplan Apt No 1/5, Muratpasa, 07230, Antalya, Turkiye
Tel.: (90) 242324751011
Web Site: https://www.astranova.com.tr
Agrochemical Mfr & Distr
N.A.I.C.S.: 325320

Astrachem Turkey **(1)**
Astrachem Agricultural pesticide Seed Fertilizer Trd and Eng Ltd STI, A1 Complex Apt No 50 Seyhan Onur Tekel Street Kiza Business Center Sit, Adana, Turkiye
Tel.: (90) 3224571060
Sales Range: $25-49.9 Million
Emp.: 11
Agrochemicals Mfr & Sales
N.A.I.C.S.: 325320
S. Ihsan Yildirim (Country Mgr)

International Building Systems Factory Co. Ltd. **(1)**
Riyadh 2nd Industrial City Opposite Police/Fire Station Al Kharj Road, PO Box 1737, Riyadh, 11441, Saudi Arabia
Tel.: (966) 112650004
Web Site: https://www.ibsf.com
Sales Range: $100-124.9 Million
Emp.: 500
Pre-Engineered Steel Buildings Mfr
N.A.I.C.S.: 332311

Tabuk Pharmaceutical Manufacturing Company **(1)**
Al-Madinah Highway Road, PO Box 3844, Tabuk, 9222-47532, Saudi Arabia
Tel.: (966) 44283030
Web Site:
http://www.tabukpharmaceuticals.com
Emp.: 2,000
Generic Pharmaceutical Mfr
N.A.I.C.S.: 325412

Tabuk Pharmaceuticals Ltd. **(1)**
Astra Industrial Group Building No 2 First Floor King Abdulaziz Street, Riyadh, Saudi Arabia
Tel.: (966) 114774946
Web Site:
https://www.tabukpharmaceuticals.com
Pharmaceuticals Mfr

ASTRA INDUSTRIAL GROUP
COMPANY—(Continued)

N.A.I.C.S.: 325412

ASTRA MICROWAVE PRODUCTS LIMITED

Astra Towers Survey No 12P Kothaguda Post Kondapur Hitechcity,
Hyderabad, 500084, Telangana, India
Tel.: (91) 4046618000
Web Site: https://www.astramwp.com
532493—(BOM)
Rev.: $88,967,096
Assets: $129,032,972
Liabilities: $52,769,521
Net Worth: $76,263,451
Earnings: $3,938,257
Emp.: 980
Fiscal Year-end: 03/31/21
Consumer Electronics Industry
N.A.I.C.S.: 334220
C. Prameelamma *(Co-Founder)*

Subsidiaries:

Astra Microwave Products Limited -
Unit-I
ASTRA Towers Survey No 12 P Kothaguda
Post Kondapur, Hitechcity, Hyderabad,
500084, Telangana, India
Tel.: (91) 4046618000
Web Site: https://wdwp.astramwp.com
Sales Range: $100-124.9 Million
Emp.: 500
Microwave Systems Mfr
N.A.I.C.S.: 334419

Astra Microwave Products Limited -
Unit-II   **(1)**
Plot No 56A Anrich Indus Estate IDA
Bollarum, Miyapur Medak Dist, Hyderabad,
502325, Andhra Pradesh, India
Tel.: (91) 4030618200
Sales Range: $25-49.9 Million
Emp.: 60
Defense & Telecommunication Devices Mfr
N.A.I.C.S.: 334290
B. Malla Reddy *(Mng Dir)*

ASTRAKHAN POWER SALE COMPANY PAO

Street John Reid 3, Astrakhan,
414000, Russia
Tel.: (7) 8512338613   **RU**
ASSB—(MOEX)
Sales Range: Less than $1 Million
Electricity Meter Installation & Maintenance Services
N.A.I.C.S.: 238210
Oleg A. Statsenko *(Gen Dir)*

ASTRAL ASIA BERHAD

Level 12 Menara TSR No 12 Jalan
PJU 7/3, Mutiara Damansara, 47810,
Petaling Jaya, Selangor, Malaysia
Tel.: (60) 322766138
Web Site: http://www.astralasia.com
AASIA—(KLS)
Rev.: $3,115,019
Assets: $74,288,813
Liabilities: $21,601,279
Net Worth: $52,687,534
Earnings: ($2,609,167)
Emp.: 189
Fiscal Year-end: 12/31/23
Civil Engineering & Building Construction Services
N.A.I.C.S.: 541330

Subsidiaries:

Tasja Development Sdn. Bhd.   **(1)**
Level 12 Menara TSR No 12 Jalan PJU 7/3
Mutiara Damansara, 47810, Petaling Jaya,
Selangor, Malaysia
Tel.: (60) 377175588
Construction Property Development Services
N.A.I.C.S.: 237210

ASTRAL FOODS LIMITED

Lanseria Corporate Estate 13 Thunderbolt Lane Ext 26, Doringkloof,
Lanseria, 1748, South Africa
Tel.: (27) 126675468
Web Site:
https://www.astralfoods.com
ARL—(JSE)
Rev.: $1,082,532,950
Assets: $534,581,027
Liabilities: $250,662,965
Net Worth: $283,918,062
Earnings: $32,322,120
Emp.: 9,088
Fiscal Year-end: 09/30/21
Animal Feeds, Animal Feed Pre-
Mixes, Broiler Genetic Breeding &
Broiler Operations; Broilers & Hatching Eggs Producer & Sales
N.A.I.C.S.: 311119
Daniel Dirk Ferreira *(CFO)*

Subsidiaries:

Astral Operations Limited   **(1)**
92 Koranna Avenue, Centurion, 157, Centurion, South Africa
Tel.: (27) 126675468
Web Site: http://www.astralfoods.com
Emp.: 1,200
Broiler Chicken Production & Distr
N.A.I.C.S.: 112320
Nick Borain *(CEO)*

Division (Domestic):

Astral Operations Limited - Earlybird
Farm Division   **(2)**
15 Industry Road, PO Box 237, Olifantsfontein, 1665, South Africa
Tel.: (27) 11 206 0600
Web Site: http://www.earlybirdfarm.com
Sales Range: $600-649.9 Million
Broiler Chicken Production Services
N.A.I.C.S.: 112320
Theo Delport *(Mng Dir-Poultry Div)*

Subsidiary (Domestic):

County Fair Foods (Pty) Ltd   **(2)**
Admiral Crescent Bofors Circle Epping 2,
PO Box 94, Cape Town, 7475, Western
Cape, South Africa
Tel.: (27) 21 505 8000
Web Site: http://www.countyfair.co.za
Rev.: $153,708,000
Emp.: 200
Broiler Chicken Production & Distr
N.A.I.C.S.: 112320

Earlybird Farm (Pty) Ltd.   **(1)**
15 Industry Road, PO Box 237, Olifantsfontein, 1665, South Africa
Tel.: (27) 112060600
Web Site: http://www.astralpoultry.com
Sales Range: $700-749.9 Million
Emp.: 8,000
Poultry Products Mfr
N.A.I.C.S.: 112390

Meadow Feeds Eastern Cape (Pty)
Limited   **(1)**
5B Lindsay Road, Neave Township, Port
Elizabeth, 6020, Eastern Cape, South Africa
Tel.: (27) 414025000
Animal Food Distr
N.A.I.C.S.: 424490
Jaco Wyk *(COO)*

Meadow Feeds Pty. Ltd.   **(1)**
Lanseria Corporate Estate Malibongwe
Drive Ext 23, Lanseria Ext 23, Lanseria,
1737, Gauteng, South Africa
Tel.: (27) 11 991 6000
Web Site: https://www.meadowfeeds.co.za
Animal Feed Mfr
N.A.I.C.S.: 311119

Division (Non-US):

Meadow Feed Mauritius   **(2)**
Richeterre Road, Port Louis, Mauritius
Tel.: (230) 9230 249 3860
Animal Feed Mfr
N.A.I.C.S.: 311119

Division (Domestic):

Meadow Feeds Cape   **(2)**

Westhoven Street Dal Josafat, Paarl, 7646,
South Africa
Tel.: (27) 21 807 8700
Web Site: http://www.meadowcape.co.za
Sales Range: $25-49.9 Million
Emp.: 111
Animal Feed Mfr
N.A.I.C.S.: 311119

Division (Non-US):

Meadow Feeds Delmas   **(2)**
Tel.: (27) 13 665 5011
Web Site: http://www.meadowfeeds.com
Sales Range: $25-49.9 Million
Emp.: 94
Animal Feed Mfr
N.A.I.C.S.: 311119

Division (Domestic):

Meadow Feeds Kwa-Zulu Natal   **(2)**
56 Ohrtmann Road, Pietermaritzburg, 3200,
South Africa
Tel.: (27) 33 387 2403
Web Site: https://www.meadowfeeds.co.za
Sales Range: $25-49.9 Million
Emp.: 120
Animal Feed Mfr
N.A.I.C.S.: 311119
Tiaan Auret *(COO)*

Meadow Feeds Port Elizabeth   **(2)**
5B Lindsay Road, Neave Township, Port
Elizabeth, 6020, East Cape, South Africa
Tel.: (27) 41 402 5000
Web Site: https://www.meadowfeeds.co.za
Sales Range: $25-49.9 Million
Emp.: 90
Animal Feed Mfr
N.A.I.C.S.: 311119
Jaco van Wyk *(COO)*

Division (Non-US):

Meadow Feeds Randfontein   **(2)**
Tel.: (27) 11 693 5120
Web Site: https://www.meadowfeeds.co.za
Sales Range: $25-49.9 Million
Emp.: 100
Animal Feed Mfr
N.A.I.C.S.: 311119
Mark Surendorff *(COO)*

Meadow Feeds Zambia   **(2)**
Plot 8537 Mwembeshi Road, Lusaka Light
Industrial Area, 10101, Lusaka, Zambia
Tel.: (260) 128 6262
Web Site: https://www.tigerfeeds.com
Sales Range: $25-49.9 Million
Emp.: 150
Animal Feed Mfr
N.A.I.C.S.: 311119

Meadow Mozambique LDA   **(2)**
Av Abel Babtista, 1277 RC, Bairro Sicauma
NT, 40009 4047, Matola, Mozambique
Tel.: (258) 21747022
Sales Range: $10-24.9 Million
Emp.: 38
Animal Feed Mfr
N.A.I.C.S.: 311119
Mark Stratford *(Mgr-Ops)*

Meadow Mocambique Limitada   **(1)**
Av Abel Baptista Bairro Sicauma, Matola,
Mozambique
Tel.: (258) 21747022
Animal Feed Mfr
N.A.I.C.S.: 311119

National Chick Limited   **(1)**
Umlaas Road, PO Box 105, Camperdown,
Durban, 3730, South Africa
Tel.: (27) 317859100
Web Site: https://www.natchix.co.za
Sales Range: $150-199.9 Million
Emp.: 753
Poultry Mfr
N.A.I.C.S.: 112340

National Chicks Swaziland (Pty)
Limited   **(1)**
PO Box 1124, Matsapha, Eswatini
Tel.: (268) 25507086
Chick Distr
N.A.I.C.S.: 424590

NuTec Southern Africa (Pty) Ltd.   **(1)**
234 Royston Road, Willowton, 3201, Pietermaritzburg, South Africa   **(25%)**

Tel.: (27) 333979405
Web Site: http://www.nutecsa.co.za
Sales Range: $25-49.9 Million
Emp.: 50
Animal Vitamin & Mineral Premix Mfr
N.A.I.C.S.: 311119

Ross Poultry Breeders (Pty) Ltd.   **(1)**
Welverdiend Farm Heidelberg/Meyerton
Roads, Meyerton, 1960, South Africa
Tel.: (27) 163660249
Sales Range: $75-99.9 Million
Emp.: 270
Poultry Breeding Services
N.A.I.C.S.: 112390
Ray Stinbury *(CEO)*

ASTRAL LIMITED

Astral House 207/1 Bh Rajpath Club
Off S G Highway, Ahmedabad,
380059, India
Tel.: (91) 7966212000
Web Site:
https://www.astralpipes.com
532830—(BOM)
Rev.: $604,544,850
Assets: $462,352,800
Liabilities: $139,612,200
Net Worth: $322,740,600
Earnings: $66,939,600
Emp.: 1,982
Fiscal Year-end: 03/31/22
Plastics Industry
N.A.I.C.S.: 326122
Hiranand A. Savlani *(CFO)*

Subsidiaries:

Resinova Chemie Limited   **(1)**
Astral House 207/1 Behind Rajpath Club
Off S G Highway, Ahmedabad, 380059, Gujarat, India
Tel.: (91) 7311103331
Web Site: https://www.astraladhesives.com
Adhesive Mfr
N.A.I.C.S.: 325520

ASTRAL RESOURCES NL

Principal Place of Business Suite 2 6
Lyall Street, South Perth, 6151, WA,
Australia
Tel.: (61) 893828822
Web Site:
https://astralresources.com.au
AAR—(ASX)
Rev.: $16,068
Assets: $23,731,677
Liabilities: $686,492
Net Worth: $23,045,186
Earnings: ($1,725,336)
Fiscal Year-end: 06/30/24
Gold Ore & Silver Ore Mining
N.A.I.C.S.: 212220
Marc Ducler *(Mng Dir)*

ASTRALIS A/S

Otto Busses Vej 7 OBV 028, 2450,
Copenhagen, Denmark
Tel.: (45) 31763313
Web Site: https://www.astralis.gg
Year Founded: 2019
ASTRLS—(CSE)
Rev.: $12,563,138
Assets: $14,253,712
Liabilities: $3,645,187
Net Worth: $10,608,525
Earnings: ($1,387,358)
Emp.: 94
Fiscal Year-end: 12/31/22
Sports Club Operator
N.A.I.C.S.: 711211
Nikolaj Nyholm *(Founder)*

Subsidiaries:

Astralis Nexus ApS   **(1)**
Tivoli Hjornet Vesterbrogade 3, 1620, Copenhagen, Denmark
Tel.: (45) 31411516
Web Site: https://astralisnexus.gg
Online Game Development Services
N.A.I.C.S.: 518210

ASTRAZENECA PLC
1 Francis Crick Avenue, Cambridge
Biomedical Campus, Cambridge, CB2
0AA, United Kingdom
Tel.: (44) 2037495000   UK
Web Site:
   https://www.astrazeneca.com
Year Founded: 1999
AZN—(NASDAQ)
Rev.: $45,811,000,000
Assets: $101,119,000,000
Liabilities: $61,953,000,000
Net Worth: $39,166,000,000
Earnings: $5,961,000,000
Emp.: 89,900
Fiscal Year-end: 12/31/23
Holding Company; Pharmaceutical
Researcher, Developer, Mfr & Mar-
keter
N.A.I.C.S.: 551112
David Fredrickson (Exec VP-
Oncology Bus Unit)

Subsidiaries:

Acerta Pharma B.V.   (1)
Kloosterstraat 9, 5349 AB, Oss, Nether-
lands
Tel.: (31) 412700574
Web Site: https://www.astrazeneca.nl
Pharmaceuticals Product Mfr
N.A.I.C.S.: 325412
Jurriaan Dekkers (CEO)

Alexion Pharmaceuticals, Inc.   (1)
121 Seaport Blvd, Boston, MA 02210
Tel.: (475) 230-2596
Web Site: http://www.alexion.com
Rev.: $45,811,000,000
Assets: $101,119,000,000
Liabilities: $61,953,000,000
Net Worth: $39,166,000,000
Earnings: $5,961,000,000
Emp.: 89,900
Fiscal Year-end: 12/31/2023
Bio-Pharmaceutical Products Developer, Mfr
& Whslr
N.A.I.C.S.: 325412
Rana Strellis (Sr VP-Global Culture & Corp
Social Responsibility)

Subsidiary (Domestic):

Achillion Pharmaceuticals, Inc.   (2)
300 George St, New Haven, CT 06511
Tel.: (203) 724-6000
Web Site: http://www.achillion.com
Sales Range: $1-9.9 Million
Emp.: 88
Pharmaceutical Developer
N.A.I.C.S.: 325412
Aradhana Sarin (Pres)

Subsidiary (Non-US):

Alexion Ilac Ticaret Limited
Sirketi   (2)
Icerenkoy Mah Umut Sok Quick Tower No
10-12/73, Atasehir, 34752, Istanbul, Turkiye
Tel.: (90) 2162517000
Biopharmaceutical Product Distr
N.A.I.C.S.: 424210

Alexion Pharma GmbH   (2)
Giesshubelstrasse 30, 8045, Zurich, Swit-
zerland
Tel.: (41) 444574000
Biopharmaceutical Product Mfr
N.A.I.C.S.: 325412

Alexion Pharma International Opera-
tions Unlimited Company   (2)
College Business Technology Park
Blanchardstown 15, Dublin, D15 R925, Ire-
land
Tel.: (353) 12546400
Biopharmaceutical Product Mfr
N.A.I.C.S.: 325412

Alexion Pharma International
Sarl   (2)
Avenue du Tribunal Federal 34, 1005, Lau-
sanne, Switzerland
Tel.: (41) 213184000
Web Site: http://www.alexion.com
Emp.: 17
Pharmaceutical Preparation Distr

N.A.I.C.S.: 325412

Alexion Pharma International
Trading   (2)
Block 10A Beckett Way Park West Business
Park Nangor Rd, Dublin, Ireland
Tel.: (353) 12546400
Pharmaceutical Products Distr
N.A.I.C.S.: 424210

Alexion Pharma Middle East
FZ-LLC   (2)
EIB-02 Suite 501 Media City, PO Box
500594, Dubai, United Arab Emirates
Tel.: (971) 45671800
Pharmaceutical Products Distr
N.A.I.C.S.: 424210

Alexion Pharma UK   (2)
3 Furzeground Way Stockley Park, Ux-
bridge, UB11 1EZ, Middlesex, United King-
dom
Tel.: (44) 2087446600
Sales Range: $25-49.9 Million
Emp.: 20
Biopharmaceutical Product Mfr
N.A.I.C.S.: 541715

Alexion Pharmaceuticals (Shanghai)
Company Limited   (2)
No 199 Liangjing Road, Shanghai, 200041,
China
Tel.: (86) 2132201760
Biopharmaceutical Product Mfr
N.A.I.C.S.: 325412

Alexion Pharmaceuticals Australasia
PTY LTD   (2)
66 Talavera Rd, Macquarie Park, 2113,
NSW, Australia
Tel.: (61) 290910500
Web Site: http://www.alexion.com
Sales Range: $25-49.9 Million
Emp.: 40
Biopharmaceutical Product Mfr
N.A.I.C.S.: 541715

Subsidiary (Domestic):

Alexion Services Latin America,
Inc.   (2)
600 Brickell Ave, Miami, FL 33131
Tel.: (305) 755-7500
Medical Product Distr
N.A.I.C.S.: 424210

LogicBio Therapeutics, Inc.   (2)
65 Hayden Ave 2nd Fl, Lexington, MA
02421
Tel.: (617) 245-0399
Web Site: http://www.logicbio.com
Rev.: $5,410,000
Assets: $62,770,000
Liabilities: $32,043,000
Net Worth: $30,727,000
Earnings: ($40,029,000)
Emp.: 62
Fiscal Year-end: 12/31/2021
Biopharmaceutical Product Research & De-
velopment Services
N.A.I.C.S.: 325412
Adi Barzel (Co-Founder)

Subsidiary (Non-US):

Portola Italia S.r.l.   (2)
Via Melchiorre Gioia 8, 20124, Milan, Italy
Tel.: (39) 0277679211
Pharmaceutical Products Distr
N.A.I.C.S.: 424210

Portola Osterreich GmbH   (2)
DC Tower 30th Floor Donau-City-Strasse 7,
1220, Vienna, Austria
Tel.: (43) 444574000
Pharmaceutical Products Distr
N.A.I.C.S.: 424210

Portola Pharma UK Ltd.   (2)
3 Furzeground Way Stockley Park, Uxbridge, UB11 1EZ, Middlesex, United Kingdom
Tel.: (44) 2087446600
Pharmaceutical Products Distr
N.A.I.C.S.: 424210

Portola Pharmaceuticals Espana
S.L.   (2)
Av Diagonal 601 1o, 08028, Barcelona,
Spain

Tel.: (34) 932723005
Pharmaceutical Products Distr
N.A.I.C.S.: 424210

Subsidiary (Domestic):

Portola Pharmaceuticals, LLC   (2)
270 E Grand Ave, South San Francisco, CA
94080
Tel.: (650) 246-7000
Pharmaceutical Research & Development
Services
N.A.I.C.S.: 541715
Glenn Brame (Chief Technical Ops Officer
& Exec VP)

Subsidiary (Non-US):

Portola Schweiz GmbH   (2)
Giesshubelstrasse 30, 8045, Zurich, Swit-
zerland
Tel.: (41) 444574000
Pharmaceutical Products Distr
N.A.I.C.S.: 424210

AstraZeneca (Israel) Ltd.   (1)
Atir Yeda street 1 building O-Tech-2 Floor 5,
POB - 8044, Kfar Saba, 4464301, Israel
Tel.: (972) 732226099
Pharmaceutical Products Distr
N.A.I.C.S.: 424210

AstraZeneca (Philippines) Inc.   (1)
16th Floor Inoza Tower 40th Street, Bonifa-
cio Global City, Taguig, 1634, Metro Manila,
Philippines   (100%)
Tel.: (63) 287778700
Sales Range: $200-249.9 Million
Emp.: 270
Pharmaceuticals & Medical Equipment Distr
N.A.I.C.S.: 325412

AstraZeneca (Singapore) Pte.
Ltd.   (1)
10 Kallang Avenue 12-10 Aperia Tower 2,
Singapore, 339510, Singapore   (100%)
Tel.: (65) 68124700
Sales Range: $25-49.9 Million
Emp.: 100
Pharmaceuticals & Medical Equipment Distr
N.A.I.C.S.: 325412

AstraZeneca (Thailand) Ltd.   (1)
Asia Centre Building 19th Floor 173/20
South Sathorn Road, Thungmahamek
Sathorn, Bangkok, 10120,
Thailand   (100%)
Tel.: (66) 27397400
Web Site: http://www.astrazeneca.co.th
Sales Range: $50-74.9 Million
Emp.: 120
Pharmaceuticals & Medical Equipment Distr
N.A.I.C.S.: 325412

AstraZeneca - Produtos Farmaceuti-
cos, Lda.   (1)
Rua Humberto Madeira 7 Queluz de Baixo,
Barcarena, 2730-097, Lisbon,
Portugal   (100%)
Tel.: (351) 214346100
Web Site: http://www.astrazeneca.com
Sales Range: $75-99.9 Million
Emp.: 110
Pharmaceuticals & Medical Equipment Distr
N.A.I.C.S.: 424210

AstraZeneca A/S   (1)
Johanne Mollers Passage 1 4th floor, 1799,
Copenhagen, Denmark   (100%)
Tel.: (45) 43666462
Web Site: https://www.astrazeneca.dk
Sales Range: $25-49.9 Million
Emp.: 100
Pharmaceuticals & Medical Equipment Mfr
& Distr
N.A.I.C.S.: 325412

AstraZeneca AB   (1)
Astraallen, 151 85, Sodertalje,
Sweden   (100%)
Tel.: (46) 855326000
Web Site: https://www.astrazeneca.se
Sales Range: $250-299.9 Million
Emp.: 7,800
Pharmaceuticals & Medical Equipment Mfr
& Distr
N.A.I.C.S.: 325412

Division (Domestic):

AstraZeneca R&D Molndal   (2)

Pepparedsleden 1, 431 83, Molndal,
Sweden   (100%)
Tel.: (46) 855326000
Web Site: http://www.astrazeneca.com
Pharmaceuticals R&D
N.A.I.C.S.: 541715

AstraZeneca R&D Sodertalje   (2)
AstraZeneca AB Karlebyhus, Astraallen,
Sodertalje, 15185, Sweden   (100%)
Tel.: (46) 855326000
Web Site: http://www.astrazeneca.se
Pharmaceuticals R&D
N.A.I.C.S.: 541715

AstraZeneca AB, o.z.   (1)
Lazaretska 8, SK 811 08, Bratislava,
Slovakia   (100%)
Tel.: (421) 257377777
Web Site: http://www.astrazeneca.sk
Sales Range: $50-74.9 Million
Emp.: 84
Pharmaceuticals & Medical Equipment Distr
N.A.I.C.S.: 423450

AstraZeneca AG   (1)
Neuhofstrasse 34, 6340, Baar,
Switzerland   (100%)
Tel.: (41) 417257575
Web Site: https://www.astrazeneca.ch
Sales Range: $25-49.9 Million
Emp.: 74
Pharmaceuticals & Medical Equipment Mfr
& Distr
N.A.I.C.S.: 325412

AstraZeneca AS   (1)
Karvesvingen 7, 0579, Oslo,
Norway   (100%)
Tel.: (47) 21006400
Web Site: https://www.astrazeneca.no
Sales Range: $50-74.9 Million
Emp.: 75
Pharmaceuticals & Medical Equipment Mfr
& Distr
N.A.I.C.S.: 325412

AstraZeneca B.V.   (1)
Louis Pasteurlaan 5, NL 2719 EE, Zoeter-
meer, Netherlands   (100%)
Tel.: (31) 793632222
Web Site: http://www.astrazeneca.com
Sales Range: $150-199.9 Million
Emp.: 400
Marketer of Prescription Drugs
N.A.I.C.S.: 424210

AstraZeneca Belgium   (1)
Rue Egide Van Ophem 110, 1180, Brussels,
Belgium   (100%)
Tel.: (32) 23704811
Web Site: https://www.astrazeneca.be
Sales Range: $50-74.9 Million
Emp.: 250
Pharmaceuticals & Medical Equipment Mfr
& Distr
N.A.I.C.S.: 325412

AstraZeneca Bulgaria   (1)
Cherni Vrah Blvd No 51 Business Garden
Office X fl 10, 1407, Sofia, Bulgaria
Tel.: (359) 24455000
Web Site: https://www.astrazeneca.bg
Sales Range: $50-74.9 Million
Emp.: 115
Pharmaceuticals Product Mfr
N.A.I.C.S.: 325412

AstraZeneca Corporate IS   (1)
2 Kindom St, London, W26 BD, United
Kingdom   (100%)
Tel.: (44) 1625582828
Sales Range: $50-74.9 Million
Emp.: 100
Investor Services
N.A.I.C.S.: 523150

AstraZeneca Czech Republic   (1)
U Trezorky 921/2 Jinonice, Ptzenska 3217
3218, 158 00, Prague, 5, Czech
Republic   (100%)
Tel.: (420) 222807111
Web Site: http://www.aztrazeneca.cz
Sales Range: $75-99.9 Million
Emp.: 180
Pharmaceuticals & Medical Equipment Mfr
& Distr
N.A.I.C.S.: 423450

AstraZeneca Dominican
Republic   (1)

AstraZeneca PLC—(Continued)

Calle Roberto Pastoriza Esq Manuel de Jesus Troncoso, Edificio Plaza Dorada Piso 3, Santo Domingo, Dominican Republic
Tel.: (809) 5496639
Pharmaceuticals & Medical Equipment Distr
N.A.I.C.S.: 423450

AstraZeneca FZ-LLC (1)
2nd Floor Building 27 - Block D Dubai Healthcare City, Dubai, United Arab Emirates
Tel.: (971) 43624888
Pharmaceuticals Product Mfr
N.A.I.C.S.: 325412

AstraZeneca Farmaceutica Spain S.A. (1)
C Serrano Galvache 56 CE Parque Norte, Edificio Roble, 28033, Madrid, Spain (100%)
Tel.: (34) 913019100
Web Site: http://www.astrazeneca.com
Sales Range: $50-74.9 Million
Emp.: 200
Pharmaceuticals & Medical Equipment Mfr & Distr
N.A.I.C.S.: 325412

AstraZeneca France (1)
31 place des Corolles, Tour Carpe Diem, 92400, Courbevoie, Cedex, France (100%)
Tel.: (33) 141294000
Web Site: https://www.astrazeneca.fr
Sales Range: $125-149.9 Million
Emp.: 300
Pharmaceuticals & Medical Equipment Mfr & Distr
N.A.I.C.S.: 325412

AstraZeneca GmbH (1)
Tinsdaler Weg 183, 22880, Wedel, Germany (100%)
Tel.: (49) 8002288660
Web Site: https://www.astrazeneca.de
Sales Range: $125-149.9 Million
Emp.: 400
Pharmaceuticals & Medical Equipment Mfr & Distr
N.A.I.C.S.: 325412

AstraZeneca Gulf FZ LLC (1)
2nd Floor Building 27 - Block D Dubai Healthcare City, PO Box 505070, Dubai, United Arab Emirates
Tel.: (971) 43624888
Web Site: https://www.astrazeneca.com
Pharmaceuticals Product Mfr
N.A.I.C.S.: 325412

AstraZeneca Holding GmbH (1)
Tinsdaler Weg 183, 22880, Wedel, Germany
Tel.: (49) 8001015482
Sales Range: $350-399.9 Million
Emp.: 1,000
Investment Management Service
N.A.I.C.S.: 523999
Dirk Greshake (Gen Mgr)

AstraZeneca Hong Kong Ltd. (1)
Rm 2301 Casco Tower, 183 Queens Road, Central, China (Hong Kong)
Tel.: (852) 24207388
Web Site: https://www.astrazeneca.com.hk
Sales Range: $25-49.9 Million
Emp.: 80
Pharmaceuticals & Medical Equipment Distr
N.A.I.C.S.: 325412

AstraZeneca Iceland (1)
Horgatuni 2, 210, Gardabaer, Iceland
Tel.: (354) 535 7151
Web Site: http://www.vistor.is
Sales Range: $50-74.9 Million
Emp.: 6
Pharmaceutical Products Distr
N.A.I.C.S.: 424210

AstraZeneca India Pvt Limited (1)
Block N1 12th Floor Manyata Embassy Business Park Rachenahalli, Outer Ring Road, Bengaluru, 560045, India (100%)
Tel.: (91) 8067748000
Web Site: https://www.astrazeneca.in
Sales Range: $50-74.9 Million
Emp.: 120
Pharmaceuticals & Medical Equipment Mfr & Distr

N.A.I.C.S.: 325412

AstraZeneca KK (1)
Grand Front Osaka Tower B 3-1 Ofuka-cho, Kita-ku, Osaka, 530-0011, Japan
Tel.: (81) 648023600
Web Site: https://www.astrazeneca.co.jp
Emp.: 3,600
Pharmaceuticals & Medical Equipment Distr
N.A.I.C.S.: 423450

AstraZeneca KK (1)
Osaka Kitaku Oayodonaka, 531 0076, Osaka, Japan (100%)
Tel.: (81) 664537500
Web Site: http://www.astrazeneca.co.jp
Rev.: $240,000,000
Emp.: 3,000
Pharmaceuticals & Medical Equipment Distr
N.A.I.C.S.: 325412

AstraZeneca Kft. (1)
Aliz utca 4 Building B 1st floor, 1117, Budapest, Hungary (100%)
Tel.: (36) 18836500
Web Site: https://www.astrazeneca.hu
Sales Range: $75-99.9 Million
Emp.: 200
Pharmaceuticals & Medical Equipment Distr
N.A.I.C.S.: 423450

Unit (Domestic):

AstraZeneca Clinical Research Region CEE (HU) (2)
Park U 3, H 2045, Torokbalint, Hungary (100%)
Tel.: (36) 23517300
Web Site: http://www.astrazeneca.hu
Sales Range: $25-49.9 Million
Emp.: 75
Research Services
N.A.I.C.S.: 541715

AstraZeneca Korea (South) (1)
21st floor ASEM Tower 517 Yeongdong-daero, Gangnam-gu, Seoul, 06164, Korea (South)
Tel.: (82) 221880800
Web Site: https://www.astrazeneca.co.kr
Sales Range: $50-74.9 Million
Emp.: 100
Pharmaceuticals & Medical Equipment Distr
N.A.I.C.S.: 424210

AstraZeneca Latvia (1)
Skanstes iela 50A, Riga, 1013, Latvia
Tel.: (371) 67377100
Web Site: https://www.astrazeneca.lv
Sales Range: $25-49.9 Million
Emp.: 22
Pharmaceuticals Product Mfr
N.A.I.C.S.: 325412

AstraZeneca Lietuva UAB (1)
Spaudos str 6-1, Vilnius, 05132, Lithuania
Tel.: (370) 52660550
Pharmaceuticals Product Mfr
N.A.I.C.S.: 325412

AstraZeneca Limited (1)
Level 5 15 Hope Town St, Shortland, 1140, Auckland, New Zealand
Tel.: (64) 96236300
Web Site: http://www.astrazeneca.co.au
Pharmaceuticals & Medical Equipment Distr
N.A.I.C.S.: 424210

AstraZeneca Luxembourg S.A.R.L. (1)
7B De Am Drill, PO Box 62, L 3961, Luxembourg, Ehlange, Luxembourg (100%)
Tel.: (352) 378989
Web Site: http://www.astrazeneca.lu
Sales Range: $50-74.9 Million
Emp.: 9
Pharmaceuticals & Medical Equipment Distr
N.A.I.C.S.: 325412
Vincent Depret (Mng Dir)

AstraZeneca Osterreich GmbH (1)
Landstrasser Hauptstrasse 1A, PO Box 153, 1030, Vienna, Austria (100%)
Tel.: (43) 1711310
Web Site: https://www.astrazeneca.at
Sales Range: $50-74.9 Million
Emp.: 150
Pharmaceuticals & Medical Equipment Mfr & Distr
N.A.I.C.S.: 325412
Jonathan Hunt (Mng Dir)

AstraZeneca Oy (1)
Keilaranta 18, 02150, Espoo, Finland (100%)
Tel.: (358) 1023010
Web Site: https://www.astrazeneca.fi
Sales Range: $25-49.9 Million
Emp.: 60
Pharmaceuticals & Medical Equipment Distr
N.A.I.C.S.: 423450

AstraZeneca Pharma India Limited (1)
Block N1 12th Floor Manyata Embassy Business Park, Rachenahalli Outer Ring Road, Bengaluru, 560045, India
Tel.: (91) 8067748000
Web Site: https://www.astrazeneca.com
Rev.: $112,803,600
Assets: $105,747,915
Liabilities: $43,480,710
Net Worth: $62,267,205
Earnings: $12,735,450
Emp.: 1,283
Fiscal Year-end: 03/31/2021
Pharmaceuticals Product Mfr
N.A.I.C.S.: 325412
Narayan K. Seshadri (Chm)

AstraZeneca Pharma Poland Sp. z.o.o. (1)
ul Postepu 14, 02-676, Warsaw, Poland (100%)
Tel.: (48) 222457300
Web Site: https://www.astrazeneca.pl
Sales Range: $50-74.9 Million
Emp.: 3,000
Pharmaceuticals & Medical Equipment Distr
N.A.I.C.S.: 423450

AstraZeneca Pharmaceutical Co. Ltd. (1)
43rd Fl CITIC Sq 1168 Nun Jing Xi Rd, Shanghai, 200041, China (100%)
Tel.: (86) 152564555
Web Site: http://www.astrazeneca.com.cn
Sales Range: $50-74.9 Million
Emp.: 120
Pharmaceuticals & Medical Equipment Mfr & Distr
N.A.I.C.S.: 325412

AstraZeneca Pharmaceuticals (Ireland) Ltd. (1)
College Business and Technology Park Blanchardstown Road North, Dublin, 15, Ireland (100%)
Tel.: (353) 16097100
Web Site: https://www.astrazeneca.ie
Sales Range: $25-49.9 Million
Emp.: 60
Pharmaceuticals & Medical Equipment Distr
N.A.I.C.S.: 423450
Gerry Burke (Pres)

AstraZeneca Pharmaceuticals (Phils.) Inc. (1)
16th Floor Inoza Tower 40th Street, Bonifacio Global City, Taguig, 1634, Philippines
Tel.: (63) 27778700
Pharmaceuticals Product Mfr
N.A.I.C.S.: 325412

AstraZeneca Pharmaceuticals (Pty) Ltd (1)
Bldg 2 Northdowns Office Pk 17 Georgian Crescent West, Sunninghill, Bryanston, 2191, Gauteng, South Africa
Tel.: (27) 2538043074
Pharmaceuticals Product Mfr
N.A.I.C.S.: 325412

AstraZeneca Pharmaceuticals LP (1)
1800 Concord Pike, Wilmington, DE 19850 (100%)
Tel.: (302) 886-3000
Web Site: http://www.astrazeneca-us.com
Sales Range: $5-14.9 Billion
Emp.: 12,500
Pharmaceuticals & Specialty Products Mfr & Distr
N.A.I.C.S.: 325412

Subsidiary (Non-US):

AstraZeneca Argentina S.A. (2)
Argerich 536, 1706, Haedo, Buenos Aires, Argentina (100%)
Tel.: (54) 146504071

Web Site: http://www.astrazeneca.com
Sales Range: $50-74.9 Million
Emp.: 217
Pharmaceuticals & Medical Equipment Mfr & Distr
N.A.I.C.S.: 325412

AstraZeneca Canada Inc. (2)
1004 Middlegate Road Suite 5000, Mississauga, L4Y 1M4, ON, Canada (100%)
Tel.: (905) 277-7111
Web Site: http://www.astrazeneca.ca
Emp.: 900
Pharmaceuticals & Medical Equipment Mfr & Distr
N.A.I.C.S.: 325412
Gaby Bourbara (VP)

AstraZeneca Chile S.A. (2)
Isidora Goyenechea 3477 Piso 2 Las Condes, Santiago, Chile
Tel.: (56) 27980800
Pharmaceuticals Product Mfr
N.A.I.C.S.: 325412

AstraZeneca Colombia S.A. (2)
Carrera 7 71-21 Torre A Piso 19, Santafe, Bogota, Colombia (100%)
Tel.: (57) 13173020
Pharmaceuticals & Medical Equipment Mfr & Distr
N.A.I.C.S.: 325412

Subsidiary (Domestic):

AstraZeneca LP (2)
50 Otis St, Westborough, MA 01581-3323 (100%)
Tel.: (508) 366-1100
Web Site: http://www.astrazeneca-us.com
Sales Range: $450-499.9 Million
Emp.: 1,390
Pharmaceuticals, Local & Topical Anesthetics, Tocalytics, Critical Care Drugs, Dopamine & Syringes Mfr
N.A.I.C.S.: 325412

AstraZeneca LP (2)
1800 Concord Pike, Wilmington, DE 19850-5437
Tel.: (302) 886-3000
Web Site: http://www.astrazeneca-us.com
Development & Marketing of Pharmaceuticals
N.A.I.C.S.: 325412

Subsidiary (Non-US):

AstraZeneca Peru S.A. (2)
Av El Derby Nro 055 Torre 2 Ofic 503, Santiago De Surco, Lima, Peru
Tel.: (51) 16101515
Pharmaceuticals Product Mfr
N.A.I.C.S.: 325412

AstraZeneca S.A. de C.V. (2)
Av Periferico Sur 4305 Piso 5 Col Jardines en la Montana, Tlalpan, 14210, Mexico, Mexico (100%)
Tel.: (52) 5553749600
Sales Range: $125-149.9 Million
Emp.: 500
Pharmaceuticals & Medical Equipment Mfr & Distr
N.A.I.C.S.: 325412

AstraZeneca do Brasil Ltda. (2)
Rod Raposo Tavares KM 26 9 Moinho Velho, Cotia, 06707-000, SP, Brazil (100%)
Tel.: (55) 1146131200
Web Site: http://www.astrazeneca.com.br
Sales Range: $200-249.9 Million
Emp.: 800
Provider of Pharmaceuticals
N.A.I.C.S.: 325412

Subsidiary (Domestic):

IPR Pharmaceutical Inc. (2)
Rd 188 San Isidro Industrial Pk, Canovanas, PR 00729
Tel.: (787) 957-1400
Web Site: http://www.iprpharmaceuticals.com
Sales Range: $100-124.9 Million
Emp.: 500
Pharmaceuticals Mfr
N.A.I.C.S.: 325412

MedImmune LLC (2)

1 MedImmune Way, Gaithersburg, MD
20878-4021
Tel.: (877) 633-4411
Emp.: 2,500
Pharmaceuticals, Biotechnologies & Medicinal Products Developer, Mfr & Marketer
N.A.I.C.S.: 541720
Matt Bell *(COO)*

Subsidiary (Non-US):

MedImmune Limited **(3)**
Milstein Building Granta Park, Cambridge,
CB2 0AA, Cambridgeshire, United Kingdom
Tel.: (44) 1223471471
Web Site: http://www.medimmune.com
Emp.: 500
Biopharmaceutical Mfr
N.A.I.C.S.: 325412

MedImmune Pharma B.V. **(3)**
Lagelandseweg 78, 6545 CG, Nijmegen,
Netherlands
Tel.: (31) 243717310
Web Site: http://www.medimmune.com
Sales Range: $25-49.9 Million
Emp.: 65
Pharmaceutical Research & Development
N.A.I.C.S.: 541720

Subsidiary (Domestic):

MedImmune Ventures, Inc. **(3)**
1 MedImmune Way, Gaithersburg, MD
20878 **(100%)**
Tel.: (301) 398-0000
Web Site: http://www.medimmune.com
Sales Range: $450-499.9 Million
Emp.: 1,000
Equity Investment Firm Focused on Therapeutic Products & Technologies Development Companies
N.A.I.C.S.: 523999

Subsidiary (Domestic):

Omthera Pharmaceuticals, Inc. **(2)**
707 State Rd, Princeton, NJ 08540
Tel.: (908) 741-4399
Web Site: http://www.omthera.com
Sales Range: $25-49.9 Million
Emp.: 14
Pharmaceuticals Mfr
N.A.I.C.S.: 325412

ZS Pharma, Inc. **(2)**
1100 Park Pl Ste 300, San Mateo, CA
94403 **(100%)**
Tel.: (650) 458-4100
Web Site: http://www.zspharma.com
Pharmaceuticals Mfr
N.A.I.C.S.: 325412
Alvaro F. Guillem *(Pres)*

AstraZeneca Produtos Farmaceuticos, Lda.
Rua Humberto Madeira 7 Queluz de Baixo,
2730-097, Barcarena, Portugal
Tel.: (351) 214346100
Web Site: https://www.astrazeneca.pt
Emp.: 200
Pharmaceuticals Product Mfr
N.A.I.C.S.: 325412

AstraZeneca Pty. Ltd. **(1)**
47 Talavera Road, North Ryde, 2113, NSW,
Australia **(100%)**
Tel.: (61) 299783500
Web Site: https://www.astrazeneca.com.au
Sales Range: $125-149.9 Million
Emp.: 400
Pharmaceuticals & Medical Equipment Mfr
& Distr
N.A.I.C.S.: 325412

AstraZeneca Romania **(1)**
Sos Pipera-Tunari 2C, Comuna Voluntari
Judetul Ilfov, 077190, Bucharest,
Romania **(100%)**
Tel.: (40) 212432520
Web Site: http://www.astrazeneca.com
Sales Range: $50-74.9 Million
Emp.: 90
Pharmaceuticals & Medical Equipment Distr
N.A.I.C.S.: 423450

AstraZeneca Russia **(1)**
1st Krasnogvardeisky passage 21 building
1 30th floor, 123112, Moscow, Russia
Tel.: (7) 4957995699
Web Site: http://www.astrazeneca.ru

Sales Range: $125-149.9 Million
Emp.: 300
Pharmaceuticals Product Mfr
N.A.I.C.S.: 325412

AstraZeneca S.A. **(1)**
Agesilaou 6-8, PO Box 62042, 15123, Maroussi, Greece **(100%)**
Tel.: (30) 2106871500
Web Site: http://www.astrazeneca.gr
Sales Range: $125-149.9 Million
Emp.: 400
Pharmaceuticals & Medical Equipment Distr
N.A.I.C.S.: 325412
Spiros Tsioutsias *(CFO)*

AstraZeneca S.p.A. **(1)**
MIND Viale Decumano 39, Basiglio, 20157,
Milan, MI, Italy **(100%)**
Tel.: (39) 0200704500
Web Site: https://www.astrazeneca.it
Sales Range: $125-149.9 Million
Emp.: 300
Pharmaceuticals & Medical Equipment Distr
N.A.I.C.S.: 325412

AstraZeneca Sdn Bhd. **(1)**
The Bousteador Level 12 No 10 Jalan PJU
7/6, PO Box 11221, Mutiara Damansara,
47800, Petaling Jaya, Selangor,
Malaysia **(100%)**
Tel.: (60) 376243888
Sales Range: $25-49.9 Million
Emp.: 150
Pharmaceuticals & Medical Equipment Distr
N.A.I.C.S.: 325412

AstraZeneca South Africa **(1)**
Building 2 Northdowns Office Park 17 Georgian Crescent West, PO Box X30, Sunninghill, Johannesburg, 2021, Bryanston,
South Africa **(100%)**
Tel.: (27) 117976000
Sales Range: $75-99.9 Million
Emp.: 200
Pharmaceuticals & Medical Equipment Distr
N.A.I.C.S.: 424210
Guni Goolab *(Pres)*

AstraZeneca Taiwan Limited **(1)**
21st Floor Yuanqi Center No 207 Section 2,
Dunhua South Road, Taipei, 10602,
Taiwan **(100%)**
Tel.: (886) 223782390
Web Site: http://www.astrazeneca.com.tw
Sales Range: $50-74.9 Million
Emp.: 200
Pharmaceuticals & Medical Equipment Distr
N.A.I.C.S.: 325412

AstraZeneca Treasury Limited **(1)**
15 Stanhope Gate, London, W1K 1LN,
United Kingdom
Tel.: (44) 9040498229
Investment Management Service
N.A.I.C.S.: 523999

AstraZeneca UK Ltd. **(1)**
Horizon Place 600 Capability Green, Luton,
LU1 3LU, Beds, United Kingdom
Tel.: (44) 582836000
Web Site: https://www.astrazeneca.co.uk
Rev.: $560,000,000
Emp.: 600
Pharmaceuticals Mfr & Whslr
N.A.I.C.S.: 325412

AstraZeneca UK Manufacturing **(1)**
Hurdsfield Industrial Estate, Macclesfield,
SK10 2NA, Cheshire, United
Kingdom **(100%)**
Tel.: (44) 1625582828
Web Site: http://www.astrazeneca.com
Mfr of Pharmaceuticals
N.A.I.C.S.: 325412

AstraZeneca Ukraine LLC **(1)**
Pymonenko St 13 Bldg 1A 2nd Floor, 4050,
Kiev, Ukraine
Tel.: (380) 443915282
Pharmaceuticals Product Mfr
N.A.I.C.S.: 325412

AstraZeneca Uruguay SA **(1)**
Yaguaron 1407 office 1205, 11100, Montevideo, Uruguay **(100%)**
Tel.: (598) 29018900
Sales Range: $25-49.9 Million
Emp.: 30
Pharmaceuticals & Medical Equipment Mfr
& Distr

N.A.I.C.S.: 325412

AstraZeneca Venezuela S.A. **(1)**
Av Principal de La Castellana Junction with
Calle JosE Angel Lamas, Torre La Castellana Floor 5 Office 5 G Chacao, Caracas,
1062, Miranda, Venezuela
Tel.: (58) 2122673344
Healtcare Services
N.A.I.C.S.: 621610

AstraZeneca Vietnam Company Limited **(1)**
18th Floor AB Tower 76 Le Lai Street, District 1, Ho Chi Minh City, Vietnam
Tel.: (84) 2838278088
Healtcare Services
N.A.I.C.S.: 621610

AstraZeneca d.o.o. **(1)**
Radnicka cesta 80, Zagreb, Croatia
Tel.: (385) 14628000
Healtcare Services
N.A.I.C.S.: 621610

AstraZeneca kontor Eestis **(1)**
Valukoja 8, 11415, Tallinn, Estonia
Tel.: (372) 6549600
Web Site: https://www.astrazeneca.ee
Sales Range: $25-49.9 Million
Emp.: 35
Pharmaceuticals Product Mfr
N.A.I.C.S.: 325412

AstraZeneca Ilac Sanayi ve Tic. Ltd. Sti. **(1)**
Buyukdere Cad Yapi Kredi Plaza B Block K
3-4 Levent, Istanbul, Turkiye
Tel.: (90) 2123172300
Web Site: https://www.astrazeneca.com.tr
Pharmaceuticals Product Mfr
N.A.I.C.S.: 325412

Astrazeneca Egypt LLC **(1)**
133 Road 90 North 5th Settlement, Cairo,
New Cairo, Egypt
Tel.: (20) 225980222
Emp.: 650
Cancer & Neuroscience Pharmaceutical Mfr
N.A.I.C.S.: 325412

Astrazeneca Ilac Sanayi Ve Ticaret Limited **(1)**
Sti Buyukdere Cad Yapi Kredi Plaza B Blok
K 3-4, Levent, Istanbul, Turkiye
Tel.: (90) 2123172300
Web Site: https://www.astrazeneca.com.tr
Pharmaceutical Products Distr
N.A.I.C.S.: 424210

Astrazeneca Nijmegen B.V. **(1)**
Lagelandseweg 78, 6545 CG, Nijmegen,
Netherlands
Tel.: (31) 793632222
Web Site: https://www.astrazeneca.nl
Emp.: 450
Biopharmaceutical Product Mfr & Distr
N.A.I.C.S.: 325414

Astrazeneca Pharmaceuticals Pakistan (private) Limited **(1)**
Off 124 & 125 1st floor Bahria Complex III
M T Khan Road, Karachi, Pakistan
Tel.: (92) 21 35202931
Pharmaceuticals Product Mfr
N.A.I.C.S.: 325412

CinCor Pharma, Inc. **(1)**
5375 Medpace Wy, Cincinnati, OH 45227
Tel.: (844) 531-1834
Web Site: https://cinrx.com
Assets: $141,106,640
Liabilities: $204,823,650
Net Worth: ($63,717,010)
Earnings: ($50,369,074)
Emp.: 15
Fiscal Year-end: 12/31/2021
Pharmaceutical Product Mfr & Distr
N.A.I.C.S.: 325412
Michael Kalb *(CFO)*

Fusion Pharmaceuticals Inc. **(1)**
270 Longwood Road South, Hamilton, L8P
0A6, ON, Canada
Tel.: (289) 799-0891
Web Site: https://www.fusionpharma.com
Rev.: $1,461,000
Assets: $219,064,000
Liabilities: $56,843,000

Net Worth: $162,221,000
Earnings: ($87,612,000)
Emp.: 102
Fiscal Year-end: 12/31/2022
Biotechnology Research & Development
Services
N.A.I.C.S.: 541714
Eric Burak *(CTO)*

Gracell Biotechnologies Inc. **(1)**
Building 12 Block B Phase II 218 Sangtian
St Suzhou Industrial Park, Shanghai,
215123, China
Tel.: (86) 51262626701
Web Site: http://www.gracellbio.com
Rev.: $1,160,872
Assets: $147,839,990
Liabilities: $22,259,421
Net Worth: $125,580,568
Earnings: ($42,076,522)
Emp.: 160
Fiscal Year-end: 12/31/2020
Biotechnology Research & Development
Services
N.A.I.C.S.: 541714

Icosavax, Inc. **(1)**
1930 Boren Ave Ste 1000, Seattle, WA
98101
Tel.: (206) 737-0085
Web Site: https://www.icosavax.com
Rev.: $582,000
Assets: $238,677,000
Liabilities: $20,515,000
Net Worth: $218,162,000
Earnings: ($91,758,000)
Emp.: 60
Fiscal Year-end: 12/31/2022
Biotechnology Research & Development
Services
N.A.I.C.S.: 541714

NV AstraZeneca SA **(1)**
Alfons Gossetlaan 40, Groot Bijgaarden,
1702, Brussels, Belgium
Tel.: (32) 23704811
Web Site: https://www.astrazeneca.be
Sales Range: $50-74.9 Million
Emp.: 100
Pharmaceutical Products Distr
N.A.I.C.S.: 424210

PT AstraZeneca Indonesia **(1)**
Perkantoran Hijau Arkadia Tower F 3rd Fl Jl
TB Simatupang Kav 88, Bohjol No 80, Jakarta, 12520, Indonesia **(100%)**
Tel.: (62) 2129979000
Sales Range: $50-74.9 Million
Emp.: 150
Pharmaceuticals & Medical Equipment Mfr
& Distr
N.A.I.C.S.: 325412

Simesa SpA **(1)**
Via Ludovico il Moro 6/C Palazzo Ferraris,
20080, Basiglio, MI, Italy
Tel.: (39) 0298011
Pharmaceuticals Product Mfr
N.A.I.C.S.: 325412

Sofotec GmbH **(1)**
Benzstrasse 1-3, 61352, Bad Homburg,
Germany
Tel.: (49) 617268090
Web Site: http://www.sofotec.com
Inhalation Device Development Services
N.A.I.C.S.: 541714
Beatrix Fyrnys *(Mng Dir)*

Zeneca International Ltd. **(1)**
Calle 4 No 715 Entre 7ma y 6 Miramar,
Apartado 16002 Zona 16, Havana,
Cuba **(100%)**
Tel.: (53) 72042449
Pharmaceuticals & Medical Equipment Distr
N.A.I.C.S.: 423450

ASTRO ALL ASIA NETWORKS PLC

Technology Park Malaysia, Lebuhraya Puchong-Sg Besi Bukit Jalil,
57000, Kuala Lumpur, Malaysia
Tel.: (60) 3 9543 4188
Web Site: http://www.astroplc.com
Sales Range: $1-4.9 Billion
Emp.: 4,659
Television Services
N.A.I.C.S.: 441330

ASTRO ALL ASIA NETWORKS PLC

Astro All Asia Networks plc—(Continued)

Augustus Ralph Marshall (*Deputy Chm & CEO*)

Subsidiaries:

Airtime Management and Programming Sdn. Bhd. (1)
All Asia Broadcast Center Technology Park Malaysia, Lebuhraya Puchong-Sg Besi Buki, 57000, Kuala Lumpur, Malaysia **(100%)**
Tel.: (60) 395436688
Web Site: http://www.austra.com
Sales Range: $800-899.9 Million
Emp.: 4,000
Radio & Television Broadcasting & Wireless Communications Equipment Mfr
N.A.I.C.S.: 334220

Celestial Filmed Entertainment Limited (1)
8/F Exchange Tower 33 Wang Chiu Rd Kowloon Bay, Kowloon, China (Hong Kong) **(100%)**
Tel.: (852) 29271111
Web Site: http://www.celestialpictures.com
Sales Range: $25-49.9 Million
Emp.: 75
Motion Picture & Video Production
N.A.I.C.S.: 512110

Celestial Movie Channel Limited (1)
8th Floor Exchange Tower No 33, 10 Wang Chiu Road Kowloon Bay, Kowloon, China (Hong Kong) **(100%)**
Tel.: (852) 29271111
Web Site: http://www.celestialpictures.com
Sales Range: $25-49.9 Million
Emp.: 80
Other Motion Picture & Video Industries
N.A.I.C.S.: 512199

Celestial Pictures Limited (1)
Shaw Administration Building, Lot 220 Clear Water Bay Road, Kowloon, China (Hong Kong) **(100%)**
Tel.: (852) 29271111
Web Site: http://www.celestialpictures.com
Sales Range: $25-49.9 Million
Emp.: 70
Motion Picture & Video Production
N.A.I.C.S.: 512110

MEASAT Broadcast Network Systems (BVI) Ltd (1)
All Asia Broadcast Center Technology Park, Kuala Lumpur, Malaysia **(100%)**
Tel.: (60) 395436688
Web Site: http://www.astro.com.my
Sales Range: $700-749.9 Million
Emp.: 4,000
Television Broadcasting
N.A.I.C.S.: 813110

MEASAT Radio Communications Sdn. Bhd. (1)
All Asia Broadcast Centre Technology Park Malaysia Lebuhraya Puchong, Sungai Besi Bukit Jalil, Kuala Lumpur, 57000, Malaysia **(100%)**
Tel.: (60) 395436688
Web Site: http://www.astromalaysia.com.my
Sales Range: $800-899.9 Million
Emp.: 4,000
Operation of Commercial Radio Broadcasting Stations
N.A.I.C.S.: 334220
Jake Abdullah (*Mng Dir*)

Philippine Animation Studio Inc (1)
A And V Crystal Tower 105 Esteban Street, Legaspi Village Makati City, 1229, Manila, Philippines **(100%)**
Tel.: (63) 28129920
Web Site: http://www.pasi.com.ph
Sales Range: $25-49.9 Million
Emp.: 12
Photography Studios, Portrait
N.A.I.C.S.: 541921

Tayangan Unggul Sdn. Bhd. (1)
Unit 1 Level 5 Block C Mines Waterfront Bussiness Park, Seri Kembangan, 57000KL, Malaysia **(100%)**
Tel.: (60) 395436688
Sales Range: $450-499.9 Million
Emp.: 2,000

Photographic Film Paper Plate & Chemical Mfr
N.A.I.C.S.: 325992
Rohane Rozhan (*CEO*)

ASTRO MALAYSIA HOLDINGS BHD

All Asia Broadcast Centre, Technology Park Malaysia Lebuhraya Puchong-Sungai Besi Bukit Jalil, 57000, Kuala Lumpur, Malaysia
Tel.: (60) 395436688
Web Site:
https://corporate.astro.com.my
ASTRO—(KLS)
Rev.: $804,246,561
Assets: $1,206,503,492
Liabilities: $974,119,153
Net Worth: $232,384,339
Earnings: $44,547,725
Emp.: 3,623
Fiscal Year-end: 01/31/23
Media Holding Company; Pay-TV, Radio, Publications & Digital Media
N.A.I.C.S.: 551112
Henry Poh Hock Tan (*CEO*)

Subsidiaries:

Astro Digital Publications Sdn Bhd (1)
Level 3 Wisma SSP No 1 Jalan SR 8/3, 43300, Seri Kembangan, Selangor, Malaysia
Tel.: (60) 3 9543 7674
Web Site:
http://www.astropublications.com.my
Magazine Publishing & Distribution Services
N.A.I.C.S.: 513120
Craig Wagstaff (*Grp Gen Mgr-Sls*)

Astro GS Shop Sdn. Bhd. (1)
Astro All Asia Broadcast Centre Technology Park Malaysia, Lebuhraya Puchong-Sungai Besi Bukit Jalil, 57000, Kuala Lumpur, Malaysia
Tel.: (60) 395441188
Web Site: https://www.goshop.com.my
Online Shopping Services
N.A.I.C.S.: 423690

Astro Productions Sdn. Bhd. (1)
All Asia Broadcast Centre Technology Park, Bukit Jalil, 57000, Kuala Lumpur, Malaysia
Tel.: (60) 395498752
Web Site: https://www.astro.com.my
Content Creation Services
N.A.I.C.S.: 541890

Astro Radio Sdn. Bhd. (1)
All Asia Broadcast Centre Technology Park Malaysia Lebuhraya Puchong, Sg Besi Bukit Jalil, 57000, Kuala Lumpur, Malaysia
Tel.: (60) 395438888
Web Site: https://www.astroradio.com.my
Radio Broadcasting Services
N.A.I.C.S.: 516110
Kenny Ong (*CEO*)

Astro Shaw Sdn. Bhd. (1)
Unit 1 Level 5 Block C Mines Waterfront Business Park, 43300, Seri Kembangan, Selangor, Malaysia
Tel.: (60) 395436688
Web Site: https://www.astroshaw.com.my
Film Studio Services
N.A.I.C.S.: 512110
Jastina Arshad (*VP*)

ASTRO RESOURCES N.L.

Suite 6 Level 5 189 Kent Street, Sydney, 2000, NSW, Australia
Tel.: (61) 280462799 AU
Web Site: http://www.aro.com.au
ASE—(ASX)
Rev.: $63,240
Assets: $12,583,902
Liabilities: $469,591
Net Worth: $12,114,312
Earnings: ($2,681,487)
Fiscal Year-end: 06/30/24
Mineral Properties Exploration Services
N.A.I.C.S.: 212220

Vincent John paul Fayad (*Sec*)

ASTRO STROBEL KOMMU-NIKATIONSSYSTEME GMBH

Olefant 1 3, Bergisch Gladbach, 51427, Germany
Tel.: (49) 22044050
Web Site: http://www.astro-kom.de
Year Founded: 1947
Sales Range: $25-49.9 Million
Emp.: 180
Radio Reception Components Mfr & Marketer
N.A.I.C.S.: 334220
Herbert Strobel (*Mng Dir*)

ASTRO-CENTURY EDUCATION & TECHNOLOGY CO., LTD.

No 9 Tianhong Road High-tech Zone, Zibo, 255086, Shandong, China
Tel.: (86) 5333590083
Web Site: http://www.sjthedu.com
Year Founded: 2004
300654—(CHIN)
Rev.: $71,468,797
Assets: $158,245,919
Liabilities: $40,475,403
Net Worth: $117,770,516
Earnings: $5,962,955
Fiscal Year-end: 12/31/23
Online Book Publishing Services
N.A.I.C.S.: 513130
Xu Yucui (*Sec*)

ASTROCAST SA

Chemins des Ramiers 20, Chavannes-pres, 1022, Renens, Switzerland
Tel.: (41) 215080421
Web Site: https://www.astrocast.com
Year Founded: 2014
ASTRO—(EUR)
Rev.: $1,209,478
Assets: $40,467,683
Liabilities: $12,670,074
Net Worth: $27,797,609
Earnings: ($24,225,798)
Emp.: 74
Fiscal Year-end: 12/31/21
Application Development Services
N.A.I.C.S.: 541511
Eric Menard (*VP*)

ASTRON CONNECT, INC.

666 Burrard St Suite 2368, Vancouver, V6C 2X8, BC, Canada
Tel.: (604) 620-2092
Web Site:
https://www.astronconnect.ca
AST—(TSXV)
Rev.: $976,810
Assets: $1,428,647
Liabilities: $248,721
Net Worth: $1,179,927
Earnings: ($1,344,106)
Fiscal Year-end: 09/30/19
Food & Beverage Product Retailer
N.A.I.C.S.: 445298
Shixin Huang (*CEO*)

ASTRON CORPORATION LIMITED

21-23 Church Street, PO Box 49, Minyip, 3392, VIC, Australia
Tel.: (61) 353857088
Web Site:
https://www.astronlimited.com.au
ATR—(ASX)
Rev.: $8,157,666
Assets: $83,468,927
Liabilities: $29,940,262
Net Worth: $53,528,665
Earnings: ($16,603,689)
Fiscal Year-end: 06/30/24
Chemical & Metal Products Mfr
N.A.I.C.S.: 325180

Kang Rong (*CMO & Head-China Ops*)

Subsidiaries:

Coast Resources Limited (1)
3035 Tutor Dr 2nd Fl, Regina, S4W 1B5, SK, Canada
Tel.: (306) 757-3001
Mineral Exploration Services
N.A.I.C.S.: 213114

Donald Mineral Sands Pty. Ltd. (1)
67-71 Main St, PO Box 49, Minyip, 3392, VIC, Australia
Tel.: (61) 353857088
Web Site:
http://www.donaldmineralsands.com.au
Sales Range: $200-249.9 Million
Emp.: 10
Mineral Exploration Services
N.A.I.C.S.: 212390

Yingkou Astron Mineral Resources Co., Ltd. (1)
Level 18 Building B Fortune Plaza, 53 Beizhan Road, Shenhe District, Shenyang, 110016, Liaoning, China
Tel.: (86) 2431286222
Web Site: http://www.astronlimited.com
Emp.: 15
Mineral Mining Services
N.A.I.C.S.: 212390
Alex Brown (*Mng Dir*)

ASTRON PAPER & BOARD MILL LIMITED

Ganesh Meridian D-702 7th Floor Opposite High Court S-G Highway, Ahmedabad, 380 060, Gujarat, India
Tel.: (91) 7940081221 In
Web Site:
https://www.astronpaper.com
Year Founded: 2010
540824—(BOM)
Rev.: $53,985,341
Assets: $42,576,916
Liabilities: $20,846,212
Net Worth: $21,730,704
Earnings: ($3,268,725)
Emp.: 329
Fiscal Year-end: 03/30/23
Paper Product Mfr & Distr
N.A.I.C.S.: 322130
Kirit Patel (*Founder, Chm & Mng Dir*)

Subsidiaries:

Balaram Papers Pvt Ltd (1)
256 and 258 Dhanali Road Nr Deem Roll at Ganeshpura, Ta Kadi Dist Mehsana, Gujarat, 384001, India
Tel.: (91) 9879512254
Web Site: http://balaram-papers-pvt-ltd.business.site
Paper Mfr
N.A.I.C.S.: 322120

ASTRUM FINANCIAL HOLDINGS LIMITED

Room 2704 27th Floor Tower 1 Admiralty Centre 18 Harcourt Road, Central, China (Hong Kong)
Tel.: (852) 36658111 Ky
Web Site: http://www.astrum-capital.com
Year Founded: 2015
8333—(HKG)
Rev.: $1,109,888
Assets: $24,673,418
Liabilities: $5,626,958
Net Worth: $19,046,460
Earnings: ($4,349,790)
Emp.: 26
Fiscal Year-end: 12/31/22
Security Brokerage Services
N.A.I.C.S.: 523150
Chik Pan (*Chm & CEO*)

Subsidiaries:

Astrum Capital Management Limited (1)

Room 2704 27/F Tower 1 Admiralty Centre 18 Harcourt Road, Admiralty, Hong Kong, China (Hong Kong)
Tel.: (852) 36658111
Web Site: https://www.astrum-capital.com
Brokerage Services
N.A.I.C.S.: 523150

ASTURIANA DE LAMINADOS SA
Poligono Industrial de Villall Parcela 1, Pola de Lena, 33695, Asturias, 33695, Spain
Tel.: (34) 985676000
Web Site: https://elzinc.es
Year Founded: 2006
ELZ—(MAD)
Rev.: $112,169,755
Assets: $188,220,435
Liabilities: $139,311,846
Net Worth: $48,908,589
Earnings: ($2,988,242)
Emp.: 156
Fiscal Year-end: 12/31/23
Metal Products Mfr
N.A.I.C.S.: 331110
Macario Fernandez Fernandez *(Chm & CEO)*

ASUKANET COMPANY LIMITED
3-28-14 Gion, Asaminami-ku, Hiroshima, 731-0138, Japan
Tel.: (81) 828501200
Web Site: https://www.asukanet.co.jp
Year Founded: 1995
2438—(TKS)
Rev.: $46,521,180
Assets: $46,864,900
Liabilities: $6,173,740
Net Worth: $40,691,160
Earnings: $1,414,540
Emp.: 435
Fiscal Year-end: 04/30/24
Digital Processing Services
N.A.I.C.S.: 323111
Yukio Fukuda *(Pres & CEO)*

ASUNTOSALKKU OY
Ilmalankuja 2, 00240, Helsinki, Finland
Tel.: (358) 102327505
Web Site: https://www.asuntosalkku.fi
Year Founded: 2018
ASUNTO—(HEL)
Rev.: $18,578,210
Assets: $318,655,481
Liabilities: $169,831,107
Net Worth: $148,824,374
Earnings: ($11,877,691)
Emp.: 13
Fiscal Year-end: 09/30/23
Real Estate Development Services
N.A.I.C.S.: 531190
Jaakko Sinnemaa *(CEO)*

ASURANSI DAYIN MITRA TBK
Wisma Hayam Wuruk 7th Floor Jl Hayam Wuruk No 8, Jakarta, 10120, Indonesia
Tel.: (62) 2180868888
Web Site:
   https://www.asuransidayinmitra.com
Year Founded: 1982
ASDM—(INDO)
Rev.: $84,630,471
Assets: $63,832,138
Liabilities: $39,692,378
Net Worth: $24,139,759
Earnings: $1,366,207
Emp.: 232
Fiscal Year-end: 12/31/23
General Insurance Services
N.A.I.C.S.: 524210
Dewi Mandrawan *(Chm)*

ASURANSI MULTI ARTHA GUNA TBK
The City Center Batavia Tower One Lt 17 Jl KH Mas Mansyur Kav 126, Jakarta Pusat, 10220, Indonesia
Tel.: (62) 212700590   Id
Web Site: https://www.mag.co.id
Year Founded: 1980
AMAG—(INDO)
Rev.: $60,025,582
Assets: $3,319,473,092
Liabilities: $3,208,707,742
Net Worth: $110,765,349
Earnings: $9,615,918
Emp.: 596
Fiscal Year-end: 12/31/23
Insurance Management Services
N.A.I.C.S.: 524298
Dedi Setiawan *(Sec)*

ASUSTEK COMPUTER INC.
15 Li-Te Rd, Beitou District, Taipei, 112, Taiwan
Tel.: (886) 228943447
Web Site: https://www.asus.com
Year Founded: 1989
ACMR1—(LUX)
Rev.: $15,080,337,335
Assets: $15,010,530,594
Liabilities: $6,913,041,866
Net Worth: $8,097,488,728
Earnings: $559,355,001
Emp.: 7,656
Fiscal Year-end: 12/31/23
Computer Hardware Equipment Mfr
N.A.I.C.S.: 332510
Che-Wei Lin *(VP-Motherboard Business Unit)*

Subsidiaries:

AAEON Technology Inc.   (1)
5F No 135 Lane 235 Pao Chiao Rd, Hsin-Tien Dist, New Taipei City, 231, Taiwan
Tel.: (886) 28 919 1234
Web Site: https://www.aaeon.com
Sales Range: $25-49.9 Million
Emp.: 400
Single Board Computers Mfr
N.A.I.C.S.: 334111

Subsidiary (US):

AAEON Electronics   (2)
324 W Blueridge Ave, Orange, CA 92865
Tel.: (714) 996-1800
Web Site: http://www.netappliance.us
Sales Range: $25-49.9 Million
Emp.: 30
Computer Peripheral Equipment Distr
N.A.I.C.S.: 423430

AAEON Electronics, Inc.   (2)
11 Crown Plz, Hazlet, NJ 07730-2441
Tel.: (732) 203-9300
Web Site: http://www.aaeon.com
Emp.: 15
Computer Peripheral Equipment Distr
N.A.I.C.S.: 423430
Y. S. Chung *(Pres)*

Subsidiary (Non-US):

AAEON Technology (Europe) B.V.   (2)
Ekkersrijt 4002, 5692 DA, Son, North Brabant, Netherlands
Tel.: (31) 499462020
Computer Circuit Boards Distr
N.A.I.C.S.: 423690
Fabrizio Del Maffeo *(Mng Dir)*

AAEON Technology (Suzhou) Inc.   (2)
Room12 2F Building B No 5 Xing Han Street, Industrial Park, Suzhou, 215021, Jiangsu Province, China
Tel.: (86) 5126 762 5700
Web Site: http://www.aaeon.com.cn
Computer Circuit Boards Distr
N.A.I.C.S.: 423430

AAEON Technology GmbH   (2)
Monzastrasse 4e, 63225, Langen, Germany
Tel.: (49) 6103 374 7900

Web Site: http://www.aaeon.com
Sales Range: $25-49.9 Million
Emp.: 10
Computer Circuit Boards Distr
N.A.I.C.S.: 334418

AAEON Technology Singapore PTE LTD   (2)
57 Genting Lane 07-00, Singapore, 349564, Singapore
Tel.: (65) 67498749
Sales Range: $25-49.9 Million
Emp.: 8
Computer Circuit Boards Distr
N.A.I.C.S.: 423690
Seng Kim Soon *(Gen Mgr)*

Acbz Importacao E Comercio Ltda.   (1)
Rua Passadena 104 Sala 109, Parque Industrial San Jose, Cotia, 06715-864, Sao Paulo, Brazil
Tel.: (55) 1135492499
Web Site: http://www.loja.asus.com.br
Mobile Phone Mfr
N.A.I.C.S.: 334220

Askey Computer Corp.   (1)
10F No 119 Jiankang Rd, Zhonghe Dist, New Taipei City, 23585, Taiwan
Tel.: (886) 22 228 7588
Web Site: https://www.askey.com.tw
Emp.: 7,000
Wireless Communication Equipment Mfr
N.A.I.C.S.: 327910

Subsidiary (Non-US):

Askey Do Brasil Tecnologia Ltda.   (2)
Rua George Ohm 230 Torre A Conjunto 71 Cidade Moncoes, Sao Paulo, 04576-020, Brazil
Tel.: (55) 1144203180
Wireless Communication Equipment Mfr
N.A.I.C.S.: 334220

Subsidiary (US):

Askey International Corp.   (2)
4017 Clipper Ct, Fremont, CA 94538
Tel.: (510) 573-1259
Wireless Communication Equipment Mfr
N.A.I.C.S.: 334220

Subsidiary (Non-US):

Askey Technology (Jiangsu) Ltd.   (2)
NO 1388 Jiao Tong Road, Wu Jiang Economic-Technological Development Area, Suzhou, 215200, Jiangsu, China
Tel.: (86) 51263487188
Wireless Communication Equipment Mfr
N.A.I.C.S.: 334220

Siligence SAS   (2)
11-13 avenue de Friedland, 75008, Paris, France
Tel.: (33) 177685090
Modem Mfr
N.A.I.C.S.: 334210

Asus Computer Czech Republic S. R. O.   (1)
Gemini Building Na Pankraci 127, 140 00, Prague, 4, Czech Republic
Tel.: (420) 274774872
N.A.I.C.S.: 332510

Asus Computer GmbH   (1)
Harkortstrasse 21 - 23, 40880, Ratingen, Germany
Tel.: (49) 1805010920
Web Site: http://www.asus.de
Computer Software Whslr
N.A.I.C.S.: 423430

Asus Computer International, Inc.   (1)
48720 Kato Rd, Fremont, CA 94538
Tel.: (510) 739-3777
Sales Range: $150-199.9 Million
Emp.: 300
Computer Peripheral Products Mfr & Distr
N.A.I.C.S.: 423430

Asus Czech Service S. R. O.   (1)
Na Rovince 887, Hrabova, 720 00, Ostrava, Czech Republic
Tel.: (420) 596766317
N.A.I.C.S.: 332510

Asus Europe B.V.   (1)
Paasheuvelweg 25, 1105 BP, Amsterdam, Netherlands
Tel.: (31) 207871100
Computer Storage Device Mfr
N.A.I.C.S.: 334112

Asus France SARL   (1)
10 Allee Bienvenue, 93160, Noisy-le-Grand, France
Tel.: (33) 149329650
N.A.I.C.S.: 332510

Asus Holland B.V.   (1)
Nw Amsterdamsestraat 44, 7814VA, Emmen, Netherlands
Tel.: (31) 591570290
Electronic Computer Mfr
N.A.I.C.S.: 334111

Asus Korea Co., Ltd.   (1)
1F Wonhyo B/D 46-1 Wonhyoro 3-Ga, YoungSan-Gu, Seoul, 140-848, Korea (South)
Tel.: (82) 215666868
N.A.I.C.S.: 332510

Asus Mexico, S. A. De C. V.   (1)
Av Insurgentes Sur 1647 Piso 10 Col San Jose Insurgentes, 03900, Mexico, Mexico
Tel.: (52) 5546242426
N.A.I.C.S.: 332510

Asus Nordic AB   (1)
Finlandsgatan 16 4 Tr, 16474, Kista, Sweden
Tel.: (46) 858898900
N.A.I.C.S.: 332510

Asus Polska Sp. Z O. O.   (1)
Al Jerozolimskie 200, 4 Floor, 02-222, Warsaw, Poland
Tel.: (48) 225718000
N.A.I.C.S.: 332510

Asus Service Australia Pty Limited   (1)
Unit 12a Gateway Business Park 63-79 Parramatta Rd, Silverwater, 2128, NSW, Australia
Tel.: (61) 1300278788
N.A.I.C.S.: 332510

Asus Technology (Hong Kong) Limited   (1)
5/F Ming Tak Commercial Building 101 Wan Chai Road, Wan Chai, Hong Kong, China (Hong Kong)
Tel.: (852) 35824738
N.A.I.C.S.: 332510
Wei Gang Chung *(Chm)*

Asus Technology (Vietnam) Co., Ltd.   (1)
110 Nguyen Chi Thanh, District 10, Ho Chi Minh City, Vietnam
Tel.: (84) 88300446
N.A.I.C.S.: 332510

Asus Technology Licensing Inc.   (1)
No 115 Lide Rd, Beitou Dist, Taipei, 112, Taiwan
Tel.: (886) 228943447
Web Site: https://www.asuslicensing.com
Mobile Communication Technology Research Services
N.A.I.C.S.: 541715

Asus Technology Pte. Limited   (1)
15A Changi Business Park Central 1 05-01 Eightrium, Singapore, 486035, Singapore
Tel.: (65) 66228888
N.A.I.C.S.: 332510
Jonathan Tsang *(Chm)*

Asustek (UK) Limited   (1)
1st Floor Focus 31 West Wing Mark Road, Hemel Hempstead, HP2 7BW, United Kingdom
Tel.: (44) 1442202700
N.A.I.C.S.: 332510

Asustek Computer (S) Pte. Ltd.   (1)
No 1 Coleman Street 04-18 The Adelphi, Singapore, 179803, Singapore
Tel.: (65) 66221766
N.A.I.C.S.: 332510

Asustek Computer Malaysia Sdn. Bhd.   (1)
Suite 28-03 28th Floor Menara Keck Seng

ASUSTeK Computer Inc.—(Continued)

203 Jalan Bukit Bintang, 55100, Kuala
Lumpur, Malaysia
Tel.: (60) 321416650
N.A.I.C.S.: 332510

Asustek Computers (Pty) Limited **(1)**
6th Floor Twin Towers West, Johannesburg,
Sandton, 2196, Gauteng, South Africa
Tel.: (27) 117835450
N.A.I.C.S.: 332510

Asustek Italy S. R. L. **(1)**
Via Piero Gobetti 2/B Centro Direzionale
Villa Fiorita, Cernusco Sul Naviglio, 20063,
Milan, Italy
Tel.: (39) 0220231101
N.A.I.C.S.: 332510

**International United Technology Co.,
Ltd.** **(1)**
No 921 Po Ai St, Chupei, Hsinchu, Taiwan
Tel.: (886) 35539199
Inkjet Print Cartridge Mfr
N.A.I.C.S.: 325910

Medus Technology Inc. **(1)**
5th Floor No 115 Lide Road, Beitou District,
Taipei, 112, Taiwan
Tel.: (886) 228943447
Web Site: https://www.medus.com.tw
Software Development Services
N.A.I.C.S.: 541511

Onyx Healthcare Europe B.V. **(1)**
Primulalaan 42, 5582 GL, Waalre, Nether-
lands
Tel.: (31) 499745600
Medicinal Product Mfr
N.A.I.C.S.: 339112

Onyx Healthcare USA, Inc. **(1)**
324 W Blueridge Ave, Orange, CA 92865
Tel.: (714) 792-0774
Web Site:
 https://www.onyxhealthcareusa.com
Computer Peripheral Equipment Mfr
N.A.I.C.S.: 334118

Shinewave International Inc. **(1)**
10F 218 Sec 6 Roosevelt Rd, Taipei,
11674, Taiwan
Tel.: (886) 28 662 1680
Web Site: https://www.shinewave.com
Emp.: 100
Utility Package Software Development Ser-
vices
N.A.I.C.S.: 541511
Alan Chang *(VP)*

Shinyoptics Corp. **(1)**
No 748 Zhongzheng Rd, Yongkang Dist,
Tainan City, 710, Taiwan
Tel.: (886) 62437000
Web Site: https://www.shinyoptics.com.tw
Software Development Services
N.A.I.C.S.: 541511

Taiwan Web Service Corporation **(1)**
3rd Floor No 177 Section 2 Zhongzheng
East Road, Tamsui District, New Taipei City,
251, Taiwan
Tel.: (886) 289796199
Web Site: https://tws.twcc.ai
Software Development Services
N.A.I.C.S.: 541511

Unimax Electronics Incorporation **(1)**
No 15 Lide Rd, Beitou Dist, Taipei, 112,
Taiwan
Tel.: (886) 22 897 0689
Web Site: https://www.unimax.com.tw
Automotive Electronic Product Mfr
N.A.I.C.S.: 336320

ASUTOSH ENTERPRISES LIM-
ITED

84/1A Topsia Road Southtrinity Plaza
3Rd Floor, Kolkata, 700046, India
Tel.: (91) 3340556800
Web Site: https://www.asutosh.co.in
Year Founded: 1981
512433—(BOM)
Rev.: $457,944
Assets: $1,652,260
Liabilities: $2,791
Net Worth: $1,649,468
Earnings: $208,066

Fiscal Year-end: 03/31/21
Investment Management Service
N.A.I.C.S.: 523940
Narayan Baheti *(Sec & Compliance
Officer)*

ASX LIMITED

Exchange Centre 20 Bridge Street,
Sydney, 2000, NSW, Australia
Tel.: (61) 29227000 AU
Web Site: https://www.asx.com.au
Year Founded: 1987
ASXFF—(OTCIQ)
Rev.: $829,630,532
Assets: $13,973,390,125
Liabilities: $11,057,730,699
Net Worth: $2,915,659,426
Earnings: $389,607,615
Emp.: 790
Fiscal Year-end: 06/30/22
Holding Company; Securities & De-
rivatives Exchange
N.A.I.C.S.: 551112
Peter D. Hiom *(Deputy CEO)*

Subsidiaries:

**ASX Clearing Corporation
Limited** **(1)**
Exchange Centre 20 Bridge St, Sydney,
2000, NSW, Australia **(100%)**
Tel.: (61) 292270027
Web Site: http://www.asxgroup.com.au
Sales Range: $200-249.9 Million
Emp.: 500
Securities Exchange Clearing Services
N.A.I.C.S.: 522320
Elmer Funke Kupper *(Mng Dir)*

ASX Operations Pty. Limited **(1)**
Exchange Centre 20 Bridge Street, Sydney,
2000, NSW, Australia **(100%)**
Tel.: (61) 292270885
Stock Market Operation Services
N.A.I.C.S.: 561499

**ASX Settlement Corporation
Limited** **(1)**
Exchange Centre 20 Bridge Street, Sydney,
2000, NSW, Australia
Tel.: (61) 292270027
Web Site: http://www.asxgroup.com.au
Sales Range: $200-249.9 Million
Emp.: 500
Payment Settlement Services
N.A.I.C.S.: 522320
Robert Woods *(Chm)*

**Australian Securities Exchange
Limited** **(1)**
20 Bridge Street, Sydney, 2000, NSW,
Australia **(100%)**
Tel.: (61) 28 298 8260
Web Site: https://www2.asx.com.au
Emp.: 530
Securities & Derivatives Exchange
N.A.I.C.S.: 523210

ASYA INFOSOFT LTD.

4th floor HN House Nidhi Complex,
Navrangpura, Ahmedabad, 380 009,
Gujarat, India
Tel.: (91) 07926462335
Web Site: http://www.sayait.com
511144—(BOM)
Rev.: $5,656,439
Assets: $13,021,688
Liabilities: $8,383,194
Net Worth: $4,638,494
Earnings: $36,198
Emp.: 2
Fiscal Year-end: 03/31/21
Information Technology Services
N.A.I.C.S.: 541511
Ketan Shah *(CEO & Mng Dir)*

ASYAD HOLDING GROUP

Kingdom of Saudi Arabia, PO Box
14552, Jeddah, 21434, Saudi Arabia
Tel.: (966) 126687441 SA
Web Site: https://asyadgroup.com
Diversified Holding Company

N.A.I.C.S.: 551112

Subsidiaries:

Wafi Energy Co. **(1)**
Othman Bin Affan Road Al Mughrizat,
11564, Riyadh, Saudi Arabia
Tel.: (966) 114191913
Web Site: https://wafienergy.com
Fuel Stations Operator & Oil & Gas Distr
N.A.I.C.S.: 457210

Subsidiary (Non-US):

Shell Pakistan Limited **(2)**
Shell House 6 Ch Khaliquzzaman Road,
PO Box 3901, Clifton, Karachi, 75530,
Pakistan **(88.71%)**
Tel.: (92) 21111888222
Web Site: https://www.shell.com.pk
Sales Range: $50-74.9 Million
Emp.: 200
Chemicals Whslr
N.A.I.C.S.: 424690
Haroon Rashid *(CEO & Mng Dir)*

ASYMCHEM LABORATORIES
TIAN JIN CO LTD

No 6 Dongting 3rd Avenue TEDA,
Tianjin, 300457, China
Tel.: (86) 2128166638 CN
Year Founded: 1998
002821—(SSE)
Rev.: $1,439,848,332
Assets: $2,560,793,508
Liabilities: $357,215,508
Net Worth: $2,203,578,000
Earnings: $463,550,256
Emp.: 10,000
Fiscal Year-end: 12/31/22
Pharmaceutical Drug Mfr
N.A.I.C.S.: 325412

AT AUTOMOBILES

Z I Noirefontaine Rn 75, Montagnat,
01250, Bourg-en-Bresse, France
Tel.: (33) 474239330
Web Site: http://www.at-
 automobiles.fr
Rev.: $20,900,000
Emp.: 26
New & Used Car Dealers
N.A.I.C.S.: 441110
Jean-Christophe Roure *(Mgr-Comml)*

AT CAPITAL PTE LIMITED

16-04/05 Samsung Hub 3 Church
Street, Singapore, 049483, Singapore
Tel.: (65) 6226 2174 SG
Web Site:
 http://www.atcapital.com.sg
Year Founded: 2011
Sales Range: $1-4.9 Billion
Privater Equity Firm
N.A.I.C.S.: 523999
Arvind Tiku *(Founder & Chm)*

Subsidiaries:

Capital Aviation Pte Ltd **(1)**
Church Street 3, Singapore, Singapore
Tel.: (65) 62262174
Financial Services
N.A.I.C.S.: 541611
Rudolf Debest *(VP)*

**Orange Power T & D Equipments
Pvt. Ltd.** **(1)**
No 2 1st Cross S S I Area Rajaji Nagar,
Bengaluru, India
Tel.: (91) 8023356615
Web Site: http://www.orangepower.co.in
Industrial Electrical Product Distr
N.A.I.C.S.: 423610

Unioil Petroleum Philippines, Inc. **(1)**
2445 Pedro Gil St Sta Ana, Manila, Philip-
pines
Tel.: (63) 25645227
Web Site: http://www.unioil.com
Fuel Distr
N.A.I.C.S.: 424720
Edgar Bungalon *(Mgr-Distr)*

AT GLOBAL MARKETS (UK)
LIMITED

1st Floor 32 Cornhill, London, EC3V
3SG, United Kingdom
Tel.: (44) 2039577777 UK
Web Site: https://www.atfx.com
Online Trading Services
N.A.I.C.S.: 523999
Joe Li *(Chm)*

Subsidiaries:

**Rakuten Securities Australia Pty.
Ltd.** **(1)**
Suite 5 Level 9 3 Spring Street, Sydney,
2000, NSW, Australia
Tel.: (61) 292472483
Web Site: http://www.sec.rakuten.com.au
Financial Services
N.A.I.C.S.: 523999

AT SEMICON CO., LTD.

138 Seoicheon-ro Majang-myeon,
Icheon, Gyeonggi-do, Korea (South)
Tel.: (82) 316457553
Web Site: http://www.itestsem.com
Year Founded: 2001
089530—(KRS)
Rev.: $13,075,241
Assets: $74,981,944
Liabilities: $19,710,846
Net Worth: $55,271,099
Earnings: ($70,224,047)
Emp.: 160
Fiscal Year-end: 12/31/22
Semiconductor Testing Equipment
Mfr
N.A.I.C.S.: 334413
Hyung Joon Kim *(CEO)*

AT SYSTEMATIZATION BER-
HAD

Lot 11 2 Level 11 Menara Lien Hoe
No 8 Persiaran Tropicana, Tropicana
Golf and Country Resort, 47410, Pet-
aling Jaya, Selangor, Malaysia
Tel.: (60) 378878330
Web Site: https://www.atsys.com.my
Year Founded: 2005
AT—(KLS)
Rev.: $12,867,315
Assets: $75,114,061
Liabilities: $20,663,672
Net Worth: $54,450,390
Earnings: ($17,512,204)
Emp.: 213
Fiscal Year-end: 03/31/23
Eletric Power Generation Services
N.A.I.C.S.: 221118
Choong Lee Aun *(Mng Dir)*

Subsidiaries:

**AT Engineering Solution Sdn.
Bhd.** **(1)**
Plot 82 Lintang Bayan Lepas, Bayan Lepas
Industrial Park Phase IV, 11900, Bayan
Lepas, Penang, Malaysia
Tel.: (60) 46374363
Industrial Automation Machinery Mfr
N.A.I.C.S.: 333998

AT Precision Tooling Sdn. Bhd. **(1)**
Plot 49 Hilir Sungai Kluang2 Bayan Lepas
Free Industrial Zone Phase 4, 11900,
Bayan Lepas, Malaysia
Industrial & Engineering Parts Fabrication
N.A.I.C.S.: 332999

AT&S AUSTRIA TECHNOLO-
GIE & SYSTEMTECHNIK AK-
TIENGESELLSCHAFT

Fabriksgasse 13, 8700, Leoben, Aus-
tria
Tel.: (43) 38422000 AT
Web Site: https://www.ats.net
AUS—(VIE)
Rev.: $1,952,738,244
Assets: $4,601,384,990
Liabilities: $3,063,268,635

Net Worth: $1,538,116,354
Earnings: $126,864,910
Emp.: 13,995
Fiscal Year-end: 03/31/22
Printed Circuit Board Mfr
N.A.I.C.S.: 334412
Heinz Moitzi *(COO & Member-Mgmt Bd)*

Subsidiaries:

AT & S Skandinavia AB **(1)**
Regus Frosunda Port Gustav III Boulevard 34 Solna, 16973, Stockholm, Sweden
Tel.: (46) 762283731
Printed Circuit Board & IC Distr
N.A.I.C.S.: 423690

AT&S (Taiwan) Co., Ltd. **(1)**
Rm 2213 22F No 333 Sec 1 Keelung Rd, Xinyi Dist, Taipei, Taiwan
Tel.: (886) 277520750
Printed Circuit Board Mfr
N.A.I.C.S.: 334412

AT&S Americas LLC **(1)**
1735 N 1st St Ste 250, San Jose, CA 95112
Tel.: (408) 454-5295
Printed Circuit Board Mfr
N.A.I.C.S.: 334412

AT&S Asia Pacific Limited **(1)**
1617-19 16F Tower 3, Hong Kong, China (Hong Kong)
Tel.: (852) 35566800
Printed Circuit Board Mfr
N.A.I.C.S.: 334412

AT&S China Co. Ltd. **(1)**
5000 Jin Du Road, Minhang District, Shanghai, 201108, China
Tel.: (86) 2124080000
Sales Range: $800-899.9 Million
Emp.: 3,634
Bare Printed Circuit Board Mfr
N.A.I.C.S.: 334412

AT&S Deutschland GmbH **(1)**
Am Ellernbusch 18-20, 52355, Duren, Germany
Tel.: (49) 24214404900
Printed Circuit Board Mfr
N.A.I.C.S.: 334412

AT&S India Private Limited **(1)**
207 S N S Manor 2 Brunton Road, Bengaluru, 560025, India
Tel.: (91) 8221244040
Printed Circuit Board Mfr
N.A.I.C.S.: 334412

AT&S Klagenfurt Leiterplatten GmbH **(1)**
Ebentaler Strasse 140, 9020, Klagenfurt, Austria
Tel.: (43) 463311000
Sales Range: $50-74.9 Million
Emp.: 150
Other Electronic Component Mfr
N.A.I.C.S.: 334419

Tofic Co. Ltd **(1)**
452 Mongnae-Dong, Danwon-Gu, Ansan, Korea (South) **(86%)**
Tel.: (82) 314952277
Sales Range: $100-124.9 Million.
Emp.: 296
Electron Tube Mfr
N.A.I.C.S.: 334419

AT-TAHUR LTD.
CB House 182-Abubakar Block, New Garden Town, Lahore, Pakistan
Tel.: (92) 4235845901
Web Site: https://www.at-tahur.com
Year Founded: 2007
PREMA—(PSX)
Rev.: $17,626,662
Assets: $26,224,916
Liabilities: $8,945,784
Net Worth: $17,279,132
Earnings: $4,488,901
Emp.: 701
Fiscal Year-end: 06/30/23
Dairy Milk Product Mfr
N.A.I.C.S.: 311511

Rasikh Elahi *(CEO)*

ATA BYGG-OCH MARK-PRODUKTER AB
Staffans v 7, Box 7051, 192 07, Sollentuna, Sweden
Tel.: (46) 8988070
Web Site: http://www.ata.se
Emp.: 100
Road Safety Barrier Mfr
N.A.I.C.S.: 332312

ATA CREATIVITY GLOBAL
1/F East Gate Building No 2 Jian Wai Soho, No 39 Dong San Huan Zhong Road Chao Yang District, Beijing, 100022, China
Tel.: (86) 1065181133   Ky
Web Site: https://ir.atai.net.cn
Year Founded: 1999
AACG—(NASDAQ)
Rev.: $31,687,026
Assets: $72,692,747
Liabilities: $50,704,938
Net Worth: $21,987,809
Earnings: ($7,337,673)
Emp.: 536
Fiscal Year-end: 12/31/22
Computer-Based Testing & Education Services
N.A.I.C.S.: 611710
Kevin Xiaofeng Ma *(Co-Founder, Chm & CEO)*

Subsidiaries:

ATA Testing Authority (Beijing) Limited **(1)**
East door Fl 1 Building No 2 Jianwai SOHO No 39 Dongsanhuan Zhonglu, Chaoyang District, Beijing, 100022, China
Tel.: (86) 1065181122
Computer Testing & Education Services
N.A.I.C.S.: 541519

ATA GAYRIMENKUL YATIRIM ORTAKLIGI AS
Dikilitas Mah Emirhan Street No 109 Atakule Balmumcu, Besiktas, 34349, Istanbul, Turkiye
Tel.: (90) 2123106450
Web Site: https://www.atagyo.com.tr
Year Founded: 2012
ATAGY—(IST)
Sales Range: Less than $1 Million
Investment Management Service
N.A.I.C.S.: 525990
Bedri Kurdoglu *(Gen Mgr)*

ATA IMS BERHAD
No 6 Jalan Dewani 1 Kawasan Perindustrian Dewani, 81100, Johor Bahru, Johor, Malaysia
Tel.: (60) 73340911   MY
Web Site: https://www.ataims.com.my
Year Founded: 1972
ATAIMS—(KLS)
Rev.: $193,816,508
Assets: $164,291,005
Liabilities: $61,878,942
Net Worth: $102,412,063
Earnings: ($53,889,312)
Emp.: 3,967
Fiscal Year-end: 03/31/23
Investment Holding Company; Industrial Products Mfr & Marketer
N.A.I.C.S.: 551112
Chee Yin Wong *(Co-Sec)*

Subsidiaries:

Lean Teik Soon Sdn. Bhd. **(1)**
No 1589 Lorong Perusahaan Utama 2 Plot P 112B MK 11, 14000, Bukit Mertajam, Penang, Malaysia
Tel.: (60) 45072288

Sales Range: $25-49.9 Million
Emp.: 27
Convenience Foods Mfr
N.A.I.C.S.: 311230

Winsheng Plastic Industry Sdn. Bhd. **(1)**
16 Jalan Hasil Dua Kawasan Perindustrian Tampoi, 81200, Johor Bahru, Johor, Malaysia
Tel.: (60) 72333333
Web Site: https://wsp.my
Sales Range: $150-199.9 Million
Emp.: 2,000
Plastic Component Mfr
N.A.I.C.S.: 326199

ATAI LIFE SCIENCES AG
KrausenstraSSe 9-10, Berlin, 10117, Germany
Tel.: (49) 89 2153 9035
Web Site: http://www.atai.life
Research & Development in the Physical & Life Sciences
N.A.I.C.S.: 541715
Christian Angermayer *(Co-Founder)*

ATAI LIFE SCIENCES N.V.
Wallstrasse 16, 10179, Berlin, Germany
Tel.: (49) 8921539035   NL
Web Site: https://www.atai.life
Year Founded: 2020
ATAI—(NASDAQ)
Rev.: $233,000
Assets: $305,441,000
Liabilities: $39,675,000
Net Worth: $265,766,000
Earnings: ($152,385,000)
Emp.: 133
Fiscal Year-end: 12/31/22
Holding Company
N.A.I.C.S.: 551112
Lars Wilde *(Co-Founder)*

Subsidiaries:

Atai Life Sciences US Inc. **(1)**
524 Broadway 11th Fl, New York, NY 10012
Heal Mental Health Disorder Services
N.A.I.C.S.: 621112

ATAKULE GAYRIMENKUL YATIRIM ORTAKLIGI AS
Cankaya Street No 1B/68, Cankaya District, Ankara, Turkiye
Tel.: (90) 3124476500
Web Site: https://www.atakulegyo.com.tr
Year Founded: 2000
AGYO—(IST)
Rev.: $6,780,603
Assets: $123,167,434
Liabilities: $879,527
Net Worth: $122,287,907
Earnings: $21,898,715
Fiscal Year-end: 12/31/23
Real Estate Investment Services
N.A.I.C.S.: 523999
Ismail Tarman *(Chm)*

ATAL REALTECH LIMITED
Unit No 301 & 302 ABH Town Square, Near City Centre Mall, Nashik, 422002, Maharashtra, India
Tel.: (91) 2532993859
Web Site: https://www.atalrealtech.com
Year Founded: 2012
543911—(BOM)
Rev.: $5,536,467
Assets: $6,641,312
Liabilities: $2,082,198
Net Worth: $4,559,114
Earnings: $294,158
Fiscal Year-end: 03/30/22
Engineeering Services
N.A.I.C.S.: 541330
Amit Atal *(Gen Mgr & Exec Dir)*

ATAL S.A.
ul Stawowa 27, 43-400, Cieszyn, Poland
Tel.: (48) 338575901
Web Site: https://www.atal.pl
Year Founded: 1990
1AT—(WAR)
Rev.: $381,221,036
Assets: $899,314,276
Liabilities: $467,682,418
Net Worth: $431,631,859
Earnings: $86,721,544
Fiscal Year-end: 12/31/23
Residential Real Estate Services
N.A.I.C.S.: 531390
Grzegorz Minczanowski *(Co-Chm-Supervisory Bd)*

ATALAYA MINING PLC
Tel.: (357) 22442705   CY
Web Site: https://www.atalayamining.com
Year Founded: 2004
ATYM—(LSE)
Rev.: $365,334,908
Assets: $719,803,564
Liabilities: $191,259,124
Net Worth: $528,544,440
Earnings: $39,354,873
Emp.: 488
Fiscal Year-end: 12/31/23
Gold & Copper Mining Services
N.A.I.C.S.: 212220
Alberto Lavandeira *(CEO)*

Subsidiaries:

Atalaya Financing Limited **(1)**
121 Prodromou Street Office 705, Strovolos, Nicosia, Cyprus
Tel.: (357) 22442705
Copper Mining Services
N.A.I.C.S.: 212230

EMED Tartessus S.L.U. **(1)**
La Dehesa s/n, 21660, Minas de Riotinto, Huelva, Spain
Tel.: (34) 959 592 850
Web Site: http://www.emed-tartessus.com
Copper Ore Mining Services
N.A.I.C.S.: 212230
Alberto Lavandeira *(Mng Dir-EMED Tartessus)*

Eastern Mediterranean Resources (Slovakia) SRO **(1)**
Zelezniciarska 1724/11, 96901, Banska Stiavnica, Slovakia
Tel.: (421) 456720069
Web Site: http://www.emed-slovakia.com
Sales Range: $50-74.9 Million
Emp.: 7
Gold Ore Mining Services
N.A.I.C.S.: 212220
Demetrios Constantinides *(Mng Dir)*

ATALIAN GLOBAL SERVICES
111-113 Quai jules Guesde, 94400, Vitry-sur-Seine, France
Tel.: (33) 155530300
Web Site: http://www.atalian.com
Year Founded: 1944
Sales Range: $550-599.9 Million
Property Management & Security Services
N.A.I.C.S.: 561210
Matthieu De Baynast *(CEO)*

Subsidiaries:

Temco Service Industries, Inc. **(1)**
417 5th Ave 9th Fl, New York, NY 10016
Tel.: (212) 889-6353
Web Site: http://www.temcoservices.com
Facility Management Services
N.A.I.C.S.: 561720
Sanjiv Bhatia *(VP-IT)*

Division (Domestic):

Spartan Security Services, Inc. **(2)**
417 5th Ave 9th Fl, New York, NY 10016
Tel.: (212) 251-7888

ATALIAN Global Services—(Continued)

Web Site:
http://www.spartansecurityservices.com
Emp.: 1,000
Fire Safety Directors, Fire Watch Guards,
Investigative Services, Mobile Patrols, Spe-
cial Surveillance Techniques, Uniformed &
Plainclothes Guards
N.A.I.C.S.: 561612
Vincent Dalsass (COO & VP)

Spartan Security Services, Inc. - New Jersey (2)
1 Madison St, East Rutherford, NJ 07073-1611
Tel.: (973) 472-9393
Web Site: http://www.atalian.us
Janitorial Services
N.A.I.C.S.: 561720

ATALLAH GROUP, INC.
333 Chabanel Street W #900, Mon-
treal, H2N 2G1, QC, Canada
Tel.: (514) 384-1906   QC
Web Site: http://www.ssense.com
Electronic Shopping Services
N.A.I.C.S.: 458110
Afshan Samani (Dir-Product Mgmt)

ATAM VALVES LIMITED
1051 Outside Industrial Area, Jaland-
har, 144004, India
Tel.: (91) 1815001111
Web Site: https://www.atamvalves.in
Year Founded: 1982
543236—(BOM)
Rev.: $6,722,407
Assets: $5,232,687
Liabilities: $1,821,142
Net Worth: $3,411,545
Earnings: $1,046,627
Emp.: 4
Fiscal Year-end: 03/31/23
Valve Mfr
N.A.I.C.S.: 332919
Natisha Choudhary (Compliance Offi-
cer & Sec)

ATAMEKEN-AGRO JSC
Vostochnaya industrial zone road 20
building 30, 020000, Kokshetau, Ka-
zakhstan
Tel.: (7) 7162775625
Web Site: https://www.atameken-
agro.com
Year Founded: 2003
KATR—(KAZ)
Rev.: $117,899,695
Assets: $241,583,829
Liabilities: $168,349,918
Net Worth: $73,233,910
Earnings: $39,303,457
Fiscal Year-end: 12/31/22
Grain Farming Services
N.A.I.C.S.: 111199
Kintal K. Islamov (Chm-Mgmt Bd &
CEO)

ATAR URGUU JSC
Khan-Uul District, Ulaanbaatar, Mon-
golia
Tel.: (976) 11 342130
ATR—(MONG)
Rev.: $3,970,808
Assets: $4,588,084
Liabilities: $307,979
Net Worth: $4,280,104
Earnings: $106,560
Fiscal Year-end: 12/31/19
Grocery & Related Product Whslr
N.A.I.C.S.: 424490

ATARI, SA
25 Rue Godot de Mauroy, 75009,
Paris, France
Tel.: (33) 183646158   FR
Web Site: https://www.atari.com
Year Founded: 1983

ATA—(EUR)
Rev.: $232,137,360
Assets: $496,208,960
Liabilities: $198,974,880
Net Worth: $297,234,080
Earnings: ($146,160,560)
Emp.: 25
Fiscal Year-end: 03/31/21
Holding Company; Interactive Enter-
tainment Software Developer & Li-
censor
N.A.I.C.S.: 551112
Frederic Chesnais (Chm & CEO)

Subsidiaries:

Atari, Inc. (1)
286 Madison Ave, New York, NY
10017 **(60%)**
Tel.: (212) 726-6500
Web Site: https://www.atari.com
Emp.: 50
Interactive Entertainment Software Devel-
oper & Licensor
N.A.I.C.S.: 533110
Wade Rosen (CEO)

ATASAY KUYUMCULUK
Merkez Mahallesi Sedir Sok No 7,
34530, Istanbul, Turkiye
Tel.: (90) 2126523366
Web Site: http://www.atasay.com
Year Founded: 1989
Sales Range: $250-299.9 Million
Emp.: 1,200
Jewelry Mfr
N.A.I.C.S.: 339910
Cihan Kamer (Pres)

ATC ALLOYS LTD.
Level 11 52 Phillip Street, Sydney,
NSW, Australia
Tel.: (61) 2 8316 3993
Web Site: http://www.atcalloys.com
Sales Range: $1-9.9 Million
Ferro-Tungsten Mfr
N.A.I.C.S.: 331110
Trent Franklin (Sec)

ATCO LTD.
5302 Forand Street SW, Calgary,
T3E 8B4, AB, Canada
Tel.: (403) 292-7500   AB
Web Site: https://www.atco.com
Year Founded: 1947
8A60—(DEU)
Rev.: $3,629,861,840
Assets: $19,148,332,960
Liabilities: $12,731,323,200
Net Worth: $6,417,009,760
Earnings: $618,443,280
Emp.: 20,100
Fiscal Year-end: 12/31/23
Electric & Natural Gas Distr; Electri-
cal Generation & Transmission
N.A.I.C.S.: 221122
George J. Lidgett (Exec VP & Gen
Mgr)

Subsidiaries:

ATCO Blue Flame Kitchen (1)
Commons Building 5302 Forand St SW,
Calgary, T3E 8B4, AB, Canada
Tel.: (403) 245-7630
Web Site:
http://www.atcoblueflamekitchen.com
Emp.: 35
Natural Gas Distr
N.A.I.C.S.: 221210

ATCO Energy Ltd. (1)
Stn Main, PO Box 1240, Edmonton, T5J
2M4, AB, Canada
Electricity Generation Services
N.A.I.C.S.: 221111

ATCO EnergySense (1)
10035 - 105 Street, Edmonton, T5J 2V6,
AB, Canada
Tel.: (780) 420-7310
Web Site: http://www.atcoenergysense.com

Energy Efficiency Program Consulting Services
N.A.I.C.S.: 541618

ATCO Structures & Logistics Ltd. (1)
115 Peacekeepers Drive SW, Calgary, T3E
7X4, AB, Canada **(75.5%)**
Tel.: (403) 292-7600
Web Site: https://structures.atco.com
Sales Range: $1-4.9 Billion
Emp.: 3,000
Prefabricated Infrastructure Construction,
Logistics & Support Services
N.A.I.C.S.: 332311

Subsidiary (Non-US):

**ATCO Frontec Europa Kft-Sucursal
em Portugal** (2)
Avenida Do Infante 50, 9004-521, Funchal,
Madeira, Portugal
Tel.: (351) 291 239370
Emp.: 3
Prefabricated Infrastructure Construction,
Logistics & Support Services
N.A.I.C.S.: 332311
Roland Kemperman (Gen Mgr)

ATCO Frontec Europe Ltd. (2)
Esztergaly u 28, Csomad, 2161, Budapest,
Hungary
Tel.: (36) 28566440
Emp.: 13
Prefabricated Infrastructure Construction,
Logistics & Support Services
N.A.I.C.S.: 332311

Subsidiary (US):

**ATCO Structures & Logistics (USA)
Inc.** (2)
1106 N Temple Dr, Diboll, TX 75941
Tel.: (936) 829-2325
Web Site: http://www.atcosl.com
Sales Range: $50-74.9 Million
Emp.: 200
Prefabricated Infrastructure Construction,
Logistics & Support Services
N.A.I.C.S.: 332311

Unit (Domestic):

**ATCO Structures & Logistics (USA)
Inc. - Alaska** (3)
425 G St Ste 707, Anchorage, AK 99501
Tel.: (907) 677-6983
Web Site: http://www.atco.com
Sales Range: $25-49.9 Million
Emp.: 2
Prefabricated Infrastructure Construction,
Logistics & Support Services
N.A.I.C.S.: 332311

Subsidiary (Non-US):

**ATCO Structures & Logistics Pty
Ltd.** (2)
55 Tonka Street, Luscombe, Gold Coast,
4207, QLD, Australia
Tel.: (61) 734128600
Web Site: http://www.atcosl.com
Emp.: 6
Prefabricated Infrastructure Construction,
Logistics & Support Services
N.A.I.C.S.: 332311

**ATCO Structures & Logistics UK
Ltd.** (2)
Clearway House Industrial Estate Over-
thorpe Road, Banbury, OX16 4US, Oxford-
shire, United Kingdom
Tel.: (44) 129 526 5953
Sales Range: $25-49.9 Million
Emp.: 29
Prefabricated Infrastructure Construction,
Logistics & Support Services
N.A.I.C.S.: 332311
Campbell Rodden (Gen Mgr)

ATCO Water, Ltd. (1)
Ste 800 909- 11 Ave SW, Calgary, T2R
1L8, AB, Canada
Tel.: (403) 245-7106
Web Site: http://www.atcowater.com
Sales Range: $75-99.9 Million
Emp.: 10
Water Treatment & Distribution Services
N.A.I.C.S.: 221310

Canadian Utilities Limited (1)

5302 Forand St SW, Calgary, T3E 8B4, AB,
Canada **(52.7%)**
Tel.: (403) 292-7500
Web Site: https://www.canadianutilities.com
Rev.: $2,529,111,240
Assets: $15,877,154,880
Liabilities: $10,551,392,640
Net Worth: $5,325,762,240
Earnings: $339,509,520
Emp.: 4,479
Fiscal Year-end: 12/31/2020
Holding Company; Utilities Distribution &
Energy Solutions Services
N.A.I.C.S.: 551112
Wayne K. Stensby (Exec VP-Puerto Rico)

Subsidiary (Non-US):

ATCO Australia Pty. Ltd. (2)
Level 12 2 Mill Street, Perth, 6000, WA,
Australia **(100%)**
Tel.: (61) 861635400
Web Site: https://www.atco.com
Emp.: 5
Holding Company; Energy & Infrastructure
Services
N.A.I.C.S.: 551112
Patrick Creaghan (Mng Dir & COO)

Subsidiary (Domestic):

ATCO Gas Australia Pty. Ltd. (3)
81 Prinsep Road, Perth, Jandakot, 6164,
WA, Australia
Tel.: (61) 131356
Web Site: https://www.atco.com
Natural Gas Pipeline Transportation & Distr
N.A.I.C.S.: 486210

ATCO I-Tek Australia (3)
Level 12 2 Mill Street, Perth, 6000, WA,
Australia
Tel.: (61) 861635400
Web Site: http://www.atcoaustralia.com.au
Sales Range: $10-24.9 Million
Information Technology Consulting Services
N.A.I.C.S.: 541512

ATCO Power Australia Pty Ltd (3)
Level 12 2 Mill St, Perth, 6000, WA, Austra-
lia
Tel.: (61) 861635400
Web Site: http://www.atco.com.au
Sales Range: $50-74.9 Million
Emp.: 50
Eletric Power Generation Services
N.A.I.C.S.: 221118

Subsidiary (Domestic):

ATCO Energy Solutions Ltd (2)
200 919 11th Ave, Calgary, T2R 1N6, AB,
Canada
Tel.: (403) 245-7106
Web Site:
http://www.atcoenergysolutions.com
Emp.: 25
Electrical & Industrial Pipeline Mfr
N.A.I.C.S.: 332996

Subsidiary (Domestic):

ATCO Midstream NWT Ltd. (3)
919 11th Avenue Suite 200, Calgary, T2R
1P3, AB, Canada
Tel.: (403) 513-3700
Natural Gas Distribution Services
N.A.I.C.S.: 221210
Craig Grant (Controller)

Subsidiary (Domestic):

ATCO Power Ltd. (2)
5302 Forand Street SW, Calgary, T3E 8B4,
AB, Canada **(100%)**
Tel.: (403) 292-7500
Web Site: http://www.atcopower.com
Sales Range: $25-49.9 Million
Emp.: 111
Independent Power Projects Developer,
Project Manager, Owner & Operator
N.A.I.C.S.: 335311

Subsidiary (Domestic):

ASHCOR Technologies Ltd. (3)
5302 Forand St SW, Calgary, T3E 8B4, AB,
Canada
Tel.: (403) 209-6011
Web Site: http://www.atco.com
Emp.: 6

Coal Combustion Products Distr
N.A.I.C.S.: 423520

Subsidiary (Domestic):

CU Inc.   **(2)**
4th Floor West Building 5302 Forand Street
SW, Calgary, T3E 8B4, AB,
Canada   **(100%)**
Tel.: (403) 292-7500
Web Site: http://www.canadianutilities.com
Sales Range: $1-4.9 Billion
Emp.: 3,850
Utilities Holding Company
N.A.I.C.S.: 551112

Subsidiary (Domestic):

ATCO Electric Ltd.   **(3)**
10035 - 105 Street, Edmonton, T5J 1C8,
AB, Canada   **(100%)**
Tel.: (780) 420-3770
Web Site: http://www.atco.com
Sales Range: $450-499.9 Million
Emp.: 900
Electric Utility Services
N.A.I.C.S.: 221122

Subsidiary (Domestic):

Northland Utilities Enterprises
Ltd.   **(4)**
1 66 Woodland Drive, Hay River, X0E 1G1,
NT, Canada   **(76%)**
Tel.: (867) 874-6879
Web Site: http://www.northlandutilities.com
Sales Range: $50-74.9 Million
Emp.: 30
Natural Gas Distr
N.A.I.C.S.: 221210

Subsidiary (Domestic):

Northland Utilities (NWT) Limited   **(5)**
1-66 Woodland Drive, Hay River, X0E 1G1,
NT, Canada   **(100%)**
Tel.: (867) 874-6879
Web Site: http://www.northlandutilities.com
Natural Gas Distr
N.A.I.C.S.: 221210

Northland Utilities (Yellowknife)
Limited   **(5)**
481 Range Lake Road, Yellowknife, X1A
3R9, NT, Canada   **(100%)**
Tel.: (867) 873-4865
Web Site: http://www.northlandutilities.com
Natural Gas Distr
N.A.I.C.S.: 221210

Subsidiary (Domestic):

The Yukon Electrical Co. Ltd.   **(4)**
100-1100 Front Street, Whitehorse, Y1A
3T4, YT, Canada   **(100%)**
Tel.: (867) 633-7000
Web Site: http://www.atcoelectricyukon.com
Sales Range: $50-74.9 Million
Emp.: 45
Electricity Distr
N.A.I.C.S.: 221122

Subsidiary (Domestic):

ATCO Gas & Pipelines Ltd.   **(3)**
10035 105 Street, Edmonton, T5J 2V6, AB,
Canada
Tel.: (780) 420-7310
Web Site: http://www.atcogas.com
Holding Company; Natural Gas Pipeline
Transportation & Distr
N.A.I.C.S.: 551112

Division (Domestic):

ATCO Gas   **(4)**
10035 105th St, Edmonton, T5J 2V6, AB,
Canada   **(100%)**
Tel.: (780) 424-5222
Web Site: http://www.atcogas.com
Sales Range: $750-799.9 Million
Emp.: 1,800
Natural Gas Transmission & Distribution
Services
N.A.I.C.S.: 221210
Dean Reeve *(Sr VP & Gen Mgr)*

ATCO Pipelines   **(4)**
1200 909 11th Ave SW, Calgary, T2R 1L8,
AB, Canada   **(100%)**
Tel.: (403) 245-7060

Web Site: http://www.atcopipelines.com
Sales Range: $25-49.9 Million
Emp.: 75
Natural Gas Pipeline Transportation Ser-
vices
N.A.I.C.S.: 486210
Jason Sharpe *(Sr VP & Gen Mgr)*

ATCO MINING INC.
303-750 West Pender Street, Van-
couver, V6C 2T7, BC, Canada
Tel.: (604) 681-0084   BC
Web Site:
    https://www.atcomining.com
Year Founded: 2021
ATMGF—(OTCIQ)
Assets: $938,406
Liabilities: $72,041
Net Worth: $866,365
Earnings: ($496,677)
Fiscal Year-end: 12/31/22
Mineral Mining Services
N.A.I.C.S.: 213115
Brian Shin *(CFO)*

ATCOAT GMBH
Katharinenstr 61, 52353, Duren, Ger-
many
Tel.: (49) 242199990
Web Site: http://en.atcoat.com
Synthetic Resin Mfr
N.A.I.C.S.: 325211
Monika Schneider *(Mng Dir)*

Subsidiaries:

ATCOAT Hamburg GmbH   **(1)**
Ottensener Strasse 20 22, 22525, Ham-
burg, Germany   **(100%)**
Tel.: (49) 405472250
Sales Range: $25-49.9 Million
Emp.: 30
Resin Mfr
N.A.I.C.S.: 325211

ATCOM TECHNOLOGIES LTD.
6/A Lalwani Industrial Estate 14 G D
Ambekar Road, Wadala, Mumbai,
400031, Maharashtra, India
Tel.: (91) 22 24117080   In
Electronic Weighing Scale Mfr
N.A.I.C.S.: 333993
Sanjay Nimbalkar *(Mng Dir)*

ATE ENERGY INTERNA-
TIONAL CO., LTD.
Bldg C 22F No 96 Hsin-Tai 5th Rd
Sec 1, Hsichih, Taipei, Taiwan
Tel.: (886) 286961585
Web Site:
    https://www.ateenergy.com.tw
Year Founded: 1995
6179—(TPE)
Rev.: $82,423,069
Assets: $149,231,529
Liabilities: $100,949,817
Net Worth: $48,281,712
Earnings: ($2,988,400)
Fiscal Year-end: 12/31/22
Engineeering Services
N.A.I.C.S.: 541330
Yuan-Jui Lu *(Chm & CEO)*

ATEA ASA
Karvesvingen 5, 0579, Oslo, Norway
Tel.: (47) 22095000
Web Site: https://www.atea.com
MKL—(DEU)
Rev.: $2,992,518,012
Assets: $1,649,547,386
Liabilities: $1,305,191,206
Net Worth: $344,356,180
Earnings: $78,329,946
Emp.: 8,073
Fiscal Year-end: 12/31/22
Consulting, Technology & Outsourc-
ing Services
N.A.I.C.S.: 541611
Ib Kunoe *(Chm)*

Subsidiaries:

Atea A/S   **(1)**
Lautrupvang 6, 2750, Ballerup, Denmark
Tel.: (45) 70252550
Web Site: https://www.atea.dk
Sales Range: $250-299.9 Million
Emp.: 800
Computer & Peripheral Equipment & Soft-
ware Whslr
N.A.I.C.S.: 423430

Atea AS   **(1)**
Karvesvingen 5, 0579, Oslo,
Norway   **(100%)**
Tel.: (47) 22095000
Web Site: https://www.atea.com
Sales Range: $150-199.9 Million
Emp.: 600
Computer & Peripheral Equipment & Soft-
ware Whslr
N.A.I.C.S.: 423430

Atea Baltic UAB   **(1)**
J Rutkausko st 6, LT-05132, Vilnius, Lithu-
ania
Tel.: (370) 52397830
Web Site: https://www.atea.lt
Software Development Services
N.A.I.C.S.: 541511

Atea Finland Oy   **(1)**
Jaakonkatu 2, 01620, Vantaa, Finland
Tel.: (358) 10806088
Web Site: https://www.atea.fi
Enterprise Management Software Develop-
ment Services
N.A.I.C.S.: 541511

Atea Global Services SIA.   **(1)**
Mukusalas Street 15, Riga, LV-1004, Latvia
Tel.: (371) 67359600
Web Site: https://www.ateaglobal.com
Software Development Services
N.A.I.C.S.: 541511
Maksims Pisculins *(CEO)*

Atea Logistics AB   **(1)**
Nylandavagen 8A, 352 50, Vaxjo,
Sweden   **(100%)**
Tel.: (46) 470771600
Web Site: https://www.atea.se
Sales Range: $75-99.9 Million
Emp.: 160
Computer & Peripheral Equipment & Soft-
ware Whslr
N.A.I.C.S.: 423430
Frank Svensson *(Mng Dir)*

Atea SIA.   **(1)**
Unijas Street 15, Riga, LV-1039, Latvia
Tel.: (371) 67819050
Web Site: https://www.atea.lv
Software Development Services
N.A.I.C.S.: 541511

Atea Sverige AB   **(1)**
Kronborgsgrand 1, 164 46, Kista,
Sweden   **(100%)**
Tel.: (46) 84774700
Web Site: https://www.atea.se
Sales Range: $250-299.9 Million
Emp.: 800
Computer & Peripheral Equipment & Soft-
ware Whslr
N.A.I.C.S.: 423430
Carl-Johan Hultenheim *(CEO)*

Atea UAB   **(1)**
J Rutkausko g 6, 05132, Vilnius, Lithuania
Tel.: (370) 52397830
Web Site: https://www.atea.lt
Information Technology Services
N.A.I.C.S.: 541519

BCC Finland Oy   **(1)**
Mechelininkatu 13, 00100, Helsinki, Finland
Tel.: (358) 104213600
Web Site: https://www.bcc.fi
Business Coaching Services
N.A.I.C.S.: 541611
Tiina Harmaja *(Partner)*

BMK UAB   **(1)**
J Rutkausko G 6, LT-05132, Vilnius, Lithu-
ania
Tel.: (370) 852125559
Web Site: https://www.bmk.lt
Software Development Services
N.A.I.C.S.: 541511

EIT Sprendimai UAB   **(1)**
J Rutkausko g 6, LT-05132, Vilnius, Lithu-
ania
Tel.: (370) 852688111
Web Site: https://www.eit.lt
Software Development Services
N.A.I.C.S.: 541511

Serveriai Verslui UAB   **(1)**
Brastos g 14, Kaunas, 47185, Lithuania
Tel.: (370) 64594032
Web Site: http://www.serveriaiverslui.lt
Software Development Services
N.A.I.C.S.: 541511
Aurimas Verbickas *(CEO)*

Solver UAB   **(1)**
A Rotundo g 5-3, LT-01400, Vilnius, Lithu-
ania
Tel.: (370) 852496426
Web Site: https://www.solver.lt
Software Development Services
N.A.I.C.S.: 541511

Top Nordic Finland Oy   **(1)**
Konninkuja 3, Veikkola, 02880, Kirkkon-
ummi, Finland
Tel.: (358) 92565272
Web Site: http://www.topnordic.fi
Gift Item Whslr
N.A.I.C.S.: 424990
Timo Kyllonen *(Designer)*

ATEAM INC.
Dai Nagoya Building 32F 28-12
Meieki 3-chome, Nakamura-ku, Na-
goya, 4516032, Japan
Tel.: (81) 527475550
Web Site: https://www.a-tm.co.jp
Year Founded: 2000
3662—(TKS)
Rev.: $148,763,740
Assets: $101,330,020
Liabilities: $37,425,740
Net Worth: $63,904,280
Earnings: $5,927,660
Emp.: 813
Fiscal Year-end: 07/31/24
Entertainment & Lifestyle Support
Computer Products Developer
N.A.I.C.S.: 513210
Takao Hayashi *(Pres)*

Subsidiaries:

Ateam Connect Inc.   **(1)**
Nagoya Lucent Tower 21F 6-1 Ushijima-
cho, Nishi, Nagoya, 451-6021, Japan
Tel.: (81) 525332085
Web Site: http://connect.a-tm.co.jp
Information Technology Services
N.A.I.C.S.: 541512
Hiroyuki Kumazawa *(Pres)*

ATECH OEM, INC.
7F AAEON Building No 43 Sec 4
Keelung Rd, Taipei, 10607, Taiwan
Tel.: (886) 223770282
Web Site: https://www.atechoem.com
Year Founded: 1990
6109—(TPE)
Rev.: $41,420,598
Assets: $41,537,035
Liabilities: $17,449,708
Net Worth: $24,087,328
Earnings: $2,090,548
Fiscal Year-end: 12/31/22
Electrical Component Mfr
N.A.I.C.S.: 335999
Wei-Chun Yen *(Chm & Pres)*

ATECT CORPORATION
3275-1 Kami-haneda-cho, Higashi-
omi, Shiga, Japan
Tel.: (81) 748203400
Web Site: https://www.atect.co.jp
Year Founded: 1959
4241—(TKS)
Rev.: $20,986,750
Assets: $33,902,690
Liabilities: $22,249,260
Net Worth: $11,653,430

Atect Corporation—(Continued)
Earnings: ($1,612,840)
Emp.: 101
Fiscal Year-end: 03/31/24
Buttons Mfr
N.A.I.C.S.: 339993
Norio Kodaka *(Pres & CEO)*

Subsidiaries:

atect korea Corporation **(1)**
452 - 2 Hyungok-Ri Chungbuk-Myeon,
4518831, Pyeongtaek, Gyeonggi-do, Korea
(South)
Tel.: (82) 316826990
Electronic Components Mfr
N.A.I.C.S.: 334419

ATELIER DE PRODUCTION ET DE CREATION
39 rue Madame, 75006, Paris,
France
Tel.: (33) 144398787
Web Site: http://www.apc.fr
Year Founded: 1987
Sales Range: $25-49.9 Million
Emp.: 200
Clothing & Accessories Mfr & Retailer
N.A.I.C.S.: 315990
Jean Touitou *(Pres & Mng Dir)*

ATELIER GARDEUR GMBH
Alsstrasse 155, Monchengladbach,
41063, Germany
Tel.: (49) 7252304337
Web Site: http://www.atelier-gardeur.de
Pants Mfr
N.A.I.C.S.: 315250
Steef Duijindam *(Mng Dir)*

ATELIERS PERRAULT FRERES
30 Rue Sebastien Cady, CS 60057,
St Laurent de la Plaine, 49290, Avignon, France
Tel.: (33) 241223722
Web Site:
http://www.atelierspettault.com
Rev.: $23,900,000
Emp.: 42
Carpentry Work, Iron & Locksmith
Services
N.A.I.C.S.: 337212
Francois Perrault *(Gen Mgr)*

Subsidiaries:

Atelier d'Oeuvres de Forge **(1)**
Les Pres, 24390, Hautefort, France
Tel.: (33) 5 53 51 72 75
Web Site: http://www.atelier-forge.com
Locksmith Services
N.A.I.C.S.: 337212
Nicolas Henry *(Pres)*

Ateliers Ferignac SA **(1)**
La Gare, 24390, Hautefort, France
Tel.: (33) 5 53 51 72 72
Web Site: http://www.ateliers-ferignac.com
Locksmith Services
N.A.I.C.S.: 337212
Antonio Morisset *(Pres)*

ATELJE A.D.
Partizanskih baza br 7, Novi Sad, 21
000, Serbia
Tel.: (381) 21 520 057
Web Site: http://www.ateljead.co.rs
Year Founded: 1957
ATLJM—(BEL)
Sales Range: Less than $1 Million
Emp.: 2
Construction Engineering Services
N.A.I.C.S.: 541330
Kostic Milan *(Exec Dir)*

ATEME S.A.
6 rue Dewoitine, 78140, Velizy-Villacoublay, France

Tel.: (33) 169358989 **FR**
Web Site: https://www.ateme.com
Year Founded: 1991
ATEME—(EUR)
Rev.: $97,726,095
Assets: $109,576,948
Liabilities: $65,393,913
Net Worth: $44,183,035
Earnings: ($49,644)
Emp.: 431
Fiscal Year-end: 12/31/22
Video Compression Equipment &
Software
N.A.I.C.S.: 334310
Michel Artieres *(Founder, Pres & CEO)*

Subsidiaries:

Anevia SA **(1)**
79 rue Benoit malon, 94250, Gentilly,
France **(100%)**
Tel.: (33) 141983240
Web Site: http://www.anevia-group.com
Sales Range: $1-9.9 Million
Software Publisher
N.A.I.C.S.: 513210
Damien Lucas *(Co-Founder & CTO)*

ATEMPO S.A.
Immeuble Illiad-23 Avenue Carnot,
91300, Massy, France
Tel.: (33) 164868300 **FR**
Web Site: http://www.atempo.com
Year Founded: 1992
Sales Range: $10-24.9 Million
Emp.: 170
Database Development Services
N.A.I.C.S.: 541511
Swamy Viswanathan *(Chief Product
Officer & Exec VP)*

Subsidiaries:

Atempo Deutschland GmbH **(1)**
Curiestrasse 2, D-70563, Stuttgart, Germany
Tel.: (49) 71167400331
Web Site: http://www.atempo.com
Data Backup & Recovery Software
N.A.I.C.S.: 513210

Atempo, Inc. **(1)**
2465 E Bayshore Rd Ste 400, Palo Alto, CA
94303
Tel.: (650) 494-2600
Web Site: http://www.atempo.com
Data Backup & Recovery Software
N.A.I.C.S.: 513210

ATEN INTERNATIONAL CO., LTD.
3F No 125 Sec 2 Datung Road,
Sijhih District, New Taipei City, 221,
Taiwan
Tel.: (886) 286926789
Web Site: http://www.aten.com
Year Founded: 1979
Sales Range: $125-149.9 Million
Emp.: 357
Computer Equipment & Peripheral
Mfr
N.A.I.C.S.: 334118
Shang Zhong Chen *(Chm)*

Subsidiaries:

ATEN China Co., Ltd. **(1)**
18/F Tower A Horizon International Tower
No 6 Zhichun Road, Beijing, 100088, China
Tel.: (86) 1052550110
Electronic Components Distr
N.A.I.C.S.: 423690

ATEN Technology Inc. **(1)**
19641 Da Vinci, Foothill Ranch, CA 92610-2603
Tel.: (949) 428-1111
Web Site: http://www.aten-usa.com
Sales Range: $50-74.9 Million
Emp.: 70
Computer Peripherals & Software Distr
N.A.I.C.S.: 423430
May Wang *(Office Mgr)*

Atech Peripherals, Inc. **(1)**
6F No 133 Sec 2 Datong Rd, Sijhih District,
New Taipei City, Taiwan
Tel.: (886) 226926969
Electronic Components Distr
N.A.I.C.S.: 423690

Aten Advance Co.,Ltd **(1)**
Eagle Town 3rd Floor # 303 278-20,
Seongsu-dong 2-ga 3-Dong, Seoul, Korea
(South) **(100%)**
Tel.: (82) 24676789
Sales Range: $25-49.9 Million
Emp.: 15
Computer Related Services
N.A.I.C.S.: 541519

Aten Canada Technologies Inc. **(1)**
11784 Hammersmith Way, Richmond, V6V
2J1, BC, Canada
Tel.: (604) 207-0809
Electronic Components Distr
N.A.I.C.S.: 423690

Aten Infotech N.V. **(1)**
Mijnwerkerslaan, Heusden, 3550,
Belgium **(100%)**
Tel.: (32) 11531543
Web Site: http://www.aten.eu
Sales Range: $25-49.9 Million
Emp.: 18
Electronic Computer Mfr
N.A.I.C.S.: 334111
Jackie Chan *(Mng Dir)*

Aten Japan Co., Ltd **(1)**
803 Tatsumi Bldg 16-6 Nishi-shinjuku
6-Chome, Shinjuku-ku, 160-0023, Tokyo,
Japan
Tel.: (81) 353237170
Web Site: http://www.atenjapan.jp
Sales Range: $25-49.9 Million
Emp.: 20
Computer Related Services
N.A.I.C.S.: 541519

Aten New Jersey Inc **(1)**
155 Pierce St, Somerset, NJ 08873
Tel.: (732) 356-1703
Web Site: http://www.aten-usa.com
Sales Range: $25-49.9 Million
Emp.: 35
Computer Related Services
N.A.I.C.S.: 541519

Aten U.K. Limited **(1)**
466 Malton Avenue, Slough, SL1 4QU,
United Kingdom **(100%)**
Tel.: (44) 1753539121
Web Site: http://www.aten.com
Sales Range: $25-49.9 Million
Emp.: 10
Computer Related Services
N.A.I.C.S.: 541519
James Liu *(Mng Dir)*

ATENDE S.A.
10a Koneser Square, 03-736, Warsaw, Poland
Tel.: (48) 222957300
Web Site: https://www.atende.pl
Year Founded: 1991
ATD—(WAR)
Rev.: $56,668,844
Assets: $41,205,848
Liabilities: $22,345,626
Net Worth: $18,860,222
Earnings: $330,855
Emp.: 371
Fiscal Year-end: 12/31/22
IT Solutions
N.A.I.C.S.: 541519
Dariusz Niedziolka *(Dir-IR)*

Subsidiaries:

A 2 Customer Care Sp. z o.o. **(1)**
Ul Aleksandra Ostrowskiego 7, 53-238,
Wroclaw, Poland
Tel.: (48) 713336913
Web Site: http://www.a2cc.eu
Software Services
N.A.I.C.S.: 541511
Krzysztof Biezmienow *(CEO & Mng Partner)*

Atende Medica Sp. z o.o. **(1)**

Al Wilanowska 313, 02-665, Warsaw, Poland
Tel.: (48) 223506410
Web Site: http://www.atendemedica.pl
Information Technology Services
N.A.I.C.S.: 541511

Atende Software Sp. z o.o. **(1)**
Ostrobramska 86, 04-163, Warsaw, Poland
Tel.: (48) 222551100
Web Site: http://www.atendesoftware.pl
Software Development Services
N.A.I.C.S.: 541511
Pawel Pisarczyk *(CEO)*

Energy Data Lab Sp. z o.o. **(1)**
Grzybowska 87, 00-844, Warsaw, Poland
Tel.: (48) 668193677
Web Site: http://www.codeshine.com
Information Technology Services
N.A.I.C.S.: 541511
Arkadiusz Kalemba *(Founder & CEO)*

OmniChip Sp. z o.o. **(1)**
ul Bobrowiecka 8, 00-728, Warsaw, Poland
Tel.: (48) 223759148
Web Site: https://www.omni-chip.com
Semiconductor Mfr
N.A.I.C.S.: 334413
Alicja Droszcz *(CTO)*

Phoenix Systems Sp. z o.o. **(1)**
Ostrobramska 86, 04-163, Warsaw, Poland
Tel.: (48) 222440630
Web Site: https://www.phoenix-rtos.com
Software Development Services
N.A.I.C.S.: 541511
Pawel Pisarczyk *(Co-Pres & CEO)*

Trust IT Sp. z o.o. **(1)**
ul Wroblewskiego 18/103, 93-578, Lodz,
Poland
Tel.: (48) 422801100
Web Site: http://www.trustit.com
Information Technology Services
N.A.I.C.S.: 541511

ATENOR S.A.
92 Avenue Reine Astrid, 1310, La
Hulpe, Belgium
Tel.: (32) 23872299 **FR**
Web Site: https://www.atenor.eu
Year Founded: 1997
ATEB—(EUR)
Rev.: $44,256,421
Assets: $1,376,508,742
Liabilities: $1,081,216,275
Net Worth: $295,292,467
Earnings: ($909,778)
Emp.: 110
Fiscal Year-end: 12/31/22
Real Estate Support Services
N.A.I.C.S.: 531390
Stephan Sonneville *(CEO & Mng Dir)*

ATERIAN PLC
Eastcastle House 27-28 Eastcastle
Street, London, W1W 8DH, United
Kingdom **UK**
Web Site: https://www.aterianplc.com
Year Founded: 2011
ATN—(LSE)
Assets: $5,164,100
Liabilities: $941,681
Net Worth: $4,222,419
Earnings: ($5,532,694)
Emp.: 22
Fiscal Year-end: 12/31/22
Mining Services
N.A.I.C.S.: 212290
Charles Bray *(Chm)*

ATESCO INDUSTRIAL CATERING JOINT STOCK COMPANY
Phu Long Ba village Long Xuyen
commune, Phuc Tho district, Hanoi,
Vietnam
Tel.: (84) 2473059886
ATS—(HNX)
Rev.: $1,975,293
Assets: $2,076,315
Liabilities: $286,010

Net Worth: $1,790,305
Earnings: $9,517
Fiscal Year-end: 12/31/23
Catering Services
N.A.I.C.S.: 722320
Pham Anh Tuan *(Chm)*

ATEVIA AG
Amalienbadstr 41, D-76227,
Karlsruhe, Germany
Tel.: (49) 72151602701   De
Web Site: http://www.atevia.com
Sales Range: $1-9.9 Million
Business Consulting & Investment
Management Services
N.A.I.C.S.: 541611
Michael Greve *(Chm-Mgmt Bd &
CEO)*

ATEX RESOURCES, INC.
50 Richmond Street East Lower
Level, Toronto, M5C 1N7, ON,
Canada
Tel.: (604) 684-7160
Web Site:
     https://www.atexresources.com
Year Founded: 1981
ATX—(TSXV)
Assets: $3,056,988
Liabilities: $70,656
Net Worth: $2,986,332
Earnings: ($738,557)
Fiscal Year-end: 09/30/21
Gold Exploration Services
N.A.I.C.S.: 212220
Carl B. Hansen *(Chm)*

ATHA ENERGY CORP.
1240-1066 Hastings St W, Vancou-
ver, V6E 3X1, BC, Canada
Tel.: (236) 521-0526
Web Site:
     https://www.athaenergy.com
Year Founded: 2021
X5U—(DEU)
Rev.: $873,476
Assets: $74,876,489
Liabilities: $8,601,830
Net Worth: $66,274,659
Earnings: ($10,553,275)
Emp.: 7
Fiscal Year-end: 12/31/23
Mineral Exploration Services
N.A.I.C.S.: 212390
Troy Boisjoli *(CEO)*

Subsidiaries:

92 Energy Limited   **(1)**
Level 3 16 Milligan Street, Perth, 6000, WA,
Australia
Tel.: (61) 893227600
Web Site: https://www.92energy.com
Rev.: $1,761,771
Assets: $3,580,660
Liabilities: $174,082
Net Worth: $3,406,579
Earnings: ($5,939,539)
Emp.: 4
Fiscal Year-end: 06/30/2023
Uranium Exploration Services
N.A.I.C.S.: 212290
Siobhan Lancaster *(Mng Dir)*

Subsidiary (Domestic):

Thunderbird Metals Pty. Ltd.   **(2)**
11 Industrial Ave, Mudgee, 2850, NSW,
Australia
Tel.: (61) 263723600
Web Site: https://thunderbird.net.au
Metal Products Mfr
N.A.I.C.S.: 332999

Labrador Uranium Inc.   **(1)**
401-217 Queen St West, Toronto, M5V
0R2, ON, Canada
Web Site: https://www.labradoruranium.com
Metal Exploration Services
N.A.I.C.S.: 213114
Greg Duras *(CFO)*

ATHABASCA MINERALS INC.
Canada Place Suite 1730 407 2
Street SW, Calgary, T2P 2Y3, AB,
Canada
Tel.: (587) 392-5862   Ca
Web Site:
     https://www.athabascaminerals.com
ABCAF—(OTCIQ)
Rev.: $25,471,431
Assets: $51,104,630
Liabilities: $29,463,087
Net Worth: $21,641,543
Earnings: $8,962,467
Fiscal Year-end: 12/31/22
Mineral Exploration Services
N.A.I.C.S.: 213114
Don Paulencu *(Chm)*

ATHABASCA OIL CORP.
Suite 1200 215 9th Avenue South-
west, Calgary, T2P 1K3, AB, Canada
Tel.: (403) 237-8227
Web Site: https://www.atha.com
Year Founded: 2006
ATH—(TSX)
Rev.: $365,804,298
Assets: $1,115,518,764
Liabilities: $671,946,447
Net Worth: $443,572,317
Earnings: ($514,368,657)
Emp.: 140
Fiscal Year-end: 12/31/20
Oil Exploration Services
N.A.I.C.S.: 211120
Ronald J. Eckhardt *(Chm)*

ATHARV ENTERPRISES LIM-
ITED
Office No 1 Yogi Kripa C H S L D/27
Central Road Yogi Nagar Borivali,
Mumbai, 400091, Maharastra, India
Tel.: (91) 9324543395
Web Site:
     https://www.atharventerprises.biz
Year Founded: 1990
530187—(BOM)
Rev.: $89,153
Assets: $2,775,653
Liabilities: $111,497
Net Worth: $2,664,156
Earnings: $497
Fiscal Year-end: 03/31/21
Yarn Distr
N.A.I.C.S.: 424310
Kaushal Ameta *(Chm)*

ATHEEB GROUP
27 Al Baz Street, PO Box 7947, Su-
laimaniya District, Riyadh, 11472,
Saudi Arabia
Tel.: (966) 14646142
Web Site: http://www.atheeb.com
Year Founded: 1985
Holding Company
N.A.I.C.S.: 551112
Abdulaziz Ahmed Abdulaziz Al-Saud
(Chm)

Subsidiaries:

Atheeb (UK) Ltd.   **(1)**
23 Wood's Mews, London, W1K 7DH,
United Kingdom
Tel.: (44) 20 74910070
Web Site: http://www.atheeb.co.uk
Investment Management Service
N.A.I.C.S.: 523940

Etihad Atheeb Telecom
Company   **(1)**
PO Box 250398, Riyadh, 11391, Saudi Ara-
bia
Tel.: (966) 12882666
Web Site: http://www.go.com.sa
Sales Range: $25-49.9 Million
Emp.: 140
Telecommunication Servicesb
N.A.I.C.S.: 517111

Abdulaziz Bin Ahmed Bin Abdulaziz Al-Saud
(Chm)

Ithraa Capital LLC   **(1)**
King Fahad Road Tatweer Building No 1 6th
floor, PO Box No 64230, Riyadh, 11536,
Saudi Arabia
Tel.: (966) 112072626
Web Site: https://ithraacap.com
Investment Banking Services
N.A.I.C.S.: 523150
Venkateshwar Rao *(CFO)*

Pannesma Company Ltd.   **(1)**
PO Box 99813, Riyadh, 11625, Saudi Ara-
bia
Tel.: (966) 1 462 23 50
Web Site: http://www.pannesma.com
Aircraft Repair & Maintenance Services
N.A.I.C.S.: 488190

ATHELNEY TRUST PLC
Waterside Court Falmouth Road,
Penryn, TR10 8AW, Cornwall, United
Kingdom
Tel.: (44) 1326378288   UK
Web Site:
     https://www.athelneytrust.co.uk
ATY—(LSE)
Rev.: $218,425
Assets: $7,501,943
Liabilities: $23,593
Net Worth: $7,478,350
Earnings: ($18,097)
Emp.: 1
Fiscal Year-end: 12/31/20
Investment Trust Services
N.A.I.C.S.: 523999
Emmanuel Clive Pohl *(Mng Dir)*

ATHENA CONSEIL LUX S.A.
29 rue de, Bertrange, 8077, Luxem-
bourg, Luxembourg
Tel.: (352) 27397725   LU
Web Site:
     http://www.athenaconseillux.com
Year Founded: 2008
Sales Range: $1-9.9 Million
Emp.: 20
Business Consulting Services
N.A.I.C.S.: 541611
Philippe Gros *(Gen Mgr)*

ATHENA CONSTRUCTIONS
LIMITED
A/203 Shyam Kamal Tejpal Road Op-
posite Vile Parle Railway Station, Vile
Parle East, Mumbai, 400057, India
Tel.: (91) 2242091000
Web Site:
     https://www.athenaindia.co.in
Year Founded: 2006
Rev.: $6,825
Assets: $2,233,071
Liabilities: $1,246,535
Net Worth: $986,536
Earnings: ($41,480)
Fiscal Year-end: 03/31/20
Construction Services
N.A.I.C.S.: 236116
Santhosh Chandrashekhar Nagar
(Mng Dir)

ATHENA GLOBAL TECHNOLO-
GIES LTD.
Gowra Palladium 2nd Floor Unit 203,
Madhapur, Hyderabad, 500 081, Te-
langana, India
Tel.: (91) 4023119633   In
Web Site: https://www.athenagt.com
517429—(BOM)
Rev.: $3,994,481
Assets: $10,549,867
Liabilities: $9,343,193
Net Worth: $1,206,674
Earnings: ($1,101,350)
Emp.: 77
Fiscal Year-end: 03/31/22

Information Technology Consulting
Services
N.A.I.C.S.: 541512
Manchala Satyendra *(Chm & Mng
Dir)*

ATHENA INVESTMENTS A/S
Harbour House Sundkrogsgade 21,
DK-2100, Copenhagen, Denmark
Tel.: (45) 33364202
Web Site:
     http://athenainvestments.com
Year Founded: 1924
ATHENA—(CSE)
Rev.: $57,865
Assets: $19,228,056
Liabilities: $8,283,877
Net Worth: $10,944,180
Earnings: ($7,008,592)
Emp.: 26
Fiscal Year-end: 12/31/19
Electric Power Generation Services;
Operating Renewable Energy Proj-
ects
N.A.I.C.S.: 221118
Peter Hostgaard-Jensen *(Chm)*

Subsidiaries:

Energia Alternativa Srl.   **(1)**
Via Stazione Supino n 102, 03013, Feren-
tino, Frosinone, Italy
Tel.: (39) 0775 725005
Web Site: http://www.energialternativa.eu
Eletric Power Generation Services
N.A.I.C.S.: 221118

Energia Verde Srl.   **(1)**
Via De Magistris Edmondo 8, Cagliari,
Italy   **(100%)**
Tel.: (39) 08 65 45 11 73
Web Site: http://www.energia-verde.it
Eletric Power Generation Services
N.A.I.C.S.: 221118

Eolica Polczyno Sp. z o.o.   **(1)**
Jaskowa Dolina 81, Gdansk, 80-286, Po-
land
Tel.: (48) 586612260
Eletric Power Generation Services
N.A.I.C.S.: 221118

Gehlenberg ApS   **(1)**
Marielundvej 48 1 tv, 2730, Herlèv, Den-
mark
Tel.: (45) 33364202
Eletric Power Generation Services
N.A.I.C.S.: 221118

Greentech Energy Systems Polska
Sp. z o.o.   **(1)**
ul Jaskowa Dolina 81, 80-286, Gdansk,
Poland
Tel.: (48) 586612260
Web Site: http://www.greentech.pk
Sales Range: $25-49.9 Million
Emp.: 10
Wind Power Plant Construction Services
N.A.I.C.S.: 237130
Slawomir Sikorski *(Chm-Mgmt Bd)*

Wiatropol Smolecin Sp. z o.o.   **(1)**
Jaskowa Dolina 81, Gdansk, 80-286, Po-
land
Tel.: (48) 586612260
Eletric Power Generation Services
N.A.I.C.S.: 221118

Wiatropol Ustka Sp. z o.o.   **(1)**
Jaskowa Dolina 81, Gdansk, 80-286, Po-
land
Tel.: (48) 586612260
Web Site: http://www.greentech.dk
Emp.: 5
Eletric Power Generation Services
N.A.I.C.S.: 221118
Slawomir Sikorski *(Pres)*

ATHENA RESOURCES LIM-
ITED
Level 33 Mia Yellagonga Tower 3 1
Spring Street, Perth, 6000, WA, Aus-
tralia
Tel.: (61) 862850456

ATHENA RESOURCES LIMITED

Athena Resources Limited—(Continued)

Web Site:
https://www.athenaresources.com
AHN—(ASX)
Assets: $8,804,814
Liabilities: $307,796
Net Worth: $8,497,019
Earnings: ($464,896)
Emp.: 1
Fiscal Year-end: 06/30/24
Mineral Exploration Services
N.A.I.C.S.: 213115
Edmond William Edwards *(Co-Sec)*

ATHENA S.A.
Amarousiou - Chalandriou 16, Marousi, 15125, Athens, Greece
Tel.: (30) 210 63 75 000
Web Site: https://www.athena-sa.gr
Year Founded: 1966
Emp.: 83
Construction Engineering Services
N.A.I.C.S.: 237990
Christos Joannou *(Chm)*

Subsidiaries:

Athena Emirates LLC **(1)**
PO Box 54008, Abu Dhabi, United Arab Emirates
Tel.: (971) 2 679 7666
Web Site: http://www.athena-sa.gr
Engineering Construction Services
N.A.I.C.S.: 237990
Nicolas Giatsos *(Area Mgr)*

Athena Fujairah LLC **(1)**
PO Box 3894, Fujairah, United Arab Emirates
Tel.: (971) 9 228 1838
Engineering Construction Services
N.A.I.C.S.: 237990

ATHENEE PALACE HILTON BUCHAREST HOTEL
Bd Poligrafiei 1C Et 1 Sectorul 1
Birou 10, 010292, Bucharest, Romania
Tel.: (40) 21 202 11 99
Web Site: http://www.athenee-palace.ro
Year Founded: 1914
Sales Range: Less than $1 Million
Emp.: 4
Hotel & Motel Services
N.A.I.C.S.: 721110

ATHENS INTERNATIONAL AIRPORT S.A.
19019 Spata Eleftherios Venizelos,
Spata, 190 19, Athens, Greece
Tel.: (30) 210 3530000
Web Site: http://www.aia.gr
Airline Services
N.A.I.C.S.: 488119
Paraschis Ioannis *(CEO)*

ATHENS MEDICAL CENTERS SA
Distomou Str 5-7, Maroussi, 15125,
Athens, Greece
Tel.: (30) 2106198100
Web Site: http://www.iatriko.gr
Year Founded: 1983
IATR—(ATH)
Sales Range: $200-249.9 Million
Emp.: 3,034
Hospitals & Healthcare Services
N.A.I.C.S.: 622110
George V. Apostolopoulos *(Chm)*

Subsidiaries:

Iatriki Techniki S.A. **(1)**
1 Filadelfias St, 14562, Athens,
Greece **(100%)**
Tel.: (30) 2106287132
Sales Range: $10-24.9 Million
Emp.: 20
Medical Laboratories

N.A.I.C.S.: 621511

Medsana Srl **(1)**
Str Dr Muscel Nanu 12 Sector 5, Bucuresti,
Bucharest, Romania **(78.9%)**
Tel.: (40) 214108643
Web Site: http://www.medsana.ro
Sales Range: $25-49.9 Million
Emp.: 150
Other Individual & Family Services
N.A.I.C.S.: 624190

ATHENS WATER SUPPLY & SEWERAGE S.A.
156 Oropou Str Galatsi, 11146, Athens, Greece
Tel.: (30) 2102144444
Web Site: https://www.eydap.gr
Year Founded: 1980
EYDAP—(ATH)
Rev.: $377,417
Assets: $1,587,641
Liabilities: $678,174
Net Worth: $909,467
Earnings: $21,763,632
Emp.: 2,286
Fiscal Year-end: 12/31/23
Water Supply & Sewerage Services
N.A.I.C.S.: 221310
Constantinos Vougiouklakis *(Gen Mgr & Exec Dir-Sewerage Network)*

ATHEZZA
ZI Mas Meze-Chemin de l'ancienne
gare, 30700, Uzes, Gard, France
Tel.: (33) 466030013
Web Site: http://www.athezza.com
Home Furnishing Distr
N.A.I.C.S.: 423220

ATHLETIC CLUB AJACCIEN ACA FOOTBALL
Stade Francois Coti Route De
Vazzio, 20000, Ajaccio, Corse,
France
Tel.: (33) 495203252
Web Site: http://www.ac-ajaccio.com
Rev.: $20,300,000
Emp.: 53
Sports Clubs, Managers & Promoters
N.A.I.C.S.: 711410
Alain Orsoni *(Mng Partner)*

ATHON SA
Via penate 4, 6850, Mendrisio, Switzerland
Tel.: (41) 91 6117070
Web Site: http://www.athon.ch
Sales Range: $10-24.9 Million
Emp.: 15
Information Technology Consulting
Services
N.A.I.C.S.: 541512
Lorenzo Medici *(CEO)*

ATHOS IMMOBILIEN AG
Waltherstrasse 11, 4020, Linz, Austria
Tel.: (43) 7326044770
Web Site: https://www.athos.at
Year Founded: 1989
ATH—(VIE)
Sales Range: Less than $1 Million
Real Estate Development Services
N.A.I.C.S.: 531390

ATHOS SERVICE GMBH
Römermauer 3 Bitburg, Rheinland-
Pfalz, 54634, Germany
Tel.: (49) 894613810
Financial Services
N.A.I.C.S.: 523999

ATHRIS HOLDING AG
Bundesplatz 14, 63002, Zug, Switzerland
Tel.: (41) 415601100
Web Site: http://www.athris.ch
Sales Range: $100-124.9 Million

Emp.: 700
Investment Services
N.A.I.C.S.: 523999
Georg von Opel *(Chm)*

ATI AIRTEST TECHNOLOGIES INC.
9 1520 Cliveden Avenue, Delta, V3M
0J0, DC, Canada
Tel.: (604) 517-3888
Web Site: https://www.airtest.com
Year Founded: 1996
AAT—(TSXV)
Rev.: $1,761,172
Assets: $1,229,301
Liabilities: $4,493,211
Net Worth: ($3,263,910)
Earnings: ($306,269)
Fiscal Year-end: 12/31/22
Air Testing Equipment Mfr
N.A.I.C.S.: 335999

ATI TELECOM INTERNATIONAL COMPANY
4336 97th St, Edmonton, T6E 5R9,
AB, Canada
Tel.: (780) 424-9100
Web Site:
http://www.altatelecom.com
Sales Range: $100-124.9 Million
Emp.: 550
Telecommunications
N.A.I.C.S.: 517121
Ron Edward *(Pres)*

ATICO MINING CORPORATION
Suite 501 543 Granville St, Vancouver, V6C 1X8, BC, Canada
Tel.: (604) 633-9022 **BC**
Web Site:
https://www.aticomining.com
Year Founded: 2010
ATCMF—(OTCQX)
Rev.: $65,166,471
Assets: $121,016,887
Liabilities: $54,069,154
Net Worth: $66,947,733
Earnings: ($3,671,632)
Fiscal Year-end: 12/31/22
Copper & Gold Mining
N.A.I.C.S.: 212230
A. Jorge Ganoza *(VP-Ops)*

Subsidiaries:

Atico Mining Corporation Colombia
SAS **(1)**
Carrera 43 N 1A SUR-69 Oficina 701 Edificio, Medellin, Colombia
Tel.: (57) 42660811
Copper & Gold Mining Services
N.A.I.C.S.: 212230

Toachi Mining Inc. **(1)**
2400 120 Adelaide Street West, Toronto,
M5H 1T1, ON, Canada
Tel.: (416) 365-2428
Web Site: http://www.toachimining.com
Assets: $1,544,223
Liabilities: $341,305
Net Worth: $1,202,919
Earnings: ($5,393,348)
Fiscal Year-end: 07/31/2018
Iron Ore Mining Services
N.A.I.C.S.: 212210
Joseph Fazzini *(CFO)*

ATIF HOLDINGS LIMITED
Dachong 1St RoadRoom 2803 Dachong Business Centre Building A
Ste 200, Nanshan District, Shenzhen,
China
Tel.: (86) 75586950818 **VG**
Web Site: https://www.ipoex.com
Year Founded: 2015
ATIF—(NASDAQ)
Rev.: $936,935
Assets: $11,397,763
Liabilities: $1,713,915
Net Worth: $9,683,848

Earnings: ($8,563,774)
Emp.: 24
Fiscal Year-end: 07/31/21
Holding Company
N.A.I.C.S.: 551112
Jun Liu *(Chm, Pres & CEO)*

ATILIM FAKTORING A.S.
Morkozi No 1 6 Kat 6 D 25-26-27-
28-29 Esentepe Mahallesi Kore, Sehitleri Caddesi Propa Plaza Sisli, Istanbul, Turkiye
Tel.: (90) 2122173401
Web Site:
http://www.atilimfaktoring.com.tr
Year Founded: 1993
ATLFA—(IST)
Sales Range: Less than $1 Million
Financial Management Services
N.A.I.C.S.: 551112
Dogan Daniyel Dinler *(Chm)*

ATINUM INVESTMENT CO., LTD
9 Teheran-ro 103-gil, Gangnam-Gu,
Seoul, 6173, Korea (South)
Tel.: (82) 25550781
Web Site:
https://www.atinuminvest.co.kr
Year Founded: 1988
021080—(KRS)
Rev.: $77,457,550
Assets: $149,255,423
Liabilities: $21,177,855
Net Worth: $128,077,568
Earnings: $21,635,344
Emp.: 31
Fiscal Year-end: 12/31/22
Financial Consulting Services
N.A.I.C.S.: 523999
Chang-Seok Hwang *(Exec VP)*

Subsidiaries:

Atinum E&P, Inc. **(1)**
333 Clay St Ste 700, Houston, TX 77002-
4115
Tel.: (713) 850-1880
Web Site: http://www.atinumenergy.com
Emp.: 25
Oil & Gas Energy Services
N.A.I.C.S.: 213112

ATISHAY LIMITED
14-15 Khatau Building 44 Bank
Street, Mumbai, 462011, India
Tel.: (91) 2249739081
Web Site: https://www.atishay.com
Year Founded: 1989
538713—(BOM)
Rev.: $3,733,289
Assets: $5,490,590
Liabilities: $475,197
Net Worth: $5,015,392
Earnings: $338,192
Emp.: 129
Fiscal Year-end: 03/31/21
Information Technology Database
Management & E-Governance Services
N.A.I.C.S.: 518210
Akhilesh Jain *(Chm & Mng Dir)*

ATKA KUNSTSTOFFVERARBEITUNG GMBH
Suedring 25, Lohne, 49393, Germany
Tel.: (49) 444292680
Web Site: http://www.atka.de
Year Founded: 1981
Rev.: $18,621,900
Emp.: 90
Industrial Product Distr
N.A.I.C.S.: 423830
Gregor Sieve *(Mgr)*

ATKINSREALIS GROUP INC.
455 boul Rene-Levesque Ouest,
Montreal, H2Z 1Z3, QC, Canada

Tel.: (514) 393-1000   Ca
Web Site: https://www.snclavalin.com
Year Founded: 1911
SNC—(OTCIQ)
Rev.: $7,281,725,396
Assets: $8,911,008,594
Liabilities: $6,066,284,756
Net Worth: $2,844,723,837
Earnings: ($738,307,184)
Emp.: 46,490
Fiscal Year-end: 12/31/19
Holding Company; Engineering, Procurement, Construction, Project Management & Technical Consulting Services
N.A.I.C.S.: 551112
Alexander Taylor *(Pres-Nuclear)*

Subsidiaries:

Atkins Danmark A/S   (1)
Arne Jacobsens Alle 17, 2300, Copenhagen, Denmark
Tel.: (45) 5 251 9000
Web Site: https://www.atkins.dk
Civil Engineering Services
N.A.I.C.S.: 541330

Data Transfer Solutions, LLC   (1)
3680 Avalon Park Blvd E Ste 200, Orlando, FL 32828
Tel.: (407) 382-5222
Web Site: https://www.dtsgis.com
Computer Related Services
N.A.I.C.S.: 541519
Allen Ibaugh *(CEO & Dir-Bus Unit)*

Protrans BC Operations Ltd.   (1)
9851 Van Horne Way, Richmond, V6X 1W4, BC, Canada
Tel.: (604) 247-5757
Information Technology Services
N.A.I.C.S.: 485113

SNC-Lavalin Inc.   (1)
455 Rene-Levesque Blvd West, Montreal, H2Z 1Z3, QC, Canada
Tel.: (514) 393-1000
Web Site: http://www.snclavalin.com
Engineering, Procurement, Construction, Project Management & Technical Consulting Services
N.A.I.C.S.: 541330
Jean-Pierre Dumont *(Sr VP-Project Mgmt Office-Infrastructure Div)*

Subsidiary (Domestic):

Aqua Data Inc.   (2)
95 5th Avenue, Pincourt, Quebec, J7W 5K8, QC, Canada
Tel.: (514) 425-1010
Web Site: https://www.aquadata.com
Sales Range: $10-24.9 Million
Emp.: 100
Water Treatment Consulting Services
N.A.I.C.S.: 611710

Arcturus Realty Corporation   (2)
425 Bloor St E Ste 400, Toronto, M4W 3R4, ON, Canada
Tel.: (416) 862-6100
Web Site: http://www.arcturusrealty.com
Sales Range: $200-249.9 Million
Emp.: 350
Commercial Property Management & Leasing Services
N.A.I.C.S.: 531190

BAE-Newplan Group Limited   (2)
1133 Topsail Road, Mount Pearl, A1N 5G2, NL, Canada   (100%)
Tel.: (709) 368-0118
Sales Range: $25-49.9 Million
Emp.: 80
Provider of Engineering Services
N.A.I.C.S.: 541330

Candu Energy Inc.   (2)
2285 Speakman Drive, Mississauga, L5K 1B1, ON, Canada
Tel.: (905) 823-9040
Web Site: http://www.candu.com
Sales Range: $400-449.9 Million
Emp.: 140
Nuclear Reactors Mfr
N.A.I.C.S.: 332410

Plant (Non-US):

Candu-Argentina   (3)
Nunez 1567 Piso 6, Buenos Aires, C1429BVA, Argentina
Tel.: (54) 1147013545
Web Site: http://www.candu.com
Sales Range: $75-99.9 Million
Emp.: 4
Nuclear Electric Power Generation
N.A.I.C.S.: 221113

Candu-China   (3)
Avic Plaza 1140 B, Dongsanhuan Zhonglu Yi No 10, 100022, Beijing, China
Tel.: (86) 1065669490
Sales Range: $75-99.9 Million
Emp.: 2
Nuclear Electric Power Generation
N.A.I.C.S.: 221113

Subsidiary (Domestic):

DBA Engineering Ltd.   (2)
401 Hanlan Road, Vaughan, L4L 3T1, ON, Canada
Tel.: (905) 851-0090
Web Site: http://www.dbaeng.com
Sales Range: $10-24.9 Million
Emp.: 100
Engineering Consulting Services
N.A.I.C.S.: 541690
Param Dhillon *(Pres)*

Groupe Stavibel Inc.   (2)
1271 7th St, Val d'Or, J9P 3S1, QC, Canada
Tel.: (819) 825-2233
Web Site: http://www.stavibel.qc.ca
Emp.: 250
Engineering Services
N.A.I.C.S.: 541330
Gilles Marcotte *(Pres & CEO)*

MDH Engineered Solutions Corp. (2)
232-111 Research Drive, Saskatoon, S7N 3R2, SK, Canada
Tel.: (306) 934-7527
Web Site: http://www.mdhsolutions.com
Emp.: 10
Environmental Consulting Services
N.A.I.C.S.: 541620
Moir D. Haug *(Founder)*

Nexacor Realty Management Inc. (2)
87 Ontario St W Ste 200, Montreal, H2X 0A7, QC, Canada
Tel.: (514) 840-8334
Web Site: http://www.nexacor.ca
Sales Range: $50-74.9 Million
Emp.: 75
Real Estate Agency Services
N.A.I.C.S.: 531210

Branch (Domestic):

SNC Lavalin Inc. - Ottawa   (2)
170 Laurier Ave, Ottawa, K1P 5V5, ON, Canada
Tel.: (613) 567-8517
Web Site: http://www.snclavalin.com
Sales Range: $25-49.9 Million
Emp.: 110
N.A.I.C.S.: 541330

Subsidiary (Domestic):

SNC-Lavalin Agro   (2)
8000 Boul Decarie 3e Etage, Montreal, H4P 2S4, QC, Canada
Tel.: (514) 735-5651
Web Site: http://www.snclavalin.com
Construction Engineering Services
N.A.I.C.S.: 541330

SNC-Lavalin Capital Inc.   (2)
455 Boulevard Rene-Levesque Ouest, Montreal, H2Z 1Z3, QC, Canada
Tel.: (514) 393-1000
Corporate Investment & Financing Services
N.A.I.C.S.: 523999

SNC-Lavalin Construction (Atlantic) Inc.   (2)
99 Lincoln Road, PO Box 1462, Fredericton, E3B 5G2, NB, Canada   (100%)
Tel.: (506) 459-2645
Web Site: http://www.snclavalin.com
Sales Range: $25-49.9 Million
Emp.: 15
N.A.I.C.S.: 541330

SNC-Lavalin Construction (Ontario) Inc.   (2)
195 The West Mall, Toronto, M9C 5K1, ON, Canada
Tel.: (416) 252-8677
Web Site: http://www.snclavalin.com
Construction Engineering Services
N.A.I.C.S.: 541330

SNC-Lavalin Defence Programs Inc.   (2)
170 Laurier Avenue West Suite 1100, Ottawa, K1P 5V5, ON, Canada
Tel.: (613) 907-7100
Business Management Consulting Services
N.A.I.C.S.: 561499
Dave Rooke *(VP)*

SNC-Lavalin Environment Inc   (2)
8648 Commerce Court, Burnaby, V5A 4N6, BC, Canada
Tel.: (604) 515-5151
Web Site: http://www.snclavalin.com
Emp.: 10
Environmental Consulting Services
N.A.I.C.S.: 541620

Branch (Domestic):

SNC-Lavalin Inc. - Calgary   (2)
605 5th Ave SW, Calgary, T2P 3H5, AB, Canada
Tel.: (403) 294-2100
Web Site: http://www.snclavalin.com
Sales Range: $150-199.9 Million
Emp.: 700
N.A.I.C.S.: 541330
Richard Neale *(Sr VP & Gen Mgr-Hydrocarbons & Chemicals-Calgary)*

SNC-Lavalin Inc. - Edmonton   (2)
8915 - 51St Ave, Sprucewoods Business Park, Edmonton, T6E 5J3, AB, Canada
Tel.: (780) 426-1000
Web Site: http://www.snclavalin.com
Sales Range: $25-49.9 Million
Emp.: 250
N.A.I.C.S.: 541330

SNC-Lavalin Inc. - Halifax   (2)
32 McQuade Lake Crescent, Halifax, B3S 1G8, NS, Canada
Tel.: (902) 492-4544
Web Site: http://www.snc.lavalin.com
Sales Range: $25-49.9 Million
Emp.: 65
N.A.I.C.S.: 541330

Division (Domestic):

SNC-Lavalin Inc. - Hydro Division (2)
1801 McGill College Ave 12th Floor, Montreal, H3A 2N4, QC, Canada
Tel.: (514) 393-1000
Hydroelectric Power Generation Services
N.A.I.C.S.: 221111
Sebastien Mousseau *(VP-Engrg)*

Branch (Domestic):

SNC-Lavalin Inc. - Levis   (2)
5955 Rue St Laurent Bureau 300, Levis, G6V 3P5, QC, Canada
Tel.: (418) 837-3621
Web Site: http://www.snclavalin.com
Sales Range: $10-24.9 Million
Emp.: 30
N.A.I.C.S.: 541330

SNC-Lavalin Inc. - Longueuil   (2)
2271 boulevard Fernand Lafontaine, Longueuil, J4G 2R7, QC, Canada
Tel.: (450) 651-6710
Web Site: http://www.snclavalin.com
Provider of Engineering Services
N.A.I.C.S.: 541330

SNC-Lavalin Inc. - Rimouski   (2)
84 rue St-Germain Est, Rimouski, G5L 1A6, QC, Canada
Tel.: (418) 723-4717
Sales Range: $25-49.9 Million
Emp.: 24
N.A.I.C.S.: 541330

SNC-Lavalin Inc. - Sarnia   (2)
St Clair Corporate Ctr 265 Front St N, Sarnia, N7T 7X1, ON, Canada
Tel.: (519) 336-0201
Web Site: http://www.snclavalin.com

Sales Range: $75-99.9 Million
Emp.: 300
Provider of Engineering Services
N.A.I.C.S.: 541330

SNC-Lavalin Inc. - Thetford Mines   (2)
69 rue Notre-Dame Ouest, Thetford Mines, G6G 1J4, QC, Canada
Tel.: (418) 338-4631
Web Site: http://www.snclavalin.com
N.A.I.C.S.: 541330

SNC-Lavalin Inc. - Toronto   (2)
Westmetro Corporate Centre 195 The West Mall, Toronto, M9C 5K1, ON, Canada
Tel.: (416) 252-5311
Web Site: http://www.snclavalin.com
Sales Range: $150-199.9 Million
Emp.: 650
N.A.I.C.S.: 541330

SNC-Lavalin Inc. - Vancouver   (2)
745 Thurlow St Suite 1100, Vancouver, V6E 0C5, BC, Canada
Tel.: (604) 662-3555
Web Site: http://www.snclavalin.com
Sales Range: $75-99.9 Million
Emp.: 500
Provider of Engineering Services; Thermal Power, Transportation & Hydro Power
N.A.I.C.S.: 541330

SNC-Lavalin Inc. - Winnipeg   (2)
148 Nature Park Way, Winnipeg, R3P 0X7, MB, Canada
Tel.: (204) 786-8080
Web Site: http://www.snclavalin.com
Sales Range: $10-24.9 Million
Emp.: 50
Engineeering Services
N.A.I.C.S.: 541330

Subsidiary (Domestic):

SNC-Lavalin International Inc.   (2)
455 Rene-Levesque Blvd West, Montreal, H2Z 1Z3, QC, Canada   (100%)
Tel.: (514) 393-1000
Web Site: http://www.snclavalin.com
Holding Company; Engineering, Procurement, Construction, Project Management & Technical Consulting Services
N.A.I.C.S.: 551112

Subsidiary (Non-US):

Kentz Corporation Limited   (3)
Gurtnafleur Clonmel, Tipperary, E91WR29, Ireland
Tel.: (353) 526122811
Web Site: http://www.kentz.com
Emp.: 15,500
Heavy Engineering & Construction Services
N.A.I.C.S.: 237990

Marte Engenharia Ltda   (3)
Buenos Aires 15 9th Fl, Rio de Janeiro, 20070-021, Brazil
Tel.: (55) 2137992000
Sales Range: $125-149.9 Million
Emp.: 20
Eletric Power Generation Services
N.A.I.C.S.: 221118
Jeffrey Hilton *(Gen Mgr)*

P.T. SNC-Lavalin TPS   (3)
Graha Aktiva 11th Floor Suite 401 Jl H R Rasuna Said, Jakarta, 12950, Selatan, Indonesia   (95%)
Tel.: (62) 215203528
Web Site: http://www.snclavalin.com
Sales Range: $25-49.9 Million
Emp.: 17
N.A.I.C.S.: 541330

Branch (Non-US):

SNC Lavalin International Inc. - Beijing Representative Office   (3)
C605 Beijing Lufthansa Center 50 Liangmaqiao Road, Chaoyang District, Beijing, 100125, China
Tel.: (86) 1064639640
Web Site: http://www.snclavalin.com
Emp.: 3
Engineeering Services
N.A.I.C.S.: 541330

SNC Lavalin International Inc. - Russia   (3)

AtkinsRealis Group Inc.—(Continued)

1st Kozhevnicheskiy pereulok 6 Bldg 1 Office 404, Office 603, 115114, Moscow, Russia
Tel.: (7) 495 604 1877
Web Site: http://www.snclavalin.com
Emp.: 3
Engineeering Services
N.A.I.C.S.: 541330

Subsidiary (Non-US):

SNC-Lavalin (Malaysia) Sdn. Bhd.   (3)
7th Floor Menara RKT No 36 Jalan Raja Abdullah, Kuala Lumpur, 50300, Malaysia   (100%)
Tel.: (60) 3 2692 0202
Web Site: http://www.snclavalin.com
Sales Range: $25-49.9 Million
Emp.: 100
Construction Management & Engineering Services
N.A.I.C.S.: 541330

SNC-Lavalin (Pty) Ltd   (3)
Block C Cullinan Place 2 Cullinan Close, PO Box 784593, Morningside, Sandton, 2146, South Africa
Tel.: (27) 115354900
Web Site: http://www.snclavalin.com
Sales Range: $200-249.9 Million
Emp.: 122
Mineral Mining Services
N.A.I.C.S.: 212390

SNC-Lavalin (Shanghai) International Trading Co. Ltd.   (3)
Huawen Plaza Suite 401 405 999 Zhong Shan Xi Road, Shanghai, 200051, China
Tel.: (86) 21 3251 5666
Web Site: http://www.snclavalin.com.cn
Engineering Consulting Services
N.A.I.C.S.: 541330

SNC-Lavalin Algerie EURL   (3)
18 Rue Mustapha Khalef, Ben Aknoun, Algiers, Algeria   (100%)
Tel.: (213) 21911750
Engineeering Services
N.A.I.C.S.: 541330

Subsidiary (US):

SNC-Lavalin America, Inc.   (3)
300 Woodcliff Dr Ste 211, Canonsburg, PA 15317
Tel.: (412) 363-9000
Web Site: http://www.snclavalin.com
Emp.: 30
Engineeering Services
N.A.I.C.S.: 541330
Scott Thruston (Gen Mgr)

Subsidiary (Domestic):

SNC-Lavalin Capital Engineering LLC   (4)
6933 Indianpolis Blvd, Hammond, IN 46324
Tel.: (219) 844-1984
Construction Engineering Services
N.A.I.C.S.: 541330

SNC-Lavalin Constructors Inc.   (4)
19015 N Creek Pkwy Ste 300, Bothell, WA 98011-8029
Tel.: (425) 489-8000
Web Site: http://www.slthermal.com
Sales Range: $125-149.9 Million
Emp.: 200
Electric Power Transmission Services
N.A.I.C.S.: 221121

SNC-Lavalin Engineers & Constructors, Inc.   (4)
919 Mylon Street, Houston, TX 77002
Tel.: (713) 667-9162
Emp.: 500
Construction Engineering Services
N.A.I.C.S.: 541330
Meg Leachman (Dir-Mktg)

SNC-Lavalin Project Services, Inc.   (4)
436 Creamery Way Ste 100, Exton, PA 19341
Tel.: (610) 524-5920
Web Site: http://www.snclavalin.com

Sales Range: $25-49.9 Million
Emp.: 50
Engineeering Services
N.A.I.C.S.: 541330
Mike Leader (Dir-Engrg)

Subsidiary (Non-US):

SNC-Lavalin Arabia Engineering Consultancy   (3)
NSH Group Tower 3rd Fl Khobar Dammam Express Highway, PO Box 30851, Al Khobar, 31952, Saudi Arabia
Tel.: (966) 38108900
Engineeering Services
N.A.I.C.S.: 541330

SNC-Lavalin Arabia, LLC   (3)
NSH Group Tower 3rd Floor, PO Box 30851, Khobar Dammam Express Highway, Al Khobar, 31952, Saudi Arabia
Tel.: (966) 38108900
Engineering & Construction Services
N.A.I.C.S.: 541330

SNC-Lavalin Australia Pty. Ltd.   (3)
191 St Georges Terrace Level 17, Perth, 6000, WA, Australia   (100%)
Tel.: (61) 893220900
Sales Range: $10-24.9 Million
Emp.: 50
N.A.I.C.S.: 541330

SNC-Lavalin Chile S.A.   (3)
2343 Luis Uribe Presitendb Risco Ave 5335 FL2, Santiago, Chile   (100%)
Tel.: (56) 24312800
Web Site: http://www.snclavalin.com
Sales Range: $75-99.9 Million
Emp.: 400
N.A.I.C.S.: 541330

SNC-Lavalin Construction International SAS   (3)
15-17 Avenue Lacassagne, 16 Avenue Tony Garnier, 69365, Lyon, France
Tel.: (33) 478470168
Sales Range: $75-99.9 Million
Emp.: 30
Engineering Construction Services
N.A.I.C.S.: 541330

SNC-Lavalin Dominicana S.A.   (3)
Av Sarasota No 18 La Julia, Santo Domingo, Dominican Republic
Tel.: (809) 2861600
Web Site: http://www.snclavalin.com
Sales Range: $25-49.9 Million
Marine Cargo Transportation Services
N.A.I.C.S.: 488390

SNC-Lavalin Egypt LLC   (3)
4 Abou Bakre El Sedeak Street Section 1144 Sheraton Area, Heliopolis, Cairo, Egypt
Tel.: (20) 222679003
Sales Range: $25-49.9 Million
Emp.: 4
Engineeering Services
N.A.I.C.S.: 541330
Eprhaim Guemei (Mng Dir)

SNC-Lavalin Engineering & Technology Pvt Limited   (3)
Mirchandani Business Pk 6th Fl, Sakinaka Andheri E, Mumbai, 400072, Maharashtra, India
Tel.: (91) 2267207000
Sales Range: $25-49.9 Million
Emp.: 80
Engineering Construction Services
N.A.I.C.S.: 541330
N. T. Balraj (Pres)

SNC-Lavalin Engineering India Private Limited   (3)
TRADE STAR A Wing 2nd Floor Kondivita Lane J B Nagar Off, Andheri-Kurla Rd Andheri E, Mumbai, 400 059, Maharashtra, India
Tel.: (91) 2267892600
Engineeering Services
N.A.I.C.S.: 541330

SNC-Lavalin Eurasia OOO   (3)
1st Kozhevnicheskiy Pereulok 6 Building 1 Office 404, Moscow, 115114, Russia
Tel.: (7) 495 604 1877
Web Site: http://www.snsLavalin.com
Sales Range: $25-49.9 Million
Emp.: 11
Engineeering Services

N.A.I.C.S.: 541330
Juan Jose (Reg Mgr)

SNC-Lavalin Europe S.A.S.   (3)
16 Cours Jean-Baptiste Langlet, 51723, Reims, France
Tel.: (33) 3 26 77 60 00
Sales Range: $100-124.9 Million
Emp.: 30
Industrial Building Construction Services
N.A.I.C.S.: 236210
Jacqui Christin (Gen Mgr)

SNC-Lavalin Gulf Contractors LLC   (3)
Abu Dhabi Trade Center Bldg West Tower 4th Floor, PO Box 54130, Abu Dhabi, 54130, United Arab Emirates   (100%)
Tel.: (971) 26440001
Web Site: http://www.snclavalin.com
Sales Range: $25-49.9 Million
Emp.: 90
Engineeering Services
N.A.I.C.S.: 541330

SNC-Lavalin Infrastructure Pvt. Ltd.   (3)
3rd floor carnoustie 1 Bldg Plot 1 Sector 16 A flim city, Noida, 201 301, Uttar Pradesh, India
Tel.: (91) 1204687400
Sales Range: $25-49.9 Million
Emp.: 17
Engineering Construction Services
N.A.I.C.S.: 541330
Ian Edwards (Exec VP-Infrastructure Construction)

SNC-Lavalin International   (3)
16 cours Jean-Baptiste Langlet, 51723, Reims, France   (100%)
Tel.: (33) 326776000
Web Site: http://www.snclavalin.com
Sales Range: $200-249.9 Million
Emp.: 600
Holding Company; Regional Managing Office
N.A.I.C.S.: 551112

Subsidiary (Domestic):

SNC-Lavalin S.A.S.   (4)
16 Cours J B Langlet, 51723, Reims, Cedex, France   (100%)
Tel.: (33) 326776000
Sales Range: $75-99.9 Million
Emp.: 300
Agrifood
N.A.I.C.S.: 541330

Subsidiary (Non-US):

SNC-Lavalin International Co. Inc.   (3)
Ave Paseo Colon Torre Polar Oeste Piso 9 Oficina 9C, Urbanizacion Los Caobos Plaza, Caracas, 1050, Venezuela
Tel.: (58) 2127941441
Sales Range: $25-49.9 Million
Emp.: 60
Engineeering Services
N.A.I.C.S.: 541330

Branch (Non-US):

SNC-Lavalin International Inc. - Cameroon   (3)
PO Box 6111, Yaounde, Cameroon
Tel.: (237) 22 200183
Web Site: http://www.sncl-avalin.com
N.A.I.C.S.: 541330

SNC-Lavalin International Inc. - Honduras   (3)
Edificio Galerias La Paz Avenida La Paz, Tegucigalpa, Honduras
Tel.: (504) 2204393
Web Site: http://www.snclavalin.com
Sales Range: $25-49.9 Million
Emp.: 12
N.A.I.C.S.: 541330

SNC-Lavalin International Inc. - Kazakhstan   (3)
205 2/2 Kabanbay Batyr Str, Nur-Sultan, Kazakhstan
Tel.: (7) 7172 912070
Web Site: http://www.snclavalin.com
Emp.: 40
Engineeering Services

N.A.I.C.S.: 541330

SNC-Lavalin International Inc. - Libya   (3)
Anbasibn Malek St Garyounes Area, PO Box 9404, Benghazi, G S P L A G, Libya
Tel.: (218) 612225242
Web Site: http://www.snclavalin.com
Sales Range: $25-49.9 Million
Emp.: 145
Engineeering Services
N.A.I.C.S.: 541330

SNC-Lavalin International Inc. - Thailand   (3)
10th Fl Ste 115 Lake Rajada Office Complex, 193 37 Rachadapisek Rd, Bangkok, 10110, Thailand
Tel.: (66) 2 654 0105
Web Site: http://www.snclavalin.com
Engineeering Services
N.A.I.C.S.: 541330

SNC-Lavalin International Inc. - Tunisia   (3)
4 Abdelhamid Ibn Badis Rd, Tunis, 1002, Tunisia
Tel.: (216) 71285466
Web Site: http://www.snclavalin.com
Sales Range: $10-24.9 Million
Emp.: 35
Business Services
N.A.I.C.S.: 561499

SNC-Lavalin International Inc. - Vietnam   (3)
Binh Minh Hotel Suite 430, 27 Ly Thai To Street, Hanoi, Vietnam
Tel.: (84) 439345521
Web Site: http://www.snclavalin.com
Sales Range: $25-49.9 Million
Emp.: 25
Engineeering Services
N.A.I.C.S.: 541330

Subsidiary (Non-US):

SNC-Lavalin International Maroc S.A.S.   (3)
62 Doulevard d'Anfa 5e Etage, 20000, Casablanca, Morocco
Tel.: (212) 522273622
Web Site: http://www.snclavalin.com
Oil & Gas Exploration Services
N.A.I.C.S.: 213112

SNC-Lavalin Korea Limited   (3)
4F Joong-pyeong building 748-15 Yeoksam-dong, Gangnam-gu, Seoul, 135-925, Korea (South)
Tel.: (82) 25661400
Web Site: http://www.snclavalin.com
Sales Range: $25-49.9 Million
Emp.: 13
Engineering Consulting Services
N.A.I.C.S.: 541330

SNC-Lavalin Kuwait General Trading and Contracting Co.   (3)
Dar Al-Awadi Tower 23rd Floor Ahmad Al Jaber Street, PO Box 4323, Safat, Kuwait, 13104, Kuwait
Tel.: (965) 22322190
Oil & Gas Exploration Services
N.A.I.C.S.: 213112

SNC-Lavalin Magyarorszag KFT   (3)
Ilka Utca 31, 1143, Budapest, Hungary
Tel.: (36) 12250197
Web Site: http://www.snclavalin.com
Sales Range: $25-49.9 Million
Emp.: 7
Environmental Consulting Services
N.A.I.C.S.: 541620

SNC-Lavalin Minerconsult Ltda   (3)
Av Raja Gabaglia 2 664 4th Floor - Estoril, 30494-170, Belo Horizonte, Minas Gerais, Brazil
Tel.: (55) 31 3348 9300
Web Site: http://www.snclavalin.com
Sales Range: $150-199.9 Million
Emp.: 100
Engineering Consulting Services
N.A.I.C.S.: 541690

Subsidiary (Domestic):

Minerconsult Engenharia Ltda   (4)
Av Raja Gabaglia 1255 Andar - Estoril 1st

Fl, Belo Horizonte, 30380435, Minas
Gerais, Brazil
Tel.: (55) 3132984000
Web Site: http://www.snclavalin.com
Sales Range: $150-199.9 Million
Emp.: 100
Mining & Metallurgy Industry Consulting
Services
N.A.I.C.S.: 541690

Subsidiary (Non-US):

SNC-Lavalin Muhendislik Ve Taahhut
Limited Sirketi   (3)
Sehit Cevdet Ozdemir Mah 203 Sokak 1/6
Dikmen, 06460, Ankara, Turkiye
Tel.: (90) 3124782222
Web Site: http://www.snclavalin.com
Engineeering Services
N.A.I.C.S.: 541330

SNC-Lavalin Panama, S.A.   (3)
Tower C 33 Fl Office 3302, Punta Pacifica,
Panama, Panama
Tel.: (507) 204 5790
Web Site: http://www.snclavalin.com
Emp.: 15
Copper Ore Mining Services
N.A.I.C.S.: 212230

SNC-Lavalin Peru S.A.   (3)
Edificio Polanco Calle Mariano De Los San-
tos 183 Oficina 301, San Isidro, 27, Lima,
Peru   (100%)
Tel.: (51) 12226502
Sales Range: $50-74.9 Million
Emp.: 15
Consulting, Design, Engineering & Con-
struction of Mining Facilities; Treatment of
Ores; Recovery of Minerals & Metals
N.A.I.C.S.: 212390

SNC-Lavalin Pharma S.A.   (3)
Berkenhoekstraat 2, Onze-Lieve-Vrouw-
Waver, 2861, Saint-Katelijne-Waver, Bel-
gium
Tel.: (32) 15768870
Sales Range: $25-49.9 Million
Emp.: 18
Engineeering Services
N.A.I.C.S.: 541330

SNC-Lavalin Polska Sp. Z o.o.   (3)
Horizon Plaza Ul Domaniewska 39a, War-
saw, 02-672, Poland
Tel.: (48) 222082500
Sales Range: $50-74.9 Million
Emp.: 10
Thermal Power Generation Services
N.A.I.C.S.: 221118
Alejandro Quintero (VP)

SNC-Lavalin Projetos Ltda.   (3)
Avenida Paulista 688 Bela Vista, Sao
Paulo, 01310-909, SP, Brazil   (100%)
Tel.: (55) 1130771202
Web Site: http://www.snclavalin.com
Sales Range: $10-24.9 Million
Emp.: 12
Business Services
N.A.I.C.S.: 561499

SNC-Lavalin South Africa (Pty)
Ltd.   (3)
Block C Cullinan Pl 2 Cullinan Close, Morn-
ingside, Sandton, 2146, South Africa
Tel.: (27) 115354900
Web Site: http://www.snclavalin.com
Sales Range: $75-99.9 Million
Emp.: 146
Engineering & Construction Services
N.A.I.C.S.: 541330

SNC-Lavalin Spain SL   (3)
Santa Leonor 32, 28037, Madrid, Spain
Tel.: (34) 915673800
Web Site: http://www.snclavalin.com
Sales Range: $75-99.9 Million
Emp.: 400
Construction Engineering Services
N.A.I.C.S.: 541330

Subsidiary (Domestic):

Intecsa-Inarsa, S.A.   (4)
Gulian Camarillo 53, 28037, Madrid, Spain
Tel.: (34) 915673800
Web Site: http://www.intecsa-
inarsa.snclavalin.com

Sales Range: $75-99.9 Million
Emp.: 35
Engineering Consulting Services
N.A.I.C.S.: 541330
Diego Ibanez Lopez (CEO)

SNC-Lavalin Health   (4)
Santa Leonor 32, Madrid, 28037, Spain
Tel.: (34) 915673800
Women Healthcare Services
N.A.I.C.S.: 621610

Subsidiary (Non-US):

SNC-Lavalin Transportation Korea
Inc.   (3)
207 Innoplex 13 yangpyeongdong-3ga,
Yeongdeungpo-gu, Seoul, Korea (South)
Tel.: (82) 236678174
Web Site: http://www.snclavalin.com
Sales Range: $25-49.9 Million
Emp.: 10
Transportation Services
N.A.I.C.S.: 488999

Societe d'Expertise et d'Ingenierie
LGL S.A.   (3)
29 Rue Oge, PO Box 15427 PV, Petion
Ville, 6141, Haiti   (100%)
Tel.: (509) 257 1746
Sales Range: $25-49.9 Million
Emp.: 15
N.A.I.C.S.: 541330

Subsidiary (Domestic):

SNC-Lavalin Nuclear Inc.   (2)
2275 Upper Middle Rd E, Oakville, L6H
OC3, ON, Canada
Tel.: (905) 829-8808
Web Site: http://www.slnuclear.com
Sales Range: $50-74.9 Million
Emp.: 100
Nuclear Power Plant Engineering, Construc-
tion & Project Management Services
N.A.I.C.S.: 541330
Barry Ward (Mgr)

SNC-Lavalin Operations & Mainte-
nance Inc.   (2)
304 E Mall Ste 900, Etobicoke, M9B 6E2,
ON, Canada   (100%)
Tel.: (416) 207-4700
Web Site: http://www.snclavalinom.com
Sales Range: $100-124.9 Million
Emp.: 400
Facilities, Infrastructure & Real Estate Man-
agement Services
N.A.I.C.S.: 561210

SNC-Lavalin Rural Development   (2)
455 Rene Levesque Blvd W 14th Fl, Mon-
treal, H2Z 1Z3, QC, Canada
Tel.: (514) 393-1000
Web Site: http://www.snclavalin.com
Environmental Consulting Services
N.A.I.C.S.: 541620

SNC-Lavalin Telecom Inc.   (2)
625 Rene Levesque Blvd West Suite 1000,
Montreal, H3B 1R2, QC, Canada
Tel.: (514) 392-3000
Web Site: http://www.snclavalin.com
Sales Range: $25-49.9 Million
Emp.: 75
Telecommunication Servicesb
N.A.I.C.S.: 517810
Alain Briere (VP & Gen Mgr)

SNC-Lavalin Transmission &
Distribution   (2)
Suite 300 640 5th Avenue SW, Calgary,
T2P 3G4, AB, Canada
Tel.: (403) 539-4550
Web Site: http://www.snclavalin.com
Emp.: 80
Hydroelectric Power Generation Services
N.A.I.C.S.: 221111

SNC-Lavalin Romania S.A.   (1)
Hermes Business Campus 5-7 Dimitrie
Pompei Blvd, Bucharest, Romania
Tel.: (40) 21 210 9459
Information Technology Services
N.A.I.C.S.: 485113

WS Atkins & Partners Overseas   (1)

WS Atkins & Partners Overseas Engineering Consultants   (1)

WS Atkins Ireland Limited   (1)
AtkinsRealis House 150 Airside Business
Park, Swords, Dublin, K67 K5W4, Ireland
Tel.: (353) 18108000
Web Site: https://atkinsrealis.ie
Emp.: 350
Civil Engineering & Design Services
N.A.I.C.S.: 541330

WS Atkins Limited   (1)
Woodcote Grove Ashley Road, Epsom,
KT18 5BW, Surrey, United Kingdom (100%)
Tel.: (44) 20 7121 2000
Web Site: http://www.atkinsglobal.com
Engineering & Project Management Con-
sulting & Support Services
N.A.I.C.S.: 541690
Philip Hoare (Pres-Atkins)

Subsidiary (Domestic):

ATK Energy EU Limited   (2)
Woodcote Grove Ashley Road, Epsom,
London, KT18 5BW, Surrey, United King-
dom
Tel.: (44) 1372726140
Web Site: http://www.atkinsglobal.com
Nuclear Material Recycling & Disposal Ser-
vices
N.A.I.C.S.: 562211

Subsidiary (Non-US):

Atkins Australasia Pty Ltd.   (2)
Level 17 191 St Georges Terrace, Perth,
6000, WA, Australia
Tel.: (61) 894422500
Web Site: http://www.atkinsglobal.com
Engineeering Services
N.A.I.C.S.: 541330

Atkins China Limited   (2)
13th Floor Wharf T&T Centre Harbour City,
Tsim Sha Tsui, Kowloon, China (Hong
Kong)
Tel.: (852) 29721000
Web Site: http://www.atkinsglobal.com
Engineering Consulting Services
N.A.I.C.S.: 541330

Subsidiary (US):

Atkins North America Inc.   (2)
4030 W Boy Scout Blvd Ste 700, Tampa,
FL 33607
Tel.: (813) 282-7275
Web Site: http://www.atkinsglobal.com
Civil & Transportation Engineering Services
N.A.I.C.S.: 541330

Subsidiary (Domestic):

Atkins Energy Government Group,
Inc.   (3)
100 Ctr Point Cir Ste 100 Ctr Point II, Co-
lumbia, SC 29210
Tel.: (803) 873-9103
Web Site: http://www.atkinsglobal.com
Nuclear Material Recycling & Disposal Ser-
vices
N.A.I.C.S.: 562211

Branch (Domestic):

Atkins North America   (3)
Dominion Plz 17304 Preston Rd Ste 1310,
Dallas, TX 75252
Tel.: (972) 818-7275
Web Site: http://www.atkinsglobal.com
Civil Engineering & Design Consulting Ser-
vices
N.A.I.C.S.: 541330

Atkins North America   (3)
11801 Domain Blvd Ste 500, Austin, TX
78758
Tel.: (512) 327-6840
Web Site: http://www.atkinsglobal.com
Engineering & Design Services
N.A.I.C.S.: 541330

Subsidiary (Domestic):

Atkins Nuclear Solutions US, Inc. (3)
5600 Seventy-Seven Ctr Dr Ste 340, Char-
lotte, NC 28217
Tel.: (704) 522-7275
Web Site: http://www.atkinsglobal.com
Nuclear Safety Engineering & Technical So-
lutions Services
N.A.I.C.S.: 541690

Faithful+Gould Inc.   (3)
10 E 40th St 13 Fl, New York, NY 10016
Tel.: (212) 252-7070
Web Site: http://www.fgould.com
Software Consulting Services
N.A.I.C.S.: 541512
Niel Clemson (Dir-Comml & Project Mgmt)

Houston Offshore Engineering,
LLC   (3)
200 Westlake Park Blvd Ste 1100, Houston,
TX 77099
Tel.: (713) 576-8500
Web Site: http://www.atkinsglobal.com
Engineeering Services
N.A.I.C.S.: 541330
John W. Chianis (Dir-Global)

ATL LEASING
Ennour Building Center Urbain Nord,
1082, Tunis, Tunisia
Tel.: (216) 70135000
Web Site: https://www.atl.com.tn
ATL—(BVT)
Sales Range: Less than $1 Million
Banking Services
N.A.I.C.S.: 522110

ATL TELECOM LIMITED
Lakeside Fountain Lane, St Mellons,
Cardiff, CF3 0FB, United Kingdom
Tel.: (44) 3303338250
Web Site: http://www.atltelecom.com
Year Founded: 2001
Sales Range: $25-49.9 Million
Emp.: 30
Convergent Voice & Data Product for
Telecommunication Industry Mfr
N.A.I.C.S.: 517112
Johnathan Nicholas Harrison (CEO)

ATLAN HOLDINGS BERHAD
17th Floor Menara Atlan 161-B Jalan
Ampang, 50450, Kuala Lumpur, Ma-
laysia
Tel.: (60) 321792000   MY
Web Site: https://www.atlan.com.my
Year Founded: 1988
ATLAN—(KLS)
Rev.: $98,728,777
Assets: $175,877,015
Liabilities: $65,413,583
Net Worth: $110,463,431
Earnings: $5,510,448
Emp.: 1,225
Fiscal Year-end: 02/29/24
Property Investment & Development
Services
N.A.I.C.S.: 531311
Sze Siang Lee (Exec Dir)

Subsidiaries:

Blossom Time Sdn. Bhd.   (1)
no 1 Jalan TropikaTropika Serringhi Batu
Serringhi, Bandar Batu Ferringhi, 11100,
Penang, Malaysia
Tel.: (60) 48811340
Web Site: http://www.blossomtime.com.my
Sales Range: $50-74.9 Million
Emp.: 5
Residential Property Development Services
N.A.I.C.S.: 531210
B. S. Ong (Exec Dir)

Duty Free International Limited   (1)
138 Cecil Street 12-01A Cecil Court, Singa-
pore, 069538, Singapore   (81.15%)
Tel.: (65) 65340181
Web Site: http://www.dfi.com.sg
Rev.: $34,229,865
Assets: $104,841,751
Liabilities: $29,029,822
Net Worth: $75,811,929
Earnings: $3,056,378
Emp.: 275
Fiscal Year-end: 02/28/2024
Duty-Free Stores Operator
N.A.I.C.S.: 459999
Sze Siang Lee (Exec Dir-Fin & Corp Svcs)

Subsidiary (Non-US):

DFZ Capital Berhad   (2)

Atlan Holdings Berhad—(Continued)

Wisma Atlan 8 Persiaran Kampung Jawa,
11900, Bayan Lepas, Penang,
Malaysia **(100%)**
Tel.: (60) 46413200
Web Site: https://www.dfzcapital.com.my
Sales Range: $150-199.9 Million
Holding Company; Real Estate & Travel
Services
N.A.I.C.S.: 551112

Subsidiary (Domestic):

Drinks Hub Asia Pte Ltd **(2)**
361 Ubi Road 3 02-04, Singapore, 408664,
Singapore
Tel.: (65) 91788322
Web Site: http://www.drinkshub.asia
Alcoholic Beverage Distr
N.A.I.C.S.: 424820
Justin Frizelle *(CEO)*

Naluri Corporation Berhad **(1)**
16th Floor Menara Naluri 161B Jalan Am-
pang, Kuala Lumpur, 50450, Malaysia
Tel.: (60) 321792000
Web Site: http://www.naluri.com.my
Sales Range: $50-74.9 Million
Emp.: 70
Real Estate Property Development Services
N.A.I.C.S.: 531210

Naluri Properties Sdn. Bhd. **(1)**
161-D Jalan Ampang, 50450, Kuala Lum-
pur, Malaysia
Tel.: (60) 321648000
Real Estate Property Development & Hotel
Management Services
N.A.I.C.S.: 531210

ATLAN MEDIA INC.
Level 19 1 OConnell Street, Sydney,
2000, NSW, Australia
Tel.: (61) 2 8520 3912 **NV**
Web Site: http://www.atlanmedia.com
Year Founded: 2016
Emp.: 3
Advertising Agency Operator
N.A.I.C.S.: 541810
William Atlan *(Pres & CEO)*

ATLANTA ASSURANCES
181 Bd d'Anfa, Casablanca, Morocco
Tel.: (212) 522957676
Web Site: http://www.atlanta.ma
ATL—(CAS)
Sales Range: Less than $1 Million
Art Insurance Services
N.A.I.C.S.: 524126

ATLANTA DEVCON LIMITED
1009 Hemkunth Behind LIC Office
Ashram Road, Ahmedabad, 380006,
Gujarat, India
Tel.: (91) 7965401222
Web Site:
https://www.atlantadevcon.com
Year Founded: 1994
Assets: $2,932,825
Liabilities: $39,613
Net Worth: $2,893,212
Earnings: ($6,780)
Emp.: 1
Fiscal Year-end: 03/31/18
Construction Engineering Services
N.A.I.C.S.: 541330

ATLANTA GOLD INC.
First Cdn Place 5600 - 100 King St
West, Toronto, M5X 1C9, ON,
Canada
Tel.: (416) 777-0013
Web Site: https://www.atgoldinc.com
ATG—(OTCIQ)
Gold Ore Mining
N.A.I.C.S.: 212220
R. David Russell *(Interim Pres & In-
terim CEO)*

Subsidiaries:

Atlanta Gold Inc. **(1)**

2417 Bank Dr Ste 101, Boise, ID 83705
Tel.: (208) 424-3343
Web Site: http://www.atgoldinc.com
Emp.: 2
Gold Mining Services
N.A.I.C.S.: 212220
Peili Miao *(CFO)*

ATLANTA LIMITED
504 Samarpan New Link Road
Chakala, Near Mirador Hotel Andheri
East, Mumbai, 400099, India
Tel.: (91) 2228382715
Web Site: http://www.atlantalimited.in
ATLANTA—(NSE)
Rev.: $46,504,799
Assets: $77,676,908
Liabilities: $121,386,324
Net Worth: ($43,709,416)
Earnings: ($54,937,646)
Emp.: 24
Fiscal Year-end: 03/30/22
Infrastructure Development, Mining &
Real Estate Services
N.A.I.C.S.: 236220
Rajhoo Bbarot *(Chm)*

Subsidiaries:

Atlanta Energy Private Limited **(1)**
340/1 1st Floor, Sultanpur Mahrauli, New
Delhi, 110030, India
Tel.: (91) 1126503691
Web Site: http://www.atlantaenergy.in
Solar Product Mfr
N.A.I.C.S.: 333414

ATLANTA POLAND S.A.
ul Zalogowa 17, 80-557, Gdansk,
Poland
Tel.: (48) 585220600 **PL**
Web Site:
https://www.atlantapoland.com.pl
Year Founded: 1990
ATP—(WAR)
Rev.: $106,963,537
Assets: $48,543,517
Liabilities: $26,169,734
Net Worth: $22,373,782
Earnings: $2,402,955
Fiscal Year-end: 06/30/23
Dried Fruit & Nut Processor & Distr
N.A.I.C.S.: 311999
Wojciech Sztuka *(Mgr-Pur)*

ATLANTIC AIRWAYS
Vagar Airport, Sorvagur, FO380,
Faroe Islands
Tel.: (298) 341000
Web Site: http://www.atlantic.fo
Sales Range: $25-49.9 Million
Emp.: 111
Oil Transportation Services
N.A.I.C.S.: 481111
Marius Davidsen *(CFO)*

ATLANTIC BRIDGE VEN-
TURES
22 Fitzwilliam Square South, Dublin,
D02 FH68, Ireland
Tel.: (353) 16034450
Web Site: http://www.abven.com
Year Founded: 2005
Sales Range: $25-49.9 Million
Emp.: 10
Privater Equity Firm
N.A.I.C.S.: 523999
Peter McManamon *(Chm)*

ATLANTIC CHINA WELDING
CONSUMABLES, INC.
Zigong, Sichuan, 643010, China
Tel.: (86) 13350101931
Web Site: https://www.chinaweld-
atlantic.com
600558—(SHG)
Rev.: $468,939,636
Assets: $440,738,836
Liabilities: $108,285,634

Net Worth: $332,453,202
Earnings: $9,609,229
Fiscal Year-end: 12/31/22
Welding Product Mfr
N.A.I.C.S.: 333992
Xinyu Li *(Chm)*

Subsidiaries:

Elite Tools Ltd. **(1)**
PO Box 64466-00620, Nairobi, Kenya
Tel.: (254) 788600500
Web Site: https://elitekenya.com
Lifting Equipment Mfr & Distr
N.A.I.C.S.: 333923

Eram Eilia, Inc. **(1)**
183 Fatemi Ave, 1414657685, Tehran, Iran
Tel.: (98) 2188954573
Welding Material Mfr & Distr
N.A.I.C.S.: 332312

Fengda Company Limited **(1)**
No 8439 off Mumbwa Road, PO Box
36373, Lusaka, Zambia
Tel.: (260) 1287145
Welding Materials Mfr & Distr
N.A.I.C.S.: 333992

IAW de Mexico, S.A. de C.V. **(1)**
Regio Avenida No 152 Regio Parque Indus-
trial, 66600, Apodaca, Mexico
Tel.: (52) 8113340012
Web Site: https://www.iaw.com.mx
Welding Materials Mfr & Distr
N.A.I.C.S.: 333992

Jiangsu Atlantic Welding Consum-
ables Limited Liability Company **(1)**
Qidong Xigang Industrial Park, Jiangsu,
226222, China
Tel.: (86) 51383819933
Steel Products Mfr
N.A.I.C.S.: 331110

SHEZHEN ATLANTIC WELDING
CONSUMABLES CO., LTD **(1)**
No 99 Industrial Road Pinghu Fucheng'ao
Industrial Park, Longgang District, Shen-
zhen, China
Tel.: (86) 75528326262
Welding Equipment Distr
N.A.I.C.S.: 423830

Star Group Pvt. Ltd. **(1)**
Buddhi Sagar Marg 3 EPC 6000, Po Box
8975, Panipokhari Balwatar, Kathmandu,
Nepal
Tel.: (977) 14421252
Information Technology Services
N.A.I.C.S.: 541519

Tianjin Atlantic Welding Consumables
Sales Co., Ltd **(1)**
No C14 Building Jiahe Nanyuan Modern
Industrial District Ninghe, Tianjin, 301508,
China
Tel.: (86) 2269283999
Steel Product Distr
N.A.I.C.S.: 423510

Tianjin Herong Titanium Industry co.,
LTD. **(1)**
Tianjin Economic Development Zone, The
First Road Of The Cross Of No 3 Jing Road
And No 12 Jing Road, Tianjin, 301505,
China
Tel.: (86) 2269623999
Titanium Product Mfr
N.A.I.C.S.: 331110

Top Electrodes Sdn. Bhd. **(1)**
No 19 Lorong Teng Kung Suk 3, 96000,
Sibu, Sarawak, Malaysia
Tel.: (60) 84214598
Welding Materials Mfr & Distr
N.A.I.C.S.: 333992

ATLANTIC GROUP
Tonningsgt 19, 6006, Alesund, Nor-
way
Tel.: (47) 70101800
Web Site: http://www.atlantic.no
Sales Range: $25-49.9 Million
Emp.: 20
Holding Company
N.A.I.C.S.: 551112
Ove Godo *(Gen Mgr)*

Subsidiaries:

Atlantic Packaging AS **(1)**
Lerstadvegen 517, 6018, Alesund, Norway
Tel.: (47) 70101810
Web Site: http://www.atlpack.no
Food Packaging Services
N.A.I.C.S.: 561910

Atlantic Seafood AS **(1)**
Tonningsgatan 19, 6006, Alesund, Norway
Tel.: (47) 70101800
Web Site: http://www.atlantic.no
Sales Range: $25-49.9 Million
Emp.: 4
Seafood Purchaser & Whslr
N.A.I.C.S.: 445250

ATLANTIC GRUPA D.D.
Miramarska 23, 10000, Zagreb, Croa-
tia
Tel.: (385) 12413900
Web Site:
https://www.atlanticgrupa.com
ATGR—(ZAG)
Rev.: $1,089,614,748
Assets: $1,002,016,779
Liabilities: $509,403,908
Net Worth: $492,612,871
Earnings: $34,462,965
Emp.: 5,275
Fiscal Year-end: 12/31/23
Pharmaceutical Preparation Manufac-
turing
N.A.I.C.S.: 325412
Zdenko Adrovic *(Chm-Supervisory
Bd)*

Subsidiaries:

Atlantic Argeta d.o.o. **(1)**
Donji Hadzici br 138, Hadzici, 71000, Sara-
jevo, Bosnia & Herzegovina
Tel.: (387) 33476600
Food & Beverage Mfr & Distr
N.A.I.C.S.: 311999

Atlantic Cedevita d.o.o. **(1)**
Planinska 15, 10000, Zagreb, Croatia
Tel.: (385) 8000009
Web Site: https://www.cedevita.com
Beverage Mfr & Distr
N.A.I.C.S.: 312111

Atlantic Droga Kolinska d.o.o. **(1)**
Kolinska Ulica 1, 1000, Ljubljana, Slovenia
Tel.: (386) 14721500
Food & Beverage Mfr & Distr
N.A.I.C.S.: 311999

Atlantic Multipower GmbH & Co.
OHG **(1)**
Moorfuhrtweg 17, 22301, Hamburg, Ger-
many
Tel.: (49) 402986601
Web Site: http://www.atlantic-multipower.de
Sales Range: $75-99.9 Million
Emp.: 200
Sports Foods Distr
N.A.I.C.S.: 424490
Neven Vrankovic *(Mng Dir)*

Subsidiary (Non-US):

Atlantic Multipower Srl **(2)**
Via Profilis Don A Dalla Torre 8/5 Zl Levada,
31047, Ponte di Piave, Treviso, Italy
Tel.: (39) 0422852076
Sales Range: $25-49.9 Million
Emp.: 8
Sports Foods Distr
N.A.I.C.S.: 424490
Giuseppe Virzi *(Dir-Comml)*

Atlantic Multipower UK Ltd **(2)**
Robert Denholm House Bletchingley Road,
Nutfield, RH1 4 HW, Surrey, United King-
dom
Tel.: (44) 1737821840
Web Site: http://www.multipoweruk.com
Sales Range: $25-49.9 Million
Emp.: 14
Sports Foods Distr
N.A.I.C.S.: 424490

Atlantic Stark d.o.o. **(1)**
Bulevar Peka Dapcevica 29, 11000, Belgrade, Serbia

Tel.: (381) 113956000
Food & Beverage Mfr & Distr
N.A.I.C.S.: 311999

Atlantic Trade d.o.o., Ljubljana (1)
Kolinska ulica 1, 1000, Ljubljana, Slovenia
Tel.: (386) 15305570
Web Site: http://www.atlantic.hr
Sales Range: $25-49.9 Million
Emp.: 12
Sports Foods Distr
N.A.I.C.S.: 424490

Atlantic s.r.l. (1)
Via Giambologna 1, 20096, Pioltello, Milan,
Italy
Tel.: (39) 02923671
Dietary Drinks Distr
N.A.I.C.S.: 311514

Cedevita d.o.o. (1)
Planinska bb 15, 10000, Zagreb, Croatia
Tel.: (385) 12413600
Web Site: http://www.cedevita.hr
Nutritional Drinks Mfr
N.A.I.C.S.: 311514

Subsidiary (Non-US):

Multivita d.o.o. (2)
Beogradski put bb, Vrsac, 26300, Vojvo-
dina, Serbia (100%)
Tel.: (381) 13 803 448
Web Site: http://www.multivita.co.rs
Mfr & Distr of Vitamin Instant Drinks &
Supplements
N.A.I.C.S.: 456191

Droga Kolinska d.d. (1)
Kolinska ulica 1, 1000, Ljubljana, Slovenia
Tel.: (386) 14721500
Web Site: http://www.atlanticgrupa.com
Sales Range: $250-299.9 Million
Emp.: 447
Food Processing Services
N.A.I.C.S.: 311423
Enzo Smrekar (Gen Mgr)

Farmacia Plus d.o.o. (1)
Avenija Gojka Suska 6, 10000, Zagreb,
Croatia
Tel.: (385) 12988684
Sales Range: $25-49.9 Million
Emp.: 2
Nutritional Drinks Mfr
N.A.I.C.S.: 311514

Fidifarm d.o.o. (1)
Obrtnicka 37, Bestovje, 10437, Rakitje, Za-
greb, Croatia
Tel.: (385) 1 241 3800
Web Site: https://www.dietpharm.com
Sales Range: $25-49.9 Million
Emp.: 79
Nutritional & Dietary Drinks Mfr
N.A.I.C.S.: 311514

ATLANTIC INSURANCE COMPANY PUBLIC LTD
15 Esperidon Str, 2001, Strovolos,
Cyprus
Tel.: (357) 22886000   CY
Web Site: http://www.atlantic.com.cy
Year Founded: 1983
ATL—(CYP)
Rev.: $26,427,576
Assets: $78,910,935
Liabilities: $35,339,422
Net Worth: $43,571,513
Earnings: $7,709,116
Emp.: 121
Fiscal Year-end: 12/31/19
Insurance Services
N.A.I.C.S.: 524298
Emilios Pyrishis (Chm & Mng Dir)

Subsidiaries:

Atlantic Securities Ltd. (1)
37 Prodromou Str, 1090, Nicosia, Cyprus
Tel.: (357) 22445400
Web Site: https://www.atlanticfs.com
Financial Brokerage Services
N.A.I.C.S.: 523999
Andreas Nicolaou (Head-Asset Mgmt)

ATLANTIC LEAF PROPERTIES LIMITED

26 New Street, Saint Helier, JE2
3RA, Jersey
Tel.: (44) 1534507000   MU
Web Site: http://www.atlanticleaf.mu
Year Founded: 2013
ALP—(MAU)
Rev.—$38,354,003
Assets: $502,244,715
Liabilities: $244,568,272
Net Worth: $257,676,443
Earnings: $27,011,048
Fiscal Year-end: 02/28/20
Real Estate Investment Trust
N.A.I.C.S.: 525990
Paul Leaf-Wright (CEO)

ATLANTIC LITHIUM LIMITED
Level 17 Angel Place 123 Pitt Street,
Sydney, 2000, NSW, Australia
Tel.: (61) 280720640
Web Site:
https://www.ironridgeresources.com
A11—(ASX)
Rev.: $479,343
Assets: $27,501,482
Liabilities: $3,829,521
Net Worth: $23,671,961
Earnings: ($8,443,581)
Fiscal Year-end: 06/30/24
Iron Ore Mining
N.A.I.C.S.: 212210
Vincent Mascolo (CEO)

ATLANTIC LUMPUS AS
Moflaget, Sleneset, 8762, Oslo, Nor-
way
Tel.: (47) 46683812
Fishing Farm Operator
N.A.I.C.S.: 112511
Dan Kristian Larssen (CEO)

ATLANTIC NAVIGATION HOLDINGS (SINGAPORE) LIMITED
30 Cecil Street 19-08 Prudential
Tower, Singapore, 49909, Singapore
Tel.: (65) 68121611   SG
Web Site:
https://www.atlanticnavigation.com
Year Founded: 1997
5UL—(CAT)
Rev.: $64,858,000
Assets: $152,704,000
Liabilities: $70,871,000
Net Worth: $81,833,000
Earnings: $11,208,000
Emp.: 176
Fiscal Year-end: 12/31/22
Holding Company
N.A.I.C.S.: 551112
Kok Liang Chew (Co-Sec)

Subsidiaries:

Atlantic Maritime Group FZE (1)
Plot-HD02 Hamriyah Free Zone, PO Box
6653, Sharjah, United Arab Emirates
Tel.: (971) 65263577
Ship Repair Services
N.A.I.C.S.: 336611

ATLANTIC PACKAGING PRODUCTS LTD.
111 Progress Ave, Scarborough, M1P
2Y9, ON, Canada
Tel.: (416) 298-8101
Web Site: http://www.atlantic.ca
Sales Range: $200-249.9 Million
Emp.: 2,500
Mfr & Distribution Services
N.A.I.C.S.: 561910
Irving Granovsky (Chm)

ATLANTIC POULTRY INC.
791 Belcher Street RR 1, Port Williams, B0P 1T0, NS, Canada
Tel.: (902) 678-1335

Web Site:
http://www.atlanticpoultry.com
Year Founded: 1943
Chicken, Turkey & Egg Products
N.A.I.C.S.: 112310

Subsidiaries:

**Atlantic Poultry Inc. - Egg
Division** (1)
830 Belcher Street, Port Williams, B0P 1T0,
NS, Canada
Tel.: (902) 679-4910
Web Site: http://www.atlanticpoultry.com
Egg Hatching Services
N.A.I.C.S.: 112310

Atlantic Poultry Inc. - Feed Mill (1)
34 Highway 358, Greenwich, B0P 1T0, NS,
Canada
Tel.: (902) 542-3821
Poultry Feed Mfr
N.A.I.C.S.: 311119

**Atlantic Poultry Inc. - Hatchery
Division** (1)
9565 Commercial Street, New Minas, B4N
3G3, NS, Canada
Tel.: (902) 678-0480
Web Site: http://www.atlanticpoultry.com
Emp.: 20
Hatchery Services
N.A.I.C.S.: 112340
Bob Cudmore (VP-Fin & Admin)

ATLANTIC PROMOTIONS INC.
770 Guimond blvd, Longueuil, J4G
1V6, QC, Canada
Tel.: (514) 871-1095
Web Site:
http://atlanticpromotionsinc.com
Year Founded: 1965
Rev.: $25,000,000
Emp.: 100
Kitchen Products Distr
N.A.I.C.S.: 423220
Juanita Coumbias (VP-Starfrit USA)

ATLANTIC SOCIETE FRANCAISE DEVELOP THERMIQUE S.A.
44 Boulevard des Etats Unis, BP 65,
F-85000, La Roche-sur-Yon, France
Tel.: (33) 251443434   FR
Web Site: http://www.atlantic.fr
Holding Company; Residential, Com-
mercial & Industrial Heating, Ventila-
tion, Air-Conditioning & Water Heat-
ing Equipment Designer & Mfr
N.A.I.C.S.: 551112
Pierre-Louis Francois (Dir-Publ)

Subsidiaries:

Atlantic SFDT (1)
58 avenue du General Leclerc, F-92340,
Bourg-la-Reine, France
Tel.: (33) 146836000
Web Site: http://www.atlantic.tm.fr
Sales Range: $800-899.9 Million
Residential, Commercial & Industrial Heat-
ing, Ventilation, Air-Conditioning & Water
Heating Equipment Designer & Mfr
N.A.I.C.S.: 333415

Unit (Domestic):

**Atlantic Climatisation Et Ventilation
S.A.S.** (2)
13 Blvd Monge, BP 71, F-69330, Meyzieu,
Cedex, France
Tel.: (33) 4 72 45 11 45
Web Site: http://www.atlantic-
climatisation.com
Air Conditioning Equipment Mfr & Distr
N.A.I.C.S.: 333415
Pierre Louis Francois (Dir-Publ)

Atlantic Franco Belge (2)
58 Ave du General Leclerc, F-92340,
Bourg-la-Reine, France
Tel.: (33) 146836000
Web Site: http://www.atlantic.fr
Hot Water Heaters & Boilers Mfr, Distr &
Services

N.A.I.C.S.: 332410

Atlantic Guillot (2)
58 avenue du General Leclerc, F-92340,
Bourg-la-Reine, France
Tel.: (33) 146836000
Web Site: http://www.atlantic-comfort.com
Sales Range: $25-49.9 Million
Emp.: 200
Commercial & Industrial Boilers Mfr, Distr &
Services
N.A.I.C.S.: 332410
Jilles Romagne (Mgr-Intl Sls)

Atlantic Ventilation (2)
13 Boulevard Monge, BP 71, F-69882,
Meyzieu, Cedex, France
Tel.: (33) 4 7245 1100
Web Site: http://www.atlantic-ventilation.fr
Ventilation Equipment Mfr & Distr
N.A.I.C.S.: 333413

Cotherm S.A.S. (1)
Z I Les Levees, Vinay, 38470, Isre, France
Tel.: (33) 476368297
Web Site: http://www.cotherm.com
Electromechanical Thermostat Mfr
N.A.I.C.S.: 334419

Hamworthy Heating Limited (1)
Fleets Corner, Poole, BH17 7LA, Dorset,
United Kingdom
Tel.: (44) 1202662500
Web Site: http://www.hamworthy-
heating.com
Sales Range: $25-49.9 Million
Emp.: 150
Commercial Heating Equipment Designer &
Mfr
N.A.I.C.S.: 332410

Thermor (1)
17 rue Croix Fauchet, BP 46, Saint-Jean-
de-la-Ruelle, F-45141, France
Tel.: (33) 238713871
Web Site: http://www.thermor.tm.fr
Sales Range: $50-74.9 Million
Emp.: 100
Electric Heaters & Bathroom Products Mfr &
Distr
N.A.I.C.S.: 333414

Ygnis Industrie (1)
Route De Solesmes, 59400, Cauroir, Nord,
France
Tel.: (33) 327731875
Web Site: http://www.ygnis.com
Sales Range: $50-74.9 Million
Emp.: 200
Residential & Commercial Boilers Mfr
N.A.I.C.S.: 332410

ATLANTIC SUPER MARKET S.A.
516 Vouliagmenis Ave, 17456, Alimos
Attikis, Greece
Tel.: (30) 2109971500
Web Site: http://www.atlantic.gr
Sales Range: $800-899.9 Million
Emp.: 3,400
Supermarket Owner & Operator
N.A.I.C.S.: 445110
Christos Sideris (Dir-Fin)

Subsidiaries:

VITA PI S.A. (1)
13th Klm Thessaloniki-Veria Old National
Road, 54623, Thessaloniki, Greece
Tel.: (30) 2310722799
Soft Drink Whslr
N.A.I.C.S.: 424490

ATLANTIC WIND & SOLAR, INC.
2 Bloor St Suite 3500, Toronto, M4W
1A8, ON, Canada
Tel.: (416) 900-0380   WV
Web Site:
http://www.atlanticwindandsolar.com
AWSL—(OTCIQ)
Rev.: $2,331,000
Assets: $936,000
Liabilities: $3,599,000
Net Worth: ($2,663,000)
Earnings: ($1,117,000)

Atlantic Wind & Solar, Inc.—(Continued)

Fiscal Year-end: 12/31/20
Wind & Solar Electric Power
N.A.I.C.S.: 221115
Kevin Bagnall *(Chm, Pres & CEO)*

Subsidiaries:

KB Industries, Inc.　　　　　　　　**(1)**
4600 140th Ave N Ste 200, Clearwater, FL 33762
Tel.: (727) 723-3300
Web Site: http://www.kbius.com
Flexible Paving System Mfr
N.A.I.C.S.: 324121

ATLANTIC ZEISER GMBH & CO.

Bogenstrasse 6 8, Emmengen, 78576, Germany
Tel.: (49) 74652910
Web Site:
　http://www.atlanticzeiser.com
Year Founded: 1997
Sales Range: $50-74.9 Million
Emp.: 350
Supplier of Technology Solutions for the Numbering, Printing, Encoding & Information Processing Industries
N.A.I.C.S.: 561910
Manfred Minich *(CEO)*

Subsidiaries:

Atlantic Zeiser (Asia) Sdn. Bhd.　**(1)**
17 Jalan PJS 7/19 Bandar Sunway, 46150, Petaling Jaya, Selangor, Malaysia
Tel.: (60) 356210906
Web Site: http://www.atlanticzeiser-asia.com.my
Printing Machinery Distr
N.A.I.C.S.: 423830

Atlantic Zeiser Ltd　　　　　　　　**(1)**
53 Central Way, Andover, SP10 5AN, Hampshire, United Kingdom
Tel.: (44) 1264324222
Web Site: http://www.atlanticzeiserUK.com
Sales Range: $25-49.9 Million
Emp.: 19
Photographic Equipment & Supplies Whslr
N.A.I.C.S.: 423410

Atlantic Zeiser S.A.　　　　　　　　**(1)**
C/ Manuel Pombo Angulo 12 3a Planta Oficina 6, 28050, Madrid, Spain
Tel.: (34) 914336661
Web Site: http://www.atlanticzeiser.es
Sales Range: $50-74.9 Million
Emp.: 10
Industrial Machinery Whslr
N.A.I.C.S.: 423830

Atlantic Zeiser S.A.S.　　　　　　　**(1)**
21-23 rue Eugene Dupuis-Europarc, 94043, Creteil, France
Tel.: (33) 156711309
Web Site: http://www.atlanticzeiser.fr
Sales Range: $50-74.9 Million
Emp.: 10
Industrial Machinery Whslr
N.A.I.C.S.: 423830

Atlantic Zeiser Srl　　　　　　　　**(1)**
Via Varesina 174, 20156, Milan, Italy
Tel.: (39) 0233497740
Web Site: http://www.atlanticzeiser.it
Sales Range: $25-49.9 Million
Emp.: 10
Durable Goods Merchant Whslr
N.A.I.C.S.: 423990
Luigi Rescaldani *(Gen Mgr)*

Atlantic Zeiser, Inc.　　　　　　　**(1)**
15 Patton Dr, West Caldwell, NJ 07006-6404
Tel.: (973) 228-0800
Web Site: http://www.atlanticzeiserusa.com
Sales Range: $25-49.9 Million
Emp.: 23
Supplier of Technology for The Numbering, Printing, Encoding & Information Processing Industries
N.A.I.C.S.: 333310
Thomas Coco *(Pres)*

Beijing Atlantic Zeiser Tech Co. Ltd.　　　　　　　　　　　　　　　**(1)**
2nd Fl Unit C Jing Chang High-Tech Info Industrial Pk No 97, ChangPing Rd Chang Ping Dist, 102206, Beijing, China
Tel.: (86) 1082893051
Web Site: http://www.atlanticzeiser.com
Sales Range: $25-49.9 Million
Emp.: 13
Industrial Maohinory Mfr
N.A.I.C.S.: 333310

ATLANTICA HOTELS & RESORTS LTD

PO Box 52 001, Potamos Yermasoyias, 4060, Limassol, Cyprus
Tel.: (357) 25 883 500　　　　　**CY**
Web Site:
　http://www.atlanticahotels.com
Year Founded: 1980
Hotels & Resorts
N.A.I.C.S.: 721110

Subsidiaries:

Kermia Hotels Ltd　　　　　　　　**(1)**
74 Cavo Greco Avenue, Ayia Napa, 5330, Cyprus
Tel.: (357) 23721401
Web Site: http://www.atlanticahotels.com
Hotels & Motels
N.A.I.C.S.: 721110
Charalambos Paytis *(Mgr)*

ATLANTICA SUSTAINABLE INFRASTRUCTURE PLC

Great West House Gw1 Great West Road, Middlesex, Brentford, TW8 9DF, Greater London, United Kingdom
Tel.: (44) 2034990465　　　　　**UK**
Web Site:
　https://www.atlanticayield.com
Year Founded: 2013
AY—(NASDAQ)
Rev.: $1,099,894,000
Assets: $8,714,333,000
Liabilities: $7,125,524,000
Net Worth: $1,588,809,000
Earnings: $36,448,000
Emp.: 1,366
Fiscal Year-end: 12/31/23
Renewable Energy Services
N.A.I.C.S.: 221118
Santiago Seage Medela *(CEO)*

ATLANTIS S.A.

Harju maakond Kesklinna linnaosa Tornimae tn 5, 10145, Tallinn, Estonia
Tel.: (372) 243673131
Web Site: https://www.atlantis-sa.pl
ATS—(WAR)
Rev.: $49,898,160
Assets: $770,009,640
Liabilities: $2,772,120
Net Worth: $767,237,520
Earnings: $45,739,980
Fiscal Year-end: 12/31/22
Wind Electric Power Generation Services
N.A.I.C.S.: 221115
Damian Patrowicz *(Pres & CEO)*

ATLANTIS SUBMARINES INTERNATIONAL INC.

210 W 6th Ave Ste 200, Vancouver, V5Y 1K8, BC, Canada
Tel.: (604) 875-1367
Web Site:
　http://www.atlantissubmarines.com
Year Founded: 1983
Sales Range: $25-49.9 Million
Emp.: 400
Holding Company; Undersea Tour Services
N.A.I.C.S.: 551112
Dennis Hurd *(Founder, Pres & CEO)*

Subsidiaries:

Atlantis Adventures, LLC.　　　　**(1)**
252 Paoa Pl, Honolulu, HI 96815
Web Site:
　http://www.atlantisadventures.com
Tour Operator
N.A.I.C.S.: 561520
Dennis Hurd *(Founder, Pres & CEO)*

Atlantis Submarines Hawaii, Inc.　**(1)**
1600 Kapiolani Blvd, Honolulu, HI 96814
Tel.: (808) 973-9800
Web Site:
　http://www.atlantisadventures.com
Sales Range: $25-49.9 Million
Undersea Tour Services
N.A.I.C.S.: 561520

ATLANTIS YATIRIM HOLDING A.S.

Bostanci District Bagdat Street Catalcesme Palace B Block, N478 Interior Door No 16 Kadikoy, Istanbul, Turkiye
Tel.: (90) 2163561621
Web Site:
　https://www.atlantisholding.com.tr
Year Founded: 1994
ATSYH—(IST)
Rev.: $1,586,228
Assets: $1,286,177
Liabilities: $710,914
Net Worth: $575,263
Earnings: $326,566
Fiscal Year-end: 12/31/22
Holding Company
N.A.I.C.S.: 551112
Necdet Deniz *(Chm)*

ATLAS BANGLADESH LIMITED

256-267 Tongi Industrial Area, Tongi Gazipur, Dhaka, 1710, Bangladesh
Tel.: (880) 29802327
Web Site: https://www.atlas.gov.bd
Year Founded: 1966
ATLASBANG—(DHA)
Rev.: $3,928,481
Assets: $58,327,370
Liabilities: $9,807,025
Net Worth: $48,520,345
Earnings: ($563,999)
Emp.: 147
Fiscal Year-end: 06/30/22
Motor Vehicle Parts Distr
N.A.I.C.S.: 441227
Shahidul Hoque Bhuia *(Chm)*

ATLAS CLEAN AIR LTD.

Unit 6 Millennium City Park Bluebell Way, Preston, PR2 5PY, Lancashire, United Kingdom
Tel.: (44) 1772 707500
Web Site:
　http://www.atlascleanair.com
Cleanroom Design & Installation Services
N.A.I.C.S.: 238990

Subsidiaries:

Clean Modules Ltd　　　　　　　　**(1)**
MillHouse Business Centre Station Rd, Castle Donington, DE74 2NJ, Derbyshire, United Kingdom
Tel.: (44) 1332696970
Web Site: http://www.cleanmodules.co.uk
Cleanroom Construction Services
N.A.I.C.S.: 236220
Nigel Coles *(Project Mgr-Engrg)*

ATLAS CONSOLIDATED MINING & DEVELOPMENT CORPORATION

503-P Pacific Tower 5F Five E-Com Center, Palm Coast Ave Corner Pacific Drive Mall of Asia Complex, Pasay, 1300, Philippines
Tel.: (63) 284030813

Web Site:
　https://www.atlasmining.com.ph
Year Founded: 1953
ACMDY—(OTCEM)
Rev.: $340,615,922
Assets: $1,231,899,564
Liabilities: $413,217,799
Net Worth: $818,681,765
Earnings: $20,177,954
Fiscal Year-end: 12/31/23
Copper, Silver & Gold Mining
N.A.I.C.S.: 212230
Martin C. Buckingham *(Exec VP)*

Subsidiaries:

ACMDC Ventures, Inc. (AVI)　　**(1)**
125 Velez Street Corner of Osmena Street, Cebu, Philippines
Tel.: (63) 322530790
Mining
N.A.I.C.S.: 212230

ATLAS CONVERTING EQUIPMENT LIMITED

8 Wolseley Road Woburn Road Industrial Estate, Bedford, Kempston, MK42 7XT, Bedfordshire, United Kingdom
Tel.: (44) 1234852553
Web Site:
　http://www.atlasconverting.com
Year Founded: 1976
Sales Range: $50-74.9 Million
Emp.: 180
Converting Equipment Mfr
N.A.I.C.S.: 333243
Alan Johnson *(Mng Dir)*

Subsidiaries:

A.C.E. (Shanghai) Trading Co. Ltd.　　　　　　　　　　　　　　　**(1)**
6P New Shanghai International Tower 360 South Pudong Road, Shanghai, 200120, China
Tel.: (86) 21 6886 2501
Sales Range: $100-124.9 Million
Emp.: 4
Slitter Rewinder Distr
N.A.I.C.S.: 333998
Raymond Chan *(Reg Mgr-Sls)*

Atlas Converting Equipment (India) Pvt. Ltd.　　　　　　　　　　　**(1)**
Plant No 13 Extension Office Building Eastern Express Highway, Pirojsha Nagar Vikhroli East, Mumbai, 400 079, India
Tel.: (91) 992 081 9791
Web Site: http://www.atlasconverting.com
Sales Range: $25-49.9 Million
Emp.: 4
Slitter Rewinder Distr
N.A.I.C.S.: 333998
Kavish Shah *(Area Mgr-Sls)*

Atlas Converting North America, Inc.　　　　　　　　　　　　　　**(1)**
9801-F Southern Pine Bvld, Charlotte, NC 28273
Tel.: (704) 587-2450
Slitter Rewinder Distr
N.A.I.C.S.: 333998

ATLAS COPCO AB

Sickla Industrivag 19 Nacka, 105 23, Stockholm, Sweden
Tel.: (46) 87439000　　　　　　**SE**
Web Site:
　https://www.atlascopco.com
Year Founded: 1873
ATCO—(NASDAQ)
Rev.: $16,172,038,177
Assets: $17,110,530,407
Liabilities: $8,540,466,624
Net Worth: $8,570,063,784
Earnings: $2,627,403,598
Emp.: 53,000
Fiscal Year-end: 12/31/23
Industrial Equipmnt Mfr
N.A.I.C.S.: 423830

Subsidiaries:

ABAC Aria Compressa S.p.A **(1)**
Via Cristoforo Colombo 3, 10070, Robassomero, Turin, Italy
Tel.: (39) 01 19 24 64 00
Web Site:
http://www.abacaircompressors.com
Sales Range: $125-149.9 Million
Emp.: 250
Industrial Air Compressor Mfr & Distr
N.A.I.C.S.: 333912
Uwe Schraader *(Gen Mgr)*

Subsidiary (US):

ABAC AMERICAN IMC Inc **(2)**
1623 Cedar Line Dr, Rock Hill, SC 29730
Tel.: (803) 980-6570
Air Compressor Mfr
N.A.I.C.S.: 333912

Subsidiary (Non-US):

ABAC Air Compressors s.a Pty Ltd. **(2)**
5 Hesketh Road, Westmead, 4001, Durban, South Africa
Tel.: (27) 31 700 6501
Sales Range: $25-49.9 Million
Emp.: 14
Air Compressor Distr
N.A.I.C.S.: 423830

ABAC CATALUNYA S.L. **(2)**
C/Barcelona 21-23, Casserres, 8693, Spain
Tel.: (34) 938 22 51 80
Air Compressor Distr
N.A.I.C.S.: 423730

ABAC DMS Air Compressors Pte Ltd **(2)**
25 Defu Ln, 539266, Singapore, Singapore
Tel.: (65) 64636531
Air Compressor Mfr
N.A.I.C.S.: 333912

ABAC France S.A.S. **(2)**
9 Rue Laurent de Lavoisier - ZI des Aureats, BP 179, 26800, Portes-les-Valence, France
Tel.: (33) 4 75 41 81 51
Web Site: http://www.abac-france.fr
Air Compressor Mfr
N.A.I.C.S.: 333912

ABAC UK Ltd **(2)**
Unit 5 Westway 21 Chesford Grange, Warrington, WA1 4SZ, Cheshire, United Kingdom
Tel.: (44) 1869 326 226
Web Site:
http://www.abacaircompressors.com
Air Compressor Mfr & Distr
N.A.I.C.S.: 333912

ALUP Kompressoren GmbH **(2)**
Nurtinger Str 50, 73257, Kongen, Germany
Tel.: (49) 7024 9612 100
Sales Range: $25-49.9 Million
Emp.: 15
Air Compressor Mfr
N.A.I.C.S.: 333912

ALUP Kompressoren B.V. **(1)**
Biezenwade 10, Postbus 1312, 3430 BH, Nieuwegein, Netherlands
Tel.: (31) 30 2809000
Sales Range: $25-49.9 Million
Emp.: 33
Air Compressor Mfr
N.A.I.C.S.: 333912
J. Neelen *(Gen Mgr)*

Subsidiary (Non-US):

ALUP CZ spol. S.r.o **(2)**
U Stadionu 4, Breclav, 690 02, Czech Republic
Tel.: (420) 519 322 980
Web Site: http://www.alup.com
Emp.: 8
Air Compressor Mfr
N.A.I.C.S.: 333912
Vitezslav Typner *(Acct Mgr)*

ALUP Kompressoren Polska Sp. Z.o.o. **(2)**
Al Krakowska 26 Janki, Raszyn, 05-090, Warsaw, Poland
Tel.: (48) 22 720 65 90

Web Site: http://www.alup.com
Sales Range: $50-74.9 Million
Emp.: 7
Air Compressor Sales & Installation Services
N.A.I.C.S.: 423730

Alup Grassair Kompressoren BV **(1)**
Galliersweg 27, 5349 AT, Oss, Netherlands
Tel.: (31) 412664190
Web Site: http://www.alupgrassair.nl
Compressor Mfr
N.A.I.C.S.: 333912

Atlas Copco (Botswana) (Pty) Ltd **(1)**
Unit 1 Plot 175 Gaborone International Commerce Park, Gaborone, 00267, Botswana
Tel.: (267) 395 9155
Sales Range: $25-49.9 Million
Emp.: 77
Air Compressor Mfr
N.A.I.C.S.: 333912
Obbie Muntwmo *(Mgr-Bus Line)*

Atlas Copco (China) Investment Co., Ltd. **(1)**
Floor 12 Building 36 No 1888 New Jinqiao Road, Shanghai, 201206, China
Tel.: (86) 4006169018
Web Site: https://www.atlascopco.com.cn
N.A.I.C.S.: 335999

Atlas Copco (Cyprus) Ltd **(1)**
39 Tripoleos Street, Latsia, 2235, Nicosia, Cyprus
Tel.: (357) 22 48 07 40
Web Site: http://www.atlascopco.com
Sales Range: $50-74.9 Million
Emp.: 10
Compressor & Generator Distr
N.A.I.C.S.: 423830

Atlas Copco (India) Ltd. **(1)**
Sveanagar Dapodi, Pune, 411 012, Maharashtra, India
Tel.: (91) 2039852100
Web Site: http://www.atlascopco.com
Air & Gas Compressor & Vacuum Pumps Mfr
N.A.I.C.S.: 333248
Umesh Oza *(Sec & Head-Legal)*

Atlas Copco (Ireland) Ltd **(1)**
Unit G15 Calmount Business Park, Bluebell, Dublin, 12, Ireland
Tel.: (353) 1 4505978
Web Site: http://www.atlascopco.ie
Sales Range: $25-49.9 Million
Emp.: 35
Industrial Machinery Mfr & Distr
N.A.I.C.S.: 333248
Alexander Pavlov *(Gen Mgr-Compressor Technique Bus)*

Atlas Copco (Malaysia) Sdn. Bhd. **(1)**
26 Jalan Anggerik Mokara 31/47 Kota Kemuning Section 31, Shah Alam, 40460, Selangor, Malaysia
Tel.: (60) 3 5123 8888
Web Site: http://www.atlascopco.com.my
Construction & Mining Machinery Distr
N.A.I.C.S.: 423810

Atlas Copco (N.Z.) Ltd **(1)**
50 Carbine Road Mt Wellington, Private Bag 92-814, Penrose, Auckland, New Zealand
Tel.: (64) 9 5794069
Web Site: http://www.atlascopco.co.nz
Emp.: 25
Construction & Mining Equipment Rental Services
N.A.I.C.S.: 532412

Subsidiary (Domestic):

Intermech Ltd **(2)**
Level 3 Building 10 666 Great South Road, PO Box 204013, Ellerslie Highbrook, 2161, Auckland, New Zealand
Tel.: (64) 9 525 2220
Web Site: http://www.intermech.co.nz
Compressed Natural Gas Refueling Solution Mfr
N.A.I.C.S.: 333248

Atlas Copco (Philippines) Inc. **(1)**

North Main Avenue Lot 12 Block 2 Laguna Techno Park, Binan, 4024, Laguna, Philippines
Tel.: (63) 2 8430535
Web Site: http://www.atlascopco.com.ph
Air Compressor Mfr & Distr
N.A.I.C.S.: 333912

Atlas Copco (Schweiz) AG **(1)**
Buetigenstrasse 80, 2557, Studen, Switzerland
Tel.: (41) 32 374 19 00
Web Site: http://www.atlascopco.com
Sales Range: $25-49.9 Million
Emp.: 80
Air Compressor Mfr & Distr
N.A.I.C.S.: 333912
Ricardo Timperi *(Gen Mgr)*

Subsidiary (Domestic):

GreenField AG **(2)**
Sternenfeldstrasse 14, 4127, Birsfelden, Switzerland
Tel.: (41) 61 827 35 35
Web Site: http://www.greenfield-comp.com
Compressor Machinery Installation Services
N.A.I.C.S.: 238220

Servatechnik AG **(2)**
Aeschwuhrstrasse 54, 4665, Oftringen, Switzerland
Tel.: (41) 62 789 75 95
Web Site: http://www.servatechnik.ch
Emp.: 6
Industrial Machinery Distr
N.A.I.C.S.: 423830

Atlas Copco (Shanghai) Equipment Rental Co Ltd **(1)**
T72-2 No 1100 Jinsui Road Jinqiao Export Processing Zone, Shanghai, 201206, China
Tel.: (86) 21 6108 2388
Industrial Equipment Rental Services
N.A.I.C.S.: 532490

Atlas Copco (Shanghai) Process Equipment Co Ltd **(1)**
No 899 Cenglin Road Lingang New City, Pudong New Area, 201306, Shanghai, China
Tel.: (86) 21 60 97 81 00
Emp.: 150
Industrial Machinery Mfr
N.A.I.C.S.: 333248

Atlas Copco (Shanghai) Trading Co., Ltd. **(1)**
No 26 Building No 518 Xinzhuan Road, Songjiang, Shanghai, 201612, China
Tel.: (86) 2124037500
Industrial Machinery & Mining Equipment Mfr
N.A.I.C.S.: 333131

Atlas Copco (Shenyang) Construction and Mining Equipment Ltd **(1)**
No 12 Kunminghu Street Shenyang Economic, Technological Development Zone, Shenyang, 110027, China
Tel.: (86) 24 25811769
Web Site: http://www.shenyangcm.com
Industrial Drilling Machinery Mfr
N.A.I.C.S.: 333248

Atlas Copco (South East Asia) Pte Ltd **(1)**
25 Tuas Avenue 2, Singapore, 639456, Singapore
Tel.: (65) 62 10 80 00
Web Site: http://www.atlascopco.com.sg
Emp.: 60
Construction Equipment Mfr & Distr
N.A.I.C.S.: 333120

Atlas Copco (Thailand) Ltd **(1)**
125 Moo 9 Wellgrow Industry Estate Bangna-Trad Km 36, Bangwua, Bang Pakong, 24130, Chachoengsao, Thailand
Tel.: (66) 38 56 29 00
Web Site: http://www.atlascopco.co.th
Emp.: 200
Air Compressor Mfr
N.A.I.C.S.: 333912
Chanwit Choon *(Mgr-Bus Line-Portable Air & Specialty Rental)*

Atlas Copco (Zambia) Ltd **(1)**
No 210 Kabundi Road, PO Box 11291, Chingola, 10101, Zambia

Tel.: (260) 212 311281
Web Site: http://www.atlascopco.co.zm
Sales Range: $50-74.9 Million
Emp.: 126
Industrial Machinery Mfr & Distr
N.A.I.C.S.: 333248
Andy Ndulubila *(Mgr-Mktg)*

Atlas Copco A/S **(1)**
Berghagan 5, 1405, Langhus, Norway
Tel.: (47) 64860300
Construction Machinery Rental Services
N.A.I.C.S.: 532412

Subsidiary (Domestic):

Atlas Copco Anlegg- og Gruveteknikk A/S **(2)**
Berghagan 5, Langhus, 1405, Norway
Tel.: (47) 64 86 03 00 00
Sales Range: $50-74.9 Million
Emp.: 6
Construction Machinery Rental Services
N.A.I.C.S.: 532412
Erik Presthus *(Gen Mgr)*

Atlas Copco Kompressorteknikk AS **(2)**
Berghagan 5, Langhus, 1405, Norway
Tel.: (47) 64860860
Web Site: http://www.atlascopco.com
Emp.: 100
Industrial Machinery Maintenance Services
N.A.I.C.S.: 811310

Atlas Copco Tools A/S **(2)**
Berghagan 5, Langhus, 1405, Norway
Tel.: (47) 64860400
Machine Tool Distr
N.A.I.C.S.: 423830

Atlas Copco Angola Lda **(1)**
Polo de Desenvolvimento Industrial de Viana Armazem 29, Estrada do Calumbo Zango, Viana, Luanda, Angola
Tel.: (244) 929 30 31 39
Web Site: http://www.atlascopco.com
Construction Machinery Mfr & Distr
N.A.I.C.S.: 333120

Atlas Copco Argentina S.A.C.I. **(1)**
Estados Unidos 5335 Malvinas Argentinas, 1667, Buenos Aires, Argentina
Tel.: (54) 3327413800
Web Site: https://www.atlascopco.com
N.A.I.C.S.: 335999

Atlas Copco Assistance Technique **(1)**
34 Rue Belkacem Amani, BP 161, 16035, Hydra, Algeria
Tel.: (213) 21693558
N.A.I.C.S.: 331513

Atlas Copco Australia Pty Ltd **(1)**
3 Bessemer Street, Blacktown, 2148, NSW, Australia
Tel.: (61) 2 9621 9707
Web Site: http://www.atlascopco.com.au
Emp.: 1,000
Construction Equipment Mfr & Distr
N.A.I.C.S.: 333120
James Cameron *(Mgr-Industrial Tool)*

Atlas Copco BH d.o.o. **(1)**
Safeta Zajke 266, 71000, Sarajevo, Bosnia & Herzegovina
Tel.: (387) 33 67 43 91
Emp.: 7
Air Compressor Mfr & Distr
N.A.I.C.S.: 333912
Armin Kremo *(Mgr-Sls-Construction & Mining Technique)*

Atlas Copco BLM S.r.l. **(1)**
Via Guglielmo Pepe 11, 20037, Paderno Dugnano, Milan, Italy
Tel.: (39) 02990351
Industrial Machinery & Mining Equipment Mfr
N.A.I.C.S.: 333131

Atlas Copco Baltic SIA **(1)**
Kalvarijos G 38, 46346, Kaunas, Lithuania
Tel.: (370) 37228861
Web Site: https://www.atlascopco.com
N.A.I.C.S.: 335999

Atlas Copco Bangladesh Ltd. **(1)**
Impetus Level 6 242/B Tejgaon-Gulshan

Atlas Copco AB—(Continued)

Link Road Tejgaon I/A, Dhaka, 1208, Bangladesh
Tel.: (880) 2887894145
Industrial Machinery & Mining Equipment Mfr
N.A.I.C.S.: 333131
Deepak Varshney *(Gen Mgr)*

Atlas Copco Belgium n.v. **(1)**
Brusselsesteenweg 346, B-3090, Overijse, Belgium
Tel.: (32) 26890511
Web Site: http://www.atlascopco.be
Emp.: 130
Holding Company
N.A.I.C.S.: 551112

Subsidiary (Domestic):

Atlas Copco ASAP n.v. **(2)**
Boomsesteenweg 957b 93, Antwerp, 2610, Belgium
Tel.: (32) 38702111
Internet Providing Services
N.A.I.C.S.: 517810
Anna-Karin Stenberg *(Gen Mgr)*

Atlas Copco Airpower n.v. **(2)**
Boomsesteenweg 957, Wilrijk, 2610, Belgium **(99%)**
Tel.: (32) 38702111
Web Site: http://www.atlascopco.com
Develop, Market & Manufacture of Stationary & Portable Compressors, in Both Standard & Specially Designed Versions
N.A.I.C.S.: 333912

Division (Domestic):

Atlas Copco Airtec **(3)**
Boomsesteenweg 957, PO Box 101, 2610, Wilrijk, 2610, Belgium
Tel.: (32) 38702111
Web Site: http://www.atlascopco.com
Sales Range: $350-399.9 Million
Emp.: 10
Production, Development & Sales of Compressors
N.A.I.C.S.: 333912
Ronnie Leten *(CEO)*

Atlas Copco Industrial Air **(3)**
Boomsesteenweg 957, PO Box 103, Wilrijk, 2610, Belgium
Tel.: (32) 38702111
Web Site: http://www.meetatlascopco.com
Sales Range: $350-399.9 Million
Emp.: 2,300
Mfr of Mobile Air Compressors, Power Generators & Light Towers
N.A.I.C.S.: 333912

Atlas Copco Oil-free Air **(3)**
Boomsesteenweg 957, PO Box 101, BE 2610, Wilrijk, Belgium
Tel.: (32) 038702111
Web Site: http://www.atlascopco.com
Sales Range: $350-399.9 Million
Emp.: 2,300
Mfr of Mobile Air Compressors, Power Generators & Light Towers
N.A.I.C.S.: 333912

Atlas Copco Portable Air **(3)**
Boomsesteenweg 957, PO Box 102, 2610, Wilrijk, Belgium
Tel.: (32) 34506011
Web Site: http://www.atlascopco.com
Sales Range: $150-199.9 Million
Emp.: 600
Mfr of Mobile Air Compressors, Power Generators & Light Towers
N.A.I.C.S.: 333912

Subsidiary (Domestic):

Atlas Copco Rental Europe n.v. **(2)**
Antwerpsesteenweg 50, 2840, Rumst, 2840, Belgium
Tel.: (32) 15 30 73 30
Sales Range: $25-49.9 Million
Emp.: 43
Industrial Machinery Rental Services
N.A.I.C.S.: 532490
Tom Deckers *(Gen Mgr)*

International Compressor Distribution n.v.
Boomsesteenweg 957, 2610, Wilrijk, Belgium

Tel.: (32) 38702111
Emp.: 1
Air Compressor Distr
N.A.I.C.S.: 423730
Amit Sharma *(Gen Mgr)*

Atlas Copco Boliviana SA **(1)**
Av 20 de Octubre 2665 Esquina Campos Edificio, Torre Azul 2do Piso Of 201, La Paz, Bolivia
Tel.: (591) 2 211 20 00
Construction Machinery Mfr & Distr
N.A.I.C.S.: 333120
Gianfranco Barbera *(Engr-Sls-Construction & Mining-Surface Mining)*

Atlas Copco Brasil Ltda **(1)**
Alameda Araguaia 2700 Tambore, Barueri, 06455-000, Sao Paulo, Brazil
Tel.: (55) 1134788700
Web Site: http://www.atlascopco.com
Industrial Machinery & Mining Equipment Mfr
N.A.I.C.S.: 333131

Atlas Copco Bulgaria Eood **(1)**
7 Iskarsko Shose Blvd Building 3 Office 4, 1528, Sofia, Bulgaria
Tel.: (359) 2 489 3178
Web Site: http://www.atlascopco.com
Sales Range: $25-49.9 Million
Emp.: 35
Construction Machinery Mfr & Distr
N.A.I.C.S.: 333120
Predrag Ilibasic *(Reg Mgr-Bus Line)*

Atlas Copco CMT Sweden AB **(1)**
Sickla Industrivag 19, Nacka, 131 54, Sweden
Tel.: (46) 87439230
Sales Range: $50-74.9 Million
Emp.: 10
Construction & Mining Machinery Distr
N.A.I.C.S.: 423810

Atlas Copco Central Asia LLP **(1)**
39 Kabdolova street, 06005, Atyrau, Kazakhstan
Tel.: (7) 7019716626
Web Site: http://www.atlascopco.com
Emp.: 200
Air Compressor Mfr & Distr
N.A.I.C.S.: 333912

Atlas Copco Chilena S.A.C. **(1)**
Panamericana Norte No 5001, Conchali, Santiago, Chile
Tel.: (56) 229973500
Web Site: http://www.atlascopco.com
Construction Machinery Mfr & Distr
N.A.I.C.S.: 333120

Atlas Copco China/Hong Kong Ltd **(1)**
Unit 1018 Tower 2 Grand Central Plaza No 138, Shatin Rural Committee Road, Sha Tin, New Territories, China (Hong Kong)
Tel.: (852) 27 97 66 00
Sales Range: $25-49.9 Million
Emp.: 3
Air Compressor Mfr
N.A.I.C.S.: 333912

Atlas Copco Colombia Ltda **(1)**
Cra 85 D No 46A-65 Bod 6 y 7, Bogota, Colombia
Tel.: (57) 1 4199200
Air Compressor Mfr
N.A.I.C.S.: 333912
Marcela Bohorquez *(Comm Mgr)*

Atlas Copco Compressor AB **(1)**
Sicklaw Industry No 19, Nacka, 131 34, Sweden
Tel.: (46) 87 43 90 00
Web Site: http://www.atlascopco.com
Emp.: 1,000
Air Compressor Distr
N.A.I.C.S.: 423720
Vladimir Kozlovski *(Engr-Quality)*

Atlas Copco Construction Tools AB **(1)**
Sickla Industrivag 19, 131 54, Nacka, Sweden **(100%)**
Tel.: (46) 87439600
Web Site: http://www.atlascopco.com
Sales Range: $50-74.9 Million
Emp.: 200

Mfr, Marketer & Distributor of Fuel-Powered Drills
N.A.I.C.S.: 333991

Subsidiary (Non-US):

Atlas Copco Construction Tools GmbH **(2)**
Helenstrasse 149, 45143, Essen, Germany **(100%)**
Tel.: (49) 2016331569
Sales Range: $75-99.9 Million
N.A.I.C.S.: 331513

Atlas Copco Construction Tools sarl **(2)**
6 Rue Ferdinand De Lesseps, Goussainville, 95190, France **(100%)**
Tel.: (33) 134047070
Sales Range: $25-49.9 Million
Emp.: 50
N.A.I.C.S.: 331513

Atlas Copco Craelius **(1)**
Bristagatan 13, 195 82, Marsta, Sweden **(100%)**
Tel.: (46) 858778500
Web Site: http://www.atlascopco.com
Sales Range: $25-49.9 Million
Emp.: 90
Equipment Supplier for Core Drilling & Ground Engineering Applications
N.A.I.C.S.: 333131

Atlas Copco Customer Finance AB **(1)**
Sickla Industrivag 19 Nacka, 105 23, Stockholm, Sweden
Tel.: (46) 8 743 83 00
Financial Management Services
N.A.I.C.S.: 523999
Ronnie Leten *(Gen Mgr)*

Subsidiary (Non-US):

Atlas Copco Customer Finance Australia Pty Ltd **(2)**
3 Bessemer St, Blacktown, 2148, NSW, Australia
Tel.: (61) 2 9621 9999
Web Site: http://www.atlascopco.com
Sales Range: $100-124.9 Million
Emp.: 25
Financial Management Services
N.A.I.C.S.: 523999
Joseph Varga *(Mng Dir)*

Atlas Copco Customer Finance Chile Ltda **(2)**
Panamericana Norte 5001, Conchali, 6553935, Santiago, Chile
Tel.: (56) 2 442 36 00
Web Site: http://www.atlascopco.cl
Financial Management Services
N.A.I.C.S.: 523999

Atlas Copco DRC sprl **(1)**
8 Avenue Lukafu Quartier Golf, Lubumbashi, Katanga, Congo, Democratic Republic of
Tel.: (243) 99 100 44 30
Sales Range: $75-99.9 Million
Emp.: 13
Construction Machinery Distr
N.A.I.C.S.: 423810
Lawrence van der Veeken *(Country Mgr)*

Atlas Copco Eastern Africa Ltd **(1)**
Airport North Road, PO Box 40900, 01000, Nairobi, Kenya
Tel.: (254) 206605000
Web Site: http://www.atlascopco.com
Sales Range: $50-74.9 Million
Emp.: 100
Industrial Machinery Distr
N.A.I.C.S.: 423830

Atlas Copco Equipment Egypt S.A.E. **(1)**
El Obour City 1st Industrial Zone - Part 7 - Block No 13024, 11828, Cairo, Egypt
Tel.: (20) 2 46100337
Web Site: http://www.atlascopco.com.eg
Emp.: 3
Compressor & Generator Machinery Distr
N.A.I.C.S.: 423830

Atlas Copco Finance DAC **(1)**
8th Floor Block E Iveagh Court Harcourt Road, Dublin, 2, Ireland

Tel.: (353) 860621258
N.A.I.C.S.: 335999

Atlas Copco France Holding S.A. **(1)**
Zone Industrielle du Vert Galant 2 Avenue de l'Eguillette, Saint-Ouen-l'Aumone, 95310, France
Tel.: (33) 1 3909 3000
Web Site: http://www.atlascopco.com
Emp.: 150
Holding Company
N.A.I.C.S.: 551112

Subsidiary (Domestic):

Atlas Copco Applications Industrielles S.A.S. **(2)**
2 Avenue de l Eguillette, Saint-Ouen-l'Aumone, 95310, France
Tel.: (33) 1 39 09 32 50
Web Site: http://www.atlascopco.com
Industrial Machinery Mfr
N.A.I.C.S.: 333248

Atlas Copco Compresseurs S.A.S **(2)**
2 Avenue de l'Eguillette - ZI du Vert Galant, Saint-Ouen-l'Aumone, 95310, France
Tel.: (33) 1 39 09 31 00
Web Site: http://www.atlascopco.com
Air Compressor Mfr
N.A.I.C.S.: 333912

Subsidiary (Domestic):

Compresseurs Mauguiere S.A.S. **(3)**
2 Avenue des Gros Chevaux, 95004, Cergy-Pontoise, France
Tel.: (33) 1 34 32 94 50
Web Site: http://www.mauguiere.com
Sales Range: $25-49.9 Million
Emp.: 9
Air Compressor Mfr
N.A.I.C.S.: 333912

Compresseurs Worthington Creyssensac S.A.S. **(3)**
2 Avenue des Gros Chevaux, BP 40616, 95004, Saint-Ouen-l'Aumone, France
Tel.: (33) 1 34 32 95 00
Sales Range: $25-49.9 Million
Emp.: 100
Air Compressor Mfr
N.A.I.C.S.: 333912

Subsidiary (Domestic):

Atlas Copco Crepelle S.A.S. **(2)**
2 Place Guy De Dampierre, BP 29, 59000, Lille, France
Tel.: (33) 3 20 52 47 11
Sales Range: $25-49.9 Million
Emp.: 92
Air Compressor Mfr
N.A.I.C.S.: 333912

Atlas Copco Forage et Construction S.A.S. **(2)**
Zone Industrielle du Vert Galant 2 avenue de l'Eguillette, 95310, Saint-Ouen-l'Aumone, France
Tel.: (33) 139093222
Construction & Mining Machinery Whslr
N.A.I.C.S.: 423810

ETS Georges Renault S.A.S. **(2)**
38 Rue Bobby Sands, BP 13627, Zac De La Lorie, Saint-Herblain, 44818, France
Tel.: (33) 2 40802000
Web Site: http://www.cp.com
Industrial Machinery Mfr
N.A.I.C.S.: 333248

Georges Renault S.A. **(2)**
ZAC de la Lorie 38, Rue Bobby Sands, BP 13627, 44236, Saint-Herblain, France **(100%)**
Tel.: (33) 240802000
Rev.: $22,000,000
Emp.: 200
Industrial Tools & Assembly Systems
N.A.I.C.S.: 333991

Atlas Copco France SAS **(1)**
2 Avenue de l Eguillette-ZI Du Vert Galant, 95310, Saint-Ouen-l'Aumone, France
Tel.: (33) 139093068
Air Compressor & Equipment Rental Services
N.A.I.C.S.: 532490

Atlas Copco Ges.m.b.H. (1)
Office Park 1 Top B02 A Flughafen, 1300,
Vienna, Austria
Tel.: (43) 1760120
Web Site: http://www.atlascopco.com
Sales Range: $25-49.9 Million
Emp.: 10
Air Compressor Mfr
N.A.I.C.S.: 333912

Subsidiary (Domestic):

AGRE Kompressoren GmbH (2)
A-4451 Garsten-St, Sankt Ulrich bei Steyr,
4442, Austria
Tel.: (43) 7252 52341 0
Air Compressor Mfr
N.A.I.C.S.: 333912

**Atlas Copco Powercrusher
GmbH** (2)
Gollensdorf 24, 4300, Sankt Valentin, Aus-
tria
Tel.: (43) 7238 293 50
Web Site: http://www.atlascopco.com
Construction Machinery Mfr & Distr
N.A.I.C.S.: 333120

Atlas Copco Ghana Ltd (1)
No 19 Akosombo Street Airport Residential
Area, PO Box 10071, Accra, Ghana
Tel.: (233) 302 77 45 12
Web Site: http://www.atlascopco.com
Sales Range: $75-99.9 Million
Emp.: 126
Construction & Mining Equipment Distr
N.A.I.C.S.: 423810

Atlas Copco Hellas AE (1)
82 Koropiou Vari Street, Koropi, 19400, Ath-
ens, Greece
Tel.: (30) 210 349 96 00
Web Site: http://www.atlascopco.com
Emp.: 56
Compressor & Generator Equipment Distr
N.A.I.C.S.: 423830
Thrasivoulos Pitsilos *(Mgr-Bus Dev)*

Atlas Copco Holding GmbH (1)
Langemarckstr 35, Essen, 45141, Germany
Tel.: (49) 20121770
Emp.: 400
Investment Management Service
N.A.I.C.S.: 523999
Alex Bongaerts *(Gen Mgr)*

Subsidiary (Domestic):

**Atlas Copco Application Center Eu-
rope GmbH** (2)
Langemarckstr 35, Essen, 45141, Germany
Tel.: (49) 20121770
Emp.: 300
Construction Machinery Mfr
N.A.I.C.S.: 333120
Piet Leas *(Pres)*

Atlas Copco Energas Gmbh (2)
Schlehenweg 15, Cologne, 50999, Ger-
many
Tel.: (49) 22369650855
Web Site: http://www.atlascopco.com
Emp.: 150
Air & Gas Compressor Manufacturing
N.A.I.C.S.: 333912

**Atlas Copco Kompressoren und
Drucklufttechnik GmbH** (2)
Langemarckstr 35, Essen, 45141, Germany
Tel.: (49) 20121770
Emp.: 200
Construction Machinery Distr
N.A.I.C.S.: 423810
Piet Leys *(Gen Mgr)*

Atlas Copco MCT GmbH (2)
Langemarckstr 35, Essen, 45141, Germany
Tel.: (49) 20121770
Emp.: 500
Air & Gas Compressor Mfr
N.A.I.C.S.: 333912

**Atlas Copco Tools Central Europe
GmbH** (2)
Langemarckstrasse 35, Essen, 45141, Ger-
many
Tel.: (49) 20121770
Web Site: http://www.atlascopco.com
Compressor Machinery Mfr
N.A.I.C.S.: 333912

Atlas Copco Tools GmbH (2)
Bayernwerkstrasse 112, D-84130, Dingolf-
ing, Germany
Tel.: (49) 873137580
Web Site: http://www.atlascopco.com
Rev.: $7,500,000
Emp.: 87
Tightening Technology Consulting, Testing &
Calibration Services
N.A.I.C.S.: 333248

**IRMER + ELZE Kompressoren
GmbH** (2)
Mindener Strasse 29, 32547, Bad Oeyn-
hausen, Germany
Tel.: (49) 5731 1801 60
Web Site: http://www.irmair.com
Sales Range: $25-49.9 Million
Emp.: 5
Portable Diesel Driven Screw Compressor
Mfr & Distr
N.A.I.C.S.: 333912
Kai Altvater *(Gen Mgr)*

**Atlas Copco Holdings South Africa
(Pty) Ltd** (1)
10 Innes Road Jet Park, Witfield, Boksburg,
1459, South Africa
Tel.: (27) 11 821 9000
Investment Management Service
N.A.I.C.S.: 523999

Subsidiary (Domestic):

**Atlas Copco South Africa (Pty)
Ltd** (2)
Innes Road Jet Park, Witfield, Boksburg,
1459, South Africa
Tel.: (27) 118219800
Web Site: http://www.atlascopco.com
Industrial Machinery Mfr & Distr
N.A.I.C.S.: 333248

Atlas Copco IAS GmbH (1)
Gewerbestrasse 52, 75015, Bretten, Ger-
many
Tel.: (49) 725255600
Industrial Machinery & Mining Equipment
Mfr
N.A.I.C.S.: 333131
Rainer Schmidt *(Mgr-Key Acct)*

**Atlas Copco Industrial Technique
AB** (1)
Sickla Industrivag 19, 10523, Stockholm,
Sweden
Tel.: (46) 87439500
Web Site: https://www.atlascopco.com
N.A.I.C.S.: 335999

**Atlas Copco Industrial Zambia
Limited** (1)
Vibhav Business Complex Plot 2810 Chin-
gola Road, Kitwe, Zambia
Tel.: (260) 212211242
Industrial Machinery & Mining Equipment
Mfr
N.A.I.C.S.: 333131
Michael Musenge *(Country Mgr)*

Atlas Copco Iran AB (1)
236 Avenue Azadi, Tehran, Iran
Tel.: (98) 21 6693 77 11
Web Site: http://www.atlascopco.ir
Construction & Mining Equipment Distr
N.A.I.C.S.: 423810

Atlas Copco Iraq LLC (1)
Gazna Road, Anikwa, Erbil, Iraq
Tel.: (964) 7510322681
N.A.I.C.S.: 335999

Atlas Copco Italia S.p.A. (1)
Via Galileo Galilei no 40, 20092, Ciniselo
Balsamo, Milan, Italy
Tel.: (39) 02 617991
Web Site: http://www.atlascopco.com
Air Compressor Mfr
N.A.I.C.S.: 333912

Subsidiary (Domestic):

Ceccato Aria Compressa S.p.A. (2)
Via Soastene 34, 36040, Brendola, Vice-
nza, Italy
Tel.: (39) 0444 703911
Web Site: http://www.ceccato-
compressors.com
Air Compressor Mfr & Distr
N.A.I.C.S.: 333912

MultiAir Italia S.r.l. (2)
39 Via Gracchi Fratelli, 20092, Ciniselo
Balsamo, Milan, Italy
Tel.: (39) 0266 018 368
Sales Range: $50-74.9 Million
Emp.: 200
Air Compressor Mfr
N.A.I.C.S.: 333912

Atlas Copco KK (1)
Shiba Koen 1-chome No 1 No 1 Sumitomo
Fudosan Onarimon 8 floor tower, Minato-ku,
Tokyo, 105-0011, Japan
Tel.: (81) 368091739
Web Site: http://www.atlascopco.com
Sales Range: $25-49.9 Million
Emp.: 30
Pneumatic Tool Mfr
N.A.I.C.S.: 333991

Subsidiary (Domestic):

Fuji Air Tools Co., Ltd (2)
2-1-14 Kamiji Higashinari-ku, Higashinari-
Ku, Osaka, 537-0003, Japan
Tel.: (81) 669722335
Web Site: http://www.fujiairtools.com
Air Powered Tools & Accessories Mfr &
Distr
N.A.I.C.S.: 333515

Atlas Copco Kft (1)
Vendel Park Huber u 1, Biatorbagy, 2051,
Hungary
Tel.: (36) 23 803 600
Web Site: http://www.atlascopco.com
Sales Range: $25-49.9 Million
Emp.: 40
Pneumatic Power Tools Mfr
N.A.I.C.S.: 333517

**Atlas Copco Kompressorteknik
A/S** (1)
Djursvang 5B, 2620, Albertslund, Denmark
Tel.: (45) 43454611
Web Site: http://www.atlascopco.com
Air Compressor Mfr
N.A.I.C.S.: 333912
Dalila Assous *(Country Mgr)*

Atlas Copco Korea Co., Ltd. (1)
Yemiji Building 14-1 Pangyo Station-ro
192beon-gil, Bundang-gu, Seongnam,
13524, Korea (South)
Tel.: (82) 316200600
Industrial Machinery & Mining Equipment
Mfr
N.A.I.C.S.: 333131
Eric Langmans *(Gen Mgr)*

Atlas Copco LLC (1)
6 Oleny Telihy Str Building 8, 04112, Kiev,
Ukraine
Tel.: (380) 443918241
Industrial Machinery & Mining Equipment
Mfr
N.A.I.C.S.: 333131

Atlas Copco Latvija SIA (1)
Martinmuiza, Marupe, 2167, Latvia
Tel.: (371) 67609190
Web Site: http://www.atlascopco.lv
Sales Range: $25-49.9 Million
Emp.: 12
Construction & Mining Machinery Mfr
N.A.I.C.S.: 333120

Atlas Copco Levant S.A.L (1)
Jdeideh 19 Building 12th Floor Pierre Ge-
mayel AVE, Jdeidet Al Maten, Beirut, Leba-
non
Tel.: (961) 1876782
Industrial Machinery & Mining Equipment
Mfr
N.A.I.C.S.: 333131

Atlas Copco Lietuva UAB (1)
Kalvarijos g 38, 46346, Kaunas, Lithuania
Tel.: (370) 37 228 861
Web Site: http://www.atlascopco.com
Winding Machinery Distr
N.A.I.C.S.: 423810

Atlas Copco Lifton Eood (1)
Tutrakan Boulevard 100, 7000, Ruse, Bul-
garia
Tel.: (359) 8281 05 55
Emp.: 120
Construction Machinery Mfr
N.A.I.C.S.: 333120

**Atlas Copco Makinalari Imalat
AS** (1)
Istasyon Mah Ibis Aga Cad No 6, Tuzla,
34940, Istanbul, Turkiye
Tel.: (90) 216 581 0 581
Web Site: http://www.atlascopco.com
Sales Range: $50-74.9 Million
Emp.: 250
Construction Machinery Mfr
N.A.I.C.S.: 333120

Atlas Copco Maroc SA (1)
2-6 Rue Ibn AL Adara Marrakouchi, Casa-
blanca, 20350, Morocco
Tel.: (212) 522634000
Web Site: http://www.atlascopco.com
Industrial Machinery & Mining Equipment
Mfr
N.A.I.C.S.: 333131

**Atlas Copco Mexicana S.A. de
C.V.** (1)
Blvd Abraham Lincoln No 13 Col, Los
Reyes Industrial Zone, Tlalnepantla, 54073,
State of Mexico, Mexico
Tel.: (52) 5522820600
Industrial Machinery & Mining Equipment
Mfr
N.A.I.C.S.: 333131

Atlas Copco Namibia (Pty) Ltd (1)
Nguni Str Northern Industrial Area, Wind-
hoek, 9000, Namibia
Tel.: (264) 61 26 13 96
Web Site: http://www.atlascopco.co.za
Sales Range: $25-49.9 Million
Emp.: 13
Construction Machinery Mfr
N.A.I.C.S.: 333120
Kobie Koekemoer *(Country Mgr)*

Atlas Copco Nederland B.V. (1)
Merwedeweg 7, 3336 LG, Zwijndrecht,
Netherlands
Tel.: (31) 78 623 02 30
Web Site: http://www.atlascopco.com
Sales Range: $25-49.9 Million
Emp.: 40
Oil & Gas Industrial Equipment Distr
N.A.I.C.S.: 423830

Subsidiary (Domestic):

Atlas Copco Beheer B.V. (2)
Merwedeweg 7, Zwijndrecht, 3336LG, Neth-
erlands
Tel.: (31) 786 23 02 30
Web Site: http://www.atlascopco.com
Sales Range: $50-74.9 Million
Emp.: 145
Air Compressor Mfr
N.A.I.C.S.: 333912
Bob van Wijnen *(Gen Mgr)*

Atlas Copco Rental B.V. (2)
Merwedeweg 7, 3336 LG, Zwijndrecht,
Netherlands
Tel.: (31) 10 23 10 110
Web Site: http://www.atlascopco.com
Sales Range: $50-74.9 Million
Emp.: 2
Construction Machinery Rental & Leasing
Services
N.A.I.C.S.: 532412

Cirmac International B.V. (2)
Lan Van Westenenk 541, 7334 DT, Apel-
doorn, Netherlands
Tel.: (31) 555340110
Web Site: http://www.cirmac.com
Sales Range: $50-74.9 Million
Gas Treatment & Generation Services
N.A.I.C.S.: 213112
Rob van Den Hout *(Gen Mgr)*

Creemers Compressors B.V. (2)
Galliersweg 27, 5349 AT, Oss, Netherlands
Tel.: (31) 412 66 79 99
Web Site: http://www.creemers.nl
Sales Range: $25-49.9 Million
Emp.: 30
Air Compressor Equipment Installation Ser-
vices
N.A.I.C.S.: 238220

Grass-Air Holding B.V. (2)
Galliersweg 27, Oss, 5349 AT, Netherlands
Tel.: (31) 412632956
Web Site: http://www.grassair.nl

Atlas Copco AB—(Continued)

Sales Range: $50-74.9 Million
Emp.: 6
Investment Management Service
N.A.I.C.S.: 523999

Atlas Copco Nigeria Ltd. (1)
110/114 Oshodi Apapa Expressway Isolo,
Lagos, Nigeria
Tel.: (234) 8090500045
Industrial Machinery & Mining Equipment
Mfr
N.A.I.C.S.: 333131
Olawale Adewunmi *(Mgr-Logistics)*

Subsidiary (Non-US):

Grass-Air Compressoren B.V. (2)
Galliersweg 27, Oss, 5349 AT, Netherlands
Tel.: (31) 412 664100
Web Site: http://www.grassair.nl
Sales Range: $25-49.9 Million
Air Compressor Equipment Installation Services
N.A.I.C.S.: 238220
John Neelen *(Gen Mgr)*

Atlas Copco North America LLC (1)
34 Maple Ave, Pine Brook, NJ
07058　　　　　　　　　　　　　　　(100%)
Tel.: (973) 439-3494
Web Site: http://www.atlascopco.com
Sales Range: $5-14.9 Billion
Emp.: 8,200
Holding Company; Industrial, Mining & Construction Equipment & Supplies Distr
N.A.I.C.S.: 551112

Subsidiary (Domestic):

Air Power of Nebraska, Inc. (2)
5401 S 72nd St, Omaha, NE 68127
Tel.: (402) 339-0500
Web Site: http://www.air-power.com
Sales Range: $1-9.9 Million
Emp.: 15
Industrial Machinery & Equipment Merchant
Whslr
N.A.I.C.S.: 423830

Atlas Copco CMT USA Inc. (2)
3700 E 68th Ave, Commerce City, CO
80022-2243
Tel.: (801) 974-5544
Sales Range: $25-49.9 Million
Emp.: 4
Mining & Drilling Equipment Mfr
N.A.I.C.S.: 333131
Torbjorn Redaelli *(Pres & Gen Mgr)*

Atlas Copco Compressors LLC (2)
300 Technology Ctr Way Ste 550, Rock Hill,
SC 29730
Tel.: (866) 546-3588
Web Site: http://www.atlascopco.us
Air & Gas Compressor Mfr
N.A.I.C.S.: 333912
Jerry Geenen *(Gen Mgr-Industrial Vacuum)*

Subsidiary (Domestic):

Accurate Air Engineering
Incorporated (3)
16207 Parmenita Rd, Cerritos, CA 90703
Tel.: (310) 537-1350
Web Site: http://www.accurateair.com
Rev.: $14,503,892
Emp.: 100
Compressors, Except Air Conditioning
N.A.I.C.S.: 423830
John Lague *(Pres)*

Quincy Compressor Inc. (3)
3501 Wisman Ln, Quincy, IL 62301-1257
Tel.: (217) 222-7700
Web Site: http://www.quincycompressor.com
Sales Range: $125-149.9 Million
Emp.: 220
Rotary & Reciprocating Air Compressors
Mfr
N.A.I.C.S.: 333618

Subsidiary (Domestic):

MidState Air Compressor, Inc. (4)
384 Deming Rd Unit C, Berlin, CT 06037-
1550
Tel.: (860) 357-5513
Web Site:
　http://www.midstateaircompressor.com

Commercial, Industrial Machinery & Equipment Repair & Maintenance
N.A.I.C.S.: 811310
Salvatore Calvo *(Treas)*

Subsidiary (Domestic):

Woodward Compressor Sales
Inc (3)
4429 South Blvd, Charlotte, NC 28209
Tel.: (704) 525-0124
Web Site: http://www.woodwardsales.com
Business to Business Electronic Markets
N.A.I.C.S.: 425120
Bill Simmons *(Mgr)*

Subsidiary (Domestic):

Atlas Copco Comptec LLC (2)
46 School Rd, Voorheesville, NY
12186-9608　　　　　　　　　　　(100%)
Tel.: (518) 765-3344
Web Site: http://www.atlascopco.com
Sales Range: $25-49.9 Million
Emp.: 200
Mfr of Custom-Built Turbomachinery
N.A.I.C.S.: 333912
Alan Keybart *(Project Mgr)*

Atlas Copco Hurricane LLC (2)
1015 Hurricane Rd, Franklin, IN 46131
Tel.: (317) 736-3800
Web Site: http://www.atlascopco.us
Sales Range: $25-49.9 Million
Emp.: 80
Portable Air & Gas Compressors Mfr
N.A.I.C.S.: 333912

Atlas Copco Mafi-Trench Company
LLC (2)
3037 Industrial Pkwy, Santa Maria, CA
93455
Tel.: (805) 928-5757
Web Site: http://www.atlascopco.com
Rev.: $1,500,000
Emp.: 85
Air & Gas Compressor Manufacturing
N.A.I.C.S.: 333912
Brian Humbles *(Dir-Ops)*

Perceptron, Inc. (2)
47827 Halyard Dr, Plymouth, MI 48170-
2461
Tel.: (734) 414-6100
Web Site: http://www.perceptron.com
Rev.: $62,262,000
Assets: $65,582,000
Liabilities: $27,281,000
Net Worth: $38,301,000
Earnings: ($3,971,000)
Emp.: 295
Fiscal Year-end: 06/30/2020
Automotive Test Products Mfr
N.A.I.C.S.: 334419
Heribert Viehweber *(VP-Quality & Ops-Global)*

Subsidiary (Non-US):

Coord3 s.r.l (3)
Strada Statale 25 No 3, Bruzolo, 10050,
Turin, Italy
Tel.: (39) 0119635511
Web Site: https://www.coord3.com
N.A.I.C.S.: 333248

Perceptron (Europe) GmbH (3)
Wamslerstrasse 2 - 4, 81829, Munich,
Germany　　　　　　　　　　　　(100%)
Tel.: (49) 89960980
Web Site: http://www.perceptron.de
Sales Range: $25-49.9 Million
Emp.: 55
Automotive Test Products Mfr
N.A.I.C.S.: 336320

Perceptron Asia Pacific Ltd. (3)
Twin Truss Building 1F 1-4-4 Yanagibashi,
Taito-ku, Tokyo, 111-0052, Japan
Tel.: (81) 362409177
Web Site: http://www.perceptron.co.jp
Sales Range: $150-199.9 Million
Emp.: 5
Automotive Test Products Whslr
N.A.I.C.S.: 423120

Perceptron Asia Pte. Ltd. (3)
18 Boon Lay Way, #10-143 TradeHub 21,
Singapore, 609966, Singapore
Tel.: (65) 67955280
Web Site: http://www.perceptron.com

Sales Range: $75-99.9 Million
Emp.: 200
Automotive Test Products Whslr
N.A.I.C.S.: 423120

Perceptron Italia, s.r.l (3)
Strada Statale 25 n3, 10050, Turin, Italy
Tel.: (39) 0119635511
Measuring & Controlling Device Mfr
N.A.I.C.S.: 334519

Perceptron Metrology Technology
(Shanghai) Co. Ltd. (3)
Room 1005 Building 22 No 368 Zhangjiang
Road, Pudong New District, Shanghai,
201203, China
Tel.: (86) 2133932262
Industrial Machinery & Equipment Whslr
N.A.I.C.S.: 423830

Perceptron Metrology UK Ltd. (3)
Fort Dunlop Fort Parkway, Birmingham,
B24 9FE, United Kingdom
Tel.: (44) 1216297794
Measuring & Controlling Device Mfr
N.A.I.C.S.: 334519

Perceptron Non Contact Metrology
Solutions Pvt Ltd. (3)
12/2 McNichols Road, Chetpet, Chennai,
600 031, India
Tel.: (91) 4442849610
Measuring & Controlling Device Mfr
N.A.I.C.S.: 334519

Perceptron Trading (Shanghai) Co.,
Ltd. (3)
Room 1005 Building 22, No 368 Zhangjiang
Road Pudong New District, Shanghai,
201203, China
Tel.: (86) 2133932262
Measuring & Controlling Device Mfr
N.A.I.C.S.: 334519
Lianlin Jiang *(Acct Mgr)*

Perceptron do Brasil Ltda. (3)
Rua Helena 218 Suite 205, Vila Olimpia,
Sao Paulo, Brazil
Tel.: (55) 1130441950
Measuring & Controlling Device Mfr
N.A.I.C.S.: 334519

Atlas Copco Pakistan (Pvt) Ltd (1)
18 XX Khayaban e Iqbal DHA, Lahore,
Pakistan
Tel.: (92) 42 35 749 406
Web Site: http://www.atlascopco.com
Sales Range: $25-49.9 Million
Emp.: 40
Industrial Machinery Mfr & Distr
N.A.I.C.S.: 333248

Atlas Copco Peru S.A.C. (1)
Los Frutales Avenue 115-Ate, Lima, Peru
Tel.: (51) 80077877
Industrial Machinery & Mining Equipment
Mfr
N.A.I.C.S.: 333131

Atlas Copco Peruana SA (1)
Francisco Grana 150-152 Urb, Santa Catalina, Lima, Peru
Tel.: (51) 1 411 6126
Web Site: http://www.atlascopco.com.pe
Sales Range: $125-149.9 Million
Emp.: 550
Construction Machinery Mfr & Distr
N.A.I.C.S.: 333120
Luciano Wolfarth *(Gen Mgr)*

Atlas Copco Polska Sp. Z.o.o. (1)
Badylarska 25, 02-484, Warsaw, Poland
Tel.: (48) 22 572 68 00
Web Site: http://www.atlascopco.com
Sales Range: $75-99.9 Million
Emp.: 150
Air Compressor Sales & Maintenance Services
N.A.I.C.S.: 423730

Atlas Copco Power Technique
GmbH (1)
Langemarckstr 35, Essen, 45141, Germany
Tel.: (49) 20121770
Industrial Machinery & Mining Equipment
Mfr
N.A.I.C.S.: 333131

Atlas Copco Reinsurance SA (1)
74 Rue de Merl, 2146, Luxembourg, Luxembourg

Tel.: (352) 24 69 53 1
Sales Range: $50-74.9 Million
Emp.: 2
Insurance Management Services
N.A.I.C.S.: 524298

Atlas Copco Rental LLC (1)
2306 S Battleground Rd, La Porte, TX
77571
Industrial Machinery & Mining Equipment
Mfr
N.A.I.C.S.: 333131

Atlas Copco Rock Drills AB (1)
Klerkgatan 21, Orebro, 702 25, Sweden
Tel.: (46) 196700000
Web Site: http://www.atlascopco.com
Sales Range: $450-499.9 Million
Emp.: 1,800
Rock Drilling Equipment Mfr & Distr
N.A.I.C.S.: 333131

Atlas Copco Romania S.R.L (1)
Sos Bucuresti-Ploiesti Nr 135 Sector 1,
013686, Bucharest, Romania
Tel.: (40) 213523622
Web Site: http://www.atlascopco.com
Sales Range: $25-49.9 Million
Emp.: 50
Construction & Mining Machinery Distr
N.A.I.C.S.: 423810
Andrei Murvai *(Reg Mgr-Bus Line)*

Subsidiary (Domestic):

Atlas Copco Industrial Technique
S.R.L. (2)
Str Nicolae Dobrin Nr 83, Arges, 110408,
Pitesti, Romania
Tel.: (40) 248210270
Web Site: http://www.atlascopco.com
Emp.: 20
Air Compressor Mfr
N.A.I.C.S.: 333912

Atlas Copco S.A.E. (1)
Avda Jose Garate no 3, 28823, Coslada,
Madrid, Spain
Tel.: (34) 91 6279100
Web Site: http://www.atlascopco.com
Emp.: 15
Construction Equipment Mfr & Distr
N.A.I.C.S.: 333120

Atlas Copco S.r.o. (1)
Prumyslova 10, 102 00, Prague, Czech
Republic
Tel.: (420) 225 434 000
Air Compressor Mfr
N.A.I.C.S.: 333912
Richerd Jaesk *(Office Mgr)*

Atlas Copco Secoroc AB (1)
Bjombacksvagan 2, PO Box 521, Fagersta,
73730, Sweden　　　　　　　　　(100%)
Tel.: (46) 22346100
Web Site: http://www.atlascopco.com
Sales Range: $200-249.9 Million
Emp.: 650
Rock Drilling Tools
N.A.I.C.S.: 333131
Ann Fvensson *(Sec)*

Atlas Copco Secoroc LLC (1)
1600 S Great SW Pkwy, Grand Prairie, TX
75051
Tel.: (972) 337-9700
Web Site: http://www.atlascopco.com
Sales Range: $75-99.9 Million
Emp.: 160
Mining Tools Mfr
N.A.I.C.S.: 423830

Atlas Copco Services Middle East
OMC (1)
The Address Tower Office 1001 10th Floor,
Manama, Bahrain
Tel.: (973) 17221551
N.A.I.C.S.: 335999

Atlas Copco Services Middle East
SPC (1)
17th Street Office 15 Plot 3 Sector M2, PO
Box 91070, Mussafah, Abu Dhabi, United
Arab Emirates
Tel.: (971) 23042777
N.A.I.C.S.: 335999

Atlas Copco Specialty Rental
LLC (1)

5810 Wilson Rd, Humble, TX 77396-2899
Tel.: (281) 454-2200
Construction Machinery Rental Services
N.A.I.C.S.: 532412
Thierry Monart *(Gen Mgr-North America)*

Atlas Copco Srbija doo   **(1)**
Milutina Milankovica 23, 11070, Belgrade,
Serbia
Tel.: (381) 114003710
Industrial Machinery & Mining Equipment
Mfr.
N.A.I.C.S.: 333131
Vlastimir Jovanovic *(Mgr-Natl Svc)*

Atlas Copco Taiwan Ltd   **(1)**
No 8 Alley 80 Lane 298 Gong 2nd Road,
Longtan, 32559, Tao Yuan, Taiwan
Tel.: (886) 3 479 6838
Web Site: http://www.atlascopco.com
Construction Machinery Mfr & Distr
N.A.I.C.S.: 333120

Atlas Copco Tanzania Ltd   **(1)**
Plot 35 Nyakato Industrial Area, PO Box
505, Mwanza, Tanzania
Tel.: (255) 28 2570289
Web Site: http://www.atlascopco.com
Construction & Mining Equipment Distr
N.A.I.C.S.: 423810
Jessie Kamau *(Mgr-Bus Line-Compressor
Technique)*

**Atlas Copco Tools & Assembly Sys-
tems LLC**   **(1)**
3301 Cross St Pkwy, Auburn Hills, MI
48326   **(100%)**
Tel.: (248) 373-3000
Web Site: http://www.atlascopco.com
Sales Range: $25-49.9 Million
Emp.: 100
Customer Service for the Pneumatic Pow-
ered Tools
N.A.I.C.S.: 423830

Subsidiary (Domestic):

**Atlas Copco Assembly Systems
LLC**   **(2)**
3301 Cross Creek Pkwy, Auburn Hills, MI
48326
Tel.: (248) 373-3000
Web Site: http://www.atlascopco.com
Sales Range: $25-49.9 Million
Machine Tool Builders
N.A.I.C.S.: 333912
Anders Hoberg *(Pres)*

Subsidiary (Non-US):

Atlas Copco Canada Inc.   **(2)**
5060 rue Levy, Saint Laurent, H4R 2P1,
QC, Canada   **(100%)**
Tel.: (514) 421-4121
Web Site: http://www.atlascopco.com
Sales Range: $25-49.9 Million
Emp.: 7
Mining Machinery, Compressors & Tools Mfr
& Distr
N.A.I.C.S.: 333131

Subsidiary (Domestic):

**Atlas Copco Compressor
Canada**   **(3)**
30 Montrose, Dollard des Ormeaux, H9B
3J9, QC, Canada   **(100%)**
Tel.: (514) 421-4121
Web Site: http://www.atlascopco.com
Sales Range: $50-74.9 Million
Marketing & Sales of Compressors
N.A.I.C.S.: 423830

Subsidiary (Domestic):

Beacon Medical Products LLC   **(2)**
1800 Overview Dr, Rock Hill, SC 29730
Tel.: (803) 817-5600
Web Site: http://www.beaconmedaes.com
Sales Range: $50-74.9 Million
Emp.: 100
Medical Gas Supplying System Distr
N.A.I.C.S.: 423450

**Chicago Pneumatic Tool Company
LLC**   **(2)**
1800 Overview Dr, Rock Hill, SC
29730-7463   **(100%)**
Tel.: (704) 936-4000
Web Site: http://www.chicagopneumatic.com

Sales Range: $25-49.9 Million
Emp.: 100
Vehicle Service Tools, Vehicle Assembly
Tools, Pneumatic Tools
N.A.I.C.S.: 333991
Philip Warmbier *(Mgr-Bus Line)*

Subsidiary (Non-US):

CP Tools Korea Co. Ltd   **(3)**
4/F Phoong Cheon Bldg 949 Hogye-Dong,
Dongan-gu, Anyang, 431080, Gyeonggi-Do,
Korea (South)
Tel.: (82) 314608463
Sales Range: $25-49.9 Million
Emp.: 1
Machine Tools Mfr
N.A.I.C.S.: 333517

**Chicago Pneumatic Construction
Equipment AB**   **(3)**
Sickla Industrivag 19, 105 23, Stockholm,
Sweden
Tel.: (46) 766 28 40 35
Sales Range: $50-74.9 Million
Emp.: 60
Construction Equipment Distr
N.A.I.C.S.: 423810
Kevin Cook *(Mgr-Sls-Western US)*

Subsidiary (Domestic):

Henrob Corporation   **(2)**
30000 S Hill Rd, New Hudson, MI 48165
Tel.: (248) 493-3800
Web Site: http://www.henrob.com
Self-Pierce Riveting Services
N.A.I.C.S.: 561990
Stuart Blacket *(Mng Dir)*

Branch (Domestic):

Henrob Corporation   **(3)**
9805 NorthCross Ctr Ct Ste A, Huntersville,
NC 28078
Tel.: (704) 987-8005
Web Site: http://www.henrob.com
Self-Pierce Riveting Services
N.A.I.C.S.: 561990

Subsidiary (Domestic):

**Mining, Rock Excavation & Construc-
tion LLC**   **(2)**
3700 E 68th Ave, Commerce City, CO
80022
Tel.: (303) 217-2834
Web Site: http://www.atlascopco.com
Sales Range: $50-74.9 Million
Emp.: 60
Construction & Mining Machinery Rental
Services
N.A.I.C.S.: 532412
Peter Redaelli *(Mgr-Product-Rock Drilling
Tools Bus)*

Division (Domestic):

American Pneumatic Tools   **(3)**
1000 S Grand Ave, Santa Ana, CA 92705
Tel.: (714) 285-2828
Web Site: http://www.apt-tools.com
Sales Range: $10-24.9 Million
Emp.: 15
Pneumatic Tools Mfr & Distr
N.A.I.C.S.: 333991

Subsidiary (Domestic):

**Atlas Copco Drilling Solutions
LLC**   **(3)**
7500 Shadwell Dr, Roanoke, VA 24019-
5106
Tel.: (540) 362-3321
Web Site: http://www.atlascopco.com
Sales Range: $25-49.9 Million
Mfr of Drilling Equipment
N.A.I.C.S.: 332999

Plant (Domestic):

Atlas Copco Drilling Solutions   **(4)**
2100 N 1st St, Garland, TX 75040-4102
Tel.: (972) 496-7400
Web Site: http://www.atlascopco.us
Sales Range: $100-124.9 Million
Mfr Drills & Drilling Tools
N.A.I.C.S.: 333517

Atlas Copco Tools AB   **(1)**

Sickla Industrivag 17, Nacka, 131 34, Swe-
den
Tel.: (46) 8 743 95 00
Web Site: http://www.atlascopca.com
Sales Range: $75-99.9 Million
Emp.: 700
Machine Tool Distr
N.A.I.C.S.: 423830

Atlas Copco UK Holdings Ltd   **(1)**
Swallowdale Lane, Hemel Hempstead, HP2
7EA, Hertfordshire, United Kingdom
Tel.: (44) 8456010001
Web Site: http://www.atlascopco.com
Construction & Mining Machinery Distr
N.A.I.C.S.: 423810

Subsidiary (Domestic):

Atlas Copco (NI) Ltd   **(2)**
Unit 4 Ballinderry Business Park, Lisburn,
BT28 2BP, Antrim, United Kingdom
Tel.: (44) 28 92 606400
Air Compressor Mfr
N.A.I.C.S.: 333912
Harry McDowell *(Mgr-Compressor Tech-
nique)*

Atlas Copco Ltd   **(2)**
Swallowdale Lane, Hemel Hempstead, HP2
7EA, Hertfordshire, United Kingdom
Tel.: (44) 845 6010001
Web Site: http://www.atlascopco.com
Sales Range: $25-49.9 Million
Emp.: 250
Compressor Machinery Mfr & Distr
N.A.I.C.S.: 333912

Medaes Limited   **(2)**
Telford Crescent, Staveley, Chesterfield,
S43 3PF, Derbyshire, United
Kingdom   **(100%)**
Tel.: (44) 1246474242
Web Site: http://www.medaes.com
Sales Range: $10-24.9 Million
Emp.: 80
Medical Gas Delivery Systems Mfr
N.A.I.C.S.: 339112

Subsidiary (US):

**Medigas Service & Testing Co.,
Inc.**   **(3)**
2071 5th Ave, Ronkonkoma, NY 11779
Tel.: (631) 563-4040
Web Site: http://www.medigasservice.com
Sales Range: $1-9.9 Million
Emp.: 18
Laboratory Equipment Installation & Verifi-
cation Services
N.A.I.C.S.: 238990
Frank Rudiliosso *(Pres)*

Subsidiary (Domestic):

Walker Filtration Limited   **(2)**
Birtley Road, Washington, NE38 9DA, Tyne
& Wear, United Kingdom
Tel.: (44) 191 417 7816
Web Site: http://www.walkerfiltration.co.uk
Filtration Products Mfr
N.A.I.C.S.: 333413
Brian Walker *(Mng Dir)*

Subsidiary (US):

Walker Filtration Inc.   **(3)**
4748 Pacific Ave, Erie, PA 16506-4926
Tel.: (814) 836-2900
Web Site: http://www.walkerfiltration.com
Filtration Products Mfr & Whslr
N.A.I.C.S.: 333413
Richard P. Taylor *(Pres)*

Atlas Copco Venezuela SA   **(1)**
Conjunto Industrial Unicentro del Norte Gal-
pon 8 Calle 99, Zona Industrial Castillito,
San Diego, Venezuela
Tel.: (58) 2416145917
Web Site: http://www.atlascopco.com
Construction & Mining Machinery Whslr
N.A.I.C.S.: 423810

**Atlas Copco Vietnam Company
Ltd**   **(1)**
Lot F Str 12 Song Than II Industrial Zone,
Di An, Binh Duong, Vietnam
Tel.: (84) 650 373 8484
Web Site: http://www.atlascopco.com.vn

Sales Range: $50-74.9 Million
Emp.: 70
Construction & Mining Equipment Distr
N.A.I.C.S.: 423810

Atlas Copco d.o.o.   **(1)**
Peske 7, 1236, Trzin, Slovenia
Tel.: (386) 15600710
Industrial Machinery & Mining Equipment
Mfr
N.A.I.C.S.: 333131

Atlas Copco s.r.o.   **(1)**
Elektrarenska 4, Bratislava, 831 04, Slova-
kia
Tel.: (421) 32 7438 001
Web Site: http://www.atlascopco.com
Air Compressor Mfr & Distr
N.A.I.C.S.: 333912

Atlas Copco s.r.o.   **(1)**
Elektrarenska 4, 831 04, Bratislava, Slova-
kia
Tel.: (421) 264 462 636
Web Site:
  http://atlascopco.industrialtechnique.com
Machine Tool Maintenance Services
N.A.I.C.S.: 811310

Berema A/S   **(1)**
Svarthagsveien 8, 1543, Vestby, Norway
Tel.: (47) 64860500
Web Site: https://www.berema.no
N.A.I.C.S.: 333248

**Bolaite (Shanghai) Compressor Co.,
Ltd.**   **(1)**
602-607 Building 9 Excellence Times
Square Lane 60 Hulan West Road,
Baoshan District, Shanghai, China
Tel.: (86) 4006690106
N.A.I.C.S.: 333248

CSK Inc.   **(1)**
4F Hanwon Building 19 Hwangsaeul-Ro
258beon-Gil, Bundang-gu, Seongnam,
13595, Gyeonggi-do, Korea (South)
Tel.: (82) 317813761
Web Site: https://www.csk.kr
N.A.I.C.S.: 333242

CSKTS Inc.   **(1)**
42487 Complex Blvd, Pablo, MT 59855
Tel.: (406) 675-2700
Web Site: http://www.csktribes.org
Disaster Emergency Services
N.A.I.C.S.: 624230

Chicago Pneumatic Brasil Ltda   **(1)**
Alameda Mamore 503 Sala 31/34, 06454-
040, Barueri, Sao Paulo, Brazil
Tel.: (55) 1121893900
Web Site: http://www.cp.com
Construction Equipment Mfr
N.A.I.C.S.: 333120

Compressed Air Products, Inc.   **(1)**
200 Parcade Ct, Peachtree City, GA 30269
Tel.: (770) 487-9292
Rev.: $3,700,000
Emp.: 21
Business to Business Electronic Markets
N.A.I.C.S.: 425120
Steve Rusmisell *(Pres)*

Compressed Air Systems, Inc.   **(1)**
9303 Stannum St, Tampa, FL 33619-2658
Tel.: (813) 626-8177
Web Site:
  http://www.compressedairsystems.com
Emp.: 55
Industrial Machinery And Equipment
N.A.I.C.S.: 423830
Brint Waring *(Pres & CEO)*

**Compressed Air Technologies,
Inc.**   **(1)**
1758 Hwy 49 S, Richland, MS 39073
Tel.: (601) 932-0536
Web Site: http://www.catms.net
Industrial Machinery & Equipment Merchant
Whslr
N.A.I.C.S.: 423830
Allen Cox *(Mgr)*

**Dekker Vacuum Technologies,
Inc.**   **(1)**
935 S Woodland Ave, Michigan City, IN
46360
Tel.: (219) 861-0661
Web Site: http://www.dekkervacuum.com

Atlas Copco AB—(Continued)

Emp.: 70
Business to Business Electronic Markets
N.A.I.C.S.: 425120
Rick Dekker *(Chm & Pres)*

Desoutter GmbH (1)
Edmund-Seng-Str 3-5, 63477, Maintal, Germany
Tel.: (49) 6181 411 0
Industrial Machinery Mfr
N.A.I.C.S.: 333248

Desoutter Italiana S.r.l. (1)
Viale della Repubblica 65, 20035, Lissone, Italy
Tel.: (39) 0 39 244 101
Web Site: http://www.desouttertools.com
Pneumatic System & Tool Mfr
N.A.I.C.S.: 333991

Desoutter S.A. (1)
Avenida de la Industria 9 Poligono Industrial de Alcobendas, 28108, Alcobendas, Spain
Tel.: (34) 915 90 31 52
Emp.: 21
Machine Tools Mfr
N.A.I.C.S.: 333517

EDMAC Europe N.V. (1)
Moerelei 123A, 2610, Antwerp, Belgium
Tel.: (32) 37508011
Web Site: http://www.edmac.eu
Compressor & Vacuum Pump Mfr
N.A.I.C.S.: 333912
Stephane Heyde *(Gen Mgr)*

Edwards Group Limited (1)
Manor Royal, Crawley, RH10 9LW, W Sussex, United Kingdom
Tel.: (44) 1293528844
Web Site: http://www.edwardsvacuum.com
Sales Range: $900-999.9 Million
Emp.: 3,300
Microelectronics Industry Gases, Vacuum & Specialist Equipment Distr
N.A.I.C.S.: 335999
Mike Allison *(Pres-Semiconductor Div)*

Subsidiary (Non-US):

Edwards GmbH (2)
Ammerthalstr 36, D85551, Kirchheim, Germany
Tel.: (49) 899919180
Web Site: http://www.edwardsvacuum.com
Microelectronics Industry Gases, Vacuum & Specialist Equipment Distr
N.A.I.C.S.: 333248

Edwards Japan Limited (2)
1078-1 Yoshihashi, Yachiyo, 276-8523, Japan
Tel.: (81) 474588836
Web Site: http://www.jp.edwardsvacuum.com
Sales Range: $25-49.9 Million
Emp.: 300
Semiconductor & Vacuum-Dependent Processing Products Whslr & Services
N.A.I.C.S.: 423610

Edwards S.p.A. (2)
Via Carpaccio 35, Trezzano San Naviglio, 20090, Milan, Italy
Tel.: (39) 0248442217
Web Site: http://www.edwardsvacuum.com
Sales Range: $10-24.9 Million
Emp.: 25
Semiconductor & Vacuum-Dependent Processing Products & Services
N.A.I.C.S.: 334413

Subsidiary (US):

Edwards Vacuum, LLC (2)
6416 Inducon Dr W, Sanborn, NY 14132
Tel.: (978) 658-5410
Web Site: http://www.edwardsvacuum.com
Sales Range: $10-24.9 Million
Emp.: 100
Mfr & Marketing of Vacuum Dry Pumps, Turbo Pumps, Instrumentation
N.A.I.C.S.: 334515

Subsidiary (Domestic):

Brooks Automation, Inc. CTI-Cryogenics Products Center (3)
15 Elizabeth Dr, Chelmsford, MA 01824

Tel.: (978) 262-2400
Vacuum Technology Solutions Mfr & Developer (for Semiconductor, Data Storage & Flat Panel Display Markets)
N.A.I.C.S.: 333912

Ceres Technologies, Inc. (3)
5 Tower Dr, Saugerties, NY 12477-4386
Tel.: (845) 247-4701
Web Site: http://www.cerestechnologies.com
Instruments & Related Products Mfr
N.A.I.C.S.: 334513
Sharon Burton *(Supvr-AR)*

Edwards India Private Ltd. (1)
Pune Service Technology Centre T97/2 Opp St Gobain Glass Works, MIDC Bhosar, Pune, 411026, India
Tel.: (91) 8002126474
N.A.I.C.S.: 333310

Edwards Israel Vacuum Ltd. (1)
Sderot HaBarzel 5, Kiryat Gat, Israel
Tel.: (972) 83741111
N.A.I.C.S.: 333310

Edwards Korea Ltd. (1)
4F/5F Hanwon B/D 19 Hwangseul-ro 258beon-gil, Bundang-gu, Seongnam, Gyeonggi-do, Korea (South)
Tel.: (82) 317167070
Vacuum System Product Mfr
N.A.I.C.S.: 335210

Edwards Ltd. (1)
Innovation Drive, Burgess Hill, RH15 9TW, West Sussex, United Kingdom
Tel.: (44) 3459212223
N.A.I.C.S.: 333310

Edwards SAS (1)
23 Rue du Gros Murger, 95220, Herblay, France
Tel.: (33) 141211256
Vaccum Pump Mfr
N.A.I.C.S.: 333912
Henri Pierre Martinez *(Dir-Sls)*

Edwards Technologies Singapore Pte. Ltd. (1)
42 Loyang Drive, Loyang Industrial Estate, Singapore, 508962, Singapore
Tel.: (65) 65468408
Vacuum System Product Mfr
N.A.I.C.S.: 335210

Edwards Vacuo Ltda (1)
Rua Bernardo Wrona 222, Bairro do Limao, Sao Paulo, 02710-060, SP, Brazil
Tel.: (55) 1139525000
Web Site: http://www.edwardsvacuum.com
Sales Range: $10-24.9 Million
Emp.: 50
Semiconductor & Vacuum-Dependent Processing Products & Services Mfr
N.A.I.C.S.: 334413

Edwards s.r.o. (1)
Jana Sigmunda 300, 783 49, Lutin, Czech Republic
Tel.: (420) 533441045
N.A.I.C.S.: 333310

Ekomak Endustriyel Kompresor Makine SanayiveTicaret A.S (1)
Serifali Mevkii Hat Boyu Caddesi Turgut Ozal Bulvari No 168 Umraniye, Istanbul, Turkiye
Tel.: (90) 2165401133
Web Site: http://www.ekomak.com
Air Compressor Mfr
N.A.I.C.S.: 333912
Eric Van Meel *(Mng Dir)*

Exlair (NZ) Limited (1)
11 Saturn Place, Rosedale, Auckland, 0632, New Zealand
Tel.: (64) 94448486
Web Site: http://www.ashair.co.nz
Air Compressor Mfr
N.A.I.C.S.: 333912

FIAC S.p.A. (1)
Via Vizzano 23, Pontecchio Marconi, 40037, Bologna, Italy
Tel.: (39) 051 678 6811
Web Site: http://www.fiac.it
Air Compressor Mfr
N.A.I.C.S.: 333912
Fabio Lucchi *(Mgr-Sls Mktg-Asia & N America)*

Hydra Flow West Inc. (1)
885 Fairway Dr, Walnut, CA 91789
Tel.: (909) 444-9880
Web Site: http://hfwinc.com
Industrial Supplies Merchant Whslr
N.A.I.C.S.: 423840
Mike King *(Mgr-Sls)*

ISRA VISION AG (1)
Industriestrasse 14, 64297, Darmstadt, Germany (100%)
Tel.: (49) 61519480
Web Site: http://www.isravision.com
Rev.: $172,347,574
Assets: $386,516,319
Liabilities: $146,063,340
Net Worth: $240,452,980
Earnings: $25,264,042
Emp.: 772
Fiscal Year-end: 09/30/2019
Industrial Image Processing & Surface Inspection System Mfr
N.A.I.C.S.: 333310
Enis Ersu *(CEO & Member-Exec Bd)*

Subsidiary (Domestic):

3D-Shape GmbH (2)
Am Weichselgarten 21, 91058, Erlangen, Germany
Tel.: (49) 91319779590
Web Site: http://www.3d-shape.com
Optical Product Mfr & Distr
N.A.I.C.S.: 334413

ISRA SURFACE VISION GmbH (2)
Albert Einstein Allee 36 40, 45699, Herten, Germany
Tel.: (49) 236693000
Sales Range: $25-49.9 Million
Emp.: 80
Engineeering Services
N.A.I.C.S.: 541330
Rudolf Kramper *(Mng Dir)*

Subsidiary (US):

ISRA SURFACE VISION Inc. (2)
4470 Peachtree Lakes Dr, Atlanta, GA 30096
Tel.: (770) 449-7776
Web Site: http://www.isravision.com
Sales Range: $25-49.9 Million
Emp.: 25
Surface Inspection System Mfr
N.A.I.C.S.: 333310

Subsidiary (Non-US):

ISRA VISION BRASIL (2)
Av Marques de Sao Vicente 587 Barra Funda, 01139-001, Sao Paulo, Brazil
Tel.: (55) 11 3476 1132
Web Site: http://www.isravision.com
Sales Range: $25-49.9 Million
Emp.: 9
Industrial Automation Software Development Services
N.A.I.C.S.: 541511

ISRA VISION FRANCE S.A (2)
Tour Suisse 1 Bd Vivier Merle, 69443, Lyon, France
Tel.: (33) 472114067
Software Development Services
N.A.I.C.S.: 541511

ISRA VISION ITALY (2)
PO Box 115, 38068, Rovereto, Trentino, Italy
Tel.: (39) 0464490603
Sales Range: $25-49.9 Million
Emp.: 10
Industrial Automation Software Development Services
N.A.I.C.S.: 541511

Subsidiary (Domestic):

ISRA VISION LASOR GmbH (2)
Rudolf Diesel Str 24, 33813, Oerlinghausen, Germany (100%)
Tel.: (49) 52027080
Web Site: http://www.isravision.com
Sales Range: $25-49.9 Million
Emp.: 50
Industrial Machinery & Equipment Whslr
N.A.I.C.S.: 423830

Subsidiary (Non-US):

ISRA VISION Ltd. (2)

56 Greenwich Avenue, Crayford, TN16 3LN, Kent, United Kingdom
Tel.: (44) 1322520410
Web Site: http://www.isravision.com
Sales Range: $25-49.9 Million
Emp.: 6
Industrial Image Processing Equipment Mfr
N.A.I.C.S.: 333310
John Claridge *(Mng Dir)*

Subsidiary (Domestic):

ISRA VISION PARSYTEC AG (2)
Pascalstrasse 16, 52076, Aachen, Germany
Tel.: (49) 2408927000
Web Site: http://www.isra-parsytec.com
Surface Inspection System Designer & Mfr
N.A.I.C.S.: 334513
Hans Jurgen Christ *(Chm-Mgmt Bd)*

Subsidiary (Non-US):

Isra Vision Korea Co. Ltd. (3)
B-301 Imi-ro 40, Uiwang, 16006, Gyeonggi-do, Korea (South)
Tel.: (82) 3180697300
Image Processing Inspection System Distr
N.A.I.C.S.: 423460

Subsidiary (US):

ISRA VISION SYSTEMS Inc. (2)
281 Enterprise Ct Ste 300, Bloomfield Hills, MI 48302-0312
Tel.: (517) 887-8878
Web Site: http://www.isravision.com
Industrial Image Processing Equipment Mfr
N.A.I.C.S.: 333310

Subsidiary (Non-US):

ISRA VISION TURKEY (2)
Resitpasa Mah Katar Cad Teknokent Ari 1 Sit No 2/5/3, Sanyer, 34467, Istanbul, Turkiye
Tel.: (90) 2122859745
Web Site: http://www.isravision.com
Sales Range: $25-49.9 Million
Emp.: 1
Industrial Automation Software Development Services
N.A.I.C.S.: 541511

Subsidiary (Domestic):

Isra Parsytec GMBH (2)
Pascalstr 16, 52076, Aachen, Germany
Tel.: (49) 2408927000
Web Site: http://www.parsytec.com
Software Development Services
N.A.I.C.S.: 541511

Subsidiary (Non-US):

Isra Vision (Shanghai) Corp Ltd (2)
Ground Floor No 4 Building Zone A No 38 Dongsheng Road, Pudong, Shanghai, 201201, China
Tel.: (86) 21689162860
Industrial Automation Software Development Services
N.A.I.C.S.: 541511

Subsidiary (Domestic):

Isra Vision GmbH (2)
Frankfurter Strasse 112, 64293, Darmstadt, Germany
Tel.: (49) 61519480
Web Site: https://www.isravision.com
N.A.I.C.S.: 333248

Isra Vision Graphikon Gmbh (2)
Max-Planck-Str 3, Berlin, 12489, Germany
Tel.: (49) 30 42 10 47 00
Web Site: http://www.graphikon.de
Photovoltaic Device Mfr
N.A.I.C.S.: 334413

Subsidiary (Non-US):

Isra Vision India Private Limited (2)
Haware Parekh Chambers A 202, 400071, Mumbai, Maharashtra, India
Tel.: (91) 2026741000
Image Processing Inspection System Distr
N.A.I.C.S.: 423460

Isra Vision Iran (2)
Dr Shariati Ave Opp Kolahdouz Farhang Bldg No 1564 5th Fl Apt 14, 1913964595, Tehran, Iran

Tel.: (98) 2122616169
Image Processing Inspection System Distr
N.A.I.C.S.: 423460

Isra Vision Japan Corp Ltd **(2)**
Benex S-3 3-20-8 Shin, Kohokuku, Yoko-
hama, 222-0033, Kanagawa, Japan
Tel.: (81) 455349911
Web Site: http://www.isravision.com
Industrial Machinery Distr
N.A.I.C.S.: 423830

Isra Vision LLC **(2)**
Prospekt Andropova 18 Korpus 6 Office
5-05, 115432, Moscow, Russia
Tel.: (7) 4994180032
Image Processing Inspection System Distr
N.A.I.C.S.: 423460

Subsidiary (US):

Isra Vision Parsytec Inc **(2)**
Bldg 9 Unit 60 245 W Roosevelt Rd, West
Chicago, IL 60185
Tel.: (630) 293-9500
Web Site: http://www.parsytec.de
Surface Inspection Systems Mfr
N.A.I.C.S.: 334519

Subsidiary (Domestic):

Isra Vision Polymetric GmbH **(2)**
Rundeturmstrasse 12, 64283, Darmstadt,
Germany
Tel.: (49) 6151155482
Web Site: http://www.polymetric.de
Scanning Product Mfr
N.A.I.C.S.: 334118

Subsidiary (Non-US):

Isra Vision Taiwan **(2)**
Jhongjheng Rd 15F-6 No 1071, 330,
Taoyuan, Taiwan
Tel.: (886) 32500148
Image Processing Inspection System Distr
N.A.I.C.S.: 423460

Isra Vision Vistek A.S. **(2)**
ITU Ayazaga Campus Teknokent ARI 1
Building No 24-3, Maslak, 34469, Istanbul,
Turkiye
Tel.: (90) 2122859745
Web Site: http://www.isravision-vistek.com
Table Ware Glass Inspection System Mfr
N.A.I.C.S.: 333310

Subsidiary (Domestic):

Metronom Automation Gmbh **(2)**
Max-hufschmidt-str 4a, 55130, Mainz, Ger-
many
Tel.: (49) 61312508380
Web Site: http://www.metronom-
automation.de
Software Development Services
N.A.I.C.S.: 541511

Vision Experts GmbH **(2)**
Am Sandfeld 15, 76149, Karlsruhe, Ger-
many
Tel.: (49) 721978390
Web Site: http://www.vision-experts.de
Print Inspection System Mfr
N.A.I.C.S.: 333248

**Innovative Vacuum Solutions,
Inc.** **(1)**
11461 N US Hwy 301 Ste 110, Thonoto-
sassa, FL 33592
Web Site: http://www.ivsonline.com
Vacuum Pump & Component Mfr
N.A.I.C.S.: 333912

**Itubombas Locacao Comercio Impor-
tacao E Exportacao Ltda.** **(1)**
Av Caetano Rugieri 5170-A, Why of Indus-
tries, Itú, 13309-710, Sao Paulo, Brazil
Tel.: (55) 1140131116
Web Site: http://www.itubombas.com.br
Pumps Mfr
N.A.I.C.S.: 333914

James E. Watson & Co. **(1)**
29 Doran Ave SE, Marietta, GA 30060-2046
Tel.: (251) 610-0061
Web Site: http://www.jwatsonco.com
Pump & Pumping Equipment Mfr
N.A.I.C.S.: 333914
R. J. Berger *(Pres)*

**KDS Kompressoren- und Druck-
luftservice GmbH** **(1)**
Pleidelsheimerstr 47 A, Bietgheim-
Bissingen, 74321, Ludwigsburg, Germany
Tel.: (49) 714277780
Web Site: http://www.hb-kompressoren.de
Air Compressor & Equipment Rental Ser-
vices
N.A.I.C.S.: 532490
Frank Kurney *(Gen Mgr)*

KRACHT GmbH **(1)**
Gewerbestrasse 20, 58791, Werdohl, Ger-
many
Tel.: (49) 23929350
Web Site: http://www.kracht.eu
Rev.: $27,588,000
Emp.: 270
Motors & Pumps Mfr
N.A.I.C.S.: 333996
Heiko Zahn *(Mng Dir)*

LLC Atlas Copco Ukraine **(1)**
9 Moskovskiy Ave Building 3, Kiev, 4073,
Ukraine
Tel.: (380) 44 499 18 70
Web Site: http://www.atlascopco.com
Sales Range: $25-49.9 Million
Emp.: 70
Industrial Machinery Mfr & Distr
N.A.I.C.S.: 333248

**Leybold (Tianjin) International Trade
Co., Ltd.** **(1)**
Zhang Run Building Room301 No2 Building
No 158 JinQiu Road, Pudong New Area,
Shanghai, China
Tel.: (86) 2131167080
Vacuum Pump & Component Mfr
N.A.I.C.S.: 333912

Leybold France SAS **(1)**
640 Rue Aristide Berges, 26500, Bourg-les-
Valence, Cedex, France
Tel.: (33) 475823300
Vacuum Pump & Component Mfr
N.A.I.C.S.: 333912

Leybold Hispanica S.A. **(1)**
C/Huelva 7, Cornella de Llobregat, 08940,
Barcelona, Spain
Tel.: (34) 9366664311
Vacuum Pump & Component Mfr
N.A.I.C.S.: 333912
Marcos Sanchez Alameda *(Country Mgr)*

Leybold India Pvt Ltd. **(1)**
T-97/2 MIDC Bhosari, 411 026, Pune, India
Tel.: (91) 2040752254
Vacuum Pump & Component Mfr
N.A.I.C.S.: 333912
Navin Mule *(Reg Sls Mgr)*

Leybold Italia Srl **(1)**
Via Filippo Brunelleschi 2, 20093, Cologno
Monzese, Italy
Tel.: (39) 02272231
Vacuum Pump & Component Mfr
N.A.I.C.S.: 333912
Claudio Longhi *(Country Mgr)*

Leybold Japan Co., Ltd. **(1)**
Shin-Yokohama A K Bldg 3-23-3, Shin-
Yokohama Kohoku-ku, Yokohama, 222-
0033, Japan
Tel.: (81) 454713330
Vacuum Pump & Component Mfr
N.A.I.C.S.: 333912

Leybold Korea Ltd. **(1)**
7F Sunae Finance Tower 25 Hwangsaeul-ro
258beon-gil, Bundang-gu, Seongnam,
13595, Gyeonggi-do, Korea (South)
Tel.: (82) 317851367
Vacuum Pump & Component Mfr
N.A.I.C.S.: 333912

Leybold Nederland B.V. **(1)**
Floridadreef 102, 3565 AM, Utrecht, Nether-
lands
Tel.: (31) 302426320
Vacuum Pump & Component Mfr
N.A.I.C.S.: 333912
Ferry Jansen *(Mgr-Sls)*

Leybold Schweiz AG **(1)**
Hinterbergstrasse 56, 6312, Steinhausen,
Switzerland
Tel.: (41) 443084050
Vacuum Pump & Component Mfr
N.A.I.C.S.: 333912

JAVAC Pty. Ltd. **(2)**

Leybold Singapore Pte Ltd **(1)**
42 Loyang Drive, Loyang Industrial Estate,
Singapore, 508962, Singapore
Tel.: (65) 63037030
Vacuum Pump & Component Mfr
N.A.I.C.S.: 333912

Leybold do Brasil Ltda. **(1)**
Av Tambore 937 Tambore, Distrito Indus-
trial, 06460-000, Barueri, Sao Paulo, Brazil
Tel.: (55) 1133764604
Vacuum Pump & Component Mfr
N.A.I.C.S.: 333912

**Liuzhou Tech Machinery Co.,
Ltd.** **(1)**
B-22-1 Guangxi, Yanghe Industrial Develop-
ment Zone, Liuzhou, 545006, China
Tel.: (86) 7723172247
Web Site: http://www.liutechportable.com.cn
Air Compressor Mfr
N.A.I.C.S.: 333912

**Mid South Engine & Power Systems,
LLC** **(1)**
2201 E Hwy 80, White Oak, TX 75693
Tel.: (903) 297-0199
Web Site: http://www.midsouthmach.com
Electronic & Precision Equipment Repair &
Maintenance Services
N.A.I.C.S.: 811210
Greg Hulett *(Pres & CEO)*

**Montana Instruments
Corporation** **(1)**
101 Evergreen Dr, 59715, Bozeman, MT
Tel.: (406) 551-2796
Web Site:
    http://www.montanainstruments.com
Analytical Laboratory Instrument Mfr
N.A.I.C.S.: 334516
Brian Smithgall *(Dir-Bus Dev)*

MultiAir BELUX NV **(1)**
E3-Laan 25, De Prijkels industrial zone,
Deinze, 9800, East Flanders, Belgium
Tel.: (32) 93866196
Web Site: http://www.maescompressoren.be
Compressor Rental Services
N.A.I.C.S.: 532490

National Pump & Energy Ltd. **(1)**
3A/6 Innovation Parkway, Birtinya, 4575,
QLD, Australia
Tel.: (61) 754384300
Web Site: http://www.nationalpump.com.au
Sales Range: $50-74.9 Million
Oil, Gas & Construction Equipment Rental
Services
N.A.I.C.S.: 532412
Michael Shelby *(Gen Mgr-Oil & Gas)*

Oerlikon Leybold Vacuum GmbH **(1)**
Bonner Strasse 498, 50968, Cologne,
50968, Germany
Tel.: (49) 2213471261
Sales Range: $400-449.9 Million
Emp.: 12,184
Fiscal Year-end: 12/31/2022
Vacuum Technologies
N.A.I.C.S.: 333996

Subsidiary (Non-US):

Drescher Asociados SRL **(2)**
Zapiola 3535, Buenos Aires, C1429ANM,
Argentina
Tel.: (54) 1147016200
Web Site: https://drescherasociados.com
Pumping Equipment Mfr
N.A.I.C.S.: 333914

FINN-LEY VAKUUM, s.r.o. **(2)**
Simackova 2, Brno-Lisen, 62800, Brno,
Czech Republic
Tel.: (420) 544211339
Web Site: https://finn-ley.cz
Textile Machinery Mfr
N.A.I.C.S.: 333248

Gertner Service GmbH **(2)**
Bul Lesi Ukrainki k 40 14a, 1133, Kiev,
Ukraine
Tel.: (380) 442357574
Web Site: https://www.leybold.com
Machine Tools Mfr
N.A.I.C.S.: 333517

36 Enterprise Drive, Rowville, 3178, VIC,
Australia
Tel.: (61) 397637633
Web Site: http://www.javac.com.au
Vacuum & Refrigeration Equipment Mfr
N.A.I.C.S.: 333912

Leybold France S.A.S. **(2)**
3 Avenue du Canada Parc du Technopolis
Batiment Beta, Les Ulis, 91940, France
Tel.: (33) 169824800
Web Site: http://www.leybold.com
Industrial Vacuum Pump Mfr
N.A.I.C.S.: 333912

Leybold Hispánica, S.A. **(2)**
Huelva, 7 E-08940 Cornellá de Llobregat,
Barcelona, Spain
Tel.: (34) 936664311
Engineeering Services
N.A.I.C.S.: 541330

Leybold Ireland **(2)**
Kerlogue Industrial Estate Rosslare Road,
Wexford, Ireland
Tel.: (353) 539146708
Web Site: http://www.provac.ie
Industrial Vacuum Mfr
N.A.I.C.S.: 333912

Leybold Italia S.r.l. **(2)**
Via Trasimeno 8, 20128, Milan, Italy
Tel.: (39) 02272231
Precision Turned Product Mfr
N.A.I.C.S.: 332721

Leybold Japan Co., Ltd. **(2)**
23-3 Shin-Yokohama 3-chome Tobu A K
Bldg 4th Floor, Kohoku-ku, Yokohama, 222-
0033, Japan
Tel.: (81) 454713330
Industrial Vacuum Pump Mfr
N.A.I.C.S.: 333912

Leybold Taiwan Ltd **(2)**
10F No 32 Chenggong 12th St County 302,
Zhubei City, Hsin-chu, 31054, Taiwan
Tel.: (886) 35001688
Vaccum Pump Mfr
N.A.I.C.S.: 333912

Leybold UK Ltd. **(2)**
Unit 9 Silverglade Business Park Leather-
head Road, Chessington, KT9 2QL, United
Kingdom
Tel.: (44) 1372737310
Web Site: https://www.leybold.com
Precision Turned Product Mfr
N.A.I.C.S.: 332721

Subsidiary (US):

Leybold USA Inc. **(2)**
6005 Enterprise Dr,, Export, PA 15632
Tel.: (800) 764-5369
Web Site: https://www.leybold.com
Vacuum Equipment Mfr
N.A.I.C.S.: 333912

Subsidiary (Non-US):

**Oerlikon Leybold Vacuum (Tianjin)
International Trade Co. Ltd.** **(2)**
1-908 Beijing Landmark Towers North
Dongsanhuan Road 8, Beijing, 100004,
China
Tel.: (86) 4000388989
Precision Turned Product Mfr
N.A.I.C.S.: 332721

Subsidiary (Domestic):

**Oerlikon Leybold Vacuum Dresden
GmbH** **(2)**
Zur Wetterwarte 50 Haus 304, 1109, Dres-
den, Germany
Tel.: (49) 351885500
Web Site: https://www.leybold.com
Industrial Vacuum Equipment Mfr
N.A.I.C.S.: 333912

Subsidiary (Non-US):

**Oerlikon Leybold Vacuum India Pvt.
Ltd** **(2)**
EL 22 J-Block MIDC Bhosari, Pune, 411
026, India
Tel.: (91) 2030616000
Web Site:
    https://oerlikonleybold.tradeindia.com
Vaccum Pump Mfr

Atlas Copco AB—(Continued)

N.A.I.C.S.: 333912

Oerlikon Leybold Vacuum Korea Ltd. (2)
3F, Jellzone 2 Tower Jeongja-dong 159-4 Bundang-gu Sungnam-si, Bundang, 463-384, Gyeonggi-do, Korea (South)
Tel.: (82) 415893035
Vacuum Pump Sales & Maintenance Services
N.A.I.C.S.: 423830

Subsidiary (Domestic):

Oerlikon Vacuum Holding GmbH (2)
Bonner Str 498, Cologne, 50968, Germany
Tel.: (49) 2213470
Investment Management Service
N.A.I.C.S.: 523999

Subsidiary (Non-US):

Oerlikon Vacuum Romania KON TRADE SRL (2)
Str Vidului nr 5, Floresti, 400236, Cluj-Napoca, Romania
Tel.: (40) 264403590
Web Site: http://www.kon-trade.ro
Pumping Equipment Distr
N.A.I.C.S.: 423830

Oerlikon Vacuum Russian Federation GERTNER Service GmbH (2)
Sadovnichskaya St 20 Bld 1, 115035, Moscow, Russia
Tel.: (7) 495 931 9645
Textile Machinery Mfr
N.A.I.C.S.: 333248

Oerlikon Vacuum Turkey TEKSER A.S. (2)
Kayisdagi Inonu Mah Kartal Cad No 55/3, Atasehir, 34755, Istanbul, Turkiye
Tel.: (90) 216 573 64 70
Vacuum Pump Distr
N.A.I.C.S.: 423830

Pneumax Co. Ltd (2)
107/1 Chaloem Phrakiat R 9 Rd, Pravet, Bangkok, 10250, Thailand
Tel.: (66) 27268000
Web Site: https://www.eng.pneumax.co.th
Industrial Pump Mfr
N.A.I.C.S.: 333996

Saengvith 2000 Co. Ltd. (2)
66/701-702 Moo 5 Soi Charansanitwong 13 Saibangwaek Road Khlongkhwang, Phasicharoen, Bangkok, 10160, Thailand
Tel.: (66) 286194469
Web Site: https://www.leybold.com
Industrial Pumping Equipment Distr
N.A.I.C.S.: 423830

TEVAK s.r.o. (2)
K Horkam 421/28, 102 00, Prague, Czech Republic
Tel.: (420) 281924711
Web Site: https://www.tevak.cz
Industrial Vacuum Pump Mfr
N.A.I.C.S.: 333912

YTM-Industrial Oy (2)
Tiilenlyojankuja 9 B, 01720, Vantaa, Finland
Tel.: (358) 29006230
Web Site: http://www.ytm.fi
Sales Range: $25-49.9 Million
Emp.: 75
Industrial Vacuum Mfr
N.A.I.C.S.: 333912
Jyrki Lehtinen (Mgr-Sls-Pressure & Dust Explosion Prevention Sys)

Oy Atlas Copco Ab (1)
Tuupakankuja 1, 01740, Vantaa, Finland
Tel.: (358) 20 718 9200
Sales Range: $25-49.9 Million
Emp.: 71
Air Compressor Mfr
N.A.I.C.S.: 333912

Subsidiary (Domestic):

Oy Atlas Copco Kompressorit Ab (2)
Itainen Valkoisenlahteentie 14 A, 01380, Vantaa, Finland
Tel.: (358) 20 718 92 00
Web Site: http://www.atlascopco.com

Sales Range: $25-49.9 Million
Emp.: 100
Compressor Machinery Mfr
N.A.I.C.S.: 333912

Oy Atlas Copco Louhintatekniikka Ab (2)
Tuupakankuja 1, 01740, Vantaa, Finland
Tel.: (358) 20 718 93 00
Sales Range: $25-49.9 Million
Emp.: 25
Winding Machinery Distr
N.A.I.C.S.: 423830
Ilkka Eskola (Gen Mgr-Construction & Mining Technique)

Oy Atlas Copco Rotex Ab (2)
Pihtisulunkatu 1a, Tampere, 33330, Finland
Tel.: (358) 207189350
Web Site: http://www.atlascopco.com
Sales Range: $25-49.9 Million
Emp.: 20
Machine Tools Mfr
N.A.I.C.S.: 333515

Oy Atlas Copco Tools Ab (2)
Itainen Valkoisenlahteentie 14 A, 01380, Vantaa, Finland
Tel.: (358) 207189200
Web Site: http://www.atlascopco.com
Sales Range: $50-74.9 Million
Emp.: 10
Construction & Mining Tool Machinery Distr
N.A.I.C.S.: 423810

PMH Druckluft GmbH (1)
Konrad-Zuse-Str 12, Moers, 47445, Germany
Tel.: (49) 2841788480
Web Site: http://www.pneumatech.com
Air Compressor & Receiver Mfr
N.A.I.C.S.: 333912

PT Atlas Copco Indonesia (1)
Cilandak Commercial Estate Kav 203 Jl Cilandak Kko, Jakarta, 12560, Indonesia
Tel.: (62) 21 7801008
Web Site: http://www.atlascopco.co.id
Sales Range: $75-99.9 Million
Emp.: 15
Construction & Mining Equipment Distr
N.A.I.C.S.: 423810

Subsidiary (Domestic):

PT Atlas Copco Fluidcon (2)
Cilandak Commercial Estate Building 201 Jl Raya Cilandak KKO, Jakarta, 12560, Indonesia
Tel.: (62) 21 7890550
Web Site: http://www.fluidcon.co.id
Emp.: 60
Oil & Gas Exploration Services
N.A.I.C.S.: 213112
Mustafa Dahlan (Mgr-HR)

Power Technique North America LLC (1)
1059 Paragon Way, Rock Hill, SC 29730
Industrial Machinery & Mining Equipment Mfr
N.A.I.C.S.: 333131
Rob Sulver (VP-PTS Ops)

Power Tools Distribution N.V. (1)
Industrielaan 14, Hoeselt, Brussels, 3730, Belgium
Tel.: (32) 89510411
Emp.: 220
Tool & Spare Parts Distr
N.A.I.C.S.: 423120
Miguel Martinez (Mgr-Fin)

Pressure Compressores Ltda. (1)
Rodovia PR 317-Km 8, Parque Industrial Sul, 87065-005, Maringa, Brazil
Tel.: (55) 4432188500
Web Site: http://www.ns1.pressure.com.br
Air Compressor Mfr
N.A.I.C.S.: 333912

QUISS Qualitats-Inspektionssystemeund Service AG (1)
Lilienthalstrasse 5, 82178, Puchheim, Germany
Tel.: (49) 89894590
Web Site: http://www.quiss.net
Adhesive & Sealant Mfr
N.A.I.C.S.: 325520

Stephan Roskothen (CEO)

Rand Air South Africa Pty Ltd (1)
10 Innes Road Jet Park, Boksburg, South Africa
Tel.: (27) 113450700
Web Site: http://www.randair.co.za
Portable Air & Power Rental Services
N.A.I.C.S.: 532490

Reno A/S (1)
Nymarksvej 2 Thyregod, 7323, Give, Denmark
Tel.: (45) 76708500
Web Site: http://www.en.reno.dk
Emp.: 60
Air Compressor Mfr & Distr
N.A.I.C.S.: 333912
Fabio Roberto Do Rego (Gen Mgr)

SCS Filtration Pty Ltd (1)
16-18 Lindon Court, Tullamarine, 3043, VIC, Australia
Tel.: (61) 1300665258
Web Site: http://www.scsfiltration.com.au
Compressed Air Filtration Product Mfr
N.A.I.C.S.: 333413

SPA Atlas Copco Algerie (1)
Route de Sidi Menif Tranche 3 Lot 119, Zeralda, Algiers, Algeria
Tel.: (213) 21 32 83 25
Sales Range: $25-49.9 Million
Emp.: 80
Construction Equipment Mfr & Distr
N.A.I.C.S.: 333120
Faouzi Ben Gharbia (Gen Mgr)

Saltus Industrial Technique GmbH (1)
Schaberger Strasse 49-53, Solingen, 42659, Germany
Tel.: (49) 2125960220
Industrial Machinery & Mining Equipment Mfr
N.A.I.C.S.: 333131

Scales Industrial Technologies, Inc. (1)
110 Voice Rd, Carle Place, NY 11514 **(100%)**
Tel.: (516) 248-9096
Web Site: http://www.scalesair.com
Emp.: 180
Design, Sale, Installation, Service & Distr of Industrial Compressed Air Solutions
N.A.I.C.S.: 333912

Schneider Bohemia Spol s.r.o. (1)
V Zahradkach 555, Line, 330 21, Plzen, Czech Republic
Tel.: (420) 377911314
Compressor Mfr
N.A.I.C.S.: 333912

Schneider Druckluft GmbH (1)
Ferdinand-Lassalle-Strasse 43, 72770, Reutlingen, Germany
Tel.: (49) 7121959222
Web Site: http://www.schneider-airsystems.com
Compressor & Pneumatic Tool Mfr
N.A.I.C.S.: 333912

Schneider-Slovensko tlakova vzduchotechnika spol. s r.o. (1)
Novozamocka 165, 949 05, Nitra, Slovakia
Tel.: (421) 376522775
Web Site:
  http://www.kompresoryschneider.sk
Air Compressor Mfr
N.A.I.C.S.: 333912

Shanghai Bolaite Compressor Co Ltd (1)
No 528 Laodong Road, Jiading Dist, Shanghai, China
Tel.: (86) 2159946511
Compressor Machinery Mfr
N.A.I.C.S.: 333912

Sociedade Atlas Copco de Portugal Lda (1)
Avenida do Forte n3, 2790-073, Carnaxide, Portugal
Tel.: (351) 2 14 16 85 73
Web Site: http://www.atlascopco.pt
Emp.: 4
Construction & Mining Equipment Distr
N.A.I.C.S.: 423810

Milton Carvalho (Mgr-Svc-Ports Sines, Setubal & Lisboa)

Synatec GmbH (1)
Bruhlhofstrasse 4, 70771, Leinfelden-Echterdingen, Germany
Tel.: (49) 71175859560
Industrial Machinery & Mining Equipment Mfr
N.A.I.C.S.: 333131
Nicolas Lebreton (Mng Dir)

Taylor Air Center (1)
4389 Commerce Dr, Whitehall, PA 18052-2507
Tel.: (610) 262-5431
Web Site: http://www.tayloraircenter.com
Sales Range: $25-49.9 Million
Emp.: 35
Provider of Industrial Machinery & Equipment
N.A.I.C.S.: 423830
Robert Abadessa (Pres)

Techfluid Nord S.A.S. (1)
34 Bis rue de la Distillerie - Parc de La Plaine, 59650, Villeneuve d'Ascq, France
Tel.: (33) 3 20 41 04 92
Compressor Mfr
N.A.I.C.S.: 333912

Tooltec (Qingdao) Tool Co Ltd (1)
No 192 Zhuzhou Road, Qingdao, 266101, China
Tel.: (86) 532 88706530
Web Site: http://www.atlascopco.com
Sales Range: $25-49.9 Million
Emp.: 6
Machine Tools Mfr
N.A.I.C.S.: 333515

Varisco S.r.l. (1)
Prima strada 37, Zona Industriale Nord, 35129, Padua, Italy
Tel.: (39) 0498294111
Web Site: http://www.varisco.it
Pump Mfr & Distr
N.A.I.C.S.: 333914
Carlo Recaldini (Mgr-Industry Sls)

Varisco Wellpoint srl (1)
Viale dell Industria 49, Industrial Area North, 35129, Padua, Italy
Tel.: (39) 0498079622
Web Site: http://www.variscowellpoint.it
Groundwater Drainage Services
N.A.I.C.S.: 221310

Vibratechniques S.A.S. (1)
Rue Du Bourgtheroulde, 76460, Saint Valery-en-Caux, France
Tel.: (33) 2 35 57 91 91
Construction Machinery Distr
N.A.I.C.S.: 423830

Wuxi Pneumatech Air/Gas Purity Equipment Co Ltd (1)
No 36 ZhuJiang Road New District, Wuxi, 214028, Jiangsu, China
Tel.: (86) 510 8521 1442
Web Site: http://www.pneumatech.com.cn
Sales Range: $50-74.9 Million
Emp.: 100
Compressor Machinery Mfr & Distr
N.A.I.C.S.: 333912
Shirley Zhang (Mgr-Personnel)

ZAO Atlas Copco (1)
15 Vashutinskoe Road, Khimki, 141402, Moscow, Russia
Tel.: (7) 495 933 55 50
Compressor Machinery Maintenance Services
N.A.I.C.S.: 811310

Zahroof Valves, Inc. (1)
8515-R Jackrabbit Rd, Houston, TX 77095
Tel.: (713) 554-2678
Web Site: http://www.zahroofvalves.com
Industrial Valve Mfr
N.A.I.C.S.: 332911
Bindu Nayar (Treas & Sec)

ATLAS CORPORATION S.R.L.
59 Pipera Street, District 2, 020111, Bucharest, Romania
Tel.: 21230878285   RO
Web Site: http://www.atlas-corp.ro
Year Founded: 1994

Sales Range: $25-49.9 Million
Emp.: 100
Construction Material Mfr & Distr
N.A.I.C.S.: 327999
John Sitinas *(Owner)*

Subsidiaries:

Atlas Corporation S.R.L. - Apla
Division   **(1)**
59 Sos Pipera, Bucharest, Romania
Tel.: (40) 21 230 8777
Web Site: http://www.apla.ro
Sales Range: $100-124.9 Million
Emp.: 20
Construction Materials Mfr & Distr
N.A.I.C.S.: 423320

ATLAS CYCLES (HARYANA) LTD.
Atlas Premises Atlas Road, Post Box
No 20, Sonipat, 131001, Haryana,
India
Tel.: (91) 1302200001
Web Site: https://atlasbicycles.com
Rev.: $102,057,070
Assets: $59,976,132
Liabilities: $44,811,998
Net Worth: $15,164,134
Earnings: ($251,721)
Emp.: 426
Fiscal Year-end: 03/31/18
Bicycle & Steel Tube Mfr
N.A.I.C.S.: 336991
Vikram Kapur *(Co-Pres)*

ATLAS ELEVATORS GENERAL TRADING & CONTRACTING COMPANY
Eastern Ring Road, PO Box 35598,
Al Quds district, Riyadh, 11383,
Saudi Arabia
Tel.: (966) 920000259
Web Site: https://www.atlaslifts-sa.net
Year Founded: 2010
9578—(SAU)
Rev.: $19,010,509
Assets: $30,957,346
Liabilities: $6,314,154
Net Worth: $24,643,191
Earnings: $2,693,000
Emp.: 351
Fiscal Year-end: 12/31/23
Elevator Product Distr
N.A.I.C.S.: 423830
Mohsen Ali Dali Alotaibi *(CEO)*

ATLAS ENGINEERED PRODUCTS LTD.
2005 Boxwood Rd, Nanaimo, V9S
5X9, BC, Canada
Tel.: (250) 754-1400   BC
Web Site:
   https://www.atlasproducts.com
Year Founded: 1984
APEUF—(OTCIQ)
Rev.: $46,177,117
Assets: $37,666,543
Liabilities: $16,127,506
Net Worth: $21,539,036
Earnings: $6,587,431
Fiscal Year-end: 12/31/22
Truss Mfr
N.A.I.C.S.: 321215
Hadi Abassi *(Founder, Pres & CEO)*

Subsidiaries:

Coastal Windows Ltd.   **(1)**
67 Queen Street W, Saint Stephen, E3L
2K7, NB, Canada
Tel.: (506) 271-4027
Web Site: http://www.coastalwindows.ca
Metal Window Product Mfr
N.A.I.C.S.: 332321

Pacer Building Components Inc.   **(1)**
200 King Street, Ilderton, N0M 2A0, ON,
Canada
Tel.: (519) 666-1360

Web Site:
   https://www.pacerbuildingcomponents.ca
Industrial Material Mfr
N.A.I.C.S.: 333120

South Central Building Systems
Ltd.   **(1)**
170 2nd St NE, PO Box 328, Carman, R0G
0J0, MB, Canada
Tel.: (204) 745-6677
Web Site:
   https://www.southcentralsystems.ca
Industrial Material Mfr
N.A.I.C.S.: 333120
Devon Hillmer *(Ops Mgr)*

ATLAS ESTATES LIMITED
3rd Floor 1 Le Truchot, Saint Peter
Port, GY1 1WD, Guernsey
Tel.: (44) 148 174 9360   GY
Web Site: http://www.atlasestates.pl
ATL—(WAR)
Rev.: $43,059,737
Assets: $302,713,836
Liabilities: $143,085,632
Net Worth: $159,628,204
Earnings: $36,644,059
Emp.: 224
Fiscal Year-end: 12/31/19
Real Estate Investment Services
N.A.I.C.S.: 523999
Mark Chasey *(Chm)*

Subsidiaries:

Atlas Estates Cooperatief U.A.   **(1)**
PO Box 15651, 1019 DT, Amsterdam, Netherlands
Tel.: (31) 206704455
Sales Range: $50-74.9 Million
Emp.: 12
Real Estate Services
N.A.I.C.S.: 531390
Lena Mariam *(Acct Mgr)*

Capital Art Apartments Sp. z o.o. **(1)**
Stock Exchange 4, 02017, Warsaw, Poland
Tel.: (48) 223405400
Web Site: http://www.caapartments.pl
Real Estate Services
N.A.I.C.S.: 531390

Grzybowska Centrum Sp. z o.o.   **(1)**
11 Walicow, 00 851, Warsaw, Poland
Tel.: (48) 225839253
Real Estate Services
N.A.I.C.S.: 531390

Ligetvaros Kft   **(1)**
Damjanich u 11-15, 1071, Budapest, Hungary
Tel.: (36) 14795800
Web Site: http://www.ligetvaros.hu
Real Estate Services
N.A.I.C.S.: 531390

World Real Estate S.R.L.   **(1)**
Via Paolo Emilio 7, 00192, Rome, Italy
Tel.: (39) 0632110998
Web Site: http://www.romepower.com
Sales Range: $50-74.9 Million
Emp.: 3
Houses & Flats Rental Services
N.A.I.C.S.: 531110

ATLAS FOR LAND RECLAMATION & AGRICULTURAL PROCESSING
Km 43 West Cairo-Alexandria Desert
Road, Giza, Egypt
Tel.: (20) 239103165
Web Site: http://www.atlasegypt.com
Year Founded: 1997
Agricultural Product Mfr
N.A.I.C.S.: 111998
Hosni Abbas Hosni Mohamed
(Founder & CEO)

ATLAS GROUP OF COMPANIES
2nd Floor Federation House
Shahrah-e-Firdousi, Karachi, 75600,
Pakistan
Tel.: (92) 215369471

Web Site:
   http://www.atlasgrouppk.com
Sales Range: $1-4.9 Billion
Emp.: 7,000
Holding Company
N.A.I.C.S.: 551112
Yusuf H. Shirazi *(Chm)*

Subsidiaries:

Atlas Asset Management Limited   **(1)**
Ground Floor Federation House Sharae
Firdousi, Clifton, Karachi, 75600, Pakistan
Tel.: (92) 21 35379501
Web Site: http://www.atlasfunds.com.pk
Asset Management Services
N.A.I.C.S.: 523940
Yusuf H. Shirazi *(Chm)*

Atlas Autos (Private) Limited   **(1)**
15th Mile National Highway, Landhi, Karachi, Pakistan
Tel.: (92) 21350169214
Web Site: https://atlasautos.com.pk
Automobile Mfr
N.A.I.C.S.: 611692
Aamir H. Shirazi *(Chm)*

Atlas Autos (Private) Limited - Karachi Plant   **(1)**
15th Mile National Highway, Landhi, Karachi, Pakistan
Tel.: (92) 2135002305
Automotive Products Mfr
N.A.I.C.S.: 334290

Atlas Autos (Private) Limited -
Sheikhupura plant   **(1)**
26/27 Km Lhr-Skp road, Sheikhupura, Pakistan
Tel.: (92) 563406501
Automotive Products Mfr
N.A.I.C.S.: 334290

Atlas Battery Ltd.   **(1)**
D-181 Central Avenue, SITE, Karachi,
75730, Pakistan
Tel.: (92) 2132567990
Web Site: http://www.atlasbattery.com.pk
Rev.: $155,431,605
Assets: $67,054,735
Liabilities: $28,590,722
Net Worth: $38,464,013
Earnings: $4,281,404
Emp.: 346
Fiscal Year-end: 06/30/2022
Battery Mfr; Owned by GS Yuasa International Ltd. & by Atlas Group of Companies
N.A.I.C.S.: 335910
Ali H. Shirazi *(Pres & CEO)*

Atlas Engineering Limited   **(1)**
15th Mile National Highway, Landhi, Karachi, 75120, Pakistan
Tel.: (92) 2135016921
Web Site:
   http://www.atlasengineering.com.pk
Sales Range: $10-24.9 Million
Emp.: 224
Cast Iron Process Pig Iron & Aluminum Alloys Producer; Automotive Components Mfr
N.A.I.C.S.: 336390
Yusuf H. Shirazi *(Chm)*

Atlas Global FZE   **(1)**
Office 708A 7th Floor JAFZA Building 18
Sheikh Zayed Road, PO Box 117442,
Dubai, United Arab Emirates
Tel.: (971) 48816966
Web Site: https://www.atlasglobal.ae
Machine & Equipment Distr
N.A.I.C.S.: 423830

Atlas Hitec (Pvt). Limited   **(1)**
15th Mile National Highway, Landhi, Karachi, 75120, Pakistan
Tel.: (92) 3500230304
Fund Management Services
N.A.I.C.S.: 523999

Atlas Honda Limited   **(1)**
1 Mcleod Road, Lahore, 54000, Pakistan
Tel.: (92) 423 722 5015
Web Site: http://www.atlashonda.com.pk
Rev.: $819,286,499
Assets: $294,494,942
Liabilities: $163,913,310
Net Worth: $130,581,632
Earnings: $34,683,875
Emp.: 2,299

Fiscal Year-end: 03/31/2022
Motorcycle Mfr & Distr; Joint Venture of Atlas Group & Honda Motor Co., Ltd.
N.A.I.C.S.: 336991
Suhail Ahmed *(VP-Mktg)*

Atlas Power Limited   **(1)**
26-27 KM Lahore Sheikhupura Road,
Sheikhupura, Punjab, Pakistan
Tel.: (92) 563406194
Web Site: https://www.atlaspower.com.pk
Power Generation Services
N.A.I.C.S.: 221118
Frahim Ali Khan *(Chm)*

Atlas Worldwide General Trading
LLC   **(1)**
Suite No 311 Nasir Ahmed Nasir Lootah
Bldg Khalid bin Al Waleed Road, PO Box
117059, Dubai, United Arab Emirates
Tel.: (971) 4 3570774
Web Site: http://www.atlasworldwide.info
Automotive Part Whslr
N.A.I.C.S.: 423120

Honda Atlas Cars Pakistan Ltd.   **(1)**
43 km Multan Road Manga Mandi, Lahore,
Pakistan
Tel.: (92) 423 538 4671
Web Site: http://www.honda.com.pk
Rev.: $670,977,149
Assets: $436,333,528
Liabilities: $312,377,426
Net Worth: $123,956,102
Earnings: $15,586,516
Emp.: 2,274
Fiscal Year-end: 03/31/2022
Car Mfr; Owned by Honda Motor Co., Ltd.
& Atlas Group of Companies
N.A.I.C.S.: 336110
Aamir H. Shirazi *(Chm)*

Shirazi Investments (Private)
Limited   **(1)**
2nd Floor Federation House Sharae Firdousi, Clifton, Karachi, Pakistan
Tel.: (92) 21353694714
Web Site:
   https://www.shiraziinvestments.com.pk
Fund Management Services
N.A.I.C.S.: 523150
Iftikhar H. Shirazi *(Chm)*

Shirazi Trading Company Private
Limited   **(1)**
Plot No 114C Al-Murtaza Commercial
Lane-3 Khayaban-e-Iqbal, Phase VIII DHA,
Karachi, Pakistan
Tel.: (92) 2135170851
Web Site: http://www.stc.atlas.pk
Information Technology Consulting Services
N.A.I.C.S.: 541512
Farooq Saleem *(CEO)*

ATLAS GROWTH ACQUISITION LTD.
Suite 3522 Level 35 Two Pacific
Place 88 Queensway, Central, China
(Hong Kong)
Tel.: (852) 22187558   Ky
Year Founded: 2021
ATLAU—(NASDAQ)
Investment Services
N.A.I.C.S.: 523999
Sung June Hwang *(Chm & CEO)*

ATLAS INSURANCE LIMITED
63/A Block-XX Phase III Commercial
Khayaban-e-Iqbal DHA, Lahore, Pakistan
Tel.: (92) 42111245000
Web Site: https://ail.atlas.pk
Year Founded: 1934
ATIL—(KAR)
Rev.: $9,372,879
Assets: $45,299,733
Liabilities: $21,428,327
Net Worth: $23,871,406
Earnings: $4,013,769
Emp.: 173
Fiscal Year-end: 12/31/19
General Insurance Services
N.A.I.C.S.: 524210
Muhammad Afzal *(Sec)*

Atlas Insurance Limited—(Continued)

ATLAS IRON LIMITED
Level 17 Raine Square 300 Murray Street, Perth, 6000, WA, Australia
Tel.: (61) 86 228 8000   **AU**
Web Site:
http://www.atlasiron.com.au
Year Founded: 2004
AGO—(OTCIQ)
Sales Range: $650-699.9 Million
Emp.: 75
Iron Ore Mining
N.A.I.C.S.: 212210
Mark Hancock *(Chief Comml Officer)*

ATLAS JEWELLERY INDIA LIMITED
No 1518 15th Floor Hemkunt Chambers 89 Nehru Road, Plot No 11 Jasola, New Delhi, 110 025, India
Tel.: (91) 1141041149
Web Site:
https://www.atlasjewelleryindia.com
514394—(BOM)
Rev.: $195,874
Assets: $22,822,331
Liabilities: $760,180
Net Worth: $22,062,152
Earnings: ($682,699)
Emp.: 11
Fiscal Year-end: 03/31/21
Jewellery Mfr & Whslr
N.A.I.C.S.: 339910
Chandan Mahapatra *(CFO, Compliance Officer & Sec)*

ATLAS LITHIUM CORPORATION
Rua Vereador Joao Alves Praes n 95-A, Olhos D'Agua, 39398-000, MG, Brazil
Tel.: (55) 2135902500   **NV**
Web Site: https://atlas-lithium.com
Year Founded: 2011
ATLX—(NASDAQ)
Rev.: $6,765
Assets: $5,684,231
Liabilities: $2,876,931
Net Worth: $2,807,300
Earnings: ($4,628,520)
Emp.: 30
Fiscal Year-end: 12/31/22
Diamond, Gold & Sand Mining & Production
N.A.I.C.S.: 212220
Marc Fogassa *(Chm & CEO)*

Subsidiaries:

Jupiter Gold Corporation   **(1)**
Rua Vereador Joao Alves Praes n 95-A, Olhos D'Agua, MG 39398-000, Minas Gerais, Brazil
Tel.: (55) 3139561109
Web Site: https://www.jupitergoldcorp.com
Assets: $78,866
Liabilities: $20,583
Net Worth: $58,283
Earnings: ($657,375)
Emp.: 5
Fiscal Year-end: 12/31/2022
Gold Exploration & Mining Services
N.A.I.C.S.: 212220
Marc Fogassa *(Founder, Chm, CEO & CFO)*

ATLAS MARA LIMITED
Ritter House 6th Floor Wickhams Cay II, PO Box 4041, Road Town, VG1110, Tortola, Virgin Islands (British)
Tel.: (284) 8834330   **VG**
Web Site: http://www.atlasmara.com
Year Founded: 2013
ATMA—(OTCIQ)
Rev.: $329,293,000
Assets: $2,608,578,000
Liabilities: $2,278,103,000

Net Worth: $330,475,000
Earnings: ($57,281,000)
Emp.: 4,820
Fiscal Year-end: 02/28/21
Holding Company
N.A.I.C.S.: 551112
Robert E. Diamond Jr. *(Founder)*

Subsidiaries:

ABC Holdings Limited   **(1)**
Plot 62433 Fairgrounds Office Park, Gaborone, Botswana   **(58.09%)**
Tel.: (267) 367 4325
Web Site: https://www.bancabc.com
Rev.: $209,643,000
Assets: $2,040,297,000
Liabilities: $1,926,947,000
Net Worth: $113,350,000
Earnings: ($1,369,000)
Emp.: 1,200
Fiscal Year-end: 12/31/2016
Financial Holding Company
N.A.I.C.S.: 551111

Subsidiary (Domestic):

African Banking Corporation Botswana Limited   **(2)**
BancABC House Plot 62433 Fairgrounds office Park, Gaborone, Botswana   **(100%)**
Tel.: (267) 3674300
Web Site: http://www.bancabc.co.bw
Banking Services
N.A.I.C.S.: 523150

Subsidiary (Non-US):

African Banking Corporation Mozambique Limited   **(2)**
Avenida Julius Nyerere n999 Polana Cimento, Maputo, Mozambique   **(100%)**
Tel.: (258) 21 487 474
Web Site: http://www.bancabc.co.mz
Banking Services
N.A.I.C.S.: 523150
Benjamin Alfredo *(Dir)*

African Banking Corporation Tanzania Limited   **(2)**
5th & 6th Floor Uhuru Heights Bibi Titi Mohammed Road, PO Box 31, Dar es Salaam, Tanzania   **(94%)**
Tel.: (255) 222111990
Web Site: http://www.bancabc.co.tz
Banking Services
N.A.I.C.S.: 523150
Roger Lamlembe *(Head-Banking Ops & IT)*

African Banking Corporation Zambia Limited   **(2)**
Arcades Shopping Mall, PO Box 37102, Lusaka, 10101, Zambia
Tel.: (260) 211256458
Web Site: http://www.atlasmarazambia.com
Emp.: 220
Banking Services
N.A.I.C.S.: 522110

ADC African Development Corporation AG   **(1)**
Gruneburgweg 18, 60322, Frankfurt am Main, Germany   **(100%)**
Tel.: (49) 69719 128 0119
Web Site: https://www.african-development.com
Financial Investment Services
N.A.I.C.S.: 523999

ATLAS MENKUL KIYMETLER YATIRIM ORTAKLIGI A.S.
Buyukdere Cad No 171 Metro City A Blok Kat 17 1, Levent, Istanbul, Turkiye
Tel.: (90) 2123441289
Web Site: https://www.atlasyo.com.tr
Year Founded: 1994
ATLAS—(IST)
Sales Range: $75-99.9 Million
Portfolio Management Services
N.A.I.C.S.: 523940
Burcu Hilal Kaplan *(Mgr-Investor Relations)*

ATLAS PEARLS LTD.

26 Railway Road, Subiaco, 6004, WA, Australia
Tel.: (61) 892844249   **AU**
Web Site:
https://www.atlaspearls.com.au
Year Founded: 1993
ATP—(ASX)
Rev.: $27,848,298
Assets: $46,643,379
Liabilities: $9,573,710
Net Worth: $37,069,669
Earnings: $21,012,965
Emp.: 1,200
Fiscal Year-end: 06/30/24
Pearl Farming
N.A.I.C.S.: 114210
Susan Patricia Hunter *(Sec)*

Subsidiaries:

Essential Oils Of Tasmania Pty Ltd   **(1)**
1520 Channel Highway, Margate, 7054, TAS, Australia
Tel.: (61) 362294222
Web Site: http://www.eotasmania.com
Emp.: 11
Essential Oils & Plant Extract Mfr
N.A.I.C.S.: 325411
Derek Zwart *(Mgr-Agronomy Svcs & Special Projects)*

ATLAS TECHNOLOGIES CORPORATION
2-5 Kasumigaseki 3-chome, Chiyoda-ku, Tokyo, 100-6036, Japan
Tel.: (81) 368211612
Web Site: https://www.atlstech.com
Year Founded: 2018
9563—(TKS)
Rev.: $18,356,010
Assets: $19,540,040
Liabilities: $1,850,490
Net Worth: $17,689,550
Earnings: $531,750
Fiscal Year-end: 12/31/23
Information Technology Services
N.A.I.C.S.: 541512

ATLASINVEST
Chaussee de la Hulpe 120, 1000, Brussels, Belgium
Tel.: (32) 2663 1750
Web Site: http://www.atlasinvest.be
Year Founded: 2007
Sales Range: $25-49.9 Million
Emp.: 20
Privater Equity Firm
N.A.I.C.S.: 523999
Marcel Q. H. van Poecke *(Founder & Chm)*

Subsidiaries:

Varo Energy Holding S.A.   **(1)**
c/o Vitol Boulevard du Pont d'Arve 28, CH-1205, Geneva, Switzerland   **(25%)**
Tel.: (41) 22 322 1111
Web Site: http://www.varoenergy.com
Holding Company; Petroleum Refining & Marketing Services
N.A.I.C.S.: 551112

Subsidiary (Domestic):

Varo Energy Marketing AG   **(2)**
Industriestrasse 24, Postfach 4713, Zug, 6304, Switzerland
Tel.: (41) 747 23 00
Web Site: http://www.varoenergy.com
Sales Range: $50-74.9 Million
Petroleum Wholesale Trade Distr
N.A.I.C.S.: 425120
Flitch Andras *(Mgr)*

Varo Refining Cressier S.A.   **(2)**
Zone Industrielle Les Hugues, Case Postale 72, CH-2088, Cressier, Switzerland
Tel.: (41) 32 758 6111
Web Site: http://www.varoenergy.com
Sales Range: $50-74.9 Million
Petroleum Refiner
N.A.I.C.S.: 324110

Jilles Vollin *(Dir-Ops)*

ATLASSIAN CORPORATION
Exchange House Primrose Street, London, EC2A 2EG, United Kingdom
Tel.: (44) 4157011110
Web Site: http://www.atlassian.com
TEAM—(NASDAQ)
Rev.: $3,534,617,000
Assets: $4,106,779,000
Liabilities: $3,452,107,000
Net Worth: $654,672,000
Earnings: ($486,761,000)
Emp.: 10,726
Fiscal Year-end: 06/30/23
Software Development Services
N.A.I.C.S.: 541511
Sridatta Viswanath *(CTO)*

Subsidiaries:

Atlassian B.V.   **(1)**
Singel 236 1016 AB, Amsterdam, Netherlands
Tel.: (31) 207960060
Collaboration & Development Software Developer
N.A.I.C.S.: 513210

Atlassian K.K.   **(1)**
Landmark Tower Suite 1407 2-2-1 Minatomirai, Nishi-ku, Yokohama, 220-8114, Kanagawa, Japan
Tel.: (81) 453309080
Collaboration & Development Software Developer
N.A.I.C.S.: 513210

Atlassian Philippines, Inc.   **(1)**
2nd Floor B3 Bonifacio High Street, Taguig, Manila, Philippines
Tel.: (63) 27557700
Collaboration & Development Software Developer
N.A.I.C.S.: 513210

Atlassian Pty. Ltd.   **(1)**
Level 6 341 George Street, Sydney, 2000, NSW, Australia
Tel.: (61) 292621443
Web Site: http://www.atlassian.com
Sales Range: $150-199.9 Million
Emp.: 450
Collaboration & Development Software Developer
N.A.I.C.S.: 513210
Jay Simons *(Pres)*

Atlassian, Inc.   **(1)**
350 Bush St Fl 13, San Francisco, CA 94104
Tel.: (414) 701-1110
Collaboration & Development Software Developer
N.A.I.C.S.: 513210

KSASHMTSSI GmbH   **(1)**
Liesingbachstrasse 224, Vienna, Austria
Tel.: (43) 17109904
IT & Consulting Services
N.A.I.C.S.: 541690

Loom Inc.   **(1)**
140 2nd St 3rd Fl, San Francisco, CA 94105
Tel.: (941) 365-3346
Web Site: http://www.loom.com
Video Messaging Services
N.A.I.C.S.: 518210
Joe Thomas *(CEO)*

MITT Australia Pty. Ltd.   **(1)**
Level 1 / 113 Burgundy Stree, Heidelberg, Melbourne, 3084, VIC, Australia
Tel.: (61) 394500500
Web Site: https://www.mitt.edu.au
Career Development Services
N.A.I.C.S.: 611430

Trello, Inc   **(1)**
55 Broadway 25th Fl, New York, NY 10006
Tel.: (844) 873-5561
Web Applications
N.A.I.C.S.: 513199
Michael Pryor *(CEO)*

ATLATSA RESOURCES CORPORATION

2nd Floor North Wing 90 Rivonia Road, 2146, Sandton, South Africa
Tel.: (27) 102861150　　　BC
Web Site:
http://www.atlatsaresources.co.za
Year Founded: 1983
Rev.: $4,051,044
Assets: $105,088,594
Liabilities: $304,769,660
Net Worth: ($199,681,066)
Earnings: ($98,235,333)
Emp.: 12
Fiscal Year-end: 12/31/18
Platinum Mining
N.A.I.C.S.: 212290
Tumelo M. Motsisi *(Chm)*

Subsidiaries:

Pelawan Investments (Proprietary) Limited　　　(1)
82 Grayston Dr, PO Box 782103, Sandton, Johannesburg, 2196, Gauteng, South Africa
Tel.: (27) 118830831
Web Site:
http://www.anooraqresources.co.za
Sales Range: $50-74.9 Million
Platinum Group Metals Exploration & Development Services
N.A.I.C.S.: 212290

Plateau Resources (Proprietary) Limited　　　(1)
4th Fl 82 Grayston Dr, PO Box 782103, Sandton, 2196, Johannesburg, South Africa
Tel.: (27) 118830831
Web Site:
http://www.anooraqresources.co.za
Emp.: 11
Platinum Group Metals Exploration & Development Services
N.A.I.C.S.: 212290

ATLINKS GROUP LIMITED
Unit 1818 18/F Nan Fung Commercial Centre 19 Lam Lok Street, Kowloon Bay, Kowloon, China (Hong Kong)
Tel.: (852) 21527600　　　Ky
Web Site: https://www.atlinks.com
Year Founded: 2013
8043—(HKG)
Rev.: $32,022,655
Assets: $35,623,057
Liabilities: $27,309,021
Net Worth: $8,314,036
Earnings: ($951,121)
Emp.: 46
Fiscal Year-end: 12/31/22
Electronic Product Mfr & Distr
N.A.I.C.S.: 334210
Hak Kan Long *(Chm)*

ATM CONSTRUCT S.A.
Str Romana 150, Prahova, Ploiesti, Romania
Tel.: (40) 244543843
Web Site:
https://www.atmconstruct.com
Year Founded: 1991
AUXI—(BUC)
Rev.: $3,163,137
Assets: $2,811,751
Liabilities: $458,557
Net Worth: $2,353,195
Earnings: $234,334
Emp.: 48
Fiscal Year-end: 12/31/23
Highway Construction Services
N.A.I.C.S.: 237310
Stefan Ion Popescu *(CEO)*

ATM GRUPA S.A.
ul Dwa Swiaty 1, 55-040, Bielany Wroclawskie, Poland
Tel.: (48) 717764700
Web Site: https://www.atmgrupa.pl
Year Founded: 1992
ATG—(WAR)
Rev.: $59,842,225

Assets: $98,035,823
Liabilities: $20,035,061
Net Worth: $78,000,762
Earnings: $7,137,195
Fiscal Year-end: 12/31/23
Film Production Services
N.A.I.C.S.: 512110
Tomasz Kurzewski *(Chm-Supervisory Bd)*

Subsidiaries:

ATM Inwestycje Sp. Z.o.o.　　　(1)
ul Dwa Swiaty 1, Kobierzyce, 55-040, Bielany Wroclawskie, Poland
Tel.: (48) 697660342
Web Site: https://www.atminwestycje.pl
Portfolio Investment Services
N.A.I.C.S.: 525110

ATM Rozrywka Sp. Z.o.o.　　　(1)
ul Two Worlds 1, 55-040, Bielany Wroclawskie, Poland
Tel.: (48) 717764700
Web Site: https://www.atmrozrywka.pl
Film Television Operator
N.A.I.C.S.: 561492

ATM Studio Sp. Z.o.o.　　　(1)
Ul Wal Miedzeszynski 384, 03-994, Warsaw, Poland
Tel.: (48) 222956110
Web Site: https://www.atmstudio.eu
Sound Stage Rental Services
N.A.I.C.S.: 512110

ATM System Sp. Z.o.o.　　　(1)
Blekitna 3, Bielany Wroclawskie, 55-040, Kobierzyce, Poland
Tel.: (48) 717855300
Web Site: https://atmsystem.pl
Film Equipment Rental Services
N.A.I.C.S.: 532490

ATMA PARTICIPACOES S.A.
Av Paulista 407 - 8 Floor, 1311000, Sao Paulo, Brazil
Tel.: (55) 1131315136
Web Site: http://www.liq.com.br
Year Founded: 2000
Business Support Services
N.A.I.C.S.: 561499
Luciano Bressan *(CFO)*

ATMIRA ESPACIO DE CONSULTORIA S.L.
Santiago de Compostela 94 8th pl, Madrid, 28035, Spain
Tel.: (34) 91 447 18 47
Web Site: http://www.atmira.com
Year Founded: 2005
Sales Range: $25-49.9 Million
Emp.: 350
Information Technology Consulting Services
N.A.I.C.S.: 541512
Joan Cardona *(CEO & Mng Partner)*

ATMOKY GMBH
Schubertstrasse 6a, 8010, Graz, Austria
Tel.: (43) 6505206003
Web Site: https://atmoky.com
Software Development Services
N.A.I.C.S.: 541511

ATN HOLDINGS, INC.
Unit 902 9th Floor Summit One Office Tower 530 Shaw Blvd, Mandaluyong, 1500, Philippines
Tel.: (63) 27170523　　　PH
Web Site:
https://www.atnholdings.com
Year Founded: 1961
ATN—(PHI)
Rev.: $215,294
Assets: $67,666,450
Liabilities: $22,011,756
Net Worth: $45,654,694
Earnings: ($128,934)
Emp.: 36

Fiscal Year-end: 03/31/24
Holding Company; Mining & Oil Exploration & Development Services
N.A.I.C.S.: 551112
Arsenio T. Ng *(Chm, Pres & CEO)*

Subsidiaries:

Advanced Home Concept Development Corp.　　　(1)
9th Floor Summit One Tower Building 530 Shaw Boulevard, Mandaluyong, 1552, Philippines
Tel.: (63) 27170523
Real Estate Manangement Services
N.A.I.C.S.: 531390

Palladian Land Development Inc　(1)
9th Floor Summit One Tower Building 530 Shaw Boulevard, Mandaluyong, 1552, Philippines
Tel.: (63) 27170523
Sales Range: $50-74.9 Million
Emp.: 7
Real Estate Manangement Services
N.A.I.C.S.: 531390

ATN INTERNATIONAL LIMITED
10 Princep Street 2nd Floor, Kolkata, 700 072, India
Tel.: (91) 3322256851
Web Site:
https://www.atninternational.in
ATNINTER—(NSE)
Rev.: $11,903
Assets: $709,977
Liabilities: $1,632,581
Net Worth: ($922,604)
Earnings: ($50,082)
Emp.: 8
Fiscal Year-end: 03/31/22
Investment Banking & Television Broadcasting Services
N.A.I.C.S.: 523150
Santosh Kumar Jain *(Mng Dir)*

ATOK-BIG WEDGE CO., INC.
Alphaland Makati Place 7232 Ayala Avenue corner Malugay Street, Makati, 1209, Philippines
Tel.: (63) 25 310 7100
Web Site:
http://www.atokbigwedge.com
Year Founded: 1931
AB—(PHI)
Rev.: $2,754
Assets: $17,552,336
Liabilities: $23,559
Net Worth: $17,528,777
Earnings: ($621,562)
Emp.: 3
Fiscal Year-end: 12/31/21
Support Activities for Mining
N.A.I.C.S.:
Roberto V. Ongpin *(Chm & CEO)*

ATOM CORPORATION
2-2-1 Minatomirai Kanagawa Landmark Tower 12th floor, Nishi-ku, Yokohama, 220-8112, Aichi, Japan
Tel.: (81) 528575225
Web Site: https://www.atom-corp.co.jp
Year Founded: 1972
7412—(TKS)
Rev.: $301,028,640
Assets: $234,991,680
Liabilities: $134,474,560
Net Worth: $100,517,120
Earnings: $3,116,960
Fiscal Year-end: 03/31/22
Restaurant Operators
N.A.I.C.S.: 722511
Tsuyoshi Yamakado *(Pres)*

ATOM EMPREENDIMENTOS E PARTICIPACOES S.A.
Rua Messias Pereira de Paula 333

Jd Elton Ville, Sorocaba, 18046-640, Sao Paulo, Brazil
Tel.: (55) 1530316100
Web Site: http://www.atompar.com.br
ATOM3—(BRAZ)
Rev.: $3,797,215
Assets: $4,638,101
Liabilities: $1,612,771
Net Worth: $3,025,330
Earnings: ($92,061)
Fiscal Year-end: 12/31/23
Financial Management Services
N.A.I.C.S.: 541611
Jose Joaquim Paifer *(Chm)*

ATOM LIVIN TECH CO., LTD.
1-27-4 Iriya, Taito-Ku, Tokyo, 110-8680, Japan
Tel.: (81) 338760600
Web Site: https://www.atomlt.com
Year Founded: 1954
3426—(TKS)
Sales Range: $100-124.9 Million
Architectural Hardware Distr
N.A.I.C.S.: 541310
Ryoichi Takahashi *(Pres)*

ATOME ENERGY PLC
Building 5 Carrwood Park Selby Road, Leeds, LS15 4LG, United Kingdom
Tel.: (44) 1133372210　　　UK
Web Site: https://www.atomeplc.com
Year Founded: 2021
ATOM—(AIM)
Rev.: $62,000
Assets: $6,620,000
Liabilities: $1,649,000
Net Worth: $4,971,000
Earnings: ($5,479,000)
Emp.: 2
Fiscal Year-end: 12/31/22
Natural Gas Distribution
N.A.I.C.S.: 221210

ATOMENERGOREMONT PLC
Kozloduy NPP site, 3321, Kozloduy, 3321, Bulgaria
Tel.: (359) 97380018
Web Site: https://www.aer-bg.com
Year Founded: 1974
ATOM—(BUL)
Sales Range: Less than $1 Million
Industrial Equipment Maintenance & Repair Services
N.A.I.C.S.: 811310

ATOMIC ENERGY OF CANADA LIMITED
Chalk River Laboratories 286 Plant Rd Stn 508A, Chalk River, K0J 1J0, ON, Canada
Tel.: (613) 584-3311　　　ON
Web Site: http://www.aecl.ca
Year Founded: 1952
Rev.: $731,069,676
Assets: $359,453,272
Liabilities: $6,346,174,435
Net Worth: ($5,986,721,163)
Earnings: ($794,997)
Emp.: 42
Fiscal Year-end: 03/31/18
Design & Construction of Nuclear Power Plants & Research Reactors; Servicing All Types of Nuclear Power Plants
N.A.I.C.S.: 237130
Claude Lajeunesse *(Chm)*

ATOMIC MINERALS CORPORATION
830 - 1100 Melville St, Vancouver, V6E 4A6, BC, Canada
Tel.: (604) 341-6870
Web Site:
https://www.atomicminerals.ca

Atomic Minerals Corporation—(Continued)

ATMMF—(OTCIQ)
Assets: $761,278
Liabilities: $433,259
Net Worth: $328,019
Earnings: ($1,135,651)
Fiscal Year-end: 08/31/23
Mineral Exploration Services
N.A.I.C.S.: 213114
Clive Massey (Pres & CEO)

ATOMIX CO., LTD.
3-9-6 Funato, Itabashi-Ku, Tokyo,
174-0041, Japan
Tel.: (81) 339693111
Web Site: https://www.atomix.co.jp
Year Founded: 1948
4625—(TKS)
Rev.: $80,126,420
Assets: $100,405,900
Liabilities: $33,063,220
Net Worth: $67,342,680
Earnings: $1,579,790
Emp.: 222
Fiscal Year-end: 03/31/24
Painting Material Mfr & Distr
N.A.I.C.S.: 325510
Toshikazu Jimbo (Pres)

ATOMO DIAGNOSTICS LIMITED
Level 1 3-5 George Street, Leichhardt, 2040, NSW, Australia
Tel.: (61) 290994750　　　　AU
Web Site:
https://www.atomodiagnostics.com
Year Founded: 2010
AT1—(ASX)
Rev.: $1,658,549
Assets: $10,741,057
Liabilities: $1,097,573
Net Worth: $9,643,484
Earnings: ($6,492,555)
Fiscal Year-end: 06/30/23
Pharmaceutical Preparation Manufacturing
N.A.I.C.S.: 325412
Chandra Sukumar (COO)

ATOMOS
700 Swanston Street, Carlton, 3053,
VIC, Australia
Tel.: (61) 399995908
Web Site: https://www.atomos.com
AMS—(ASX)
Rev.: $56,147,936
Assets: $83,326,227
Liabilities: $41,766,549
Net Worth: $41,559,678
Earnings: ($7,940,027)
Emp.: 100
Fiscal Year-end: 06/30/22
Camera Accessory Mfr
N.A.I.C.S.: 334310
James Cody (CFO)

ATOMSYSTEM CO., LTD.
5-9 Minami-Fujisawa Asahi-Seimei
Bldg 8-9F, Fujisawa, 251-8543, Kanagawa, Japan
Tel.: (81) 466291248
Web Site:
http://www.atomsystem.co.jp
Year Founded: 1981
Sales Range: $1-4.9 Billion
Emp.: 226
System Developer
N.A.I.C.S.: 541511
Tetsuya Hosono (Pres)

ATON GMBH
Leopoldstrasse 53, 80802, Munich,
Germany
Tel.: (49) 89 970515 0　　　　De
Web Site: http://www.aton.de

Year Founded: 2001
Rev.: $2,284,851,478
Assets: $2,892,663,332
Liabilities: $1,822,223,874
Net Worth: $1,070,439,458
Earnings: $331,631,981
Emp.: 17,330
Fiscal Year-end: 12/31/19
Investment Holding Company
N.A.I.C.S.: 551112
Jorg Fahrenbach (Mng Dir & CFO)

Subsidiaries:

AspiAir GmbH　　　　　　　　(1)
Wohraer Strasse 37, 35285, Gemunden,
Germany
Tel.: (49) 64535853042
Emp.: 4
Pharmaceuticals Product Mfr
N.A.I.C.S.: 325412
Sebastian Canisius (Chief Medical Officer)

BBZ Mitte GmbH　　　　　　　(1)
Goerdelerstr 139, 36100, Petersberg, Germany
Tel.: (49) 66162080
Web Site: http://www.bbz-mitte.de
Educational Support Services
N.A.I.C.S.: 611710

DC Aviation GmbH　　　　　　(1)
Stuttgart Airport, 70629, Stuttgart, Germany
Tel.: (49) 711 933 06 0
Web Site: http://www.dc-aviation.com
Emp.: 330
Aircraft Management Services
N.A.I.C.S.: 488119
Michael K. Kuhn (CEO & Mng Dir)

Subsidiary (Non-US):

DC Aviation Flight Crew Ltd.　(2)
Triq Il-Mediterran Kyle Apartment No 3 The
Village, San Giljan, Malta
Tel.: (356) 21 373 546
Web Site: http://www.dc-aviation-
flightcrew.com
Aircraft Charter Services
N.A.I.C.S.: 481211
Birgit Friedrich (Mng Dir)

Jet-Link AG　　　　　　　　(2)
Ops Center Flughofstrasse 54, 8152, Glattbrugg, Switzerland
Tel.: (41) 848 22 10 00
Web Site: http://www.jet-link.ch
Aircraft Charter Services
N.A.I.C.S.: 481211

DC Aviation Ltd.　　　　　　(1)
Malta International Airport, PO Box 23,
Gudja, LQA 5000, Malta
Tel.: (356) 21375973
Web Site: http://www.dc-aviation.com.mt
Emp.: 11
Aircraft Charter Services
N.A.I.C.S.: 481211
Sandy Cassar Cardona (Mgr-FBO)

Deilmann-Haniel International Mining
& Tunneling GmbH　　　　　(1)
Haustenbecke 1, 44319, Dortmund,
Germany　　　　　　　　　(100%)
Tel.: (49) 2312891395
Web Site: http://www.deilmann-haniel.com
Sales Range: $650-699.9 Million
Emp.: 240
Holding Company; Mine & Tunnel Construction
N.A.I.C.S.: 551112
Thomas Steinbrecher (Co-Mng Dir)

Subsidiary (Domestic):

Deilmann-Haniel Mining Systems
GmbH　　　　　　　　　　(2)
Haustenbecke 1, Dortmund, 44319,
Germany　　　　　　　　　(100%)
Tel.: (49) 2312891289
Web Site: http://www.dhms.com
Sales Range: $50-74.9 Million
Emp.: 200
Mining & Civil Engineering Machinery Mfr
N.A.I.C.S.: 333131
Hubert Koch (Mgr-Svc)

Deilmann-Haniel Shaft Sinking
GmbH　　　　　　　　　　(2)

Haustenbecke 1, 44319, Dortmund,
Germany　　　　　　　　　(100%)
Tel.: (49) 2312891396
Web Site: http://www.deilmann-haniel.com
Emp.: 210
Shaft Sinking for Civil Engineering & Tunneling Projects
N.A.I.C.S.: 237990
Jochen Greinacher (CEO)

Subsidiary (US):

Frontier-Kemper Constructors,
Inc.　　　　　　　　　　　(2)
1695 Allen Rd, Evansville, IN
47710　　　　　　　　　　(98.97%)
Tel.: (812) 426-2741
Web Site: https://www.frontierkemper.com
Sales Range: $100-124.9 Million
Emp.: 85
Underground & Heavy Civil Construction
Services
N.A.I.C.S.: 237990
W. David Rogstad (Pres & CEO)

Subsidiary (Non-US):

The Redpath Group　　　　　(2)
710 McKeown Ave, North Bay, P1B 7M2,
ON, Canada
Tel.: (705) 474-2461
Web Site: http://www.redpathmining.com
Holding Company; Ore Mining Contractor
N.A.I.C.S.: 551112
George B. Flumerfelt (CEO)

Subsidiary (US):

J.S. Redpath Corporation　　(3)
1410 Greg St Ste 404, Sparks, NV 89431
Tel.: (775) 359-0444
Engineeering Services
N.A.I.C.S.: 541330
Mark Imnonen (Mgr)

Subsidiary (Non-US):

P.T Redpath Indonesia　　　(3)
Plaza 89 3rd Floor Suite 306 Jl H R Rasuna Said Kav X-7 No 6, Jakarta, 12940,
Indonesia
Tel.: (62) 21 520 7547
Engineeering Services
N.A.I.C.S.: 541330

Redpath Argentina Construcciones
S.A.　　　　　　　　　　　(3)
Av Cordoba E 226 5, San Juan, Argentina
Tel.: (54) 264 420 2126
Engineeering Services
N.A.I.C.S.: 541330

Redpath Australia Pty Limited　(3)
2/267 Great Eastern Highway, Belmont,
6104, WA, Australia
Tel.: (61) 8 9477 3700
Engineeering Services
N.A.I.C.S.: 541330

Subsidiary (Domestic):

Redpath Canada Limited　　(3)
710 McKeown Avenue, North Bay, P1B
7M2, ON, Canada　　　　　(100%)
Tel.: (705) 474-2461
Web Site: http://www.redpathmining.com
Ore Mining Contractor Services
N.A.I.C.S.: 238990

Subsidiary (Non-US):

Redpath Chilena Construcciones Y
Cia. Limitada　　　　　　　(3)
Av Kennedy 5454 Of 701, Santiago, Vitacura, Chile
Tel.: (56) 2 29383800
Emp.: 40
Engineeering Services
N.A.I.C.S.: 541330
George Flumerfelt (CEO)

Redpath Mining (S.A.) (Pty.) Ltd.　(3)
18 Industry Road Isando Ext 2, 1600,
Kempton Park, South Africa
Tel.: (27) 11 570 4300
Engineeering Services
N.A.I.C.S.: 541330

Redpath Mining Australia Pty.
Ltd.　　　　　　　　　　　(3)
63 Lavarack Avenue, Eagle Farm, 4009,

QLD, Australia　　　　　　(100%)
Tel.: (61) 738685000
Web Site: http://www.redpathmining.com
Sales Range: $25-49.9 Million
Ore Mining Contractor Services
N.A.I.C.S.: 238990

Redpath Mining Zambia Limited　(3)
6004 Sibweni Rd, PO Box 32001, Northmead, Lusaka, Zambia
Tel.: (260) 212 248132
Engineeering Services
N.A.I.C.S.: 541330

Redpath Mongolia LLC　　　(3)
Khair Tokhoi Building 3rd floor Chinggis Avenue, PO Box 1947, 1st Horoo Sukhbaatar
District, Ulaanbaatar, 211213, Mongolia
Tel.: (976) 11 310709
Engineeering Services
N.A.I.C.S.: 541330

EDAG Engineering Group AG　(1)
Schlossgasse 2, 9320, Arbon,
Switzerland　　　　　　　　(62.89%)
Tel.: (41) 715443311
Web Site: https://www.edag.com
Rev.: $932,527,299
Assets: $806,465,345
Liabilities: $627,053,354
Net Worth: $179,411,991
Earnings: $31,901,843
Emp.: 8,642
Fiscal Year-end: 12/31/2023
Holding Company; Engineering Services
N.A.I.C.S.: 551112
Holger Merz (CFO)

Subsidiary (Non-US):

EDAG Engineering GmbH　　(2)
Kreuzberger Ring 40, 65205, Wiesbaden,
Germany
Tel.: (49) 61173750
Web Site: http://www.edag.de
Automobile Mfr
N.A.I.C.S.: 336110
Cosimo De Carlo (CEO-Grp)

Subsidiary (Domestic):

BFFT Gesellschaft fur Fahrzeugtechnik mbH　　　　　　　　　　(3)
Dr Ludwig-Kraus-Strasse 2, 85080, Gaimersheim, Germany
Tel.: (49) 8458 3238 0
Web Site: http://www.bfft.de
Software Development Services
N.A.I.C.S.: 541511
Markus Fichtner (Mng Dir)

Subsidiary (Non-US):

EDAG Engineering & Design India
Priv. Ltd.　　　　　　　　　(3)
No 201 A B C D Delta 2 Building Giga
Space IT Park, Viman Nagar, Pune,
411014, India
Tel.: (91) 20 41466700
Automotive Distr
N.A.I.C.S.: 423110
Tristan Pfurr (Mng Dir)

EDAG Engineering AB　　　(3)
Fabriksgatan 13, 41250, Gothenburg, Sweden
Tel.: (46) 31 6464 00
Web Site: http://www.edag.se
Automobile Mfr
N.A.I.C.S.: 336110
Jurgen Vogt (CFO)

EDAG Engineering CZ spol.
s.r.o.　　　　　　　　　　　(3)
Konevova 134-135, 29301, Mlada Boleslav,
Czech Republic
Tel.: (420) 326 374 580
Automotive Distr
N.A.I.C.S.: 423110
Dirk Keller (Mng Dir)

EDAG Engineering Polska
Sp.z.o.o.　　　　　　　　　(3)
Zygmunta Slominskiego 4, 00-204, Warsaw,
Poland
Tel.: (48) 22 510 69 00
Web Site: http://www.pl.edag.com
Automobile Parts Mfr
N.A.I.C.S.: 336390
Jan Gierej (Founder)

EDAG Engineering S.R.L. (3)
Str Ignat Nr 15 et 1, '700381, Iasi, Romania
Tel.: (40) 332 101 889
Emp.: 3
Automotive Distr
N.A.I.C.S.: 423110
Stefan Alde *(Mng Dir)*

EDAG Engineering Schweiz GmbH (3)
Schlossgasse 2, 9320, Arbon, Switzerland
Tel.: (41) 714473658
Web Site: http://www.edag.ch
Automotive Distr
N.A.I.C.S.: 423110
Jochen Seifert *(Mng Dir)*

EDAG Holding Sdn. Bhd. (3)
Unit 2 2 Level 2 Block E Peremba Square
Saujana Resort Seksyen U2, 40150, Shah
Alam, Malaysia
Tel.: (60) 3 7846 0895
Automotive Distr
N.A.I.C.S.: 423110
Philipp Kersting *(Mng Dir)*

EDAG Hungary Kft. (3)
Zrinyi Str 11, 9024, Gyor, Hungary
Tel.: (36) 96 401 800
Web Site: http://www.hu.edag.com
Emp.: 200
Automotive Distr
N.A.I.C.S.: 423110
Rainer Schon *(Mng Dir)*

Subsidiary (US):

EDAG Inc. (3)
1875 Research Dr Ste 200, Troy, MI 48083
Tel.: (248) 588-3134
Automotive Distr
N.A.I.C.S.: 423110
Kimberly Martinez *(Mgr-HR)*

Subsidiary (Domestic):

CKGP/PW & Associates, Inc. (4)
1650 Research Dr Ste 300, Troy, MI
48083 (100%)
Tel.: (248) 577-0400
Web Site: http://www.ckgppw.com
Mfr & Paint Process Engineering Services
N.A.I.C.S.: 541330
Greg Garringer *(Pres & CEO)*

Subsidiary (Non-US):

EDAG Japan Co., Ltd. (3)
6-chome-145 Hanasakicho, Nishi-ku, Yoko-
hama, 220-0022, Japan
Tel.: (81) 45 320 2670
Web Site: http://www.jp.edag.com
Automotive Distr
N.A.I.C.S.: 423110
Hitoshi Yamaoka *(Mng Dir)*

EDAG Mexico, S.A. de C.V. (3)
Avenida Ebano S/N Lote A Edificio de Ofici-
nas FINSA II Parque, Industrial FINSA
Cuautlancingo, Puebla, 72710, Mexico
Tel.: (52) 222 641 3581
Automotive Distr
N.A.I.C.S.: 423110
Rainer Hofmann *(CEO & Mng Dir)*

EDAG Production Solution CZ s.r.o. (3)
tr Vaclava Klementa 1459, 29301, Mlada
Boleslav, Czech Republic
Tel.: (420) 326719091
Web Site: http://www.edag-ps.de
Emp.: 50
Automotive Distr
N.A.I.C.S.: 423110

Subsidiary (Domestic):

EDAG Production Solutions GmbH & Co. KG (3)
Reesbergstrasse 1, 36039, Fulda, Germany
Tel.: (49) 6616000150
Web Site: http://www.edag-ps.de
Automobile Mfr
N.A.I.C.S.: 336110
Dirk Keller *(Member-Mgmt Bd)*

Subsidiary (Non-US):

EDAG Production Solutions Korea Ltd. (3)
1001 Daeryung Technotown 8 cha Gasan-

dong, Geumcheon-gu, 481-11, Seoul, Korea
(South)
Tel.: (82) 70 76636 282
Automotive Distr
N.A.I.C.S.: 423110
Rainer Wittich *(Mng Dir)*

EDAG Technologies India Priv. Ltd. (3)
8 IMT Manesar Sector 6, Gurgaon, 122001,
Haryana, India
Tel.: (91) 1244367132
Automotive Distr
N.A.I.C.S.: 423110

EDAG do Brasil Ltda. (3)
Av do Taboao no 1 195, 09655-000, Sao
Bernardo do Campo, Brazil
Tel.: (55) 11 4173 96 00
Automotive Distr
N.A.I.C.S.: 423110
Martin Vollmer *(Mng Dir)*

Subsidiary (Domestic):

Haus Kurfurst GmbH (3)
Schlossstrasse 2, 36037, Fulda, Germany
Tel.: (49) 6 61 83 39 0
Web Site: http://www.kurfuerst-fulda.de
Restaurant Operators
N.A.I.C.S.: 722511
Harald Poeschke *(Mng Dir)*

Subsidiary (Non-US):

Rucker Italia S.R.L. (3)
Via Pavia Street 11, Rivoli, 10038, Italy
Tel.: (39) 011 957 2414
Web Site: http://www.rucker.it
Emp.: 5
Investment Management Service
N.A.I.C.S.: 523999
Giovanni Pulina *(Gen Mgr)*

Rucker Lypsa S.L.U. (3)
Poligono Industrial Almeda Carretera del
Prat 65, 08940, Barcelona, Spain
Tel.: (34) 93 377 61 61
Web Site: http://www.rueckerlypsa.es
Emp.: 500
Automobile Mfr
N.A.I.C.S.: 336110

Rucker SR spol.s.r.o. i.L. (3)
Panonska cesta 17, 85104, Bratislava, Slo-
vakia
Tel.: (421) 2 6820 1210
Investment Management Service
N.A.I.C.S.: 523999

EDAG Italia S.R.L. (1)
Corso Vittorio Emanuele II 48, 10123, Turin,
Italy
Tel.: (39) 051957115
Web Site: http://it.edag.com
Emp.: 115
Automobile Parts Mfr
N.A.I.C.S.: 336390
Giovanni Pulina *(CEO & Dir-Vehicle Engrg)*

EDAG Netherlands B.V. (1)
Schootense Dreef 21, 5708 HZ, Helmond,
Netherlands
Tel.: (31) 492594050
Web Site: http://nl.edag.com
Automobile Parts Mfr
N.A.I.C.S.: 336390
Franz Lorey *(CEO)*

EDAG Production Solutions India Priv. Ltd. (1)
14th Floor Block II Vatika Business Park
Sohna Road, Gurgaon, 122018, India
Tel.: (91) 1244323232
Web Site: http://www.edag-ps.de
Engineeering Services
N.A.I.C.S.: 541330
Janak Patel *(Mng Dir)*

Flexible Fertigungstechnik GmbH (1)
Stuckweg 4, 35325, Mucke, Germany
Tel.: (49) 6400 580
Investment Management Service
N.A.I.C.S.: 523999
Manfred Hahl *(Gen Mgr)*

Jota GmbH (1)
Am Trippelsberg 110, 40589, Dusseldorf,
Germany
Tel.: (49) 21199963682
Web Site: http://www.jota-gmbh.com

Software Development Services
N.A.I.C.S.: 541511

Muller HRM Engineering AB (1)
Eriksbergstorget 11, 417 64, Gothenburg,
Sweden
Tel.: (46) 767666710
Web Site: http://www.mullerhrm.isvorg.com
Oil & Gas Services
N.A.I.C.S.: 213112
Jorgen Thornquist *(Sr Mgr)*

OOO EDAG Production Solutions RU (1)
3-iy Akademicheskiy Proezd 19 Gebaude
Nr 2, 248000, Kaluga, Russia
Tel.: (7) 9112938446
Automobile Parts Mfr
N.A.I.C.S.: 336390
Pavel Vasiliev *(Mng Dir)*

Parkmotive GmbH (1)
Reesbergstrasse 1, 36043, Fulda, Germany
Tel.: (49) 66160008000
Web Site: http://www.parkmotive.com
Software Services
N.A.I.C.S.: 541511

Redpath Mining Inc. (1)
101 Worthington Street East Suite 304,
North Bay, P1B 1G5, ON, Canada
Tel.: (705) 474-2461
Web Site: http://www.redpathmining.com
Metal & Mining Services
N.A.I.C.S.: 213114
George B. Flumerfelt *(CEO)*

**Reform Maschinenfabrik Adolf Ra-
benseifner GmbH & Co. KG** (1)
Weserstr 24 u 26, 36043, Fulda, Germany
Tel.: (49) 661 4959 00
Web Site: http://www.reform.de
Emp.: 200
Industrial Machinery Mfr & Distr
N.A.I.C.S.: 333248

Scherwo Steuerungstechnik GmbH (1)
Grubmuhlerfeldstr 54, 82131, Gauting, Ger-
many
Tel.: (49) 89 850 8123
Web Site: http://www.scherwo.de
Welding Equipment Mfr
N.A.I.C.S.: 333992

**TSO Industrieanlagen Planung und
Vertrieb GmbH** (1)
Ludwig-Erhard-Strasse 9, 91486, Uehlfeld,
Germany
Tel.: (49) 9163 96 88 47
Web Site: http://www.tso-
industrieanlagen.de
Emp.: 17
Construction Engineering Services
N.A.I.C.S.: 541330
Martin Schwarzmeier *(Mng Dir)*

Ziehm Imaging Austria GmbH (1)
Ziegelfeldstrasse 10, Tulln an der Donau,
3430, Tulln, Austria
Tel.: (43) 720569501
Medical Equipment Device Mfr
N.A.I.C.S.: 339112

Ziehm Imaging GmbH (1)
Lina-Ammon-Strasse 10, 90471, Nurem-
berg, Germany
Tel.: (49) 911 217 20
Web Site: http://www.ziehm.com
Emp.: 500
Diagnostic Imaging Services
N.A.I.C.S.: 621512
Klaus Horndler *(CEO)*

Subsidiary (Non-US):

Ziehm Imaging Finnland (OY) (2)
Kumitehtaankatu 5, 04260, Kerava, Finland
Tel.: (358) 40 5 02 31 75
Diagnostic Imaging Services
N.A.I.C.S.: 621512

Subsidiary (US):

Ziehm Imaging Inc. (2)
6280 Hazeltine National Dr, Orlando, FL
32882
Tel.: (407) 615-8560
Diagnostic Imaging Services
N.A.I.C.S.: 621512
Nelson Mendes *(Pres & CEO)*

Subsidiary (Domestic):

Orthoscan, Inc. (3)
14555 N 82nd St, Scottsdale, AZ 85260
Tel.: (480) 503-8010
Web Site: http://www.orthoscan.com
Emp.: 80
Medical Device Distr
N.A.I.C.S.: 423450

Subsidiary (Non-US):

Ziehm Imaging SA (2)
Unit D1 Tillbury Business Park 16th Road,
Randjespark, Midrand, 1683, South Africa
Tel.: (27) 113143108
Web Site: http://www.ziehm.com
Diagnostic Imaging Services
N.A.I.C.S.: 621512

Ziehm Imaging Sarl (2)
1 Allee de Londres, 91140, Villejust, France
Tel.: (33) 1 69 07 16 65
Diagnostic Imaging Services
N.A.I.C.S.: 621512

Ziehm Imaging Singapore Pte. Ltd. (2)
No 7030 Ang Mo Kio Ave 5 Northstar AMK
08-53, Singapore, 569880, Singapore
Tel.: (65) 65705211
Web Site: http://www.ziehm.com
Emp.: 7
Diagnostic Imaging Services
N.A.I.C.S.: 621512

Ziehm Medical (Shanghai) Co. Ltd. (2)
Rm 06-07 25 / F 83 Loushanguan Road,
Shanghai, 200336, China
Tel.: (86) 21 62 36 99 03
Diagnostic Imaging Services
N.A.I.C.S.: 621512

Ziehm Medical Do Brasil (2)
Av Roque Petroni Junior 1089 cj 904, Cen-
tro Profissional Morumbi Shopping, 04707-
000, Sao Paulo, Brazil
Tel.: (55) 11 30 33 59 99
Web Site: http://www.ziehm.com
Emp.: 3
Diagnostic Imaging Services
N.A.I.C.S.: 621512

Subsidiary (US):

Ziehm Medical LLC (2)
888 Veterans Hwy, Hauppauge, NY 11788-
2950
Tel.: (631) 348-2512
Diagnostic Imaging Services
N.A.I.C.S.: 621512

Ziehm Imaging Spain S.L.U. (1)
Avenida Perez Galdos 13 - 14, 46007, Va-
lencia, Spain
Tel.: (34) 960911152
Medical Equipment Device Mfr
N.A.I.C.S.: 339112

Ziehm Imaging Srl (1)
Via Paolo Borsellino 22/24, 42124, Reggio
Emilia, Italy
Tel.: (39) 0522610894
Medical Equipment Device Mfr
N.A.I.C.S.: 339112

ATON GREEN STORAGE S.P.A.
Via Guido Rossa 5, Spilamberto,
41057, Bologna, MO, Italy
Tel.: (39) 059783939
Web Site:
https://www.atonstorage.com
Year Founded: 2014
ATON—(EUR)
Battery Mfr
N.A.I.C.S.: 335910
Ettore Uguzzoni *(Chm)*

ATON LLC
20 Ovchinnikovskaya Naberezhnaya
Building 1, 115035, Moscow, Russia
Tel.: (7) 4957776677
Web Site: http://www.aton.ru
Year Founded: 1991

ATON LLC—(Continued)

Financial Management & Investment Services
N.A.I.C.S.: 523999

ATON RESOURCES INC.
Suite 1700 666 Burrard Street, Vancouver, V6C 2X8, BC, Canada
Tel.: (604) 331-5092
Web Site:
https://www.atonresources.com
Year Founded: 2006
AAN—(TSXV)
Assets: $622,737
Liabilities: $8,169,036
Net Worth: ($7,546,299)
Earnings: ($7,507,961)
Fiscal Year-end: 12/31/23
Metal Exploration Services
N.A.I.C.S.: 213114
Javier Orduna (Mgr-Exploration)

ATORKA GROUP HF
Hlidasmari 1, 201, Kopavogur, Iceland
Tel.: (354) 5406200   IS
Web Site: http://www.atorka.is
Sales Range: $25-49.9 Million
Emp.: 2
Investment Services
N.A.I.C.S.: 523999
Thordur Olasur Thordarson (Chm)

ATOS SE
River Ouest 80 quai Voltaire, 95877, Bezons, Cedex, France
Tel.: (33) 173260000
Year Founded: 2000
ATO—(EUR)
Rev.: $12,239,369,739
Assets: $17,692,639,758
Liabilities: $13,592,704,511
Net Worth: $4,099,935,247
Earnings: ($1,092,164,904)
Emp.: 110,797
Fiscal Year-end: 12/31/22
Information Technology Services
N.A.I.C.S.: 541512
Gilles Arditti (Head-IR & Internal Audit)

Subsidiaries:

Air Lynx SAS   (1)
1 Avenue de l'Atlantique, 91940, Les Ulis, France
Tel.: (33) 981434646
Web Site: https://www.air-lynx.com
Emp.: 25
Telecommunication Servicesb
N.A.I.C.S.: 517810
Philippe Saenz (Co-Founder & Pres)

Atos (Australia) Pty. Ltd.   (1)
885 Mountain Highway, Bayswater, 3153, VIC, Australia
Tel.: (61) 397216400
Information Technology Services
N.A.I.C.S.: 541512
Mike Green (Mng Dir)

Atos AG   (1)
Freilagerstrasse 28, 8047, Zurich, Switzerland
Tel.: (41) 587021111
Web Site: https://atos.net
Emp.: 800
Information Technology Consulting Services
N.A.I.C.S.: 541690

Atos Argentina SA   (1)
Virrey Liniers No 2250, Distrito Tecnologico Parque Patricios, C1241ABV, Buenos Aires, Argentina
Tel.: (54) 1151935690
Web Site: https://atos.net
Emp.: 1,200
Information Technology Solutions & Consulting Services
N.A.I.C.S.: 541690

Atos Belgium SA   (1)

Da Vincilaan 5, 1930, Zaventem, Belgium
Tel.: (32) 26902800
Web Site: https://atos.net
Emp.: 500
Information Technology Consulting Services
N.A.I.C.S.: 541512
Patrick Gyseling (Chief Comml Officer)

Atos Bilisim Danismanlik ve Musteri Hizmetleri Sanavi ve Ticaret A/S   (1)
Yakacik Caddesi No 111 - 18, Kartal, 34870, istanbul, Turkiye
Tel.: (90) 2165002000
Information Technology Services
N.A.I.C.S.: 541512

Atos Consluting Canaroias, SA   (1)
Subida al Mayorazgo 24B Planta 1, 38110, Santa Cruz de Tenerife, Spain
Tel.: (34) 674329144
Information Technology Services
N.A.I.C.S.: 541512

Atos Consulting France   (1)
Nous Ecrire River Ouest 80 Quai Voltaire, Bezons, France
Tel.: (33) 173260000
Web Site: http://www.fr.atosconsulting.com
Sales Range: $700-749.9 Million
Emp.: 4,000
Information Technology Consulting Services
N.A.I.C.S.: 541611

Atos Convergence Creators GmbH   (1)
Autokaderstrasse 29, 1210, Vienna, Austria
Tel.: (43) 506180
Web Site: http://atos.net
Communication & Enterprise Security Software
N.A.I.C.S.: 513210
Giuseppe Di Franco (Head-Central & Eastern Europe)

Subsidiary (Non-US):

Atos Convergence Creators SRL   (2)
21 Mihail Kogalniceanu Bloc C-6, 500090, Brasov, Romania
Tel.: (40) 213058600
Communication & Enterprise Security Software
N.A.I.C.S.: 513210
Giuseppe Di Franco (Head-Central & Eastern Europe)

Atos Covics Business Solutions Co., Ltd.   (1)
Suite 1207 Unicom International Tower No 547, West Tianmu Road, Shanghai, 200070, China
Tel.: (86) 2163171122
Web Site: http://www.covics.cn
Software System Consultancy Services
N.A.I.C.S.: 541512

Atos France S.A.S.   (1)
River Ouest 80 Quai Voltaire, 95877, Bezons, cedex, France
Tel.: (33) 173260000
Digital Transformation Services
N.A.I.C.S.: 541810

Atos Global Delivery Center Mexico, S. de R.L. de C.V.   (1)
Sevilla 40 Piso 9 Col Juarez Delegacion, Cuauhtemoc, 06600, Ciudad de Mexico, Mexico
Tel.: (52) 5513287300
Information Technology Services
N.A.I.C.S.: 541512
Paul Maya (CEO)

Atos Global Delivery Center Philippines, Inc.   (1)
7F One Ecom Building Harbor Drive Sunset Ave Mall of Asia Complex, Pasay, 1300, Philippines
Tel.: (63) 9829600
Information Technology Services
N.A.I.C.S.: 541512

Atos IT Services Private Ltd   (1)
Gate No 2 Plant No 5 Pirojshahnagar LBS Marg, Vikhroli W, Mumbai, 400079, Maharashtra, India
Tel.: (91) 22 6733 3400
Web Site: http://www.in.atos.net
Software Development & IT Consulting Services

N.A.I.C.S.: 541511

Atos IT Services SARL   (1)
Angle Avenues Mehdi Benbaraka et Annakhil Hay Ryad-Plateau n 3-4eme, Etage Espace Les Palmiers, Rabat, Morocco
Tel.: (212) 529014200
Information Technology Services
N.A.I.C.S.: 541512

Atos IT Services UK Limited   (1)
Second Floor Mid City Place 71 High Holborn, Regents Place, London, WC1V 6EA, United Kingdom
Tel.: (44) 8007833040
Web Site: https://atos.net
Information Technology Services
N.A.I.C.S.: 541519

Atos IT Servicios do Brazil LTDA   (1)
Avenue Maria Coelho Aguiar 215 bl E 5 andar, Sao Luis, 05804-900, Maranhao, Brazil
Tel.: (55) 11 2183 2344
Software Development Services
N.A.I.C.S.: 541511

Atos IT Solutions & Services A/S   (1)
Dybendalsvaenget 3, 2630, Taastrup, Denmark
Tel.: (45) 43311400
Information Technology Services
N.A.I.C.S.: 541512

Atos IT Solutions & Services LLC   (1)
Andropov Avenue Building 18 Building 5 Floor 19 Room 23, Moscow, 115432, Russia
Tel.: (7) 4957372610
Information Technology Services
N.A.I.C.S.: 541512

Atos IT Solutions & Services Ltd.   (1)
Charn Issara Tower II 36th Floor 2922/339 New Petchaburi Rd, Bangkapi Huay Kwang, Bangkok, 10310, Thailand
Tel.: (66) 27879000
Information Technology Services
N.A.I.C.S.: 541512
Kasiphon Aphimukkhunanon (Mng Dir & Head-SIs)

Atos IT Solutions & Services OY   (1)
Kalkkipellontie 6, 026050, Espoo, Finland
Tel.: (358) 106885000
Information Technology Services
N.A.I.C.S.: 541512

Atos IT Solutions & Services S.A.S.   (1)
Autopista Norte-Carrera 45 No 108-27 Edificio Paralelo 108-Oficina, 1505, Bogota, Colombia
Tel.: (57) 15190233
Information Technology Services
N.A.I.C.S.: 541512

Atos IT Solutions & Services s.r.o   (1)
Doudlebska 1699/5, 140 00, Prague, 4, Czech Republic
Tel.: (420) 705899989
Information Technology Services
N.A.I.C.S.: 541512
Tomas Hlavsa (Head-Big Data & Security Div)

Atos IT Solutions and Services GmbH   (1)
Otto-Hahn-Ring 6, Munich, 81739, Germany
Tel.: (49) 89 636 02
Holding Company; Information Technology Products & Services
N.A.I.C.S.: 551112
Winfried Holz (CEO)

Subsidiary (Domestic):

Atos IT-Dienstleistung und Beratung GmbH   (2)
Bruchstrasse 5, 45883, Gelsenkirchen, Germany
Tel.: (49) 20994560
Sales Range: $125-149.9 Million
Emp.: 702
Information Technology Services
N.A.I.C.S.: 541513

Science + Computing AG   (2)

Hagellocher Weg 73, 72070, Tubingen, Germany
Tel.: (49) 707194570
Information Technology Services
N.A.I.C.S.: 541512

applied international informatics GmbH   (2)
Am Studio 16, 12489, Berlin, Germany   (100%)
Tel.: (49) 3025928300
Web Site: https://www.aiinformatics.com
Sales Range: $75-99.9 Million
Emp.: 150
Information Technology Solutions
N.A.I.C.S.: 541512
Josef Durmoser (Mng Dir)

Atos IT Solutions and Services GmbH   (1)
Siemensstrasse 92, 1210, Vienna, Austria
Tel.: (43) 506180
Web Site: https://atos.net
Software Development & IT Consulting Services
N.A.I.C.S.: 541511

Atos IT Solutions and Services d.o.o.   (1)
Poslovni centar Almeria Heinzelova 69 5 kat, 10000, Zagreb, Croatia
Tel.: (385) 12867000
Web Site: https://atos.net
Emp.: 3
IT Consulting & Software Development Services
N.A.I.C.S.: 541690

Atos IT Solutions and Services, Inc.   (1)
2500 Westchester Ave Ste 300, Purchase, NY 10577
Tel.: (914) 881-3000
Web Site: http://www.atos.net
Emp.: 30
IT Solutions & Consulting Services
N.A.I.C.S.: 541690
Chad Harris (Pres-North America)

Atos ITS Nearshore Center Maroc S.A.R.L.   (1)
Shore 7 Casablanca Nearshore Park 11 000 Bd Alqods Sidi Maarouf, Casablanca, Morocco
Tel.: (212) 529014200
Digital Transformation Services
N.A.I.C.S.: 541810

Atos India Private Limited   (1)
1402 /1403 Supremus E Wing Techno Campus, Kanjurmarg, Mumbai, 400042, Maharashtra, India
Tel.: (91) 2262194000
Information Technology Services
N.A.I.C.S.: 541512
Sujata Salunkhe (Gen Mgr)

Atos Information Technology (China) Co., Ltd.   (1)
Building B No 7 Zhonghuan South Road, Wangjing Chaoyang District, Beijing, 100102, China
Tel.: (86) 1069115500
Web Site: https://atos.net
Information Technology Services
N.A.I.C.S.: 541512

Atos Information Technology (Nanjing) Co., Ltd.   (1)
12th Floor Chuangzhi Building 17 Xinghuo Road, Pukou District, Nanjing, 210061, China
Tel.: (86) 2552129888
Information Technology Services
N.A.I.C.S.: 541512

Atos Information Technology (Singapore) Pte. Ltd.   (1)
988 Toa Payoh North 08-01, Singapore, 319002, Singapore
Tel.: (65) 67308888
Digital Transformation Services
N.A.I.C.S.: 541810

Atos Information Technology GmbH   (1)
Otto-Hahn-Ring 6, 81739, Munich, Germany
Tel.: (49) 2113990
Web Site: https://atos.net

Information Technology Services
N.A.I.C.S.: 541511

Atos Information Technology HK Ltd. (1)
8/F Octa Tower 8 Lam Chak Street, Kowloon Bay, Kowloon, China (Hong Kong)
Tel.: (852) 22806008
Emp.: 400
Information Technology Services
N.A.I.C.S.: 541512
Paul Wong (Mng Dir)

Atos Information Technology Inc. (1)
23/F Cyber One Building, Eastwood City - Cyberpark Libis, Quezon City, 1110, Philippines
Tel.: (63) 9829600
Information Technology Services
N.A.I.C.S.: 541512
James Linsangan (Mgr-IT)

Atos Information Technology SAE (1)
50 Abbas El Akad Street, Nasr City, Cairo, Egypt
Tel.: (20) 12888 02555
Software Development & IT Consulting Services
N.A.I.C.S.: 541690

Atos International Germany GmbH (1)
Otto-Hahn-Ring 6, 81739, Munich, Germany
Tel.: (49) 2113990
Cloud Computing Services
N.A.I.C.S.: 518210

Atos KK (1)
6th floor Daisan Toranomon Electric Building 1-2-20 Toranomon, Minato-ku, Tokyo, 105-0001, Japan
Tel.: (81) 345888214
Web Site: https://atos.net
Information Technology Services
N.A.I.C.S.: 541512
Yawara Hirata (Mng Dir)

Atos Luxembourg PSF S.A. (1)
17 r Edmond Reuter, 5326, Contern, Luxembourg
Tel.: (352) 31 36 37 1
Web Site: http://atos.net
Emp.: 100
Information Technology Solutions & Consulting Services
N.A.I.C.S.: 541512

Atos Luxembourg SF S.A. (1)
Altitude Lhassa building 12 Rue du Chateau d'Eau, 3364, Leudelange, Luxembourg
Tel.: (352) 3136371
Cloud Computing Services
N.A.I.C.S.: 518210

Atos Magyarorszag Kft. (1)
Infopark A epulet 1 emelet Neumann J u 1, 1117, Budapest, Hungary
Tel.: (36) 14375100
Web Site: https://atos.net
Information Technology Services
N.A.I.C.S.: 541512

Atos Nederland B.V. (1)
Burgemeester Rijnderslaan 30, 1185 MC, Amstelveen, Netherlands
Tel.: (31) 882655555
Web Site: https://atos.net
Information Technology Services
N.A.I.C.S.: 541512

Atos Origin Brasil Ltda (1)
Maria Coelho Aguiar 215 Bloco E 50 Andar, Sao Paulo, 05804-900, Brazil
Tel.: (55) 1121832344
Software Development Services
N.A.I.C.S.: 513210

Atos Origin FZ LLC (1)
The One Tower 31st Floor Sheikh Zayed Road, PO Box 500437, Barsha Heights Tecom, Dubai, United Arab Emirates
Tel.: (971) 44402300
Web Site: https://atos.net
Information Technology Services
N.A.I.C.S.: 541511

Atos Origin Formation S.A (1)
13 Rue De Bucarest, Paris, 75008, France
Tel.: (33) 155306200
Web Site: http://www.formation.fr.atos.net

Sales Range: $10-24.9 Million
Emp.: 35
Information Technology Training Services
N.A.I.C.S.: 611710

Atos Origin Indonesia PT (1)
Plaza Central 19 Floor Suite 1902 Jalan Jenderal Sudirman 47, Jakarta, 12930, Indonesia
Tel.: (62) 215724373
Web Site: http://ap.atos.net
Emp.: 12
Information Technology Solutions & Consulting Services
N.A.I.C.S.: 541690
Magnus Alvarsson (Head-Bus & Platform Solutions)

Atos Origin Information Technology (China) Co. Ltd (1)
11 F Unicom Mansion No 547 Tianmu West Road, Zhabei District, Shanghai, 200070, China
Tel.: (86) 2163541616
Information Technology Consulting Services
N.A.I.C.S.: 541618

Atos Origin Integration SAS (1)
Le Millenium Sophia Antipo, Valbonne, 06560, Alpes Maritimes, France
Tel.: (33) 492952300
General Management Consulting Services
N.A.I.C.S.: 541611

Atos Origin Management France SAS (1)
80 quai Voltaire River Ouest, Bezons, 95877, France
Tel.: (33) 173262215
Web Site: http://www.atos.net
Sales Range: $700-749.9 Million
Emp.: 5,000
Information Technology Consulting Services
N.A.I.C.S.: 541611

Atos Origin Servicos de Tecnologia da Informacao do Brasil Ltda (1)
Avenida Maria Coelho Aguiar 215 Bloco E 50 e 70, Andares Cep Jardim Sao Luis, Sao Paulo, 05804 900, Brazil
Tel.: (55) 11 2183 2344
Information Technology Consulting Services
N.A.I.C.S.: 541512

Atos Poland Global Service Sp Zoo (1)
ul Pulawska 180, 02-670, Warsaw, Poland
Tel.: (48) 224446500
Information Technology Services
N.A.I.C.S.: 541512
Lukasz Laskowski (Head-SAP Functional Team)

Atos Polska SA (1)
Biuro P180 ul Pulawska 180, 02 - 670, Warsaw, Poland
Tel.: (48) 223899999
Web Site: https://atos.net
Information Technology Services
N.A.I.C.S.: 541512
Daniel Sowinski (Mgr-Svc Delivery)

Atos Pty. Ltd. (1)
Ground Floor Building 31 Woodlands Office Park Woodlands Drive, Woodmead, South Africa
Tel.: (27) 110467300
Information Technology Services
N.A.I.C.S.: 541512

Atos Qatar LLC (1)
QFIB Building Al Sadd Area Zone 38, PO 202378, Doha, Qatar
Tel.: (974) 44478183
Web Site: https://atos.net
Software Development & IT Consulting Services
N.A.I.C.S.: 541690

Atos Saudi Company (1)
PO Box 8772, Riyadh, 11492, Saudi Arabia
Tel.: (966) 11 4666 555
Software Development & IT Consulting Services
N.A.I.C.S.: 541690

Atos Services (Malaysia) Sdn Bhd (1)
G01 Ground Floor 2310 Century Square, Jalan Usahawan, 63000, Cyberjaya, Selan-

gor, Malaysia
Tel.: (60) 383160288
Web Site: https://atos.net
Emp.: 400
Information Technology Solutions & Consulting Services
N.A.I.C.S.: 541519

Atos Singapore (1)
988 Toa Payoh North 08-01, Singapore, 319002, Singapore
Tel.: (65) 6730 8888
Web Site: http://www.atos.net
Information Technology Services
N.A.I.C.S.: 541519
See Wee Goh (Mng Dir & Head-Bus & Platform Solutions)

Atos Solucoes e Serivcos Para Tecnologias de Informacao, Unipessoal, Ltda. (1)
Av Jose Malhoa n 16-7 B2 Edificio Europa, 1070-159, Lisbon, Portugal
Tel.: (351) 210971400
Information Technology Services
N.A.I.C.S.: 541512

Atos Solucoes e Servicos para Tecnologias de Informacao, Unipessoal, Ltda. (1)
Av Jose Malhoa N 16 - 7 B2 Edificio Europa, 1070-159, Lisbon, Portugal
Tel.: (351) 210971400
Digital Transformation Services
N.A.I.C.S.: 541810

Atos Spain SA (1)
Calle Albarracin 25, 28037, Madrid, Spain
Tel.: (34) 912148800
Web Site: https://atos.net
Information Technology Consulting Services
N.A.I.C.S.: 541512

Subsidiary (Domestic):

Atos Origin Consulting Canarias, SA (2)
C/ Galicia 25 - 1 H, 35006, Las Palmas, Gran Canaria, Spain
Tel.: (34) 928296006
Web Site: http://www.atos.net
Sales Range: $25-49.9 Million
Emp.: 150
Information Technology Consulting Services
N.A.I.C.S.: 541611

Cantabria - Mundivia S.A (2)
C Real Consulado s n Poligono Industrial Candina, Santander, 39011, Cantabria, Spain
Tel.: (34) 942355931
Information Technology Consulting Services
N.A.I.C.S.: 541512

Cetisa, S.A. (2)
Condesa de Sagasta 6 Entreplanta B, Leon, 24001, Spain
Tel.: (34) 987276910
Information Technology Consulting Services
N.A.I.C.S.: 541512

Infoservicios S.A (2)
Calle Albarracin 25, Madrid, 28037, Spain
Tel.: (34) 912148800
Sales Range: $150-199.9 Million
Emp.: 1,000
Information Technology Consulting Services
N.A.I.C.S.: 541611

SM2 Baleares SA (2)
Cami dels Reis 308 Edificio Mapfre 2 Planta, 07010, Palma de Mallorca, Spain
Tel.: (34) 971750324
Web Site: http://www.sm2baleares.es
Sales Range: $25-49.9 Million
Emp.: 100
System Integration & Consulting Services
N.A.I.C.S.: 541512
Alejandro Forcades Pons (CEO)

Tempos21 S.A (2)
Avda Diagonal 200, Barcelona, 08018, Spain
Tel.: (34) 934861818
Web Site: http://www.tempos21.com
Sales Range: $25-49.9 Million
Emp.: 25
Information Technology Consulting Services
N.A.I.C.S.: 541512

Atos Taiwan Ltd (1)
5F No 100 Sec 3 Min Sheng East Road, Taipei, 10596, Taiwan
Tel.: (886) 225142500
Web Site: https://atos.net
Information Technology Consulting Services
N.A.I.C.S.: 541690

Atos UK IT Limited (1)
4 Triton Square, Regents Place, London, NW1 3HG, United Kingdom
Tel.: (44) 2078304444
Web Site: http://www.uk.atos.net
Information Technology Consulting Services
N.A.I.C.S.: 541511

Bull S.A. (1)
68 Rue Jean Jaures, BP 68, 78340, Les Clayes-sous-Bois, France
Tel.: (33) 130807000
Sales Range: $1-4.9 Billion
Emp.: 9,236
Computer Integrated Systems Design; IT Consultancy Services
N.A.I.C.S.: 541512

Subsidiary (Domestic):

Agarik SAS (2)
20 rue Dieumegard, 93400, Saint-Ouen, France
Tel.: (33) 825602601
Web Site: http://www.agarik.com
Web Hosting Services
N.A.I.C.S.: 518210

Amesys S.A. (2)
655 Avenue Galilee, BP 20140, 13794, Aix-en-Provence, cedex 3, France (100%)
Tel.: (33) 4 42 24 62 00
Web Site: http://www.amesys-conseil.fr
Sales Range: $200-249.9 Million
Emp.: 750
Information Technology Products Developer & Technical Services
N.A.I.C.S.: 541512

Subsidiary (Non-US):

Amesys Canada Inc. (3)
137 rue Saint-Pierre Suite 206, Montreal, H2Y 3T5, QC, Canada
Tel.: (514) 875-9755
Web Site: http://www.amesys-conseil.fr
IT Consulting Services
N.A.I.C.S.: 541690

Subsidiary (Non-US):

Bull Algerie (2)
Rue Yahia El-Mazouni Lotissement la Fumee, Villa 16A El-Biar, 16000, Algiers, Algeria
Tel.: (213) 21798854
Web Site: https://www.bull.com
Internet Publishing Services
N.A.I.C.S.: 513199

Bull Cote d'ivoire SA (2)
31 avenue Nogues - 01, BP 1580, Abidjan, Cote d'Ivoire (100%)
Tel.: (225) 20213904
Information Technology Services
N.A.I.C.S.: 541512

Bull Cyprus Ltd (2)
18 Kyriakou Matsis Ave, PO Box 27299, 1643, Nicosia, Cyprus
Tel.: (357) 22 44 99 33
Designer of Information Technology Infrastructure
N.A.I.C.S.: 541512

Bull Gabon (2)
Immeuble ABIALI, Zl d'Oloumi, BP 2260, Libreville, Gabon (100%)
Tel.: (241) 5306000
Emp.: 15
IT Consulting & Computer Services
N.A.I.C.S.: 541519

Bull GmbH (2)
Von-der-Wettern-Strasse 27, 51149, Cologne, Germany (100%)
Tel.: (49) 22033050
Web Site: https://de.atos.net
Sales Range: $50-74.9 Million
Emp.: 230
Designer & Developer of Servers & Software
N.A.I.C.S.: 541519

Atos SE—(Continued)

Bull Indian Ocean Ltd. (2)
1st Floor Beau Bebe Building Trianon, Quatre Bornes, Mauritius
Tel.: (230) 467 0889
Sales Range: $25-49.9 Million
Emp.: 1
Security Software Development Services
N.A.I.C.S.: 541511

Bull Information Systems (Hong Kong) Ltd. (2)
Room 25 Radio City 505-511 Hennessey Road, Causeway Bay, China (Hong Kong)
Tel.: (852) 28367512
Web Site: http://www.bull.com
IT Consulting Services
N.A.I.C.S.: 541690

Subsidiary (Non-US):

Bull Information Systems Co. Limited (Beijing) (3)
11 Floor Jing Guang Centre Office Building Hu Jia Lou, Mail Box 8806, 100020, Beijing, Chaoyang District, China
Tel.: (86) 10 6597 8001
Web Site: http://www.bull.com
Information Technology Solutions & Consulting Services
N.A.I.C.S.: 541690

Subsidiary (Non-US):

Bull Information Systems Ireland (2)
Office 5B Level 5 Block 4 Dundrum Town Centre, Sandyford Road, Dublin, 16, Ireland
Tel.: (353) 1 246 9704
Web Site: http://uk.atos.net
Sales Range: $25-49.9 Million
Emp.: 10
Software Development Services
N.A.I.C.S.: 541511

Bull Madagascar S.A. (2)
12 Rue Indira Gandhi, BP 252, Tsaralalana, 101, Antananarivo, Madagascar (100%)
Tel.: (261) 202222407
Emp.: 26
Information Technology Solutions & Consulting Services
N.A.I.C.S.: 541690

Bull Morocco (2)
Boulevard Al Qods Casanearshore, Quartier Sidi Maarouf, Casablanca, Morocco (100%)
Tel.: (212) 529014200
Web Site: https://www.bull.com
Emp.: 50
Information Technology Solutions & Consulting Services
N.A.I.C.S.: 541690

Bull Polska sp. z.o.o. (2)
Saski Crescent ul Krolewska 16, Warsaw, 00-103, Poland
Tel.: (48) 224334900
Software Development Services
N.A.I.C.S.: 541511
Miron Niewiadomski *(Mgr-Mktg)*

Bull SAL (2)
Rue Jal el Dib 69 - Secteur 1, BP 60208, Beirut, 12412020, Lebanon (95%)
Tel.: (961) 4712855
Web Site: https://www.bull.com
Emp.: 15
Computer Integrated Systems Design; IT Consultancy Services
N.A.I.C.S.: 541690

Bull Senegal SARL (2)
Coeur 3 Pyrotechnie Cite Keur Gorgui -Immeuble Khadim Rassoul, BP 3183, Dakar, Senegal (100%)
Tel.: (221) 338649800
Information Technology Services
N.A.I.C.S.: 541512

Bull Uruguay SA (2)
(100%)
Tel.: (698) 24871169
Information Technology Solutions & Consulting Services
N.A.I.C.S.: 541690
Javier Suhr *(Mgr-Dev)*

Bull do Brasil Sistemas de Informacao Ltda (2)

Avenida Angelica 903, Sao Paulo, 01227-901, Brazil
Tel.: (55) 11 3824 4700
Web Site: http://www.bull.com
Emp.: 200
Designer of Information Technology Infrastructure Systems & Consulting Services
N.A.I.C.S.: 541512

Subsidiary (Domestic):

Elexo S.A. (2)
20 Rue de Billancourt, 92100, Boulogne-Billancourt, France
Tel.: (33) 141221000
Web Site: http://www.atos.net
Sales Range: $25-49.9 Million
Emp.: 25
Computer Peripheral Equipment Distr
N.A.I.C.S.: 423430

Evidian SA (2)
rue Jean Jaures, BP 68, 78340, Les Clayes-sous-Bois, France (100%)
Tel.: (33) 130803777
Web Site: https://www.evidian.com
Sales Range: $200-249.9 Million
Emp.: 1,000
Security Software Services
N.A.I.C.S.: 541511

Subsidiary (US):

Evidian Systems Inc. (3)
160 Broadway Ste 10RE, New York, NY 10038
Tel.: (646) 233-1239
Web Site: http://www.evidian.com
Software Development Services
N.A.I.C.S.: 541511

Subsidiary (Non-US):

UAB Bull Baltija (2)
Gostauto Street 40, 01112, Vilnius, Lithuania
Tel.: (370) 52487460
Web Site: https://www.bull.com
Sales Range: $25-49.9 Million
Emp.: 28
Software Development Services
N.A.I.C.S.: 541511

DataSentics a.s. (1)
Washingtonova 1599/17, Nove Mesto, 110 00, Prague, Czech Republic
Tel.: (420) 608005432
Web Site: https://datasentics.com
Emp.: 57,000
Software Development Services
N.A.I.C.S.: 541511

Eagle Creek Software Services, Inc. (1)
10050 Crosstown Cir, Eden Prairie, MN 55344
Tel.: (925) 230-2111
Web Site: http://eaglecrk.com
Sales Range: Less than $1 Million
Computer Integrated Systems Design
N.A.I.C.S.: 541512
Ken Behrendt *(Pres)*

EcoAct S.A.S. (1)
35 Rue de Miromesnil, 75008, Paris, France
Tel.: (33) 183640870
Environmental Consulting Services
N.A.I.C.S.: 541620

Econocom Digital Security SAS (1)
50 Avenue Daumesnil Building B 8th Floor, 75012, Paris, France
Tel.: (33) 170838585
IT Security Services
N.A.I.C.S.: 561621
Nicolas Planson *(Mgr-Practice)*

Edifixio S.A.S. (1)
River Ouest 80 Quai Voltaire, 95870, Bezons, Cedex, France
Tel.: (33) 173260000
Web Site: https://www.eviden.com
Information Technology Services
N.A.I.C.S.: 518210

Energy4u GmbH (1)
Albert-Nestler-Str 17, 76131, Karlsruhe, Germany
Tel.: (49) 72161052100
Web Site: https://energy4u.org

Computer Related Services
N.A.I.C.S.: 541519
Jan Schinnerling *(Mgr-Bus Unit)*

Evidian-Bull Japan KK (1)
6F Daisan Toranomon Electric Building 1-2-20 Toranomon, Minato-ku, Tokyo, 105-0001, Japan
Tel.: (81) 354567691
Web Site: https://www.evidian.com
Information Technology Services
N.A.I.C.S.: 541512

FastvViewer GmbH (1)
Schwesterhausgasse 11, 92318, Neumarkt, Germany
Tel.: (49) 9181509560
Web Site: http://www.fastviewer.com
Emp.: 20
Information Technology Services
N.A.I.C.S.: 541512

Ipsotek Ltd. (1)
Tuition House 27-37 St Georges Road, Wimbledon, London, SW19 4EU, United Kingdom
Tel.: (44) 2089718300
Web Site: https://www.ipsotek.com
Artificial Intelligence Video Analytics Services
N.A.I.C.S.: 541715

Kynectis SA (1)
175 rue Jean-Jacques Rousseau, 92138, Issy-les-Moulineaux, Cedex, France
Tel.: (33) 155642200
Web Site: http://www.idnomic.com
Software Development Services
N.A.I.C.S.: 541511
Coralie Heritier *(CEO)*

Maven Wave Partners, LLC (1)
71 S Wacker Dr Ste 2040, Chicago, IL 60606
Tel.: (312) 878-4100
Web Site: http://www.mavenwave.com
Management Consulting Services
N.A.I.C.S.: 541618
Brian Farrar *(Co-Founder & Partner)*

Paladion Networks Private Limited (1)
Shilpa Vidya 49 1st Main 3rd Phase JP Nagar, Bengaluru, 560078, India
Tel.: (91) 80 42543444
Web Site: http://www.paladion.net
Sales Range: $400-449.9 Million
Emp.: 800
Security System Services
N.A.I.C.S.: 561621
Rajat Mohanty *(Co-Founder & CEO)*

Processia Solutions Inc. (1)
3111 Boulevard St-Martin West Suite 220, Laval, H7T 0K2, QC, Canada
Tel.: (450) 786-0400
Web Site: https://www.processia.com
Fabricated Metal & Tire Mfr.
N.A.I.C.S.: 332215

SEC Consult Austria AG (1)
Wagramer Strasse 19 / Stock 16, 1220, Vienna, Austria
Tel.: (43) 189030430
Web Site: https://www.sec-consult.com
Business Management Consulting Services
N.A.I.C.S.: 541618

Sema GMBH (1)
Kolner Street 9, Langenfeld, 40764, Nordrhein-Westfalen, Germany
Tel.: (49) 217391750
Information Technology Consulting Services
N.A.I.C.S.: 541611

Syntel, Inc. (1)
525 E Big Beaver Rd Ste 300, Troy, MI 48083
Tel.: (248) 619-2800
Web Site: https://www.syntelinc.com
Rev.: $923,828,000
Assets: $483,716,000
Liabilities: $496,638,000
Net Worth: ($12,922,000)
Earnings: $166,268,000
Emp.: 22,114
Fiscal Year-end: 12/31/2017
Computer Software & Services; IT Outsourcing
N.A.I.C.S.: 541511

Daniel M. Moore *(Chief Admin Officer, Gen Counsel & Sec)*

Subsidiary (Non-US):

Syntel Deutschland GmbH (2)
Landsberger Strasse 302, 80687, Munich, Germany
Tel.: (49) 8990405234
Web Site: http://www.syntelinc.com
Emp.: 1
Business Processing Services
N.A.I.C.S.: 518210

Syntel Europe Ltd. (2)
Bolsover House 5 Clipstone Street, London, W1W 6BB, United Kingdom (100%)
Tel.: (44) 2076363587
Sales Range: $150-199.9 Million
Emp.: 60
Information Technology Services
N.A.I.C.S.: 541511

Syntel International Pvt. Ltd. (2)
Plot No H7 & H8 SIPCOT IT Park, Siruseri Kanchipuram Dist, Chennai, 603103, India (100%)
Tel.: (91) 44 4742 3800
Web Site: http://www.atos-syntel.net
Sales Range: $200-249.9 Million
Emp.: 800
Computer Programming
N.A.I.C.S.: 541511

Syntel Ltd. (2)
Unit 112 SDF IV SEEPZ Andheri, Mumbai, 400096, Maharashtra, India (100%)
Tel.: (91) 22 4047 0100
Web Site: http://www.atos-syntel.net
Sales Range: $500-549.9 Million
Emp.: 2,000
Flexible, Custom Information Technology & Knowledge Process Outsourcing Solutions
N.A.I.C.S.: 541511

Syntel Private Limited (2)
Unit 112 Sdf Iv Seepz Andheri, Mumbai, 400 096, India
Tel.: (91) 2240470100
Software Development Services
N.A.I.C.S.: 541511
Renuka Sridar *(Sr Mgr)*

TSG EDV-Terminal Service GmbH (1)
Modecenterstrasse 1, 1030, Vienna, Austria
Tel.: (43) 5061840000
Computer Related Services
N.A.I.C.S.: 541519
Andreas Zemanek *(CEO)*

X Perion Consulting AG (1)
Nikolaus-Otto-Str 1, 22946, Trittau, Germany
Tel.: (49) 4154989590
Web Site: http://www.x-perion.de
Business Management Consulting Services
N.A.I.C.S.: 541618

ATOSS SOFTWARE AG

Rosenheimer Strasse 141 h, 81671, Munich, Germany
Tel.: (49) 89427710
Web Site: https://www.atoss.com
AOF—(DEU)
Rev.: $166,905,144
Assets: $126,282,728
Liabilities: $57,986,291
Net Worth: $68,296,437
Earnings: $39,485,430
Emp.: 775
Fiscal Year-end: 12/31/23
Software Consulting & Training Services
N.A.I.C.S.: 541512
Rolf Baron Vielhauer von Hohenhau *(Deputy Chm-Supervisory Bd)*

Subsidiaries:

ATOSS CSD Software GmbH (1)
Rodinger Strasse 19, 93413, Cham, Germany
Tel.: (49) 997185180
Web Site: http://www.atoss-csd.de
Sales Range: $25-49.9 Million
Emp.: 30
Management Software Solutions

N.A.I.C.S.: 541511

ATOSS Software AG (1)
Luggwegstrasse 9, 8048, Zurich, Switzerland
Tel.: (41) 44 501 5300
Web Site: https://www.atoss.com
Sales Range: $25-49.9 Million
Emp.: 200
Management Software Solutions
N.A.I.C.S.: 541511
Andreas F. J. Obereder *(Founder, CEO & Member-Mgmt Bd)*

ATOSS Software Gesellschaft m.b.H. (1)
Am Moosfeld 3, 81829, Modling, Munchendorf, Austria
Tel.: (43) 171728334
Sales Range: $25-49.9 Million
Emp.: 100
Customized Software Solutions
N.A.I.C.S.: 541511

ATOSS Software S.R.L. (1)
Calea Torontalului 69, 300668, Timisoara, Timis, Romania
Tel.: (40) 356710170
Web Site: http://www.atoss.ro
Sales Range: $25-49.9 Million
Emp.: 70
Workforce Management Software Solutions
N.A.I.C.S.: 541511

ATOUR LIFESTYLE HOLDINGS LIMITED
18th Floor Wuzhong Building 618 Wuzhong Road, Shanghai, China
Tel.: (86) 2164059928   Ky
Web Site: https://ir.yaduo.com
Year Founded: 2012
ATAT—(NASDAQ)
Rev.: $346,711,625
Assets: $729,590,003
Liabilities: $547,667,530
Net Worth: $181,922,473
Earnings: $15,029,748
Emp.: 3,255
Fiscal Year-end: 12/31/22
Holding Company
N.A.I.C.S.: 551112
Haijun Wang *(Founder, Chm & CEO)*

ATPI LIMITED
Rivercastle House 10 Leake Street, London, SE1 7NN, United Kingdom
Tel.: (44) 207 111 8500
Web Site: http://www.atpi.com
Year Founded: 1936
Sales Range: $25-49.9 Million
Emp.: 1,244
Travel Management Services
N.A.I.C.S.: 561520
Graham Ramsey *(Chm)*

ATRACK TECHNOLOGY, INC.
8F No 13 Ln 120 Sec 1 Neihu Rd, Neihu Dist, Taipei, 11493, Taiwan
Tel.: (886) 227975852
Web Site: https://www.atrack.com.tw
Year Founded: 2010
6465—(TPE)
Rev.: $5,964,387
Assets: $17,085,577
Liabilities: $9,293,844
Net Worth: $7,791,733
Earnings: ($2,840,790)
Fiscal Year-end: 12/31/22
Telematric Hardware Product Mfr
N.A.I.C.S.: 332510
Jun-Kuo Tang *(Chm & Pres)*

Subsidiaries:

ATrack Technology (Tokyo) Inc. (1)
7 Chome-4-9 Ueno, Taito, Tokyo, 110-0005, Japan
Tel.: (81) 364035237
Hardware Mfr
N.A.I.C.S.: 332510

ATRAE, INC.

8th Floor Joule A 1-10-10 Azabu-juban, Minato-ku, 106-0045, Tokyo, 106-0045, Japan
Tel.: (81) 364353210
Web Site: https://www.atrae.co.jp
Year Founded: 2003
6194—(TKS)
Rev.: $54,997,130
Assets: $50,686,410
Liabilities: $11,329,820
Net Worth: $39,356,590
Earnings: $2,368,060
Fiscal Year-end: 09/30/23
Management Software Development Services
N.A.I.C.S.: 541511
Shigeki K. *(Project Mgr & Mgr)*

ATRATO ONSITE ENERGY PLC
The Scalpel 52 Lime Street 18th Floor, London, EC3M 7AF, United Kingdom
Tel.: (44) 2038809800   UK
Web Site: https://www.atratoroof.com
Year Founded: 2021
ROOF—(LSE)
Rev.: $11,444,940
Assets: $176,581,796
Liabilities: $824,952
Net Worth: $175,756,843
Earnings: $8,187,142
Fiscal Year-end: 09/30/23
Investment Management Service
N.A.I.C.S.: 523999
Juliet Davenport *(Chm)*

ATREM S.A.
ul Czolgowa 4, 62-002, Zlotniki, Poland
Tel.: (48) 785992002
Web Site: https://www.atrem.pl
ATR—(WAR)
Rev.: $36,180,132
Assets: $28,875,254
Liabilities: $18,683,689
Net Worth: $10,191,565
Earnings: $1,512,703
Fiscal Year-end: 12/31/23
Engineeering Services
N.A.I.C.S.: 541330
Przemyslaw Szmyt *(CTO)*

ATRENEW INC.
12th Floor Building 6 No 433 Songhu Road, Yangpu District, Shanghai, 200000, China
Tel.: (86) 2152907031   Ky
Web Site: https://www.atrenew.com
Year Founded: 2011
RERE—(NYSE)
Rev.: $1,614,186,143
Assets: $760,561,448
Liabilities: $246,679,497
Net Worth: $513,881,951
Earnings: ($21,634,083)
Emp.: 2,055
Fiscal Year-end: 12/31/23
Refurbished Electronic Product On-line Retailer
N.A.I.C.S.: 541519
Kerry Xuefeng Chen *(Founder, Chm & CEO)*

ATRESMEDIA CORPORACION DE MEDIOS DE COMUNICA-CION, S.A.
Graciosa Island Avenue 13 San Sebastian de los Reyes, 28703, Madrid, Spain
Tel.: (34) 916230500
Web Site:
https://www.atresmediacorp.com
Year Founded: 1988
A3M—(MAD)
Rev.: $771,289,326

Assets: $1,422,707,805
Liabilities: $701,067,447
Net Worth: $721,640,358
Earnings: $175,954,300
Emp.: 2,558
Fiscal Year-end: 12/31/23
Television & Radio Broadcasting; Advertising Services
N.A.I.C.S.: 516120
Silvio Gonzalez Moreno *(CEO)*

Subsidiaries:

A3 MULTIMEDIA S.L.U. (1)
rue des pagannes, 49300, Cholet, France
Tel.: (33) 241463855
Web Site: http://www.a3multimedia.com
Barcode Terminals Whslr
N.A.I.C.S.: 423690

ANTENA 3 EVENTOS S.L.U. (1)
Calle Fuerteventura 12-12, San Sebastian de los Reyes, 28703, Spain
Tel.: (34) 916232750
Web Site: http://www.a3eventos.es
Sales Range: $25-49.9 Million
Emp.: 20
Television Broadcasting Services
N.A.I.C.S.: 516120
Alvaro Pitto *(Mng Dir)*

ANTENA 3 FILMS S.L.U. (1)
Calle Isla de Graciosa 13, San Sebastian de los Reyes, 28703, Spain
Tel.: (34) 916230500
Web Site: http://www.antena3films.com
Motion Picture Production Services
N.A.I.C.S.: 512110

ATRES ADVERTISING S.L.U. (1)
Fuerteventura 12, 28700, San Sebastian de los Reyes, Spain
Tel.: (34) 916230500
Web Site: http://www.atresadvertising.com
Advertising Agencies
N.A.I.C.S.: 541810

MOVI ERECORD CINE S.A.U. (1)
Calle Isla de Graciosa 13, San Sebastian de los Reyes, 28703, Spain
Tel.: (34) 916230102
Web Site: http://www.movierecord.com
Cinema Advertising Services
N.A.I.C.S.: 541810

MUSICA APARTE S.A.U. (1)
Calle Fuerteventura 12, San Sebastian de los Reyes, 28703, Spain
Tel.: (34) 916232534
Emp.: 3
Television Broadcasting Services
N.A.I.C.S.: 516120
Nuria Rodriguez *(Mgr)*

UNIPUBLIC S.A. (1)
Fuerteventura 12, 28703, San Sebastian de los Reyes, Madrid, Spain
Tel.: (34) 916232750
Web Site: http://www.unipublic.es
Sales Range: $50-74.9 Million
Emp.: 10
Bicycling Race Organizers
N.A.I.C.S.: 711310

ATREYU CAPITAL MARKETS LTD.
21 Ha arbaa St, Tel Aviv, 64739, Israel
Tel.: (972) 36845500   Il
ATRY—(TAE)
Rev.: $54,704
Assets: $59,117,557
Liabilities: $114,933
Net Worth: $59,002,624
Earnings: $20,167,979
Fiscal Year-end: 12/31/23
Investment Banking Services
N.A.I.C.S.: 523150

ATRIA PLC
Itikanmaenkatu 3, PO Box 900, FI-60060, Seinajoki, Finland
Tel.: (358) 204728111
Web Site: https://www.atria.fi

ATRAV—(HEL)
Rev.: $1,831,110,512
Assets: $1,122,197,280
Liabilities: $620,949,709
Net Worth: $501,247,572
Earnings: ($4,159,292)
Emp.: 3,698
Fiscal Year-end: 12/31/22
Food Processing Services
N.A.I.C.S.: 311612
Juha Grohn *(CEO)*

Subsidiaries:

A-Pihvi Kauhajoki Oy (1)
Rahikkatie 95, Kauhajoki As, Seinajoki, Finland
Tel.: (358) 64168218
Food Processing Services
N.A.I.C.S.: 311612

Atria Concept AB (1)
Planiavagen 17 2 tr, Nacka, 13134, Sweden
Tel.: (46) 8 55 63 06 50
Food Processing Services
N.A.I.C.S.: 311612

Atria Concept SP Z.o.o (1)
ul Czestochowska 24, 32-085, Modlnica, Poland
Tel.: (48) 126612033
Web Site: https://www.sibylla.pl
Food Processing Services
N.A.I.C.S.: 311612

Atria Danmark A/S (1)
Langmarksvej 1, 8700, Horsens, Denmark
Tel.: (45) 76282500
Web Site: https://www.atria.dk
Restaurant Services
N.A.I.C.S.: 721110

Atria Eesti AS (1)
Metsa 19, 68206, Valga, 68206, Estonia
Tel.: (372) 7679900
Web Site: https://atria.ee
Food Processing Services
N.A.I.C.S.: 311612
Olle Horm *(CEO & Member-Mgmt Bd)*

Atria Finland Ltd. (1)
Atriantie 1, Box 900, Nurmo, 60060, Seinajoki, Finland
Tel.: (358) 204728111
Web Site: https://www.atria.fi
Food Processing Services
N.A.I.C.S.: 311612

Atria Scandinavia AB (1)
Augustendalsvagen 19, SE 131 52, Nacka, Sweden
Tel.: (46) 19300300
Web Site: http://www.atria.se
Sales Range: $550-599.9 Million
Emp.: 1,691
Food Processing
N.A.I.C.S.: 311612
Tomas Back *(Exec VP)*

Subsidiary (Non-US):

3-STJERNET A/S (2)
Langmarksvej 1, 8700, Horsens, Denmark
Tel.: (45) 76282500
Web Site: http://www.3-stjernet.dk
Sales Range: $25-49.9 Million
Emp.: 140
Meat Toppings
N.A.I.C.S.: 112320

Subsidiary (Domestic):

Atria Foodservice AB (2)
Florettgatan 18, 254 67, Helsingborg, Sweden
Tel.: (46) 10 482 3000
Web Site: https://www.atriafoodservice.se
Frozen Fish & Meat
N.A.I.C.S.: 311710

Subsidiary (Domestic):

Gourmet Service AB (3)
Vindkraftsvagen 5, S-135 70, Stockholm, Sweden
Tel.: (46) 856649000
Web Site: http://www.gourmet-service.com

Atria Plc—(Continued)

Sales Range: $25-49.9 Million
Emp.: 25
Fish Pate & Sandwiches
N.A.I.C.S.: 311999

Subsidiary (Domestic):

Atria Retail AB (2)
Drottninggatan 14, SE-697 80, Skullersta, Sweden
Tel.: (46) 19300300
Deli Products
N.A.I.C.S.: 311999

Subsidiary (Domestic):

Charkdelikatesser I Halmstad AB (3)
Svetsaregatan 6, Halmstad, 302 50, Sweden
Tel.: (46) 35172600
Web Site: http://www.charkdelikatesser.se
Deli Products
N.A.I.C.S.: 311999

Subsidiary (Domestic):

Charkdelikatesser Produktion AB (4)
Svetsaregatan 6, S-302 50, Halmstad, Sweden
Tel.: (46) 35172600
Web Site: http://www.charkdelikatesser.se
Food Production
N.A.I.C.S.: 311919

Moheda Chark AB (4)
Ostanakravagen 2, S-340 36, Moheda, Sweden
Tel.: (46) 47272660
Web Site: http://www.atria.com
Sales Range: $10-24.9 Million
Emp.: 20
Deli Products
N.A.I.C.S.: 311999

Subsidiary (Domestic):

G A Carlsson AB - Gea's (3)
Prastkragens vag 9, Box 188, SE-132 26, Saltsjo-Boo, Sweden
Tel.: (46) 19 300 300
Web Site: http://www.atriagroup.com
Deli Products
N.A.I.C.S.: 311999

Pastejkoket AB (3)
c/o Charkdelikatesser Produktion AB, Svetsaregatan 6, 302 50, Halmstad, Sweden
Tel.: (46) 14057300
Web Site: http://www.pastejkoket.se
Sales Range: $25-49.9 Million
Emp.: 187
Deli Meat Products
N.A.I.C.S.: 311999

Subsidiary (Domestic):

AB Carl A Carlson Charkuterier (4)
Jadersvagen, Box 11, S-732 21, Arboga, Sweden
Tel.: (46) 589 128 50
Deli Products
N.A.I.C.S.: 311999

Delikatess Skinkor AB (4)
Grenvagen 1-3, S-577 39, Hultsfred, Sweden
Tel.: (46) 495249600
Web Site: http://www.atria.com
Deli Products
N.A.I.C.S.: 311999

Norrboda Charkuterifabrik AB (4)
Tryckerigatan 12, S-571 34, Nassjo, Sweden
Tel.: (46) 38016993
Deli Products
N.A.I.C.S.: 311999

Subsidiary (Domestic):

Sardus Latta Maltider AB (2)
Hanholmsvagen 51, SE 602 28, Norrkoping, Sweden
Tel.: (46) 19 300 300
Web Site: http://www.sarduslattamaltider.se
Light Meals & Sandwiches
N.A.I.C.S.: 311991

Subsidiary (Domestic):

Allt Smorgas (3)

Speditionsvagen 25, S-142 50, Skogas, Sweden
Tel.: (46) 87715535
Sandwiches & Salads
N.A.I.C.S.: 311999

Best-In Oy (1)
PL 147, 70100, Kuopio, Finland
Tel.: (358) 204728111
Web Site: https://www.best-in.fi
Pet Food Distr
N.A.I.C.S.: 424490

Domretor Oy (1)
Leipomonkuja 6, 62200, Kauhava, Finland
Tel.: (358) 403590441
Web Site: https://www.domretor.fi
Packaging Food Product Mfr & Distr
N.A.I.C.S.: 311999

F-Logistiikka Oy (1)
Pusurinkatu 48, Forssa, 30100, Kanta-Hame, Finland
Tel.: (358) 341541
Logistics Consulting Servies
N.A.I.C.S.: 541614

KB Joddlaren (1)
Sodra Langebergsgatan 12, 421 32, Vastra Frolunda, Sweden
Tel.: (46) 31 722 55 00
Food Processing Services
N.A.I.C.S.: 311612

Korv-Gorans Kebab Oy (1)
Foretagarvagen 24, 68600, Jakobstad, Finland
Tel.: (358) 67232818
Web Site: https://gorans.fi
Frozen Meat Mfr
N.A.I.C.S.: 311412

OOO Campomos (1)
Ryabinovaya Street 32, RUS 121471, Moscow, Russia
Tel.: (7) 4954486704
Web Site: http://www.campomos.ru
Sales Range: $100-124.9 Million
Emp.: 300
Processed Food
N.A.I.C.S.: 311612

Ridderheims AS (1)
Per Kroghs vei 4C, 1065, Oslo, Norway
Tel.: (47) 22422443
Food Processing Services
N.A.I.C.S.: 311612

ATRIUM BIRE, SIGI, S.A.
Lugar do Espido Via Norte, 4470-177, Maia, Portugal
Tel.: (351) 229401700
Web Site: https://www.atrium-sigi.com
Year Founded: 2022
MLATR—(EUR)
Real Estate Investment Services
N.A.I.C.S.: 531190
Luis Mota Duarte *(Vice Chm)*

ATRIUM LJUNGBERG AB
Smedjegatan 2C, Box 4200, SE-131 04, Nacka, Sweden
Tel.: (46) 86158900
Web Site: http://www.al.se
Year Founded: 1946
ATRLJ.B—(OMX)
Rev.: $376,616,800
Assets: $6,627,112,800
Liabilities: $3,509,067,520
Net Worth: $3,118,045,280
Earnings: $458,654,560
Emp.: 329
Fiscal Year-end: 12/31/21
Real Estate Development Services
N.A.I.C.S.: 531390
Johan Ljungberg *(Chm)*

Subsidiaries:

Fastighets AB Osterbotten (1)
Magnus Ladulasgatan 67, PO Box 4050, 118 27, Stockholm, Sweden
Tel.: (46) 8 743 59 99
Real Estate Development Services
N.A.I.C.S.: 531390

KB Arbetsstolen 3 (1)
PO Box 4808, 116 93, Stockholm, Sweden
Tel.: (46) 73 026 93 30
Real Estate Development Services
N.A.I.C.S.: 531390

Ljungberg Gruppen Holding AB (1)
Tegelviksgatan 22, Stockholm, 116 93, Sweden
Tel.: (46) 86 10 19 00
Holding Company
N.A.I.C.S.: 551112

ATRIUM MORTGAGE INVESTMENT CORPORATION
1010 18 King Street East, Toronto, M5C 1C4, ON, Canada
Tel.: (416) 867-1053   ON
Web Site: https://www.atriummic.com
Year Founded: 2001
AMIVF—(OTCIQ)
Rev.: $74,435,199
Assets: $662,902,480
Liabilities: $298,779,086
Net Worth: $364,123,395
Earnings: $38,877,353
Fiscal Year-end: 12/31/23
Real Estate Mortgage & Investment Services
N.A.I.C.S.: 522310
Robert G. Goodall *(Founder, Pres & CEO)*

ATRIUM REAL ESTATE INVESTMENT TRUST
36-2 Jalan 5/101C Off Jalan Kaskas Jalan Cheras, 56100, Kuala Lumpur, Wilayah Persekutuan, Malaysia
Tel.: (60) 391322810   MY
Web Site:
   https://www.atriumreit.com.my
Year Founded: 2006
ATRIUM—(KLS)
Rev.: $8,612,386
Assets: $140,166,746
Liabilities: $62,492,359
Net Worth: $77,674,387
Earnings: $5,596,758
Fiscal Year-end: 12/31/23
Real Estate Investment Trust Services
N.A.I.C.S.: 531110
Mohamad Khir Harun *(Chm)*

ATRUM COAL LIMITED
Level 5 126 Phillip St, Sydney, 2000, NSW, Australia
Tel.: (61) 386784091
Web Site: https://www.atrumcoal.com
ATU—(ASX)
Rev.: $372,103
Assets: $6,103,420
Liabilities: $3,128,083
Net Worth: $2,975,337
Earnings: ($6,368,099)
Fiscal Year-end: 12/31/22
Coal Mining
N.A.I.C.S.: 212115
Max Wang *(Mng Dir)*

ATRYA SAS
ZI Le Moulin, 67110, Gundershoffen, France
Tel.: (33) 3 8880 2929   FR
Web Site: http://www.atrya.com
Year Founded: 1980
Sales Range: $500-549.9 Million
Emp.: 1,900
PVC Window & Door Mfr
N.A.I.C.S.: 332321

Subsidiaries:

AMCC Fenetres et Portes SAS (1)
9-11 rue du Rondeau ZI les Fadeaux, 36000, Chateauroux, France
Tel.: (33) 820 22 31 02
Web Site: http://www.amcc-fenetres.fr
Window & Door Mfr & Distr

N.A.I.C.S.: 321911

Guttomat Sektionaltore GmbH (1)
Wiener Strasse 58, 7540, Gussing, Austria
Tel.: (43) 3322 42 372 0
Web Site: http://www.guttomat.at
Door Mfr
N.A.I.C.S.: 321911
Marc Burger *(CEO)*

Hasler Fenster AG (1)
Oberwilerstrasse 73, 4106, Therwil, Switzerland
Tel.: (41) 726 96 26
Web Site: http://www.haslerfenster.ch
Door Mfr
N.A.I.C.S.: 321911

Norba SA (1)
Route de Lausanne 46, 1610, Oron, Switzerland
Tel.: (41) 21 908 00 30
Web Site: http://www.norba.ch
Window & Door Mfr
N.A.I.C.S.: 321911

SOPROFEN (1)
Rue de Wallonie 1, 6200, Chatelet, Belgium
Tel.: (32) 71 24 34 34
Web Site: http://www.soprofen.be
Door Mfr
N.A.I.C.S.: 321911

TRYBA ENERGIES SAS (1)
22a rue de Gumbrechtshoffen, 67110, Gundershoffen, France
Tel.: (33) 1 30 05 16 91
Web Site: http://www.tryba-energies.fr
Heat Pump Mfr
N.A.I.C.S.: 333415

ATRYS HEALTH SA
Calle Provenca 392 planta baixa, 08025, Barcelona, Spain
Tel.: (34) 934581561
Web Site:
   https://www.atryshealth.com
Year Founded: 2007
ATRY—(MAD)
Sales Range: Less than $1 Million
Diagnostic & Medical Treatment Services
N.A.I.C.S.: 621999
Santiago De Torres Sanahuja *(Chm & Pres)*

ATS CORPORATION
730 Fountain St N Building 2, Cambridge, N3H 4R7, ON, Canada
Tel.: (519) 653-6500
Web Site:
   https://www.atsautomation.com
Year Founded: 1978
ATS—(NYSE)
Rev.: $2,240,439,536
Assets: $3,020,461,698
Liabilities: $1,776,502,918
Net Worth: $1,243,958,780
Earnings: $143,444,633
Emp.: 7,000
Fiscal Year-end: 03/31/24
Turnkey Factory Automation Systems Mfr & Designer
N.A.I.C.S.: 541512
David L. McAusland *(Chm)*

Subsidiaries:

ACE Automation (Tianjin) Co. Ltd. (1)
157 Huang Hai Road TEDA, Tianjin, 300457, China
Tel.: (86) 11 22 532 2007
Web Site: http://www.atsautomation.com
N.A.I.C.S.: 541512

ATS Advanced Manufacturing Division (1)
730 Fountain St N Bldg 2, Cambridge, N3H 4R7, ON, Canada   (100%)
Tel.: (519) 650-2332
Web Site: http://www.atsautomation.com
Sales Range: $25-49.9 Million
Emp.: 150
Mfr of Microelectronics Components

N.A.I.C.S.: 541512

ATS Assembly & Test, Inc. (1)
1 ATS Dr, Wixom, MI 48393
Tel.: (734) 522-1900
Emp.: 15
Automation Tooling Systems
N.A.I.C.S.: 423420

Plant (Domestic):

**ATS Assembly & Test, Inc. -
Dayton** (2)
313 Mound St, Dayton, OH 45402
Tel.: (937) 222-3030
Web Site: http://www.assembly-testww.com
Emp.: 145
Developer & Mfr of Custom Assembly, Automation & Test Systems
N.A.I.C.S.: 333248

ATS Automation (1)
Plot 221 Lorong Perindustrian Bukit Minyak 11, Mukim 13 Kawasam Perindustrian, Bukit Mertajam Seberang Perind, 14000, Penang, Malaysia (100%)
Tel.: (60) 45098585
Web Site: http://www.atsautomaton.com
Sales Range: $25-49.9 Million
Emp.: 65
N.A.I.C.S.: 541512

**ATS Automation Asia (Tianjin) Co.,
Ltd.** (1)
NO 12-2 XEDA Century Road, Xiqing Economic Development Area, Tianjin, 300385, China
Tel.: (86) 2258882888
Web Site: http://www.atsautomation.com
Sales Range: $50-74.9 Million
Emp.: 130
Electric Equipment Mfr
N.A.I.C.S.: 335999

ATS Automation Asia Pte Ltd (1)
38A Jalan Pemimpin 01 01 Wisdom Ind Bldg, Singapore, 577178, Singapore (100%)
Tel.: (65) 62995988
Web Site: http://www.atsautomation.com
Sales Range: $25-49.9 Million
Emp.: 100
N.A.I.C.S.: 541512

**ATS Automation Malaysia SDN.
BHD.** (1)
Plot 221 Lorong Perindustrian Bukit Minyak 11 Mukim 13, Seberang Perai Tengah, 14000, Bukit Mertajam, Penang, Malaysia
Tel.: (60) 45098585
Emp.: 55
Conveyor Machinery Mfr
N.A.I.C.S.: 333922
Benoit Goeurit (Gen Mgr)

**ATS Automation Tooling Systems
GmbH** (1)
Marsstrasse 2, Munich, 85551, Heimstetten, Germany
Tel.: (49) 894272210
Web Site:
https://lifescienceeurope.automation.com
Emp.: 200
Turnkey Factory Automation Systems Mfr & Designer
N.A.I.C.S.: 541512
Christian Debus (Mng Dir)

Branch (Domestic):

**ATS Automation Tooling Systems
GmbH - Winnenden** (2)
Birkenstrasse 1-7, 71364, Winnenden, Germany
Tel.: (49) 7195 702 0
Web Site: http://www.atsautomation.com
Sales Range: $75-99.9 Million
Emp.: 70
Cutting Tool Mfr
N.A.I.C.S.: 333515
Hans-Werner Bongers (Mng Dir)

ATS Carolina Inc. (1)
1510 Cedar Line Dr, Rock Hill, SC 29730 (100%)
Tel.: (803) 324-9300
Web Site: http://www.atsautomation.com
Sales Range: $25-49.9 Million
Emp.: 100

Mfr & Designer of Turnkey Factory Automation Systems
N.A.I.C.S.: 333998
Stew Wiedersprecher (Gen Mgr)

ATS Machine Tool Division (1)
730 Fountain Street North Building 2, Cambridge, N3H 4R7, ON, Canada (100%)
Tel.: (519) 653-6500
Web Site: https://www.atsautomation.com
Sales Range: $25-49.9 Million
Emp.: 100
Machine Tooling
N.A.I.C.S.: 333517
Jordi Brown (Gen Mgr)

ATS Ohio Inc. (1)
425 Enterprise Dr, Lewis Center, OH 43035
Tel.: (614) 888-2344
Web Site: http://www.ats-ohio.com
Sales Range: $50-74.9 Million
Emp.: 120
Provider of Automated Tooling Systems
N.A.I.C.S.: 333998

**ATS Precision Metal
Components** (1)
80 Alpine Rd, Kitchener, N2E 1A1, ON, Canada (100%)
Tel.: (519) 744-6661
Web Site: http://www.atsautomation.com
Sales Range: $25-49.9 Million
Emp.: 150
N.A.I.C.S.: 541512

**ATS Precision Plastic
Components** (1)
730 Fountain St Bldg 1, Cambridge, N3H 4R7, ON, Canada (100%)
Tel.: (519) 650-6600
Web Site: http://www.ats.com
Sales Range: $25-49.9 Million
Emp.: 250
N.A.I.C.S.: 541512

ATS Sortimat USA LLC (1)
5655 Meadowbrook Industrial Ct, Rolling Meadows, IL 60008-3833
Tel.: (847) 925-1234
Sales Range: $25-49.9 Million
Emp.: 40
General Purpose Machinery Mfr
N.A.I.C.S.: 333998

ATS Systems Oregon Inc. (1)
2121 NE Jack London St, Corvallis, OR 97330-6916 (100%)
Tel.: (541) 758-3329
Web Site: http://www.atsautomation.com
Sales Range: $25-49.9 Million
Emp.: 100
Factory Automation Systems, Custom Automation Equipment, Standard Automation Products & Turnkey Assembly Machinery, as well as High-Volume Precision Components
N.A.I.C.S.: 333998
Stewart Wiedersprecher (Gen Mgr)

ATS Test Inc. (1)
600 Chrislea Rd, Woodbridge, L4L 8K9, ON, Canada (100%)
Tel.: (905) 850-8600
Web Site: http://www.atsautomation.com
Sales Range: $25-49.9 Million
Emp.: 50
Testing Services
N.A.I.C.S.: 541380

**ATS Wickel-und Montagetechnik
AG** (1)
Grosszelgstrasse 21, Wurenlos, 5436, Switzerland (100%)
Tel.: (41) 564368585
Web Site:
http://www.switzerland.atsautomation.com
Sales Range: $25-49.9 Million
Emp.: 35
N.A.I.C.S.: 541512
Tony Lang (Gen Mgr)

**Assembly & Test - Europe
GmbH** (1)
Carl-Borgward Strasse 11, Neuwied, Germany
Tel.: (49) 26313820
Web Site: http://www.atsautomation.com
Sales Range: $25-49.9 Million
Emp.: 80
Automated Production Equipment Mfr

N.A.I.C.S.: 333248
Anthony Caputo (CEO)

Automation Tooling Systems Enterprises, Inc. (1)
1510 Cedar Line Dr, Rock Hill, SC 29730-7442
Tel.: (803) 324-9300
Industrial Machinery Mfr
N.A.I.C.S.: 333248

Biodot, Inc. (1)
2852 Alton Pwy, Irvine, CA 92606
Tel.: (949) 440-3685
Web Site: https://www.biodot.com
Sales Range: $1-9.9 Million
Emp.: 30
Process Control Instruments
N.A.I.C.S.: 334513
Thomas C. Tisone (Pres)

CFT S.p.A. (1)
Via Paradigna 94/A, 43122, Parma, Italy
Tel.: (39) 052 127 7111
Web Site: https://www.cft-group.com
Food Processing Equipment Mfr
N.A.I.C.S.: 333241
Roberto Catelli (Pres)

Subsidiary (Non-US):

CFT DO BRASIL LTD (2)
Rua Joaquim Galvao 588, 05627-010, Sao Paulo, Brazil
Tel.: (55) 1137394860
Food Processing Equipment Mfr
N.A.I.C.S.: 333241

CFT Ukraine Ltd (2)
81100 Lviv Region, Pustomyty, Ukraine
Tel.: (380) 933906737
Food Processing Equipment Mfr
N.A.I.C.S.: 333241
Eugenia Onyshko (Mng Dir)

Subsidiary (US):

Cft Packaging Usa Inc. (2)
1033 Butterfield Rd, Vernon Hills, IL 60061
Tel.: (847) 247-0233
Web Site: http://www.cft-group.com
Food Processing Equipment Mfr
N.A.I.C.S.: 333241

Subsidiary (Domestic):

Levati Food Tech S.r.l. (2)
Via Lega Dei Carrettieri 14, 43038, Sala Baganza, Parma, Italy
Tel.: (39) 0521 838311
Web Site: http://www.gealevati.com
Vegetable Handling System Mfr
N.A.I.C.S.: 333241

Raytec Vision S.p.A. (2)
Via Paradigna 94/A, 43122, Parma, Italy
Tel.: (39) 0521303427
Web Site: https://www.raytecvision.com
Emp.: 50
Development & Production of Fruit & Vegetable Sorting Equipment
N.A.I.C.S.: 333241
Raffaele Pezzoli (CEO)

Comecer S.p.A. (1)
Via Maestri del Lavoro 90, Castel Bolognese, 48014, Ravenna, Italy
Tel.: (39) 0546656375
Web Site: https://www.comecer.com
Pharmaceuticals Mfr
N.A.I.C.S.: 325412

IPCOS NV (1)
Geldenaaksebaan 329, 3001, Leuven, Belgium
Tel.: (32) 16393083
Web Site: http://www.ipcos.com
Emp.: 60
Automation & Optimization Solutions for Continuous & Batch Processes; Digital Oilfield Solutions for Oil & Gas Industry
N.A.I.C.S.: 513210
Peter Van Overschee (CEO)

Subsidiary (Non-US):

IPCOS (UK) Ltd. (2)
Second Floor Suite D 4 Adkins Corner, Perne Road, Cambridge, CB1 3RU, United Kingdom
Tel.: (44) 1223 246 450

Web Site: http://www.ipcos.com
Emp.: 6
Information Technology Consulting Services
N.A.I.C.S.: 541512
Michelle Flynn (Gen Mgr)

IPCOS BV (2)
Bosscheweg 135B, 5282 WV, Boxtel, Netherlands
Tel.: (31) 411 613 500
Web Site: http://www.ipcos.com
Sales Range: $25-49.9 Million
Emp.: 15
Automation & Optimization Engineering Services
N.A.I.C.S.: 541519
Sam Dhaliwal (Mng Dir)

**IPCOS Engineering Solutions Pvt.
Ltd.** (2)
SCO-120-121 1st Floor Sector 8C Madhya Marg, Chandigarh, India
Tel.: (91) 172 2541210
Web Site: http://www.ipcos.com
Sales Range: $25-49.9 Million
Emp.: 12
Automation & Optimization Engineering Services
N.A.I.C.S.: 541519
Gundeep Gill (Mng Dir)

IWK Packaging Systems, Inc. (1)
2 Cranberry Rd Ste A1b, Parsippany, NJ 07054
Tel.: (973) 404-9300
Industrial Machinery Mfr
N.A.I.C.S.: 333248

IWK Verpackungstechnik GmbH (1)
Lorenzstrasse 6, 76297, Stutensee, Germany (100%)
Tel.: (49) 7 244 9680
Web Site: https://www.iwk.de
Sales Range: $75-99.9 Million
Emp.: 450
Packaging Machinery Mfr
N.A.I.C.S.: 333993
Svend Weidemann (Co-Mng Dir)

NCC Automated Systems, Inc. (1)
255 Schoolhouse Rd, Souderton, PA 18964
Tel.: (215) 721-1900
Web Site: http://www.nccas.com
Rev.: $2,600,000
Emp.: 25
Conveyor & Conveying Equipment Mfr
N.A.I.C.S.: 333922
Les Patkos (Dir)

**Process Automation Solutions
GmbH** (1)
Am Herrschaftsweiher 25, 67071, Ludwigshafen, Germany
Tel.: (49) 62379320
Web Site: https://pa-ats.com
Automation Machinery Mfr
N.A.I.C.S.: 336110
Christian Debus (Pres)

Subsidiary (Non-US):

ZI-ARGUS LTD. (2)
278 B1 Fl 1-2 Raintree Office Garden Soi Soonvijai 4 Rama IX Road, Kwaeng Bangkapi Khet Huaykwang, Bangkok, 10310, Thailand
Tel.: (66) 23199933
Industrial Machinery & Equipment Distr
N.A.I.C.S.: 423830

**ROLEC Prozess - und Brautechnik
GmbH** (1)
Eichfeldstrasse 2, Chieming, 83339, Traunstein, Germany
Tel.: (49) 866492720
Web Site: https://www.rolec-gmbh.com
Beverage Machine Mfr
N.A.I.C.S.: 333241

Siapi S.R.L. (1)
Via Ferrovia Nord 45, San Vendemiano, 31020, Treviso, Italy
Tel.: (39) 04384096
Web Site: https://www.siapi.it
Pet Container Moulding Machine Mfr
N.A.I.C.S.: 332439

Sortimat Technology Pvt. Ltd. (1)
191/A1 Station Road, Chinchwad, Pune, 411 033, India

ATS Corporation—(Continued)

Tel.: (91) 20 30700333
Web Site: http://www.sortimat.in
Emp.: 6
Cutting Tool Mfr
N.A.I.C.S.: 333517
Philippe Lutgen (Mng Dir)

ATS ENGINEERING LTD.
5 Hata'siya Street, Migdal Ha'Emeq,
2310801, Israel
Tel.: (972) 46061450
Web Site: http://www.ats-eng.com
Software Development Services
N.A.I.C.S.: 541511

ATS-TANNER BANDING SYSTEMS AG
Poststrasse 30, CH-6300, Zug, Switzerland
Tel.: (41) 417100603
Web Site: https://www.ats-tanner.com
Year Founded: 1988
Logistic Services
N.A.I.C.S.: 541614

ATSUGI CO., LTD.
1-3-2 Ohyakita, Ebina, Kanagawa,
Japan
Tel.: (81) 462311111
Web Site: https://www.atsugi.co.jp
Year Founded: 1947
3529—(TKS)
Rev.: $140,191,490
Assets: $277,712,540
Liabilities: $56,667,530
Net Worth: $221,045,010
Earnings: $8,797,910
Emp.: 137
Fiscal Year-end: 03/31/24
Textile Product Mfr & Whslr
N.A.I.C.S.: 315250
Hiroshi Kudo (Pres)

Subsidiaries:

Renown Inx Incorporated   (1)
8-8-20 Nishigotanda Dist, Shinagawa Ward,
Tokyo, Japan   (100%)
Tel.: (81) 354968330
Apparel Whslr
N.A.I.C.S.: 424350

ATTACQ LIMITED
Nexus 1 Ground Floor, 37 Magwa
Crescent Waterfall City, Midrand,
2090, South Africa
Tel.: (27) 105491050
Web Site: https://www.attacq.co.za
ATT—(JSE)
Rev.: $128,665,755
Assets: $1,153,363,840
Liabilities: $496,240,296
Net Worth: $657,123,544
Earnings: $27,476,315
Emp.: 156
Fiscal Year-end: 06/30/23
Real Estate Development Services
N.A.I.C.S.: 531390
Louis van der Watt (Founder)

ATTANA AB
Engelbrekts vag 6, Sollentuna, 191
62, Stockholm, Sweden
Tel.: (46) 841020000
Web Site: https://www.attana.com
Year Founded: 2002
Medical Equipment Mfr
N.A.I.C.S.: 339112
Anders Ulriksson (CFO)

ATTARD & CO. LTD.
Canter Business Centre Patri Felicjan
Bilocca Street, Marsa, MRS 1521,
Malta
Tel.: (356) 21237555
Web Site: http://www.attardco.com
Year Founded: 1921

Sales Range: $10-24.9 Million
Emp.: 100
Provider of High Performance Liquid
Chromotography (HPLC), Thermal
Analysis & Mass Spectrometry (MS)
Instruments, Columns & Related Services
N.A.I.C.S.: 334516
Cecilia Pellogrini (Mgr Mktg)

Subsidiaries:

Attard & Co. Foodstuffs Ltd.   (1)
Canter House Patri Felicjan Bilocca Street,
Marsa, MRS 1524, Malta
Tel.: (356) 2123 7555
Web Site: http://www.attardcofood.com
Food & Alcoholic Beverage Whslr
N.A.I.C.S.: 424490
Susanne Fsadni (Coord-Office)

Attard & Co. Industrial Ltd.   (1)
Building Materials Center, Qormi, QRM
3618, Malta
Tel.: (356) 21 485 629
Construction Materials Whslr
N.A.I.C.S.: 423320

Subsidiary (Domestic):

Evolve Ltd.   (2)
P F Bilocca Street, Marsa, MRS 1524,
Malta
Tel.: (356) 25692120
Web Site: http://www.evolveltd.eu
Laboratory Equipment & Supplies Distr
N.A.I.C.S.: 423490
Hugh Arrigo (Mng Dir)

T4B Ltd.   (2)
Canter Business Centre Patri Felicja
Bilocca Str, Marsa, MRS 1524, Malta
Tel.: (356) 25 692121
Web Site: http://www.t4bservices.com
Building Contracting & Finishing Services
N.A.I.C.S.: 238390
Patrick Spiteri (Mng Dir)

World Express Logistics Ltd.   (2)
Canter Business Centre P Felicja Bilocca
Str, Marsa, 1524, Malta
Tel.: (356) 21442295
Web Site: http://www.wel.com.mt
Freight Forwarding Services
N.A.I.C.S.: 488510
Geraldine Naudi (Coord-Logistics)

ATTENDO AB
Tel.: (46) 858625200
Web Site: http://www.attendo.com
Year Founded: 1985
Women Healthcare Services
N.A.I.C.S.: 456199
Martin Tiveus (Pres & CEO)

Subsidiaries:

Mikeva Oy   (1)
Metsolantia 4, Vantaa, 1450, Finland
Tel.: (358) 207400440
Web Site: http://www.mikeva.fi
Sales Range: $25-49.9 Million
Residential Care & Rehabilitation Facility
Operator
N.A.I.C.S.: 623311
Patri Pitkaranta (Gen Mgr)

ATTESTOR LIMITED
7 Seymour Street, London, W1H
7JW, United Kingdom
Tel.: (44) 2070749610
Web Site: https://www.attestor.com
Year Founded: 2019
Value Investment Firm
N.A.I.C.S.: 523940

ATTI-KAT SA
109-111 Mesogion Avenue Building
G1, 11526, Athens, Greece
Tel.: (30) 2106971100
Web Site: http://www.attikat.gr
Year Founded: 1980
Sales Range: $10-24.9 Million
Emp.: 60
Heavy Construction Services

N.A.I.C.S.: 236220
Sofia Alexiadou (CFO)

ATTICA BANK S.A.
3-5 Palaion Patron Germanou, 106-
72, Athens, Greece
Tel.: (30) 2103669000
Web Site: https://www.atticabank.gr
TATT—(ATI I)
Rev.: $70,765,163
Assets: $3,343,385,495
Liabilities: $3,402,299,806
Net Worth: ($58,914,310)
Earnings: ($417,188,647)
Emp.: 600
Fiscal Year-end: 12/31/22
Banking Services
N.A.I.C.S.: 522110
Athanasios Ch. Tsadaris (Deputy
CEO)

Subsidiaries:

Attica Consulting S.A.   (1)
8 Mavromichali Str, 106 79, Athens, Greece
Tel.: (30) 210 3667003
Web Site: http://www.atticabank.gr
Financial Investment Advisory Services
N.A.I.C.S.: 523940

Attica Ventures S.A.   (1)
18 Omirou St, 10672, Athens, Greece
Tel.: (30) 2103637663
Web Site: http://www.attica-ventures.com
Sales Range: $50-74.9 Million
Emp.: 3
Venture Capital Fund Management Services
N.A.I.C.S.: 523910

Attica Wealth Management S.A.   (1)
2 Christou Lada Street, 105 61, Athens,
Greece
Tel.: (30) 2103396860
Web Site: http://www.atticawealth.gr
Sales Range: $50-74.9 Million
Emp.: 14
Wealth Management Services
N.A.I.C.S.: 522180

AtticaBank Properties S.A   (1)
Omirou 8, 105 64, Athens, Greece
Tel.: (30) 2103669290
Web Site: http://www.atticabankproperties.gr
Sales Range: $50-74.9 Million
Emp.: 11
Investment Banking Services
N.A.I.C.S.: 523150

ATTICA GROUP
1-7 Lysikratous and Evripidou Street,
17674, Athens, Greece
Tel.: (30) 2108919500
Web Site: https://www.attica-group.com
Year Founded: 1918
ATTICA—(ATH)
Rev.: $489,201,269
Assets: $903,916,427
Liabilities: $573,856,277
Net Worth: $330,060,150
Earnings: $15,733,098
Emp.: 1,596
Fiscal Year-end: 12/31/22
Ferry Transportation Services
N.A.I.C.S.: 483112
Michael G. Sakellis (VP)

Subsidiaries:

Anek Lines SA   (1)
148 Karamanli Ave, 73100, Chania, Greece
Tel.: (30) 2104197400
Web Site: http://www.anek.gr
Rev.: $184,232,315
Assets: $345,026,127
Liabilities: $394,748,967
Net Worth: ($49,722,840)
Earnings: ($49,402,269)
Emp.: 658
Fiscal Year-end: 12/31/2021
Shipping Transportation & Communication
Services
N.A.I.C.S.: 483112
Georgios S. Katsanevakis (Chm & Pres)

Subsidiary (Domestic):

CHAMPION FERRIES L.T.D.   (2)
63 Dragatsaniou Str, 18545, Piraeus,
Greece
Tel.: (30) 2104619106
Web Site: http://www.championferries.gr
Sales Range: $25-49.9 Million
Emp.: 14
Shipping Agency Services
N.A.I.C.S.: 488510

LEFKA ORI S.A.   (2)
Stylos Apokoronou, Kalyves, Chania,
73003, Greece
Tel.: (30) 2825083310
Web Site: http://www.etanap.gr
Sales Range: $25-49.9 Million
Emp.: 30
Plastics Bottle Mfr
N.A.I.C.S.: 326160
Emmanouil Apostolakis (Mng Dir)

Blue Star Maritime S.A.   (1)
1-7 Lysikratous & Evripidou Street, Kallithea, 17674, Voula, Athens, Greece
Tel.: (30) 2108919500
Web Site: http://www.attica-group.com
Sales Range: $150-199.9 Million
Emp.: 725
Maritime Transportation Services
N.A.I.C.S.: 483112

Hellenic Seaways Single Member
Maritime S.A.   (1)
1-7 Lysikratous and Evripidou str, Kallithea,
176 74, Athens, Greece
Tel.: (30) 2108919800
Web Site: https://www.hellenicseaways.gr
Ferry Service
N.A.I.C.S.: 483111

SUPERFAST DEKA MC.   (1)
Vouliagmenis 70, Voula, 166 73, Greece
Tel.: (30) 21 0891 9040
Marine Transportation Services
N.A.I.C.S.: 483111

Superfast Ferries Single Member
Maritime S.A.   (1)
Lysikratous 1-7 and Evripidou str, Kallithea,
176 74, Athens, Greece
Tel.: (30) 2108919700
Web Site: https://www.superfast.com
Ferry Service
N.A.I.C.S.: 483114

ATTICA PUBLICATIONS S.A.
Kifisias Ave 40, 190 18, Athens,
Greece
Tel.: (30) 2106199080
Web Site: http://www.atticamedia.gr
Year Founded: 1994
ATEK—(ATH)
Sales Range: Less than $1 Million
Newspaper Publishing Services
N.A.I.C.S.: 513110
Nikolaos Panopoulos (CEO)

ATTILAN GROUP LIMITED
22 Cross Street 03-54/61 South
Bridge Court, China Square Central,
Singapore, 048421, Singapore
Tel.: (65) 6226 3771
Web Site: http://asiasons.com
Year Founded: 1999
Sales Range: $1-9.9 Million
Emp.: 250
Investment Holding Company
N.A.I.C.S.: 523999
Jared Chih Li Lim (Mng Dir)

ATTIVO GROUP
158 Leinster Road, Merivale,
Christchurch, 8014, New Zealand
Tel.: (64) 33531300
Web Site: https://attivogroup.co
Emp.: 100
Advertising Services
N.A.I.C.S.: 541810

Subsidiaries:

Deutsch New York   (1)
387 Park Ave S, New York, NY 10016-

Tel.: (212) 981-7600
Web Site: https://deutschny.com
Emp.: 569
Advertising Services
N.A.I.C.S.: 541810
Val DiFebo (CEO)

Harvey Cameron Group Limited (1)
93-95 Cambridge Terrace, Christchurch, New Zealand
Tel.: (64) 33531300
Web Site: http://www.hca.co.nz
Emp.: 29
Advertising Services
N.A.I.C.S.: 541810
Iain Harvey (Mng Dir)

Hill Holliday (1)
2 Drydock Ave, Boston, MA 02210
Tel.: (617) 366-4000
Web Site: https://www.hhcc.com
Sales Range: $800-899.9 Million
Emp.: 350
Advertising Agency & Direct Mail Advertising
N.A.I.C.S.: 541810
Karen Kaplan (Chm & CEO)

Subsidiary (Domestic):

Erwin Penland and Company (2)
110 E Court St Ste 400, Greenville, SC 29601
Tel.: (864) 271-0500
Web Site: https://www.epandcompany.com
Advetising Agency
N.A.I.C.S.: 541810
Karen Mawhinney (Mng Dir)

Gray Matter Agency Inc. (2)
24 Shipyard Dr, Hingham, MA 02043
Tel.: (781) 740-4001
Web Site: http://www.graymatteragency.com
Sales Range: $10-24.9 Million
Emp.: 10
Advertising Agencies
N.A.I.C.S.: 541810
Karl Thompson (Partner & Dir-Creative)

Branch (Domestic):

Hill Holliday/New York (2)
104 W 40th St Fl 7, New York, NY 10018
Tel.: (212) 905-7000
Web Site: http://www.hhcc.com
Rev.: $180,000,000
Emp.: 170
Advertising Agencies
N.A.I.C.S.: 541810

ATTOCK CEMENT PAKISTAN LIMITED
D-70 Block-4 Kehkashan-5 Clifton, Karachi, 75600, Pakistan
Tel.: (92) 2135309773
Web Site: https://www.attockcement.com
Year Founded: 1981
ACPL—(KAR)
Rev.: $177,616,042
Assets: $238,421,455
Liabilities: $98,446,528
Net Worth: $139,974,928
Earnings: $14,771,094
Emp.: 945
Fiscal Year-end: 06/30/21
Cement Mfr & Sales
N.A.I.C.S.: 327120
Irfan Amanullah (CFO & Sec)

ATTOCK REFINERY LTD
Morgah, Rawalpindi, Pakistan
Tel.: (92) 515487041
Web Site: https://www.arl.com.pk
Year Founded: 1922
ATRL—(PSX)
Rev.: $1,659,454,805
Assets: $692,819,659
Liabilities: $252,031,180
Net Worth: $440,788,479
Earnings: $100,937,578
Emp.: 623
Fiscal Year-end: 06/30/23
Oil Refinery
N.A.I.C.S.: 324110

Asif Saeed (Asst Gen Mgr-Comml & Materials Mgmt)

Subsidiaries:

Attock Petroleum Limited (1)
9th Floor Attock House Morgah, Rawalpindi, 4400, Pakistan
Tel.: (92) 512611600
Web Site: http://www.apl.com.pk
Emp.: 100
Petroleum Refineries
N.A.I.C.S.: 324110
Shoiab A. Malik (CEO)

Capgas Private Limited (1)
POL House Morgah, Rawalpindi, 46600, Pakistan
Tel.: (92) 51548758996
Storage, Filling & Distribution of Liquefied Petroleum Gas
N.A.I.C.S.: 457210

National Refinery Limited (1)
7-B Korangi Industrial Area, Karachi, 74900, Pakistan
Tel.: (92) 2135064135
Web Site: https://www.nrlpak.com
Rev.: $1,268,468,730
Assets: $402,128,708
Liabilities: $277,659,820
Net Worth: $124,468,888
Earnings: ($16,055,970)
Emp.: 971
Fiscal Year-end: 06/30/2023
Crude Oil Refining Services
N.A.I.C.S.: 211120
Shuaib Anwer Malik (Chm)

Pakistan Oilfields Limited (1)
POL House Morgah, Rawalpindi, Pakistan
Tel.: (92) 515487589
Web Site: https://www.pakoil.com.pk
Rev.: $243,642,372
Assets: $596,459,599
Liabilities: $333,321,899
Net Worth: $263,137,700
Earnings: $134,189,085
Emp.: 687
Fiscal Year-end: 06/30/2023
Oil & Gas Support Services
N.A.I.C.S.: 333132
Shuaib A. Malik (Chm & CEO)

ATTRELL AUTO HOLDINGS LIMITED
100 Canam Crescent, Brampton, L7A 1A9, ON, Canada
Tel.: (905) 451-1699
Web Site: http://www.attrelltoyota.com
Rev.: $20,148,043
Emp.: 44
New & Used Car Dealers
N.A.I.C.S.: 441110
John Attrell (Gen Mgr)

ATTURRA LTD.
Level 2, 10 Bond Street, Sydney, 2000, NSW, Australia
Tel.: (61) 296570999
Web Site: https://atturra.com
Year Founded: 2015
ATA—(ASX)
Rev.: $162,494,657
Assets: $189,962,606
Liabilities: $89,678,151
Net Worth: $100,284,455
Earnings: $6,497,730
Emp.: 900
Fiscal Year-end: 06/30/24
Software Publisher
N.A.I.C.S.: 513210
Stephen Kowal (CEO)

Subsidiaries:

Atturra Holdings Pty Ltd (1)
Level 2 10 Bond Street, Sydney, 2000, Australia
Tel.: (61) 296570999
IT Consulting Services
N.A.I.C.S.: 513210

ATUL AUTO LTD.

8B National Highway Nr Microwave Tower Shapar, Veraval, 360024, Rajkot, India
Tel.: (91) 2827252999
Web Site: https://www.atulauto.co.in
531795—(BOM)
Rev.: $43,232,280
Assets: $74,415,705
Liabilities: $36,661,170
Net Worth: $37,754,535
Earnings: ($3,478,020)
Emp.: 700
Fiscal Year-end: 03/31/22
Transportation Services
N.A.I.C.S.: 488999
Jayantibai J. Chandra (Chm & Mng Dir)

Subsidiaries:

Atul Green Automotive Private Limited (1)
Survey No 86 Plot No 1 to 4 Near Microwave Tower 8B National Highway, Shapar Veraval Dist, Rajkot, 360024, Gujarat, India
Tel.: (91) 2827235500
Web Site: https://www.atulgreen.co.in
Automobile Parts Mfr
N.A.I.C.S.: 336390

ATV PROJECTS INDIA LIMITED
1201 12th Floor Windfall Building Sahar Plaza Complex, Andheri Kurla Road Andheri E, Mumbai, 400059, India
Tel.: (91) 9219400853
Web Site:
  https://www.atvprojects.co.in
Year Founded: 1978
500028—(BOM)
Rev.: $4,656,288
Assets: $35,751,930
Liabilities: $10,716,287
Net Worth: $25,035,642
Earnings: $943,543
Fiscal Year-end: 03/31/21
Engineeering Services
N.A.I.C.S.: 541330
Mahesh V. Chaturvedi (Chm)

ATVEXA AB
Brovagen 9, 182 76, Stocksund, Sweden
Tel.: (46) 733019666
Web Site: http://www.atvexa.se
ATVEXA.B—(OMX)
Rev.: $249,287,360
Assets: $238,178,080
Liabilities: $182,265,440
Net Worth: $55,912,640
Earnings: $9,033,920
Emp.: 3,890
Fiscal Year-end: 08/31/21
Real Estate Development Services
N.A.I.C.S.: 531390
Anna Katarina Sjogren (CEO)

ATW TECH INC.
1050 de la Montagne Suite 400, Montreal, H3G 1Y8, QC, Canada
Tel.: (514) 935-5959
Web Site: https://atwtech.com
Year Founded: 2007
ATW—(TSXV)
Sales Range: Less than $1 Million
Healthcare Software Developer
N.A.I.C.S.: 513210
Michel Guay (Founder, Pres & CEO)

Subsidiaries:

VoxTel RNIS Telecommunications Inc. (1)
1050 de la Montagne Suite 400, Montreal, H3G 1Y8, QC, Canada
Web Site: http://www.voxtel.com
Telecommunication Servicesb
N.A.I.C.S.: 517810

AU MIN AFRICA PTY LTD
Fairview Office Park Regus House 3rd Floor Ring Road, Greenacres, 6045, Port Elizabeth, South Africa
Tel.: (27) 82 709 4988
Web Site: http://www.auminerals.biz
GRYEF—(OTCIQ)
Sales Range: Less than $1 Million
Gold, Precious Metals, Diamonds & Other Precious Gems Mining & Trading
N.A.I.C.S.: 212220
Martin F. Bernstein (Chm)

AU MINERA CORP
2 Bloor Street East Suite 3500, Toronto, M4W 1A8, ON, Canada
Tel.: (416) 915-4128
Web Site: http://www.auminera.com
Gold & Copper Mining Services
N.A.I.C.S.: 212290
Alejandro Diaz (Pres & CEO)

AU SMALL FINANCE BANK LIMITED
19-A Dhuleshwar Garden Ajmer Road, Jaipur, 302 001, Rajasthan, India
Tel.: (91) 1414110060
Web Site: https://www.aubank.in
Year Founded: 1996
AUBANK—(NSE)
Rev.: $943,955,513
Assets: $9,429,119,755
Liabilities: $407,914,853
Net Worth: $9,021,204,902
Earnings: $154,222,368
Emp.: 27,817
Fiscal Year-end: 03/31/22
Banking & Financial Services
N.A.I.C.S.: 522291
Sanjay Agarwal (CEO & Mng Dir)

AU VIET SECURITIES CORPORATION
6th Floor 130 Nguyen Cong Tru, Nguyen Thai Binh quarter 1st District, Ho Chi Minh City, Vietnam
Tel.: (84) 838216789
Web Site: http://www.avsc.com.vn
Year Founded: 2007
Emp.: 80
Investment Banking & Securities Brokerage Services
N.A.I.C.S.: 523150
Vinh Duc Doan (Chm)

AUB GROUP LIMITED
Level 14 141 Walker Street, Sydney, 2060, NSW, Australia
Tel.: (61) 299352222   AU
Web Site:
  https://www.aubgroup.com.au
Year Founded: 2000
AUB—(ASX)
Rev.: $644,222,086
Assets: $2,703,826,111
Liabilities: $1,535,816,634
Net Worth: $1,168,009,477
Earnings: $111,963,808
Emp.: 5,500
Fiscal Year-end: 06/30/24
Financial Advisory Services
N.A.I.C.S.: 523940
Michael P. C. Emmett (CEO & Mng Dir)

Subsidiaries:

AEI Insurance Group Pty Ltd (1)
Level 10 1 Elizabeth Plaza, North Sydney, 2060, NSW, Australia
Tel.: (61) 289131600
Web Site: https://aei.com.au
Sales Range: $50-74.9 Million
Emp.: 25
Automobile Insurance & Mortgage Services
N.A.I.C.S.: 524298

AUB Group Limited—(Continued)

Tim Wedlock (Mng Dir)

AUB Group NZ Limited (1)
Level 7 110 Symonds Street, Grafton, Auckland, 1010, New Zealand
Tel.: (64) 223467929
Insurance Brokerage Services
N.A.I.C.S.: 524210

Austagencies Pty. Ltd. (1)
Level 14 141 Walker St, North Sydney, 2060, NSW, Australia
Tel.: (61) 299309500
Web Site: https://www.austagencies.com.au
Insurance Brokerage Services
N.A.I.C.S.: 524210

Austbrokers CE McDonald Pty. Ltd. (1)
Level 1 2 Westlink Court 10 station Rd, Darra, Brisbane, 4075, QLD, Australia
Tel.: (61) 734236000
Automobile Insurance Services
N.A.I.C.S.: 524298

Austbrokers Canberra Pty. Ltd. (1)
Cnr Lyell Newcastle Streets, PO Box 727, Fyshwick, 2609, ACT, Australia (85%)
Tel.: (61) 262146700
Web Site:
https://www.austbrokerscanberra.com.au
Brokerage Services
N.A.I.C.S.: 524210

Austbrokers Central Coast Pty. Ltd. (1)
Unit 4 3 Pioneer Avenue, PO Box 3009, Tuggerah, 2259, NSW, Australia
Tel.: (61) 1300662714
Web Site:
https://www.abcentralcoast.com.au
Sales Range: $50-74.9 Million
Emp.: 20
Insurance & Brokerage Services
N.A.I.C.S.: 524210
Bob White (Mng Dir)

Austbrokers Corporate Pty. Ltd. (1)
Level 14 141 Walker St, North Sydney, 2060, NSW, Australia
Tel.: (61) 293468050
Web Site:
https://www.austbrokerscorporate.com.au
Insurance Advisory Services
N.A.I.C.S.: 524298

Austbrokers Life Pty Ltd (1)
Suite 15 02 Level 15 56 Pitt Street, PO Box 103, Sydney, 2000, NSW, Australia
Tel.: (61) 1300225433
Web Site:
https://www.austbrokerslife.com.au
Mortgage Brokerage Services
N.A.I.C.S.: 522310

Austbrokers Premier Pty. Ltd. (1)
280 Montague Rd, PO Box 3290, West End, Brisbane, 4101, QLD, Australia
Tel.: (61) 730101821
Web Site:
http://www.premier.austbrokers.com
Sales Range: $50-74.9 Million
Emp.: 20
Insurance Brokerage Services
N.A.I.C.S.: 524210

Austbrokers Professional Services Pty. Ltd. (1)
Level 14 44 Market Street, Sydney, 2000, NSW, Australia
Tel.: (61) 285673110
Web Site:
https://www.professionalrisks.com.au
Brokerage Services
N.A.I.C.S.: 523150

Austbrokers Pty. Ltd. (1)
Level 14 141 Walker Street, North Sydney, 2060, NSW, Australia
Tel.: (61) 299352222
Web Site: https://www.austbrokers.com.au
General & Life Insurance Services
N.A.I.C.S.: 524298

Austbrokers RWA Pty. Ltd. (1)
22 Darley Rd, PO Box 485, Manly, 2095, NSW, Australia
Tel.: (61) 299762511

Web Site:
http://www.austbrokersrwa.com.au
Sales Range: $50-74.9 Million
Emp.: 20
Insurance Services
N.A.I.C.S.: 524210
Paul George (Gen Mgr)

Austbrokers Sydney Pty. Ltd. (1)
Level 14 44 Market Street, Sydney, 2000, NSW, Australia
Tel.: (61) 289131600
Web Site: https://www.absyd.com.au
Sales Range: $50-74.9 Million
Emp.: 100
Brokerage Services
N.A.I.C.S.: 523150
Jeff Howells (Gen Mgr)

Austbrokers Terrace Insurance Brokers Pty. Ltd. (1)
1/187A Henley Beach Road, Mile End, 5031, SA, Australia
Tel.: (61) 882389200
Web Site: https://www.abterrace.com.au
Sales Range: $50-74.9 Million
Emp.: 21
Insurance Services
N.A.I.C.S.: 524210

Austbrokers Terrace Insurance Pty Ltd (1)
1/192 Argyle Street, PO Box 203, Fitzroy, 3065, VIC, Australia
Tel.: (61) 882389200
Web Site: http://www.abterrace.com.au
Sales Range: $50-74.9 Million
Emp.: 26
Insurance Brokerage Services
N.A.I.C.S.: 524210
Rob Morrell (Mng Dir)

Austbrokers Trade Credit Pty. Ltd. (1)
Level 14 44 Market Street, Sydney, 2000, NSW, Australia
Tel.: (61) 285673110
Web Site: https://abtradecredit.com
Insurance Brokerage Services
N.A.I.C.S.: 524210

Carriers Insurance Brokers Pty. Ltd. (1)
Unit 2 1725 Pittwater Road, Mona Vale, 2103, NSW, Australia
Tel.: (61) 299132002
Web Site:
https://www.carriersbrokers.com.au
Sales Range: $25-49.9 Million
Emp.: 8
Automobile Insurance & Mortage Services
N.A.I.C.S.: 327910
Kevin Hill (Founder)

Experien Insurance Services Pty. Ltd. (1)
Level 11 151 Castlereagh St, Sydney, 2000, NSW, Australia
Tel.: (61) 300796577
Web Site: https://www.experien.com.au
Insurance Brokerage Services
N.A.I.C.S.: 524210

Finsura Holdings Pty. Ltd. (1)
Suite 7 11 Level 7 12 Century Circuit, Baulkham Hills, 2153, NSW, Australia
Tel.: (61) 298992999
Web Site: https://www.finsura.com.au
Sales Range: $50-74.9 Million
Emp.: 25
Insurance & Financial Planning Services
N.A.I.C.S.: 523999
Matthew Driscoll (Mng Dir)

McNaughton Gardiner Insurance Brokers Pty. Ltd. (1)
91 Victoria Street, Bunbury, 6230, WA, Australia
Tel.: (61) 897223700
Web Site: https://www.mgib.com.au
Sales Range: $50-74.9 Million
Emp.: 20
Insurance Brokerage Services
N.A.I.C.S.: 524210
Antony Gallagher (Mng Dir)

Runacres Limited (1)
Runacres Hou se 1st Floor Suite 146 Somerfield Street, Beckenham,

Christchurch, 8024, New Zealand
Tel.: (64) 33791001
Web Site: https://runacres.co.nz
Business & Personal Insurance Services
N.A.I.C.S.: 524210

SPT Financial Services Pty. Ltd. (1)
Ste 5 18 Gibbs St, Miranda, 2228, NSW, Australia
Tel.: (61) 295404240
Web Site:
http://www.sptfinancialservices.com
Sales Range: $50-74.9 Million
Emp.: 5
Financial Planning Services
N.A.I.C.S.: 523999
Philip Budin (Gen Mgr)

Terrace Insurance Brokers Pty. Ltd. (1)
1/187A Henley Beach Road, Mile End, 5031, SA, Australia
Tel.: (61) 882389200
Web Site: https://www.abterrace.com.au
General Insurance Services
N.A.I.C.S.: 524210

WRI Insurance Brokers Pty Ltd (1)
26 Hunter St, Parramatta, 2150, NSW, Australia
Tel.: (61) 288313800
Web Site: https://www.wrib.com.au
Insurance Broker Services
N.A.I.C.S.: 524210

AUBAY SA
13 rue Louis Pasteur, 92100, Boulogne-Billancourt, France
Tel.: (33) 146106767   FR
Web Site: https://www.aubay.com
Year Founded: 1997
AUB—(EUR)
Rev.: $523,699,428
Assets: $468,892,902
Liabilities: $219,687,919
Net Worth: $249,204,983
Earnings: $32,096,368
Emp.: 6,562
Fiscal Year-end: 12/31/20
Information & Communication Technology Consulting & Technical Support Services
N.A.I.C.S.: 541990
Christian Aubert (Chm)

Subsidiaries:

Aedian SA (1)
2/4 rue Helene, 75017, Paris, France
Tel.: (33) 156353000
Web Site: http://www.aedian.com
Sales Range: $50-74.9 Million
Information Technology Management & Consulting Services
N.A.I.C.S.: 541513
Vincent Gauthier (Chm)

Aubay Italia S.p.A. (1)
Via Giotto 36, 20145, Milan, Italy (88%)
Tel.: (39) 026556761
Web Site: https://www.aubay.it
Information & Communication Technology Consulting & Technical Support Services
N.A.I.C.S.: 541990
Paolo Riccardi (Mgr)

Aubay Luxembourg S.A. (1)
38 Parc d'activites, 8308, Capellen, Luxembourg
Tel.: (352) 2992501
Web Site: http://www.aubay.com
Emp.: 120
Information & Communication Technology Consulting & Technical Support Services
N.A.I.C.S.: 541990

Aubay Spain S.L. (1)
2a pl Dr Zamenhof 36 Dupl, 28027, Madrid, Spain
Tel.: (34) 913269270
Web Site: https://aubay.es
Information & Communication Technology Consulting & Technical Support Services
N.A.I.C.S.: 541990

Subsidiary (Non-US):

Aubay Portugal (2)

Duque d'Avila Building Avenida Duque d'Avila n 46 - 7 C, 1050-083, Lisbon, Portugal
Tel.: (351) 211928417
Information & Communication Technology Consulting & Technical Support Services
N.A.I.C.S.: 541990

Aubay UK Limited (1)
One Canada Square Level39 Canary Wharf, London, EL4 5AB, United Kingdom
Tel.: (44) 208 194 7971
Web Site: https://www.aubay.co.uk
Staffing & Recruiting Services
N.A.I.C.S.: 561311
Phumlani Mbuqe (Project Mgr)

Offis SA/NV (1)
Boulevard Paepsem Paapsemlaan 11/B, 1070, Brussels, Belgium
Tel.: (32) 2609 1111
Information & Communication Technology Consulting & Technical Support Services
N.A.I.C.S.: 541990
Christophe Andrieux (Mng Dir)

Promotic Belgium SA/NV (1)
Rue Chaude Voie 39, Naninne, Namur, 5100, Belgium
Tel.: (32) 81408200
Web Site: http://www.aubay.com
Emp.: 45
Information & Communication Technology Consulting & Technical Support Services
N.A.I.C.S.: 541990
Michel Soetens (Mng Dir)

Quantic SA (1)
5 avenue de Verdun, 94200, Ivry-sur-Seine, France
Tel.: (33) 185330130
Web Site: http://www.quantic.fr
Information Technology Services
N.A.I.C.S.: 541519

AUBEX CORPORATION
Hulic Ryogoku Building 9F 4-31-11 Ryogoku, Sumida-ku, Tokyo, 130-0026, Japan
Tel.: (81) 367013200
Web Site: https://www.aubex.co.jp
Year Founded: 1893
3583—(TKS)
Rev.: $35,608,070
Assets: $64,255,810
Liabilities: $22,903,650
Net Worth: $41,352,160
Earnings: $2,881,960
Fiscal Year-end: 03/31/24
Pen Mfr & Whlsr
N.A.I.C.S.: 339940
Norigi Kurihara (Pres)

Subsidiaries:

FARO INTERNATIONAL, INC. (1)
151 Kalmus Dr M6, Costa Mesa, CA 92626
Tel.: (714) 432-8780
Web Site: https://www.farotools.com
Stationery Product Distr
N.A.I.C.S.: 424120

AUBRY LOGISTIQUE
N 4 Zone Industrielle, 88700, Rambervillers, France
Tel.: (33) 329653246
Web Site: http://aubry-logistique.fr
Sales Range: $10-24.9 Million
Emp.: 150
Trucking Service
N.A.I.C.S.: 484121
Philippe Aubry (Chm)

AUCFAN CO., LTD.
Sumitomo Fudosan Osaki Twin Bldg East 7F 5-1-18 Kitashinagawa, Shinagawa-ku, Tokyo, 141-0001, Japan
Tel.: (81) 368090951
Web Site: https://www.aucfan.co.jp
Year Founded: 2007
3674—(TKS)
Rev.: $36,478,050
Assets: $50,339,000

Liabilities: $17,512,300
Net Worth: $32,826,700
Earnings: $120,530
Emp.: 165
Fiscal Year-end: 09/30/23
Electronic Auction Website Operator
N.A.I.C.S.: 455219
Keisuke Yamada *(Exec Officer)*

Subsidiaries:

Smart Sourcing Co., Ltd. **(1)**
2-13-30 Kamiosaki Oak Meguro 3rd Floor,
Shinagawa-ku, Tokyo, 141-0021, Japan
Tel.: (81) 364525885
Web Site: http://www.smartsourcing.co.jp
Software Development Services
N.A.I.C.S.: 541511

Synabiz Co., Ltd. **(1)**
7th floor East Building Sumitomo Fudosan
Osaki Twin Building, 5-1-18 Kitashinagawa
Shinagawa-ku, Tokyo, 141-0001, Japan
Tel.: (81) 364160931
Software Development Services
N.A.I.C.S.: 541511

AUCHAN HOLDING S.A.
40 avenue de Flandre, 59170, Croix,
Cedex, France
Tel.: (33) 1 58 063080　　　　　FR
Web Site: http://www.auchan-holding.com
Year Founded: 1961
Rev.: $51,978,301,900
Assets: $38,620,611,820
Liabilities: $27,586,631,240
Net Worth: $11,033,980,580
Earnings: ($1,405,424,300)
Emp.: 331,099
Fiscal Year-end: 12/31/19
Holding Company; Hypermarket &
Supermarket Operator
N.A.I.C.S.: 551112
Edgard Bonte *(Chm-Retail)*

Subsidiaries:

ATAC SAS **(1)**
94 rue Albert Calmette, Jouy-en-Josas,
78350, France
Tel.: (33) 130672626
Supermarket Operator
N.A.I.C.S.: 445110

Accord Finance S.A. **(1)**
Ogrodowa 58, 00-876, Warsaw, Poland
Tel.: (48) 717997001
Commercial Banking Services
N.A.I.C.S.: 522110
Stephane Schersach *(CEO)*

Alcampo **(1)**
Calle de Santiago de Compostela Sur s/n
Edificio Oficinas La Vaguada, 28029, Madrid, Spain **(100%)**
Tel.: (34) 917306666
Web Site: http://www.alcampo.es
Supermarket
N.A.I.C.S.: 445110

Atak OOO **(1)**
6 Pr 4-I Voikovski, Moscow, 125171, Russia
Tel.: (7) 4956609870
Web Site: http://www.ataksupermarket.ru
Supermarket Operator
N.A.I.C.S.: 445110
Alina Gerber *(Sr Mgr-HR)*

Auchan **(1)**
23 Blvd Louis XI, PO Box 1805, ZI Menneton, 37018, Tours, Cedex, France **(100%)**
Tel.: (33) 247777777
Sales Range: $5-14.9 Billion
Emp.: 32,000
Hypermarket & Supermarket Operator
N.A.I.C.S.: 457110

Auchan **(1)**
Travessa Teixeira Junior No 1, Lisbon,
1300-388, Portugal **(100%)**
Tel.: (351) 21 360 2100
Web Site: http://www.auchan.pt
Hypermarket Business
N.A.I.C.S.: 445110
Fernando Ereio *(Dir-Logistics)*

Auchan **(1)**
5 rue Alphonse Weicker, 2721, Luxembourg, Luxembourg **(100%)**
Tel.: (352) 4377431
Web Site: http://www.auchan.lu
Sales Range: $200-249.9 Million
Emp.: 800
Hypermarket Business
N.A.I.C.S.: 445110
Marc Gueuzuria *(Gen Mgr)*

Auchan Coordination Services
S.A. **(1)**
Rue de la Terre a Briques 29 - Bat E Centre Futur Orcq, 7522, Marquain, Belgium
Tel.: (32) 69789690
Supermarket Operator
N.A.I.C.S.: 445110

Auchan E-Commerce France
S.A.S **(1)**
rue du Marechal de Lattre de Tassigny,
59170, Croix, France
Tel.: (33) 969325959
Web Site: http://www.auchan.fr
Online Shopping Services
N.A.I.C.S.: 425120

Auchan E-Commerce Polska Sp. z
o.o. **(1)**
ul Pulawska 46, 05-500, Piaseczno, Poland
Tel.: (48) 227263300
Web Site: http://www.auchandirect.pl
Online Shopping Services
N.A.I.C.S.: 425120

Auchan Hungary **(1)**
Sport utca 2-4, 2040, Budaors,
Hungary **(100%)**
Tel.: (36) 80109010
Web Site: http://www.auchan.hu
Sales Range: $800-899.9 Million
Hypermarket & Supermarket Businesses
N.A.I.C.S.: 445110

Auchan Polska **(1)**
Pulawska 46, 05-500, Piaseczno,
Poland **(100%)**
Tel.: (48) 227158671
Web Site: http://www.auchan.pl
Emp.: 150
Hypermarket Business
N.A.I.C.S.: 445110

Auchan Romania S.A. **(1)**
Sector 6 str Brasov no 25 Room 1 floor 4,
Bucharest, Romania
Tel.: (40) 219141
Web Site: http://www.auchan.ro
Supermarket Operator
N.A.I.C.S.: 445110
Francois Remy *(Pres)*

Auchan Shanghai Hypermarket **(1)**
3rd Floor 1750 Chang Yang Road, Shanghai, 200090, China **(100%)**
Tel.: (86) 2165432211
Web Site: http://www.auchan.com.cn
Hypermarket Business
N.A.I.C.S.: 445110

Auchan Ukraine **(1)**
Avenue Moskovskiy 15A, Kiev, 04073,
Ukraine **(100%)**
Tel.: (380) 443913825
Web Site: http://www.auchan.ua
Hypermarket Business
N.A.I.C.S.: 445110

BA Finans AS **(1)**
Holtlivegen 88, 2611, Lillehammer, Norway
Tel.: (47) 61255683
Commercial Banking Services
N.A.I.C.S.: 522110

Ceetrus Hungary Kft. **(1)**
Soroksari ut 44 Mill Park A Epulet, 1095,
Budapest, Hungary
Tel.: (36) 18874520
Web Site: http://www.ceetrus.hu
Shopping Mall Operator
N.A.I.C.S.: 531120

Ceetrus Italy SPA **(1)**
Galleria Buenos Aires 8/12, 20124, Milan,
MI, Italy
Tel.: (39) 03440861171
Web Site: http://www.ceetrus.it
Asset Management Services
N.A.I.C.S.: 523940

Ceetrus Polska SP ZOO **(1)**
Ul Pulawska 38, 05-500, Piaseczno, Poland
Tel.: (48) 223198785
Web Site: http://www.ceetrus.pl
Shopping Mall Operator
N.A.I.C.S.: 531120
Kinga Zablocka Jr. *(Mgr-Commercialization)*

ELO **(1)**
3A Rue Verkhniaya Krasnoselskaya,
107140, Moscow, Russia **(100%)**
Tel.: (7) 4957212090
Web Site: http://www.auchan.ru
Hypermarket Business
N.A.I.C.S.: 445110

Eurauchan SAS **(1)**
200 Rue De La Recherche, Villeneuve
d'Ascq, 59650, France
Tel.: (33) 328376700
Supermarket Operator
N.A.I.C.S.: 445110

Immochan Magyarorszag Kft. **(1)**
Soroksari ut 44 A building 2nd Flr, 1095,
Budapest, Hungary
Tel.: (36) 18874520
Web Site: http://www.ceetrus.com
Real Estate Consulting Service
N.A.I.C.S.: 531210
Balazs Gabosy *(Dir-Comml)*

MGV Distri-Hiper S.A. Auchan **(1)**
Str Barbu Delavrance a 13, Sector 1,
011351, Bucharest, Romania **(100%)**
Tel.: (40) 212227887
Web Site: http://www.auchan.ro
Hypermarket Business
N.A.I.C.S.: 445110

Oney - Instituicao Financeira de
Credito, S.A. **(1)**
Av Jose Gomes Ferreira 9 Sala 01, 1495-139, Alges, Portugal
Tel.: (351) 214126800
Financial Consulting Services
N.A.I.C.S.: 523940

Oney Magyarorszag Zrt. **(1)**
Tolgyfa u 28, Budapest, 1027, Hungary
Tel.: (36) 18880000
Commercial Banking Services
N.A.I.C.S.: 522110

AUCHAN SPA
8/N Milano Fiori, Rozzano, 20089,
MI, Italy
Tel.: (39) 0257581　　　　　　IT
Web Site: http://www.auchan.it
Sales Range: $100-124.9 Million
Emp.: 300
Hypermarket & Supermarket Business
N.A.I.C.S.: 445110
Patrick Espasa *(Pres-Romania)*

AUCKLAND INTERNATIONAL AIRPORT LIMITED
Auckland Airport offices 4 Leonard
Isitt Drive, PO Box 73020, Manukau,
2150, New Zealand
Tel.: (64) 92750789　　　　　NZ
Web Site:
https://www.aucklandairport.co.nz
Year Founded: 1966
AIA—(ASX)
Rev.: $374,342,105
Assets: $6,476,854,067
Liabilities: $1,466,387,560
Net Worth: $5,010,466,507
Earnings: $25,837,321
Emp.: 579
Fiscal Year-end: 06/30/23
International Airport
N.A.I.C.S.: 488119
Adrian Littlewood *(CEO)*

AUCKLAND REAL ESTATE TRUST
Level 9 117 Macquarie Street, Sydney, 2000, NSW, Australia
Tel.: (61) 292228100

Web Site:
http://www.quattroplusrealestate.com
AKL—(ASX)
Rev.: $8,173,771
Assets: $132,344,171
Liabilities: $70,029,221
Net Worth: $62,314,950
Earnings: $6,662,389
Fiscal Year-end: 06/30/20
Real Estate Services
N.A.I.C.S.: 531210
Andrew Saunders *(Sec)*

AUCLERT SAS
Z I Les Rochettes 12 Rue Des
Rochettes, 91150, Morigny
Champigny, Essonne, France
Tel.: (33) 169921260
Web Site:
http://concessions.peugeot.fr
Rev.: $17,000,000
Emp.: 48
N.A.I.C.S.: 441110
Frederic Thiou *(Dir-Fin)*

AUCMA CO., LTD.
No 315 Qianwangang Road Economic and Technological Development Zone, Qingdao, 266555, Shandong, China
Tel.: (86) 53286765129
Web Site: https://www.aucma.com.cn
Year Founded: 1987
600336—(SHG)
Rev.: $1,343,171,756
Assets: $1,066,260,920
Liabilities: $685,441,491
Net Worth: $380,819,430
Earnings: $20,523,489
Emp.: 5,500
Fiscal Year-end: 12/31/22
Refrigeration Equipment Mfr & Distr
N.A.I.C.S.: 335220

AUCNET INC.
Aoyama OM Square 5-8 Kita-Aoyama
2-chome, Minato-ku, Tokyo, 107-8349, Japan
Tel.: (81) 364402500
Web Site: https://www.aucnet.co.jp
Year Founded: 1984
3964—(TKS)
Rev.: $307,018,270
Assets: $267,037,760
Liabilities: $108,859,860
Net Worth: $158,177,900
Earnings: $30,969,120
Emp.: 878
Fiscal Year-end: 12/31/23
Online Used Car Auctions
N.A.I.C.S.: 441120
Kiyotaka Fujisaki *(Chm & CEO)*

Subsidiaries:

AUCNET HK LIMITED **(1)**
Flat/Rm 1103 11/F The Metropolis Tower 10
Metropolis Drive, Hunghom, Kowloon,
China (Hong Kong)
Tel.: (852) 35251288
Electronic Auction Services
N.A.I.C.S.: 455219

Advance Car Technology Company
Limited **(1)**
Sanbancho Annex Building 1-4 Fl, Sanbancho Chiyoda-ku, Tokyo, Japan
Tel.: (81) 352169762
Web Site: http://www.act-x.co.jp
Sales Range: $25-49.9 Million
Emp.: 20
New Car Dealers
N.A.I.C.S.: 441110
Nariyuki Sawanobori *(Gen Mgr)*

Advanced Core Technology Co.,
Ltd. **(1)**
NihonTV yonbancho Bldg 1go 5F 8-1
YonSanban-cho, Chiyoda-ku, Tokyo, 102-0081, Japan
Tel.: (81) 3 5216 9762

Aucnet Inc.—(Continued)

Web Site: http://www.act-x.co.jp
Advanced Core Technology Co., Ltd.
N.A.I.C.S.: 541512

Artnex Inc. (1)
Harifaxkudan Bldg 3F 2-4-4, Kudanminami
Chiyoda-ku, Tokyo, 102-0074, Japan
Tel.: (81) 3 3512 6146
Web Site: http://www.artnex.co.jp
Art Auction Services
N.A.I.C.S.: 459920

Auc Financial Partners Inc (1)
2-5-8 Kita-Aoyama, Minato-ku, Tokyo, 107-0061, Japan
Tel.: (81) 36 440 2255
Web Site: https://www.auc-fp.co.jp
Automobile Assurance Services
N.A.I.C.S.: 541990

Auc Service Inc. (1)
Sanbancho Tokyu Building 8-1, Chiyoda-ku,
102-8349, Tokyo, Sanbancho, Japan
Tel.: (81) 335126111
Web Site: http://www.aucnet-nyukai.com
Business Auctions of Automobiles, Motor-
cycles & Other Business Services
N.A.I.C.S.: 424930

Aucnet Advance Inc. (1)
Aoyama OM Square Bldg 7F 2-5-8 Kita-
Aoyama, Minato-ku, Tokyo, 107-0061, Ja-
pan
Tel.: (81) 364402340
Consulting Business Services
N.A.I.C.S.: 541618

**Aucnet Consumer Products USA,
LLC** (1)
222 Pacific Coast Hwy Fl 23, El Segundo,
CA 90245
Tel.: (310) 746-5629
Auction Services
N.A.I.C.S.: 561990

Aucnet Digital Products Inc. (1)
Gaien Blsg 9F 2-23-8 Minamiaoyama,
Minato-ku, Tokyo, 107-0062, Japan
Tel.: (81) 3 5413 6251
Electronic Auction Services
N.A.I.C.S.: 455219

Aucnet IBS Inc. (1)
2-5-8 Kita-Aoyama, Minato-ku, Tokyo, 107-
0061, Japan
Tel.: (81) 364402680
Information Technology Services
N.A.I.C.S.: 541511

Aucnet Medical Inc. (1)
Aoyama Om Square Bldg 8F 2-5-8 Kita-
Aoyama, Minato-ku, Tokyo, 107-0061, Ja-
pan
Tel.: (81) 36 440 2610
Web Site: http://www.aucnet-medical.com
Medical Equipment Maintenance Services
N.A.I.C.S.: 811210

Aucnet Sales and Support Inc. (1)
Sanbancho Tokyu Building, 8-1 Sanban-cho
Chiyoda-ku, 102-8349, Tokyo, Japan
Tel.: (81) 335126544
Web Site: http://www.aucnet-nyukai.com
Motor Vehicle Supplies & New Parts Whslr
N.A.I.C.S.: 423120

**Automobile Inspection System
Inc.** (1)
3F Sanbancho Tokyu Bldg 8-1 Sanbancho,
Chiyoda-ku, Tokyo, 102-8349, Japan
Tel.: (81) 33 512 6118
Web Site: https://www.ais-inc.jp
Commercial Sectors Regulation Licensing &
Inspection
N.A.I.C.S.: 926150
Hirufumi Goto (Pres & Dir)

Gallery Rare Ltd. (1)
Maruito Minamihorie Paros Building 6F
1-7-4 Minamihorie, Nishi-ku, Osaka, 550-
0015, Japan
Tel.: (81) 662516653
Emp.: 90
Fashion Miscellaneous Goods Distr
N.A.I.C.S.: 424990
Kenichi Morimoto (Sr Mng Exec Officer)

Hello Net Inc. (1)
Nihonterebi-Yonbancho Building 1 3F, 5-6

Yonban-cho Chiyoda-ku, Tokyo, 102-0081,
Japan
Tel.: (81) 335126300
Web Site: http://www.hellonet.co.jp
Sales Range: $50-74.9 Million
Emp.: 20
Real Estate Agents & Brokers
N.A.I.C.S.: 531210

I-Auc Inc. (1)
8-1 Sanbancho, Chiyoda-ku, Tokyo, 102-
0075, Japan
Tel.: (81) 335126123
Web Site: https://www.iauc.co.jp
Sales Range: $50-74.9 Million
Emp.: 60
Motor Vehicle Supplies & New Parts Whslr
N.A.I.C.S.: 423120

Ing Communications Corp (1)
Nakanoya Building 2F 2-12-16 Shiroyama-
cho, Shiroyama-cho Oyama-city, Oyama,
323-0025, Tochigi, Japan
Tel.: (81) 285203811
New Car Dealers
N.A.I.C.S.: 441110

Jbtv, Inc. (1)
10-7 Gobancho JBTV Gobancho Building,
Chiyoda-ku, Tokyo, 102-0076, Japan
Tel.: (81) 335126311
Business Process Outsourcing Services
N.A.I.C.S.: 541611

Kinuta Flower Auction Co., Ltd. (1)
7F South Building Tokyo Central Wholesale
Market 1-4-1 Okura, Setagaya-ku, Tokyo,
157-0074, Japan
Tel.: (81) 357279101
Web Site: https://www.kinuta-kaki.co.jp
Emp.: 34
Motorcycle Product Mfr & Distr
N.A.I.C.S.: 336991

Menergia Inc. (1)
2-11-3 Yaesu Line View Kyobashi 5th Floor,
Chuo-ku, Tokyo, 104-0028, Japan
Tel.: (81) 366656975
Media Services
N.A.I.C.S.: 541840

Runmart Inc. (1)
6/F No 5 Akiyama Bldg Higashi 1-3-10,
Shibuya-ku, Tokyo, 150-0011, Japan
Tel.: (81) 35 766 8460
Web Site: http://www.runmart.co.jp
Sales Range: $75-99.9 Million
Emp.: 250
Motor Vehicle Supplies & Parts Whslr
N.A.I.C.S.: 423120
John Cook (Mng Dir)

AUCTION TECHNOLOGY GROUP PLC
Harlequin Building 65 Southwark
Street, London, SE1 0HR, United
Kingdom
Tel.: (44) 2037255500
Web Site:
https://www.auctiontechnology.com
ATG—(LSE)
Other Computer Related Services
N.A.I.C.S.: 541519
John-Paul Savant (CEO)

Subsidiaries:

Live Auctioneers, LLC (1)
10 E 38th St 4th Fl, New York, NY 10016
Tel.: (212) 947-4112
Web Site: http://www.liveauctioneers.com
Business Support Services
N.A.I.C.S.: 561499
Phil Michaelson (CEO)

AUCTUS CAPITAL PARTNERS AG
Prinzregentenstrasse 18, 80538, Mu-
nich, Germany
Tel.: (49) 8915907000
Web Site: http://www.auctus.com
Year Founded: 2001
Sales Range: $200-249.9 Million
Emp.: 900
Privater Equity Firm
N.A.I.C.S.: 523999

Ingo Krocke (Founder, CEO & Mng
Partner)

Subsidiaries:

Babcock & Wilcox Volund AB (1)
Anders Carlssons gata 14, PO Box 8876,
402 72, Gothenburg, Sweden
Tel.: (46) 31501960
Power & Heating Equipment Whslr
N.A.I.C.S.: 423720
Ulf Hagg (Mgr-Process)

Hobatex GmbH (1)
Driburger Str 39, 33034, Brakel, Germany
Tel.: (49) 52 72 37 77 0
Web Site: http://www.hobatex.de
Wood Product Distr
N.A.I.C.S.: 423310

PharmaLex GmbH (1)
Bahnstrasse 42-46, 61381, Friedrichsdorf,
Germany
Tel.: (49) 6172764640
Web Site: http://www.pharmalex.com
Research & Development in the Physical,
Engineering & Life Sciences
N.A.I.C.S.: 541715
Thomas Dobmeyer (CEO)

AUCTUS INVESTMENT GROUP LIMITED
Level 23 101 Collins Street, Mel-
bourne, 3000, VIC, Australia
Tel.: (61) 399599888   AU
Web Site: https://auctusinvest.com
Year Founded: 2011
AVC—(ASX)
Rev.: $2,514,022
Assets: $22,966,747
Liabilities: $5,104,834
Net Worth: $17,861,912
Earnings: $1,343,483
Fiscal Year-end: 06/30/24
Investment Management Service
N.A.I.C.S.: 551112
Campbell Mccomb (Mng Dir)

AUDACIA SA
58 Rue d Hauteville, 75010, Paris,
France
Tel.: (33) 156434800
Web Site: https://www.audacia.fr
Year Founded 2006
ALAUD—(EUR)
Software Development Services
N.A.I.C.S.: 541511
Charles Beigbeder (CEO)

AUDALIA RESOURCES LIMITED
Level 1 1139 Hay Street, West Perth,
6005, WA, Australia
Tel.: (61) 893210715
Web Site:
https://www.audalia.com.au
ACP—(ASX)
Rev.: $2,379
Assets: $8,276,956
Liabilities: $6,898,335
Net Worth: $1,378,620
Earnings: ($625,911)
Fiscal Year-end: 06/30/24
Lead, Zinc & Copper Mining Services
N.A.I.C.S.: 212230
Karen Logan (Sec)

AUDANT INVESTMENTS PTY. LTD.
Level 11 151 Macquarie St, Sydney,
2000, NSW, Australia
Tel.: (61) 292471500
Web Site:
http://www.audantinvestments.com
Investment Services
N.A.I.C.S.: 523999
Syd Cassimaty (Controller-Fin)

AUDAX RENOVABLES, S.A.
Calle de la Electronica n 19 7th floor

door C, 8915, Barcelona, Spain
Tel.: (34) 932405306   ES
Web Site:
https://www.audaxrenovables.com
Year Founded: 2000
ADX—(MAD)
Rev.: $2,528,356,331
Assets: $1,429,708,577
Liabilities: $1,238,460,095
Net Worth: $191,248,482
Earnings: $34,639,585
Emp.: 666
Fiscal Year-end: 12/31/23
Renewable Energy Producer
N.A.I.C.S.: 237130

Subsidiaries:

Eolica el Pedregoso, S.L. (1)
Calle Arenal 21, Malaga, 29016, Spain
Tel.: (34) 952226604
Eletric Power Generation Services
N.A.I.C.S.: 221118

Fercom Eolica, S.L. (1)
Calle Travessera De Gracia 30 - Pis 5, Bar-
celona, 08021, Spain
Tel.: (34) 934960200
Electric Power Generation
N.A.I.C.S.: 221118

AUDAX-KECK GMBH
Weiherstrasse 10, Calw, 75365, Ger-
many
Tel.: (49) 705116250   De
Web Site: http://www.audax.de
Year Founded: 1982
Rev.: $10,847,073
Emp.: 16
Building Protection Products Distr
N.A.I.C.S.: 424690
Gunther Keck (Mng Dir)

Subsidiaries:

AUDAX Ltd. (1)
Ha Tsuen Tin Ha Road 1D San Uk Tsuen
Yuen Long, Hong Kong, New Territories,
China (Hong Kong)
Tel.: (852) 69323165
Building Protection Product Distr
N.A.I.C.S.: 424950

AUDEARA LIMITED
Level 1 North Tower 527 Gregory
Terrace, Bowen Hills, 4006, QLD,
Australia
Tel.: (61) 1300251539   AU
Web Site: https://www.audeara.com
Year Founded: 2015
AUA—(ASX)
Rev.: $1,894,755
Assets: $3,087,078
Liabilities: $1,020,428
Net Worth: $2,066,650
Earnings: ($2,440,456)
Fiscal Year-end: 06/30/23
Electronic Products Mfr
N.A.I.C.S.: 334419
James Fielding (Mng Dir)

AUDEMARS PIGUET & CIE
Route de France 16, 1348, Le Bras-
sus, Switzerland
Tel.: (41) 216423266
Web Site:
http://www.audemarspiguet.com
Year Founded: 1875
Sales Range: $75-99.9 Million
Emp.: 1,200
Jewelry & Watch Mfr
N.A.I.C.S.: 339910
Antonio Seward (CEO-North
America)

Subsidiaries:

**Audemars Piguet (North
America)** (1)
65 E 57th St, New York, NY 10022
Tel.: (212) 758-8400
Web Site: http://www.audemarspiguet.com

Sales Range: $25-49.9 Million
Emp.: 33
Jewelry & Watches
N.A.I.C.S.: 339910

Audemars Piguet (Suisse) S.A. (1)
Route de France 16, Le Brassus, 1348,
Switzerland
Tel.: (41) 218112280
Web Site: http://www.audemarspiguet.com
Sales Range: $25-49.9 Million
Emp.: 20
Jewelry & Watches
N.A.I.C.S.: 339910
Nicolas Kappenverger *(Mgr)*

Audemars Piguet Deutschland (1)
Bahnhofstrasse 44 46, Wiesbaden, 65185,
Germany (100%)
Tel.: (49) 611341750
Web Site: http://www.audemarspiguet.com
Sales Range: $25-49.9 Million
Emp.: 15
Jewelry & Watches
N.A.I.C.S.: 339910
Nicolas de Quatrebarbes *(Mng Dir)*

Audemars Piguet France (1)
2 Rue Duphot, Paris, F 75008,
France (100%)
Tel.: (33) 153576760
Web Site: http://www.audemarspiguet.com
Jewelry & Watches
N.A.I.C.S.: 339910

Audemars Piguet Italia S.p.A. (1)
Via Melchiorre Gioia 168, 20125, Milan,
Italy
Tel.: (39) 0266985117
Web Site: http://www.audemarspiguet.com
Jewelry & Watches
N.A.I.C.S.: 339910
Alessandro Bogliolo *(Chm)*

AUDEN TECHNO CORP.
No 19 Ln 772 Heping Rd, Bade Dist,
Taoyuan, 334, Taiwan
Tel.: (886) 33631901
Web Site: https://www.auden.com.tw
Year Founded: 1981
3138—(TAI)
Emp.: 384
Communication Equipment Mfr
N.A.I.C.S.: 334290
Chang Yu-Pin *(Chm)*

AUDERA
Rue Alfred Nobel, Ifs, 14123, Caen,
France
Tel.: (33) 231356666
Web Site: http://www.audera.fr
Rev.: $21,800,000
Emp.: 28
New & Used Car Dealers
N.A.I.C.S.: 441110
Serge Foucher *(Pres)*

AUDIENCE LABS SA
2 place Louis Pradel, 69001, Lyon,
France
Tel.: (33) 478985853
Web Site: http://www.alabs.io
Online Marketing Services
N.A.I.C.S.: 541890
Hakim Labiod *(CEO)*

AUDIENCEVIEW TICKETING CORPORATION
200 Wellington Street West 2nd
Floor, Toronto, M5V 3C7, ON,
Canada
Tel.: (416) 687-2000
Web Site:
http://www.audienceview.com
Year Founded: 2002
Live Events & Entertainment Services
N.A.I.C.S.: 711310
Mark Fowlie *(CEO)*

Subsidiaries:

TheaterMania.com, Inc. (1)
550 7th Ave 16th Fl, New York, NY 10018

Tel.: (212) 352-0255
Web Site: http://www.theatermania.com
Theater Information & Web Based Ticketing
Services
N.A.I.C.S.: 711110

Vendini, Inc. (1)
55 Francisco St Ste 350, San Francisco,
CA 94133
Tel.: (800) 901-7173
Web Site: http://www.vendini.com
Ticketing, Marketing, Fundraising & Patron
Management
N.A.I.C.S.: 541613
Keith Goldberg *(COO)*

AUDINATE GROUP LIMITED
Level 7 64 Kippax Street, Surry Hills,
2010, NSW, Australia
Tel.: (61) 280901000 AU
Web Site: https://www.audinate.com
Year Founded: 2003
AD8—(ASX)
Rev.: $61,086,405
Assets: $126,518,429
Liabilities: $12,678,953
Net Worth: $113,839,476
Earnings: ($228,365)
Emp.: 225
Fiscal Year-end: 06/30/24
Information Technology Services
N.A.I.C.S.: 541511
David A. Krall *(Chm)*

Subsidiaries:

Audinate Limited (1)
Future Business Centre Kings Hedges Rd,
Cambridge, CB4 2HY, United Kingdom
Tel.: (44) 1273921695
Computer Networking Services
N.A.I.C.S.: 541511

Audinate Limited (1)
Suite 1106-08 11/F Tai Yau Building No 181
Johnston Road, Wanchai, China (Hong
Kong)
Tel.: (852) 35880030
Computer Networking Services
N.A.I.C.S.: 541511

Audinate Pty Limited (1)
Level 7 64 Kippax Street, Surry Hills, 2010,
NSW, Australia
Tel.: (61) 280901000
Computer Networking Services
N.A.I.C.S.: 541511

Audinate, Inc. (1)
4380 S Macadam Ave Ste 255, Portland,
OR 97239
Tel.: (503) 224-2998
Computer Networking Services
N.A.I.C.S.: 541511

AUDIO GROUP GREECE B.V.
321 Mesogion Avenue, 15231, Halan-
dri, Athens, Greece
Tel.: (30) 210 6721200 NL
Web Site: http://www.aggbv.gr
Holding Company; Electronics Distr
N.A.I.C.S.: 551112
Andreas Tsolias *(Mgr-Technical)*

Subsidiaries:

Eisagogiki Emporiki Ellados A.E. (1)
321 Mesogion Ave, 15231, Halandri, Ath-
ens, Greece
Tel.: (30) 210 672 1200
Web Site: http://www.isembel.gr
Electronics Distr
N.A.I.C.S.: 423620
Christina Argyropoulou *(Mng Dir)*

AUDIO PIXELS HOLDINGS LIMITED
Suite 3 Level 12 75 Elizabeth Street,
Sydney, 2000, NSW, Australia
Tel.: (61) 292333915 AU
Web Site:
https://www.audiopixels.com.au
Year Founded: 2006
ADPXF—(OTCIQ)
Rev.: $322,345

Assets: $3,547,161
Liabilities: $3,448,218
Net Worth: $98,943
Earnings: ($1,626,086)
Emp.: 13
Fiscal Year-end: 12/31/22
Electronic & Precision Equipment Re-
pair & Maintenance
N.A.I.C.S.: 811210
Frederick Bart *(Chm & CEO)*

AUDIO-TECHNICA CORPORA-TION
2206 Naruse, Machida, Tokyo, 194-
8666, Japan
Tel.: (81) 3 6801 2001
Web Site: http://www.audio-
technica.co.jp
Professional Sound Equipment Mfr
N.A.I.C.S.: 334310
Kazuo Matsushita *(Pres)*

Subsidiaries:

Audio-Technica (Greater China)
Limited (1)
Room K 9th Floor Kaiser Est Ph 2 51 Man
Yue Street, Hung Hom, Kowloon, China
(Hong Kong)
Tel.: (852) 23569268
Web Site: http://www.audio-technica.com.hk
Professional Audio Equipment
N.A.I.C.S.: 334310

Audio-Technica (S.E.A.) Pte. Ltd. (1)
1 Ubi View 01-14 focus 1, Singapore,
408555, Singapore
Tel.: (65) 67495686
Web Site: http://www.audio-technica.com.sg
Sales Range: $25-49.9 Million
Emp.: 20
Professional Audio Equipment
N.A.I.C.S.: 334310
Vincent Heng Fai Chan *(Mng Dir)*

Audio-Technica Central Europe
Ltd (1)
Fogado u 3, 1107, Budapest, Hungary
Tel.: (36) 1 433 34 08
Audio Equipment Distr
N.A.I.C.S.: 423620
Zsolt Zold *(Dir-Technical)*

Audio-Technica Limited (UK) (1)
Technica House Royal London Industrial
Estate, Old Lane, Leeds, LS11 8AG, United
Kingdom
Tel.: (44) 1132771441
Web Site: http://www.audio-technica.co.uk
Sales Range: $25-49.9 Million
Emp.: 30
Professional Audio Equipment
N.A.I.C.S.: 334310
Lee Barnes *(Mgr-Customer Svcs)*

Audio-Technica Niederlassung
Deutschland (1)
Lorenz Schott Strasse 5, 55252, Mainz-
Kastel, Germany
Tel.: (49) 6134 25734 0
Audio Equipment Distr
N.A.I.C.S.: 423620
Jorg Rader *(Gen Mgr)*

Audio-Technica SAS (1)
11 rue des Pyramides, 75001, Paris, France
Tel.: (33) 1 43 72 82 82
Audio Equipment Distr
N.A.I.C.S.: 423620

Audio-Technica Taiwan Co., Ltd. (1)
No 6 Lane 322 Section 2 Duanda LiFuda
Road, Zhongli, 32050, Taoyuan, Taiwan
Tel.: (886) 34985831
Web Site: http://www.audio-technica.com.tw
Audio Equipment Distr
N.A.I.C.S.: 423620

Audio-Technica U.S., Inc. (1)
1221 Commerce Dr, Stow, OH 44224
Tel.: (330) 686-2600
Web Site: http://www.audio-technica.com
Sales Range: $10-24.9 Million
Emp.: 115
Professional Sound Equipment Distr
N.A.I.C.S.: 334310
Greg Pinto *(VP-Mktg & Customer Sls)*

AUDIOBOOM GROUP PLC
Forum 4 Grenville Street, PO Box
264, Saint Helier, JE4 8TQ, Jersey
Web Site:
https://www.audioboomplc.com
BOOM—(AIM)
Rev.: $65,030,000
Assets: $23,177,000
Liabilities: $21,008,000
Net Worth: $2,169,000
Earnings: ($19,426,000)
Emp.: 39
Fiscal Year-end: 12/31/23
Audio & Podcasting Distr
N.A.I.C.S.: 541870
Brad Clarke *(CFO)*

Subsidiaries:

Audioboom Limited (1)
Morocco Store 1a - 1b Leathermarket St,
London, SE1 3JA, United Kingdom
Tel.: (44) 2074036688
Web Site: https://www.audioboom.com
Advertising Services
N.A.I.C.S.: 541810
Stuart Last *(CEO)*

AUDIOCODES LTD.
1 Hayarden Street Airport City, Lod,
7019900, Israel
Tel.: (972) 39764099 II
Web Site:
https://www.audiocodes.com
AUDC—(NASDAQ)
Rev.: $275,093,000
Assets: $323,831,000
Liabilities: $134,071,000
Net Worth: $189,760,000
Earnings: $28,466,000
Emp.: 966
Fiscal Year-end: 12/31/22
Voice Compression Chips & Related
Products Mfr
N.A.I.C.S.: 334210
Eyal Frishberg *(VP-Ops)*

Subsidiaries:

AudioCodes Argentina S.A. (1)
Bulnes 747 Piso 4 Of A, C1176ABM, Bue-
nos Aires, Argentina (100%)
Tel.: (54) 91156192242
Web Site: http://www.audiocodes.com
Sales Range: $100-124.9 Million
Emp.: 334
Information Retrieval Services
N.A.I.C.S.: 517810

AudioCodes Brasil Equipamentos de
Voz sobre IP Ltda. (1)
Av das Nacoes Unidas 12551 17 andar, Jd
Paulistano, Sao Paulo, 04578-000, SP,
Brazil (100%)
Tel.: (55) 1182059077
Web Site: http://www.audiocodes.com
Equipment Sales of Voice Gateways to
Communication Services
N.A.I.C.S.: 517810

AudioCodes California (1)
27 Worlds Fair Dr Ste 1, Somerset, NJ
08873-1353 (100%)
Tel.: (858) 625-2400
Web Site: http://www.audiocodes.com
Sales Range: $25-49.9 Million
Emp.: 100
Designs, Manufactures & Sells Packet
Voice Gateways to Communication Services
N.A.I.C.S.: 334210

AudioCodes Europe Limited (1)
37 Broadhurst Gardens, London, NW6 3QT,
Hants, United Kingdom (100%)
Tel.: (44) 1252759150
Telecommunication Research & Develop-
ment
N.A.I.C.S.: 541715

AudioCodes GmbH (1)
Hanauer Landstrasse 148a, 60314, Frank-
furt am Main, Germany (100%)
Tel.: (49) 6967830530
Mfr & Sales of Packet Voice Gateways to
Communication Companies

AudioCodes Ltd.—(Continued)

N.A.I.C.S.: 517121

AudioCodes India Pvt. Ltd. (1)
Unit no 306 III Floor Tower B Millennium Plaza Sushant Lok Phase 1, Gurgaon, 122002, Haryana, India (100%)
Tel.: (91) 1244994550
Emp.: 10
Mfr & Sales of Packet Voice Gateways to Communication Companies
N.A.I.C.S.: 517121

AudioCodes Korea Ltd. (1)
302 Landmark building 607 Yeongdong-daero, Gangnam-gu, Seoul, 06087, Korea (South) (100%)
Tel.: (82) 27825377
Web Site: http://www.audiocodes.com.kr
Sales Range: $25-49.9 Million
Emp.: 4
Mfr & Sales of Packet Voice Gateways Systems
N.A.I.C.S.: 517121

AudioCodes Ltd. (1)
104 Avenue Albert 1er - Les Passerelles, 92500, Rueil-Malmaison, France (100%)
Tel.: (33) 664043021
Mfr & Sales of Voice Gateways to Communication Companies
N.A.I.C.S.: 517121

AudioCodes Mexico (1)
Av Miguel de Cervantes Saavedra 301 Edificio Terret Torre Sur Piso 14, Col Granada Ciudad de, 11520, Mexico, CP, Mexico (100%)
Tel.: (52) 5515556625
Web Site: http://www.audiocodes.com
Sales of Voice Gateways Systems
N.A.I.C.S.: 517121

AudioCodes Singapore (1)
8 Kallang Avenue Aperia Tower 1 06-04, Singapore, 339509, Singapore (100%)
Tel.: (65) 64936688
Web Site: http://www.audiocodes.com
Sales Range: $25-49.9 Million
Emp.: 10
Packet Voice Gateways Systems Mfr & Sales
N.A.I.C.S.: 517121

AudioCodes USA (1)
27 World's Fair Dr, Somerset, NJ 08873 (100%)
Tel.: (732) 469-0880
Web Site: http://www.ai-logix.com
Sales Range: $25-49.9 Million
Emp.: 60
Designer & Mfr of Computer Hardware & Software Communication Solutions Products
N.A.I.C.S.: 334118

AudioCodes, Beijing (1)
Room 602 Beijing Air China Plaza No 36 Xiaoyun Road, Chaoyang District, Beijing, 100027, China (100%)
Tel.: (86) 1065974260
Web Site: http://www.audiocodes.com
Sales Range: $25-49.9 Million
Emp.: 5
Mfr & Sales of Voice Gateways to Communication Services
N.A.I.C.S.: 334290

AudioCodes, Inc. (1)
27 Worlds Fair Dr Ste 2, Somerset, NJ 08873-1353 (100%)
Tel.: (408) 441-1175
Web Site: http://www.audiocodes.com
Sales Range: $25-49.9 Million
Emp.: 20
Voice Network Solutions
N.A.I.C.S.: 517810

Nuera Communications Singapore Pte Ltd.
8 Kallang Ave Aperia Tower 1 No 06-04, Singapore, 339509, Singapore
Tel.: (65) 64936688
Electronic Parts & Equipment Mfr
N.A.I.C.S.: 334419

AUDIOTECH HEALTHCARE CORPORATION
175 2nd Ave Ste 760, Kamloops, V2C 5W1, BC, Canada   AB
Tel.: (250) 372-5847
Web Site: http://www.audiotech.org
Year Founded: 1998
Sales Range: $1-9.9 Million
Hearing Centers Operator & Manager
N.A.I.C.S.: 456199
Osvaldo Iadarola (Pres & CEO)

Subsidiaries:

Canadian Hearing Care (1)
#760 - 175 Second Ave, Kamloops, V2C 5W1, BC, Canada (100%)
Tel.: (250) 372-5847
Web Site:
  http://www.canadianhearingcare.com
Hearing Services
N.A.I.C.S.: 456199

AUDIOVALLEY
Route de Lennik 451, 1070, Brussels, Belgium
Tel.: (32) 2 466 31 60
Web Site: http://www.audiovalley.com
ALAVY—(EUR)
Sales Range: $10-24.9 Million
Emp.: 105
Digital Audio Services
N.A.I.C.S.: 512290
Alexandre Saboundjian (CEO)

AUDIUS AG
Mercedesstrasse 31, D-71384, Weinstadt, Germany
Tel.: (49) 71 51 36 900 0
Web Site: http://www.audius.de
Year Founded: 1991
IT Services & Software Mfr
N.A.I.C.S.: 513210
Rainer Francisi (Chm)

Subsidiaries:

Audius SE (1)
Mercedesstrasse 31, D - 71384, Weinstadt, Germany (100%)
Tel.: (49) 7151369000
Web Site: https://www.audius.de
Rev.: $79,160,371
Assets: $40,394,992
Liabilities: $17,817,829
Net Worth: $22,577,164
Earnings: $3,723,289
Emp.: 591
Fiscal Year-end: 12/31/2022
Information Technology Services
N.A.I.C.S.: 541519
Rainer Francisi (Chm)

AUDIX CORPORATION
No 8 Lane 120 Section 21 Neihu Road, Taipei, Taiwan
Tel.: (886) 287976688
Web Site: https://www.audix.com
2459—(TAI)
Rev.: $242,655,277
Assets: $328,579,012
Liabilities: $143,036,785
Net Worth: $185,542,228
Earnings: $19,712,024
Emp.: 3,000
Fiscal Year-end: 12/31/23
Optoelectronic Products & Components Mfr
N.A.I.C.S.: 334413

Subsidiaries:

AHC Warehouse & Trading (Shenzhen) Co., Ltd. (1)
4/F Bldg 25 Kezhi Road West, Science and Technology Industrial Park Nanshan Area, Shenzhen, 518057, Guangdong, China
Tel.: (86) 75526631938
General Warehousing & Storage Services
N.A.I.C.S.: 493110

AHI Electronics Warehouse (Hang Zhou) Co., Ltd. (1)
Room 610 Huadu Building No 137 Qingc-

hun Road, Hangzhou, 310006, Zhejiang, China
Tel.: (86) 571 8724 4671
Web Site: http://www.audix.com
Electronic Components Distr
N.A.I.C.S.: 423690

AHI Electronics Warehouse (Shanghai) Co., Ltd. (1)
3F 34 Building No 806 Guiping Road, Gaohejing Development Zone, Shanghai, 200233, China
Tel.: (86) 2164950798
Web Site: http://www.audix.com
General Warehousing & Storage Services
N.A.I.C.S.: 493110

AHI Electronics Warehouse (Wu Jiang) Co., Ltd. (1)
No 1289 Jiang Xing East Road, Eastern Wujiang Economic Development Zone, Wujiang, 215200, Jiangsu, China
Tel.: (86) 51263439990
Web Site: http://www.audix.com
Electronic Components Distr
N.A.I.C.S.: 423690

Audix Hi-Tech Investment Co., Ltd. (1)
Unit E 18/F Infotech Centre No 21 Hung To Road, Kwun Tong, Kowloon, China (Hong Kong)
Tel.: (852) 27997575
Emp.: 8
Electronic Components Mfr
N.A.I.C.S.: 334416
Ken Chung (Mgr)

Audix Technology (Wujiang) Co., Ltd. (1)
No 1289 Jiang Xing East Road, the Eastern Part of Wujiang Economic Development Zone, Wujiang, 215200, Jiangsu, China
Tel.: (86) 51263403993
Sales Range: $50-74.9 Million
Emp.: 50
Electronic Components Mfr
N.A.I.C.S.: 334413

Audix Technology (Xiamen) Co., Ltd. (1)
No 7 Rixin Road, Jimei, Xiamen, 361022, Fujian, China
Tel.: (86) 5926663666
Web Site: http://www.audix.com
Sales Range: $400-449.9 Million
Emp.: 2,500
Electronic Components Mfr
N.A.I.C.S.: 334419
James Chung (Chm)

Lily Medical Corporation (1)
No 28-2 Shun Jeau Diann, Chunan Town, Miao-li, 35056, Taiwan
Tel.: (886) 3 761 2625
Web Site: https://www.lily-medical.com
Sales Range: $25-49.9 Million
Emp.: 100
Surgical Supplies Mfr
N.A.I.C.S.: 339113

Toyo Kuni Electronics Co. Ltd. (1)
Unit E 18/F Infotech Centre No 21 Hung To Road, Kwun Tong, Kowloon, China (Hong Kong)
Tel.: (852) 27997575
Sales Range: $50-74.9 Million
Emp.: 10
Electronic Components Distr
N.A.I.C.S.: 423690

YUKA Precision (Wujiang) Co., Ltd. (1)
No 66 Jiang Xing East Road, The Eastern Part of Wujiang Economic Development Zone, Wujiang, 215200, Jiangsu, China
Tel.: (86) 5126 343 9780
Web Site: http://www.audix.com
Industrial Mold Mfr
N.A.I.C.S.: 333511
Chenghung Chung (Chm)

AUDLEY CAPITAL ADVISORS LLP
7 Vigo Street, London, W1S 3HF, United Kingdom
Tel.: (44) 20 7529 6900

Web Site:
  http://www.audleycapital.com
Investment Services
N.A.I.C.S.: 523999
John MacKenzie (CEO)

AUG. LAUKHUFF GMBH & CO. KG
Aug Laukhuff Strasse 1, Weikersheim, 97990, Germany
Tel.: (49) 793491600
Web Site: http://www.laukhuff.de
Year Founded: 1823
Rev.: $15,173,400
Emp.: 150
Musical Instrument Mfr
N.A.I.C.S.: 339992
Magnus Windelen (Mng Dir)

AUGA GROUP, AB
Konstitucijos pr 21C, Quadrum North, 08130, Vilnius, Lithuania
Tel.: (370) 52335340   SE
Web Site: https://www.auga.lt
Year Founded: 2003
AUG1L—(VSE)
Rev.: $88,090,601
Assets: $260,975,207
Liabilities: $163,968,812
Net Worth: $97,006,395
Earnings: ($18,957,884)
Emp.: 1,199
Fiscal Year-end: 12/31/21
Holding Company; Organic Farming & Agricultural Products Whslr
N.A.I.C.S.: 551112
Dalius Misiunas (Chm-Mgmt Bd)

Subsidiaries:

AUGA Gruduva, UAB (1)
Mokyklos str 2, Gotlybiskiai village, 71372, Sakiai, Lithuania
Tel.: (370) 345 51139
Emp.: 70
Mixed Crop & Livestock Farming Services
N.A.I.C.S.: 111998
Remigijus Kromelis (Chm)

AUGA Jurbarkai, ZUB (1)
Vytauto Didziojo str 99, Klisiu village, 74205, Jubarkas, Lithuania
Tel.: (370) 447 72290
Mixed Crop & Livestock Farming Services
N.A.I.C.S.: 111998
Julius Laurinaitis (Chm)

AUGA Lankesa, ZUB (1)
Lankesos str 2, Bukoniu village, 55418, Jonava, Lithuania
Tel.: (370) 349 49794
Mixed Crop & Livestock Farming Services
N.A.I.C.S.: 111998
Arturas Narkevicius (Chm)

AUGA Mantviliskis, ZUB (1)
Liepos 6-osios str 18, Mantviliskio village Dotnuva parish, 58332, Kedainiai, Lithuania
Tel.: (370) 347 59623
Mixed Crop Farming Services
N.A.I.C.S.: 111998
Aloyzas Vazgys (Chm)

AUGA Nausode, ZUB (1)
Nausodes str 55, Kirmeliai village Troskunai parish, 29308, Anyksciai, Lithuania
Tel.: (370) 381 47592
Mixed Corp & Livestock Farming Services
N.A.I.C.S.: 111998
Ceslovas Valiuskevicius (Chm)

AUGA Skemiai, ZUB (1)
Kedainiu str 13, Skemiai village, 82350, Radviliskis, Lithuania
Tel.: (370) 422 45123
Mixed Crop & Livestock Farming Services
N.A.I.C.S.: 111998
Aloyzas Vazgys (Chm)

AUGA Smilgiai, ZUB (1)
Panevezio str 23 Smilgiai, Smilgiai parrish, 38375, Panevezys, Lithuania
Tel.: (370) 455 53 526
Mixed Crop & Livestock Farming Services
N.A.I.C.S.: 111998

AUGA Spindulys, ZUB (1)
Spindulio str 13, Vaitiekunai village Grinkiskis parish, 82380, Radviliskis, Lithuania
Tel.: (370) 422 47274
Mixed Crop Farming Services
N.A.I.C.S.: 111998
Adolfas Sniauka (Chm)

AUGA Zelsvele, ZUB (1)
Zelsveles str 12, Zelsvos village Liudvinavo parrish, 69193, Marijampole, Lithuania
Tel.: (370) 343 22047
Mixed Crop & Livestock Farming Services
N.A.I.C.S.: 111998
Paulus Actraukac (CEO)

Baltic Champs, UAB (1)
Poviliskes village 15, Gruzdziu sen, 81411, Siauliai, Lithuania
Tel.: (370) 4 137 2494
Web Site: https://champs.lt
Mushroom Farming, Packaging & Whslr
N.A.I.C.S.: 111411
Arunas Radzevicius (Gen Mgr)

UAB Agro Management Team (1)
Smolensko str 10 A, 3201, Vilnius, Lithuania
Tel.: (370) 52595657
Web Site: http://www.agromt.lt
Agricultural Property Management Services
N.A.I.C.S.: 531312

UAB Agross (1)
Smolensko st 10, 03201, Vilnius, Lithuania
Tel.: (370) 52335340
Agricultural Supplies Distr
N.A.I.C.S.: 424590

UAB Agrotechnikos centras (1)
Konstitucijos ave 21C Quadrum North, 08130, Vilnius, Lithuania
Tel.: (370) 66554599
Web Site: https://augatech.lt
New & Used Tractor Distr
N.A.I.C.S.: 423820

AUGE TECHNOLOGY CORPO-RATION
Bldg 1281 Nishi Gotanda 7 Chome, Shinagawa-ku, Tokyo, 141-0031, Japan
Tel.: (81) 368210265
Web Site: http://www.auge-tech.com
Year Founded: 2007
Sales Range: Less than $1 Million
Software Product Sales & Support Services
N.A.I.C.S.: 513210
Akira Tomitani (Owner)

AUGMENTUM FINTECH PLC
4 Chiswell Street, London, EC1Y 4UP, United Kingdom
Tel.: (44) 2039615420   UK
Web Site: https://www.augmentum.vc
Year Founded: 2017
AUGM—(LSE)
Rev.: $12,746,097
Assets: $367,055,325
Liabilities: $2,022,993
Net Worth: $365,032,332
Earnings: $6,068,979
Emp.: 5
Fiscal Year-end: 03/31/23
Portfolio Management & Investment Advice
N.A.I.C.S.: 523940
Tim Levene (CEO & Partner)

AUGROS COSMETIC PACK-AGING
ZA du Londeau rue de l'expansion, Cerise, 61000, Alencon, France
Tel.: (33) 233817200
Web Site: https://www.augros.fr
Year Founded: 1919
AUGR—(EUR)
Sales Range: $10-24.9 Million
Cosmetics Capping & Packaging Product Mfr
N.A.I.C.S.: 339999
Jacques Bourgine (CEO)

AUGUR CAPITAL AG
Westendstrasse 16-22, Frankfurt, 60325, Germany
Tel.: (49) 69 716 799 0   De
Web Site:
   http://www.augurcapital.com
Privater Equity Firm
N.A.I.C.S.: 523940

Subsidiaries:

LRI Invest S.A. (1)
9A rue Gabriel Lippmann, 5365, Munsbach, Luxembourg
Tel.: (352) 2615001
Web Site: http://www.lri-invest.lu
Investment Management Service
N.A.I.C.S.: 523150
Udo Stadler (Mgr-Principal Relationship)

AUGURE SA
5 Boulevard Montmartre, 75002, Paris, France
Tel.: (33) 1 70 98 24 00
Web Site: http://www.augure.com
Year Founded: 2002
Software Mfr
N.A.I.C.S.: 513210
Michael Jais (CEO)

Subsidiaries:

Fashion GPS, Inc. (1)
515 W 20th St Ste 7W, New York, NY 10011
Tel.: (212) 594-2138
Web Site: http://www.fashiongps.com
Software Publisher
N.A.I.C.S.: 513210
Edwin Mullon (Founder & CEO)

AUGUST EQUITY LLP
10 Slingsby Place St Martin's Courtyard, London, WC2E 9AB, United Kingdom
Tel.: (44) 2076328200
Web Site:
   http://www.augustequity.com
Sales Range: $25-49.9 Million
Emp.: 14
Privater Equity Firm
N.A.I.C.S.: 523999
Aatif Hassan (Partner)

Subsidiaries:

Active Assistance (1)
1 Suffolk Way, Kent, Sevenoaks, TN13 1YL, United Kingdom
Tel.: (44) 844 846 1616
Web Site: http://www.activeassistance.com
Health Care Srvices
N.A.I.C.S.: 621999
Ejaz Nabi (CEO)

Compass Fostering (1)
Mountfields House Squirrel Way, Loughborough, LE11 3GE, Leicestershire, United Kingdom
Tel.: (44) 1452 399199
Web Site: http://www.compassfostering.com
Health Care Srvices
N.A.I.C.S.: 624110
Bernie Gibson (COO)

The Old Deanery Care Village (1)
Deanery Hill, Bocking, Braintree, CM7 5SR, Essex, United Kingdom
Tel.: (44) 1376 328600
Web Site: http://www.olddeanery.com
Residential Care Services
N.A.I.C.S.: 623210

Westpoint Veterinary Group (1)
Dawes Farm Bognor Road, Warnham, RH12 3SH, Sussex, United Kingdom
Tel.: (44) 1306 628 086
Web Site:
   http://www.westpointveterinarygroup.com
Pharmaceuticals Product Mfr
N.A.I.C.S.: 325412
Jon Mouncey (Dir-Clinical & Member-Exec Bd)

AUGUST FALLER GMBH & CO. KG
Freiburger Strasse 25, 79183, Waldkirch, Germany
Tel.: (49) 76814050
Web Site: http://www.august-faller.com
Year Founded: 1882
Pharmaceutical Packaging Product Mfr
N.A.I.C.S.: 322212
Michael Faller (Mng Dir-Digital Pkg Svc)

AUGUST HILDEBRANDT GMBH
Siemensplatz 1, 19057, Schwerin, Germany
Tel.: (49) 385645300
Web Site: http://www.cabledrum.com
Year Founded: 1868
Rev.: $38,456,437
Emp.: 105
Wooden Cable Drums Mfr
N.A.I.C.S.: 321999
Uwe Wenkel (Mng Dir)

Subsidiaries:

Hildebrandt Netherlands B.V. (1)
Spinnerstraat 15, 7481 KJ, Haaksbergen, Netherlands
Tel.: (31) 535732255
Wooden Cable Drum Distr
N.A.I.C.S.: 424990

Hildebrandt USA, inc. (1)
1077 Mecklenburg Hwy, Mooresville, NC 28115
Tel.: (704) 664-7630
Wooden Cable Drum Distr
N.A.I.C.S.: 424990

AUGUST RUEGGEBERG GMBH & CO. KG PFERD-WERKZEUGE
Hauptstrasse 13, 51709, Marienheide, Germany
Tel.: (49) 8042187117
Web Site:
   http://www.rueggeberg.com
Year Founded: 1897
Sales Range: $250-299.9 Million
Emp.: 1,900
Mfr of Files, Burs, Mounted Points, Polishing & Fine Grinding Tools, Cutting & Grinding Wheels; Chain Saw Accessories
N.A.I.C.S.: 332216
Jorn Bielenberg (CEO & Mng Dir)

Subsidiaries:

D.O.O. Tehnoalat (1)
Pitagorina 1, Novi Sad, 21000, Serbia   (100%)
Tel.: (381) 21504273
Web Site: http://www.tehnoalat.rs
Sales Range: $25-49.9 Million
Emp.: 10
Machine Tool, grinding, cutting Tool Distr
N.A.I.C.S.: 423830
Baljana Maeskov (Gen Mgr)

PFERD Australia (Pty.) Ltd. (1)
No 1 3 Coniser Crescent, 3172, Dingley, VIC, Australia   (100%)
Tel.: (61) 395581177
Web Site: http://www.pferd.com.au
Sales Range: $25-49.9 Million
Emp.: 100
Sales of Machine Tools, Metal Cutting Types.
N.A.I.C.S.: 333517

PFERD CANADA INC. (1)
5570 McAdam Road, Mississauga, L4Z 1P1, ON, Canada
Tel.: (905) 501-1555
Web Site: http://www.pferdcanada.ca
Abrasive & Cutting Tool Mfr
N.A.I.C.S.: 327910
Rick Hatelt (Mgr-Territory)

PFERD Rueggeberg France (1)
2 Ave De La Concorde, Zone DActivites Economiques, 67129, Molsheim, France   (100%)
Tel.: (33) 388495872
Web Site: http://www.pferd.com
Sales Range: $25-49.9 Million
Emp.: 20
Sales of Machine Tools, Metal Cutting Types.
N.A.I.C.S.: 333517

PFERD, Inc. (1)
30 Jytek Dr, Leominster, MA 01453-5932   (100%)
Tel.: (978) 840-6420
Web Site: http://www.pferdusa.com
Sales Range: $25-49.9 Million
Emp.: 30
Distr of Cutting Tools
N.A.I.C.S.: 423840
Peter Skaalen (VP-Ops-Milwaukee)

PFERD-Rueggeberg B.V. (1)
Hekven 15 Bis, PO Box 2070, Breda, 4800, Netherlands
Tel.: (31) 765937090
Web Site: http://www.pferd.nl
Machine Tools Mfr
N.A.I.C.S.: 333517

PFERD-Rueggeberg Ges.m.b.H (1)
Prinz Eugen Str 17, 4020, Linz, Austria   (100%)
Tel.: (43) 732796411
Web Site: http://www.pferdrueggeberg.at
Sales Range: $25-49.9 Million
Emp.: 10
Sales of Machine Tools, Metal Cutting Types.
N.A.I.C.S.: 333517
Hoegner Dietmar (Mgr)

PFERD-Rueggeberg bvba (1)
Waterranonkelstraat 2 a, 1130, Brussels, Belgium
Tel.: (32) 2 2470590
Web Site: http://www.pferd.be
Cutting Tools, Machine Tool Accessories & Machinists Precision Measuring Devices Mfr
N.A.I.C.S.: 333515

PFERD-Tools Pvt. Ltd. (1)
115/116 MIDC Estate Satpur, 422007, Nasik, India
Tel.: (91) 253350665
Sales of Machine Tools, Metal Cutting Types.
N.A.I.C.S.: 333517

PFERD-VSM Sp.z.o.o. (1)
Ul Polna 1 A, 62025, Kastryzyn Wielkopolski, Kastryzyn Wielkopols, Poland (100%)
Tel.: (48) 618970480
Web Site: http://www.ferdvsm.pl
Sales Range: $25-49.9 Million
Emp.: 30
Distr of Cutting Tools.
N.A.I.C.S.: 333515
Grzegorz Koczur (Pres)

Rotea D.O.O. (1)
Badaliceva 26 b, HR 10000, Zagreb, Croatia
Tel.: (385) 3820113
Machine Tools, Metal Cutting Types Sales
N.A.I.C.S.: 333517

AUGUSTA GOLD CORP.
Suite 555999 Canada Place, Vancouver, V6C 3E1, BC, Canada
Tel.: (604) 687-1717   DE
Web Site:
   https://www.augustagold.com
Year Founded: 2007
G—(TSX)
Assets: $60,668,959
Liabilities: $44,179,448
Net Worth: $16,489,511
Earnings: ($19,720,212)
Emp.: 12
Fiscal Year-end: 12/31/22
Gold Exploration Services
N.A.I.C.S.: 212220
Donald R. Taylor (Pres & CEO)

Subsidiaries:

Bullfrog Mines LLC (1)

Augusta Gold Corp.—(Continued)

1 Boiling Pot Rd, Beatty, NV 89003
Tel.: (604) 687-1717
Gold & Silver Exploration Services
N.A.I.C.S.: 541612

Standard Gold Corp.
International Environment House 2 Chemin
de Balexert 7-9, Chatelaine, 1219, Geneva,
Switzerland
Tel.: (41) 227887080
Web Site: https://www.goldstandard.org
Environmental Services
N.A.I.C.S.: 541620

AUGUSTUS MARTIN LTD.
St Andrews Way Bromley By Bow,
London, E3 3PB, United Kingdom
Tel.: (44) 2075374200
Web Site:
    http://www.augustusmartin.com
Sales Range: $50-74.9 Million
Emp.: 500
Format Printing Services
N.A.I.C.S.: 323111
Lascelle Barrow (Co-Mng Dir)

AUGWIND ENERGY TECH STORAGE LTD.
Europark, PO Box 33, Yakum,
6097200, Israel
Tel.: (972) 93081210
Web Site: https://www.aug-wind.com
Year Founded: 2012
AUGN—(TAE)
Rev.: $594,328
Assets: $20,424,055
Liabilities: $4,411,908
Net Worth: $16,012,147
Earnings: ($7,193,753)
Fiscal Year-end: 06/30/23
Advanced Technology Services
N.A.I.C.S.: 811210
Seligsohn Gabriel (Chm)

AUJAN INDUSTRIES CO., L.L.C.
PO Box 990, Dammam, 31421, Saudi
Arabia
Tel.: (966) 38570777
Web Site: http://www.aujan.com
Year Founded: 1905
Sales Range: $150-199.9 Million
Emp.: 1,100
Beverages & Confectionery Products
N.A.I.C.S.: 311352
Adel Aujan (Chm)

Subsidiaries:

Ansari & Aujan Company L.L.C. (1)
PO Box 5721, Doha, Qatar
Tel.: (974) 4601 230
Beverage Mfr & Distr
N.A.I.C.S.: 312111
Prebaharen Jeevaretnam (Key Acct Mgr)

Rani Soft Drinks Private Ltd. (1)
402 Dev Plaza 4th Floor S V Road,
Andheri-West, Mumbai, 400058, Maharashtra, India
Tel.: (91) 22 26249783
Beverage Mfr & Distr
N.A.I.C.S.: 312111
Atanu Gangoly (Country Mgr)

Saud Aujan & Bros. Co. (1)
PO Box 29, Kuwait, Kuwait
Tel.: (965) 4336131
Sales Range: $75-99.9 Million
Emp.: 120
Food, Beverage & Cigarette Importer &
Distr
N.A.I.C.S.: 424820

AUKETT SWANKE GROUP PLC
10 Bonhill Street, London, EC2A
4PE, United Kingdom
Tel.: (44) 2078433000

Web Site:
https://www.aukettswanke.com
AUK—(AIM)
Rev.: $18,255,824
Assets: $18,968,743
Liabilities: $14,678,497
Net Worth: $4,290,246
Earnings: ($330,998)
Fiscal Year-end: 09/30/23
Professional & Management Services
N.A.I.C.S.: 541320
Suzette Vela Burkett (Mng Dir-UK
Practice)

Subsidiaries:

Anders + Kern (U.K.) Limited (1)
Norderstedt House James Carter Road,
Mildenhall, IP28 7RQ, Suffolk, United Kingdom
Tel.: (44) 1638510900
Web Site: http://www.anders-kern.co.uk
Audio Visual Equipment Distr
N.A.I.C.S.: 423690
Barrie Meehan (Mng Dir)

Aukett Fitzroy Robinson Limited (1)
Tel.: (44) 2076368033
Sales Range: $25-49.9 Million
Emp.: 90
Building Architectural Designing & Construction Services
N.A.I.C.S.: 236220

Aukett Fitzroy Robinson Sp.
z.o.o. (1)
Ul Emilii Plater 18, 00688, Warsaw, Poland
Tel.: (48) 223923350
Web Site: http://www.afr.com.pl
Sales Range: $25-49.9 Million
Emp.: 12
Architectural & Construction Services
N.A.I.C.S.: 541310

Aukett sro (1)
Janackovo Nabrezi 471/49, 150 00, Prague,
Czech Republic
Tel.: (420) 22 422 0025
Web Site: https://www.arch.cz
Sales Range: $25-49.9 Million
Emp.: 10
Building Architectural & Construction Services
N.A.I.C.S.: 541310

Shankland Cox Limited (1)
1301 Sidra Tower Sheikh Zayed Road, PO
Box 37133, 2nd Interchange Al Quoz,
Dubai, 37133, United Arab Emirates
Tel.: (971) 43380144
Web Site: https://shanklandcox.com
Building Architectural Services
N.A.I.C.S.: 541310

Swanke Hayden Connell Mimarlik
AS (1)
Kore Sehitleri 34/6 Deniz Is Hani, Zincirlikuyu, 34394, Istanbul, Turkiye
Tel.: (90) 212 318 0400
Web Site:
    https://www.turkey.aukettswanke.com
Landscape Architectural & Designing Services
N.A.I.C.S.: 541320
Burcu Senparlak (Gen Mgr)

Torpedo Factory Group Limited (1)
The Old Torpedo Factory St Leonard's
Road, London, NW10 6ST, United Kingdom
Tel.: (44) 2085371000
Web Site: https://www.tfg.com
System Design Services
N.A.I.C.S.: 541512

Veretec Limited (1)
10 Bonhill Street, London, EC2A 4PE,
United Kingdom
Tel.: (44) 2078433199
Web Site: https://veretec.co.uk
Sales Range: $25-49.9 Million
Emp.: 130
Architectural & Construction Design Services
N.A.I.C.S.: 541310

AUKING MINING LIMITED
Level 8 Waterfront Place 1 Eagle
Street, Brisbane, 4000, QLD, Australia
Tel.: (61) 735351208
Web Site:
    https://www.aukingmining.com
Year Founded: 1995
Rev.: $6,783
Assets: $407,852
Liabilities: $266,998
Net Worth: $140,854
Earnings: ($1,754,644)
Fiscal Year-end: 12/31/17
Mineral Exploration Services
N.A.I.C.S.: 212230
Paul Marshall (CFO & Sec)

AULBACH ENTGRATUNG-STECHNIK GMBH
Kreuzfeldring 5, 63820, Miltenberg,
Germany
Tel.: (49) 602220880
Web Site: http://www.aulbach-com.de
Rev.: $12,069,750
Emp.: 27
Industrial Machinery Mfr
N.A.I.C.S.: 333248
Walter Aulbach (Gen Mgr-Sls-Design)

AULD PHILLIPS LTD.
46199 Yale Road, Chilliwack, V2P
2P2, BC, Canada
Tel.: (604) 792-0158
Web Site: http://www.auldphillips.com
Year Founded: 1965
Rev.: $16,781,424
Emp.: 250
Women Clothing Distr
N.A.I.C.S.: 458110
Roderick A. Cooper (Pres)

AUMA RIESTER GMBH & CO. KG
Aumastr 1, 79379, Mullheim, Germany
Tel.: (49) 76318090
Web Site: https://www.auma.com
Year Founded: 1965
Sales Range: $250-299.9 Million
Emp.: 2,600
Electric Actuator & Valve Gearbox Mfr
N.A.I.C.S.: 332911
Jorg Hoffmann (Chm & Mng Dir)

Subsidiaries:

AUMA (Schweiz) AG (1)
Chorrenmattstrasse 43, 8965, Berikon,
Switzerland
Tel.: (41) 566400945
Actuator Distr
N.A.I.C.S.: 423610

AUMA ACTUATORS (Singapore) Pte
Ltd. (1)
Blk 5048 Ang Mo Kio Industrial Park 2 01 -
627, Singapore, 569551, Singapore
Tel.: (65) 64818750
Web Site: http://www.aumacom.sg
Actuator Distr
N.A.I.C.S.: 423610

AUMA ACTUATORS Ltd. (1)
Genration House Yeo Bank 3 Kenn Road,
North Somerset, Clevedon, BS21 6TH,
United Kingdom
Tel.: (44) 1275871141
Web Site: http://www.auma.co.uk
Actuator Distr
N.A.I.C.S.: 423610
Kerry Harris (Head-Sls)

AUMA Actuators (China) Co.,
Ltd. (1)
171 North Renmin Road, 215499, Taicang,
China
Tel.: (86) 51233026900
Web Site: http://www.auma-china.com
Actuator Distr
N.A.I.C.S.: 423610

AUMA Actuators (S) Pte. Ltd. (1)
38 Ang Mo Kio Industrial Park 2 01-07, Singapore, 569511, Singapore
Tel.: (65) 64818750
Electric Actuator Mfr
N.A.I.C.S.: 333995
Stefan Kolbe (Sls Dir-Asia Pacific)

AUMA BENELUX B.V. (1)
Le Pooleweg 9, 2314 XT, Leiden, Netherlands
Tel.: (31) 715814040
Web Site: http://www.auma.nl
Actuator Distr
N.A.I.C.S.: 423610

AUMA BENELUX B.V.BA. (1)
Kwadestraat 149, 8800, Roeselare, Belgium
Tel.: (32) 51242480
Web Site: http://www.auma.nl
Actuator Distr
N.A.I.C.S.: 423610

AUMA Endustri Kontrol Sistemleri
Limited Sirketi (1)
Yasamkent Mah 3207 Cad 3204 Sokak No
8, Cayyolu, 06810, Ankara, Turkiye
Tel.: (90) 3122173288
Actuator Distr
N.A.I.C.S.: 423610

AUMA Finland Oy (1)
Tiistinniityntie 2, 02230, Espoo, Finland
Tel.: (358) 9584022
Web Site: http://www.auma.fi
Actuator Distr
N.A.I.C.S.: 423610

AUMA France S.A.R.L. (1)
Z A C Les Chataigniers III - 10 Rue Constantin Pecqueur, 95157, Taverny, Cedex,
France
Tel.: (33) 139327272
Web Site: http://www.auma.fr
Actuator Distr
N.A.I.C.S.: 423610

AUMA INDIA PRIVATE LIMITED (1)
Plot No 38 A & 39 B II Phase Peenya Industrial Area, 560 058, Bengaluru, India
Tel.: (91) 8028394365
Web Site: http://www.auma.co.in
Actuator Distr
N.A.I.C.S.: 423610
Arvind Goel (Mng Dir)

AUMA ITALIANA S.r.l. (1)
Via delle Arnasche 6, Cerro Maggiore,
20023, Milan, Italy
Tel.: (39) 033151351
Web Site: http://www.auma.it
Actuator Distr
N.A.I.C.S.: 423610

AUMA JAPAN Co., Ltd. (1)
199 Ichinotsubo Nakaharaku, Kawasaki,
211-0016, Kanagawa, Japan
Tel.: (81) 448638371
Actuator Distr
N.A.I.C.S.: 423610

AUMA Mexico S. de R.L. de C.V. (1)
Col Anahuac I Seccion Del Miguel Hidalgo
Laguna de Terminos No 221, Floor 8 Office
B 603, 11320, Mexico, Mexico
Tel.: (52) 5525815516
Electric Actuator Mfr
N.A.I.C.S.: 333995

AUMA Polska Sp. Z o.o. (1)
ul Komuny Paryskiej 1 d, 41-219, Sosnowiec, Poland
Tel.: (48) 327835200
Web Site: http://www.auma.com.pl
Actuator Distr
N.A.I.C.S.: 423610

AUMA Servopohony spol. s.r.o. (1)
Boleslavska 1467, 250 01, Brandys had
Labem, Czech Republic
Tel.: (420) 326396993
Web Site: http://www.auma.cz
Actuator Distr
N.A.I.C.S.: 423610
Tomas Budka (Engr-Sls & Svc)

AUMA Technology Automations
Ltd (1)
Boripolskaya str 7, 02099, Kiev, Ukraine
Tel.: (380) 445865303
Actuator Distr
N.A.I.C.S.: 423610

AUMA-Armaturenantriebe Ges.m.b.H. **(1)**
Handelsstrasse 14, 2512, Tribuswinkel, Austria
Tel.: (43) 225282540
Web Site: http://www.auma.at
Actuator Distr
N.A.I.C.S.: 423610

AUMA-LUSA Representative Office, Lda. **(1)**
Rua D Joao II 8A-8B, 2730-061, Barcarena, Portugal
Tel.: (351) 211307100
Electric Actuator Mfr
N.A.I.C.S.: 333995

Auma Actuators Middle East WLL **(1)**
No 84 Business Bay Building No 1260 Block 324 Road 2421, PO Box 15268, Manama, Bahrain
Tel.: (973) 317896585
Actuator Distr
N.A.I.C.S.: 423610
Mohammed Al-Halwachi *(Engr-Svc)*

Auma Automacao do Brasil ltda. **(1)**
Rua Indochina 159 Jardim Fontana, Cotia, Sao Paulo, Brazil
Tel.: (55) 1146123477
Actuator Distr
N.A.I.C.S.: 423610
Bernardo Itzicovitch *(Mng Dir)*

Auma South Africa (Pty) Ltd. **(1)**
PO Box 1283, 1560, Springs, South Africa
Tel.: (27) 113632880
Actuator Distr
N.A.I.C.S.: 423610
Mark Majatovic *(Mgr-Sls & Mktg)*

Erichs Armatur AB **(1)**
Travbanegatan 8, PO Box 9144, Malmo, 21377, Sweden
Tel.: (46) 40 31 15 50
Web Site: http://www.auma.se
Emp.: 60
Valve & Actuator Mfr
N.A.I.C.S.: 332911
Ulf Elowsson *(Mng Dir)*

Fabo Kereskedelmi es Szolgaltato Kft. **(1)**
Recsei u 4, 8800, Nagykanizsa, Hungary
Tel.: (36) 93324666
Web Site: http://www.fabo.hu
Gearbox Mfr & Distr
N.A.I.C.S.: 333612

GFC AntriebsSysteme GmbH **(1)**
Grenzstrasse 5, Coswig, 1640, Germany
Tel.: (49) 3523 94 60
Web Site: http://www.gfc-antriebe.de
Gear Mfr
N.A.I.C.S.: 333612

Haselhofer Feinmechanik GmbH **(1)**
Eichendorffstrasse 42-48, 78054, Villingen-Schwenningen, Germany
Tel.: (49) 7720 8540 0
Web Site: http://www.haselhofer.de
Electric Actuator Mfr
N.A.I.C.S.: 335314

OOO AumaPrivodService **(1)**
Respubliki street 61 office 604, 625000, Tyumen, Russia
Tel.: (7) 3452696351
Actuator Distr
N.A.I.C.S.: 423610

OOO PRIWODY AUMA **(1)**
Stroitelny proezd 7a bldg 28 office 132-136, 125362, Moscow, Russia
Tel.: (7) 4957877821
Web Site: http://www.auma.com
Actuator Distr
N.A.I.C.S.: 423610
Alexandr Smirnov *(Engr-Sls)*

SIPOS Aktorik GmbH **(1)**
Im Erlet 2, 90518, Altdorf, Germany
Tel.: (49) 9187 9227 0
Web Site: http://www.sipos.de
Emp.: 90
Electric Actuator & Control System Mfr
N.A.I.C.S.: 335314
Thomas Suckut *(Mng Dir)*

AUMAKE LIMITED
Suite 1552 Level 15 60 Station Street East, Parramatta, 2150, NSW, Australia
Tel.: (61) 283308844   AU
Web Site:
   https://www.aumake.com.au
Year Founded: 2011
AUK—(ASX)
Rev.: $17,329,538
Assets: $2,914,863
Liabilities: $2,537,661
Net Worth: $377,202
Earnings: ($4,168,862)
Emp.: 80
Fiscal Year-end: 06/30/24
Consumer Products Distr
N.A.I.C.S.: 423620
Keong Chan *(Chm)*

Subsidiaries:

Jumbuck Australia Pty. Ltd. **(1)**
9 French Street CBD, Adelaide, 5000, SA, Australia
Tel.: (61) 881001600
Web Site: https://www.jumbuck.com.au
Emp.: 200
Farming Product Distr
N.A.I.C.S.: 424910

AUMEGA METALS LTD.
Emerald House 1202 Hay Street, West Perth, 6005, WA, Australia
Tel.: (61) 861170478   AU
Web Site: https://aumegametals.com
Year Founded: 2016
AAM—(ASX)
Rev.: $1,256,542
Assets: $37,591,234
Liabilities: $5,191,254
Net Worth: $32,399,981
Earnings: ($2,774,848)
Fiscal Year-end: 06/30/21
Mineral Exploration Services
N.A.I.C.S.: 213114
Ian Murray *(Chm)*

AUN CONSULTING, INC.
6F Kishimoto Building 2-2-1 Marunouchi, Chiyoda-ku, Tokyo, 100-0005, Japan
Tel.: (81) 570052459
Web Site: https://www.auncon.co.jp
Year Founded: 1998
2459—(TKS)
Rev.: $2,915,010
Assets: $6,299,330
Liabilities: $3,305,000
Net Worth: $2,994,330
Earnings: ($912,180)
Emp.: 26
Fiscal Year-end: 05/31/24
Information Technology Consulting Services
N.A.I.C.S.: 541512
Akira Shida *(Pres & CEO)*

Subsidiaries:

AUN Global Marketing Pte. Ltd. **(1)**
20th Floor One Marina Boulevard, Singapore, 18989, Singapore
Tel.: (65) 6 978 4042
Web Site: https://aun-singapore.com.sg
Information Technology Consulting Services
N.A.I.C.S.: 541512

AUN Hong Kong Marketing Co., Ltd. **(1)**
Rm 703 Unit F 7/F Block B Hop Hing Industrial Building, 704 Castle Peak Road, Kowloon, China (Hong Kong)
Tel.: (852) 2368 0528
Web Site: http://www.aun-hongkong.com.hk
Emp.: 6
Information Technology Consulting Services
N.A.I.C.S.: 541512
Akira Shida *(CEO)*

AUN Thai Laboratories Co., Ltd. **(1)**
Thaniya Building Suite no 1105 11th Floor

No 62 Silom Road, Suriyawongse Bangrak, Bangkok, 10500, Thailand
Tel.: (66) 2 652 5090
Web Site: https://www.aun-thai.co.th
Emp.: 17
Information Technology Consulting Services
N.A.I.C.S.: 541512
Akira Shida *(Pres & CEO)*

AUNA S.A.A.
Avenida Republica de Panama 3461, San Isidro, Lima, Peru
Tel.: (51) 12053500   Pe
Year Founded: 1989
Rev.: $413,760,527
Assets: $566,008,453
Liabilities: $392,785,590
Net Worth: $173,222,863
Earnings: $22,107,973
Emp.: 6,761
Fiscal Year-end: 12/31/19
Holding Company
N.A.I.C.S.: 551112
Jesus Zamora Leon *(Chm)*

AUNDE ACHTER & EBELS GMBH
Waldnieler Str 151, 41068, Monchengladbach, Germany
Tel.: (49) 21619350   De
Web Site:
   http://interimsseite.aundedata.de
Year Founded: 1982
Sales Range: $200-249.9 Million
Emp.: 257
Automotive Parts Mfr & Distr
N.A.I.C.S.: 811114
Rolf Konigs *(CEO & Chm)*

Subsidiaries:

AUNDE Brazil S.A. **(1)**
Rua Itapolis 85 - Vila Ibar, Poa, 08559-450, Sao Paulo, Brazil
Tel.: (55) 11 4634 7100
Web Site: http://www.aunde.com.br
Automobile Seat Cover Mfr & Distr
N.A.I.C.S.: 336360
Reginaldo Nogueira *(Acct Mgr)*

AUNDE Corporation **(1)**
3000 Town Ctr Ste 1385, Southfield, MI 48075
Tel.: (248) 358-0810
Emp.: 4
Automotive Parts Mfr & Distr
N.A.I.C.S.: 336390
Gerwald Meilen *(VP)*

AUNDE Kft **(1)**
Almos u 2, 5000, Szolnok, Hungary
Tel.: (36) 5 6 37 16 06
Web Site: http://www.aunde.hu
Automobile Parts Distr
N.A.I.C.S.: 423120
Peter Erzsebet *(Gen Mgr)*

AUNDE Kulmbach GmbH **(1)**
Vorwerkstrasse 4, 95326, Kulmbach, Germany
Tel.: (49) 92 21 508 0
Emp.: 30
Automobile Parts Mfr
N.A.I.C.S.: 336390
Karin Niechziol *(Office Mgr)*

AUNDE Mexico S.A. de C.V. **(1)**
Calle 2 Manzana C Lote 1 Parque Industrial San Miguel, Huejotzingo, 74169, Mexico
Tel.: (52) 227 275 99 00
Automobile Parts Distr
N.A.I.C.S.: 423120
Antonio Ruiz *(Mgr-Pur, Traffic & Customs)*

AUNDE Poland Sp. z o.o. **(1)**
ul Senatorska 70, Lodz, 93-192, Poland
Tel.: (48) 42 6808950
Web Site: http://www.aunde.pl
Automobile Parts Distr
N.A.I.C.S.: 423120

AUNDE S.A. **(1)**
Carrer Emporda s/n, Sant Celoni, 08470, Barcelona, Spain
Tel.: (34) 93 848 41 00
Web Site: http://www.aunde.es

Automobile Parts Mfr
N.A.I.C.S.: 336390
Amador Gonzalez Moreta *(CFO)*

Aunde France Sa **(1)**
41 Rue de Picardie, 02100, Saint-Quentin, France
Tel.: (33) 3 23 06 61 61
Web Site: http://www.aunde.fr
Emp.: 100
Automobile Parts Distr
N.A.I.C.S.: 423120
Karine Coulon *(Office Mgr)*

De Witte Lietaer International Textiles NV **(1)**
Koningin Astridlaan 48, Lauwe, 8930, Belgium   **(100%)**
Tel.: (32) 56430211
Web Site: http://www.dwl.be
Sales Range: $150-199.9 Million
Emp.: 85
Automotive Textiles Mfr
N.A.I.C.S.: 314999
Hubert Thaury *(Gen Mgr)*

Faze Three Autofab Limited **(1)**
63-64 C Wing Mitttal Court, Nriman Point, Mumbai, 400 021, India
Tel.: (91) 226 242 1313
Web Site: http://fazethreeautofab.com
Rev.: $18,408,390
Assets: $16,425,045
Liabilities: $11,422,320
Net Worth: $5,002,725
Earnings: $1,516,515
Fiscal Year-end: 03/31/2021
Automotive Fabric Mfr
N.A.I.C.S.: 332999
Ajay Anand *(Founder, Chm & Mng Dir)*

ISRINGHAUSEN GmbH & Co. KG **(1)**
Isringhausen-Ring 58, 32657, Lemgo, Germany
Tel.: (49) 52 61 2100
Web Site: http://www.isri.de
Automobile Parts Mfr
N.A.I.C.S.: 336390
Rolf Konigs *(Mng Dir)*

Subsidiary (Domestic):

ISRI GmbH **(2)**
Rather Strasse 51 Halle 301 2 OG, 40476, Dusseldorf, Germany
Tel.: (49) 2 11 169 759 0
Automotive Parts Mfr & Distr
N.A.I.C.S.: 336390
Eckart Warnke *(Gen Mgr)*

Subsidiary (Non-US):

ISRINGHAUSEN AB **(2)**
Magasinsgatan 2, Kungsbacka, 434 37, Sweden
Tel.: (46) 30 03 57 30
Automobile Parts Distr
N.A.I.C.S.: 423120

ISRINGHAUSEN Assentos, Lda. **(2)**
Zona Industrial Da Coelheira - Inst mitsubishi Truck Europe, 2205-697, Tramagal, Portugal
Tel.: (351) 241 890 706
Emp.: 5
Automobile Parts Distr
N.A.I.C.S.: 423120
Luis Senhora *(Gen Mgr)*

ISRINGHAUSEN B.V.B.A. **(2)**
Kaarderslaan 12, Lokeren, 9160, Belgium
Tel.: (32) 93485012
Emp.: 120
Automobile Parts Distr
N.A.I.C.S.: 423120
Rolf Konigs *(Gen Mgr)*

ISRINGHAUSEN Industrial Ltda. **(2)**
Rua Jacui 370 - Campanario, Diadema, Sao Paulo, 09930-280, Brazil
Tel.: (55) 11 4093 9304
Web Site: http://www.isri.com.br
Automobile Parts Mfr
N.A.I.C.S.: 336390

ISRINGHAUSEN Koltuk Sistemleri Ltd. **(2)**
Mustafa Kareer Cad Acelya Sk No 2, Dosab, Bursa, Turkiye
Tel.: (90) 224 219 00 30

AUNDE Achter & Ebels GmbH—(Continued)

Automobile Parts Distr
N.A.I.C.S.: 423120

**ISRINGHAUSEN Mexico S.A.de
C.V.** **(2)**
Calle Sierra del Paseo 851, 25300, Saltillo,
Coahuila, Mexico
Tel.: (52) 844 450 3200
Automobile Parts Distr
N.A.I.C.S.: 423120
Enrique Sastre *(Mgr-Plant)*

**ISRINGHAUSEN OTO YAN SANAYI,
YEDEK PARCA ve KOLTUK
SISTEMLERI SANAYI VE TICARET
A.S.**
Demirtas Organize Sanayi Bolgesi Acelya
Sk No 2, Osmangazi, Bursa, Turkiye
Tel.: (90) 2242 19 00 30
Web Site: http://www.isri.com.tr
Automobile Parts Distr
N.A.I.C.S.: 423120

ISRINGHAUSEN Pty. Ltd. **(2)**
510 Victoria Street, Wetherill Park, 2164,
NSW, Australia
Tel.: (61) 2 9756 6199
Web Site: http://www.isri.com.au
Automobile Parts Distr
N.A.I.C.S.: 423120

**ISRINGHAUSEN Queretaro S.A. de
C.V.** **(2)**
Avenida Las Misiones 23 Fracc Ind Ber-
nardo Quintana, 76240, El Marques, Quere-
taro, Mexico
Tel.: (52) 442 221 5123
Web Site:
http://www.eseestebanmex.com.mx
Automobile Parts Mfr
N.A.I.C.S.: 336390
Federico Arreaga *(Gen Mgr)*

ISRINGHAUSEN S.A. **(2)**
Avenida Aragon 402, 28022, Madrid, Spain
Tel.: (34) 917462510
Automobile Parts Distr
N.A.I.C.S.: 423120

ISRINGHAUSEN S.p.A. **(2)**
Via Nibbia 2/4, San Pietro Mosezzo Fraz
Nibbia, 28060, Novara, Italy
Tel.: (39) 0321 486100
Automobile Parts Distr
N.A.I.C.S.: 423120

ISRINGHAUSEN Spain S.L.U. **(2)**
Pol Industrial Landaben C/L, Navarra,
31012, Pamplona, Spain
Tel.: (34) 948 286 030
Web Site: http://www.isri.es
Emp.: 100
Automotive Parts Mfr & Distr
N.A.I.C.S.: 336390
Juan Cordova *(Gen Mgr)*

ISRINGHAUSEN Umea AB **(2)**
Larlingsgatan 10, 904 22, Umea, Sweden
Tel.: (46) 90 71 51 60
Automobile Parts Distr
N.A.I.C.S.: 423120

**ISRINGHAUSEN of South Africa (Pty)
Ltd.** **(2)**
14 Napier Road Settlers Heights, East Lon-
don, Eastern Cape, South Africa
Tel.: (27) 43 736 3545
Web Site: http://www.isri.co.za
Automotive Parts Mfr & Distr
N.A.I.C.S.: 336390

Subsidiary (US):

ISRINGHAUSEN, Inc. **(2)**
1458 S 35th st, Galesburg, MI 49053
Tel.: (269) 484-5333
Web Site: http://www.isringhausen.com
Automobile Parts Mfr
N.A.I.C.S.: 336390
Gary Slater *(Gen Mgr-Key Account- Truck)*

AUO CORPORATION
No 1 Li-Hsin Rd 2, Hsinchu Science
Park, Hsin-chu, Taiwan
Tel.: (886) 35008800 **TW**
Web Site: https://www.auo.com
Year Founded: 1996

AUOTY—(OTCIQ)
Rev.: $8,177,125,366
Assets: $12,540,329,066
Liabilities: $7,132,777,159
Net Worth: $5,407,551,907
Earnings: ($593,582,305)
Emp.: 54,645
Fiscal Year-end: 12/31/23
Display Panels Mfr & Developer
N.A.I.C.S.: 334413
Andy Yang *(VP-Strategic Investment
& New Bus Ops)*

Subsidiaries:

AFPD Pte., Ltd. **(1)**
10 Tampines Industrial Avenue 3, Singa-
pore, 528798, Singapore
Tel.: (65) 64249888
Web Site: http://www.afpd.com.sg
Electronic Components Mfr
N.A.I.C.S.: 334419

**AU Optronics (Shanghai) Co.,
Ltd.** **(1)**
No 3 Ln 58 San Zhuang Rd Songjiang Ex-
port Processing Zone, Shanghai, 201613,
China
Tel.: (86) 21 3781 8800
Electronic Components Mfr
N.A.I.C.S.: 334419

AU Optronics (Slovakia) s.r.o. **(1)**
Bratislavska 517, 911 05, Trencin, Slovakia
Tel.: (421) 326578800
Web Site: http://www.auo.com
Liquid Crystal Display Panel Mfr
N.A.I.C.S.: 334419

**AU Optronics Corporation
America** **(1)**
9720 Cypresswood Dr. Ste 241, Houston,
TX 77070
Tel.: (281) 807-2630
Web Site: http://auo.com
Sales Range: $50-74.9 Million
Emp.: 5
Plasma Display Panels (PDP) & TFT LCD
Modules Sales
N.A.I.C.S.: 423690

AU Optronics Corporation Japan **(1)**
Web Site: http://www.auo.com
Sales Range: $25-49.9 Million
Emp.: 25
Electric Appliances Mfr
N.A.I.C.S.: 335220

AU Optronics Europe B.V. **(1)**
Zekeringstraat 39, 1014 BV, Amsterdam,
Netherlands
Tel.: (31) 207940825
Sales Range: $25-49.9 Million
Emp.: 15
Plasma Display Panels (PDP) & TFT LCD
Modules Sales
N.A.I.C.S.: 423690

AU Optronics Korea Ltd. **(1)**
3F MJL B/D 204 5 Non Hyeon 1 Dong,
GangNam-Gu, Seoul, 135-011, Korea
(South)
Tel.: (82) 2 515 8092
Electronic Components Mfr
N.A.I.C.S.: 334419

**AU Optronics Manufacturing (Shang-
hai) Corp.** **(1)**
No 3 Lane 58 Sanzhuang Rd Export Pro-
cessing Zone, Songjiang, Shanghai, China
Tel.: (86) 2137818800
Electronic Components Mfr
N.A.I.C.S.: 334419

**AUO Green Energy America
Corp.** **(1)**
1525 McCarthy Blvd Ste 218, Milpitas, CA
95035
Tel.: (408) 518-8800
Web Site: http://www.auo.com
Emp.: 14
Electronic Components Mfr
N.A.I.C.S.: 334419

AUO Green Energy Europe B.V. **(1)**
Zekeringstraat 39, 1014 BV, Amsterdam,
Netherlands
Tel.: (31) 207940825
Electronic Components Mfr

N.A.I.C.S.: 334419

Behr-Hella Thermocontrol GmbH **(1)**
Hansastrasse 40, 59557, Lippstadt,
Germany **(100%)**
Tel.: (49) 2941666000
Web Site: http://www.bhtcgroup.de
Automobiles

ComQi Inc. **(1)**
134 W 26th St Ste 900, New York, NY
10001
Tel.: (347) 276-7931
Construction Contracting Services
N.A.I.C.S.: 236220

**Darwin Precisions (Suzhou)
Corp.** **(1)**
No 11 Tingxin Street Suzhou Industry Zone,
Suzhou, China
Tel.: (86) 51262758800
Electronic Components Mfr
N.A.I.C.S.: 334419

**Darwin Precisions (Xiamen)
Corp.** **(1)**
No 3089 Xiangan North Road TorchHigh-
Tech Industrial Development Zone, Xiangan
District, Xiamen, 361102, Fujian, China
Tel.: (86) 5927168800
Electronic Components Mfr
N.A.I.C.S.: 334419

M.Setek Co., Ltd. **(1)**
Shinagawa East One Tower 14F 2-16-1 Ko-
nan, Minato-ku, Tokyo, 108-0075, Japan
Tel.: (81) 3 3474 8800
Web Site: http://www.msetek.com
Sales Range: $200-249.9 Million
Emp.: 718
Polysilicon & Single Crystal Silicon Wafer
Mfr
N.A.I.C.S.: 334413

AUPLATA SAS
Zone Industrielle de Degrad des
Cannes-Immeuble Simeg Remire-
Montjoly, 97354, Paris, France
Tel.: (33) 0172748187
Web Site:
https://auplataminggroup.com
Rev.: $5,956,958
Assets: $133,197,241
Liabilities: $54,603,250
Net Worth: $78,593,990
Earnings: ($14,485,721)
Emp.: 58
Fiscal Year-end: 12/31/17
Gold Mining Services
N.A.I.C.S.: 212220
Luc Gerard Nyafe *(Chm)*

Subsidiaries:

Brexia GoldPlata Peru S.A.C. **(1)**
Av Alfredo Benavides Nro 1555 Int 403,
Lima, Peru
Tel.: (51) 16355321
Web Site: http://www.brexia.pe
Mineral & Mining Services
N.A.I.C.S.: 212290
Fernando Valdez *(Country Mgr)*

AUPU HOME STYLE CORPO-
RATION LTD.
No 210 No 21 Street, Economic &
Technological Development Zone,
Hangzhou, 310018, Zhejiang, China
Tel.: (86) 57188177925
Web Site: http://www.aupu.net
Year Founded: 2004
603551—(SHG)
Rev.: $263,983,000
Assets: $337,474,861
Liabilities: $114,734,894
Net Worth: $222,739,967
Earnings: $33,709,282
Emp.: 800
Fiscal Year-end: 12/31/22
Household Appliance Mfr & Distr
N.A.I.C.S.: 335220
James Fang *(Chm)*

AUQ GOLD MINING INC.

United Kingdom Bldg 409 Granville
St, Vancouver, V6C 1T2, BC, Canada
Tel.: (604) 719-8129
Web Site: https://www.auqgold.com
NSVLF—(OTCIQ)
Assets: $608,206
Liabilities: $787,168
Net Worth: ($178,962)
Earnings: ($777,307)
Fiscal Year-end: 02/29/24
Mineral Exploration Services
N.A.I.C.S.: 213114
Glen MacDonald *(CEO)*

AURA ENERGY LIMITED
Level 30 35 Collins Street, Mel-
bourne, 3000, VIC, Australia
Tel.: (61) 391018551
Web Site:
https://www.auraenergy.com.au
AURA—(AIM)
Rev.: $70,870
Assets: $26,746,832
Liabilities: $991,777
Net Worth: $25,755,055
Earnings: ($2,607,951)
Emp.: 3
Fiscal Year-end: 06/30/22
Uranium Exploring
N.A.I.C.S.: 212290
Peter D. Reeve *(Chm)*

AURA INVESTMENTS LTD.
132 Menachem Begin Road Azrieli
Center Triangle Tower, Tel Aviv,
6701101, Israel
Tel.: (972) 37181910
Web Site: https://www.auraisrael.co.il
Year Founded: 1992
AURA—(TAE)
Rev.: $287,296,860
Assets: $868,109,946
Liabilities: $619,455,993
Net Worth: $248,653,954
Earnings: $32,696,228
Emp.: 3
Fiscal Year-end: 12/31/23
Miscellaneous Financial Investment
Activities
N.A.I.C.S.: 523999

AURA OSIGURANJE A.D.
Veljka Mladenovica 7d, 78000, Banja
Luka, Bosnia & Herzegovina
Tel.: (387) 51 490 490
Web Site:
http://www.auraosiguranje.com
Year Founded: 2007
AURO—(BANJ)
Sales Range: Less than $1 Million
General Insurance Services
N.A.I.C.S.: 524210

AURA RENEWABLE ACQUISI-
TIONS PLC
Holborn Gate 330 High Holborn, Lon-
don, WC1V 7QH, United KingdomUK
Web Site:
https://www.aurarenewables.com
Year Founded: 2021
ARA—(LSE)
Investment Management Service
N.A.I.C.S.: 523999

AURANGABAD DISTILLERY
LIMITED
Walchandnagar, Tal Indapur, Pune,
413114, Maharashtra, India
Tel.: (91) 2118252407
Web Site:
https://www.aurangabaddistillery.com
Year Founded: 2000
AURDIS—(NSE)
Rev.: $14,662,442
Assets: $19,274,120
Liabilities: $11,304,346

Net Worth: $7,969,774
Earnings: $2,009,676
Emp.: 55
Fiscal Year-end: 03/31/23
Distilleries Mfr
N.A.I.C.S.: 312140
Dharampal Kalani *(Chm & Mng Dir)*

AURANIA RESOURCES LTD.

36 Toronto Street Suite 1050, Toronto, M5C 1B5, ON, Canada
Tel.: (416) 367-3200   BM
Web Site: https://www.aurania.com
Year Founded: 2007
ARU—(TSXV)
Rev.: $2,912
Assets: $536,138
Liabilities: $8,217,474
Net Worth: ($7,681,336)
Earnings: ($7,529,672)
Emp.: 15
Fiscal Year-end: 12/31/23
Gold, Uranium & Copper Mining
N.A.I.C.S.: 212220
Jean Paul Pallier *(VP-Exploration)*

Subsidiaries:

AuroVallis Sarl   **(1)**
Chemin de Champlan 32 1997 Haute-Nendaz, 1997, Haute-Nendaz, Switzerland
Tel.: (41) 272883256
Mineral Exploration Services
N.A.I.C.S.: 213114

AURAS TECHNOLOLGY CO., LTD.

242 Taiwan, Xinzhuang District, New Taipei City, 24891, Taiwan
Tel.: (886) 289901653
Web Site: https://www.auras.com.tw
Year Founded: 1998
3324—(TPE)
Rev.: $433,261,139
Assets: $367,155,708
Liabilities: $185,511,397
Net Worth: $181,644,311
Earnings: $40,229,653
Emp.: 795
Fiscal Year-end: 12/31/22
Computer Component Mfr & Distr
N.A.I.C.S.: 334118
Yu-Shen Lin *(Chm & Pres)*

AURCANA SILVER CORPORATION

2751 Graham Street, Victoria, V8T 3Z1, BC, Canada
Tel.: (604) 331-9333
Web Site: https://www.aurcana.com
AUN—(TSXV)
Rev.: $475,234
Assets: $119,401,708
Liabilities: $45,310,748
Net Worth: $74,090,960
Earnings: ($35,454,268)
Fiscal Year-end: 12/31/21
Mining Exploration Services
N.A.I.C.S.: 212290
Donna M. Moroney *(Sec)*

Subsidiaries:

Ouray Silver Mines, Inc.   **(1)**
1900 Main St Unit 1, Ouray, CO 81427
Tel.: (970) 325-9830
Web Site: http://www.ouraysilvermines.com
Silver Mining Services
N.A.I.C.S.: 212220
Brian Briggs *(CEO)*

AUREA, S.A.

3 avenue Bertie Albrecht, F-75008, Paris, France
Tel.: (33) 153838545   FR
Web Site: https://www.aurea-france.com
Year Founded: 1988
AURE—(EUR)

Sales Range: $200-249.9 Million
Emp.: 277
Holding Company; Waste Motor Oil, Polyvinyl Chloride & Worn Tire Processing & Recycling Services; Water Decontamination Services
N.A.I.C.S.: 551112
Joel Picard *(Chm & Dir Gen)*

Subsidiaries:

Aluminium Regeal Affimet   **(1)**
Avenue du Vermandois, PO Box 80419, 60204, Compiegne, France   **(100%)**
Tel.: (33) 344238200
Web Site: http://www.recovco.fr
Sales Range: $100-124.9 Million
Emp.: 100
Aluminum Reprocessing Services
N.A.I.C.S.: 331314

Broplast S.A.R.L   **(1)**
Za Pierre Fondelle Route De Perignat, BP 7, 1580, Izernore, Ain, France
Tel.: (33) 474 49 10 37
Web Site: http://www.broplast.com
Sales Range: $25-49.9 Million
Emp.: 25
Thermoplastic Recycling Services
N.A.I.C.S.: 325612
Alexandre Bernardin *(Gen Mgr)*

Compagnie Francaise Eco Huile S.A.   **(1)**
3 avenue Bertie Albrecht, F-78008, Paris, France   **(100%)**
Tel.: (33) 153838555
Web Site: http://www.aurea.com
Waste Motor Oil Processing & Recycling Services
N.A.I.C.S.: 562920

Eco Huile SA   **(1)**
Zone Industrielle Avenue De Port Jerome, Lillebonne, 76170, Seine Maritime, France   **(100%)**
Tel.: (33) 235395847
Motor Oil Recycling Services
N.A.I.C.S.: 324110
Lett Richard *(Pres)*

Flaurea Chemicals S.A.   **(1)**
12 Quai des Usines, B-7800, Ath, Belgium
Tel.: (32) 68281912
Web Site: http://www.flaureachemicals.com
Chemical Products & Metal Salts Mfr
N.A.I.C.S.: 325998
Robert Van Quickelberghe *(Mgr-Pur Dept)*

M Lego   **(1)**
Rue du Cuivre, 72400, Boesse le Sec, Cedex, France
Tel.: (33) 2 43 60 60 65
Web Site: http://www.m-lego.com
Sales Range: $25-49.9 Million
Emp.: 100
Alloy Mfr
N.A.I.C.S.: 331110
Romary Sertelet *(Gen Mgr)*

Roll-Gom S.A.   **(1)**
Rue Laennec, F-62217, Tilloy-les-Mofflaines, France   **(100%)**
Tel.: (33) 321249495
Web Site: http://www.roll-gom.com
Sales Range: $25-49.9 Million
Emp.: 95
Worn Tires Processing & Recycling Services
N.A.I.C.S.: 562920
Richard Lett *(Mng Dir)*

Rulo N.V.   **(1)**
Chaussee d'Audenarde 82, BE-7742, Herinnes, Belgium   **(80%)**
Tel.: (32) 69559371
Web Site: http://www.rulo.be
Sales Range: $25-49.9 Million
Emp.: 2
Polyvinyl Chloride & Other Plastic Material Recycling Services
N.A.I.C.S.: 562920

AURELIA METALS LTD

Tel.: (61) 731805000   AU
Web Site: https://aureliametals.com
Year Founded: 2009

AMI—(ASX)
Rev.: $206,926,616
Assets: $315,518,502
Liabilities: $103,945,750
Net Worth: $211,572,751
Earnings: ($3,828,821)
Emp.: 322
Fiscal Year-end: 06/30/24
Gold & Copper Mining
N.A.I.C.S.: 212220
Angus Wyllie *(Gen Mgr-Cobar Region)*

Subsidiaries:

Dargues Gold Mines Pty. Ltd.   **(1)**
920 Majors Creek Road, Majors Creek, 2622, NSW, Australia
Tel.: (61) 1800732002
Gold & Base Metals Mining Services
N.A.I.C.S.: 213114

AURELIUS EQUITY OPPORTUNITIES SE & CO. KGAA

Ludwig-Ganghofer-Strasse 6, 82031, Grunwald, Germany
Tel.: (49) 895447990   De
Web Site: https://www.aurelius-group.com
AR4—(DEU)
Rev.: $3,145,276,992
Assets: $2,801,861,088
Liabilities: $2,074,128,888
Net Worth: $727,732,200
Earnings: $186,446,832
Emp.: 12,094
Fiscal Year-end: 12/31/21
Privater Equity Firm
N.A.I.C.S.: 523999
Dirk Markus *(Chm)*

Subsidiaries:

Armstrong Metalldecken GmbH   **(1)**
Bundesstrasse 70, 6830, Rankweil, Austria
Tel.: (43) 552234440
Sales Range: $50-74.9 Million
Metal Ceiling Systems Mfr & Distr
N.A.I.C.S.: 332311

Armstrong World Industries Ltd.   **(1)**
Harman House 1 George St, Uxbridge, UB8 1QQ, Mddx, United Kingdom
Tel.: (44) 800371849
Sales Range: $125-149.9 Million
Emp.: 40
Ceiling Tile & Systems Mfr & Distr
N.A.I.C.S.: 327999

Aurelius Active Management Holding GmbH   **(1)**
Ludwig-Ganghofer-Street 6, Grunwald, 82031, Germany
Tel.: (49) 895447990
Web Site: http://www.aureliusinvest.de
Investment Management Service
N.A.I.C.S.: 523999

Aurelius Alpha Limited   **(1)**
6th Floor 33 Glasshouse Street, London, W1B 5DG, United Kingdom
Tel.: (44) 20 7440 0480
Web Site: http://www.aureliusinvest.co.uk
Investment Services
N.A.I.C.S.: 523999
Tristan Nagler *(Mng Dir)*

Aurelius Beteiligungsberatungs AG   **(1)**
Unterer Anger 3, Munich, 80331, Germany
Tel.: (49) 895447990
Investment Management Consulting Services
N.A.I.C.S.: 541618

Aurelius Commercial Beteiligungs GmbH   **(1)**
Ludwig-Ganghofer-Str 6, Grunwald, 82031, Germany
Tel.: (49) 89 5447990
Consumer Goods Distr
N.A.I.C.S.: 424990

Aurelius Finance Company Ltd.   **(1)**
6th Floor 33 Glasshouse Street, London, W1B 5DG, United Kingdom

Tel.: (44) 2074400480
Capital Investment Services
N.A.I.C.S.: 523940
Karun Dhir *(Mng Dir)*

Aurelius Nederland B.V.   **(1)**
Parnassusweg 819, 1082 LZ, Amsterdam, Netherlands
Tel.: (31) 208546468
Capital Investment Services
N.A.I.C.S.: 523940
Gilles Van Kooten *(Principal & Head)*

Aurelius Nordics AB   **(1)**
Sturegatan 34, 114 36, Stockholm, Sweden
Tel.: (46) 844683596
Capital Investment Services
N.A.I.C.S.: 523940

Aurelius Transaktionsberatungs AG   **(1)**
Unterer Anger 3, Munich, 80331, Germany
Tel.: (49) 89 5447990
Investment Advisory Services
N.A.I.C.S.: 523940

BCA Beteiligungs GmbH   **(1)**
Ludwig-Ganghofer-Str 6, Grunwald, 82031, Germany
Tel.: (49) 895447990
Human Resource Consulting Services
N.A.I.C.S.: 541612

BPG Building Partners Group GmbH   **(1)**
Industriestrasse 4, Wandlitz District Schonerlinde, 16348, Brandenburg, Germany
Tel.: (49) 3094030322
Web Site: http://www.buildingpartners.de
Construction Scaffolding Services
N.A.I.C.S.: 238990

Subsidiary (Domestic):

B+P Gerustbau GmbH   **(2)**
Industriestrasse 4 OT, Wandlitz Schonerlinde, 16348, Brandenburg, Germany
Tel.: (49) 309403030
Scaffolding Services
N.A.I.C.S.: 238990

Subsidiary (Domestic):

B+P Gerustbau Hamburg GmbH   **(3)**
Bosteler Feld 3, 21218, Seevetal, Germany
Tel.: (49) 41058699690
Scaffolding Services
N.A.I.C.S.: 238990

BSB Bau- und Spezialgerustbau GmbH   **(1)**
Industriering 4, 04626, Schmolln, Germany
Tel.: (49) 344913220
Construction Scaffolding Services
N.A.I.C.S.: 238990

BT Fleet Limited   **(1)**
Unit 4520 Sollihill Parkway Birmingham Business Park, Solihull, B37 7YN, United Kingdom
Tel.: (44) 800 028 4387
Web Site: http://www.btfleet.com
Sales Range: $250-299.9 Million
Emp.: 950
Fleet Management Services
N.A.I.C.S.: 561499

Bertram Group Ltd.   **(1)**
1 Broadland Business Park, Norwich, NR7 0WF, United Kingdom
Tel.: (44) 1603648400
Web Site: http://www.bertramgroup.co.uk
Book Whslr & Retailer
N.A.I.C.S.: 424920
Frances Staton *(Mgr-Category)*

Blaupunkt International GmbH & Co. KG   **(1)**
Robert Bosch Strasse 200, 31139, Hildesheim, Germany
Tel.: (49) 512199810
Web Site: http://www.blaupunkt.de
Sales Range: $250-299.9 Million
Car Radios, Traffic Warning & Routing Systems Mfr
N.A.I.C.S.: 334220

Subsidiary (Domestic):

Blaupunkt AudioVision GmbH & Co. KG   **(2)**

Aurelius Equity Opportunities SE & Co. KGaA—(Continued)

Robert-Bosch-Str 200, 31139, Hildesheim, Germany
Tel.: (49) 5121 9981 0
Web Site: http://www.blaupunkt.de
Automotive Audio System Mfr
N.A.I.C.S.: 334310

Blaupunkt Car Audio Systems GmbH & Co. KG (2)
Robert-Bosch-Str 200, Hildesheim, 31139, Germany
Tel.: (49) 5121 99810
Car Audio System Mfr
N.A.I.C.S.: 334310

Blaupunkt International Services AG (2)
Robert-Bosch-Str 200, Hildesheim, Germany
Tel.: (49) 5121 99810
Business Management Consulting Services
N.A.I.C.S.: 541611

CalaChem Ltd. (1)
Earls Rd, Grangemouth, FK3 8XG, United Kingdom
Tel.: (44) 1324 498 300
Web Site: http://www.calachem.com
Sales Range: $50-74.9 Million
Emp.: 20
Specialty Chemicals Mfr
N.A.I.C.S.: 325180
Ian C. Brown (Head-Ops)

Calumet Photographic Ltd. (1)
Promandis House Bradbourne Drive, Tilbrook, Milton Keynes, MK7 8AJ, United Kingdom
Tel.: (44) 1908 366 344
Web Site: http://www.calphoto.co.uk
Photographic Equipment Retailer
N.A.I.C.S.: 449210
Jonathan Maisey (Acct Mgr-Police Sls & Support)

Subsidiary (Domestic):

Bowens International Ltd. (2)
Unit 6 Gilberd Court, Colchester, CO4 9WN, Essex, United Kingdom (100%)
Tel.: (44) 1206 832650
Web Site: http://www.bowens.co.uk
Photographic Equipment Mfr
N.A.I.C.S.: 335139

Subsidiary (Non-US):

Calumet Photographic BV (2)
Keienbergweg 13, 1101 EZ, Amsterdam, Netherlands
Tel.: (31) 205640700
Web Site: http://www.calumetphoto.nl
Photographic Product Mfr
N.A.I.C.S.: 333310
Bart Kuijpers Wentink (Branch Mgr)

Calumet Photographic GmbH (2)
Bahrenfelder Strasse 260, 22765, Hamburg, Germany
Tel.: (49) 404231600
Web Site: http://www.calumetphoto.de
Photographic Product Mfr
N.A.I.C.S.: 333310
Stefan Schreck (Mktg Mgr)

Conaxess Trade Austria GmbH (1)
Ared Strasse 29/2/223, 2544, Leobersdorf, Austria
Tel.: (43) 225662099
Food & Confectionery Product Distr
N.A.I.C.S.: 424490
Alice Stockinger (CFO)

Conaxess Trade Sweden AB (1)
Lofstroms Alle 5, 172 66, Sundbyberg, Sweden
Tel.: (46) 87251400
Food & Confectionery Product Distr
N.A.I.C.S.: 424490
Irene Skogster (Mgr-HR)

Conaxess Trade Switzerland AG (1)
Industriestrasse 9, 4623, Neuendorf, Switzerland
Tel.: (41) 625313700
Emp.: 80
Food & Confectionery Product Distr
N.A.I.C.S.: 424490

Ursula Hinden (Head-HR)

Create & Craft Ltd. (1)
Ideal Home House Newark Road, Peterborough, PE1 5WG, United Kingdom
Tel.: (44) 8717123455
Web Site: http://www.createandcraft.com
Craft Product Retailer
N.A.I.C.S.: 459999

DFA - Transport und Logistik GmbH (1)
Brunnenstrasse 82, 07580, Ronneburg, Germany
Tel.: (49) 3660239910
Web Site: http://www.dfa-logistik.de
Sales Range: $25-49.9 Million
Emp.: 200
Hazardous Waste Transport Services
N.A.I.C.S.: 562211
Michael Hulm (Owner)

Dawson France SAS (1)
3 rue Galvani, 91745, Massy, Cedex, France
Tel.: (33) 169192150
Web Site: http://www.dawson.fr
Book Distr
N.A.I.C.S.: 424920

Education Umbrella Ltd. (1)
Ashton Road, Beckford, Tewkesbury, GL20 7AU, Gloucestershire, United Kingdom
Tel.: (44) 1242604408
Web Site:
    http://www.educationumbrella.com
Book Distr & Retailer
N.A.I.C.S.: 424920

Erasmus Antiquariaat en Boekhandel B.V. (1)
Veemarkt 207, 1019 CJ, Amsterdam, Netherlands
Tel.: (31) 205353433
Web Site: http://www.erasmusbooks.nl
Book Distr
N.A.I.C.S.: 424920
Joleen McFarlane (Reg Sls Mgr)

Fixation UK Ltd. (1)
Unit C 250 Kennington Lane, London, SE11 5RD, United Kingdom
Tel.: (44) 2075823294
Web Site: http://www.fixationuk.com
Camera & Photographic Product Repair Services & Retailer
N.A.I.C.S.: 811210
Melanie Stanton (Mgr-Svc Support)

Footasylum PLC (1)
Sandbrook House Sandbrook Park, Rochdale, OL11 1RY, United Kingdom
Tel.: (44) 1706714299
Web Site: http://www.footasylum.com
Sportswear Retailer
N.A.I.C.S.: 459110
Barry Bown (Chm)

Foto-Video Sauter GmbH & Co. KG (1)
Sonnenstrasse 26, 80331, Munich, Germany
Tel.: (49) 895515040
Web Site: http://www.foto-video-sauter.de
Camera & Related Product Retailer
N.A.I.C.S.: 449210

GIP Development SARL (1)
2-4 rue du Chateau d Eau, 3364, Leudelange, Luxembourg
Tel.: (352) 27768340
Web Site: http://www.gip-development.net
Intellectual Property Investment & Management Services
N.A.I.C.S.: 523999
Andrzej Cebrat (Mgr)

GTM Development Ltd. (1)
16 Fitzwilliam Street Upper, Dublin, D02 Y221, Ireland
Tel.: (353) 15252443
Web Site: http://www.gtmdevelopment.ie
Intellectual Property Management Services
N.A.I.C.S.: 541199

Getronics Global Services BV (1)
Gustav Mahlerplein 23A Symphony Building - 5th Floor, 1082 MS, Amsterdam, Netherlands
Tel.: (31) 707 703950

Web Site: http://www.getronics.com
Information Systems; Communications Services
N.A.I.C.S.: 519290
Christian Schmehl (Chief Transformation Officer)

Subsidiary (Non-US):

Connectis ICT Services S.A.U. (2)
Parque Empresarial Cristalia calle Via de los Poblados 3, Edificio 5 plantas 5 y 6, 28033, Madrid, Spain (100%)
Tel.: (34) 913 827 500
Web Site: http://www.connectis.es
Sales Range: $75-99.9 Million
Emp.: 500
IT Consultancy, Outsourcing & Technical Services
N.A.I.C.S.: 541512
Graham T. Johnson (Mng Dir)

Subsidiary (Non-US):

Connectis ICT Services S.A. (3)
Bulnes 2756 Piso 5, Buenos Aires, C1425 DKX, Argentina (100%)
Tel.: (54) 11 5556 5100
Web Site: http://www.connectis-ict.com.ar
Sales Range: $25-49.9 Million
Emp.: 155
IT Consultancy, Outsourcing & Technical Services
N.A.I.C.S.: 541512

Subsidiary (Non-US):

Getronics (Schweiz) AG (2)
Industriestrasse 50a, 8304, Wallisellen, Switzerland
Tel.: (41) 58 301 12 12
Web Site: http://www.connectis.ch
Sales Range: $25-49.9 Million
Emp.: 12
Information Technology Consulting Services
N.A.I.C.S.: 541512
Kurt Bylang (Gen Mgr)

Getronics (UK) Limited (2)
200 Brook Drive Green Park, Reading, RG2 6UB, Berkshire, United Kingdom
Tel.: (44) 870 906 8000
Web Site: http://www.getronics.com
Sales Range: $25-49.9 Million
Emp.: 100
Information Technology & Business Communications Services
N.A.I.C.S.: 561499

Getronics Deutschland GmbH (2)
Robert-Bosch-Strasse 13, 64293, Darmstadt, Germany
Tel.: (49) 6151 1370 0
Web Site: http://www.getronics.de
Information Technology Consulting Services
N.A.I.C.S.: 541512
Thomas Brenneis (Gen Mgr)

Getronics Hungary Kft (2)
Henger u 2/B, Budapest, 1027, Hungary
Tel.: (36) 1 371 7500
Information Technology Consulting Services
N.A.I.C.S.: 541512

Getronics Solutions (S) Pte Ltd (2)
20 Anson Road 07-03/04, Twenty Anson, Singapore, 79912, Singapore
Tel.: (65) 6890 2828
Sales Range: $25-49.9 Million
Emp.: 160
System Integration & Consulting Services
N.A.I.C.S.: 541512
John Maloch (Mng Dir-Asia Pacific)

Subsidiary (US):

Pomeroy IT Solutions Sales Company, Inc. (2)
1020 Petersburg Rd, Hebron, KY 41048-8222
Tel.: (859) 586-0600
Web Site: http://www.pomeroy.com
Hardware, Software, Technical Staffing, Computer Infrastructure & Lifecycle Services
N.A.I.C.S.: 541512
Kristi Nelson (Chief Admin Officer & Gen Counsel)

Gustav Raetz Gerustbau GmbH (1)

Lerchenstrasse 16, 80995, Munich, Germany
Tel.: (49) 893515511
Construction Scaffolding Services
N.A.I.C.S.: 238990

H&F Shoes (Thailand) Co., Ltd. (1)
159/35 Sermmit Tower Building Floor 21 Sukhumvit 21 Asoke Road, Khlong Toei Nuea Wattana, Bangkok, 10110, Thailand
Tel.: (66) 28208999
Web Site:
    http://www.schollshoesthailand.com
Slipper & Shoe Retailer
N.A.I.C.S.: 458210
Paul Tuerlings (Mng Dir)

HanseYachts AG (1)
Ladebower Chaussee 11, 17493, Greifswald, Germany (73.68%)
Tel.: (49) 3834579200
Web Site: https://www.hansegroup.com
Rev.: $187,415,488
Assets: $124,974,065
Liabilities: $136,582,499
Net Worth: ($11,608,434)
Earnings: ($13,886,279)
Emp.: 1,500
Fiscal Year-end: 06/30/2023
Yacht Builder
N.A.I.C.S.: 336612
Gert Purkert (Chm-Supervisory Bd)

Subsidiary (Domestic):

Hanse (Deutschland) Vertriebs GmbH & Co. KG (2)
Holzteichstr 7, 17489, Greifswald, Germany
Tel.: (49) 38347755700
Web Site:
    http://www.hanseyachtsvertrieb.de
Sailing & Motor Yacht Boat Distr
N.A.I.C.S.: 441222

Hellanor AS (1)
Industriveien 26, 1481, Hagan, Norway
Tel.: (47) 67066000
Web Site: http://www.hellanor.no
Sales Range: $75-99.9 Million
Emp.: 250
Automotive Spare Parts Distr
N.A.I.C.S.: 423120
Aase Sollid (Mgr-HR)

Houtschild Internationale Boekhandel BV (1)
Sir Winston Churchilllaan 281, 2288 DA, Rijswijk, Netherlands
Tel.: (31) 704130600
Web Site: http://www.houtschild.com
Book Distr
N.A.I.C.S.: 424920
Hans McIlveen (Head-Ops)

ISOCHEM Holding GmbH (1)
Ludwig-Ganghofer-Str 6, Grunwald, 82031, Germany
Tel.: (49) 895447990
Investment Management Service
N.A.I.C.S.: 523999

Subsidiary (Domestic):

ISOCHEM Beteiligungs GmbH (2)
Ludwig-Ganghofer-Str 6, Grunwald, 82031, Germany
Tel.: (49) 89 5447990
Specialty Chemicals Distr
N.A.I.C.S.: 424690

Ideal Shopping Direct Ltd. (1)
Ideal Home House, Newark Road, Peterborough, PE1 5WG, Cambridgeshire, United Kingdom
Tel.: (44) 8431 688 888
Web Site: http://www.ideal.shopping
Online & Television Retailer
N.A.I.C.S.: 455219
Michael Hancox (CEO)

Ideal World Home Shopping Ltd. (1)
Ideal Home House Newark Road, Peterborough, PE1 5WG, Cambridgeshire, United Kingdom
Tel.: (44) 8717123456
Web Site: http://www.idealworld.tv
Home Shopping Retailer
N.A.I.C.S.: 455219
Jamie Martin (CEO)

LD Didactic GmbH (1)

Leyboldstr 1, Hurth, 50354, Germany
Tel.: (49) 22 33 604 430
Web Site: http://www.ld-didactic.de
Sales Range: $50-74.9 Million
Emp.: 130
Educational & Research Equipment Mfr &
Whslr
N.A.I.C.S.: 333310
Eric Blumenthal (Gen Mgr)

Subsidiary (US):

Feedback Education, Inc. **(2)**
437 Dimmocks Mill Rd, Hillsborough, NC
27278-0400 **(100%)**
Tel.: (919) 644-6466
Web Site: http://www.fbk.com
Sales Range: $25-49.9 Million
Emp.: 10
Educational Electronic Equipment Mfr &
Distr
N.A.I.C.S.: 423490

Subsidiary (Non-US):

Feedback Instruments Limited **(2)**
Park Road, Units 5 & 6 Warren Court,
Crowborough, TN6 2QX, East Sussex,
United Kingdom **(100%)**
Tel.: (44) 1892653322
Web Site:
http://www.feedback-Instruments.com
Rev.: $7,745,000
Emp.: 40
Educational Electronic Equipment Mfr
N.A.I.C.S.: 334519

LoXite GmbH **(1)**
Kienhorststrasse 60, 13403, Berlin, Germany
Tel.: (49) 3094030321
Construction Services
N.A.I.C.S.: 236220

MEZ GmbH **(1)**
Hauptstrasse 78, 79336, Herbolzheim, Germany
Tel.: (49) 76433330
Web Site: http://www.mezcrafts.de
Handcraft Product Retailer
N.A.I.C.S.: 459130

Subsidiary (Non-US):

MEZ Crafts Hungary Kft. **(2)**
Gyar utca 21, Nagyatad, 7500, Kaposvar,
Hungary
Tel.: (36) 82504300
Web Site: http://www.mezcrafts.hu
Handcraft Product Retailer
N.A.I.C.S.: 459130

MEZ Crafts Lithuania UAB **(2)**
A Juozapaviciaus g 6/2, LT-09310, Vilnius,
Lithuania
Tel.: (370) 52072002
Web Site: http://www.mezcrafts.lt
Handcraft Product Retailer
N.A.I.C.S.: 459130

MEZ Crafts Portugal Lda. **(2)**
Quinta de Cravel, 4430-968, Vila Nova de
Gaia, Portugal
Tel.: (351) 223770700
Web Site: http://www.mezcrafts.pt
Handcraft Product Retailer
N.A.I.C.S.: 459130

MEZ Crafts Tekstil Anonim Sirket **(2)**
Kavacik Mah Ekinciler Caddesi Elbistan
Cikmazi N 8/6, Beykoz, Istanbul, Turkiye
Tel.: (90) 2162170020
Handcraft Product Retailer
N.A.I.C.S.: 459130

MEZ Crafts UK Ltd. **(2)**
17F Brooke's Mill, Armitage Bridge, Huddersfield, HD4 7NR, United Kingdom
Tel.: (44) 1484950630
Web Site: http://www.mezcrafts.co.uk
Handcraft Product Retailer
N.A.I.C.S.: 459130

MEZ Fabra Spain S.A. **(2)**
Av Meridiana 354 pta 4 B, 08027, Barcelona, Spain
Tel.: (34) 932908400
Handcraft Product Retailer
N.A.I.C.S.: 459130

Minova International Limited **(1)**

1 Nicholson Street, East Melbourne, 3002,
VIC, Australia
Tel.: (61) 396657209
Web Site:
http://www.minovainternational.com
Sales Range: $450-499.9 Million
Emp.: 1,200
Rock Anchoring Systems & Products Mfr
N.A.I.C.S.: 325211

Office Depot Europe B.V. **(1)**
Columbusweg 33, 5928 LA, Venlo, Netherlands
Tel.: (31) 77 3265000
Web Site: http://www.officedepot.eu
Holding Company
N.A.I.C.S.: 551112

Subsidiary (Non-US):

Guilbert Luxembourg S.A.R.L. **(2)**
ZI ZARE Ilot Est, L-4385, Ehlerange, Luxembourg
Tel.: (352) 4017011
Web Site: http://www.gilbert.lu
Office Supply & Stationery Product Distr
N.A.I.C.S.: 459410

Subsidiary (Domestic):

Office Depot B.V. **(2)**
Columbusweg 33, 5928 LA, Venlo, Netherlands
Tel.: (31) 773238888
Web Site: http://www.officedepot.nl
Office Supply & Stationery Product Distr
N.A.I.C.S.: 459410

Subsidiary (Non-US):

Office Depot BS **(2)**
126 Avenue du Poteau, 60300, Senlis,
France
Tel.: (33) 344545454
Web Site: http://www.officedepot-bs.fr
Office Supply & Stationery Product Distr
N.A.I.C.S.: 459410

Office Depot Deutschland GmbH **(2)**
Linuos Paulin Strasse 2, 63762, Grossostheim, Germany **(100%)**
Tel.: (49) 602697345550
Web Site: http://www.officedepot.eu
Sells Office Products to Small & Medium
Sized Businesses Through Direct Marketing
Catalogs & Programs
N.A.I.C.S.: 459410

Subsidiary (Domestic):

Office Depot Service- und
Beteiligungs-GmbH & Co. KG **(3)**
Linus Pauling Strasse 2, 63762, Grossostheim, Germany
Tel.: (49) 602697340
Office Supplies Stationery Stores
N.A.I.C.S.: 459410

Subsidiary (Non-US):

Office Depot France SNC **(2)**
126 Avenue du Poteau, 60300, Senlis,
France
Tel.: (33) 344 545 454
Web Site: http://www.officedepot.fr
Office Supplies & Furniture
N.A.I.C.S.: 459410

Office Depot GmbH **(2)**
Sagestrasse 50-52, 5600, Lenzburg, Switzerland
Tel.: (41) 844110000
Web Site: http://www.officedepot.eu
Office Supply & Stationery Product Distr
N.A.I.C.S.: 459410

Office Depot International (UK)
Ltd **(2)**
501 Beaumont Leys Lane, Leicester, LE4
2BN, United Kingdom
Tel.: (44) 8444120042
Office Products to Small & Medium Sized
Businesses Through Direct Marketing Catalogs & Programs
N.A.I.C.S.: 459410

Office Depot International BVBA **(2)**
Antwerpen Harmonie Lange Lozanastraat
142, 2018, Antwerp, Belgium
Tel.: (32) 70220140
Web Site: http://www.officedepot.eu

Stationery & Office Supplies
N.A.I.C.S.: 459410

Office Depot Ireland Limited **(2)**
10 Earlsfort Terrace, Dublin, D02 T380,
Ireland **(100%)**
Tel.: (353) 18150701
Stationery & Office Supplies
N.A.I.C.S.: 459410

Subsidiary (Domestic):

Office Depot Netherlands B.V. **(2)**
Columbus Weg 33, 5928 LA, Venlo,
Netherlands **(100%)**
Tel.: (31) 773265000
Web Site: http://www.officedepot.nl
Sells Office Products to Small & Medium
Sized Businesses Through Direct Marketing
Catalogs & Programs
N.A.I.C.S.: 459410

Subsidiary (Non-US):

Office Depot UK Limited **(2)**
501 Beaumont Leys Lane, Leicester, LE4
2BN, United Kingdom
Tel.: (44) 8444120042
Office Supply & Stationery Product Distr
N.A.I.C.S.: 459410

Subsidiary (Domestic):

Viking Direct B.V. **(2)**
Columbusweg 33, 5928 LA, Venlo, Netherlands
Tel.: (31) 773238900
Office Supply & Stationery Product Distr
N.A.I.C.S.: 459410

Subsidiary (Non-US):

Viking Direct (Holdings) Limited **(3)**
510 Beaumont Leys Lane, Leicester, LE4
2BN, United Kingdom
Tel.: (44) 3301281399
Web Site: http://www.viking-direct.co.uk
Office Supply & Stationery Product Distr
N.A.I.C.S.: 459410
Stewart Roland Hussey (Dir)

Viking Direct (Ireland) Limited **(3)**
10 Earlsfort Terrace, Dublin, D02 T380,
Ireland
Tel.: (353) 1890818130
Web Site: http://www.vikingdirekt.ie
Office Supply & Stationery Product Distr
N.A.I.C.S.: 459410

Viking Direkt GesmbH **(3)**
Tragweiner Strasse 57, 4230, Freistadt,
Austria
Tel.: (43) 810955012
Web Site: http://www.vikingdirekt.at
Catalog & Mail Order Distr
N.A.I.C.S.: 449129
Arjan Lammers (Mng Dir)

Subsidiary (Domestic):

Viking Netherlands B.V. **(3)**
Columbusweg 33, 5928 LA, Venlo, Netherlands
Tel.: (31) 773238900
Web Site: http://www.vikingdirect.nl
Office Stationery Product Whslr
N.A.I.C.S.: 459410

Subsidiary (Non-US):

Warehouse Express Ltd. **(2)**
13 Frensham Road, Sweet Briar Industrial
Estate, Norwich, NR3 2BT, Norfolk, United
Kingdom
Tel.: (44) 1603486413
Web Site: http://www.wexphotovideo.com
Consumer Electronic Product Retailer
N.A.I.C.S.: 449210
Stewart Fielder (Sls Dir)

Oy Conaxess Trade Finland AB **(1)**
Malmin Kauppatie 18, 00700, Helsinki, Finland
Tel.: (358) 207411220
Food Product Whslr
N.A.I.C.S.: 424490
Riku Lahdensuo (Mng Dir)

Pohland-Herrenkleidung GmbH & Co.
KG **(1)**
Schildergasse 1, 50667, Cologne, Germany
Tel.: (49) 2212580232

Web Site: http://www.pohland.de
Sales Range: $75-99.9 Million
Emp.: 468
Men's Clothing Retailer
N.A.I.C.S.: 458110

RH Retail Holding GmbH **(1)**
Ludwig-Ganghofer-Str 6, Grunwald, 82031,
Germany
Tel.: (49) 89 5447990
Investment Management Service
N.A.I.C.S.: 523999

Richard Scherpe GmbH & Co. **(1)**
Grafische Betriebe, 47800, Krefeld, Germany
Tel.: (49) 21515390
Web Site: http://www.scherpe.de
Sales Range: $10-24.9 Million
Emp.: 91
Forms, Labels & Packaging Printing Services
N.A.I.C.S.: 323111

SSE Contracting Ltd. **(1)**
1 Forbury Place 43 Forbury Road, Reading,
RG1 3JH, Berks, United Kingdom
Tel.: (44) 1189580100
Web Site: http://www.ssecontracting.co.uk
Eletric Power Generation Services
N.A.I.C.S.: 221118
Colin Nicol (Gen Mgr)

Silvan A/S **(1)**
Edwin Rahrs Vej 88, 8220, Brabrand, Denmark
Tel.: (45) 87308730
Web Site: http://www.silvan.dk
Building Material Retailer
N.A.I.C.S.: 444180
Christiana Rasmussen (Head-HR)

Technologie Tworzyw Sztucnych
Spol. Zoo. **(1)**
ul Prosta 28 Lozienica, 72-100, Goleniow,
Poland
Tel.: (48) 918862150
Web Site: http://www.yachtech.pl
Shipbuilding Construction Services
N.A.I.C.S.: 336611
Maciej Twardowski (Mng Dir)

The Body Shop International
Limited **(1)**
Watersmead, Littlehampton, BN17 6LS, W
Sussex, United Kingdom
Tel.: (44) 2083882328
Web Site: https://www.thebodyshop.in
Natural Skin & Hair Care Products Mfr
N.A.I.C.S.: 325620

Subsidiary (Non-US):

A. Christenssen Engros A/S **(2)**
Gamle Ringeriksvei 74, PO Box 80,
Bekkestua, 1356, Baerum, Norway
Tel.: (47) 67592850
Web Site: http://www.thebodyshop.no
Skin & Hair Care Products Retailer
N.A.I.C.S.: 456120

BS Denmark A/S **(2)**
Ostergade 33 3 sal, DK-1100, Copenhagen,
K, Denmark
Tel.: (45) 70252226
Web Site: http://www.thebodyshop.com
Skin & Hair Care Products Retailer
N.A.I.C.S.: 456120

Affiliate (Non-US):

Bodim Port Oy **(2)**
Web Site: http://www.thebodyshop.fi
Skin & Hair Care Products Importer & Distr
N.A.I.C.S.: 456120

Subsidiary (Non-US):

Cosmenatura SA **(2)**
Calle Hermosilla 30 4 dcha, 28001, Madrid,
Spain
Tel.: (34) 91 114 7205
Web Site: http://www.thebodyshop.es
Skin & Hair Care Products Retailer
N.A.I.C.S.: 456120

Gingko Ltd. **(2)**
Empedokleous St, 57-59 Pagrati, 11633,
Athens, Greece
Tel.: (30) 2109315907
Web Site: http://www.thebodyshop.gr

Aurelius Equity Opportunities SE & Co. KGaA—(Continued)

Skin & Hair Care Products Retailer
N.A.I.C.S.: 456120

National Marketing & Trading Co LLC (2)
PO Box 1475, Ruwi, 112, Oman
Tel.: (968) 247 85 770
Web Site: http://www.thebodyshop.com
Skin & Hair Care Products Retailer
N.A.I.C.S.: 456120

Obon Sai Cosmetics Ltd (2)
8 Monemvasias Street, 4152, Limassol, Cyprus
Tel.: (357) 25343590
Web Site: https://thebodyshop.cy
Skin & Hair Care Products Retailer
N.A.I.C.S.: 456120

Rampai-Niaga Sdn Bhd (2)
No 5 Jalan USJ10/1C, 47620, Subang Jaya, Selangor, Malaysia
Tel.: (60) 356324313
Web Site: https://www.thebodyshop.com.my
Cosmetic Product Retailer
N.A.I.C.S.: 456120
Mina Cheah-Foong (Mng Dir)

The Body Shop (France) SARL (2)
4th floor 51 rue Le Peletier, 75009, Paris, France
Tel.: (33) 170712148
Web Site: https://www.thebodyshop.com
Skin & Hair Care Products Mfr
N.A.I.C.S.: 456120

The Body Shop (Singapore) Pte Ltd (2)
3 Killiney Road Winsland House I #06-02/06, Singapore, 239519, Singapore
Tel.: (65) 68362322
Web Site: http://www.thebodyshop.com
Skin & Hair Care Products Retailer
N.A.I.C.S.: 456120

Subsidiary (Non-US):

Mighty Ocean Company Ltd (3)
Tel.: (852) 25426322
Web Site: http://www.thebodyshop.com
Skin & Hair Care Products Retailer
N.A.I.C.S.: 456120

Subsidiary (Non-US):

The Body Shop Beteiligungs-GmbH (2)
Georg Glock Strasse 8, 40474, Dusseldorf, Germany
Tel.: (49) 21154417003
Cosmetics Whslr
N.A.I.C.S.: 456120

The Body Shop Germany GmbH (2)
Georg Glock Strasse 8, 40474, Dusseldorf, Germany
Tel.: (49) 21154417003
Web Site: https://www.thebodyshop.com
Cosmetics Products Mfr
N.A.I.C.S.: 325620
Kerstin Kranz (Mng Dir)

The Body Shop International (PTE) Ltd. (2)
3 Killiney Rd Winsland House I 06-02/06, Singapore, 239519, Singapore
Tel.: (65) 68362322
Web Site: http://www.thebodyshop.com
Natural Skin & Hair Care Products Mfr
N.A.I.C.S.: 325620

Subsidiary (US):

The Body Shop International Inc. (2)
5036 One World Way, Wake Forest, NC 27587
Tel.: (919) 554-4900
Web Site: http://www.thebodyshop.com
Skin & Hair Care Products Retailer
N.A.I.C.S.: 456120

Branch (Non-US):

The Body Shop Canada Limited (3)
1 Yorkdale Road Suite 510, Toronto, M6A 3A1, ON, Canada
Web Site: https://www.thebodyshop.com
Skin & Hair Care Products Retailer

N.A.I.C.S.: 456120

Subsidiary (Non-US):

The Body Shop Svenska AB (2)
PO Box 17040, 104 62, Stockholm, Sweden
Skin & Hair Care Products Retailer
N.A.I.C.S.: 456120

The Body Shop Switzerland AG (2)
Bahnstrasse 21, CH-8610, Uster, Switzerland
Tel.: (41) 44 905 85 85
Web Site: http://www.thebodyshop.ch
Skin & Hair Care Products Retailer
N.A.I.C.S.: 456120

The Body Shop a Islandi (2)
Dalvegur 16d, PO Box 375, 200, Kopavogur, Iceland
Tel.: (354) 5646555
Web Site: http://www.thebodyshop.com
Skin & Hair Care Products Retailer
N.A.I.C.S.: 456120

Transform Hospital Group Ltd. (1)
192 Altrincham Road, Manchester, M22 4RZ, United Kingdom
Tel.: (44) 3300539115
Web Site: http://www.transforminglives.co.uk
Hospital & Health Care Services
N.A.I.C.S.: 622110
Tony Veverka (CEO-Grp)

VAG GmbH (1)
Carl-Reuther-Str 1, 68305, Mannheim, Germany
Tel.: (49) 6217490
Industrial Valve Mfr
N.A.I.C.S.: 332911

Subsidiary (Non US):

VAG Middle East DMCC (2)
Unit No 2O-00-A2 J and GPlexS Jumeirah Lakes Towers, PO Box 337675, Dubai, United Arab Emirates
Tel.: (971) 48769133
Industrial Equipment Whsr
N.A.I.C.S.: 423840

VAG Valves India (Private) Ltd. (2)
Plot No 57 and 56 Phase-III TSIIC, Pashamylaram Patancheru Sangareddy, 502307, Telangana, India
Tel.: (91) 9100054249
Industrial Equipment Whsr
N.A.I.C.S.: 423840

Wychem Ltd. (1)
Bury Road, Stradishall, Newmarket, CB8 8YN, Suffolk, United Kingdom
Tel.: (44) 1440820338
Web Site: http://www.wychem.com
Chemical Products Mfr
N.A.I.C.S.: 325998
Federico Vidili (Mgr-Comml-Global)

ZIM Flugsitze GmbH (1)
Rontgenstrasse 7, 88677, Markdorf, Germany
Tel.: (49) 754495720
Web Site: http://www.zim-flugsitz.de
Aircraft Seat Mfr
N.A.I.C.S.: 336413
Heiko Fricke (CEO)

brightONE GmbH (1)
Dusseldorfer Strasse 40, 65760, Eschborn, Germany
Tel.: (49) 6196 93 29 0
Web Site: http://www.tieto.de
Sales Range: $150-199.9 Million
Emp.: 800
Information Technology Consulting Services
N.A.I.C.S.: 541512
Rolf Lindenberg (Head-Comm)

Subsidiary (Non-US):

brightONE Healthcare Solutions B.V. (2)
Basicweg 24, 3821 BR, Amersfoort, Netherlands
Tel.: (31) 334536200
Web Site: http://www.brightone.nl
Emp.: 24
Information Technology Consulting Services
N.A.I.C.S.: 541519
Oedse de Boer (Mng Dir)

iKan Paper Crafts Ltd. (1)
2nd Floor New Mill Wellington Mills Quebec Street, Elland, HX5 9AS, West Yorkshire, United Kingdom
Tel.: (44) 1422310919
Web Site: http://www.kanbancrafts.com
Paper Stationery Product Mfr
N.A.I.C.S.: 322230

nestor Hotel Objekt Ludwigsburg GmbH (1)
Stuttgarter Strasse 35/2, 71638, Ludwigsburg, Germany
Tel.: (49) 71419670
Hotel Services
N.A.I.C.S.: 721110

nestor Hotel Objekt Neckarsulm GmbH (1)
Sulmstrasse 2, 74172, Neckarsulm, Germany
Tel.: (49) 71323880
Hotel Services
N.A.I.C.S.: 721110

sit-up Ltd. (1)
11 Acton Park Estate Eastman Road Acton, London, W3 7QE, United Kingdom
Tel.: (44) 20 8600 9700
Web Site: http://www.sit-up.tv
Home Shopping Network Retailer
N.A.I.C.S.: 516120

AURELIUS MINERALS LIMITED
110 Yonge Street Suite 1900, Toronto, M5C 1T4, ON, Canada
Tel.: (416) 304-9095   **BC**
Web Site:
    https://www.aureliusminerals.com
Year Founded: 2007
AUL—(TSXV)
Assets: $6,417,227
Liabilities: $2,992,404
Net Worth: $3,424,823
Earnings: ($3,516,870)
Fiscal Year-end: 12/31/20
Mineral Exploration Services
N.A.I.C.S.: 213114
Randy Turner (Chm)

AURES TECHNOLOGIES
24 bis rue Leonardo de Vinci, 91090, Lisses, France
Tel.: (33) 169111660
Web Site: https://www.aures.com
ALAUR—(EUR)
Rev.: $112,500,663
Assets: $108,353,507
Liabilities: $68,344,512
Net Worth: $40,008,995
Earnings: $2,939,828
Emp.: 382
Fiscal Year-end: 12/31/21
Computerized & Electronic Point-of-Sale Products Distr
N.A.I.C.S.: 423690
Patrick Cathala (Founder, Chm & CEO)

Subsidiaries:

Aures GmbH (1)
Dr-von-Fromm-Str 12, 92637, Weiden, Germany
Tel.: (49) 96129369
Business Support Services
N.A.I.C.S.: 561499

Aures Technologies GmbH (1)
Frauenstrasse 28, 82216, Maisach, Germany
Tel.: (49) 8141227150
Web Site: https://aures.com
Computer Hardware Mfr & Distr
N.A.I.C.S.: 334111
Hilmar Buchwald (Exec Dir)

Aures Technologies Inc. (1)
1671 Fenton Business Park Ct, Fenton, MO 63026
Tel.: (714) 669-3111
Web Site: https://aures.com
Computer Hardware Mfr & Distr

N.A.I.C.S.: 334111
Jeff Burroughs (Mng Dir & VP-Sls & Mktg)

Aures Technologies Ltd. (1)
2 Sycamore Court Manor Park Warrington Road, Runcorn, WA7 1RS, Cheshire, United Kingdom
Tel.: (44) 1928599966
Web Site: https://aures.com
Sales Range: $25-49.9 Million
Emp.: 12
Computerized & Electronic Point-of-Sale Products Distr
N.A.I.C.S.: 423690

Aures Technologies Pty. Ltd. (1)
Unit 6 83/85 Boundary Road, Mortdale, 2223, NSW, Australia
Tel.: (61) 295845222
Web Site: https://aures.com
Computer Hardware Mfr & Distr
N.A.I.C.S.: 334111
Phillip Wild (Mng Dir)

Aures USA Inc (1)
8599 Prairie Trail Dr Unit A 300, Englewood, CO 80112
Tel.: (303) 495-5643
Web Site: http://www.aures.com
Sales Range: $50-74.9 Million
Emp.: 5
Electronic Product Distr
N.A.I.C.S.: 423430

AUREX ENERGY CORP.
Suite 101A 2366 Avenue C North, Saskatoon, S7L 5X5, SK, Canada
Tel.: (306) 242-7363   **AB**
Web Site:
    https://www.aurexenergy.ca
Year Founded: 2008
AURX—(TSXV)
Sales Range: Less than $1 Million
Investment Services
N.A.I.C.S.: 523999
Gary Billingsley (Pres & CEO)

AURIANT MINING AB
Box 55696, 102 15, Stockholm, Sweden
Tel.: (46) 86242680
Web Site: https://www.auriant.com
Year Founded: 2004
AUR—(OMX)
Rev.: $37,343,000
Assets: $47,319,000
Liabilities: $69,400,000
Net Worth: ($22,081,000)
Earnings: ($7,022,000)
Emp.: 460
Fiscal Year-end: 12/31/23
Mineral Exploration Services
N.A.I.C.S.: 213114
Lord Daresbury (Chm)

AURIC MINING LIMITED
Level 1 1 Tully Road, East Perth, 6004, WA, Australia
Tel.: (61) 895489997   **AU**
Web Site:
    https://www.auricmining.com.au
Year Founded: 2019
AWJ—(ASX)
Rev.: $3,124,230
Assets: $8,677,924
Liabilities: $897,226
Net Worth: $7,780,698
Earnings: $856,520
Fiscal Year-end: 12/31/23
Mining Services
N.A.I.C.S.: 212290
Mark English (Mng Dir)

AURIGA INDUSTRIES A/S
Finlandsgade 14, 8200, Arhus, Denmark
Tel.: (45) 70237988   **DK**
Web Site: http://www.auriga-industries.com
Year Founded: 1938
Sales Range: $1-4.9 Billion

Holding Company Services
N.A.I.C.S.: 551112
Ole Ohlenschlaeger Madsen *(Chm)*

AURIN INVESTMENT GROUP GMBH

Hochstrasse 29, 60313, Frankfurt am Main, Germany
Tel.: (49) 69 348 754 51
Web Site: http://www.aurin-investment.com
Year Founded: 2020
Investment Services
N.A.I.C.S.: 523999
Kerim Chouaibi *(Mng Partner)*

Subsidiaries:

Wirecard Central Eastern Europe GmbH   **(1)**
Primoschgasse 3, 9020, Klagenfurt, Austria
Tel.: (43) 316 81 36 81 40
Web Site: http://www.wirecard.at
Electronic Money Transfer Services
N.A.I.C.S.: 522320

AURINIA PHARMACEUTICALS INC.

1203 4464 Markham Street, Victoria, V8Z 7X8, BC, Canada
Tel.: (250) 708-4272
Web Site:
https://www.auriniapharma.com
Year Founded: 1993
AUPH—(NASDAQ)
Rev.: $134,030,000
Assets: $470,860,000
Liabilities: $65,425,000
Net Worth: $405,435,000
Earnings: ($108,180,000)
Emp.: 300
Fiscal Year-end: 12/31/22
Immunosuppressant Therapies Developer & Mfr
N.A.I.C.S.: 325412
Peter S. Greenleaf *(Pres & CEO)*

AURION RESOURCES LTD.

120 Torbay Road Suite W220, Saint John's, A1A 2G8, NL, Canada
Tel.: (709) 722-4128
Web Site:
https://www.aurionresources.com
Year Founded: 2006
AIRRF—(OTCQX)
Rev.: $263,009
Assets: $48,192,838
Liabilities: $1,958,721
Net Worth: $46,234,117
Earnings: ($3,516,794)
Fiscal Year-end: 12/31/22
Mineral Exploration Services
N.A.I.C.S.: 213114
Mike Basha *(Pres)*

Subsidiaries:

Aurion Resources AB   **(1)**
Ambetsgatan 8, 776 30, Hedemora, Sweden
Tel.: (46) 705913998
Mineral Exploration Services
N.A.I.C.S.: 213114

AURIONPRO SOLUTIONS LIMITED

Synergia IT Park Rabale, Near Rabale Police Station Rabale, Navi Mumbai, 400701, Maharashtra, India
Tel.: (91) 2240407070
Web Site: https://www.aurionpro.com
Year Founded: 1997
532668—(BOM)
Rev.: $90,590,068
Assets: $115,840,329
Liabilities: $45,535,827
Net Worth: $70,304,502
Earnings: $13,907,398
Emp.: 2,000

Fiscal Year-end: 03/30/23
Banking Software Development Services
N.A.I.C.S.: 541511
Amit R. Sheth *(Co-Chm)*

Subsidiaries:

AurionPro Solutions (HK) Ltd.   **(1)**
20/F Champion Building 287-291 Des Voeux Road, Central, Sheung Wan, China (Hong Kong)
Tel.: (852) 28542812
Sales Range: $25-49.9 Million
Emp.: 4
Supply Chain Software Publisher
N.A.I.C.S.: 513210

AurionPro Solutions, SPC   **(1)**
PO Box 20658, Manama, Bahrain
Tel.: (973) 17217991
Web Site: http://www.aurionpro.com
Sales Range: $25-49.9 Million
Emp.: 100
Information Technology Consulting Services
N.A.I.C.S.: 541512

Aurionpro SCM Pte Ltd.   **(1)**
438B Alexandra Road Alexandra Technopark 05-11, Singapore, 119968, Singapore
Tel.: (65) 65364852
Web Site: https://www.aurionpro.com
Supply Chain Software Development Services
N.A.I.C.S.: 541511

Aurionpro Solutions PTY Ltd.   **(1)**
Level 2 215 Spring Street, Melbourne, 3000, VIC, Australia
Tel.: (61) 411703688
Information Technology Consulting Services
N.A.I.C.S.: 541512

Aurionpro Transit Pte. Ltd.   **(1)**
Block 438B Alexandra Road Alexandra Technopark 01-08, Singapore, 119968, Singapore
Tel.: (65) 67186690
Transportation Management Services
N.A.I.C.S.: 541614

Integro Technologies (Vietnam) LLC   **(1)**
12th floor Diamond Flower Tower 48 Le Van Luong, Nhan Chinh Thanh Xuan District, Hanoi, Vietnam
Tel.: (84) 2466668858
Information Technology Services
N.A.I.C.S.: 541519

Integro Technologies Co. Ltd.   **(1)**
30th Floor Singha Complex Unit 3001-3003 3009-3014 Office no 3006, 1788 New Petchaburi Road Bangkapi Huai Kwang, Bangkok, 10310, Thailand
Tel.: (66) 20883617
Information Technology Services
N.A.I.C.S.: 541519

Integro Technologies Pte Ltd.   **(1)**
438B Alexandra Road Block B Alexandra Technopark 05-11, Singapore, 119968, Singapore
Tel.: (65) 65366438
Web Site: https://www.integrosys.com
Sales Range: $25-49.9 Million
Emp.: 90
Banking Software Development Services
N.A.I.C.S.: 541511
Shekhar Mullatti *(CEO & Mng Dir)*

Integro Technologies Sdn. Bhd.   **(1)**
Suite 3 Level 21 Block 2B Plaza Sentral Jalan Stesen Sentral 5, 50470, Kuala Lumpur, Malaysia
Tel.: (60) 327704847
Information Technology Services
N.A.I.C.S.: 541519

SC Soft Americas LLC   **(1)**
Easy Work Space 2295 S Hiawassee Rd 104, Orlando, FL 32835
Tel.: (321) 333-8680
Web Site: https://scsoftusa.com
Information Technology Services
N.A.I.C.S.: 541519

Sena Systems (India) Pvt. Ltd.   **(1)**
A-3 Abhimanshree Society 1st Floor East

Wing, Pashan Road, Pune, 411 008, Maharashtra, India
Tel.: (91) 2030641500
Sales Range: $25-49.9 Million
Emp.: 150
Information Technology Consulting Services
N.A.I.C.S.: 561499

Spikes, Inc.   **(1)**
536 N Santa Cruz Ave, Los Gatos, CA 95030
Tel.: (408) 755-5713
Web Site: http://www.spikes.com
Emp.: 50
Software Development & Information Technology Services
N.A.I.C.S.: 513210

AURIS AG

Hirschgasslein 30, 4051, Basel, Switzerland
Tel.: (41) 61 271 27 70
Web Site: http://www.aurisag.ch
Year Founded: 2009
Gold Mining Services
N.A.I.C.S.: 212220
Peter Geoggel *(Chm)*

AURIS MINERALS LIMITED

Level 1 / 18 Richardson Street, West Perth, 6005, WA, Australia
Tel.: 861094333
Web Site:
https://www.aurisminerals.com.au
AUR—(ASX)
Rev.: $182,103
Assets: $10,389,179
Liabilities: $150,654
Net Worth: $10,238,525
Earnings: ($2,955,371)
Emp.: 1
Fiscal Year-end: 06/30/24
Gold & Copper Exploration
N.A.I.C.S.: 212220
Mark Clements *(Sec)*

AURISCO PHARMACEUTICAL CO., LTD.

Badu Industrial Park Zone, Tiantai, Taizhou, 317200, Zhejiang, China
Tel.: (86) 57683177319
Web Site: https://www.aurisco.com
Year Founded: 1998
605116—(SHG)
Rev.: $141,533,941
Assets: $285,411,115
Liabilities: $48,955,248
Net Worth: $236,455,867
Earnings: $29,609,672
Emp.: 1,600
Fiscal Year-end: 12/31/22
Pharmaceutical Product Mfr & Distr
N.A.I.C.S.: 325412
Zhien Peng *(Chm)*

AURIZON HOLDINGS LIMITED

Aurizon 900 Ann Street, Fortitude Valley, 4006, QLD, Australia
Tel.: (61) 730199000
Web Site:
https://www.aurizon.com.au
AZJ—(ASX)
Rev.: $2,566,773,494
Assets: $7,743,055,524
Liabilities: $4,779,647,416
Net Worth: $2,963,408,108
Earnings: $271,100,426
Emp.: 5,930
Fiscal Year-end: 06/30/24
Holding Company; Rail Freight Services
N.A.I.C.S.: 551112
Dominic D. Smith *(Sec)*

Subsidiaries:

Aurizon Operations Limited   **(1)**
900 Ann Street, Fortitude Valley, 4006, QLD, Australia   **(100%)**
Tel.: (61) 730199000

Web Site: https://www.aurizon.com.au
Rail Freight Transportation Services
N.A.I.C.S.: 482111

Aurizon Port Services NSW Pty. Ltd.   **(1)**
72- 76 Archer Street, South Townsville, 4814, QLD, Australia
Tel.: (61) 747216112
Warehousing & Logistics Services
N.A.I.C.S.: 541614

Aurizon Port Services Pty Ltd   **(1)**
72- 76 Archer Street, South Townsville, Townsville, 4814, QLD, Australia
Tel.: (61) 747216112
Web Site: http://www.tbsh.com.au
Transportation Services
N.A.I.C.S.: 485999

CRT Group Pty. Ltd.   **(1)**
1 Chambers Road, Altona, 3025, VIC, Australia
Tel.: (61) 392901700
Logistic Services
N.A.I.C.S.: 488999
Richard Spall *(CEO)*

AURO HOLDINGS BERHAD

No 5-7 Level 5 Menara MBMR No 1 Jalan Syed Putra, 58000, Kuala Lumpur, Selangor, Malaysia
Tel.: (60) 322763213
Web Site: https://auro.com.my
AURO—(KLS)
Rev.: $1,513,559
Assets: $7,477,700
Liabilities: $1,918,086
Net Worth: $5,559,614
Earnings: ($438,576)
Emp.: 81
Fiscal Year-end: 02/29/24
Molded Timbers Mfr & Sales
N.A.I.C.S.: 321215
Chong Voon Wah *(Co-Sec)*

Subsidiaries:

NWP Industries Sdn. Bhd.   **(1)**
B-2-08 Jalan SS6/20 Dataran Glomac Pusat Bandar Kelana Jaya, 47301, Petaling Jaya, Selangor, Malaysia
Tel.: (60) 378801155
Emp.: 100
Timber Product Mfr & Distr
N.A.I.C.S.: 321215

AURO IMPEX & CHEMICALS LIMITED

32 K L Saigal Sarani 740A Block P, New Alipore, Kolkata, 700053, India
Tel.: (91) 983003029
Web Site:
https://www.auroimpex.com
Year Founded: 1994
AUROIMPEX—(NSE)
Rev.: $28,235,406
Assets: $9,972,445
Liabilities: $7,845,434
Net Worth: $2,127,012
Earnings: $727,103
Fiscal Year-end: 03/31/23
Automation Product Mfr
N.A.I.C.S.: 335314
Madhusudan Goenka *(Mng Dir)*

AURO LABORATORIES LIMITED

314 TV Industrial Estate S K Ahire Marg, Worli, Mumbai, 400 030, India
Tel.: (91) 2266635456   In
Web Site: https://www.aurolabs.com
Year Founded: 1992
530233—(BOM)
Rev.: $7,092,310
Assets: $7,502,069
Liabilities: $3,199,451
Net Worth: $4,302,617
Earnings: $388,299
Emp.: 72
Fiscal Year-end: 03/31/22
Pharmaceuticals Product Mfr

Auro Laboratories Limited—(Continued)
N.A.I.C.S.: 325412
Sharat Deorah *(Chm & Mng Dir)*

AUROBINDO PHARMA LTD.
Galaxy Floors 2224 Plot No 1 Survey
No 831, Hyderabad Knowledge City
Raidurg Panmaktha Ranga Reddy
District, Hyderabad, 500 032, Telangana, India
Tel.: (91) 4066725000
Web Site: https://www.aurobindo.com
Year Founded: 1986
AUROPHARMA—(NSE)
Rev.: $3,245,402,160
Assets: $4,630,314,780
Liabilities: $1,275,956,955
Net Worth: $3,354,357,825
Earnings: $361,330,515
Emp.: 7,849
Fiscal Year-end: 03/31/22
Generic Pharmaceuticals & Active
Pharmaceutical Ingredient Mfr
N.A.I.C.S.: 325412
K. Nityananda Reddy *(Vice Chm)*

Subsidiaries:

APL Chemi Natura Ltd. **(1)**
Plot No 2 Maitrivihar, Ameerpet, Hyderabad,
500 038, India
Tel.: (91) 40 5572 5000
Pharmaceutical Preparations
N.A.I.C.S.: 325412

APL Research Centre Limited **(1)**
Plot No 2 Maitrivihar, Ameerpet, Hyderabad,
500038, India
Tel.: (91) 40 66725333
Web Site: http://www.aurobindo.com
Pharmaceutical Products Mfr & Whslr
N.A.I.C.S.: 325412

APL Swift Services (Malta) Ltd. **(1)**
HF26 Hal Far Industrial Estate, Birzebbuga,
BBG 3000, Malta
Tel.: (356) 22294000
Pharmaceuticals Product Mfr
N.A.I.C.S.: 325412

APL Thai Limited **(1)**
438 Phattanakaran 30 Road, Sunluang,
Bangkok, 10250, Thailand
Tel.: (66) 27195512
Pharmaceutical Preparations
N.A.I.C.S.: 325412

Acrotech Biopharma LLC **(1)**
279 Princeton Hightstown Rd, East Windsor, NJ 08520
Web Site: https://acrotechbiopharma.com
Pharmaceuticals Product Mfr
N.A.I.C.S.: 325412
Ashish Anvekar *(Pres)*

All Pharma (Shanghai) Trading Company Limited **(1)**
Room No 3304 No 8 Xingly Rd, Changning,
Shanghai, 200051, China
Tel.: (86) 2152080981
Web Site: http://www.aurobindo.com
Sales Range: $50-74.9 Million
Emp.: 10
Pharmaceutical Products Mfr & Whslr
N.A.I.C.S.: 325412

Apotex Europe B.V. **(1)**
Postbus 408, 2300 AK, Leiden, Netherlands
Tel.: (31) 715243100
Pharmaceuticals Product Mfr
N.A.I.C.S.: 325412

Apotex Polska sp. z.o.o. **(1)**
ul Ostrobramska 95, 04-118, Warsaw, Poland
Tel.: (48) 223112000
Web Site: http://www.apotex.pl
Pharmaceutical Products Distr
N.A.I.C.S.: 424210

Auro Health LLC **(1)**
2572 Brunswick Pike, Lawrenceville, NJ
08648
Web Site: https://www.aurohealth.com
Pharmaceuticals Product Mfr
N.A.I.C.S.: 325412

Aurobindo (Datong) Bio-Pharma Co.
Ltd. **(1)**
Economic & Technology Development
Zong, Datong, Shanxi, China
Tel.: (86) 3526108710
Pharmaceutical Preparations
N.A.I.C.S.: 325412

Aurobindo (H.K.) Limited **(1)**
Warehouse-B Venton Mfg 1 Wo Hing Road,
Wo Hop Shek Santsuen, Hong Kong, China
(Hong Kong)
Tel.: (852) 23675053
Pharmaceutical Preparations
N.A.I.C.S.: 325412

Aurobindo Ilac Sanayi Ve Ticaret
Ltd **(1)**
Egitim Mh Poyraz Sk Sadikoglu Plaza 5 No
27 Kadikoy, Istanbul, 34722, Türkiye
Tel.: (90) 2163481076
Pharmaceutical Products Mfr & Whslr
N.A.I.C.S.: 325412

Aurobindo Pharma (Italia) S.r.l **(1)**
Via Pergolesi 15, 20124, Milan, Italy
Tel.: (39) 0289289800
Pharmaceutical Products Mfr & Whslr
N.A.I.C.S.: 325412

Aurobindo Pharma (Malta)
Limited **(1)**
Vault-14 Level 2 Valletta Waterfront, Floriana, FRN 1913, Malta
Tel.: (356) 9999 1441
Web Site: http://www.aurobindo.com
Sales Range: $25-49.9 Million
Emp.: 20
Pharmaceutical Products Distr
N.A.I.C.S.: 424210

Subsidiary (Domestic):

Agile Malta Holdings Limited **(2)**
Vault-14 Level 2 Valletta Waterfront, Floriana, FLN 1913, Malta
Tel.: (356) 99991441
Web Site: http://www.aurobindo.com
Emp.: 17
Holding Company; Pharmaceutical Products
Distr
N.A.I.C.S.: 551112

Subsidiary (Domestic):

Agile Pharma (Malta) Limited **(3)**
Vault-14 Level 2 Valletta Waterfront, Floriana, FLN 1913, Malta
Tel.: (356) 99991441
Pharmaceutical Products Distr
N.A.I.C.S.: 424210

Aurobindo Pharma (Portugal) Unipessoal LDA **(1)**
Av do Forte n 3 Parque Suecia Ed IV 2 ste
4, 2794-038, Carnaxide, Portugal
Tel.: (351) 214185104
Sales Range: $50-74.9 Million
Emp.: 9
Pharmaceutical Products Mfr & Distr
N.A.I.C.S.: 325412

Subsidiary (Domestic):

Aurovitas Unipessoal Lda. **(2)**
Rua Joao De Deus 19, 2700-487, Amadora,
Portugal
Tel.: (351) 214967120
Web Site: http://www.aurovitas.pt
Sales Range: $25-49.9 Million
Emp.: 53
Pharmaceutical Preparation Mfr
N.A.I.C.S.: 325412
Duarte Sinoes *(Mng Dir)*

Aurobindo Pharma (Pty) Limited **(1)**
53 Phillip Engelbrecht Avenue Woodhill Office Park Buiding No1, Meyersdal ext 12,
Johannesburg, 1448, South Africa
Tel.: (27) 118679100
Web Site: http://www.aurobindo.com
Pharmaceuticals Product Mfr
N.A.I.C.S.: 325412

Aurobindo Pharma B.V. **(1)**
Baarnsche Dijk 1, 3741 LN, Baarn, Netherlands
Tel.: (31) 35 542 9933
Web Site: http://www.aurobindo.nl
Emp.: 60

Pharmaceutical Products Mfr & Whslr
N.A.I.C.S.: 325412
Kalman Petro *(Mng Dir & Grp VP-South
West Europe)*

Subsidiary (Domestic):

Aurex B.V. **(2)**
Baarnsche Dijk 1, 3741 LN, Baarn, Netherlands
Tel.: (31) 35 303 4950
Web Site: http://www.aurex-pharma.com
Emp.: 5
Generic Pharmaceutical Mfr
N.A.I.C.S.: 325412
Nicole Veen *(Mgr-Supply Chain)*

Subsidiary (Non-US):

Helix Healthcare B.V. **(2)**
Tel.: (31) 20 521 4769
Pharmaceutical Preparations
N.A.I.C.S.: 325412

Subsidiary (Domestic):

Pharmacin B.V. **(2)**
Molenvliet 103, 3335 LH, Zwijndrecht, Netherlands
Tel.: (31) 786101836
Web Site: http://www.pharmacin.nl
Sales Range: $25-49.9 Million
Emp.: 20
Pharmaceutical Products Mfr & Whslr
N.A.I.C.S.: 325412

Aurobindo Pharma Colombia
SAS **(1)**
Calle 100 No 17 36 Office 1003 One Hundred Building, Bogota, Colombia
Tel.: (57) 15208438
Web Site: http://www.aurobindo.com.co
Pharmaceuticals Product Mfr
N.A.I.C.S.: 325412

Aurobindo Pharma France SARL **(1)**
22 - 26 rue des Gaudines, Saint Germain-
en-Laye, 78100, France
Tel.: (33) 609318105
Pharmaceutical Products Mfr & Whslr
N.A.I.C.S.: 325412

Aurobindo Pharma GmbH **(1)**
Willy-Brandt-Allee 2, 81829, Munich, Germany
Tel.: (49) 89 3700 338 0
Web Site: http://www.aurobindo-pharma.de
Sales Range: $50-74.9 Million
Emp.: 5
Pharmaceutical Products Mfr & Distr
N.A.I.C.S.: 325412

Aurobindo Pharma Industria Pharmaceutica Ltda **(1)**
VP 6E S/N Qd 09 Mod 12 a 15, Bloco B,
DAIA, Anapolis, 75132-135, Goias, Brazil
Tel.: (55) 6240153400
Web Site: http://www.aurobindo.ind.br
Emp.: 100
Pharmaceuticals Product Mfr
N.A.I.C.S.: 325412

Subsidiary (Domestic):

Aurobindo Pharma Productos Farmaceuticos Ltda **(2)**
Vp-06E Qd 09 Mod 12/15, Daia, Anapolis,
75132-135, Goias, Brazil
Tel.: (55) 62 40153400
Web Site: http://www.aurobindo.ind.br
Pharmaceutical Products Mfr & Whslr
N.A.I.C.S.: 325412

Aurobindo Pharma Japan K.K **(1)**
9th Floor Youth Building 1-3-8
Nihonbashibakuro-cho, Cho-ku, Tokyo, 103-
0002, Japan
Tel.: (81) 33 249 2261
Web Site: http://www.aurobindo.com
Sales Range: $25-49.9 Million
Emp.: 4
Pharmaceuticals Product Mfr
N.A.I.C.S.: 325412

Aurobindo Pharma Produtos Farmaceuticos Ltda. **(1)**
VP 6E S/N Qd 09 Mod 12 a 15 Bloco B
DAIA, Anapolis, 75132-135, Goias, Brazil
Tel.: (55) 62992315858
Pharmaceuticals Product Mfr
N.A.I.C.S.: 325412

Aurobindo Pharma Romania
SRL **(1)**
Paneologu Street No 24 2nd Floor Room
No E02, 3rd District, Bucharest, Romania
Tel.: (40) 213118815
Pharmaceutical Products Mfr & Whslr
N.A.I.C.S.: 325412
Daniela Iaru *(Mgr-Corp Sec)*

Aurobindo Pharma USA Inc. **(1)**
2400 Rte 130 N, Dayton, NJ 08810
Tel.: (732) 839-9400
Web Site: http://www.aurobindo.com
Sales Range: $50-74.9 Million
Emp.: 200
Pharmaceutical Preparations
N.A.I.C.S.: 325412

Subsidiary (Domestic):

Aurolife Pharma LLC **(2)**
2400 US Hwy 130 N, Dayton, NJ 08810
Tel.: (732) 839-9400
Web Site: https://www.aurolifepharma.com
Pharmaceuticals Product Mfr
N.A.I.C.S.: 325412

Affiliate (Domestic):

Cephazone Pharma LLC **(2)**
250 E Bonita Ave, Pomona, CA 91767-1924
Tel.: (909) 392-8900
Web Site: http://www.cephazone.com
Pharmaceutical Preparations
N.A.I.C.S.: 325412
Gerald Macedo *(Owner)*

Subsidiary (Domestic):

Natrol, LLC **(2)**
21411 Prairie St, Chatsworth, CA 91311-
5829
Tel.: (818) 739-6000
Web Site: https://www.natrol.com
Dietary Supplements, Herbal Teas & Sports
Nutrition Products Mfr & Marketer
N.A.I.C.S.: 325411
Tom Zimmerman *(CEO)*

Subsidiary (Domestic):

Prolab Nutrition Inc. **(3)**
21411 Prairie St, Chatsworth, CA 91311
Tel.: (818) 739-6000
Web Site: http://www.prolab.com
Nutritional Products Whslr
N.A.I.C.S.: 456191
Jenia Khudagulyan *(COO)*

Aurobindo Switzerland AG **(1)**
Alpenstrasse 15, 6304, Zug, Switzerland
Tel.: (41) 41 726 82 06
Pharmaceutical Products Mfr & Distr
N.A.I.C.S.: 325412

Aurobindo Tongling (Datong) Pharmaceutical Co. Ltd. **(1)**
Economic & Technology Development
Zone, Datong, Shanxi, China
Tel.: (86) 3526108710
Pharmaceutical Preparations
N.A.I.C.S.: 325412

Auromedics Pharma LLC **(1)**
279 Princeton Hightstown Rd, East Windsor, NJ 08520
Tel.: (732) 355-9449
Web Site: https://auromedics.com
Pharmaceutical Products Distr
N.A.I.C.S.: 424210

Auropharma Inc. **(1)**
3700 Steeles Avenue West Suite 402,
Woodbridge, L4L 8K8, ON, Canada
Tel.: (905) 856-8063
Web Site: https://www.auropharma.ca
Pharmaceutical Products Distr
N.A.I.C.S.: 424210

Aurovida Farmaceutica S.A, De
C.V **(1)**
Rio Tiber 91-401 Col Cuauhtemoc, 06500,
Cuauhtemoc, Mexico
Tel.: (52) 5531312985
Pharmaceuticals Product Mfr
N.A.I.C.S.: 325412

Aurovitas Pharma Polska Sp. z
o.o. **(1)**
ul Sokratesa 13D/27, 01-909, Warsaw, Poland

Tel.: (48) 223112000
Web Site: http://www.aurovitas.pl
Pharmaceuticals Product Mfr
N.A.I.C.S.: 325412

Aurovitas Spain SA. (1)
Avenida de Burgos 16 D 5th floor Building
Euromor, 28036, Madrid, Spain
Tel.: (34) 916308645
Web Site: http://www.aurovitas.es
Pharmaceuticals Product Mfr
N.A.I.C.S.: 325412

Aurovitas Spol s.r.o (1)
Karlovarska 77/12, 161 00, Prague, Czech
Republic
Tel.: (420) 234705721
Web Site: http://www.aurovitas.cz
Pharmaceuticals Product Mfr
N.A.I.C.S.: 325412

**CuraTeQ Biologics Private
Limited** (1)
Galaxy Towers Floors 22-24 Plot No 1 Sur-
vey No 83/1, Hyderabad Knowledge City
Raidurg Panmaktha Ranga Reddy District,
Hyderabad, 500032, Telangana, India
Tel.: (91) 8455255222
Web Site: https://curateqbio.com
Biopharmaceutical Healthcare Services
N.A.I.C.S.: 541714

GENERIS Farmaceutica, S.A. (1)
Rua Joao de Deus n 19, Venda Nova,
2700-487, Amadora, Portugal
Tel.: (351) 21 496 7120
Web Site: https://www.generis.pt
Pharmaceuticals Product Mfr
N.A.I.C.S.: 325412

GLS Pharma Limited (1)
F-30 Phase-1 Okhla Industrial Estate, New
Delhi, 110020, India
Tel.: (91) 1145586751
Web Site: https://glspharma.com
Pharmaceutical Product Mfr & Distr
N.A.I.C.S.: 325412

**Generis Phar, Unipessoal Ld
WOS** (1)
Rua Joao De Deus No19, 2700-487, Ama-
dora, Portugal
Tel.: (351) 214967120
Pharmaceuticals Product Mfr
N.A.I.C.S.: 325412

Milpharm Limited (1)
Ares Block Odyssey Business Park South
Ruislip, Middlesex, London, HA4 6QD,
United Kingdom
Tel.: (44) 208 845 8811
Web Site: http://www.aurobindo.com
Sales Range: $25-49.9 Million
Emp.: 40
Pharmaceutical Products Mfr & Whslr
N.A.I.C.S.: 325412

Puren Pharma GmbH & Co. KG. (1)
Willy-Brandt-Allee 2, 81829, Munich, Ger-
many
Tel.: (49) 895589090
Web Site: http://www.puren-pharma.de
Pharmaceutical Product Mfr
N.A.I.C.S.: 325412

Tergene Biotech Private Limited (1)
Suite 121 and 122 Building 450, Genome
Valley Turkapally V Shamirpet M RR Dist,
Hyderabad, 500078, Telangana, India
Tel.: (91) 4023480075
Web Site: http://www.tergene.com
Vaccines Mfr
N.A.I.C.S.: 325412
M. Kuppusamy (Co-Founder & Mng Dir)

Vespyr Brands LLC (1)
279 Princeton Hightstown Rd, East Wind-
sor, NJ 08520
Web Site: https://www.vespyrbrands.com
Health & Wellness Services
N.A.I.C.S.: 812199

AUROMA COKE LIMITED
Suit No 706 Shantiniketan 8 Camac
Street, Kolkata, 700 017, West Ben-
gal, India
Tel.: (91) 3322822310
Web Site: http://www.auroma.in
Year Founded: 1977

531336—(BOM)
Sales Range: $1-9.9 Million
Coal Product Mfr & Whslr
N.A.I.C.S.: 324199
Subhash Srivastava (Compliance
Officer)

**AURORA ABSOLUTE RETURN
FUND**
Level 6 Suite 613 370 St Kilda Road,
Melbourne, 3004, VIC, Australia
Tel.: (61) 1300553431
Investment Fund Management Ser-
vices
N.A.I.C.S.: 523940
John Patton (Mng Dir)

AURORA CANNABIS INC.
500-10355 Jasper Avenue, Edmon-
ton, T5J 1Y6, AB, Canada   BC
Web Site: http://www.auroramj.com
Year Founded: 2013
ACB—(NASDAQ)
Rev.: $227,228,089
Assets: $2,037,628,967
Liabilities: $443,577,011
Net Worth: $1,594,051,956
Earnings: ($543,754,223)
Emp.: 1,643
Fiscal Year-end: 06/30/21
Medical Cannabis Mfr
N.A.I.C.S.: 325411
Glen Ibbott (CFO)

Subsidiaries:

Aurora Deutschland GmbH (1)
Wilmersdorfer Strasse 98/99, 10629, Berlin,
Germany
Tel.: (49) 30983216010
Pharmaceutical Product Whslr
N.A.I.C.S.: 424210

CanniMed Ltd. (1)
1 Plant Technology Road, PO Box 19A
RR#5, Saskatoon, S7K 3J8, SK, Canada
Tel.: (855) 787-1577
Web Site: http://www.cannimed.ca
Pharmaceutical-Grade Cannabis Mfr
N.A.I.C.S.: 325412
Andre Jerome (Interim CEO)

ICC Labs Inc. (1)
c/o 1500-1055 West Georgia Street, Van-
couver, V6E 4N7, BC, Canada
Tel.: (604) 362-5207
Sales Range: Less than $1 Million
Investment Services
N.A.I.C.S.: 523999
David Shpilt (CEO)

**Whistler Medical marijuana
Corporation** (1)
Unit 113 1330 Alpha Lake Road, Whistler,
V8E 0R6, BC, Canada
Tel.: (604) 962-3440
Web Site:
http://www.whistlermedicalmarijuana.com
Organic Medical Product Distr
N.A.I.C.S.: 424690

AURORA CORPORATION
16th Floor No 2 Section 5 Xinyi
Road, Taipei, Taiwan
Tel.: (886) 223458088
Web Site: https://www.aurora.com.tw
Year Founded: 1965
2373—(TAI)
Rev.: $377,768,193
Assets: $586,661,249
Liabilities: $301,887,493
Net Worth: $284,773,756
Earnings: $38,401,810
Emp.: 4,075
Fiscal Year-end: 12/31/23
Office Machinery & Furniture Mfr &
Distr
N.A.I.C.S.: 333310
Hui-hua Yuan (Chm)

Subsidiaries:

Aurora Corp. of America (1)

3500 Challenger St, Torrance, CA 90503
Tel.: (310) 793-5650
Web Site: https://www.auroracorp.com
Sales Range: $25-49.9 Million
Emp.: 35
Consumer Electronics Mfr
N.A.I.C.S.: 423420

Aurora Japan Corp. (1)
8-12-1 Nishi-Shinjuku, Shinjuku-ku, Tokyo,
160-0023, Japan
Tel.: (81) 33 369 6171
Web Site: https://www.aurora-japan.co.jp
Sales Range: $50-74.9 Million
Emp.: 9
Electrical Apparatus & Equipment Wiring
Supplies & Construction Material Whslr
N.A.I.C.S.: 423610

**Aurora Office Automation
Corporation** (1)
7th Floor No 2 Sec 5, Shinyi Rd, 110, Tai-
pei, Taiwan
Tel.: (886) 223458018
Web Site: http://www.oa-world.com.tw
Sales Range: $25-49.9 Million
Emp.: 20
Equipment Whslr
N.A.I.C.S.: 423420

**Aurora Office Automation Sales Co.,
Ltd.** (1)
11th Floor No 99 Fucheng Rd, Pudong New
Area, Shanghai, China
Tel.: (86) 2158828999
Web Site: http://www.aurora.com.cn
Equipment Whslr
N.A.I.C.S.: 423420
Yuntai Chen (Pres & Gen Mgr)

Aurora Office Furniture Co., Ltd. (1)
10th Floor Aurora Plaza No 99, Fucheng Rd
Pudong Dist, Shanghai, China
Tel.: (86) 2159161010
Web Site: http://www.aurora.com.tw
Office Furniture Mfr
N.A.I.C.S.: 337214

Aurora Singapore Corp. (1)
50 Genting Lane 08-01 Cideco Industrial
Complex, Singapore, 349558, Singapore
Tel.: (65) 68416641
Web Site: http://www.aurora.com.sg
Sales Range: $25-49.9 Million
Emp.: 7
Machinery Mfr
N.A.I.C.S.: 333310

Aurora Systems Corporation (1)
3rd Floor No 156 Jiankang Road, Song-
shan District, 105, Taipei, Taiwan
Tel.: (886) 227476789
Web Site: http://www.eosasc.com.tw
Computer Programming Services
N.A.I.C.S.: 541511

Aurora Telecom Corporation (1)
3rd Floor No 423 Rueiguang Rd, Neihu
Dist, 114, Taipei, Taiwan   **(60%)**
Tel.: (886) 226560668
Web Site: http://www.auroracomm.tw
Cellular Telecommunication Retail Stores
N.A.I.C.S.: 517112

**AURORA DESIGN PUBLIC
COMPANY LIMITED**
444 Soi Udomsuk 26, Bangna Nuea
Bangna, Bangkok, 10260, Thailand
Tel.: (66) 27495044
Web Site:
https://www.auroradesign.co.th
Year Founded: 1973
AURA—(THA)
Rev.: $873,573,497
Assets: $391,519,491
Liabilities: $225,774,491
Net Worth: $165,745,000
Earnings: $24,814,050
Fiscal Year-end: 12/31/23
Jewelry Product Mfr
N.A.I.C.S.: 339910
Prasit Srirungthum (Chm)

AURORA EIENDOM AS
Oravegen 4, 6650, Surnadal, Norway
Tel.: (47) 46448411   NO

Web Site: https://www.aurora.no
Year Founded: 2021
AURA—(EUR)
Rev.: $13,925,677
Assets: $856,206,943
Liabilities: $485,542,773
Net Worth: $370,664,170
Earnings: ($14,882,110)
Emp.: 158
Fiscal Year-end: 12/31/23
Real Estate Investment Services
N.A.I.C.S.: 531190
Lars Ove Loseth (CEO)

**AURORA FUNDS MANAGE-
MENT LIMITED**
Suite 613 Level 6 370 St Kilda Road,
Melbourne, 3004, VIC, Australia
Tel.: (61) 1300 553 431   AU
Web Site:
http://www.aurorafunds.com.au
Year Founded: 2000
Investment Fund Management Ser-
vices
N.A.I.C.S.: 523940
Donna Dwyer (Sr Mgr-Ops)

Subsidiaries:

**Aurora Property Buy-Write Income
Trust** (1)
Suite 613 Level 6 370 St Kilda Road, PO
Box 33281, Melbourne, 3004, VIC, Australia
Tel.: (61) 1300 553 431
Web Site: http://www.aurorafunds.com.au
Rev.: $234,680
Assets: $5,700,337
Liabilities: $280,976
Net Worth: $5,419,361
Earnings: ($1,301,167)
Fiscal Year-end: 06/30/2018
Closed-End Investment Fund
N.A.I.C.S.: 525990
John Patton (Mng Dir)

Subsidiary (Domestic):

RNY Property Trust (2)
The Huntley Group 37 Bligh Street Suite
301 Level 3, Sydney, 2000, NSW,
Australia   **(80.96%)**
Tel.: (61) 292335444
Real Estate Investment Trust
N.A.I.C.S.: 525990

**AURORA GLOBAL INCOME
TRUST**
Suite 613 Level 6 370 St Kilda Road,
Melbourne, 3004, VIC, Australia
Tel.: (61) 1300553431   AU
Web Site:
http://www.aurorafunds.com.au
Year Founded: 2007
AIB—(ASX)
Rev.: $82,715
Assets: $674,172
Liabilities: $13,349
Net Worth: $660,824
Fiscal Year-end: 06/30/21
Investment Management Service
N.A.I.C.S.: 523940
John Patton (Mng Dir)

**AURORA INVESTMENT TRUST
PLC**
64-66 Glentham Road, London,
SW13 9JJ, United Kingdom
Tel.: (44) 2086000100
Web Site:
https://www.aurorainvestmenttrust.com
ARR—(LSE)
Rev.: $1,638,768
Assets: $221,589,408
Liabilities: $388,308
Net Worth: $221,201,100
Earnings: ($2,999,203)
Fiscal Year-end: 12/31/20

Aurora Investment Trust PLC—(Continued)

Portfolio Management & Investment Advice
N.A.I.C.S.: 523940
Gary Channon (Partner)

AURORA LABS LIMITED
41-43 Wittenberg Drive, Canning Vale, 6155, WA, Australia
Tel.: (61) 894341934   AU
Web Site:
https://www.auroralabs3d.com
Year Founded: 2014
A3D—(ASX)
Rev.: $116,293
Assets: $2,055,975
Liabilities: $866,448
Net Worth: $1,189,527
Earnings: ($1,873,673)
Emp.: 10
Fiscal Year-end: 06/30/24
Metal Printer Mfr & Distr
N.A.I.C.S.: 333248
David Budge (Founder & Mng Dir)

AURORA MOBILE LIMITED
14/F China Certification and Inspection Building, No 8 Keji South 12th Road Nanshan District, Shenzhen, 518057, Guangdong, China
Tel.: (86) 75583881462   Ky
Web Site: https://ir.jiguang.cn
Year Founded: 2012
JG—(NASDAQ)
Rev.: $40,184,980
Assets: $48,486,237
Liabilities: $34,125,222
Net Worth: $14,361,016
Earnings: ($8,676,894)
Emp.: 371
Fiscal Year-end: 12/31/23
Data Analysis & Development services
N.A.I.C.S.: 518210
Fei Chen (Co-Founder & Pres)

AURORA OPTOELECTRONICS CO., LTD.
No 21 Tianxingqiao, Shapingba District, Harbin, 150431, China
Tel.: (86) 45151775068
Web Site: http://www.aurora-sapphire.cn
Sales Range: $150-199.9 Million
Pharmaceutical Product Mfr & Distr
N.A.I.C.S.: 325412
Hongbo Zuo (Chm & Gen Mgr)

AURORA ROYALTIES INC.
15 Polson Street, Toronto, M5A 1A4, ON, Canada
Tel.: (647) 749-9035   BC
Year Founded: 2007
AUR.H—(TSXV)
Assets: $40,007
Liabilities: $10,170
Net Worth: $29,838
Earnings: ($49,392)
Fiscal Year-end: 11/30/22
Metal Mining & Exploration Services
N.A.I.C.S.: 212290
Kieran Prashad (Pres & CEO)

AURORA S.A.
Str Stefan cel Mare nr 8, Targu Frumos, 6750, Iasi, Romania
Tel.: (40) 232710910
Web Site: http://www.aurorashoes.ro
Year Founded: 1991
AUR—(BUC)
Rev.: $719,859
Assets: $717,080
Liabilities: $405,364
Net Worth: $311,716
Earnings: $76,125
Emp.: 58

Fiscal Year-end: 12/31/19
Textile Products Mfr
N.A.I.C.S.: 314999

AURORA SOLAR TECHNOLOGIES INC.
100 - 788 Harbourside Drive, North Vancouver, V7P 3R7, BC, Canada
Tel.: (778) 241-5000   BC
Web Site:
https://www.aurorasolartech.com
Year Founded: 2006
A82—(DEU)
Rev.: $8,062,807
Assets: $7,531,343
Liabilities: $3,234,655
Net Worth: $4,296,688
Earnings: ($160,772)
Fiscal Year-end: 03/31/24
Production Measurement & Control Systems
N.A.I.C.S.: 334513
Joseph Lee (Interim CFO)

AURORA WORLD CORPORATION
Aurora World Building 624 Teheran-ro, Gangnam-gu, Seoul, Korea (South)
Tel.: (82) 234204114
Web Site: https://kor.auroraworld.com
Year Founded: 1985
039830—(KRS)
Rev.: $177,709,497
Assets: $355,860,897
Liabilities: $252,710,730
Net Worth: $103,150,167
Earnings: $5,627,258
Emp.: 153
Fiscal Year-end: 12/31/22
Toy Mfr & Game Developing Services
N.A.I.C.S.: 339930
Kim Yong Yeon (Dir)

AUROS TECHNOLOGY CO., LTD.
15-23 Dongtan Sandan 6-Gil, Dongtan-myeon, Hwaseong, 18487, Gyeonggi-do, Korea (South)
Tel.: (82) 3180468800
Web Site: https://www.aurostech.com
Year Founded: 2009
322310—(KRS)
Rev.: $27,150,422
Assets: $53,461,382
Liabilities: $6,618,574
Net Worth: $46,842,808
Earnings: ($2,284,128)
Emp.: 168
Fiscal Year-end: 12/31/22
Measuring Equipment Mfr
N.A.I.C.S.: 334515
Junwoo Lee (CEO)

AUROTEK CORPORATION
1Fl No 60 Jhouzih St, Neihu District, Taipei, 114, Taiwan
Tel.: (886) 287523311   TW
Web Site:
https://www.aurotek.com.tw
Year Founded: 1980
6215—(TAI)
Rev.: $32,164,196
Assets: $60,355,699
Liabilities: $10,424,605
Net Worth: $49,931,095
Earnings: $2,596,815
Emp.: 214
Fiscal Year-end: 12/31/23
Automation & Safety Systems Mfr & Distr
N.A.I.C.S.: 541512
Cody Yung-Chang Chang (Chm & CEO)

Subsidiaries:

Aurotek (Japan) Inc.   (1)
VORT Akihabara IV 2F 1-7-8 Kandasuda-cho, Mail No 101-0041, Chiyoda-ku, Tokyo, 101-0041, Japan
Tel.: (81) 352977028
Emp.: 4
Office Equipments Mfr
N.A.I.C.S.: 333216

Aurotek Corporation - Taoyuan Factory   (1)
1st Floor No 61 Lioufu Road, Lujhu Township, Taoyuan, 338, Taiwan
Tel.: (886) 33223788
Circuit Board Cutting Machinery Mfr & Distr
N.A.I.C.S.: 333517
Natalia Chang (Mgr-Sls)

Plenty Island (Thai) Co., Ltd.   (1)
3 Soi Charoenrat 10 Charoenrat Rd, Bangkhlo Bangkhorlaem, Bangkok, 10120, Thailand
Tel.: (66) 2 291 9933
Web Site: https://www.aurotek.com.tw
Sales Range: $25-49.9 Million
Emp.: 28
Industrial Machinery Whslr
N.A.I.C.S.: 423830

AURRIGO INTERNATIONAL PLC
Unit 33 Bilton Industrial Estate Humber Avenue, Coventry, CV3 1JL, United Kingdom
Tel.: (44) 2476635818   UK
Web Site: https://www.aurrigo.com
Year Founded: 2019
AURR—(AIM)
Automotive Parts Mfr & Distr
N.A.I.C.S.: 336310

Subsidiaries:

Aurrigo Pte. Ltd.   (1)
CAVE Changi Airport T2 B16-30 60 Boulevard S, Singapore, 819 643, Singapore
Tel.: (65) 86530881
Autonomous Passenger Vehicle Mfr & Distr
N.A.I.C.S.: 336999

AURSKOG SPAREBANK
Senterveien 15, 1930, Aurskog, 1930, Norway
Tel.: (47) 63854440
Web Site: https://www.aurskog-sparebank.no
Year Founded: 1846
AURG—(OSL)
Sales Range: Less than $1 Million
Commercial Banking Services
N.A.I.C.S.: 522110
Evy Ann Hagen (CEO & Mgr-Mng)

AURUBIS AG
Hovestrasse 50, 20539, Hamburg, Germany
Tel.: (49) 4078830   De
Web Site: http://www.aurubis.com
Year Founded: 1866
NDA—(DEU)
Rev.: $18,415,398,230
Assets: $7,834,697,820
Liabilities: $3,253,420,030
Net Worth: $4,581,277,790
Earnings: $152,097,993
Emp.: 7,230
Fiscal Year-end: 09/30/23
Copper Melting Mfr
N.A.I.C.S.: 551112
Fritz Vahrenholt (Chm-Supervisory Bd)

Subsidiaries:

Aurubis Berango S.L.U.   (1)
Arana Bidea 20, 48640, Berango, Bizkaia, Spain
Tel.: (34) 946689100
Web Site: https://www.aurubis.com
Emp.: 90
Solid Waste Recycling Services

N.A.I.C.S.: 562111

Aurubis Buffalo, Inc.   (1)
70 Sayre St, Buffalo, NY 14207-2299
Tel.: (716) 879-6700
Sales Range: $150-199.9 Million
Emp.: 650
Copper Product Distr
N.A.I.C.S.: 423510
Brad Groff (Dir-Sls)

Aurubis Engineering EAD   (1)
3 D-r Hristo Stambolski Str, Sofia, 1463, Bulgaria
Tel.: (359) 2 954 95 60
Copper Product Mfr
N.A.I.C.S.: 332999
Angel Kostov (Gen Mgr)

Aurubis Finland Oy   (1)
Kuparitie, PO Box 60, 28101, Pori, Finland
Tel.: (358) 26266111
Web Site: https://www.aurubis.fi
Sales Range: $25-49.9 Million
Emp.: 290
Steel Copper Mfr
N.A.I.C.S.: 331529
Hannu Heiskanen (Mng Dir)

Aurubis Metal Products (Shanghai) Co., Ltd   (1)
Unit20 Floor16 Lande Dongting Building No 319 Middle Zhenghe Road, Taicang, 215400, Jiangsu, China
Tel.: (86) 2158683370
Web Site: http://www.auribis.com
Emp.: 7
Copper Product Mfr & Distr
N.A.I.C.S.: 332999
Rich Wang (Gen Mgr)

Aurubis Middle East FZE   (1)
Jafza One Tower Office No 606 Jebel Ali Free Zone, PO Box 263498, Dubai, United Arab Emirates
Tel.: (971) 43366704
Non Ferrous Metal Mfr
N.A.I.C.S.: 331491
Majed Joumaa (Mng Dir)

Aurubis Netherlands B.V.   (1)
Oostzeestraat 1, 7202 CM, Zutphen, Netherlands
Tel.: (31) 575 594 594
Emp.: 220
Copper & Copper Alloy Mfr
N.A.I.C.S.: 331420
Ad van Trier (Mgr-Production)

Aurubis Slovakia s.r.o.   (1)
Mokradska 2931, 026 01, Dolny Kubin, Slovakia
Tel.: (421) 435832111
Web Site: http://www.aurubis.sk
Sales Range: $25-49.9 Million
Emp.: 8
Rolled Non-Ferrous Alloy Mfr
N.A.I.C.S.: 331420
Tadeusz Kipiel (Mng Dir)

Aurubis Stolberg GmbH & Co. KG   (1)
Zweifaller Strasse 150, 52224, Stolberg, Germany
Tel.: (49) 240212410
Web Site: http://www.aurubis-stolberg.com
Sales Range: $100-124.9 Million
Emp.: 400
Producer of Semi-Finished Products of Copper & Copper Alloys
N.A.I.C.S.: 331529

Aurubis Stolberg Verwaltungs GmbH   (1)
Zweifaller Strasse 150, 52224, Stolberg, Germany
Tel.: (49) 240212410
Web Site: https://www.aurubis.com
Emp.: 40
Copper Product Mfr
N.A.I.C.S.: 331410

Aurubis Sweden AB   (1)
Trefasgatan 1, 721 30, Vasteras, Sweden
Tel.: (46) 21198000
Sales Range: $25-49.9 Million
Emp.: 113
Copper & Copper-Alloy Sheets, Strips & Plates Products Mfr & Sales
N.A.I.C.S.: 331420

Per Bjorklund *(Mng Dir)*

Branch (Domestic):

Aurubis Sweden (2)
Slottsvagen 1, SE 61281, Finspang, Sweden
Tel.: (46) 12283700
Sales Range: $25-49.9 Million
Copper & Copper Alloy Products Sales
N.A.I.C.S.: 423510

Aurubis UK Limited (1)
Rabone Lane, Rabone Park, Smethwick, B66 2NN, West Midlands, United
Kingdom (100%)
Tel.: (44) 1215551199
Web Site: http://www.aurubis.co.uk
Sales Range: $25-49.9 Million
Emp.: 25
Rolled Copper & Brass Products Mfr
N.A.I.C.S.: 331420
Brian Middleton *(Mng Dir)*

Aurubis nv/sa (1)
Broekstraat 31 Rue du Marais, 1000, Brussels, Belgium
Tel.: (32) 22271222
Web Site: http://www.aurubis.com
Sales Range: $1-4.9 Billion
Emp.: 1,443
Holding Company; Copper Smelting, Refining & Recycling
N.A.I.C.S.: 551112

Subsidiary (Non-US):

Aurubis Bulgaria AD (2)
Industrial Zone, Pirdop, 2070, Sofia, Bulgaria
Tel.: (359) 72862280
Web Site: https://www.aurubis.com
Sales Range: $1-4.9 Billion
Emp.: 850
Copper Smelting & Refining
N.A.I.C.S.: 331410

Aurubis Italia Srl (2)
Nucleo Industriale, Pianodardine, 83100, Avellino, Italy
Tel.: (39) 0825625507
Web Site: http://www.aurubis.com
Sales Range: $25-49.9 Million
Emp.: 100
Copper Smelting & Refining
N.A.I.C.S.: 331410

Aurubis Mortara S.p.A. (2)
Via Enrico Fermi 52, 27036, Mortara, Italy
Tel.: (39) 0384 90156
Copper Product Mfr & Distr
N.A.I.C.S.: 332999

Aurubis Rus LLC (2)
19-ya Liniya 34 Korp 1 Liter B, 199178, Saint Petersburg, Russia
Tel.: (7) 812 4492797
Copper Product Mfr
N.A.I.C.S.: 332999
Victoria Kuznechenkova *(Gen Mgr)*

Plant (Domestic):

Aurubis nv/sa - Olen (2)
Watertorenstraat 35, 2250, Olen, Belgium
Tel.: (32) 14243111
Web Site: http://belgium.aurubis.com
Sales Range: $150-199.9 Million
Emp.: 530
Copper Processing
N.A.I.C.S.: 331410

CABLO Metall-Recycling und Handel GmbH (1)
Flugplatzstrasse 1-2, 16833, Fehrbellin, Germany (100%)
Tel.: (49) 339326190
Web Site: http://www.cablo.de
Sales Range: $25-49.9 Million
Emp.: 60
Cable Metal Recycling Services
N.A.I.C.S.: 423930
Claudia Borgwardt *(Asst Mgr-Logistics)*

Deutsche Giessdraht GmbH (1)
Kupferstr 5, 46446, Emmerich am Rhein, Germany (100%)
Tel.: (49) 28227800
Web Site: http://www.deutsche-giessdraht.de

Sales Range: $25-49.9 Million
Emp.: 110
Copper Processing & Mfg
N.A.I.C.S.: 331420
Alexander Khoury *(Mng Dir)*

E.R.N. Elektro-Recycling NORD GmbH (1)
Peutestrasse 21-23, 20539, Hamburg, Germany
Tel.: (49) 407804780
Emp.: 15
Electronic Equipment Recycling Services
N.A.I.C.S.: 562998

Huttenbau Gesellschaft Peute mbH (1)
Hovestr 50, Hamburg, 20539, Germany
Tel.: (49) 4078830
Copper Mining Services
N.A.I.C.S.: 212230

Peute Baustoff GmbH (1)
Peutestrasse 79, 20539, Hamburg, Germany (100%)
Tel.: (49) 407891600
Web Site: http://www.peute.de
Emp.: 12
Stone Construction Products Mfr & Distr
N.A.I.C.S.: 327991
Marc Waltemathe *(Mng Dir)*

RETORTE GmbH (1)
Selenium Chemicals Metals Sulzbacher Strasse 45, a d Pegnitz, 90552, Rothenbach, Germany (100%)
Tel.: (49) 9119533740
Web Site: https://www.retorte.com
Sales Range: $25-49.9 Million
Emp.: 35
Chemical & Metal Products Mfr
N.A.I.C.S.: 325180

Schwermetall Halbzeugwerk GmbH & Co. KG (1)
Breiniger Berg 165, 52223, Stolberg, Germany
Tel.: (49) 24027610
Web Site: https://www.schwermetall.de
Sales Range: $125-149.9 Million
Emp.: 320
Metal Pre-Rolled Strips Mfr
N.A.I.C.S.: 331420

AURUM PACIFIC (CHINA) GROUP LIMITED
21st Floor Henan Building 90 Jaffe Road, Wanchai, China (Hong Kong)
Tel.: (852) 31027188 Ky
Web Site:
  http://www.aurumpacific.com.hk
8148—(HKG)
Rev.: $2,733,090
Assets: $2,495,175
Liabilities: $1,777,988
Net Worth: $717,188
Earnings: ($2,718,938)
Emp.: 52
Fiscal Year-end: 12/31/22
Software Development Services
N.A.I.C.S.: 541511

Subsidiaries:

KanHan Technologies Limited (1)
22/F Hua Fu Commercial Building 111 Queen's Road West, Hong Kong, China (Hong Kong)
Tel.: (852) 2 865 3800
Web Site: https://www.kanhan.com
Application Software Development Services
N.A.I.C.S.: 541511

AURUM PROPTECH LTD.
Aurum Q1 Aurum Q Parc Thane Belapur Road, Mumbai, 400 710, Maharashtra, India
Tel.: (91) 2261501800
Web Site:
  https://www.aurumproptech.in
539289—(BOM)
Sales Range: $1-9.9 Million
Software Publishing Services
N.A.I.C.S.: 513210
Kunal Karan *(CFO)*

Subsidiaries:

Aurum Analytica Private Limited (1)
A-33 3rd Floor A-Block Sector 2 Near Sector 15 Metro Station, Noida, 201301, Uttar Pradesh, India
Tel.: (91) 1204565098
Web Site: https://www.aurumanalytica.in
Real Estate Investment Services
N.A.I.C.S.: 531210

Aurum Softwares And Solutions Private Limited (1)
Aurum Building Q1 Thane - Belapur Rd, Ghansoli Thane, Navi Mumbai, 400710, India
Tel.: (91) 27781271
Web Site:
  https://www.aurumsoftwaresolutions.com
Information Technology Consulting Services
N.A.I.C.S.: 518210

Helloworld Technologies India Private Limited (1)
375 5th Main Rd Sector 6 HSR Layout, Bengaluru, 560102, Karnataka, India
Tel.: (91) 8880008888
Web Site: https://thehelloworld.com
Real Estate Management Services
N.A.I.C.S.: 531311

NestAway Technologies Private Limited (1)
1471 Nestaway 13th Cross Road HSR Layout Sector 1, Urban, Bengaluru, 560102, Karnataka, India
Tel.: (91) 8904242424
Web Site: https://www.nestaway.com
Property Rental Services
N.A.I.C.S.: 531110

AURUM RESOURCES LIMITED
Suite 11 23 Railway Road, Perth, 6008, WA, Australia
Tel.: (61) 865591792 AU
Web Site:
  https://www.aurumres.com.au
Year Founded: 2021
AUE—(ASX)
Rev.: $9,030
Assets: $1,448,379
Liabilities: $39,619
Net Worth: $1,408,760
Earnings: ($787,244)
Emp.: 2
Fiscal Year-end: 06/30/23
Gold & Metal Exploration Services
N.A.I.C.S.: 213114
Mauro Piccini *(Sec)*

AURUMIN LIMITED
Suite 2 Ground Floor 17 Ord Street, West Perth, 6005, WA, Australia
Tel.: (61) 865552950 AU
Web Site:
  https://www.aurumin.com.au
AUN—(ASX)
Rev.: $70,518
Assets: $11,326,448
Liabilities: $4,035,712
Net Worth: $7,290,736
Earnings: ($4,013,168)
Fiscal Year-end: 06/30/23
Mineral Exploration Services
N.A.I.C.S.: 212390
Bradley Tristan Jurganas Valiukas *(Mng Dir)*

AURWEST RESOURCES CORPORATION
Suite 650 340 - 12th Avenue S W, Calgary, T2R 1L5, AB, Canada
Tel.: (403) 585-9875 BC
Web Site:
  https://aurwestresources.com
Year Founded: 2008
AURWF—(OTCIQ)
Assets: $4,858,575
Liabilities: $290,892
Net Worth: $4,567,684
Earnings: ($550,796)

Fiscal Year-end: 12/31/21
Gold Mining Services
N.A.I.C.S.: 212220

AUS ASIA MINERALS LIMITED
125 Royal Street, Perth, 6005, WA, Australia
Tel.: (61) 8 9325 3000
Web Site:
  http://www.ausasiaminerals.com
Sales Range: Less than $1 Million
Coal Exploration & Mining Services
N.A.I.C.S.: 212115
Hirotaka Suzuki *(Chm & Mng Dir)*

AUSCANN GROUP HOLDINGS PTY LTD
PO Box 1976, West Perth, 6872, WA, Australia
Tel.: (61) 64441720 AU
Web Site:
  https://www.auscann.com.au
Year Founded: 2014
AC8—(ASX)
Rev.: $1,404,927
Assets: $34,570,003
Liabilities: $529,947
Net Worth: $34,040,056
Earnings: ($6,620,947)
Fiscal Year-end: 06/30/21
Wine Mfr & Distr
N.A.I.C.S.: 312130
Mal Washer *(Chm)*

Subsidiaries:

CannPal Animal Therapeutics Limited (1)
Level 3 45a Bay Street, Double Bay, 2028, NSW, Australia
Tel.: (61) 261083622
Web Site: http://www.cannpal.com
Rev.: $535,212
Assets: $1,361,106
Liabilities: $233,753
Net Worth: $1,127,353
Earnings: ($1,191,461)
Fiscal Year-end: 06/30/2020
Biomedical Research Services
N.A.I.C.S.: 541715
Layton Patrick Mills *(Founder, CEO & Mng Dir)*

AUSGOLD LIMITED
Level 1 307 Murray Street, Perth, 6000, WA, Australia
Tel.: (61) 892209890
Web Site:
  https://www.ausgoldlimited.com
AU4—(DEU)
Rev.: $294,681
Assets: $56,676,437
Liabilities: $1,682,616
Net Worth: $54,993,821
Earnings: ($1,981,654)
Fiscal Year-end: 06/30/22
Gold Ore & Silver Ore Mining
N.A.I.C.S.: 212220
Denis Ivan Rakich *(Sec & Exec Dir)*

AUSGROUP LIMITED
3 Shenton Way 21-04 Shenton House, Singapore, 068805, Singapore
Tel.: (65) 62264222 SG
Web Site:
  http://www.ausgroupltd.com
Year Founded: 2004
5GJ—(SES)
Rev.: $187,756,392
Assets: $106,125,743
Liabilities: $101,339,354
Net Worth: $4,786,389
Earnings: ($24,275,198)
Emp.: 1,000
Fiscal Year-end: 06/30/22
Construction Services
N.A.I.C.S.: 236210

AusGroup Limited—(Continued)

Subsidiaries:

AGC Australia Pty Ltd   **(1)**
Level 1 18-32 Parliament Place, West Perth, 6005, WA, Australia
Tel.: (61) 800570532
Web Site: http://www.ausgroupltd.com
Emp.: 200
Construction Engineering Services
N.A.I.C.S.: 541330

AGC Industries Pty Ltd   **(1)**
Level 2 251 Saint Georges Terrace, Perth, 6000, WA, Australia
Tel.: (61) 894391934
Construction Engineering Services
N.A.I.C.S.: 541330

Access Australasia Sdn. Bhd.   **(1)**
B1-6-2 The Soho Suites Klcc Jalan Perak, Kuala Lumpur, 50450, Malaysia
Tel.: (60) 321817991
Building Construction Services
N.A.I.C.S.: 236220

AusGroup Corporation Co., Ltd.   **(1)**
209/36 M 10 T Tungsukhla A, Si Racha, Chon Buri, 20230, Thailand
Tel.: (66) 33047009
Building Construction Services
N.A.I.C.S.: 236220

MAS Australasia Pty Ltd   **(1)**
34 Clune St, Bayswater, Perth, 6053, WA, Australia
Tel.: (61) 893797222
Sales Range: $25-49.9 Million
Emp.: 40
Construction Engineering Services
N.A.I.C.S.: 541330

Modern Access Services Singapore Pte. Ltd.   **(1)**
12 Tuas Avenue 1, Singapore, 639497, Singapore
Tel.: (65) 68631971
Building Construction Services
N.A.I.C.S.: 236220
Mohamad Tahir *(Mgr-Contracts)*

NT Port & Marine Pty. Ltd.   **(1)**
31 Muramats Road, East Arm, Darwin, 0822, NT, Australia
Tel.: (61) 889306500
Marine Chartering Services
N.A.I.C.S.: 483111
Lindsay Whiting *(Mgr-Port)*

AUSMANI LIMITED
16 James Street, Geelong, 3220, VIC, Australia
Tel.: (61) 352255400   AU
Sales Range: $1-9.9 Million
Emp.: 18
Web Entertainment Services
N.A.I.C.S.: 516210
Vincent Sweeney *(Chm)*

Subsidiaries:

World Wide Entertainment Production & Sales Pty. Ltd.   **(1)**
Level 5 83 Moorabool St, Geelong, 3220, VIC, Australia
Tel.: (61) 352255400
Television Program Production & Broadcasting Services
N.A.I.C.S.: 516120

Subsidiary (Domestic):

Genr8 Digital Media Pty Ltd.   **(2)**
16 James St, Geelong, 3220, VIC, Australia
Tel.: (61) 3 5225 5475
Online Digital Media Services
N.A.I.C.S.: 513199

AUSMON RESOURCES LIMITED
Suite 1312 87-89 Liverpool Street, Sydney, 2000, NSW, Australia
Tel.: (61) 292646988
Web Site:
https://www.ausmonresources.com

AOA—(ASX)
Rev.: $131,054
Assets: $1,888,205
Liabilities: $644,603
Net Worth: $1,243,602
Earnings: ($243,821)
Emp.: 50
Fiscal Year-end: 06/30/24
Metal Exploration & Mining Services
N.A.I.C.S.: 212290
John Qiang Wang *(Mng Dir)*

AUSOM ENTERPRISE LIMITED
606-Swagat Building Near Lal Bunglow CG Road, Ahmedabad, 380 006, India
Tel.: (91) 7926421455
Web Site: https://www.ausom.in
509009—(BOM)
Rev.: $4,593,116
Assets: $18,312,990
Liabilities: $2,402,304
Net Worth: $15,910,686
Earnings: $732,623
Emp.: 3
Fiscal Year-end: 03/30/22
Gold & Silver Distr
N.A.I.C.S.: 423520
Kishor Pranjivandas Mandalia *(CEO & Mng Dir)*

AUSON AB
Verkstadsgatan 3, Kungsbacka, 43442, Sweden
Tel.: (46) 300562000
Web Site: http://www.auson.se
Year Founded: 1928
Emp.: 50
Mfr of Rust Protection, Sound Damping, Roof Care & Wood Protection Products
N.A.I.C.S.: 325194

AUSQUEST LIMITED
8 Kearns Crescent, Ardross, Ardross, 6153, WA, Australia
Tel.: (61) 893643866
Web Site:
https://www.ausquest.com.au
AQD—(ASX)
Rev.: $149,938
Assets: $5,663,946
Liabilities: $458,331
Net Worth: $5,205,615
Earnings: ($555,421)
Emp.: 8
Fiscal Year-end: 06/30/24
Mineral Exploration Services
N.A.I.C.S.: 213115
Graeme Drew *(Mng Dir)*

AUSSIE BROADBAND LTD.
Tel.: (61) 1300880905
Web Site:
https://www.aussiebroadband.com
Year Founded: 2008
ABB—(ASX)
Rev.: $667,572,397
Assets: $826,499,859
Liabilities: $445,819,950
Net Worth: $380,679,909
Earnings: $17,614,313
Fiscal Year-end: 06/30/24
Internet Service Provider
N.A.I.C.S.: 517121
Phillip Britt *(Co-Founder & Mng Dir)*

Subsidiaries:

Symbio Holdings Limited   **(1)**
Level 4 580 George Street, Sydney, 2000, NSW, Australia
Tel.: (61) 280088000
Web Site: http://www.symbio.global
Rev.: $156,103,551
Assets: $160,623,305
Liabilities: $45,654,964
Net Worth: $114,968,342
Earnings: $11,935,708

Emp.: 400
Fiscal Year-end: 06/30/2021
VoIP Broadband Phone Services & IP Convergent Solutions
N.A.I.C.S.: 517112
Catherine Ly *(Treas & Sec)*

Subsidiary (Domestic):

My Net Fone Australia Pty Limited   **(2)**
L 2 10-14 Waterloo St, Surry Hills, 2010, NSW, Australia
Tel.: (61) 280088000
Web Site: http://www.mynetfone.com.au
Emp.: 1,000
Internet Telecommunication Services
N.A.I.C.S.: 517810
Rene Sugo *(CEO)*

AUST & HACHMANN E.K.
Neumann Reichardt Strasse 27 33, DE-22041, Hamburg, Germany
Tel.: (49) 403116700
Web Site: http://www.hachmann-vanilla.de
Year Founded: 1881
Rev.: $16,925,238
Emp.: 20
Vanilla Beans Distr
N.A.I.C.S.: 424510
Berend Hachmann *(Owner)*

AUSTAL LIMITED
100 Clarence Beach Road, Henderson, 6166, WA, Australia
Tel.: (61) 894101111
Web Site: https://www.austal.com
Year Founded: 1988
AUTLF—(OTCIQ)
Rev.: $1,094,919,222
Assets: $1,294,435,865
Liabilities: $586,257,940
Net Worth: $708,177,924
Earnings: $60,961,907
Emp.: 5,000
Fiscal Year-end: 06/30/22
Ship Building & Repairing
N.A.I.C.S.: 336611
David Patrick Alexander Singleton *(CEO & Mng Dir)*

Subsidiaries:

Austal Cairns Pty. Ltd.   **(1)**
61-79 Cook Street, Cairns, QLD, Australia
Tel.: (61) 740419700
Ship Repairing Services
N.A.I.C.S.: 541350

Austal Muscat LLC   **(1)**
Al Zubair Commercial Complex Mina Al Fahal, PO Box 896, 116, Muscat, Oman
Tel.: (968) 24498532
Transportation Equipment Distr
N.A.I.C.S.: 423860

Austal USA LLC   **(1)**
1 Dunlap Dr, Mobile, AL 36602
Tel.: (251) 434-8000
Web Site: https://usa.austal.com
Emp.: 2,500
Transportation Equipment Distr
N.A.I.C.S.: 423860

Austal Viet Nam Co., Ltd.   **(1)**
Street No 12 Dong Xuyen Industrial Zone, Rach Dua Ward, Vung Tau, Bia Ria-Vung Tau, Vietnam
Tel.: (84) 2543857572
Web Site: https://vietnam.austal.com
Emp.: 450
Transportation Equipment Distr
N.A.I.C.S.: 423860

ElectraWatch Inc.   **(1)**
660 Hunters Pl Ste 102, Charlottesville, VA 22911
Tel.: (434) 970-7878
Web Site: http://www.electrawatch.com
Engineering Services
N.A.I.C.S.: 541330
Ryan Dunn *(Gen Mgr)*

AUSTAR GOLD LIMITED

Bridge Street, Woods Point, Melbourne, 3723, VIC, Australia
Tel.: (61) 57778268   AU
Web Site: http://www.austargold.com
AUL—(ASX)
Rev.: $4,709,218
Assets: $1,355,115
Liabilities: $2,150,960
Net Worth: ($795,845)
Earnings: ($1,160,323)
Fiscal Year-end: 06/30/20
Minerals Exploration
N.A.I.C.S.: 213115
Paul McNally *(Chm)*

AUSTAR LIFESCIENCES LIMITED
Room 1801 Building B Chaowai Men Office Building 26 Chaowai Street, Chaoyang District, Beijing, China
Tel.: (86) 4008121586
Web Site: http://www.austar.com.hk
6118—(HKG)
Rev.: $312,901,618
Assets: $335,382,325
Liabilities: $211,327,553
Net Worth: $124,054,772
Earnings: $9,511,258
Emp.: 1,913
Fiscal Year-end: 12/31/22
Chemical & Pharmaceutical Equipment
N.A.I.C.S.: 333248
Mars Kwok Keung Ho *(Founder, Chm & CEO)*

AUSTASIA GROUP LTD.
No 9 Guangbei Road Agricultural High-tech Zone, Guangrao, Dongying, Shandong, China
Tel.: (86) 5466435337   SG
Web Site:
https://www.austasiadairy.com
Year Founded: 1997
2425—(HKG)
Rev.: $562,786,000
Assets: $1,542,141,000
Liabilities: $741,837,000
Net Worth: $800,304,000
Earnings: $23,394,000
Emp.: 2,388
Fiscal Year-end: 12/31/22
Investment Management Service
N.A.I.C.S.: 523999
Yong Nang Tan *(Chm)*

AUSTCHINA HOLDINGS LTD
Level 7 344 Queen Street, Brisbane, 4000, QLD, Australia
Tel.: (61) 732296606   AU
Web Site:
https://www.austchinaholdings.com
AUH—(ASX)
Rev.: $13,724
Assets: $11,444,730
Liabilities: $1,090,325
Net Worth: $10,354,405
Earnings: ($941,718)
Fiscal Year-end: 06/30/24
Low Carbon Emission Coal Exploration & Production Services
N.A.I.C.S.: 212115
Bruce Patrick *(COO)*

AUSTEM CO., LTD.
739 Susin-ro Susin-myeon, Dongnam-gu, Cheonan, Chungnam, Korea (South)
Tel.: (82) 415592500
Web Site: https://www.austem.com
Year Founded: 1990
031510—(KRS)
Rev.: $85,054,605
Assets: $143,626,169
Liabilities: $70,520,343
Net Worth: $73,105,826
Earnings: ($10,415,786)

Emp.: 300
Fiscal Year-end: 12/31/22
Automobile Parts Mfr
N.A.I.C.S.: 336390
Kim Jeong-U *(Dir-Rep)*

Subsidiaries:

Austem Co., Ltd. - Sejong Plant
1   **(1)**
35 Sandan-gil, Jeonui-myeon, Sejong, Korea (South)
Tel.: (82) 448606411
Automobile Parts Distr
N.A.I.C.S.: 441330

Austem Co., Ltd. - Sejong Plant
2   **(1)**
105 Sandan-gil, Jeonui-myeon, Sejong, Korea (South)
Tel.: (82) 448608200
Automobile Parts Distr
N.A.I.C.S.: 441330

LLC JV O'Zauto-Austem   **(1)**
73 Bobur Shoh Street, Andijan, 170127,
Uzbekistan
Tel.: (998) 742280701
Automotive Parts Services
N.A.I.C.S.: 811121

POS-AUSTEM Kunshan Automotive
Co., Ltd.   **(1)**
1368 Fengxing Rd, Husqiao Town, Kunshan, Jiangsu, China
Tel.: (86) 51257600111
Automobile Parts Distr
N.A.I.C.S.: 441330

POS-AUSTEM Suzhou Automotive
Co., Ltd.   **(1)**
No 168 Longquan Road Automotive Park
Ceda, Logquanyi, Chengdu, 610100, China
Tel.: (86) 2888495152
Automobile Parts Distr
N.A.I.C.S.: 441330

POS-AUSTEM Wuhan Automotive
Co., Ltd.   **(1)**
No 8 Henger Road, Qingling Industrial Park
Hongshan District, Wuhan, Hubei, China
Tel.: (86) 2781521885
Automobile Parts Distr
N.A.I.C.S.: 441330

POS-AUSTEM Yantai Automotive
Co., Ltd.   **(1)**
ChangJiang Road Yeda, Yantai, Shandong,
China
Tel.: (86) 5353978300
Automobile Parts Distr
N.A.I.C.S.: 441330

AUSTEVOLL SEAFOOD ASA
Alfabygget, 5392, Storebo, Norway
Tel.: (47) 56181000   NO
Web Site: https://www.auss.no
Z85—(DEU)
Rev.: $2,879,087,382
Assets: $4,439,497,506
Liabilities: $1,838,167,375
Net Worth: $2,601,330,131
Earnings: $230,001,847
Emp.: 7,235
Fiscal Year-end: 12/31/22
Commercial Fishing & Fish Processing
N.A.I.C.S.: 114119
Helge Singelstad *(Chm)*

Subsidiaries:

Austevoll Fiskeindustri AS   **(1)**
Alfabygget, 5392, Storebo, Norway
Tel.: (47) 5618 1000
Web Site: http://www.aufi.no
Processing of Salmon & Pelagic Products
N.A.I.C.S.: 311710

Austral Group S.A.A.   **(1)**
Av Victor A Belaunde No 147 Torre Real 1
Piso 3-Centro, Torre Real 7 Centro Empresarial, Empresarial Real San Isidro, 15073,
Lima, Peru   **(89.26%)**
Tel.: (51) 17085900
Web Site: https://www.austral.com.pe
Emp.: 1,200

Production of Fishmeal, Fish Oil, Canned
Fish & Frozen Fish
N.A.I.C.S.: 114111
Luis A. Gonzalez *(Founder)*

Dragoy Grossist AS   **(1)**
Huldervegen 18, 9016, Tromso, Norway
Tel.: (47) 91339479
Fish & Seafood Distr
N.A.I.C.S.: 424460

Epax Norway AS   **(1)**
Aarsaethervegen 17, 6006, Alesund, Norway
Tel.: (47) 70135960
Web Site: https://www.epax.com
Chemical & Pharmaceutical Product Mfr
N.A.I.C.S.: 325412

FoodCorp S.A.   **(1)**
Av Pedro Aguirre Cerda 995, Coronel,
Chile   **(100%)**
Tel.: (56) 412922411
Web Site: https://www.fcc.cl
Production of Fishmeal, Fishoil, Canned
Fish & Frozen Fish
N.A.I.C.S.: 114111

Leroy Bulandet AS   **(1)**
Hellersoyvegen 88, 6987, Bulandet, Norway
Tel.: (47) 57733030
Fish & Seafood Distr
N.A.I.C.S.: 424460

Leroy Norge AS   **(1)**
Stanseveien 33, 0976, Oslo, Norway
Tel.: (47) 22821800
Fish & Seafood Distr
N.A.I.C.S.: 424460

Leroy Seafood Danmark A/S   **(1)**
Soren Nordbysvej 27-29, 9850, Hirtshals,
Denmark
Tel.: (45) 98945777
Web Site: https://leroyseafood.dk
Frozen Fish Product Retailer
N.A.I.C.S.: 445250

Leroy Seafood Group ASA   **(1)**
Thormohlens gate 51 B, 5006, Bergen,
Norway   **(70.59%)**
Tel.: (47) 55213650
Web Site: http://www.leroyseafood.com
Rev.: $3,034,653,829
Assets: $4,071,657,605
Liabilities: $2,115,723,372
Net Worth: $1,955,934,233
Earnings: $20,698,459
Emp.: 6,000
Fiscal Year-end: 12/31/2023
Distribution, Sales, Marketing & Processing
of Seafood; Production of Salmon, Trout &
Other Fish
N.A.I.C.S.: 311710
Helge Singelstad *(Chm)*

Subsidiary (Domestic):

Finnmark Havfiske AS   **(2)**
Lovenvoldgt 11, 6001, Alesund, Norway
Tel.: (47) 70118600
Seafood Whslr
N.A.I.C.S.: 424460
Ari Theodor Josefsson *(Mng Dir)*

Hammerfest Industrifiske AS   **(2)**
Harbor Road 44, Rypefjord, 9610, Hammerfest, Norway
Tel.: (47) 70118600
Seafood Whslr
N.A.I.C.S.: 424460
Ronny Vagsholm *(Mng Dir)*

Havfisk ASA   **(2)**
Keiser Wilhelmsgate 23, 6002, Alesund,
Norway
Tel.: (47) 70 11 86 00
Web Site: http://www.havfisk.no
Finfish Fishing; Seafood Products Export
Services
N.A.I.C.S.: 114111
Eldar Kare Farstad *(CFO)*

Laks- & Vildtcentralen AS   **(2)**
Stanseveien 33, 0976, Oslo, Norway
Tel.: (47) 2 282 1800
Web Site: https://www.laksogvilt.no
Emp.: 60
Seafood Distr
N.A.I.C.S.: 424460
Thorbjornsen Ole *(Mgr-Pur)*

Leroy Alfheim AS   **(2)**
Skuteviksboder 1-2, PO Box 7600, 5020,
Bergen, Norway
Tel.: (47) 55303900
Seafood Whslr
N.A.I.C.S.: 424460

Leroy Aurora AS   **(2)**
Kystens Hus Stortorget 1, PO Box 2123,
9267, Tromso, Norway
Tel.: (47) 77609300
Seafood Whslr
N.A.I.C.S.: 424460
Anna Hanssen *(Project Mgr-Cleaner Fish)*

Leroy Delico AS   **(2)**
Varabergmyra 2, 4051, Sola, Norway
Tel.: (47) 51718900
Seafood Whslr
N.A.I.C.S.: 424460
Bjorn Jakobsen *(Gen Mgr)*

Subsidiary (Non-US):

Leroy Finland OY   **(2)**
Pajakatu 2, 20320, Turku, Finland
Tel.: (358) 2 434 9800
Web Site: https://www.leroy.fi
Fish Product Distr
N.A.I.C.S.: 424460
Monika Nars *(Mng Dir)*

Subsidiary (Domestic):

Leroy Fossen AS   **(2)**
Reigstadvegen 39, 5281, Valestrandsfossen, Norway
Tel.: (47) 56193230
Seafood Whslr
N.A.I.C.S.: 424460
Oystein Vie *(Gen Mgr)*

Leroy Midt AS   **(2)**
Industriparken 31, Sandstad, 7246, Hitra,
Norway
Tel.: (47) 72465000
Seafood Whslr
N.A.I.C.S.: 424460
Robert Sandslett *(Reg Mgr)*

Leroy Norway Seafoods AS   **(2)**
Buoyveien 7, 8340, Stamsund, Norway
Tel.: (47) 76062000
Seafood Whslr
N.A.I.C.S.: 424460
Borge Soleng *(CEO)*

Subsidiary (Domestic):

Melbu Fryselager AS   **(3)**
Villaveien 1, 8445, Melbu, Norway
Tel.: (47) 7 615 4400
Web Site: https://www.melbufrys.no
Seafood Whslr
N.A.I.C.S.: 424460

Subsidiary (Non-US):

Leroy Portugal Lda.   **(2)**
Escritorio 11/12 Marl Lugar Di Ouintanilho
Pavilhao R-07, S Juliao Do Tojal, 2670-838,
Loures, Portugal
Tel.: (351) 219369960
Seafood Whslr
N.A.I.C.S.: 424460
Rita Costa *(Mgr-HR)*

Leroy Processing Spain SL   **(2)**
C/ Artisans 4, Pinto, 28320, Madrid, Spain
Tel.: (34) 91 691 8678
Web Site: https://www.leroyseafood.com
Seafood Whslr
N.A.I.C.S.: 424460
Antonio Diez Sanchez *(CEO)*

Subsidiary (Domestic):

Leroy Seafood AS   **(2)**
Thormohlens Gate 51 B, 5006, Bergen,
Norway
Tel.: (47) 55213650
Seafood Whslr
N.A.I.C.S.: 424460
Henning Beltestad *(CEO)*

Leroy Seafood AS   **(2)**
Thormohlens Gate 51 B, 5006, Bergen,
Norway
Tel.: (47) 55213650
Seafood Whslr
N.A.I.C.S.: 424460

Henning Beltestad *(CEO)*

Subsidiary (US):

Leroy Seafood USA Inc.   **(3)**
1289 Fordham Blvd Ste 406, Chapel Hill,
NC 27514
Tel.: (919) 967-1895
Seafood Whslr
N.A.I.C.S.: 424460

Subsidiary (Non-US):

SAS Leroy Seafood France   **(3)**
640 Rue Commios, 62223, Saint-Laurent-
Blangy, France
Tel.: (33) 321156907
Web Site: https://www.leroyseafood.fr
Seafood Whslr
N.A.I.C.S.: 424460
Jean Pierre Gonda *(CEO)*

Subsidiary (Domestic):

SAS Eurosalmo   **(4)**
127 Rue des Mures, 69220, Saint-Jean-
d'Ardieres, France
Tel.: (33) 474077070
Seafood Whslr
N.A.I.C.S.: 424460

Subsidiary (Non-US):

Leroy Seafood Holding B.V.   **(2)**
Schulpengat 10, PO Box 54, 8320 AB, Urk,
Netherlands
Tel.: (31) 527685357
Seafood Whslr
N.A.I.C.S.: 424460
Gerrit Wakker *(CFO)*

Leroy Sverige AB   **(2)**
Odegarden 10, Box 24, Smogen, 456 25,
Sotenas, Sweden
Tel.: (46) 8811400
Seafood Whslr
N.A.I.C.S.: 424460

Subsidiary (Domestic):

Leroy Seafood AB   **(3)**
Arntorpsgatan 18, 442 45, Kungalv, Sweden
Tel.: (46) 31857500
Seafood Whslr
N.A.I.C.S.: 424460

Leroy Smogen Seafood AB   **(3)**
PO Box 24, Smogan, 456 25, Sotenas,
Sweden
Tel.: (46) 523667000
Seafood Whslr
N.A.I.C.S.: 424460

Subsidiary (Domestic):

Leroy Trondheim AS   **(2)**
Pir 1-Nr 7 Hurtigrutekaien, 7010, Trondheim, Norway
Tel.: (47) 55334106
Seafood Whslr
N.A.I.C.S.: 424460

Subsidiary (Non-US):

Leroy Turkey Su Urunleri San. Ve Tic
A.S   **(2)**
Ataturk Mah Girne Cad No 33, PO Box
34752, Atasehir, Istanbul, Turkiye
Tel.: (90) 2166290685
Seafood Whslr
N.A.I.C.S.: 424460
Umit Guvenc *(Mng Dir)*

Subsidiary (Domestic):

Leroy Vest AS   **(2)**
Sjotrollbygget Skipavika 54, 5397, Bekkjarvik, Norway
Tel.: (47) 91911800
Seafood Whslr
N.A.I.C.S.: 424460

Nordland Havfiske AS   **(2)**
Lovenvoldgata 11, 6002, Alesund, Norway
Tel.: (47) 70118600
Seafood Whslr
N.A.I.C.S.: 424460
Ari T. Josefsson *(Mng Dir)*

Norsk Oppdrettsservice AS   **(2)**
Abelnes 60, 4404, Flekkefjord, Norway

Austevoll Seafood ASA—(Continued)

Tel.: (47) 9 402 2444
Web Site:
https://www.norskoppdrettsservice.no
Fish Cleaning & Distr
N.A.I.C.S.: 424460

Sjotroll Havbruk AS (2)
C-O Sjotroll AS, 5397, Bekkjarvik, Horda-
land, Norway (50.7%)
Tel.: (47) 91911800
Web Site: http://www.sjotroll.no
Sales Range: $25-49.9 Million
Emp.: 120
Salmon & Trout Farming
N.A.I.C.S.: 112511
Hans Jorgen Runshaug (CEO)

Leroy Seafood Italy S.R.L. (1)
Via del Gelso 110, 45014, Porto Viro, Italy
Tel.: (39) 04261883366
Fish & Seafood Distr
N.A.I.C.S.: 424460

Leroy Seafood Netherlands B.V. (1)
Schulpengat 10, 8321 WC, Urk, Nether-
lands
Tel.: (31) 527685357
Web Site: https://www.leroyseafood.nl
Fish & Seafood Distr
N.A.I.C.S.: 424460

Leroy Seafood UK Ltd. (1)
Office Suite F8 Innovation Centre Innova-
tion Way, Grimsby, United Kingdom
Tel.: (44) 7775673280
Fish & Seafood Distr
N.A.I.C.S.: 424460

Leroy Sjomatgruppen AS (1)
Postboks 7600, 5020, Bergen, Norway
Tel.: (47) 55213650
Web Site:
https://www.leroysjomatgruppen.no
Fish & Seafood Whslr
N.A.I.C.S.: 424460

Norsk Oppdrettservice AS (1)
Abelnes 60, 4404, Flekkefjord, Norway
Tel.: (47) 94022444
Web Site: https://norskoppdrettsservice.no
Fish & Seafood Whslr
N.A.I.C.S.: 424460

Pelagia AS (1)
Bradbenken 1, 5003, Bergen,
Norway (50%)
Tel.: (47) 5 784 4400
Web Site: https://www.pelagia.com
Emp.: 709
Pelagic Fish Products Mfr
N.A.I.C.S.: 424460
Egil Magne Haugstad (CEO)

Subsidiary (Non-US):

United Fish Industries (UK)
Limited (2)
Gilbey Road, Grimsby, DN31 2SL, Lincs,
United Kingdom
Tel.: (44) 1472263450
Sales Range: $50-74.9 Million
Emp.: 35
Animal Aquaculture
N.A.I.C.S.: 112519
Thomas Tynan (COO)

Scan Fish Danmark A/S
Industrihojen 5, 7730, Hanstholm, Denmark
Tel.: (45) 97962122
Emp.: 80
Frozen Fish Product Whslr
N.A.I.C.S.: 445250

AUSTEX OIL LIMITED
Suite 2 Level 10 70 Phillip Street,
Sydney, 2000, NSW, Australia
Tel.: (61) 292382363
Web Site: http://www.austexoil.com
Oil & Gas Producer
N.A.I.C.S.: 213112
Richard A. Adrey (Mng Dir-USA)

Subsidiaries:

Well Enhancement Services LLC (1)
1544 Sawdust Rd Ste 100, The Woodlands,
TX 77380
Tel.: (281) 367-0386

Web Site: http://www.wellenhancement.com
Sales Range: $50-74.9 Million
Emp.: 11
Well Enhancement & Oil Recovery Tech-
nologies Provider
N.A.I.C.S.: 213111
Chris D. Nelson (CFO)

AUSTIN ENGINEERING CO.
LTD.
Village Patla Bhesan, Junagadh, 362
030, Gujarat, India
Tel.: (91) 2873252223
Web Site: https://www.aec.com
522005—(BOM)
Rev.: $12,565,166
Assets: $13,314,033
Liabilities: $6,065,159
Net Worth: $7,248,873
Earnings: $227,491
Emp.: 473
Fiscal Year-end: 03/31/22
Roller Bearing Mfr
N.A.I.C.S.: 332991
Rajan Ramniklal Bambhania (CEO &
Mng Dir)

Subsidiaries:

Accurate Engineering Inc. (1)
8710 Telfair Ave, Sun Valley, CA 91352
Tel.: (818) 768-3919
Web Site: https://www.accueng.com
Industrial Ball & Roller Bearing Whslr
N.A.I.C.S.: 423840

AUSTIN ENGINEERING LTD.
100 Chisholm Crescent, Kewdale,
6105, WA, Australia
Tel.: (61) 893340666
Web Site: https://www.austineng.com
ANG—(ASX)
Rev.: $209,161,324
Assets: $195,646,367
Liabilities: $108,611,111
Net Worth: $87,035,256
Earnings: $19,827,724
Emp.: 1,446
Fiscal Year-end: 06/30/24
Industrial Machinery Manufacturing,
Repair & Support Services
N.A.I.C.S.: 811310
Brad Higgins (Mgr-Bus Dev-Africa)

Subsidiaries:

Austbore Pty. Ltd. (1)
Tel.: (61) 74 952 6222
Web Site: http://www.austbore.com.au
Sales Range: $25-49.9 Million
Emp.: 50
Mining Engineering Services
N.A.I.C.S.: 541330
Frank Deponte (Gen Mgr)

Austin Canada Inc. (1)
125 Mackay Crescent, Wood Buffalo, Fort
McMurray, T9H 4C9, AB, Canada
Tel.: (307) 690-7489
Mining Machinery Mfr & Distr
N.A.I.C.S.: 333131
Cory Wassan (Reg Acct Mgr)

Austin ETT Africa Limited (1)
Unit 21 Circle Square Business Park, For-
bach, Riviere du Rempart, Mauritius
Tel.: (230) 244 3210
Web Site: https://www.austin-ett.com
Mining Machinery Mfr & Distr
N.A.I.C.S.: 333131

PT Austin Engineering Indonesia (1)
Jl Mas Surya Negara Kav B2, Kawasan In-
dustrial Terpadu Kabil Batu Besar Nongsa,
Batam, 29467, Indonesia
Tel.: (62) 77 871 1999
Mining Industry Equipment Mfr & Distr
N.A.I.C.S.: 333131
Nry Nuriyanto (Gen Mgr)

Western Technology Services
Inc. (1)
415 1st St, Mills, WY 82644
Tel.: (307) 235-6475

Sales Range: $50-74.9 Million
Emp.: 200
Industrial Machinery Manufacturing, Repair
& Support Services
N.A.I.C.S.: 811310
Shane Fox (CFO)

AUSTIN FRASER LIMITED
Thames Tower Station Road, Read-
ing, RG1 1LX, Berkshire, United
Kingdom
Tel.: (44) 118 959 6689
Web Site:
http://www.austinfraser.com
Year Founded: 2007
Sales Range: $10-24.9 Million
Emp.: 47
Employee Recruitment Services
N.A.I.C.S.: 561311
Peter Hart (CEO)

Subsidiaries:

Austin Fraser GmbH (1)
Sternstrasse 5, 80538, Munich, Germany
Tel.: (49) 8927373800
Web Site: http://www.austinfraser.de
Employee Placement Services
N.A.I.C.S.: 561311
Lara Louisa Ridder (Mgr-Ops)

Austin Fraser Inc (1)
401 Congress Ave, Austin, TX 78701
Tel.: (512) 823-0011
Employee Placement Services
N.A.I.C.S.: 561311
Don Townsend (Mgr-Dev-Dallas)

AUSTIN GOLD CORP.
1021 West Hastings Street 9th Floor,
Vancouver, V6C 0C3, BC, Canada Ca
Tel.: (604) 644-6579
Web Site: https://www.austin.gold
Year Founded: 2020
AUST—(NYSEAMEX)
Assets: $12,005,240
Liabilities: $676,605
Net Worth: $11,328,635
Earnings: ($4,000,671)
Emp.: 3
Fiscal Year-end: 12/31/23
Exploration & Mining Services
N.A.I.C.S.: 213114
Joseph J. Ovsenek (Chm)

AUSTIN LAZ & COMPANY
PLC.
Km8 Sapele Rd, Benin City, Nigeria
Tel.: (234) 8021124095
Web Site:
https://www.austinlaz.com.ng
AUSTINLAZ—(NIGE)
Assets: $964,166
Liabilities: $36,619
Net Worth: $927,546
Earnings: ($32,989)
Emp.: 150
Fiscal Year-end: 12/31/23
Refrigerator Equipment Mfr
N.A.I.C.S.: 333415
Pat Utomi (Chm)

AUSTIN RESOURCES LTD.
82 Richmond Street East Suite 200,
Toronto, M5C 1P1, ON, Canada
Tel.: (416) 848-9888 AB
Web Site:
http://www.austinresources.ca
Year Founded: 2007
AUT.H—(TSXV)
Assets: $15,124
Liabilities: $274,011
Net Worth: ($258,883)
Earnings: ($58,974)
Fiscal Year-end: 12/31/22
Investment Services
N.A.I.C.S.: 523999
Zhigang Xie (CEO)

AUSTIN-SMITH:LORD LLP
Port of Liverpool Building Pier Head,
Liverpool, L3 1BY, Merseyside,
United Kingdom
Tel.: (44) 151 227 1083
Web Site:
http://www.austinsmithlord.com
Year Founded: 1949
Sales Range: $10-24.9 Million
Emp.: 50
Architectural Services
N.A.I.C.S.: 541310
Neil Chapman (Partner)

Subsidiaries:

Austin-Smith:Lord Abu Dhabi (1)
Al Nasr Street Qasr Al Hosn Cultural Quar-
ter, PO Box 129743, Abu Dhabi, United
Arab Emirates
Tel.: (971) 2 631 7072
Web Site: http://www.austinsmithlord.com
Architectural Services
N.A.I.C.S.: 541310

Austin-Smith:Lord LLP (1)
One Dunleavy Drive, Cardiff, CF11 0SN,
United Kingdom
Tel.: (44) 2920 225 208
Web Site: http://www.austinsmithlord.com
Emp.: 15
Architectural Services
N.A.I.C.S.: 541310

Austin-Smith:Lord LLP (1)
296 St Vincent Street, Glasgow, G2 5RU,
United Kingdom
Tel.: (44) 141 223 8500
Web Site: http://www.austinsmithlord.com
Emp.: 15
Architectural Services
N.A.I.C.S.: 541310
Munirah Khairuddin (Partner)

Austin-Smith:Lord LLP (1)
Port of Liverpool Building, Pier Head, Liver-
pool, L3 1BY, United Kingdom
Tel.: (44) 151 227 1083
Web Site: http://www.austinsmithlord.com
Emp.: 5
Architectural Services
N.A.I.C.S.: 541310

Austin-Smith:Lord LLP (1)
4 Jordan Street, Manchester, M15 4PY,
United Kingdom
Tel.: (44) 161 228 7569
Architectural Services
N.A.I.C.S.: 541310

AUSTOFIX GROUP LIMITED
18 Kinkaid Avenue, Plympton, 5037,
SA, Australia
Tel.: (61) 883510644
Web Site: http://www.austofix.com.au
Year Founded: 1993
Sales Range: $1-9.9 Million
Specialty Medical Device Designer,
Mfr & Distr
N.A.I.C.S.: 339112
Mark Neilson Balnaves (Chm)

Subsidiaries:

Austofix Surgical Pty Ltd (1)
18 Kinkaid Ave, Plympton, 5037, SA, Aus-
tralia
Tel.: (61) 883510644
Web Site: http://www.austofix.com.au
Sales Range: $25-49.9 Million
Emp.: 20
Surgical Instruments Suppliers
N.A.I.C.S.: 339113
Chris Henry (Gen Mgr)

Australian Orthopaedic Fixations Pty
Ltd (1)
18 Kinkaid Ave, Plympton, 5037, SA, Aus-
tralia
Tel.: (61) 883510644
Web Site: http://www.austofix.com.au
Sales Range: $10-24.9 Million
Emp.: 15
Medical Orthopaedic Services
N.A.I.C.S.: 622110
Chris Henry (Gen Mgr)

AUSTON CAPITAL CORP.

2025 Graveley Street, Vancouver,
V5L 3B6, BC, Canada
Tel.: (604) 642-0115
ASTN.P—(TSXV)
Rev.: $1,517
Assets: $141,370
Liabilities: $11,891
Net Worth: $129,479
Earnings: ($56,896)
Fiscal Year-end: 07/31/21
Financial Services
N.A.I.C.S.: 523999
Mark Fekete *(CEO & CFO)*

AUSTPAC RESOURCES N.L.

Level 5 37 Pitt Street, Sydney, 2000,
NSW, Australia
Tel.: (61) 292522599
Web Site:
   http://www.austpacresources.com
Assets: $2,027,664
Liabilities: $751,595
Net Worth: $1,276,069
Earnings: ($600,277)
Emp.: 6
Fiscal Year-end: 06/30/19
Mineral Processing & Exploration
Services
N.A.I.C.S.: 213115
Nicholas J. Gaston *(Sec)*

Subsidiaries:

Austpac Resources NL - Newcastle
Demonstration Plant   **(1)**
240 Cormorant Rd, Kooragang Island,
Newcastle, 2304, NSW, Australia
Tel.: (61) 249284338
Web Site: http://www.austpacresources.com
Sales Range: $50-74.9 Million
Emp.: 10
Mineral Exploration Services
N.A.I.C.S.: 213115
John Winter *(Gen Mgr)*

AUSTRAL GOLD LIMITED

Level 5 137-139 Bathurst Street, Syd-
ney, 2000, NSW, Australia
Tel.: (61) 466892307   **AU**
Web Site:
   https://www.australgold.com
AGD—(ASX)
Rev.: $47,729,000
Assets: $104,284,000
Liabilities: $62,711,000
Net Worth: $41,573,000
Earnings: ($7,243,000)
Emp.: 103
Fiscal Year-end: 12/31/23
Gold & Other Precious Metal Ore Ex-
ploration & Mining Services
N.A.I.C.S.: 212220
Raul Guerra *(VP)*

Subsidiaries:

Guanaco Compania Minera SpA   **(1)**
2065 of 1103, Antofagasta, Chile
Tel.: (56) 552892241
Web Site: http://www.minaguanaco.cl
Mining Services
N.A.I.C.S.: 213114

Revelo Resources Corp.   **(1)**
Suite 501 - 543 Granville Street, Vancouver,
V6C 1X8, BC, Canada
Tel.: (604) 687-5544
Web Site: http://www.reveloresources.com
Rev.: $95,298
Assets: $2,027,976
Liabilities: $4,862,827
Net Worth: ($2,834,851)
Earnings: ($1,753,213)
Emp.: 443
Fiscal Year-end: 01/31/2020
Iron & Other Metal Ore Exploration & Min-
ing Services
N.A.I.C.S.: 213114

Subsidiary (Non-US):

Compania Minera Mena Resources
(Chile) Limitada   **(2)**

Don Carlos 2939 of 707, Las Condes,
7550171, Chile
Tel.: (56) 2327125
Web Site: http://www.ironcreekcapital.com
Emp.: 10
Mineral Exploration Services
N.A.I.C.S.: 213115

AUSTRAL RESOURCES AUS-TRALIA LTD.

RACQ House Level 9 Suite 902 60
Edward Street, Brisbane, 4000, QLD,
Australia
Tel.: (61) 735202500   **AU**
Web Site: https://www.australres.com
Year Founded: 2010
AR1—(ASX)
Rev.: $42,008,665
Assets: $102,899,317
Liabilities: $117,207,915
Net Worth: ($14,308,598)
Earnings: ($22,832,462)
Fiscal Year-end: 12/31/22
Other Nonmetallic Mineral Mining &
Quarrying
N.A.I.C.S.: 212390
Dan Jauncey *(Mng Dir)*

AUSTRALASIAN METALS LIM-ITED

Unit 34 Level 5 123B Colin St, West
Perth, 6005, WA, Australia
Tel.: (61) 865073082   **AU**
Web Site:
   https://www.australasiangold.com
Year Founded: 2018
8ON—(DEU)
Rev.: $198,125
Assets: $4,829,208
Liabilities: $142,830
Net Worth: $4,686,377
Earnings: ($163,104)
Fiscal Year-end: 06/30/23
Gold & Metal Exploration Services
N.A.I.C.S.: 213114
Qingtao Zeng *(Mng Dir)*

AUSTRALIA & INTERNA-TIONAL HOLDINGS LIMITED

GPO Box 1398, Brisbane, 4001,
QLD, Australia
Tel.: (61) 730067200   **AU**
Year Founded: 1985
AID—(NSXA)
Rev.: $137,943
Assets: $4,462,629
Liabilities: $419,731
Net Worth: $4,042,898
Earnings: $81,539
Fiscal Year-end: 06/30/21
Investment Management Service
N.A.I.C.S.: 523940
Saskia R. Jo *(Co-Sec)*

AUSTRALIA & NEW ZEALAND BANKING GROUP LIMITED

ANZ Centre Melbourne Level 9 833
Collins Street, Docklands, Melbourne,
3008, VIC, Australia
Tel.: (61) 392735555   **AU**
Web Site: https://www.anz.com.au
Year Founded: 1970
ANZ—(ASX)
Rev.: $41,933,959,020
Assets: $849,753,897,650
Liabilities: $802,234,549,250
Net Worth: $47,519,348,400
Earnings: $4,581,926,700
Emp.: 42,142
Fiscal Year-end: 09/30/24
Financial Investment Services
N.A.I.C.S.: 551111
Kevin Corbally *(Chief Risk Officer)*

Subsidiaries:

ANZ (Delaware) Inc.   **(1)**

277 Park Ave, New York, NY
10172   **(100%)**
Tel.: (212) 801-9800
Web Site: http://www.anz.com
Sales Range: $1-4.9 Billion
Emp.: 105
Bank Holding Company
N.A.I.C.S.: 551111

Subsidiary (Domestic):

ANZ Securities Inc.   **(2)**
277 Park Ave, New York, NY
10172   **(100%)**
Tel.: (212) 801-9800
Web Site: http://www.anz.com
Sales Range: $50-74.9 Million
Emp.: 85
Investment Banking
N.A.I.C.S.: 522110
Charles Lachman *(Head-Markets-Global)*

ANZ Asia Pacific Division   **(1)**
Level 6 100 Queen Street, Melbourne,
3000, VIC, Australia
Tel.: (61) 392736141
Web Site: http://www.anz.com
Sales Range: $900-999.9 Million
Emp.: 4,394
Banking Operations Management Services
N.A.I.C.S.: 551114

Subsidiary (Non-US):

ANZ Bank (Samoa) Limited   **(2)**
Beach Road, PO Box L1855, Apia, Samoa
(Western)   **(100%)**
Tel.: (685) 69999
Web Site: http://www.anz.com
Personal & Commercial Banking Services
N.A.I.C.S.: 522110

ANZ Bank Solomon Islands   **(2)**
Level 1 Ranadi - Prince Philip Highway, PO
Box 10, Honiara, Solomon Islands   **(100%)**
Tel.: (677) 21111
Web Site: http://www.anz.com
Personal & Commercial Banking Services
N.A.I.C.S.: 522110

ANZ Cook Islands   **(2)**
ANZ House Maire Nui Drive, PO Box 907,
Avarua, Rarotonga, Cook Islands
Tel.: (682) 21750
Web Site: http://www.anz.com
Sales Range: $50-74.9 Million
Emp.: 40
Personal & Commercial Banking Services
N.A.I.C.S.: 522110
Glen Stewart *(CEO)*

ANZ Fiji   **(2)**
ANZ House 25 Victoria Parade, PO Box
179, Suva, Fiji   **(100%)**
Tel.: (679) 3316644
Web Site: http://www.anz.com
Personal & Commercial Banking Services
N.A.I.C.S.: 522110

Group (Non-US):

ANZ International (Hong Kong)
Ltd.   **(2)**
22/F Three Exchange Square 8 Connaught
Place, Central, China (Hong Kong) **(100%)**
Tel.: (852) 39182000
Web Site: http://www.anz.com
Sales Range: $150-199.9 Million
Emp.: 400
Bank Holding Company; Commercial Bank-
ing Services
N.A.I.C.S.: 551111

Subsidiary (Domestic):

ANZ Asia Limited   **(3)**
Suites 3101-5 One Exchange Square, 8
Connaught Place, Central, China (Hong
Kong)   **(100%)**
Tel.: (852) 28437111
Web Site: http://www.anz.com
Sales Range: $75-99.9 Million
Emp.: 4
Personal & Commercial Banking Services
N.A.I.C.S.: 522110

Subsidiary (Non-US):

ANZ Bank (Vanuatu) Limited   **(3)**
Kumul Highway, Port-Vila, Vanuatu **(100%)**
Tel.: (678) 26355

Web Site: http://www.anz.com
Sales Range: $50-74.9 Million
Emp.: 100
Banking Services
N.A.I.C.S.: 522110

Representative Office (Non-US):

ANZ Japan   **(3)**
33rd Floor Marunouchi Building
4-1Marunouchi 2-chome, Chiyoda, Tokyo,
100-6333, Japan   **(100%)**
Tel.: (81) 362127770
Web Site: http://institutional.anz.com
Sales Range: $200-249.9 Million
Emp.: 300
Personal & Commercial Banking Services
N.A.I.C.S.: 522110

ANZ Korea   **(3)**
22nd Fl Kyobo Building 1 Chongro 1, Seoul,
Korea (South)   **(100%)**
Tel.: (82) 27303151
Web Site: http://www.anz.com
Sales Range: $50-74.9 Million
Emp.: 70
Corporate Banking
N.A.I.C.S.: 522110

ANZ Shanghai   **(3)**
15th Floor Mirae Asset Tower 166 Lujiazui
Ring Road, Pudong, Shanghai, 200120,
China   **(100%)**
Tel.: (86) 2161696000
Web Site: http://institutional.anz.com
Sales Range: $100-124.9 Million
Emp.: 200
Personal & Commercial Banking Services
N.A.I.C.S.: 522110

ANZ Taiwan   **(3)**
39F and 40F No 68 Sec 5 Zhongxiao E Rd,
Xinyi Dist, Taipei, 110, Taiwan   **(100%)**
Tel.: (886) 287225000
Web Site: http://institutional.anz.com
Sales Range: $50-74.9 Million
Emp.: 40
Personal & Commercial Banking Services
N.A.I.C.S.: 522110

Group (Non-US):

ANZ International Pte. Ltd.   **(2)**
1 Raffles Place, #32-00 OUB Centre, Sin-
gapore, 049315, Singapore   **(100%)**
Tel.: (65) 65358355
Web Site: http://www.anz.com
Bank Holding Company; Commercial Bank-
ing Services
N.A.I.C.S.: 551111

Representative Office (Non-US):

ANZ Malaysia   **(3)**
Level 2 02-02 Menara Dion 27 Jalan Sultan
Ismail, 50250, Kuala Lumpur,
Malaysia   **(100%)**
Tel.: (60) 3 2078 1588
Web Site: http://institutional.anz.com
Sales Range: $75-99.9 Million
Emp.: 3
Personal & Commercial Banking Services
N.A.I.C.S.: 522110

ANZ Philippines   **(3)**
Solaris One Level 14 130 Dela Rosa Street,
Legaspi Village, Makati, 1229, Philippines
Tel.: (63) 28417773
Web Site: http://institutional.anz.com
Personal & Commercial Banking Services
N.A.I.C.S.: 522110

Subsidiary (Domestic):

ANZ Singapore Limited   **(3)**
10 Collyer Quay Ocean Financial Centre
Level 30, Singapore, 049315,
Singapore   **(100%)**
Tel.: (65) 66818033
Web Site: http://institutional.anz.com
Financial Services
N.A.I.C.S.: 522299

Representative Office (Non-US):

ANZ Thailand   **(3)**
9th Floor GPF Witthayu Tower A, 93-1
Wireless Road, Bangkok, 10330, Thailand
Tel.: (66) 22566350

Australia & New Zealand Banking Group Limited—(Continued)

Sales Range: $50-74.9 Million
Emp.: 3
Trade Financing Services
N.A.I.C.S.: 522299

Subsidiary (Non-US):

P.T. ANZ Panin Bank **(3)**
ANZ Tower Jl Jend Sudirman Kav 33A, Jakarta, 10220, Indonesia **(85%)**
Tel.: (62) 215750300
Web Site: http://www.anz.com
Banking Services
N.A.I.C.S.: 522299

Subsidiary (Non-US):

ANZ Tonga **(2)**
Taufa'ahau Road, PO Box 910, Nuku'alofa, Tonga **(100%)**
Tel.: (676) 67620500
Web Site: http://www.anz.com
Sales Range: $50-74.9 Million
Emp.: 80
Personal & Commercial Banking Services
N.A.I.C.S.: 522110

ANZ Australian Capital Territory **(1)**
25 Petrie Plaza, Canberra, 2600, ACT, Australia
Tel.: (61) 6 276 4100
Banking & Financial Investments
N.A.I.C.S.: 522299

ANZ Bank (Europe) Limited **(1)**
40 Bank Street, London, E14 5EJ, United Kingdom
Tel.: (44) 203 229 2121
Emp.: 300
Commercial Banking Services
N.A.I.C.S.: 522110

ANZ Bank (Thai) Public Company Limited **(1)**
Level 8 Athenee Tower 63 Wireless Road Lumpini, Pathumwan, Bangkok, 10330, Thailand
Tel.: (66) 22639700
Financial Investment Services
N.A.I.C.S.: 523999

ANZ Germany **(1)**
Friedrich-Ebert-Anlage 35-37, 60327, Frankfurt am Main, Germany **(100%)**
Tel.: (49) 697100080
Web Site: http://www.anz.com
Sales Range: $75-99.9 Million
Emp.: 10
Corporate Banking Services
N.A.I.C.S.: 522110

ANZ Guam Inc. **(1)**
424 W O'Brien Dr 112 Julale Ctr, Hagatna, GU 96910
Tel.: (671) 479-9000
Commercial Banking Services
N.A.I.C.S.: 522110

ANZ Institutional Division **(1)**
Level 6 100 Queen Street, Melbourne, 3000, VIC, Australia
Tel.: (61) 392736141
Web Site: http://www.anz.com
Sales Range: $5-14.9 Billion
Emp.: 6,051
Corporate & Institutional Banking Services
N.A.I.C.S.: 522110
Shayne Cary Elliott *(Member-Mgmt Bd)*

ANZ Lenders Mortgage Insurance Pty. Limited **(1)**
Level 6 100 Queen Street, Melbourne, 3000, VIC, Australia
Tel.: (61) 132599
N.A.I.C.S.: 522310

ANZ National Bank Ltd. **(1)**
Level 14 ANZ Tower 215-229 Lambton Quay, PO Box 1492, Wellington, 6011, New Zealand **(100%)**
Tel.: (64) 44967000
Web Site: http://www.anz.co.nz
Emp.: 9,178
Bank Holding Company
N.A.I.C.S.: 551111

Co-Headquarters (Domestic):

ANZ National Bank Ltd. **(2)**

Level 24 ANZ Centre 23-29 Albert Street, Auckland, New Zealand
Tel.: (64) 93744051
Web Site: http://www.anznational.co.nz
Corporate Office; Banking Services
N.A.I.C.S.: 551114

Subsidiary (Non-US):

ANZ Bank (Kiribati) Limited **(3)**
PO Box 66, Bairiki, Tarawa, Kiribati
Tel.: (686) 21095
Sales Range: $50-74.9 Million
Emp.: 7
Commercial Banking Services
N.A.I.C.S.: 522110
Isikeli Tuituku *(CEO)*

Subsidiary (Domestic):

ANZ Investment Services (New Zealand) Limited **(3)**
Level 6 1 Victoria Street, Wellington, 6011, New Zealand
Tel.: (64) 44967000
Financial Investment Services
N.A.I.C.S.: 523999

ANZ New Zealand Securities Limited **(3)**
PO Box 1790, Wellington, 6140, New Zealand
Tel.: (64) 44996655
Web Site: http://www.anzsecurities.co.nz
Online Securities Trading Service
N.A.I.C.S.: 518210
Lance Cook *(Mgr-Compliance)*

Arawata Assets Limited **(3)**
Ground Floor Anz Centre 23-29 Albert Street, Auckland, 1010, New Zealand
Tel.: (64) 44968071
Financial Management Services
N.A.I.C.S.: 523999
Sharon McDonald *(Head-Property)*

The National Bank of New Zealand Ltd. **(3)**
Level 14 ANZ Tower 215-229 Lambton Quay, PO Box 1492, Wellington, 6011, New Zealand **(100%)**
Tel.: (64) 44967000
Web Site: https://www.anz.co.nz
Sales Range: $800-899.9 Million
Emp.: 2,000
Personal & Commercial Banking Services
N.A.I.C.S.: 522110

ANZ New Zealand Investments Limited **(1)**
Level 17 23-29 ANZ Centre Albert Street, PO Box 92210, Victoria St West, Auckland, 1142, New Zealand
Tel.: (64) 44703142
Web Site: http://www.anz.co.nz
Sales Range: $100-124.9 Million
Emp.: 15
Investment Management Service
N.A.I.C.S.: 523999
Stuart Millar *(Head-Diversified Portfolio Mgmt)*

ANZ Northern Territory **(1)**
69 Smith St, Darwin, 0800, NT, Australia **(100%)**
Tel.: (61) 889823510
Sales Range: $50-74.9 Million
Emp.: 30
Banking Services
N.A.I.C.S.: 522299
Steve Straub *(Reg Mgr)*

ANZ Private Bank **(1)**
Fl 1 324 Queen St, Brisbane, 4000, QLD, Australia **(100%)**
Tel.: (61) 732285513
Web Site: http://www.anz.com
Sales Range: $75-99.9 Million
Emp.: 30
Investment Banking Services
N.A.I.C.S.: 522299

ANZ Securities Limited **(1)**
Level 12 530 Collins Street, Melbourne, 3000, VIC, Australia **(100%)**
Tel.: (61) 36401400
Stock Brokerage & Related Services
N.A.I.C.S.: 523150

ANZ UK **(1)**

40 Bank Street, Canary Wharf, London, E14 5EJ, United Kingdom
Tel.: (44) 2032292121
Web Site: http://www.anz.com
Sales Range: $125-149.9 Million
Emp.: 250
Personal, Commercial & Investment Banking Services
N.A.I.C.S.: 522110

Australian Commercial Property Management Limited **(1)**
Level 6 492 Saint Kilda Road, Melbourne, 3004, VIC, Australia **(100%)**
Tel.: (61) 398677200
Web Site: http://www.ribinob.com.au
Sales Range: $25-49.9 Million
Emp.: 35
Property Management Services
N.A.I.C.S.: 531312

OnePath Funds Management Limited **(1)**
L 13 347 Kent St, Sydney, 2000, NSW, Australia
Tel.: (61) 292348111
Web Site: http://www.onepath.com.au
Emp.: 1,000
Investment Management Service
N.A.I.C.S.: 523999
Gavin Pearce *(Gen Mgr)*

PT Bank ANZ Indonesia **(1)**
WTC 3 Level 30-31 Jl Jendral Sudirman Kav 29-31, Jakarta, 12920, Indonesia
Tel.: (62) 8041000269
Financial Investment Services
N.A.I.C.S.: 523999
Hong Swee Lau *(Commissioner)*

Share Investing Limited **(1)**
Level 20, Tower Three International Towers Sydney 300 Barangaroo Avenu, Barangaroo, 2000, NSW, Australia
Tel.: (61) 3 8541 0458
Web Site: http://www.anz.com.au
Online Securities Trading Service
N.A.I.C.S.: 518210

AUSTRALIA CHINA HOLDINGS LIMITED
Level 4 45 Murray Street, Prymont, Sydney, 2009, NSW, Australia
Tel.: (61) 32431977
Web Site: http://www.aakch.com
Year Founded: 1995
Investment Holding Services
N.A.I.C.S.: 523940
Stonely W. T. Sek *(Sec)*

AUSTRALIA FINANCE GROUP LTD
Level 4 100 Havelock Street, West Perth, 6005, WA, Australia
Tel.: (61) 1300130987
Web Site:
https://www.afgonline.com.au
AFG—(ASX)
Rev.: $718,000,131
Assets: $3,991,268,012
Liabilities: $3,853,013,472
Net Worth: $138,254,540
Earnings: $20,332,532
Emp.: 311
Fiscal Year-end: 06/30/24
Mortgage Banker
N.A.I.C.S.: 522310
Anthony Gill *(Chm)*

Subsidiaries:

AFG Home Loans Pty Ltd **(1)**
PO Box 710, West Perth, 6872, WA, Australia
Tel.: (61) 1800629948
Web Site:
https://www.afghomeloans.com.au
Home Loan Services
N.A.I.C.S.: 522310

Broli Finance Pty. Ltd. **(1)**
Level 1 Fintelligence Suites 2 Boston Court, Varsity Lakes, 4227, QLD, Australia
Tel.: (61) 1300131373
Web Site: https://www.brolifinance.com.au

Motor Vehicle Finance Services
N.A.I.C.S.: 522220

Fintelligence Pty. Ltd. **(1)**
Level 1 Fintelligence Suites 2 Boston Court, Varsity Lakes, 4227, QLD, Australia
Tel.: (61) 1300131388
Web Site: https://www.fintelligence.com.au
Information Technology Services
N.A.I.C.S.: 541512

AUSTRALIA SANDSTONE MERCHANTS PTY. LTD.
465 Halcrows Road, Glenorie, Sydney, 2157, NSW, Australia
Tel.: (61) 2 9980 7941 AU
Web Site:
http://www.australiansandstone.com
Sales Range: $10-24.9 Million
Sandstone Quarrying, Processing & Distr
N.A.I.C.S.: 212311
Buddy Francis *(Co-Owner)*

AUSTRALIA UNITED MINING LIMITED
Suite 502, Sydney, 206, NSW, Australia
Tel.: (61) 292524525
Web Site:
https://www.australiaunited.com
AYM—(ASX)
Rev.: $4,888
Assets: $2,816,429
Liabilities: $1,292,871
Net Worth: $1,523,558
Earnings: ($1,144,220)
Emp.: 1
Fiscal Year-end: 06/30/24
Gold & Other Metal Mining
N.A.I.C.S.: 212220
Robert Ng *(CFO)*

AUSTRALIA ZOO PTY LTD
163A Steve Irwin Way, Beerwah, 4519, QLD, Australia
Tel.: (61) 754362000
Web Site:
http://www.australiazoo.com.au
Year Founded: 1970
Sales Range: $100-124.9 Million
Emp.: 400
Zoo Operations
N.A.I.C.S.: 712130
Terri Irwin *(Owner)*

AUSTRALIAN AGRICULTURAL COMPANY LIMITED
Tel.: (61) 733684400
Web Site: https://www.aaco.com.au
AAC—(ASX)
Rev.: $211,519,775
Assets: $1,574,436,935
Liabilities: $530,449,427
Net Worth: $1,043,987,508
Earnings: $104,914,397
Emp.: 423
Fiscal Year-end: 03/31/22
Beef & Agricultural Products
N.A.I.C.S.: 112111
Bruce Bennett *(Gen Counsel & Sec)*

Subsidiaries:

Chefs Partner Pty Ltd. **(1)**
30 Manton St, Morningside, Brisbane, 4170, QLD, Australia
Tel.: (61) 739025900
Web Site: http://www.chefspartner.com.au
Sales Range: $25-49.9 Million
Emp.: 30
Meat Product Whslr
N.A.I.C.S.: 424420

AUSTRALIAN AGRICULTURAL PROJECTS LTD
Suite 19 456 St Kilda Road, Melbourne, 3004, VIC, Australia
Tel.: (61) 417001446 AU

Web Site: https://www.voopl.com.au
AAP—(ASX)
Rev.: $3,157,061
Assets: $14,945,864
Liabilities: $6,491,550
Net Worth: $8,454,314
Earnings: $837,894
Fiscal Year-end: 06/30/24
Olive Oil Mfr
N.A.I.C.S.: 311224
Kimberley Arnold Hogg *(Sec)*

Subsidiaries:

AOX Pty Ltd (1)
31 Lakewood Blvd, Braeside, 3195, VIC, Australia
Tel.: (61) 385871400
Sales Range: $25-49.9 Million
Emp.: 10
Olive Oil Mfr & Distr
N.A.I.C.S.: 311225

AUSTRALIAN ASSOCIATED MOTOR INSURERS LIMITED

PO Box 14180, Melbourne, 8001, Victoria, Australia
Tel.: (61) 61385201300
Web Site: http://www.aami.com.au
Sales Range: $1-4.9 Billion
Emp.: 2,900
Insurance Services
N.A.I.C.S.: 524298

AUSTRALIAN ASSOCIATED PRESS PTY LTD

AAP News Ctr 3 Rider Blvd Rhodes Waterside, Rhodes, 2138, NSW, Australia
Tel.: (61) 293228000
Web Site: http://www.aap.com.au
Year Founded: 1935
Sales Range: $125-149.9 Million
Emp.: 600
News Syndicates
N.A.I.C.S.: 516210
Bruce Davidson *(CEO)*

Subsidiaries:

Medianet (1)
Level 6 3 Rider Boulevard, Rhodes, 2138, NSW, Australia
Tel.: (61) 1300 616 813
Web Site: http://www.medianet.com.au
Media & Communication Services
N.A.I.C.S.: 541840

Pagemasters Pty Ltd. (1)
Collins St East, PO Box 4, Melbourne, 8003, VIC, Australia
Tel.: (61) 3 8413 3200
Web Site: http://www.pagemasters.com
Newspaper Publishers
N.A.I.C.S.: 513110
Antony Phillips *(Gen Mgr)*

AUSTRALIAN BOND EX-CHANGE HOLDINGS LIMITED

Level 19 15 Castlereagh Street, Sydney, 2000, NSW, Australia
Tel.: (61) 1800319769   AU
Web Site:
  https://www.bondexchange.com.au
Year Founded: 2015
ABE—(ASX)
Rev.: $3,056,554
Assets: $7,745,610
Liabilities: $2,318,885
Net Worth: $5,426,725
Earnings: ($3,282,638)
Fiscal Year-end: 06/30/23
Holding Company
N.A.I.C.S.: 551112
Michael Vander Donk *(CTO)*

Subsidiaries:

Australian Bond Exchange Pty Ltd. (1)
Level 19 15 Castlereagh Street, Sydney, 2000, NSW, Australia

Tel.: (61) 1800319769
Web Site:
  https://www.bondexchange.com.au
Financial Advisory Services
N.A.I.C.S.: 522320

AUSTRALIAN CAREERS NET-WORK LIMITED

7 Raleigh Street, Spotswood, 3015, VIC, Australia
Tel.: (61) 383317890   AU
Education Training Services
N.A.I.C.S.: 611710
Ivan Robert Brown *(CEO & Mng Dir)*

AUSTRALIAN CENTRAL CREDIT UNION LTD

50 Flinders Street, GPO Box 1942, Adelaide, 5000, SA, Australia
Tel.: (61) 2 8299 9101
Web Site:
  http://www.peopleschoicecu.com.au
Year Founded: 1949
Rev.: $243,083,464
Assets: $6,195,500,405
Liabilities: $5,760,327,476
Net Worth: $435,172,929
Earnings: $14,826,690
Emp.: 1,049
Fiscal Year-end: 06/30/19
Banking & Credit Services
N.A.I.C.S.: 522130
Steven Peter William Laidlaw *(CEO & Mng Dir)*

AUSTRALIAN DAIRY NUTRI-TIONALS GROUP

160 Depot Road, Camperdown, 3260, VIC, Australia
Tel.: (61) 386927284   AU
Web Site: https://adnl.com.au
AHF—(ASX)
Rev.: $4,182,072
Assets: $20,263,486
Liabilities: $2,417,220
Net Worth: $17,846,267
Earnings: ($4,967,398)
Fiscal Year-end: 06/30/24
Farm Owner & Operator
N.A.I.C.S.: 112120
Sundaranathan Mahinthan *(CEO)*

AUSTRALIAN ENERGY MAR-KET OPERATOR LIMITED

Level 22 530 Collins Street, Melbourne, 3000, VIC, Australia
Tel.: (61) 396098000   AU
Web Site: http://www.aemo.com.au
Year Founded: 1996
Rev.: $533,134,991
Assets: $211,879,483
Liabilities: $203,594,848
Net Worth: $8,284,635
Earnings: ($44,214,957)
Fiscal Year-end: 06/30/19
Gas & Electricity Markets Administrative Services
N.A.I.C.S.: 926130
Brett Hausler *(Chief Governance Officer & Gen Counsel)*

AUSTRALIAN ETHICAL IN-VESTMENT LIMITED

Level 8 130 Pitt Street, Sydney, 2000, NSW, Australia
Tel.: (61) 1800021227   AU
Web Site:
  https://www.australianethical.com
Year Founded: 1986
AEF—(ASX)
Rev.: $67,101,362
Assets: $34,210,737
Liabilities: $14,082,532
Net Worth: $20,128,205
Earnings: $7,699,653
Emp.: 49

Fiscal Year-end: 06/30/24
Investment Managing
N.A.I.C.S.: 523940
Tom May *(Gen Counsel & Co-Sec)*

Subsidiaries:

Australian Ethical Superannuation Pty Limited (1)
PO Box 1916, Wollongong, 2500, NSW, Australia
Tel.: (61) 1300134337
Pension Fund Management Services
N.A.I.C.S.: 523940

AUSTRALIAN FILM INSTITUTE

236 Dorcas St, Melbourne, 3205, VIC, Australia
Tel.: (61) 396961844
Web Site: http://www.afi.org.au
Year Founded: 1958
Sales Range: $1-9.9 Million
Emp.: 11
Film Promoter
N.A.I.C.S.: 512199
Damian Trewhella *(CEO)*

AUSTRALIAN FOOD & FIBRE LTD.

Suite 3 50 Auburn Street, Moree, 2400, Australia
Tel.: (61) 2 6752 5795
Emp.: 60
Cotton & Miscellaneous Agricultural Product Production Services
N.A.I.C.S.: 111920
David Robinson *(Exec Chm)*

Subsidiaries:

Auscott Limited (1)
Level 12 6 O'Connell St, Sydney, 2000, NSW, Australia
Tel.: (61) 2 9295 4800
Web Site: http://www.auscott.com.au
Sales Range: $50-74.9 Million
Emp.: 255
Cotton, Farming, Warehousing, Marketing & Shipping Services
N.A.I.C.S.: 115111
Ashley Power *(CEO)*

AUSTRALIAN FOUNDATION INVESTMENT COMPANY LIM-ITED

Level 21 101 Collins Street, Melbourne, 3000, VIC, Australia
Tel.: (61) 396509911   AU
Web Site: https://www.afi.com.au
Year Founded: 1928
AFI—(ASX)
Rev.: $226,532,451
Assets: $6,622,508,653
Liabilities: $1,106,091,075
Net Worth: $5,516,417,579
Earnings: $197,925,346
Emp.: 18
Fiscal Year-end: 06/30/24
Provider of Investment Services
N.A.I.C.S.: 523940
John Paterson *(Chm)*

Subsidiaries:

Australian Investment Company Services Limited (1)
Level 21 101 Collins St, Melbourne, 3000, VIC, Australia
Tel.: (61) 396509911
Web Site: http://www.afi.com.au
Financial Investment Services
N.A.I.C.S.: 523999

AUSTRALIAN GAS NET-WORKS LIMITED

Level 6 400 King William Street, Adelaide, 5000, SA, Australia
Tel.: (61) 8 8227 1500   AU
Web Site:
  http://www.australiangas.com.au
Year Founded: 1997

Sales Range: $450-499.9 Million
Natural Gas Distribution Services
N.A.I.C.S.: 221210
Paul May *(CFO)*

AUSTRALIAN GOLD & COP-PER LIMITED

14 Edward Street, Orange, 2800, NSW, Australia
Tel.: (61) 861888181
Web Site:
  https://www.austgoldcopper.com.au
Year Founded: 2019
AGC—(ASX)
Rev.: $62,126
Assets: $10,745,248
Liabilities: $98,622
Net Worth: $10,646,626
Earnings: ($1,080,074)
Fiscal Year-end: 06/30/23
Gold & Metal Exploration Services
N.A.I.C.S.: 213114
Glen Diemar *(Mng Dir)*

AUSTRALIAN GOLDFIELDS LIMITED

1681 Chestnut St Suite 400, Vancouver, V6J 4M6, BC, Canada
Tel.: (604) 834-2968
Web Site:
  https://www.ozlithiumcorp.com
GRXX—(OTCIQ)
Assets: $3,127,953
Liabilities: $165,969
Net Worth: $2,961,984
Earnings: ($1,964,142)
Fiscal Year-end: 06/30/21
Metal Exploration Services
N.A.I.C.S.: 212390
Sheri Rempel *(CFO)*

Subsidiaries:

Pilbara Gold Group Pty. Ltd. (1)

AUSTRALIAN GRAND PRIX CORPORATION PTY. LTD.

Level 5 616 St Kilda Road, Melbourne, 3004, VIC, Australia
Tel.: (61) 3 9258 7100
Web Site:
  http://www.grandprix.com.au
Rev.: $99,030,253
Assets: $34,040,771
Liabilities: $14,816,845
Net Worth: $19,223,925
Earnings: ($1,212,351)
Emp.: 73
Fiscal Year-end: 06/30/19
Sports Club Managers & Promoters
N.A.I.C.S.: 711211
John Harnden *(Chm)*

AUSTRALIAN MEAT INDUS-TRY SUPERANNUATION TRUST PTY LTD.

Parramatta Square Level 22 Tower 6 10 Darcy Place, Parramatta, 2150, NSW, Australia
Tel.: (61) 285715453   AU
Web Site:
  https://www.ausfoodsuper.com.au
Financial Services
N.A.I.C.S.: 523999

AUSTRALIAN MINES LIMITED

Level 34 1 Eagle Street, Brisbane, 4000, QLD, Australia
Web Site:
  http://www.australianmines.com.au
AUZ—(ASX)
Rev.: $92,815
Assets: $31,368,857
Liabilities: $172,276
Net Worth: $31,196,581
Earnings: ($2,536,725)
Emp.: 3

Australian Mines Limited—(Continued)

Fiscal Year-end: 06/30/24
Nickel Mining Services
N.A.I.C.S.: 212230
Michael Ramsden (Chm)

Subsidiaries:

Norwest Minerals Limited   (1)
Tel.: (61) 861170457
Web Site:
  https://www.norwestminerals.com.au
Rev.: $398
Assets: $14,522,884
Liabilities: $663,866
Net Worth: $13,859,018
Earnings: ($694,912)
Fiscal Year-end: 06/30/2024
Metal & Mineral Exploration Services
N.A.I.C.S.: 212220
Michael Tilley (Chm)

AUSTRALIAN OIL & GAS CORP.

Level 21 500 Collins Street, Melbourne, 3000, VIC, Australia
Tel.: (61) 386104701   DE
AOGC—(OTCIQ)
Sales Range: Less than $1 Million
Oil & Gas Exploration Services
N.A.I.C.S.: 213112
E. Geoffrey Albers (Pres & Treas)

AUSTRALIAN OILSEEDS HOLDINGS LIMITED

126 -142 Cowcumbla Street, Cootamundra, 2590, NSW, Australia
Tel.: (61) 0269424347   Ky
Web Site:
  https://www.australianoilseeds.au
COOT—(NASDAQ)
Rev.: $22,521,015
Assets: $20,030,043
Liabilities: $19,424,023
Net Worth: $606,020
Earnings: ($14,176,575)
Emp.: 21
Fiscal Year-end: 06/30/24
Holding Company
N.A.I.C.S.: 551112

Subsidiaries:

Australian Oilseeds Investments Pty
Ltd.   (1)
100 Park Rd 2, Slacks Creek, 4127, QLD,
Australia
Tel.: (61) 738062268
Food & Beverage Mfg
N.A.I.C.S.: 311999

Edoc Acquisition Corp.   (1)
7612 Main St Fishers Ste 200, Victor, NY
14564
Tel.: (585) 678-1198
Web Site: http://www.edocmed.net
Assets: $21,405,267
Liabilities: $25,708,930
Net Worth: ($4,303,663)
Earnings: ($7,686,390)
Emp.: 2
Fiscal Year-end: 12/31/2022
Investment Services
N.A.I.C.S.: 523999
Kevin Chen (Chm & CEO)

AUSTRALIAN PACIFIC COAL LTD.

Level 15 344 Queen Street, Brisbane,
4000, QLD, Australia
Tel.: (61) 732210679   AU
Web Site: http://www.aqcltd.com
Year Founded: 1999
AQC—(ASX)
Rev.: $1,694,011
Assets: $68,417,924
Liabilities: $55,852,478
Net Worth: $12,565,447
Earnings: ($8,434,094)
Fiscal Year-end: 06/30/24
Coal Exploration Services

N.A.I.C.S.: 212115
Craig McPherson (Sec)

AUSTRALIAN POSTAL CORPORATION

111 Bourke Street, Melbourne, 3000,
VIC, Australia
Tel.: (61) 392047171   AU
Web Site: http://auspost.com.au
Rev.: $4,915,367,156
Assets: $3,892,744,632
Liabilities: $2,266,126,450
Net Worth: $1,626,618,182
Earnings: $28,761,698
Emp.: 36,000
Fiscal Year-end: 06/30/19
Postal Service
N.A.I.C.S.: 491110
Bob Black (COO-Grp)

Subsidiaries:

Australian Air Express Pty. Ltd.   (1)
440 Elizabeth St Level 7, Melbourne, 3000,
Australia   (50%)
Tel.: (61) 386333100
Web Site: http://www.aae.com.au
Freight Air Transportation Services
N.A.I.C.S.: 481112

Star Track Express Pty. Ltd.   (1)
51 Sargents Road, Minchinbury, Sydney,
2770, NSW, Australia   (100%)
Tel.: (61) 2 8801 4000
Web Site:
  http://www.startrackexpress.com.au
Sales Range: $100-124.9 Million
Freight Transportation & Logistics Services
N.A.I.C.S.: 488510

AUSTRALIAN POTASH LIMITED

Suite 31 22 Railway Road, Subiaco,
6008, WA, Australia
Tel.: (61) 893221003
Web Site:
  https://www.australianpotash.com
APC—(ASX)
Rev.: $223,214
Assets: $1,041,856
Liabilities: $543,466
Net Worth: $498,390
Earnings: $318,812
Fiscal Year-end: 06/30/24
Gold Mining
N.A.I.C.S.: 212220
Matt Shackleton (CEO & Mng Dir)

AUSTRALIAN RARE EARTHS LIMITED

Level 10 111 Gawler Place, Adelaide,
5000, SA, Australia
Tel.: (61) 1300646100   AU
Web Site: https://wwww.ar3.com.au
Year Founded: 2019
AR3—(ASX)
Rev.: $127,582
Assets: $17,578,689
Liabilities: $1,347,869
Net Worth: $16,230,820
Earnings: ($1,577,037)
Fiscal Year-end: 06/30/23
Mineral Exploration Services
N.A.I.C.S.: 212390
Rick Pobjoy (Mng Dir & CTO)

AUSTRALIAN RUGBY UNION

Ground Floor 29-57 Christie Street,
Saint Leonards, 2065, NSW, Australia
Tel.: (61) 280055555
Web Site: http://www.rugby.com.au
Sales Range: $25-49.9 Million
Emp.: 100
Management of the Australian National Rugby Team
N.A.I.C.S.: 711211
Paul McLean (Chm)

AUSTRALIAN STRATEGIC MA-

TERIALS LIMITED

Level 4 66 Kings Park Road, West
Perth, 6005, WA, Australia
Tel.: (61) 892001681   AU
Web Site: https://www.asm-au.com
Year Founded: 2000
ASM—(ASX)
Rev.: $6,748,544
Assets: $106,067,512
Liabilities: $77,891,657
Net Worth: $328,175,855
Earnings: ($39,970,039)
Emp.: 70
Fiscal Year-end: 06/30/23
Metal Exploration Services
N.A.I.C.S.: 213114
Jason Clifton (CFO)

Subsidiaries:

KSM Metals Co., Ltd.   (1)
83 Gwahaksaneop-4-ro Oksan-myeon,
Heungdeok-gu, Cheongju,
Chungcheongbuk-do, Korea (South)
Tel.: (82) 432189396
Web Site: https://www.ksm-kr.com
Solar Electric Power Generation Services
N.A.I.C.S.: 221114

AUSTRALIAN TRADE AND INVESTMENT COMMISSION

Level 23 Aon Tower 201 Kent Street,
Sydney, 2000, NSW, Australia
Tel.: (61) 132878   AU
Web Site: http://www.austrade.gov.au
Year Founded: 1985
Rev.: $144,001,172
Assets: $93,659,762
Liabilities: $45,692,423
Net Worth: $47,967,339
Earnings: ($9,675,604)
Emp.: 1,073
Fiscal Year-end: 06/30/19
Australian Export & International
Business Facilitation Services
N.A.I.C.S.: 926110
Kelly Ralston (Deputy CEO-Digital
Svcs & Outreach)

Subsidiaries:

Australian Consulate General   (1)
150 E 42nd St 34th Fl, New York, NY
10017
Tel.: (646) 344-8111
Web Site: http://www.austrade.gov.au
Sales Range: $25-49.9 Million
Emp.: 15
Consular & Trade Services
N.A.I.C.S.: 921190

AUSTRALIAN TURF CLUB (ATC)

Alison Rd, Locked Bag 3, Randwick,
2031, NSW, Australia
Tel.: (61) 1300 729 668
Web Site:
  http://www.australianturfclub.com.au
Year Founded: 1840
Rev.: $187,850,559
Assets: $284,132,083
Liabilities: $82,151,748
Net Worth: $201,980,335
Earnings: ($6,370,744)
Emp.: 2,000
Fiscal Year-end: 07/31/19
Racetrack Operator
N.A.I.C.S.: 711212
Matthew Galanos (Chief Fin & Ops
Officer)

Subsidiaries:

Thoroughbred Racing Productions
(Victoria) Pty Ltd   (1)
Unit 11 331 Ingles Street, Port Melbourne,
3207, VIC, Australia
Tel.: (61) 3 9646 7322
Web Site: http://www.trpbroadcast.com.au
Television Broadcasting Services
N.A.I.C.S.: 516120

Charles Cole (Mgr-Engrg & Technical)

AUSTRALIAN UNITED INVESTMENT COMPANY LTD

Level 20 101 Collins Street, Melbourne, 3000, VIC, Australia
Tel.: (61) 396540499
Web Site: https://www.aui.com.au
Year Founded: 1950
AUI—(ASX)
Rev.: $38,569,044
Assets: $1,024,423,740
Liabilities: $218,649,839
Net Worth: $805,773,902
Earnings: $32,797,810
Fiscal Year-end: 06/30/24
Portfolio Management & Investment
Advice
N.A.I.C.S.: 523940
Andrew J. Hancock (Sec)

AUSTRALIAN UNITED RETAILERS LIMITED

Level 9 South Wharf Tower 30 Convention Centre Place, South Wharf,
Melbourne, 3006, VIC, Australia
Tel.: (61) 398098600
Web Site:
  http://www.foodworks.com.au
Rev.: $42,375,341
Assets: $15,648,851
Liabilities: $13,535,994
Net Worth: $2,112,857
Earnings: ($307,732)
Emp.: 50
Fiscal Year-end: 06/30/19
Food Stores Owner & Operator
N.A.I.C.S.: 445110
Rick Wight (CEO & Mng Dir)

Subsidiaries:

Australian United Grocers Pty
Ltd   (1)
18 Jaybel Street, Slacks Creek, Salisbury,
4107, QLD, Australia
Tel.: (61) 733405200
Groceries Retailer
N.A.I.C.S.: 424410

FoodWorks Retail Pty Ltd   (1)
1601 Malvern Road, Glen Iris, Melbourne,
3146, VIC, Australia
Tel.: (61) 398098600
Sales Range: $25-49.9 Million
Supermarkets Operation Services
N.A.I.C.S.: 445110

AUSTRALIAN UNITY LIMITED

271 Spring Street, Melbourne, 3000,
VIC, Australia
Tel.: (61) 386827000
Web Site:
  https://www.australianunity.com.au
Year Founded: 1840
AYUPA—(ASX)
Rev.: $480,148,235
Assets: $6,649,425,721
Liabilities: $5,817,464,586
Net Worth: $831,961,134
Earnings: ($15,184,963)
Emp.: 9,500
Fiscal Year-end: 06/30/24
Health Insurance
N.A.I.C.S.: 921130
David Bryant (Chief Investment Officer & CEO-Wealth & Capital Markets)

Subsidiaries:

Australian Unity Bowral Development
Pty Ltd   (1)
149 Castlereagh Street, Sydney, 2000,
NSW, Australia
Tel.: (61) 386826801
Financial Advisory Services
N.A.I.C.S.: 523999

Australian Unity Care Services Pty
Ltd   (1)
114 Albert Road, South Melbourne, 3205,

VIC, Australia
Tel.: (61) 386826237
Financial Advisory Services
N.A.I.C.S.: 523940

Australian Unity Funds Management Limited (1)
L 14 114 Albert Road, South Melbourne, 3205, VIC, Australia
Tel.: (61) 386827000
Emp.: 30
Financial Management Services
N.A.I.C.S.: 523999
Frank Salmann *(Gen Mgr)*

Australian Unity Group Services Proprietary Limited (1)
114 Albert Road, South Melbourne, 3205, VIC, Australia
Tel.: (61) 386827000
Emp.: 800
Financial Management Services
N.A.I.C.S.: 523999

Australian Unity Health Care Limited (1)
L 14 114 Albert Road, South Melbourne, 3205, VIC, Australia
Tel.: (61) 386824288
Financial Management Services
N.A.I.C.S.: 523999

Australian Unity Health Limited (1)
271 Spring Street, Melbourne, 3000, VIC, Australia
Tel.: (61) 386827000
Web Site: http://www.australianunity.com
Health Insurance Services
N.A.I.C.S.: 524114

Australian Unity Investment Bonds Limited (1)
114 Albert Rd, South Melbourne, 3205, VIC, Australia
Tel.: (61) 386825000
Financial Advisory Services
N.A.I.C.S.: 523999

Australian Unity Nominees Pty Ltd (1)
114 Albert Road, South Melbourne, 3205, VIC, Australia
Tel.: (61) 386825000
Fund Management Services
N.A.I.C.S.: 524292

Australian Unity Property Limited (1)
114 Albert Road, South Melbourne, 3205, VIC, Australia
Tel.: (61) 386827000
Financial Management Services
N.A.I.C.S.: 523999
Rohan Mead *(Gen Mgr)*

Australian Unity Retirement Living Services Limited (1)
Unit 30 Karagi Ct 2 Pheasant Ave, Bateau Bay, Wyong, 2261, NSW, Australia
Tel.: (61) 243342602
Web Site: http://www.australianunity.net
Financial Advisory Services
N.A.I.C.S.: 523999

IOOF Ltd (1)
Level 06 161 Collins Street, Melbourne, 3001, VIC, Australia
Tel.: (61) 800913118
Sales Range: $200-249.9 Million
Emp.: 300
Investment Management Service
N.A.I.C.S.: 523999

Lifeplan Australia Building Society Limited (1)
111 Gawler Place, Adelaide, 5000, SA, Australia
Tel.: (61) 882123838
Sales Range: $50-74.9 Million
Emp.: 13
Financial Management Services
N.A.I.C.S.: 523999

Lifeplan Australia Friendly Society Limited (1)
111 Gawler Pl, Adelaide, 5000, SA, Australia
Tel.: (61) 882123838
Web Site: http://www.lifeplan.com.au
Fund Management Services
N.A.I.C.S.: 524292

Remedy Healthcare Group Pty Ltd (1)
11 Lt Lonsdale Street, GPO Box 2219, Melbourne, 3001, VIC, Australia
Tel.: (61) 130 022 4334
Web Site:
https://www.remedyhealthcare.com.au
Health Care Management Services
N.A.I.C.S.: 621999

The Governor s Retirement Resort Pty Ltd (1)
166 River Park Road, Port Macquarie, 2444, NSW, Australia
Tel.: (61) 1300149290
Sales Range: $50-74.9 Million
Emp.: 12
Financial Management Services
N.A.I.C.S.: 523999

Willandra Village Management Pty Ltd (1)
81 Willandra Road and 51 Little Willandra Road, Cromer, 2099, NSW, Australia
Tel.: (61) 1300295832
Web Site:
https://www.australianunity.com.au
Financial Management Services
N.A.I.C.S.: 523999
Robert Smith *(Mgr)*

AUSTRALIAN VANADIUM LIMITED
Level 2 50 Kings Park Road, West Perth, 6005, WA, Australia
Tel.: (61) 893215594
Web Site:
https://www.australianvanadium.com
AVL—(ASX)
Rev.: $562,901
Assets: $113,737,980
Liabilities: $19,623,397
Net Worth: $94,114,583
Earnings: ($10,152,244)
Fiscal Year-end: 06/30/24
Vanadium Exploration Services
N.A.I.C.S.: 212290
Leslie Ingraham *(Exec Dir)*

Subsidiaries:

Australian Uranium Ltd (1)
70 Aberdeen St, Northbridge, Perth, 6003, WA, Australia
Tel.: (61) 8 9228 1827
Uranium Mining Services
N.A.I.C.S.: 212290

Technology Metals Australia Limited (1)
Suite 9 330 Churchill Avenue, Subiaco, 6008, WA, Australia
Tel.: (61) 864891600
Web Site: http://www.tmtlimited.com.au
Rev.: $27,771
Assets: $25,693,584
Liabilities: $511,220
Net Worth: $25,182,364
Earnings: ($1,201,742)
Fiscal Year-end: 06/30/2021
Vanadium Exploration Services
N.A.I.C.S.: 212290
Ian Prentice *(Mng Dir)*

AUSTRALIAN VINTAGE LTD.
275 Sir Donald Bradman Drive, Cowandilla, Adelaide, 5033, SA, Australia
Tel.: (61) 881728333　　　AU
Web Site: https://avlwines.com.au
Year Founded: 2002
AVG—(ASX)
Rev.: $174,007,745
Assets: $277,399,171
Liabilities: $134,767,628
Net Worth: $142,631,543
Earnings: ($62,122,729)
Emp.: 442
Fiscal Year-end: 06/30/24
Wine Producer
N.A.I.C.S.: 312130
Michael H. Noack *(CFO)*

Subsidiaries:

Australian Vintage (UK) Ltd. (1)

2nd Floor Stephenson House 2 Cherry Orchard Road, Croydon, London, CR0 6BA, United Kingdom
Tel.: (44) 207 924 8850
Grape & Wine Mfr
N.A.I.C.S.: 312130
Julian Dyer *(COO)*

Miranda Wines Pty. Ltd. (1)
57 Jondaryan Avenue, Griffith, 2680, Australia　　　　　　　　　　(100%)
Tel.: (61) 269624033
Web Site: http://www.mirandawines.com.au
Sales Range: $25-49.9 Million
Emp.: 65
Beverages Mfr
N.A.I.C.S.: 424820

AUSTRALIAN WOOL INNOVATION LIMITED (AWI)
Level 6 68 Harrington Street The Rocks, Sydney, 2000, NSW, Australia
Tel.: (61) 282953100
Web Site: http://www.wool.com
Rev.: $71,130,703
Assets: $100,504,202
Liabilities: $13,510,966
Net Worth: $86,993,237
Earnings: $1,319,241
Emp.: 1,800
Fiscal Year-end: 06/30/19
Wool Production & Marketing Services
N.A.I.C.S.: 112410
Stuart K. McCullough *(CEO)*

AUSTRALIAN WOOL TESTING AUTHORITY LTD.
70 Robertson St, Kensington, 3031, VIC, Australia
Tel.: (61) 3 9371 4100
Web Site: http://www.awta.com.au
Emp.: 400
Agricultural Product Testing Services
N.A.I.C.S.: 541380
Michael Jackson *(Mng Dir)*

Subsidiaries:

Agrifood Technology Pty Ltd. (1)
260 Princes Hwy, PO Box 728, Werribee, 3030, VIC, Australia　　　　(100%)
Tel.: (61) 397420555
Web Site: http://www.agrifood.com.au
Sales Range: $25-49.9 Million
Emp.: 25
Agricultural Product Testing Services
N.A.I.C.S.: 541380
Robert Rantino *(Mgr-Customer Rels)*

Australian Wool Testing Authority Ltd. - AWTA Product Testing Division (1)
1st Floor 191 Racecourse Road, Flemington, 3031, VIC, Australia
Tel.: (61) 393712400
Web Site:
http://www.awtaproducttesting.com.au
Hydrostatic Testing Services
N.A.I.C.S.: 541380
Craig Wales *(Mgr-Product Testing)*

Australian Wool Testing Authority Ltd. - AWTA Raw Wool Division (1)
24 Robertson St, Kensington, 3031, VIC, Australia
Tel.: (61) 393712100
Web Site:
http://www.awtawooltesting.com.au
Hydrostatic Testing Services
N.A.I.C.S.: 541380

NZWTA Ltd (1)
22 Bridge Street Ahuriri, Napier, 4110, New Zealand
Tel.: (61) 68351086
Web Site: http://www.nzwta.co.nz
Hydrostatic Testing Services
N.A.I.C.S.: 541380
Duane Knowles *(CEO)*

AUSTRALIANSUPER PTY LTD
GPO Box 1901, Melbourne, 3001, VIC, Australia
Tel.: (61) 300 300 273

Web Site:
https://www.australiansuper.com
Emp.: 100
Superannuation, Pension Fund & Insurance Services
N.A.I.C.S.: 525110
Paul Schroder *(CEO)*

Subsidiaries:

Axicom Pty Limited (1)
Level 1 110 Pacific Highway, Saint Leonards, 2065, NSW, Australia
Tel.: (61) 294959000
Web Site: http://www.axicom.com.au
Wireless Telecommunications Operator
N.A.I.C.S.: 517112

AUSTRALIE SASU
199 rue Championnet, 75018, Paris, France
Tel.: (33) 1 7577 9200　　　　FR
Year Founded: 1984
Sales Range: $10-24.9 Million
Emp.: 150
Advetising Agency
N.A.I.C.S.: 541810
Vincent Leclabart *(Co-Founder)*

AUSTRALIS OIL & GAS LIMITED
Ground Floor 215 Hay Street, PO Box 8225, Subiaco, 6008, WA, Australia
Tel.: (61) 892208700　　　AU
Web Site:
https://www.australisoil.com
Year Founded: 2015
ATS—(ASX)
Rev.: $20,712,000
Assets: $70,777,000
Liabilities: $17,578,000
Net Worth: $53,199,000
Earnings: ($15,315,000)
Fiscal Year-end: 12/31/23
Oil & Gas Exploration Services
N.A.I.C.S.: 213112
Ian Lusted *(CEO & Mng Dir)*

Subsidiaries:

Australis TMS Inc. (1)
3 Allen Ctr 333 Clay St Ste 3680, Houston, TX 77002
Tel.: (346) 229-2525
Oil & Gas Exploration Services
N.A.I.C.S.: 211130

AUSTRIA HOTELS INTERNATIONAL BETRIEBS-GMBH
Hessgasse 7, 1010, Vienna, Austria
Tel.: (43) 1 316 65 0
Web Site: http://www.austria-hotels.at
Year Founded: 1955
Sales Range: $75-99.9 Million
Emp.: 700
Home Management Services
N.A.I.C.S.: 721110
Oliver W. Braun *(Owner & CEO)*

AUSTRIACARD HOLDINGS AG
Lamezanstrasse 4-8, 1230, Vienna, Austria
Tel.: (43) 1610650
Web Site:
https://www.austriacard.com
Year Founded: 1897
ACAG—(ATH)
Rev.: $402,426,847
Assets: $355,103,940
Liabilities: $237,652,172
Net Worth: $117,451,768
Earnings: $17,452,185
Emp.: 2,739
Fiscal Year-end: 12/31/23
Holding Company
N.A.I.C.S.: 551112
Emmanouil Kontos *(Deputy CEO)*

Austriacard Holdings AG—(Continued)

Subsidiaries:

**Austria Card Turkey Kart Operasyon-
lari AS** (1)
Ikitelli Organize Sanayi Bolgesi Ataturk Bul-
vari Deposite Is Merkezi, A6 Blok Kat 2 No
209 Basaksehir, Istanbul, Turkiye
Tel.: (90) 2124070019
Web Site: https://actkart.com.tr
Information Technology Services
N.A.I.C.S.: 541511

**TAG Systems Smart Solutions
S.L.U.** (1)
Madrid 48, Torres de la Alameda, 28813,
Madrid, Spain
Tel.: (34) 918863127
Credit Card Distr
N.A.I.C.S.: 424120

TSG Norway AS (1)
Mellomvika 1, 8622, Mo i Rana, Norway
Tel.: (47) 75199005
Information Technology Services
N.A.I.C.S.: 541511

**AUSUPREME INTERNATIONAL
HOLDINGS LIMITED**
Flat E 28/F EGL Tower 83 Hung To
Road Kwun Tong, Kowloon, China
(Hong Kong)
Tel.: (852) 81082733   Ky
Web Site: http://www.ausupreme.com
Year Founded: 2001
Rev.: $27,155,836
Assets: $27,690,200
Liabilities: $4,258,920
Net Worth: $23,431,281
Earnings: $1,553,822
Emp.: 208
Fiscal Year-end: 03/31/20
Personal Care Product Mfr & Distr
N.A.I.C.S.: 325620
Chi Fai Choy (Chm & Co-CEO)

AUSWIDE BANK LTD.
16-20 Barolin Street, PO Box 1063,
Bundaberg, 4670, QLD, Australia
Tel.: (61) 741504000
Web Site:
https://www.auswidebank.com.au
Year Founded: 1979
ABA—(ASX)
Rev.: $81,190,856
Assets: $3,451,351,125
Liabilities: $3,235,238,041
Net Worth: $216,113,084
Earnings: $20,022,077
Emp.: 239
Fiscal Year-end: 06/30/22
Commercial Banking & Financial Ser-
vices
N.A.I.C.S.: 522110
William R. Schafer (CFO & Sec)

Subsidiaries:

Wide Bay Australia (1)
16-20 Barolin Street, PO Box 508, 73 Victo-
ria Street, Bundaberg, 4670, QLD, Australia
Tel.: (61) 300138831
Web Site: https://www.auswidebank.com.au
Banking & Financial Services
N.A.I.C.S.: 522110

AUTECH CORPORATION
Yedeok-ro Godeok-myeon, Yesan,
Choongchungnam-Do, Korea (South)
Tel.: (82) 226280660
Web Site: https://www.autech.co.kr
Year Founded: 2000
067170—(KRS)
Rev.: $781,933,365
Assets: $468,985,876
Liabilities: $359,962,200
Net Worth: $109,023,676
Earnings: ($29,741,058)
Emp.: 95
Fiscal Year-end: 12/31/22

Motor Vehicle Body Mfr
N.A.I.C.S.: 336211
Sung-hee Kang (CEO)

Subsidiaries:

**Autech Corporation - Gyeongju
Factory** (1)
689-4 Naengcheon-ri Eoidong-eup, Gyeo-
ngju, Gyeongsanghuk-do, Korea (South)
Tel.: (82) 547410795
Automobile & Spare Parts Mfr
N.A.I.C.S.: 336211

**Autech Corporation - Yesan
Factory** (1)
930 Hoeum-ri Godeuk-myeon, Yesan,
Chungcheongnam, Korea (South)
Tel.: (82) 413393300
Web Site: https://www.autech.co.kr
Automobile & Spare Parts Mfr
N.A.I.C.S.: 336211

AUTECO MINERALS LTD.
Suite 3 Level 3 24 Outram Street,
West Perth, 6005, WA, Australia
Tel.: (61) 892209030
Web Site:
http://www.autecominerals.com.au
FFM—(ASX)
Rev.: $313,835
Assets: $166,274,038
Liabilities: $28,899,573
Net Worth: $137,374,465
Earnings: ($14,990,652)
Emp.: 97
Fiscal Year-end: 06/30/24
Metals Exploration & Mining Services
N.A.I.C.S.: 212210
Ray Shorrocks (Chm)

Subsidiaries:

Marmota Ltd. (1)
Unit 6 79-81 Brighton Road, PO Box 117,
Adelaide, 5045, SA, Australia
Tel.: (61) 882940899
Web Site: https://www.marmota.com.au
Rev.: $91,402
Assets: $13,681,398
Liabilities: $547,944
Net Worth: $13,133,453
Earnings: ($267,781)
Fiscal Year-end: 06/30/2024
Uranium Exploration & Mining
N.A.I.C.S.: 212290
Colin Rose (Chm)

Subsidiary (Domestic):

Marmosa Pty Ltd (2)
Warehouse 1 5 Butler Blvd Burbridge Busi-
ness Park, Adelaide, 5950, SA, Australia
Tel.: (61) 883753900
Sales Range: $50-74.9 Million
Mineral Exploration Services
N.A.I.C.S.: 213115

**AUTEL INTELLIGENT TECH-
NOLOGY CORP., LTD.**
Rainbow Technology Building No 36
Gaoxin North 6th Road, Songping-
shan Community Xili Subdistrict Nan-
shan District, Shenzhen, 518055,
Guangdong, China
Tel.: (86) 75581593644
Web Site: http://www.autel.com
Year Founded: 2004
688208—(SHG)
Rev.: $318,083,950
Assets: $734,789,746
Liabilities: $309,725,110
Net Worth: $425,064,636
Earnings: $14,325,475
Emp.: 508
Fiscal Year-end: 12/31/22
Medical Product Mfr & Distr
N.A.I.C.S.: 339112
Hongjing Li (Chm & Gen Mgr)

**AUTHEN-TECH COMMUNICA-
TIONS CANADA INC.**

895 Edgeley Boulevard, Concord,
L4K 4V9, ON, Canada
Tel.: (905) 738-3528
Web Site: http://www.authentech.ca
Rev.: $17,041,210
Emp.: 100
Telecommunication Servicesb
N.A.I.C.S.: 517810
Len Stanmore (CEO)

**AUTHORISED INVESTMENT
FUND LTD.**
Level 40 140 William Street, Mel-
bourne, 3000, VIC, Australia
Tel.: (61) 390988624
Web Site:
http://www.authorisedinvest.com
Investment Management Service
N.A.I.C.S.: 525990
Ben Genser (Chm)

**AUTHUM INVESTMENT INFRA-
STRUCTURE LTD.**
707 Raheja Centre Free Press Jour-
nal Marg, Nariman Point, Mumbai,
400021, India
Tel.: (91) 2261786000
Web Site: http://www.authum.com
011262—(KOL)
Rev.: $123,844,007
Assets: $548,601,499
Liabilities: $122,542,779
Net Worth: $426,058,719
Earnings: $912,827,097
Emp.: 11
Fiscal Year-end: 03/31/22
Financial Support Services
N.A.I.C.S.: 523999
Navin Kumar Jain (Mng Dir)

AUTINS GROUP PLC
Central Point One Central Park Drive,
Rugby, CV23 0WE, Warwickshire,
United Kingdom
Tel.: (44) 1788578300   UK
Web Site: https://autins.com
Year Founded: 1966
AUTG—(AIM)
Rev.: $31,812,737
Assets: $34,093,707
Liabilities: $16,759,696
Net Worth: $17,334,011
Earnings: ($1,471,768)
Emp.: 182
Fiscal Year-end: 09/30/21
Polystyrene Foam Product Manufac-
turing
N.A.I.C.S.: 326140
Gareth Kaminski-Cook (CEO)

Subsidiaries:

Autins AB (1)
Hamneviksvagen 12, 41879, Gothenburg,
Sweden
Tel.: (46) 738177233
Automotive Parts Mfr & Distr
N.A.I.C.S.: 336390

Autins Gmbh (1)
Siemensstrasse 9a, 40721, Hilden, Ger-
many
Tel.: (49) 21039903148
Automotive Parts Mfr & Distr
N.A.I.C.S.: 336390

Autins Limited (1)
Central Point One Central Park Drive,
Rugby, CV23 0WE, Warwickshire, United
Kingdom
Tel.: (44) 1788578300
Automotive Parts Mfr & Distr
N.A.I.C.S.: 336390

Autins Technical Centre Limited (1)
Workshop 5 NW05 Horiba Mira Technology
Park Watling Street, Nuneaton, CV13 6DE,
Warwickshire, United Kingdom
Tel.: (44) 1788578300
Automotive Parts Mfr & Distr
N.A.I.C.S.: 336390

AUTO CENTER SA
Bd Iuliu Maniu 105c S 6, Bucharest,
Romania
Tel.: (40) 21 2115251
Sales Range: Less than $1 Million
Emp.: 10
Motor Vehicle Repair & Maintenance
Services
N.A.I.C.S.: 811114

**AUTO CLEARING CHRYSLER
DODGE JEEP RAM**
331 Circle Drive West, Saskatoon,
S7L 5S8, SK, Canada
Tel.: (306) 244-2186
Web Site:
http://www.autoclearing.com
Year Founded: 1982
New & Used Car Dealers
N.A.I.C.S.: 441110
Paul Savoie (Gen Mgr)

AUTO HRVATSKA D.D.
Heinzelova 70, 10000, Zagreb, Croa-
tia
Tel.: (385) 16449991
Web Site:
https://www.autohrvatska.hr
Year Founded: 1952
AUHR—(ZAG)
Rev.: $266,956,193
Assets: $132,638,919
Liabilities: $44,535,128
Net Worth: $88,103,792
Earnings: $2,766,873
Emp.: 780
Fiscal Year-end: 12/31/23
Car Rental Services
N.A.I.C.S.: 532111
Bogdan Tihava (Chm)

**AUTO IMPEX JOINT STOCK
COMPANY**
Sonsoglon-2 Auto Impex Building,
Ulaanbaatar, Mongolia
Tel.: (976) 70171315
AOI—(MONG)
Rev.: $77,378
Assets: $970,717
Liabilities: $2,147,996
Net Worth: ($1,177,278)
Earnings: ($26,186)
Fiscal Year-end: 12/31/19
Motor Vehicle Parts Whslr
N.A.I.C.S.: 423120

**AUTO ITALIA HOLDINGS LIM-
ITED**
28 F Viva Place 36 Heung Yip Road,
Wong Chuk Hang, Hong Kong, China
(Hong Kong)
Tel.: (852) 23650269   BM
Web Site:
https://www.autoitalia.com.hk
ATTGF—(OTCIQ)
Rev.: $10,232,886
Assets: $116,380,073
Liabilities: $52,528,266
Net Worth: $63,851,807
Earnings: ($810,252)
Emp.: 7
Fiscal Year-end: 12/31/21
Holding Company; Luxury Car Deal-
erships Owner & Operator; Car Whslr
N.A.I.C.S.: 551112
Benny Tin Lung Chong (CEO & Chm)

Subsidiaries:

Auto Italia Limited (1)
3S Center Unit C Ground Floor 2 Yuen
Shun Circuit, Sha Tin, NT, China (Hong
Kong)
Tel.: (852) 2365 0269
Web Site: http://www.autoitalia.com.hk
Luxury Car Distr & Dealerhips Operator
N.A.I.C.S.: 441110

Dalian Auto Italia Car Trading Co.,
Ltd.   **(1)**
No 2-7 Yi Pin Xing Hai B3 Area Xing Hai
Square, Dalian, 116023, Liaoning,
China   **(75.4%)**
Tel.: (86) 411 84804789
Sales Range: $25-49.9 Million
Emp.: 21
Luxury Car Dealer
N.A.I.C.S.: 441110

Nanjing Auto Italia Car Trading Co.,
Ltd.   **(1)**
No 48 Ningnan Avenue, Yuhua District,
Nanjing, 210012, Jiangsu, China **(75.4%)**
Tel.: (86) 25 58077888
Luxury Car Dealer
N.A.I.C.S.: 441110

AUTO KUCA 21. MAJ A.D.
Patrijarha Dimitrija 24, Rakovica,
11000, Belgrade, Serbia
Tel.: (381) 11 3564 420
Web Site:
    http://www.dmbautokuca.co.rs
Year Founded: 1994
AKDM—(BEL)
Sales Range: Less than $1 Million
Emp.: 11
Automobile Maintenance & Repair
Services
N.A.I.C.S.: 811111
Milutin Dobrilovic (Exec Dir)

AUTO KUCA LESKOVAC A.D.
Dorda Stamenkovica bb, Leskovac,
Serbia
Tel.: (381) 16252464
Year Founded: 1982
AKLE—(BEL)
Assets: $375,390
Liabilities: $55
Net Worth: $375,335
Earnings: ($1,693)
Emp.: 3
Fiscal Year-end: 12/31/22
Car & Motor Vehicle Whslr
N.A.I.C.S.: 423110
Mile Stojiljkovic (Exec Dir)

AUTO KUCA VOZDOVAC A.D.
Vojvode Stepe 318, Belgrade, Serbia
Tel.: (381) 11 2492 038
Year Founded: 1966
Sales Range: $1-9.9 Million
Emp.: 72
Motor Vehicle Maintenance & Repair
Services
N.A.I.C.S.: 811111

AUTO KUCA ZEMUN A.D.
Prvomajska 70, Zemun, Serbia
Tel.: (381) 113169489
Year Founded: 2001
AKZM—(BEL)
Sales Range: Less than $1 Million
Motor Vehicle Maintenance & Repair
Services
N.A.I.C.S.: 811111
Zeljko Jankovic (Exec Dir)

AUTO NEJMA MAROC SA
Km 10 Route d'El Jadida, 20 230,
Casablanca, 20 230, Morocco
Tel.: (212) 522650990
Web Site: https://www.autonejma.ma
Year Founded: 1963
NEJ—(CAS)
Sales Range: $200-249.9 Million
Car Dealer
N.A.I.C.S.: 441110
Abdellatif Hakam (Chm)

AUTO NETWORKS INTERNATIONAL CORPORATION
81 Fu Hsing Road, Section 1 South
District, Taichung, 403, Taiwan
Tel.: (886) 963080887   NV

Year Founded: 2009
Automotive Wheels Distr
N.A.I.C.S.: 423120
Chi Shing Huang (Pres, CEO, CFO,
Treas & Sec)

AUTO ONE AUSTRALIA PTY. LTD.
Unit 1 40 Carrington Road, Castle
Hill, 2154, NSW, Australia
Tel.: (61) 288451111
Web Site: http://www.autoone.com.au
Year Founded: 1988
Automobile Parts Distr
N.A.I.C.S.: 441330
Andrew Boath (Mng Dir)

AUTO PARTNER SA
Ekonomiczna 20, 43-150, Bierun,
Poland
Tel.: (48) 323251500
Web Site: https://en.autopartner.com
Year Founded: 1993
APR—(WAR)
Rev.: $712,129,076
Assets: $394,483,746
Liabilities: $182,750,842
Net Worth: $211,732,905
Earnings: $52,069,537
Emp.: 2,327
Fiscal Year-end: 12/31/22
Automobile Parts Distr
N.A.I.C.S.: 423120
Aleksander Gorecki (Founder & Pres)

Subsidiaries:

Maxgear Sp. z o.o. Sp.
komandytowa   **(1)**
Ul Ekonomiczna 20, 43-150, Bierun, Poland
Tel.: (48) 323251500
Web Site: https://www.maxgear.pl
Automobile Parts Distr
N.A.I.C.S.: 423120

AUTO PINS INDIA LTD.
16 Industrial Area Rajiv Gandhi
Colony, Faridabad, 121001, Haryana,
India
Tel.: (91) 1294155691
Web Site:
    https://www.autopinsindia.com
Year Founded: 1953
531994—(BOM)
Rev.: $3,894,686
Assets: $1,947,555
Liabilities: $1,119,218
Net Worth: $828,337
Earnings: $124,406
Emp.: 70
Fiscal Year-end: 03/31/21
Automobile Parts Mfr
N.A.I.C.S.: 336110
Rajbir Singh (Mng Dir)

AUTO RELAIS SAGLIO
232 Avenue De Colmar, 67100,
Strasbourg, Bas Rhin, France
Tel.: (33) 388791679
Sales Range: $10-24.9 Million
Emp.: 27
New & Used Car Dealers
N.A.I.C.S.: 441110
Jean-Pierre Wolf (Pres)

AUTO SENATEUR INC
255 Saint Martin E, Laval, H7M 1Z1,
QC, Canada
Tel.: (450) 668-2710
Web Site:
    http://www.vimonttoyotalaval.com
Rev.: $68,274,666
Emp.: 70
New & Used Car Dealers
N.A.I.C.S.: 441110

AUTO WEST GROUP

10780 Cambie Rd, Richmond, V6X
1K8, BC, Canada
Tel.: (604) 273-2217
Web Site:
    https://www.autowestgroup.ca
Year Founded: 1986
Emp.: 200
Motor Vehicles Mfr
N.A.I.C.S.: 441110

Subsidiaries:

M.T.K. Auto West Ltd.   **(1)**
10780 Cambie Road, Richmond, V6X 1K8,
BC, Canada
Tel.: (604) 273-2217
Web Site: https://www.autowestbmw.com
Emp.: 200
New & Used Car Dealers
N.A.I.C.S.: 441110

AUTO1 GROUP SE
Bergmannstrasse 72, 10961, Berlin,
Germany
Tel.: (49) 30201638360
Web Site: https://www.auto1-
group.com
Year Founded: 2012
AG1—(DEU)
Rev.: $5,895,569,825
Assets: $1,839,722,642
Liabilities: $1,216,533,564
Net Worth: $623,189,078
Earnings: ($125,691,776)
Emp.: 5,356
Fiscal Year-end: 12/31/23
Car Retailer
N.A.I.C.S.: 441120
Christian Bertermann (CEO)

Subsidiaries:

AUTO1 Czechia s.r.o.   **(1)**
Na Maninach 876/7, Holesovice, 170 00,
Prague, Czech Republic
Tel.: (420) 228881443
Used Car Distr
N.A.I.C.S.: 441120

AUTO1.com GmbH   **(1)**
Bergmannstrasse 72, 10961, Berlin, Germany
Tel.: (49) 3020163405
Web Site: https://www.auto1.com
Used Car Distr
N.A.I.C.S.: 441120

Agenzia1 S.r.l.   **(1)**
Corso Unione Sovietica 612/3A, 10135, Turin, Italy
Tel.: (39) 01119505045
Web Site: https://www.agenzia1.it
Vehicle Insurance Services
N.A.I.C.S.: 524126

Autohero Belgium B.V.   **(1)**
Uitbreidingstraat 82, 2600, Berchem, Belgium
Tel.: (32) 33930650
Web Site: https://www.autohero.com
Used Car Distr
N.A.I.C.S.: 441120

Autohero GmbH   **(1)**
Bergmannstr 72, 10961, Berlin, Germany
Tel.: (49) 8006646640
Used Car Distr
N.A.I.C.S.: 441120

Autohero Italia S.R.L.   **(1)**
Via Perin Del Vaga 2, 20156, Milan, Italy
Tel.: (39) 03408263066
Used Car Distr
N.A.I.C.S.: 441120

Autohero NL B.V.   **(1)**
Hoogoorddreef 11, 1101 BA, Amsterdam,
Netherlands
Tel.: (31) 850003355
Used Car Distr
N.A.I.C.S.: 441120

Autohero Osterreich GmbH   **(1)**
Rennweg 97-99, 1030, Vienna, Austria
Tel.: (43) 800202320
Used Car Distr
N.A.I.C.S.: 441120

Autohero Plus Spain S.L.   **(1)**
Rosario Pino No 14-16 1a Planta, 28020,
Madrid, Spain
Tel.: (34) 911675783
Used Car Distr
N.A.I.C.S.: 441120

Autohero Poland Sp. z o.o.   **(1)**
Polczynska 31A, 01-377, Warsaw, Poland
Tel.: (48) 882000404
Used Car Distr
N.A.I.C.S.: 441120

WKA B.V.   **(1)**
Uitbreidingstraat 82, 2600, Antwerp, Belgium
Tel.: (32) 78484070
Web Site: https://www.wijkopenautos.be
Used Car Distr
N.A.I.C.S.: 441120

WKDA Osterreich GmbH   **(1)**
Rennweg 97-99, 1030, Vienna, Austria
Tel.: (43) 800999144
Web Site: https://www.wirkaufendeinauto.at
Automobile Parts Distr
N.A.I.C.S.: 423140

WijkopenAutos B.V.   **(1)**
Hoogoorddreef 11, 1101 BA, Amsterdam,
Netherlands
Tel.: (31) 858887799
Web Site: https://www.wijkopenautos.nl
Automotive Distr
N.A.I.C.S.: 483212

AUTOBACS SEVEN CO., LTD.
5-6-52 Toyosu Koto-ku Tokyo NBF
Toyosu Canal Front, Koto-ku, Tokyo,
135-8717, Japan
Tel.: (81) 362198787   JP
Web Site: https://www.autobacs.co.jp
Year Founded: 1947
9832—(TKS)
Rev.: $1,519,348,160
Assets: $1,288,606,280
Liabilities: $434,911,560
Net Worth: $853,694,720
Earnings: $42,006,550
Emp.: 4,385
Fiscal Year-end: 03/31/24
Holding Company; Automotive Accessories Stores Owner & Operator
N.A.I.C.S.: 551112
Kiomi Kobayashi (Pres, CEO & Chief
Autobacs Chain Officer)

Subsidiaries:

AudioXtra Pty. Ltd.   **(1)**
10 Stoddart Road, Prospect, 2148, NSW,
Australia
Tel.: (61) 288419000
Web Site: https://www.audioxtra.com.au
Emp.: 50
Automotive Products Whslr
N.A.I.C.S.: 423110
Shannon Mcintosh (Branch Mgr)

Autobacs Car Service Malaysia Sdn.
Bhd.   **(1)**
No 7B and No 7 Jalan Camar 1/3, Taman
Perling, 81200, Johor Bahru, Johor, Malaysia
Tel.: (60) 72448298
Web Site: http://www.autobacs.com.my
Automotive Products Whslr
N.A.I.C.S.: 423110
Hidemitsu Ansai (CEO)

Autobacs Financial Service Co.,
Ltd.   **(1)**
5-6-52 Toyosu NBF Toyosu Canal Front 3rd
floor, Koto-ku, Tokyo, 135-0061, Japan
Tel.: (81) 362196001
Web Site: https://www.autobacs-afs.com
Emp.: 30
Financial Services
N.A.I.C.S.: 523210

Autobacs France Sas   **(1)**
254 ter boulevard du Havre, 95480, Pierrelaye, France
Tel.: (33) 175720260
Web Site: http://www.autobacs.fr
Automotive Products Whslr
N.A.I.C.S.: 423110

Autobacs Seven Co., Ltd.—(Continued)

Agnes Darnac *(CEO)*

Autobacs Management Service Co., Ltd. (1)
1-9-4 Edagawa Sumitomo Real Estate Toyosu TK Building 3rd Floor, Koto, Tokyo, Japan
Tel.: (81) 368624510
Automotive Products Whslr
N.A.I.C.S.: 423110

Autobacs Nagasaki Co., Ltd. (1)
2844-12 Hiucho, Sasebo, 857-1151, Nagasaki, Japan
Tel.: (81) 956338100
Web Site: http://www.ab-nagasaki.com
Automobile Whslr
N.A.I.C.S.: 423110

Autobacs Venture Singapore Pte. Ltd. (1)
10 Ubi View, Singapore, 408543, Singapore
Tel.: (65) 67495600
Web Site: https://www.autobacs.com.sg
Car Maintenance Services
N.A.I.C.S.: 811198
Jia Cherng Khoo *(Supvr-Mechanic)*

BACS Boots Co., Ltd. (1)
2-1 Makinohara, Inzai, 270-1331, Japan
Tel.: (81) 476469221
Web Site: https://bacsboots.com
Emp.: 83
Automobile Maintenance Services
N.A.I.C.S.: 811198

Chain Growth Co., Ltd. (1)
5-6-52 Toyosu, Koto-ku, Tokyo, 135-0061, Japan
Tel.: (81) 362196916
Web Site: https://www.chain-growth.com
Human Resouce Services
N.A.I.C.S.: 541612

FATRASTYLING Inc. (1)
1157-812 Hodozawa, Gotemba, 412-0046, Japan
Tel.: (81) 550896979
Web Site: https://www.fatrastyling.jp
Emp.: 10
Automotive Parts Mfr & Distr
N.A.I.C.S.: 336390

Kumamoto Autobacs Inc. (1)
1-11-7 Nishihara, Higashi-ku, Kumamoto, 861-8029, Japan
Tel.: (81) 963846466
Web Site: https://www.ab-autostars.com
Automotive Products Whslr
N.A.I.C.S.: 423110

SIAM Autobacs Co., Ltd. (1)
729/170 Ratchadaphisek Road, Bang Phongphang Subdistrict Yannawa, Bangkok, 10120, Thailand
Tel.: (66) 229507327
Web Site: http://www.autobacs.co.th
Car Related Product Whslr
N.A.I.C.S.: 423110
Krisnun Tiraganon *(Gen Mgr-Sls & Mktg)*

SK Automobile Pte. Ltd. (1)
23 Kaki Bukit Ave 4 03-01 Vicom Inspection Centre South Wing, Singapore, Singapore
Tel.: (65) 67895155
Web Site: http://www.skauto.com.sg
Emp.: 30
Automobile Maintenance Services
N.A.I.C.S.: 811198
Shaun Martin Plunkett *(Mgr-Bus Dev)*

Shaken-Bankin DEPOT Inc. (1)
3-1-6 Steel Street, Urayasu, 279-0025, Japan
Tel.: (81) 473818150
Web Site: https://www.shaken-depot.jp
Emp.: 23
Automobile Maintenance Services
N.A.I.C.S.: 811198

Yumesho Ltd. (1)
304-6 Kamifukawa-cho, Asakita, Hiroshima, 739-1752, Japan
Tel.: (81) 825622624
Web Site: http://www.yumesho.co.jp
Drainage Sanitary Equipment Mfr
N.A.I.C.S.: 332999

AUTOBANK AG

Gertrude-Frohlich-Sandner-Strasse 3, 1100, Vienna, Austria
Tel.: (43) 1601900
Web Site: https://www.autobank.at
Emp.: 50
Motor Vehicle Financing & Leasing Services
N.A.I.C.S.: 522220
Markus Beuchert *(CFO & Member-Mgmt Bd)*

AUTOBIO DIAGNOSTICS CO., LTD

No 87 Jingbei Yi Rd National Eco&Tech Zone, Zhengzhou, 450016, Henan, China
Tel.: (86) 37162007036
Web Site: https://www.autobio.com.cn
Year Founded: 1998
603658—(SHG)
Rev.: $623,604,487
Assets: $1,470,313,602
Liabilities: $359,443,445
Net Worth: $1,110,870,156
Earnings: $163,908,169
Emp.: 5,000
Fiscal Year-end: 12/31/22
Diagnostic Product Mfr & Distr
N.A.I.C.S.: 334510
Miao Yongjun *(Chm)*

AUTOCANADA INC.

Suite 200-15511 123 Avenue NW, Edmonton, T5V 0C3, AB, Canada
Tel.: (780) 732-3135
Web Site: https://www.autocan.ca
Year Founded: 2009
ACQ—(TSX)
Rev.: $2,604,596,566
Assets: $1,486,630,831
Liabilities: $1,202,804,001
Net Worth: $283,826,830
Earnings: ($5,181,040)
Emp.: 4,030
Fiscal Year-end: 12/31/20
Holding Company; Car Dealerships Owner & Operator
N.A.I.C.S.: 551112
Paul W. Antony *(Chm)*

Subsidiaries:

1053038 ONTARIO LIMITED (1)
1495 Upper James St, Hamilton, L9B 1K2, ON, Canada
Tel.: (905) 574-8200
Web Site: https://www.sterlinghonda.com
Rev.: $23,208,505
Emp.: 49
New & Used Car Dealers
N.A.I.C.S.: 441110
Tony Reed *(Gen Mgr-Sls)*

4236009 MANITOBA LTD (1)
1445 18th St N, Brandon, R7C 1A6, MB, Canada
Tel.: (204) 728-8554
Web Site: https://www.kelleherford.com
Rev.: $13,594,008
Emp.: 60
New & Used Car Dealers
N.A.I.C.S.: 441110
Mike Boutilier *(Mgr-Sls)*

Dodge City Auto (1)
2200 Eighth Street East, Saskatoon, S7H 0V3, SK, Canada
Tel.: (306) 700-3355
Web Site: http://www.dodgecityauto.com
New & Used Car Dealers
N.A.I.C.S.: 441110

Haldimand Motors Ltd. (1)
42 Talbot St E Hwy 3, Cayuga, N0A 1E0, ON, Canada
Tel.: (905) 772-3636
Web Site: http://www.haldimandmotors.com
Used Car Dealers
N.A.I.C.S.: 441120
Arda Edelman *(Treas & Sec)*

Hunt Club Nissan Ltd. (1)

275 West Hunt Club Rd, Nepean, K2E 1A6, ON, Canada (90%)
Tel.: (888) 375-8413
Web Site: http://www.huntclubnissan.com
New & Used Car Dealers
N.A.I.C.S.: 441110

Lakewood Chevrolet (1)
9150 34 Avenue, Edmonton, T6E 5P2, AB, Canada (75%)
Tel.: (780) 462-5959
Web Site: http://www.lakewoodchev.com
Sales Range: $25-49.9 Million
New & Used Car Dealer
N.A.I.C.S.: 441110
Blair MacPherson *(Mgr-Parts)*

Saskatoon Motor Products Ltd. (1)
715 Circle Drive East, Saskatoon, S7K 0V1, SK, Canada (70%)
Tel.: (306) 242-0276
Web Site: http://www.smpchev.ca
Sales Range: $25-49.9 Million
Emp.: 75
New & Used Car Dealers
N.A.I.C.S.: 441110
Corey Risling *(Mgr-Sls)*

Toronto Dodge Chrysler Ltd. (1)
321 Front Street East, Toronto, M5A 1G3, ON, Canada
Tel.: (416) 368-7000
Web Site: http://www.torontododge.ca
New & Used Car Dealer
N.A.I.C.S.: 441110

AUTOCAPITAL CANADA INC.

11 Church Street, Toronto, M5E1W1, ON, Canada
Web Site: http://www.autocapitalcanada.ca
Year Founded: 2012
Art Finance Services
N.A.I.C.S.: 522220
Voke Natasza Ararile *(Sr Mgr-Talent & HR)*

AUTOCONT CONTROL SYSTEMS, S.R.O.

Kafkova 1853/3, Moravska, 702 00, Ostrava, Czech Republic
Tel.: (420) 595691150
Web Site: http://www.accs.cz
Sales Range: $10-24.9 Million
Emp.: 25
Information & Communication Technology Mfr
N.A.I.C.S.: 334118

Subsidiaries:

AutoCont Online A/S (1)
Podebradska 88 55, 190 02, Prague, 9, Czech Republic
Tel.: (420) 251022102
Web Site: http://www.acol.cz
Provider of Telecommunications Services
N.A.I.C.S.: 517112

AutoCont a.s. (1)
Schneidra Trnavskeho 6, 84101, Bratislava, Slovakia (100%)
Tel.: (421) 264287881
Web Site: http://www.autocont.sk
Information & Communication Technologies Distr
N.A.I.C.S.: 334118

AUTOCORP HOLDING PUBLIC COMPANY LIMITED

1111 Moo 1 Maliwan Road, Bantum Muang, Khon Kaen, 40000, Thailand
Tel.: (66) 43306333
Web Site: https://www.autocorpgroup.com
Year Founded: 2015
ACG—(THA)
Rev.: $53,144,416
Assets: $39,973,519
Liabilities: $19,676,261
Net Worth: $20,297,257
Earnings: $506,684
Emp.: 430
Fiscal Year-end: 12/31/23

Holding Company
N.A.I.C.S.: 551112
Phanumast Rungkakulnuwat *(CEO)*

Subsidiaries:

Autoclik by ACG Company Limited (1)
1111 Moo 1 Maliwan Road Tambon Ban Thum, Mueang District, Khon Kaen, 40000, Thailand
Tel.: (66) 20278889
Web Site: https://www.autoclikfastfit.com
Automotive Repair & Maintenance Services
N.A.I.C.S.: 811198

Honda Maliwan Company Limited (1)
1111 Moo 1 Maliwan Road Bantum, Mueang, Khon Kaen, 40000, Thailand
Tel.: (66) 43306444
Car Dealing Services
N.A.I.C.S.: 441110

AUTOCOUNT DOTCOM BERHAD

B2-3A-01 Level 3A Block B2 Meritus Oasis Corporate Park No 2, Jalan PJU 1A/2 Ara Damansara, 47301, Petaling Jaya, Selangor, Malaysia
Tel.: (60) 30003000
Web Site: https://www.autocountsoft.com
Year Founded: 2022
0276—(KLS)
Rev.: $9,031,620
Assets: $15,477,376
Liabilities: $3,763,494
Net Worth: $11,713,881
Earnings: $2,826,072
Fiscal Year-end: 12/31/23
Software Development Services
N.A.I.C.S.: 541511
Wee Kong Tan *(CFO)*

AUTOFEED CORPORATION

47 Ditton Drive Unit 7, Hamilton, L8W 2E5, ON, Canada
Tel.: (905) 648-8200
Web Site: http://www.autofeed.ca
Sales Range: $150-199.9 Million
Emp.: 16
Feeder Equipment Mfr & Service
N.A.I.C.S.: 335999
Bill Chamberlain *(VP)*

AUTOGRANA A.D.

12 januara 5, Priboj, Serbia
Tel.: (381) 33455381
Year Founded: 1999
ATGR—(BEL)
Sales Range: Less than $1 Million
Emp.: 28
Automotive Part Whslr
N.A.I.C.S.: 423110
Mima Alajbegovic *(Exec Dir)*

AUTOHAUS HEINRICH SENDEN GMBH

Sittarder Str 25-29, 52511, Geilenkirchen, Germany
Tel.: (49) 245162080
Web Site: http://www.ah-senden.de
Sales Range: $25-49.9 Million
New & Used Car Dealers
N.A.I.C.S.: 441120
Ingo Diapers *(Co-Mng Partner)*

AUTOHAUS KRETTER GMBH

Otto-von-Guericke-Strasse 1, 7552, Gera, Germany
Tel.: (49) 365437700
Web Site: http://www.autohaus-kretter.de
Rev.: $64,170,011
Emp.: 75
New & Used Car Dealers
N.A.I.C.S.: 441110
Jurgen Munzel *(Mng Dir)*

AUTOHAUS WIDMANN + WINTERHOLLER GMBH

Rudolf-Diesel-Str 18, Dachau, 85221, Germany
Tel.: (49) 8131 3121 0
Web Site: http://www.widmann-winterholler.de
Emp.: 250
Motor Vehicle Dealership Operator
N.A.I.C.S.: 441110
Erwin Winterholler *(Mng Dir)*

Subsidiaries:

Autohaus Widmann + Winterholler GmbH - Farchant **(1)**
Partenkirchner Str 34, 82490, Farchant, Bavaria, Germany
Tel.: (49) 8821 96676 0
Web Site: http://www.oberlandautomobile.de
Sales Range: $25-49.9 Million
Emp.: 18
Car Dealer
N.A.I.C.S.: 441110
Erwen Winterholler *(Mgr)*

AUTOHELLAS S.A.

31 Viltanioti Str, Kifissia, 145 64, Athens, Greece
Tel.: (30) 2106264000
Web Site: https://www.hertz.gr
Year Founded: 1962
0AH1—(DEU)
Rev.: $826,203,354
Assets: $1,294,648,459
Liabilities: $922,363,607
Net Worth: $372,284,852
Earnings: $89,088,815
Emp.: 1,562
Fiscal Year-end: 12/31/22
Car Rental Services
N.A.I.C.S.: 532111
Theodoros Emmanuella Vasilakis *(Chm)*

Subsidiaries:

Autotechnica Fleet Services S.R.L. **(1)**
MULTIGALAXY MG2 Building Str George Constantinescu No 2C Floor 3, No 2C Floor 3 sector 2 Pipera, 020339, Bucharest, Romania
Tel.: (40) 214078200
Web Site: https://www.hertz.ro
Sales Range: $50-74.9 Million
Emp.: 20
Car Rental Services
N.A.I.C.S.: 532111

Autotechnica Ltd. **(1)**
Tel.: (359) 24390220
Web Site: https://www.autotechnica.bg
Car Rental Services
N.A.I.C.S.: 532111

Autotechnica Montenegro doo **(1)**
Oktobarske Revolucije 114, 81000, Podgorica, Montenegro
Tel.: (382) 68882201
Web Site: https://www.hertz.me
Car Rental Services
N.A.I.C.S.: 532111

Autotechnica Serbia doo **(1)**
31 Omladinskih Brigada, 11070, Belgrade, Serbia
Tel.: (381) 112028200
Web Site: https://www.hertz.rs
Car Rental Services
N.A.I.C.S.: 532111

Demstar Rentals 2005 Ltd. **(1)**
16 Aikaterini Kornarou Strovolos, PO Box 27752, Engomi, Nicosia, 2015, Cyprus
Tel.: (357) 22208888
Web Site: http://www.hertz.com.cy
Sales Range: $50-74.9 Million
Emp.: 25
Car Rental Services
N.A.I.C.S.: 532111
Pambos Danos *(Gen Mgr)*

Fasttrack S.A. **(1)**
28 Vouliagmenis Avenue, Ellinikon, 16777, Athens, Greece

Tel.: (30) 2109638849
Web Site: https://www.fasttrackingreece.com
Airport Concierge & Booking Services
N.A.I.C.S.: 561599

Hyundai Hellas S.A. **(1)**
31 Viltanioti, 14564, Kifissia, Greece
Tel.: (30) 2105507000
Web Site: https://www.hyundai.gr
Car Dealer
N.A.I.C.S.: 441110

KINEO S.A. **(1)**
Viltanioti 31, 14564, Kifissia, Greece
Tel.: (30) 2111986219
Web Site: https://kineo.gr
Electric Vehicle Dealer
N.A.I.C.S.: 441227

Kia Hellas S.A. **(1)**
Viltanioti 31, Kato Kifisia, Mandra-Attikis, Greece
Tel.: (30) 2105507000
Automotive Distr
N.A.I.C.S.: 423110

Technokar S.A. **(1)**
Viltanioti 31 K, 14564, Kifissia, Greece
Tel.: (30) 2106263701
Web Site: https://www.seat.gr
Car Dealer
N.A.I.C.S.: 441110

AUTOKOMERC A.D.

Nikole Pasica 5, 74000, Doboj, Bosnia & Herzegovina
Tel.: (387) 53241594
AUTK—(BANJ)
Sales Range: $1-9.9 Million
Emp.: 40
Land Transportation Services
N.A.I.C.S.: 485999
Uros Krulj *(Chm-Mgmt Bd)*

AUTOKORAN A.D.

IV Sandzacke brigade bb, Priboj, Serbia
Tel.: (381) 3352600
Web Site: http://www.autokoranadpriboj.co.rs
Year Founded: 2002
ATKR—(BEL)
Sales Range: Less than $1 Million
Emp.: 9
Automotive Repair & Maintenance Services
N.A.I.C.S.: 811111
Aco Radovic *(Exec Dir & Dir)*

AUTOKRAZ HOLDING CO.

2 Yaroslavskiy proyezd Str, Kremenchuk, 39631, Poltava, Ukraine
Tel.: (380) 536 76 6210
Web Site: http://www.autokraz.com.ua
Sales Range: $10-24.9 Million
Emp.: 17,800
Heavy-Duty Trucks & Special-Purpose Vehicles Mfr
N.A.I.C.S.: 336120
Sergey Sazonov *(Gen Dir)*

Subsidiaries:

FTF KrAZ **(1)**
9 V Boyko Str, Kremenchuk, 39602, Poltavskaya, Ukraine
Tel.: (380) 536798221
Web Site: http://www.autokraz.com.ua
Heavy-Duty Trucks Exporter
N.A.I.C.S.: 336120

Foreign Trade Firm KrAZ LLC **(1)**
2 Yaroslavskiy Proyizd Str, 39631, Kremenchuk, Ukraine
Tel.: (380) 536766210
Truck & Trailer Mfr & Distr
N.A.I.C.S.: 336212

AUTOKUCA RAKETA AD

Prvomajska 63, 31205, Sevojno, Serbia
Tel.: (381) 31531799

Web Site: https://www.ak-raketa.rs
Year Founded: 1999
RKSV—(BEL)
Rev.: $87,582
Assets: $433,217
Liabilities: $584,530
Net Worth: ($151,313)
Earnings: ($17,207)
Emp.: 1
Fiscal Year-end: 12/31/23
Automotive Repair & Maintenance Services
N.A.I.C.S.: 811198
Dragan Radosavljevic *(Gen Mgr)*

AUTOKUHLER GMBH & CO. KG

Am Hohlen Weg 31, 34369, Hofgeismar, Germany
Tel.: (49) 56718830
Web Site: http://www.akg-group.com
Year Founded: 1919
Sales Range: $250-299.9 Million
Emp.: 2,400
Heat Exchanger Mfr
N.A.I.C.S.: 332410
Hartwig Pietzcker *(Chm-Mgmt Bd)*

Subsidiaries:

AKG France S.A.S **(1)**
Parc Industriel Sud - ZI Remy 4 Rue des Freres Remy, PO Box 20416, 57200, Sarreguemines, France
Tel.: (33) 3 87 95 11 11
Web Site: http://www.akg-france.com
Heat Exchanger Distr
N.A.I.C.S.: 423720

AKG India Private Ltd. **(1)**
7/294 Pollachi Main Road, Solvampalayam Kinathukadavu, Coimbatore, 642 109, Tamil Nadu, India
Tel.: (91) 124 4 22 24 51
Web Site: http://www.akg-india.in
Heat Exchanger Mfr & Distr
N.A.I.C.S.: 332410
Subash Ganeshan *(Asst Mgr)*

AKG Japan Ltd. **(1)**
NISSO 12 Bldg 10F Shin-Yokohama 3-6-12, Kohoku, Yokohama, 222-0033, Japan
Tel.: (81) 45 4 70 54 22
Heat Exchanger Distr
N.A.I.C.S.: 423720

AKG Korea Ltd. **(1)**
Suite 1903 Halla Sigma Valley Gasan-dong 345-90, Geumchun-gu, Seoul, 153-706, Korea (South)
Tel.: (82) 263 43 63 80
Heat Exchanger Distr
N.A.I.C.S.: 423720

AKG North American Operations, Inc. **(1)**
7315 Oakwood St Ext, Mebane, NC 27302-0370
Tel.: (919) 563-4286
Web Site: http://www.akg-of-america.com
Heat Exchanger Distr
N.A.I.C.S.: 423720
Traci Bond-White *(Dir-HR)*

AKG Termoteknik Sistemler San. ve Tic. Ltd. **(1)**
Istiklal Mahallesi 40 Sokak No 4, 35735, Izmir, Turkiye
Tel.: (90) 232 877 2199
Web Site: http://www.akg-turkey.com
Emp.: 67
Heat Exchanger Distr
N.A.I.C.S.: 423720
Ibrahim Ozdemir *(Mng Dir)*

AKG Thermal Systems (Taicang) Co., Ltd. **(1)**
No 100 East Beijing Rd Taicang Economic Development Zone, 215400, Taicang, Jiangsu, China
Tel.: (86) 512 53 56 94 18
Heat Exchanger Mfr & Distr
N.A.I.C.S.: 332410
Jane Xiong *(Mgr-Pur)*

AKG Thermal Systems, Inc. **(1)**

809 Mattress Factory Rd, Mebane, NC 27302-0189
Tel.: (919) 563-4871
Web Site: http://www.akgts.com
Emp.: 25
Business to Business Electronic Markets
N.A.I.C.S.: 425120
Rick White *(Pres)*

AKG Thermotechnik GmbH & Co. KG **(1)**
Steinmuhlenweg 3, 34369, Hofgeismar, Germany
Tel.: (49) 5671 8 83 0
Web Site: http://www.akg.de
Heat Exchanger Mfr & Distr
N.A.I.C.S.: 332410

AKG UK Limited **(1)**
Unit B Parc Eirin, Tonyrefail, CF 39 8WW, United Kingdom
Tel.: (44) 1443 67 33 55
Heat Exchanger Distr
N.A.I.C.S.: 423720
Laurence Grubb *(Mng Dir)*

AKG Verwaltungsgesellschaft mbH **(1)**
Am Hohlen Weg 31, 34369, Hofgeismar, Germany
Tel.: (49) 56718830
Heat Exchanger Mfr
N.A.I.C.S.: 332410

AKG do Brasil **(1)**
Alameda Armenio Gomes 105, Bairro Parque das Rodovias, Lorena, 12605-470, Sao Paulo, Brazil
Tel.: (55) 1231523557
Heat Exchanger Distr
N.A.I.C.S.: 423720

SIA AKG Thermotechnik Latvia **(1)**
Aviacijas iela 34, 3004, Jelgava, Latvia
Tel.: (371) 630 1 22 00
Web Site: http://www.akg-gruppe.de
Heat Exchanger Distr
N.A.I.C.S.: 423720
Gerhard Ritzmann *(Mng Dir)*

AUTOLINE INDUSTRIES LIMITED

S No 313 314 320 to 323 Nanekarwadi Chakan, Taluka Khed, Pune, 410501, India
Tel.: (91) 2135635865 In
Web Site: https://www.autolineind.com
Year Founded: 1996
532797—(BOM)
Rev.: $77,808,153
Assets: $66,487,976
Liabilities: $49,361,307
Net Worth: $17,126,669
Earnings: $1,050,040
Emp.: 799
Fiscal Year-end: 03/31/22
Design, Engineering & Manufacturing of Automotive Mechanical Systems
N.A.I.C.S.: 336390
Prakash B. Nimbalkar *(Chm)*

Subsidiaries:

Autoline Design Software Limited **(1)**
S Nos 313 314 320 to 323, Nanekarwadi Chakan Taluka - Khed Dist, Pune, 410 501, India
Tel.: (91) 9665065637
Emp.: 50
Automotive Component Mfr & Distr
N.A.I.C.S.: 336390
Naresh Naik *(Engr-Product)*

Autoline Industries Limited - Bhosari Unit I **(1)**
T-135 MIDC, Bhosari, Pune, 411 026, India
Tel.: (91) 20 66306570
Automotive Components Mfr
N.A.I.C.S.: 336390

Autoline Industries Limited - Bhosari Unit II **(1)**
E-12-17 7 & 8 MIDC, Bhosari, Pune, 411 026, India
Tel.: (91) 20 30632555
Automotive Components Mfr

Autoline Industries Limited—(Continued)

N.A.I.C.S.: 336390

Autoline Industries Limited - Bhosari Unit III (1)
F-II 24/25 MIDC, Pimpri, Pune, 411 018, India
Tel.: (91) 20 66306502
Automotive Components Mfr
N.A.I.C.S.: 336390

Autoline Industries Limited - Chakan Unit I (1)
Gat No 291 to 296 Plot No 6, Nanekarwadi Khed, Pune, 410 501, India
Tel.: (91) 2135664946
Automotive Components Mfr
N.A.I.C.S.: 336390

Autoline Industries Limited - Chakan Unit III (1)
S No 613 Mahalunge, Chakan Taluka-Khed, Pune, 410 501, India
Tel.: (91) 2135 664891
Automotive Components Mfr
N.A.I.C.S.: 336390

SZ Design SRL (1)
Via Arese 30, Terrazzano di Rho, 20017, Milan, Italy
Tel.: (39) 029346621
Automotive Components Mfr
N.A.I.C.S.: 336390

AUTOLITE (INDIA) LIMITED
D-469 Road No 9A Vishwakarma Industrial Area, Jaipur, 302013, Rajasthan, India
Tel.: (91) 1412333994
Web Site: http://www.autopal.com
Rev.: $17,358,642
Assets: $15,723,939
Liabilities: $9,860,026
Net Worth: $5,863,913
Earnings: $53,273
Fiscal Year-end: 03/31/19
Automotive Head Lamp Mfr
N.A.I.C.S.: 335132
Mahi Pal Gupta (Chm & Co-Mng Dir)

Subsidiaries:

Autolite Manufacturing Limited (1)
D-469 Road No 9a VKI Area, Jaipur, 203013, India
Tel.: (91) 1412333994
Web Site: http://www.autopal.com
Emp.: 150
Automotive Lighting Product Mfr
N.A.I.C.S.: 336320
Dinesh Sharma (Gen Mgr-Export)

Autopal Inc (1)
7316 Lavery Dr, Plano, TX 75025
Tel.: (214) 227-1762
Web Site: http://www.autopal.com
Emp.: 2
Automotive Lighting Parts Distr
N.A.I.C.S.: 423120

AUTOLIV, INC.
Klarabergsviadukten 70 Section B7, 111 64, Stockholm, Sweden
Tel.: (46) 858720600   SE
Web Site: https://www.autoliv.com
Year Founded: 1997
ALV—(NYSE)
Rev.: $10,475,000,000
Assets: $8,332,000,000
Liabilities: $5,762,000,000
Net Worth: $2,570,000,000
Earnings: $488,000,000
Emp.: 52,500
Fiscal Year-end: 12/31/23
Automotive Safety Equipment Mfr & Sales
N.A.I.C.S.: 333310
Svante Mogefors (Exec VP-Quality)

Subsidiaries:

3G Yatirim ve Gayrimenkul Ticaret A.S (1)
30 Haziran 2005, Persembe, Turkiye

Tel.: (90) 212 347 06 47
Automotive Safety System Mfr
N.A.I.C.S.: 336390

AS Norma (1)
Laki 14, 10621, Tallinn, Estonia
Tel.: (372) 6500442
Web Site: https://www.norma.ee
Automotive Parts & Accessory Mfr
N.A.I.C.S.: 336390

Airbags International Ltd. (1)
Viking Way, Congleton, CW12 1TT, Cheshire, United Kingdom (100%)
Tel.: (44) 1260294300
Web Site: https://careerunitedkingdom.autoliv.com
Sales Range: $75-99.9 Million
Emp.: 250
Mfr & Distr of Automotive Airbags
N.A.I.C.S.: 336110

Autoliv (Changchun) Mawhung Vehicle Safety Systems Co., Ltd. (1)
No 1831 Century Street Changchun Economic Development Zone, Changchun, 130033, China (59%)
Tel.: (86) 4314634388
Web Site: http://www.autoliv.com
Sales Range: $75-99.9 Million
Emp.: 120
Mfr & Distr of Automotive Safety Systems
N.A.I.C.S.: 336340

Autoliv (China) Electronics Co., Ltd. (1)
No 318 Huancheng East Road Fengxian District, Shanghai, 201401, China
Tel.: (86) 2167109300
Motor Vehicle Body Mfr
N.A.I.C.S.: 336111
Thierry Masson (Gen Mgr)

Autoliv (China) Steering Wheel Co., Ltd. (1)
No 1808 Chenqiao Rd Fengpu Development Zone, Fengxian Distric, Shanghai, 201401, China
Tel.: (86) 2167107660
Motor Vehicle Parts Mfr
N.A.I.C.S.: 423120

Autoliv (Shanghai) Management Co., Ltd. (1)
No 1000 Beihe Highway, Jiading, Shanghai, 201807, China
Tel.: (86) 2169925583
Motor Vehicle Body Mfr
N.A.I.C.S.: 336211

Autoliv (Shanghai) Vehicle Safety Systems Co., Ltd. (1)
Gaotai Rd No 820 Jiading Industrial Zone, Shanghai, 201821, China
Tel.: (86) 2169169699
Automotive Parts & Components Mfr
N.A.I.C.S.: 441330
Jason Zhang (Project Mgr)

Autoliv AB (1)
Klarabergsviadukten 70 Section B7, PO Box 70381, 107 24, Stockholm, Sweden (100%)
Tel.: (46) 858720600
Emp.: 80
Automotive Safety Equipment Designer, Mfr & Whslr
N.A.I.C.S.: 336390
Jan Carlson (Chm)

Subsidiary (Domestic):

Autoliv Development AB (2)
Wallentinsvagen 22, 447 37, Vargarda, Sweden (100%)
Tel.: (46) 322626300
Web Site: http://www.autoliv.com
Sales Range: $25-49.9 Million
Emp.: 50
Car-Seat Belts
N.A.I.C.S.: 336340

Autoliv Electronics AB (2)
Medevivagen 55, PO Box 383, Motala, 591 33, Sweden (100%)
Tel.: (46) 141223000
Web Site: http://www.autoliv.se
Sales Range: $125-149.9 Million
Emp.: 350

Automotive Safety Equipment Designer, Mfr & Whslr
N.A.I.C.S.: 336320
Bo Wass (Mng Dir)

Autoliv Electronics AB (2)
Teknikringen 9, Linkoping, 583 30, Sweden (100%)
Tel.: (46) 134804400
Web Site: http://www.autoliv.com
Sales Range: $25-49.9 Million
Emp.: 70
Automotive Safety Equipment Designer, Mfr & Whslr
N.A.I.C.S.: 336320

Autoliv Mekan AB (2)
N Kringelvagen 13-15, PO Box 34, Hassleholm, 281 21, Sweden (100%)
Tel.: (46) 45142500
Web Site: http://www.autoliv.com
Sales Range: $50-74.9 Million
Emp.: 150
Automotive Safety Equipment Designer, Mfr & Whslr
N.A.I.C.S.: 336390

Svensk Airbag AB (2)
Smedmastaregatan 3, Kungalv, 442 34, Sweden
Tel.: (46) 303204500
Web Site: http://www.autoliv.com
Sales Range: $25-49.9 Million
Emp.: 20
Automotive Airbags Mfr & Whslr
N.A.I.C.S.: 336390

Autoliv ASP B.V. (1)
Schouwrooij 15, 5281 RE, Boxtel, Noord-Brabant, Netherlands
Tel.: (31) 411617961
Automobile Component Mfr & Distr
N.A.I.C.S.: 336390

Autoliv Argentina S.A. (1)
Parque Industrial Pilar 1629 Lote 7 Fraccion 7, Calle 7 y del Canal, Mar del Plata, Argentina
Tel.: (54) 2322 537400
Automobile Parts & Accessories Mfr
N.A.I.C.S.: 336340

Autoliv Asia Pacific (1)
Unit 1405 7 14th Fl 2 Pacific Pl 142 Sukhumvit Rd Klongtoey, Bangkok, 10110, Thailand (100%)
Tel.: (66) 26598500
Web Site: http://www.autoliv.com
Sales Range: $50-74.9 Million
Emp.: 15
Mfr of Seatbelt Webbing Products
N.A.I.C.S.: 336110

Autoliv Australia Pty. Ltd. (1)
1521 Hume Hwy, Campbellfield, 3061, VIC, Australia (100%)
Tel.: (61) 393555500
Web Site: http://www.autoliv.com
Sales Range: $150-199.9 Million
Emp.: 310
Mfr & Distr of Seat Belts, Passenger & Side Impact Airbags & Steering Wheels
N.A.I.C.S.: 336340

Autoliv B.V. & Co. KG, Werk Nord (1)
Otto Hahn Strasse 4, PO Box 109, Elmshorn, 25333, Germany (100%)
Tel.: (49) 41217970
Web Site: http://www.autoliv.com
Sales Range: $600-649.9 Million
Emp.: 1,200
Automotive Seat Belts Mfr
N.A.I.C.S.: 336360

Autoliv BKI S.A. (1)
Carrer d' Ausias March 5, La Pobla de Vallbona, 46185, Valencia, Spain
Tel.: (34) 962799600
Web Site: https://careerspain.autoliv.com
Sales Range: $75-99.9 Million
Emp.: 120
Mfr of Automotive Seat Belts
N.A.I.C.S.: 336360

Autoliv BV & Co. KG (1)
Otto Hahn Strasse 4, 25337, Elmshorn, D-25333, Germany
Tel.: (49) 41217970
Leather Good & Allied Product Mfr

N.A.I.C.S.: 316990
Wolf Ulrich Wachter (Mgr-Engrg)

Autoliv Beijing Safety Systems (1)
38 Yongan Road, Changping, Beijing, 102200, China (45%)
Tel.: (86) 10 588 23890
Web Site: http://www.autoliv.com
Sales Range: $50-74.9 Million
Emp.: 80
Seatbelt Production
N.A.I.C.S.: 326220

Autoliv Cankor (1)
Gebze Osb2, 41400, Gebze, Turkiye (100%)
Tel.: (90) 2626484600
Sales Range: $150-199.9 Million
Emp.: 460
Mfr of Automotive Seat Belts & Airbags
N.A.I.C.S.: 336360

Autoliv Cankor Otomotiv Emniyet Sistemleri Sanayi Ve Ticaret A.S. (1)
Gebze Organize Sanayi Bolgesi Ihsan Dede Cad 800 Sokak No 801, Gebze, 41480, Kocaeli, Turkiye
Tel.: (90) 2626484600
Automobile Equipment Mfr
N.A.I.C.S.: 336211

Autoliv Corporation (1)
Song Ri 436-1 Dong Tan-Myun, Hwaseong, 445812, Kyung Ki-Do, Korea (South)
Tel.: (82) 313796500
Automotive Safety Equipment Mfr
N.A.I.C.S.: 336390

Autoliv Electronics SAS, Rouen (1)
Bd Lenine, PO Box 76807, Saint Etienne-du-Rouvray, France (100%)
Tel.: (33) 232914343
Web Site: http://www.autoliv.com
Sales Range: $150-199.9 Million
Emp.: 500
Mfr of Automotive Electrical Systems
N.A.I.C.S.: 336110

Autoliv Electronics, Pontoise (1)
Rue Du Petit Albi Parc Silic Batiment D, PO Box 28 529, 95801, Cergy, France (100%)
Tel.: (33) 130178500
Web Site: http://www.autoliv.com
Sales Range: $50-74.9 Million
Emp.: 150
Mfr of Automotive Electronic Systems
N.A.I.C.S.: 811198

Autoliv France (1)
2 Rue Villaret De Joyeuse, 75017, Paris, France (100%)
Tel.: (33) 153812100
Web Site: http://www.autoliv.com
Sales Range: $25-49.9 Million
Emp.: 30
Mfr of Automotive Airbags & Seat Belts
N.A.I.C.S.: 336360

Autoliv France, Gournay (1)
Ave De I Europe, BP 99, 76220, Gournay-en-Bray, France (100%)
Tel.: (33) 232894000
Web Site: https://careerfrance.autoliv.com
Sales Range: $600-649.9 Million
Emp.: 1,100
Mfr of Car Safety Equipment
N.A.I.C.S.: 336340

Autoliv GmbH, Braunschweig (1)
Hansestrasse 46, Braunschweig, 38112, Germany (100%)
Tel.: (49) 5312181152
Web Site: http://www.autoliv.com
Sales Range: $150-199.9 Million
Emp.: 400
Mfr & Distr of Automotive Airbag Systems
N.A.I.C.S.: 336110

Autoliv GmbH, Werk Sud (1)
Theodor Heuss Strasse 2, 85221, Dachau, Germany (100%)
Tel.: (49) 81312950
Web Site: http://www.autoliv.com
Sales Range: $300-349.9 Million
Emp.: 850
Development & Production of Automotive Airbags
N.A.I.C.S.: 336110

Autoliv Hirotako Sdn. Bhd. (1)
Lebuh Taming, Jalan Balakong, 43300, Seri

Kembangan, Selangor Darul Ehsan,
Malaysia   **(49%)**
Tel.: (60) 389612020
Web Site: http://www.hirotako.com.my
Sales Range: $125-149.9 Million
Emp.: 400
Automotive Restraint Systems Mfr
N.A.I.C.S.: 336360

Subsidiary (Domestic):

**Autoliv Hirotako Safety Sdn.
Bhd.**   **(2)**
Lot 1989 Lebuh Tanming Taman Tanming,
Jalan Balakong, 43300, Seri Kembangan,
Selangor Darul Ehsan, Malaysia
Tel.: (60) 389612020
Sales Range: $75-99.9 Million
Mfr of Automotive Airbags & Other Safety
Systems
N.A.I.C.S.: 336390

Subsidiary (Domestic):

Autoliv Hirotako SRS Sdn. Bhd.   **(3)**
Lot 1989 Lebuh Tanming Taman Tanming,
Jalan Balakong, Seri Kembangan, 43300,
Selangor Darul Ehsan, Malaysia
Tel.: (60) 389623576
Sales Range: $100-124.9 Million
Emp.: 400
Mfr of Automotive Safety Restraint Systems
N.A.I.C.S.: 336390
Looi Kokloon *(Mng Dir)*

Autoliv Holding AB   **(1)**
Vasagatan 11, 111 20, Stockholm, Sweden
Tel.: (46) 858720600
Web Site: http://www.autoliv.com
Holding Company
N.A.I.C.S.: 551112

Autoliv Isodelta   **(1)**
Zi Chire En Montreuil, Vouille, 86190,
France   **(100%)**
Tel.: (33) 549396000
Web Site: http://www.autoliv.com
Sales Range: $10-24.9 Million
Emp.: 225
Automotive Safety System Mfr
N.A.I.C.S.: 336110

Autoliv Isodelta SAS   **(1)**
Zone Industrielle Chire en, Chire-en-
Montreuil, Montreuil, 86190, France
Tel.: (33) 549396000
Automotive Parts & Components Mfr
N.A.I.C.S.: 441330
David Guilloineau *(Dir-Logistics)*

Autoliv Italia SpA   **(1)**
Strada Torino 27, Orbassano, 10043, TO,
Italy
Tel.: (39) 0119022511
Web Site: http://www.autoliv.com
Sales Range: $50-74.9 Million
Emp.: 20
Mfr of Automotive Safety Systems
N.A.I.C.S.: 336110

Autoliv Izumi Philippines, Inc. **(1)**
Third Street Mactan Economic Zone, Lapu-
Lapu, 6015, Philippines   **(100%)**
Tel.: (63) 323400502
Web Site: http://www.autolivasp.com
Sales Range: $300-349.9 Million
Emp.: 936
Mfr of Automotive Safety Systems
N.A.I.C.S.: 336110

Autoliv Japan Ltd.   **(1)**
23-3 Jinta Taketoyo-cho, Chita, 470-2372,
Aichi, Japan   **(100%)**
Tel.: (81) 569740862
Web Site: http://www.autoliv.com
Sales Range: $75-99.9 Million
Emp.: 150
Mfr of Automotive Safety Systems
N.A.I.C.S.: 336110

Division (Domestic):

**Autoliv Japan Ltd. - Atsugi
Facility**   **(2)**
704-1 Kamiechi, Atsugi, 243-0801, Kana-
gawa, Japan   **(100%)**
Tel.: (81) 462041200
Sales Range: $50-74.9 Million
Emp.: 200
Steering Wheels & Components Mfr

N.A.I.C.S.: 336330

Autoliv KK   **(1)**
3-17-6 Shinyokohama, Kohoku-ku, Yoko-
hama, 222-8580, Japan   **(100%)**
Tel.: (81) 454753501
Sales Range: $25-49.9 Million
Emp.: 30
Mfr & Assembly of Automotive Night Vision
Safety Systems
N.A.I.C.S.: 336110

Division (Domestic):

**Autoliv Japan Ltd. - Fujisawa
Facility**   **(2)**
12 Kiriharacho, Fujisawa, 252 0811, Kana-
gawa, Japan
Tel.: (81) 466441711
Web Site: http://www.autoliv.com
Sales Range: $25-49.9 Million
Mfr & Distr of Automotive Locking Seat Belt
Retractors
N.A.I.C.S.: 336360

Autoliv KLE S.A.   **(1)**
Can Batzacs Crta C 17 Km 17 5 0 24, PO
Box 242, Granollers, 08403, Spain **(100%)**
Tel.: (34) 938615000
Web Site: http://www.autoliv.com
Sales Range: $150-199.9 Million
Emp.: 300
Mfr of Automotive Seat Belts & Buckles
N.A.I.C.S.: 336360
Eloe Ruez *(CFO)*

Autoliv KLE S.A.U.   **(1)**
Carretera C-17 Km 17 5 Poligono Industrial
Batzacs, 08400, Granollers, Barcelona,
Spain
Tel.: (34) 938615000
Automotive Parts & Components Whslr
N.A.I.C.S.: 441330
Jesus Arribas *(Plant Mgr)*

Autoliv Kft.   **(1)**
Iskola u 38, Sopronkovesd, 9483, Sopron,
Hungary   **(100%)**
Tel.: (36) 99536300
Web Site: https://careerhungary.autoliv.com
Sales Range: $10-24.9 Million
Emp.: 1,000
Mfr of Automotive Belt Assemblies
N.A.I.C.S.: 326220

Autoliv Mando Corporation   **(1)**
Song Ri 436-3 Dong Tan Myun Kangnam-
ku, Seoul, 445-810, Korea (South)
Tel.: (82) 313796500
Web Site: http://www.autoliv.com
Sales Range: $150-199.9 Million
Emp.: 500
Mfr of Automotive Safety Systems
N.A.I.C.S.: 336340

Autoliv North America   **(1)**
3350 Airport Rd, Ogden, UT 84405
Tel.: (801) 625-4800
Web Site: http://www.autoliv.com
Sales Range: $1-4.9 Billion
Emp.: 10,500
Motor Vehicle Parts & Accessories
N.A.I.C.S.: 336340

Subsidiary (Domestic):

Aerotest Operations, Inc.   **(2)**
3455 Fostoria Way, San Ramon, CA
94583   **(100%)**
Tel.: (925) 866-1212
Web Site:
https://www.aerotestoperations.com
Sales Range: $50-74.9 Million
Provides Services for Neutron Radiography,
Activation Analysis & Irradiation
N.A.I.C.S.: 541380

Unit (Domestic):

Autoliv - Airbag Inflator Facility **(2)**
250 American Way, Brigham City, UT
84302
Tel.: (435) 734-6100
Web Site: http://www.alliedsecurity.com
Sales Range: $250-299.9 Million
Emp.: 1,200
Mfr of Car Safety Equipment Airbags
N.A.I.C.S.: 561499

Subsidiary (Domestic):

Autoliv ASP, Inc.   **(2)**

3350 Airport Rd, Ogden, UT 84405
Tel.: (801) 625-8200
Web Site: http://www.autoliv.com
Sales Range: $600-649.9 Million
Emp.: 4,000
Mfr of Air Bags
N.A.I.C.S.: 541380

Subsidiary (Non-US):

Autoliv Canada, Inc.   **(2)**
20 Autoliv Dr, PO Box 1090, Tilbury, NOP
2LO, ON, Canada   **(100%)**
Tel.: (519) 682-1083
Web Site: http://www.autoliv.com
Sales Range: $50-74.9 Million
Emp.: 200
Automotive Air Bags Mfr
N.A.I.C.S.: 336390

Subsidiary (Domestic):

Autoliv Electronics Canada, Inc. **(3)**
7455 Birchmount Rd, Markham, L3R 5C2,
ON, Canada   **(100%)**
Tel.: (905) 475-8510
Web Site: http://www.autoliv.com
Sales Range: $25-49.9 Million
Emp.: 370
Mfr of Automotive Parts
N.A.I.C.S.: 336340

Unit (Domestic):

Autoliv Electronics America   **(2)**
26545 American Dr, Southfield, MI 48034
Tel.: (248) 223-0600
Sales Range: $100-124.9 Million
Emp.: 300
Automotive Safety Equipment Designer, Mfr
& Whslr
N.A.I.C.S.: 336320
Wendell Lane *(VP)*

Autoliv Inflators   **(2)**
250 N 900 W, Brigham City, UT 84302
Tel.: (435) 734-6849
Web Site: http://www.autoliv.com
Sales Range: $150-199.9 Million
Emp.: 1,100
Air Bags & Inflators Mfr
N.A.I.C.S.: 541380

Autoliv Initiators   **(2)**
1360 N 1000 W, Tremonton, UT
84337-9336   **(100%)**
Web Site: http://www.autoliv.com
Sales Range: $75-99.9 Million
Emp.: 400
Mfr of Automotive Safety Products & Pro-
pellant
N.A.I.C.S.: 336390

**Autoliv North America Airbag Inflator
Facility**   **(2)**
3350 Airport Rd, Ogden, UT 84405-1563
Tel.: (801) 625-8200
Web Site: http://www.autoliv.com
Sales Range: $150-199.9 Million
Emp.: 700
Mfr of Air Bags
N.A.I.C.S.: 541380

**Autoliv North America Airbag Module
Facility**   **(2)**
1000 W 3300 S, Ogden, UT 84401-3855
Tel.: (801) 629-9800
Sales Range: $700-749.9 Million
Emp.: 4,000
Car Safety Equipment Mfr
N.A.I.C.S.: 336360

**Autoliv North America Seat Belt
Facility**   **(2)**
410 Autoliv Beltway, Madisonville, KY
42431-8783
Tel.: (270) 326-3300
Web Site: http://www.autoliv.com
Sales Range: $100-124.9 Million
Emp.: 310
Mfr & Distr of Automotive Seat Belts
N.A.I.C.S.: 336360

**Autoliv North America Service Parts
Facility**   **(2)**
1000 W 3300 S, Ogden, UT 84401-3855
Tel.: (801) 629-9800
Web Site: http://www.autoliv.com
Mfr Car Safety Equipments
N.A.I.C.S.: 423120

**Autoliv North America Steering Wheel
Facility**   **(2)**
4868 E Park 30 Dr, Columbia City, IN
46725-8861
Tel.: (260) 244-4941
Web Site: http://www.autoliv.com
Sales Range: $25-49.9 Million
Emp.: 26
Mfr of Steering Wheels
N.A.I.C.S.: 336390

**Autoliv North America, American
Technical Center**   **(2)**
1320 Pacific Dr, Auburn Hills, MI 48326-
1569
Tel.: (248) 475-9000
Emp.: 400
Automotive Safety Systems Developer, Mfr
& Seller
N.A.I.C.S.: 336390
Leif Berntsson *(VP-Quality)*

Autoliv Safety Technology   **(2)**
2475 Paseo De Las Americas A, San Di-
ego, CA 92154
Tel.: (619) 662-8000
Sales Range: $150-199.9 Million
Emp.: 900
Automotive Safety Equipment Mfr
N.A.I.C.S.: 336390
Ken Henehan *(Mng Dir)*

Pyrotechnic Processing Facility **(2)**
167000 W Hwy 83, Corinne, UT 84307
Tel.: (435) 471-3001
Web Site: http://www.autoliv.com
Sales Range: $75-99.9 Million
Emp.: 200
Mfr of Pyrotechnic Products for the Airbag
Industry
N.A.I.C.S.: 336110

**Autoliv Poland Restraint
Systems**   **(1)**
Belgijska 2, 55-220, Jelcz-Laskowice,
Poland   **(100%)**
Tel.: (48) 713810700
Web Site: https://careerpoland.autoliv.com
Sales Range: $300-349.9 Million
Emp.: 600
Mfr of Automotive Passenger Seat Re-
straints
N.A.I.C.S.: 336360

Autoliv Poland Sp.zo.o.   **(1)**
Ul Polna 49, 55-200, Olawa,
Poland   **(100%)**
Tel.: (48) 713010100
Sales Range: $650-699.9 Million
Emp.: 1,500
Mfr of Automotive Power Trains & Safety
Systems
N.A.I.C.S.: 336350

Autoliv QB, Inc.   **(1)**
Blk 7 Lot 8 LIIP Ave Laguna International
Industrial Park, Mampalasan, 4024, Binan
Laguna, Philippines   **(100%)**
Tel.: (63) 495390119
Sales Range: $1-9.9 Million
Emp.: 100
Mfr of Automotive Safety Systems
N.A.I.C.S.: 336110

Autoliv Romania S.A.   **(1)**
Bucegi Street 8, 500053, Brasov,
Romania   **(100%)**
Tel.: (40) 268508108
Web Site: https://careerromania.autoliv.com
Sales Range: $600-649.9 Million
Emp.: 1,100
Automobile Mfr
N.A.I.C.S.: 336110

**Autoliv Sicherheitstechnik GmbH,
Werk Ost**   **(1)**
Eichbergstrasse 10 13, 04720, Dobeln,
Germany   **(100%)**
Tel.: (49) 343166010
Web Site: http://www.autoliv.com
Sales Range: $25-49.9 Million
Emp.: 250
Mfr of Automotive Safety Systems
N.A.I.C.S.: 336110

Autoliv Southern Africa (Pty) Ltd. **(1)**
19 Fransen st, Chamdor, Krugersdorp,
1754, Gauteng, South Africa   **(100%)**
Tel.: (27) 112792600

Autoliv, Inc.—(Continued)

Web Site:
https://careersouthafrica.autoliv.com
Sales Range: $10-24.9 Million
Emp.: 150
Mfr of Automotive Safety Systems
N.A.I.C.S.: 336340

Autoliv Spring Dynamics **(1)**
Maidstone Road, Milton Keynes, MK10
0BH, Bucks, United Kingdom **(100%)**
Tel.: (44) 1908286900
Web Site: http://www.autoliv.com
Sales Range: $75-99.9 Million
Emp.: 120
Mfr of Automotive Seat Springs
N.A.I.C.S.: 336360

Autoliv Steering Wheels Mexico S. de
R.L. de C.V. **(1)**
Circuito El Marques Norte Suite 25 Parque
Industrial El Marques, Poblado El Colorado,
El Marques, Queretaro, Mexico
Tel.: (52) 4421018500
Automotive Parts & Components Mfr
N.A.I.C.S.: 441330
Adriana Chavez Duran (Coord-QMS)

Autoliv Steering Wheels S.R.L. de
C.V. **(1)**
Av Tepeyac No 1120 Chichimequillas El
Marques, Chichimequallas Km 4 5, 76240,
Queretaro, Mexico **(100%)**
Tel.: (52) 2781159
Sales Range: $300-349.9 Million
Emp.: 800
Mfr of Automotive Steering Wheels & Other
Safety Systems
N.A.I.C.S.: 336330

Autoliv Textiles **(1)**
Viking Way, Congleton, CW12 1TT, Chesh-
ire, United Kingdom **(100%)**
Tel.: (44) 1260294300
Web Site: http://www.autoliv.com
Sales Range: $50-74.9 Million
Emp.: 250
Automotive Fabrics Mfr
N.A.I.C.S.: 313310

Autoliv Thailand Limited **(1)**
700 415 M 7 Amata Nakorn Industrial Es-
tate, Chon Buri, 20000, Thailand **(100%)**
Tel.: (66) 38456000
Sales Range: $200-249.9 Million
Emp.: 900
Mfr & Sales of Automotive Components
N.A.I.C.S.: 336330

Autoliv de Mexico S.A. de C.V. **(1)**
Av De Los Sauces No 9 Parque Industrial,
Lerma, Mexico **(100%)**
Tel.: (52) 7282827600
Sales Range: $600-649.9 Million
Emp.: 1,200
Mfr of Automotive Airbags & Other Safety
Systems
N.A.I.C.S.: 336360

Autoliv do Brasil **(1)**
Av Marginal a Rodovia Floriano Area Ind do
Piracangagua, Rodrigues Pinheiro 551,
12043-000, Taubate, SP, Brazil
Tel.: (55) 1236271077
Web Site: http://www.autoliv.com
Sales Range: $1-4.9 Billion
Emp.: 6,000
Mfr of Automotive Seats.
N.A.I.C.S.: 336360

Autoliv do Brasil Ltda **(1)**
Av Roberto Bertoletti 551, Taubate, Sao
Paulo, 12042-045, Brazil
Tel.: (55) 1221251077
Automotive Parts & Components Mfr
N.A.I.C.S.: 441330
Juliano De Carvalho (Acct Mgr)

Livbag SAS **(1)**
2 Rue Villaret De Joyeuse, 75017, Paris,
France **(100%)**
Tel.: (33) 298813000
Web Site: http://www.autoliv.com
Sales Range: $600-649.9 Million
Emp.: 1,300
Mfr of Automotive Safety Systems
N.A.I.C.S.: 336110

Mei-An Autoliv Co., Ltd. **(1)**

No706 Fu Kao Rd, 330, Taoyuan,
Taiwan **(100%)**
Tel.: (886) 33012612
Web Site: http://www.autoliv.com.tw
Sales Range: $10-24.9 Million
Emp.: 90
Mfr of Automotive Seat Belts & Other Safety
Systems
N.A.I.C.S.: 336360

N.C.S. Pyrotechnie et Technologies
SAS **(1)**
Rue De La Cartoucherie, 95470, Survilliers,
France
Tel.: (33) 134317000
Sales Range: $25-49.9 Million
Emp.: 5
Motor Vehicle Body Mfr
N.A.I.C.S.: 336211
Mark Neyret (Gen Dir)

Nanjing Hongguang Autoliv Ltd. **(1)**
18 Hengda Rd Nanjing Economic Devolp-
ment zone, Nanjing, 210038,
China **(70%)**
Tel.: (86) 2585803900
Sales Range: $300-349.9 Million
Emp.: 515
Mfr of Automotive Safety Systems
N.A.I.C.S.: 336110
Jennfer Gen (Gen Mgr)

Norma A/S **(1)**
Laki 14, 10621, Tallinn, Estonia **(100%)**
Tel.: (372) 6500444
Web Site: http://www.norma.ee
Sales Range: $75-99.9 Million
Emp.: 600
Mfr of Automotive Safety Systems
N.A.I.C.S.: 336110

Subsidiary (Non-US):

ZAO Norma-Osvar **(2)**
Zheleznodorozhnaya Str 13, Vyazniki,
601446, Vladimir, Russia
Tel.: (7) 4923331123
Web Site: http://www.rubelts.ru
Automotive Safety System Mfr
N.A.I.C.S.: 336390

P.T. Autoliv Indonesia **(1)**
BPSP Bldg 2nd Fl No.8 Pulo Buaran V Blok
JJ4, Jakarta Industrial Estate, Pulo Gadung,
Jakarta, 13920, Indonesia
Tel.: (62) 214604245
Web Site: http://www.autoliv.com
Sales Range: $75-99.9 Million
Emp.: 105
N.A.I.C.S.: 336340

Taicang van Oerle Alberton Shenda
Special Type Textile Products Co.,
Ltd. **(1)**
Taicang van Oerle Alberton Shenda Special
Type Textile Products Co., L, Taicang,
215400, Jiangsu, China
Tel.: (86) 51253129188
Motor Vehicle Body Mfr
N.A.I.C.S.: 336211

VOA Canada **(1)**
190 Macdonald Road, Collingwood, L9Y
4N6, ON, Canada **(100%)**
Tel.: (705) 444-2561
Sales Range: $25-49.9 Million
Emp.: 100
Mfr of Automotive Seat Belt Webbing
N.A.I.C.S.: 336360

VOA Canada, Inc. **(1)**
190 MacDonald Rd, Collingwood, L9Y 4N6,
ON, Canada
Tel.: (705) 444-2561
Leather Good & Allied Product Mfr
N.A.I.C.S.: 316990
Jill Stewart (Dir-Fin)

Van Oerle Alberton B.V. **(1)**
Schouwrooij 15, PO Box 52, Boxtel, 5281
RE, Netherlands **(100%)**
Tel.: (31) 411617961
Web Site: http://www.autoliv.com
Sales Range: $100-124.9 Million
Emp.: 170
Mfr of Safety Belts Webbing
N.A.I.C.S.: 326220

AUTOLUS THERAPEUTICS
PLC

The Mediaworks 191 Wood Lane,
White City, London, W12 7FP, United
Kingdom
Tel.: (44) 2038296230 **UK**
Web Site: https://www.autolus.com
Year Founded: 2018
AUTL—(NASDAQ)
Rev.: $6,360,000
Assets: $490,274,000
Liabilities: $191,600,000
Net Worth: $298,674,000
Earnings: ($148,839,000)
Emp.: 399
Fiscal Year-end: 12/31/22
Biopharmaceutical Product Research
& Development Services
N.A.I.C.S.: 541714
Matthias Alder (Chief Bus Officer, Sec
& Sr VP)

AUTOMAKEDONIJA A.D.
Ul 16 Macedonian Brigade No 2,
1000, Skopje, North Macedonia
Tel.: (389) 23103130 **MK**
Web Site:
https://www.automakedonija.com.mk
Year Founded: 1946
AUMK—(MAC)
Rev.: $9,282,325
Assets: $12,515,550
Liabilities: $5,720,430
Net Worth: $6,795,120
Earnings: $478,997
Fiscal Year-end: 12/31/23
Motor Vehicle Whslr
N.A.I.C.S.: 423110

AUTOMATED TOUCHSTONE
MACHINES LIMITED
7th Bldg Nangang 1st Industry Park
Xili Songbai Rd, Nashan, Shenzhen,
518057, China
Tel.: (86) 75526711320
Web Site: http://www.tis.com.cn
Sales Range: $25-49.9 Million
Emp.: 197
Banking Equipment & Software Ser-
vices
N.A.I.C.S.: 561499
Weidong Yuan (Mgr-Overseas Mar-
ket)

AUTOMATIC ELECTRIC EU-
ROPE B.V.
Witte Paal 320 D, 1742 LE, Schagen,
Netherlands
Tel.: (31) 224296077 **Nl**
Web Site:
http://www.aeetransformers.com
Year Founded: 1972
Electronic Component Mfr & Distr
N.A.I.C.S.: 334416

AUTOMATION & CONTROLS
ENGINEERING LTD.
3 Royal Rd, Le Hochet Terre Rouge,
Port Louis, Mauritius
Tel.: (230) 2488210
Web Site: http://www.automation.mu
Measuring Displaying & Controlling
Industrial Process Variables Instru-
ments & Related Products Mfr
N.A.I.C.S.: 334513
Guy Lee (Mng Dir)

AUTOMATION TECHNIQUE SA
Chios 46, 104 39, Athens, Greece
Tel.: (30) 2108823464 **GR**
Web Site:
http://www.automationtechnique.gr
Automation Product Mfr
N.A.I.C.S.: 334512

AUTOMOBILE & PCB INC.
248 Namdong-daero, Namdong-gu,
Incheon, Gyeonggi-do, Korea (South)

Tel.: (82) 326769700
Web Site: https://www.anpcb.co.kr
Year Founded: 1977
015260—(KRS)
Rev.: $82,420,883
Assets: $81,914,979
Liabilities: $58,864,987
Net Worth: $23,049,992
Earnings: ($23,284,550)
Emp.: 288
Fiscal Year-end: 12/31/22
Printed Circuit Board Mfr & Sales
N.A.I.C.S.: 334412
Jeon Un-Gwan (Dir-Rep)

AUTOMOBILE CORPORATION
OF GOA LTD
G3WH 6GC Sattari, Buimpal, Goa,
403530, India
Tel.: (91) 8322383044
Web Site: https://www.acglgoa.com
Year Founded: 1980
505036—(BOM)
Rev.: $39,458,369
Assets: $39,065,290
Liabilities: $16,006,782
Net Worth: $23,058,508
Earnings: $469,751
Emp.: 480
Fiscal Year-end: 03/31/22
Sheet Metal Components Mfr
N.A.I.C.S.: 332322
Ajay O. V. (CEO)

AUTOMOBILE PROVENCE IN-
NOVATION
Route De Miramas 870 Allee De
Szentendre, 13300, Avignon,
Provence, France
Tel.: (33) 490423939
Web Site: http://www.citroen.fr
Sales Range: $10-24.9 Million
Emp.: 32
New & Used Car Dealers
N.A.I.C.S.: 441110
Jean-Luc Rousselet (Sls Mgr)

AUTOMOBILES CHATENET
Theillou, BP 9, Pierre-Buffiere, Limo-
ges, 87260, France
Tel.: (33) 555009158
Web Site: http://www.automobiles-
chatenet.com
Rev.: $23,400,000
Emp.: 60
Motor Vehicles & Car Bodies
N.A.I.C.S.: 336110
Yannick Tourat (Dir)

AUTOMOBILES MAUGER
FORD
119 Grande Allee Est, Grande-
Riviere, G0C1V0, QC, Canada
Tel.: (418) 385-2118
Web Site: http://maugerford.com
Rev.: $32,517,411
Emp.: 65
New & Used Car Dealers
N.A.I.C.S.: 441110
Ghislaine Coulombe (Dir-Sls)

AUTOMOBILES ORTHEZI-
ENNES
Route De Pau 208 Avenue Pierre
Mendes France, 64300, Orthez,
France
Tel.: (33) 559670000
Web Site: http://www.edenauto.com
New & Used Car Dealers
N.A.I.C.S.: 441110
(S)

AUTOMOTIVE FINCO CORP.
8 King Street E Suite 1800, Toronto,
M5B 1C5, ON, Canada
Tel.: (647) 351-8870 **ON**
Web Site: https://autofincocorp.com

Year Founded: 1986
AFCC.H—(TSXV)
Rev.: $2,019,049
Assets: $18,298,558
Liabilities: $12,463
Net Worth: $18,286,095
Earnings: $1,374,839
Fiscal Year-end: 12/31/23
High Growth Specialty Finance Company; Auto Retail Sector
N.A.I.C.S.: 523999

AUTOMOTIVE PROPERTIES REAL ESTATE INVESTMENT TRUST

133 King Street East Suite 300, Toronto, M5C 1G6, ON, Canada
Tel.: (647) 789-2440   ON
Web Site:
https://www.automotiveproperties.ca
Year Founded: 2015
APR.UN—(TSX)
Rev.: $58,768,003
Assets: $732,489,443
Liabilities: $426,423,175
Net Worth: $306,066,268
Earnings: $21,094,180
Fiscal Year-end: 12/31/20
Real Estate Related Services
N.A.I.C.S.: 531390
Kapil Dilawri (Chm)

AUTOMOTIVE TRIM DEVELOPMENTS

Priory Mill Charter Avenue, Coventry, CV4 8AF, Warwickshire, United Kingdom
Tel.: (44) 2476 695 150
Web Site:
http://www.autotrimdev.com
Year Founded: 2000
Sales Range: $10-24.9 Million
Emp.: 85
Leather Product Mfr
N.A.I.C.S.: 316990

AUTOMOVILISMO Y TURISMO SA

Avda Andres Bello 1863, Santiago, Chile
Tel.: (56) 2125702
Year Founded: 1943
ATSA—(SGO)
Sales Range: Less than $1 Million
Vehicle Rental Services
N.A.I.C.S.: 441110
Eduardo Silva Araya (Pres)

AUTONEUM HOLDING LTD.

Schlosstalstrasse 43, 8406, Winterthur, Switzerland
Tel.: (41) 522448282
Web Site: https://www.autoneum.com
AUTN—(SWX)
Rev.: $2,736,272,890
Assets: $1,986,213,462
Liabilities: $1,347,991,449
Net Worth: $638,222,014
Earnings: $72,617,067
Emp.: 16,519
Fiscal Year-end: 12/31/23
Motor Vehicle Seating & Interior Trim Manufacturing
N.A.I.C.S.: 336360
Hans-Peter Schwald (Chm)

Subsidiaries:

Autoneum (Chongqing) Sound-Proof Parts Co. Ltd. **(1)**
Block A85-1/02 Xipeng Industrial Park, Jiu Long Po District, Chongqing, 401326, Jiangsu, China
Tel.: (86) 2366010159
Emp.: 54
Motor Vehicle Interior Product Mfr
N.A.I.C.S.: 336360

Autoneum (Shanghai) Management Co. Ltd. **(1)**
Building 9 No 659 Yinxing Road, Pu Tuo District, Shanghai, 201802, China
Tel.: (86) 2166275522
Automotive Components Mfr
N.A.I.C.S.: 336390

Autoneum Belgium N.V. **(1)**
Oosterring 14, 3600, Genk, Limburg, Belgium
Tel.: (32) 89620100
Sales Range: $50-74.9 Million
Emp.: 250
Automotive Interior Materials Mfr
N.A.I.C.S.: 336360

Autoneum CZ s.r.o. **(1)**
U Dvoriska 1721, 565 01, Chocen, Czech Republic
Tel.: (420) 465732111
Web Site: https://www.autoneum.com
Sales Range: $50-74.9 Million
Automotive Interior Materials Mfr
N.A.I.C.S.: 336360

Autoneum Erkurt Otomotive AS **(1)**
Minarelicavus OSB Mahallesi Ataturk Bulvari No 1, Nilufer, 16220, Bursa, Türkiye
Tel.: (90) 224483272930
Automotive Components Mfr
N.A.I.C.S.: 336390

Autoneum Feltex (Pty) Ltd. **(1)**
Automotive Supplier Park Unit A9 30 Helium Road, Rosslyn, Pretoria, 0200, Gauteng, South Africa **(51%)**
Tel.: (27) 873546671
Motor Vehicle Interior Product Mfr
N.A.I.C.S.: 336360

Autoneum France S.A.S.U. **(1)**
Rue des Chevries, CS 40509, 78416, Aubergenville, France **(100%)**
Tel.: (33) 130950960
Sales Range: $50-74.9 Million
Motor Vehicle Interior Product Mfr
N.A.I.C.S.: 336360

Autoneum Germany GmbH **(1)**
Im Mittelbruch 1, Gundernhausen, 64380, Rossdorf, Germany **(100%)**
Tel.: (49) 60714910
Sales Range: $100-124.9 Million
Emp.: 300
Supplier of Noise Control & Thermal Insulation Systems for Motor Vehicles
N.A.I.C.S.: 336360
Bennett Meyer (Gen Mgr)

Autoneum Great Britain Ltd. **(1)**
Keller House Hereward Rise, Halesowen, B62 8AN, West Midlands, United Kingdom **(100%)**
Tel.: (44) 1216190590
Web Site: https://www.autoneum.com
Sales Range: $50-74.9 Million
Supplier of Noise Control & Thermal Insulation Systems for Motor Vehicles
N.A.I.C.S.: 336360

Plant (Domestic):

Autoneum Great Britain Ltd. - Heckmondwike **(2)**
Flush Mills Westgate, PO Box 22, Heckmondwike, WF16 0EP, West Yorkshire, United Kingdom **(100%)**
Tel.: (44) 192 473 8000
Web Site: http://www.autoneum.com
Sales Range: $25-49.9 Million
Automotive Interiors Mfr
N.A.I.C.S.: 336360

Autoneum India Pvt. Ltd. **(1)**
SP-1 RIICO Industrial Area Phase 2, Behror, 301 701, Alwar, 301 701, India
Tel.: (91) 1494297603
Automotive Components Mfr
N.A.I.C.S.: 336390

Autoneum Korea Ltd. **(1)**
1904-1 Trade Tower 511 Yeongdong-Daero, Gangnam-gu, Seoul, 06164, Korea (South)
Tel.: (82) 260007351
Automotive Components Mfr
N.A.I.C.S.: 336390

Autoneum Management AG **(1)**
Schlosstalstrasse 43, 8406, Winterthur, Switzerland **(100%)**

Tel.: (41) 522448388
Sales Range: $25-49.9 Million
Motor Vehicle Interior Product Mfr
N.A.I.C.S.: 336360

Autoneum Mexico Operations, S.A. de C.V. **(1)**
Juan Salvador Agraz No 61 Building Euro Ten Office No 1102, Santa Fe Cuajimalpa, 05348, Mexico, Mexico
Tel.: (52) 5510000200
Automotive Components Mfr
N.A.I.C.S.: 336390

Autoneum Mexico, S. de R.L. de C.V. **(1)**
Blvd G Morales 257 Parque Ind La Labor Edif 6 Col El llano, 83210, Hermosillo, Mexico
Tel.: (52) 662184282
Automotive Components Mfr
N.A.I.C.S.: 336390

Autoneum Netherlands B.V. **(1)**
Graafschap Hornelaan 140, Weert, 6004 HT, Limburg, Netherlands
Tel.: (31) 654222691
Automotive Interior Materials Mfr
N.A.I.C.S.: 336360

Autoneum Nittoku (Guangzhou) Sound-Proof Co. Ltd. **(1)**
Xinhua Industrial Area Yongjun Road, Xinhua Town Huadu District, Guangzhou, 510800, China
Tel.: (86) 2061815333
Automotive Components Mfr
N.A.I.C.S.: 336390

Autoneum Nittoku Sound Proof Products India Pvt. Ltd. **(1)**
RNS - 15 Sipcot Industrial Growth Centre Vadakapattu Post, Oragadam, 603 204, Chennai, 603204, India
Tel.: (91) 4467120000
Automotive Components Mfr
N.A.I.C.S.: 336390

Autoneum North America, Inc. **(1)**
34705 W 12 Mile Rd Ste 100, Farmington Hills, MI 48331 **(100%)**
Tel.: (248) 848-0100
Sales Range: $150-199.9 Million
Automotive & Commercial Sound Control Materials Mfr
N.A.I.C.S.: 336390

Subsidiary (Non-US):

Autoneum Canada Ltd. **(2)**
1451 Bell Mill Sideroad, PO Box 400, Tillsonburg, N4G 4H8, ON, Canada **(100%)**
Tel.: (519) 842-6411
Sales Range: $75-99.9 Million
Motor Vehicle Interior Product Mfr
N.A.I.C.S.: 336360

Plant (Domestic):

Autoneum North America, Inc. - Aiken **(2)**
Powderhouse Rd, Aiken, SC 29803
Tel.: (803) 649-1371
Web Site: http://www.autoneum.com
Sales Range: $25-49.9 Million
Emp.: 50
Automotive & Commercial Sound Control Materials Mfr
N.A.I.C.S.: 336390

Autoneum North America, Inc. - Bloomsburg **(2)**
480 W 5th St, Bloomsburg, PA 17815-1563
Tel.: (570) 784-4100
Web Site: http://www.autoneum.com
Sales Range: $150-199.9 Million
Automobile Carpeting & Acoustical Parts
N.A.I.C.S.: 336390

Joint Venture (Domestic):

UGN, Inc. **(2)**
18410 Crossing Dr Ste C, Tinley Park, IL 60487 **(50%)**
Tel.: (773) 437-2400
Web Site: http://ugn.com
Sales Range: $300-349.9 Million
Automotive Acoustic, Interior Trim & Thermal Management Product Mfr

N.A.I.C.S.: 336390
Peter Anthony (Pres & CEO)

Autoneum Poland Sp. z.o.o. **(1)**
ul Owsiana 60A, 40-780, Katowice, Poland
Tel.: (48) 322015800
Automotive Interior Materials Mfr
N.A.I.C.S.: 336360

Autoneum Portugal Lda. **(1)**
Rua Dr Manuel Goncalves Martins, Alto da Guerra, 2910-021, Setubal, Portugal **(86%)**
Tel.: (351) 265730420
Motor Vehicle Interior Product Mfr
N.A.I.C.S.: 336360

Autoneum Rus LLC **(1)**
Stankozavodskaya Street 7, 390042, Ryazan, Russia
Tel.: (7) 4912778611
Automotive Components Mfr
N.A.I.C.S.: 336390
Nistratov Vadim (Gen Mgr)

Autoneum Spain Northwest S.L.U. **(1)**
Pol Ind As Pedreiras Pista de Roblido, A Rua, Spain
Tel.: (34) 988 336 134
Motor Vehicle Interior Product Mfr
N.A.I.C.S.: 336360

Autoneum Spain S.A.U. **(1)**
Poligono As Pedreiras s/n, 32350, A Rua, Spain
Tel.: (34) 988336134
Motor Vehicle Interior Product Mfr
N.A.I.C.S.: 336360

Autoneum Switzerland AG **(1)**
Bahnweg Sud 43, 9475, Sevelen, Switzerland **(100%)**
Tel.: (41) 817860100
Sales Range: $100-124.9 Million
Motor Vehicle Interior Product Mfr
N.A.I.C.S.: 336360

Autoneum Technologies AG **(1)**
Schlosstalstrasse 43, Winterthur, 8406, Zürich, Switzerland
Tel.: (41) 522087171
Automotive Components Mfr
N.A.I.C.S.: 336390

Borgers SE & Co. KGaA **(1)**
Borgersstrasse 2-10, 46397, Bocholt, Germany
Tel.: (49) 28713450
Web Site: http://www.borgers-group.com
Sales Range: $700-749.9 Million
Emp.: 5,052
Automobile Textile Component Mfr
N.A.I.C.S.: 336360

Rieter Automotive (International) AG **(1)**
Schlosstalstrasse 43, Winterthur, 8406, Zürich, Switzerland
Tel.: (41) 522087171
Holding Company
N.A.I.C.S.: 551112

Tianjin Rieter Nittoku Automotive Sound-Proof Co. Ltd **(1)**
No 9 Saida5 Sub Rd Xiqing Economic Development Zone, Tianjin, 300385, China **(51%)**
Tel.: (86) 2223889388
Motor Vehicle Interior Product Mfr
N.A.I.C.S.: 336360

UGN de Mexico, S. de R.L. de C.V. **(1)**
Av Paseo de Las Colinas No 104, Parque Industrial Y de Nogocios Las Colina, 36270, Silao, Mexico
Tel.: (52) 4445005500
Automotive Components Mfr
N.A.I.C.S.: 336390

AUTOPREVOZ AD BANJA LUKA

Put Srpskih Branilaca 35, 78 000, Banja Luka, Bosnia & Herzegovina
Tel.: (387) 51 308 855
Web Site: http://www.autoprevoz.org
Year Founded: 1945
APBL—(BANJ)

Autoprevoz AD Banja Luka—(Continued)

Sales Range: $1-9.9 Million
Emp.: 150
Transportation Services
N.A.I.C.S.: 488999
Nebojsa Glamocak *(Chm-Mgmt Bd)*

AUTOPREVOZ GORNJI MILANOVAC A.D.

Vojvode Misica 26, 32300, Gornji Milanovac, Serbia
Tel.: (381) 32 711 254
Web Site: http://www.autoprevoz.rs
Year Founded: 1962
Sales Range: $1-9.9 Million
Emp.: 100
Passenger Transportation Services
N.A.I.C.S.: 485999

AUTOPREVOZ JANJUSEVIC A.D.

Jarmovac BB, 31331, Priboj, Serbia
Tel.: (381) 33455662
Web Site: https://www.janjusevic.com
Year Founded: 1973
APJP—(BEL)
Sales Range: $1-9.9 Million
Passenger Transportation Services
N.A.I.C.S.: 485999
Vinko Janjusevic *(Exec Dir & Dir)*

AUTOPREVOZTURIST A.D.

Zupana Stracimira 29, Cacak, Serbia
Tel.: (381) 32 222 727
Web Site:
http://www.autoprevozturist.co.rs
Year Founded: 2008
Sales Range: $1-9.9 Million
Emp.: 9
Travel Agency Services
N.A.I.C.S.: 561510

AUTORIDERS INTERNATIONAL LTD.

4A 104 Vikas Center Swami Vivekanand Road BEST Colony, Santacruz West, Mumbai, 400 054, India
Tel.: (91) 9871646688
Web Site: http://www.autoriders.in
Year Founded: 1994
Rev.: $4,610,983
Assets: $5,960,364
Liabilities: $3,727,544
Net Worth: $2,232,820
Earnings: $401,219
Emp.: 265
Fiscal Year-end: 03/31/22
Car Rental Services
N.A.I.C.S.: 532111
Tapan Mukesh Patel *(CEO & Mng Dir)*

AUTOSERVER CO., LTD.

14F Harumi Island Triton Square Office Tower W Bldg, 1-8-8 Harumi Chuo-ku, Tokyo, 104-0053, Japan
Tel.: (81) 351448501
Year Founded: 1997
5589—(TKS)
Rev.: $40,503,564
Assets: $108,069,912
Liabilities: $42,066,621
Net Worth: $66,003,291
Earnings: $9,114,057
Fiscal Year-end: 12/31/22
Information Technology Services
N.A.I.C.S.: 541512
Noriaki Takada *(Pres)*

AUTOSPORTS GROUP LIMITED

565 Parramatta Road, Leichhardt, 2040, NSW, Australia
Tel.: (61) 287532873   AU

Web Site:
http://www.autosportsgroup.com.au
Year Founded: 2016
ASG—(ASX)
Rev.: $1,767,336,398
Assets: $1,154,103,227
Liabilities: $824,467,812
Net Worth: $329,635,415
Earnings: $42,365,117
Emp.: 200
Fiscal Year-end: 06/30/24
Automobile Vehicle Distr
N.A.I.C.S.: 441110
James Evans *(Chm)*

Subsidiaries:

Modena Trading Pty Ltd   (1)
Unit 1A 64-66 Mentmore Avenue, Rosebery, 2018, NSW, Australia
Tel.: (61) 296980080
Web Site:
https://www.molinaricoffee.com.au
Grocery Product Distr
N.A.I.C.S.: 424490

Prestige Auto Traders Australia Pty Ltd   (1)
180 Mullens Street, Rozelle, 2039, NSW, Australia
Tel.: (61) 287552200
Web Site:
http://www.prestigeautotraders.com.au
Used Car Distr
N.A.I.C.S.: 441120

Stillwell Motor Group   (1)
1508 Centre Road Building 41 Clayton Business Park, Clayton, 3168, VIC, Australia
Tel.: (61) 395505300
Web Site: http://www.stillwellgroup.com.au
Emp.: 400
Automotive Retailer
N.A.I.C.S.: 441110
Chris Stillwell *(Chm)*

AUTOSTORE HOLDINGS LTD.

Stokkastrandvegen 85, 5578, Nedre Vats, Norway
Tel.: (47) 52763500
Web Site:
https://www.autostoresystem.com
Year Founded: 1996
AUTO—(OSL)
Rev.: $645,700,000
Assets: $2,131,800,000
Liabilities: $856,900,000
Net Worth: $1,274,900,000
Earnings: ($32,600,000)
Emp.: 973
Fiscal Year-end: 12/31/23
Holding Company
N.A.I.C.S.: 551112
Anette Matre *(CIO)*

AUTOTEHNA A.D

Bulevar Aleksandra 94, 11000, Belgrade, Serbia
Tel.: (381) 11 2431 687
Web Site: http://www.autotehna.com
Year Founded: 1969
ATHN—(BEL)
Sales Range: Less than $1 Million
Car Rental Services
N.A.I.C.S.: 532111
Milisav Rasic *(Founder)*

AUTOTEHNA A.D.

Solunskih ratnika br 11, 34310, Topola, Serbia
Tel.: (381) 34811720
Web Site:
http://www.autotehnatopola.rs
Year Founded: 2001
AUTP—(BEL)
Rev.: $70,806
Assets: $130,628
Liabilities: $28,456
Net Worth: $102,172
Earnings: ($6,425)

Emp.: 5
Fiscal Year-end: 12/31/20
Automobile Repair & Maintenance Services
N.A.I.C.S.: 811114
Zarko Rekovic *(Exec Dir)*

AUTOTRANSPORT A.D.

Staro Sajmiste 29, Novi Beograd, Belgrade, Serbia
Tel.: (381) 112136190
Year Founded: 2003
AUTT—(BEL)
Rev.: $113,915
Assets: $440,530
Liabilities: $13,775
Net Worth: $426,755
Earnings: ($38,506)
Emp.: 3
Fiscal Year-end: 12/31/22
Food Transportation Services
N.A.I.C.S.: 484121
Milan Narancic *(Exec Dir)*

AUTOTRANSPORT A.D.

Georgi Dimitrova 13, Bosilegrad, Serbia
Tel.: (381) 17 877 271
Year Founded: 2005
Sales Range: Less than $1 Million
Emp.: 1
Passenger Transportation Services
N.A.I.C.S.: 485999
Stojne Nikolov *(Exec Dir)*

AUTOTRANSPORT A.D.

Adrani 578A, 36000, Kraljevo, Serbia
Tel.: (381) 36 391 520
Web Site: http://www.autotransport-kv.com
Year Founded: 1949
Sales Range: $10-24.9 Million
Emp.: 380
Passenger Transportation Services
N.A.I.C.S.: 485999
Zoran Maricic *(Exec Dir)*

AUTOVEICOLI ERZELLI S.P.A.

Via Enrico Melen 73, 16152, Genoa, GE, Italy
Tel.: (39) 010 656 7600   IT
Web Site:
http://www.autoveicolierzelli.it
Year Founded: 1973
New & Used Car Dealer
N.A.I.C.S.: 441110
Bruno Boieri *(CEO)*

AUTOVENTIL A.D.

Milosa Obrenovica 2, 31000, Uzice, Serbia
Tel.: (381) 31563401
Web Site:
https://www.autoventil.co.rs
Year Founded: 1957
AVEN—(BEL)
Rev.: $6,116,943
Assets: $8,005,893
Liabilities: $943,299
Net Worth: $7,062,594
Earnings: $477,901
Emp.: 169
Fiscal Year-end: 12/31/23
Valves & Valve Guide Mfr
N.A.I.C.S.: 336310

AUTOWALLIS PUBLIC LIMITED COMPANY

Honved utca 20, 1055, Budapest, 1055, Hungary
Tel.: (36) 15515773
Web Site: https://www.autowallis.hu
Year Founded: 2012
AUTOWALLIS—(BUD)
Rev.: $740,342,883
Assets: $366,338,200

Liabilities: $269,152,242
Net Worth: $97,185,959
Earnings: $22,743,423
Emp.: 860
Fiscal Year-end: 12/31/22
Asset Management Services
N.A.I.C.S.: 523940
Zsolt Mullner *(Chm)*

Subsidiaries:

AVTO AKTIV SLO d.o.o.   (1)
Ljubljanska Cesta 24, 1236, Trzin, Slovenia
Tel.: (386) 15605800
Web Site: https://www.avto-aktiv.si
Car Dealer
N.A.I.C.S.: 441110

Inicial Autohaz Kft.   (1)
Kulso Veszpremi u 6, 9028, Gyor, Hungary
Tel.: (36) 96998080
Web Site: https://inicial.hu
Emp.: 140
Car Dealer
N.A.I.C.S.: 441110

WallisMotor Ljubljajna d.o.o.   (1)
Celovska Cesta 182, 1000, Ljubljana, Slovenia
Tel.: (386) 15833500
Web Site: https://www.bmw-wallis.si
Car Dealer
N.A.I.C.S.: 441110

AUTOWAVE CO., LTD.

1850 Miyanoki-cho, Inage-ku, Chiba, 263-0054, Japan
Tel.: (81) 432502669
Web Site: https://www.auto-wave.co.jp
Year Founded: 1960
2666—(TKS)
Rev.: $71,883,680
Assets: $73,335,680
Liabilities: $39,910,640
Net Worth: $33,425,040
Earnings: $1,316,480
Fiscal Year-end: 03/31/22
Automobile Parts Distr
N.A.I.C.S.: 423120
Daisuke Hirooka *(Pres & CEO)*

AUTUMN BUILDERS LIMITED

29A Weston Street 2nd Floor Room No B3, Kolkata, 700 012, India
Tel.: (91) 3340048979
Web Site:
http://www.autumnbuilders.in
Year Founded: 2009
Rev.: $167,194
Assets: $2,018,841
Liabilities: $30,040
Net Worth: $1,988,802
Earnings: $1,120
Fiscal Year-end: 03/31/18
Real Estate Manangement Services
N.A.I.C.S.: 531390
Deepak Kumar Singh *(Mng Dir)*

AUX INTERNATIONAL HOLDINGS LIMITED

Unit 1 10/F Emperor Group Centre, 288 Hennessy Road, Wanchai, China (Hong Kong)
Tel.: (852) 28016623
Web Site: https://www.auxint.com
2080—(HKG)
Rev.: $46,076,686
Assets: $77,689,555
Liabilities: $46,232,623
Net Worth: $31,456,932
Earnings: ($13,930)
Emp.: 1,089
Fiscal Year-end: 03/31/22
Night Club Owner
N.A.I.C.S.: 722410
Sandy Kwok Shan Tsang *(Co-Sec)*

AUXICO RESOURCES CANADA, INC.

201 Notre Dame West Suite 500, Montreal, H2Y 1T4, QC, Canada
Tel.: (514) 296-1641
Web Site:
https://www.auxicoresources.com
Year Founded: 2014
AUAG—(OTCIQ)
Rev.: $601,217
Assets: $3,907,627
Liabilities: $22,630,742
Net Worth: ($18,723,115)
Earnings: ($24,017,629)
Fiscal Year-end: 09/30/21
Mineral Exploration & Mining Services
N.A.I.C.S.: 213115
Pierre Gauthier *(Chm & CEO)*

AUXLY CANNABIS GROUP INC.
777 Richmond St W Unit 002, Toronto, M6J 0C2, ON, Canada
Tel.: (647) 812-0121 BC
Web Site: https://www.auxly.com
Year Founded: 1987
3KF—(DEU)
Rev.: $76,350,183
Assets: $197,768,948
Liabilities: $159,222,338
Net Worth: $38,546,611
Earnings: ($33,611,146)
Emp.: 369
Fiscal Year-end: 12/31/23
Investment Services
N.A.I.C.S.: 523150
Chuck Rifici *(Founder)*

Subsidiaries:

Knightswood Holdings Ltd. **(1)**
Four Bentall Centre Suite 732 1055 Dunsmuir Street, PO Box 49256, Vancouver, V7X 1L2, BC, Canada
Tel.: (778) 668-7783
Web Site: http://www.knightswood.ca
Investment Banking Services
N.A.I.C.S.: 523150

AV CONCEPT HOLDINGS LTD
6th Floor Enterprise Square Three 39 Wang Chiu Road, Kowloon Bay, China (Hong Kong)
Tel.: (852) 23347333
Web Site:
https://www.avconcept.com
0595—(HKG)
Rev.: $134,455,072
Assets: $225,129,947
Liabilities: $15,919,485
Net Worth: $209,210,461
Earnings: $29,797,089
Emp.: 137
Fiscal Year-end: 03/31/22
Electronic Products & Internet Appliances Semiconductors Distr, Designer & Mfr
N.A.I.C.S.: 334419
Yuk Kwan So *(Founder, Chm & CEO)*

Subsidiaries:

AV Concept Limited **(1)**
6 F Enterprise Square Three 39 Wang Chiu Road, Kowloon, China (Hong Kong)
Tel.: (852) 23347333
Emp.: 100
Electronic Components Distr
N.A.I.C.S.: 423690
Pilly So *(CEO)*

AV Concept Singapore Pte Ltd. **(1)**
219 Henderson Road 10-01 Henderson Industrial Park, Singapore, 159556, Singapore **(100%)**
Tel.: (65) 62765130
Web Site: http://www.avconcept.com
Sales Range: $25-49.9 Million
Emp.: 30
Semiconductor & Related Device Mfr
N.A.I.C.S.: 334310
John Lee *(Pres)*

AVC Technology (International) Limited **(1)**
6 F Enterprise Square Three 39 Wang Chiu Road, Kowloon, China (Hong Kong)
Tel.: (852) 23347334
Web Site: http://www.avconcept.com
Electronic Components Distr
N.A.I.C.S.: 423690

AV PROMOTIONS HOLDINGS LIMITED
13/F Shing Dao Industrial Building No 232 Aberdeen Main Road, Aberdeen, China (Hong Kong)
Tel.: (852) 25270918 Ky
Web Site:
http://www.avpromotions.com
Year Founded: 1991
8419—(HKG)
Rev.: $12,032,685
Assets: $31,385,018
Liabilities: $22,298,985
Net Worth: $9,086,033
Earnings: ($6,824,948)
Emp.: 159
Fiscal Year-end: 12/31/22
visual Design Services
N.A.I.C.S.: 541490
Man Por Wong *(Founder, Chm & Compliance Officer)*

AV TECH CORPORATION
10F E Building No 1911 San Chung Rd, Nankang, Taipei, 115, Taiwan
Tel.: (886) 226553866
Web Site: https://www.avtech.com.tw
8072—(TAI)
Rev.: $37,918,864
Assets: $81,370,905
Liabilities: $5,757,644
Net Worth: $75,613,261
Earnings: $2,252,199
Fiscal Year-end: 12/31/23
Video Surveillance Systems Mfr & Distr
N.A.I.C.S.: 334220
Shih-Chung Chen *(Chm & Pres)*

Subsidiaries:

Av Tech Corporation - CCTV Product Division **(1)**
10 F E Building No 19-11 San Chung Road, Nankang, Taipei, 115, Taiwan
Tel.: (886) 2 2655 3866
Web Site: http://www.avtech.com.tw
Emp.: 100
Closed Circuit Television Mfr
N.A.I.C.S.: 334511

Av Tech Corporation - Sanchong Factory **(1)**
No 193-2 Zhongxing North Street, Sanchong, Taipei, Taiwan
Tel.: (886) 2 8511 2266
Web Site: http://www.avtech.com.tw
Sales Range: $100-124.9 Million
Emp.: 300
Surveillance Equipment Mfr
N.A.I.C.S.: 334290

Chieftron International Inc. **(1)**
12F B-Building No 106 Sec 1 Xintai 5th Rd, Xizhi District, New Taipei City, 221, Taiwan
Tel.: (886) 22 696 1696
Web Site: https://www.chieftron.com.tw
Sales Range: $25-49.9 Million
Emp.: 35
Electronic Components Distr
N.A.I.C.S.: 423690

AVA RISK GROUP LIMITED
10 Hartnett Close, Mulgrave, 3170, VIC, Australia
Tel.: (61) 64089318
Web Site:
https://www.theavagroup.com
Year Founded: 1994
AVA—(ASX)
Rev.: $20,177,617
Assets: $24,076,522

Liabilities: $5,413,996
Net Worth: $18,662,527
Earnings: ($3,474,225)
Fiscal Year-end: 06/30/24
Fibre Optic Intrusion System Provider
N.A.I.C.S.: 561621
Robert Broomfield *(CEO)*

Subsidiaries:

Bqt Solutions (Australia) Pty. Ltd. **(1)**
10 Hartnett Close, Mulgrave, 3170, VIC, Australia
Tel.: (61) 288172800
Access Control Services
N.A.I.C.S.: 561621

Bqt Solutions (NZ) Ltd. **(1)**
Unit 4 101 Diana Drive, Wairau Valley, Auckland, 0627, New Zealand
Tel.: (64) 94417630
Web Site: https://www.bqtsolutions.com
Access Control Services
N.A.I.C.S.: 561621

Bqt Solutions (UK) Ltd. **(1)**
Regus Castle Court 41 London Road, Reigate, RH2 9RJ, United Kingdom
Tel.: (44) 1737735071
Access Control Services
N.A.I.C.S.: 561621

Fft India Pvt. Ltd. **(1)**
Unit No 718 Seventh Floor Ocus Quantum Sector 51, Gurgaon, 122003, Haryana, India
Tel.: (91) 1247177347
Optical Fibber Technology Services
N.A.I.C.S.: 541512

MaxSec Group Limited **(1)**
Unit 29 1 Talavera Road, North Ryde, 2113, NSW, Australia
Tel.: (61) 288172800
Investment, Development & Marketing of Smart Card Based Security Access Control Systems
N.A.I.C.S.: 541511
Donny Tsui *(Grp Mgr-Fin)*

AVAC, LTD.
Suite 220 6815 8 St NE, Calgary, T2E 7H7, AB, Canada
Tel.: (403) 274-2774 AB
Web Site: https://www.avacgrp.com
Investment Firm
N.A.I.C.S.: 523999
Mark Carlson *(Mng Dir & Founding Partner)*

Subsidiaries:

Botaneco Specialty Ingredients Inc. **(1)**
2985 23rd Ave NE Ste 134, Calgary, T1Y 7L3, AB, Canada
Tel.: (403) 668-6685
Web Site: http://www.botaneco.ca
Pharmaceuticals Product Mfr
N.A.I.C.S.: 325412
David Dzisiak *(COO)*

AVACO CO., LTD
160-7 Seongseo4chacheomdan-ro, Dalseo-Gu, Daegu, 42724, Korea (South)
Tel.: (82) 535838150
Web Site: https://avaco.com
Year Founded: 2000
083930—(KRS)
Rev.: $166,641,538
Assets: $213,560,561
Liabilities: $84,086,093
Net Worth: $129,474,468
Earnings: $13,887,091
Emp.: 404
Fiscal Year-end: 12/31/22
Flat Panel Display Equipment Mfr
N.A.I.C.S.: 334419
Kwang-Hyun Kim *(CEO)*

Subsidiaries:

AVACO CO., Ltd - Daegu 1st Factory **(1)**

160-7 Seongseo4chacheomdan-ro, Dalseo-gu, Daegu, Korea (South)
Tel.: (82) 53 583 8150
Web Site: http://www.avaco.co.kr
Vacuum Equipment & Clean Transfer System Mfr
N.A.I.C.S.: 333248

DaeMyong ENG Co., Ltd **(1)**
135 Seongseo-ro, Dalseo-gu, Daegu, Korea (South)
Tel.: (82) 535834050
Web Site: https://www.daemyung-eng.co.kr
Vacuum Equipment Mfr
N.A.I.C.S.: 333248

Plant (Domestic):

DaeMyong ENG Co., Ltd - Gumi Factory **(2)**
59-9 Cheomdangieop 7-ro, Sandong-eup, Gumi, 730-853, Gyeongsangbuk-do, Korea (South)
Tel.: (82) 7086608848
Sales Range: $25-49.9 Million
Emp.: 13
Vacuum Equipment Mfr
N.A.I.C.S.: 333248

AVACTA GROUP PLC
Unit 20 Ash Way, Thorp Arch Estate, Wetherby, LS23 7FA, United Kingdom
Tel.: (44) 1904217070
Web Site: https://www.avacta.com
AVCT—(AIM)
Rev.: $11,623,425
Assets: $111,596,925
Liabilities: $89,385,945
Net Worth: $22,210,980
Earnings: ($46,240,755)
Fiscal Year-end: 12/31/22
Bio-Analytical Technology Services
N.A.I.C.S.: 541714
Alastair Smith *(CEO)*

Subsidiaries:

Avacta Animal Health Limited **(1)**
Unit 651 Street 5 Thorp Arch Estate, Wetherby, LS23 7FZ, United Kingdom
Tel.: (44) 190 421 7071
Web Site:
https://www.avactaanimalhealth.com
Animal Health Care Services
N.A.I.C.S.: 541940

Avacta Life Sciences Limited **(1)**
Unit 20 Ash Way Thorp Arch Estate, Wetherby, LS23 7FA, United Kingdom
Tel.: (44) 190 421 7070
Web Site: https://avacta.com
Pharmaceuticals Product Mfr
N.A.I.C.S.: 325412
Eliot Richard Forster *(Chm)*

Launch Diagnostics Limited **(1)**
Ash House Ash Road New Ash Green, Longfield, DA3 8JD, Kent, United Kingdom
Tel.: (44) 1474874426
Web Site:
https://www.launchdiagnostics.com
Emp.: 60
Diagnostics Development Mfr
N.A.I.C.S.: 325413

AVADA GROUP LIMITED
Suite 1 Level 2 116 Ipswich Road, Woolloongabba, 4102, QLD, Australia
Tel.: (61) 1300321995
Web Site:
https://www.avadagroup.com.au
Year Founded: 2021
AVD—(ASX)
Rev.: $115,408,489
Assets: $84,887,527
Liabilities: $54,596,075
Net Worth: $30,291,452
Earnings: ($3,670,861)
Emp.: 2,100
Fiscal Year-end: 06/30/23
Engineeering Services
N.A.I.C.S.: 541330
Dan Crowley *(CEO)*

AVADA Group Limited—(Continued)

Subsidiaries:

D&D Services (Australia) Pty Ltd.   **(1)**
Level 2 65 Market Street, Wollongong, 2500, NSW, Australia
Tel.: (61) 242209500
Web Site: https://www.dd-group.com.au
Emp.: 350
Traffic Management Services
N.A.I.C.S.: 561990

D&D Traffic Management Pty Ltd.   **(1)**
Level 2 65 Market Street, Wollongong, 2500, NSW, Australia
Tel.: (61) 242209500
Web Site: https://www.dd-group.com.au
Emp.: 300
Traffic Management Services
N.A.I.C.S.: 926120

Linemark Traffic Control Pty Ltd.   **(1)**
12 Heidi Street, Paget, 4740, QLD, Australia
Tel.: (61) 1300717471
Web Site:
   https://www.linemarktraffic.com.au
Traffic Control Services
N.A.I.C.S.: 926120

Platinum Traffic Services Pty Ltd.   **(1)**
Unit 2/6 Waler Crescent, Smeaton Grange, Sydney, 2567, NSW, Australia
Tel.: (61) 1300787835
Web Site:
   https://www.platinumtraffic.com.au
Emp.: 521
Traffic Management Services
N.A.I.C.S.: 926120

The Traffic Marshal Pty Ltd.   **(1)**
132 Toongabbie Road, Girraween, 2145, NSW, Australia
Tel.: (61) 299661900
Web Site:
   https://www.thetrafficmarshal.com.au
Transportation Services
N.A.I.C.S.: 561599

Verifact Traffic Pty Ltd.   **(1)**
PO Box 826, Springwood, 4127, QLD, Australia
Tel.: (61) 1300685879
Web Site: https://www.verifacttraffic.com.au
Emp.: 750
Traffic Management Services
N.A.I.C.S.: 926120

Wilsons TM Limited   **(1)**
2 Lakeside Place, Harewood, Christchurch, 8051, New Zealand
Tel.: (64) 800400986
Web Site: https://www.wilsonstm.nz
Emp.: 134
Traffic Management Services
N.A.I.C.S.: 561990

AVADEL PHARMACEUTICALS PLC
10 Earlsfort Terrace, Dublin, D02 T380, Ireland
Tel.: (353) 1114851200   **IE**
Web Site: https://www.avadel.com
Year Founded: 1990
AVDL—(NASDAQ)
Assets: $132,785,000
Liabilities: $153,930,000
Net Worth: ($21,145,000)
Earnings: ($137,464,000)
Emp.: 41
Fiscal Year-end: 12/31/22
Polymer-Based Delivery Systems for Medical Applications
N.A.I.C.S.: 325412
Geoffrey M. Glass *(Chm)*

Subsidiaries:

Eclat Pharmaceuticals, LLC   **(1)**
16640 Chesterfield Grove Rd Ste 200, Chesterfield, MO 63005
Tel.: (636) 449-1830
Web Site: https://www.eclatpharma.com
Pharmaceutical Product Mfr & Distr

N.A.I.C.S.: 325412

FSC Holdings, LLC   **(1)**
9951 Horn Rd, Sacramento, CA 95827-1955
Tel.: (916) 857-1349
Holding Company
N.A.I.C.S.: 551112
Robert Cunard *(CEO)*

Flamel Technologies Inc.   **(100%)**
2121 K St NW Ste 650, Washington, DC 20037-3600
Tel.: (202) 862-8400
Sales Range: $50-74.9 Million
Emp.: 4
Drug Delivery Method Mfr
N.A.I.C.S.: 424210

AVADH SUGAR & ENERGY LIMITED
Birla Building 5th Floor 9/1 R N Mukherjee Road, Kolkata, 700 001, India
Tel.: (91) 3322430497
Web Site: https://www.birla-sugar.com
Year Founded: 2015
AVADHSUGAR—(NSE)
Rev.: $375,071,820
Assets: $331,758,240
Liabilities: $221,138,982
Net Worth: $110,619,259
Earnings: $16,981,869
Emp.: 722
Fiscal Year-end: 03/31/22
Organic Chemical Product Mfr & Distr
N.A.I.C.S.: 325199
Devendra Kumar Sharma *(Exec Dir)*

AVAILABLE FINANCE LIMITED
Agarwal House Ground Floor 5 Yeshwant Colony, Indore, 452003, Madhya Pradesh, India
Tel.: (91) 7314714082
Web Site:
   https://www.availablefinance.in
Year Founded: 1993
531310—(BOM)
Sales Range: Less than $1 Million
Financial Services
N.A.I.C.S.: 523999
Rakesh Sahu *(CFO)*

AVALA A.D.
Lenjinova 3, 12000, Pozarevac, Serbia
Tel.: (381) 12 7 160 056
Web Site: http://www.hoteldunav.rs
Year Founded: 1947
Sales Range: Less than $1 Million
Emp.: 39
Home Management Services
N.A.I.C.S.: 721110

AVALANCHE SEARCH MARKETING INC.
34219 Neil Rd, Lucan, N0M 2J0, ON, Canada
Tel.: (519) 964-3738   **Ca**
Web Site:
   https://www.avalanchesearch.com
Sales Range: $10-24.9 Million
Software Developer, Marketer & Sales
N.A.I.C.S.: 334610
Bruce Lamb *(Pres & CEO)*

AVALAND BERHAD
Lot C-02 Level 2 Skypark One City, Jalan USJ 25/1, 47650, Subang Jaya, Selangor, Malaysia
Tel.: (60) 358789000
Web Site:
   https://www.avaland.com.my
Year Founded: 1971
AVALAND—(KLS)
Rev.: $47,602,148
Assets: $294,421,774

Liabilities: $110,026,783
Net Worth: $184,394,990
Earnings: $102,152
Emp.: 293
Fiscal Year-end: 12/31/22
Holding Company
N.A.I.C.S.: 551112
Apollo Bello Tanco *(COO)*

Subsidiaries:

Eco Green City Sdn. Bhd.   **(1)**
12A-3 Jalan PJU 8/5C Perdana Business Centre Bandar Damansara Perdana, 47820, Petaling Jaya, Selangor, Malaysia
Tel.: (60) 351159988
Property Developer Services
N.A.I.C.S.: 531390
Simon Sim *(Mgr-M&E)*

Lakefront Residence Sdn. Bhd,   **(1)**
Persiaran Semarak Api, 63000, Cyberjaya, Selangor, Malaysia
Tel.: (60) 1117226000
Web Site: http://www.lakefront.my
Property Developer Services
N.A.I.C.S.: 531390

AVALDATA CORPORATION
1-25-10 Asahi-machi Machida, Tokyo, 194-0023, Japan
Tel.: (81) 427321000
Web Site: https://www.avaldata.co.jp
Year Founded: 1959
6918—(TKS)
Sales Range: Less than $1 Million
Emp.: 170
Industrial Embedded Computer & Electronics Equipment Mfr
N.A.I.C.S.: 334111
Yutaka Kikuchi *(Pres)*

AVALON ADVANCED MATERIALS INC.
130 Adelaide St W Suite 2060, Toronto, M5H 3P5, ON, Canada
Tel.: (416) 364-4938   **Ca**
Web Site:
   https://www.avalonadvanced.com
Year Founded: 1991
AVLNF—(OTCQB)
Rev.: $8,800
Assets: $92,676,014
Liabilities: $3,789,202
Net Worth: $88,886,812
Earnings: ($2,937,558)
Emp.: 7
Fiscal Year-end: 08/31/21
Metal Exploration & Mining Services
N.A.I.C.S.: 212290
Donald S. Bubar *(Pres & CEO)*

AVALON FORD SALES LTD.
621 Kenmount Rd, Saint John's, A1B0G2, NL, Canada
Tel.: (709) 754-7500
Web Site:
   http://www.avalon.dealer.com
Year Founded: 1990
New & Used Car Dealers
N.A.I.C.S.: 441110
Doug Lester *(Gen Mgr-Sls)*

AVALON TECHNOLOGIES LIMITED
B7 & B8 First Main Road, MEPZ-SEZ Tambaram, Chennai, 600045, India
Tel.: (91) 4442220400
Web Site: https://www.avalontec.com
Year Founded: 1999
AVALON—(NSE)
Rev.: $130,912,919
Assets: $161,112,998
Liabilities: $87,809,904
Net Worth: $73,303,094
Earnings: $7,166,660
Fiscal Year-end: 03/31/23
Electronic Components Mfr
N.A.I.C.S.: 334419

R. M. Subramanian *(CFO)*

AVANCE GAS HOLDING LTD.
Par-la-Ville Place 14 Par-la-Ville Road, PO Box HM 1593, HM 08, Hamilton, HM 08, Bermuda
Tel.: (441) 4723114000
Web Site:
   https://www.avanceogas.com
Year Founded: 2007
A07—(DEU)
Rev.: $352,310,000
Assets: $1,153,585,000
Liabilities: $549,791,000
Net Worth: $603,794,000
Earnings: $163,577,000
Emp.: 9
Fiscal Year-end: 12/31/23
Liquefied Petroleum Gas Transportation
N.A.I.C.S.: 483111
Kenneth Aasvang *(Head-Ops)*

Subsidiaries:

Avance Gas AS   **(1)**
Bryggegata 3, PO Box 1327, Vika, 0112, Oslo, Norway
Tel.: (47) 23114000
Web Site: https://www.avancegas.com
Oil & Gas Services
N.A.I.C.S.: 237120

AVANCE TECHNOLOGIES LTD.
D-603 6th Floor Opp Infinity Mall New Link Road, Crystal Plaz Premises Co-op Soc Andheri West, Mumbai, 400 053, India
Tel.: (91) 22 65264891
Web Site: http://www.avance.in
Year Founded: 1985
Rev.: $4,555,812
Assets: $93,124,468
Liabilities: $32,945,530
Net Worth: $60,178,938
Earnings: $18,688
Emp.: 4
Fiscal Year-end: 03/31/18
Telecommunication Servicesb
N.A.I.C.S.: 517810
Srikrishna Bhamidipati *(Chm, Mng Dir & Compliance Officer)*

AVANGARDCO INVESTMENTS PUBLIC LIMITED
121 V Prospect Peremohy, 03115, Kiev, Ukraine
Tel.: (380) 443934050
Web Site: http://avangard.co.ua
Year Founded: 2003
AVGR—(LSE)
Sales Range: $150-199.9 Million
Shell Eggs Production & Sales
N.A.I.C.S.: 112310
Oleg Bakhmatyuk *(Founder & Chm)*

AVANI RESOURCES PTE LTD.
143 Cecil St, GB Building Level 24 Singapore 069542, Singapore, 069542, Singapore
Tel.: (65) 62211270
Web Site: https://avani.sg
Year Founded: 2010
Wholesale Import & Export
N.A.I.C.S.: 423520

AVANT BRANDS INC.
1632 Dickson Avenue Suite 335, Kelowna, V1Y7T2, BC, Canada
Tel.: (778) 760-8338   **BC**
Web Site: https://avantbrands.ca
Year Founded: 2012
AVTBF—(OTCQX)
Rev.: $17,682,657
Assets: $52,437,011
Liabilities: $14,697,477
Net Worth: $37,739,534

Earnings: ($5,177,129)
Emp.: 220
Fiscal Year-end: 11/30/22
Investment Services
N.A.I.C.S.: 523999
Jeremy Wright *(CFO)*

AVANT CORPORATION
Shinagawa Intercity B Building 13F
2-15-2 Konan, Minato-ku, Tokyo, 108-6113, Japan
Tel.: (81) 357828600
Web Site: https://www.avantcorp.com
Year Founded: 1997
3836—(TKS)
Rev.: $151,886,180
Assets: $136,193,120
Liabilities: $53,510,660
Net Worth: $82,682,460
Earnings: $17,727,000
Emp.: 1,055
Fiscal Year-end: 06/30/24
Software Package Development &
Consulting Services
N.A.I.C.S.: 513210
Tetsuji Morikawa *(Pres & CEO-Grp)*

Subsidiaries:

DIVA CORPORATION OF UK   **(1)**
7 35-37 Ludgate Hill, London, United Kingdom
Tel.: (44) 2074195088
Software Development Services
N.A.I.C.S.: 541511

Diva Corporation of America   **(1)**
533 Airport Blvd Ste 400, Burlingame, CA 94010
Tel.: (650) 373-2012
Software Development Services
N.A.I.C.S.: 541511

Fierte Corporation   **(1)**
Shinjuku i-Land Tower 22F/42F/43F Reception 43F 6-5-1 Nishi-Shinjuku, Shinjuku-ku, Tokyo, 163-1343, Japan
Tel.: (81) 35 909 5177
Web Site: https://www.fiertecorp.com
Treasury Management Solution Services
N.A.I.C.S.: 541611
Gen Nagata *(CEO)*

Internet Disclosure Co., Ltd.   **(1)**
Toranomon Toyo-Kyodo Building 13-3 Toranomon 1-Chome, Minato-Ku, Tokyo, 105-0001, Japan
Tel.: (81) 355321613
Web Site: http://www.internet-disclosure.com
Data Processing Services
N.A.I.C.S.: 518210
Hiroshi Takizawa *(Pres & CEO)*

AVANT IMAGING & INFORMATION MANAGEMENT, INC.
205 Industrial Parkway North, Aurora, L4G 4C4, ON, Canada
Tel.: (416) 798-7110
Web Site: http://www.aiim.com
Year Founded: 1990
Sales Range: $10-24.9 Million
Emp.: 100
Commercial Printing Services
N.A.I.C.S.: 323111
Mario Giorgio *(Chm & CEO)*

AVANTAZH GROUP
20- Kultury Str, 61058, Kharkiv, Ukraine
Tel.: (380) 577004410
Web Site: http://www.avantazh.eu
Year Founded: 1998
Residential & Commercial Real Estate Development, Construction, Ownership, Management, Sales & Leasing Services
N.A.I.C.S.: 531390
Anatoliy Denisenko *(Pres)*

AVANTE CORP

1959 Leslie Street, North York, M3B 2M3, ON, Canada
Tel.: (416) 923-6984
Web Site:
    https://www.avantelogixx.com
Year Founded: 1996
ALXXF—(OTCIQ)
Rev.: $18,430,905
Assets: $18,593,259
Liabilities: $8,613,826
Net Worth: $9,979,433
Earnings: ($2,252,650)
Fiscal Year-end: 03/31/24
Security System Services
N.A.I.C.S.: 561621
Francis Michaud *(VP-Fin)*

Subsidiaries:

Avante Security Inc.   **(1)**
1959 Leslie St, Toronto, M3B 2M3, ON, Canada
Tel.: (416) 923-6984
Web Site: http://www.avantesecurity.com
Security Firm Services
N.A.I.C.S.: 561621

Citywide Locksmiths Ltd.   **(1)**
1750 Avenue Road, Toronto, M5M 3Y9, ON, Canada
Tel.: (416) 789-1213
Web Site: http://www.citywidelocksmith.ca
Locksmith Services
N.A.I.C.S.: 561622

AVANTE SYSTEMS, INC.
Room 709-710 7/F Tower 1, Silvercord Centre Tsim Sha Tsui, Kowloon, China (Hong Kong)
Tel.: (852) 311 3951   NV
Year Founded: 2010
Emp.: 1
Video Camera Mfr & Whslr
N.A.I.C.S.: 334310

AVANTEC ZERSPANTECHNIK GMBH
Wilhelmstrasse 123, 75428, Illingen, Germany
Tel.: (49) 704282220
Web Site: http://www.avantec.de
Year Founded: 1989
Sales Range: $10-24.9 Million
Emp.: 140
Cutting Tool Mfr
N.A.I.C.S.: 333515
Gustav Werthwein *(Founder)*

Subsidiaries:

AVANTEC Austria GmbH   **(1)**
Knoppen 93, 8984, Bad Mitterndorf, Austria
Tel.: (43) 362427915
Industrial Tool Mfr & Distr
N.A.I.C.S.: 333515
Mathias Schneider *(Mgr-Sls)*

AVANTEC Italy S.r.l.   **(1)**
Via Gramsci 157, 24069, Rome, Italy
Tel.: (39) 0354258369
Industrial Tools Distr
N.A.I.C.S.: 423830
Mathias Schneider *(Mgr-Sls)*

AVANTEC USA, LLC   **(1)**
50 S Chestnut St, Boyertown, PA 19512
Tel.: (610) 473-2872
Industrial Tools Distr
N.A.I.C.S.: 423830
Mathias Schneider *(Mgr-Sls)*

AVANTEL LTD.
Plot No 68 & 69 4th Floor Jubilee Heights, Survey No 66 & 67 Jubilee Enclave Madhapur, Hyderabad, 500 081, India
Tel.: (91) 4066305000
Web Site: https://www.avantel.in
Year Founded: 1990
532406—(BOM)
Rev.: $18,575,589
Assets: $17,921,156
Liabilities: $5,034,422

Net Worth: $12,886,733
Earnings: $3,217,781
Emp.: 175
Fiscal Year-end: 03/31/23
Communication Equipment Mfr
N.A.I.C.S.: 334290
Abburi Vidyasagar *(Chm & Mng Dir)*

AVANTHA GROUP
First India Place Tower-C 5th Floor, Mehrauli - Gurgaon Road, Gurgaon, 122 022, Haryana, India
Tel.: (91) 1244099436
Web Site:
    http://www.avanthagroup.com
Year Founded: 2007
Sales Range: $1-4.9 Billion
Emp.: 22,000
Holding Company
N.A.I.C.S.: 551112
Gautam Thapar *(Founder & Chm)*

Subsidiaries:

Avantha Business Solutions
Limited   **(1)**
Bestech Business Tower Ist Floor Sector-48 Sohna Road, Gurgaon, 122018, Haryana, India
Tel.: (91) 124 4343434
Web Site: http://www.avanthabsl.com
Financial Services
N.A.I.C.S.: 522320
Kuljit Hooda *(Asst VP-IT)*

Subsidiary (US):

Avantha Business Solutions USA, Inc.   **(2)**
14141 46th St N Ste 1212, Clearwater, FL 33762-0389
Tel.: (877) 340-6940
Financial Services
N.A.I.C.S.: 522320

Avantha Power & Infrastructure
Limited   **(1)**
6th & 7th floor Vatika City Point, MG Road, Gurgaon, 122 002, Haryana, India
Tel.: (91) 1244392000
Web Site: http://www.avanthapower.com
Power Generation & Distribution Services
N.A.I.C.S.: 221118
Sudhir Mohan Trehan *(Chm)*

Subsidiary (Domestic):

Korba West Power Company
Limited   **(2)**
, Village - Chhote Bhandar PO - Bade Bhandar, Raigarh, 496 100, Chhattisgarh, India
Tel.: (91) 7762 251514
Power Generation Services
N.A.I.C.S.: 221118

Malanpur Captive Power Limited   **(2)**
H-3 Industrial Area, Malanpur District, Bhind, 477116, Madhya Pradesh, India
Tel.: (91) 7539 400276
Eletric Power Generation Services
N.A.I.C.S.: 221118

Ballarpur Industries Limited   **(1)**
First India Place Tower C Mehrauli - Gurgaon Road, Gurgaon, 122 002, Haryana, India   **(49.24%)**
Tel.: (91) 1242804242
Web Site: http://www.bilt.com
Rev.: $45,855,810
Assets: $500,959,095
Liabilities: $667,766,190
Net Worth: ($166,807,095)
Earnings: ($175,631,820)
Emp.: 1,072
Fiscal Year-end: 03/31/2020
Paper Mfr
N.A.I.C.S.: 322120
R. R. Vederah *(Vice Chm)*

Biltech Building Elements
Limited   **(1)**
232-B Okhla Industrial Estate Area Phase-III, New Delhi, 110 020, India
Tel.: (91) 1149696600
Web Site: http://www.biltechindia.com

Autoclaved Aerated Concrete Building Material Mfr & Marketer
N.A.I.C.S.: 327390
Manish Tiwari *(CEO)*

CG Power and Industrial Solutions
Ltd.   **(1)**
CG House 6th Floor Dr Annie Besant Road, Worli, Mumbai, 400 030, Maharashtra, India   **(42.67%)**
Tel.: (91) 2224237777
Web Site: http://www.cgglobal.com
Rev.: $722,121,400
Assets: $938,816,200
Liabilities: $953,331,400
Net Worth: ($14,515,200)
Earnings: ($303,371,600)
Emp.: 2,802
Fiscal Year-end: 03/31/2020
Power Distribution & Industrial Equipment Mfr; Household Appliance Mfr
N.A.I.C.S.: 335311
Natarajan Srinivasan *(Mng Dir)*

Subsidiary (US):

CG Automation Solutions USA
Inc.   **(2)**
60 Fadem Rd, Springfield, NJ 07081-3116
Tel.: (973) 379-7400
Web Site: http://www.cgautomationusa.com
Sales Range: $10-24.9 Million
Emp.: 50
Telemetering & Computer Interfacing Equipment Mfr
N.A.I.C.S.: 334513
Normand Lavoie *(Pres)*

Subsidiary (Domestic):

CG Capital And Investments
Limited   **(2)**
6th Floor CG House, Dr Annie Besant Road Worli, Mumbai, 400030, India   **(100%)**
Tel.: (91) 2224237777
Miscellaneous Financial Investment Activities
N.A.I.C.S.: 523999
S. M. Threhan *(Chm)*

Subsidiary (Non-US):

CG Electric Systems Hungary
Zrt   **(2)**
Mariassy utca 7, 1095, Budapest, Hungary   **(100%)**
Tel.: (36) 1 4836600
Web Site: http://www.cgglobal.com
Power Distribution & Specialty Transformer Mfr
N.A.I.C.S.: 335311

CG Holdings Belgium NV   **(2)**
Antwerpsesteenweg 167, 2800, Mechelen, Belgium   **(100%)**
Tel.: (32) 15283333
Web Site: http://www.cgglobal.com
Sales Range: $200-249.9 Million
Emp.: 1,000
Electrical Transmission & Distribution Equipment Mfr
N.A.I.C.S.: 335311
Dhilip Patel *(CTO & Exec VP)*

Subsidiary (Domestic):

CG Motors Private Ltd   **(2)**
6th Floor CG House, Dr Annie Besant Road Worli, 400030, Mumbai, India   **(100%)**
Tel.: (91) 2224237777
Web Site: http://www.cgglobal.com
Sales Range: $25-49.9 Million
Emp.: 48
Other Specialized Design Services
N.A.I.C.S.: 541490
S. M. Threhan *(Mng Dir)*

Subsidiary (US):

CG Power Solutions USA Inc.   **(2)**
7 Cen Hill Dr, Latham, NY 12110
Tel.: (518) 452-7718
Web Site: http://www.cgglobal.com
Sales Range: $25-49.9 Million
Emp.: 62
Power Transmission & Distribution Systems Engineering & Construction Services
N.A.I.C.S.: 237130
Brian Carroll *(Project Mgr)*

Avantha Group—(Continued)

Subsidiary (Non-US):

CG Power Systems Belgium NV **(2)**
Antwerpsesteenweg 167, 2800, Mechelen, Belgium **(100%)**
Tel.: (32) 15283333
Emp.: 700
Electronic Coil Transformer & Other Inductor Mfr
N.A.I.C.S.: 334416

CG Power Systems Canada Inc. **(2)**
101 Rockman Street, Winnipeg, R3T 0L7, MB, Canada **(100%)**
Tel.: (204) 452-7446
Web Site: http://www.cgglobal.com
Sales Range: $100-124.9 Million
Emp.: 300
Power Distribution & Specialty Transformer Mfr
N.A.I.C.S.: 335311

CG Power Systems Ireland Ltd. **(2)**
Dublin Road, Cavan, Ireland **(100%)**
Tel.: (353) 494331588
Web Site: http://www.cgglobal.com
Sales Range: $100-124.9 Million
Emp.: 450
Electronic Coil Transformer & Other Inductor Mfr
N.A.I.C.S.: 334416
James McMahon *(Mng Dir)*

Subsidiary (Domestic):

CG Ppi Adhesive Products Limited **(2)**
215 Kundaim Industrial Estate, Kundaim, 403115, Goa, India **(100%)**
Tel.: (91) 8322395210
Web Site: http://www.cgppi.com
Sales Range: $25-49.9 Million
Emp.: 100
Adhesive Mfr
N.A.I.C.S.: 325520
Murali Dhar Nikam *(CEO)*

Subsidiary (Non-US):

CG Sales Networks France S.A. **(2)**
Immeuble Arago 1, 41 Boulevard Vauban, F-78280, Guyancourt, France **(100%)**
Tel.: (33) 134521080
Web Site: http://www.pauwels.com
Sales Range: $50-74.9 Million
Emp.: 4
Electrical Apparatus & Equipment Wiring Supplies & Construction Materials Sales
N.A.I.C.S.: 423610

CG Service Systems Curacao NV **(2)**
Sans Souci 47 C, Willemstad, Curacao **(100%)**
Tel.: (599) 98883355
Sales Range: $25-49.9 Million
Emp.: 6
Computer System Design Services
N.A.I.C.S.: 541512

Subsidiary (Domestic):

Malapur Captive Power LTD **(2)**
Vandana Building 11, Tolstoy Marg, 11001, New Delhi, India **(100%)**
Tel.: (91) 1130416300
Web Site: http://www.cgglobal.com
Computer System Design Services
N.A.I.C.S.: 541512

Solaris ChemTech Industries Limited **(1)**
First India Place Tower-C 1st Floor, Mehrauli-Gurgaon Road, Gurgaon, 122 002, India
Tel.: (91) 1242804242
Web Site: http://www.solarischemtech.com
Bromine Chemicals Mfr
N.A.I.C.S.: 325998
S. Hariharan *(Mng Dir)*

The Global Green Company Limited **(1)**
No 68 Oblapura Village Anugondanahalli Hobli, Hoskote, Bengaluru, 560 067, India
Tel.: (91) 80 27945181
Web Site: http://www.globalgreengroup.com
Food Product Mfr & Distr

N.A.I.C.S.: 311412
Attila Zakuczki *(Assoc VP-Agricultural Ops-Europe)*

Subsidiary (Non-US):

Global Green International **(2)**
Unit No 308 Dubai Arch Tower Plot No PH1 - G1 Jumeirah Lake Towers, Dubai, United Arab Emirates
Tel.: (971) 4 454 8528
Food Products Mfr
N.A.I.C.S.: 311412

Global Green International NV **(2)**
Bergemeersenstraat 118, 9300, Aalst, Belgium
Tel.: (32) 53 59 01 00
Food Products Distr
N.A.I.C.S.: 424420

Subsidiary (US):

Global Green USA Ltd. **(2)**
19 Spear Rd SE 308, Ramsey, NJ 07446
Tel.: (201) 327-2228
Web Site: http://www.globalgreen.org
Food Products Distr
N.A.I.C.S.: 424420

Subsidiary (Non-US):

Puszta Konzerv Kft. **(2)**
PO Box 49, 4060, Balmazujvaros, Hungary
Tel.: (36) 52377355
Food Products Distr
N.A.I.C.S.: 424420

Unit (Domestic):

The Global Green Company Limited - Hyderabad Unit **(2)**
Kohir Mandal Venkatapur village, Medak, 502321, Andhra Pradesh, India
Tel.: (91) 8451 287632
Food Products Distr
N.A.I.C.S.: 424420

AVANTI ACQUISITION CORP.
Boundary Hall Cricket Square, PO Box 1093, Georgetown, KY1-1102, Cayman Islands　　　　　　Ky
Tel.: (345) 814 5831
Web Site: http://www.avanti-acquisition.com
Year Founded: 2020
AVAN—(NYSE)
Rev.: $47,898,102
Assets: $600,489,194
Liabilities: $648,634,480
Net Worth: ($48,145,286)
Earnings: $46,559,048
Emp.: 2
Fiscal Year-end: 12/31/21
Investment Services
N.A.I.C.S.: 523999
Nassef Sawiris *(Chm & CEO)*

AVANTI CAPITAL PLC
73 Cornhill, London, EC3V 3QQ, United Kingdom
Tel.: (44) 20 7299 1459
Web Site: http://www.avanticap.com
Sales Range: Less than $1 Million
Emp.: 492
Investment Services
N.A.I.C.S.: 523940
Philip J. Crawford *(Chm)*

AVANTI COMMUNICATIONS GROUP PLC
Cobham House 20 Black Friars Lane, London, EC4V 6EB, United Kingdom
Tel.: (44) 2077491600
Web Site: http://www.avantiplc.com
Rev.: $56,600,000
Assets: $807,800,000
Liabilities: $674,100,000
Net Worth: $133,700,000
Earnings: ($65,700,000)
Emp.: 254
Fiscal Year-end: 06/30/17

Holding Company; Satellite Communications Services
N.A.I.C.S.: 551112
Kyle Whitehill *(CEO)*

Subsidiaries:

Avanti Broadband Limited **(1)**
Cobham House 20 Black Friars Lane, London, EC4V 6EB, United Kingdom
Tel.: (44) 2077491600
Web Site: http://www.avantepic.com
Sales Range: $25-49.9 Million
Broadband Service Provider
N.A.I.C.S.: 517810
David Williams *(Mng Dir)*

Avanti Communications Limited **(1)**
20 Black Friars Lane, London, EC4V 6EB, United Kingdom
Tel.: (44) 2077491600
Web Site: http://www.avantiplc.com
Sales Range: $25-49.9 Million
Emp.: 100
Satellite Communication Services
N.A.I.C.S.: 517410
Paul Bedford *(Mgr)*

Avanti Space Limited **(1)**
20 Black Prairie Lane Bldg Cobham House, London, EC4V 6EB, United Kingdom
Tel.: (44) 2077491600
Web Site: http://www.avantiplc.com
Sales Range: $25-49.9 Million
Emp.: 100
Satellite Television Network Services
N.A.I.C.S.: 516120
David Williams *(CEO)*

AVANTI FEEDS LTD.
G-2 Concorde Apartment 6-3-658 Somajiguda, Hyderabad, 500082, Telangana, India
Tel.: (91) 4023310260
Web Site:
　　https://www.avantifeeds.com
Year Founded: 1993
AVANTI—(NSE)
Rev.: $698,556,386
Assets: $343,462,488
Liabilities: $50,344,162
Net Worth: $293,118,326
Earnings: $33,473,486
Emp.: 1,162
Fiscal Year-end: 03/31/21
Shrimp & Fish Feed Mfr
N.A.I.C.S.: 311119
Alluri Indra Kumar *(Chm & Co-Mng Dir)*

Subsidiaries:

Avanti Feeds Ltd. - Prawn Feed/Fish Feed Factories **(1)**
15-11-24 Near Railway Station, W G District, Kovvur, 534 350, Andrapradesh, India
Tel.: (91) 8813 231541
Web Site: http://www.avantifeeds.com
Emp.: 600
Fish Feed Mfr
N.A.I.C.S.: 311119
Paresh Kumar Shetty *(Gen Mgr-Mktg)*

Avanti Thai Aqua Feeds Private Limited **(1)**
Block-498/1 & 501 Balda Village, Valsad Dist, Pardi, 396125, India
Tel.: (91) 2602995480
Shrimp Feed Mfr
N.A.I.C.S.: 311119

AVANTI GOLD CORPORATION
2380 - 1055 W Hastings Street, Vancouver, V6E 2E9, BC, Canada
Tel.: (604) 808-6300　　　　　BC
Web Site:
　　https://www.avantigoldcorp.com
Year Founded: 2014
VALU—(CNSX)
Assets: $44,404
Liabilities: $844,284
Net Worth: ($799,881)
Earnings: ($2,729,671)
Fiscal Year-end: 04/30/22

Metal Mining
N.A.I.C.S.: 212290

AVANTI HELIUM CORP.
Tel.: (403) 384-0401　　　　　BC
Web Site: https://avantihelium.com
Year Founded: 2011
ARGYF—(OTCIQ)
Assets: $1,396,006
Liabilities: $11,625
Net Worth: $1,384,381
Earnings: ($418,329)
Fiscal Year-end: 12/31/20
Energy Exploration Services
N.A.I.C.S.: 211120
Genga Nadaraju *(VP-Subsurface)*

AVANTIA CO., LTD.
Sanyo Honsha Bldg 3-31-1 Myoontori, Mizuho-ku, Nagoya, 467-0842, Aichi, Japan
Tel.: (81) 528590034
Web Site: http://www.sanyo-hn.co.jp
Year Founded: 1989
8904—(TKS)
Rev.: $441,750,620
Assets: $419,072,500
Liabilities: $246,467,500
Net Worth: $172,605,000
Earnings: $3,663,580
Emp.: 593
Fiscal Year-end: 08/31/24
Building Construction Services
N.A.I.C.S.: 236115
Yasunari Sawada *(Pres & CEO)*

AVANTIUM HOLDING BV
Zekeringstraat 29, 1014 BV, Amsterdam, Netherlands
Tel.: (31) 20 586 8080
Web Site: http://www.avantium.com
Year Founded: 2000
Emp.: 135
Chemical Technologies Processes
N.A.I.C.S.: 325998
Tom B. van Aken *(CEO)*

AVANZA BANK HOLDING AB
Regeringsgatan 103, PO Box 1399, 111 93, Stockholm, Sweden
Tel.: (46) 840942000
Web Site: https://www.avanza.se
Year Founded: 1999
AZA—(OMX)
Rev.: $278,456,827
Assets: $22,581,040,958
Liabilities: $22,117,320,895
Net Worth: $463,720,063
Earnings: $156,040,724
Emp.: 635
Fiscal Year-end: 12/31/22
Financial Services
N.A.I.C.S.: 523999
Rikard Josefson *(CEO)*

AVARGA LIMITED
1 Kim Seng Promenade 1310 Great World City West Lobby, Singapore, 237994, Singapore
Tel.: (65) 68365522
Web Site: https://www.avarga.com.sg
Year Founded: 1967
U09—(SES)
Rev.: $1,287,569,491
Assets: $536,197,076
Liabilities: $196,843,899
Net Worth: $339,353,177
Earnings: $20,586,230
Emp.: 436
Fiscal Year-end: 12/31/23
Investment Holding Company; Waste Paper Recycling & Paper Products Mfr
N.A.I.C.S.: 551112
Kooi Ong Tong *(Chm)*

Subsidiaries:

Taiga Building Products Ltd.   **(1)**
800-4710 Kingsway, Burnaby, V5H 4M2,
BC, Canada   **(65.1%)**
Tel.: (604) 438-1471
Web Site: https://www.taigabuilding.com
Rev.: $1,243,139,140
Assets: $370,929,014
Liabilities: $210,546,751
Net Worth: $160,382,263
Earnings: $55,405,763
Emp.: 584
Fiscal Year-end: 12/31/2020
Lumber, Panel Products & Related Building
Products Distr
N.A.I.C.S.: 321999
Trent Balog *(Pres)*

Subsidiary (US):

Taiga Building Products USA Ltd.   **(2)**
2685 Index St, Washougal, WA 98501
Tel.: (800) 663-1470
Mouldings, Composite Decking, Panels, Engineered Wood, Preserved Wood & Accessories & Other Building Products Mfr
N.A.I.C.S.: 321211

Subsidiary (Domestic):

Exterior Wood Inc.   **(3)**
2685 Index St, Washougal, WA 98671
Tel.: (360) 835-8561
Web Site: https://www.exteriorwood.com
Wood Preserving
N.A.I.C.S.: 321114
Damien Fallin *(Mgr-Pur & Production)*

AVARN SECURITY GROUP HOLDING AS
Rajatorpantie 8, 01600, Vantaa, Fin-
land
Tel.: (358) 2042828   FI
Web Site:
  https://www.avarnsecurity.com
Year Founded: 2021
Security technology, Security Ser-
vices & Solutions
N.A.I.C.S.: 561621
Amund Skarholt *(Chm)*

Subsidiaries:

Avarn Security OY   **(1)**
Pitajanmaentie 14, Helsinki, 00380,
Finland   **(100%)**
Tel.: (358) 2042828
Web Site: http://www.avarn.fi
Commercial Security Services
N.A.I.C.S.: 561612
Juha Murtopuro *(Mng Dir)*

Nokas AS   **(1)**
Trleborgodden 6, Tonsberg, 3112, Norway
Tel.: (47) 33308800
Web Site: http://www.nokas.no
Sales Range: $125-149.9 Million
Emp.: 5,000
Security System & Guard Services
N.A.I.C.S.: 561621
Heine Wang *(CEO)*

Subsidiary (Non-US):

Nokas Sverige   **(2)**
Vastberga Alle 11, PO Box 42182, 126 17,
Stockholm, Sweden
Tel.: (46) 102226000
Web Site: http://www.nokas.com
Security Services
N.A.I.C.S.: 541690
Vidar Berg *(CEO)*

AVARONE METALS INC.
Suite 610 700 West Pender Street,
Vancouver, V6C 1G8, BC, Canada
Tel.: (604) 669-9788
Web Site: http://www.avarone.com
Year Founded: 1993
AVM—(CNSX)
Rev.: $99,217
Assets: $34,848
Liabilities: $1,032,298
Net Worth: ($997,450)
Earnings: ($120,160)

Fiscal Year-end: 07/31/23
Metal Exploration Services
N.A.I.C.S.: 212290
Marc Levy *(CEO)*

AVASARA FINANCE LIMITED
Bandra Hill View CHS 3rd Floor 85
Hill Road Opp Yoko Sizzlers, Bandra
W, Mumbai, 400 050, India
Tel.: (91) 2226414725
Web Site: https://www.trcfin.in
Year Founded: 1994
511730—(BOM)
Rev.: $85,517
Assets: $359,896
Liabilities: $8,545
Net Worth: $351,351
Earnings: $36,336
Emp.: 6
Fiscal Year-end: 03/31/21
Financial Management Services
N.A.I.C.S.: 523999
Giddaiah Koteswar *(Exec Dir)*

AVATEC CO., LTD.
100 Dalseodaero 85-gil, Dalseo-gu,
Daegu, Korea (South)
Tel.: (82) 535924060
Web Site: https://www.avatec.co.kr
Year Founded: 2000
149950—(KRS)
Rev.: $56,132,046
Assets: $114,962,025
Liabilities: $10,070,410
Net Worth: $104,891,615
Earnings: ($3,313,819)
Emp.: 531
Fiscal Year-end: 12/31/22
Electronic Components Mfr
N.A.I.C.S.: 334419
Myeong-Seop Park *(Co-CEO)*

AVATION PLC
65 Kampong Bahru Road 01-01, Sin-
gapore, 169370, Singapore
Tel.: (65) 62522077   UK
Web Site: https://www.avation.net
Year Founded: 2006
AVAP—(LSE)
Rev.: $99,250,000
Assets: $1,179,596,000
Liabilities: $937,964,000
Net Worth: $241,632,000
Earnings: $12,192,000
Emp.: 23
Fiscal Year-end: 06/30/23
Aircraft Leasing Services
N.A.I.C.S.: 532411
Robert Jeffries Chatfield *(Chm)*

AVAX S.A.
16 Amarousiou-Halandriou Street,
151 25, Maroussi, Greece
Tel.: (30) 2106375000
Web Site: https://avax.gr
Year Founded: 1986
AVAX—(ATH)
Rev.: $486,847,042
Assets: $1,291,063,095
Liabilities: $1,119,613,650
Net Worth: $171,449,445
Earnings: $10,762,339
Emp.: 1,928
Fiscal Year-end: 12/31/23
Civil Engineering Contract Services
N.A.I.C.S.: 541330
Christos Joannou *(Chm)*

Subsidiaries:

Athens Marina S.A.   **(1)**
New Faliro, 185 47, Piraeus, Greece
Tel.: (30) 2104853200
Web Site: https://www.athens-marina.com
Yacht Mooring Services
N.A.I.C.S.: 713930
Stavros Karnakis *(Gen Mgr)*

Volterra SA   **(1)**

16 Marousiou Chalandriou, 151 25, Ma-
roussi, Greece
Tel.: (30) 2130883000
Web Site: http://www.volterra.gr
Oil & Energy Services
N.A.I.C.S.: 213112

AVBA HI TECH SERVICES LTD.
1 Hatzmicha St, PO Box 512,
Yoqne'am Illit, 2069208, Israel
Tel.: (972) 46449000   II
Web Site: http://www.avba.co.il
Year Founded: 1987
Laboratory Equipment Distr
N.A.I.C.S.: 423490
Victor Orland *(CEO)*

AVC IMMEDIA LIMITED
Grandholm Mill, Grandholm Crescent,
Aberdeen, AB22 8BB, Scotland,
United Kingdom
Tel.: (44) 1224392828
Web Site: http://www.avcmedia.com
Year Founded: 1976
Advetising Agency
N.A.I.C.S.: 541810

Subsidiaries:

Immedia Broadcast Limited   **(1)**
729 The Broadway, Newbury, RG14 1AS,
Berkshire, United Kingdom
Tel.: (44) 1635556200
Sales Range: $25-49.9 Million
Emp.: 100
Radio Broadcasting Services
N.A.I.C.S.: 516210
Bruno Brookes *(CEO)*

AVCON INFORMATION TECH-NOLOGY CO., LTD.
Building A6 Bay Valley Technology
Park 1688 Guoquan North Road,
Yangpu District, Shanghai, 200433,
China
Tel.: (86) 2155666588
Web Site: https://www.avcon.com.cn
Year Founded: 2003
300074—(CHIN)
Rev.: $57,955,716
Assets: $225,093,492
Liabilities: $71,917,092
Net Worth: $153,176,400
Earnings: ($14,859,936)
Emp.: 300
Fiscal Year-end: 12/31/22
Video Conferencing & Video Monitor-
ing Control Systems & Software
N.A.I.C.S.: 334220
Lui Wen Fai *(Chm & Gen Mgr)*

AVE S.A.
Paradisou 35, 151 25, Maroussi,
Greece
Tel.: (30) 2108092000
Web Site: https://www.ave.gr
Year Founded: 1982
AVE—(ATH)
Rev.: $20,788,917
Assets: $52,504,131
Liabilities: $59,058,460
Net Worth: ($6,554,329)
Earnings: ($9,824,703)
Emp.: 189
Fiscal Year-end: 12/31/23
Home Video Distr
N.A.I.C.S.: 512120
Ioannis T. Bardinogiannis *(Chm)*

Subsidiaries:

Officemart Office Professional Solu-
tions SA   **(1)**
Hefaistou 9, 19442, Koropi, Greece
Tel.: (30) 2105152052
Web Site: https://www.officemart.gr
Office Equipment Merchant Whslr
N.A.I.C.S.: 424120

Ster Cinemas A.E.   **(1)**

Tompazi 15 Pylea, 55535, Thessaloniki,
Greece
Tel.: (30) 8018017837
Motion Picture Theater Operator
N.A.I.C.S.: 512131

AVECHO BIOTECHNOLOGY LTD.
Unit A8 2A Westall Road, Clayton,
3168, VIC, Australia
Tel.: (61) 390025000
Web Site:
  https://www.avecho.com.au
AVE—(ASX)
Rev.: $322,560
Assets: $4,985,566
Liabilities: $641,332
Net Worth: $4,344,234
Earnings: ($2,340,822)
Emp.: 20
Fiscal Year-end: 12/31/23
Pharmaceutical & Nutraceutical Re-
searcher, Developer & Mfr
N.A.I.C.S.: 325412
Paul Gavin *(CEO)*

Subsidiaries:

Vital Health Sciences Pty Ltd   **(1)**
11 Duerdin St, Clayton, 3168, VIC, Australia
Tel.: (61) 395651119
Health Science Services
N.A.I.C.S.: 541715

AVECIA LTD.
Hexagon House Old Market St, PO
Box 42, Blackley, Manchester, M9
8ZS, United Kingdom
Tel.: (44) 1617211013
Web Site: http://www.avecia.com
Year Founded: 1999
Sales Range: $350-399.9 Million
Emp.: 2,529
Specialty Chemicals Mfr
N.A.I.C.S.: 325412
Detlef Rethage *(Pres)*

Subsidiaries:

Avecia Ltd. - Cincinnati Facility   **(1)**
8560 Reading Rd, Cincinnati, OH 45215
Tel.: (513) 679-3000
Pharmaceuticals Product Mfr
N.A.I.C.S.: 325412

Avecia Ltd. - Milford Facility   **(1)**
125 Fortune Blvd, Milford, MA 01757
Tel.: (508) 532-2500
Pharmaceuticals Product Mfr
N.A.I.C.S.: 325412

Avecia NV/SA   **(1)**
Av De Tervueren 13 B, 1040, Brussels,
Belgium   **(100%)**
Tel.: (32) 27430090
Web Site: http://www.avecia.com
N.A.I.C.S.: 325998

Avecia Spain S.L.   **(1)**
Palou 2 Y 4 Poligono Industrial, Parets Del
Valles, Barcelona, Spain   **(100%)**
Tel.: (34) 935620047
Basic Inorganic Chemical Mfr
N.A.I.C.S.: 325180

AVEMIO AG
Konigsallee 60F, 40212, Dusseldorf,
Germany
Tel.: (49) 21188284118
Web Site: https://www.avemio.com
Year Founded: 2018
3D6—(DUS)
Rev.: $109,448,710
Assets: $55,833,745
Liabilities: $30,102,535
Net Worth: $25,731,210
Earnings: ($3,620,694)
Emp.: 174
Fiscal Year-end: 12/31/23
Software Development Services
N.A.I.C.S.: 541511
Norbert Gunkler *(CFO)*

Avemio AG—(Continued)

Subsidiaries:

BPM Broadcast & Professional Media
GmbH **(1)**
Obenhauptstrasse 15, D-22335, Hamburg,
Germany
Tel.: (49) 4055762455
Web Site: https://www.bpm-media.de
Emp.: 30
Broadcast Camera Mfr
N.A.I.C.S.: 334310

MoovIT GmbH **(1)**
Schanzenstrasse 29, 51063, Cologne, Germany
Tel.: (49) 22130200210
Web Site: https://www.moovit.de
Information Technology Services
N.A.I.C.S.: 541512

MoovIT Software Products
GmbH **(1)**
Schanzenstrasse 29, 51063, Cologne, Germany
Tel.: (49) 22129218690
Web Site: https://www.moovit-sp.com
Software Development Services
N.A.I.C.S.: 541511

VCT Videocation Creative Tools
GmbH **(1)**
Kohlentwiete 14, 22761, Hamburg, Germany
Tel.: (49) 408515070
Web Site: https://www.creativetools.de
Software Production Services
N.A.I.C.S.: 512110

AVENG LIMITED

3rd Floor 10 The High Street Melrose
Arch, Johannesburg, 2076, South
Africa
Tel.: (27) 117792800
Web Site: https://www.aveng.co.za
AEG—(JSE)
Rev.: $1,786,124,940
Assets: $851,169,250
Liabilities: $597,353,650
Net Worth: $253,815,600
Earnings: $67,411,240
Emp.: 5,211
Fiscal Year-end: 06/30/22
Construction & Engineering Services
N.A.I.C.S.: 236220
Hercu Aucamp (Mng Dir-Steel)

Subsidiaries:

Aveng E+PC Engineering & Projects
Company Limited **(1)**
The Highlands Bldg 30 The Woodlands,
Woodlands Dr Woodmead, 2191, Sandton,
2191, Gauteng, South Africa
Tel.: (27) 10 205 1000
Web Site: http://www.avengegroup.com
Sales Range: $200-249.9 Million
Emp.: 100
Industrial Engineering, Design & Project
Delivery Services
N.A.I.C.S.: 541330
Vishal Maharaj (Dir-Fin)

Dynamic Fluid Control (Pty) Ltd. **(1)**
32 Lincoln Road, Benoni, South Africa
Tel.: (27) 103004900
Web Site: https://dfc.co.za
Construction Steel & Concrete Materials Mfr
N.A.I.C.S.: 327320
Mlungisi Cele (COO)

Fraser & Chalmers Siyakha (Pty)
Limited **(1)**
1 Belfast Rd, Bayhead, Durban, 4026,
Kwazulu-Natal, South Africa
Tel.: (27) 312051525
Industrial Engineering Services
N.A.I.C.S.: 541330

Grinaker-LTA (Namibia) (Pty)
Limited **(1)**
13 Cullinan Street, Northern Industrial Area,
Windhoek, Namibia
Tel.: (264) 61228411
Web Site: http://www.grinaker-lta.com

Sales Range: $25-49.9 Million
Emp.: 200
Construction Engineering Services
N.A.I.C.S.: 541330

Grinaker-LTA Engineering and Mining
Services Limited **(1)**
41 Scott Street, Bramley, Johannesburg,
1459, Gauteng, South Africa
Tel.: (27) 119235000
Web Site: https://grinaker-lta.co.za
Industrial & Mining Engineering Services
N.A.I.C.S.: 541330

McConnell Dowell Corporation
Limited **(1)**
Level 3 109 Burwood Road, Hawthorn,
3122, VIC, Australia
Tel.: (61) 39 816 2400
Web Site: http://www.macdow.com.au
Sales Range: $50-74.9 Million
Emp.: 200
Construction Engineering Services
N.A.I.C.S.: 237990

Subsidiary (Non-US):

Dutco McConnell Dowell Qatar
LLC **(2)**
Ofc No 12 2 Fl Al Hilal Bldg 114 Dring Rd,
PO Box 30933, Doha, Qatar
Tel.: (974) 4675 491
Sales Range: $25-49.9 Million
Emp.: 29
Commercial Building Construction Services
N.A.I.C.S.: 236220

Subsidiary (Domestic):

McConnell Dowell Constructors
(Aust.) Pty Limited **(2)**
Level 4 230 Brunswick Street, PO Box 161,
Fortitude Valley, 4006, QLD, Australia
Tel.: (61) 734218200
Web Site: https://www.mcconnelldowell.com
Sales Range: $25-49.9 Million
Emp.: 100
Construction Engineering Services
N.A.I.C.S.: 237990
Mario Russo (Mng Dir)

Subsidiary (Non-US):

McConnell Dowell Constructors
Limited **(2)**
Building B Level 3 600 Great South Road,
Ellerslie, Auckland, 1051, New Zealand
Tel.: (64) 95735891
Emp.: 60
Mining Engineering Services
N.A.I.C.S.: 541330

McConnell Dowell Constructors Thai
Limited **(2)**
Bangkok Business Center Building 11th
Floor Room 1101, 29 Sukhumvit 63 Road
Klongton Nua Wattana, Bangkok, 10110,
Thailand
Tel.: (66) 23915406
Sales Range: $50-74.9 Million
Emp.: 200
Oil & Gas Pipeline Construction Services
N.A.I.C.S.: 237120

McConnell Dowell Philippines
Inc. **(2)**
Level 4NOL Tower Madrigal Business Park
Commerce Avenue, Alabang, Muntinlupa,
1780, Philippines
Tel.: (63) 2 809 6328
Web Site: https://www.mcconnelldowell.com
Sales Range: $75-99.9 Million
Emp.: 6
Industrial Engineering Services
N.A.I.C.S.: 541330

PT. McConnell Dowell Indonesia **(2)**
Parama Building 1st FloorJl KH Achmad
Dahlan No 69 A-B, Kebayoran Baru, Jakarta, 12130, Indonesia
Tel.: (62) 217253051
Web Site: http://www.macdow.com.au
Sales Range: $25-49.9 Million
Emp.: 50
Construction Engineering Services
N.A.I.C.S.: 237990

Mcconnell Dowell South East Asia
Private Limited **(1)**
750 Chai Chee Road No 03-18 ESR Biz-

Park Chai Chee, Singapore, 469000, Singapore
Tel.: (65) 431366
Industrial Building Construction Services
N.A.I.C.S.: 236210

Moolman Mining Botswana (Pty)
Limited **(1)**
Private Bag F449, Francistown, Botswana
Tel.: (267) 2418849
Web Site: http://www.aveng.com
Sales Range: $200-249.9 Million
Emp.: 500
Mining Support Services
N.A.I.C.S.: 213113
Brian Wilmot (Mng Dir)

Trident Steel (Pty) Limited **(1)**
Marthunisen Road Roodekop, Germiston,
1401, Gauteng, South Africa
Tel.: (27) 118617111
Web Site: https://avengtridentsteel.co.za
Steel Processing Services
N.A.I.C.S.: 331110
Raven Brijrajh (Dir-Fin)

Trident Steel Intellectual Property
(Pty) Limited **(1)**
Marthunisen Road Roodekop, Germiston,
1450, Gauteng, South Africa
Tel.: (27) 118617111
Web Site: https://www.trident.co.za
Steel Warehousing Services
N.A.I.C.S.: 493110
Hercu Aucamp (CEO)

AVENG WATER PTY LTD

Building 10 Country Club Estate
Woodland Dr, Woodmead, Woodmead, 2191, South Africa
Tel.: (27) 102051000
Web Site:
http://www.avengwater.co.za
Year Founded: 1989
Sales Range: $25-49.9 Million
Emp.: 40
Water Treatment Plant Installation
Services
N.A.I.C.S.: 237110
K. Njobe (Mng Dir)

AVENGA

Sky Tower 66 Gwiazdzista Street,
53-413, Wroclaw, Poland
Tel.: (48) 713424658
Web Site: http://www.itkontrakt.com
Year Founded: 2004
Recruitment & Outsourcing Services
N.A.I.C.S.: 518210
Natalia Faccio (Bus Line Mgr)

Subsidiaries:

CoreValue **(1)**
PO Box 971, Lebanon, NH 03766
Tel.: (603) 678-8353
Web Site:
http://www.corevaluesoftware.com
Engineeering Services
N.A.I.C.S.: 541330
Chuck Richards (Founder)

AVENIR ELECTRIQUE DE LI-MOGES

99 Rue Henri Giffard, 87020, Limoges, France
Tel.: (33) 555358383
Web Site: http://www.avenirelec.fr
Year Founded: 1920
Sales Range: $25-49.9 Million
Emp.: 192
General Electric Services
N.A.I.C.S.: 238210

AVENIR ENERGIE SA

13 rue Emmanuel Chabrier, Valence,
26905, France
Tel.: (33) 475822890
Sales Range: $10-24.9 Million
Emp.: 50
Geothermal Heating Systems
N.A.I.C.S.: 333414

AVENIR TELECOM S.A.

Les Rizeries 208 Boulevard de Plombieres, 13581, Marseilles, Cedex 20,
France
Tel.: (33) 488006000 **FR**
Web Site: https://www.avenir-
telecom.com
AVT—(EUR)
Sales Range: $1-9.9 Million
Emp.: 1,982
Mobile Phones & Cellular Accessories Distr
N.A.I.C.S.: 423690
Jean-Daniel Beurnier (Co-Founder,
Pres & CEO)

Subsidiaries:

Avenir Telecom France **(1)**
2008 bd de Plombieres, Marseille, 13581,
Marseilles, Cedex 20, France
Tel.: (33) 488006000
Emp.: 25
Mobile Telephony Products Distr
N.A.I.C.S.: 334220

Avenir Telecom Romania **(1)**
Sos Bucuresti-Ploiesti Nr 67 Sector 1,
13685, Bucharest, Romania
Tel.: (40) 212012900
Web Site: https://www.internity.ro
Mobile Telephony Products Mfr
N.A.I.C.S.: 334220

Avenir Telecom Spain **(1)**
Pine Ave s n The Oak Park, 48170, Zamudio, Biscay, Spain
Tel.: (34) 944521516
Web Site: http://www.avenir-telecom.com
Telecom Distr
N.A.I.C.S.: 334220

AVENIRA LIMITED

Tel.: (61) 892647000
Web Site: https://www.avenira.com
Year Founded: 2006
AEV—(ASX)
Rev.: $59,819
Assets: $14,619,198
Liabilities: $4,061,726
Net Worth: $10,557,472
Earnings: ($2,085,239)
Fiscal Year-end: 06/30/24
Phosphate Rock Mining Services
N.A.I.C.S.: 212390
Brett Clark (Chm & CEO)

Subsidiaries:

Minemakers Australia Pty Ltd **(1)**
19 100 Hay St Subiaco, West Perth, 6008,
WA, Australia
Tel.: (61) 8 9264 7000
Web Site: http://www.avenira.com
Emp.: 7
Phosphate Exploration Services
N.A.I.C.S.: 212390
Andrew Drummond (Mng Dir)

AVENSIA AB

Vavaregatan 21, 222 36, Lund, 222
29, Sweden
Tel.: (46) 46373000
Web Site: https://www.avensia.com
Year Founded: 1998
AVEN—(OMX)
Rev.: $17,119,522
Assets: $40,414,173
Liabilities: $39,278,991
Net Worth: $1,135,182
Earnings: $2,850,132
Emp.: 350
Fiscal Year-end: 12/31/22
Software Development Services
N.A.I.C.S.: 541511
Robin Gustafsson (CEO)

AVENTAS MANUFACTURING GROUP LIMITED

Castle Buildings Paget Square, Enniskillen, BT74 7HS, Co Fermanagh,
United Kingdom

Tel.: (44) 28 9592 2041 UK
Web Site: http://www.aventas.com
Year Founded: 2011
Holding Company; Plastic Products Mfr
N.A.I.C.S.: 551112
Paul O'Brien (CEO)

AVENTURA GROUP AB
David Bagares gata 7, 111 36, Stockholm, Sweden
Tel.: (46) 850301550
Web Site:
  https://www.aventura.group
Year Founded: 2011
69R—(DEU)
Emp.: 100
Online Shopping Services
N.A.I.C.S.: 425120
Ariel Tang (VP)

AVENUE CARS OF GLOUCESTER LIMITED
City Business Centre, Hempsted, Gloucester, GL2 5JH, United Kingdom
Tel.: (44) 1452528181
Web Site:
  http://www.avenuecars.com
Year Founded: 1989
Sales Range: $10-24.9 Million
Emp.: 9
Car Retailer
N.A.I.C.S.: 441120
Nick Broady (Mng Dir)

AVENUE MOVING AND STORAGE LIMITED
992 Rangeview Road, Mississauga, L5E 1H3, ON, Canada
Tel.: (905) 891-2041
Web Site:
  http://www.avenuemoving.com
Year Founded: 1914
Rev.: $21,253,210
Emp.: 30
Transportation & Storage Services
N.A.I.C.S.: 484122
Jeff Stone (Gen Mgr)

AVENUE NISSAN SALES LTD.
1661 Avenue Road, Toronto, M5M 3Y2, ON, Canada
Tel.: (416) 783-3303
Web Site:
  http://www.avenuenissan.com
Year Founded: 1980
Rev.: $14,367,170
Emp.: 32
New & Used Car Dealers
N.A.I.C.S.: 441110

AVENUE SUPERMARTS LIMITED
B 72 and B 72A Wagle Industrial Estate, Road No 33 Kamgar Hospital Road, Thane, 400 604, Maharashtra, India
Tel.: (91) 2233400500
Web Site: http://www.dmartindia.com
Year Founded: 2000
540376—(BOM)
Rev.: $5,151,837,420
Assets: $2,170,887,836
Liabilities: $243,092,141
Net Worth: $1,927,795,696
Earnings: $285,155,566
Emp.: 12,108
Fiscal Year-end: 03/31/23
Department Store Retailer
N.A.I.C.S.: 445110
Radhakishan Damani (Founder)

AVENZA HOLDINGS INC.
124 Merton Street Suite 400, Toronto, M4S 2Z2, ON, Canada

Tel.: (416) 487-5116
Web Site: http://www.avenza.com
Holding Company; Mapping & Spatial Imaging Software Developer, Publisher & Marketer
N.A.I.C.S.: 551112
Ted Florence (Pres & CEO)

Subsidiaries:

Avenza Systems Inc. (1)
84 Merton St, Toronto, M4S 1A1, ON, Canada
Tel.: (416) 487-5116
Web Site: http://www.avenza.com
Mapping & Spatial Imaging Software Developer, Publisher & Marketer
N.A.I.C.S.: 513210
Ted Florence (Pres & CEO)

AVER INFORMATION INC.
8F No157 Da-An Rd, Tucheng Dist, New Taipei City, 23673, Taiwan
Tel.: (886) 222698535
Web Site: https://www.averusa.com
Year Founded: 2008
3669—(TAI)
Rev.: $81,258,246
Assets: $140,730,038
Liabilities: $35,268,385
Net Worth: $105,461,653
Earnings: $8,174,433
Emp.: 620
Fiscal Year-end: 12/31/23
Multimedia Surveillance Products Mfr
N.A.I.C.S.: 334511
Michael Kuo (Founder & Chm)

Subsidiaries:

AVer Information Inc. (1)
Rotterdamseweg 402 A2, 2629 HH, Delft, Netherlands
Tel.: (31) 157112337
Electronic Products Mfr & Distr
N.A.I.C.S.: 334111

AVer Information, Inc. (1)
668 Mission Ct, Fremont, CA 94539
Tel.: (408) 263-3828
Web Site: https://www.aver.com
Sales Range: $25-49.9 Million
Emp.: 52
Surveillance Product Mfr & Distr
N.A.I.C.S.: 334419
Arthur S. Pait (Founder & Pres)

AVERBUCH FORMICA CENTER LTD.
Har Azmon 25, Ramla, Israel
Tel.: (972) 89131900
Web Site: https://www.averbuch.co.il
Year Founded: 1958
AVER—(TAE)
Rev.: $4,885,481
Assets: $26,925,265
Liabilities: $6,282,359
Net Worth: $20,642,906
Earnings: ($794,309)
Emp.: 100
Fiscal Year-end: 12/31/23
All Other Miscellaneous Wood Product Manufacturing
N.A.I.C.S.: 321999

Subsidiaries:

Arpa Industriale S.p.A. (1)
Via Piumati 91 Corso Monviso 8, Bra, 12042, Cuneo, Italy
Tel.: (39) 017 243 6111
Web Site: https://www.arpaindustriale.com
High Quality Panel Mfr
N.A.I.C.S.: 335999

AVERMEDIA TECHNOLOGIES INC.
No 135 Jian 1st Rd, Zhonghe Dist, Taipei, 23585, Taiwan
Tel.: (886) 222263630
Web Site:
  https://www.avermedia.com

Year Founded: 1990
2417—(TAI)
Rev.: $105,962,781
Assets: $192,566,722
Liabilities: $54,546,517
Net Worth: $138,020,205
Earnings: $4,151,378
Emp.: 468
Fiscal Year-end: 12/31/23
Computer & Peripheral Equipment Mfr & Distr
N.A.I.C.S.: 334118
Michael Chung Song Kuo (Chm, Pres & CEO)

AVERNA TECHNOLOGIES INC.
87 Prince St Suite 510, Montreal, H3C 2M7, QC, Canada
Tel.: (514) 842-7577 Ca
Web Site: http://www.averna.com
Year Founded: 1999
Sales Range: $25-49.9 Million
Emp.: 400
Communications & Electronics Testing Solutions Developer & Mfr
N.A.I.C.S.: 334515
Lori Seidman (Chief Legal Officer)

Subsidiaries:

Averna Test Systems Inc. (1)
1011 Mansell Rd Ste B, Roswell, GA 30076
Tel.: (770) 643-1878
Web Site: http://www.averna.com
Communications & Electronics Testing Solutions Developer & Mfr
N.A.I.C.S.: 334515
Michael Ciporkin (Engr-Support)

Nexjen Systems (1)
5933 Brookshire Blvd, Charlotte, NC 28216-3386
Tel.: (704) 969-7070
Web Site: http://www.nexjen.com
Automated Equipment Manufacturer
N.A.I.C.S.: 335999
Brian Esque (VP)

AVERON PARK LIMITED
The Shard 32 London Bridge Street, London, SE1 9SG, United Kingdom
Tel.: (44) 2036678181 UK
Web Site:
  https://www.averonpark.co.uk
Year Founded: 2013
Diversified Holding Company
N.A.I.C.S.: 551112
Graham Ross Russell (Chm)

Subsidiaries:

Foresight Sustainable Forestry Company Plc (1)
The Shard 32 London Bridge Street, London, SE1 9SG, United Kingdom
Tel.: (44) 2036678100
Web Site: https://fsfc.foresightgroup.eu
Assets: $214,657,915
Liabilities: $1,013,633
Net Worth: $213,644,282
Earnings: ($14,312,042)
Fiscal Year-end: 09/30/2023
Investment Management Service
N.A.I.C.S.: 523999

Subsidiary (Domestic):

Fordie Estates Limited (2)
Fordie Estate, Comrie, Crieff, PH6 2LT, United Kingdom
Tel.: (44) 1764679060
Web Site: https://www.fordieestate.co.uk
Environmental Stewardship Services
N.A.I.C.S.: 541620

AVEROX INC.
Office 104 1st Floor Green Trust Tower Jinnah Avenue Blue Area, Islamabad, 44000, Pakistan
Tel.: (92) 518357574 NV
Web Site: http://www.averox.com
Sales Range: Less than $1 Million
Emp.: 80

Software Solutions, Engineering, Telecommunications Network Deployment Services, Systems Integration & Related Support Services
N.A.I.C.S.: 541690
Salmon Mahmood (Pres & CEO)

Subsidiaries:

Averox (Pvt.) Ltd. (1)
509-B St 9 F 10/2, Islamabad, 44000, Pakistan
Tel.: (92) 51 211 0755
Telecommunication Software Development Services
N.A.I.C.S.: 541511

AVERTEX UTILITY SOLUTIONS INC.
205235 County Road 109, Amaranth, L9W 0T8, ON, Canada
Tel.: (519) 942-3030
Web Site: https://www.avertex.ca
Year Founded: 2003
Rev.: $18,123,139
Emp.: 85
Construction & Network Installation Services
N.A.I.C.S.: 541330
Andy Blokker (Co-Founder)

AVES ONE AG
Grosse Elbstrasse 61, 22767, Hamburg, Germany
Tel.: (49) 40238304600 De
Web Site: https://www.avesone.com
Year Founded: 1898
AVES—(DEU)
Rev.: $111,305,849
Assets: $1,016,665,228
Liabilities: $1,011,437,513
Net Worth: $5,227,714
Earnings: ($5,345,349)
Emp.: 32
Fiscal Year-end: 12/31/21
Logistics Equipment Leasing Services
N.A.I.C.S.: 532411
Ralf Wohltmann (Chm-Supervisory Bd)

Subsidiaries:

CH2 Contorhaus Hansestadt Hamburg AG (1)
Kallmorgen Tower Willy-Brandt-Str 23, 20457, Hamburg, Germany
Tel.: (49) 40881414900
Web Site: http://www.ch2-ag.de
Financial Investment Services
N.A.I.C.S.: 523999

CH2 Logistica Portfolioverwaltung GmbH & Co. KG (1)
Kallmorgen Tower Willy-Brandt-Str 23, 20457, Hamburg, Germany
Tel.: (49) 40881414955
Web Site: http://www.ch2-portfolioverwaltung.de
Financial Investment Services
N.A.I.C.S.: 523999

AVESCO MARKETING CORPORATION
810 Aurora Blvd cor Yale Street, PO Box 3531, Cubao, Quezon City, 1109, Manila, Philippines
Tel.: (63) 29128881
Web Site: http://www.avesco.com.ph
Year Founded: 1948
Sales Range: $10-24.9 Million
Emp.: 500
Measuring & Controlling Device Mfr
N.A.I.C.S.: 334513
Robinson Tang (Gen Mgr)

AVESORO HOLDINGS LIMITED
3rd Floor Le Gallais Building 54 Bath Street, Saint Helier, JE2 4SU, Jersey
Tel.: (44) 203 405 9170
Web Site: http://avesoroholdings.com
Holding Company

Avesoro Holdings Limited—(Continued)

N.A.I.C.S.: 551112

Subsidiaries:

Avesoro Jersey Limited **(1)**
3rd Floor Le Gallais Building 54 Bath
Street, Saint Helier, JE2 4SU, Jersey
Tel.: (44) 203 405 9170
Mineral Exploration Services
N.A.I.C.S.: 212220

Subsidiary (Non-US):

Avesoro Resources Inc. **(2)**
1st Floor Octagon Point 5 Cheapside St
Pauls, London, EC2V 6AA, United
Kingdom **(72.9%)**
Tel.: (44) 20 3405 9160
Web Site: http://www.avesoro.com
Rev.: $282,798,000
Assets: $310,088,000
Liabilities: $211,491,000
Net Worth: $98,597,000
Earnings: ($26,862,000)
Fiscal Year-end: 12/31/2018
Gold Mining Services
N.A.I.C.S.: 212220
Serhan Umurhan (CEO)

AVESTHAGEN LIMITED

Discoverer 9th FI International Tech-
nology Park, Whitefield Rd, Benga-
luru, 560066, India
Tel.: (91) 8028411665
Web Site:
http://www.avesthagen.com
Year Founded: 1998
Sales Range: $200-249.9 Million
Emp.: 650
Biopharmaceuticals & Nutritional
Products Mfr
N.A.I.C.S.: 325412
Villoo Morawala-Patell (Founder, Chm
& Mng Dir)

Subsidiaries:

AVETHAGEN M-E FZ-LLC **(1)**
Dubiotech Business Center, PO Box
122819, Academic City, Dubai, United Arab
Emirates
Tel.: (971) 506445324
Pharmaceutical Products Distr
N.A.I.C.S.: 424210

Avesthagen Pte. Ltd. **(1)**
50 Raffles Place 17-01 Singapore Land
Tower, 048623, Singapore, Singapore
Tel.: (65) 6532 2122
Pharmaceutical Products Distr
N.A.I.C.S.: 424210

Avesthagen Pvt. Ltd. **(1)**
Chivers Way, Cambridge, CB24 9AD,
United Kingdom
Tel.: (44) 1223 257719
Pharmaceutical Products Distr
N.A.I.C.S.: 424210

Avesthagen, Inc. **(1)**
9588 Topanga Canyon Blvd, Chatsworth,
CA 91311
Tel.: (818) 709-2411
Web Site: http://www.avesthagen.com
Pharmaceutical Products Distr
N.A.I.C.S.: 424210
Alex Moffett (Pres & CEO)

Dhanvantari Botanicals, Pvt.,
Ltd. **(1)**
593 10th Cross 7th main JP Nagar 3rd
Phase, Bengaluru, 560078, India
Tel.: (91) 8026591529
Biological Product Mfr
N.A.I.C.S.: 325414
Deva Kumar (COO)

AVEX INC.

Sumitomo Fudosan Azabu-Juban
Building 1-4-1 Mita, Minato-ku, Tokyo,
108-0073, Japan
Tel.: (81) 354138550 JP
Web Site: https://www.avex.com
Year Founded: 1988

7860—(TKS)
Rev.: $881,688,070
Assets: $726,353,070
Liabilities: $355,538,680
Net Worth: $370,814,390
Earnings: $6,524,070
Emp.: 1,514
Fiscal Year-end: 03/31/24
Holding Company; Music & Visual
Media Publishing, Production & Distri-
bution Services; Music Artist Manage-
ment Services
N.A.I.C.S.: 551112
Masato Matsuura (Chm)

Subsidiaries:

Avex & Hirotsu Bio Empower
LLC **(1)**
Sumitomo Fudosan Azabu Juban Building
4-1 Mita 1-chome, Minato-ku, Tokyo, Japan
Tel.: (81) 367145260
Web Site: https://avex-healthcare.jp
Advertising Agency Services
N.A.I.C.S.: 541810

Avex Asia Pte. Ltd. **(1)**
3 Fraser Street 05-21 Duo Tower, Singa-
pore, 189352, Singapore
Tel.: (65) 65364321
Music Concert Services
N.A.I.C.S.: 711320
Shunta Takahashi (Pres)

Avex Classics International Inc. **(1)**
Tel.: (81) 570020050
Music Concert Services
N.A.I.C.S.: 711320

Avex Entertainment Inc. **(1)**
Sumitomo Fudosan Azabu-Juban Building
1-4-1 Mita, Minato-ku, Tokyo, 108-0073,
Japan
Tel.: (81) 354138550
Web Site: http://www.avexnet.jp
Sales Range: $650-699.9 Million
Music & Visual Media Publishing, Produc-
tion & Distribution Services
N.A.I.C.S.: 512230

Subsidiary (Domestic):

Binyl Records Inc. **(2)**
3-1-30 Minamiaoyama, Minato-ku, Tokyo,
Japan
Tel.: (81) 354138550
Sales Range: $25-49.9 Million
Emp.: 9
Music Publishers
N.A.I.C.S.: 512230

Avex Hong Kong Ltd. **(1)**
Suite 1501 Millennium City, Kowloon Bay,
Kowloon, China (Hong Kong)
Tel.: (852) 25042181
Web Site: http://www.avexasia.com
Sales Range: $150-199.9 Million
Emp.: 320
Music & Entertainment Services
N.A.I.C.S.: 711130
Puddy Marini (Mng Dir)

Avex Management Inc. **(1)**
3-1-30 Minami-Aoyama, Minato-ku, Tokyo,
107-0062, Japan
Tel.: (81) 354138557
Sales Range: $150-199.9 Million
Emp.: 400
Music Artist Management Services
N.A.I.C.S.: 711410

Avex Marketing Inc. **(1)**
NBF Minamiaoyama Bldg 4 5F 3-1-31 Mi-
namiaoyama, Minata-ku, Minami,
Tokushima, Japan
Tel.: (81) 354138670
Web Site: http://www.avexnet.jp
Sales Range: $400-449.9 Million
Emp.: 1,000
Music & Entertainment Marketing Services
N.A.I.C.S.: 711320

Subsidiary (Domestic):

Para. TV Inc. **(2)**
Oriental Bldg 1-2-22 Mita 4F, Minato-ku,
Tokyo, 108-0073, Japan
Tel.: (81) 354844736
Web Site: http://www.paratv.co.jp

Internet & Mobile Broadcasting Services
N.A.I.C.S.: 516210

MEE Inc. **(1)**
13805 1st Ave N Ste 400, Plymouth, MN
55441
Tel.: (763) 449-8870
Rev.: $1,106,000
Emp.: 7
Laboratory Instrument Mfr
N.A.I.C.S.: 334516
Larry Hanke (CEO & Principal)

AVG LOGISTICS LTD.

102 1st Floor Jhilmil Metro Complex,
Delhi, 110095, India
Tel.: (91) 8527291034
Web Site:
https://www.avglogistics.com
AVG—(NSE)
Rev.: $45,670,238
Assets: $31,405,592
Liabilities: $20,676,651
Net Worth: $10,728,941
Earnings: $240,690
Emp.: 408
Fiscal Year-end: 03/31/21
Logistic Services
N.A.I.C.S.: 488510
Sanjay Gupta (CEO & Mng Dir)

AVI GLOBAL TRUST PLC

2 Cavendish Square, London, W1G
0PU, Devon, United Kingdom
Tel.: (44) 2076594800
Web Site: https://www.aviglobal.co.uk
AGT—(LSE)
Assets: $1,246,869,216
Liabilities: $149,189,994
Net Worth: $1,097,679,222
Earnings: ($125,708,166)
Fiscal Year-end: 09/30/22
Closed-End Investment Trust
N.A.I.C.S.: 525920
Joe Bauernfreund (CEO, Chief In-
vestment Officer & Portfolio Mgr)

AVI JAPAN OPPORTUNITY
TRUST PLC

2 Cavendish Square, London, W1G
0PU, Devon, United Kingdom
Tel.: (44) 2076594800
Web Site: https://www.ajot.co.uk
Year Founded: 2018
AJOT—(LSE)
Assets: $207,547,395
Liabilities: $19,163,595
Net Worth: $188,383,800
Earnings: ($8,419,455)
Fiscal Year-end: 12/31/22
Financial Investment Services
N.A.I.C.S.: 523999

AVI LIMITED

2 Harries Road, Illovo, Johannesburg,
South Africa
Tel.: (27) 115021300
Web Site: http://www.avi.co.za
AVI—(JSE)
Rev.: $944,664,819
Assets: $637,575,235
Liabilities: $310,501,084
Net Worth: $327,074,151
Earnings: $119,484,376
Emp.: 8,412
Fiscal Year-end: 06/30/22
Food, Beverage & Apparels Mfr
N.A.I.C.S.: 311514
James R. Hersov (Co-Chm)

Subsidiaries:

A&D Spitz (Pty) Limited **(1)**
30 Sloane Street, Bryanston, 2021, Johan-
nesburg, South Africa
Tel.: (27) 117077300
Web Site: https://www.spitz.co.za
Sales Range: $25-49.9 Million
Emp.: 60
Apparel & Accessories Distr

N.A.I.C.S.: 458110
Simon Crutchley (Mng Dir)

AVI Financial Services (Pty)
Limited **(1)**
2 Harries Road, PO Box 1897, Illovo, Jo-
hannesburg, 2196, Gauteng, South Africa
Tel.: (27) 115021300
Web Site: http://www.avi.co.za
Sales Range: $50-74.9 Million
Emp.: 30
Financial Investment Advisory Services
N.A.I.C.S.: 523940

Hampton Sportswear (Pty)
Limited **(1)**
2 Harries Rd, Illovo, Johannesburg, 2196,
Gauteng, South Africa
Tel.: (27) 115021340
Sales Range: $50-74.9 Million
Emp.: 6
Sportswear Whslr
N.A.I.C.S.: 424350

Indigo Brands **(1)**
16 - 20 Evans Ave, Epping Industria 1,
Cape Town, 7460, South Africa
Tel.: (27) 215078500
Web Site: https://www.indigobrands.com
Emp.: 450
Yardley Cosmetics Mfr & Distr
N.A.I.C.S.: 325620

Irvin & Johnson Holding Company
(Pty) Limited **(1)**
I J House 1 Davidson Street, Woodstock,
Cape Town, 7925, Western Cape, South
Africa
Tel.: (27) 214407800
Web Site: https://www.ij.co.za
Sales Range: $400-449.9 Million
Emp.: 2,000
Convenience Food Mfr & Distr
N.A.I.C.S.: 311412

National Brands Limited **(1)**
30 Sloane Street, Bryanston, 2021, Gau-
teng, South Africa
Tel.: (27) 117077200
Web Site: http://www.avi.com
Sales Range: $50-74.9 Million
Emp.: 300
Chips & Snacks Mfr & Distr
N.A.I.C.S.: 311919
Simon L. Crutchley (CEO)

National Brands Limited **(1)**
30 Sloane Street, Bryanston, 2021, Gau-
teng, South Africa
Tel.: (27) 117077200
Web Site: http://www.avi.com
Sales Range: $50-74.9 Million
Emp.: 300
Chips & Snacks Mfr & Distr
N.A.I.C.S.: 311919
Simon L. Crutchley (CEO)

National Brands Limited **(1)**
30 Sloane Street, Bryanston, 2021, Gau-
teng, South Africa
Tel.: (27) 117077200
Web Site: http://www.avi.com
Sales Range: $50-74.9 Million
Emp.: 300
Chips & Snacks Mfr & Distr
N.A.I.C.S.: 311919
Simon L. Crutchley (CEO)

National Brands Limited **(1)**
30 Sloane Street, Bryanston, 2021, Gau-
teng, South Africa
Tel.: (27) 117077200
Web Site: http://www.avi.com
Sales Range: $50-74.9 Million
Emp.: 300
Chips & Snacks Mfr & Distr
N.A.I.C.S.: 311919
Simon L. Crutchley (CEO)

AVI POLYMERS LIMITED

103 Nalanda Complex Premchand
Nagar Road Vastrapur, Ahmedabad,
380 015, India
Tel.: (91) 7048360390
Web Site:
https://www.avipolymers.com
Year Founded: 1993

539288—(BOM)
Rev.: $573,846
Assets: $695,099
Liabilities: $118,059
Net Worth: $577,040
Earnings: $46,424
Emp.: 4
Fiscal Year-end: 03/31/21
Polymer Product Mfr & Distr
N.A.I.C.S.: 325211
Mansukh Patel *(Chm & Mng Dir)*

AVI PRODUCTS INDIA LIMITED

110 Manish Ind Est No 4 Navghar
Rd, Vasai E Dist, Thane, 401 210,
Maharashtra, India
Tel.: (91) 2502390707
Web Site: http://www.aviphoto.in
523896—(BOM)
Rev.: $460,127
Assets: $654,515
Liabilities: $61,917
Net Worth: $592,598
Earnings: $15,812
Emp.: 6
Fiscal Year-end: 03/31/22
Photographic & Specialty Chemical
Mfr
N.A.I.C.S.: 325992
Avinash Dhirajlal Vora *(Chm & Mng
Dir)*

AVI-TECH HOLDINGS LIMITED

19A Serangoon North Avenue 5, Singapore, 554859, Singapore
Tel.: (65) 64826168
Web Site: https://www.avi-
tech.com.sg
1R6—(SES)
Rev.: $25,858,466
Assets: $44,009,633
Liabilities: $5,699,148
Net Worth: $38,310,485
Earnings: $2,414,969
Emp.: 144
Fiscal Year-end: 06/30/23
Semiconductor Circuit Mfr
N.A.I.C.S.: 334413
Alvin Tai Meng Lim *(COO)*

Subsidiaries:

Avi-Tech Electronics Pte. Ltd.   **(1)**
19A Serangoon North Avenue 5, Singapore,
554859, Singapore
Tel.: (65) 64826168
Web Site: https://www.avi-tech.com.sg
Printed Circuit Board Assembly Mfr
N.A.I.C.S.: 334418

Avi-Tech, Inc.   **(1)**
500 N Gulph Rd Ste 520, King of Prussia,
PA 19406
Tel.: (610) 450-4191
Web Site: https://www.avitechinc.com
Information Technology Services
N.A.I.C.S.: 541512

AVIA SOLUTIONS GROUP AB

Smolensko st 10, LT-03201, Vilnius,
Lithuania
Tel.: (370) 63100959
Web Site: http://www.aviasg.com
Rev.: $417,504,520
Assets: $182,556,260
Liabilities: $107,524,705
Net Worth: $75,031,555
Earnings: $5,983,311
Emp.: 2,297
Fiscal Year-end: 12/31/17
Integrated Fleet Management, Crew
Training, Charter Flight Management,
Aircraft Rental, Aircraft Maintenance
& Other Related Services
N.A.I.C.S.: 488190
Gediminas Ziemelis *(Founder & Chm)*

Subsidiaries:

Aviator Airport Alliance Europe
AB   **(1)**
Generatorgatan 11, Box 118, Stockholm-
Arlanda, 190 46, Stockholm, Sweden
Tel.: (46) 8 58 55 42 00
Web Site: http://www.aviator.eu
Airport Ground Handling Services
N.A.I.C.S.: 488119
Paul Nord *(CIO)*

Subsidiary (Non-US):

Aviator Denmark A/S   **(2)**
Vestvej 4, 2770, Kastrup, Denmark
Tel.: (45) 3247 4700
Web Site: http://www.aviator.eu
Emp.: 650
Airport Ground Handling Services
N.A.I.C.S.: 488119
Lars Wrist-Elkjaer *(Mng Dir)*

Roros Flyserice AS   **(2)**
ditt lokale Reisebyra, Roros, 7374, Norway
Tel.: (47) 72 41 39 00
Web Site: http://www.rorostravel.no
Aircraft Support & Ground Handling Services
N.A.I.C.S.: 488190

AVIAAM LEASING AB

Smolensko St 10, LT-03201, Vilnius,
Lithuania
Tel.: (370) 5 252 55 25
Web Site: http://www.aviaam.com
Sales Range: $1-9.9 Million
Aircraft Leasing & Management
N.A.I.C.S.: 532411

AVIAOK INTERNATIONAL LLC

Grecheskaya ulitsa 74, Taganrog,
347900, Rostov Oblast, Russia
Tel.: (7) 8634311770
Web Site: http://www.aviaok.com
Year Founded: 1998
Sales Range: $25-49.9 Million
Emp.: 200
Aviation Equipment Mfr
N.A.I.C.S.: 334511
Amerey Chmykhov *(Dir Gen)*

AVIAREPS AG

Josephspitalstrasse 15, 80331, Munich, Germany
Tel.: (49) 8955253373
Web Site: http://www.aviareps.de
Emp.: 100
Aviation & Tourism Agency
N.A.I.C.S.: 561510
Nico Ortmann *(Gen Mgr-Tourism)*

AVIAREPS MARKETING GARDEN LTD.

International Place Yotsuya Sanei-cho
11-16, Shinjuku-ku, Tokyo, 160-0008,
Japan
Tel.: (81) 3 3225 0008   JP
Web Site: http://www.aviareps.jp
Emp.: 780
Public Relations & Advertising Services
N.A.I.C.S.: 541820
Yoichi Hayase *(Gen Mgr)*

Subsidiaries:

AVIAREPS Marketing Garden   **(1)**
Dongwha Building 14F 58-7 Seosomun-
Dong, Joong-Gu, Seoul, 100-814, Korea
(South)
Tel.: (82) 2 777 8178
Web Site: http://www.aviareps.com
Emp.: 30
Public Relations & Advertising Services
N.A.I.C.S.: 541820
Irene Lee *(Country Mgr)*

AVIAREPS Marketing Garden
Ltd.   **(1)**
8F No 271 Sinyi Road, Section 2, Taipei,
100, Taiwan
Tel.: (886) 2 2377 5630

Web Site: http://www.aviareps.com
Public Relations & Advertising Services
N.A.I.C.S.: 541820

Marketing Garden Ltd.   **(1)**
Novel Plz Ste 1605 128 Nanjing Rd W,
Shanghai, 200003, China
Tel.: (86) 21 6359 1535
Web Site: http://www.aviareps.com
Public Relations & Advertising Services
N.A.I.C.S.: 541820
Jane Dong *(Mgr-Consumer Promos)*

AVIATION INDUSTRY CORPORATION OF CHINA

Building 19 No 5 Courtyard
Shuguang Xili, Chaoyang District,
Beijing, 100028, China
Tel.: (86) 1058356984
Web Site: http://www.avic.com
Year Founded: 2008
Sales Range: $50-74.9 Billion
Emp.: 450,000
Aircraft, Helicopter, Attack Aircraft &
General Aviation Aircraft Mfr
N.A.I.C.S.: 336411
Yuanxian Chen *(Exec VP)*

Subsidiaries:

AVIC Aviation High-Technology Co.,
Ltd.   **(1)**
No 1 Yonghe Road, Gangzha District, Nantong, 226011, Jiangsu, China
Tel.: (86) 51385516141
Web Site: http://www.tontec.net
Rev.: $624,234,223
Assets: $1,070,862,530
Liabilities: $279,114,007
Net Worth: $791,748,524
Earnings: $107,448,232
Emp.: 1,968
Fiscal Year-end: 12/31/2022
Machinery Tool Mfr & Whslr
N.A.I.C.S.: 333517
Jiang Bo *(Chm)*

AVIC Electromechanical Systems
Co., Ltd.   **(1)**
25F Building 16 Yard Jia District B, No 5
Shuguang West Lane Chaoyang District,
Beijing, 100028, China
Tel.: (86) 1058354876
Web Site: http://www.avicem.com
Rev.: $2,296,954,962
Assets: $5,346,057,649
Liabilities: $2,705,403,629
Net Worth: $2,640,654,019
Earnings: $194,731,442
Fiscal Year-end: 12/31/2021
Electro Mechanical Product Mfr
N.A.I.C.S.: 334419

AVIC Heavy Machinery Co., Ltd.   **(1)**
5F Building No 1 Duocai Aviation Headquarters, Shuanglong Airport Economic
Zone, Guiyang, 550008, Guizhou, China
Tel.: (86) 85188600765
Web Site: http://www.hm.avic.com
Rev.: $1,483,984,602
Assets: $2,960,287,865
Liabilities: $1,444,709,822
Net Worth: $1,515,578,042
Earnings: $168,728,297
Emp.: 9,000
Fiscal Year-end: 12/31/2022
Hydraulic Product Mfr
N.A.I.C.S.: 332912
Ran Xing *(Chm)*

AVIC Helicopter Co., Ltd.   **(1)**
7th Floor Building A No 14 Xiaoguandongli,
Chaoyang District, Beijing, 100029, China
Tel.: (86) 1058354758
Web Site: https://avicopter.avic.com
Rev.: $2,733,989,333
Assets: $3,888,272,152
Liabilities: $2,476,421,757
Net Worth: $1,411,850,396
Earnings: $54,344,768
Emp.: 6,200
Fiscal Year-end: 12/31/2022
Aircraft & Aircraft Parts Mfr
N.A.I.C.S.: 336411
Yan Lingxi *(Chm)*

AVIC Industry-Finance Holdings Co.,
Ltd.   **(1)**

20 layer AVIC building No 10 East Third
Ring Road, Chaoyang District, Beijing,
100022, China
Tel.: (86) 1065675160
Web Site: http://www.aviccapital.com
Rev.: $2,345,308,720
Assets: $70,129,146,987
Liabilities: $61,008,667,756
Net Worth: $9,120,479,231
Earnings: $40,178,791
Fiscal Year-end: 12/31/2023
Real Estate Investment Services
N.A.I.C.S.: 523999

AVIC Jonhon Optronic Technology
Co., Ltd.   **(1)**
No 10 Zhoushan Road, Luoyang, 471003,
China
Tel.: (86) 37964323017
Web Site: https://www.jonhon.cn
Rev.: $2,223,672,048
Assets: $4,466,226,492
Liabilities: $1,868,600,448
Net Worth: $2,597,626,044
Earnings: $381,485,052
Fiscal Year-end: 12/31/2022
Electrical Products Mfr
N.A.I.C.S.: 335999

Subsidiary (Domestic):

Avic forstar Science & technology
Co., Ltd.   **(2)**
No 71 Jinye Road high-tech District, Xi'an,
Shaanxi, China
Tel.: (86) 2968903600
Web Site: http://www.forstar.com.cn
Coaxial Connector Mfr
N.A.I.C.S.: 334417

AVIC Xian Aircraft Industry Group
Company Ltd.   **(1)**
No 1 Xifei Avenue, Yanliang District, Xi'an,
710089, Shaanxi, China
Tel.: (86) 2986847885
Web Site: http://www.aircraft_co.avic.com
Rev.: $5,287,468,212
Assets: $11,537,166,420
Liabilities: $9,271,923,336
Net Worth: $2,265,243,084
Earnings: $73,478,340
Fiscal Year-end: 12/31/2022
Aircraft Product Mfr
N.A.I.C.S.: 336412
Wu Zhipeng *(Chm)*

AviChina Industry & Technology Co.,
Ltd.   **(1)**
Building A No 14 Xiaoguandongli Anding-
menwai, Chaoyang District, Beijing, 100029,
China   **(56.04%)**
Tel.: (86) 1058354335
Web Site: http://www.avichina.com
Rev.: $11,730,849,944
Assets: $25,617,273,432
Liabilities: $13,425,231,699
Net Worth: $12,192,041,732
Earnings: $926,088,461
Emp.: 74,584
Fiscal Year-end: 12/31/2023
Aviation Products Development & Mfr
N.A.I.C.S.: 336411
Yuanxian Chen *(Chm)*

Cirrus Design Corporation   **(1)**
4515 Taylor Cir, Duluth, MN 55811
Tel.: (800) 921-2737
Web Site: http://www.cirrusaircraft.com
Aircraft Mfr
N.A.I.C.S.: 336411
Patrick Waddick *(Pres-Innovation & Ops)*

Continental Aerospace Technologies
Holding Limited   **(1)**
Unit A 20/F Tower 2 Admiralty Centre 18
Harcourt Road Admiralty, Hong Kong,
China (Hong Kong)
Tel.: (852) 29150143
Rev.: $212,353,163
Assets: $484,480,620
Liabilities: $125,072,018
Net Worth: $359,408,603
Earnings: $6,481,080
Emp.: 380
Fiscal Year-end: 12/31/2022
Holding Company
N.A.I.C.S.: 551112
Weixuan Lai *(Chm)*

Continental Motors, Inc.   **(1)**

Aviation Industry Corporation of China—(Continued)

2039 S Broad St, Mobile, AL 36615
Tel.: (251) 438-3411
Web Site:
http://www.genuinecontinental.aero
Sales Range: $125-149.9 Million
Emp.: 375
Manned & Unmanned Aircraft, New & Re-built General Aviation Piston Engines Mfr
N.A.I.C.S.: 336412
Dancyl Washington (Dir-Design Engrg)

Henniges Automotive, Inc. (1)
2750 High Meadow Cir, Auburn Hills, MI 48326
Tel.: (248) 340-4100
Web Site:
http://www.hennigesautomotive.com
Vehicle Sealing System & Anti-Vibration Product Mfr
N.A.I.C.S.: 339991
Larry Williams (Pres & CEO)

Plant (Non-US):

Henniges Automotive Inc. - Gomez Palacio (2)
Boulevard Gomez Palacio 265 3a Etapa Parque Industrial Lagunero, 35078, Gomez Palacio, Durango, Mexico
Tel.: (52) 871 729 3800
Web Site:
http://www.hennigesautomotive.com
Vehicle Sealing Systems & Anti-Vibration Products Mfr
N.A.I.C.S.: 339991

Henniges Automotive Inc. - Guadalajara (2)
Calle Paseo del Valle 4910 Fracciona-miento Guadalajara Tech Park, 45080, Za-popan, Jalisco, Mexico
Tel.: (52) 333 777 9000
Web Site:
http://www.hennigesautomotive.com
Vehicle Sealing Systems & Anti-Vibration Products Mfr
N.A.I.C.S.: 339991

Henniges Automotive Inc. - Torreon (2)
Alberto N Swain 150 Ciudad Industrial, 27016, Torreon, Coahuila, Mexico
Tel.: (52) 871 228 8003
Web Site:
http://www.hennigesautomotive.com
Vehicle Sealing Systems & Anti-Vibration Products Mfr
N.A.I.C.S.: 339991

Plant (Domestic):

Henniges Automotive, Inc. - Frederick (2)
1801 Flying Fortress, Frederick, OK 73542
Tel.: (580) 335-5503
Web Site:
http://www.hennigesautomotive.com
Fiberglass Products Mfr & Distr
N.A.I.C.S.: 313210

Henniges Automotive, Inc. - New Haven (2)
101 Danny Scott Dr, New Haven, MO 63068
Tel.: (573) 237-1300
Web Site:
http://www.hennigesautomotive.com
Vehicle Sealing Systems & Anti-Vibration Products Mfr
N.A.I.C.S.: 339991

Plant (Non-US):

Henniges Automotive, Inc. - Oakville (2)
4445 Fairview Street, Oakville, L7L 2A4, ON, Canada
Tel.: (289) 636-4461
Web Site:
http://www.hennigesautomotive.com
Vehicle Sealing Systems & Anti-Vibration Products Mfr
N.A.I.C.S.: 339991

Plant (Domestic):

Henniges Automotive, Inc. - Reidsville Plant (2)

226 Watlington Industrial Dr, Reidsville, NC 27320
Tel.: (336) 342-9300
Web Site:
http://www.hennigesautomotive.com
Vehicle Sealing Systems & Anti-Vibration Products Mfr
N.A.I.C.S.: 339991

Hilite Germany GmbH (1)
Am Schlossfeld 5, 97828, Marktheidenfeld, Germany
Tel.: (49) 9391 911 0
Web Site: http://www.hilite.com
Sales Range: $500-549.9 Million
Emp.: 1,700
Motor Vehicle Transmission & Power Train Part Mfr
N.A.I.C.S.: 336350
Karl Hammer (CEO)

Unit (Domestic):

Hilite Germany GmbH (2)
Weberstrasse 17, 72622, Nurtingen, Germany
Tel.: (49) 702292260
Web Site: http://www.hilite.com
Motor Vehicle Transmission & Power Train Part Mfr
N.A.I.C.S.: 336350

Unit (US):

Hilite International, Inc. - Whitehall (2)
2001 Peach St, Whitehall, MI 49461
Tel.: (231) 894-3200
Web Site: http://www.hilite.com
Motor Vehicle Transmission & Power Train Part Mfr
N.A.I.C.S.: 336350

Pacific Century Motors (1)
Beijing E-Town Economic Development Area, Beijing, China (51%)
Tel.: (86) 1067886732
Auto Parts & Components Mfr & Distr
N.A.I.C.S.: 336390
Tianbao Zhou (Pres)

Subsidiary (US):

Nexteer Automotive Group Ltd. (2)
3900 E Holland Rd, Saginaw, MI 48601-9494 (67%)
Tel.: (989) 757-5000
Web Site: http://www.nexteer.com
Rev.: $3,032,210,000
Assets: $3,305,741,000
Liabilities: $1,384,756,000
Net Worth: $1,920,985,000
Earnings: $122,303,000
Emp.: 12,100
Fiscal Year-end: 12/31/2020
Motor Vehicle Steering & Driveline System Mfr
N.A.I.C.S.: 336330
Doug Owenby (VP-Ops-North America)

AVIATION LINKS LTD.
2 Nirim Street, Tel Aviv, 6706037, Israel
Tel.: (972) 35209000 II
AVIA—(TAE)
Rev.: $60,855,973
Assets: $22,429,369
Liabilities: $14,902,663
Net Worth: $7,526,707
Earnings: $1,688,357
Fiscal Year-end: 12/31/22
Travel Tour Operator
N.A.I.C.S.: 561520
Amit Zeldman (CFO)

AVIC AIRBORNE SYSTEMS CO., LTD.
8F 9F Building 20 No 5A Shuguangxili, Chaoyang District, Beijing, 100028, China
Tel.: (86) 1058355270
Web Site:
http://www.aviconics.com.cn
600372—(SHG)
Rev.: $1,570,550,862
Assets: $3,987,706,521

Liabilities: $2,215,262,144
Net Worth: $1,772,444,377
Earnings: $122,416,529
Fiscal Year-end: 12/31/22
Aircraft Electronic Product Mfr
N.A.I.C.S.: 334511
Wang Jiangang (Pres)

AVIC INTERNATIONAL HOLD-INGS LIMITED
39/F AVIC Center Building No 1018 Huafu Road, Futian District, Shenzhen, 518031, China
Tel.: (86) 755 21246901 CN
Web Site: http://www.avic161.com
Year Founded: 1997
Rev.: $7,893,276,313
Assets: $14,726,159,820
Liabilities: $9,101,779,947
Net Worth: $5,624,379,873
Earnings: $51,105,312
Emp.: 61,874
Fiscal Year-end: 12/31/18
Holding Company; Investment Management Services
N.A.I.C.S.: 551112
Lei You (Sr Exec VP)

Subsidiaries:

AVIC International Beijing Company Limited (1)
Tenth - 15 Floors L1 Building AVIC Plaza 13 Ronghua South Road, Daxing, Beijing, 100176, China
Tel.: (86) 1087091000
Web Site: http://www.en.intl-bj.avic.com
International Trade Services
N.A.I.C.S.: 522299
Gong Jiayan (Chm)

AVIC Weihai Shipyard Co., Ltd. (1)
Zaobei Bay Economic Technical Development Zone, Weihai, 264207, Shandong, China
Tel.: (86) 6315386099
Web Site: http://www.wh-shipyard.com
Emp.: 4,500
Shipbuilding & Maintenance Services
N.A.I.C.S.: 336611

Align Aerospace Holdings, Inc. (1)
9401 De Soto Ave, Chatsworth, CA 91311
Tel.: (818) 727-7800
Web Site: http://www.alignaero.com
Holding Company; Aerospace & Defense Industry Hardware & Related Components, Distr
N.A.I.C.S.: 551112
Jerome De Truchis (CEO)

Subsidiary (Domestic):

Align Aerospace LLC (2)
9401 De Soto Ave, Chatsworth, CA 91311
Tel.: (818) 727-7800
Web Site: http://alignaero.com
Aerospace & Defense Industry Hardware & Related Components Distr
N.A.I.C.S.: 423860
Jerome De Truchis (Pres & CEO)

Subsidiary (Non-US):

Align Aerospace France SAS (3)
26 Allee du Clos des Charmes, 77090, Collegien, France
Tel.: (33) 160069650
Web Site: http://www.alignaero.com
Emp.: 50
Aerospace & Defense Industry Hardware & Related Components Distr
N.A.I.C.S.: 423860

China Merchants Property Operation & Service Co., Ltd. (1)
Tel.: (86) 75583244582
Web Site: http://www.cmpo1914.com
Rev.: $1,828,538,066
Assets: $2,501,225,775
Liabilities: $1,193,940,189
Net Worth: $1,307,285,586
Earnings: $83,328,958
Fiscal Year-end: 12/31/2022
Real Estate Development Services
N.A.I.C.S.: 531390

Lv Bin (Chm)

China National Aero-Technology Guangzhou Company Limited (1)
China Guangdong Guangzhou Poly International Plaza, No 1 Haizhuqu District Road East Pazhou South Tower 3 4 floor, Guangzhou, China
Tel.: (86) 2089899984
Web Site: http://www.intl-gz.avic.com
Electrical Equipment & Component Mfr
N.A.I.C.S.: 335999
Deng Kai (Chm)

Shennan Circuit Company Limited (1)
No 99 Qiaocheng East Road, Nanshan District, Shenzhen, 518053, China
Tel.: (86) 75586001818
Web Site: http://www.scc.com.cn
Printed Circuit Board Mfr
N.A.I.C.S.: 334412
You Lei (Chm)

Plant (Domestic):

Shennan Circuit Company Limited - Longgang Factory (2)
East Gaoqiao Industrial Zone Pingdi Street, Longgang District, Shenzhen, 518117, China
Tel.: (86) 755 89300000
Printed Circuit Board Mfr
N.A.I.C.S.: 334412

Shennan Circuits Co., Ltd. (1)
No 1639 Yanlong Avenue Pingdi Street, Longgang District, Shenzhen, 518117, China
Tel.: (86) 75589300000
Web Site: https://www.scc.com.cn
Medical Equipment Mfr
N.A.I.C.S.: 339112

Tianma Micro-electronics Co., Ltd. (1)
No 88 Daxin Road Tianma Building, Nan-shan District, Shenzhen, China
Tel.: (86) 75536351000
Web Site: http://www.en.tianma.com
Liquid Crystal Display Mfr
N.A.I.C.S.: 334419

Subsidiary (Non-US):

Tianma Europe GmbH (2)
Peter-Muller-Strasse 22, 40468, Dusseldorf, Germany
Tel.: (49) 21168818100
Web Site: http://www.tianma.eu
Liquid Crystal Display Mfr
N.A.I.C.S.: 334419

Subsidiary (US):

Tianma Microelectronics (USA) Inc. (2)
13949 Central Ave, Chino, CA 91710
Tel.: (909) 590-5833
Web Site: http://www.tianma-usa.com
Emp.: 15
Electronic Product Distr
N.A.I.C.S.: 423690
Eric Cheng (Gen Mgr)

Subsidiary (Non-US):

Tianma Microelectronics Korea Co., LTD (2)
158 8/F Mido Plaza Bldg, Bundang-Ku, Seongnam, Kyunggi-Do, Korea (South)
Tel.: (82) 31 717 8770 1
Emp.: 17
Electronic Product Distr
N.A.I.C.S.: 423690
Ben Yang (Gen Mgr)

AVIC JOY HOLDINGS (HK) LIMITED
Unit 1905A Level 19 International Commerce Centre 1 Austin Road West, Hong Kong, China (Hong Kong)
Tel.: (852) 29700220 HK
0260—(HKG)
Rev.: $406,598
Assets: $89,105,798
Liabilities: $167,052,540

Net Worth: ($77,946,743)
Earnings: ($6,305,385)
Emp.: 29
Fiscal Year-end: 12/31/21
Investment Holding Company
N.A.I.C.S.: 551112
Chang Chien *(Chm)*

AVICANNA, INC.
480 University Ave Suite 1502, MaRS Centre, Toronto, M5G 1V2, ON, Canada
Tel.: (647) 243-5283
Web Site: https://www.avicanna.com
AVCN—(TSX)
Rev.: $1,228,227
Assets: $23,590,092
Liabilities: $12,708,710
Net Worth: $10,881,382
Earnings: ($25,707,051)
Fiscal Year-end: 12/31/20
Pharmaceutical Product Mfr & Distr
N.A.I.C.S.: 325412
Aras Azadian *(Co-Founder & CEO)*

AVICOLA BRASOV S.A.
Str Cucului Nr 5, 500484, Brasov, Romania
Tel.: (40) 268257741
Web Site:
   http://www.avicolabrasov.ro
Sales Range: $25-49.9 Million
Emp.: 490
Poultry Raising & Processing
N.A.I.C.S.: 112340

AVICOLA SLOBOZIA SA
Soseaua Constantei Km 5-6, Lal-omita, Slobozia, Romania
Tel.: (40) 243 221200
Web Site: http://www.avicola-slobozia.ro
Sales Range: $25-49.9 Million
Emp.: 378
Poultry Farming Services
N.A.I.C.S.: 112340
Stanoiu Dumitru *(Gen Mgr)*

AVICOR CONSTRUCTION
5325 Jean Talcon East St Suite 256, Saint Leonard, H1S 1L4, QC, Canada
Tel.: (514) 744-1700
Web Site: http://www.avicor.ca
Rev.: $20,372,500
Emp.: 13
General Building Contracting Services
N.A.I.C.S.: 236220
Rode Callegari *(Pres)*

AVID LIFE MEDIA INC.
20 Eglinton Ave Ste 1200, Toronto, M4R 1K8, ON, Canada
Tel.: (416) 480-2334   ON
Web Site: https://www.rubylife.com
Sales Range: $25-49.9 Million
Emp.: 90
Holding Company; Dating & Other Social Websites Owner & Operator
N.A.I.C.S.: 551112
Evan Black *(VP-Sls-Ashley Madison)*

Subsidiaries:

Avid Dating Life Inc.   **(1)**
20 Eglinton Avenue Suite 1200, Toronto, M4R 1K8, ON, Canada
Tel.: (416) 480-2334
Web Site: http://www.ashleymadison.com
Adult Dating Website Operator
N.A.I.C.S.: 513140
Evan Black *(VP-Sls)*

Cougar Life Inc.   **(1)**
20 Eglinton Avenue Suite 1200, Toronto, M4R 1K8, ON, Canada
Tel.: (416) 480-2334
Web Site: http://www.cougarlife.com

Adult Dating Website Operator
N.A.I.C.S.: 513140

AVID PROPERTY GROUP
Level 35 259 George St, Sydney, NSW, Australia
Tel.: (61) 2 8316 7700
Web Site: http://www.avid.com.au
Real Estate Property Development
N.A.I.C.S.: 531390
Cameron Holt *(CEO)*

Subsidiaries:

Villa World Limited   **(1)**
Level 1 Oracle West 19 Elizabeth Avenue, PO Box 1899, Broadbeach, 4218, QLD, Australia
Tel.: (61) 755888888
Web Site: http://www.villaworld.com.au
Rev.: $344,643,311
Assets: $458,864,120
Liabilities: $217,130,757
Net Worth: $241,733,363
Earnings: $34,055,901
Fiscal Year-end: 06/30/2018
Property Investment & Development
N.A.I.C.S.: 523940
Bradley Scale *(Gen Counsel & Sec)*

Subsidiary (Domestic):

GEO Property Group Limited   **(2)**
600 Victoria St, Richmond, 3121, Victoria, Australia
Tel.: (61) 3 94278332
Real Estate Agency Services
N.A.I.C.S.: 531210

Villa World (Vic) Pty Ltd   **(2)**
99 Coventry St, Southbank, 3006, VIC, Australia
Tel.: (61) 396937800
Housing Construction Services
N.A.I.C.S.: 236117
Robin Valmadre *(Mgr-Sls)*

Villa World Developments Pty Ltd   **(2)**
Level 1 Oracle West 19 Elizabeth Avenue, Broadbeach, 4218, QLD, Australia **(100%)**
Tel.: (61) 755888888
Web Site: http://www.villaworld.com.au
Real Estate Property Development Services
N.A.I.C.S.: 531390
Guy Farrands *(Mng Dir)*

Villa World Group   **(2)**
Level 1 Oracle West 19 Elizabeth Ave, Broadbeach, Bundall, 4218, QLD, Australia
Tel.: (61) 7 5588 8888
Web Site: http://www.villaworldgroup.com.au
Emp.: 60
Investment Management Service
N.A.I.C.S.: 541618
Craig Treasure *(Mng Dir)*

Villa World Homes   **(2)**
Level 1 Oracle W 19 Elizabeth Ave, Broadbeach, 4218, QLD, Australia
Tel.: (61) 755888888
Web Site: http://www.villaworld.com.au
Sales Range: $25-49.9 Million
Emp.: 80
Real Estate Property Development Services
N.A.I.C.S.: 531390

AVIDIAN GOLD CORP.
110 Yonge St Suite 1601, Toronto, M5C 1T4, ON, Canada
Tel.: (905) 741-5458
Web Site:
   https://www.avidiangold.com
Year Founded: 2011
AVG—(TSXV)
Assets: $5,517,069
Liabilities: $3,207,247
Net Worth: $2,309,822
Earnings: ($5,831,666)
Fiscal Year-end: 06/30/21
Gold Exploration & Mining Services
N.A.I.C.S.: 212220
John Schaff *(VP-Exploration)*

AVIGNON CAPITAL LIMITED

28 Margaret Street, London, W1W 8RZ, United Kingdom
Tel.: (44) 207 299 7850   UK
Web Site:
   http://www.avignoncapital.com
Year Founded: 2011
Commercial Property Investment Management Services
N.A.I.C.S.: 531312
Eric Mounier *(CEO)*

AVILEN, INC.
Akihabara First Square 9F 2-3-3 Ni-honbashi Bakurocho, Chuo-ku, To-kyo, 103-0002, Japan
Tel.: (81) 358234694
Web Site: https://avilen.co.jp
Year Founded: 2018
5591—(TKS)
Emp.: 46
Software Development Services
N.A.I.C.S.: 541511
Takefumi Yoshikawa *(CTO)*

AVILLION BERHAD
Unit 8E Level 8 Wisma YPR No 1 Lorong Kapar, Off Jalan Syed Putra, 58000, Kuala Lumpur, Malaysia
Tel.: (60) 322620100
Web Site:
   https://www.avillionberhad.com
AVI—(KLS)
Rev.: $7,938,563
Assets: $89,175,240
Liabilities: $36,298,350
Net Worth: $52,876,890
Earnings: ($2,252,745)
Fiscal Year-end: 03/31/22
Travel Services
N.A.I.C.S.: 561520
Angeline Set Fui Chong *(CFO)*

Subsidiaries:

Admiral Cove Development Sdn Bhd   **(1)**
Unit 8E Level 8 Wisma YPR No 1 Lorong Kapar Syed Putra Off Jalan, 58000, Kuala Lumpur, Malaysia
Tel.: (60) 322620100
Web Site: http://www.admiralcove.com.my
Hotel Operator
N.A.I.C.S.: 721110

Subsidiary (Domestic):

Admiral Marina Berhad   **(2)**
Batu 5 1/2 Jalan Pantai, 71050, Port Dick-son, Negeri Sembilan, Malaysia
Tel.: (60) 66482514
Web Site: http://www.admiralmarina.com.my
Hotel Operator
N.A.I.C.S.: 721110

Avi Spa Sdn Bhd   **(1)**
Avillion Port Dickson 3rd Mile Jalan Pantai, 71000, Port Dickson, Negeri Sembilan, Malaysia
Tel.: (60) 66475740
Web Site: http://www.avispa.com.my
Spa Services
N.A.I.C.S.: 812112

Vacation Asia (HK) Limited   **(1)**
Suite 905 9/F Tower 6 China Hong Kong City 33 Canton Road, Tsimshatsui, Kow-loon, China (Hong Kong)
Tel.: (852) 27312038
Web Site: http://www.vahk.com.hk
Hotel Operator
N.A.I.C.S.: 721110

AVINCO LTD.
Adelaide House 7 Haddington Ter Dun Laoghaire, Dublin, Ireland
Tel.: (353) 1 6637440
Web Site: http://www.avinco.net
Year Founded: 2003
Sales Range: $10-24.9 Million
Aircraft Operating Services
N.A.I.C.S.: 488119
Francois Gautier *(Founder & CEO)*

AVINGTRANS PLC
Chatteris Business Park, Chatteris, PE16 6SA, Cambridgeshire, United Kingdom
Tel.: (44) 1354692391
Web Site:
   https://www.avingtrans.plc.uk
AVG—(LSE)
Rev.: $133,757,144
Assets: $193,628,522
Liabilities: $59,264,478
Net Worth: $134,364,044
Earnings: $36,929,984
Emp.: 704
Fiscal Year-end: 05/31/21
All Other Miscellaneous Fabricated Metal Product Manufacturing
N.A.I.C.S.: 332999
Steve McQuillan *(CEO)*

Subsidiaries:

Booth Industries Ltd.   **(1)**
Nelson Street, PO Box 50, Bolton, BL3 2AP, Greater Manchester, United Kingdom
Tel.: (44) 120 436 6333
Web Site: https://www.booth-industries.co.uk
Sales Range: $25-49.9 Million
Emp.: 140
Secure Doors, Windows & Wall Systems Mfr
N.A.I.C.S.: 236210

C & H Precision Limited   **(1)**
Precision House Derby Road Industrial Es-tate, Sandiacre, Nottingham, NG10 5HU, Nottinghamshire, United Kingdom
Tel.: (44) 115 939 4707
Web Site: https://www.chprecision.co.uk
Sales Range: $25-49.9 Million
Emp.: 100
Machine Tools Mfr
N.A.I.C.S.: 333515
Philip Akrill *(Gen Mgr)*

Composite Products Limited   **(1)**
16 Top Angel, Buckingham, MK18 1TH, United Kingdom
Tel.: (44) 128 082 4498
Web Site: https://www.composite-products.co.uk
Programmable Material Cutting Table Mfr
N.A.I.C.S.: 333515

Crown UK Limited   **(1)**
Old Mill Road Portishead, Bristol, BS20 7BX, United Kingdom
Tel.: (44) 127 581 8008
Web Site: https://www.crown-international.co.uk
Sales Range: $25-49.9 Million
Emp.: 7
Fabrication Units Mfr
N.A.I.C.S.: 541420
Mark Stacey *(Mng Dir)*

Hayward Tyler Group Plc   **(1)**
1 Kimpton Road, Luton, LU1 3LD, United Kingdom
Tel.: (44) 1582 731144
Web Site: http://www.haywardtyler.com
Emp.: 354
Electric Motors & Pumps Designer & Mfr
N.A.I.C.S.: 333996
Savio Dias *(Mgr-Quality Assurance)*

Subsidiary (Domestic):

Hayward Tyler Group Limited   **(2)**
1 Kimpton Road, Luton, LU1 3LD, United Kingdom
Tel.: (44) 1582 731144
Web Site: http://www.haywardtyler.com
Electric Motor & Pumps Mfr
N.A.I.C.S.: 333996

Subsidiary (US):

Energy Steel and Supply Company   **(3)**
3123 John Conley Dr, Lapeer, MI 48446
Tel.: (810) 538-4990
Web Site: http://www.energysteel.com
Emp.: 65
Pump & Pumping Equipment Mfr
N.A.I.C.S.: 333914

Avingtrans plc—(Continued)

Division (Domestic):

Hayward Tyler Fluid Handling Ltd **(3)**
1 Kimpton Road, Luton, LU1 3LD, United Kingdom
Tel.: (44) 1582 731144
Web Site: http://www.haywardtyler.com
Electric Motor & Pumps Mfr
N.A.I.C.S.: 333996

Subsidiary (US):

Hayward Tyler Inc. **(3)**
480 Roosevelt Hwy, Colchester, VT 05446
Tel.: (802) 655-4444
Web Site: http://www.haywardtyler.com
Motor & Pumps Mfr
N.A.I.C.S.: 333996
Michael C. Turmelle (Pres & Mng Dir)

Subsidiary (Non-US):

Hayward Tyler India Private Limited **(2)**
509-510 Charmwood Plaza EROS Garden Surajkund Road, Faridabad, 121009, Haryana, India
Tel.: (91) 129 4118 744
Web Site: http://www.haywardtyler.com
Industrial Pumps & Motors Mfr
N.A.I.C.S.: 333996
Ratish Balachandran (Gen Mgr)

Hayward Tyler Pumps (Kunshan) Co., Ltd **(2)**
Factory B3 No 111 Nan Song Road, Yu Shan Town, Kunshan, 215300, Jiangsu, China
Tel.: (86) 5125 790 6257
Web Site: http://haywardtyler.com
Electric Motor & Pumps Designer & Mfr
N.A.I.C.S.: 333996

Hayward Tyler Holdings Limited **(1)**
1 Kimpton Road, Luton, LU1 3LD, United Kingdom
Tel.: (44) 158 273 1144
Web Site: https://www.haywardtyler.com
Motor Pump Mfr
N.A.I.C.S.: 333996

Maloney Metalcraft Ltd. **(1)**
Westgate, Aldridge, Walsall, WS9 8EX, West Midlands, United Kingdom
Tel.: (44) 192 245 0200
Web Site: https://www.maloney-metalcraft.com
Sales Range: $10-24.9 Million
Emp.: 85
Mfr of Equipment for Oil & Natural Gas Production
N.A.I.C.S.: 423830
Austin Adams (Mng Dir)

Scientific Magnetics Limited **(1)**
7 Suffolk Way, Abingdon, OX14 5JX, United Kingdom
Tel.: (44) 123 553 5000
Web Site: https://www.scientificmagnetics.co.uk
Bespoke Superconducting Magnet System Mfr
N.A.I.C.S.: 334610
Clint Gouveia (Mng Dir)

Stainless Metalcraft (Chatteris) Limited **(1)**
Chatteris Business Park, Chatteris, PE16 6SA, Cambridgeshire, United Kingdom
Tel.: (44) 135 469 2391
Web Site: https://www.metalcraft.co.uk
Bespoke Mfr
N.A.I.C.S.: 337212
Stephen Buttriss (Sls Mgr)

Tecmag, Inc. **(1)**
10161 Harwin Dr Ste 150, Houston, TX 77036
Tel.: (713) 667-8747
Web Site: https://tecmag.com
Electronic Components, Nec, Nsk
N.A.I.C.S.: 334419

AVINO SILVER & GOLD MINES LTD.

Suite 900 570 Granville Street, Vancouver, V6C 3P1, BC, Canada
Tel.: (604) 682-3701 **BC**
Web Site: https://www.avino.com
Year Founded: 1968
ASM—(NYSEAMEX)
Rev.: $44,187,000
Assets: $121,196,000
Liabilities: $23,175,000
Net Worth: $98,021,000
Earnings: $3,096,000
Emp.: 239
Fiscal Year-end: 12/31/22
Silver & Gold Exploration & Mining
N.A.I.C.S.: 212220
Gary R. Robertson (Chm)

AVINOR AS
Oslo Atrium Dronning Eufemias Gate 6, 0191, Oslo, Norway
Tel.: (47) 67030000 **NO**
Web Site: http://www.avinor.no
Year Founded: 2003
Rev.: $1,338,209,460
Assets: $5,014,617,810
Liabilities: $3,279,687,360
Net Worth: $1,734,930,450
Earnings: $79,734,810
Emp.: 3,012
Fiscal Year-end: 12/31/19
Airport Operator
N.A.I.C.S.: 488119
Petter Johannessen (CFO)

Subsidiaries:

Avinor Flysikring AS **(1)**
Bringeland, Bygstad, 6977, Sogn Og Fjordane, Norway
Tel.: (47) 67031930
Air Navigation Services
N.A.I.C.S.: 488330

Oslo Lufthavn AS **(1)**
PO Box 100, 2061, Gardermoen, Norway
Tel.: (47) 64812000
Web Site: http://www.osло.no
Sales Range: $125-149.9 Million
Emp.: 500
Other Airport Operations
N.A.I.C.S.: 488119
Nick Nilsen (CEO)

Sola Hotel Eiendom AS **(1)**
Dronning Eufemias gate 6, 0191, Oslo, Norway
Tel.: (47) 67033340
Real Estate Consulting Service
N.A.I.C.S.: 531210

AVIO S.P.A.
Via Latina snc SP 600 Ariana Km 5 2, 00034, Colleferro, RM, Italy
Tel.: (39) 0697285111 **IT**
Web Site: https://www.avio.com
Year Founded: 2015
AVIO—(ITA)
Rev.: $402,533,200
Assets: $1,393,189,279
Liabilities: $1,064,486,454
Net Worth: $328,702,826
Earnings: $1,423,885
Emp.: 1,119
Fiscal Year-end: 12/31/22
Missile & Space Vehicle Propulsion Systems & Components Designer & Mfr
N.A.I.C.S.: 336415
Roberto Italia (Chm)

Subsidiaries:

Temis S.R.L. **(1)**
Corbetta Via G Donizetti 20, Corbetta, 20011, Milan, MI, Italy
Tel.: (39) 0290380812
Web Site: https://temissrl.com
Aerospace Product Mfr & Distr
N.A.I.C.S.: 336413

AVIOANE CRAIOVA S.A.

10 Aviatorilor Street, 207280, Ghercesti, Dolj, Romania
Tel.: (40) 251402000 **RO**
Web Site: https://www.acv.ro
Year Founded: 1972
AVIO—(BUC)
Rev.: $20,515,849
Assets: $60,681,402
Liabilities: $50,094,893
Net Worth: $10,586,509
Earnings: $24,559
Emp.: 273
Fiscal Year-end: 12/31/23
Military Aircraft & Related Machinery Mfr
N.A.I.C.S.: 336411
Cristiana Motataianu (Deputy Dir)

AVIRA RESOURCES LTD.
Level 3 88 William Street, Perth, 6000, WA, Australia
Tel.: (61) 894632463
Web Site: https://www.aviraresourcesltd.com
AVW—(ASX)
Rev.: $23,797
Assets: $1,198,808
Liabilities: $2,666
Net Worth: $1,196,142
Earnings: ($475,638)
Fiscal Year-end: 06/30/24
Gold Exploration & Mining Services
N.A.I.C.S.: 212220
David Deloub (Exec Dir)

AVIS FINANCIAL CORP.
Talstrasse 20, Zurich, 8001, Switzerland
Tel.: (41) 445007171 **NV**
AVFP—(OTCIQ)
Sales Range: Less than $1 Million
Business Development Services
N.A.I.C.S.: 541613

AVISA DIAGNOSTICS INC.
36 Toronto Street Suite 1000, Toronto, M5C 2C5, ON, Canada
Tel.: (416) 848-7744 **ON**
Web Site: http://www.mukubaresources.com
Year Founded: 1984
MKU—(TSXV)
Rev.: $277,830
Assets: $122,155
Liabilities: $647,940
Net Worth: ($525,785)
Earnings: ($715,762)
Emp.: 3
Fiscal Year-end: 12/31/20
Base Metal, Copper, Cobalt, Gold, Uranium, Nickel, Lead, Zinc, Iron & Manganese Mining Services
N.A.I.C.S.: 212290
Daniel Gray Crandall (CEO & CFO)

AVISION INC.
No 20 Creation Rd 1 Hsinchu Science Park, Hsin-chu, 30077, Taiwan
Tel.: (886) 35782388
Web Site: https://www.avision.com
2380—(TAI)
Rev.: $64,265,964
Assets: $81,265,114
Liabilities: $55,147,289
Net Worth: $26,117,825
Earnings: ($13,414,565)
Emp.: 239
Fiscal Year-end: 12/31/23
Computer Equipments Mfr & Distr
N.A.I.C.S.: 334118
Eric Kuo (Mgr)

Subsidiaries:

Avision (Suzhou) Co., Ltd. **(1)**
No 9 Suhong West Road Suzhou Industrial Park, Suzhou, 215021, Jiangsu, China
Tel.: (86) 51262565888

Office Equipment Distr
N.A.I.C.S.: 423420

Avision Brasil Ltda. **(1)**
Rua Forida 1670 - CJ 22 Berrini, Sao Paulo, Brazil
Tel.: (55) 1127376558
Web Site: https://www.avision.com.br
Scanner Mfr & Distr
N.A.I.C.S.: 334510

Avision Europe GmbH **(1)**
Siemensring 91, 47877, Willich, Germany
Tel.: (49) 2154888500
Web Site: https://avision-europe.co.uk
Sales Range: $50-74.9 Million
Emp.: 15
Scanners Sales & Support Services
N.A.I.C.S.: 423450

Avision Labs., Inc. **(1)**
6815 Mowry Ave, Newark, CA 94560
Tel.: (510) 739-2369
Sales Range: $25-49.9 Million
Emp.: 25
Office Equipment Distr
N.A.I.C.S.: 423420

AVISON YOUNG (CANADA) INC.
18 York Street Suite 400, Toronto, M5J 2T8, ON, Canada
Tel.: (416) 955-0000 **Ca**
Web Site: http://www.avisonyoung.com
Year Founded: 1978
Sales Range: $200-249.9 Million
Emp.: 800
Real Estate Brokerage Services
N.A.I.C.S.: 531210
Mark E. Rose (Chm, CEO & Principal)

Subsidiaries:

Aguer Havelock Associates, Inc. **(1)**
2485 Natomas Park Dr Ste 150, Sacramento, CA 95833
Tel.: (916) 563-7555
Real Estate Manangement Services
N.A.I.C.S.: 531390

Avison Young (USA) Inc. **(1)**
120 N LaSalle Ste 850, Chicago, IL 60602
Tel.: (312) 957-7600
Web Site: http://www.avisonyoung.com
Real Estate Brokerage Services
N.A.I.C.S.: 531210
Earl E. Webb (Pres-Ops)

Branch (Domestic):

Avison Young (USA) Inc. - Los Angeles, North **(2)**
6711 Forest Lawn Dr, Los Angeles, CA 90068
Tel.: (323) 851-6666
Web Site: http://www.avisonyoung.com
Sales Range: $50-74.9 Million
Emp.: 10
Real Estate Brokerage Services
N.A.I.C.S.: 531210
Christopher Bonbright (Principal)

Avison Young (USA) Inc. - New Jersey **(2)**
1120 Headquarters Plz N Tower 8th Fl, Morristown, NJ 07960
Tel.: (973) 898-6360
Web Site: http://www.avisonyoung.us
Sales Range: $50-74.9 Million
Emp.: 53
Real Estate Brokerage & Construction Management Services
N.A.I.C.S.: 531210
Christopher K. Richter (Principal & Sr VP-Dev)

Avison Young (USA) Inc. - Raleigh-Durham **(2)**
1511 Sunday Dr Ste 200, Raleigh, NC 27607
Tel.: (919) 785-3434
Web Site: http://www.avisonyoung.com
Sales Range: $50-74.9 Million
Emp.: 61
Commercial Real Estate Brokerage Services

N.A.I.C.S.: 531210
Gina Ide *(Principal & Sr VP-Property Mgmt)*

Avison Young (USA) Inc. - South Florida-Fort Lauderdale (2)
515 E Las Olas Blvd Ste 400, Fort Lauderdale, FL 33301
Tel.: (954) 903-1800
Web Site: http://www.avisonyoung.com
Sales Range: $25-49.9 Million
Emp.: 35
Commercial Real Estate Brokerage, Property Management & Asset Solution Services
N.A.I.C.S.: 531210
S. Pike Rowley *(Mng Dir & Principal)*

Avison Young (USA) Inc. - Tampa (2)
1715 N Westshore Blvd Ste 130, Tampa, FL 33607
Tel.: (813) 288-1800
Web Site: http://www.lwccommercial.com
Sales Range: $50-74.9 Million
Emp.: 19
Commercial Real Estate Services
N.A.I.C.S.: 531390
Clay Witherspoon *(Mng Dir)*

Commercial Texas, LLC (1)
515 Congress Ave Ste 1500, Austin, TX 78701
Tel.: (512) 474-2411
Real Estate Manangement Services
N.A.I.C.S.: 531390

R7 Real Estate Inc. (1)
555 S Flower St Ste 3200, Los Angeles, CA 90071
Tel.: (213) 300-8776
Web Site: http://www.r7re.com
Real Estate Manangement Services
N.A.I.C.S.: 531390
Stan Yoshihara *(Chief Visionary Officer)*

Roy et Tremblay Inc. (1)
445 boul Sainte-Foy bureau 10445 boul Sainte-Foy bureau 10, Longueuil, J4J 1X9, QC, Canada
Tel.: (450) 646-2111
Engineeering Services
N.A.I.C.S.: 541330

The Eidson Group, LLC (1)
3525 Piedmont Rd NE 6 Piedmont Ctr Ste 310, Atlanta, GA 30305
Tel.: (404) 262-0996
Web Site: http://www.eidsongroup.com
Real Estate Manangement Services
N.A.I.C.S.: 531390
Doug Eidson *(Principal)*

The Remington Group Inc (1)
351 E Conestoga Rd, Wayne, PA 19087
Tel.: (610) 995-9330
Web Site: http://www.remingtongroup.com
Emp.: 10
Business Consulting Services
N.A.I.C.S.: 541611
William F. Conner *(Pres)*

AVISTA OIL AG
Bahnhofstrasse 82, 31311, Uetze, Germany
Tel.: (49) 5177850
Web Site: http://www.avista-oil.de
Year Founded: 1951
Sales Range: $50-74.9 Million
Emp.: 700
Used Oil Recycling Services
N.A.I.C.S.: 562119
Marc Verfurth *(Chm-Exec Bd & CEO)*

Subsidiaries:

Avista Oil Danmark A/S (1)
Juelsmindevej 6, 4400, Kalundborg, Denmark
Tel.: (45) 59 56 56 44
Web Site: http://www.avista-oil.dk
Oil Recycling Services
N.A.I.C.S.: 562119
Claus Hauge Hansen *(Mgr-Ops)*

RECUP-OIL b.v.b.a. (1)
Meulebekestraat 145, 8770, Ingelmunster, Belgium
Tel.: (32) 51 487 547
Waste Oil Collection Services
N.A.I.C.S.: 562119

Refining & Trading Holland N.V. (1)
Oosterwierum 25, Delfzijl, 9936 HJ, Farmsum, Netherlands
Tel.: (31) 596 67 33 00
Web Site: http://www.northrefinery.nl
Oil Recycling Services
N.A.I.C.S.: 562119
H. P. Yntema *(Dir-Ops)*

Universal Environmental Services, LLC (1)
411 Dividend Dr, Peachtree City, GA 30269
Tel.: (770) 486-8816
Web Site: http://www.universalservices.com
Sales Range: $10-24.9 Million
Waste Material Recycling Services
N.A.I.C.S.: 325211
Brian Sager *(District Mgr)*

Wubben Handelsmij B.V. (1)
Tussenriemer 21, 4704 RT, Roosendaal, Netherlands
Tel.: (31) 165 555888
Web Site: http://www.wubben.nl
Waste Oil Collection Services
N.A.I.C.S.: 562119

AVIT LTD.
15th Floor, Block A, Phase 1, Shenzhen International Innovation Valley, Xingke 1st Street, Shenzhen, 518055, China
Tel.: (86) 7553575018   CN
Web Site: https://www.avit.com.cn
Year Founded: 2000
300264—(CHIN)
Rev.: $18,402,000
Assets: $51,953,873
Liabilities: $40,164,746
Net Worth: $11,789,127
Earnings: ($9,383,028)
Fiscal Year-end: 12/31/23
Cable Digital Television Software & Terminal Hardware Products Mfr & Distr
N.A.I.C.S.: 513210
Kunjiang Chen *(Chm)*

AVIVA INDUSTRIES LIMITED
C-3/1001 Anushruti Tower Near Jain Temple Opp New York Tower, Nr Thaltej Cross Road S G Highway, Ahmedabad, 380 054, India
Tel.: (91) 7926856815
Web Site:
https://www.avivaindustries.com
Year Founded: 1984
512109—(BOM)
Rev.: $12,968
Assets: $659,978
Liabilities: $53,590
Net Worth: $606,388
Earnings: $437
Fiscal Year-end: 03/31/21
Electrical Product Mfr & Whslr
N.A.I.C.S.: 335999
Bharvinbhai Sureshbhai Patel *(Chm & Mng Dir)*

AVIVA PLC
80 Fenchurch Street, London, EC3M 4AE, United Kingdom
Tel.: (44) 2072832000   UK
Web Site: https://www.aviva.com
Year Founded: 1998
AIVAF—(OTCIQ)
Rev.: $45,054,580,480
Assets: $486,707,319,280
Liabilities: $460,294,234,400
Net Worth: $26,413,084,880
Earnings: $2,764,317,920
Emp.: 22,062
Fiscal Year-end: 12/31/21
Financial Investment Services
N.A.I.C.S.: 524210
Kristine Cooper *(Gen Counsel & Sec)*

Subsidiaries:

AssureWeb Limited (1)
Eagle Tower, Montpellier Dr, Cheltenham,

GL50 1TA, Glos, United Kingdom
Tel.: (44) 8704584561
Web Site: http://www.assureweb.co.uk
Sales Range: $25-49.9 Million
Emp.: 100
Financial Software Services
N.A.I.C.S.: 334610
Andrew Simon *(CEO)*

Aviva Annuity UK Limited (1)
2 Rougier Street, York, YO90 1UU, United Kingdom
Tel.: (44) 1904 628982
Insurance Management Services
N.A.I.C.S.: 524298

Aviva Canada Inc. (1)
10 Aviva Way Suite 100, Markham, L6G 0G1, ON, Canada   (100%)
Tel.: (416) 288-1800
Web Site: https://www.aviva.ca
Sales Range: $1-4.9 Billion
Emp.: 3,100
Insurance Provider
N.A.I.C.S.: 524128
Colin Simpson *(CFO)*

Subsidiary (Domestic):

Aviva Insurance Company of Canada (2)
2206 Eglinton Ave E, Scarborough, M1L 4S8, ON, Canada
Tel.: (416) 288-1800
Web Site: http://www.avivacanada.com
Property & Casualty Insurance Services
N.A.I.C.S.: 524126

Pilot Insurance Company (2)
191 Bloor St E Unit 11, Oshawa, L1H 3M3, ON, Canada
Tel.: (905) 723-1103
Web Site: http://www.pilot.ca
Sales Range: $50-74.9 Million
Emp.: 13
Insurance Management Services
N.A.I.C.S.: 524298

Scottish & York Insurance Co. Limited (2)
2206 Eglinton Ave E Ste 160, Scarborough, M1L 4S8, ON, Canada
Tel.: (416) 288-1800
Insurance Agency Services
N.A.I.C.S.: 524210

Aviva Equity Release UK Limited (1)
Po Box No 520 Surrey Street, Norwich, NR1 3WG, United Kingdom
Tel.: (44) 1603 622 200
Mortgage Brokerage Services
N.A.I.C.S.: 522310

Aviva Group Holdings Limited (1)
8 Surrey Street, Norwich, NR1 3ST, United Kingdom
Tel.: (44) 16 0362 2200
Investment Management Service
N.A.I.C.S.: 523999

Subsidiary (Domestic):

Aviva Central Services UK Limited (2)
8 Surrey Street, Norwich, NR1 3ST, Norfolk, United Kingdom
Tel.: (44) 1603 622200
Web Site: http://www.aviva.co.uk
Insurance Agency Services
N.A.I.C.S.: 524210

Aviva Group Ireland plc (1)
One Park Place Hatch Street, Dublin, 2, Ireland
Tel.: (353) 16078000
Sales Range: $1-4.9 Billion
Emp.: 177
Holding Company; Insurance Products & Services
N.A.I.C.S.: 551112
John Quinlan *(CEO)*

Subsidiary (Domestic):

Aviva Insurance Europe SE (2)
One Park Place Hatch Street, Dublin, 2, Ireland   (100%)
Tel.: (353) 18988000
Web Site: http://www.aviva.ie

Sales Range: $400-449.9 Million
Title, Property & Casualty Insurance Products & Services
N.A.I.C.S.: 524126

Aviva Life & Pensions Ireland Ltd. (2)
Building 12 Cherrywood Business Park, Loughlinstown, Dublin, D18 W2P5, Ireland   (100%)
Tel.: (353) 1 898 7950
Web Site: https://www.aviva.ie
Sales Range: $300-349.9 Million
Life Insurance & Pension Provider
N.A.I.C.S.: 524128

Aviva Health UK Limited (1)
8 Surrey Street, PO Box 520, Norwich, NR1 3NG, United Kingdom
Tel.: (44) 8001455744
Insurance Services
N.A.I.C.S.: 524298

Aviva Insurance Ireland Designated Activity Company (1)
One Park Place Hatch Street, Dublin, D02 E651, Ireland
Tel.: (353) 18332211
Web Site: https://www.aviva.ie
Insurance Services
N.A.I.C.S.: 524298

Aviva Insurance Limited (1)
Pitheavlis, Perth, PH2 0NH, United Kingdom
Tel.: (44) 3450307041
Web Site: https://www.aviva.co.uk
Insurance Services
N.A.I.C.S.: 524298

Aviva Insurance UK Limited (1)
8 Surrey Street, Norwich, NR1 3NG, United Kingdom
Tel.: (44) 1603 684 506
Insurance Management Services
N.A.I.C.S.: 524298
Andy Briggs *(CEO)*

Aviva Investors Canada Inc. (1)
100 King Street West Floor 49, Toronto, M5X 2A2, ON, Canada
Tel.: (416) 360-2770
Web Site: https://www.avivainvestors.com
Asset Investment Services
N.A.I.C.S.: 523940
Susan Ebenston *(Pres & COO)*

Aviva Investors France SA (1)
14 rue Roquepine, 75008, Paris, France
Tel.: (33) 176629000
Asset Investment Services
N.A.I.C.S.: 523940
Stephane Echardour *(Head-Euro Mandates)*

Aviva Investors Holdings Limited (1)
Saint Helens 1 Undershaft, London, EC3P 3DQ, United Kingdom
Tel.: (44) 20 7283 2000
Investment Management Service
N.A.I.C.S.: 523999
Paul Abberley *(Head-Investments)*

Subsidiary (Domestic):

Aviva Investors Global Services Limited (2)
St Helen's 1 Undershaft, London, EC3P 3DQ, United Kingdom
Tel.: (44) 207 809 6000
Web Site: https://www.avivainvestors.com
Investment Management Service
N.A.I.C.S.: 523999

Subsidiary (US):

Aviva Investors North America, Inc. (2)
215 10th St Ste 1000, Des Moines, IA 50309
Tel.: (515) 657-8563
Web Site: http://www.avivainvestors.us
Sales Range: $75-99.9 Million
Emp.: 80
Asset Management Services
N.A.I.C.S.: 523940
Kevin Mathews *(Head-High Yield-Global)*

Subsidiary (Domestic):

Aviva Investors UK Fund Services Limited (2)

Aviva plc—(Continued)

Surrey Street, Norwich, NR1 3GG, Norfolk, United Kingdom
Tel.: (44) 1603 622200
Investment Management Service
N.A.I.C.S.: 523999

Aviva Investors Real Estate France S.A. **(1)**
24-26 rue de la Pepiniere, 75008, Paris, France
Tel.: (33) 176628660
Web Site:
http://www.airef.avivainvestors.com
Asset Investment Services
N.A.I.C.S.: 523940
Jean-Baptiste Toxe *(Mgr-Asset)*

Aviva Investors Schweiz GmbH **(1)**
Stockerstrasse 38, 8002, Zurich, Switzerland
Tel.: (41) 442159010
Asset Investment Services
N.A.I.C.S.: 523940
Viviana Negrinotti *(Mgr-Mktg)*

Aviva Italia Holding S.p.A **(1)**
Via Scarsellini 14, 20161, Milan, Italy
Tel.: (39) 0227751
Insurance Management Services
N.A.I.C.S.: 524298

Aviva Life & Pensions UK Limited **(1)**
2 Rougier Street, York, YO90 1UU, United Kingdom **(100%)**
Tel.: (44) 1603622200
Web Site: http://www.aviva.co.uk
Sales Range: $50-74.9 Million
Emp.: 100
Life Insurance, Annuity & Pensions
N.A.I.C.S.: 524128

Aviva Limited **(1)**
4 Shenton Way 01-01 SGX Centre 2, Singapore, 068807, Singapore
Tel.: (65) 6827 9933
Web Site: http://www.aviva.com.sg
Insurance Management Services
N.A.I.C.S.: 524298

Aviva Powszechne Towarzystwo Emerytalne Aviva BZ WBK S.A. **(1)**
Ul Domaniewska 44, 02-672, Warsaw, Poland
Tel.: (48) 225574050
Investment Management Service
N.A.I.C.S.: 523999

Aviva Risk Management Solutions UK Limited **(1)**
1 Friars Gate Stratford Rd, Solihull, B90 4BN, West Midlands, United Kingdom
Tel.: (44) 845 3016030
Sales Range: $25-49.9 Million
Emp.: 150
Business Consulting Services
N.A.I.C.S.: 541618
Simon Bramall *(Mgr-Ops & Trading)*

Aviva Towarzystwo Ubezpieczen Na Zycie SA **(1)**
Ul Domaniewska 44, 02-672, Warsaw, Poland
Tel.: (48) 22 557 40 50
Web Site: http://www.aviva.pl
Emp.: 1,000
Insurance Management Services
N.A.I.C.S.: 524298

Aviva Towarzystwo Ubezpieczen Ogolnych SA **(1)**
Ul Domaniewska 44, 02-672, Warsaw, Poland
Tel.: (48) 22 557 40 50
Web Site: http://www.aviva.pl
Emp.: 150
General Insurance Management Services
N.A.I.C.S.: 524298

Bay Mill Specialty Insurance Adjusters Inc. **(1)**
328 Mill Street, Beaverton, L0K 1A0, ON, Canada
Web Site: http://www.bay-mill.com
Recreational Vehicle Insurance Services
N.A.I.C.S.: 524298

CGU Underwriting Limited **(1)**

1 Undershaft, London, EC3P 3DQ, United Kingdom
Tel.: (44) 2072837500
Web Site: http://www.aviva.com
Insurance Management Services
N.A.I.C.S.: 524298

CNP Vita Assicura S.p.A. **(1)**
Centro Direzionale Loreto, Viale Abruzzi 94, 20131, Milan, Italy **(51%)**
Tel.: (39) 0227751
Fire Insurance Services
N.A.I.C.S.: 524113

Criterion Tec Limited **(1)**
7 Lochside View, Edinburgh, EH12 9DH, United Kingdom
Tel.: (44) 1313570100
Web Site: https://www.criterion.org.uk
Financial Services
N.A.I.C.S.: 522320

Expander Advisors Sp. z o.o. **(1)**
Gdanski Business Center ul Inflancka 4B building C 6th floor, 00-189, Warsaw, Poland
Tel.: (48) 222954444
Web Site: https://www.expander.pl
Financial Advisors
N.A.I.C.S.: 525990

Focus Mall Zielona Gora Sp. Z o.o. **(1)**
ul Wroclawska 17, 65-427, Zielona Gora, Poland
Tel.: (48) 68 410 7000
Web Site: https://www.focusmall-zielonagora.pl
Supermarket & Grocery Product Distr
N.A.I.C.S.: 445110

Friends Life Group Limited **(1)**
Aviva Centre, PO Box 582, Bristol, BS34 9FX, United Kingdom **(76%)**
Tel.: (44) 1392844407
Web Site: http://www.aviva.co.uk
Sales Range: $15-24.9 Billion
Holding Company; Financial Investment & Consolidation
N.A.I.C.S.: 551112

Subsidiary (Domestic):

Friends Life Management Services Limited **(2)**
Wellington Row, York, YO90 1WR, United Kingdom
Tel.: (44) 03456029189
Web Site: http://www.friendslife.co.uk
General Insurance Services
N.A.I.C.S.: 524210

Sesame Bankhall Group Limited **(2)**
Jackson House Sibson Road, Sale, M33 7RR, Manchester, United Kingdom
Tel.: (44) 345 230 6000
Web Site: https://www.sbg.co.uk
Holding Company; Mortgage & Investment Services
N.A.I.C.S.: 551112
Lisa Winnard *(Dir-HR & Dev)*

Subsidiary (Domestic):

Bankhall Support Services Limited **(3)**
Jackson House Sibson Road Sale, Manchester, M33 7RR, Cheshire, United Kingdom
Tel.: (44) 3453005326
Web Site: https://www.bankhall.co.uk
Financial Services
N.A.I.C.S.: 523999
Ross Liston *(Mng Dir)*

Sesame Services Ltd **(3)**
Independence House Holly Bank Road, Huddersfield, HD3 3HN, United Kingdom
Tel.: (44) 1484422224
Web Site: http://www.sesame.co.uk
Financial Services
N.A.I.C.S.: 525990

Heath Farm Energy Limited **(1)**
Metheringham Heath Lane, Nocton, Lincoln, LN4 2AL, United Kingdom
Tel.: (44) 1522810740
Web Site: https://www.heathfarmenergy.com
Electric Power Distribution Services
N.A.I.C.S.: 221122

IPE BV **(1)**
Metaalweg 20, Weurt, 6551 AD, Beuningen, Netherlands
Tel.: (31) 24 677 7357
Web Site: https://www.ipebv.nl
Sheet Metal Work Mfg
N.A.I.C.S.: 332322

Life Plus Sp. z o.o. **(1)**
Ul Artwinskiego 24/1, 25-734, Kielce, Poland
Tel.: (48) 7381932772
Web Site: https://life-plus.pl
N.A.I.C.S.: 423450

London and Edinburgh Insurance Company Limited **(1)**
The Warren Warren Road, Worthing, BN14 9QD, United Kingdom
Tel.: (44) 1903 820 820
General Insurance Services
N.A.I.C.S.: 524210

Navigator Investment Services Limited **(1)**
6 Shenton Way 09-08, Downtown 2, Singapore, 068809, Singapore
Tel.: (65) 68277555
Web Site: https://grow.singlife.com
N.A.I.C.S.: 523940

Origo Services Limited **(1)**
7 Lochside View Edinburgh Park, Edinburgh, EH12 9DH, United Kingdom
Tel.: (44) 1314515181
Web Site: https://origo.com
Financial Services
N.A.I.C.S.: 522320

Porowneo.Pl Sp. z o.o **(1)**
Ul Inflancka 4B, 00-189, Warsaw, Poland
Tel.: (48) 519902560
Web Site: https://www.porowneo.pl
Automobile Insurance Services
N.A.I.C.S.: 524126

Premier Mortgage Service Limited **(1)**
Wellington Row, York, YO90 1WR, United Kingdom
Tel.: (44) 3452308000
Web Site: https://www.trustpms.com
N.A.I.C.S.: 551112
Stephanie Charman *(Dir-Strategic Relationships)*

Professional Investment Advisory Services Pte. Ltd. **(1)**
6 Shenton Way OUE Downtown 2 09-08, Singapore, 068809, Singapore
Tel.: (65) 6 372 5700
Web Site: https://www.proinvest.com.sg
Emp.: 700
Financial Advisory Services
N.A.I.C.S.: 523940
Nishit Majmudar *(Chm)*

Reschop Carre Hattingen GmbH **(1)**
Reschop-Carre Platz 1, 45525, Hattingen, Germany
Tel.: (49) 2324 686 5435
Web Site: https://www.reschop-carre.de
Supermarket & Grocery Product Distr
N.A.I.C.S.: 445110

Reschop Carre Marketing GmbH **(1)**
Thurn-und-Taxis-Platz 6, 60313, Frankfurt am Main, Germany
Tel.: (49) 23246865435
Supermarket & Grocery Store Distr
N.A.I.C.S.: 445110

Sesame Bankhall Valuation Services Limited **(1)**
Wellington Row, York, YO90 1WR, United Kingdom
Tel.: (44) 1156719634
Web Site: https://www.sbvaluationservices.co.uk
N.A.I.C.S.: 522320
Stephanie Charman *(Dir-Strategic Relationships)*

Singlife Financial Advisers Pte. Ltd **(1)**
51 Cuppage Road 03-09, Singapore, 229469, Singapore
Tel.: (65) 68279980
Web Site: https://singlifefa.com
Bond Investment Services

N.A.I.C.S.: 525910
Koh Wei Lee *(CEO)*

AVIX, INC.

6-85 Benten-dori, Naka-ku, Yokohama, 231-0007, Kanagawa, Japan
Tel.: (81) 456707711
Web Site: https://www.avix.co.jp
Year Founded: 1989
7836—(TKS)
Rev.: $24,635,470
Assets: $18,488,170
Liabilities: $8,216,230
Net Worth: $10,271,940
Earnings: $528,800
Emp.: 41
Fiscal Year-end: 03/31/24
LED Equipment Mfr
N.A.I.C.S.: 335139
Tomohisa Kumazaki *(Chm)*

AVK HOLDING A/S

Sondergade 33, DK-8464, Galten, Denmark
Tel.: (45) 8694 3888
Web Site: http://www.avkvalves.com
Year Founded: 1941
Sales Range: $100-124.9 Million
Emp.: 3,800
Water Supply & Valve Equipment Mfr
N.A.I.C.S.: 332911
Niels Aage Kjaer *(Owner & CEO)*

Subsidiaries:

AVF Gulf JLT **(1)**
Office No 1101 - SABA Tower 1 Jumeirah Lake Off Sheikh Zayed Road, Dubai, United Arab Emirates
Tel.: (971) 44 22 76 68
Valve & Fitting Distr
N.A.I.C.S.: 423720

AVK Armadan Sp. z o.o. **(1)**
ul Jakubowska 1, 62-045, Pniewy, Poland
Tel.: (48) 61 29 12 001
Web Site: http://www.avk.com.pl
Valve & Fitting Distr
N.A.I.C.S.: 423720

AVK Australia Pty Ltd **(1)**
559A Grand Junction Road, Wingfield, Adelaide, 5013, SA, Australia
Tel.: (61) 8 8368 0900
Web Site: http://www.avkvalves.com.au
Emp.: 20
Valve & Fitting Distr
N.A.I.C.S.: 423830

AVK Belgium NV **(1)**
Zoomstraat 6a, 9160, Lokeren, Belgium
Tel.: (32) 9 348 13 13
Web Site: http://www.avkvalves.be
Emp.: 20
Valve & Fitting Distr
N.A.I.C.S.: 423720
Dira Gamsegers *(Gen Mgr)*

AVK FLOW CONTROL A/S **(1)**
Karetmagervej 21, 7100, Vejle, Denmark
Tel.: (45) 76 40 88 47
Valve & Fitting Distr
N.A.I.C.S.: 423720

AVK Finland Oy **(1)**
Pyharanta 7 D, 33250, Tampere, Finland
Tel.: (358) 3 389 1822
Web Site: http://www.avkvalves.fi
Valve & Fitting Distr
N.A.I.C.S.: 423720

AVK France S.A.S. **(1)**
ZI de Villebarou 4 rue de la Garbotiere - CS 2904, 41029, Blois, Cedex, France
Tel.: (33) 2 54 74 23 13
Web Site: http://www.avk.fr
Valve & Fitting Distr
N.A.I.C.S.: 423720

AVK GUMMI A/S **(1)**
Mosegardsvej 1, 8670, Lasby, Denmark
Tel.: (45) 8695 1311
Web Site: http://www.avkgummi.com
Emp.: 150
Rubber Component Mfr
N.A.I.C.S.: 326299

Peter Lorentzen *(Mng Dir)*

Subsidiary (Non-US):

AVK Sealing Technology (Kunshan) Co. Ltd. **(2)**
Building 8 No 78 Gucheng M Rd, Suzhou, 215300, Jiangsu, China
Tel.: (86) 51257558818
Rubber Product Distr
N.A.I.C.S.: 424690

AVK Haut Marnaise S.A.S. **(1)**
14 B Rue Irma Masson, 52300, Joinville, France
Tel.: (33) 3 25 94 48 00
Web Site: http://www.avkfrance.fr
Emp.: 25
Industrial Valve Mfr
N.A.I.C.S.: 332911
Morten Nielsen *(Pres)*

AVK Industrial Pty Ltd **(1)**
Unit 1 15 Dunstan Road, Wingfield, Adelaide, 5013, SA, Australia
Tel.: (61) 8 8262 8885
Web Site: http://www.avkindustrial.com.au
Valve & Fitting Distr
N.A.I.C.S.: 423720
Craig Wright *(Mgr-Bus Dev)*

AVK Industrial Valve Singapore Pte. Ltd. **(1)**
11 Changi North Street 1 03-11, 498823, Singapore, Singapore
Tel.: (65) 6542 0451
Valve & Fitting Distr
N.A.I.C.S.: 423720
Irene Quek Hwee Lin *(Sr Mgr-Sls & Mktg)*

AVK Italia s.r.l. **(1)**
Via Gramsci 29, Pero, 20016, Milan, Italy
Tel.: (39) 02 339371
Web Site: http://www.avkvalves.it
Valve & Fitting Distr
N.A.I.C.S.: 423720

AVK Mittelmann Armaturen GmbH **(1)**
Schillerstrasse 50, 42489, Wulfrath, Germany
Tel.: (49) 2058 901 01
Web Site: http://www.avkmittelmann.com
Valve & Fitting Mfr
N.A.I.C.S.: 332911

AVK Nederland B.V. **(1)**
Radeweg 12, 8171 MD, Vaassen, Netherlands
Tel.: (31) 578574490
Web Site: http://www.avknederland.nl
Valve & Fitting Distr
N.A.I.C.S.: 423720
Albert Dokter *(Mgr-Sls)*

AVK Norge AS **(1)**
Hagasletta 7, 3236, Sandefjord, Norway
Tel.: (47) 33 48 29 99
Web Site: http://www.avk.no
Valve & Fitting Distr
N.A.I.C.S.: 423720

AVK Philippines Inc. **(1)**
No 70 West ave Bgy West Triangle, 1104, Quezon City, Philippines
Tel.: (63) 2 376 6400
Valve & Fitting Distr
N.A.I.C.S.: 423720

AVK Plastics B.V. **(1)**
Gaaikemastraat 62, 8561 AN, Balk, Netherlands
Tel.: (31) 514 604604
Web Site: http://www.avkplastics.com
Plastics Product Mfr
N.A.I.C.S.: 333511

Subsidiary (Non-US):

AVK Plast A/S **(2)**
Oster Vedstedvej 26A, 6760, Ribe, Denmark
Tel.: (45) 75 420 144
Web Site: http://www.avkplast.dk
Plastic Product Mfr & Distr
N.A.I.C.S.: 333511
Henrik Lund-Olesen *(Mng Dir)*

AVK Sverige AB **(1)**
Kanslihusvagen 13A, 28135, Hassleholm, Sweden

Tel.: (46) 451 45800
Web Site: http://www.avkvalves.se
Valve & Fitting Distr
N.A.I.C.S.: 423720

AVK Syntec (Anhui) Co. Ltd. **(1)**
Wujiang Industry Park, Hexian, Ma'anshan, Anhui, China
Tel.: (86) 555 5968701
Web Site: http://www.avksyntec.com
Industrial Valve Mfr
N.A.I.C.S.: 332911

AVK Tooling A/S **(1)**
Granlyvej 2, 9300, Saeby, Denmark
Tel.: (45) 9846 1711
Web Site: http://www.avktool.dk
Emp.: 80
Air Engine Mfr & Distr
N.A.I.C.S.: 336390

AVK UK Limited **(1)**
Rushmills, Northampton, NN4 7YB, United Kingdom
Tel.: (44) 1604601188
Web Site: http://www.avkuk.co.uk
Valve & Fitting Distr
N.A.I.C.S.: 423720
Kieran Fitzpatrick *(Head-Mktg)*

Subsidiary (Domestic):

AVK Syddal Ltd. **(2)**
Dunkirk Lane, Hyde, Manchester, SK14 4PL, Cheshire, United Kingdom
Tel.: (44) 1246 479140
Web Site: http://www.avkfittings.co.uk
Emp.: 40
Valve & Fitting Mfr & Distr
N.A.I.C.S.: 332911
Sean Brody *(Gen Mgr)*

Aqua-Gas Manufacturing Ltd. **(2)**
Arnsley Road, Weldon North Ind Est, Corby, NN17 5QW, England, United Kingdom
Tel.: (44) 1536 275910
Valve & Fitting Mfr
N.A.I.C.S.: 332911

Bryan Donkin Valves Ltd. **(2)**
Colliery Close Ireland Ind Est, Staveley, Chesterfield, S43 3FH, England, United Kingdom
Tel.: (44) 1246 479100
Web Site: http://www.avkuk.co.uk
Industrial Valve Mfr
N.A.I.C.S.: 332911

Glenfield Valves Limited **(2)**
Lifeways House 22 Shaw Road, Prestwick, KA9 2LP, Ayrshire, United Kingdom
Tel.: (44) 1292670404
Web Site: http://www.glenfield.co.uk
Valve & Fitting Mfr
N.A.I.C.S.: 332911
Greg Morris *(Mgr-Technical-Water)*

Invicta Valves Ltd. **(2)**
Units 9-12 Boxmend Parkwood Industrial Estate, Maidstone, ME15 9XT, Kent, United Kingdom
Tel.: (44) 1622 754613
Web Site: http://www.invictavalves.co.uk
Emp.: 71
Valve & Actuator Distr
N.A.I.C.S.: 423830
Alex Philo *(Mgr-Bus Dev-Water Industry)*

AVK VOD-KA a.s. **(1)**
Lodni namesti 7, 412 01, Litomerice, Czech Republic
Tel.: (420) 416 734 980
Web Site: http://www.avkvodka.cz
Valve & Fitting Distr
N.A.I.C.S.: 423720

AVK Valves (Anhui) Co., Ltd. **(1)**
No 2 Heng Jiang Street, Hexian, Chaohu, Anhui, China
Tel.: (86) 565 535 1327
Valve & Fitting Mfr
N.A.I.C.S.: 332911
Soeren Kjaer *(Gen Mgr)*

AVK Valves (Beijing) Co Ltd **(1)**
Room 2704 Building 11 Jianwai Soho 39 East 3rd-ring Road, Chaoyang District, 100022, Beijing, China
Tel.: (86) 10 5869 9649
Valve & Fitting Distr

N.A.I.C.S.: 423720

AVK Valves (Shanghai) Co. Ltd. **(1)**
Room 302 Warner Business Center No 1733 Lianhua Road, Minhang, 201100, Shanghai, China
Tel.: (86) 21 5789 1222
Valve & Fitting Distr
N.A.I.C.S.: 423720
Bo Frank Nielsen *(Mng Dir)*

AVK Valves Company Hong Kong Ltd. **(1)**
Units C & D 10th floor Centre 600 82 King Lam Street, Cheung Sha Wan, Kowloon, China (Hong Kong)
Tel.: (852) 2773 0846
Valve & Fitting Distr
N.A.I.C.S.: 423720

AVK Valves India Pvt. Ltd. **(1)**
179 KIADB Industrial Area 3rd Phase, Kolar, Malur, 563130, Karnataka, India
Tel.: (91) 8151324743
Web Site: http://www.avkindia.com
Valve & Fitting Mfr & Distr
N.A.I.C.S.: 332911

AVK Valves Korea Co., Ltd. **(1)**
Suite E8 8/F KNN Tower 30 Centumseo-ro, Haeundae-gu, Busan, 612-020, Korea (South)
Tel.: (82) 51 664 8808
Web Site: http://www.avkvalves.co.kr
Valve & Fitting Distr
N.A.I.C.S.: 423720

AVK Valves Manufacturing Malaysia Sdn. Bhd. **(1)**
Lot No 1 Jalan Sg Chadong 8 Batu 5 1/2 miles Jalan Kapar, 42100, Klang, Selangor, Malaysia
Tel.: (60) 3291 8270
Web Site: http://www.avkvalves.com.my
Valve & Fitting Mfr & Distr
N.A.I.C.S.: 332911
Kenny Tan Keng Gee *(Sls Mgr-Export Market)*

AVK Valves Southern Africa Pty. Ltd. **(1)**
PO Box 1025, Brackenfell, 7561, Cape Town, South Africa
Tel.: (27) 21 981 4414
Web Site: http://www.avkvalves.co.za
Valve & Fitting Distr
N.A.I.C.S.: 423720
Brian McGugan *(Mng Dir)*

Subsidiary (Non-US):

Wouter Witzel EuroValve B.V. **(2)**
Industrieterrein De Pol 12, 7581 CZ, Losser, Netherlands
Tel.: (31) 53 536 95 36
Web Site: http://www.wouterwitzel.nl
Industrial Valve Mfr
N.A.I.C.S.: 332911

AVK Valvulas S.A. **(1)**
Pol Industrial Francoli parcela 27, 43006, Tarragona, Spain
Tel.: (34) 977 54 30 08
Web Site: http://www.avkvalvulas.com
Valve & Fitting Distr
N.A.I.C.S.: 423720

AVK Valvulas do Brasil Ltda. **(1)**
Av Vitoria Rossi Martini 435, 13347-613, Indaiatuba, Sao Paulo, Brazil
Tel.: (55) 19 3936 5936
Web Site: http://www.avkvalvulas.com.br
Valve & Fitting Distr
N.A.I.C.S.: 423720

AVK Vietnam Co. Ltd. **(1)**
No 32 Road No 11 Him Lam 6A Residential Area Hamlet 4, Binh Hung Ward Binh Chanh District, Ho Chi Minh City, Vietnam
Tel.: (84) 8 5431 9511
Valve & Fitting Distr
N.A.I.C.S.: 423720
Rasmus Moller Martensen *(Gen Mgr)*

American AVK Co. **(1)**
2155 Meridian Blvd, Minden, NV 89423
Tel.: (775) 552-1400
Web Site: http://www.americanavk.com
Valve & Fitting Mfr
N.A.I.C.S.: 423720
Michael Enos *(Controller)*

CYL Knife Valves S.L. **(1)**
Pol Ibarluze B-1 2, Hernani, 20120, Spain
Tel.: (34) 943 33 31 30
Web Site: http://www.cyl.es
Valve & Fitting Mfr
N.A.I.C.S.: 332911

Damper Technology Ltd. **(1)**
Meadowbank House Meadowbank Court, Eastwood, Nottingham, NG16 3SL, United Kingdom
Tel.: (44) 1159324046
Web Site: http://www.dampertechnology.com
Valve & Fitting Mfr & Distr
N.A.I.C.S.: 332911
Mark Hancock *(Mng Dir)*

Subsidiary (Non-US):

Damper Technology Canada **(2)**
2050 Dagenais Blvd, Laval, H7L 5W2, QC, Canada
Tel.: (450) 622-9694
Valve & Fitting Distr
N.A.I.C.S.: 332911

Damper Technology India Pvt. Ltd. **(2)**
No 608/3A2B 608/3A1B Eachanari - Chettipalayam Road, Eachanari Post, Coimbatore, 641021, India
Tel.: (91) 422 669 1261
Valve & Fitting Distr
N.A.I.C.S.: 423720

Plant (Domestic):

Damper Technology Ltd. - Leicester Plant **(2)**
Silverdale Drive, Thurmaston, Leicester, LE4 8NN, United Kingdom
Tel.: (44) 116 2604179
Valve & Fitting Distr
N.A.I.C.S.: 332911

Fusion Group Ltd. **(1)**
Fusion House Chesterfield Trading Estate, Chesterfield, S41 9PZ, Derbs, United Kingdom
Tel.: (44) 1246 260111
Web Site: http://www.fusiongroup.co.uk
Industrial Machinery Mfr
N.A.I.C.S.: 333998
Kevin Raine *(Dir)*

Subsidiary (Non-US):

Fusion Group Holdings Pty Limited **(2)**
146 Crockford Street, Northgate, Brisbane, 4013, QLD, Australia
Tel.: (61) 733935770
Web Site: http://www.fusionplast.com.au
Plastic Pipe & Fitting Distr
N.A.I.C.S.: 423720

Fusion Italia S.R.L **(2)**
Localita Chiazza SP 29, Dego, 17058, Savona, Italy
Tel.: (39) 019 577 8018
Web Site: http://www.fusionitalia.net
Industrial Machinery Mfr
N.A.I.C.S.: 333998
Francesca Nari *(Coord-Comml)*

Fusion Polska Sp. z o.o. **(2)**
Bodycha 97 Reguly, 05-816, Michalowice, Poland
Tel.: (48) 227238872
Web Site: http://www.fusiongroup.com
Industrial Machinery & Equipment Distr
N.A.I.C.S.: 423830

Fusion Romania Srl **(2)**
Str Stefan cel Mare nr 152-154, 550321, Sibiu, Romania
Tel.: (40) 269253217
Web Site: http://www.fusion.ro
Plastic Pipe & Fitting Distr
N.A.I.C.S.: 423720

PT Fusion Technologies Indonesia **(2)**
Ruko Hybrida Utama Jln Hybrida Raya Blok RB 1 kav 7, Kelapa Gading, Jakarta, 14250, Indonesia
Tel.: (62) 214516966
Web Site: http://www.fusiongroup.com
Industrial Machinery & Equipment Distr

AVK Holding A/S—(Continued)
N.A.I.C.S.: 423830

G+W GmbH (1)
Industriestr 4, 74933, Neidenstein, Germany
Tel.: (49) 7263 919696
Web Site: http://www.gw-strassenkappen.de
Plastic Product Mfr & Distr
N.A.I.C.S.: 333511

Indva Sverige AB (1)
Vaxthusvagen 5, 281 51, Hassleholm, Sweden
Tel.: (46) 451 74 69 00
Web Site: http://www.indva.se
Valve & Fitting Distr
N.A.I.C.S.: 423720

InterApp AG (1)
Grundstrasse 24, 6343, Rotkreuz, Switzerland
Tel.: (41) 41 798 22 33
Web Site: http://www.interapp.net
Emp.: 180
Valve & Fitting Mfr
N.A.I.C.S.: 332911
Guido Baldini (Mng Dir)

Subsidiary (Non-US):

InterApp Deutschland GmbH (1)
Schillerstrasse 50, 42489, Wulfrath, Germany
Tel.: (49) 2058 890 92 50
Valve & Fitting Distr
N.A.I.C.S.: 423720

Plant (Domestic):

InterApp Ges.m.b.H. (2)
Kolpingstrasse 19, 1230, Vienna, Austria
Tel.: (43) 1 616 2371 0
Valve & Fitting Distr
N.A.I.C.S.: 423720

InterApp Valcom S.A. (2)
Calle De Calderon De La Barca, Paracuelios de Jarama, 28860, Spain
Tel.: (34) 916584128
Valve & Fitting Distr
N.A.I.C.S.: 423720

Orbinox Brasil Industria e Comercio Ltda. (1)
Rua Alberto Magnusson no 162, Vitoria Martini, 13347-633, Indaiatuba, Sao Paulo, Brazil
Tel.: (55) 19 3935 5369
Valve & Fitting Distr
N.A.I.C.S.: 423720

Orbinox S.A. (1)
Pol Industrial s/n, 20270, Anoeta, Spain
Tel.: (34) 943 69 80 30
Valve & Fitting Distr
N.A.I.C.S.: 423720

Subsidiary (Non-US):

Orbe Canada Inc. (2)
2050 Dagenais Blvd West, Laval, H7L 5W2, QC, Canada
Tel.: (450) 622-8775
Web Site: http://www.orbinox.com
Valve & Fitting Mfr & Distr
N.A.I.C.S.: 332911

Subsidiary (US):

Orbe Valve Inc. (2)
311 N Fron St, Amory, MS 38821
Tel.: (662) 256-2227
Web Site: http://www.orbinox.com
Valve & Fitting Distr
N.A.I.C.S.: 423720

Subsidiary (Domestic):

Orbinox Comercial S.L. (2)
Pol Industrial Beotibar s/n, 20491, Belauntza, Spain
Tel.: (34) 943 69 80 33
Valve & Fitting Distr
N.A.I.C.S.: 423720

Subsidiary (Non-US):

Orbinox Deutshland GmbH (2)
Kurzer Morgen 3, 58239, Schwerte, Germany
Tel.: (49) 2304 957 057
Industrial Valve Distr

N.A.I.C.S.: 423840

Subsidiary (Domestic):

Orbinox Valves International SA (2)
Parque Tecnologico de San Sebastian P Mikeletegui 56-planta 3, 20009, San Sebastian, Spain
Tel.: (34) 943 69 80 30
Valve & Fitting Distr
N.A.I.C.S.: 423720

PV Engineering SA Pty Ltd (1)
3 Potgieter St, Alrode, Alberton, Gauteng, South Africa
Tel.: (27) 118649950
Industrial Valve Distr
N.A.I.C.S.: 423840

Saudi Valves Manufacturing Co. Ltd. (1)
Street 45 Phase 4 Industrial Area, PO Box 10830, Jeddah, 21433, Saudi Arabia
Tel.: (966) 12 637 1570
Web Site: http://www.avksvmc.com
Valve & Fitting Mfr
N.A.I.C.S.: 332911
Imtiyaz Damad (Mgr-Key Acct-Aramco Unit)

TEC artec GmbH (1)
Am Heidering 7a, 16515, Oranienburg, Germany
Tel.: (49) 3301 20 32
Web Site: http://www.tec-artec.de
Industrial Valve Mfr & Distr
N.A.I.C.S.: 332911

Vatech 2000 ApS (1)
Vaerkstedsvej 15, 5500, Middelfart, Denmark
Tel.: (45) 64 40 20 60
Web Site: http://www.vatech.dk
Valve & Fitting Distr
N.A.I.C.S.: 423720

World Valve B.V. (1)
Leusinkweg 5a, 7582 CM, Losser, Netherlands
Tel.: (31) 53 5381295
Web Site: http://www.worldvalve.com
Emp.: 25
Valve & Fitting Mfr & Distr
N.A.I.C.S.: 332911
Danny Muller (Gen Mgr)

AVL LIST GMBH
Hans-List-Platz 1, 8020, Graz, Austria
Tel.: (43) 3167870
Web Site: http://www.avl.com
Year Founded: 1948
Sales Range: $800-899.9 Million
Emp.: 9,500
Diesel Powertrain Engineering, Simulation & Powertrain Testing Systems
N.A.I.C.S.: 336310
Helmut O. List (Chm & CEO)

Subsidiaries:

AVL AST d.o.o. (1)
Strojarska Street 22, Zagreb, 10000, Croatia
Tel.: (385) 16598600
Web Site: http://www.avl.com
Sales Range: $25-49.9 Million
Emp.: 150
Powertrain Engine Design, Development & Testing
N.A.I.C.S.: 333618
Goran Mirkovic (Mng Dir)

AVL Autokut Engineering Ltd. (1)
Csoka utca 7-13, 1115, Budapest, Hungary
Tel.: (36) 14643950
Web Site: http://www.avl.com
Engine & Powertrain Development & Testing
N.A.I.C.S.: 333618

AVL Cechy spol. s r.o. (1)
Tovarni 605, 753 01, Hranice, Czech Republic
Tel.: (420) 581653352
Web Site: http://www.avlcechy.cz
Engine & Powertrain Development & Testing Mfr
N.A.I.C.S.: 333618

AVL Deutschland GmbH (1)

Peter-Sander-Strasse 32, Mainz-Kastel, 55252, Germany
Tel.: (49) 613471790
Web Site: http://www.avl.com
Sales Range: $125-149.9 Million
Emp.: 100
Engine & Powertrain Development & Testing
N.A.I.C.S.: 333618
Sabine Mueller (Sec)

AVL France S.A. (1)
Espace Claude Monet 2-4 rue Hans List, 78290, Croissy-sur-Seine, France
Tel.: (33) 130157500
Web Site: http://www.avl.com
Sales Range: $25-49.9 Million
Emp.: 79
Powertrain Engineering Sales, Marketing & Support; Instrumentation & Test Systems Sales & Marketing
N.A.I.C.S.: 336310
Gilbert Lemieux (Mng Dir)

AVL Iberica S.A. (1)
Paseo Arco de Ladrillo 68 pl 5, 47007, Valladolid, Spain
Tel.: (34) 983548073
Web Site: http://www.avl.com
Sales Range: $25-49.9 Million
Emp.: 45
Engine & Powertrain Development & Testing
N.A.I.C.S.: 333618
Joan Anton Mikuel (Mng Dir)

AVL Italy S.r.l. (1)
Corso Francesco Ferrucci 112, 10138, Turin, Italy
Tel.: (39) 0114705111
Web Site: http://www.avl.com
Powertrain Engineering Support & Instrumentation & Test Systems Design, Development, Sales & Distribution
N.A.I.C.S.: 333618

AVL List Nordiska AB (1)
Transmissionsvagen 2, PO Box 223, Sodertalje, 15148, Sweden
Tel.: (46) 850065600
Web Site: http://www.avl.com
Sales Range: $25-49.9 Million
Emp.: 20
Powertrain Engine Design Testing & Sales Mfr
N.A.I.C.S.: 333618

AVL Michigan Holding Corporation (1)
47519 Halyard Dr, Plymouth, MI 48170-2438
Tel.: (734) 414-9600
Web Site: http://www.avlna.com
Sales Range: $50-74.9 Million
Emp.: 300
Holding Company; Diesel Engine Design & Testing
N.A.I.C.S.: 551112
Werner Schuster (CFO)

Subsidiary (Domestic):

AVL North America Inc. (2)
47603 Halyard Dr, Plymouth, MI 48170-2438
Tel.: (734) 414-9600
Web Site: http://www.avl.com
Sales Range: $75-99.9 Million
Powertrain & Engine Testing Services
N.A.I.C.S.: 541380
Bob Nemeth (Dir-IT)

AVL Powertrain Engineering, Inc. (2)
47519 Halyard Dr, Plymouth, MI 48170-2438
Tel.: (734) 414-9600
Web Site: http://www.avl.com
Engine Design & Development
N.A.I.C.S.: 336310

AVL United Kingdom Limited (1)
Avon House Hartlebury Trading Estate, Hartlebury, DY10 4JB, Worcestershire, United Kingdom
Tel.: (44) 1299254600
Web Site: http://www.avl.com
Sales Range: $25-49.9 Million
Emp.: 70
Powertrain Engine Design, Development, Testing & Sales
N.A.I.C.S.: 333618

Antonio Ciriello (Mng Dir)

AVLA PERU COMPANIA DE SEGUROS SA
Calle Las Begonias No 415 Tercer Piso, San Isidro, Lima, Peru
Tel.: (51) 7154400
AVLASGC1—(LIM)
Rev.: $35,634,901
Assets: $78,034,977
Liabilities: $49,256,201
Net Worth: $28,778,776
Earnings: $5,844,601
Fiscal Year-end: 12/31/23
Insurance Services
N.A.I.C.S.: 524298

AVMAX GROUP INC.
2055 Pegasus Road, Calgary, T2E 8C3, AB, Canada
Tel.: (403) 291-2464
Web Site: https://www.avmax.com
Year Founded: 1976
Airline Support Services & Aircraft Spares Distr
N.A.I.C.S.: 488190
Al Davies (Chief Sls Officer)

Subsidiaries:

Avmax Avionics (1)
275 Palmer Road NE, Calgary, T2E 7G4, AB, Canada
Tel.: (403) 250-2644
Web Site: http://avionics.avmaxgroup.com
Electronic Equipment Distr
N.A.I.C.S.: 423690

Avmax Engineering (1)
3691 - 19th Street N E, Calgary, T2E 6S8, AB, Canada
Tel.: (403) 250-3185
Aircraft Engineering Services
N.A.I.C.S.: 488190

Avmax Montana, Inc. (1)
1930 Airport Ct, Great Falls, MT 59404
Tel.: (406) 453-2344
Sales Range: $25-49.9 Million
Emp.: 50
Support Activities for Air Transportation
N.A.I.C.S.: 488190

Avmax Spares East Africa Limited (1)
Wilson Airport Langata Rd, PO Box 1054-00517, Nairobi, Kenya
Tel.: (254) 20 600 5732
Emp.: 17
Aircraft Parts Distr
N.A.I.C.S.: 423860
David Kuria (Mng Dir)

R1 Airlines Ltd. (1)
100 - 680 Palmer Road NE, Calgary, T2E 7R3, AB, Canada
Tel.: (403) 250-3079
Web Site: http://www.r1airlines.ca
Aircraft Charter Services
N.A.I.C.S.: 481212
John Binder (CEO & Exec VP)

AVMOR LTEE
950 Michelin, Laval, H7L 5C1, QC, Canada
Tel.: (450) 629-8074
Web Site: http://www.avmor.com
Year Founded: 1948
Rev.: $15,561,000
Emp.: 100
Cleaning Chemicals & Sanitation Systems Mfr
N.A.I.C.S.: 325612
Irene O'Nei (Mgr-Western Canada)

AVOCET HARDWARE LTD.
Brookfoot Mills Elland Rd, Brighouse, HD6 2RW, W Yorkshire, United Kingdom
Tel.: (44) 1484750000
Web Site: http://www.avocet-hardware.co.uk
Sales Range: $50-74.9 Million

Emp.: 80
Hardware Product Designer Mfr & Distr
N.A.I.C.S.: 332510
Rythm Jain Saigal *(CEO)*

AVOCET MINING PLC
5th Floor 15 Old Bailey, London, EC4M 7EF, United Kingdom
Tel.: (44) 20 3709 2570
Web Site: http://www.avocet.co.uk
Sales Range: $75-99.9 Million
Emp.: 567
Gold Mining Services
N.A.I.C.S.: 212220
David Cather *(CEO)*

Subsidiaries:

Avocet Gold Limited **(1)**
5th Floor 15 Old Bailey, London, EC4M 7EF, United Kingdom **(100%)**
Tel.: (44) 2077667676
Web Site: http://www.avocetmining.com
Sales Range: $50-74.9 Million
Emp.: 15
Gold Ore Mining
N.A.I.C.S.: 212220
David Cather *(CEO)*

Wega Mining Mali S.A. **(1)**
Korofina Nord Rue 110 Porte 329, Bamako, Mali
Tel.: (223) 20245039
Sales Range: $50-74.9 Million
Emp.: 4
Gold Mining Services
N.A.I.C.S.: 212220
Saidou Diallo *(Mgr)*

AVOLTA AG
Brunngasslein 12, CH - 4010, Basel, Switzerland
Tel.: (41) 612664444 CH
Web Site:
https://www.avoltaworld.com
Year Founded: 1865
AVOL—(SWX)
Rev.: $14,094,029,000
Assets: $18,199,419,800
Liabilities: $15,449,599,200
Net Worth: $2,749,820,600
Earnings: $238,472,800
Emp.: 76,962
Fiscal Year-end: 12/31/23
International Travel Retailer
N.A.I.C.S.: 561510
Juan Carlos-Torres Carretero *(Chm)*

Subsidiaries:

Aldeasa Chile, Ltd. **(1)**
Comodoro Arturo Merino Benitez Airport-Access North, Pudahuel, Santiago, Chile
Tel.: (56) 228967100
Travel Shopping Services
N.A.I.C.S.: 561599

Autogrill S.p.A. **(1)**
Centro Direzionale Milano Fiori Strada 5 Palazzo Z, 20089, Milan, Rozzano, Italy **(100%)**
Tel.: (39) 0248261
Web Site: http://www.autogrill.com
Rev.: $3,540,566,384
Assets: $5,058,994,051
Liabilities: $3,862,497,914
Net Worth: $1,196,496,137
Earnings: ($25,197,344)
Emp.: 12,638
Fiscal Year-end: 12/31/2021
Holding Company; Restaurant Food & Beverage Services & In-Flight Catering Services Contractor
N.A.I.C.S.: 551112
Gianmario Tondato Da Ruos *(CEO)*

Subsidiary (Non-US):

Autogrill Catering UK Limited **(2)**
5 Pond Street, London, NW3 2PN, United Kingdom
Tel.: (44) 845 0949 094
Web Site:
http://www.autogrillcateringuk.com

Food & Beverage Services Contractor
N.A.I.C.S.: 722310

Autogrill Iberia S.L.U **(2)**
Mendez Alvaro 1 Estatción Puerta de Atocha AVE, 28045, Madrid, Spain
Tel.: (34) 91 423 0200
Web Site: http://www.autogrill.es
Food & Beverage Services Contractor
N.A.I.C.S.: 722310

Subsidiary (US):

HMSHost Corporation **(2)**
6905 Rockledge Dr, Bethesda, MD 20817-1828
Tel.: (240) 694-4100
Web Site: https://www.hmshost.com
Sales Range: $1-4.9 Billion
Emp.: 26,000
Food & Beverage Services Contractor
N.A.I.C.S.: 722310
Sarah Naqvi *(CIO)*

Subsidiary (Domestic):

Stellar Partners Inc. **(3)**
12750 Citrus Park Ln Ste 210, Tampa, FL 33625
Tel.: (813) 396-3639
Web Site:
http://www.stellarairportstores.com
Airport News & Gifts Specialty Retailer
N.A.I.C.S.: 455219
Susan Stackhouse *(Founder)*

Dufrital SpA **(1)**
Viale Lancetti 43, 20158, Milan, Italy
Tel.: (39) 02698151
Web Site: https://www.dufry.it
Food Products Distr
N.A.I.C.S.: 424490
Tiziana DAleo *(Mgr-Retail)*

Dufry BaBasel Mulhouse Ltd. **(1)**
Basel Lulhouse 80, Euro Airport, 4030, Basel, Switzerland
Tel.: (41) 613252880
Sales Range: $50-74.9 Million
Emp.: 60
Commercial Products Retailer
N.A.I.C.S.: 423990

Dufry France SA **(1)**
Nice Cote d'Azur Airport, Nice, France
Web Site: http://www.dufry.com
Sales Range: $10-24.9 Million
Emp.: 70
Travel Retailer
N.A.I.C.S.: 561599

Dufry Holdings & Investments AG **(1)**
Brunngjasslein No 12, Basel, 4052, Switzerland
Tel.: (41) 612664444
Sales Range: $100-124.9 Million
Emp.: 130
Investment Management Service
N.A.I.C.S.: 523999

Dufry Management Ltd. **(1)**
Brunngasslein 12, Basel, CH 4020, Switzerland
Tel.: (41) 612664444
Web Site: http://www.dufry.ch
Sales Range: $25-49.9 Million
Emp.: 140
Business Management Services
N.A.I.C.S.: 561499

Dufry Samnaun Ltd. **(1)**
Plan Bell, Samnaun, 7563, Graubunden, Switzerland
Tel.: (41) 818618020
Sales Range: $25-49.9 Million
Emp.: 5
Commercial Products Retailer
N.A.I.C.S.: 455110

Dufry Shop Finance Limited Srl. **(1)**
Viale Vincenzo Lancetti 43, Milan, 20158, Italy
Tel.: (39) 02698151
Web Site: http://www.dufry.com
Fur & Leather Apparels Retailer
N.A.I.C.S.: 458110

Duty Free Caribbean Holdings Ltd. **(1)**

24 Broad St, Bridgetown, Barbados **(60%)**
Tel.: (246) 227 1325
Web Site: http://www.dutyfreecaribbean.com
Emp.: 300
Holding Company; Duty Free Retail Stores Owner & Operator
N.A.I.C.S.: 551112
Peter Allan *(CEO)*

Hudson Ltd. **(1)**
1 Meadowlands Plz, East Rutherford, NJ 07073
Tel.: (201) 939-5050
Web Site: https://www.hudsongroup.com
Travel Management Services
N.A.I.C.S.: 561510
Brian Quinn *(Deputy CEO & Exec VP)*

Hudson News Company **(1)**
1 Meadowlands Plz, East Rutherford, NJ 07073
Tel.: (201) 939-5050
Web Site: http://www.hudsongroup.com
Sales Range: $450-499.9 Million
Distr of Magazines & Books
N.A.I.C.S.: 424920

Regstaer-SP LLC **(1)**
1st Krasnogvardeisky Proezd 21 Building 1, OKO Business Center Floor 40, 123112, Moscow, Russia
Tel.: (7) 4951508851
Web Site: https://regstaer.ru
Clothing Retailer
N.A.I.C.S.: 458110

The Nuance Group AG **(1)**
Hohenbuhlstrasse 2, 8152, Glattbrugg, Switzerland
Tel.: (41) 584408000
Web Site: http://www.thenuancegroup.com
Duty Free Retailer
N.A.I.C.S.: 459999

Subsidiary (Non-US):

The Nuance Group (Australia) Pty Ltd **(2)**
190 Bourke Road, Alexandria, 2015, NSW, Australia
Tel.: (61) 293844777
Web Site: http://www.thenuancegroup.com
Duty Free Retailing
N.A.I.C.S.: 459999

The Nuance Group (Malta) Limited **(2)**
Malta International Airport Administration Building 2nd Floor, Luqa, LQA 4000, Malta
Tel.: (356) 21323412
Web Site: http://www.thenuancegroup.com
Airport Concession Services
N.A.I.C.S.: 488119

World Duty Free S.p.A. **(1)**
Via Greppi 2, 28100, Novara, Italy **(100%)**
Tel.: (39) 0639967700
Web Site:
http://www.worlddutyfreegroup.com
Holding Company; Airport Retail Stores Operator
N.A.I.C.S.: 551112
Chris Bouttle *(Dir-Fin & IR)*

Subsidiary (Non-US):

World Duty Free Group S.A.U. **(2)**
Edificio Merrimack IV Calle Josefa Valcarcel 30, 28027, Madrid, Spain **(100%)**
Tel.: (34) 912742200
Web Site:
http://www.worlddutyfreegroup.com
Holding Company; Airport Retail Stores Operator
N.A.I.C.S.: 551112
Isabel Zarza *(Dir-Strategy & Corp Dev)*

Subsidiary (Non-US):

WDFG UK Limited **(3)**
4 New Square Bedfont Lakes, Feltham, TW14 8HA, Middlesex, United Kingdom
Tel.: (44) 1784475509
Web Site: https://worlddutyfree.com
Airport Retail Stores Operator
N.A.I.C.S.: 459999
Frederick Robert Creighton *(COO & Dir-Retail)*

Subsidiary (Domestic):

World Duty Free Group Espana S.A. **(3)**
Edificio Merrimack IV Calle Josefa Valcarcel 30, 28027, Madrid, Spain
Tel.: (34) 912742200
Web Site:
http://www.worlddutyfreegroup.com
Airport Retail Stores Operator
N.A.I.C.S.: 459999
Isabel Zarza *(Dir-Strategy & Corp Dev)*

Subsidiary (Non-US):

World Duty Free Group Germany GmbH **(3)**
Terminal-Ring 1 ZGO/Room 4036, 40474, Dusseldorf, Germany
Tel.: (49) 21142177472
Travel Shopping Services
N.A.I.C.S.: 561599
Bettina Kuhnrich *(Mng Dir)*

AVON CORPORATION LTD.
15/B 2nd Floor Kamal kunj Opp Vijay S V Road Irla Bridge, Andheri West, Mumbai, 400058, Maharashtra, India
Tel.: (91) 2266804049
Web Site: http://www.avon.co.in
Sales Range: $10-24.9 Million
Emp.: 70
Electronic Weighing Balances Mfr
N.A.I.C.S.: 333998

AVON LIPPIATT HOBBS (CONTRACTING) LIMITED
114 Station Road, Westbury, BA13 4TW, Wiltshire, United Kingdom
Tel.: (44) 1373855122
Year Founded: 1986
Rev.: $80,000,000
Emp.: 300
Utility Contractor; Pipework Installation; Heater Installation & Servicing
N.A.I.C.S.: 238220
John H.A. Clarke *(Chm)*

Subsidiaries:

FlowMole **(1)**
Unit C Edison Courtyard, Earlstrees Industrial Estate, Corby, NN17 4LS, Northamptonshire, United Kingdom **(100%)**
Tel.: (44) 1536400141
Sales Range: $25-49.9 Million
Emp.: 27
Underground Utility Installation & Replacement Services
N.A.I.C.S.: 237120

AVON MERCANTILE LIMITED
Upper Basement Smart Bharat Mall Plot Nol-2, Sector - 25A Gautam Buddha Naga, Noida, 201301, Uttar Pradesh, India
Tel.: (91) 1203355131
Web Site:
https://www.avonmercantile.co.in
Year Founded: 1985
11138—(CSE)
Sales Range: Less than $1 Million
Emp.: 3
Financial Investment Services
N.A.I.C.S.: 523999
Rakesh Kumar Gupta *(Chm & Compliance Officer)*

AVON PROTECTION PLC
Hampton Park West Semington Road, Melksham, SN12 6NB, Wiltshire, United Kingdom
Tel.: (44) 1225896800
Web Site: https://www.avon-protection-plc.com
Year Founded: 1890
AVON—(LSE)
Rev.: $243,800,000
Assets: $348,100,000
Liabilities: $188,700,000
Net Worth: $159,400,000

Avon Protection plc—(Continued)

Earnings: ($16,400,000)
Emp.: 928
Fiscal Year-end: 09/30/23
Rubber Products Mfr
N.A.I.C.S.: 326299
David Evans (Chm)

Subsidiaries:

Avon Engineered Fabrications, Inc   (1)
113 St A, Picayune, MS 39466-5427
Tel.: (601) 889-9050
Web Site: https://www.aef-performance.com
Rubber Products Mfr
N.A.I.C.S.: 326220

Avon Hi-Life Inc.   (1)
110 Lincoln St, Johnson Creek, WI 53038-0009
Tel.: (920) 699-3431
Web Site: https://www.milkrite-interpuls.com
Sales Range: $50-74.9 Million
Emp.: 140
Rubber Product & Glass Mfr
N.A.I.C.S.: 326299

Avon Milk-Rite USA Inc.   (1)
110 Lincoln St, Johnson Creek, WI 53038-0009
Tel.: (920) 699-3431
Web Site: http://www.avon-rubber.com
Sales Range: $50-74.9 Million
Emp.: 140
Rubber Product & Glass Mfr
N.A.I.C.S.: 326299
Larry Gunderson (Gen Mgr)

Avon Polymer Products Limited   (1)
Hampton Park West, Semington Rd, Melksham, SN12 6NB, Wiltshire, United Kingdom   **(100%)**
Tel.: (44) 1225896811
Web Site: http://www.milkrite-interpuls.com
Sales Range: $50-74.9 Million
Emp.: 150
Rubber & Plastics Hoses & Belting Mfr
N.A.I.C.S.: 326220

Avon Protection Systems, Inc.   (1)
503 8th St, Cadillac, MI 49601-9282
Tel.: (231) 779-6200
Web Site: http://www.avon-protection.com
Sales Range: $100-124.9 Million
Emp.: 300
Respiratory Protection Mask Mfr
N.A.I.C.S.: 339113

Avon Rubber & Plastics Inc.   (1)
    (100%)
Tel.: (231) 775-6571
Web Site: http://www.avon-rubber.com
Sales Range: $150-199.9 Million
Emp.: 500
Rubber Products Mfr
N.A.I.C.S.: 326199
Scott Marish (Controller)

Avon Rubber Overseas Limited   (1)
Hampton Park West, Semington Road, Melksham, SN12 6NB, Wiltshire, United Kingdom   **(100%)**
Tel.: (44) 1225896300
Sales Range: $50-74.9 Million
Emp.: 150
Rubber & Plastics Hoses & Belting Mfr
N.A.I.C.S.: 326220

Avon Rubber Pension Trust Limited   (1)
Hampton Park West, Melksham, SN12 6NB, Wiltshire, United Kingdom
Tel.: (44) 1225896300
Web Site: http://www.avon-rubber.com
Sales Range: $100-124.9 Million
Emp.: 150
Pension Investment Advisory Services
N.A.I.C.S.: 525110

AVONDALE FOOD STORES LIMITED
4520 Jordan Rd, Jordan Station, Lincoln, L0R 1S0, ON, Canada
Tel.: (905) 562-4173
Web Site:
   http://www.avondalestores.com

Sales Range: $100-124.9 Million
Emp.: 800
Convenience Store
N.A.I.C.S.: 445131
Frank Stewart (Head-Pur)

AVONMORE CAPITAL & MANAGEMENT SERVICES LTD.
F-33/3 Okhla Industrial Area Phase II, New Delhi, 110020, India
Tel.: (91) 1143500700
Web Site: https://avonmorecapital.in
Year Founded: 1991
AVONMORE—(NSE)
Rev.: $11,902,036
Assets: $51,060,637
Liabilities: $12,259,229
Net Worth: $38,801,408
Earnings: $5,521,466
Emp.: 10
Fiscal Year-end: 03/31/22
Financial Management Services
N.A.I.C.S.: 523999
Shilpa Bhatia (Compliance Officer & Sec)

AVONSIDE GROUP SERVICES LIMITED
The Courtyard Green Lane, Heywood, OL10 2EX, Lancs, United Kingdom
Tel.: (44) 800 731 5982   UK
Web Site:
   http://www.avonsidegroup.co.uk
Year Founded: 1988
Envelope Contractors; Roofing Services (Solar Photovoltaic & Solar Thermal Roof Panels)
N.A.I.C.S.: 238160
Eddie Stanton (CEO)

Subsidiaries:

Bracknell Roofing Ltd.   (1)
Lichfield Road Branston, Burton-on-Trent, DE14 3HD, Staffordshire, United Kingdom
Tel.: (44) 8705 626800
Web Site: http://www.bracknellroofing.com
Roofing Contracting Services
N.A.I.C.S.: 238160
Simon Smith (Mng Dir)

AVRASYA GAYRIMENKUL YATIRIM ORTAKLIGI A.S.
Buyukdere Cad No 171 Metrocity A Blok K 17 1, Levent - Sisli, Istanbul, Turkiye
Tel.: (90) 2123441288
Web Site:
   http://www.avrasyayo.com.tr
Year Founded: 1994
AVGYO—(IST)
Rev.: $1,036,386
Assets: $37,887,196
Liabilities: $630,355
Net Worth: $37,256,841
Earnings: $530,781
Fiscal Year-end: 12/31/23
Portfolio Management Services
N.A.I.C.S.: 523940
Fatma Ozturk Gumussu (Chm)

AVRASYA PETROL VE TURISTIK TESISLER YATIRIMLAR AS
Resadiye Caddesi Cumhuriyet Koyu No 18, Beykoz, 34829, Istanbul, Turkiye
Tel.: (90) 2165533454
Web Site: https://www.avtur.com.tr
AVTUR—(IST)
Rev.: $392,337
Assets: $23,348,045
Liabilities: $3,318,237
Net Worth: $20,029,809
Earnings: $2,861,669
Fiscal Year-end: 12/31/23
Financial Investment Services
N.A.I.C.S.: 523999

Ayten Ozturk Unal (Chm)

AVRICORE HEALTH INC.
1120-789 West Pender Street, Vancouver, V6C1H2, BC, Canada
Tel.: (604) 613-4336   BC
Web Site: https://avricore.com
Year Founded: 2000
AVCNF   (OTCQB)
Rev.: $2,574,534
Assets: $1,875,013
Liabilities: $390,942
Net Worth: $1,484,071
Earnings: ($517,999)
Emp.: 1
Fiscal Year-end: 12/31/23
Pharmaceutical Technology Services
N.A.I.C.S.: 325412
David M. Hall (Chm)

AVRIL SCA
11 Rue Monceau CS 60003, 75378, Paris, Cedex 08, France
Tel.: (33) 1 4069 4800   FR
Web Site: http://www.groupeavril.com
Year Founded: 2013
Holding Company; Renewable Chemistry, Renewable Energy, Animal Nutrition & Human Nutrition Products & Services
N.A.I.C.S.: 551112
Jean-Philippe Puig (CEO)

Subsidiaries:

Biogemma S.A.S.   (1)
5 rue Saint-Germain l'Auxerrois, 75001, Paris, France
Tel.: (33) 155349400
Web Site: http://www.biogemma.com
Emp.: 80
Agricultural Seed Genetic Research & Development
N.A.I.C.S.: 541715

Oleon N.V.   (1)
Assenedestraat 2, 9940, Ertvelde, Belgium
Tel.: (32) 93411011
Web Site: http://www.oleon.com
Sales Range: $500-549.9 Million
Oleochemical Products Mfr & Developer of Biodiesel Production Systems
N.A.I.C.S.: 311225
Moussa Naciri (Mng Dir)

Sofiproteol S.A.   (1)
11 rue de Monceau, CS 60003, 75378, Paris, Cedex 08, France
Tel.: (33) 140694800
Web Site: http://www.sofiproteol.com
Agricultural Investment Holding Company
N.A.I.C.S.: 551112
Claire Maingon (Mng Dir & Asst Dir-Commitments)

Holding (Domestic):

Doux SA   (2)
ZI Lospars, BP 22, 29150, Chateaulin, France   **(52.5%)**
Tel.: (33) 298866900
Web Site: http://www.doux.com
Poultry & Poultry Products Production, Processing & Marketing
N.A.I.C.S.: 311615
Severine Martinez (Mgr-Publi)

AVRIO VENTURES LTD.
Crowfoot West Business Centre Suite 235 600 Crowfoot Crescent NW, Calgary, T3G 0B4, AB, Canada
Tel.: (403) 215-5492
Web Site:
   http://www.avriocapital.com
Year Founded: 2006
Privater Equity Firm
N.A.I.C.S.: 523999
Aki Georgacacos (Co-Founder & Mng Dir)

AVRO INDIA LIMITED
A-7/36-39 South of GT Road Industrial Areas Opp, Rathi Udyog Ltd

Electrosteel Casting Compound, Ghaziabad, 201009, India
Tel.: (91) 9910039125
Web Site:
   https://www.avrofurniture.com
Year Founded: 2002
AVROIND—(NSE)
Rev.: $7,312,551
Assets: $3,043,158
Liabilities: $983,496
Net Worth: $2,059,662
Earnings: $247,311
Emp.: 44
Fiscal Year-end: 03/31/21
Plastics Product Mfr
N.A.I.C.S.: 326111

AVROT INDUSTRIES LTD.
Kibbutz, Be'erot Yitzhak, 60905, Israel
Tel.: (972) 39375027
Web Site: https://www.avrot.co.il
Year Founded: 1984
AVRT—(TAE)
Rev.: $40,573,283
Assets: $65,528,387
Liabilities: $36,645,116
Net Worth: $28,883,271
Earnings: $411,935
Fiscal Year-end: 12/31/23
All Other Miscellaneous Fabricated Metal Product Manufacturing
N.A.I.C.S.: 332999

Subsidiaries:

Paladex Ltd.   (1)
Kibbut Beerot, Be'erot Yitzhak, 60905, Israel
Tel.: (972) 39375065
Steel Pipe Mfr & Distr
N.A.I.C.S.: 331210

AVRUPA MINERALS LTD.
410-325 Howe Street, Vancouver, V6C 1Z7, BC, Canada
Tel.: (604) 687-3520   BC
Web Site:
   https://www.avrupaminerals.com
Year Founded: 2008
AVU—(TSXV)
Rev.: $363
Assets: $706,812
Liabilities: $73,974
Net Worth: $632,839
Earnings: ($41,945)
Emp.: 2
Fiscal Year-end: 12/31/23
Mineral Exploration Services
N.A.I.C.S.: 213114
Paul W. Kuhn (Pres & CEO)

AVRUPA YATIRIM HOLDING AS
Senlikkoy Mah Florya Cad Yeni Baglar Sok No 6, Istanbul, Turkiye
Tel.: (90) 2129141246
Web Site:
   https://www.avrupayatirimholding.com.tr
Year Founded: 1998
AVHOL—(IST)
Rev.: $3,197,935
Assets: $8,918,991
Liabilities: $2,707,267
Net Worth: $6,211,724
Earnings: $200,476
Fiscal Year-end: 12/31/22
Investment Holding Company Services
N.A.I.C.S.: 551112
Ramazan Burak Telli (Chm)

AVSL INDUSTRIES LTD.
1001 10th Floor NDM Tower - II NSP, Pitampura, Delhi, 110034, India
Tel.: (91) 1145561234
Web Site: https://www.avsl.co.in
Year Founded: 2003

AVSL—(NSE)
Rev.: $13,859,200
Assets: $10,310,268
Liabilities: $5,866,988
Net Worth: $4,443,280
Earnings: $803,971
Emp.: 291
Fiscal Year-end: 03/31/22
Power Cable Raw Material Mfr
N.A.I.C.S.: 335929
Sanjay Bansal (Founder & Mng Dir)

AVT NATURAL PRODUCTS LTD.
Plot No 225 /1A 5-7, Kaipoorikkara
Vazhakulam Marampilly Post, Aluva,
683 105, Kerala, India
Tel.: (91) 4842677262
Web Site: https://www.avtnatural.com
519105—(BOM)
Rev.: $77,748,967
Assets: $61,256,491
Liabilities: $10,922,225
Net Worth: $50,334,266
Earnings: $9,944,066
Emp.: 320
Fiscal Year-end: 03/31/22
Grinding Spices Mfr
N.A.I.C.S.: 311942
Alex K. Abraham (CMO & Sr VP)

Subsidiaries:

AVT Tea Services North America
LLC   (1)
8805 Tamiami Trl N Ste 160, Naples, FL
34108
Tel.: (201) 218-5936
Web Site: http://www.avttea.com
Tea Mfr
N.A.I.C.S.: 311920

AVTECH SWEDEN AB
Farogatan 33, 164 51, Kista, Sweden
Tel.: (46) 854410480
Web Site: https://avtech.aero
AVT.B—(OMX)
Rev.: $1,497,922
Assets: $3,731,986
Liabilities: $498,086
Net Worth: $3,233,899
Earnings: ($242,939)
Emp.: 8
Fiscal Year-end: 12/31/20
Digital Air Traffic Management
N.A.I.C.S.: 488190
Christer Fehrling (Mktg Dir)

Subsidiaries:

AVTECH France SARL   (1)
Aeropole 3 5 Avenue Albert Durand, 31700,
Blagnac, France
Tel.: (33) 561300400
Oil Transportation Services
N.A.I.C.S.: 488190

AVTECH Middle East LLC   (1)
Al Garhoud 57th Street Bu Shaqar Building
Office # 301, PO Box 97332, Dubai, United
Arab Emirates
Tel.: (971) 4 250 44 66
Oil Transportation Services
N.A.I.C.S.: 488190

AviaQ AB   (1)
Lonnvagen 2, SE-184 43, Akersberga, Swe-
den
Tel.: (46) 8 544 104 80
Web Site: http://www.aviaq.com
Oil Transportation Services
N.A.I.C.S.: 488190

AVTIL ENTERPRISE LIMITED
1/204 Navjivan Society 2nd Floor,
Lamington Road, Mumbai, 400 008,
India
Tel.: (91) 22 23071996
Web Site:
http://www.avtradeinvest.com
Year Founded: 1982
Rev.: $497,793

Assets: $1,296,962
Liabilities: $130,460
Net Worth: $1,166,501
Earnings: ($2,777,764)
Emp.: 2
Fiscal Year-end: 03/31/19
Financial Services
N.A.I.C.S.: 523999
Gautam R. Bhandari (CFO)

AVTODOM OAO
Zorge Street 17 bld 1, Moscow,
125252, Russia
Tel.: (7) 495145685
Web Site: https://avtodom.ru
Emp.: 100
Motor Vehicles Mfr
N.A.I.C.S.: 336211

Subsidiaries:

Mercedes-Benz Russia SAO   (1)
Leningradsky Prospek 39a, 125167, Mos-
cow, Russia
Tel.: (7) 4957452600
Web Site: http://www.mercedes-benz.ru
Sales Range: $200-249.9 Million
Emp.: 800
New Car Dealers
N.A.I.C.S.: 441110
Evgenia Schwaljowa (Head-Fleet Sls-Cars)

AVTOTEHNA, D.D.
Litijska 259, Ljubljana, 1000, Slovenia
Tel.: (386) 15853800
Web Site: http://www.avtotehna.si
Year Founded: 1953
Sales Range: $350-399.9 Million
Emp.: 1,200
Holding Company
N.A.I.C.S.: 551112
Jordan Kocjancic (Chm)

Subsidiaries:

AT Adria d.o.o.   (1)
Litijska 259, 1261, Ljubljana, Dobrunje, Slo-
venia
Tel.: (386) 15853728
Web Site: http://www.atadria.com
Wholesale Trade Agents & Brokers
N.A.I.C.S.: 425120

Advertus d.o.o.   (1)
Slovenceva ulica 24, 1000, Ljubljana, Slo-
venia
Tel.: (386) 15853711
Sales Range: $25-49.9 Million
Emp.: 15
Wholesale Trade Agents & Brokers
N.A.I.C.S.: 425120

Atrik d.o.o.   (1)
Litijska Cesta 261, 1261, Ljubljana, Slove-
nia
Tel.: (386) 15208700
Web Site: http://www.atrik.si
Wholesale Trade Agents & Brokers
N.A.I.C.S.: 425120

Avtera d.o.o.   (1)
Smartinska 106, 1000, Ljubljana, Slovenia
Tel.: (386) 15853610
Web Site: http://www.avtera.si
Sales Range: $75-99.9 Million
Emp.: 120
Wholesale Trade Agents & Brokers
N.A.I.C.S.: 425120
Damjan Celofiga (Mng Dir)

Avtotehna Oprema d.o.o.   (1)
Litijska cesta 259, 1261, Ljubljana, Slovenia
Tel.: (386) 15853700
Web Site: http://www.at-oprema.si
Emp.: 10
Wholesale Trade Agent & Broker Services
N.A.I.C.S.: 425120

Avtotehna VIS d.o.o.   (1)
Celovska Cesta 228, 1000, Ljubljana, Slo-
venia
Tel.: (386) 15818510
Web Site: http://www.avtotehna-vis.si
Automobile Sales
N.A.I.C.S.: 336110
Bojan Muravec (Gen Mgr)

Birotehna d.o.o.   (1)
Smartinska 106, Ljubljana, Slovenia
Tel.: (386) 15853410
Web Site: http://www.birotehna.si
Wholesale Trade Agents & Brokers
N.A.I.C.S.: 425120

Istra Avto d.o.o.   (1)
Smarska Cesta 5A, Koper, 6000, Slovenia
Tel.: (386) 56682300
Web Site: http://www.istra-avto.si
Sales Range: $25-49.9 Million
Emp.: 30
Wholesale Trade Agents & Brokers
N.A.I.C.S.: 425120
Iztok Klabjan (Gen Mgr)

Repro-MS 03 d.o.o.   (1)
Dolenjska cesta 242 C, 1000, Ljubljana,
Slovenia
Tel.: (386) 15853577
Web Site: http://www.reproms.si
Sales Range: $50-74.9 Million
Emp.: 10
Wholesale Trade Agents & Brokers
N.A.I.C.S.: 425120
Ivo Rojec (CEO)

Swaty d.d.   (1)
Titova cesta 60, 2000, Maribor,
Slovenia   (73%)
Tel.: (386) 23331600
Web Site: http://www.swatycomet.si
Sales Range: $25-49.9 Million
Emp.: 610
Grinding Wheel Mfr
N.A.I.C.S.: 333517
Ales Mikeln (Gen Mgr)

AVVAA WORLD HEALTH CARE PRODUCTS INC.
#4 4602 31st Street, Vernon, V1T
5J9, BC, Canada   NV
Web Site: http://www.avvaa.com
Year Founded: 1998
AVVH—(OTCIQ)
Sales Range: Less than $1 Million
Emp.: 2
Skin Care & Animal Care Pharma-
ceuticals Mfr & Distr
N.A.I.C.S.: 325412
Lance Loose (CEO)

AVY PRECISION TECHNOL-OGY, INC.
10F No 101 Fu-Hsing North Road,
Taipei, Taiwan
Tel.: (886) 225472089
Web Site: http://www.avy.com.tw
Year Founded: 1975
Sales Range: $75-99.9 Million
Emp.: 5,080
Professional Camera Parts Distr
N.A.I.C.S.: 449210
Mincheng Li (Gen Mgr-Garments)

Subsidiaries:

AVY Co., Ltd.   (1)
No 56 Sec 2 Yatan Rd, Tanzi Dist, Taic-
hung, 42752, Taiwan
Tel.: (886) 425342600
Aluminium Ore Mfr
N.A.I.C.S.: 331314
Jiong-Xiong Dong (Chm)

Avy Precision Metal Components
(Suzhou) Co., Ltd   (1)
No 7 Chunqiu Road Panyang Industr, Su-
zhou, 215143, China
Tel.: (86) 51265718899
Metal Stamping Distr
N.A.I.C.S.: 424610

Dong Guan Cheng Guang Metal
Products Co., Ltd.   (1)
Xin Tang Industrial Park, Houjie, Dongguan,
Guangdong, China
Tel.: (86) 7695926110
Aluminium Ore Mfr
N.A.I.C.S.: 331314
Jun-Yi Dong (Chm)

Dong Guang Ying Hua Precision
Metal Co., Ltd.   (1)

No 8 Songbai Rd, South China Industrial
Park Liaobu Town, Dongguan, Guangdong,
China
Tel.: (86) 76982316661
Aluminium Ore Mfr
N.A.I.C.S.: 331314
Jun-Yi Dong (Chm)

AWA PAPER & TECHNOLOGI-CAL COMPANY INC.
3-10-18 Minamiyaso-cho, Tokushima,
770-0005, Tokushima, Japan
Tel.: (81) 886318100
Web Site:
https://www.awapaper.co.jp
Year Founded: 1916
3896—(TKS)
Rev.: $106,520,150
Assets: $140,436,060
Liabilities: $94,939,430
Net Worth: $45,496,630
Earnings: $343,720
Emp.: 640
Fiscal Year-end: 03/31/24
Paper Products Mfr
N.A.I.C.S.: 322120
Yasuo Yoshii (Auditor)

Subsidiaries:

AWA PAPER (SHANGHAI) Co.,
LTD.   (1)
No 355 Liantang Road Spark Development
Zone, Pudong New Zone, Shanghai,
201419, China
Tel.: (86) 21 5750 5800
Paper Products Mfr
N.A.I.C.S.: 322120
S. Azuma (Gen Mgr)

Thai United Awa Paper Co., Ltd. (1)
36 Moo 7 Bangna-Trad Rd T Bangkaew,
Bang Phli, 10540, Samutprakarn, Thailand
Tel.: (66) 27517026
Web Site: https://www.tuapaper.com
Paper Products Mfr
N.A.I.C.S.: 322120

AWAKN LIFE SCIENCES CORP.
301-217 Queen Street W, Toronto,
M5V 0R2, ON, Canada
Tel.: (604) 240-3114   BC
Web Site:
https://www.awaknlifesciences.com
Year Founded: 2018
AWKNF—(OTCQB)
Rev.: $1,115,526
Assets: $3,277,646
Liabilities: $3,314,754
Net Worth: ($37,108)
Earnings: ($7,288,404)
Emp.: 44
Fiscal Year-end: 01/31/23
Biotechnology Research & Develop-
ment Services
N.A.I.C.S.: 541714
Anthony Tennyson (CEO)

AWALE RESOURCES LTD.
8681 Clay Street, Mission, V4S 1E7,
BC, Canada
Tel.: (604) 410-2277
Web Site:
https://www.awaleresources.com
ARIC—(TSXV)
Rev.: $18,907
Assets: $6,915,485
Liabilities: $1,386,240
Net Worth: $5,529,245
Earnings: ($1,045,475)
Fiscal Year-end: 12/31/23
Metal Exploration Services
N.A.I.C.S.: 213114
Glen Parsons (CEO)

AWANBIRU TECHNOLOGY BERHAD
Block 11B Star Central Lingkaran Cy-

AwanBiru Technology Berhad—(Continued)

ber Point Timur Cyber 1, 63000, Cyberjaya, Selangor, Malaysia
Tel.: (60) 386897000
Web Site: https://www.awantec.my
Year Founded: 2003
AWANTEC—(KLS)
Rev.: $8,458,836
Assets: $89,039,153
Liabilities: $49,101,587
Net Worth: $39,937,566
Earnings: ($1,388,783)
Emp.: 131
Fiscal Year-end: 06/30/23
IT Training Services
N.A.I.C.S.: 611420
Abu Hasan Ismail *(Founder, Pres & CEO)*

AWARDIT AB
Snickarbacken 2, 111 39, Stockholm, 111 39, Sweden
Tel.: (46) 84114000
Web Site: https://www.awardit.com
Year Founded: 1999
AWRD—(OMX)
Rev.: $34,012,709
Assets: $37,233,179
Liabilities: $18,738,059
Net Worth: $18,495,120
Earnings: $2,673,552
Emp.: 50
Fiscal Year-end: 12/31/20
Advertising & Marketing Services
N.A.I.C.S.: 541810
Niklas Lundqvist *(Founder)*

AWARE SUPER PTY LTD
Level 22 388 George Street, Sydney, 2000, NSW, Australia
Tel.: (61) 1300650873   **AU**
Web Site: http://aware.com.au
Superannuation Fund; Investment Advice & Wealth Managemmt Services
N.A.I.C.S.: 524292
Deanne Stewart *(CEO)*
Subsidiaries:

Vocus Group Ltd.   **(1)**
Level 12 60 Miller Street, North Sydney, 2060, NSW, Australia
Tel.: (61) 289998999
Web Site: http://www.vocus.com.au
Sales Range: $550-599.9 Million
Telecommunication Servicesb
N.A.I.C.S.: 517810
Ashe-lee Jegathesann *(Gen Counsel & Sec)*

Subsidiary (Domestic):

Amnet Broadband Pty. Ltd.   **(2)**
Level 6 202 Pier St, Perth, 6000, WA, Australia
Tel.: (61) 1300539986
Web Site: http://www.amnet.com.au
Emp.: 150
Broadband Internet Providers
N.A.I.C.S.: 517810
Ryan Punter *(Bus Mgr)*

Eftel Pty Limited   **(2)**
Level 10 452 Flinders Street, Melbourne, 3000, VIC, Australia
Tel.: (61) 3 9090 2525
Web Site: http://www.eftel.com.au
Broadband Network Operator
N.A.I.C.S.: 517810

Subsidiary (Domestic):

Engin Limited   **(3)**
Level 3 28 Rodborough Road, French's Forest, 2086, NSW, Australia
Tel.: (61) 290044444
Web Site: http://www.engin.com.au
Sales Range: $10-24.9 Million
VoIP Services
N.A.I.C.S.: 517810

OntheNet   **(3)**

165 Varsity Parade Level 1, PO Box 102, Varsity Lakes, Gold Coast, 4227, QLD, Australia
Tel.: (61) 7 55539222
Web Site: http://www.onthenet.com.au
Internet Services, DSL & Broadband Services
N.A.I.C.S.: 517111

Subsidiary (Domestic):

LSP Communications Pty Limited   **(2)**
U 3a 100 Station St, Nunawading, VIC, Australia
Tel.: (61) 398722935
Electronic Parts & Equipment Merchant Whslr
N.A.I.C.S.: 423690

M2 Commander Pty. Ltd.   **(2)**
76 Berry Street, Sydney, 2060, NSW, Australia
Tel.: (61) 2 9030 1605
Web Site: http://www.commander.com.au
Business Telecommunications Products & Services
N.A.I.C.S.: 561499

Multelink Services Pty Limited   **(2)**
Suite101 29-31 Solent Circuit, 2153, Baulkham Hills, NSW, Australia
Tel.: (61) 1300309360
Web Site: http://www.multelink.com.au
Telecommunications
N.A.I.C.S.: 517810
Vaughan Bowen *(CEO & Mng Dir)*

Perth International Exchange Pty Ltd   **(2)**
1 William Street, Perth, 6000, WA, Australia
Tel.: (61) 892166600
Web Site: http://www.perthix.com
Information Technology Consulting Services
N.A.I.C.S.: 541512

Primus Telecom Pty. Ltd.   **(2)**
Level 3 538 Collins Street West, Melbourne, 3000, VIC, Australia
Tel.: (61) 399230785
Web Site: http://www.iprimus.com.au
Holding Company; Telecommunications & Internet Services
N.A.I.C.S.: 551112

Subsidiary (Domestic):

0014 Pty. Ltd.   **(3)**
GPO Box 4618, Melbourne, 3001, VIC, Australia
Tel.: (61) 1300140014
Web Site: http://www.0014.com.au
Discounted International Telecommunications Services
N.A.I.C.S.: 517810

Primus Telecommunications (Australia) Pty. Ltd.   **(3)**
Level 3 538 Collins Street West, Melbourne, 3000, VIC, Australia
Tel.: (61) 300854485
Web Site: http://www.iprimus.com.au
Telecommunication Servicesb
N.A.I.C.S.: 517112

Subsidiary (Domestic):

Vocus Fibre Pty Limited   **(2)**
L 1 189 Miller St, North Sydney, North Sydney, 2060, NSW, Australia
Tel.: (61) 1300889988
Web Site: http://www.vocus.com.au
Sales Range: $25-49.9 Million
Emp.: 80
Telecommunication & Data Centre Services
N.A.I.C.S.: 517810
Alex West *(Mng Dir)*

Vocus Group Limited   **(2)**
L 1 Vocus House 189 Miller St, North Sydney, Sydney, 2060, NSW, Australia
Tel.: (61) 2 8999 8999
Web Site: http://www.vocus.com.au
Emp.: 55
Telecommunication Servicesb
N.A.I.C.S.: 517810
Robert Mansfield *(Chm)*

Vocus Pty Limited   **(2)**
L 1 Vocus House 189 Miller St, North Sydney, Sydney, 2060, NSW, Australia

Tel.: (61) 289998999
Web Site: http://www.vocus.com.au
Emp.: 12
Telecommunication Servicesb
N.A.I.C.S.: 517810
Doug Sayce *(CEO)*

AWAX S.P.A.
Otrada Quaglia 20, 10020, Cantena, TO, Italy
Tel.: (39) 011 945 5511   **IT**
Web Site: https://www.awax.it
Emp.: 100
Wax Mfr & Distr
N.A.I.C.S.: 424690
Giuseppe Ambroggio *(CEO)*

Subsidiaries:

Hywax GmbH   **(1)**
Worthdamm 13-27, 20457, Hamburg, Germany
Tel.: (49) 40781150
Web Site: https://www.hywax.com
Specialty Chemicals Mfr & Distr
N.A.I.C.S.: 325998

AWC BERHAD
Tel.: (60) 380244505
Web Site: https://www.awc.com.my
AWC—(KLS)
Rev.: $80,699,406
Assets: $93,863,050
Liabilities: $31,082,024
Net Worth: $62,781,026
Earnings: $2,283,997
Emp.: 1,081
Fiscal Year-end: 06/30/23
Building Automation System Mfr
N.A.I.C.S.: 238210
Sor Hua Tea *(Sec)*

Subsidiaries:

Ambang Wira Sdn. Bhd.   **(1)**
20-2 Subang Business Centre Jalan USJ 9/5T, 47620, Subang Jaya, Selangor, Malaysia
Tel.: (60) 380244505
Web Site: https://www.awc.com.my
Sales Range: $75-99.9 Million
Emp.: 300
Industrial Engineering Services
N.A.I.C.S.: 541330

DD Techniche Sdn. Bhd.   **(1)**
No 11-3 Jalan USJ 21/1, 47630, Subang Jaya, Selangor, Malaysia
Tel.: (60) 380818630
Web Site: https://www.ddtechniche.com
Building Construction Services
N.A.I.C.S.: 236220

Environmental and Landscape Services Sdn. Bhd.   **(1)**
18-5 Subang Business Centre Jalan USJ 9/5T UEP, 47620, Subang Jaya, Selangor, Malaysia
Tel.: (60) 380244505
Landscaping Services
N.A.I.C.S.: 561730

Infinite QL Sdn. Bhd.   **(1)**
A-19-01 Tower A Pinnacle Petaling Jaya Lorong Utara C, 46300, Petaling Jaya, Selangor, Malaysia   **(51%)**
Tel.: (60) 122312388
Web Site: https://www.infiniteql.com
Sales Range: $25-49.9 Million
Emp.: 60
Surveillance & Communication System Mfr
N.A.I.C.S.: 334220
P. Deivindran *(Mng Dir)*

Subsidiary (Domestic):

Cardax Sales & Services Sdn. Bhd.   **(2)**
G 02 Ground Floor Block A Dataran Hamodal, No 4 Jalan 13/4 Section 13, 46300, Petaling Jaya, Selangor Darul Ehsan, Malaysia
Tel.: (60) 379626688
Sales Range: $50-74.9 Million
Emp.: 70

Industrial Electronic Systems Sales & Maintenance Services
N.A.I.C.S.: 423690

Device 4U Sdn. Bhd.   **(2)**
G 02 Block A Dataran Hamodal No 4 Jalan 13/4, 4 Jalan 13 4, 46200, Petaling Jaya, Selangor, Malaysia
Tel.: (60) 379626688
Sales Range: $25-49.9 Million
Surveillance & Communication System Mfr
N.A.I.C.S.: 334511

Meps Devices Sdn. Bhd.   **(2)**
G 02 Block A Dataran Hamodal, No 4 Jalan 13 4 Section 13, 46200, Petaling Jaya, Selangor, Malaysia
Tel.: (60) 379626688
Web Site: http://www.infiniteql.com
Sales Range: $25-49.9 Million
Emp.: 60
Surveillance & Communication System Mfr
N.A.I.C.S.: 334511

Vdosoft Sdn. Bhd.   **(2)**
A-19-01 Pinnacle Petaling Jaya Lorong Utara C Pjs 52, 46200, Petaling Jaya, Selangor, Malaysia
Tel.: (60) 379626688
Web Site: https://www.vdosoft.com
Sales Range: $25-49.9 Million
Emp.: 70
Digital Video Technological Research & Development Services
N.A.I.C.S.: 541715

M&C Engineering & Trading Sdn. Bhd.   **(1)**
79 Jalan SS25 2, Taman Bukit Emas, 47301, Petaling Jaya, Selangor, Malaysia
Tel.: (60) 378039511
Electrical Engineering Services
N.A.I.C.S.: 541330

Qudotech Sdn. Bhd.   **(1)**
11-3 Jalan USJ 21/1 UEP, 47640, Subang Jaya, Selangor Darul Ehsan, Malaysia
Tel.: (60) 380246566
Web Site: https://www.qudotech.com.my
Building Construction Services
N.A.I.C.S.: 236220
Chee Kar Ming *(Mng Dir)*

STREAM Environment Sdn. Bhd. **(1)**
11 Jalan Sungai Besi Indah 5/2, Taman Sungai Besi Indah, 43300, Seri Kembangan, Selangor Darul Ehsan, Malaysia   **(51%)**
Tel.: (60) 389418118
Web Site: http://www.nexaldes.com
Emp.: 80
Automated Waste Collection System Mfr
N.A.I.C.S.: 221320

Subsidiary (Non-US):

STREAM Environment (S) Pte. Ltd.   **(2)**
Block 9002 Tampines Street 93 02-38, Singapore, 528836, Singapore
Tel.: (65) 68484366
Web Site: https://www.stream-environment.com
Emp.: 20
Waste Collection Services
N.A.I.C.S.: 562111

Stream Environment Sdn. Bhd.   **(1)**
11 Jalan Sungai Besi Indah 5/2 Taman Sungai Besi Indah, 43300, Seri Kembangan, Selangor Darul Ehsan, Malaysia
Tel.: (60) 389418118
Web Site: https://www.stream-environment.com
Full Vacuum System Mfr
N.A.I.C.S.: 335210
Skanda Rajah *(Exec Dir)*

Trackwork & Supplies Sdn. Bhd. **(1)**
No 31-5 Level 5 Dataran Prima Block F2 Jalan PJU 1/42A, 47301, Petaling Jaya, Selangor, Malaysia   **(60%)**
Tel.: (60) 378049799
Web Site: https://www.trackwork.com.my
Rail Welding Services
N.A.I.C.S.: 811310

AWE PLC

Aldermaston, Reading, RG7 4PR, Berkshire, United Kingdom
Tel.: (44) 1189814111
Web Site: http://www.awe.co.uk
Sales Range: $550-599.9 Million
Emp.: 8,000
Nuclear Warhead Maintenance Services
N.A.I.C.S.: 928110
Lindsey Appleton *(Sec)*

AWEA MECHANTRONIC CO., LTD.
629 Suezhetou Section KwanPu Rd, Wenshan Li Xinpu, Hsinchu, 305043, Taiwan
Tel.: (886) 35885191
Web Site: https://www.awea.com
Year Founded: 1986
1530—(TAI)
Rev.: $77,239,835
Assets: $194,966,833
Liabilities: $84,185,157
Net Worth: $110,781,676
Earnings: $6,223,421
Fiscal Year-end: 12/31/23
Boring & Milling Machinery Mfr
N.A.I.C.S.: 333517

Subsidiaries:

Awea Mechantronic (Suzhou) Ltd.   (1)
No 4888 East Lake Taihu Avenue, Wujiang Economic & Technological Development Zone, Jiangsu, 215200, China
Tel.: (86) 51282868200
Computer Numerical Control Machine Tool Mfr & Distr
N.A.I.C.S.: 333517

Awea Mechantronic Co., Ltd. - Taiwan Taichung Factory   (1)
No 15 Keyuan 2nd Road Central Taiwan, Science Park, Taichung, 407, Taiwan
Tel.: (886) 424629698
Industrial Machine Tool Mfr
N.A.I.C.S.: 333517

Best Way Mechantronic Co.   (1)
No 7801 Song Ze Road Qingpu Industrial Zone, Shanghai, 201700, China
Tel.: (86) 2169210588
Machine Tools Mfr
N.A.I.C.S.: 333517

AWF MADISON GROUP LIMITED
Level 6 51 Shortland Street, Auckland, 1010, New Zealand
Tel.: (64) 95268770
Web Site:
http://www.awfmadison.co.nz
Year Founded: 1988
Rev.: $179,415,960
Assets: $63,992,954
Liabilities: $40,665,295
Net Worth: $23,327,659
Earnings: $1,348,609
Emp.: 330
Fiscal Year-end: 03/31/19
Temporary Help Service
N.A.I.C.S.: 561320
Ross B. Keenan *(Chm)*

Subsidiaries:

Allied Work Force Christchurch Limited   (1)
320-324 Cashel St, Christchurch, 8011, Canterbury, New Zealand
Tel.: (64) 33729540
Web Site: http://www.aws.co.nz
Sales Range: $25-49.9 Million
Emp.: 4
Labor Hiring Services
N.A.I.C.S.: 561311

Allied Work Force Dunedin Limited   (1)
163 Hillside Road, Dunedin, 9012, Otago, New Zealand
Tel.: (64) 34555511

Web Site: http://www.awf.co.nz
Sales Range: $25-49.9 Million
Emp.: 3
Labor Hiring Services
N.A.I.C.S.: 561311

Allied Work Force Hamilton Limited   (1)
Unit 3 27 norten road, Te Rapa, Hamilton, 3204, Waikato, New Zealand
Tel.: (64) 78481815
Web Site: http://www.awf.co.nz
Sales Range: $25-49.9 Million
Emp.: 4
Labor Hiring Services
N.A.I.C.S.: 561311

Allied Work Force Nelson Limited   (1)
101 Bolt Rd, Tahunanui, Nelson, 7011, New Zealand
Tel.: (64) 35475467
Web Site: http://www.awf.co.nz
Sales Range: $25-49.9 Million
Emp.: 3
Labor Hiring Services
N.A.I.C.S.: 561311

Allied Work Force Palmerston North Limited   (1)
49 Victoria Ave, Palmerston North, 4410, New Zealand
Tel.: (64) 63558080
Web Site: http://www.awf.co.nz
Sales Range: $25-49.9 Million
Emp.: 3
Labor Hiring Services
N.A.I.C.S.: 561311

Allied Work Force Tauranga Limited   (1)
6 Marsh St, Tauranga, 3110, New Zealand
Tel.: (64) 75718575
Labor Hiring Services
N.A.I.C.S.: 561311

Allied Work Force Wellington Limited   (1)
182 Thorndon Quay, Petone, Wellington, 6011, New Zealand
Tel.: (64) 45665171
Web Site: http://www.awf.co.nz
Emp.: 9
Labor Hiring Services
N.A.I.C.S.: 561311

Allied Work Force Whangarei Limited   (1)
33b Commerce St, Whangarei, 0110, New Zealand
Tel.: (64) 94597272
Web Site: http://www.awf.co.nz
Sales Range: $25-49.9 Million
Emp.: 101
Labor Hiring Services
N.A.I.C.S.: 561311

Quin Workforce Limited   (1)
89 Thorndon Quay, Wellington, 6011, New Zealand
Tel.: (64) 45862761
Web Site: http://www.quin.co.nz
Sales Range: $25-49.9 Million
Emp.: 12
Labor Hiring Services
N.A.I.C.S.: 561311
Alex Parks *(Gen Mgr)*

AWILCO DRILLING PLC
7th Floor Suite 1 50 Broadway, Arnhall Business Park, London, SW1H 0BL, Aberdeen, United Kingdom
Tel.: (44) 1224737900   UK
Web Site:
https://www.awilcodrilling.com
Year Founded: 2009
AWLCF—(OTCEM)
Assets: $14,299,327
Liabilities: $171,952,046
Net Worth: ($157,652,719)
Earnings: ($180,503,081)
Emp.: 13
Fiscal Year-end: 12/31/22
Oil & Gas Drilling Services
N.A.I.C.S.: 213111
Sigurd E. Thorvildsen *(Chm)*

AWILCO LNG ASA
Beddingen 8 Aker Brygge, NO-0250, Oslo, Norway
Tel.: (47) 22014200
Web Site: http://www.awilcolng.no
0Q4G—(LSE)
Rev.: $51,541,000
Assets: $348,107,000
Liabilities: $221,720,000
Net Worth: $126,387,000
Earnings: $5,800,000
Emp.: 7
Fiscal Year-end: 12/31/22
LNG Vessel Owner & Operator
N.A.I.C.S.: 488510
Sigurd E. Thorvildsen *(Co-Chm)*

Subsidiaries:

Awilco LNG 1 AS   (1)
Beddingen 8, 250, Oslo, Norway
Tel.: (47) 22014200
Web Site: http://www.awilco.no
Liquefied Natural Gas Transportation Services
N.A.I.C.S.: 483111

Awilco LNG 2 AS   (1)
Beddingen 8, 250, Oslo, Norway
Tel.: (47) 22014200
Sales Range: $25-49.9 Million
Liquefied Natural Gas Transportation Services
N.A.I.C.S.: 483111

Awilco LNG 3 AS   (1)
Beddingen 8, 250, Oslo, Norway
Tel.: (47) 22014200
Sales Range: $25-49.9 Million
Liquefied Natural Gas Transportation Services
N.A.I.C.S.: 483111

Awilco LNG 4 AS   (1)
Beddingen 8, 0250, Oslo, Norway
Tel.: (47) 22014200
Emp.: 52
Liquefied Natural Gas Transportation Services
N.A.I.C.S.: 483111

Awilco LNG 5 AS   (1)
Beddingen 8 Aker Brygge, NO-0250, Oslo, Norway
Tel.: (47) 22014200
Liquefied Natural Gas Transportation Services
N.A.I.C.S.: 483111

Awilco LNG 6 AS   (1)
Beddingen 8, Oslo, 250, Norway
Tel.: (47) 22014200
Web Site: http://www.awilcolng.no
Sales Range: $25-49.9 Million
Liquefied Natural Gas Transportation Services
N.A.I.C.S.: 483111

Awilco LNG 7 AS   (1)
Beddingen 8, Oslo, 250, Norway
Tel.: (47) 22014200
Liquefied Natural Gas Transportation Services
N.A.I.C.S.: 483111

AWN HOLDINGS LIMITED
Level 11 153 Walker Street, North Sydney, 2060, NSW, Australia
Tel.: (61) 280839800   AU
Web Site: http://arowanaco.com
AWN—(ASX)
Rev.: $88,430,021
Assets: $137,821,332
Liabilities: $45,957,315
Net Worth: $91,864,017
Earnings: $42,976,917
Fiscal Year-end: 06/30/21
Investment Services
N.A.I.C.S.: 523999
Kevin Tser Fah Chin *(Founder, Exec Chm & CEO)*

Subsidiaries:

Auldhouse Computer Training Limited   (1)

Ground Floor 338 Ponsonby Road, PO Box 214, Ponsonby, Auckland, 1140, New Zealand
Tel.: (64) 93600338
Web Site: https://www.lumifywork.com
Information Technology Training Services
N.A.I.C.S.: 611420

Cool or Cosy (QLD) Pty. Ltd.   (1)
36 Computer Rd, Yatala, Gold Coast, 4207, QLD, Australia
Tel.: (61) 7 3804 6666
Web Site: http://www.coolorcosy.com.au
Air Condition Equipment Whslr
N.A.I.C.S.: 423730

Cool or Cosy Perth   (1)
109 Garling St O'Connor Unit 2, Perth, 6163, Western Australia, Australia
Tel.: (61) 893389000
Web Site:
http://www.coolorcosyperth.com.au
Supplier & Installer of Environmentally Friendly Cellulose Fiber Insulation
N.A.I.C.S.: 423330

ENS International Pty. Ltd.   (1)
Level 11 153 Walker St, North Sydney, 2060, NSW, Australia
Tel.: (61) 292999688
Web Site: https://www.negotiate.org
Negotiation Training Services
N.A.I.C.S.: 926150

EdventureCo Pty Ltd   (1)
Level 14 97 Creek Street, Brisbane, QLD, Australia
Tel.: (61) 7 3154 3236
Vocational & Professional Education & Training
N.A.I.C.S.: 923110
Lucas West *(Mgr-Digitl Strategy & Ops)*

Subsidiary (Domestic):

DDLS Australia Pty Ltd   (2)
Level 24 477 Pitt Street, Sydney, 2000, NSW, Australia
Tel.: (61) 2 8069 6280
Web Site: http://www.ddls.com.au
IT Technical Training, Certification & Professional Development Services
N.A.I.C.S.: 611420
Jon Lang *(CEO)*

Everthought Education Pty. Ltd.   (1)
Building 3 / 92 Mallard Way, Cannington, 6107, WA, Australia
Tel.: (61) 1300656498
Web Site: https://everthought.edu.au
Building & Construction Training Services
N.A.I.C.S.: 611519

Lumify Learn Pty. Ltd.   (1)
Level 24 477 Pitt Street, Sydney, 2000, NSW, Australia
Tel.: (61) 1800936230
Web Site: https://lumifylearn.com
Information Technology Training Services
N.A.I.C.S.: 611420

AWS ACHSLAGERWERK STASSFURT GMBH
An der Liethe 5, 39418, Stassfurt, Germany
Tel.: (49) 3925960402
Web Site: http://www.silbitz-group.com
Year Founded: 1896
Rev.: $33,409,084
Emp.: 175
Industrial Machinery Mfr
N.A.I.C.S.: 333248
Thomas Heb *(Mng Dir)*

Subsidiaries:

Proconnex GmbH   (1)
Eisenberg 27, Sachsen-Anhalt, 38855, Wernigerode, Germany
Tel.: (49) 1736756710
Web Site: https://www.proconnex.de
Industrial Machinery Distr
N.A.I.C.S.: 423830

AWWAL MODARABA MANAGEMENT LIMITED

AWWAL MODARABA MANAGEMENT LIMITED

Awwal Modaraba Management Limited—(Continued)

6th Floor Horizon Vista Plot No Commercial 10 Block No 4 Scheme No 5, Clifton, Karachi, Pakistan
Tel.: (92) 213 877 1685
Web Site: http://www.awwal.com.pk
Year Founded: 2014
AWWAL—(KAR)
Rev.: $1,193,855
Assets: $7,949,099
Liabilities: $319,261
Net Worth: $7,629,838
Earnings: $717,307
Fiscal Year-end: 06/30/19
Financial & Advisory Services
N.A.I.C.S.: 541611
Khalid Aziz Mirza *(Chm)*

AX INVESTMENTS PLC

AX House Mosta Road, Lija, LJA 9010, Malta
Tel.: (356) 23312114
Web Site:
http://www.axinvestmentsplc.com
Year Founded: 2001
AX24A—(MAL)
Rev.: $3,484,004
Assets: $73,783,183
Liabilities: $52,210,880
Net Worth: $21,572,303
Earnings: $748,401
Fiscal Year-end: 10/31/19
Investment Management Service
N.A.I.C.S.: 523940
Angelo Xuereb *(Chm)*

Subsidiaries:

AX Construction Limited **(1)**
Hardrocks Industrial Park, Burmarrad, Malta
Tel.: (356) 22584900
Web Site:
https://www.axconstruction.com.mt
Civil Engineering & Construction Services
N.A.I.C.S.: 541330

Hilltop Gardens Retirement Village Limited **(1)**
Triq l-Inkwina, In-Naxxar, Malta
Tel.: (356) 22351000
Web Site:
https://www.hilltopgardens.com.mt
Apartment Rental Services
N.A.I.C.S.: 531110

AXA COOPERATIVE INSURANCE COMPANY

Al Malik Abdullah Ibn Abdulaziz Rd, PO Box 753, Al Nuzha District, Riyadh, 11421, Saudi Arabia
Tel.: (966) 112730501
Web Site: https://www.gig.sa
Year Founded: 2009
8250—(SAU)
Rev.: $377,567,064
Assets: $770,208,039
Liabilities: $545,354,172
Net Worth: $224,853,867
Earnings: $36,882,816
Emp.: 370
Fiscal Year-end: 12/31/20
Insurance Agency Services
N.A.I.C.S.: 524210
Babar Ali Khan *(CFO)*

AXA S.A.

25 Avenue Matignon, 75008, Paris, France
Tel.: (33) 140755700 **FR**
Web Site: https://www.axa.com
Year Founded: 1816
AXAHF—(OTCQX)
Rev.: $92,313,721,174
Assets: $711,390,882,095
Liabilities: $653,550,060,805
Net Worth: $57,840,821,291
Earnings: $8,138,867,426
Emp.: 94,705
Fiscal Year-end: 12/31/23

Holding Company; Insurance & Financial Products, Including Reinsurance, Asset Management & Real Estate Services
N.A.I.C.S.: 551112
Helen Browne *(Gen Counsel-Grp)*

Subsidiaries:

AXA ART Versicherung AG **(1)**
Limmatstrasse 250, Zurich, 8005, Switzerland
Tel.: (41) 44 874 84 84
Web Site: http://www.axa-art.ch
Art Insurance Services
N.A.I.C.S.: 524298
David Saillen *(Mng Dir)*

Subsidiary (Non-US):

AXA ART **(2)**
Via Lazzaro Palazzi 2/A, 20124, Milan, Italy
Tel.: (39) 02 888 965 1
Web Site: http://www.axa-art.lt
Art Insurance Services
N.A.I.C.S.: 524298

AXA ART **(2)**
Chlodna 51, 00-867, Warsaw, Poland
Tel.: (48) 225999000
Art Insurance Services
N.A.I.C.S.: 524298

AXA ART - NEDERLAND **(2)**
Ginnekenweg 213, 4835 NA, Breda, Netherlands
Tel.: (31) 76 514 85 58
Web Site: http://www.axa-art.nl
Art Insurance Services
N.A.I.C.S.: 524298
Leo Kamp *(Mng Dir)*

AXA ART FRANCE **(2)**
19 Rue d'Orleans, 92200, Neuilly-sur-Seine, France
Tel.: (33) 1 46 40 85 85
Web Site: http://www.axa-art.fr
Art Insurance Services
N.A.I.C.S.: 524298
Christian Muller *(Mng Dir)*

AXA ART LUXEMBOURG **(2)**
1 Place de l Etoile, 1479, Luxembourg, Luxembourg
Tel.: (352) 4424241
Web Site: http://www.axa-art.lu
Art Insurance Services
N.A.I.C.S.: 524298

Subsidiary (US):

AXA Art Insurance Corporation **(2)**
3 W 35th St 11th Fl, New York, NY 10001
Tel.: (212) 415-8400
Web Site: http://www.axa-art-usa.com
Emp.: 25
Art Insurance Services
N.A.I.C.S.: 524298
Christiane Fischer *(Pres & CEO)*

Division (Non-US):

AXA Art Insurance Corporation - Canada **(3)**
500 King Street West Floor 3, Toronto, M5V 1L9, ON, Canada
Tel.: (437) 836-3566
Web Site: http://www.axa-art.ca
Sales Range: $50-74.9 Million
Emp.: 5
Art & Collectable Insurance Services
N.A.I.C.S.: 524298
Ann-Louise Seago *(VP)*

Subsidiary (Non-US):

AXA Fine Art China **(2)**
China Diamond Exchange Building 555 Pudian Rd, Pudong Xinqu, Shanghai, China
Tel.: (86) 2161563500
Art Insurance Services
N.A.I.C.S.: 524298

AXA Fine Art Hong Kong **(2)**
1204-05 Dch Commercial Centre 25 Westlands Road, Quarry Bay, China (Hong Kong)
Tel.: (852) 25272020
Web Site: http://www.axa.com.hk

Sales Range: $50-74.9 Million
Art Insurance Services
N.A.I.C.S.: 524298

AXA Fine Art Singapore **(2)**
8 Shenton Way 27-01 AXA Tower, Singapore, 068811, Singapore
Tel.: (65) 68804957
Sales Range: $200-249.9 Million
Emp.: 35
Art Insurance Services
N.A.I.C.S.: 524298
Charles Liu *(Mgr-Bus Dev)*

AXA Assicurazioni **(1)**
Corso Como 17, 20154, Milan, Italy **(100%)**
Tel.: (39) 02480841
Web Site: http://www.axa.it
Sales Range: $200-249.9 Million
Emp.: 400
Insurance
N.A.I.C.S.: 524128

AXA Assistance S.A. **(1)**
6 rue Andre Gide, 92321, Chatillon, Cedex, France **(100%)**
Tel.: (33) 155924000
Web Site: http://www.axa-assistance.com
Sales Range: $250-299.9 Million
Emp.: 1,000
Holding Company
N.A.I.C.S.: 551112

Subsidiary (Non-US):

AXA ASSISTANCE (BEIJING) Co., LTD. **(2)**
RM 2801 Palaze Eagle Tower B No 26 Xiao Yun Rd, Chaoyang District, Beijing, 100016, China
Tel.: (86) 1084685899
Web Site: http://www.axa-assistance.com.cn
Medical Assistance Services
N.A.I.C.S.: 923130

AXA Assistance **(2)**
Hvezdova 1689/2a, 140 62, Prague, Czech Republic
Tel.: (420) 272101099
Web Site: https://www.axa-assistance.cz
General Insurance Services
N.A.I.C.S.: 524298

AXA Assistance (UK) Ltd **(2)**
The Quadrangle 106-118 Station Road, Redhill, RH1 1PR, Surrey, United Kingdom
Tel.: (44) 1737815023
Web Site: http://www.axa-assistance.co.uk
Sales Range: $150-199.9 Million
Emp.: 442
General Insurance Services
N.A.I.C.S.: 524298

AXA Assistance Canada Inc. **(2)**
2001 Robert-Bourassa Bd Suite 1850, Montreal, H3A 2L8, QC, Canada
Tel.: (514) 285-9053
Web Site: http://www.axa-assistance.ca
Roadside Medical Assistance Services
N.A.I.C.S.: 923130

AXA Assistance Chile S.A **(2)**
Josue Smith Solar 280, Santiago, Chile
Tel.: (56) 229418903
Web Site: http://www.axa-assistance.cl
Sales Range: $25-49.9 Million
General Insurance Services
N.A.I.C.S.: 524298

AXA Assistance Deutschland GmbH **(2)**
Colonia-Allee 10-20, 51067, Cologne, Germany
Tel.: (49) 22180247000
Web Site: http://www.axapartners.de
General Insurance Services
N.A.I.C.S.: 524298

Subsidiary (Domestic):

AXA Assistance France **(2)**
6 Rue Andre Gide, 92320, Chatillon, Cedex, France **(100%)**
Tel.: (33) 155924000
Web Site: http://www.axa-assistance.com
Emp.: 2,941
Insurance
N.A.I.C.S.: 524128
Yves Masson *(Pres & Dir Gen)*

Subsidiary (Domestic):

Pluridis **(3)**
87 Rue Saint-Lazare, 75009, Paris, France **(60%)**
Tel.: (33) 155319595
Web Site: http://www.pluridis.tm.fr
Emp.: 5
Employee Support Services
N.A.I.C.S.: 561499

Subsidiary (Non-US):

AXA Assistance Japan Co., Ltd. **(2)**
1-3-13 Takanawa NBF Takanawa Building 7F, Minato-ku, Tokyo, 108-0074, Japan
Tel.: (81) 367448570
Web Site: https://www.axa-assistance.co.jp
Sales Range: $50-74.9 Million
General Insurance Services
N.A.I.C.S.: 524298

AXA Assistance Mexico SA de CV **(2)**
Insurgentes Sur 601 Piso 6 Col Napoles Del, Benito Juarez, Mexico, Mexico
Tel.: (52) 5552559426
Web Site: http://www.axa-assistance.com.mx
General Insurance Services
N.A.I.C.S.: 524210

AXA Assistance Ocean Indien Ltd **(2)**
No 8 DBM Building Industrial Zone Coromandel, Port Louis, Mauritius
Tel.: (230) 2330340
Web Site: http://www.axa-assistance-mauritius.com
General Insurance Services
N.A.I.C.S.: 524210

AXA Assistance Panama SA. **(2)**
Ave Via Espana Plaza Comercial San Fernando Local 1 y 2, Panama, Panama
Tel.: (507) 2049200
Web Site: http://www.axa-assistance.com.pa
Sales Range: $50-74.9 Million
Emp.: 6
General Insurance Services
N.A.I.C.S.: 524298

Unit (US):

AXA Assistance USA, Inc. **(2)**
122 S Michigan Ave Ste 1100, Chicago, IL 60603
Tel.: (312) 935-3500
Web Site: http://www.axa-assistance-usa.com
Sales Range: $25-49.9 Million
Emp.: 150
Personal Service Agents Brokers & Bureaus
N.A.I.C.S.: 812990
Bernard Ferrand *(Sr VP-North America)*

Subsidiary (Non-US):

Inter Partner Assistance S.A. **(2)**
Avenue Regent 7, 1000, Brussels, Belgium **(100%)**
Tel.: (32) 25500400
Web Site: https://www.ip-assistance.be
Sales Range: $150-199.9 Million
Emp.: 320
Personal insurance services
N.A.I.C.S.: 524298

Subsidiary (Non-US):

Call Us Assistance International GmbH **(3)**
Waschhausgasse 2, 1020, Vienna, Austria
Tel.: (43) 1316700
Web Site: https://www.call-us-assistance.com
Emp.: 30
Business Process Outsourcing Services
N.A.I.C.S.: 561499

Inter Partner Asistencia Servicios Espana SA **(3)**
C/ Arequipa 1, 28043, Madrid, Spain
Tel.: (34) 91 468 87 00
Web Site: http://www.corp.axa-assistance.es
General Assistance Services
N.A.I.C.S.: 561990

Inter Partner Assistance Algerie Spa **(3)**

Lot 16/18 Agefa activity zone, Said Ham-
dine Bir Mourad Rais, 16078, Algiers, Alge-
ria
Tel.: (213) 21980000
Web Site: https://www.ip-assistance.dz
Sales Range: $10-24.9 Million
General Assistance Services
N.A.I.C.S.: 561990

Inter Partner Assistance Co., Ltd. (3)
Unit 2012-14 54 Sukhumvit 21 Asoke Road,
North Klongtoey Wattan, 10100, Bangkok,
Thailand
Tel.: (66) 22065400
Medical Assistance Services
N.A.I.C.S.: 923130

Inter Partner Assistance Greece (3)
Dimitressa 15 Ionos Dragoumi, Palio
Phaliro, 11528, Athens, Greece
Tel.: (30) 2109475900
Web Site: http://www.inter-partner.gr
Medical Assistance Services
N.A.I.C.S.: 923130

**Inter Partner Assistance Hong-Kong
Ltd**
Unit 1015-1018 Tower 1 Millennium City 1
388 KWUN Tong Rd, Kwun Tong, Kowloon,
China (Hong Kong)
Tel.: (852) 28510620
Web Site: http://www.ipahk.com.hk
Sales Range: $10-24.9 Million
Emp.: 30
General Assistance Services
N.A.I.C.S.: 561990
Joseph Lee *(Gen Mgr)*

Inter Partner Assistance Ltd (3)
17/F-1 No 77 Sec 2 Tun Hua S Rd, Taipei,
10682, Taiwan
Tel.: (886) 227007700
Web Site: http://www.ipassistance.com.tw
Medical Assistance Services
N.A.I.C.S.: 923130

**Inter Partner Assistance Polska
S.A.** (3)
Prosta 68, 00838, Warsaw, Poland
Tel.: (48) 225298400
Web Site: http://www.ipa.com.pl
General Assistance Services
N.A.I.C.S.: 561990
Jan Cupa *(CEO)*

Inter Partner Assistance S.A. (3)
Cours de Rive 2, 1204, Geneva, Switzer-
land
Tel.: (41) 228194400
Web Site: http://www.inter-partner.ch
Medical Assistance Services
N.A.I.C.S.: 923130
Serge Morelli *(Gen Mgr)*

Inter Partner Assistance Turkey (3)
Kisikli Mah Bosna Bulvari No 39 Camlica,
Uskudar, 34760, Istanbul, Turkiye
Tel.: (90) 2165243636
Web Site: http://www.ipaistanbul.com
General Assistance Services
N.A.I.C.S.: 561990

Inter Partner Assistance s/c Ltda (3)
Al Rio Negro 433 - 5 Andar Alphaville, Ba-
rueri, 06454-904, Sao Paulo, Brazil
Tel.: (55) 11 41965922
Web Site: http://www.interpartner.com.br
General Assistance Services
N.A.I.C.S.: 561990

**Inter Partner Assistenza Servizi
Spa** (3)
Via Bernardino Alimena 111, 00173, Rome,
Italy
Tel.: (39) 06421181
Web Site: http://www.axa-assistance.it
General Insurance Services
N.A.I.C.S.: 524210

AXA Assurance Maroc (1)
120-122 Avenue Hassan II, Casablanca,
21000, Morocco
Tel.: (212) 522889292
Web Site: http://www.axa.ma
Sales Range: $350-399.9 Million
Emp.: 514
Life Insurance Products & Services
N.A.I.C.S.: 524113

AXA Assurances (1)

313 Terrasses de l Arche, 75458, Nanterre,
Cedex, France **(100%)**
Tel.: (33) 147741001
Web Site: http://www.axa.fr
Sales Range: $200-249.9 Million
Emp.: 280
N.A.I.C.S.: 524128

AXA Assurances Gabon (1)
BP 4047, Libreville, Gabon **(99%)**
Tel.: (241) 762897
Web Site: http://www.axa.com
Sales Range: $100-124.9 Million
Emp.: 118
Insurance Provider
N.A.I.C.S.: 524128

**AXA Assurances Luxembourg
S.A.** (1)
1 Place de l Etoile, 1479, Luxembourg,
Luxembourg **(100%)**
Tel.: (352) 4424241
Web Site: http://www.axa.lu
Sales Range: $100-124.9 Million
Reinsurance
N.A.I.C.S.: 524130

Subsidiary (Domestic):

**AXA Assurances Vie
Luxembourg** (2)
1 Place de l Etoile, 1479, Luxembourg,
Luxembourg **(100%)**
Tel.: (352) 4424241
Web Site: http://www.axa.lu
Sales Range: $100-124.9 Million
Emp.: 180
Insurance Services
N.A.I.C.S.: 524128

AXA Assurances Senegal (1)
5 Place De L'independance, BP 182, Da-
kar, Senegal **(100%)**
Tel.: (221) 338491010
Web Site: http://www.axagroup.com
Sales Range: $75-99.9 Million
Emp.: 60
Insurance Services
N.A.I.C.S.: 524128

**AXA Bank Europe Czech
Republic** (1)
Uzka 8/488, 602 00, Brno, Czech Republic
Tel.: (420) 494 945 240
Web Site: http://www.axabank.cz
Commercial Banking Services
N.A.I.C.S.: 522110
Ladislav Krocak *(CEO)*

AXA Bank Europe Slovakia (1)
Kolarska 6, Bratislava, 81106, Slovakia
Tel.: (421) 229292929
Web Site: http://www.axabanka.sk
Commercial Banking Services
N.A.I.C.S.: 522110

AXA Banque (1)
Les Fontaines Axa 203-205 Rue Carnot,
94138, Fontenay-sous-Bois, Cedex,
France **(100%)**
Tel.: (33) 970808088
Web Site: http://www.axa.fr
Sales Range: $200-249.9 Million
Emp.: 500
Asset Management & Financial Services
N.A.I.C.S.: 522320

**AXA Business Services Private
Limited** (1)
1st and 2nd Floor Mfar Manyata Tech Park
Phase IV, Rachenahalli Village Nagawara,
Bengaluru, 560045, India
Tel.: (91) 8041830000
Web Site: http://www.axaindia.com
Sales Range: $300-349.9 Million
Emp.: 250
Business Process Outsourcing Services
N.A.I.C.S.: 561499

AXA Ceska republika s.r.o (1)
Lazarska 13/8, 120 00, Prague, Czech Re-
public
Tel.: (420) 292 292 292
Web Site: http://www.axa.cz
General Insurance Services
N.A.I.C.S.: 524210

AXA Cessions (1)
61 rue Mstislav Rostropovitch, 75017, Paris,
France

Tel.: (33) 156437917
Web Site: https://reinsurance-general-
conditions.axa.com
Insurance Service Provider
N.A.I.C.S.: 524298

**AXA China Region Insurance Com-
pany (Bermuda) Limited** (1)
Avenida Do Infante D Henrique No 43-53A
20 Andar The Macau Square, Macau, China
(Macau)
Tel.: (853) 2878 1188
Web Site: http://www.axa.com.hk
Insurance Management Services
N.A.I.C.S.: 524298

**AXA China Region Insurance Com-
pany Limited** (1)
151 Gloucester Road, Wanchai, China
(Hong Kong)
Tel.: (852) 25191111
Web Site: http://www.axa.com.hk
Emp.: 100
Financial Protection & Wealth Management
Services
N.A.I.C.S.: 523940
Etienne Bouas-Laurent *(CEO)*

AXA China Region Ltd. (1)
18 F Axa Ctr 151 Gloucester Rd, Wanchai,
China (Hong Kong) **(100%)**
Tel.: (852) 25191111
Web Site: http://www.axa.com.hk
Sales Range: $200-249.9 Million
Emp.: 500
N.A.I.C.S.: 524128

Subsidiary (Domestic):

**AXA Wealth Management (HK)
Limited** (2)
18 Harbour Road 33rd Floor Central Plaza,
Wanchai, 652, China (Hong Kong)
Tel.: (852) 21173000
Web Site: http://www.axa.com.hk
Financial Services
N.A.I.C.S.: 523999

AXA Colonia Insurance Limited (1)
Wolfe Tone House Wolfe Tone Street, Dub-
lin, 1, Ireland **(100%)**
Tel.: (353) 18726444
Web Site: http://www.axa.ie
Insurance Services
N.A.I.C.S.: 524128

AXA Conseil (1)
21 Rue De Chateaudun, 75009, Paris,
France **(100%)**
Tel.: (33) 156023000
Web Site: http://www.axa.fr
N.A.I.C.S.: 524128

AXA Corporate Solutions (1)
24 Rue Jules Lefebvre, Paris, 75009,
France **(100%)**
Tel.: (33) 156928000
Web Site: http://www.axa-
corporatesolutions.com
Sales Range: $400-449.9 Million
Emp.: 777
N.A.I.C.S.: 524128
Phillip Araotard *(CEO)*

AXA Corporate Solutions (1)
Via Della Moscova 18, 20121, Milan, Italy
Tel.: (39) 02 65538 1
Property & Casualty Insurance Manage-
ment Services
N.A.I.C.S.: 524298

AXA Corporate Solutions (1)
143 Cecil Street 09-02 GB Building, Singa-
pore, 069542, Singapore
Tel.: (65) 63 38 72 88
Property & Casualty Insurance Services
N.A.I.C.S.: 524126

**AXA Corporate Solutions Assurance
S.A** (1)
2-4 Jules Lefebvre, 75009, Paris, France
Tel.: (33) 156928000
General Insurance Services
N.A.I.C.S.: 524298

**AXA Corporate Solutions
Australia** (1)
Level 21 Australia Square 264 George
Street, PO Box 3973, Sydney, 2001, NSW,
Australia

Tel.: (61) 2 9274 3000
Web Site: http://www.axa-
corporatesolutions.com
Sales Range: $50-74.9 Million
Emp.: 2
Property & Casualty Insurance Manage-
ment Services
N.A.I.C.S.: 524298
Hubert Jumel *(CEO)*

AXA Corporate Solutions Dubai (1)
Wafi Residential Centre Ground Floor, PO
Box 290, Dubai, United Arab Emirates
Tel.: (971) 4 3150205
Property & Casualty Insurance Services
N.A.I.C.S.: 524126
Xavier Luscan *(Mgr-Underwriting-Property &
Engrg Corp Solutions)*

**AXA Corporate Solutions
Germany** (1)
Colonia-Allee 10-20, 51067, Cologne,
51067, Germany
Tel.: (49) 221 148 21180
Property & Casualty Insurance Services
N.A.I.C.S.: 524126
Juergen Kurth *(CEO)*

**AXA Corporate Solutions Hong
Kong** (1)
Unit 1204-05 DCH Commercial Centre 25
Westlands Road, Quarry Bay, China (Hong
Kong)
Tel.: (852) 2161 0000
Web Site: http://www.axa-
corporatesolutions.com
Property & Casualty Insurance Services
N.A.I.C.S.: 524126
Pierre Martelly *(CEO)*

**AXA Corporate Solutions
Switzerland** (1)
General Guisan-Strasse 40, PO Box 4600,
8401, Winterthur, Switzerland
Tel.: (41) 52 261 63 00
Web Site: http://www.axa-
corporatesolutions.com
Emp.: 20
Property & Casualty Insurance Manage-
ment Services
N.A.I.C.S.: 524298
Thomas Baumgartner *(Reg Mgr-Comml)*

AXA Corporate Solutions UK (1)
140 Fenchurch Street, London, EC3M 6BL,
United Kingdom
Tel.: (44) 2077026600
Web Site: http://www.axa-
corporatesolutions.com
Emp.: 5
Property & Casualty Insurance Services
N.A.I.C.S.: 524126
Paul Lowin *(COO)*

AXA Cote D'Ivoire (1)
Avenue Lamine Fadiga Prolonge, Abidjan,
Cote d'Ivoire **(100%)**
Tel.: (225) 20318888
Web Site: http://www.axa.ci
Sales Range: $50-74.9 Million
Emp.: 15
Insurance Services
N.A.I.C.S.: 524128

AXA Customer Services Ltd (1)
8 DBM Industrial Estate Coromandel, Port
Louis, Mauritius
Tel.: (230) 2067900
Web Site: http://www.axa-
customerservices.com
Sales Range: $75-99.9 Million
Emp.: 50
Business Process Outsourcing Services
N.A.I.C.S.: 561499
Martin A. Weintz *(CEO)*

AXA Czech Republic Insurance (1)
Lazarska 8/13, 12000, Prague, Czech Re-
public
Tel.: (420) 225021295
Web Site: http://www.axa.cz
Emp.: 150
Insurance Management Services
N.A.I.C.S.: 524298

**AXA Czech Republic Pension
Funds** (1)
Uzka 8/488, 602 00, Brno, Czech Republic
Tel.: (420) 292 292 292
Pension Fund Management Services

AXA S.A.—(Continued)

N.A.I.C.S.: 525110

AXA Direct (1)
Chlodna 51, 00-867, Warsaw, Poland
Tel.: (48) 225999000
Web Site: http://www.axadirect.pl
Insurance Management Services
N.A.I.C.S.: 524298

AXA Direct Korea (1)
11F 4 Hangang-daero 71-gil, Yongsan-gu,
04322, Seoul, Korea (South)
Tel.: (82) 234793030
Web Site: http://www.axa.co.kr
Online Insurance Services
N.A.I.C.S.: 524298

AXA Framlington (1)
7 Newgate Street, London, EC1A 7NX,
United Kingdom
Tel.: (44) 2073306400
Web Site: http://www.axa.com
Sales Range: $100-124.9 Million
Investment Management Service
N.A.I.C.S.: 523999

AXA France Assurance SAS (1)
313 Gerrasses de l'Arche, 92727, Nanterre,
Cedex, France (100%)
Tel.: (33) 147741001
Web Site: http://www.axa.fr
Sales Range: $100-124.9 Million
Emp.: 200
N.A.I.C.S.: 524128
Francois Pierson *(Chm & CEO)*

Subsidiary (Domestic):

AXA Epargne Entreprise (2)
313 Terrasses de l'Arche, 92727, Nanterre,
France
Tel.: (33) 147741001
Web Site:
http://www.epargneretraiteentreprise.axa.fr
General Insurance Services
N.A.I.C.S.: 524298

AXA France IARD (2)
26 rue Drouot, 75009, Paris, France
Tel.: (33) 3 23 53 27 64
Reinsurance Services
N.A.I.C.S.: 524130

AXA France Vie S.A (2)
313 Terrasses de l'Arche, 92727, Nanterre,
Cedex, France
Tel.: (33) 140506070
Web Site: https://www.axa.fr
General Insurance Services
N.A.I.C.S.: 524210
Nicolas Moreau *(CEO)*

AXA General Insurance Co., Ltd. (1)
Kairaku Building Kotobuki 2-1-13 Kotobuki,
Taito-ku, Tokyo, 111-8633, Japan
Tel.: (81) 3 4335 8570
Web Site: http://www.axa-direct.co.jp
General Insurance Services
N.A.I.C.S.: 524298

**AXA General Insurance Hong
Kong** (1)
21/F Manhattan Pl 23 Wang Tai Road, Kow-
loon Bay, Kowloon, China (Hong
Kong) (100%)
Tel.: (852) 25233061
Web Site: http://www.axa-insurance.com.hk
Sales Range: $100-124.9 Million
Emp.: 200
Life Insurance
N.A.I.C.S.: 524113

AXA Global Re SA (1)
9 Avenue De Messine, 75008, Paris,
France
Tel.: (33) 156437800
Reinsurance Carrier Services
N.A.I.C.S.: 524130

**AXA Group Operations Switzerland
AG**
Paulstrasse 12, PO Box 357, 8401, Winter-
thur, Switzerland
Tel.: (41) 522611111
Web Site: http://www.axa.com
Sales Range: $800-899.9 Million
Information Technology & Telecommunica-
tion Services
N.A.I.C.S.: 541512

AXA Holding Maroc S.A. (1)
120-122 Av Hassan Ii, Casablanca, Mo-
rocco
Tel.: (212) 5228892
Investment Management Service
N.A.I.C.S.: 523940

AXA Holdings Belgium (1)
Troonplein 1, 1000, Brussels,
Belgium (100%)
Tel.: (32) 25500555
Web Site: http://www.axa.be
Sales Range: $1-4.9 Billion
Emp.: 6,000
Holding Company
N.A.I.C.S.: 551112

Subsidiary (Domestic):

**AXA Bank Belgium Sabelgium
SA** (2)
Place du Trone 1, 1000, Brussels,
Belgium (100%)
Tel.: (32) 26786111
Web Site: http://www.axa.be
Sales Range: $50-74.9 Million
Commercial Bank
N.A.I.C.S.: 522110

AXA Belgium S.A. (2)
Place du Trone 1, 1000, Brussels,
Belgium (100%)
Tel.: (32) 3226786111
Web Site: http://www.axa.be
Sales Range: $1-4.9 Billion
Life Insurance
N.A.I.C.S.: 524113
Giovanni D'Aniello *(Grp CTO)*

AXA Insurance (1)
Chemin De Primerose 11, PO Box 7753,
1002, Lausanne, Switzerland
Tel.: (41) 213195363
General Insurance Services
N.A.I.C.S.: 524210

**AXA Insurance (Saudi Arabia)
B.S.C.** (1)
Kanoo Tower King Abdul Aziz Road 2nd
Floor, PO Box 753, Riyadh, 11421, Saudi
Arabia (100%)
Tel.: (966) 14776706
Web Site: http://www.axa-gulf.com
Sales Range: $350-399.9 Million
Emp.: 550
Insurance Provider
N.A.I.C.S.: 524128

AXA Insurance Gulf (1)
2nd Floor Kanoo Building Abu Obeidah Av-
enue, PO Box 45, Manama, Bahrain
Tel.: (973) 17 210 778
Sales Range: $50-74.9 Million
Emp.: 5
General Insurance Services
N.A.I.C.S.: 524298
Gerome Droesch *(Gen Mgr)*

AXA Insurance Gulf (1)
Kanoo Tower King Abdul Aziz Road 2nd
Floor, PO Box 753, 11421, Riyadh, Saudi
Arabia
Tel.: (966) 1 477 6706
Web Site: http://www.axa-cooperative.com
General Insurance Services
N.A.I.C.S.: 524210

AXA Insurance Limited (1)
Unit 4 Blanchardstown Plaza Main Street
15, Blanchardstown, Dublin, Ireland
Tel.: (353) 18179733
Web Site: http://www.axa.ie
Emp.: 3
Insurance Management Services
N.A.I.C.S.: 524298

**AXA Insurance Singapore Pte
Ltd** (1)
143 Cecil Street 03-01/10 Gb Building, Sin-
gapore, 069542, Singapore (100%)
Tel.: (65) 68805500
Web Site: http://www.axa.com
Sales Range: $100-124.9 Million
Emp.: 200
Life Insurance
N.A.I.C.S.: 524113

AXA Insurance pcl (1)
1168/67 Lumpini Tower 23 Fl Rama 4 rd
Thung Mahamek, Sathorn, Bangkok,

10120, Thailand (100%)
Tel.: (66) 21188111
Web Site: http://www.axa.co.th
Sales Range: $200-249.9 Million
Emp.: 260
Retail & Commercial Insurance
N.A.I.C.S.: 524128

AXA Investment Managers S.A. (1)
Tour Majunga -La Defense 9, 6 Place de la
Pyramide, 92800, Puteaux, Cedex,
France (100%)
Tel.: (33) 144457000
Web Site: http://www.axa-im.com
Sales Range: $800-899.9 Million
Emp.: 2,500
Holding Company; Investment Advisory &
Asset Management Services
N.A.I.C.S.: 551112
Viktoria Orhamn *(Mgr-Client Svc)*

Subsidiary (Non-US):

**AXA Investment Managers Asia (Sin-
gapore) Ltd.** (2)
1 George St 14-02/03, Singapore, 049145,
Singapore
Tel.: (65) 62362288
Web Site: http://www.axa.com
Asset Management Services
N.A.I.C.S.: 523940

**AXA Investment Managers Asia
Limited** (2)
Suite 3603-3605 One Taikoo Place 979
King's Road, Quarry Bay, China (Hong
Kong)
Tel.: (852) 22852000
Web Site: https://www.axa-im.com.hk
Sales Range: $25-49.9 Million
Asset Management Services
N.A.I.C.S.: 523940
Terence Lam *(Mng Dir & Head-Client Grp
Core-Asia Pacific)*

**AXA Investment Managers Benelux
SA/NV** (2)
Place du Trone 1 Troonplein, 1000, Brus-
sels, Belgium
Tel.: (32) 26796350
Web Site: https://www.axa-im.be
Emp.: 16
Investment Management & Real Estate In-
vestment Services
N.A.I.C.S.: 523940
Stephan Deceulaer *(Head-Product Mgmt &
Grp Distr)*

Branch (Non-US):

**AXA Investment Managers Benelux
SA/NV - Netherlands** (3)
Beethovenstraat 518, 1082 PR, Amsterdam,
Netherlands
Tel.: (31) 203011175
Web Site: http://www.axa-im.nl
Sales Range: $50-74.9 Million
Asset Management Services
N.A.I.C.S.: 523940
Hanneke Veringa *(Country Mgr)*

Subsidiary (Non-US):

**AXA Investment Managers
Deutschland GmbH** (2)
Thurn-und-Taxis-Platz 6, 60313, Frankfurt
am Main, Germany
Tel.: (49) 69900252049
Web Site: https://www.axa-im.de
Emp.: 9
Investment Management & Real Estate In-
vestment Services
N.A.I.C.S.: 523940
Sven Krumpholz *(Mng Dir)*

**AXA Investment Managers Italia
S.p.A.** (2)
68 Corso Di Porta Romana, 20122, Milan,
Italy
Tel.: (39) 025829911
Web Site: http://www.axa-im.it
Asset Management Services
N.A.I.C.S.: 523940

**AXA Investment Managers Japan
Ltd.** (2)
NBF Platinum Tower 14F 17-3 Shirokane
1-chome, Minato-ku, Tokyo, 108-0072, Japan

Tel.: (81) 354473100
Web Site: http://www.axa-im.co.jp
Asset Management Services
N.A.I.C.S.: 523940

AXA Investment Managers LLC (2)
PO Box 22415, Doha, Qatar
Tel.: (974) 44967200
Emp.: 2
Investment Management Service
N.A.I.C.S.: 523999
Fadi Salibi *(Head-Middle East)*

Subsidiary (Domestic):

**AXA Investment Managers Paris
S.A.** (2)
Majunga Tower - La Defense 9, 6 Place de
la Pyramide, 92800, Puteaux,
France (100%)
Tel.: (33) 144457000
Web Site: https://www.axa-im.fr
Sales Range: $350-399.9 Million
Emp.: 1,000
Asset Management & Financial Services
N.A.I.C.S.: 523940
Lionel Pernias *(Head-Fixed-Income Solu-
tions)*

Subsidiary (Non-US):

**AXA Investment Managers Schweiz
AG** (2)
Affolternstrasse 42, Postfach 6949, 8050,
Zurich, Switzerland
Tel.: (41) 58 360 7800
Web Site: https://www.axa-im.ch
Asset Management Services
N.A.I.C.S.: 523940

**AXA Investment Managers UK
Limited** (2)
22 Bishopsgate, London, EC2N 4BQ,
United Kingdom (100%)
Tel.: (44) 1268448667
Web Site: http://www.axa-im.co.uk
Sales Range: $200-249.9 Million
Emp.: 500
Asset Management Services
N.A.I.C.S.: 524128

Division (Domestic):

AXA Framlington (3)
7 Newgate Street, London, EC1A 7NX,
United Kingdom
Tel.: (44) 20 7003 1000
Web Site: http://www.axa-framlington.com
Sales Range: $100-124.9 Million
Emp.: 150
Specialty Investment Fund Management
Services
N.A.I.C.S.: 523940
Mark Tinker *(Portfolio Mgr)*

Subsidiary (Domestic):

**AXA Investment Managers GS
Limited** (3)
22 Bishopsgate, London, EC2N 4BQ,
United Kingdom
Tel.: (44) 2070031000
Emp.: 400
Holding Company; Investment Management
Services
N.A.I.C.S.: 551112

Branch (Non-US):

**AXA Investment Managers GS Ltd.,
Sucursal en Espana** (4)
Paseo De La Castellana 93 6 Planta,
28046, Madrid, Spain
Tel.: (34) 914067200
Web Site: http://www.axa-im.es
Emp.: 7
Investment Management Service
N.A.I.C.S.: 523940

Subsidiary (US):

AXA Investment Managers, Inc. (2)
100 W Putnam Ave 3 Fl, Greenwich, CT
06830
Tel.: (203) 983-4238
Web Site: https://www.axa-im-usa.com
Asset Management Services
N.A.I.C.S.: 523940
James Wallace *(Head-Wholesale Distr &
Sub-Advisory)*

Subsidiary (Domestic):

AXA Real Estate Investment Managers S.A. (2)
6 Place de la Pyramide, La Defense, Paris, 92908, France
Tel.: (33) 144459500
Web Site: http://www.axa-realestate.com
Sales Range: $550-599.9 Million
Emp.: 1,500
Real Estate Portfolio Management Services
N.A.I.C.S.: 531390
Pascal Aujoux (Head-Asset Mgmt-Southern Europe)

Unit (Non-US):

AXA Real Estate Investment Managers - Hungary (3)
Kalman Imre Utca 1 2nd Floor, 1054, Budapest, Hungary
Tel.: (36) 12885090
Web Site: http://www.axa-realestate.com
Emp.: 3
Real Estate Investment Services
N.A.I.C.S.: 531390
Jake Lodge (Sr Mgr-Asset)

AXA Real Estate Investment Managers - Spain (3)
Edificio Cadagua Paseo de la Castellana 93 6 Planta, 28046, Madrid, Spain
Tel.: (34) 914067200
Real Estate Investment Services
N.A.I.C.S.: 531390

AXA Real Estate Investment Managers - Switzerland (3)
42 Affolternstrasse, 8050, Zurich, Switzerland
Tel.: (41) 432991199
Emp.: 10
Real Estate Investment Services
N.A.I.C.S.: 531390
Nigel Volkart (Head-Asset Mgmt)

AXA Real Estate Investment Managers - UK (3)
155 Bishopsgate, London, EC2M 3XJ, United Kingdom
Tel.: (44) 2073744100
Emp.: 200
Real Estate Investment Services
N.A.I.C.S.: 531390
Huw Stephens (Head-Local Transactions)

Subsidiary (Non-US):

AXA Real Estate Investment Managers Italia S.r.l. (3)
Corso Di Porta Romana 68, 20122, Milan, Italy
Tel.: (39) 025844201
Real Estate Investment Services
N.A.I.C.S.: 531390
Alessio Lucentini (Head-Local Asset Mgmt)

AXA Real Estate Investment Managers Japan KK (3)
Nbf Platinum Tower 14f 1-17-3 Shirokane, Minato-ku, Tokyo, 108-0072, Japan
Tel.: (81) 357932200
Web Site: http://www.axa.com
Sales Range: $50-74.9 Million
Real Estate Investment Services
N.A.I.C.S.: 531390

AXA Real Estate Investment Managers Nederland B.V. (3)
Strawinskylaan 2701 Atrium Tower A - 14th Floor, 1077 ZZ, Amsterdam, Netherlands
Tel.: (31) 203011150
Web Site: http://www.axa-realestate.com
Real Estate Manangement Services
N.A.I.C.S.: 531390
Alphons Spaninks (Head-Asset Mgmt)

Joint Venture (Domestic):

Dunkerque LNG SAS (3)
30 Rue Lhemitte Centre Tertiaire Des Trois Ponts, 59140, Dunkerque, France (15.19%)
Tel.: (33) 328241663
Web Site: http://www.dunkerquelng.com
Liquefied Natural Gas Terminal Operator
N.A.I.C.S.: 424710

Subsidiary (US):

NorthStar Realty Europe Corp. (3)

590 Madison Ave 34th Fl, New York, NY 10022
Tel.: (212) 547-2600
Sales Range: $100-124.9 Million
Real Estate Investment Services
N.A.I.C.S.: 525990
Sven Rein (Mgr)

AXA Ireland Limited (1)
Wolfe Tone House Wolfe Tone Street, Dublin, 1, Ireland
Tel.: (353) 18726444
Emp.: 12
General Insurance Services
N.A.I.C.S.: 524210

AXA Italia S.p.A. (1)
Via Leopardi 15, 20123, Milan, Italy
Tel.: (39) 02480841
Web Site: http://www.axa.it
General Insurance Services
N.A.I.C.S.: 524298

Subsidiary (Domestic):

AXA Interlife S.p.A. (2)
Via Leopardi 15, 20123, Milan, Italy
Tel.: (39) 02480841
Web Site: http://www.axa.it
Life Insurance Management Services
N.A.I.C.S.: 524113

AXA Japan Holding Co. (1)
NBF Platinum Tower 1-17-3 Shirokane, Minato-ku, Tokyo, 108 8020, Japan (100%)
Tel.: (81) 367377700
Web Site: http://www.axa.co.jp
Sales Range: $1-4.9 Billion
Emp.: 7,000
Insurance Holding Company
N.A.I.C.S.: 524298

Subsidiary (Domestic):

NEXTIA Life Insurance Co., Ltd. (2)
8th Floor Kojimachi Building 3-3-4KDX Kojimachi, Chiyoda-ku, Tokyo, 102-0083, Japan
Tel.: (81) 120953831
Web Site: http://www.axa-direct-life.co.jp
Life Insurance Management Services
N.A.I.C.S.: 524113

AXA Konzern AG (1)
Colonia Allee 10-20, 51067, Cologne, Germany (100%)
Tel.: (49) 8003203205
Web Site: http://www.axa.de
Sales Range: $1-4.9 Billion
Emp.: 4,500
General Insurance Services
N.A.I.C.S.: 524128
Jens Warkentin (Member-Mgmt Bd)

Subsidiary (Domestic):

AXA ART Versicherung AG (2)
Colonia-Allee 10-20, 51067, Cologne, Germany
Tel.: (49) 89540618120
Web Site: http://www.axa-art.de
Sales Range: $50-74.9 Million
Emp.: 4,500
Art Insurance Services
N.A.I.C.S.: 524298

AXA Bank AG. (2)
Colonia-Allee 10-20, 51067, Cologne, Germany
Tel.: (49) 805771089
Commercial Banking Services
N.A.I.C.S.: 522110

AXA Krankenversicherung AG (2)
Colonia-Allee 10-20, 51067, Cologne, Germany
Tel.: (49) 8003203205
Web Site: http://www.axa.de
General Insurance Services
N.A.I.C.S.: 524210

AXA Liabilities Managers Belgium (1)
25 Boulevard du Souverain, 1170, Brussels, Belgium
Tel.: (32) 26786111
Reinsurance Management Services
N.A.I.C.S.: 524130

AXA Liabilities Managers SAS (1)
39 Rue du Colisee, 75008, Paris, France

Tel.: (33) 1 58 36 75 00
Web Site: http://www.axa-lm.com
Sales Range: $200-249.9 Million
Emp.: 30
Liability Management Services
N.A.I.C.S.: 523940
John Byrne (Head-Bus Dev)

AXA Liabilities Managers UK Limited (1)
Civic Drive, Ipswich, IP1 2AN, Suffolk, United Kingdom
Tel.: (44) 1473212422
Reinsurance Management Services
N.A.I.C.S.: 524130

AXA Life Europe Limited (1)
Wolfe Tone House Wolfe Tone Street, Dublin, 1, Ireland
Tel.: (353) 14711716
Web Site: http://www.axa-lifeeurope.com
Sales Range: $50-74.9 Million
Emp.: 2
Insurance Management Services
N.A.I.C.S.: 524298
Roel Voogt (Mng Dir)

AXA Life Insurance Company Limited (1)
NBF Platinum Tower 1-17-3 Shirokane, Minato-ku, Tokyo, 108 8020, Japan (100%)
Tel.: (81) 367377777
Web Site: http://www.axa.co.jp
Sales Range: $1-4.9 Billion
Emp.: 8,000
Life Insurance
N.A.I.C.S.: 524113

AXA Life Ltd. (1)
General-Guisan-Strasse 40, 8401, Winterthur, Switzerland
Tel.: (41) 800809809
Life Insurance Management Services
N.A.I.C.S.: 524113

AXA Luxembourg SA (1)
1 Place de l Etoile, 1479, Luxembourg, Luxembourg
Tel.: (352) 4424241
Web Site: http://www.axa.lu
Emp.: 300
Health Insurance Services
N.A.I.C.S.: 524114

AXA MBASK IC OJSC (1)
Hazi Aslanov 80/9, Baku, Azerbaijan
Tel.: (994) 12950
Web Site: http://www.axambask.az
Sales Range: $50-74.9 Million
Insurance Management Services
N.A.I.C.S.: 524298
Selcuk Adiguzel Ayhan (Chm-Mgmt Bd)

AXA Mansard Insurance PLC (1)
Santa Clara Court Plot 1412 Ahmadu Bello Way, Victoria Island, Lagos, Nigeria (77%)
Tel.: (234) 7006267273
Web Site: http://www.axamansard.com
Rev.: $51,058,886
Assets: $78,627,032
Liabilities: $54,125,532
Net Worth: $24,501,500
Earnings: $1,802,190
Emp.: 343
Fiscal Year-end: 12/31/2022
Insurance Products & Services
N.A.I.C.S.: 524298
Tosin Runsewe (Exec Dir-Client Svcs)

Subsidiary (Domestic):

AXA Mansard Health Limited (2)
177 Ikorodu Road Onipanu, Lagos, Nigeria
Tel.: (234) 1 4606655
Health Insurance Services
N.A.I.C.S.: 524114

AXA Mansard Investments Limited (2)
2nd Floor 927/928 Bishop Aboyade Cole Street, Victoria Island, Lagos, Nigeria
Tel.: (234) 12701559
Investment Services
N.A.I.C.S.: 523999

Tangerine Pensions Limited (2)
No 21B Olosa Street, Victoria Island, Lagos, Nigeria

Tel.: (234) 14485490
Pension Services
N.A.I.C.S.: 524292

AXA Mediterranean Holding, S.A. (1)
Camino fuente de la Mora 1, 28050, Madrid, Spain (100%)
Tel.: (34) 915388437
Web Site: http://www.axa.com
Insurance Services
N.A.I.C.S.: 524128

Subsidiary (Domestic):

AXA Aurora Iberica S.A. de Seguros y Reaseguros (2)
Camino fuente de la Mora 1, 28050, Madrid, Spain (100%)
Tel.: (34) 915388200
Web Site: http://www.axa.es
Sales Range: $600-649.9 Million
Emp.: 2,500
Insurance Provider
N.A.I.C.S.: 524298

AXA Aurora Vida SA de Seguros y Reaseguros (2)
Place Federico Moyua 4, Bilbao, 48009, Spain
Tel.: (34) 944 20 62 00
General Insurance Services
N.A.I.C.S.: 524210

Subsidiary (Non-US):

AXA Insurance A.E. (2)
48 Michalakopoulou Str, 11528, Athens, Greece
Tel.: (30) 2107268000
Web Site: http://www.axa.gr
General Insurance Services
N.A.I.C.S.: 524298

Subsidiary (Domestic):

AXA Seguros Generales SA de Seguros y Reaseguros (2)
Place Federico Moyua 4, Bilbao, 48009, Spain
Tel.: (34) 944 20 62 00
General Insurance Services
N.A.I.C.S.: 524298

Hilo Direct Seguros y Reaseguros S.A. (2)
Calle Emilio Vargas 6, 28043, Madrid, Spain (100%)
Tel.: (34) 900300100
Web Site: https://www.directseguros.es
Sales Range: $200-249.9 Million
Emp.: 320
Insurance Services
N.A.I.C.S.: 524128

Subsidiary (Non-US):

Seguro Directo Gere Companhia de Seguros SA (2)
Rua Goncalo Sampaio 39 Apartado, 4076, Porto, Portugal
Tel.: (351) 218612323
Web Site: https://www.segurodirecto.pt
General Insurance Services
N.A.I.C.S.: 524210

AXA Merkens Fonds Gmbh (1)
Colonia-Allee 10-20, 51067, Cologne, Germany
Tel.: (49) 221161515800
Pension Fund Management Services
N.A.I.C.S.: 525110

AXA Middle East (1)
Jal El Dib Highway Axa Middle East Bldg, PO Box 11-550, 11072050, Beirut, Lebanon
Tel.: (961) 4 716 333
Web Site: http://www.axa-middleeast.com
General Insurance Services
N.A.I.C.S.: 524298
Roger Nasnas (Chm & CEO)

AXA Pension Solutions AG (1)
Gertrudstrasse 15, Postfach 300, 8401, Winterthur, Switzerland
Tel.: (41) 522612838
Pension Fund Services
N.A.I.C.S.: 525110

AXA Philippines (1)
34th Floor GT Tower Ayala Ave corner H V

AXA S.A.—(Continued)

Dela Costa, Makati, Philippines
Tel.: (63) 285815292
Web Site: http://www.axa.com.ph
General Insurance Services
N.A.I.C.S.: 524298
Ronaldo C. San Jose (CFO)

AXA Poland Pension Funds (1)
ul Chlodna 51, Warsaw, 00-867, Poland
Tel.: (48) 225550000
Pension Fund Services
N.A.I.C.S.: 525110

AXA Polska S.A. (1)
ul Chlodna 51 Budynek Warsaw Trade
Tower, 00-867, Warsaw, Poland
Tel.: (48) 225550000
Asset Management Services
N.A.I.C.S.: 523940

AXA Portugal - Companhia de Se-
guros S.A. (1)
Praca Marques De Pombal No 14 Ap 1953,
1058 801, Lisbon, Portugal (100%)
Tel.: (351) 213506100
Sales Range: $200-249.9 Million
Emp.: 300
Insurance Provider
N.A.I.C.S.: 524128

AXA Portugal Companhia de Seguros
de Vida SA (1)
Praca Marques de Pombal n 14, 1250-162,
Lisbon, Portugal
Tel.: (351) 707 281 281
Life Insurance Management Services
N.A.I.C.S.: 524113

AXA Powszechne Towarzystwo Em-
erytalne S.A. (1)
ul Chlodna 51, 00-867, Warsaw, Poland
Tel.: (48) 225550050
Pension Fund Services
N.A.I.C.S.: 525110

AXA Protection juridique (1)
1 Place Victorien Sardou, 78166, Marly-le-
Roi, Cedex, France
Tel.: (33) 130099000
Web Site: http://www.axa.com
Insurance Management Services
N.A.I.C.S.: 524298

AXA Rosenberg Canada Co. (1)
5700 Yonge Street Suite 1400, North York,
M2M 4K2, ON, Canada
Tel.: (416) 250-1992
Investment Management Service
N.A.I.C.S.: 523999

AXA Rosenberg Investment Manage-
ment Asia Pacific Ltd. (1)
57/F One Island East 18 Westlands Road,
Quarry Bay, China (Hong Kong)
Tel.: (852) 2285 2000
Investment Management Service
N.A.I.C.S.: 523999

AXA Rosenberg Investment Manage-
ment Limited (1)
7 Newgate Street, London, EC1A 7NX,
United Kingdom
Tel.: (44) 2070031800
Web Site: http://www.axa-im.co.uk
Sales Range: $200-249.9 Million
Emp.: 30
Investment Management Service
N.A.I.C.S.: 523999
Gideon Smith (Chief Investment Officer-
Europe)

AXA SPDB Investment Managers
Co., Ltd (1)
38/F Shanghai Central Plaza 381 Middle
Huai Hai Road, Shanghai, 200020, China
Tel.: (86) 4008828999
Web Site: https://www.py-axa.com
Financial Investment Services
N.A.I.C.S.: 523999

AXA SR (1)
Kolarska 6, 811 06, Bratislava, Slovakia
Tel.: (421) 259491111
Web Site: http://www.axa.sk
General Insurance Services
N.A.I.C.S.: 524210

AXA Seguros SA de CV (1)
Av Periferico Sur 3325, San Jeronimo Ac-

ulco, 10400, Mexico, DF, Mexico
Tel.: (52) 5551692500
Web Site: http://www.axa.com.mx
Sales Range: $1-4.9 Billion
Emp.: 4,200
Insurance Services
N.A.I.C.S.: 524210

AXA Seguros Uruguay SA (1)
Missiones 1549, Montevideo, 11000,
Uruguay (100%)
Tel.: (598) 29160850
Web Site: http://www.axa-seguros.com
Sales Range: $50-74.9 Million
Emp.: 20
N.A.I.C.S.: 524128

AXA Services SAS (1)
76 route de la Demi-lune, La Defense,
92057, Paris, Cedex, France
Tel.: (33) 155672000
Information Technology Management Services
N.A.I.C.S.: 541512

AXA Technology Services
Australia (1)
Level 5 750 Collins St, Docklands, Mel-
bourne, 3008, VIC, Australia
Tel.: (61) 3 8688 2204
Information Technology Consulting Services
N.A.I.C.S.: 541512

AXA Technology Services Germany
Gmbh (1)
Colonia-Allee 10-20, 51067, Cologne, Ger-
many
Tel.: (49) 221148105
Information Technology & Telecommunica-
tion Services
N.A.I.C.S.: 541512

AXA Technology Services Japan
K.K (1)
NBF Platinum Tower 21F 1-17-3 Shirokane,
Minato-ku, Tokyo, 108-8020, Japan
Tel.: (81) 3 6737 5284
Web Site: http://www.axa-tech.com
Emp.: 10
Information Technology & Telecommunica-
tion Services
N.A.I.C.S.: 541512
Norbert Juettner (Pres)

AXA Technology Services
Portugal (1)
Praca Jose Queiros n 1 Edificio Entreposto
Porta 2 3 Piso, Lisbon, 1800-237, Portugal
Tel.: (351) 21 85 47 429
Web Site: http://www.axa-tech.com
Information Technology Consulting Services
N.A.I.C.S.: 541512
Edurado Caria (Gen Mgr)

AXA Technology Services SAS. (1)
76 Route de la Demi-Lune, Paris, 92057,
France
Tel.: (33) 1 55 67 20 00
Web Site: http://www.axa-tech.com
Data Processing Services
N.A.I.C.S.: 518210

AXA Technology Services South East
Asia (1)
27/F Cambridge House TaiKoo Place 979
King's Road, Quarry Bay, China (Hong
Kong)
Tel.: (852) 25 19 11 11
Web Site: http://www.axa-tech.com
Information Technology & Telecommunica-
tion Services
N.A.I.C.S.: 541512

AXA Technology Services UK
Plc (1)
Spectrum Building Bond Street, Bristol, BS1
3LG, United Kingdom
Tel.: (44) 125 685 2000
Web Site: http://www.axa-tech.com
Information Technology & Telecommunica-
tion Services
N.A.I.C.S.: 541512

AXA Towarzystwo Ubezpieczen
S.A. (1)
Chlodna 51, 00-867, Warsaw, Poland
Tel.: (48) 225550050
Fire Insurance Services
N.A.I.C.S.: 524113

AXA Turkey Holding A.S. (1)
Meclis-i Mebusan Cad Oyak Yp Hany No
15 Salypazary, Istanbul, 34433, Turkiye
Tel.: (90) 212 334 24 24
Investment Management Service
N.A.I.C.S.: 523940

Subsidiary (Domestic):

AXA Sigorta A.S. (2)
Kilic Ali Pasa Mah Meclis-i Mebusan Cad
No 15, Salipazari, 34433, Istanbul, Turkiye
Tel.: (90) 2123342424
Web Site: https://www.axasigorta.com.tr
Sales Range: $300-349.9 Million
Emp.: 588
General Insurance Services
N.A.I.C.S.: 524210

AXA UK plc (1)
20 Gracechurch Street, London, EC3V
0BG, United Kingdom (100%)
Tel.: (44) 2079205900
Web Site: http://www.axa.co.uk
Emp.: 4,500
Holding Company; Life Insurance, Pen-
sions, Investment
N.A.I.C.S.: 524128
Scott Wheway (Chm)

Subsidiary (Domestic):

AXA Insurance PLC (2)
20 Gracechurch Street, London, EC3V
0BG, United Kingdom (100%)
Tel.: (44) 1892512345
Sales Range: $150-199.9 Million
Emp.: 350
Life Insurance
N.A.I.C.S.: 524113

AXA Insurance UK plc (2)
5 Old Broad Street, London, EC2N 1AD,
United Kingdom
Tel.: (44) 20 7920 5101
General Insurance Services
N.A.I.C.S.: 524298

Division (Domestic):

AXA PPP Healthcare Group PLC (2)
Crescent Road, Tunbridge Wells, TN1 2PL,
Kent, United Kingdom (100%)
Tel.: (44) 1892512345
Web Site:
http://www.axapphealthcare.co.uk
Emp.: 2,000
Healtcare Services
N.A.I.C.S.: 524114
Fergus Craig (Dir-Comml)

Subsidiary (Domestic):

AXA Sun Life Plc (2)
AXA Center, Brierly Furlong Stoke Gifford,
Bristol, BS34 8SW, United
Kingdom (100%)
Tel.: (44) 2079205900
Sales Range: $1-4.9 Billion
Emp.: 3,500
Life Insurance
N.A.I.C.S.: 524128

Bluefin Group Limited (2)
5 Old Broad Street, London, EC2N 1AD,
United Kingdom
Tel.: (44) 207 338 0111
Web Site: http://www.bluefingroup.co.uk
General Insurance Services
N.A.I.C.S.: 524298

Guardian Royal Exchange plc (2)
5 Old Broad Street, London, EC2N 1AD,
United Kingdom
Tel.: (44) 20 7920 5900
General Insurance Services
N.A.I.C.S.: 524210
Robin D. Pagden (Exec Dir)

AXA Ubezpieczenia Towarzystwo
Ubezpieczen i Reasekuracji S.A. (1)
Ul Chlodna 51, 00-867, Warsaw, Poland
Tel.: (48) 225550000
Web Site: http://www.axa.pl
Insurance Management Services
N.A.I.C.S.: 524210
Grzegorz Anczewski (Member-Mgmt Bd)

AXA Ukraine (1)
Bratska Str 14 6th Floor 3rd Entrance, Kiev,
4070, Ukraine

Tel.: (380) 44 391 1122
Web Site: http://www.axa-ukraine.com
General Insurance Services
N.A.I.C.S.: 524210
Philippe Wautelet (CEO)

AXA Versicherung AG (1)
Coloniaallee 10-20, 51067, Cologne,
Germany (100%)
Tel.: (49) 8003203205
Web Site: http://www.axa.de
Sales Range: $100-124.9 Million
Emp.: 170
General Insurance Services
N.A.I.C.S.: 524128

AXA Versicherungen AG (1)
General Guisan Strasse 40, PO Box 4600,
8401, Winterthur, Switzerland
Tel.: (41) 522616300
Web Site: http://www.axa-winterthur.ch
Sales Range: $200-249.9 Million
Emp.: 23,000
Life & Other Insurance Services
N.A.I.C.S.: 524298

Subsidiary (Non-US):

AXA Seguros Mexico (2)
Av Periferico Sur 3325, San Jeronimo Ac-
ulco, 10400, Mexico, DF, Mexico
Tel.: (52) 55 5169 2500
Web Site: http://www.axa.mx
Sales Range: $150-199.9 Million
Emp.: 493
Insurance Services
N.A.I.C.S.: 524128
Ismael Gomez Gordillo (Gen Mgr)

AXA Tianping Property & Casualty
Insurance Company Ltd.
(AXATP) (2)
China Diamond Exchange Building 555 Pu-
dian Rd, Pudong Xinqu, Shanghai, Pudong,
China (100%)
Tel.: (86) 2161563500
Web Site: http://www.axa-ins.com.cn
Foreign-Capital Property & Casualty Insur-
ance Services
N.A.I.C.S.: 524126
Raymond Chan (CEO & Gen Mgr)

AXA Winterthur Pensiones (2)
Avenida Diagonal 575 2nd Floor, 08029,
Barcelona, Spain
Tel.: (34) 902404084
Web Site: http://www.axa.es
Insurance
N.A.I.C.S.: 524128

DBV-Winterthur Holding AG (2)
Abraham Lincoln Park 5, 65172, Wies-
baden, Germany
Tel.: (49) 22114835800
Web Site: http://www.axa.de
Sales Range: $600-649.9 Million
Emp.: 2,000
Insurance Services
N.A.I.C.S.: 524210

Subsidiary (Domestic):

Technopark Immobilien AG (2)
Technoparkstrasse 1, 8005, Zurich, Switzer-
land
Tel.: (41) 444451000
Web Site: https://www.technopark.ch
Sales Range: $25-49.9 Million
Emp.: 8
Technology Services
N.A.I.C.S.: 517810

Winterthur Insurance Co (2)
General-Guisan-Strasse 40, 8400, Winter-
thur, Switzerland
Tel.: (41) 582181100
Web Site: http://www.axa-winterthur.ch
Sales Range: $700-749.9 Million
Emp.: 2,500
Insurance
N.A.I.C.S.: 524128

Winterthur Life & Pensions AG (2)
General Guisan Strasse 40, PO Box 357,
8401, Winterthur, Switzerland
Tel.: (41) 522611111
Web Site: http://www.winterthur-leben.ch
Insurance Provider
N.A.I.C.S.: 524128

AXA Vie Gabon (1)

1935 Boulevard de l independance, BP
4047, Libreville, Gabon
Tel.: (241) 1798080
Web Site: http://www.axa.ga
Sales Range: $50-74.9 Million
Emp.: 16
Insurance Provider
N.A.I.C.S.: 524128

AXA Wealth Ltd (1)
Winterthur Way, Basingstoke, RG21 6SZ,
Hants, United Kingdom
Tel.: (44) 1256470707
Web Site: http://www.axawealth.co.uk
Sales Range: $350-399.9 Million
Emp.: 850
General Insurance Services
N.A.I.C.S.: 524298
Paul Riddell (Head-Strategic Comm)

**AXA Wealth Management Singapore
Pte Ltd** (1)
143 Cecil Streee 03-01/10 GB Building, Sin-
gapore, 069542, Singapore
Tel.: (65) 68805500
Web Site: http://www.axalife.com.sg
Life Insurance Management Services
N.A.I.C.S.: 524113
Glenn Williams (CEO)

**AXA Zycie Towarzystwo Ubezpieczen
S.A.** (1)
Ul Chlodna 51, 00-867, Warsaw, Poland
Tel.: (48) 225550052
Web Site: http://www.axa.pl
Life Insurance
N.A.I.C.S.: 524113

AXA d.d.s., a.s. (1)
Laurinska 18, 811 01, Bratislava, Slovakia
Tel.: (421) 2 2929 2929
Pension Fund Management Services
N.A.I.C.S.: 327910

AXA investicni spolecnost a.s. (1)
Laurinska 18, 811 01, Bratislava, Slovakia
Tel.: (421) 229292929
Financial Investment Services
N.A.I.C.S.: 523999

Branch (Non-US):

AXA investicni spolecnost a.s. (2)
Lazarska 8/13, 12000, Prague, Czech Re-
public
Tel.: (420) 225021295
Web Site: http://www.axa.cz
Financial Investment Services
N.A.I.C.S.: 523999

AXA pojisovna a.s. (1)
Lazarska 13/8, 120 00, Prague, Czech Re-
public
Tel.: (420) 292 292 292
Web Site: http://www.axa.cz
General Insurance Services
N.A.I.C.S.: 524298

AXA zivotni pojistovna a.s. (1)
Kolarska 6, 811 06, Bratislava, Slovakia
Tel.: (421) 259491111
Web Site: http://www.axa.sk
General Insurance Services
N.A.I.C.S.: 524210

Branch (Non-US):

AXA zivotni pojistovna, a.s. (2)
Lazarska 13/8, 120 00, Prague, Czech Re-
public
Tel.: (420) 225021109
Life Insurance Management Services
N.A.I.C.S.: 524113

**AXA-ARAG Protection juridique
SA** (1)
Birmensdorferstrasse 108, PO Box 9829,
8036, Zurich, Switzerland
Tel.: (41) 848111100
Web Site: http://www.axa.ch
Asset Management Services
N.A.I.C.S.: 523940

AXA-ARAG Rechtsschutz AG. (1)
Affolternstrasse 42, Postfach 9829, 8050,
Zurich, Switzerland
Tel.: (41) 848111100
Web Site: http://www.axa.ch
Sales Range: $100-124.9 Million
General Insurance Services
N.A.I.C.S.: 524210

Asuransi AXA Indonesia (1)
Jl Prof Dr Satrio Kav 18 Kuningan City, Ja-
karta, 12940, Indonesia (80%)
Tel.: (62) 2130058000
Web Site: http://www.axa.co.id
Sales Range: $100-124.9 Million
Emp.: 113
Insurance Provider
N.A.I.C.S.: 524128

Avanssur S.A. (1)
oddzial W polsce Ul Street Chlodna 51, 00-
867, Warsaw, Poland
Tel.: (48) 225999000
General Insurance Services
N.A.I.C.S.: 524210

Axa General Insurance - Ltd. (1)
11F 4 Hangang-Daero 71-Gil, Yongsan-gu,
Seoul, 04322, Korea (South)
Tel.: (82) 15661566
Web Site: https://www.axa.co.kr
Fire Insurance Services
N.A.I.C.S.: 524210

Axa XL Group Ltd. (1)
OHara House One Bermudiana Road, PO
Box HM 2245, Hamilton, HM 08, Bermuda
Tel.: (441) 2928515
Insurance & Reinsurance Services
N.A.I.C.S.: 524130

Bluefin Advisory Services Limited (1)
1 Aldgate 1st Floor, London, EC3N 1LP,
United Kingdom
Tel.: (44) 2077094500
Sales Range: $200-249.9 Million
Emp.: 5
General Insurance Services
N.A.I.C.S.: 524298
William F. Ruprecht (CEO)

**DBV Deutsche Beamtenversicherung
AG** (1)
Frankfurter Strasse 50, 65189, Wiesbaden,
Germany
Tel.: (49) 1803552233
Web Site: http://www.dbv.de
General Insurance Services
N.A.I.C.S.: 524210

Subsidiary (Domestic):

**DBV Deutsche Beamtenversicherung
Lebensversicherung AG** (2)
Colonia-Allee 10-20, 51067, Kolin, Germany
Tel.: (49) 221 14841011
Web Site: http://www.dbv.de
General Insurance Services
N.A.I.C.S.: 524210

Direct Assurance (1)
Parc Des Fontaines 163-167 Avenue
Georges-clemenceau, 92742, Nanterre, Ce-
dex, France
Tel.: (33) 146144500
Web Site: http://www.direct-assurance.fr
Rev.: $179,795,000
Insurance
N.A.I.C.S.: 524128

GIE AXA (1)
25 Avenue Matignon, 75008, Paris, France
Tel.: (33) 140755700
General Insurance Services
N.A.I.C.S.: 524210

GIG Gulf (1)
Safeway BuildWay No 3303, PO Box 833,
Al Khuwair, 112, Muscat, Oman
Tel.: (968) 24400100
Web Site: http://www.axa-gulf.com
General Insurance Services
N.A.I.C.S.: 524210

Gulf Insurance Group (GIG) Gulf (1)
Showroom 4 Plot 514-0 Makani 19694
80701 Sheikh Zayed Road, PO Box 290,
Next to metropolitan Hotel Um Al Sheif,
Dubai, United Arab Emirates (100%)
Tel.: (971) 45074085
Web Site: http://www.axa-gulf.com
Insurance Services
N.A.I.C.S.: 524128

**HAYAH Insurance Company
P.J.S.C** (1)
Floor 16 Sheikh Sultan Bin Hamdan Build-
ing Corniche Road, PO Box 63323, Abu
Dhabi, United Arab Emirates
Tel.: (971) 24084700

Web Site: https://hayah.com
Rev.: $12,598,423
Assets: $48,878,844
Liabilities: $16,045,146
Net Worth: $32,833,698
Earnings: $44,098
Fiscal Year-end: 12/31/2019
General Insurance Services
N.A.I.C.S.: 524210
Mishal Kanoo (Vice Chm)

ICBC-AXA Life Assurance (1)
Unit E 18th and 19th Floor No 166 Lujiazui
Ring Road, Shanghai, 200120, Pudong,
China
Tel.: (86) 215 879 2288
Web Site: https://www.icbc-axa.com
Medical Insurance Services
N.A.I.C.S.: 524114

**ICBC-AXA-Minmetals Assurance Co.,
Ltd.** (1)
12/F China Merchants Tower 161 Lu Jai Zui
Road, Pudong New District, Shanghai,
200120, China (27.5%)
Tel.: (86) 2158792288
Web Site: http://www.icbc-axa.com
Sales Range: $10-24.9 Million
Insurance Services in Life, Education, Re-
tirement, Health & Wealth Management
N.A.I.C.S.: 524113

IPA SINGAPORE PTE LTD (1)
11 Pepper Road 12 01 Ebi Plaza, Singa-
pore, 089057, Singapore
Tel.: (65) 6322 2600
Web Site: http://www.axa-assistance.com.sg
Sales Range: $50-74.9 Million
Emp.: 40
General Insurance Services
N.A.I.C.S.: 524210
Matthew Chew (Acct Mgr)

Juridica (1)
1 Place Victorien Sardou, 78160, Marly-le-
Roi, France (100%)
Tel.: (33) 130099000
Web Site: https://www.juridica.fr
Sales Range: $100-124.9 Million
Emp.: 150
Insurance Services
N.A.I.C.S.: 524128

**Krungthai-AXA Life Insurance Co.,
Ltd.** (1)
Pcl 9 G Tower Grand Rama 9 Floor 1 20-27
Rama 9 Road, Bangkok, 10310,
Thailand (50%)
Tel.: (66) 27231159
Web Site: http://www.krungthai-axa.co.th
Sales Range: $200-249.9 Million
Emp.: 526
Life Insurance Products & Services
N.A.I.C.S.: 524113

**Kyobo AXA General Insurance Co.
Ltd.** (1)
395-70 Shindaebang-Dong, Dongjak-gu,
Seoul, 156-714, Korea (South)
Tel.: (82) 2 3479 4888
General Insurance Services
N.A.I.C.S.: 524298

Laya Healthcare Limited (1)
Eastgate Road Eastgate Business Park,
Little Island, T45 E181, Cork, Ireland
Tel.: (353) 212022000
Web Site: https://www.layahealthcare.ie
Emp.: 450
Property & Casualty Insurance Services
N.A.I.C.S.: 524210

Maxis GBN S.A.S. (1)
Terrasse 4 7 Boulevard Des Bouvets,
92000, Nanterre, France (50%)
Tel.: (33) 157321864
Web Site: http://www.maxis-gbn.com
Sales Range: $75-99.9 Million
Employee Benefits Services
N.A.I.C.S.: 524298

Mutuelle Saint-Christophe (1)
277 Rue Saint Jacques, 75256, Paris, Ce-
dex 05, France (100%)
Tel.: (33) 156247600
Web Site: https://www.saint-christophe-
assurances.fr
Sales Range: $100-124.9 Million
Emp.: 120
Insurance

N.A.I.C.S.: 524128

Outpost Wines LLC (1)
2075 Summit Lake Dr, Angwin, CA 94508-
9778
Tel.: (707) 965-1718
Web Site: https://www.outpostwines.com
Wineries
N.A.I.C.S.: 312130

**PT AXA Mandiri Financial
Services** (1)
AXA Tower 9th Floor Jl Prof Dr Satrio Kav
18 Kuningan City, Kav 36-38, Jakarta,
12940, Indonesia
Tel.: (62) 2130058888
Financial Services; Joint Venture Owned
51% by AXA S.A. & 49% PT Bank Mandiri
(Persero) Tbk.
N.A.I.C.S.: 523999

**ROLAND Rechtsschutz Versich-
erungs AG** (1)
Deutz-Kalker Strasse 46, 50679, Cologne,
Germany (60%)
Tel.: (49) 2218277500
Web Site: http://www.roland-rechtsschutz.de
Legal & Business Support Services
N.A.I.C.S.: 541199

Subsidiary (Domestic):

**Jurpartner Services Gesellschaft fur
Rechtsschutz-Schadenregulierung
mbH** (2)
Eumeniusstrase 15-17, 50679, Cologne,
Germany
Tel.: (49) 221 80264 0
Web Site: http://www.jurpartner.de
General Insurance Services
N.A.I.C.S.: 524210
Daniel Halmer (Mng Dir)

ROLAND Assistance GmbH (2)
Deutz Kalker Strasse 46, 50679, Cologne,
Germany
Tel.: (49) 22182778277
Web Site: https://www.roland-assistance.de
Automotive & Insurance Services
N.A.I.C.S.: 524126

Subsidiary (Non-US):

**ROLAND Rechtsschutz-
Versicherungs-AG - Amsterdam** (2)
Herengracht 141, 1015 BH, Amsterdam,
Netherlands
Tel.: (31) 205538 000
Legal & Business Support Services
N.A.I.C.S.: 541199

**ROLAND Rechtsschutz-
Versicherungs-AG - Vienna** (2)
Mariannengasse 14, 1090, Vienna, Austria
Tel.: (43) 171877330
Legal & Business Support Services
N.A.I.C.S.: 541199

Subsidiary (Domestic):

**ROLAND Schutzbrief-Versicherung
AG** (2)
Deutz-Kalker Strasse 46, 50679, Cologne,
Germany
Tel.: (49) 2218277377
Web Site: http://www.roland-schutzbrief.de
Accidental Insurance Services
N.A.I.C.S.: 524113
Frank Feist (CEO)

U A Vie (1)
9 Ave Houdaille, PO Box 2016, Abidjan,
Cote d'Ivoire (100%)
Tel.: (225) 20310400
Web Site: http://www.uavie.ci
Sales Range: $100-124.9 Million
Emp.: 103
Insurance Services
N.A.I.C.S.: 524128

UAT (1)
169 boulevard du 13 Janvier, BP 495,
Lome, Togo
Tel.: (228) 2211034
Insurance Services
N.A.I.C.S.: 524128

UGAR (1)
BP 179, Conakry, Papua New
Guinea (40%)

AXA S.A.—(Continued)

Tel.: (675) 414841
Sales Range: $75-99.9 Million
Emp.: 91
Insurance Services
N.A.I.C.S.: 524128

XL Group Ltd. (1)
O'Hara House One Bermudiana Road,
Hamilton, HM 08, Bermuda
Tel.: (441) 2928515
Web Site: http://www.xlgroup.com
Rev.: $11,328,157,000
Assets: $63,436,236,000
Liabilities: $62,290,104,000
Net Worth: $1,146,132,000
Earnings: ($560,398,000)
Emp.: 7,304
Fiscal Year-end: 12/31/2017
Holding Company; Insurance Services
N.A.I.C.S.: 524126
Craig Langham (Reg Mgr-APAC)

Subsidiary (US):

Allied International Holdings Inc. (2)
10451 Gulf Blvd, Treasure Island, FL 33706
Tel.: (727) 367-6900
Web Site: http://www.alliedspecialty.com
Emp.: 70
Insurance Agents, Brokers & Services
N.A.I.C.S.: 524210
Mary Chris Smith (Chm & Pres)

Subsidiary (Domestic):

Allied Specialty Insurance Inc. (3)
10451 Gulf Blvd, Treasure Island, FL
33706-4814
Tel.: (727) 367-6900
Web Site: http://www.alliedspecialty.com
Emp.: 70
Insurance Agents
N.A.I.C.S.: 524210

T.H.E. Insurance Co. Inc. (3)
10451 Gulf Blvd, Treasure Island, FL
33706-4814
Tel.: (727) 367-6900
Web Site: http://www.theinsco.com
Amusement & Entertainment Insurance
Services
N.A.I.C.S.: 524210

Subsidiary (Non-US):

Angel Risk Management Limited (2)
Ground Floor Marlborough House Victoria
Road South, Chelmsford, CM1 1LN, Essex,
United Kingdom
Tel.: (44) 1245343630
Web Site:
https://www.angelriskmanagement.com
Insurance Underwriting Services
N.A.I.C.S.: 524126
Paul Norman (Office Mgr)

**Brooklyn Underwriting Pty
Limited** (2)
Angel Place Level 28 123 Pitt Street, Sydney, 2000, NSW, Australia
Tel.: (61) 282701790
Web Site:
https://www.brooklynunderwriting.com.au
Insurance Underwriting Services
N.A.I.C.S.: 524126
Alex Coombes (Mgr-Professional Risk)

**Catlin (North American) Holdings
Ltd.** (2)
20 Gracechurch Street Fenchurch Street,
London, EC3V 0BG, United Kingdom
Tel.: (44) 2076488124
Property & Casualty Insurance Services
N.A.I.C.S.: 524126

Subsidiary (Domestic):

Catlin Insurance Company Ltd. (2)
O Hara House One Bermudiana Road,
Hamilton, HM 08, Bermuda
Tel.: (441) 296 0060
Web Site: http://xlcatlin.com
Property & Casualty Insurance Products &
Services
N.A.I.C.S.: 524126
Patrick Tannock (CEO-XL Insurance (Bermuda) Ltd)

Subsidiary (Non-US):

Catlin Australia Pty Limited (3)
123 Pitt Street Angel Place, Sydney, 2000,
NSW, Australia
Tel.: (61) 282701400
Web Site: http://www.axaxl.com
General Insurance Services
N.A.I.C.S.: 524113

Catlin Canada Inc. (3)
First Canadian Place 100 King Street West
Suite 3020, PO Box 310, Toronto, M5X
1C9, ON, Canada
Tel.: (416) 644-3312
Web Site: http://www.axaxl.com
General Insurance Services
N.A.I.C.S.: 524113
Nick Greggains (CEO & Country Mgr)

Catlin Europe SE (3)
Herzog-Friedrich-Strasse 10, 6020,
Innsbruck, Austria
Tel.: (43) 150602235
Web Site: http://xlcatlin.com
General Insurance Services
N.A.I.C.S.: 524126

Catlin Guernsey (3)
Carinthia House 9-11 The Grange, Saint
Peter Port, GY1 2QL, Guernsey
Tel.: (44) 1481 720 003
Web Site: http://xlcatlin.com
General Insurance Services
N.A.I.C.S.: 524113

Catlin Hong Kong Ltd. (3)
Unit 3601-02 36F Central Plaza 18 Harbour
Road, Wanchai, China (Hong Kong)
Tel.: (852) 2820 5888
Web Site: http://xlcatlin.com
General Insurance Services
N.A.I.C.S.: 524113

Catlin Insurance Company Ltd. (3)
20 Gracechurch st, London, EC3V 0BG,
United Kingdom
Tel.: (44) 2076260486
Web Site: http://www.xlcatlin.com
Emp.: 900
General Insurance Services
N.A.I.C.S.: 524126

Catlin Singapore Pte Ltd. (3)
138 Market Street 10-01 CapitaGreen, Singapore, 048946, Singapore
Tel.: (65) 65388710
Property & Casualty Insurance Services
N.A.I.C.S.: 524126
Daryl Lee Gomez (Head-Compliance &
Regulatory Affairs-Asia Pacific)

Subsidiary (US):

Catlin, Inc. (3)
3340 Peachtree Rd N E Tower Pl 100 Ste
2800 & 2950, Atlanta, GA 30326
Tel.: (404) 443-4910
Web Site: http://xlcatlin.com
General Insurance Services
N.A.I.C.S.: 524126
Mike McGavick (CEO)

Catlin, Inc. (3)
4900 N Scottsdale Rd Ste 3600, Scottsdale, AZ 85251
Tel.: (480) 755-6700
Web Site: http://xlcatlin.com
General Insurance Services
N.A.I.C.S.: 524126
Stephanie TerMeer (Head-US Shared Svcs)

Subsidiary (Non-US):

XL Catlin Middle East (3)
Gate Village Building 4 Level 1 Office 106,
Dubai International Financial Centre,
506947, Dubai, United Arab Emirates
Tel.: (971) 43739373
Emp.: 12
Property & Casualty Insurance Services
N.A.I.C.S.: 524126
Hazel Beso (Office Mgr)

Subsidiary (Non-US):

Catlin Re Schweiz AG (2)
Limmatstrasse 250, 8005, Zurich, Switzerland
Tel.: (41) 432682363
Web Site: http://www.xlcatlin.com

Property & Casualty Insurance Services
N.A.I.C.S.: 524126

Subsidiary (Non-US):

**XL Re Latin America (Argentina
SA)** (3)
Ave Del Libertador 6250, Buenos Aires,
Argentina
Tel.: (54) 1148967600
Property & Casualty Insurance Services
N.A.I.C.S.: 524126

Subsidiary (US):

**Global Asset Protection Services,
LLC** (2)
100 Constitution Plz Ste 12, Hartford, CT
06103
Tel.: (860) 246-1863
Web Site: http://www.xlgroup.com
Emp.: 115
General Insurance Services
N.A.I.C.S.: 524210
Michael S. McGavick (CEO)

New Energy Risk, Inc. (2)
3555 Alameda De Las Pulgas 2nd Fl,
Menlo Park, CA 94025
Tel.: (650) 617-0222
Web Site: https://www.newenergyrisk.com
Underwriting Insurance Solution Provider
N.A.I.C.S.: 524128
Tom Hutton (Chm)

Subsidiary (Domestic):

**New Ocean Capital Management
Limited** (2)
3 Bermudiana Road, Hamilton, HM08, Bermuda
Tel.: (441) 4412947530
Web Site: http://www.newoceancap.com
General Insurance Services
N.A.I.C.S.: 524210

XL Bermuda Ltd. (2)
O'Hara House One Bermudiana Road,
Hamilton, HM 08, Bermuda
Tel.: (441) 2928515
Web Site: http://www.xlcatlin.com
Property Catastrophe Insurance Services
N.A.I.C.S.: 524126

Subsidiary (Non-US):

XL Catlin Japan KK (2)
Tokyo Sankei Building 1-7-2 Otemachi,
Chiyoda-ku, Tokyo, 100-0004, Japan
Tel.: (81) 368802050
Property & Casualty Insurance Services
N.A.I.C.S.: 524126

**XL Financial Services (Ireland)
Ltd** (2)
8 St Stephens Green 2 D02 VK30, Dublin,
Ireland
Tel.: (353) 16075300
Web Site: http://www.xlgroup.com
Emp.: 59
Financial Services
N.A.I.C.S.: 523999

Subsidiary (US):

XL Group - Insurance (2)
505 Eagleview Blvd, Exton, PA 19341
Tel.: (610) 968-9500
Web Site: http://www.axaxl.com
Insurance Management Services
N.A.I.C.S.: 524298
Elie Hanna (Head-Broker Mgmt-Global)

Division (Non-US):

XL Group - Insurance - Environmental International Division (3)
XL House 70 Gracechurch Street, London,
EC3V 0XL, United Kingdom
Tel.: (44) 20 7933 7000
Web Site: http://www.xlenvironmental.com
Emp.: 70
Insurance Management Services
N.A.I.C.S.: 524298

Division (Domestic):

XL Group - Insurance - New York Environmental Division (3)
1 World Financial Ctr 200 Liberty St 22nd
Fl, New York, NY 10281

Tel.: (212) 915-7000
Web Site: http://www.xlenvironmental.com
Insurance Management Services
N.A.I.C.S.: 524298
Joseph Moylan (Mgr-Northeast Reg)

Subsidiary (Non-US):

**XL India Business Services Private
Limited** (2)
12th 14th 15th Block B2 B3 IT/ITES SEZ of
DLF Limited Sector - 30, Village Silokhera,
Gurgaon, 122004, Haryana, India
Tel.: (91) 1244138000
General Insurance Services
N.A.I.C.S.: 524210

**XL India Business Services Pvt
Ltd** (2)
8/5th Flr Dlt F Cyber City, Gurgaon,
122002, Haryana, India
Tel.: (91) 1244178000
Web Site: http://www.xlgroup.com
Emp.: 10
Insurance Management Services
N.A.I.C.S.: 524298

Subsidiary (US):

XL Innovate, LLC (2)
3555 Alameda De Las Pulgas 2nd Fl,
Menlo Park, CA 94025
Tel.: (650) 817-7434
Web Site: http://www.xlinnovate.com
Property & Casualty Insurance Services
N.A.I.C.S.: 524126
G. Thompson Hutton (Mng Partner)

XL Insurance (2)
Brookfield Pl 200 Liberty St, New York, NY
10281
Tel.: (212) 915-7000
Web Site: http://www.axaxl.com
Insurance
N.A.I.C.S.: 524210

Subsidiary (Non-US):

**XL Insurance (China) Company
Limited** (2)
HSBC Building Units 1013-14 Level 10
Shanghai Ifc 8, Century Avenue Pudong,
Shanghai, 200120, China
Tel.: (86) 2160583900
Web Site: http://www.axaxl.cn
Emp.: 20
Insurance Management Services
N.A.I.C.S.: 524298
Phil Xue (CEO & Gen Mgr)

**XL Insurance (UK) Holdings
Limited** (2)
XL House 70 Gracechurch Street, London,
EC3V 0XL, United Kingdom
Tel.: (44) 2079337000
Holding Company
N.A.I.C.S.: 551112

XL Insurance Argentina S.A. (2)
Maitu 942 19th Fl, 1006, Buenos Aires,
Argentina (100%)
Tel.: (54) 01143231111
Web Site: http://www.xlinsurance.com
Emp.: 10
N.A.I.C.S.: 524128

XL Insurance Company (2)
8 St Stephens Green 2 D02 VK30, Dublin,
Ireland (100%)
Tel.: (353) 16075300
Web Site: http://www.xlgroup.com
Insurance Services
N.A.I.C.S.: 524298

XL Insurance Company Limited (2)
40 Ashford Road, Parkwood, Johannesburg, 2193, South Africa (100%)
Tel.: (27) 114421111
Web Site: http://www.xlgroup.com
Emp.: 4
Insurance Carrier
N.A.I.C.S.: 524128

XL Insurance Company SE (2)
Plaza De La Lealtad 4, 28014, Madrid,
Spain
Tel.: (34) 917023300
Web Site: http://xlcatlin.com
General Insurance Services
N.A.I.C.S.: 524126

XL Insurance Company SE **(2)**
138 Market St Ste 10-01 Capita Green, Singapore, 048946, Singapore
Tel.: (65) 65388718
Web Site: http://xlcatlin.com
General Insurance Services
N.A.I.C.S.: 524126

XL Insurance Company SE **(2)**
50 rue Taitbout, 75320, Paris, France
Tel.: (33) 155500999
Web Site: http://www.xlcatlin.com
General Insurance Services
N.A.I.C.S.: 524210

Subsidiary (US):

XL Insurance Company of New York, Inc **(2)**
70 Seaview Ave Seaview House, Stamford, CT 06902
Tel.: (203) 964-5200
Web Site: http://www.xlgroup.com
Emp.: 1,000
Insurance Management Services
N.A.I.C.S.: 524298

Subsidiary (Non-US):

XL Insurance Switzerland **(2)**
Limmatstrasse 250 Brewery Building, PO Box 3032, 8005, Zurich, Switzerland **(100%)**
Tel.: (41) 435554000
Web Site: http://www.xlgroup.com
Emp.: 200
N.A.I.C.S.: 524128

XL Insurance Switzerland Ltd **(2)**
Limmatstrasse 250, PO Box 2361, 8005, Zurich, 8005, Switzerland
Tel.: (41) 435554000
General Insurance Services
N.A.I.C.S.: 524210

Subsidiary (Domestic):

XL Investment Management Ltd **(2)**
XL House One Bermudiana Road Hamilton 08, Hamilton, HM 08, Bermuda
Tel.: (441) 292 8515
Emp.: 120
Investment Management Service
N.A.I.C.S.: 523999
Patrick Tannock (Pres)

Subsidiary (Non-US):

XL London Market Group Ltd **(2)**
Fitzwilliam Ho, London, EC3A 8AE, United Kingdom
Tel.: (44) 1212317170
General Insurance Services
N.A.I.C.S.: 524210

XL London Market Ltd. **(2)**
XL House, 70 Gracechurch St, London, EC3V 0XL, United Kingdom
Tel.: (44) 2079337000
Web Site: http://www.xlin.com
Emp.: 1,500
Insurance Services
N.A.I.C.S.: 524298

XL Re Europe SE **(2)**
8 St Stephen's Green, Dublin, Ireland
Tel.: (353) 97143739373
Web Site: http://www.xlcatlin.com
International Property & Specialty Reinsurance Services
N.A.I.C.S.: 524126

Subsidiary (US):

XL Reinsurance America Inc. **(2)**
70 Seaview Ave Seaview House, Stamford, CT 06902-6040 **(100%)**
Tel.: (203) 964-5200
Web Site: http://www.axaxl.com
Rev.: $7,439,000
Emp.: 400
Property & Casualty Reinsurance
N.A.I.C.S.: 524130
Richard H. Miller (Treas)

Subsidiary (Domestic):

Greenwich Insurance Company **(3)**
Seaview House 70 Seaview Ave, Stamford, CT 06902-6040
Tel.: (203) 964-5200

General Insurance Services
N.A.I.C.S.: 524210

XL Design Professional **(3)**
30 Ragsdale Dr Ste 201, Monterey, CA 93940
Tel.: (831) 657-2508
Web Site: http://www.xldp.com
Emp.: 3
Professional Liability Insurance for Architects & Engineers
N.A.I.C.S.: 524298

XL Insurance America Inc. **(3)**
190 S LaSalle St, Chicago, IL 60603-3410 **(100%)**
Tel.: (312) 444-6500
Web Site: http://www.axaxl.com
Emp.: 50
Insurance Services for Business
N.A.I.C.S.: 524298
Ronald E. Beauregard Jr. (Chief Underwriting Officer & Sr VP-Excess & Surplus Property Bus)

Division (Domestic):

XL Reinsurance Corporation **(3)**
70 Seaview Ave Seaview House, Stamford, CT 06902 **(100%)**
Tel.: (203) 964-5200
Web Site: http://www.nacre.com
Holding Company for Property & Casualty Reinsurance Company
N.A.I.C.S.: 524126
Micheal McGavick (CEO)

Subsidiary (Domestic):

Indian Harbor Insurance Company **(4)**
Seaview House 70 Seaview Ave, Stamford, CT 06902 **(100%)**
Tel.: (800) 622-7311
Web Site: http://www.xlgroup.com
Rev.: $1,380,000
Emp.: 250
Surplus Lines Insurance
N.A.I.C.S.: 524210
Richard H. Miller (Treas)

Subsidiary (Non-US):

XL Re Ltd **(4)**
70 Grace Church Street XL House, London, EC3V 0XL, United Kingdom **(100%)**
Tel.: (44) 2079337000
Web Site: http://www.xlgroup.com
Emp.: 600
N.A.I.C.S.: 524298

Subsidiary (Domestic):

XL Reinsurance America **(4)**
190 S Lasalle St, Chicago, IL 60603 **(100%)**
Tel.: (312) 876-7200
Web Site: http://www.axaxl.com
Emp.: 15
General Insurance Services
N.A.I.C.S.: 524298

XL Reinsurance America **(4)**
10 Glenlake Pkwy Ste 910, Atlanta, GA 30328-1276
Tel.: (770) 677-4200
Emp.: 6
N.A.I.C.S.: 524298
Jamie Veghte (CEO)

XL Reinsurance American **(4)**
100 Constitution Plz, Hartford, CT 06103-4306
Tel.: (860) 293-6200
Web Site: http://www.axaxl.com
Property Casualty Underwriting
N.A.I.C.S.: 524126

XL Reinsurance Inc. **(4)**
1331 N California Blvd Ste 200, Walnut Creek, CA 94596 **(100%)**
Tel.: (925) 937-9600
Emp.: 5
Insurance Services
N.A.I.C.S.: 524130

Subsidiary (Domestic):

XL Reinsurance Limited **(2)**
O Hara House One Bermudiana Road, PO Box HM 2245, Hamilton, HM 08, Bermuda

Tel.: (441) 2921358
Web Site: http://www.axaxl.com
Emp.: 300
Reinsurance
N.A.I.C.S.: 524130

Subsidiary (Non-US):

XL Seguros Brasil S.A. **(2)**
Av Brigadeiro Faria Lima 4300 4 andar Edificio FL Corporate, 04538-132, Sao Paulo, 04538-132, Brazil
Tel.: (55) 1135139200
Web Site: https://www.axaxl.com
Insurance Underwriting Services
N.A.I.C.S.: 524113

XL Seguros Mexico S.A. de C.V. **(2)**
Lazaro Cardenas 2400 5th floor Office No 9, San Pedro Garcia, 66278, Monterrey, NL, Mexico
Tel.: (52) 5590009234
Web Site: http://www.axaxl.com
Insurance Services
N.A.I.C.S.: 524298

XL Services UK Ltd. **(2)**
XL House 70 Gracechurch St, London, EC3V 0XL, United Kingdom
Tel.: (44) 2079337000
Web Site: http://www.xlinsurance.com
Emp.: 700
Insurance Services
N.A.I.C.S.: 524298

Yuzzu SA **(1)**
Havenlaan 86C, Box 117, 1000, Brussels, Belgium
Tel.: (32) 25056700
Web Site: https://www.yuzzu.be
Insurance Services
N.A.I.C.S.: 524298

AXACTOR SE
Drammensveien 167, 0277, Oslo, Norway
Tel.: (47) 32755000
Web Site: https://www.axactor.no
Year Founded: 2015
AXA—(OSL)
Rev.: $32,379,804
Assets: $155,740,184
Liabilities: $112,860,752
Net Worth: $42,879,432
Earnings: $2,381,030
Emp.: 1,150
Fiscal Year-end: 12/31/19
Debt Collection & Debt Purchase Services
N.A.I.C.S.: 522390
Bjorn Erik Naess (Chm)

Subsidiaries:

Axactor Espana Platform SA **(1)**
C/Alcala 63 4th Floor, 28014, Madrid, Spain
Tel.: (34) 910120462
Web Site: http://www.axactor.es
Emp.: 702
Credit Management Services
N.A.I.C.S.: 561450
David Martin (Country Mgr)

Axactor Finland OY **(1)**
Porkkalankatu 20 aA, 00180, Helsinki, Finland
Tel.: (358) 143623300
Web Site: https://www.axactor.com
Debt Collection Services
N.A.I.C.S.: 561440
Jarkko Jalonen (Country Mgr)

Axactor Germany Holding GmbH **(1)**
Im Breitspiel 13, 69126, Heidelberg, Germany
Tel.: (49) 622198760
Web Site: http://www.axactor.de
Fiduciary Claim Processing Services
N.A.I.C.S.: 523991

Axactor Italy SpA **(1)**
Via Cascina Colombaro 36a, 12100, Cuneo, CN, Italy
Tel.: (39) 017165694
Web Site: http://www.axactor.it
Emp.: 135
Credit Management Services
N.A.I.C.S.: 561450

Maurizio Nannini (Mgr-ICT)

Axactor Norway AS **(1)**
Tel.: (47) 32755000
Web Site: https://www.axactor.com
Debt Collection Services
N.A.I.C.S.: 561440
Stian Brekke (Acct Mgr)

Axactor Sweden AB **(1)**
Nordstadstorget 6, 411 05, Gothenburg, Sweden
Tel.: (46) 313833810
Web Site: https://www.axactor.com
Emp.: 30
Credit Management Services
N.A.I.C.S.: 561450
Lisa Sohtell (Country Mgr)

SPT Inkasso OU **(1)**
Lootsa 8a, Tallinn, 11415, Estonia
Tel.: (372) 6580100
Debt Collection Services
N.A.I.C.S.: 561440

VABA GmbH **(1)**
Heidestr 159, 42549, Velbert, Germany
Tel.: (49) 205156633
Web Site: http://www.vaba-velbert.de
Aluminium & Wood Door Mfr
N.A.I.C.S.: 321911

AXARA
152 rue Paris, Monteuil, 93100, Montreuil, France
Tel.: (33) 143631313
Web Site: http://www.axara.com
Rev.: $15,700,000
Emp.: 30
Women's Clothing Mfr
N.A.I.C.S.: 315250
Bernard Bouten (Mgr-Personnel)

AXAS HOLDINGS CO., LTD.
4-2 Yamashironishi, Tokushima, 770-8054, Japan
Tel.: (81) 88 623 6666   JP
Web Site: http://www.axas-hd.jp
Year Founded: 2016
Holding Company; Consumer Products Retailer
N.A.I.C.S.: 551112
Takuji Hisaoka (Pres & CEO)

Subsidiaries:

AXAS Corporation **(1)**
4-2 Yamashironishi, Tokushima, 770-8054, Japan
Tel.: (81) 88 654 0077
Web Site: http://www.axas.co.jp
Consumer Products Retailer
N.A.I.C.S.: 455219
Takuji Hisaoka (Pres)

Zakkaya Bulldog Co., Ltd. **(1)**
1-3-15 Minamihonmachi, Chuo-ku, Osaka, 541-0054, Japan
Tel.: (81) 6 6260 5505
Web Site: http://www.z-bulldog.co.jp
Consumer Products Retailer
N.A.I.C.S.: 455219
Takuji Hisaoka (Pres & CEO)

AXCAP VENTURES INC.
800 West Pender Street Suite 1430, Vancouver, V6C2V6, BC, Canada
Tel.: (604) 363-0411   BC
Web Site: http://www.netcoins.ca
Year Founded: 1987
1WJ—(DEU)
Rev.: $13,297
Assets: $2,004,041
Liabilities: $177,952
Net Worth: $1,826,089
Earnings: ($665,732)
Fiscal Year-end: 12/31/22
Investment Services
N.A.I.C.S.: 523999
Mark Binns (CEO-Acting)

AXCEL MANAGEMENT A/S
Sankt Annae Plads 10, 1250, Copenhagen, Denmark

Axcel Management A/S—(Continued)

Tel.: (45) 33366999   DK
Web Site: http://www.axcel.dk
Year Founded: 1994
Asset Management & Private Equity
Investment Firm
N.A.I.C.S.: 523940
Lars Cordt *(Partner)*

Subsidiaries:

Aidian Oy   **(1)**
Koivu Mankkaantie 6 B, 02200, Espoo,
Finland
Tel.: (358) 10 309 3000
Web Site: http://www.aidian.fi
Biotechnogical & Medical Laboratory Testing Services
N.A.I.C.S.: 621999
Antti Koivula *(COO & CFO)*

Subsidiary (Non-US):

Aidian Denmark ApS   **(2)**
Orestads Boulevard 73, 2300, Copenhagen,
Denmark   **(100%)**
Tel.: (45) 86103020
Web Site: http://www.aidian.dk
Testing Laboratory Products Mfr
N.A.I.C.S.: 621999
Bitten Stender *(Head-Reg & Mgr-Sls)*

Aidian Germany GmbH   **(2)**
Mergenthaler Allee 15-21, 65760, Eschborn,
Germany
Tel.: (49) 6196 77 00 146
Web Site: http://www.aidian.de
Diagnostic Health Care Services
N.A.I.C.S.: 621999
Gabriele Rech *(Head-Reg)*

Aidian Norway AS   **(2)**
Fredrik Selmers vei 6, 0663, Oslo,
Norway   **(100%)**
Tel.: (47) 66785630
Web Site: http://www.aidian.no
Biotechnogical & Medical Laboratory Testing Services
N.A.I.C.S.: 541380
Bitten Stender *(Head-Reg)*

Aidian Sweden AB   **(2)**
Svardvagen 21, 182 33, Danderyd,
Sweden   **(100%)**
Tel.: (46) 86230400
Web Site: http://www.aidian.se
Biotechnogical & Medical Laboratory Testing Services
N.A.I.C.S.: 541380
Bitten Stender *(Head-Reg)*

BALL WHOLESALE ApS   **(1)**
Klovermarken 29, 7190, Billund, Denmark
Tel.: (45) 76 98 11 00
Apparel Distr
N.A.I.C.S.: 458110

Subsidiary (Non-US):

BALL GROUP Norge AS   **(2)**
Sjolyst Plass 3 Rom 108, Oslo, Norway
Tel.: (47) 24 11 83 00
Apparel Distr
N.A.I.C.S.: 458110

BALL GROUP Sverige AB   **(2)**
Bryggaregatan 19-21, 503 38, Boras, Sweden
Tel.: (46) 33 12 77 80
Apparel Distr
N.A.I.C.S.: 458110

Delete Sweden AB   **(1)**
Hiomotie 19, 00380, Helsinki, Finland
Tel.: (358) 10 656 1000
Web Site: http://www.delete.fi
Construction Engineering Services
N.A.I.C.S.: 541330
Jussi Niemela *(CEO)*

Mita-Teknik A/S   **(1)**
Handvaerkervej 1, DK-8840, Rodkaersbro,
Denmark
Tel.: (45) 8665 8600
Web Site: http://www.mita-teknik.com
Emp.: 100
Wind Energy Equipment Mfr
N.A.I.C.S.: 333248
Jesper Andersen *(CEO)*

Subsidiary (Non-US):

Mita-Teknik (Ningbo) Co. Ltd.   **(2)**
Nordic Industrial Park No 5 Jinxi Road,
Zhenhai, Ningbo, 315221, China
Tel.: (86) 574 8630 6728
Web Site: http://www.mita-teknik.com
Emp.: 100
Electronic Equipment & Component Distr
N.A.I.C.S.: 423690

Subsidiary (US):

Mita-Teknik LLC   **(2)**
John Hancock Ctr 875 N Michigan Ave Ste
3950, Chicago, IL 60611
Tel.: (312) 261-6009
Electronic Equipment & Component Distr
N.A.I.C.S.: 423690

Subsidiary (Non-US):

**Mita-Teknik Technology Private
Ltd**   **(2)**
No 1/62-15 Ravi Colony 1st Street Paul
Wells Road, St Thomas Mount, Chennai,
600 016, India
Tel.: (91) 44 2231 2278
Web Site: http://www.mita-teknik.com
Electronic Equipment & Component Distr
N.A.I.C.S.: 423690

Nordic Waterproofing AB   **(1)**
Bruksgatan, PO Box 22, Hoganas, 263 21,
Sweden   **(100%)**
Tel.: (46) 42 36 22 40
Web Site:
   http://www.nordicwaterproofing.com
Sales Range: $250-299.9 Million
Roofing
N.A.I.C.S.: 423330
Mats Limdborg *(Mgr)*

Subsidiary (Non-US):

Makati Oy   **(2)**
Liekokuja 6, FIN 03100, Nummela,
Finland   **(100%)**
Tel.: (358) 9 2242 850
Web Site:
   http://web.nordicwaterproofing.com
Sales Range: $25-49.9 Million
Emp.: 20
Construction Waterproofing Materials Mfr
N.A.I.C.S.: 423390

Subsidiary (Domestic):

Trebolit AB   **(2)**
PO Box 22, 263 21, Hoganas,
Sweden   **(100%)**
Tel.: (46) 41048000
Web Site: http://www.trebolit.se
Develops & Markets Waterproofing Products & Other Construction Products
N.A.I.C.S.: 423390

Royal Scandinavia A/S   **(1)**
Sondre Fasanvej 9, DK 2000, Frederiksberg, Denmark
Tel.: (45) 38 14 48 48
Web Site: http://www.royalscandinavia.com
Holding Company
N.A.I.C.S.: 551112
Christian Frigast *(Vice Chm)*

Subsidiary (Domestic):

Illums Bolighus A/S   **(2)**
Amagertorv 10, 1160, Copenhagen,
Denmark   **(100%)**
Tel.: (45) 33141941
Web Site: http://www.illumsbolighus.dk
Sales Range: $25-49.9 Million
Retail Sale of Porcelain, Silver & Glass
Distr
N.A.I.C.S.: 449129
Henrik Ypkendanz *(CEO)*

Subsidiary (US):

Orrefors Kosta Boda, Inc.   **(2)**
1317 Route 73 Ste 201, Mount Laurel, NJ
08054
Tel.: (856) 768-5400
Web Site: http://www.orrefors.us
Emp.: 10
Porcelain Silverware & Glassware Distr
N.A.I.C.S.: 423220
Roy Bodnar *(VP-Fin)*

TMK A/S   **(1)**
Skautrupvej 16, Tvis, 7500, Holstebro, Denmark
Tel.: (45) 9743 5200
Web Site: http://www.tmk.dk
Household Furniture Distr
N.A.I.C.S.: 423210
Ole Lund Andersen *(CEO)*

AXCEN PHOTONICS CORPORATION

6F No 119 Baozhong Rd, Xindian
Dist, New Taipei City, 231, Taiwan
Tel.: (886) 289111840
Web Site: https://www.axcen.com.tw
Year Founded: 2002
6530—(TPE)
Rev.: $8,573,523
Assets: $16,869,337
Liabilities: $2,298,440
Net Worth: $14,570,897
Earnings: $1,681,393
Fiscal Year-end: 12/31/22
Photonic Integration & Electrical Device Mfr
N.A.I.C.S.: 334419

AXEL JOHNSON GRUPPEN AB

Villagatan 6, PO Box 26008, 100 41,
Stockholm, Sweden
Tel.: (46) 87016100   SE
Web Site: http://www.axeljohnson.se
Year Founded: 1873
Sales Range: $5-14.9 Billion
Commodity Trading Services
N.A.I.C.S.: 551112
Mia Brunell Livfors *(Pres & CEO)*

Subsidiaries:

AxFast AB   **(1)**
Drottninggatan 78, PO Box 216, 101 24,
Stockholm, Sweden
Tel.: (46) 87525300
Web Site: http://www.axfast.se
Sales Range: $25-49.9 Million
Emp.: 15
Commercial Property Acquisition, Development & Management Services
N.A.I.C.S.: 531390
Erik Lindvall *(Pres & CEO)*

Axel Johnson AB   **(1)**
Villagatan 6, Box 26008, 100 41, Stockholm, Sweden   **(100%)**
Tel.: (46) 87016100
Web Site: http://www.axeljohnson.se
Rev.: $8,181,630,240
Assets: $2,915,215,520
Liabilities: $1,458,569,280
Net Worth: $1,456,646,240
Earnings: $349,314,560
Emp.: 19,342
Fiscal Year-end: 12/31/2016
Holding Company; Retail Trade & Trade-Related Businesses Developer, Owner &
Operator
N.A.I.C.S.: 551112
Caroline Morner Berg *(Chm)*

Subsidiary (Non-US):

**AKO Armaturen - Separation
GmbH**   **(2)**
Adam-Opel-Strasse 5, Astheim, 65468,
Trebur, Germany
Tel.: (49) 614791590
Web Site: http://www.ako-armaturen.de
Sales Range: $25-49.9 Million
Emp.: 20
Diaphragm Valves Squash Valve Collar
Valve Worm-Gear Pump Dosing Pump &
Silt Sieve Mfr
N.A.I.C.S.: 332911
Helmut Hessinger *(Mgr-Sls)*

AxPro France S.A.   **(2)**
40 Ave Des Terroirs De France, 75012,
Paris, France
Tel.: (33) 144745300
Carpet Mfr
N.A.I.C.S.: 314110

Subsidiary (Domestic):

Axel Johnson International AB   **(2)**
Sveawvajen 166 Floor 17, 11346, Stockholm, Sweden
Tel.: (46) 84537700
Web Site: http://www.axinter.se
Sales Range: $50-74.9 Million
Emp.: 5
Steel Wire Rope, Wind Turbine Servicing,
Bearings, Imaging Solutions & Components
for Heavy Vehicles
N.A.I.C.S.: 331222
Mats R. Karlsson *(Pres & CEO)*

Subsidiary (Domestic):

AxFlow Holding AB   **(3)**
Sveavagen 166 14th Floor, SE-113 46,
Stockholm, Sweden   **(100%)**
Tel.: (46) 854547670
Web Site: http://www.axflow.com
Sales Range: $150-199.9 Million
Emp.: 397
Holding Company; Industrial Pumps Mfr &
Distr
N.A.I.C.S.: 551112
Ole Weiner *(Pres & CEO)*

Subsidiary (Non-US):

AxFlow A/S   **(4)**
Solvang 6, 3450, Allerod, Denmark
Tel.: (45) 70103550
Web Site: http://www.axflow.dk
Sales Range: $25-49.9 Million
Emp.: 25
Mfr of Pumping Equipment
N.A.I.C.S.: 333914

Subsidiary (Non-US):

Widni Oy   **(5)**
Valokaari 8, 00750, Helsinki, Finland
Tel.: (358) 975180500
Web Site: http://www.widni.fi
Sales Range: $75-99.9 Million
Emp.: 20
N.A.I.C.S.: 333310
Johan Karlberg *(Mng Dir)*

Subsidiary (Domestic):

AxFlow AB   **(4)**
Byangsgrand 6, SE-120 40, Arsta,
Sweden   **(100%)**
Tel.: (46) 86022200
Web Site: http://www.axflow.se
Sales Range: $25-49.9 Million
Emp.: 10
Industrial Pump Distr
N.A.I.C.S.: 423830

Subsidiary (Non-US):

AxFlow DC B.V.   **(5)**
Pascallaan 69, 8218 NJ, Lelystad, Netherlands
Tel.: (31) 320 27 66 33
Industrial Pump Distr
N.A.I.C.S.: 423830

AxFlow GesmbH   **(5)**
Seering 2/2 OG, 8141, Unterpremstatten,
Austria
Tel.: (43) 316 68 35 09
Web Site: http://www.axflow.at
Emp.: 10
Industrial Pump Distr
N.A.I.C.S.: 423830
Andreas Lippitsch *(Mng Dir)*

AxFlow Kft   **(5)**
Billk Centre B1 Europa utca 6 room 209,
1239, Budapest, Hungary
Tel.: (36) 1 454 3080
Industrial Pump Distr
N.A.I.C.S.: 423830
Laszlo Vago *(Mng Dir)*

AxFlow Limited   **(5)**
Unit 3 10B Stadium business park Ballycoolin Road, Dublin, Ireland
Tel.: (353) 188 298 64
Web Site: http://www.axflow.ie
Emp.: 5
Industrial Pump Distr
N.A.I.C.S.: 423830
Stuart Flood *(Mng Dir)*

AxFlow SRL   **(5)**

Str Henri Barbusse nr 19, 400616, Cluj-
Napoca, Romania
Tel.: (40) 726 304 180
Web Site: http://www.axflow.ro
Emp.: 3
Industrial Pump Distr
N.A.I.C.S.: 423830
Laszlo Vago *(Mng Dir)*

AxFlow Sp. z o.o.　　　　　　　　　　**(5)**
ul Floriana 3/5, 04 664, Warsaw, Poland
Tel.: (48) 22 613 00 12
Industrial Pump Distr
N.A.I.C.S.: 423830
Mariusz Krawczyk *(Mng Dir)*

AxFlow n.v. / s.a.　　　　　　　　　　**(5)**
PO Box 233, 8200 AE, Lelystad, Nether-
lands
Tel.: (31) 36 538 12 11
Industrial Pump Distr
N.A.I.C.S.: 423830
Joep Verhagen *(Mng Dir)*

AxFlow s.r.o., o.z.p.z.o.　　　　　　**(5)**
M R Stefanika 39, 920 01, Hlohovec, Slova-
kia
Tel.: (421) 911 769 788
Industrial Pump Distr
N.A.I.C.S.: 423830
Renata Borovenova *(Mng Dir)*

OE Solutions AS　　　　　　　　　　**(5)**
Kobberveien 2, 4313, Sandnes, Norway
Tel.: (47) 5197 3933
Web Site: http://www.oe-solutions.no
Industrial Equipment Mfr
N.A.I.C.S.: 333998
Egil Fosse *(Mgr-Technical)*

Subsidiary (Non-US):

AxFlow AS　　　　　　　　　　　　**(4)**
Lilleakerveien 10, PO Box 98, 0283, Oslo,
Norway
Tel.: (47) 22736700
Web Site: http://www.axflow.no
Sales Range: $10-24.9 Million
Emp.: 45
Provider of Pumping Equipment
N.A.I.C.S.: 333914
Gunnar Oedegaard *(Mng Dir)*

AxFlow B.V.　　　　　　　　　　　**(4)**
Dosiderwg No 2, 1332 AT, Almere, Nether-
lands
Tel.: (31) 365381211
Web Site: http://www.axflow.nl
Sales Range: $10-24.9 Million
Emp.: 50
Distr of Pumps, Measuring & Control Equip-
ment; Provider of Engineering Services
N.A.I.C.S.: 541330

AxFlow GmbH　　　　　　　　　　**(4)**
Seering 2 / 2nd Floor, 8141, Unterpremstat-
ten, Austria
Tel.: (43) 3166835090
Web Site: http://www.axflow.com
Sales Range: $1-9.9 Million
Emp.: 15
Mfr & Distributor of Pumps
N.A.I.C.S.: 333914
Andreas Lippitsch *(Gen Mgr)*

AxFlow Lda.　　　　　　　　　　　**(4)**
Ave Duarte Pacheco 2, PO Box 92, Santo
Amaro De Oeiras, 2780316, Oeiras, Codex,
Portugal
Tel.: (351) 214461590
Web Site: http://www.axflow.pt
Sales Range: $25-49.9 Million
Emp.: 6
Mfr of Pumping Equipment
N.A.I.C.S.: 333914
Jose Vargas *(Mng Dir)*

AxFlow Ltd.　　　　　　　　　　　**(4)**
Orion Park Northfield Ave, Ealing, London,
W13 9SJ, United Kingdom
Tel.: (44) 2085792111
Web Site: http://www.axflow.co.uk
Sales Range: $25-49.9 Million
Emp.: 25
Distr of Positive Displacement Pumps &
Related Products & Services
N.A.I.C.S.: 423830
Tony Peters *(Mng Dir)*

Branch (Domestic):

AxFlow Ltd.　　　　　　　　　　　**(5)**

Unit 3 Harlaw Centre Howe Moss Crescent,
Kirkhill Industrial Estate, Aberdeen, AB21
OGN, United Kingdom
Tel.: (44) 1224729367
Web Site: http://www.axflow.co.uk
Sales Range: $100-124.9 Million
Emp.: 4
Pumps & Valves Distr
N.A.I.C.S.: 423830

Division (Domestic):

Meller Flow Trans Limited　　　　**(5)**
Millersdale Close Euroway Industrial Estate,
Bradford, BD4 6RX, United Kingdom
Tel.: (44) 1274687687
Web Site: http://www.mellerflowtrans.com
Sales Range: $75-99.9 Million
Emp.: 25
Provider of Transport Services for Liquid
Powder Chemical & Gas
N.A.I.C.S.: 488510

Subsidiary (Non-US):

AxFlow Oy　　　　　　　　　　　**(4)**
Jokinsunkuja 3, 00560, Helsinki, Finland
Tel.: (358) 97771930
Web Site: http://www.axflow.fi
Sales Range: $25-49.9 Million
Emp.: 10
Steel Wire Rope, Wind Turbine Servicing,
Bearings, Imaging Solutions & Components
for Heavy Vehicles
N.A.I.C.S.: 331222

AxFlow SA　　　　　　　　　　　**(4)**
Avenida de la Industria 53, 280 34, Madrid,
Spain
Tel.: (34) 917291818
Web Site: http://www.axflow.es
Sales Range: $1-9.9 Million
Emp.: 29
Provider of Pumping Equipment
N.A.I.C.S.: 333914

AxFlow SAS　　　　　　　　　　　**(4)**
87 Rue des Poiriers ZA Sainte Apolline, PO
Box 72, 78370, Plaisir, France
Tel.: (33) 130684141
Web Site: http://www.axflow.com
Sales Range: $25-49.9 Million
Emp.: 23
Industrial Pumps Mfr & Distr
N.A.I.C.S.: 333996

AxFlow SpA　　　　　　　　　　　**(4)**
Via Del Commercio 15 - 15/A, 20090, Mi-
lan, Italy
Tel.: (39) 02484801
Web Site: http://www.axflow.com
Sales Range: $25-49.9 Million
Emp.: 20
Marketing, Sales & Service of Ice Equip-
ment
N.A.I.C.S.: 423740

AxFlow s.r.o.　　　　　　　　　　**(4)**
Tovaren 256 14, Prague, 10200, Czech
Republic
Tel.: (420) 272101180
Web Site: http://www.axflow.cz
Sales Range: $50-74.9 Million
Emp.: 13
Steel Wire Rope, Wind Turbine Servicing,
Bearings, Imaging Solutions & Components
for Heavy Vehicles
N.A.I.C.S.: 331222

Subsidiary (Domestic):

AxIndustries AB　　　　　　　　　**(3)**
Villagatan 6, PO Box 5174, SE-10244,
Stockholm, Sweden
Tel.: (46) 84537700
Web Site: http://www.axindustries.se
Sales Range: $150-199.9 Million
Holding Company; Automotive Bearings,
Transmissions & Heavy-Duty Vehicle Com-
ponents Mfr & Distr
N.A.I.C.S.: 551112

Subsidiary (Domestic):

AB Karosseritillbehor　　　　　　**(4)**
Olsgardsgatan 3, PO Box 9095, 21579,
Malmo, Sweden
Tel.: (46) 40220020
Web Site: http://www.abkatl.se

Sales Range: $25-49.9 Million
Emp.: 25
Consumer Goods Trading
N.A.I.C.S.: 425120

Eigenbrodt AB　　　　　　　　　　**(4)**
Optimusvagen 14, PO Box 704, Upplands
Vasby, 19427, Sweden
Tel.: (46) 859463400
Web Site: http://www.eigenbrodt.se
Rev.: $13,815,000
Emp.: 30
Commercial Vehicle Component Industrial
Component & Tool Mfr
N.A.I.C.S.: 336330
Johan Karlberg *(Mng Dir)*

Subsidiary (Non-US):

Eigenbrodt Widni Baltic OU　　　**(5)**
Laki 5, 10621, Tallinn, Estonia
Tel.: (372) 6 532 430
Automobile Component Distr
N.A.I.C.S.: 423120
Johan Karlberg *(Mng Dir)*

Eigenbrodt Widni OY　　　　　　**(5)**
Sahkotie 8, 01510, Vantaa, Finland
Tel.: (358) 9 751 80 500
Automobile Component Distr
N.A.I.C.S.: 423120
Johan Karlberg *(Mng Dir)*

Subsidiary (Domestic):

Elektro-Dynamo AB　　　　　　　**(4)**
Exportgatan 33, 422 46, Hisings Backa,
Sweden
Tel.: (46) 31 742 17 17
Web Site: http://www.lastvagnsdelar.com
Automobile Component Distr
N.A.I.C.S.: 423120
Leif Bohlenius *(Mng Dir)*

**GISAB Gallivare Industriservice
AB**　　　　　　　　　　　　　　　**(4)**
Hertiggatan 26, 983 35, Malmberget, Swe-
den
Tel.: (46) 970 142 70
Web Site: http://www.gisab.net
Industrial Machinery Mfr
N.A.I.C.S.: 333998
Thomas Johansson *(Mng Dir)*

Subsidiary (Non-US):

Jens S. Transmisjoner AS　　　　**(4)**
Enebakkveien 117, PO Box 9, Manglerud,
0612, Oslo, Norway
Tel.: (47) 23 06 04 00
Web Site: http://www.jens-s.no
Industrial Machinery Distr
N.A.I.C.S.: 423830
Rune Blichfeldt *(Mng Dir)*

Jens S. Transmissioner A/S　　　**(4)**
Brogrenen 5, 2635, Ishoj, Denmark
Tel.: (45) 70 13 83 33
Web Site: http://www.jens-s.dk
Industrial Machinery Mfr
N.A.I.C.S.: 333998
Anders Lassen *(Mng Dir)*

Subsidiary (Domestic):

Jens S. Transmissioner AB　　　**(4)**
Koppargatan 9, 602 23, Norrkoping,
Sweden　　　　　　　　　　　　　**(100%)**
Tel.: (46) 11198000
Web Site: http://www.jens-s.se
Sales Range: $25-49.9 Million
Emp.: 50
Motor Vehicle Power Transmission Parts
Distr
N.A.I.C.S.: 423120
Erik Carlsson *(Mng Dir)*

Nomo AB　　　　　　　　　　　　**(4)**
Gribbylundsvagen 2, 187 62, Taby, Sweden
Tel.: (46) 8 630 28 00
Web Site: http://www.nomo.se
Emp.: 40
Bearing Product Distr
N.A.I.C.S.: 423840
Asa Bergstrom *(Dir-Supply Chain)*

Nomo Kullager AB　　　　　　　**(4)**
Gribbylundsvagen 2, 187 62, Taby,
Sweden　　　　　　　　　　　　　**(100%)**
Tel.: (46) 86302800
Web Site: http://www.nomo.se

Sales Range: $50-74.9 Million
Emp.: 70
Ball Bearing Importer & Distr
N.A.I.C.S.: 423120
Leif Bexelius *(Mgr-Warehouse)*

Subsidiary (Non-US):

Oy Jens S. AB　　　　　　　　　**(4)**
Pl 95, 022 71, Espoo, Finland
Tel.: (358) 9 8676730
Web Site: http://www.jens-s.fi
Emp.: 7
Power Transmission Product Distr
N.A.I.C.S.: 333612
Par Nylund *(Mng Dir)*

Porin Laakeri Oy　　　　　　　　**(4)**
Helmentie 5, 28360, Pori, Finland
Tel.: (358) 2 631 9500
Web Site: http://www.porinlaakeri.fi
Emp.: 10
Bearing Product Distr
N.A.I.C.S.: 423840
Jari Ylinen *(Mng Dir)*

Spruit Transmissies BV　　　　　**(4)**
Ivoorstraat 4, 1812 RE, Alkmaar, Nether-
lands
Tel.: (31) 72 5412000
Web Site: http://www.spruit.nl
Power Transmission Product Distr
N.A.I.C.S.: 333612
Dick Winkelhuis *(Mng Dir)*

Subsidiary (Domestic):

Sundquist Components AB　　　　**(4)**
Skrittgatan 1, PO Box 50579, SE-213 77,
Malmo, Sweden
Tel.: (46) 40180075
Web Site: http://www.sundquistcomp.se
Polymer Material Die-Cutting & Processing
Services
N.A.I.C.S.: 326199
Johnny Meltzer *(Mng Dir)*

Sverull AB　　　　　　　　　　　**(4)**
Fridhemsvagen 17, 553 02, Jonkoping,
Sweden
Tel.: (46) 36312600
Web Site: http://www.sverull.se
Sales Range: $25-49.9 Million
Emp.: 80
Motor Vehicle Bearings & Power Transmis-
sion Parts Distr
N.A.I.C.S.: 423120
Goran Hegestig *(Mng Dir)*

Subsidiary (Domestic):

AxLoad AB　　　　　　　　　　　**(3)**
Sveavagen 166 floor 15, 113 46, Stock-
holm, Sweden
Tel.: (46) 8 453 77 50
Web Site: http://www.axload.com
Lifting Equipment Distr
N.A.I.C.S.: 423830
Martin Malmvik *(CEO)*

Subsidiary (Non-US):

ACK Forankra SAS　　　　　　　**(4)**
8 rue Jacques de Vaucanson ZAC de la
Pesseliere, 69780, Mions, France
Tel.: (33) 4 72 45 01 20
Web Site: http://www.ackforankra.fr
Cargo Handling Services
N.A.I.C.S.: 488320

AxFlow Systems B.V.　　　　　　**(4)**
Bedrijfsweg 14, 8251 KK, Dronten, Nether-
lands
Tel.: (31) 321 313 540
Industrial Pump Distr
N.A.I.C.S.: 423830

Cables y Eslingas, S.A.　　　　　**(4)**
c/Montclar s/n Poligono Polizur, 08290, Cer-
danyola del Valles, Barcelona, Spain
Tel.: (34) 93 592 42 00
Web Site: http://www.cyesa.com
Sales Range: $10-24.9 Million
Emp.: 100
Steel Wire Ropes, Lifting Slings & Lifting
Accessories Mfr
N.A.I.C.S.: 331222
Silvia Ramirez *(Mgr-Export)*

Certex Danmark A/S　　　　　　**(4)**
Trekanten 6-8, 6500, Vojens, Denmark

Axel Johnson Gruppen AB—(Continued)

Tel.: (45) 74 54 14 37
Web Site: http://www.certex.dk
Lifting Equipment Distr
N.A.I.C.S.: 423830
Majbritt Petersen (Mng Dir)

Certex Eesti OU (4)
Peterburi tee 47, 11415, Tallinn, Estonia
Tel.: (372) 6062 599
Web Site: http://www.certex.ee
Lifting Equipment Distr
N.A.I.C.S.: 423830

Certex Finland Oy (4)
Juvan teollisuuskatu 25 C, 02920, Espoo,
Finland
Tel.: (358) 201 550 220
Web Site: http://www.certex.fi
Emp.: 40
Lifting Equipment Distr
N.A.I.C.S.: 423830
Eero Era-Esko (Controller)

Certex Latvija SIA (4)
Ritausmas iela 11B, 1058, Riga, Latvia
Tel.: (371) 761 18 82
Web Site: http://www.certex.lv
Lifting Equipment Distr
N.A.I.C.S.: 423830
Vidas Valavicius (Mng Dir)

Certex Lietuva UAB (4)
Titnago str 14, Vilnius, 02300, Lithuania
Tel.: (370) 5 2322297
Web Site: http://www.certex.lt
Emp.: 11
Lifting Equipment Distr
N.A.I.C.S.: 423830
Vidas Valavicius (Mng Dir)

Certex Lifting & Service GmbH (4)
Hansaallee 321 Halle 23, 40549, Dussel-
dorf, Germany
Tel.: (49) 211 67 00 90
Web Site: http://www.certex.de
Lifting Equipment Distr
N.A.I.C.S.: 423830
Herr Philip Bruls (Mng Dir)

Certex Lifting Ltd (4)
Unit C1 Harworth Industrial Estate Bryans
Close, Doncaster, Harworth, DN11 8RY,
United Kingdom
Tel.: (44) 1302756777
Web Site: http://www.certex.co.uk
Lifting Equipment Distr
N.A.I.C.S.: 423830
Kevin Smith (Mng Dir)

Division (Domestic):

**Certex Lifting Ltd - Oil & Gas
Division** (5)
Broadfold House Broadfold Road Bridge of
Don, Aberdeen, AB23 8EE, United Kingdom
Tel.: (44) 224 251 080
Lifting Equipment Mfr
N.A.I.C.S.: 333998

**Certex Lifting Ltd - Renewables
Division** (5)
Brittania House Admiralty Road, Norfolk,
NR30 3PQ, United Kingdom
Tel.: (44) 493 857 705
Lifting Equipment Mfr
N.A.I.C.S.: 333998

Subsidiary (Non-US):

Certex Norge AS (4)
Eternitveien 44, 3470, Slemmestad, Norway
Tel.: (47) 66 79 95 00
Web Site: http://www.certex.no
Lifting Equipment Distr
N.A.I.C.S.: 423830
Harald Hope (Mng Dir)

Certex Offshore Services AS (4)
PO Box 2277, 6503, Kristiansund, Norway
Tel.: (47) 715 88 700
Web Site: http://www.certexoffshore.no
Logistics Consulting Servies
N.A.I.C.S.: 541614
Ole Ersvik (Mng Dir)

Certex Rus ZAO (4)
Kubinskaja ul 82, 196240, Saint Petersburg,
Russia
Tel.: (7) 812 3350965

Web Site: http://www.certex.ru
Lifting Equipment Mfr & Distr
N.A.I.C.S.: 333998
Dennis Jakovlev (Mng Dir)

Subsidiary (Domestic):

Certex Svenska AB (4)
Pentavagen 3, 183 02, Taby, Sweden
Tel.: (46) 8 758 00 10
Web Site: http://www.certex.se
Lifting Equipment Distr
N.A.I.C.S.: 423830
Stefan Jagelid (CEO)

Subsidiary (Non-US):

Erling Haug AS (4)
Vestre Kanalkai 24, 7010, Trondheim, Nor-
way
Tel.: (47) 73 53 97 00
Web Site: http://www.haug.no
Emp.: 30
Automotive Component Mfr & Distr
N.A.I.C.S.: 336390
Kristian Steinshylla (Mng Dir)

Forankra Espana SL (4)
Avda Universidad Autonoma 15 Parque
tecnologico del Valles, 08290, Barcelona,
Spain
Tel.: (34) 93 580 06 60
Lifting Equipment Distr
N.A.I.C.S.: 423830
Phillipe Plossu (Mng Dir)

Forankra Pol Sp. z o.o. (4)
ul Tartaczna 1, 72-100, Goleniow, Poland
Tel.: (48) 91 418 25 91
Web Site: http://www.forankra.pl
Emp.: 50
Textile Product Mfr & Distr
N.A.I.C.S.: 316990
Maciej Nowoswiecki (Mng Dir)

GPI Forankra SAS (4)
ZA la Bohalle, 49800, La Bohalle, France
Tel.: (33) 2 41 54 90 60
Web Site: http://www.gpi-int.fr
Textile Products Mfr
N.A.I.C.S.: 316990
Philippe Plossu (Mng Dir)

Haklift ABT Oy (4)
Asessorinkatu 3-7, 207 80, Kaarina, Finland
Tel.: (358) 25 11 55 11
Web Site: http://www.haklift.com
Lifting Equipment Distr
N.A.I.C.S.: 423830
Jorma Tuominen (Mng Dir)

Haklift Baltic OU (4)
Artelli 8, 10621, Tallinn, Estonia
Tel.: (372) 6 567 018
Web Site: http://www.forankra.ee
Emp.: 10
Lifting Equipment Distr
N.A.I.C.S.: 423830
Rain Kallas (Mng Dir)

**L-EX Equipments Transports
Logistics** (4)
C/Boters 6u000bES, 08290, Cerdanyola del
Valles, Spain
Tel.: (34) 93 594 91 99
Web Site: http://www.l-ex.es
Logistics Consulting Servies
N.A.I.C.S.: 541614
Fransesc Pros (Mng Dir)

Mennens Amsterdam BV (4)
Contactweg 40, 1014 AN, Amsterdam,
Netherlands
Tel.: (31) 20 5811811
Web Site: http://www.mennens.nl
Emp.: 75
Lifting Equipment Distr
N.A.I.C.S.: 423830
Frits van Boetzelaer (Member-Mgmt Bd)

Mennens Belgium (4)
Vitshoekstraat 10 Havennummer 1037,
A1003ABV, Zwijndrecht, Belgium
Tel.: (32) 3 253 23 23
Web Site: http://www.mennensbelgium.be
Emp.: 50
Lifting Equipment Distr
N.A.I.C.S.: 423830
Wim Cools (Mng Dir)

Mennens Dongen BV (4)

Metaalstraat 5, 5107 ND, Dongen, Nether-
lands
Tel.: (31) 162 383800
Lifting Equipment Distr
N.A.I.C.S.: 423830
Danny van Deuzen (Mng Dir)

Mennens Groningen BV (4)
Duinkerkenstraat 33, 9723 BP, Groningen,
Netherlands
Tel.: (31) 50 3183031
Web Site: http://www.mennens.nl
Emp.: 70
Lifting Equipment Distr
N.A.I.C.S.: 423830
David Posthumus (Member-Mgmt Bd)

Mennens Hengelo BV (4)
Oosterveldsingel 35, 7558 PJ, Hengelo,
Netherlands
Tel.: (31) 74 2503504
Web Site: http://www.mennens.au
Emp.: 50
Lifting Equipment Distr
N.A.I.C.S.: 423830
Marshal Stockner (CEO)

Mennens Schiedam BV (4)
Kommiezenlaan 16, 3125 AN, Schiedam,
Netherlands
Tel.: (31) 10 4373033
Lifting Equipment Distr
N.A.I.C.S.: 423830

Subsidiary (Domestic):

Ro-Ro International TM AB (4)
Arods Industrivag 74, 422 43, Gothenburg,
Sweden
Tel.: (46) 31 51 50 10
Web Site: http://www.roroint.se
Emp.: 200
Logistics Consulting Servies
N.A.I.C.S.: 541614

Subsidiary (Non-US):

Axel Johnson International AS (3)
Lilleakerveien 10, PO Box 144, N 0216,
Oslo, Norway
Tel.: (47) 22736030
Web Site: http://www.fujifilm.no
Steel Wire Rope, Wind Turbine Servicing,
Bearings, Imaging Solutions & Components
for Heavy Vehicles
N.A.I.C.S.: 331222
Rolf Erik Smith (CEO)

Subsidiary (Domestic):

FUJIFILM Sverige AB (3)
Sveavagen 167, PO Box 23086, SE-104
35, Stockholm, Sweden
Tel.: (46) 850614100
Web Site: http://www.fujifilm.se
Sales Range: $50-74.9 Million
Emp.: 55
Photographic Equipment & Supplies Sales
& Distr
N.A.I.C.S.: 333310
Nils-Petter Tetlie (Mng Dir)

Forankra AB (3)
Arods Industrivag 72, SE-422 43, Gothen-
burg, Sweden
Tel.: (46) 31509080
Web Site: http://www.forankra.com
Sales Range: $75-99.9 Million
Industrial Lifting & Material Handling Equip-
ment Mfr
N.A.I.C.S.: 333924
Erik Eklov (Mng Dir)

Subsidiary (Non-US):

Axel Johnson Lab Systems A/S (2)
Bygstubben 12, Copenhagen, 2950, Vid-
baek, Denmark
Tel.: (45) 35431881
Sales Range: $1-9.9 Million
Emp.: 6
Distribution of Scientific Equipment
N.A.I.C.S.: 423490

Subsidiary (Domestic):

Axfood AB (2)
Solnavagen 4, 113 65, Stockholm,
Sweden (50.1%)
Tel.: (46) 855399000

Web Site: https://www.axfood.se
Rev.: $8,051,998,470
Assets: $2,979,927,384
Liabilities: $2,266,662,735
Net Worth: $713,264,650
Earnings: $235,570,914
Emp.: 6,774
Fiscal Year-end: 12/31/2023
Holding Company; Food Retailer & Trade
Whslr
N.A.I.C.S.: 551112
Antonia Axson Johnson (Founder)

Subsidiary (Domestic):

Axfood IT AB (3)
Norra stationsgatan 80, Stockholm, 10769,
Sweden
Tel.: (46) 855399000
Information Technology Consulting Services
N.A.I.C.S.: 541512
Anders Strealman (CEO)

Axfood Narlivs AB (3)
Handelsgatan 5, 70117, Orebro,
Sweden (100%)
Tel.: (46) 196030350
Web Site: http://www.narlivs.se
Grocery Distr & Convenience Stores Opera-
tor
N.A.I.C.S.: 424410

Axfood Sverige AB (3)
Norra Stationsgatan 80C, Stockholm, 107
69, Sweden (100%)
Tel.: (46) 855399000
Web Site: http://www.axfood.se
Sales Range: $150-199.9 Million
Emp.: 600
Food Retailer & Trade Whslr
N.A.I.C.S.: 445110
Anders Stralman (Pres & CEO)

Subsidiary (Domestic):

Dagab AB (4)
Norra stationsgatan 80C, Stockholm,
10769, Sweden (100%)
Tel.: (46) 8 553 99 000
Web Site: http://www.axfood.se
Grocery Distr
N.A.I.C.S.: 424410

Hemkopskedjan AB (4)
Norra Stationsgatan 80C, 107 69, Stock-
holm, Sweden (100%)
Tel.: (46) 771554400
Web Site: http://www.hemkop.se
Sales Range: $800-899.9 Million
Retail Grocery Stores Operator
N.A.I.C.S.: 445110
Anders Fahlgren (Mgr-HR)

Subsidiary (Domestic):

PrisXtra AB (3)
Norra Stationsgatan 58-60, Stockholm, 113
33, Sweden
Tel.: (46) 8 441 51 60
Web Site: http://www.prisxtra.se
Food Store Operating Services
N.A.I.C.S.: 445298

Willys AB (3)
Falkenbergsgatan 3, 412 86, Gothenburg,
Sweden (100%)
Tel.: (46) 771717000
Web Site: http://www.willys.se
Sales Range: $1-4.9 Billion
Emp.: 2,886
Discount Retail Grocery Stores Operator
N.A.I.C.S.: 445110
Thomas Evertsson (Pres)

Subsidiary (Domestic):

Willys Hemma AB (4)
Falkenbergsgatan 3 Van 6, 412 87, Gothen-
burg, Sweden (100%)
Tel.: (46) 771717000
Web Site: http://www.willys.se
Small Discount Retail Grocery Stores Op-
erator
N.A.I.C.S.: 445110

Subsidiary (Domestic):

Axstores AB (2)
Ringvagen 100 Hus A2 Vaning 6, 118 90,
Stockholm, Sweden
Tel.: (46) 8 402 80 00

Web Site: http://www.axstores.se
Departmental Store Operator
N.A.I.C.S.: 455110

Subsidiary (Domestic):

Ahlens AB (3)
Ringvagen 100, 118 90, Stockholm, Sweden
Tel.: (46) 84028000
Web Site: http://www.ahlens.se
Sales Range: $800-899.9 Million
Emp.: 2,900
Departmental Store Operator
N.A.I.C.S.: 455110
Thomas Axen *(Pres)*

Subsidiary (Non-US):

Kildair Service ULC (2)
1000 Montee des Pionniers Bureau 110, Terrebonne, J6V 1S8, QC, Canada
Tel.: (450) 756-8091
Web Site: https://www.spragueenergy.com
Fuel Mfr
N.A.I.C.S.: 324199
Francois Guay *(VP-Oil Supply & Trading)*

Subsidiary (Domestic):

Mercator International AB (2)
Regeringsgatan 82, SE 11139, Stockholm, Sweden
Tel.: (46) 86679330
Assisting Swedish Export Companies with Counter-Purchase & Barter Transactions
N.A.I.C.S.: 561990

Subsidiary (Non-US):

Normaco Ltd. (2)
45 Conduit Street, London, SW1H 9AA, United Kingdom
Tel.: (44) 207 287 7355
Trusts
N.A.I.C.S.: 523999

Subsidiary (Domestic):

Novax AB (2)
Villakatan 6, PO Box 26008, Stockholm, 100 41, Sweden
Tel.: (46) 87006660
Web Site: http://www.novax.se
Sales Range: $25-49.9 Million
Emp.: 4
Consumer Goods Trading
N.A.I.C.S.: 425120
Eric Persson *(Mng Dir)*

Ranas Bilfjadrar AB (2)
Fjadervagen 11, 76296, Ranas, Sweden
Tel.: (46) 175 74851
Web Site: http://www.ranasbilfjadrar.nu
Automobile Parts Mfr
N.A.I.C.S.: 336390

Subsidiary (Non-US):

S.A. Cebelor (2)
Researchpark Zone 1 Nr 10, 1731, Zellik, Belgium
Tel.: (32) 24269966
Web Site: http://www.cebelor.be
Sales Range: $25-49.9 Million
Emp.: 40
Orthopedic Device Mfr
N.A.I.C.S.: 339112
Jan Ruysschaert *(Gen Mgr)*

Svenska Teknisk Byra AB (2)
ul Floriana 3 5, PL 04 664, Warsaw, Poland
Tel.: (48) 226130012
Web Site: http://www.axflow.pl
Pumping Components
N.A.I.C.S.: 333914

Weir Canada Inc. (2)
8600 Rue Street Patrick, La Salle, H8N 1V1, QC, Canada
Tel.: (514) 366-5757
Web Site: http://www.weirservices.com
Sales Range: $25-49.9 Million
Emp.: 100
Distr of Industrial Products & Instrumentations
N.A.I.C.S.: 424130
Maria Bellinei *(Mgr-HR)*

Weir Canada, Inc. (2)
2715 18th St Northeast, Calgary, T2E 7E6,

AB, Canada
Tel.: (403) 250-9458
Web Site: http://www.weirminerals.com
Sales Range: $25-49.9 Million
Emp.: 60
Distribution of Industrial Instrumentation
N.A.I.C.S.: 425120
Russell Mackie *(Reg Mgr)*

Axel Johnson Inc. (1)
155 Spring St 6th Fl, New York, NY 10012
Tel.: (646) 291-2445
Web Site: http://www.axeljohnson.com
Sales Range: $1-4.9 Billion
Emp.: 1,000
Investment Services
N.A.I.C.S.: 523999
Michael D. Milligan *(Pres & CEO)*

Subsidiary (Domestic):

Kinetico Incorporated (2)
10845 Kinsman Rd, Newbury, OH 44065
Tel.: (800) 944-9283
Web Site: http://www.kinetico.com
Water Treatment System Mfr
N.A.I.C.S.: 333310

Subsidiary (Non-US):

Kinetico Belgium Holdings NV (3)
Industrieweg Daelemveld 1026, 3540, Herk-de-Stad, Belgium
Tel.: (32) 13 55 17 01
Water Treatment System Distr
N.A.I.C.S.: 423830

Kinetico Denmark ApS (3)
Sandvadsvej 7, Koge, 4600, Denmark
Tel.: (45) 56 65 14 00
Web Site: http://www.kinetico.dk
Water Treatment System Mfr
N.A.I.C.S.: 333310

Kinetico France SARL (3)
ZAC des Beaux Soleils - Parc GVIO d'Osny 9 Chaussee Jules Cesar, 95520, Osny, France
Tel.: (33) 1 34 46 87 78
Web Site: http://www.kinetico.fr
Water Treatment System Mfr
N.A.I.C.S.: 333310

Kinetico Germany GmbH (3)
Bunzlauer Strasse 12, 56203, Hohr-Grenzhausen, Germany
Tel.: (49) 26249529734
Web Site: http://www.kinetico.de
Water Treatment System Mfr
N.A.I.C.S.: 333310

Kinetico Incorporated (3)
10-21 Parr Boulevard, Bolton, L7E 4G3, ON, Canada
Tel.: (905) 857-9583
Web Site: http://www.kinetico.ca
Water Treatment System Mfr
N.A.I.C.S.: 333310

Kinetico UK Limited (3)
Bridge House Chandler's Way Park Gate, Southampton, SO31 1FQ, Hampshire, United Kingdom
Tel.: (44) 1489 566970
Web Site: http://www.kinetico.co.uk
Water Treatment System Mfr
N.A.I.C.S.: 333310

Subsidiary (Domestic):

Nimbus Water Systems (3)
42445 Avenida Alvarado, Temecula, CA 92590
Tel.: (951) 894-2800
Web Site: http://www.nimbuswater.com
Mfg Water Purification Systems
N.A.I.C.S.: 333310

Selecto Inc. (3)
3980 Lakefield Ct, Suwanee, GA 30024-1256
Tel.: (678) 574-0799
Web Site: http://www.selectoinc.com
Water Filtration Product Manufacturer
N.A.I.C.S.: 339999
Terry Libin *(Co-Founder & Pres)*

Holding (Non-US):

La Fantana SRL (2)

B-dul Garii Obor nr 8C sect 2, Bucharest, Romania
Tel.: (40) 212007200
Web Site: http://www.lafantana.ro
Drinking Water Distr
N.A.I.C.S.: 424490
Cristian Amza *(CEO)*

Subsidiary (Domestic):

Parkson Corporation (2)
1401 W Cypress Creek Rd, Fort Lauderdale, FL 33309-1721
Tel.: (954) 974-6610
Web Site: http://www.parkson.com
Sales Range: $25-49.9 Million
Emp.: 70
Mfr of Process Equipment & Instrumentation for Water & Wastewater Treatment
N.A.I.C.S.: 561110
Mark Turpin *(VP-Strategic Mktg & Bus Dev)*

Subsidiary (Non-US):

Parkson Canada Corporation (3)
301 B Saint Johns, Box 126, Pointe-Claire, H9R 3J1, QC, Canada
Tel.: (514) 636-8712
Web Site: http://www.parkson.com
Sales Range: $1-9.9 Million
Emp.: 1
Waste Treatment Services
N.A.I.C.S.: 423830
Jean Grenier *(Mgr-Sls)*

Subsidiary (Domestic):

Schreiber LLC (3)
100 Schreiber Dr, Trussville, AL 35173-1876
Tel.: (205) 655-7466
Web Site: http://www.schreiberwater.com
Miscellaneous General Purpose Machinery Mfr
N.A.I.C.S.: 333998
P. Thacher Worthen *(Pres & CEO)*

AXEL LINDGREN AB
133 33 Saltsjobaden, Stockholm, Sweden
Tel.: (46) 70 222 3122   SE
Web Site: http://www.axellindgren.se
Investment Services
N.A.I.C.S.: 523999
Lars Lindgren *(Owner)*

AXEL MARK INC.
Harmony Tower 17F 1-32-2 Honcho Nakano-ku, Tokyo, 164-0012, Japan
Tel.: (81) 353543351
Web Site: https://www.axelmark.co.jp
Year Founded: 1994
3624—(TKS)
Rev.: $26,949,120
Assets: $7,889,200
Liabilities: $9,544,480
Net Worth: ($1,655,280)
Earnings: ($7,986,000)
Emp.: 40
Fiscal Year-end: 09/30/20
Mobile Phone Content Distr; Mobile Internet Advertising Production & Planning Services
N.A.I.C.S.: 541890
Junji Oshita *(Pres & CEO)*

AXEL POLYMERS LIMITED
309 Moxi Sankarda - Savli Road, Tal Savli Dist, Vadodara, 391780, Gujarat, India
Tel.: (91) 2667244395
Web Site: https://www.axelindia.com
Year Founded: 1992
513642—(BOM)
Rev.: $10,028,259
Assets: $7,556,804
Liabilities: $5,874,646
Net Worth: $1,682,158
Earnings: $125,048
Fiscal Year-end: 03/31/22
Specialty Polymer Mfr
N.A.I.C.S.: 325211
B. K. Bodhanwala *(Chm)*

AXEL SPRINGER SE
Axel Springer Strasse 65, 10888, Berlin, Germany
Tel.: (49) 3025910   De
Web Site:
  https://www.axelspringer.com
Year Founded: 1946
Rev.: $3,485,116,306
Assets: $7,672,720,790
Liabilities: $4,446,964,060
Net Worth: $3,225,756,730
Earnings: $150,733,156
Emp.: 16,120
Fiscal Year-end: 12/31/19
Newspapers, Magazines, Books & Electronic Media Publisher
N.A.I.C.S.: 513120
Mathias Dopfner *(Chm & CEO)*

Subsidiaries:

APM Print d.o.o. (1)
III Bulevar 29, 11070, Belgrade, Serbia
Tel.: (381) 113130438
Web Site: http://www.apmprint.rs
Newspaper Publishers
N.A.I.C.S.: 513110

AWIN AG (1)
Eichhornstrasse 3, 10785, Berlin, Germany   **(80%)**
Tel.: (49) 30 5096 910
Web Site: http://www.awin.com
Advertising Publishing Support Services
N.A.I.C.S.: 541830
Mark Walters *(CEO & Member-Exec Bd)*

Subsidiary (Non-US):

AWIN AB (2)
Gotgatan 78, 118 30, Stockholm, Sweden
Tel.: (46) 84415230
Advertising & Marketing Agency
N.A.I.C.S.: 541810
Tim Lomborg *(Regional Mgr-Nordic, Central & Eastern Europe)*

AWIN B.V. (2)
Entrepotdok 86, 1018 AD, Amsterdam, Netherlands
Tel.: (31) 205558900
Advertising & Marketing Agency
N.A.I.C.S.: 541810
Ian Charlesworth *(Reg Mgr)*

Subsidiary (US):

AWIN Inc. (2)
8 Market Pl Ste 600, Baltimore, MD 21202
Tel.: (443) 252-8830
Web Site: http://www.awin.com
Advertising Publishing Support Services
N.A.I.C.S.: 541830
Alexandra Forsch *(Pres)*

Subsidiary (Domestic):

ShareASale.com, Inc. (3)
15 W Hubbard St Ste 500, Chicago, IL 60654
Tel.: (312) 321-0487
Web Site: http://www.shareasale.com
Advertising Publishing Support Services
N.A.I.C.S.: 541890
Brian Littleton *(Founder & CEO)*

Subsidiary (Non-US):

AWIN SAS (2)
117-119 Quai de Valmy, 75010, Paris, France
Tel.: (33) 177454600
Digital Marketing & Advertising Services
N.A.I.C.S.: 541810
Frank Surena *(Gen Mgr)*

AWIN SRL (2)
Via Vincezo Monti 8, 20123, Milan, Italy
Tel.: (39) 023705971
Digital Marketing & Advertising Svcs
N.A.I.C.S.: 541810

AWIN Sp. z.o.o. (2)
ul Domaniewska 48, 02-672, Warsaw, Poland
Tel.: (48) 223769319
Digital Marketing & Advertising Svcs
N.A.I.C.S.: 541810
Ewa Kalata *(Head-Publisher Sls)*

Axel Springer SE—(Continued)

**AWIN VEICULACAO DE PUBLICI-
DADE NA INTERNET LTDA** (2)
Av Paulista 37, 01311-000, Sao Paulo, Bra-
zil
Tel.: (55) 1131423400
Digital Marketing & Advertising Svcs
N.A.I.C.S.: 541810
Rodrigo Genoveze (Country Mgr)

Awin Ltd. (2)
2 Thomas More Square, London, E1W
1YN, United Kingdom
Tel.: (44) 2075530400
Digital Markeitng & Advertising Services
N.A.I.C.S.: 541810
James Bentley (Dir-Strategy)

Admiral Strand Feriehuse ApS (1)
Houstrupvej 170, Lonne, 6830, Norre
Nebel, Denmark
Tel.: (45) 70204606
Web Site: http://www.admiralstrand.dk
Cottage Home Operator
N.A.I.C.S.: 721199

Axel Springer Budapest GmbH (1)
Varosmajor Ut 11, Budapest, 1122,
Hungary　　　　　　　　　(92.93%)
Tel.: (36) 14885766
Web Site: http://www.axelspringer.hu
Sales Range: $50-74.9 Million
Emp.: 400
Publisher
N.A.I.C.S.: 513110
Gabriella Udvari (Office Mgr)

**Axel Springer Corporate Solutions
GmbH & Co. KG** (1)
Axel-Springer-Strasse 65, 10969,
Germany
Tel.: (49) 30259174539
Web Site: http://www.as-corporate-
solutions.de
Emp.: 90
Newspaper Publishers
N.A.I.C.S.: 513110
Frank Parlow (Mng Dir)

**Axel Springer Digital Ventures
GmbH** (1)
Axel-Springer-Strasse 65, 10888, Berlin,
Germany　　　　　　　　　(100%)
Tel.: (49) 30 2591 78000
Investment Assistance
N.A.I.C.S.: 523940
Ulrich Schmitz (Mng Dir)

Axel Springer Espana S.A. (1)
Santiago de composcela 94 2nd Fl, 28035,
Madrid, Spain　　　　　　　(100%)
Tel.: (34) 915140600
Web Site: http://www.axelspringer.es
Sales Range: $50-74.9 Million
Emp.: 65
Computer Magazines Publisher
N.A.I.C.S.: 513110

**Axel Springer Ideas Engineering
GmbH** (1)
65 Axel-Springer-StraSSe, Berlin, 10888,
Germany　　　　　　　　　(100%)
Tel.: (49) 30 259178100
Web Site: http://www.axelspringerideas.de
Information Technology And Services
N.A.I.C.S.: 519290
Dat Tran (Head-AI)

Subsidiary (Non-US):

Bonial SAS (2)
117 quai de Valmy, 75010, Paris, France
Tel.: (33) 184880140
Web Site: http://www.bonial.fr
Digital Drive to Store Marketing
N.A.I.C.S.: 449210
Laurent Landel (Assoc Dir)

**Axel Springer Mediahouse Berlin
GmbH** (1)
Mehringdamm 33, 10961, Berlin,
Germany　　　　　　　　　(100%)
Tel.: (49) 0 30 3088188 222
Web Site: http://www.axel-springer-
mediahouse-berlin.de
Publishing Services
N.A.I.C.S.: 513120
Petra Kalb (Mng Dir)

Axel Springer Norway AS (1)
Prinsensgt 22, 0157, Oslo, Norway (100%)
Tel.: (47) 2164 0550
Web Site: http://www.axelspringer.no
Online Job Search Portal Data Services
N.A.I.C.S.: 518210
Tom Moller (Mng Dir)

Axel Springer Polska Sp.z o.o. (1)
Al Jerozolimskie 181, 02 222, Warsaw,
Poland　　　　　　　　　　(100%)
Tel.: (48) 226084100
Web Site: http://www.axelspringer.pl
Sales Range: $200-249.9 Million
Emp.: 700
Publisher
N.A.I.C.S.: 513110

Axel Springer Syndication GmbH (1)
Schutzenstrasse 15-17, 10117, Berlin,
Germany　　　　　　　　　(100%)
Tel.: (49) 30259171275
Web Site: https://www.axelspringer-
syndication.de
Media And Content Publishing
N.A.I.C.S.: 513199
Alexandra Braun (Co-Mng Dir)

Axel Springer hy GmbH (1)
Axel-Springer-Strasse 65, 10888, Berlin,
Germany　　　　　　　　　(100%)
Tel.: (49) 30 25 91 78150
Web Site: http://www.hy.co
Digital Media Services And Solutions Pro-
vider
N.A.I.C.S.: 561499
Christoph Keese (CEO)

**Bilanz Deutschland Wirtschaftsmaga-
zin GmbH** (1)
Kaiser-Wilhelm-Strasse 20, 20355, Ham-
burg, Germany
Tel.: (49) 4034723447
Web Site: http://www.abo.bilanz.de
Newspaper Publishers
N.A.I.C.S.: 513110
Tina Krantz (Dir-Adv)

Bonial International GmbH (1)
Hussitenstrasse 32-33, 13355, Berlin, Ger-
many
Tel.: (49) 3060989600
Web Site: http://www.bonial.com
Online Shopping Services
N.A.I.C.S.: 561621
Christian Gaiser (Founder & Chm)

**Buch- und Presse-GroSSvertrieb
Hamburg GmbH & Co. KG** (1)
Neuer Holtigbaum 2, 22143, Hamburg,
Germany　　　　　　　　　(80.5%)
Tel.: (49) 040 67590 111
Web Site: http://www.bphh.de
Newspapers, Magazines And Press-Related
Products Wholesalers
N.A.I.C.S.: 424920
Michael Fischer (Mng Dir)

City-Nav Sp. z o.o. (1)
Ul Grunwaldzka 43/4, 60-784, Poznan, Po-
land
Tel.: (48) 534890617
Web Site: http://www.city-nav.com
Travel Planning Services
N.A.I.C.S.: 561510

Contact Impact GmbH (1)
Dr-Leo-Ritter-StraSSe 2, D-93049, Regens-
burg, Germany　　　　　　(75.1%)
Tel.: (49) 941 78304 200
Web Site: http://www.contactimpact.de
Digital Advertising Services
N.A.I.C.S.: 541810
Sven Moller (CEO)

DanCenter A/S (1)
Lyngbyvej 20, 2100, Copenhagen,
Denmark　　　　　　　　　(100%)
Tel.: (45) 70 13 00 00
Web Site: http://www.dancenter.eu
Recreational Home Rental Services
N.A.I.C.S.: 236115
Steen Seitner (CEO)

EPROFESSIONAL GmbH (1)
Heidenkampsweg 74-76, 20097, Hamburg,
Germany
Tel.: (49) 403992780
Web Site: http://www.eprofessional.de
Online Advertising, Marketing & Consulting
Services

N.A.I.C.S.: 541613
Thomas Nuss (Mng Dir)

Elmshorner Nachrichten (1)
Schulstrasse 62, Elmshorn, 25335,
Germany　　　　　　　　　(100%)
Tel.: (49) 41212970
Web Site: http://www.shz.de
Sales Range: $25-49.9 Million
Emp.: 32
Newspapers
N.A.I.C.S.: 513110

Immosolve GmbH (1)
Tegelberg 43, 24576, Bad Bramstedt, Ger-
many
Tel.: (49) 4192816840
Web Site: http://www.immosolve.de
Real Estate Software Development Ser-
vices
N.A.I.C.S.: 327910

Immowelt Holding AG (1)
Nordostpark 3-5, 90411, Nuremberg, Ger-
many
Tel.: (49) 911520250
Web Site: http://www.immowelt-group.com
Emp.: 600
Online Estate Agencies
N.A.I.C.S.: 531390
Cai-Nicolas Ziegler (CEO)

Subsidiary (Domestic):

Immowelt AG (2)
Nordostpark 3-5, 90411, Nuremberg, Ger-
many
Tel.: (49) 91152025 0
Real Estate Digital Marketing & Advertising
Agency
N.A.I.C.S.: 531390

Immowelt Hamburg GmbH (2)
Spaldingstr 64, 20097, Harburg, Germany
Tel.: (49) 408221075 0
Web Site: http://www.immonet.de
Digital Real Estate Marketing Svcs
N.A.I.C.S.: 531390
Boris Z. (Sr Mgr-Bus Dev & Media Sls)

Journalistenschule Axel Springer (1)
Axel Springer Strasse 65, D 10888, Berlin,
Germany　　　　　　　　　(100%)
Tel.: (49) 30259172801
Web Site: http://www.axelspringer.de
Sales Range: $50-74.9 Million
Emp.: 8
Provider of Journalism Training
N.A.I.C.S.: 711510
Mathias Dopfner (Chm & CEO)

**MAZ & More TV-Produktion
GmbH** (1)
Stralauer Allee 8a, Box 040423 10062,
10245, Berlin, Germany
Tel.: (49) 30 2591 70601
Television Broadcasting
N.A.I.C.S.: 516120
Torsten Rossmann (Chm & CEO)

Media Impact Inc. (1)
286 Madison Ave Ste 2001, New York, NY
10017
Tel.: (212) 972-1720
Web Site: http://www.asgmedia.com
Emp.: 7
Media Representatives
N.A.I.C.S.: 541840
Micheal Monheim (VP)

Subsidiary (Domestic):

Insider, Inc. (2)
150 5th Ave 8th Fl, New York, NY
10011　　　　　　　　　　(100%)
Tel.: (646) 484-6610
Web Site: http://www.businessinsider.com
Emp.: 325
Business News, Analysis & Commentary
Publisher
N.A.I.C.S.: 513120
Mathias Dopfner (Owner)

Livingly Media, Inc. (2)
990 Industrial Rd Ste 204, San Carlos, CA
94070
Tel.: (650) 366-4715
Web Site: http://www.livingly.com
Sales Range: $10-24.9 Million
Emp.: 65
Interactive Online Publisher

N.A.I.C.S.: 513199
Tony Mamone (Co-Founder)

eMarketer Inc. (2)
11 Times Sq, New York, NY 10036
Web Site: http://www.emarketer.com
Market Research & Trend Analysis Services
N.A.I.C.S.: 541910
Geoff Ramsey (Founder & Chief Content
Officer)

N24 Media GmbH (1)
Marlene-Dietrich-Platz 5, 10785, Berlin,
Germany
Tel.: (49) 3020902400
Web Site: http://www.n24-media.de
Sales Range: $125-149.9 Million
Emp.: 150
Television Broadcasting Network
N.A.I.C.S.: 516120
Torsten Rossmann (Chm-Mgmt Bd)

**PACE Paparazzi Catering & Event
GmbH** (1)
Axel-Springer-Strasse 65, 10888, Berlin,
Germany
Tel.: (49) 30259177668
Web Site: http://www.pace-berlin.de
Catering Services
N.A.I.C.S.: 722320

**Ringier Axel Springer Magyarorszag
Kft** (1)
11 Varosmajor Street, 1122, Budapest, Hun-
gary
Tel.: (36) 14885700
Web Site: http://www.ringieraxelspringer.hu
Newspaper Publishers
N.A.I.C.S.: 513110

Rodacom SARL (1)
26 rue Colonel Dumont, 38000, Grenoble,
France
Tel.: (33) 476461369
Web Site: http://www.rodacom.fr
Real Estate Software Services
N.A.I.C.S.: 531390

Sales Impact GmbH (1)
Axel-Springer-Platz 1, 20350, Hamburg,
Germany
Tel.: (49) 4034700
Web Site: http://www.salesimpact.de
Newspaper Publishers
N.A.I.C.S.: 513110

Saongroup Limited (1)
South Block The Malthouse Grand Canal
Quay, Dublin, Ireland
Tel.: (353) 16709900
Web Site: http://www.saongroup.com
Recruitment Services
N.A.I.C.S.: 561311

Scubia GbR (1)
Templiner Strasse 16, 10119, Berlin, Ger-
many
Tel.: (49) 30568370503
Web Site: http://www.scubia.de
Online Marketing Services
N.A.I.C.S.: 541613

Sokoweb Technologies, S.L. (1)
Plaza del Doctor Letamendi No 1-2 7th
Floor, 08007, Barcelona, Spain
Tel.: (34) 935516260
Web Site: http://www.ofertia.com
Online Marketing Platform Design Services
N.A.I.C.S.: 541511

StepStone GmbH (1)
Axel-Springer-Strasse 65, 10969, Berlin,
Germany
Tel.: (49) 30 398 0620
Holding Company; Online Job Search Por-
tal Publisher & Data Services
N.A.I.C.S.: 551112
Ralf Baumann (CEO)

Subsidiary (US):

Appcast, Inc. (2)
10 Water St, Lebanon, NH 03766 (85%)
Tel.: (800) 570-5430
Web Site: https://www.appcast.io
Recruitment Advertising Technology & En-
terprise Managed Services
N.A.I.C.S.: 518210
Chris Forman (CEO & Founder)

Subsidiary (Domestic):

Bayard Advertising Agency, Inc. (3)

902 Broadway 10th Fl, New York, NY
10010-6002
Tel.: (212) 228-9400
Web Site: http://www.bayardad.com
Emp.: 150
N.A.I.C.S.: 541810
Louis Naviasky (CEO)

Branch (Domestic):

Bayard Advertising Agency, Inc.   (4)
902 Broadway, New York, NY 10010
Tel.: (212) 228-9400
Emp.: 70
N.A.I.C.S.: 541810
Mary Anne Kozack (VP)

Bayard Advertising Agency, Inc.   (4)
8401 Colesville Rd Ste 502, Silver Spring,
MD 20910-6365
Tel.: (301) 589-9125
Emp.: 10
N.A.I.C.S.: 541810
Rosemary Petreikis (Sr VP & Gen Mgrr)

Bayard Advertising Agency, Inc.   (4)
550 S Wadsworth Blvd Ste 500, Lakewood,
CO 80226
Tel.: (303) 571-2000
Web Site: http://www.bayardad.com
Sales Range: $10-24.9 Million
Emp.: 8
N.A.I.C.S.: 541810
Phil Roberts (Reg Mgr-Western)

Bayard Advertising Agency, Inc.   (4)
40 Fairway Trl, Covington, GA 30014-3972
Tel.: (404) 266-9991
N.A.I.C.S.: 541810

Bayard Advertising Agency, Inc.   (4)
902 Broadway, New York, NY 10010
Tel.: (212) 228-9400
Emp.: 70
N.A.I.C.S.: 541810
Debra Pastalove (VP)

Bayard Advertising Agency, Inc.   (4)
4929 Wilshire Blvd Ste 770, Los Angeles,
CA 90010-3817
Tel.: (323) 930-9300
Emp.: 5
N.A.I.C.S.: 541810
Don Sabatino (Sr VP-New Bus Dev)

Bayard Advertising Agency, Inc.   (4)
8777 E Via de Ventura, Scottsdale, AZ
85258
Tel.: (480) 922-8808
Emp.: 4
N.A.I.C.S.: 541810
Linda Kooltonow (Dir)

Bayard Advertising Agency, Inc.   (4)
1035 Greenwood Blvd Ste 211, Lake Mary,
FL 32746
Tel.: (407) 804-1013
Web Site: http://www.bayardad.com
Emp.: 6
N.A.I.C.S.: 541810
Carol Wyka (VP & Gen Mgr)

Bayard Advertising Agency, Inc.   (4)
9801 Dupont Ave S Ste 300, Minneapolis,
MN 55431
Tel.: (952) 881-4411
Web Site: http://www.bayardad.com
Emp.: 5
N.A.I.C.S.: 541810
Rebecca Gish (Branch Mgr)

Subsidiary (Non-US):

Jobsite UK (Worldwide) Limited   (2)
Langstone Technology Park, Langstone
Road, Havant, PO9 1SA, United Kingdom
Tel.: (44) 2392457575
Web Site: http://www.jobsite.co.uk
Emp.: 169
Online Recruitment Consultancy Services
N.A.I.C.S.: 541612
Nick Gold (CEO)

Subsidiary (Domestic):

StepStone Deutschland GmbH   (2)
Volklinger Strasse 1, 40219, Dusseldorf,
Germany
Tel.: (49) 211 93 4930
Web Site: http://www.stepstone.de
Emp.: 20

Online Job Search Portal Publisher & Data
Services
N.A.I.C.S.: 518210
Simone Reif (Mng Dir)

Subsidiary (Non-US):

StepStone NV   (2)
Koningsstraat 47 Rue Royale, 1000, Brus-
sels, Belgium   (100%)
Tel.: (32) 2209 9800
Web Site: http://www.stepstone.be
Online Job Search Portal Publisher & Data
Services
N.A.I.C.S.: 518210
Christophe de Rassenfosse (Chief Product
Officer)

StepStone Osterreich GmbH   (2)
Prinz-Eugen Strasse-8-10, A-1040, Vienna,
Austria
Tel.: (43) 40500680
Online Job Portals
N.A.I.C.S.: 519290
Nikolai Durhammer (Mng Dir)

StepStone Services Sp. z o.o.   (2)
Domaniewski 50, 02-672, Warsaw, Poland
Tel.: (48) 668821872
Online Recruitment & Staffing Services
N.A.I.C.S.: 513199

StepStone pl Sp. z o.o.   (2)
ul Domaniewska 49, 02-672, Warsaw, Po-
land
Tel.: (48) 504201404
Web Site: http://www.stepstone.pl
Emp.: 2,500
Online Job Portals
N.A.I.C.S.: 519290
Istvan Martis (CEO)

TotalJobs Group Limited   (2)
Rathbone Place Holden House, London,
W1T 1JU, United Kingdom   (100%)
Tel.: (44) 207 572 4200
Web Site: http://www.totaljobsgroup.com
Online Job Search Portal Publisher & Data
Services
N.A.I.C.S.: 518210
Mark Little (CEO)

Tecoloco El Salvador S.A. de
C.V.   (1)
Pasaje Bella Vista Block 118 #3-138 9a
Calle Poniente Bis, San Salvador, El Salva-
dor
Tel.: (503) 2257 8300
Recruitment Solutions
N.A.I.C.S.: 541612

Topreality.sk s.r.o.   (1)
Odborarska 1381/18, 915 01, Nove Mesto
nad Vahom, Slovakia
Tel.: (421) 948964550
Web Site: http://www.realestates.sk
Real Estate Services
N.A.I.C.S.: 531390

TraderFox GmbH   (1)
Obere Wassere 1, 72764, Reutlingen, Ger-
many
Tel.: (49) 71218208028
Web Site: http://www.traderfox.de
Trading Services
N.A.I.C.S.: 523160

Transfermarkt GmbH & Co. KG   (1)
Wandsbeker Zollstrasse 5a, 22041, Ham-
burg, Germany
Tel.: (49) 40670482120
Web Site: http://www.transfermarkt.co.in
Trading Services
N.A.I.C.S.: 523160
Matthias Seidel (Co-CEO)

Umzugsauktion GmbH & Co. KG   (1)
Brandhof 10, 79227, Freiburg, Germany
Tel.: (49) 7664 404676.0
Web Site: http://www.umzugsauktion.de
Logistic Services
N.A.I.C.S.: 541614
Christian Gimbel (Mng Dir)

United Classifieds s.r.o.   (1)
Prievozska 14, 821 09, Bratislava, Slovakia
Tel.: (421) 269298298
Web Site: http://www.unitedclassifieds.sk
Real Estate Services
N.A.I.C.S.: 531390

Vertical Media GmbH   (1)
Wallstrasse 27, 10179, Berlin, Germany
Tel.: (49) 30921025300
Web Site: http://www.verticalmedia.com
Newspaper Publishers
N.A.I.C.S.: 513110
Luisa Vroomen (Mgr-Fin)

Visual Meta GmbH   (1)
Alexanderstrasse 1-5, 10178, Berlin, Ger-
many
Tel.: (49) 30609848898
Web Site: http://www.visual-meta.com
Online Shopping Solutions
N.A.I.C.S.: 513210
Johannes Kotte (Mng Dir)

Yourcareergroup Austria GmbH   (1)
Prinz-Eugen-Strasse 8-10, 1040, Vienna,
Austria
Tel.: (43) 13100371
Web Site: http://www.hotelcareer.at
E-Recruiting Online Services
N.A.I.C.S.: 561312

Yourcareergroup GmbH   (1)
Volklinger Strasse 1, 40219, Dusseldorf,
Germany
Tel.: (49) 2119388970
Web Site: http://www.yourcareergroup.com
Online Recruiting Services
N.A.I.C.S.: 561311
Pierre-Emmanuel Derriks (Mng Dir)

affilinet Schweiz GmbH   (1)
Flurstrasse 55, 8048, Zurich, Switzerland
Tel.: (41) 445631930
Online Advertising Services
N.A.I.C.S.: 541810

meinestadt.de GmbH   (1)
Waidmarkt 11, 50676, Cologne,
Germany   (100%)
Tel.: (49) 221 99533 0
Web Site: http://www.meinestadt.de
Portal Operator
N.A.I.C.S.: 519290
Mark Hoffmann (Mng Dir)

upday GmbH & Co. KG   (1)
Axel-Springer-Strasse 65, 10888, Berlin,
Germany
Tel.: (49) 30259138652
Web Site: http://www.upday.com
Mobile Phone Product Services
N.A.I.C.S.: 516210

AXELERO SPA

Via A Stradivari 1, 20131, Milan, Italy
Tel.: (39) 02 5468620
Web Site: http://www.axelero.it
Year Founded: 2008
Digital Advertising & Web Marketing
Solutions
N.A.I.C.S.: 541890
Leonardo Cucchiarini (Chm & CEO)

AXELL CORPORATION

Akihabara UDX SouthWing 10F,
4-14-1 Sotokanda, Chiyoda-ku, To-
kyo, 101-8973, Japan
Tel.: (81) 352981670   JP
Web Site: https://www.axell.co.jp
Year Founded: 1996
6730—(TKS)
Rev.: $116,137,700
Assets: $102,944,140
Liabilities: $17,734,630
Net Worth: $85,209,510
Earnings: $11,706,310
Emp.: 128
Fiscal Year-end: 03/31/24
Semiconductor, Circuit Board, Gam-
ing, Office, Graphics & Sound Equip-
ment & Technology Products De-
signer, Mfr & Sales
N.A.I.C.S.: 334413
Nobuhiro Sendai (Gen Mgr-Mgmt
Dept)

Subsidiaries:

ax Inc.   (1)
4F Tosokaikan 19-22 Uguisudanicho,
Shibuya-ku, Tokyo, Japan   (90%)

Web Site: http://axinc.jp
Software Publisher
N.A.I.C.S.: 513210
Takehiko Terada (Pres & CEO)

Subsidiary (Domestic):

MotionPortrait, Inc.   (2)
7F Mitsuisumitomo Bank Gotanda Bldg
1-14-10 Higashi Gotanda, Shinagawa-ku,
Tokyo, 141-0022, Japan   (100%)
Tel.: (81) 334407500
Sales Range: $25-49.9 Million
Emp.: 15
Imaging Software Publisher
N.A.I.C.S.: 513210
Junichi Fujita (Pres)

AXEREAL UNION DE COOP-
ERATIVES AGRICOLES

5 rue Leonard de Vinci, 45100, Or-
leans, France
Tel.: (33) 2 37 97 59 00
Web Site: http://www.axereal.com
Sales Range: $1-4.9 Billion
Emp.: 3,225
Grain Collection & Processing Ser-
vices
N.A.I.C.S.: 111199
Jean-Francois Loiseau (Chm)

Subsidiaries:

Axiane Meunerie   (1)
20 Rue de la Gare, 35330, Maure-de-
Bretagne, France
Tel.: (33) 2 99 34 87 20
Web Site: http://www.axiane.com
Grain Milling
N.A.I.C.S.: 311211
Tanguy Poupart (CEO)

Boortmalt N.V.   (1)
Zandvoort 2 Haven 350 Bus 1, 2030, Ant-
werp, Belgium
Tel.: (32) 3 545 04 11
Web Site: http://www.boortmalt.com
Emp.: 385
Malt Mfr
N.A.I.C.S.: 311213
Yvan Schaepman (CEO)

Subsidiary (Domestic):

Belgomalt S.A.   (2)
Chaussee de Charleroi 40, 5030, Gem-
bloux, Belgium   (100%)
Tel.: (32) 81625840
Sales Range: $25-49.9 Million
Emp.: 30
Malt Mfr
N.A.I.C.S.: 311213

Cargill Malt   (1)
704 S 15th St, Sheboygan, WI 53081-4341
Tel.: (920) 459-4148
Malt Producers
N.A.I.C.S.: 311213
Bart DeRoher (Gen Mgr)

Cargill Malt   (1)
3349 94th Ave SE, Spiritwood, ND
58481   (100%)
Tel.: (701) 253-7890
Malt Related Services
N.A.I.C.S.: 311213
Matt AbuAyed (Plant Mgr)

Granit Negoce SA   (1)
27 Quai de la Fontaine, Nimes, 30900,
France
Tel.: (33) 4 66 36 92 36
Grain Distr
N.A.I.C.S.: 424510

AXF RESOURCES PTY LTD.

188 Ballarat Road, Footscray, Mel-
bourne, 3011, VIC, Australia
Tel.: (61) 3 8680 4800
Web Site:
     http://www.axfgroup.com.au
Year Founded: 2005
Property Development & Interior Ser-
vices
N.A.I.C.S.: 531390
Richard Mingfeng Gu (Mng Dir)

AXF Resources Pty Ltd.—(Continued)

AXIAL RETAILING INC.

18-2 Nakakono, Nagaoka, 954-0131, Niigata, Japan
Tel.: (81) 258666711
Web Site: https://www.axial-r.com
Year Founded: 1967
8255—(TKS)
Rev.: $1,786,180,640
Assets: $868,487,900
Liabilities: $317,888,120
Net Worth: $550,599,780
Earnings: $49,191,620
Fiscal Year-end: 03/31/24
Supermarket Store Operator
N.A.I.C.S.: 445110
Kazuhiko Hara (Pres & CEO)

AXIATA GROUP BERHAD

Level 5 Corporate Headquarters Axiata Tower 9 Jalan Stesen Sentral 5, Kuala Lumpur Sentral, 50470, Kuala Lumpur, Wilayah Persekutuan, Malaysia
Tel.: (60) 322638888
Web Site: https://www.axiata.com
Year Founded: 2001
AXIATA—(KLS)
Rev.: $5,819,274,074
Assets: $17,278,461,587
Liabilities: $10,785,265,820
Net Worth: $6,493,195,767
Earnings: $2,120,510,899
Emp.: 14,341
Fiscal Year-end: 12/31/22
Telecommunications & Internet Services
N.A.I.C.S.: 517112
Jamaludin Ibrahim (Pres, CEO-Grp & Mng Dir)

Subsidiaries:

Axiata Business Services Sdn Bhd **(1)**
Axiata Tower 9 Jalan Stesen Sentral 5 Kuala Lumpur Sentral, 50470, Kuala Lumpur, Malaysia
Tel.: (60) 322638888
Web Site: https://iot.xpand.asia
Information Technology Services
N.A.I.C.S.: 541512

Axiata Digital Capital Sdn Bhd **(1)**
Axiata Tower Level 32 9 Jalan Stesen Sentral 5, Kuala Lumpur Sentral, 50470, Kuala Lumpur, Malaysia
Tel.: (60) 322609404
Web Site: https://credit.myboost.co
Financial Payment Services
N.A.I.C.S.: 522320

Axiata Digital Labs (Private) Limited **(1)**
Level 11 Parkland 33 Park Street, Colombo, Western, Sri Lanka
Tel.: (94) 766766300
Web Site: https://www.axiatadigitallabs.com
Software Development Services
N.A.I.C.S.: 541511

Axiata Digital Labs Sdn. Bhd. **(1)**
Axiata Tower Level 25c No 9, Jalan Stesen Sentral 5 Kuala Lumpur Sentral, 50470, Kuala Lumpur, Malaysia
Tel.: (60) 124168738
Software Development Services
N.A.I.C.S.: 541511

Axiata Digital Services Sdn Bhd **(1)**
Level 32 Axiata Tower 9 Jalan Stesen Sentral 5, 50470, Kuala Lumpur, Wilayah Persekutuan, Malaysia
Tel.: (60) 322609400
Web Site: https://www.axiatadigital.com
Digital Marketing & Advertising Services
N.A.I.C.S.: 541613

Subsidiary (Domestic):

Apigate Sdn Bhd **(2)**
Level 29 Axiata Tower 9 Jalan Stesen Sentral 5 Kuala Lumpur Sentral, 50470, Kuala Lumpur, Malaysia

Tel.: (60) 322609400
Web Site: https://connect.myboost.co
Telecommunication Provider Services
N.A.I.C.S.: 517810

Axiata Digital Advertising Sdn Bhd **(2)**
Level 32 Axiata Tower 9 Jalan Stesen Sentral 5 Kuala Lumpur Sentral, 50470, Kuala Lumpur, Malaysia
Tel.: (60) 322609400
Integrated Digital Advertising Agency Services
N.A.I.C.S.: 541810

Axiata Digital eCode Sdn Bhd **(2)**
Level 29 Axiata Tower 9 Jalan Stesen Sentral 5 Kuala Lumpur Sentral, 50470, Kuala Lumpur, Malaysia
Tel.: (60) 322609400
Digital Financial Services
N.A.I.C.S.: 522320
Gavin Teo (Head-Fin)

Celcom (Malaysia) Berhad **(1)**
Menara Celcom No 82, Jalan Raja Muda Abdul Aziz, 50300, Kuala Lumpur, Malaysia **(100%)**
Tel.: (60) 326883939
Web Site: http://www.celcom.com.my
Sales Range: $1-4.9 Billion
Emp.: 3,600
Mobile Telecommunications Services
N.A.I.C.S.: 517112

Subsidiary (Domestic):

Technology Resources Industries **(2)**
Menara Celcom 82 Jalan Raja Muda Abdul Azis, Kuala Lumpur, 50300, Malaysia **(20.99%)**
Tel.: (60) 326883939
Web Site: http://www.celcom.com.my
N.A.I.C.S.: 238210

Dialog Axiata PLC **(1)**
475 Union Place, Colombo, 02, Sri Lanka **(85%)**
Tel.: (94) 777678700
Web Site: http://www.dialog.lk
Telecommunications & Internet Services
N.A.I.C.S.: 517112
Azzat Kamaludin (Chm)

Subsidiary (Domestic):

Dialog Broadband Networks (Private) Limited **(2)**
No 221/1 Dharmapala Mawatha, Colombo, Sri Lanka
Tel.: (94) 777678700
Telecommunication Servicesb
N.A.I.C.S.: 517810

Edotco Bangladesh Co. Ltd. **(1)**
Uday Tower 13th & 14th Floor 57 and 57/A, Gulshan Avenue Gulshan-1, Dhaka, 1212, Bangladesh
Tel.: (880) 1871006767
Telecommunication & Information Services
N.A.I.C.S.: 517810

Edotco Towers (Bangladesh) Limited **(1)**
Uday Tower 13th and 14th Floor 57 and 57/A Gulshan Avenue, Gulshan-1, Dhaka, Bangladesh
Tel.: (880) 1871006767
Telecommunication Infrastructure Services
N.A.I.C.S.: 517111

H One (Private) Limited **(1)**
The Hub No 245 Ven Muruththettuwe Ananda Nahimi Mawatha, 05, Colombo, Sri Lanka
Tel.: (94) 117434100
Web Site: https://www.h-oneonline.com
Software Development Services
N.A.I.C.S.: 541511

Headstart (Private) Limited **(1)**
No 475 Union Place, Colombo, Sri Lanka
Tel.: (94) 117727577
Web Site: https://www.headstart.lk
Software Development Services
N.A.I.C.S.: 541511

Infront Consulting Group (S) Pte Ltd. **(1)**
65 Ubi Road 1 03-56 Oxley Bizhub, Singapore, 408729, Singapore

Tel.: (65) 67023970
Information Technology Consulting Services
N.A.I.C.S.: 541512

Multinet Pakistan (Private) Limited **(1)**
1D 203 Sector 30, Korangi Industrial Area, Karachi, 74900, Pakistan **(89%)**
Tel.: (92) 2111 102 1021
Web Site: https://www.multinet.com.pk
Sales Range: $1-9.9 Million
Telecommunication Servicesb
N.A.I.C.S.: 517111
Adnan Asdar (CEO)

Ncell Private Limited **(1)**
Lalitpur Sub-metropolitan City, Ward No 4 Nakkhu, Patan, Nepal
Tel.: (977) 9805554444
Web Site: http://www.ncell.axiata.com
Emp.: 25,000
Mobile Telecom Operator
N.A.I.C.S.: 517112

PT Axiata Digital Labs Indonesia **(1)**
Av Manuel Bandeira 291 - Bloco B - 2 andar conjuntos 33 e 34, Kuningan, South Jakarta, Indonesia
Tel.: (62) 87777339164
Information Technology Services
N.A.I.C.S.: 541511

PT Hipernet Indodata **(1)**
Jl Makaliwe Raya No 24-24A Grogol Kec Grogol petamburan, Kota Jakarta Barat Daerah Khusus Ibukota, Jakarta, Indonesia
Tel.: (62) 2129393939
Web Site: https://hypernet.co.id
Information Technology Services
N.A.I.C.S.: 541511

PT XL Axiata Tbk **(1)**
XL Axiata Tower Jl HR Rasuna Said X5 Kav 11-12, Kuningan Timur Setiabudi, Jakarta, 12950, Indonesia **(83.8%)**
Tel.: (62) 215761881
Web Site: https://www.xl.co.id
Rev.: $1,820,636,650
Assets: $4,742,135,790
Liabilities: $3,402,520,170
Net Worth: $1,339,615,620
Earnings: $26,011,860
Fiscal Year-end: 12/31/2020
Mobile Telecommunications Services
N.A.I.C.S.: 517112
Dian Siswarini (Chm)

Robi Axiata Limited **(1)**
Nafi Tower 53 Gulsan Avenue Gulsan1, Dhaka, Bangladesh **(68.7%)**
Tel.: (880) 1819000123
Web Site: http://www.robi.com.bd
Mobile Telecommunications Services
N.A.I.C.S.: 517112

Smart Axiata Co., Ltd. **(1)**
No 464A Monivong Blvd, Sangkat Tonle Bassac Khan Chamkarmorn, Phnom Penh, Cambodia
Tel.: (855) 10200888
Web Site: https://www.smart.com.kh
Emp.: 1,000
Mobile Telecommunication Operator
N.A.I.C.S.: 517112

Suvitech Co., Ltd. **(1)**
555/60-61 SSP Tower 1 22 Floor Soi Sukhumvit 63 Ekkamai Road, Klongton Nua Wattana, Bangkok, Thailand
Tel.: (66) 271143357
Web Site: https://suvitech.com
Information Technology Services
N.A.I.C.S.: 541512

Tanjung Digital Sdn Bhd **(1)**
No 9173 Jalan Negara, Taman Melawati, 53100, Kuala Lumpur, Malaysia
Tel.: (60) 341019019
Web Site: https://www.tanjungdigital.com
Information Technology Services
N.A.I.C.S.: 541512

Telekom Malaysia International (Cambodia) Co. Ltd. **(1)**
No 56 Preah Norodom Blvd Sangkat Chey Chumneah, Khan Doun Penh, Phnom Penh, 23, Cambodia **(100%)**
Tel.: (855) 16810001
Sales Range: $50-74.9 Million
Emp.: 100
Mobile Telecommunications Services

N.A.I.C.S.: 517112

edotco Group Sdn Bhd **(1)**
Level 30 Axiata Tower 9 Jalan Stesen Sentral 5 Kuala Lumpur Sentral, 50470, Kuala Lumpur, Malaysia
Tel.: (60) 322621388
Web Site: https://www.edotcogroup.com
Integrated Telecommunication Services
N.A.I.C.S.: 517810

AXICHEM AB

Sodergatan 26, 211 34, Malmo, Sweden
Tel.: (46) 467800673
Web Site: https://www.axichem.com
AXIC.A—(OMX)
Rev.: $150,158
Assets: $6,805,960
Liabilities: $256,368
Net Worth: $6,549,592
Earnings: ($1,649,301)
Emp.: 6
Fiscal Year-end: 12/31/20
Biochemical Mfr
N.A.I.C.S.: 325998
Jan Gustavsson (Chm)

AXIELL GROUP AB

Faltspatvagen 4, Lund, 224 78, Sweden
Tel.: (46) 462700400
Web Site: http://www.axiell.com
Year Founded: 1982
Books & Archives Management System Services
N.A.I.C.S.: 519290
Joel Sommerfeldt (Pres & CEO)

AXINGTON INC.

2 03 2nd Floor Wisma Academy No 4A Jalan 19/1, 67 Jalan Raja Chulan, 46300, Petaling Jaya, Selangor Darul Ehsan, Malaysia
Tel.: (60) 379551768
Web Site: https://serialachieva.com
Year Founded: 2015
42U—(SES)
Rev.: $6,063,521
Assets: $9,043,704
Liabilities: $1,440,075
Net Worth: $7,603,630
Earnings: $349,761
Emp.: 100
Fiscal Year-end: 12/31/18
Business Support Services
N.A.I.C.S.: 561499
Ranjit Singh (Reg Mng Dir)

Subsidiaries:

Tricor Axcelasia (SG) Pte Ltd **(1)**
80 Robinson Road 02-00, Singapore, Singapore
Tel.: (65) 62363333
Management Consulting Services
N.A.I.C.S.: 541618

Tricor Axcelasia Sdn Bhd **(1)**
Unit 30-01 Level 30 Tower A Vertical Business Suite Avenue 3, Bangsar South No 8 Jalan Kerinchi, 59200, Kuala Lumpur, Malaysia
Tel.: (60) 327839191
Management Consulting Services
N.A.I.C.S.: 541618

Tricor Roots Sdn Bhd **(1)**
Unit 30-01 Level 30 Tower A Vertical Business Suite Avenue 3, Bangsar South No 8 Jalan Kerinchi, 59200, Kuala Lumpur, Malaysia
Tel.: (60) 327839211
Management Consulting Services
N.A.I.C.S.: 541618

AXIOM CAPITAL ADVISORS, INC.

1600 333 7th Ave SW, Calgary, T2P 2Z1, AB, Canada
Tel.: (604) 940-8826

Web Site:
http://www.axiomadvisors.ca
ACA—(CNSX)
Rev.: $31,291
Assets: $4,446
Liabilities: $39,015
Net Worth: ($34,569)
Earnings: ($120,859)
Fiscal Year-end: 06/30/21
Financial Management Services
N.A.I.C.S.: 541611
L. Evan Baergen *(Fin Dir)*

AXIOM CORP.
380 Van Sickle Road Unit 600, Saint
Catharines, L2S 0B5, ON, Canada
Tel.: (905) 646-8787   CO
Web Site:
http://www.axiompaper.com
Year Founded: 2012
Sales Range: Less than $1 Million
Emp.: 6
Packaging Solutions
N.A.I.C.S.: 561910
Scott MacRae *(Pres)*

AXIOM MINING LIMITED
Level 6 15 Astor Terrace, Spring Hill,
4000, QLD, Australia
Tel.: (61) 7 3319 4100   HK
Web Site: http://www.axiom-
mining.com
Rev.: $140,419
Assets: $5,749,623
Liabilities: $3,175,278
Net Worth: $2,574,345
Earnings: ($3,652,400)
Fiscal Year-end: 09/30/17
Mineral Exploration Services
N.A.I.C.S.: 212290
Ryan Richard Mount *(CEO)*

AXIOM PROPERTIES LIMITED
Level 1 Leigh Chambers 20 Leigh
Street, Adelaide, 5000, SA, Australia
Tel.: (61) 881202400
Web Site: http://www.axiompl.com.au
AXI—(ASX)
Rev.: $1,054,354
Assets: $12,415,198
Liabilities: $5,436,031
Net Worth: $6,979,167
Earnings: ($3,508,280)
Emp.: 10
Fiscal Year-end: 06/30/24
Investment Management
N.A.I.C.S.: 523940
Paul Rouvray *(Gen Mgr-Operations-
South Australian)*

AXIOMTEK CO., LTD
8th Floor 55 Nanxing Road, Xizhi
District, New Taipei City, 221026,
Taiwan
Tel.: (886) 286462111
Web Site: https://www.axiomtek.com
Year Founded: 1990
3088—(TPE)
Rev.: $219,120,270
Assets: $224,271,223
Liabilities: $86,806,498
Net Worth: $137,464,726
Earnings: $23,794,891
Emp.: 872
Fiscal Year-end: 12/31/23
Computer & Computer Peripheral
Equipment & Software Whslr
N.A.I.C.S.: 423430
Yu-Te Yang *(Chm)*

Subsidiaries:

Axiom Technology Inc   **(1)**
18138 Rowland St, City of Industry, CA
91748   **(100%)**
Tel.: (626) 581-3232
Web Site: http://www.axiomtek.com

Sales Range: $25-49.9 Million
Emp.: 45
Computer & Computer Peripheral Equip-
ment & Software Whslr
N.A.I.C.S.: 423430

Axiomtek (M) Sdn. Bhd.   **(1)**
No 16 Jalan Tandang 51/205A Seksen 51,
Batu 6/12 Off Jalan Klang Lama, 46000,
Petaling Jaya, Selangor, Malaysia
Tel.: (60) 377731203
Web Site: https://www.axiomtek.com.my
Computer Equipment Distr
N.A.I.C.S.: 423430

Axiomtek (Thailand) Co., Ltd.   **(1)**
7/17 Moo 6 Tumbol Banmai, Amphur
Pakkret, Nonthaburi, 11120, Thailand
Tel.: (66) 25734725
Computer Equipment Distr
N.A.I.C.S.: 423430

Axiomtek Deutschland GmbH   **(1)**
Elisabeth-Selbert-Str 21a, 40764, Langen-
feld, Germany
Tel.: (49) 2173399360
Computer Equipment Distr
N.A.I.C.S.: 423430

Axiomtek ITALIA S.r.l   **(1)**
Via Pavia 21, 20835, Muggio, Italy
Tel.: (39) 026642991
Web Site: http://www.axiomtek.it
Computer Equipment Mfr
N.A.I.C.S.: 334111

Axiomtek Technology (Shen Zheng)
Co., Ltd.   **(1)**
Unit GH 6F Building 7 Baoneng Science
and Technology Park, Qinghu Community
Qinghu Village Longhua District, Shenzhen,
518040, China
Tel.: (86) 75566865899
Web Site: http://www.axiomtek.com.cn
Computer Equipment Distr
N.A.I.C.S.: 423430

Axiomtek Tekdeutschland Gmbh **(1)**
Elisabeth-Selbert-Strasse 21a, 40764, Lan-
genfeld, Germany
Tel.: (49) 2173399360
Web Site: https://www.axiomtek.de
Industrial Computer Mfr
N.A.I.C.S.: 334111

AXION VENTURES INC.
1400-400 Burrard Street, Vancouver,
V6C 2T6, BC, Canada
Tel.: (604) 687-7767   BC
Web Site:
https://www.axionventures.com
Year Founded: 2011
AXV—(TSXV)
Sales Range: Less than $1 Million
Investment Services
N.A.I.C.S.: 523999
Grant Kim *(Exec Dir)*

Subsidiaries:

Longroot (Thailand) Ltd.   **(1)**
57 Wireless Road, Bangkok, Thailand
Tel.: (66) 23093667
Web Site: http://www.longroot.co.th
Financial Services
N.A.I.C.S.: 561499

AXIS AUTO FINANCE INC.
165 Galaxy Blvd 2nd Floor, Etobi-
coke, M9W 0C8, ON, Canada
Tel.: (226) 212-5106   Ca
Web Site:
https://www.axisfinancegroup.com
Year Founded: 2008
X7D—(DEU)
Rev.: $28,394,419
Assets: $126,597,576
Liabilities: $125,649,231
Net Worth: $948,345
Earnings: ($16,931,714)
Emp.: 140
Fiscal Year-end: 06/30/24
Financial Services
N.A.I.C.S.: 523999
Richard Lloyd *(CFO)*

Subsidiaries:

Pivotal Capital Corp.   **(1)**
165 Galaxy Blvd 2nd Floor, Toronto, M9W
0C8, ON, Canada
Web Site: https://pivotalcapitalcorp.com
Financial Services
N.A.I.C.S.: 522320

AXIS BANK LIMITED
Trishul 3rd Floor Opp Samartheshwar
Temple Law Garden, Ellisbridge,
Ahmedabad, 380 006, India
Tel.: (91) 7966306161   In
Web Site: https://www.axisbank.com
Year Founded: 1994
AXISBANK—(NSE)
Rev.: $11,035,743,960
Assets: $137,909,407,149
Liabilities: $123,745,150,565
Net Worth: $14,164,256,584
Earnings: $982,185,231
Emp.: 78,307
Fiscal Year-end: 03/31/21
Commercial Banking
N.A.I.C.S.: 522110
Rajesh Kumar Dahiya *(Exec Dir-Corp
Centre)*

Subsidiaries:

A.Treds Ltd.   **(1)**
A3 11th Floor Ashar IT Park Road No 16Z
Wagle Industrial Estate, Thane, 400604,
Maharashtra, India
Tel.: (91) 2262357373
Web Site: https://www.invoicemart.com
N.A.I.C.S.: 561440
Prakash Sankaran *(Mng Dir)*

Axis Asset Management Company
Ltd.   **(1)**
112 1st Floor Yusuf Building Plot No 49
Veer Nariman Road, Hutatma Chowk Fort,
Mumbai, 400 001, Maharashtra, India
Tel.: (91) 8108622211
Web Site: https://www.axisamc.com
Banking Services
N.A.I.C.S.: 523150
Meghna Gupta *(Head-HR)*

Axis Bank Limited - Corporate
Office   **(1)**
Axis House C-2 Wadia International Centre,
Pandurang Budhkar Marg Worli, Mumbai,
400 025, India
Tel.: (91) 2224252525
Web Site: https://www.axisbank.com
Corporate Office
N.A.I.C.S.: 551114

Subsidiary (Domestic):

Axis Private Equity Limited   **(2)**
146 Maker Chamber VI 14th Fl, Nariman
Point, 400021, Mumbai, Maharashtra, India
Tel.: (91) 2222895300
Sales Range: $50-74.9 Million
Emp.: 10
Equity Investment Management Services
N.A.I.C.S.: 523999

Axis Bank UK Ltd.   **(1)**
Unit No G 06 Eagle House 167 City Road,
London, EC1V 1AW, United Kingdom
Tel.: (44) 2073972522
Web Site: https://www.axisbankuk.co.uk
Banking Services
N.A.I.C.S.: 523150
Rajiv Anand *(Chm)*

Axis Capital USA LLC   **(1)**
10000 Avalon Blvd Ste 200, Alpharetta, GA
30009
Tel.: (678) 746-9000
Web Site: https://www.axiscapital.com
N.A.I.C.S.: 522291
W. Marston Becker *(Chm)*

Axis Finance Ltd.   **(1)**
Axis House C - 2 Wadia International Cen-
tre, Pandurang Budhkar Marg Worli, Mum-
bai, 400 025, India
Tel.: (91) 2224252525
Web Site: https://www.axisfinance.in
N.A.I.C.S.: 522299
Amitabh Chaudhry *(Chm)*

Axis Mutual Fund Trustee Ltd. **(1)**
Narain Manzil Barakhamba Rd Connaught
Place, New Delhi, Delhi, 110001, India
Tel.: (91) 8108622211
Web Site: https://www.axismf.com
N.A.I.C.S.: 523150

Axis Securities Ltd.   **(1)**
Unit 002 A Building - A Agastya Corporate
Park Piramal Realty, Kamani Junction Kurla
West, Navi Mumbai, 400070, India
Tel.: (91) 2240508080
Web Site: https://simplehai.axisdirect.in
Investment Banking Services
N.A.I.C.S.: 523150

Freecharge Payment Technologies
Pvt. Ltd.   **(1)**
DLF Cyber Green 11th Floor Tower-C DLF
Cyber City DLF Phase-3, Gurgaon, 122002,
Haryana, India
Tel.: (91) 9773840200
Web Site: https://www.freecharge.in
N.A.I.C.S.: 561422

**AXIS CAPITAL HOLDINGS
LIMITED**
AXIS House 92 Pitts Bay Road, Pem-
broke, HM 08, Bermuda
Tel.: (441) 4962600   BM
Web Site:
https://www.axiscapital.com
Year Founded: 2001
AXS—(NYSE)
Rev.: $5,643,388,000
Assets: $30,250,672,000
Liabilities: $24,987,476,000
Net Worth: $5,263,196,000
Earnings: $346,042,000
Emp.: 2,048
Fiscal Year-end: 12/31/23
Holding Company; Specialty Insur-
ance & Reinsurance Products & Ser-
vices
N.A.I.C.S.: 551112
Conrad D. Brooks *(Gen Counsel)*

Subsidiaries:

AXIS Capital Holdings Limited - AXIS
Global Accident & Health
Division   **(1)**
1 University Sq Dr Ste 200, Princeton, NJ
08540
Tel.: (609) 375-9200
Web Site:
http://www.axisaccidenthealth.com
Emp.: 300
Insurance Management Services
N.A.I.C.S.: 524298
Chris DiSipio *(CEO)*

AXIS Group Services, Inc.   **(1)**
10000 Avalon Blvd Ste 200, Alpharetta, GA
30009
Tel.: (678) 746-9000
Emp.: 300
Insurance Brokerage Services
N.A.I.C.S.: 524210

AXIS Insurance Company   **(1)**
233 S Wacker Dr Ste 4930, Chicago, IL
60606
Tel.: (312) 977-0700
Insurance Brokerage Services
N.A.I.C.S.: 524210
Peter W. Wilson *(CEO)*

AXIS Re Limited   **(1)**
34 Upper Mount St, Dublin, Ireland
Tel.: (353) 16325900
Web Site: http://www.axiscapital.com
Provider of Reinsurance Services
N.A.I.C.S.: 524298
Steve Arora *(CEO)*

AXIS Re SE   **(1)**
Mount Herbert Court 34 Upper Mount
Street, Dublin, Ireland
Tel.: (353) 16325900
Emp.: 42
Fire Insurance Services
N.A.I.C.S.: 524113
William A. Fischer *(Chief Underwriting Offi-
cer)*

AXIS Reinsurance Company   **(1)**

AXIS Capital Holdings Limited—(Continued)

1211 Ave of the Americas 26th Fl, New York, NY 10036
Tel.: (212) 500-7600
Web Site: http://www.axiscapital.com
Sales Range: $50-74.9 Million
Emp.: 100
Provider of Reinsurance Services
N.A.I.C.S.: 524126
Jason Busti *(Pres-North America)*

AXIS Specialty Europe Limited **(1)**
Sixth Floor 20 Kildare Street, Dublin, Ireland
Tel.: (353) 16325900
Web Site: https://www.axiscapital.com
Sales Range: $50-74.9 Million
Emp.: 30
Provider of Non-Life Insurance Services
N.A.I.C.S.: 524298

AXIS Specialty Finance LLC **(1)**
11680 Great Oaks Way Ste 500, Alpharetta, GA 30022
Tel.: (678) 746-9000
Sales Range: $100-124.9 Million
Emp.: 250
Insurance Management Services
N.A.I.C.S.: 524298

AXIS Specialty Insurance Co. **(1)**
9 Farm Springs Rd, Farmington, CT 06032-2569
Tel.: (860) 674-6600
Provider of Insurance Services
N.A.I.C.S.: 524210

AXIS Specialty Limited **(1)**
Axis House 92 PittsBay Road, Pembroke, HM 08, Bermuda
Tel.: (441) 4962600
Web Site: http://www.axiscapital.com
Provider of General Insurance & Reinsurance Services
N.A.I.C.S.: 524298

AXIS Specialty UK Holdings Limited **(1)**
60 Great Tower St, London, EC3R 5AZ, United Kingdom
Tel.: (44) 2078773800
Investment Management Service
N.A.I.C.S.: 523999

AXIS Surplus Insurance Company **(1)**
10000 Avalon Blvd Ste 200, Alpharetta, GA 30009
Tel.: (678) 746-9000
Sales Range: $200-249.9 Million
Emp.: 300
Provider of Property & Casualty Insurance
N.A.I.C.S.: 524210

Compagnie Belge dAssurances Aviation NV/SA **(1)**
Avenue Louise 54, 1050, Brussels, Belgium
Tel.: (32) 23491211
Web Site: http://www.aviabel.com
Insurance Services
N.A.I.C.S.: 524298

Contessa Limited **(1)**
Unit 61 Enniskillen Business Centre Lackaghboy, Enniskillen, BT74 4RL, United Kingdom
Tel.: (44) 2866347918
Property & Casualty Insurance Services
N.A.I.C.S.: 524126

Ternian Insurance Group LLC **(1)**
7310 N 16th St Ste 100, Phoenix, AZ 85020
Tel.: (602) 216-0006
Insurance Agency Services
N.A.I.C.S.: 524113
Craig A. Smith *(Pres)*

AXIS CONSULTING CORPORATION

6F Kojimachi Crystal City 4-8 Kojimachi, Chiyoda-ku, Tokyo, 102-0083, Japan
Tel.: (81) 335561812
Web Site: https://www.axc-g.co.jp
Year Founded: 2002
9344—(TKS)
Rev.: $29,016,300

Assets: $25,576,640
Liabilities: $5,871,680
Net Worth: $19,704,960
Earnings: $3,122,440
Emp.: 137
Fiscal Year-end: 06/30/24
Management Consulting Services
N.A.I.C.S.: 541611
Yukihiro Yamao *(Pres)*

AXIS INFORMATION SYSTEMS

2nd floor Umutako Plaza opposite I&M bank, Kigali, 1382, Gikondo, Rwanda
Tel.: (250) 788 611902
Web Site: http://www.axis.rw
Year Founded: 2006
Sales Range: $10-24.9 Million
Emp.: 20
Development & Implementation of Web & Mobile Applications & Solutions
N.A.I.C.S.: 513210
Clement Uwajeneza *(Founder & Chm)*

AXIS REAL ESTATE INVESTMENT TRUST

Penthouse Menara Axis No 2 Jalan 51A/223 Section 51A, 46100, Petaling Jaya, Selangor Darul Ehsan, Malaysia
Tel.: (60) 79584882 **MY**
Web Site: https://www.axis-reit.com.my
Year Founded: 2005
AXREIT—(KLS)
Rev.: $60,205,503
Assets: $900,671,534
Liabilities: $356,366,984
Net Worth: $544,304,550
Earnings: $40,289,312
Emp.: 78
Fiscal Year-end: 12/31/22
Real Estate Investment Trust Services
N.A.I.C.S.: 531110
Kit May Leong *(CEO)*

AXISCADES TECHNOLOGIES LTD.

Kirloskar Business Park Block-C 2nd Floor Hebbal, Bengaluru, 560 024, India
Tel.: (91) 8041939000
Web Site: https://www.axiscades.com
532395—(BOM)
Rev.: $84,548,127
Assets: $108,435,873
Liabilities: $62,488,512
Net Worth: $45,947,361
Earnings: $3,095,697
Emp.: 1,223
Fiscal Year-end: 03/31/22
Engineering Design & Software Development Services
N.A.I.C.S.: 541330
Shweta Agarwal *(Compliance Officer & Sec)*

Subsidiaries:

AXISCADES GmbH **(1)**
Hein-Sass-Weg 36, 21129, Hamburg, Germany
Tel.: (49) 4074382399
Web Site: http://www.axiscades.com
Engineering Design Services
N.A.I.C.S.: 541330
Oliver Brotzki *(Gen Mgr)*

AXISCADES Inc. **(1)**
3008 W Willow Knolls Dr, Peoria, IL 61614
Tel.: (309) 691-3988
Rev.: $2,784,773
Engineering Design Services
N.A.I.C.S.: 541330
Srinivas Pulikam *(Pres & CEO)*

Subsidiary (Non-US):

AXISCADES UK Limited **(2)**
The Pump House - 15, Narborough Wood Park, Enderby, LE19 4XT, Leicestershire, United Kingdom
Tel.: (44) 1162394343
Rev.: $102,525
Engineering Design Services
N.A.I.C.S.: 541330

AXISCADES Technology Canada Inc. **(1)**
1200 McGill College Avenue Suite 1100, Montreal, H3B 4G7, QC, Canada
Tel.: (514) 380-2341
Rev.: $2,121,248
Engineering Design Services
N.A.I.C.S.: 541330

Cades Studec Technologies (India) Private Limited **(1)**
11 3rd Road Near by CBI office Ganga Nagar North R T Nagar Post, Bengaluru, 560 032, India
Tel.: (91) 8031906654
Web Site: https://www.cadesstudec.co.in
Engineering Design Services
N.A.I.C.S.: 541330
Adarsh Patil *(Mgr-Technical)*

AXITA COTTON LTD.

Servey No 324 357 358 Kadi Thol Rod Borisana, Kadi, Mehsana, 382 715, Gujarat, India
Tel.: (91) 6358747514
Web Site: https://www.axitacotton.com
Year Founded: 2013
542285—(BOM)
Rev.: $84,485,430
Assets: $14,636,356
Liabilities: $11,657,951
Net Worth: $2,978,405
Earnings: $509,640
Emp.: 23
Fiscal Year-end: 03/31/21
Textile Products Mfr
N.A.I.C.S.: 313310
Nitinbhai Govindbhai Patel *(Chm & Mng Dir)*

AXMIN, INC.

1111 Alberni Street Suite 2209, Vancouver, V6E 4V2, BC, Canada
Tel.: (604) 488-8878
Web Site: https://www.axmininc.com
AXMIF—(OTCEM)
Rev.: $7,669
Assets: $147,098
Liabilities: $669,505
Net Worth: ($522,407)
Earnings: ($635,441)
Fiscal Year-end: 12/31/22
Gold Mining Services
N.A.I.C.S.: 212220
Lucy Yan *(Chm & CEO)*

AXOLOT SOLUTIONS HOLDING AB

Hamntorget 3 1 tr, 252 21, Helsingborg, Sweden
Tel.: (46) 102115010
Web Site: https://www.axolotsolutions.com
Year Founded: 2014
AXOLOT—(OMX)
Rev.: $191,070
Assets: $2,526,998
Liabilities: $221,979
Net Worth: $2,305,019
Earnings: ($1,751,478)
Emp.: 5
Fiscal Year-end: 12/31/22
Holding Company
N.A.I.C.S.: 551112
Lennart Holm *(Chm)*

Subsidiaries:

Flocon Technologies Oy **(1)**

Tekniikantie 2, 02150, Espoo, Finland
Tel.: (358) 405159109
Web Site: https://www.flocon.fi
Water Purification Services
N.A.I.C.S.: 221310

AXON ACTIVE AG

Schlossli Schonegg, Wilhelmshohe, Luceme, 0000, Switzerland
Tel.: (41) 412492570 **CH**
Web Site: http://www.axonactive.com
Sales Range: $50-74.9 Million
Emp.: 150
Holding Company Business Services
N.A.I.C.S.: 551112
Peter Delfosse *(CEO)*

Subsidiaries:

Kompass International Neuenschwander SA **(1)**
Saint Laurent, F 73800, Cruet, France
Tel.: (33) 479652508
Web Site: http://www.kompass.com
Business Directories Publisher
N.A.I.C.S.: 513140

AXON HOLDINGS S.A.

2 Ermou St, Syntgama, 10563, Athens, Greece
Tel.: (30) 2103216000
AXON—(ATH)
Sales Range: $350-399.9 Million
Emp.: 2,740
Holding Company; Healthcare & Financial Services
N.A.I.C.S.: 551112
Panagiotis N. Doumanoglou *(Gen Mgr)*

Subsidiaries:

AXON Securities S.A. **(1)**
Stadiou Str 48, 10564, Athens, Greece
Tel.: (30) 2103363800
Web Site: http://www.axonsec.gr
Sales Range: $50-74.9 Million
Emp.: 20
Securities Trading Services
N.A.I.C.S.: 523150
Adamopoulou Efi *(Mgr)*

Data Design S.A. **(1)**
Messogion Ave 249, 154 51, Athens, Greece
Tel.: (30) 2106537422
Web Site: http://www.datadesign.gr
Sales Range: $25-49.9 Million
Emp.: 15
Medical Software Development Services
N.A.I.C.S.: 541511

Euromedica Palaiou Falirou S.A. **(1)**
Leoforos Amfitheas 107, Palaion Faliron, 17563, Athens, Greece
Tel.: (30) 2109803370
Web Site: http://www.euromedica.gr
Sales Range: $10-24.9 Million
Emp.: 24
Healtcare Services
N.A.I.C.S.: 622110
Michael Stamatakis *(Mgr)*

Ippokratis Magnetic Tomography S.A. **(1)**
Saint George 88, Korydallos, 18454, Piraeus, Greece
Tel.: (30) 2104941000
Web Site: http://www.ippokratis-medical.gr
Sales Range: $10-24.9 Million
Emp.: 7
Diagnostic Center Services
N.A.I.C.S.: 621512

SONAK S.A. **(1)**
Govatsi Str, PO Box 60, Lofos Aghios Georgios, 19003, Markopoulon, Greece
Tel.: (30) 2299021000
Web Site: http://www.sonak.gr
Sales Range: $25-49.9 Million
Emp.: 25
Defense Software & Electronic Systems Development Services
N.A.I.C.S.: 541511
George Giavroutas *(Mgr-IT)*

AXON PARTNERS GROUP SA
Calle Sagasta 18 3, 28004, Madrid,
Spain
Tel.: (34) 913102894
Web Site:
https://www.axonpartnersgroup.com
Year Founded: 2006
APG—(MAD)
Emp.: 25
Management Consulting Services
N.A.I.C.S.: 541618
Javier Martinez de Irujo *(Partner)*

AXON VENTURES LIMITED
Shop No 26 Meera Co. Op Hsg Soc
New Link Road Green Park, Andheri
West, Mumbai, 400053, India
Tel.: (91) 22 65368222
Web Site:
http://axonfinance.wordpress.com
Year Founded: 1982
Software Development Services
N.A.I.C.S.: 541511

AXP ENERGY LIMITED
Level 10 84 Pitt Street, Sydney,
2000, NSW, Australia
Tel.: (61) 292999580
Web Site:
https://www.fremontpetroleum.com
Year Founded: 2006
AUNXF—(OTCIQ)
Rev.: $20,752,162
Assets: $30,584,500
Liabilities: $13,906,205
Net Worth: $16,678,295
Earnings: $606,945
Fiscal Year-end: 06/30/22
Crude Petroleum Extraction Services
N.A.I.C.S.: 211120
Guy T. Goudy *(Chm)*

AXPO HOLDING AG
Parkstrasse 23, Baden, 5401, Switzerland
Tel.: (41) 562003111   CH
Web Site: http://www.axpo.com
Sales Range: $5-14.9 Billion
Emp.: 4,200
Holding Company; Electric Power
Generation & Distribution Services
N.A.I.C.S.: 551112
Andrew Walo *(CEO & Member-Exec Bd)*

Subsidiaries:

Axpo Benelux S.A.   **(1)**
Avenue Louise 480 14th Floor, 1050, Brussels, Belgium
Tel.: (32) 26 27 49 50
Electric Power & Natural Gas Distr.
N.A.I.C.S.: 221122
Domenico Franceschino *(Gen Mgr)*

Axpo DOOEL MK   **(1)**
Karposovo Vostanie 4/2-3 Karpos, 1000,
Skopje, North Macedonia
Tel.: (389) 44 749 41 41
Electric Power Distribution Services
N.A.I.C.S.: 221122

Axpo France S.A.S.   **(1)**
27 Avenue de l'Opera, 75001, Paris, France
Tel.: (33) 1 70 38 54 23
Electric Power & Natural Gas Distribution
Services
N.A.I.C.S.: 221122
Joanna Juszczak *(Mng Dir)*

Axpo Holz + Energie AG   **(1)**
Flughofstrasse 54, Glattbrugg, 8152, Switzerland
Tel.: (41) 44 809 74 80
Web Site: http://www.axpo-holz.ch
Engineering & Operating Biomass Power
Plants
N.A.I.C.S.: 541330

Axpo Informatik AG   **(1)**
Bruggerstrasse 68, Baden, Switzerland
Tel.: (41) 56 200 33 66

Information Technology Consulting Services
N.A.I.C.S.: 541512

Axpo International S.A.   **(1)**
74 Grand Rue, Luxembourg, 1660, Luxembourg
Tel.: (352) 262 003 80
Web Site: http://www.axpo.com
Electric Power Distribution Services
N.A.I.C.S.: 221122
Marc Linnenbaum *(Mng Dir)*

Axpo Kompogas AG   **(1)**
Flughofstrasse 54, 8152, Glattbrugg,
Switzerland   **(100%)**
Tel.: (41) 44 809 77 77
Web Site: http://www.axpo-kompogas.ch
Operation & Management of Biomass
Plants
N.A.I.C.S.: 221118

Axpo Singapore Pte. Ltd.   **(1)**
1 Wallich Street 15-02A Guoco Tower, Singapore, 078881, Singapore
Tel.: (65) 6 322 1410
Web Site: https://www.axpo.com
Hydropower Energy Services
N.A.I.C.S.: 221111

Axpo Slovensko, s.r.o.   **(1)**
Pribinova 4, Bratislava, 811 09, Slovakia
Tel.: (421) 23 231 0137
Web Site: https://www.axpo.com
Hydropower Energy Services
N.A.I.C.S.: 221111

Axpo Solutions AG   **(1)**
Parkstrasse 23, CH-5401, Baden,
Switzerland   **(100%)**
Tel.: (41) 56 200 31 11
Web Site: http://www.axpo.com
Holding Company; Energy Production, Distribution & Trading Services
N.A.I.C.S.: 551112
Domenico De Luca *(CEO)*

Corporate Headquarters (Domestic):

Axpo Trading AG - Head Office &
Trading Center   **(2)**
Lerzenstrasse 10, CH-8953, Dietikon, Switzerland
Tel.: (41) 447494141
Web Site: http://www.axpo.com
Corporate Office
N.A.I.C.S.: 551114

Subsidiary (Non-US):

Axpo Albania Sh.a.   **(3)**
Rruga "Reshit Petrela" Pallati Usluga 17,
Tirana, Albania
Tel.: (355) 4 24 20448
Web Site: http://www.axpo.com
Electric Power Generation
N.A.I.C.S.: 221118

Axpo Austria GmbH   **(3)**
Eschenbachgasse 11/8, 1010, Vienna, Austria
Tel.: (43) 1 585 09 09 0
Sales Range: $75-99.9 Million
Emp.: 5
Electric Power Distribution
N.A.I.C.S.: 221122
Roman Stutz *(Gen Mgr)*

Axpo BH doo   **(3)**
UNITIC building B office B6/16 Fra Andjela
Zvizdovica 1, 71000, Sarajevo, Bosnia &
Herzegovina
Tel.: (387) 33 295 788
Electric Power Distribution Services
N.A.I.C.S.: 221122
Boris Jurkovic *(Mng Dir)*

Axpo Bulgaria EAD   **(3)**
19 Yanko Sakazov blvd Apart 5, Oborishte
Residential Area, Sofia, 1756, Bulgaria
Tel.: (359) 29461294
Web Site: http://www.axpo.com
Sales Range: $75-99.9 Million
Electric Power Trading Services
N.A.I.C.S.: 221122
Miroslav Damianov *(Mng Dir)*

Axpo Deutschland GmbH   **(3)**
Messehaus am Markt-Markt 16, 04109,
Leipzig, Germany
Tel.: (49) 341 2 61 79 0
Web Site: http://www.axpo.com

Sales Range: $75-99.9 Million
Electric Power Distribution
N.A.I.C.S.: 221122
Rudolf Anderegg *(Mng Dir)*

Axpo Energy Romania S.A.   **(3)**
79-81 Popa Savu Street, Bucharest,
011432, Romania
Tel.: (40) 21 230 33 23
Emp.: 13
Electric Power & Gas Distribution
N.A.I.C.S.: 221122
Catalin Iordache *(Mng Dir)*

Axpo Iberia S.L.   **(3)**
Paseo de la Castellana 66 6 planta, Madrid,
28046, Spain
Tel.: (34) 915947170
Sales Range: $50-74.9 Million
Electric Power Generation
N.A.I.C.S.: 221118
Ignacio Soneira *(Mng Dir)*

Axpo Italia S.p.A.   **(3)**
via Enrico Albareto 21, Genoa, 16153, Italy
Tel.: (39) 010291041
Web Site: http://www.axpo.com
Sales Range: $75-99.9 Million
Emp.: 250
Electric Power Generation
N.A.I.C.S.: 221122
Salvatore Pinto *(Chm)*

Subsidiary (Domestic):

Axpo Gas Service Italia SpA   **(4)**
Via Di Vittorio 41, 20068, Peschiera Borromeo, Italy
Tel.: (39) 02 87 38 971
Electric Power & Natural Gas Distribution
Services
N.A.I.C.S.: 221122

Calenia Energia S.p.A.   **(4)**
Via Enrico Albareto 21, 16153, Genoa,
Italy   **(85%)**
Tel.: (39) 010 2910 41
Web Site: http://www.caleniaenergia.eu
Electric Power Generation
N.A.I.C.S.: 221118
Simone Demarchi *(Gen Mgr)*

Rizziconi Energia SpA   **(4)**
Via Enrico Albareto 21, Genoa, 16153,
Italy   **(100%)**
Tel.: (39) 010 2910 41
Electricity Power Plant; Electricity Generation
N.A.I.C.S.: 221118
Giuseppe Brancato *(Mng Dir)*

Subsidiary (Non-US):

Axpo Nordic AS   **(3)**
Dronning Eufemias Gate 6B, 0190, Oslo,
Norway
Tel.: (47) 22018400
Sales Range: $50-74.9 Million
Electric Power Trading
N.A.I.C.S.: 221118
Hakon Rohne *(Mng Dir)*

Subsidiary (Non-US):

Axpo Finland Oy   **(4)**
Teknobulevardi 3-5, 1530, Vantaa, Finland
Tel.: (358) 20 775 60 50
Electric Power Distribution Services
N.A.I.C.S.: 221122
Matti Ahtosalo *(Mng Dir)*

Axpo Sverige AB   **(4)**
Stortorget 29, 211 34, Malmo, Sweden
Tel.: (46) 40107770
Web Site: http://www.axpo.com
Sales Range: $50-74.9 Million
Emp.: 10
Electric Power Distribution
N.A.I.C.S.: 221122
Tomas Sjoberg *(Mng Dir)*

Subsidiary (Non-US):

Axpo Polska Sp.z.o.o.   **(3)**
Al Jerozolimskie 123, 02-017, Warsaw, Poland
Tel.: (48) 224525300
Web Site: http://www.axpo.com
Sales Range: $75-99.9 Million
Emp.: 3
Electric Power Trading

N.A.I.C.S.: 221122

Axpo Trgovina d.o.o.   **(3)**
Bosutska 30, Zagreb, 10000, Croatia
Tel.: (385) 1 611 7592
Electric Power Distribution Services
N.A.I.C.S.: 221122
Boris Jurkovic *(Mng Dir)*

Axpo UK Ltd.   **(3)**
38 Threadneedle Street, London, EC2R
8AY, United Kingdom
Tel.: (44) 20 7448 3570
Web Site: http://www.axpo.com
Electricity & Gas Distribution
N.A.I.C.S.: 221122
Kamal Khoury *(Mng Dir)*

Axpo d.o.o. Beograd   **(3)**
Milutina Milankovica 11a, 11070, Belgrade,
Serbia
Tel.: (381) 11 260 3767
Web Site: http://www.axpo.com
Sales Range: $75-99.9 Million
Emp.: 2
Electric Power Distribution
N.A.I.C.S.: 221122
Veljko Cvijovic *(Gen Mgr)*

Subsidiary (Domestic):

Calancasca AG   **(3)**
C/o Studio Legale E Notarile, 6535, Roveredo, Switzerland
Tel.: (41) 918271385
Hydropower Plant
N.A.I.C.S.: 221111

Affiliate (Domestic):

Kernkraftwerk Gosgen-Daniken
AG   **(2)**
Kraftwerkstrasse, 4658, Daniken,
Switzerland   **(37.5%)**
Tel.: (41) 622882000
Web Site: http://www.kkg.ch
Sales Range: $200-249.9 Million
Emp.: 550
Nuclear Power Plant Operator
N.A.I.C.S.: 221113
Patrick Gehri *(Head-Electrical Engrg Dept)*

Axpo Tegra AG   **(1)**
Via Innovativa 11, CH 7013, Domat/Ems,
Switzerland
Tel.: (41) 81 632 33 33
Web Site: http://www.axpo.com
Biomass Power Plant
N.A.I.C.S.: 221118

Axpo Turkey Enerji A.S.   **(1)**
Aytar Cad Fecri Ebcioglu Sok RSD Ofis No
4 Kat 2 Nisbetiye Besiktas, 34340, Istanbul,
Turkiye
Tel.: (90) 212 269 9080
Web Site: https://www.axpo.com
Hydropower Energy Services
N.A.I.C.S.: 221111

Axpo U.S. LLC   **(1)**
575 5th Ave Ste 2801, New York, NY 10017
Tel.: (212) 847-1212
Web Site: https://www.axpo.com
Hydropower Energy Services
N.A.I.C.S.: 221111

Axpo Ukraine LLC   **(1)**
19-21a Bohdana Khmelnytskogo Street,
01054, Kiev, Ukraine
Tel.: (380) 44 391 1424
Web Site: https://www.axpo.com
Hydropower Energy Services
N.A.I.C.S.: 221111

Axpo d.o.o.   **(1)**
Bulevar Mihajla Pupina 117, 11070, Belgrade, Serbia
Tel.: (381) 11 260 3767
Web Site: https://www.axpo.com
Hydropower Energy Services
N.A.I.C.S.: 221111
Veljko Cvijovic *(Mng Dir)*

Centralschweizerische Kraftwerke
AG   **(1)**
Taschmattstrasse 4, 6015, Lucerne, Switzerland
Tel.: (41) 412495111
Web Site: http://www.ckw.ch
Emp.: 1,780
Electric Power Services

Axpo Holding AG—(Continued)

N.A.I.C.S.: 221122
Andrew Walo *(Chm)*

AXTEL INDUSTRIES LIMITED

Vadodara Halol Highway, Dist Panch-
mahal, Halol, 389350, Gujarat, India
Tel.: (91) 2676247900
Web Site: https://www.axtelindia.com
523850—(BOM)
Rev.: $25,091,498
Assets: $24,439,056
Liabilities: $11,313,584
Net Worth: $13,125,471
Earnings: $2,361,832
Emp.: 205
Fiscal Year-end: 03/31/23
Engineering Equipment Mfr & Distr
N.A.I.C.S.: 333248
Ajay Naishad Desai *(Exec Dir)*

AXTERIA GROUP BERHAD

Suite 02-01 Level 2 Wisma Teras Eco
No 56, Jalan Setia Tropika 1/14 Ta-
man Setia Tropika, 81200, Johor
Bahru, Johor, Malaysia
Tel.: (60) 72330911   MY
Web Site: https://agb.my
Year Founded: 1999
AXTERIA—(KLS)
Rev.: $14,231,817
Assets: $42,975,025
Liabilities: $10,753,723
Net Worth: $32,221,303
Earnings: ($214,213)
Emp.: 27
Fiscal Year-end: 12/31/23
Holding Company; Audio & Electrical
Equipment Mfr
N.A.I.C.S.: 551112
Ahmad Rahizal Ahmad Rasidi *(Exec Dir)*

Subsidiaries:

Teras Eco Sdn. Bhd.   (1)
Suite 02-01 Level 2 Wisma Teras Eco No
56 Jalan Setia Tropika 1/14, Taman Setia
Tropika, 81200, Johor Bahru, Johor, Malaysia
Tel.: (60) 72330911
Web Site: http://www.teraseco.com.my
Real Estate & Property Management Services
N.A.I.C.S.: 531390

AXWAY SOFTWARE SA

Tour W 102 terrasse Boieldieu La
Defense, 92805, Paris, Cedex,
France
Tel.: (33) 147172424   FR
Web Site: https://www.axway.com
Year Founded: 2001
AXW—(EUR)
Rev.: $308,167,494
Assets: $629,088,064
Liabilities: $227,382,905
Net Worth: $401,705,159
Earnings: $10,362,616
Emp.: 1,689
Fiscal Year-end: 12/31/21
Software Publisher
N.A.I.C.S.: 513210
Kathleen Clark Bracco *(Deputy Chm)*

Subsidiaries:

Appcelerator Inc.   (1)
2811 Mission College Blvd 8th Fl, Santa
Clara, CA 95054
Tel.: (480) 627-8777
Web Site: http://www.appcelerator.com
Mobile Applications
N.A.I.C.S.: 513210

Axway Asia Pacific Pte Ltd   (1)
SGX Centre 2 No 04-03 4 Shenton Way,
Singapore, 068807, Singapore
Tel.: (65) 67787055
Software Development Services
N.A.I.C.S.: 541511

Axway BV   (1)
Hogeweg 37 D, 5301 LJ, Zaltbommel,
Gelderland, Netherlands
Tel.: (31) 418 576090
Web Site: http://www.axway.com
Sales Range: $350-399.9 Million
Emp.: 1,700
Software Development Services
N.A.I.C.S.: 541512

Axway Belgium SA   (1)
Avenue Arnaud Fraiteur 15-23, Ixelles,
1050, Brussels, Belgium
Tel.: (32) 26419662
Sales Range: $25-49.9 Million
Emp.: 20
Software Publishing Services
N.A.I.C.S.: 513210
Jo van Audenhove *(Gen Mgr)*

Axway Bulgaria   (1)
Business Park Sofia Mladost 4 Build 11B Fl
2, 1766, Sofia, Bulgaria
Tel.: (359) 28178300
Sales Range: $75-99.9 Million
Emp.: 170
Secure Messaging Systems Software Products for Enterprises & Government
N.A.I.C.S.: 513210

Axway GmbH   (1)
Mainzer Landstr 61, 60329, Frankfurt, Germany
Tel.: (49) 692 44 50 80
Sales Range: $50-74.9 Million
Emp.: 150
Software Publishing Services
N.A.I.C.S.: 513210

Axway Inc.   (1)
16220 N Scottsdale Rd Ste 500, Scottsdale, AZ 85254
Tel.: (480) 627-1800
Sales Range: $50-74.9 Million
Collaborative Business Solutions & Services
N.A.I.C.S.: 541512
Patrick Donovan *(CEO)*

Subsidiary (Domestic):

Axway   (2)
2600 Bridge Pkwy Ste 201, Redwood City,
CA 94065
Tel.: (650) 801-3100
Web Site: http://www.axway.com
Sales Range: $50-74.9 Million
Emp.: 120
Secure Messaging Systems Software Products for Enterprises & Government
N.A.I.C.S.: 334610

Axway Ireland Limited   (1)
1st Floor 8-34 Percy Place, Dublin, 4, Ireland
Tel.: (353) 16080100
Integrated Information Technology Services
N.A.I.C.S.: 541519
Colin McGovern *(Product Mgr)*

Axway Ltd.   (1)
28/F AIA Central No 1 Connaught Road,
Central, China (Hong Kong)
Tel.: (852) 35200535
Integrated Information Technology Services
N.A.I.C.S.: 541519
Elton Chung *(Dir-Bus Dev)*

Axway Nordic AB   (1)
Knarrarnasgatan 7, 164 29, Kista, Sweden
Tel.: (46) 852254527
Business Networking Services
N.A.I.C.S.: 561499

Axway Pte. Ltd.   (1)
77 Robinson Road 11-01/02, Singapore,
068896, Singapore
Tel.: (65) 67787055
Sales Range: $25-49.9 Million
Collaborative Business Solutions & Services
N.A.I.C.S.: 513210

Subsidiary (Non-US):

Axway Limited   (2)
28/F AIA Central No 1 Connaught Road,
Central, China (Hong Kong)
Tel.: (852) 35200535
Web Site: http://www.axway.com
Sales Range: $25-49.9 Million
Collaborative Business Solutions & Services
N.A.I.C.S.: 513210

Axway Software Malaysia Sdn Bhd   (2)
Quill 7 27 Floor Jalan Stesen 5 Kuala Lumpur Sentral, 50470, Kuala Lumpur, Malaysia
Tel.: (60) 27766800
Web Site: http://www.axway.com
Collaborative Business Solutions & Services
N.A.I.C.S.: 513210

Axway Pty Ltd   (1)
Level 13 99 Mount Street, North Sydney,
2065, NSW, Australia
Tel.: (61) 294969496
Web Site: http://www.axway.com
Sales Range: $25-49.9 Million
Software Programming Services
N.A.I.C.S.: 541511

Axway Romania Srl   (1)
Calea Serban Voda nr 133 et 3, Sector 4,
040205, Bucharest, Romania
Tel.: (40) 212076565
Integrated Information Technology Services
N.A.I.C.S.: 541519
Madalina Popescu *(Sr Mgr)*

Axway Software China   (1)
5/F Tower C Lei Shing Hong Plaza No 8
Wangjing Street, Chaoyang District, Beijing,
100102, China
Tel.: (86) 1065630081
Software Publishing Services
N.A.I.C.S.: 513210

Axway Software Do Brasil Ltda.   (1)
Rua Verbo Divino 2001 Torre B cj 1309
Chacara Santo Antonio, Sao Paulo, 04719-
002, SP, Brazil
Tel.: (55) 1137049900
Integrated Information Technology Services
N.A.I.C.S.: 541519
Marcelo Ramos *(CEO, Sr VP & Gen Mgr)*

Axway Software GmbH   (1)
Kurfurstendamm 119, 10711, Berlin, Germany
Tel.: (49) 30690100
Web Site: http://www.axway.com
Collaborative Business Solutions & Services
N.A.I.C.S.: 513210

Axway Software Iberia   (1)
Avenida de Manoteras 48, 28050, Madrid,
Spain
Tel.: (34) 913547739
Integrated Information Technology Services
N.A.I.C.S.: 541519

Axway Srl   (1)
Strada 4, 20090, Assago, Milan, Italy
Tel.: (39) 0248048901
Web Site: http://www.axway.it
Software Development Services
N.A.I.C.S.: 541511

Axway UK Ltd   (1)
Beaufort House Cricketfield Road, Uxbridge, UB8 1QG, Middlesex, United Kingdom
Tel.: (44) 1895202780
Web Site: http://www.axway.com
Sales Range: $25-49.9 Million
Information Technology Consulting Services
N.A.I.C.S.: 541512

Sopra Banking Software   (1)
3 rue du Pre Faucon PAE - Les Glaisins,
CS 30238, 74942, Annecy-le-Vieux, Cedex,
France
Tel.: (33) 450333030
Web Site: https://www.soprabanking.com
Service Providers to Banking Industry
N.A.I.C.S.: 561990
Eric Pasquier *(CEO)*

Subsidiary (Non-US):

Apak Group Ltd.   (2)
Apak House Badminton Court Station Road,
Bristol, BS37 5HZ, United
Kingdom   (100%)
Tel.: (44) 1454 871000
Web Site: http://www.sword-apak.com
Sales Range: $25-49.9 Million
Emp.: 90
Financial Software Development Services
N.A.I.C.S.: 541511
Tony Allen *(Pres & CEO)*

Subsidiary (Non-US):

Apak Beam Ltd   (3)

119-120 Building 13 Dubai Internet City, PO
Box 500406, Dubai, United Arab Emirates
Tel.: (971) 4367 0375
Web Site: http://www.apakbeam.com
Software Development Services
N.A.I.C.S.: 541511

Subsidiary (Non-US):

Sopra Banking Software Belgium   (2)
Quatuor-Tour C Bld Roi Albert II 4, B-1000,
Brussels, Belgium   (100%)
Tel.: (32) 27774111
Software Development Services
N.A.I.C.S.: 541511

Syncplicity LLC   (1)
2811 Mission College Blvd 7th Fl, Santa
Clara, CA 95054
Tel.: (888) 908-4276
Web Site: http://www.syncplicity.com
Software Publisher
N.A.I.C.S.: 513210
Patrick Gibbons *(VP-Customer Success Engrg)*

Systar SA   (1)
171 bureaux de la Colline, 92213, Saint-
Cloud, France   (100%)
Tel.: (33) 149114500
Web Site: http://www.systar.com
Sales Range: $25-49.9 Million
Emp.: 150
Performance Management Software Publisher
N.A.I.C.S.: 513210
Laurent van Huffel *(Exec VP-North American Ops)*

AXXESS CAPITAL

33 Aviatorilor Blvd, Bucharest,
011853, Romania
Tel.: (40) 212077100
Web Site:
http://www.axxesscapital.net
Sales Range: $25-49.9 Million
Emp.: 20
Privater Equity Firm
N.A.I.C.S.: 523999
Horia D. Manda *(Mng Partner)*

Subsidiaries:

Frigotehnica S.A.   (1)
24 Delea Veche Building A 11th Floor, 2nd
District, 021806, Bucharest, Romania
Tel.: (40) 212503441
Web Site: http://www.frigotehnica.ro
Sales Range: $50-74.9 Million
Commercial & Industrial Refrigeration
Equipment Mfr
N.A.I.C.S.: 333415

AXXIOME AG

Multergasse 2A, 9000, Saint Gallen,
Switzerland
Tel.: (41) 71 222 75 17
Web Site: http://www.axxiome.com
Year Founded: 2009
Emp.: 300
IT Services
N.A.I.C.S.: 541512
Michael Mauk *(Founder & CEO)*

Subsidiaries:

Axxiome Americas, Inc.   (1)
815 NW 57th Ave, Miami, FL 33126
Tel.: (305) 264-1057
IT Services
N.A.I.C.S.: 541512
Alberto Garda *(Mng Dir)*

Axxiome Asia Pacific Pte. Ltd.   (1)
#17-01 Marina Bay Financial Centre Tower
3 12 Marina Boulevard, Singapore, 18982,
Singapore
Tel.: (65) 6809 5251
IT Services
N.A.I.C.S.: 541512
Stefan Afendoulis *(Mng Dir)*

Axxiome Benelux BV   (1)
Ringwade 1, 3439 LM, Nieuwegein, Netherlands
Tel.: (31) 6 5191 0270
IT Services

N.A.I.C.S.: 541512
Christian Schmidt *(Mng Dir)*

Axxiome Brasil Ltda. **(1)**
Av Roque Petroni Jr. 999, Sao Paulo, CP
04707 - 910, Brazil
Tel.: (55) 11 5185 8700
Web Site: http://www.axiome.com
IT Services
N.A.I.C.S.: 541512
Alejandro Iribarnegaray *(Mng Dir)*

Axxiome CIS LLC. **(1)**
Presnenskaya emb 10C, Moscow, 123317,
Russia
Tel.: (7) 495 967 7904
IT Services
N.A.I.C.S.: 541512
Andrey Kuznetsov *(Mng Dir)*

Axxiome Canada Ltd. **(1)**
2 Bloor Street W Suite 700, Toronto, M4W
3R1, ON, Canada
Tel.: (416) 642-6508
IT Services
N.A.I.C.S.: 541512

Axxiome Colombia S.A.S. **(1)**
Carrera 6 No. 115-65 Centro Comercial Ha-
cienda Santa Barbara Ofc. F201, Bogota,
Colombia
Tel.: (57) 1 620 5630
IT Services
N.A.I.C.S.: 541512

Axxiome Deutschland GmbH **(1)**
Hauptstr 1, 82008, Unterhaching, Germany
Tel.: (49) 89 2000 180 566
IT Services
N.A.I.C.S.: 541512
Roger Kellenberger *(Mng Dir)*

Axxiome Polska Sp. z o.o **(1)**
ul Ozynowa 32, 53-009, Wroclaw, Poland
Tel.: (48) 71 750 40 50
IT Services
N.A.I.C.S.: 541512
Pawel Midon *(Mng Dir)*

Axxiome S.A. **(1)**
Lavalle 348 3rd Floor, Buenos Aires, 1047,
Argentina
Tel.: (54) 11 5272 3560
Web Site: http://www.axxiome.com
Emp.: 30
IT Services
N.A.I.C.S.: 541512
Marcos Chialva *(Mng Dir)*

Axxiome UK Ltd. **(1)**
Regus House Windmill Hill Business Park
Whitehill Way, Swindon, SN5 6QR, United
Kingdom
Tel.: (44) 1793 441 420
IT Services
N.A.I.C.S.: 541512
Ameet Dave *(Mng Dir)*

Axxiome USA LLC **(1)**
100 Park Ave 16th Fl, New York, NY 10017
Tel.: (212) 351-5013
IT Services
N.A.I.C.S.: 541512
Al Wasserberger *(Sr VP-Corp Dev)*

Subsidiary (Domestic):

J9 Technologies, Inc. **(2)**
25 Broadway 9th Fl, New York, NY 10004
Tel.: (866) 221-8109
Web Site: http://www.j9tech.com
Computer Facilities Management Services
N.A.I.C.S.: 541513
Clay Roach *(CEO)*

Axxiome Uruguay S.A. **(1)**
Juncal 1305 apto 108 (Edificio TUPI), Mon-
tevideo, C.P.11000, Uruguay
Tel.: (598) 2 916 25 05
IT Services
N.A.I.C.S.: 541512

HartterGruppe GmbH **(1)**
Raimundgasse 25, 7400, Oberwart, Austria
Tel.: (43) 3352334400
Web Site: http://www.hartter.com
Banking & Financial Services
N.A.I.C.S.: 523150
Manfred Joseph *(Mng Dir)*

Nixil Pty. Ltd. **(1)**
2nd Floor 122 Walker Street, North Sydney,

2060, NSW, Australia
Tel.: (61) 24272227
Web Site: http://www.nixil.com.au
IT Services
N.A.I.C.S.: 541512

quSqu intelligence GmbH **(1)**
Krugerstr 3a, 85716, Unterschleissheim,
Germany
Tel.: (49) 1622044284
Web Site: http://www.qusqu-intelligence.de
Business Consulting Services
N.A.I.C.S.: 541611

**AXXION ASSET MANAGE-
MENT SAC**
Av Primavera 517 Centro Empre-
sarial Primavera Oficina 105, San
Borja, Lima, Peru
Tel.: (51) 1 647 0629
Web Site: http://www.axxion.com.pe
Private Investment Firm
N.A.I.C.S.: 523999
Karl Reusche *(Pres & CEO)*

Subsidiaries:

Industria Textil Piura S.A. **(1)**
Km 3.5 Carretera Piura, Piura, Sullana,
Peru **(69.23%)**
Tel.: (51) 74 327 741
Web Site: http://www.textilpiura.com.pe
Cotton Textile Mfr & Sales
N.A.I.C.S.: 111920

**AXXON WERTPAPIERHAN-
DELSBANK AG**
Hafenstrasse 54, 60327, Frankfurt,
Germany
Tel.: (49) 6924702880
Web Site: http://www.axxon-
wphbank.de
Sales Range: $25-49.9 Million
Emp.: 12
Bank
N.A.I.C.S.: 522299

AXXZIA, INC.
35F Shinjuku Sumitomo Building
2-6-1 Nishi-Shinjuku, Shinjuku-Ku,
Tokyo, 160-0023, Japan
Tel.: (81) 363045840
Web Site: https://www.axxzia.co.jp
Year Founded: 2011
4936—(TKS)
Rev.: $75,834,240
Assets: $65,577,460
Liabilities: $12,483,540
Net Worth: $53,093,920
Earnings: $4,938,680
Fiscal Year-end: 07/31/24
Dietary Supplement Mfr & Distr
N.A.I.C.S.: 325412
Duan Zhuo *(Founder & Pres)*

**AXYZ AUTOMATION GROUP
INC.**
5330 South Service Road, Burlington,
L7L 5L1, ON, Canada
Tel.: (905) 634-4940
Web Site:
http://www.axyzautomationgroup.com
Year Founded: 1990
Holding Company; Industrial Cutting
& Router Equipment Mfr & Whslr
N.A.I.C.S.: 551112
Luke Hansen-Macdonald *(Pres)*

Subsidiaries:

AXYZ Automation Inc. **(1)**
5330 South Service Road, Burlington, V7X
1L2, ON, Canada
Tel.: (905) 634-4940
Web Site: http://www.axyz.com
Industrial Cutting & Router Equipment Mfr &
Whslr
N.A.I.C.S.: 333517

Subsidiary (US):

AXYZ Ohio Valley Region, Inc. **(2)**

2844 E Kemper Rd, Cincinnati, OH 45241-
1820
Tel.: (513) 771-7444
Web Site: http://www.axyz.com
Industrial Cutting & Router Equipment
Whslr
N.A.I.C.S.: 423830
Jim Heenan *(Specialist-Technical Sls)*

WARDJet, Inc. **(1)**
180 South Ave, Tallmadge, OH 44278
Tel.: (330) 677-9100
Web Site: http://www.wardjet.com
Industrial Waterjet Cutting Machinery Mfr &
Whslr
N.A.I.C.S.: 333517
Richard Ward *(Pres)*

AXYZ CO., LTD.
2-1-8 Somuta 3F Showa Shitsunai
Bldg, Kagoshima, 890-0014, Japan
Tel.: (81) 992237385   JP
Web Site: http://www.axyz-grp.co.jp
Year Founded: 1962
1381—(TKS)
Rev.: $160,699,920
Assets: $152,085,220
Liabilities: $23,188,160
Net Worth: $128,897,060
Earnings: $7,706,580
Fiscal Year-end: 06/30/24
Poultry Products, Seasoned & Frozen
Foods Mfr & Sales
N.A.I.C.S.: 311612

AYA GOLD & SILVER INC.
1320 Graham suite 132 Ville Mont-
Royal, Montreal, H3P 3C8, QC,
Canada
Tel.: (514) 951-4411
Web Site: https://ayagoldsilver.com
Year Founded: 2007
AYA—(TSX)
Rev.: $34,301,914
Assets: $161,257,878
Liabilities: $21,256,189
Net Worth: $140,001,689
Earnings: $1,272,142
Emp.: 285
Fiscal Year-end: 12/31/21
Gold & Silver Mining Services
N.A.I.C.S.: 212220
Benoit La Salle *(Co-Pres & CEO)*

Subsidiaries:

Algold Resources Ltd. **(1)**
1320 Graham Blvd 132, Ville Marie, H3P
3C8, QC, Canada
Tel.: (514) 747-4653
Web Site: http://www.algold.com
Mineral Exploration Services
N.A.I.C.S.: 213114

Aya Gold & Silver Maroc S.A. **(1)**
Boulevard Ibnou Sina and Rue Abou
Rayane Al Falaki, 20370, Casablanca, Mo-
rocco
Tel.: (212) 522949011
Copper Ore Mining Services
N.A.I.C.S.: 212230

AYA KITCHENS & BATHS, LTD.
1551 Caterpillar Road, Mississauga,
L4X 2Z6, ON, Canada
Tel.: (905) 848-1999
Web Site:
https://www.ayakitchens.com
Year Founded: 2000
Rev.: $11,979,030
Emp.: 150
Wood Kitchen Cabinet Mfr
N.A.I.C.S.: 337110
Dave Marcus *(Founder & CEO)*

AYALA CORPORATION
32F-35F Tower One and Exchange
Plaza Ayala Triangle Ayala Avenue,
Makati, 1226, Philippines
Tel.: (63) 29083000
Web Site: http://www.ayala.com.ph

Year Founded: 1834
AYYLF—(OTCIQ)
Rev.: $6,092,617,656
Assets: $28,667,270,828
Liabilities: $16,639,815,775
Net Worth: $12,027,455,053
Earnings: $983,242,700
Emp.: 40,372
Fiscal Year-end: 12/31/23
Holding Company
N.A.I.C.S.: 551112
Fernando Zobel de Ayala *(Pres &
COO)*

Subsidiaries:

AC Energy Holdings, Inc. **(1)**
4F 6750 Building Ayala Avenue, Makati,
1226, Philippines
Tel.: (63) 7306300
Web Site: http://www.acenergy.com.ph
Investment Holding Company; Energer
Company
N.A.I.C.S.: 551112
Eric T. Francia *(Prea & CEO)*

Subsidiary (Domestic):

ACEN Corporation **(2)**
35F Ayala Triangle Gardens Tower 2,
Paseo de Roxas cor Makati Avenue,
Makati, 1226, Philippines **(51.48%)**
Tel.: (63) 277306300
Web Site: https://acenrenewables.com
Rev.: $627,009,324
Assets: $4,141,786,854
Liabilities: $1,480,029,181
Net Worth: $2,661,757,673
Earnings: $259,744,275
Emp.: 713
Fiscal Year-end: 12/31/2022
Power Generation Services
N.A.I.C.S.: 213112
Jaime Alfonso Eder Zobel de Ayala *(Vice
Chm)*

Subsidiary (Domestic):

**Trans-Asia Petroleum
Corporation** **(3)**
11th Floor The PHINMA Plaza 39 Plaza
Drive Rockwell Center, Makati, 1210, Philip-
pines
Tel.: (63) 2 870 0100
Oil & Gas Exploration, Development & Pro-
duction
N.A.I.C.S.: 211120

AC Energy, Inc. **(1)**
Tel.: (63) 277306300
Power Generation Services
N.A.I.C.S.: 221118

**Ayala Automotive Holdings
Corporation** **(1)**
34F Tower One, Ayala Triangle Ayala Av-
enue, Makati, 1226, Philippines
Tel.: (63) 28485643
Web Site: http://www.ayala.com.ph
Holding Company; Car Dealerships
N.A.I.C.S.: 551112

Subsidiary (Domestic):

Honda Cars Makati, Inc. **(2)**
1 Pres Sergio Osmena Highway, Makati,
1232, Philippines
Tel.: (63) 84244994
Web Site: https://acmotors.com.ph
Car Dealership
N.A.I.C.S.: 441110

**Isuzu Automotive Dealership,
Inc.** **(2)**
Alabang-Zapote Road corner Acacia Av-
enue, Ayala Alabang, Muntinlupa, 1780,
Philippines
Tel.: (63) 28071788
Web Site:
http://www.isuzuautodealer.com.ph
Sales Range: $25-49.9 Million
Car Dealership
N.A.I.C.S.: 441110

Ayala Aviation Corporation **(1)**
Ayala Hangar, Domestic Airport, Pasay,
1301, Philippines **(100%)**
Tel.: (63) 28323595

Ayala Corporation—(Continued)

Sales Range: $25-49.9 Million
Emp.: 20
Aviation Services
N.A.I.C.S.: 488190

Ayala Foundation, Inc. (1)
8F 111 Paseo Building Paseo de Roxas corner Legaspi Street, Legaspi Village, Makati, 1229, Metro Manila, Philippines (100%)
Tel.: (63) 77598288
Web Site: https://www.ayalafoundation.org
Sales Range: $25-49.9 Million
Emp.: 50
Charitable Grant Services
N.A.I.C.S.: 813211

Ayala Hotels, Inc. (1)
19 Fl Tower 1 Bldg, Ayala Ave, 1226, Makati, Philippines (76.8%)
Tel.: (63) 27517711
Web Site: http://www.ayalahotels.com.ph
Sales Range: $25-49.9 Million
Emp.: 6
N.A.I.C.S.: 721199
Jose Emmanuel Jalandoni (Pres)

Ayala International Pte. Ltd. (1)
Raffles City Twr 32 03A, 250 Northbridge Rd, Singapore, 179101, Singapore
Tel.: (65) 63392886
Web Site: http://www.ayala.com
Sales Range: $50-74.9 Million
Emp.: 6
Holding Company
N.A.I.C.S.: 551112

Ayala Land, Inc. (1)
Tower 1 Exchange Plaza Ayala Triangle, PO Box 1902, Ayala Avenue, Makati, 1226, Metro Manila, Philippines (53.5%)
Tel.: (63) 28485643
Web Site: https://www.ayalaland.com.ph
Sales Range: $75-99.9 Million
Emp.: 25
Property Development
N.A.I.C.S.: 531210
Jaime E. Ysmael (Sr VP)

Affiliate (Domestic):

Cebu Holdings Inc. (2)
20/F Ayala Center Cebu Tower Bohol Street, Cebu Business Park, Cebu, 6000, Philippines (47.06%)
Tel.: (63) 328883700
Web Site: http://www.cebuholdings.com
Rev.: $94,406,003
Assets: $575,492,990
Liabilities: $336,875,726
Net Worth: $238,617,264
Earnings: $32,855,386
Emp.: 14,537
Fiscal Year-end: 12/31/2019
Real Estate Ownership, Development, Marketing & Management
N.A.I.C.S.: 531210
Anna Ma. Margarita B. Dy (Chm)

Subsidiary (Domestic):

Cebu Property Ventures and Development Corporation (3)
20/F Ayala Center Cebu Tower Bohol Street, Cebu Business Park, Cebu, 6000, Philippines (76.26%)
Tel.: (63) 328883700
Web Site: http://www.cpvdc.com
Rev.: $16,058,752
Assets: $115,098,428
Liabilities: $72,238,498
Net Worth: $42,859,930
Earnings: $4,939,498
Emp.: 51,611
Fiscal Year-end: 12/31/2017
Property Management & Development Services
N.A.I.C.S.: 531311
June Vee D. Monteclaro-Navarro (Sec)

Darong Agricultural & Development Corporation (1)
33rd Fl Twr One Ayala Triangle Ave, Makati, Philippines (100%)
Tel.: (63) 8415421
Agricultural Production Services
N.A.I.C.S.: 115116

GNPower Kauswagan Co., Ltd. (1)

28F Orient Square Building Don Francisco Ortigas, Jr Road Ortigas Center, Pasig, Philippines
Tel.: (63) 25707205
Power Generation Services
N.A.I.C.S.: 221118
Daniel E. Chalmers (Chm)

Honda Cars Cebu, Inc. (1)
A Soriano Ave North Reclamation Area, Cebu, 6000, Philippines
Tel.: (63) 322313502
Web Site: http://www.hondacebu.com.ph
Car Maintenance Services
N.A.I.C.S.: 811111

Integrated Microelectronics, Inc. (1)
North Science Avenue Special Export Processing Zone Laguna Technopark, Binan, 4024, Laguna, Philippines (67.8%)
Tel.: (63) 27566840
Web Site: https://www.global-imi.com
Rev.: $23,963,400
Assets: $17,958,428
Liabilities: $12,350,677
Net Worth: $5,607,750
Earnings: ($2,135,429)
Emp.: 12,659
Fiscal Year-end: 12/31/2023
Integrated Electronics Mfr
N.A.I.C.S.: 334418
Arthur R. Tan (Vice Chm & CEO)

Subsidiary (Domestic):

PSi Technologies Holdings, Inc. (2)
Electronics Ave FTI Industrial Complex, Taguig, 1604, Philippines (100%)
Tel.: (63) 28384966
Web Site: http://www.psitechnologies.com
Sales Range: $75-99.9 Million
Emp.: 2,567
Semiconductor Assembly & Test Services
N.A.I.C.S.: 334413
Helen G. Tiu (Sec)

Subsidiary (Non-US):

VIA optronics GmbH (2)
Unterer Markt 12, 90518, Altdorf, Germany (76%)
Tel.: (49) 9187 90681 0
Web Site: http://www.via-optronics.com
Emp.: 290
LCD Display Mfr
N.A.I.C.S.: 335999

Subsidiary (Non-US):

VIA optronics (Suzhou) Co., Ltd (3)
158-50 Huashan Rd, FengQiao Industry Park, Suzhou, Jiangsu, China
Tel.: (86) 51266610700
Electronic Product Distr
N.A.I.C.S.: 423690

Via Optronics, Ltd. (3)
2F No 97 Sec 2 Dunhua S Rd, PO Box 96343, Da'an Dist, Taipei, 106, Taiwan
Tel.: (886) 227036660
Emp.: 12
Electronic Product Distr
N.A.I.C.S.: 423690

Division (US):

Via optronics LLC (3)
21333 NW Jacobson Rd, Hillsboro, OR 97124
Tel.: (503) 690-2460
Web Site: http://www.via-optronics.com
Sales Range: $25-49.9 Million
Emp.: 80
Contrast Optical Filters
N.A.I.C.S.: 449210

LiveIt Investments, Inc. (1)
33/F Tower One Ayala Triangle, Ayala Avenue, Makati, Philippines
Tel.: (63) 848 5643
Sales Range: $300-349.9 Million
Holding Company; Business Process Outsourcing Products & Services
N.A.I.C.S.: 551112
Alfredo I. Ayala (CEO)

Subsidiary (US):

Affinity Express, Inc. (2)
2250 Point Blvd Ste 150, Elgin, IL 60123
Tel.: (847) 930-3200

Sales Range: $10-24.9 Million
Emp.: 1,000
Advertising, Graphic Designing & Marketing Services
N.A.I.C.S.: 541890
David Grant (Exec VP)

Subsidiary (Domestic):

HRMall Inc. (2)
2nd Level Street Market, Fort Bonitacio Global City, Taguig, 1634, Philippines
Tel.: (63) 2 9760308
Web Site: http://www.hrmall.asia
Sales Range: $75-99.9 Million
Emp.: 30
Human Resources Business Process Outsourcing Services
N.A.I.C.S.: 561499

Subsidiary (US):

IQ BackOffice, Inc. (3)
2121 Rosecrans Ave Ste 3350, El Segundo, CA 90245
Tel.: (310) 322-2758
Web Site: https://www.iqbackoffice.com
Sales Range: $25-49.9 Million
Emp.: 40
Finance, Accounting & Human Resources Outsourcing Services
N.A.I.C.S.: 561499
Larry Coleman (Dir-Sls & Mktg)

Merlin Solar Technologies, Inc. (1)
Tel.: (408) 321-8258
Web Site: http://www.merlinsolar.com
Solar Power Generation Services
N.A.I.C.S.: 221114
Olaf Gresens (Pres)

AYALALAND LOGISTICS HOLDINGS CORP.

3rd Floor Glorietta Ayala Center, 1226, Makati, 1224, Philippines
Tel.: (63) 288841106
Web Site:
　　https://www.ayalalandlogistics.com
Year Founded: 1989
ALLHC—(PHI)
Rev.: $89,368,573
Assets: $424,014,989
Liabilities: $175,087,973
Net Worth: $248,927,016
Earnings: $16,223,293
Emp.: 53
Fiscal Year-end: 12/31/21
Investment Holding Company
N.A.I.C.S.: 551112
Felipe U. Yap (Vice Chm)

Subsidiaries:

FLT PRIME Insurance Corporation (1)
16th Floor PearlBank Center 146 Valero Street, Salcedo Village, Makati, 1226, Philippines
Tel.: (63) 28922826
Web Site: http://www.fltprime.com
Sales Range: $50-74.9 Million
Emp.: 50
General Insurance Services
N.A.I.C.S.: 524113
Yuen Po Seng (Pres & CEO)

Orion Solutions, Inc. (1)
20th Floor LKG Tower 6801 Ayala Avenue, Makati, 1226, Philippines
Tel.: (63) 28367650
Web Site: http://www.orionsolutionsinc.com
Sales Range: $25-49.9 Million
Emp.: 15
Computer Software Consulting Services
N.A.I.C.S.: 541512
Jerdy Augusto (Head-Bus Unit)

Tutuban Properties, Inc. (1)
Tutuban Center CM Recto, Manila, Philippines
Tel.: (63) 22511661
Web Site: http://www.tutuban.com.ph
Sales Range: $50-74.9 Million
Emp.: 100
Shopping Mall Operation Services
N.A.I.C.S.: 531120
Jocelyn Niu (Mgr)

AYALON INSURANCE COMPANY LTD.

Beyit Aiyalon Bituah Aba Hilel Silver 12 Ta Do'ar 10957, Ramat Gan, 52008, Israel
Tel.: (972) 37569090
Web Site: http://www.ayalon-ins.co.il
AYAL—(TAE)
Rev.: $947,392,995
Assets: $4,404,238,362
Liabilities: $4,209,413,113
Net Worth: $194,825,249
Earnings: $20,187,318
Fiscal Year-end: 12/31/23
Offices of Other Holding Companies
N.A.I.C.S.: 551112
Aaron Fogel (Chm)

AYCO GRUPO INMOBILIARIO, S.A.

Almagro 14 Floor 5, 28010, Madrid, 28010, Spain
Tel.: (34) 917812775
Web Site: https://www.ayco.es
Year Founded: 1941
AYC—(MAD)
Sales Range: Less than $1 Million
Real Estate Development Services
N.A.I.C.S.: 531390
Jose Palma Garcia (Pres)

AYDEM YENILENEBILIR ENERJI A.S.

Adalet Mahallesi Hasan Gonullu Bulvari No 15/1, Merkezefendi, Denizli, Turkiye
Tel.: (90) 2582422776
Web Site:
　　https://www.aydemyenilenebilir.com.tr
Year Founded: 1995
AYDEM—(IST)
Rev.: $117,615,011
Assets: $1,093,101,424
Liabilities: $565,595,998
Net Worth: $527,505,426
Earnings: $31,445,711
Emp.: 556
Fiscal Year-end: 12/31/22
Electric Power Distribution Services
N.A.I.C.S.: 221122
Omer Fatih Keha (Gen Mgr)

AYEN ENERJI AS

Hulya Sokak No 37 G O P, 06700, Ankara, Turkiye
Tel.: (90) 3124450464
Web Site: https://www.ayen.com.tr
AYEN—(IST)
Rev.: $209,735,761
Assets: $297,239,543
Liabilities: $163,976,044
Net Worth: $133,263,499
Earnings: $49,209,117
Emp.: 265
Fiscal Year-end: 12/31/22
Electric Power Distribution Services
N.A.I.C.S.: 221122
Mehmet Aydiner (Chm)

Subsidiaries:

Ayen Electric Trading Inc. (1)
Hulya Sokak No 37 G O P, Ankara, Turkiye
Tel.: (90) 3124450464
Electric Power Distribution Services
N.A.I.C.S.: 221122

Ayen Elektrik Ticaret A.S. (1)
Hulya Sokak No 37, Gaziosmanpasa, 06700, Ankara, Turkiye
Tel.: (90) 3124450464
Web Site: https://www.ayenelektrik.com
Electrical Equipment Whslr
N.A.I.C.S.: 423830

Ayen Energija D.O.O (1)
Kosanicev Venac 20, 11000, Belgrade, Serbia
Tel.: (381) 44316685

Electric Power Distribution Services
N.A.I.C.S.: 221122

Ayen Energy Trading D.O.O (1)
Dolenjska Cesta 148, 1000, Ljubljana, Slovenia
Tel.: (386) 40164776
Electric Power Distribution Services
N.A.I.C.S.: 221122

Ayen Energy Trading Sha (1)
Blv Deshmoret e Kombit Twin Towers Tower
No 2 Floor 10, 1019, Tirana, Albania
Tel.: (355) 42280272
Electric Power Distribution Services
N.A.I.C.S.: 221122

Tasfiye Halinde Arakli Dogalgaz Uretim Sanayi ve Ticaret A.S. (1)
Hulya Sokak No 37, Gaziosmanpasa, 06700, Ankara, Turkiye
Tel.: (90) 3124450464
Renewable Energy Consulting Services
N.A.I.C.S.: 541690

AYEPEE LAMITUBES LIMITED
B-1 MIDC P O Murbad, Thane, 421 401, Maharashtra, India
Tel.: (91) 9765405761 In
Web Site:
http://www.ayepeelamitubes.net
Year Founded: 1984
Rev.: $75,779
Assets: $950,562
Liabilities: $2,121,930
Net Worth: ($1,171,368)
Earnings: ($145,638)
Fiscal Year-end: 03/31/18
Paper Product Mfr & Distr
N.A.I.C.S.: 322211

AYER HOLDINGS BERHAD
5th Floor Bangunan Yee Seng, No 15 Jalan Raja Chulan, 50200, Kuala Lumpur, Malaysia
Tel.: (60) 320342366
Web Site: https://ayer.com.my
Year Founded: 1907
AYER—(KLS)
Rev.: $22,644,021
Assets: $135,259,259
Liabilities: $15,303,704
Net Worth: $119,955,556
Earnings: $7,479,577
Emp.: 67
Fiscal Year-end: 12/31/22
Property Development & Plantation Business
N.A.I.C.S.: 111191
Jeannie Khoo Poh Gaik (COO-Grp)

Subsidiaries:

Bukit Hitam Development Sdn. Bhd. (1)
Lot 59244 Jalan, BP 7/15, Bandar Bukit Puchong, 47120, Puchong, Selangor Darul Ehsan, Malaysia
Tel.: (60) 380683388
Web Site: http://www.bukitpuchong.com.my
Real Estate Development Services
N.A.I.C.S.: 531390

AYERS EXPLORATION INC.
6 Harston Avenue, Mosman, Sydney, 2088, NSW, Australia
Tel.: (61) 411199319 NV
Year Founded: 2006
Mineral Clay Exploration Services
N.A.I.C.S.: 212323
Bruce Drury (Pres, CEO, CFO, Treas, Sec & VP-Exploration)

AYES CELIK HASIR VE CIT SANAYI A.S.
Ali Riza Gurcan St Metropol Center No 31/21, Merter, 34173, Istanbul, Turkiye
Tel.: (90) 5312608882
Web Site: https://www.ayescelik.com
Year Founded: 1978

AYES—(IST)
Rev.: $182,822,395
Assets: $60,744,422
Liabilities: $43,431,910
Net Worth: $17,312,512
Earnings: $2,747,764
Fiscal Year-end: 12/31/23
Steel Products Mfr
N.A.I.C.S.: 331110

AYFIE GROUP AS
Sjolyst Plass 2, 278, Oslo, Norway
Tel.: (47) 48310800 NO
Web Site: https://www.ayfie.com
Year Founded: 2016
AYFIE—(OSL)
Rev.: $1,902,365
Assets: $970,164
Liabilities: $1,203,492
Net Worth: ($233,327)
Earnings: ($2,398,116)
Emp.: 12
Fiscal Year-end: 12/31/23
Software Development Services
N.A.I.C.S.: 541511
Lars Rahbaek Boilesen (Chm)

AYNGARAN INTERNATIONAL LTD.
Unit 19 Riverside Bus Park Lyon Rd, Wimbledon, London, SW19 2 RL, United Kingdom
Tel.: (44) 2085434477 IM
Web Site: http://www.ayngaran.com
Year Founded: 1987
Tamil Movies Production & Distribution Services
N.A.I.C.S.: 512110

Subsidiaries:

Ayngaran International Media Pvt. Ltd. (1)
No 147 11 3rd Fl Rajparis Trimeni Towers G N Chetty Rd, T Nagar, Chennai, 600 017, Tamil Nadu, India
Tel.: (91) 4428153344
Web Site: http://www.ayngaran.com
Film Production & Distribution Services
N.A.I.C.S.: 512110

AYO TECHNOLOGY SOLUTIONS LTD.
Waterway House 3 Dock Road, V&A Waterfront, Cape Town, 8001, South Africa
Tel.: (27) 218791527
Web Site: https://www.ayotsl.com
Year Founded: 1996
AYOE—(JSE)
Rev.: $119,755,863
Assets: $260,033,741
Liabilities: $48,015,703
Net Worth: $212,018,038
Earnings: ($18,153,547)
Emp.: 1,151
Fiscal Year-end: 08/31/22
Software Development Services
N.A.I.C.S.: 541511

Subsidiaries:

Afrinat Proprietary Limited (1)
10th Floor Convention Towers Heerengracht Street, Cape Town, 8001, South Africa
Tel.: (27) 214271400
Web Site: https://www.afrinat.co.za
Hand Sanitizer Mfr
N.A.I.C.S.: 325611
Abdusamad Sidar (CEO)

Headset Solutions Africa Proprietary Limited (1)
Communication Centre Urtell Crescent Somerset Mall, Cape Town, 7137, Somerset West, South Africa
Tel.: (27) 210012667
Web Site: http://www.headsetsolutions.co
Electronic Equipment Distr
N.A.I.C.S.: 423690
Nielle Truter (COO)

Orleans Cosmetics Proprietary Limited (1)
20 Bell Close, Westlake Business Park Tokai, Cape Town, South Africa
Tel.: (27) 217012900
Web Site: https://orleanscosmetics.co.za
Cosmetic Product Whslr
N.A.I.C.S.: 456120

Puleng Technologies Proprietary Limited (1)
Block A Knightsbridge Office Park 33 Sloane Street, Bryanston, 2191, Gauteng, South Africa
Tel.: (27) 112054300
Web Site: http://www.puleng.co
Data Security Services
N.A.I.C.S.: 561621
Leigh Mayr (Sls Dir)

SGT Solutions Proprietary Limited (1)
58 Oak Ave Highveld Techno Park, Centurion, 0169, South Africa
Tel.: (27) 126728000
Web Site: https://sgtsolutions.co.za
Network Field Services
N.A.I.C.S.: 518210

SGT Solutions Proprietary Limited (1)
58 Oak Ave Highveld Techno Park, Centurion, 0169, South Africa
Tel.: (27) 126728000
Web Site: https://sgtsolutions.co.za
Network Field Services
N.A.I.C.S.: 518210

SGT Solutions Proprietary Limited (1)
58 Oak Ave Highveld Techno Park, Centurion, 0169, South Africa
Tel.: (27) 126728000
Web Site: https://sgtsolutions.co.za
Network Field Services
N.A.I.C.S.: 518210

SGT Solutions Proprietary Limited (1)
58 Oak Ave Highveld Techno Park, Centurion, 0169, South Africa
Tel.: (27) 126728000
Web Site: https://sgtsolutions.co.za
Network Field Services
N.A.I.C.S.: 518210

Tripos Travel Proprietary Limited (1)
2nd Floor Old Warehouse Building Black River Park 2 Fir Street, Observatory, Cape Town, 7925, South Africa
Tel.: (27) 214626104
Web Site: http://www.tripostravel.com
Travel Services
N.A.I.C.S.: 561510
Mark Cromhout (Ops Mgr)

esp Afrika Proprietary Limited (1)
1st Floor Waterway House North 3 Dock Road V A Waterfront, Cape Town, 8001, South Africa
Tel.: (27) 21 671 0506
Web Site: https://www.espafrika.com
Event Management Services
N.A.I.C.S.: 561920
Billy Domingo (COO)

AYONDO LTD.
20 Collyer Quay 01-02, Singapore, 049319, Singapore
Tel.: (65) 800 9999 94150
Web Site: http://www.ayondo.com
1I5—(SES)
Trade Financing Services
N.A.I.C.S.: 522299
Dominic Anthony Morris (CEO & CTO)

AYOUBCO GENERAL CONTRACTING
31a Ahmed Hishmat St, Zamalek, Cairo, 11211, Egypt
Tel.: (20) 27363900
Web Site: http://www.ayoubco.com
Year Founded: 1941
Sales Range: $75-99.9 Million
Emp.: 400

Construction Services
N.A.I.C.S.: 237310
Ayoub Adly Ayoub (Chm)

AYR MOTOR EXPRESS INC.
46 Poplar Street, Woodstock, E7M 4G2, NB, Canada
Tel.: (506) 325-2205
Web Site: http://www.ayrmotor.com
Year Founded: 1990
Rev.: $35,613,600
Emp.: 300
Truck Transportation Services
N.A.I.C.S.: 484122
Sandy Keenan (VP)

AYR WELLNESS INC.
199 Bay Street Suite 5300, Toronto, M5L 1B9, ON, Canada
Tel.: (949) 574-3860
AYRWF—(OTCQX)
Rev.: $465,618,000
Assets: $1,763,880,000
Liabilities: $928,556,000
Net Worth: $835,324,000
Earnings: ($245,466,000)
Emp.: 2,800
Fiscal Year-end: 12/31/22
Cannabis Product Mfr & Distr
N.A.I.C.S.: 325411
David Goubert (Pres & CEO)

Subsidiaries:

Liberty Health Sciences Inc. (1)
18770 N County Rd 225, Gainesville, FL 32609
Tel.: (833) 254-4877
Web Site:
http://www.libertyhealthsciences.com
Flower, Nursery Stock & Florists' Supplies Merchant Whslr
N.A.I.C.S.: 424930
George Gremse (Interim CEO)

AYRTON DRUGS MANUFACTURING COMPANY LIMITED
PO Box 2149, Accra, Ghana
Tel.: (233) 21245090
Web Site:
http://www.ayrtondrugs.com
Year Founded: 1965
AYRTN—(GHA)
Sales Range: $10-24.9 Million
Pharmaceuticals Mfr
N.A.I.C.S.: 325412
Samuel Adjepong (CEO)

AYS VENTURES BERHAD
Lot 6488 Jalan Haji Abdul Manan, 42100, Klang, Selangor Darul Ehsan, Malaysia
Tel.: (60) 333775597 MY
Web Site: https://www.ays-group.com
Year Founded: 1982
5021—(KLS)
Rev.: $276,330,285
Assets: $270,883,553
Liabilities: $169,094,970
Net Worth: $101,788,583
Earnings: $28,839,690
Emp.: 255
Fiscal Year-end: 03/31/22
Investment Holding Services
N.A.I.C.S.: 551112
Chiew Ho Oh (Founder & Grp Mng Dir)

Subsidiaries:

AYS (FZ) Sdn. Bhd. (1)
P407-408 part of 409 Jalan FZ1-P4 Port Klang Free Trade Zone/KS12, 42920, Pulau Indah, Selangor Darul Ehsan, Malaysia
Tel.: (60) 333775597
Steel Component Mfr & Distr
N.A.I.C.S.: 332312

AYS Metal Products & Engineering Sdn. Bhd. (1)
Lot 3846 7 1/2th Mile Jalan Kapar, 42200,

AYS Ventures Berhad—(Continued)

Klang, Selangor Darul Ehsan, Malaysia
Tel.: (60) 3 3291 9888
Web Site: http://www.ays-metal.com
Press Steel Sectional Tank Mfr & Distr
N.A.I.C.S.: 332420
Oh Chiew Ho (Founder)

AYS Wire Products Sdn. Bhd.　　(1)
24B Tingkat 2 Jalan Dato Yusof Shahbudin
28 Taman Sentosa, Klang, Selangor, Malaysia
Tel.: (60) 332919911
Steel Fabric Mfr
N.A.I.C.S.: 332312
Wong Kian Hwa (Exec Dir)

CH Yodoform Sdn. Bhd.　　(1)
Lot 3846 7th Mile Jalan Kapar, 42200, Klang, Malaysia
Tel.: (60) 3 329 18800
Purlin & Steel Product Mfr & Distr
N.A.I.C.S.: 332323
Tong Seng Won (Dir-Grp Engrg & Mfg)

Steelaris Pte. Ltd.　　(1)
3 International Business Park, Singapore, 609927, Singapore
Tel.: (65) 65925945
Commercial & Institutional Building Construction Services
N.A.I.C.S.: 236220

AYYAN INVESTMENT CO.
Office No 101 First Floor Macro Business Center Tariq Bin Ziad Street, PO Box 77411, Al Rakah Al Janubiyah, Al Khobar, 31952, Saudi Arabia
Tel.: (966) 138822130
Web Site: https://www.ahsa-dev.com.sa
Year Founded: 1993
2140—(SAU)
Rev.: $70,984,343
Assets: $436,273,258
Liabilities: $237,874,812
Net Worth: $198,398,447
Earnings: ($11,900,034)
Fiscal Year-end: 12/31/22
Industrial Project Development Services
N.A.I.C.S.: 541330
Saad Amash Al-Shammary (Vice Chm)

AZ-COM MARUWA HOLDINGS INC.
7-1 Asahi, Yoshikawa, 342-0008, Saitama, Japan
Tel.: (81) 489911000
Web Site: https://www.az-com-maruwa-hd.co.jp
Year Founded: 1970
9090—(TKS)
Rev.: $1,312,441,940
Assets: $889,666,340
Liabilities: $509,313,720
Net Worth: $380,352,620
Earnings: $60,276,590
Emp.: 19,523
Fiscal Year-end: 03/31/24
Land Transportation
N.A.I.C.S.: 484121
Masaru Wasami (Pres & CEO)

Subsidiaries:

AZ-COM Data Security Co., Ltd.　(1)
35 Midorigaoka, Chichibu, 368-0067, Saitama, Japan
Tel.: (81) 494631313
Web Site: https://www.azcom-data.co.jp
Emp.: 110
Data Security Services
N.A.I.C.S.: 541519
Masayuki Iizuka (Pres)

Chu-Shikoku Maruwa Logistics Co., Ltd.　　(1)
4666-1 Asahigaoka Niida, Kochi, 781-0112, Japan
Tel.: (81) 888376376

Web Site: http://www.chushikoku-maruwa.com
Freight Transportation Services
N.A.I.C.S.: 488510

Japan Logistics Development Co., Ltd.　　(1)
Seino Fushimi Building 2-8-11 Nishiki, Naka-ku, Nagoya, 460 0003, Aichi, Japan
Tel.: (81) 522220881
Web Site: http://www.jld.co.jp
Custom Computer Programming Services
N.A.I.C.S.: 541511

Kansai Maruwa Logistics Co., Ltd.　　(1)
1-1 Yawata Kaitori, Yawata, 614-8302, Kyoto, Japan
Tel.: (81) 756327900
Web Site: https://www.az-com.co.jp
Emp.: 2,226
General Trucking Services
N.A.I.C.S.: 484121
Akira Yoshii (Pres)

Kyushu Maruwa Logistics Co., Ltd.　　(1)
3-9-70 Kamata, Higashi-ku, Fukuoka, 813-0023, Japan
Tel.: (81) 926636222
Web Site: https://www.kyushu-maruwa.co.jp
General Trucking Services
N.A.I.C.S.: 484121

NS Maruwa Logistics Co., Ltd.　(1)
3rd floor Sanoh Building 1-37-8 Higashi Nippori, Arakawa-ku, Tokyo, 116-0014, Japan
Tel.: (81) 364583431
Web Site: https://www.ns-maruwa.co.jp
Emp.: 515
General Trucking Services
N.A.I.C.S.: 484121

PHYZ Holdings Inc.　　(1)
Mainichi Intecio 13F Umeda 3-4-5, Kita-ku, Osaka, 530-0001, Japan　　(58.44%)
Tel.: (81) 664530250
Web Site: https://www.phyz.co.jp
Rev.: $181,973,300
Assets: $51,181,230
Liabilities: $29,037,730
Net Worth: $22,143,500
Earnings: $5,638,330
Emp.: 676
Fiscal Year-end: 03/31/2024
Logistics Management Consulting Services
N.A.I.C.S.: 541614
Takashi Ohsawa (Pres & CEO)

Tohoku Maruwa Logistics Co., Ltd.　　(1)
3F Sendai Nagamachi Future Co-creation Center 6-7-21 Koriyama, Taihaku-ku, Sendai, 982-0003, Miyagi, Japan
Tel.: (81) 222267117
Web Site: https://www.tohokumaruwa.co.jp
Emp.: 626
General Trucking Services
N.A.I.C.S.: 484121
Kenji Hirano (Pres)

AZABACHE ENERGY INC.
Suite 1600 Dome Tower 333 7th Ave SW Cleo TD Square, Calgary, T2P 2Z1, AB, Canada
Tel.: (403) 264-1915　　ON
Web Site: http://www.azaenergy.com
Year Founded: 2005
Sales Range: Less than $1 Million
Oil & Gas Exploration & Development Services
N.A.I.C.S.: 211120
Claudio A. Larotonda (Pres & CEO)

Subsidiaries:

Argenta Energia S.A.　　(1)
Florida 890 Fl 18, C1003ABV, Buenos Aires, Argentina
Tel.: (54) 1148934004
Web Site: http://www.acaenergia.com
Sales Range: $50-74.9 Million
Emp.: 15
Oil & Gas Field Exploration Services
N.A.I.C.S.: 213112
Tlauvio Larotonda (Mgr)

Argenta Oil and Gas T&T Limited　　(1)
81 A Bel Air Dr, PO Box 7743, La Romaine, San Fernando, Trinidad & Tobago
Tel.: (868) 6521786
Oil & Gas Field Exploration Services
N.A.I.C.S.: 213112

AZAD ENGINEERING LIMITED
90/C 90/D Phase-1 I D A Jeedimetla, Hyderabad, 500055, India
Tel.: (91) 4023097007
Web Site: https://www.azad.in
Year Founded: 1983
544061—(BOM)
Rev.: $31,696,345
Assets: $71,386,921
Liabilities: $46,658,364
Net Worth: $24,728,557
Earnings: $1,031,170
Fiscal Year-end: 03/31/23
Metal Products Mfr
N.A.I.C.S.: 332311

AZAR INTERNATIONAL CORP.
Carretera Turistica Luperon 12th km No 7 Grand Parada, San Felipe de Puerto Plata, 57000, Dominican Republic
Tel.: (809) 7028057778　　NV
Web Site: http://www.azartravel.net
Year Founded: 2018
Rev.: $4,000
Assets: $7,159
Liabilities: $13,122
Net Worth: ($5,963)
Earnings: ($29,503)
Fiscal Year-end: 08/31/21
Investment Services
N.A.I.C.S.: 523999
Hilario Lopez Vargas (Founder, Pres, CEO, CFO, Treas & Sec)

AZAR REFRACTORIES CO.
Isfahan-Saadat Abad St -Boali Sina Alley-Yasman Alley-Plak 15, Babashykhaly Industrial zone Steel, Isfahan, Iran
Tel.: (98) 3136643367
Web Site: https://www.azarref.ir
Year Founded: 1992
NSAZ—(THE)
Sales Range: Less than $1 Million
Emp.: 917
Dolomite Product Mfr
N.A.I.C.S.: 327410

AZARAB INDUSTRIES
No 15 MollaSadra Ave Vanak sq, PO Box 38135-835, 1991913981, Tehran, Iran
Tel.: (98) 2184921
Web Site: https://www.azarab.ir
Industrial Equipment Mfr
N.A.I.C.S.: 333248
Ali Sheikhzadeh (Mng Dir)

AZARBAIJAN INVESTMENT DEVELOPMENT COMPANY
No3 6th 10m st Next to Talaiyeh Complex Parvin Etesami st, Manzariyeh, Tabriz, Iran
Tel.: (98) 411 4784057　　IR
Web Site: http://www.azarbayjanid.com
Year Founded: 1996
Investment Services
N.A.I.C.S.: 523999
Khalil Gholipour Khalili (Mng Dir)

Subsidiaries:

Coolack Shargh Company (P.J.S)　　(1)
KM24 Tehran Road, 54951-18657, Tabriz, Iran
Tel.: (98) 411 6306434
Web Site: http://www.coolackshargh.com

Soft Drinks Mfr
N.A.I.C.S.: 312111
Seyed Mohammad Majdoleslami (Mng Dir)

AZARGA METALS CORP.
Unit 1 - 15782 Marine Drive, White Rock, V4B 1E6, BC, Canada
Tel.: (604) 536-2711
Web Site: https://www.azargametals.com
EUUNF—(OTCIQ)
Assets: $756,582
Liabilities: $762,766
Net Worth: ($6,184)
Earnings: ($550,581)
Fiscal Year-end: 09/30/23
Uranium Exploration & Development Services
N.A.I.C.S.: 212290
Michael J. Hopley (Co-CEO)

AZARGA URANIUM CORP.
Unit 1 15782 Marine Drive, White Rock, V4B1E6, BC, Canada
Tel.: (604) 536-2711　　BC
Web Site: http://www.azargauranium.com
AZZ—(TSX)
Assets: $41,850,626
Liabilities: $4,608,095
Net Worth: $37,242,531
Earnings: ($7,737,996)
Emp.: 6
Fiscal Year-end: 12/31/19
Uranium Exploration, Development & Mining Services
N.A.I.C.S.: 213114

Subsidiaries:

Powertech (USA) Inc.　　(1)
310 2nd Ave, Edgemont, SD 57735
Tel.: (605) 662-8308
Web Site: http://www.azargauranium.com
Emp.: 2
Uranium Ore Exploration, Development & Mining
N.A.I.C.S.: 213114
John M. Mays (COO)

AZARIT COMPANY
9 Unit - 3rd Floor - 17 No - Toward To Shariati St Taleghani St, Postal Code 15636-74843, Tehran, Iran
Tel.: (98) 21 77536836
Web Site: http://www.azaritco.com
Year Founded: 1974
Fiber Cement Product Mfr
N.A.I.C.S.: 327310
Javad SaatSaz Maghrebi (Mgr & Head)

AZBIL CORPORATION
Tokyo Building 2-7-3 Marunouchi, Chiyoda-ku, Tokyo, 100-6419, Japan
Tel.: (81) 368101000　　JP
Web Site: https://www.azbil.com
Year Founded: 1995
6845—(TKS)
Rev.: $1,923,100,180
Assets: $2,073,742,080
Liabilities: $587,239,010
Net Worth: $1,486,503,070
Earnings: $199,668,270
Emp.: 9,909
Fiscal Year-end: 03/31/24
Holding Company
N.A.I.C.S.: 551112
Tadayuki Sasaki (Chm)

Subsidiaries:

Azbil (Thailand) Co., Ltd.　　(1)
No 9 G Tower Grand Praram 9 14th Floor Rama 9 Road, Huay Kwang, Bangkok, 10310, Thailand
Tel.: (66) 20119000
Web Site: http://www.th.azbil.com

Sales Range: $25-49.9 Million
Emp.: 100
Building & Industrial Automation System Mfr
N.A.I.C.S.: 541350
Kiyoshi Kurata *(Mng Dir)*

Azbil Brazil Limited (1)
Rua Sampaio Viana 277 -1 andar-
Conjuntos 11 e 13, Sao Paulo, 04004-000,
Brazil
Tel.: (55) 1130513476
Web Site: http://www.br.azbil.com
Industrial Equipment Distr
N.A.I.C.S.: 423840
Tetsuya Chikaraishi *(Mng Dir)*

**Azbil Control Instrument Trading (Da-
lian) Co., Ltd.** (1)
No 18 Dong Bei Second Street Dalian
Econmy Technical Development, Dalian,
China
Tel.: (86) 41187623552
Web Site: http://www.acnp.cn.azbil.com
Emp.: 430
Construction Services
N.A.I.C.S.: 236220

**Azbil Control Instruments (Dalian)
Co., Ltd.** (1)
No 18 Dong Bei Second St, Dalian Econ
Tech Dev, Dalian, Liaoning, China
Tel.: (86) 41187623555
Industrial & Airconditioning Valves &
Switches Mfr
N.A.I.C.S.: 332911

**Azbil Control Solutions (Shanghai)
Co., Ltd.** (1)
B2-8F No 700 Yishan Road, Xuhui District,
Shanghai, 200233, China
Tel.: (86) 2150906661
Web Site: http://www.acn.cn.azbil.com
Sales Range: $100-124.9 Million
Emp.: 300
Building Automation & Industrial Automation
System Installation & Maintenance Services
N.A.I.C.S.: 238210

Azbil Europe NV (1)
Bosdellestraat 120/2, Zaventem, B-1933,
Belgium
Tel.: (32) 27850710
Web Site: http://eu.azbil.com
Sales Range: $25-49.9 Million
Emp.: 18
Building Automation System Mfr
N.A.I.C.S.: 238290
Masami Watanabe *(Mng Dir)*

Azbil Europe NV (1)
Lilienthalstrasse 29, 85399, Hallbergmoos,
Germany
Tel.: (49) 81154154310
Web Site: http://www.eu.azbil.com
Emp.: 18
Industrial Equipment Mfr
N.A.I.C.S.: 333248
Masami Watanabe *(Mng Dir)*

Azbil Hong Kong Limited (1)
3/F Richwealth Industrial Building 77-87
Wang Lung Street, Tsuen Wan, China
(Hong Kong)
Tel.: (852) 21496622
Industrial Equipment Mfr
N.A.I.C.S.: 333248

Azbil India Private Limited (1)
1901 Cyber One Plot No 4 & 6 S Prana-
vanandji Marg Sector 30A, Vashi, Navi
Mumbai, 400703, India
Tel.: (91) 2227815700
Web Site: http://www.in.azbil.com
Industrial Equipment Mfr
N.A.I.C.S.: 333248
Shailendra Sharma *(Mng Dir)*

**Azbil Information Technology Center
(Dalian) Co., Ltd.** (1)
Unit 22 ST2 Dalian Center Yujing Building 5
No 280 Changjiang Road, Zhongshan Dis-
trict, Dalian, 116000, China
Tel.: (86) 41183679010
Web Site: http://acni.cn.azbil.com
Sales Range: $25-49.9 Million
Emp.: 30
Data Processing Services
N.A.I.C.S.: 518210

Azbil Kimmon Co., Ltd. (1)

1-14-3 Kita-Otsuka, Toshima-ku, Tokyo,
170-0004, Japan
Tel.: (81) 359803735
Web Site: http://www.ak.azbil.com
Emp.: 1,300
Water Meters & Electrical Equipments Mfr
N.A.I.C.S.: 334514
Mitsuharu Miyazawa *(Chm)*

**Azbil Kimmon Technology
Corporation** (1)
237-12 Wen-Shan, Wen-Sheng Village,
Miao-li, Taiwan
Tel.: (886) 37321886
Industrial Equipment Mfr
N.A.I.C.S.: 333248

Azbil Korea Co., Ltd. (1)
6F Yusu Holdings Building 25 International
Finance-ro 2-gil, Yeongdeungpo-gu, Seoul,
07327, Korea (South)
Tel.: (82) 221687800
Web Site: http://www.kr.azbil.com
Sales Range: $25-49.9 Million
Emp.: 80
Building Automation Industrial Automation
System Mfr
N.A.I.C.S.: 541350

Azbil Kyoto Co., Ltd. (1)
1-3-3 Kamoya Shimoichinotani, Kyotamba-
cho Funai-gun, Kyoto, 622-0442, Japan
Tel.: (81) 771870560
Web Site: http://www.akt.azbil.com
Flow Measurement Instruments Mfr &
Flowmeter Calibration Facility
N.A.I.C.S.: 334514
Yutaka Higuchi *(Pres & CEO)*

Azbil Malaysia Sdn. Bhd. (1)
Lot 19 07 Level 19 Tower 2 Faber Towers
Jalan Desa Bahagia Taman Desa, 58100,
Kuala Lumpur, Malaysia
Tel.: (60) 379726106
Web Site: http://www.my.azbil.com
Emp.: 55
Building Automation & Industrial Automation
Systems Mfr
N.A.I.C.S.: 541350
Vivian Long *(Mgr-HR)*

Azbil Mexico, S. de R.L.de C.V. (1)
Blvd Adolfo Lopez Mateos 2500E Loc 2B
Col San Isidro de Jerez, 37530, Leon, Gua-
najuato, Mexico
Tel.: (52) 4777840948
Industrial Equipment Mfr
N.A.I.C.S.: 333248

**Azbil North America Research & De-
velopment, Inc.** (1)
2334 Walsh Ave, Santa Clara, CA 95051
Tel.: (408) 245-3121
Industrial Equipment Mfr
N.A.I.C.S.: 333248
Judy Jackson *(CFO)*

Azbil North America, Inc. (1)
9033 N 24th Ave Ste 6, Phoenix, AZ 85021
Tel.: (602) 216-8199
Web Site: http://www.us.azbil.com
Sales Range: $25-49.9 Million
Emp.: 20
Sensor Instruments Mfr
N.A.I.C.S.: 334519
Gary Johnson *(Pres)*

Subsidiary (Domestic):

Vortek Instruments, LLC (2)
8475 W I 25 Ste 300, Longmont, CO 80504
Tel.: (303) 682-9999
Web Site: http://www.vortekinst.com
Sales Range: $10-24.9 Million
Emp.: 6
Precision Multivariable Flowmeters Mfr
N.A.I.C.S.: 334514
Jim Storer *(Owner)*

Azbil Philippines Corporation (1)
3rd floor Pilgrim Building 111 Aguirre Street,
Legaspi Village, Makati, 1229, Philippines
Tel.: (63) 28110916
Web Site: http://ph.azbil.com
Sales Range: $25-49.9 Million
Emp.: 50
Building Automation & Industrial Automation
Systems Mfr
N.A.I.C.S.: 238210
Takaaki Kawamura *(Mng Dir)*

**Azbil Production (Thailand) Co.,
Ltd.** (1)
700 /1013 Moo 9, T Mabpong A Phanthong,
Chon Buri, 20160, Thailand
Tel.: (66) 38109300
Industrial Equipment Mfr
N.A.I.C.S.: 333248

Azbil RoyalControls Co., Ltd. (1)
1-14-3 Kitaotsuka, Toshima-ku, Tokyo, 170-
0004, Japan
Tel.: (81) 3 3576 6951
Web Site: http://www.arc.azbil.com
Sales Range: $75-99.9 Million
Emp.: 129
Automation & Control Equipment Whslr
N.A.I.C.S.: 423830

Azbil Saudi Limited (1)
PO Box 68683, Dammam 2nd Industrial
City, Dammam, 31537, Saudi Arabia
Tel.: (966) 920011091
Industrial Equipment Mfr
N.A.I.C.S.: 333248

Azbil Singapore Pte. Ltd. (1)
No 2 International Business Park The Strat-
egy Tower 1 04-12, Singapore, 609930,
Singapore
Tel.: (65) 67785966
Web Site: http://www.sg.azbil.com
Sales Range: $25-49.9 Million
Emp.: 43
Building Automation & Industrial Automation
Systems Mfr
N.A.I.C.S.: 238210

Azbil Taishin Co., Ltd. (1)
200-7 Nakano, Nakano, 383-0013, Nagano,
Japan
Tel.: (81) 269263320
Web Site: http://www.ats.azbil.com
Electric Device Mfr
N.A.I.C.S.: 334419

Azbil Taiwan Co., Ltd. (1)
9th Floor No 44 Section 2 Zhongshan North
Road, Zhongshan District, Taipei, Taiwan
Tel.: (886) 225216800
Web Site: http://www.tw.azbil.com
Industrial Equipment Mfr
N.A.I.C.S.: 333248

Azbil Telstar, S.L.U. (1)
Av/ Font i Sague 55, Orbital 40, 8227, Ter-
rassa, Spain (100%)
Tel.: (34) 937361600
Web Site: https://www.etelstar.com
Sales Range: $125-149.9 Million
Emp.: 900
Life Science & Industrial Pumps, Equipment
& Instrument Designer & Mfr
N.A.I.C.S.: 333912
Jordi Puig *(CEO)*

Subsidiary (Domestic):

Telstar Industrial, S.L. (2)
Josep Tapiolas 120, 8226, Terrassa, Spain
Tel.: (34) 937361600
Web Site: http://www.telstar-vacuum.com
Industrial Pumps & Equipment Designer &
Mfr
N.A.I.C.S.: 333912

Telstar Instrumat, S.L. (2)
Av Font i Sague 55 Parc Cientific i Tecno-
logic, Orbital 40, Terrassa, 8227, Spain
Tel.: (34) 935 442 320
Web Site: http://www.telstar-instrumat.com
Industrial & Scientific Instrument Mfr
N.A.I.C.S.: 334516

Division (Domestic):

Telstar Life Science Solutions (2)
Av Font i Sague 55 Parc Cientific i Tecno-
logic, Orbital 40, Terrassa, 8227, Spain
Tel.: (34) 937 361 600
Web Site: http://www.telstar-
lifesciences.com
Emp.: 400
Medical, Pharmaceutical & Laboratory
Pumps & Equipment Mfr
N.A.I.C.S.: 334510
Jordi Puig *(Mng Dir)*

Azbil Trading Co., Ltd. (1)
1-14-3 Kita-Otsuka Otsuka Asami Building,
Toshima-ku, Tokyo, 170-8421, Japan
Tel.: (81) 3 5961 2140

Web Site: http://www.as.azbil.com
Sales Range: $75-99.9 Million
Emp.: 354
Automation & Control Equipment Distr
N.A.I.C.S.: 423830
Keiichi Fuwa *(Chm)*

Azbil Vietnam Co., Ltd. (1)
2nd Floor 17T2 Hapulico Complex No 1
Nguyen Huy Tuong Street, Thanh Xuan
Trung Ward Thanh Xuan District, Hanoi,
Vietnam
Tel.: (84) 2473012224
Web Site: http://www.vn.azbil.com
Emp.: 80
Industrial Equipment Mfr
N.A.I.C.S.: 333248
Yusaku Michinobu *(Mng Dir)*

**Azbil Yamatake Friendly Co.,
Ltd.** (1)
1-12-2 Kawana Fujisawa Techno Center,
Fujisawa, 251-8522, Kanagawa, Japan
Tel.: (81) 466202108
Web Site: http://www.ayf.azbil.com
Courier Service
N.A.I.C.S.: 492110

Japan Facility Solutions, Inc. (1)
17th floor Shin-Osaki Kogyo Building 1-6-4
Osaki, Shinagawa-ku, Tokyo, 141-0032,
Japan (10%)
Tel.: (81) 363712500
Web Site: http://www.j-facility.com
Sales Range: $25-49.9 Million
Emp.: 200
Facilities Environmental Management Con-
sulting Services
N.A.I.C.S.: 541620

P.T. Azbil Berca Indonesia (1)
Jalan Cikini Raya No 95 RT 10/RW 4 CCM
Building 3rd & 5th Floors, Jakarta Pusat,
10330, Indonesia
Tel.: (62) 212305538
Web Site: http://www.berca.azbil.com
Sales Range: $25-49.9 Million
Emp.: 249
Building Automation & Industrial Automation
Services
N.A.I.C.S.: 238210
Kiyoshi Kurata *(Pres)*

**Shanghai Azbil Automation Co.,
Ltd.** (1)
Room 803 Building B2 No 700 Yishan
Road, Xuhui District, Shanghai, 200030,
China
Tel.: (86) 2168732581
Web Site: http://sacn.cn.azbil.com
Building Automation & Industrial Automation
System Designing & Maintenance Services
N.A.I.C.S.: 238210

TACO Co., Ltd. (1)
9-27-9 Takashimadaira, Itabashi-ku, Tokyo,
175-0082, Japan (100%)
Tel.: (81) 3 3936 2311
Web Site: http://www.azbil.com
Emp.: 150
Fluid Control Equipment Designer & Mfr
N.A.I.C.S.: 333996
Hirano Masashi *(Pres)*

**Yamatake Automation Products
(Shanghai) Co., Ltd.** (1)
8th Floor Building B2 No 700 Yishan Road,
Xuhui District, Shanghai, 200235, China
Tel.: (86) 2150905580
Web Site: http://www.yas-yamatake.com
Automobile & Industrial Control Products
Whslr
N.A.I.C.S.: 423610

**Yamatake Engineering (M) Sdn.
Bhd.** (1)
Lot 19 08 Level 19 Tower 2 Faber Towers
Jalan Desa Bahagia Taman Desa, 58100,
Kuala Lumpur, Malaysia
Tel.: (60) 379880106
Construction Materials Mfr
N.A.I.C.S.: 333120

**Yamatake Environmental Control
Technology (Beijing) Co., Ltd.** (1)
Rm No 706 Liangziyinzuo Bldg 23 Zhichun
Rd, Haidian Dist, Beijing, 100191, China
Tel.: (86) 1082358248
Web Site: http://www.yeco-yamatake.com

Azbil Corporation—(Continued)

Sales Range: $25-49.9 Million
Emp.: 10
Building Automation Industrial Automation
System Mfr
N.A.I.C.S.: 238210

AZEARTH CORPORATION

4-13-7 Kuramae, Taito-ku, Tokyo,
111-8623, Japan
Tel.: (81) 338651311
Web Site: https://www.azearth.co.jp
Year Founded: 1947
3161—(TKS)
Rev.: $54,479,620
Assets: $56,264,320
Liabilities: $11,818,680
Net Worth: $44,445,640
Earnings: $1,236,070
Emp.: 211
Fiscal Year-end: 04/30/24
Textile & Piece Goods Products
Wholesale Trader
N.A.I.C.S.: 424310
Hiroo Suzuki (Chm)

Subsidiaries:

DALIAN FREE TRADE ZONE
NICHIURA TRADING CO., LTD. (1)
No 10 Wanbao Street Dalian E&T Develop-
ment Zone, Dalian, China
Tel.: (86) 41187643972
Protective Clothing & Equipment Mfr & Distr
N.A.I.C.S.: 339113

NICHIURA TRADING (SHANGHAI)
CO., LTD. (1)
Room 1405 Everbright Convention & Exhi-
bition Center, E Building No 82 Caobao
Road Xuhui, Shanghai, China
Tel.: (86) 2154885999
Protective Clothing & Equipment Mfr & Distr
N.A.I.C.S.: 339113

AZENN SA

23 rue du Champ Morin, 3560, Mon-
tauban, France
Tel.: (33) 806800021　　　　　　FR
Web Site: http://www.azenn.com
Year Founded: 2000
Cables & Networking Products Mfr &
Distr
N.A.I.C.S.: 335921
Philippe Berthelot (Pres)

AZERION GROUP N.V.

Boeing Avenue 30, 1119 PE,
Schiphol-Rijk, Netherlands
Tel.: (31) 207602040
Web Site: https://www.azerion.com
Year Founded: 2014
AZRN—(EUR)
Rev.: $568,495,419
Assets: $719,726,239
Liabilities: $598,741,583
Net Worth: $120,984,656
Earnings: $27,707,252
Emp.: 1,200
Fiscal Year-end: 12/31/23
Software Development Services
N.A.I.C.S.: 541511

Subsidiaries:

AdPlay S.r.l. (1)
Via Procaccini 33, 20154, Milan, Italy
Tel.: (39) 0236752408
Web Site: https://www.adplay.it
Digital Transformation Services
N.A.I.C.S.: 518210

Azerion Portugal Lda. (1)
Edificio LACS Rocha Conde de Obidos S 1
5, 1350-352, Lisbon, Portugal
Tel.: (351) 210539176
Digital Entertainment Services
N.A.I.C.S.: 541810

Delta Projects GmbH (1)
Sonnenstrasse 26b, Feldkirchen b, 85622,
Munich, Germany

Tel.: (49) 8942017360
Web Site: https://deltaprojects.de
Information Technology Services
N.A.I.C.S.: 541512

KeyGames Network B.V. (1)
Beechavenue 182, 1119PX, Schiphol-Rijk,
Netherlands
Tel.: (31) 207602040
Digital Entertainment Services
N.A.I.C.S.: 541810

Playcade Interactive GmbH (1)
Bleichbrucke 10, 20354, Hamburg, Ger-
many
Tel.: (49) 40609437230
Web Site: https://www.playcade.de
Digital Gaming & Entertainment Services
N.A.I.C.S.: 541810

Sulake Oy (1)
Dagmarinkatu 6, 00100, Helsinki, Finland
Tel.: (358) 106567000
Web Site: https://www.sulake.com
Online Game Entertainment Services
N.A.I.C.S.: 713290

Vlyby Digital GmbH (1)
Schwanthalerstr 22, 80336, Munich, Ger-
many
Tel.: (49) 89200006780
Web Site: https://www.vlyby.com
Programmatic Video Advertising Services
N.A.I.C.S.: 541810

Voidu B.V. (1)
Boeing Avenue 30, 1119 PE, Schiphol-Rijk,
Netherlands
Tel.: (31) 207602040
Web Site: https://www.voidu.com
Digital Entertainment Services
N.A.I.C.S.: 541810

WHOW Games GmbH (1)
Bleichbrucke 10, 20354, Hamburg, Ger-
many
Tel.: (49) 4060943720
Web Site: https://www.whow.net
Online Game Distr
N.A.I.C.S.: 423920

Woozworld Inc. (1)
55 ave Mont-Royal Ouest bureau 720,
Montreal, H2T 2S6, QC, Canada
Tel.: (514) 281-8999
Web Site: https://www.woozworld.com
Virtual Gaming Network Services
N.A.I.C.S.: 518210

sMeets Communications GmbH (1)
Engeldamm 62-64b, D-10179, Berlin, Ger-
many
Tel.: (49) 3023257936
Web Site: https://www.smeet.com
3D Social Chat Game Operator
N.A.I.C.S.: 713290

AZERKOSMOS OJSC

72 Uzeyir Hajibeyli Street, AZ1000,
Baku, Azerbaijan
Tel.: (994) 123100055
Web Site: http://www.azercosmos.az
Satellite Telecommunication Services
N.A.I.C.S.: 517410
Dunay Badirkhanov (Vice Chm)

AZEUS SYSTEMS HOLDINGS LTD.

33F Cambridge House Taikoo Place
979 Kings Road, North Point, China
(Hong Kong)
Tel.: (852) 28933673
Web Site: https://www.azeus.com
BBW—(SES)
Rev.: $28,073,529
Assets: $33,475,082
Liabilities: $13,523,553
Net Worth: $19,951,529
Earnings: $6,249,081
Fiscal Year-end: 03/31/22
Software Programming Services
N.A.I.C.S.: 513210
Wai Ming Yap (Sec)

Subsidiaries:

Azeus Pty Ltd (1)

Level 46 Tower One - International Towers
Sydney, 100 Barangaroo Avenue, Baranga-
roo, 2000, NSW, Australia
Tel.: (61) 431395477
Software Development Services
N.A.I.C.S.: 513210

Azeus Systems (Dalian) Co.,
Ltd. (1)
Room 502-D Building 17 No 267 Wuvi
Road, Shahekou District, Dalian, Liaoning,
China
Tel.: (86) 41184756901
Software Development Services
N.A.I.C.S.: 513210

Azeus Systems Limited (1)
22/F Olympia Plaza 255 Kings Road, North
Point, China (Hong Kong)
Tel.: (852) 28933673
Software Development Services
N.A.I.C.S.: 513210

Azeus UK Limited (1)
2 017 Azeus Convene WeWork 3 Water-
house Square 138-142 Holborn, London,
EC1N 2SW, United Kingdom
Tel.: (44) 2037553591
Web Site: https://uk.azeus.com
Software Development Services
N.A.I.C.S.: 513210

Convene India Private Limited (1)
8th Floor B Tower Logix Cyber Park C-28
C-29 C Block, Industrial Area Sector-62
Gautam Buddha Nagar, Noida, 201 301,
UP, India
Tel.: (91) 9015599399
Information Technology Services
N.A.I.C.S.: 541511

Convene Pty Ltd (1)
Level 46 Tower One-International Towers
Sydney 100 Barangaroo Avenue, Baranga-
roo, 2000, NSW, Australia
Tel.: (61) 421072206
Information Technology Services
N.A.I.C.S.: 541511

Convene SG Pte Ltd (1)
600 North Bridge Road 23-01 Parkview
Square, Singapore, 188778, Singapore
Tel.: (65) 68567330
Information Technology Services
N.A.I.C.S.: 541511

Convene UK Limited (1)
Munro House Portsmouth Road, Surrey,
Cobham, KT11 1PP, United Kingdom
Tel.: (44) 2080045940
Software Development Services
N.A.I.C.S.: 513210

AZEVEDO & TRAVASSOS S.A.

Rua Vicente Antonio de Oliveira 1
050, Pirituba, 02955-080, Sao Paulo,
02955-080, SP, Brazil
Tel.: (55) 1139737787
Web Site:
　　https://www.azevedotravassos.com
Year Founded: 1922
AZEV4—(BRAZ)
Rev.: $76,834,341
Assets: $129,507,335
Liabilities: $72,819,040
Net Worth: $56,688,295
Earnings: ($9,081,890)
Fiscal Year-end: 12/31/23
Civil Engineering Services
N.A.I.C.S.: 541330
Abelardo Gomes Parente Jr. (Dir-IR)

AZGARD NINE LIMITED

Ismail Aiwan-e-Science Shahrah-e-
Roomi, Lahore, 54600, Pakistan
Tel.: (92) 4235761794
Web Site: https://www.azgard9.com
ANL—(KAR)
Rev.: $105,006,749
Assets: $142,714,036
Liabilities: $135,759,009
Net Worth: $6,955,027
Earnings: ($2,418,479)
Emp.: 5,605
Fiscal Year-end: 06/30/20

Denim & Yarn Mfr
N.A.I.C.S.: 313110
Ahmed H. Shaikh (CEO)

Subsidiaries:

Hazara Phosphate Fertilizers (Pri-
vate) Limited (1)
Hattar Rd, Haripur, Islamabad, 22620, Paki-
stan
Tel.: (92) 995616124
Sales Range: $25-49.9 Million
Emp.: 100
Phosphate Mfr
N.A.I.C.S.: 325312

Montebello SRL (1)
Martiri Delle Foibe No 9, Montebello Vicen-
tino, Lonigo, VI 36045, Italy
Tel.: (39) 0444449422
Web Site: http://www.montebellodenim.com
Sales Range: $25-49.9 Million
Emp.: 30
Textile & Apparel Products & Accessories
Mfr
N.A.I.C.S.: 313310

AZIA AVTO JSC

101/1 Bazhov St, Oskemen, 070000,
Kazakhstan
Tel.: (7) 232772440
Web Site: http://www.aziaavto.kz
Year Founded: 2002
ASAV—(KAZ)
Rev.: $47,465,165
Assets: $171,957,806
Liabilities: $155,856,093
Net Worth: $16,101,714
Earnings: $3,093,338
Fiscal Year-end: 12/31/19
Motor Car Parts Mfr
N.A.I.C.S.: 336390
Erik Sagymbaev (Gen Dir)

AZIENDA BRESCIANA PETROLI NOCIVELLI S.P.A.

Via Padana Superiore 67, 25045,
Castegnato, BS, Italy
Tel.: (39) 0302142011
Web Site:
　　https://www.abpnocivelli.com
Year Founded: 1963
ABP—(EUR)
Construction Engineering Services
N.A.I.C.S.: 541330
Beatrice Bonfadini (Pres)

AZIENDA ELETTRICA TICINESE

Casella Postale 1041, 6501, Bellin-
zona, Switzerland
Tel.: (41) 91 822 27 11
Web Site: http://www.aet.ch
Electric Power Distribution
N.A.I.C.S.: 221122
Giovanni Leonardi (Pres)

Subsidiaries:

AET Italia SpA (1)
Via Adele Martignoni 25, Milan, 20124, Italy
Tel.: (39) 0266823374
Web Site: http://www.aetitalia.net
Eletric Power Generation Services
N.A.I.C.S.: 221111

Calore SA (1)
Piazza Grande 5, 6601, Locarno, Switzer-
land
Tel.: (41) 917569200
Web Site: http://www.calore.ch
Eletric Power Generation Services
N.A.I.C.S.: 221111
Vinicio Curti (CEO)

Lucendro SA (1)
Impianto Lucendro, 6780, Airolo,
Switzerland (100%)
Tel.: (41) 918222711
Hydroelectric Power Generation
N.A.I.C.S.: 221111
Roberto Pronini (Pres)

Parco eolico del San Gottardo SA **(1)**
Casella Postale 1041, 6501, Bellinzona, Switzerland
Tel.: (41) 918222711
Wind Power Structure Installation Services
N.A.I.C.S.: 333611

Societa Elettrica Sopracenerina SA **(1)**
Via Gen Guisan 10, 6710, Biasca, Switzerland
Tel.: (41) 917569191
Web Site: http://www.ses.ch
Eletric Power Generation Services
N.A.I.C.S.: 221111

AZIMUT EXPLORATION INC.
110 De La Barre Street Suite 224, Longueuil, J4K 1A3, QC, Canada
Tel.: (450) 646-3015   QC
Web Site: https://www.azimut-exploration.com
AZM—(TSXV)
Rev.: $104,108
Assets: $34,817,548
Liabilities: $2,341,449
Net Worth: $32,476,099
Earnings: $1,365,901
Fiscal Year-end: 08/31/23
Mineral Exploration Services
N.A.I.C.S.: 213115
Jean-Marc Lulin *(Pres & CEO)*

AZIMUT HOLDING SPA
Via Cusani 4, 20121, Milan, Italy
Tel.: (39) 0288981   IT
Web Site: https://www.azimut-group.com
Year Founded: 1989
HDB—(MUN)
Assets: $10,135,979,568
Liabilities: $8,635,409,688
Net Worth: $1,500,569,880
Earnings: $429,006,894
Emp.: 1,476
Fiscal Year-end: 12/31/22
Asset Management Services
N.A.I.C.S.: 523940
Pietro Giuliani *(Chm)*

Subsidiaries:

AZ Investment Management **(1)**
Zhong Rong Jasper Tower 8 Yin Cheng Middle Road-Suite 706, Lujiazui Pudong, Shanghai, China
Tel.: (86) 21 3813 9258
Web Site: http://www.anzhongim.com
Emp.: 18
Financial Advisory & Investment Services
N.A.I.C.S.: 523940

AZ Life Ltd **(1)**
Block 3-The Oval Shelbourne Road, Dublin, Ireland
Tel.: (353) 1 6602292
Asset Management Services
N.A.I.C.S.: 523940
Marco Malcontenti *(Chm)*

AZ Swiss S.a. **(1)**
Via Luciano Zuccoli 19, 6900, Paradiso, Switzerland
Tel.: (41) 91 985 26 26
Asset Management Services
N.A.I.C.S.: 523940

Azimut (DIFC) Limited **(1)**
Office Unit 45 Floor 16 Central Park Towers, PO Box 506944, Dubai International Financial Centre, Dubai, United Arab Emirates
Tel.: (971) 47038111
Asset Management Services
N.A.I.C.S.: 541611

Azimut (ME) Limited **(1)**
Office Unit 2 Floor 7 Al Khatem Tower ADGM Square Al Maryah Island, PO Box 764630, Abu Dhabi, United Arab Emirates
Tel.: (971) 26740063
Asset Management Services
N.A.I.C.S.: 541611

Azimut Consulenza Sim Spa **(1)**
VI Regina Pacis 16, 41049, Sassuolo, Italy
Tel.: (39) 0536 803513
Asset Management Services
N.A.I.C.S.: 523940
Pietro Giuliani *(Chm)*

Azimut Egypt Asset Management S.A.E. **(1)**
Smart Village Building B 16, PO Box 12577, Giza, Egypt
Tel.: (20) 235353535
Web Site: https://azimut.eg
Asset Management Services
N.A.I.C.S.: 541611

Azimut Financial Insurance S.p.A. **(1)**
Via Cusani 4, 20121, Milan, Italy
Tel.: (39) 0288981
Insurance Services
N.A.I.C.S.: 524210

Azimut Investments S.A. **(1)**
2A Rue Eugene Ruppert, 2453, Luxembourg, 2163, Luxembourg
Tel.: (352) 2663811
Web Site: https://www.azimutinvestments.com
Asset Management Services
N.A.I.C.S.: 523940
Pietro Giuliani *(Chm)*

Azimut Investments SA **(1)**
2A Rue Eugene Ruppert, 2453, Luxembourg, Luxembourg
Tel.: (352) 2663811
Web Site: https://www.azimutinvestments.com
Asset Management Services
N.A.I.C.S.: 523940

Azimut Investments SA AGF **(1)**
Espoz 3150 Of 101 Vitacura, 7630266, Santiago, Chile
Tel.: (56) 232242385
Investment Management Service
N.A.I.C.S.: 525910

Azimut Life DAC **(1)**
1st Floor Block C One Park Place Hatch Street Upper, Dublin, D02 E762, Ireland
Tel.: (353) 187268167
Web Site: https://www.azimutlife.ie
Financial Services
N.A.I.C.S.: 524113

Azimut Portfoy Yonetimi A.S. **(1)**
Buyukdere Cad Kempinski Residence Astoria B Kule No127 K9 Esentepe, Sisli, Istanbul, Turkiye
Tel.: (90) 2122446200
Web Site: https://azimutportfoy.com
Asset Management Services
N.A.I.C.S.: 541611

Blackwood Advisory Pty. Ltd. **(1)**
Millson Business Centre 43 Williamson Street, Bendigo, 3550, VIC, Australia
Tel.: (61) 1300609590
Web Site: https://www.blackwoodadvisory.au
Investment Management Service
N.A.I.C.S.: 541611

Catalina Consultants Pty. Ltd. **(1)**
Suite 1 Level 7 6-10 O'Connell Street, Sydney, 2000, NSW, Australia
Tel.: (61) 292515638
Web Site: https://catalinaconsultants.com.au
Human Resource Outsourcing Services
N.A.I.C.S.: 561311

Certe Wealth Protection Pty. Ltd. **(1)**
Level 7 72 Pitt Street, Sydney, 2000, NSW, Australia
Tel.: (61) 291325900
Web Site: https://www.certe.com.au
Financial Planning Services
N.A.I.C.S.: 541611

Compagnie de Gestion Privee Monegasque SAM **(51%)**
8 Boulevard des, 98000, Monte Carlo, Monaco
Tel.: (377) 97 97 41 00
Emp.: 30
Asset Management Services
N.A.I.C.S.: 523940

Cranage Financial Group Pty. Ltd. **(1)**
Level 1 4 Riverside Quay, Southbank, 3006, VIC, Australia
Tel.: (61) 390976000
Web Site: https://www.cranagegroup.com.au
Financial Planning Services
N.A.I.C.S.: 541611

Dunsford Finance Planning Pty. Ltd. **(1)**
41 Lathams Road, Carrum Downs, 3201, VIC, Australia
Tel.: (61) 397885788
Web Site: https://www.dunsfordfp.com.au
Financial Planning Services
N.A.I.C.S.: 541611

Dunsford Financial Planning Pty. Ltd. **(1)**
41 Lathams Road, Carrum Downs, 3201, VIC, Australia
Tel.: (61) 397885788
Web Site: https://www.dunsfordfp.com.au
Financial Planning Services
N.A.I.C.S.: 541611

Electa Ventures S.R.L. **(1)**
Via Brera 16, 24121, Milan, Italy
Tel.: (39) 027214231
Web Site: https://www.groupelecta.com
Investment Management Service
N.A.I.C.S.: 525910

Eureka Financial Group Pty. Ltd. **(1)**
Aurora Place Level 10 88 Phillip Street, Sydney, 2000, NSW, Australia
Tel.: (61) 294602288
Web Site: https://eurekawhittakermacnaught.com.au
Emp.: 20
Investment Management Service
N.A.I.C.S.: 541611

Foster Raffan Iplan Pty. Ltd. **(1)**
Level 6/8 West St, North Sydney, 2060, NSW, Australia
Tel.: (61) 283505850
Web Site: https://fosterraffaniplan.com.au
Financial Planning Services
N.A.I.C.S.: 541611

Harvest WealthPty. Ltd. **(1)**
13 Flinders Terrace, PO Box 28, Port Augusta, 5700, SA, Australia
Tel.: (61) 886321900
Web Site: https://harvestwealthsa.com.au
Financial Advice Services
N.A.I.C.S.: 541611

Hurwitz Geller Pty. Ltd. **(1)**
Level 10 Aurora Place 88 Phillip Street, Sydney, 2000, NSW, Australia
Tel.: (61) 292623800
Web Site: https://hgpl.com.au
Accounting Services
N.A.I.C.S.: 541219

Katarsis Capital Advisors Sa **(1)**
Via Carlo Frasca 5, 6900, Lugano, Switzerland
Tel.: (41) 912613850
Web Site: http://www.katarsiscapital.ch
Financial Advisory Services
N.A.I.C.S.: 523940

Kellaway Cridland Pty. Ltd. **(1)**
Level 12 95 Pitt Street, Australia Square Plaza Building, Sydney, 2000, NSW, Australia
Tel.: (61) 292338800
Web Site: https://www.kellcrid.com.au
Accounting Services
N.A.I.C.S.: 541219

Kingsbridge Private Pty. Ltd. **(1)**
Level 10 88 Phillip Street, Sydney, 2000, NSW, Australia
Tel.: (61) 292990599
Web Site: https://kingsbridgeprivate.com
Financial Planning Services
N.A.I.C.S.: 541611

Matthews Steer Pty. Ltd. **(1)**
Essendon Fields House Level 2 7 English Street, Essendon Fields, 3041, VIC, Australia
Tel.: (61) 393256300
Web Site: https://www.matthewssteer.com.au
Emp.: 60
Financial Advice Services
N.A.I.C.S.: 541611

Menico Tuck Parrish Financial Services Pty. Ltd. **(1)**
192 Mulgrave Road, Westcourt, 4870, QLD, Australia
Tel.: (61) 740447888
Web Site: https://mtpfinancial.com.au
Financial Planning Services
N.A.I.C.S.: 541611

Nestworth Financial Strategists Pty. Ltd. **(1)**
Level 4 Transport House 230 Brunswick Street, Fortitude Valley, 4006, QLD, Australia
Tel.: (61) 1800678984
Web Site: https://nestworth.com.au
Financial Advice Services
N.A.I.C.S.: 541611

On-Track Financial Solutions Pty. Ltd. **(1)**
Suite 40 11 Preston Street, Como, 6152, WA, Australia
Tel.: (61) 893671611
Web Site: https://www.on-trackfinancial.com
Financial Planning Services
N.A.I.C.S.: 541611

People & Partners Pty. Ltd. **(1)**
Aurora Place Level 10 88 Phillip Street, Sydney, 2000, NSW, Australia
Tel.: (61) 290931311
Web Site: https://www.peopleandpartners.com.au
Financial Planning Services
N.A.I.C.S.: 541611

People & Partners Wealth Management Pty. Ltd. **(1)**
Aurora Place Level 10 88 Phillip Street, Sydney, 2000, NSW, Australia
Tel.: (61) 290931311
Web Site: https://www.peopleandpartners.com.au
Financial Advice Services
N.A.I.C.S.: 541611

Pride Advice Pty. Ltd. **(1)**
Ground Floor 420 King William St, Adelaide, 5000, SA, Australia
Tel.: (61) 881688450
Web Site: https://prideadvice.com.au
Investment Management Service
N.A.I.C.S.: 541611

SCM Financial Group Pty. Ltd. **(1)**
L2 917 Riversdale Road, Surry Hills, 3127, VIC, Australia
Tel.: (61) 398489811
Web Site: https://scmfg.com.au
Financial Planning Services
N.A.I.C.S.: 541611

Sage Business Group Pty. Ltd. **(1)**
43 Gap Road, Sunbury, 3429, VIC, Australia
Tel.: (61) 397447144
Web Site: https://www.sagegroup.com.au
Financial Advice Services
N.A.I.C.S.: 541611

Sanctuary Wealth Group LLC **(1)**
3815 River Crossing Pkwy Ste 200, Indianapolis, IN 46240
Tel.: (317) 975-7729
Web Site: https://sanctuarywealth.com
Financial Advice Services
N.A.I.C.S.: 541611

Sterling Planners Pty. Ltd. **(1)**
Level 9 75 Miller Street, North Sydney, 2060, NSW, Australia
Tel.: (61) 289049793
Web Site: https://www.sterlingplanners.com.au
Financial Advice Services
N.A.I.C.S.: 541611

Tempus Wealth Group Pty. Ltd. **(1)**
Level 1 550 Princes Highway, Kirrawee, 2232, NSW, Australia
Tel.: (61) 291953770
Web Site: https://www.tempuswealth.com.au
Financial Advice Services
N.A.I.C.S.: 541611

Wealthmed Australia Pty. Ltd. **(1)**
Ground Floor 11 Eccles Blvd Cnr Florey Blvd & Shine Court, Birtinya, 4575, QLD, Australia

Azimut Holding SpA—(Continued)
Tel.: (61) 1300887137
Web Site: https://www.wealthmed.com.au
Emp.: 28
Financial Planning Services
N.A.I.C.S.: 541611

Wealthwise Pty. Ltd. (1)
Suite 4 Level 2 Building C The Garden Office Park, 355 Scarborough Beach Road, Osborne Park, 6017, WA, Australia
Tel.: (61) 893806333
Web Site: https://www.wealthwise.com.au
Financial Advice Services
N.A.I.C.S.: 541611

AZIMUT-BENETTI S.P.A.
Via M Coppino 104, 55049, Viareggio, Italy
Tel.: (39) 05843821   IT
Web Site: http://www.azimutbenetti.it
Yacht Builder & Whslr
N.A.I.C.S.: 336611
Paolo Vitelli *(Chm & CEO)*

Subsidiaries:

Azimut Benetti Services USA, Inc. (1)
1883 W State Rd 84 Ste 103, Fort Lauderdale, FL 33315-2232
Tel.: (954) 727-0584
Yacht Whslr
N.A.I.C.S.: 423910
Maria Baget *(Mgr)*

AZINCOURT ENERGY CORP.
Suite 1430 800 West Pender Street, Vancouver, V6C 2V6, BC, Canada
Tel.: (604) 638-8063   BC
Web Site:
  http://www.azincourturanium.com
Year Founded: 2011
AZURF—(OTCQB)
Rev.: $536,149
Assets: $11,340,477
Liabilities: $141,862
Net Worth: $11,198,615
Earnings: ($7,548,606)
Fiscal Year-end: 09/30/22
Metal Mining
N.A.I.C.S.: 212290
Alex Klenman *(Pres & CEO)*

AZINCOURT ENERGY CORP.
Suite 1430-800 West Pender Street, Vancouver, V6C 2V6, BC, Canada
Tel.: (604) 638-8063
Web Site:
  https://www.azincourtenergy.com
A0U2—(BER)
Rev.: $92,099
Assets: $11,622,098
Liabilities: $1,001,217
Net Worth: $10,620,881
Earnings: ($2,631,015)
Fiscal Year-end: 09/30/21
Oil & Gas Exploration Services
N.A.I.C.S.: 213112
C. Trevor Perkins *(VP)*

AZION CORP.
5F No 30 Beiping East Road, Zhongzheng District, Taipei, Taiwan
Tel.: (886) 223563996
Web Site: https://www.azion.com.tw
6148—(TPE)
Rev.: $15,773,755
Assets: $30,529,375
Liabilities: $13,766,063
Net Worth: $16,763,312
Earnings: $1,184,629
Emp.: 150
Fiscal Year-end: 12/31/22
Information Technology Services
N.A.I.C.S.: 541512
Wen-To Liao *(Chm & Pres)*

Subsidiaries:

Jetit Corporation (1)
5th Floor No 30 Beiping East Road, Zhongzheng District, New Taipei City, Taiwan
Tel.: (886) 223563595
Web Site: https://www.jetit.com.tw
Software Development Services
N.A.I.C.S.: 541511

AZIZ PIPES LIMITED
Aziz Bhaban 93 Motijheel Commercial Area 3rd Floor, Dhaka, 1000, Bangladesh
Tel.: (880) 29562691
Web Site: https://www.azizpipes.com
Year Founded: 1981
AZIZPIPES—(DHA)
Rev.: $540,092
Assets: $3,425,462
Liabilities: $4,714,340
Net Worth: ($1,288,878)
Earnings: ($334,872)
Emp.: 25
Fiscal Year-end: 06/30/23
PVC Pipe Mfr
N.A.I.C.S.: 326122
Mohammed Nurul Absar *(Mng Dir & CFO)*

AZKOYEN S.A
Avda San Silvestre s/n, 31350, Peralta, Navarra, Spain
Tel.: (34) 948709709
Web Site: https://www.azkoyen.com
Year Founded: 1945
AZK—(MAD)
Rev.: $212,461,640
Assets: $237,212,717
Liabilities: $109,104,758
Net Worth: $128,107,959
Earnings: $19,313,390
Emp.: 887
Fiscal Year-end: 12/31/23
Payment Systems & Vending Machines Technological Solutions Seller & Mfr
N.A.I.C.S.: 333310

Subsidiaries:

Azkoyen Comercial Deutschland GmbH (1)
Am Turm 86, 53721, Siegburg, 53721, Nordrhein-Westfalen, Germany
Tel.: (49) 224159570
Web Site: http://www.azkoyen.com
Sales Range: $25-49.9 Million
Emp.: 4
Vending Machine Mfr
N.A.I.C.S.: 333310

Azkoyen Industrial, S.A. (1)
Avda San Silvestre s/n, 31350, Peralta, Navvara, Spain
Tel.: (34) 948709709
Web Site: http://industrial.azkoyen.com
Sales Range: $50-74.9 Million
Emp.: 150
Vending Machine Mfr
N.A.I.C.S.: 333310

Azkoyen Medios de Pago, S.A. (1)
Av San Silvestre S N, 31350, Peralta, Navarra, Spain
Tel.: (34) 948709709
Web Site:
  http://www.azkoyenmediosdepago.com
Sales Range: $50-74.9 Million
Emp.: 108
Electric Device Mfr
N.A.I.C.S.: 334419
Juan Manuel Prieto *(Mgr-Sls)*

Subsidiary (Domestic):

Coges Espana Medios de Pago, S.L. (2)
C/ Isla de Hierro 7 Modulo 3 2, 28703, San Sebastian de los Reyes, Madrid, Spain
Tel.: (34) 948709709
Web Site: http://www.coges.es
Vending Machine Mfr

N.A.I.C.S.: 333310

Subsidiary (Non-US):

Coges S.p.A. (2)
Via Giacomo Leopardi 23, 36030, Caldogno, VI, Italy
Tel.: (39) 0445502811
Web Site: https://www.coges.es
Sales Range: $25-49.9 Million
Emp.: 75
Electronic Payment Systems & Vending Machines Mfr
N.A.I.C.S.: 333310

Coges France, S.A.S. (1)
3 Avenue De La Foire Aux Vins Lot No 2, 68000, Colmar, France
Tel.: (33) 389277007
Cash Machines Mfr
N.A.I.C.S.: 333998

Impulsa Soluciones Tecnologicas, S.L. (1)
Paseo de La Habana 27 Piso 2 Izquierda, 28036, Madrid, Spain
Tel.: (34) 91 411 7326
Vending Machine Mfr
N.A.I.C.S.: 333310

primion Technology AG (1)
Steinbeisstr 2-5, 72510, Stetten am kalten Markt, Germany   (88.5%)
Tel.: (49) 75739520
Web Site: http://www.primion.de
Sales Range: $50-74.9 Million
Emp.: 250
Security, Time Recording & Access Control Systems & Services
N.A.I.C.S.: 561621
Jorge Pons Vorberg *(Mng Dir)*

AZMAYESH INDUSTRIAL FACTORIES COMPANY
Shariati Street Two-Way Above Ghalhak Bon Post Shareef, Tehran, Iran
Tel.: (98) 2122925910
Year Founded: 1959
Industrial Machinery & Equipment Mfr
N.A.I.C.S.: 333998
Asdoallah Amini *(Chm)*

AZN CAPITAL CORP.
Suite 3123 595 Burrard Street, Vancouver, V7X 1J1, BC, Canada
Tel.: (604) 609-6125
AZN.H—(TSXV)
Assets: $330,543
Liabilities: $8,434,660
Net Worth: ($8,104,117)
Earnings: ($27,985,369)
Fiscal Year-end: 12/31/20
Micro-Mobility Solutions
N.A.I.C.S.: 488999
Maxwell Smith *(CEO & Acting CFO)*

AZO GMBH & CO. KG
Rosenberger Str 28 Industriegebiet Ost, 74706, Osterburken, Germany
Tel.: (49) 6291920
Web Site: http://www.azo.com
Year Founded: 1949
Sales Range: $10-24.9 Million
Emp.: 1,062
Industrial Machinery Mfr
N.A.I.C.S.: 333310
Adolf Zimmermann *(Co-Founder)*

Subsidiaries:

AZO CONTROLS GmbH (1)
Rosenberger Str 28, 74706, Osterburken, Germany
Tel.: (49) 6291 92 60 00
Web Site: http://www.azo-controls.com
Emp.: 150
Industrial Machinery Mfr
N.A.I.C.S.: 333248
Dieter Herzig *(Founder & Mng Dir)*

AZO EURL (1)
9 rue de la Fontaine Grillee, La Haye-Fouassiere, 44690, Nantes, France
Tel.: (33) 49629192445

N.A.I.C.S.: 333310
Sales Range: $25-49.9 Million
Emp.: 20
Industrial Machinery Mfr
N.A.I.C.S.: 333248

AZO Ingredients Automation System (Tianjin) Co., Ltd. (1)
3-D-501 Ziyuan Road 13 Huayuan Hi-Tech Industry Park, 300384, Tianjin, China
Tel.: (86) 22 58627521
Industrial Machinery & Equipment Distr
N.A.I.C.S.: 423830

AZO LIQUIDS GmbH (1)
Gottlieb-Daimler-Strasse 4, 79395, Neuenburg am Rhein, Germany
Tel.: (49) 7631 9739 0
Web Site: http://www.azo-liquids.com
Emp.: 40
Industrial Machinery & Equipment Distr
N.A.I.C.S.: 423830
Patrick Weisser *(Mng Dir)*

AZO Ltd. (1)
410 137 Soi Ratchrada 22, Ratchradapisek Road, Samsennok Huay Kwang, 10310, Bangkok, Thailand
Tel.: (66) 25415192
Web Site: http://www.azo.com
Inorganic Dye & Pigment Mfr
N.A.I.C.S.: 325130

AZO N.V. (1)
Katwilgweg 15, Antwerp, 2050, Belgium
Tel.: (32) 32501600
Web Site: http://www.azo.be
Sales Range: $25-49.9 Million
Emp.: 80
Industrial Machinery Mfr
N.A.I.C.S.: 333248
Erik Kwanten *(Branch Mgr)*

AZO UK Ltd. (1)
11C Farady Court Centrum 100, Burton, DE14 2WX, United Kingdom
Tel.: (44) 870 606 0642
Industrial Equipment Distr
N.A.I.C.S.: 423830

AZO, Inc. (1)
4445 Malone Rd, Memphis, TN 38118-1070
Tel.: (901) 794-9480
Web Site: http://www.azo.com
Sales Range: $25-49.9 Million
Emp.: 30
Material Handling Machinery Mfr
N.A.I.C.S.: 333249
Chuck Kerwin *(Dir)*

HSH-Systeme Fur Prozess-IT GmbH (1)
Heiner-Fleischmann-Str 7, 74172, Neckarsulm, Germany
Tel.: (49) 713293420
Web Site: http://www.hsh-systeme.com
Sales Range: $50-74.9 Million
Emp.: 130
Measuring Displaying & Controlling & Industrial Process & Variables Instruments & Related Products Mfr
N.A.I.C.S.: 334513
Hendrick Langer *(Mgr-Sls)*

OOO AZO Rus (1)
Prospect Andropova 18 Building 6 6-17 Office, 115432, Moscow, Russia
Tel.: (7) 495 641 75 30
Web Site: http://www.azo.com.ru
Emp.: 4
Industrial Machinery & Equipment Distr
N.A.I.C.S.: 423830
Evgenia Ivanova *(Mgr-Svc)*

AZOOM CO., LTD.
211 Shinjuku Minds Tower 19F, Yoyogi Shibuya-ku, Tokyo, 151-0053, Japan
Tel.: (81) 353651235
Web Site: https://www.azoom.jp
3496—(TKS)
Rev.: $58,655,570
Assets: $28,239,470
Liabilities: $9,982,720
Net Worth: $18,256,750
Earnings: $6,225,020
Fiscal Year-end: 09/30/23
Real Estate Manangement Services
N.A.I.C.S.: 531390

Yoji Sugata *(Founder, Chm & Pres)*

**AZOREAN-AQUATIC TECH-
NOLOGIES SA**
Rua da Pranchinha N 92, 9500-331,
Ponta Delgada, Portugal
Tel.: (351) 210314000
Web Site: https://www.azorean.eu
Year Founded: 2011
MLAAT—(EUR)
Sales Range: Less than $1 Million
Marine Robotics System Mfr
N.A.I.C.S.: 336611
Vinod Karuvat *(Head-Hardware)*

**AZORIM INVESTMENT DEVEL-
OPMENT & CONSTRUCTION
CO., LTD.**
32 Arania Street, Tel Aviv, Israel
Tel.: (972) 35632632
Web Site: https://www.azorim.co.il
AZRM—(TAE)
Rev.: $406,189,799
Assets: $1,895,064,758
Liabilities: $1,324,118,504
Net Worth: $570,946,254
Earnings: $48,736,565
Fiscal Year-end: 12/31/23
Residential Property Managers
N.A.I.C.S.: 531311
Eran Ezra Anavim *(VP-Fin)*

AZPECT PHOTONICS AB
Aminogatan 34, Molndal, 431 53,
Sweden
Tel.: (46) 855442480
Web Site: http://www.azpect.com
Year Founded: 1994
Sales Range: $10-24.9 Million
Emp.: 13
Measurement Instrument Mfr
N.A.I.C.S.: 334516

AZPLANNING CO., LTD.
2-12-20 Totsuka, Kawaguchi, 333-
0811, Japan
Tel.: (81) 482981720
Web Site: https://www.azplan.co.jp
Year Founded: 1989
3490—(TKS)
Rev.: $81,577,540
Assets: $70,410,790
Liabilities: $52,721,240
Net Worth: $17,689,550
Earnings: $4,395,800
Fiscal Year-end: 02/29/24
Real Estate Development Services
N.A.I.C.S.: 531311
Toshihito Matsumoto *(Chm & Pres)*

AZRIELI GROUP LTD.
Azrieli Center 1, Tel Aviv, 67021, Is-
rael
Tel.: (972) 36081126   II
Web Site:
     https://www.azrieligroup.com
Year Founded: 1983
AZRG—(TAE)
Rev.: $1,419,256,781
Assets: $14,939,079,750
Liabilities: $8,427,683,250
Net Worth: $6,511,396,500
Earnings: $612,791,812
Emp.: 435
Fiscal Year-end: 12/31/23
Offices of Other Holding Companies
N.A.I.C.S.: 551112
Danna Azrieli *(Chm)*

Subsidiaries:

Granite Hacarmel Investments
Ltd.   (1)
Hagavish St Industrial Area Kiryat Sapir, PO
Box 8401, Netanya, 42507, Israel   **(60%)**
Tel.: (972) 98637700
Web Site: http://www.granitehacarmel.co.il

Sales Range: $1-4.9 Billion
Emp.: 15
Investment Holding Company
N.A.I.C.S.: 551112
Joseph Singer *(CEO)*

Subsidiary (Domestic):

Global Environmental Solutions
Ltd.   (2)
Askar site Akko Industrial Zone Akko, POB
2408, Acre, 24123, Israel   **(100%)**
Tel.: (972) 732823600
Web Site: https://www.ges.co.il
Sales Range: $200-249.9 Million
Emp.: 400
Environmental Solution
N.A.I.C.S.: 221310

Supergas Israel Gas Distribution Co.
Ltd   (2)
36 Yad Harutzim Street, South IZ, Netanya,
Israel   **(100%)**
Tel.: (972) 98308101
Web Site: http://www.supergas.co.il
Sales Range: $75-99.9 Million
Liquefied Petroleum Gas Distr
N.A.I.C.S.: 221210

Green Mountain AS   (1)
Hodneveien 260, 4016, Stavanger, Norway
Tel.: (47) 46903139
Web Site: https://greenmountain.no
Renewable Energy Generation Services
N.A.I.C.S.: 221118

AZTEC MINERALS CORP.
1130 - 609 Granville Street, PO Box
10328, Vancouver, V7Y 1G5, BC,
Canada
Tel.: (604) 685-9770
Web Site:
     http://www.aztecminerals.com
AZZTF—(OTCQB)
Rev.: $2,440
Assets: $2,330,766
Liabilities: $74,619
Net Worth: $2,256,147
Earnings: ($426,148)
Fiscal Year-end: 12/31/19
Mineral Exploration Services
N.A.I.C.S.: 213114
Joey Wilkins *(Pres & CEO)*

AZTECH GROUP LTD.
31 Ubi Road 1 09-01 Aztech Building,
Singapore, 408694, Singapore
Tel.: (65) 65942288
Web Site: http://www.aztech-
     group.com
Year Founded: 1986
Sales Range: $300-349.9 Million
Multimedia Products & Computer Pe-
ripherals Mfr
N.A.I.C.S.: 334419
Michael Hong Yew Mun *(Chm &
CEO)*

Subsidiaries:

AZ-Technology Sdn Bhd   (1)
Unit 179 7th Floor Block A Jalan Business
Center #97 Jalan SS7/2, Kelana Business
Centre Selango, Petaling Jaya, 47301, Se-
langor, Malaysia   **(100%)**
Tel.: (60) 378048450
Sales Range: $25-49.9 Million
Emp.: 10
Telephone Apparatus Mfr
N.A.I.C.S.: 334210
Michael Mun *(CEO)*

Azfin Semiconductors Pte Ltd   (1)
31 Ubi Rd 1 Aztech Bldg, 408694, Singa-
pore, Singapore   **(82%)**
Tel.: (65) 67479855
Semiconductor & Related Device Mfr
N.A.I.C.S.: 334413

Aztech Labs Inc.   (1)
4005 Clipper Ct, Fremont, CA
94538   **(100%)**
Tel.: (510) 683-9800
Web Site: http://www.aztech.com

Sales Range: $25-49.9 Million
Emp.: 50
Other Computer Peripheral Equipment Mfr
N.A.I.C.S.: 334118

Shiro Corporation Pte Ltd   (1)
31 Ubi Road 1, #08-00 Aztech Building,
408694, Singapore, Singapore   **(100%)**
Tel.: (65) 65942233
Web Site: http://www.shirocorp.com
Sales Range: $50-74.9 Million
Emp.: 7
Computer & Computer Peripheral Equip-
ment & Software Whslr
N.A.I.C.S.: 423430

AZTECHWB CO., LTD.
652-1 Shinyung-dong, saha-gh, Bu-
san, Korea (South)
Tel.: (82) 512023101
Web Site: https://www.aztechwb.co.kr
Year Founded: 1969
032080—(KRS)
Rev.: $34,878,403
Assets: $108,938,666
Liabilities: $24,577,526
Net Worth: $84,361,141
Earnings: ($1,089,645)
Emp.: 98
Fiscal Year-end: 12/31/22
Textile Products Mfr
N.A.I.C.S.: 313310
William Schmidt *(Head-Clinical Dev)*

AZUL AZUL SA
Av El Parron 0939, La Cisterna, San-
tiago, Chile
Tel.: (56) 28999900
AZUL.AZUL—(SGO)
Sales Range: Less than $1 Million
Professional Soccer Club Operator
N.A.I.C.S.: 711211
Felipe Andres De Pablo Jerez *(COO)*

AZUL S.A.
Edificio Jatoba 8th Floor Castelo
Branco Office Park Avenida Marcos,
Penteado de Ulhoa Rodrigues 939
Tambore Barueri, Sao Paulo, 06460-
040, SP, Brazil
Tel.: (55) 1148312880   BR
Web Site:
     http://www.ir.voeazul.com.br
Year Founded: 2008
AZUL4—(BRAZ)
Rev.: $3,700,154,552
Assets: $4,094,707,149
Liabilities: $8,347,942,367
Net Worth: ($4,253,235,218)
Earnings: ($474,714,528)
Emp.: 16,017
Fiscal Year-end: 12/31/23
Oil Transportation Services
N.A.I.C.S.: 481111
David Gary Neeleman *(Founder &
Chm)*

AZULIS CAPITAL
24 rue Royale, 75008, Paris, France
Tel.: (33) 142987020
Web Site: https://www.azuliscapital.fr
Clothing Accessory Retailer
N.A.I.C.S.: 458110

AZUMA HOUSE CO., LTD.
3F Azuma House Bldg 1-2-17
Kuroda, Wakayama, 640-8341, Japan
Tel.: (81) 120801406
Web Site: https://azumahouse.com
Year Founded: 1977
3293—(TKS)
Rev.: $86,505,070
Assets: $214,401,960
Liabilities: $104,768,500
Net Worth: $109,633,460
Earnings: $5,268,170
Emp.: 195
Fiscal Year-end: 03/31/24

Real Estate Services
N.A.I.C.S.: 531390
Yukio Azuma *(Pres & CEO)*

AZUMA SHIPPING CO., LTD.
8-12 Harumi 1-chome Harumi Island
Triton Square Office Tower Z 33rd Fl,
Chuo-ku, Tokyo, 104-6233, Japan
Tel.: (81) 362212201
Web Site:
     https://www.azumaship.co.jp
Year Founded: 1917
9380—(TKS)
Rev.: $262,721,060
Assets: $255,998,690
Liabilities: $143,741,060
Net Worth: $112,257,630
Earnings: $2,095,370
Emp.: 824
Fiscal Year-end: 03/31/24
Shipping Transportation Services
N.A.I.C.S.: 488320
Yasuo Nagashima *(Pres)*

Subsidiaries:

Azuma CIS, LLC   (1)
5th Floor Savvinskaya Naberezhnoi Busi-
ness Center, 15 Savvinskaya Nab, 119435,
Moscow, Russia
Tel.: (7) 4956516724
Web Site: http://www.azumaship.co.jp
Freight Forwarding Services
N.A.I.C.S.: 488510

Azuma Logitec Co., Ltd.   (1)
3-17-16 Tatsumi, Koto-ku, Tokyo, Japan
Tel.: (81) 335220018
Web Site: https://www.azuma-logitec.com
Truck Transportation Services
N.A.I.C.S.: 484110

Azuma Shipping (Qingdao) Co.,
Ltd.   (1)
Room 807 Building A No 19 Zhanzhou Er
Road Shinan District, Qingdao, China
Tel.: (86) 53282868908
Freight Forwarding Services
N.A.I.C.S.: 488510

Azuma Shipping Co., Ltd. - Chubu
Business Division   (1)
8-10 Meiko 2-chome, Minato-ku, Nagoya,
Aichi, Japan
Tel.: (81) 526615207
Transportation Services
N.A.I.C.S.: 488330

Azuma Shipping Co., Ltd. - Kanto
Business Division   (1)
138-2 Higashishinmachi, Ota, Gunma, Ja-
pan
Tel.: (81) 276502771
Transportation Services
N.A.I.C.S.: 488330

Azuma Shipping Co., Ltd. - Kanto
Business Division   (1)
Sompo Japan Nipponkoa Chiba Bldg 5F
8-4 Chibaminato, Chuo-ku, Chiba, Japan
Tel.: (81) 432461187
Transportation Services
N.A.I.C.S.: 488330

Azuma Shipping Co., Ltd. - Keihin
Business Division   (1)
51-1 Miyamae Ohkumajumonji-aza Watar-
icho, Watari-gun, Miyagi, Japan
Tel.: (81) 223348213
Transportation Services
N.A.I.C.S.: 488330

Azuma Shipping Co., Ltd. - Keihin
Business Division   (1)
8-15 Tokai 4-Chome, Ohta-ku, Tokyo, Japan
Tel.: (81) 357551525
Transportation Services
N.A.I.C.S.: 488330

Azuma Shipping Co., Ltd. - Kyushu
Business Division   (1)
2 Higashiminatomachi 4-chome, Moji-ku,
Kitakyushu, 801-0853, Fukuoka, Japan
Tel.: (81) 933213137
Web Site: http://www.azumaship.co.jp
Emp.: 520
Transportation Services

Azuma Shipping Co., Ltd.—(Continued)

N.A.I.C.S.: 488330
Akihiro Shibata *(CEO)*

Azuma Shipping Co., Ltd. - Maritime Transportation Division (1)
87 Fugane Akasakicho Ohfunato, Iwate, Japan
Tel.: (81) 192272141
Transportation Services
N.A.I.C.S.: 488330

Azuma Shipping Mongolia LLC (1)
Erkhi Center 409, Bayangol District, Ulaanbaatar, Mongolia
Tel.: (976) 70115333
Transportation Services
N.A.I.C.S.: 488330

Azuma Transport Services (Thailand) Co., Ltd. (1)
5 Sitthivorakit Building 12th Fl Soi Pipat Silom Road, Bangrak, Bangkok, 10500, Thailand
Tel.: (66) 2 238 5303
General Transport Services
N.A.I.C.S.: 484110

Buzen kubota kaiun Co., Ltd. (1)
4-2 Higashi-Minato-machi Moji-ku, Kitakyushu, Fukuoka, Japan
Tel.: (81) 362212230
Freight Forwarding Services
N.A.I.C.S.: 488510

Eastern Marine System Co., Ltd. (1)
Tekkou Bldg 3rd Fl 3-1-11 Matsubara-cho, Oita, Ohita, Japan
Tel.: (81) 335367781
Web Site: https://eastern-marinesystem.co.jp
Ship Leasing Services
N.A.I.C.S.: 532411

Kanto Air Cargo Co., Ltd. (1)
3-7-2 Sakurada, Sakura-ku, Saitama, 338-0833, Japan
Tel.: (81) 487623561
Web Site: http://www.kanto-aircargo.co.jp
Emp.: 126
Marine Transportation Services
N.A.I.C.S.: 488490

Kinki Transport & Terminal Co., Ltd. (1)
4-1-6 Chikko, Minato-ku, Osaka, 552-0021, Japan
Tel.: (81) 665712801
Web Site: https://www.kinki-koun.com
Marine Transportation Services
N.A.I.C.S.: 488320

Qingdao Sinotrans-Azuma Logistics Co., Ltd. (1)
Room 1203 No 5 Henan Road, Qingdao, China
Tel.: (86) 53282891157
Container Transportation Services
N.A.I.C.S.: 484110

Siam Azuma Multi-Trans Co., Ltd. (1)
5 Sitthivorakit Building 12th fl Soi Pipat Silom Road, Silom Bangrak, Bangkok, 10500, Thailand
Tel.: (66) 22385303
Emp.: 38
Freight Forwarding Services
N.A.I.C.S.: 488510

Tandem Global Logistics (HK) Limited (1)
Flat J 3 / F HK Spinners Industrial Building Phase 6, 481 Castle Peak Road Cheung Sha Wan, Kowloon, China (Hong Kong)
Tel.: (852) 27416018
Web Site: http://tandemgloballogistics.net
Freight Forwarding Services
N.A.I.C.S.: 488510
Eric Yau *(Gen Mgr)*

Tandem Global Logistics (India) Pvt. Ltd. (1)
143 Adarsh Industrial Estate Sahar Chakala Road, Andheri E, Mumbai, 400 099, India
Tel.: (91) 2242291500
Web Site: http://tandemgloballogistics.net
Freight Forwarding Services
N.A.I.C.S.: 488510
Lavin Shetty *(Exec Dir)*

Tandem Global Logistics (Shanghai) Co., Ltd. (1)
Room 1202 Shanghai Plaza 138 Huaihai M Rd, Shanghai, 200021, China
Tel.: (86) 2164747537
Web Site: http://tandemgloballogistics.net
Freight Forwarding Services
N.A.I.C.S.: 488510
Helen Wong *(Mgr-Accounts & Admin)*

Tandem Global Logistics Japan Co., Ltd. (1)
8F Oak Building 6-113 Aioi-cho, Naka-ku, Yokohama, 231-0012, Kanagawa, Japan
Tel.: (81) 452287174
Freight Forwarding Services
N.A.I.C.S.: 488510
Toshiyuki Sakurai *(Pres)*

Subsidiary (Domestic):

Japan Aircargo Forwarders Association (2)
Asteer Kayabacho Bldg 4F 6-1 Shinkawa 1-chome Chuo-ku, Tokyo, Japan
Tel.: (81) 362227571
Web Site: http://www.jafa.or.jp
Freight Forwarding Services
N.A.I.C.S.: 488510
Yutaka Ito *(Chm)*

Japan International Freight Forwarders Association, Inc. (2)
4F Across Shinkawa Bldg Annex 16-14 Shinkawa 1-chome, Chuo-ku, Tokyo, 104-0033, Japan
Tel.: (81) 332970351
Web Site: http://www.jiffa.or.jp
Freight Forwarding Services
N.A.I.C.S.: 488510

The Yokohama Chamber of Commerce & Industry (2)
Sangyo Boeki Center Building 8F 2 Yamashita-cho, Naka-ku, Yokohama, 231-8524, Japan
Tel.: (81) 456717400
Web Site: http://www.yokohama-cci.or.jp
Freight Forwarding Services
N.A.I.C.S.: 488510
Takashi Uyeno *(Chm)*

Tandem Global Logistics Netherlands B.V. (1)
Vlaardingweg 63, 3044 CJ, Rotterdam, Netherlands
Tel.: (31) 102404875
Web Site: http://tandemgloballogistics.net
Freight Forwarding Services
N.A.I.C.S.: 488510
Joep Stijns *(Mng Dir)*

Yokohama Liquified Gas Terminal Co., Ltd. (1)
12-14 Daikoku-cho, Tsurumi-ku, Yokohama, 230-0053, Kanagawa, Japan
Tel.: (81) 45 505 5550
Liquefied Petroleum Gas Services
N.A.I.C.S.: 221210

AZUMAH RESOURCES LIMITED

Suite 2 11 Ventnor Avenue, West Perth, 6005, WA, Australia
Tel.: (61) 894867911
Web Site:
http://www.azumahresources.com
AZM—(ASX)
Rev.: $22,098
Assets: $616,194
Liabilities: $173,813
Net Worth: $442,381
Earnings: ($1,554,466)
Emp.: 2
Fiscal Year-end: 06/30/19
Gold Mining
N.A.I.C.S.: 212220

AZUR INDUSTRIES

Z I La Feuillane 42 Zi La Feuillane, 13270, Fos-sur-Mer, Bouches Du Rhone, France
Tel.: (33) 442051228

Web Site:
http://www.azurindustries.com
Rev.: $14,400,000
Emp.: 100
Fabricated Structural Metal Mfr
N.A.I.C.S.: 332312
Patrick Chatelier *(Dir)*

AZURE HEALTHCARE LIMITED

1/31 Sabre Drive Port Melbourne, Melbourne, 3207, VIC, Australia
Tel.: (61) 3 9209 9688
Web Site:
http://www.azurehealthcare.com.au
Rev.: $22,168,565
Assets: $13,796,167
Liabilities: $6,428,093
Net Worth: $7,368,074
Earnings: $445,511
Emp.: 101
Fiscal Year-end: 06/30/19
Nursecall Systems & Clinical Workflow Solutions
N.A.I.C.S.: 561499
Clayton Astles *(CEO)*

Subsidiaries:

Austco Communications Systems Pty. Ltd. (1)
1/31 Sabre Drive, Port Melbourne, 3207, VIC, Australia
Tel.: (61) 392099688
Web Site: http://www.austco.ca
Sales Range: $25-49.9 Million
Emp.: 25
Electronic Communication Systems Mfr
N.A.I.C.S.: 334290
Robert Grey *(Founder)*

Austco Marketing & Service (Asia) Pte. Ltd. (1)
Blk 5014 Ang Mo Kio Ave 5 05-07/08 TECHplace II, Singapore, 569881, Singapore
Tel.: (65) 64818400
Web Site: http://www.austco.com.sg
Sales Range: $25-49.9 Million
Emp.: 20
Electronic Communication Systems Mfr
N.A.I.C.S.: 334290
Michael Chia *(Mng Dir)*

Austco Marketing & Service (Canada) Ltd. (1)
940 The East Mall Suite 101, Etobicoke, M9B 6J7, ON, Canada
Tel.: (416) 620-1830
Web Site: http://www.austco.ca
Electronic Communication Systems Mfr
N.A.I.C.S.: 334290

Austco Marketing & Service (UK) Ltd. (1)
6 West Court Buntsford Park Rd, Bromsgrove, B60 3DX, Worcestershire, United Kingdom
Tel.: (44) 1527877778
Web Site: http://www.austco.com
Sales Range: $25-49.9 Million
Emp.: 10
Electronic Communication Systems Mfr
N.A.I.C.S.: 334290

Austco Marketing & Service (USA) Ltd. (1)
9155 Sterling St Ste 100, Irving, TX 75063
Tel.: (972) 929-0974
Web Site: http://www.austco.us
Sales Range: $25-49.9 Million
Emp.: 5
Electronic Communication Systems Mfr
N.A.I.C.S.: 334290
Judy Whitehead *(Mgr-HR)*

Calltec Pty. Ltd. (1)
Unit 21 35 Dunlop Rd, Mulgrave, 3170, Victoria, Australia
Tel.: (61) 385627575
Web Site: http://www.tsvaustralia.com.au
Electronic Communication Solutions & Services
N.A.I.C.S.: 517810

Tecsound (QLD) Pty. Ltd. (1)

Unit 11 Northport Bus Park, 441 Nudgee Rd, Hendra, 4011, QLD, Australia
Tel.: (61) 738684900
Web Site: http://www.tecsound.com.au
Audio System Design & Integrated Services
N.A.I.C.S.: 541490

Tecsound (VIC) Pty. Ltd. (1)
Unit 21 35 Dunlop Rd, PO Box 5083, Mulgrave, 3170, Victoria, Australia
Tel.: (61) 385627575
Web Site: http://www.tecsound.com.au
Sales Range: $25-49.9 Million
Emp.: 55
Audio System Design & Integration Services
N.A.I.C.S.: 541490

Tecsound (West Australia) Pty. Ltd. (1)
78B Collingwood St, Osborne Park, 6017, Western Australia, Australia
Tel.: (61) 894458844
Web Site: http://www.tecsound.com.au
Sales Range: $25-49.9 Million
Emp.: 15
Audio Systems Design & Integration Services
N.A.I.C.S.: 541490
Ron Anderson *(Mgr-Sls)*

AZURE POWER GLOBAL LIMITED

DSC-304 Second Floor DLF South Court, Saket, New Delhi, 110017, India
Tel.: (91) 1149409800
Web Site:
https://www.azurepower.com
Year Founded: 2008
AZRE—(NYSE)
Rev.: $252,400,000
Assets: $2,318,300,000
Liabilities: $1,886,000,000
Net Worth: $432,300,000
Earnings: ($27,800,000)
Emp.: 427
Fiscal Year-end: 03/31/23
Solar Electric Power Generation Services
N.A.I.C.S.: 221114
Samitla Subba *(Head-Policy & Comm)*

AZUREWAVE TECHNOLOGIES, INC.

8F No 94 Baozhong Road, Xindian District, New Taipei City, Taiwan
Tel.: (886) 255995599
Web Site:
https://www.azurewave.com
3694—(TAI)
Rev.: $311,694,288
Assets: $180,537,944
Liabilities: $84,044,276
Net Worth: $96,493,668
Earnings: $10,904,182
Fiscal Year-end: 12/31/23
Wireless Communication Products
N.A.I.C.S.: 334220
Jason Cheng *(Chm)*

AZZALIN SRL

Strada Marziana 9, 27020, Parona, Pavia, Italy
Tel.: (39) 0384 253136
Web Site: http://www.azzalinsrl.it
Year Founded: 1970
Sales Range: $1-9.9 Million
Emp.: 16
Industrial Valves, Gears, Actuators & Tools Mfr & Distr
N.A.I.C.S.: 332911
Luciano Azzalin *(CEO)*

Subsidiaries:

Valvesource Ltd (1)
31 Hampstead Ave, Mildenhall, IP28 7AS, Suffolk, United Kingdom
Tel.: (44) 1638 711 500

Web Site: http://www.valvesource.co.uk
Supplier of Industrial Valves to Oil, Gas, Petrochemical & Other Related Industries
N.A.I.C.S.: 423830
Brian Whiles *(Dir)*

AZZEDINE ALAIA S.A.S.
7 Rue De Moussy, 75004, Paris, France
Tel.: (33) 142721919
Web Site: http://www.alaia.fr
Rev.: $13,000,000
Emp.: 45
N.A.I.C.S.: 424350
Azzedine Alaia *(Pres)*

AZZURRO SOLUTIONS CORP.
V Osikach 24 Dolni Mecholupy, 10900, Prague, Czech Republic
Tel.: (420) 7027036003   NV
Year Founded: 2019
Rev.: $7,982
Assets: $2,499
Liabilities: $45,859
Net Worth: ($43,360)
Earnings: ($23,302)
Emp.: 1
Fiscal Year-end: 09/30/23
Investment Services
N.A.I.C.S.: 523999

B & A LIMITED
113 Park Street 9th Floor, Kolkata, 700 016, West Bengal, India
Tel.: (91) 3322657389
Web Site: https://www.barooahs.com
Year Founded: 1915
508136—(BOM)
Rev.: $33,927,075
Assets: $25,338,290
Liabilities: $11,108,957
Net Worth: $14,229,333
Earnings: $2,360,672
Emp.: 3,462
Fiscal Year-end: 03/31/21
Tea Mfr
N.A.I.C.S.: 311920
Somnath Chatterjee *(Mng Dir)*

B & A PACKAGING INDIA LIMITED
113 Park Street 9th Floor, Kolkata, 700 016, India
Tel.: (91) 3322269582
Web Site: https://www.bampl.com
Year Founded: 1915
523186—(BOM)
Rev.: $17,600,583
Assets: $11,785,192
Liabilities: $4,190,550
Net Worth: $7,594,642
Earnings: $1,245,317
Emp.: 146
Fiscal Year-end: 03/31/22
Paper Sack Mfr
N.A.I.C.S.: 322220
Somnath Chatterjee *(Exec Dir)*

B & D STRATEGIC HOLDINGS LIMITED
Units 2803-2803A Asia Trade Centre No 79 Lei Muk Road, Kwai Chung, New Territories, China (Hong Kong)
Tel.: (852) 2 409 2783   Ky
Web Site: http://www.bnd-strategic.com.hk
Year Founded: 1995
1780—(HKG)
Rev.: $28,213,859
Assets: $36,662,436
Liabilities: $8,149,343
Net Worth: $28,513,093
Earnings: ($5,152,235)
Emp.: 56
Fiscal Year-end: 03/31/21
Holding Company
N.A.I.C.S.: 551112

Wing Kwok Tang *(Chm)*

B & S INTERNATIONAL HOLDINGS LTD.
Unit 911 9th Floor Tai Yau Building 181 Johnston Road, Wan Chai, Hong Kong, China (Hong Kong)
Tel.: (852) 2 893 6632   Ky
Web Site: http://www.bandshk.com
1705—(HKG)
Rev.: $62,306,111
Assets: $35,557,722
Liabilities: $18,703,390
Net Worth: $16,854,333
Earnings: $208,432
Emp.: 721
Fiscal Year-end: 03/31/21
Food & Beverage Distr
N.A.I.C.S.: 424820
Andrew Kam Chuen Chan *(Chm & CEO)*

B C HOUSING MANAGEMENT COMMISSION
4555 Kingsway Ste 1701, Burnaby, V5H 4V8, BC, Canada
Tel.: (604) 433-1711
Web Site: http://www.bchousing.org
Sales Range: $200-249.9 Million
Emp.: 550
Subsidized Housing & Housing Assistance Services
N.A.I.C.S.: 624229
Stephanie Allen *(VP)*

B GAON HOLDINGS LTD.
Ariel Sharon 8, PO Box 266, Or Yehuda, 6039730, Israel
Tel.: (972) 37954100
Web Site: https://www.gaon.com
Year Founded: 1951
GAON—(TAE)
Investment Holding Company Services
N.A.I.C.S.: 551112
Nissim Lachem *(CFO)*

B INVESTMENTS HOLDING SAE
Cinema Radio Building 24 Talaat Harb Street 1st Floor Downtown, 11956, Cairo, Egypt
Tel.: (20) 25763012
Web Site: https://binvestmentsegypt.com
Year Founded: 2005
BINV—(EGX)
Private Equity
N.A.I.C.S.: 523999
Hazem Barakat *(Co-Founder)*

Subsidiaries:

Orascom Financial Holding SAE   **(1)**
Nile City Towers South Tower 2005 A Corniche El Nile, Boulaq, Egypt   **(90%)**
Tel.: (20) 24617300
Web Site: http://orascomfh.com
Privater Equity Firm
N.A.I.C.S.: 523940
Nils Bachtler *(CEO)*

B L KASHYAP & SONS LIMITED
409 4th Floor DLF Tower - A Jasola, New Delhi, 110 025, India
Tel.: (91) 1140500300
Web Site: https://www.blkashyap.com
532719—(BOM)
Rev.: $158,297,207
Assets: $195,529,657
Liabilities: $137,795,057
Net Worth: $57,734,600
Earnings: $5,998,738
Emp.: 933
Fiscal Year-end: 03/31/22
Construction Engineering Services
N.A.I.C.S.: 541330

Vinod Kashyap *(Chm)*

Subsidiaries:

Soul Space Projects Limited   **(1)**
409 4th floor DLF Tower - A Jasola, New Delhi, 110025, India
Tel.: (91) 1143058345
Web Site: https://www.soulspace.co.in
Sales Range: $650-699.9 Million
Emp.: 150
Real Estate Development Services
N.A.I.C.S.: 531390

B N RATHI SECURITIES LTD.
6-3-652 4th Floor Kautilya Amrutha Estates Somajiguda, Hyderabad, 500 082, India
Tel.: (91) 4040527777
Web Site: https://www.bnrsecurities.com
523019—(BOM)
Rev.: $5,899,909
Assets: $20,185,695
Liabilities: $15,181,446
Net Worth: $5,004,249
Earnings: $683,466
Emp.: 60
Fiscal Year-end: 03/31/22
Financial Security Services
N.A.I.C.S.: 523150
M. V. Rao *(Compliance Officer & Head-Ops)*

Subsidiaries:

B N Rathi Comtrade Private Limited   **(1)**
6-3-652 IV Floor Kautilya Amrutha Estates, Somajiguda, Hyderabad, 500 082, Telangana, India
Tel.: (91) 4030527777
Commodity Trading Services
N.A.I.C.S.: 523210
H. N. Rathi *(Mng Dir)*

B NANJI ENTERPRISES LIMITED
Moorti Bunglow No 5 Ashok Nagar Co Op Soc Ltd, B/h Sundarvan ISRO Satelite, Ahmedabad, 380 015, India
Tel.: (91) 7965214174
Web Site: http://www.bnanji.com
Real Estate Related Services
N.A.I.C.S.: 531390
Bhikhubhai Nanjibhai Padsala *(Chm & Mng Dir)*

B!FERRAZ
Rua Iguatemi 236, Itaim Bibi, Sao Paulo, 01451-010, Brazil
Tel.: (55) 11 3377 7945
Web Site: http://www.bferraz.com.br
Year Founded: 1999
Marketing & Advertising Services
N.A.I.C.S.: 541613
Bazinho Ferraz *(Pres)*

B&B INVESTMENT PARTNERS LLP
Third Floor 55 Blandford Street, London, W1U 7HW, United Kingdom
Tel.: (44) 20 7022 6660
Web Site: http://bandbinvestment.com
Privater Equity Firm
N.A.I.C.S.: 523999
Chris Britton *(Principal)*

Subsidiaries:

Aromatherapy Associates Ltd.   **(1)**
5 Montpelier Street, Knightsbridge, London, SW7 1EX, Middlesex, United Kingdom
Tel.: (44) 20 7838 1117
Web Site: http://www.aromatherapyassociates.com
Sales Range: $1-9.9 Million
Emp.: 5
Aromatherapy Product Mfr
N.A.I.C.S.: 325620
Geraldine Howard *(Co-Founder)*

B&B REALTY LIMITED
17 4th Floor Shah Sultan Cunningham Road, Bengaluru, 560 052, Karnataka, India
Tel.: (91) 8022203274
Web Site: https://www.bbrl.in
Rev.: $149,376
Assets: $3,470,814
Liabilities: $1,234,188
Net Worth: $2,236,626
Earnings: $747
Fiscal Year-end: 03/31/18
Real Estate Manangement Services
N.A.I.C.S.: 531390
Bharat Kumar Bhandari *(Chm & Mng Dir)*

B&B TRADE DISTRIBUTION CENTRE
675 York St, London, N5W 2S6, ON, Canada
Tel.: (519) 679-1770
Web Site: http://www.bbtrade.com
Rev.: $15,389,256
Emp.: 70
Heating Ventilation Air conditioning Refrigeration Whslr
N.A.I.C.S.: 238220
Tom Boutette *(Pres)*

B&B TRIPLEWALL CONTAINERS LIMITED
Sy No 263/2/3 Marsur Madiwal Village Kasaba Hobli, Anekal Taluk, Bengaluru, 562106, India
Tel.: (91) 7353751661
Web Site: https://www.boxandboard.in
Year Founded: 1992
543668—(BOM)
Rev.: $46,069,064
Assets: $37,374,191
Liabilities: $23,064,132
Net Worth: $14,310,059
Earnings: $2,471,646
Emp.: 400
Fiscal Year-end: 03/30/23
Paper Container Packaging Mfr & Distr
N.A.I.C.S.: 322219
Manish Gupta *(Chm)*

B&C SPEAKERS SPA
Via Poggiomoro 1 - Vallina, 50012, Florence, Italy
Tel.: (39) 03905565721
Web Site: https://www.bcspeakers.com
Year Founded: 1944
BEC—(ITA)
Rev.: $103,784,444
Assets: $95,317,379
Liabilities: $44,306,965
Net Worth: $51,010,414
Earnings: $15,447,361
Emp.: 344
Fiscal Year-end: 12/31/23
Audio Equipment Mfr & Distr
N.A.I.C.S.: 334310
Roberto Coppini *(Founder & Chm)*

Subsidiaries:

B&C Speakers Brasil Comercio de Equipamentos de Audio Ltda.   **(1)**
Sergio Jungblut Dieterich 1011 Dep 3 Sao Joao, Porto Alegre, 91060-410, RS, Brazil
Tel.: (55) 5131031539
Loudspeaker Transducer Mfr
N.A.I.C.S.: 334310

B&C Speakers NA (USA), LLC   **(1)**
220 W Pkwy Unit 11, Pompton Plains, NJ 07444
Tel.: (973) 248-0955
Loudspeaker Transducer Mfr
N.A.I.C.S.: 334310
Bennett Prescott *(Dir-Sls & Ops-North America)*

B&C Speakers SpA—(Continued)

Eighteen Sound S.r.l. (1)
Via Botticelli 8, 42124, Reggio Emilia, Italy
Tel.: (39) 05221861800
Web Site: https://www.eighteensound.it
Audio Loudspeaker Product Mfr
N.A.I.C.S.: 334310

Eminence Speaker LLC. (1)
838 Mulberry Pike, Eminence, KY 40019
Tel.: (502) 845-5622
Web Site: http://www.eminence.com
Emp.: 90
Loudspeaker Mfr
N.A.I.C.S.: 334310
Chris Rose (Pres)

B&D LIFE HEALTH CO.,LTD.
73 Seodal-ro 298beon-gil Bupyeong-gu, Incheon, Korea (South)
Tel.: (82) 25528481
Web Site: http://www.e-seje.com
Year Founded: 2012
Household Care Product Mfr & Distr
N.A.I.C.S.: 325611
Daniel Lee (CEO)

B&M EUROPEAN VALUE RE-TAIL S.A.
9 Allee Scheffer, 2520, Luxembourg, Luxembourg
Tel.: (352) 246130207   LU
Web Site:
http://www.bandmretail.com
Year Founded: 1978
BME—(LSE)
Rev.: $6,187,889,400
Assets: $4,454,336,600
Liabilities: $5,348,432,600
Net Worth: ($894,096,000)
Earnings: $432,146,400
Emp.: 43,505
Fiscal Year-end: 03/31/23
Grocery Products Retailer
N.A.I.C.S.: 424410
Simon Arora (CEO)

Subsidiaries:

Heron Foods Ltd. (1)
The Vault Dakota Drive, Estuary Commerce Park Speke, Liverpool, L24 8RJ, United Kingdom
Tel.: (44) 3456037300
Web Site: https://www.heronfoods.com
Frozen Specialty Food Mfr
N.A.I.C.S.: 311412

J.A. Woll Handels GmbH (1)
Am Hornberg 6, 29614, Soltau, Germany
Tel.: (49) 519198030
Packaged Frozen Food Merchant Whslr
N.A.I.C.S.: 424420

B&S GROUP S.A.
14 Rue Strachen Mensdorf G D,
L-6933, Luxembourg, Luxembourg
Tel.: (352) 26870881
Web Site: https://www.bs-group-sa.com
Year Founded: 1872
BSGR—(EUR)
Rev.: $2,450,374,214
Assets: $1,018,456,783
Liabilities: $731,010,045
Net Worth: $287,446,738
Earnings: $53,034,551
Emp.: 1,699
Fiscal Year-end: 12/31/23
Holding Company
N.A.I.C.S.: 551112
Anke Bongers (Dir-Corp Comm & IR)

Subsidiaries:

Anker Amsterdam Spirits B.V. (1)
Slego 2, 1046 BM, Amsterdam, Netherlands
Tel.: (31) 206840329
Web Site:
https://www.ankeramsterdamspirits.nl
Wine & Soft Drink Whslr
N.A.I.C.S.: 424820

B&S HTG B.V. (1)
Rondeboslaan 35, 9936 BJ, Delfzijl, Netherlands
Tel.: (31) 596635100
Web Site: https://www.bs-htg.com
Health & Beauty Product Distr
N.A.I.C.S.: 424820

Capi-Lux Netherlands B.V. (1)
Robijnlaan 14, 2132 WX, Hoofddorp, Netherlands
Tel.: (31) 235699500
Web Site: https://www.capi.com
Electronic Product Distr
N.A.I.C.S.: 423690

Checkpoint Distribution B.V. (1)
Rondeboslaan 35, Farmsum, 9936 BJ, Delfzijl, Netherlands
Tel.: (31) 596635130
Web Site:
https://www.checkpointdistribution.nl
Skin Care & Cosmetic Whslr
N.A.I.C.S.: 424210

Checkpoint Trading B.V. (1)
Rondeboslaan 35, 9936 BJ, Delfzijl, Netherlands
Tel.: (31) 596635100
Web Site: https://checkpoint-trading.com
Perfume Product Distr
N.A.I.C.S.: 424210

JTG Trading BV (1)
Rijksstraatweg 7, 3316 EE, Dordrecht, Netherlands   (91.8%)
Tel.: (31) 787507300
Web Site: http://www.jtg.nl
Beauty Product Distr
N.A.I.C.S.: 456120

Lagaay Medical Group B.V. (1)
Rijksstraatweg 7, 3316 EE, Dordrecht, Netherlands
Tel.: (31) 104123871
Web Site: https://www.lagaay.com
Emp.: 50
Medical Product Distr
N.A.I.C.S.: 423450

Signature Beauty B.V. (1)
Rijksstraatweg 7, 3316 EE, Dordrecht, Netherlands
Tel.: (31) 786534370
Web Site: https://www.signature.beauty
Food & Electronic Distr
N.A.I.C.S.: 424820

Square Dranken Nederland B.V. (1)
Hereplein 4, 9711 GA, Groningen, Netherlands
Tel.: (31) 503180463
Web Site: https://www.squaredranken.com
Rum & Wine Whslr
N.A.I.C.S.: 424810

Topbrands Europe B.V. (1)
Aston Martinlaan 1, 3261 NB, Oud-Beijerland, Netherlands
Tel.: (31) 186577188
Web Site: https://www.topbrands.nl
Emp.: 230
Cosmetic & Home Care Product Distr
N.A.I.C.S.: 424590

Worldbrands Europe B.V. (1)
Rondeboslaan 35, 9936 BJ, Farmsum, Netherlands
Tel.: (31) 655794247
Web Site:
https://www.worldbrandseurope.com
Makeup Product Distr
N.A.I.C.S.: 424210

B&T EXACT GMBH
Gewerbestrasse 31, 52825, Gevelsberg, Germany
Tel.: (49) 233275530
Web Site: http://www.but-exact.de
Year Founded: 1997
Rev.: $15,175,995
Emp.: 67
Vehicle Repair & Spare Parts Services
N.A.I.C.S.: 811198
Jorg-Peter Tepel (Mng Partner)

B+B VAKMEDIANET GROEP B.V.

Prinses Margrietlaan 3, 2404 HA, Alphen aan den Rijn, Netherlands
Tel.: (31) 88 584 0800   NI
Web Site: http://www.vakmedianet.nl
Emp.: 250
Holding Company; Business-to-Business Media Publisher & Events Organizer
N.A.I.C.S.: 551112
Ruud Bakker (Founder & Mng Dir)

Subsidiaries:

B+B Vakmedianet B.V. (1)
Prinses Margrietlaan 3, 2404 HA, Alphen aan den Rijn, Netherlands
Tel.: (31) 88 584 0800
Web Site: http://www.vakmedianet.nl
Emp.: 100
Business-to-Business Media Publisher & Events Organizer
N.A.I.C.S.: 425120
Ruud Bakker (Founder & Mng Dir)

B+F DORSTEN GMBH
Barbarastrasse 50, 46282, Dorsten, Germany
Tel.: (49) 23629260
Web Site: http://www.fuchs-dorsten.de
Rev.: $45,492,612
Emp.: 120
Prefabricated Construction Services
N.A.I.C.S.: 332311
Hartmut Brandstrup (Bus Mgr)

B+H OCEAN CARRIERS LTD.
3rd Floor Par La Ville Place 14 Par La Ville Road, Hamilton, HM 08, Bermuda
Tel.: (441) 295 6875   LR
Web Site: http://www.bhocean.com
Year Founded: 1988
Sales Range: $50-74.9 Million
Emp.: 175
Operates & Sells Vessels for Dry Bulk & Liquid Cargo
N.A.I.C.S.: 483111

Subsidiaries:

B+H Equimar Singapore Pte. Ltd. (1)
78 Shenton Way # 20-02, 079120, Singapore, Singapore
Tel.: (65) 63235253
Web Site: http://www.bhocean.com
Sales Range: $25-49.9 Million
Emp.: 20
Inland Water Freight Transportation
N.A.I.C.S.: 483211

B+H Management Ltd. (1)
3rd Floor Par La Ville PI, Hamilton, HM08, Bermuda
Tel.: (441) 2956875
Web Site: http://www.bhocean.com
Holding Company
N.A.I.C.S.: 551112
Michael Hutner (Mng Dir)

Equimar Shipholdings, Ltd. (1)
3rd Floor ParLaVille Place 14 Par-La-Ville Road, Hamilton, HM JX, Bermuda (100%)
Tel.: (441) 2956875
Sales Range: $25-49.9 Million
Operates & Sells Vessels for Dry Bulk & Liquid Cargo
N.A.I.C.S.: 561990

Product Transport (S) Pte. Ltd (1)
78 Shenton Way No 20-02, 079120, Singapore, Singapore
Tel.: (65) 63237330
Web Site: http://www.bhocean.com
Sales Range: $25-49.9 Million
Emp.: 20
Marine Cargo Handling
N.A.I.C.S.: 488320

Product Transport (US) Inc (1)
19 Burnside St, Bristol, RI 02809
Tel.: (401) 410-1140
Freight Transportation Arrangement
N.A.I.C.S.: 488510

B+S BANKSYSTEME AG
Elsenheimerstrasse 57, 80687, Munich, Germany
Tel.: (49) 89741190   De
Web Site: https://www.bs-ag.com
Year Founded: 1992
DTD2—(DEU)
Rev.: $13,608,899
Assets: $30,939,366
Liabilities: $15,291,588
Net Worth: $15,647,778
Earnings: $24,565
Emp.: 116
Fiscal Year-end: 06/30/22
Electronic Banking Software & Other Applications for Secure Internet Banking
N.A.I.C.S.: 541512
Peter Bauch (Member-Exec Bd)

Subsidiaries:

B+S Banksysteme Aktiengesellschaft (1)
Elsenheimerstrasse 57, 80687, Munich, Germany
Tel.: (49) 89741190
Web Site: https://www.bs-ag.com
Sales Range: $25-49.9 Million
Emp.: 20
Banking Software Solutions Provider
N.A.I.C.S.: 541511

B+S Banksysteme Aktiengesellschaft (1)
Bichl Feld St 11, Salzburg, 5020, Austria
Tel.: (43) 6624305910
Sales Range: $25-49.9 Million
Emp.: 50
Banking Software Solutions Provider
N.A.I.C.S.: 541511

B+S Banksysteme Deutschland GmbH (1)
Bichlfeldstrabe 11, 80686, Salzburg, Germany
Tel.: (49) 89741190
Sales Range: $25-49.9 Million
Emp.: 20
Banking Software Solutions Provider
N.A.I.C.S.: 541511
Peter Bauch (CEO)

B+S Banksysteme Schweiz AG (1)
Frutigen St 2, 3600, Thun, Switzerland
Tel.: (41) 332230444
Banking Software Solutions Provider
N.A.I.C.S.: 541511

B-52 CAPITAL PUBLIC COMPANY LIMITED
973 President Tower Floor 7 th, Phloen Chit Rd Lumpini Pathumwan, Bangkok, 10330, Thailand
Tel.: (66) 26560189
Web Site: https://www.b52.co.th
Year Founded: 1964
B52—(THA)
Rev.: $2,236,689
Assets: $6,534,622
Liabilities: $1,406,761
Net Worth: $5,127,861
Earnings: ($908,746)
Emp.: 2,544
Fiscal Year-end: 12/31/23
Sock Mfr & Distr; Real Estate Property Developer
N.A.I.C.S.: 315120
Suthep Pongpitak (Chm)

B-A-L GERMANY AG
Poststrasse 5, 01662, Meissen, Germany
Tel.: (49) 35214596539
Web Site: https://www.bal-ag.de
Year Founded: 2014
BAM—(STU)
Rev.: $384,191
Assets: $3,748,542
Liabilities: $1,254,711
Net Worth: $2,493,830
Earnings: $38,582

Emp.: 2
Fiscal Year-end: 12/31/23
Real Estate Manangement Services
N.A.I.C.S.: 531210
Falko Zschunke *(Chm & CEO)*

B-FLEXION GROUP HOLD-INGS SA
Avenue Giuseppe-Motta 31-33, CH-1211, Geneva, Switzerland
Tel.: (41) 58 944 0400   CH
Web Site:
   http://www.areslifesciences.com
Year Founded: 2008
Life Sciences Investment Holding Company
N.A.I.C.S.: 551112
Jacques Theurillat *(CEO & Partner)*

Subsidiaries:

Affidea Group B.V.   (1)
Prins Bernhardplein 200, 1097 JB, Amsterdam, Netherlands
Tel.: (31) 20 679 0026
Web Site: http://www.affidea.com
Sales Range: $350-399.9 Million
Emp.: 5,000
Holding Company; Radiological Diagnostic, Clinical Laboratory & Cancer Care Medical Centers Operator
N.A.I.C.S.: 551112
Dimitris Moulavasilis *(CEO)*

Subsidiary (Domestic):

Affidea B.V.   (2)
Prins Bernhardplein 200, 1097 JB, Amsterdam, Netherlands
Tel.: (31) 20 521 4777
Web Site: http://www.affidea.com
Radiological Diagnostic, Clinical Laboratory & Cancer Care Medical Centers Operator
N.A.I.C.S.: 621512
Dimitris Moulavasilis *(CEO)*

Co-Headquarters (Non-US):

Affidea B.V. - Operations Headquarters   (3)
West End Business Center 22-24 Vaci St, 1132, Budapest, Hungary
Tel.: (36) 1 815 3500
Web Site: http://www.affidea.com
Corporate Operations Office
N.A.I.C.S.: 551114
Eva Kovari *(Office Mgr)*

Stallergenes Greer plc   (1)
40 Bernard Street 3rd Floor, London, WC1N 1LE, United Kingdom   (100%)
Tel.: (44) 2031415000
Web Site: http://www.stallergenesgreer.com
Holding Company; Pharmaceutical Product Mfr & Whslr
N.A.I.C.S.: 551112
Paola Ricci *(Head-Pharmaceutical Affairs)*

Subsidiary (US):

Stallergenes Greer Holdings Inc.   (2)
55 Cambridge Pkwy Ste 400, Cambridge, MA 02142   (100%)
Tel.: (617) 225-8000
Web Site:
   http://www.stallergenesgreerus.com
Holding Company; Regional Managing Office
N.A.I.C.S.: 551112
Richard Russell *(Pres & CEO)*

Subsidiary (Domestic):

Greer Laboratories, Inc.   (3)
639 Nuway Cir NE, Lenoir, NC 28645   (100%)
Tel.: (828) 754-5327
Web Site: http://www.greerlabs.com
Sales Range: $25-49.9 Million
Emp.: 210
Vaccines
N.A.I.C.S.: 325414
Craig Kennedy *(VP-Opers)*

Stallergenes, Inc.   (3)
55 Cambridge Pkwy Ste 400, Cambridge, MA 02142   (100%)
Tel.: (617) 225-8000

Web Site:
   http://www.stallergenesgreerus.com
Allergen Biopharmaceutical Distr
N.A.I.C.S.: 424210
Thomas Lang *(Pres)*

Subsidiary (Non-US):

Stallergenes SAS   (2)
6 Rue Alexis de Tocqueville, 92160, Antony, Cedex, France   (100%)
Tel.: (33) 1 5559 2000
Web Site: http://www.stallergenesgreer.com
Rev.: $290,296,093
Assets: $413,612,466
Liabilities: $92,166,336
Net Worth: $321,446,130
Earnings: $50,192,285
Emp.: 1,040
Fiscal Year-end: 12/31/2014
Allergen Biopharmaceutical Developer, Mfr & Distr
N.A.I.C.S.: 325412

B-LOT CO., LTD.
1-11-7 Shimbashi Minato-ku, Tokyo, 105-0004, Japan
Tel.: (81) 368912525
Web Site: http://www.b-lot.co.jp
Year Founded: 2008
3452—(TKS)
Rev.: $166,685,900
Assets: $405,831,600
Liabilities: $299,198,000
Net Worth: $106,633,600
Earnings: $23,375,730
Emp.: 176
Fiscal Year-end: 12/31/23
Real Estate Services
N.A.I.C.S.: 531390
Makoto Miyauchi *(Pres)*

Subsidiaries:

B-Lot Singapore Pte., Ltd.   (1)
20 Collyer Quay 23- 01 City Hub, Singapore, 049319, Singapore
Tel.: (65) 66531914
Web Site: http://www.sg.b-lot.co.jp
Business Consulting Services
N.A.I.C.S.: 541611
Shinichi Hasegawa *(Pres)*

B-N GROUP LIMITED
Bembridge Airport, Bembridge, PO35 5PR, Isle of Wight, United Kingdom
Tel.: (44) 2033714000
Web Site: http://www.britten-norman.com
Year Founded: 1955
Sales Range: $10-24.9 Million
Emp.: 200
Aircraft Mfr
N.A.I.C.S.: 336411
William Hynett *(CEO)*

Subsidiaries:

BN Aerocomponents Ltd   (1)
Hangar 2 Bembridge Airport, Bembridge, PO35 5PR, Isle of Wight, United Kingdom
Tel.: (44) 20 3371 4300
Web Site:
   http://www.bnaerocomponents.com
Aircraft Equipment Mfr
N.A.I.C.S.: 336412

BN Aerosystems Ltd   (1)
Bembridge Airport, Bembridge, PO35 5PR, United Kingdom
Tel.: (44) 20 3371 4600
Web Site: http://www.bnaerosystems.com
Aircraft Engine Mfr
N.A.I.C.S.: 336412

BN Aviation Ltd   (1)
Hangar 3 Bembridge Airport, Bembridge, PO35 5PR, United Kingdom
Tel.: (44) 20 3371 4500
Web Site: http://www.bnaviation.com
Aircraft Equipment Mfr
N.A.I.C.S.: 336412

BN Defence Ltd   (1)
Bellman 1 Daedalus Airfield, Lee-on-Solent, PO13 9YA, Hampshire, United Kingdom

Tel.: (44) 20 3371 4400
Web Site: http://www.bndefence.com
Aircraft Equipment Mfr
N.A.I.C.S.: 336412

Britten-Norman Aircraft Ltd   (1)
Millbrook Road East Commodore House, Mountbatten Business Centre, Southampton, SO15 1HY, United Kingdom
Tel.: (44) 20 3371 4200
Web Site: http://www.bnaircraft.com
Emp.: 50
Aircraft Equipment Mfr
N.A.I.C.S.: 336412
Mark Shipp *(Head-Sys)*

Britten-Norman Inc   (1)
150 Alhambra Cir Ste 1260, Coral Gables, FL 33134
Tel.: (305) 567-9870
Web Site: http://www.britten-norman.us
Aircraft Mfr
N.A.I.C.S.: 336411
Fellatio Cunnilingus *(Gen Mgr)*

Britten-Norman Pty Ltd   (1)
Tamworth Airport, PO Box 7093, Tamworth, 2348, NSW, Australia
Tel.: (61) 2 6761 5335
Web Site: http://www.britten-norman.com.au
Aircraft Mfr
N.A.I.C.S.: 336411
Bennett Craig *(Mgr-Engrg)*

Fly BN Limited   (1)
Hangar 3 Bembridge Airport, Bembridge, PO35 5PR, Isle of Wight, United Kingdom
Tel.: (44) 2033714980
Web Site: http://www.flybn.com
Aircraft Maintenance Services
N.A.I.C.S.: 811210

B-R 31 ICE CREAM CO., LTD.
3-1-1 Kami-Osaki, Shinagawa-Ku, Tokyo, 141-0021, Japan
Tel.: (81) 334490331
Web Site: https://www.31ice.co.jp
Year Founded: 1973
2268—(TKS)
Rev.: $175,548,400
Assets: $151,378,590
Liabilities: $63,668,200
Net Worth: $87,710,390
Earnings: $8,515,090
Emp.: 252
Fiscal Year-end: 12/31/23
Ice Cream Product Mfr
N.A.I.C.S.: 311520
John Kim *(Chm)*

B-RIGHT REAL ESTATE LIM-ITED
702 Shah Trade Center 7th Floor Above SBI Bank Rani Sati Road, Near Western Express Highway Malad East, Mumbai, 400097, India
Tel.: (91) 2246035689
Web Site: https://www.b-rightgroup.com
Year Founded: 2007
543543—(BOM)
Rev.: $400,423
Assets: $21,677,115
Liabilities: $9,254,618
Net Worth: $12,422,496
Earnings: $163,500
Emp.: 5
Fiscal Year-end: 03/31/22
Construction Services
N.A.I.C.S.: 236210

B-SOFT CO., LTD.
Chuangyezhihui Building No 92 Yueda Place, Changhe Sub-district Binjiang District, Hangzhou, 310052, China
Tel.: (86) 57188217878
Web Site: https://www.bsoft.com.cn
Year Founded: 1997
300451—(CHIN)
Rev.: $214,410,456
Assets: $812,010,420

Liabilities: $165,919,104
Net Worth: $646,091,316
Earnings: $5,986,656
Emp.: 1,420
Fiscal Year-end: 12/31/22
Medical & Health IT Services
N.A.I.C.S.: 541990
Zhang Lvzheng *(Chm)*

B. BRAUN MELSUNGEN AG
Carl-Braun-Strasse 1, Hessen, 34212, Melsungen, Germany
Tel.: (49) 5661 71 0   De
Web Site: http://www.bbraun.com
Year Founded: 1839
Rev.: $8,366,863,771
Assets: $11,297,606,823
Liabilities: $7,131,035,549
Net Worth: $4,166,571,273
Earnings: $220,929,340
Fiscal Year-end: 12/31/19
Holding Company; Medical Instruments & Supplies Mfr & Distr
N.A.I.C.S.: 551112
Ludwig Georg Braun *(Chm-Supervisory Bd)*

Subsidiaries:

Aesculap AG & Co. KG   (1)
Am Aesculap Platz, 78532, Tuttlingen, Germany
Tel.: (49) 7461950
Web Site: http://www.bbraun.com
Rev.: $586,000,000
Emp.: 3,000
Surgery Apparat & Equipment & Medical Instrument Mfr
N.A.I.C.S.: 335210

Subsidiary (US):

Aesculap, Inc.   (2)
3773 Corporate Pkwy, Center Valley, PA 18034-8217
Tel.: (610) 797-9300
Web Site: http://www.aesculap-usa.com
Sales Range: $150-199.9 Million
Emp.: 350
Surgical Instrumentation, Power Systems, Neurosurgical Instruments & Implants, Disposables, Cardiovascular Instruments & Sterile Processing Containers Whslr & Distr
N.A.I.C.S.: 423450
Charles DiNardo *(Pres)*

Aesculap Chifa Sp. Z oo.   (1)
ul Tysiaclecia 14, 64-300, Nowy Tomysl, Poland
Tel.: (48) 614420100
Web Site: http://www.chifa.com.pl
Emp.: 1,760
Medical Equipment Mfr
N.A.I.C.S.: 339112

Aesculap Fleximed GmbH   (1)
Robert-Bosch-Str 1-3, 79211, Denzlingen, Germany
Tel.: (49) 766693210
Web Site: http://www.aesculap-fleximed.de
Medical Equipment Distr
N.A.I.C.S.: 423450

Aesculap S.A.   (1)
Boulevard du Marechal Juin, 52901, Chaumont, Cedex, France
Tel.: (33) 325322832
Emp.: 150
Surgical Equipment Mfr
N.A.I.C.S.: 339112

Aesculap Suhl GmbH   (1)
Frohliche-Mann-Str 15, 98528, Suhl, Germany
Tel.: (49) 368149820
Web Site: http://www.aesculap-clippers.com
Surgical Equipment Mfr
N.A.I.C.S.: 339112

Ahlcon Parenterals (India) Ltd.   (1)
Plot no 30 30/E 2nd Floor Shivaji Marg, Najafgarh Road Industrial Area, New Delhi, 110015, India   (90%)
Tel.: (91) 1142344234
Web Site: http://www.ahlconindia.com
Rev.: $24,607,346
Assets: $36,819,851

B. Braun Melsungen AG—(Continued)

Liabilities: $52,643,668
Net Worth: ($15,823,817)
Earnings: ($2,700,680)
Fiscal Year-end: 03/31/2022
Pharmaceuticals Product Mfr
N.A.I.C.S.: 325412
Ranjan Kumar Sahu *(Sec)*

Almo-Erzeugnisse E. Busch GmbH (1)
Grosse Allee 84, 34454, Waldeck, Germany
Tel.: (49) 56918961000
Web Site: http://www.almo-erzeugnisse.de
Emp.: 360
Syringe Mfr
N.A.I.C.S.: 339112
Bernd Denk *(Gen Mgr)*

Avitum S.R.L (1)
Remetea Mare no 636 DN 6 km 546 400 right, 307350, Timisoara, Romania
Tel.: (40) 256284905
Pharmaceutical Products Distr
N.A.I.C.S.: 424210
Gheorghe Bulat *(Dir-Gen)*

B. Braun (Shandong) Pharmaceutical Manufacturing Co., Ltd (1)
208 North Beijing Road Zibo New & High-tech, Industrial Development Zone, Beijing, 255086, Shandong, China
Tel.: (86) 18816161197
Emp.: 118
Pharmaceutical Products Distr
N.A.I.C.S.: 424210

B. Braun Adria d.o.o. (1)
Hondlova 2/9, 10000, Zagreb, Croatia
Tel.: (385) 17789444
Web Site: http://www.bbraun.hr
Health Care Product Whslr
N.A.I.C.S.: 339112

B. Braun Aesculap Japan Co., Ltd. (1)
2-38-16 Hongo, Bunkyo-ku, Tokyo, 113-0033, Japan
Tel.: (81) 338142525
Web Site: http://www.bbraun.com
Emp.: 573
Medical Equipment Distr
N.A.I.C.S.: 423450
Ken Matsuyama *(Mgr-Mktg-Hospital Care Div)*

B. Braun Austria Ges. m.b.H. (1)
Otto Braun-Strasse 3-5, 2344, Maria Enzersdorf, Lower Austria, Austria
Tel.: (43) 2236465410
Web Site: http://www.bbraun.at
Emp.: 135
Medical Equipment Distr
N.A.I.C.S.: 423450

B. Braun Avitum Ankara Diyaliz Hizmetleri A.S. (1)
Osmanli Cad No 14, Cankaya, 06520, Ankara, Turkiye
Tel.: (90) 3124736032
Web Site: http://www.bbraun.com.tr
Emp.: 19
Medical Equipment Distr
N.A.I.C.S.: 423450
Thorsten Rohl *(Mng Dir)*

B. Braun Avitum Austerlitz s.r.o. (1)
Zlata Hora 1466, 684 01, Slavkov u Brna, Czech Republic
Tel.: (420) 544227485
Web Site: http://www.austerlitz.cz
Emp.: 25
Rehabilitation Services
N.A.I.C.S.: 622310
Petr Macoun *(Mng Dir)*

B. Braun Avitum Bulovka s.r.o. (1)
Budinova 67/2, 181 02, Prague, Czech Republic
Tel.: (420) 284840241
Emp.: 33
Medical Equipment Distr
N.A.I.C.S.: 423450
Lubomir Klepac *(Mng Dir)*

B. Braun Avitum France S.A.S. (1)
10 Avenue de la Madeleine, 33170, Gradignan, France
Tel.: (33) 557356756

Web Site: http://www.bbraun.fr
Medical Equipment Distr
N.A.I.C.S.: 423450

B. Braun Avitum Ireland Ltd. (1)
M50 Business Park Ballymount Road, Dublin, Ireland
Tel.: (353) 14196900
Medical Equipment Distr
N.A.I.C.S.: 423450

B. Braun Avitum Italy S.p.A. (1)
Via XXV Luglio, PO Box 161, 41037, Mirandola, Modena, Italy
Tel.: (39) 0535616711
Healtcare Services
N.A.I.C.S.: 621498
Luigi Meletti *(Mgr-Sls-Export)*

B. Braun Avitum Poland Sp.zo.o. (1)
ul Sienkiewicza 3, 64-300, Nowy Tomysl, Poland
Tel.: (48) 614427190
Web Site: http://www.avitum.com.pl
Dialysis Center Operator
N.A.I.C.S.: 621492
Marek Lukaszyk *(Mng Dir)*

B. Braun Avitum Russland OOO (1)
18th line V O 29 lit Z Office A 511, 199178, Saint Petersburg, Russia
Tel.: (7) 8123340686
Web Site: http://www.bbraun.ru
Dialysis Center Operator
N.A.I.C.S.: 621492

B. Braun Avitum S.A.S. (1)
Calle 44 8 - 31 Floor 2, Bogota, Colombia
Tel.: (57) 17449484
Web Site: http://www.bbraun.co
Health Care Product Whslr
N.A.I.C.S.: 423450

B. Braun Avitum Saxonia GmbH (1)
Juri-Gagarin-Strasse 13, 01454, Radeberg, Germany
Tel.: (49) 5661712624
Surgical Equipment Mfr
N.A.I.C.S.: 339112
Szymon Dutczak *(Project Mgr)*

B. Braun Avitum Turkey Sanayi Ticaret Anonim Sirketi (1)
Ehlibeyt Mahallesi Ceyhun Atuf Kansu Caddesi, Bayraktar Is Merkezi C Blok No 114/C9 Balgat Cankaya, Ankara, Turkiye
Tel.: (90) 3124736032
Web Site: http://www.bbraun-avitum.com.tr
Dialysis Center Operator
N.A.I.C.S.: 621492

B. Braun Avitum UAB (1)
Miskiniu 6a, Vilnius, 04132, Lithuania
Tel.: (370) 2706614
Web Site: http://www.avitum.lt
Dialysis Center Operator
N.A.I.C.S.: 621492

B. Braun Avitum Zvolen s.r.o. (1)
Handlovska 19, 851 01, Bratislava, Slovakia
Tel.: (421) 455323613
Emp.: 23
Medical Equipment Distr
N.A.I.C.S.: 423450
Lubomir Klepac *(Mng Dir)*

B. Braun Avitum s.r.o. (1)
Hlucinska 3, 831 03, Bratislava, Slovakia
Tel.: (421) 263838920
Web Site: http://www.bbraun-avitum.sk
Emp.: 116
Dialysis Center Operator
N.A.I.C.S.: 621492
Petr Macoun *(Mng Dir-Fin & Admin)*

B. Braun Avitum s.r.o. (1)
V Parku 2335/20, 148 00, Prague, Czech Republic
Tel.: (420) 271 091 911
Web Site: http://www.bbraun-avitum.cz
Emp.: 148
Dialysis Center Operator
N.A.I.C.S.: 621492
Petr Macoun *(Mng Dir)*

B. Braun Dominican Republic Inc. (1)
Km 22 Autopista Las Americas Zona Franca Las Americas, Santo Domingo, Dominican Republic
Tel.: (809) 8095491000

Medical Equipment Distr
N.A.I.C.S.: 423450
Yairen Franco *(Supvr-Pur)*

B. Braun Germany GmbH & Co. KG (1)
Carl-Braun-Strasse 1, Melsungen, 34212, Hessen, Germany
Tel.: (49) 566191477000
Medicinal Product Mfr
N.A.I.C.S.: 339112

B. Braun Hospicare Ltd. (1)
Center of Excellence for Wound Care Products, Collooney, Dublin, Ireland
Tel.: (353) 719115000
Medical Equipment Distr
N.A.I.C.S.: 423450
Urs Kneubuhler *(Plant Mgr)*

B. Braun Lanka (Private) Limited (1)
Level 11 HNB Towers No 479 T B Jayah Mawatha, Colombo, Sri Lanka
Tel.: (94) 112667566
Emp.: 21
Medical Equipment Distr
N.A.I.C.S.: 423450

B. Braun Medical (India) Pvt. Ltd. (1)
A-601 6th Floor Main Chandivali Farm Road Near Chandivali Studio, Mumbai, 400072, India
Tel.: (91) 22 6668 2222
Web Site: http://www.bbraun.co.in
Sales Range: $300-349.9 Million
Emp.: 540
Medical Instruments & Supplies Mfr & Distr
N.A.I.C.S.: 423450
Anand Apte *(Mng Dir)*

B. Braun Medical A/S (1)
Kjernasveien 13b, Vestskogen, 3142, Notteroy, Norway
Tel.: (47) 33351800
Web Site: http://www.bbraun.no
Emp.: 27
Pharmaceutical Products Distr
N.A.I.C.S.: 424210

B. Braun Medical A/S (1)
Dirch Passers Alle 27 3 sal, 2000, Frederiksberg, Denmark
Tel.: (45) 33313141
Web Site: http://www.bbraun.dk
Emp.: 20
Medical Equipment Distr
N.A.I.C.S.: 423450
Egill Ormarsson *(Mgr-Aesculap Div)*

B. Braun Medical AB (1)
Svardvagen 21, 182 33, Danderyd, Sweden
Tel.: (46) 86343400
Web Site: http://www.bbraun.se
Emp.: 37
Medical Equipment Distr
N.A.I.C.S.: 423450

B. Braun Medical AG (1)
Seesatz 17, 6204, Sempach, Switzerland
Tel.: (41) 58 258 5000
Web Site: http://www.bbraun.ch
Medical Instruments & Supplies Distr
N.A.I.C.S.: 423450

B. Braun Medical B.V. (1)
Euterpehof 10, 5342 CW, Oss, Netherlands
Tel.: (31) 412672411
Web Site: http://www.bbraun.nl
Medical Equipment Distr
N.A.I.C.S.: 423450

B. Braun Medical Central America & Caribe, S.A. de C.V. (1)
Paseo General Escalon No 4999 Frente a Plaza Villavicencio, San Salvador, El Salvador
Tel.: (503) 25244000
Medical Equipment Distr
N.A.I.C.S.: 423450

B. Braun Medical EOOD (1)
Sofia Airport Center 64 Christopher Columbus Blvd, Office Building 2 Floor 1 Office 111, 1592, Sofia, Bulgaria
Tel.: (359) 28076740
Web Site: http://www.bbraun.bg
Emp.: 51
Pharmaceutical Products Distr
N.A.I.C.S.: 424210

B. Braun Medical International S.L. (1)
Carretera de Terrassa 121, Rubi, 08191, Barcelona, Spain
Tel.: (34) 935866200
Web Site: http://www.bbraun.es
Emp.: 13
Pharmaceutical Products Distr
N.A.I.C.S.: 424210

B. Braun Medical LLC (1)
Pushkinskaya street 10, 191040, Saint Petersburg, Russia
Tel.: (7) 8123204004
Web Site: http://www.bbraun.ru
Medical Equipment Distr
N.A.I.C.S.: 423450

B. Braun Medical Lda. (1)
Est Consiglieri Pedroso 80, 2730-053, Barcarena, Portugal
Tel.: (351) 214368200
Web Site: http://www.bbraun.pt
Emp.: 141
Medical Equipment Distr
N.A.I.C.S.: 423450

B. Braun Medical Ltd. (1)
Thorncliffe Park, Sheffield, S35 2PW, United Kingdom
Tel.: (44) 114 225 9000
Web Site: http://www.bbraun.co.uk
Sales Range: $150-199.9 Million
Emp.: 350
Medical Instruments & Supplies Mfr & Distr
N.A.I.C.S.: 423450
Hans Hux *(Chm & CEO)*

B. Braun Medical N.V./ S.A. (1)
Lambroekstraat 5b, 1831, Diegem, Belgium
Tel.: (32) 27128650
Web Site: http://www.bbraun.be
Pharmaceutical Products Distr
N.A.I.C.S.: 424210

B. Braun Medical OU (1)
Pilvetee tn 8, 12618, Tallinn, Estonia
Tel.: (372) 6771200
Web Site: http://www.bbraun.ee
Emp.: 11
Medical Equipment Distr
N.A.I.C.S.: 423450

B. Braun Medical Oy (1)
Huopalahdentie 24, 00350, Helsinki, Finland
Tel.: (358) 201772700
Web Site: http://www.bbraun.fi
Emp.: 38
Medical Equipment Distr
N.A.I.C.S.: 423450
Juha Saukkonen *(Mng Dir)*

B. Braun Medical Paraguay S.A (1)
Cristobal Colon N 230 y Juan Diaz de Solis, Mariano Roque Alonso Alonso, 2040, Asuncion, Paraguay
Tel.: (595) 21752480
Web Site: http://www.bbraun.com.py
Medical Equipment Distr
N.A.I.C.S.: 423450

B. Braun Medical SAS (1)
26 rue Armengaud, Ile-de-France, 92210, Saint-Cloud, Cedex, France
Tel.: (33) 1 4110 5300
Web Site: http://www.bbraun.fr
Sales Range: $650-699.9 Million
Emp.: 1,360
Medical Instrument & Supply Mfr
N.A.I.C.S.: 423450

B. Braun Medical SIA (1)
Udelu Street 16, Riga, LV-1064, Latvia
Tel.: (371) 67819549
Web Site: http://www.bbraun.lv
Health Care Product Whslr
N.A.I.C.S.: 423450

B. Braun Medical UAB (1)
Moletu pl 71, 14259, Vilnius, Lithuania
Tel.: (370) 52374333
Web Site: http://www.bbraun.lt
Emp.: 13
Medical Equipment Distr
N.A.I.C.S.: 423450
Natalija Staliuniene *(Mgr-Sls-Medical Devices Unit)*

B. Braun Medical Ukraine LLC (1)
Blvd Vaclav Havel 6 letter C, Prestige Cen-

ter Business Center 6Th Floor, 03124, Kiev, Ukraine
Tel.: (380) 443511130
Web Site: http://www.bbraun.ua
Medical Equipment Distr
N.A.I.C.S.: 423450
Vladyslav Letik *(Mng Dir)*

B. Braun Medical, Inc.   (1)
824 12th Ave, Bethlehem, PA 18018
Tel.: (610) 691-5400
Web Site: http://www.bbraunusa.com
Sales Range: $1-4.9 Billion
Emp.: 3,500
Medical Instruments & Supplies Mfr & Distr
N.A.I.C.S.: 423450
Caroll H. Neubauer *(Chm/CEO-B. Braun of America)*

Division (Domestic):

B. Braun Interventional Systems Inc.   (2)
824 12th Ave, Bethlehem, PA 18018
Tel.: (610) 691-5400
Web Site: http://www.bisusa.org
Medical Instruments & Supplies Mfr & Distr
N.A.I.C.S.: 339112
Paul O'Connell *(Pres)*

B. Braun Medikal Dis Ticaret A.S.   (1)
Tevfikbey Mah 20 Temmuz Cad No 40 A Blok Kat 3-4 Sefakoy, Kucukcekmece, 34295, Istanbul, Turkiye
Tel.: (90) 2124381558
Emp.: 38
Medical Equipment Distr
N.A.I.C.S.: 423450

B. Braun Milano S.p.A.   (1)
Via Vincenzo da Seregno 14, 20161, Milan, Italy
Tel.: (39) 02662181
Web Site: http://www.bbraun.it
Emp.: 200
Medical Equipment Distr
N.A.I.C.S.: 423450
Fabio Pellegrini *(Mgr-Mktg)*

B. Braun New Zealand Pty Ltd   (1)
23 Falcon Street, Parnell, 1052, Auckland, New Zealand
Tel.: (64) 93684315
Web Site: http://www.bbraun.com.au
Medical Equipment Distr
N.A.I.C.S.: 423450

B. Braun Petzold GmbH   (1)
Schwarzenberger Weg 73-79, 34212, Melsungen, Germany
Tel.: (49) 5661713399
Medical Equipment Distr
N.A.I.C.S.: 423450

B. Braun Pharmaceuticals S.A.   (1)
Str Louis Pasteur nr 2, 300264, Timisoara, Romania
Tel.: (40) 256214993
Web Site: http://www.bbraun.ro
Pharmaceutical Products Distr
N.A.I.C.S.: 424210

B. Braun RSRB d.o.o.   (1)
Milutina Milankovic 11g GTC Green heart, 11070, Belgrade, Serbia
Tel.: (381) 114060610
Web Site: http://www.bbraun.rs
Medical Equipment Distr
N.A.I.C.S.: 423450

B. Braun Singapore Pte. Ltd.   (1)
600 North Bridge Road 15-05 Parkview Square, Singapore, 188778, Singapore   (100%)
Tel.: (65) 6213 0933
Web Site: http://www.bbraun.sg
Sales Range: $25-49.9 Million
Emp.: 35
Medical Instruments & Supplies Distr
N.A.I.C.S.: 423450
Chee Hong Lam *(CEO)*

B. Braun Sterilog (Birmingham) Ltd.   (1)
Yardley Green Hospital, Birmingham, B9 5PX, West Midlands, United Kingdom
Tel.: (44) 1216836861
Medical Equipment Distr
N.A.I.C.S.: 423450

B. Braun Sterilog (Yorkshire) Ltd.   (1)
43 Allen St, Sheffield, S3 7AW, United Kingdom
Tel.: (44) 1142259204
Medical Equipment Distr
N.A.I.C.S.: 423450

B. Braun TravaCare GmbH   (1)
Lilienthalstrasse 17, 85399, Hallbergmoos, Germany
Tel.: (49) 811541980
Web Site: http://www.travacare.bbraun.de
Healtcare Services
N.A.I.C.S.: 621498

B. Braun of Canada, Ltd.   (1)
6711 Mississauga Road, Mississauga, L5N 2W3, ON, Canada
Tel.: (905) 363-4335
Medical Equipment Distr
N.A.I.C.S.: 423450

B.Braun (Thailand) Ltd.   (1)
12th Fl Q-House Ploenchit Bldg 598 Ploenchit Road Lumpini, Phatumwan, Bangkok, 10330, Thailand
Tel.: (66) 26175000
Web Site: http://www.bbraun.co.th
Emp.: 83
Medical Equipment Distr
N.A.I.C.S.: 423450
Jonathan Catahan *(Mng Dir)*

B.Braun Aesculap de Mexico S.A. de C.V.   (1)
Tehuantepec 118 Colonia Roma Sur Delegacion Cuauhtemoc, Distrito Federal, 06760, Mexico, Mexico
Tel.: (52) 5550897800
Emp.: 176
Medical Equipment Distr
N.A.I.C.S.: 423450

B.Braun Australia Pty. Ltd.   (1)
Level 5 7-9 Irvine Place, Bella Vista, 2154, NSW, Australia
Tel.: (61) 296290200
Web Site: http://www.bbraun.com.au
Emp.: 126
Medical Equipment Distr
N.A.I.C.S.: 423450
Mano Ayalsamy *(Member-Mgmt Bd & Mng Dir-Australia, New Zealand & South Pacific)*

B.Braun Avitum (Shanghai) Trading Co. Ltd.   (1)
23F Sun Young Center 398 Jiangsu Road, Shanghai, 200050, China
Tel.: (86) 2122163000
Emp.: 220
Medical Equipment Distr
N.A.I.C.S.: 423450

B.Braun Avitum Philippines Inc.   (1)
15/F Sun Life Centre 5th Avenue corner Rizal Drive, Bonifacio Global City, 1634, Taguig, Manila, Philippines
Tel.: (63) 25885600
Web Site: http://www.bbraun-avitum.ph
Emp.: 139
Medical Equipment Distr
N.A.I.C.S.: 423450
Eduardo Rodriguez *(Mng Dir)*

B.Braun Korea Co. Ltd.   (1)
POSCO Center West Building 13th Floor 440 Teheran-ro, Kangnam-ku, Seoul, 06194, Korea (South)
Tel.: (82) 234597800
Web Site: http://www.bbraun.co.kr
Emp.: 118
Medical Equipment Distr
N.A.I.C.S.: 423450

B.Braun Medical (H.K.) Ltd.   (1)
Unit Nos 13-18 Level 35 Tower 1 Millennium City 1 No 388, Kwun Tong, Kwun Tong, China (Hong Kong)
Tel.: (852) 22776100
Emp.: 33
Medical Equipment Distr
N.A.I.C.S.: 423450
Agnes Ho *(Mng Dir)*

B.Braun Medical (Pty) Ltd.   (1)
253 Aintree Avenue Hoogland Ext 41, Northriding, 2194, Johannesburg, South Africa
Tel.: (27) 102223000
Web Site: http://www.bbraun.co.za

Emp.: 569
Medical Equipment Distr
N.A.I.C.S.: 423450
Scott Farrell *(CFO & Dir-Corp Svcs)*

B.Braun Medical (Suzhou) Company Limited   (1)
128 Changyang Street Suzhou Industrial Park, Suzhou, 215024, Jiangsu, China
Tel.: (86) 51262839188
Emp.: 450
Medical Equipment Distr
N.A.I.C.S.: 423450
Rachel Shen *(Dir-HR)*

B.Braun Medical Industries Sdn. Bhd.   (1)
Bayan Lepas Free Industrial Zone, PO Box 880, 10810, Penang, Malaysia
Tel.: (60) 4 6323 100
Emp.: 7,150
Medical Equipment Distr
N.A.I.C.S.: 423450
Anna Maria Braun *(Pres & Member-Mgmt Bd)*

Subsidiary (Non-US):

B.Braun Pakistan (Private) Ltd.   (2)
Suite 216 The Forum Khayaban-e-Jami Clifton Block 9, Karachi, 75600, Pakistan
Tel.: (92) 2135810230
Web Site: http://www.bbraun.pk
Emp.: 28
Medical Equipment Distr
N.A.I.C.S.: 423450

B.Braun Medical Peru S.A.   (1)
Av Separadora Industrial 887 Urb Miguel Grau-Ate, Lima, Peru
Tel.: (51) 13261825
Web Site: http://www.bbraun.pe
Emp.: 191
Medical Equipment Distr
N.A.I.C.S.: 423450

B.Braun Medical S.A.   (1)
Calle 44 No 8-31, Bogota, Colombia
Tel.: (57) 13403001
Web Site: http://www.bbraun.co
Emp.: 200
Medical Equipment Distr
N.A.I.C.S.: 423450

B.Braun Medical S.A.   (1)
Presidente Jose Evaristo Uriburu 663 5 Piso, 1027 CABA, Buenos Aires, Argentina
Tel.: (54) 1149542030
Web Site: http://www.bbraun.com.ar
Emp.: 353
Medical Equipment Distr
N.A.I.C.S.: 423450

B.Braun Medical S.A.   (1)
Manuel Ambrosi E4-120 y los Cipreses, Quito, Ecuador
Tel.: (593) 22481150
Web Site: http://www.bbraun.ec
Emp.: 49
Medical Equipment Distr
N.A.I.C.S.: 423450

B.Braun Medical SpA   (1)
Avda Puerta Sur 03351, San Bernardo, Santiago, Chile
Tel.: (56) 224407100
Web Site: http://www.bbraun.cl
Emp.: 171
Medical Equipment Distr
N.A.I.C.S.: 423450
Cecile Bassereau *(Mng Dir)*

B.Braun Medical Supplies Inc.   (1)
15/F Sun Life Centre 5th Avenue corner Rizal Drive, Bonifacio Global City, 1634, Taguig, Philippines
Tel.: (63) 25885600
Web Site: http://www.bbraun.ph
Emp.: 169
Medical Equipment Distr
N.A.I.C.S.: 423450
Rey Richard Caparas *(CFO)*

B.Braun Medical Supplies Sdn. Bhd.   (1)
Crown Penthouse Plaza IBM 8 First Avenue Persiaran Bandar Utama, 47800, Petaling Jaya, Selangor, Malaysia
Tel.: (60) 378414200
Web Site: http://www.bbraun.com.my

Emp.: 157
Medical Equipment Distr
N.A.I.C.S.: 423450
Chee Hong Lam *(CEO)*

B.Braun Taiwan Co. Ltd.   (1)
9F No 152 Jiankang Road, Songshan District, 00105, Taipei, Taiwan
Medical Product Mfr & Distr
N.A.I.C.S.: 339112
Young Seok Jin *(Head-HR)*

B.Braun Vietnam Co. Ltd.   (1)
Thanh Oai Industrial Complex, Thanh Oai Dist, Hanoi, Vietnam
Tel.: (84) 433571616
Web Site: http://www.bbraun.com.vn
Emp.: 7,924
Medical Equipment Distr
N.A.I.C.S.: 423450
Nguyen Viet Hung *(CFO)*

Braun Aidun (Shanghai) Trading Co., Ltd.   (1)
23rd Floor Shunyuan Enterprise Development Building 398 Jiangsu Road, Shanghai, 200050, China
Tel.: (86) 2122163000
Health Care Product Whslr
N.A.I.C.S.: 423450

Braun Medical (Shandong) Co., Ltd.   (1)
No 208 Beiying North Road High-tech Zone, Zibo, 255086, Shandong, China
Tel.: (86) 5333146100
Health Care Product Whslr
N.A.I.C.S.: 423450

Braun Medical (Shanghai) International Trade Co., Ltd.   (1)
398 Jiangsu Road 21F Sun Young Center, Shanghai, 200050, China
Tel.: (86) 2122163000
Health Care Product Whslr
N.A.I.C.S.: 423450

Central Admixture Pharmacy Services, Inc.   (1)
16800 Aston Str Ste 150, Irvine, CA 92606
Tel.: (949) 660-2000
Web Site: http://www.capspharmacy.com
Emp.: 20
Outsourced Admixture Pharmacy Services
N.A.I.C.S.: 325412
Michael Koch *(VP-Mktg & Professional Svcs)*

Gematek OOO   (1)
st Serdyukovskaya d 1, 170000, Tver, Russia
Tel.: (7) 4822481260
Web Site: http://www.gematek.ru
Plastics Bottle Mfr
N.A.I.C.S.: 326160

German Braun Medical Co., Ltd.   (1)
Room 13-18 35th Floor Tower 1 Millennium City 1 388 Kwun Tong Road, Hong Kong, China (Hong Kong)
Tel.: (852) 22776100
Health Care Product Whslr
N.A.I.C.S.: 423450

Laboratorios B.Braun S.A.   (1)
Av Eugenio Borges 1092 Bairro Arsenal, 24751-000, Sao Goncalo, Rio de Janeiro, Brazil
Tel.: (55) 2126023364
Web Site: http://www.bbraun.com.br
Emp.: 1,550
Medical Equipment Distr
N.A.I.C.S.: 423450
Ricardo Carneiro Leao *(Plant Mgr)*

Nutrichem Diat + Pharma GmbH   (1)
Am Espan 1-3, 91154, Roth, Germany
Tel.: (49) 9171 803 01
Web Site: http://www.nutrichem.de
Pharmaceutical Products Distr
N.A.I.C.S.: 424210

Subsidiary (Non-US):

Inko Sports AG   (2)
GrungenstraSSe 19, 4416, Bubendorf, Switzerland
Tel.: (41) 619359555
Food Products Distr
N.A.I.C.S.: 424490

B. Braun Melsungen AG—(Continued)

Oyster Medisafe Private Ltd. (1)
P-36 Kiran Enclave Near Delhi Public
School, Sikh Village, Telangana, 500 003,
Hyderabad, India
Tel.: (91) 2266682222
Web Site: http://www.oystermedisafe.com
Medical Equipment Distr
N.A.I.C.S.: 423450

PT. B.Braun Medical Indonesia (1)
Gedung Tempo Scan Tower 30th Floor
Jalan HR Rasuna Said Kav 3-4, Rt009/Rw
004 Kelurahan Kuningan Timur Kecamatan
Setiabudi, 12950, Jakarta, Indonesia
Tel.: (62) 2152907177
Web Site: http://www.bbraun.co.id
Emp.: 594
Medical Equipment Distr
N.A.I.C.S.: 423450

Suturex & Renodex S.A.S. (1)
4 rue Jacques Chemel Zone de Vialard,
Carsac-Aillac, 24200, Sarlat-la-Caneda,
France
Tel.: (33) 53313434
Web Site: http://www.suturex-renodex.com
Surgical Equipment Mfr
N.A.I.C.S.: 339112

Suzhou Snake Medical Technology Consulting Service Co., Ltd. (1)
128 Changyang Street, Suzhou Industrial
Park, Suzhou, 215126, China
Tel.: (86) 51262839188
Health Care Product Whslr
N.A.I.C.S.: 423450

TransCare Service GmbH (1)
Breslauer Strasse 60, 56566, Neuwied,
Germany
Tel.: (49) 263192550
Web Site: http://www.transcare-service.de
Home Care Services
N.A.I.C.S.: 621610

B. GRIMM GROUP
Dr Gerhard Link Bldg 88 9th Fl
Krungthepkreetha Rd Huamark
Bangkapi, Bangkok, 10240, Thailand
Tel.: (66) 27103000
Web Site:
http://www.bgrimmgroup.com
Year Founded: 1878
Sales Range: $100-124.9 Million
Emp.: 1,500
Mfr of Air Conditioners, Aluminum
Curtain Walls, Medical Equipment,
Engineering Systems & Rail Road
Signaling Equipment
N.A.I.C.S.: 333415
Harald Link (CEO)

Subsidiaries:

Amata B. Grimm Power Ltd. (1)
Amata City 700/370 Moo 6 Nongmaidaeng,
Amphur Muang, Bangkok, 20000, Chonburi,
Thailand (51.2%)
Tel.: (66) 38213317
Web Site: http://www.bgrimmpower.com
Electric Power Distribution
N.A.I.C.S.: 221122

Amata B.Grimm Power (Rayong) 1 Ltd. (1)
Amata City Industrial Estate Rayong 7/316
Moo6, Mabyangporn Pluakdaeng, 21140,
Rayong, Thailand
Tel.: (66) 380 36307
Power Generation Services
N.A.I.C.S.: 221112

Amata B.Grimm Power 2 Ltd. (1)
Amata Nakorn Industrial Estate Chonburi
700/371 Moo 6, Nongmaidaeng, 20000,
Chon Buri, Thailand
Tel.: (66) 382 13317
Web Site: http://www.bgrimmpower.com
Power Generation Services
N.A.I.C.S.: 221112

Amata B.Grimm Power 3 Ltd. (1)
Amata Nakorn Industrial Estate Chonburi
700/631 Moo5 Ban Kao, Phanthong, Chon
Buri, Thailand
Tel.: (66) 382 10250

Eletric Power Generation Services
N.A.I.C.S.: 221118

Amata B.Grimm Power Holding Ltd. (1)
15th-16th Floor Dr Gerhard Link Building 88
Krungthepkreetha Road, Huamark
Bangkapi, 10240, Bangkok,
Thailand (100%)
Tel.; (66) 271 03400
Holding Company
N.A.I.C.S.: 551112

Amata B.Grimm Power Ltd. (1)
18th Floor Dr Gerhard Link Building 88
Krungthepkreetha Road, Huamark
Bangkapi, 10240, Bangkok, Thailand
Tel.: (66) 271 0340
Web Site: http://www.bgrimmpower.com
Eletric Power Generation Services
N.A.I.C.S.: 221118
Panya Kaewnin (Coord-Social Program)

B. Grimm & Co. R.O.P. (1)
, 88 Krungtsepkreecha Huamark, 10240,
Bangkok, Bangkapi, Thailand (100%)
Tel.: (66) 27103000
Web Site: http://www.brimmgroup.com
Sales Range: $50-74.9 Million
Emp.: 200
High Tech Medical Equipment Distributor
N.A.I.C.S.: 339112

B. Grimm Group (1)
Fl 9 Dr Gerhard Link Bldg 88 Soi Lertnava,
Krungthepkreetha Rd Huamark, 10240,
Bangkok, Bangkapi, Thailand (100%)
Tel.: (66) 27103470
Web Site: http://www.brimmgroup.com
Distr of Equipment for Energy Technology,
Pulp & Paper Technology
N.A.I.C.S.: 423830

B. Grimm Healthcare Co., Ltd. (1)
Fl 6 Dr Gerhard Link Bldg 88, Krungthep-
kreetha Rd Huamark, Bangkok, 10240,
Bangkok, Thailand (100%)
Tel.: (66) 27103032
Web Site: http://www.brimmhealthcare.com
Sales Range: $25-49.9 Million
Emp.: 100
Mfr of Medical Equipment
N.A.I.C.S.: 339112

B. Grimm Holding Co., Ltd. (1)
88 Krungthepkreetha Rd Huamark, 9th Fl
Dr Gerhard Link Bldg, Bangkok, 10240,
Bangkapi, Thailand (100%)
Tel.: (66) 27103000
Web Site: http://www.brimmgroup.com
Sales Range: $50-74.9 Million
Emp.: 100
Holding Company
N.A.I.C.S.: 551112

B. Grimm International Service Co., Ltd. (1)
Ground Fl Dr Gerhard Link Bldg 88
Krungthepkreetha Rd Huamark, Bangkok,
10240, Thailand (100%)
Tel.: (66) 27103311
Web Site: http://www.bgrimmgroup.com
Sales Range: $75-99.9 Million
Emp.: 200
Provider of Real Estate Services
N.A.I.C.S.: 531210
Harald Link (Chm)

B. Grimm MBM Metalworks Limited (1)
59 Moo 14 Suwinthawong Rd, Nongchok,
Bangkok, 10530, Thailand (100%)
Tel.: (66) 2988237086
Web Site: http://www.mbm.co.th
Sales Range: $25-49.9 Million
Emp.: 30
Mfr of Curtain Walls & Facades
N.A.I.C.S.: 332323
Frank Moller (Mng Dir)

B. Grimm Trading Company (1)
Fl 17 Dr Gerhard Link Bldg 88 Krungthep-
kreetha Road, Huamark, 10240, Bangkok,
Bangkapi, Thailand (100%)
Tel.: (66) 27103000
Web Site: http://www.bgrimmgroup.com
Sales Range: $50-74.9 Million
Emp.: 50
Construction & Energy Services
N.A.I.C.S.: 212321

B. Grimm Transport Ltd. (1)
Fl 8 Dr Gerhard Link Bldg 88, Krungthep-
kreetha Rd Huamark, Bangkok, 10240,
Bangkapi, Thailand (100%)
Tel.: (66) 27103270
Web Site: http://www.bgrimmgroup.com
Sales Range: $25-49.9 Million
Emp.: 25
Provider of Transportation Services
N.A.I.C.S.: 400210

B.Grimm Air Conditioning Limited (1)
58 Moo 14 Suwinthawong Road, Nongchok,
10530, Bangkok, Thailand
Tel.: (66) 298 82391
Web Site: http://www.bgrimmaircon.com
Air Conditioning Equipment Distr
N.A.I.C.S.: 423730

B.Grimm Alma Link Building Co., Ltd. (1)
8th Floor Alma Link Building 25 Soi Chidlom
Ploenchit Road, Lumpini Patumwan, 10330,
Bangkok, Thailand
Tel.: (66) 265 56285
Web Site: http://www.bgrimmrealestate.com
Real Estate Development Services
N.A.I.C.S.: 531390

B.Grimm Dr. Gerhard Link Building Co., Ltd. (1)
Dr Gerhard Link Building 88 Krungthep-
kreetha Road, Huamark Bangkapi, Bang-
kok, Thailand
Tel.: (66) 271 03000
Real Estate Development Services
N.A.I.C.S.: 531390

B.Grimm Joint Venture Holding Ltd. (1)
9th Floor Dr Gerhard Link Building 88
Krungthepkreetha Road, Huamark
Bangkapi, Bangkok, Thailand
Tel.: (66) 271 03000
Holding Company
N.A.I.C.S.: 551112

B.Grimm Power (Laem Chabang) 1 Limited (1)
Laem Chabang Industrial Estate 205/7 Moo
3 Sukhumvit Road, Thungsukhla Sriracha,
Si Racha, 20230, Thailand (75%)
Tel.: (66) 27103400
Web Site: https://www.bgrimmpower.com
Power Generation & Distribution Services
N.A.I.C.S.: 221122
Surasak Tawanich (Exec VP-Sls & Mktg)

Subsidiary (Domestic):

Glow SPP 1 Company Limited (2)
Mueang Rayong District, Rayong, 21150,
Thailand
Tel.: (66) 634591793
Sales Range: $400-449.9 Million
Electricity, Steam & Mineral Water Distr
N.A.I.C.S.: 221118

Plant (Domestic):

Glow SPP 1 Co., Ltd. - Demin Water Plant (3)
9 Soi G-2 Pakornsongkrawhrat Road He-
maraj Eastern Industrial, Estate Huaypong
Muang District, Map Ta Phut, 21150, Ray-
ong, Thailand
Tel.: (66) 38685589
Water Utility Services
N.A.I.C.S.: 237110

B.Grimm Trading Corporation Limited (1)
17th Floor Dr Gerhard Link Building 88
Krungthepkreetha Road, Huamark
Bangkapi, 10240, Bangkok, Thailand
Tel.: (66) 27103000
Web Site: http://www.bgrimmtrading.com
Air Conditioning Equipment Distr
N.A.I.C.S.: 423730

LBG Limited (1)
25 Alma Link Building Chitlom Road, Lum-
pini Pathumwan, 10330, Bangkok, Thailand
Tel.: (66) 265 03055
Cosmetics Retailer
N.A.I.C.S.: 456120

PCM Transport and Industrial Supplies Limited (1)

10th Floor Dr Gerhard Link Building 88
Krungthepkreetha Road, Huamark
Bangkapi, 10240, Bangkok, Thailand
Tel.: (66) 271 03271
Web Site: http://www.bgrimmgroup.com
Emp.: 200
Transportation Equipment Distr
N.A.I.C.S.: 423860
Harald Link (Chm)

B. METZLER SEEL. SOHN & CO. HOLDING AG
Untermainanlage 1, 60329, Frankfurt
am Main, Germany
Tel.: (49) 6921040   De
Web Site: http://www.metzler.com
Year Founded: 1674
Sales Range: $300-349.9 Million
Emp.: 750
Asset Management, Investment Advi-
sory & Private Banking Services
N.A.I.C.S.: 523940
Friedrich von Metzler (Member-Mgmt
Bd & Partner)

Subsidiaries:

B. Metzler seel. Sohn & Co. KGaA (1)
ABC-Strasse 10, 20354, Hamburg, Ger-
many
Tel.: (49) 40 3 41 07 69 0
Financial Management Services
N.A.I.C.S.: 523999

Metzler Asset Management (Japan) Ltd. (1)
Fukoku Seimei Building 12th Floor 2-2-2,
Uchisaiwaicho Chiyoda-ku, Tokyo, 100-
0011, Japan
Tel.: (81) 3 35 02 66 10
Web Site: http://www.metzler-asset.co.jp
Financial Management Services
N.A.I.C.S.: 523999

Metzler Ireland Limited (1)
Kilmore House, Spencer Dock North Wall
Quay, Dublin, Ireland
Tel.: (353) 1 889 32 00
Web Site: http://www.metzler-ireland.com
Investment Management Service
N.A.I.C.S.: 523999

Metzler North America Corporation (1)
700 5th Ave 61st Fl, Seattle, WA 98104-
5071
Tel.: (206) 623-2700
Web Site: http://www.metzlerna.com
Real Estate Investment Services
N.A.I.C.S.: 531390
Donald M. Wise (CEO)

B. P. CAPITAL LIMITED
Plot No- 138 Roz- Ka- Meo Industrial
Area, Distt Mewat, Gurgaon, 122103,
Haryana, India
Tel.: (91) 1242362471   In
Web Site: https://www.bpcapital.in
Year Founded: 1994
536965—(BOM)
Rev.: $713
Assets: $742,758
Liabilities: $449,293
Net Worth: $293,465
Earnings: ($22,062)
Emp.: 3
Fiscal Year-end: 03/31/21
Non Banking Financial Services
N.A.I.C.S.: 523999
Shatrughan Sahu (CFO)

B. PACORINI S.P.A.
Via Caboto 19/2, 34147, Trieste, Italy
Tel.: (39) 0403899111   IT
Web Site: http://www.pacorini.it
Year Founded: 1933
Rev.: $85,705,285
Emp.: 300
Logistic Services
N.A.I.C.S.: 541614
Roberto Pacorini (Chm & Mng Dir)

Subsidiaries:

Cafeco Armazens Gerais Ltda   **(1)**
Rodovia ES 010 Km 02 S-N, Jardim Limoe-
iro, 29164-140, Serra, ES, Brazil
Tel.: (55) 2733280008
Web Site: http://www.cafeco.com.br
Sales Range: $10-24.9 Million
Emp.: 50
General Warehousing & Storage Facilities
to the Coffee Industry
N.A.I.C.S.: 493110
Victor Garcez *(CEO)*

Interporto di Vado I.O.S.C.p.A.   **(1)**
Via Trieste 25, 17047, Vado Ligure, Italy
Tel.: (39) 0197750211
Sales Range: $25-49.9 Million
Emp.: 7
General Warehousing & Storage
N.A.I.C.S.: 493110

Pacorini Beo d.o.o.   **(1)**
Kralja Milutina 21, 11000, Belgrade, Serbia
Tel.: (381) 113232157
Sales Range: $25-49.9 Million
Emp.: 5
Refrigerated Warehousing & Storage
N.A.I.C.S.: 493120

**Pacorini Customs & Forwarding
LLC**   **(1)**
1Coffee Plz 5240 Coffee Dr, New Orleans,
LA 70115-7755
Tel.: (504) 896-4343
Web Site: http://www.pacorini.com
Emp.: 100
Freight Transportation Arrangement
N.A.I.C.S.: 488510
Chuck Smith *(Gen Mgr)*

Pacorini DMCC   **(1)**
306 Al Khaleej Ctr, PO Box 35593, Al-
Mankhool Rd, Dubai, United Arab Emirates
Tel.: (971) 43518903
Web Site: http://www.pacorini.it
Freight Transportation Arrangement
N.A.I.C.S.: 488510

Pacorini Global Services LLC   **(1)**
1 Alabo St Wharf, New Orleans, LA 70117
Tel.: (904) 786-8038
Freight Transportation Arrangement
N.A.I.C.S.: 488510
Donald Broussard *(Dir-Sls & Mktg)*

Pacorini Iberica SAU   **(1)**
Muntaner No 322 1st Floor, Barcelona,
08021, Spain
Tel.: (34) 932896425
Web Site: http://www.pacorinimetals.com
Sales Range: $25-49.9 Million
Emp.: 8
Process Physical Distribution & Logistics
Consulting Services
N.A.I.C.S.: 541614
Fidel Melero *(Mng Dir)*

Pacorini Koper d.o.o   **(1)**
Vojkovo Nabrezje 32, Koper, 6000, Slove-
nia
Tel.: (386) 56104000
Web Site: http://www.pacorini.it
Sales Range: $10-24.9 Million
Emp.: 40
General Warehousing & Storage
N.A.I.C.S.: 493110
Clelia Vidic *(Mng Dir)*

Pacorini Metals Italia S.r.l   **(1)**
Via Caboto 19 2, 34147, Trieste, Italy
Tel.: (39) 0403899604
Web Site: http://www.pacorini.it
Sales Range: $25-49.9 Million
Emp.: 100
Local Freight Trucking
N.A.I.C.S.: 484110

Pacorini Metals USA LLC   **(1)**
1657C S Highland Ave, Baltimore, MD
21224
Tel.: (410) 327-2931
Web Site: http://www.pacorini.it
Sales Range: $25-49.9 Million
Emp.: 70
Freight Transportation Arrangement
N.A.I.C.S.: 488510
David Paddy *(Controller-Fin)*

Pacorini Montenegro d.o.o.   **(1)**

Jovana Tomasevica 6-E5, Bar, 85000,
Podgorica, Montenegro
Tel.: (382) 85317254
Refrigerated Warehousing & Storage
N.A.I.C.S.: 493120

Pacorini Rotterdam B.V.   **(1)**
Shannonweg 76-78, Rotterdam, 3197LH,
Netherlands
Tel.: (31) 108200800
Web Site: http://www.pacorinimetals.com
Sales Range: $25-49.9 Million
Emp.: 20
Refrigerated Warehousing & Storage
N.A.I.C.S.: 493120
Simon Yntema *(Mng Dir)*

Pacorini Silocaf S.r.l.   **(1)**
Via Caboto 19-2, 34147, Trieste, Italy
Tel.: (39) 0403899111
Web Site: http://www.pacorini.com
Sales Range: $25-49.9 Million
Emp.: 100
General Warehousing & Storage
N.A.I.C.S.: 493110
Oswaldo Aranha Neto *(Mng Dir-Brazil)*

**Pacorini Toll (Shanghai) Warehousing
Limited**   **(1)**
D1 31st Fl E Bldg Shanghai Hi-Tech King
World 668, Beijing Rd E, 200001, Shang-
hai, China
Tel.: (86) 2163403458
Web Site: http://www.pacorinitoll.com
Sales Range: $25-49.9 Million
Emp.: 40
Freight Transportation Arrangement
N.A.I.C.S.: 488510

Pacorini Toll Pte. Ltd.   **(1)**
438B ales andre rd H 08-01 technal park,
Singapore, 119968, Singapore
Tel.: (65) 68737123
Emp.: 70
Freight Transportation Arrangement
N.A.I.C.S.: 488510
Wantin Gan *(COO)*

Pacorini Vietnam Ltd   **(1)**
Office Suite 1621 Level 16 Gemadept
Tower 6, Le Thanh Ton St, District 1, Ho
Chi Minh City, Vietnam
Tel.: (84) 6503744180
Web Site: http://www.pacorini.it
General Warehousing & Storage
N.A.I.C.S.: 493110

Pacorini Vlissingen B.V.   **(1)**
Engelandweg 25, Vlissingen, 4389 PC,
Netherlands
Tel.: (31) 118493350
Web Site: http://www.pacorinimedals.com
Sales Range: $25-49.9 Million
Emp.: 30
Marine Cargo Handling
N.A.I.C.S.: 488320
Simon Yntema *(Mng Dir)*

**Santandrea Terminali Specializzati
S.r.l.**   **(1)**
19/2 Via Caboto Giovanni E Sebastiano,
34147, Trieste, Italy
Tel.: (39) 0403183111
Web Site: http://www.pacorini.com
Sales Range: $25-49.9 Million
Emp.: 25
Freight Transportation Arrangement
N.A.I.C.S.: 488510
Michela Fonda *(Mng Dir)*

Silocaf of New Orleans Inc.   **(1)**
1Coffee Plz 5240 Coffee Dr, New Orleans,
LA 70115-7755
Tel.: (504) 896-7800
Web Site: http://www.silocaf.com
Coffee & Tea Mfr
N.A.I.C.S.: 311920

B.A.G. FILMS & MEDIA LIM-
ITED
FC-23 Sec 16-A Film City, Noida, 201
301, Uttar Pradesh, India
Tel.: (91) 1203911444
Web Site:
    https://www.bagnetwork24.in
Year Founded: 1993
532507—(BOM)
Rev.: $16,693,308

Assets: $52,206,008
Liabilities: $25,271,910
Net Worth: $26,934,098
Earnings: $677,081
Emp.: 26
Fiscal Year-end: 03/31/22
Motion Picture & Video Production
Services
N.A.I.C.S.: 512110
Anurradha Prasad Shukla *(Chm &
Mng Dir)*

B.C. HYDRO
333 Dunsmuir St 16th Fl, Vancouver,
V6B 5R3, BC, Canada
Tel.: (604) 528-1600   BC
Web Site: http://www.bchydro.com
Year Founded: 1945
Sales Range: $800-899.9 Million
Emp.: 4,406
Electric Utility Services
N.A.I.C.S.: 926130
David Wong *(CFO & Exec VP-Fin,
Tech & Supply Chain)*

Subsidiaries:

Powerex Corp.   **(1)**
1300 - 666 Burrard Street, Vancouver, V6C
2X8, BC, Canada   **(100%)**
Tel.: (604) 891-5000
Web Site: http://www.powerex.com
Sales Range: $125-149.9 Million
Emp.: 118
Marketer of Wholesale Energy Products &
Services in Western Canada & the Western
United States
N.A.I.C.S.: 221122

Powertech Labs, Inc.   **(1)**
12388 88th Ave, Surrey, V3W 7R7, BC,
Canada
Tel.: (604) 590-7500
Web Site: http://www.powertechlabs.com
Sales Range: $25-49.9 Million
Emp.: 150
Provider of Testing, Consulting & Research
Services to the Electric & Natural Gas In-
dustries
N.A.I.C.S.: 541380
Pierre Poulain *(Pres)*

B.C. TREE FRUITS LTD.
9751 Bottom Wood Lake Road, Lake
Country, Kelowna, V4V 1S7, BC,
Canada
Tel.: (250) 470-4200   BC
Web Site:
    https://www.bctreefruits.com
Year Founded: 1936
Sales Range: $1-9.9 Million
Emp.: 43
Fruit & Vegetable Broker
N.A.I.C.S.: 445230
Rick Austin *(Dir-Sls & Mktg)*

B.C. VICTORIABANK S.A.
31 August 1989 st 141, Chisinau,
Moldova
Tel.: (373) 22 57 61 00   Md
Web Site: http://www.victoriabank.md
Year Founded: 1989
Banking Services
N.A.I.C.S.: 522110

Subsidiaries:

**Banca Comerciala Romana Chisinau
S.A.**   **(1)**
str Puskin 60/2 mun, Chisinau, MD-2005,
Moldova
Tel.: (373) 22852000
Web Site: https://www.bcr.md
Commercial Banking Services
N.A.I.C.S.: 522110
Sergiu Cristian Manea *(Chm-Supervisory
Bd)*

B.DUCK SEMK HOLDINGS IN-
TERNATIONAL LIMITED
Unit A6 25/F Tml Tower 3 Hoi Shining

Road, New Territories, Tsuen Wan,
China (Hong Kong)   Ky
Web Site: https://www.semk.net
Year Founded: 2001
2250—(HKG)
Rev.: $24,842,580
Assets: $53,262,033
Liabilities: $7,950,456
Net Worth: $45,311,577
Earnings: $9,745,084
Emp.: 181
Fiscal Year-end: 12/31/22
Holding Company
N.A.I.C.S.: 551112
Hui Ha Lam *(CEO)*

B.F. LORENZETTI & ASSOCI-
ATES
2001 McGill College Suite 2200,
Montreal, H3A 1G1, QC, Canada
Tel.: (514) 843-3632
Web Site: http://www.bflcanada.ca
Year Founded: 1987
Rev.: $13,209,735
Emp.: 82
Commercial Insurance Brokerage
Services
N.A.I.C.S.: 524298
Barry F. Lorenzetti *(Pres)*

B.F. MODARABA
Plot No 43-1-E P E C H S Block-6
Off Razi Road Shahrah-e-Faisal, Ka-
rachi, Pakistan
Tel.: (92) 21111229269
Web Site:
    https://www.bfmodaraba.com.pk
Year Founded: 1989
BFMOD—(PSX)
Rev.: $37,629
Assets: $409,072
Liabilities: $12,903
Net Worth: $396,169
Earnings: ($21,582)
Emp.: 8
Fiscal Year-end: 06/30/23
Financial Services
N.A.I.C.S.: 523999
Muhammad Omar Amin Bawany
(CEO)

Subsidiaries:

Sind Particle Board Mills Ltd.   **(1)**
43-1-E B Block 6 PECHS off Razi Road
Shahrah-e-Faisal, Karachi, Pakistan
Tel.: (92) 21111229269
Web Site: https://www.spbm.com.pk
Wood Product Distr
N.A.I.C.S.: 423310

B.G.E. SERVICE & SUPPLY
LTD.
5711 103 A Street, Edmonton, T6H
2J6, AB, Canada
Tel.: (780) 436-6960
Web Site:
    http://www.thefiltershop.com
Year Founded: 1968
Rev.: $37,200,000
Emp.: 130
Industrial Filter Mfr
N.A.I.C.S.: 423840
Roberta MacGillivray *(Pres)*

B.I.G. INDUSTRIES BERHAD
19-D 4th Floor Block 2 Worldwide
Business Centre, Jalan Tinju 13/50
Section 13, 40675, Shah Alam, Se-
langor, Malaysia
Tel.: (60) 355129999
Web Site: https://www.bigind.com.my
Year Founded: 1982
BIG—(KLS)
Rev.: $7,878,541
Assets: $11,953,327
Liabilities: $3,365,931
Net Worth: $8,587,395

B.I.G. Industries Berhad—(Continued)

Earnings: $566,992
Fiscal Year-end: 06/30/23
Industrial Gases Mfr & Distr
N.A.I.C.S.: 325120
Ban Tin Lau *(Chm)*

Subsidiaries:

Alpha Billion Sdn. Bhd. **(1)**
Lot 2225 Section 66, Jalan Dermaga Pending Industrial Estate, 93450, Kuching, Sarawak, Malaysia
Tel.: (60) 82486321
Industrial Gas Mfr
N.A.I.C.S.: 325120

B.I.G. Industrial Gas Sdn. Bhd. **(1)**
Lot 2225 Section 66 Jalan Dermaga Pending Industrial Estate, 93450, Kuching, Sarawak, Malaysia
Tel.: (60) 82486321
Sales Range: $25-49.9 Million
Emp.: 50
Industrial Gases Mfr & Distr
N.A.I.C.S.: 325120

B.I.G. Marketing Sdn. Bhd. **(1)**
19-D 4th Floor Block 2 Worldwide Business Centre, Jalan Tinju 13/50 Section 13, 40675, Shah Alam, Selangor Darul Ehsan, Malaysia
Tel.: (60) 355129999
Sales Range: $150-199.9 Million
Emp.: 300
Industrial Gas Distr
N.A.I.C.S.: 424690

Kinalaju Supply Sdn. Bhd. **(1)**
Lot 6 2nd Floor Wisma KKM Jalan Tuaran, Inanam, 88450, Kota Kinabalu, Sabah, Malaysia
Tel.: (60) 88437422
Cement Distr
N.A.I.C.S.: 423320

Puncak Luyang Sdn. Bhd. **(1)**
19-D 4th Floor Block 2 Worldwide Business Centre, Jalan Tinju 13/50 Section 13, 40675, Shah Alam, Selangor Darul Ehsan, Malaysia
Tel.: (60) 355129999
Web Site: http://www.bigind.com.my
Sales Range: $50-74.9 Million
Emp.: 100
Residential Condominium Management Services
N.A.I.C.S.: 531311

Uni-Mix Concrete Products Sdn. Bhd. **(1)**
Lot 6 2nd Floor Wisma KKM Jalan Tuaran, Inanam, 88450, Kota Kinabalu, Sabah, Malaysia
Tel.: (60) 88437422
Industrial Gas Mfr
N.A.I.C.S.: 325120

Uni-Mix Sdn. Bhd. **(1)**
Lot 6 2nd F Wisma KKM Jalan Tuaran, 88450, Kota Kinabalu, Sabah, Malaysia
Tel.: (60) 88437422
Sales Range: $50-74.9 Million
Emp.: 150
Readymix Concrete Mfr
N.A.I.C.S.: 327320

B.L.L. HOLDINGS LTD
8 Veridion Way, Erith, DA18 4AL, United Kingdom
Tel.: (44) 44 13 2252 6262
Web Site: http://www.bll.co.uk
Presentation & Marketing Products Mfr
N.A.I.C.S.: 424120

Subsidiaries:

W.E. Baxter Limited **(1)**
8 Veridion Way, Erith, DA18 4AL, Kent, United Kingdom
Tel.: (44) 2086851234
Web Site: http://www.we-baxter.co.uk
Ring Binder Printer Services
N.A.I.C.S.: 323111

B.O.S. BETTER ONLINE SO-LUTIONS LTD.

20 Freiman Street, Rishon le Zion, 7535825, Israel
Tel.: (972) 39542000
Web Site: https://www.boscom.com
BOSC—(NASDAQ)
Rev.: $41,511,000
Assets: $30,595,000
Liabilities: $13,961,000
Net Worth: $16,634,000
Earnings: $1,276,000
Emp.: 86
Fiscal Year-end: 12/31/22
Middleware Connectivity Device Mfr
N.A.I.C.S.: 334118
Benny Katz *(CTO-Robotics)*

Subsidiaries:

Lynk USA, Inc. **(1)**
6280 Manchester Blvd Ste 200, Buena Park, CA 90621-2294
Tel.: (714) 443-4000
Web Site: http://www.telelynk.com
N.A.I.C.S.: 541512

B.P. MARSH & PARTNERS PLC
4 Matthew Parker Street, London, SW1H 9NP, United Kingdom
Tel.: (44) 2072333112
Web Site: https://www.bpmarsh.co.uk
BPM—(AIM)
Rev.: $40,208,242
Assets: $212,489,365
Liabilities: $5,596,793
Net Worth: $206,892,573
Earnings: $29,608,237
Emp.: 16
Fiscal Year-end: 01/31/23
Financial Services
N.A.I.C.S.: 525990
Jonathan Newman *(Dir-Fin Grp)*

Subsidiaries:

ZON Re-USA, LLC **(1)**
2 Corporate Dr Ste 636, Shelton, CT 06484
Tel.: (203) 225-6278
Web Site: http://www.zondigital.com
Accident Reinsurance Products & Services
N.A.I.C.S.: 524130
W. Brian Harrigan *(Chm, Pres & CEO)*

B.R.R. GUARDIAN MO-DARABA
18th Floor BRR Towers Hassan Ali Street off I I Chundrigar Road, Karachi, 74000, Pakistan
Tel.: (92) 2132602401
Web Site:
http://www.firstdawood.com
BRR—(KAR)
Rev.: $1,379,246
Assets: $13,199,096
Liabilities: $3,335,601
Net Worth: $9,863,495
Earnings: $321,975
Emp.: 78
Fiscal Year-end: 06/30/19
Investment & Financial Management Services
N.A.I.C.S.: 523940
Tariq Masood *(CFO)*

Subsidiaries:

Dawood Family Takaful Limited **(1)**
1701-A Saima Trade Towers II Chundrigar Road, Karachi, 74000, Pakistan
Tel.: (92) 111338786
Web Site: https://www.dawoodtakaful.com
Insurance Services
N.A.I.C.S.: 524210
Ayaz Dawood *(Chm)*

B.S.D. CROWN LTD.
7 Menachem Begin Road, Gibor Sport Tower 8th Floor, Ramat Gan, 5268102, Israel
Tel.: (972) 3 7401791
Web Site: http://www.bsd-c.com

Sales Range: $50-74.9 Million
Investment Services
N.A.I.C.S.: 523999
Joseph Williger *(Chm)*

Subsidiaries:

Emblaze Mobile Ltd. **(1)**
1 Emblaze Square Emblaze House, PO Box 2220, 43662, Ra'anana, Israel **(100%)**
Tel.: (972) 97699302
Web Site: http://www.emblazemobile.com
Mobile Devices & Mobile Related Technologies Mfr
N.A.I.C.S.: 517112

emoze Ltd. **(1)**
Hamenofim St Ste 9, PO Box 2216, Herzliyya, 43725, Israel **(100%)**
Tel.: (972) 97699333
Web Site: http://www.emoze.com
Sales Range: $25-49.9 Million
Emp.: 30
Push E-mail & Personal Information Management Services
N.A.I.C.S.: 517112

B2B SOFTWARE TECHNOLO-GIES LIMITED
6-3-1112 3rd 4th Floor AVR Towers Behind Westside Show Room, Near Somajiguda Circle Begumpet, Hyderabad, 500 016, Telangana, India
Tel.: (91) 4023372522
Web Site:
https://www.b2bsoftech.com
531268—(BOM)
Rev.: $2,794,578
Assets: $2,426,874
Liabilities: $267,376
Net Worth: $2,159,498
Earnings: $364,946
Emp.: 94
Fiscal Year-end: 03/31/22
Software Development Services
N.A.I.C.S.: 541511
Ramachandra Rao Nemani *(CEO)*

Subsidiaries:

B2B Softech Inc. **(1)**
9001 San Fernando Rd, Sun Valley, CA 91352
Tel.: (818) 504-3787
Software Development Services
N.A.I.C.S.: 541511

B2B Software Technologies Kassel GmbH **(1)**
Ludwig-Erhard-Str 12, 34131, Kassel, Germany
Tel.: (49) 5619538487
Software Development Services
N.A.I.C.S.: 541511

B2EN CO., LTD.
2th floor 146 Seonyu-ro, Yeongdeungpo-gu, Seoul, 07255, Korea (South)
Tel.: (82) 226360090
Web Site: https://www.b2en.com
Year Founded: 2004
307870—(KRS)
Rev.: $20,772,661
Assets: $30,442,503
Liabilities: $17,268,179
Net Worth: $13,174,325
Earnings: ($1,699,476)
Emp.: 198
Fiscal Year-end: 12/31/22
Information Technology Services
N.A.I.C.S.: 541512

B2GOLD CORP.
Suite 3400 - 666 Burrard Street, Vancouver, V6C 2X8, BC, Canada
Tel.: (604) 681-8371   BC
Web Site: https://www.b2gold.com
Year Founded: 2006
BTG—(NYSEAMEX)
Rev.: $1,732,590,000

Assets: $3,681,233,000
Liabilities: $569,444,000
Net Worth: $3,111,789,000
Earnings: $252,873,000
Emp.: 4,050
Fiscal Year-end: 12/31/22
Gold Ore Exploration, Development & Mining Services
N.A.I.C.S.: 212220
Robert Melvin Douglas Cross *(Chm)*

Subsidiaries:

Oklo Resources Limited **(1)**
Level 5 56 Pitt Street, Sydney, 2000, NSW, Australia
Tel.: (61) 2 8823 3110
Web Site: http://www.okloresources.com
Rev.: $103,694
Assets: $54,834,032
Liabilities: $1,524,772
Net Worth: $53,309,261
Earnings: ($5,154,117)
Emp.: 4
Fiscal Year-end: 06/30/2021
Uranium Exploration Services
N.A.I.C.S.: 212290
Louisa Martino *(Sec)*

Sabina Gold & Silver Corporation **(1)**
No 1800 - 555 Burrard Street, Box 220, Vancouver, V7X 1M9, BC, Canada
Tel.: (604) 998-4175
Web Site: http://www.sabinagoldsilver.com
Rev.: $240,160
Assets: $503,770,328
Liabilities: $74,655,327
Net Worth: $429,115,000
Earnings: $6,280,926
Emp.: 26
Fiscal Year-end: 12/31/2021
Mineral Exploration & Development
N.A.I.C.S.: 212220
Elaine Bennett *(CFO & VP-Fin)*

B2HOLDING AS
Stortingsgaten 22, Oslo, 0121, Norway
Tel.: (47) 22 83 39 50
Web Site: http://www.b2holding.no
Debt Management Services
N.A.I.C.S.: 523999
Olav Dalen Zah *(CEO)*

Subsidiaries:

B2 Kaptial d.o.o **(1)**
Leskoskova cesta 2, 1102, Ljubljana, Slovenia
Tel.: (386) 59082461
Web Site: http://www.b2kapital.si
Financial Services
N.A.I.C.S.: 523999

Creditreform Latvija SIA **(1)**
Skanstes 52, Riga, 1013, Latvia
Tel.: (371) 67501030
Web Site: http://www.creditreform.lv
Debt Collection Services
N.A.I.C.S.: 561440
Maris Baidekalns *(CEO)*

Interkreditt AS **(1)**
Lorkenesgata 3, 6002, Alesund, Norway
Tel.: (47) 70300500
Web Site: http://www.interkreditt.no
Emp.: 4
Debt Collection Services
N.A.I.C.S.: 561440
Jens Ivar Grytten Skarboe *(CEO)*

OK Perinta Oy **(1)**
Tiilitehtaankatu 7 A, 65100, Vaasa, Finland
Tel.: (358) 30 603 5600
Web Site: http://www.okperinta.fi
Emp.: 131
Debt Collection Services
N.A.I.C.S.: 561440
Ahlstrom Kari *(Mng Dir)*

Subsidiary (Non-US):

OK Incure OU **(2)**
Mustamae tee 16, 10617, Tallinn, Estonia
Tel.: (372) 6755820
Web Site: http://www.incure.ee
Debt Collection Services

N.A.I.C.S.: 561440
Eric Noormets *(Mgr-Intl Collection)*

Sileo Kapital AB   **(1)**
Stora Nygatan 17, 411 08, Gothenburg,
Sweden
Tel.: (46) 105507800
Web Site: http://www.sileokapital.com
Emp.: 33
Debt Collection Services
N.A.I.C.S.: 561440
Jan Pettersson *(CEO)*

ULTIMO Sp. z o.o.   **(1)**
58-68 Braniborska Str, 53-680, Wroclaw,
Poland
Tel.: (48) 71 359 41 60
Web Site: http://www.ultimo.pl
Sales Range: $75-99.9 Million
Emp.: 550
Debt Collection Services
N.A.I.C.S.: 561440
Janusz Tchorzewski *(Chm-Supervisory Bd)*

B3 CONSULTING GROUP AB
Kungsbron 2, PO Box 8, 101 20,
Stockholm, Sweden
Tel.: (46) 841014340
Web Site: https://www.b3.se
Year Founded: 2003
B3—(OMX)
Rev.: $106,849,495
Assets: $59,250,517
Liabilities: $44,573,698
Net Worth: $14,676,820
Earnings: $5,666,545
Emp.: 781
Fiscal Year-end: 12/31/23
Information Technology Consulting
Services
N.A.I.C.S.: 541512
Sven Uthorn *(Founder & CEO)*

B3 S.A.
Praca Antonio Prado 48 Centro, Sao
Paulo, 01010-010, SP, Brazil
Tel.: (55) 1125654000   BR
Web Site: https://www.b3.com.br_us
Year Founded: 2017
B3SA3—(BRAZ)
Rev.: $1,978,512,514
Assets: $9,855,742,746
Liabilities: $5,810,254,861
Net Worth: $4,045,487,885
Earnings: $823,996,211
Fiscal Year-end: 12/31/23
Investment Management Service
N.A.I.C.S.: 523210
Cicero Augusto Vieira Neto *(COO &*
Member-Exec Bd)

Subsidiaries:

BLK Sistemas Financeiros Ltda. **(1)**
Rua Libero Badaro 377 20 andar, Centro,
Sao Paulo, 01009-000, Brazil
Tel.: (55) 1132951522
Web Site: http://www.blk.com.br
Information Technology Development Ser-
vices
N.A.I.C.S.: 541511
Leonardo Alvarez *(Mgr-Sls & Bus Dev)*

BM&F USA Inc.   **(1)**
61 Broadway 26th Fl Ste 2605, New York,
NY 10006-2828
Tel.: (212) 750-4197
Investment Management Service
N.A.I.C.S.: 523999

Banco B3 S.A   **(1)**
Joao Bricola Street 59 - 4 Floor, Sao Paulo,
01014-010, SP, Brazil
Tel.: (55) 1125655784
Web Site: https://www.bancob3.com.br
N.A.I.C.S.: 522320

Portal de Documentos S.A   **(1)**
Av Tucunare 550 3 andar Tambore, Barueri,
06460-020, Sao Paulo, Brazil
Tel.: (55) 1133771000
Web Site:
    http://www.portaldedocumentos.com.br
Information Technology Development Ser-
vices

N.A.I.C.S.: 541511

B3SYSTEM S.A.
Ul Marszalkowska 53/5, 00-676, War-
saw, Poland
Tel.: (48) 22 480 89 00
Web Site: http://www.b3system.pl
Information Technology Security Ser-
vices
N.A.I.C.S.: 561621
Pawel Tomasz Paluchowski *(Chm-*
Mgmt Bd)

B4S SOLUTIONS PVT LTD.
S-40 Harsha Compound Site-2, Loni
Road Industrial Area Mohan Nagar,
Ghaziabad, 201007, Uttar Pradesh,
India
Tel.: (91) 120 418 8300
Web Site:
    http://www.bhardwajservices.com
Year Founded: 1989
Human Resouce Services
N.A.I.C.S.: 541612
Ramakant Sharma *(Founder)*

Subsidiaries:

SAL Automotive Limited   **(1)**
PhaseIV Industrial Area S A S Nagar, Mo-
hali, 160055, Punjab, India
Tel.: (91) 1722234940
Web Site: https://www.swarajenterprise.com
Rev.: $156,675,806
Assets: $62,981,755
Liabilities: $21,257,009
Net Worth: $41,724,747
Earnings: $14,943,242
Emp.: 335
Fiscal Year-end: 03/31/2022
Automobile Seat Cover Mfr
N.A.I.C.S.: 336360
Jai Bhagwan Kapil *(Chm)*

B90 HOLDINGS PLC
33-37 Athol Street, Douglas, IM1
1LB, Isle of Man
Tel.: (44) 1624647979   IM
Web Site:
    https://www.b90holdings.com
B90—(AIM)
Rev.: $3,823,751
Assets: $13,340,610
Liabilities: $3,182,126
Net Worth: $10,158,485
Earnings: ($6,914,311)
Fiscal Year-end: 12/31/23
Investment Services
N.A.I.C.S.: 523999
Marcel Wilhelmus Johannes Noorde-
loos *(Dir-Fin)*

BA CONSULTING GROUP LTD.
45 St Clair Ave West Ste 300, To-
ronto, M4V 1K9, ON, Canada
Tel.: (416) 961-7110
Web Site: http://www.bagroup.com
Rev.: $18,600,000
Emp.: 50
Transportation Planning & Engineer-
ing Services
N.A.I.C.S.: 541330
Mark Jamieson *(Principal)*

BA GLASS B.V.
Avenida Vasco de Gama 8001, Av-
intes, 4434-508, Vila Nova de Gaia,
Portugal
Tel.: (351) 22 7860 500   NL
Web Site: http://www.baglass.com
Rev.: $1,043,201,363
Assets: $1,650,739,013
Liabilities: $974,084,963
Net Worth: $676,654,050
Earnings: $162,373,368
Emp.: 3,699
Fiscal Year-end: 12/31/19
Holding Company; Glass Container
Mfr

N.A.I.C.S.: 551112
Sandra Maria Santos *(CEO &*
Member-Exec Bd)

Subsidiaries:

Anchor Glass Container
Corporation   **(1)**
3001 N Rocky Point Dr E Ste 300, Tampa,
FL 33607
Tel.: (813) 884-0000
Web Site: http://www.anchorglass.com
Glass Container Products Mfr
N.A.I.C.S.: 327213
Robert Stewart *(Chief Compliance Officer)*

BA Glass Portugal S.A.   **(1)**
Avenida Vasco de Gama 8001, Avintes,
4434-508, Vila Nova de Gaia, Portugal
Tel.: (351) 22 7860 500
Web Site: http://www.baglass.com
Glass Container Mfr
N.A.I.C.S.: 327213

Subsidiary (Non-US):

BA Glass Bulgaria S.A.   **(2)**
1 Prof Ivan Georgov Str, 1220, Sofia, Bul-
garia
Tel.: (359) 2 921 6500
Glass Container Mfr
N.A.I.C.S.: 327213

Ba Glass Germany GmbH   **(1)**
Dr-Kurt-Becker-Str 1, 39638, Gardelegen,
Germany
Tel.: (49) 3907775780
Glass Container Mfr
N.A.I.C.S.: 327213

Ba Glass Greece , S.A.   **(1)**
5 Orizomilon St, Egaleo, 122 44, Athens,
Greece
Tel.: (30) 2105403400
Glass Container Mfr
N.A.I.C.S.: 327213

Ba Glass I - Servicos De Gestao E
Investimentos, S.A.   **(1)**
Avenida Vasco da Gama 8001, 4434-508,
Porto, Portugal
Tel.: (351) 227860500
Glass Container Mfr
N.A.I.C.S.: 327213

Ba Glass Poland Sp.Z.O.O.   **(1)**
Ulica Ostroroga 8/1, 60-349, Poznan, Po-
land
Tel.: (48) 515867443
Glass Container Mfr
N.A.I.C.S.: 327213

BA RIA - VUNG TAU HOUSE
DEVELOPMENT JOINT STOCK
COMPANY
3rd Floor Hodeco Plaza 36 Nguyen
Thai Hoc Street, Ward 7, Vung Tau,
Vietnam
Tel.: (84) 643856274
Web Site: https://hodeco.vn
HDC—(HOSE)
Rev.: $27,416,828
Assets: $193,923,650
Liabilities: $114,983,514
Net Worth: $78,610,136
Earnings: $5,423,692
Emp.: 107
Fiscal Year-end: 12/31/23
Real Estate Services
N.A.I.C.S.: 531390
Doan Huu Ha Vinh *(Deputy Gen Dir*
& Sec)

BAADER BANK AG
Weihenstephaner Str 4, 85716, Un-
terschleissheim, Germany
Tel.: (49) 8951500
Web Site: https://www.baaderbank.de
BWB—(MUN)
Assets: $4,347,128,370
Liabilities: $4,165,254,748
Net Worth: $181,873,621
Earnings: $3,123,952
Emp.: 560
Fiscal Year-end: 12/31/23

Brokerage & Investment Banking
Services
N.A.I.C.S.: 523999
Dieter Brichmann *(Deputy Chm)*

Subsidiaries:

Baader & Heins Capital Management
AG   **(1)**
Weihenstephaner Strasse 4, 85716, Unter-
schleissheim, Germany
Tel.: (49) 892318000
Web Site: https://baaderheins.de
Sales Range: $50-74.9 Million
Emp.: 10
Financial Support Services
N.A.I.C.S.: 523999
Andree Heins *(Member-Mgmt Bd)*

Baader Heins & Seitz Capital Man-
agement AG   **(1)**
Weihenstephaner Strasse 4, 85716, Unter-
schleissheim, Germany   **(70%)**
Tel.: (49) 892318000
Web Site: http://www.baaderheinsseitz.de
Sales Range: $50-74.9 Million
Emp.: 15
Investment Management Service
N.A.I.C.S.: 523999
Andree Heins *(Founder & CEO)*

Baader Helvea AG   **(1)**
Freigutstrasse 12, 8002, Zurich, Switzerland
Tel.: (41) 433889200
Banking Services
N.A.I.C.S.: 522110
Morgan Deane *(CEO)*

Subsidiary (US):

Baader Helvea Inc.   **(2)**
420 Lexington Ave Ste 804, New York, NY
10170
Tel.: (212) 935-5150
Banking Services
N.A.I.C.S.: 522110
Francis Grevers *(Pres)*

Subsidiary (Non-US):

Baader Helvea Ltd.   **(2)**
5 Royal Exchange Buildings, London, EC3V
3NL, United Kingdom
Tel.: (44) 2070547100
Banking Services
N.A.I.C.S.: 522110
Ralf Schmidgall *(Head-Sls)*

Conservative Concept AG   **(1)**
Lussiweg 37, 6300, Zug,
Switzerland   **(100%)**
Tel.: (41) 417267552
Web Site: http://www.ccag.com
Sales Range: $50-74.9 Million
Emp.: 8
Real Estate Agents & Brokers Offices
N.A.I.C.S.: 531210
Mitzler Hins *(Gen Mgr)*

Conservative Concept Portfolio Man-
agement AG   **(1)**
Borsenstrasse 1, 60313, Frankfurt am Main,
Germany   **(49.96%)**
Tel.: (49) 6913881260
Web Site: http://www.ccpm.de
Sales Range: $50-74.9 Million
Emp.: 12
Portfolio Management
N.A.I.C.S.: 523940

KA.DE.GE KG   **(1)**
Weihenstephaner Strasse 4, 85716, Unter-
schleissheim, Germany
Tel.: (49) 89 216300
Web Site: http://www.kadege.de
Emp.: 6
Financial Management Consulting Services
N.A.I.C.S.: 541611

Selan Holding GmbH   **(1)**
Weihenstephaner Str 4, 85716, Unter-
schleissheim, Germany
Tel.: (49) 8951501901
Banking Services
N.A.I.C.S.: 522110
Dirk Freitag *(Mng Dir)*

direcct AG   **(1)**
Schillerstrasse 30-40, 60313, Frankfurt am
Main, Germany   **(75%)**

Baader Bank AG—(Continued)

Tel.: (49) 6913881180
Web Site: http://www.directtag.de
Sales Range: $50-74.9 Million
Emp.: 3
Investment Management Service
N.A.I.C.S.: 523999

BAAN ROCK GARDEN PUBLIC COMPANY LIMITED

601 Ramkhamhaeng 39 Pracha-Uthit Road, Wangthonglang, Bangkok, 10310, Thailand
Tel.: (66) 29347000
Web Site:
https://www.rockgarden.co.th
Year Founded: 1990
BROCK—(THA)
Rev.: $2,106,811
Assets: $37,795,906
Liabilities: $847,847
Net Worth: $36,948,060
Earnings: ($264,516)
Fiscal Year-end: 12/31/23
Real Estate Development Services
N.A.I.C.S.: 531390
Virat Chinprapinporn *(Chm)*

BAANX GROUP LTD.

Level 18 40 Bank Street Canary Wharf, London, E14 5NR, United Kingdom
Tel.: (44) 2071297484
Web Site: http://baanx.com
Banking Services
N.A.I.C.S.: 522110
Birendra Roy *(Head-Global Acquiring)*

BAAZEEM TRADING COMPANY

7095 King Faisal Road Al Murabba 3613, PO Box 2156, Riyadh, 12613, Saudi Arabia
Tel.: (966) 114129999
Web Site: https://www.baazeem.com
Year Founded: 1978
Household Product Distr
N.A.I.C.S.: 424410
Ali Musleh Al Waqidi *(CEO)*

BABA ARTS LTD.

B1 & B4 Baba House 86 M V Road, Andheri East, Mumbai, 400093, Maharashtra, India
Tel.: (91) 2226733131
Web Site:
https://www.babaartslimited.com
532380—(BOM)
Rev.: $1,981,736
Assets: $2,695,571
Liabilities: $50,514
Net Worth: $2,645,057
Earnings: $382,690
Emp.: 5
Fiscal Year-end: 03/31/21
Film Production Services
N.A.I.C.S.: 512110

BABCOCK INTERNATIONAL GROUP PLC

33 Wigmore Street, London, W1U 1QX, United Kingdom
Tel.: (44) 2073555300   UK
Web Site:
https://www.babcocknational.com
Year Founded: 1989
BCKIF—(OTCIQ)
Rev.: $5,511,853,480
Assets: $4,110,233,820
Liabilities: $3,649,650,200
Net Worth: $460,583,620
Earnings: ($41,351,940)
Emp.: 26,000
Fiscal Year-end: 03/31/23

Defense Systems, Materials Handling, Marine & Rail Refurbishing & Engineering Services
N.A.I.C.S.: 541330
Jack Borrett *(Gen Counsel & Sec-Grp)*

Subsidiaries:

Appledore Shipbuilders (2004) Limited   **(1)**
H M Dockyard, Plymouth, PL1 4SG, Devonshire, United Kingdom
Tel.: (44) 1752 605665
Web Site:
http://www.babcockinternational.com
Emp.: 5,000
Ship Building Services
N.A.I.C.S.: 336611
Archie Bethal *(Gen Mgr)*

BNS Nuclear Services Limited   **(1)**
Cambridge Road Whetstone, Leicester, LE8 6LH, Leicestershire, United Kingdom
Tel.: (44) 1162 750750
Engineeering Services
N.A.I.C.S.: 541330

Babcock (NZ) Ltd   **(1)**
Queens Parade, Devonport, Auckland, 0624, New Zealand
Tel.: (64) 9 4461999
Web Site: http://www.babcock.com.au
Emp.: 20
Marine Engineering Services
N.A.I.C.S.: 541330

Babcock Africa (Pty) Ltd   **(1)**
1 Osborne Lane, Bedfordview, 2007, Gauteng, South Africa   **(100%)**
Tel.: (27) 0116011000
Web Site: http://www.babcock.co.za
Sales Range: $25-49.9 Million
Emp.: 100
Industrial & Civil Engineering Equipment Mfr
N.A.I.C.S.: 541330
Roger O'Callaghan *(CEO)*

Babcock Africa Services (Pty) Limited   **(1)**
49 Great North Road, Benoni, 1501, Gauteng, South Africa
Tel.: (27) 1 000 12561
Engineering Support Services
N.A.I.C.S.: 541330

Babcock Airports   **(1)**
Cambridge Rd, Whetstone, LE8 6LH, Leics, United Kingdom
Tel.: (44) 1162750750
Sales Range: $75-99.9 Million
Emp.: 150
Airport Baggage Handling Systems Developer & Mfr
N.A.I.C.S.: 488119

Babcock Canada Inc.   **(1)**
75 Albert Street Suite 800, Ottawa, K1P 5E7, ON, Canada
Tel.: (613) 567-2764
Web Site: http://www.babcockcanada.com
Emp.: 102
Asset Management Services
N.A.I.C.S.: 523940
Mike Whalley *(Pres)*

Babcock Defence & Security Services   **(1)**
Pembroke House Herald Way Pegasus Business Park, Castle Donington, Derby, DE74 2TZ, United Kingdom
Tel.: (44) 1509676869
Sales Range: $10-24.9 Million
Emp.: 50
Aircraft Flight Training & Maintenance Services
N.A.I.C.S.: 611512

Babcock Design & Technology Limited   **(1)**
Building 1020 Rosyth Royal Dockyard, Dunfermline, KY11 2YL, Fife, United Kingdom
Tel.: (44) 1383 412131
Engineering Support Services
N.A.I.C.S.: 541330
Ian Lindsay *(Mng Dir-Design & Tech)*

Babcock Eagleton Inc.   **(1)**
2900 N Loop W Ste 1000, Houston, TX 77092

Tel.: (713) 871-8787
Web Site: http://www.eagletoninc.com
Sales Range: $100-124.9 Million
Emp.: 150
Oil & Gas Pipeline Engineering & Support Services
N.A.I.C.S.: 213112
Duain Cagle *(Pres)*

Babcock Education & Skills Limited   **(1)**
33 Wigmore Street, London, W1U 1QX, United Kingdom
Tel.: (44) 1372834444
Educational Support Services
N.A.I.C.S.: 611710

Babcock Integrated Technology Limited   **(1)**
Ashton House Ashton Vale Road, Bristol, BS3 2HQ, Avon, United Kingdom
Tel.: (44) 1179 664677
Engineering Support Services
N.A.I.C.S.: 541330

Babcock International France Aviation SAS   **(1)**
Lieu-dit le Portaret, 83340, Le Cannet-des-Maure, France
Tel.: (33) 498107272
Engineeering Services
N.A.I.C.S.: 541330

Babcock International Holdings BV   **(1)**
Bezuidenhoutseweg 1 S, Hague, 2594 AB, Netherlands
Tel.: (31) 703814411
Emp.: 3
Investment Management Service
N.A.I.C.S.: 523999
R. J. Zerdonk *(Dir)*

Babcock International Italy S.p.A.   **(1)**
Via Mario Mameli snc Ciampino International Airport, 00134, Rome, Italy
Tel.: (39) 06798915500
Engineeering Services
N.A.I.C.S.: 541330

Babcock International Limited   **(1)**
223-224 Newfields Rd Walton Summit Bamber Bridge, Preston, PR5 8AL, Lancashire, United Kingdom
Tel.: (44) 1772404400
Sales Range: $75-99.9 Million
Emp.: 300
Engineering Support Services
N.A.I.C.S.: 541330

Babcock International Spain S.L.U.   **(1)**
Complejo Triada Avenida de Burgos N 17 Planta 7, 28036, Madrid, Spain
Tel.: (34) 913442038
Engineeering Services
N.A.I.C.S.: 541330

Babcock International Support Services Limited   **(1)**
1000 Lakeside North Harbour Western Road, Portsmouth, PO6 3EN, Hampshire, United Kingdom
Tel.: (44) 2392316244
Web Site:
http://www.babcockinternational.com
Sales Range: $25-49.9 Million
Emp.: 100
Business Support Services
N.A.I.C.S.: 561499
Gavin Hopgood *(Mgr-Ops)*

Babcock Land Limited   **(1)**
Bournemouth International Airport, Christchurch, BH2 36BS, United Kingdom
Tel.: (44) 1202 365200
Sales Range: $75-99.9 Million
Emp.: 140
Real Estate Manangement Services
N.A.I.C.S.: 531390

Babcock Marine   **(1)**
33 Wigmore St, London, W1U 1QX, United Kingdom
Tel.: (44) 2073555300
Sales Range: $125-149.9 Million
Emp.: 300
Naval Base Management Services, Submarine & Warship Systems Developer & Marine Equipment Mfr

N.A.I.C.S.: 336611
Archie Bethel *(CEO)*

Subsidiary (Domestic):

Babcock Engineering Services Ltd.   **(2)**
Rosyth Dockyards, Rosyth, Dunfermline, KY11 2YD, Fife, United Kingdom   **(100%)**
Tel.: (44) 1383412131
Emp.: 2,000
Repair, Refitting & Servicing of Military & Civilian Ships; Small Boat Construction & Outfitting & Rail Rolling Stock Refurbishment
N.A.I.C.S.: 336611
Ken Munro *(Gen Mgr)*

Babcock International Group   **(2)**
Devonport Royal Dockyard, Plymouth, PL1 4SG, United Kingdom
Tel.: (44) 1752605665
Ship & Boat Design, Construction & Support Services
N.A.I.C.S.: 336612

Babcock Marine (Clyde) Limited   **(1)**
Rosyth Dockyard, Dunfermline, KY112YD, United Kingdom
Tel.: (44) 1383 412131
Marine Engineering Services
N.A.I.C.S.: 541330

Babcock Ntuthuko Engineering (Pty) Limited   **(1)**
5 6 Bickley Rd, Nigel, 1491, Gauteng, South Africa
Tel.: (27) 117398200
Web Site: http://www.babcock.co.za
Emp.: 16
Engineeering Services
N.A.I.C.S.: 541330
Madhu Kumar *(Gen Mgr)*

Babcock Pty Ltd   **(1)**
Level 9 70 Franklin Street, Adelaide, 5000, SA, Australia
Tel.: (61) 884401400
Web Site: http://www.babcock.com.au
Engineeering Services
N.A.I.C.S.: 541330
David Ruff *(CEO)*

Babcock Rail   **(1)**
Kintail House 3 Lister Way, Hamilton International Technology Park, Glasgow, G72 0FT, United Kingdom
Tel.: (44) 1698203005
Sales Range: $25-49.9 Million
Emp.: 250
Railway Engineering, Systems Design & Maintenance Services
N.A.I.C.S.: 541330
Bobby Forbes *(Dir-Comml)*

Babcock West Sussex Careers Limited   **(1)**
1 The Chambers Chapel St, Chichester, PO19 1DL, West Sussex, United Kingdom
Tel.: (44) 1243771666
Web Site: http://www.vtplc.com
Sales Range: $25-49.9 Million
Emp.: 20
Human Resource Consulting Services
N.A.I.C.S.: 541612

Devonport Royal Dockyard Limited   **(1)**
Devonport Royal Dockyard, Plymouth, PL1 4SG, United Kingdom
Tel.: (44) 1752 323 652
Ship Repair & Maintenance Services
N.A.I.C.S.: 336611

Dounreay Site Restoration Limited   **(1)**
Dounreay, Thurso, KW14 7TZ, Caithness, United Kingdom
Tel.: (44) 1847 802121
Web Site: http://www.dounreay.com
Rev.: $244,671,000
Emp.: 900
Engineering Support Services
N.A.I.C.S.: 541330
Stephen White *(Chm)*

LSC Group Limited   **(1)**
Lincoln House Wellington Crescent, Lichfield, WS138RZ, Staffordshire, United Kingdom

Tel.: (44) 1543 446 800
Web Site: http://www.lsc.co.uk
Sales Range: $25-49.9 Million
Emp.: 130
Business Management Consulting Services
N.A.I.C.S.: 541611
Kieron Bramall (Bus Dir)

Liquid Gas Equipment Limited　　(1)
Young House 42 Discovery Ter Heriot Watt
University Research Park, Edinburgh, EH14
4AP, Scotland, United Kingdom
Tel.: (44) 131 317 8787
Sales Range: $25-49.9 Million
Emp.: 75
Engineering Design & System Integration
Services
N.A.I.C.S.: 541330
Gary Robinson (Dir-Fin)

Marine Industrial Design Limited　(1)
HMNZ Dockyard Queens Parade, Devonport, Auckland, 0624, New Zealand
Tel.: (64) 94198440
Web Site: http://www.marinedesign.co.nz
Marine Engineering Services
N.A.I.C.S.: 541330
Peter Allan (Project Mgr)

National Training Institute LLC　　(1)
PO Box 267, Madinat Al Sultan Qaboos,
115, Muscat, Oman
Tel.: (968) 24228600
Web Site: http://www.ntioman.com
Vocational Training Services
N.A.I.C.S.: 624310
Turkiya Al Hassani (CEO)

**Research Sites Restoration
Limited**
Harwell Oxford, Didcot, OX11 0DF, United
Kingdom
Tel.: (44) 1235 820220
Web Site: http://www.research-sites.com
Engineering Support Services
N.A.I.C.S.: 541330
Andy Staples (Dir-Ops)

Rosyth Royal Dockyard Limited　(1)
Babcock International Rosyth Business
Park, Rosyth, KY11 2YD, Fife, United Kingdom
Tel.: (44) 1383 412131
Web Site:
　http://www.babcockinternational.com
Emp.: 3,000
Ship Repair & Maintenance Services
N.A.I.C.S.: 336611
Archie Bethel (Gen Mgr)

VT Griffin Services, Inc.　　　　(1)
72919 Carter St, Fort Huachuca, AZ 85670
Tel.: (520) 533-1722
Sales Range: $25-49.9 Million
Emp.: 8
Facilities Management Services
N.A.I.C.S.: 561210
Karl Greenman (Bus Mgr)

**BABELON INVESTMENTS CO.
P.L.C.**
Abdali Boulevard 14 Rafic Hariri Avenue Kawar Building, PO Box 9207,
Shumaisani, Amman, 11191, Jordan
Tel.: (962) 65885203
Year Founded: 2006
SALM—(AMM)
Investment Management Service
N.A.I.C.S.: 523940
Amer Aref Mustafa Al Daas (Mgr-Fin)

**BABIS VOVOS INTERNA-
TIONAL CONSTRUCTION S.A.**
340 Kifissias Ave, 15451, Neo Psichico, Greece
Tel.: (30) 2106726036
Web Site: http://www.babisvovos.gr
VOVOS—(ATH)
Sales Range: $50-74.9 Million
Emp.: 20
Real Estate Property Development &
Construction Services
N.A.I.C.S.: 531312
Armodios C. Vovos (Vice Chm &
CEO)

**BABY BUNTING GROUP LIM-
ITED**
153 National Drive, Dandenong
South, 3175, VIC, Australia
Tel.: (61) 387958100　　　　　　　AU
Web Site:
　https://www.babybunting.com.au
Year Founded: 1979
BBN—(ASX)
Rev.: $332,790,463
Assets: $221,824,919
Liabilities: $154,634,748
Net Worth: $67,190,171
Earnings: $1,132,479
Emp.: 1,590
Fiscal Year-end: 06/30/24
Infant Care Products Retailer
N.A.I.C.S.: 459999
Darin Hoekman (CFO & Sec)

BABY CALENDAR, INC.
Miyata Building 10F 1-38-2 Yoyogi,
Shibuya-Ku, Tokyo, 1510053, Japan
Tel.: (81) 366313600
Web Site: https://www.corp.baby-
　calendar.jp
Year Founded: 1991
7363—(TKS)
Information Technology Services
N.A.I.C.S.: 541512
Keiji Yasuda (Chm & Pres)

BABYLON BANK S.A.
Bank of Babylon Building, Karada,
Baghdad, Iraq
Tel.: (964) 7182252　　　　　　　　IQ
Web Site: https://bbk.iq
Year Founded: 1999
BBAY—(IRAQ)
Sales Range: $10-24.9 Million
Commercial Banking Services
N.A.I.C.S.: 522110
Tariq Abdul-Baki Al-Ani (Gen Dir)

BABYLON HOTEL
Jadiriyah, Baghdad, Iraq
Tel.: (964) 1 7781964
Year Founded: 1990
HBAY—(IRAQ)
Sales Range: Less than $1 Million
Home Management Services
N.A.I.C.S.: 721110

BABYLON LTD.
4 HaNehoshet St, Tel Aviv, Israel
Tel.: (972) 35382103　　　　　　　　II
Web Site: http://www.babylon.com
Year Founded: 1997
ABRA—(TAE)
Rev.: $112,723,026
Assets: $162,741,536
Liabilities: $80,075,976
Net Worth: $82,665,560
Earnings: $4,117,419
Emp.: 1,000
Fiscal Year-end: 12/31/23
Software Publisher
N.A.I.C.S.: 513210
Noam Lanir (Chm)

Subsidiaries:

Babylon Software Ltd.　　　　　　(1)
Tchernikhovski St 35, Haifa, 3570901, Israel
Tel.: (972) 48335562
Web Site: http://www.babylon-software.com
Translation Program Services
N.A.I.C.S.: 541930

**BABYLON PUMP & POWER
LIMITED**
1 Port Place High Wycombe, Perth,
6057, WA, Australia
Tel.: (61) 894546309　　　　　　　AU
Web Site:
　https://www.babylonpump.com
BPP—(ASX)
Rev.: $27,870,014

Assets: $22,312,274
Liabilities: $14,908,132
Net Worth: $7,404,142
Earnings: $339,227
Fiscal Year-end: 06/30/24
Industrial Equipment Rental Services
N.A.I.C.S.: 532490
Michael Shelby (Chm)

Subsidiaries:

Primepower Queensland Pty Ltd　(1)
14 Len Shield Street, Paget, MacKay, 4740,
QLD, Australia
Tel.: (61) 749523922
Web Site:
　https://www.primepowerqld.com.au
Engine Repair Services
N.A.I.C.S.: 811111

BABYTREE GROUP
6th Floor Building A Borui Plaza No
26 North Road of East Third Ring,
Chaoyang District, Beijing, China
Tel.: (86) 1061138080　　　　　　Ky
Web Site: http://www.babytree.com
Year Founded: 2007
1761—(HKG)
Rev.: $39,567,949
Assets: $288,139,550
Liabilities: $22,881,409
Net Worth: $265,258,141
Earnings: ($54,350,806)
Emp.: 502
Fiscal Year-end: 12/31/21
Advertising Agency Services
N.A.I.C.S.: 541810
Huainan Wang (Chm)

**BAC GIANG EXPLOITABLE
MINERAL JOINT STOCK COM-
PANY**
Cau Sat hamlet Son Hai Commune,
Luc Ngan, Bac Giang, Vietnam
Tel.: (84) 240 3518 073
Coal Mining Services
N.A.I.C.S.: 212115

**BAC HOLDING INTERNA-
TIONAL CORP.**
Carrera 7 No. 116 - 50 Office 04 -
139, Usaquén,, 110111, Bogota, Colombia
Tel.: (57) 018000111901
Web Site:
　https://www.baccredomatic.com
Year Founded: 1972
BHI—(COLO)
Rev.: $2,633,228,606
Assets: $35,694,538,321
Liabilities: $31,696,691,759
Net Worth: $3,997,289,036
Earnings: $553,543,095
Emp.: 20,142
Fiscal Year-end: 12/31/23
Bank Holding Company
N.A.I.C.S.: 551111
Rodolfo Tabash Espinach (Pres &
CEO)

**BAC KAN MINERAL JOINT
STOCK CORPORATION**
Group 4 Duc Xuan Ward, Bac Kan,
Bac Kan, Vietnam
Tel.: (84) 2813871779
Web Site: http://www.backanco.com
Year Founded: 2000
BKC—(HNX)
Rev.: $24,029,900
Assets: $38,504,300
Liabilities: $20,711,300
Net Worth: $17,793,000
Earnings: $296,800
Emp.: 1,008
Fiscal Year-end: 12/31/22
Metal & Mineral Products Mfr & Distr
N.A.I.C.S.: 332999

**BAC LIEU FISHERIES JOINT
STOCK COMPANY**
89 Road 1A Hamlet 2, Gia Rai Town
Gia Rai District, Bac Lieu, Vietnam
Tel.: (84) 781849567
Web Site: http://www.baclieufis.vn
Year Founded: 2000
BLF—(HNX)
Sales Range: $10-24.9 Million
Processed Seafood Distr
N.A.I.C.S.: 445250

BACANORA LITHIUM LTD.
The Clubhouse 8 St Jamess Square,
London, SW1Y 4JU, United Kingdom
Tel.: (44) 4032376122　　　　　　AB
Web Site:
　http://www.bacanoralithium.com
Year Founded: 2008
BCN—(AIM)
Rev.: $845,963
Assets: $180,424,899
Liabilities: $46,144,845
Net Worth: $134,280,054
Earnings: $20,141,891
Emp.: 15
Fiscal Year-end: 12/31/21
Borate & Lithium Exploration & Mining
N.A.I.C.S.: 213114
Peter Secker (CEO)

BACARDI LIMITED
65 Pitts Bay Rd, Pembroke, HM 08,
Bermuda
Tel.: (441) 2954345
Web Site:
　http://www.bacardilimited.com
Year Founded: 1862
Sales Range: $1-4.9 Billion
Emp.: 6,000
Holding Company: Distilleries
N.A.I.C.S.: 551112
Ned Duggan (CMO-Global)

Subsidiaries:

Bacardi & Company Limited　　　(1)
1000 Bacardi Road, PO Box N-4880, Nassau, Bahamas
Tel.: (242) 3623100
Distilled & blended Liquors
N.A.I.C.S.: 312140

Bacardi AB　　　　　　　　　　(1)
Wallingatan 2 Plan 5, 111 60, Stockholm,
Sweden
Tel.: (46) 85 664 8000
Alcoholic Beverages Services
N.A.I.C.S.: 722410

Bacardi Canada, Inc.　　　　　　(1)
3250 Bloor Street West East Tower Suite
1050, Toronto, M8X 2X9, ON,
Canada　　　　　　　　　　(100%)
Tel.: (905) 451-6100
Web Site: http://www.bacardi.ca
Sales Range: $25-49.9 Million
Emp.: 150
Distilled & Blended Liquors
N.A.I.C.S.: 312140

Bacardi Capital Limited　　　　　(1)
65 Pitts Bay Road, Pembroke, HM 08, Bermuda
Tel.: (441) 2954345
Web Site: http://www.bacardi.com
Sales Range: $25-49.9 Million
Emp.: 70
N.A.I.C.S.: 312130

Bacardi China Limited　　　　　(1)
Unit 3009-3012 Raffles City Changning
Tower 1 No 1133 Changning Road, Shanghai, 200051, China
Tel.: (86) 213 428 4999
Alcoholic Beverages Services
N.A.I.C.S.: 722410

Bacardi Corporation　　　　　　(1)
PO Box 363549, San Juan, PR 00936-3549
Tel.: (787) 788-1500

Bacardi Limited—(Continued)

Web Site: http://www.barcardi.com
Sales Range: $100-124.9 Million
Emp.: 300
Distillation, Aging, Bottling & Wholesale Distributor of Rum; Marketing of Home Appliances; Refreshment Bottlers; Environmental Testing; Distribution of Liquors & Food Stuffs
N.A.I.C.S.: 312140
Jose Melendez (Dir-Fin)

Subsidiary (Domestic):

Bacardi Bottling Corporation (2)
12200 N Main St, Jacksonville, FL
32218-3819 (100%)
Tel.: (904) 757-1290
Web Site: http://www.ashgrove.com
Sales Range: $125-149.9 Million
Emp.: 300
Rectifies & Bottles Rum
N.A.I.C.S.: 424810
Michelle Adams (Coord-Environmental Health & Safety)

Holding (Non-US):

Bacardi Centroamerica, S.A. (2)
Calle 50 y Aquilino de la Guardia Edifico American International, Piso 5 Officina 1, Panama, Panama (100%)
Tel.: (507) 2697002
Sales Range: $25-49.9 Million
Emp.: 12
Distilled & Blended Liquors
N.A.I.C.S.: 312130
Peter Bachel (Dir)

Bacardi Espana S.A. (1)
Calle Facundo Bacardi 14, Mollet Del Valles, 08100, Barcelona, Spain (100%)
Tel.: (34) 935657100
Web Site: http://www.bacardi.com
Sales Range: $100-124.9 Million
Emp.: 400
Distilled & Blended Liquors
N.A.I.C.S.: 312140

Bacardi France S.A.S. (1)
19 Ave Michelet, F 93400, Saint-Ouen, France (100%)
Tel.: (33) 49454800
Sales Range: $25-49.9 Million
Emp.: 250
Distilled & Blended Liquors
N.A.I.C.S.: 312140

Bacardi Global Brands Inc. (1)
866 Ponce De Leon Blvd Fl 2, Coral Gables, FL 33134-3039
Tel.: (305) 446-9050
Web Site: http://www.knight-sec.com
Sales Range: $25-49.9 Million
Emp.: 20
Distilled & Blended Liquors
N.A.I.C.S.: 424820

Bacardi Global Brands Limited (1)
205 Brooklands Rd, Weybridge, KT13 0BG, Surrey, United Kingdom (100%)
Tel.: (44) 1932826400
Web Site: http://www.bacardi.co.uk
Sales Range: $25-49.9 Million
Emp.: 40
Distilled & Blended Liquors
N.A.I.C.S.: 312140
Ned Duggan (Pres)

Bacardi GmbH (1)
Hindenburg Strasse 49, D 22297, Hamburg, Germany (100%)
Tel.: (49) 40339500
Web Site: http://www.bacardi-deutschland.de
Sales Range: $100-124.9 Million
Emp.: 300
Distilled & Blended Liquors
N.A.I.C.S.: 312140

Bacardi International Limited (1)
65 Pitts Bay Road, Pembroke, HM 08, Bermuda
Tel.: (441) 2954345
Web Site: http://www.onebacardi.com
Sales Range: $25-49.9 Million
Emp.: 65
N.A.I.C.S.: 312130
Facundo L. Bacardi (Chm & Pres)

Bacardi Martini Patron International GmbH (1)

Quaistrasse 11, 8200, Schaffhausen, Switzerland
Tel.: (41) 52 630 0510
Alcoholic Beverages Services
N.A.I.C.S.: 722410

Bacardi Nederland N.V. (1)
Groningenweg 8, 2803 PV, Gouda, Netherlands (100%)
Tel.: (31) 182569999
Web Site: http://www.bacardi.nl
Sales Range: $25-49.9 Million
Emp.: 75
Distilled & Blended Liquors
N.A.I.C.S.: 312140
Francis Debeuckelaere (Gen Mgr)

Bacardi Norge AS (1)
Ovre Slottsgate 17, 0157, Oslo, Norway
Tel.: (47) 2 288 7950
Alcoholic Beverages Services
N.A.I.C.S.: 722410

Bacardi Rus LLC (1)
4th Lesnoy Per 4 BC White Stone 3rd Floor, Bacardi Moscow and Central Federal District, 125047, Moscow, Russia
Tel.: (7) 84957559785
Alcoholic Beverages Services
N.A.I.C.S.: 722410

Bacardi Shanghai Limited (1)
19f Shanghai Arch Tower 2 No.533 Loushandun Road, Shanghai, 200031, Xuhui, China (100%)
Tel.: (86) 2164660299
Web Site: http://www.bacardilimited.com
Sales Range: $25-49.9 Million
Emp.: 50
Distilled & Blended Liquors
N.A.I.C.S.: 312140
Adam Zhu (Chm-Greater China)

Bacardi USA, Inc. (1)
2701 Le Jeu Rd, Coral Gables, FL 33134-5014
Tel.: (305) 573-8511
Web Site: http://www.bacardi.com
Sales Range: $1-4.9 Billion
Emp.: 400
Wholesale Spirits & Liquor
N.A.I.C.S.: 424820
Mauricio Vergara (Sr VP-Comml)

Bacardi Venezuela C.A. (1)
Ave Venezuela Clement, El Rosal, Caracas, 1060, Miranda, Venezuela
Tel.: (58) 2129515987
Sales Range: $25-49.9 Million
Emp.: 20
Distilled & Blended Liquors
N.A.I.C.S.: 312140

Bacardi y Compania, S.A. de C.V. (1)
Autopista Mexico Queretaro No 4431, 54900, Tultitlan, Mexico (100%)
Tel.: (52) 5558990900
Sales Range: $150-199.9 Million
Emp.: 700
Distilled & Blended Liquors
N.A.I.C.S.: 312140
John Grey (Reg Pres-Alvia Pacific)

Bacardi-Martini Asia-Pacific Limited (1)
Fl 18 Bank Of E Asia Harbour View Center, 56 Gloucester Rd, Wanchai, China (Hong Kong) (100%)
Tel.: (852) 25280009
Web Site: http://www.bacardiltd.com
Sales Range: $25-49.9 Million
Emp.: 25
Distilled & Blended Liquors
N.A.I.C.S.: 312140
Jon Grey (Pres)

Bacardi-Martini BV (1)
Groningenweg 8, NL 2800 AX, Gouda, Netherlands (100%)

Tel.: (31) 182390000
Web Site: http://www.bacardinederland.nl
Sales Range: $25-49.9 Million
Emp.: 20
Distilled & Blended Liquors
N.A.I.C.S.: 312140

Bacardi-Martini Belgium NV (1)
Medialaan No 50, B-1800, Brussels, Belgium (100%)
Tel.: (32) 24234811
Web Site: http://www.bacardi-martini.com
Sales Range: $75-99.9 Million
Emp.: 75
Wines, Brandy & Brandy Spirits; Distilled & Blended Liquors
N.A.I.C.S.: 312130
Francis Debeuckelaere (Gen Mgr)

Bacardi-Martini Chile S.A. (1)
595 Ureta Cox, San Miguel, Santiago, Chile (99%)
Tel.: (56) 25522194
Sales Range: $25-49.9 Million
Emp.: 16
Distilled & Blended Liquors
N.A.I.C.S.: 312140

Bacardi-Martini Danmark A/S (1)
Baltorpbakken 1, DK 2750, Ballerup, Denmark (100%)
Tel.: (45) 44866644
Web Site: http://www.bacardi.dk
Sales Range: $25-49.9 Million
Emp.: 20
Distilled & Blended Liquors
N.A.I.C.S.: 312140

Subsidiary (Non-US):

Bacardi-Martini Finland (2)
Punavuorenkatu 17, 00150, Helsinki, Finland (100%)
Tel.: (358) 96980610
Web Site: http://www.bacardi.fi
Sales Range: $25-49.9 Million
Emp.: 4
Distilled & Blended Liquors Sales & Marketing
N.A.I.C.S.: 424820
Sami Savolainen (Acct Mgr)

Bacardi-Martini France (1)
19 Ave Michelet, 93400, Saint-Ouen, France (100%)
Tel.: (33) 149454800
Web Site: http://www.bacardi-martini.fr
Sales Range: $25-49.9 Million
Emp.: 200
Distilled & Blended Liquors
N.A.I.C.S.: 312140

Bacardi-Martini GmbH (1)
Handelskai, 94296, A 1200, Vienna, Austria (100%)
Tel.: (43) 610310
Web Site: http://www.bacardi.at
Sales Range: $25-49.9 Million
Emp.: 35
Distilled & Blended Liquors
N.A.I.C.S.: 312140

Bacardi-Martini Hungary Kft. (1)
Retkoz Utca 5, H 1118, Budapest, Hungary (80%)
Tel.: (36) 12464283
Web Site: http://www.bacardi.hu
Sales Range: $25-49.9 Million
Emp.: 50
Provider of Distilled & Blended Liquors
N.A.I.C.S.: 312140

Bacardi-Martini India Limited (1)
227 Ground Fl Okhla Industrial Estate Phase III, New Delhi, 110020, India (100%)
Tel.: (91) 11 6310422
Web Site: http://www.bacardilimited.com
Sales Range: $25-49.9 Million
Emp.: 35
Distilled & Blended Liquors
N.A.I.C.S.: 312140
Vijay Subramaniam (Mng Dir-Asia Pacific & Middle East & Africa)

Bacardi-Martini Pacific Pty. Ltd. (1)
Level 8 Kent St 201, Sydney, 2000, NSW, Australia (100%)
Tel.: (61) 1800357994
Web Site: http://www.bacardilion.com.au

Sales Range: $25-49.9 Million
Emp.: 40
Distilled & Blended Liquors
N.A.I.C.S.: 312140
Ray Noble (Dir-Mktg)

Bacardi-Martini Polska Sp z o.o. (1)
ul Woloska 22, 02-675, Warsaw, Poland
Tel.: (48) 22 452 0200
Alcoholic Beverages Services
N.A.I.C.S.: 722410

Bacardi-Martini Russia (1)
Riverside Towers Kosmodamianskaya Naberezhnaya 22 4, Moscow, 115054, Russia (100%)
Tel.: (7) 0957559785
Sales Range: $25-49.9 Million
Emp.: 100
Distilled & Blended Liquors
N.A.I.C.S.: 312140
Robert Furniss Roe (Gen Mgr)

Bacardi-Martini UK Limited (1)
W Bay Rd, Western Docks, Southampton, SO15 1DT, United Kingdom (100%)
Tel.: (44) 2380318000
Web Site: http://www.bacardi.co.uk
Sales Range: $150-199.9 Million
Emp.: 600
Distilled & Blended Liquors
N.A.I.C.S.: 312140
Stella Julie David (CMO-Global)

Bacardi-Martini Uruguay S.A. (1)
Eduardo Pondal 782, Montevideo, 12900, Uruguay (100%)
Tel.: (598) 23091416
Sales Range: $25-49.9 Million
Emp.: 50
Wines, Brandy & Brandy Spirits
N.A.I.C.S.: 312130
Selvena Deresa (CFO)

Leblon Holdings LLC. (1)
41 W 25th St, New York, NY 10010
Tel.: (212) 741-2675
Web Site: http://lebloncachaca.com
Sales Range: $1-9.9 Million
Emp.: 35
Cachaca & Cedilla Mfr
N.A.I.C.S.: 312140

S.A. Bacardi-Martini Belgium N.V. (1)
Medialaan 50, 1800, Vilvoorde, Belgium
Tel.: (32) 2 897 9099
Alcoholic Beverages Services
N.A.I.C.S.: 722410

BACHEM HOLDING AG
Hauptstrasse 144, 4416, Bubendorf, Switzerland
Tel.: (41) 585952021   CH
Web Site: https://www.bachem.com
Year Founded: 1971
BANB—(SWX)
Rev.: $686,137,393
Assets: $2,000,095,088
Liabilities: $430,659,617
Net Worth: $1,569,435,471
Earnings: $132,943,904
Emp.: 2,006
Fiscal Year-end: 12/31/23
Offices of Other Holding Companies
N.A.I.C.S.: 551112
Stephan Schindler (CFO)

Subsidiaries:

Bachem (UK) Ltd. (1)
Delph Court Sullivans Way, Saint Helens, WA9 5GL, Merseyside, United Kingdom (100%)
Tel.: (44) 1744612108
Sales Range: $25-49.9 Million
Emp.: 46
Mfr & Reseach of Peptides & Solid Phase Synthesis
N.A.I.C.S.: 325998
Julie Marley (Mgr-Site)

Bachem AG (1)
Hauptstrasse 144, 4416, Bubendorf, Switzerland (100%)
Tel.: (41) 585952021
Sales Range: $100-124.9 Million
Emp.: 600

Mfr of Technical Equipment for Solid Phase Synthesis & Purification of Peptides
N.A.I.C.S.: 333248

Bachem Americas, Inc. (1)
3132 Kashiwa St, Torrance, CA 90505
Tel.: (310) 539-4171
Sales Range: $25-49.9 Million
Emp.: 183
Mfr of Active Pharmaceutical Ingredients, Peptides & Organic Molecules Mfr
N.A.I.C.S.: 325412

Bachem Distribution Services GmbH (1)
Hegenheimer Strasse 5, 79576, Weil am Rhein, Germany (100%)
Tel.: (49) 41619352323
Sales Range: $25-49.9 Million
Emp.: 5
Mfr of Peptide Active Pharmaceutical Ingredients
N.A.I.C.S.: 325998

Bachem Japan K.K. (1)
Nihonbashi Life Science Building 7 8F
1-9-10 Nihonbashi-Horidome cho, Chuo-ku, Tokyo, 103-0012, Japan
Tel.: (81) 366610774
Emp.: 3
Pharmaceuticals Product Mfr
N.A.I.C.S.: 325412

Bachem SA (1)
Succursale Vionnaz Route du Simplon 22, 1895, Vionnaz, Switzerland
Tel.: (41) 58 595 3990
Pharmaceuticals Product Mfr
N.A.I.C.S.: 325412

Sochinaz SA (1)
Rte Du Samtlon 22, Vionnaz, CH 1895, Switzerland (100%)
Tel.: (41) 244824444
Web Site: http://www.bachem.com
Sales Range: $25-49.9 Million
Emp.: 92
Mfr of Organic Intermediates & Active Pharmaceutical Ingredients
N.A.I.C.S.: 325412

BACIL PHARMA LIMITED
71 Laxmi Building Sir P M Road, Fort, Mumbai, 400001, India
Tel.: (91) 2222661541
Web Site:
    http://www.bacilpharma.com
524516—(BOM)
Rev.: $7,858
Assets: $173,569
Liabilities: $6,440
Net Worth: $167,129
Earnings: ($526,864)
Emp.: 3
Fiscal Year-end: 03/31/22
Agro Product Whslr
N.A.I.C.S.: 424510
Jayesh Ramchandra Patil (CFO)

BACKA A.D.
Novosadski put 10, 21400, Backa Palanka, Serbia
Tel.: (381) 216040976
Web Site: https://adbacka.rs
Year Founded: 1989
BCKA—(BEL)
Rev.: $3,008,740
Assets: $27,043,516
Liabilities: $13,239,204
Net Worth: $13,804,312
Earnings: ($1,615,310)
Emp.: 27
Fiscal Year-end: 12/31/23
Farming Services
N.A.I.C.S.: 111140
Zoran Scekic (CEO)

BACKA PALANKA A.D.
Zdravka elara 37, 21400, Beograd, Serbia
Tel.: (381) 212101113
Web Site: https://backapalanka.rs
Year Founded: 1968

Sales Range: $10-24.9 Million
Emp.: 145
Meat Processing Services
N.A.I.C.S.: 311615

BACKSTAGEPLAY INC.
Suite 350-409 Granville Street, Vancouver, V6C 1T2, BC, Canada
Tel.: (604) 241-8400
Web Site:
    https://www.backstageplay.com
BP—(CNSX)
Assets: $373,008
Liabilities: $252,831
Net Worth: $120,177
Earnings: ($152,861)
Fiscal Year-end: 12/31/21
Software Development Services
N.A.I.C.S.: 334610
Scott F. White (Chm & CEO)

Subsidiaries:

Parlay Entertainment (1)
2305 Wye Croft Road 2nd Floor, Oakville, L6L 6R2, ON, Canada (100%)
Tel.: (905) 337-8524
Web Site: http://www.parlaygroup.com
Internet Gaming Software
N.A.I.C.S.: 334610

BACTECH ENVIRONMENTAL CORPORATION
37 King Street East Suite 409, Toronto, M5C 1E9, ON, Canada
Tel.: (416) 813-0303   Ca
Web Site:
    https://www.bactechgreen.com
Year Founded: 2010
BCCEF—(OTCQB)
Assets: $840,428
Liabilities: $2,280,813
Net Worth: ($1,440,384)
Earnings: ($2,490,105)
Emp.: 5
Fiscal Year-end: 12/31/22
Biotechnology Researcher & Developer
N.A.I.C.S.: 541714
M. Ross Orr (Pres & CEO)

BACTIGUARD HOLDING AB
Alfred Nobels Alle 150, Stockholm, Sweden
Tel.: (46) 84405880
Web Site:
    https://www.bactiguard.com
BACTI.B—(OMX)
Rev.: $22,710,054
Assets: $82,430,980
Liabilities: $36,852,534
Net Worth: $45,578,446
Earnings: ($4,686,407)
Emp.: 163
Fiscal Year-end: 12/31/20
Medical Chemical Product Mfr
N.A.I.C.S.: 325998
Cecilia Edstrom (CEO)

BACTIQUANT A/S
Blokken 75, 3460, Birkerod, Denmark
Tel.: (45) 69884000
Web Site:
    https://www.bactiquant.com
Year Founded: 1999
9JX—(DEU)
Biotechnology Research & Development Services
N.A.I.C.S.: 541714
Mette Juhl Jorgensen (COO)

BACUI TECHNOLOGIES INTERNATIONAL LTD.
138 Robinson Road 26-03 Oxley Tower, Singapore, 068906, Singapore
Tel.: (65) 75722683288   SG
Web Site: https://www.egl.com.sg
Year Founded: 1994

YYB—(SES)
Rev.: $636,949
Assets: $11,622,271
Liabilities: $9,848,603
Net Worth: $1,773,668
Earnings: $322,553
Emp.: 1,569
Fiscal Year-end: 03/31/23
Special Interest Magazines Publisher
N.A.I.C.S.: 513120
Abdul Jabbar Karam Din (Co-Sec)

Subsidiaries:

Lifestyle Magazines Publishing Pte Ltd (1)
8 Kaki Bukit Ave 1 01-01/02, Singapore, 417941, Singapore
Tel.: (65) 62505817
Web Site: http://www.wineanddine.com.sg
Lifestyle & Special Interest Magazine Publishers
N.A.I.C.S.: 323111
Alison Ang (Exec Dir)

BACVIET STEEL JSC
53 Duc Giang, Long Bien District, Hanoi, Vietnam
Tel.: (84) 436559257
Web Site:
    http://www.bacvietgroup.com
Emp.: 330
Steel Products Mfr
N.A.I.C.S.: 331110
Vuong Anh Tran (Chm)

Subsidiaries:

BACVIET Furniture Company Limited (1)
Lot 8 9 B1 5 Phan Dang Luu Str, Khue Trung Cam Le, Da Nang, Vietnam
Tel.: (84) 5113699777
Steel Whslr
N.A.I.C.S.: 423510

BACVIET Industry Joint Stock Company (1)
Gia Le Industrial Park, Dong Hung, Thai Binh, Vietnam
Tel.: (84) 363795392
Industrial Steel Mfr
N.A.I.C.S.: 333511

BACVIET Structure Steel Building Company Limited (1)
Km7 National Highway No 18, Que Vo, Phuong Lieu, Bac Ninh, Vietnam
Tel.: (84) 2413617331
Industrial Steel Mfr
N.A.I.C.S.: 333511

BAD BOY FURNITURE WAREHOUSE LIMITED
500 Fenmar Drive, Weston, M9L 2V5, ON, Canada
Tel.: (416) 667-7546
Web Site: http://www.badboy.ca
Year Founded: 1991
Rev.: $36,062,400
Emp.: 200
Furniture & Appliance Supplier
N.A.I.C.S.: 449110
Blayne Lastman (Chm & CEO)

BADANAI MOTORS LTD
399 Memorial Ave, Thunder Bay, P7B 3Y4, ON, Canada
Tel.: (807) 683-4900
Web Site: http://badanaimotors.com
Rev.: $29,039,613
Emp.: 60
New & Used Car Dealers
N.A.I.C.S.: 441110
Kelly Badanai (Owner)

BADARO NO.19 SHIP INVESTMENT COMPANY
16F Standard Chartered Bank Korea Head Office Building 47 Jong-ro, Jongno-gu, Seoul, 03160, Korea (South)

Tel.: (82) 232103333
Web Site:
    http://www.globalmarifin.com
155900—(KRS)
Rev.: $8,906,156
Assets: $39,747,039
Liabilities: $3,566,645
Net Worth: $36,180,393
Earnings: $8,676,060
Fiscal Year-end: 12/31/22
Investment Management Service
N.A.I.C.S.: 523999
Jae Boong Lee (CEO)

BADECO ADRIA D.D.
Branilaca Sarajeva 20, Sarajevo, Bosnia & Herzegovina
Tel.: (387) 33278805
Web Site: http://www.badeco.ba
FDSSR—(SARE)
Rev.: $696,016
Assets: $159,369,443
Liabilities: $37,700,111
Net Worth: $121,669,332
Earnings: $56,541
Emp.: 5
Fiscal Year-end: 12/31/21
Tobacco Product Mfr
N.A.I.C.S.: 312230

BADEL 1862 D.D.
Vlaska 116, 10000, Zagreb, Croatia
Tel.: (385) 14609555
Web Site: http://www.badel1862.hr
Year Founded: 1862
BD62-R-A—(ZAG)
Sales Range: $50-74.9 Million
Emp.: 500
Wine & Spirits Mfr & Distr
N.A.I.C.S.: 312130
Zlatko Spoljar (Dir-Export)

Subsidiaries:

Badel 1862 d.o.o (1)
Bulevar Mihajla Pupina 121, Novi, Belgrade, 10070, Serbia
Tel.: (381) 112137832
Sales Range: $25-49.9 Million
Emp.: 10
Wine & Spirits Mfr
N.A.I.C.S.: 312130
Mirko Babic (Gen Mgr)

Badel Sarajevo d.o.o. (1)
Fetaha Beirbegovica 45, Sarajevo, 2326, Bosnia & Herzegovina
Tel.: (387) 33712470
Sales Range: $25-49.9 Million
Emp.: 13
Wine & Spirits Mfr
N.A.I.C.S.: 312130
Koricic Samir (Mgr)

Badel d.o.o.e.l. (1)
Kolektorska bb, 91000, Skopje, North Macedonia
Tel.: (389) 23175114
Sales Range: $25-49.9 Million
Emp.: 10
Wine & Spirits Mfr
N.A.I.C.S.: 312130
Lobco Bavlovske (Mng Dir)

BADER GMBH
Robert-Bosch-Strasse 2, 89250, Senden, Germany
Tel.: (49) 73 07 83 0
Web Site:
    http://www.badergruppe.com
Year Founded: 1952
Emp.: 1,000
Custom Machinery Manufacturing
N.A.I.C.S.: 333998
Karl Schmidberger (Mng Dir)

Subsidiaries:

Baltic Metalltechnik GmbH (1)
Gruner Weg 5, 23936, Grevesmuhlen, Germany
Tel.: (49) 3881 7240
Web Site: http://www.balticmetall.de

Bader GmbH—(Continued)

Metal Working Services
N.A.I.C.S.: 332999
Rainer Gsell (Mng Dir)

BADGER INFRASTRUCTURE SOLUTIONS LTD.

ATCO Building II 4th Floor 919 11th Ave SW, Calgary, T2R1P3, AB, Canada
Tel.: (403) 264-8500
Web Site: https://www.badgerinc.com
Year Founded: 1992
6BD0—(DEU)
Rev.: $683,799,000
Assets: $633,014,000
Liabilities: $388,020,000
Net Worth: $244,994,000
Earnings: $41,771,000
Emp.: 2,433
Fiscal Year-end: 12/31/23
Excavation Services
N.A.I.C.S.: 213111
Stephen J. Jones (Chm)

Subsidiaries:

Badger Daylighting   (1)
777 Orchard, Bayfield, CO 81122
Tel.: (970) 884-7380
Web Site: http://www.badgerinc.com
Sales Range: $25-49.9 Million
Emp.: 12
Excavation Work
N.A.I.C.S.: 238910

BADR INVESTMENT GROUP LLC

Way No 5007 Bldg 587, Opp Savoy Hotel Apts Ghala, Muscat, Oman
Tel.: (968) 2200 4100   **OM**
Web Site: http://www.badrinvest.com
Holding Company
N.A.I.C.S.: 551112
Ali Hassan Sulaiman (Chm)

Subsidiaries:

AATCO LLC   (1)
Falaj Al Qabail, PO Box 130, Sohar Industrial Estate, 322, Sohar, Oman
Tel.: (968) 2675 1591
Web Site: http://www.aakgc.com
Condiment Mfr & Distr
N.A.I.C.S.: 311941
Ali Hassan Sulaiman (Chm)

Automatic Terrazzo Tiles Factory LLC   (1)
P C 100, PO Box 965, Rusayl, Muscat, Oman
Tel.: (968) 24446902
Tiles Mfr
N.A.I.C.S.: 327390
Abdul Karim Hassan Sulaiman (Chm)

BAE SYSTEMS PLC

6 Carlton Gardens, London, SW1Y 5AD, United Kingdom
Tel.: (44) 1252373232   **UK**
Web Site:
https://www.baesystems.com
Year Founded: 1977
BAESF—(OTCIQ)
Rev.: $29,131,532,441
Assets: $40,474,627,619
Liabilities: $26,938,904,317
Net Worth: $13,535,723,302
Earnings: $2,448,876,546
Emp.: 99,800
Fiscal Year-end: 12/31/23
Holding Company; Aereospace Mfr, Cyber security & intelligence, and Electronics Services
N.A.I.C.S.: 551112
Brod Greve (Fin Dir)

Subsidiaries:

Aircraft Research Association Limited   (1)

Manton Lane, Bedford, MK41 7PF, United Kingdom
Tel.: (44) 1234324600
Web Site: http://www.ara.co.uk
Emp.: 150
Aircraft Mfr
N.A.I.C.S.: 336411
Paul Hutchings (CFO)

BAE SYSTEMS OMC   (1)
12 Barnsley Road Industrial Sites, Benoni, 1501, Gauteng, South Africa
Tel.: (27) 117473300
Armored Vehicle Mfr
N.A.I.C.S.: 336992
Johan Steyn (CEO)

BAE Systems   (1)
Warton Aerodrome, Preston, PR4 1AX, United Kingdom   (100%)
Tel.: (44) 1772633333
Web Site: http://www.baesystems.com
Sales Range: $1-4.9 Billion
Emp.: 7,000
Aircraft Mfr
N.A.I.C.S.: 336411

BAE Systems   (1)
Prestwick International Airport, Prestwick, KA9 2RW, United Kingdom   (100%)
Tel.: (44) 1292675000
Sales Range: $100-124.9 Million
Emp.: 450
Aircraft Design, Research & Development, Build Testing, Manufacture & Sales Services
N.A.I.C.S.: 336411
Neil McManus (Mng Dir & VP)

BAE Systems (Malaysia) Sdn Bhd   (1)
Level 28 Menara Binjai 2 Jalan Binjai, Kuala Lumpur, 50450, Malaysia
Tel.: (60) 321913000
Aircraft Parts & Auxiliary Equipment Mfr
N.A.I.C.S.: 336413

BAE Systems (Overseas Holdings) Limited   (1)
Warwick Ho, Farnborough, GU14 6YU, Hampshire, United Kingdom
Tel.: (44) 1252 373232
Investment Management Service
N.A.I.C.S.: 523940

BAE Systems Applied Intelligence   (1)
Waterside House 170 Priestley Road Surrey Research Park, Guildford, GU2 7RQ, Surrey, United Kingdom
Tel.: (44) 1483 816000
Web Site: http://www.baesystems.com
Emp.: 1,500
Information Technology Consulting Services
N.A.I.C.S.: 541512

BAE Systems Australia Limited   (1)
Level 12 20 Bridge Street, Sydney, 2000, NSW, Australia   (100%)
Tel.: (61) 292404600
Web Site: http://www.baesystems.com.au
Sales Range: $25-49.9 Million
Emp.: 65
Electronic System Mfr
N.A.I.C.S.: 334511

BAE Systems C-ITS AB   (1)
Repslagaregatan 25, 582 22, Linkoping, Sweden
Tel.: (46) 852802600
Aircraft Parts & Auxiliary Equipment Mfr
N.A.I.C.S.: 336413

BAE Systems Electronics Limited   (1)
6 Carlton Gardens, London, SW1Y 5AD, United Kingdom
Tel.: (44) 1252 373 232
Electronic Components Mfr
N.A.I.C.S.: 334419

BAE Systems Enterprises Limited   (1)
Chester House, Farnborough, GU14 6TQ, Hampshire, United Kingdom
Tel.: (44) 1252 373232
Electronic Security Equipment Mfr
N.A.I.C.S.: 334290

Subsidiary (Domestic):

BAE Systems (Operations) Limited   (2)

Warton Aerodrome, Preston, PR4 1AX, Lancashire, United Kingdom
Tel.: (44) 1772 633333
Sales Range: $1-4.9 Billion
Emp.: 9,000
Aerospace Software Development Services
N.A.I.C.S.: 541511
Christopher George Boardman (Mng Dir)

BAE Systems Hagglunds AB   (1)
Bjornavagen 2, Ornskoldsvik, 891 41, Sweden
Tel.: (46) 66080000
Aircraft Parts & Auxiliary Equipment Mfr
N.A.I.C.S.: 336413
Dan Lindell (Dir-Combat Vechiles)

BAE Systems India (Services) Pvt. Ltd   (1)
2nd Floor Hotel Le-Meridien Commercial Tower Raisina Road, New Delhi, 110 001, India
Tel.: (91) 11 4341 2345
Web Site: http://www.baesystems.com
Aviation & Defense Security Device Mfr
N.A.I.C.S.: 334511
Indu Anand (Head-Comm)

BAE Systems Integrated System Technologies   (1)
Victory Point Lyon Way, Frimley, GU16 7EX, Surrey, United Kingdom   (100%)
Tel.: (44) 1252373232
Web Site: http://www.baesystems.com
Emp.: 500
Aircraft Sensor & Electronic Systems Mfr
N.A.I.C.S.: 334511

BAE Systems Regional Aircraft   (1)
Prestwick International Airport, Prestwick, KA9 2RW, Ayrshire, United Kingdom
Tel.: (44) 1292 675000
Web Site: http://www.regional-services.com
Emp.: 220
Aircraft Repair & Maintenance Services
N.A.I.C.S.: 488190

BAE Systems Saudi Arabia   (1)
Po Box 1732, Riyadh, 11441, Saudi Arabia
Tel.: (966) 1445 9100
Electric Equipment Mfr
N.A.I.C.S.: 334419

BAE Systems Surface Ships (Holdings) Limited   (1)
Warwick House, Farnborough, GU14 6TQ, United Kingdom
Tel.: (44) 1252 373232
Investment Management Service
N.A.I.C.S.: 523999

BAE Systems, Inc.   (1)
1601 Research Blvd, Rockville, MD 20850-3173   (100%)
Tel.: (301) 838-6000
Web Site: http://www.baesystems.com
Sales Range: $5-14.9 Billion
Emp.: 52,000
Developer of Military Electronics, Radar Systems, Artillery, Ballistic Missiles, Airplanes & Armored Vehicles
N.A.I.C.S.: 336413
Ian T. Graham (Gen Counsel, Sec & Sr VP)

Group (Domestic):

BAE Systems Applied Intelligence & Security   (2)
8500 Heckscher Dr, Jacksonville, FL 32226
Tel.: (904) 251-3111
Web Site: http://www.baesystems.com
Sales Range: $1-4.9 Billion
Emp.: 8,150
Security, Business Intelligence Solutions & Ship Repair Services
N.A.I.C.S.: 336611

Subsidiary (Domestic):

BAE Systems Mobility & Protection Systems   (3)
7822 S 46th St, Phoenix, AZ 85044
Tel.: (602) 643-7603
Web Site: http://www.baesystems.com
Sales Range: $250-299.9 Million
Emp.: 800
Energy Absorbing Seating & Systems
N.A.I.C.S.: 423490

Subsidiary (Domestic):

Stewart & Stevenson Services, Inc.   (4)
1000 Louisiana Ste 5900, Houston, TX 77002-1051
Tel.: (713) 751-2600
Web Site: http://www.ssss.com
Sales Range: $900-999.9 Million
Diesel Engines, Diesel Generators, Irrigation Equipment, Pumps, Aircraft Ground Support Equipment & Oil Field Equipment Mfr
N.A.I.C.S.: 333618
John Merrifield (Pres)

Subsidiary (Domestic):

BAE Systems   (5)
5000 I-10 W, Sealy, TX 77474
Tel.: (979) 885-2977
Web Site: http://www.baesystems.com
Sales Range: $900-999.9 Million
Tactical Vehicles Designer & Mfr
N.A.I.C.S.: 336992

Subsidiary (Domestic):

BAE Systems Survivability Systems LLC   (3)
9113 Le Saint Dr, Fairfield, OH 45014-5453
Tel.: (513) 881-9800
Web Site: http://www.baesystems.com
Sales Range: $150-199.9 Million
Emp.: 700
Armored Vehicles; Personal, Industrial, Corporate & Government Security
N.A.I.C.S.: 561613

Bianchi International Inc.   (3)
3120 E. Mission Blvd, Ontario, CA 91761
Tel.: (904) 741-5400
Web Site: http://www.bianchi-intl.com
Sales Range: $75-99.9 Million
Emp.: 280
Leather Goods Mfr & Sales
N.A.I.C.S.: 314910

Break-Free   (3)
13386 International Pkwy, Jacksonville, FL 32218-2383
Tel.: (904) 741-5400
Web Site: http://www.break-free.com
Sales Range: $25-49.9 Million
Emp.: 50
Gun Cleaning Lubricants & Preservatives
N.A.I.C.S.: 324191

Monadnock Lifetime Products, Inc.   (3)
126 NH Route 12 N, Fitzwilliam, NH 03447
Tel.: (603) 585-6810
Web Site: http://www.batons.com
Develops, Manufactures & Sells Police Equipment, Primarily Police Batons
N.A.I.C.S.: 423490

PROTECH Armored Products   (3)
13386 International Pkwy, Jacksonville, FL 32218
Tel.: (904) 741-5400
Web Site: http://www.protecharmored.com
Hard Armor Products Including Ballistic Shields, Bullet Resistant Vests, Visors & Accessories; Mfrs. Protective Armor Products for Helicopters, Automobiles & Riot Control Vehicles
N.A.I.C.S.: 423490

Group (Domestic):

BAE Systems Customer Solutions   (2)
4075 Wilson Blvd, Arlington, VA 22203
Tel.: (703) 387-2200
Web Site: http://www.baesystems.com
Sales Range: $1-4.9 Billion
Emp.: 14,000
Developer of Radar Communication Equipment & Information Technology Services & Operator of Non-Nuclear Ship Repair Facilities
N.A.I.C.S.: 334511

Division (Domestic):

BAE Systems Information Technology   (3)
8201 Greensboro Dr Ste 1200, McLean, VA 22102-3846   (100%)

Tel.: (703) 847-5820
Web Site: http://www.bae.com
Sales Range: $100-124.9 Million
Emp.: 330
Systems Engineering, Technical Assistance,
Software Development, Communications
Engineering, Training to the U.S. Defense &
Intelligence Community
N.A.I.C.S.: 541611

Branch (Domestic):

**BAE Systems Information
Technology   (4)**
2525 Network Pl, Herndon, VA
20171-3514   **(100%)**
Tel.: (703) 563-7500
Web Site: http://www.digitalnet.com
Network Infrastructure & Information Assur-
ance Solutions Developer
N.A.I.C.S.: 541511

Division (Domestic):

BAE Systems Ship Repair   (3)
750 W Berkley Ave, Norfolk, VA 23523-
1032
Tel.: (757) 494-4000
Web Site: http://www.baesystems.com
Sales Range: $450-499.9 Million
Emp.: 2,200
Non-Nuclear Ship Repair, Modernization,
Overhaul & Conversion Services
N.A.I.C.S.: 336611
Joe Kampbell *(Pres)*

Subsidiary (Domestic):

BAE Systems Hawaii Shipyards   (4)
Cushing St Drydock No 4, Pearl Harbor, HI
96810
Tel.: (808) 423-8888
Sales Range: $25-49.9 Million
Emp.: 200
Ship Repair Services
N.A.I.C.S.: 336611

**BAE Systems Norfolk Ship
Repair   (4)**
750 W Berkley Ave, Norfolk, VA 23523-
1032
Tel.: (757) 494-4000
Web Site: http://www.baesystems.com
Sales Range: $150-199.9 Million
Emp.: 1,000
Ship Building, Conversion & Repair Ser-
vices
N.A.I.C.S.: 336611

**BAE Systems San Diego Ship
Repair   (4)**
2205 E Belt, San Diego, CA 92113
Tel.: (619) 238-1000
Web Site: http://www.baesystems.com
Sales Range: $150-199.9 Million
Emp.: 1,000
Ship Building & Repairing Services
N.A.I.C.S.: 336611
David Thomas *(Gen Mgr)*

**BAE Systems Southeast Shipyards
AMHC Inc.   (4)**
8500 Heckscher Dr, Jacksonville, FL 32226-
2434
Tel.: (904) 251-1790
Sales Range: $300-349.9 Million
Emp.: 300
Maintenance, Repair, Overhaul & Conver-
sion Services for Commercial & Military
Vessels
N.A.I.C.S.: 336611
Kevin E. Wilson *(VP-Sls & Mktg)*

Subsidiary (Domestic):

**BAE Systems Southeast Shipyards
Alabama, LLC   (5)**
Main Gate Dunlap Dr, Mobile, AL 36652
Tel.: (251) 690-7100
Sales Range: $400-449.9 Million
Ship Building & Repair Services
N.A.I.C.S.: 336611

**BAE Systems Southeast Shipyards
Jacksonville, LLC   (5)**
8500 Heckscher Ave, Jacksonville, FL 32226-
2434
Tel.: (904) 251-1545

Sales Range: $400-449.9 Million
Ship Building & Repair Services
N.A.I.C.S.: 336611

Division (Domestic):

**BAE Systems-Technology Solutions &
Services Sector   (3)**
1601 Research Blvd, Rockville, MD
20850-3173   **(100%)**
Tel.: (301) 838-6000
Web Site:
     http://www.tss.na.baesystems.com
Sales Range: $150-199.9 Million
Emp.: 600
Systems Engineering, Technical & Analytical
Services
N.A.I.C.S.: 541512

Subsidiary (Domestic):

Advanced Concepts, Inc.   (4)
9861 Broken Land Pkwy Ste 150, Colum-
bia, MD 21046
Tel.: (410) 381-3780
Web Site: http://www.baesystems.com
Sales Range: $75-99.9 Million
Emp.: 300
Information Technology, Network Security
Solutions & Systems Engineering & Devel-
opment Services for US Intelligence & Mili-
tary
N.A.I.C.S.: 541511

Division (Domestic):

**BAE Systems Performance Based
Solutions   (4)**
520 Gaither Rd, Rockville, MD 20850
Tel.: (301) 738-4000
Web Site:
     http://www.tss.na.baesystems.com
Sales Range: $25-49.9 Million
Emp.: 50
Designer of Submarine Based Ballistic Mis-
sile Technology
N.A.I.C.S.: 336414

**BAE Systems-Analytical & Ordinance
Solutions   (4)**
308 Voyager Way, Huntsville, AL 35806-
3560
Tel.: (256) 890-8000
Sales Range: $25-49.9 Million
Emp.: 250
Engineeering Services
N.A.I.C.S.: 541715

Plant (Domestic):

**BAE Systems-Ordnance
Systems   (5)**
4509 W Stone Dr, Kingsport, TN
37660-1048   **(100%)**
Tel.: (423) 578-8010
Ordnance Systems
N.A.I.C.S.: 541611
Todd Hayes *(VP & Gen Mgr)*

Division (Domestic):

**BAE Systems-Applied
Technologies   (4)**
4545A Viewridge Ave, San Diego, CA
92123   **(100%)**
Tel.: (858) 569-1886
Web Site: http://www.bae-
     systemsmarine.co.uk
Sales Range: $10-24.9 Million
Emp.: 60
Aircraft Mfr
N.A.I.C.S.: 541330

**BAE Systems-Applied
Technologies   (4)**
16541 Commerce Dr, King George, VA
22485-5806   **(100%)**
Tel.: (540) 663-6300
Aircraft Mfr
N.A.I.C.S.: 238990

**BAE Systems-Applied
Technologies   (4)**
1844 Poulsbo Ave, Keyport, WA
98345   **(100%)**
Tel.: (360) 598-8800
Aircraft Systems Mfr
N.A.I.C.S.: 336413

**BAE Systems-Integrated Electronic
Solutions   (4)**
23481 Cottonwood Pkwy, California, MD
20619-2038   **(100%)**
Tel.: (301) 863-0888
Developer & Mfr of Naval Radio Communi-
cations Systems
N.A.I.C.S.: 334220

**BAE Systems-Integrated O & M
Solutions   (4)**
Industrial Park 557 Mary Esther Cut Off,
Fort Walton Beach, FL
32548-4090   **(100%)**
Tel.: (850) 244-7711
Sales Range: $10-24.9 Million
Emp.: 55
Engineeering Services
N.A.I.C.S.: 561210

Subsidiary (Domestic):

Bae Systems Spectal LLC   (4)
1875 Campus Commons Dr Ste 100, Res-
ton, VA 20191
Tel.: (703) 860-6180
Web Site: http://www.baesystems.com
Sales Range: $650-699.9 Million
Security & Intelligence Solutions, Specializ-
ing in Government Consulting, Training &
Technology Development
N.A.I.C.S.: 541690

McClendon, LLC   (4)
14900 Bogle Dr Ste 300, Chantilly, VA
20151
Tel.: (703) 263-0490
Web Site: http://www.baesystems.com
Sales Range: $50-74.9 Million
Technical & Professional Services to Intelli-
gence & Military Communities
N.A.I.C.S.: 541690

Subsidiary (Domestic):

BAE Systems Imaging Solutions   (2)
1801 McCarthy Blvd, Milpitas, CA 95035
Tel.: (408) 433-2500
Web Site: http://www.fairchildimaging.com
Sales Range: $50-74.9 Million
Emp.: 160
Electronic Imaging Components & Systems
Mfr & Developer
N.A.I.C.S.: 334413

**BAE Systems Information and Elec-
tronic Systems Integration Inc.   (2)**
65 Spit Brook Rd, Nashua, NH 03060-6909
Tel.: (603) 885-4321
Electric Equipment Mfr
N.A.I.C.S.: 334419

Group (Domestic):

**BAE Systems Platforms &
Services   (2)**
2000 N 15th St 11th Fl, Arlington, VA 22201
Tel.: (703) 907-8200
Web Site: http://www.baesystems.com
Holding Company; Armored Combat Ve-
hicles, Artillery Systems & Intelligent Muni-
tions Developer & Mfr
N.A.I.C.S.: 551112

Subsidiary (Domestic):

**BAE Systems Land & Armaments
Inc.   (3)**
1300 N 17th St Ste 1400, Arlington, VA
22209
Tel.: (703) 907-8200
Web Site: http://www.baesystems.com
Landing Craft & Armored Vehicles Mfr
N.A.I.C.S.: 336992

Division (Domestic):

BAE Systems   (4)
1205 Coleman Ave, Santa Clara, CA 95050
Tel.: (408) 289-0111
Research & Development of Military Weap-
onry
N.A.I.C.S.: 541715
John Morrow *(Mgr-Bradley Survivability
Tech)*

**BAE Systems Armament Systems
Division   (4)**
4800 E River Rd, Minneapolis, MN 55421-
1498

Tel.: (763) 571-9201
Web Site: http://www.uniteddefense.com
Sales Range: $450-499.9 Million
Emp.: 2,000
Designer & Mfr of Artillery & Missile
Launching Systems
N.A.I.C.S.: 336415

**BAE Systems Ground Systems
Division   (4)**
1100 Bairs Rd, York, PA 17408
Tel.: (717) 225-8000
Web Site: http://www.uniteddefense.com
Sales Range: $350-399.9 Million
Emp.: 2,500
Designer & Mfr of Manned Armored Combat
Vehicles & Unmanned Robotic Weapons
Systems
N.A.I.C.S.: 336992

**BAE Systems Steel Products
Division   (4)**
2101 W 10th St, Anniston, AL 36201-4223
Tel.: (256) 237-2841
Sales Range: $200-249.9 Million
Emp.: 550
Mfr of Steel Components & Suspension
Equipment for Tracked Combat Vehicles
N.A.I.C.S.: 336992

Subsidiary (Domestic):

BAE Systems TVS Inc.   (2)
5000 Interstate 10, Sealy, TX 77474-9506
Tel.: (979) 885-2977
Automobile Parts Mfr
N.A.I.C.S.: 336390

Group (Domestic):

**BAE Systems-Electronics & Inte-
grated Solutions   (2)**
65 Spit Brook Rd, Nashua, NH
03060   **(100%)**
Tel.: (603) 885-4321
Web Site:
     http://www.eis.na.baesystems.com
Sales Range: $1-4.9 Billion
Emp.: 15,000
Mfr of Electronic Systems & Subsystems for
Military & Commercial Applications
N.A.I.C.S.: 334511

Division (Domestic):

BAE Systems   (3)
10920 Technology Pl, San Diego, CA
92127   **(100%)**
Tel.: (858) 675-2600
Web Site: http://www.baesystems.com
Sales Range: $450-499.9 Million
Emp.: 2,000
Developer of Information Technology Sys-
tems & Geospatial Exploitation Software
N.A.I.C.S.: 518210

BAE Systems   (3)
95 Canal St, Nashua, NH 03061
Tel.: (603) 885-4321
Web Site: http://www.baesystems.com
Developer of Aircraft Radar & Electronic
Countermeasure Systems
N.A.I.C.S.: 334511

Branch (Domestic):

BAE Systems   (4)
6500 Tracor Ln, Austin, TX
78725-2151   **(100%)**
Tel.: (512) 926-2800
Web Site: http://www.baesystems.com
Sales Range: $125-149.9 Million
Emp.: 550
Developer of Situational Awareness Sensor
Systems
N.A.I.C.S.: 334511

BAE Systems-Flight Systems   (4)
116880 Flight Systems Dr, Mojave, CA
93501
Tel.: (661) 824-6438
Web Site:
     http://www.eis.na.baesystems.com
Sales Range: $25-49.9 Million
Emp.: 170
Commercial & Military Aircraft Modification
Services
N.A.I.C.S.: 336411

Division (Domestic):

BAE Systems-ADR   (3)

BAE Systems plc—(Continued)

124 Gaither Dr Ste 100, Mount Laurel, NJ 08054
Tel.: (856) 866-9700
Sales Range: $25-49.9 Million
Emp.: 100
Digital Mapping & Surveying Services
N.A.I.C.S.: 541360

BAE Systems-Communications, Navigation, Identification & Reconnaissance (3)
150 Parish Dr, Wayne, NJ 07474 **(100%)**
Tel.: (973) 633-6000
Web Site:
http://www.eis.na.baesystems.com
Sales Range: $350-399.9 Million
Emp.: 1,300
Providing Technological Support for Aerospace Engineering
N.A.I.C.S.: 334511

Branch (Domestic):

BAE Systems-Communication, Navigation, Identification & Reconnaissance (4)
450 Pulaski Rd, Greenlawn, NY 11740-1606 **(100%)**
Tel.: (631) 261-7000
Web Site:
http://www.eis.na.baesystems.com
Sales Range: $125-149.9 Million
Emp.: 600
Avionics, Navigation & Military Communication Services
N.A.I.C.S.: 334511

Division (Domestic):

BAE Systems-Information Warfare (3)
144 Daniel Webster Hwy N, Merrimack, NH 03054 **(100%)**
Tel.: (603) 885-4321
Web Site: http://www.baesystems.com
Sales Range: $800-899.9 Million
Emp.: 4,500
Developer of Signal Management & Electronic Attack Systems
N.A.I.C.S.: 334511

Branch (Domestic):

BAE Systems (4)
4075 Wilson Blvd Ste 900, Arlington, VA 22203 **(100%)**
Tel.: (703) 387-2200
Web Site:
http://www.eis.na.baesystems.com
Sales Range: $125-149.9 Million
Emp.: 450
Aircraft Systems Mfr
N.A.I.C.S.: 334511
Ann Ackerson (Chief Procurement Officer-Global)

Division (Domestic):

BAE Systems-Platform Solutions (3)
600 Main St, Johnson City, NY 13790-1806 **(100%)**
Tel.: (607) 770-2000
Web Site:
http://www.eis.na.baesystems.com
Sales Range: $450-499.9 Million
Emp.: 1,500
Mfr of Aircraft & Vehicle Control & Guidance Systems
N.A.I.C.S.: 336413

Subsidiary (Domestic):

Bae Systems IAP Research, Inc. (2)
2763 Culver Ave, Dayton, OH 45429
Tel.: (937) 296-1806
Web Site: http://www.iap.com
Research & Development in the Physical, Engineering & Life Sciences
N.A.I.C.S.: 541715
John Barber (Co-Founder & Pres)

Signal Innovations Group Inc. (2)
4721 Emperor Blvd Ste 330, Durham, NC 27703
Tel.: (919) 323-3453
Web Site: http://www.siginnovations.com
Emp.: 25

Federal Defense, Intelligence & Security Services
N.A.I.C.S.: 541330
Lawrence Carin (CTO)

Bohemia Interactive Simulations k.s. (1)
Vltavska 3101/24 Smichov, 150 00, Prague, Czech Republic
Tel.: (420) 226 219 964
Web Site: http://www.bisimulations.com
Game Development Services
N.A.I.C.S.: 541511
Colin Hillier (COO)

Subsidiary (US):

TerraSim, Inc. (2)
1 Gateway Ctr Ste 2050 420 Ft Duquesne Blvd, Pittsburgh, PA 15222
Tel.: (412) 232-3646
Web Site: http://www.terrasim.com
Emp.: 23
Software Development Services
N.A.I.C.S.: 541511

Detica Group Limited (1)
Surrey Research Park, Guildford, GU2 7YP, Surrey, United Kingdom
Tel.: (44) 1483816000
Web Site: http://www.baesystemsdetica.com
Sales Range: $300-349.9 Million
Emp.: 1,464
Business & Information Technology Consulting Services
N.A.I.C.S.: 541690
Neil Medley (COO)

Subsidiary (Non-US):

BAE Systems Applied Intelligence (2)
Level 5 Block 4 Dundrum Town Centre, Dublin, 14, Dundrum, Ireland
Tel.: (353) 18739600
Web Site: http://www.baesystems.com
Sales Range: $50-74.9 Million
Emp.: 301
Fraud Detection & Compliance Software Developer
N.A.I.C.S.: 513210
Julian Cracknell (Mng Dir)

Subsidiary (US):

Detica Consulting LLC (2)
260 Madison Ave Ste 8057, New York, NY 10016
Tel.: (646) 216-2143
Web Site: http://www.baesystemsdetica.com
Sales Range: $10-24.9 Million
Emp.: 50
Technical Consulting Services
N.A.I.C.S.: 541690

Subsidiary (Domestic):

Detica Limited (2)
Surrey Research Park, Guildford, GU25YP, Surrey, United Kingdom
Tel.: (44) 1483442000
Web Site: http://www.baesystemsdetica.com
Management Consulting Services
N.A.I.C.S.: 541618
Kevin Taylor (CEO)

Division (Domestic):

Detica System Integration Limited (3)
Surrey Research Park, Guildford, GU25YP, Surrey, United Kingdom
Tel.: (44) 1483442000
Management Consulting Services
N.A.I.C.S.: 541618

Detica-StreamShield (3)
St Marys Court The Broadway, Amersham, HP7 0UT, Bucks, United Kingdom
Tel.: (44) 8701149465
Web Site: http://www.baesystemsdetica.com
Sales Range: $25-49.9 Million
Emp.: 65
Data Processing Services
N.A.I.C.S.: 518210

Subsidiary (US):

Detica Solutions, Inc. (2)
265 Franklin St Ste 5, Boston, MA 02110
Tel.: (617) 737-4170

Web Site: http://www.baesystemsdetica.com
Developer of Fraud Detection & Compliance Software
N.A.I.C.S.: 513210
Joe Friscia (Exec VP & Gen Mgr)

Hagglunds Vehicle GmbH (1)
Hoher Holzweg 12, 30966, Hemmingen, Germany
Tel.: (49) 5101991800
Web Site: http://www.haegglunds-vehicle.de
Automobile Parts Mfr
N.A.I.C.S.: 336110
Anders Lundgren (Mng Dir)

Heckler & Koch GmbH (1)
Heckler and Koch-Str 1, PO Box 1329, 78727, Oberndorf, Germany **(100%)**
Tel.: (49) 7423790
Web Site: http://www.heckler-koch.com
Small Arms Mfr
N.A.I.C.S.: 332994

Subsidiary (US):

Heckler & Koch Inc. (2)
19980 Highland Vista Dr Ste 190, Ashburn, VA 20147
Tel.: (703) 450-1900
Web Site: http://www.hecklerkoch-usa.com
Sales Range: $25-49.9 Million
Emp.: 13
Distr of Military & Federal Law Enforcement Sporting Firearms
N.A.I.C.S.: 423910

Hunter Aerospace Corporation Pty Limited (1)
604 New England Hwy, Rutherford, 2320, NSW, Australia
Tel.: (61) 249320000
Web Site:
https://www.hunteraerospace.com.au
N.A.I.C.S.: 811198

MBDA Holdings S.A.S. (1)
37 Boulevard de Montmorency, 75016, Paris, France **(37.5%)**
Tel.: (33) 142242424
Web Site: http://www.mbda-systems.com
Holding Company; Guided Missiles & Missile Systems Mfr
N.A.I.C.S.: 551112
Antoine Bouvier (CEO)

Subsidiary (Non-US):

MBDA Deutschland GmbH (2)
Hagenauer Forst 27, Schrobenhausen, 86529, Germany
Tel.: (49) 8252 99 0
Aircraft Machinery Mfr
N.A.I.C.S.: 336413
Thomas Homberg (Mng Dir)

Subsidiary (Domestic):

Bayern-Chemie Gesellschaft fur Flugchemische Antriebe mbH (3)
Liebigstrasse 17, PO Box 11, 84544, Aschau, Germany
Tel.: (49) 86386010
Web Site: http://bayern-chemie.com
Sales Range: $50-74.9 Million
Emp.: 160
Rocket Propulsion Systems Mfr
N.A.I.C.S.: 336415

TDW-Gesellschaft fur verteidigungstechnische Wirksysteme GmbH (3)
Hagenauer Forst 27, 86529, Schrobenhausen, Germany
Tel.: (49) 8252 99 0
Web Site: http://www.eads.com
Sales Range: $200-249.9 Million
Emp.: 1,000
Aircraft Part Mfr
N.A.I.C.S.: 336413
Thomas Homberg (Gen Mgr)

Subsidiary (Domestic):

MBDA France SAS (2)
1 ave Reaumur, 92350, Le Plessis-Robinson, France
Tel.: (33) 171541000
Web Site: http://www.mbda-systems.com
Sales Range: $25-49.9 Million
Emp.: 100
Missiles & Missile Systems

N.A.I.C.S.: 336412

Joint Venture (Domestic):

EUROSAM (3)
Centre d'affaires de la Boursidiere Batiment Kerguelen, Le Plessis-Robinson, 92357, France
Tel.: (33) 1 4187 1416
Web Site: http://www.eurosam.com
Emp.: 70
Missile Defense Systems Mfr
N.A.I.C.S.: 336414
Michelle Vigneras (Mng Dir)

ROXEL S.A.S. (3)
La Boursidi Immeuble Jura, 92357; Le Plessis-Robinson, France **(50%)**
Tel.: (33) 141 07 82 95
Web Site: http://www.roxelgroup.com
Propulsion System Mfr
N.A.I.C.S.: 336415

Subsidiary (Domestic):

ROXEL France (4)
Route D Ardon, 45240, La Ferte-Saint-Aubin, France
Tel.: (33) 238516666
Sales Range: $100-124.9 Million
Emp.: 300
Rocket Propulsion Systems Mfr
N.A.I.C.S.: 335312

Subsidiary (Non-US):

MBDA Italia SpA (3)
Via Monte Flavio 45, 00131, Rome, Italy
Tel.: (39) 06 87711
Web Site: http://www.mbda-systems.com
Missile Systems Mfr
N.A.I.C.S.: 336414

MBDA UK Ltd. (2)
Six Hills Way, Stevenage, SG1 2DA, United Kingdom
Tel.: (44) 1438312422
Web Site: http://www.mbda.co.uk
Sales Range: $350-399.9 Million
Emp.: 2,000
Missile Mfr
N.A.I.C.S.: 336414

Branch (Domestic):

MBDA UK (3)
Six Hills Way, Stevenage, SG1 2DA, Hertfordshire, United Kingdom
Tel.: (44) 1438752000
Web Site: http://www.mbda.co.uk
Emp.: 4,000
Missile Mfr
N.A.I.C.S.: 336414
Chris Allam (Mng Dir)

Panavia Aircraft GmbH (1)
Am Soeldnermoos 17, 85399, Hallbergmoos, Germany **(42.5%)**
Tel.: (49) 811800
Web Site: http://www.panavia.de
Sales Range: $25-49.9 Million
Emp.: 100
Military Aircraft Designer & Mfr
N.A.I.C.S.: 336411

Pitch Technologies AB (1)
Repslagaregatan 25, 582 22, Linkoping, Sweden
Tel.: (46) 134705500
Web Site: http://www.pitchtechnologies.com
Information Technology & Services
N.A.I.C.S.: 541511
Bjorn Moller (Pres)

Pitch Technologies Limited (1)
5 Upper Montagu Street, London, W1H 2AG, United Kingdom
Tel.: (44) 2072585135
Information Technology & Services
N.A.I.C.S.: 541511

Port Solent Marina Limited (1)
South Lockside Port Solent, Portsmouth, PO6 4TJ, Hampshire, United Kingdom
Tel.: (44) 2392210765
Web Site: http://www.premiermarinas.com
Travel & Tourism Services
N.A.I.C.S.: 561510

Prismatic Ltd. (1)
2 Omega Park, Alton, GU34 2QE, Hamp-

shire, United Kingdom
Tel.: (44) 1420571417
Web Site: http://www.prismaticltd.co.uk
Solar Power Generation Services
N.A.I.C.S.: 221114
Dave Corfield *(CEO)*

Saudi Maintenance & Supply Chain
Management Company Limited **(1)**
Ar Rimal, Riyadh, 13454, Saudi Arabia
Tel.: (966) 114459100
Web Site: https://www.smscmc.com
N.A.I.C.S.: 541614

Saudi Technology & Logistics Ser-
vices Limited **(1)**
Tashkeel Tower 3rd Floor, Alworood District,
Riyadh, Saudi Arabia
Tel.: (966) 504466188
Web Site: http://www.lts.sa
Petrochemical Mfr
N.A.I.C.S.: 325110

BAFANG ELECTRIC SUZHOU CO., LTD.
No 9 Heshun Road, Suzhou Indus-
trial Park, Suzhou, 215122, China
Tel.: (86) 51265975996
Web Site: https://bafang-e.com.cn
Year Founded: 2003
603489—(SHG)
Rev.: $400,134,889
Assets: $504,088,636
Liabilities: $102,743,597
Net Worth: $401,345,039
Earnings: $71,903,080
Emp.: 1,000
Fiscal Year-end: 12/31/22
Electrical Equipment Mfr & Distr
N.A.I.C.S.: 335999
Qinghua Wang *(Chm & Gen Mgr)*

BAFGH MINING COMPANY
Syed Jamaluddin Asadabadi Yousef
Abad Street 16th Ansari Street, Plate
10, 1431893493, Tehran, Iran
Tel.: (98) 2188717520
Web Site: https://bmc.co.ir
Year Founded: 1966
BAFG—(THE)
Sales Range: Less than $1 Million
Emp.: 329
Metal Ore Mining Services
N.A.I.C.S.: 212290

BAFNA PHARMACEUTICALS LIMITED
Bafna Towers 299 Thambu Chetty
Street, Chennai, 600 001, India
Tel.: (91) 4425267517
Web Site:
   https://www.bafnapharma.com
Year Founded: 1981
532989—(BOM)
Rev.: $14,222,481
Assets: $15,536,623
Liabilities: $6,729,645
Net Worth: $8,806,978
Earnings: $1,359,391
Emp.: 588
Fiscal Year-end: 03/31/23
Pharmaceuticals Mfr
N.A.I.C.S.: 325412
Paras Bafna *(Exec Dir)*

BAGATELLE INTERNATIONAL INC.
8225 Mayrand Street Suite 200, Mon-
treal, H4P 2C7, QC, Canada
Tel.: (514) 587-2580
Web Site: http://www.bagatelle.ca
Year Founded: 1968
Sales Range: $10-24.9 Million
Emp.: 15
Women Apparel Mfr
N.A.I.C.S.: 315250
Michael Litvack *(CEO)*

BAGHDAD FOR PACKING MATERIALS
Al-Zaafrania Industrial Strip, Bagh-
dad, Iraq
Tel.: (964) 1 7731151
Year Founded: 1962
Paper Packaging Product Mfr
N.A.I.C.S.: 322219

BAGHDAD MOTOR CARS SERVICING CO.
Hai Al-Wahda Sec 902 St 40 Buld 10,
Baghdad, Iraq
Tel.: (964) 7192097
Year Founded: 1984
SBMC—(IRAQ)
Sales Range: Less than $1 Million
Automotive Repair Services
N.A.I.C.S.: 811198

BAGHDAD SOFT DRINKS CO.
Industrial Strip Al-Zaafrania, Bagh-
dad, Iraq
Tel.: (964) 17734145
Web Site:
   http://www.pepsibaghdad.com
Year Founded: 1989
Soft Drinks Mfr
N.A.I.C.S.: 312111

Subsidiaries:

Baghdad of Iraq Company for Public
Transport & Real Estate
Investments **(1)**
Amiriyah Abu Ghraib Old Way, Baghdad,
Iraq **(90%)**
Tel.: (964) 1 5556611
Sales Range: Less than $1 Million
Food Transportation Services
N.A.I.C.S.: 488490

Iraqi Land Transport Co. **(1)**
Nahda Square Maared Road Near To
Nahda Garage, Baghdad, Iraq **(80%)**
Tel.: (964) 1 8866491
Sales Range: Less than $1 Million
Land Transportation Services
N.A.I.C.S.: 488490

BAGO GROUP
Bernardo de Irigoyen 248, Capital
Federal, Buenos Aires, C1072AAF,
Argentina
Tel.: (54) 11 4344 2000
Web Site: http://www.bago.com.ar
Sales Range: $1-4.9 Billion
Emp.: 3,850
Holding Company: Pharmaceuticals,
Animal Husbandry & Farming
N.A.I.C.S.: 551112

Subsidiaries:

Armstrong Laboratorios de Mexico
S.A. de C.V. **(1)**
Division del Norte No 3311 Colonia Can-
delaria Delegacion, Coyoacan, 04380,
Mexico
Tel.: (52) 3000 1500
Web Site:
   http://www.laboratoriosarmstrong.mx
Pharmaceutical Product Mfr & Distr
N.A.I.C.S.: 325412

Biogenesis Bago S.A. **(1)**
Ruta Panamericana Km 38 5, Garin, 1619,
Argentina
Tel.: (54) 33 2744 8300
Web Site: http://www.biogenesisbago.com
Pharmaceutical Product Mfr & Distr
N.A.I.C.S.: 325412

Gramon Bago de Uruguay S.A. **(1)**
Av Joaquin Suarez 3359, 11 700, Montevi-
deo, Uruguay
Tel.: (598) 2 200 46 11
Web Site: http://www.gramonbago.com.uy
Pharmaceutical Product Mfr & Distr
N.A.I.C.S.: 325412

Laboratorios Bago Colombia **(1)**
Carrera 51 No 96-11 B La Castellana, Bogota, Colombia

Tel.: (57) 1 6360303
Web Site: http://www.bago.com.co
Pharmaceutical Product Mfr & Distr
N.A.I.C.S.: 325412

Laboratorios Bago S.A. **(1)**
Bernardo de Irigoyen 248, Autonoma de
Buenos Aires, Buenos Aires, C 1072 AAF
Cdad, Argentina
Tel.: (54) 1143442000
Web Site: http://www.bago.com.ar
Sales Range: $450-499.9 Million
Emp.: 1,050
Mfr of Pharmaceutical Products
N.A.I.C.S.: 325412
Sebastian Bago *(Pres)*

Joint Venture (Domestic):

Nutricia Bago S.A. **(2)**
Marcelo T de Alvear 590 Piso 1,
C1058AAF, Buenos Aires, Argentina
Tel.: (54) 1153545400
Web Site: https://nutriciaoverseas.com.ar
Sales Range: $10-24.9 Million
Emp.: 40
Newly Developed Baby & Clinical Nutrition
Products Marketer; Owned 51% by Danone
Baby & Medical Nutrition B.V. & 49% by
Laboratorios Bago S.A.
N.A.I.C.S.: 541613
Sandra Slavkis *(Gen Mgr-Bus Dev)*

Laboratorios Bago de Bolivia
S.A. **(1)**
Calle 9 de Calacoto 21 entre Av Los
Sauces y Costanera, La Paz, Bolivia
Tel.: (591) 2770337
Web Site: http://www.bago.com.bo
Pharmaceutical Product Mfr & Distr
N.A.I.C.S.: 325412

Laboratorios Bago de Guatemala
S.A. **(1)**
20 Calle Final Km 6 8 Carretera a Muxbal
Complejo Pradera, Ofibodega No 5, Guate-
mala, Guatemala
Tel.: (502) 2375 2365
Web Site: http://www.bago.com.gt
Pharmaceutical Product Mfr & Distr
N.A.I.C.S.: 325412

Laboratorios Bago del Ecuador
S.A. **(1)**
Lizardo Garcia E1080 y Av 12 de Octubre
Edificio Alto, Aragon, Quito, Ecuador
Tel.: (593) 24 002400
Web Site: http://www.bago.com.ec
Pharmaceutical Product Mfr & Distr
N.A.I.C.S.: 325412
Mauricio Teran *(Product Mgr)*

Laboratorios Bago del Peru S.A. **(1)**
Av Jorge Chavez 154 - oficina 401, Miraflo-
res, Lima, Peru
Tel.: (51) 1 611 2900
Web Site: http://www.bago.com.pe
Pharmaceutical Product Mfr & Distr
N.A.I.C.S.: 325412
Irving Lopez Franco *(Mgr-District)*

Laboratorios Bago do Brasil S.A. **(1)**
R Conego Felipe 365 - Taquara, Rio de Ja-
neiro, 22713-010, Brazil
Tel.: (55) 21 2159 2600
Web Site: http://www.bago.com.br
Pharmaceutical Product Mfr & Distr
N.A.I.C.S.: 325412

Victoria Seguros S.A. **(1)**
Calle Florida 556, Buenos Aires, Argentina
Tel.: (54) 1143221100
Web Site: http://www.victoria.com.ar
Pharmaceutical Product Mfr & Distr
N.A.I.C.S.: 325412

BAGS-ENERGOTEHNIKA D.D.
Ul Igmanska bb, Vogosca, 71 320,
Sarajevo, Bosnia & Herzegovina
Tel.: (387) 3 343 2632
BAGSR—(SARE)
Rev.: $1,908,725
Assets: $6,679,977
Liabilities: $4,406,597
Net Worth: $2,273,380
Earnings: ($75,832)
Emp.: 26
Fiscal Year-end: 12/31/20

Media Production & Distr
N.A.I.C.S.: 541830

BAGUIO GREEN GROUP LIMITED
UnitA 4/F Dragon Industrial Building
No 93 King Lam Street, Lai Chi Kok,
Kowloon, China (Hong Kong)
Tel.: (852) 25413388
Web Site: http://www.baguio.com.hk
1397—(HKG)
Rev.: $228,622,928
Assets: $114,261,420
Liabilities: $71,407,268
Net Worth: $42,854,153
Earnings: $6,554,138
Emp.: 8,894
Fiscal Year-end: 12/31/22
Cleaning Services, Pest Control,
Landscaping Services & Waste Man-
agement
N.A.I.C.S.: 561740
Wing Hong Ng *(Chm)*

Subsidiaries:

Baguio Waste Management & Recy-
cling Limited **(1)**
Unit A 4/F Dragon Industrial Building No 93
King Lam Street, Lai Chi Kok, Kowloon,
New Territories, China (Hong Kong)
Tel.: (852) 25413388
Waste Recycling Services
N.A.I.C.S.: 562920

Modern Automobile Company
Limited **(1)**
G/F Dd 124 Lot 673-674, Yuen Long, China
(Hong Kong)
Tel.: (852) 24886005
Automotive Repair & Maintenance Services
N.A.I.C.S.: 811111

Tak Tai Enviroscape Limited **(1)**
Unit A 4/F No 93 King Lam Street, Dragon
Industrial Building Lai Chi Kok, Kowloon,
China (Hong Kong)
Tel.: (852) 26861025
Web Site: https://taktai.hk
Landscaping Services
N.A.I.C.S.: 561730

BAHAMAS INTERNATIONAL SECURITIES EXCHANGE
Ste 201 Fort Nassau Centre British
Colonial Hilton Bay St, PO Box EE-
15672, Nassau, Bahamas
Tel.: (242) 323 2330
Web Site:
   http://www.bisxbahamas.com
Emp.: 4
Stock Exchange Operator
N.A.I.C.S.: 523210
Keith Davies *(CEO & Sec)*

BAHAMASAIR HOLDINGS LIMITED
Windsor Field, N-4881, Nassau, Ba-
hamas
Tel.: (242) 3778451
Web Site:
   http://www.bahamasair.com
Year Founded: 1970
Sales Range: $150-199.9 Million
Emp.: 700
Oil Transportation Services
N.A.I.C.S.: 481111
Barry Farrington *(Chm)*

BAHEMA EDUCACAO SA
340 Room 1, Vila Olimpia, Sao
Paulo, 04549-002, SP, Brazil
Tel.: (55) 1130817142 **BR**
Web Site:
   https://www.bahema.com.br
Year Founded: 1953
BAHI3—(BRAZ)
Rev.: $67,517,025
Assets: $106,426,411
Liabilities: $84,503,314

Bahema Educacao SA—(Continued)

Net Worth: $21,923,097
Earnings: ($1,196,260)
Fiscal Year-end: 12/31/23
Holding Company
N.A.I.C.S.: 551112
Guilherme Affonso Ferreira *(CEO-IR)*

Subsidiaries:

Centro de Formacao de Educadores
da Vila Ltda.   **(1)**
Av Brg Faria Lima 1656-9, Andar Pinheiros,
01451-001, Sao Paulo, Brazil
Tel.: (55) 1137519677
Web Site: http://www.cfvila.com.br
Educational Training Center Services
N.A.I.C.S.: 611699

BAHIA LAS MINAS CORP.
PH Towers Building the Americas
Mezzanine Darien Street Punta
Punta, Coronado Construction Punta
Pacifica, Panama, Panama
Tel.: (507) 216 9900
Year Founded: 1998
BLMI—(PAN)
Sales Range: Less than $1 Million
Eletric Power Generation Services
N.A.I.C.S.: 221111

BAHIA PRODUTOS DE MA-DEIRA S.A.
Rodovia BR 418 km 37, Posto da
Mata, Nova Vicosa, 45928 000, Ba-
hia, Brazil
Tel.: (55) 73 209 8333   BR
Web Site: http://www.lyptus.com.br
Year Founded: 1999
Sales Range: $200-249.9 Million
Wood Products Mfr
N.A.I.C.S.: 321211

BAHLSEN GMBH & CO. KG
Podbielskistrasse 11, 30163, Han-
nover, Germany   De
Web Site: http://www.bahlsen.de
Year Founded: 1889
Sales Range: $700-749.9 Million
Emp.: 3,652
Cookie & Candy Mfr
N.A.I.C.S.: 311821
Werner Michael Bahlsen *(Co-Mng
Dir)*

BAHMAN INVESTMENT COM-PANY
Vali Asr St Higher Vank Square Lida
St, Tehran, 15875-1846, Iran
Tel.: (98) 2188784603
Year Founded: 2002
SBAH—(THE)
Sales Range: Less than $1 Million
Emp.: 29
Investment Management Service
N.A.I.C.S.: 523940

BAHRAIN BOURSE
Harbour Gate 4th Floor, PO Box
3203, Manama, Bahrain
Tel.: (973) 17261260   BH
Web Site:
    http://www.bahrainbourse.com
Year Founded: 1989
Rev.: $8,226,666
Assets: $15,954,492
Liabilities: $3,559,493
Net Worth: $12,394,999
Earnings: ($1,314,038)
Emp.: 97
Fiscal Year-end: 12/31/19
Stock Exchange
N.A.I.C.S.: 523210
Abdulla Jaffar Abdin *(Sr Dir-Ops)*

BAHRAIN CAR PARK COM-PANY B.S.C.

128 Government Avenue Amakin
building 2nd Floor office 2009, PO
Box 5298, Manama, Bahrain
Tel.: (973) 17224477
Web Site: https://amakin.bh
Year Founded: 1961
CPARK—(BAH)
Rev.: $5,792,297
Assets: $54,612,687
Liabilities: $1,788,777
Net Worth: $52,823,909
Earnings: $2,146,248
Emp.: 60
Fiscal Year-end: 12/31/22
Car Parking Services
N.A.I.C.S.: 812930
Tariq Ali Al Jowder *(CEO)*

BAHRAIN CINEMA COMPANY B.S.C.
Floor 27 Building 470 Road 1010
Block 410 Fakhro Tower, PO Box
26573, Sanabis, Manama, Bahrain
Tel.: (973) 17258900
Web Site:
    https://www.bahraincinema.com
Year Founded: 1967
CINECO—(BAH)
Rev.: $13,179,609
Assets: $191,595,769
Liabilities: $41,604,098
Net Worth: $149,991,671
Earnings: ($4,980,559)
Emp.: 252
Fiscal Year-end: 12/31/23
Movie Screening Services
N.A.I.C.S.: 512131
Ahmed A. Rahman Rashed *(CEO)*

BAHRAIN COMMERCIAL FA-CILITIES COMPANY BSC
PO Box 1175, Manama, Bahrain
Tel.: (973) 17786000   BH
Web Site:
    https://www.bahraincredit.com.bh
Year Founded: 1983
BCFC—(BAH)
Rev.: $66,852,338
Assets: $791,697,833
Liabilities: $426,617,331
Net Worth: $365,080,502
Earnings: $9,721,228
Emp.: 747
Fiscal Year-end: 12/31/22
Financial Services
N.A.I.C.S.: 523999
Ali Aburwais *(VP-Compliance &
MLRO)*

Subsidiaries:

National Motor Company W.L.L.   **(1)**
PO Box 11722, Manama, Bahrain
Tel.: (973) 17457100
Web Site: http://www.nmc.com.bh
Automobile Vehicle Distr
N.A.I.C.S.: 423110
Biju James *(Mgr-Comml)*

Tasheelat Automotive Company
WLL   **(1)**
Building 857 Road 31 Block 608, Wadiyan,
1175, Sitra, Bahrain
Tel.: (973) 17734000
Web Site: https://tac.com.bh
Automotive Parts Mfr & Distr
N.A.I.C.S.: 336390

Tasheelat Car Leasing Company
W.L.L.   **(1)**
PO Box 1175, Manama, Bahrain
Tel.: (973) 17899799
Web Site: https://www.tcl.bh
Car Rental & Leasing Services
N.A.I.C.S.: 532112
Najib Hussain *(Mgr-Rental Sls & Ops)*

BAHRAIN DUTY FREE SHOP COMPLEX BSC
Al Barsha Building Bldg No 145,

Road 2403 Muharraq 224, Manama,
Bahrain
Tel.: (973) 17723100
Web Site: https://www.bdutyfree.com
Year Founded: 1990
DUTYF—(BAH)
Rev.: $13,647,939
Assets: $118,661,468
Liabilities: $840,893
Net Worth: $117,820,574
Earnings: $11,371,956
Emp.: 2
Fiscal Year-end: 12/31/23
Operator of Duty Free Shopping in
Bahrain International Airport
N.A.I.C.S.: 561499
Farouk Yousuf Almoayyed *(Chm)*

Subsidiaries:

Almoayyed Contracting Group
Y.K.   **(1)**
Bldg 115 Road 383 Manama Centre 304,
PO Box 143, Manama, Bahrain
Tel.: (973) 17211211
Web Site: https://www.almoayyed.com
Property Development Services
N.A.I.C.S.: 531390

BAHRAIN FAMILY LEISURE COMPANY B.S.C.
10th Floor Gulf Executive Offices
Adliya Block 338, PO Box 11612, Ma-
nama, Bahrain
Tel.: (973) 17292973   BH
Web Site: https://www.bflc.com.bh
Year Founded: 1994
FAMILY—(BAH)
Rev.: $2,537,283
Assets: $6,053,561
Liabilities: $1,406,313
Net Worth: $4,647,248
Earnings: ($2,113,321)
Emp.: 46
Fiscal Year-end: 12/31/22
Restaurant Operating Services
N.A.I.C.S.: 722511
Abdul Latif Khalid Al-Aujan *(Chm)*

BAHRAIN ISLAMIC BANK
Road 1708 Block 317 Building 722 Al
Salam Tower Diplomatic Area, PO
Box 5240, Manama, Bahrain
Tel.: (973) 17515151   BH
Web Site: https://www.bisb.com
Year Founded: 1979
BISB—(BAH)
Rev.: $164,581,841
Assets: $3,612,150,871
Liabilities: $2,057,393,703
Net Worth: $1,554,757,168
Earnings: $33,335,986
Emp.: 324
Fiscal Year-end: 12/31/22
Banking Services
N.A.I.C.S.: 522110
Hassan Amir Jarrar *(CEO)*

Subsidiaries:

Abaad Real Estate Company
B.S.C.   **(1)**
PO Box 20714, 20714, Manama, Bahrain
Tel.: (973) 17511999
Web Site: http://www.abaadrealestate.com
Sales Range: $50-74.9 Million
Emp.: 8
Real Estate Manangement Services
N.A.I.C.S.: 531390
Ahmed Ahmed Abdulla *(CEO)*

BAHRAIN MIDDLE EAST BANK BSC
BMB Centre / Diplomatic Area Build-
ing 135 Road 1702 Block, PO Box
797, 317, Manama, Bahrain
Tel.: (973) 17532345   BH
Web Site: https://www.bmb.com.bh
Year Founded: 1982
Rev.: $11,948,000

Assets: $245,639,000
Liabilities: $163,857,000
Net Worth: $81,782,000
Earnings: $5,228,000
Emp.: 30
Fiscal Year-end: 12/31/17
Investment Banking Services
N.A.I.C.S.: 523150
Alwyn William Rodrigues *(I lead-IT &
-Acting & Sr Mgr)*

Subsidiaries:

BMB Property Services   **(1)**
Block 317 Building 135 Road 1702 Diplo-
matic Area, 135, Manama, Bahrain
Tel.: (973) 1752 8127
Emp.: 16
Construction Engineering Services
N.A.I.C.S.: 541330
Hamid Shah *(Mgr)*

BAHRAIN MUMTALAKAT HOLDING COMPANY B.S.C.
Arcapita Building 4th Floor Building
No 551 Road 4612, PO Box 820,
Sea Front 346 Bahrain Bay, Ma-
nama, Bahrain
Tel.: (973) 17561111   BH
Web Site: http://www.bmhc.bh
Year Founded: 2006
Investment Holding Company
N.A.I.C.S.: 551112
Suha Karzoon *(CFO)*

BAHRAIN NATIONAL HOLD-ING COMPANY BSC
9th Floor BNH Tower Seef Business
District, PO Box 843, Manama, Bah-
rain
Tel.: (973) 17587300
Web Site: https://www.bnhgroup.com
BNH—(BAH)
Rev.: $111,307,392
Assets: $335,349,195
Liabilities: $155,295,616
Net Worth: $180,053,579
Earnings: $18,575,104
Emp.: 205
Fiscal Year-end: 12/31/22
Insurance & Risk Management Ser-
vices
N.A.I.C.S.: 524298
Farooq Yusuf Almoayyed *(Chm)*

Subsidiaries:

Bahrain National Insurance Company
B.S.C.   **(1)**
2491 Road 2832 Block 428, Seef Area, Ma-
nama, Bahrain
Tel.: (973) 17 587 444
Web Site: http://www.bnidirect.com
Emp.: 110
General Insurance Services
N.A.I.C.S.: 524210
Abdulhussain Khalil Dawani *(Chm)*

Bahrain National Life Assurance
Company B.S.C.   **(1)**
BNH Tower 2491 Road 2832, PO Box 843,
Seef Business District, 428, Manama,
Bahrain   **(75%)**
Tel.: (973) 17587333
Web Site: http://www.bnl4life.com
Emp.: 15
General Insurance Services
N.A.I.C.S.: 524210

BAHRAIN SHIP REPAIR AND ENGINEERING COMPANY
Mina Salman Industrial Area, PO Box
568, Manama, Bahrain
Tel.: (973) 17725300
Web Site: https://www.basrec.com
BASREC—(BAH)
Rev.: $18,096,541
Assets: $94,403,403
Liabilities: $10,253,932
Net Worth: $84,149,471
Earnings: $2,769,688

Emp.: 265
Fiscal Year-end: 12/31/22
Ship Repair & Engineering Services
N.A.I.C.S.: 336611
Fawzi Ahmed Kanoo *(Chm)*

BAHRAIN TELECOMMUNICA-TIONS COMPANY BSC

PO Box 14, Manama, Bahrain
Tel.: (973) 17884888   BH
Web Site: https://batelco.com
Year Founded: 1981
BEYON—(BAH)
Rev.: $1,127,036,418
Assets: $3,091,071,855
Liabilities: $1,545,905,944
Net Worth: $1,545,165,911
Earnings: $217,596,350
Emp.: 2,567
Fiscal Year-end: 12/31/23
Telecommunication Servicesb
N.A.I.C.S.: 517111
Shaikh Abdulla bin Khalifa Al Khalifa *(Chm)*

Subsidiaries:

Batelco Middle East Company
SPC   **(1)**
PO BOX 14, Manama, kingdom of Bahrain, Bahrain
Tel.: (973) 17884424
Telecommunication Servicesb
N.A.I.C.S.: 517112

Dhivehi Raajjeyge Gulhun Plc   **(1)**
Ameenee Magu, PO Box 2082, Magu, Male, 20403, Maldives   **(52%)**
Tel.: (960) 3322802
Web Site: https://www.dhiraagu.com.mv
Sales Range: $150-199.9 Million
Emp.: 500
Telecommunication Servicesb
N.A.I.C.S.: 517111
Ismail Rasheed *(CEO & Mng Dir)*

Monaco Telecom SAM   **(1)**
9 Rue du Gabian, Monaco, Monaco   **(55%)**
Tel.: (377) 99666300
Web Site: http://www.monaco-telecom.mc
Sales Range: $125-149.9 Million
Emp.: 438
Cable & Wireless Telecommunications Services
N.A.I.C.S.: 517112

Subsidiary (Non-US):

Epic Ltd.   **(2)**
87 Kenedy Ave, 1077, Nicosia, Cyprus
Tel.: (357) 96136136
Web Site: http://www.mtn.com.cy
Telecommunication Servicesb
N.A.I.C.S.: 517111

Vodafone Malta Ltd.   **(2)**
Vodafone House Msida Rd, Birkirkara, BKR 9024, Malta   **(100%)**
Tel.: (356) 21482820
Cellular Communications Network Operator
N.A.I.C.S.: 517112
Tamas Banyai *(CEO)*

Sure (Guernsey) Limited   **(1)**
Tel.: (44) 1481700700
Web Site: https://www.sure.com
Telecommunication Servicesb
N.A.I.C.S.: 517810
Justin Bellinger *(Chief Digital Officer)*

Subsidiary (Non-US):

Foreshore Limited   **(2)**
The Powerhouse Queens Road, Saint Helier, JE2 3AP, Jersey
Tel.: (44) 1534752300
Web Site: http://www.foreshore.net
Internet Services & Data Center
N.A.I.C.S.: 517110

Umniah Mobile Company PSC   **(1)**
Queen Nour St Al-Shmeisani, PO Box 942481, Amman, 11194, Jordan
Tel.: (962) 62002000
Web Site: https://www.umniah.com

Wired & Wireless Telecommunication Services
N.A.I.C.S.: 517112
Ziad Shatara *(CEO)*

BAHVEST RESOURCES BER-HAD

Block Q6 Lot 81-2 Kubota Sentral, PO Box 2112, 91000, Tawau, Sabah, Malaysia
Tel.: (60) 89747747   MY
Web Site: https://bahvest.com
Year Founded: 2004
BAHVEST—(KLS)
Rev.: $42,510,055
Assets: $36,317,537
Liabilities: $10,185,575
Net Worth: $26,131,962
Earnings: $213,992
Emp.: 219
Fiscal Year-end: 09/30/23
Aquaculture Services
N.A.I.C.S.: 112519
Fui Ming Lo *(CEO & Mng Dir)*

BAI COMMUNICATIONS PTY LTD

Level 10, Tower A 799 Pacific Highway, Chatswood, 2067, NSW, Australia
Tel.: (61) 2 8113 4666
Web Site:
https://www.baicommunications.com
Emp.: 800
Telecommunications Infrastructure
N.A.I.C.S.: 517111
Igor Leprince *(Grp CEO)*

Subsidiaries:

Mobilitie, LLC   **(1)**
660 Newport Center Dr Ste 200, Newport Beach, CA 92660
Tel.: (949) 999-1515
Web Site: http://www.mobilitie.com
Sales Range: $10-24.9 Million
Emp.: 60
Wireless Telecommunications Infrastructure Services
N.A.I.C.S.: 517810
Christos Karmis *(CEO)*

Subsidiary (Domestic):

Signal Point Systems Inc.   **(2)**
1270 Shiloh Rd Ste 100, Kennesaw, GA 30144-1390
Tel.: (770) 499-0439
Web Site: http://www.sigpoint.com
Sales Range: $10-24.9 Million
Emp.: 170
Water, Sewer & Utility Contracting Services
N.A.I.C.S.: 237110
Gordon Harris *(CFO)*

BAI SHA TECHNOLOGY CO., LTD.

No 116 Sec 1 Xiangshun Rd, Taiping, Taichung, 411042, Taiwan
Tel.: (886) 436083888
Web Site: https://www.bsbs.com.tw
Year Founded: 1992
8401—(TPE)
Rev.: $48,030,985
Assets: $46,309,196
Liabilities: $14,600,350
Net Worth: $31,708,845
Earnings: $4,160,648
Emp.: 494
Fiscal Year-end: 12/31/22
Paper Products Mfr
N.A.I.C.S.: 322299
Lin Yen-Shu *(Chm)*

BAIADA POULTRY PTY LIM-ITED

642 Great Western Highway, Pendle Hill, 2145, NSW, Australia
Tel.: (61) 2 9842 1000
Web Site: http://www.baiada.com.au

Sales Range: $200-249.9 Million
Emp.: 2,200
Poultry Producer
N.A.I.C.S.: 311615
John Camilleri *(Mng Dir)*

BAIC BLUEPARK NEW ENERGY TECHNOLOGY CO., LTD.

No 5 Donghuan Middle Road, Beijing Economic and Technological Development Zone Blue Valley, Beijing, 100176, Sichuan, China
Tel.: (86) 4000008899
Web Site: https://www.bjev.com.cn
600733—(SHG)
Rev.: $1,335,803,564
Assets: $4,402,159,431
Liabilities: $3,516,925,160
Net Worth: $885,234,271
Earnings: ($767,268,633)
Fiscal Year-end: 12/31/22
Real Estate Lending Services
N.A.I.C.S.: 531110

BAID FINSERV LIMITED

Baid House IInd Floor 1 Tara Nagar Ajmer Road, Jaipur, 302006, Rajasthan, India
Tel.: (91) 9116133220
Web Site:
     https://www.baidfinserv.com
Year Founded: 1991
511724—(BOM)
Rev.: $7,385,844
Assets: $43,201,765
Liabilities: $24,422,818
Net Worth: $18,778,947
Earnings: $1,020,945
Emp.: 141
Fiscal Year-end: 03/31/21
Financial Services
N.A.I.C.S.: 523999
Panna Lal Baid *(Founder, Chm & Mng Dir)*

BAIDA GROUP CO., LTD.

34F Building No 2 Xizi International No 22 Nanyuan Street, Yuhang District, Hangzhou, 311100, Zhejiang, China
Tel.: (86) 57185158800
Web Site: http://www.baidagroup.com
Year Founded: 1992
600865—(SHG)
Rev.: $31,889,136
Assets: $375,988,743
Liabilities: $42,460,596
Net Worth: $333,528,147
Earnings: $25,240,045
Fiscal Year-end: 12/31/22
Departmental Store Operator
N.A.I.C.S.: 455110
Wu Nanping *(Chm)*

BAIDU, INC.

No 10 Shangdi 10th Street, Haidian District, Beijing, 100085, China
Tel.: (86) 1059928888   Ky
Web Site: https://ir.baidu.com
Year Founded: 2000
BIDU—(NASDAQ)
Rev.: $19,536,000,000
Assets: $59,636,000,000
Liabilities: $25,614,000,000
Net Worth: $34,022,000,000
Earnings: $1,605,000,000
Emp.: 45,500
Fiscal Year-end: 12/31/21
Software Development Services
N.A.I.C.S.: 551112
Robin Yanhong Li *(Co-Founder, Chm & CEO)*

Subsidiaries:

Baidu (China) Co., Ltd.   **(1)**

7-8/F Building B Guangzhou Information Port No 16 Keyun Rd, Guangzhou, China
Tel.: (86) 2085658800
Internet Service Provider
N.A.I.C.S.: 517810

Baidu (Hong Kong) Limited   **(1)**
15/F Prosperity Millennia Plaza 663 King's Road, Quarry Bay, China (Hong Kong)
Tel.: (852) 37009282
Web Site: https://www.baiduhk.com.hk
Advertisement Optimization Services
N.A.I.C.S.: 541890

Baidu Holdings Limited   **(1)**
PO Box 957, Road Town, Virgin Islands (British)   **(100%)**
Tel.: (284) 4948184
Holding Company
N.A.I.C.S.: 551112
Robin Yanhong Li *(CEO)*

Subsidiary (Non-US):

Baidu Online Network Technology (Beijing) Co. Ltd.   **(2)**
12/F Ideal International Plaza, No 58 West-North 4th Ring, Beijing, 100080, China   **(100%)**
Tel.: (86) 1082621188
Web Site: http://ir.baidu.com
Chinese Language Internet Search Engine
N.A.I.C.S.: 517810

Baidu International Technology (Shenzhen) Co., Ltd.   **(1)**
Fuhong road Futian district Huaqiang Garden 9E, Futian Dist, Shenzhen, 51800, Guangdong, China
Tel.: (86) 75582567896
Web Site: http://www.baidu.en.alibaba.com
Emp.: 2
Online Marketing Services
N.A.I.C.S.: 541613

Baidu Japan Inc.   **(1)**
Roppongi Hills Mori Tower 39F Roppongi 6-10-1, Minato-ku, Tokyo, 106-6139, Japan
Tel.: (81) 368112080
Web Site: https://www.baidu.jp
Search Engine Optimization Services
N.A.I.C.S.: 541512

Baidu.com Times Technology (Beijing) Co., Ltd.   **(1)**
Baidu Campus No 10 Shangdi No 10 Street, Haidian Dist, Beijing, China
Tel.: (86) 1059928888
Web Site: http://www.baidu.com
Internet Search Portal Operator
N.A.I.C.S.: 519290

Qunar Cayman Islands Limited   **(1)**
17th Floor Viva Plaza Building 18 Yard 29 Suzhou Street, Haidian District, Beijing, 100080, China   **(37%)**
Tel.: (86) 1089676966
Web Site: http://www.qunar.com
Internet Travel Search Services
N.A.I.C.S.: 561599
Haijun Yang *(Pres)*

iQIYI, Inc.   **(1)**
4/F iQIYI Youth Center Yoolee Plaza No 21 North Road of, Workers Stadium Chaoyang District, Beijing, 100027, China
Tel.: (86) 1062677171
Web Site: http://www.iqiyi.com
Rev.: $4,442,714,329
Assets: $7,055,067,550
Liabilities: $6,083,189,261
Net Worth: $971,878,289
Earnings: ($20,869,041)
Emp.: 4,981
Fiscal Year-end: 12/31/2022
Online Entertainment Service Provider
N.A.I.C.S.: 516210
Robin Yanhong Li *(Chm)*

BAIJIAYUN GROUP LTD

24F A1 South Building No 32 Fengzhan Road, Yuhuatai District, Nanjing, 210000, China
Tel.: (86) 258222159   Ky
Web Site: https://www.baijiayun.com
Year Founded: 2004
RTC—(NASDAQ)
Rev.: $59,794,661

Baijiayun Group Ltd—(Continued)

Assets: $61,203,045
Liabilities: $36,791,174
Net Worth: $24,411,871
Earnings: ($83,084,079)
Emp.: 219
Fiscal Year-end: 06/30/24
Holding Company; Plastic Film Developer, Mfr & Distr
N.A.I.C.S.: 551112
Gangjiang Li *(Chm & CEO)*

Subsidiaries:

Fuwei Films (Shandong) Co.,
Ltd. **(1)**
No 387 Donming Road, Weifang, 261061,
Shandong, China **(100%)**
Tel.: (86) 8601068522612
Web Site: http://en.fuweifilms.com
Plastic Film Developer, Mfr & Distr
N.A.I.C.S.: 326113

BAIKALINVESTBANK JSC

5 Oktyabrskoy Revolyutsil Str, Irkutsk, 664007, Russia
Tel.: (7) 3952258800
Web Site:
http://www.baikalrosbank.ru
Sales Range: Less than $1 Million
Commercial Banking Services
N.A.I.C.S.: 522110

BAIKANG BIOLOGICAL GROUP HOLDINGS LIMITED

Ginkgo Biomedical Science & Technology Industrial Park, Xuzhou,
221300, Jiangsu, China
Tel.: (86) 51686989727 **VG**
Year Founded: 2017
Rev.: $26,762,733
Assets: $17,996,229
Liabilities: $9,428,303
Net Worth: $8,567,926
Earnings: $14,901,240
Emp.: 106
Fiscal Year-end: 04/30/18
Holding Company
N.A.I.C.S.: 551112

BAIKSAN CO., LTD.

47 Gongdan 1-daero 27beon-gil, Siheung, Gyeonggi, Korea (South)
Tel.: (82) 314990044
Web Site: https://www.baiksan.co.kr
Year Founded: 1984
035150—(KRS)
Rev.: $365,011,650
Assets: $259,915,953
Liabilities: $121,735,291
Net Worth: $138,180,662
Earnings: $34,735,396
Emp.: 237
Fiscal Year-end: 12/31/22
Synthetic Leather Mfr
N.A.I.C.S.: 339920
Kim Hanjun *(CEO)*

BAILADOR TECHNOLOGY INVESTMENTS LIMITED

Suite 3 Level 20 20 Bond Street,
Sydney, 2000, NSW, Australia
Tel.: (61) 292232344
Web Site: http://www.bailador.com.au
BTI—(ASX)
Rev.: $2,906,651
Assets: $178,591,078
Liabilities: $22,930,689
Net Worth: $155,660,389
Earnings: $13,804,754
Emp.: 100
Fiscal Year-end: 06/30/24
Investment Management Service
N.A.I.C.S.: 523999
David Kirk *(Co-Founder & Partner)*

Subsidiaries:

Lendi Pty. Ltd. **(1)**
Level 9 37 Pitt St, Sydney, 2000, NSW,
Australia
Tel.: (61) 1300323181
Web Site: http://www.lendi.com.au
Emp.: 400
Home Loan Services
N.A.I.C.S.: 522310

Siteminder Limited **(1)**
Bond Store 3 30 Windmill Street, Millers
Point, 2000, NSW, Australia
Tel.: (61) 1300736198
Web Site: http://www.siteminder.com
Hotel Booking Services
N.A.I.C.S.: 561599

Stackla Pty. Ltd. **(1)**
Level 1 71 Alexander Street, Crows Nest,
2065, NSW, Australia
Tel.: (61) 289990555
Web Site: http://www.stackla.com
Asset Management Services
N.A.I.C.S.: 523940
Damien Mahoney *(Co-Founder)*

BAILEY METAL PRODUCTS LIMITED

1 Caldari Road, Concord, L4K 3Z9,
ON, Canada
Tel.: (905) 738-9267
Web Site: http://www.bmp-group.com
Year Founded: 1950
Sales Range: $25-49.9 Million
Emp.: 300
Steel Products Mfr
N.A.I.C.S.: 331513
David Hunt *(Chm & CEO)*

Subsidiaries:

Bailey Metal Processing Limited **(1)**
1211 Heritage Road, Burlington, L7L 4Y1,
ON, Canada
Tel.: (905) 336-5111
Web Site:
http://www.baileymetalprocessing.com
Emp.: 50
Metal Processing Services
N.A.I.C.S.: 331513

Bailey Metal Products Limited **(1)**
101 - 5710 Roper Road NW, Edmonton,
T6B 3G7, AB, Canada
Tel.: (780) 462-5757
Web Site: http://www.bmp-group.com
Sales Range: $10-24.9 Million
Emp.: 25
Mfr of Fabricated Structural Metal
N.A.I.C.S.: 332312

Bailey West Inc. **(1)**
7715 Anvil Way, Surrey, V3W 6A2, BC,
Canada
Tel.: (604) 590-5100
Steel Products Mfr
N.A.I.C.S.: 331513

BAILIAN GROUP CO., LTD.

315 Zhongshan South Road,
Huangpu District, Shanghai, 200010,
China
Tel.: (86) 21 633 23636 **CN**
Web Site: http://www.bailiangroup.cn
Year Founded: 2003
Holding Company Supermarket Department Store Pharmacies & Convenience Store Owner & Operator
N.A.I.C.S.: 551112
Xin-Sheng Ma *(Chm)*

Subsidiaries:

Shanghai Bailian Group Co., Ltd. **(1)**
Level 10 518 Shangcheng Road, Pudong,
Shanghai, 200120, China
Tel.: (86) 2163223344
Web Site: http://www.shfriendship.com.cn
Rev.: $4,530,571,952
Assets: $8,097,674,682
Liabilities: $5,281,999,267
Net Worth: $2,815,675,415
Earnings: $96,083,625
Emp.: 54,599

Fiscal Year-end: 12/31/2022
Commodities Retailing; Commercial Real
Estate Developer
N.A.I.C.S.: 445110

Unit (Domestic):

Bailian Nanqiao Shopping Mall **(2)**
No 588 Baiqi Road, Fengxian District,
Shanghai, China
Tel.: (86) 2133610000
Web Site: http://www.blnqmall.com
Shopping Mall Facility Leasing & Property
Management Services
N.A.I.C.S.: 531120

Bailian Outlets Plaza **(2)**
No 2888 Hu-Qing-Ping Highway, Qingpu
District, Shanghai, 201703, China
Tel.: (86) 2159756655
Web Site: http://www.bloqp.com
Brand Outlet Shopping Plaza Leasing &
Property Management Services
N.A.I.C.S.: 531120

Bailian Youyicheng Shopping
Mall **(2)**
No 8 Songhu Road, Shanghai, China
Tel.: (86) 2155529900
Web Site: http://www.blyycmall.com
Shopping Mall Leasing & Property Management Services
N.A.I.C.S.: 531120

Holding (Non-US):

Lianhua Supermarket Holdings Co.,
Ltd. **(2)**
3 Lockhart Road, 39 Gloucester Road,
Wanchai, China (Hong Kong) **(34.03%)**
Tel.: (852) 2152629922
Web Site: https://lianhua.todayir.com
Rev.: $3,793,427,355
Assets: $3,497,772,962
Liabilities: $3,305,586,798
Net Worth: $192,186,164
Earnings: ($56,895,453)
Emp.: 27,780
Fiscal Year-end: 12/31/2021
Supermarket Services
N.A.I.C.S.: 445110
Li-Ping Hu *(Sec)*

Holding (Domestic):

Orient Shopping Centre Ltd. **(2)**
No 8 North Caoxi Road, Shanghai, 200030,
China
Tel.: (86) 2164870000
Web Site: http://www.bldfqj.com
Sales Range: $350-399.9 Million
Emp.: 600
Shopping Mall Facility Leasing & Property
Management Services
N.A.I.C.S.: 531120

Unit (Domestic):

Orient Shopping Centre -
Huaihai **(3)**
No 755 Middle Huaihai Road, Luwan District, Shanghai, China
Tel.: (86) 21 6445 8000
Shopping Mall Facility Leasing & Property
Management Services
N.A.I.C.S.: 531120

Orient Shopping Centre - Jiading **(3)**
No 66 Shanghai Road, Shanghai, 201800,
China
Tel.: (86) 2160941688
Web Site: http://www.bldfjd.com
Shopping Mall Facility Leasing & Property
Management Services
N.A.I.C.S.: 531120

Orient Shopping Centre -
Nandong **(3)**
No 800 East Nanjing Road, Huangpu District, Shanghai, 200001, China
Tel.: (86) 21 6322 3344
Web Site: http://www.bldfnd.com
Shopping Mall Facility Leasing & Property
Management Services
N.A.I.C.S.: 531120

Orient Shopping Centre - Ningbo **(3)**
No 151 E Zhongshan Rd, Haishu District,
Ningbo, 315000, Zhejiang, China
Tel.: (86) 57487255700

Shopping Mall Facility Leasing & Property
Management Services
N.A.I.C.S.: 531120

Orient Shopping Centre -
Yangpu **(3)**
No 2500 Siping Road, Yangpudian District,
Shanghai, 200433, China
Tel.: (86) 2155053888
Web Site: http://www.bldfyp.com
Shopping Mall Facility Leasing & Property
Management Services
N.A.I.C.S.: 531120

Unit (Domestic):

Shanghai Fashion Store **(2)**
No 650-690 East Nanjing Road, Huangpu
District, Shanghai, 200001, China
Tel.: (86) 2163225445
Web Site: http://www.blszsd.com
Department Store Facility Leasing & Property Management Services
N.A.I.C.S.: 531120

Shanghai Hualian Commercial Building - Huangpu **(2)**
No 340 East Nanjing Road, Huangpu District, Shanghai, 200001, China
Tel.: (86) 2163515300
Web Site: http://www.blhlss.com
Commercial Facility Leasing & Property
Management Services
N.A.I.C.S.: 531120

Shanghai Lady Fashion Department
Store **(2)**
22F Hao Xin Yibai Dasha Road 58, Shanghai, China
Tel.: (86) 2163223344
Web Site: http://www.blfnsd.com
Department Store Facility Leasing & Property Management Services
N.A.I.C.S.: 531120

Shanghai No. 1 Department Store -
Huangpu **(2)**
No 830 East Nanjing Road, Huangpu District, Shanghai, China
Tel.: (86) 2163223344
Web Site: http://www.bldybh.com
Department Store Facility Leasing & Property Management Services
N.A.I.C.S.: 531120

Shanghai No. 1 Department Store -
Songjiang **(2)**
No 98-116 Zhongshan Road, Songjiang
District, Shanghai, China
Tel.: (86) 57713090
Web Site: http://www.bldysj.com
Department Store Facility Leasing & Property Management Services
N.A.I.C.S.: 531120

Holding (Domestic):

Shanghai No. 1 Yaohan Co., Ltd. **(2)**
Shanghai New Building 22nd Fl 58 Hundred
Liuhe Road, Shanghai, 200001,
China **(64%)**
Tel.: (86) 21 6322 3344
Web Site: http://www.bldybbb.com
Commercial & Shopping Facility Leasing &
Property Management Services
N.A.I.C.S.: 531120

Unit (Domestic):

Yong'an Department Store **(2)**
58 New Hundred Liuhe Road Shanghai
Building 22 Fl, Shanghai, 200001, China
Tel.: (86) 21 6322 3344
Web Site: http://www.blyabh.com
Department Store Facility Leasing & Property Management Services
N.A.I.C.S.: 531120

BAILLIE GIFFORD & CO.

Calton Sq 1 Greenside Row, Edinburgh, EH1 3AN, Scotland, United
Kingdom
Tel.: (44) 1312752000
Web Site:
http://www.bailliegifford.com
Year Founded: 1908
Sales Range: $200-249.9 Million
Emp.: 670

Manager of Pension Funds & Investment Trusts & Provider of Retail Financial Products
N.A.I.C.S.: 524292
Charles Plowden *(Joint Sr Partner)*

Subsidiaries:

Baillie Gifford International LLC **(1)**
780 3rd Ave 47th Fl, New York, NY 10017
Tel.: (212) 319-4633
Financial Investment Management Services
N.A.I.C.S.: 523940
Larysa M. Bemko *(Dir-Mktg)*

Baillie Gifford Ltd. **(1)**
Calton Square 1 Greenside Row, Edinburgh, EH1 3AN, Scotland, United Kingdom
Tel.: (44) 1312752000
Web Site: http://www.bailliegifford.com
Sales Range: $300-349.9 Million
Emp.: 650
Insurance & Annuities; Joint Venture of The Guardian Life Insurance Company of America & Baillie Gifford & Co.
N.A.I.C.S.: 524128
Richard Barry *(Dir-HR)*

BAILLIE GIFFORD CHINA GROWTH TRUST PLC
Calton Square 1 Greenside Row, Edinburgh, EH1 3AN, United Kingdom
Tel.: (44) 8009172112   **UK**
Web Site:
   https://www.bailliegifford.com
Year Founded: 1907
BGCG—(LSE)
Assets: $253,583,385
Liabilities: $7,937,655
Net Worth: $245,645,730
Earnings: ($15,116,475)
Fiscal Year-end: 01/31/23
Investment Trust Management Services
N.A.I.C.S.: 523940
Susan Platts-Martin *(Chm)*

BAILLIE GIFFORD JAPAN TRUST PLC
Calton Square 1 Greenside Row, Edinburgh, EH1 3AN, United Kingdom
Tel.: (44) 1312752000
Web Site:
   http://www.bailliegifford.com
Year Founded: 1981
BGFD—(LSE)
Rev.: $19,973,458
Assets: $1,130,575,074
Liabilities: $184,696,663
Net Worth: $945,878,411
Earnings: $80,585,187
Fiscal Year-end: 08/31/24
Investment Management Service
N.A.I.C.S.: 523940
Matthew Brett *(Mgr)*

BAILLIE GIFFORD SHIN NIPPON PLC
Calton Square 1 Greenside Row, Edinburgh, EH1 3AN, United Kingdom
Tel.: (44) 1312752000
Web Site:
   http://www.bailliegifford.com
BGS—(LSE)
Assets: $765,965,640
Liabilities: $108,971,115
Net Worth: $656,994,525
Earnings: ($8,491,725)
Emp.: 900
Fiscal Year-end: 01/31/23
Investment Services
N.A.I.C.S.: 523999
Neil Donaldson *(Chm)*

BAIN ALNAHRAIN INVESTMENT COMPANY
Arasat Al-Hindiya Building 132 Street 30, District 929, Baghdad, Iraq
Tel.: (964) 17760759

Web Site: http://www.bain-alnahrain.com
Year Founded: 2001
VMES—(IRAQ)
Sales Range: Less than $1 Million
Financial Investment Services
N.A.I.C.S.: 523999

BAINE JOHNSTON CORPORATION
410 East White Hills, Saint John's, A1A 5J7, NL, Canada
Tel.: (709) 576-1780
Web Site:
   http://www.bainejohnston.com
Year Founded: 1780
Rev.: $18,904,585
Emp.: 150
Fishing Industry
N.A.I.C.S.: 114119
Chris Collingwood *(Chm & CEO)*

BAINULTRA INC.
956 chemin Olivier, Saint-Nicolas, G7A 2N1, QC, Canada
Tel.: (418) 831-7701
Web Site: http://www.bainultra.com
Year Founded: 1977
Rev.: $27,926,240
Emp.: 100
Bathroom Furniture & Products Mfr
N.A.I.C.S.: 327110
Henry Brunelle *(Pres)*

BAIOO FAMILY INTERACTIVE LIMITED
35 Floor Goldchi Building 120 Huangpu W Ave, Tianhe District, Guangzhou, 510620, Guangdong, China
Tel.: (86) 2085536367
Web Site: http://www.baioo.com.hk
2100—(HKG)
Rev.: $131,801,764
Assets: $288,699,887
Liabilities: $50,288,893
Net Worth: $238,410,994
Earnings: $1,451,596
Emp.: 1,050
Fiscal Year-end: 12/31/22
Children's Interactive Internet Games
N.A.I.C.S.: 513210
Jian Dai *(Co-Founder, Chm & CEO)*

BAIRAHA FARMS PLC
2nd Floor No 407 Galle Road, 3, Colombo, 3, Sri Lanka
Tel.: (94) 112575255
Web Site: https://www.bairaha.com
BFL—(COL)
Rev.: $35,868,752
Assets: $32,991,797
Liabilities: $7,536,180
Net Worth: $25,455,617
Earnings: $4,071,646
Emp.: 991
Fiscal Year-end: 03/31/22
Poultry Services
N.A.I.C.S.: 112340
M. T. A. Furkhan *(Chm)*

BAIRD MACGREGOR INSURANCE BROKERS LP
825 Queen Street East, Toronto, M4M 1H8, ON, Canada
Tel.: (416) 778-8000
Web Site:
   http://www.bairdmacgregor.com
Year Founded: 1979
Rev.: $23,413,936
Emp.: 85
Insurance Brokerage Services
N.A.I.C.S.: 524210

BAIRONG INC.
1-3/F Tower A No 10 Furong Street,

Chaoyang District, Beijing, China
Tel.: (86) 1064718828   **Ky**
Web Site:
   https://www.baironginc.com
Year Founded: 2014
6608—(HKG)
Rev.: $371,194,478
Assets: $762,318,481
Liabilities: $146,328,783
Net Worth: $615,989,699
Earnings: $46,419,334
Emp.: 1,354
Fiscal Year-end: 12/31/23
Software Development Services
N.A.I.C.S.: 541511
Hongqiang Zhao *(CFO)*

BAIYANG INVESTMENT GROUP, INC.
No 9 Gaoxin 4th Road High-tech Industrial Development Zone, Guangxi, Nanning, 530004, China
Tel.: (86) 7713210585   **CN**
Web Site: https://www.baiyang.com
Year Founded: 2000
002696—(SSE)
Rev.: $451,244,196
Assets: $405,816,372
Liabilities: $192,978,396
Net Worth: $212,837,976
Earnings: $8,752,536
Emp.: 1,640
Fiscal Year-end: 12/31/22
Fish Production & Distribution
N.A.I.C.S.: 112511
Li Fengqiang *(Chm)*

BAIYE TRADING (SHANGHAI) CO., LTD.
Room 806 Building 2 No 500 Jianyun Road Tianna Shanghui, Zhoupu Town, Shanghai, China
Tel.: (86) 2150800969   **CN**
Web Site: http://www.bioneercn.com
Diagnostic Raw Material Mfr
N.A.I.C.S.: 325413

BAIYIN NONFERROUS METAL (GROUP) CO., LTD.
96 Youhao Road, Baiyin, 730900, Gansu, China
Tel.: (86) 9438811954   **CN**
Web Site: http://www.bynmc.com
Year Founded: 1954
Holding Company; Nonferrous Metal Products Mfr
N.A.I.C.S.: 551112
Messrs Wang Bin *(Deputy Gen Mgr)*

Subsidiaries:

Gold One Africa Limited **(1)**
Constantia Office Park Bridgeview House Ground Fl, Weltevreden Park, Johannesburg, 1709, South Africa
Tel.: (27) 117261047
Web Site: http://www.gold1.co.za
Gold Resource Exploration, Development & Mining
N.A.I.C.S.: 212220
Jost Barenberg *(VP-Mining)*

Subsidiary (Domestic):

New Kleinfontein Mining Company Limited **(2)**
Clover Field Ave Outenikua Rd East Vail, Private Bag X17, Weltevreden Park, Springs, 1560, South Africa **(100%)**
Tel.: (27) 11730760
Holding Company; Gold Ore Exploration & Mining Services
N.A.I.C.S.: 551112
Izak Marais *(Gen Mgr)*

Subsidiary (Domestic):

New Kleinfontein Goldmine (Proprietary) Limited **(3)**
Postnet Suite 115, Private Bag X17, Welte-

vreden Park, Johannesburg, 1715, South Africa **(100%)**
Tel.: (27) 10 591 5200
Gold Ore Mining Services
N.A.I.C.S.: 212220

BAIYING HOLDINGS GROUP LIMITED
30/F Huijin International Centre No 77 Tainan Road, Xiamen, Fujian, China
Tel.: (86) 5922273555   **Ky**
Web Site: http://www.byleasing.com
Year Founded: 2010
8525—(HKG)
Rev.: $3,955,410
Assets: $44,781,570
Liabilities: $8,967,129
Net Worth: $35,814,441
Earnings: ($3,695,505)
Emp.: 84
Fiscal Year-end: 12/31/22
Sales Financing & Leasing Services
N.A.I.C.S.: 522220
Shiyuan Zhou *(Chm)*

BAIYU HOLDINGS, INC.
25th Floor Block C Tairan Building No 31 Tairan 8th Road, Futian District, Shenzhen, 518000, Guangdong, China
Tel.: (86) 75588898711   **DE**
Web Site: http://www.tdglg.com
Year Founded: 2011
BYU—(NASDAQ)
Rev.: $156,835,301
Assets: $363,097,798
Liabilities: $65,123,629
Net Worth: $297,974,169
Earnings: $4,525,127
Emp.: 58
Fiscal Year-end: 12/31/22
Holding Company; Commercial Banking
N.A.I.C.S.: 551111
Renmei Ouyang *(Chm, Pres & CEO)*

BAJAJ AUTO LTD.
Akurdi, Pune, 411035, India
Tel.: (91) 7219821111   **In**
Web Site: https://www.bajajauto.com
Year Founded: 1926
532977—(NSE)
Rev.: $4,513,266,591
Assets: $4,212,751,034
Liabilities: $692,392,542
Net Worth: $3,520,358,492
Earnings: $726,600,324
Emp.: 6,831
Fiscal Year-end: 12/31/23
Automobile Mfr & Distr
N.A.I.C.S.: 336991
Rajiv Bajaj *(Mng Dir)*

Subsidiaries:

Bajaj Allianz General Insurance Co. Ltd. **(1)**
1st Floor GE Plaza Airport Road, Yerwada, Pune, 411006, Maharashtra, India
Tel.: (91) 2056026666
Web Site: http://www.bajajallianz.co.in
Sales Range: $250-299.9 Million
Emp.: 1,371
Insurance Services; Owned by Allianz AG & by Bajaj Auto Limited
N.A.I.C.S.: 524298

Subsidiary (Domestic):

Bajaj Allianz Life Insurance Co. Ltd. **(2)**
Ground Floor GE Plaza Airport Road, Yerwada, Pune, 411006, Maharashtra, India
Tel.: (91) 2066026666
Web Site: http://www.bajajallianz.com
Fire Insurance Services
N.A.I.C.S.: 524113
Chandramohan Mehra *(CMO)*

Bajaj Auto Ltd. - Akurdi Plant **(1)**

Bajaj Auto Ltd.—(Continued)

Mumbai Pune Rd, Akurdi, Pune, 411035,
Maharashtra, India
Tel.: (91) 2027472851
Sales Range: $1-4.9 Billion
Mfr of Scooters, M80 Motorcycles & Front
Engine Three-Wheelers
N.A.I.C.S.: 336991
Rajiv Bajaj *(Mng Dir)*

Bajaj Auto Ltd. - Waluj Plant   **(1)**
Waluj Industrial Area, Aurangabad, Maha-
rashtra, India
Sales Range: $1-4.9 Billion
Mfr of Scooters, Motorcycles, Scooterettes,
Rear Engine Three-Wheelers
N.A.I.C.S.: 336991

Bajaj Electricals Limited   **(1)**
45/47 Veer Nariman Road, Mumbai,
400001, Maharashtra, India
Tel.: (91) 2222043841
Web Site: https://www.bajajelectricals.com
Rev.: $666,304,398
Assets: $544,849,564
Liabilities: $312,087,826
Net Worth: $232,761,738
Earnings: $16,981,501
Emp.: 2,272
Fiscal Year-end: 03/31/2022
Consumer Electronic Appliances Mfr & Distr
N.A.I.C.S.: 335999
Shekhar Bajaj *(Chm & Mng Dir)*

Bajaj Finance Ltd.   **(1)**
Akurdi, Pune, 411 035, India
Tel.: (91) 2030186403
Web Site: https://www.bajajfinserv.in
Rev.: $4,318,915,965
Assets: $29,006,981,640
Liabilities: $23,040,199,455
Net Worth: $5,966,782,185
Earnings: $959,353,395
Emp.: 31,542
Fiscal Year-end: 03/31/2022
Financial Services
N.A.I.C.S.: 525990
Rajeev Jain *(Mng Dir)*

Bajaj Finserv Limited   **(1)**
Bajaj Auto Limited Complex Mumbai - Pune
Road, Mumbai - Pune Road Akurdi, Pune,
411035, Maharashtra, India
Tel.: (91) 2071576064
Web Site: http://www.bajajfinserv.in
Rev.: $9,840,178,646
Assets: $48,619,290,210
Liabilities: $39,315,521,851
Net Worth: $9,303,768,359
Earnings: $769,411,906
Emp.: 105
Fiscal Year-end: 03/31/2023
Financial Investment Services
N.A.I.C.S.: 523999
Ranjit Gupta *(Pres-Insurance)*

Bajaj Holdings & Investment
Limited   **(1)**
Mumbai-Pune Road, Akurdi, Pune, 411 035,
India
Tel.: (91) 2071576066
Web Site: https://www.bhil.in
Rev.: $205,922,937
Assets: $7,831,032,530
Liabilities: $263,199,333
Net Worth: $7,567,833,197
Earnings: $885,111,938
Emp.: 19
Fiscal Year-end: 03/31/2024
Holding Company
N.A.I.C.S.: 551112
Anant Marathe *(CFO)*

Subsidiary (Domestic):

Maharashtra Scooters Limited   **(2)**
Mumbai-Pune Road Akurdi, Pune, 411 035,
India
Tel.: (91) 2071576066
Web Site: https://www.mahascooters.com
Rev.: $26,543,244
Assets: $3,371,350,219
Liabilities: $251,922,462
Net Worth: $3,119,427,757
Earnings: $19,480,393
Emp.: 102
Fiscal Year-end: 03/31/2022
Automobile Parts Mfr
N.A.I.C.S.: 336110

R. B. Laddha *(CFO)*

Hercules Hoists Limited   **(1)**
43/2B Savroli-Kharpada Road Dhamani,
Khalapur, 410 202, Maharashtra, India
Tel.: (91) 2192662502
Web Site: http://www.indef.com
Rev.: $13,367,595
Assets: $48,072,338
Liabilities: $2,038,791
Net Worth: $46,033,547
Earnings: $1,771,674
Emp.: 137
Fiscal Year-end: 03/31/2020
Material Handling Equipment Mfr
N.A.I.C.S.: 339999
Shekhar Bajaj *(Chm)*

Mukand Engineers Ltd   **(1)**
Thane-Belapur Road Dighe Kalwe, Thane,
400 605, Maharshtra, India
Tel.: (91) 2221727500
Web Site: http://www.mukandengineers.com
Rev.: $7,891,790
Assets: $25,280,961
Liabilities: $22,844,380
Net Worth: $2,436,581
Earnings: ($3,174,159)
Emp.: 200
Fiscal Year-end: 03/31/2019
Alloy & Stainless Steel Mfr
N.A.I.C.S.: 331513
K. P. Jotwani *(CEO)*

Mukand Ltd.   **(1)**
Bajaj Bhawan 3rd Floor 226 Nariman Point,
Mumbai, 400021, India
Tel.: (91) 2261216666
Web Site: https://www.mukand.com
Rev.: $418,730,200
Assets: $624,384,600
Liabilities: $530,490,800
Net Worth: $93,893,800
Earnings: ($33,583,200)
Emp.: 1,628
Fiscal Year-end: 03/31/2020
Alloy & Stainless Steel Mfr
N.A.I.C.S.: 331110
Suketu V. Shah *(Co-Mng Dir)*

PT. Bajaj Auto Indonesia   **(1)**
Menara Imperium LT 12X JL H R Rauna
Said Kav 1, Jakarta, Jakarta Selatan,
12980, Indonesia
Tel.: (62) 218281787
N.A.I.C.S.: 336991

BAJAJ GLOBAL LIMITED
Imambada Road, Civil Lines, Nagpur,
440 008, Maharashtra, India
Tel.: (91) 7122720071   In
Web Site:
   https://www.bajajgloballtd.com
Year Founded: 1985
512261—(BOM)
Rev.: $106,456
Assets: $1,718,276
Liabilities: $140,404
Net Worth: $1,577,872
Earnings: $149,904
Fiscal Year-end: 03/31/21
Financial Services
N.A.I.C.S.: 523999
Bhanupriya Sharma *(CFO & Sec)*

BAJAJ HEALTHCARE LIMITED
602606 Bhoomi Velocity Infotech
Park Plot No B39 B39A B39 A1,
Wagle Industrial Estate Above ICICI
Bank Road No 23, Thane, 400 604,
India
Tel.: (91) 2266177400   In
Web Site:
   https://www.bajajhealth.com
Year Founded: 1993
BAJAJHCARE—(NSE)
Rev.: $93,002,077
Assets: $98,430,614
Liabilities: $53,592,343
Net Worth: $44,838,271
Earnings: $9,744,175
Emp.: 1,052
Fiscal Year-end: 03/31/22
Pharmaceutical Product Mfr & Distr

N.A.I.C.S.: 325412
Sajankumar R. Bajaj *(Chm & Co-Mng
Dir)*

**BAJAJ HINDUSTAN SUGAR
LIMITED**
Bajaj Bhawan B-10 Sector 3 Jamna-
lal Bajaj Marg, Noida, 201 301, Delhi,
India
Tel.: (91) 1202543939   in
Web Site:
   https://www.bajajhindusthan.com
Year Founded: 1931
500032—(BOM)
Rev.: $868,186,410
Assets: $2,175,719,910
Liabilities: $1,570,369,710
Net Worth: $605,350,200
Earnings: ($18,392,010)
Emp.: 7,493
Fiscal Year-end: 03/31/23
Sugar & Ethanol Mfr
N.A.I.C.S.: 325193
Kushagra Nayan Bajaj *(Chm & Mng
Dir)*

Subsidiaries:

Bajaj Consumer Care Limited   **(1)**
Old Station Road, Udaipur, 313001, Rajast-
han, India   **(84.75%)**
Tel.: (91) 2266919477
Web Site:
   https://www.bajajconsumercare.com
Rev.: $110,136,850
Assets: $111,678,329
Liabilities: $14,605,755
Net Worth: $97,072,574
Earnings: $20,338,709
Emp.: 480
Fiscal Year-end: 03/31/2022
Hair Care Products Mfr
N.A.I.C.S.: 325620
Dilip Kumar Maloo *(CFO)*

Bajaj Hindusthan Ltd. - Kinauni -
Sugar Unit   **(1)**
Kaithwari Link Road, Kinauni, Meerut,
250502, India
Tel.: (91) 1212418829
Sugar Products Mfr
N.A.I.C.S.: 325199

Bajaj Hindusthan Ltd. - Rudauli -
Sugar Unit   **(1)**
Rudra Nagar, Rudauli, 272001, India
Tel.: (91) 5542206791
Sugar Products Mfr
N.A.I.C.S.: 325199

Bajaj Hindusthan Sugar Ltd. -
Khambhar Khera - Sugar Unit   **(1)**
Sarda Nagar Road, Khambhar Khera, Sri-
nagar, 261 502, India
Tel.: (91) 5871233410
Web Site: https://www.bajajhindusthan.com
Sugar Products Mfr
N.A.I.C.S.: 311314

**BAJAJ STEEL INDUSTRIES
LTD.**
Plot No C-108 MIDC Industrial Area
Hingna, Nagpur, 440028, Maharash-
tra, India
Tel.: (91) 7104238101
Web Site: http://www.bajajngp.com
012132—(KOL)
Rev.: $61,450,689
Assets: $53,918,961
Liabilities: $25,688,085
Net Worth: $28,230,875
Earnings: $4,981,335
Emp.: 285
Fiscal Year-end: 03/31/22
Cotton Ginning Machinery Mfr
N.A.I.C.S.: 333111
Rohit Bajaj *(Chm & Mng Dir)*

Subsidiaries:

Bajaj Coneagle LLC   **(1)**
1900 Market St, Millbrook, AL 36054
Tel.: (334) 517-6139

Web Site: https://bajajconeagle.com
Winding Machinery Distr
N.A.I.C.S.: 423830
Venkatachalam Sankar *(Pres)*

BAJINOVAC A.D.
Milan Obrenovic 4, Bajina Basta,
Serbia
Tel.: (381) 31863780
Web Site: https://bajinovac.ls.rs
Year Founded: 1989
BAJI—(BEL)
Sales Range: Less than $1 Million
Emp.: 1
Cereal Crop Farming Services
N.A.I.C.S.: 111998
Miladin Jankovic *(Exec Dir)*

**BAK AMBALAJ SANAYI VE
TICARET A.S.**
AOSB 10002 Sokak No 45, Cigli,
35620, Izmir, Turkiye
Tel.: (90) 2323767450
Web Site:
   https://www.bakambalaj.com.tr
Year Founded: 1973
BAKAB—(IST)
Rev.: $60,427,531
Assets: $59,865,337
Liabilities: $40,217,645
Net Worth: $19,647,692
Earnings: $5,025,728
Emp.: 700
Fiscal Year-end: 12/31/22
Packaging Products Mfr
N.A.I.C.S.: 326112
Ali Enver Bakioglu *(Chm)*

BAK INTERNATIONAL LTD.
BAK Industrial Park Kuichong Town,
Lonngang District, Shenzhen,
518119, China
Tel.: (86) 75589770088
Sales Range: $1-4.9 Billion
Rechargeable Batteries
N.A.I.C.S.: 335910
Xiangqian Li *(Gen Mgr)*

Subsidiaries:

BAK Battery (Shenzhen) Co.,
Ltd.   **(1)**
Bike Industry Park Kuichong Town, Long-
gang District, Shenzhen, 51811-9, China
Tel.: (86) 75 5897 70088
Lithium Battery Cell Mfr
N.A.I.C.S.: 335910

BAK Battery Canada Ltd.   **(1)**
1750 Coast Meridian Road, Port Coquitlam,
V3C 6R8, BC, Canada
Tel.: (604) 464-5221
Battery Mfr
N.A.I.C.S.: 335910

BAK Battery Ltd.   **(1)**
BAK Industrial Park, 1 BAK Street
Kuichong, Shenzhen, 518119, China
Tel.: (86) 75589770060
Web Site: http://www.bak.com.cn
Rechargeable Battery
N.A.I.C.S.: 335910
Xiangqian Li *(Gen Mgr)*

BAK Europe GmbH   **(1)**
Max Nonne Str 45, 22419, Hamburg, Ger-
many
Tel.: (49) 40 533 27 36 88
Web Site: http://www.bak-europe.de
Telecommunication Equipment Mfr & Distr
N.A.I.C.S.: 334290

BAKANLAR MEDYA A.S.
Tepeoren Mah Istanbul Tuzla Orga-
nize Sanayii Bolgesi 3 Cadde No 23,
Tuzla, Istanbul, Turkiye
Tel.: (90) 216 316 11 56
Web Site:
   http://www.bakanlarmedya.fc
Year Founded: 1996
Paper Bag Mfr
N.A.I.C.S.: 322220

Ahmet Bakan (Gen Mgr)

BAKED GAMES S.A.
Street Henryka Sienkiewicza 16, 41-250, Czeladz, Poland
Tel.: (48) 512509192
Web Site:
https://www.bakedgames.pl
Year Founded: 2015
BKD—(WAR)
Software Development Services
N.A.I.C.S.: 541511

BAKER & PROVAN PTY. LTD.
9-11 Power St, Saint Marys, 2760, NSW, Australia
Tel.: (61) 288019000   AU
Web Site:
http://www.bakerprovan.com.au
Sales Range: $25-49.9 Million
Emp.: 51
Mechanical Engineering Services
N.A.I.C.S.: 541330
Peter Allan Baker (Chm & Mng Dir)

Subsidiaries:

Air & Hydraulic Power Centre   (1)
8 Monash Gate, Jandakot, 6164, WA, Australia
Tel.: (61) 8 9417 2933
Web Site: http://www.airhyd.com.au
Hydraulic Equipment Repair & Maintenance Services
N.A.I.C.S.: 811310

BAKER STEEL RESOURCES TRUST LIMITED
Arnold House St Julian's Avenue, Saint Peter Port, GY1 3NF, Guernsey
Tel.: (44) 2073890009   GY
Web Site:
http://www.bakersteelresources.com
BSRT—(LSE)
Rev.: $763,810
Assets: $104,860,999
Liabilities: $265,735
Net Worth: $104,595,263
Earnings: ($681,584)
Fiscal Year-end: 12/31/23
Investment Trust Management Services
N.A.I.C.S.: 523940
Howard Miles (Chm)

BAKER TECHNOLOGY LIMITED
10 Jalan Samulun, Singapore, 629124, Singapore
Tel.: (65) 62621380   SG
Web Site:
https://www.bakertech.com.sg
Year Founded: 1981
BTP—(SES)
Rev.: $69,238,052
Assets: $211,659,471
Liabilities: $27,919,412
Net Worth: $183,740,059
Earnings: $2,705,446
Emp.: 171
Fiscal Year-end: 12/31/23
Truck & Trailer Components Mfr & Distr
N.A.I.C.S.: 336390
Wee Lee Tan (Mng Dir-Baker Engrg Pte Ltd)

Subsidiaries:

Baker Engineering Pte. Ltd.   (1)
10 Jalan Samulun, Singapore, 629124, Singapore
Tel.: (65) 66379799
Web Site:
https://www.bakerengineering.com.sg
Shipyard Offshore Lifeboat Mfr
N.A.I.C.S.: 336611
Deryck Chan (Mgr-Bus Dev)

CH Offshore Ltd   (1)

12A Jalan Samulun, Singapore, 629131, Singapore   **(52.72%)**
Tel.: (65) 64109018
Web Site: https://www.choffshore.com.sg
Rev.: $24,094,000
Assets: $54,479,000
Liabilities: $14,197,000
Net Worth: $40,282,000
Earnings: ($8,249,000)
Emp.: 27
Fiscal Year-end: 12/31/2023
Offshore Oil & Gas Marine Services
N.A.I.C.S.: 213112
Mee Fun Lim (Sec)

Sea Deep Shipyard Pte. Ltd   (1)
6 Pioneer Sector One, Singapore, 628418, Singapore
Tel.: (65) 68613255
Web Site: https://www.seadeep.com.sg
Sales Range: $25-49.9 Million
Emp.: 100
Crane Design & Mfr
N.A.I.C.S.: 333923

Subsidiary (Domestic):

Interseas Shipping (Private) Limited   (2)
No 6 Pioneer Sector One, 628418, Singapore
Tel.: (65) 68613255
Web Site: http://www.seadeep.com.sg
Sales Range: $25-49.9 Million
Emp.: 10
Crane Design & Mfr
N.A.I.C.S.: 333923

BAKER TILLY INTERNATIONAL LIMITED
New Bridge Street House 30-34 New Bridge Street, London, EC4V 6BJ, United Kingdom
Tel.: (44) 2038822000   UK
Web Site: http://www.bakertilly.global
Sales Range: $1-4.9 Billion
Emp.: 26,000
Accountancy & Business Network Services Organization
N.A.I.C.S.: 813920

BAKER TILLY UK HOLDINGS LIMITED
6th Floor 25 Farringdon Street, London, EC4A 4AB, United Kingdom
Tel.: (44) 2032018000   UK
Web Site: http://www.bakertilly.co.uk
Year Founded: 2006
Sales Range: $250-299.9 Million
Emp.: 1,600
Holding Company; Accounting & Business Advisory Services
N.A.I.C.S.: 551112
Martin Rodgers (Chm)

Subsidiaries:

Baker Tilly Investment Solutions Limited   (1)
6th Floor 25 Farringdon Street, London, EC4A 4AB, United Kingdom   **(100%)**
Tel.: (44) 2075351400
Sales Range: $200-249.9 Million
Emp.: 400
Financial Management Services
N.A.I.C.S.: 523940

Baker Tilly UK Audit LLP   (1)
25 Farringdon Street, London, EC4A 4AB, United Kingdom
Tel.: (44) 20 3201 8000
Web Site: http://www.bakertilly.co.uk
Accountancy & Business Advisory Services
N.A.I.C.S.: 541211
Martin Rodgers (Chm)

BAKHTAR CABLE
No 45 2nd Fl West 2nd St Golha Sq, Tehran, Iran
Tel.: (98) 88004859
Electrical Component Mfr
N.A.I.C.S.: 335999
Seyed Naser Sobhani (CEO)

BAKKAVOR GROUP PLC
Fitzroy Place 5th Floor 8 Mortimer Street, London, W1T 3JJ, United Kingdom
Tel.: (44) 1775663800   UK
Web Site: https://www.bakkavor.com
Year Founded: 2017
BAKK—(LSE)
Rev.: $2,576,666,400
Assets: $1,856,616,300
Liabilities: $1,112,476,200
Net Worth: $744,140,100
Earnings: $14,815,350
Fiscal Year-end: 12/31/22
Holding Company; Prepared Food Mfr
N.A.I.C.S.: 551112
Agust Gudmundsson (Founder & Grp CEO)

Subsidiaries:

Bakkavor Holdings Limited   (1)
Fitzroy Place 5th Floor 8 Mortimer Street, London, W1T 3JJ, United Kingdom
Tel.: (44) 177 576 1111
Web Site: http://www.bakkavor.com
Holding Company; Prepared Food Mfr
N.A.I.C.S.: 551112
Agust Gudmundsson (CEO)

Subsidiary (Domestic):

Alresford Salads Ltd.   (2)
The Nythe, Alresford, SO24 9DZ, Hampshire, United Kingdom
Tel.: (44) 1962734084
Web Site: http://www.bakkavor.co.uk
Sales Range: $25-49.9 Million
Emp.: 100
Watercress, Leafy Salads & Herbs Producer
N.A.I.C.S.: 445298

Subsidiary (Non-US):

Bakkavor European Marketing BV   (2)
Fred Roeskestraat 123-1, 1076 EE, Amsterdam, Netherlands
Tel.: (31) 205771177
Food Distr
N.A.I.C.S.: 424480

Bakkavor Iberica S.A.   (2)
Calle Cartagena 57 1 izq, Torre Pacheco, 30700, Murcia, Spain
Tel.: (34) 968576508
Emp.: 25
Food Mfr
N.A.I.C.S.: 311412

Subsidiary (Domestic):

Bakkavor Limited   (2)
Fitzroy Place 5th Floor 8 Mortimer Street, London, W1T 3JJ, United Kingdom
Tel.: (44) 1775761111
Web Site: http://www.bakkavor.com
Fresh Prepared Foods Preparer, Marketer & Distr
N.A.I.C.S.: 311991
Agust Gudmundsson (CEO)

Subsidiary (Domestic):

Bakkavor Fresh Cook Limited   (3)
Sluice Road Holbeach St Marks, Spalding, PE12 8HF, United Kingdom
Tel.: (44) 1406703200
Emp.: 533
Food Mfr
N.A.I.C.S.: 311412
Jonathon Wheatley (Mgr-Factory)

Plant (Domestic):

Bakkavor Limited - Bakkavor Desserts Highbridge Facility   (3)
Isleport Business Park, Highbridge, Somerset, TA9 4JU, United Kingdom
Tel.: (44) 1278558100
Emp.: 450
Food Mfr
N.A.I.C.S.: 311412

Bakkavor Limited - Bakkavor Desserts Newark Facility   (3)

Jessop Way Newark Industrial Estate, Newark, NG24 2ER, Nottinghamshire, United Kingdom
Tel.: (44) 1636553000
Emp.: 1,400
Food Mfr
N.A.I.C.S.: 311412

Bakkavor Limited - Bakkavor Meals London Facility   (3)
40 Cumberland Avenue Park Royal, London, NW10 7RQ, United Kingdom
Tel.: (44) 2087285000
Emp.: 2,500
Food Mfr
N.A.I.C.S.: 311412

Bakkavor Limited - Bakkavor Meals Sutton Bridge Facility   (3)
Langley Park Chalk Lane, Sutton Bridge, PE12 9YF, Lincolnshire, United Kingdom
Tel.: (44) 1406439200
Food Mfr
N.A.I.C.S.: 311412
Jago Yearsley (Mgr-Technical)

Bakkavor Limited - Melrow Salads Facility   (3)
Melrow Nursery Rydings Lane Banks, Southport, PR9 8EB, Merseyside, United Kingdom
Tel.: (44) 1772812088
Emp.: 19
Food Mfr
N.A.I.C.S.: 311412

Bakkavor Limited - Tilmanstone Salads Facility   (3)
Millyard Way Pike Road Industrial Estate, Tilmanstone, London, CT15 4NL, United Kingdom
Tel.: (44) 1304808000
Emp.: 750
Food Mfr
N.A.I.C.S.: 311412
John Rowe (Mgr-Continuous Improvement)

Subsidiary (Domestic):

Bakkavor London Limited   (3)
Forward Drive Christchurch Avenue, Harrow, HA3 8NT, United Kingdom
Tel.: (44) 2084242666
Food Mfr
N.A.I.C.S.: 311412

Unit (Domestic):

Bakkavor Pizza   (3)
Forward Drive Christchurch Avenue, Christchurch Ave, Harrow, HA3 8NT, Middlesex, United Kingdom
Tel.: (44) 2039629396
Sales Range: $150-199.9 Million
Emp.: 1,000
Pre-Prepared Pizza Mfr
N.A.I.C.S.: 311999

Subsidiary (Domestic):

Bakkavor Spalding Ltd   (3)
West Marsh Road, Spalding, PE11 2BB, United Kingdom
Tel.: (44) 1775663800
Emp.: 2,000
Food Mfr
N.A.I.C.S.: 311412

Subsidiary (US):

Bakkavor USA Inc   (2)
18201 Central Ave, Carson, CA 90746
Tel.: (310) 436-1600
Emp.: 600
Food Distr
N.A.I.C.S.: 424480
Pete Laport (Pres)

Subsidiary (Domestic):

B Robert's Foods LLC   (3)
2700 Westinghouse Blvd, Charlotte, NC 28273
Tel.: (704) 522-1977
Web Site: http://www.brobertsfoods.com
Frozen Fruit, Juice & Vegetable Mfr
N.A.I.C.S.: 311411
Sharon Lothian (Mgr-HR)

Unit (Domestic):

Bourne Prepared Produce   (2)

Bakkavor Group plc—(Continued)

Spalding Road, Bourne, PE10 0AT, Lincolnshire, United Kingdom
Tel.: (44) 1778 393222
Web Site: http://www.bakkavor.com
Sales Range: $150-199.9 Million
Emp.: 1,000
Salad Production Services: Leafy Salads, Prepared Fruit, Stir Fry & Prepared Vegetables
N.A.I.C.S.: 311999
Jennie Beasley (Mgr-HR)

Bourne Stir Fry   **(2)**
Tunnel Bank, Cherry Holt Road, Bourne, PE10 0DJ, Lincolnshire, United Kingdom
Tel.: (44) 778571211
Web Site: http://www.geest.co.uk
Sales Range: $25-49.9 Million
Emp.: 250
Beansprouts Mfr
N.A.I.C.S.: 311999

Caledonian Produce   **(2)**
Carriden Indus Estate, Bo'ness, EH51 9SJ, West Lothian, United Kingdom
Tel.: (44) 1506823491
Web Site: http://www.bakkavor.co.uk
Sales Range: $125-149.9 Million
Emp.: 1,500
Vegetables & Potatoes Retailer
N.A.I.C.S.: 424490
Philip Kealey (Gen Mgr)

Subsidiary (Non-US):

Creative Food Group Limited   **(2)**
279 Jianqian Road Nanxiang Devp Area, Jiading, Shanghai, 201802, China
Tel.: (86) 2169170101
Web Site: http://www.creative-food.com
Emp.: 1,100
Food Distr
N.A.I.C.S.: 424480

Subsidiary (Domestic):

Cucina Sano Ltd   **(2)**
Laburnum Farm Old Leake, Boston, PE22 9PN, United Kingdom
Tel.: (44) 1205878000
Emp.: 535
Food Mfr
N.A.I.C.S.: 311412
Grzegorz Kiraga (Sr Mgr-Section)

English Village Salads Limited   **(2)**
Camblesforth Road, Selby, YO8 8ND, North Yorkshire, United Kingdom
Tel.: (44) 1757617161
Food Mfr
N.A.I.C.S.: 311412

Subsidiary (Non-US):

Gastro Primo Limited   **(2)**
Units 1906-1912 19/F Eight Commercial Tower 8 Sun Yip Street, Chaiwan, Hong Kong, China (Hong Kong)
Tel.: (852) 28890287
Web Site: http://www.gastroprimo.com
Emp.: 170
Food Distr
N.A.I.C.S.: 424480
Walter Kern (Dir-Food Dev)

Subsidiary (Domestic):

Hitchen Foods Ltd   **(2)**
Dobson Park Way Manchester Road Ince in Makerfield, Wigan, WN2 2DX, Lancashire, United Kingdom
Tel.: (44) 1942824100
Emp.: 800
Food Mfr
N.A.I.C.S.: 311412
Terry McCormick (Mgr-Engrg Section)

Subsidiary (Non-US):

ITALPIZZA S.r.l.   **(2)**
Str Gherbella 454 / A, 41126, Modena, Italy
Tel.: (39) 05 946 5611
Web Site: https://www.italpizza.it
Food Mfr
N.A.I.C.S.: 311412
Cristian Pederzini (Mng Dir)

Subsidiary (Domestic):

International Produce Ltd.   **(2)**

Spade Lane Cold Store, Sittingbourne, ME9 7TT, Kent, United Kingdom   **(76%)**
Tel.: (44) 1634371371
Web Site: http://www.internationalproduce.com
Sales Range: $75-99.9 Million
Emp.: 300
Fruit & Vegetable Importer, Exporter & Whslr
N.A.I.C.S.: 445298
Steve Smith (Gen Mgr)

New Primebake Ltd   **(2)**
Whitchurch Road, Newhall, Nantwich, CW5 8DL, Cheshire, United Kingdom
Tel.: (44) 1270780900
Emp.: 500
Food Mfr
N.A.I.C.S.: 311412
Ian Robertson (Dir-Ops)

Unit (Domestic):

The Pizzeria   **(2)**
Sluice Road, Holbeach Saint Marks, Spalding, PE12 8HF, Lincolnshire, United Kingdom
Tel.: (44) 1406703000
Sales Range: $75-99.9 Million
Emp.: 350
Pre-Prepared Pizza Mfr
N.A.I.C.S.: 311999

Subsidiary (Domestic):

Welcome Food Ingredients Ltd   **(2)**
Brookside Way, Huthwaite, NG17 2NL, Nottinghamshire, United Kingdom
Tel.: (44) 1623551552
Emp.: 300
Food Mfr
N.A.I.C.S.: 311412

Unit (Domestic):

Wingland Foods   **(2)**
Wingland Enterprise Park Millennium Way, Sutton Bridge, Spalding, PE12 9TD, Lincs, United Kingdom
Tel.: (44) 1406352500
Web Site: http://www.bakkavor.co.uk
Sales Range: $75-99.9 Million
Emp.: 400
Pre-Prepared Leafy Salads Mfr
N.A.I.C.S.: 311999
Katherine Rowney (Mgr-HR)

BAKKEN ENERGY, LLC
Carrera 40 No 10A-65 Barrio El Poblado, Medellin, Colombia
Tel.: (57) 42682451   NV
Web Site:
   http://www.bakkenenergycorp.com
Year Founded: 2005
Sales Range: Less than $1 Million
Gold & Other Precious Metals Mining & Exploration Services
N.A.I.C.S.: 212220

BAKU STOCK EXCHANGE
19 Bul-Bul Ave, AZ1000, Baku, Azerbaijan
Tel.: (994) 4989820
Web Site: http://www.bse.az
Year Founded: 2000
Stock Exchange Services
N.A.I.C.S.: 523210
Vugar Namazov (Chm-Exec Bd)

BAKUER S.P.A.
Via Montecascioli 1, Firenze, 50018, Scandicci, Italy
Tel.: (39) 0335325391
Web Site: http://www.bakuer.it
Year Founded: 1940
Sales Range: $10-24.9 Million
Emp.: 70
Tooling System for CNC Machine Tool & FMS Traditional Machine Tool & Fixture System Mfr
N.A.I.C.S.: 333517

Subsidiaries:

Bakuer American Co.   **(1)**

c/o Teledyne Firth Stering 1 Teledyne Place, La Vergne, TN 37086   **(100%)**
Machine Tool Parts
N.A.I.C.S.: 425120

BAL PHARMA LTD
5th Floor Lakshmi Narayan Complex 10/1 Palace Road, Bengaluru, 560 099, Karnataka, India
Tel.: (91) 8041379500
Web Site:
   https://www.balpharma.com
BALPHARMA—(NSE)
Rev.: $39,089,027
Assets: $35,562,714
Liabilities: $27,578,542
Net Worth: $7,984,172
Earnings: $778,719
Emp.: 837
Fiscal Year-end: 03/31/22
Pharmaceutical Company
N.A.I.C.S.: 325412
Shailesh Dheerajmal Siroya (Mng Dir)

Subsidiaries:

Lifezen Healthcare Private
Limited   **(1)**
5th Floor Laxminarayan Complex 10/1 Palace Road, Opp to Shangri la Hotel, Bengaluru, 560052, India
Tel.: (91) 8041379505
Web Site: https://www.lifezen.in
Healthcare Product Distr
N.A.I.C.S.: 423450

BALA TECHNO GLOBAL LTD.
P-22 CIT Road Scheme - 55, Kolkata, 700014, West Bengal, India
Tel.: (91) 33 22658157
Web Site:
   http://www.balatechnoglobal.com
Sales Range: $10-24.9 Million
Cotton Yarn Distr
N.A.I.C.S.: 313110
Tapas Kar (Compliance Officer)

BALAI NI FRUITAS INC.
68 Data St Don Manuel, Quezon City, Philippines
Tel.: (63) 287128361
Web Site:
   https://www.balainifruitas.com
BALAI—(PHI)
Rev.: $9,663,368
Assets: $10,143,141
Liabilities: $1,836,642
Net Worth: $8,306,499
Earnings: $1,058,800
Emp.: 233
Fiscal Year-end: 12/31/23
Food & Beverage Product Mfr
N.A.I.C.S.: 312130

BALAJI AMINES LIMITED
Balaji Tower No 9/1A/1 Hotgi Road Asara Chowk, Sholapur, 413 224, Maharashtra, India
Tel.: (91) 2172451500
Web Site:
   https://www.balajiamines.com
530999—(BOM)
Rev.: $323,592,633
Assets: $267,923,237
Liabilities: $36,124,466
Net Worth: $231,798,772
Earnings: $55,375,730
Emp.: 1,111
Fiscal Year-end: 03/31/23
Specialty Chemicals Mfr
N.A.I.C.S.: 325180
A. Prathap Reddy (Chm)

Subsidiaries:

Kalinganagar Special Steel Private
Limited   **(1)**
2nd Floor Balaji Towers 9/1A/1 Hotgi Road, Solapur, 413224, Maharashtra, India
Tel.: (91) 2172451500

Web Site:
   http://www.balajispecialitychemicals.com
Chemical Products Mfr
N.A.I.C.S.: 325998

BALAJI TELEFILMS LTD.
C-13 Balaji House Dalia Industrial Estate Opposite Laxmi Indus Industrial, Estate New Link Road Andheri West, Mumbai, 400 053, India
Tel.: (91) 912240698000
Web Site:
   https://www.balajitelefilms.com
BALAJITELE—(NSE)
Rev.: $41,924,501
Assets: $104,673,469
Liabilities: $26,397,790
Net Worth: $78,275,679
Earnings: ($16,232,416)
Emp.: 93
Fiscal Year-end: 03/31/21
Television Software Producer
N.A.I.C.S.: 513210
Jeetendra Kapoor (Chm)

Subsidiaries:

Balaji Motion Pictures Ltd   **(1)**
C-13 Balaji House Dalia Indus Estate Opposite Laxmi Indus Estate, New Link Rd Andheri W, Mumbai, 400 053, India
Tel.: (91) 2240698000
Web Site:
   http://www.balajimotionpictures.com
Television Programming Services
N.A.I.C.S.: 512110
Sakett Saawhney (Gen Mgr-Production)

BALAMARA RESOURCES LIMITED
Level 2 Spectrum 100 Railway Road, Subiaco, 6008, WA, Australia
Tel.: (61) 8 9367 8133
Web Site:
   http://www.balamara.com.au
Rev.: $2,056
Assets: $3,744,714
Liabilities: $18,575,904
Net Worth: ($14,831,190)
Earnings: ($5,911,586)
Fiscal Year-end: 06/30/19
Zinc Exploration Services
N.A.I.C.S.: 212230
Derek Lenartowicz (Chm)

BALASORE ALLOYS LIMITED
Balgopalpur, Balasore Dist, 756 020, Baleshwar, Orissa, India
Tel.: (91) 6782 2757 81   In
Web Site:
   http://www.balasorealloys.com
Year Founded: 1984
Rev.: $182,630,827
Assets: $248,674,414
Liabilities: $115,479,905
Net Worth: $133,194,509
Earnings: ($4,122,090)
Emp.: 860
Fiscal Year-end: 03/31/19
Ferro Alloys Production Services
N.A.I.C.S.: 339999
Trilochan Sharma (Officer-Nodal)

BALATACILAR - BALATACILIK SANAYI VE TICARET A.S.
Konak Mahallesi Cumhuriyet Bulvar Gumruk is Merkezi No 38 Daire 708, Konak, Izmir, Turkiye
Tel.: (90) 2324464649   TR
Web Site: http://www.balatacilar.com
Year Founded: 1988
BALAT—(IST)
Rev.: $149,439
Assets: $2,108,250
Liabilities: $1,018,666
Net Worth: $1,089,584
Earnings: ($61,926)
Emp.: 130
Fiscal Year-end: 12/31/22

Brake System Mfr & Whslr
N.A.I.C.S.: 336340

BALAXI PHARMACEUTICALS LIMITED
Plot No 409 H No 8-2-293 MAPS Towers 3rd Floor, Phase-III Road No 81 Jubilee Hills, Hyderabad, 500 096, Telangana, India
Tel.: (91) 4023555300
Web Site: https://balaxipharma.in
Year Founded: 1942
BALAXI—(NSE)
Rev.: $38,815,072
Assets: $24,088,237
Liabilities: $8,641,324
Net Worth: $15,446,913
Earnings: $6,505,290
Emp.: 450
Fiscal Year-end: 03/31/22
Tea Plantation Services
N.A.I.C.S.: 111998
Ashish Maheshwari *(Mng Dir & CFO)*

BALCO GROUP AB
Algvagen 4, 352 45, Vaxjo, Sweden
Tel.: (46) 470533000
Web Site: https://www.balcogroup.se
Year Founded: 1987
BALCO—(NASDAQ)
Rev.: $122,420,716
Assets: $119,027,605
Liabilities: $51,918,959
Net Worth: $67,108,646
Earnings: $7,628,305
Emp.: 536
Fiscal Year-end: 12/31/22
Software Development Services
N.A.I.C.S.: 541511
Ingalill Berglund *(Chm)*

Subsidiaries:

RK Teknik i Gusum AB **(1)**
Dalangsvagen 1, 615 71, Gusum, Sweden
Tel.: (46) 12321020
Web Site: https://rkteknik.se
Steel Balcony Mfr & Distr
N.A.I.C.S.: 331110

Stora Fasad AB **(1)**
Fallskarmsvagen 3, 721 31, Vasteras, Sweden
Tel.: (46) 708451042
Web Site: https://storafasad.se
Plastering & General Contracting Services
N.A.I.C.S.: 541611

TBO-Haglinds AB **(1)**
Jadersvagen 10, 732 34, Arboga, Sweden
Tel.: (46) 58986600
Web Site: https://www.tbo.se
Construction Services
N.A.I.C.S.: 541330

BALDER DANMARK A/S
Vesterbrogade 1 E 5 Sal, 1620, Copenhagen, Denmark
Tel.: (45) 88136151
Web Site: http://www.balder.dk
Real Estate
N.A.I.C.S.: 531390
Jakob Jensen *(Mgr-Quality)*

Subsidiaries:

HPG Inc. **(1)**
29 Brownridge Rd, Georgetown, L7G 0C6, ON, Canada
Tel.: (365) 877-9315
Web Site: http://www.precinmac.com
Sales Range: $1-9.9 Million
Emp.: 115
gas turbine & Industrial Compressor Mfr
N.A.I.C.S.: 333248
Paul Watts *(Gen Mgr)*

BALDERTON CAPITAL
20 Balderton St, London, W1K 6TL, United Kingdom
Tel.: (44) 2070166800
Web Site: http://www.balderton.com

Sales Range: $1-4.9 Billion
Emp.: 35
Privater Equity Firm
N.A.I.C.S.: 523999
Bernard Liautaud *(Mng Partner)*

BALEA ESTIVAL 2002 S.A.
Hotel Balea Neptun, Constanta, Romania
Tel.: (40) 241491073
BLEA—(BUC)
Rev.: $3,140,426
Assets: $3,146,553
Liabilities: $332,568
Net Worth: $2,813,985
Earnings: $2,102,287
Emp.: 1
Fiscal Year-end: 12/31/22
Restaurant & Hotel Operator
N.A.I.C.S.: 722511
Maria Durbac *(Gen Mgr)*

BALFOUR BEATTY PLC
5 Churchill Place Canary Wharf, London, E14 5HU, United Kingdom
Tel.: (44) 2072166800   UK
Web Site:
    https://www.balfourbeatty.com
Year Founded: 1909
BLFBY—(OTCIQ)
Rev.: $9,189,130,500
Assets: $6,170,653,500
Liabilities: $4,715,617,500
Net Worth: $1,455,036,000
Earnings: $345,691,500
Fiscal Year-end: 12/31/22
Engineeering Services
N.A.I.C.S.: 541330
Eric Stenman *(Pres-US)*

Subsidiaries:

Balfour Beatty Campus Solutions LLC **(1)**
1 Country View Rd, Malvern, PA 19355
Tel.: (610) 355-8220
Web Site:
    https://www.bbcampussolutions.com
Property Development & Management Services
N.A.I.C.S.: 531210
Amy Aponte *(VP)*

Balfour Beatty Capital Group Inc **(1)**
1 Country View Rd, Malvern, PA 19355
Tel.: (610) 355-8100
Web Site: http://www.bbcgrp.com
Asset Management Services
N.A.I.C.S.: 523940
Marina Dikos *(Chief Acctg Officer & Sr VP)*

Subsidiary (Domestic):

Balfour Beatty Communities LLC **(2)**
1 Country View Rd, Malvern, PA 19355
Tel.: (610) 355-8100
Emp.: 80
Real Estate Development Services
N.A.I.C.S.: 531390
Kellie Ajjan *(Sr VP-HR)*

Balfour Beatty Group Ltd **(1)**
130 Wilton Road, London, SW1V 1LQ, United Kingdom
Tel.: (44) 2072166800
Emp.: 1,000
Civil Engineering Services
N.A.I.C.S.: 237990

Subsidiary (Domestic):

Balfour Beatty Building Management & Services **(2)**
130 Wilton Road, London, SW1V 1LQ, United Kingdom
Tel.: (44) 2072166800
Sales Range: $25-49.9 Million
Emp.: 200
Building Management & Services
N.A.I.C.S.: 561790
Peter John Louis Zinkin *(Dir-Plng & Dev)*

Subsidiary (Non-US):

Mansell Plc **(3)**

Tel.: (44) 2086548191
Web Site: http://www.mansell.plc.uk
Sales Range: $25-49.9 Million
Emp.: 200
Building Services
N.A.I.C.S.: 561790

Subsidiary (Non-US):

Balfour Beatty Construction Services UK **(4)**
Tel.: (44) 161 741 6100
Web Site: http://www.balfourbeattycsuk.com
Sales Range: $25-49.9 Million
Emp.: 200
Construction & Management Services
N.A.I.C.S.: 236220

Subsidiary (Domestic):

Balfour Beatty Civil Engineering Ltd **(2)**
86 Station Road, Redhill, RH1 1PQ, Surrey, United Kingdom
Tel.: (44) 1737785000
Web Site: http://www.balfourbeattycsuk.com
Civil Engineering & Project Management
N.A.I.C.S.: 541330

Subsidiary (Non-US):

BPH Equipment Limited **(3)**
Web Site: http://www.bphequipment.co.uk
Sales Range: $50-74.9 Million
Emp.: 15
Crane, Plant & Machinery Equipment Rental
N.A.I.C.S.: 532490

Subsidiary (Domestic):

Balfour Beatty Rail **(3)**
Lyndon House 58-62 Hagley Rd 15th Fl, Birmingham, B16 8PE, Edgbaston, United Kingdom
Tel.: (44) 1214564200
Web Site: http://www.bbrail.co.uk
Sales Range: $25-49.9 Million
Emp.: 100
Railway Engineering & Construction
N.A.I.C.S.: 237990
Nigel Claxton *(Dir-Comml)*

Balvac, Ltd. **(3)**
Sherwood House, Gadbrook Business Centre, Rudheath, Northwich, CW9 7UQ, United Kingdom
Tel.: (44) 1606333036
Web Site: http://www.balvac.co.uk
Civil Enginering & Building Refurbishment Contractor
N.A.I.C.S.: 237990

Birse Group **(3)**
Humber Road, Barton-upon-Humber, United Kingdom
Tel.: (44) 1652633222
Sales Range: $550-599.9 Million
Emp.: 60
Building, Civil & Process Engineering Services; Plant Hire Services & Equipment Rental Services
N.A.I.C.S.: 541330

Division (Domestic):

Birse Group Services **(4)**
Humber Rd, Barton-upon-Humber, DN18 5BW, United Kingdom
Tel.: (44) 1652633222
Sales Range: $10-24.9 Million
Business Services
N.A.I.C.S.: 561499
Christine Jaeckel *(Mng Dir)*

Subsidiary (Domestic):

Birse Metro Limited **(3)**
Lyon House, 160-166 Borough High Street, London, SE1 1LB, United Kingdom
Tel.: (44) 2071735250
Sales Range: $10-24.9 Million
Emp.: 50
Construction Services for London Underground Network
N.A.I.C.S.: 237990

Birse Process Engineering Limited **(3)**
Alexander House 4 Station Road, Cheadle

Hulme, SK8 5AE, Cheshire, United Kingdom
Tel.: (44) 1619624880
Sales Range: $25-49.9 Million
Emp.: 20
Engineering & Construction for the Process, Energy & Environmental Sectors
N.A.I.C.S.: 541330

Connect Roads Sunderland Ltd **(3)**
13 Tiley Road Crowther Industrial Estate, Washington, NE38 0AE, Tyne & Wear, United Kingdom
Tel.: (44) 191 418 3100
Web Site: http://www.bbcap.co.uk
Sales Range: $25-49.9 Million
Emp.: 22
Road Construction Engineering Services
N.A.I.C.S.: 237310

Joint Venture (Non-US):

Gammon Construction Ltd. **(3)**
22/F Tower 1 The Quayside 77 Hoi Bun Road, Kwun Tong, Kowloon, China (Hong Kong) **(50%)**
Tel.: (852) 25168823
Sales Range: $1-4.9 Billion
Emp.: 7,000
Construction Services
N.A.I.C.S.: 236220
Patricia Or *(Exec Dir-Fin, Risk Mgmt & Information Mgmt-Gammon Capital)*

Subsidiary (Domestic):

Balfour Beatty Construction Limited **(2)**
Dean House, 24 Ravelston Terrace, Edinburgh, EH4 3TP, United Kingdom
Tel.: (44) 1313329411
Sales Range: $1-4.9 Billion
Emp.: 150
Construction Services
N.A.I.C.S.: 236220
Dean Banks *(Mng Dir)*

Subsidiary (US):

Balfour Beatty Construction Group Inc **(3)**
3100 McKinnon St, Dallas, TX 75201
Tel.: (214) 451-1000
Construction Engineering Services
N.A.I.C.S.: 541330
Martin Welton *(Dir-Bus Dev-Charlotte)*

Subsidiary (Domestic):

Balfour Beatty Construction LLC **(4)**
3100 McKinnon St, Dallas, TX 75201-1593
Tel.: (214) 451-1000
Web Site: https://www.balfourbeattyus.com
Sales Range: $300-349.9 Million
Emp.: 1,496
Commercial & Industrial Building Construction
N.A.I.C.S.: 236210
Eric Stenman *(Pres)*

Subsidiary (Domestic):

Balfour Beatty Construction LLC **(5)**
7901 SW 6th Ct, Plantation, FL 33324-3282
Tel.: (954) 585-4000
Web Site: http://www.balfourbeattyus.com
Sales Range: $75-99.9 Million
Emp.: 90
General Construction Services
N.A.I.C.S.: 236220

Subsidiary (Domestic):

Balfour Beatty Construction Northern Limited **(3)**
Cavendish House, Cross Street, Sale, M33 7BU, United Kingdom
Tel.: (44) 1619727501
Sales Range: $25-49.9 Million
Emp.: 80
Construction Services
N.A.I.C.S.: 236220

Balfour Beatty Construction Scottish & Southern Limited **(3)**
Dean House, 24 Ravelston Terrace, Edinburgh, EH4 3TP, United Kingdom
Tel.: (44) 1313329411
Web Site: http://www.bbrl.co.uk
Construction Services

Balfour Beatty plc—(Continued)

N.A.I.C.S.: 236220

Balfour Beatty-Construction Services UK (3)
5 Churchill Place Canary Wharf, London, E14 5HU, United Kingdom
Tel.: (44) 2072166800
Web Site: http://www.balfourbeattyuk.com
Sales Range: $250-299.9 Million
Commercial Building Contractor
N.A.I.C.S.: 236220

Subsidiary (Domestic):

Cowlin Timber Frame (4)
Duffryn Bach Terrace, Church Village, Pontypridd, United Kingdom
Tel.: (44) 3209953
Timber Frame Mfr
N.A.I.C.S.: 236220

Subsidiary (Domestic):

Balfour Beatty Engineering Services Limited (2)
5 Chuch Hill Place, Canarywall, London, E14 5HU, United Kingdom
Tel.: (44) 207 216 6800
Web Site: http://www.balfourbeattycsuk.com
Sales Range: $25-49.9 Million
Emp.: 200
Mechanical Engineering Services
N.A.I.C.S.: 541330

Balfour Beatty Ground Engineering Ltd (2)
Pavilion C2 Ashwood Park Ashwood Way, Basingstoke, RG23 8BG, Hampshire, United Kingdom
Tel.: (44) 1256365200
Web Site: http://www.bbge.com
Sales Range: $25-49.9 Million
Emp.: 7
Ground Engineering Services
N.A.I.C.S.: 541330

Balfour Beatty Infrastructure Investments Ltd (2)
5 Churchill Place Canary Wharf, London, E14 5HU, United Kingdom
Tel.: (44) 2072166800
Web Site: http://www.balfourbeatty.com
Real Estate Development Services
N.A.I.C.S.: 531390

Subsidiary (Non-US):

Balfour Beatty Investment Holdings Ltd (2)
Tel.: (44) 2072166800
Emp.: 100
Investment Management Service
N.A.I.C.S.: 523999

Subsidiary (Domestic):

Balfour Beatty Investments Limited (2)
Focus Point 3rd Floor 21 Caledonian Road, London, N1 9GB, United Kingdom
Tel.: (44) 2071213700
Web Site:
   https://www.balfourbeattyinvestments.com
Financial Management Services
N.A.I.C.S.: 523999

Balfour Beatty Homes Ltd. (1)
RCI Building Haylock House Kettering Venture Park, Kettering, NN15 6EY, United Kingdom
Tel.: (44) 1536608654
Web Site:
   https://www.balfourbeattyhomes.com
Residential Home Development Services
N.A.I.C.S.: 236115

Balfour Beatty Investments Inc. (1)
1 Country View Rd, Malvern, PA 19355
Tel.: (610) 355-8100
Investment Management Service
N.A.I.C.S.: 523940
Jennifer Shannon (VP-IT)

Gwynt y Mor OFTO plc (1)
Q14 Quorum Business Park Benton Lane, Newcastle upon Tyne, NE12 8BU, United Kingdom
Tel.: (44) 2071213700
Wind Electric Power Generation Services

N.A.I.C.S.: 221115

HSW Inc. (1)
23311 Madero, Mission Viejo, CA 92691
Tel.: (949) 380-4161
Web Site: http://www.hswcorp.com
Water & Sewer System Inspection Services
N.A.I.C.S.: 237110
Mark Burel (CEO)

Painter Drothers Ltd. (1)
Holmer Road, Hereford, HR4 9SW, United Kingdom
Tel.: (44) 1432374400
Structural Steel Mfr
N.A.I.C.S.: 332312
David Spencer (Mgr-SHEQS)

Scotland TranServ (1)
150 Polmadie Road Glasgow, Glasgow, G5 0HD, Scotland, United Kingdom
Tel.: (44) 141 218 3800
Web Site: http://www.scotlandtranserv.co.uk
Emp.: 300
Highway Maintenance, Street Lighting & Other Transportation Infrastructure Support Services
N.A.I.C.S.: 488490

BALGOPAL COMMERCIAL LIMITED
Flat No B-002 Dreamax Vega Upadhyay Compound Pump House, Jijamata Road Andheri East, Mumbai, 400093, MH, India
Tel.: (91) 9324922533
Web Site:
   https://www.bcommercial.org
Year Founded: 1982
539834—(BOM)
Rev.: $121,766,094
Assets: $256,227,699
Liabilities: $48,160,544
Net Worth: $208,067,155
Earnings: $4,156,398
Fiscal Year-end: 03/31/22
Investment Management Service
N.A.I.C.S.: 523150
Banwarilal Mahansaria (Mng Dir & Officer-Compliance)

BALHOUSIE HOLDINGS LIMITED
Earn House Broxden Business Park Lamberkine Drive, Perth, PH1 1RA, United Kingdom
Tel.: (44) 1738 254 254   **UK**
Web Site:
   http://www.balhousiecare.co.uk
Sales Range: $10-24.9 Million
Emp.: 850
Holding Company; Nursing Care Facilities Owner & Operator
N.A.I.C.S.: 551112
Tony Banks (Founder & Chm)

Subsidiaries:

Alastrean Care Home Aboyne (1)
Tarland, Aboyne, AB34 4TA, Aberdeenshire, United Kingdom
Tel.: (44) 1339 881235
Nursing Care Facility
N.A.I.C.S.: 623110

Antiquary Care Home Arbroath (1)
Westway, Arbroath, DD11 2BW, Scotland, United Kingdom
Tel.: (44) 1241 434969
Nursing Care Facility
N.A.I.C.S.: 623110

Auchterarder Care Home (1)
Abbey Road, Auchterarder, PH3 1DN, Scotland, United Kingdom
Tel.: (44) 1764 664192
Nursing Care Facility
N.A.I.C.S.: 623110

Clement Park Care Home Dundee (1)
4 Clement Park Place, Dundee, DD2 3JN, United Kingdom
Tel.: (44) 1382 610960
Web Site: http://www.balhousiecare.co.uk

Emp.: 80
Nursing Care Facility
N.A.I.C.S.: 623110
Margrate Stephen (Mgr-Care Home)

Coupar Angus Care Home (1)
Meadowside Close, Coupar Angus, PH13 9FB, Perthshire, United Kingdom
Tel.: (44) 1828 424930
Web Site: http://www.balhousiecare.co.uk
Nursing Care Facility
N.A.I.C.S.: 623110

Crieff Care Home (1)
Comrie Road, Crieff, PH7 4BJ, Perth and Kinross, United Kingdom
Tel.: (44) 1764 655231
Nursing Care Facility
N.A.I.C.S.: 623110

Forthview Care Home (1)
6 Sea Road, Methil, KY8 3DE, Fife, United Kingdom
Tel.: (44) 1592 716500
Web Site: http://www.balhousiecare.co.uk
Emp.: 60
Nursing Care Facility
N.A.I.C.S.: 623110
Maria Hutchinson (Mgr-Care Home)

Glens Care Home Brechin (1)
18-20 Church Street, Edzell, Brechin, DD9 7TQ, Dundee and Angus, United Kingdom
Tel.: (44) 1356 648888
Web Site: http://www.balhousiecare.co.uk
Nursing Care Facility
N.A.I.C.S.: 623110
Elaine Dickson (Mgr)

Lisden Care Home Kirriemuir (1)
63 Brechin Road, Kirriemuir, DD8 4DE, Angus, United Kingdom
Tel.: (44) 1575 574499
Nursing Care Facility
N.A.I.C.S.: 623110
Terry Starbuck (Mgr)

Luncarty Care Home (1)
Scarth Road, Luncarty, PH1 3HE, Perth and Kinross, United Kingdom
Tel.: (44) 1738 828163
Web Site: http://www.balhousie.com
Emp.: 33
Nursing Care Facility
N.A.I.C.S.: 623110
Tracy McEwan (Mgr-Care Home)

Methven Care Home Perth (1)
31 Lynedoch Road, Methven, Perth, PH1 3PH, United Kingdom
Tel.: (44) 1738 840644
Emp.: 2
Nursing Care Facility
N.A.I.C.S.: 623110
Lars Arne Hoff (Mgr)

Monkbarns Care Home Arbroath (1)
14 Monkbarns Drive, Arbroath, DD11 2DS, United Kingdom
Tel.: (44) 1241 871713
Nursing Care Facility
N.A.I.C.S.: 623110
Joyce Chalmers (Mgr-Care Home)

Moyness Care Home Dundee (1)
76 Grove Road, Broughty Ferry, Dundee, DD5 1JP, Dundee and Angus, United Kingdom
Tel.: (44) 1382 480899
Nursing Care Facility
N.A.I.C.S.: 623110

North Grove Care Home Perth (1)
101 Hay Street, Perth, PH1 5HS, Perth and Kinross, United Kingdom
Tel.: (44) 1738 628771
Nursing Care Facility
N.A.I.C.S.: 623110

North Inch Care Home Perth (1)
99 Hay Street, Perth, PH1 5HS, Perth and Kinross, United Kingdom
Tel.: (44) 1738 632233
Nursing Care Facility
N.A.I.C.S.: 623110

Pitlochry Care Home (1)
Burnside Road, Pitlochry, PH16 5BP, United Kingdom
Tel.: (44) 1796 473280
Nursing Care Facility

N.A.I.C.S.: 623110

Rigifa Care Home Perth (1)
College Road, Perth, PH1 3PB, United Kingdom
Tel.: (44) 1738 840747
Nursing Care Facility
N.A.I.C.S.: 623110

Rumbling Bridge Care Home Kinross (1)
Crook of Devon, Kinross, KY13 0PX, United Kingdom
Tel.: (44) 1577 840478
Web Site: http://www.balhousiecare.co.uk
Nursing Care Facility
N.A.I.C.S.: 623110

Stormont Care Home Blairgowrie (1)
Kirk Wynd, Blairgowrie, PH10 6HN, Perth and Kinross, United Kingdom
Tel.: (44) 1250 872853
Web Site: http://www.balhousiecare.co.uk
Emp.: 26
Nursing Care Facility
N.A.I.C.S.: 623110
Helen Norrie (Mgr-Care Home)

The Dalguise Centre Care Home Perth (1)
Balbeggie, Perth, PH2 6AT, United Kingdom
Tel.: (44) 1821 650591
Nursing Care Facility
N.A.I.C.S.: 623110

The Grange Care Home Perth (1)
Balbeggie, Perth, PH2 6AT, United Kingdom
Tel.: (44) 1821 650690
Emp.: 21
Nursing Care Facility
N.A.I.C.S.: 623110
Karen Austin (Mgr-Care Home)

Wheatlands Care Home Bonnybridge (1)
Larbert Road, Bonnybridge, FK4 1ED, Stirlingshire, United Kingdom
Tel.: (44) 1324 814561
Web Site: http://www.balhousie.co.uk
Emp.: 4
Nursing Care Facility
N.A.I.C.S.: 623110
Grace Sloan (Mgr-Care Home)

Willowbank Care Home Carnoustie (1)
56 Maule Street, Carnoustie, DD7 6AB, Dundee and Angus, United Kingdom
Tel.: (44) 1241 852160
Nursing Care Facility
N.A.I.C.S.: 623110
Jan Robertson (Mgr-Care Home)

BALKAN & SEA PROPERTIES REIT
14 General Kolev Blvd Ent B floor 1 Ap 4, 9000, Varna, 9000, Bulgaria
Tel.: (359) 52603830
Web Site:
   https://www.bsproperties.eu
BSP—(BUL)
Sales Range: Less than $1 Million
Real Estate Development Services
N.A.I.C.S.: 531390
Liudmilla Ivanova Daskalova (CEO)

BALKAN MINING & MINERALS LIMITED
Tel.: (61) 861888181   **AU**
Web Site:
   https://www.balkanmin.com
Year Founded: 2020
7JL—(DEU)
Rev.: $291
Assets: $2,650,149
Liabilities: $304,757
Net Worth: $2,345,392
Earnings: ($3,249,267)
Fiscal Year-end: 06/30/23
Mineral Exploration Services
N.A.I.C.S.: 212390
Ross Cotton (CFO)

BALKANCAR ZARYA PLC

1 Tosho Kutev Str, 5200, Pavlikeni,
Bulgaria
Tel.: (359) 61053061
Web Site:
　　https://www.balkancarzarya.com
Year Founded: 1964
4BUA—(BUL)
Sales Range: Less than $1 Million
Steel Wheels & Rims Mfr
N.A.I.C.S.: 331221
E. Marinova *(Dir-IR)*

BALKRISHNA INDUSTRIES LIMITED

BKT House C/15 Trade World Ka-
mala Mills Compound, Senapati
Bapat Marg Lower Parel W, Mumbai,
400013, India
Tel.: (91) 2266663800
Web Site: https://www.bkt-tires.com
BALKRISIND—(NSE)
Rev.: $1,211,685,151
Assets: $1,480,446,016
Liabilities: $574,393,621
Net Worth: $906,052,395
Earnings: $126,778,970
Emp.: 3,472
Fiscal Year-end: 03/31/23
Pneumatic Tire Mfr
N.A.I.C.S.: 326211
Arvind Poddar *(Chm & Co-Mng Dir)*

BALKRISHNA PAPER MILLS LIMITED

A/7 Trade World Kamala City Sena-
pati Bapat Marg Lower Parel, Mum-
bai, 400 013, India
Tel.: (91) 2261207900
Web Site: https://www.bpml.in
Year Founded: 1975
BALKRISHNA—(NSE)
Rev.: $33,386,453
Assets: $25,530,742
Liabilities: $38,977,821
Net Worth: ($13,447,079)
Earnings: ($639,871)
Fiscal Year-end: 03/31/22
Paper Products Mfr
N.A.I.C.S.: 322299
Anurag P. Poddar *(Chm & Mng Dir)*

BALLARD POWER SYSTEMS, INC.

9000 Glenlyon Parkway, Burnaby,
V5J 5J8, BC, Canada
Tel.: (604) 454-0900　　　　　Ca
Web Site: https://www.ballard.com
Year Founded: 1979
BLDP—(NASDAQ)
Rev.: $83,786,000
Assets: $1,247,077,000
Liabilities: $88,166,000
Net Worth: $1,158,911,000
Earnings: ($173,494,000)
Emp.: 1,296
Fiscal Year-end: 12/31/22
Fuel Cell & Fuel Cell Systems Mfr
N.A.I.C.S.: 335999
R. Randall MacEwen *(Pres & CEO)*

Subsidiaries:

Ballard Material Products Inc.　　**(1)**
2 Industrial Ave, Lowell, MA
01851-5107　　　　　　　　　**(100%)**
Tel.: (978) 934-7522
Sales Range: $25-49.9 Million
Emp.: 50
Broadwoven Fabric Mills
N.A.I.C.S.: 313210

Ballard Power Systems
Corporation　　　　　　　　　**(1)**
9000 Glenlyon Pkwy, Burnaby, V5J 5J8,
BC, Canada　　　　　　　　　**(100%)**
Tel.: (604) 454-0900
Web Site: http://www.ballard.com

Sales Range: $75-99.9 Million
Physical Engineering & Life Sciences Re-
search & Development
N.A.I.C.S.: 541715

Ballard Power Systems Europe
A/S　　　　　　　　　　　　**(1)**
Majsmarken 1, 9500, Hobro,
Denmark　　　　　　　　　　**(43%)**
Tel.: (45) 88435500
Web Site: https://www.ballard.com
Sales Range: Less than $1 Million
Emp.: 42
Fuel Cell & Hydrogen Technology Devel-
oper
N.A.I.C.S.: 335312
Jesper Themsen *(Pres & CEO)*

BALLERINA-KUCHEN H.-E. ELLERSIEK GMBH

Bruchstrasse 49-51, D-32289, Rod-
ing, Germany
Tel.: (49) 52265990
Web Site: http://www.ballerina.de
Year Founded: 1978
Rev.: $55,176,000
Emp.: 250
Kitchenware Mfr
N.A.I.C.S.: 337110
Heinz Erwin Ellersiek *(Mng Dir)*

BALLI GROUP PLC

33 Cavendish Square, London, W1G
0PW, United Kingdom
Tel.: (44) 2073062000
Web Site: http://www.balli.co.uk
Year Founded: 1991
Sales Range: $1-4.9 Billion
Emp.: 2,000
Steel, Aluminum, Chemicals & Other
Commodity Trader & Distr
N.A.I.C.S.: 425120
Hassan Alaghband *(Owner)*

Subsidiaries:

Balli Klockner GmbH　　　　　**(1)**
Schifferstrasse 200, 47059, Duisburg, Ger-
many
Tel.: (49) 2032896000
Web Site: http://www.balli-germany.de
Sales Range: $50-74.9 Million
Emp.: 10
Metal Service Centers & Metal Merchant
Whslr
N.A.I.C.S.: 423510
Axel Kopp *(Mng Dir)*

Balli Klockner Middle East FZE　**(1)**
Jebel Ali Free Zone, PO Box 16936, Dubai,
United Arab Emirates
Tel.: (971) 48816549
Web Site: http://www.balli.co.uk
Iron & Steel Mills
N.A.I.C.S.: 331110

Balli Steel Inc　　　　　　　　**(1)**
1100 Louisiana St Ste 5300, Houston, TX
77002-5215
Tel.: (713) 627-7310
Metal Service Centers & Metal Merchant
Whslr
N.A.I.C.S.: 423510

Balli Steel Pipe LLC　　　　　　**(1)**
1100 Louisiana St Ste 5300, Houston, TX
77002-5215
Tel.: (713) 627-7310
Web Site: http://www.balli.co.uk
Purchased Steel & Iron & Steel Pipe &
Tube Mfr
N.A.I.C.S.: 331210

Balli West Africa Limited　　　　**(1)**
57 Ring Rd Central, PO Box AN 5144, Ac-
cra, Ghana
Tel.: (233) 21270167
Web Site: http://www.balli.co.uk
Sales Range: $50-74.9 Million
Emp.: 7
Metal Service Centers & Metal Merchant
Whslr
N.A.I.C.S.: 423510

WeBco International LLC　　　　**(1)**

210 3rd Springs Dr Ste 2, Weirton, WV
26062
Tel.: (304) 723-6101
Sheet Metal Work Mfg
N.A.I.C.S.: 332322

BALLIN, INC.

2825 Brabant-Marineau, Montreal,
H4S 1R8, QC, Canada
Tel.: (514) 333-5501
Web Site: http://www.ballin.com
Rev.: $23,334,211
Emp.: 351
Men's Dress Slacks Marketer & Mfr
N.A.I.C.S.: 315250
Joseph Balinsky *(Pres)*

BALLY WULFF AUTOMATEN GMBH

Maybachufer 48-51, 12045, Berlin,
Germany
Tel.: (49) 30620020　　　　　De
Web Site: http://www.ballywulff.de
Year Founded: 1950
Sales Range: $75-99.9 Million
Emp.: 325
Wall & Touch-Screen Game Ma-
chines Mfr & Distr
N.A.I.C.S.: 333310
Sascha Blodau *(CEO)*

BALLY, CORP.

Rm 401 Bldg 2 Weishijiu Rd Xi-
aoshan D, Pudong, Hangzhou,
311215, China
Tel.: (86) 18258830915　　　　NV
Year Founded: 2013
BLYQ—(OTCIQ)
Assets: $6,750
Liabilities: $184,082
Net Worth: ($177,332)
Earnings: ($35,385)
Fiscal Year-end: 09/30/23
Online Garden Products Retailer
N.A.I.C.S.: 459999
George T. Papanier *(Pres-Retail)*

BALLYMORE RESOURCES LIMITED

Suite 606 Level 6 10 Market St, Bris-
bane, 4000, QLD, Australia
Tel.: (61) 732126299　　　　　AU
Web Site:
　　https://www.ballymoreresource.com
Year Founded: 2019
BMR—(ASX)
Rev.: $540
Assets: $7,945,258
Liabilities: $284,060
Net Worth: $7,661,197
Earnings: ($562,152)
Fiscal Year-end: 06/30/22
Mining Services
N.A.I.C.S.: 212290
Duncan Patrick Cornish *(CFO)*

BALLYVESEY HOLDINGS LIM-ITED

607 Antrim Road, Newtownabbey,
BT36 4RF, United Kingdom
Tel.: (44) 2890849321
Web Site:
　　http://www.ballyveseyholdings.com
Year Founded: 1970
Sales Range: $550-599.9 Million
Emp.: 1,857
Investment Management Service
N.A.I.C.S.: 523940
Paul Jones *(Gen Mgr-Truck & Plant)*

Subsidiaries:

Ballyvesey Finance Ltd　　　　　**(1)**
Unit 7 Penmaen Business Centre Penmaen
Road, Pontllanfraith, Blackwood, NP12
2DZ, United Kingdom
Tel.: (44) 1495238300
Web Site: http://www.ballyveseyfinance.com

Automobile Financing Services
N.A.I.C.S.: 522220
Gareth Young *(Gen Mgr)*

Ballyvesey Holdings Polska Ltd　**(1)**
Podmiejska 95, 44-207, Rybnik, Poland
Tel.: (48) 327396285
Web Site: http://www.ballyvesey.pl
Office Building Rental Services
N.A.I.C.S.: 531120
Tom Harrison *(Project Mgr)*

Ballyvesey Recycling Solutions
Ltd　　　　　　　　　　　　**(1)**
50 Trench Road, Newtownabbey, BT36
4TY, Antrim, United Kingdom
Tel.: (44) 2890021000
Web Site:
　　http://www.ballyveseyrecyclingsolution.com
Scrap Metal Recycling Services
N.A.I.C.S.: 423930
Dennis Monaghan *(Mng Dir)*

Birds Transport & Logistics Ltd　**(1)**
Parsonage Street, Oldbury, B69 4PH, West
Midland, United Kingdom
Tel.: (44) 1215529666
Web Site:
　　http://www.ballyveseyholdings.com
Logistics Consulting Servies
N.A.I.C.S.: 541614
Justin Dankenbring *(Fin Mgr)*

Centurion Truck Rental Ltd　　　**(1)**
Stakehill Industrial Park, Middleton, Man-
chester, M24 2RW, United Kingdom
Tel.: (44) 1616539700
Web Site:
　　http://www.centuriontruckrental.co.uk
Truck Rental Services
N.A.I.C.S.: 532490
Warren Fletcher *(Mng Dir)*

Commercial Vehicle Auctions Ltd　**(1)**
Carr Hill Industrial Estate, Doncaster, DN4
8DE, South Yorkshire, United Kingdom
Tel.: (44) 1302732600
Web Site: http://www.cva-auctions.co.uk
Automobile Auction Services
N.A.I.C.S.: 425120

Contract Plant Rental Ltd　　　　**(1)**
Little Wigston Tamworth Rd, Appleby
Magna, Swadlincote, DE12 7BJ,
Derbyshire, United Kingdom
Tel.: (44) 1933232663
Web Site:
　　http://www.contractplantrental.com
Construction Equipment Rental Services
N.A.I.C.S.: 532412
John Tull *(Gen Mgr)*

Heathrow Truck Centre Ltd　　　**(1)**
Lakeside Industrial Estate, Colnbrook, SL3
0ED, Berks, United Kingdom
Tel.: (44) 1753681818
Web Site: https://www.htc-heathrow.com
Truck Dealership
N.A.I.C.S.: 532120

Htc Van Centre Ltd　　　　　　　**(1)**
Crabtree Manorway North, Belvedere, DA17
6BT, Kent, United Kingdom
Tel.: (44) 20 8319 7812
Web Site: http://www.htcvancentre.co.uk
Automotive Distr
N.A.I.C.S.: 423110
Peter Gibbons *(Dir-After Sls)*

Midlands Truck & Van Ltd　　　　**(1)**
1 Dorset Road Saltley Business Park, Salt-
ley, Birmingham, B8 1BG, United Kingdom
Tel.: (44) 1212211071
Web Site: http://www.midlandstruckvan.com
New & Used Truck Dealer
N.A.I.C.S.: 441110
Nigel Simmons *(Mgr-Svc)*

TDL Equipment Ltd　　　　　　　**(1)**
Wentworth Way Wentworth Industrial Park,
Tankersley, S75 3DH, South Yorkshire,
United Kingdom
Tel.: (44) 8444994499
Web Site: http://www.tdlequipment.com
Construction Equipment Distr
N.A.I.C.S.: 423810
Andrew Taylor *(Principal)*

Trafford Van Centre Ltd　　　　　**(1)**
Unit 5 Circle South John Gilbert Way Traf-

Ballyvesey Holdings Limited—(Continued)

ford Park, Manchester, M17 1NF, United Kingdom
Tel.: (44) 1618773445
Web Site: http://www.trafforvancentre.com
Automotive Distr
N.A.I.C.S.: 423110
Andy Clarke *(Mgr-Bus Dev)*

BALMAIN CORP.
Level 14 60 Castlereagh Street, Sydney, 2000, NSW, Australia
Tel.: (61) 292328888
Web Site: http://www.balmain.com.au
Year Founded: 1979
Sales Range: $50-74.9 Million
Emp.: 130
Commercial Lending Services
N.A.I.C.S.: 522310
Michael Holm *(Chm)*

Subsidiaries:

AMAL Asset Management
Limited **(1)**
Level 9 Castlereagh Street, Sydney, 2000, NSW, Australia
Tel.: (61) 2 9230 6700
Web Site: http://www.amal.com.au
Financial Services
N.A.I.C.S.: 522390
Kent McPhee *(CEO)*

Subsidiary (Non-US):

AMAL New Zealand Limited **(2)**
Level 31 Vero Centre 48 Shortland Street, Auckland, 1143, New Zealand
Tel.: (64) 9 966 7585
Financial Services
N.A.I.C.S.: 522390

Scottish Pacific Business Finance
Pty. Limited **(1)**
L 2 50 Carrington St, Sydney, 2000, NSW, Australia
Tel.: (61) 293729999
Web Site: http://www.spbf.com.au
Factoring & Business Finance Services
N.A.I.C.S.: 522220

Trilogy Funds Management
Limited **(1)**
Level 13 56 Pitt Street, Sydney, 2000, NSW, Australia
Tel.: (61) 2 8028 2828
Web Site: http://www.trilogyfunds.com.au
Emp.: 30
Fund Management Services
N.A.I.C.S.: 525910
Rodger Bacon *(Deputy Chm)*

BALMER LAWRIE & CO. LTD.
21 Netaji Subash Road, Kolkata, 700 001, India
Tel.: (91) 3322225218
Web Site:
https://www.balmerlawrie.com
Year Founded: 1867
BALMLAWRIE—(NSE)
Rev.: $321,883,189
Assets: $363,326,636
Liabilities: $129,640,329
Net Worth: $233,686,307
Earnings: $22,882,178
Emp.: 989
Fiscal Year-end: 03/30/23
Diversified Products Manufacturing & Trading Including Greases, Lubricants, Leather, Functional Chemicals, Packaging, Turnkey Projects, Tea Exports, Travel, Tourism, Cargo & Logistics
N.A.I.C.S.: 339999
Adika Ratna Sekhar *(Chm, Mng Dir & Dir-HR & Corp Affairs)*

BALMER LAWRIE INVESTMENTS LTD.
21 Netaji Subhas Road, Kolkata, 700001, India
Tel.: (91) 3322225227

Web Site: https://www.blinv.com
532485—(BOM)
Rev.: $287,402,374
Assets: $351,613,803
Liabilities: $112,634,968
Net Worth: $238,978,836
Earnings: $18,832,072
Fiscal Year-end: 03/31/22
Investment Management Service
N.A.I.C.S.: 523999
Abhishek Lahoti *(Officer-Pub Information & Sec)*

BALMORAL GROUP LTD.
Balmoral Park, Loirston, Aberdeen, AB12 3GY, United Kingdom
Tel.: (44) 1224859000
Web Site: http://www.balmoral-group.com
Year Founded: 1980
Sales Range: $50-74.9 Million
Emp.: 600
Lightweight Plastic Composites Mfr; Liquid Storage & Treatment Products Designer & Mfr; Marine Equipment Supplier
N.A.I.C.S.: 326199
Jim Milne *(Chm & Mng Dir)*

Subsidiaries:

Balmoral Advanced Composites
Limited **(1)**
Balmoral Park Loirston, Loriston, Aberdeen, AB12 3GY, United Kingdom
Tel.: (44) 1224859000
Web Site: http://www.balmoral.co.uk
Sales Range: $125-149.9 Million
Emp.: 400
Lightweight Plastic Composites Mfr
N.A.I.C.S.: 326199
James S. Milne *(Chm & Mng Dir)*

Balmoral Marine Ltd. **(1)**
Balmoral Park, Loriston, Aberdeen, AB12 3GY, United Kingdom
Tel.: (44) 1224859000
Web Site: http://www.balmoral-group.com
Emp.: 500
Marine Equipment Supplier
N.A.I.C.S.: 488320
Allen Robertson *(Dir-Ops)*

Balmoral Tanks Limited **(1)**
Unit 2 Coomber Way Industrial Estate, Croydon, CR0 4TQ, Surrey, United Kingdom
Tel.: (44) 2086654100
Web Site: http://www.balmoral-group.com
Sales Range: $25-49.9 Million
Emp.: 10
Liquid Storage & Treatment Tanks & Other Related Products
N.A.I.C.S.: 332420
Norman Ross *(Dir-Sls)*

Balmoral Wellbeing Ltd. **(1)**
Longdon Manor, Shipston-on-Stour, CV36 4PW, Warwickshire, United Kingdom
Tel.: (44) 1608 682888
Web Site: http://www.the-egg.co.uk
Relaxation Chamber
N.A.I.C.S.: 326199

BALMORAL INTERNATIONAL LAND HOLDINGS PLC
29 North Anne Street, Dublin, Ireland
Tel.: (353) 18872788
Web Site: http://www.bilplc.com
Year Founded: 2011
Holding Company
N.A.I.C.S.: 551112
Niall Quigley *(Sec)*

Subsidiaries:

Balmoral International Land
Limited **(1)**
29 North Anne Street, Dublin, Ireland **(100%)**
Tel.: (353) 18872788
Web Site: http://www.bilplc.com

Sales Range: $10-24.9 Million
Emp.: 9
Real Estate Development Services
N.A.I.C.S.: 531390

Subsidiary (Non-US):

Balmoral International Land UK
Ltd **(2)**
Fairbourne Drive, Atterbury Lakes, Milton Keynes, MK10 9RG, Buckinghamshire, United Kingdom
Tel.: (44) 1908488627
Web Site: http://www.bilplc.com
Real Estate Property Management Services
N.A.I.C.S.: 531311

Subsidiary (Domestic):

Balmoral Land Naul Ltd **(2)**
29 North Anne Street, Dublin, 7, Ireland
Tel.: (353) 18872788
Emp.: 6
Real Estate Property Development Services
N.A.I.C.S.: 531210
Robert Knox *(Gen Mgr)*

Balmoral International Land Property
Holdings BV **(1)**
Claude Debussylaan 24, 1082 MD, Amsterdam, Netherlands
Tel.: (31) 205222555
Holding Company
N.A.I.C.S.: 551112

BALMUDA, INC.
5-1-21 Kyonancho Musashino, Tokyo, 180-0023, Japan
Tel.: (81) 2119350422
Web Site: https://www.balmuda.com
Year Founded: 2003
6612—(TKS)
Rev.: $92,247,990
Assets: $55,323,270
Liabilities: $25,084,420
Net Worth: $30,238,850
Earnings: ($14,683,390)
Emp.: 137
Fiscal Year-end: 12/31/23
Home Appliance Mfr & Distr
N.A.I.C.S.: 335220
Gen Terao *(Founder, Chm & Pres)*

BALNIBARBI CO., LTD.
6F Nakazawa Karaki Building 1-14-26 Minamihorie, Nishi-ku, Osaka, 550-0015, Japan
Tel.: (81) 643906544
Web Site: https://www.balnibarbi.com
Year Founded: 1991
3418—(TKS)
Rev.: $83,671,440
Assets: $63,263,620
Liabilities: $41,941,460
Net Worth: $21,322,160
Earnings: $3,346,360
Emp.: 641
Fiscal Year-end: 07/31/24
Restaurant Management
N.A.I.C.S.: 722511
Bungo Ando *(Pres)*

BALOCCO S.P.A.
Santa Lucia 51, Fossano, 12045, Cuneo, Italy
Tel.: (39) 0172 653411
Web Site: http://www.balocco.it
Year Founded: 1927
Sales Range: $150-199.9 Million
Emp.: 323
Bakery Products Mfr
N.A.I.C.S.: 311821
Silvia Caffetti *(Mgr-Export)*

BALOCHISTAN GLASS LIMITED
12-KM Sheikhupura Road Kot Abdul Malik, Lahore, Pakistan
Tel.: (92) 4237164424 PK
Web Site:
https://www.balochistanglass.com

BGL—(PSX)
Rev.: $669,157
Assets: $9,122,306
Liabilities: $6,029,363
Net Worth: $3,092,943
Earnings: ($485,861)
Emp.: 6
Fiscal Year-end: 06/30/23
Glass Products Mfr
N.A.I.C.S.: 327215
Muhammad Tousif Paracha *(CEO)*

BALOCHISTAN PARTICLE BOARD LIMITED
3rd Floor Imperial Court Dr Ziauddin Ahmed Road, Karachi, 75530, Pakistan
Tel.: (92) 2135680036
Web Site: http://www.bpbl.net
BPBL—(LAH)
Rev.: $17,088
Assets: $46,921
Liabilities: $100,240
Net Worth: ($53,319)
Earnings: ($6,512)
Emp.: 1
Fiscal Year-end: 06/30/19
Particle Board, Formaldehyde & Formaldehyde Based Resins Mfr
N.A.I.C.S.: 325211
Muslim R. Habib *(CEO)*

BALOG AUCTION SERVICES INC.
PO Box 786, Lethbridge, T1J 3Z6, AB, Canada
Tel.: (403) 320-1980
Web Site:
http://www.balogauction.com
Rev.: $27,300,714
Emp.: 40
Hosts Livestock & Machinery Auction Services
N.A.I.C.S.: 459420
Robert C. Balog *(Co-Owner)*

BALOISE HOLDING AG
Aeschengraben 21, CH-4001, Basel, Switzerland
Tel.: (41) 582858585 CH
Web Site: https://www.baloise.com
Year Founded: 1863
BLHEF—(OTCIQ)
Rev.: $6,000,443,459
Assets: $86,333,481,153
Liabilities: $82,720,066,519
Net Worth: $3,613,414,634
Earnings: $261,862,528
Emp.: 6,016
Fiscal Year-end: 12/31/23
Holding Company
N.A.I.C.S.: 551112
Carsten Stolz *(CFO & Head-Fin)*

Subsidiaries:

AboDeinAuto GmbH **(1)**
Havel-Center Room 239 Am Industriegelande 3, 14772, Brandenburg, Germany
Tel.: (49) 304 036 6758
Web Site: https://www.abodeinauto.de
Car Dealing Services
N.A.I.C.S.: 441110
Alexander Thieme *(CEO)*

Baloise (Luxembourg) Holding
S.A. **(1)**
Rue Du Puits Romanian 23, 8070, Bertrange, Luxembourg
Tel.: (352) 2901901
Investment Management Service
N.A.I.C.S.: 523999
Romain Braas *(Mng Dir)*

Baloise Asset Management International AG **(1)**
Aeschengraben 21, Basel, 4002, Switzerland
Tel.: (41) 58 285 85 85
Asset Management Services

N.A.I.C.S.: 523940

Baloise Asset Management Schweiz AG   **(1)**
Aeschengraben 21, 4002, Basel, Switzerland
Tel.: (41) 582857299
Web Site: http://www.baloise-asset-management.com
Asset Management Services
N.A.I.C.S.: 523940

Baloise Assurances Luxembourg S.A.   **(1)**
23 rue du Puits Romain Bourmicht BP28, 2010, Bertrange, Luxembourg   **(100%)**
Tel.: (352) 2901901
Web Site: http://www.baloise.lu
Sales Range: $650-699.9 Million
Emp.: 250
Insurance & Pension Services
N.A.I.C.S.: 524128

Subsidiary (Domestic):

Baloise Assurances IARD S.A.   **(2)**
BP 28, 2010, Luxembourg, Luxembourg
Tel.: (352) 290 190 530
Web Site: http://www.baloise.lu
Sales Range: $200-249.9 Million
Emp.: 270
Insurance Management Services
N.A.I.C.S.: 524298
Andre Bredimus *(Gen Mgr)*

Baloise Europe Vie SA   **(2)**
23 Rue Du Roman Wells, 8070, Bertrange, Bourmicht, Luxembourg
Tel.: (352) 2901901
Web Site: http://wwwbaloise.lu
Sales Range: $100-124.9 Million
Emp.: 350
Fire Insurance Services
N.A.I.C.S.: 524128
Braas Omain *(CEO)*

Baloise Vie Luxembourg S.A   **(2)**
8 rue du Chateau d'Eau, 3364, Leudelange, Luxembourg
Tel.: (352) 2901901
Web Site: http://www.baloise.lu
Emp.: 370
General Insurance Services
N.A.I.C.S.: 524210
Braas Romain *(CEO)*

Baloise Bank SoBa   **(1)**
Amthausplatz 4, PO Box 262, 4502, Solothurn, Switzerland
Tel.: (41) 848800806
Web Site: http://www.baloise.ch
Sales Range: $100-124.9 Million
Emp.: 220
Banking & Financial Support Services
N.A.I.C.S.: 522110

Baloise Belgium SA   **(1)**
Posthofbrug 16, 2600, Antwerp, Belgium
Tel.: (32) 3 247 21 11
Web Site: http://www.baloise.be
Emp.: 1,362
Life Insurance Carrier
N.A.I.C.S.: 524113
Christophe Hamal *(CEO)*

Subsidiary (Domestic):

Amazon Insurance nv   **(2)**
City Link, Posthofbrug 14, 2600, Antwerp, Belgium
Tel.: (32) 32 47 23 80
Web Site: http://www.amazon.be
General Insurance Services
N.A.I.C.S.: 524210

Baloise Belgium SA - Brussel   **(2)**
Koning Albert II-laan 19, 1210, Brussels, Belgium
Tel.: (32) 27730311
Web Site: http://www.baloise.be
Property & Casualty Insurance Services
N.A.I.C.S.: 524298
Chris Staes *(Mng Dir)*

Baloise Delta Holding S.a.r.l.   **(1)**
Rue Du Puits Romain 23, 8070, Strassen, Luxembourg
Tel.: (352) 2901901
Investment Management Service
N.A.I.C.S.: 523999

Baloise Fund Invest   **(1)**
Lautengartenstrasse 6, PO Box 2275, 4002, Basel, Switzerland
Tel.: (41) 612857032
Web Site: http://www.baloise.ch
Financial Investment Services
N.A.I.C.S.: 523999

Baloise Fund Invest Advico   **(1)**
Rue Emile Bian 1, Luxembourg, 1235, Luxembourg
Tel.: (352) 2901901
Investment Management Service
N.A.I.C.S.: 523999

Baloise Insurance Company (I.O.M.) Ltd.   **(1)**
3 Fl IOMA House, Hope St, Douglas, IM1 1AP, Isle of Man   **(100%)**
Sales Range: $50-74.9 Million
Emp.: 10
Reinsurance
N.A.I.C.S.: 524130

Baloise Lebensversicherung AG   **(1)**
Ludwig-Erhard-Strasse 22, 20459, Hamburg, Germany
Tel.: (49) 4035997711
Life Insurance Agencies Services
N.A.I.C.S.: 524210

Baloise Life (Liechtenstein) AG   **(1)**
Alte Landstrasse 6, Balzers, 9496, Liechtenstein
Tel.: (423) 3889000
Web Site: http://www.baloise-life.com
Emp.: 25
Insurance Services
N.A.I.C.S.: 524298

Baloise Life Ltd.   **(1)**
Aeschengraben 21, PO Box 2275, 4002, Basel, Switzerland
Tel.: (41) 582852828
N.A.I.C.S.: 524113

Baloise Sachversicherung AG   **(1)**
Basler Strasse 4, 61352, Bad Homburg, Germany
Tel.: (49) 61721254600
Life Insurance Agencies Services
N.A.I.C.S.: 524210

Basler Versicherungs-Gesellschaft   **(1)**
Aeschengraben 21, 4051, Basel, Switzerland   **(100%)**
Tel.: (41) 582852828
Web Site: http://www.baloise.ch
Sales Range: $1-4.9 Billion
Emp.: 3,300
Non-Life Insurance Services
N.A.I.C.S.: 524298

Basler Versicherungs-Gesellschaft   **(1)**
Basler Strasse 4, 61352, Bad Homburg, Germany   **(100%)**
Tel.: (49) 61721254600
Web Site: http://www.basler.de
Sales Range: $800-899.9 Million
Emp.: 1,300
Life Insurance
N.A.I.C.S.: 524113

Subsidiary (Domestic):

Avetas Versicherungs-Aktiengesellschaft   **(2)**
Postfach 11 53, 61281, Bad Homburg, Germany
Tel.: (49) 1803181851
Automotive & Accidental Insurance Services
N.A.I.C.S.: 524113

Basler Lebensversicherungs-AG   **(2)**
Ludwig Erhard Strasse 22, 20459, Hamburg, 22797, Germany
Tel.: (49) 4035997711
Web Site: http://www.basler.de
Sales Range: $1-4.9 Billion
Emp.: 1,900
Life Insurance & Pension Products & Services
N.A.I.C.S.: 524113

Basler Securitas Versicherungs-Aktiengesellschaft   **(2)**
Basler Strasse 4, 61352, Bad Homburg, Germany

Tel.: (49) 61721254600
Web Site: https://www.baloise.de
Non-Life Insurance Services
N.A.I.C.S.: 524298

Deutscher Ring Beteiligungsholding GmbH   **(2)**
Ludwig Erhard Strasse 22, 20459, Hamburg, Germany
Tel.: (49) 4035990
Web Site: http://www.basler.de
Investment Management Service
N.A.I.C.S.: 523999
Frank Grund *(Gen Mgr)*

Deutsche Niederlassung der Friday Insurance S.A.   **(1)**
Friedrichstrasse 70, 10117, Berlin, Germany
Tel.: (49) 30959983200
Web Site: https://www.friday.de
Car & Household Insurance Services
N.A.I.C.S.: 524298

Deutscher Ring Financial Services GmbH   **(1)**
Ludwig-Erhard-Strasse 22, Hamburg, 22797, Germany
Tel.: (49) 4035993020
Web Site: http://www.desler.de
Financial Management Services
N.A.I.C.S.: 523999

Deutscher Ring Sachversicherungs-AG   **(1)**
Ludwig Erhard Strasse 22, D 20459, Hamburg, Germany   **(100%)**
Tel.: (49) 4035990
Web Site: http://www.deutscherring.de
Sales Range: $800-899.9 Million
Emp.: 1,600
Property Insurance Products & Services
N.A.I.C.S.: 524126

Euromex N.V.   **(1)**
Generaal Lemanstraat 82-92, 2600, Berchem, Antwerp, Belgium   **(100%)**
Tel.: (32) 34514400
Web Site: http://www.euromex.be
Sales Range: $10-24.9 Million
Emp.: 120
Non-Life Insurance
N.A.I.C.S.: 524128
Rob Vromen *(CEO)*

Fidea NV   **(1)**
Van Eycklei 14, 2018, Antwerp, Belgium
Tel.: (32) 32038511
Web Site: http://www.fidea.be
Rev.: $364,964,330
Assets: $3,140,191,804
Liabilities: $2,649,199,990
Net Worth: $490,991,814
Earnings: $19,673,721
Emp.: 360
Fiscal Year-end: 12/31/2017
Insurance Services
N.A.I.C.S.: 524298
Edwin Schellens *(CEO)*

GROCON Erste Grundstucksgesellschaft mbH   **(1)**
Ludwig Erhard Strasse 22, 20459, Hamburg, Germany
Tel.: (49) 40 35992874
Property Management Services
N.A.I.C.S.: 531312

PAX ANLAGE AG   **(1)**
Aeschengraben 21, Basel, 4051, Switzerland   **(70.96%)**
Tel.: (41) 582858329
Web Site: http://www.artires.ch
Real Estate Development Services
N.A.I.C.S.: 531390
Urs Bienz *(CEO)*

ROLAND Rechtsschutz Beteiligungs GmbH   **(1)**
Deutz-Kalker Strasse 46, 50679, Cologne, Germany   **(60%)**
Tel.: (49) 2218277500
Holding Company
N.A.I.C.S.: 551112

BALRAMPUR CHINI MILLS LIMITED
FMC Fortuna 2nd floor 234/3A AJC Bose Road, Kolkata, 700 020, India

Tel.: (91) 3322874749
Web Site: https://www.chini.com
Year Founded: 1965
500038—(BOM)
Rev.: $665,989,274
Assets: $613,148,309
Liabilities: $235,082,416
Net Worth: $378,065,893
Earnings: $63,422,746
Emp.: 6,350
Fiscal Year-end: 03/31/22
Sugar, Molasses, Alcohol, Bagasse, Power & Organic Manure Mfr
N.A.I.C.S.: 311314
Vivek Saraogi *(Mng Dir)*

Subsidiaries:

Balrampur Overseas Pvt. Ltd.   **(1)**
FMC Fortuna 234 3A, A J C Bose Rd, Kolkata, 700020, India
Tel.: (91) 3322874749
Web Site: http://www.chini.in
Sales Range: $25-49.9 Million
Emp.: 100
Sugar Mfr
N.A.I.C.S.: 311313
Vivek I Saraog *(Mng Dir)*

BALS CORPORATION
5-53-67 Jingumae, Shibuya-ku, Tokyo, 1500001, Japan
Tel.: (81) 354597500
Sales Range: $350-399.9 Million
Emp.: 588
Interior Designer
N.A.I.C.S.: 541410
Fumio Takashima *(Pres & CEO)*

Subsidiaries:

BALS Hong Kong Limited   **(1)**
Shop 1032 Elements 1 Austin Rd W, Kowloon, China (Hong Kong)
Tel.: (852) 23021961
Web Site: http://www.balseokyo.com
Sales Range: $25-49.9 Million
Emp.: 20
Interior Goods Mfr
N.A.I.C.S.: 337212

REALFLEET Co., Ltd.   **(1)**
Cosmos Aoyama B1F 5-53-67 Jingumae, Shibuya-ku, Tokyo, 150-0001, Japan
Tel.: (81) 357740641
Web Site: http://www.realfleet.co.jp
Home & Electrical Appliances Whslr
N.A.I.C.S.: 423620

BALTA GROUP NV
Wakkensteenweg 2, St-Baafs-Vijve, 8710, Wielsbeke, Belgium
Tel.: (32) 56622211
Web Site:
    https://www.baltagroup.com
Year Founded: 1964
BALTA—(EUR)
Rev.: $690,065,764
Assets: $986,968,219
Liabilities: $708,809,935
Net Worth: $278,158,285
Earnings: ($15,457,400)
Emp.: 3,838
Fiscal Year-end: 12/31/20
Textile Floor Covering Distr
N.A.I.C.S.: 449121
Cyrille Ragoucy *(Chm & CEO)*

Subsidiaries:

Balta Floorcovering Yer Das, emeleri San.ve Tic A.S.   **(1)**
Cadde No 563, Organized Industrial Zone 123, 64100, Usak, Turkiye
Tel.: (90) 276 266 7025
Web Site:
    https://www.floorcovering.balta.com.tr
Woven Carpet Machinery Mfr
N.A.I.C.S.: 314110

Balta Floorcovering Yer Dos, emeleri San.ve Tic A.S.   **(1)**
Organize Sanayi Bolgesi 123 Cadde No 563, 64100, Usak, Turkiye

Balta Group NV—(Continued)

Tel.: (90) 2762667025
Web Site: http://floorcovering.balta.com.tr
Home Furnishing & Houseware Mfr
N.A.I.C.S.: 337122
Ceylan Eroglu *(Mgr-Health Safety Environmental)*

Balta Orient Tekstil Sanayi Ve Ticaret **(1)**
A.S.
Organize Sanayi Bolgesi 109 Cadde No 351, 64100, Usak, Türkiye
Tel.: (90) 2762667740
Web Site: http://orient.balta.com.tr
Home Furnishing & Houseware Mfr
N.A.I.C.S.: 337122

Balta Oudenaarde NV **(1)**
Industriepark De Bruwaan 4, 9700, Oudenaarde, Belgium
Tel.: (32) 55335211
Web Site: http://www.captiqs.com
Technical Non-Woven Product Mfr
N.A.I.C.S.: 313230

Balta USA, Inc. **(1)**
6739 New Calhoun Hwy Bld Ste 100, Rome, GA 30161
Tel.: (706) 278-8008
Home Furnishing & Houseware Mfr
N.A.I.C.S.: 337122
Hans Fossez *(Pres)*

Modulyss NV **(1)**
Zevensterrestraat 21, 9240, Zele, Belgium
Tel.: (32) 52808080
Web Site: http://www.modulyss.com
Carpet Tile Mfr
N.A.I.C.S.: 314110
Kristof Weyn *(Mgr-Logistics)*

BALTCAP AS
Tartu mnt 2, 10145, Tallinn, Estonia
Tel.: (372) 665 0280
Web Site: http://www.baltcap.com
Year Founded: 1995
Emp.: 28
Privater Equity Firm
N.A.I.C.S.: 523999
Peeter Saks *(Mng Partner)*

BALTEC MASCHINENBAU AG
Obermattstrasse 65, 8330, Pfaffikon, Switzerland
Tel.: (41) 44 953 13 33
Web Site: http://www.baltec.com
Year Founded: 1983
Sales Range: $10-24.9 Million
Emp.: 50
Riveting Machines Mfr & Distr
N.A.I.C.S.: 333517
Walter Graenicher *(Chm)*

Subsidiaries:

BalTec (UK) Ltd. **(1)**
BalTec House Unit 1 Heron Industrial Estate Basingstoke Road, Spencers Wood, Reading, RG7 1PJ, Berkshire, United Kingdom **(100%)**
Tel.: (44) 118 9311191
Web Site: http://www.baltec.co.uk
Emp.: 10
Riveting Machine Distr
N.A.I.C.S.: 423830
Dave Abbott *(Gen Mgr-Sls)*

BalTec Corporation **(1)**
121 Hillpointe Dr Ste 900, Canonsburg, PA 15317-9563 **(100%)**
Tel.: (724) 873-5757
Web Site: http://www.baltecorporation.com
Riveting Machine Distr
N.A.I.C.S.: 423830

BALTIC BRIDGE S.A.
Ul Marszalkowska 89, 00-693, Warsaw, Poland
Tel.: (48) 221166666
Web Site: http://www.wi.pl
Sales Range: $75-99.9 Million
Emp.: 160

Investment Holding Company; Information, Communication Technology & Telecommunications Services
N.A.I.C.S.: 551112
Leszek Wisniewski *(CEO)*

BALTIC CLASSIFIEDS GROUP PLC
Saltoniskiu St 9b, 00105, Vilnius, Lithuania
Tel.: (370) 52075061 UK
Web Site:
    https://www.balticclassifieds.com
Year Founded: 2021
BCG—(LSE)
Rev.: $65,631,340
Assets: $450,856,896
Liabilities: $91,854,090
Net Worth: $359,002,806
Earnings: $25,053,961
Emp.: 131
Fiscal Year-end: 04/30/23
Real Estate Development Services
N.A.I.C.S.: 531190
Justinas Simkus *(CEO)*

BALTIC I ACQUISITION CORP.
25th Floor 700 West Georgia St, Vancouver, V7Y 1B3, BC, Canada
Tel.: (604) 363-7742 BC
Year Founded: 2018
BLTC.P—(TSXV)
Assets: $204,439
Liabilities: $126,452
Net Worth: $77,987
Earnings: ($20,597)
Fiscal Year-end: 12/31/23
Business Consulting Services
N.A.I.C.S.: 522299
Harry Pokrandt *(CEO)*

BALTIC INVESTMENT BANK PJSC
Ul Divenskaya 1 Gorkovskaya Street, 197101, Saint Petersburg, Russia
Tel.: (7) 8123261326
Web Site:
    http://www.baltinvestbank.com
Year Founded: 1994
Sales Range: Less than $1 Million
Mortgage Banking Services
N.A.I.C.S.: 522292

BALTIC REEFERS LTD.
Vvendenskaya St 7, Saint Petersburg, Russia
Tel.: (7) 812 380 67 07
Web Site: http://www.baltic-reefers.com
Shipping Services
N.A.I.C.S.: 483111

Subsidiaries:

Cool Carriers AB **(1)**
Katarinavagen 17, 116 45, Stockholm, Sweden
Tel.: (46) 8 753 90 00
Web Site: http://www.cool.se
Sales Range: $25-49.9 Million
Emp.: 23
Marine Freight Transportation Services; Logistics Services for Perishable Cargo; Cold Storage Facilities
N.A.I.C.S.: 483111
Boris Gersling *(CEO)*

Subsidiary (Non-US):

Cool Carriers Chile S.A. **(2)**
Avda Errazuriz 755 Of 605-A, Valparaiso, Chile
Tel.: (56) 32 3815 000
Web Site: http://www.cool.se
Marine Freight Transportation Services; Logistics Services for Perishable Cargo; Cold Storage Facilities
N.A.I.C.S.: 483111
Ricardo Barckhahn *(Mng Dir)*

Cool Carriers New Zealand Ltd **(2)**

56A Maskell Street, St Heliers, Auckland, 1071, New Zealand
Tel.: (64) 21 422321
Web Site: http://www.cool.se
Marine Freight Transportation Services; Logistics Services for Perishable Cargo; Cold Storage Facilities
N.A.I.C.S.: 483111
Lesley Sloper *(Mgr-Transport Mgmt Svcs)*

Subsidiary (US):

Cool Carriers USA Inc. **(2)**
319 Ponoma Rd, Port Hueneme, CA 93041
Tel.: (805) 488-1222
Web Site: http://www.cool.se
Sales Range: $25-49.9 Million
Emp.: 3
Marine Freight Transportation Services; Logistics Services for Perishable Cargo; Cold Storage Facilities
N.A.I.C.S.: 483111

BALTIC SEA PROPERTIES AS
Apotekergata 10, 180, Oslo, Norway
Tel.: (47) 93094319
Web Site: https://www.balticsea.no
BALT—(OSL)
Rev.: $9,437,399
Assets: $118,180,963
Liabilities: $73,937,617
Net Worth: $44,243,346
Earnings: $2,847,706
Emp.: 16
Fiscal Year-end: 12/31/23
Real Estate Manangement Services
N.A.I.C.S.: 531210

BALTIC TELEKOM AS
Rupniecibas iela 1-5, Riga, LV-1010, Latvia
Tel.: (371) 67783611
BTE1R—(RSE)
Telecommunication Servicesb
N.A.I.C.S.: 517810
Janis Mellups *(Chm)*

BALTICON SA
ul Tadeusza Wendy 15, 81-341, Gdynia, Poland
Tel.: (48) 586630079
Web Site: https://www.balticon.pl
Year Founded: 1991
Emp.: 280
Containers Handling Services
N.A.I.C.S.: 488320
Katarzyna Lysak *(Sec)*

BALTO RESOURCES LTD.
600 850 West Hastings St, Vancouver, V6C 1E1, BC, Canada
Tel.: (604) 662-8130 BC
Year Founded: 1973
BAL.H—(TSXV)
Assets: $76,143
Liabilities: $2,327,419
Net Worth: ($2,251,275)
Earnings: ($437,101)
Fiscal Year-end: 03/31/23
Metal Ore Mining Services
N.A.I.C.S.: 212290
Danielle Alleyn *(CFO)*

BALU FORGE INDUSTRIES LTD.
506 Imperial Palace 45 Telly Park Road, Andheri E, Mumbai, 400069, Maharashtra, India
Tel.: (91) 26839916
Web Site:
    https://www.baluindustries.com
Year Founded: 1989
531112—(BOM)
Rev.: $40,213,637
Assets: $38,825,214
Liabilities: $17,172,574
Net Worth: $21,652,640
Earnings: $4,073,747
Emp.: 119

Fiscal Year-end: 03/31/22
Information Technology Business
N.A.I.C.S.: 541512
Yatin Hasmukhbhai Mehta *(Mng Dir & Officer-Compliance)*

BALUCHISTAN WHEELS LIMITED
1st Floor State Life Building 3 Di Ziauddin Ahmed Road, Karachi, Pakistan
Tel.: (92) 2135689259
Web Site: http://www.bwheels.com
Year Founded: 1980
BWHL—(PSX)
Rev.: $6,028,902
Assets: $8,481,594
Liabilities: $1,085,230
Net Worth: $7,396,364
Earnings: $490,721
Emp.: 207
Fiscal Year-end: 06/30/23
Automobile Steel Wheel Mfr
N.A.I.C.S.: 336390
Razak H. M. Bengali *(CEO & Mng Dir)*

BALURGHAT TECHNOLOGIES LTD.
170/2C Acharya Jagdish Chandra Bose Rd, Kolkata, 700014, West Bengal, India
Tel.: (91) 8022290289
Web Site: https://www.balurghat.co.in
Year Founded: 1952
520127—(BOM)
Rev.: $12,646,859
Assets: $4,255,322
Liabilities: $2,810,639
Net Worth: $1,444,683
Earnings: ($124,088)
Emp.: 46
Fiscal Year-end: 03/31/21
Transportation Services
N.A.I.C.S.: 488999
Pawan Kumar Sethia *(Mng Dir)*

BALVER ZINN JOSEF JOST GMBH & CO. KG
Blintroper Weg 11, 58802, Balve, Germany
Tel.: (49) 23759150
Web Site: http://www.balverzinn.com
Year Founded: 1976
Rev.: $26,132,956
Emp.: 100
Electronic Components Mfr
N.A.I.C.S.: 334419
Josef Jost *(Dir-Comml Mgmt)*

Subsidiaries:

Cobar Europe B.V. **(1)**
Aluminiumstraat 2, Breda, Netherlands
Tel.: (31) 765445566
Electronic Parts Distr
N.A.I.C.S.: 423690
Manfred Bult *(Mng Dir & COO)*

BALWIN PROPERTIES LIMITED
105 Corlett Drive, Melrose, Johannesburg, South Africa
Tel.: (27) 114502818
Web Site: https://www.balwin.co.za
Year Founded: 1996
BWN—(JSE)
Rev.: $128,323,227
Assets: $415,548,698
Liabilities: $197,215,835
Net Worth: $218,332,863
Earnings: $11,838,079
Emp.: 325
Fiscal Year-end: 02/29/24
Real Estate Manangement Services
N.A.I.C.S.: 531390
Jonathan Weltman *(CFO)*

BALYO SA
74 Avenue Vladimir Ilitch Lenine,
94110, Arcueil, France
Tel.: (33) 155264310
Web Site: http://www.balyo.com
Year Founded: 2004
BALYO—(EUR)
Sales Range: $25-49.9 Million
Industrial Robot Mfr & Distr
N.A.I.C.S.: 334513
Pascal Rialland *(CEO)*

Subsidiaries:

Balyo Apac Pte Ltd (1)
76C Duxton Road, Singapore, Singapore
Tel.: (65) 88625218
Industrial Machinery Products Mfr
N.A.I.C.S.: 333998

Balyo Inc. (1)
78 B-Olympia Ave, Woburn, MA 01801
Tel.: (781) 281-7957
Industrial Machinery Products Mfr
N.A.I.C.S.: 333998

BALZAC CARAVANES
Ratarieux Rn 82, 42580, L'Etrat,
Loire, France
Tel.: (33) 477740424
Web Site: http://balzaccaravanes.fr
Sales Range: $10-24.9 Million
Emp.: 14
Car Rental Services
N.A.I.C.S.: 532111
Gilbert Goubatian *(Gen Mgr)*

BALZER'S CANADA INC.
North Service Road Emerald Park,
Regina, S4L 1B6, SK, Canada
Tel.: (306) 781-2400
Web Site:
http://www.balzerscanada.com
Year Founded: 1937
Rev.: $59,700,000
Emp.: 350
Industrial & commercial Building Con-
structionWaste Water & Themal
Power Plant Construction
N.A.I.C.S.: 236210
C. H. Balzer *(Founder)*

BAM STRATEGY
420 McGill Ste 400, Montreal, H2Y
2G1, QC, Canada
Tel.: (514) 875-1500 QC
Web Site:
http://www.bamstrategy.com
Year Founded: 1996
Sales Range: $10-24.9 Million
Emp.: 70
Advetising Agency
N.A.I.C.S.: 541810
Chris Emergui *(Pres)*

BAMA COMPANY
Bama Complex-Baharan City-
Kelishad-Zobeahan Express Way, PO
Box 81785-363, 81747-54754, Isfa-
han, Iran
Tel.: (98) 3117252743
Web Site: http://www.bamaco.ir
Year Founded: 1951
BAMA—(THE)
Sales Range: Less than $1 Million
Lead & Zinc Ore Mining Services
N.A.I.C.S.: 212230

BAMA GRUPPEN AS
Nedre Kalbakkvei 40, PO Box 263Al-
nabru, Oslo, 0614, Alnabru, Norway
Tel.: (47) 22880500
Web Site: http://www.bama.no
Food Manufacturing
N.A.I.C.S.: 311999
Rune Flaen *(CEO)*

Subsidiaries:

Saba Fresh Cuts AB (1)

Torbornavagen 13 B, Helsingborg, 25015,
Sweden
Tel.: (46) 42 24 96 00
Web Site: http://www.saba.se
Sales Range: $25-49.9 Million
Emp.: 150
Vegetable Salad Mfr
N.A.I.C.S.: 311991
Stefan Grahn *(Mng Dir)*

BAMBERGER KALIKO GMBH
Kronacher Strasse 59, Bamberg,
96052, Germany
Tel.: (49) 95140990 De
Web Site: http://www.bamberger-
kaliko.com
Year Founded: 1963
Sales Range: $25-49.9 Million
Emp.: 175
Mfr of Industrial Textile Products
N.A.I.C.S.: 313210
Bert Krieger *(Chief Comml Officer)*

BAMBI-BANAT AD
Djure Djakovica bb, 12000, Pozare-
vac, Serbia
Tel.: (381) 12539800
Web Site: http://ukusnidani.bambi.rs
Year Founded: 1967
Snack Food Mfr
N.A.I.C.S.: 311919

BAMBINO AGRO INDUSTRIES LIMITED
4E Surya Towers Sardar Patel Road,
Secunderabad, 500 003, Telangana,
India
Tel.: (91) 4044363322 In
Web Site: https://bambinoagro.com
Year Founded: 1982
519295—(BOM)
Rev.: $35,168,070
Assets: $26,199,984
Liabilities: $15,871,877
Net Worth: $10,328,107
Earnings: $1,208,341
Emp.: 294
Fiscal Year-end: 03/31/22
Food Products Mfr
N.A.I.C.S.: 311999
Ritu Tiwary *(Compliance Officer &
Sec-Legal)*

BAMBOO CAPITAL JSC
27C Quoc Huong Street, Thao Dien
Ward Thu Duc City, Ho Chi Minh
City, Vietnam
Tel.: (84) 2862680680
Web Site:
https://www.bamboocap.com.vn
Year Founded: 2011
BCG—(HNX)
Building Construction Services
N.A.I.C.S.: 236210
Nguyen Ho Nam *(Chm & CEO)*

BAMBOOS HEALTH CARE HOLDINGS LIMITED
4/F Star House 3 Salisbury Road,
Tsim Sha Tsui, Kowloon, China (Hong
Kong)
Tel.: (852) 25755893
Web Site:
http://www.bamboos.com.hk
2293—(HKG)
Rev.: $18,095,249
Assets: $45,316,994
Liabilities: $18,153,419
Net Worth: $27,163,575
Earnings: $7,560,808
Emp.: 67
Fiscal Year-end: 06/30/22
Healthcare Staffing Services
N.A.I.C.S.: 561311
Hiu Chu Hai *(Chm & CEO)*

Subsidiaries:

Bamboos Education- School for Tal-
ents Limited (1)
15/F Bamboos Centre 52 Hung To Road,
Kwun Tong, China (Hong Kong)
Tel.: (852) 25755689
Web Site: https://bamboos.com.hk
Healthcare Training Services
N.A.I.C.S.: 611519

Bamboos Professional Nursing Ser-
vices Limited (1)
Room 204 2/F Wing On Plaza 62 Mody
Road, Tsim Sha Tsui, Kowloon, China
(Hong Kong)
Tel.: (852) 25755893
Web Site: https://www.bamboos.com.hk
Emp.: 27,000
Healthcare Staffing Services
N.A.I.C.S.: 621610
Hai Hiu Chu *(Chm & CEO)*

Garden Medical Centre Limited (1)
Room 204 2/F Wing On Plaza 62 Mody
Road, Tsim Sha Tsui, Kowloon, China
(Hong Kong)
Tel.: (852) 21539989
Web Site: https://www.gardenclinic.com.hk
Aesthetic Medicine Services
N.A.I.C.S.: 541219

BAMBU AG
Lowenstrasse 16, Postfach 1031,
8280, Kreuzlingen, Switzerland
Tel.: (41) 718883288
Web Site: http://www.bambu-ag.ch
Financial Advisory Services
N.A.I.C.S.: 523940

BAMBUSER AB
Malmskillnadsgatan 13, 111 57,
Stockholm, Sweden
Tel.: (46) 768822502
Web Site: https://bambuser.com
Year Founded: 2007
BUSER—(OMX)
Rev.: $18,709,671
Assets: $37,165,208
Liabilities: $5,510,553
Net Worth: $31,654,655
Earnings: ($27,637,144)
Emp.: 102
Fiscal Year-end: 12/31/23
Internet Broadcasting Services
N.A.I.C.S.: 516210
Maryam Ghahremani *(CEO)*

BAMCARD D.D.
Trg heroja 10 / II, 71000, Sarajevo,
Bosnia & Herzegovina
Tel.: (387) 3 365 2888
Web Site: http://www.bamcard.ba
Year Founded: 1999
BMCDRK2—(SARE)
Rev.: $1,579,663
Assets: $3,225,931
Liabilities: $153,348
Net Worth: $3,072,584
Earnings: $275,191
Emp.: 27
Fiscal Year-end: 12/31/20
Banking Card Issuing Services
N.A.I.C.S.: 522210

BAMESA ACEROS
Angli 92, Barcelona, 8017, Spain
Tel.: (34) 932541950
Web Site: http://www.bamesa.com
Year Founded: 1962
Sales Range: $75-99.9 Million
Emp.: 500
Steel Services
N.A.I.C.S.: 331221
Alejandro Quintanilla Cornudella
(Chm)

Subsidiaries:

Aceros Chapa Industrial S.L. (1)
Poligono Cantarranas, Pancorbo, 09280,

Burgos, Spain
Tel.: (34) 947 347 500
Steel Products Mfr
N.A.I.C.S.: 332111

Aceros Chapa Industrial, S.L. (1)
Estrada do Poceirao - Palmela Gare, 2950-
951, Palmela, Portugal
Tel.: (351) 1 233 02 68
Steel Product Distr
N.A.I.C.S.: 423510

Bamesa Celik A.S. (1)
Karadenizliler Mah Basyigit Cad No 202,
Kullar-Basiskele, Kocaeli, Kocaeli, Turkiye
Tel.: (90) 262 349 38 51
Steel Product Distr
N.A.I.C.S.: 423510

Bamesa Celik Muradiye Demir
Sanayi ve Ticaret (1)
Muradiye Sanayi Bolgesi Inonu Mah Dr
Orhan Aksoy Cad No 24, Muradiye, Manisa,
Turkiye
Tel.: (90) 236 214 00 54
Steel Product Distr
N.A.I.C.S.: 423510

Bamesa Celik Servis S.V.T.A.S. (1)
Umurbey Sanayi Bolgesi Yalova Yolu 3 Km,
Umurbey Gemlik, 16600, Bursa, Turkiye
Tel.: (90) 224 513 35 85
Steel Product Distr
N.A.I.C.S.: 423510

Bamesa France, S.A. (1)
8-10 Route de Stains, 94381, Bonneuil-sur-
Marne, Cedex, France
Tel.: (33) 1 45 13 44 20
Steel Product Distr
N.A.I.C.S.: 423510

Bamesa Otel, S.A. (1)
Str Depozitelor Nr 2 cod, 115500, Topolo-
veni, Judetul Arges, Romania
Tel.: (40) 372 487 800
Web Site: http://www.bamesa.com
Emp.: 100
Steel Product Distr
N.A.I.C.S.: 423510
Gabriel Gahete *(Gen Mgr)*

Barcelonesa de Metales, S.A. (1)
Poligono Cal Alayo Ronda Ponent 14, El
Prat de Llobregat, 08820, Barcelona, Spain
Tel.: (34) 934 792 990
Steel Products Mfr
N.A.I.C.S.: 332111

BAMPSL SECURITIES LIMITED
100-A Cycle Market Jhandewalan
Extension, New Delhi, 110 055, India
Tel.: (91) 1123556436 In
Web Site:
https://www.bampslsecurities.co.in
Year Founded: 1995
531591—(BOM)
Rev.: $75,130
Assets: $5,094,058
Liabilities: $33,198
Net Worth: $5,060,860
Earnings: $2,717
Fiscal Year-end: 03/31/21
Financial Investment Services
N.A.I.C.S.: 523999
Bhisham Kumar Gupta *(Mng Dir)*

BAN LEONG TECHNOLOGIES LIMITED
150 Ubi Avenue 4 Ubi BizHub 0401,
Singapore, 408825, Singapore
Tel.: (65) 65129221
Web Site:
https://www.banleong.com.sg
B26—(SES)
Rev.: $150,956,814
Assets: $58,619,674
Liabilities: $25,568,691
Net Worth: $33,050,983
Earnings: $4,496,937
Emp.: 5,000
Fiscal Year-end: 03/31/23
Computer Peripheral Distr
N.A.I.C.S.: 423430
You Hong Tan *(Deputy Mng Dir)*

Ban Leong Technologies Limited—(Continued)

Subsidiaries:

Ban Leong Chin Inter Co., Ltd. **(1)**
534 Soi Preeyanuch Rama 9 Road,
Bangkapi Huaykwang, Bangkok, 10310,
Thailand
Tel.: (66) 23144143
Web Site: http://www.chininter.co.th
Electronic Product Distr
N.A.I.C.S.: 423690
Artit Thonapan *(Product Mgr)*

Ban Leong Technologies Sdn
Bhd **(1)**
3 02 Level 3 Wisma Academy 4A Jalan
19/1, Petaling Jaya, 46300, Selangor, Ma-
laysia
Tel.: (60) 3 79566300
Computer Peripheral Equipment Distr
N.A.I.C.S.: 423430
Wang Chinchin *(Gen Mgr)*

Cooler Master Technology Inc. **(1)**
7F No 398 Xinhu 1st Rd, Neihu Dist, Taipei,
114065, Taiwan
Tel.: (886) 222253517
Web Site: https://www.coolermaster.com
Software Product Mfr & Distr
N.A.I.C.S.: 334419

Digital Hub Pte Ltd **(1)**
No 150 Ubi Avenue 4 Level 4, Singapore,
408825, Singapore
Tel.: (65) 6512 9206
Web Site: http://www.digitalhub.com.sg
Multimedia Equipment & Accessories Distr
N.A.I.C.S.: 423430
Dennin AP *(Mgr-Bus)*

Hotway Technology Corporation **(1)**
3F-4 No81 Sec 1 Xin-tai 5th Road, Xizhi
Dist, New Taipei City, 22101, Taiwan
Tel.: (886) 226980818
Web Site: https://www.hotway.com.tw
Computer Peripheral Equipment Mfr
N.A.I.C.S.: 334118

ScreenBeam Inc. **(1)**
220 Devcon Dr, San Jose, CA 95112
Tel.: (408) 752-7700
Web Site: https://www.screenbeam.com
Wireless Modem & Router Distr
N.A.I.C.S.: 423690

TP-Link Corporation Limited **(1)**
No 150 Ubi Avenue 4 04-01, Singapore,
408825, Singapore
Tel.: (65) 65129250
Web Site: https://www.tp-link.com
Networking Device Distr
N.A.I.C.S.: 423410

BAN LOONG HOLDINGS LTD.
Room 2709-10 27/F China Re-
sources Building, No 26 Harbour
Road, Wanchai, China (Hong Kong)
Tel.: (852) 2 710 0333
Web Site: http://www.0030hk.com
0030—(HKG)
Rev.: $156,931,819
Assets: $186,067,105
Liabilities: $76,165,938
Net Worth: $109,901,167
Earnings: $1,703,858
Emp.: 33
Fiscal Year-end: 03/31/21
Mobile Communications Services
N.A.I.C.S.: 334220
Wang Chow *(Deputy Chm & CEO)*

**BANADER HOTELS COMPANY
BSC**
Flat 52 building 1006 Road 2813
Block 428, PO Box 2474, Manama,
Bahrain
Tel.: (973) 17200064
Web Site: http://banaderhotels.com
BANADER—(BAH)
Rev.: $7,343,161
Assets: $86,769,653
Liabilities: $59,419,525
Net Worth: $27,350,129
Earnings: ($6,296,424)

Emp.: 3
Fiscal Year-end: 12/31/22
Hotel Operator
N.A.I.C.S.: 721110
Abdulla Hasan Buhindi *(Chm)*

BANARAS BEADS LIMITED
A-1 Industrial Estate, Varanasi,
221106, India
Tel.: (91) 5422370161
Web Site:
https://www.banarasbead.com
Year Founded: 1940
526849—(BOM)
Rev.: $2,995,879
Assets: $7,656,750
Liabilities: $825,648
Net Worth: $6,831,102
Earnings: $326,635
Emp.: 257
Fiscal Year-end: 03/31/21
Glass Beads Mfr & Distr
N.A.I.C.S.: 339910
Ashok Kumar Gupta *(Chm & Mng
Dir)*

BANAS FINANCE LIMITED
E109 Crystal Plaza New Link Road
Opp Infinity Mall, Andheri W, Mumbai,
400 053, India
Tel.: (91) 9152096140
Web Site:
https://www.banasfinance.com
Year Founded: 1983
509053—(BOM)
Rev.: $1,975,140
Assets: $14,232,751
Liabilities: $1,540,647
Net Worth: $12,692,104
Earnings: $1,591,462
Emp.: 23
Fiscal Year-end: 03/31/21
Share Trading Services
N.A.I.C.S.: 523150
Amit Gulecha *(Mng Dir)*

BANAT ESTIVAL 2002 SA
Str Plopilor nr 16B, Neptun Municipiul
Mangalia, Constanta, Romania
Tel.: (40) 241491073
BNAT—(BUC)
Rev.: $73,258
Assets: $792,058
Liabilities: $398,905
Net Worth: $393,152
Earnings: $23,951
Emp.: 1
Fiscal Year-end: 12/31/20
Accommodation Services
N.A.I.C.S.: 721110

BANATSKI DESPOTOVAC A.D.
trg Dusana Cubica 1, 23242,
Banatski Despotovac, Serbia
Tel.: (381) 23 3879 013
Web Site:
http://www.bdespotovac.co.rs
Year Founded: 1946
Sales Range: $1-9.9 Million
Emp.: 41
Cereal Crop Farming Services
N.A.I.C.S.: 111998

BANBAO CO., LTD.
Block 13-09 Jinyuan Industry Area
Chaoshan Road, Shantou, Guang-
dong, China
Tel.: (86) 13502955331
Web Site:
https://www.banbaoglobal.com
Year Founded: 2003
603398—(SHG)
Rev.: $132,582,893
Assets: $446,050,252
Liabilities: $345,511,666
Net Worth: $100,538,587
Earnings: ($32,118,199)

Fiscal Year-end: 12/31/22
Educational Toy Mfr & Distr
N.A.I.C.S.: 339930

BANCA CARIGE S.P.A.
Via Cassa Di Risparmio 15, 16100,
Genoa, Italy
Tel.: (39) 0105791   **IT**
Web Site: http://www.gruppocarige.it
Banking & Insurance Services
N.A.I.C.S.: 522110
Giuseppe Bocuzzi *(Pres)*

Subsidiaries:

Carige Reoco SpA **(1)**
Via del Colle 95R, 16128, Genoa, Italy
Tel.: (39) 0105795106
Web Site: https://www.carigereoco.it
Building Construction Services
N.A.I.C.S.: 236220

**BANCA CENTRALE DELLA
REPUBBLICA DI SAN MARINO**
Via del Voltone 120, San Marino,
47890, San Marino
Tel.: (378) 0549 882 325
Web Site: http://www.bcsm.sm
Sales Range: $25-49.9 Million
Emp.: 59
Central Bank
N.A.I.C.S.: 521110
Mario Giannini *(Dir Gen)*

**BANCA COMERCIALA CAR-
PATICA SA**
Soseaua Pipera nr 42 cladirea
Globalworth Plaza etajele 8 si 10,
Sector 2, 550135, Sibiu, Bucuresti,
Romania
Tel.: (40) 747045464
Web Site: http://www.carpatica.ro
Year Founded: 1999
Sales Range: $25-49.9 Million
Monetary Intermediation Services
N.A.I.C.S.: 521110
Daniela Elena Iliescu *(Gen Mgr)*

BANCA DE ECONOMII S.A.
Columna str nr 115, Chisinau, 2012,
Moldova
Tel.: (373) 22 218 005   **Md**
Web Site: http://www.bem.md
Year Founded: 1940
Banking Services
N.A.I.C.S.: 522110

BANCA DI CIVIDALE S.P.A.
Via sen Guglielmo Pelizzo 8-1,
33043, Cividale del Friuli, Italy
Tel.: (39) 0432707111
Web Site: https://www.civibank.it
Year Founded: 1886
Commercial Banking Services
N.A.I.C.S.: 522110

**BANCA FARMAFACTORING
S.P.A.**
Via Domenichino 5, 20149, Milan,
Italy
Tel.: (39) 02 499051   **IT**
Web Site: http://www.bffgroup.com
Year Founded: 1985
Rev.: $264,905,735
Assets: $5,652,066,428
Liabilities: $5,397,126,081
Net Worth: $254,940,347
Earnings: $105,403,556
Emp.: 413
Fiscal Year-end: 12/31/18
Factoring & Credit Management Ser-
vices
N.A.I.C.S.: 522299
Salvatore Messina *(Chm)*

Subsidiaries:

IOS Finance EFC, S.A. **(1)**
Edifici Caravel la Caravel·la La Nina 12 4

Planta, 08034, Barcelona, Spain
Tel.: (34) 93 511 40 25
Web Site: http://www.iosfinance.es
Financial Management Services
N.A.I.C.S.: 523999

Magellan S.A. **(1)**
Al Marszalka Jozefa Pilsudskiego 76, 90-
330, Lodz, Poland
Tel.: (48) 422723100
Web Site: http://www.magellansa.pl
Rev.: $39,992,887
Assets: $503,711,682
Liabilities: $407,204,092
Net Worth: $96,507,589
Earnings: $7,362,331
Emp.: 182
Fiscal Year-end: 12/31/2016
Financial Services
N.A.I.C.S.: 522291
Urban Kielichowski *(COO & Member-Mgmt
Bd)*

**BANCA FINNAT EURAMERICA
S.P.A.**
Palazzo Altieri Piazza del Gesu 49,
00186, Rome, Italy
Tel.: (39) 06699331
Web Site: http://www.bancafinnat.it
BFE—(ITA)
Rev.: $20,988,416
Assets: $2,348,516,639
Liabilities: $2,061,894,071
Net Worth: $286,622,568
Earnings: $3,921,750
Emp.: 353
Fiscal Year-end: 12/31/19
Investment, Insurance & Banking
Services
N.A.I.C.S.: 551111
Arturo Nattino *(CEO & Gen Mgr)*

Subsidiaries:

Calipso SpA **(1)**
Via Meravigli 3, 20123, Milan, Italy **(80.3%)**
Tel.: (39) 02876836
Web Site: http://www.calipso-gbf.it
Sales Range: $50-74.9 Million
Emp.: 7
Corporate Asset & Liability Solutions
N.A.I.C.S.: 524298

Finnat Fiduciaria SpA **(1)**
Piazza del Gesu 49, Rome, 186,
Italy   **(95%)**
Tel.: (39) 066783956
Web Site: http://www.finnat.it
Emp.: 15
Fiduciary Services
N.A.I.C.S.: 523991

Finnat Investments SpA **(1)**
Piazza Del Gesu 49, 00186, Rome,
Italy   **(100%)**
Tel.: (39) 0669940038
Web Site: http://www.finnat.it
Sales Range: $50-74.9 Million
Investment Services
N.A.I.C.S.: 523150

Finnat Servizi Assicurativi S.r.l. **(1)**
Viale Liegi 10, 00198, Rome, Italy
Tel.: (39) 0685304484
Insurance Services
N.A.I.C.S.: 524298

Investire Immobiliare SGR S.p.A. **(1)**
Palazzo Altieri Piazza del Gesu n 49,
00186, Rome, Italy
Tel.: (39) 06 699 331
Web Site:
http://www.investireimmobiliaresgr.com
Real Estate Fund Management Services
N.A.I.C.S.: 531390

Investire SGR S.p.A. **(1)**
Largo Donegani 2, 20121, Milan, Italy
Tel.: (39) 0669 6291
Web Site: https://www.investiresgr.it
Asset Management Services
N.A.I.C.S.: 523999
Dario Valentino *(CEO)*

Natam Management Company S.A. (1)
11 Rue Beatrix de Bourbon, 1225, Luxembourg, Luxembourg
Tel.: (352) 288091
Web Site: https://www.natam.lu
Asset Management Services
N.A.I.C.S.: 523999
Alberto Alfiero (Chm)

BANCA IFIS S.P.A.
Via Terraglio 63, Mestre, 30174, Venice, Italy
Tel.: (39) 0415027511
Web Site: https://www.bancaifis.it
Year Founded: 1983
IF—(ITA)
Rev.: $589,088,469
Assets: $15,939,964,842
Liabilities: $13,945,440,645
Net Worth: $1,994,524,197
Earnings: $123,538,836
Emp.: 1,849
Fiscal Year-end: 12/31/21
Financial Services
N.A.I.C.S.: 523999
Sebastien Egon Von Furstenberg (Chm)

Subsidiaries:

Banca Credifarma S.p.A. (1)
Via Mario Bianchini 13, 00142, Rome, Italy
Tel.: (39) 023490020
Web Site: https://www.bancacredifarma.it
Credit Management Services
N.A.I.C.S.: 541611

Capital Fin S.p.A. (1)
Corso Umberto I 381, 80138, Naples, Italy
Tel.: (39) 0815635606
Banking Services
N.A.I.C.S.: 522110

Credifarma S.p.A. (1)
Via dei Caudini 2, 00185, Rome, Italy
Tel.: (39) 06444851
Web Site: http://www.credifarma.it
Financial Services
N.A.I.C.S.: 523999

FBS Real Estate S.p.A. (1)
Via Senato 6, 20121, Milan, Italy
Tel.: (39) 0287211330
Web Site: http://fbsre.blupixelit.eu
Real Estate Services
N.A.I.C.S.: 531390
Federico Strocchi (Pres)

IFIS Finance Sp. Z o.o. (1)
Ul Wspolna 70, 00-687, Warsaw, Poland
Tel.: (48) 225258200
Web Site: https://www.ifisfinance.pl
Factory Services
N.A.I.C.S.: 522299

IFIS Rental Services S.r.l. (1)
Via Borghetto 5, 20122, Milan, Italy
Tel.: (39) 02241291
Banking Services
N.A.I.C.S.: 522110

Ifis Finance I.F.N. S.A. (1)
Strada Teheran nr 2 et 7 Sector 1, 011932, Bucharest, Romania
Tel.: (40) 213274729
Web Site: https://www.ifisfinance.ro
Credit Management Services
N.A.I.C.S.: 541611

Ifis Npl Investing S.p.A. (1)
via G S Mercadante 2/A Nero, 50144, Florence, Italy
Tel.: (39) 0553446411
Loan Management Services
N.A.I.C.S.: 522390

Ifis Npl Servicing S.p.A. (1)
via Terraglio 63, 30174, Venezia Mestre, Italy
Tel.: (39) 0415027511
Loan Management Services
N.A.I.C.S.: 522390

Revalea S.p.A. (1)
Via Borghetto 5, 20122, Milan, Italy
Tel.: (39) 0277311
Loan Management Services

N.A.I.C.S.: 522390

BANCA INTERMOBILIARE DI INVESTIMENTI E GESTIONI S.P.A.
Via Gramsci 7, 10121, Turin, Italy
Tel.: (39) 01108281   IT
Web Site:
http://www.bancaintermobiliare.com
Year Founded: 1981
Investment & Private Banking Services
N.A.I.C.S.: 523150
Claudio Moro (CEO)

Subsidiaries:

Banca Consulia S.p.a. (1)
Corso Monforte n 52, Milan, 20122, Italy
Tel.: (39) 02 85906 1
Web Site: http://www.bancaconsulia.it
Financial Advisory Services
N.A.I.C.S.: 523940
Cesare Castelbarco Albani (Pres)

Bim Immobiliare Srl (1)
Largo Vittorio Emanuele II 84, 10121, Turin, Italy
Tel.: (39) 011 5536500
Web Site: http://www.bimimmobiliare.com
Real Estate Development Services
N.A.I.C.S.: 531210

Bim Insurance Broker SpA (1)
Via Gramsci 7, Turin, Italy
Tel.: (39) 011 0828416
Web Site: http://www.bimbrokers.it
Insurance Brokerage Services
N.A.I.C.S.: 524210

BANCA INTESA JSC
2 Petroverigskiy Lane, 101000, Moscow, Russia
Tel.: (7) 4954118070
Web Site: http://www.bancaintesa.ru
Year Founded: 1992
Rev.: $52,283,940
Assets: $1,016,109,746
Liabilities: $836,074,656
Net Worth: $180,035,090
Earnings: $559,032
Fiscal Year-end: 12/31/20
Commercial Banking Services
N.A.I.C.S.: 522110
Lein Olga Vadimovna (Deputy Chm-Mgmt Bd)

BANCA MEDIOLANUM S.P.A.
Via Ennio Doris Palazzo Meucci, 20079, Basiglio, Milano, Italy
Tel.: (39) 0290451625   IT
Web Site:
https://www.bancamediolanum.it
BMED—(ITA)
Rev.: $1,720,409,279
Assets: $72,501,835,459
Liabilities: $71,764,526,672
Net Worth: $737,308,787
Earnings: $533,623,607
Emp.: 3,092
Fiscal Year-end: 12/31/20
Investment & Financial Management Services
N.A.I.C.S.: 523940
Ennio Doris (Chm)

Subsidiaries:

Alboran S.p.A. (1)
Via Larga 8, 20122, Milan, Italy
Tel.: (39) 0227321211
Web Site: http://www.alboran.it
Television Program Production
N.A.I.C.S.: 516120

Banco Mediolanum, S.A. (1)
Av Diagonal 668-670, 08034, Barcelona, Spain
Tel.: (34) 932 535 400
Web Site: http://www.bancomediolanum.es
Commercial Banking Services
N.A.I.C.S.: 522110

Bankhaus August Lenz & Co. AG (1)
Holbeinstr 11, Munich, 81679, Germany
Tel.: (49) 1805170070
Web Site: http://www.banklenz.de
Commercial Banking Services
N.A.I.C.S.: 522110

Fibanc Pensiones S.G.F.P. S.A. (1)
Calle Entenca 321, Barcelona, 08029, Spain
Tel.: (34) 932535400
Sales Range: $100-124.9 Million
Emp.: 210
Commercial Banking Services
N.A.I.C.S.: 522110

Fibanc SA (1)
Av Diagonal 668-670, 08034, Barcelona, Spain
Tel.: (34) 932535400
Web Site: http://www.fibancmediolanum.es
Sales Range: $100-124.9 Million
Emp.: 250
Banking & Fund Management Services
N.A.I.C.S.: 522110
Carlos Tusquets (Pres)

Ges Fibanc S.G.I.I.C. S.A. (1)
Calle Entenza 321, Barcelona, 8029, Spain
Tel.: (34) 932535400
Commercial Banking Services
N.A.I.C.S.: 522110

Mediolanum Asset Management Ltd (1)
Iona Building Shelbourne Road, Dublin, 4, Ireland
Tel.: (353) 1 2310800
Asset Management Services
N.A.I.C.S.: 523940

Mediolanum Comunicazione S.p.A. (1)
Palazzo Meucci Via Francesco Sforza, 20080, Basiglio, Milano, Italy
Tel.: (39) 0290491
Financial Support Services
N.A.I.C.S.: 523999

Mediolanum Corporate University S.p.A. (1)
Palazzo Archimede Ludovico il Moro 4/A, Basiglio, Milano, Italy
Tel.: (39) 0290496050
Web Site:
https://www.mediolanumuniversity.it
Emp.: 2,500
Educational Support Services
N.A.I.C.S.: 611710
Mark Mobius (Chm)

Mediolanum Distribuzione Finanziaria S.p.A. (1)
Via Francesco Sforza 15, Basiglio, 20080, Milano, Italy
Tel.: (39) 0290491
Sales Range: $700-749.9 Million
Emp.: 2,000
Commercial Banking Services
N.A.I.C.S.: 522110
Pirovano Giovanni (Mng Dir)

Mediolanum Gestione Fondi SGRpA (1)
Palazzo Meucci, Via Francesco Sforza, Milan, Basiglio, Italy
Tel.: (39) 0290491
Web Site:
http://www.mediolanumgestionefondi.it
Asset Management Services
N.A.I.C.S.: 541611

Mediolanum International Funds Ltd (1)
2 Shelbourne Buildings Shelbourne Road Ballsbridge, Dublin, D04 W3V6, Ireland
Tel.: (353) 1 2310800
Web Site: http://www.mediolanum.ie
Sales Range: $25-49.9 Million
Emp.: 70
Asset Management Services
N.A.I.C.S.: 541618
Furiol Pietribiasi (CEO)

Mediolanum International Life (1)
Palazzo Fermi Via Ennio Doris, Basiglio, 20080, Milan, Italy
Tel.: (39) 0290491

Web Site:
http://www.mediolanuminternationallife.it
Sales Range: $50-74.9 Million
Emp.: 5
Insurance Services
N.A.I.C.S.: 524298

Mediolanum Vita SpA (1)
Palazzo Meucci - Via F Sforza, Basiglio, 20079, Milan, Italy
Tel.: (39) 0290491
Web Site: https://www.mediolanumvita.it
Sales Range: $700-749.9 Million
Emp.: 2,500
Insurance Services
N.A.I.C.S.: 524298
Giovanni Pirovano (Gen Mgr)

BANCA MONTE DEI PASCHI DI SIENA S.P.A.
Piazza Salimbeni 3, 53100, Siena, SI, Italy
Tel.: (39) 0577294111   IT
Web Site: https://www.gruppomps.it
Year Founded: 1472
BMPS—(ITA)
Rev.: $4,709,873,732
Assets: $132,326,452,622
Liabilities: $121,556,855,169
Net Worth: $10,769,597,453
Earnings: $2,214,311,461
Emp.: 16,737
Fiscal Year-end: 12/31/23
Commercial Banking Services
N.A.I.C.S.: 522110
Leonardo Bellucci (Chief Risk Officer)

Subsidiaries:

Monte paschi fiduciaria S.p.A. (1)
Via Aldo Moro 11/13, 53100, Siena, Italy
Tel.: (39) 0577279301
Web Site: https://www.mpsfiduciaria.it
Trust Fund Management Services
N.A.I.C.S.: 525920

Mps Capital Services Banca per le imprese S.p.A. (1)
Via Panciatichi 48, 50127, Florence, Italy
Tel.: (39) 05524981
Web Site: https://www.mpscapitalservices.it
Investment Banking Services
N.A.I.C.S.: 541513

BANCA NATIONALA A MOLDOVEI
1 Grigore Vieru Avenue, 2005, Chisinau, Moldova
Tel.: (373) 22221679
Web Site: http://www.bnm.org
Banking Services
N.A.I.C.S.: 521110
Eugeniu Prodan (Head-Security Svc)

BANCA POPOLARE DELL'ETRURIA E DEL LAZIO S.C.
Via Calamandrei 255, 52100, Arezzo, Italy
Tel.: (39) 0575 33 73 17   IT
Web Site: http://www.bancaetruria.it
Year Founded: 1882
Sales Range: $550-599.9 Million
Emp.: 1,686
Banking Services
N.A.I.C.S.: 522110
Lorenzo Rosi (Chm)

Subsidiaries:

Etruria Informatica Srl (1)
Via Calamandrei 255, 52100, Arezzo, Italy
Tel.: (39) 0575 398255
Software Development Services
N.A.I.C.S.: 541511

BANCA POPOLARE DI SONDRIO S.P.A.
Piazza Garibaldi 16, 23100, Sondrio, Italy
Tel.: (39) 0342528111   IT
Web Site: https://www.popso.it

Banca Popolare di Sondrio S.p.A.—(Continued)

Year Founded: 1871
BPSA—(ITA)
Rev.: $1,624,732,311
Assets: $63,717,590,251
Liabilities: $59,494,706,930
Net Worth: $4,222,883,321
Earnings: $509,065,018
Emp.: 3,033
Fiscal Year-end: 12/31/23
Banking & Financial Services
N.A.I.C.S.: 522110
Mario Alberto Pedranzini (CEO & Mng Dir)

Subsidiaries:

Banca Popolare di Sondrio (SUISSE) S.A.   **(1)**
Via Maggio 1, 6900, Lugano, Switzerland
Tel.: (41) 588553100
Web Site: http://www.bps-suisse.ch
Sales Range: $200-249.9 Million
Emp.: 150
Banking Services
N.A.I.C.S.: 523150
Andrea Romano (First VP & Head-Mktg & PR)

Factorit S.p.A.   **(1)**
Via Cino del Duca 12, 20122, Milan, Italy   **(100%)**
Tel.: (39) 02581501
Web Site: http://www.factorit.it
Sales Range: $50-74.9 Million
Emp.: 20
Corporate Loan Services
N.A.I.C.S.: 522299
Mario Torchia (Mgr-Intl)

Pirovano Stelvio SpA   **(1)**
Via delle Prese 8, 23100, Sondrio, Italy
Tel.: (39) 034 221 0040
Web Site: https://www.pirovano.it
Travel Agency Services
N.A.I.C.S.: 561510

BANCA POPOLARE DI SPO-LETO S.P.A.
Piazza Luigi Pianciani, 06049, Spo-leto, Italy
Tel.: (39) 07432151   **IT**
Web Site: http://www.bpspoleto.it
Banking Services
N.A.I.C.S.: 522110
Tommaso Cartone (Pres)

BANCA POPOLARE PUG-LIESE S.C.P.A.
Via Luzzatti 8, 73046, Matino, Italy
Tel.: (39) 0833500111
Web Site: https://www.bpp.it
Year Founded: 1994
Insurance Services
N.A.I.C.S.: 524298

BANCA PRIVADA D'ANDORRA, SA
Av Carlemany 119, AD700, Escaldes-Engordany, Andorra
Tel.: (376) 873500
Web Site: http://www.bpa.ad
Year Founded: 1958
Sales Range: $10-24.9 Million
Emp.: 149
Banking Services
N.A.I.C.S.: 522110
Ramon Cierco Noguer (Co-Chm)

Subsidiaries:

BPA Assegurances, SA   **(1)**
Calle de la Unio 1 1r, AD700, Escaldes-Engordany, Andorra   **(100%)**
Tel.: (376) 873555
Web Site: http://www.bpa.ad
Insurance Services
N.A.I.C.S.: 524298

BPA Fons, SA   **(1)**
Aravina Cafef Unio 3, AD 500, Andorra La Vella, Andorra   **(100%)**

Tel.: (376) 808696
Sales Range: $50-74.9 Million
Emp.: 50
Fund Management Services
N.A.I.C.S.: 525910

BPA Gestio, SA   **(1)**
C de la Unio 3 5a, AD700, Escaldes-Engordany, Andorra   **(100%)**
Tel.: (376) 873500
Financial Services
N.A.I.C.S.: 523999
Ramon Cierco Noguer (Chm)

BPA IPWM (Suisse), S.A.   **(1)**
33c Avenue de Miremont, 1206, Geneva, Switzerland
Tel.: (41) 22 782 58 86
Investment Advisory Services
N.A.I.C.S.: 523930
Jose Corral (Mng Dir)

BPA Serveis, SA   **(1)**
119 Carlamin Ave, AD700, Escaldes-Engordany, Andorra   **(100%)**
Tel.: (376) 876359
Web Site: http://www.bpa.ad
Sales Range: $25-49.9 Million
Business Services
N.A.I.C.S.: 561499

Banca Privada d'Andorra (Panama), S.A.   **(1)**
C 50 edificio Banca Privada d'Andorra, 0833-00088, Panama, Panama
Tel.: (507) 297 56 00
Investment Advisory Services
N.A.I.C.S.: 523940

Banco de Madrid, S.A.   **(1)**
Paseo de la Castellana 2, 28046, Madrid, Spain
Tel.: (34) 902 42 33 33
Web Site: http://www.bancomadrid.com
Investment Banking Services
N.A.I.C.S.: 523150
Jose Perez Fernandez (Chm)

Interdin, S.A.   **(1)**
P Castellana 93, 28046, Madrid, Spain
Tel.: (34) 915559433
Web Site: http://www.interdin.com.ec
Investment Banking Services
N.A.I.C.S.: 523150
Oscar Serra (Gen Mgr)

BANCA PROFILO S.P.A.
Via Cerva 28, 20122, Milan, Italy
Tel.: (39) 02584081
Web Site: https://www.bancaprofilo.it
Year Founded: 1992
PRO—(LSE)
Sales Range: $10-24.9 Million
Emp.: 202
Retail & Investment Banking Services
N.A.I.C.S.: 523150
Luigi Spaventa (VP)

BANCA SELLA HOLDINGS S.P.A.
Piazza Gaudenzio Sella 1, 13900, Biella, Italy
Tel.: (39) 015 35011   **IT**
Web Site: http://sellagroup.eu
Sales Range: $600-649.9 Million
Bank Holding Company
N.A.I.C.S.: 551111
Maurizio Sella (Chm)

BANCA SISTEMA S.P.A.
Largo Augusto 1/A, ang via Verziere 13, 20122, Milan, Italy
Tel.: (39) 02802801
Web Site:
     https://www.bancasistema.it
BST—(ITA)
Rev.: $124,658,991
Assets: $4,509,324,717
Liabilities: $4,220,265,802
Net Worth: $289,058,915
Earnings: $31,065,874
Emp.: 269
Fiscal Year-end: 12/31/21
Banking Services

N.A.I.C.S.: 522110
Gianluca Garbi (CEO & Gen Mgr)

BANCA TRANSILVANIA S.A.
Calea Dorobantilor no 30-36, Cluj County, 400117, Cluj-Napoca, Romania
Tel.: (40) 264407150
Web Site:
     https://www.bancatransilvania.ro
Year Founded: 1993
TLV—(BUC)
Rev.: $1,817,268,185
Assets: $36,455,967,988
Liabilities: $33,461,212,113
Net Worth: $2,994,755,875
Earnings: $643,159,966
Fiscal Year-end: 12/31/23
Banking & Financial Services
N.A.I.C.S.: 523150
Horia Ciorcila (Chm)

Subsidiaries:

BT Asset Management SAI S.A.   **(1)**
Str Emil Racovita nr 22, Cluj-Napoca, Romania
Tel.: (40) 264301036
Web Site:
     https://www.btassetmanagement.ro
Financial Investment Services
N.A.I.C.S.: 523999

BT Capital Partners S.A.   **(1)**
Brancusi Business Center 74-76 Constantin Brancusi St 1st Floor, Cluj-Napoca, Romania
Tel.: (40) 264430564
Web Site: http://www.btcapitalpartners.ro
Emp.: 800
Investment Banking Services
N.A.I.C.S.: 523150
Dragos Darabut (Mgr-Investment Banking)

BT Direct IFN S.A.   **(1)**
Str Constantin Brancusi nr 74-76 etaj 3, Cluj-Napoca, Romania
Tel.: (40) 264302000
Web Site: https://www.btdirect.ro
Financial Investment Services
N.A.I.C.S.: 523999
Gabriel Gogu (Deputy Gen Mgr)

BT Investments S.R.L.   **(1)**
B-Dul Eroilor 36, Cluj-Napoca, Cluj, Romania
Tel.: (40) 264407150
Financial Investment Services
N.A.I.C.S.: 523940

BT Leasing MD SRL   **(1)**
Mun Str A Puskin nr 60/2, Chisinau, MD-2005, Moldova
Tel.: (373) 22260780
Web Site: http://www.btleasing.md
Sales Range: $50-74.9 Million
Emp.: 11
Consumer Lending Services
N.A.I.C.S.: 522291

BT Leasing Transilvania IFN S.A.   **(1)**
B-dul C Brancusi nr 74-76 etaj 1, Cluj-Napoca, Cluj, Romania
Tel.: (40) 264438816
Web Site: https://www.btleasing.ro
Sales Range: $50-74.9 Million
Emp.: 100
Vehicles Financial Leasing Services
N.A.I.C.S.: 525990

BT Operational Leasing SA   **(1)**
Calea Floreasca nr 131-137 et 7 sector 1, 013685, Bucharest, Romania
Tel.: (40) 751600100
Web Site: http://www.btopleasing.ro
Operational Leasing Services
N.A.I.C.S.: 532112

BT Securities S.A.   **(1)**
No 74-76 Constantin Brancusi, Cluj-Napoca, 400462, Cluj, Romania
Tel.: (40) 26 443 0564
Web Site: http://www.btsecurities.ro
Sales Range: $50-74.9 Million
Emp.: 45
Financial Investment Services

N.A.I.C.S.: 523940
Nicolae Moroianu (Exec Mgr)

OTP Bank Romania S.A.   **(1)**
Buzesti Street no 66-68 sector 1, 11017, Bucharest, Romania
Tel.: (40) 213085711
Web Site: https://www.otpbank.ro
Commercial Banking Services
N.A.I.C.S.: 522110
Pongracz Antal (Chm-Supervisory Bd)

dea Leasing IFN S.A.   **(1)**
Sos Bucuresti-Ploiesti 19-21 et 2 Sector 1, Bucharest, Romania
Tel.: (40) 212044444
Web Site: https://www.idealeasing.ro
Financial Lending Services
N.A.I.C.S.: 522220

BANCO ALFA DE INVESTI-MENTO SA
Alameda Santos 466 - 4th floor, Cerqueira Cesar, Sao Paulo, 01418-000, Brazil
Tel.: (55) 1140043344
Web Site: http://www.alfanet.com.br
Year Founded: 1925
Sales Range: $100-124.9 Million
Banking Services
N.A.I.C.S.: 522110
Adilson Herrero (Dir-IR)

Subsidiaries:

FINANCEIRA ALFA S.A.   **(1)**
Al Santos 466 - 4 Floor/parte, 1418000, Sao Paulo, Brazil
Tel.: (55) 1131755606
Web Site: http://www.alfanet.com.br
Sales Range: Less than $1 Million
Financial Investment Services
N.A.I.C.S.: 523999
Antonio Jose Ambrozano Neto (Member-Exec Bd & Dir-IR)

BANCO BAC DE PANAMA, S.A.
Avenida Balboa Calle 42 y 43 Bella Vista, PO Box 0816-03396, Panama, Panama
Tel.: (507) 207 2100
Web Site: http://www.bancobac.com
Emp.: 378
Commercial Banking Services
N.A.I.C.S.: 522110
Ernesto Castegnaro Hate (Pres)

BANCO BIC PORTUGUES S.A.
Av Antonio Augusto Aguiar no 132 Building Frontier, 1050-020, Lisbon, Portugal
Tel.: (351) 213 598 000   **PT**
Web Site: http://www.bancobic.pt
Year Founded: 2008
Corporate & Investment Banking
N.A.I.C.S.: 523150
Luis Mira Amaral (CEO)

BANCO BILBAO VIZCAYA AR-GENTARIA, S.A.
Calle Azul 4, 28050, Madrid, Spain
Tel.: (34) 913746000   **ES**
Web Site: https://www.bbva.com
Year Founded: 1999
BBVA—(NYSE)
Rev.: $51,640,405,785
Assets: $836,993,308,871
Liabilities: $777,350,528,815
Net Worth: $59,642,780,056
Earnings: $8,654,219,728
Emp.: 121,486
Fiscal Year-end: 12/31/23
Financial Investment Services
N.A.I.C.S.: 522110
Carlos Torres Vila (Chm)

Subsidiaries:

AFP Horizonte SA   **(1)**
Avda Republica de Panama, San Isidro, 3055, Lima, Peru   **(24.85%)**

Tel.: (51) 12154082
Web Site: http://www.afphorizonte.com.pe
Pension Fund Management Services
N.A.I.C.S.: 524292

ANIDAPORT - Investimentos Imobiliarios, Unipessoal, LTDA (1)
Av Duque D' Avila n 46-4 C, 1050-083, Lisbon, Portugal
Tel.: (351) 219362349
Real Estate Services
N.A.I.C.S.: 531390

Aplica Soluciones Tecnologicas Chile Limitada (1)
Moneda 1096 Piso 5 Santiago Centro, Santiago, Chile
Tel.: (56) 23516800
Financial Management Services
N.A.I.C.S.: 523999

BBV Bilbao (1)
Gran Via 12, 48001, Bilbao, Vizcaya, Spain **(100%)**
Tel.: (34) 944876000
Web Site: http://www.bbva.com
Sales Range: $350-399.9 Million
Emp.: 1,000
Investment Banking Services
N.A.I.C.S.: 523150

BBV Interactivos (1)
Clara Del Rey 26, Madrid, 28002, Spain **(100%)**
Tel.: (34) 913748515
Web Site: http://www.bbva.com
Sales Range: $350-399.9 Million
Emp.: 1,000
Investment Banking Services
N.A.I.C.S.: 523150

BBV Madrid (1)
Paseo De La Castellana 81, 28046, Madrid, Spain **(100%)**
Tel.: (34) 913746000
Web Site: http://www.bbva.com
Sales Range: $50-74.9 Million
Emp.: 100
Investment Banking Services
N.A.I.C.S.: 523150

BBV Privanza (1)
Padilla 17, 28006, Madrid, Spain **(100%)**
Tel.: (34) 913748700
Web Site: http://www.bbva.es
Sales Range: $50-74.9 Million
Emp.: 100
Investment Banking Services
N.A.I.C.S.: 523150

BBVA (Suiza) S.A. (1)
Selnaustrasse 32/36 4th floor, PO Box 3930, 8021, Zurich, Switzerland **(100%)**
Tel.: (41) 900265951
Web Site: https://www.bbva.ch
Sales Range: $100-124.9 Million
Emp.: 110
N.A.I.C.S.: 522299

BBVA Banco Provincial, S.A. (1)
Caracas San Bernardino urbanization Volmer Avenue with East Avenue 0, Provincial Financial Center, Caracas, 1011, Venezuela **(55.14%)**
Tel.: (58) 2125045689
Web Site: https://www.provincial.com
Sales Range: $450-499.9 Million
Emp.: 5,544
Commercial Banking Services
N.A.I.C.S.: 522110
Aura Marina Kolster *(Sec)*

BBVA Brasil Banco de Investimento SA (1)
Rua Campos Bicudo 98-15-cj 152 Jardim Europa, Sao Paulo, 04536-010, Brazil
Tel.: (55) 1137074900
N.A.I.C.S.: 522320

BBVA Colombia S.A. (1)
Carrera Novena no 72-21 Apdo, 53851, Bogota, Colombia **(73.7%)**
Tel.: (57) 13124666
Web Site: https://www.bbva.com.co
Commercial & Financial Banking Services
N.A.I.C.S.: 522110
Oscar Cabrera *(Pres)*

BBVA Information Technology Espana, S.L. (1)

Ed Bilma - C/ Maria Tubau 9 - 5th floor, 28050, Madrid, Spain
Tel.: (34) 914552642
Web Site: https://www.bbvaitspain.com
Emp.: 637
Software Development Services
N.A.I.C.S.: 541511

BBVA Instituicao Financeira de Credito, S.A. (1)
Av D Joao II No 35 F/G/H 2nd Floor Infante Building, Parque das Nacoes, 1990-083, Lisbon, Portugal
Tel.: (351) 217985700
Web Site: https://www.bbvacf.pt
Financial Management Services
N.A.I.C.S.: 523999

BBVA Ireland plc (1)
3 Georges Dock IFSC, Dublin, 1, Ireland
Tel.: (353) 16702847
Sales Range: $50-74.9 Million
Emp.: 4
Financial Management Services
N.A.I.C.S.: 523999
Pablo Vallejo *(Mng Dir)*

BBVA Leasing Mexico SA de CV (1)
Av Paseo de la Reforma No 510, Colonia Juarez, 06600, Cuauhtemoc, Mexico
Tel.: (52) 555621
Web Site: https://www.bbvaleasing.mx
Financial Lending Services
N.A.I.C.S.: 522220

BBVA Luxinvest, S.A. (1)
76 Avenue de la Liberte, 1930, Luxembourg, Luxembourg
Tel.: (352) 4830711
Sales Range: $50-74.9 Million
Emp.: 3
Investment Management Service
N.A.I.C.S.: 523999

BBVA Paraguay SA (1)
Yegros 435 y 25 de Mayo, Asuncion, Paraguay
Tel.: (595) 21492072
Banking Financial Services
N.A.I.C.S.: 523150

BBVA Provincial Overseas NV (1)
Kaya WFG Jombi Mensing 18 Building E 3rd Floor, Willemstad, Curacao
Tel.: (599) 97376010
Web Site:
https://www.bbvaprovincialoverseas.com
N.A.I.C.S.: 522320

BBVA Seguros Colombia SA (1)
Carrera 9 No 72-21 Floor 8, Bogota, Colombia
Tel.: (57) 6012191100
Web Site: http://www.bbvaseguros.com.co
Banking Financial Services
N.A.I.C.S.: 523150

BBVA Servicios, S.A. (1)
Monforte De Lemos, Madrid, 28029, Spain
Tel.: (34) 913746417
Sales Range: $50-74.9 Million
Emp.: 3
Consumer Goods Distr
N.A.I.C.S.: 424990
Fernando de la Rica *(CEO)*

BBVA Sociedad Titulizadora S.A (1)
Av Republica de Panama 3055 27, San Isidro, 15036, Lima, Peru
Tel.: (51) 2092137
Web Site: https://titulizadora.bbva.pe
N.A.I.C.S.: 523999

BBVA Transfer Services Inc. (1)
16825 Northchase Dr, Houston, TX 77060
Tel.: (281) 765-1500
Web Site:
http://www.bbvatransferservices.com
Money Transfer Services
N.A.I.C.S.: 522320
Aurora Garza Hagan *(Pres & CEO)*

BBVA Wealth Solutions, Inc. (1)
1300 Post Oak Blvd Ste 1500, Houston, TX 77056
Tel.: (713) 552-9277
Web Site:
http://www.bbvawealthsolutions.com
Financial Advisory Services
N.A.I.C.S.: 523999

Bahia Sur Resort S.C (1)
Cano Herrera S/N, San Fernando, 11100, Cadiz, Spain
Tel.: (34) 956880086
Web Site: http://www.hotelbahiasur.com
Hotel Services
N.A.I.C.S.: 721110

Banco BBVA Argentina S.A. (1)
Av Cordoba 111, C1054AAA, Buenos Aires, Argentina **(76%)**
Tel.: (54) 1143464000
Web Site: http://www.bbva.com.ar
Rev.: $7,482,966,922
Assets: $23,208,573,829
Liabilities: $18,911,511,088
Net Worth: $4,297,062,741
Earnings: $699,622,962
Emp.: 5,888
Fiscal Year-end: 12/31/2022
Provider of Commercial Banking Services
N.A.I.C.S.: 522110
Martin Ezequiel Zarich *(CEO)*

Banco Bilbao Vizcaya Argentaria (Portugal), S.A. (1)
Avenida da Liberdade 222, Lisbon, 1250-148, Portugal
Tel.: (351) 213117200
Commercial Banking Services
N.A.I.C.S.: 522110

Banco Bilbao Vizcaya Argentaria Uruguay S.A. (1)
25 de Mayo 401, 11000, Montevideo, Uruguay
Tel.: (598) 24098835
Web Site: https://www.bbva.com.uy
N.A.I.C.S.: 522320

Banco Depositario BBVA, S.A. (1)
Calle Clara Del Rey 26, Madrid, 28002, Spain
Tel.: (34) 915377000
Commercial Banking Services
N.A.I.C.S.: 522110

Banco Occidental SA (1)
Calle Almagro 8, 28010, Madrid, Spain
Tel.: (34) 612256632
Web Site: https://bancooccidentalb.com
N.A.I.C.S.: 522320

Banco Provincial Overseas N.V. (1)
Sta Rosaweg 51-53-55, Willemstad, Curacao
Tel.: (599) 97376010
Commercial Banking Services
N.A.I.C.S.: 522110

CB Transport, Inc. (1)
8506 Cedarhome Dr NW, Stanwood, WA 98292
Tel.: (360) 629-4542
General Freight Trucking Services
N.A.I.C.S.: 484110
Bruce Carlson *(Gen Mgr)*

Casa De Bolsa Bbva Mexico, S.A. de C.V. (1)
Av Paseo de la Reforma 510 Colonia Juarez, Alcaldia Cuauhtemoc, CP 06600, Mexico, Mexico
Tel.: (52) 5556217050
Investment Banking Services
N.A.I.C.S.: 523150

Catalunya Banc, S.A. (1)
Placa Antoni Maura 6, 08003, Barcelona, Spain **(100%)**
Tel.: (34) 93 484 5000
Web Site: http://www.catalunyacaixa.com
Savings Bank
N.A.I.C.S.: 522180

Subsidiary (Domestic):

Gestio D'Actius Titulitzats, S.G.F.T.H. (2)
C/Roure 6, 08820, El Prat de Llobregat, Spain **(100%)**
Tel.: (34) 93 484 73 36
Web Site: http://www.gat-sgft.info
Mortgage Backed Securitization & Asset Backed Securitization
N.A.I.C.S.: 524126

Continental S.A. Sociedad Administradora de Fondos (1)
Primer Piso 3055 Av Republica De

Panama, San Isidro, Lima, Peru
Tel.: (51) 1 211 1970
Insurance & Pension Fund Services
N.A.I.C.S.: 524298

Copromed S.A. de C.V. (1)
Bosque de Duraznos 61 Piso 11 A, Bosques de las Lomas, 11700, Mexico, Mexico
Tel.: (52) 5552452760
Financial Services
N.A.I.C.S.: 523999

Crea Madrid Nuevo Norte S.A. (1)
Paseo de la Castellana 216 15t Floor, 28046, Madrid, Spain
Tel.: (34) 913449021
Web Site:
https://creamadridnuevonorte.com
N.A.I.C.S.: 531390

Data Architecture & Technology S.L. (1)
Avenida de Europa 26 Atica 5 3rd Fl, Pozuelo de Alarcon, 28224, Madrid, Spain
Tel.: (34) 673681105
Web Site: https://www.datio.com
Software Development Services
N.A.I.C.S.: 541511

Distrito Castellana Norte, S.A. (1)
216 Castellana Avenue 15th floor, Madrid, Spain
Tel.: (34) 913449021
Web Site:
http://www.distritocastellananorte.com
Urban Development Services
N.A.I.C.S.: 925120

El Milanillo, S.A. (1)
Cl Factor 5, Madrid, 28013, Spain
Tel.: (34) 918900459
Real Estate Development Services
N.A.I.C.S.: 531390

Emprendimientos de Valor S.A (1)
25 de Mayo 401 esquina Zabala, 11000, Montevideo, Uruguay
Tel.: (598) 29161444
Banking Financial Services
N.A.I.C.S.: 523150

Europea de Titulizacion, S.A., S.G.F.T. (1)
Sociedad Gestora de Fondos de Titulizacion Jorge Juan 68, 28009, Madrid, Spain
Tel.: (34) 914118467
Web Site: https://edt-sg.com
Fund Management Services
N.A.I.C.S.: 523940
Ignacio Echevarria Soriano *(Vice Chm)*

Facileasing S.A. de C.V. (1)
61 Bosque de Duraznos 11th Floor, Bosques de las Lomas, Mexico, 11700, Mexico
Tel.: (52) 55 52 45 27 60
Web Site: http://www.facileasing.com.mx
Motor Vehicle Leasing Services
N.A.I.C.S.: 532120

Subsidiary (Domestic):

Facileasing Equipment, S.A. de C.V. (2)
Av Universidad No 1200 Xoco Benito Juarez, Mexico, 03339, Mexico
Tel.: (52) 5552012000
Financial Services
N.A.I.C.S.: 523999

Financiera Ayudamos S.A. de C.V., SOFOMER (1)
Av Canal de Miramontes 2600 Local E-11 Colonia Avante, Delegacion Coyoacan, 04460, Mexico, Mexico
Tel.: (52) 55991550
Web Site: https://www.financieraayudamos.mx
Financial Services
N.A.I.C.S.: 523999

Finanzia AutoRenting, S.A. (1)
Almogavers St No 183 185 2nd Fl, Barcelona, 08010, Spain
Tel.: (34) 902117300
Automotive Financial Leasing Services
N.A.I.C.S.: 522220

Garanti BBVA AS (1)
Levent Nispetiye Mah Aytar Cad No 2, Be-

Banco Bilbao Vizcaya Argentaria, S.A.—(Continued)

siktas, 34340, Istanbul, Türkiye
Tel.: (90) 2123181818
Web Site: http://www.garantibbva.com.tr
Banking Financial Services
N.A.I.C.S.: 523150
Recep Bastug (Pres & CEO)

Garanti BBVA Emeklilik AS (1)
Mete Cad No 30, Taksim, 34437, Istanbul,
Türkiye
Tel.: (90) 2123347000
Web Site:
http://www.garantibbvaemeklilik.com.tr
Pension Services
N.A.I.C.S.: 525110
Recep Bastug (Chm)

Garanti BBVA Filo AS (1)
Camcesme Mahallesi Tersane Caddesi No
15 K 3, Pendik, 34899, Istanbul, Türkiye
Tel.: (90) 2166254300
Web Site: http://www.garantibbvafilo.com.tr
Car Lending Services
N.A.I.C.S.: 532111
Aysegul Gulgor (Gen Mgr)

Garanti BBVA Leasing AS (1)
Camcesme Mahallesi Tersane Caddesi No
15, Pendik, 34899, Istanbul, Türkiye
Tel.: (90) 2166254150
Web Site:
https://www.garantibbvaleasing.com.tr
Financial Lending Services
N.A.I.C.S.: 522220

Garanti BBVA Portfoy AS (1)
Levent Nispetiye Mah Aytar Cad No 2, Be-
siktas, 34340, Istanbul, Türkiye
Tel.: (90) 2123841300
Web Site:
http://www.garantibbvaportfoy.com.tr
Asset Management Services
N.A.I.C.S.: 523920
Maria Paloma Piqueras Hernandez (Chm)

Garanti BBVA Yatirim As (1)
Etiler Mahallesi Tepecik Yolu Demirkent Sok
No 1, Besiktas, 34337, Istanbul, Türkiye
Tel.: (90) 2123841010
Web Site:
http://www.garantibbvayatirim.com.tr
Investment Banking Services
N.A.I.C.S.: 523150

Garanti Bank SA (1)
5 Fabrica de Glucoza Street Business Cen-
ter Novo Park 3 F Building, 5th and 6th
Floors District 2, Bucharest, Romania
Tel.: (40) 212089260
Web Site: http://www.garantibbva.ro
Banking Financial Services
N.A.I.C.S.: 523150

Garanti Bbva Factoring AS (1)
Camcesme Mahallesi Tersane Caddesi No
15, Pendik, 34899, Istanbul, Türkiye
Tel.: (90) 2166254000
Web Site:
https://www.garantibbvafactoring.com
Financial Investment Advice Services
N.A.I.C.S.: 523940

Garanti Odeme Sistemleri As (1)
15 Temmuz Mah Kocman Ca No 38,
Bagcilar, Istanbul, Türkiye
Tel.: (90) 2124782705
Web Site:
http://www.garantiodemesistemleri.com
Credit Card Marketing Services
N.A.I.C.S.: 522210

Garantibank Bbva International N.V. (1)
Keizersgracht 569-575, 1017 DR, Amster-
dam, Netherlands
Tel.: (31) 205539999
Web Site: https://garantibank.nl
N.A.I.C.S.: 522320

Grupo Financiero BBVA-Bancomer, S.A.
Avenida Universidad 1200 N1 CNCE M,
At'n Al Publico, Col Xco, 03339, Mexico,
DF, Mexico
Tel.: (52) 5556 210399
Web Site: http://www.bancomer.com.mx
Emp.: 29,000
Retail & Commercial Banking; Other Finan-
cial Services

N.A.I.C.S.: 522110
Division (Domestic):

BBVA Bancomer Afore (2)
Montes Urales 424 1er Piso Col Lomas de
Chapultepec, CP 11000, Mexico, D.F.,
Mexico
Tel.: (52) 91 71 40 00
Web Site: http://www.bancomer.com
Banking & Financial Services
N.A.I.C.S.: 523150

Banca Hipotecaria (2)
Montes Urales 424 2o Piso Col Lomas de
Chapultepec, Deleg Miguel Hidalgo,
Mexico, CP 11000, DF, Mexico
Tel.: (52) 55 9178 4600
Web Site: http://www.hipnal.com.mx
N.A.I.C.S.: 522299

Subsidiary (US):

Bancomer Transfer Services, Inc. (2)
16825 Northchase Dr Ste 1525, Houston,
TX 77060
Tel.: (281) 765-1525
Sales Range: $50-74.9 Million
Emp.: 55
Financial Transfer Services
N.A.I.C.S.: 522320
Aurora Garza Hagan (CEO)

Division (Domestic):

Casa de Cambio Bancomer (2)
Av Manuel L Barragan, DF, 00860, Mexico,
Mexico
Tel.: (52) 53760399
N.A.I.C.S.: 522299

Factoraje Bancomer (2)
J Balmes 11 Torre C Mezzanine Piso 3 Col
Los Morales, Polanco, DF, 11510, Mexico,
Mexico
Tel.: (52) 52833000
N.A.I.C.S.: 522299

Sistema de Ahorro para el Retiro (2)
Ave Universidad 1200 Col Xoco, DF,
03339, Mexico, Mexico
Branches & Agencies of Foreign Bank
N.A.I.C.S.: 522110

Inverahorro, S.L. (1)
Paseo Castellana 81, Madrid, 28046, Spain
Tel.: (34) 915377000
Investment Management Service
N.A.I.C.S.: 523999

Madiva Soluciones, S.L. (1)
Avenida de Manoteras 44 Floor 3 - Module
D, Hortaleza, 28050, Madrid, Spain
Tel.: (34) 917568487
Web Site: http://www.madiva.com
Software Development Services
N.A.I.C.S.: 541511

Openpay Argentina, S.A. (1)
Av Cordoba No 111 Piso 30, 1054, Buenos
Aires, Argentina
Tel.: (54) 8003336736
Web Site:
https://www.openpayargentina.com.ar
N.A.I.C.S.: 522320

Openpay Colombia SAS (1)
Calle 81 11 -08, Bogota, Colombia
Tel.: (57) 17945461
Web Site: https://www.openpay.co
Data Hosting Services
N.A.I.C.S.: 518210

Openpay Peru, S.A. (1)
Av Andres Reyes No 338 Piso 7, 15046,
San Isidro, Lima, Peru
Tel.: (51) 15950005
Web Site: https://www.openpay.pe
N.A.I.C.S.: 522320

Openpay S.A. De C.V. (1)
Av 5 de Febrero 1351 Sequoia 102 Col,
Felipe Carrillo Puerto, 76138, Queretaro,
Mexico
Tel.: (52) 5550220404
Web Site: https://www.openpay.mx
Data Hosting Services
N.A.I.C.S.: 518210

Psa Finance Argentina Compania Financiera SA (1)

Av Roque Saenz Pena 1211 Piso 2, Bue-
nos Aires, Argentina
Tel.: (54) 8003337777
Web Site: https://www.psafinance.com.ar
N.A.I.C.S.: 524126

Qipro Soluciones S.L. (1)
Severo Ochoa Street 55 Edf Alei Center II,
29590, Malaga, Spain
Tel.: (34) 951503770
Web Site: http://qiprosoluciones.negocio.site
Business Process Outsourcing Services
N.A.I.C.S.: 541611

River Oaks Bank Building, Inc. (1)
2001 Kirby Dr, Houston, TX 77019
Tel.: (713) 526-6211
Financial Services
N.A.I.C.S.: 523999

Seguros Bbva Bancomer Sa De Cv (1)
Avenida Paseo de la Reforma 510 Cuauh-
temoc Mayor's Office, Colonia Juarez,
06600, Mexico, Mexico
Tel.: (52) 5552262663
Web Site: http://www.bbva.mx
Insurance Services
N.A.I.C.S.: 524210

Seguros Provincial CA (1)
Av San Juan Bosco with 2da Transversal
de Altamira Altamira Center, Building Floor
1 Altamira Urbanization, Caracas, Venezu-
ela
Tel.: (58) 2122745111
Web Site: http://www.segurosprovincial.com
Insurance Services
N.A.I.C.S.: 524210

Societe Inmobiliere BBV D (1)
29 Rue DeE Masure, 64100, Bayonne,
France
Tel.: (33) 559582244
Real Estate Manangement Services
N.A.I.C.S.: 531390

Sport Club 18, S.A. (1)
Paseo Castellana 81, Madrid, 28046, Spain
Tel.: (34) 915377000
Real Estate Development Services
N.A.I.C.S.: 531390

Veridas Digital Authentication Solu-tions S.L. (1)
M-10 Tajonar, Poligono Industrial Talluntxe
II, 31192, Navarra, Spain
Tel.: (34) 948246295
Web Site: https://veridas.com
Emp.: 100
Digital Authentication Services
N.A.I.C.S.: 561990

Volkswagen Financial Services Com-pania Financiera SA (1)
Av Cordoba 111 Piso 31, C1054AAA, Bue-
nos Aires, Argentina
Tel.: (54) 56509650
Web Site: https://www.vwfs.com.ar
N.A.I.C.S.: 524126

BANCO BMG S.A.
Juscelino Kubitschek 1830 Tower 2
10th Floor, Sao Paulo, 04543-900,
Brazil
Tel.: (55) 8009799099
Web Site:
https://www.bancobmg.com.br
Year Founded: 1930
BMGB4—(BRAZ)
Rev.: $891,795
Assets: $5,308,087
Liabilities: $4,270,603
Net Worth: $1,037,484
Earnings: $94,647
Fiscal Year-end: 12/31/19
Commercial Banking Services
N.A.I.C.S.: 522110
Ana Karina Bortoni Dias (Chm & Pres)

BANCO BPM S.P.A.
Piazza F Meda 4, 20121, Milan, Italy
Tel.: (39) 0277001   IT
Web Site: https://gruppo.bancobpm.it

BAMI—(ITA)
Rev.: $3,139,122
Assets: $202,736,285
Liabilities: $189,087,419
Net Worth: $13,648,866
Earnings: $750,927
Emp.: 16,749
Fiscal Year-end: 12/31/22
Bank Holding Company
N.A.I.C.S.: 551111
Giuseppe Castagna (CEO)

Subsidiaries:

Arena Broker S.r.l. (1)
Via Pancaldo 70, 37138, Verona, Italy
Tel.: (39) 045 8185 411
Web Site: http://www.arenabroker.it
Insurance Brokerage Services
N.A.I.C.S.: 524210

Auto Trading Leasing IFN s.a. (1)
Sector 2 Str C A Rosetti Nr 17 Parterul Si
Supanta Cladirii, Mezanin, Bucharest, Ro-
mania
Tel.: (40) 21 312 70 52
Sales Range: $50-74.9 Million
Emp.: 25
Automobile Leasing Services
N.A.I.C.S.: 522220

Banca Aletti & C. S.p.A. (1)
Via Roncaglia 12, IT-20146, Milan, Italy
Tel.: (39) 02433581
Web Site: http://www.alettibank.it
Rev.: $238,169,567
Assets: $16,976,794,225
Liabilities: $16,038,010,235
Net Worth: $938,783,990
Earnings: $66,067,241
Fiscal Year-end: 12/31/2016
Private & Investment Banking
N.A.I.C.S.: 523150
Maurizio Zancanaro (CEO)

Subsidiary (Domestic):

Alletti Gestielle SGR S.p.A. (2)
Via Roncaglia 12, 20146, Milan, Italy
Tel.: (39) 0249967340
Web Site: http://www.gestielle.it
Sales Range: $50-74.9 Million
Emp.: 70
Asset Management
N.A.I.C.S.: 525990

Banca Italease S.p.A. (1)
Via Sile 18, IT-20139, Milan, Italy (100%)
Tel.: (39) 0277651
Web Site: http://www.bancaitalease.it
Sales Range: $1-4.9 Billion
Emp.: 1,120
Bank Holding Company
N.A.I.C.S.: 551111

Subsidiary (Domestic):

Italease Finance S.p.A. (2)
Via Sile 18, IT-20139, Milan, Italy (70%)
Tel.: (39) 0277651
Lease Financing Services
N.A.I.C.S.: 525990

Italease Gestione Beni S.p.A. (2)
Via Sile 18, IT-20139, Milan, Italy (100%)
Tel.: (39) 0277651
Web Site: http://www.italeasegestionebeni.it
Holding Company; Evaluation, Management
& Sale of Formerly Leased Assets
N.A.I.C.S.: 551112

Subsidiary (Domestic):

Essegibi Finanziaria S.p.A. (3)
Via Sile 18, IT-20139, Milan, MI,
Italy (100%)
Tel.: (39) 02 7765 1
Web Site: http://www.essegibi.it
Secondary Market Financing Services
N.A.I.C.S.: 522299

Essegibi Promozioni Immobiliari S.r.l. (3)
Via Sile 18, IT-20139, Milan, Italy (100%)
Tel.: (39) 02 7765 1
Web Site: http://www.essegibi.it
Real Estate Intermediation Services
N.A.I.C.S.: 522292

Branch (Domestic):

Italease Gestione Beni - Operational Headquarters (3)
Via Milano 110, IT-26025, Pandino, CR, Italy
Tel.: (39) 0373975411
Web Site: http://www.italeasegestionebeni.it
Evaluation, Management & Sale of Formerly Leased Assets
N.A.I.C.S.: 561499

Subsidiary (Domestic):

Italease Network S.p.A. (2)
Piazza Monsignor G Almici 15, IT-25124, Brescia, Italy (100%)
Tel.: (39) 030 22851
Corporate Lending Services
N.A.I.C.S.: 522299

Mercantile Leasing S.p.A. (2)
Viale Don Minzoni 1, IT-50129, Florence, Italy (100%)
Tel.: (39) 05556701
Sales Range: $100-124.9 Million
Emp.: 220
Real Estate, Vehicle & Capital Goods Leasing Services
N.A.I.C.S.: 531190

Release S.p.A. (2)
Via Sile 18, Milan, 20139, Italy
Tel.: (39) 02 367031
Financial Management Services
N.A.I.C.S.: 523999
Murcelini Diunpuolo (Gen Mgr)

Banca Popolare di Cremona S.p.A. (1)
Via Cesare Battisti, Cremona, Italy
Tel.: (39) 0372 404 1
Investment Banking Services
N.A.I.C.S.: 523150

Banca Popolare di Lodi S.p.A. (1)
Via Polenghi Lombardo 13, Bipielle City, 26900, Lodi, Italy
Tel.: (39) 0371580111
Web Site: http://www.bancobolare.it
Sales Range: $1-4.9 Billion
Emp.: 8,579
Retail & Commercial Loans & Deposit Products, Credit Cards, Insurance & Online Brokerage Services
N.A.I.C.S.: 523150
Vittorio Coda (Deputy Chm)

Banca Popolare di Novara S.p.A. (1)
Via Negroni 11, IT-26100, Novara, Italy
Tel.: (39) 0321 662 111
Web Site: http://www.bpn.it
Commericial Banking
N.A.I.C.S.: 522110

Banca Popolare di Verona - S. Geminiano e S. Prospero S.p.A. (1)
Piazza Nogara 2, IT-37121, Verona, Italy
Tel.: (39) 0458675111
Web Site: http://www.bpv.it
Sales Range: $1-4.9 Billion
Emp.: 14,000
Banking Services
N.A.I.C.S.: 522110
Alberto Bauli (Chm)

Bipiemme Vita S.p.A. (1)
Via del Lauro 1, 20121, Milan, Italy
Tel.: (39) 02 7700 2405
Web Site: http://www.bipiemmevita.it
Emp.: 72
Life & Health Insurance Services
N.A.I.C.S.: 524210

Bormioli Rocco Glass Co. Inc. (1)
41 Madison Ave 17th Fl Ofc Showroom, New York, NY 10010
Tel.: (212) 719-0606
Web Site: http://www.bormioliroccousa.com
Glass Products Mfr
N.A.I.C.S.: 327212

Credito Bergamasco S.p.A. (1)
Largo Porta Nuova 2, IT-24122, Bergamo, Italy
Tel.: (39) 035393111
Web Site: http://www.bancopopolare.it
Commercial & Merchant Banking & Asset Management Services
N.A.I.C.S.: 522110

Tecmarket Servizi S.p.A. (1)
Via Antonio Meucci 5, Verona, 37135, Italy
Tel.: (39) 0458274790
Marketing Consulting Services
N.A.I.C.S.: 541613

BANCO BPM SPA
Piazza F, Meda, 4, Milan, 20121, Italy
Tel.: (39) 02 77 00 3515
Web Site:
http://www.bancobpmspa.com
Year Founded: 2017
Emp.: 16,626
Private & Corporate Banking Services
N.A.I.C.S.: 522110
Giuseppe Castagna (CEO)

BANCO BRADESCO S.A.
Cidade de Deus s/n - Vila Yara, Osasco, 06029-900, SP, Brazil
Tel.: (55) 1136844011   BR
Web Site: https://banco.bradesco
Year Founded: 1943
BBD—(NYSE)
Rev.: $38,567,884,816
Assets: $345,976,113,519
Liabilities: $315,458,105,515
Net Worth: $30,518,008,004
Earnings: $4,079,005,931
Emp.: 88,381
Fiscal Year-end: 12/31/22
Banking Services
N.A.I.C.S.: 522110
Marcelo de Araujo Noronha (VP)

Subsidiaries:

Agora Corretora de Titulos e Valores Mobiliarios S.A. (1)
Praia De Botafogo 300 Salas 601 301 Parte e Loja 101, Rio de Janeiro, 02225-040, Brazil
Tel.: (55) 21 2529 0800
Web Site: http://www.agorainvest.com.br
Securities Brokerage Services
N.A.I.C.S.: 523150

BAC Florida Bank (1)
169 Miracle Mile R10, Coral Gables, FL 33134
Tel.: (305) 789-7000
Web Site: http://www.bacflorida.com
Sales Range: $50-74.9 Million
Emp.: 114
State Commercial Banks
N.A.I.C.S.: 522110
Julio Rojas (Co-Pres & Co-CEO)

Subsidiary (Domestic):

BAC Florida Investments (2)
3011 Ponce de Leon Blvd PH1, Coral Gables, FL 33134
Tel.: (305) 789-7000
Web Site: https://bradescobank.com
Rev.: $3,742,894
Emp.: 12
Full Service Broker Dealer
N.A.I.C.S.: 524210
Marcella Correa (Pres & CEO)

BAC Insurance Corp (2)
2600 Douglas Rd, Coral Gables, FL 33134
Tel.: (305) 442-8420
Rev.: $1,415,350
Emp.: 4
Life Insurance
N.A.I.C.S.: 524113

Credomatic of Florida Inc. (2)
9150 S Dadeland Blvd Ste 800, Miami, FL 33156
Tel.: (305) 372-3000
Web Site:
http://www.credomaticmerchants.com
Rev.: $3,900,000
Emp.: 60
Data Processing & Preparation
N.A.I.C.S.: 522320
Ricardo Horvilleur (Pres)

Banco Boavista S.A. (1)
Rua Min Edgard Costa 68 Centro, Nova Iguacu, 22430-190, Rio de Janeiro, Brazil
Tel.: (55) 21 2668 2720
Commercial & Retail Banking Services

N.A.I.C.S.: 522110

Banco Bradesco Argentina S.A. (1)
JUANA MANSO 555 PISO 2 DPTO, 1002, Buenos Aires, Argentina (100%)
Tel.: (54) 1141146111
Web Site: http://www.bradesco.com
Sales Range: $50-74.9 Million
Emp.: 15
N.A.I.C.S.: 522299

Banco Bradesco Europa S.A. (1)
Tel.: (352) 2541311
Web Site: http://www.bradesco.lu
Sales Range: $50-74.9 Million
Emp.: 39
Commercial Banking Services
N.A.I.C.S.: 522110

Banco Bradesco Financiamentos S.A. (1)
Cidade de Deus s/n - Prata Building - 4th Floor, Yara Village Osasco, Sao Paulo, 06029-900, Brazil
Tel.: (55) 40044433
Web Site:
https://www.bradescofinanciamentos.com
Commercial Banking Services
N.A.I.C.S.: 522110

Banco Bradesco New York (1)
450 Park Ave 32nd Fl, New York, NY 10022 (100%)
Tel.: (212) 688-9855
Web Site: http://www.bradesco.com
Sales Range: $75-99.9 Million
Emp.: 26
International Banking
N.A.I.C.S.: 522299

Bradesco Argentina de Seguros S.A (1)
Paraguay 610 Piso 5 Dto B, Buenos Aires, Argentina
Tel.: (54) 1143137867
Insurance Management Services
N.A.I.C.S.: 524298

Bradesco Auto/RE Companhia de Seguros (1)
Rua Barao de Itapagipe 225, Rio Comprido, Rio de Janeiro, 20261-901, RJ, Brazil
Tel.: (55) 2125031199
Web Site:
http://www.bradescoautore.com.br
General Insurance Services
N.A.I.C.S.: 524298

Subsidiary (Domestic):

Atlantica Companhia de Seguros S.A. (2)
Rua Barao de Itapagipe no 225 - parte, Rio Comprido, Rio de Janeiro, 20261-901, Brazil
Tel.: (55) 2125031199
General Insurance Services
N.A.I.C.S.: 524298

Bradesco Capitalizacao S.A. (1)
Av Alphaville 779, Barueri, Sao Paulo, 06472-900, SP, Brazil
Tel.: (55) 1132655433
Web Site:
http://www.bradescocapitalizacao.com.br
Fire Insurance Services
N.A.I.C.S.: 524298

Bradesco Corretora T.V.M. (1)
Av Paulista 1450 7th Floor, 01310-917, Sao Paulo, Brazil
Tel.: (55) 11 2178 5757
Web Site:
http://www.bradescocorretora.com.br
Commercial Banking Services
N.A.I.C.S.: 522110

Bradesco Leasing S.A. Arrendamento Mercantil (1)
Tel.: (55) 1141972906
Web Site:
http://www.bradescoleasing.com.br
Financial Management Services
N.A.I.C.S.: 523999

Bradesco Saude S.A. (1)
Rua Barao de Itapagipe 225, Rio Comprido, Rio de Janeiro, 20261-901, Brazil
Tel.: (55) 2125031101
Web Site: http://www.bradescosaude.com.br

Health Insurance Services
N.A.I.C.S.: 524114

Bradesco Securities, Inc., (1)
450 Park Ave, New York, NY 10022-3084
Tel.: (212) 888-9141
Web Site: http://www.bradescori.b.br
Securities Brokerage Services
N.A.I.C.S.: 523150
Marcelo Cabral (CEO)

Bradesco Vida E Previdencia S.A. (1)
Av Alphaville 779 18 do Forte, Empresarial, Barueri, 06472-900, SP, Brazil
Tel.: (55) 1136845760
Web Site:
http://www.bradescoprevidencia.com.br
Fire Insurance Services
N.A.I.C.S.: 524298

Columbus Holdings (1)
750 Shaw Boulevard, Mandaluyong, 1552, Philippines
Tel.: (63) 28183601
Investment Management Service
N.A.I.C.S.: 523940

Companhia Brasileira de Solucoes e Servicos S.A. (1)
Alameda Rio Negro 161 17th Fl, Barueri, 06454, Brazil
Tel.: (55) 1121881845
Sales Range: $200-249.9 Million
Emp.: 300
Credit Card Processing Services
N.A.I.C.S.: 522320

Subsidiary (Domestic):

IBI promotora de vendas ltda (2)
Estr do Portela 77 - Madureira, 21351-050, Rio de Janeiro, Brazil
Tel.: (55) 2121060008
Commercial Banking Services
N.A.I.C.S.: 522110

RCB Investimentos S.A. (1)
Praca General Gentil Falcao 108 13 andar conj 132, Sao Paulo, 04571-150, Brazil (65%)
Tel.: (55) 1128741180
Web Site: http://www.rcbinv.com.br
Financial Management Services
N.A.I.C.S.: 541611

Scopus Tecnologia Ltda (1)
Avenida Mutinga 4 105 Jd Santo Elias - Pirituba, Sao Paulo, 05110-000, Brazil
Tel.: (55) 11 3909 3400
Web Site: http://www.scopus.com.br
Sales Range: $700-749.9 Million
Emp.: 3,000
Information Technology Consulting Services
N.A.I.C.S.: 541512

Uniao Participacoes Ltda (1)
Rua Araujo Porto Alegre 36 - Castelo, Rio de Janeiro, 20030-013, Brazil
Tel.: (55) 1155046500
Commercial Banking Services
N.A.I.C.S.: 522110

BANCO CENTRAL DE CHILE
Agustinas N 1180, PO Box 967, 8340454, Santiago, Chile
Tel.: (56) 26702000
Web Site: http://www.bcentral.cl
Year Founded: 1926
Sales Range: $1-4.9 Billion
Emp.: 562
Central Bank
N.A.I.C.S.: 521110
Miguel Angel Nacrur Gazali (Gen Counsel)

BANCO CENTRAL DE CUBA
Municipio Habana Vieja La Habana, PO Box 746, Havana, 402, Cuba
Tel.: (53) 78668003
Web Site: http://www.bc.gov.cu
Year Founded: 1950
Sales Range: $125-149.9 Million
Emp.: 450
Central Bank
N.A.I.C.S.: 521110
Gustavo Roca Sanchez (Mgr-London)

Banco Central de Cuba—(Continued)

BANCO CENTRAL DE HONDU-RAS

Barrio El Centro Avenida Juan Ramon Molina Primera Calle, Apartado Postal 3165, Septima Avenida, Tegucigalpa, Honduras
Tel.: (504) 2237 2270   HN
Web Site: http://www.bch.hn
Year Founded: 1950
Sales Range: $200-249.9 Million
Banking Services
N.A.I.C.S.: 521110
Manuel de Jesus Bautista (Chm)

BANCO CENTRAL DE LA RE-PUBLICA ARGENTINA

Reconquista 266, C1003ABF, Buenos Aires, Argentina
Tel.: (54) 1143483500
Web Site: http://www.bcra.gov.ar
Central Bank
N.A.I.C.S.: 521110
Federico Sturzenegger (Pres)

BANCO CENTRAL DE LA RE-PUBLICA DOMINICA

Calle Pedro Henriquez Urena, esq Leopoldo Navarro, Santo Domingo, Dominican Republic
Tel.: (809) 2219111
Web Site:
  http://www.bancentral.gov.do
Year Founded: 1947
Central Bank
N.A.I.C.S.: 521110
Fabiola M. Herrera De Valdez (Dir-Payment Sys Dept)

BANCO CENTRAL DE RESERVA DE EL SALVADOR

Alameda Juan Pablo II entre 15 y 17 Av Norte, Apartado Postal 106, San Salvador, El Salvador
Tel.: (503) 2281 8000
Web Site: http://www.bcr.gob.sv
Sales Range: $75-99.9 Million
Central Bank
N.A.I.C.S.: 521110
Marta Evelyn de Rivera (First VP)

BANCO CENTRAL DE RESERVA DEL PERU

Jr Santa Rosa 441-445, Lima, 1, Peru
Tel.: (51) 16132000   Pe
Web Site: http://www.bcrp.gob.pe
Year Founded: 1922
Rev.: $1,595,626,837
Assets: $75,330,369,473
Liabilities: $70,602,115,057
Net Worth: $4,728,254,416
Earnings: $555,537,295
Emp.: 974
Fiscal Year-end: 12/31/19
Central Bank
N.A.I.C.S.: 521110
Carlos Lopez Obregon (Deputy Mgr-HR)

BANCO CENTRAL DE VEN-EZUELA

Av Urdaneta esq Las Carmelitas, 1010, Caracas, Venezuela
Tel.: (58) 2128015111
Web Site: http://www.bcv.org.ve
Sales Range: $450-499.9 Million
Emp.: 2,000
Central Bank
N.A.I.C.S.: 521110
Calixto Ortega (Pres)

BANCO CENTRAL DEL ECUA-DOR

Avenue Amazonas N34-451 y Av-

enue Atahualpa, Quito, Ecuador
Tel.: (593) 2 2255777
Web Site: http://www.bce.fin.ec
Sales Range: $200-249.9 Million
Emp.: 780
Central Bank
N.A.I.C.S.: 521110
Eduardo Cabezas Molina (Chm)

BANCO CENTRAL DEL PARA-GUAY

Federacion Rusa y Cabo 1 Marecos, Santo Domingo, Asuncion, Paraguay
Tel.: (595) 21608011
Web Site: http://www.bcp.gov.py
Sales Range: $200-249.9 Million
Emp.: 900
Central Bank
N.A.I.C.S.: 521110
Carlos Gustavo Fernandez Valdovinos (Pres)

BANCO CENTRAL DEL URU-GUAY

Diagonal Fabini 777, Montevideo, Uruguay
Tel.: (598) 219671658
Web Site: http://www.bcu.gub.uy
Central Bank
N.A.I.C.S.: 521110
Alberto Grana (Mgr-Policy)

BANCO CENTRAL DO BRASIL

Setor Bancario Sul SBS Quadra 3 Bloco B Ed, Caixa Postal 08670, 70074-900, Brasilia, Brazil
Tel.: (55) 6134143980
Web Site: http://www.bcb.gov.br
Sales Range: $1-4.9 Billion
Central Bank
N.A.I.C.S.: 521110
Henrique de Campos Meirelles (Governor)

BANCO COMAFI S.A.

Avenida Presidente Roque Saenz Pena 660, Buenos Aires, 1035 AR, Argentina
Tel.: (54) 1143793333   Ar
Web Site: http://www.comafi.com.ar
Year Founded: 1984
Sales Range: $100-124.9 Million
Retail, Commercial & Investment Banking, Brokerage & Trust Services
N.A.I.C.S.: 522110
Guillermo Alejandro Cervino (Chm)

BANCO COMERCIAL PORTU-GUES, S.A.

Praca Dom Joao I n 28, 4000-295, Porto, Portugal
Tel.: (351) 211131080   PT
Web Site:
  http://www.ind.millenniumbcp.pt
Year Founded: 1985
BCP—(EUR)
Rev.: $2,217,689,264
Assets: $105,399,476,209
Liabilities: $96,327,363,944
Net Worth: $9,072,112,265
Earnings: $255,922,228
Emp.: 17,331
Fiscal Year-end: 12/31/20
Commercial, Investment & Personal Banking, Insurance & Asset Management
N.A.I.C.S.: 522110
Ana Isabel dos Santos de Pina Cabral (Sec)

Subsidiaries:

Bank Millennium S.A.   (1)
Ul Stanislawa Zaryna 2A, 02-593, Warsaw, Poland   (50%)
Tel.: (48) 225984161
Web Site: https://www.bankmillennium.pl
Rev.: $1,334,727,893

Assets: $31,890,244,837
Liabilities: $30,138,493,063
Net Worth: $1,751,751,774
Earnings: $146,269,563
Emp.: 6,700
Fiscal Year-end: 12/31/2023
Commercial Banking
N.A.I.C.S.: 522110
Boguslaw Kott (Chm-Supervisory Bd)

EURO BANK SPOLKA AKCYJNA   (1)
ul Sw Mikolaja 72, Wroclaw, 50-126, Poland
Tel.: (48) 717955500
Commercial Banking Services
N.A.I.C.S.: 522110

Millennium bcp Gestao de Activos - Sociedade Gestora de Fundos de Investimento, S.A.   (1)
Av Professor Doutor Cavaco Silva Tagus Park Edif 3 Piso 1 Ala A, 2744-002, Porto Salvo, Portugal
Tel.: (351) 211132000
Web Site:
  http://www.fundos.millenniumbcp.pt
Asset Management Services
N.A.I.C.S.: 541618

BANCO CRUZEIRO DO SUL SA

Rua Funchal 418 7-9 andares Ed E-Tower, Vila Olimpia, CEP-04551-060, Sao Paulo, SP, Brazil
Tel.: (55) 1138481800
Web Site: http://www.bcsul.com.br
Sales Range: $750-799.9 Million
Emp.: 600
Banking Services
N.A.I.C.S.: 522110
Luis Octavio Azeredo Lopes Indio da Costa (Chm & CEO)

BANCO DA AMAZONIA S/A

Av Presidente Vargas 800 14 Floor, 66017000, Belem, PA, Brazil
Tel.: (55) 9140083888
Web Site:
  http://www.bancoamazonia.com.br
BAZA3—(BRAZ)
Rev.: $737,236,533
Assets: $8,082,144,187
Liabilities: $7,030,442,422
Net Worth: $1,051,701,765
Earnings: $256,594,083
Fiscal Year-end: 12/31/23
Financial Banking Services
N.A.I.C.S.: 522110
Luiz Fernando Pires Augusto (Chm)

BANCO DAYCOVAL S.A.

Avenida Paulista 1793 Bela Vista, 1311200, Sao Paulo, SP, Brazil
Tel.: (55) 113138 1025   BR
Web Site:
  http://www.daycoval.com.br
Year Founded: 1968
Rev.: $1,148,576,419
Assets: $7,463,730,492
Liabilities: $6,630,031,355
Net Worth: $833,699,137
Earnings: $166,334,804
Emp.: 1,994
Fiscal Year-end: 12/31/18
Banking Services
N.A.I.C.S.: 522110
Morris Dayan (Member-Exec Bd)

BANCO DE BOGOTA SA

Calle 52 No 27 35, Barrancabermeja, 2047, Colombia
Tel.: (57) 6214773
Commercial Banking Services
N.A.I.C.S.: 522110
Alejandro Figueroa Jaramillo (CEO)

BANCO DE COMERCIO S.A.

Av Canaval y Moreyra N 452 - 454, San Isidro, 15036, Lima, Peru
Tel.: (51) 5136000

Web Site: https://www.bancom.pe
Year Founded: 2004
BANCOMC1—(LIM)
Rev.: $68,876,744
Assets: $620,412,382
Liabilities: $512,233,017
Net Worth: $108,179,365
Earnings: $1,131,892
Fiscal Year-end: 12/31/23
Commercial Banking Services
N.A.I.C.S.: 522110
Carlos Titto Almora Ayona (Chm)

BANCO DE ESPANA

C Alcala 48, 28014, Madrid, Spain
Tel.: (34) 91 338 5000   ES
Web Site: http://www.bde.es
Year Founded: 1782
Sales Range: $1-4.9 Billion
Banking Services
N.A.I.C.S.: 521110
Luis M. Linde (Governor)

BANCO DE GUATEMALA

7a Av 22-01 zona 1, Guatemala, Guatemala
Tel.: (502) 2429 6000
Web Site: http://www.banguat.gob.gt
Banking Services
N.A.I.C.S.: 521110
Julio Roberto Suarez Guerra (Pres)

BANCO DE LA NACION AR-GENTINA

Bartolome Mitre 326, C1036AAF, Buenos Aires, Argentina
Tel.: (54) 1143478452   Ar
Web Site: http://www.bna.com.ar
Year Founded: 1891
Sales Range: $1-4.9 Billion
Emp.: 16,000
Retail Commercial & Investment Banking Leasing & International Trade Financing Services
N.A.I.C.S.: 522110
Alicia Ines Caballero (Sec)

Subsidiaries:

Banco de la Nacion Argentina   (1)
777 Brickell Ave Ste 802, Miami, FL 33131
Tel.: (305) 371-7500
International Trade Financing
N.A.I.C.S.: 522299
Claudio R. Alemann (Gen Mgr)

Branch (Domestic):

Banco de la Nacion Argentina - New York   (2)
230 Park Ave Frnt B, New York, NY 10169-0017
Tel.: (212) 303-0600
Web Site: http://www.bna.com.ar
Sales Range: $25-49.9 Million
Emp.: 42
International Trade Financing
N.A.I.C.S.: 522299
Miguel Angel Mandrile (Gen Mgr)

Nacion Bursatil S.A   (1)
Florida 238 Piso 3, Buenos Aires, Argentina
Tel.: (54) 1160760200
Web Site: https://nacionbursatil.com.ar
Portfolio Management Services
N.A.I.C.S.: 523150

Nacion Reaseguros S.A   (1)
San Martin 913, C1004AAS, Buenos Aires, Argentina
Tel.: (54) 1143199900
Web Site:
  https://www.nacionreaseguros.com.ar
Reinsurance Services
N.A.I.C.S.: 524130

Nacion Servicios S.A   (1)
Dr T M de Anchorena 454, C1170ACH, Buenos Aires, Argentina
Tel.: (54) 1145102100
Commercial Banking Services
N.A.I.C.S.: 522110

Pellegrini S.A   (1)

Av Corrientes 345 2, C1043AAD, Buenos Aires, Argentina
Tel.: (54) 1143131412
Commercial Banking Services
N.A.I.C.S.: 522110

BANCO DE LA PROVINCIA DE BUENOS AIRES

San Martin 137, C1004AAC, Buenos Aires, Argentina
Tel.: (54) 1143470000
Web Site:
http://www.bancoprovincia.com.ar
Year Founded: 1882
Sales Range: $1-4.9 Billion
Emp.: 14,000
International Banking
N.A.I.C.S.: 522299
Carlos Francisco Dellepiane *(Vice Chm)*

Subsidiaries:

Grupo Banco Provincia S.A. **(1)**
San Martin 108-Piso 17-18 y 20, Buenos Aires, C1004AAD, Argentina
Tel.: (54) 11 4347 0096
Commercial Banking Services
N.A.I.C.S.: 522110

Subsidiary (Domestic):

Bapro Mandatos y Negocios S.A. **(2)**
Carlos Pellegrini 91 1009, Buenos Aires, Argentina
Tel.: (54) 11 5167 6099
Commercial Banking Services
N.A.I.C.S.: 522110

Provincia Seguros S.A. **(2)**
Carlos Pellegrini 71, Buenos Aires, C1009ABA, Argentina
Tel.: (54) 11 4346 7300
Web Site:
http://www.provinciaseguros.com.ar
Commercial Banking Services
N.A.I.C.S.: 522110

Provincia Bursatil S.A. **(1)**
San Martin 108 - Piso 12, C1004AAD, Buenos Aires, Argentina
Tel.: (54) 11 4347 0132
Web Site:
http://www.provinciabursatil.com.ar
Commercial Banking Services
N.A.I.C.S.: 522110
Eduardo Andres Eleta *(Pres)*

Provincia Microempresas S.A. **(1)**
Av P Luro 3869 PB Mar del Plata, Buenos Aires, Argentina
Tel.: (54) 223 476 0139
Commercial Banking Services
N.A.I.C.S.: 522110

BANCO DE LA REPUBLICA COLOMBIA

Carrera 7 14-78, PO Box 3551, Bogota, 111711, Colombia
Tel.: (57) 13431111
Web Site: http://www.banrep.gov.co
Year Founded: 1923
Sales Range: $450-499.9 Million
Central Bank
N.A.I.C.S.: 521110

BANCO DE MOCAMBIQUE

Av 25 de Setembro 1695, PO Box 423, Maputo, 258, Mozambique
Tel.: (258) 21354600
Web Site: http://www.bancomoc.mz
Sales Range: $1-9.9 Million
Banking Services
N.A.I.C.S.: 521110
Ernesto Gouveia Gove *(Governor)*

BANCO DE OCCIDENTE

Piso 15, No 7-61 Carrera 4a, Cali, Colombia
Tel.: (57) 92 886 1111   CL
Web Site:
http://www.bancodeoccidente.com

Sales Range: $100-124.9 Million
Banking & Financial Services
N.A.I.C.S.: 522110

BANCO DE PORTUGAL

R do Ouro 27, 1100-150, Lisbon, Portugal
Tel.: (351) 213213200
Web Site: http://www.bportugal.pt
Sales Range: $1-4.9 Billion
Emp.: 1,689
Banking Services
N.A.I.C.S.: 521110
Carlos da Silva Costa *(Governor)*

BANCO DE SABADELL, S.A.

Avda Oscar Espla 37, 03007, Alicante, Barcelona, Spain
Tel.: (34) 963085000   ES
Web Site:
https://www.bancsabadell.com
Year Founded: 1881
SAB—(MAD)
Rev.: $9,344,653,572
Assets: $253,802,023,527
Liabilities: $238,823,385,495
Net Worth: $14,978,638,032
Earnings: $1,439,243,471
Emp.: 19,316
Fiscal Year-end: 12/31/23
Financial Investment Services
N.A.I.C.S.: 523999

Subsidiaries:

BanSabadell Correduria de Seguros SA **(1)**
Calle Del Sena Pg Ind Can Sant Joan, Barcelona, Spain
Tel.: (34) 937289459
Sales Range: $50-74.9 Million
Emp.: 100
Insurance Agencies & Brokerages
N.A.I.C.S.: 524210

BanSabadell Finanziaria SpA. **(1)**
Corso Venezia 5, 20121, Milan, Italy
Tel.: (39) 0276007552
Web Site:
http://www.grupobancosabadell.com
Commericial Banking
N.A.I.C.S.: 522110

BanSabadell Fincom, E.F.C., S.A. **(1)**
Sant Cugat Of Valles, 08190, Barcelona, Spain
Tel.: (34) 935916300
Web Site:
http://www.bansabadellfincom.com
Sales Range: $50-74.9 Million
Emp.: 100
Financial Investment Activities
N.A.I.C.S.: 523999

BanSabadell Holding, S.L. **(1)**
C Del Seine Pq AE Can Sant Joan 12, Sant Cugat del Valles, 08172, Spain
Tel.: (34) 937289289
Web Site: http://www.bancsabadell.com
Investment Management Service
N.A.I.C.S.: 523999

BanSabadell Inversion, S.A., S.G.I.I.C. **(1)**
Calle Del Sena Pq Activ Economicas Can San Joa, Sant Cugat Del Valles, Barcelona, Spain
Tel.: (34) 937289289
Nondepository Credit Intermediation
N.A.I.C.S.: 522299

BancSabadell d'Andorra, S.A. **(1)**
Av del Fener 7, AG500, Escaldes-Engordany, Andorra
Tel.: (376) 735600
Web Site: http://www.bsandorra.com
Sales Range: $50-74.9 Million
Emp.: 100
Commericial Banking
N.A.I.C.S.: 522110

Banco Guipuzcoano S.A. **(1)**
Avenida de la Libertad 21, San Sebastian, 28004, Spain

Tel.: (34) 943418100
Sales Range: $500-549.9 Million
Banking Services
N.A.I.C.S.: 522110
Antonio Salvador Serrats Iriarte *(Vice Chm)*

Subsidiary (Domestic):

Ederra, S.A. **(2)**
Camino de Portuetxe 35-A Igara, San Sebastian, 20018, Guipuzcoa, Spain
Tel.: (34) 943 21 79 10
Web Site: http://www.ederra.com.ar
Real Estate Services
N.A.I.C.S.: 531210

Grao Castalia, S.L. **(2)**
Haygon La Almazara SL San Vicente del Raspe, Valencia, 46004, Spain
Tel.: (34) 963528181
Real Estate Property Management Services
N.A.I.C.S.: 531312

Guipuzcoano Capital, S.A. **(2)**
Avenida de la Libertad 2, 20004, San Sebastian, Guipuzcoa, Spain
Tel.: (34) 943 418 564
Sales Range: $75-99.9 Million
Emp.: 200
Securities Brokerages & Banking Services
N.A.I.C.S.: 523150

Guipuzcoano Correduria de Seguros del Grupo Banco Guipuzcoano, S.A. **(2)**
Camino de Portuetxe 35-A Igara, 20018, San Sebastian, Guipuzcoa, Spain
Tel.: (34) 943 41 85 85
Commercial Banking Services
N.A.I.C.S.: 522110

Guipuzcoano Entidad Gestora de Fondos de Pensiones , S.A. **(2)**
Paseo De La Concha 11, San Sebastian, 20007, Guipuzcoa, Spain
Tel.: (34) 943418692
Sales Range: $50-74.9 Million
Emp.: 3
Pension Fund Management Services
N.A.I.C.S.: 523940

Banco Urquijo S.A. **(1)**
Serrano 71, 28006, Madrid, Spain
Tel.: (34) 913372000
Web Site: http://www.bancourquijo.com
Sales Range: $100-124.9 Million
Emp.: 200
Banking Services
N.A.I.C.S.: 522110

Bansabadell Factura, S.L. **(1)**
C Del Sena Pq Actividades Economicas Cant San 12, 8174, Sant Cugat del Valles, Barcelona, Spain
Tel.: (34) 937289289
Commercial Banking Services
N.A.I.C.S.: 522110

Easo Bolsa, S.A. **(1)**
Portuetxe Street 35, 20018, San Sebastian, Spain
Tel.: (34) 943418564
Financial Management Services
N.A.I.C.S.: 523999

Espais SL **(1)**
Ave Diagonal 67 6th floor, 8019, Barcelona, Spain
Tel.: (34) 932920000
Web Site: http://www.espais.es
Sales Range: $50-74.9 Million
Emp.: 14
Real Estate Agents & Brokers
N.A.I.C.S.: 531210
Consejero Delegado *(Pres)*

Financiera Iberoamericana, S.A. **(1)**
5th Ave 78-80 St Miramar Trade Center Edificio Barcelona office 314, Playa La Habana, Havana, Cuba
Tel.: (53) 72043196
Financial Investment Activities
N.A.I.C.S.: 523999

Geysers International Inc. **(1)**
4811 Beach Blvd Ste 401, Jacksonville, FL 32207-4867
Tel.: (904) 356-1100
Web Site: http://www.geysers.net
Software Publisher
N.A.I.C.S.: 513210

Landscape Parcsud SL **(1)**
Calle Sant Vicenc 51, Sabadell, Spain
Tel.: (34) 932473957
Land Subdivision
N.A.I.C.S.: 237210

Sabadell Corporate Finance, S.L. **(1)**
Principe de Vergara 125, Madrid, 28002, Spain
Tel.: (34) 913 19 88 07
Web Site:
http://www.sabadellcorporatefinance.com
Sales Range: $75-99.9 Million
Emp.: 10
Investment Banking & Financial Advisory Services
N.A.I.C.S.: 523150
Pablo Hernandez Sampelayo *(Mng Dir-ECM)*

SabadellCAM **(1)**
San Fernando 40, 03001, Alicante, Spain
Tel.: (34) 902100112
Web Site: http://www.cam.es
Banking Services
N.A.I.C.S.: 522110

Subsidiary (Domestic):

CAM Capital, S.A.U. **(2)**
Avenida Oscar Espla 37, 03007, Alicante, Spain
Tel.: (34) 965143791
Banking Services
N.A.I.C.S.: 522110

Mediterraneo Vida S.A. **(2)**
Avda de Elche N 178 Edificio Centro Administrativo, 03008, Alicante, Spain
Tel.: (34) 965905344
General Insurance Services
N.A.I.C.S.: 524210

Meserco, S.L. **(2)**
Consell de Cent 284, Barcelona, 08022, Spain
Tel.: (34) 934342210
Business Management Consulting Services
N.A.I.C.S.: 541611

Tabimed Gestion de Proyectos, S.L **(2)**
Avenida General Marva 8, 03004, Alicante, Spain
Tel.: (34) 965901400
Web Site: http://www.tabimed.es
Engineering Consulting Services
N.A.I.C.S.: 541330

Servicios Reunidos, S.A. **(1)**
Avenida Pena De Francia, La Alberca, 37624, Spain
Tel.: (34) 923415093
Insurance Management Services
N.A.I.C.S.: 524298

Spanish Power, S.L. **(1)**
Juan De Mena 10, 28014, Madrid, Spain
Tel.: (34) 915313907
Web Site: http://wwwfusgar.com
Sales Range: $25-49.9 Million
Emp.: 10
Automotive Mechanical & Electrical Repair & Maintenance
N.A.I.C.S.: 811114
Don Ricardo Fuster *(Mgr)*

TSB Banking Group plc **(1)**
20 Gresham Street, London, EC2V 7JE, United Kingdom
Tel.: (44) 3459758758
Web Site: http://www.tsb.co.uk
Rev.: $1,483,762,176
Assets: $57,372,002,560
Liabilities: $54,679,698,688
Net Worth: $2,692,303,872
Earnings: $160,140,544
Emp.: 8,296
Fiscal Year-end: 12/31/2017
Bank Holding Company
N.A.I.C.S.: 551111
Ralph Coates *(CFO)*

Subsidiary (Domestic):

TSB Bank plc **(2)**
Henry Duncan House 120 George Street, Edinburgh, EH2 4LH, United Kingdom **(100%)**
Tel.: (44) 3459758758

Banco de Sabadell, S.A.—(Continued)

Web Site: http://www.tsb.co.uk
Commericial Banking
N.A.I.C.S.: 522110
Helen Rose (COO)

Tecnocredit, S.A. (1)
Plz Catalunya 1, Sabadell, Spain
Tel.: (34) 934194440
Management Consulting Services
N.A.I.C.S.: 541618

BANCO DEL BAJIO, S.A.
Av Manuel J Clouthier 402 Col, Leon,
Guanajuato, 37128, Leon, Guana-
juato, Mexico
Tel.: (52) 4777104632
Web Site: http://www.bb.com.mx
Year Founded: 1994
BBAJIO—(MEX)
Rev.: $1,466,824,538
Assets: $20,284,445,895
Liabilities: $17,836,887,248
Net Worth: $2,447,558,647
Earnings: $648,868,826
Emp.: 6,422
Fiscal Year-end: 12/31/23
Commercial Banking Services
N.A.I.C.S.: 522110
Edgardo Del Rincon Gutierrez (CEO)

**BANCO DEL CARIBE, C.A.
BANCO UNIVERSAL**
Dr Paul a Salvador del Leon Edif
Banco del Caribe, Piso 10, 101A, Ca-
racas, Venezuela
Tel.: (58) 2125055511
Web Site:
    http://www.bancaribe.com.ve
ABC.A—(BVC)
Sales Range: $50-74.9 Million
Emp.: 2,000
Banking Services
N.A.I.C.S.: 522110
Juan Carlos Dao (Pres)

BANCO DELTA S.A.
Via Spain Torre Delta Old Bank Build-
ing Boston Ground Floor, PO Box
0816-07831, Panama, Panama
Tel.: (507) 340 0000
Web Site: http://www.bandelta.com
Year Founded: 1972
BDEL—(PAN)
Sales Range: Less than $1 Million
Commercial Banking Services
N.A.I.C.S.: 522110
Arturo Muller Norman (Pres)

BANCO DI CARIBE N.V.
Schottegatweg Oost 205, PO Box
3785, Willemstad, Curacao
Tel.: (599) 9 432 3000   CW
Web Site:
    http://www.bancodicaribe.com
Year Founded: 1973
Rev.: $56,860,973
Assets: $1,020,975,172
Liabilities: $920,527,546
Net Worth: $100,447,627
Earnings: $7,360,904
Fiscal Year-end: 12/31/19
Financial Services
N.A.I.C.S.: 523999
Percival N. Virginia (Mng Dir-Ops)

Subsidiaries:

Banco di Caribe (Aruba) N.V. (1)
Vondellaan 31, Oranjestad, Aruba
Tel.: (297) 5 232000
Emp.: 75
Commercial Banking Services
N.A.I.C.S.: 522110

Ennia Caribe Holding NV (1)
JB Gorsiraweg 6, PO Box 581, Willemstad,
Curacao   (100%)
Tel.: (599) 94343800
Web Site: http://www.ennia.com

Sales Range: $100-124.9 Million
Emp.: 180
Holding Company; Life Insurance Products
& Services
N.A.I.C.S.: 551112

**BANCO DI DESIO E DELLA
BRIANZA S.P.A.**
Via E Hovagnati 1, 20832, Desio,
Italy
Tel.: (39) 03626131   IT
Web Site: http://www.bancodesio.it
Year Founded: 1909
Sales Range: $300-349.9 Million
Emp.: 1,397
Banking Services
N.A.I.C.S.: 522110
Agostino Gavazzi (Chm)

Subsidiaries:

Banco Desio Lazio S P A (1)
Via Po 6 8, 00198, Rome, Italy
Tel.: (39) 06852571
Web Site: http://www.bancodesiolazio.it
Commercial Banking Services
N.A.I.C.S.: 522110

Brianfid-Lux S A (1)
6 placedenacy, L-1840, Luxembourg, Lux-
embourg
Tel.: (352) 2602881
Emp.: 10
Commercial Banking Services
N.A.I.C.S.: 522110

Chiara Assicurazioni S P A (1)
Via Galileo Galilei 7, Milan, 20124, Italy
Tel.: (39) 026328811
Web Site: http://www.chiaraassicurazioni.it
Sales Range: $50-74.9 Million
Emp.: 42
Non-Life Insurance Services
N.A.I.C.S.: 524128

BANCO DO BRASIL S.A.
Saun Qd 5 Lt B Asa Norte, Brasilia,
CEP 70040-911, DF, Brazil
Tel.: (55) 40035285   BR
Web Site: https://www.bb.com.br
Year Founded: 1808
BBAS3—(BRAZ)
Rev.: $53,358,608,527
Assets: $446,941,158,318
Liabilities: $419,132,454,993
Net Worth: $27,808,703,325
Earnings: $2,562,142,016
Emp.: 100,622
Fiscal Year-end: 12/31/16
Commercial Banking & Financial Ser-
vices
N.A.I.C.S.: 522110
Andre Guilherme Brandao (CEO)

Subsidiaries:

BB Administradora de Cartoes de
Credito S.A.   (1)
SBS Quadra 1 Bloco A Lote 25 Ed Sede I
Fl 9, 70073-900, Brasilia, Brazil (100%)
Tel.: (55) 6133101300
Sales Range: $75-99.9 Million
Emp.: 100
Credit & Financial Services
N.A.I.C.S.: 522299

BB Banco de Investimento S.A. (1)
R Senador Dantas, 105 36 Andar, Rio de
Janeiro, RJ, Brazil   (100%)
Tel.: (55) 2138083625
Web Site: https://www.bancobrasil.com.br
Investment & Financial Services
N.A.I.C.S.: 523150

BB Leasing-Arrendamento
Mercantil   (1)
Setor Bancario Sul Quadra 4 Bloco C Ed
Sede III, 7 Andar, 70089 900, Brasilia, DF,
Brazil   (100%)
Tel.: (55) 6133103253
Sales Range: $50-74.9 Million
Emp.: 25
Credit & Financial Services
N.A.I.C.S.: 522299

BB Seguridade Participacoes
S/A   (1)
SAUN Quadra 05 Bloco B 3 andar Edificio
BB, Asa Norte, Brasilia, 70040-912, DF,
Brazil
Tel.: (55) 34932929
Web Site:
    http://www.bancodobrasilseguridade.com
Rev.: $1,023,912,157
Assets: $2,550,050,007
Liabilities: $1,159,806,761
Net Worth: $1,399,852,226
Earnings: $756,160,968
Emp.: 167
Fiscal Year-end: 12/31/2021
Holding Company; Financial Services
N.A.I.C.S.: 551112
Rafael Augusto Sperendio (Dir-Investor Re-
lations)

Banco Patagonia Sudameris
S.A.   (1)
Teneiente General J d peron 500 - 3 piso,
Buenos Aires, Argentina
Tel.: (54) 11 4323 5000
Web Site:
    http://www.bancopatagonia.com.ar
Sales Range: $450-499.9 Million
Emp.: 2,240
Commercial Banking Services
N.A.I.C.S.: 522110
Joao Carlos Nobrega Pecego (Chm)

Banco do Brasil AG Austria (1)
Praterstrasse 31 4th Floor Galaxy Tower,
1020, Vienna, Austria   (100%)
Tel.: (43) 151266630
Web Site: http://www.bancodobrasil.at
Sales Range: $1-9.9 Million
Emp.: 20
Banking Activities
N.A.I.C.S.: 522299
Guilherme Andre Frantz (Mng Dir)

Banco do Brasil S.A. - New York (1)
600 5th Ave Fl 3, New York, NY
10020-2302   (100%)
Tel.: (212) 626-7000
Sales Range: $50-74.9 Million
Emp.: 100
International Banking
N.A.I.C.S.: 522110

Brasilian American Merchant
Bank   (1)
Elizabethan Sq Phase 3 Bldg 4th Fl, PO
Box 1360 GT, Shedden Rd, Georgetown,
Grand Cayman, Cayman Islands (100%)
Tel.: (345) 9495907
Sales Range: $50-74.9 Million
Emp.: 12
Merchant Banking Activities
N.A.I.C.S.: 522299

Subsidiary (Non-US):

BB Securities Ltd. (2)
16 St Martins Le Trand Fl 7, EC1A 4NA,
London, United Kingdom -
England   (100%)
Tel.: (44) 2073675800
Sales Range: $50-74.9 Million
Securities House
N.A.I.C.S.: 523999

Brasilprev Seguros e Previdencia
S.A.   (1)
Rua Alexandre Dumas 1671, Sao Paulo,
04717-004, Brazil
Tel.: (55) 11 2162 6600
Web Site: http://www.brasilprev.com.br
Pension Fund Management Services
N.A.I.C.S.: 523940
Walter Malieni (CEO)

Cobra Technologia S.A. (1)
Estrada Dos Bandeirantes 7966 Curicica,
Jacarepagua, 22783 110, Rio de Janeiro,
Brazil   (100%)
Tel.: (55) 2124428800
Sales Range: $300-349.9 Million
Emp.: 450
Computer Industry
N.A.I.C.S.: 518210

**BANCO DO ESTADO DO RIO
GRANDE DO SUL SA**

Rua Capitao Montanha 177 4th Floor,
Porto Alegre, 90010-040, Brazil
Tel.: (55) 5132153232   BR
Web Site:
    https://www.banrisul.com.br
Year Founded: 1928
BRSR5—(BRAZ)
Rev.: $2,664,385,442
Assets: $22,164,204,011
Liabilities: $20,700,600,798
Net Worth: $1,763,603,214
Earnings: $180,982,459
Fiscal Year-end: 12/31/23
Banking Services
N.A.I.C.S.: 522110
Odir Alberto Pinheiro Tonollier (Chm)

Subsidiaries:

Banrisul S.A. Corretora de VM e
Cambio   (1)
Rua Caldas Junior 108 - 2 andar, Centro,
Porto Alegre, 90010-260, Brazil
Tel.: (55) 5132151062
Web Site:
    https://www.banrisulcorretora.com.br
Real Estate Asset Management Services
N.A.I.C.S.: 531390

BANCO FIBRA S.A.
Av Presidente Juscelino Kubitschek
360-5th to 9th Floor, Vila Nova Con-
ceicao, 04543-000, Sao Paulo, Brazil
Tel.: (55) 1138476500
Web Site:
    http://www.bancofibra.com.br
Sales Range: $550-599.9 Million
Emp.: 1,051
Credit Operation & Banking Services
N.A.I.C.S.: 522110
Ricardo Steinbruch (Chm)

BANCO GENERAL, S.A.
Ave Aquilino De La Guardia y Ave
5ta B Sur Torre Banco General, Apar-
tado Postal 0816-00843, Panama,
Panama
Tel.: (507) 303 7000
Web Site: http://www.bgeneral.com
Year Founded: 1955
BGEN—(PAN)
Sales Range: Less than $1 Million
Banking Services
N.A.I.C.S.: 522110
Juan Raul Humbert Arias (VP)

Subsidiaries:

Banco General (Costa Rica),
S.A.   (1)
Torre Banco General Trejos Montealegre
Escazu, Contiguo Centro Corporativo El
Cedral, San Jose, Costa Rica
Tel.: (506) 25884600
Web Site: http://www.bgeneral.fi.cr
Private Banking Services
N.A.I.C.S.: 522110

General de Seguros, S. A. (1)
50th Street and Aquilino de La Guardia
10th Floor, Panama, Panama
Tel.: (507) 3032222
Web Site: http://www.generaldeseguros.com
Insurance Services
N.A.I.C.S.: 524210

Vale General, S.A. (1)
Ave Aquilino de la Guardia y Calle 50 PH
Plaza Banco General Piso 12, Panama,
Panama
Tel.: (507) 3005001
Web Site: http://www.valegeneral.com
Finance Consulting Services
N.A.I.C.S.: 541611

BANCO GNB SUDAMERIS S.A.
Carrera 7 No 75-85/87, Bogota, Co-
lombia
Tel.: (57) 1 275 0000   Co
Web Site:
    http://www.gnbsudameris.com.co
Year Founded: 1920

Sales Range: $1-4.9 Billion
Emp.: 3,487
Banking Services
N.A.I.C.S.: 522110
Camilo Verastegui Carvajal *(Pres)*

Subsidiaries:

Banco GNB Colombia S.A. **(1)**
Carrera 8 N 15-60, Bogota, Colombia
Tel.: (57) 1 334 5088
Web Site: http://www.bancognb.com.co
Emp.: 744
Commericial Banking
N.A.I.C.S.: 522110

Banco GNB Paraguay S.A. **(1)**
Avenida Aviadores del Chaco 2351 esq,
Herib Campos Cervera, Asuncion, Para-
guay
Tel.: (595) 21 618 3000
Web Site: http://www.bancognb.com.py
Emp.: 200
Commercial Banking
N.A.I.C.S.: 522110

Banco GNB Peru S.A. **(1)**
Jr Carabaya No 891 -899, Lima, Peru
Tel.: (51) 1 616 3000
Web Site: http://www.bancognb.com.pe
Emp.: 800
Commercial Banking Services
N.A.I.C.S.: 522110

Servibanca S.A. **(1)**
Carrera 8 No 15-42, Bogota, Colombia
Tel.: (57) 1 344 1600
Web Site: http://www.servibanca.com.co
Automated Teller Machine Network Opera-
tor
N.A.I.C.S.: 522110

BANCO GUAYAQUIL SA

Pichincha 107 and P Icaza, Guaya-
quil, Ecuador
Tel.: (593) 3730100
Web Site:
https://www.bancoguayaquil.com
GYL—(GUA)
Sales Range: Less than $1 Million
Commercial Banking Services
N.A.I.C.S.: 522110
Danilo Carrera Drouet *(Chm)*

BANCO HIPOTECARIO SA

Reconquista 151, 1003, Buenos Ai-
res, 1003, Argentina
Tel.: (54) 1143475000
Web Site:
https://www.hipotecario.com.ar
Commercial Banking Services
N.A.I.C.S.: 522210
Eduardo Sergio Elsztain *(CEO)*

BANCO INTER S.A.

Avenida do Contorno 7777-Lourdes,
Belo Horizonte, 30110-051, Minas
Gerais, Brazil
Tel.: (55) 3121017000
Web Site:
http://www.bancointer.com.br
BIDI4—(BRAZ)
Sales Range: Less than $1 Million
Commercial Banking Services
N.A.I.C.S.: 522110
Joao Vitor Nazareth Menin Teixeira
de Souza *(CEO)*

BANCO INTERAMERICANO DE FINANZAS SA

Av Rivera Navarrete 600, San Isidro,
Peru
Tel.: (51) 16319000
Web Site: https://www.banbif.com.pe
Year Founded: 1990
BIFC1—(LIM)
Sales Range: Less than $1 Million
Investment Banking Services
N.A.I.C.S.: 523150
Sandro Gustavo Fuentes Acurio
(Chm)

BANCO INTERNACIONAL

Moneda 818, Santiago, Chile
Tel.: (56) 229897000
Commercial Banking Services
N.A.I.C.S.: 522110
Segismundo Schulin-Zeuthen Ser-
rano *(Chm)*

BANCO INTERNACIONAL DE COSTA RICA, S.A.

50th Floor Balboa Ave Aquilino De La
Guardia Street, Panama, Panama
Tel.: (507) 208 9500
Web Site: http://www.bicsa.com
Year Founded: 1976
BICSA—(PAN)
Sales Range: $100-124.9 Million
Emp.: 170
Banking Services
N.A.I.C.S.: 522110
Daniel Gonzalez Santiesteban *(CEO)*

BANCO LATINOAMERICANO DE COMERCIO EXTERIOR, S.A.

Torre V Business Park Avenida La
Rotonda Urb Costa del Este, PO Box
0819-08730, Panama, Panama
Tel.: (507) 2108500
Web Site: https://www.bladex.com
Year Founded: 1979
BLX—(NYSE)
Rev.: $166,672,000
Assets: $9,283,910,000
Liabilities: $8,214,563,000
Net Worth: $1,069,347,000
Earnings: $92,040,000
Emp.: 238
Fiscal Year-end: 12/31/22
International Banking Services
N.A.I.C.S.: 522299
Ana Graciela de Mendez *(CFO & Exec VP)*

Subsidiaries:

Bladex Representacao Ltda. **(1)**
R Leopoldo Couto de Magalhaes Junior 110
1 Fl, Sao Paulo, 04542-000, Brazil
Tel.: (55) 1121989602
Commercial Banking Services
N.A.I.C.S.: 522110

BANCO MACRO S.A.

Avenida Eduardo Madero 1182, Bue-
nos Aires, Argentina
Tel.: (54) 1152226500 Ar
Web Site: https://www.macro.com.ar
BMA—(NYSE)
Rev.: $7,282,213,297
Assets: $24,851,528,679
Liabilities: $18,761,127,355
Net Worth: $6,090,401,324
Earnings: $484,798,889
Emp.: 7,796
Fiscal Year-end: 12/31/22
Banking Services
N.A.I.C.S.: 522110
Delfin Jorge Ezequiel Carballo *(Vice Chm)*

Subsidiaries:

Argentina Clearing S.A. **(1)**
Paraguay 777 15th Floor, Rosario, Argen-
tina
Tel.: (54) 3415302900
Web Site: https://argentinaclearing.com.ar
Sales Range: $50-74.9 Million
Emp.: 10
Investment Advice
N.A.I.C.S.: 523940

Banco Itau Argentina S.A. **(1)**
Cerrito 740, 1309 CF, Buenos Aires, Argen-
tina
Tel.: (54) 43728421
Web Site: http://www.itau.com.ar
Full Banking Services
N.A.I.C.S.: 522299

Garantizar S.G.R. **(1)**
Sarmiento 663 Piso 6, C1041AAM, Buenos
Aires, Argentina
Tel.: (54) 1143252898
Web Site: http://www.garantizar.com.ar
Scientific & Technical Consulting Services
N.A.I.C.S.: 541690

Macro Bank Ltd **(1)**
PO Box N-4444, Nassau, Bahamas
Tel.: (242) 3236418
Trusts Estates & Agency Accounts
N.A.I.C.S.: 525920
Gustavo Alejandro Manriquez *(CEO & Gen Mgr)*

Macro Securities S.A. **(1)**
Sales Range: $50-74.9 Million
Emp.: 30
Commercial Banking
N.A.I.C.S.: 522110

Nuevo Banco Suquia S.A. **(1)**
25 de Mayo 160, Cordoba, Argentina
Tel.: (54) 3514200200
Web Site: http://www.bancosuquia.com.ar
Commericial Banking
N.A.I.C.S.: 522110

Proin S.A. **(1)**
Apartado Postal 319 6150, Santa Ana, San
Jose, Costa Rica
Tel.: (506) 22395271
Real Estate Property Lessors
N.A.I.C.S.: 531190

Visa Argentina S.A. **(1)**
Web Site: http://www.visa.com.ar
Retail Electronic Payment Operator
N.A.I.C.S.: 522299

Subsidiary (Domestic):

Banelco S.A. **(2)**
Mexico 444, Buenos Aires, Argentina
Tel.: (54) 1143455678
Scientific & Technical Consulting Services
N.A.I.C.S.: 541690

BANCO MASTER S.A.

Brigadier Faria Lima Avenue, 3,477
Tower B 5th Floor Itaim Bibi, 04538-
133, Sao Paulo, Brazil
Tel.: (55) 1140031117
Web Site: https://bancomaster.com.br
Year Founded: 1973
Banking Services
N.A.I.C.S.: 522110

Subsidiaries:

Banco Voiter S.A. **(1)**
Pres. Juscelino Kubitschek Avenue, 50 4th,
5th and 6th floors, 04543-000, Sao Paulo,
Brazil
Tel.: (55) 1133156777
Web Site: https://www.voiter.com
Banking Services
N.A.I.C.S.: 523150

Unit (Domestic):

Banco Indusval Multistock **(2)**
Rua Boa Vista 356-5-10 andar, Centro,
CEP 01014-000, Sao Paulo, SP, Brazil
Tel.: (55) 0800 704 0418
Web Site: http://www.bip.b.br
Commercial Banking Services
N.A.I.C.S.: 522110
Marcelo Hiroshi *(CIO)*

Banco Indusval Multistock - Porto
Alegre Unit **(2)**
Rua Furriel Luiz Antonio Vargas 250 - sala
802, 90470-130, Porto Alegre, Rio Grande
do Sul, Brazil
Tel.: (55) 5134069100
Commercial Banking Services
N.A.I.C.S.: 522110

Banco Indusval Multistock - Recife
Unit **(2)**
Av Engenheiro Domingos Ferreira 2589 -
sala 204, 51020-031, Recife, Pernambuco,
Brazil
Tel.: (55) 81 3092 2150
Commercial Banking Services
N.A.I.C.S.: 522110

Banco Indusval Multistock - Rio de
Janeiro Unit **(2)**
Rua Lauro Muller 116 - sala 3501, 22290-
160, Rio de Janeiro, Brazil
Tel.: (55) 2135783200
Sales Range: $50-74.9 Million
Emp.: 10
Commercial Banking Services
N.A.I.C.S.: 522110
Andres Pedrera *(Gen Mgr)*

Subsidiary (Domestic):

Banco Smartbank S.A. **(2)**
Rua Tabapua 841, Itaim Bibi, Sao Paulo,
04533-010, SP, Brazil
Tel.: (55) 8008780630
Web Site: http://www.smartbank.com.br
Banking Services
N.A.I.C.S.: 522210

BANCO MERCANTIL DO BRA- SIL S.A.

Avenida do Contorno 5800 14 andar,
Savassi, Belo Horizonte, 30110-042,
Minas Gerais, Brazil
Tel.: (55) 30575242 BR
Web Site:
http://www.mercantildobrasil.com.br
Year Founded: 1940
BMEB4—(BRAZ)
Rev.: $970,136,010
Assets: $4,055,247,594
Liabilities: $3,723,016,992
Net Worth: $332,230,602
Earnings: $81,479,031
Emp.: 3,000
Fiscal Year-end: 12/31/23
Banking Services
N.A.I.C.S.: 523150
Roberto Godoy Assumpcao *(Dir-IR)*

Subsidiaries:

Banco Mercantil de Investimentos
S.A. **(1)**
R Rio de Janeiro 654 - 6 Floor, 30160912,
Belo Horizonte, MG, Brazil
Tel.: (55) 3130576336
Sales Range: $1-9.9 Million
Financial Services
N.A.I.C.S.: 523999
Athaide Vieira Dos Santos *(Dir-IR)*

Mercantil do Brasil Financeira
S.A. **(1)**
R Rio de Janeiro 654 - 6 Floor, 30160912,
Belo Horizonte, MG, Brazil
Tel.: (55) 3130576336
Sales Range: $10-24.9 Million
Consumer Financial Services
N.A.I.C.S.: 522291
Athaide Vieira Dos Santos *(Dir-IR)*

BANCO NACIONAL DE PANAMA

Via Spain Tower Banconal, PO Box
0816-05220, Panama, Panama
Tel.: (507) 5052900
Web Site:
http://www.banconal.com.pa
Year Founded: 1904
BNAL—(PAN)
Rev.: $361,079,412
Assets: $16,872,936,999
Liabilities: $15,910,719,873
Net Worth: $962,217,126
Earnings: $125,253,694
Emp.: 3,516
Fiscal Year-end: 12/31/20
Commercial Banking Services
N.A.I.C.S.: 522110
Lizbeth Ann Henriquez Leonard
(Pres)

BANCO OPPORTUNITY S/A

Av Presidente Wilson n 231 28 Andar, Centro, 20030-905, Rio de Janeiro, Brazil
Tel.: (55) 2138043434

Banco Opportunity S/A—(Continued)

Web Site:
http://www.opportunity.com.br
Year Founded: 1994
Sales Range: $25-49.9 Million
Emp.: 100
Asset Management Services
N.A.I.C.S.: 523940
Dorio Ferman *(Chm & CEO)*

BANCO PINE S.A.
Avenida Presidente Juscelino Ku-
bitschek 1.830 - 6 andar, Sao Paulo,
04543-900, Brazil
Tel.: (55) 1133725333
Web Site: http://www.pine.com
PINE4—(BRAZ)
Rev.: $143,337,184
Assets: $2,510,538,445
Liabilities: $2,302,310,048
Net Worth: $208,228,397
Earnings: ($29,265,937)
Emp.: 434
Fiscal Year-end: 12/31/19
Banking, Financial & Investment Ser-
vices
N.A.I.C.S.: 522110
Noberto Nogueira Pinheiro *(Chm)*

BANCO PRODUCTS (I) LTD.
Bil Near Bhaili Railway Station Padra
Road, Dist Vadodara, Baroda, 391
410, Gujarat, India
Tel.: (91) 2652318100
Web Site:
https://www.bancoindia.com
500039—(BOM)
Rev.: $267,949,118
Assets: $209,096,037
Liabilities: $75,090,779
Net Worth: $134,005,258
Earnings: $20,805,330
Emp.: 622
Fiscal Year-end: 03/31/22
Gaskets & Radiators Mfr
N.A.I.C.S.: 339991
Dinesh Kavthekar *(Officer-
Compliance & Sec)*

Subsidiaries:

NRF BVBA　　　　　　　　　　**(1)**
Boomsesteenweg 2, 2627, Schelle, Belgium
Tel.: (32) 3 8877 676
Web Site: http://www.nrf.eu
Automobile Radiator Mfr
N.A.I.C.S.: 336390

NRF Deutschland GmbH　　　**(1)**
Werner-Heisenberg-Strasse 22, 46446, Em-
merich am Rhein, Germany
Tel.: (49) 282296740
Sales Range: $25-49.9 Million
Emp.: 11
Heat Exchanger Mfr
N.A.I.C.S.: 332410
Alok Gupta *(Gen Mgr)*

NRF France SAS　　　　　　**(1)**
ZI 2-Batterie 500-145 rue Elsa Triolet,
59125, Trith-Saint-Leger, France
Tel.: (33) 327211717
Automobile Radiator Mfr
N.A.I.C.S.: 336390

NRF Handelsges. GmbH　　　**(1)**
Breitenleerstrasse 101/Halle 3, 1220, Vi-
enna, Austria
Tel.: (43) 1259 335 5
Web Site: http://www.nrf.eu
Automotive Air Conditioning System Mfr
N.A.I.C.S.: 336390

NRF Poland Spolka. Z.O.O　　**(1)**
Magazynowa 40, Jankowo Gdanskie, 80-
180, Kolbudy, Poland
Tel.: (48) 583431477
Emp.: 20
Radiator & Air Conditioning Component Mfr
N.A.I.C.S.: 333414

Nederlandse Radiateuren Fabriek
BV　　　　　　　　　　　　　**(1)**

Langenboomseweg 64, 5451 JM, Mill en
Sint Hubert, Netherlands
Tel.: (31) 485476476
Web Site: https://www.nrf.eu
Sales Range: $50-74.9 Million
Emp.: 200
Radiator & Air Conditioning Equipment Mfr
N.A.I.C.S.: 333414
Frank Toebes *(Mng Dir)*

Subsidiary (Non-US):

NRF Espana S.A.　　　　　　**(2)**
Avda Asegra 22, 18210, Peligros, Granada,
Spain
Tel.: (34) 31485476430
Emp.: 50
Automotive Air Conditioning System & Ra-
diator Distr
N.A.I.C.S.: 423120
Eduardo Gijon *(Mng Dir)*

BANCO SAFRA S.A.
Avenida Paulista 2100 8 Andar, Sao
Paulo, 01310 930, Brazil
Tel.: (55) 11 3175 7575　　　BR
Web Site: http://www.safra.com.br
Year Founded: 1955
Rev.: $3,608,563,441
Assets: $46,917,093,079
Liabilities: $43,880,151,046
Net Worth: $3,036,942,033
Earnings: $552,639,973
Emp.: 8,070
Fiscal Year-end: 12/31/18
Commericial Banking
N.A.I.C.S.: 522110
Alberto Corsetti *(CEO)*

Subsidiaries:

Chiquita Brands International,
Inc.　　　　　　　　　　　　**(1)**
4757 The Grove Drive Ste 260, Wind-
ermere, FL 34786
Tel.: (800) 468-9716
Web Site: http://www.chiquita.com
Rev.: $3,090,224,000
Assets: $1,612,038,000
Liabilities: $1,288,704,000
Net Worth: $323,334,000
Earnings: ($62,536,000)
Emp.: 120
Fiscal Year-end: 12/31/2014
Food Producer, Processor & Distr
N.A.I.C.S.: 311411
Stephen Coale *(Sr VP-Supply Chain)*

Subsidiary (Non-US):

Chiquita Brands International
Sarl　　　　　　　　　　　　**(2)**
Batiment B4 A-One Business Center Route
de l'Etraz, 1180, Rolle, Switzerland
Tel.: (41) 58 272 2000
Holding Company; Regional Managing Of-
fice; Fruit Distr
N.A.I.C.S.: 551112
Mario Pacheco *(Sr VP-Global Logistics)*

Subsidiary (Non-US):

Boeckmans Belgie NV　　　　**(3)**
Van Meterenkaai 1 bus 4, B-2000, Antwerp,
Belgium
Tel.: (32) 3202 0202
Web Site: http://www.boeckmans.be
Maritime Freight Transport Services
N.A.I.C.S.: 483111
Thierry Denave *(Gen Mgr)*

Boeckmans Nederland b.v.　　**(3)**
Spui 16, 3161 ED, Rhoon, Netherlands
Tel.: (31) 10 5030000
Web Site: http://www.boeckmans.nl
Shipping & Forwarding Freight Services
N.A.I.C.S.: 483111
Caroline Naaktgeboren *(Gen Mgr-Customer
Svc)*

Chiquita Banana Company BV　**(3)**
Franklinweg 35, 4207 HX, Gorinchem,
Netherlands
Tel.: (31) 183 69 31 11
Web Site: http://www.chiquita.nl
Sales Range: $125-149.9 Million
Banana Import & Export
N.A.I.C.S.: 111339

Subsidiary (Non-US):

Chiquita Deutschland GmbH　**(4)**
Neue Groninger Strasse 13, D-20457, Ham-
burg, Germany
Tel.: (49) 40 360239 200
Web Site: http://www.chiquita.de
Fruit & Vegetable Canning Services
N.A.I.C.S.: 311421
Marc Speidel *(Mng Dir, Member-Mgmt Bd &
Country Dir-Germany)*

Subsidiary (Domestic):

Chiquita Fruit Bar (Germany)
GmbH　　　　　　　　　　　**(5)**
Trankgasse 11, 50667, Cologne, Germany
Tel.: (49) 221 1608711
Web Site: http://www.chiquita-fruitbar.com
Emp.: 20
Fresh Fruit & Vegetable Juices & Smooth-
ies
N.A.I.C.S.: 311421
Christiane Kruse *(Office Mgr)*

Subsidiary (Non-US):

Processed Fruit Ingredients,
BVBA　　　　　　　　　　　**(4)**
Rijnkaai 37, Antwerp, 2000, Belgium
Tel.: (32) 26494961
Fruit & Vegetable Canning Services
N.A.I.C.S.: 311421

Subsidiary (Non-US):

Great White Fleet, Ltd.　　　　**(3)**
Van Meterenkaai 1, B-2000, Antwerp, Bel-
gium
Tel.: (32) 3 2020202
Web Site: http://www.boeckmans.be
Air Freight & Shipping Cargo Transport Ser-
vices
N.A.I.C.S.: 484230
Thierry de Nave *(Gen Mgr-Agency)*

Subsidiary (Domestic):

Chiquita Brands LLC　　　　　**(2)**
2051 SE 35th St, Fort Lauderdale, FL
33316-4019
Tel.: (954) 453-1201
Web Site: http://www.chiquita.com
Tree Fruits
N.A.I.C.S.: 111339
Darcilo Santos *(CEO & CFO)*

Plant (Domestic):

Chiquita Brands LLC -
Bethlehem　　　　　　　　　**(3)**
2777 Brodhead Rd, Bethlehem, PA 18020-
9448
Tel.: (610) 866-1851
Web Site: http://www.chiquita.com
Sales Range: $50-74.9 Million
Emp.: 14
Banana Ripening & Distribution Center
N.A.I.C.S.: 424480
Alvaro Alevedo *(Branch Mgr)*

Chiquita Brands LLC - Fort
Lauderdale　　　　　　　　　**(3)**
DCOTA Office Center 1855 Griffin Rd Ste
C436, Fort Lauderdale, FL 33004-2275
Tel.: (954) 527-7816
Web Site: http://www.chiquita.com
Sales Range: $75-99.9 Million
Emp.: 80
Fresh Fruit & Vegetable Service
N.A.I.C.S.: 424480

Chiquita Brands LLC - Freeport　**(3)**
1100 Cherry St, Freeport, TX 77541-5863
Tel.: (979) 233-0844
Web Site: http://www.chiquita.com
Sales Range: $50-74.9 Million
Emp.: 7
Bananas Ripening & Freight Transportation
N.A.I.C.S.: 483111
Tony Caranna *(Gen Mgr)*

Chiquita Brands LLC - Gulfport　**(3)**
1000 30th Ave, Gulfport, MS 39501
Tel.: (228) 864-5046
Web Site: http://www.chiquita.com
Sales Range: $10-24.9 Million
Emp.: 16
Bananas Freight Transportation
N.A.I.C.S.: 488510

Chiquita Brands LLC -
Wilmington　　　　　　　　　**(3)**
101 River Rd, Wilmington, DE 19801
Tel.: (302) 571-9781
Web Site: http://www.chiquita.com
Sales Range: $50-74.9 Million
Emp.: 100
Import & Distribution of Bananas
N.A.I.C.S.: 424480
Mario Pacheco *(Sr VP Global Logistics)*

Subsidiary (Domestic):

Chiquita Fresh North America
LLC　　　　　　　　　　　　**(3)**
2051 SE 35th St, Fort Lauderdale, FL
33316-4019
Tel.: (954) 453-1201
Web Site: http://www.chiquita.com
Sales Range: $100-124.9 Million
Fresh Fruit Distr
N.A.I.C.S.: 424480
Darcilo Santos *(CEO & CFO)*

Fresh Express Incorporated　　**(3)**
950 E Blanco Rd, Salinas, CA 93901-4409
Tel.: (831) 775-2300
Sales Range: $50-74.9 Million
Fresh Salads & Vegetables Mfr & Whslr
N.A.I.C.S.: 424480
Kenneth Diveley *(CEO-Chiquita Fruit Solu-
tions & Fresh Express)*

Plant (Domestic):

Fresh Express Inc. - Chicago　**(4)**
9501 Nevada Ave, Franklin Park, IL 60131
Tel.: (847) 451-1452
Sales Range: $125-149.9 Million
Emp.: 300
Pre-Cut Vegetable Supplier to Fast-Food
Chains
N.A.I.C.S.: 424480
Kevin Drves *(Plant Mgr)*

Fresh Express Inc. - Grand
Prairie　　　　　　　　　　　**(4)**
2370 W Warrior Trail, Grand Prairie, TX
75052-7254
Tel.: (972) 595-3600
Wholesale Produce
N.A.I.C.S.: 424480

Subsidiary (Domestic):

TransFRESH Corporation　　　**(3)**
40 Ragsdale Dr Ste 200, Monterey, CA
93940
Tel.: (831) 772-6086
Web Site: http://www.transfresh.com
Sales Range: Less than $1 Million
Emp.: 17
Transportation of Fresh Fruits & Vegetables
N.A.I.C.S.: 311421
Jean-Yves Pamart *(Gen Mgr-Europe)*

Subsidiary (Non-US):

Chiquita Guatemala, S.A.　　　**(2)**
9a Calle entre 1ra y 2da av Puerto Barrios,
Izabal, Guatemala, Guatemala
Tel.: (502) 24 793 17000
Web Site: http://www.chiquita.com
Fruit & Vegetable Freight & Shipping Ser-
vices
N.A.I.C.S.: 311421
Manrique Bermudez *(Dir-Latin American
Logistics)*

Chiquita Logistic Services El Salva-
dor Ltda.　　　　　　　　　　**(2)**
Paseo General Escalon Villas Espanolas,
San Salvador, El Salvador
Tel.: (503) 22638017
Fruit & Vegetable Logistics & Canning Ser-
vices
N.A.I.C.S.: 311421
Edwin Polanco *(Country Mgr)*

J. Safra Sarasin Holding AG　　**(1)**
Elisabethenstrasse 62, 4002, Basel, Swit-
zerland
Tel.: (41) 58 317 4444
Web Site: http://www.jsafrasarasin.com
Rev.: $2,575,006,529
Assets: $37,717,470,555
Liabilities: $32,415,607,028
Net Worth: $5,301,863,526
Earnings: $391,544,615
Emp.: 2,178

Fiscal Year-end: 12/31/2019
Bank Holding Company
N.A.I.C.S.: 551111
Jacob J. Safra *(Chm)*

Subsidiary (Domestic):

Bank J. Safra Sarasin AG **(2)**
Elisabethenstrasse 62, 4002, Basel, Switzerland
Tel.: (41) 58 317 44 44
Web Site: http://www.sarasin.ch
Rev.: $725,333,389
Assets: $21,857,767,199
Liabilities: $19,781,436,080
Net Worth: $2,076,331,119
Earnings: $144,416,678
Emp.: 1,100
Fiscal Year-end: 12/31/2016
Private & Institutional Investment Banking
N.A.I.C.S.: 523150
Pierre-Alain Bracher *(Vice Chm)*

Subsidiary (Non-US):

Bank J. Safra Sarasin (Gibraltar)
Ltd. **(3)**
First Floor Neptune House Marina Bay, PO
Box 542, Gibraltar, Gibraltar **(100%)**
Tel.: (350) 2000 2500
Web Site: http://www.jsafrasarasin.com.gi
Private & Institutional Banking
N.A.I.C.S.: 523150

Subsidiary (Non-US):

Banque J. Safra Sarasin (Monaco)
SA **(2)**
La Belle Epoque 15 Bis / 17 Avenue
d'Ostende, BP 347, 98006, Monaco, Cedex,
Monaco **(100%)**
Tel.: (377) 93106655
Web Site: http://www.jsafrasarasin.com
Private & Institutional Banking
N.A.I.C.S.: 523150

BANCO SANTANDER, S.A.
Ciudad Grupo Santander, 28660,
Boadilla del Monte, Spain
Tel.: (34) 912596514   ES
Web Site: https://www.santander.com
Year Founded: 1857
SAN—(NYSE)
Rev.: $57,067,715,120
Assets: $1,960,068,380,400
Liabilities: $1,840,864,003,680
Net Worth: $119,204,376,720
Earnings: $9,978,221,760
Emp.: 197,070
Fiscal Year-end: 12/31/21
Bank Holding Company
N.A.I.C.S.: 551111
Jose Antonio Alvarez Alvarez *(Vice
Chm & CEO)*

Subsidiaries:

Aevis Europa, S.L. **(1)**
Tel.: (34) 913626300
Financial Services
N.A.I.C.S.: 523999

Attijariwafa Bank **(1)**
2 Boulevard Moulay Youssef, 20000, Casablanca, Morocco
Tel.: (212) 522224169
Web Site: https://www.attijariwafabank.com
Rev.: $2,387,432,394
Assets: $62,516,038,119
Liabilities: $52,298,662,250
Net Worth: $10,217,375,869
Earnings: $601,469,839
Emp.: 8,094
Fiscal Year-end: 12/31/2022
Commercial Banking Services
N.A.I.C.S.: 522110
Mohamed El Kettani *(CEO)*

Subsidiary (Non-US):

Attijariwafa bank Egypt S.A.E **(2)**
Web Site:
  http://www.attijariwafabank.com.eg
Retail & Corporate Banking Services
N.A.I.C.S.: 522299
Mohamed Hamilili *(CFO-Acting, COO &
Deputy Mng Dir)*

Autodescuento, S.L. **(1)**
c/ Alcala number 4 5th Floor, 28014, Madrid, Spain
Tel.: (34) 917026389
Web Site: https://www.autodescuento.com
Car Retailer
N.A.I.C.S.: 441110

Autohaus24 GmbH **(1)**
Dr-Carl-von-Linde-Str 2, 82049, Pullach,
Germany
Tel.: (49) 8970808484
Web Site: https://www.autohaus24.de
Emp.: 35
Car Retailer
N.A.I.C.S.: 441110

Aviacion Intercontinental, A.I.E. **(1)**
Avenida Cantabria Ed Amazonia S/N-Piso
2, Boadilla del Monte, 28660, Spain
Tel.: (34) 912894714
Sales Range: $50-74.9 Million
Emp.: 200
Airline Transportation Services
N.A.I.C.S.: 488190
Aneen Catalan *(Gen Mgr)*

Aviacion Regional Cantabra,
A.I.E. **(1)**
Avenida De Cantabria S/N-Ed Amazonia,
Boadilla del Monte, 28660, Spain
Tel.: (34) 912894714
Industrial Machinery & Equipment Whslr
N.A.I.C.S.: 423830

Banco Madesant - Sociedade Unipessoal, S.A. **(1)**
2nd Floor Avenida Arriaga 73 2 Sala 211,
Funchal, 9000-060, Portugal
Tel.: (351) 291203110
Financial Management Services
N.A.I.C.S.: 523999

Banco Rio de la Plata S.A. **(1)**
Bartolome Mitre 480, 1036, Buenos Aires,
Argentina
Tel.: (54) 1143411000
Sales Range: $1-4.9 Billion
Emp.: 4,640
Commercial & Investment Banking Services
N.A.I.C.S.: 522110

Banco Santander (Panama),
S.A. **(1)**
Piso 7 Edificio PH Torre ADR Local 700B,
Avenida Samuel Lewis y C 58, Santo Domingo Obarrio, Panama, Panama **(100%)**
Tel.: (507) 2636577
Web Site:
  http://www.bancosantander.com.pa
Sales Range: $50-74.9 Million
Emp.: 5
Banking Services
N.A.I.C.S.: 522110

Banco Santander (Suisse), S.A. **(1)**
(99.96%)
Tel.: (41) 229092222
Web Site: http://www.pb-santander.com
Banking Services
N.A.I.C.S.: 522110

Banco Santander Central Hispano
(Guernsey), Ltd. **(1)**
Dorey Court Atmiral Park Elizabeth Avenue,
PO Box 191, Saint Peter Port, GY1 4HW,
Guernsey **(99.98%)**
Tel.: (44) 1481715424
Web Site: http://www.confiance.gg
Sales Range: $50-74.9 Million
Emp.: 24
Banking Services
N.A.I.C.S.: 522110

Banco Santander Consumer Portugal, S.A. **(1)**
Rua de Cantabria 42 - Edificio 2, Carcavelos, 2775-711, Cascais, Portugal
Tel.: (351) 707200103
Web Site: http://www.santanderconsumer.pt
Financial Insurance Services
N.A.I.C.S.: 524210

Banco Santander Peru S.A. **(1)**
Av Ricardo Rivera Navarrete N 475 Piso
14, San Isidro, Peru
Tel.: (51) 2158160
Web Site: http://www.santander.com.pe
Sales Range: Less than $1 Million
Commercial Banking Services
N.A.I.C.S.: 522110

Cesar Emilio Rodriguez Larrain Salinas
(Chm)

Banco Santander Portugal, S.A. **(1)**
Praca Marqes de Pombal No 2, Lisbon,
P-1250 161, Portugal
Tel.: (351) 707212424
Web Site: http://www.santander.pt
Sales Range: $700-749.9 Million
Emp.: 1,287
Banking Services
N.A.I.C.S.: 522110

Banco Santander Rio S.A. **(1)**
Bartolome Mitre 480, 1036, Buenos Aires,
Argentina
Tel.: (54) 1143411000
Web Site: https://www.santanderrio.com.ar
Sales Range: $1-4.9 Billion
Emp.: 6,281
Banking Services
N.A.I.C.S.: 522110
Sergio Lew *(CEO)*

Banco Santander Totta, S.A. **(1)**
Rua do Ouro n 88, 1100-063, Lisbon, Portugal
Tel.: (351) 217807364
Web Site: http://www.santander.pt
Banking Services
N.A.I.C.S.: 522110

Banco Santander de Negocios Colombia S.A. **(1)**
Calle 93 A No 13-24 piso 4 oficina 401, Bogota, Colombia
Web Site: http://www.santander.com.co
Financial Services
N.A.I.C.S.: 523999

Banco Santander de Negocios Portugal, S.A. **(1)**
Avenida Eng Duarte Pacheco, Amoreiras
Torre 1 Piso 6, P-1099 024, Lisbon,
Portugal **(99.35%)**
Tel.: (351) 213801500
Web Site: http://www.santander.pt
Sales Range: $50-74.9 Million
Emp.: 100
Banking Services
N.A.I.C.S.: 522110

Banco Santander-Chile **(1)**
Bandera 140 20th Floor, Santiago,
Chile **(83.94%)**
Tel.: (56) 23202000
Web Site: http://www.santander.cl
Rev.: $1,962,830,179
Assets: $72,529,142,478
Liabilities: $67,078,451,257
Net Worth: $5,450,691,221
Earnings: $605,863,388
Emp.: 9,229
Fiscal Year-end: 12/31/2023
Banking Services
N.A.I.C.S.: 522320
Claudio Melandri Hinojosa *(Chm & Pres)*

Banco de Venezuela, S.A. **(1)**
Web Site:
  http://www.bancodevenezuela.com
Sales Range: $1-4.9 Billion
Emp.: 5,189
Banking Services
N.A.I.C.S.: 522110

Banif Banco Internacional do Funchal
SA **(1)**
Avenida Jose Malhoa 22, 1099-012, Lisbon,
Portugal
Tel.: (351) 217211200
Web Site: http://www.banif.pt
Sales Range: $600-649.9 Million
Emp.: 3,196
Banking Services
N.A.I.C.S.: 522110

Subsidiary (Non-US):

Banif-Banco Internacional do Funchal
(Brasil), SA **(2)**
Av Juscelino Kubitscheck 1 700, Sao Paulo,
Brazil
Tel.: (55) 1131652000
Commercial Bank
N.A.I.C.S.: 522110

Subsidiary (Domestic):

Companhia de Seguros Asoreana,
SA **(2)**

Largo da Matriz 45-52, 9501-922, Ponta
Delgada, Portugal **(100%)**
Tel.: (351) 296201400
Sales Range: $300-349.9 Million
Emp.: 600
Miscellaneous Financial Investment Activities
N.A.I.C.S.: 523999

InvestaCor - Sociedade Gestora de
Participacoes Sociais, S A **(2)**
Rue lisboa Roalt Garden Hotel, Ponta Delgada, 9500216, Portugal
Tel.: (351) 296307300
Web Site: http://www.investacor.com
Sales Range: $10-24.9 Million
Emp.: 65
Hotels (except Casino Hotels) & Motels
N.A.I.C.S.: 721110

CC-Bank Aktiengesellschaft **(1)**
Santander-Platz 1, Monchengladbach,
41061, Germany **(100%)**
Tel.: (49) 21616900
Web Site: http://www.santander.de
Sales Range: $700-749.9 Million
Emp.: 2,080
Banking Services
N.A.I.C.S.: 522299

CCAP Auto Lease Ltd. **(1)**
PO Box 660335, Dallas, TX 75266-0335
Web Site: http://www.chryslercapital.com
Vehicle Financing Services
N.A.I.C.S.: 522220

CCB Finance, s.r.o. **(1)**
Safrankova 1, 155 00, Prague, Czech
Republic **(100%)**
Tel.: (420) 225285111
Sales Range: $125-149.9 Million
Emp.: 301
Leasing Services
N.A.I.C.S.: 561499

Cableuropa, S.A.U. **(1)**
Calle Basauri 7-9, Urbanizacion la Florida,
Aravaca, 28023, Madrid, Spain **(19%)**
Tel.: (34) 911809300
Web Site: http://www.ono.es
Sales Range: $500-549.9 Million
Emp.: 500
Internet & Cable Services
N.A.I.C.S.: 541512

Carfinco Financial Group Inc. **(1)**
Suite 200 4245 97th Street, Edmonton, T6E
5Y7, AB, Canada
Tel.: (780) 413-7549
Web Site: http://www.carfinco.com
Holding Company; Automobile Financing
Services
N.A.I.C.S.: 551112

Subsidiary (Domestic):

Carfinco Inc. **(2)**
200 4245 97 Street NW, Edmonton, T6E
5Y7, AB, Canada
Tel.: (780) 413-7549
Web Site:
  https://www.santanderconsumer.ca
Automobile Financing Services
N.A.I.C.S.: 522220
Tracy A. Graf *(Pres & CEO)*

Companhia Geral de Credito Predial
Portuges, S.A. **(1)**
(99.36%)
Web Site: http://www.cpp.pt
Banking Services
N.A.I.C.S.: 522110

Diners Club Spain, S.A. **(1)**
C/ Josefa Valcarcel 26 5 Planta Modulo B,
28027, Madrid, Spain
Tel.: (34) 912114300
Web Site: http://www.dinersclub.es
Financial Payment Services
N.A.I.C.S.: 522320

Grupo Financiero Santander Mexico,
S.A.B. de C.V. **(1)**
Avenida Prolongacion Paseo de la Reforma
500, Colonia Lomas de Santa Fe Alcaldia
Alvaro Obregon, 01219, Mexico, CP,
Mexico
Tel.: (52) 5552578000
Web Site: https://www.santander.com.mx
Rev.: $3,715,769,720

Banco Santander, S.A.—(Continued)

Assets: $64,833,290,250
Liabilities: $59,684,635,110
Net Worth: $5,148,655,140
Earnings: $792,026,960
Emp.: 16,793
Fiscal Year-end: 12/31/2016
Bank Holding Company
N.A.I.C.S.: 551112
Hector Blas Grisi Checa (Pres & CEO)

Subsidiary (Domestic):

Banca Serfin, S.A. (2)
Prolongacion Paseo de la Reforma, Mod 409 Nivel 4, Colonia Lomas de Santa Fe, CP 01219, Mexico, Mexico (100%)
Tel.: (52) 5552598860
Web Site: http://www.serfin.com.mx
Banking Services
N.A.I.C.S.: 522110

Casa de Bolsa Santander Serfin, S.A. de C.V. (2)
Prolongacion Paseo de la Reforma 500, Modulo 206, Colonia Lomas de Santa Fe, 01210, Mexico, DF, Mexico (73.95%)
Tel.: (52) 5552615435
Sales Range: $700-749.9 Million
Emp.: 1,200
Investment Services
N.A.I.C.S.: 523160

Grupo Taper, S.A. (1)
Ave Avenida De La Industria No 49 Bldg Egifizio Fresno 1st Fl, 28108, Alcobendas, Madrid, Spain (27.77%)
Tel.: (34) 914841960
Web Site: http://www.grupotaper.com
Sales Range: $50-74.9 Million
Emp.: 70
Medical Equipment Distr
N.A.I.C.S.: 456191
Fernando Gumuzio Iniguez de Onzono (Chm)

Iberica de Compras Corporativas, S.L. (1)
Aquanima Grupo Santander Avenida de Cantabria s/n, Edificio Arrecife Planta 0 Boadilla Del Monte, 28660, Madrid, Spain
Tel.: (34) 912895314
Web Site: https://www.aquanima.com
Sales Range: $50-74.9 Million
Emp.: 100
Financial Management Services
N.A.I.C.S.: 523999

Ingenieria de Software Bancario, S.L. (1)
Avenida Cantabria 3 S/N, Boadilla del Monte, 28660, Spain
Tel.: (34) 914704001
Web Site: http://www.isban.es
Sales Range: $700-749.9 Million
Emp.: 300
Software Development Services
N.A.I.C.S.: 541511

Laparanza, S.A. (1)
Carretera De Colmenar Viejo 21, Tres Cantos, 28760, Spain
Tel.: (34) 916521233
Agricultural Farming Services
N.A.I.C.S.: 115112

Luri 4, S.A. (1)
Plaza Independencia 8, Madrid, 28001, Spain
Tel.: (34) 915315405
Web Site: http://www.lurisa.com
Sales Range: $50-74.9 Million
Emp.: 1
Real Estate Administration
N.A.I.C.S.: 522110

Mercury Trade Finance Solutions, S.L. (1)
Tel.: (34) 913291645
Web Site: http://www.mercury-tfs.com
Trading Finance Services
N.A.I.C.S.: 522299

Meridian Capital Group, LLC (1)
1 Battery Park Plz 26th Fl, New York, NY 10004
Tel.: (212) 972-3600
Web Site: https://www.meridiancapital.com
Commercial Mortgage Brokerage Services

N.A.I.C.S.: 522310
Ralph Herzka (Co-Founder, Chm & CEO)

Naviera Trans Gas, A.I.E. (1)
Calle Goya Tafira Alta 7 Las Palmas De Gran Canari, Las Palmas, 35017, Spain
Tel.: (34) 928472515
Natural Gas Transportation Services
N.A.I.C.S.: 486210

Open Bank, S.A. (1)
Tel.: (34) 913421000
Web Site: http://www.bancoonline.openbank.es
Commercial Banking Services
N.A.I.C.S.: 522110

Optimal Investment Services S.A. (1)
Beccolat 8, 1201, Geneva, Switzerland
Tel.: (41) 229097474
Financial Management Services
N.A.I.C.S.: 523999

PSA Bank Deutschland GmbH (1)
Siemensstrasse 10, 63263, Neu-Isenburg, Germany
Tel.: (49) 61023020
Banking Services
N.A.I.C.S.: 522110

PSA Banque France SA (1)
Tel.: (33) 146396633
Banking Services
N.A.I.C.S.: 522110

PSA Finance Polska Sp. z o.o. (1)
Ul Domaniewska 44A, 02-672, Warsaw, Poland
Tel.: (48) 801512131
Web Site: http://www.e-psafinance.pl
Financial Insurance Services
N.A.I.C.S.: 524210

PSA Finance UK Limited (1)
61 London Road, Redhill, RH1 1QA, Surrey, United Kingdom
Tel.: (44) 3453455449
Web Site: https://www.stellantisfinancialservices.com
Financial Insurance Services
N.A.I.C.S.: 524210

Patagon Bank, S.A. (1) (100%)
Tel.: (34) 913421000
Web Site: http://www.openbank.es
Banking Services
N.A.I.C.S.: 522110

Santander Asset Management Chile S.A. (1)
Bandera 140 piso 3 Santiago Centro, Santiago, Chile
Tel.: (56) 228476103
Financial Assets Management Services
N.A.I.C.S.: 523940

Santander Asset Management S.A. (1)
Tel.: (56) 25500357
Web Site: http://www.santandermanagement.com
Asset Management Services
N.A.I.C.S.: 523940
Diego Ceballos (Chief Investment Officer)

Santander Asset Management UK Limited (1)
287 St Vincent Street, Glasgow, G2 5NB, United Kingdom
Tel.: (44) 8000284174
Financial Assets Management Services
N.A.I.C.S.: 523940

Santander Asset Management, S.A., S.G.I.I.C. (1)
Calle Serrano 69, 28006, Madrid, Spain
Tel.: (34) 915123123
Web Site: http://www.santanderassetmanagement.es
Financial Assets Management Services
N.A.I.C.S.: 523940

Santander Banespa Grupo (1)
Praca Antonio Prado 6, Centro, Sao Paulo, 01602-900, SP, Brazil
Tel.: (55) 112499338
Holding Company
N.A.I.C.S.: 551111

Subsidiary (Domestic):

Banco Santander (Brasil) S.A. (2)
Avenida Presidente Juscelino Kubitschek, 2041 & 2235 Bloco A Vila Olimpia, Sao Paulo, 04543-011, Brazil (88.65%)
Tel.: (55) 1135533300
Web Site: https://www.santander.com.br
Rev.: $22,152,028,936
Assets: $189,452,921,875
Liabilities: $168,174,658,039
Net Worth: $21,276,263,636
Earnings: $2,746,693,629
Emp.: 52,603
Fiscal Year-end: 12/31/2022
Banking Services
N.A.I.C.S.: 522110
Jose Antonio Alvarez (Vice Chm)

Santander Bank & Trust, Ltd. (1)
Goodmans Bay Corporate Centre Sea View Dr 3rd Fl W Bay St, Nassau, N1682, Bahamas (100%)
Tel.: (242) 322 3588
Investment & Banking Services
N.A.I.C.S.: 523150

Santander Bank Polska S.A. (1)
Aleja Jana Pawta II 17, 00-854, Warsaw, Poland (76.5%)
Tel.: (48) 618119999
Web Site: https://www.santander.pl
Rev.: $4,677,275,903
Assets: $70,287,572,229
Liabilities: $61,727,862,393
Net Worth: $8,559,709,836
Earnings: $1,257,070,373
Fiscal Year-end: 12/31/2023
Offices of Bank Holding Companies
N.A.I.C.S.: 551111
Michal Gajewski (CEO & Member-Mgmt Bd)

Subsidiary (Domestic):

BZ WBK Asset Management S.A. (2)
Plac Wolnosci 16, 61-739, Poznan, Poland
Tel.: (48) 618519268
Web Site: http://www.am.bzwbk.pl
Sales Range: $50-74.9 Million
Emp.: 100
Investment Advisory Services
N.A.I.C.S.: 523940

BZ WBK Finanse & Leasing S.A. (2)
Poznanskie Centrum Finansowe Placa Andersa 5, 61 894, Poznan, Poland (100%)
Tel.: (48) 618503500
Web Site: http://www.leasing24.pl
Sales Range: $50-74.9 Million
Emp.: 100
Lease & Rental of Fixed Assets & Selling Goods on Instalments
N.A.I.C.S.: 531110

Dom Maklerski BZ WBK S.A. (2)
Pl Wolnosci 15, Poznan, 60-967, Poland
Tel.: (48) 618564880
Online Brokerage Services
N.A.I.C.S.: 523150

WBK Nieruchomosci S.A. (2)
Palac W Zakrzewie, Zakrzewo, 62 270, Poznan, Klecko, Poland (100%)
Tel.: (48) 614270203
Web Site: http://www.zakrzewo.bzwbk.pl
Sales Range: $50-74.9 Million
Emp.: 20
Investment Banking
N.A.I.C.S.: 523150
Diana Matlosz (Gen Mgr)

Santander Bank and Trust (Bahamas), Ltd. (1)
Goodmans Bay Corporate Center, PO Box 1682, Nassau, Bahamas (100%)
Tel.: (242) 3223588
Banking Services
N.A.I.C.S.: 522299
Michael Richard (Sr VP & Head-Seafood Indus Banking)

Santander Benelux SA/NV (1)
Avenue Des Larciviens 85, 1040, Brussels, Belgium
Tel.: (32) 22865411
Sales Range: $50-74.9 Million
Emp.: 18
Banking Services
N.A.I.C.S.: 522110

Guillermo Sanz Murat (Mng Dir)

Santander Consumer Bank AG (1)
Santander-Platz 1, Monchengladbach, 41061, Germany
Tel.: (49) 21616900
Sales Range: $700-749.9 Million
Emp.: 200
Financial Services
N.A.I.C.S.: 523999
Ulrich Andrews (Gen Mgr)

Joint Venture (Domestic):

Hyundai Capital Bank Europe GmbH (2)
Friedrich-Ebert-Anlage 35-37, 60327, Frankfurt am Main, Germany
Tel.: (49) 6992 038 3000
Web Site: https://www.hyundaicapitalbank.eu
Private Banking Services
N.A.I.C.S.: 523150
Martin Liehr (Mng Dir)

Subsidiary (Domestic):

Allane SE (3)
Dr -Carl-von-Linde-Str 2, 82049, Pullach, Germany (92.07%)
Tel.: (49) 897080810
Web Site: https://allane-mobility-group.com
Rev.: $918,355,048
Assets: $1,591,307,744
Liabilities: $1,329,078,504
Net Worth: $262,229,240
Earnings: $2,702,128
Emp.: 693
Fiscal Year-end: 12/31/2020
Auto Leasing Services
N.A.I.C.S.: 532112
Michael Martin Ruhl (Chm-Mgmt Bd & CEO)

Subsidiary (Non-US):

Sixt Mobility Consulting AG (4)
Grossmattstr 9, 8902, Urdorf, Switzerland
Tel.: (41) 848111144
Automobile Parts Distr
N.A.I.C.S.: 423120

Subsidiary (Domestic):

Sixt Mobility Consulting GmbH (4)
Zugspitzstr 1, 82049, Pullach, Germany
Tel.: (49) 89744440
Web Site: http://www.mobility-consulting.com
Automobile Parts Distr
N.A.I.C.S.: 423120

Subsidiary (Non-US):

Sixt Mobility Consulting S.a.R.L. (4)
1 rue Francois Jacob, 92500, Rueil-Malmaison, France
Tel.: (33) 182732646
Automobile Parts Distr
N.A.I.C.S.: 423120

Santander Consumer Bank AS (1)
Strandvn 18, PO Box 177, 1325, Lysaker, Norway
Tel.: (47) 21083000
Sales Range: $200-249.9 Million
Emp.: 300
Commercial Banking Services
N.A.I.C.S.: 522110
Michael Hvidsten (CEO)

Santander Consumer Bank GmbH (1)
Wagramer Strasse 19, PO Box 200, 1220, Vienna, Austria
Tel.: (43) 502031800
Web Site: https://www.santanderconsumer.at
Emp.: 43
Automobile Financial Management Services
N.A.I.C.S.: 525990
Olaf Peter Poenisch (Chm-Mgmt Bd & CEO)

Santander Consumer Bank S.A. (1)
Ul Legnicka 48 B, 54-202, Wroclaw, Poland
Tel.: (48) 713589909
Web Site: http://www.santanderconsumer.pl
Banking Services
N.A.I.C.S.: 522110

Santander Consumer Banque S.A. (1)
26 quai Charles Pasqua, CS 80174, 92309, Levallois-Perret, France
Tel.: (33) 170949300
Web Site: http://www.santanderconsumer.fr
Banking Services
N.A.I.C.S.: 522110

Santander Consumer Finance, S.A. (1)
Sales Range: $700-749.9 Million
Emp.: 1,126
Banking Services
N.A.I.C.S.: 522110

Subsidiary (Domestic):

Financiera El Corte Ingles E.F.C., S.A. (2)
Calle Hermosilla 112, 28009, Madrid, Spain (51%)
Tel.: (34) 913779779
Web Site:
  https://www.financieraelcorteingles.es
Financial Management
N.A.I.C.S.: 541611

Subsidiary (Non-US):

Santander Consumer Finance Benelux B.V. (2)
Winthontlaan 171, Utrecht, 3526 KV, Netherlands
Tel.: (31) 306388100
Financial Management Services
N.A.I.C.S.: 523999

Santander Consumer Holding GmbH (1)
Nordrhein-Westfalen, Monchengladbach, 41061, Germany
Tel.: (49) 21616900
Sales Range: $1-4.9 Billion
Emp.: 500
Investment Management Service
N.A.I.C.S.: 523999
Ulrich Leuschner *(Mng Dir)*

Santander Consumer Leasing GmbH (1)
Santander-Platz 1, Monchengladbach, 41061, Germany
Tel.: (49) 21616907808
Sales Range: $50-74.9 Million
Emp.: 2
Leasing Services
N.A.I.C.S.: 532112

Santander Consumer Leasing s.r.o. (1)
Safrankova 1 Praha 5, Prague, 190 00, Czech Republic
Tel.: (420) 2 8301 9550
Automobile Leasing Services
N.A.I.C.S.: 532112

Santander Consumer Renting, S.L. (1)
Calle de Santa Barbara 1, Torrelaguna, 28180, Madrid, Spain
Tel.: (34) 902151601
Vehicle Rental & Automotive Services
N.A.I.C.S.: 532111

Santander Consumer S.A.S. (1)
Calle 70 No 11-83, Bogota, Colombia
Tel.: (57) 6017434301
Web Site:
  https://www.santanderconsumer.co
Financial Services
N.A.I.C.S.: 523999

Santander Consumer, EFC, S.A. (1)
Avenida De Cantabria S/N-Ciudad Grupo Santander Ed Dehesa, Boadilla del Monte, 28660, Spain
Tel.: (34) 912892547
Web Site: http://www.santanderconsumer.es
Financial Management Services
N.A.I.C.S.: 523999

Santander Corporate & Investment Banking (1)
9, place Vendôme, 75001, Paris, France
Tel.: (33) 53537000
Web Site: https://www.santandercib.com
Emp.: 7,638
Financial Services

N.A.I.C.S.: 523999

Santander Financial Products, Ltd. (1)
Block 8 Harcourt Centre, Dublin, 2, Ireland (100%)
Tel.: (353) 14757850
Sales Range: $50-74.9 Million
Emp.: 6
Financial Services
N.A.I.C.S.: 561499

Santander Global Property, S.L. (1)
Paseo Castellana 93-PLT 13, Madrid, 28046, Spain
Tel.: (34) 911773780
Sales Range: $50-74.9 Million
Emp.: 2
Real Estate Manangement Services
N.A.I.C.S.: 531390
Juan Antonio Guitart *(Gen Mgr)*

Santander Holdings USA, Inc. (1)
75 State St, Boston, MA 02109
Tel.: (617) 346-7200
Web Site: https://www.santanderus.com
Rev.: $15,819,939,000
Assets: $164,972,575,000
Liabilities: $149,471,666,000
Net Worth: $15,500,909,000
Earnings: $932,902,000
Emp.: 11,800
Fiscal Year-end: 12/31/2023
Bank Holding Company
N.A.I.C.S.: 551111
Javier Maldonado *(Vice Chm)*

Subsidiary (Domestic):

Capital Street Delaware LP (2)
900 N Michigan Ave, Chicago, IL 60611-1542
Tel.: (312) 915-2400
Investment Management Service
N.A.I.C.S.: 523940

Independence Community Commercial Reinvestment Corp. (2)
103 Foulk Rd, Wilmington, DE 19803
Tel.: (302) 691-6408
Investment Management Service
N.A.I.C.S.: 523940

PBE Companies, LLC (2)
2711 Centerville Rd, Wilmington, DE 19808-1660
Tel.: (617) 346-7459
Investment Management Service
N.A.I.C.S.: 523940

Santander Bank, N.A. (2)
824 N Market St, Wilmington, DE 19801
Tel.: (302) 654-5182
Web Site: http://www.santanderbank.com
Emp.: 9,800
Savings, Loans, Commercial & Investment Banking Services
N.A.I.C.S.: 522180
Duke Dayal *(Co-Pres)*

Santander Consumer USA Holdings Inc. (2)
1601 Elm St Ste 800, Dallas, TX 75201 (80.2%)
Tel.: (214) 634-1110
Web Site:
  http://www.santanderconsumerusa.com
Rev.: $8,090,906,000
Assets: $48,887,493,000
Liabilities: $43,265,532,000
Net Worth: $5,621,961,000
Earnings: $910,911,000
Emp.: 5,576
Fiscal Year-end: 12/31/2020
Financial Holding Company; Consumer Lending & Sales Financing
N.A.I.C.S.: 551111
Christopher Keith Pfirrman *(Gen Counsel)*

Subsidiary (Domestic):

Santander Consumer USA Inc. (3)
PO Box 961245, Fort Worth, TX 76161-1245
Tel.: (214) 634-1110
Web Site:
  https://santanderconsumerusa.com
Sales Range: $350-399.9 Million
Emp.: 820

N.A.I.C.S.: 523999

Purchasing, Securitization & Servicing of Automobile Retail Installment Contracts for Non-Prime Consumers
N.A.I.C.S.: 522291

Subsidiary (Domestic):

Santander Insurance Agency, U.S., LLC (2)
75 State St, Boston, MA 02109
Tel.: (770) 248-3546
Insurance Brokerage Services
N.A.I.C.S.: 524210

Sovereign Delaware Investment Corporation (2)
103 Foulk Rd, Wilmington, DE 19803
Tel.: (302) 691-6123
Investment Management Service
N.A.I.C.S.: 523940

Sovereign REIT Holdings, Inc. (2)
103 Foulk Rd Ste 236, Wilmington, DE 19803-3742
Tel.: (302) 421-9003
Investment Management Service
N.A.I.C.S.: 551112

Sovereign Real Estate Investment Trust (2)
103 Foulk Rd Ste 200, Wilmington, DE 19803
Tel.: (302) 654-7584
Real Estate Investment Services
N.A.I.C.S.: 531390

Sovereign Securities Corporation, LLC (2)
1500 Market St, Philadelphia, PA 19102-2106
Tel.: (267) 256-2818
Security Brokerage Services
N.A.I.C.S.: 523150

Synergy Abstract, LP (2)
25 W Moreland Ave, Hatboro, PA 19040
Tel.: (215) 441-5177
Web Site: http://www.beaconabstract.com
Insurance Agencies
N.A.I.C.S.: 524210

Waypoint Insurance Group, Inc. (2)
1805 Loucks Rd Ste 400, York, PA 17408
Tel.: (717) 767-9006
Insurance Brokerage Services
N.A.I.C.S.: 524210

Santander Investment Securities Inc. (1)
45 E 53rd St, New York, NY 10022-4604
Tel.: (212) 350-3500
Web Site: http://www.santander.us
Sales Range: $100-124.9 Million
Emp.: 200
International Banking
N.A.I.C.S.: 522110

Santander Seguros y Reaseguros, Compania Aseguradora, S.A. (1)
Avenida de Cantabria s/n Ciudad Grupo Santander, Boadilla del Monte, 28860, Madrid, Spain
Tel.: (34) 915123123
Web Site: https://www.santanderseguros.es
Financial Insurance Services
N.A.I.C.S.: 524210

Santander Totta Seguros, Companhia de Seguros de Vida, S.A. (1)
Rua dos Sapateiros 174-4, 1100-580, Lisbon, Portugal
Tel.: (351) 217807369
Web Site:
  http://www.santandertottaseguros.pt
Financial Insurance Services
N.A.I.C.S.: 524210

Santander Towarzystwo Funduszy Inwestycyjnych S.A. (1)
Pl Wladyslawa Andersa 5, 61-894, Poznan, Poland
Tel.: (48) 801123801
Web Site: https://www.santander.pl
Investment Management Service
N.A.I.C.S.: 523940
Jacek Marcinowski *(Pres)*

Santander UK Group Holdings plc (1)
2 Triton Square Regents Place, London,

NW1 3AN, United Kingdom
Tel.: (44) 8706076000
Web Site: http://www.santander.co.uk
Rev.: $14,962,130,775
Assets: $356,075,485,988
Liabilities: $337,183,791,972
Net Worth: $18,891,694,017
Earnings: $2,014,642,767
Emp.: 19,800
Fiscal Year-end: 12/31/2023
Holding Company
N.A.I.C.S.: 551111
Nathan Bostock *(CEO)*

Subsidiary (Domestic):

Santander UK plc (2)
2 Triton Square Regent's Place, London, NW1 3AN, United Kingdom (100%)
Tel.: (44) 8706076000
Web Site: https://www.santander.co.uk
Rev.: $9,107,585,760
Assets: $387,239,394,360
Liabilities: $367,678,722,320
Net Worth: $19,560,672,040
Earnings: $1,892,661,680
Emp.: 18,123
Fiscal Year-end: 12/31/2022
Offices of Bank Holding Companies
N.A.I.C.S.: 551111
Nathan Bostock *(CEO)*

Subsidiary (Non-US):

Cater Allen Limited (3)
Tel.: (44) 2077564500
Web Site: http://www.caterallen.co.uk
Commercial Banking Services
N.A.I.C.S.: 522110

Subsidiary (Domestic):

Santander Cards UK Ltd. (3)
6 Agar Street, London, WC2N 4HR, United Kingdom
Tel.: (44) 113 280 7080
Web Site: http://www.santandercards.com
Sales Range: $1-4.9 Billion
Emp.: 3,000
Credit Card Services
N.A.I.C.S.: 522210

Santander Consumer Credit Services Limited (3)
Malvern House Hatters Lane, Watford, WD18 8YF, Herts, United Kingdom
Tel.: (44) 1923426426
Credit Management Services
N.A.I.C.S.: 522299

Santander Financial Services Plc (3)
2 Triton Square, Regent's Place, London, NW1 3AN, United Kingdom
Tel.: (44) 8706076000
Web Site: http://www.santander.co.uk
Rev.: $78,171,360
Assets: $8,831,002,800
Liabilities: $8,412,602,400
Net Worth: $418,400,400
Earnings: $8,787,720
Emp.: 1,047
Fiscal Year-end: 12/31/2019
Treasury & Wholesale Banking Services
N.A.I.C.S.: 522320
Susan Allen *(Exec Dir)*

Santander Insurance Services UK Limited (3)
2 Triton Square Regents Place, London, NW1 3AN, United Kingdom
Tel.: (44) 8706076000
Insurance Management Services
N.A.I.C.S.: 524298

Branch (Non-US):

Santander UK plc - Isle of Man Branch (3)
19/21 Prospect Hill, PO Box 123, British Isles, Douglas, IM99 1ZZ, Isle of Man
Tel.: (44) 1624 641 888
Web Site: http://www.santander.co.im
Commericial Banking
N.A.I.C.S.: 522110
James Geldart *(Mng Dir)*

Services and Promotions Miami LLC (1)
1401 Brickell Ave 810, Miami, FL 33131-3506

Banco Santander, S.A.—(Continued)

Tel.: (305) 358-1401
Scientific & Technical Consulting Services
N.A.I.C.S.: 541690
Julio Covas *(Gen Mgr)*

Sistema 4B, S.A. **(1)**
C/Francisco Sancha 12, Madrid, 28034, Spain
Tel.: (34) 913626300
Financial Management Services
N.A.I.C.S.: 523999

Totta & Acores Inc. **(1)**
71 Ferry St A, Newark, NJ 07105-1830
Tel.: (973) 578-8633
Credit Intermediation Services
N.A.I.C.S.: 522390

Totta (Ireland), PLC **(1)**
AIB International Cntr IFSC 1 Co, Dublin, Ireland
Tel.: (353) 18291208
Financial Management Services
N.A.I.C.S.: 523999

URO Property Holdings Socimi SA **(1)**
Calle Serrano No 21 2nd Left, Madrid, Spain
Tel.: (34) 917814618
Rev.: $117,749,923
Assets: $1,732,072,166
Liabilities: $1,532,008,952
Net Worth: $200,063,214
Earnings: $21,591,514
Emp.: 2
Fiscal Year-end: 12/31/2019
Real Estate Management Services
N.A.I.C.S.: 531390
Simon Blaxland *(CEO)*

Universia Brasil S.A. **(1)**
Av Juscelino Kubitscheck 2235-19th Floor, Sao Paulo, 04543-011, Brazil
Tel.: (55) 1135535215
Education Services
N.A.I.C.S.: 611710

Vista Desarrollo, S.A. SCR de Regimen Simplificado **(1)**
Calle Serrano 67, Madrid, 28006, Spain
Tel.: (34) 914360781
Emp.: 12
Investment Management Service
N.A.I.C.S.: 523999
Rafael Garabito *(Mgr)*

BANCO SOFISA S.A.
Alameda Santos 1496 10 andar, 01418-100, Sao Paulo, Brazil
Tel.: (55) 1131765836
Web Site: http://www.sofisa.com.br
Sales Range: $150-199.9 Million
Emp.: 502
Banking Services
N.A.I.C.S.: 522110
Gilberto Maktas Meiches *(Chm)*

BANCOLOMBIA S.A.
Carrera 48 Ste 26-85 Avenida Los Industriales, Medellin, Colombia
Tel.: (57) 6014885950　　　　Co
Web Site:
　　https://www.grupobancolombia.com
Year Founded: 1998
CIB—(NYSE)
Rev.: $9,656,908,922
Assets: $88,854,781,406
Liabilities: $78,736,777,192
Net Worth: $10,118,004,213
Earnings: $1,610,333,909
Emp.: 34,756
Fiscal Year-end: 12/31/23
Financial Investment Services
N.A.I.C.S.: 523999
Mauricio Rosillo Rojas *(VP)*

Subsidiaries:

Bancolombia Capital LLC **(1)**
1221 Brickell Ave Ste 2010, Miami, FL 33131
Tel.: (786) 551-9122

Web Site:
　　https://www.bancolombiacapital.com
Securities Brokerage & Advisory Services
N.A.I.C.S.: 523150

Bancolombia Panama S.A. **(1)**
Calle 47 y Aquilino de la Guardia Plaza Marbella-Edificio, Bancolombia Apartado, 0816-03320, Panama, Panama
Tel.: (507) 2089700
Web Site:
　　https://panama.grupobancolombia.com
Foreign Currency Investment Services
N.A.I.C.S.: 523150

Bancolombia Puerto Rico Internacional Inc **(1)**
270 Muoz Rivera Ave, San Juan, PR 00918
Tel.: (787) 756-5511
Web Site:
　　http://www.bancolombiapuertorico.com
Sales Range: $50-74.9 Million
Emp.: 15
Commercial Banking Services
N.A.I.C.S.: 522110

Banistmo S.A. **(1)**
47 Avenida Aquilino de la Guardia, Panama, Panama
Sales Range: $400-449.9 Million
Commercial & Investment Banking
N.A.I.C.S.: 522110

Ecosistemas Digitales S.A.S. **(1)**
Calle 8 Ste 43C - 68 CoWork Latam Astorga, Medellin, Colombia
Tel.: (57) 3228814826
Web Site: https://edncolombia.com
Computer Systems Design & Related Services
N.A.I.C.S.: 541512

Negocios Digitales Colombia S.A.S. **(1)**
Calle 77b 57-103 Oficina 2201 Edificio Green Towers, Barranquilla, Colombia
Tel.: (57) 3012783620
Web Site: https://negociosdigitales.com.co
Digital Marketing & Advertising Services
N.A.I.C.S.: 541810

Valores Bancolombia S.A. **(1)**
Carrera 48 Ste 26 - 85, Medellin, Colombia
Tel.: (57) 6045109000
Web Site:
　　https://valores.grupobancolombia.com
Investment Banking & Securities Brokerage Services
N.A.I.C.S.: 523150

WOMPI S.A.S. **(1)**
48 18a 14 Ed FIC 48 11th floor, Antioquia, Medellin, Colombia
Tel.: (57) 6013430006
Web Site: https://wompi.com
Financial Transaction Processing Services
N.A.I.C.S.: 522320

BANCORP WEALTH MANAGEMENT NEW ZEALAND LTD.
11th Floor 191 Queen Street, Auckland, 1010, New Zealand
Tel.: (64) 9 309 8270
Web Site: http://www.bancorp.co.nz
Merchant & Investment Banking
N.A.I.C.S.: 523150

BANCROFT MOTORS LTD
29668 Hwy 62 N, PO Box 1420, Bancroft, K0L 1C0, ON, Canada
Tel.: (833) 942-1539
Web Site:
　　https://www.boyergmbancroft.com
New & Used Car Dealers
N.A.I.C.S.: 441110
Margaret Macdonald *(Mgr-Bus)*

BAND REP MANAGEMENT, INC.
8th Floor Tower Five 33 Canton Road, Tsim Sha Tsui, Hong Kong, China (Hong Kong)
Tel.: (852) 7753218207　　　　NV
Web Site:
　　http://www.bandmanagement.com

Year Founded: 2012
Emp.: 1
Band Management Services
N.A.I.C.S.: 711410

BANDAI NAMCO HOLDINGS INC.
Bandai Namco miraikenkyusho
5-37-8 Shiba, Minato-ku, Tokyo, 108-0014, Japan
Tel.: (81) 357835500　　　　JP
Web Site:
　　https://www.bandainamco.co.jp
Year Founded: 2005
7832—(TKS)
Rev.: $6,941,888,100
Assets: $6,423,849,180
Liabilities: $1,798,019,150
Net Worth: $4,625,830,030
Earnings: $670,868,730
Emp.: 11,159
Fiscal Year-end: 03/31/24
Holding Company
N.A.I.C.S.: 551112
Mitsuaki Taguchi *(Chm)*

Subsidiaries:

Actas Inc. **(1)**
4F Torikona 3-36-1, Shimorenjaku Mitaka, Tokyo, 181-0013, Japan
Tel.: (81) 422268016
Web Site: https://www.actas-inc.co.jp
Emp.: 22
Animation Production Services
N.A.I.C.S.: 512191

Artpresto Co., Ltd. **(1)**
3-13-16 Mita, Minato-ku, Tokyo, 108-0073, Japan
Tel.: (81) 354396270
Web Site: https://www.artpresto.co.jp
Emp.: 80
Stationery Product Mfr
N.A.I.C.S.: 322230
Shuhei Tamaya *(Pres)*

B. B. STUDIO Co., Ltd. **(1)**
11th floor Mita 43MT Building 3-13-16 Mita, Minato-ku, Tokyo, 108-0073, Japan
Tel.: (81) 367443920
Web Site: https://www.bbst.co.jp
Emp.: 189
Gaming Software Development Services
N.A.I.C.S.: 541511

BANDAI Co., Ltd. **(1)**
1-4-8 Komagata, Taito-Ku, Tokyo, 111-8081, Japan
Tel.: (81) 338475011
Web Site: http://www.bandai.co.jp
Sales Range: $1-4.9 Billion
Emp.: 1,157
Toys, Model Kits & Video Games Mfr
N.A.I.C.S.: 339930
Kazunori Ueno *(Pres & CEO)*

Subsidiary (Non-US):

BANDAI (GUANGZHOU) CO., LTD. **(2)**
Unit 2001 20 F Pearl River International Bldg No 112 Yuehua Rd, Guangzhou, 510030, Guangdong, China
Tel.: (86) 2083033428
Web Site: http://www.gundambase.com.cn
Emp.: 30
Gaming Toys Whslr
N.A.I.C.S.: 423920

BANDAI (H.K.) CO., LTD. **(2)**
28 F MG 133 Tower Hoi Bun Road, Kwun Tong, Kowloon, China (Hong Kong)
Tel.: (852) 28660229
Web Site: http://www.bandai.com.hk
Emp.: 150
Toys Whslr
N.A.I.C.S.: 423920
Yamazaki S. *(Gen Mgr)*

Subsidiary (Domestic):

BANDAI Channel Co., Ltd. **(2)**
5-10-2 Minamiaoyama Dai 2 Kuyo Bldg 6f, Minato-Ku, Tokyo, 107-0062, Japan
Tel.: (81) 354686211
Web Site: http://www.b-ch.com

Animated Film Production Services
N.A.I.C.S.: 512110

Subsidiary (Non-US):

BANDAI ESPANA S.A. **(2)**
Avda Partenon 10, 28042, Madrid, Spain
Tel.: (34) 917211616
Web Site: https://www.bandai.es
Toy & Hobby Goods Distr
N.A.I.C.S.: 423920

BANDAI Korea Co., Ltd. **(2)**
11th Fl Ls Yongsan Tower 191 Hangangno 2-ga, Yongsan-gu, Seoul, 140-702, Korea (South)　　　　**(66.67%)**
Tel.: (82) 2 795 6111
Web Site: http://www.bandai.co.kr
Toy & Hobby Goods Whslr
N.A.I.C.S.: 423920

Subsidiary (Domestic):

BANDAI LOGIPAL INC. **(2)**
4-42-5 Higashiyotsugi, Katsushika-ku, Tokyo, 124-8585, Japan
Tel.: (81) 3 3695 5151
Web Site: http://www.blpinc.com
Logistics & Warehouse Services
N.A.I.C.S.: 541614

Subsidiary (Non-US):

BANDAI Polska Sp. z o.o. **(2)**
ul Cybernetyki 7, 02-677, Warsaw, Poland
Tel.: (48) 22 321 94 60
Web Site: http://www.bandai.nationalnet.pl
Sales Range: $50-74.9 Million
Emp.: 8
Toys & Hobby Goods Whslr,
N.A.I.C.S.: 423920

BANDAI S.A. **(2)**
21/23 Rue du Petit Albi, PO 48470, Cergy, 95808, France
Tel.: (33) 134303030
Web Site: http://www.bandai.fr
Toy & Hobby Goods Whslr
N.A.I.C.S.: 423920

BANDAI U.K. LTD. **(2)**
37 - 39 Kew Foot Road, Richmond, TW9 2SS, Surrey, United Kingdom
Tel.: (44) 2083246160
Web Site: https://www.bandai.co.uk
Emp.: 18
Toy & Hobby Goods Distr
N.A.I.C.S.: 423920

Subsidiary (Domestic):

BANDAI VISUAL CO., LTD. **(2)**
Shinagawa Seaside Park Tower 4-12-4 Higashi-Shinagawa, Shinagawa-ku, Tokyo, 140-0002, Japan
Tel.: (81) 3 6720 1601
Web Site: http://www.bandaivisual.co.jp
Visual Software Development Services
N.A.I.C.S.: 541511

Subsidiary (US):

Bandai Namco Toys & Collectibles America Inc. **(2)**
23 Odyssey, Irvine, CA 92618
Tel.: (714) 816-9500
Web Site: http://www.bandai.com
Toys & Model Kits Distr
N.A.I.C.S.: 423920
Kotaro Hama *(CEO)*

Joint Venture (Domestic):

Tsuburaya Productions Co., Ltd. **(2)**
16-17 Nampeidai-cho, Shibuya-ku, Tokyo, 150-0036, Japan
Tel.: (81) 354897860
Web Site: https://tsuburaya-prod.com
Sales Range: $25-49.9 Million
Emp.: 90
Television Show & Movie Production Services
N.A.I.C.S.: 512110

BANDAI NAMCO Arts Inc. **(1)**
Ebisu First Square 1-18-14 Ebisu, Shibuya-ku, Tokyo, 150-0013, Japan
Tel.: (81) 358287582
Web Site: http://www.bandainamcoarts.co.jp
Emp.: 344
Live Event Production Services

N.A.I.C.S.: 711320

BANDAI NAMCO Business Arc Inc. (1)
2nd floor West Building Sumitomo Fudosan Sanda Twin Building, 3-5-27 Mita Minato-ku, Tokyo, 108-6302, Japan
Tel.: (81) 357811500
Web Site: https://www.bandainamco-ba.co.jp
Business Support Services
N.A.I.C.S.: 561499

BANDAI NAMCO Games Inc. (1)
4-5-15 Higashi-shinagawa, Shinagawa-ku, Tokyo, 140-8590, Japan
Tel.: (81) 357835500
Sales Range: $900-999.9 Million
Emp.: 1,700
Holding Company; Consumer Video Game Software, Commercial Amusement Machinery & Network Entertainment Media Designer & Mfr
N.A.I.C.S.: 551112

Subsidiary (US):

BANDAI NAMCO Entertainment America Inc. (2)
2051 Mission Clg Blv, Santa Clara, CA 95054
Tel.: (408) 235-2000
Web Site: http://www.bandainamcoent.com
Sales Range: $25-49.9 Million
Emp.: 180
Video Game Software Publisher & Distr
N.A.I.C.S.: 513210
Hide Irie (COO & Exec VP)

Subsidiary (Non-US):

BANDAI NAMCO Games France S.A.S. (2)
49-51 Rue Des Docks, 69009, Lyon, France
Tel.: (33) 4 37 64 30 00
Web Site: http://www.bandainamcgames.fr
Video Games Whslr
N.A.I.C.S.: 423920

Subsidiary (Domestic):

D3 Inc. (2)
KDX Kajicho Building 3-5-2 Kanda Kajicho, Chiyoda-ku, Tokyo, 101-0045, Japan
Tel.: (81) 570012789
Web Site: https://www.d3p.co.jp
Sales Range: $125-149.9 Million
Emp.: 17
Holding Company; Computer & Mobile Device Video Game Designer, Publisher & Distr
N.A.I.C.S.: 551112

Subsidiary (Domestic):

D3Publisher Inc. (3)
8-3F Daiwa Jimbocho 3-chome Building 2-3-2 Kanda Jimbocho, Chiyoda-ku, Tokyo, 101-0051, Japan (100%)
Tel.: (81) 570012789
Web Site: http://www.d3p.co.jp
Emp.: 22
Computer & Mobile Device Video Game Designer, Publisher & Distr
N.A.I.C.S.: 513210
Toshihiro Nada (Pres & CEO)

BANDAI NAMCO Holdings (USA) Inc. (1)
5551 Katella Ave, Cypress, CA 90630
Tel.: (714) 816-9500
Web Site: http://www.bandainamco.com
Emp.: 70
Holding Company
N.A.I.C.S.: 551112

Subsidiary (Domestic):

BANDAI NAMCO Amusement America Inc. (2)
951 Cambridge Dr, Elk Grove Village, IL 60007
Tel.: (847) 264-5610
Web Site: http://www.bandainamco-am.com
Coin Operated Gaming Machine Mfr
N.A.I.C.S.: 339999
Frank Cosentino (Sr VP)

BANDAI NAMCO Holdings UK Ltd. (1)

Namco House Acton Park Industrial Estate Vale, London, W3 7QE, United Kingdom
Tel.: (44) 2083246000
Sales Range: $50-74.9 Million
Emp.: 5
Holding Company
N.A.I.C.S.: 551112
Phil Brannelly (Mgr-Mktg)

Subsidiary (Domestic):

BANDAI NAMCO Amusement Europe Ltd. (2)
37-39 Kew Foot Road, Richmond, London, TW9 2SS, United Kingdom
Tel.: (44) 1212306666
Web Site: http://www.bandainamco-am.co.uk
Sales Range: $25-49.9 Million
Arcade Machine Distr
N.A.I.C.S.: 423990

BANDAI NAMCO Online Inc. (1)
5-37-8 Shiba, Minato-ku, Tokyo, Japan (100%)
Tel.: (81) 570022262
Web Site: http://www.bandainamco-ol.co.jp
Emp.: 120
Online Gambling Services
N.A.I.C.S.: 517810
Takashi Tokai (Pres & Dir)

BANPRESTO (H.K.) LTD. (1)
28th FL MG Tower 133 Hoi Bun Road Kwun Tong, Kwai Fong, Kowloon, China (Hong Kong)
Tel.: (852) 24186100
Web Site: http://www.banpresto.com.hk
Emp.: 20
Gaming Toys Mfr
N.A.I.C.S.: 339930

Banpresto Sales Co., Ltd. (1)
4-12-2 Higashishinagawa Shinagawa Seaside West Tower 1f, Shinagawa-Ku, Tokyo, 140-0002, Japan
Tel.: (81) 367443930
Stationery Product Distr
N.A.I.C.S.: 424120

CCP Co., Ltd. (1)
3-14-11 Kotobuki Kuramae Chiyoda Building 3F, Taito-ku, Tokyo, 111-0042, Japan
Tel.: (81) 3 5806 3501
Web Site: http://www.ccp-jp.com
Sales Range: $25-49.9 Million
Emp.: 20
Gaming Toys Mfr & Whslr
N.A.I.C.S.: 339930

Italian Tomato Ltd. (1)
9-6-24 Akasaka Minatu-Ku, Tokyo, 107 0052, Japan (30.6%)
Tel.: (81) 334042681
Sales Range: $25-49.9 Million
Emp.: 50
N.A.I.C.S.: 334310

LOGIPAL EXPRESS INC (1)
4-42-5 Higashiyotsugi, Katsushika-Ku, Tokyo, 124-8585, Japan
Tel.: (81) 3 3695 5151
Logistics Consulting Servies
N.A.I.C.S.: 541614

Lantis Co., Ltd. (1)
1-3-14 Hiroo Asaxhiro Bldg 4f, Shibuya-Ku, Tokyo, 150-0012, Japan
Tel.: (81) 354758131
Web Site: http://www.lantis.jp
Music Publishing Services
N.A.I.C.S.: 512230

Megahouse Corporation (1)
2-5-4 Komagata Bandai Dai 2 Bldg 5 6f, Taito-Ku, Tokyo, 111-0043, Japan
Web Site: http://www.megahouse.co.jp
Gaming Toys Mfr & Distr
N.A.I.C.S.: 339930

NAMCO Ltd. (1)
Tel.: (81) 337562311
Web Site: http://www.namco.co.jp
Sales Range: $1-4.9 Billion
Emp.: 2,431
Arcade, Pool Hall, Bowling Center, Amusement Park & Health Spa Operator
N.A.I.C.S.: 713990

Subsidiary (Non-US):

NAMCO Enterprises Asia Ltd. (2)

28/F Mg Tower 133 Hoi Pun Rd Kwun Tong, 280 Gloucester Road, Kowloon, China (Hong Kong)
Tel.: (852) 25166610
Web Site: http://www.namco.com
Sales Range: $25-49.9 Million
Emp.: 30
Arcade & Amusement Facilities Operator
N.A.I.C.S.: 713120
Masafumi Suzuki (Mng Dir)

Subsidiary (US):

NAMCO Entertainment Inc. (2)
877 Supreme Dr, Bensenville, IL 60106-1106
Tel.: (630) 238-2200
Web Site: http://www.namcoarcade.com
N.A.I.C.S.: 334310
Curt Lindbert (Mgr-Redemption & Mdsg)

Subsidiary (Non-US):

NAMCO Operations Europe Ltd. (2)
8 Acton Park Estate, The Vale, London, W3 7QE, United Kingdom
Tel.: (44) 20 8324 6150
Web Site: http://www.namcofunscape.com
Sales Range: $25-49.9 Million
Emp.: 90
Amusement Facility Operating Services
N.A.I.C.S.: 561210
James Cullens (Mng Dir)

NAMCO Operations Spain S.L. (2)
Buenavista 3, 28220, Majadahonda, Spain
Tel.: (34) 916342961
Web Site: http://www.namco.es
Sales Range: $50-74.9 Million
Emp.: 3
Arcade & Amusement Facilities Operator
N.A.I.C.S.: 713120

Unit (Non-US):

Yokohama Creative Center (2)
Sales Range: $25-49.9 Million
Emp.: 5
N.A.I.C.S.: 334310

Unit (Domestic):

Yokohama Mirai-Kenkyusho (2)
15 1 Shinei Cho Tsuzuki Ku, Yokohama, 221 Japan
Tel.: (81) 455930711
Web Site: http://www.namco.com
N.A.I.C.S.: 334310

Pleasure Cast Co., Ltd. (1)
3F 3-35 Shibaura, Minato-ku, Tokyo, 108-0023, Japan
Tel.: (81) 368918540
Web Site: http://www.pleasurecast.co.jp
Amusement Facility Operating Services
N.A.I.C.S.: 713990

Plex Co., Ltd. (1)
2-5-4 Komagata Bandai 2nd Building, Taito-Ku, Tokyo, 111-0043, Japan
Tel.: (81) 358275210
Web Site: https://www.plex-web.com
Gaming Toys Mfr & Distr
N.A.I.C.S.: 339930

Reflector Entertainment Ltd. (1)
2200 Stanley Street, Montreal, H3A1R6, QC, Canada
Tel.: (438) 792-5100
Web Site: https://reflectorentertainment.com
N.A.I.C.S.: 516210
Herve Hoerdt (CEO)

SOTSU CO.,LTD. (1)
2-4-1Hamamatsu-Cho, Minato-Ku, Tokyo, 105-6126, Japan (82.05%)
Tel.: (81) 363860311
Web Site: http://www.sotsu-co.jp
Rev.: $149,832,240
Assets: $236,874,000
Liabilities: $44,497,680
Net Worth: $192,376,320
Earnings: $16,596,720
Emp.: 35
Fiscal Year-end: 08/31/2018
Animated Product Producer
N.A.I.C.S.: 512110
Hideyuki Namba (Pres)

Subsidiary (Domestic):

Sotsu Music Publishing Co., Ltd. (2)

Densokan 5-9-5 Ginza, Chuo-Ku, Tokyo, 104-0061, Japan
Tel.: (81) 355375215
Web Site: https://www.sotsu.co.jp
Emp.: 1
Music Production Services
N.A.I.C.S.: 512250
Hideyuki Nanba (Pres)

Seeds Co., Ltd. (1)
93 Chudojiawatacho Kyoto Research Park 6 Gokan 215, Shimogyo-Ku, Kyoto, 600-8815, Japan
Tel.: (81) 753261240
Gaming Toys Mfr & Distr
N.A.I.C.S.: 339930

Sun-Star Stationery Co., Ltd. (1)
5-20-8 Asakusabashi CS Tower 9th floor, Taito-ku, Tokyo, 111-0053, Japan
Web Site: http://www.sun-star-st.jp
Emp.: 170
Stationery Product Mfr & Distr
N.A.I.C.S.: 322230

Sunrise Music Publishing Co., Ltd. (1)
2-44-10 Kamiigusa, Suginami-Ku, Tokyo, 167-0023, Japan (100%)
Tel.: (81) 333957821
Web Site: http://www.gunboy.net
Music Publishing Services
N.A.I.C.S.: 512230
Sashida Eiji (CEO)

VIBE Inc. (1)
4-12-4 Higashishinagawa Seaside Park Tower 19f, Shinagawa-Ku, Tokyo, 140-0002, Japan
Tel.: (81) 367201700
Web Site: http://www.vibe.co.jp
Advertising Agency Services
N.A.I.C.S.: 541810

WiZ Co., Ltd. (1)
3 Chome-14 Kotobuki, Taito-ku, Tokyo, 111-0042, Japan (87.37%)
Tel.: (81) 358300411
Web Site: http://www.wizinc.com
Game Mfr
N.A.I.C.S.: 339930

BANDAR RAYA DEVELOPMENTS BERHAD
Level 11 Menara BRDB 285 Jalan Maarof, Bukit Bandaraya, 59000, Kuala Lumpur, Malaysia
Tel.: (60) 3 26882888
Web Site: http://www.brdb.com.my
Year Founded: 1965
Sales Range: $200-249.9 Million
Residential & Commercial Properties Development Services
N.A.I.C.S.: 236115
Kim Seng Low (Dir-Asset & Property Mgmt)

Subsidiaries:

Capital Square Sdn. Bhd. (1)
11 Menara BRDB 285 Jalan Maarof Bukit Bandaraya, 50100, Kuala Lumpur, Malaysia
Tel.: (60) 326981288
Sales Range: $50-74.9 Million
Emp.: 12
Real Estate Management & Development Services
N.A.I.C.S.: 531210
Krishnan Periasamy (CEO)

Midwest Profits Sdn. Bhd. (1)
B Capsquare Centre Psn Capsquare, 50100, Kuala Lumpur, Malaysia
Tel.: (60) 3 2698 0128
Sales Range: $25-49.9 Million
Emp.: 50
Gourmet Delicatessen & Supermarkets Operation Services
N.A.I.C.S.: 445110

Permas Jaya Sdn. Bhd. (1)
G 33 Blok A Permas Mall No 3 Jalan Permas Utara, Bandar Baru Permas Jaya, 81750, Johor Bahru, Johor, Malaysia
Tel.: (60) 73871333
Sales Range: $50-74.9 Million
Emp.: 15
Property Management Services

Bandar Raya Developments Berhad—(Continued)

N.A.I.C.S.: 531311
Teh Ku Yong (COO)

BANDHAN FINANCIAL SERVICES LTD.

DN-32 Sector-V Salt Lake City, Kolkata, 700 091, West Bengal, India
Tel.: (91) 33 6609 0909
Web Site: http://www.bandhanmf.com
Year Founded: 2001
Financial Services
N.A.I.C.S.: 522291
Asit Pal (Chm)

Subsidiaries:

Bandhan Financial Holdings
Limited **(1)**
DN 32 Sector V, Salt Lake City, Kolkata, 700091, West Bengal, India
Tel.: (91) 33 6609 0909
Holding Company; Financial Services
N.A.I.C.S.: 551112

Subsidiary (Domestic):

Bandhan Bank Limited **(2)**
DN 32 Sector V, Salt Lake City, Kolkata, 700091, West Bengal, India
Tel.: (91) 3366090909
Web Site: https://www.bandhanbank.com
Rev.: $1,740,856,709
Assets: $12,840,491,879
Liabilities: $12,615,057,181
Net Worth: $225,434,698
Earnings: $423,323,257
Emp.: 39,750
Fiscal Year-end: 03/31/2020
Banking Services
N.A.I.C.S.: 522110
Deepankar Bose (Head-Corp Centre)

BANDIRMA GUBRE FABRIKALARI A.S.

Susam Sk No 22 Bagfas Binasi Cihangir, Beyoglu, 34433, Istanbul, Turkiye
Tel.: (90) 2122930885
Web Site: https://www.bagfas.com.tr
Year Founded: 1968
BAGFS—(IST)
Rev.: $97,598,056
Assets: $306,935,003
Liabilities: $147,759,115
Net Worth: $159,175,888
Earnings: ($51,045,155)
Fiscal Year-end: 12/31/23
Chemical Fertilizer Mfr & Whslr
N.A.I.C.S.: 325314
Buket Gencer Sahin (Deputy CEO)

BANDO CHEMICAL INDUSTRIES, LTD.

4-6-6 Minatojima Minamimachi, Chuo-ku, Kobe, 650-0047, Japan
Tel.: (81) 783042923
Web Site: https://www.bandogrp.com
Year Founded: 1906
5195—(TKS)
Rev.: $715,717,580
Assets: $830,361,420
Liabilities: $265,133,710
Net Worth: $565,227,710
Earnings: $40,849,800
Emp.: 4,023
Fiscal Year-end: 03/31/24
Mfr of Transmission Belts & V-Belts
N.A.I.C.S.: 326220
Mitsutaka Yoshii (Pres)

Subsidiaries:

Aimedic MMT Co., Ltd. **(1)**
Shinagawa Season Terrace 25F 1-2-70 Konan, Minato-Ku, Tokyo, 108-0075, Japan
Tel.: (81) 357155211
Web Site: http://www.aimedicmmt.co.jp
Orthopedic Implant Product Mfr
N.A.I.C.S.: 339113
Takayuki Hirooka (Pres & CEO)

BL Autotec, Ltd. **(1)**
3-3- 17 Meiwa-dori, Hyogo-ku, Kobe, 652-0883, Japan
Tel.: (81) 786822611
Web Site: http://www.bl-autotec.co.jp
Robot Mfr & Distr
N.A.I.C.S.: 333998
Hisashi Izumi (Pres)

Bando (India) Pvt. Ltd. **(1)**
Plot No 436 Sector-8 IMT Manesar, Gurgaon, 122050, Haryana, India
Tel.: (91) 1244305600
Sales Range: $25-49.9 Million
Emp.: 10
Plastic & Rubber Belt Mfr
N.A.I.C.S.: 326220

Bando (Shanghai) Management Co., Ltd. **(1)**
3rd Floor Building H Linkong Economic Park 787 Xiehe Road, Changning District, Shanghai, 200335, China
Tel.: (86) 2163917222
Web Site: http://www.bando.cn
Automotive Products Whslr
N.A.I.C.S.: 423120

Bando (Singapore) Pte. Ltd. **(1)**
No 1 Toh Tuck Link 04-02, Singapore, 596222, Singapore **(100%)**
Tel.: (65) 64752233
Web Site: https://www.bando.com.sg
Sales Range: $50-74.9 Million
Emp.: 25
Mfr of Semiconductors & Related Devices
N.A.I.C.S.: 326150

Bando Belt Manufacturing(Turkey), Inc. **(1)**
Gebze OSB2 Mahallesi 1000Cadde No1018/1, Cayirova, 41420, Kocaeli, Turkiye
Tel.: (90) 8507772687
Web Site: https://www.bandoturkey.com.tr
Automotive Belt Mfr
N.A.I.C.S.: 336340

Bando Chemical Industries, Ltd. - Ashikaga Plant **(1)**
188-6 Arakane-cho, Ashikaga, 326-0832, Tochigi, Japan
Tel.: (81) 284724121
Industrial Rubber Belt Mfr
N.A.I.C.S.: 326220

Bando Chemical Industries, Ltd. - Kakogawa Plant **(1)**
648 Komoikenouchi Tsuchiyama-aza Hiraoka-cho, Kakogawa, 675-0198, Hyogo, Japan
Tel.: (81) 789423232
Industrial Rubber Belt Mfr
N.A.I.C.S.: 326220

Bando Chemical Industries, Ltd. - Nankai Plant **(1)**
20-1 Onosato 5-chome, Sennan, 590-0526, Osaka, Japan
Tel.: (81) 72 482 7711
Web Site: http://www.bandogrp.com
Industrial Rubber Belt Mfr
N.A.I.C.S.: 326220

Bando Chemical Industries, Ltd. - Wakayama Plant **(1)**
1242-5 Mogami Momoyama-cho, Kinokawa, 649-6111, Wakayama, Japan
Tel.: (81) 736 66 0999
Web Site: http://www.bandogrp.com
Industrial Rubber Belt Mfr
N.A.I.C.S.: 326220

Bando Elastomer Co., Ltd. **(1)**
3-17 Meiwadori 3-chome, Hyogo-ku, Kobe, 652-0883, Japan
Tel.: (81) 786525650
Rubber Products Mfr
N.A.I.C.S.: 326291

Bando Europe GmbH **(1)**
Krefelder Str 671, 41066, Monchengladbach, Germany
Tel.: (49) 2161901040
Web Site: https://www.bando.de
Sales Range: $25-49.9 Million
Emp.: 20
Industrial Rubber Belt Mfr
N.A.I.C.S.: 326220
Yoshida Ryota (Mng Dir)

Bando Iberica S.A. **(1)**
Francesc Layret Street 12-14 warehouses 4-5, Sant Ermengol II Industrial Park, 08630, Abrera, Barcelona, Spain
Tel.: (34) 937778740
Web Site: https://bando-iberica.es
Sales Range: $50-74.9 Million
Emp.: 13
Mfr of Semiconductors & Related Devices
N.A.I.C.S.: 326150

Bando Industrial Components & Services, Ltd. **(1)**
Shinosaka Prime Tower 9F 1-1 Nishinakajima 6-chome, Yodogawa-ku, Osaka, 532-0011, Japan
Tel.: (81) 648063058
Rubber Products Mfr
N.A.I.C.S.: 326291

Bando Korea Co., Ltd. **(1)**
38 Eogokgongdan 1-gil, Yangsan, 50591, Gyeongsangnam, Korea (South)
Tel.: (82) 553719200
Web Site: http://www.bandokorea.co.kr
Rubber & Plastic Mfr
N.A.I.C.S.: 326299

Bando Kosan Co., Ltd. **(1)**
3-17 Meiwa-dori 3-chome, Hyogo-ku, Kobe, 652-0883, Japan
Tel.: (81) 786515353
Rubber Products Mfr
N.A.I.C.S.: 326291

Bando Manufacturing (Dongguan) Co., Ltd. **(1)**
Building ZF8 ZhenAn Industrial Park ZhenAn Road, ChangAn Town, Dongguan, GuangDong, China
Tel.: (86) 76985645075
Web Site: http://www.bando.com.sg
Rubber & Plastic Belt Mfr
N.A.I.C.S.: 326220

Bando Manufacturing (Thailand) Ltd. **(1)**
47/7 Village No 4 Bang Pla Road, Ban Ko Subdistrict Mueang Samut Sakhon District, Bangkok, 74000, Thailand
Tel.: (66) 34468410
Web Site: https://www.bandothai.co.th
Emp.: 944
Passport Issuing Services
N.A.I.C.S.: 336340

Bando Manufacturing (Vietnam) Co., Ltd. **(1)**
M-6 Plot Thang Long II Industrial Park, Di Su Ward, My Hao, Hung Yen, Vietnam
Tel.: (84) 2213974986
Web Site: http://www.bando-bmvn.com
Automotive Belt Mfr
N.A.I.C.S.: 336340
Koj Ikoma (Gen Dir)

Bando Sakata, Ltd. **(1)**
Suite No 10A 9/F Tower 2 33 Canton Road Kowloon, Tsim Sha Tsui, Kowloon, China (Hong Kong) **(100%)**
Tel.: (852) 24944815
Sales Range: $50-74.9 Million
Emp.: 56
N.A.I.C.S.: 336340

Bando Siix Ltd. **(1)**
Suite No 10A 9/F Tower 2 China Hong Kong City 33 Canton Road, Tsimshatsui, Kowloon, China (Hong Kong)
Tel.: (852) 24944815
Web Site: https://www.bando.com.sg
Rubber Belt Mfr
N.A.I.C.S.: 326220

Bando Trading Co., Ltd. **(1)**
2-4-60, Kanazawa, 770-0871, Tokushima, Japan
Tel.: (81) 886641355
Web Site: http://bando-j.com
Emp.: 16
Trading Services
N.A.I.C.S.: 425120
Hideyo Bando (Pres)

Bando USA, Inc. **(1)**
1149 W Bryn Mawr, Itasca, IL 60143-1508 **(100%)**
Tel.: (630) 773-6600
Web Site: http://www.bandousa.com

Sales Range: $25-49.9 Million
Emp.: 40
Automotive & Industrial V-Belts Distr
N.A.I.C.S.: 326220
Joseph Laudadio (Pres & CEO)

Division (Domestic):

Bando USA, Inc. **(2)**
2720 Pioneer Dr, Bowling Green, KY 42101 **(90%)**
Tel.: (630) 773-6600
Web Site: http://www.bandousa.com
Sales Range: $75-99.9 Million
Emp.: 150
Mfr of Fan Belts
N.A.I.C.S.: 326220

Bando-Scholtz Corporation **(1)**
648 Komoikenouchi Tsuchiyama-aza, Hiraoka-cho, Kakogawa, 675-0104, Hyogo, Japan
Tel.: (81) 789433933
Rubber Products Mfr
N.A.I.C.S.: 326291

Dongil-Bando Co., Ltd. **(1)**
38 Eogokgongdan1-gil, Gyeongsangnamdo, Yangsan, 50591, Korea (South) **(100%)**
Tel.: (82) 553719200
Sales Range: $50-74.9 Million
Emp.: 100
Chemicals Mfr
N.A.I.C.S.: 325180

East Japan Belt Products, Inc. **(1)**
6-13 Aiya-cho 4-chome Taira, Iwaki, 970-8026, Fukushima, Japan
Tel.: (81) 246222696
Rubber Products Mfr
N.A.I.C.S.: 326291

Fukuibelt. Industries, Ltd. **(1)**
23-1-7 Shimoemori-cho, Fukui, 918-8037, Japan
Tel.: (81) 776363100
Rubber Products Mfr
N.A.I.C.S.: 326291

Hokuriku Bando, Inc. **(1)**
2-19 Tonyamachi 3-chome, Toyama, 930-0834, Japan
Tel.: (81) 764512525
Power Transmission Belt Product Mfr
N.A.I.C.S.: 333613

Kee Fatt Industries, Sdn. Bhd. **(1)**
No 1 Jalan Kee Fatt Batu 23 Kulai, 81000, Kulai, Johor, Malaysia **(39%)**
Tel.: (60) 76612888
Web Site: https://www.keefatt.com
Sales Range: $1-9.9 Million
Emp.: 400
Mfr of Roller Chain
N.A.I.C.S.: 326150
Chai Woo Sien (Founder & Chm)

Koyo Sangyo Co., Ltd. **(1)**
Yubinbango Yanagibashi 2-19-6 Yanagibashi First Building, Taito-ku, Tokyo, 111-0052, Japan
Tel.: (81) 356896900
Web Site: http://www.koyo-sg.co.jp
Chemical & Resin Product Mfr
N.A.I.C.S.: 325998

P.T. Bando Indonesia **(1)**
Jl Gajah Tunggal Km 7 Tangerang Kel, Pasir Jaya Kecamatan Jati Uwung Kotamadya, Tangerang, 15135, Indonesia
Tel.: (62) 215903920
Web Site: https://home.bandoindonesia.com
Power Transmission Belt Mfr
N.A.I.C.S.: 336350

Pengeluaran Getah Bando (Malaysia) Sdn. Bhd. **(1)**
No 2 Jalan Sengkang Batu 22, Kulai, 81000, Johor, Malaysia **(100%)**
Tel.: (60) 76635021
Sales Range: $75-99.9 Million
Emp.: 180
N.A.I.C.S.: 336340

Philippine Belt Manufacturing Corp. **(1)**
2nd Floor Siemkang Bldg 280 Dasmarinas St, Binondo, Manila, 1006, Philippines
Tel.: (63) 282410794
Web Site: https://www.philbelt.com
Rubber Belt Mfr & Distr

N.A.I.C.S.: 326220

Philippine Belt Mfg. Corp. (1)
2nd Floor Siemkang Bldg 280 Dasmarinas St, PO Box 205, Binondo, Manila, 1099, Philippines
Tel.: (63) 282410794
Web Site: https://www.philbelt.com
Sales Range: $25-49.9 Million
Emp.: 30
Sales of Trencher Parts
N.A.I.C.S.: 326220

Sanwu Bando Inc. (1)
11FL-2 No51 Sec 1 Min Sheng E Road, Zhongshan, Taipei, Taiwan (50%)
Tel.: (886) 225678255
Web Site: http://www.bando.com.tw
Sales Range: $50-74.9 Million
Emp.: 8
Automotive Parts & Materials Handling Systems
N.A.I.C.S.: 326220

Vann Corporation (1)
2-27-1 Higashinihonbashi, Chuo-ku, Tokyo, 103-0004, Japan
Tel.: (81) 338617411
Web Site: http://vann-co-jp.secure-web.jp
Industrial Distr
N.A.I.C.S.: 423840

BANDSTRA TRANSPORTATION SYSTEMS LTD.
3394 Hwy 16 E, Box 95, Smithers, V0J 2N0, BC, Canada
Tel.: (250) 847-2057
Web Site: https://www.bandstra.com
Year Founded: 1955
Emp.: 400
Household Goods Carrier Services
N.A.I.C.S.: 484210
John Bandstra Jr. (Pres)

BANDVULC TYRES LTD.
Gillard Way Lee Mill Industrial Estate Ivybridge, Devon, PL21 9LN, United Kingdom
Tel.: (44) 1752 893559
Web Site: http://www.bandvulc.com
Year Founded: 1971
Sales Range: $75-99.9 Million
Emp.: 320
Tire Rebuilding Services
N.A.I.C.S.: 326212
Patrick O'Connell (Head-Hot Retread Tech)

BANENG HOLDINGS BHD.
Lot 4979 2 1/2 Miles Jalan Tanjong Laboh, 83000, Batu Pahat, Johor Darul Takzim, Malaysia
Tel.: (60) 74355730
Web Site: http://www.bhb.net.my
Sales Range: $25-49.9 Million
Fabrics & Garments Mfr
N.A.I.C.S.: 315250
Choon Hiok Lim (Mng Dir)

Subsidiaries:

Chenille International Pte. Ltd. (1)
120 Lower Delta Road 07-11 Cendex Centre, Singapore, 169208, Singapore
Tel.: (65) 67352511
Clothing Apparels Mfr & Distr
N.A.I.C.S.: 315250

Maxlin Garments Sdn. Bhd. (1)
Lot 4979 2 1/2 Miles Km 4 Jalan Tanjung Labuh, 83000, Batu Pahat, Johor, Malaysia
Tel.: (60) 74355701
Sales Range: $100-124.9 Million
Emp.: 400
Apparels Mfr & Distr
N.A.I.C.S.: 315120

BANESCO BANCO UNIVERSAL C.A.
Principal de Bello Monte Avenue, Lincoln St & Sorbona St, Banesco City Bldg, Caracas, Venezuela
Tel.: (58) 212 501 7111

Web Site: http://www.banesco.com
Sales Range: $1-4.9 Billion
Banking Services
N.A.I.C.S.: 522110

BANESCO S.A.
Avenida Aquilino de la Guardia y Calle 47, Bella Vista Edificio Ocean Business Plaza Piso 28, Panama, Panama
Tel.: (507) 2822000
Web Site:
http://www.banesco.com.pa
Year Founded: 2007
BANE—(PAN)
Rev.: $75,259,441
Assets: $1,935,369,939
Liabilities: $1,767,271,191
Net Worth: $168,098,748
Earnings: $12,607,189
Fiscal Year-end: 12/31/20
Commercial Banking Services
N.A.I.C.S.: 522110
Miguel Angel Marcano (Pres & Dir)

BANESTES S.A. BANCO DO ESTADO DO ESPIRITO SANTO
Av Princesa Isabel 574 Bloco B 9 Andar, Centro, Vitoria, 29010-930, ES, Brazil
Tel.: (55) 2733831083
Web Site:
http://www.banestes.com.br
Year Founded: 1937
BEES4—(BRAZ)
Rev.: $917,158,947
Assets: $7,402,977,941
Liabilities: $7,023,861,024
Net Worth: $379,116,917
Earnings: $57,882,947
Fiscal Year-end: 12/31/23
Commercial Banking Services
N.A.I.C.S.: 522110
Bruno Curty Vivas (Chief Legal & Admin Officer)

BANG & OLUFSEN A/S
Bang and Olufsen Alle 1, DK-7600, Struer, Denmark
Tel.: (45) 96841122
Web Site: https://www.bang-olufsen.com
Year Founded: 1925
BGOUF—(OTCIQ)
Rev.: $374,470,065
Assets: $332,363,887
Liabilities: $194,035,687
Net Worth: $138,328,200
Earnings: ($2,459,811)
Emp.: 998
Fiscal Year-end: 05/31/24
Televisions, Radios, Audio/Visual Recorders, Gramophones, Compact Disc Players, Complete Music Systems, Digital Switching Systems, Telephones & Shop-Profiling Solutions Mfr
N.A.I.C.S.: 334310
Juha Christensen (Deputy Chm)

Subsidiaries:

Bang & Olufsen A/S (1)
PO Box 645, Skoyen, N 0214, Oslo, Norway (100%)
Tel.: (47) 80010532
Web Site: http://www.bang-olufsen.com
Sales Range: $50-74.9 Million
Emp.: 8
Sale of Electrical Products
N.A.I.C.S.: 423620

Bang & Olufsen AG (1)
Grindelstrasse 15, CH 8303, Bassersdorf, Switzerland (100%)
Tel.: (41) 844727272
Web Site: http://www.bangolufsen.com
Sales Range: $50-74.9 Million
Emp.: 8

Markets Telecommunications Products & Accessories
N.A.I.C.S.: 423620

Bang & Olufsen America, Inc. (1)
780 W Dundee Rd, Arlington Heights, IL 60004-1562 (100%)
Tel.: (847) 590-4900
Web Site: http://www.bang-olufsen.com
Sales Range: $25-49.9 Million
Emp.: 35
Consumer Electronics; Audio, Video & Multimedia Products
N.A.I.C.S.: 423620

Bang & Olufsen Asia Pte. Ltd. (1)
10 -12 Scotts Rd 01 05 Grand Hyatt, Singapore, 228211, Singapore (100%)
Tel.: (65) 67377500
Sales Range: $25-49.9 Million
Emp.: 4
N.A.I.C.S.: 334310

Bang & Olufsen Danmark a/s (1)
Peter Bangs Vej 15, 7600, Struer, Denmark (100%)
Tel.: (45) 96841122
Sales Range: $400-449.9 Million
Emp.: 2,000
Audio & Video Equipment Mfr
N.A.I.C.S.: 334310

Subsidiary (Domestic):

Bang & Olufsen ICEpower a/s (2)
Gl Lundtoftevej 1b, 2800, Lyngby, Denmark
Tel.: (45) 96 84 11 22
Web Site: http://www.icepower.bang-olufsen.com
Sales Range: $25-49.9 Million
Emp.: 3
Audio Power Conversion Equipment Mfr
N.A.I.C.S.: 334310
Keld Anderson (Gen Mgr)

Bang & Olufsen Deutschland GmbH (1)
Dr Carl von Linde-Strasse 2, 82049, Pullach, Germany
Tel.: (49) 89759050
Audio & Video Equipment Mfr
N.A.I.C.S.: 334310

Bang & Olufsen Espana S.A. (1)
Avenida Europa 2, Parque Empresarial La Moraleja, 28108, Alcobendas, Madrid, Spain (100%)
Tel.: (34) 916616575
Web Site: http://www.bang-olufsen.com
Sales Range: $25-49.9 Million
Emp.: 28
Audio & Video Products
N.A.I.C.S.: 334310

Bang & Olufsen Finance A/S (1)
Peter Bangs Vej 15, 7600, Struer, Denmark (100%)
Tel.: (45) 96841122
Web Site: http://www.bang-olufsen.dk
Sales Range: $400-449.9 Million
Emp.: 300
Promotes & Supports the Distribution of Company Products
N.A.I.C.S.: 449210

Bang & Olufsen France S.A. (1)
141 Rue Jules Guesde, 92304, Levallois-Perret, France (100%)
Tel.: (33) 55212155
Web Site: http://www.bang-olufsen.com
Sales Range: $25-49.9 Million
Emp.: 30
Audio & Video Products
N.A.I.C.S.: 334310

Bang & Olufsen Italia S.p.A. (1)
Via Meravigli 2, 20123, Milan, Italy (100%)
Tel.: (39) 0027259141
Sales Range: $25-49.9 Million
Emp.: 20
Electrical Appliances, Television & Radio
N.A.I.C.S.: 449210

Bang & Olufsen Japan K.K. (1)
Shiba Boat Bldg 9th Fl 3 1 15 Shiba, Minato Ku, Tokyo, 1050014, Japan (100%)
Tel.: (81) 354401844
Web Site: http://www.bang-olufsen.com
Sales Range: $25-49.9 Million
Emp.: 45
N.A.I.C.S.: 334310

Bang & Olufsen Operations a/s (1)
Alle 1, 7600, Struer, Denmark
Tel.: (45) 96841122
Web Site: http://www.bang-olufsen.dk
Sales Range: $350-399.9 Million
Emp.: 200
Logistics Consulting Servies
N.A.I.C.S.: 541614

Subsidiary (Domestic):

Bang & Olufsen Expansion a/s (2)
Peter Bangs Vej 15, 7600, Struer, Denmark
Tel.: (45) 96841122
Web Site: http://www.bang-olufsen.com
Sales Range: $350-399.9 Million
Emp.: 100
Audio Equipment Mfr
N.A.I.C.S.: 334310
Tue Mantoni (Gen Mgr)

Bang & Olufsen Svenska AB (2)
Gl Lundtoftevej 1B, 2800, Lyngby, Denmark
Tel.: (45) 96841122
Emp.: 100
Audio Product Mfr
N.A.I.C.S.: 334310
Yasuyuki Tanaka (Pres & CEO)

Bang & Olufsen Telecom a/s (1)
Peter Bangs Vej 15, 7600, Struer, Denmark (100%)
Tel.: (45) 96841122
Web Site: http://www.telecom.bang-olufsen.com
Sales Range: $400-449.9 Million
Emp.: 2,000
Develops, Produces & Markets Telecommunications Products & Accessories
N.A.I.C.S.: 517810

Bang & Olufsen United Kingdom Ltd. (1)
630 Wharfdale Rd, Winnersh Triangle, Wokingham, RG41 5TP, Berks, United Kingdom (100%)
Tel.: (44) 1189692288
Web Site: http://www.bang-olufsen.com
Emp.: 30
Sale of Electrical Products
N.A.I.C.S.: 423620
Karen Watts (Dir-Mktg)

Bang & Olufsen n.v./s.a. (1)
Louizalaan 331-333, 1050, Brussels, Belgium (100%)
Tel.: (32) 24560811
Web Site: http://www.bang-olufsen.com
Sales Range: $25-49.9 Million
Emp.: 12
Sale of Electrical Products
N.A.I.C.S.: 423620

Bright Future International Limited (1)
Shop 2008 Podium Level 2 IFC Mall, Hong Kong, China (Hong Kong)
Tel.: (852) 2 526 8800
Audio Visual Equipment Whslr
N.A.I.C.S.: 423690

OU BO-Soft (1)
Parnu Mnt 139, Tallinn, 11317, Estonia
Tel.: (372) 6283614
Audio Equipment Mfr
N.A.I.C.S.: 334310

BANG OVERSEAS LTD.
405/406 Kewal Industrial Estate Senapati Bapat Marg, Lower Parel West, Mumbai, 400 001, Maharashtra, India
Tel.: (91) 2266607965
Web Site:
https://www.banggroup.com
Year Founded: 1992
BANG—(NSE)
Rev.: $11,661,222
Assets: $19,729,137
Liabilities: $6,557,037
Net Worth: $13,172,100
Earnings: $673,314
Emp.: 285
Fiscal Year-end: 03/30/22
Men's Clothing Mfr & Exporter
N.A.I.C.S.: 315250

Bang Overseas Ltd.—(Continued)

Brijgopal Balaram Bang *(Chm & Mng Dir)*

Subsidiaries:

Thomas Scott (India) Limited **(1)**
405-406 Kewal Industrial Estate Senapati
Bapat Marg, Lower Parel West, Mumbai,
400 001, Maharashtra, India
Tel.: (91) 2266607965
Web Site: https://www.thomasscott.org
Rev.: $2,942,063
Assets: $4,973,567
Liabilities: $4,424,868
Net Worth: $548,699
Earnings: ($15,635)
Emp.: 162
Fiscal Year-end: 03/31/2021
Garments Mfr
N.A.I.C.S.: 315250
Brijgopal Balaram Bang *(Mng Dir)*

Vedanta Creations Limited **(1)**
No 50 Kewal Indl Estate Ground Fl Lowr
Parel W, Mumbai, 400013, Maharashtra,
India
Tel.: (91) 2230402212
Readymade Garments Whslr
N.A.I.C.S.: 315210

BANGALORE FORT FARMS LIMITED
16A Brabourne Road 6th Floor, Kolkata, 700001, India
Tel.: (91) 9073933003
Web Site:
https://www.bangalorefortfarms.com
539120—(BOM)
Rev.: $2,829,431
Assets: $2,318,247
Liabilities: $1,344,080
Net Worth: $974,167
Earnings: $21,821
Emp.: 3
Fiscal Year-end: 03/31/21
Jute Mfr
N.A.I.C.S.: 313210
Parmeshwar Singh *(Exec Dir)*

BANGALORE STOCK EXCHANGE LIMITED
51 Stock Exchange Towers, 1st
Cross JC Road, Bengaluru, 560 027,
India
Tel.: (91) 8041575235
Web Site: http://www.bgse.co.in
Year Founded: 1963
Stock Exchange Services
N.A.I.C.S.: 523210
Sudhakar Rao *(Chm)*

BANGAS LIMITED
South Avenue Tower 6th Floor House
No 50 Road No 3 7 Gulshan Avenue,
Dhaka, 1212, Bangladesh
Tel.: (880) 29847926
Web Site:
https://www.bangas.com.bd
Year Founded: 1980
BANGAS—(CHT)
Rev.: $1,663,992
Assets: $2,053,819
Liabilities: $596,087
Net Worth: $1,457,731
Earnings: $20,182
Emp.: 191
Fiscal Year-end: 06/30/23
Grocery Product Mfr & Whslr
N.A.I.C.S.: 311821
Atiqul Haque *(CEO)*

BANGCHAK CORPORATION PUBLIC COMPANY LIMITED
2098 M Tower Building 8th Floor
Sukhumvit Road, Phra Khanong Tai
Phra Khanong, Bangkok, 10260,
Thailand
Tel.: (66) 23358888

Web Site:
https://www.bangchak.co.th
BCP—(THA)
Rev.: $4,546,523,625
Assets: $4,942,108,763
Liabilities: $2,999,005,468
Net Worth: $1,943,103,295
Earnings: ($232,142,761)
Emp.: 1,230
Fiscal Year-end: 12/31/20
Petroleum Exploration & Development
N.A.I.C.S.: 211120
Chaiwat Kovavisarach *(Pres & CEO)*

Subsidiaries:

BBGI Public Company Limited **(1)**
2098 M Tower Building 5th Floor Sukhumvit
Road, Phra Khanong Tai Phra Khanong,
Bangkok, 10260, Thailand
Tel.: (66) 23358899
Web Site: https://www.bbgigroup.com
Bio Fuel Mfr & Distr
N.A.I.C.S.: 325199
Pichai Chunhavajira *(Chm)*

BCPG Public Company Limited **(1)**
2098 M Tower Building 12th Floor
Sukhumvit Road, Phra Khanong Tai Phra
Khanong, Bangkok, 10260, Thailand
Tel.: (66) 23358999
Web Site: https://www.bcpggroup.com
Rev.: $155,679,963
Assets: $2,167,198,279
Liabilities: $1,302,771,663
Net Worth: $864,426,615
Earnings: $32,292,870
Emp.: 153
Fiscal Year-end: 12/31/2023
Electric Power Distribution Services
N.A.I.C.S.: 221122
Pichai Chunhavajira *(Chm)*

Bangchak Retail Co., Ltd. **(1)**
3195/28 Vibulthani Tower 24th Floor Rama
IV Road, Klong Ton Klong Toey District,
Bangkok, 10260, Thailand
Tel.: (66) 23354995
Bio Fuel Mfr & Distr
N.A.I.C.S.: 325199

Esso (Thailand) Public Company
Limited **(1)**
3195/17-29 Rama 4 Road Klong Ton, Klong
Toey District, Bangkok, 10110,
Thailand **(76.34%)**
Tel.: (66) 24074000
Web Site: https://www.esso.co.th
Rev.: $6,497,025,387
Assets: $2,061,560,917
Liabilities: $1,245,265,335
Net Worth: $816,295,583
Earnings: $62,536,264
Emp.: 596
Fiscal Year-end: 12/31/2023
Petroleum Mfr
N.A.I.C.S.: 211120
Ratrimani Pasiphol *(Mgr)*

Nido Petroleum Limited **(1)**
Tower One - International Towers Sydney
Level 46, 100 Barangaroo Avenue, Sydney,
2000, NSW, Australia
Tel.: (61) 8 9474 0000
Web Site: http://www.nido.com.au
Oil & Gas Exploration Services
N.A.I.C.S.: 213112
Michael Fischer *(CEO & Mng Dir)*

The Bangchak Biofuel Co., Ltd. **(1)**
28 Moo 9, Bang Krasan Subdistrict Bang
Pa-in District, Phra Nakhon Si Ayutthaya,
13160, Thailand
Tel.: (66) 3 527 6500
Web Site: https://www.bangchakbiofuel.co.th
Emp.: 65
Biodiesel Mfr
N.A.I.C.S.: 324110

The Bangchak Green Net Co.
Ltd **(1)**
2098 M Tower Building 17th Floor
Sukhumvit Road, Phra Khanong Tai Phra
Khanong, Bangkok, 10260,
Thailand **(100%)**
Tel.: (66) 23672699
Sales Range: $200-249.9 Million
Emp.: 1,000
Fuel Dealers

N.A.I.C.S.: 457210

BANGKO SENTRAL NG PILIPINAS
A Mabini St Cor P Ocampo St
Malate, Manila, 1004, Philippines
Tel.: (63) 27087701
Web Site: http://www.bsp.gov.ph
Year Founded: 1993
Sales Range: $1-4.9 Billion
Emp.: 5,234
Banking Services
N.A.I.C.S.: 521110
Leny I. Silvestre *(Mng Dir-Supervision & Examination Sector)*

BANGKOK AIRWAYS PUBLIC COMPANY LIMITED
99 Mu 14 Vibhavadirangsit Rd Chom
Phon Chatuchak, Bangkok, 10900,
Thailand
Tel.: (66) 22655678
Web Site: http://www.bangkokair.com
BA—(THA)
Rev.: $634,414,856
Assets: $1,689,668,600
Liabilities: $1,196,101,707
Net Worth: $493,566,893
Earnings: $90,741,583
Emp.: 2,294
Fiscal Year-end: 12/31/23
Oil Transportation Services
N.A.I.C.S.: 481111
Puttipong Prasarttong-Osoth *(Vice Chm, Pres, CEO, Exec VP-Ops, Sr VP-Comml & VP-HR)*

Subsidiaries:

Bangkok Air Aviation Training Center
Co., Ltd. **(1)**
6th Floor 99 Mu 14 Vibhavadi Rangsit Road
Chomphon, Chatuchak, Bangkok, 10900,
Thailand
Tel.: (66) 22655678
Web Site: https://www.batc.co.th
Flight Training Services
N.A.I.C.S.: 611512

Bangkok Air Catering Co., Ltd. **(1)**
888 Moo1 Tambon Nongprue Amphur,
Bangplee, Samut Prakan, 10540, Thailand
Tel.: (66) 21317500
Web Site:
https://www.bangkokaircatering.com
Emp.: 600
Catering Services
N.A.I.C.S.: 722320
Linus A. E. Knobel *(Mng Dir)*

Subsidiary (Domestic):

BAC Gourmet House Co., Ltd. **(2)**
2194 Asiatique The Riverfront Charoenkrung Rd, Watprayakrai Bang Kho Leam,
Bangkok, 10120, Thailand
Tel.: (66) 21317500
Web Site: https://www.gourmethouse.co.th
Hotel Operator
N.A.I.C.S.: 721110
Tien Koosuwan *(Gen Mgr)*

Bangkok Air Catering Phuket Co.,
Ltd. **(2)**
138 Sakhu Si Sunthon, Thalang District,
Phuket, 83110, Thailand
Tel.: (66) 21317500
Emp.: 160
Catering Services
N.A.I.C.S.: 722320

Bangkok Air Catering Samui Co.,
Ltd. **(2)**
99/13 Moo 4 Tambon Bophut, Amphoe Koh
Samui, Surat Thani, Thailand
Tel.: (66) 21317500
Emp.: 87
Catering Services
N.A.I.C.S.: 722320

Bangkok Airways Ground Services
Co. Ltd. **(1)**
99 Moo 4 Bo Phut, Koh Samui, Surat
Thani, 84320, Thailand

Tel.: (66) 652691515
Web Site: https://www.pg-gs.com
Emp.: 199
Ground Handling Services
N.A.I.C.S.: 561990
Nijjapat Piyapant *(Gen Mgr)*

Gourmet Primo Co., Ltd. **(1)**
129 Sukhapiban 2 Road Kwaeng Dokmai,
Khet Prawet, Bangkok, 10250, Thailand
Tel.: (66) 23285997
Web Site: https://www.gourmetprimo.com
Food Mfr
N.A.I.C.S.: 311999
Hassan Farran *(Production Mgr)*

Worldwide Flight Services Bangkok
Air Ground Handling Co., Ltd. **(1)**
777 Moo 1, Nong Prue Bang Phli, Samut
Prakan, 10540, Thailand
Tel.: (66) 21315000
Web Site:
http://www.bangkokflightservices.com
Flight Services
N.A.I.C.S.: 488190
Stewart Sinclair *(Mng Dir)*

Subsidiary (Domestic):

BFS Cargo DMK Co., Ltd. **(2)**
777 Moo 1, Racha Thewa Bang Phli, Samut
Prakan, 10540, Thailand
Tel.: (66) 21315555
Flight Services
N.A.I.C.S.: 488190

BANGKOK AVIATION FUEL SERVICES PUBLIC COMPANY LIMITED
171/2 Kamphang Phet 6 Rd Don
Mueang Don Mueang, Bangkok,
10210, Thailand
Tel.: (66) 28348900
Web Site: https://www.bafsthai.com
BAFS—(THA)
Rev.: $89,737,472
Assets: $663,445,432
Liabilities: $467,849,413
Net Worth: $195,596,019
Earnings: ($7,761,385)
Emp.: 527
Fiscal Year-end: 12/31/23
Aviation Fuel Services
N.A.I.C.S.: 457210
Palakorn Suwanrath *(Chm)*

Subsidiaries:

BAFS Pipeline Transportation
Ltd **(1)**
424 Kamphaeng Phet 6 Rd, Don Muang,
Bangkok, 10210, Thailand
Tel.: (66) 25746180
Web Site: https://fpt.co.th
Pipeline Transportation Services
N.A.I.C.S.: 486990

Thai Aviation Refuelling Company
Limited **(1)**
99 Moo 10 Srisa Jorakhanol, BangSaothong, Samut Prakan, 10570, Thailand
Tel.: (66) 21 344 0216
Web Site: https://www.tarco.co.th
Sales Range: $25-49.9 Million
Pipeline Network Operating Services
N.A.I.C.S.: 486990
Pariwat Vattanasup *(Mng Dir)*

BANGKOK BANK PUBLIC COMPANY LIMITED
333 Silom Road Silom Bangrak,
Bangkok, 10500, Thailand
Tel.: (66) 26455555   TH
Web Site:
https://www.bangkokbank.com
Year Founded: 1944
BBL—(THA)
Rev.: $5,586,044
Assets: $129,746,281
Liabilities: $114,490,226
Net Worth: $15,256,055
Earnings: $965,927
Fiscal Year-end: 12/31/23
Commercial Banking Services

N.A.I.C.S.: 522110
Deja Tulananda *(Vice Chm)*

Subsidiaries:

BSL Leasing Co., Ltd.   **(1)**
175 Sathorn City Tower 19th Floor South
Sathorn Rd, Bangkok, 10120, Thailand
Tel.: (66) 26704700
Web Site: http://www.bsl.co.th
Investment Services
N.A.I.C.S.: 523940

Bangkok Bank (China) Co., Ltd.   **(1)**
No 7 Zhongshan East-1 Road, Shanghai,
200002, China
Tel.: (86) 2123290100
Sales Range: $100-124.9 Million
Emp.: 130
Commercial Banking Services
N.A.I.C.S.: 522110

Bangkok Bank Berhad   **(1)**
1-45-01 Menara Bangkok Bank Laman
Sentral Berjaya No 105 Jalan Ampang,
50450, Kuala Lumpur, Malaysia   **(100%)**
Tel.: (60) 3 2174 6888
Web Site: http://www.bangkokbank.com.my
Rev.: $59,241,566
Assets: $1,271,734,858
Liabilities: $965,143,727
Net Worth: $306,591,130
Earnings: ($351,395)
Emp.: 75
Fiscal Year-end: 12/31/2019
Commercial Bank
N.A.I.C.S.: 522110

Bangkok Industrial Gas Co., Ltd.   **(1)**
183 Rajanakarn Building 11th Floor South
Sathorn Road, Yannawa, Bangkok, 10120,
Thailand
Tel.: (66) 26856789
Web Site: http://www.bigth.com
Sales Range: $25-49.9 Million
Emp.: 70
Industrial Gas Mfr
N.A.I.C.S.: 325120
Piyabut Charuphen *(Mng Dir)*

Bualuang Securities Public Company
Limited   **(1)**
29th Floor Silom Complex Office Building
Bang Rak 191 Silom Road, Bangkok,
10500, Thailand   **(99.7%)**
Tel.: (66) 22313777
Web Site: http://www.bualuang.co.th
Sales Range: $100-124.9 Million
Emp.: 200
Securities Brokerage Services
N.A.I.C.S.: 523150

Bualuang Ventures Ltd.   **(1)**
Asia Centre Building 15th Floor 173/10
South Sathorn Road, Thung Maha Mek,
Bangkok, Thailand
Tel.: (66) 20118730
Web Site: http://www.bualuangventures.com
Investment Services
N.A.I.C.S.: 523999

M.K. Real Estate Development Public
Company Limited   **(1)**
No 345 Building 345 Surawong Floors 6-8
Surawong Road, Suriyawong Subdistrict
Bangrak District, Bangkok, 10500, Thailand
Tel.: (66) 22348888
Web Site: https://www.mk.co.th
Rev.: $114,836,545
Assets: $599,268,432
Liabilities: $377,991,090
Net Worth: $221,277,342
Earnings: ($113,975)
Fiscal Year-end: 12/31/2020
Real Estate Development Services
N.A.I.C.S.: 531390
Suthep Wongvorazathe *(Chm & Chm)*

Subsidiary (Domestic):

Prospect Development Co., Ltd.   **(2)**
16 th Floor Tisco Tower 48/29 North
Sathorn Road Silom Bangrak, Bangkok,
10500, Thailand
Tel.: (66) 26973852
Web Site: http://www.prospectd.com
Property Rental & Leasing Services
N.A.I.C.S.: 531120

PT Bank Permata Tbk   **(1)**

Gedung World Trade Center II WTC II Lt
21-30 JI JI Jend Sudirman Kav, 29-31 Pon-
dok Pinang Kebayoran Lama RT 8/RW 3
Kuningan Karet Setia, Jakarta, 12920,
Indonesia   **(89.12%)**
Tel.: (62) 2129850611
Web Site: http://www.permatabank.com
Rev.: $821,944,410
Assets: $11,301,588,130
Liabilities: $9,618,973,560
Net Worth: $1,682,614,570
Earnings: $105,029,400
Emp.: 7,806
Fiscal Year-end: 12/31/2019
Financial Banking Services
N.A.I.C.S.: 521110
Katharine Grace *(Sec)*

Subsidiary (Domestic):

PT Sahabat Finansial Keluarga   **(2)**
Metropolitan Tower Lantai 3 JI RA Kartini
TB Simatuoang Kav 14, Cilandak, Jakarta
Selatan, 12430, Indonesia
Tel.: (62) 2127652020
Web Site: http://www.sfk.co.id
Financial Banking Services
N.A.I.C.S.: 522110

Sinnsuptawee Asset Management
Co., Ltd.   **(1)**
323 United Center Building Unit No 3001
30th Floor Silmon Road, Bangkok, 10500,
Thailand
Tel.: (66) 2635 5001
Web Site: http://www.stamc.com
Sales Range: $50-74.9 Million
Emp.: 9
Asset Management Services
N.A.I.C.S.: 533110
Kulathida Sivaya Thorn *(Mng Dir)*

BANGKOK BROADCASTING & TV CO., LTD.
No 998/1 Soi Ruamsirimit Phahony-
othin Road, Chomphon Subdistrict
Chatuchak District, Bangkok, 10900,
Thailand
Tel.: (66) 2495 7777
Web Site: http://www.ch7.com
Year Founded: 1967
Broadcasting Services
N.A.I.C.S.: 516120

Subsidiaries:

BBTV Productions Co., Ltd.   **(1)**
998/1 Phaholyothin Road Jomphol
Chatuchak, Bangkok, 10900, Thailand
Tel.: (66) 2 272 0201
Broadcasting Services
N.A.I.C.S.: 512110

Subsidiary (Domestic):

Matching Maximize Solution PLC   **(2)**
305/12 Soi Sukhothai 6 Sukhothai Rd,
Dusit, Bangkok, 10300, Thailand   **(87.6%)**
Tel.: (66) 22436543
Web Site: https://matchinggroup-test.com
Rev.: $13,159,299
Assets: $44,943,644
Liabilities: $7,700,603
Net Worth: $37,243,041
Earnings: $587,657
Emp.: 443
Fiscal Year-end: 12/31/2023
Commercial Film Production Services
N.A.I.C.S.: 512110
Chanintorn Ulit *(Sr VP-Rental Equipment Bus)*

Subsidiary (Domestic):

Book Maker Co., Ltd.   **(3)**
305/10 Sok Sukhothai 6 Sukhothai Road,
Dusit, Bangkok, 10300, Thailand
Tel.: (66) 2669 4200
Motion Picture Production Services
N.A.I.C.S.: 512110

Gear Head Co., Ltd.   **(3)**
999 Moo 2, Bangbor, Samut Prakan,
10560, Thailand
Tel.: (66) 2020393999
Web Site: http://www.gearheadthailand.com
Motion Picture Production Services
N.A.I.C.S.: 512110

Goody Film (Thailand) Co., Ltd.   **(3)**
1213/513 Lat Phrao 94 Plab Pla, Wangth-
onglang, Bangkok, 10310, Thailand
Tel.: (66) 25593997
Web Site: http://www.goodyfilmthailand.com
Motion Picture Production Services
N.A.I.C.S.: 512110

Matching Broadcast Co., Ltd.   **(3)**
305/10 Soi Sukhothai 6 Sukhothai Road,
Dusit, Bangkok, 10300, Thailand
Tel.: (66) 2243 6543
Broadcasting Services
N.A.I.C.S.: 516120

Matching Entertainment Co., Ltd.   **(3)**
305/10 Soi Sukhothai 6 Sukhothai Road,
Dusit, Bangkok, 10300, Thailand
Tel.: (66) 2243 6543
Web Site:
    http://www.matchingentertainment.com
Film Production Services
N.A.I.C.S.: 512110

Matching Motion Pictures Co.,
Ltd.   **(3)**
305/10 Soi Sukhothai 6 Sukhothai Road,
Dusit, Bangkok, Thailand
Tel.: (66) 2243 6543
Motion Picture Production Services
N.A.I.C.S.: 512110

Matching Movie Town Co., Ltd.   **(3)**
305/10 Soi Sukhothai 6 Sukhothai Road,
Dusit, Bangkok, 10300, Thailand
Tel.: (66) 2243 6543
Motion Picture Production Services
N.A.I.C.S.: 512110

BANGKOK BUSINESS EQUIP-MENT AUTOMATION CO., LTD.
199/82-84 Vipawadee-Rungsit Road,
Samsennai Phayathai, Bangkok,
10400, Thailand
Tel.: (66) 22710213   TH
Web Site: http://www.bbe-group.com
Year Founded: 1970
Sales Range: $50-74.9 Million
Emp.: 200
Office & Other Professional Equip-
ment Distr
N.A.I.C.S.: 423420
Dej Churdsuwanrak *(Mng Dir-Security Sys)*

Subsidiaries:

Bangkok OA Coms Co., Ltd.   **(1)**
199-82-84 Vipavadee Rangsit Highway,
Bangkok, 10400, Thailand   **(100%)**
Tel.: (66) 22710213
Web Site: http://www.bbe-group.com
Security Equipment Distr
N.A.I.C.S.: 423610

BANGKOK CHAIN HOSPITAL PUBLIC COMPANY LIMITED
44 Moo 4 Chaengwattana Road,
Pakkred, Nonthaburi, 11120, Thailand
Tel.: (66) 28369907
Web Site:
    https://www.bangkokhospital.com
BCH—(THA)
Rev.: $345,338,148
Assets: $517,593,781
Liabilities: $117,533,635
Net Worth: $400,060,146
Earnings: $43,171,452
Emp.: 8,591
Fiscal Year-end: 12/31/23
Healtcare Services
N.A.I.C.S.: 423450
Chalerm Harnphanich *(Chm)*

BANGKOK COMMERCIAL AS-SET MANAGEMENT PUBLIC COMPANY LIMITED
99 Surasak Road, Silom Sub-District
Bangrak District, Bangkok, 10500,
Thailand
Tel.: (66) 26300700   TH
Web Site: https://www.bam.co.th

Year Founded: 1998
BAM—(THA)
Rev.: $267,905,130
Assets: $4,008,480,911
Liabilities: $2,734,858,525
Net Worth: $1,273,622,385
Earnings: $44,794,961
Emp.: 1,334
Fiscal Year-end: 12/31/23
Investment Management Service
N.A.I.C.S.: 523999
Bundit Anantamongkol *(CEO, Pres-Supporting Grp & Exec Dir)*

BANGKOK DEC-CON PUBLIC COMPANY LIMITED
52/3 Moo 8 Bangbuathong-
Suphanburi Road T Lahan, Bangbua-
thong, Nonthaburi, 11110, Thailand
Tel.: (66) 29255777
Web Site:
    https://www.bangkokdeccon.co.th
Year Founded: 1992
BKD—(THA)
Rev.: $24,366,829
Assets: $59,049,809
Liabilities: $16,502,804
Net Worth: $42,547,004
Earnings: $489,257
Fiscal Year-end: 12/31/23
Hotel & Commercial Furniture Mfr
N.A.I.C.S.: 337127
Nuchanart Ratanasuwanachart *(Mng Dir)*

BANGKOK DUSIT MEDICAL SERVICES PUBLIC COMPANY LIMITED
2 Soi Soonvijai 7 New Petchaburi
Road, Huay Khwang, Bangkok,
10310, Thailand
Tel.: (66) 23103000   TH
Web Site: https://www.bdms.co.th
Year Founded: 1969
BDULF—(OTCIQ)
Rev.: $2,982,070,514
Assets: $4,191,848,569
Liabilities: $1,305,566,054
Net Worth: $2,886,282,515
Earnings: $434,885,947
Emp.: 36,339
Fiscal Year-end: 12/31/23
Holding Company; Hospitals Owner &
Operator
N.A.I.C.S.: 551112
Poramaporn Prasarttong-osoth
(Founder)

Subsidiaries:

A.N.B. Laboratories Co., Ltd.   **(1)**
557 Ramintra Rd, Kannayao, Bangkok,
10230, Thailand
Tel.: (66) 25100021
Web Site: https://www.anblab.com
Pharmaceutical Product Mfr & Distr
N.A.I.C.S.: 325412

A.N.B. Laboratory Co., Ltd.   **(1)**
557 Ramintra Rd, Kannayao, Bangkok,
10230, Thailand
Tel.: (66) 25100021
Web Site: http://www.anblab.com
Pharmaceutical Product Mfr & Distr
N.A.I.C.S.: 325412
Wisanu Assawes *(Mng Dir)*

BDMS Wellness Clinic Co., Ltd.   **(1)**
2/4 Wireless Road, Lumpini Pathumwan,
Bangkok, 10330, Thailand
Tel.: (66) 28269999
Web Site: https://www.bdmswellness.com
Clinical Healthcare Services
N.A.I.C.S.: 622110
Tanupol Virunhagarun *(Acting CEO)*

BNH Medical Center Co., Ltd.   **(1)**
9/1 Convent Road, Bang Rak, Bangkok,
10500, Thailand
Tel.: (66) 2 632 0550
Health Care Srvices

Bangkok Dusit Medical Services Public Company Limited—(Continued)

N.A.I.C.S.: 621498

Bangkok Helicopter Services Co., Ltd. (1)
5th Floor 2301/2 New Petchburi Rd, Bangkapi Huaykwang, Bangkok, 10310, Thailand
Tel.: (66) 27624192
Web Site: https://www.bangkokhelicopter.co.th
Air Ambulance Services
N.A.I.C.S.: 621910
Chula Sukmanop *(Gen Dir)*

Bangkok Hospital Chiangmai Co., Ltd. (1)
88/8-9 Moo 6, Nong Pa Khrang Mueang Chiang Mai, Chiang Mai, 50000, Thailand
Tel.: (66) 52089888
Web Site: https://www.bangkokhospital-chiangmai.com
Clinical Healthcare Services
N.A.I.C.S.: 622110

Bangkok Hospital Chiangrai Co., Ltd. (1)
369 Moo 13 Phahonyothin Road, Nang Lae Mueang Chiang Rai, Chiang Rai, 57100, Thailand
Tel.: (66) 52051800
Web Site: https://www.bangkokhospital-chiangrai.com
Clinical Healthcare Services
N.A.I.C.S.: 622110

Bangkok Hospital Hat Yai Co., Ltd. (1)
75 Soi 15 Petchkasem Road, Hat Yai Sub-district, Hat Yai, 90110, Songkhla, Thailand **(98.78%)**
Tel.: (66) 7 427 2800
Web Site: https://bangkokhatyai.com
Hospital Operations
N.A.I.C.S.: 622110

Bangkok Hospital Medical Center (1)
2 Soi Soonvijai 7 New Petchburi Rd, Bangkapi Huaykwang, Bangkok, 10310, Thailand
Tel.: (66) 2 310 3000
Web Site: https://www.bangkokhospital.com
Hospital Operator
N.A.I.C.S.: 622110
Chatree Duangnet *(CEO)*

Bangkok Hospital Pattaya Co., Ltd. (1)
301 Moo 6 Sukhumvit Road Km 143, ban-glamung, Pattaya, 20150, Chonburi, Thailand **(97.22%)**
Tel.: (66) 3 825 9999
Web Site: https://www.bangkokpattayahospital.com
Hospital Operator
N.A.I.C.S.: 622110
Chirotchana Sucharto *(Chm)*

Bangkok Hospital Phuket Co., Ltd. (1)
2/1 Hongyok Utis Road, Muang, Phuket, 83000, Thailand **(99.67%)**
Tel.: (66) 7 625 4425
Web Site: https://www.phukethospital.com
Hospital Operator
N.A.I.C.S.: 622110
Pongsak Viddayakorn *(Chm)*

Bangkok Hospital Prapadaeng Co., Ltd. (1)
288 Moo 1 Suksawat Road Km 18, Prasa-mutjadee District, Samut Prakan, 10290, Thailand **(79%)**
Tel.: (66) 2818 9000
Web Site: http://www.bpdhospital.com
Hospital Operator
N.A.I.C.S.: 622110

Bangkok Hospital Ratchasima Co., Ltd. (1)
1308/9 Mitrapap Road, Nai Muang, Nakhon Ratchasima, 30130, Thailand **(89.53%)**
Tel.: (66) 4 401 5999
Web Site: http://www.bkh.co.th
Hospital Operator
N.A.I.C.S.: 622110

Bangkok Hospital Samui Co., Ltd. (1)
57 Moo 3 Thaweerat Phakdee Road, Ko Samui, 84320, Suratthani, Thailand
Tel.: (66) 7742 9500
Web Site: http://www.bangkokhospitalsamui.com
Health Care Srvices
N.A.I.C.S.: 621498
Oomkid Udomkijmongkol *(Dir-I Hospital)*

Bangkok Hospital Surat Co., Ltd. (1)
179 - 179/1 Village No 1, Wat Pradu Mueang Surat Thani District, Surat Thani, 84000, Thailand
Tel.: (66) 77956789
Web Site: https://www.bangkokhospitalsurat.com
Clinical Healthcare Services
N.A.I.C.S.: 622110

Bangkok Hospital Trat Co., Ltd. (1)
376 Moo 2 Sukhumvit Road, Wang Krachae Subdistrict Mueang District, Trat, 23000, Thailand **(99.76%)**
Tel.: (66) 3 961 2000
Web Site: https://www.bth.co.th
Hospital Operator
N.A.I.C.S.: 622110

Bangkok Khon Kaen Hospital Co., Ltd. (1)
888 Village No 16 Mallwan Road, Nai Mueang Subdistrict Mueang District, Khon Kaen, 40000, Thailand
Tel.: (66) 43042888
Web Site: https://www.bangkokhospitalkhonkaen.com
Clinical Healthcare Services
N.A.I.C.S.: 622110

Bangkok Pattaya Hospital Co., Ltd. (1)
301 Moo 6 Sukhumvit Road Km 143, Ban-glamung, Chon Buri, 20150, Thailand
Tel.: (66) 38259999
Web Site: https://www.bangkokpattayahospital.com
Clinical Healthcare Services
N.A.I.C.S.: 622110

Bangkok Phuket Hospital Co., Ltd. (1)
2/1 Hongyok Utis Road, Muang District, Phuket, 83000, Thailand
Tel.: (66) 76254425
Web Site: https://www.phukethospital.com
Clinical Healthcare Services
N.A.I.C.S.: 621498
Kongkiat Kespechara *(Acting CEO)*

Bangkok Premier Life Insurance Broker Co., Ltd. (1)
2301/2 New Petchburi Rd, Bangkok, 10310, Thailand
Tel.: (66) 2 769 7751
Web Site: http://www.bpib.co.th
Life & Health Insurance Services
N.A.I.C.S.: 524210

Bangkok Ratchasima Hospital Co., Ltd. (1)
308/9 Mitrapap Road, Nai Muang, Nakhon Ratchasima, 30000, Thailand
Tel.: (66) 44015999
Web Site: https://www.bkh.co.th
General Hospital Services
N.A.I.C.S.: 622110

Bangkok Rayong Hospital Co., Ltd. (1)
8 Village No 2 Saengchannamit Road, Noen Phra Subdistrict Mueang Rayong Dis-trict, Rayong, 21000, Thailand
Tel.: (66) 38921999
Web Site: https://www.bangkokhospitalrayong.com
Clinical Healthcare Services
N.A.I.C.S.: 622110

Bangkok Samui Hospital Co., Ltd. (1)
57 Moo 3 Thaweerat Phakdee Rd, Amphoe Koh Sa-mui, Surat Thani, 84320, Thailand
Tel.: (66) 77429500
Web Site: https://bangkokhospitalsamui.com
Clinical Healthcare Services
N.A.I.C.S.: 622110

Bdms Silver Co., Ltd. (1)

Prime Estate on the corner of Sarasin and Lang Suan Road Lumpini, Bangkok, Thai-land
Tel.: (66) 27551793
Web Site: https://bdms.listedcompany.com
Wellness & Medical Services
N.A.I.C.S.: 812199

General Hospital Products PCL (1)
101/99 Soi Navanakorn 7 Phaholyothin Road, Khlong Luang, 12120, Pathum Thani, Thailand
Tel.: (66) 20 730 4906
Web Site: https://www.ghp.co.th
Pharmaceutical Product Mfr & Distr
N.A.I.C.S.: 325412

Greenline Synergy Co., Ltd. (1)
488 7th Floor Samitivej Srinakarin Hospital Srinakarin Road, Suanluang, Bangkok, 10250, Thailand
Tel.: (66) 27628000
Web Site: https://www.glsict.com
Information Technology Services
N.A.I.C.S.: 541511

Paolo Medic Co., Ltd. (1)
670/1 Phaholyothin Rd Samsen Nai, Phayathai, Bangkok, 10400, Thailand
Tel.: (66) 22797000
Web Site: http://www.paolohealthcare.com
Emp.: 2,000
Health Care Srvices
N.A.I.C.S.: 621498
Somboon Pornpaiboonstid *(Mgr-Fin)*

Phyathai 1 Hospital Co., Ltd. (1)
364/1 Thanon Si Ayutthaya, Thanon Phayathai Ratchathewi, Bangkok, 10400, Thailand
Tel.: (66) 22014600
Web Site: https://www.phyathai.com
Clinical Healthcare Services
N.A.I.C.S.: 622110

Phyathai 2 Hospital Co., Ltd. (1)
943 Phaholyothin Road, Phyathai, Bangkok, 10400, Thailand
Tel.: (66) 26172444
Heart & Musculoskeletal Centre Services
N.A.I.C.S.: 813212

Samitivej Public Company Limited (1)
133 Sukhumvit 49 Road Klongtan Nua Wadhana, Bangkok, 10110, Thailand
Tel.: (66) 20222222
Web Site: https://www.samitivejhospitals.com
Health Care Srvices
N.A.I.C.S.: 621999

Subsidiary (Domestic):

Samitivej Chonburi Co., Ltd. (2)
888 88 Moo 3 Sukhumvit Rd, Ban Suan Mueang Chon Buri, Chon Buri, 20000, Thai-land
Tel.: (66) 33038888
Web Site: https://www.samitivejchonburi.com
Clinical Healthcare Services
N.A.I.C.S.: 622110

Subsidiary (Non-US):

Samitivej International Co., Ltd. (2)
9E/2 Kabar Aye Pagoda Road, Ward No 7 Mayangone Township, Yangon, Myanmar
Tel.: (95) 18660545
Clinical Services
N.A.I.C.S.: 621498

Subsidiary (Domestic):

Samitivej Sriracha Co., Ltd. (2)
8 Soi Laemket Jermjomphol Rd, Si Racha, 20110, Chon Buri, Thailand
Tel.: (66) 38320300
Web Site: https://www.samitivejsriracha.com
General Hospital Services
N.A.I.C.S.: 622110

Save Drug Center Co., Ltd. (1)
1/2 Soi Soonvijai 2 New Petchaburi Road, Huaykwang Bangkapi, Bangkok, 10310, Thailand
Tel.: (66) 641810179
Web Site: https://www.savedrug.co.th
Pharmaceutical Products Distr
N.A.I.C.S.: 456110

Sodexo Healthcare Support Service (Thailand) Co., Ltd. (1)
23/52-54 Sorachai Building 17th Floor Soi Sukhumvit 63 Sukhumvit Road, Klongtan Nua Vadhana, Bangkok, 10110, Thailand
Tel.: (66) 2714 1661
Web Site: http://www.th.sodexo.com
Emp.: 2,250
Health Care Srvices
N.A.I.C.S.: 621498
Stuart Winters *(CEO)*

Thai Medical Center PCL (1)
Soi Borommaratchachonnani 4, Bang Bamru Subdistrict Bang Phlat District, Bangkok, 10700, Thailand
Tel.: (66) 804492233
Web Site: https://www.thaimedical.center
Health Care Srvices
N.A.I.C.S.: 621498

The Phya Thai II Hospital Co., Ltd. (1)
943 Phaholyothin Road, Phyathai, Bangkok, 10400, Thailand
Tel.: (66) 2 617 2444
Web Site: https://www.phyathai2international.com
Clinical Healthcare Services
N.A.I.C.S.: 622110

BANGKOK INSURANCE PUBLIC COMPANY LTD.

Bangkok Insurance Building 25 Sa-thon Tai Road Thung Maha Mek, Sa-thon, Bangkok, 10120, Thailand
Tel.: (66) 22858888
Web Site: http://www.bangkokinsurance.com
Year Founded: 1947
BKI—(THA)
Rev.: $873,298,450
Assets: $2,218,744,291
Liabilities: $1,245,836,446
Net Worth: $972,907,845
Earnings: $88,853,029
Emp.: 1,647
Fiscal Year-end: 12/31/23
Insurance Services
N.A.I.C.S.: 524298
Paveena Juchuan *(Exec VP)*

BANGKOK LAND PUBLIC COMPANY LIMITED

47/569-576 Moo 3 10th Floor New Geneva Building Popular 3 Road, Tambol Bannmai Amphur Pakkred, Nonthaburi, 11120, Thailand
Tel.: (66) 25044940
Web Site: https://www.bangkokland.co.th
Year Founded: 1973
BLAND—(THA)
Rev.: $108,448,148
Assets: $1,782,341,116
Liabilities: $539,158,760
Net Worth: $1,243,182,356
Earnings: $17,989,165
Emp.: 1,508
Fiscal Year-end: 03/31/23
Property Development Services
N.A.I.C.S.: 531390
Anant Kanjanapas *(Chm & CEO)*

Subsidiaries:

Bangkok Land (Cayman Islands) Limited (1)
G/F Caledonian House Mary Street, PO Box 1043, Georgetown, KY1-1102, Cayman Islands
Tel.: (345) 9490050
Web Site: http://www.sterlingtrustco.com
Financial Services
N.A.I.C.S.: 522299
Benjamin Booker *(Mng Dir)*

Bangkok Land Agency Limited (1)
47/217-222 9/F Kimpo Building Chaengwat-tana Road, Pakkred, Nonthaburi, 11120, Thailand
Tel.: (66) 25035040
Property Rental Services

N.A.I.C.S.: 531210

Impact Exhibition Management Company Limited **(1)**
10th Fl Bangkok Land Building 47/569-576 Popular 3 Road, Banmai Sub-district Pakkred District, Nonthaburi, 11120, Thailand
Tel.: (66) 2 833 4455
Web Site: https://www.impact.co.th
Property Rental Services
N.A.I.C.S.: 531120
Anant Kanjanapas *(Chm)*

BANGKOK POST PUBLIC COMPANY LIMITED
Bangkok Post Building 136 Sunthorn Kosa Road, Klong Toey, Bangkok, 10110, Thailand
Tel.: (66) 26164000
Web Site:
   https://www.bangkokpost.co.th
Year Founded: 1946
POST—(THA)
Rev.: $10,300,943
Assets: $6,850,622
Liabilities: $17,219,614
Net Worth: ($10,368,992)
Earnings: ($1,685,438)
Emp.: 319
Fiscal Year-end: 12/31/23
Newspaper Publishing Services
N.A.I.C.S.: 513110
Suthikiati Chirathivat *(Chm)*

BANGKOK RANCH PUBLIC COMPANY LIMITED
18/1 Moo 12 Lang Wat Bangplee Yai Nai Rd Bangplee Yai, Bangplee, Samut Prakan, 10540, Thailand
Tel.: (66) 21757200
Web Site:
   https://www.bangkokranch.com
Year Founded: 1984
BR—(THA)
Rev.: $234,530,095
Assets: $314,325,645
Liabilities: $176,011,169
Net Worth: $138,314,476
Earnings: $8,602,877
Emp.: 1,772
Fiscal Year-end: 12/31/23
Duck Producer & Processor
N.A.I.C.S.: 112390
Joseph Suchaovanich *(Co-Chm & CEO)*

Subsidiaries:

Lucky Duck International Food B.V. **(1)**
Rietdekkerstraat 5, 5405 AX, Uden, Netherlands
Tel.: (31) 413256125
Web Site: http://www.luckyduck-bv.com
Meat Product Distr
N.A.I.C.S.: 424470
Bas Timmer *(Sls Mgr)*

Tomassen Duck-To B.V. **(1)**
Fokko Kortlanglaan 116, 3853 KH, Ermelo, Netherlands
Tel.: (31) 341553675
Web Site: http://www.tomassen.com
Sales Range: $25-49.9 Million
Emp.: 90
Poultry Farming Services
N.A.I.C.S.: 112340

Tomassen Transport B.V. **(1)**
Voorsterweg 117, 7371 EK, Loenen, Netherlands
Tel.: (31) 55 505 8600
Web Site: https://www.thomassen-transport.nl
Logistic Services
N.A.I.C.S.: 488510

BANGKOK RUBBER PUBLIC CO., LTD.
611/40 Soi Watchannai Rajuthit 2 Bangklo, Bangkolaem, Bangkok, 10120, Thailand
Tel.: (66) 2689950020   TH
Web Site: http://www.pan-group.com
Year Founded: 1974
Emp.: 18,000
Sports Shoes & Other Footwear Mfr
N.A.I.C.S.: 316210

Subsidiaries:

Bangkok Athletic Co., Ltd. **(1)**
611/210-213 Soi Watchannai Rajuthit 2, Bangklo Bangkholeam, Bangkok, 10120, Thailand **(99.9%)**
Tel.: (66) 2689834559
Web Site: http://www.pan-sportswear.com
Rev.: $7,000,000
Emp.: 450
Sporting Goods Mfr
N.A.I.C.S.: 339920

Innovation Footwear Co., Ltd. **(1)**
82 Mu9 Samkok-Sena Road Bangnomko Sena, Ayutthaya, 13110, Thailand
Footwear Mfr
N.A.I.C.S.: 316210

BANGKOK SHEET METAL PUBLIC COMPANY LTD.
149 Village No 6 Soi Suksawat 78 Suksawat Road, Bangjak Subdistrict Phra Pradaeng District, Samut Prakan, 10130, Thailand
Tel.: (66) 281755557
Web Site: https://www.bmplc.co.th
Year Founded: 1995
BM—(THA)
Rev.: $41,755,318
Assets: $47,792,801
Liabilities: $20,716,665
Net Worth: $27,076,136
Earnings: $1,172,641
Fiscal Year-end: 12/31/23
Metal Products Mfr
N.A.I.C.S.: 332312
Damnoen Kaewthawee *(Chm)*

Subsidiaries:

BM Innotech Industry Company Limited **(1)**
149 Moo 6 Suksawad Road, Prapadang, Bangkok, 10130, Samutprakarn, Thailand
Tel.: (66) 281755557
Fabricated Metal Products Mfr
N.A.I.C.S.: 332999

BANGKOK STEEL INDUSTRY PUBLIC COMPANY LIMITED
205 United Flour Mill Bldg 7th Floor, Rajawongse Rd Chakkrawad Samphanthawongse, Bangkok, 10100, Thailand
Tel.: (66) 22260680
Web Site:
   http://www.bangkoksteel.co.th
Year Founded: 1964
Sales Range: $300-349.9 Million
Emp.: 1,345
Steel Bar & Galvanized Steel Sheet Mfr
N.A.I.C.S.: 331110
Jaray Bhumichitra *(CEO)*

BANGKOK UNION INSURANCE PUBLIC COMPANY LIMITED
Bangkok Insurance Building Surawong Road, Suriyawong Subdistrict Bang Rak District, Bangkok, 10500, Thailand
Tel.: (66) 22336920
Web Site: https://www.bui.co.th
Year Founded: 1929
Sales Range: $10-24.9 Million
Insurance Management Services
N.A.I.C.S.: 524298
Malinee Leopairat *(Board of Directors & Chm)*

BANGLADESH AUTOCARS LIMITED
110 Tejgaon I/A, Dhaka, 1208, Bangladesh
Tel.: (880) 28870467   BD
Web Site:
   https://www.bdautocars.com
Year Founded: 1979
BDAUTOCA—(DHA)
Rev.: $600,633
Assets: $628,971
Liabilities: $274,450
Net Worth: $354,521
Earnings: $24,607
Emp.: 21
Fiscal Year-end: 06/30/22
Natural Gas Refuelling Services
N.A.I.C.S.: 424710

BANGLADESH BANK
PO Box 325, Dhaka, Bangladesh
Tel.: (880) 27122566
Web Site:
   http://www.bangladeshbank.org.bd
Sales Range: $400-449.9 Million
Emp.: 3,848
Banking Services
N.A.I.C.S.: 521110
Md. Sadrul Huda *(Gen Mgr-Internal Audit)*

Subsidiaries:

Security Printing Corporation (Bangladesh) Ltd. **(1)**
Bangladesh Ordnance Factory Shimultoly, Gazipur, 1703, Bangladesh
Tel.: (880) 2 9205110 5
Web Site: http://www.spcbl.org.bd
Emp.: 579
Banknote Printing Services
N.A.I.C.S.: 323111
Ehteshamul Karim *(Sec & Gen Mgr-Fin & Accts)*

BANGLADESH BUILDING SYSTEM LTD.
Ga-64 3rd Floor Configure Bepari Tower Middle Badda Progoti Swarani, Dhaka, 1212, Bangladesh
Tel.: (880) 2222295915
Web Site: https://www.bbspeb.com
Year Founded: 2003
BBS—(CHT)
Rev.: $8,553,827
Assets: $44,237,272
Liabilities: $19,414,778
Net Worth: $24,822,494
Earnings: ($1,506,533)
Emp.: 595
Fiscal Year-end: 06/30/23
Steel Building Construction Services
N.A.I.C.S.: 332311
Hasan Morshed Chowdhury *(Mng Dir)*

BANGLADESH EXPORT IMPORT CO. LTD.
Beximco Industrial Park Sarabo Kashimpur, Gazipur, Bangladesh
Tel.: (880) 8618220
Web Site: https://www.bextex.net
BEXIMCO—(DHA)
Rev.: $870,913,675
Assets: $2,129,211,130
Liabilities: $1,193,981,201
Net Worth: $935,229,929
Earnings: $145,560,754
Emp.: 5,498
Fiscal Year-end: 06/30/22
Textile Sales
N.A.I.C.S.: 314999
Sardar Ahmed Khan *(COO)*

Subsidiaries:

Beximco Engineering Ltd. **(1)**
Beximco Tejgaon Complex Building Level-7 149-150 Tejgaon I/A, Dhaka, 1208, Bangladesh
Tel.: (880) 9609100220
Web Site:
   https://www.beximcoengineering.com
Industrial Building Construction Services
N.A.I.C.S.: 236210

Bextex Limited **(1)**
Beximco Industrial Park, Sarabo Kashimpur, Gazipur, Bangladesh
Tel.: (880) 28618220
Web Site: http://www.bextex.net
Sales Range: $150-199.9 Million
Yarn & Denim Fabrics Mfr
N.A.I.C.S.: 313210

BANGLADESH FINANCE LIMITED
Baitul Hossain Building 2nd Floor, 27 Dilkusha C/A, Dhaka, 1000, Bangladesh
Tel.: (880) 29559146
Web Site: https://www.bdfinance.net
Year Founded: 2000
BDFINANCE—(DHA)
Rev.: $17,989,209
Assets: $214,288,525
Liabilities: $177,774,745
Net Worth: $36,513,780
Earnings: $3,756,025
Emp.: 124
Fiscal Year-end: 12/31/21
Financial & Investment Services
N.A.I.C.S.: 522291
Md. Sajjadur Rahman Bhuiyan *(CFO)*

Subsidiaries:

BD Finance Capital Holdings Limited **(1)**
64 Motijheel C/A 2nd Floor, Dhaka, 1000, Bangladesh
Tel.: (880) 29588186
Web Site: http://www.bdcapital.com.bd
Financial Brokerage Services
N.A.I.C.S.: 523999
Hossain Khaled *(Vice Chm)*

BD Finance Securities Limited **(1)**
64 Motijheel C/A 2nd Floor, Dhaka, 1000, Bangladesh
Tel.: (880) 29554592
Web Site: http://www.bdsecurities.com.bd
Financial Brokerage Services
N.A.I.C.S.: 523999
Anwar Hossain *(Chm)*

Bangladesh Finance Capital Limited **(1)**
64 Motijheel C/A 2nd Floor, Dhaka, 1000, Bangladesh
Tel.: (880) 2223384592
Web Site: https://bfcl.bd.finance
Investment Banking Services
N.A.I.C.S.: 523150

Bangladesh Finance Securities Limited **(1)**
64 Motijheel C/A 2nd Floor, Dhaka, 1000, Bangladesh
Tel.: (880) 2223384592
Web Site: https://bfsl.bd.finance
Financial Future Brokerage Services
N.A.I.C.S.: 523160

BANGLADESH GENERAL INSURANCE COMPANY LIMITED
42 Dilkusha C/A, Dhaka, Bangladesh
Tel.: (880) 2223383056
Web Site:
   https://www.bgicinsure.com
Year Founded: 1985
BGIC—(CHT)
Rev.: $1,611,271
Assets: $16,613,898
Liabilities: $6,955,571
Net Worth: $9,658,327
Earnings: $625,419
Emp.: 101
Fiscal Year-end: 12/31/23
Insurance Services
N.A.I.C.S.: 524298
Md. Towhid Samad *(Chm)*

Bangladesh General Insurance Company Limited—(Continued)

BANGLADESH INDUSTRIAL FINANCE COMPANY LIMITED

Police Plaza Concord Tower-2
Level-8 Plot-2 Road-144, Dhaka,
1212, Bangladesh
Tel.: (880) 255045123
Web Site: https://www.bifcol.com
Year Founded: 1996
BIFC—(CHT)
Rev.: $411,389
Assets: $105,296,285
Liabilities: $230,605,110
Net Worth: ($125,308,825)
Earnings: ($11,475,794)
Emp.: 33
Fiscal Year-end: 12/31/21
Lease Finance & Loan Services
N.A.I.C.S.: 522291
Mahbubur Rahman (Sr Asst VP)

BANGLADESH LAMPS LIMITED

Flat A4 Level-5 House 10, Road 90
Gulshan-2, Dhaka, 1212, Bangladesh
Tel.: (880) 29855371   BD
Web Site: https://www.bll.com.bd
Year Founded: 1960
BDLAMPS—(CHT)
Rev.: $16,707,818
Assets: $21,118,090
Liabilities: $13,421,720
Net Worth: $7,696,371
Earnings: $101,750
Emp.: 257
Fiscal Year-end: 06/30/23
Electric Bulb Mfr
N.A.I.C.S.: 335139
Latifur Rahman (Mng Dir)

BANGLADESH NATIONAL INSURANCE CO., LTD.

Rashid Tower 3rd floor House No 11
Road No 18, Gulshan-1, Dhaka,
1212, Bangladesh
Tel.: (880) 8832234
Web Site: https://www.bnicl.net
Year Founded: 1996
BNICL—(DHA)
Rev.: $2,600,069
Assets: $22,727,487
Liabilities: $12,095,287
Net Worth: $10,632,200
Earnings: $1,581,199
Emp.: 691
Fiscal Year-end: 12/31/22
General Insurance Services
N.A.I.C.S.: 524210
Sana Ullah (CEO & Mng Dir)

BANGLADESH SERVICES LIMITED

1 Minto Road, Dhaka, 1000, Bangladesh
Tel.: (880) 258316000
Web Site: https://www.bsl.gov.bd
Year Founded: 1973
BDSERVICE—(DHA)
Rev.: $15,419,814
Assets: $348,545,897
Liabilities: $139,579,181
Net Worth: $208,966,716
Earnings: ($7,820,079)
Emp.: 502
Fiscal Year-end: 06/30/23
Home Management Services
N.A.I.C.S.: 721110
Md. Mohibul Haque (Chm)

BANGLADESH SHIPPING CO., LTD. BSC

BSC Tower 22nd Floor Rajuk Avenue
Plot No 2 3 Dainik Banglar Moor, PO

Box No 641, Dhaka, 1000, Bangladesh
Tel.: (880) 29553524
Web Site:
https://www.bsc.portal.gov.bd
Year Founded: 1972
BSC—(CHT)
Rev.: $47,718,838
Assets: $317,127,186
Liabilities: $194,733,099
Net Worth: $122,394,087
Earnings: $22,801,673
Emp.: 489
Fiscal Year-end: 06/30/23
Cargo Shipping Services
N.A.I.C.S.: 488320

BANGLADESH STEEL RE-ROLLING MILLS LTD.

Ali Mansion 1207/1099 Sadarghat
Road, Chittagong, Bangladesh
Tel.: (880) 2333354901
Web Site: https://www.bsrm.com
Year Founded: 1952
BSRMLTD—(CHT)
Rev.: $1,049,545,216
Assets: $949,029,449
Liabilities: $566,486,665
Net Worth: $382,542,784
Earnings: $26,576,349
Emp.: 1,932
Fiscal Year-end: 06/30/23
Metal Products Mfr
N.A.I.C.S.: 331110
Gautam Bandopadhyay (COO)

BANGLADESH SUBMARINE CABLE CO., LTD.

Level-7 191 Rahmans Regnum Center, Tejaon-Gulshan Link Roa, Dhaka,
1208, Bangladesh
Tel.: (880) 226603315
Web Site: https://www.bsccl.com
Year Founded: 2008
BSCCL—(CHT)
Rev.: $47,020,998
Assets: $189,995,492
Liabilities: $62,060,497
Net Worth: $127,934,995
Earnings: $25,451,939
Emp.: 133
Fiscal Year-end: 06/30/23
Cable Telecommunication Services
N.A.I.C.S.: 516210

BANGLADESH THAI ALUMINIUM LIMITED

BTA Tower 29 Kemal Ataturk Avenue
Banani C/A Road No 17, Dhaka,
1213, Bangladesh
Tel.: (880) 29821574
Web Site: https://www.btaalu.com
Year Founded: 1979
BDTHAI—(CHT)
Rev.: $8,527,694
Assets: $54,474,718
Liabilities: $22,029,936
Net Worth: $32,444,781
Earnings: ($607,578)
Emp.: 644
Fiscal Year-end: 06/30/23
Aluminum Mfr
N.A.I.C.S.: 331313
Zahid Maleque (Chm)

BANGLADESH WELDING ELECTRODES LIMITED

87 Motijheel Com Area Red Crescent
Chamber 2nd Floor, Dhaka, 1000,
Bangladesh
Tel.: (880) 29551490
Web Site: http://www.bwelbd.com
Year Founded: 1969
BDWELDING—(DHA)
Welding Electrode Mfr
N.A.I.C.S.: 333992

S. M. Islam (Mng Dir)

BANGO PLC

326 Cambridge Science Park, Cambridge, CB4 0WG, United Kingdom
Tel.: (44) 3330770247
Web Site: https://www.bango.com
BGO—(AIM)
Rev.: $28,490,000
Assets: $71,539,000
Liabilities: $40,095,000
Net Worth: $31,444,000
Earnings: ($2,140,000)
Emp.: 187
Fiscal Year-end: 12/31/22
Business Services
N.A.I.C.S.: 541511
Ray Anderson (Co-Founder & Chm)

Subsidiaries:

Bango.net Limited   (1)
326 Cambridge Science Park, Cambridge,
CB4 0WG, Cambridgeshire, United Kingdom
Tel.: (44) 1223472777
Web Site: https://web.bango.net
Mobile Payment Solutions
N.A.I.C.S.: 522320

DOCOMO Digital Limited   (1)
57-63 Scrutton Street, London, EC2A 4PF,
United Kingdom
Tel.: (44) 20 7096 9089
Web Site: http://www.docomodigital.com
Emp.: 1,000
Wireless Telecommunication Services
N.A.I.C.S.: 517112
Fernando Gonzalez-Mesones (Pres-Solutions Bus)

Subsidiary (Non-US):

DOCOMO Digital Germany
GmbH   (2)
Fritz-Vomfelde-Str 18, 40547, Dusseldorf,
Germany
Tel.: (49) 211970200
Web Site: http://www.docomodigital.com
Sales Range: $125-149.9 Million
Emp.: 200
Wireless Telecommunication Services
N.A.I.C.S.: 517112
Edgar Schnorpfeil (Grp COO & Head-B2O
Ops)

BANGSAPHAN BARMILL PUBLIC COMPANY LIMITED

8th Floor Prapawit Building No 28/1
Surasak Road, Silom Bangrak, Bangkok, 10500, Thailand
Tel.: (66) 263005905   TH
Web Site: https://www.bsbm.co.th
Year Founded: 1994
BSBM—(THA)
Rev.: $17,947,223
Assets: $56,825,965
Liabilities: $3,741,243
Net Worth: $53,084,722
Earnings: ($1,405,885)
Fiscal Year-end: 12/31/23
Steel Product Mfr & Distr
N.A.I.C.S.: 331221

BANJA LAKTASI A.D.

Karadordeva 44, 78250, Laktasi, Bosnia & Herzegovina
Tel.: (387) 51 532 256
Web Site: http://www.banja-laktasi.info
Emp.: 45
Home Management Services
N.A.I.C.S.: 721110
Dragan Jevtovic (Chm-Mgmt Bd)

BANK AGROROS JSC

90 Chernyshevskogo Str, Saratov,
410017, Russia
Tel.: (7) 8452441919
Web Site: http://www.agroros.ru
Sales Range: Less than $1 Million

Commercial Banking Services
N.A.I.C.S.: 522110

BANK AL-MAGHRIB

277 Avenue Mohammed V Boite,
postale 445, Rabat, Morocco
Tel.: (212) 37702626
Web Site: http://www.bkam.ma
Sales Range: $400-449.9 Million
Banking Services
N.A.I.C.S.: 521110

BANK AL-SHARQ S.A.S

Hafez Ibrahim Street Bank Al-Sharq
Building, PO Box 7732, Shaalan, Damascus, Syria
Tel.: (963) 11 66 803 000
Web Site:
http://www.bankalsharq.com
Year Founded: 2008
Sales Range: $1-9.9 Million
Commercial Banking Services
N.A.I.C.S.: 522110
Naji Chaoui (Chm)

BANK ALBILAD

8229 Al Mutamarat Unit 2, Riyadh,
12711 - 3952, Saudi Arabia
Tel.: (966) 14798888   SA
Web Site:
http://www.bankalbilad.com
Year Founded: 2004
1140—(SAU)
Rev.: $1,325,569,124
Assets: $34,540,156,246
Liabilities: $30,967,579,789
Net Worth: $3,572,576,456
Earnings: $555,042,794
Emp.: 4,494
Fiscal Year-end: 12/31/22
Retail & Investment Banking Services
N.A.I.C.S.: 523150
Nasser Mohammad AlSubeaei (Vice
Chm)

Subsidiaries:

Albilad Investment Company   (1)
King Fahad Street, PO Box 140, Riyadh,
Saudi Arabia
Tel.: (966) 92 000 3636
Web Site: https://www.albilad-capital.com
Investment Management Service
N.A.I.C.S.: 523210
Zaid Almufarih (CEO)

Enjaz Payment Services Company
Ltd.   (1)
PO Box 140, Riyadh, 11411, Saudi Arabia
Tel.: (966) 920011541
Web Site: https://www.enjaz.com
Fund Transfer Services
N.A.I.C.S.: 522320

BANK ALEXANDROVSKY PJSC

Zagorodny Prospect 46/2 Lit B, Saint
Petersburg, 191119, Russia
Tel.: (7) 8123248777
Web Site: http://www.alexbank.ru
Sales Range: Less than $1 Million
Commercial Banking Services
N.A.I.C.S.: 522110

BANK ALJAZIRA

King Abdulaziz Road Al Nahda Building No 7845, Jeddah, 23523, Saudi
Arabia
Tel.: (966) 126098888   SA
Year Founded: 1975
1020—(SAU)
Rev.: $1,044,034,395
Assets: $30,888,894,014
Liabilities: $27,260,300,227
Net Worth: $3,628,593,787
Earnings: $295,777,371
Emp.: 2,421
Fiscal Year-end: 12/31/22
Banking Services

N.A.I.C.S.: 522110
Abdulmajeed Ibrahim AlSultan (Vice Chm)

Subsidiaries:

Aljazira Capital Company (1)
King Fahd Road, PO Box 20438, Riyadh, 11455, Saudi Arabia
Tel.: (966) 8001169999
Web Site: https://www.aljaziracapital.com.sa
Financial Services
N.A.I.C.S.: 541611
Ziad Aba Al-Khail (CEO & Mng Dir)

BANK ASIA LIMITED

Rangs Tower 68 Purana Paltan, Dhaka, 1000, Bangladesh
Tel.: (880) 27110062
Web Site: http://www.bankasia-bd.com
BANKASIA—(CHT)
Rev.: $188,736,200
Assets: $4,293,734,661
Liabilities: $4,034,099,181
Net Worth: $259,635,480
Earnings: $18,253,658
Emp.: 2,865
Fiscal Year-end: 12/31/22
Banking Services
N.A.I.C.S.: 522180
A. Rouf Chowdhury (Chm)

Subsidiaries:

BA Exchange Company (UK) Limited (1)
131 Whitechapel Road, London, E1 1DT, United Kingdom
Tel.: (44) 2030054845
Web Site: https://www.baexchange.co.uk
Financial Transaction Processing Services
N.A.I.C.S.: 522320
Kamrul Huda Azad (CEO)

BA Express USA Inc. (1)
168-29 Hillside Ave Ste 2B, Jamaica, NY 11432
Tel.: (718) 565-5052
Web Site: https://www.baexpress.net
Financial Transaction Processing Services
N.A.I.C.S.: 522320

Bank Asia Securities Limited (1)
Hadi Mansion 2nd Floor 2, Dilkusha Commercial Area, Dhaka, 1000, Bangladesh
Tel.: (880) 247119242
Web Site: https://www.basl-bd.com
Security Broking Services
N.A.I.C.S.: 523150
Abdur Rouf Chowdhury (Chm)

BANK AUDI SAL

Bank Audi Plaza - Bab Idriss, PO Box 11-2560, 2021 8102, Beirut, 2021 8102, Lebanon
Tel.: (961) 1994000   LB
Web Site:
https://www.bankaudi.com.lb
Year Founded: 1962
AUDI—(BEY)
Rev.: $67,298,289
Assets: $3,110,692,552
Liabilities: $2,819,417,176
Net Worth: $291,275,376
Earnings: ($11,063,796)
Emp.: 3,136
Fiscal Year-end: 12/31/23
Retail, Commercial, Investment Banking & Wealth Management Services
N.A.I.C.S.: 522110
Samir N. Hanna (Chm, CEO & Gen Mgr)

Subsidiaries:

Audi Capital (KSA) cjsc (1)
     (99.99%)
Tel.: (966) 112199300
Web Site: https://www.audicapital.com
Investment Banking & Wealth Management Services
N.A.I.C.S.: 523150

Audi Saradar Investment Bank sal (1)
Bank Audi Plaza Block D France Street, Bab Idriss, Beirut, 2021-8102, Lebanon (99.99%)
Tel.: (961) 1994000
Web Site: http://www.asib.com
Sales Range: $1-4.9 Billion
Emp.: 4,000
Investment Banking & Securities Dealing
N.A.I.C.S.: 523150

Subsidiary (Domestic):

Infi Gamma Holding sal (2)
Clover Building Charles Malik Avenue Mar Nicolas Sector, Beirut, Lebanon
Tel.: (961) 1 977488
Emp.: 5
Investment Management Service
N.A.I.C.S.: 523999
Jocelyne Jalkh (Gen Mgr)

Audi Saradar Private Bank sal (1)
Clover Bldg Charles Malek Ave, PO Box 11-1121, Riad El-Solh, 1107-2805, Beirut, Lebanon (99.99%)
Tel.: (961) 1205400
Web Site: http://www.audisaradarpb.com
Sales Range: $75-99.9 Million
Emp.: 500
Wealth Management & Investment Banking Services
N.A.I.C.S.: 523991
Fady Georges Amatoury (Chm & Gen Mgr)

Subsidiary (Domestic):

Agence Saradar d'Assurances sal (2)
Clover Bldg Charles Malek Avenue Ashrafieh, PO Box 11-1121, Beirut, 1107-2805, Lebanon (100%)
Tel.: (961) 1338676
Sales Range: $50-74.9 Million
Emp.: 12
Insurance Agents
N.A.I.C.S.: 524210

Societe Libanaise de Factoring sal (2)
Zen Building, Beirut, 11-1121, Lebanon (91%)
Tel.: (961) 1209200
Web Site: http://www.solifac.com
Sales Range: $50-74.9 Million
Emp.: 18
Factoring & Credit Intermediation Services
N.A.I.C.S.: 522299
Pierre Najjear (Chm & Gen Mgr)

Bank Audi France S.A. (1)
73 Avenue des Champs-Elysees, 75008, Paris, France (99.99%)
Tel.: (33) 153835000
Web Site: https://www.bankaudi.fr
Sales Range: $75-99.9 Million
Emp.: 100
Retail, Commercial & Investment Banking
N.A.I.C.S.: 522110
Sherine R. Audi (CEO & Gen Mgr)

Bank Audi LLC (1)
Qatar Financial Centre Office 1801 18th Floor Qatar Financial Centre, PO Box 23270, Tower Diplomatic Area, Doha, Qatar (100%)
Tel.: (974) 44051000
Sales Range: $75-99.9 Million
Emp.: 25
Retail, Commercial & Private Banking Services
N.A.I.C.S.: 522110

Bank Audi S.A.M. (1)
24 Boulevard des Moulins, BP 23, 98001, Monaco, Monaco
Tel.: (377) 97701701
Web Site: http://www.bankaudimonaco.com
Sales Range: $50-74.9 Million
Emp.: 19
Investment Services
N.A.I.C.S.: 523999

Bank Audi Syria sa (1)
Mohafaza Bldg Youssef Al-Azmeh Square, PO Box 6228, Damascus, Syria (47%)
Tel.: (963) 1123888000
Retail & Commercial Banking
N.A.I.C.S.: 522110

Subsidiary (Domestic):

Audi Capital (Syria) LLC (2)
Tanzeem kafarsouseh - Cham City Center - plaza 86 Bldg 2nd Floor, PO Box 6228, Damascus, Syria
Tel.: (963) 11 23888630
Web Site: http://www.audicapitalsyria.com
Sales Range: $50-74.9 Million
Emp.: 3
Security Brokerage Services
N.A.I.C.S.: 523150

Bank Audi sal - Jordan Branches (1)
Le Royal Hotel Complex Zahran Street 3rd Circle 4th Floor, Jabal Amman, Amman, Jordan
Tel.: (962) 64604000
Sales Range: $50-74.9 Million
Emp.: 60
Retail & Commercial Banking Services
N.A.I.C.S.: 522110
Yousef A. Ensour (Gen Mgr)

Banque Audi (Suisse) sa (1)
Cours des Bastions 18, PO Box 384, 1211, Geneva, Switzerland (100%)
Tel.: (41) 227041111
Web Site: http://www.bankaudi.ch
Sales Range: $75-99.9 Million
Emp.: 80
Investment Banking & Trust Services
N.A.I.C.S.: 523150
Philippe R. Sednaoui (Chm)

National Bank of Sudan (1)
National Bank of Sudan Bldg Block 1, Kasr Avenue, Khartoum, Sudan (76.56%)
Tel.: (249) 183797993
Retail & Commercial Banking
N.A.I.C.S.: 522110

BANK AUSTRALIA LIMITED

222 High Street, Private Bag 12, Kew, 3101, VIC, Australia
Tel.: (61) 398544666   AU
Web Site:
http://www.bankmecu.com.au
Rev.: $158,591,581
Assets: $4,452,973,284
Liabilities: $4,078,003,722
Net Worth: $374,969,562
Earnings: $16,048,887
Emp.: 386
Fiscal Year-end: 06/30/19
Banking & Financial Services
N.A.I.C.S.: 522110
John P. Yardley (Deputy CEO)

BANK BTB OJSC

Y Safarov str 27, Baku, Azerbaijan
Tel.: (994) 124997995
Web Site: https://www.btb.az
Year Founded: 2010
BKTBN—(BAK)
Rev.: $15,589,170
Assets: $209,994,703
Liabilities: $180,382,578
Net Worth: $29,612,125
Earnings: ($502,060)
Fiscal Year-end: 12/31/21
Commercial Banking Services
N.A.I.C.S.: 522110

BANK CENTERCREDIT JSC

38 Al-Farabi Avenue, Medeu district, A25D5G0, Almaty, Kazakhstan
Tel.: (7) 272443030
Web Site: http://www.bcc.kz
CCBN—(KAZ)
Rev.: $201,993,881
Assets: $9,335,442,594
Liabilities: $8,744,198,285
Net Worth: $591,244,309
Earnings: $313,333,511
Fiscal Year-end: 12/31/22
Banking Services
N.A.I.C.S.: 522110
Bakhytbek B. Baiseitov (Chm)

Subsidiaries:

BCC Invest JSC (1)

st Al-Farabi 38 1st floor, Almaty, 050059, Kazakhstan (100%)
Tel.: (7) 7272443232
Web Site: http://www.bcc-invest.kz
Sales Range: $50-74.9 Million
Emp.: 60
Investment Banking & Securities Dealing
N.A.I.C.S.: 523150

BANK CENTRALI TA' MALTA

Castille Place, Valletta, VLT 1060, Malta
Tel.: (356) 25500000   Mt
Web Site:
http://www.centralbankmalta.org
Year Founded: 1968
Rev.: $65,428,940
Assets: $10,401,471,334
Liabilities: $9,949,100,527
Net Worth: $452,370,807
Earnings: $35,275,590
Emp.: 334
Fiscal Year-end: 12/31/19
Central Bank
N.A.I.C.S.: 521110
Raymond Filletti (Chief Fin Control & Risk Officer)

BANK DHOFAR SAOG

Ruwi Sultanate Of Oman, PO Box 1507, 112, Ruwi, Oman
Tel.: (968) 24790466   OM
Web Site:
https://www.bankdhofar.com
Year Founded: 1990
BKDB—(MUS)
Rev.: $570,926,517
Assets: $12,171,217,415
Liabilities: $10,267,391,344
Net Worth: $1,903,826,070
Earnings: $100,672,745
Emp.: 1,689
Fiscal Year-end: 12/31/23
Banking Services
N.A.I.C.S.: 522110
Abdul Hafidh Salim Rajab Al Aujaili (Chm)

BANK DOM.RF JSC

10 Vozdvizhenka Str, 125009, Moscow, Russia
Tel.: (7) 8007758686
Web Site: http://www.domrfbank.ru
Year Founded: 1993
Sales Range: Less than $1 Million
Mortgage Banking Services
N.A.I.C.S.: 522292
Artem Fedorko (Chm)

BANK ESKHATA OJSC

Ul Gagarin 135, Khujand, Dushanbe, 735700, Tajikistan
Tel.: (992) 342266999
Web Site: http://www.eskhata.com
Year Founded: 1993
Emp.: 100
Investment Banking Services
N.A.I.C.S.: 523150
Nazarov Akbar Abdushukurovich (Chm-Mgmt Bd)

BANK FOR INTERNATIONAL SETTLEMENTS

Centralbahnplatz 2, 4051, Basel, Switzerland
Tel.: (41) 612808080   CH
Web Site: http://www.bis.org
Year Founded: 1930
Rev.: $775,222,746
Assets: $295,642,513,272
Liabilities: $275,381,605,206
Net Worth: $20,260,908,066
Earnings: $468,302,382
Emp.: 584
Fiscal Year-end: 03/31/19

Bank for International Settlements—(Continued)

International Monetary & Financial Cooperation Promoter Between Central Banks & International Organisations
N.A.I.C.S.: 522320
Agustin Carstens *(Gen Mgr)*

Subsidiaries:

Financial Stability Institute **(1)**
Centralbahnplatz 2, Basel, 4002, Switzerland **(100%)**
Tel.: (41) 612808080
Web Site: http://www.bis.org
Sales Range: $300-349.9 Million
Promoter of Financial Stability
N.A.I.C.S.: 711310

BANK FUR TIROL UND VORARLBERG AG

Stadtforum, PO Box 573, 6020, Innsbruck, Austria
Tel.: (43) 5053330
Web Site: http://www.btv.at
Sales Range: $200-249.9 Million
Emp.: 1,195
Banking Services
N.A.I.C.S.: 522110
Heinrich Treichl *(Chm)*

Subsidiaries:

BKS Bank AG **(1)**
St Veiter Ring 43, 9020, Klagenfurt, Austria
Tel.: (43) 4635858
Web Site: https://www.bks.at
Rev.: $274,474,004
Assets: $11,781,724,254
Liabilities: $9,901,021,085
Net Worth: $1,880,703,168
Earnings: $197,668,617
Emp.: 1,146
Fiscal Year-end: 12/31/2023
Banking Services
N.A.I.C.S.: 522110
Franz Gasselsberger *(Vice Chm-Supervisory Bd)*

Subsidiary (Domestic):

BKS Immobilien-Service Gesellschaft mbH **(2)**
St Veiter Ring 43, 9020, Klagenfurt, Austria **(100%)**
Tel.: (43) 4635858
Web Site: http://www.bks.at
Sales Range: $50-74.9 Million
Emp.: 100
Nonresidential Buildings Lessors
N.A.I.C.S.: 531120

BKS Zentrale-Errichtungs- u. Vermietungsgesellschaft mbH **(2)**
St Veiter Ring 43, 9020, Klagenfurt, Austria **(50%)**
Tel.: (43) 46358580
Web Site: http://www.bks.at
Sales Range: $75-99.9 Million
Emp.: 200
Nonresidential Buildings Lessors
N.A.I.C.S.: 531120
Herta Stockbauer *(Mng Dir)*

BKS-Immobilienleasing Gesellschaft mbH **(2)**
St. Veiter Ring 43, 9020, Klagenfurt, Austria **(100%)**
Tel.: (43) 4635858790
All Other Nondepository Credit Intermediation
N.A.I.C.S.: 522299

BKS-Leasing Gesellschaft mbH **(2)**
St Veiter Ring 43, 9020, Klagenfurt, Austria **(100%)**
Tel.: (43) 4635858795
Web Site: http://www.bks.at
All Other Nondepository Credit Intermediation
N.A.I.C.S.: 522299

BTV Anlagenleasing 2 GmbH **(1)**
Stadtsorun 1, 6020, Innsbruck, Austria **(100%)**
Tel.: (43) 505333
Web Site: http://www.btv.at

Sales Range: $200-249.9 Million
Emp.: 400
Other Activities Related to Credit Intermediation
N.A.I.C.S.: 522390

BTV Anlagenleasing 3 GmbH **(1)**
Stadtsorun 1, 6020, Innsbruck, Austria **(100%)**
Tel.: (43) 5125333
Web Site: http://www.btv-leasing.com
Other Activities Related to Credit Intermediation
N.A.I.C.S.: 522390

BTV Leasing Deutschland GmbH **(1)**
Neuhauser Strasse 5, 80331, Munich, Germany **(100%)**
Tel.: (49) 8925544730
Web Site: http://www.btv-leasing.com
Investment Banking & Securities Dealing
N.A.I.C.S.: 523150
Gehart Schwab *(Mng Dir)*

BTV Leasing GmbH **(1)**
Sradtforum 1, 6020, Innsbruck, Austria **(100%)**
Tel.: (43) 5 05 333
Web Site: http://www.btv-leasing.com
Emp.: 28
Commericial Banking
N.A.I.C.S.: 522110
Gerd Schwab *(CEO)*

BTV Leasing Schweiz AG **(1)**
Hauptstrasse 19, 9422, Bern, Switzerland
Tel.: (41) 71 858 10 74
Web Site: http://www.btv-leasing.com
Real Estate Lending Services
N.A.I.C.S.: 522292

BTV Mobilien Leasing GmbH **(1)**
Stadtsorun 1, 6020, Innsbruck, Austria **(100%)**
Tel.: (43) 505333
Sales Range: $200-249.9 Million
Emp.: 400
Other Activities Related to Credit Intermediation
N.A.I.C.S.: 522390

BTV Real-Leasing GmbH **(1)**
Stadtsorun 1, 6020, Innsbruck, Austria **(100%)**
Tel.: (43) 1534817780
Web Site: http://www.btv-leasing.com
Sales Range: $50-74.9 Million
Emp.: 15
Real Estate Agents & Brokers Offices
N.A.I.C.S.: 531210

BTV Real-Leasing I GmbH **(1)**
Stadtsorun 1, 6020, Innsbruck, Austria **(100%)**
Tel.: (43) 51253330
Web Site: http://www.btv-leasing.com
All Other Miscellaneous Mfr
N.A.I.C.S.: 339999

BTV Real-Leasing II GmbH **(1)**
Stadtsorun 1, Innsbruck, 6020, Austria **(100%)**
Tel.: (43) 5053332028
Web Site: http://www.btv-leasing.com
Sales Range: $50-74.9 Million
Emp.: 15
Office Machinery & Equipment Rental & Leasing
N.A.I.C.S.: 532420

BTV Real-Leasing III Nachfolge GmbH And Co KG **(1)**
Stadtsorun 1, Innsbruck, 6020, Austria **(100%)**
Tel.: (43) 505333
Web Site: http://www.btv-leasing.com
All Other Nondepository Credit Intermediation
N.A.I.C.S.: 522299

Drei-Banken-Versicherungs AG **(1)**
Wiener Strasse 32, Linz, 4020, Austria **(20%)**
Tel.: (43) 73265445550
Web Site: http://www.dbvag.at
Sales Range: $50-74.9 Million
Emp.: 50
Direct Life Insurance Carriers
N.A.I.C.S.: 524113

Oberbank AG **(1)**

Untere Donaulande 28, A-4020, Linz, Austria
Tel.: (43) 73278020
Web Site: https://www.oberbank.at
Rev.: $583,753,507
Assets: $28,920,964,818
Liabilities: $25,093,077,919
Net Worth: $3,827,886,898
Earnings: $261,336,067
Emp.: 2,139
Fiscal Year-end: 12/31/2022
Banking Services
N.A.I.C.S.: 522110
Franz Gasselsberger *(Chm-Mgmt Bd & CEO)*

Subsidiary (Non-US):

Oberbank Geschaftsbereich Tschechien spol S.r.o. **(2)**
I P Pavlova 5, 120 00, Prague, Czech Republic
Tel.: (420) 224190100
Web Site: http://www.oberbank.cz
Sales Range: $75-99.9 Million
Emp.: 250
Commericial Banking
N.A.I.C.S.: 522110
Robert Cokorne *(Mng Dir)*

Oberbank Leasing S.r.o. **(2)**
Galvaniho 7-B, 82104, Bratislava, Slovakia
Tel.: (421) 248214320
Web Site: http://www.oberbank.sl
Sales Range: $50-74.9 Million
Emp.: 22
Commericial Banking
N.A.I.C.S.: 522110

Oberbank Leasing spol S.r.o. **(2)**
Namesti I P Pavlova 1789-5, 120 00, Prague, Czech Republic
Tel.: (420) 224190160
Web Site: http://www.oberbankleasing.cz
Sales Range: $50-74.9 Million
Emp.: 30
Commericial Banking
N.A.I.C.S.: 522110
Ludek Knypl *(Mng Dir)*

BANK INDONESIA

JI MH Thamrin 2, Jakarta, 10350, Indonesia
Tel.: (62) 213817317
Web Site: http://www.bi.go.id
Sales Range: $1-4.9 Billion
Emp.: 6,000
Banking Services
N.A.I.C.S.: 522110
Hartadi A. Sarwono *(Deputy Governor)*

BANK KERJASAMA RAKYAT MALAYSIA BERHAD

Tower 1 Bank Rakyat Twin Tower No 33 Jalan Travers, 50470, Kuala Lumpur, Malaysia
Tel.: (60) 3 26129600
Web Site:
http://www.bankrakyat.com.my
Year Founded: 1954
Sales Range: $1-4.9 Billion
Banking Services
N.A.I.C.S.: 522110
Zulkiflee Abbas Abdul Hamid *(Pres & Mng Dir)*

Subsidiaries:

Rakyat Hartanah Sdn Bhd **(1)**
Lot P T 34060 Jalan Sungai Ramal Luar, 43000, Kajang, Malaysia
Tel.: (60) 387365573
Business Management Services
N.A.I.C.S.: 561110

Rakyat Holdings Sdn Bhd **(1)**
Tingkat 12 Menara 2 Menara Kembar Bank Rakyat No 33 Jalan Rakyat, 50470, Kuala Lumpur, Malaysia
Tel.: (60) 322657500
Web Site: http://www.rakyatholdings.com
Property Development Services
N.A.I.C.S.: 236116
Syed Abdul Aziz Bin Syed Hassan *(CEO)*

Rakyat Management Services Sdn Bhd **(1)**
Suite 8-2 Tingkat 8 Bangunan Perhim No 150 Jalan Ipoh, 51200, Kuala Lumpur, Malaysia
Tel.: (60) 340418700
Business Management Services
N.A.I.C.S.: 561110
Mokharzinim Mokhtar *(Gen Mgr)*

Rakyat Niaga Sdn Bhd **(1)**
No 155 Ground Floor Wisma Perkeso Jalan Tun Razak, 50400, Kuala Lumpur, Malaysia
Tel.: (60) 326815255
Business Management Services
N.A.I.C.S.: 561110
Rizalruzaimal Jamaludin *(Gen Mgr)*

Rakyat Travel Sdn Bhd **(1)**
Tkt 11 Menara 2 Menara Kembar Bank Rakyat 33 Jalan Rakyat, 50470, Kuala Lumpur, Malaysia
Tel.: (60) 322657600
Web Site: http://www.rakyatravel.com.my
Emp.: 47
Travel Arrangement Services
N.A.I.C.S.: 561599

BANK KUZNECKIY

Krasnaya St 104, Penza, 440000, Russia
Tel.: (7) 8412450267
Web Site: https://www.kuzbank.ru
Year Founded: 2015
KUZB—(MOEX)
Sales Range: Less than $1 Million
Commercial Banking Services
N.A.I.C.S.: 522110

BANK LEUMI LE-ISRAEL B.M.

24-32 Yehuda Halevi St, Tel Aviv, 65546, Israel
Tel.: (972) 768858111
Web Site: https://english.leumi.co.il
Year Founded: 1902
LUMI—(TAE)
Rev.: $4,337,346,131
Assets: $198,334,417,873
Liabilities: $183,558,375,359
Net Worth: $14,776,042,514
Earnings: $1,905,265,441
Emp.: 7,893
Fiscal Year-end: 12/31/23
Commercial Banking Services
N.A.I.C.S.: 522110
Ronen Agassi *(Executives)*

Subsidiaries:

Bank Leumi (Luxembourg) S.A. **(1)**
6 D route de Treves, Senningerberg, L 2633, Luxembourg **(100%)**
Tel.: (352) 346390
Web Site: http://www.pt.lu
Sales Range: $50-74.9 Million
Emp.: 30
International Banking
N.A.I.C.S.: 522299
Uri Rom *(Chm)*

Bank Leumi (UK) plc **(1)**
12th Floor 1 Angel Court, London, EC2R 7HJ, United Kingdom **(78.4%)**
Tel.: (44) 2037721500
Web Site: https://www.leumiuk.com
Sales Range: $100-124.9 Million
Emp.: 130
International Banking
N.A.I.C.S.: 522299
Gil Karni *(CEO)*

Subsidiary (Non-US):

Bank Leumi (Jersey) Ltd. **(2)**
2 Hill St, PO Box 510, Saint Helier, JE4 5TR, Jersey **(100%)**
Tel.: (44) 1534702525
Web Site: http://www.leumijersey.com
Sales Range: $50-74.9 Million
Emp.: 20
Banking Services
N.A.I.C.S.: 522110
David Cooper *(Mng Dir)*

Bank Leumi Le-Israel Trust Co. Ltd. **(1)**

8 Rothschild Blvd, Tel Aviv, 66881, Israel **(100%)**
Tel.: (972) 35170777
Web Site: http://www.trust.co.il
Sales Range: $50-74.9 Million
Emp.: 20
Financial Services
N.A.I.C.S.: 523940

Bank Leumi USA **(1)**
579 5th Ave, New York, NY 10017-1917 **(99.8%)**
Tel.: (917) 542-2343
Web Site: https://www.leumiusa.com
Sales Range: $150-199.9 Million
Emp.: 447
International Banking
N.A.I.C.S.: 522110
John P. McGann (Chief Admin Officer)

Bank Leumi USA **(1)**
19495 Biscayne Blvd Ste 500, Aventura, FL 33180-2320
Tel.: (305) 702-3500
Web Site: https://www.leumiusa.com
Sales Range: $50-74.9 Million
Emp.: 20
Banking Services
N.A.I.C.S.: 522110
Charles D. Johnston (Chm)

Leumi & Co. Investment House Ltd. **(1)**
25 Kalisher St, Tel Aviv, 65156, Israel **(100%)**
Tel.: (972) 35141222
Web Site: http://www.leumico.co.il
Sales Range: $50-74.9 Million
Emp.: 40
N.A.I.C.S.: 522299

Leumi (Latin America) **(1)**
Luis A de Herrera 1248, Torre A Piso 10, 11000, Montevideo, Uruguay **(100%)**
Tel.: (598) 26285838
Web Site: http://www.leumi.com.uy
Sales Range: $50-74.9 Million
Emp.: 18
International Banking
N.A.I.C.S.: 522299

Leumi (Schweiz) AG **(1)**
Dianastrasse 5, 8002, Zurich, Switzerland
Tel.: (41) 58 207 91 11
Web Site: http://www.leumi.ch
Sales Range: $100-124.9 Million
Emp.: 120
International Banking
N.A.I.C.S.: 522299
Amnon Zaidenberg (Co-Chm)

Leumi Finance Co., Ltd. **(1)**
35 Yehuda Halevi St, Tel Aviv, 65136, Israel **(100%)**
Tel.: (972) 35149908
Web Site: http://www.leumi.com
Sales Range: $75-99.9 Million
Emp.: 10
N.A.I.C.S.: 522299

Leumi Industrial Development Ltd. **(1)**
13 Ahad Haam St, Tel Aviv, 65136, Israel **(100%)**
Tel.: (972) 35149951
Web Site: http://www.leumi.co.il
Sales Range: $75-99.9 Million
Emp.: 5
N.A.I.C.S.: 522299

Leumi L.P. Ltd. **(1)**
Dizengoff 55 Fl 17, Tel Aviv, 64332, Israel **(100%)**
Tel.: (972) 36217333
Web Site: http://www.leumi.co.il
N.A.I.C.S.: 522299

Leumi Leasing Ltd. **(1)**
13 Ehad Haam St, Tel Aviv, 65546, Israel **(100%)**
Tel.: (972) 35148111
Web Site: http://www.leumi.co.il
Sales Range: $50-74.9 Million
Emp.: 35
N.A.I.C.S.: 522299

Leumi Leasing and Investments Ltd. **(1)**
13 Ahad Haam, Tel Aviv, 65151, Israel
Tel.: (972) 35149908

Investment Management Service
N.A.I.C.S.: 523999

Leumi Mortgage Bank Ltd. **(1)**
43 Alenby St, Tel Aviv, Israel **(100%)**
Tel.: (972) 3 514 7676
Sales Range: $50-74.9 Million
Emp.: 20
N.A.I.C.S.: 522299

Leumi Overseas Trust Corporation Ltd **(1)**
2 Hill St, PO Box 510, Saint Helier, Jersey **(100%)**
Tel.: (44) 1534702500
Web Site: http://www.leumijersey.com
Sales Range: $50-74.9 Million
Emp.: 40
Trust & Fiduciary Services
N.A.I.C.S.: 523991
John Germain (Dir-Trust Svcs)

Leumi Partners Ltd. **(1)**
Azrieli Center 5 36th Floor 132, Menachem Begin Rd, Tel Aviv, 67025, Israel
Tel.: (972) 35141212
Web Site: https://www.leumipartners.com
Investment Banking Services
N.A.I.C.S.: 523999

LeumiTech Ltd. **(1)**
HaMenofim St 15, Herzliya, 076-88-56297, Israel
Tel.: (972) 768856297
Web Site: https://www.leumitech.com
Financial Services
N.A.I.C.S.: 523999

BANK LEVOBEREZHNY PJSC
Ul Plakhotnogo 25/1, Novosibirsk, 630054, Russia
Tel.: (7) 3833600900
Web Site: http://www.nskbl.ru
Sales Range: Less than $1 Million
Commercial Banking Services
N.A.I.C.S.: 522110

BANK LINTH LLB AG
Zurcherstrasse 3, 8730, Uznach, Switzerland
Tel.: (41) 844114411
Web Site: http://www.banklinth.ch
LINN—(SWX)
Sales Range: Less than $1 Million
Banking Services
N.A.I.C.S.: 522110
Ralph P. Siegl (Pres)

BANK MAKRAMAH LIMITED
Ein Munjed Abraj House 2nd floor, PO Box 4444, Ramallah, Palestine
Tel.: (970) 22947070
Web Site: https://www.altakaful-ins.ps
Year Founded: 2006
TIC—(PAL)
Rev.: $60,515,882
Assets: $69,031,006
Liabilities: $45,137,613
Net Worth: $23,893,393
Earnings: $2,031,393
Fiscal Year-end: 12/31/23
Insurance Agency Services
N.A.I.C.S.: 524210
Yaccub Kalouti (Chm)

BANK MELLAT
327 Taleghani Ave, 15817, Tehran, Iran
Tel.: (98) 21 82961
Web Site: http://en.bankmellat.ir
Sales Range: $1-4.9 Billion
Emp.: 24,737
Banking Services
N.A.I.C.S.: 522110
Hadi Akhlaghi Feizasar (CEO)

Subsidiaries:

Persia International Bank PLC London **(1)**
6 Lothbury, London, EC2R 7HH, United Kingdom
Tel.: (44) 2076068521

Web Site: http://www.persiabank.co.uk
Sales Range: $50-74.9 Million
Emp.: 20
Banking Services
N.A.I.C.S.: 522110
M. R. Meskarian (CEO)

BANK MUSCAT SAOG
Building No 120/4 Block No 311 Street No 62 Airport Heights - Seeb, PO Box 134, 112, Ruwi, Oman
Tel.: (968) 24795555
Web Site: https://www.bankmuscat.com
Year Founded: 1993
BKMB—(MUS)
Rev.: $1,215,844,979
Assets: $33,186,092,784
Liabilities: $27,388,066,913
Net Worth: $5,798,025,871
Earnings: $521,463,453
Emp.: 3,973
Fiscal Year-end: 12/31/22
Commercial Banking Services
N.A.I.C.S.: 522110
Khalid Mustahail Al Mashani (Chm)

Subsidiaries:

Muscat Security House LLC **(1)**
Opposite Al Faisaliya Foundation King Fahad Road, PO Box No 54488, Riyadh, 11514, Saudi Arabia
Tel.: (966) 12799888
Securities Trading & Custodial Services
N.A.I.C.S.: 523150

BANK NEGARA MALAYSIA
Jalan Dato Onn, PO Box 10922, Kuala Lumpur, 50929, Malaysia
Tel.: (60) 326988044
Web Site: http://www.bnm.gov.my
Year Founded: 1959
Rev.: $2,706,350,220
Assets: $109,820,088,000
Liabilities: $74,980,662,120
Net Worth: $34,839,425,880
Earnings: $2,170,624,680
Emp.: 2,838
Fiscal Year-end: 12/31/19
Central Bank
N.A.I.C.S.: 521110
Nor Shamsiah Mohd Yunus (Chm)

Subsidiaries:

The Credit Counselling and Debt Management Agency **(1)**
Level 5 and 6 Menara Bumiputra Commerce Jalan Raja Laut, 50350, Kuala Lumpur, Malaysia
Tel.: (60) 3 2616 7766
Web Site: http://www.akpk.org.my
Financial Management Services
N.A.I.C.S.: 541611
Azman Hasim (Gen Mgr-Corp Dev Div)

BANK NIZWA SAOG
PO Box 1423, Al Khuwair, 133, Muscat, Oman
Tel.: (968) 24950500
Web Site: https://www.banknizwa.om
Year Founded: 2012
BKNZ—(MUS)
Rev.: $114,908,842
Assets: $3,640,079,020
Liabilities: $3,018,624,992
Net Worth: $621,454,028
Earnings: $32,456,494
Emp.: 415
Fiscal Year-end: 12/31/21
Commercial Banking Services
N.A.I.C.S.: 522110
Khalid Jamal Al Kayed (CEO)

BANK OCHRONY SRODOW-ISKA S.A.
ul Zelazna 32, 00-832, Warsaw, Poland
Tel.: (48) 228508735

Web Site: https://www.bosbank.pl
Year Founded: 1997
BOS—(WAR)
Rev.: $406,173,779
Assets: $5,597,675,545
Liabilities: $5,051,786,318
Net Worth: $545,889,226
Earnings: $19,912,093
Emp.: 324
Fiscal Year-end: 12/31/23
Banking Services
N.A.I.C.S.: 522180
Stanislaw Kolasinski (Vice Chm-Mgmt Bd)

BANK OF AFRICA
Lotissement Mandarona Lot N 1 Imm Promoffice Sidi Maarouf, 20000, Casablanca, Morocco
Tel.: (212) 522586365 Ma
Web Site: https://bank-of-africa.net
Year Founded: 1959
BOA—(CAS)
Sales Range: $1-4.9 Billion
Emp.: 11,000
Retail, Corporate Banking, Financial Advisory & Asset Management Services
N.A.I.C.S.: 522110
Othman Benjelloun (Chm & CEO)

Subsidiaries:

BMCE Capital **(1)**
Tour BMCE Rond Point Hassan II, Casablanca, 20200, Morocco **(100%)**
Tel.: (212) 522498978
Web Site: http://www.bmcecapital.com
Sales Range: $500-549.9 Million
Emp.: 700
Investment Banking, Securities Brokerage, Advisory & Asset Management Services
N.A.I.C.S.: 523150
Khalid Nasr (Pres)

Division (Domestic):

BMCE Capital Bourse **(2)**
Tour BMCE Rond Point Hassan II, 20 000, Casablanca, Morocco **(100%)**
Tel.: (212) 522481001
Web Site: http://www.bmcecapitalbourse.com
Sales Range: $50-74.9 Million
Emp.: 20
Brokerage Services
N.A.I.C.S.: 523150
Anas Mikou (CEO)

Unit (Domestic):

BMCE Capital Conseil **(2)**
30 Boulevard Moulay Youssef, 20 000, Casablanca, Morocco
Tel.: (212) 522429100
Web Site: http://www.bmcecapital.com
Sales Range: $25-49.9 Million
Emp.: 36
Investment Advisory Services
N.A.I.C.S.: 523940
Mehdi Drafate (Gen Mgr)

Division (Domestic):

BMCE Capital Gestion **(2)**
63 Boulevard Moulay Youssef, 20 000, Casablanca, Morocco **(100%)**
Tel.: (212) 522470847
Sales Range: $50-74.9 Million
Emp.: 25
Asset Management Services
N.A.I.C.S.: 523940
Amine Amor (CEO)

BMCE International, S.A.U. **(1)**
Calle Serrano 59, 28006, Madrid, Spain
Tel.: (34) 915756800
Web Site: http://www.bmce-intl.com
Retail & Commercial Banking
N.A.I.C.S.: 522110

Maghrebail SA **(1)**
45 Boulevard Moulay Youssef, 20070, Casablanca, 20070, Morocco
Tel.: (212) 522203304
Web Site: https://www.maghrebail.ma

Bank of Africa—(Continued)

Sales Range: $25-49.9 Million
Investment Management Service
N.A.I.C.S.: 523999
Reda Daifi (Gen Mgr-Comml & Commitments)

Maroc Factoring (1)
Residence Adriana 1er etage 63 boulevard Moulay Yuussef, 20000, Casablanca, Morocco (100%)
Tel.: (212) 520427632
Web Site: http://www.marocfactoring.ma
Sales Range: $50-74.9 Million
Emp.: 14
Factoring Services
N.A.I.C.S.: 522299
Nezha Azzouzi (Dir-Sls)

MediCapital Bank Plc (1)
Juxon House 2nd Floor 100 St Pauls Churchyard, London, EC4M 8BU, United Kingdom
Tel.: (44) 207 429 5500
Web Site: http://www.medicapitalbank.com
Sales Range: $50-74.9 Million
Emp.: 30
Commercial Banking Services
N.A.I.C.S.: 522110
David Suratgar (Chm)

Salafin SA (1)
Zenith Millenium immeuble 8 Sidi Maarouf, Casablanca, Morocco
Tel.: (212) 522974455
Web Site: http://www.salafin.com
Sales Range: $25-49.9 Million
Commercial Banking Services
N.A.I.C.S.: 522110
Mohammed Amine Bouabid (Chm-Mgmt Bd)

BANK OF ALBANIA
Sheshi Skenderbej 1, Tirana, Albania
Tel.: (355) 4222152
Web Site:
   http://www.bankofalbania.org
Sales Range: $50-74.9 Million
Emp.: 427
Banking Services
N.A.I.C.S.: 521110
Ardian Fullani (Chm-Supervisory Bd & CEO)

BANK OF BAKU OJSC
Ataturk Ave 42, Baku, Azerbaijan
Tel.: (994) 124470055
Web Site:
   http://www.bankofbaku.com
Year Founded: 1994
BOBAK—(BAK)
Sales Range: Less than $1 Million
Commercial Banking Services
N.A.I.C.S.: 522110
Elchin Isayev (Chm-Supervisory Bd)

BANK OF BARODA
Baroda Bhawan 7th floor RC Dutt Road, Vadodara, 390 007, India
Tel.: (91) 2652316792   In
Web Site:
   https://www.bankofbaroda.in
Year Founded: 1908
532134—(BOM)
Rev.: $11,981,995,553
Assets: $182,928,712,444
Liabilities: $170,285,281,980
Net Worth: $12,643,430,463
Earnings: $1,071,483,013
Emp.: 79,173
Fiscal Year-end: 03/31/22
Banking Services
N.A.I.C.S.: 522110
Rathi Prakash Vir (Gen Mgr)

Subsidiaries:

BOB Capital Markets Ltd. (1)
1704 B Wing 17th Floor Parinee Crescenzo Plot No C - 38/39 G Block, Bandra Kurla Complex Bandra East, Mumbai, 400 051, Maharashtra, India (100%)
Tel.: (91) 2261389300

Web Site: https://www.bobcaps.in
Sales Range: $50-74.9 Million
Investment Banking
N.A.I.C.S.: 523150
Sanjiv Chadha (Chm)

BOB Financial Solutions Limited (1)
2 Floor Baroda SP Road Behind Shopping Centre, Colaba, Mumbai, 400102, India (100%)
Tel.: (91) 22 4206 8500
Web Site: http://www.bobfinancial.com
Credit Card Issuer
N.A.I.C.S.: 522210
R. K. Arora (VP-Accts, Audit Inspection, CRM & Billing)

Bank of Baroda (Botswana) Ltd. (1)
Plot 14456 Post Net Kgale View G-West Gaborone Industrial, Gaborone, Botswana
Tel.: (267) 3992710
Web Site: https://www.bankofbaroda.co.bw
Sales Range: $50-74.9 Million
Banking Services
N.A.I.C.S.: 522110
Seretse Bagopi (Chm)

Bank of Baroda (Ghana) Ltd. (1)
Kwame Nkrumah Avenue Next to Melcom, Post Mail Bag No 298 AN, Adabraka, Accra, Ghana
Tel.: (233) 21250072
Web Site: http://www.bankofbaroda.com
Sales Range: $50-74.9 Million
Banking Services
N.A.I.C.S.: 522110

Bank of Baroda (Guyana) Inc. (1)
10 Ave of the Republic and Regent St, PO Box 10768, Lacytown, Georgetown, Guyana
Tel.: (592) 2264005
Web Site: https://www.bankofbaroda.gy
Sales Range: $50-74.9 Million
Banking Services
N.A.I.C.S.: 522110

Bank of Baroda (Kenya) Ltd. (1)
Baroda House 90 Muthithi road, PO Box 30033-100, 29 Koinage St, Nairobi, 100, Kenya
Tel.: (254) 202248402
Web Site:
   https://www.bankofbarodakenya.co.ke
Sales Range: $50-74.9 Million
Emp.: 70
Banking Services
N.A.I.C.S.: 522110
Vindhya Vittal Ramesh (Gen Mgr)

Bank of Baroda (New Zealand) Ltd. (1)
114 Dominion Road, Mount Eden, Auckland, 1024, New Zealand
Tel.: (64) 96321020
Web Site: https://barodanzltd.co.nz
Commercial Banking Services
N.A.I.C.S.: 522110
Anupam Srivastava (Mng Dir)

Bank of Baroda (Tanzania) Ltd. (1)
Plot No 149/32 Ohio / Sokoine Drive, PO Box 5356, Dar es Salaam, Tanzania
Tel.: (255) 222124472
Web Site: https://www.bankofbaroda.co.tz
Banking Services
N.A.I.C.S.: 522110

Bank of Baroda (Trinidad & Tobago) Ltd. (1)
Furness House 90 Independence Square, Port of Spain, Trinidad & Tobago
Tel.: (868) 6253964
Web Site: http://www.bankofbaroda.com
Sales Range: $50-74.9 Million
Banking Services
N.A.I.C.S.: 522110

Bank of Baroda (UK) Limited (1)
32 City Road, London, EC1Y 2BD, United Kingdom
Tel.: (44) 2074481556
Web Site: https://www.bankofbarodauk.com
Banking Services
N.A.I.C.S.: 522110
Sanjay Kumar Grover (Mng Dir)

Bank of Baroda (Uganda) Ltd. (1)
18 Kampala Road, Kampala, Uganda
Tel.: (256) 414233680

Web Site: https://www.bankofbaroda.ug
Sales Range: $50-74.9 Million
Banking Services
N.A.I.C.S.: 522110
Vastina Rukimirana Nsanze (Chm)

Baroda Asset Management India Ltd (1)
501 Titanium 5th Floor Western Express Highway Gorgaun E, Mumbai, 400063, India (51%)
Tel.: (91) 2230741000
Web Site: http://www.barodamf.com
Investment Advice
N.A.I.C.S.: 523940
Sanjay Chawla (Chief Investment Officer)

Baroda Global Shared Services Ltd. (1)
5th Floor Baroda Sun Tower C-34 G-Block Bandra Kurla Complex, Bandra East, Mumbai, 400051, Maharashtra, India
Tel.: (91) 7961800330
Web Site: https://www.bgss.in
Banking Services
N.A.I.C.S.: 522110

India Infradebt Ltd. (1)
The Capital B Wing 1101-A Bandra Kurla Complex, Mumbai, 400 051, India
Tel.: (91) 2268196900
Web Site: http://www.infradebt.in
Refinance Banking Services
N.A.I.C.S.: 522110
Suvek Nambiar (CEO & Mng Dir)

Indo Zambia Bank Ltd. (1)
Plot No 6907 Cairo Road, PO Box 35411, Lusaka, Zambia (20%)
Tel.: (260) 211225080
Web Site: http://www.izb.co.zm
Banking Services
N.A.I.C.S.: 522110
Michael Gondwe (Chm)

The Nainital Bank Ltd. (1)
Naini Bank House 7 Oaks, Kolkata, 263001, India
Tel.: (91) 5942235823
Web Site: http://www.nainitalbank.co.in
Sales Range: $350-399.9 Million
Emp.: 800
Commericial Banking
N.A.I.C.S.: 522110
Naresh Bhardwaj (Deputy Gen Mgr)

BANK OF BEIJING CO., LTD.
Bank of Beijing Tower C 17 26 Financial St, Xicheng District, Beijing, China
Tel.: (86) 1066426500   CN
Web Site:
   https://www.bankofbeijing.com.cn
Year Founded: 1996
601169—(SHG)
Rev.: $9,305,150,400
Assets: $475,668,460,800
Liabilities: $432,057,834,000
Net Worth: $43,610,626,800
Earnings: $3,476,304,000
Emp.: 17,980
Fiscal Year-end: 12/31/22
Banking Services
N.A.I.C.S.: 522110

Subsidiaries:

Bank of Xian Co., Ltd . (1)
116 Heping Road Jinding Building, Beilin District, Xi'an, 710061, Shaanxi, China
Tel.: (86) 2985766951
Web Site: http://www.bankofbeijing.com.cn
Rev.: $922,084,020
Assets: $56,979,732,139
Liabilities: $52,873,318,134
Net Worth: $4,106,414,005
Earnings: $340,391,797
Fiscal Year-end: 12/31/2022
Commercial Banking Services
N.A.I.C.S.: 522110

BANK OF BEIRUT S.A.L.
Bank of Beirut sal Bldg Foch Street, Beirut Central District, Beirut, Lebanon
Tel.: (961) 1958483   LB

Web Site:
   https://www.bankofbeirut.com
Year Founded: 1973
BOB—(BEY)
Rev.: $1,416,589,680
Assets: $16,217,733,840
Liabilities: $14,649,766,560
Net Worth: $1,567,967,280
Earnings: ($121,475,640)
Emp.: 1,611
Fiscal Year-end: 12/31/19
Banking Services
N.A.I.C.S.: 522110
Salim G. Sfeir (Chm & CEO)

Subsidiaries:

Bank of Beirut (UK) Ltd (1)
17 A Curzon St, London, W1J 5HS, United Kingdom (100%)
Tel.: (44) 2074938342
Web Site: http://www.bankofbeirut.co.uk
Sales Range: $50-74.9 Million
Emp.: 40
Commercial Banking
N.A.I.C.S.: 522110

BANK OF BOTSWANA
Khama Crescent, Private Bag 154, Gaborone, Botswana
Tel.: (267) 3606000
Web Site:
   http://www.bankofbotswana.bw
Sales Range: $125-149.9 Million
Emp.: 500
Banking Services
N.A.I.C.S.: 521110
A. M. Motsomi (Deputy Governor)

BANK OF CEYLON
No 1 BOC Square Bank of Ceylon Mawatha, Colombo, 01, Sri Lanka
Tel.: (94) 11 2446790   LK
Web Site: http://www.boc.lk
Year Founded: 1939
Rev.: $1,252,860,456
Assets: $12,628,558,897
Liabilities: $11,907,070,970
Net Worth: $721,487,927
Earnings: $106,552,735
Emp.: 8,724
Fiscal Year-end: 12/31/18
Banking Services
N.A.I.C.S.: 522110
M. T. S. A. Perera (Asst Gen Mgr-Product Dev & Bus Process Re-Engrg Project)

Subsidiaries:

BOC Property Development & Management (Pvt) Ltd (1)
19th Fl BOC Head Ofc Bldg, No 4 Bank of Ceylon Mw, Colombo, Sri Lanka
Tel.: (94) 112388229
Residential Property Managers
N.A.I.C.S.: 531311

BOC Travels (Private) Limited (1)
1st Floor Bank of Ceylon Super Grade Branch Building Baseline Road, Colombo, Sri Lanka
Tel.: (94) 112 688 154
Web Site: http://www.boctravels.com
Travel Tour Operator
N.A.I.C.S.: 561520
K. H. Wilfred (Chm)

Bank of Ceylon (UK) Limited (1)
No 1 Devonshire Square, London, EC2M 4WD, United Kingdom
Tel.: (44) 207 377 1888
Web Site: http://www.bankofceylon.co.uk
Banking Services
N.A.I.C.S.: 522110
Sampath Perera (Mgr-Credit)

Ceybank Holiday Homes (Pvt) Ltd (1)
12th Floor BoC Head Office BOC Square, No 01 Bank Of Ceylon Mw, Colombo, 01, Sri Lanka (100%)
Tel.: (94) 112447845

Web Site:
http://www.ceybankholidayhomes.com
Sales Range: $25-49.9 Million
Emp.: 9
Travel Arrangement & Reservation Services
N.A.I.C.S.: 561599

Hotels Colombo (1963) Limited **(1)**
No 02 York Street, Colombo, Sri Lanka
Tel.: (94) 112320320
Banking Services
N.A.I.C.S.: 522110

Lanka Securities Pvt. Ltd. **(1)**
228/1 Galle Road, 04, Colombo, Sri Lanka
Tel.: (94) 114706757
Web Site: https://www.lsl.lk
Securities Trading & Brokerage Services;
Owned by First Capital Securities Corporation & Bank of Ceylon
N.A.I.C.S.: 523150

Merchant Bank of Sri Lanka & Finance PLC **(1)**
No 28 BOC Merchant Tower St Michael's
Road, Colombo, Sri Lanka
Tel.: (94) 114711711
Web Site: https://www.mbslbank.com
Financial Services
N.A.I.C.S.: 921130
Dammika Hapuhinna *(CEO)*

Merchant Bank of Sri Lanka Ltd **(1)**
No 28 St Michael's Road Boc Merchant
Tower, Colombo, 03, Sri Lanka
Tel.: (94) 114711711
Web Site: http://www.mbslbank.com
Sales Range: $100-124.9 Million
Emp.: 150
Securities Brokerage
N.A.I.C.S.: 523150
Nishaman Karunapala *(CEO)*

Subsidiary (Domestic):

MBSL Insurance Company
Limited **(2)**
Kew Road No 122, Colombo, 02, Sri Lanka
Tel.: (94) 112 304500
Web Site: http://www.mbslinsurance.lk
General Insurance Services
N.A.I.C.S.: 524210
Sujeewa Lokuhewa *(Chm)*

MBSL Savings Bank Limited **(2)**
No 519 T B Jayah Mawawatha, Colombo,
10, Sri Lanka
Tel.: (94) 11 2 374000
Web Site: http://www.mbslsavingsbank.com
Banking Services
N.A.I.C.S.: 522110
M. R. Shah *(Chm)*

Merchant Credit of Sri Lanka Ltd **(1)**
11th Floor 28 St Michaels Rd, BoC Merchant Tower, Colombo, Sri Lanka **(87.76%)**
Tel.: (94) 112301501
Web Site: http://www.mcsl.lk
Sales Range: $50-74.9 Million
Emp.: 100
Real Estate Credit
N.A.I.C.S.: 522292

Property Development Ltd **(1)**
19th Floor BOC Head Office Building, No 4
Bank of Ceylon Mw, Colombo, Sri Lanka
Tel.: (94) 112448549
Emp.: 100
Administrative Management & General
Management Consulting Services
N.A.I.C.S.: 541611
Kirthi Basnayake *(Head-HR)*

BANK OF CHANGSHA CO., LTD.
Block B Kailin Commercial Cent 53
Binjiang Road, Yuelu Distric, Changsha, 410005, China
Tel.: (86) 73189934772
Web Site:
https://www.bankofchangsha.com
601577—(SHG)
Rev.: $3,210,613,006
Assets: $127,024,582,417
Liabilities: $118,295,597,534
Net Worth: $8,728,984,883
Earnings: $956,300,202
Fiscal Year-end: 12/31/22

Commercial Banking Services
N.A.I.C.S.: 522110
Yuguo Zhu *(Chm)*

BANK OF CHENGDU CO., LTD.
Building No 16 Xiyu Street, Qingyang
District, Chengdu, 610000, China
Tel.: (86) 95507
Web Site: https://www.bocd.com.cn
Year Founded: 1996
601838—(SHG)
Rev.: $2,841,880,205
Assets: $128,838,102,822
Liabilities: $120,213,852,970
Net Worth: $8,624,249,852
Earnings: $1,409,949,731
Emp.: 6,000
Fiscal Year-end: 12/31/22
Commercial Banking Services
N.A.I.C.S.: 522110

BANK OF CHINA, LTD.
1 Fuxingmen Nei Dajie, Beijing,
100818, China
Tel.: (86) 1066596688   CN
Web Site: https://www.boc.cn
Year Founded: 1912
601988—(SSE)
Rev.: $106,209,821,700
Net Worth: $282,865,197,600
Earnings: $28,890,602,100
Emp.: 309,384
Fiscal Year-end: 12/31/19
Commercial Banking Services
N.A.I.C.S.: 522110
Jingzhen Lin *(Exec VP)*

Subsidiaries:

BOC Aviation **(1)**
8 Shenton Way 18-01, Singapore, 068811,
Singapore **(100%)**
Tel.: (65) 63235559
Web Site: http://www.bocaviation.com
Sales Range: $250-299.9 Million
Emp.: 100
Aircraft & Fleet Leasing Services
N.A.I.C.S.: 532411
Siqing Chen *(Chm)*

BOC Financial Asset Investment
Company Limited **(1)**
8/F No 110 Xidan North Street, Xicheng
District, Beijing, 100032, China
Tel.: (86) 1083262479
Financial Assets Management Services
N.A.I.C.S.: 523940

BOC Financial Leasing Co., Ltd. **(1)**
No 13 Zourong Road, Yuzhong District,
Chongqing, 400010, China
Tel.: (86) 2363031966
Financial Investment Services
N.A.I.C.S.: 523999

BOC Financial Technology Co., Ltd. **(1)**
No 288 Kayuan 2nd Road, Pudong New
District, Shanghai, 201201, China
Tel.: (86) 2120408162
Financial Investment Services
N.A.I.C.S.: 523999

BOC Fullerton Community Bank Co., Ltd. **(1)**
9/F No 110 Xidan North Street, Xicheng
District, Beijing, 100032, China
Tel.: (86) 1057765000
Financial Investment Services
N.A.I.C.S.: 523999

BOC Group Life Assurance Co., Ltd. **(1)**
13th Floor 1111 King's Road, Taikoo Shing,
China (Hong Kong)
Tel.: (852) 28600688
Web Site: https://www.boclife.com.hk
Financial Insurance Services
N.A.I.C.S.: 524210

BOC Hong Kong (Holdings)
Limited **(1)**
53/F Bank of China Tower 1 Garden Road,
Hong Kong, China (Hong Kong) **(66.06%)**
Tel.: (852) 228462700

Web Site: https://www.bochk.com
Rev.: $6,439,713,440
Assets: $428,340,129,380
Liabilities: $387,111,027,480
Net Worth: $41,229,101,900
Earnings: $3,671,802,640
Emp.: 14,915
Fiscal Year-end: 12/31/2020
Bank Holding Company
N.A.I.C.S.: 522110
Man Chan *(Deputy CEO)*

Subsidiary (Non-US):

Bank Of China (Malaysia)
Berhad **(2)**
Web Site: http://www.bankofchina.com
Commericial Banking
N.A.I.C.S.: 522110

Subsidiary (Domestic):

Bank of China (Hong Kong)
Limited **(2)**
Bank of China Tower 1 Garden Road, Hong
Kong, China (Hong Kong)
Tel.: (852) 2 826 6888
Web Site: https://www.bochk.com
Sales Range: $50-74.9 Million
Emp.: 90
Commericial Banking
N.A.I.C.S.: 522110
Gao Yingxin *(Vice Chm & CEO)*

BOC International Holdings
Limited **(1)**
26/F Bank of China Tower 1 Garden Road,
Hong Kong, China (Hong Kong)
Tel.: (852) 3 988 6000
Web Site: https://www.bocigroup.com
Investment Banking
N.A.I.C.S.: 523150
Tong Li *(CEO)*

BOC Wealth Management Co., Ltd. **(1)**
10/F Tower A Corporate Square No 35 Finance Street, Xicheng District, Beijing,
100033, China
Tel.: (86) 1083937333
Health Insurance Services
N.A.I.C.S.: 524128

BOC-Samsung Life Insurance Co., Ltd. **(1)**
9th Floor Xidanhui Building 110 Xidan North
Street, West District, Beijing, 100032, China
Tel.: (86) 1083262688
Web Site: http://www.boc-samsunglife.cn
Financial Insurance Services
N.A.I.C.S.: 524210

Banco da China Brasil S.A. **(1)**
Av Paulista 901-14 Andar-Bela Vista, Sao
Paulo, SP, Brazil
Tel.: (55) 1135083200
Banking Services
N.A.I.C.S.: 522110

Bank Of China (Mauritius)
Limited **(1)**
5th floor Dias Pier Building Caudan, Port
Louis, Mauritius
Tel.: (230) 2034878
Banking Services
N.A.I.C.S.: 522110

Bank Of China Consumer Finance
Co., Ltd. **(1)**
1409 BOC Building 200 Mid Yicheng Road,
Pudong New District, Shanghai, 200120,
China
Tel.: (86) 2163291680
Banking Investment Services
N.A.I.C.S.: 523150

Bank of China (Central & Eastern
Europe) Limited **(1)**
Jozsef Nador ter 7, 1051, Budapest, Hungary
Tel.: (36) 14299200
Banking Services
N.A.I.C.S.: 522110

Bank of China (Europe) S.A. **(1)**
55 Boulevard Royal, 2449, Luxembourg,
Luxembourg
Tel.: (352) 268688
Web Site: https://www.bankofchina.com
Commercial Banking Services

N.A.I.C.S.: 522110

Bank of China (Luxembourg)
S.A. **(1)**
Tel.: (352) 268688
Banking Services
N.A.I.C.S.: 522110

Bank of China (Macau) Limited **(1)**
Bank of China Tower Avenida Doutor Mario
Soares, Macau, China (Macau)
Tel.: (853) 28781828
Commercial Banking Services
N.A.I.C.S.: 522110

Bank of China (New Zealand)
Limited **(1)**
Level 17 205 Queen Street, Auckland, New
Zealand
Tel.: (64) 99809000
Web Site: https://www.bankofchina.com
Commercial Banking Services
N.A.I.C.S.: 522110

Bank of China (Peru) S.A. **(1)**
Av Republica de Panama 3461 Torre
Panama piso 29, San Isidro, Lima, Peru
Tel.: (51) 7037700
Banking Services
N.A.I.C.S.: 522110

Bank of China (Thai) Public Company
Limited **(1)**
179/4 Bangkok City Tower South Sathorn
Rd Tungmahamek, Sathorn, Bangkok,
10120, Thailand
Tel.: (66) 22861010
Web Site: http://www.bankofchina.co.th
Banking Services
N.A.I.C.S.: 522110

Bank of China (Zambia) Limited **(1)**
Plot No 2339 Kabelenga Road, PO Box
34550, Lusaka, Zambia
Tel.: (260) 211233271
Banking Services
N.A.I.C.S.: 522110

Bank of China Group Investment
Limited **(1)**
23rd Floor Bank of China Tower 1 Garden
Road, Central, China (Hong Kong)
Tel.: (852) 22007500
Web Site: https://www.bocgi.com
Investment Management Service
N.A.I.C.S.: 523940

Bank of China Investment Management Co., Ltd. **(1)**
26/F Bank of China Tower 200 Mid Yin
Cheng Rd, Pudong, Shanghai, 200120,
China
Tel.: (86) 213883499
Web Site: https://www.bocim.com
Banking Investment Services
N.A.I.C.S.: 523150

Bank of China Limited
(Singapore) **(1)**
4 Battery Rd, Singapore, 049908, Singapore
Tel.: (65) 65352411
Web Site: http://www.bankofchina.com
Sales Range: $200-249.9 Million
Emp.: 500
N.A.I.C.S.: 522299

Bank of China Mexico, S.A. **(1)**
Paseo de la Reforma 243 Piso 24, Colonia
Cuauhtemoc, Mexico, Mexico
Tel.: (52) 5541705800
Banking Services
N.A.I.C.S.: 522110

Bank of China Srbija A.D. **(1)**
Bulevar Zorana Dindica 2a, 11070, Belgrade, Serbia
Tel.: (381) 116351000
Banking Services
N.A.I.C.S.: 522110

Bank of China Turkey A.S. **(1)**
Esentepe Mah Buyukdere Cad No 209 Kat
21, 343944, Istanbul, Turkiye
Tel.: (90) 2122608888
Web Site: http://www.bankofchina.com.tr
Banking Services
N.A.I.C.S.: 522110

Bank of China-New York **(1)**

Bank of China, Ltd.—(Continued)

1045 Avenue of the Americas, New York, NY 10018
Tel.: (212) 935-3101
Web Site: http://www.bocusa.com
Sales Range: $100-124.9 Million
Emp.: 400
International Banking
N.A.I.C.S.: 522299
Shiqianj Wu (Gen Mgr)

Banque De Chine (Djibouti) S.A. (1)
Zone Industrielle Sud Lot Numero 219B, BP 2119, Djibouti, Djibouti
Tel.: (253) 21336666
Banking Services
N.A.I.C.S.: 522110

Kiu Kwong Investment Co. Ltd. (1)
8/F Chiao Shang Building, 92 104 Queen's Road, Central, China (Hong Kong)
Tel.: (852) 25 22 7339
Provider of Investment Services
N.A.I.C.S.: 523940

Tai Fung Bank Limited (1)
Building 418 Alameda Dr Carlos d' Assumpcao, Macau, China (Macau)
Tel.: (853) 28322323
Web Site: http://www.taifungbank.com
Financial Investment Services
N.A.I.C.S.: 523999
Ho Hao Tong (Chm)

BANK OF CHONGQING CO., LTD.
No 6 Yongpingmen Street, Jiangbei District, Chongqing, 400024, China
Tel.: (86) 2363799024
Web Site: https://www.cqcbank.com
1963—(HKG)
Rev.: $3,916,361,459
Assets: $105,212,099,856
Liabilities: $97,001,612,068
Net Worth: $8,210,487,788
Earnings: $723,991,333
Emp.: 5,284
Fiscal Year-end: 12/31/23
Commercial Banking Services
N.A.I.C.S.: 522110
Hailing Ran (Exec Dir)

BANK OF COMMUNICATIONS CO., LTD.
No 188 Yin Cheng Zhong Lu, Pudong New Area, Shanghai, 200120, China
Tel.: (86) 2158766688   CN
Web Site:
https://www.bankcomm.com
Year Founded: 1908
3328—(HKG)
Rev.: $686,811,664
Assets: $48,104,876,341
Liabilities: $42,027,707,237
Net Worth: $6,077,169,104
Earnings: $187,068,594
Emp.: 87,828
Fiscal Year-end: 12/31/20
Banking Services
N.A.I.C.S.: 522110
Wanfu Zhou (Exec VP)

Subsidiaries:

BOCOM International Holdings Co., Ltd. (1)
9 101115/F Man Yee Building 68 Des Voeux Road, Central, China (Hong Kong) (100%)
Tel.: (852) 3 710 3328
Web Site: http://www.bocomgroup.com
Investment Banking & Securities Dealing
N.A.I.C.S.: 523150

BOCOM MSIG Life Insurance Company Limited (1)
Floor 22-23 No 333 Lujiazui Ring Road, Pudong New Area, Shanghai, 200120, China
Tel.: (86) 2122192288
Web Site: https://www.bocommlife.com
Fire Insurance Services
N.A.I.C.S.: 524113

Bank of Communications Trustee Limited (1)
1/F Far East Consortium Building 121 Des Voeux Road, Central, China (Hong Kong) (100%)
Tel.: (852) 2 239 5559
Web Site: https://www.bocomtrust.com.hk
Retirement Scheme Management Services
N.A.I.C.S.: 524292

BoCommlife Insurance Company Limited (1)
Floor 22-23 No 333 Lujiazui Ring Road, Pudong New Area, Shanghai, 200120, China
Tel.: (86) 2122192288
Web Site: https://www.bocommlife.com
Insurance Providing Services
N.A.I.C.S.: 524210

China BOCOM Insurance Co., Ltd. (1)
18/F Fairmont House 8 Cotton Tree Drive, Central, China (Hong Kong) (100%)
Tel.: (852) 2 591 2938
Web Site: https://www.cbic.hk
Insurance Agencies & Brokerages
N.A.I.C.S.: 524210

BANK OF CYPRUS HOLDINGS PUBLIC LIMITED COMPANY
51 Stassinos Street Strovolos, PO Box 21472, 2002, Nicosia, Cyprus
Tel.: (357) 22128000   CY
Web Site:
https://www.bankofcyprus.com
Year Founded: 1899
BOCH—(LSE)
Rev.: $1,178,682,259
Assets: $28,460,623,098
Liabilities: $25,801,084,237
Net Worth: $2,659,538,861
Earnings: $522,583,347
Emp.: 2,830
Fiscal Year-end: 12/31/23
Banking Services
N.A.I.C.S.: 522110
Charis Pouangare (Deputy CEO)

Subsidiaries:

BOC Asset Management Ltd. (1)
134 Limassol Ave 3rd floor Cyfield bldg, Strovolos, 2015, Nicosia, Cyprus
Tel.: (357) 22121790
Web Site:
http://www.am.bankofcyprus.com.cy
Asset Management Services
N.A.I.C.S.: 523940
Michalis Athanasiou (Chm)

Bank of Cyprus (Channel Islands) Ltd (1)
Canada Court, PO Box 558, Upland Road, Saint Peter Port, GY1 6JF, Guernsey
Tel.: (44) 1481716026
Commericial Banking
N.A.I.C.S.: 522110

Bank of Cyprus Romania Ltd (1)
Calea Dorobantilor 187B, Sector 1, Bucharest, Romania
Tel.: (40) 214099100
Web Site: http://www.bankofcyprus.ro
Sales Range: $50-74.9 Million
Emp.: 100
Commericial Banking
N.A.I.C.S.: 522110
Ehrastos Hadjichrascodoulou (Gen Mgr)

Battersee Real Estate SRL (1)
Spl Independentei 52, Bucharest, 50085, Romania
Tel.: (40) 21409919
Real Estate Manangement Services
N.A.I.C.S.: 531390

Blindingqueen Properties SRL (1)
Spl Independentei nr 52, Bucharest, Romania
Tel.: (40) 756085649
Real Estate Property Management Services
N.A.I.C.S.: 531390

Cobhan Properties Ltd (1)
5 Woodend Park, Cobham, KT11 3BX, Surrey, United Kingdom

Tel.: (44) 1932 576444
Property Management Services
N.A.I.C.S.: 531312

Cyprialife Ltd. (1)
17 Acropoleos Avenue, 2006, Strovolos, Cyprus
Tel.: (357) 22111213
Web Site: http://www.cnpcyprialife.com
Insurance Services
N.A.I.C.S.: 524298
Xavier Larnaudie-Eiffel (Chm)

Cyprus Leasing Romania IFN SA (1)
Calea Dorobantilor nr 187, Bucharest, 10565, Romania
Tel.: (40) 214099258
Web Site: http://www.bankofcyprus.ro
Sales Range: $50-74.9 Million
Emp.: 9
Real Estate & Vehicle Leasing Services
N.A.I.C.S.: 531390
Anca Petcu (Gen Mgr)

Drysdale Properties Ltd (1)
3385 Senkler Rd, Belcarra, V3H 4S3, BC, Canada
Tel.: (604) 936-1000
Real Estate Management Services
N.A.I.C.S.: 531390
Matt Keenan (Dir-Agent Dev-Central Valley)

EuroLife Ltd (1)
Evrou 4, PO Box 21655, Strovolos, 2003, Nicosia, Cyprus
Tel.: (357) 22124000
Web Site: https://www.eurolife.com.cy
Emp.: 100
Direct Life Insurance Carriers
N.A.I.C.S.: 524113

General Insurance of Cyprus Ltd (1)
Evrou Strovolos 4, 2003, Nicosia, Cyprus
Tel.: (357) 22128700
Web Site: https://genikesinsurance.com.cy
Insurance Services
N.A.I.C.S.: 524126

JCC Payment Systems Ltd (1)
Stadiou 1, PO Box 21043, 1500, Nicosia, Cyprus
Tel.: (357) 22868000
Web Site: https://www.jcc.com.cy
Credit Card Issuing
N.A.I.C.S.: 522210

Kermia Ltd (1)
51 Stasinos Street Ayia Paraskevi, Strovolos, 2002, Nicosia, Cyprus
Tel.: (357) 22663692
Sales Range: $100-124.9 Million
Emp.: 150
Commericial Banking
N.A.I.C.S.: 522110

Kermia Properties & Investments Ltd (1)
51 Stasinos Street Ayia Paraskevi, Strovolos, 2002, Nicosia, Cyprus
Tel.: (357) 25343658
Web Site: http://www.kermia.com.cy
Sales Range: $50-74.9 Million
Emp.: 2
Real Estate Investment Services
N.A.I.C.S.: 531390
Stavros Stavrinides (Gen Mgr)

Kyprou Finance (NL) B.V. (1)
Teleportboulevard, Amsterdam, 1043 EJ, Netherlands
Tel.: (31) 20 5405800
Financial Management Services
N.A.I.C.S.: 523999

Kyprou Insurance Services Ltd (1)
170 Alexandras Ave, 11521, Athens, Greece
Tel.: (30) 2106418012
Web Site: http://www.bankofcyprus.gr
Sales Range: $50-74.9 Million
Emp.: 25
Insurance Related Activities
N.A.I.C.S.: 524298

Kyprou Mutual Fund Management Company S.A. (1)
170 Alexandras Ave, 11527, Athens, Greece
Tel.: (30) 2106418888
Web Site: http://www.bankofcyprus.gr
Sales Range: $25-49.9 Million
Emp.: 15
Management Consulting Services

N.A.I.C.S.: 541618

Kyprou Securities SA (1)
Fidippidou St 26, 11527, Athens, Greece
Tel.: (30) 2108701000
Web Site: http://www.kyprousecurities.gr
Sales Range: $50-74.9 Million
Emp.: 22
Investment Banking & Securities Dealing
N.A.I.C.S.: 523150

LCP Holdings and Investments Public Ltd. (1)
1 Agiou Prokopiou and Posidonos 1st Floor, 2406, Nicosia, Cyprus
Tel.: (357) 22121700
Web Site: https://www.lcp-holdings.com
Assets: $9,469,425
Liabilities: $6,072,468
Net Worth: $3,396,957
Earnings: ($266,584)
Fiscal Year-end: 12/31/2022
Financial Investment Services
N.A.I.C.S.: 523999

Subsidiary (Domestic):

Laiki Financial Services Ltd (2)
Laiki Capital House 26 Vyronos Street, PO Box 24616, 1096, Nicosia, Cyprus
Tel.: (357) 22 718501
Web Site: http://www.laikifs.com
Asset Management, Investment & Brokerage Services
N.A.I.C.S.: 523940
Michael Xiouros (Gen Mgr)

Ledra Estate Ltd. (1)
6-8 Acheon Road Achaia Court Office No 8e, Nicosia, Cyprus
Tel.: (357) 22776538
Web Site: http://www.ledraestates.com
Real Estate Services
N.A.I.C.S.: 531210

Limestone Properties Ltd (1)
115 Cave Springs Dr, Hunt, TX 78024
Tel.: (830) 238-3232
Web Site: http://www.limestoneproperties.us
Real Estate Manangement Services
N.A.I.C.S.: 531390

Thames Properties Ltd (1)
6 Forge Lane Petersham Road, Richmond, TW10 7BF, Surrey, United Kingdom
Tel.: (44) 2089487982
Real Estate Management Services
N.A.I.C.S.: 531390

The Cyprus Investment and Securities Corporation Ltd (1)
1 Agiou Prokopiou and Posidonos 1 st Floor, Engomi, 2406, Nicosia, Cyprus
Tel.: (357) 22121700
Web Site: https://www.cisco-online.com.cy
Sales Range: $50-74.9 Million
Emp.: 36
Financial Investment Activities
N.A.I.C.S.: 523999

BANK OF ENGLAND
Threadneedle Street, London, EC2R 8AH, United Kingdom
Tel.: (44) 2076014444
Web Site:
http://www.bankofengland.co.uk
Year Founded: 1694
Sales Range: $1-4.9 Billion
Emp.: 1,613
Banking Services
N.A.I.C.S.: 521110
Chris Salmon (Exec Dir-Markets)

BANK OF GANSU CO., LTD.
Gansu Bank Building 525-1 Donggang West Road, Lanzhou, Gansu, China
Tel.: (86) 9318770491   CN
Web Site:
https://www.gsbankchina.com
Year Founded: 2017
2139—(HKG)
Rev.: $1,924,655,793
Assets: $53,803,258,197
Liabilities: $49,209,207,466
Net Worth: $4,594,050,731

Earnings: $89,529,242
Emp.: 4,505
Fiscal Year-end: 12/31/23
Commercial Banking Services
N.A.I.C.S.: 522110
Jinhu Qiu *(VP)*

BANK OF GEORGIA GROUP PLC

29 Farm Street, London, W1J 5RL, United Kingdom
Tel.: (44) 2031784052   UK
Web Site:
https://www.bankofgeorgia.com
Year Founded: 2011
BGEO—(LSE)
Assets: $10,705,263,760
Liabilities: $9,131,500,832
Net Worth: $1,573,762,928
Earnings: $534,579,800
Fiscal Year-end: 12/31/22
Commercial Banking Services
N.A.I.C.S.: 551111
Neil Janin *(Chm)*

Subsidiaries:

JSC Liberty Consumer   **(1)**
27 Pekini Str, Tbilisi, 0160, Georgia
Tel.: (995) 32 444 263
Web Site: http://www.libertyconsumer.ge
Holding Company
N.A.I.C.S.: 551112
Giorgi Vakhtangishvili *(CEO)*

Subsidiary (Domestic):

JSC Prime Fitness   **(2)**
78 Chavchavadze Ave, Tbilisi, Georgia
Tel.: (995) 32 225 626
Web Site: http://www.primefitness.ge
Fitness Center Operator
N.A.I.C.S.: 713940

JSC Teliani Valley   **(1)**
A Tsereteli Ave 118, 0119, Tbilisi, Georgia   **(75%)**
Tel.: (995) 322313249
Web Site: https://www.telianivalley.com
Rev.: $10,981,104
Assets: $41,123,577
Liabilities: $17,024,342
Net Worth: $24,099,235
Earnings: ($130,109)
Fiscal Year-end: 12/31/2016
Wine Producer
N.A.I.C.S.: 312130

Subsidiary (Domestic):

Global Beer Georgia, LLC   **(2)**
A Isaklani Blind Alley, Tbilisi, 0172, Georgia
Tel.: (995) 322313247 48
Web Site: http://icy.ge
Alcohol & non-alcoholic Beverages Mfr & Distr
N.A.I.C.S.: 424820
Zdenek Radil *(CEO)*

Subsidiary (Domestic):

Kazbegi JSC   **(3)**
7 Martskhena Sanapiro Str, 0112, Tbilisi, Georgia
Tel.: (995) 32 294 2388
Web Site: https://www.kazbegi.com
Beer Mfr
N.A.I.C.S.: 312120

Subsidiary (Non-US):

Ltd Park MV   **(2)**
15 25 Jurkalnes St, Riga, 1046, Latvia
Tel.: (371) 67790100
Sales Range: $50-74.9 Million
Emp.: 90
Liquors & Spirits Distr
N.A.I.C.S.: 424820

Teliani Trading Ukraine Ltd.   **(2)**
st Vikentiya Khvoyki 18 14 office 225, 04080, Kiev, Ukraine
Tel.: (380) 445370232
Web Site: https://telianitrading.kiev.ua
Wine Distr
N.A.I.C.S.: 424820

Unifree Duty Free Isletmeciligi A.S.   **(2)**
Caddesi No 1 Arnavutkoy, Gayrettepe, Istanbul, 34394, Turkiye
Tel.: (90) 212 211 6045
Web Site: https://www.unifree.com.tr
Sales Range: $25-49.9 Million
Emp.: 100
Wines & Liquors Distr
N.A.I.C.S.: 445320
Ali Senher *(Gen Mgr)*

Tree of Life Foundation NPO   **(1)**
29a Gagarini str, Tbilisi, 0160, Georgia
Tel.: (995) 322444493
Web Site: http://www.tree.ge
Social Activity Services
N.A.I.C.S.: 624120

BANK OF GHANA

One Thorpe Road, PO Box 2674, Accra, Ghana
Tel.: (233) 3026661746
Web Site: http://www.bog.gov.gh
Year Founded: 1957
Sales Range: $125-149.9 Million
Emp.: 500
Banking Services
N.A.I.C.S.: 522110
Ernest K. Addison *(Chm)*

Subsidiaries:

Ghana Interbank Payment and Settlement Systems Ltd   **(1)**
23 Seventh Avenue Ridge West, Accra, Ghana
Tel.: (233) 302 610800
Web Site: http://www.ghipss.com
Commercial Banking Services
N.A.I.C.S.: 522110

Ghana International Bank plc   **(1)**
67 Cheapside 1st Fl, London, EC2V 6AZ, United Kingdom   **(51%)**
Tel.: (44) 2076530350
Web Site: http://www.ghanabank.co.uk
Sales Range: $50-74.9 Million
Emp.: 46
Banking Services
N.A.I.C.S.: 522110

BANK OF GREECE S.A.

21 El Venizelos Str, GR 102 50, Athens, Greece
Tel.: (30) 2103201111   GR
Web Site:
https://www.bankofgreece.gr
Year Founded: 1927
TELL—(ATH)
Rev.: $3,515,092,470
Assets: $244,409,558,310
Liabilities: $240,584,005,394
Net Worth: $3,825,552,916
Earnings: $106,525,990
Fiscal Year-end: 12/31/23
Banking Services
N.A.I.C.S.: 522110

BANK OF GUIYANG CO., LTD.

Zone B Zhongtian Exhibition City Changling North Road, Building 1-6 East Area Financial Business District Guanshanhu District, Guiyang, 550081, China
Tel.: (86) 4001196033
Web Site: https://www.bankgy.cn
Year Founded: 1997
601997—(SHG)
Rev.: $2,196,272,426
Assets: $90,698,184,767
Liabilities: $82,463,363,377
Net Worth: $8,234,821,390
Earnings: $857,372,537
Emp.: 5,716
Fiscal Year-end: 12/31/22
Commercial Banking Services
N.A.I.C.S.: 522110
Zhenghai Zhang *(Chm)*

BANK OF GUIZHOU CO., LTD.

Building No 9 Yongchang Road, Guanshanhu District, Guiyang, 550081, Guizhou, China
Tel.: (86) 85186987798   CN
Web Site: http://www.bgzchina.com
Year Founded: 2012
6199—(HKG)
Rev.: $3,110,747,120
Assets: $73,906,365,059
Liabilities: $67,818,288,796
Net Worth: $6,088,076,263
Earnings: $530,219,179
Emp.: 5,418
Fiscal Year-end: 12/31/22
Commercial Banking Services
N.A.I.C.S.: 522110
Zhiming Li *(Chm)*

BANK OF GUYANA

1 Church Street & Avenue of the Republic, PO Box 1003, Georgetown, Guyana
Tel.: (592) 2263250
Web Site:
http://www.bankofguyana.org.gy
Sales Range: $10-24.9 Million
Emp.: 260
Banking Services
N.A.I.C.S.: 521110
G. N. Ganga *(Chm)*

BANK OF HANGZHOU CO., LTD.

46 hangzhou qingchun road, Hangzhou, 310003, Zhejiang, China
Tel.: (86) 57185151339   CN
Web Site: https://www.hccb.com.cn
Year Founded: 1996
600926—(SHG)
Rev.: $4,623,583,442
Assets: $226,961,942,360
Liabilities: $213,122,261,570
Net Worth: $13,839,680,790
Earnings: $1,639,777,932
Fiscal Year-end: 12/31/22
Banking Services
N.A.I.C.S.: 523150

BANK OF INDIA

Star House C-5 G Block Bandra Kurla Complex Bandra East, Mumbai, 400 051, India
Tel.: (91) 2266684444   In
Web Site: https://bankofindia.co.in
Year Founded: 1906
BANKINDIA—(NSE)
Rev.: $6,611,457,011
Assets: $99,039,116,336
Liabilities: $91,774,629,195
Net Worth: $7,264,487,141
Earnings: $460,159,607
Emp.: 49,767
Fiscal Year-end: 03/31/23
Banking Services
N.A.I.C.S.: 522110
Kollegal Venkatasheshan Raghavendra *(Gen Mgr)*

Subsidiaries:

BOI Merchant Bankers Ltd.   **(1)**
Star House-II First Floor Plot No C-4, G-Block Bandra-Kurla Complex, Bandra E, Mumbai, 400 051, India
Tel.: (91) 2261312906
Web Site: http://www.boimb.com
Investment Banking Services
N.A.I.C.S.: 523150
P. R. Rajagopal *(Chm)*

BOI Shareholding Limited   **(1)**
70/80 Bank of India bulding 4th floor M G Road Fort, Versova Andheri W, Mumbai, 400 001, MH, India
Tel.: (91) 2256684444
Web Site: https://www.boislindia.com
Investment Advice
N.A.I.C.S.: 523940

Bank of India (New Zealand) Ltd.   **(1)**

10 Manukau Road, PO Box No 99491, Epsom, Auckland, 1023, New Zealand
Tel.: (64) 99265710
Web Site: https://www.bankofindia.co.nz
Banking Services
N.A.I.C.S.: 522110
Onkar Nath Thakur *(Mng Dir)*

Bank of India (Tanzania) Ltd.   **(1)**
Maktaba Street, PO Box 7581, Dar es Salaam, Tanzania
Tel.: (255) 222135362
Web Site: https://www.boitanzania.co.tz
Banking Services
N.A.I.C.S.: 522110
C. G. Chaitanya *(Chm)*

Bank of India (Uganda) Ltd.   **(1)**
Picfare House Plot No 37 Next to NWSC Head Offices Jinja Road, Kampala, Uganda
Tel.: (256) 200901484
Web Site: https://www.boiuganda.co.ug
Banking Services
N.A.I.C.S.: 522110
Wenceslaus Rama Makuza *(Chm)*

Indo Zambia Bank Ltd.   **(1)**
Plot No 6907 Cairo Road, PO Box 35411, Lusaka, Zambia   **(20%)**
Tel.: (260) 211225080
Web Site: http://www.izb.co.zm
Banking Services
N.A.I.C.S.: 522110
Michael Gondwe *(Chm)*

PT Bank Swadesi Tbk   **(1)**
Jalan KH Samanhudi 37, Jakarta, 10710, Indonesia   **(76%)**
Tel.: (62) 213500007
Web Site: http://www.bankswadesi.co.id
Sales Range: $200-249.9 Million
Emp.: 370
Banking Services
N.A.I.C.S.: 522110

PT Bank of India Indonesia, Tbk.   **(1)**
JI K H Samanhudi No 37, Jakarta, 10710, Indonesia
Tel.: (62) 213500007
Web Site: https://boiindonesia.co.id
Rev.: $23,055,320
Assets: $397,988,820
Liabilities: $178,592,861
Net Worth: $219,395,959
Earnings: $3,171,111
Emp.: 230
Fiscal Year-end: 12/31/2023
Commercial Banking Services
N.A.I.C.S.: 522110
Sindbad R. Hardjodipuro *(Chm)*

BANK OF INNOVATION, INC.

Shinjuku East Side Square 3F 6-27-30 Shinjuku, Shinjuku-Ku, Tokyo, 160-0022, Japan
Tel.: (81) 344001817
Web Site: https://www.boi.jp
Year Founded: 2006
4393—(TKS)
Rev.: $151,250,970
Assets: $57,379,370
Liabilities: $31,302,350
Net Worth: $26,077,020
Earnings: $23,347,370
Fiscal Year-end: 09/30/23
Software Development Services
N.A.I.C.S.: 541511
Tomohiro Higuchi *(Founder, Pres & CEO)*

BANK OF IRELAND GROUP PLC

Baggot Plaza 27-33 Upper Baggot St, Dublin, D04 VX58, Ireland
Tel.: (353) 16615933   IE
Web Site:
https://www.bankofireland.com
Year Founded: 2017
BIRG—(ISE)
Rev.: $6,830,347,507
Assets: $168,042,305,202
Liabilities: $154,486,293,978
Net Worth: $13,556,011,224
Earnings: $1,727,822,145
Emp.: 10,845

Bank of Ireland Group plc—(Continued)

Fiscal Year-end: 12/31/23
Commercial Banking Services
N.A.I.C.S.: 551111
Patrick Kennedy (Chm)

Subsidiaries:

First Rate Exchange Services
Limited   (1)
Great West House Great West Road, Brentford, TW8 9DF, Middlesex, United Kingdom
Tel.: (44) 3458503050
Web Site: https://www.firstrate.co.uk
Foreign Currency Exchange Services
N.A.I.C.S.: 523160

The Governor and Company of the
Bank of Ireland   (1)
40 Mespil Road, Dublin, 4, Ireland
Tel.: (353) 1 661 5933
Web Site: http://www.bankofireland.com
Rev.: $3,060,526,140
Assets: $131,716,016,460
Liabilities: $121,658,320,980
Net Worth: $10,057,695,480
Earnings: $848,303,820
Emp.: 11,208
Fiscal Year-end: 12/31/2016
International & Retail Banking Services
N.A.I.C.S.: 522110
Archie G. Kane (Governor)

Subsidiary (Non-US):

Avondale Securities S.A.   (2)
Val Sainte Croix 7, Luxembourg, 1371, Luxembourg
Tel.: (352) 2020 4100
Securities Brokerage Services
N.A.I.C.S.: 523150

Unit (Domestic):

Bank of Ireland Corporate
Banking   (2)
50 - 55 Lr Baggot Street, Dublin, D02 Y754, Ireland   (100%)
Tel.: (353) 1 661 5255
Web Site: http://www.boi.ie
Sales Range: $200-249.9 Million
Emp.: 350
Corporate Banking
N.A.I.C.S.: 522110
Peter Mullen (Head-Leveraged Acq Fin)

Unit (Non-US):

Bank of Ireland Corporate Banking -
Belfast   (3)
1 Donegall Square, Belfast, BT1 5LR, United Kingdom
Tel.: (44) 289 043 3000
Web Site:
   http://corporatebanking.bankofireland.com
Sales Range: $75-99.9 Million
Emp.: 180
Corporate Banking Services
N.A.I.C.S.: 522110

Bank of Ireland Corporate Banking -
Frankfurt   (3)
Taunusanlage 17, 60325, Frankfurt am Main, Frankfurt, Germany
Tel.: (49) 69716733910
Emp.: 7
Commercial Banking Services
N.A.I.C.S.: 522110
Thomas Grau (Head-Acq Fin)

Bank of Ireland Corporate Banking -
London   (3)
Bow Bells House 1 Bread Street, London, EC4M 9BE, United Kingdom
Tel.: (44) 20 7236 2000
Commercial Banking Services
N.A.I.C.S.: 522110

Subsidiary (Domestic):

Bank of Ireland International Finance
Ltd.   (2)
La Touche House International Financial Services Center, Custom House Docks, Dublin, 1, Ireland   (100%)
Tel.: (353) 16701400
Web Site: http://www.boi.ie

Sales Range: $50-74.9 Million
Emp.: 80
International Asset Financing
N.A.I.C.S.: 522110

Bank of Ireland Mortgage Bank
PLC   (2)
New Century House Mayor Street Lower IFSC, Dublin, Ireland
Tel.; (353) 1 611 3333
Web Site: http://www.bim-online.co.uk
Mortgage Loan Services
N.A.I.C.S.: 522310

Bank of Ireland Private Banking
Limited   (2)
40 Mespil Road, Dublin, 4, Ireland
Tel.: (353) 1 637 8600
Web Site: https://www.privatebanking.com
Sales Range: $50-74.9 Million
Emp.: 75
Banking Services
N.A.I.C.S.: 522110
Gabriel Bannigan (Mng Dir)

Subsidiary (Domestic):

Bank of Ireland   (3)
40 Mespil Road, Dublin, 4, Ireland   (100%)
Tel.: (353) 1 637 8600
Web Site:
   http://www.privatebanking.ireland.com
Sales Range: $25-49.9 Million
Emp.: 50
Trust Services
N.A.I.C.S.: 523991
Sean O. Murchu (Mng Dir)

Division (Domestic):

Bank of Ireland Retail (Ireland & UK)
Division   (2)
40 Mespil Rd, Dublin, 4, Ireland
Tel.: (353) 16615933
Web Site: http://www.boi.ie
Sales Range: $700-749.9 Million
Emp.: 1,500
Retail Banking
N.A.I.C.S.: 523150
Richard P. Boucher (Mng Dir)

Subsidiary (Non-US):

Bank of Ireland (I.O.M.) Limited   (3)
4 Christian Rd, PO Box 246, Douglas, IM99 1XF, Isle of Man   (100%)
Tel.: (44) 1624644200
Web Site:
   http://boioffshore.bankofireland.com
Sales Range: $25-49.9 Million
Emp.: 35
Banking Services
N.A.I.C.S.: 522110

Bank of Ireland (UK) plc   (3)
Bow Bells House 1 Bread Street, London, EC4M 9BE, United Kingdom   (100%)
Tel.: (44) 2072362000
Web Site: http://www.bankofirelanduk.com
Rev.: $925,989,600
Assets: $35,326,634,400
Liabilities: $32,729,666,400
Net Worth: $2,596,968,000
Earnings: $127,225,200
Emp.: 277
Fiscal Year-end: 12/31/2019
Retail & Commercial Banking Services
N.A.I.C.S.: 522110
Thomas McAreavey (CFO)

Unit (Domestic):

Bank of Ireland Business Banking UK
- Belfast   (4)
1 Donegal Square South, Belfast, BT1 5LR, United Kingdom
Tel.: (44) 28 9043 3000
Commercial Banking Services
N.A.I.C.S.: 522110
David McGowan (Mng Dir)

Bank of Ireland Business Banking UK
- London   (4)
Bow Bells House 1 Bread Street, London, EC4M 9BE, United Kingdom
Tel.: (44) 20 7236 2000
Web Site: http://www.bank-of-ireland.co.uk
Sales Range: $50-74.9 Million
Emp.: 100
Business Banking Services

N.A.I.C.S.: 522110

Bank of Ireland Consumer Banking
UK   (4)
One Temple Quay, PO Box 27, Bristol, BS99 7AX, United Kingdom
Tel.: (44) 117 979 2222
Mortgage Loan Brokerage Services
N.A.I.C.S.: 522310
Brendan Nevin (Mng Dir)

Subsidiary (Domestic):

Bank of Ireland Home Mortgages
Limited   (3)
1 Temple Quay, PO Box 3191, Bristol, BS1 9HY, United Kingdom   (100%)
Tel.: (44) 117 979 2222
Web Site:
   http://www.bankofirelandmortgages.co.uk
Sales Range: $75-99.9 Million
Emp.: 240
Mortgage Financing
N.A.I.C.S.: 522299
Mike Joyce (Mng Dir)

Unit (Domestic):

Bank of Ireland UK Financial
Services   (4)
One Temple Quay, PO Box 27, Bristol, BS99 7AX, United Kingdom
Tel.: (44) 11 7909 0900
Sales Range: $350-399.9 Million
Emp.: 800
Commercial Banking Services
N.A.I.C.S.: 522110
Des Crowley (CEO)

Post Office Financial & Travel
Services   (4)
Eastcheap Court 11 Philpot Lane, London, EC3M 8BA, United Kingdom
Tel.: (44) 845 641 8931
Sales Range: $75-99.9 Million
Emp.: 250
Financial Management Services
N.A.I.C.S.: 523999
Patrick Waldron (CEO)

Unit (Domestic):

Bank of Ireland - Business On
Line   (3)
1st Floor The Operation Center, Dublin, 18, Ireland
Tel.: (353) 12361265
Sales Range: $50-74.9 Million
Emp.; 100
Online Commercial Banking Services
N.A.I.C.S.: 522110

Bank of Ireland 365   (3)
Tallaght Square, Dublin, 24, Ireland   (100%)
Tel.: (353) 1 460 6400
Web Site: http://www.365online.com
Credit Card & Banking Services
N.A.I.C.S.: 522320

Subsidiary (Domestic):

Bank of Ireland Commercial Finance
Ltd.   (3)
40 Mestil Rd, Dublin, 4, Ireland   (100%)
Tel.: (353) 16140300
Web Site: http://www.bif.ie
Sales Range: $50-74.9 Million
Emp.: 100
Current Asset Financing
N.A.I.C.S.: 523940
Ricky Boucher (CEO)

Unit (Domestic):

Bank of Ireland Consumer
Lending   (3)
New Century House IFSC Mayor Street Lower, Dublin, 1, Ireland
Tel.: (353) 1 611 3333
Web Site: http://www.bankofireland.com
Sales Range: $150-199.9 Million
Emp.: 500
Consumer Lending Services
N.A.I.C.S.: 522291

Bank of Ireland Credit Card
Services   (3)
33-35 Nassau St, Dublin, 2, Ireland   (100%)

Tel.: (353) 567757747
Sales Range: $75-99.9 Million
Emp.: 150
Credit Card Services
N.A.I.C.S.: 522299

Subsidiary (Domestic):

Bank of Ireland Finance Ltd.   (3)
40 Mespil Road, Ballsbridge, Dublin, 4, Ireland   (100%)
Tel.: (353) 76 623 4900
Web Site: https://bankofireland.com
Installment Credit & Leasing
N.A.I.C.S.: 522110
Pat Creed (Mng Dir)

Bank of Ireland Insurance & Investments Ltd.   (3)
33-35 Nassau Street, Dublin, 2, Ireland
Tel.: (353) 1 703 9500
Web Site: https://www.bankofireland.com
Insurance & Investment Services
N.A.I.C.S.: 524210
Shawn Casey (Mng Dir)

Subsidiary (Domestic):

Bank of Ireland Insurance Services
Ltd   (4)
Arena Bldg White Town Way Tallaght, Dublin, 24, Ireland   (100%)
Tel.: (353) 17039800
Web Site: http://www.boi.ie
Sales Range: $50-74.9 Million
Emp.: 60
N.A.I.C.S.: 522110
Eamon Slevin (Mng Dir)

Subsidiary (Domestic):

First Rate Enterprises Limited   (3)
3-4 South Frederick Street, Dublin, 2, Ireland   (100%)
Tel.: (353) 1 863 8500
Sales Range: $25-49.9 Million
Emp.: 30
Retail Foreign Exchange Services
N.A.I.C.S.: 523160

Subsidiary (Non-US):

NIIB Group Limited   (3)
1 Donegall Square South, Belfast, BT1 5LR, United Kingdom   (100%)
Tel.: (44) 289 043 3000
Web Site: https://www.bankofireland.com
Installment Credit & Leasing
N.A.I.C.S.: 522110
James McGee (Mng Dir)

Subsidiary (Domestic):

Marshall Leasing Limited   (4)
Bridge House Orchard Lane, Huntingdon, PE29 3QT, United Kingdom   (99%)
Tel.: (44) 1480414541
Web Site: http://www.marshall-leasing.co.uk
Motor Vehicle Leasing Services
N.A.I.C.S.: 532112
Greg McDowell (Mng Dir)

Subsidiary (Domestic):

New Ireland Assurance Company
plc   (3)
5-9 South Frederick Street, Dublin, D02 DF29, Ireland
Tel.: (353) 1 617 2000
Web Site: https://www.newireland.ie
Emp.: 700
Life Insurance Products & Services
N.A.I.C.S.: 524113
Sean Casey (Mng Dir)

Unit (Domestic):

Bank of Ireland Life   (4)
Baggot Plaza 27-33 Upper Baggot St, Dublin, D04 VX58, Ireland
Tel.: (353) 189 030 9309
Web Site: https://www.bankofireland.com
Sales Range: $150-199.9 Million
Emp.: 300
Life Insurance Policies & Pension Administration Services
N.A.I.C.S.: 524292

Subsidiary (Domestic):

Bank of Ireland Treasury & International Banking Limited   (2)

2 Burlington Plaza Burlington Road, Dublin,
4, Ireland
Tel.: (353) 76 624 4100
Sales Range: $200-249.9 Million
Emp.: 500
International Banking
N.A.I.C.S.: 522299

Unit (Non-US):

Bank of Ireland Global Markets -
London　　　　　　　　　　　　(3)
Bow Bells House 1 Bread Street, London,
EC4M 9BE, United Kingdom
Tel.: (44) 203 201 6000
Financial Management Services
N.A.I.C.S.: 523999

Unit (US):

Bank of Ireland Global Markets -
Stamford　　　　　　　　　　　(3)
300 1st Stamford Pl, Stamford, CT 06902
Tel.: (203) 391-5555
Web Site:
　http://corporatebanking.bankofireland.com
Commercial Banking Services
N.A.I.C.S.: 522110
Darsh Mariyappa *(Head-Global Markets)*

Subsidiary (Domestic):

Bank of Ireland Trasury Limited　(3)
2 Burlington Plaza Burlington Road, Dublin,
4, Ireland　　　　　　　　　　(100%)
Tel.: (353) 766 244 100
Web Site:
　http://corporatebanking.bankofireland.com
Sales Range: $150-199.9 Million
Emp.: 500
International Finance Services
N.A.I.C.S.: 522299

Subsidiary (Domestic):

Life Assurance Bank of Ireland Life
Holdings Plc　　　　　　　　　(2)
50-55 Lower Baggot Street, Dublin, Ireland
Tel.: (353) 1 703 9500
Web Site: http://www.bankofireland.com
Insurance Management Services
N.A.I.C.S.: 524298
Mick Sweeney *(Interim CEO)*

Subsidiary (Non-US):

Northridge Finance Ltd.　　　　(2)
5th Floor Bank of Ireland 1 Donegal Square
South, Belfast, BT1 5LR, United Kingdom
Tel.: (44) 844 8921846
Web Site: http://www.northridgefinance.com
Financial Management Services
N.A.I.C.S.: 523999

Subsidiary (Domestic):

Partholon CDO 1 plc　　　　　(2)
5 Harbourmaster Place International Finan-
cial Services Centre, Dublin, Ireland
Tel.: (353) 16806016
Commercial Banking Services
N.A.I.C.S.: 522110

BANK OF JAMAICA
Nethersole Place, PO Box 621,
Kingston, Jamaica
Tel.: (876) 9220750
Web Site: http://www.boj.org.jm
Sales Range: $350-399.9 Million
Emp.: 490
Banking Services
N.A.I.C.S.: 521110
Livingstone Morrison *(Investment &
Risk Mgmt)*

BANK OF JAPAN
2-1-1 Nihonbashi-Hongokucho, Chuo-
ku, Tokyo, 103-0021, Japan
Tel.: (81) 3 3279 1111
Web Site: http://www.boj.or.jp
Year Founded: 1882
Rev.: $16,324,382,355
Net Worth: $35,070,073,384
Earnings: $6,791,422,052
Emp.: 4,653
Fiscal Year-end: 03/31/18
Banking Services

N.A.I.C.S.: 522110
Shigehiro Kuwabara *(Exec Dir)*

BANK OF JERUSALEM, LTD.
Tel.: (972) 768096000
Web Site:
　https://www.bankjerusalem.co.il
Year Founded: 1963
Commercial Banking Services
N.A.I.C.S.: 522110
Gil Topaz *(CEO)*

BANK OF JIANGSU COMPANY LIMITED
No 26 China Road, Nanjing, 210001,
Jiangsu, China
Tel.: (86) 95319　　　　　　　CN
Web Site: https://www.jsbchina.cn
Year Founded: 2006
600919—(SHG)
Rev.: $9,908,087,249
Assets: $418,433,374,757
Liabilities: $388,186,814,761
Net Worth: $30,246,559,996
Earnings: $3,564,193,417
Emp.: 15,000
Fiscal Year-end: 12/31/22
Commercial Banking Services
N.A.I.C.S.: 522110
Ping Xia *(Chm)*

BANK OF JINZHOU CO., LTD.
No 68 Keji Road, Jinzhou, 121013,
Liaoning, China
Tel.: (86) 4163220109　　　　CN
Web Site:
　https://www.jinzhoubank.com
0416—(HKG)
Rev.: $5,517,337,831
Assets: $119,292,545,081
Liabilities: $109,322,700,505
Net Worth: $9,969,844,576
Earnings: $14,368,396
Emp.: 4,997
Fiscal Year-end: 12/31/21
Commercial Banking Services
N.A.I.C.S.: 522110
Wei Xuekun *(Chm)*

BANK OF JIUJIANG CO., LTD.
No 619 Changhong Avenue, Lianxi
District, Jiujiang, 332000, Jiangxi,
China
Tel.: (86) 7927783000　　　　CN
Web Site: https://www.jjccb.com
Year Founded: 2000
6190—(HKG)
Rev.: $2,800,654,693
Assets: $67,350,377,016
Liabilities: $62,237,531,164
Net Worth: $5,112,845,852
Earnings: $235,923,386
Emp.: 4,967
Fiscal Year-end: 12/31/22
Commercial Banking Services
N.A.I.C.S.: 522110
Xianting Liu *(Chm)*

BANK OF JORDAN PLC
Al-Shmeisani-Abdul Hameed Sharaf
St Building No 15, PO Box 2140, Am-
man, 11181, Jordan
Tel.: (962) 65609200
Web Site:
　https://www.bankofjordan.com
BOJX—(AMM)
Rev.: $216,477,942
Assets: $3,825,697,184
Liabilities: $3,173,499,787
Net Worth: $652,197,397
Earnings: $50,024,163
Emp.: 1,497
Fiscal Year-end: 12/31/20
Banking Services
N.A.I.C.S.: 522110
Shaker Tawfiq Fakhouri *(Chm)*

Subsidiaries:

Bank of Jordan Syria　　　　　(1)
Bagdad Street Sabaa Bahrat Square, PO
Box 8058, Damascus, Syria
Tel.: (963) 1122900000
Web Site: http://www.bankofjordan.com
Rev.: $261,131,567
Assets: $4,280,231,615
Liabilities: $3,522,465,437
Net Worth: $757,766,178
Earnings: $62,648,234
Emp.: 1,823
Fiscal Year-end: 12/31/2023
Commercial Banking Services
N.A.I.C.S.: 522110
Jawad F. Al Halbouni *(Gen Mgr)*

Excel for Financial Investment Com-
pany Ltd.　　　　　　　　　　(1)
Amman - Mecca St - Al- Husseini Complex
- Bldg No 164 - First Floor, PO Box 942453,
Amman, 11194, Jordan
Tel.: (962) 65519309
Web Site: https://excelinvest.jo
Emp.: 6
Brokerage & Financial Services
N.A.I.C.S.: 523150

BANK OF KAOHSIUNG CO., LTD.
168 Po Ai 2nd Road, Tsoying District,
Kaohsiung, 813, Taiwan
Tel.: (886) 75570535
Web Site: https://www.bok.com.tw
Year Founded: 1982
2836—(TAI)
Rev.: $221,338,165
Assets: $10,036,142,497
Liabilities: $9,429,515,063
Net Worth: $606,627,434
Earnings: $28,294,351
Emp.: 1,098
Fiscal Year-end: 12/31/23
Financial Banking Services
N.A.I.C.S.: 522320

BANK OF KATHMANDU LIMITED
Kamalpokhari, Kathmandu, Nepal
Tel.: (977) 14414541
Web Site: http://www.bok.com.np
BOKL—(NEP)
Rev.: $84,933,366
Assets: $873,955,370
Liabilities: $753,009,611
Net Worth: $120,945,759
Earnings: $16,427,639
Emp.: 776
Fiscal Year-end: 07/16/19
Banking Services
N.A.I.C.S.: 522110
Manish Kumar Singh *(Head-CASA,
Retail Lending & DCU)*

Subsidiaries:

Bank of Kathmandu Lumbini Ltd.　(1)
Kamal Pokhari, Kathmandu, Nepal
Tel.: (977) 4414541
Web Site: http://www.bok.com.np
Banking Services
N.A.I.C.S.: 522110

BANK OF KHARTOUM
PO Box 1008, Khartoum, Sudan
Tel.: (249) 156661000
Web Site:
　http://www.bankofkhartoum.com
Year Founded: 1913
KHBA—(KHAR)
Rev.: $98,027,962
Assets: $4,621,988,791
Liabilities: $1,447,500,743
Net Worth: $3,174,488,048
Earnings: $21,355,424
Fiscal Year-end: 12/31/20
Banking Services
N.A.I.C.S.: 522110
Mohamed Saeed Ahmed Abdulla
Alsharif *(Chm)*

Subsidiaries:

Al Fahed Valuable Assets In Transit
United Co. Ltd.　　　　　　　(1)
Al-Jamaa Street Building 2/4, Khartoum,
Sudan
Tel.: (249) 156661751
Transportation Services
N.A.I.C.S.: 485999

Canar Telecommunications Co.
Ltd.　　　　　　　　　　　　(1)
Canar Tower Al-Mashtal Street Riyadh Area
Block No 15, Khartoum, Sudan
Tel.: (249) 151515151
Web Site: http://www.canar.sd
Telecommunication Servicesb
N.A.I.C.S.: 517810
Mohamed Siddig Nasir Osman *(CTO)*

National Trading & Services Co.
Ltd.　　　　　　　　　　　　(1)
Al-Amarat- Street 59, PO Box 12348, Khar-
toum, Sudan
Tel.: (249) 156666501
Trading Services
N.A.I.C.S.: 523160
Mohammed Gindeel *(Mgr-Comml)*

Sanabel Security Co.　　　　　(1)
AL Waha Towers 3rd Floor suit 302, Khar-
toum, Sudan
Tel.: (249) 156667091
Web Site: http://www.sanabelfs.com
Financial Services
N.A.I.C.S.: 523210
Dima Awad A. Hameed *(Gen Mgr)*

BANK OF LANZHOU CO., LTD.
No 211 Jiuquan Road, Chengguan,
Lanzhou, 730030, Gansu, China
Tel.: (86) 4008896799
Web Site: https://www.lzbank.com
Year Founded: 1997
001227—(SSE)
Rev.: $1,109,857,236
Assets: $62,778,370,251
Liabilities: $58,170,261,797
Net Worth: $4,608,108,454
Earnings: $258,063,594
Fiscal Year-end: 12/31/23
Commercial Banking Services
N.A.I.C.S.: 522110
Jianping Xu *(Chm)*

BANK OF MALDIVES PLC
11 Boduthakurufaanu Magu, Male,
20094, Maldives
Tel.: (960) 332 2948
Web Site:
　http://www.bankofmaldives.com.mv
Year Founded: 1982
Sales Range: $10-24.9 Million
Emp.: 190
Banking Services
N.A.I.C.S.: 522110
Fathimath Manike *(Dir-Islamic Bank-
ing)*

BANK OF MAURITIUS
Sir William Newton Street, Port Louis,
Mauritius
Tel.: (230) 2023800
Web Site: http://www.bom.mu
Year Founded: 1967
Rev.: $650,414,041
Assets: $8,680,614,891
Liabilities: $8,371,830,542
Net Worth: $308,784,349
Earnings: $551,939,147
Emp.: 395
Fiscal Year-end: 06/30/21
Banking Services
N.A.I.C.S.: 521110
Hemlata Sadhna Sewraj-Gopal
(Deputy Governor)

BANK OF MONTREAL
100 King Street West 1 First Canadian Place 21st Floor, Toronto, M5X
1A1, ON, Canada

Bank of Montreal—(Continued)

Tel.: (416) 867-6785   Ca
Web Site: https://www.bmo.com
Year Founded: 1817
BMO—(NYSE)
Rev.: $73,030,029,600
Assets: $1,042,180,220,040
Liabilities: $979,865,894,520
Net Worth: $62,314,325,520
Earnings: $5,416,997,640
Emp.: 56,000
Fiscal Year-end: 10/31/24
Commercial Banking & Investment
Services
N.A.I.C.S.: 522110
Cameron Fowler (Chief Ops & Strategy Officer)

Subsidiaries:

BMO Capital Markets (1)
1 First Canadian Place 100 King Street
West, Toronto, M5X 2A1, ON, Canada
Tel.: (416) 359-4000
Web Site: http://www.bmocm.com
Risk Management & Investment Banking
Services
N.A.I.C.S.: 523150
Peter Myers (Head-Investment & Corp.
Banking-Global)

Subsidiary (US):

BMO Capital Markets Corp. (2)
3 Times Sq, New York, NY 10036-6564
Tel.: (212) 702-1900
Web Site: http://www.bmocm.com
Investment Banking & Financial Advisory
Services
N.A.I.C.S.: 523150
Deland Kamanga (Head-Global Markets)

Subsidiary (Domestic):

**BMO Capital Markets Equity Group
(U.S.), Inc.** (3)
115 S La Salle St 1200, Chicago, IL 60603-3801
Tel.: (312) 845-4019
Commercial Banking Services
N.A.I.C.S.: 522110

Subsidiary (Domestic):

BMO Nesbitt Burns Inc. (2)
1 First Canadian Place 100 King Street
West, Toronto, M5X 1A1, ON,
Canada   **(100%)**
Tel.: (416) 359-4000
Web Site: http://www.bmo.com
Sales Range: $600-649.9 Million
Emp.: 2,500
Investment Advisory Services
N.A.I.C.S.: 523940

Affiliate (Domestic):

**BMO Global Water Solutions TACTIC
Fund** (3)
1 First Canadian Place 100 King Street
West 3rd Floor Podium, Toronto, M5X 1H3,
ON, Canada
Tel.: (416) 359-4597
Rev.: $7,215,190
Assets: $25,199,967
Liabilities: $3,919,425
Net Worth: $21,280,542
Earnings: $6,596,823
Fiscal Year-end: 12/31/2017
Closed-End Investment Fund
N.A.I.C.S.: 525990

**DoubleLine Income Solutions
Trust** (3)
1 First Canadian Place 100 King Street
West 3rd Floor Podium, Toronto, M5X 1H3,
ON, Canada
Tel.: (416) 359-4597
Rev.: $4,549,901
Assets: $37,047,933
Liabilities: $8,741,866
Net Worth: $28,306,066
Earnings: $3,639,121
Fiscal Year-end: 12/31/2017
Closed-End Investment Fund
N.A.I.C.S.: 525990
Youse E. Guia (Chief Compliance Officer)

Subsidiaries:

Subsidiary (Domestic):

**BMO Private Equity (Canada)
Inc.** (2)
1 First Canadian Place 100 King Street
West 50th Floor, Toronto, M5X 1H3, ON,
Canada
Tel.: (416) 359-4000
Web Site: http://www.bmocm.com
Privator Equity Firm
N.A.I.C.S.: 523999

BMO Capital Trust (1)
100 King St W First Canadian Pl, Toronto,
M5X 1A1, ON, Canada
Tel.: (416) 867-5000
Rev.: $4,833,749
Nondeposit Trust Facilities
N.A.I.C.S.: 523991

**BMO Finance Company I, S.A
R.L.** (1)
9 Rue Gabriel Lippmann, 5365, Munsbach,
Luxembourg
Tel.: (352) 27 69 35
Commercial Banking Services
N.A.I.C.S.: 522110

BMO Financial Corp. (1)
111 W Monroe St, Chicago, IL 60603-4096
Tel.: (312) 461-2121
Web Site: http://www.bmo.com
Sales Range: $1-4.9 Billion
Emp.: 6,638
Bank Holding Company
N.A.I.C.S.: 551111
Darrel Hackett (Pres-Wealth Mgmt US)

Subsidiary (Domestic):

BMO Asset Management Corp. (2)
190 S LaSalle St 4th Fl, Chicago, IL 60603
Tel.: (312) 461-7699
Mutual Fund Management Services
N.A.I.C.S.: 523940
David Walker (Dir-Investment-F&C Private
Equity Funds)

Subsidiary (Non-US):

**BMO Global Asset Management
(EMEA)** (2)
8th Floor Exchange House Primrose Street,
London, EC2A2NY, United Kingdom
Tel.: (44) 2076288000
Web Site: http://www.bmo.com
Investment Management Service
N.A.I.C.S.: 523999
James Edwards (Dir-Institutional SIs)

Subsidiary (Domestic):

BMO Harris Bank N.A. (2)
111 W Monroe St, Chicago, IL 60603-4096
Tel.: (312) 461-2121
Web Site: http://www.bmoharris.com
Sales Range: $650-699.9 Million
Emp.: 6,850
Commercial Banking Services
N.A.I.C.S.: 522110
Darrel Hackett (Executives, Bd of Dirs)

Subsidiary (Domestic):

**BMO Harris Equipment Finance
Company** (3)
250 E Wisconsin Ave Ste 1400, Milwaukee,
WI 53202-4219   **(100%)**
Tel.: (414) 272-2374
Web Site: http://www4.harrisbank.com
Sales Range: $10-24.9 Million
Emp.: 60
Lease Financing of Business Equipment &
Machinery to Commercial, Industrial & Institutional Customers
N.A.I.C.S.: 532490
Jud Snyder (Pres)

**BMO Harris Financial Advisors,
Inc.** (3)
111 W Monroe St, Chicago, IL 60603
Tel.: (312) 461-2121
Web Site: http://www4.harrisbank.com
Investment Advice & Securities Brokerage
Services
N.A.I.C.S.: 523940
Darrel Hackett (Pres)

BMO Harris Financing, Inc. (3)
111 W Monroe St, Chicago, IL 60603

Tel.: (312) 461-2121
Web Site: http://www.bmoharris.com
Sales Range: $600-649.9 Million
Emp.: 2,000
Commercial Banking Services
N.A.I.C.S.: 522110

Harris RIA Holdings, Inc. (3)
111 W Monroe St Ste 1200, Chicago, IL
60603-4014
Tel.: (312) 461-2121
Investment Management Service
N.A.I.C.S.: 523999

Harris myCFO, Inc. (3)
1080 Mars Rd Ste 100, Menlo Park, CA
94025
Tel.: (312) 461-3754
Sales Range: $50-74.9 Million
Emp.: 100
Financial Management Services
N.A.I.C.S.: 523940

Subsidiary (Domestic):

CTC Consulting LLC (4)
4380 SW Macadam Ave Ste 400, Portland,
OR 97239
Tel.: (503) 228-4300
Web Site: http://www.ctcconsultinginc.com
Rev.: $23,000,000,000
Emp.: 60
Financial Investment Consulting Services
N.A.I.C.S.: 523940
Garbis P. Mechigian (Mng Dir)

Subsidiary (Domestic):

M&I Servicing Corp. (2)
3993 Howard Hughes Pkwy Ste 100, Las
Vegas, NV 89109-0961
Tel.: (702) 735-1832
Sales Range: $10-24.9 Million
Emp.: 2
Management Investment Services
N.A.I.C.S.: 525910

**Stoker Ostler Wealth Advisors,
Inc.** (2)
4900 N Scottsdale Rd Ste 2600, Scottsdale, AZ 85251-7658
Tel.: (480) 890-8088
Web Site: http://www.stokerostler.com
Emp.: 20
Wealth Management Services
N.A.I.C.S.: 523940
Michelle Decker (Mng Dir & Sr Portfolio
Mgr)

**BMO Group Retirement Services
Inc.** (1)
181 Bay St Suite 2820, Toronto, ON,
Canada
Tel.: (877) 446-8347
Web Site: http://www.bmo.com
Administrative Services
N.A.I.C.S.: 561110

BMO Investorline, Inc. (1)
1st Canadian Pl 100 King St W B1 Fl, Toronto, M5X 1H3, ON, Canada   **(100%)**
Tel.: (416) 867-4000
Web Site: http://www.bmoinvestorline.com
Sales Range: $1-9.9 Million
Emp.: 120
Investment Management & Brokerage Services
N.A.I.C.S.: 523150

BMO Life Assurance Company (1)
60 Yonge Street, Toronto, M5E 1H5, ON,
Canada
Tel.: (416) 596-3900
Web Site: http://www.bmolifeinsurance.com
Sales Range: $200-249.9 Million
Emp.: 30
Fire Insurance Services
N.A.I.C.S.: 524298

BMO Life Insurance Company (1)
60 Yonge St, Toronto, M5E 1H5, ON,
Canada
Tel.: (416) 596-3900
Web Site: http://www.bmo.com
Rev.: $14,323,020
Emp.: 250
Insurance Agents Brokers & Service
N.A.I.C.S.: 524298

BMO Reinsurance Limited (1)

Cedar Court Wildey Business Park, Saint
Michaels, MD 14006
Tel.: (246) 622-6673
Web Site: http://www.bmoreinsurance.com
Reinsurance Services
N.A.I.C.S.: 524130
Paula Codrington (Gen Mgr)

BMO Trust Company (1)
1 1st Canadian Pl 41 Fl, Toronto, M5X 1A1,
ON, Canada   **(100%)**
Tel.: (416) 359-5901
Web Site: http://bmoharris.com
Sales Range: $50-74.9 Million
Emp.: 70
Trust & Fiduciary Services
N.A.I.C.S.: 523991

**Bank of Montreal (China) Co.
Ltd.** (1)
Unit 01 27th Floor Tower 3 China Central
Place No 77 Jianguo Road, Chaoyang District, Beijing, 100025, China
Tel.: (86) 10 8588 1688
Emp.: 100
Commercial Banking Services
N.A.I.C.S.: 522110

Bank of Montreal Assessoria e Servicos Ltda. (1)
Av Rio Branco 143 1801, Rio de Janeiro,
20040-006, Brazil
Tel.: (55) 21 3852 6407
Sales Range: $50-74.9 Million
Emp.: 5
Commercial Banking Services
N.A.I.C.S.: 522110

**Bank of Montreal Capital Markets
(Holdings) Limited** (1)
95 Queen Victoria St, London, EC4V 4HG,
United Kingdom
Tel.: (44) 20 7236 1010
Web Site: http://www.bmo.com
Sales Range: $100-124.9 Million
Emp.: 20
Investment Management Service
N.A.I.C.S.: 523999

Subsidiary (Domestic):

BMO Capital Markets Limited (2)
95 Queen Victoria Street 2nd Floor, London, EC4V 4HG, United Kingdom
Tel.: (44) 20 7236 1010
Web Site: http://www.bmocm.com
Investment Banking Services
N.A.I.C.S.: 523150

Pyrford International Limited (2)
95 Wigmore Street, London, W1U 1FD,
United Kingdom
Tel.: (44) 20 7495 4641
Web Site: http://www.pyrford.co.uk
Sales Range: $50-74.9 Million
Emp.: 35
Asset Management Services
N.A.I.C.S.: 523940

Bank of Montreal Finance Ltd. (1)
100 King Street West 21st Floor First Canadian Place, Toronto, M5X 1A1, ON, Canada
Tel.: (416) 867-4711
Web Site: http://www.bmo.com
Commercial Banking Services
N.A.I.C.S.: 522110

Bank of Montreal Ireland plc (1)
6th Floor 2 Harbourmaster Place, Dublin,
Ireland
Tel.: (353) 1 6629300
Web Site: http://www.bmo.com
Sales Range: $50-74.9 Million
Emp.: 19
Banking Services
N.A.I.C.S.: 522110

Columbia Threadneedle AM (Holdings) Plc (1)
Exchange House Primrose Street, London,
EC2A 2NY, United Kingdom
Tel.: (44) 2076288000
Sales Range: $250-299.9 Million
Asset Management Services
N.A.I.C.S.: 523940
Bart Kuijpers (Mng Dir & Head-Fiduciary
Mgmt Bus)

Subsidiary (Domestic):

BMO Global Asset Management (2)

8th Fl Exchange House Primrose St, London, EC2A 2NY, United Kingdom
Tel.: (44) 2076288000
Web Site: http://www.bmo.com
Asset Management Services
N.A.I.C.S.: 541618
David Logan *(Head-Distr)*

BMO Real Estate Partners LLP   **(2)**
5 Wigmore Street, London, W1U 1PB, United Kingdom
Tel.: (44) 20 7499 2244
Web Site: http://www.bmorep.com
Sales Range: $50-74.9 Million
Emp.: 80
Real Estate Manangement Services
N.A.I.C.S.: 531390
Richard Kirby *(Dir-Property Funds)*

Subsidiary (Non-US):

BMO Real Estate Partners GmbH & Co. KG   **(3)**
Oberanger 34-36, 80331, Munich, Germany
Tel.: (49) 89 61 46 51 0
Web Site: http://www.bmorep.com
Emp.: 40
Real Estate Manangement Services
N.A.I.C.S.: 531390
Iris Schoeberl *(Mng Dir & Head-Institutional Clients)*

Subsidiary (Domestic):

Columbia Threadneedle Investment Services Limited   **(2)**
8th Floor Exchange House Primrose Street, London, EC2A2NY, United Kingdom
Tel.: (44) 2076288000
Sales Range: $350-399.9 Million
Emp.: 400
Investment Services
N.A.I.C.S.: 523999
Jonanthan Mann *(Head-Emerging Market Debt)*

F&C (CI) Limited   **(2)**
8th Floor Exchange House Primrose Street, London, EC2A2NY, United Kingdom
Tel.: (44) 1314651000
Web Site: http://www.unitmanagement.co.uk
Sales Range: $250-299.9 Million
Emp.: 800
Holding Company
N.A.I.C.S.: 551112

F&C Asset Managers Limited   **(2)**
8th Floor Exchange House Primrose Street, London, EC2A2NY, United Kingdom
Tel.: (44) 1314651000
Sales Range: $150-199.9 Million
Asset Management Services
N.A.I.C.S.: 523940

F&C Emerging Markets Limited   **(2)**
8th Floor Exchange House Primrose Street, London, EC2A2NY, United Kingdom
Tel.: (44) 2076288000
Sales Range: $350-399.9 Million
Financial Investment Activities
N.A.I.C.S.: 523999

F&C Group (Holdings) Limited   **(2)**
8th Floor Exchange House Primrose Street, London, EC2A2NY, United Kingdom
Tel.: (44) 2076288000
Sales Range: $250-299.9 Million
Emp.: 800
Holding Company
N.A.I.C.S.: 551112
Richard Wilson *(CEO)*

F&C Group Management Limited   **(2)**
8th Fl Exchange House Primrose St, London, EC2A2NY, United Kingdom
Tel.: (44) 2076288000
Web Site: http://www.unitmanagement.co.uk
Sales Range: $250-299.9 Million
Emp.: 800
Holding Company
N.A.I.C.S.: 551112

F&C Management Limited   **(2)**
8th Floor Exchange House Primrose Street, London, EC2A 2NY, United Kingdom
Tel.: (44) 2076288000
Sales Range: $350-399.9 Million
Emp.: 800
Securities & Commodity Exchanges
N.A.I.C.S.: 523210

Richard Wilson *(CEO)*

Subsidiary (Non-US):

F&C Netherlands B.V.   **(2)**
Jachthavenweg 109 E, 1081 KM, Amsterdam, Netherlands
Tel.: (31) 205823000
Web Site: http://www.bmogam.nl
Sales Range: $50-74.9 Million
Emp.: 60
Investment Advice
N.A.I.C.S.: 523940
Ben Kramer *(Mng Dir)*

F&C Portugal Gestao de Patrimonios S.A.   **(2)**
Rua de Campolide 372-1, 1070-040, Lisbon, Portugal
Tel.: (351) 21 003 3200
Web Site: http://www.bmogam.com
Sales Range: $50-74.9 Million
Emp.: 35
Investment Management Service
N.A.I.C.S.: 523999
Ana Moura Serra *(Head-Client Svcs-Institutional)*

Subsidiary (Domestic):

F&C Property Limited   **(2)**
8th Floor Exchange House Primrose Street, London, EC2A2NY, United Kingdom
Tel.: (44) 2076288000
Web Site: http://www.fandc.com
Sales Range: $200-249.9 Million
Development of Building Projects
N.A.I.C.S.: 531390

F&C REIT Corporate Finance Limited   **(2)**
5 Wigmore Street, London, W1U 1PB, United Kingdom
Tel.: (44) 20 7499 2244
Real Estate Investment Services
N.A.I.C.S.: 531390

FP Asset Management Holdings Limited   **(2)**
Exchange House, Primrose Street, London, EC2A 2NY, United Kingdom   **(100%)**
Tel.: (44) 2076288000
Holding Company
N.A.I.C.S.: 551112

FP Fund Managers Limited   **(2)**
Exchange House, Primrose Street, London, United Kingdom   **(100%)**
Tel.: (44) 20 7628 8000
Fund Management Services
N.A.I.C.S.: 525910

REIT Asset Management Limited   **(2)**
5 Wigmore Street, London, W1U 1PB, United Kingdom
Tel.: (44) 20 7499 2244
Emp.: 60
Real Estate Manangement Services
N.A.I.C.S.: 531390
Lynn Peters *(Office Mgr)*

Thames River Capital UK Limited   **(2)**
51 Berkeley Square, London, W1J 5BB, United Kingdom
Tel.: (44) 2073601200
Sales Range: $100-124.9 Million
Emp.: 150
Investment Management Service
N.A.I.C.S.: 523999
Ros Smyth *(Head-Legal)*

Subsidiary (Domestic):

Thames River Multi-Capital LLP   **(3)**
51 Berkeley Square, London, W1J 5BB, United Kingdom
Tel.: (44) 20 7360 1200
Investment Management Service
N.A.I.C.S.: 523999

Greene Holcomb & Fisher, LLC   **(1)**
90 S 7th St Wells Fargo Ctr 54th Fl, Minneapolis, MN 55402   **(100%)**
Tel.: (612) 904-5700
Web Site: http://www.bmocm.com
Sales Range: $1-9.9 Million
Emp.: 50
Investment Banking Services
N.A.I.C.S.: 523150

Philip I. Smith *(Mng Dir)*

Lloyd George Management (Hong Kong) Limited   **(1)**
Suite 3808 1 Exchange Square, Central, China (Hong Kong)
Tel.: (852) 28454433
Web Site: http://www.lloydgeorge.com
Sales Range: $75-99.9 Million
Emp.: 80
Asset Management & Investment Banking Services
N.A.I.C.S.: 523150
Robert Lloyd George *(Founder, Chm & CIO)*

Subsidiary (Non-US):

Lloyd George Management (Europe) Limited   **(2)**
95 Wigmore Street, London, W1U 1FD, United Kingdom
Tel.: (44) 207 408 7688
Web Site: http://www.lgminvestment.com
Sales Range: $50-74.9 Million
Emp.: 2
Portfolio Management Services
N.A.I.C.S.: 523940
Irina Hunter *(Sr Portfolio Mgr)*

Lloyd George Management (Singapore) Pte Ltd.   **(2)**
11a Stanley St, Downtown, Singapore, 68730, Singapore
Tel.: (65) 62223877
Sales Range: $50-74.9 Million
Emp.: 2
Asset Management Services
N.A.I.C.S.: 523940
How Teng Chiou *(Gen Mgr)*

Monarch Industries Limited   **(1)**
51 Burmac Rd, Winnipeg, R2J 4J3, MB, Canada
Tel.: (204) 786-7921
Web Site: http://www.monarchindustries.com
Hydraulic Cylinders & Metal Casting Mfr
N.A.I.C.S.: 333517
Roy Cook *(Pres & CEO)*

Moneris Solutions Corporation   **(1)**
3300 Bloor Street West, Toronto, M8X 2X2, ON, Canada
Tel.: (416) 734-1000
Web Site: https://www.moneris.com
Sales Range: $700-749.9 Million
Emp.: 1,500
Payment Processing Services; Owned by RBC Financial Group & Bank of Montreal
N.A.I.C.S.: 522320
Malcolm Fowler *(Chief Product & Partnership Officer)*

Division (Domestic):

Ernex   **(2)**
4259 Canada Way Ste 225, Burnaby, V5G 1H1, BC, Canada
Tel.: (604) 415-1500
Web Site: http://www.ernex.com
Sales Range: $1-9.9 Million
Emp.: 65
Electronic Marketing Services
N.A.I.C.S.: 541512
Grant Finnighan *(Gen Mgr)*

Subsidiary (Domestic):

MSC Moneris Services Corp.   **(2)**
7350 Rue Transcanadienne, Saint Laurent, H4T 1A3, QC, Canada
Tel.: (514) 733-5403
Web Site: http://www.msposcorp.com
Sales Range: $150-199.9 Million
Emp.: 300
Payment Processing Services
N.A.I.C.S.: 522320
Shalini Desa *(Reg Mgr-Ops)*

BANK OF NAMIBIA
71 Robert Mugabe Ave, PO Box 2882, Windhoek, Namibia
Tel.: (264) 612835111
Web Site: http://www.bon.com.na
Year Founded: 1990
Sales Range: $50-74.9 Million
Emp.: 298

Banking Services
N.A.I.C.S.: 522110
Lea Namoloh *(Dir-HR)*

BANK OF NANJING CO., LTD.
No 88 Jiangshan Street, Jianye District, Nanjing, 210019, China
Tel.: (86) 95302
Web Site: https://www.njcb.com.cn
Year Founded: 1996
601009—(SHG)
Rev.: $6,262,744,176
Assets: $289,151,516,956
Liabilities: $267,010,600,522
Net Worth: $22,140,916,434
Earnings: $2,584,488,676
Emp.: 2,700
Fiscal Year-end: 12/31/22
Banking Services
N.A.I.C.S.: 522110
Shengrong Hu *(Chm)*

BANK OF NINGBO CO., LTD.
No 345 Ningdong Road, Yinzhou District, Ningbo, 315042, Zhejiang, China
Tel.: (86) 57487050028   **CN**
Web Site: https://www.nbcb.com.cnglish
Year Founded: 1997
002142—(SSE)
Rev.: $8,674,247,250
Assets: $381,937,592,700
Liabilities: $353,456,314,200
Net Worth: $28,481,278,500
Earnings: $3,596,604,750
Emp.: 27,000
Fiscal Year-end: 12/31/23
Commercial Banking Services
N.A.I.C.S.: 522110
Huayu Lu *(Chm)*

Subsidiaries:

Huarong Consumer Finance Co., Ltd.   **(1)**
12/F Block A Xiangyuan Square No 310 Suixi Road, Luyang District, Hefei, 230001, Anhui, China   **(76.6%)**
Tel.: (86) 55162882391
Financial Services
N.A.I.C.S.: 541611

BANK OF PAPUA NEW GUINEA
Douglas St, PO Box 121, Port Moresby, 121, Papua New Guinea
Tel.: (675) 3227200
Web Site: http://www.bankpng.gov.pg
Sales Range: $100-124.9 Million
Emp.: 300
Banking Services
N.A.I.C.S.: 521110
Loi Martin Bakani *(Chm)*

BANK OF QINGDAO CO., LTD.
No 6 Qinling Road, Laoshan District, Qingdao, 266061, Shandong, China
Tel.: (86) 4006696588   **CN**
Web Site: https://www.qdccb.com
Year Founded: 1996
002948—(SSE)
Rev.: $1,726,888,015
Assets: $84,180,517,833
Liabilities: $78,650,604,924
Net Worth: $5,529,912,910
Earnings: $491,332,383
Emp.: 4,861
Fiscal Year-end: 12/31/23
Commercial Banking Services
N.A.I.C.S.: 522110
Shaoquan Guo *(Chm)*

BANK OF QUEENSLAND LIMITED
Level 6 100 Skyring Terrace, Newstead, 4006, QLD, Australia
Tel.: (61) 732123844   **AU**
Web Site: https://www.boq.com.au

Bank of Queensland Limited—(Continued)

Year Founded: 1874
BKQNF—(OTCIQ)
Rev.: $2,649,149,117
Assets: $68,691,399,883
Liabilities: $64,694,529,569
Net Worth: $3,996,870,314
Earnings: $80,850,231
Emp.: 3,163
Fiscal Year-end: 08/31/23
Banking Services
N.A.I.C.S.: 522320
Matthew Baxby (Co-CFO)

Subsidiaries:

BOQ Equipment Finance Limited   (1)
Level 17 259 Queens St, Brisbane, 4000,
QLD, Australia
Tel.: (61) 733362420
Web Site: http://www.boq.com.au
Sales Range: $75-99.9 Million
Emp.: 38
Banking
N.A.I.C.S.: 522210

Boq Finance (Aust) Limited   (1)
Level 6 100 Skyring Terrace, Newstead,
4006, QLD, Australia
Tel.: (61) 800245614
Web Site: https://www.boqfinance.com.au
Financial Investment Services
N.A.I.C.S.: 523999

BANK OF SHANGHAI CO., LTD

No 168 Middle Yincheng Road, Pilot
Free Trade Zone, Shanghai, 200120,
China
Tel.: (86) 2168475888   **CN**
Web Site: https://www.bosc.cn
Year Founded: 1995
601229—(SHG)
Rev.: $7,456,991,911
Assets: $404,144,876,164
Liabilities: $373,025,423,394
Net Worth: $31,119,452,770
Earnings: $3,128,142,186
Emp.: 14,333
Fiscal Year-end: 12/31/22
Banking Services
N.A.I.C.S.: 522110

Subsidiaries:

BOSC International Company
Limited   (1)
34th Floor Champion Building 3 Garden
Road, Central, China (Hong Kong)
Tel.: (852) 31218300
Web Site: https://www.boscinternational.com
Financial Investment Services
N.A.I.C.S.: 523940

Bank of Shanghai (Hong Kong)
Limited   (1)
34/F Champion Tower Three Garden Road,
Central, China (Hong Kong)
Tel.: (852) 31218222
Web Site:
   http://www.bankofshanghai.com.hk
Banking Services
N.A.I.C.S.: 522110

BANK OF SHARJAH P.S.C.

Al Khan Street, PO Box 1394,
Sharjah, United Arab Emirates
Tel.: (971) 65694411
Web Site:
   https://www.bankofsharjah.com
Year Founded: 1973
BOS—(ABU)
Rev.: $479,829,837
Assets: $10,743,759,679
Liabilities: $9,789,306,660
Net Worth: $954,453,019
Earnings: ($74,942,824)
Emp.: 313
Fiscal Year-end: 12/31/23
Banking Services
N.A.I.C.S.: 522110
Mohammed Saud Al Qasimi (Chm)

Subsidiaries:

Emirates Lebanon Bank S.A.L.   (1)
Bourj El Ghazal Avenue Fouad Chehab-
Tabaris, BP 11-1608, Beirut, Lebanon
Tel.: (961) 1200601
Web Site: https://www.elbank.com.lb
Commercial Banking Services
N.A.I.C.S.: 522110
Varouj Narguizian (Chm & Gen Mgr)

BANK OF SIERRA LEONE

Siaka Stevens Street, Freetown,
Western Area, Sierra Leone
Tel.: (232) 22 226501
Web Site: http://www.bsl.gov.sl
Sales Range: $10-24.9 Million
Emp.: 572
Banking Services
N.A.I.C.S.: 521110
A.R. Coker (Sr Dir-Res)

BANK OF ST. VINCENT & THE GRENADINES

Tel.: (784) 4571844
Web Site: http://www.svgncb.com
Sales Range: $10-24.9 Million
Emp.: 182
Banking Services
N.A.I.C.S.: 522110
Phillip H. Hernandez (CEO)

BANK OF SUZHOU CO., LTD.

No 728 Zhongyuan Road, Suzhou
Industrial Park, Suzhou, 215028, Ji-
angsu, China
Tel.: (86) 51269868023
Web Site:
   https://www.suzhoubank.com
Year Founded: 2010
002966—(SSE)
Rev.: $1,651,519,584
Assets: $73,646,636,076
Liabilities: $67,965,768,468
Net Worth: $5,680,867,608
Earnings: $550,148,976
Fiscal Year-end: 12/31/22
Commercial Banking Services
N.A.I.C.S.: 522110
Lanfeng Wang (Chm)

BANK OF SYRIA & OVER-SEAS S.A.

Harika - Bab Barid - Lawyers Syndi-
cate Bldg, Damascus, Syria
Tel.: (963) 11 226 0560
Web Site: http://www.bso.com.sy
Year Founded: 2003
BSO—(DSE)
Sales Range: $10-24.9 Million
Commercial Banking Services
N.A.I.C.S.: 522110
Ahmad Rateb Al Shallah (Chm)

BANK OF THAILAND

273 Samsen Road Watsamphraya,
Phra Nakhon District, Bangkok,
10200, Thailand
Tel.: (66) 22835353
Web Site: http://www.bot.or.th
Year Founded: 1942
Sales Range: $1-4.9 Billion
Emp.: 3,461
Banking Services
N.A.I.C.S.: 521110
Mathee Supapongse (Asst Governor)

BANK OF THE PHILIPPINE IS-LANDS

Ayala Triangle Gardens Tower 2
Paseo de Roxas corner Makati Av-
enue, Legaspi Village, Makati, 1226,
Philippines
Tel.: (63) 88910000   **PH**
Web Site: http://bpi.com.ph
Year Founded: 1851

BPHLY—(OTCIQ)
Rev.: $1,760,033,600
Assets: $50,375,832,000
Liabilities: $44,236,587,200
Net Worth: $6,139,244,800
Earnings: $501,488,000
Emp.: 18,619
Fiscal Year-end: 12/31/21
Bank Holding Company
N.A.I.C.S.: 551111
Jaime Augusto Zobel de Ayala (Chm)

Subsidiaries:

BPI Capital Corporation   (1)
23/F Ayala Triangle Gardens Tower 2
Paseo De Roxas Cor Makati Avenue,
Makati, 1226, Philippines   (100%)
Tel.: (63) 285800888
Sales Range: $50-74.9 Million
Emp.: 20
Investment Banking & Securities Dealing
N.A.I.C.S.: 523150

Subsidiary (Domestic):

BPI Asset Management   (2)
7/F BPI Buendia Center Sen Gil J Puyat
Avenue, Makati, 1206, Philippines   (45%)
Tel.: (63) 25803930
Web Site:
   http://www.bpiassetmanagement.com
Sales Range: $10-24.9 Million
Investment & Asset Management Services
N.A.I.C.S.: 523940
Antonio Jose U. Periquet (Chm)

BPI Securities Corporation   (2)
8/F BPI Building 6768 Ayala Avenue,
Makati, 1226, Philippines   (100%)
Tel.: (63) 28169190
Sales Range: $50-74.9 Million
Emp.: 20
Securities Brokerage Services
N.A.I.C.S.: 523150

BPI Card Corporation   (1)
8753 Paseo de Roxas 8th Fl BPI Card Cen-
ter, Makati, 1226, Metro Manila, Philippines
Tel.: (63) 28169562
Web Site: http://www.bpiexpressonline.com
Credit Card Services
N.A.I.C.S.: 522110

BPI Century Tokyo Lease & Finance
Corporation   (1)
21F NEX Tower 6786 Ayala Avenue, Brgy
Bel-Air Metro Manila, Makati, 1229,
Philippines   (49%)
Tel.: (63) 285395000
Automobile Leasing Services
N.A.I.C.S.: 532112

BPI Computer Systems Corp   (1)
BPI Card Center Building Ayala Ave And
Paseo De Roxas, Makati, 1226, Philippines
Tel.: (63) 28169578
Commercial Banking Services
N.A.I.C.S.: 522110

BPI Direct BanKo Inc.   (1)
220 Ortigas Avenue BanKo Center North
Greenhills Metro Manila, San Juan, Philip-
pines
Tel.: (63) 277549980
Web Site: http://www.banko.com.ph
Bank Services
N.A.I.C.S.: 522110

BPI Direct Savings Bank   (1)
8/F BPI Card Center, 8753 Paseo de
Roxas, Makati, 1226, Philippines   (100%)
Tel.: (63) 2 816 9562
Web Site: http://www.bpidirect.com
Sales Range: Less than $1 Million
Emp.: 20
Internet & Mobile Banking Services
N.A.I.C.S.: 522180
Carlos B. Aquino (Sec)

BPI Express Remittance Corp.   (1)
875 3rd Ave, New York, NY 10022
Tel.: (212) 644-6700
Web Site: http://www.bpi.com
Sales Range: $50-74.9 Million
Emp.: 4
Commercial Banking Services
N.A.I.C.S.: 522110

BPI Express Remittance Spain
S.A   (1)
Calle Joaquin Costa 50, 08001, Barcelona,
Spain
Tel.: (34) 933011537
Sales Range: $50-74.9 Million
Emp.: 6
Commercial Banking Services
N.A.I.C.S.: 522110
Sharon Dionola (Mng Dir)

BPI Family Savings Bank, Inc.   (1)
109 Paseo De Roxas Avenue cor Dela
Rosa St, Paseo de Roxas, corner Dela
Rosa Street, Makati, 1229,
Philippines   (100%)
Tel.: (63) 28910000
Web Site: http://www.bpiexpressonline.com
Sales Range: $75-99.9 Million
Emp.: 15
Savings & Loan Services
N.A.I.C.S.: 522180
Maria Cristina L. Go (Pres)

BPI Forex Corporation   (1)
6Fl Ayala Wing BPI Head Office Bldg, Ayala
Ave cor Paseo de Roxas, Makati, 1201,
Metro Manila, Philippines
Tel.: (63) 28169476
Web Site: http://www.bpiexpressonline.com
Sales Range: $25-49.9 Million
Emp.: 20
Currency Exchange Services
N.A.I.C.S.: 561499

BPI Foundation, Inc.   (1)
16/F BPI Building Ayala Avenue, Makati,
1226, Philippines   (100%)
Tel.: (63) 28169288
Web Site: http://www.bpifoundation.org
Sales Range: $25-49.9 Million
Emp.: 5
Charitable Grant Services
N.A.I.C.S.: 813211
Cezar P. Consing (Vice Chm)

BPI Leasing Corporation   (1)
15 floor BPI Buendia Center 372 Senator
Gil Puyat Avenue, Belair, Makati, 1226,
Philippines   (100%)
Tel.: (63) 2 816 9124
Web Site: http://www.bpiexpressonline.com
Sales Range: $50-74.9 Million
Emp.: 30
Lease Financing Services
N.A.I.C.S.: 522220
Samuel Tang (Pres)

BPI Operations Management
Corporation   (1)
5/F BPI Intramuros Operations Center Mu-
ralla Street, Solana Street Intramuros, Ma-
nila, Philippines   (100%)
Tel.: (63) 25286988
Sales Range: Less than $1 Million
Emp.: 450
Management Consulting Services
N.A.I.C.S.: 541611
Rafael Pertierra (Gen Mgr)

BPI PHILAM LIFE ASSURANCE
CORPORATION   (1)
12th 14th 15th Floor Ayala Life-FGU Center
6811 Ayala Avenue, Makati, 1226, Philip-
pines
Tel.: (63) 288885433
Web Site: http://www.ayalalife.com.ph
General Insurance Services
N.A.I.C.S.: 524210

BPI Wealth Hong Kong Limited   (1)
5/F LHT Tower 31 Queens Road, Central,
China (Hong Kong)
Tel.: (852) 25211155
Sales Range: $50-74.9 Million
Emp.: 12
Commercial Banking Services
N.A.I.C.S.: 522110
Jonathan Paul Back (Exec Dir)

BPI-Philam Life Assurance
Corporation   (1)
   (49%)
Sales Range: $500-549.9 Million
Life Insurance Products & Services
N.A.I.C.S.: 524113
Spencer Yap (CFO)

BPI/MS Insurance Corporation   (1)
18TH Floor BPI Philam Life Building Ayala

Avenue, 6811 Ayala Avenue, Makati, 1209, Philippines
Tel.: (63) 288409700
Web Site: https://www.bpims.com
Sales Range: $300-349.9 Million
Non-Life Insurance Products & Services; Owned by Bank of the Philippine Islands & by Mitsui Sumitomo Insurance Co., Ltd.
N.A.I.C.S.: 524126
Cezar P. Consing *(Chm)*

Bank of the Philippine Islands (Europe) Plc **(1)**
26A 27A Earl's Court Gardens, London, SW5 0SZ, United Kingdom
Tel.: (44) 2078350088
Web Site: http://www.bpiexpressonline.com
Sales Range: $50-74.9 Million
Emp.: 21
Commercial Banking Services
N.A.I.C.S.: 522110
Alex Tan *(Mng Dir)*

Prudential Investments, Inc **(1)**
100 Mulberry St Gateway Ctr 3 14th Fl, Newark, NJ 07102
Tel.: (973) 802-2991
Investment Management Service
N.A.I.C.S.: 523999

Robinsons Bank Corporation **(1)**
17th Floor Galleria Corporate Center EDSA corner Ortigas Avenue, Quezon City, Philippines
Tel.: (63) 286372273
Web Site:
  https://www.robinsonsbank.com.ph
Financial Services
N.A.I.C.S.: 541611
Lance Y. Gokongwei *(Chm)*

Speed International, Inc **(1)**
1460 Military Rd, Kenmore, NY 14217-1308
Tel.: (716) 876-2235
Commercial Banking Services
N.A.I.C.S.: 522110

BANK OF THE RYUKYUS, LTD.
2-1 Higashimachi, PO Box 310, Naha, 900-0034, Okinawa, Japan
Tel.: (81) 988661212
Web Site: https://www.ryugin.co.jp
Year Founded: 1948
8399—(FKA)
Rev.: $435,936,110
Assets: $20,272,982,370
Liabilities: $19,330,634,330
Net Worth: $942,348,040
Earnings: $37,353,110
Fiscal Year-end: 03/31/24
Banking Services
N.A.I.C.S.: 522110
Hitoshi Kinjo *(Auditor)*

Subsidiaries:

Okinawa Credit Service Co., Ltd. **(1)**
2-3-10 Matsuyama OCS Building, Naha, 900-8609, Okinawa, Japan
Tel.: (81) 12 011 0404
Web Site: https://www.ocsnet.co.jp
Emp.: 131
Individual Credit Purchase Mediation Services
N.A.I.C.S.: 522390

Ryugin Business Service Co., Ltd. **(1)**
9-17 Kumoji 1-chome, Naha, 900-0015, Okinawa, Japan
Tel.: (81) 988634572
Web Site: http://www.ryugin.co.jp
Sales Range: $25-49.9 Million
Emp.: 100
All Other Business Support Services
N.A.I.C.S.: 561499

Ryugin DC Co., Ltd. **(1)**
6th floor 1-7-1 Kumoji Ryukyu Lease General Building, Naha, 900-0015, Japan
Tel.: (81) 988621525
Web Site: http://www.ryugindc.co.jp
Sales Range: $50-74.9 Million
Emp.: 35
Credit Card Issuing
N.A.I.C.S.: 522210

Ryugin Hosho Co., Ltd. **(1)**
1-9 Tsubokawa 1-chome, Naha, 900-0015, Okinawa, Japan
Tel.: (81) 988321200
Web Site: http://www.ryugin.co.jp
Sales Range: $50-74.9 Million
Emp.: 50
Housing Loans, Debt Guaranty & Insurance Services
N.A.I.C.S.: 524210

Ryugin Office Service Co., Ltd. **(1)**
4-1-1 Uchima Urasoe, Urasoe, 901-2121, Okinawa, Japan
Tel.: (81) 988767130
Sales Range: $25-49.9 Million
Emp.: 100
Clerical Services
N.A.I.C.S.: 561110

Ryugin Research Institute., Ltd. **(1)**
1-9 Tsubokawa 1-chome, Naha, 900-0025, Okinawa, Japan
Tel.: (81) 988354650
Sales Range: $25-49.9 Million
Emp.: 10
Suryveying & Research Consulting Services
N.A.I.C.S.: 541611
Tamotsu Teruya *(CEO)*

Ryugin Sougo Kenkyusho., Ltd. **(1)**
1/1-9 Tsubokawa, Naha, 900-0025, Japan
Tel.: (81) 988354650
Web Site: http://www.ryugin-ri.co.jp
Sales Range: $25-49.9 Million
Emp.: 9
All Other Information Services
N.A.I.C.S.: 519290

Ryukyu Leasing Co., Ltd. **(1)**
Ryukyu Lease General Building 10F 1-7-1Kumoji, Naha, 900-8550, Okinawa, Japan **(49.92%)**
Tel.: (81) 988665500
Web Site: https://www.rlease.co.jp
Equipment Rental & Leasing
N.A.I.C.S.: 532420
Katsuo Yasuda *(Pres)*

BANK OF TIANJIN CO., LTD.
No 15 Youyi Road, Hexi District, Tianjin, 300201, China
Tel.: (86) 2228405262   CN
Web Site:
  https://www.bankoftianjin.com
Year Founded: 1996
1578—(HKG)
Rev.: $4,321,601,684
Assets: $116,411,644,329
Liabilities: $107,407,759,747
Net Worth: $9,003,884,581
Earnings: $521,557,239
Emp.: 6,699
Fiscal Year-end: 12/31/23
Commercial Banking Services
N.A.I.C.S.: 522110
Furong Zhang *(Sec & VP)*

BANK OF TOYAMA LTD.
3-1 Shimonoseki-cho, Takaoka, 933-8606, Toyama, Japan
Tel.: (81) 766213535
Web Site:
  https://www.toyamabank.co.jp
8365—(TKS)
Rev.: $67,065,060
Assets: $3,650,015,560
Liabilities: $3,443,102,730
Net Worth: $206,912,830
Earnings: $165,250
Emp.: 333
Fiscal Year-end: 03/31/24
Banking Services
N.A.I.C.S.: 522110
Yuu Nakaoki *(Deputy Pres)*

BANK OF UGANDA
37-43 Kampala Rd, PO Box 7120, 710, Kampala, Uganda
Tel.: (256) 41258441
Web Site: http://www.bou.or.ug
Year Founded: 1966
Sales Range: $50-74.9 Million

Emp.: 957
Banking Services
N.A.I.C.S.: 522110
Emmanuel Tumusiime Mutebile *(Chm)*

BANK OF VALLETTA P.L.C.
BOV Centre Triq il-Kanun, Zone 4 Central Business District, Santa Vennera, CBD 4060, Malta
Tel.: (356) 22753700   Mt
Web Site: https://www.bov.com
Year Founded: 1974
BOV—(MAL)
Rev.: $486,810,906
Assets: $16,013,851,421
Liabilities: $14,614,433,162
Net Worth: $1,399,418,258
Earnings: $185,380,285
Emp.: 2,102
Fiscal Year-end: 12/31/23
Banking Services
N.A.I.C.S.: 522110
Elvia George *(CFO)*

Subsidiaries:

BOV Asset Management Limited **(1)**
Premium Banking Centre PBC 475, Triq il-Kbira San Guzepp, Santa Vennera, SVR 1011, Malta
Tel.: (356) 21227311
Web Site:
  https://www.bovassetmanagement.com
Sales Range: $50-74.9 Million
Emp.: 10
Fund Management Services
N.A.I.C.S.: 525190
Mark Agius *(Gen Mgr)*

BOV Fund Services Ltd. **(1)**
Premium Banking Centre 475, Triq il-Kbira San Guzepp, Santa Vennera, SVR 1011, Malta
Tel.: (356) 21227148
Web Site: https://www.bovfundservices.com
Sales Range: $50-74.9 Million
Emp.: 45
Fund Administration Services
N.A.I.C.S.: 524292

BANK OF ZAMBIA
Bank Square Cairo Road, PO Box 30080, Lusaka, Zambia
Tel.: (260) 1228888
Web Site: http://www.boz.zm
Banking Services
N.A.I.C.S.: 521110
Caleb M. Fundanga *(Chm & Governor)*

BANK OF ZHENGZHOU CO., LTD.
22 Shangwu Waihuan Road, Zhengdong New District, Zhengzhou, Henan, China
Tel.: (86) 37167009199   CN
Web Site: https://en.zzbank.cn
Year Founded: 1996
6196—(HKG)
Rev.—$3,518,025,545
Assets: $83,048,511,967
Liabilities: $75,659,928,833
Net Worth: $7,388,583,134
Earnings: $365,032,699
Emp.: 5,888
Fiscal Year-end: 12/31/22
Commercial Banking Services
N.A.I.C.S.: 522110
Tianyu Wang *(Chm)*

BANK PASARGAD
No 430 Mirdamad Blvd, Tehran, 1969774511, Iran
Tel.: (98) 21 82890
Web Site: http://bpi.ir
Sales Range: $1-4.9 Billion
Financial & Banking Services
N.A.I.C.S.: 522110

Subsidiaries:

Pasargad Group International Trading Company **(1)**
Unit 110 Armineh Tower No 2 Bakhshi Ally Khovardin Avenue, Ghods town, Tehran, Iran
Tel.: (98) 21 88573880
Web Site: http://www.pasargaditc.com
Steel Products Mfr
N.A.I.C.S.: 332999
Keumars Mokhtari *(Mgr-Fin)*

BANK POLSKA KASA OPIEKI SPOLKA AKCYJNA
Zubra 1, 01-066, Warsaw, Poland
Tel.: (48) 226560000   PL
Web Site: https://www.pekao.com.pl
Year Founded: 1929
PEO—(WAR)
Rev.: $4,543,284,932
Assets: $76,803,245,742
Liabilities: $69,181,027,986
Net Worth: $7,622,217,756
Earnings: $1,653,017,133
Emp.: 14,363
Fiscal Year-end: 12/31/23
Commercial Banking Services
N.A.I.C.S.: 522110
Tomasz Kubiak *(Vice Chm-Mgmt Bd)*

Subsidiaries:

Centrala Pekao Factoring Sp. z o.o. **(1)**
ul Krakowskie Przedmiescie 64, 20-076, Lublin, Poland
Tel.: (48) 814452000
Web Site: http://www.pekaofaktoring.com.pl
Sales Range: $50-74.9 Million
Emp.: 50
Financial Services
N.A.I.C.S.: 525990

Centralny Dom Maklerski Pekao S.A. **(1)**
ul Woloska 18, PL-02 675, Warsaw, Poland **(100%)**
Tel.: (48) 226402840
Web Site: http://www.cdmpekao.com.pl
Sales Range: $150-199.9 Million
Emp.: 400
Brokerage Services
N.A.I.C.S.: 523150
Piotr Teleon *(Pres-Mgmt Bd)*

Centrum Kart S.A. **(1)**
ul Grzybowska 53/57, 00-844, Warsaw, Poland
Tel.: (48) 226561710
Web Site: https://www.centrumkart.pl
Financial Support
N.A.I.C.S.: 525990

Dom Inwestycyjny Xelion Sp. z o.o. **(1)**
ul Pulawska 107, 02-595, Warsaw, Poland
Tel.: (48) 225654400
Web Site: https://www.xelion.pl
Financial Advisory Services
N.A.I.C.S.: 523940

PEKAO BANK HIPOTECZNY S.A. **(1)**
10A Skierniewicka Str, 01-230, Warsaw, Poland
Tel.: (48) 228521900
Web Site: https://www.pekaobh.pl
Commercial Banking Services
N.A.I.C.S.: 522110

PEKAO FAKTORING SP. ZOO **(1)**
ul Krakowskie Przedmiescie 64, 20-076, Lublin, Poland
Tel.: (48) 814452000
Web Site: https://www.pekaofaktoring.pl
Financial Factoring Services
N.A.I.C.S.: 522299

PEKAO LEASING HOLDING S.A. **(1)**
Pulawska 182, Warsaw, Poland
Tel.: (48) 225209557
Investment Management Service
N.A.I.C.S.: 523999

PEKAO PROPERTY SA **(1)**

Bank Polska Kasa Opieki Spolka
Akcyjna—(Continued)

ul Grzybowska 53/57, 00-950, Warsaw,
Poland
Tel.: (48) 226243320
Web Site: http://www.pekaoproperty.pl
Real Estate Development Services
N.A.I.C.S.: 531390

Pekao Direct Sp. z o.o
ul Josepha Conrada 37, 31-357, Krakow,
Poland
Tel.: (48) 693719729
Web Site: https://www.pekaodirect.pl
Customer Care Services
N.A.I.C.S.: 561422
Maciej Grela (Project Mgr)

Pekao Financial Services Sp. z
o.o. **(1)**
21 Postepu Street, 02-676, Warsaw, Poland
Tel.: (48) 226400901
Web Site: https://www.pekao-fs.com.pl
Sales Range: $75-99.9 Million
Emp.: 200
Financial Services
N.A.I.C.S.: 525990
Waldemar Kasinow (Pres-Mgmt Bd)

Pekao Fundusz Kapitalowy Sp. z
o.o. **(1)**
ul. Grzybowska 53/57, 00-950, Warsaw,
Poland
Tel.: (48) 226560700
Web Site: http://www.pekaofk.pl
Financial Services
N.A.I.C.S.: 525990

Pekao Investment Banking S.A. **(1)**
Zwirki i Wigury 31 Bud A I pietro, 02-091,
Warsaw, Poland
Tel.: (48) 604109109
Web Site: https://www.pekaoib.pl
Financial Advisory Services
N.A.I.C.S.: 523940
Maciej Jacenko (Pres)

Pekao Investment Management
S.A. **(1)**
Ul Zubra 1, 01-066, Warsaw, Poland
Tel.: (48) 604109109
Web Site: https://www.pekaoib.pl
N.A.I.C.S.: 541611

Pekao Leasing Sp. z o.o. **(1)**
Armii Ludowej 26, 00-609, Warsaw, Poland
Tel.: (48) 225482100
Web Site: http://www.pekaoleasing.com.pl
Auto Leasing
N.A.I.C.S.: 532112

Pekao Pioneer Powszechned To-
warzystwo Emerytalne S.A. **(1)**
ul Domaniewska 41A, Warsaw, 2672, Po-
land
Tel.: (48) 228744610
Web Site: http://www.pekaopte.pl
Sales Range: $50-74.9 Million
Emp.: 25
Financial Services
N.A.I.C.S.: 525990

Pekao TFI S.A. **(1)**
ul Marynarska 15, 02-674, Warsaw, Poland
Tel.: (48) 226404040
Web Site: https://www.pekaotfi.pl
Investment Management Service
N.A.I.C.S.: 523940

Pioneer Pekao Investment Manage-
ment S.A. **(1)**
ul Marynarska 15, 02-674, Warsaw, Poland
Tel.: (48) 226404000
Web Site: http://www.pioneer.com.pl
Investment Management Service
N.A.I.C.S.: 523940

BANK RBK JSC
84 Adi Sharipov Street, Almaty, Ka-
zakhstan
Tel.: (7) 27 330 90 30
Banking Services
N.A.I.C.S.: 522110
Marpu Zhakubayeva (CEO)

BANK SADERAT OF IRAN
Panzdah Khordad Ave, Tehran, Iran

Tel.: (98) 33907224
Web Site: http://in.bsi.ir
Year Founded: 1961
Sales Range: $1-4.9 Billion
Banking Services
N.A.I.C.S.: 522110
Hassan Khodayari (Mgr-Branches
Affairs & Mktg)

BANK SADERAT PLC
5 Lothbury, London, EC2R 7HD,
United Kingdom
Tel.: (44) 2076000133
Web Site: http://www.saderat-plc.com
Year Founded: 1973
Sales Range: $10-24.9 Million
Emp.: 29
Banking & International Trade Financ-
ing Services
N.A.I.C.S.: 522110
C. R. Wakefield (Asst Mng Dir)

BANK SIAB PJSC
Chernigovskaya St 8 lit A 1, 196084,
Saint Petersburg, Russia
Tel.: (7) 8123808130
Web Site: http://www.siab.ru
Year Founded: 1995
Sales Range: Less than $1 Million
Commercial Banking Services
N.A.I.C.S.: 522110
Galina Vanchikova (Chm-Mgmt Bd &
Pres)

BANK TEJARAT
No 247 corner of Shahid Nejat Elahi
St Ayatollah Taleghani St, PO Box
14157, Taleghani Ave, 1598617818,
Tehran, Iran
Tel.: (98) 81041
Web Site: https://www.tejaratbank.ir
Year Founded: 1887
Banking Services
N.A.I.C.S.: 522110
R. Dolat Abadi (Mng Dir)

**BANK VAN DE NEDER-
LANDSE ANTILLEN**
Simon Bolivar Plein 1, Willemstad,
Curacao
Tel.: (599) 94345500
Web Site: http://www.centralbank.cw
Sales Range: $50-74.9 Million
Emp.: 220
Central Bank
N.A.I.C.S.: 521110
E. D. Tromp (Pres)

BANK ZARECHYE JSC
2 Luknitskogo Str, 420032, Kazan,
Tatarstan, Russia
Tel.: (7) 8435575903
Web Site: http://www.zarech.ru
Year Founded: 1990
Sales Range: Less than $1 Million
Commercial Banking Services
N.A.I.C.S.: 522110

BANK ZENIT PJSC
Odesskaya St 2, 117638, Moscow,
Russia
Tel.: (7) 4959671111
Web Site: http://www.zenit.ru
Year Founded: 1994
Mortgage Banking Services
N.A.I.C.S.: 522292
Oleg A. Mashtalyar (Chm-Mgmt Bd)

BANKA BIOLOO LIMITED
5th Floor Prestige Phoenix 1405 Uma
Nagar, Begumpet, Hyderabad,
500016, India
Tel.: (91) 8209525579
Web Site: https://www.bankabio.com
Year Founded: 2012

BANKA—(NSE)
Rev.: $5,876,448
Assets: $8,900,810
Liabilities: $3,427,310
Net Worth: $5,473,500
Earnings: $346,560
Emp.: 621
Fiscal Year-end: 03/30/23
Waste Management Services
N.A.I.C.S.: 562119
Sanjay Banka (Chm)

**BANKA POSTANSKA STE-
DIONICA A.D.**
Ulica kraljice Marije 3, 11120, Bel-
grade, Serbia
Tel.: (381) 11 20 20 292
Web Site: http://www.posted.co.rs
Year Founded: 1921
Sales Range: $75-99.9 Million
Financial Banking Services
N.A.I.C.S.: 523150

BANKA SLOVENIJE
Slovenska 35, 1505, Ljubljana, Slove-
nia
Tel.: (386) 14719000
Web Site: http://www.bsi.si
Sales Range: $300-349.9 Million
Emp.: 417
Banking Services
N.A.I.C.S.: 521110
Janko Tratnik (Dir-Banking Ops)

BANKHAUS ERBE JSC
26 Bld 1 Zoologicheskaya Str,
123056, Moscow, Russia
Tel.: (7) 4992547200
Web Site: http://www.erbebank.com
Year Founded: 1991
Sales Range: Less than $1 Million
Commercial Banking Services
N.A.I.C.S.: 522110

**BANKHAUS WOLBERN AG &
CO. KG**
Am Sandtorkai 54, 20457, Hamburg,
Germany
Tel.: (49) 40376080
Web Site: http://www.woelbern.de
Sales Range: $25-49.9 Million
Emp.: 90
Banking Services
N.A.I.C.S.: 522110
Hans Detlef Boesel (Chm)

BANKINTER, S.A.
Paseo de la Castellana 29, 28046,
Madrid, Spain
Tel.: (34) 913397500　　　　ES
Web Site: https://www.bankinter.com
Year Founded: 1965
BKT—(BAR)
Rev.: $3,969,055,687
Assets: $121,963,783,725
Liabilities: $116,219,190,589
Net Worth: $5,744,593,136
Earnings: $911,706,238
Emp.: 6,541
Fiscal Year-end: 12/31/23
Commercial Banking Services
N.A.I.C.S.: 522110
Pedro Guerrero Guerrero (Chm)

Subsidiaries:

Bankinter Consultoria, Asesoramiento
y Atencion Telefonica, S.A. **(1)**
Avenida de Bruselas No 12, 28108, Al-
cobendas, Madrid, Spain
Tel.: (34) 916234322
Web Site: http://www.bankinter.es
Sales Range: $25-49.9 Million
Emp.: 25
Telebanking Services
N.A.I.C.S.: 517810

Bankinter Consumer Finance, EFC,
S.A. **(1)**

Avenida De Bruselas Arroyo Vega 7, 28108,
Alcobendas, Madrid, Spain
Tel.: (34) 916578729
Commercial Banking Services
N.A.I.C.S.: 522110

Bankinter Emisiones, S.A. **(1)**
Paseo Castellana 29, Madrid, 28046, Spain
Tel.: (34) 913397500
Web Site: http://www.bankinter.com
Banking Services
N.A.I.C.S.: 522110

Bankinter Gestao De Ativos, S.A. **(1)**
Praca Marques de Pombal No 13 1 o Piso,
1250-162, Lisbon, Portugal
Tel.: (351) 211144281
Commercial & Investment Banking Services
N.A.I.C.S.: 522110

Bankinter Luxembourg, S.A. **(1)**
37 Avenue J F Kennedy, L-1855, Luxem-
bourg, Luxembourg
Tel.: (352) 20210120
Web Site: https://www.bankinter.lu
Banking Customer Services
N.A.I.C.S.: 522110

Bankinter Seguros de Vida, de Se-
guros y Reaseguros SA **(1)**
Pico de San Pedro 2, Tres Cantos, 28760,
Madrid, Spain
Tel.: (34) 913398424
Insurance Related Activities
N.A.I.C.S.: 524298

Bankinter, S.A. - Sucursal em
Portugal **(1)**
Praca Marques de Pombal 13 2 andar,
1250-162, Lisbon, Portugal
Tel.: (351) 707505050
Web Site: http://www.bankinter.pt
Retail & Corporate Banking Services
N.A.I.C.S.: 522110

Evo Banco S.A. **(1)**
Calle Don Ramon de la Cruz Numero 84,
28006, Madrid, Spain
Tel.: (34) 912752666
Web Site: https://www.evobanco.com
N.A.I.C.S.: 522110

Intermobiliaria, S.A. **(1)**
Residencial Puerto Alto Calle del Naranjo
49 B2 - 11, Estepona, Malaga, Spain
Tel.: (34) 951977004
Web Site: https://intermobiliaria.es
Real Estate Investment Services
N.A.I.C.S.: 531190

**BANKISLAMI PAKISTAN LIM-
ITED**
11th Floor Executive Tower Dolmen
City Marine Drive, Block-4 Clifton,
Karachi, 74000, Pakistan
Tel.: (92) 21111475264　　　　PK
Web Site:
　　https://www.bankislami.com.pk
Year Founded: 2004
BIPL—(KAR)
Rev.: $80,008,029
Assets: $1,831,948,244
Liabilities: $1,700,227,601
Net Worth: $131,720,643
Earnings: $7,108,504
Emp.: 3,447
Fiscal Year-end: 12/31/19
Commercial & Investment Banking
N.A.I.C.S.: 522110
Ali Hussain (Chm)

**BANNARI AMMAN SUGARS
LTD.**
1212 Trichy Road, Coimbatore, 641
018, India
Tel.: (91) 4222204100
Web Site: https://www.bannari.com
500041—(BOM)
Rev.: $273,496,928
Assets: $350,603,499
Liabilities: $156,309,590
Net Worth: $194,293,909
Earnings: $10,917,802
Emp.: 1,898

Fiscal Year-end: 03/31/22
Sugar & Alcohol Mfr
N.A.I.C.S.: 111991
C. Palaniswamy *(Officer-Compliance & Sec)*

BANNER CHEMICALS LIMITED
Hampton Court Tudor Road, Manor Park, Runcorn, WA71TU, United Kingdom
Tel.: (44) 1928597000   UK
Web Site: http://www.bannerchemicals.com
Year Founded: 1860
Chemical Mfr & Distr
N.A.I.C.S.: 325998
Mordechai Kessler *(Chm & CEO)*

Subsidiaries:

Banner Chemicals-Biocides   (1)
Hampton Court, Tudor Road Manor Park, Runcorn, WA7 1TU, Cheshire, United Kingdom
Tel.: (44) 1928597000
Web Site: http://www.bannerchemicals.com
Sales Range: $25-49.9 Million
Emp.: 20
Chemicals Manufacturing
N.A.I.C.S.: 325998
Graham Cauchois *(Dir-Ops)*

Banner Chemicals-BlueCat-AdBlue Solutions   (1)
Hampton Court Manor Park, Runcorn, WA7 1TU, Cheshire, United Kingdom
Tel.: (44) 1928597010
Web Site: http://www.bannerchemicals.com
Sales Range: $25-49.9 Million
Emp.: 30
Chemicals Distribution
N.A.I.C.S.: 424690
Collin Boyle *(Dir-Fin)*

Banner Chemicals-Cosmetics & Personal Care   (1)
Hampton Ct Tudor Rd Manor Pk, Runcorn, WA7 1TU, Cheshire, United Kingdom
Tel.: (44) 1928597025
Web Site: http://www.bannerchemicals.com
Sales Range: $25-49.9 Million
Emp.: 59
Chemicals Manufacturing
N.A.I.C.S.: 325998
Graham Cauchois *(Dir-Specialty Bus)*

Banner Chemicals-Hydrocarbon Solvents   (1)
Hampton Court Manor Park, Runcorn, WA7 1TU, Cheshire, United Kingdom
Tel.: (44) 1928597020
Web Site: http://www.bannerchemicals.com
Sales Range: $25-49.9 Million
Emp.: 50
Chemicals Manufacturing
N.A.I.C.S.: 325998
Mottie Kessler *(Mng Dir)*

Banner Chemicals-Oil Field Applications   (1)
Hampton Ct Manor Pk, Runcorn, WA7 1TU, Cheshire, United Kingdom
Tel.: (44) 1928597024
Web Site: http://www.bannerchemicals.com
Sales Range: $50-74.9 Million
Emp.: 80
Chemicals Manufacturing
N.A.I.C.S.: 424690

Banner Chemicals-Oxygenated Solvents & Intermediates   (1)
Hampton Court Tudor Rd Manor Park, Runcorn, WA7 1TU, Cheshire, United Kingdom
Tel.: (44) 1928597020
Web Site: http://www.bannerchemicals.com
Sales Range: $25-49.9 Million
Emp.: 92
Pharmaceutical, Food & Personal Care Solvents
N.A.I.C.S.: 325199
Chris Hall *(Bus Dir)*

Banner Chemicals-Pharmaceutical Products   (1)
Hampton Court Manor Park, Runcorn, WA7 1TU, Cheshires, United Kingdom

Tel.: (44) 1928597020
Web Site: http://www.bannerchemicals.com
Sales Range: $25-49.9 Million
Emp.: 30
Pharmaceutical Preparations
N.A.I.C.S.: 325412
David Stringer *(Dir-Sls & Mktg)*

Banner Chemicals-Precision & Electronics Cleaning   (1)
Hampton Court Tudor Road Manor Park, Runcorn, WA7 1TU, Cheshire, United Kingdom
Tel.: (44) 1928597030
Web Site: http://www.bannerchemicals.com
Sales Range: $25-49.9 Million
Emp.: 80
Cleaning & Degreasing Solvents
N.A.I.C.S.: 325998

Banner Chemicals-Specialty Chemicals   (1)
Hampton Court Tudor Road Manor Park, Runcorn, WA7 1TU, Cheshire, United Kingdom
Tel.: (44) 1928597000
Web Site: http://www.bannerchemicals.com
Sales Range: $50-74.9 Million
Emp.: 80
Specialty Chemicals
N.A.I.C.S.: 424690
Graham Cauchois *(Bus Dir)*

MP Storage & Blending   (1)
Dockside Rd, Middlesbrough, TS3 8AS, Cleveland, United Kingdom
Tel.: (44) 1642244125
Web Site: http://www.mpstorage.com
Sales Range: $25-49.9 Million
Emp.: 25
Chemical Storage & Blending
N.A.I.C.S.: 493190
Darran Lemson *(Mgr-Bus Dev)*

Prism Chemicals   (1)
59-61 Sandhills Lane, Liverpool, L5 9XL, Merseyside, United Kingdom
Tel.: (44) 1642 244 125
Web Site: http://www.bannerchemicals.com
Sales Range: $25-49.9 Million
Emp.: 7
Pigment Formulations
N.A.I.C.S.: 325130

Samuel Banner & Co.   (1)
Hampton Court Manor Park, Runcorn, WA7 1TU, Cheshire, United Kingdom
Tel.: (44) 1928597021
Web Site: http://www.bannerchemicals.com
Sales Range: $50-74.9 Million
Emp.: 75
Chemicals Transportation
N.A.I.C.S.: 424690
Mark Johnson *(Mgr-Supply Chain)*

BANNERMAN ENERGY LTD
Suite 7 245 Churchill Ave, Subiaco, 6008, WA, Australia
Tel.: (61) 893811436
Web Site: https://bannermanenergy.com
BMN—(ASX)
Rev.: $1,083,066
Assets: $71,974,492
Liabilities: $1,387,553
Net Worth: $70,586,939
Earnings: ($6,384,882)
Emp.: 10
Fiscal Year-end: 06/30/24
Other Metal Ore Mining
N.A.I.C.S.: 212290
Brandon Munro *(CEO & Mng Dir)*

Subsidiaries:

Bannerman Mining Resources (Namibia) (Pty.) Ltd.   (1)
45 Mandume Ya Ndemufayo St, Swakopmund, 28454, Erongo, Namibia
Tel.: (264) 64416200
Web Site: http://www.bannermanresources.com
Sales Range: $50-74.9 Million
Emp.: 5
Mineral Exploration Services
N.A.I.C.S.: 212390

BANNERS CO., LTD.
102 Ishihara 1-chome, Kumagaya, 360-0816, Saitama, Japan
Tel.: (81) 485232018
Web Site: https://www.banners.jp
Year Founded: 1950
3011—(TKS)
Rev.: $30,961,240
Assets: $57,520,220
Liabilities: $41,061,320
Net Worth: $16,458,900
Earnings: $1,216,240
Emp.: 86
Fiscal Year-end: 03/31/24
Automotive Distr
N.A.I.C.S.: 423110

BANNU WOOLLEN MILLS LIMITED
D I Khan Road, Bannu, Karachi, Pakistan
Tel.: (92) 928613151
Web Site: https://www.bwm.com.pk
Year Founded: 1953
BNWM—(PSX)
Rev.: $4,917,661
Assets: $23,541,339
Liabilities: $4,862,554
Net Worth: $18,678,784
Earnings: ($122,656)
Emp.: 467
Fiscal Year-end: 06/30/19
Woollen Products Mfr
N.A.I.C.S.: 314999
Mushtaq Ahmad Khan *(Exec Dir)*

BANNY COSMIC INTERNATIONAL HOLDINGS, INC.
Flat 12 14/F Tower 1 Silvercord 30 Canton Road, Kowloon, China (Hong Kong)
Tel.: (852) 2516 5060   NV
Assets: $22,502
Liabilities: $88,348
Net Worth: ($65,846)
Earnings: ($191,392)
Fiscal Year-end: 06/30/18
Metal Mining
N.A.I.C.S.: 212290
Wenxin Liu *(Pres)*

BANPU POWER PCL
26th Floor Thanapoom Tower 1550 New Petchburi Road, Makkasan Ratchathewi, Bangkok, 10400, Thailand
Tel.: (66) 20076000
Web Site: https://www.banpupower.com
Year Founded: 1996
BPP—(THA)
Rev.: $888,692,427
Assets: $2,887,169,293
Liabilities: $1,291,040,737
Net Worth: $1,596,128,556
Earnings: $187,929,729
Emp.: 1,033
Fiscal Year-end: 12/31/23
Electric Power Distribution Services
N.A.I.C.S.: 221118

Subsidiaries:

Banpu Japan K.K.   (1)
Kasumigaseki Building 33rd Floor 3-2-5, PO Box 116, Chiyoda-ku, Tokyo, 100-6001, Japan
Tel.: (81) 362054665
Web Site: https://banpu-japan.com
Solar Energy Distribution Services
N.A.I.C.S.: 221122

Banpu Power (Japan) Co., Ltd.   (1)
Kasumigaseki Building 33rd Floor 3-2-5, PO Box 116, Kasumigaseki Chiyoda-ku, Tokyo, Japan
Tel.: (81) 362054665
Web Site: http://www.banpu-japan.com
Solar Power Services

N.A.I.C.S.: 221114
Wataru Shima *(CEO)*

FOMM Corporation   (1)
1-7 Kinko-cho, Kanagawa-ku, Yokohama, Kanagawa, Japan
Tel.: (81) 452863476
Web Site: https://www.fomm.co.jp
Electric Vehicle Mfr
N.A.I.C.S.: 336320

BANPU PUBLIC COMPANY LIMITED
27th Floor Thanapoom Tower 1550 New Petchburi Road Makkasan, Ratchathewi, Bangkok, 10400, Thailand
Tel.: (66) 26946600   TH
Web Site: http://www.banpu.com
BNPJY—(OTCIQ)
Rev.: $4,939,612,408
Assets: $12,235,310,205
Liabilities: $7,691,594,863
Net Worth: $4,543,715,343
Earnings: $350,975,030
Emp.: 6,116
Fiscal Year-end: 12/31/23
Coal Mining & Coal-Fired Power Generation Services
N.A.I.C.S.: 212115
Chanin Vongkusolkit *(Chm)*

Subsidiaries:

Akira Energy Ltd.   (1)
9th Floor York House The Landmark 15 Queen's Road, Central, China (Hong Kong)
Tel.: (852) 25228101
Coal Mining Services
N.A.I.C.S.: 213113

Asian American Coal Inc.   (1)
Geneva Place 2nd Floor 333 Waterfront Drive, Road Town, Tortola, Virgin Islands (British)
Tel.: (284) 2844944388
Coal Mining Services
N.A.I.C.S.: 213113

Subsidiary (Non-US):

Banpu Singapore Pte. Ltd.   (2)
One Marina Boulevard 28-00, Singapore, 018989, Singapore
Tel.: (65) 68907188
Coal Mining Services
N.A.I.C.S.: 213113

BLCP Power Ltd.   (1)
No 9 I-8 Road, Map Ta Phut Industrial Estate Tumbol Map Ta Phut Amphur Muang, Rayong, 21150, Thailand   (50%)
Tel.: (66) 3 892 5100
Web Site: https://www.blcp.co.th
Other Electric Power Generation
N.A.I.C.S.: 221118
Yuthana Charoenwong *(Mng Dir)*

BPP Renewable Investment (China) Co., Ltd.   (1)
Unit 108 No 26 Jiafeng Road, Pilot Free Trade Zone, Shanghai, China
Tel.: (86) 1057580388
Coal Mining Services
N.A.I.C.S.: 213113

Banpu Coal Power Ltd.   (1)
1550 Thanapoom Tower 26th Floor New Petchburi Road, Makkasan Ratchathewi, Bangkok, 10400, Thailand   (100%)
Tel.: (66) 20076000
Sales Range: $125-149.9 Million
Emp.: 250
Other Electric Power Generation
N.A.I.C.S.: 221118

Banpu Energy Services (Thailand) Co., Ltd.   (1)
1550 Thanapoom Tower 27th Floor New Petchburi Road, Makkasan Ratchathewi, Bangkok, 10400, Thailand
Tel.: (66) 26946600
Coal Mining Services
N.A.I.C.S.: 213113

Banpu Infinergy Co., Ltd.   (1)
29th Floor Thanapoom Tower 1550 New

Banpu Public Company Limited—(Continued)

Petchburi Road, Makkasan Ratchathewi,
Bangkok, 10400, Thailand
Tel.: (66) 20956595
Web Site: http://www.banpuinfinergy.co.th
Solar Power Generation Services
N.A.I.C.S.: 221114

Banpu International Ltd. (1)
(99.99%)
Tel.: (66) 26946600
Web Site: http://www.banpu.co.th
Sales Range: $100-124.9 Million
Emp.: 200
Support Activities for Coal Mining
N.A.I.C.S.: 213113

**Banpu Investment (China) Co.,
Ltd.** (1)
Unit 508 5th Floor Tower 21 No 10 Jiuxi-
anqiao Road, Chaoyang District, Beijing,
China
Tel.: (86) 1057580388
Coal Mining Services
N.A.I.C.S.: 213113

Banpu Minerals Co., Ltd. (1)
1550 Thanapoom Tower 26th Floor New
Petchburi Road, Makkasan Ratchathewi,
Bangkok, 10400, Thailand (99.99%)
Tel.: (66) 26946600
Sales Range: $200-249.9 Million
Emp.: 300
Support Activities for Coal Mining
N.A.I.C.S.: 213113

Subsidiary (Non-US):

Banpu Australia Co., Pty Ltd. (2)
Level 12 31 Queen Street, Melbourne,
3000, VIC, Australia
Tel.: (61) 3 8613 8888
Coal Mining Services
N.A.I.C.S.: 213113

Banpu Power International Ltd. (1)
One Cathedral Square, Level 11, Port
Louis, Mauritius (100%)
Tel.: (230) 2104000
Web Site: http://www.mitco.mu
Sales Range: $75-99.9 Million
Emp.: 75
Other Electric Power Generation
N.A.I.C.S.: 221118

**Banpu Power Investment (China)
Ltd.** (1)
9A 9th Floor Tower B Gateway Plaza No 18
Xia Guang Li North Road, East Third Ring,
100027, Beijing, Chaoyang, China (100%)
Tel.: (86) 10 57580388
Eltric Power Generation Services
N.A.I.C.S.: 221118

**Centennial Coal Company
Limited** (1)
Level 20 1 Market Street, Sydney, 2000,
NSW, Australia
Tel.: (61) 292662700
Sales Range: $700-749.9 Million
Emp.: 1,700
Coal Mining Services
N.A.I.C.S.: 212115
Robert G. Cameron (Founder)

Subsidiary (Domestic):

Berrima Coal Pty Limited (2)
Level 20 1 Market Street, Medway, Sydney,
2000, NSW, Australia (100%)
Tel.: (61) 292662700
Sales Range: $50-74.9 Million
Emp.: 22
Coal Mining Services
N.A.I.C.S.: 213113

Subsidiary (Non-US):

Centennial Airly Pty Limited (2)
Tel.: (61) 292662700
Coal Mining Services
N.A.I.C.S.: 213113

Subsidiary (Domestic):

**Centennial Angus Place Pty
Limited** (2)
Level 20 1 Market Street, Sydney, 2000,
NSW, Australia
Tel.: (61) 292662700

Coal Mining Services
N.A.I.C.S.: 212115

Centennial Clarence Pty Limited (2)
Level 20 1 Market Street, Sydney, 2000,
NSW, Australia
Tel.: (61) 292662700
Coal Mining Services
N.A.I.C.S.: 213113

**Centennial Mandalong Pty
Limited** (2)
177 Mandalong Rd, Hunter Valley, Manda-
long, 2264, NSW, Australia
Tel.: (61) 2 4973 090
Coal Mining Services
N.A.I.C.S.: 213113

**Centennial Mannering Pty
Limited** (2)
Rutleys Road, Doyalson, NSW, Australia
Tel.: (61) 2 4358 0580
Coal Mining Services
N.A.I.C.S.: 213113

Subsidiary (Non-US):

**Centennial Munmorah Pty
Limited** (2)
Tel.: (61) 292662700
Web Site: http://www.centenniacoal.com.au
Sales Range: $25-49.9 Million
Emp.: 28
Coal Mining Services
N.A.I.C.S.: 213113

Subsidiary (Domestic):

Centennial Myuna Pty Limited (2)
Level 20 1 Market Street, Sydney, 2000,
NSW, Australia
Tel.: (61) 292662700
Sales Range: $25-49.9 Million
Emp.: 28
Coal Mining Services
N.A.I.C.S.: 213113
Robert Cameron (Mng Dir)

Centennial Newstan Pty Limited (2)
Level 20 1 Market Street, Sydney, 2000,
NSW, Australia
Tel.: (61) 292662700
Sales Range: $25-49.9 Million
Emp.: 28
Coal Mining Services
N.A.I.C.S.: 213113

Subsidiary (Non-US):

Charbon Coal Pty Limited (2)
Tel.: (61) 292662700
Sales Range: $25-49.9 Million
Emp.: 30
Coal Mining Services
N.A.I.C.S.: 213113
David Moult (CEO & Mng Dir)

Clarence Coal Pty Limited (2)
Tel.: (61) 292662700
Web Site: http://www.centennialcoal.com.au
Sales Range: $25-49.9 Million
Emp.: 28
Coal Mining Services
N.A.I.C.S.: 213113

Clarence Colliery Pty Limited (2)
Web Site: http://www.centennialcoal.com.au
Sales Range: $25-49.9 Million
Emp.: 28
Coal Mining Services
N.A.I.C.S.: 213113

Subsidiary (Domestic):

Coalex Pty Limited (2)
Level 20 1 Market Street, Sydney, 2000,
NSW, Australia
Tel.: (61) 292662700
Sales Range: $25-49.9 Million
Emp.: 28
Coal Mining Services
N.A.I.C.S.: 213113

Subsidiary (Non-US):

Ivanhoe Coal Pty Limited (2)
Tel.: (61) 292662700
Web Site: http://www.centennialcoal.com.au
Sales Range: $25-49.9 Million
Emp.: 28
Coal Mining Services

N.A.I.C.S.: 213113

Subsidiary (Domestic):

Powercoal Pty Limited (2)
Level 20 1 Market Street, Sydney, 2000,
NSW, Australia
Tel.: (61) 292662700
Sales Range: $25-49.9 Million,
Emp.: 30
Coal Mining Services
N.A.I.C.S.: 213113

Springvale Coal Pty Limited (2)
Castlereagh Hwy, Lidsdale, 2790, NSW,
Australia
Tel.: (61) 2 6350 1600
Coal Mining Services
N.A.I.C.S.: 213113

Hunnu Coal Limited (1)
Level 1 33 Richardson Street, West Perth,
6005, WA, Australia
Tel.: (61) 892004267
Web Site: http://www.hunnucoal.com
Sales Range: Less than $1 Million
Coal Mining Services
N.A.I.C.S.: 212115
Chinbat Duger (Gen Mgr-Ops)

**PT. IndoTambangraya Megah
Tbk** (1)
Pondok Indah Office Tower III 3rd floor
Jalan Sultan Iskandar Muda, Pondok Indah
Kav V-TA South Jakarta, Jakarta, 12310,
Indonesia
Tel.: (62) 2129328100
Web Site: https://itmg.co.id
Emp.: 2,500
Coal Mining Services
N.A.I.C.S.: 213113

Subsidiary (Domestic):

PT. Bharinto Ekatama (2)
Desa Muara Begai Kecamatan Muara
Lawa, Kabupaten Kutai Barat, Kalimantan,
75775, Kalimantan Timur, Indonesia
Tel.: (62) 29328100
Coal Distr
N.A.I.C.S.: 423520

**Shijiazhuang Chengfeng Cogen Co.,
Ltd.** (1)
East of Jingshen Express Way, Zhengding
County, Shijiazhuang, 050800, Hebei,
China (100%)
Tel.: (86) 31185176918
Sales Range: $125-149.9 Million
Emp.: 250
Other Electric Power Generation
N.A.I.C.S.: 221118

Zouping Peak CHP Co., Ltd. (1)
Handian Town, Zouping County, Binzhou,
256209, Shandong, China (70%)
Tel.: (86) 5434615655
Other Electric Power Generation
N.A.I.C.S.: 221118

Zouping Peak Pte. Ltd. (1)
8 Marina Boulevard 05-02 Marina Bay Financial Centre, Singapore, 018981, Singapore
Tel.: (65) 63381888
Eltric Power Generation Services
N.A.I.C.S.: 221118

BANQUE BEMO S.A.L.
Elias Sarkis Ave BEMO Bldg, PO Box
16-6353, Ashrafieh, Beirut, Lebanon
Tel.: (961) 1200505   LB
Web Site:
https://www.bemobank.com
Year Founded: 1964
BEMO—(BEY)
Rev.: $1,363,465
Assets: $37,959,679
Liabilities: $35,454,162
Net Worth: $2,505,517
Earnings: ($968,536)
Fiscal Year-end: 12/31/22
Banking Services
N.A.I.C.S.: 522110
Samih H. Saadeh (Vice Chm & Gen
Mgr)

Subsidiaries:

BSEC S.A. (1)
3rd Floor Two Park Avenue Building Park
Avenue, Beirut Central District, Beirut,
Lebanon
Tel.: (961) 1997998
Web Site: http://www.bsec-sa.com
Sales Range: $50-74.9 Million
Emp.: 15
Financial Services
N.A.I.C.S.: 523999

BANQUE BEMO SAUDI
FRANSI S.A.
29 Ayyar Street, Damascus, Syria
Tel.: (963) 11 231 77 78
Web Site: http://www.bbsfbank.com
Year Founded: 2004
BBSF—(DSE)
Sales Range: $10-24.9 Million
Commercial Banking Services
N.A.I.C.S.: 522110
Riad Obegi (Chm)

BANQUE CANTONALE DE GE-
NEVE S.A.
Quai de I Ile 17, PO Box 2251, 1211,
Geneva, Switzerland
Tel.: (41) 582112100
Web Site: https://www.bcge.ch
Year Founded: 1816
BCGE—(SWX)
Rev.: $701,064,895
Assets: $35,975,237,854
Liabilities: $33,380,127,313
Net Worth: $2,595,110,541
Earnings: $274,827,669
Emp.: 916
Fiscal Year-end: 12/31/23
Miscellaneous Financial Investment
Activities
N.A.I.C.S.: 523999
Jean-Marc Joris (Member-Exec Bd &
Head-Ops Div)

Subsidiaries:

**Banque Cantonale de Geneve
(France) SA** (1)
20 place Louis-Pradel, 69001, Lyon,
France (100%)
Tel.: (33) 472073150
Web Site: https://www.bcgef.fr
Sales Range: $50-74.9 Million
Emp.: 29
Banking Services
N.A.I.C.S.: 522110

Capital Transmission S.A. (1)
Quai de Ille 17 Case postale 2251, 1211,
Geneva, Switzerland
Tel.: (41) 582112142
Web Site:
https://www.capitaltransmission.ch
Equity Investment Services
N.A.I.C.S.: 523940

Dimension SA (1)
Avenue de la Gare 20, 1003, Lausanne,
Switzerland
Tel.: (41) 21 317 5210
Web Site: https://www.dimension.ch
Specializing Distr
N.A.I.C.S.: 455219
Arthur Magis (Mng Dir)

Loyal Finance AG (1)
Gessnerallee 38, 8001, Zurich, Switzerland
Tel.: (41) 442155090
Web Site: https://www.loyalfinance.ch
Asset Management Services
N.A.I.C.S.: 523940

**Synchrony Asset Management
SA** (1)
7 Rue du Mont-Blanc, PO Box 2196, 1211,
Geneva, Switzerland (100%)
Tel.: (41) 229097575
Web Site: https://www.synchrony.ch
Sales Range: $50-74.9 Million
Emp.: 15
Asset Management Services
N.A.I.C.S.: 523999

BANQUE CANTONALE DU JURA S.A.
Rue de la Chaumont 10, 2900, Porrentruy, 2900, Switzerland
Tel.: (41) 324651301
Web Site: https://www.bcj.ch
BCJ—(SWX)
Sales Range: Less than $1 Million
Commercial Banking Services
N.A.I.C.S.: 522110
Bertrand Valley (CEO)

BANQUE CANTONALE VAUDOISE
Place Saint-Francois 14, Case postale 300, 1001, Lausanne, Switzerland
Tel.: (41) 212121000
Web Site: https://www.bcv.ch
Year Founded: 1845
BCVN—(SWX)
Rev.: $1,037,694,013
Assets: $65,266,075,388
Liabilities: $60,992,239,468
Net Worth: $4,273,835,920
Earnings: $520,177,384
Emp.: 1,982
Fiscal Year-end: 12/31/23
Commercial Banking Services
N.A.I.C.S.: 522110
Thomas W. Paulsen (CFO, Member-Exec Bd & Head-Fin & Risks)

Subsidiaries:

Asesores y Gestores Financieros SA   (1)
Paseo de la Castellana 92, 28046, Madrid, Spain   (50%)
Tel.: (34) 91 590 2121
Web Site: https://www.ayg.es
Sales Range: $50-74.9 Million
Emp.: 65
Credit Intermediation Services
N.A.I.C.S.: 522390

BCV Italia Srl   (1)
Viale Spagna 88, 20093, Cologno Monzese, Italy   (100%)
Tel.: (39) 022544055
Web Site: http://www.bcv-vacuum.com
Credit Intermediation
N.A.I.C.S.: 522299
Vaghi Sesano (Mng Dir)

Banque Piguet Galland & Cie SA   (1)
Avenue 41, PO Box 3456, CH 1211, Geneva, Switzerland   (75%)
Tel.: (41) 583104000
Web Site: http://www.banque-piguet.ch
Rev.: $1,000,000,000
Emp.: 180
Private Banking
N.A.I.C.S.: 523150
Calloud Olivier (CEO)

Cerifonds (Luxembourg) SA   (1)
43 Boulevard Prince Henri, 1724, Luxembourg, Luxembourg
Tel.: (352) 286648352
N.A.I.C.S.: 525190

Gerifonds S.A.   (1)
Rue du Maupas 2, Case postale 6249, 1002, Lausanne, Switzerland   (100%)
Tel.: (41) 213213200
Web Site: https://www.gerifonds.ch
Emp.: 38
Investment Management
N.A.I.C.S.: 523940
Christian Carron (CEO)

Groupe Baumgartner Holding SA   (1)
Rue de la Vernie 12, Crissier, Lausanne, Switzerland
Tel.: (41) 448866181
Web Site: http://www.baumgartnerholding.ch
Holding Company
N.A.I.C.S.: 551112

Office Vaudois de Cautionnement Agricole SA   (1)
Ave Des Jordils 1, Lausanne, Switzerland
Tel.: (41) 216142433
Credit Intermediation

N.A.I.C.S.: 522299

Piguet Galland & Cie SA   (1)
Rue de la Plaine 18, 1400, Yverdon-les-Bains, Switzerland
Tel.: (41) 58 310 4511
Web Site: https://www.piguetgalland.ch
Emp.: 155
Banking Services
N.A.I.C.S.: 523150
Olivier Calloud (CEO)

Societe Pour la Gestion de Placements Collectifs GEP SA   (1)
Rue Du Maupas 2, 1004, Lausanne, Switzerland   (100%)
Tel.: (41) 213187272
Open-End Investment Funds
N.A.I.C.S.: 525910

BANQUE CENTRALE DES COMORES
Place de France, BP 405, Moroni, Comoros
Tel.: (269) 7731814
Web Site: http://www.banque.comoros.org
Sales Range: $25-49.9 Million
Emp.: 50
Banking Services
N.A.I.C.S.: 522110

BANQUE CENTRALE DES ETATS DE L'AFRIQUE DE L'OUEST
Avenue Abdoulaye Fadiga, BP 3108, Dakar, Senegal
Tel.: (221) 338390500
Web Site: http://www.bceao.int
Sales Range: $200-249.9 Million
Central Bank
N.A.I.C.S.: 521110
Tiemoko Meyliet Kone (Governor)

BANQUE CENTRALE DU LUXEMBOURG
Boulevard Royal 2, 2983, Luxembourg, Luxembourg
Tel.: (352) 477441
Web Site: http://www.bcl.lu
Central Bank
N.A.I.C.S.: 521110
Yves Mersch (Pres)

BANQUE CENTRALE POPULAIRE S.A.
101 Boulevard Mohamed Zerktouni, BP 10 622, 20100, Casablanca, Morocco
Tel.: (212) 522224111
Web Site: https://www.groupebcp.com
Year Founded: 1926
BCP—(CAS)
Rev.: $1,997,415,644
Assets: $52,654,286,753
Liabilities: $47,132,320,087
Net Worth: $5,521,966,666
Earnings: $418,337,022
Emp.: 2,569
Fiscal Year-end: 12/31/23
Banking Services
N.A.I.C.S.: 522110

Subsidiaries:

BCP Bank (Mauritius) Ltd   (1)
9th Floor Maeva Tower Corner Bank Street & Silicon Avenue, Ebene, 72201, Mauritius
Tel.: (230) 2071000
Web Site: http://www.bcpbank.mu
Rev.: $19,659,789
Assets: $541,456,395
Liabilities: $473,916,347
Net Worth: $67,540,048
Earnings: ($3,275,275)
Fiscal Year-end: 12/31/2018
Banking Services
N.A.I.C.S.: 522110
Abdelwafi Atif (Exec Dir & Mng Dir)

Banque Malgache de l'Ocean Indien   (1)
Place de l'Idependance Antaninarenina, Antananarivo, 101, Madagascar
Tel.: (261) 202234609
Web Site: http://www.bmoinet.net
Retail & International Banking Services
N.A.I.C.S.: 522110
Alain Merlot (Gen Mgr)

BANQUE COMMERCIALE DU CONGO S.A.R.L.
Boulevard du 30 juin, PO Box 2798, Kinshasa, Congo, Democratic Republic of
Tel.: (243) 815181768
Web Site: http://www.bcdc.cd
Year Founded: 1909
Sales Range: $50-74.9 Million
Emp.: 400
Commercial Banking Services
N.A.I.C.S.: 522110

BANQUE D'ALGERIE
Immeuble Joly 38 Avenue Franklin Roosevelt, Algiers, Algeria
Tel.: (213) 21 230023
Web Site: http://www.bank-of-algeria.dz
Central Bank
N.A.I.C.S.: 521110
Mohammed Laksaci (Governor)

BANQUE DE KIGALI S.A.
63 Avenue du Commerce, BP 175, Kigali, 175, Rwanda
Tel.: (250) 252593100   RW
Web Site: http://www.bk.rw
Year Founded: 1966
Sales Range: $25-49.9 Million
Emp.: 1,200
Commercial Banking & Lending Services
N.A.I.C.S.: 522110
Marc Holtzman (Chm)

Subsidiaries:

BK Securities Limited   (1)
Plot No 6112 Avenue de la Paix, PO Box 175, Kigali, Rwanda
Tel.: (250) 252593100
Stock Brokerage Services
N.A.I.C.S.: 523150

BANQUE DE TUNISIE ET DES EMIRATS
5bis rue Mohamed Badra, 1002, Tunis, Tunisia
Tel.: (216) 71112000
Web Site: https://www.bte.com.tn
Year Founded: 1982
Banking Services
N.A.I.C.S.: 522110
Jabr Zaal Albuflassa (Chm)

BANQUE DEGROOF S.A.
Rue de l'Industrie 44, Brussels, 1040, Belgium
Tel.: (32) 22879111   BE
Web Site: http://www.degroof.be
Year Founded: 1871
Sales Range: $100-124.9 Million
Emp.: 1,012
Bank Holding Company
N.A.I.C.S.: 551111
Regnier Haegelsteen (Co-Mng Dir)

Subsidiaries:

Aforge Degroof Finance SA   (1)
44 rue de Lisbonne, 75008, Paris, France
Tel.: (33) 1 73 44 56 50
Investment Banking Services
N.A.I.C.S.: 523150

Banque Degroof Luxembourg S.A.   (1)
2 Rue Eugene Ruppert, Zone d'activite La

Cloche d'or, Luxembourg, 2453, Luxembourg   (100%)
Tel.: (352) 4535451
Web Site: http://www.degroof.lu
Sales Range: $200-249.9 Million
Emp.: 300
Commercial Banking
N.A.I.C.S.: 522110
Geert de Bruyne (Mng Dir)

Bearbull International Ltd   (1)
Charlotte House 2nd Floor, Charlotte Street New Providenc, 2453, Nassau, Bahamas   (100%)
Tel.: (242) 3237376
Sales Range: $50-74.9 Million
Emp.: 5
Miscellaneous Financial Investment Activities
N.A.I.C.S.: 523999

Degroof Petercam Corporate Finance SA/NV   (1)
Rue Guimard 18, 1040, Brussels, Belgium
Tel.: (32) 2 287 97 11
Web Site: http://www.degroofpetercam.be
Investment Banking Services
N.A.I.C.S.: 523150

PrivatBank Degroof, S.A.U.   (1)
Avenida Diagonal 464, 08006, Barcelona, Spain
Tel.: (34) 93 445 85 00
Investment Banking Services
N.A.I.C.S.: 523150

BANQUE DU CAIRE
6 Dr Mostafa Abu Zahra St, PO Box 9022, Nasr City, 11371, Cairo, Egypt
Tel.: (20) 222646401
Web Site: https://www.banqueducaire.com
BQDC.CA—(EGX)
Rev.: $1,588,446,895
Assets: $12,995,079,417
Liabilities: $11,934,979,954
Net Worth: $1,060,099,463
Earnings: $215,511,836
Emp.: 8,581
Fiscal Year-end: 12/31/23
Financial Banking Services
N.A.I.C.S.: 522110
Tarek Fayed (Chm & CEO)

BANQUE DU LIBAN
Masraf Lubnan Street, PO Box 11-5544, Beirut, 11/1/5544, Lebanon
Tel.: (961) 1750000
Web Site: http://www.bdl.gov.lb
Sales Range: $450-499.9 Million
Emp.: 1,500
Central Bank
N.A.I.C.S.: 521110
Riad T. Salame (Governor)

BANQUE ET CAISSE D'EPARGNE DE L'ETAT
1 Place de Metz, L 2954, Luxembourg, Luxembourg
Tel.: (352) 40151   LU
Web Site: http://www.spuerkeess.lu
Year Founded: 1856
BCEE—(LUX)
Rev.: $490,269,124
Assets: $61,696,165,950
Liabilities: $56,036,812,714
Net Worth: $5,659,353,236
Earnings: $406,754,622
Emp.: 1,881
Fiscal Year-end: 12/31/21
Commercial & Private Banking Services
N.A.I.C.S.: 522110
Elisabeth Mannes-Kieffer (Vice Chm)

BANQUE HERITAGE (SUISSE) S.A.
61 route de Chene, PO Box 6600, 1211, Geneva, Switzerland
Tel.: (41) 58 220 00 00

Banque Heritage (Suisse) S.A.—(Continued)

Web Site: http://www.heritage.ch
Rev.: $7,597,935,000
Private Banking Services & Asset Management
N.A.I.C.S.: 523150
Carlos Esteve *(CEO & Gen Mgr)*

Subsidiaries:

Banque Heritage (Uruguay) S.A.   (1)
Rincon 530, 11000, Montevideo, Uruguay
Tel.: (598) 2916 0177
Web Site: http://www.heritage.com.uy
Sales Range: $50-74.9 Million
Emp.: 50
Private Banking Services & Asset Management
N.A.I.C.S.: 523150
Graciela Reybaud Pallas *(Gen Mgr)*

HFT Intl. (Guernsey) LTD   (1)
Dorey Court Admiral Park, Saint Peter Port, GY1 3GB, Guernsey
Tel.: (44) 1481726014
Financial Management Services
N.A.I.C.S.: 551112

BANQUE INTERNATIONALE ARABE DE TUNISIE

7072 Avenue Habib Bourguiba, 1001, Tunis, Tunisia
Tel.: (216) 71131000
Web Site: https://www.biat.com.tn
Year Founded: 1976
BIAT—(BVT)
Rev.: $366,631,422
Assets: $6,855,765,023
Liabilities: $6,221,549,146
Net Worth: $634,215,877
Earnings: $99,031,434
Emp.: 1,966
Fiscal Year-end: 12/31/22
Investment Banking Services
N.A.I.C.S.: 523150
Ismail Mabrouk *(Chm)*

Subsidiaries:

Assurances BIAT   (1)
Les jardins du Lac II, Les Berges du Lac II, 1053, Tunis, Tunisia
Tel.: (216) 31300100
Web Site: http://www.assurancesbiat.com.tn
Sales Range: $50-74.9 Million
Emp.: 92
General Insurance Services
N.A.I.C.S.: 524298

Compagnie Internationale Arabe de Recouvrement   (1)
7 Rue Alain Savary, 1002, Tunis, Tunisia
Tel.: (216) 71783712
Commercial Banking Services
N.A.I.C.S.: 522110

Societe de pole de competitivite de Monastir - El Fejja   (1)
Mfcpole Grand Boulevard du Lac Immeuble BIAT 2eme etage, Les Berges du Lac, Tunis, Tunisia
Tel.: (216) 71 138 543
Commercial Banking Services
N.A.I.C.S.: 522110

BANQUE INTERNATIONALE POUR LAFRIQUE AU TOGO SA

13 Rue du Commerce, BP 346, Lome, Togo
Tel.: (228) 221 3286   TG
Web Site: http://www.biat.tg
Sales Range: $10-24.9 Million
Retail & Commercial Banking
N.A.I.C.S.: 522110
Jean-Paul Le Calm *(Dir Gen)*

BANQUE LIBANO-FRANCAISE S.A.L.

5 Rome Street Beirut Liberty Plaza Building Hamra, Beirut, 1808, Lebanon

Tel.: (961) 1791332
Web Site: http://www.eblf.com
Year Founded: 1967
Sales Range: $200-249.9 Million
Emp.: 700
Investment Banking Services
N.A.I.C.S.: 523150
Farid Raphael *(Founder, Chm & Gen Mgr)*

Subsidiaries:

BANK AL-SHARQ S.A.S.   (1)
Bank Al-Sharq Building Hafez Ibrahim Street Shaalan, 7732, Damascus, Syria
Tel.: (963) 11 668 03 000
International Banking
N.A.I.C.S.: 522299

BANQUE SBA S.A.   (1)
68 Champs Elysees Avenue, 75008, Paris, France
Tel.: (33) 1 53 93 25 00
Web Site: http://www.banque-sba.com
Sales Range: $50-74.9 Million
Emp.: 66
Financial Management Services
N.A.I.C.S.: 523999
Nagi Letayf *(Deputy CEO)*

Subsidiary (Non-US):

LF FINANCE (SUISSE) S.A.   (2)
86 Rhone Street, 1211, Geneva, Switzerland
Tel.: (41) 22 319 72 00
Web Site: http://www.lffinance.com
Sales Range: $50-74.9 Million
Emp.: 8
Financial Management Services
N.A.I.C.S.: 523999
Dory Hage *(Mng Dir)*

LIBANO-FRANCAISE FINANCE S.A.L.   (1)
The Floor Commerce & Finance Building Kantari, 113-6243, Beirut, Lebanon
Tel.: (961) 1 364 443
International Banking
N.A.I.C.S.: 522299

BANQUE MAURITANIENNE POUR LE COMMERCE INTERNATIONAL

Avenue Gamal abdel Nasser, BP 628, Nouakchott, Mauritania
Tel.: (222) 5252826
Web Site: http://www.bmci.mr
Sales Range: $1-9.9 Million
Emp.: 260
Banking Services
N.A.I.C.S.: 522110

BANQUE MISR

151 Mohamed Farid Street, Cairo, Egypt
Tel.: (20) 223912106   EG
Web Site:
http://www.banquemisr.com.eg
Year Founded: 1920
Sales Range: $650-699.9 Million
Emp.: 13,000
Commercial Bank
N.A.I.C.S.: 522110
Mohamed Kamal El-Din Barakat *(Chm)*

BANQUE NATIONALE DE BELGIQUE S.A.

Boulevard de Berlaimont 14, 1000, Brussels, Belgium
Tel.: (32) 22212111   BE
Web Site: http://www.nbb.be
Year Founded: 1850
Sales Range: $1-4.9 Billion
Banking Services
N.A.I.C.S.: 522110
Jean Hilgers *(Treas)*

BANQUE NATIONALE DU RWANDA

PO Box 531, Kigali, Rwanda

Tel.: (250) 574282
Web Site: http://www.bnr.rw
Sales Range: $125-149.9 Million
Emp.: 500
Banking Services
N.A.I.C.S.: 521110
Monique Nsanzabaganwa *(Vice Chm)*

BANQUE PROFIL DE GESTION SA

Cours de Rive 11, 1204, Geneva, Switzerland
Tel.: (41) 228183131
Web Site: http://www.bpdg.ch
BPDG—(SWX)
Rev.: $2,347,689
Assets: $278,158,150
Liabilities: $278,158,149
Net Worth: $1
Earnings: ($601,459)
Emp.: 39
Fiscal Year-end: 12/31/19
Banking Services
N.A.I.C.S.: 522110
Silvana Cavanna *(CEO)*

Subsidiaries:

Dynamic Assets Management Company (Luxembourg) SA   (1)
15 rue du Fort Bourbon, 1249, Luxembourg, Luxembourg
Tel.: (352) 26480264
Web Site: http://www.dmcfund.lu
Fund Management Services
N.A.I.C.S.: 523940
Christian Wolf *(Officer-Conducting)*

BANQUE SAUDI FRANSI

King Saud Road, PO Box 56006, Riyadh, 11554, Saudi Arabia
Tel.: (966) 112891136
Web Site: http://www.alfransi.com.sa
Year Founded: 1977
1050—(SAU)
Rev.: $2,137,654,979
Assets: $61,879,247,834
Liabilities: $51,548,538,595
Net Worth: $10,330,709,239
Earnings: $953,240,901
Emp.: 3,105
Fiscal Year-end: 12/31/22
International Banking Services
N.A.I.C.S.: 522299
Mazin Abdulrazzak AlRomaih *(Chm)*

Subsidiaries:

Saudi Fransi Capital LLC   (1)
8092 King Fahd Road, Riyadh, 12313-3735, Saudi Arabia
Tel.: (966) 112826828
Web Site: https://www.sfc.sa
Financial Services
N.A.I.C.S.: 523210
Waleed Fatani *(CEO)*

BANRO CORPORATION

1 First Canadian Place 100 King Street West Suite 7070, Toronto, M5X 1E3, ON, Canada
Tel.: (416) 366-2221   Ca
Web Site: http://www.banro.com
Sales Range: $200-249.9 Million
Emp.: 1,476
Gold Mining, Exploration & Development Services
N.A.I.C.S.: 212220
John U. Clarke *(Pres & CEO)*

BANSAL ROOFING PRODUCTS LIMITED

3/2 Labdhi Industrial Estate Acid Mill Compound Ranmukteshwar Road, Pratapnagar, Vadodara, 390 004, Gujarat, India
Tel.: (91) 9925050913
Web Site:
https://www.bansalroofing.com
Year Founded: 2008

538546—(BOM)
Rev.: $12,753,195
Assets: $5,159,700
Liabilities: $1,876,875
Net Worth: $3,282,825
Earnings: $761,670
Emp.: 31
Fiscal Year-end: 03/31/23
Roofing Produot Mfr
N.A.I.C.S.: 339999
Kaushalkumar S. Gupta *(Chm & Mng Dir)*

BANSARD INTERNATIONAL

40 rue d Arcueil, PO Box 70163, 94533, Rungis, France
Tel.: (33) 141731060
Web Site: http://www.bansard.com
Year Founded: 1963
Sales Range: $100-124.9 Million
Emp.: 600
Transport & Logistics Services
N.A.I.C.S.: 488999
Simon Pinto *(Pres)*

Subsidiaries:

Bansard Bangladesh   (1)
Jahangir Tower 5th floor 10 Kazi Nazrul Islam avenue, Karwan Bazar, 1215, Dhaka, Bangladesh
Tel.: (880) 2 91 22 707
Freight Transportation Services
N.A.I.C.S.: 488510

BANSEI ROYAL RESORTS HIKKADUWA PLC

4th Floor West Tower World Trade Centre, 01, Colombo, Sri Lanka
Tel.: (94) 112339135
Year Founded: 1976
BRR—(COL)
Rev.: $328,128
Assets: $1,036,300
Liabilities: $91,772
Net Worth: $944,528
Earnings: $54,832
Emp.: 38
Fiscal Year-end: 03/31/23
Consumer Services
N.A.I.C.S.: 561990
H. Ota *(CEO & Exec Dir)*

BANSISONS TEA INDUSTRIES LIMITED

33 M G Road, Siliguri, 734 405, West Bengal, India
Tel.: (91) 3532501808   In
519353—(BOM)
Rev.: $27,708
Assets: $848,997
Liabilities: $20,246
Net Worth: $828,752
Earnings: $10,765
Fiscal Year-end: 03/31/21
Cultivation Services
N.A.I.C.S.: 111998
Sandeep Agrawal *(Exec Dir)*

BANSWARA SYNTEX LIMITED

Industrial Area Dohad Road, Banswara, 327 001, Rajasthan, India
Tel.: (91) 2962257676
Web Site:
https://www.banswarasyntex.com
503722—(BOM)
Rev.: $164,720,911
Assets: $120,255,722
Liabilities: $65,817,829
Net Worth: $54,437,893
Earnings: $6,227,185
Emp.: 13,326
Fiscal Year-end: 03/31/22
Yarn & Fabric Mfr
N.A.I.C.S.: 313110
Ravindra Kumar Toshniwal *(Co-Mng Dir)*

Subsidiaries:

Banswara Fabrics Limited **(1)**
Dohad Road Industrial Area, Banswara, 327
001, India
Tel.: (91) 29 6225 7676
Web Site: http://www.banswarasyntex.com
Emp.: 1,000
Fabric Yarn Mfr
N.A.I.C.S.: 313110
Shyam Sunder Sajal *(Pres)*

BANTAM CAPITAL CORP.
25-106-4480 West Saanich Road,
Victoria, V8Z 3E9, BC, Canada
Tel.: (250) 384-0751 **AB**
Web Site:
http://www.idgholdings.com
Year Founded: 1995
IDH.H—(TSXV)
Assets: $131,577
Liabilities: $17,950
Net Worth: $113,627
Earnings: ($128,142)
Fiscal Year-end: 06/30/22
Holding Company; Outdoor Leisure
Products Mfr; Protective Services
N.A.I.C.S.: 551112
Glynn Jones *(CFO & Sec)*

Subsidiaries:

Integral Designs **(1)**
202B 1012 Douglas Street, Victoria, V8W
2C3, BC, Canada
Tel.: (250) 384-0751
Outdoor Sporting & Camping Equipment
Mfr
N.A.I.C.S.: 339920

**BANTAS BANDIRMA AM-
BALAJ SANAYI VE TICARET
AS**
Balikesir Asfalt 8 km P K 77,
Bandirma, Balikesir, Turkiye
Tel.: (90) 2667338787
Web Site: https://www.bantas.com.tr
Year Founded: 1986
BNTAS—(IST)
Sales Range: Less than $1 Million
Packaging Product Services
N.A.I.C.S.: 561910
Adnan Erdan *(Chm)*

BANTREL CO.
600 1201 Glenmore Trail SW, Cal-
gary, T2P 0T8, AB, Canada
Tel.: (403) 290-5000
Web Site: http://www.bantrel.com
Year Founded: 1983
Sales Range: $200-249.9 Million
Emp.: 1,400
Engineeering Services
N.A.I.C.S.: 541330
Darren Curran *(Pres)*

Subsidiaries:

Bantrel Constructors Co. **(1)**
2010 700 6 Avenue SW, Calgary, T2P 0T8,
AB, Canada
Tel.: (403) 515-8800
Industrial Building Construction Services
N.A.I.C.S.: 236210
Tony Fanelli *(VP)*

Bantrel Management Services
Co. **(1)**
400 700 6 Avenue SW, Calgary, T2P 0T8,
AB, Canada
Tel.: (403) 290-2750,
Construction Engineering Services
N.A.I.C.S.: 541330

Bemac Construction Corp. **(1)**
500 800 5 Avenue SW, Calgary, T2P 3T2,
AB, Canada
Tel.: (587) 233-6000
Industrial Building Construction Services
N.A.I.C.S.: 236210

BANVIDA SA

Bucarest 150 piso 6 oficina 601,
Providencia, Santiago, Chile
Tel.: (56) 223939003
Web Site: https://www.banvida.cl
Year Founded: 1998
BANVIDA—(SGO)
Sales Range: Less than $1 Million
Investment Management Service
N.A.I.C.S.: 525990
Martin Ducci Cornu *(CEO & Gen
Mgr)*

**BANVIT BANDIRMA VITAMINLI
YEM SANAYII ANONIM SIR-
KETI**
Omerli Mah Omerli Sok No 208,
Bandirma, 10201, Balikesir, Turkiye
Tel.: (90) 2667338600
Web Site: https://www.banvitas.com
Year Founded: 1968
BANVT—(IST)
Rev.: $339,572,330
Assets: $216,849,082
Liabilities: $150,647,066
Net Worth: $66,202,016
Earnings: ($13,672,552)
Emp.: 5,221
Fiscal Year-end: 12/31/22
Chicken Production Services
N.A.I.C.S.: 112320
Patricio Santiago Rohner *(Chm)*

BANYAN GOLD CORP.
Suite 1000 1050 W Pender Street,
Vancouver, V6E3S7, BC, Canada **AB**
Web Site:
https://www.banyangold.com
Year Founded: 2010
BYAGF—(OTCQB)
Rev.: $518,235
Assets: $44,174,047
Liabilities: $7,203,601
Net Worth: $36,970,446
Earnings: $277,814
Emp.: 8
Fiscal Year-end: 09/30/23
Gold Mining
N.A.I.C.S.: 212220
Mark Ayranto *(Chm)*

**BANYAN TREE HOLDINGS
LTD.**
211 Upper Bukit Timah Road, Singa-
pore, 588182, Singapore
Tel.: (65) 68495888
Web Site:
https://www.banyantree.com
BYNEF—(OTCIQ)
Rev.: $248,360,978
Assets: $1,311,625,387
Liabilities: $732,254,033
Net Worth: $579,371,355
Earnings: $24,884,496
Emp.: 13,169
Fiscal Year-end: 12/31/23
Holding Company; Hotels & Resorts
N.A.I.C.S.: 551112
Claire See Ngoh Chiang *(Sr VP)*

Subsidiaries:

Architrave Design & Planning Ser-
vices Pte. Ltd. **(1)**
24 A/B Angsana House Cheong Chin Nam
Road, Singapore, 599747, Singapore
Tel.: (65) 68495800
Web Site: http://www.architrave.com
Architectural Services
N.A.I.C.S.: 541310
Dharmali Kusumadi *(Mng Dir)*

Banyan Tree Gallery (Thailand)
Limited **(1)**
21/13 Thai Wah Tower 1 South Sathorn
Road, Bangkok, 10120, Thailand
Tel.: (66) 2285 0040
Handmade Craft Retailer
N.A.I.C.S.: 459420

Banyan Tree Hotels & Resorts Korea
limited **(1)**
60 JangChungdan-Ro, Jung-gu, Seoul,
100-857, Korea (South)
Tel.: (82) 222508000
Home Management Services
N.A.I.C.S.: 721110
Yuna Lee *(Mgr-Mktg & Comm)*

Banyan Tree Hotels & Resorts Pte.
Ltd. **(1)**
211 Upper Bukit Timah Road, Singapore,
588182, Singapore
Hotel & Resort Operator
N.A.I.C.S.: 721110
Claire See Ngoh Chiang *(Founder)*

Banyan Tree Resorts & Spas (Thai-
land) Company Limited **(1)**
51st -54th Floor 21/100 South Sathon Road
Thai Wah Tower II Building, Sathon, Bang-
kok, 10120, Thailand
Tel.: (66) 2 679 1052
Resort & Spa Operator
N.A.I.C.S.: 721110
Waralee Rungruangkanokkul *(Mgr-Admin)*

Laguna Resorts & Hotels Public
Company Limited **(1)**
No 21/9 21/31 and 21/33 Thai Wah Tower 1
5th and 12th Floor, South Sathorn Road,
Bangkok, 10120, Thailand
Tel.: (66) 26774455
Web Site: https://www.lagunaresorts.com
Rev.: $178,554,760
Assets: $877,235,541
Liabilities: $432,695,525
Net Worth: $444,540,016
Earnings: $10,966,082
Emp.: 84
Fiscal Year-end: 12/31/2023
Home Management Services
N.A.I.C.S.: 721110
Kwonping Ho *(Chm & CEO)*

Subsidiary (Domestic):

Laguna Holiday Club Limited **(2)**
61 Moo 4 Srisoonthorn Road, Thalang Dis-
trict, Phuket, 83110, Thailand
Tel.: (66) 7 635 8500
Web Site:
https://www.lagunaholidayclubresort.com
Hotel & Resort Operator
N.A.I.C.S.: 721120
Ben Lhcr *(Mgr-Sls)*

Thai Wah Plaza Limited **(1)**
21/100 South Sathorn Road, Bangkok,
10120, Thailand
Tel.: (66) 26791200
Hotel & Resort Operator
N.A.I.C.S.: 721110
Nopparat Aumpa *(Gen Mgr)*

**BAO MINH INSURANCE COR-
PORATION**
No 26 Ton That Dam Nguyen Thai
Binh Ward, District 1, Ho Chi Minh
City, Vietnam
Tel.: (84) 838294180
Web Site:
http://www.baominh.com.vn
Year Founded: 1995
Sales Range: $75-99.9 Million
Insurance Services
N.A.I.C.S.: 524298
Vinh Duc Tran *(Chm)*

BAO VIET HOLDINGS
No 8 Le Thai To, Hanoi, Vietnam
Tel.: (84) 439289898
Web Site:
https://www.baoviet.com.vn
Year Founded: 1964
BVH—(HOSE)
Rev.: $2,384,286,766
Assets: $9,109,386,044
Liabilities: $8,192,314,296
Net Worth: $917,071,748
Earnings: $76,631,547
Emp.: 7,000
Fiscal Year-end: 12/31/23
Financial Services
N.A.I.C.S.: 523999

Dao Dinh Thi *(Chm-Mgmt Bd)*

Subsidiaries:

Bao Viet Commercial Joint Stock
Bank **(1)**
16 Phan Chu Trinh, Phan Chu Trinh Ward
Hoan Kiem District, Hanoi, Vietnam
Tel.: (84) 2439288989
Web Site: http://www.baovietbank.vn
Banking Services
N.A.I.C.S.: 522110

Bao Viet Fund Management
Company **(1)**
8 Le Thai To, Hoan Kiem District, Hanoi,
Vietnam
Tel.: (84) 4 3928 9898
Investment Services
N.A.I.C.S.: 523999

Bao Viet Insurance Corporation **(1)**
104 Tran Hung Dao, Cua Nam Ward Hoan
Kiem District, Hanoi, 10000, Vietnam
Tel.: (84) 2438262614
Web Site: http://baoviet.com.vn
Emp.: 350
General Insurance Services
N.A.I.C.S.: 524210

Bao Viet Securities Joint Stock
Company **(1)**
8 Le Thai To, Hoan Kiem District, Hanoi,
Vietnam
Tel.: (84) 4 3928 9898
Brokerage Services
N.A.I.C.S.: 523150

Baoviet Tokio Marine Insurance Joint
Venture Company **(1)**
Room 601 6th Floor Sun Red River Building
23 Phan Chu Trinh, Hoan Kiem District, Ha-
noi, Vietnam
Tel.: (84) 439330704
Web Site:
http://www.baoviettokiomarine.com
Sales Range: $1-9.9 Million
Emp.: 50
Non-Life Insurance Products & Services
N.A.I.C.S.: 524128
Hidaki Mishima *(Gen Mgr)*

**BAODING DONGLI MACHIN-
ERY CO., LTD.**
No 29 East QianjinStreet, Baoding,
071100, Hebei, China
Tel.: (86) 3125802961
Web Site: https://www.bddlm.com
Year Founded: 1998
301298—(CHIN)
Rev.: $78,951,457
Assets: $153,284,005
Liabilities: $26,449,407
Net Worth: $126,834,598
Earnings: $11,861,376
Fiscal Year-end: 12/31/23
Automobile Parts Mfr & Distr
N.A.I.C.S.: 336110
Zheng Wang *(Chm)*

**BAODING LUCKY INNOVATIVE
MATERIALS CO., LTD.**
No 569 Herun Road, Baoding,
071051, China
Tel.: (86) 15712525800
Web Site:
https://maginfo.luckyfilm.com
Year Founded: 2005
300446—(CHIN)
Rev.: $23,839,920
Assets: $114,496,200
Liabilities: $18,518,760
Net Worth: $95,977,440
Earnings: $703,404
Emp.: 240
Fiscal Year-end: 12/31/22
Magnetic & Thermosensitive Record-
ing Materials Mfr
N.A.I.C.S.: 334610
Chen Fanzhang *(Chm)*

**BAODING TECHNOLOGY CO.,
LTD.**

Baoding Technology Co., Ltd.—(Continued)

China Town Industrial Park, Tangxi, Hangzhou, 311106, China
Tel.: (86) 57186318908
Web Site: https://www.baoding-tech.com
Year Founded: 1989
002552—(SSE)
Rev.: $193,832,028
Assets: $729,813,240
Liabilities: $357,396,624
Net Worth: $372,416,616
Earnings: ($4,840,992)
Emp.: 480
Fiscal Year-end: 12/31/22
Iron & Steel Products Mfr & Engineering Services
N.A.I.C.S.: 332111
Zhang Xufeng (Chm)

BAODING TIANWEI BAOBIAN ELECTRIC CO., LTD.
No2222 West Tianwei Road, Baoding, 071056, Hebei, China
Tel.: (86) 3123308341
Web Site:
https://www.btwelectric.com
600550—(SHG)
Rev.: $483,766,845
Assets: $761,897,560
Liabilities: $641,216,825
Net Worth: $120,680,736
Earnings: $4,140,382
Emp.: 1,000
Fiscal Year-end: 12/31/22
Power Transmission Product Mfr & Distr
N.A.I.C.S.: 333612

BAOFENG GROUP CO., LTD.
13F Shouheng Technology Mansion No 51 Xueyuan Road, Haidian District, Beijing, 100191, China
Tel.: (86) 1062309066
Rev.: $163,854,530
Assets: $180,574,380
Liabilities: $304,592,050
Net Worth: ($124,017,670)
Earnings: ($294,123,970)
Fiscal Year-end: 12/31/18
Software Development Services
N.A.I.C.S.: 541511
Xin Feng (Chm, Pres, CEO & Sec)

BAOFENG GROUP CO., LTD.
3-3-1267 Xijing Road, Beijing, China
Tel.: (86) 10 62309066
Web Site: http://www.baofeng.com
Sales Range: $50-74.9 Million
Emp.: 660
Entertainment Related Software Publisher
N.A.I.C.S.: 513210
Xin Feng (Chm, Pres, CEO & Sec)

BAOJI TITANIUM INDUSTRY CO., LTD.
No 88 Gaoxin Avenue High-tech Development Zone, Baoji, 721014, Shaanxi, China
Tel.: (86) 9173382666
Web Site: http://www.baoti.com
Year Founded: 1999
600456—(SHG)
Rev.: $931,502,319
Assets: $1,749,261,810
Liabilities: $799,483,033
Net Worth: $949,778,776
Earnings: $78,224,983
Fiscal Year-end: 12/31/22
Titanium Product Mfr
N.A.I.C.S.: 331491
Wang Jian (Chm)

BAOLINGBAO BIOLOGY CO., LTD.
No 1 East Outer Ring Road High-tech Industrial Development Zone, Dezhou, Yucheng, 251200, Shandong, China
Tel.: (86) 5348918699
Web Site: https://www.blb-cn.com
Year Founded: 1997
002286—(SSE)
Rev.: $380,870,100
Assets: $422,062,056
Liabilities: $140,652,720
Net Worth: $281,409,336
Earnings: $18,697,068
Emp.: 560
Fiscal Year-end: 12/31/22
Oligosaccharide, High Fructose Syrup & Tetrahydroxy Butane Mfr & Sales
N.A.I.C.S.: 325414
Dai Sijue (Chm)

BAOLONG INTERNATIONAL CO., LTD.
No 25 Shisan N Rd, Yunlin County, Douliu, 640106, Yunlin, Taiwan
Tel.: (886) 255811777
Web Site: http://www.baolongintl.com
1906—(TAI)
Rev.: $110,922,328
Assets: $221,944,594
Liabilities: $79,782,789
Net Worth: $142,161,805
Earnings: $984,270
Fiscal Year-end: 12/31/23
Industrial Paper Distr
N.A.I.C.S.: 424130
Fu-Yuan Li (Chm & Gen Mgr)

BAOSHENG MEDIA GROUP HOLDINGS LIMITED
Room 901 Block B Jinqiu International Building No 6 Zhichun Road, Haidian District, Beijing, China
Tel.: (86) 1082088021
Web Site: https://ir.bsacme.com
Year Founded: 2018
BAOS—(NASDAQ)
Rev.: $921,834
Assets: $48,827,742
Liabilities: $6,467,631
Net Worth: $42,360,111
Earnings: ($1,845,170)
Emp.: 32
Fiscal Year-end: 12/31/23
Holding Company
N.A.I.C.S.: 551112
Wenxiu Zhong (Founder, Chm & CEO)

BAOSHENG SCIENCE & TECHNOLOGY INNOVATION CO., LTD
No 1 Suzhong Road, Anyi Town, Baoying, 225800, Jiangsu, China
Tel.: (86) 51488238888
Web Site:
https://www.baoshengcable.com
Year Founded: 2000
600973—(SHG)
Rev.: $5,824,012,933
Assets: $2,975,471,254
Liabilities: $2,294,179,805
Net Worth: $681,291,449
Earnings: $9,091,153
Emp.: 2,000
Fiscal Year-end: 12/31/22
Electric Cables & Wires Mfr
N.A.I.C.S.: 335929
Sheng Changshan (Chm)

Subsidiaries:

Changzhou Jinyuan Copper Co., Ltd. **(1)**
776 Zhongwu Road, Changzhou, Jiangsu, China
Tel.: (86) 51988830226
Web Site: http://www.jinyuan-copper.com
Copper Wire & Rod Mfr

N.A.I.C.S.: 331420

Dongguan Nistar Transmitting Technology Co., Inc. **(1)**
Qiao Xin Xi'er Road, Eastern Industrial Park Qiao tou Town, Dongguan, China
Tel.: (86) 76982803333
Web Site: https://www.nistarwire.com
Weir & Cable Mfr & Distr
N.A.I.C.S.: 335929

BAOSHIDA INTERNATIONAL HOLDING GROUP CO., LTD.
8 Kaiyuan Road, Licheng District, Jinan, 250101, Shandong, China
Tel.: (86) 531 8888 6788
Web Site: http://www.baoshida.com
Year Founded: 2002
Holding Company; Investment, Real Estate, Trade & Industrial Services
N.A.I.C.S.: 551112
Xingjun Shang (CEO)

Subsidiaries:

Baoshida Swissmetal Ltd. **(1)**
Weidenstrasse 50, Dornach, 4143, Switzerland
Tel.: (41) 617053212
Web Site: http://www.baoshida-swissmetal.net
Sales Range: $50-74.9 Million
Emp.: 10
Holding Company; Copper Wire, Rods, Extruded Strips & Copper Alloy Products Mfr
N.A.I.C.S.: 551112
Mitchel Philippe (Chm)

Subsidiary (US):

Avins USA, Inc. **(2)**
19528 Ventura Blvd Ste 812, Tarzana, CA 91356
Web Site: http://www.avins.com
Sales Range: $25-49.9 Million
Emp.: 9
Precious Metal Product Mfr
N.A.I.C.S.: 331410

Subsidiary (Non-US):

Swissmetal East Asia Ltd. **(2)**
One Peking Unit 1202 Level 12, 1 Peking Road Tsim Sha Tsue, Kowloon, China (Hong Kong)
Tel.: (852) 3980 9286
Metal Products Mfr
N.A.I.C.S.: 332999

Shandong Baoshida Cable Co., Ltd. **(1)**
Baoshida Scientific Industrial Park, Gongye North Road Licheng District, Jinan, Shandong, China
Tel.: (86) 531 8868 1868
Web Site: http://en.baoshidacable.com
Emp.: 2,000
Cable Mfr
N.A.I.C.S.: 331222
Xing Shang (CEO)

BAOTA INDUSTRY CO., LTD.
No 388 Liupanshan West Road Economic & Technological Development Zone, West District of Yinchuan Ningxia Hui Autonomous Region Xixia District, Yinchuan, 750021, Ningxia, China
Tel.: (86) 9518697187
Web Site: http://www.nxz.com.cn
Year Founded: 1996
000595—(SSE)
Rev.: $35,157,564
Assets: $174,663,216
Liabilities: $72,466,056
Net Worth: $102,197,160
Earnings: ($12,612,132)
Fiscal Year-end: 12/31/22
Bearing Products Mfr
N.A.I.C.S.: 332991
Du Zhixue (Chm)

BAOTAILONG NEW MATERIALS CO., LTD.

No 16 Baotailong Road, Xinxing District, Qitaihe, 154600, Heilongjiang, China
Tel.: (86) 4642924567
Web Site: https://www.btlgf.com
Year Founded: 2003
601011—(SHG)
Rev.: $529,716,789
Assets: $1,880,443,104
Liabilities: $704,420,819
Net Worth: $1,176,022,285
Earnings: $21,304,675
Fiscal Year-end: 12/31/22
Coke Product Mfr & Distr
N.A.I.C.S.: 324199
Qin Huai (Pres)

BAOTOU DONGBAO BIO-TECH CO., LTD.
No 46 Huanghe Street Rare Earth High-tech Development Zone, Inner Mongolia, Baotou, 014030, China
Tel.: (86) 4726208697
Web Site:
https://www.dongbaoshengwu.com
Year Founded: 1997
300239—(CHIN)
Rev.: $132,453,360
Assets: $324,058,644
Liabilities: $77,535,900
Net Worth: $246,522,744
Earnings: $15,365,376
Emp.: 300
Fiscal Year-end: 12/31/22
Gelatin & Collagen Products Mfr
N.A.I.C.S.: 325998
Wang Aiguo (Chm)

BAOTOU HUAZI INDUSTRY CO., LTD.
Inner Mongolia Autonomous Region, Donghe District, Baotou, 014045, China
Tel.: (86) 4726957544
Web Site: http://www.huazi.com
Year Founded: 1998
600191—(SHG)
Rev.: $51,733,665
Assets: $270,906,068
Liabilities: $62,942,541
Net Worth: $207,963,527
Earnings: ($23,176,951)
Fiscal Year-end: 12/31/22
Sugar Products Mfr
N.A.I.C.S.: 311314
Li Yanyong (Chm)

BAOTOU IRON & STEEL (GROUP) COMPANY LIMITED
Hexi Industrial Zone, Kun District, Baotou, 014010, Inner Mongolia, China
Tel.: (86) 4722183163
Web Site: http://www.btsteel.com
Year Founded: 1954
Sales Range: $5-14.9 Billion
Emp.: 80,000
Iron & Steel Mfr
N.A.I.C.S.: 332111
Bingli Zhou (Chm)

Subsidiaries:

China Northern Rare-Earth Group Highi-Tech Company Limited **(1)**
No 83 Huanghe Road Rare-earth Hi-tech Industrial Development Zone, Inner Mongolia, Baotou, 014030, China
Tel.: (86) 4722207799
Web Site: http://www.reht.com
Rev.: $4,637,931,034
Assets: $5,607,091,133
Liabilities: $1,882,388,555
Net Worth: $3,724,702,578
Earnings: $328,248,255
Fiscal Year-end: 12/31/2023
Rare Earth Mineral Mining
N.A.I.C.S.: 212290
Jinling Li (Chm)

Inner Mongolia Baotou Steel Union
Company Limited **(1)**
Inner Mongolia Queensland, Baotou, Hexi,
China
Tel.: (86) 4722189515
Web Site: https://www.baoganggf.com
Rev.: $10,132,914,248
Assets: $20,599,781,197
Liabilities: $11,979,933,924
Net Worth: $8,619,847,273
Earnings: ($102,485,935)
Fiscal Year-end: 12/31/2022
Iron & Steel Mfr
N.A.I.C.S.: 332111
Li Degang *(Chm)*

BAOTOU TOMORROW TECH-NOLOGY CO., LTD.
No 22 Shuguang Road Rare Earth
High-tech Industrial Dev Zn, Baotou,
041030, China
Tel.: (86) 472 220 7068
600091—(SHG)
Rev.: $2,793,018
Assets: $177,262,438
Liabilities: $40,726,282
Net Worth: $136,536,156
Earnings: ($2,694,964)
Fiscal Year-end: 12/31/20
Chemical Product Mfr & Distr
N.A.I.C.S.: 325199
Guochun Li *(Chm & Pres)*

BAOWU MAGNESIUM TECH-NOLOGY CO., LTD.
No 11 Kaiping Road, Dongping Sub-
district Lishui District, Nanjing,
211212, Jiangsu, China
Tel.: (86) 2557234888
Web Site: https://www.rsm.com.cn
Year Founded: 1993
002182—(SSE)
Rev.: $1,278,287,244
Assets: $1,272,484,512
Liabilities: $624,167,856
Net Worth: $648,316,656
Earnings: $85,827,924
Fiscal Year-end: 12/31/22
Nonferrous Metal Products Mfr
N.A.I.C.S.: 331410
Naijuan Fan *(CFO & Deputy Gen
Mgr)*

BAOXINIAO HOLDING CO., LTD.
No 2299 Shuangta Road Oubei
Street, Yongjia County, Wenzhou,
325102, Zhejiang, China
Tel.: (86) 57767379161
Web Site: http://www.bxn.com
Year Founded: 2001
002154—(SSE)
Rev.: $605,511,504
Assets: $841,060,584
Liabilities: $272,606,256
Net Worth: $568,454,328
Earnings: $64,411,308
Fiscal Year-end: 12/31/22
Jean Apparel Mfr
N.A.I.C.S.: 315250
Zhi Ze Wu *(Chm)*

BAOYE GROUP COMPANY LIMITED
No 1687 Guazhu East Road, Keqiao,
Shaoxing, 312030, Zhejiang, China
Tel.: (86) 57584135837   CN
Web Site:
http://www.baoyegroup.com
Year Founded: 1974
2355—(HKG)
Rev.: $3,429,319,140
Assets: $6,854,395,954
Liabilities: $5,190,010,816
Net Worth: $1,664,385,138
Earnings: $101,285,262
Emp.: 6,560
Fiscal Year-end: 12/31/22

Construction Services
N.A.I.C.S.: 236220
Baogen Pang *(Chm & Chm)*

Subsidiaries:

Anhui Baoye Construction Engineer-
ing Group Co., Ltd. **(1)**
Intersection of Lihe Road and Xiaocheng
Road, Xinzhan Industrial Park Xinzhan Dis-
trict, Hefei, 230000, Anhui, China
Tel.: (86) 55164286117
Web Site: http://www.ahbaoye.com
Real Estate Services
N.A.I.C.S.: 531390

BAOZUN INC.
NO 510 West Jiangchang RD, JingAn
District, Shanghai, 200436, China
Tel.: (86) 2180266000   Ky
Web Site: https://www.baozun.com
BZUN—(NASDAQ)
Rev.: $1,287,060,676
Assets: $1,550,863,629
Liabilities: $901,520,427
Net Worth: $649,343,202
Earnings: ($100,090,561)
Emp.: 7,588
Fiscal Year-end: 12/31/22
Ecommerce Services
N.A.I.C.S.: 459999
Vincent Wenbin Qiu *(Co-Founder,
Chm & CEO)*

BAPCOR LIMITED
127-139 Link Road, Melbourne Air-
port, Melbourne, 3045, VIC, Australia
Tel.: (61) 384707300   NZ
Web Site: http://www.bapcor.com.au
Year Founded: 1971
BAP—(ASX)
Rev.: $1,360,134,877
Assets: $1,271,905,043
Liabilities: $674,721,552
Net Worth: $597,183,491
Earnings: ($105,919,471)
Emp.: 5,500
Fiscal Year-end: 06/30/24
Automotive Aftermarket Supplies &
Accessories Distr
N.A.I.C.S.: 441330
Margaret Anne Haseltine *(Chm)*

Subsidiaries:

AADi Australia Pty Ltd **(1)**
57 Meadow Ave, Coopers Plains, 4108,
QLD, Australia
Tel.: (61) 732779960
Web Site: https://www.aadiaustralia.com.au
Automotive Parts Mfr & Distr
N.A.I.C.S.: 336390

Australian Automotive Electrical
Wholesale Pty Ltd **(1)**
Unit 3 32-34 Wodonga Street, Beverley,
5009, SA, Australia
Tel.: (61) 882680988
Web Site: https://www.aaewholesale.com.au
Automotive Electrical Parts Distr
N.A.I.C.S.: 423610

Bapcor New Zealand Limited **(1)**
21-27 Omega Street, Rosedale, Auckland,
0632, New Zealand **(100%)**
Tel.: (64) 94143200
Web Site: http://www.bapcor.com.au
Investment Holding Company
N.A.I.C.S.: 551112

Subsidiary (Domestic):

Brake & Transmission NZ
Limited **(2)**
21-27 Omega Street, Albany, Auckland,
0632, New Zealand **(100%)**
Tel.: (64) 94143200
Web Site: https://www.bntnz.co.nz
Automobile Parts Distr
N.A.I.C.S.: 423610
Martin Storey *(Gen Mgr)*

Subsidiary (Non-US):

Diesel Distributors Australia Pty
Limited **(2)**

Unit 1 12 Selhurst Street, Coopers Plains,
Brisbane, 4108, QLD, Australia **(100%)**
Tel.: (61) 733455633
Web Site:
http://www.dieseldistributors.com.au
Diesel Engine Components Distr
N.A.I.C.S.: 423860
Lloyd Richardson *(Branch Mgr)*

Holding (Domestic):

Diesel Distributors Limited **(2)**
2/103 Cryers Road, East Tamaki, Auckland,
2013, New Zealand **(100%)**
Tel.: (64) 9265 0622
Web Site: http://www.dieseldistributors.co.nz
Diesel Fuel Injection Parts & Equipment
Distr
N.A.I.C.S.: 423120

Subsidiary (Domestic):

HCB Technologies Limited **(2)**
19 Timberly Rd, Mangere, Auckland, 2022,
New Zealand **(100%)**
Tel.: (64) 96220033
Web Site: https://www.hcb.co.nz
Automotive & Industrial Batteries Whslr
N.A.I.C.S.: 423610
Paul Eden *(Gen Mgr)*

Holding (Domestic):

Number 1 Shoes Limited **(2)**
Level 3 South Annex 1-7 The Strand, Taka-
puna, Auckland, 0622, New
Zealand **(100%)**
Tel.: (64) 800 661 7463
Web Site:
http://www.numberoneshoes.co.nz
Footwear Retailer
N.A.I.C.S.: 424340
Gary Rohloff *(CEO)*

Subsidiary (Domestic):

R Hannah & Co Limited **(2)**
15 John Unit G Seddon Drive Elsdon, PO
Box 50146, Porirua, Wellington, 5240, New
Zealand **(100%)**
Tel.: (64) 4 237 5499
Web Site: http://www.hannahs.co.nz
Footwear Retailer
N.A.I.C.S.: 424340

Bapcor Retail Pty. Ltd. **(1)**
327 Ferntree Gully Road, Mount Waverley,
3149, VIC, Australia
Tel.: (61) 388781111
Vehicle Parts & Accessories Distr
N.A.I.C.S.: 423140

Baxters Pty Ltd **(1)**
327 Ferntree Gully Rd, Mount Waverley,
3149, VIC, Australia
Tel.: (61) 397307000
Web Site: https://www.baxters.com.au
Automotive Electrical Parts Distr
N.A.I.C.S.: 423610

Don Kyatt Spare Parts (Qld) Pty
Ltd **(1)**
1912 Ipswich Road, Rocklea, 4108, QLD,
Australia
Tel.: (61) 732775966
Web Site: http://www.donkyattqld.com.au
Automotive Electrical Parts Distr
N.A.I.C.S.: 423610

Federal Batteries Qld Pty Ltd **(1)**
Unit G/10-16 South St, Rydalmere, 2116,
NSW, Australia
Tel.: (61) 296385222
Web Site:
https://www.federalbatteries.com.au
Automotive Electrical Parts Distr
N.A.I.C.S.: 423610

I Know Parts & Wrecking Pty Ltd **(1)**
171-173 Military Road, Guildford, 2161,
NSW, Australia
Tel.: (61) 732774076
Web Site: http://www.iknowparts.com.au
Automotive Electrical Parts Distr
N.A.I.C.S.: 423610

JAS Oceania Pty Ltd **(1)**
54-58 Lillee Crescent, Tullamarine, 3043,
VIC, Australia
Tel.: (61) 393172600
Web Site: https://www.jasoceania.com.au

Automotive Electrical Parts Distr
N.A.I.C.S.: 423610

Low Voltage Pty Ltd **(1)**
72 Butler Way, Tullamarine, 3043, VIC,
Australia
Tel.: (61) 393357100
Web Site: http://www.lowvoltage.net.au
Electrical Product Mfr & Distr
N.A.I.C.S.: 335999

MTQ Engine Systems (Aust) Pty
Ltd **(1)**
111 Beenleigh Road, Acacia Ridge, 4110,
QLD, Australia
Tel.: (61) 737234400
Web Site: https://www.mtqes.com.au
Diesel Engine Components Distr
N.A.I.C.S.: 423860

Midas Australia Pty Ltd **(1)**
327 Ferntree Gully Road, Mount Waverley,
3149, VIC, Australia
Tel.: (61) 388781111
Web Site: https://www.midas.com.au
Automotive Services
N.A.I.C.S.: 811111

Premier Auto Trade Pty Ltd **(1)**
36-40 Shearson Crescent, Mentone, 3194,
VIC, Australia
Tel.: (61) 395819100
Web Site:
https://www.premierautotrade.com.au
Automotive Engine Parts Distr
N.A.I.C.S.: 441330

BAQUS GROUP LIMITED
2/3 North Mews, London, WC1N 2JP,
United Kingdom
Tel.: (44) 2078311283   UK
Web Site: http://www.baqus.co.uk
Year Founded: 2006
Construction & Property Consultancy
Services
N.A.I.C.S.: 236220
Rob McNeill *(CEO)*

Subsidiaries:

Baqus Group - Oxford **(1)**
31 West Way Botley, Oxford, OX2 0JE, Ox-
fordshire, United Kingdom
Tel.: (44) 1865241159
Web Site: http://www.baqus.co.uk
Sales Range: $25-49.9 Million
Emp.: 6
Chartered Quantity Surveying & Construc-
tion Cost Consultant Services
N.A.I.C.S.: 541620

Fletcher McNeill & Partners
Limited **(1)**
Quantum House 23 Roscoe St, Liverpool,
L1 2SX, Merseyside, United Kingdom
Tel.: (44) 1517085896
Web Site: http://www.baqus.co.uk
Emp.: 11
Quantity Surveying Services
N.A.I.C.S.: 541990
Robert McNeill *(Exec Dir)*

BAR 2 LIMITED
Victoria House 49 Clarendon Road,
Watford, WD17 1HX, United Kingdom
Tel.: (44) 1923690910
Web Site: http://www.bar2.co.uk
Year Founded: 2001
Sales Range: $1-9.9 Million
Emp.: 13
Staffing Services
N.A.I.C.S.: 561320
Jason Hargreaves *(Mng Dir)*

BAR PACIFIC GROUP HOLD-INGS LIMITED
Room D2 11/F Phase 2 Hang Fung
Industrial Building, Kowloon, China
(Hong Kong)
Tel.: (852) 2 356 1126   Ky
Web Site:
http://www.barpacific.com.hk
Year Founded: 2016

Bar Pacific Group Holdings Limited—(Continued)

8432—(HKG)
Rev.: $15,316,375
Assets: $25,285,110
Liabilities: $23,098,770
Net Worth: $2,186,340
Earnings: ($1,347,841)
Emp.: 337
Fiscal Year-end: 03/31/22
Bar Operator
N.A.I.C.S.: 722410
Eva Ying Sin Tse *(Chm & CEO)*

BARAK VALLEY CEMENTS LIMITED
Unit Nos DSM 450-451-452 DLF
Towers 15 Shivaji Marg Moti Nagar,
Delhi, 110015, India
Tel.: (91) 1141212600
Web Site:
https://www.barakcement.com
532916—(BOM)
Rev.: $24,325,638
Assets: $31,445,915
Liabilities: $16,708,255
Net Worth: $14,737,659
Earnings: ($617,103)
Emp.: 276
Fiscal Year-end: 03/30/22
Cement Mfr
N.A.I.C.S.: 327310
Santosh Kumar Bajaj *(Exec Dir)*

Subsidiaries:

Valley Strong Cements (Assam)
Limited   (1)
Devendra Nagar Jhoombasti, PO Badar-
purghat Distt, Assam, 110034, India
Tel.: (91) 3843269435
Emp.: 6
Cement Mfr
N.A.I.C.S.: 327310

BARAKA POWER LIMITED
6/A/1 1st and 2nd Floor Segunbagi-
cha, Dhaka, 1000, Bangladesh
Tel.: (880) 2223352305   BD
Web Site: https://barakapower.com
Year Founded: 2007
BARKAPOWER—(DHA)
Rev.: $21,032,072
Assets: $81,418,981
Liabilities: $22,192,974
Net Worth: $59,226,007
Earnings: $5,527,096
Emp.: 132
Fiscal Year-end: 06/30/22
Eletric Power Generation Services
N.A.I.C.S.: 221118
Faisal Ahmed Chowdhury *(Chm)*

Subsidiaries:

Baraka Fashions Limited   (1)
06 Shing Bari Road Boro Dewara, Tongi,
Gazipur, 1700, Bangladesh
Tel.: (880) 1713363663
Web Site: https://www.barakafashions.com
Emp.: 1,038
Garment Product Mfr
N.A.I.C.S.: 315250
Faisal Ahmed Chowdhry *(Chm)*

Baraka Patenga Power Limited   (1)
6/A/1 2nd Floor Segunbagicha, Dhaka,
1000, Bangladesh
Tel.: (880) 29560339
Web Site: http://www.bpplbd.com
Eletric Power Generation Services
N.A.I.C.S.: 221118
Gulam Rabbani Chowdhury *(Chm)*

BARAKAH OFFSHORE PE-TROLEUM BERHAD
No.28 Jln PJU 5/4 Dataran Sunway,
Petaling Jaya, Kota Damansara, Ma-
laysia
Tel.: (60) 3 6141 8820

Web Site:
http://www.barakahpetroleum.com
Emp.: 100
Offshore Petroleum Transport
N.A.I.C.S.: 486910
Firdauz Edmin Moktar *(CFO & VP)*

Subsidiaries:

PBJV Group Sdn. Bhd   (1)
No 4 1st Floor Wisma NDP Jln Besar, Dun-
gun, 23100, Paka, Malaysia
Tel.: (60) 827 7171
Web Site:
http://www.pbjv.barakahpetroleum.com
Ship Management Services
N.A.I.C.S.: 532411
Rasdee Abdullah *(Pres & CEO)*

BARAN GROUP LTD.
Eshkolot 3 Omer Industrial Park,
Omer, 50200, Israel
Tel.: (972) 39775000
Web Site:
https://www.barangroup.com
Year Founded: 1979
BRAN—(TAE)
Rev.: $188,065,476
Assets: $201,613,479
Liabilities: $136,849,563
Net Worth: $64,763,917
Earnings: $10,420,224
Emp.: 950
Fiscal Year-end: 12/31/23
Engineeering Services
N.A.I.C.S.: 541330
Meir Dor *(Founder & Chm)*

Subsidiaries:

BARTEC Engineering LLC   (1)
4-B Afrosiab Str Mirobod Dist, Tashkent,
Uzbekistan
Tel.: (998) 71 256 9503
Engineeering Services
N.A.I.C.S.: 541330

BTN Baran Telecom Networks
GmbH   (1)
Am Lichtbogen 51, 45141, Essen, Germany
Tel.: (49) 20 186 6200
Web Site: https://www.bt-networks.de
Engineeering Services
N.A.I.C.S.: 541330

Baran Chile SpA   (1)
Av del Valle #961 Oficina 5710, Ciudad Em-
presarial Comuna Huechuraba, Santiago,
Chile
Tel.: (56) 95207 4790
Engineeering Services
N.A.I.C.S.: 541330
Daniel Bardin *(Gen Mgr)*

Baran Construction and Infrastructure
Ltd.   (1)
Baran House 5 Menachem Begin Boule-
vard, Beit Dagan, 50200, Israel
Tel.: (972) 39775110
Construction Engineering Services
N.A.I.C.S.: 541330

Baran Engineering South Africa (Pty)
Ltd.   (1)
22nd 11 Avenue Edenburg, Sandton, 2128,
Gauteng, South Africa
Tel.: (27) 79 445 4573
Engineeering Services
N.A.I.C.S.: 541330

Baran Industries (91) Ltd.   (1)
Baran House 5 Menachem Begin Boule-
vard, Beit Dagan, 50200, Israel
Tel.: (972) 39775000
Construction Engineering Services
N.A.I.C.S.: 541330
Nahman Tsabar *(CEO)*

Baran Projects South Africa (Pty)
Ltd.   (1)
22nd 11 Avenue Edenburg, Sandton, 2128,
Gauteng, South Africa
Tel.: (27) 97239775022
Construction Management Services
N.A.I.C.S.: 541330

Baran South East Asia Ltd.   (1)

889 Thai CC Tower 6th Floor 64 Shouth
Sathorn Rd, Yannawa Sathorn, Bangkok,
10120, Thailand
Tel.: (66) 97239775022
Construction Management Services
N.A.I.C.S.: 541330

Baran Telecom, Inc.   (1)
2355 Industrial Park Blvd, Cumming, GA
30041-6463
Tel.: (678) 455-1181
Web Site: http://www.barantelecom.com
Sales Range: $125-149.9 Million
Emp.: 475
Network Wireless Telecommunications Ser-
vices
N.A.I.C.S.: 237130

Baran Vietnam Ltd.   (1)
418 Ly Thai So St Hoan Kiem District 6/F,
Hanoi, Vietnam
Tel.: (84) 4 9365871
Engineeering Services
N.A.I.C.S.: 541330

Baran-Oil & Petrochemical (1987)
Projects Ltd.   (1)
9 Hashalom Avenue, Nesher, 36651, Israel
Tel.: (972) 48304888
Web Site: http://www.barangroup.com
Sales Range: $25-49.9 Million
Emp.: 80
Engineering & Construction Services
N.A.I.C.S.: 541330
Zvika Achrai *(Mng Dir)*

Baran-Romania LLC   (1)
1 N Titulescu, Bucharest, 011131, Romania
Tel.: (40) 213165542
Construction Management Services
N.A.I.C.S.: 541330

BaranMex, S.A. de C.V.   (1)
Av Mariano Escobedo No 476 Oficina 1218,
Col Nueva Anzures Del Cuauhtemoc,
11590, Mexico, DF, Mexico
Tel.: (52) 1 55 4739 2570
Engineeering Services
N.A.I.C.S.: 541330
Shabtay Mizrahi *(Gen Dir)*

BARBADOS SHIPPING & TRADING CO. LTD.
1st Floor The AutoDome, Warrens,
Saint Michael, BB11000, Barbados
Tel.: (246) 4175110
Sales Range: $350-399.9 Million
Emp.: 2,032
Diversified Holding Company
N.A.I.C.S.: 551112

Subsidiaries:

Agro Chemicals Inc   (1)
41 Warrens Industrial Park, Saint Michael,
Barbados
Tel.: (246) 4253939
Web Site: http://www.agro-chemicals.com
Sales Range: $25-49.9 Million
Emp.: 30
Chemicals & Agricultural Products Distr
N.A.I.C.S.: 325320
Lisa G. Mustor *(Gen Mgr)*

BCB Communications   (1)
First Fl The Massy Dome Warrens, Saint
Michael, Barbados
Tel.: (246) 417 5010
Sales Range: $25-49.9 Million
Emp.: 13
Marketing & Advertising Services
N.A.I.C.S.: 541910
C A Clarke *(Mng Dir)*

DaCosta Mannings Inc.   (1)
The Auto Dome Warrens, Saint Michael,
Barbados
Tel.: (246) 4318700
Household Appliance Retailer
N.A.I.C.S.: 423620

Knights Limited   (1)
Prescod Blvd, Saint Michael, Barbados
Tel.: (246) 4297700
Paper Products Mfr & Distr
N.A.I.C.S.: 322299

Peronne Manufacturing Company
Ltd   (1)

Peronne Complex Worthing, Christchurch,
Barbados
Tel.: (246) 4356921
Sales Range: $25-49.9 Million
Emp.: 20
Food Products Mfr
N.A.I.C.S.: 311991

Roberts Manufacturing Company
Ltd   (1)
Lower Estate, Saint Michael, Barbados
Tel.: (246) 4292131
Web Site: http://www.rmco.com
Sales Range: $25-49.9 Million
Emp.: 160
Animal Feed Mfr
N.A.I.C.S.: 311111
Jason Sambrano *(Mng Dir)*

United Insurance Company   (1)
Lower Broad St, United Insurance Bldg,
Bridgetown, Barbados
Tel.: (246) 4301900
Web Site: http://www.unitedinsure.com
Sales Range: $50-74.9 Million
Emp.: 80
General Non-Life Insurance Services
N.A.I.C.S.: 524210
Howard Hall *(CEO)*

Warrens Motors Inc.   (1)
The Auto Dome Warrens, Saint Michael,
Barbados
Tel.: (246) 4175000
Web Site: http://www.warrensmotors.com
Sales Range: $25-49.9 Million
Emp.: 50
Motor Industrial Services
N.A.I.C.S.: 333612

BARBADOS STOCK EX-CHANGE INC.
8th Avenue, Belleville, Saint Michael,
BB11114, Barbados
Tel.: (246) 4369871
Web Site: http://www.bse.com.bb
Sales Range: $25-49.9 Million
Emp.: 19
Stock Exchange Services
N.A.I.C.S.: 523210
Kerry Greene *(Sec)*

BARBARA BUI SA
Route De Vannes Zi Du Pigeon
Blanc, Locmine, 56500, Lorient,
France
Tel.: (33) 153018805
Web Site: http://www.barbarabui.fr
Rev.: $24,800,000
Emp.: 121
Womens & Misses Suits & Coats
N.A.I.C.S.: 315250
William Halimi *(CEO)*

BARBARA PERSONNEL INC.
200 Montcalm St, Gatineau, J8Y 3B5,
QC, Canada
Tel.: (613) 236-9689
Web Site:
http://www.barbarapersonnel.com
Year Founded: 1973
Rev.: $35,607,965
Emp.: 300
Employment Agencies
N.A.I.C.S.: 561311
Barbara Cloutier *(Pres)*

BARBER GLASS RETAIL
167 Suffolk St W, Guelph, N1H 2J7,
ON, Canada
Tel.: (519) 824-0310
Web Site:
http://www.barberglassretail.ca
Year Founded: 1883
Rev.: $15,202,452
Emp.: 12
Fabricated Glass Products Mfr
N.A.I.C.S.: 444180

BARCELO CORPORACION EMPRESARIAL S.A.

Jose Rover Motta 27, 07006, Palma
de Mallorca, Baleares, Spain
Tel.: (34) 971771700   ES
Web Site: http://www.barcelo.com
Rev.: $2,686,139,109
Assets: $3,292,512,789
Liabilities: $1,698,980,758
Net Worth: $1,593,532,031
Earnings: $208,257,715
Emp.: 33,378
Fiscal Year-end: 12/31/18
Hotels & Resorts Operator
N.A.I.C.S.: 721110
Simon Barcelo Tous *(Co-Chm)*

Subsidiaries:

BCLO Brisa Punta Cana, BV   **(1)**
Evert van de Beekstraat 310, 1118 CX,
Schiphol, Netherlands
Tel.: (31) 205214777
Holding Company
N.A.I.C.S.: 551112

Barcelo Condal Hoteles, S.A.   **(1)**
Placa dels Paisos Catalans, 8014, Barce-
lona, Catalonia, Spain
Tel.: (34) 935035300
Hotel Operator
N.A.I.C.S.: 721110

Barcelo Gestion Hoteles Italia,
SRL   **(1)**
Contrada Chiusa, Rome, 88050, Italy
Tel.: (39) 0961 791373
Hotel Operator
N.A.I.C.S.: 721110

Barcelo Pyramids LLC   **(1)**
229 Al Ahram Street, Gizah, 12111, Cairo,
Egypt
Tel.: (20) 35823300
Hotel Operator
N.A.I.C.S.: 721110

Barcelo Switzerland, S.A   **(1)**
Chemin des Primeveres 45, 1700, Fribourg,
Switzerland
Tel.: (41) 264258484
Holding Company
N.A.I.C.S.: 551112

Barcelo Turizm Otelcilik Limited   **(1)**
186 Millet Caddesi Topkapi, Fatih, Istanbul,
Turkiye
Tel.: (90) 2126311212
Hotel Operator
N.A.I.C.S.: 721110

Crestline Hotels & Resorts, LLC   **(1)**
3950 University Dr Ste 301, Fairfax, VA
22030
Tel.: (571) 529-6100
Web Site: http://www.crestlinehotels.com
Hotel Management
N.A.I.C.S.: 721110
Pierre Donahue *(Gen Counsel & Exec VP)*

Escalatur Viagens, Lda.   **(1)**
R Tomas Ribeiro 89, 1050, Lisbon, Portugal
Tel.: (351) 213175900
Web Site: http://www.barceloviagens.pt
Tour Operator
N.A.I.C.S.: 561520

Hotel Campos de Guadalmina
S.L.   **(1)**
Av Alcalde Alfonso Molina - Ed Fadesa,
15008, A Coruna, Spain
Tel.: (34) 981179200
Hotel Operator
N.A.I.C.S.: 721110

Hotel Fuerteventura Playa, S.L   **(1)**
Av Jahn Reisen 1, Costa Calma, 35627,
Las Palmas, Spain
Tel.: (34) 928547344
Web Site:
  http://www.fuerteventuraplayahotel.com
Hotel Operator
N.A.I.C.S.: 721110

Montecastillo Sport Catering, S.L **(1)**
Crtra de Arcos Km 9 6, Jerez de la Fron-
tera, 11406, Cadiz, Spain
Tel.: (34) 956151200
Hotel Operator
N.A.I.C.S.: 721110
Ignacio Martin *(Gen Mgr)*

Servicios Hoteleros de Manzanillo
SRL de CV   **(1)**
Av Vista Hermosa No 13 Peninsula de San-
tiago, Manzanillo, 28867, Colima, Mexico
Tel.: (52) 3143311300
Hotel Operator
N.A.I.C.S.: 721110
Miquel Calsat *(Gen Mgr)*

Viajes Interopa, S.A   **(1)**
Calle de Alcala 165, 28009, Madrid, Spain
Tel.: (34) 902200400
Tour Operator
N.A.I.C.S.: 561520

BARCLAYS PLC
1 Churchill Place, Canary Wharf,
London, E14 5HP, United Kingdom
Tel.: (44) 2076232323   UK
Web Site: https://www.ib.barclays
BARC—(LSE)
Rev.: $10,960,873,560
Assets: $1,879,471,430,200
Liabilities: $1,784,144,551,280
Net Worth: $95,326,878,920
Earnings: $9,810,884,720
Emp.: 43,000
Fiscal Year-end: 12/31/21
Financial Investment Services
N.A.I.C.S.: 551111
Timothy R. M. Main *(Head-
Investment Banking-EMEA)*

Subsidiaries:

54 Lombard Street Investments
Limited   **(1)**
1 Churchill Place, London, E14 5HP, United
Kingdom
Tel.: (44) 2076261567
Investment Management Service
N.A.I.C.S.: 523999

Aros Mineral AB   **(1)**
Observatoriegatan 23, PO Box 70426, 107
25, Stockholm, Sweden
Tel.: (46) 854542630
Mineral Mining Services
N.A.I.C.S.: 213115

B D & B Investments Limited   **(1)**
1 Church Place, London, E14 5HP, United
Kingdom
Tel.: (44) 2076261567
Investment Management Service
N.A.I.C.S.: 523999

BBSA Servicos e Participacoes
Limitada   **(1)**
Praca Prf Jose Lannes 40, Sao Paulo,
04571-100, Brazil
Tel.: (55) 9 3270
Investment Management Service
N.A.I.C.S.: 523999

BEIF Management Limited   **(1)**
High Street, Hoddesdon, EN11 8HD, Hert-
ford, United Kingdom
Tel.: (44) 8456 000200
Investment Management Service
N.A.I.C.S.: 523999

BIE Executive Limited   **(1)**
First Floor Queen's House 8 Queen Street,
London, EC4N 1SP, United Kingdom
Tel.: (44) 2034405250
Web Site: http://www.bie-executive.com
Executive Search & Advisory Services
N.A.I.C.S.: 561312
Robert Walker *(CEO)*

BPB Holdings S.A.   **(1)**
1820 Chemin Grange Canal, 1204, Ge-
neva, Switzerland
Tel.: (41) 22819 51 11
Investment Management Service
N.A.I.C.S.: 523999

Banco Barclays S.A.   **(1)**
Av Faria Lima 4440 - 12th Floor Itaim Bibi,
Sao Paulo, 04552-040, Brazil
Tel.: (55) 11 3757 7000
Web Site: http://www.barcap.com
Commercial Banking Services
N.A.I.C.S.: 522110

Bankfil Limited   **(1)**
170 Main Street, Johannesburg, 2001, Gau-

---

teng, South Africa
Tel.: (27) 113504000
Web Site: http://www.absa.co.za
Investment Management Service
N.A.I.C.S.: 523999

Barafor Limited   **(1)**
1 Churchill Place, London, E14 5HP, United
Kingdom
Tel.: (44) 20 7116 1000
Investment Management Service
N.A.I.C.S.: 523999

Barclays (Security Realisation)
Limited   **(1)**
1 Churchill Place, London, E14 5HP, United
Kingdom
Tel.: (44) 2071161000
Securities Brokerage Services
N.A.I.C.S.: 523150

Barclays Aldersgate Investments
Limited   **(1)**
1 Churchill Place, London, E14 5HP, United
Kingdom
Tel.: (44) 2071161000
Investment Management Service
N.A.I.C.S.: 523999

Barclays Alma Mater General Partner
Limited   **(1)**
1 Churchill Place, London, E14 5HP, United
Kingdom
Tel.: (44) 2071161000
Asset Management Services
N.A.I.C.S.: 523940

Barclays Asia Limited   **(1)**
41/F Cheung Kong Center 2 Queen's Road,
Central, China (Hong Kong)
Tel.: (852) 2903 2938
Commercial Banking Services
N.A.I.C.S.: 522110

Barclays Bank PLC   **(1)**
1 Churchill Place, London, E14 5HP, United
Kingdom   **(100%)**
Tel.: (44) 2071161000
Rev.: $23,059,833,375
Assets: $1,496,043,928,301
Liabilities: $1,419,669,275,436
Net Worth: $76,374,652,865
Earnings: $4,495,077,001
Emp.: 23,900
Fiscal Year-end: 12/31/2023
Retail & Commercial Banking, Loans, Insur-
ance & Credit Card Services
N.A.I.C.S.: 522110
C. S. Venkatakrishnan *(Co-Pres)*

Subsidiary (Domestic):

Barclay Leasing Limited   **(2)**
Churchill Plaza Churchill Way, Basingstoke,
RG21 7GP, Hampshire, United Kingdom
Tel.: (44) 1256791245
Financial Lending Services
N.A.I.C.S.: 522220

Barclaycard Funding PLC   **(2)**
54 Lombard Street, London, EC3P 4AH,
United Kingdom
Tel.: (44) 20 7699 5000
Fund Management Services
N.A.I.C.S.: 523940

Unit (Domestic):

Barclays Asset Finance   **(2)**
Churchill Plaza Churchill Way, Basingstoke,
RG21 7GL, United Kingdom   **(100%)**
Tel.: (44) 256797000
Web Site: http://www.barclays.co.uk
Sales Range: $600-649.9 Million
Emp.: 1,005
Finance House Providing Leasing & Other
Financial Facilities to Business Customers
N.A.I.C.S.: 522299

Subsidiary (Non-US):

Barclays Bank   **(2)**
183 Ave Daumesnil, 75012, Paris,
France   **(100%)**
Tel.: (33) 55787878
Web Site: http://www.barclays.fr
Sales Range: $50-74.9 Million
Emp.: 96
Retail & Corporate Banking Services
N.A.I.C.S.: 522299

Barclays Bank   **(2)**
Regal House, PO Box 187, Gibraltar, Gi-
braltar
Tel.: (350) 52378
Web Site: http://www.barclays.com
Retail & Corporate Banking Services
N.A.I.C.S.: 522299

Barclays Bank   **(2)**
Via Della Moscova 18, 20121, Milan,
Italy   **(100%)**
Tel.: (39) 0263721
Web Site: http://www.barclays.it
Sales Range: $50-74.9 Million
Emp.: 60
Retail Banking Services
N.A.I.C.S.: 522110

Barclays Bank   **(2)**
24/F Ferrum Tower 66 Suha-dong Jung-gu,
Seoul, 100-210, Korea (South)   **(100%)**
Tel.: (82) 221262600
Web Site: http://www.barclaysbank.com
Sales Range: $25-49.9 Million
Emp.: 50
Retail & Corporate Banking Services
N.A.I.C.S.: 522299
John Chang *(Head-Equities Distr-Asia Pa-
cific)*

Barclays Bank   **(2)**
23 Church St 13 08 Capital Sq, Singapore,
049481, Singapore   **(100%)**
Tel.: (65) 63953000
Web Site: http://www.barclays.com.sg
Retail & Corporate Banking Services
N.A.I.C.S.: 522299

Barclays Bank   **(2)**
601/603 Ceejay House Shivsagar Estate Dr
Annie Besant Road, Mumbai, 400018,
Worli, India   **(100%)**
Tel.: (91) 2267196000
Web Site: http://www.barclays.in
Sales Range: $50-74.9 Million
Emp.: 75
Retail & Corporate Banking Services
N.A.I.C.S.: 522299

Barclays Bank   **(2)**
Rm 1211 Scitech Tower, 22 Jianquomenwai
Dajie, Beijing, 100004, China
Tel.: (86) 1065150006
Retail & Corporate Banking Services
N.A.I.C.S.: 522299

Representative Office (US):

Barclays Bank   **(2)**
1111 Brickell Ave, Miami, FL 33131-3112
Tel.: (305) 533-3333
Web Site: http://www.barcap.com
Retail & Corporate Banking Services
N.A.I.C.S.: 522110

Subsidiary (Non-US):

Barclays Bank (Seychelles) Ltd.   **(2)**
Independence Ave, PO Box 167, Victoria,
Mahe, Seychelles
Tel.: (248) 383838
Web Site: http://www.barclays.com
Sales Range: $75-99.9 Million
Emp.: 249
Retail & Corporate Banking Services
N.A.I.C.S.: 522299

Barclays Bank (South East Asia)
Nominees Private Limited   **(2)**
23 Church Street 13-08 Capital Square,
Singapore, 049481, Singapore
Tel.: (65) 63953388
Commercial Banking Services
N.A.I.C.S.: 522110

Barclays Bank - Mauritius   **(2)**
Sir William Newton Street, PO Box 284,
Port Louis, Mauritius
Tel.: (230) 402 1000
Web Site: http://www.barclays.mu
Sales Range: $50-74.9 Million
Emp.: 300
Retail & Corporate Banking Services
N.A.I.C.S.: 522299

Barclays Bank Ireland PLC   **(2)**
Two Park Place Hatch St, Dublin,
Ireland   **(100%)**
Tel.: (353) 16182626
Web Site:
  http://www.business.barclays.co.uk

Barclays PLC—(Continued)

Sales Range: $50-74.9 Million
Emp.: 75
Retail & Corporate Banking Services
N.A.I.C.S.: 522299
Kevin Wall *(CEO)*

Barclays Bank Mexico, S.A. (2)
Paseo De La Reforma 505 Piso 41 Col,
Ouaultemoc, 00500, Mexico
Tel.: (52) 55 5241 3200
Commercial Banking Services
N.A.I.C.S.: 522110
Raul Martinez-Ostos *(Country Mgr)*

Division (Domestic):

Barclays Bank PLC - Wealth & Investment Management Division (2)
43 Brook Street, PO Box 391, Knightsbridge, London, W1K 4HJ, United Kingdom
Tel.: (44) 1624 684 316
Investment Management Service
N.A.I.C.S.: 523940
Vivian Chan *(Head-North Asia)*

Subsidiary (Non-US):

Barclays Bank Tanzania Ltd. (2)
TDFL Building, PO Box 5137, Ohio St, Dar es Salaam, Tanzania
Tel.: (255) 222129581
Web Site: http://www.barclays.com
Retail & Corporate Banking Services
N.A.I.C.S.: 522299

Barclays Bank of Botswana Ltd. (2)
Barclays House Khama Crescent, PO Box 478, Gaborone, Botswana
Tel.: (267) 2673905575
Web Site: http://www.barclays.com
Sales Range: $100-124.9 Million
Emp.: 947
Banking Services
N.A.I.C.S.: 522110
Oduetse Motshidisi *(Chm-Interim)*

Barclays Bank of Ghana Ltd. (2)
High St, PO Box 2949, Accra, Ghana (100%)
Tel.: (233) 216649014
Web Site: http://www.barclays.com
Sales Range: $50-74.9 Million
Emp.: 100
Banking Services
N.A.I.C.S.: 522110

Barclays Bank of Kenya Ltd. (2)
Barclays Plaza, PO Box 30120, Loita Street, Nairobi, Kenya (68.5%)
Tel.: (254) 2213915
Banking Services
N.A.I.C.S.: 522110
Jeremy Awori *(Mng Dir)*

Barclays Bank of Uganda Ltd. (2)
16 Kampala Rd, PO Box 2971, Kampala, Uganda
Tel.: (256) 412309726
Web Site: http://www.barclays.com
Sales Range: $75-99.9 Million
Emp.: 150
Retail & Corporate Banking Services
N.A.I.C.S.: 522299

Barclays Bank of Zambia Ltd. (2)
PO Box 31936, Cairo Rd, Lusaka, Zambia
Tel.: (260) 211228858
Web Site: http://www.barclays.com
Sales Range: $300-349.9 Million
Emp.: 750
Retail & Corporate Banking Services
N.A.I.C.S.: 522299

Barclays Capital (2)
7 Rue des Alpes, CH 1201, Geneva, Switzerland (100%)
Tel.: (41) 227150240
Web Site: http://www.barcap.com
Sales Range: $75-99.9 Million
Emp.: 200
Investment Banking Services
N.A.I.C.S.: 523150

Barclays Capital (2)
World Trade Centre Tower C 14th Floor, Strawinskylaan 1453, NL-1077 XX, Amsterdam, Netherlands (100%)
Tel.: (31) 205707840
Web Site: http://www.barcap.nl

Investment Banking
N.A.I.C.S.: 523150

Barclays Capital Canada Inc (2)
333 Bay Street Suite 4910, Toronto, M5H 2R2, ON, Canada
Tel.: (416) 863-8900
Commercial Banking Services
N.A.I.C.S.: 522110

Subsidiary (US):

Barclays Capital Inc. (2)
745 7th Ave, New York, NY 10019 (100%)
Tel.: (212) 526-7000
Web Site:
http://www.investmentbank.barclays.com
Sales Range: $600-649.9 Million
Emp.: 1,600
Investment Banking & Securities Dealing Services
N.A.I.C.S.: 523150
Rick Landgarten *(Head-Healthcare & Real Estate Investment Banking-Global)*

Subsidiary (Domestic):

BCAP LLC (3)
200 Park Ave, New York, NY 10166
Tel.: (212) 412-4000
Asset Management Services
N.A.I.C.S.: 523940

Barclays Capital Energy Inc. (3)
200 Park Ave, New York, NY 10166
Tel.: (212) 412-1000
Investment Management Service
N.A.I.C.S.: 523999

Barclays Commercial Mortgage Securities LLC (3)
745 7th Ave, New York, NY 10019
Tel.: (212) 412-4000
Mortgage Loan Brokerage Services
N.A.I.C.S.: 522310

Barclays Services LLC (3)
40 Wall St 28th Fl, New York, NY 10005
Tel.: (212) 412-4000
Financial Management Services
N.A.I.C.S.: 523999

Subsidiary (Non-US):

Barclays Capital Japan Limited (2)
31 Floor Roppongi Hills Mori Tower 6-10-1 Roppongi, Minato-ku, Tokyo, 106-6131, Japan (100%)
Tel.: (81) 345301100
Web Site: http://www.barclayscapital.com
Sales Range: $300-349.9 Million
Emp.: 1,000
Corporate & Retail Banking Services
N.A.I.C.S.: 522299

Subsidiary (Domestic):

Barclays Capital Securities Limited (2)
5 The North Colonnade, Canary Wharf, London, E14 4BB, United Kingdom (100%)
Tel.: (44) 2076232323
Web Site: http://www.barcap.com
Investment Banking & Securities Dealing Services
N.A.I.C.S.: 523150

Barclays Funds Ltd. (2)
54 Lombard St, London, EC3P 3AH, United Kingdom (100%)
Tel.: (44) 8457660936
Web Site: http://www.barclays.co.uk
Sales Range: $150-199.9 Million
Emp.: 500
Unit Trust Management
N.A.I.C.S.: 523991

Subsidiary (Non-US):

Barclays Global Investors Canada Ltd. (2)
161 Bay Street Suite 2500, PO Box 614, Toronto, M5J 2S1, ON, Canada (100%)
Tel.: (416) 643-4000
Sales Range: $25-49.9 Million
Emp.: 50
Investment Advice & Products
N.A.I.C.S.: 525910

Subsidiary (Domestic):

Barclays Global Investors Limited (2)
Murray House 1 Royal Mint Court, London, EC3N 4HH, United Kingdom
Tel.: (44) 2076688000
Asset Management
N.A.I.C.S.: 523999

Unit (Domestic):

Barclays Group Property Services (2)
Northwest House 119 - 127 Marylebone, London, NW15 PX, United Kingdom
Tel.: (44) 2077237668
Sales Range: $50-74.9 Million
Emp.: 60
Manager of Barclays' Property Portfolio
N.A.I.C.S.: 531120

Barclays Home Finance (2)
Meridian House Anchor Boulevard, Crossways, Dartford, DA2 6QH, United Kingdom
Tel.: (44) 1322426426
Web Site: http://www.barclays.co.uk
Sales Range: $300-349.9 Million
Emp.: 400
Loan Processing Services; Owned 20% by Barclays PLC
N.A.I.C.S.: 531390

Subsidiary (Domestic):

Barclays Insurance Services Co. Ltd. (2)
8 Bedford Park, Croydon, CR9 2XX, United Kingdom (100%)
Tel.: (44) 2082533000
Sales Range: $50-74.9 Million
Emp.: 100
Insurance Brokers
N.A.I.C.S.: 524210

Subsidiary (Non-US):

Barclays Investments & Loans (India) Limited (2)
Ganesh Chs Sector 1 Vashi, Mumbai, 400703, India
Tel.: (91) 22 65977313
Web Site: http://www.barclaysfinance.in
Financial Management Services
N.A.I.C.S.: 523999

Barclays Private Bank & Trust Company (2)
39-41 Broad St, Saint Helier, JE4 8PU, Jersey
Tel.: (44) 1534873741
Web Site: http://www.barclayswells.co.uk
Sales Range: $150-199.9 Million
Emp.: 300
Investment & Corporate Banking Services
N.A.I.C.S.: 523150
Adele Bohlen *(Head-Fiduciaries)*

Barclays Private Bank & Trust Ltd. (2)
Le Marchant House Le Truchot, PO Box 41, Saint Peter Port, GY1 3BE, Guernsey
Tel.: (44) 1481724500
Web Site: http://www.barclays.com
Private Banking, Trust & Fiduciary Services
N.A.I.C.S.: 522110

Barclays Securities (India) Private Limited (2)
Units 1305 & 1306 12th Floor Prestige Meridian II M G Road, Bengaluru, 560001, India
Tel.: (91) 80 6648 5200
Web Site: http://www.barclayswealth.com
Sales Range: $50-74.9 Million
Emp.: 10
Investment & Security Services
N.A.I.C.S.: 523150

Barclays Shared Services Private Limited (2)
Unitech Infospace Park Tower A 5th to 10th floor B-2, Sector-62, Noida, 201307, India
Tel.: (91) 120 3895000
Web Site:
http://www.barclayssharedservices.com
Operational Support Services
N.A.I.C.S.: 561499

Subsidiary (Domestic):

Barclays Stockbrokers Ltd. (2)
Tay House 300 Bath Street, Glasgow, G2 4LN, Strathclyde, United Kingdom (100%)
Tel.: (44) 8456089000
Web Site:
http://www.stockbrokers.barclays.co.uk
Sales Range: $300-349.9 Million
Emp.: 800
Stock Broking Services
N.A.I.C.S.: 523910

Barclays Venture Nominees Limited (2)
1 Churchill Place, London, E14 5HP, United Kingdom
Tel.: (44) 20 7441 4213
Web Site: http://www.barclayscorporate.com
Sales Range: $25-49.9 Million
Emp.: 50
Venture Capital Firm
N.A.I.C.S.: 523999

FIRSTPLUS Financial Group PLC (2)
The Avenue Business Park, Pentwyn, Cardiff, CF23 8FF, United Kingdom
Tel.: (44) 29 2030 3020
Web Site: http://www.firstplus.co.uk
Financial Investment Services
N.A.I.C.S.: 523999

Subsidiary (Non-US):

Standard Life Bank Limited (2)
Tel.: (44) 1312252552
Web Site: http://www.standardlife.co.uk
Sales Range: $1-4.9 Billion
Emp.: 300
Banking Services
N.A.I.C.S.: 522110

Subsidiary (Domestic):

The Northview Group Limited (2)
Ascot House, Maidenhead Office Park, Maidenhead, SL6 3QQ, United Kingdom
Tel.: (44) 2070256592
Web Site: http://www.northviewgroup.com
Holding Company; Mortgage Lending Services
N.A.I.C.S.: 551112
Alex Maddox *(Dir-Bus Origination & Dev)*

Subsidiary (Domestic):

Acenden Limited (3)
Ascot House Maidenhead Office Park, Maidenhead, SL6 3QQ, United Kingdom
Tel.: (44) 3333000426
Web Site: http://www.acenden.com
Mortgage Services
N.A.I.C.S.: 522310
Amamy Attia *(Dir)*

Kensington Mortgages Limited (3)
Ascot House, Maidenhead Office Park, Maidenhead, SL6 3QQ, United Kingdom
Tel.: (44) 3333000921
Web Site:
https://www.kensingtonmortgages.co.uk
Mortgage Lending Services
N.A.I.C.S.: 522292
Sarah Green *(Head-Sls & Mktg)*

Barclays CCP Funding LLP (1)
1 Churchill Place, London, E14 5HP, United Kingdom
Tel.: (44) 20 7116 5695
Fund Management Services
N.A.I.C.S.: 523940

Barclays Capital Asia Limited (1)
41/F Cheung Kong Ctr 2 Queen's Road, Central, China (Hong Kong)
Tel.: (852) 2903 2938
Investment Management Service
N.A.I.C.S.: 523999

Barclays Capital Charitable Trust (1)
19-21 Broad St, Saint Helier, Jersey
Tel.: (44) 1534 602901
Charitable Trust Management Services
N.A.I.C.S.: 813211

Barclays Capital Finance Limited (1)
5 The North Colonnade, Canary Wharf, London, E14 4BB, United Kingdom
Tel.: (44) 20 7623 2323
Financial Investment Services

N.A.I.C.S.: 523999

Barclays Capital Global Services Singapore Pte. Limited (1)
St Marina Blvd Marina Bay Financial Centre
Tower 2 Level 23-01, Singapore, 18983,
Singapore
Tel.: (65) 6828 5000
Investment Management Service
N.A.I.C.S.: 523999

Barclays Capital Luxembourg S.a r.l. (1)
9 Allee Scheffer, Luxembourg, 2520, Luxembourg
Tel.: (352) 26 63 5100
Asset Management Services
N.A.I.C.S.: 523940

Barclays Capital Margin Financing Limited (1)
1 Churchill Place, London, E14 5HP, United Kingdom
Tel.: (44) 2071161000
Venture Capital Services
N.A.I.C.S.: 523999

Barclays Capital Markets Malaysia Sdn Bhd. (1)
Mexis Tower, 50888, Kuala Lumpur, Malaysia
Tel.: (60) 3 2170 0000
Financial Management Services
N.A.I.C.S.: 523999

Barclays Capital Principal Investments Limited (1)
1 Churchill Place, London, E14 5HP, United Kingdom
Tel.: (44) 20 7116 1000
Investment Management Service
N.A.I.C.S.: 523999

Barclays Capital Services Limited (1)
5 The North Colonnade Canary Wharf, London, E14 4BB, United Kingdom
Tel.: (44) 20 7623 2323
Investment Banking Services
N.A.I.C.S.: 523150

Barclays Capital Strategic Advisers Limited (1)
1 Churchill Place, London, E14 5HP, United Kingdom
Tel.: (44) 2071161000
Web Site: http://www.barclays.com
Investment Management Service
N.A.I.C.S.: 523999

Barclays Converted Investments (No.2) Limited (1)
1 Churchill Place, London, E14 5HP, United Kingdom
Tel.: (44) 2071161000
Investment Management Service
N.A.I.C.S.: 523999

Barclays Covered Bond Funding LLP (1)
1 Churchill Place, London, E14 5HP, United Kingdom
Tel.: (44) 2071165695
Fund Management Services
N.A.I.C.S.: 523940

Barclays Covered Bonds Limited Liability Partnership (1)
1 Churchill Place, London, E14 5HP, United Kingdom
Tel.: (44) 2071165695
Asset Management Services
N.A.I.C.S.: 523940

Barclays Darnay Euro Investments Limited (1)
1 Churchill Place, London, E14 5HP, United Kingdom
Tel.: (44) 2071161000
Investment Management Service
N.A.I.C.S.: 523999

Barclays Directors Limited (1)
1 Churchill Place, London, E14 5HP, United Kingdom
Tel.: (44) 2071161000
Investment Management Service
N.A.I.C.S.: 523999

Barclays Diversification SA. (1)

183 Avenue Daumesnil, Paris, 75012,
France
Tel.: (33) 1 55 78 78 78
Financial Management Services
N.A.I.C.S.: 523999
Tony Blanco *(Gen Mgr)*

Barclays Fiduciary Services (UK) Limited (1)
Osborne Court Gadbrook Park, Northwich,
CW9 7UE, United Kingdom
Tel.: (44) 84 5766 0936
Fiduciary Services
N.A.I.C.S.: 523991

Barclays Finance Europe Limited (1)
1 Churchill Place, London, E14 5HP, United Kingdom
Tel.: (44) 20 7116 1000
Financial Management Services
N.A.I.C.S.: 523999

Barclays Financial Planning Ltd (1)
30 Tower View, West Malling, ME19 4WA,
Kent, United Kingdom
Tel.: (44) 1732849748
Financial Management Services
N.A.I.C.S.: 523999

Barclays Financial Services Italia S.p.A. (1)
Via Della Moscova 18, Milan, Italy
Tel.: (39) 0263721
Financial Management Services
N.A.I.C.S.: 523999

Subsidiary (Domestic):

Barclays Family S.p.A (2)
Via Costanza Arconati 1, Milan, 20135, Italy
Tel.: (39) 025 4151
Credit Management Services
N.A.I.C.S.: 522390

Iveco Finanziaria S.p.A. (2)
Lungo Stura Lazio 49, 10156, Turin, Italy
Tel.: (39) 0110078078
Financial Management Services
N.A.I.C.S.: 523999

Barclays Financial Services Limited (1)
Barclays Plaza M6 Loita Street, Nairobi,
00100, Kenya
Tel.: (254) 20310843
Financial Management Services
N.A.I.C.S.: 523999

Barclays France SA (1)
32 Avenue George V, Paris, 75008, France
Tel.: (33) 1 55 78 78 78
Web Site: http://www.barclays.fr
Investment Banking Services
N.A.I.C.S.: 523150

Barclays Funds Investments Limited (1)
1 Churchill Place, London, E14 5HP, United Kingdom
Tel.: (44) 2071161000
Investment Management Service
N.A.I.C.S.: 523999

Barclays GBP Funding Limited (1)
1 Churchill Place, London, E14 5HP, United Kingdom
Tel.: (44) 20 7116 1000
Fund Management Services
N.A.I.C.S.: 523940

Barclays Group Holdings Limited (1)
1 Churchill Place, London, E14 5HP, United Kingdom
Tel.: (44) 2071161000
Investment Management Service
N.A.I.C.S.: 523999

Barclays Holdings (Isle of Man) Limited (1)
4th Floor Queen Victoria House 41 Victoria
St, Douglas, IM1 2LF, Isle of Man
Tel.: (44) 1624 683828
Investment Management Service
N.A.I.C.S.: 523999
Lesley Corlett *(VP & Head-Compliance-Wealth & Investment Mgmt)*

Barclays International Fund Managers Limited (1)
28-30 The Parade, JE4 8RA, Saint Helier,
Jersey

Tel.: (44) 1534 812700
Fund Management Services
N.A.I.C.S.: 523940

Barclays Leasing (No.9) Limited (1)
Churchill Plaza, Basingstoke, RG21 7GP,
Hampshire, United Kingdom
Tel.: (44) 1256791245
Financial Lending Services
N.A.I.C.S.: 522220

Barclays Long Island Limited (1)
1 Churchill Place, London, E14 5HP, United Kingdom
Tel.: (44) 2071165695
Investment Management Service
N.A.I.C.S.: 523999

Barclays Marlist Limited (1)
Churchill Plaza Churchill Way, Basingstoke,
RG21 7GP, Hampshire, United Kingdom
Tel.: (44) 1256817777
Financial Management Services
N.A.I.C.S.: 523999

Barclays Mercantile Business Finance Limited (1)
Churchill Plaza Churchill Way 5th Floor,
Basingstoke, RG21 7GP, Hampshire, United Kingdom
Tel.: (44) 1256 817 777
Investment Management Service
N.A.I.C.S.: 523999

Barclays Mercantile Limited (1)
Churchill Way, Basingstoke, RG21 7GP,
Hampshire, United Kingdom
Tel.: (44) 1256 817777
Investment Management Service
N.A.I.C.S.: 523999

Barclays Metals Limited (1)
1 Churchill Place, London, E14 5HP, United Kingdom
Tel.: (44) 2071161000
Investment Management Service
N.A.I.C.S.: 523999

Barclays Patrimoine S.C.S. (1)
2 Boulevard De Strasbourg, Toulouse,
31000, Haute-Garonne, France
Tel.: (33) 562737373
Sales Range: $50-74.9 Million
Emp.: 24
Investment Management Service
N.A.I.C.S.: 523940
Christen Varley *(Mng Dir)*

Barclays Physical Trading Limited (1)
1 Churchill Place, London, E14 5HP, United Kingdom
Tel.: (44) 2071161000
Financial Management Services
N.A.I.C.S.: 523999

Barclays Private Bank & Trust (Isle of Man) Limited (1)
Floor 4 Queen Victoria House 41 Victoria
Street, Douglas, IM1 2LF, Isle of Man
Tel.: (44) 1624 682 828
Commercial Banking Services
N.A.I.C.S.: 522110

Barclays Private Bank Ltd (1)
43 Brook Street, London, W1K 4HJ, United Kingdom
Tel.: (44) 20 7487 2000
Commercial Banking Services
N.A.I.C.S.: 522110

Barclays Private Banking Services Limited (1)
56 Grosvenor Street West Central, London,
W1K 3HZ, United Kingdom
Tel.: (44) 20 7487 2000
Commercial Banking Services
N.A.I.C.S.: 522110

Barclays Private Trust Limited (1)
1 Churchill Place, London, E14 5HP, United Kingdom
Tel.: (44) 2071161000
Investment Trust Management Services
N.A.I.C.S.: 523940

Barclays Secured Funding (LM) Limited (1)
1 Churchill Place, London, E14 5HP, United Kingdom
Tel.: (44) 2071161000

Fund Management Services
N.A.I.C.S.: 523940

Barclays Secured Notes Finance LLP (1)
1 Churchill Place, London, E14 5HP, United Kingdom
Tel.: (44) 2071161000
Financial Management Services
N.A.I.C.S.: 523999

Barclays Sharedealing Limited (1)
1 Churchill Place, London, E14 5HP, United Kingdom
Tel.: (44) 2071161000
Securities Brokerage Services
N.A.I.C.S.: 523150

Barclays Unquoted Investments Limited (1)
1 Churchill Place, London, E14 5HP, United Kingdom
Tel.: (44) 2071161000
Investment Management Service
N.A.I.C.S.: 523999

Barclays Unquoted Property Investments Limited (1)
1 Churchill Place, London, E14 5HP, United Kingdom
Tel.: (44) 2071161000
Real Estate Manangement Services
N.A.I.C.S.: 531390

Barclays Vie SA (1)
183 Avenue Daumesnil, Paris, 75012,
France
Tel.: (33) 1 55 78 77 00
General Insurance Services
N.A.I.C.S.: 524210

Barclays Wealth Asset Management (Monaco) S.A.M (1)
31 Avenue de la Costa, 98000, Monte
Carlo, Monaco
Tel.: (377) 93 10 51 51
Emp.: 200
Asset Management Services
N.A.I.C.S.: 523940
Antony Jenkins *(Gen Mgr)*

Barclays Wealth Corporate Services (Guernsey) Limited (1)
Level 1 Regency Court Glategny Esplanade
Saint Peter Port, Saint Peter Port, GY1
3ST, Guernsey
Tel.: (44) 1534 711 111
Investment Management Service
N.A.I.C.S.: 523999
Justine Gaudion *(Head-Local Markets)*

Barclays Wealth Managers France SA (1)
183 Avenue Daumesnil, Paris, 75012,
France
Tel.: (33) 155787878
Asset Management Services
N.A.I.C.S.: 523940

Barclays Wealth Nominees (Jersey) Limited (1)
66-68 Esplanade, Saint Helier, JE4 5PS,
Jersey
Tel.: (44) 15347 111 11
Financial Management Services
N.A.I.C.S.: 523999

Barclays Wealth Nominees Limited (1)
1 Churchill Place, London, E14 5HP, United Kingdom
Tel.: (44) 2071161000
Asset Management Services
N.A.I.C.S.: 523940

Barclays Wealth Trustees (Guernsey) Limited (1)
Level 1 Regency Court Glategny Esplanade, Saint Peter Port, GY1 3ST, Guernsey
Tel.: (44) 1534 711 111
Fund Management Services
N.A.I.C.S.: 523940

Barclays Wealth Trustees (Hong Kong) Limited (1)
42/F Citibank Tower 3 Garden Road, Central, China (Hong Kong)
Tel.: (852) 2903 4692
Fund Management Services
N.A.I.C.S.: 523940

Barclays PLC—(Continued)

Barclays Wealth Trustees (India) Private Limited (1)
Titanium 2nd Floor Western Express Highway Plot No 201, Goregaon East, Mumbai, 400063, India
Tel.: (91) 22 6731 5000
Fund Management Services
N.A.I.C.S.: 523940

Barclays Zimbabwe Nominees (Pvt) Limited (1)
Floor 2 Three Anchor Hse Jason Moyo Ave, PO Box 1279, Harare, Zimbabwe
Tel.: (263) 4 75 8281
Investment Management Service
N.A.I.C.S.: 523999

Barclayshare Nominees Limited (1)
1 Churchill Place, London, E14 5HP, United Kingdom
Tel.: (44) 2071161000
Investment Management Service
N.A.I.C.S.: 523999

Barclaytrust (Suisse) SA (1)
Chemin De Grange-Canal 18-20, Chene-Bougeries, 1224, Switzerland
Tel.: (41) 22 819 59 00
Commercial Banking Services
N.A.I.C.S.: 522110

Barclaytrust Channel Islands Limited (1)
39-41 Broad St, Saint Helier, JE4 8PU, Jersey
Tel.: (44) 1534873741
Financial Management Services
N.A.I.C.S.: 523999

Barclaytrust International (Jersey) Limited (1)
39-41 Broad Street, Saint Helier, JE4 8PU, Jersey
Tel.: (44) 1534 873741
Web Site: http://www.barclays.com
Financial Management Services
N.A.I.C.S.: 523999

Barmac (Construction) Limited (1)
Churchill Plaza Churchill Way, Basingstoke, RG21 7GP, Hampshire, United Kingdom
Tel.: (44) 1256 817777
Construction Engineering Services
N.A.I.C.S.: 541330

BauBeCon Assets GmbH (1)
Erik-Blumenfeld-Platz 27b, Hamburg, 22587, Germany
Tel.: (49) 51184000
Asset Management Services
N.A.I.C.S.: 523940

BauBeCon BIO GmbH (1)
Schuetzenallee 3, Hannover, 30519, Germany
Tel.: (49) 51184000
Real Estate Rental Services
N.A.I.C.S.: 531110

BauBeCon Immobilien GmbH (1)
Schutzenallee 3, Hannover, 30519, Germany
Tel.: (49) 51184000
Real Estate Development Services
N.A.I.C.S.: 531390

Baubecon Holding 1 GmbH (1)
Schuetzenallee 3, Hannover, 30519, Germany
Tel.: (49) 511 84000
Investment Management Service
N.A.I.C.S.: 523999

Capital Property Fund Nominees Proprietary Limited (1)
4th Floor Rivonia Village Rivonia Boulevard Rivonia, PO Box 2555, Johannesburg, 2128, Gauteng, South Africa
Tel.: (27) 11 612 6870
Emp.: 80
Real Estate Management Services
N.A.I.C.S.: 531390
Dazray Tarr (Office Mgr)

Chapelcrest Investments Limited (1)
1 Churchill Place, London, E14 5HP, United Kingdom
Tel.: (44) 2076261567
Investment Management Service

N.A.I.C.S.: 523999

Chewdef GP GmbH (1)
Eysseneckstr 4, Frankfurt am Main, Germany
Tel.: (49) 8969381680
Investment Management Service
N.A.I.C.S.: 523999

Clearlybusiness.com Limited (1)
1 Churchill Place, London, E14 5HP, United Kingdom
Tel.: (44) 845 601 5962
Web Site: http://www.clearlybusiness.com
Software Development Services
N.A.I.C.S.: 541511

Cobalt Investments Limited (1)
1 Churchill Place, London, E14 5HP, United Kingdom
Tel.: (44) 2076261567
Investment Management Service
N.A.I.C.S.: 523999

Crescendo Investment Holdings Limited (1)
Tropic Isle, PO Box 438, Road Town, Virgin Islands (British)
Tel.: (284) 4942616
Investment Management Service
N.A.I.C.S.: 523999

Denham Investments Limited (1)
1 Churchill Place, London, E14 5HP, United Kingdom
Tel.: (44) 2076261567
Investment Management Service
N.A.I.C.S.: 523999

Ebbgate Investments Limited (1)
1 Churchill Place, London, E14 5HP, United Kingdom
Tel.: (44) 2076261567
Investment Management Service
N.A.I.C.S.: 523999

Eldfell Investments Limited (1)
1 Churchill Place, London, E14 5HP, United Kingdom
Tel.: (44) 2076261567
Investment Management Service
N.A.I.C.S.: 523999

Equity Value Investments No.1 Limited (1)
1 Churchill Place, London, E14 5HP, United Kingdom
Tel.: (44) 2076261567
Investment Management Service
N.A.I.C.S.: 523999

Euromedica Ltd. (1)
5 Chancery Lane, London, EC4A 1BL, United Kingdom
Tel.: (44) 2034405300
Web Site: http://www.euromedica.com
Sales Range: $10-24.9 Million
Emp.: 20
Healthcare & Life Sciences Industry Executive Search & Management Consultancy Services
N.A.I.C.S.: 541612

Subsidiary (Non-US):

Euromedica Executive Search GmbH (2)
Lessingstrasse 5, D-60325, Frankfurt am Main, Germany
Tel.: (49) 69271030
Web Site: http://www.euromedica.com
Healthcare & Life Sciences Industry Executive Search & Management Consultancy Services
N.A.I.C.S.: 541612

Euromedica International Ltd. (2)
Pegasuslaan 5, BE-1831, Diegem, Belgium
Tel.: (32) 27092950
Web Site: http://www.euromedica.com
Healthcare & Life Sciences Industry Executive Search & Management Consultancy Services
N.A.I.C.S.: 541612

Euromedica SARL (2)
18 rue de Marignan, F-75008, Paris, France
Tel.: (33) 149530511
Web Site: http://www.euromedica.com
Healthcare & Life Sciences Industry Executive Search & Management Consultancy Services

N.A.I.C.S.: 541612

Gerrard Financial Planning Limited (1)
1a-1b Greenfield Crescent, B15 3BE, Birmingham, United Kingdom - England
Tel.: (44) 800 5875800
Financial Management Services
N.A.I.C.S.: 523999

Gerrard Investment Management Limited (1)
1 Churchill Place, London, E14 5HP, United Kingdom
Tel.: (44) 20 7114 1000
Web Site: http://www.gerrard.com
Investment Management Service
N.A.I.C.S.: 523999

Gerrard Management Services Limited (1)
1 Churchill Place, London, E14 5HP, United Kingdom
Tel.: (44) 2031342000
Investment Management Service
N.A.I.C.S.: 523999

Gordon Holdings (Netherlands) B.V. (1)
Fred Roeskestraat 123-1, Amsterdam, 1076 EE, Noord-Holland, Netherlands
Tel.: (31) 20 577 1177
Investment Management Service
N.A.I.C.S.: 523999

Greig Middleton Holdings Limited (1)
Old Mutual Place 2 Lambeth Hill, London, EC4V 4GG, United Kingdom
Tel.: (44) 904 049 8229
Investment Management Service
N.A.I.C.S.: 523999

Grupo Financiero Barclays Mexico, S.A. de C.V. (1)
Eje 3 Sur Av Morelos 41 Artes Graficas Cuauhtemoc, Mexico, Mexico
Tel.: (52) 1 55 5241 3200
Securities Brokerage Services
N.A.I.C.S.: 523150

Hamnes Investments BV (1)
Dam 7F-6e Etage, 1012 JS, Amsterdam, Netherlands
Tel.: (31) 204867646
Financial Management Services
N.A.I.C.S.: 523999

Hoardburst Limited (1)
54 Lombard Street, London, EC3P 3AH, United Kingdom
Tel.: (44) 904 049 8229
Financial Management Services
N.A.I.C.S.: 523999

ISB CANARIAS SA (1)
Calle Albareda 5, Las Palmas, 35007, Spain
Tel.: (34) 913 362 055
Commercial Banking Services
N.A.I.C.S.: 522110

Iveco Capital Limited (1)
Iveco House Station Road, Watford, WD17 1SR, Hertfordshire, United Kingdom
Tel.: (44) 19 2325 9777
Web Site: http://web.iveco.com
Investment Management Service
N.A.I.C.S.: 523999

Iveco Finance AG (1)
Oberfeldstrasse 20, Kloten, 8302, Switzerland
Tel.: (41) 44804 30 00
Financial Lending Services
N.A.I.C.S.: 522220

Iveco Finance GmbH (1)
Salzstrasse 185, 74076, Heilbronn, Germany
Tel.: (49) 71 31 27 88 0
Web Site: http://www.ivecocapital.de
Financial Management Services
N.A.I.C.S.: 523999

Iveco Finance Holdings Limited (1)
Iveco House Station Road, Watford, WD17 1ZS, United Kingdom
Tel.: (44) 1923 259777
Emp.: 100
Investment Management Service
N.A.I.C.S.: 523999

Staurt Webster (Gen Mgr)

Kafue House Limited (1)
Cairo Rd, PO Box 31936, Lusaka, 10101, Zambia
Tel.: (260) 211 366100
Commercial Banking Services
N.A.I.C.S.: 522110

Limited Liability Company Barclays Capital (1)
125047 G Moskva Ul Tverskaya-Yamskaya 1-Ya d 21, Moscow, Russia
Tel.: (7) 495 786 84 00
Web Site: http://www.barcap.com
Investment Banking Services
N.A.I.C.S.: 523150

Maloney Investments Limited (1)
1 Churchill Place, London, E14 5HP, United Kingdom
Tel.: (44) 2076261567
Investment Management Service
N.A.I.C.S.: 523999

Mercantile Credit Company Limited (1)
Churchill Plaza Churchill Way, Basingstoke, RG21 7GP, Hampshire, United Kingdom
Tel.: (44) 1256817777
Financial Lending Services
N.A.I.C.S.: 522220

Mercantile Industrial Leasing Limited (1)
Churchill Plaza Churchill Way, Basingstoke, RG21 7GP, Hampshire, United Kingdom
Tel.: (44) 1256817777
Financial Lending Services
N.A.I.C.S.: 522220

Merque Financial Services Proprietary Limited (1)
104 Park St, Klerksdorp, 2571, North West, South Africa
Tel.: (27) 437014200
Financial Management Services
N.A.I.C.S.: 523999

Murray House Investments Limited (1)
1 Churchill Place, London, E14 5HP, United Kingdom
Tel.: (44) 2076261567
Investment Management Service
N.A.I.C.S.: 523999

Myers Grove Investments Limited (1)
1 Churchill Place, London, E14 5HP, United Kingdom
Tel.: (44) 2076261567
Investment Management Service
N.A.I.C.S.: 523999

Newfunds Proprietary Limited (1)
180 Commissioner St, Johannesburg, 2000, South Africa
Tel.: (27) 11 895 5517
Fund Management Services
N.A.I.C.S.: 523940
Michael Mgwaba (Office Mgr)

Ou Skip Beleggings Proprietary Limited (1)
401 Parkgebou Durbanweg 49, Bellville, 7530, Western Cape, South Africa
Tel.: (27) 113504000
Investment Management Service
N.A.I.C.S.: 523999

Patus 216 GmbH (1)
Erik-Blumfeld-Platz 27b, Hamburg, 22587, Germany
Tel.: (49) 511 84000
Financial Management Services
N.A.I.C.S.: 523999

Red House Management Company (Norfolk) Limited (1)
9 Sewell Cottages Redhouse Buxton, Norwich, NR10 5PF, Norfolk, United Kingdom
Tel.: (44) 904 049 8229
Property Management Services
N.A.I.C.S.: 531311

Relative Value Investments UK Limited Liability Partnership (1)
1 Churchill Place, London, E14 5HP, United Kingdom

Tel.: (44) 2076261567
Investment Management Service
N.A.I.C.S.: 523999

Ruthenium Investments Limited (1)
1 Churchill Place, London, E14 5HP, United
Kingdom
Tel.: (44) 2076261567
Investment Management Service
N.A.I.C.S.: 523999

Ruval SA (1)
Plaza Colon 1, Madrid, 28046, Spain
Tel.: (34) 913361000
Building Maintenance Services
N.A.I.C.S.: 236118

**Societe Francaise de Gestion et de
Construction (SFGC) SA** (1)
183 Av Daumesnil, 75012, Paris, France
Tel.: (33) 1 42 47 82 47
Property Management Services
N.A.I.C.S.: 531311

**Somerset West Autopark Proprietary
Limited** (1)
75 Hartshorne Street, Benoni, South Africa
Tel.: (27) 115109900
Property Management Services
N.A.I.C.S.: 531311

Svenska Kaolin AB (1)
Drottningg 92-94, 111 36, Stockholm, Swe-
den
Tel.: (46) 8 545426 30
Web Site: http://www.svenskakaolin.se
Clay Mining Services
N.A.I.C.S.: 212323

UB Group Limited (1)
33 Sloane Dr, Johannesburg, 2191, South
Africa
Tel.: (27) 113507071
Investment Management Service
N.A.I.C.S.: 523999

Westferry Investments Limited (1)
1 Churchill Place, London, E14 5HP, United
Kingdom
Tel.: (44) 2076261567
Investment Management Service
N.A.I.C.S.: 523999

Woolwich Homes Limited (1)
54 Lombard Street, London, EC3P 3AH,
United Kingdom
Tel.: (44) 904 049 8229
Real Estate Manangement Services
N.A.I.C.S.: 531390

**Woolwich Surveying Services
Limited** (1)
Drake House Anchor Boulevard Crossways,
Dartford, DA2 6QH, United Kingdom
Tel.: (44) 845 605 1111
Surveying & Mapping Services
N.A.I.C.S.: 541360

Zeban Nominees Limited (1)
54 Lombard Street, London, EC3P 3AH,
United Kingdom
Tel.: (44) 904 049 8229
Financial Management Services
N.A.I.C.S.: 523999

BARCO MATERIALS HAN-
DLING LTD.

24 Kerr Crescent Keer Industrial
Park, Guelph, N1H 6H9, ON, Canada
Tel.: (519) 763-1037
Web Site: http://www.barco.ca
Rev.: $31,944,472
Emp.: 146
Pallet & Box Mfr
N.A.I.C.S.: 321920

BARCO N.V.

Beneluxpark 21, BE-8500, Kortrijk,
Belgium
Tel.: (32) 56233211
Web Site: https://www.barco.com
Year Founded: 1934
BAR—(EUR)
Rev.: $945,846,744
Assets: $1,250,597,653
Liabilities: $394,382,951
Net Worth: $856,214,702

Earnings: ($5,395,658)
Emp.: 3,519
Fiscal Year-end: 12/31/20
Display Monitor, Projector, Lighting
Solutions & Visual System Control
Software Mfr
N.A.I.C.S.: 335139
Inge Govaerts *(Officer-Corp Comm)*

Subsidiaries:

Advan Int'l Corp. (1)
47817 Fremont Blvd, Fremont, CA 94538
Tel.: (510) 490-1005
Web Site: http://www.advancorp.com
Sales Range: $10-24.9 Million
Emp.: 45
Medical Display Instruments Mfr
N.A.I.C.S.: 334118
Kenzo Sudo *(Pres & CEO)*

Barco Co., Ltd. (1)
Yamato International Bldg 8F 5-1-1 Heiwa-
jima, Ota-ku, Tokyo, 143-0006,
Japan **(100%)**
Tel.: (81) 357628720
Sales Range: $25-49.9 Million
Emp.: 55
Data Processing Services
N.A.I.C.S.: 518210
Mark Poot *(CEO)*

Barco Colombia SAS (1)
Carrera 15 n 88-64Torre Zimma Oficina
610, 110221, Bogota, Colombia
Tel.: (57) 17564550
Electric Equipment Mfr
N.A.I.C.S.: 335999

Barco Control Rooms (1)
Greschbachstrasse 5 a, 76229, Karlsruhe,
Germany **(100%)**
Tel.: (49) 72162010
Sales Range: $50-74.9 Million
Emp.: 150
N.A.I.C.S.: 518210
Carl Peetrs *(CFO)*

Barco Coordination Center NV (1)
Tel.: (32) 56233211
Sales Range: $150-199.9 Million
Emp.: 100
Software Development Services
N.A.I.C.S.: 541511
Eric Van Zele *(CEO)*

Barco Electronic Systems Ltd. (1)
(100%)
Tel.: (91) 1204020300
Sales Range: $100-124.9 Million
Emp.: 500
Data Processing Hosting & Related Ser-
vices
N.A.I.C.S.: 518210
Rajiv Bhalla *(Mng Dir)*

Barco Electronic Systems S.A. (1)
Travessera de les Corts 241-Entlo 3,
08028, Barcelona, Spain **(100%)**
Tel.: (34) 934442103
Sales Range: $25-49.9 Million
Emp.: 20
Data Processing Services
N.A.I.C.S.: 518210

**Barco Elektronik Sistemleri San.Tic.
A.S** (1)
Ivedik OSB 1435 Cad No 4, Yenimahalle,
06378, Ankara, Turkiye
Tel.: (90) 3124429257
Web Site: https://barkoelektronik.com
Electronic & Mechanical Mfr
N.A.I.C.S.: 334513

Barco Fredrikstad AS (1)
Mossevelen 63, 1610, Fredrikstad, Norway
Tel.: (47) 69304550
Electric Equipment Mfr
N.A.I.C.S.: 335999

Barco GmbH (1)
Greschbachstrasse 5 a, 76229, Karlsruhe,
Germany **(100%)**
Tel.: (49) 72162010
Sales Range: $50-74.9 Million
Emp.: 180
Data Processing Services
N.A.I.C.S.: 518210

Barco Ltd. (1)

Building 329 Doncastle Road, Bracknell,
RG12 8PE, Berkshire, United
Kingdom **(100%)**
Tel.: (44) 134 492 3941
Web Site: https://www.barco.com
Sales Range: $25-49.9 Million
Emp.: 23
Mfr & Sales of Bearings
N.A.I.C.S.: 518210

Barco Ltd. (1)
Suite 2607-2610 26/F Prosperity Center 25
Chong Yip Street, Kwun Tong, Kowloon,
China (Hong Kong) **(100%)**
Tel.: (852) 2 397 0752
Web Site: http://www.barco.com
Sales Range: $25-49.9 Million
Emp.: 20
Data Processing Services
N.A.I.C.S.: 518210

Barco Ltd. (1)
165 2 Samsong Pong Gangnangu, Kang-
nam Ku, Seoul, 135-090, Korea
(South) **(99%)**
Tel.: (82) 234458900
Sales Range: $1-9.9 Million
Emp.: 20
N.A.I.C.S.: 518210

Barco Ltd. (1)
8F No 665 Bannan Rd, Zhonghe Dist, New
Taipei City, 235, Taiwan **(94%)**
Tel.: (886) 277150299
Web Site: https://www.barco.com
Sales Range: $25-49.9 Million
Emp.: 14
Designs & Develops Visualization Solutions
for Professional Markets
N.A.I.C.S.: 518210

Barco Ltd. (1)
65 42 Tower 19th Fl Rm 1902 Sukhumvit
42 Rd, Prakanong Klongtoey, Bangkok,
10110, Thailand **(100%)**
Tel.: (66) 27122533
Sales Range: $25-49.9 Million
Emp.: 2
N.A.I.C.S.: 518210

Barco Ltda. (1)
Av Ibirapuera 2332 8 andar conj 82 Torre II
Moema, Vila Olimpia, Sao Paulo, 04028-
002, Brazil **(100%)**
Tel.: (55) 1135131000
Web Site: https://www.barco.com.br
Sales Range: Less than $1 Million
Emp.: 12
N.A.I.C.S.: 518210

Barco Manufacturing s.r.o. (1)
Billundska 2756, Kladno, 272 01, Czech
Republic
Tel.: (420) 312 818 411
Sales Range: $25-49.9 Million
Emp.: 100
Electronic Components Mfr
N.A.I.C.S.: 334419

Barco Pte. Ltd. (1)
No 10 Changi South Lane, Singapore,
486162, Singapore **(100%)**
Tel.: (65) 62437610
Web Site: http://www.barco.com
Sales Range: $25-49.9 Million
Emp.: 20
Data Processing Services
N.A.I.C.S.: 518210

Barco S.A. (1)
177 Avenue Georges Clemenceau Im-
meuble Le Plein Ouest, 92000, Nanterre,
France **(100%)**
Tel.: (33) 15 569 1020
Web Site: https://www.barco.com
Emp.: 30
Data Processing Services
N.A.I.C.S.: 518210

Barco S.r.L. (1)
Via Monferrato 7, 20094, Corsico, MI,
Italy **(100%)**
Tel.: (39) 02 458 7981
Web Site: https://www.barco.com
Sales Range: $25-49.9 Million
Emp.: 20
Developer of Imaging Technologies
N.A.I.C.S.: 518210

Barco SAS (1)

Immeuble Le Plein Ouest 177 Avenue
Georges Clemenceau, 92000, Nanterre,
France
Tel.: (33) 155691020
Electronic Components Mfr
N.A.I.C.S.: 334419

Barco Sdn Bhd (1)
27-1 and 27-2 Block D1 Jalan Pju 1/41 Dat-
aran Prima, Selangor Darul, 47301, Petal-
ing Jaya, Selangor Darul Ehsan,
Malaysia **(100%)**
Tel.: (60) 378803362
Sales Range: $25-49.9 Million
Emp.: 7
N.A.I.C.S.: 518210

Barco Services OOO (1)
Office 17/2 Building 1 Zvezdny Boulevard,
Moscow, 129085, Russia
Tel.: (7) 4957855255
Electric Equipment Mfr
N.A.I.C.S.: 335999

Barco Silex N.V. (1)
Scientific Park, Rue du Bosquet 7, 1348,
Louvain-la-Neuve, Belgium **(99%)**
Tel.: (32) 10454904
Web Site: http://www.barco.com
Sales Range: $1-9.9 Million
Emp.: 20
N.A.I.C.S.: 518210
Watteyn Thierru *(Mng Dir)*

Barco Silex SAS (1)
Zone Industrielle Rousset Immeuble CCE 6
Route De Trets, 13790, Peynier, France
Tel.: (33) 4 42 16 41 06
Web Site: http://www.barco-silex.com
Emp.: 9
Electronic Engineering Services
N.A.I.C.S.: 541330
Jean-Eric Leroy *(Gen Mgr)*

Barco Singapore Private Limited (1)
100G Pasir Panjang Road Interlocal Centre
05-27/28/29, Singapore, 118523, Singapore
Tel.: (65) 877356
Electronic Component Mfr & Distr
N.A.I.C.S.: 334513

Barco Sp. Z o.o. (1)
Annopol 17, 03-236, Warsaw,
Poland **(100%)**
Tel.: (48) 222703160
Sales Range: Less than $1 Million
Emp.: 10
Data Processing Services
N.A.I.C.S.: 518210

Barco Sverige AB (1)
Tel.: (46) 86268905
Computer Peripheral Equipment Mfr
N.A.I.C.S.: 334118

Barco Systems Pty Ltd. (1)
Unit 1 A 11 Lord Street, Botany, 2019,
NSW, Australia **(100%)**
Tel.: (61) 296951146
Sales Range: $25-49.9 Million
Emp.: 2
N.A.I.C.S.: 518210
George Hoiuros *(Mgr-Sls)*

**Barco Trading (Shanghai) Co.,
Ltd.** (1)
Room 702 No 138 Fenyang Road, Shang-
hai, 200031, China **(100%)**
Tel.: (86) 2160912222
Sales Range: $25-49.9 Million
Emp.: 35
N.A.I.C.S.: 518210
Diana Lu *(Dir-HR)*

**Barco Visual (Beijing) Electronics
Co., Ltd.** (1)
No 16 Changsheng Rd Changping Technol-
ogy Park, Changping Dist, Beijing, 102200,
China
Tel.: (86) 1080101166
Projector Mfr
N.A.I.C.S.: 334118

**Barco Visual (Beijing) Trading Co.,
Ltd.** (1)
12F Citychamp Building No 12 Tai Yang
Gong Zhong Lu, Chao Yang District,
100028, Beijing, China
Tel.: (86) 10 5650 2288
Electronic Components Mfr

Barco Ltd. (1)

Barco N.V.—(Continued)

N.A.I.C.S.: 334419

Barco Visual Solutions S.A. de C.V. (1)
Av Paseo de la Reforma 250 Piso 9 Oficina 991 ABCD, Del Cuauhtemoc, CP 06600, Mexico, Mexico
Tel.: (52) 5536007083
Electronic Equipment Distr
N.A.I.C.S.: 423690

Barco Visual Solutions, Inc. (1)
5925 Airport Rd Suite 200, Mississauga, L4V 1W1, ON, Canada
Tel.: (905) 405-6225
Microfilm Equipment Whslr
N.A.I.C.S.: 423690

Barco, Inc. (1)
3059 Premiere Pkwy Ste 400, Duluth, GA 30097
Tel.: (678) 475-8000
Sales Range: $50-74.9 Million
Emp.: 250
Communication & Visualization Equipment Mfr
N.A.I.C.S.: 334290

Subsidiary (Domestic):

Barco Federal Systems LLC (2)
3059 Premiere Pkwy, Duluth, GA 30097
Tel.: (678) 475-8000
Web Site: http://www.barco.com
Search & Navigation System Mfr
N.A.I.C.S.: 334511

Unit (Domestic):

Barco Simulations (2)
600 Bellbrook Ave, Xenia, OH 45385-4053 (100%)
Tel.: (937) 372-7579
Sales Range: $50-74.9 Million
Emp.: 110
Mfr & Distributor of Cailigraphic Projectors for Flight Simulation
N.A.I.C.S.: 334220
Greg Packet (VP-Ops)

Barco Visual Solutions, LLC (2)
3059 Premiere Pkwy, Duluth, GA 30097-4905
Tel.: (770) 218-3200
Distr of Large Screen Projectors
N.A.I.C.S.: 541511

BarcoView Avionics (1)
Beneluxpark 21, 8500, Kortrijk, Belgium (79.99%)
Tel.: (32) 5 623 3211
Web Site: http://www.barcoaerospace.com
Sales Range: $400-449.9 Million
Emp.: 2,000
N.A.I.C.S.: 518210

BarcoView Texen SAS (1)
Parc Techn Basso Cambo 7 Rue Roger Camboulives, Toulouse, 31100, France
Tel.: (33) 534637000
Computer Peripheral Equipment Mfr & Distr
N.A.I.C.S.: 334118

Cinionic BVBA (1)
Beneluxpark 21, 8500, Kortrijk, Belgium (80%)
Tel.: (32) 5 636 8877
Web Site: https://www.cinionic.com
Technology Development Services
N.A.I.C.S.: 541511

Cinionic Inc. (1)
3078 Prospect Park Dr, Rancho Cordova, CA 95670
Technology Development Services
N.A.I.C.S.: 541511
Ivan Cannau (Exec VP)

Dermicus AB (1)
Kungsgatan 4, 411 19, Gothenburg, Sweden
Tel.: (46) 317118000
Web Site: https://dermicus.com
Tele Dermatology Skincare Services
N.A.I.C.S.: 812112

FIMI S.r.l. (1)
Via Saul Banfi 1, Saronno, 21047, Varese, Italy
Tel.: (39) 02 961751

Emp.: 9
Medical Device Mfr
N.A.I.C.S.: 334510
Ian Yates (Gen Mgr)

Gnosco AB (1)
Kungsgatan 4, 411 19, Gothenburg, Sweden
Tel.: (46) 317118000
Web Site: https://dermicus.com
Healtcare Services
N.A.I.C.S.: 621999

Innovative Designs (1)
Akkerstraat 1, 8020, Waardamme, Belgium (100%)
Tel.: (32) 50217042
Web Site: http://www.id-be.com
Sales Range: $25-49.9 Million
Emp.: 15
Video Technology Mfr
N.A.I.C.S.: 512110

Tulsarr Industrial Research B.V. (1)
Marinus Van Meelweg 20, 5657EN, Eindhoven, Noord Brabanc, Netherlands (100%)
Tel.: (31) 402922622
Web Site: http://www.bestsorting.com
Sales Range: $25-49.9 Million
Emp.: 45
N.A.I.C.S.: 518210

BARCOS CO., LTD.
48-1 Nakae, Kurayoshi, Tottori, 682-0002, Japan
Tel.: (81) 858481440
Web Site: https://www.barcos.jp
Year Founded: 1991
7790—(TKS)
Rev.: $27,346,130
Assets: $29,742,550
Liabilities: $26,261,360
Net Worth: $3,481,190
Earnings: $297,780
Emp.: 69
Fiscal Year-end: 12/31/23
Textile Product Mfr & Distr
N.A.I.C.S.: 314999
Takashi Yamamoto (Pres & CEO)

BARDELLA S.A. INDUSTRIAS MECANICAS
Av Antonio Bardella 525, Guarulhos, 07220-020, SP, Brazil
Tel.: (55) 1124871000
Web Site: https://www.bardella.com.br
Year Founded: 1911
BDLL4—(BRAZ)
Rev.: $4,609,678
Assets: $102,106,502
Liabilities: $136,634,844
Net Worth: ($34,528,341)
Earnings: ($14,736,955)
Fiscal Year-end: 12/31/23
Industrial Equipment Mfr & Whslr
N.A.I.C.S.: 333998
Claudio Bardella (Pres)

Subsidiaries:

DURAFERRO Industria e Comercio Ltda. (1)
Estrada Municipal Araras Elihu-Root km 3, Caixa Postal 418, 13600-970, Araras, Sao Paulo, Brazil
Tel.: (55) 19 3543 6300
Web Site: http://www.duraferro.com.br
Travelling Crane Mfr
N.A.I.C.S.: 333923

BARDOT PTY. LTD.
63 Victoria Cres, Abbotsford, Melbourne, 3067, VIC, Australia
Tel.: (61) 394207900
Web Site: http://www.bardot.com
Year Founded: 1996
Emp.: 600
Women Clothing & Accessory Distr
N.A.I.C.S.: 458110
Basil Artemides (CEO)

BAREKET CAPITAL LTD.
Hilzon 5, Ramat Gan, 5320047, Israel
Tel.: (972) 33770013
Web Site: https://bareketc.com
Year Founded: 2015
BRKT—(TAE)
Rev.: $29,996,408
Assets: $296,587,093
Liabilities: $267,864,618
Net Worth: $28,722,475
Earnings: $3,733,941
Fiscal Year-end: 12/31/23
Miscellaneous Financial Investment Activities
N.A.I.C.S.: 523999

BARENBRUG HOLDING B.V.
Stationsstraat 40, PO Box 4, 6515 AB, Nijmegen, Netherlands
Tel.: (31) 243488100
Web Site: http://www.barenbrug.nl
Year Founded: 1904
Sales Range: $150-199.9 Million
Emp.: 500
Plant Breeding, Seed Production & Seed Trade Services
N.A.I.C.S.: 111199

Subsidiaries:

Barenbrug Belgium NV/SA (1)
Uilenstraat 155a, 9100, Saint-Niklaas, Belgium (100%)
Tel.: (32) 32191947
Web Site: http://www.barenbrug.be
Sales Range: $25-49.9 Million
Emp.: 6
Plant Breeding, Seed Production & Seed Trade
N.A.I.C.S.: 111199
Bastiaan J. Barenbrug (Mng Dir)

Barenbrug China R.O. (1)
16F City Plaza 2 Shilipu, Chaoyang Dist, Beijing, 100025, China (100%)
Tel.: (86) 1065561872
Web Site: http://www.barenbrug.com.cn
Sales Range: $25-49.9 Million
Emp.: 10
Plant Breeding, Seed Production & Seed Trade
N.A.I.C.S.: 111199

Barenbrug France S.A. (1)
Parc D Activites ZAC Les Portes De La Foret, 77615, Marne-la-Vallee, Cedex, France (100%)
Tel.: (33) 0160068100
Web Site: http://www.barenbrug.fr
Sales Range: $25-49.9 Million
Emp.: 25
Plant Breeding Seed Production & Seed Trade Services
N.A.I.C.S.: 111199
Benoit Petitjean (Dir-Mktg)

Barenbrug Holland B.V. (1)
Stationsstraat 40, 6515 AB, Nijmegen, Netherlands (100%)
Tel.: (31) 243488100
Web Site: http://www.barenbrug.nl
Sales Range: $25-49.9 Million
Emp.: 100
Plant Breeding Seed Production & Seed Trade Services
N.A.I.C.S.: 111199
Paul Van Den Berg (Dir-Mktg)

Barenbrug Luxembourg S.A. (1)
Industriezone Ingeldorf Strae Diekirch, PO Box 12, Ettelbruck, L 9201, Diekirch, Luxembourg (100%)
Tel.: (352) 808484
Web Site: http://www.barenbrug.lu
Sales Range: $25-49.9 Million
Emp.: 15
Plant Breeding Seed Production & Seed Trade Services
N.A.I.C.S.: 111199

Barenbrug Polska Sp. z.o.o. (1)
Ul Sowia 15, Poznan, 62 080, Poland (100%)
Tel.: (48) 618164133
Web Site: http://www.barenbrug.pl

Sales Range: $25-49.9 Million
Emp.: 3
Plant Breeding, Seed Production & Seed Trade
N.A.I.C.S.: 111199
Eliza Kosmidr (Office Mgr)

Barenbrug Research USA (1)
33477 Hwy 99 E, Tangent, OR 97389-0239 (100%)
Tel.: (541) 926-5801
Web Site: http://www.barusa.com
Sales Range: $50-74.9 Million
Emp.: 100
Provider of Plant Breeding & Seed Production Distr
N.A.I.C.S.: 424910
John Thyssen (Pres & CEO)

Barenbrug Research Wolfheze (1)
Duitsekampweg 60, NL 6874 BX, Wolfheze, Netherlands (100%)
Tel.: (31) 264835100
Web Site: http://www.barenbrug.nl
Sales Range: $25-49.9 Million
Emp.: 13
Plant Breeding
N.A.I.C.S.: 111422
P. Arts (Gen Mgr)

Barenbrug U.K. Ltd. (1)
Rougham Industrial Estate, Bury Saint Edmunds, IP30 9ND, Suffolk, United Kingdom (100%)
Tel.: (44) 1359272000
Web Site: http://www.barenbrug.co.uk
Sales Range: $25-49.9 Million
Emp.: 20
Plant Breeding, Seed Production & Seed Trade
N.A.I.C.S.: 111199
Paul R. Johnson (Mng Dir)

Barenbrug USA (1)
33477 Hwy 99 E, Tangent, OR 97389-0239 (100%)
Tel.: (541) 926-5801
Web Site: http://www.barusa.com
Sales Range: $50-74.9 Million
Emp.: 100
Plant Breeding Seed Production & Seed Trade Distr
N.A.I.C.S.: 424910

Heritage Seeds Pty. Ltd. (1)
26 Prosperity Way, PO Box 4020, Dandenong South, 3175, VIC, Australia (92%)
Tel.: (61) 395017000
Web Site: http://www.heritageseeds.com.au
Sales Range: $25-49.9 Million
Emp.: 20
Plant Breeding, Seed Production & Seed Trade
N.A.I.C.S.: 111199
Peter Young (Mng Dir)

New Zealand Agriseeds Ltd. (1)
2547 Old West Coast Road, Christchurch, 7671, New Zealand (100%)
Tel.: (64) 33188514
Web Site: http://www.agriseeds.co.nz
Sales Range: $10-24.9 Million
Emp.: 60
Plant Breeding, Seed Production & Seed Trade
N.A.I.C.S.: 111199
Murray J. Willocks (CEO)

Palaversich Y Cia S.A. (1)
Alvarez Condarco 612, 2700, Pergamino, Argentina (100%)
Tel.: (54) 2477433230
Web Site: http://www.barenbrug.com.ar
Sales Range: $10-24.9 Million
Emp.: 50
Plant Breeding, Seed Production & Seed Trade
N.A.I.C.S.: 111199

BARILGA CORPORATION JOINT STOCK COMPANY
North East Extension 4-Th Floor, Builder'S Square-13, Ulaanbaatar, Mongolia
Tel.: (976) 1 132 1420
Web Site: http://www.barilgacor.mn
BRC—(MONG)
Sales Range: $1-9.9 Million

Building Construction Services
N.A.I.C.S.: 236220

BARILLA HOLDING S.P.A.
Via Mantova 166, 43122, Parma, Italy
Tel.: (39) 05212621
Web Site: http://www.barillagroup.it
Year Founded: 1877
Sales Range: $5-14.9 Billion
Pasta
N.A.I.C.S.: 311423
Guido M. Barilla *(Chm)*

Subsidiaries:

Barilla America N.Y. Inc. **(1)**
100 Horseshoe Blvd, Avon, NY 14414-1164
Tel.: (585) 226-5600
Food Product Mfr & Distr
N.A.I.C.S.: 311999

Barilla America, Inc. **(1)**
1200 Lakeside Dr, Bannockburn, IL
60015 **(100%)**
Tel.: (847) 405-7500
Web Site: http://www.barilla.com
Sales Range: $25-49.9 Million
Emp.: 140
Pasta Mfr
N.A.I.C.S.: 311824
Eugenio Perrier *(VP-Mktg)*

Barilla Australia Pty Ltd **(1)**
4 Annandale Street, Canberra, 2038, NSW,
Australia
Tel.: (61) 2 8585 3911
Web Site: http://www.barilla.com
Emp.: 12
Food Products Distr
N.A.I.C.S.: 424490
Terry Ryan *(Gen Mgr)*

Barilla Austria GmbH **(1)**
Grabenweg 64, 6020, Innsbruck, Austria
Tel.: (43) 512390409
Food Products Distr
N.A.I.C.S.: 424490
Frank Zobl *(Mng Dir)*

Barilla Canada Inc. **(1)**
26 Yonge Street 1500, Toronto, M5C 2W7,
ON, Canada
Tel.: (800) 922-7455
Web Site: http://www.barilla.ca
Food Products Distr
N.A.I.C.S.: 424490
Gino Rulli *(VP & Gen Mgr)*

Barilla Do Brasil LTDA **(1)**
Alameda Vicente Pinzon 144- cj 71 e 72,
Sao Paulo, 04547-130, Brazil
Tel.: (55) 1138468302
Web Site: http://www.barilla.com.br
Food Products Distr
N.A.I.C.S.: 424490
Maurizio Scarpa *(Country Mgr)*

Barilla Espana S.L. **(1)**
Zurbano 43, Madrid, Spain
Tel.: (34) 932242718
Web Site: http://www.barilla.es
Food Products Distr
N.A.I.C.S.: 424490

Barilla France SAS **(1)**
103 Rue de Grenelle, 75007, Paris, France
Tel.: (33) 1 44 11 14 00
Web Site: http://www.barilla.fr
Food Product Mfr & Distr
N.A.I.C.S.: 311999
Charlotte Oudin *(Mgr-Trade Mktg & Category Mgmt)*

Subsidiary (Domestic):

Harry's Restauration SAS **(2)**
72 Route de Chauny, 02430, Gauchy,
France
Tel.: (33) 3 23 50 68 80
Food Product Mfr & Distr
N.A.I.C.S.: 311999

Barilla Gida A.S. **(1)**
Kosifler Plaza Serin Sok No 9 A Blok
Icerenkoy, 34752, Istanbul, Turkiye
Tel.: (90) 216 469 85 85
Web Site: http://www.barillagida.com.tr
Emp.: 50
Food Product Mfr & Distr

N.A.I.C.S.: 311999
Yaman Altan *(Mgr-Mktg)*

Barilla Hellas S.A. **(1)**
26 Pappou & Akragantos Str, 10442, Athens, Greece
Tel.: (30) 210 5197800
Web Site: http://www.barilla.gr
Food Product Mfr & Distr
N.A.I.C.S.: 311999
Aris Giannakis *(Area Mgr-Technical)*

Barilla Japan K.K. **(1)**
Kyodo Bldg 8F 5-6-24 Minamiaoyama,
Minato-Ku, Tokyo, 107-0062, Japan
Tel.: (81) 364187905
Web Site: http://www.barilla.co.jp
Food Products Distr
N.A.I.C.S.: 424490

Barilla Netherlands B.V. **(1)**
Lange Dreef 13i, 4131 NJ, Vianen, Netherlands
Tel.: (31) 347 35 88 30
Web Site: http://www.wasa.nl
Food Products Distr
N.A.I.C.S.: 424490
Patrick Pol *(Key Acct Mgr)*

Subsidiary (Non-US):

Barilla Switzerland A.G. **(2)**
Ruetistrasse 32, 8702, Zollikon, Switzerland
Tel.: (41) 41 767 00 80
Web Site: http://www.barillapasta.ch
Food Products Distr
N.A.I.C.S.: 424490

Barilla Singapore Pte Ltd **(1)**
27 Kreta Ayer Road, Singapore, 088994,
Singapore
Tel.: (65) 69080750
Web Site: http://www.barilla.com.sg
Food Products Distr
N.A.I.C.S.: 424490

Barilla Sverige AB **(1)**
80 Commune, Stockholm, Sweden
Tel.: (46) 20 75 80 81
Web Site: http://www.barilla.se
Food Product Mfr & Distr
N.A.I.C.S.: 311999
Asa Hermansson *(Mgr-Mktg)*

Subsidiary (Non-US):

Barilla Danmark A/S **(2)**
Mileparken 18, 2740, Skovlunde, Denmark
Tel.: (45) 44 91 96 00
Food Products Distr
N.A.I.C.S.: 424490

Barilla Deutschland GmbH **(2)**
Gustav-Heinemann-Ufer 72 c, 50968, Cologne, Germany
Tel.: (49) 221 84618 0
Web Site: http://www.barilla.de
Food Product Mfr & Distr
N.A.I.C.S.: 311999
Torsten Prekel *(Key Acct Mgr)*

Barilla Norge AS **(2)**
Sandvikavegen 55 2312, Ottestad, 2301,
Hamar, Norway
Tel.: (47) 62 58 27 00
Web Site: http://www.barilla.no
Food Products Distr
N.A.I.C.S.: 424490

Barilla Poland Sp. Z.o.o. **(2)**
ul Poleczki 23, 02-822, Warsaw, Poland
Tel.: (48) 22 335 21 50
Web Site: http://www.barilla.pl
Food Products Distr
N.A.I.C.S.: 424490
Grzegorz Skup *(Key Acct Mgr)*

ZAO KONDI **(1)**
132 Mendelleva, Ufa, Russia
Tel.: (7) 347 2529700
Food Products Mfr
N.A.I.C.S.: 311999

BARING VOSTOK CAPITAL PARTNERS
9 Lesnaya St White Gardens Business Center Building B 6th Floor,
125196, Moscow, Russia
Tel.: (7) 4959671307
Web Site: http://baring-vostok.com

Year Founded: 1994
Sales Range: $25-49.9 Million
Emp.: 50
Privater Equity Firm
N.A.I.C.S.: 523999
Mikhail Lomtadze *(Partner)*

Subsidiaries:

Kaspi Bank JSC **(1)**
90 Adi Sharipov Street, 050012, Almaty,
Kazakhstan **(51%)**
Tel.: (7) 7272501720
Web Site: http://www.kaspibank.kz
Rev.: $4,195,518,174
Assets: $14,957,768,103
Liabilities: $12,538,863,279
Net Worth: $2,418,904,824
Earnings: $1,861,013,102
Emp.: 3,600
Fiscal Year-end: 12/31/2023
Banking Services
N.A.I.C.S.: 522110
Vyacheslav Kim *(Chm)*

Subsidiary (Non-US):

Caspian Capital B.V. **(2)**
Schouwburgplein 30-34, Rotterdam, 3012
CL, Zuid-Holland, Netherlands
Tel.: (31) 102245333
Financial Services
N.A.I.C.S.: 541611
Tim Ruoff *(Gen Mgr)*

BARINGS CORE SPAIN SOCIMI, S.A.
Calle Serrano 41 4, 28001, Madrid,
Spain
Tel.: (34) 917370407
Web Site: https://www.barings.com
Year Founded: 2016
MLBAR—(EUR)
Rev.: $22,792,100
Assets: $285,500,707
Liabilities: $177,599,511
Net Worth: $107,901,196
Earnings: $5,522,295
Fiscal Year-end: 12/31/23
Real Estate Investment Services
N.A.I.C.S.: 531210
Steve Boehm *(COO)*

BARINTHUS BIOTHERAPEU-TICS PLC
Unit 6-10 Zeus Building Rutherford
Avenue, Harwell, OX11 0DF, United
Kingdom
Tel.: (44) 1865818808 **UK**
Web Site:
https://www.barinthusbio.com
Year Founded: 2016
BRNS—(NASDAQ)
Rev.: $268,000
Assets: $280,715,000
Liabilities: $28,153,000
Net Worth: $252,562,000
Earnings: ($50,865,000)
Emp.: 72
Fiscal Year-end: 12/31/21
Biotechnology Research & Development Services
N.A.I.C.S.: 541714
William Enright *(CEO)*

BARITA INVESTMENTS LIM-ITED
15 St Lucia Way, Kingston, 5, Jamaica
Tel.: (876) 9262681
Web Site: https://www.barita.com
Year Founded: 1977
BIL—(JAM)
Rev.: $10,936,364
Assets: $717,466,939
Liabilities: $506,979,836
Net Worth: $210,487,103
Earnings: $27,607,992
Emp.: 218
Fiscal Year-end: 09/30/22

Investment Management Service
N.A.I.C.S.: 523940
Vanessa Williams *(Mgr-Mandeville)*

BARKAWI HOLDING GMBH
Baierbrunner Str 35, 81379, Munich,
Germany
Tel.: (49) 89 74 98 26 0
Web Site:
http://www.barkawigroup.com
Sales Range: $100-124.9 Million
Emp.: 300
Holding Company
N.A.I.C.S.: 551112

Subsidiaries:

B2X Care Solutions GmbH **(1)**
Baierbrunner Str 35, Munich, 81379, Germany
Tel.: (49) 89 45 23 53 0
Web Site: http://www.b2xcare.com
Sales Range: $50-74.9 Million
Emp.: 200
After-Sales Solutions
N.A.I.C.S.: 513210
Tilo Brandis *(COO)*

Barkawi Management Consultants
GmbH **(1)**
Seilerstatte 11/13, 1010, Vienna, Austria
Tel.: (43) 151215980
Management Consulting Services
N.A.I.C.S.: 541611
Gregor Gluttig *(Mgr)*

Barkawi Management Consulting
(Shanghai) Co., Ltd. **(1)**
Unit 2205 ICP Building 1318 Sichuan North
Road, Shanghai, 200080, China
Tel.: (86) 2156413837
Management Consulting Services
N.A.I.C.S.: 541611

BARKER MINERALS LTD.
17970 Lacasse Rd, Prince George,
V2K 5T4, BC, Canada
Tel.: (778) 675-0776 **BC**
Web Site:
https://barkermineralsltd.yolasite.com
Year Founded: 1993
BML—(TSXV)
Sales Range: Less than $1 Million
Mineral Exploration Services
N.A.I.C.S.: 213114

BARKING APPLICATIONS CORPORATION
5114 Lakeshore Road, Burlington,
L7L 1B9, ON, Canada
Tel.: (905) 464-5493 **NV**
Web Site:
http://www.barkingapplications.com
Year Founded: 2011
Mobile Device Software Developer
N.A.I.C.S.: 513210
Raymond Kitzul *(Pres, CEO & CFO)*

BARKMAN CONCRETE LTD.
152 Brandt Street, Steinbach, R5G
0R2, MB, Canada
Tel.: (204) 326-3445
Web Site:
https://www.barkmanconcrete.com
Year Founded: 1948
Rev.: $17,427,632
Emp.: 85
Concrete Products Mfr
N.A.I.C.S.: 327831
Brian Pries *(Gen Mgr)*

BARKSDALE RESOURCES CORP.
Suite 615-800 West Pender Street,
Vancouver, V6C 2V6, BC, Canada
Tel.: (604) 398-5385 **Ca**
Web Site:
https://www.barksdaleresources.com
BRKCF—(OTCQX)
Rev.: $41,600

Barksdale Resources Corp.—(Continued)

Assets: $16,700,819
Liabilities: $1,336,428
Net Worth: $15,364,391
Earnings: ($2,600,829)
Fiscal Year-end: 03/31/23
Mineral Exploration Services
N.A.I.C.S.: 213115
Terri Anne Welyki (VP-Corp Comm)

BARLAGE GMBH
Am Gleis 5, 49740, Haselunne, Germany
Tel.: (49) 59629390
Web Site: http://www.barlage.com
Year Founded: 1980
Rev.: $29,902,130
Emp.: 900
Welded Structures Mfr
N.A.I.C.S.: 332999
Sascha Bendleb (Head-Sls & Project Mgmt)

BARLINEK S.A.
Al Solidarnosci 36, 25-323, Kielce, Poland
Tel.: (48) 413331111
Web Site: http://www.barlinek.com.pl
Sales Range: $150-199.9 Million
Emp.: 3,321
Wood Flooring Mfr
N.A.I.C.S.: 321918
Krzysztof Kwapisz (Vice Chm-Supervisory Bd)

BARLOWORLD LTD.
61 Katherine Street, PO Box 782248, Sandton, 2196, South Africa
Tel.: (27) 114451000   ZA
Web Site:
      https://www.barloworld.com
Year Founded: 1902
BRL1—(DEU)
Rev.: $2,452,224,880
Assets: $2,620,724,120
Liabilities: $1,704,761,380
Net Worth: $915,962,740
Earnings: $92,963,220
Emp.: 6,289
Fiscal Year-end: 09/30/23
Integrated Holding Company; Earthmoving & Power Systems Equipment; Automotive; Materials Handling & Logistics Management
N.A.I.C.S.: 551112
Dumisa Buhle Ntsebeza (Co-Chm)

Subsidiaries:

Avis Southern Africa Ltd.   (1)
3 Brabazon Road, Isando, 1600, Johannesburg, South Africa
Tel.: (27) 113878230
Web Site: https://www.avis.co.za
Sales Range: $650-699.9 Million
Emp.: 1,600
Passenger Car Rental
N.A.I.C.S.: 532111
Rainer Gottschick (CEO)

Barloworld Automotive (Pty)
Limited   (1)
6 Anvil Road, Johannesburg, Isando, South Africa   (100%)
Tel.: (27) 861 225529
Web Site: http://www.barloworldmotor.co.za
Sales Range: $400-449.9 Million
Emp.: 2,000
Other Motor Vehicle Electrical & Electronic Equipment Manufacturing
N.A.I.C.S.: 336110

Barloworld Equipment (Pty)
Limited   (1)
1 Electron Ave Kempton Park, PO Box 781291, Isando, 1600, Gauteng, South Africa
Tel.: (27) 119290000
Web Site: https://www.barloworld-equipment.com

Sales Range: $25-49.9 Million
Emp.: 60
Industrial Machinery & Equipment Merchant Whslrs
N.A.I.C.S.: 333248

Barloworld Equipment - Southern
Africa   (1)
Electron Avenue Ext, Isando, 1600, Gauteng, South Africa   (100%)
Tel.: (27) 119290000
Web Site: https://www.barloworld-equipment.com
Sales Range: $550-599.9 Million
Emp.: 2,000
Dealers in Earthmoving Equipment
N.A.I.C.S.: 423830

Barloworld Equipment Martex   (1)
1226 Haile Selassie Road, Gaborone Industrial Sites, Gaborone, Botswana   (100%)
Tel.: (267) 395 1781
Web Site: https://www.barloworld-equipment.com
Sales Range: $200-249.9 Million
Emp.: 521
Distr of Earthmoving Equipment, Materials Handling Equipment, Motor Vehicles, Paint, Building Materials, Office Automation Products, Household Appliances
N.A.I.C.S.: 325510

Barloworld Finanzauto   (1)
Av de la Madrid 43, Arganda del Rey, 28500, Spain
Tel.: (34) 918 71 26 12
Web Site: http://www.finanzauto.es
Sales Range: $150-199.9 Million
Emp.: 200
Industrial Machinery Whslr
N.A.I.C.S.: 423830

Barloworld Holdings PLC   (1)
Ground Floor Statesman House, Stafferton Way, Maidenhead, SL6 1AD, Berks, United Kingdom
Tel.: (44) 1628592900
Holding Company; Investment Management Services
N.A.I.C.S.: 551112

Holding (Domestic):

Barloworld Equipment UK
Limited   (2)
1st Floor Aurora Vanwall Business Park Vanwall Road, Vanwall Rd, Maidenhead, SL6 4UB, Berkshire, United Kingdom   (100%)
Tel.: (44) 1628592900
Web Site: http://www.barloworld.co.uk
Sales Range: $25-49.9 Million
Emp.: 20
Purchasing Agent for Earthmoving & Allied Capital Equipment
N.A.I.C.S.: 333120
Anton Globus (Mng Dir)

Barloworld Information Systems (Pty)
Limited   (1)
180 Katherine Street, Sandton, 2146, Johannesburg, South Africa
Tel.: (27) 114451600
Information Systems Services
N.A.I.C.S.: 561499

Barloworld Logistics (Pty)
Limited   (1)
Route 21 Business Park 85 Regency Dr, Irene, Centurion, 0157, Johannesburg, South Africa   (75%)
Tel.: (27) 11 445 1600
Web Site: https://www.barloworld-logistics.com
Process, Physical Distr & Logistics Consulting Services
N.A.I.C.S.: 541614

Barloworld Mera SA   (1)
Avenida De Madrid 43, Arganda del Rey, 28500, Spain
Tel.: (34) 918740000
Web Site: http://www.mera-cat.com
Sales Range: $75-99.9 Million
Emp.: 20
Industrial Equipment Distr
N.A.I.C.S.: 423830
Salzmann Victor (Office Mgr)

Barloworld Netherlands   (1)

De Witboom 1, Vianen, 4131 PL, Netherlands
Tel.: (31) 347349400
Web Site: http://www.heffiq.nl
Sales Range: $75-99.9 Million
Emp.: 125
Fleet Management Services
N.A.I.C.S.: 532112
Lex Knol (Mgr)

Barloworld Plascon (Pty) Ltd.   (1)
180 Katherine St, Sandton, 2000, Johannesburg, South Africa   (100%)
Tel.: (27) 113014600
Web Site: http://www.plascon.co.za
Sales Range: $25-49.9 Million
Emp.: 60
Mfr of Paints & Protective Coatings, Surface Preparations, Printing Inks & Industrial Soaps
N.A.I.C.S.: 325510

Barloworld Siyakhula (Pty)
Limited   (1)
Block E Upper Grayston Office Park 150 Linden St, Sandton, 2196, South Africa
Tel.: (27) 878309603
Web Site:
      https://www.barloworldsiyakhula.com
Building Construction Services
N.A.I.C.S.: 236210
Don Wilson (Chm)

Barloworld South Africa (Pty)
Limited   (1)
1 Electron Ave, Kempton Park, Isando, 1600, Gauteng, South Africa
Tel.: (27) 113014000
Web Site: http://www.barloworldmotor.
Motor Vehicle Parts Distr
N.A.I.C.S.: 423120
Alma Heustis (Gen Mgr)

Finanzauto, S.A.   (1)
Calle Brass 2, Arganda del Rey, 28500, Madrid, Spain   (100%)
Tel.: (34) 90 113 0013
Web Site: https://www.finanzauto.es
Sales Range: $400-449.9 Million
Emp.: 1,200
Fully Warranted Used Machinery Mfr & Distr
N.A.I.C.S.: 333111

NMI Durban South Motors (Pty)
Ltd.   (1)
6-10 Hagart Road, PO Box 1290, Pinetown, 3610, South Africa
Tel.: (27) 31 717 1333
Web Site:
      https://mercedesbenznmidsm.co.za
Sales Range: $250-299.9 Million
Emp.: 650
Other Motor Vehicle Electrical & Electronic Equipment Manufacturing
N.A.I.C.S.: 336110

Pretoria Portland Cement Co.
Ltd.   (1)
Building 148 Katherine Street Cnr Grayston Drive, PO Box 787416, Sandton, Johannesburg, 2146, South Africa   (60%)
Tel.: (27) 113869000
Web Site: https://www.ppc.africa
Sales Range: $125-149.9 Million
Emp.: 300
Mfr of Cement, Lime & Related Building Products
N.A.I.C.S.: 327310
Phillip Jabulani Moleketi (Chm)

Robor Industrial (Pty) Limited   (1)
8 Barbara Road, Elandsfontein, 1429, South Africa   (100%)
Tel.: (27) 19711600
Web Site: http://www.robor.co.za
Sales Range: $800-899.9 Million
Emp.: 3,000
Mfr of Steel Tubing; Metals Merchant & International Shipping/Trading
N.A.I.C.S.: 331210

Sociedade Technica De Equipamentos e Tractores SA   (1)
Rua da Guine Apartado 3050, Prior Velho, 2686-401, Portugal
Tel.: (351) 21 940 9300
Ground Moving & Extraction Machinery Distr

N.A.I.C.S.: 423440
Vasque Santos (Gen Mgr)

Sonnex Investments (Pty.) Ltd.   (1)
PO Box 215, Windhoek, Namibia   (100%)
Tel.: (264) 61 26 2161
Sales Range: $100-124.9 Million
Emp.: 275
Distr of Household Appliances, Paint, Earthmoving Equipment, Cement Products & Office Automation Products
N.A.I.C.S.: 335220

Vostochnaya Technica UK Ltd   (1)
1st Floor Aurora Vanwall Business Park Vanwall Road, Maidenhead, SL6 4UB, Berkshire, United Kingdom
Tel.: (44) 1628592900
Industrial Brand Management Services
N.A.I.C.S.: 541613

Zeda Car Leasing (Pty) Limited   (1)
6 Anvil Rd, Isando, Johannesburg, 1600, South Africa
Tel.: (27) 115529000
Web Site: https://www.avisfleet.co.za
Emp.: 500
Passenger Car Leasing Services
N.A.I.C.S.: 532112
Slade Thompson (CEO)

BARNESMCINERNEY INC.
120 Adelaide St W Ste 910, Toronto, M5H 3L5, ON, Canada
Tel.: (416) 367-5000
Emp.: 30
Advertising Agencies
N.A.I.C.S.: 541810
Kenneth Barnes (Chm)

BARNIER ET FILS
Le Bas Chirat Rue De La Loire, Saint Etienne, 42160, France
Tel.: (33) 477550164
Rev.: $10,300,000
Emp.: 46
N.A.I.C.S.: 333613
Patrick Robert (Pres)

BARODA EXTRUSION LIMITED
At & Po Garadiya Jarod Samalaya Road, Tal Savli, Vadodara, Gujarat, India
Tel.: (91) 9825303113
Web Site:
      https://www.barodaextrusion.com
Year Founded: 1993
513502—(BOM)
Rev.: $14,761,547
Assets: $4,258,841
Liabilities: $9,026,199
Net Worth: ($4,767,358)
Earnings: $187,756
Emp.: 86
Fiscal Year-end: 03/31/22
Copper Product Mfr
N.A.I.C.S.: 331410
Parasmal B. Kanugo (Chm & Mng Dir)

BARODA RAYON CORP LTD.
P O Fatehnagar, Udhna, 394220, Surat, 394220, Gujarat, India
Tel.: (91) 2612899555
Web Site: https://www.brcl.in
Year Founded: 1958
Synthetic Yarn Mfr
N.A.I.C.S.: 325220
Damodarbhai B. Patel (Chm & Mng Dir)

BARON DE LEY, S.A.
Carretera Mendavia a Lodosa km 55 Mendavia, 31897, Navarra, Spain
Tel.: (34) 948694303
Web Site: http://www.barondeley.com
Year Founded: 1985
BDL—(MAD)
Sales Range: $100-124.9 Million
Emp.: 190

Wineries; Wine, Other Alcoholic &
Non-Alcoholic Beverages Sales &
Distr
N.A.I.C.S.: 312130
Eduardo Santos-Ruiz Diaz *(Chm)*

Subsidiaries:

Dehesa Baron de Ley S.A.   **(1)**
Carretera de Mendavia a, Navarra, Spain
Tel.: (34) 948694303
Sales Range: $25-49.9 Million
Emp.: 35
Wine Mfr
N.A.I.C.S.: 312130

El Coto de Rioja S.A.   **(1)**
Camino Viejo de Oyon 26, Oyon-Oion,
01320, Alava, Spain
Tel.: (34) 945622216
Web Site: http://www.elcoto.com
Sales Range: $25-49.9 Million
Emp.: 100
Wine Mfr
N.A.I.C.S.: 312130
Julio Noain *(Gen Mgr)*

Finca Museum S.L.   **(1)**
Camino Viejo De Logrono 26, Oyon Euskad
Pais Vasco Cigales, 01320, Valladolid, Vall-
adolid, Spain
Tel.: (34) 983581029
Museums
N.A.I.C.S.: 712110

BARON INFOTECH LIMITED

Off 504 Survey No 131 141 Kom-
pally, Begumpet, Secunderabad, 500
014, India
Tel.: (91) 4032492514
Web Site:
    https://www.baroninfotech.com
Year Founded: 1994
Sales Range: Less than $1 Million
Software Development Services
N.A.I.C.S.: 541511
S. Nageswara Rao *(Compliance Offi-
cer & Gen Mgr-Fin)*

BARON PARTNERS LIMITED

Level 32 Deutsche Bank Place, 126
Phillip Street, Sydney, 2000, NSW,
Australia
Tel.: (61) 292325500
Web Site:
    http://www.baronpartners.com.au
Year Founded: 1987
Sales Range: $10-24.9 Million
Emp.: 10
Investment Services
N.A.I.C.S.: 523999
Stephen Chapman *(Co-Founder &
Exec Dir)*

BARONSMEAD SECOND VEN-
TURE TRUST PLC

100 Wood Street, London, EC2V
7AN, United Kingdom
Tel.: (44) 8009231534   UK
BMD—(LSE)
Rev.: $11,785,010
Assets: $249,292,327
Liabilities: $1,756,890
Net Worth: $247,535,437
Earnings: $10,455,802
Fiscal Year-end: 09/30/20
Investment Fund Services
N.A.I.C.S.: 525910

BARONSMEAD VENTURE
TRUST PLC

The Mending Rooms Meltham Road,
Park Valley Mills, Huddersfield, HD4
7BH, United Kingdom
Tel.: (44) 1738631949   UK
Web Site:
    https://www.baronsmeadvcts.co.uk
Year Founded: 1998
BVT—(LSE)
Sales Range: $1-9.9 Million

Emp.: 217
Investment Trust Management Ser-
vices
N.A.I.C.S.: 523940
Peter Lawrence *(Chm)*

BAROQUE JAPAN LIMITED

Sumitomo Realty Development Aoba-
dai Hills 477 Aobadai, Meguro-ku,
Tokyo, 153-0042, Japan
Tel.: (81) 367309191
Web Site: https://www.baroque-
    global.com
Year Founded: 2000
3548—(TKS)
Rev.: $572,465,520
Assets: $373,957,760
Liabilities: $156,767,600
Net Worth: $217,190,160
Earnings: $17,356,240
Emp.: 1,502
Fiscal Year-end: 02/28/22
Fashion Apparels Retailer
N.A.I.C.S.: 458110
Hiroyuki Murai *(Pres & CEO)*

BAROYECA GOLD & SILVER
INC.

1020 - 800 West Pender, Vancouver,
V6C 2V6, BC, Canada
Tel.: (604) 646-8353   BC
Web Site: https://www.baroyeca.com
Year Founded: 2006
BGS—(TSXV)
Assets: $245,124
Liabilities: $374,483
Net Worth: ($129,360)
Earnings: ($289,258)
Fiscal Year-end: 05/31/24
Gold & Silver Mining Services
N.A.I.C.S.: 212220
Richard D. Wilson *(CEO)*

BARR + WRAY LIMITED

1 Buccleuch Avenue, Hillington Park,
Glasgow, G52 4NR, United Kingdom
Tel.: (44) 1418829991
Web Site:
    http://www.barrandwray.com
Year Founded: 1959
Rev.: $19,172,016
Emp.: 81
Water Treatment & Design Services
N.A.I.C.S.: 221310
Alister MacDonald *(Chm & CEO)*

Subsidiaries:

Barr + Wray (H.K.) Limited   **(1)**
Unit B 21/F 998 Canton Road, Mongkok,
Kowloon, China (Hong Kong)
Tel.: (852) 22149990
Water Treatment & Design Services
N.A.I.C.S.: 221310
Derek Barton *(Mng Dir)*

Barr + Wray FZE   **(1)**
Dubai Silicon Oasis Le Solarium Building
Office 401, PO Box 341246, Dubai, United
Arab Emirates
Tel.: (971) 43206440
Water Treatment & Design Services
N.A.I.C.S.: 221310
Corrine Sunter *(Dir-Sls)*

BARRACHD LTD.

10 Lochside Place Edinburgh Park,
Edinburgh, EH12 9RG, United King-
dom
Tel.: (44) 131 564 0575
Web Site: http://www.barrachd.co.uk
Year Founded: 2007
Sales Range: $10-24.9 Million
Emp.: 35
Software Development Services
N.A.I.C.S.: 541511
Clark Wilson *(Mng Dir)*

BARRAMUNDI GROUP LTD.

46 Woodlands Terrace, Singapore,
738459, Singapore
Tel.: (65) 62610010   SG
Web Site:
    https://www.barramundi.com
Year Founded: 2008
95Z—(DEU)
Rev.: $26,121,325
Assets: $53,575,630
Liabilities: $36,650,136
Net Worth: $16,925,494
Earnings: ($22,874,040)
Fiscal Year-end: 12/31/22
Aquaculture Product Distr
N.A.I.C.S.: 424460
James Kwan *(CEO)*

Subsidiaries:

UVAXX Pte. Ltd.   **(1)**
203 Henderson Road 12-01 Henderson In-
dustrial Park, Singapore, 159546, Singa-
pore
Tel.: (65) 69707274
Web Site: https://www.uvaxx.com
Diagnostic Services
N.A.I.C.S.: 621512

BARRAMUNDI LIMITED

Level 1 67-73 Hurstmere Road, Pri-
vate Bag 93502, Takapuna, Auckland,
0740, New Zealand
Tel.: (64) 94897074
Web Site:
    https://www.barramundi.co.nz
BRM—(NZX)
Rev.: $26,063,995
Assets: $120,343,301
Liabilities: $1,185,407
Net Worth: $119,157,895
Earnings: $22,927,033
Emp.: 900
Fiscal Year-end: 06/30/23
Investment Services
N.A.I.C.S.: 523150
Frank Jasper *(CIO)*

BARRATT DEVELOPMENTS
PLC

Barratt House Cartwright Way Forest
Business Park, Bardon Hill, Coalville,
LE67 1UF, Leicestershire, United
Kingdom
Tel.: (44) 1530278278   UK
Web Site:
    http://www.barrattdevelopment.com
Year Founded: 1958
BDEV—(LSE)
Rev.: $6,717,243,120
Assets: $10,103,509,215
Liabilities: $3,039,131,532
Net Worth: $7,064,377,682
Earnings: $669,401,666
Emp.: 6,728
Fiscal Year-end: 06/30/23
Construction Engineering Services
N.A.I.C.S.: 541330
Steven J. Boyes *(Deputy CEO &
COO)*

Subsidiaries:

BDW East Scotland Limited   **(1)**
Blairton House Old Aberdeen Road, Balme-
die, AB23 8SH, Aberdeenshire, United King-
dom
Tel.: (44) 1358741300
Web Site:
    http://www.barrattdevelopments.co.uk
Property Management Services
N.A.I.C.S.: 531311

BDW Trading Limited   **(1)**
Barratt House Cartwright Way Forest Busi-
ness Park Bardon Hill, Coalville, LE67 1UF,
Leicestershire, United Kingdom
Tel.: (44) 1530278278
Develop & Build Residential Home Services
N.A.I.C.S.: 236117

Barratt Central Limited   **(1)**
4 Brindley Road City Park, Manchester,

M16 9HQ, United Kingdom   **(100%)**
Tel.: (44) 1618720161
Web Site: http://www.barrtthomes.co.uk
Sales Range: $25-49.9 Million
Emp.: 2
House & Apartment Construction
N.A.I.C.S.: 236118
Pop Lawson *(Chm)*

Subsidiary (Domestic):

Barratt Chester Limited   **(2)**
Oak House, Ellmport, Chester, CH65 9HQ,
Cheshire, United Kingdom   **(100%)**
Tel.: (44) 513574800
Web Site: http://www.barratt.com
Sales Range: $25-49.9 Million
House & Apartment Construction
N.A.I.C.S.: 236118

Unit (Domestic):

Barratt Homes Mercia   **(2)**
Remus 2 2 Cranbrook Way, Solihull, Shir-
ley, B90 4GT, United Kingdom
Tel.: (44) 121 713 7310
Web Site:
    http://www.barrattdevelopments.co.uk
House & Apartment Construction Services
N.A.I.C.S.: 236118

Subsidiary (Domestic):

Barratt Manchester Limited   **(2)**
4 Brindley Rd, Manchester, M16 9HQ,
United Kingdom   **(100%)**
Tel.: (44) 1618720161
Web Site: http://www.barrathomes.co.uk
Sales Range: $25-49.9 Million
Emp.: 75
House & Apartment Construction Services
N.A.I.C.S.: 236118

Unit (Domestic):

Barratt Sheffield   **(2)**
Barratt House Newton Chambers Rd,
Thorncliffe Park Chapeltown, Sheffield, S35
2PH, United Kingdom   **(100%)**
Tel.: (44) 01142572500
House & Apartment Construction
N.A.I.C.S.: 236118

Subsidiary (Domestic):

Barratt West Midlands Limited   **(2)**
60 Whitehall Road, Halesowen, B63 3JS,
West Midland, United Kingdom   **(100%)**
Tel.: (44) 1215855303
Web Site: http://www.barratthomes.co.uk
Sales Range: $25-49.9 Million
House & Apartment Construction
N.A.I.C.S.: 236118
Adrian Farr *(Mng Dir)*

Barratt Commercial Ltd.   **(1)**
Unit 1a Forest Business Park Cartwright
Way, Bardon Hill, Coalville, LE67 1GL, Leic-
estershire, United Kingdom
Tel.: (44) 1530276700
Web Site:
    http://www.barrattdevelopments.co.uk
House & Apartment Construction
N.A.I.C.S.: 236118

Barratt Construction Ltd.   **(1)**
Golf Rd, Ellon, AB41 9AT, Aberdeenshire,
United Kingdom   **(100%)**
Tel.: (44) 358720765
Web Site: http://www.barratthomes.co.uk
House & Apartment Construction Services
N.A.I.C.S.: 236118

Barratt East Midlands Limited   **(1)**
16 Regan Chilwell, Beeston, Nottingham,
NG9 6RZ, Notts, United Kingdom   **(100%)**
Tel.: (44) 1590075500
House & Apartment Construction
N.A.I.C.S.: 236118

Barratt East Scotland Limited   **(1)**
Craigcrook Castle Craigcrook Rd, Edin-
burgh, EH4 3PE, United Kingdom   **(100%)**
Tel.: (44) 313363655
Emp.: 35
House & Apartment Construction
N.A.I.C.S.: 236118
Colin Dearlove *(CFO)*

Barratt Eastern Counties Limited **(1)**
7 Springfield Lyons Approach, Chelmsford,

Barratt Developments PLC—(Continued)

CM2 5EY, United Kingdom **(100%)**
Tel.: (44) 1245232200
Sales Range: $25-49.9 Million
Emp.: 70
House & Apartment Construction
N.A.I.C.S.: 236118
Keith Parrett (Mng Dir)

Barratt London Limited **(1)**
Third Floor Press Centre Here East 13 East
Bay Lane, Queen Elizabeth Olympic Park,
London, E15 2GW, United
Kingdom **(100%)**
Tel.: (44) 208 522 2700
Web Site: http://www.barratt.com.co.uk
Real Estate Developments & Investments
N.A.I.C.S.: 525990

Barratt Northampton Limited **(1)**
Barratt House Sandy Way Grange Park,
Northampton, NN4 5EJ, United
Kingdom **(100%)**
Tel.: (44) 1604664500
Web Site: http://www.barratthomes.co.uk
Sales Range: $25-49.9 Million
Emp.: 100
House & Apartment Construction
N.A.I.C.S.: 236118
Andrew Swindell (Mng Dir)

Barratt Northern Limited **(1)**
Barratt House City West Buisness Pk,
Scottswood Road, Newcastle upon Tyne,
NE4 7DF, United Kingdom **(100%)**
Tel.: (44) 1912986100
Web Site: http://www.barratthome.co.uk
Sales Range: $25-49.9 Million
Emp.: 60
House & Apartment Construction
N.A.I.C.S.: 236118
Mike Roberts (Mng Dir)

Subsidiary (Domestic):

Barratt York Limited **(2)**
6 Alpha Court Monks Cross Drive, York,
YO32 9WN, United Kingdom **(100%)**
Tel.: (44) 1904617660
House & Apartment Construction
N.A.I.C.S.: 236118

Barratt South West Limited **(1)**
Unit 1 Great Park Court Bradley Stoke,
Bristol, BS32 4PY, United Kingdom
Tel.: (44) 1454278000
Develop & Build Residential Home Services
N.A.I.C.S.: 236117

**Barratt Southern Counties
Limited** **(1)**
Barratt Southern Counties Limited, Guild-
ford, GU1 4SW, Surrey, United
Kingdom **(100%)**
Tel.: (44) 1483505533
Sales Range: $25-49.9 Million
Emp.: 60
Develop & Build Residential Home Services
N.A.I.C.S.: 236117
Kristine Johnston (Mktg Mgr)

Barratt Southern Limited **(1)**
Alexandra House Balfour Road, Hounslow,
TW3 1JX, Middlesex, United
Kingdom **(100%)**
Tel.: (44) 2086071900
House & Apartment Construction
N.A.I.C.S.: 236118

Subsidiary (Domestic):

Barratt East Anglia Limited **(2)**
Barratt House 7 Mill Tye, Great Cornard,
Sudbury, CO10 0JA, Suffolk, United King-
dom
Tel.: (44) 1787468950
Residential Construction
N.A.I.C.S.: 525990

Unit (Domestic):

Barratt Southampton **(2)**
Tollbar House Tollbar Way, Hedge End,
Southampton, SO30 2UH, Hampshire,
United Kingdom **(100%)**
Tel.: (44) 1489779200
Emp.: 50
House & Apartment Construction
N.A.I.C.S.: 236118

Barratt West **(1)**
710 Waterside Drive Aztec West, Almonds-
bury, Bristol, BS32 4UD, United
Kingdom **(100%)**
Tel.: (44) 1454202202
Web Site: http://www.barratt.com
Sales Range: $50-74.9 Million
Emp.: 120
House & Apartment Construction
N.A.I.C.S.: 236118
Richard Gregory (Mng Dir)

Subsidiary (Domestic):

Barratt Bristol Limited **(2)**
Barratt House 710 Waterside Drive Aztec
West, Almondsbury, Bristol, BS32 4UD,
United Kingdom **(100%)**
Tel.: (44) 145 420 2202
Web Site: http://www.barratthomes.co.uk
House & Apartment Construction
N.A.I.C.S.: 236118
Andrea Pilgrim (Dir-Sls)

Unit (Domestic):

Barratt Exeter **(2)**
Barratt House Hennock Rd Central, Exeter,
EX2 8LL, United Kingdom **(100%)**
Tel.: (44) 392439022
Web Site: http://www.barratt.co.uk
Sales Range: $25-49.9 Million
Emp.: 100
House & Apartment Construction
N.A.I.C.S.: 236118

Subsidiary (Domestic):

Barratt South Wales Limited **(2)**
Oak House Village Way, Tongwynlais, Car-
diff, CF15 7NE, United Kingdom **(100%)**
Tel.: (44) 292 054 4744
Web Site:
    http://www.barrattdevelopments.co.uk
House & Apartment Construction
N.A.I.C.S.: 236118

Barratt West Scotland Limited **(1)**
7 Buchanan Gate Cumbernauld Road,
Stepps, Glasgow, G33 6FB, United
Kingdom **(100%)**
Tel.: (44) 1417798300
Rev.: $41,000,000
Emp.: 50
Develop & Build Residential Home Services
N.A.I.C.S.: 236117

Broad Oak Homes Limited **(1)**
Broad Oak Lane Little Green Head Kingsley
Moor, Stoke-on-Trent, ST10 2EL, Stafford-
shire, United Kingdom
Tel.: (44) 178 255 9906
Web Site:
    https://www.broadoakhomes.co.uk
New Housing Construction Services
N.A.I.C.S.: 236117

**David Wilson Homes (North Mid-
lands) Limited** **(1)**
2 Horizon Place Mellors Way, Nottingham
Business Park, Nottingham, NG8 6PY,
United Kingdom
Tel.: (44) 1159007550
Develop & Build Residential Home Services
N.A.I.C.S.: 236117

**David Wilson Homes (South Mid-
lands) Limited** **(1)**
1a Fortune Close, Riverside Business Park,
Northampton, NN3 9HT, United Kingdom
Tel.: (44) 1604784000
Develop & Build Residential Home Services
N.A.I.C.S.: 236117

**David Wilson Homes (Southern)
Limited** **(1)**
Norgate House Tealgate, Charnham Park,
Hungerford, RG17 0YT, Berkshire, United
Kingdom
Tel.: (44) 1488680300
Develop & Build Residential Home Services
N.A.I.C.S.: 236117

**David Wilson Homes Yorkshire
Limited** **(1)**
6 Alpha Court Monks Cross Drive, York,
YO32 9WN, United Kingdom
Tel.: (44) 1904617660
Develop & Build Residential Home Services
N.A.I.C.S.: 236117

KingsOak Homes Ltd. **(1)**
Wingrove House, Ponteland Rd, Newcastle
upon Tyne, NE5 3DP, United
Kingdom **(100%)**
Tel.: (44) 1912272000
Web Site: http://www.kingsoakhomes.com
House & Apartment Construction
N.A.I.C.S.: 236118

Oregon Timber Frame Limited **(1)**
Portland Buildings Dunsdale Road Scottish
Borders, Selkirk, TD7 5EB, United Kingdom
Tel.: (44) 175 072 4940
Web Site: https://www.oregon.co.uk
Timber Frame Mfr & Distr
N.A.I.C.S.: 321215
Elaine Wilson (Dir-Sls & Mktg)

Redrow plc **(1)**
Redrow House, St David's Park, Ewloe,
CH5 3RX, Flintshire, United Kingdom
Tel.: (44) 1244520044
Web Site: https://www.redrowplc.co.uk
Rev.: $2,905,520,800
Assets: $4,313,476,440
Liabilities: $1,665,922,440
Net Worth: $2,647,554,000
Earnings: $267,470,840
Emp.: 2,239
Fiscal Year-end: 07/03/2022
Home Builders & Developers
N.A.I.C.S.: 236117
John F. Tutte (Chm)

Subsidiary (Domestic):

Harrow Estates plc **(2)**
Redrow House 6400 Cinnabar Court,
Daresbury, Warrington, WA4 4GE, United
Kingdom
Tel.: (44) 192 878 5840
Web Site: https://www.harrowestates.co.uk
Real Estate Services
N.A.I.C.S.: 531390
Julian Larkin (Mng Dir)

**Redrow Homes (Eastern)
Limited** **(2)**
2 Aurum Court Sylvan Way Southfields,
Business Park Laindon, Basildon, SS15
6TU, Essex, United Kingdom **(100%)**
Tel.: (44) 1268886400
Web Site: http://www.redrow.co.uk
Sales Range: $25-49.9 Million
Emp.: 40
Home Builders & Developers
N.A.I.C.S.: 236117

**Redrow Homes (Lancashire)
Limited** **(2)**
14 Eaton Ave Matrix Ossice Pk, Buckshaw
Village, Chorley, PR77NA, Lancashire,
United Kingdom **(100%)**
Tel.: (44) 1772643700
Web Site: http://www.redrow.co.uk
Sales Range: $25-49.9 Million
Emp.: 40
Home Builders & Developers
N.A.I.C.S.: 236117

**Redrow Homes (Midlands)
Limited** **(2)**
Redrow House Kinsall Green, Wilnecote,
Tamworth, B77 5PX, United
Kingdom **(100%)**
Tel.: (44) 827260600
Web Site: http://www.redrow.co.uk
Home Builders & Developers
N.A.I.C.S.: 236117

Redrow Homes (Northwest) Ltd. **(2)**
St Davids Park, Ewloe, CH5 3RX, Flint-
shire, United Kingdom **(100%)**
Tel.: (44) 1244520044
Web Site: http://www.redrow.co.uk
Sales Range: $25-49.9 Million
Emp.: 60
Home Builders & Developers
N.A.I.C.S.: 236117

**Redrow Homes (South Midlands)
Limited** **(2)**
Redrow House 6 Waterside Way, The
Lakes, Northampton, NN4 7XD, United
Kingdom **(100%)**
Tel.: (44) 160 460 1115
Web Site: http://www.redrow.co.uk
Sales Range: $25-49.9 Million
Emp.: 50
Home Builders & Developers

N.A.I.C.S.: 236118
John Mann (Mng Dir)

**Redrow Homes (Southern)
Limited** **(2)**
Redrow House Boundary Rd, Loudwater,
High Wycombe, HP10 9QT, United
Kingdom **(100%)**
Tel.: (44) 1628539700
Web Site: http://www.redrow.co.uk
Sales Range: $25-49.9 Million
Emp.: 50
Home Builders & Developers
N.A.I.C.S.: 236117

**Redrow Homes (Yorkshire)
Limited** **(2)**
Redrow House Brunel Rd, Wakefield, WF2
0XG, Yorkshire, United Kingdom **(100%)**
Tel.: (44) 1924822566
Web Site: http://www.redrow.co.uk
Sales Range: $25-49.9 Million
Emp.: 60
Home Builders & Developers
N.A.I.C.S.: 236117
John Handley (Dir-Comml)

**Redrow Homes South Wales
Limited** **(2)**
Redrow House Copse Walk, Cardiff Gate
Business Park Cardiff Gate, Cardiff, CF23
8RH, United Kingdom **(100%)**
Tel.: (44) 292 054 9103
Web Site: http://www.redrow.co.uk
Emp.: 70
Home Builders & Developers
N.A.I.C.S.: 531311
Tim Stone (Mng Dir)

Redrow Homes South West Ltd **(2)**
Redrow House West Point Great Park Rd,
Bradley Stoke, Bristol, BS32 4QG, United
Kingdom **(100%)**
Tel.: (44) 1454625000
Web Site: http://www.redrow.co.uk
Sales Range: $25-49.9 Million
Emp.: 60
Home Builders & Developers
N.A.I.C.S.: 236117
Parry Stiles (Mng Dir)

**Wilson Bowden Developments
Ltd.** **(1)**
Wilson Bowden Developments Forest Busi-
ness Park, Bardon Hill, LE67 1UB, Leices-
tershire, United Kingdom **(100%)**
Tel.: (44) 1530276276
Web Site: http://www.wilsonbowden.co.uk
Sales Range: $1-4.9 Billion
Emp.: 25
Commercial Property Development Services
N.A.I.C.S.: 236220
Nick Richardson (Mng Dir)

**BARRATTS TRADING
LIMITED**
BPL House 880 Harrogate Rd, Ap-
perley Bridge, Bradford, BD10 0NW,
W Yorkshire, United Kingdom
Tel.: (44) 1274617761 UK
Web Site: http://www.barratts.co.uk
Year Founded: 1907
Sales Range: $300-349.9 Million
Emp.: 1,184
Shoes & Leather Goods Retailer
N.A.I.C.S.: 458210
Ken Platt (Dir-ECommerce)

BARRAULT
521 Route De Limoges, 79000, Niort,
Deux Sevres, France
Tel.: (33) 549283311
Web Site: http://www.barrault.com
Sales Range: $25-49.9 Million
Emp.: 188
N.A.I.C.S.: 423120

BARRDAY, INC.
260 Holiday Inn Drive Unit 33 Second
Floor Building C, PO Box 790, Cam-
bridge, N3C 4E8, ON, Canada
Tel.: (519) 621-3620
Web Site: http://www.barrday.com
Year Founded: 1958
Rev.: $12,121,041

Emp.: 100
Industrial Textile, Coating Adhesives
& Sealant Mfr
N.A.I.C.S.: 325520
Michael J. Buckstein *(Owner, Pres & CEO)*

Subsidiaries:

Barrday Composite Solutions **(1)**
86 Providence Rd, Millbury, MA 01527
Tel.: (508) 581-2100
Sales Range: $10-24.9 Million
Emp.: 50
Wheels, Abrasive
N.A.I.C.S.: 327910
Jonnathan Sorkes *(Mgr-Mktg)*

BARRE LOGISTIQUE SER-VICES
Rue du Val Clair, 51683, Reims, Cedex 2, France
Tel.: (33) 326041313
Rev.: $20,100,000
Emp.: 56
Freight Transportation Arrangement
N.A.I.C.S.: 488510
Guillaume Corgie *(DP Mgr)*

BARREL CO., LTD.
2F 138 Wonhyo-Ro, Yongsan-Gu, Seoul, Korea (South)
Tel.: (82) 23353176
Web Site:
http://www.en.getbarrel.com
Year Founded: 2010
267790—(KRS)
Emp.: 82
Sewn Wearing Apparel Mfr
N.A.I.C.S.: 315250
Jong-Gil Park *(Sr Mgr)*

BARRETT CORPORATION
300 Lockhart Mill Rd, PO Box 9060, Woodstock, E7M 5C3, NB, Canada
Tel.: (506) 443-7237
Web Site:
http://www.barrettamateur.com
Year Founded: 1976
Sales Range: $150-199.9 Million
Emp.: 800
Investments & Investments Support Services to Various Holdings
N.A.I.C.S.: 561499
Edward Barrett *(Co-CEO)*

BARRETT STEEL LIMITED
Barrett House Cutler Heights Lane
Dudley Hill, Bradford, BD4 9HU, West Yorkshire, United Kingdom
Tel.: (44) 1274 682281
Web Site: http://www.barrettsteel.com
Year Founded: 1866
Sales Range: $350-399.9 Million
Emp.: 910
Steel Products Mfr
N.A.I.C.S.: 331110
Roy Butcher *(Chm & CEO)*

Subsidiaries:

Barrett Tubes Division **(1)**
Unit 8 Autobase Industrial Park Tipton Road, Tividale, Dudley, B69 3HU, West Midlands, United Kingdom
Tel.: (44) 1216015050
Web Site: http://www.barretttubes.com
Steel Products Mfr
N.A.I.C.S.: 331110

BARRICK GOLD CORPORA-TION
161 Bay Street Suite 3700, PO Box 212, Toronto, M5J 2S1, ON, Canada
Tel.: (416) 861-9911
Web Site: https://www.barrick.com
Year Founded: 1983
GOLD—(NYSE)
Rev.: $11,397,000,000
Assets: $45,811,000,000

Liabilities: $13,809,000,000
Net Worth: $32,002,000,000
Earnings: $1,272,000,000
Emp.: 24,600
Fiscal Year-end: 12/31/23
Gold Exploration & Mining Services
N.A.I.C.S.: 212220
Kevin Thomson *(Sr Exec VP-Strategic Matters)*

Subsidiaries:

Acacia Mining plc **(1)**
5th Floor No 1 Cavendish Place, London, W1G 0QF, United Kingdom **(100%)**
Tel.: (44) 2071297150
Web Site: http://www.acaciamining.com
Rev.: $663,789,000
Assets: $1,820,725,000
Liabilities: $641,114,000
Net Worth: $1,179,611,000
Earnings: $58,866,000
Emp.: 1,543
Fiscal Year-end: 12/31/2018
Gold & Copper Mining Services
N.A.I.C.S.: 212220
Peter Geleta *(CEO-Interim)*

Barrick (Niugini) Limited **(1)**
Level 2 The Lodge Building Brampton Street, PO Box 851, National Capital District, Port Moresby, Papua New Guinea
Tel.: (675) 3224800
Web Site: http://www.barrick.com
Emp.: 15
Gold Mining Services
N.A.I.C.S.: 212220

Barrick Chile Ltda. **(1)**
Av Ricardo Lyon 222, Providencia, Santiago, Chile **(100%)**
Tel.: (56) 23402022
Sales Range: $100-124.9 Million
Emp.: 200
N.A.I.C.S.: 212220
Igor Alcides Gonzales Galindo *(Pres)*

Subsidiary (Domestic):

Compania Minera Casale Limitada **(2)**
Diego De Almagro 204, Copiapo, Chile
Tel.: (56) 52221025
Gold Ore Mining Services
N.A.I.C.S.: 212220

Compania Minera Nevada Spa. **(2)**
Barrio Industrial coquimbo Sitio 58, Alto Penuelas, Coquimbo, Chile
Tel.: (56) 51202131
Web Site: http://www.barrick.com
Metal Mining Services
N.A.I.C.S.: 212290

Joint Venture (Domestic):

Compania Minera Zaldivar S.A. **(2)**
Avenida Grecia 750, Antofagasta, 1271837, Chile **(50%)**
Tel.: (56) 55433400
Web Site: http://www.barrick.com
Gold Mining Services
N.A.I.C.S.: 212220

Barrick Gold Australia Limited **(1)**
Level 9 Brookfield Pl 125 St George Terrace, Perth, 6000, WA, Australia **(100%)**
Tel.: (61) 892125777
Web Site: http://www.barrick.com
Sales Range: $200-249.9 Million
Emp.: 300
Gold, Copper & Nickel Mining & Exploration Services
N.A.I.C.S.: 212220

Subsidiary (Domestic):

Barrick (PD) Australia Limited **(2)**
125 St Georges Terrace, Perth, 6000, WA, Australia
Tel.: (61) 892125777
Web Site: http://www.barrick.com
Sales Range: $50-74.9 Million
Emp.: 300
Gold & Silver Mining
N.A.I.C.S.: 212220

Subsidiary (Non-US):

Barrick Mining Company (Australia) Limited **(2)**

Tel.: (61) 8 9212 5777
Sales Range: $200-249.9 Million
Emp.: 300
Gold Mining Services
N.A.I.C.S.: 212220

Subsidiary (Non-US):

Barrick (GSM) Ltd. **(3)**
Tel.: (61) 890882111
Sales Range: $50-74.9 Million
Emp.: 62
Miner of Gold
N.A.I.C.S.: 212220

Barrick (Plutonic) Limited **(3)**
Tel.: (61) 892125777
Gold Ore Mining Services
N.A.I.C.S.: 212220

Barrick Gold Corp. - Doyon Mine **(1)**
PO Box 970, Rouyn-Noranda, J9X 5C8, QC, Canada
Tel.: (819) 759-3611
Web Site: http://www.camdior.com
Sales Range: $200-249.9 Million
Emp.: 500
N.A.I.C.S.: 212220

Barrick Gold Finance Company **(1)**
161 Bay St Suite 3700, Toronto, M5J 2S1, ON, Canada
Tel.: (416) 861-9911
Web Site: http://www.barrick.com
Sales Range: $200-249.9 Million
Emp.: 40
Financial Management Services
N.A.I.C.S.: 523999

Barrick Gold of North America, Inc. **(1)**
136 E S Temple Ste 1800, Salt Lake City, UT 84111-1163
Tel.: (801) 741-4660
Sales Range: $50-74.9 Million
Emp.: 100
Holding Company; Gold Mining
N.A.I.C.S.: 551112

Subsidiary (Domestic):

Barrick Gold U.S. Inc. **(2)**
136 E S Temple St Ste 1800, Salt Lake City, UT 84111-1163
Tel.: (801) 741-4660
Web Site: http://www.barrick.com
Sales Range: $50-74.9 Million
Emp.: 50
Gold Ore Mining
N.A.I.C.S.: 212220

Subsidiary (Domestic):

Barrick Cortez Inc. **(3)**
8C 66 Box 1250, Crescent Valley, NV 89821
Tel.: (775) 468-4400
Gold Ore Mining Services
N.A.I.C.S.: 212220

Barrick Gold Exploration Inc. **(3)**
1655 Mountain City Hwy, Elko, NV 89801
Tel.: (775) 748-1001
Sales Range: $75-99.9 Million
Acquires, Invests in & Develops Gold Mining Projects
N.A.I.C.S.: 212220

Barrick Goldstrike Mines, Inc. **(3)**
PO Box 29, Elko, NV 89803
Tel.: (775) 778-8183
Gold Mining
N.A.I.C.S.: 212220

Branch (Domestic):

Ruby Hill Mine **(3)**
Intersection of Hwy 50 and 278, Eureka, NV 89316-0676 **(100%)**
Tel.: (775) 237-6060
Web Site: http://www.barrick.com
Sales Range: $75-99.9 Million
Gold Mine
N.A.I.C.S.: 212220

Joint Venture (Domestic):

Round Mountain Gold Corporation **(2)**
1 Smoky Valley Rd, Round Mountain, NV 89045-0480

Tel.: (775) 377-2366
Web Site: http://www.kinross.com
Sales Range: $75-99.9 Million
Emp.: 800
Gold Mining; Owned 50% by Barrick Gold Corporation & 50% by Kinross Gold Corporation
N.A.I.C.S.: 212220

Barrick International (Barbados) Corp. **(1)**
1st Floor Enfield House Upper Collymore Rock, PO Box 1395, Saint Michael, 14004, Barbados
Tel.: (246) 430 8875
Sales Range: $50-74.9 Million
Emp.: 14
Metal Mining Services
N.A.I.C.S.: 213114

Minera Barrick Misquichilca S.A. **(1)**
Av Manuel Olguin 375 Piso 11, Lima, Peru **(100%)**
Tel.: (51) 1 612 4100
Sales Range: $200-249.9 Million
Emp.: 450
N.A.I.C.S.: 212220

Nevada Gold Mines LLC **(1)**
1655 Mountain City Hwy, Elko, NV 89801
Tel.: (775) 748-1001
Gold & Copper Mfr
N.A.I.C.S.: 331491

Randgold Resources Limited **(1)**
3rd Floor Unity Chambers 28 Halkett Street, Saint Helier, JE2 4WJ, Channel Islands, Jersey
Tel.: (44) 1534 735 333
Rev.: $1,307,095,000
Assets: $4,303,469,000
Liabilities: $311,200,000
Net Worth: $3,992,269,000
Earnings: $335,047,000
Fiscal Year-end: 12/31/2017
Gold Mining Services
N.A.I.C.S.: 212220

Subsidiary (Domestic):

Mining Investments Jersey Ltd **(2)**
La Motte Chambers La Motte St, Saint Helier, JE1 1BJ, Jersey **(100%)**
Tel.: (44) 534735333
Investment Company
N.A.I.C.S.: 525910

Subsidiary (Non-US):

Randgold Resources (Cote d'Ivoire) Ltd. **(2)**
Immuble Borg Plato 8 Blvd Carde, 01 BP 725, Abidjan, Cote d'Ivoire **(100%)**
Tel.: (225) 20225012
Gold Mining
N.A.I.C.S.: 212220

Subsidiary (Domestic):

Randgold Resources Cote d'Ivoire SARL **(3)**
22 Rue de Hortensias, Boulevard Latrille, Abidjan, 1215, Cote d'Ivoire **(100%)**
Tel.: (225) 22482360
Sales Range: $50-74.9 Million
Emp.: 12
Gold Mining
N.A.I.C.S.: 212220

Subsidiary (Non-US):

Randgold Resources (Mali) Ltd **(2)**
Faladie 6448 Avenue de l'OUA, BP E1160, Bamako, Mali **(100%)**
Tel.: (223) 20203858
Gold Mining
N.A.I.C.S.: 212220

Subsidiary (Domestic):

Randgold Resources Mali SARL **(3)**
Faladie Oea Ave Door No 6448, BP E 1160, Bamako, Mali **(100%)**
Tel.: (223) 2213855
Gold Mining
N.A.I.C.S.: 212220

Subsidiary (Non-US):

Randgold Resources (Senegal) Ltd **(2)**

Barrick Gold Corporation—(Continued)

67 Ave Andre Peytavin, BP 887, Dakar,
Senegal   **(100%)**
Tel.: (221) 338491780
Gold Mining
N.A.I.C.S.: 212220

Randgold Resources (UK) Ltd   **(2)**
1st Floor 2 Savoy Court Strand, London,
WC2N 0RQW, United Kingdom
Tel.: (44) 2075577730
Sales Range: $50-74.9 Million
Emp.: 3
Gold Mining Services
N.A.I.C.S.: 212220

**Randgold Resources Burkina Faso
SARL**   **(2)**
242 Rue 13 03 Gandaogo Secteur 13 Zone
Du Bois 01, BP 4771, Ouagadougou, Bur-
kina Faso
Tel.: (226) 50 36 39 36
Web Site:
    http://www.randgoldresources.com
Gold Mining Services
N.A.I.C.S.: 212220

**Randgold Resources Tanzania
Ltd**   **(2)**
Plot 173 Block D Mwanza, PO Box 2430,
Mwanza, Tanzania   **(100%)**
Tel.: (255) 282500974
Gold Mining
N.A.I.C.S.: 212220

**Seven Bridges Trading 14 (Pty)
Ltd**   **(2)**
Level 0 Wilds View Isle Of Houghton Carse
O'Gowrie Road, Houghton Estate, Johan-
nesburg, 2198, South Africa
Tel.: (27) 11 481 72 00
Sales Range: $25-49.9 Million
Emp.: 10
Logistics Consulting Servies
N.A.I.C.S.: 541614
Lois Wark (Gen Mgr)

**BARRIE CHRYSLER DODGE
JEEP RAM LTD.**
395 Dunlop Street W, Barrie, L4N
1C3, ON, Canada
Tel.: (705) 726-0393
Web Site:
    http://www.barriechryslerjeep.com
Year Founded: 1973
Rev.: $56,179,200
Emp.: 110
New & Used Car Dealers
N.A.I.C.S.: 441110
Ray Billett (Mgr-Parts)

BARRO GROUP PTY LTD
191 Drummond Street, Carlton, 3053,
VIC, Australia
Tel.: (61) 0386563900
Web Site: https://barro.com.au
Emp.: 100
Premixed Concrete & Quarry Prod-
ucts Distr
N.A.I.C.S.: 238110

BARRY & FITZWILLIAM LTD.
50 Dartmouth Square, Dublin, Ireland
Tel.: (353) 16671755
Web Site: http://www.bandf.ie
Sales Range: $50-74.9 Million
Emp.: 120
Spirits Distr
N.A.I.C.S.: 424820
Chris Murphy (Chm)

**BARRY CULLEN CHEVROLET
CADILLAC LTD**
905 Woodlawn Road West, Guelph,
N1K 1B7, ON, Canada
Tel.: (519) 824-0210
Web Site: http://www.barrycullen.com
New & Used Cars Dealers
N.A.I.C.S.: 441110
Morris KurtzFavero (Mgr-Parts)

**BARRYROE OFFSHORE EN-
ERGY PLC**
Paramount Court Corrig Road Sandy-
ford Business Park, Dublin, D18
R9C7, Ireland
Tel.: (353) 12194074
Web Site:
    https://barryroeoffshoreenergy.com
BCY   (ISE)
Rev.: $443,395
Assets: $77,097,853
Liabilities: $16,435,079
Net Worth: $60,662,774
Earnings: ($12,722,110)
Emp.: 2
Fiscal Year-end: 12/31/20
Oil & Gas Exploration
N.A.I.C.S.: 211120
James Menton (Chm)

Subsidiaries:

Providence Resources UK
Limited   **(1)**
5 Jubilee Pl, London, SW3 3TD, United
Kingdom
Tel.: (44) 2073495284
Sales Range: $50-74.9 Million
Emp.: 12
Oil & Gas Exploration & Development Ser-
vices
N.A.I.C.S.: 213112
Bernard Gibbina (Mgr)

BARSELE MINERALS CORP.
Suite 300 - 1055 W Hastings Street,
Vancouver, V6E 2E9, BC, Canada
Tel.: (604) 687-8566   **BC**
Web Site:
    https://www.barseleminerals.com
Year Founded: 2013
BME—(OTCIQ)
Rev.: $4,583
Assets: $186,780
Liabilities: $45,878
Net Worth: $140,902
Earnings: ($873,940)
Fiscal Year-end: 12/31/20
Gold, Silver & Copper Exploration &
Mining
N.A.I.C.S.: 213114
Ben Whiting (VP-Exploration)

Subsidiaries:

Gold Line Resources Ltd.   **(1)**
Suite 3123-595 Burrard Street, Vancouver,
V7X 1J1, BC, Canada
Web Site:
    https://www.goldlineresources.com
Gold Exploration & Mining Services
N.A.I.C.S.: 212220
Adam Cegielski (CEO)

BARTLE & GIBSON CO. LTD.
13475 Fort Road NW, Edmonton,
T5A 1C6, AB, Canada
Tel.: (780) 472-2850
Web Site:
    https://www.bartlegibson.com
Year Founded: 1944
Rev.: $65,065,500
Emp.: 300
Plumbing, Heating & Electrical Prod-
ucts Whslr
N.A.I.C.S.: 423720

**BARTON GOLD HOLDINGS
LIMITED**
Level 4 12 Gilles Street, Adelaide,
5000, SA, Australia
Tel.: (61) 863119160   **AU**
Web Site:
    https://www.bartongold.com.au
Year Founded: 2019
BGD3—(DEU)
Rev.: $1,997,131
Assets: $16,361,088
Liabilities: $10,686,575
Net Worth: $5,674,513

Earnings: ($3,702,158)
Fiscal Year-end: 06/30/23
Offices of Other Holding Companies
N.A.I.C.S.: 551112
Alexander Witrak Scanlon (Founder)

**BARTON STORAGE SYSTEMS
LTD.**
Barton Industrial Park, Mount Pleas-
ant, Bilston, WV14 7NG, West Mid-
lands, United Kingdom
Tel.: (44) 1902499500
Web Site:
    http://www.bartonstorage.com
Year Founded: 1964
Sales Range: $1-9.9 Million
Emp.: 20
Shelving & Storage System Mfr
N.A.I.C.S.: 337215
Keith Bibb (Mng Dir)

BARTRONICS INDIA LTD.
Survey No 351 Raj Bollaram Village,
Medchal Mandal & District, Hydera-
bad, 501 401, Telangana, India
Tel.: (91) 4049269269
Web Site: https://www.bartronics.com
532694—(BOM)
Rev.: $7,263,970
Assets: $102,374,072
Liabilities: $30,270,595
Net Worth: $72,103,477
Earnings: $56,293,187
Emp.: 58
Fiscal Year-end: 03/30/23
Hardware Product Mfr
N.A.I.C.S.: 332510
K. Udai Sagar (Mng Dir)

BARTSCHER GMBH
Franz-Kleine-Strasse 28, D-33154,
Salzkotten, Germany
Tel.: (49) 52589710
Web Site: http://www.bartscher.de
Year Founded: 1876
Rev.: $35,864,400
Emp.: 68
Catering Equipment Mfr
N.A.I.C.S.: 332215
Susanne Hellinge (Mgr-Sls)

BARU GOLD CORP.
1021 West Hastings St 9th floor, Van-
couver, V6E 03C, BC, Canada
Tel.: (604) 684-2183   **BC**
Web Site: https://barugold.com
BARU—(OTCIQ)
Assets: $5,121,502
Liabilities: $1,115,678
Net Worth: $4,005,824
Earnings: ($3,183,832)
Fiscal Year-end: 08/31/21
Gold & Copper Mining
N.A.I.C.S.: 212220
Karen Dyczkowski (CFO & Sec)

**BARUN ELECTRONICS CO.,
LTD.**
548 Gyeonggidong-ro, Hwaseong,
Gyeonggi, Korea (South)
Tel.: (82) 3180206000
Web Site: http://www.bec.co.kr
Year Founded: 1998
064520—(KRS)
Rev.: $15,843,059
Assets: $68,598,612
Liabilities: $28,415,792
Net Worth: $40,182,820
Earnings: ($4,623,340)
Emp.: 140
Fiscal Year-end: 12/31/22
Semiconductor Mfr
N.A.I.C.S.: 334413
YoungMin An (CEO)

BARUNSON CO., LTD.

5F K-tower 1 Daehak 3-ro,
Yeongtong-gu, Suwon, 16227,
Gyeonggi-do, Korea (South)
Tel.: (82) 317279712
Web Site: https://www.barunson.co.kr
Year Founded: 1985
018700—(KRS)
Rev.: $44,997,698
Assets: $68,208,312
Liabilities: $23,033,555
Net Worth: $45,174,757
Earnings: ($19,098,655)
Emp.: 187
Fiscal Year-end: 12/31/22
Restaurant Operators
N.A.I.C.S.: 722511
Kang Sin-Beom (Dir-Rep)

**BARUNSON ENTERTAINMENT
& ARTS CORPORATION**
3F 130 Hannam-daero, Yongsan-gu,
Seoul, 04417, Korea (South)
Tel.: (82) 15886922
Web Site:
    https://www.barunsonena.com
Year Founded: 1997
035620—(KRS)
Rev.: $19,967,131
Assets: $98,233,098
Liabilities: $32,524,664
Net Worth: $65,708,435
Earnings: ($10,183,836)
Emp.: 29
Fiscal Year-end: 12/31/22
Online Game Publisher
N.A.I.C.S.: 541511
Sin Ae Gwak (Co-CEO)

BARVIC
Zac De La Cerisaie 22 Rue Des
Huleux, 93240, Stains, Seine Saint
Denis, France
Tel.: (33) 149711515
Rev.: $18,700,000
Emp.: 23
N.A.I.C.S.: 424350
Pinhas Attias (Gen Mgr)

**BARWA REAL ESTATE COM-
PANY Q.P.S.C.**
Barwa Al Sadd Towers Tower No 1
Suhaim bin Hamad Street C Ring
Road, PO Box 27777, Doha, Qatar
Tel.: (974) 97444088785
Web Site: https://www.barwa.com.qa
Year Founded: 2005
BRES—(QE)
Rev.: $396,749,488
Assets: $10,294,682,086
Liabilities: $4,266,348,853
Net Worth: $6,028,333,232
Earnings: $338,279,448
Emp.: 126
Fiscal Year-end: 12/31/23
Land Acquisition & Related Services
N.A.I.C.S.: 531390
Salah Ghanem Al Ali (Chm)

Subsidiaries:

Barwa City Real Estate Company
WLL   **(1)**
PO Box 27777, Doha, Qatar
Tel.: (974) 44998888
Real Estate Manangement Services
N.A.I.C.S.: 531390

Qatar Project Management Company
Q.P.S.C.   **(1)**
Suhaim bin Hamad Street C Ring Road
Barwa Al-Sadd-Tower 1, PO Box 27711,
Doha, Qatar
Tel.: (974) 44054444
Web Site: https://www.qpm.com.qa
Project Management Services
N.A.I.C.S.: 561110
Abdulla Jobara Alromaihi (Chm)

Qatar Real Estate Investment Com-
pany Q.P.S.C   **(1)**

Old Salata area-Museum Street, PO Box 22311, Doha, Qatar
Tel.: (974) 4408 6000
Web Site: http://www.alaqaria.com.qa
Real Estate Development Services
N.A.I.C.S.: 531390
Khalid Khalifa Jassim Al Thani *(Chm & Mng Dir)*

BAS CASTINGS LIMITED
Wharf Road Industrial Estate, Pinxton, Alfreton, NG16 6LE, Nottinghamshire, United Kingdom
Tel.: (44) 1773 812028
Web Site:
http://www.bascastings.co.uk
Year Founded: 1973
Sales Range: $10-24.9 Million
Emp.: 80
Iron Casting Mfr
N.A.I.C.S.: 331511
Robert Radford *(Mng Dir)*

BASANT AGRO TECH (INDIA) LTD.
Near S T Workshop Kaulkhed, Akola, 444 044, India
Tel.: (91) 7219203090
Web Site:
https://www.basantagro.com
524687—(BOM)
Rev.: $44,109,224
Assets: $38,387,376
Liabilities: $19,980,979
Net Worth: $18,406,397
Earnings: $1,199,193
Emp.: 275
Fiscal Year-end: 03/31/21
Agricultural Product Mfr
N.A.I.C.S.: 325320
Shashikant C. Bhartia *(Chm & Mng Dir)*

BASCOGEL
Zone Industrielle De Jalday, 64500, Saint-Jean-de-Luz, Pyrenees Atlantiques, France
Tel.: (33) 559080202
Rev.: $12,900,000
Emp.: 25
N.A.I.C.S.: 424420
Nathalie Arana *(Mgr-DP)*

BASE D'INFORMATIONS LEGALES HOLDING S.A.S.
33 Rue Sadi Carnot, 78, Rambouillet, France
Tel.: (33) 134941000
Web Site: http://www.bil.fr
Sales Range: $100-124.9 Million
Emp.: 300
Holding Company
N.A.I.C.S.: 551112
Thierry Asmar *(CEO-Altares)*

Subsidiaries:

Dun & Bradstreet France SA **(1)**
55 Ave Des Champs Pierreux, 92012, Nanterre, Cedex, France
Tel.: (33) 141375000
Web Site: http://www.altaref.fr.com
Sales Range: $25-49.9 Million
Emp.: 100
Business Information Services
N.A.I.C.S.: 519290

BASE ONE INTEGRATED MARKETING SERVICES
Harlequin House 3rd Floor, 7 High Street, Teddington, TW11 8EE, Middlesex, United Kingdom
Tel.: (44) 208 943 9999
Web Site:
http://www.baseonegroup.co.uk
Year Founded: 1987
Rev.: $19,991,400
Emp.: 50

Advertising Specialties, Brand Development, Direct Marketing, Interactive Agencies, Internet/Web Design
N.A.I.C.S.: 541810
Kingsley Reed *(Acct Dir)*

BASELLANDSCHAFTLICHE KANTONALBANK
Rheinstrasse 7, 4410, Liestal, Switzerland
Tel.: (41) 619259494
Web Site: https://www.blkb.ch
BLKB—(SWX)
Rev.: $33,526,696
Assets: $37,576,183,586
Liabilities: $34,622,686,586
Net Worth: $2,953,497,001
Earnings: $140,684,395
Emp.: 787
Fiscal Year-end: 12/31/22
Banking Services
N.A.I.C.S.: 522110
Christoph Loeb *(Head-Media)*

Subsidiaries:

ATAG Asset Management (Luxembourg) S.A. **(1)**
Blvd Grande-Duchesse Charlotte 34a, 1330, Luxembourg, Luxembourg **(100%)**
Tel.: (352) 2531311
Sales Range: $50-74.9 Million
Emp.: 16
Miscellaneous Financial Investment Activities
N.A.I.C.S.: 523999

ATAG Asset Management AG **(1)**
Centralbahnstrasse 7, 4051, Basel, Switzerland **(100%)**
Tel.: (41) 612781111
Web Site: http://www.aan.ph
Sales Range: $100-124.9 Million
Emp.: 116
Commericial Banking
N.A.I.C.S.: 522110

ATAG Private Client Services AG **(1)**
St Jakobs-Strasse 17, 4052, Basel, Switzerland **(75%)**
Tel.: (41) 615646565
Web Site: http://www.atag-pcs.ch
Sales Range: $25-49.9 Million
Emp.: 25
Other Accounting Services
N.A.I.C.S.: 541219

EVA- the Basel life sciences start-up agency **(1)**
Hochbergerstrasse 60c, CH-4057, Basel, Switzerland
Tel.: (41) 612838485
Web Site: http://www.eva-basel.ch
Business Services
N.A.I.C.S.: 561499

Graff Capital Management AG **(1)**
Fraumunsterstrasse 13, 8022, Zurich, Switzerland **(100%)**
Tel.: (41) 442153000
Web Site: http://www.graffcapital.ch
Securities & Commodity Exchanges
N.A.I.C.S.: 523210

BASELODE ENERGY CORP.
Suite 1805 - 55 University Avenue, Toronto, M5J 2H7, ON, Canada
Tel.: (416) 644-1567
Web Site: https://www.baselode.com
BSENF—(OTCQB)
Assets: $12,372,506
Liabilities: $2,337,293
Net Worth: $10,035,213
Earnings: ($6,139,505)
Fiscal Year-end: 12/31/23
Mineral Exploration Services
N.A.I.C.S.: 213115
James Sykes *(CEO)*

BASEPOINT BUSINESS CENTRES
61 Thames St, Windsor, SL4 1LQW, Berkshire, United Kingdom

Tel.: (44) 1753853515
Web Site: http://www.basepoint.co.uk
Sales Range: $10-24.9 Million
Emp.: 120
Office Space & Workshops for Small to Medium Sized Businesses
N.A.I.C.S.: 561499
Brian Andrews *(Exec Dir)*

BASER FAKTORING A.S.
Nispetiye Caddesi Akmerkez B3 Blok Kat 2, Etiler, 34340, Istanbul, Turkiye
Tel.: (90) 2122928090
Web Site:
http://www.baserfaktoring.com
Year Founded: 1995
BSRFK—(IST)
Sales Range: Less than $1 Million
Financial Management Services
N.A.I.C.S.: 551112

BASETROPHY GROUP HOLDINGS LIMITED
Unit 18 29/F New Tech Plaza 34 Tai Yau Street San Po Kong, Kowloon, China (Hong Kong)
Tel.: (852) 26982181 Ky
Web Site:
http://www.wbgroupfw.com.hk
Year Founded: 2003
8460—(HKG)
Rev.: $11,026,200
Assets: $13,451,760
Liabilities: $5,596,868
Net Worth: $7,854,893
Earnings: ($825,945)
Emp.: 54
Fiscal Year-end: 12/31/22
Civil Engineering Services
N.A.I.C.S.: 238910
Chung Ho Lau *(Chm, CEO & Officer-Compliance)*

Subsidiaries:

Workbase Engineering Limited **(1)**
Unit 18 29/F New Tech Plaza 34 Tai Yau Street, San Po Kong, Kowloon, China (Hong Kong)
Tel.: (852) 2 698 2181
Web Site: https://www.wbgroupfw.com.hk
Site Preparation Contracting Services
N.A.I.C.S.: 238910

BASF SE
Carl-Bosch-Str 38, 67056, Ludwigshafen, Germany
Tel.: (49) 621600 De
Web Site: https://www.basf.com
Year Founded: 1865
BFFAF—(OTCQX)
Rev.: $76,059,167,689
Assets: $85,434,374,667
Liabilities: $46,492,990,403
Net Worth: $38,941,384,264
Earnings: $248,371,785
Emp.: 111,991
Fiscal Year-end: 12/31/23
Holding Company; Automotive & Industrial Coatings, Chemicals, Plastics, Agricultural & Performance Products Mfr; Oil & Natural Gas Production
N.A.I.C.S.: 551112
Kurt Bock *(CFO)*

Subsidiaries:

Azuma Bussan Ltd. **(1)**
3-8-6 Saikon, Koriyama, 963-8862, Fukushima, Japan
Tel.: (81) 249240776
Chemical Products Mfr
N.A.I.C.S.: 325998

BASF (Czech) spol. s r.o. **(1)**
Sokolovska 668/136d, 186 00, Prague, Czech Republic
Tel.: (420) 235000111
Web Site: https://www.basf.com

Sales Range: $50-74.9 Million
Emp.: 70
Chemical Products Mfr
N.A.I.C.S.: 325998

BASF (Schweiz) AG **(1)**
Appital, Postfach 99, CH 8820, Wadenswil, Switzerland **(100%)**
Tel.: (41) 17819111
Web Site: http://www.basf.ch
Sales Range: $25-49.9 Million
Emp.: 40
Mfr of Chemicals
N.A.I.C.S.: 325998

Branch (Domestic):

BASF (Schweiz) AG - Basel Site **(2)**
Klybeckstrasse 141, 4057, Basel, Switzerland **(100%)**
Tel.: (41) 616361111
Web Site: https://www.basf.com
Specialty Chemical Whslr
N.A.I.C.S.: 424690

Subsidiary (Domestic):

BASF Fine Chemicals Switzerland SA **(2)**
Route Cantonale, Evionnaz, Geneva, CH-1902, VS, Switzerland **(100%)**
Tel.: (41) 277661620
Web Site: http://www.orgamol.com
Sales Range: $125-149.9 Million
Chemical & Pharmaceutical Ingredient Mfr
N.A.I.C.S.: 325998

BASF Intertrade AG **(2)**
Grafenauweg 8, 6300, Zug, Switzerland **(100%)**
Tel.: (41) 417120123
Web Site: https://www.basf-intertrade.ch
Sales Range: $25-49.9 Million
Emp.: 40
Mfr of Chemicals
N.A.I.C.S.: 325998

BASF Kaisten AG **(2)**
Hardmatt 434, CH-5082, Kaisten, Switzerland **(100%)**
Tel.: (41) 628689111
Web Site: http://www.basf.com
Chemicals Mfr
N.A.I.C.S.: 325998

BASF 3D Printing Solutions GmbH **(1)**
Speyerer Strasse 4, 69115, Heidelberg, Germany
Tel.: (49) 622167417900
Web Site: https://forward-am.com
Additive Product Mfr
N.A.I.C.S.: 339999
Oleksandra Blacka *(Mgr-Bus Dev)*

BASF A/S **(1)**
Kalvebod Brygge 45, 1560, Copenhagen, Denmark **(100%)**
Tel.: (45) 32660700
Web Site: http://www.basf.com
Sales Range: $50-74.9 Million
Emp.: 60
Sales of Chemicals
N.A.I.C.S.: 424690

Subsidiary (Domestic):

BASF A/S **(2)**
Malmparken 5, 2750, Ballerup, Denmark
Tel.: (45) 4 473 0100
Web Site: https://www.basf.com
Emp.: 300
Chemical Products Mfr
N.A.I.C.S.: 325998

BASF AB **(1)**
Sven Hultins Plats 5, 412 58, Gothenburg, Sweden **(100%)**
Tel.: (46) 31639800
Web Site: https://www.basf.com
Sales Range: $50-74.9 Million
Emp.: 60
Sales of Chemicals
N.A.I.C.S.: 424690

Joint Venture (Domestic):

Svaloef Weibull AB **(2)**
von Troils vag 1, 213 37, Malmo, Sweden **(40%)**
Tel.: (46) 10 556 5600

BASF SE—(Continued)

Web Site: http://www.swseed.com
Sales Range: $125-149.9 Million
Agricultural Seed Production & Whslr
N.A.I.C.S.: 424910

BASF AS (1)
Leangbukta 40, PO Box 233, N 1372,
Asker, Norway (100%)
Tel.: (47) 00792100
Web Site: http://www.basf.com
Sales Range: $25-49.9 Million
Emp.: 12
Sales of Chemicals
N.A.I.C.S.: 424690

Subsidiary (Domestic):

Pronova BioPharma ASA (2)
Lilleakerveien 2C, Oslo, 1327,
Norway (100%)
Tel.: (47) 22 53 48 50
Web Site: http://www.pronova.com
Sales Range: $100-124.9 Million
Emp.: 65
Omega-3 Derived Pharmaceuticals Mfr
N.A.I.C.S.: 325412

Subsidiary (Domestic):

Pronova BioPharma Norge AS (3)
Framnesveien 41, Sandefjord, 3222, Nor-
way
Tel.: (47) 33 44 68 00
Web Site: http://www.pronova.com
Sales Range: $50-74.9 Million
Emp.: 150
Mfr of Omega 3-Derived Pharmaceuticals
N.A.I.C.S.: 325412

BASF Afrique de l'Ouest
S.A.R.L. (1)
Bd Achalme No 3, BP 3761, Abidjan, 01,
Cote d'Ivoire
Tel.: (225) 21261292
Distr & Importer of Chemicals
N.A.I.C.S.: 424690

BASF Agricultural Products Group
Corporation (1)
14385 W Port Arthur Rd, Beaumont, TX
77705
Tel.: (409) 981-5000
Chemical Product Mfr & Distr
N.A.I.C.S.: 325998

BASF Agricultural Solutions Belgium
N.V. (1)
Dreve Richelle 161 E Bte 43, 1410, Water-
loo, Belgium
Tel.: (32) 23732721
Web Site: https://www.agro.basf.be
Pesticide & Fertilizer Distr
N.A.I.C.S.: 424910

BASF Agricultural Specialities
Limited (1)
50/51 Eldon Way, Lineside Industrial Estate
Wick, Littlehampton, BN17 7HE, West Sus-
sex, United Kingdom
Tel.: (44) 1903732323
Pest Control Services
N.A.I.C.S.: 561710
Peter Elliott (Mgr-EHS)

BASF Agro Trademarks GmbH (1)
Carl-Bosch-Str 38, Ludwigshafen, 67063,
Rheinland-Pfalz, Germany
Tel.: (49) 621600
Administrative Management Consulting Ser-
vices
N.A.I.C.S.: 541611

BASF Akquisitions GmbH (1)
Carl-Bosch-Str 38, Ludwigshafen, 67063,
Rheinland-Pfalz, Germany
Tel.: (49) 2501140
Web Site: http://www.basf-coatings.de
Management Consulting Services
N.A.I.C.S.: 541618

BASF Akquisitions- und Objektverw-
ertungsgesellschaft mbH (1)
Carl-Bosch-Str 38, Ludwigshafen, 67056,
Germany
Tel.: (49) 621600
Web Site: http://www.basf.com
Business Management Consulting Services
N.A.I.C.S.: 541611

BASF Americas Corporation (1)
100 Park Ave, Florham Park, NJ 07932-
1006
Tel.: (973) 245-6000
Web Site: http://www.basf.com
Chemical Products Distr
N.A.I.C.S.: 424690

BASF Argentina S.A. (1)
Tucuman 1, C1049AAA, Buenos Aires,
Argentina (100%)
Tel.: (54) 1143179600
Web Site: http://www.basf.com.ar
Sales Range: $150-199.9 Million
Emp.: 700
Distr of Styropor, Finishing Products & Crop
Protection Products
N.A.I.C.S.: 111998

Subsidiary (Domestic):

BASF Poliuretanos S.A. (2)
Cabo 10 Moreno 2370 Parque Industrial
Burzaco, Buenos Aires, Argentina
Tel.: (54) 1142996792
Web Site: http://www.basf.com.ar
Sales Range: $25-49.9 Million
Emp.: 19
Chemical Products Mfr
N.A.I.C.S.: 325998
Gustavo Fernandez (Mgr)

BASF Battery Technology Investment
GmbH & Co. KG (1)
Carl-Bosch-Str 38, Ludwigshafen, 67063,
Rheinland-Pfalz, Germany
Tel.: (49) 621 60 0
Web Site: http://www.basf.com
Emp.: 38,000
Investment Management Service
N.A.I.C.S.: 523999

BASF Bautechnik GmbH (1)
Dr-Albert-Frank-Str 32, Trostberg, 83308,
Bayern, Germany
Tel.: (49) 8621863700
Construction Chemicals Mfr
N.A.I.C.S.: 325998

BASF Belgium Coordination Center
CommV (1)
Dreve Richelle 161 bte 43, 1410, Waterloo,
Belgium
Tel.: (32) 23732225
Chemical Products Mfr
N.A.I.C.S.: 325998
Nicole Arndt (Mgr-Global Conrolling)

BASF Belgium S.A./N.V. (1)
Dreve Richelle 161, 1510, Waterloo,
Belgium (100%)
Tel.: (32) 23732111
Web Site: http://www.basf.com
Sales Range: $75-99.9 Million
Emp.: 160
Sales of Chemicals
N.A.I.C.S.: 424690

Subsidiary (Domestic):

BASF Antwerpen N.V. (2)
Scheldelaan 600-Haven 725, 2040, Ant-
werp, Belgium (100%)
Tel.: (32) 35612111
Web Site: https://www.basf.com
Basic Chemicals, Fine Chemicals, Fertiliz-
ers, Pre-Products for Polyurethanes, Fibers
& Plastics Mfr
N.A.I.C.S.: 325998

BASF Polyurethanes (2)
Dreve Richelle 161 E/F, 1180, Waterloo,
Belgium (100%)
Tel.: (32) 23732119
Web Site: http://www.basf.be
Sales Range: $25-49.9 Million
Emp.: 35
Sales of Polyurethane
N.A.I.C.S.: 424690

Unit (Domestic):

BASF SE - European Governmental
Affairs (2)
Maria van Bourgondiestraat 58, 1000, Brus-
sels, Belgium
Tel.: (32) 27400350
Web Site: http://www.basf.com
Emp.: 11
Administrative Services for Chemicals

N.A.I.C.S.: 325998

BASF Beteiligungsgesellschaft
mbH (1)
Carl-Bosch-Str 38, Ludwigshafen, 67063,
Rheinland-Pfalz, Germany
Tel.: (49) 621600
Chemical Products Mfr
N.A.I.C.S.: 325998

BASF Biorenewable Beteiligungs
GmbH & Co. KG (1)
Carl-Bosch-Str 38, Ludwigshafen, 67063,
Rheinland-Pfalz, Germany
Tel.: (49) 621600
Web Site: http://www.basf.com
Chemical Products Mfr
N.A.I.C.S.: 325998

BASF Bolivia S.R.L. (1)
Av San Martin N 1800 4 Piso, 7185, Santa
Cruz, Casilla, Bolivia
Tel.: (591) 33141080
Chemical Distr
N.A.I.C.S.: 424690

BASF Bulgaria Ltd. (1)
118 Bulgaria Blv fl 1, 1618, Sofia, Bulgaria
Tel.: (359) 29152047
Cosmetic Product Mfr & Distr
N.A.I.C.S.: 339999

BASF Catalysts Grundbesitz
GmbH (1)
Carl-Bosch-Str 38, Ludwigshafen, 67063,
Germany
Tel.: (49) 1715697125
Chemical Products Mfr
N.A.I.C.S.: 325998

BASF Catalysts India Pvt. Ltd. (1)
P 8/1 2nd Floor, Veerapuram Village Mahin-
dra World City Chengelpet Taluk
Kanchipuram, Chennai, 603002, Tamil
Nadu, India
Tel.: (91) 4467468181
Chemicals Mfr
N.A.I.C.S.: 325199

BASF Chemcat Thailand Limited (1)
64/24 Moo 4, Eastern Seaboard Industrial
Estate Pluakdaeng, Rayong, 21140, Thai-
land
Tel.: (66) 38955555
Auto Part & Accessory Mfr
N.A.I.C.S.: 333515

BASF Chemikalien GmbH (1)
Carl-Bosch-Str 38, Ludwigshafen, 67063,
Germany
Tel.: (49) 621600
Web Site: http://www.basf.com
Chemical Products Mfr
N.A.I.C.S.: 325998

BASF Chile S.A. (1)
Av Carrascal 3851, Quinta Normal,
7360081, Santiago, Chile (100%)
Tel.: (56) 226407010
Web Site: https://www.basf.com
Sales Range: $150-199.9 Million
Emp.: 500
Distr of Chemicals
N.A.I.C.S.: 424690

Subsidiary (Domestic):

Aislapol S.A. (2)
Av Carrascal 3791, 7360081, Santiago,
Chile
Tel.: (56) 26407070
Chemical Products
N.A.I.C.S.: 325998

BASF Coastings Services Sp. z
o.o. (1)
Ul Wiosenna 9, 63-100, Srem, Poland
Tel.: (48) 616366333
Chemical Product Mfr & Distr
N.A.I.C.S.: 325199

BASF Coating Services S.A.S. (1)
16 rue Jean Mermoz, 77290, Compans,
France
Tel.: (33) 160949870
Chemical Product Mfr & Distr
N.A.I.C.S.: 325998

BASF Coatings AG (1)
Glasuritstrasse 1, 48165, Munster, 48165,
Germany

Tel.: (49) 2501140
Web Site: http://www.basf-coatings.de
Holding Company; Paints & Coatings Mfr
N.A.I.C.S.: 325998
Christiane Weiser-Zimmermann (Head-
Global Comm)

Subsidiary (Non-US):

BASF Argentina S.A. (2)
Av de los Constitucionntes 1758,
B1667FYF, Tortuguitas, Argentina (100%)
Tel.: (54) 2320330000
Web Site: https://www.basf.com
Sales Range: $400-449.9 Million
Emp.: 2,000
Distr of Coatings & Paints
N.A.I.C.S.: 325510

BASF Coating Services (Pty)
Ltd. (2)
Central Park Building 2 Esplanade Road
7441 Century City, Cape Town, 7441, South
Africa
Tel.: (27) 215559800
Web Site: https://www.basf.com
Sales Range: $100-124.9 Million
Emp.: 340
Chemical Products Mfr
N.A.I.C.S.: 325998

BASF Coatings A.S. (2)
Mete Plaza Degirmenyolu Cad Huzurhoca
Sok No 84 Kat 9-17, Icerenkoy-Atasehir,
34752, Istanbul, Turkiye
Tel.: (90) 216 5703400
Web Site: http://www.basf.com.tr
Sales Range: $200-249.9 Million
Emp.: 800
Paint & Coating Mfr
N.A.I.C.S.: 325510

BASF Coatings Australia Pty.
Ltd. (2)
231-233 Newton Road, Locked Bag 101,
2164. Wetherill Park, NSW, Australia
Tel.: (61) 287870100
Web Site: http://www.glasurit.com.au
Sales Range: $25-49.9 Million
Emp.: 25
Automotive Coating Product Mfr
N.A.I.C.S.: 325510

Subsidiary (Domestic):

BASF Coatings GmbH (2)
Glasuritstrasse 1, 48165, Munster, Ger-
many
Tel.: (49) 2501140
Web Site: https://www.basf-coatings.com
Sales Range: $400-449.9 Million
Emp.: 2,300
Chemical Products Mfr
N.A.I.C.S.: 325998

Subsidiary (Non-US):

BASF Coatings Holding B.V. (2)
Industrieweg 12, Maarssen, 3606 AS, Neth-
erlands
Tel.: (31) 346581004
Web Site: http://www.basf.com
Sales Range: $50-74.9 Million
Emp.: 65
Holding Company; Chemical Product Mfr
N.A.I.C.S.: 551112

Subsidiary (Domestic):

BASF Coatings Nederland B.V. (3)
Industrieweg 12, Postbus 1015, 3606 AS,
Maarssen, Netherlands
Tel.: (31) 346573232
Web Site: http://www.glasarit.nl
Sales Range: $25-49.9 Million
Chemical Products Mfr
N.A.I.C.S.: 325998

Subsidiary (Non-US):

BASF Coatings India Private Ltd. (2)
Thurbe, Thane-Belapur Road, Navi Mum-
bai, 400 705, India
Tel.: (91) 22 6712 7600
Web Site: http://www.basf.com
Mfr of Chemicals
N.A.I.C.S.: 325998

BASF Coatings Japan Ltd. (2)
296 Shimokurata-cho, Totsuka-ku, Yoko-

hama, 244-0815, Kanagawa,
Japan **(100%)**
Tel.: (81) 45 862 7500
Web Site: http://www.basf.de
Sales Range: $100-124.9 Million
Emp.: 400
Distr of Automotive OEM Coatings
N.A.I.C.S.: 325520

BASF Coatings Private Ltd. **(2)**
302 T V Industrial Estate S K Ahire Marg,
400025, Mumbai, India
Tel.: (91) 2256618000
Web Site: http://www.basf.com
Automotive Coating Product & Solutions
Supplier
N.A.I.C.S.: 325510

BASF Coatings S.A. **(2)**
Cristobal Colon s/n Poligono Industrial del
Henares, 19004, Guadalajara, Spain
Tel.: (34) 949 209 000
Emp.: 60
Paint & Coating Mfr
N.A.I.C.S.: 325510
Luis Carboniro *(Gen Mgr)*

BASF Coatings S.A.S. **(2)**
Zone Industrielle De Breuil Merret Angre, F
60676, Clermont, France **(100%)**
Tel.: (33) 344777777
Web Site: http://www.basf.fr
Sales Range: $200-249.9 Million
Emp.: 600
Mfr of Paints & Lacquers
N.A.I.C.S.: 325510

Subsidiary (Domestic):

**BASF Coatings Services
S.A.R.L.** **(3)**
16 rue Jean Mermoz, Zac de la Feuchere,
77290, Compans, France **(100%)**
Tel.: (33) 81 010 2468
Web Site: https://www.basf.com
Sales Range: $25-49.9 Million
Emp.: 100
Automotive Coating Mfr
N.A.I.C.S.: 325510

Subsidiary (Non-US):

BASF Coatings S.p.A. **(2)**
Via Marconato 8, 20811, Cesano Maderno,
MB, Italy
Tel.: (39) 03625121
Web Site: http://www.basf-coatings.com
Chemical Products Mfr
N.A.I.C.S.: 325998

BASF Coatings Services AB **(2)**
Transportgatan 37, Box 23, Hisings Karra,
422 46, Gothenburg, Sweden **(100%)**
Tel.: (46) 31578700
Web Site: http://www.glasurit.com
Coatings & Paints Distr
N.A.I.C.S.: 424950

BASF Coatings Services AG **(2)**
Huobstrasse 3, Postfach 63, 8808,
Pfaffikon, Switzerland
Tel.: (41) 447874343
Chemical Products Mfr
N.A.I.C.S.: 325998

BASF Coatings Services GmbH **(2)**
Gewerbestrasse 25, 5301, Eugendorf, Aus-
tria
Tel.: (43) 622571180
Web Site: http://www.basf-coatings-
services.at
Sales Range: $25-49.9 Million
Emp.: 20
Automotive Coating Mfr
N.A.I.C.S.: 325510

BASF Coatings Services S.A. **(2)**
Antonio de la Pena y Lopez 13-B Pol Ind
Ctra Amarilla, Seville, 41007, Spain
Tel.: (34) 94 920 90 00
Web Site: http://www.basf-coatings-
services.es
Paint & Coating Distr
N.A.I.C.S.: 424950

**BASF Coatings Services
S.A./N.V.** **(2)**
Rijksweg 14, Terhulpsesteenweg 178, 2880,
Bornem, Belgium
Tel.: (32) 37403811
Web Site: https://www.basf.com

Automotive Coating Product Mfr
N.A.I.C.S.: 325510

BASF Coatings Services S.R.L. **(2)**
Mioveni Str Uzinei Nr 1-3 Ro-Mio-Vop P70,
Arges, Romania
Tel.: (40) 21 529 90 00
Sales Range: $25-49.9 Million
Emp.: 18
Paint & Coating Distr
N.A.I.C.S.: 424950
Luminita Teodorescu *(Gen Mgr)*

**BASF Coatings Services Sp. z
o.o.** **(2)**
Janikowo ul 19 Pilotow, 62-006, Kobylnica,
Poland
Emp.: 13
Automotive Paints & Industrial Coatings Mfr
N.A.I.C.S.: 325510

BASF Coatings Services s.r.o. **(2)**
Prievozska 2, 821 09, Bratislava, Slovakia
Tel.: (421) 258266111
Web Site: http://www.basf-sh.sk
Sales Range: $100-124.9 Million
Emp.: 40
Chemical Products Mfr
N.A.I.C.S.: 325998
Edita Hippova *(Mgr)*

**BASF Coatings de Mexico S.A. de
C.V.** **(2)**
Av 1 No 9 Parque Industrial Cartagena,
54900, Tultitlan, Estado de Mexico,
Mexico **(100%)**
Tel.: (52) 555 899 3831
Sales Range: $100-124.9 Million
Emp.: 380
Mfr of Automotive Coatings
N.A.I.C.S.: 325510

BASF Coatings, Inc. **(2)**
11/F HHIC Building 1128 University Park-
way North Bonifacio Global City, Taguig,
1634, Philippines **(100%)**
Tel.: (63) 28118000
Web Site: http://www.asiapacific.basf.com
Sales Range: $50-74.9 Million
Emp.: 210
Distr of Adhesive Coatings
N.A.I.C.S.: 325520

**BASF Coatings, storitve za avtomo-
bilske premaze, d.o.o.** **(2)**
Dunajska cesta 111A, Ljubljana, 1000, Slo-
venia
Tel.: (386) 73372144
Web Site: http://www.basf.com
Sales Range: $1-9.9 Million
Emp.: 11
Automotive Coating Mfr
N.A.I.C.S.: 325510

BASF S.A. **(2)**
Av Dr Julio Maranhao 3219, Bairro Praz-
eres, 54325 620, Jaboatao, Brazil **(100%)**
Tel.: (55) 1130433663
Web Site: http://www.basf.com.br
Sales Range: $50-74.9 Million
Emp.: 250
Mfr of Coatings & Paints
N.A.I.C.S.: 325510
Gislaine Rossetti *(Dir-Comm)*

Subsidiary (Domestic):

Chemetall GmbH **(2)**
Trakehner Strasse 3, 60487, Frankfurt am
Main, Germany
Tel.: (49) 6971650
Web Site: http://www.chemetall.com
Mfr, Developer & Sales of Products & Pro-
cesses for Surface Treatment, Fine Chemi-
cals & Polymer Chemicals
N.A.I.C.S.: 325199
Peter Fendel *(Member-Mgmt Bd)*

Subsidiary (Non-US):

**Changchun Chemetall Chemicals
Co., Ltd.** **(3)**
Building 6 Sun Science & Technology Park
Lane 399 Shengxia Road, Pudong New
Area, 201210, Shanghai, China
Tel.: (86) 2158120929
Web Site: http://www.chemetall.com.cn
Mfr of Surface Treatment & Other Chemical
Products
N.A.I.C.S.: 325998

Chemetall (Australasia) Pty. Ltd. **(3)**
17 Turbo Drive, Bayswater North, Mel-
bourne, 3153, VIC, Australia
Tel.: (61) 39 729 6253
Web Site: https://www.chemetall.com.au
Surface Chemistry Applications Mfr
N.A.I.C.S.: 325998

Chemetall (New Zealand) Ltd. **(3)**
Tel.: (64) 98203888
Web Site: https://www.chemetall.co.nz
Chemical Product Mfr & Sales
N.A.I.C.S.: 325998

Chemetall (Pty) Ltd. **(3)**
5 Seller Road, Boksburg, 1460, South Af-
rica
Tel.: (27) 119142500
Web Site: http://www.chemetall.com
Emp.: 115
Specialty Chemicals Mfr & Distr
N.A.I.C.S.: 325998

Chemetall (Thailand) Co. Ltd. **(3)**
No 88 Nimitkul Building Room No E-01 5th
Floor Soi Rama IX 57/1, Wisetsook 2 Su-
anluang Sub District Suanluang District,
Bangkok, 10250, Thailand
Tel.: (66) 218 722 3570
Web Site: https://www.chemetall.com
Chemical Products Mfr
N.A.I.C.S.: 325998

Chemetall AB **(3)**
Backa Strandgata 18, 42246, Hisings
Backa, Sweden
Tel.: (46) 313377650
Web Site: http://www.chemetall.se
Chemical Products Mfr
N.A.I.C.S.: 325998

Chemetall Asia Pte. Ltd. **(3)**
12 Loyang Crescent, Singapore, 508980,
Singapore
Tel.: (65) 6 885 7900
Web Site: https://www.chemetall.com
Chemical Products Mfr
N.A.I.C.S.: 325998

Chemetall B.V. **(3)**
IJsselstraat 41, 5347 KG, Oss, Netherlands
Tel.: (31) 412681888
Web Site: http://www.chemetall.nl
Chemical Surface Treatments, Cathodic
Protection Supplier & Sales
N.A.I.C.S.: 325998

Chemetall Finland Oy **(3)**
Kuninkaankatu 22 C, 33110, Tampere, Fin-
land
Tel.: (358) 32223401
Web Site: https://www.chemetall.com
Chemical Products Distr
N.A.I.C.S.: 424690

Chemetall Hong Kong Ltd. **(3)**
Unit 316B 3rd Floor of Enterprise Place
Phase One Hong Kong Science, Park Pak
Shek Kok, Hong Kong, New Territories,
China (Hong Kong)
Tel.: (852) 24623966
Web Site: http://www.chemetall.hk
Chemical Products Mfr
N.A.I.C.S.: 325998

Chemetall Italia S.r.l. **(3)**
Via della Tecnica 5-7, 20833, Giussano,
MB, Italy
Tel.: (39) 03623151
Web Site: http://www.chemetall.it
Production & Sales of Various Chemical
Products
N.A.I.C.S.: 325998

Chemetall Limited **(3)**
Napier House Auckland Park, Bletchley,
Milton Keynes, MK1 1BU, United Kingdom
Tel.: (44) 1908649333
Web Site: http://www.chemetall.co.uk
Chemical Product Mfr, Warehousing &
Laboratory Facilities
N.A.I.C.S.: 325998

**Chemetall Mexicana, S.A. de
C.V.** **(3)**
Avenida El Tepeyac No 1420-B, 76250, El
Marques, Queretaro, Mexico
Tel.: (52) 442 227 2000
Web Site: https://www.chemetallna.com
Chemical Products Mfr
N.A.I.C.S.: 325998

Chemetall Polska Sp.z o.o. **(3)**
Ul Przeclawska 8, 03-879, Warsaw, Poland
Tel.: (48) 22 510 1130
Web Site: https://www.chemetall.pl
Chemical Products Mfr
N.A.I.C.S.: 325998

Chemetall S.A. **(3)**
Paseo de la Ribera 107, E-08420, Barce-
lona, Spain
Tel.: (34) 93 840 67 86
Web Site: http://www.chemetall.es
Chemical Products Mfr
N.A.I.C.S.: 325998

Chemetall S.A.S. **(3)**
Carre 92 Immeuble G2, 8 avenue des Lou-
vresses, 92622, Gennevilliers, France
Tel.: (33) 14 715 3800
Web Site: https://www.chemetall.com
Chemical Product Mfr, Laboratory & Techni-
cal Center
N.A.I.C.S.: 325998

Chemetall S.R.L. **(3)**
Edificio Republica Tucuman 1 18th floor,
C1107DDA, Buenos Aires, Argentina
Tel.: (54) 114 317 9600
Web Site: https://www.chemetall.com
Chemical Products Mfr
N.A.I.C.S.: 325998

**Chemetall Sanayi Kimyasallari Ticaret
ve Sanayi A.S.** **(3)**
TOSB Organize Sanayi Bolgesi 3 Cadde
No 21, 41420, Kocaeli, Turkiye
Tel.: (90) 262 677 4900
Web Site: http://www.chemetall.com.tr
Design & Production of Surface Treatment
Chemicals & Plastisols
N.A.I.C.S.: 325998

Subsidiary (US):

Chemetall US, Inc. **(3)**
675 Central Ave, New Providence, NJ
07974
Tel.: (908) 464-6900
Web Site: http://www.chemetallna.com
Chemical Products Mfr
N.A.I.C.S.: 325998

Subsidiary (Non-US):

Chemetall Canada Limited **(4)**
Suite 110 1 Kenview Blvd, Brampton, L6T
5E6, ON, Canada
Tel.: (905) 791-1628
Web Site: http://www.chemetallna.com
Chemical Product Distr, Sales & Warehous-
ing
N.A.I.C.S.: 424690

BASF Coatings GmbH **(1)**
Glasuritstrasse 1, 48165, Munster, Ger-
many
Tel.: (49) 2501140
Web Site: https://www.basf-coatings.com
Industrial Coating Mfr
N.A.I.C.S.: 325510

BASF Coatings Services B.V. **(1)**
Industrieweg 12, 3606, Maarssen, Nether-
lands
Tel.: (31) 346573232
Automotive Coating Mfr
N.A.I.C.S.: 325510

BASF Coatings Services Itlay Srl **(1)**
Via Padule 40 Firenze, 50018, Scandicci,
Italy
Tel.: (39) 0557350121
Chemical Coating Services
N.A.I.C.S.: 325510
Andrea Amato *(Mng Dir)*

**BASF Coatings Services Pty.
Ltd.** **(1)**
Central Park Building 2 Esplanade Road,
Century City, Cape Town, 7441, South Af-
rica
Tel.: (27) 215559800
Automotive Repair Services
N.A.I.C.S.: 811111

BASF Coatings Services S.A.S. **(1)**
16 Rue Jean Mermoz, 77290, Compans,
France
Tel.: (33) 160949870
Chemical Coating Services
N.A.I.C.S.: 325510

BASF SE—(Continued)

BASF Coatings Services S.A.U. (1)
Carretera del Mig 219, L'Hospitalet de Llobregat, 08907, Barcelona, Spain
Tel.: (34) 932616100
Chemical Coating Services
N.A.I.C.S.: 325510

BASF Coatings Services Sp.
z.o.o. (1)
Pilotow 19, Janikowo, 62-006, Kobylnica, Poland
Tel.: (48) 616464872
Chemical Coating Services
N.A.I.C.S.: 325510

BASF Color Solutions Germany
GmbH (1)
Site Koeln-Muelheim Clevischer Ring 180, 51063, Cologne, Germany
Tel.: (49) 221 96498 0
Emp.: 14
Plastic Colorants Mfr
N.A.I.C.S.: 325998
Cesare Pollini (Plant Mgr)

Subsidiary (Non-US):

BASF Color Solutions France
S.A.S. (2)
Zone Industrielle de Breuil le Sec, 60676, Clermont, Oise, France
Tel.: (33) 3 44 77 77 77
Emp.: 600
Specialty Chemicals Distr
N.A.I.C.S.: 424690
K. K. Chan (Gen Mgr)

BASF Colors & Effects GmbH (1)
An der Rheinschanze 1, 67059, Ludwigshafen, Germany
Tel.: (49) 621600
Web Site: http://www.colors-effects.eu
Emp.: 2,600
Plastic & Cosmetic Product Mfr
N.A.I.C.S.: 325998
Alexander Haunschild (Mng Dir)

BASF Colors & Effects Japan
Ltd. (1)
OVOL Nihonbashi Building 3F 3 4 4 Nihonbashi Muromachi, Chuo, Tokyo, 103-0022, Japan
Tel.: (81) 352902424
Dye & Pigment Mfr
N.A.I.C.S.: 325130

BASF Colors & Effects Korea
Ltd. (1)
196 Jangsaengpo ro, Nam-gu, Ulsan, 44781, Korea (South)
Tel.: (82) 522290245
Dye & Pigment Mfr
N.A.I.C.S.: 325130

BASF Colors & Effects Switzerland
AG (1)
Standort Basel Klybeckstrasse 141, 4057, Basel, Switzerland
Tel.: (41) 616361111
Chemical Products Mfr
N.A.I.C.S.: 325998
Daniel Muller (Sr Mgr-Bus Dev)

BASF Construction Additives
GmbH (1)
Dr-Albert-Frank-Str 32, 83308, Trostberg, Germany
Chemical Products Mfr
N.A.I.C.S.: 325998

BASF Construction Chemicals
GmbH (1)
Dr-Albert-Frank-Strasse 32, Chemiepark Trostberg, D-83308, Trostberg, Germany (100%)
Tel.: (49) 86218610
Sales Range: $1-4.9 Billion
Emp.: 7,100
Holding Company; Construction Chemical Products Mfr
N.A.I.C.S.: 551112

Subsidiary (Non-US):

BASF A/S (2)
Hallandsvej 1, DK 6230, Rodekro, Denmark
Tel.: (45) 74661511

Web Site: http://www.master-builders-solutions.basf.dk
Sales Range: $25-49.9 Million
Emp.: 60
Production & Distribution of Chemical Products for the Building Industry
N.A.I.C.S.: 325998

BASF Construction Chemicals
(China) Co. Ltd. (2)
Room 1801-1802 Habour Ring Plaza 18 Xizang Zhong Road, Shanghai, China
Tel.: (86) 21 2320 3844
Web Site: http://www.basf-cc.cn
Chemical Products Distr
N.A.I.C.S.: 424690

BASF Construction Chemicals (Pty)
Ltd (2)
11 Pullinger Street, Westonaria, 1780, South Africa
Tel.: (27) 11 754 1343
Web Site: http://www.basf.co.za
Construction Chemical Mfr & Distr
N.A.I.C.S.: 325998

BASF Construction Chemicals
(Schweiz) AG (2)
Industriestrasse 26, 8207, Schaffhausen, Switzerland
Tel.: (41) 589582525
Web Site: http://www.conica.basf.com
Sales Range: $50-74.9 Million
Emp.: 150
Mfr of Sports Flooring Surfaces
N.A.I.C.S.: 326199
Karl Meyer (Dir-Sports)

Unit (Domestic):

BASF Admixture Systems
Europe (3)
Vulkanstrasse 110, CH 8048, Zurich, Switzerland
Tel.: (41) 444382361
Web Site: http://www.basf.com
Mfr of Concrete, Mortar & Pavement Additives & Admixtures
N.A.I.C.S.: 327390

Subsidiary (Non-US):

BASF Construction Chemicals Algeria
S.A.R.L. (2)
Zone Industrielle de Baba Ali, District 05-Ilot 03, 16 305, Algiers, Algeria
Tel.: (213) 2 358 9912
Web Site: https://www.basf.com
Construction Chemicals Mfr
N.A.I.C.S.: 325998

Group (Non-US):

BASF Construction Chemicals
Asia/Pacific (2)
Room 2207 Shanghai Times Square, 93 Huai Hai Zhong Road, Shanghai, 200021, China
Tel.: (86) 2151332839
Web Site: http://www.ap.cc.basf.com
Sales Range: $200-249.9 Million
Emp.: 1,000
Mfr of Concrete, Pavement & Mortar Additives & Admixtures
N.A.I.C.S.: 327390

Unit (Non-US):

BASF Construction Chemicals (Hong
Kong) Limited (3)
20 F EW International Tower, 120 124 Texaco Road, Tsuen Wan, NT, China (Hong Kong)
Tel.: (852) 24074291
Web Site: http://www.basf.com
Sales Range: $25-49.9 Million
Emp.: 30
Distr of Construction Materials
N.A.I.C.S.: 444180

BASF Construction Chemicals (Taiwan) Co., Ltd (3)
No 11 Chih-Li 1st Road, 540, Nant'ou, 540, Taiwan
Tel.: (886) 492255138
Web Site: http://www.basf.net
Sales Range: $25-49.9 Million
Emp.: 100
Distr of Construction Materials

N.A.I.C.S.: 444180

BASF Construction Chemicals Singapore Pte Ltd (3)
No 33 Tuas Ave 11, Singapore, 639090, Singapore
Tel.: (65) 68616766
Web Site: http://www.basf-cc.com.sg
Sales Range: $25-49.9 Million
Emp.: 60
Construction Supplies Mfr & Distr
N.A.I.C.S.: 444180

Subsidiary (Non-US):

BASF Construction Chemicals Australia Pty. Ltd. (4)
11 Stanton Road, Seven Hills, 2147, NSW, Australia
Tel.: (61) 288114200
Web Site: http://www.basf-cc.com.au
Sales Range: $25-49.9 Million
Emp.: 40
Distr of Construction Materials
N.A.I.C.S.: 444180

BASF Construction Chemicals Malaysia Sdn Bhd (4)
Kawasan Perindustrian Bukit Raja No 8 Jalan Keluli 2, 41050, Kelang, Selangor Darul Ehsan, Malaysia
Tel.: (60) 333443388
Web Site: http://www.basf-cc.com
Sales Range: $10-24.9 Million
Emp.: 40
Sales & Marketing of Construction Supplies
N.A.I.C.S.: 444180

Unit (Non-US):

NMB Co., Ltd. (3)
16 26 Roppongi 3 Chome, Minatu Ku, Tokyo, 106-0032, Japan
Tel.: (81) 3 3584 7099
Web Site: http://www.ap.construction-chemicals.basf.com
Sales Range: $125-149.9 Million
Emp.: 400
Distr of Concrete, Pavement & Mortar Additives & Admixtures
N.A.I.C.S.: 327390

Subsidiary (Non-US):

BASF Construction Chemicals Belgium NV (2)
Industrieterrien Ravenshout 3711, 3945, Hamme, Belgium
Tel.: (32) 11340434
Web Site: http://www.basf-cc.be
Sales Range: $25-49.9 Million
Emp.: 72
Distr of Chemical Products for the Construction Industry
N.A.I.C.S.: 444180
Tom Vanpraet (Mgr-HR)

Subsidiary (Non-US):

BASF Nederland B.V., Construction
Chemicals (3)
Karolusstraat 2, Postbus 132, Oosterhout, 4903 RJ, Netherlands
Tel.: (31) 162476660
Web Site: http://www.master-builders-solutions.basf.nl
Sales Range: $25-49.9 Million
Emp.: 40
Distr of Chemical Products for the Construction Industry
N.A.I.C.S.: 444180

Subsidiary (Non-US):

BASF Construction Chemicals
Canada Ltd. (2)
1800 Clark Blvd, Brampton, L6T 4M7, ON, Canada
Tel.: (905) 792-2012
Web Site: http://www.basf-admixtures.com
Sales Range: $25-49.9 Million
Emp.: 20
Mfr of Concrete, Pavement & Mortar Additives
N.A.I.C.S.: 327390

Subsidiary (Domestic):

BASF Construction Canada Holdings
Inc. (3)

100 Milverton Dr 5th Fl, Mississauga, L5R 4H1, ON, Canada
Tel.: (289) 360-1300
Investment Management Service
N.A.I.C.S.: 523999

Subsidiary (Non-US):

BASF Construction Chemicals Espana SA (2)
Basters 15, 08184, Barcelona, Spain
Tel.: (34) 938620000
Web Site: http://www.basf-cc.es
Sales Range: $200-249.9 Million
Emp.: 1,000
Distr of Construction Chemicals & Materials
N.A.I.C.S.: 423390

BASF Construction Chemicals Europe AG (2)
Vulkanstrasse 110, 8048, Zurich, Switzerland
Tel.: (41) 58 958 22 11
Web Site: http://www.basf-cc.ch
Construction Chemicals Mfr
N.A.I.C.S.: 325998
Luis Caporicci (Gen Mgr)

BASF Construction Chemicals France
S.A.S. (2)
Z I Petite Montagne Sud 10 Rue, F 91017, Lisses, France
Tel.: (33) 169475000
Web Site: http://www.basf.com
Sales Range: $50-74.9 Million
Emp.: 150
Distr of Chemical Products for the Construction Industry
N.A.I.C.S.: 444180

Plant (Domestic):

BASF Construction Chemicals GmbH
- Frankfurt am Main (2)
Kennedy-Allee 93, 605596, Frankfurt am Main, Germany
Tel.: (49) 69633080
Sales Range: $1-4.9 Million
Mfr of Chemicals & Products for Construction Industry
N.A.I.C.S.: 325520

Subsidiary (Non-US):

BASF Construction Chemicals Italia
SpA (2)
Via Vicinale Delle Corti 21, 31100, Treviso, Italy
Tel.: (39) 0422 304251
Web Site: http://www.basf-cc.it
Chemical Additive Mfr
N.A.I.C.S.: 325998

BASF Construction Chemicals
Ltda. (2)
Rio Palena 9665 ENEA, Pudahuel, Santiago, Chile
Tel.: (56) 2 799 4300
Web Site: http://www.basf-cc.cl
Construction Chemicals Mfr
N.A.I.C.S.: 325998

BASF Construction Chemicals Peru
S.A. (70%)
Jr Placido Jimenez No 630/790, Cercado, 01, Lima, Peru
Tel.: (51) 1 385 0109
Web Site: http://www.la.cc.basf.com
Construction Chemicals Mfr
N.A.I.C.S.: 325998

BASF Construction Chemicals Sweden AB (2)
Metalvagen 42, 19572, Stockholm, Rosersberg, Sweden
Tel.: (46) 87560165
Sales Range: $25-49.9 Million
Emp.: 15
Distr of Concrete Additives & Building Supplies
N.A.I.C.S.: 444180

BASF Construction Chemicals
UK (2)
Albany House Swinton Hall Road, Manchester, M27 4DT, United Kingdom
Tel.: (44) 161 485 6222
Web Site: https://www.basf.com
Sales Range: $25-49.9 Million
Emp.: 70
Mfr of Waterproofing & Roofing Products

N.A.I.C.S.: 313320

BASF Construction Chemicals Venezuela, S.A. (2)
Av Circunvalacion del Sol Centro Profesional Santa Paula, 1080, Caracas, Venezuela
Tel.: (58) 212 935 8306
Web Site: http://www.basf-cc-la.com
Sales Range: $25-49.9 Million
Emp.: 40
Distr of Concrete Additives
N.A.I.C.S.: 444180

Subsidiary (US):

BASF Construction Chemicals, LLC (2)
23700 Chagrin Blvd, Cleveland, OH 44122
Tel.: (216) 839-7500
Web Site: http://www.basf.com
Sales Range: $400-449.9 Million
Emp.: 200
Mfr of Expansion Joints, Exterior Insulation & Finish Systems & Concrete Repair & Construction Products
N.A.I.C.S.: 325520
Juan Alfonso Garcia (VP-Admixture Sys Bus-North America)

Subsidiary (Domestic):

BASF Corp. - Building Systems (3)
889 Valley Park Dr, Shakopee, MN 55379-1854
Tel.: (952) 496-6000
Web Site: http://www.buildingsystems.basf.com
Sales Range: $50-74.9 Million
Emp.: 113
Mfr of Sealants & Adhesives, Concrete Repair Products, Grouts, Performance Flooring, Traffic Deck Membranes & Preformed Expansion Joints
N.A.I.C.S.: 325520

BASF Wall Systems, Inc. (3)
3550 Saint Johns Bluff Rd S, Jacksonville, FL 32224-2614
Tel.: (904) 996-6000
Web Site: http://www.senergy.cc
Sales Range: $25-49.9 Million
Emp.: 30
Mfr of Exterior Insulation & Finish Systems, Stucco Systems & Architectural Finish Coatings
N.A.I.C.S.: 238190

Subsidiary (Non-US):

BASF Construction Systems (China) Co. Ltd. (2)
69 Guiquig Road Caohejing Develpment Area, 200233, Shanghai, China
Tel.: (86) 21 6485 33 00
Construction Chemicals Mfr
N.A.I.C.S.: 325998

BASF Yapi Kimyasallari San A/S (2)
Mete Plaza Degirmenyolu cad Huzurhoca Sok No 84 Kat 9 17, 34752, Istanbul, Kavacik, Turkiye
Tel.: (90) 2165703400
Web Site: http://www.basf-yks.com.tr
Sales Range: $25-49.9 Million
Emp.: 100
Distr of Construction Chemicals
N.A.I.C.S.: 424690

Subsidiary (Domestic):

PCI Augsburg GmbH (2)
Piccardstrasse 11, 86159, Augsburg, Germany
Tel.: (49) 82159010
Web Site: https://www.pci-augsburg.eu
Sales Range: $250-299.9 Million
Emp.: 750
Mfr of Chemical Products for the Building Industry
N.A.I.C.S.: 444180

BASF Construction Chemicals Grundbesitz GmbH & Co. KG (1)
Carl-Bosch-Str 38, Ludwigshafen, 67063, Rheinland-Pfalz, Germany
Tel.: (49) 621600
Web Site: http://www.basf.com
Emp.: 30,000
Chemical Products Mfr

N.A.I.C.S.: 325998

BASF Construction Solutions GmbH (1)
Dr-Albert-Frank-Str 32, 83308, Trostberg, Germany
Tel.: (49) 86218616
Chemical Products Mfr
N.A.I.C.S.: 325998

BASF Controls Ltd. (1)
St Michaels Industrial Estate, Widnes, WA8 8TJ, Cheshire, United Kingdom
Tel.: (44) 1514207151
Web Site: http://www.basf.co.uk
Pest Control Chemical Mfr
N.A.I.C.S.: 325320

BASF Coordination Center Comm.V. (1)
Haven 725 Scheldelaan 600, 2040, Antwerp, Belgium
Tel.: (32) 3 561 2167
Emp.: 300
Chemical Products Mfr
N.A.I.C.S.: 325998
Wouter de Geest (Mng Dir)

BASF Corporation (1)
100 Park Ave, Florham Park, NJ 07932 (100%)
Tel.: (973) 245-6000
Sales Range: $15-24.9 Billion
Emp.: 1,000
Holding Company; North America Regional Managing Office
N.A.I.C.S.: 551112
Juan Carlos Ordonez (Sr VP-North America)

Subsidiary (Domestic):

Automotive Refinish Technologies LLC (2)
400 Galleria Ofc Ctr Ste 217, Southfield, MI 48034
Tel.: (248) 304-5569
Automotive Paint & Coating Distr
N.A.I.C.S.: 424950
Marvin Gillfillan (VP-North America)

Subsidiary (Non-US):

BASF Canada Inc. (2)
100 Milverton Drive, Mississauga, L5R 4H1, ON, Canada (100%)
Tel.: (289) 360-6159
Web Site: https://www.basf.com
Sales Range: $50-74.9 Million
Emp.: 150
Chemicals
N.A.I.C.S.: 325998

Subsidiary (Domestic):

BASF Catalysts LLC (2)
33 Wood Ave, Iselin, NJ 08830-0770
Tel.: (732) 205-7001
Web Site: https://www.catalysts.basf.com
Sales Range: $1-4.9 Billion
Material Science Technology & Precious Metal Services
N.A.I.C.S.: 424690

Subsidiary (Non-US):

BASF Catalyst Canada ULC (3)
100 Milverton Dr 5th Fl, Mississauga, L5R 4H1, ON, Canada
Tel.: (289) 360-1300
Chemical Products Mfr
N.A.I.C.S.: 325998

BASF Catalysts (Guilin) Co. Ltd. (3)
Sub-district No 1 Guilin Hi-Tech Development Zone, No 18 Can Luan Road, Guilin, 541004, Guangxi Zhuang, China
Tel.: (86) 773 380 5678
Emission Control Catalyst Mfr & Distr
N.A.I.C.S.: 334519

BASF Catalysts (Shanghai) Co. Ltd. (3)
199 Luqiao Road, Pudong, Shanghai, 201206, China
Tel.: (86) 21 6109 1777
Chemical Products Mfr
N.A.I.C.S.: 325998

BASF Catalysts Asia B.V. (3)

Groningensingel 1, Arnhem, 6835 EA, Netherlands
Tel.: (31) 26 371 7171
Investment Management Service
N.A.I.C.S.: 523999

BASF Catalysts Canada B.V. (3)
Groningensingel 1, Arnhem, 6835 EA, Gelderland, Netherlands
Tel.: (31) 263717171
Chemical Products Mfr
N.A.I.C.S.: 325998

Subsidiary (Domestic):

BASF Catalysts Delaware LLC (3)
100 Campus Dr, Florham Park, NJ 07932-1020
Tel.: (973) 245-6000
Chemical Products Mfr
N.A.I.C.S.: 325998

Subsidiary (Non-US):

BASF Catalysts Germany GmbH (3)
Seligmannallee 1, 30173, Hannover, Germany
Tel.: (49) 511288660
Web Site: https://www.basf.com
Sales Range: $25-49.9 Million
Emp.: 75
Absorbents Mfr
N.A.I.C.S.: 339113

BASF Catalysts Holding Asia B.V. (3)
Groningensingel 1, Arnhem, 6835 EA, Gelderland, Netherlands
Tel.: (31) 263717171
Emp.: 100
Investment Management Service
N.A.I.C.S.: 523999

Subsidiary (Domestic):

BASF Catalysts Holding China LLC (3)
100 Campus Dr, Florham Park, NJ 07932-1020
Tel.: (973) 245-6000
Investment Management Service
N.A.I.C.S.: 523999

Unit (Domestic):

BASF Catalysts LLC - Appearance & Performance Technologies (3)
25 Middlesex Essex Tpke, Iselin, NJ 08830-0770
Tel.: (732) 205-5000
Pigments, Additives, Thickeners & Absorbents for Paint, Coatings, Plastic & Allied Industries
N.A.I.C.S.: 325180

Plant (Domestic):

BASF Catalysts LLC - East Windsor (3)
12 Thompson Rd, East Windsor, CT 06088-9696
Tel.: (860) 623-9901
Web Site: http://www.catalysts.basf.com
Sales Range: $10-24.9 Million
Emp.: 73
Thermal Spray Coating Mfr
N.A.I.C.S.: 325510
David Lamontagne (Plant Mgr)

Unit (Domestic):

BASF Catalysts LLC - Environmental Technologies (3)
25 Middlesex Essex Tpke, Iselin, NJ 08830
Tel.: (732) 205-5000
Web Site: http://www.basf.com
Emissions Control Technologies & Systems Mfr
N.A.I.C.S.: 333413

BASF Catalysts LLC - Material Services (3)
25 Middlesex Essex Tpke, Iselin, NJ 08830-0770
Tel.: (732) 205-5000
Web Site: http://www.basf.com
Purchase & Sale of Precious & Base Metals & Related Products; Related Services for Precious Metal Refining; Production of Salts & Solutions

N.A.I.C.S.: 331410

BASF Catalysts LLC - Paper Pigments & Additives (3)
25 Middlesex Essex Tpke, Iselin, NJ 08830-0770
Tel.: (732) 205-5000
Coatings, Extenders & Pigments for the Paper Industry
N.A.I.C.S.: 325510
Robert Spadoni (VP & Gen Mgr-Minerals Tech)

BASF Catalysts LLC - Process Technologies (3)
25 Middlesex Essex Tpke, Iselin, NJ 08830-0770
Tel.: (732) 205-5000
Mfr & Marketer of Advanced Chemical & Polymerization Catalysts, Sorbents, Separation Products & Cracking & Hydroprocessing Technologies
N.A.I.C.S.: 325998

Plant (Domestic):

BASF Catalysts LLC - Quincy (3)
1101 N Madison St, Quincy, FL 32352-0981
Tel.: (850) 627-7688
Sales Range: $10-24.9 Million
Emp.: 176
Industrial Minerals, Fullers Earth, Attapulgite Clay
N.A.I.C.S.: 325130

Unit (Domestic):

BASF Catalysts LLC - Separation Systems & Ventures (3)
25 Middlesex Essex Tpke, Iselin, NJ 08830-0770
Tel.: (732) 205-5000
Web Site: http://www.basf.com
Mfr of Pigments
N.A.I.C.S.: 325130

Subsidiary (Non-US):

BASF Catalysts NL Finance C.V. (3)
Groningensingel 1, 6835 EA, Arnhem, Netherlands
Tel.: (31) 26 3717171
Financial Management Services
N.A.I.C.S.: 523999

BASF Catalysts UK Holdings Limited (3)
63 St Mary Axe, London, EC3A 8LE, United Kingdom
Tel.: (44) 20 7456 7300
Investment Management Service
N.A.I.C.S.: 523999

Subsidiary (Domestic):

Engelhard Energy Corporation (3)
101 Wood Ave S, Iselin, NJ 08830-2703
Tel.: (732) 205-5000
Chemical Product Whslr
N.A.I.C.S.: 424690

Subsidiary (Non-US):

Engelhard Metals AG (3)
Grafenauweg 6, Zug, 6300, Switzerland
Tel.: (41) 7108277
Web Site: http://www.pasf.com
Sales Range: $25-49.9 Million
Emp.: 4
Precious Metals Dealing & Management
N.A.I.C.S.: 458310

Engelhard Metals Ltd. (3)
63 St Mary Axe, London, EC3A 8NH, United Kingdom
Tel.: (44) 2074567300
Web Site: http://www.basf.pl
Sales Range: $25-49.9 Million
Emp.: 45
Precious Metals Dealing & Management
N.A.I.C.S.: 458310

Joint Venture (Non-US):

N.E. ChemCat Corporation (3)
27th floor World Trade Center Building South Tower 2-4-1 Hamamatsucho, Minato-ku, Tokyo, 105-5127, Japan
Tel.: (81) 334355490
Sales Range: $200-249.9 Million
Emp.: 681

BASF SE—(Continued)

Chemical Catalysts, Precious Metal Coating
& Automotive Exhaust Catalysts Mfr
N.A.I.C.S.: 325998

Subsidiary (Domestic):

Ovonic Battery Company, Inc. **(3)**
2983 Waterview Dr, Rochester Hills, MI
40309
Tel.: (248) 293-7002
Web Site: http://www.catalysts.basf.com
Sales Range: $25-49.9 Million
Emp.: 45
Batteries Mfr
N.A.I.C.S.: 335910
Michael A. Fetcenko (Pres)

Plant (Domestic):

**BASF Corp. - Ambler - Care
Chemicals** **(2)**
300 Brookside Ave, Ambler, PA 19002-3498
Tel.: (215) 628-1000
Web Site: http://www.basf.com
Sales Range: $50-74.9 Million
Emp.: 1
Cosmetics, Surfactants & Related Products
Mfr
N.A.I.C.S.: 325998

BASF Corp. - Appleton Plant **(2)**
2901 N Conkey St, Appleton, WI 54911
Tel.: (920) 731-1893
Web Site: http://www2.basf.us
Chemical Products Mfr
N.A.I.C.S.: 325998

Unit (Domestic):

**BASF Corp. - Charlotte (Chesa-
peake) Site** **(2)**
4330 Chesapeake Dr, Charlotte, NC 28216
Tel.: (704) 392-4313
Web Site: http://www2.basf.us
Sales Range: $25-49.9 Million
Emp.: 20
Chemical Testing Laboratory & Product
Whslr
N.A.I.C.S.: 541380

**BASF Corp. - Charlotte (Steele
Creek) Technical Center** **(2)**
11501 Steele Creek Rd, Charlotte, NC
28273
Tel.: (704) 588-5280
Web Site: http://www.basf.com
Sales Range: $150-199.9 Million
Emp.: 270
Dispersions & Pigments, Paper Chemicals
& Hygiene Products Whslr & Technical Ser-
vices
N.A.I.C.S.: 424690
Kevin M. Murphy (Gen Mgr)

Unit (Domestic):

**BASF Corp. - Superabsorbents North
America** **(3)**
11501 Steele Creek Rd, Charlotte, NC
28273
Tel.: (704) 588-5280
Web Site:
    http://www.superabsorbents.basf.com
Superabsorbent Chemical Products Whslr &
Technical Services
N.A.I.C.S.: 424690
James C. Robinson (Mgr-Technical)

Unit (Domestic):

**BASF Corp. - Engineering Plastics
NAFTA** **(2)**
450 Clark Dr, Budd Lake, NJ 07828-1234
Tel.: (973) 426-5429
Web Site: http://www.basf.us
Sales Range: $25-49.9 Million
Emp.: 28
Engineering Plastic Materials Mfr
N.A.I.C.S.: 325211

Plant (Domestic):

BASF Corp. - Evans City Plant **(2)**
1424 Mars-Evans City Rd, Evans City, PA
16033
Tel.: (724) 538-1200
Web Site: http://www.basf.us

Sales Range: $50-74.9 Million
Emp.: 133
Inorganic Chemical Compounds Mfr
N.A.I.C.S.: 325180

BASF Corp. - Freeport Plant **(2)**
602 Copper Rd, Freeport, TX 77541
Tel.: (979) 415-6215
Web Site: http://www.basf.com
Sales Range: $550-599.9 Million
Emp.: 850
Various Chemical Products Mfr
N.A.I.C.S.: 325998

BASF Corp. - Geismar Plant **(2)**
8404 River Rd, Geismar, LA 70734
Tel.: (225) 339-7300
Web Site: http://www2.basf.us
Sales Range: $550-599.9 Million
Emp.: 1,400
Various Chemical Products Mfr
N.A.I.C.S.: 325998
Jerry Lebold (Sr VP & Gen Mgr)

BASF Corp. - Greenville Plant **(2)**
1175 Martin St, Greenville, OH 45331
Tel.: (937) 547-6700
Web Site: http://www.basf.com
Sales Range: $50-74.9 Million
Emp.: 104
Coating & Resin Products Mfr
N.A.I.C.S.: 325510

Subsidiary (Domestic):

BASF Corp. - Independence **(2)**
8001 E Pleasant Valley Rd, Independence,
OH 44131
Tel.: (216) 867-1040
Web Site: http://www.basf.com
Sales Range: $25-49.9 Million
Emp.: 12
Specialty Electrolyte Materials, High Perfor-
mance Solvents, Aryl Phosphorus Deriva-
tives & Other Custom Manufactured Prod-
ucts
N.A.I.C.S.: 325998
Martin Payne (Gen Mgr)

Plant (Domestic):

**BASF Corp. - LaGrange - Nutrition &
Health** **(2)**
5325 S 9th St, La Grange, IL 60525-3602
Tel.: (708) 579-6150
Sales Range: $25-49.9 Million
Emp.: 30
Chemicals & Vitamins Mfr
N.A.I.C.S.: 325180

BASF Corp. - Livonia Plant **(2)**
13000 Levan St, Livonia, MI 48150
Tel.: (734) 591-6200
Web Site: http://www2.basf.us
Polymers
N.A.I.C.S.: 325199

**BASF Corp. - Monaca Polymers
Plant** **(2)**
370 Frankfort Rd, Monaca, PA 15061
Tel.: (724) 728-6900
Web Site: http://www.basf.us
Sales Range: $50-74.9 Million
Emp.: 125
Chemical Polymers Mfr
N.A.I.C.S.: 325998

BASF Corp. - Newport Plant **(2)**
205 S James St, Newport, DE 19804-2424
Tel.: (302) 992-5600
Web Site: http://www.basf.com
Sales Range: $50-74.9 Million
Emp.: 250
Pigment Processing
N.A.I.C.S.: 424690

Unit (Domestic):

BASF Corp. - Southfield Site **(2)**
26701 Telegraph Rd, Southfield, MI 48033
Tel.: (248) 304-5453
Web Site: http://www.basf.com
Sales Range: $125-149.9 Million
Emp.: 275
Automotive Refinishing & Coating Products
Mfr & Marketer
N.A.I.C.S.: 325510
Christopher Toomey (Sr VP)

**BASF Corp. - Tarrytown Research
Facility** **(2)**

540 White Plains Rd, Tarrytown, NY 10591
Tel.: (914) 785-2000
Web Site: http://www.basf.com
Sales Range: $50-74.9 Million
Emp.: 150
Mfr of Additives
N.A.I.C.S.: 325180

Plant (Domestic):

**BASF Corp. - Tucson - Mining
Chemicals** **(2)**
2430 N Huachuca Dr, Tucson, AZ 85745-
8891
Tel.: (520) 622-8891
Web Site: http://www.basf.com
Sales Range: $25-49.9 Million
Emp.: 13
Distr of Chemicals for the Mining Industry
N.A.I.C.S.: 424690

BASF Corp. - Washington Plant **(2)**
2 Pleasant View Ave, Washington, NJ
07882
Tel.: (908) 689-2500
Web Site: http://www.basf.us
Emp.: 20
Chemical Products Mfr
N.A.I.C.S.: 325998

**BASF Corp. - West Memphis
Plant** **(2)**
100 Bridgeport Rd, West Memphis, AR
72301
Tel.: (870) 735-8750
Web Site: http://www2.basf.us
Sales Range: $50-74.9 Million
Emp.: 135
Specialty Industrial & Water Treatment
Chemicals Mfr
N.A.I.C.S.: 325998
Debbie Dalley (Plant Mgr)

BASF Corp. - White Stone Plant **(2)**
3455 Southport Rd, Spartanburg, SC 29302
Tel.: (864) 585-3411
Web Site: http://www.basf.com
Chemical Products Mfr
N.A.I.C.S.: 325998

BASF Corp. - Wyandotte Plant **(2)**
Wyandotte N Works 1609 Biddle Ave, Wy-
andotte, MI 48192
Tel.: (734) 324-6100
Web Site: http://www.basf.com
Sales Range: $200-249.9 Million
Emp.: 1,000
Urethane, Joncryl & Specialty Plastic Prod-
ucts Mfr
N.A.I.C.S.: 326150
Gregory Pflum (VP & Gen Mgr)

Subsidiary (Domestic):

BASF Fina Petrochemicals LP **(2)**
100 Park Ave, Florham Park, NJ 07932
Tel.: (973) 245-6000
Web Site: http://www.basf.com
Emp.: 1,000
Ehylene & Propylene Mfr
N.A.I.C.S.: 325110

Unit (Domestic):

BASF Foam Enterprises **(2)**
13630 Water Tower Cir, Plymouth, MN
55441-3704
Tel.: (763) 559-3266
Web Site: http://www.basf-pfe.com
Sales Range: $25-49.9 Million
Emp.: 10
Mfr of Rigid Polyurethane Foam Products
N.A.I.C.S.: 326150

Subsidiary (Domestic):

BASF Fuel Cell Inc. **(2)**
39 Veronica Ave, Somerset, NJ 08873-6800
Tel.: (732) 545-5100
Web Site: http://www.basf-fuelcell.com
Sales Range: $25-49.9 Million
Emp.: 31
Fuel Cell Mfr
N.A.I.C.S.: 334413

BASF Intertrade Corporation **(2)**
1111 Bagby St Ste 2630, Houston, TX
77002-2621
Tel.: (713) 759-3070
Chemical Products Distr
N.A.I.C.S.: 424690

**BASF Polyurethanes North
America** **(2)**
106 Main St, Malcom, IA 50157
Tel.: (641) 528-3000
Web Site: http://www.polyurethanes.basf.us
Sales Range: $50-74.9 Million
Emp.: 80
Cast Elastomer Polyurethane Systems &
Polyester Polyols Mfr
N.A.I.C.S.: 325211

**BASF Venture Capital America
Inc.** **(2)**
46820 Fremont Blvd, Fremont, CA 94538
Tel.: (510) 445-6141
Investment Management Service
N.A.I.C.S.: 523999
Markus Solibieda (Mng Dir-Investment)

Subsidiary (Non-US):

BASF de Mexico S.A. de C.V. **(2)**
Insurgentes Sur 975 Col Ciudad de los De-
portes, Delegacion Benito Juarez, 03710,
Mexico, Mexico **(100%)**
Tel.: (52) 555 325 2600
Web Site: https://www.basf.com
Sales Range: $650-699.9 Million
Emp.: 250
Plastic Products, Coatings & Dispersions
Mfr
N.A.I.C.S.: 325211

Joint Venture (Domestic):

Polioles S.A. de C.V. **(3)**
Fernando Montes de Oca No 71 Col Con-
desa, Del Cuauhtemoc, 06140, Mexico, DF,
Mexico **(50%)**
Tel.: (52) 559 140 0500
Web Site: https://www.polioles.com.mx
Emp.: 360
Petrochemicals Mfr & Whslr
N.A.I.C.S.: 325110

Subsidiary (Domestic):

Mustang Property Corporation **(2)**
1535 SE 17th St 107, Fort Lauderdale, FL
33316-1737
Tel.: (954) 356-5800
Property Management Services
N.A.I.C.S.: 531312

Oliver Warehouse Inc. **(2)**
260 Mutual Ave, Winchester, KY 40391
Tel.: (859) 744-7641
Commercial Storage & Warehousing Ser-
vices
N.A.I.C.S.: 493190

ProCat Testing LLC **(2)**
30844 Century Dr, Wixom, MI 48393
Tel.: (248) 926-8200
Web Site: http://www.procat-testing.com
Emission Testing Services
N.A.I.C.S.: 541380
Ashley Barrett (Gen Mgr)

**Tradewinds Chemicals
Corporation** **(2)**
1105 N Market St, Wilmington, DE 19801-
1216
Tel.: (302) 427-0263
Emp.: 4
Chemical Products Distr
N.A.I.C.S.: 424690

Watson Bowman Acme Corp. **(2)**
95 Pineview Dr, Amherst, NY 14228
Tel.: (716) 691-7566
Web Site:
    https://www.watsonbowmanacme.com
Sales Range: $25-49.9 Million
Emp.: 100
Expansion Joint Mfr
N.A.I.C.S.: 332312

Zedx, Inc. **(2)**
369 Rolling Ridge Dr, Bellefonte, PA 16823
Tel.: (814) 357-8490
Web Site: http://www.zedxinc.com
Agricultural Business Intelligence & Informa-
tion Technology Products & Services
N.A.I.C.S.: 518210

BASF Croatia d.o.o. **(1)**
Slavonska avenija 1b, 10000, Zagreb,
Croatia **(100%)**
Tel.: (385) 16000000

Web Site: https://www.basf.com
Sales Range: $25-49.9 Million
Emp.: 10
Sales of Chemicals
N.A.I.C.S.: 325211

BASF Crop Protection Division   **(1)**
Speyerer Strasse 27, D-67117, Limburger-
hof, Germany
Tel.: (49) 621600
Web Site: http://www.agro.basf.com
Sales Range: $1-4.9 Billion
Emp.: 1,350
Holding Company; Pesticides & Other Crop
Protection Chemicals Mfr
N.A.I.C.S.: 551112
Markus Heldt *(Pres)*

Subsidiary (Non-US):

**BASF Agricultural Research Founda-
tion, Inc.**   **(2)**
Sales Range: $25-49.9 Million
Emp.: 100
Agricultural Research
N.A.I.C.S.: 541715

BASF Agro B.V. - Arnhem (NL)   **(2)**
Wddenswil Branch Steinacherstrasse 101,
Postfach 69, 8820, Wadenswil, Switzerland
Tel.: (41) 7819911
Chemical Products Mfr
N.A.I.C.S.: 325998

**BASF Agro Hellas Industrial and
Commercial S.A.**   **(2)**
449 Mesogion Avenue, 15343, Athens, Agia
Paraskevi, Greece
Tel.: (30) 2106860100
Web Site: http://www.basf.com
Sales Range: $25-49.9 Million
Emp.: 80
Chemical Products Mfr
N.A.I.C.S.: 325998

BASF Agro SAS   **(2)**
21 chemin de la Sauvegarde, 69134,
Ecully, France
Tel.: (33) 472324545
Web Site: http://www.agro.basf.fr
Emp.: 150
Agricultural Chemical Mfr
N.A.I.C.S.: 325320

Subsidiary (Domestic):

BASF Agri-Production S.A.S.   **(3)**
Port 7502 7502 route du vieux chemin de
Loon, Site Industriel Leurette, 59820, Grav-
elines, France
Tel.: (33) 328235250
Web Site: https://www.basf.com
Sales Range: $50-74.9 Million
Emp.: 140
Agricultural Product Mfr
N.A.I.C.S.: 325320

Subsidiary (Non-US):

BASF Agro, Ltd.   **(2)**
Roppongi 25 Mori Bldg 23F, 1 4 30 Rop-
pongi Minato Ku, Tokyo, 106-6121,
Japan   **(100%)**
Tel.: (81) 335869911
Web Site: http://www.basf-japan.co.jp
Sales Range: $50-74.9 Million
Emp.: 170
Mfr of Agricultural Chemicals
N.A.I.C.S.: 325998

Subsidiary (Domestic):

**BASF Plant Science Company
GmbH**   **(2)**
Speyerer Strasse 2, D-67117, Limburgerhof,
Germany   **(100%)**
Tel.: (49) 621600
Web Site: http://www.agro.basf.com
Sales Range: $75-99.9 Million
Emp.: 120
Holding Company; Nitrogenous Fertilizer &
Other Agro-Chemical Product Developer &
Mfr
N.A.I.C.S.: 551112

Subsidiary (Domestic):

BASF Plant Science GmbH   **(3)**
Speyerer Strasse 2, 67117, Limburgerhof,
Germany   **(100%)**
Tel.: (49) 621600

Web Site: http://www.agro.basf.com
Sales Range: $75-99.9 Million
Emp.: 120
Nitrogenous Fertilizer & Other Agro-
Chemical Product Developer & Mfr
N.A.I.C.S.: 325311

Subsidiary (Non-US):

DNA LandMarks Inc.   **(4)**
84 richelieu Street, Saint-Jean-sur-
Richelieu, J3B 6X3, QC, Canada
Tel.: (450) 358-2621
Web Site: http://www.dnalandmarks.ca
Emp.: 47
Assisted Breeding Services
N.A.I.C.S.: 115210

Plant Science Sweden AB   **(4)**
Herman Ehles Vag 3-4, 268 31, Svalov,
Sweden
Tel.: (46) 418 66 70 80
Agricultural Chemical Mfr
N.A.I.C.S.: 325320

Subsidiary (Domestic):

SunGene GmbH   **(4)**
Corrensstr 3, 06466, Gatersleben,
Sachsen-Anhalt, Germany
Tel.: (49) 39482 760 0
Web Site: http://www.sungene.de
Sales Range: $125-149.9 Million
Biotechnology Research & Development
Services
N.A.I.C.S.: 541714

Subsidiary (US):

BASF Plant Science LP   **(3)**
26 Davis Dr, Research Triangle Park, NC
27709   **(100%)**
Tel.: (919) 547-2000
Web Site: http://www.agproducts.basf.com
Insecticide & Other Agro-Chemical Product
Developer & Mfr
N.A.I.C.S.: 325320
Paul Rea *(VP-Ops)*

Plant (Domestic):

**BASF Agricultural Products de Puerto
Rico**   **(4)**
State Rd Ste 2 KM 47 2, Manati, PR 00674
Tel.: (787) 621-1700
Web Site: http://www.basf.us
Sales Range: $25-49.9 Million
Emp.: 200
Pesticides & Other Agricultural Products Mfr
N.A.I.C.S.: 325320

**BASF Corp. - Beaumont Agricultural
Products Plant**   **(4)**
14385 W Port Arthur Rd, Beaumont, TX
77705
Tel.: (409) 981-5000
Web Site: http://www2.basf.us
Sales Range: $25-49.9 Million
Emp.: 165
Pesticides & Other Agricultural Products Mfr
N.A.I.C.S.: 325320

**BASF Corp. - Palmyra (Hannibal) Ag-
ricultural Products Plant**   **(4)**
3150 Hwy JJ, Palmyra, MO 63461
Tel.: (573) 769-2011
Web Site: http://www2.basf.us
Sales Range: $75-99.9 Million
Emp.: 310
Pesticides & Other Agricultural Products Mfr
N.A.I.C.S.: 325320

Subsidiary (US):

Becker Underwood, Inc.   **(3)**
801 Dayton Ave, Ames, IA 50010
Tel.: (515) 232-5907
Web Site: http://www.beckerunderwood.com
Colorants & Bio-Agronomics Products Mfr &
Marketer
N.A.I.C.S.: 325320

BASF Digital Farming GmbH   **(1)**
Albrecht Thaer Str 34, 48147, Munster,
Germany
Tel.: (49) 251 987 9730
Web Site: https://www.xarvio.com
Business Services
N.A.I.C.S.: 425120
Andree-Georg Girg *(Mng Dir)*

BASF Dominicana S.A.   **(1)**
Gustavo Mejia Ricart No 11, Santo Do-
mingo, 2422, Dominican Republic
Tel.: (809) 334 1026
Web Site: http://www.basf-corp.com
Sales Range: $25-49.9 Million
Emp.: 30
Sales of Chemicals & Plastics
N.A.I.C.S.: 424690

BASF EOOD   **(1)**
Blvd Bulgaria 118 Abacus Business Center
1st Floor, 1618, Sofia, Bulgaria
Tel.: (359) 2 915 20 33
Web Site: http://www.basf.bg
Chemical Products Mfr
N.A.I.C.S.: 325998
Valentina Dikanska *(Gen Mgr)*

BASF East Africa Ltd.   **(1)**
The Pavillion 6th Floor Lower Kabete Road,
Nairobi, Kenya
Tel.: (254) 204072000
Web Site: https://www.basf.com
Chemicals Mfr
N.A.I.C.S.: 327390
Lincoln Asembo *(Country Mgr & Acct Mgr)*

**BASF East Asia Regional Headquar-
ters Ltd.**   **(1)**
45th Floor Jardine House, No 1 Connaught
Place, Central, China (Hong Kong) **(100%)**
Tel.: (852) 27310111
Web Site: http://www.basf.com
Holding Company; Regional Managing Of-
fice
N.A.I.C.S.: 551112

Subsidiary (Non-US):

**BASF Asia Pacific (India) Pvt.
Ltd.**   **(2)**
Third Floor Vibgyor Towers Unit No 305 G
Block Bandra-Kurla Complex, Mumbai, 400
051, India
Tel.: (91) 22 6661 8000
Agricultural Chemical Mfr
N.A.I.C.S.: 325320

BASF Australia Ltd.   **(2)**
Level 12 28 Freshwater Place, Southbank,
3006, VIC, Australia   **(100%)**
Tel.: (61) 388556600
Web Site: https://www.basf.com
Sales Range: $450-499.9 Million
Emp.: 500
Distr & Importer of Chemicals
N.A.I.C.S.: 424690

Subsidiary (Non-US):

BASF New Zealand Ltd.   **(3)**
Shed 5E City Works Depot 77 Cook Street,
PO Box 407, Auckland Central, Auckland,
1010, New Zealand   **(100%)**
Tel.: (64) 9 255 4300
Web Site: https://www.basf.com
Sales Range: $25-49.9 Million
Emp.: 35
Distr & Importer of Chemicals
N.A.I.C.S.: 424690

Subsidiary (Domestic):

BASF China Ltd.   **(2)**
45/F Jardine House No 1 Connaught Pl,
Central, China (Hong Kong)   **(100%)**
Tel.: (852) 27311222
Web Site: http://www.basf.com.cn
Sales Range: $100-124.9 Million
Emp.: 300
Mfr of Chemicals
N.A.I.C.S.: 325998

Subsidiary (Non-US):

BASF (China) Co., Ltd.   **(3)**
333 Jiangxinsha Road, Pudong, Shanghai,
200137, China   **(100%)**
Tel.: (86) 2120391000
Web Site: https://www.basf.com
Sales Range: $125-149.9 Million
Mfr of Chemicals
N.A.I.C.S.: 325998

Branch (Domestic):

BASF (China) Co., Ltd. - Beijing   **(4)**
15/F Beijing Sunflower Tower No 37 Maizidian St, Chaoyang District, Beijing, 100125,
China

Tel.: (86) 1065876666
Chemicals Mfr
N.A.I.C.S.: 325998

**BASF (China) Co., Ltd. -
Guangzhou**   **(4)**
Suite 2808 Dongshan Plaza 69 Xianlie
Road, 69 Xian Lie Road Central,
Guangzhou, 510095, Guangzou,
China   **(100%)**
Tel.: (86) 208 713 6000
Web Site: http://www.basfchina.com.cn
Sales Range: $75-99.9 Million
Emp.: 350
Mfr of Chemicals
N.A.I.C.S.: 325998

Subsidiary (Domestic):

**BASF Auxiliary Chemicals Co.
Ltd.**   **(4)**
300 Jiangxinsha Rd Pudong, Shanghai,
200137, China   **(100%)**
Tel.: (86) 21 3865 2000
Web Site: http://www.asiapacific.basf.com
Mfr of Organic Pigments, Textile Auxiliaries,
Leather Auxiliaries, Acrylate Dispersion &
Metal Complex Dyes
N.A.I.C.S.: 325130

**BASF Care Chemicals (Shanghai)
Co. Ltd.**   **(4)**
15/F Xinmao Mansion No 99 Tianzhou Rd,
Shanghai, 200233, China
Tel.: (86) 2161953666
Chemical Products Mfr
N.A.I.C.S.: 325998

**BASF Chemicals (Shanghai) Co.,
Ltd.**   **(4)**
20/F Harbour Ring Plaza, 18 Xizang Zhong
Road, Shanghai, 200001, China
Tel.: (86) 2123203000
Web Site: http://www.basf.com
Chemical Products Mfr
N.A.I.C.S.: 325998

**BASF Polyurethanes (China) Co.,
Ltd.**   **(4)**
Suite 2801-06 Dongshan Plaza, 69 Xian Lie
Road Central, Guangzhou, 510095, Guang-
dong, China   **(100%)**
Tel.: (86) 2087136000
Web Site: http://www.basfchina.com.cn
Sales Range: $25-49.9 Million
Emp.: 200
Polyurethane Systems, Thermoplastic Poly-
urethane Elastomers & Polyurethane Pro-
cessing Equipment & Facilities
N.A.I.C.S.: 325211

**BASF Shanghai Coatings Co.
Ltd.**   **(4)**
Chu Hua Road Shanghai Chemical Industry
Park, Jinshan, Shanghai, 201507,
China   **(60%)**
Tel.: (86) 2164895250
Sales Range: $25-49.9 Million
Emp.: 180
Mfr of Coatings & Plastic Parts
N.A.I.C.S.: 325510

Joint Venture (Domestic):

BASF-YPC Company Limited   **(4)**
No 8 East Xinhua Road, Jiangbei New
Area, Nanjing, 210048, Jiangsu,
China   **(50%)**
Tel.: (86) 2558569966
Web Site: https://www.basf-ypc.com.cn
Petrochemical Products Mfr
N.A.I.C.S.: 325110

Affiliate (Domestic):

**Shanghai BASF Polyurethane Co.,
Ltd.**   **(4)**
No 25 Chu Hua Road, Shanghai Chemical
Industry Park, Shanghai, 201507,
China   **(70%)**
Tel.: (86) 2167121199
Web Site: http://www.basf.com
Polymer Product Mfr
N.A.I.C.S.: 325211

Joint Venture (Domestic):

**Shanghai Gaoqiao BASF Dispersions
Co., Ltd.**   **(4)**
No 99 Ln 1929 Pudong Bei Road, Pudong

BASF SE—(Continued)

New Area, Shanghai, 200137, China
Tel.: (86) 2158670303
Web Site: http://www.sgbd.com.cn
Sales Range: $50-74.9 Million
Emp.: 200
Adhesive Raw Material Mfr
N.A.I.C.S.: 325520

Subsidiary (Non-US):

BASF Taiwan Ltd. (3)
16F No 87 SungJiang Road, PO Box 3134,
Taipei, 104, Taiwan (100%)
Tel.: (886) 22 518 7600
Web Site: https://www.basf.com
Sales Range: $25-49.9 Million
Emp.: 85
Mfr of Chemicals
N.A.I.C.S.: 325998

Subsidiary (Domestic):

**BASF Electronic Materials
Taiwan** (4)
33 Chin Chien 1st Rd Kuan Yin Ind, 328,
Taoyuan, Taiwan
Tel.: (886) 34837701
Web Site: http://www.basf.com
Sales Range: $25-49.9 Million
Electronic Chemical Product Mfr
N.A.I.C.S.: 325998

Subsidiary (Non-US):

BASF Company Ltd. (2)
15-16F KCCI Bldg 39 Sejong-daero, Jung-
gu, Seoul, 04513, Korea (South) (100%)
Tel.: (82) 237073100
Web Site: https://www.basf.com
Sales Range: $900-999.9 Million
Emp.: 1,100
Mfr of Plastics Materials & Basic Forms
N.A.I.C.S.: 326199
Woo-Sung Shin *(Mng Dir)*

BASF India Ltd. (2)
3rd Fl VIBGYOR unit 305 Twr Plot No C 62
G Blk Bandra-Kurla Complex, Mumbai, 400
051, India (51%)
Tel.: (91) 22 6661 8000
Web Site: http://www.asiapacific.basf.com
Sales Range: $1-4.9 Billion
Emp.: 2,000
Mfr of Styropor, Colorants, Finishing Prod-
ucts & Crop Protection Products
N.A.I.C.S.: 325998
Ramkumar Dhruva *(Pres-ASEAN, Australia,
New Zealand, South & East Asia)*

Subsidiary (Non-US):

BASF Bangladesh Limited (3)
Crystal Palace 7th Floor House 22 SE D
Road - 140, PO Box 410, Gulshan South
Avenue Gulshan - 1, Dhaka, 1212,
Bangladesh (76%)
Tel.: (880) 222281981
Web Site: https://www.basf.com
Sales Range: $25-49.9 Million
Emp.: 27
Mfr of Chemicals
N.A.I.C.S.: 325998

BASF-Lanka (Pvt.) Ltd. (3)
9th Floor Orion Tower One No 736 Dr
Danister De Silva Mawatha, Colombo, 2, Sri
Lanka
Tel.: (94) 11 242 3388
Web Site: https://www.basf.com
Sales Range: $25-49.9 Million
Emp.: 65
Chemicals & Dyes Mfr
N.A.I.C.S.: 325998

Subsidiary (Non-US):

BASF Japan Ltd. (2)
3-4-4 Nihonbashi Muromachi OVOL Nihon-
bashi Building 3rd floor, Chuo-ku, Tokyo,
103-0022, Japan (100%)
Tel.: (81) 35 290 3000
Web Site: https://www.basf.com
Sales Range: $1-4.9 Billion
Emp.: 1,600
Finishing Products, Plastics, Chemicals
N.A.I.C.S.: 325998
Joerg-Christian Steck *(Pres)*

Joint Venture (Domestic):

BASF INOAC Polyurethanes Ltd. (3)
1-196 Motomiyamichi Kawata, Shinshiro,
441-1347, Aichi, Japan
Tel.: (81) 536235511
Web Site: https://www.bip-jp.com
Sales Range: $25-49.9 Million
Emp.: 100
Polyurethane Foam System Mfr; Owned
50% by BASF Asktiengesellschaft & 50%
by Inoac Corporation
N.A.I.C.S.: 326150

BASF Idemitsu Co., Ltd. (3)
OVOL Nihonbashi Building 3F 3-4-4 Nihon-
bashi Muromachi, Chuo-ku, Tokyo, 103-
0022, Japan
Tel.: (81) 352902400
Web Site: http://www.basf.com
Emp.: 1,138
Chemical Product Mfr; Owned 50% by
BASF Aktiengellschaft & 50% by Idemitsu
Petrochemical Co., Ltd.
N.A.I.C.S.: 325998

Branch (Domestic):

BASF Japan Ltd. - Osaka (3)
1-8-15 Azuchi-machi, Chuo-ku, Osaka, 541-
0052, Japan
Tel.: (81) 6 266 6825
Web Site: https://www.basf.com
Sales Range: $25-49.9 Million
Emp.: 50
Mfr of Chemicals
N.A.I.C.S.: 325998

Joint Venture (Domestic):

NISSO BASF Agro Co., Ltd. (3)
Shinko Building 1-11-4 Kudan-Kita,
Chiyoda-ku, Tokyo, 102 0073, Japan
Tel.: (81) 332370655
Herbicide Mfr
N.A.I.C.S.: 325320

Subsidiary (Non-US):

BASF South East Asia Pte. Ltd. (2)
128 Beach Road Guoco Midtown 18-01,
35-01 Suntec Tower One, Singapore,
189773, Singapore (100%)
Tel.: (65) 63370330
Web Site: https://www.basf.com
Sales Range: $1-4.9 Billion
Emp.: 1,000
Holding Company; Regional Managing Of-
fice
N.A.I.C.S.: 551112

Subsidiary (Non-US):

BASF (Malaysia) Sdn. Bhd. (3)
No 2 Jalan Astaka U8/87 Seksyen U8, Bukit
Jelutong, 40150, Shah Alam, Selangor,
Malaysia (100%)
Tel.: (60) 356283888
Web Site: https://www.basf.com
Sales Range: $50-74.9 Million
Emp.: 120
Mfr of Chemicals
N.A.I.C.S.: 325998

Subsidiary (Domestic):

**BASF Asia-Pacific Service Centre
Sdn Bhd** (4)
Level 25 Menara TM, Jalan Pantai Baharu,
59200, Kuala Lumpur, Malaysia
Tel.: (60) 322469000
Web Site: https://www.basf.com
Finance & Accounting, Information Technol-
ogy & Human Resources Services
N.A.I.C.S.: 541611

Joint Venture (Domestic):

**BASF PETRONAS Chemicals Sdn.
Bhd.** (4)
Lot 19 01 Level 19 1powerhouse No 1 Per-
siaran Bandar Utama, Bandar Utama,
47800, Petaling Jaya, Selangor, Malaysia
Tel.: (60) 376121088
Web Site: https://www.basf-
petronas.com.my
Sales Range: $25-49.9 Million
Emp.: 48
Chemical Product Mfr; Owned 60% by
BASF Aktiengellschaft & 40% by Petro-
liam Nasional Berhad

N.A.I.C.S.: 325180

Subsidiary (Domestic):

**BASF PETRONAS Chemicals Sdn.
Bhd.** (4)
Jalan Gebeng 2/1, Kawasan Perindustrian
Gebeng, 26080, Kuantan, Pahang, Malay-
sia
Tel.: (60) 95855000
Web Site: https://www.basf-
petronas.com.my
Chemical Products Mfr
N.A.I.C.S.: 325180
Sven Crone *(Mng Dir)*

**BASF Polyurethanes (Malaysia) Sdn.
Bhd.** (4)
No 2 Jln U8 87 Seksyen U8, 40706, Shah
Alam, Selangor, Malaysia
Tel.: (60) 378473196
Polyurethane Systems Mfr
N.A.I.C.S.: 326140

Subsidiary (Non-US):

BASF (Thai) Ltd. (3)
Emporium Tower 622 23rd Floor Sukhumvit
24 Road, Klongton Kongtoey, Bangkok,
10110, Thailand (100%)
Tel.: (66) 2 624 1999
Web Site: https://www.basf.com
Sales Range: $50-74.9 Million
Emp.: 250
Mfr of Chemicals
N.A.I.C.S.: 325998

Affiliate (Non-US):

BASF See Sen Sdn. Bhd. (3)
Lot PT 3940, Kawasan Perindustrian,
24000, Kemaman, Malaysia
Tel.: (60) 98634657
Emp.: 11
Chemical Product Mfr; Owned 70% by
BASF Aktiengellschaft & 30% by See
Sen Chemical Berhad
N.A.I.C.S.: 325998

Subsidiary (Domestic):

BASF Singapore Pte. Ltd. (3)
7 Temasek Blvd, Singapore, 38987,
Singapore (100%)
Tel.: (65) 63370330
Web Site: http://www.basf.com
Sales Range: $50-74.9 Million
Emp.: 550
Marketing, Sales & Distribution of Chemi-
cals
N.A.I.C.S.: 424690

Joint Venture (Domestic):

ELLBA Eastern (Pte) Ltd. (3)
61 seraya avenue, Jurong, 627879, Singa-
pore
Tel.: (65) 63370330
Sales Range: $200-249.9 Million
Emp.: 650
Styrene Monomer & Propylene Oxide Mfr;
Owned 50% by BASF SE & 50% by Royal
Dutch Shell plc
N.A.I.C.S.: 325998

Affiliate (Domestic):

Santoku BASF Pte. Ltd. (3)
35 Tuas West Avenue, 638433, Singapore
Tel.: (65) 68631211
Sales Range: $25-49.9 Million
Emp.: 25
Chemical Products
N.A.I.C.S.: 325998
Henry Tan *(Mng Dir)*

BASF Ecuatoriana S.A. (1)
Srepublida 500 Sprabbra Edisio Bldg
Pucsre, PO Box 17013255, Quito,
Ecuador (100%)
Tel.: (593) 22541100
Web Site: http://www.basf.de
Distr of Chemicals
N.A.I.C.S.: 424690

**BASF Electronic Materials (Shanghai)
Co. Ltd.** (1)
No 16 Heng Er Road Qing Pu Export Pro-
cessing Zone, Shanghai, 201707, China
Tel.: (86) 21 5970 5700

Emp.: 60
Electronic Components Mfr
N.A.I.C.S.: 334419
John Dou *(Gen Mgr)*

BASF Electronic Materials Gmbh (1)
Carl Bosch Strasse 38, 67056, Lud-
wigshafen, Germany
Tel.: (49) 6216040228
Web Site: http://www.basf.com
Electronic & Chemicals Research, Producer
& Retailer
N.A.I.C.S.: 334419

BASF Espanola S.L. (1)
C/ Can Rabia 3-5, Apartado De Correos
762, 08017, Barcelona, Spain (100%)
Tel.: (34) 934964000
Web Site: http://www.basf.es
Sales Range: $50-74.9 Million
Emp.: 160
Chemicals, Plastics, Finishing Products Mfr;
Fertilizers & Crop Protection Products Sales
N.A.I.C.S.: 325211

Joint Venture (Domestic):

**BASF SONATRACH PropanChem
S.A.** (2)
Carretera N-340 km 1 156, Apartado de
Correos 520, 43080, Tarragona, Spain
Tel.: (34) 977256703
Web Site:
http://www.basfsonatrachpropanchem.com
Propylene & Gasoline Producer; Owned
51% by BASF Aktiengesellschaft & 49% by
SONATRACH International Holding Corpo-
ration
N.A.I.C.S.: 213112

BASF FZE (1)
Downtown Jebel Ali The Galleries Budling
4, PO Box 61309, Jebel Ali Free Zone
Sheikh Zayed Road Exit 17, 61309, Dubai,
United Arab Emirates
Tel.: (971) 48072222
Web Site: https://www.basf.com
Sales Range: $25-49.9 Million
Emp.: 60
Chemical Products Mfr
N.A.I.C.S.: 325998

BASF Finance Malta GmbH (1)
Carl-Bosch-Str 38, Ludwigshafen, 67063,
Germany
Tel.: (49) 621600
Financial Management Services
N.A.I.C.S.: 523999

BASF Food (1)
W V Ivan Vasov Balscha Str 1, 1408, Sofia,
Bulgaria
Tel.: (359) 29515958
Web Site: http://www.basf.de
Sales Range: $25-49.9 Million
Emp.: 17
Mfr of Chemicals
N.A.I.C.S.: 325998

BASF France S.A.S. (1)
49 avenue Georges Pompidou, 92593,
Levallois-Perret, Cedex, France (100%)
Tel.: (33) 149645000
Web Site: https://www.basf.com
Sales Range: $100-124.9 Million
Emp.: 160
Holding Company; Chemical Products Mfr &
Distr
N.A.I.C.S.: 551112

Subsidiary (Domestic):

**BASF Beauty Care Solutions France
SAS** (2)
49 avenue Georges Pompidou, 92593,
Levallois-Perret, Cedex, France
Tel.: (33) 149645000
Web Site:
http://www.beautycaresolutions.basf.com
Sales Range: $25-49.9 Million
Emp.: 100
Cosmetic & Personal Care Biotechnology
Research, Development & Materials Mfr
N.A.I.C.S.: 325199

Plant (Domestic):

**BASF Beauty Care Solutions France
SAS - Lyon** (3)

32 rue Saint-Jean de Dieu, 69007, Lyon, France
Tel.: (33) 472766000
Web Site: https://www.basf.com
Sales Range: $50-74.9 Million
Cosmetic & Personal Care Biotechnology Research, Development & Materials Mfr
N.A.I.C.S.: 325199

Subsidiary (US):

BASF Beauty Care Solutions LLC (3)
50 Health Sciences Dr, Stony Brook, NY 11790
Tel.: (631) 689-0200
Web Site:
http://www.beautycaresolutions.basf.com
Sales Range: $25-49.9 Million
Emp.: 100
Cosmetic & Personal Care Biotechnology Research, Development & Materials Mfr
N.A.I.C.S.: 325199

Subsidiary (Domestic):

BASF Health and Care Products France S.A.S. (2)
Usine d'Estarac, 31360, Boussens, France
Tel.: (33) 561984360
Sales Range: $25-49.9 Million
Emp.: 90
Health Care Products Mfr
N.A.I.C.S.: 325412

BASF Performance Products France SA (2)
28 rue de la Chapelle, BP 151, 68331, Huningue, France (100%)
Tel.: (33) 3 8989 5959
Web Site: http://www.basf.fr
Inorganic Pigments Mfr & Whslr
N.A.I.C.S.: 325130
Olivier Ubrich (Mng Dir)

Plant (Domestic):

BASF Performance Products France - Gron Plant (3)
Zone Industrielle 9 Rue des Salcys, F-89100, Gron, France
Tel.: (33) 386652525
Chemicals Mfr
N.A.I.C.S.: 325998

Subsidiary (Domestic):

Societe Fonciere et Industrielle S.A.S. (2)
Zone Industrielle de Breuil le Sec, 60676, Clermont, 60676, France
Tel.: (33) 344777777
Web Site: http://www.basf.com
Sales Range: $100-124.9 Million
Chemical Products Mfr
N.A.I.C.S.: 325998

BASF Future Business GmbH (1)
Benckiserplatz 1, Ludwigshafen, 67059, Germany
Tel.: (49) 6216076811
Web Site: http://www.basf-fb.de
Sales Range: $1-9.9 Million
Emp.: 5
Energy Management, Electronics & Technology System Developer
N.A.I.C.S.: 541715
Stefan Blank (Sr VP Intermediates)

BASF Gastronomie GmbH (1)
Anilinstrasse 12, 67063, Ludwigshafen, Germany
Tel.: (49) 6216094243
Web Site: http://www.gastronomie.basf.de
Chemicals Mfr
N.A.I.C.S.: 325180

BASF Grenzach GmbH (1)
Kochlinstrasse 1, 79639, Grenzach-Wyhlen, Germany (100%)
Tel.: (49) 7624120
Web Site: https://www.basf.com
Chemicals Developer & Mfr
N.A.I.C.S.: 325998

BASF HOCK Mining Chemical (China) Company Ltd. (1)
South of Ershilipu Village Huangtun Town High and New Technology Zone, Jining, 272104, Shandong, China

Tel.: (86) 5373713668
Chemicals Mfr
N.A.I.C.S.: 325199

BASF Hellas Industrial and Commercial S.A. (1)
449 Mesogeion Ave, Agia Paraskevi, 15343, Athens, Greece
Tel.: (30) 210 6860 212
Emp.: 75
Specialty Chemicals Mfr
N.A.I.C.S.: 325998
Hidetaka Kai (Mgr-IT)

BASF Hellas S.A. (1)
449 Mesogion Avenue, Agia Paraskevi, 15343, Athens, Greece
Tel.: (30) 210 68 60 100
Web Site: http://www.agro.basf.gr
Agricultural Chemical Mfr
N.A.I.C.S.: 325320

BASF Holdings South Africa (Pty.) Ltd. (1)
Tel.: (27) 112032400
Web Site: https://www.basf.com
Sales Range: $50-74.9 Million
Emp.: 10
Investment Management Service
N.A.I.C.S.: 523999

BASF Hong Kong Ltd. (1)
Unit 2 20 F EW International Tower 120 124 Texaco Road, Tsuen Wan, China (Hong Kong)
Tel.: (852) 24084400
Chemicals Mfr
N.A.I.C.S.: 325199
Anthony M. Tang (Acct Mgr-Construction Sys)

BASF Hungaria Kft. (1)
Vaci ut 96-98, Pest County, 1132, Budapest, Hungary (100%)
Tel.: (36) 12509700
Web Site: https://www.basf.com
Sales Range: $25-49.9 Million
Emp.: 35
Wholesale of Chemical Products
N.A.I.C.S.: 424690

BASF IT Services Holding GmbH (1)
Jaegerstrasse 1, 67059, Ludwigshafen, 67059, Germany
Tel.: (49) 621 60 99550
Web Site:
http://www.information-services.basf.com
Rev.: $635,588,590
Investment Management Service
N.A.I.C.S.: 523999

Subsidiary (Domestic):

BASF IT Services GmbH (2)
Jaegerstrasse 1, 67059, Ludwigshafen, Germany (100%)
Tel.: (49) 216058497
Web Site: http://www.information-services.basf.com
Sales Range: $350-399.9 Million
Emp.: 2,400
Information Technology Support Services
N.A.I.C.S.: 541513

Subsidiary (Domestic):

BASF IT Services Consult GmbH (3)
Christoph-Probst-Weg 3, 20251, Hamburg, Germany
Tel.: (49) 40 41000 0
Web Site: http://www.basf.com
Information Technology Consulting Services
N.A.I.C.S.: 541512

Subsidiary (Non-US):

BASF IT Services Holding Ltd. (3)
Cheadle Hulme Earl Road, Cheadle, SK8 6QG, United Kingdom
Tel.: (44) 161 485 6222
Web Site: http://www.basf.com
Investment Management Service
N.A.I.C.S.: 523999

BASF IT Services Ltd. (3)
Malmparken 5, 2750, Ballerup, Denmark
Tel.: (45) 44730100
Web Site: http://www.information-services.basf.com

Sales Range: $25-49.9 Million
Emp.: 160
Information Technology Support Services
N.A.I.C.S.: 541513

BASF IT Services N.V./S.A. (3)
Haven 725 Scheldelaan 600, Antwerp, 2040, Belgium (100%)
Tel.: (32) 35613710
Web Site: http://www.basf.be
Information Technology Support Services
N.A.I.C.S.: 541513

Branch (Non-US):

BASF IT Services N.V./S.A. - France (4)
49 Avenue Georges Pompidou, 92593, Levallois-Perret, France (100%)
Tel.: (33) 49645164
Web Site: http://www.information-services.basf.com
Information Technology Support Services
N.A.I.C.S.: 541513

Subsidiary (Non-US):

BASF IT Services S.A. (3)
Crta N-340 Km 1 156, 43006, Tarragona, Spain
Tel.: (34) 977 256 200
Information Technology Consulting Services
N.A.I.C.S.: 541512

BASF IT Services S.p.A. (3)
Via Marconato 8, 20031, Cesano Maderno, MI, Italy (100%)
Tel.: (39) 03625121
Web Site: http://www.information-services.basf.com
Information Technology Support Services
N.A.I.C.S.: 541513

BASF Immobilien Pigment GmbH (1)
Carl-Bosch-Str 38, Ludwigshafen, 67063, Germany
Tel.: (49) 621600
Web Site: http://www.basf.com
Chemical Products Mfr
N.A.I.C.S.: 325998

BASF Immobilien-Gesellschaft mbH (1)
Carl-Bosch-Str 38, 67063, Ludwigshafen, Rheinland-Pfalz, Germany
Tel.: (49) 621 60 0
Property Management Services
N.A.I.C.S.: 531311

BASF Industrial Metals LLC (1)
Kadashevskaya Nab 14/3, 119017, Moscow, Russia
Tel.: (7) 495 225 6490
Sales Range: $25-49.9 Million
Emp.: 1
Industrial Chemicals Mfr
N.A.I.C.S.: 325998
Victor Nikitin (Gen Dir)

BASF Innovationsfonds GmbH (1)
4 Gartenweg 7a Z 34, 67063, Ludwigshafen, Germany
Emp.: 14
Research & Development Services
N.A.I.C.S.: 541715

BASF Interservicios S.A. de C.V. (1)
Av Insurgentes Sur 975 Cd de los Deportes Benito Juarez, Mexico, 3710, Mexico
Tel.: (52) 5553252600
Web Site: http://www.basfmexicana.com
Business Management Consulting Services
N.A.I.C.S.: 541611
Michael Stuntt (Pres)

BASF Iran (PJS) Co. (1)
Sohrevardi Shomali Ave Kangavar Alley-No 5 15579, 11365-4619, Tehran, Iran
Tel.: (98) 2188768237
Chemical Product Mfr & Distr
N.A.I.C.S.: 325998

BASF Iran AG (1)
Sohrevardi Shomali Ave Kangavar Aly No 5, Tehran, 15579, Iran (100%)
Tel.: (98) 218768237
Web Site: http://www.basf.de
Distr of Chemicals
N.A.I.C.S.: 424690

BASF Ireland DAC (1)
Inchera Industrial Estate Inchera, Little Island, Cork, T45 XY62, Ireland
Tel.: (353) 214517100
Plastic Material Mfr & Distr
N.A.I.C.S.: 325211

BASF Ireland Limited (1)
Inchera Industrial Estate, Inchera, Little Island, T45 XY62, Cork, Ireland
Tel.: (353) 21 451 7100
Web Site: https://www.basf.com
Sales Range: $50-74.9 Million
Emp.: 120
Mining Chemical Mfr
N.A.I.C.S.: 325998
Enda Quigley (Mng Dir)

BASF Italia S.p.A. (1)
Via Marconato 8, 20811, Cesano Maderno, MB, Italy (100%)
Tel.: (39) 03625121
Web Site: https://www.basf.com
Sales Range: $250-299.9 Million
Emp.: 1,200
Mfr & Sales of Dyestuffs & Finishing Products
N.A.I.C.S.: 424690

Subsidiary (Domestic):

BASF Coatings Services Italy Srl (2)
Via Padule 40, Scandicci, 50018, Florence, Italy
Tel.: (39) 0557350121
Web Site: http://www.europebasf.com
Emp.: 22
Automotive Coating Distr
N.A.I.C.S.: 424950

BASF Interservice Spa (2)
Via Marconato 8, 20031, Cesano Maderno, MI, Italy
Tel.: (39) 03625121
Web Site: http://www.basf.it
Chemical Products Mfr
N.A.I.C.S.: 325998

Unit (Domestic):

BASF Italia - Centro Cuoio (2)
Via Montorso 35, Vicenza, 36071, VI, Italy
Tel.: (39) 0444485311
Web Site: http://www.basf.com
Chemical Products Mfr
N.A.I.C.S.: 325998

BASF Italia - Centro Ricerca e Sviluppo (2)
Servizio Tecnico, Via Quarantola 40, 48022, Lugo di Romagna, RA, Italy
Tel.: (39) 054524110
Web Site: http://www.agro.basf.it
Sales Range: $25-49.9 Million
Emp.: 12
Chemical Products Mfr
N.A.I.C.S.: 325998

BASF Italia - Espansi (2)
Via Montesanto 46, Bibbiano, 42021, Italy
Tel.: (39) 0522251011
Web Site: http://www.basf.it
Emp.: 30
Chemical Products Mfr
N.A.I.C.S.: 325998

BASF Italia - Nutrizione Animale (2)
Via Leonardo da Vinci 2, 24040, Bergamo, BG, Italy
Tel.: (39) 035 45580 11
Animal Nutrition Products & Services
N.A.I.C.S.: 812910

BASF Jobmarkt GmbH (1)
Web Site: http://www.deutschland.basf.com
Employment Placement Services
N.A.I.C.S.: 561311

BASF Kanoo Gulf FZE (1)
Jevel Ali Free Zone, PO Box 61309, Dubai, United Arab Emirates (100%)
Tel.: (971) 48838773
Web Site: http://www.basf.ae
Sales Range: $50-74.9 Million
Emp.: 75
Distr of Chemicals
N.A.I.C.S.: 424690

BASF Kanoo Polyurethanes LLC (1)
Dubai Industrial City 3, 490001, Dubai, United Arab Emirates

BASF SE—(Continued)
Tel.: (971) 44470807
Polyurethane Products Mfr
N.A.I.C.S.: 325211

BASF Kaspian Yapi kimyasallari Sanayi mehud mesuliyyetli cemiyyeti (1)
H Zeynalabdin Tagiyev Settlement, 5022, Sumgayit, Azerbaijan
Tel.: (994) 124187950
Construction Materials Distr
N.A.I.C.S.: 423390

BASF Lampertheim GmbH (1)
Chemiestrasse 22, 68623, Lampertheim, Germany (100%)
Tel.: (49) 6206150
Web Site: https://www.basf.com
Sales Range: $250-299.9 Million
Emp.: 1,000
Chemicals Developer, Mfr & Whslr
N.A.I.C.S.: 325998

BASF Leuna GmbH (1)
Am Haupttor Bau 7302, 06237, Leuna, Germany
Tel.: (49) 341433872
Web Site: http://www.basf-leuna.de
Sales Range: $1-9.9 Million
Emp.: 140
Chemical Products Mfr
N.A.I.C.S.: 325998

BASF Lizenz GmbH (1)
Carl-Bosch-Str 38, Ludwigshafen, 67063, Germany
Tel.: (49) 621600
Web Site: http://www.basf.com
Asset Management Services
N.A.I.C.S.: 523940

BASF Logistics GmbH (1)
J 542 Carl Bosch Strasse 38, 67056, Ludwigshafen, Germany
Tel.: (49) 6216046900
Logistic Services
N.A.I.C.S.: 541614

BASF Ltd. (1)
Building A1 Business Park A, Cairo Festival City, 11431, New Cairo, Egypt (100%)
Tel.: (20) 225980800
Web Site: https://www.basf.com
Emp.: 60
Chemical Products Distr
N.A.I.C.S.: 424690

BASF Ludwigshafen Grundbesitz SE & Co. KG (1)
Carl-Bosch-Str 38, 67063, Ludwigshafen, Rheinland-Pfalz, Germany
Tel.: (49) 621 6048661
Web Site: http://www.basf.com
Emp.: 3,100
Management Consulting Services
N.A.I.C.S.: 541618

BASF Maroc S.A. (1)
7 Allee des Orchidees, PO Box 2509, Ain Sebaa, 20250, Casablanca, Morocco (100%)
Tel.: (212) 522669400
Web Site: https://www.basf.com
Sales Range: $25-49.9 Million
Emp.: 50
Distr of Chemicals, Plastic Products & Colorants for Industry & Agriculture
N.A.I.C.S.: 424690

BASF Metal Forwards Limited (1)
21st Floor 110 Bishopsgate, London, EC2N 4AY, United Kingdom
Tel.: (44) 2073982500
Emp.: 25
Commodity Contract & Brokerage Services
N.A.I.C.S.: 523160
Clive Stocker (Gen Mgr)

BASF Metals (Shanghai) Co. Ltd. (1)
239 Luqiao Road Jinqiao Export Processing Zone, Shanghai, 201206, China
Tel.: (86) 21 6109 1885
Metal Product Distr
N.A.I.C.S.: 423510
Frank Ni (Mgr-Comml)

BASF Metals GmbH (1)
Grafenauweg 6, 6300, Zug, Switzerland

Tel.: (41) 41 710 82 77
Web Site: http://www.basf.com
Sales Range: $25-49.9 Million
Emp.: 5
Industrial Chemicals Mfr
N.A.I.C.S.: 325998

BASF Metals Japan Ltd. (1)
World Trade Center Bldg 24F 2-4-1 Hamamatsu-cho, Minato-ku, Tokyo, 105-6124, Japan
Tel.: (81) 3 3578 6661
Sales Range: $25-49.9 Million
Emp.: 10
Industrial Chemicals Mfr
N.A.I.C.S.: 325998

BASF Metals Ltd. (1)
21st Floor Bishopsgate, London, EC2N 4AY, United Kingdom
Tel.: (44) 2073982500
Chemical Products Mfr
N.A.I.C.S.: 325998
Lisa Wood (Ops Mgr)

BASF Metals Recycling Ltd. (1)
Forest Vale Road, Cinderford, GL14 2PH, Gloucestershire, United Kingdom
Tel.: (44) 1594827744
Web Site: https://www.basf.com
Sales Range: $25-49.9 Million
Emp.: 7
Metal Scrap Recycling Services
N.A.I.C.S.: 562920

BASF Metasheen (1)
2 Air Care Drive, PO Box 1347, Smiths Falls, K7A 5C7, ON, Canada
Tel.: (613) 283-4400
Specialty Chemicals Distr
N.A.I.C.S.: 424690

BASF Mexicana, S.A. de C.V. (1)
Av Insurgentes Sur 975, Col Ciudad de los Deportes, 03710, Mexico, Mexico
Tel.: (52) 553252600
Web Site: https://www.basf.com
Chemicals Mfr
N.A.I.C.S.: 325199

BASF Middle East Chemicals LLC (1)
Building B 05 Siemens Building Opp Presidential Flight, Masdar City, Abu Dhabi, United Arab Emirates
Tel.: (971) 28119327
Chemicals Mfr
N.A.I.C.S.: 327390
Jens Rudolph (Mng Dir)

BASF Mobilienleasing GmbH (1)
Carl-Bosch-Str 38, Ludwigshafen, 67063, Germany
Tel.: (49) 6216099911
Chemical Products Mfr
N.A.I.C.S.: 325998

BASF Nederland B.V. (1)
(100%)
Tel.: (31) 263717171
Web Site: http://www.basf.nl
Chemical Product Mfr, Facility Management & Communications
N.A.I.C.S.: 325998

BASF Nederland B.V. (1)
Groningensingel 1, 6835 EA, Arnhem, Netherlands (100%)
Tel.: (31) 513619619
Web Site: http://www.basf.nl
Sales Range: $200-249.9 Million
Emp.: 673
Chemical Sales & Administrative Services
N.A.I.C.S.: 325998

Subsidiary (Domestic):

BASF Finance Europe N.V. (2)
Rijnkade 155, NL 6811 HD, Arnhem, Netherlands (100%)
Tel.: (31) 264456856
Web Site: http://www.basf.nl
Financial Services of Chemicals
N.A.I.C.S.: 325998

Subsidiary (Non-US):

BASF Minerals Oy (2)
Tammasaarenkatu 3, 1800, Helsinki, Finland
Tel.: (358) 9615981

Sales Range: $25-49.9 Million
Emp.: 5
Processed Kaolin Distr
N.A.I.C.S.: 423320
Mika Laukkanen (Mgr-Sls)

Subsidiary (Domestic):

BASF Operations B.V. (2)
Groningensingel 1, Arnhem, 6835 EA, Gelderland, Netherlands
Tel.: (31) 263717171
Web Site: http://www.basf.com
Emp.: 100
Chemical Products Mfr
N.A.I.C.S.: 325998

BASF New Business GmbH (1)
Benckiserplatz 1 BE01, 67059, Ludwigshafen, Germany
Tel.: (49) 6216076811
Investment Services
N.A.I.C.S.: 523999
Holger Schneider (Sr Mgr-Tech)

BASF Nutrition Animale (1)
Zone Industrielle de Bellitourne-Aze, 53200, Chateau-Gontier, France
Tel.: (33) 243074226
Web Site: http://www.basf.com
Animal Health & Nutrition Services
N.A.I.C.S.: 812910

BASF Osterreich GmbH (1)
Handelskai 94 - 96, 1200, Vienna, Austria (100%)
Tel.: (43) 1878900
Web Site: https://www.basf.com
Sales Range: $25-49.9 Million
Emp.: 175
Chemical Products Mfr
N.A.I.C.S.: 325998

BASF Oy (1)
Tammasaarenkatu 3, 00180, Helsinki, Finland (100%)
Tel.: (358) 9615981
Sales Range: $25-49.9 Million
Emp.: 30
Chemical Sales
N.A.I.C.S.: 424690

Division (Domestic):

BASF Oy - Wolman Division (2)
Patosillantie, Box 112, 45701, Kuusankoski, Finland
Tel.: (358) 5 311 0420
Web Site: http://www.basf.fi
Emp.: 1
Wood Preservative Mfr
N.A.I.C.S.: 325998

Subsidiary (Domestic):

Oy Mercantile Ab (2)
Kalevankatu 4, PO Box 301, 00101, Helsinki, Finland
Tel.: (358) 95 654 9301
Web Site: https://www.mercantile.fi
Sales Range: $10-24.9 Million
Chemical Products Mfr
N.A.I.C.S.: 325998

BASF Panama S.A. (1)
Calle 50 Torre Credicorp Bank, Corregimiento de San Francisco, Panama, Panama (100%)
Tel.: (507) 2100050
Sales Range: $50-74.9 Million
Emp.: 5
Sales of Chemicals
N.A.I.C.S.: 424690

BASF Paper Chemicals (Jiangsu) Co. Ltd. (1)
No 1 Ganghan Rd Dagang New Zone, Zhenjiang, 212132, Jiangsu, China
Tel.: (86) 51183121121
Chemical Products Mfr
N.A.I.C.S.: 325998

BASF Paraguaya S.A. (1)
Independencia Nacional No 811, Productor Piso 12, 3064, Asuncion, Casilla de Correo, Paraguay (100%)
Tel.: (595) 21498401
Sales Range: $10-24.9 Million
Emp.: 23
Chemical & Agricultural Products Whslr
N.A.I.C.S.: 424690

BASF Performance Polyamides Korea Co., Ltd. (1)
160 Gongdan-ro Onsan-eup, Ulju-gun, Ulsan, 45010, Korea (South)
Tel.: (82) 522310800
Plastic Material Mfr & Distr
N.A.I.C.S.: 325211

BASF Performance Polymers Gmbl l (1)
Breitscheidstr 137, 07407, Erfurt, Germany
Tel.: (49) 36723700
Web Site: http://www.basf.com
Sales Range: $75-99.9 Million
Emp.: 170
Polymer Product Mfr
N.A.I.C.S.: 326140

BASF Performance Products GmbH (1)
Roseggerstrasse 101, 8670, Krieglach, Austria
Tel.: (43) 3855 2371 0
Web Site: http://www.master-builders-solutions.basf.at
Construction Chemical Mfr & Distr
N.A.I.C.S.: 325998
Thomas Strobl (Mgr-Technical)

BASF Performance Products Ltd. (1)
18 Floor Xin An Building 1599 Tian Zhou Road, Caohejing Hi-Tech Park, Shanghai, 200233, China
Tel.: (86) 21 2403 2000
Chemical Products Mfr
N.A.I.C.S.: 325998

BASF Personal Care and Nutrition GmbH (1)
Rheinpromenade 1, 40789, Monheim, Germany
Tel.: (49) 217349950
Web Site: https://www.personal-care.basf.com
Personal Care Product Mfr
N.A.I.C.S.: 325620

BASF Peruana S.A. (1)
Av Oscar R Benavides No 5915 Callao, PO Box 3911, Lima, Peru (100%)
Tel.: (51) 1 513 2500
Web Site: http://www.basf.com.pe
Sales Range: $50-74.9 Million
Emp.: 160
Mfr of Chemicals, Animal Nutrition, Dispersions for Paint & Paper
N.A.I.C.S.: 325998

BASF Philippines, Inc. (1)
Main Ofc & Plant ED Carmelray Industrial Pk 1, Calamba, 4028, Philippines (100%)
Tel.: (63) 495490001
Web Site: http://www.basf.com.sg
Sales Range: $75-99.9 Million
Emp.: 150
Distr of Chemicals
N.A.I.C.S.: 424690

BASF Pigment GmbH (1)
Gustav-Siegle-Strasse 19, 74354, Besigheim, Germany (100%)
Tel.: (49) 71438080
Web Site: http://www.basf.com
Sales Range: $1-9.9 Million
Emp.: 220
Chemical Products Mfr
N.A.I.C.S.: 325998

BASF Plastic Additives Middle East S.P.C. (1)
Building 1420 Road 1518 R 1510 Block 115, 1510 Block 115, Hidd, 50993, Bahrain
Tel.: (973) 17 585 252
Web Site: http://www.basf.com
Emp.: 3
Plastic Additive Mfr
N.A.I.C.S.: 326199

BASF Polska Sp. z o o (1)
Al Jerozolimskie 142B, 02-305, Warsaw, Poland (100%)
Tel.: (48) 225709999
Web Site: https://www.basf.com
Sales Range: $50-74.9 Million
Emp.: 500
Mfr of Chemicals
N.A.I.C.S.: 325998
Andres Gietl (Pres)

BASF Polyurethane Specialties (China) Co. Ltd. (1)
2333 Gang Cheng Road, Pudong, Shanghai, 200137, China
Tel.: (86) 21 3865 2000
Chemical Products Mfr
N.A.I.C.S.: 325998

BASF Polyurethanes GmbH (1)
Elastogranstrasse 60, 49448, Lemforde, Germany
Tel.: (49) 5443120
Web Site: http://www.polyurethanes.basf.de
Polyurethane Material Mfr & Distr
N.A.I.C.S.: 326150

Subsidiary (Non-US):

BASF Poliuretani Italia SpA (2)
Strada Per Poirino 38, 14019, Villanova d'Asti, Asti, Italy
Tel.: (39) 0141 949 111
Web Site: http://www.polyurethanes.basf.de
Chemical Products Mfr
N.A.I.C.S.: 325998

BASF Poliuretany Polska Sp. z o.o. (2)
Ul Wiosenna 9, 63-100, Srem, Poland
Tel.: (48) 61 636 63 66
Sales Range: $25-49.9 Million
Emp.: 21
Polyurethane Material Mfr
N.A.I.C.S.: 326150
Slawomir Gorski (Mng Dir)

Subsidiary (Domestic):

BASF Polyurethane Licensing GmbH (2)
Elastogranstr 60, 49448, Lemforde, Germany
Tel.: (49) 5443120
Web Site: http://www.pu.basf.de
Emp.: 1,000
Chemical Products Mfr
N.A.I.C.S.: 325998

Subsidiary (Non-US):

BASF Polyurethanes (Chongqing) Co. Ltd. (1)
No 1 Huabei Second Rd Changshou Economic, Technology Development Zone, Chongqing, 401221, China
Tel.: (86) 2386626666
Chemical Products Mfr
N.A.I.C.S.: 325998
Christian Tragut (Gen Mgr)

BASF Polyurethanes Benelux B.V. (2)
Hemelrijk 11-13, 5281 PS, Boxtel, Netherlands
Tel.: (31) 411 615 615
Web Site: http://www.polyurethanes.basf.eu
Sales Range: $25-49.9 Million
Emp.: 3
Chemical Products Mfr
N.A.I.C.S.: 325998

BASF Polyurethanes France S.A.S. (2)
ZI Rue Decauville, 77292, Mitry-Mory, France
Tel.: (33) 16021 4249
Web Site: http://www.pu.basf.de
Sales Range: $25-49.9 Million
Emp.: 55
Polyurethane Material Mfr
N.A.I.C.S.: 326150
Olivier Ubrich (Pres)

BASF Polyurethanes Nordic AB (2)
Angeredsvinkeln 5, 42467, Angered, Sweden
Tel.: (46) 31 330 0050
Web Site: http://www.elastogran.se
Emp.: 23
Chemical Products Mfr
N.A.I.C.S.: 325998
Ake Lundberg (Mng Dir)

BASF Polyurethanes Pars (Private Joint Stock) Company (2)
Sohrevardi Shomali Avenue Kangavar Alley No 5, Tehran, 15579, Iran
Tel.: (98) 2188747571
Polyurethane Material Mfr & Distr
N.A.I.C.S.: 326150

BASF Polyurethanes South Africa (Pty.) Ltd. (2)
Evergreen Road Tunney Ext 7 Greenhills, PO Box 1449, Elandsfontein, Johannesburg, 1610, South Africa
Tel.: (27) 114377600
Sales Range: $25-49.9 Million
Emp.: 54
Polyurethane Material Distr
N.A.I.C.S.: 424610

BASF Polyurethanes U.K. Ltd. (2)
Wimsey Way, Somercotes, Alfreton, DE55 4NL, Derbyshire, United Kingdom
Tel.: (44) 177360 7161
Polyurethane Material Mfr & Distr
N.A.I.C.S.: 326150

BASF Portuguesa, Lda. (1)
Rua 25 De Abril 1, Prior Velho, 2685-368, Prior Velho, Portugal (100%)
Tel.: (351) 219499900
Web Site: http://www.basf-cc.pt
Sales Range: $25-49.9 Million
Emp.: 30
Chemical Sales
N.A.I.C.S.: 424690
Anabela Sousa (Sec)

BASF Pozzolith Ltd. (1)
Roppongi Hills Mori Tower 21F 6-10-1 Roppongi, Minato-ku, Tokyo, 106-6121, Japan
Tel.: (81) 3 3796 9710
Web Site: http://www.japan.basf.com
Construction Materials Distr
N.A.I.C.S.: 423390

BASF Process Catalysts GmbH (1)
Grosse Drakenburger Strasse 93-97, 31582, Nienburg, Germany
Tel.: (49) 502186530
Chemical Product Mfr & Distr
N.A.I.C.S.: 325998

BASF Properties Inc. (1)
345 Carlingview Dr, Etobicoke, M9W 6N9, ON, Canada
Tel.: (416) 675-3611
Property Management Services
N.A.I.C.S.: 531311

BASF Qtech Inc. (1)
100 Milverton Drive 5th Floor, Mississauga, L5R 4H1, ON, Canada
Tel.: (732) 205-7620
Web Site: http://www.basf-qtech.com
Catalytic Surface Coating Mfr
N.A.I.C.S.: 325510

BASF Quimica Colombiana S.A. (1)
Calle 99 69 C-32, Bogota, Colombia (100%)
Tel.: (57) 16322260
Web Site: https://www.basf.com
Chemicals, Polyester Resins, Finishing Products, Crop Protection Products & Animal Nutrition Products Mfr & Distr
N.A.I.C.S.: 424690

BASF Renewable Energy GmbH (1)
Benckiserplatz 1, 67056, Ludwigshafen, Germany
Tel.: (49) 6216046375
Electricity Energy Distr
N.A.I.C.S.: 423610

BASF Representation Belarus (1)
Pr Pobeditelej 5, 220004, Minsk, Belarus
Tel.: (375) 17 203 9024
Chemical Products Mfr
N.A.I.C.S.: 325998

BASF S.A. (1)
Av Angelo Demarchi 123, 09851-550, Sao Bernardo do Campo, SP, Brazil (100%)
Tel.: (55) 112 349 1122
Web Site: https://www.basf.com.br
Sales Range: $1-4.9 Billion
Emp.: 3,700
Chemicals, Colorants, Finishing Products, Coatings & Paints, Crop Protection Products & Styropor Mfr & Whslr
N.A.I.C.S.: 325998

Subsidiary (Domestic):

BASF Poliuretanos Ltda. (2)
Av Papa Joao XXIII 4800, 09370-904, Maua, SP, Brazil
Tel.: (55) 1145427200
Web Site: http://www.basf.com.br

Sales Range: $100-124.9 Million
Emp.: 300
Chemical Products Mfr
N.A.I.C.S.: 325998

BASF SA (2)
Av Angelo Demarchi 123, Caixa Postal 340, 09844-900, Sao Bernardo do Campo, SP, Brazil (100%)
Tel.: (55) 11 4347 1122
Web Site: http://www.basf.com.br
Mfr of Coatings
N.A.I.C.S.: 325510

BASF S.p.A. (1)
13 Rue Arezki Abri Ugra, 16035, Hydra, Algeria (100%)
Tel.: (213) 21603493
Web Site: http://www.basfsafrica.co.za
Sales Range: $25-49.9 Million
Emp.: 20
Distr of Chemicals
N.A.I.C.S.: 424690

BASF S.r.l. (1)
Soseaua Pipera nr 43 Cladirea A Etaj 1 Sector 2, 014254, Bucharest, Romania
Tel.: (40) 215299000
Web Site: https://www.basf.com
Sales Range: $50-74.9 Million
Emp.: 80
Sales of Chemicals
N.A.I.C.S.: 424690
Luminita Teodorescu (Gen Mgr)

BASF SE - Laenderbereich Vertrieb Europe (1)
Benckiserplatz 1, 67056, Ludwigshafen, Germany
Tel.: (49) 621600
Sales of Chemicals
N.A.I.C.S.: 424690

BASF Saudi Arabia Limited Company (1)
Al-Othman Office Tower Floor 14 King Saud Road, Dhahran, Saudi Arabia
Tel.: (966) 138538734
Web Site: https://www.basf.com
Chemicals Whslr
N.A.I.C.S.: 424690
Ahmad Attea (Mgr-Sys)

BASF Services (Malaysia) Sdn. Bhd. (1)
Jalan Gebeng 2/1 Kawasan Perindustrian Gebeng, 26080, Kuantan, Pahang, Malaysia
Tel.: (60) 95857000
Web Site: https://www.basf.com
Emp.: 3
Chemical Products Mfr
N.A.I.C.S.: 325998

BASF Services Europe GmbH (1)
Rotherstrasse 11, 10245, Berlin, Germany
Tel.: (49) 3020055000
Web Site: http://www.basf-services-europe.com
Sales Range: $25-49.9 Million
Emp.: 100
Finance & Accounting & Human Resources Services
N.A.I.C.S.: 541612

BASF Slovenija d.o.o. (1)
Dunajska cesta 165, 1000, Ljubljana, Slovenia (100%)
Tel.: (386) 15897500
Web Site: https://www.basf.com
Sales Range: $25-49.9 Million
Emp.: 17
Sales of Chemicals
N.A.I.C.S.: 424690

BASF Slovensko s.r.o. (1)
Einsteinova 23, 85101, Bratislava, Slovakia (100%)
Tel.: (421) 25 826 6111
Web Site: https://www.basf.com
Emp.: 130
Sales of Chemicals & Agricultural Chemicals & Plastics
N.A.I.C.S.: 424690

BASF South Africa (Pty.) Ltd. (1)
852 Sixteenth Road, Midrand, 1685, South Africa (100%)
Tel.: (27) 112032400
Web Site: https://www.basf.com

Sales Range: $75-99.9 Million
Emp.: 130
Distr & Importer of Chemicals
N.A.I.C.S.: 424690
Benoit Fricard (Mng Dir & Head)

Subsidiary (Domestic):

BASF Construction Chemicals South Africa (Pty) Ltd. (2)
852 16th Road, Midrand, 1685, South Africa
Tel.: (27) 11 203 2405
Web Site: http://www.basf-cc.co.za
Emp.: 70
Construction Chemical Distr
N.A.I.C.S.: 424690

BASF Srbija d.o.o. (1)
Omladinskih brigada 90b, 11070, Novi Beograd, Serbia (100%)
Tel.: (381) 113093410
Web Site: https://www.basf.com
Sales Range: $25-49.9 Million
Emp.: 24
Chemicals Whslr
N.A.I.C.S.: 424690
Michael Nan (Mng Dir)

BASF Stavebni hmoty Ceska republika s.r.o. (1)
K Majovu 1244, 537 01, Chrudim, Czech Republic
Tel.: (420) 469607111
Web Site: http://www.basf-cc.cz
Emp.: 200
Construction Chemical Mfr & Distr
N.A.I.C.S.: 325998

BASF Suisse S.A. (1)
Case postale 448, 1870, Monthey, Switzerland
Tel.: (41) 244744111
Electronic Material Mfr & Distr
N.A.I.C.S.: 334419

BASF Taiwan B.V. (1)
Groningensingel 1, Arnhem, 6835 EA, Gelderland, Netherlands
Tel.: (31) 263717171
Web Site: http://www.basf.com
Emp.: 100
Chemical Products Mfr
N.A.I.C.S.: 325998
Herbert Fisch (Mng Dir)

BASF Trading Egypt S.A.E. (1)
Business Park A Building A1, Cairo Festival City, Cairo, Egypt
Tel.: (20) 225980800
Chemical Product Mfr & Distr
N.A.I.C.S.: 325998

BASF Tuerk Kimya Sanayi ve Ticaret Ltd. Sti. (1)
Barbaros Mah Begonya Sok Nidakule Atasehir Kuzey C Kapisi, 34746, Karakoyunlu, Istanbul, Turkiye
Tel.: (90) 2123343400
Web Site: http://www.basf.de
Sales Range: $75-99.9 Million
Emp.: 150
Distr of Chemicals
N.A.I.C.S.: 424690

Subsidiary (Domestic):

BASF Tuerk Kimya Sanayi ve Ticaret Ltd. Sti. (2)
Beylikbagi Mh 341 Sok No1, 41400, Gebze, Kocaeli, Turkiye
Tel.: (90) 262 679 3000
Web Site: https://www.basf.com
Distr of Chemicals
N.A.I.C.S.: 424690

BASF Tunisie S.A. (1)
21 Rue Jerusalem, Belvedere, 1002, Tunis, Tunisia (100%)
Tel.: (216) 71796800
Web Site: http://www.basf.com
Sales Range: $25-49.9 Million
Emp.: 12
Distr of Chemicals
N.A.I.C.S.: 424690

BASF Turk Kimya San. ve Tic. Ltd. Sti. (1)
Barbaros Mah Begonya Sok Nidakule Atasehir Kuzey C Kapisi No 3E/ 5-22, Atasehir, 34746, Istanbul, Turkiye

BASF SE—(Continued)

Tel.: (90) 2165703400
Chemical Product Mfr & Distr
N.A.I.C.S.: 325199

BASF Turk Kimya Sanayi ve Ticaret Ltd. Sti. (1)
Barbaros Mah Begonya Sok Nidakule Atasehir Kuzey C Kapisi, No 3E/5-22 34746 Atasehir, Istanbul, Turkiye
Tel.: (90) 2165703400
Chemical Products Mfr
N.A.I.C.S.: 325998
Mubahat Akin (Reg Sls Mgr)

BASF UAB (1)
Fiausiausio 13, 01114, Vilnius, Lithuania
Tel.: (370) 52107450
Sales Range: $25-49.9 Million
Emp.: 23
Chemical Products Mfr
N.A.I.C.S.: 325998
Torban Berlin Henson (Gen Dir)

Branch (Non-US):

BASF UAB - Latvia (2)
Maza Nometnu iela 45/53, Riga, 1002, Latvia
Tel.: (371) 7508250
Web Site: http://www.basf.com
Chemical Product Whslr
N.A.I.C.S.: 424690

BASF US Verwaltung GmbH (1)
Carl-Bosch-Str 38, Ludwigshafen, 67063, Rheinland-Pfalz, Germany
Tel.: (49) 621600
Chemical Products Distr
N.A.I.C.S.: 424690

BASF Uruguaya S.A. (1) (100%)
Tel.: (598) 26281818
Sales Range: $25-49.9 Million
Emp.: 45
Mfr of Chemicals
N.A.I.C.S.: 325998

BASF Venezolana, S.A. (1)
Av Circunvalacion del Sol Centro Profesional Santa Paula Torre B, Espacio Express PB Local 4, 1080, Caracas, Macaracuay, Venezuela (100%)
Tel.: (58) 2129358306
Web Site: http://www.basf.com.ve
Sales Range: $50-74.9 Million
Emp.: 40
Chemicals Mfr
N.A.I.C.S.: 325998

BASF Venezuela S.A. (1)
Av Circunvalacion del Sol Centro Profesional Santa Paula, Caracas, 1080, Venezuela
Tel.: (58) 2129358306
Chemical Product Mfr & Distr
N.A.I.C.S.: 325998

BASF Venture Capital GmbH (1) (100%)
Tel.: (49) 6216076801
Web Site: http://www.basf-vc.de
Sales Range: $50-74.9 Million
Emp.: 12
Venture Capital & Investment Services
N.A.I.C.S.: 523910
Christoph Koehler (Mgr-Investment)

Subsidiary (Domestic):

BASF VC Beteiligungs- und Managementgesellschaft (2)
Carl-Bosch-Str 38, Ludwigshafen, 67063, Germany
Tel.: (49) 621600
Investment Management Service
N.A.I.C.S.: 523999

BASF Vietnam Co. Ltd. (1)
Suite 1101 Level 11 Saigon Trade Center 37 Ton Duc Thang Str, Dist 1, Ho Chi Minh City, Binh Duong, Vietnam
Tel.: (84) 283 824 3833
Web Site: https://www.basf.com
Sales Range: $50-74.9 Million
Emp.: 136
Chemical Products Mfr
N.A.I.C.S.: 325998

BASF Vitamins Company Ltd. (1)
No 88 Yunhai Road Shenyang Economic & Technological Development Zone, Shenyang, 110141, China
Tel.: (86) 24 2581 0788
Pharmaceuticals Product Mfr
N.A.I.C.S.: 325412

BASF West Africa Ltd. (1)
1 Illupeju Bypass, Illupeju Industrial Estate, Lagos, Nigeria
Construction Services
N.A.I.C.S.: 236220
Jean-Marc Ricca (Mng Dir)

BASF Wohnen + Bauen GmbH (1)
Brunckstrasse 49, 67063, Ludwigshafen, Germany
Chemical Products Mfr
N.A.I.C.S.: 325998

BASF Wolman GmbH (1)
Dr Wolman-Str 31-33, Sinzheim, 76547, Rastatt, Germany
Tel.: (49) 72218000
Web Site: http://www.wolman.biz
Wood Product Distr
N.A.I.C.S.: 423310
Ralf Schulz (Mng Dir)

BASF Zambia Limited (1)
Plot No 8472 Nexus Centre Malambo Road, Light Industrial Area, Lusaka, 33764, Zambia
Tel.: (260) 211244462
Agricultural Services
N.A.I.C.S.: 541690
Admore Nyaguze (Natl Sls Mgr)

BASF de Costa Rica S.A. (1)
Edificio Los Balcones Seccion A, Roble Escazu 5to Piso oficinas REGUS, 10229-1000, San Jose, Costa Rica (100%)
Tel.: (506) 22011900
Web Site: https://www.basf.com
Sales Range: $25-49.9 Million
Emp.: 50
Distr of Chemicals
N.A.I.C.S.: 424690

BASF de El Salvador, S.A. de C.V. (1)
89 Avenida Norte San Salvador, Colonia Escalon, San Salvador, El Salvador
Tel.: (503) 2640770
Sales Range: $50-74.9 Million
Emp.: 10
Importer of Agro Chemicals
N.A.I.C.S.: 424690

BASF de Guatemala, S.A. (1)
Boulevard del Sur 5to Piso, Apartado Postal 850, 1012, Guatemala, Guatemala (99%)
Tel.: (502) 2 269 7064
Web Site: http://www.basf.de
Sales Range: $25-49.9 Million
Emp.: 38
Mfr of Chemicals
N.A.I.C.S.: 325998

BASF de Nicaragua S.A. (1)
Edificio Malaga modulo No A 15 Plaza Espana, Managua, 2658, Nicaragua
Tel.: (505) 2660768
Chemical Product Mfr & Distr
N.A.I.C.S.: 325998

BASF plc (1)
Albany House Swinton Hall Road, PO Box 4, Swinton, Manchester, M27 4DT, Cheshire, United Kingdom (100%)
Tel.: (44) 1614856222
Sales Range: $150-199.9 Million
Emp.: 425
Sales of Industrial Chemicals
N.A.I.C.S.: 424690

Subsidiary (Domestic):

BASF Performance Products plc (2)
Charter Way, Macclesfield, SK10 2NX, Cheshire, United Kingdom (100%)
Tel.: (44) 1625665000
Web Site: http://www.basf.co.uk
Sales Range: $75-99.9 Million
Emp.: 200
Holding Company; Pigments, Inorganic Chemicals & Plastics Mfr & Whslr
N.A.I.C.S.: 551112

Plant (Domestic):

BASF Performance Products plc - Bradford Plant (3)

Cleckheaton Road, PO Box 38, Low Moor, Bradford, BD12 OJZ, W Yorkshire, United Kingdom
Tel.: (44) 1274417000
Web Site: http://www.basf.com
Mfr of Specialty Water Treatment Chemicals
N.A.I.C.S.: 325998

BASF Performance Products plc - Paisley Plant (3)
Hawkhead Road, Paisley, PA2 7BG, United Kingdom
Tel.: (44) 1418871144
Web Site: http://www.basf.co.uk
Mfr of Pigments
N.A.I.C.S.: 325130

Division (Domestic):

BASF Performance Products plc - Pigments Division (3)
Charter Way, Macclesfield, SK10 2NX, Cheshire, United Kingdom
Tel.: (44) 1625617878
Sales Range: $125-149.9 Million
Inorganic Pigments Mfr
N.A.I.C.S.: 325130

Subsidiary (Domestic):

BASF Pharma (Callanish) Limited (2)
Studio 87 87 Ridgway, Wimbledon Village, London, SW19 4ST, United Kingdom
Tel.: (44) 20 8946 4625
Pharmaceuticals Product Mfr
N.A.I.C.S.: 325412
Angus Morrison (Mgr-Technical)

BASF UK Limited (2)
Earl Road, PO Box 4, Cheadle Hulme, Cheadle, SK8 6QG, Cheshire, United Kingdom
Tel.: (44) 161 485 6222
Care Chemical Products Sales
N.A.I.C.S.: 424690

Sorex Holdings Ltd. (2)
Saint Michael's Industrial Estate, Widnes, WA8 8TJ, Cheshire, United Kingdom
Tel.: (44) 1514207151
Web Site: http://www.pestcontrol.basf.co.uk
Sales Range: $50-74.9 Million
Emp.: 70
Holding Company; Insecticide & Pesticide Developer & Mfr
N.A.I.C.S.: 551112

Subsidiary (US):

BASF Pest Control Solutions (3)
3568 Tree Ct Industrial Blvd, Saint Louis, MO 63122-6620
Tel.: (636) 225-5371
Web Site: http://www.pestcontrol.basf.us
Sales Range: $25-49.9 Million
Insecticides & Animal Pesticides Developer & Mfr
N.A.I.C.S.: 325320

Subsidiary (Domestic):

Sorex Ltd. (3)
Earl Road, PO Box 4, Cheadle Hulme, SK8 6QG, United Kingdom (100%)
Tel.: (44) 161 485 6222
Web Site: http://www.pestcontrol.basf.co.uk
Insecticide & Pesticide Mfr
N.A.I.C.S.: 325320

BASF spol. s.r.o. (1)
Sokolovska 668/136d, 186 00, Prague, Czech Republic (100%)
Tel.: (420) 235000111
Web Site: https://www.basf.com
Sales Range: $50-74.9 Million
Emp.: 70
Chemicals Whslr
N.A.I.C.S.: 424690

BASF watertechnologies GmbH & Co. KG (1)
Carl-Bosch-Str 38, 67063, Ludwigshafen, Germany
Tel.: (49) 621 60 0
Chemical Products Distr
N.A.I.C.S.: 424690

BASF, SIA (1)
Maza Nometnu iela 45/53, Riga, LV-1002, Latvia

Tel.: (371) 7508250
Chemical Coating Services
N.A.I.C.S.: 325510
Saulius Nainys (Mgr-Sls & Acct-Natl)

BASF-PJPC Neopentylglycol Co. Ltd. (1)
21 Fl Economic And Trade Ctr Bldg Changyi District, Jilin, 132002, China (100%)
Tel.: (86) 4322799515
Web Site: http://www.basf.com
Sales Range: $25-49.9 Million
Emp.: 50
Mfr of Powder Coatings, Unsaturated Polyester, Plasticers & Pharmaceuticals; Joint Venture of BASF AG (60%) & Jilin Chemical Industrial Company Limited (40%)
N.A.I.C.S.: 325412

BBCC - EU Government Relations BASF Group B.V. (1)
Rue Marie de Bourgogne 58, 1000, Brussels, Belgium
Tel.: (32) 27400350
Emp.: 11
Chemical Product Mfr & Distr
N.A.I.C.S.: 325998

BBCC-Business Belux-BTC (1)
Dreve Richelle 161 E boite, 43 1410, Waterloo, Belgium
Tel.: (32) 23732111
Chemical Product Mfr & Distr
N.A.I.C.S.: 325998

BTC Europe GmbH (1)
Rheinpromenade 1, 40789, Monheim am Rhein, Germany
Tel.: (49) 217333470
Web Site: https://www.btc-europe.com
Sales Range: $150-199.9 Million
Emp.: 300
Specialty Chemicals Distr
N.A.I.C.S.: 424690

Basf Toda Battery Materials LLC (1)
Shinagawa Grand Central Tower 6F 2-16-4 Konan, Minato-ku, Tokyo, 108-0075, Japan
Tel.: (81) 364514660
Cathode Material Mfr
N.A.I.C.S.: 334419

Chemcontrol Limited (1)
Cross-Crossing Centre, Cross-Crossing, San Fernando, Trinidad & Tobago
Tel.: (868) 6572000
Web Site: http://chemcontrol.co.tt
Chemical & Polymer Supplier
N.A.I.C.S.: 325180

Chemetall Danmark A/S (1)
Kalvebod Brygge 45, 1560, Copenhagen, Denmark
Tel.: (45) 44925700
Automotive Coating Mfr
N.A.I.C.S.: 325510

Chemetall Kft. (1)
Sokolovska 668/136D, 186 00, Prague, Czech Republic
Tel.: (420) 235000242
Automotive Coating Mfr
N.A.I.C.S.: 325510

Chemovator GmbH (1)
Industriestrasse 35, 68169, Mannheim, Germany
Tel.: (49) 621 602 9872
Web Site: https://www.chemovator.com
Chemicals Mfr
N.A.I.C.S.: 325998
Christoph Rathke (Co-Founder)

Chemster GmbH (1)
Elisabethstr 1, 68165, Mannheim, Germany
Tel.: (49) 62118063780
Web Site: http://www.chemster.net
Cosmetic Cream Mfr
N.A.I.C.S.: 325620
Dirk Van Roost (Mng Dir, CFO & COO)

Ciba Holding AG (1)
Klybeckstrasse 141, CH-4002, Basel, Switzerland
Tel.: (41) 616361111
Web Site: http://www.cibasc.com
Rev.: $5,085,012,900
Assets: $5,938,099,200
Liabilities: $4,522,302,400
Net Worth: $1,415,796,800

Earnings: ($484,532,400)
Emp.: 12,467
Fiscal Year-end: 12/31/2008
Holding Company; Dyes, Plastics, Performance Polymers, Pigments & Specialty Chemicals Mfr
N.A.I.C.S.: 551112

Subsidiary (Domestic):

Ciba Specialty Chemicals Holding Inc. (2)
Klybeckstrasse 141, 4057, Basel, Switzerland
Tel.: (41) 616361111
Sales Range: $5-14.9 Billion
Emp.: 19,338
Holding Company
N.A.I.C.S.: 551112

Cognis Australia Pty. Ltd. (1)
4 Saligna Dr, Tullamarine, Melbourne, 3043, VIC, Australia
Tel.: (61) 399333500
Chemical Products Mfr
N.A.I.C.S.: 325998

Cognis GmbH (1)
Rheinpromenade 1, Monheim, 40789, Germany
Tel.: (49) 21179400
Web Site: http://www.cognis.com
Sales Range: $1-4.9 Billion
Emp.: 5,500
Holding Company; Specialty Chemical Mfr; Owned by Permira Advisers LLP, The Goldman Sachs Group, Inc. & SV Life Sciences
N.A.I.C.S.: 551112

Subsidiary (Non-US):

Cognis Chemicals (China) Co. Ltd. (2)
15/F Xingmao Building 99 Tianzhou Road, Shanghai, 200233, China
Tel.: (86) 2154644666
Sales Range: $100-124.9 Million
Emp.: 400
Chemicals & Resins Mfr
N.A.I.C.S.: 325211

Cognis France S.A.S. (2)
185 Ave De Fontainebleau Saint Fargeau, 77310, Ponthierry, France
Tel.: (33) 0160652100
Sales Range: $200-249.9 Million
Emp.: 533
Mfr of Additives
N.A.I.C.S.: 325180

Plant (Domestic):

Cognis GmbH - Illertissen (2)
Robert-Hansen-Strasse 1, D-89257, Illertissen, Germany
Tel.: (49) 7303130
Web Site: http://www.cognis.com
Sales Range: $100-124.9 Million
Emp.: 374
Chemicals & Resins Mfr
N.A.I.C.S.: 325211

Subsidiary (Non-US):

Cognis Thai Ltd. (2)
71/1 Phyathai Road, Rajthevee, Bangkok, 10400, Thailand
Tel.: (66) 26547000
Sales Range: $25-49.9 Million
Emp.: 50
Production & Sale of Specialty Chemicals
N.A.I.C.S.: 325998

P.T. Cognis Indonesia (2)
Jalan Raya Jakarta Bogor Km 31-2, Jakarta, 16953, Indonesia
Tel.: (62) 218711096
Cosmetics & Adhesives Mfr
N.A.I.C.S.: 325620

Cognis S.A. (1)
Carabelas 2398, Avellaneda, B1872EQB, Argentina
Tel.: (54) 11 4001 0200
Chemical Products Mfr
N.A.I.C.S.: 325998

Construction Chemicals Division in BASF A/S (1)
Hallandsvej 1, 6230, Rodekro, Denmark
Tel.: (45) 74 66 15 11

Web Site: http://www.basf-cc.dk
Sales Range: $50-74.9 Million
Emp.: 6
Construction Chemical Distr
N.A.I.C.S.: 424690

Construction Research & Technology GmbH (1)
Dr Albert-Frank-Str 32, Trostberg, 83308, Bayern, Germany
Tel.: (49) 8621860
Sales Range: $75-99.9 Million
Emp.: 500
Construction Chemical Research & Development Services
N.A.I.C.S.: 541715

Cosmetic Rheologies Ltd. (1)
Measurement House Mancunian Way, Manchester, M12 6HN, United Kingdom
Tel.: (44) 161 705 2290
Cosmetic Chemicals Distr
N.A.I.C.S.: 424690

CropDesign N.V. (1)
Technologiepark 21 C, 9052, Zwijnaarde, 9052, Belgium
Tel.: (32) 9 242 34 00
Web Site: http://www.cropdesign.com
Sales Range: $25-49.9 Million
Emp.: 120
Agricultural Research & Development Services
N.A.I.C.S.: 541715
Wim van Camp (Mng Dir & Head-Strategic Mgmt)

DLight BVBA (1)
Antwerpseweg 1 bus 1, 2440, Geel, Belgium
Tel.: (32) 26691425
Web Site: http://www.cuxco.be
Customer Support Services
N.A.I.C.S.: 561990

De Mattos & Sullivan Limited (1)
47-1 Tigne Seafront, Sliema, SLM15, Malta
Sales Range: $75-99.9 Million
Emp.: 5
Chemicals, Gifts & Soft Toys Importer
N.A.I.C.S.: 325998
Andrew Portelli (Mgr-Sls)

Deutsche Nanoschicht GmbH (1)
Heisenbergstrasse 16, 53359, Rheinbach, Germany
Tel.: (49) 22269060300
Web Site: http://www.d-nano.de
Chemical Coating Services
N.A.I.C.S.: 325510
Michael Backer (Founder)

Dr. D.A. Delis AG (1)
Paleologou Benizelou 5, 10556, Athens, Greece
Tel.: (30) 2103297222
Web Site: http://www.delis.gr
Sales Range: $25-49.9 Million
Emp.: 70
Importer of Chemicals
N.A.I.C.S.: 424690

Dr. Wolman GmbH (1)
Dr Wolman-Str 31 33, 76547, Sinsheim, Germany (100%)
Tel.: (49) 72218000
Web Site: https://www.wolman.de
Sales Range: $25-49.9 Million
Emp.: 100
Mfr of Fire Proofing Agents, Wood Preserving Agents
N.A.I.C.S.: 321114

Elastogran GmbH (1)
Elastogran Strasse 60, 49448, Lemforde, Germany (100%)
Tel.: (49) 5443120
Web Site: http://www.pu.basf.de
Sales Range: $450-499.9 Million
Emp.: 1,200
Polyurethane Products & Systems, Specialty Elastomers & Technical Parts Mfr
N.A.I.C.S.: 326150

Subsidiary (Non-US):

BASF Espanola S.L. (2)
Poligono Industrial Can Jardi C/ Compositor Vivaldi 1-7, Rubi, 08191, Barcelona, Spain
Tel.: (34) 936806100
Web Site: http://www.polyurethanes.basf.de

Polyurethane Systems Mfr; Thermoplastic Polyurethane Elastomers & Polyurethane Processing Equipment & Facilities
N.A.I.C.S.: 325211

BASF Poliuretan Hungaria Kft. (2)
Terstyanszky ut 89, 2083, Solymar, Budapest, Hungary
Tel.: (36) 26560580
Web Site: http://www.elastogran.hu
Sales Range: $10-24.9 Million
Emp.: 22
Polyurethane Mfr
N.A.I.C.S.: 326140
Zoltan Demjen (Mng Dir)

BASF Polyurethane Industry and Trade Co., Ltd. Sti (2)
Seyhli Mah Ankara Cad No 334, 34912, Istanbul, Seyhli-Pendik, Turkiye
Tel.: (90) 216 378 6443
Web Site: http://www.polyurethanes.basf.de
Sales Range: $25-49.9 Million
Emp.: 5
Polyurethane Systems Mfr; Thermoplastic Polyurethane Elastomers & Polyurethane Processing Equipment & Facilities
N.A.I.C.S.: 325211

Subsidiary (Domestic):

BASF Schwarzheide GmbH (2)
Schipkauer Strasse 1, 01986, Schwarzheide, Germany (100%)
Tel.: (49) 3575260
Web Site: http://www.basf-schwarzheide.de
Sales Range: $400-449.9 Million
Emp.: 2,266
Mfr of Polyurethane Systems, Thermoplastic Polyurethane Elastomers & Polyurethane Processing Equipment & Facilities
N.A.I.C.S.: 325211

Subsidiary (Non-US):

Elastogran France S.A.S (2)
Rue Decauville, PO Box 207, 77292, Mitry-Mory, France (100%)
Tel.: (33) 160214249
Web Site: http://www.elastogran.de
Sales Range: $50-74.9 Million
Emp.: 160
Mfr of Polyurethane Systems, Thermoplastic Polyurethane Elastomers & Polyurethane Processing Equipment & Facilities
N.A.I.C.S.: 325211

Subsidiary (Domestic):

Elastogran Innovationsprojekte Beteiligungsgesellschaft mbH (2)
Elastogranstr 60, 49448, Lemforde, Germany
Tel.: (49) 5443122688
Chemical Products Mfr
N.A.I.C.S.: 325998

Subsidiary (Non-US):

Elastogran Italia S.p.A. (2)
Strada Per Poirino 38, I 14019, Villanova d'Asti, Italy (100%)
Tel.: (39) 0141949111
Web Site: http://www.elastogran.de
Mfr of Polyurethane Systems, Thermoplastic Polyurethane Elastomers & Polyurethane Processing Equipment & Facilities
N.A.I.C.S.: 325211

Elastogran Lagomat Nordic AB (2)
Angeredsvinkeln 5, 42467, Angered, Sweden
Tel.: (46) 313300050
Web Site: http://www.elastogran.de
Sales Range: $25-49.9 Million
Emp.: 23
Polyurethane Products & Systems, Specialty Elastomers & Technical Parts Mfr
N.A.I.C.S.: 325211

Elastogran UK Limited (2)
Alfreton Industrial Est, Somercotes Way, Derby, DE55 4NL, Derbyshire, United Kingdom (100%)
Tel.: (44) 773607161
Web Site: http://www.elastogran.de
Sales Range: $25-49.9 Million
Emp.: 75
Polyurethane Systems Mfr; Thermoplastic Polyurethane Elastomers & Polyurethane Processing Equipment & Facilities

N.A.I.C.S.: 325211

OOO Elastokam (2)
Promzona PF 52, Republik Tatarstan, Nizhnekamsk, 4, Russia
Tel.: (7) 8555383062
Web Site: http://www.polyurethanes.basf.de
Chemical Products Mfr
N.A.I.C.S.: 325998

Elfte BASF Projektentwicklungsgesellschaft mbH (1)
Carl-Bosch-Str 38, Ludwigshafen, 67056, Germany
Tel.: (49) 621600
Project Management Consulting Services
N.A.I.C.S.: 541618

Energ2 Technologies, Inc. (1)
100 NE Northlake Way Ste 300, Seattle, WA 98105
Tel.: (206) 547-0445
Web Site: http://www.energ2.com
Chemicals Mfr
N.A.I.C.S.: 325998
Kirill Bramnik (CEO)

Engelhard Arganda S.L. (1)
Doctor Fleming 3, Madrid, Spain
Tel.: (34) 914589940
Chemical Products Distr
N.A.I.C.S.: 424690

Engelhard Peru S.A. (1)
Av San Borja Norte 1302, Lima, Peru
Tel.: (51) 1 2251080
Mineral Mining Services
N.A.I.C.S.: 212390

Engelhard South Africa (Pty.) Ltd. (1)
Struan Way, Port Elizabeth, 6000, South Africa
Tel.: (27) 414011000
Sales Range: $100-124.9 Million
Emp.: 30
Catalytic Converter Machinery Mfr
N.A.I.C.S.: 333248
Paul Allday (Dir-Site)

Esuco Beheer B.V. (1)
Groningensingel 1, Arnhem, 6835 EA, Gelderland, Netherlands
Tel.: (31) 263717171
Investment Management Service
N.A.I.C.S.: 523999

FSL Flugplatz Speyer/Ludwigshafen GmbH (1)
Joachim-Becher-Strasse 2, 67346, Speyer, Germany
Tel.: (49) 623 268 7290
Web Site: https://www.flugplatz-speyer.de
Aviation Services
N.A.I.C.S.: 488190
Roland Kern (Mng Dir)

Funfzehnte BASF Erwerbsgesellschaft mbH (1)
Carl-Bosch-Str 38, Ludwigshafen, 67056, Germany
Tel.: (49) 621 600
Chemical Product Whslr
N.A.I.C.S.: 424690

Funfzehnte BASF Finanzbeteiligungsgesellschaft mbH (1)
Carl-Bosch-Str 38, Ludwigshafen, 67063, Rheinland-Pfalz, Germany
Tel.: (49) 621 60 0
Financial Management Services
N.A.I.C.S.: 523999

Funfzehnte BASF Projektentwicklungsgesellschaft mbH (1)
Carl-Bosch-Str 38, 67063, Ludwigshafen, Rheinland-Pfalz, Germany
Tel.: (49) 621 60 0
Project Management Consulting Services
N.A.I.C.S.: 541618

GASCADE Gastransport GmbH (1)
Kolnische Strasse 108-112, 34119, Kassel, Germany
Tel.: (49) 5619340
Web Site: https://www.gascade.de
Gas Transmission System Services
N.A.I.C.S.: 221210

Gewerkschaft des konsolidierten Steinkohlenbergwerks Breitenbach

BASF SE—(Continued)

GmbH (1)
Carl-Bosch-Str 38, 67063, Ludwigshafen,
Rheinland-Pfalz, Germany
Tel.: (49) 621 60 0
Coal Mining Services
N.A.I.C.S.: 213113

Grunau Illertissen GmbH (1)
Robert-Hansen-Str 1, 89257, Illertissen,
Germany
Tel.: (49) 730 31 30
Chemical Products Mfr
N.A.I.C.S.: 325998
Thomas Kuehm (Pres)

Guano-Werke GmbH & Co. KG (1)
Tel.: (49) 621600
Web Site: http://www.basf.com
Emp.: 40,000
Chemical Products Mfr
N.A.I.C.S.: 325998

HEMOMAK HEM Uros DOOEL (1)
Basino Selo, PO Box 11, Veles, 1400, North
Macedonia
Tel.: (389) 43212552
Emp.: 17
Chemical Products Mfr
N.A.I.C.S.: 325998
Goran Jovanovinc (Gen Mgr)

Inca Bronze Powders Ltd. (1)
Springfield Road, Bolton, BL1 7LQ, Lan-
cashire, United Kingdom
Tel.: (44) 1254 873 888
Industrial Chemicals Mfr
N.A.I.C.S.: 325998

Interlates Ltd. (1)
Gladden Place, Skelmersdale, WN8 9SX,
Lancashire, United Kingdom
Tel.: (44) 1695729577
Chemical Product Whslr
N.A.I.C.S.: 424690

Isobionics B.V. (1)
Urmonderbaan 22 bldg 220 0 205, 6167
RD, Geleen, Netherlands
Tel.: (31) 43 302 0212
Web Site: https://www.isobionics.com
Oil Ingredient Mfr
N.A.I.C.S.: 311225
Toine Janssen (Founder & CEO)

**Jordanian Swiss Company for Manu-
facturing & Marketing Construction
Chemicals Company Ltd.** (1)
Al Madina Al Monawarah Street, PO Box
752, Amman, 11118, Jordan
Tel.: (962) 6 5521672
Web Site: http://www.basf-cc.com.jo
Emp.: 9
Construction Chemical Mfr & Distr
N.A.I.C.S.: 325998
Yousef Abdallah (Mgr-EHS & Ops)

**Kartal Kimya Sanayi ve Ticaret
A.S.** (1)
Balcik Mah Pelitli Yolu Cad No 140, Mollafe-
nari Yolu Uzeri, 41490, Gebze, Kocaeli,
Turkiye
Tel.: (90) 2628884100
Web Site: https://en.kartal.com.tr
Chemical Products
N.A.I.C.S.: 325998

Kendell S.r.l. (1)
Via Del Lavoro 17, Rovoredo in Piano,
33080, Rovoredo, PN, Italy
Tel.: (39) 0434590422
Web Site: https://www.kendell.it
Chemical Products Mfr
N.A.I.C.S.: 325998

**LUCARA Immobilienverwaltungs
GmbH** (1)
Rheinuferstr 65-69, 67061, Ludwigshafen,
Rheinland-Pfalz, Germany
Tel.: (49) 621 6049810
Real Estate Manangement Services
N.A.I.C.S.: 531390

LUWOGE GmbH (1)
Brunckstrasse 49, 67063, Ludwigshafen,
Germany
Tel.: (49) 6216044044
Web Site: http://www.luwoge.com
Sales Range: $50-74.9 Million
Emp.: 100
Property Management

N.A.I.C.S.: 531312

Unit (Domestic):

LUWOGE GmbH Haus Breitnau (2)
Gastehaus der BASF, Im Talgrund 11,
79874, Breitnau, Germany
Tel.: (49) 765291190
Web Site: http://www.basf.com
Sales Range: $25-49.9 Million
Emp.: 26
Property Management
N.A.I.C.S.: 531312

**LUWOGE GmbH Haus
Westerland** (2)
Brunckstrasse 49, 67063, Ludwigshafen,
Germany
Tel.: (49) 6216095430
Web Site: http://www.luwoge.de
Sales Range: $25-49.9 Million
Emp.: 35
Property Management
N.A.I.C.S.: 531312

**LUWOGE GmbH Studienhaus St.
Johann** (2)
Schlossstrasse 5, Schlossstrasse 5, 76857,
Albstadt, Germany
Tel.: (49) 6345480
Property Management
N.A.I.C.S.: 531312
Thomas Herrmann (Gen Mgr)

Subsidiary (Domestic):

LUWOGE consult GmbH (1)
Donnersbergweg 2, Ludwigshafen, 67059,
Germany
Tel.: (49) 621 55 90 989 0
Web Site: http://www.luwoge-consult.de
Emp.: 25
Real Estate Development Services
N.A.I.C.S.: 531390
Ulrich Baum (Mgr)

Lig Ace Co. Ltd. (1)
1-24-43 Junka Sutoku Bldg, Fukui, 910-
0023, Japan
Tel.: (81) 776282566
Chemical Products Mfr
N.A.I.C.S.: 325998

Lipogene AB (1)
Svalof Weibull Ab, Svalov, 268 81, Skane,
Sweden
Tel.: (46) 86574200
Biotechnology Research & Development
Services
N.A.I.C.S.: 541714

Lucura Ruckversicherungs AG (1)
Wohlerstr 19, 67063, Ludwigshafen,
Rheinland-Pfalz, Germany
Tel.: (49) 621 622181
General Insurance Services
N.A.I.C.S.: 524210

M/s. Amaravati International (1)
c/o Soaltee Hotel Limited, POB 1481, Kath-
mandu, Tahachal, Nepal
Tel.: (977) 14272555
Chemical Product Whslr
N.A.I.C.S.: 424690
Nalin Mendiratta (Gen Mgr)

**Master Builders Solutions Belgium
N.V.** (1)
Nijverheidsweg 89, 3945, Ham, Belgium
Tel.: (32) 11340431
Construction Services
N.A.I.C.S.: 236220
Paul Dens (Mng Dir)

**Master Builders Solutions Polska sp.
z o.o.** (1)
Ul Casimir the Great 58, 32-400, Myslenice,
Poland
Tel.: (48) 123728000
Construction Services
N.A.I.C.S.: 236220
Cezary Urban (Mktg Mgr-Construction
Chemicals BASF-Central Europe)

**Master Builders Solutions Yapi
Kimyasallari Sanayi Ve Ticaret Lim-
ited Sirketi** (1)
Icerenkoy Mah Bahcelerarasi Sok No 43,
Atasehir, Istanbul, Turkiye
Tel.: (90) 2165703400

Construction Services
N.A.I.C.S.: 236220
Melahat Yilmaz (Mgr-HR)

**Master Builders Solutions Nederland
B.V.** (1)
Karolusstraat 2, 4903 RJ, Oosterhout, Neth-
erlands
Tel.: (31) 162425190
Construction Services
N.A.I.C.S.: 236220

MetalFX Technology Ltd. (1)
The Sidings Station Road, Guiseley, LS20
8BX, Leeds, United Kingdom
Tel.: (44) 1943 884 888
Paint & Coating Mfr
N.A.I.C.S.: 325510

Metanomics GmbH (1)
Tegeler Weg 33, Berlin, 10589, Germany
Tel.: (49) 30 34807 100
Web Site: http://www.metanomics.de
Sales Range: $25-49.9 Million
Emp.: 150
Biotechnology Research & Development
Services
N.A.I.C.S.: 541714
Thomas Ehrhardt (CEO)

NOF (Thailand) Ltd. (1)
11th Floor R 11-07/3 2034/52 Italthai Tower,
New Phetchburi Road, Huaykwang District,
Bangkok, Thailand
Tel.: (66) 27160095
Chemical Products Mfr
N.A.I.C.S.: 325998

**Nunhems (Beijing) Seed Co.,
Ltd.** (1)
No 16 Jinghaisilu, Beijing Economic-
Technological Development Area, Beijing,
100176, China
Tel.: (86) 1084315836
Nursery Product Distr
N.A.I.C.S.: 424930
Ren Baoquan (Mgr-Farm)

Nunhems Maroc SARL (1)
La Marina Tour Ivoire 32nd Floor, 20000,
Casablanca, Morocco
Tel.: (212) 661135279
Vegetable Seed Whslr
N.A.I.C.S.: 424910

Nunhems Tohumculuk A.S. (1)
Satirli Mah Merkez Sokak No 101/1, Serik,
07510, Antalya, Türkiye
Tel.: (90) 2427102244
Chemical Product Mfr & Distr
N.A.I.C.S.: 325998

Nunhems Ukraine T.O.V. (1)
19 Druzhby Narodiv Blvd, Kiev, 01042,
Ukraine
Tel.: (380) 443860998
Chemical Products Mfr
N.A.I.C.S.: 325998

OOO BASF Stroitelnye Sistemy (1)
Kadaschewskaja Nabereshnaja d 14/3,
Moscow, 119017, Russia
Tel.: (7) 4952 25 64 36
Web Site: http://www.stroysist.ru
Sales Range: $50-74.9 Million
Emp.: 15
Construction Chemical Distr
N.A.I.C.S.: 424690
Sergey Vetlov (Gen Dir)

OPAL NEL TRANSPORT GmbH (1)
Emmerichstrasse 11, 34119, Kassel, Ger-
many
Tel.: (49) 561 934 0
Web Site: http://www.opal-nel-transport.de
Natural Gas Transportation Services
N.A.I.C.S.: 486210

**P. Papas & Co. O.E. Trading
Company** (1)
5 Agias Sofias St, 12132, Peristeri, Athen,
Greece
Tel.: (30) 2105752944
Web Site: http://www.sourischemicals.gr
Sales Range: $25-49.9 Million
Emp.: 6
Chemical Products Mfr
N.A.I.C.S.: 325998
Tena Souris (Gen Mgr)

**P.T. BASF Care Chemicals
Indonesia** (1)

Jl Raya Jakarta-Bogor Km 31 2, Cimanggis,
Depok, 16452, Indonesia
Tel.: (62) 2129495200
Chemical Product Mfr & Distr
N.A.I.C.S.: 325998

P.T. BASF Indonesia (1)
DBS Bank Tower 27th Floor Ciputra World
1, Jakarta Jl Prof Dr Satrio Kav 3-5, Ja-
karta, 12940, Indonesia (100%)
Tel.: (62) 2129886000
Web Site: https://www.basf.com
Sales Range: $50-74.9 Million
Emp.: 562
Mfr of Chemicals
N.A.I.C.S.: 325998

PCI Bauprodukte AG (1)
Im Schachen 291, 5113, Holderbank, Swit-
zerland
Tel.: (41) 589582121
Web Site: https://www.pci.ch
Emp.: 1,200
Construction Materials Distr
N.A.I.C.S.: 423390
Fred Noordam (Area Mgr)

PolyAd Services GmbH (1)
Chemiestrasse Building L 31, 68623,
Lampertheim, Germany
Tel.: (49) 6206 15 2301
Web Site: http://www.polyadservices.com
Sales Range: $25-49.9 Million
Emp.: 6
Plastic Additive Mfr
N.A.I.C.S.: 325998

**Projektentwicklungs-GmbH Friesen-
heimer Insel** (1)
Lindenallee 55, Essen, 45127, Nordrhein-
Westfalen, Germany
Tel.: (49) 201820240
Chemical Products Distr
N.A.I.C.S.: 424690

**Rolic Technologies (Shanghai) Co.,
Ltd.** (1)
Room 1002 Building A 685 Huaxu Road
E-Link World South Area, Shanghai, China
Tel.: (86) 2139295680
Web Site: http://www.rolic.cn
Optical Film Mfr
N.A.I.C.S.: 333310
Wenyue Ding (Mng Dir)

Rolic Technologies AG (1)
Gewerbestrasse 18, 4123, Allschwil, Swit-
zerland
Tel.: (41) 614872222
Liquide Crystal Laboratories Mfr
N.A.I.C.S.: 334419

Rolic Technologies Ltd. (1)
Gewerbestrasse 18, 4123, Allschwil, Swit-
zerland
Tel.: (41) 61 487 2222
Web Site: https://www.basf.com
Optical Instrument Mfr
N.A.I.C.S.: 333310
Anna-Maria Cappetta (Head-HR & Admin)

S.T.I.M.A. S.A.R.L. (1)
Residence Yasmine, Les Berges du Lac,
2045, Tunis, Tunisia
Tel.: (216) 7 186 2262
Web Site: http://www.planet.tn
Sales Range: $25-49.9 Million
Emp.: 12
Agricultural Chemical Product Mfr
N.A.I.C.S.: 325320

**SGS-Schwarzheider Gastronomie
und Service GmbH** (1)
Schipkauer Strasse 1, Schwarzheide, 1986,
Germany
Tel.: (49) 35752 62397
Web Site: http://www.sgs-
gastronomieservice.de
Catering Services
N.A.I.C.S.: 722320

**Saudi BASF for Building Materials
Co. Ltd.** (1)
2nd Industrial City, Dammam, Saudi Arabia
Tel.: (966) 3 812 1140
Web Site: http://www.saudi-basf.com
Building Construction Material Distr
N.A.I.C.S.: 423390

Sculpteo SAS (1)

10 Rue Auguste Perret, 94800, Villejuif,
France
Tel.: (33) 18 364 1122
Web Site: https://www.sculpteo.com
Digital Printer Mfr
N.A.I.C.S.: 333248
Eric Carreel *(Co-Founder)*

Setup Performance SAS **(1)**
10 route du Chaffard, Frontonas, 38290,
Isere, France
Tel.: (33) 47 495 2450
Web Site: https://www.setuperformance.com
Polymer Product Mfr
N.A.I.C.S.: 325211

Styrolution Mexicana S.A. de
C.V. **(1)**
Insurgentes No 975 Ciudad De Los De-
portes Benito Ju Rez, Mexico, 03710,
Mexico
Tel.: (52) 5553252600
Chemical Products Mfr
N.A.I.C.S.: 325998

Taiko Shoji Ltd. **(1)**
Meito Bldg 2f, Tokorozawa, 359-0046, Sai-
tama, Japan
Tel.: (81) 429983056
Emp.: 15
Construction Materials Distr
N.A.I.C.S.: 423390

Thai Ethoxylate Company
Limited **(1)**
555/1 Energy Complex Center Building A
15th Floor Vibhavadi Rangsit Rd,
Chatuchak Subdistrict Chatuchak District,
Bangkok, 10900, Thailand
Tel.: (66) 22658400
Web Site: https://www.tex.co.th
Fatty Alcohol Ethylates Mfr
N.A.I.C.S.: 325180

Thermische Ruckstandsverwertung
GmbH & Co. KG **(1)**
Postfach 16 16, 50380, Wesseling, Ger-
many
Tel.: (49) 2236 722581
Special Industry Machinery
N.A.I.C.S.: 333248

TrinamiX GmbH **(1)**
Industriestrase 35, 67063, Ludwigshafen,
Germany
Tel.: (49) 6216077750
Web Site: https://trinamixsensing.com
Emp.: 150
Opto-Electronic Mfr
N.A.I.C.S.: 334413
Ingmar Bruder *(Founder, Chm & Mng Dir)*

UBench International NV **(1)**
Antoine Coppenslaan 27/bus 3, 2300, Turn-
hout, Belgium
Tel.: (32) 1 470 4077
Web Site:
    https://www.ubenchinternational.com
Automobile Mfr
N.A.I.C.S.: 336110
Brigitte Van Gerven *(Project Mgr)*

Unbench B.V. **(1)**
Antoine Coppenslaan 27 Bus 3, 2300, Turn-
hout, Belgium
Tel.: (32) 14704077
Chemical Product Mfr & Distr
N.A.I.C.S.: 325998

Untertage-Speicher-Gesellschaft mbH
(USG) **(1)**
Friedrich-Ebert-Strasse 160, 34119, Kassel,
Germany
Tel.: (49) 5613010
Web Site: http://www.wintershall.com
Sales Range: $50-74.9 Million
Emp.: 120
Chemical Products Mfr
N.A.I.C.S.: 325998

Wilhelm Rosenstein Ltd. **(1)**
14 Shenkar Street, PO Box 12691, 46733,
Herzliyya, 12691, Israel
Tel.: (972) 99718802
Web Site: https://www.wrl-ltd.com
Chemical Products Mfr
N.A.I.C.S.: 325998

Wintershall Dea AG **(1)**
Friedrich-Ebert-Strasse 160, Kassel, 34119,
Germany **(72.7%)**

Tel.: (49) 5613010
Web Site: https://www.wintershalldea.com
Rev.: $18,533,958,400
Assets: $19,256,022,400
Liabilities: $15,777,344,000
Net Worth: $3,478,678,400
Earnings: ($4,718,467,200)
Emp.: 2,314
Fiscal Year-end: 12/31/2022
Holding Company; Oil & Natural Gas Prod-
ucts & Services
N.A.I.C.S.: 551112
Mario Mehren *(CEO & Chm-Exec Bd)*

Subsidiary (Domestic):

DEA Deutsche Erdoel AG **(2)**
Uberseering 40, 22297, Hamburg, Germany
Tel.: (49) 4063750
Crude Oil, Natural Gas, Refineries & Petro-
leum Products Distr
N.A.I.C.S.: 211120
Uwe-Stephan Lagies *(Head-Corp Comm)*

Subsidiary (Non-US):

DEA Norge AS **(3)**
Lokkeveien 103, PO Box 640, Sentrum,
4007, Stavanger, Norway
Tel.: (47) 51765400
Web Site: http://www.dea-norge.com
Oil & Gas Exploration Services
N.A.I.C.S.: 213112
Hellen Ek *(Mgr-Sls)*

Subsidiary (Domestic):

Wintershall AG **(2)**
Friedrich Ebert Str 160, Kassel, 34119,
Hessen, Germany **(51%)**
Tel.: (49) 5613010
Web Site: http://www.wintershall.de
Sales Range: $125-149.9 Million
Emp.: 500
Crude Oil, Natural Gas & Petroleum Prod-
ucts
N.A.I.C.S.: 324199

Subsidiary (Domestic):

Haidkopf GmbH **(3)**
Friedrich-Ebert-Strasse 160, 34119, Kassel,
Germany
Tel.: (49) 5613010
Web Site: http://www.wintershall.com
Natural Gas Distr
N.A.I.C.S.: 221210

Joint Venture (Non-US):

OOO Wolgodeminoil **(3)**
Ul Rabotche-Krestyanskaya Street 30 A,
400074, Volgograd, Russia
Tel.: (7) 8442333420
Web Site: http://www.basf.com
Chemical Product Mfr; Owned 50% by Win-
tershall AG & 50% by OAQ Lukoil
N.A.I.C.S.: 325998

Joint Venture (Domestic):

WINGAS Holding GmbH **(3)**
Friedrich-Ebert-Strasse 160, 34119, Kassel,
Hessen, Germany **(50.04%)**
Tel.: (49) 5613010
Web Site: http://www.wintershall.com
Investment Management Service
N.A.I.C.S.: 523999

Subsidiary (Domestic):

WINGAS GmbH **(4)**
Konigstor 20, 34117, Kassel, Germany
Tel.: (49) 561998580
Web Site: https://www.wingas.com
Rev.: $2,194,307,584
Emp.: 400
Commercial & Industrial Natural Gas Supply
Services
N.A.I.C.S.: 221210

Subsidiary (Non-US):

WINGAS Belgium s.p.r.l./b.v.b.a. **(5)**
Avenue des Arts Kunstlaan 21, 1000, Brus-
sels, Belgium
Tel.: (32) 22806724
Web Site: http://www.wintershall.com
Commercial & Industrial Natural Gas Supply
Services
N.A.I.C.S.: 221210

Subsidiary (Domestic):

WINGAS Transport GmbH & Co.
KG **(5)**
Baumbachstrasse 1, 34119, Kassel, Ger-
many
Tel.: (49) 5619340
Web Site: http://www.wingas-transport.de
Sales Range: $50-74.9 Million
Emp.: 250
Commercial & Industrial Natural Gas Supply
Services
N.A.I.C.S.: 486210
Bjorn Kaiser *(Mng Dir)*

Subsidiary (Non-US):

WINGAS UK Ltd. **(5)**
Bridge House Berleith House 73-75 Sheen
Rd, 3 Heron Square, Richmond, TW9 1Yj,
Surrey, United Kingdom
Tel.: (44) 2084399680
Web Site: http://www.wingas-uk.com
Sales Range: $75-99.9 Million
Emp.: 23
Commercial & Industrial Natural Gas Supply
Services
N.A.I.C.S.: 221210

Subsidiary (Domestic):

WINGAS Verwaltungs-GmbH **(5)**
Friedrich-Ebert-Str 160, 34119, Kassel, Ger-
many
Tel.: (49) 5613010
Web Site: http://www.wingas.de
Investment Management Service
N.A.I.C.S.: 523999

Subsidiary (Non-US):

Wintershall (UK North Sea) Ltd. **(3)**
83 Baker Street, London, W1U 6AG, United
Kingdom
Tel.: (44) 2070347048
Oil & Gas Exploration Services
N.A.I.C.S.: 213112

Wintershall AG Doha **(3)**
Salam Tower 11th Fl Al Corniche St, PO
Box 2541, Doha, Qatar
Tel.: (974) 4839554
Chemical Products Mfr
N.A.I.C.S.: 325998

Wintershall AG Vertretung
Moskau **(3)**
Ul Namjotkina 16, W-420 GSP 7, 117997,
Moscow, Russia
Tel.: (7) 4957198689
Web Site: http://www.wintershall.com
Chemical Products Mfr
N.A.I.C.S.: 325998

Wintershall Chile Lda. **(3)**
Av Isidora Goyenechea 3120 Piso 3, Las
Condes, Santiago, Chile
Tel.: (56) 24312700
Natural Gas Exploration Service
N.A.I.C.S.: 213112

Wintershall Energia S.A. **(3)**
Della Paolera 265 14th Fl, C1006 ACI, Bue-
nos Aires, Argentina
Tel.: (54) 1155542700
Web Site: http://www.wintershall.com
Emp.: 60
Chemical Products Mfr
N.A.I.C.S.: 325998

Subsidiary (Domestic):

Wintershall Erdgas Handelshaus
GmbH AG **(3)**
Friedrich Ebert Strasse 160, Kassel, 10707,
Germany **(100%)**
Tel.: (49) 308859230
Web Site: http://www.wintershall.com
Sales Range: $50-74.9 Million
Emp.: 20
Oil & Gas Exploration & Production
N.A.I.C.S.: 213112

Subsidiary (Domestic):

Wintershall Erdgas Beteiligungs
GmbH **(4)**
Friedrich Ebert St 160, 34119, Kassel, Hes-
sen, Germany **(100%)**
Tel.: (49) 5613010

Web Site: http://www.wintershall.com
Oil & Gas Exploration & Production
N.A.I.C.S.: 213112

Subsidiary (Non-US):

Wintershall Erdgas Handelshaus Zug
AG **(4)**
Grafenauweg 8, Zug, 6300, Switzerland
Tel.: (41) 417114618
Web Site: http://www.wiee.ch
Emp.: 10
Oil & Gas Exploration & Production
N.A.I.C.S.: 213112
Wolf-Tieter Stucken *(Mgr)*

Wirom Gas S.A. **(4)**
Str Popa Savu 77, Bucharest, 11432,
Romania **(51%)**
Tel.: (40) 212221564
Web Site: http://www.wirom.ro
Chemical Product Mfr; Owned 51% by Win-
tershall Erdgas Handelshaus Zug AG &
49% by Distrigaz Sud S.A.
N.A.I.C.S.: 325998

Subsidiary (Non-US):

Wintershall Libya **(3)**
The Commercial Centre, Tripoli, Libya
Tel.: (218) 213350140
Web Site: http://www.wintershall.com
Sales Range: $75-99.9 Million
Emp.: 200
Oil & Gas Production & Exploration
N.A.I.C.S.: 213112

Wintershall Middle East GmbH-Abu
Dhabi **(3)**
PO Box 47193, Abu Dhabi, United Arab
Emirates
Tel.: (971) 26810517
Web Site: http://www.wintershall.com
Sales Range: $50-74.9 Million
Emp.: 2
Oil & Gas Exploration & Production
N.A.I.C.S.: 213112

Wintershall Nederland B.V. **(3)**
Bogaaretlein 47, 2284DP, Rijswijk,
Netherlands **(100%)**
Tel.: (31) 703583100
Web Site: http://www.wintershall.nl
Oil & Gas Exploration & Production
N.A.I.C.S.: 213112
R. Frimpong *(Gen Mgr)*

Subsidiary (Domestic):

Clyde Netherlands BV **(4)**
Stadhoudersplantsoen 2, 2517 JL, Hague,
Netherlands
Tel.: (31) 703560085
Mfr of Petroleum
N.A.I.C.S.: 211120

Wintershall Exploration and Produc-
tion International C.V. **(4)**
Bogaardplein 47, Rijswijk, 2284 DP, South
Holland, Netherlands
Tel.: (31) 703583100
Oil & Gas Exploration Services
N.A.I.C.S.: 213112
Gilbert Brink *(Gen Mgr)*

Wintershall Nederland Transport and
Trading B.V. **(4)**
Bogaardplein 47, Rijswijk, 2284 DP, South
Holland, Netherlands
Tel.: (31) 703583100
Web Site: http://www.wintershall.com
Emp.: 250
Oil & Gas Exploration Services
N.A.I.C.S.: 213112

Wintershall Noordzee B.V. **(4)**
Bogaardplein 47, 2284 DP, Rijswijk, Nether-
lands
Tel.: (31) 703583100
Web Site: http://www.wintershall.com
Sales Range: $150-199.9 Million
Emp.: 300
Oil & Gas Exploration & Production
N.A.I.C.S.: 213112

Wintershall Petroleum (E&P)
B.V. **(4)**
Bogaardplein 47, Rijswijk, 2284 DP, Zuid-
Holland, Netherlands
Tel.: (31) 703583100

BASF SE—(Continued)

Web Site: http://www.wintershall.com
Oil & Gas Exploration Services
N.A.I.C.S.: 213112

Wintershall Services B.V. (4)
Bogaardplein 47, Rijswijk, 2284 DP, Netherlands
Tel.: (31) 703583100
Sales Range: $200-249.9 Million
Oil & Gas Exploration Services
N.A.I.C.S.: 213112
Gilbert van den Brink (Gen Dir)

Subsidiary (Domestic):

Wintershall Norwegen Explorations-und Produktions- GmbH (3)
Friedrich-Ebert-Str 160, 34119, Kassel, Germany
Tel.: (49) 5613010
Web Site: http://www.wintershall.com
Oil & Gas Exploration Services
N.A.I.C.S.: 213112

Subsidiary (Non-US):

Wintershall Oil AG (3)
Grafenauweg 6-8, Zug, 6300, Switzerland
Tel.: (41) 417108828
Web Site: http://www.wintershall.com
Sales Range: $50-74.9 Million
Emp.: 6
Oil & Gas Exploration & Production
N.A.I.C.S.: 213112

Wintershall Petroleum Iberia S.A. (3)
Abogado Aranegui Van Ingen, Fuente Del Romero 29B, 28023, Madrid,
Spain (100%)
Tel.: (34) 913572403
Sales Range: $50-74.9 Million
Emp.: 4
Oil & Gas Exploration & Production
N.A.I.C.S.: 213112

Subsidiary (Domestic):

Wintershall Russia Holding GmbH (3)
Friedrich-Ebert-Str 160, Kassel, 34119, Hessen, Germany
Tel.: (49) 5613010
Investment Management Service
N.A.I.C.S.: 523999

Wintershall Vermogensverwaltungsgesellschaft mbH (3)
Friedrich-Ebert-Strasse 160, 34119, Kassel, Germany
Tel.: (49) 5613010
Web Site: http://www.wintershall.com
Oil & Gas Exploration Services
N.A.I.C.S.: 213112

Wintershall Wolga Petroleum GmbH (3)
Friedrich-Ebert-Strasse 160, Kassel, 34119, Hessen, Germany
Tel.: (49) 5613010
Web Site: http://www.wintershall.com
Oil & Gas Exploration Services
N.A.I.C.S.: 213112

Wintershall Holding GmbH (1)
Friedrich-Ebert-Strasse 160, 34119, Kassel, Germany
Tel.: (49) 5613010
Chemical Product Mfr & Distr
N.A.I.C.S.: 325998

Wintershall Libyen Oil & Gas GmbH (1)
Corinthia Towers Hotel, Gsplaj, Tripoli, Libya
Tel.: (218) 213350140
Agricultural Management Services
N.A.I.C.S.: 115116

Wintershall Norge AS (1)
Kanalpiren Hinna Park Laberget 28, PO Box 230, Sentrum, NO-4001, Stavanger, Norway
Tel.: (47) 51822400
Agricultural Management Services
N.A.I.C.S.: 115116

ZAO BASF (1)
Tel.: (7) 4952317176
Web Site: http://www.basf.ru

Sales Range: $75-99.9 Million
Emp.: 150
Chemical Products Mfr & Whslr
N.A.I.C.S.: 325998

Subsidiary (Domestic):

OOO BASF Wostok (2)
Mishutinskoe Shosse 72, Pavlovsky Posad, 142505, Moscow, Russia
Tel.: (7) 4964351949
Automotive Paint Mfr
N.A.I.C.S.: 325510

Zodiac Enterprises, LLC (1)
1112 Industrial Blvd, Caldwell, TX 77836
Tel.: (979) 567-9631
Web Site: http://www.zodcat.com
Smelting, Refining & Alloying of Nonferrous Metal
N.A.I.C.S.: 331492
John Larch (Pres & CEO)

Zweite BASF Immobilien-Gesellschaft mbH (1)
Carl-Bosch-Str 38, Ludwigshafen, 67063, Germany
Tel.: (49) 621600
Property Management Services
N.A.I.C.S.: 531311

baseclick GmbH (1)
Floriansbogen 2-4, Neuried, 82061, Munich, Germany
Tel.: (49) 899 699 3401
Web Site: https://www.baseclick.eu
Sales Range: $25-49.9 Million
Emp.: 6
Chemical Products Mfr
N.A.I.C.S.: 325998

hte GmbH (1)
Kurpfalzring 104, 69123, Heidelberg, Germany
Tel.: (49) 62 217 4970
Web Site: https://www.hte-company.com
Sales Range: $25-49.9 Million
Emp.: 200
Heterogeneous Catalysis Experimentation Research
N.A.I.C.S.: 541715
Wolfram Stichert (CEO)

BASHUNDHARA PAPER MILLS LTD.

Bashundhara Industrial Headquarter BIHQ Tower 1 Plot 844 Rd 12 Block I, Umme Kulsum Road Bashundhara R/A, Dhaka, 1229, Bangladesh
Tel.: (880) 2843228993
Web Site:
https://www.bashundharapaper.com
BPML—(CHT)
Rev.: $120,297,555
Assets: $345,069,424
Liabilities: $220,749,009
Net Worth: $124,320,415
Earnings: $4,150,422
Emp.: 4,445
Fiscal Year-end: 06/30/23
Paper Material Product Mfr
N.A.I.C.S.: 322299
Khijir Ahammed (Gen Mgr)

BASIC CAPITAL MANAGEMENT CO., LTD.

Yaesu Building 5F 2-4-1 Yaesu, Chuo-ku, Tokyo, 104 0028, Japan
Tel.: (81) 3 5200 8831 JP
Web Site: http://www.basic-cm.co.jp
Year Founded: 2002
Investment Fund Management Services
N.A.I.C.S.: 523999
Yuna Kaneda (Pres & CEO)

BASIC ELEMENT COMPANY

30 Rochdelskaya Street, 123022, Moscow, Russia
Tel.: (7) 4957205025
Web Site: http://www.basel.ru
Year Founded: 2008
Sales Range: $25-49.9 Billion

Investment Services
N.A.I.C.S.: 523999
Oleg Deripaska (Chm-Supervisory Bd)

Subsidiaries:

BasEl Real Estate, OJSC (1)
36-2 Kutuzovsky prospekt, Moscow, 121170, Russia
Tel.: (7) 495 935 71 85
Real Estate Management Services
N.A.I.C.S.: 531390
Vaagn Arutyunyan (CEO)

Kuban AgroHolding (1)
77 Mira st, Ust-Labinsk, Krasnodar, 352330, Russia
Tel.: (7) 86135 4 12 29
Web Site: http://www.ahkuban.ru
Emp.: 5,000
Agricultural Services
N.A.I.C.S.: 115112
Andrey Oleynik (Chm)

Russian Machines Corporation (1)
15-8 ul Rochdelskaya, Moscow, 123022, Russia
Tel.: (7) 495 653 82 07
Web Site: http://www.rm.ru
Emp.: 68,000
Automotive Components Mfr
N.A.I.C.S.: 336390
Elena Matveeva (VP-Comm Policy & Govt Rels)

BASIC ENERGY CORPORATION

UB 111 Paseo de Roxas Building Paseo de Roxas, Legaspi Village, Makati, 1229, Philippines
Tel.: (63) 232244383
Web Site:
https://www.basicenergy.ph
Year Founded: 1968
BSC—(PHI)
Oil Exploration Services
N.A.I.C.S.: 213112
Angel P. Gahol (Compliance Officer, Officer-IR & Sec)

Subsidiaries:

Basic Diversified Industrial Holdings, Inc (1)
7th Fl Basic Petroleum Bldg 104 C Palanca Jr St, Legaspi Village, Makati, 1229, Philippines
Tel.: (63) 28178596
Investment Holding & Management Services
N.A.I.C.S.: 523940

BASIC-FIT NV

Wegalaan 60, 2132 JC, Hoofddorp, Netherlands
Tel.: (31) 233022385 NI
Web Site: https://www.basic-fit.com
Year Founded: 2016
BFIT—(EUR)
Rev.: $1,156,029,363
Assets: $3,570,565,184
Liabilities: $3,124,626,339
Net Worth: $445,938,845
Earnings: ($2,957,280)
Emp.: 8,000
Fiscal Year-end: 12/31/23
Fitness Training Services
N.A.I.C.S.: 812990
Rene Moos (Chm & CEO)

Subsidiaries:

HealthCity Luxembourg S.A. (1)
Route De Luxembourg 11, 5230, Sandweiler, Luxembourg
Tel.: (352) 2615201
Fitness Training Center Operator
N.A.I.C.S.: 713940

BASICNET S.P.A.

Largo Maurizio Vitale 1, 10152, Turin, Italy
Tel.: (39) 01126171

Web Site: https://www.basic.net
Year Founded: 1983
BAN—(ITA)
Rev.: $83,858,871
Assets: $252,368,120
Liabilities: $70,652,928
Net Worth: $181,715,192
Earnings: $80,682,097
Emp.: 876
Fiscal Year-end: 12/31/21
Sportswear Mfr & Designer
N.A.I.C.S.: 424350
Marco Daniele Boglione (Chm)

Subsidiaries:

Basic Properties B.V. (1)
Strawinskylaan 3111-6e Etage, 1077ZX, Amsterdam, Netherlands (100%)
Tel.: (31) 204420266
Trusts Estates & Agency Accounts
N.A.I.C.S.: 525920

Basic Village S.p.A. (1)
Largo Maurizio Vitale 1, 10152, Turin, Italy (100%)
Tel.: (39) 01126141
Web Site: https://torino.basicvillage.com
Men's Clothing Stores
N.A.I.C.S.: 458110

BasicItalia S.r.l. (1)
Strada della Cebrosa 106, 10156, Turin, Italy (90%)
Tel.: (39) 01126177
Web Site: https://www.basicitalia.com
Mens & Boys Cut & Sew Other Outerwear Mfr
N.A.I.C.S.: 315250

Kappa France S.A.S. (1)
41 rue Bobby Sands, 44800, Saint-Herblain, France
Tel.: (33) 240928282
Web Site: https://www.kappa.fr
Cloth Distr
N.A.I.C.S.: 424350

BASICS OFFICE PRODUCTS LTD.

1040 Fountain St N, Cambridge, N3E 1A3, ON, Canada
Tel.: (519) 653-8984
Web Site: https://www.basics.com
Year Founded: 1976
Sales Range: $25-49.9 Million
Emp.: 31
Office Products Whslr
N.A.I.C.S.: 423420
Sean Macey (Pres)

BASIL READ HOLDINGS LIMITED

The Basil Read Campus 7 Romeo Street, Hughes, Boksburg, South Africa
Tel.: (27) 114186300
Web Site:
https://www.basilread.co.za
Rev.: $369,973,189
Assets: $222,007,786
Liabilities: $213,574,827
Net Worth: $8,432,959
Earnings: ($81,640,526)
Emp.: 4,675
Fiscal Year-end: 12/31/17
Civil Engineering Construction & Development Services
N.A.I.C.S.: 237310
Khathutshelo Mapasa (CEO)

Subsidiaries:

Basil Read (Pty) Limited (1)
7 Romeo Street Hughes Extension, Private Bag X 170, 1459, Boksburg, Gauteng, South Africa
Tel.: (27) 114186300
Sales Range: $50-74.9 Million
Emp.: 200
Building Construction Services
N.A.I.C.S.: 236220
Khathutshelo Mapasa (CEO)

Blasting & Excavating (Pty)
Limited   **(1)**
7 Vernier Street, Witfield Extn 33, Boksburg,
1469, Gauteng, South Africa
Tel.: (27) 113234000
Web Site: http://www.blasting.co.za
Mining Support Services
N.A.I.C.S.: 212114

Contract Plumbing and Sanitation
(Pty) Limited   **(1)**
256 Vonkprop Street Samcor Park Ext 1,
Silverton, Pretoria, 0117, Gauteng, South
Africa
Tel.: (27) 128038310
Sales Range: $25-49.9 Million
Emp.: 50
Plumbing & Sanitation Engineering Services
N.A.I.C.S.: 238220

Facets Interiors (Pty) Limited   **(1)**
Ground Fl Guild Hall 5 Anerley Rd, Park-
town, Johannesburg, 2193, Gauteng, South
Africa
Tel.: (27) 116467449
Web Site: http://www.facetsinteriors.co.za
Sales Range: $25-49.9 Million
Emp.: 8
Interior Designing Services
N.A.I.C.S.: 541410

Mvela Phanda Construction (Pty)
Limited   **(1)**
256 Vonkprop St Samcor Park Ext 1, Preto-
ria, 0184, Gauteng, South Africa
Tel.: (27) 128034099
Plumbing Services
N.A.I.C.S.: 238220

Newport Construction (Pty)
Limited   **(1)**
448 Oldsmobile St, Port Elizabeth, 6001,
Eastern Cape, South Africa
Tel.: (27) 414611488
Emp.: 20
Commercial Building Construction Services
N.A.I.C.S.: 236220
Paul Walker *(Mng Dir)*

P. Gerolemou Construction (Pty)
Limited   **(1)**
1-256 Vonkprop Samcor Park Silverton
Sydafrika, Pretoria, 0117, Gauteng, South
Africa
Tel.: (27) 128034100
Commercial Building Construction Services
N.A.I.C.S.: 236220
Panayiotis Andreou Gerolemou *(Mng Dir)*

Portal Partnership Incorporated   **(1)**
24 Third Ave, Parktown N, Sandton, 2193,
Gauteng, South Africa
Tel.: (27) 114471307
Building Architectural Design Services
N.A.I.C.S.: 541310

Roadcrete Africa (Pty) Limited   **(1)**
7 Romeo st hugen ext, Boksburg, 1459,
Gauteng, South Africa
Tel.: (27) 113234100
Web Site: http://www.roadcrete.co.za
Civil Engineering Services
N.A.I.C.S.: 541330
Ann Bernhardt *(Dir-Fin)*

TRG Trading (Pty) Limited   **(1)**
Postnet Ste 281, Private Bag X 5091, Brits,
0250, Brits, South Africa
Tel.: (27) 12 254 0999
Stone Quarrying Services
N.A.I.C.S.: 212311

BASILEA PHARMACEUTICA LTD.
Hegenheimermattweg 167b, Allschwil,
4123, Basel, Switzerland
Tel.: (41) 616061111
Web Site: https://www.basilea.com
BPMUF—(OTCEM)
Rev.: $187,347,279
Assets: $205,953,174
Liabilities: $217,841,693
Net Worth: ($11,888,519)
Earnings: $12,420,965
Emp.: 147
Fiscal Year-end: 12/31/23
Biopharmaceutical Product Mfr

N.A.I.C.S.: 325412
Steven D. Skolsky *(Vice Chm)*

Subsidiaries:

Basilea Pharmaceutica Deutschland
GmbH   **(1)**
Kistlerhofstr 75, 81379, Munich, Germany
Tel.: (49) 8978576740
Web Site: http://www.basilea.com
Sales Range: $25-49.9 Million
Emp.: 38
Pharmaceuticals Producut Sales
N.A.I.C.S.: 424210

Basilea Pharmaceutica International
Ltd.   **(1)**
Grenzacherstrasse 487, 4005, Basel, Swit-
zerland
Tel.: (41) 616061111
Web Site: http://www.basilea.com
Emp.: 160
Drug Mfr
N.A.I.C.S.: 325412

Basilea Pharmaceutica S.R.L.   **(1)**
Piazza Meda 3, 20121, Milan, Italy
Tel.: (39) 0258215592
Web Site: http://www.basilea.com
Sales Range: $50-74.9 Million
Emp.: 1
Pharmaceuticals Producut Sales
N.A.I.C.S.: 424210

BASILIC FLY STUDIO LIMITED
Tower A KRC Commerzone Mount
Poonamallee Road, Porur, Chennai,
600116, Tamil Nadu, India
Tel.: (91) 4461727700
Web Site:
https://www.basilicflystudio.com
Year Founded: 2016
BASILIC—(NSE)
Rev.: $9,568,922
Assets: $6,442,180
Liabilities: $2,603,800
Net Worth: $3,838,380
Earnings: $3,362,112
Emp.: 474
Fiscal Year-end: 03/31/23
Software Development Services
N.A.I.C.S.: 541511

BASIN CONTRACTING LIM-ITED
100 Bedrock Lane, Elmsdale, B2S
2B1, NS, Canada
Tel.: (902) 883-2235
Web Site: https://www.basin-
gallant.com
Year Founded: 1985
Rev.: $16,017,090
Emp.: 100
Paving Contract Services
N.A.I.C.S.: 324121
Fred Benere *(Pres)*

BASIN ENERGY LIMITED
Level 1 3 Ord Street, West Perth,
6000, WA, Australia
Tel.: (61) 736677449   **AU**
Web Site:
https://www.basinenergy.com.au
Year Founded: 2021
BSN—(ASX)
Rev.: $97,132
Assets: $7,994,108
Liabilities: $88,707
Net Worth: $7,905,401
Earnings: ($1,840,174)
Fiscal Year-end: 06/30/24
Mineral Exploration Services
N.A.I.C.S.: 212390
Ben Donovan *(Sec)*

BASIN URANIUM CORP.
503 905 West Pender St, Vancouver,
V6C 1L6, BC, Canada
Tel.: (604) 363-0411   **BC**
Web Site:
https://www.basinuranium.ca

Year Founded: 2017
BURCF—(OTCIQ)
Assets: $5,030,746
Liabilities: $92,732
Net Worth: $4,938,014
Earnings: ($173,276)
Fiscal Year-end: 05/31/22
Mineral Mining Services
N.A.I.C.S.: 213115
Joel Leonard *(CFO)*

BASLER AG
An der Strusbek 60-62, 22926, Ah-
rensburg, Germany
Tel.: (49) 41024630
Web Site:
https://www.baslerweb.com
Year Founded: 1988
BSL—(DEU)
Rev.: $224,195,997
Assets: $282,325,791
Liabilities: $128,689,165
Net Worth: $153,636,627
Earnings: ($15,244,445)
Emp.: 1,115
Fiscal Year-end: 12/31/23
Digital Cameras, Optical Components
& Inspection Systems Mfr
N.A.I.C.S.: 333310
Norbert Basler *(Founder & Chm-
Supervisory Bd)*

Subsidiaries:

Basler Asia Pte. Ltd.   **(1)**
35 Marsiling Industrial Estate Road 3 05-06,
Singapore, 739257, Singapore
Tel.: (65) 63671355
Sales Range: $50-74.9 Million
Emp.: 7
Vision Equipment Mfr & Distr
N.A.I.C.S.: 333310
Zhiming Lin *(Engr-Product Quality)*

Basler France S.A.   **(1)**
28 rue Jean Perrin, 33608, Pessac, Cedex,
France
Tel.: (33) 557266896
Computer Component Mfr
N.A.I.C.S.: 334118

Basler Japan KK   **(1)**
Atago Toyo Bldg 3F 1-3-4 Atago, Minato-ku,
Tokyo, 105-0002, Japan
Tel.: (81) 364324080
Photographic Equipment Mfr
N.A.I.C.S.: 316990

Basler Korea Inc.   **(1)**
No 1503 Parkview Tower 248 Jeongjail-Ro,
Bundang-Gu, Seongnam, 13554, Korea
(South)
Tel.: (82) 317143114
Photographic Equipment Mfr
N.A.I.C.S.: 316990

Basler Neumunster AG   **(1)**
Oderstr 11, 24539, Neumunster, Germany
Tel.: (49) 4321559560
Photographic Equipment Mfr
N.A.I.C.S.: 316990

Basler Vision Technologies Taiwan
Inc.   **(1)**
No 160 Zhuangjing N Rd, Zhubei, 302, Hs-
inchu, Taiwan
Tel.: (886) 35583955
Digital Camera Mfr
N.A.I.C.S.: 333310

Basler Vision Technology (Beijing)
Co., Ltd.   **(1)**
2nd Floor Building No 5 Dongsheng Inter-
national Pioneer Park No 1, Yongtaizhuang
North Road Haidian District, Beijing, China
Tel.: (86) 1062952828
Photographic Equipment Mfr
N.A.I.C.S.: 316990

Basler, Inc.   **(1)**
855 Springdale Dr Ste 203, Exton, PA
19341
Tel.: (610) 280-0171
Sales Range: $25-49.9 Million
Emp.: 16

Electrical Apparatus & Equipment, Wiring
Supplies & Related Equipment Merchant
Whslr
N.A.I.C.S.: 423610

CHROMOS Group AG   **(1)**
Niederhaslistrasse 12, CH-8157, Dielsdorf,
Switzerland
Tel.: (41) 448555000
Web Site: https://www.chromosgroup.ch
Magazine Publisher
N.A.I.C.S.: 323111

Photon-Tech Instruments Co.,
Ltd.   **(1)**
No 355 Sec 3 Zhongqing Rd, Xitun Dist,
Taichung, 40761, Taiwan
Tel.: (886) 24259955
Web Site: https://www.photon-tech.com.tw
Project Development Services
N.A.I.C.S.: 541511

BASLER KANTONALBANK AG
Aeschenvorstadt 41, 4051, Basel,
Switzerland
Tel.: (41) 612663333   **CH**
Web Site: https://www.bkb.ch
Year Founded: 1899
BSKP—(SWX)
Sales Range: Less than $1 Million
Banking Services
N.A.I.C.S.: 522110
Adrian Bult *(Chm)*

Subsidiaries:

Bank Cler AG   **(1)**
Aesenplatz 3, CH-4002, Basel,
Switzerland   **(75.8%)**
Tel.: (41) 612862121
Web Site: http://www.cler.ch
Banking Services
N.A.I.C.S.: 522110
Sandra Lienhart *(CEO)*

BASLER SACHVERSICHERUNGS-AG
Basler Strasse 4, 61352, Bad Hom-
burg, Germany
Tel.: (49) 6172 125 460
Web Site: https://www.basler.de
Emp.: 100
Insurance Services
N.A.I.C.S.: 524298
Ralph Castiglioni *(Mng Dir)*

Subsidiaries:

MedMal Direct Insurance
Company   **(1)**
245 Riverside Ave Ste 550, Jacksonville, FL
32202
Web Site: http://www.mymedmal.com
Sales Range: $10-24.9 Million
Emp.: 33
General Insurance Services
N.A.I.C.S.: 524210
Britt R. Stephens *(VP-Underwriting)*

BASLINI S.P.A.
Via Barozzi 8, 20122, Milan, Italy
Tel.: (39) 0276003161   **IT**
Web Site: http://www.ccb-baslini.it
Year Founded: 1925
Sales Range: $25-49.9 Million
Emp.: 150
Agricultural & Industrial Accessory
Material Mfr
N.A.I.C.S.: 325998
Antonio Baslini *(Pres)*

Subsidiaries:

Baslini Metalli S.p.A.   **(1)**
Via Lodi 29, 24047, Treviglio, BG, Italy
Tel.: (39) 03633101
Web Site: http://www.baslini.it
Sales Range: $25-49.9 Million
Emp.: 10
Metal Products
N.A.I.C.S.: 332999

BASS OIL LIMITED

Bass Oil Limited—(Continued)

Level 5 11-19 Bank Place, Mel-
bourne, 3000, VIC, Australia
Tel.: (61) 399273000   AU
Web Site: https://www.bassoil.com.au
BAS—(ASX)
Rev.: $6,555,475
Assets: $11,379,423
Liabilities: $4,571,377
Net Worth: $6,808,046
Earnings: $269,783
Fiscal Year-end: 12/31/23
Oil & Gas Exploration
N.A.I.C.S.: 211120
Giustino Guglielmo *(Mng Dir)*

BASSAC

50 route de la Reine, FR-92100,
Boulogne-Billancourt, France
Tel.: (33) 155604545   FR
Web Site: http://www.bassac.fr
BASS—(EUR)
Sales Range: $1-4.9 Billion
Residential Development Services
N.A.I.C.S.: 236117
Moise Mitterrand *(Chm & CEO)*

**BASSARI RESOURCES LIM-
ITED**

25 Colin Street, West Perth, 6005,
WA, Australia
Tel.: (61) 396299925
Web Site:
    http://www.bassariresources.com
Rev.: $699
Assets: $54,256,578
Liabilities: $15,515,967
Net Worth: $38,740,611
Earnings: ($2,375,128)
Fiscal Year-end: 12/31/19
Gold & Other Metal Mining & Explo-
ration Services
N.A.I.C.S.: 212220
Ian Riley *(Sec)*

**BASSETT & WALKER INTER-
NATIONAL, INC.**

2 Berkeley Street Suite 303, Toronto,
M5A 4J5, ON, Canada
Tel.: (416) 363-7070
Web Site:
    http://www.bassettwalkerinc.com
Year Founded: 1992
Agricultural Commodities Provider
N.A.I.C.S.: 926140

BASSETTI GROUP SAS

4 Avenue Doyen Louis Weil, 38000,
Grenoble, France
Tel.: (33) 47623354
Web Site: https://www.bassetti-
    group.com
Emp.: 100
Software Development Services
N.A.I.C.S.: 513210
David Bassetti *(Founder & Mng Dir)*

Subsidiaries:

MAQSIMA GmbH   (1)
Am TUV 1, 66280, Sulzbach, Germany
Tel.: (49) 6897 506 41
Web Site: http://www.maqsima.de
Software Development Services
N.A.I.C.S.: 541511

BASSILICHI CEE D.O.O.

Bulevar Mihajla Pupina 165e, 11070,
Belgrade, Serbia
Tel.: (381) 112604070
Year Founded: 2008
Financial Transaction Processing
Services
N.A.I.C.S.: 522320

**BASSO INDUSTRY CORPORA-
TION**

No 24 36th Rd Taichung Industrial
Park, Taichung, 40768, Taiwan
Tel.: (886) 423598877
Web Site: https://www.basso.com.tw
1527—(TAI)
Rev.: $91,761,630
Assets: $172,946,951
Liabilities: $18,447,071
Net Worth: $154,499,880
Earnings: $12,112,986
Emp.: 645
Fiscal Year-end: 12/31/23
Pneumatic Fastening Tools Mfr
N.A.I.C.S.: 334513
Ming-Ta Lai *(Chm)*

Subsidiaries:

Basso Industry Corporation - Plastic
Injection Plant   (1)
No 24 36th Rd, Taichung Industrial Park,
Taichung, 40768, Taiwan
Tel.: (886) 42 359 8877
Web Site: https://www.basso.com.tw
Sales Range: $200-249.9 Million
Emp.: 700
Injection Molded Plastic Products Mfr
N.A.I.C.S.: 326121

BAST JSC

Koktem 1 15A BC Koktem Square
7th floor, Microdistrict, Almaty, Ka-
zakhstan
Tel.: (7) 7273553545
Web Site: https://www.bast-mining.kz
BAST—(KAZ)
Rev.: $4,473,645
Assets: $19,754,881
Liabilities: $24,922,847
Net Worth: ($5,167,965)
Earnings: ($6,351,787)
Fiscal Year-end: 12/31/20
Mineral Mining Services
N.A.I.C.S.: 212390

BASTA FRANCE

Lieu Dit Beaulieu, 58500, Clamecy,
Nievre, France
Tel.: (33) 386270701
Web Site: http://www.bastagroup.com
Rev.: $17,300,000
Emp.: 83
Cycle Lighting & Immovable Locks
Supplier
N.A.I.C.S.: 336320
Allen Mrozinski *(Dir-Pur)*

BASTE

Route De La Schlucht, 68140, Col-
mar, France
Tel.: (33) 389778827
Rev.: $23,600,000
Emp.: 21
Groceries & Related Products
N.A.I.C.S.: 424490
Christian Scherrer *(Mgr & Fin)*

BASTEI LUBBE AG

Schanzenstrasse 6-20, 51063, Co-
logne, Germany
Tel.: (49) 22182002288
Web Site: https://www.luebbe.de
Year Founded: 1953
BST—(DEU)
Rev.: $119,069,239
Assets: $112,173,087
Liabilities: $45,974,346
Net Worth: $66,198,741
Earnings: $9,410,711
Emp.: 323
Fiscal Year-end: 03/31/24
Trade Magazine Publisher
N.A.I.C.S.: 513120
Klaus Kluge *(Member-Exec Bd & Dir-
Programme, Sls & Mktg)*

Subsidiaries:

Bastei Media GmbH   (1)

Erich-Kastner-Str 1a, 99094, Erfurt, Ger-
many
Tel.: (49) 36151143800
Media Production Services
N.A.I.C.S.: 516120

Daedalic Entertainment GmbH   (1)
Papenreye 51, 22453, Hamburg, Germany
Tel.: (49) 3054461793
Emp.: 90
Game Development & Publishing Services
N.A.I.C.S.: 513210
Carsten Fichtelmann *(Co-Founder & CEO)*

Moravska Bastei MoBa s.r.o.   (1)
Koliste 13a, 602 00, Brno, Czech Republic
Tel.: (420) 541126051
Book & Magazine Publisher
N.A.I.C.S.: 513120

Rader GmbH   (1)
Kornharpener Strasse 126, 44791, Bochum,
Germany
Tel.: (49) 234959870
Web Site: https://www.raeder.de
Home Furnishing Product Mfr & Distr
N.A.I.C.S.: 314120

Siebter Himmel Bastei Lubbe
GmbH   (1)
Brusseler Strasse 67, 50672, Cologne, Ger-
many
Tel.: (49) 22116919191
Book & Magazine Publisher
N.A.I.C.S.: 513120

BASTI SA

Str Rezervoarelor 2, Prahova,
Ploiesti, Romania
Tel.: (40) 244 573460
Sales Range: Less than $1 Million
Emp.: 5
Real Estate Prorperty Leasing Ser-
vices
N.A.I.C.S.: 531190

BASTIDE DIFFUSION

Route De Bagnols, 30340, Ales,
France
Tel.: (33) 466562727
Web Site: http://www.bastide.fr
Rev.: $20,100,000
Emp.: 83
Homefurnishings
N.A.I.C.S.: 423220
Olivier Fraquet *(Dir)*

**BASTIDE LE CONFORT MEDI-
CAL SA**

Euro 2000 activity center 12 avenue
de la dame, 30132, Caissargues,
France
Tel.: (33) 466386808   FR
Web Site:
    https://www.bastideleconfort.com
Year Founded: 1977
BLC—(EUR)
Rev.: $384,004,617
Earnings: $5,823,035
Emp.: 1,323
Fiscal Year-end: 06/30/19
Health & Personal Care Products Re-
tailer & Home Health Care Services
N.A.I.C.S.: 456199
Guy Bastide *(Chm & CEO)*

Subsidiaries:

Dorge Medic SA   (1)
Chausse de Nivelles 351, Temploux, 5020,
Namur, Belgium   (100%)
Tel.: (32) 81742884
Sales Range: $1-9.9 Million
Emp.: 15
Health & Personal Care Products Retailer &
Support Services
N.A.I.C.S.: 456199
Christine Collin *(Gen Mgr)*

BASTIDE MANUTENTION

3 rue Gutenberg, 31100, Toulouse,
France
Tel.: (33) 561315959

Web Site: http://www.fenwick-
    bastidemanutention.com
Emp.: 70
Industrial Machinery & Equipment
N.A.I.C.S.: 423830

BASTION MINERALS LIMITED

Level 6 22 Pitt Street, Sydney, 2000,
NSW, Australia
Tel.: (61) 407123143
Web Site:
    https://www.bastionminerals.com
Year Founded: 2010
BMO—(ASX)
Rev.: $88,170
Assets: $4,822,085
Liabilities: $1,303,775
Net Worth: $3,518,310
Earnings: ($2,554,571)
Fiscal Year-end: 12/31/22
Mineral Exploration Services
N.A.I.C.S.: 212390
Alan Ross Landles *(Chm)*

BASTOGI S.P.A.

Via GB Piranesi 10, 20137, Milan,
Italy
Tel.: (39) 02739831
Web Site: https://www.bastogi.com
Year Founded: 1862
Sales Range: $25-49.9 Million
Emp.: 22
Holding Company; Art Education Ser-
vices
N.A.I.C.S.: 551112
Marco Cabassi *(Chm)*

Subsidiaries:

Brioschi Finanziaria S.p.A.   (1)
Via Tamburini 13, 20123, Milan, Italy
Tel.: (39) 02 4856161
Web Site: http://www.brioschi.it
Real Estate Developers
N.A.I.C.S.: 531210

Frigoriferi Milanesi S.p.A.   (1)
Via G.B. Piranesi 10, Milan, Italy
Tel.: (39) 0273983232
Web Site: http://www.frigoriferimilanesi.it
Warehouse & Cold Storage Facility
N.A.I.C.S.: 493120

BASTY PERE ET FILS

1400 Avenue D Antibes, 45200,
Amilly, Loiret, France
Tel.: (33) 238951515
Rev.: $35,800,000
Emp.: 86
N.A.I.C.S.: 441110
Delphine Gay *(Dir-Mktg)*

BAT S.P.A.

Via Henry Ford ZI EST, Noventa di
Piave, 30020, Venice, Italy
Tel.: (39) 042165672   IT
Web Site: http://www.batgroup.com
Year Founded: 1983
Sales Range: $25-49.9 Million
Emp.: 113
Canopies & Sun Awnings Systems &
Components Designer, Mfr & Mar-
keter
N.A.I.C.S.: 339999
Amorino Barbieri *(Founder & Pres)*

Subsidiaries:

BAT Iberica, S.L.   (1)
Travesia Cuenca-3 num 2 Pol Ind Campor-
rosso Apartado de Correos n 22, Chinchilla
de Monte-Aragon, 2520, Albacete, Spain
Tel.: (34) 967261779
Web Site: http://www.batgroup.com
Canopies & Sun Awnings Systems & Com-
ponents Designer, Mfr & Marketer
N.A.I.C.S.: 339999

Durasol Awnings, Inc.   (1)
445 Delldale Rd, Chester, NY 10918-2049
Tel.: (845) 692-1100
Web Site: http://www.durasol.com

Sales Range: $25-49.9 Million
Retractable Canvas Awnings Mfr.
N.A.I.C.S.: 314910
Debra Plock *(Mgr-Customer Support)*

Floris Obdam B.V.   (1)
Poel 5, 1713 GL, Koggenland, North Hol-
land, Netherlands
Tel.: (31) 226331393
Web Site: http://www.floriszonwering.nl
Canopies & Sun Awnings Systems & Com-
ponents Designer, Mfr & Marketer
N.A.I.C.S.: 339999

KE Protezioni Solari srl   (1)
Via Calnova 160/a, Noventa di Piave,
30020, Venice, Italy
Tel.: (39) 0421307000
Web Site: http://www.keitaly.it
Canopies & Sun Awnings Systems & Com-
ponents Designer, Mfr & Marketer
N.A.I.C.S.: 339999

BATA INDIA LIMITED
418/02 Bata house Sector 17 Oppo-
site MDI, Gurgaon, 122001, Haryana,
India
Tel.: (91) 7289900000
Web Site: https://www.bata.in
Year Founded: 1931
500043—(BOM)
Rev.: $333,566,415
Assets: $481,182,293
Liabilities: $233,482,295
Net Worth: $247,699,998
Earnings: $14,058,545
Emp.: 4,357
Fiscal Year-end: 03/30/22
Footwear & Accessories Mfr & Distr
N.A.I.C.S.: 316210
Rajeev Gopalakrishnan *(Mng Dir)*

Subsidiaries:

Bata Properties Limited   (1)
6A SN Banerjee Road, Kolkata, 700013,
West Bengal, India
Tel.: (91) 3323014421
Footwear Mfr
N.A.I.C.S.: 316210

BATA PAKISTAN LIMITED
GT Road, Batapur, Lahore, 53400,
Pakistan
Tel.: (92) 42111044   PK
Web Site: https://www.bata.com.pk
Year Founded: 1942
BATA—(LAH)
Rev.: $112,216,317
Assets: $102,256,696
Liabilities: $54,313,543
Net Worth: $47,943,153
Earnings: $7,012,271
Emp.: 2,683
Fiscal Year-end: 12/31/19
Shoe Mfr & Distr
N.A.I.C.S.: 316990
Muhammad Imran Malik *(CEO)*

BATA SHOE COMPANY (BAN-GLADESH) LIMITED
Tongi, Gazipur, 1710, Dhaka, 1710,
Bangladesh
Tel.: (880) 298105015
Web Site: https://www.batabd.com
Year Founded: 1894
BATASHOE—(CHT)
Rev.: $58,980,264
Assets: $76,610,959
Liabilities: $34,092,443
Net Worth: $42,518,516
Earnings: ($15,383,865)
Emp.: 1,266
Fiscal Year-end: 12/31/20
Leather Product Mfr
N.A.I.C.S.: 316990
Rajeev Gopalakrishnan *(Chm)*

BATAILLE MATERIAUX
A 71 69 Rue Jules Ferry, 27500, Pont
Audemer, Eure, France

Tel.: (33) 232415205
Web Site: http://www.bigmat-
bataille.com
Rev.: $24,300,000
Emp.: 91
Plumbing Fixtures, Equipment & Sup-
plies
N.A.I.C.S.: 423720
Philippe Bataille *(Pres)*

BATALPHA BOBACH GMBH
Raiffeisenstrasse 17 18 Langenfeld,
40764, Langenfeld, Germany
Tel.: (49) 217385350
Web Site: http://www.batalpha.de
Sales Range: $75-99.9 Million
Emp.: 350
Musical, Theatre & Opera Stage Au-
tomation
N.A.I.C.S.: 339992
Max Gunter Bobach *(CEO & Gen
Mgr)*

BATEAUX NANTAIS
Quai de la Motte Rouge, BP 50826,
44008, Nantes, Cedex 1, France
Tel.: (33) 240145114
Web Site: http://www.bateaux-
nantais.fr
Year Founded: 1997
Sales Range: $25-49.9 Million
Emp.: 75
Tourist Boat Operator
N.A.I.C.S.: 487210
Gerard Basle *(Mng Dir)*

BATENBURG TECHNIEK N.V.
Stolwijkstraat 33, 3079 DN, Rotter-
dam, Netherlands
Tel.: (31) 102928080   NI
Web Site: http://www.batenburg.nl
Sales Range: $200-249.9 Million
Emp.: 1,000
Technical Installation & Trading Ser-
vices
N.A.I.C.S.: 238190
Ralph van den Broek *(CEO)*

BATERO GOLD CORP.
Suite 230 2 Toronto Street, Toronto,
M5C 2B5, ON, Canada
Tel.: (604) 568-6378   BC
Web Site:
https://www.baterogold.com
Year Founded: 2008
BAT—(OTCIQ)
Rev.: $3,375
Assets: $38,390,410
Liabilities: $291,620
Net Worth: $38,098,790
Earnings: ($666,346)
Fiscal Year-end: 08/31/21
Gold & Other Mineral Exploration
N.A.I.C.S.: 213114
Patricia Barbotto *(CFO)*

Subsidiaries:

Sociedad Minera Quinchia
S.A.S.   (1)
Cra 25A 1 - 31 Oficina 15-11 Parque Em-
presarial El Tesoro, Medellin, Colombia
Tel.: (57) 6046041948
Web Site: https://www.mquinchia.com
Mineral Property Exploration Services
N.A.I.C.S.: 213114

BATH BUILDING SOCIETY
15 Queen Square, Bath, BA1 2HN,
United Kingdom
Tel.: (44) 1225 423271
Web Site:
http://www.bathbuildingsociety.co.uk
Rev.: $13,925,257
Assets: $435,342,337
Liabilities: $384,921,810
Net Worth: $50,420,527
Earnings: $2,905,194

Emp.: 47
Fiscal Year-end: 12/31/19
Mortgage Lending & Other Invest-
ment Services
N.A.I.C.S.: 522310
Chris Smyth *(Vice Chm)*

Subsidiaries:

Bath Property Letting Limited   (1)
34 Southgate Street City Centre, Bath, BA1
1TP, United Kingdom
Tel.: (44) 1225314055
Web Site:
http://www.bathpropertyletting.co.uk
Property Leasing Services
N.A.I.C.S.: 531110

BATH STREET CAPITAL LIM-ITED
Level 14 191 Queen Street, Auck-
land, 1010, New Zealand
Tel.: (64) 9 366 3290   NZ
Year Founded: 2013
Privater Equity Firm
N.A.I.C.S.: 523999
Andrew Howard Barnes *(Owner &
Mng Dir)*

Subsidiaries:

Perpetual Trust Limited   (1)
Level 13 191 Queen Street, Auckland,
1010, New Zealand   (100%)
Tel.: (64) 9 366 3290
Web Site: http://www.perpetual.co.nz
Emp.: 60
Wealth Management Services
N.A.I.C.S.: 523991
Andrew Howard Barnes *(Chm)*

The New Zealand Guardian Trust
Company Limited   (1)
Level 13 191 Queen Street, Auckland,
1010, New Zealand
Tel.: (64) 9 366 3290
Web Site: http://www.guardiantrust.co.nz
Sales Range: $50-74.9 Million
Emp.: 180
Trust Management Services
N.A.I.C.S.: 523991
Andrew Howard Barnes *(Mng Dir)*

BATHURST METALS CORP.
665 Dougall Road, Gibsons, V0N
1V8, BC, Canada
Tel.: (604) 783-4273
Year Founded: 2006
BMVVF—(OTCIQ)
Assets: $992,740
Liabilities: $148,106
Net Worth: $844,633
Earnings: ($107,935)
Fiscal Year-end: 09/30/23
Mineral Exploration Services
N.A.I.C.S.: 213114
Harold Forzley *(Pres & CEO)*

BATHURST RESOURCES LIM-ITED
Level 12 1 Willeston Street, Welling-
ton, 6011, New Zealand
Tel.: (64) 44996830   NZ
Web Site: https://www.bathurst.co.nz
BRL—(ASX)
Rev.: $26,165,072
Assets: $178,284,091
Liabilities: $9,647,727
Net Worth: $168,636,364
Earnings: $54,118,421
Emp.: 620
Fiscal Year-end: 06/30/23
Coal Production Services
N.A.I.C.S.: 213113
Richard Tacon *(CEO)*

BATIC INVESTMENTS & LO-GISTICS CO
Al Faisaliah Office Tower 14th Floor
King Fahad Road, Riyadh, 11472,
Saudi Arabia

Tel.: (966) 114187800
Web Site: https://batic.sa
Year Founded: 1984
4110—(SAU)
Rev.: $113,983,500
Assets: $361,124,758
Liabilities: $233,647,841
Net Worth: $127,476,917
Earnings: ($8,519,223)
Fiscal Year-end: 12/31/22
Financial Investment Services
N.A.I.C.S.: 523999

BATICIM BATI ANADOLU CI-MENTO SANAYII A.S.
Ankara Caddesi No 335, Bornova,
35050, Izmir, 35050, Turkiye
Tel.: (90) 2324784400
Web Site: https://www.baticim.com.tr
Year Founded: 1966
BTCIM—(IST)
Rev.: $389,376,615
Assets: $678,829,127
Liabilities: $263,483,432
Net Worth: $415,345,694
Earnings: $69,596,889
Emp.: 1,000
Fiscal Year-end: 12/31/23
Cement Mfr
N.A.I.C.S.: 327310

BATIGERE NORD EST
15 Rue De Paris, 69170, Tarare,
Rhone, France
Tel.: (33) 382395050
Web Site: http://www.batigere-
nordest.fr
Rev.: $35,500,000
Emp.: 108
N.A.I.C.S.: 531110
Christophe Kiesser *(Mgr-Sls)*

BATIMENTS ET LOGEMENTS RESIDENTIELS
4 Rue De Chatillon, 25480, Besan-
con, Doubs, France
Tel.: (33) 381882626
Rev.: $16,800,000
Emp.: 19
N.A.I.C.S.: 531210
David Baudiquey *(Pres)*

BATISOKE SOKE CIMENTO SANAYII TAS
Ankara Caddesi No 335, Bornova,
Izmir, Turkiye
Tel.: (90) 2565182250
Web Site:
https://www.batisoke.com.tr
Year Founded: 1966
BSOKE—(IST)
Rev.: $65,313,153
Assets: $103,261,911
Liabilities: $101,084,987
Net Worth: $2,176,924
Earnings: ($23,774,614)
Emp.: 356
Fiscal Year-end: 12/31/22
Cement & Aggregate Mfr
N.A.I.C.S.: 327310
Mehmet Mustafa Bukey *(Chm)*

Subsidiaries:

Baticim Enerji Elektrik Uretim
A.S.   (1)
Ankara Caddesi No 335 Bornova, Izmir,
Turkiye
Tel.: (90) 2324784400
Construction Equipment Mfr
N.A.I.C.S.: 333120

BATISTYL PRODUCTION
Zi De La Fromentiniere, 49360, Mau-
levrier, Maine Et Loire, France
Tel.: (33) 241494950
Rev.: $38,600,000
Emp.: 68

Batistyl Production—(Continued)
N.A.I.C.S.: 423720
Bruno Couton (DP Mgr)

BATIVAL
Zone Industrielle Les Banardes,
25800, Valdahon, Doubs, France
Tel.: (33) 381562711
Sales Range: $10-24.9 Million
Emp.: 108
Engineeering Services
N.A.I.C.S.: 236115
Claude Pretre (Pres)

BATLA MINERALS SA
1 Rue de la Sauvagine, 34920, Le
Cres, France
Tel.: (33) 4 42 93 89 19
Web Site:
　　http://www.batlaminerals.com
MLBAT—(EUR)
Sales Range: $10-24.9 Million
Diamond Mining Services
N.A.I.C.S.: 212390

BATLIBOI LTD.
Bharat House 5th Floor 104 Bombay
Samachar Marg, Fort, Mumbai, 400
001, India
Tel.: (91) 2266378200
Web Site: https://www.batliboi.com
Year Founded: 1892
522004—(BOM)
Rev.: $27,125,321
Assets: $39,131,957
Liabilities: $22,000,538
Net Worth: $17,131,419
Earnings: ($642,260)
Emp.: 332
Fiscal Year-end: 03/31/22
Industrial Machinery Mfr
N.A.I.C.S.: 333248
Ganpat Sawant (Compliance Officer
& Sec)

Subsidiaries:

AESA Air Engineering Private
Limited　　　　　　　　　　　　(1)
357 Fie, Industrial Estate Patpar Ganj,
Delhi, 110092, India
Tel.: (91) 1143004800
Engineeering Services
N.A.I.C.S.: 541330
Sunil Mohan (Acct Mgr)

AESA Air Engineering SA　　　(1)
78 Faubourg des Vosges, 68804, Thann,
Cedex, France
Tel.: (33) 389383434
Web Site: https://www.aesa-ae.com
Air Conditioning & Ventilation Services
N.A.I.C.S.: 238220

Quickmill Inc.　　　　　　　　(1)
760 Rye Street, Peterborough, K9J 6W9,
ON, Canada
Tel.: (705) 745-2961
Web Site: https://www.quickmill.com
CNC Machinery Mfr & Distr
N.A.I.C.S.: 333248

BATM ADVANCED COMMUNI-CATIONS LTD.
Neve Neeman Ind Area 4 Haharash
Street, PO Box 7318, 4524075, Hod
Hasharon, 4524075, Israel
Tel.: (972) 98662525　　　　　ǁ
Web Site: https://www.batm.com
Year Founded: 1992
BVC—(TAE)
Rev.: $122,830,000
Assets: $174,627,000
Liabilities: $55,191,000
Net Worth: $119,436,000
Earnings: $622,000
Fiscal Year-end: 12/31/23
Other Communications Equipment
Manufacturing
N.A.I.C.S.: 334290

Zvi Marom (Founder & CEO)

Subsidiaries:

A.M.S. 2000　　　　　　　　　(1)
Strada Turturelelor no 62 Decebal Tower
Sector 3, Bucharest, 031612, Romania
Tel.: (40) 21 324 7050
Web Site: https://www.ams.ro
Sales Range: $25-49.9 Million
Emp.: 45
Medical Laboratory Equipment Distr
N.A.I.C.S.: 423450

Adaltis Srl　　　　　　　　　　(1)
Via Luigi Einaudi 7 Guidonia di Montecelio,
00012, Rome, Italy
Tel.: (39) 07745791
Web Site: http://www.adaltis.net
Sales Range: $25-49.9 Million
Emp.: 60
Diagnostic Instruments Mfr & Distr
N.A.I.C.S.: 334510
David Perry (CEO)

B.A.T.M. Germany GmbH　　　(1)
Hammerweg 4, 52074, Aachen,
Germany　　　　　　　　　(100%)
Tel.: (49) 2414635490
Computer Peripheral Equipment Mfr
N.A.I.C.S.: 334118

BATM France　　　　　　　　　(1)
6 Avenue Des Bleuets, 94380, Bonneuil-
sur-Marne, France
Tel.: (33) 156712773
Web Site: http://www.batm.fr
Sales Range: $25-49.9 Million
Emp.: 4
Telecommunication Servicesb
N.A.I.C.S.: 517810

CAT Technologies Ltd　　　　　(1)
Communication Center G G Israel Studio
Jerusalem Ltd, Neve Ilan, Jerusalem,
90850, Israel
Tel.: (972) 25704005
Web Site: http://www.cat-tc.com
Medical Equipment Mfr
N.A.I.C.S.: 334510

Critical Telecom Inc.　　　　　(1)
Ste 500 340 March Rd. K2K2E4, Ottawa,
ON, Canada　　　　　　　　(100%)
Tel.: (613) 271-1599
Web Site: https://www.criticaltelecom.com
Telephone Apparatus Mfr
N.A.I.C.S.: 334210

Telco Systems　　　　　　　　(1)
15 Berkshire Rd, Mansfield, MA
02048　　　　　　　　　　(100%)
Tel.: (781) 551-0300
Web Site: https://www.telco.com
Sales Range: $25-49.9 Million
Emp.: 75
Fiber Optic Transmission Products Mfr
N.A.I.C.S.: 334210
Reinhard Florin (Gen Mgr-North America)

Vigilant Technologies Ltd　　　(1)
4 Haharsh St, Hod Hasharon, 45240, Israel
Tel.: (972) 3 6491110
Web Site: http://www.vglnt.com
Surveillance Equipment Mfr
N.A.I.C.S.: 334511

Vigilant Technology Inc.　　　　(1)
15 Berkshire Rd, Mansfield, MA 02048
Tel.: (800) 708-0169
Web Site: http://www.vglnt.com
Surveillance Device Mfr
N.A.I.C.S.: 334419

BATTERY MINERAL RE-SOURCES CORP.
Suite 1900 - 1040 West Georgia
Street, Vancouver, V6E 4H3, BC,
Canada
Tel.: (604) 628-1100
Web Site: https://www.bmrcorp.com
Year Founded: 2007
BMR—(TSXV)
Rev.: $11,069,481
Assets: $84,289,197
Liabilities: $44,958,393
Net Worth: $39,330,803
Earnings: ($9,439,667)

Fiscal Year-end: 12/31/23
Asset Management Services
N.A.I.C.S.: 523940
Martin Kostuik (CEO)

Subsidiaries:

ESI Energy Services Inc.　　　(1)
600 Crowfoot Crescent NW, Calgary, T3G
0B4, AB, Canada　　　　　(100%)
Tel.: (403) 205-7188
Web Site:
　　https://www.energyservicesinc.com
Pipeline Equipment Rental & Sales Com-
pany
N.A.I.C.S.: 532412
Priyanka Bambaranda (CFO)

BATTERY MINERALS LIMITED
Ground Floor 10 Ord Street, West
Perth, 6005, WA, Australia
Tel.: (61) 861481000
Web Site:
　　http://www.batteryminerals.com
WTM—(ASX)
Rev.: $14,507
Assets: $16,658,414
Liabilities: $254,506
Net Worth: $16,403,908
Earnings: ($5,316,959)
Fiscal Year-end: 12/31/23
Graphite Exploration Services
N.A.I.C.S.: 212390
David Flanagan (Chm)

BATTERY X METALS INC.
5500 Wharf Avenue 207, PO Box
609, Sechelt, V0N 3A0, BC, Canada
Tel.: (778) 908-2730
Web Site:
　　http://www.straightupresources.com
ST—(CNSX)
Assets: $1,211,314
Liabilities: $82,597
Net Worth: $1,128,717
Earnings: ($450,310)
Fiscal Year-end: 12/31/20
Mineral Exploration Services
N.A.I.C.S.: 213115
Mark Brezer (Pres & CEO)

BATTIKHA SECURITY INC.
168 Shorting Road, Scarborough,
M1S 3S7, ON, Canada
Tel.: (416) 493-3939
Web Site:
　　http://www.battikhasecurity.ca
Year Founded: 2000
Rev.: $12,326,862
Emp.: 50
Commercial & Residential Security
Systems Supplier
N.A.I.C.S.: 561621
Lilian Battikha (Owner)

BATTISTELLA ADMINISTRA-CAO E PARTICIPACOES S.A.
Al Bom Pastor 3700-Sala 06, 83015-
140, Curitiba, PR, Brazil
Tel.: (55) 4132997272　　　　BR
Web Site:
　　http://www.battistella.com.br
Year Founded: 1949
EPAR3—(BRAZ)
Rev.: $94,275,322
Assets: $20,930,036
Liabilities: $4,427,409
Net Worth: $16,502,627
Earnings: $3,205,358
Fiscal Year-end: 12/31/23
Heavy Duty Truck Mfr & Forestry
Services
N.A.I.C.S.: 336120

BATTLERS CORP.
No 1 Street Sophora Court 1/27,
6021, Larnaca, Cyprus
Tel.: (357) 302111983153　　　NV

Web Site:
　　http://www.battlerscorp.com
Year Founded: 2016
Rev.: $2,980
Assets: $9,789
Liabilities: $6,140
Net Worth: $3,649
Earnings: ($12,161)
Emp.: 1
Fiscal Year-end: 06/30/18
Business Management Services
N.A.I.C.S.: 561110
Stepan Feodosiadi (Pres, Treas &
Sec)

BATU KAWAN BERHAD
Wisma Taiko No 1 Jalan S P
Seenivasagam, 30000, Ipoh, Perak
Darul Ridzuan, Malaysia
Tel.: (60) 52408000　　　　　MY
Web Site:
　　https://www.bkawan.com.my
Year Founded: 1965
BKAWAN—(KLS)
Rev.: $5,217,650,159
Assets: $6,752,917,037
Liabilities: $3,113,168,466
Net Worth: $3,639,748,571
Earnings: $229,797,460
Emp.: 49,246
Fiscal Year-end: 09/30/23
Chemical Products Mfr
N.A.I.C.S.: 325199
Hau Hian Hian Lee (Mng Dir)

Subsidiaries:

Chemical Company of Malaysia
Berhad　　　　　　　　　　(1)
Level 5 Menara KLK No 1 Jalan PJU 7/6,
Mutiara Damansara, 47810, Petaling Jaya,
Selangor, Malaysia　　　　(59.73%)
Tel.: (60) 355166888
Web Site: https://www.ccmberhad.com
Rev.: $93,677,800
Assets: $147,467,027
Liabilities: $68,177,215
Net Worth: $79,289,812
Earnings: $3,908,389
Emp.: 341
Fiscal Year-end: 12/31/2019
Fertilizers, Chlor-Alkali Chemicals, Agro-
chemicals & Paints Mfr
N.A.I.C.S.: 212390

Subsidiary (Domestic):

CCM Chemicals Sdn. Bhd.　　(2)
Level 5 Menara KLK No1 Jalan PJU 7/6,
Mutiara Damansara, 47810, Petaling Jaya,
Selangor, Malaysia　　　　(100%)
Tel.: (60) 355166888
Chemical Products Mfr
N.A.I.C.S.: 212390
Noor Aslam (Mng Dir)

CCM Innovative Solutions Sdn
Bhd　　　　　　　　　　　(2)
No 32 Jalan P10/16 Selaman Industrial
Park, Section 10, 43650, Bandar Baru
Bangi, Selangor Darul Ehsan, Malaysia
Tel.: (60) 3 8922 1828
Chemical Products Mfr
N.A.I.C.S.: 325998

CCM Marketing Sdn Bhd　　　(2)
No 12 Jalan Saudagar 1 U1/16A, HICOM
Glenmarie Industrial Park, 40150, Shah
Alam, Selangor Darul Ehsan, Malaysia
Tel.: (60) 355690533
Pharmaceutical Marketing Services
N.A.I.C.S.: 424210

CCM Polymers Sdn. Bhd.　　　(2)
No 69 Jalan P10/16 Selaman Industrial
Park Section 10, 43650, Bandar Baru
Bangi, Selangor, Malaysia
Tel.: (60) 389221828
Agrochemical & Paint Mfr
N.A.I.C.S.: 325510
Thomas Gan (Sr Mgr-Bus)

Subsidiary (Non-US):

CCM Singapore Pte Ltd　　　　(2)
25 International Business Park 02-60 Ger-

man Centre, 02-60 German Centre, Singapore, 609916, Singapore
Tel.: (65) 64685468
Chemical Products Mfr
N.A.I.C.S.: 325998

Subsidiary (Domestic):

CCM Usaha Kimia (M) Sdn Bhd   **(2)**
Lot 4 & 6 Jalan Kemajuan 16/17A, 40200, Shah Alam, Selangor Darul Ehsan, Malaysia
Tel.: (60) 355106920
Chemical Products Mfr
N.A.I.C.S.: 325998

CCM Watercare Sdn Bhd   **(2)**
Lot 4 & 6 Jalan Kemajuan 16/17A, 40200, Shah Alam, Selangor Darul Ehsan, Malaysia
Tel.: (60) 351018388
Chemical Products Mfr
N.A.I.C.S.: 325998
Norazlan Zulkifli *(Gen Mgr)*

Duopharma Biotech Berhad   **(2)**
Lot 2599 Jalan Seruling 59 Kawasan 3, Taman Klang Jaya, 41200, Klang, Selangor Darul Ehsan, Malaysia
Tel.: (60) 333232759
Web Site: https://duopharmabiotech.com
Pharmaceuticals Product Mfr
N.A.I.C.S.: 325412

Subsidiary (Non-US):

CCM Pharmaceuticals (S) Pte Ltd.   **(3)**
25 International Business Park 03-24/25 German Centre, 02-60 German Centre, Singapore, 609916, Singapore
Tel.: (65) 65628326
Pharmaceuticals Mfr
N.A.I.C.S.: 325412

Subsidiary (Domestic):

CCM Pharmaceuticals Sdn Bhd   **(3)**
Lot 2 4 6 8 10 Jalan P/7 Seksyen 13 13, Kawasan Perusahaan, 43650, Bandar Baru Bangi, Selangor Darul Ehsan, Malaysia
Tel.: (60) 389242188
Pharmaceuticals Mfr
N.A.I.C.S.: 325412

Subsidiary (Non-US):

DB (Philippines), Inc.   **(3)**
Unit 803 The Taipan Place F The Taipan Place F Ortigas Jr Ave, Ortigas, Pasig, 1600, Philippines
Tel.: (63) 26387805
Pharmaceuticals & Chemicals & Fertilizers Product Whslr
N.A.I.C.S.: 325412

Subsidiary (Domestic):

Innovax Sdn Bhd   **(3)**
No 2 Jalan Saudagar U1/16 Seksyen U1, Zon Perindustrian Hicom Glenmarie, 40150, Shah Alam, Selangor Darul Ehsan, Malaysia
Tel.: (60) 55696888
Pharmaceuticals Mfr
N.A.I.C.S.: 325412

Subsidiary (Non-US):

PT CCM Indonesia   **(2)**
Wisma GKBI 39th Floor, Jl Jend Sudirman No 28, Jakarta, 10210, Pusat, Indonesia
Tel.: (62) 2157998094
Chemical Products Mfr
N.A.I.C.S.: 325998

Subsidiary (Domestic):

Sentosa Pharmacy Sdn Bhd   **(2)**
No 64 Jln Permas 9 13 Taman Permas Jaya, Johor, Masai, 81750, Malaysia
Tel.: (60) 73887328
Sales Range: $25-49.9 Million
Emp.: 9
Pharmaceuticals Product Mfr
N.A.I.C.S.: 325412
Chong Choo *(Bus Mgr)*

Unique Pharmacy (Ipoh) Sdn Bhd   **(2)**
No 81, Jln Yang Kalsom, Ipoh, 30250,

Perak, Malaysia
Tel.: (60) 52557662
Pharmaceutical & Healthcare Products Mfr
N.A.I.C.S.: 325412

Enternal Edge Sdn. Bhd.   **(1)**
Jalan S P Seenivasagam 1, 30000, Ipoh, Perak, Malaysia
Tel.: (60) 52417844
Chemicals Mfr
N.A.I.C.S.: 325199

KLK Kolb Specialties BV   **(1)**
Langestraat 167, 7491 AE, Delden, Netherlands
Tel.: (31) 743775000
Surfactant Mfr & Distr
N.A.I.C.S.: 325613

KLK Land Sdn Bhd   **(1)**
Suite 1A-1 Level 1 Menara KLK No 1 Jalan PJU 7/6 Mutiara Damansara, 47810, Petaling Jaya, Selangor, Malaysia
Tel.: (60) 377261868
Web Site: https://www.klkland.com.my
Investment Services
N.A.I.C.S.: 523999

KLK Tensachem SA   **(1)**
Rue de Renory 28, Seraing, 4102, Ougree, Belgium
Tel.: (32) 43389389
Web Site: https://www.tensachem.com
Emp.: 100
Anionic Surfactant Mfr
N.A.I.C.S.: 325613

Klk Hardwood Flooring Sdn. Bhd.   **(1)**
No 4 Lebuh Perusahaan Kelebang 5 IGB International Industrial Park, Jalan Kuala Kangsar, 31200, Ipoh, Malaysia
Tel.: (60) 52911599
Web Site: https://www.bkbhevea.com
Wood Machinery & Equipment Mfr
N.A.I.C.S.: 333243

Malay-Sino Chemical Industries Sdn. Bhd.   **(1)**
4 1/2 Miles Jalan Lahat, 30200, Ipoh, Perak, Malaysia
Tel.: (60) 53224255
Web Site: https://www.malay-sino.com.my
Chemicals Mfr
N.A.I.C.S.: 325199

Subsidiary (Domestic):

Circular Agency Sdn. Bhd.   **(2)**
Pt 115637 - Pt 115639 Zarib Industrial Park, Off Jalan Lahat-Simpang Pulai, 31500, Ipoh, Malaysia
Tel.: (60) 53227199
Rail Transport Services
N.A.I.C.S.: 488210

Malay-Sino Chemical Industries Sdn. Bhd. - Kemaman Plant   **(2)**
Lot PT 4406 Kawasan Perindustrian Teluk Kalong, Kemaman, 24000, Terengganu, Malaysia
Tel.: (60) 98633529
Chemicals Mfr
N.A.I.C.S.: 325199

See Sen Chemical Bhd.   **(1)**
PT 3904 Kawasan Perindustrian Telok Kalong, Chukai, 24000, Kemaman, Terengganu, Malaysia
Tel.: (60) 98632142
Web Site: http://www.seesenchem.com.my
Chemical Mfr & Distr
N.A.I.C.S.: 325199

Plant (Domestic):

See Sen Chemical Bhd. - Pasir Gudang Facility   **(2)**
PLO 276 Jalan Pekeliling, Pasir Gudang Industrial Estate, 81700, Pasir Gudang, Johor, Malaysia
Tel.: (60) 72512491
Web Site: http://www.seesenchem.com.my
Chemicals Mfr
N.A.I.C.S.: 325199

Somerset Cuisine Limited   **(1)**
Tylers End Isleport Business Park, Highbridge, Somerset, TA9 4JS, United Kingdom
Tel.: (44) 1278780913

Web Site:
https://www.somersetcuisine.co.uk
Jams & Preserve Product Mfr
N.A.I.C.S.: 311421
Julie Blake *(Comml Dir)*

BATYS TRANSIT JSC
Shevchenko str 162 zh, Almaty, 050000, Kazakhstan
Tel.: (7) 7273756414
Web Site: http://www.bttr.kz
Year Founded: 2005
BTTR—(KAZ)
Rev.: $10,243,514
Assets: $103,340,246
Liabilities: $71,172,243
Net Worth: $32,168,003
Earnings: $3,289,523
Emp.: 52
Fiscal Year-end: 12/31/23
Eletric Power Generation Services
N.A.I.C.S.: 221118
Kurmangazy Beysembaevich Ibragimov *(Chm)*

BAUCH ENGINEERING GMBH & CO. KG
Robert-Bosch-Strasse 8, Eitensheim, 85117, Gaimersheim, Germany
Tel.: (49) 845832340
Web Site: http://www.bauch.biz
Year Founded: 1993
Rev.: $10,690,350
Emp.: 19
Machines & Mechanical Component Mfr
N.A.I.C.S.: 333517
Manfred Bauch *(Co-Mng Dir)*

Subsidiaries:

BAUCH Powertrain Components Co., Ltd.   **(1)**
Chengxiang Industrial Area 143 Yan Shan West Road, 215400, Taicang, China
Tel.: (86) 51281600130
Measuring Tool Distr
N.A.I.C.S.: 423830
Ni Ping *(Dir-Technical)*

BAUDOUX CONSTRUCTION METALLIQUES
12 Route De Sissonne, 02820, Saint-Erme-Outre-et-Ramecourt, Aisne, France
Tel.: (33) 323226377
Web Site:
  http://www.baudouxcm.com
Rev.: $13,900,000
Emp.: 63
N.A.I.C.S.: 332312
Pascale Raffelet *(Mgr-Pur)*

BAUDRY AUTOMOBILES
Boulevard Lavoisier, 85000, La Roche-sur-Yon, Vendee, France
Tel.: (33) 251477747
Year Founded: 1999
New & Used Car Dealers
N.A.I.C.S.: 441110
Didier Jaulin *(Dir)*

BAUER AKTIENGESELL-SCHAFT
BAUER-Strasse 1, 86529, Schrobenhausen, Germany
Tel.: (49) 8252970
Web Site: https://www.bauer.de
B5A—(DEU)
Rev.: $1,813,043,384
Assets: $1,748,278,653
Liabilities: $1,314,098,856
Net Worth: $434,179,797
Earnings: ($103,082,236)
Emp.: 11,892
Fiscal Year-end: 12/31/22
Construction Machinery Manufacturer
N.A.I.C.S.: 238910

Hartmut Beutler *(Member-Mgmt Bd)*

Subsidiaries:

BAUER (MALAYSIA) SDN. BHD.   **(1)**
Unit 506 Blk G Phileo Damansara 1 No 9 Jln 16 11 Off Jln Damansara, 46350, Petaling Jaya, Selangor, Malaysia
Tel.: (60) 379569366
Web Site: http://www.bauer.com.my
Sales Range: $25-49.9 Million
Emp.: 50
Construction Machinery Mfr
N.A.I.C.S.: 333120
Thomas Domanski *(Mng Dir)*

Subsidiary (Non-US):

BAUER Foundations Australia Pty Ltd.   **(2)**
Ground Floor 154 Enoggera Road, Newmarket, Brisbane, 4051, QLD, Australia
Tel.: (61) 733527444
Web Site: http://www.baueraustralia.com.au
Sales Range: $25-49.9 Million
Pile Driving Equipment Mfr
N.A.I.C.S.: 335999
Thomas Domanski *(Member-Mgmt Bd)*

BAUER Corporate Services Private Limited   **(1)**
12th Floor Lotus Business Park Off New Link Road, Andheri West, Mumbai, 400053, Maharashtra, India
Tel.: (91) 2240024017
Web Site: http://www.bauerindia.in
Information Technology Solutions
N.A.I.C.S.: 541512

BAUER EGYPT S.A.E.   **(1)**
197 26 July Street, El Mohandseen, 112 455, Cairo, Egypt
Tel.: (20) 233026083
Web Site: https://www.bauer-egypt.com
Sales Range: $100-124.9 Million
Emp.: 500
Foundation Contractor
N.A.I.C.S.: 238110
Ashraf Wahby *(Mgr-Technical)*

BAUER ENVIRO Kft.   **(1)**
Aradi U 16 II 2, 1062, Budapest, Hungary
Tel.: (36) 14522070
Web Site: http://www.bauerenviro.hu
Environmental Consulting Services
N.A.I.C.S.: 541620

BAUER Engineering India Private Limited   **(1)**
403-404 B Tower Millennium Plaza B Block Sushant Lok-1, Gurgaon, 122 002, Haryana, India
Tel.: (91) 1244295787
Web Site: https://www.bauer-india.com
Civil Engineering Services
N.A.I.C.S.: 541330

BAUER Foundation Corp.   **(1)**
13203 Byrd Legg Dr, Odessa, FL 33556
Tel.: (727) 531-2577
Web Site: http://www.bauerfoundations.com
Sales Range: $50-74.9 Million
Emp.: 100
Civil Engineering Services
N.A.I.C.S.: 541330

BAUER Foundations Canada Inc.   **(1)**
5050 74th Avenue SE, Calgary, T2C 3C9, AB, Canada
Tel.: (403) 723-0159
Web Site: http://www.bauerfoundations.ca
Sales Range: $25-49.9 Million
Emp.: 20
Civil Engineering Services
N.A.I.C.S.: 541330
Samir Hebib *(Mng Dir)*

BAUER Foundations Philippines, Inc.   **(1)**
12th Floor Units A-K Cyber One Building 11 Eastwood Avenue, Eastwood City Cyberpark Bagumbayan, Quezon City, 1110, Philippines
Tel.: (63) 284248760
Web Site: http://www.bauer.net.ph
Sales Range: $25-49.9 Million
Emp.: 20
Civil Engineering Services

BAUER Aktiengesellschaft—(Continued)

N.A.I.C.S.: 541330

BAUER Funderingstechniek B.V. (1)
Rendementsweg 29, 3641 SK, Mijdrecht, Netherlands
Tel.: (31) 297231150
Foundation Work Contract Services
N.A.I.C.S.: 238910
Eelco van der Velde (Mng Dir)

BAUER Hong Kong Limited (1)
Units 1604-6 16th Fl Chinachem Tsuen Wan Plaza 455-457 Castle Peak Rd, Tsuen Wan, New Territories, China (Hong Kong)
Tel.: (852) 24309928
Web Site: http://www.bauerhk.com.hk
Sales Range: $25-49.9 Million
Emp.: 10
Construction & Project Management Services
N.A.I.C.S.: 541330

BAUER Manufacturing Inc. (1)
100 N FM 3083 E 9303 New Trails Dr, Conroe, TX 77303
Tel.: (936) 539-5030
Web Site: http://www.bauer-conroe.com
Sales Range: $25-49.9 Million
Emp.: 80
Swaging Machine Mfr
N.A.I.C.S.: 333517
Thomas L. Jarboe (Pres & CEO)

BAUER Maschinen GmbH. (1)
BAUER-Strasse 1, Neuburg-Schrobenhausen Dist, 86529, Schrobenhausen, Germany
Tel.: (49) 8252970
Web Site: https://equipment.bauer.de
Sales Range: $800-899.9 Million
Emp.: 5,000
Construction Machinery Mfr
N.A.I.C.S.: 333120

Subsidiary (Non-US):

BAUER Equipment Gulf FZE. (2)
9W Bldg B-Block Office 521 Dubai Airport Freezone, PO Box 54253, Dubai, United Arab Emirates
Tel.: (971) 42555905
Web Site: https://www.bauer.ae
Foundation Equipments Sales
N.A.I.C.S.: 532412
Hermann Schrattenthaler (Reg Dir-Middle East & Africa)

Plant (Domestic):

BAUER Maschinen GmbH - Aresing Plant (2)
Sonnenhamerstrasse 55, 86561, Aresing, Germany
Tel.: (49) 8252970
Web Site: http://www.bauer.ge
Construction Machinery Mfr
N.A.I.C.S.: 333120

BAUER Maschinen GmbH - Edelshausen Plant (2)
Gewerbegebiet Edelshausen In der Scherau 1, 86529, Schrobenhausen, Germany
Tel.: (49) 8252970
Web Site: http://www.bauer.de
Sales Range: $25-49.9 Million
Emp.: 200
Construction Machinery Mfr
N.A.I.C.S.: 333120

BAUER Maschinen GmbH - Schrobenhausen Plant (2)
Burgermeister-Gotz-Strasse 36, 86529, Schrobenhausen, Germany
Tel.: (49) 8252970
Web Site: http://www.bauer.de
Sales Range: $75-99.9 Million
Emp.: 400
Construction Machinery Mfr
N.A.I.C.S.: 333243

Subsidiary (Non-US):

BAUER Technologies Far East Pte. Ltd. (2)
30 Tuas Avenue 11, Singapore, 639108, Singapore
Tel.: (65) 65766633

Web Site: https://www.bauerfe.com
Sales Range: $25-49.9 Million
Emp.: 40
Drilling Rigs & Accessories Mfr
N.A.I.C.S.: 333132
Klaus Schwarz (Mng Dir & Member-Mgmt Bd)

Subsidiary (Domestic):

BAUER EQUIPMENT SOUTH ASIA PTE. LTD. (3)
30 Tuas Avenue 11, Singapore, 639108, Singapore
Tel.: (65) 65766631
Web Site: http://www.bauerfe.com
Sales Range: $50-74.9 Million
Emp.: 4
Foundation Work Equipment & Supplies
N.A.I.C.S.: 532412

Subsidiary (Non-US):

BAUER Equipment (Malayasia) SDN. BHD. (3)
11 Jalan Seputeh Batu 3 Jalan Kelang Lama, 58000, Kuala Lumpur, Selangor, Malaysia
Tel.: (60) 379808334
Drilling Rigs Mfr
N.A.I.C.S.: 333132

BAUER Equipment (Shanghai) Co. Ltd. (3)
Block 3 No 27 Caolian Zhi Road, Jiading District, Shanghai, 201804, China
Tel.: (86) 2139123888
Web Site: http://www.bauerchina.net
Sales Range: $25-49.9 Million
Drilling Rigs Mfr
N.A.I.C.S.: 333132

BAUER Equipment Hong Kong Ltd. (3)
Unit 4A G/F Join-In Hang Sing Centre 71-75 Container Port Road, Kwai Chung, NT, China (Hong Kong)
Tel.: (852) 25449613
Web Site: http://www.bauer.de
Sales Range: $25-49.9 Million
Emp.: 7
Drilling Rigs & Accessories Mfr
N.A.I.C.S.: 333132

BAUER Tianjin Technologies Co. Ltd. (3)
No 1 Kai Yuan Road Xiqing Car Industrial Park, Xiqing Development Area, Tianjin, 300380, China
Tel.: (86) 2223807700
Rotary Drilling Rigs Mfr
N.A.I.C.S.: 333132

Bauer Technologies Thailand Co., Ltd. (3)
999 Gaysorn Plaza 5th Floor Unit 5B1 Ploenchit Rd, Patumwan Lumpini, Bangkok, 10330, Thailand
Tel.: (66) 26240647
Construction Equipment Mfr
N.A.I.C.S.: 333120

P.T. Bauer Equipment Indonesia (3)
Gading Kirana Timur Blok A 11/15, Kelapa Gading, 14240, Jakarta Utara, Indonesia
Tel.: (62) 212937385
Construction Equipment Mfr
N.A.I.C.S.: 333120
Fahri Fazri (Mgr-Mktg & Sls)

Shanghai BAUER Technologies Co. Ltd. (3)
No 28 Caolian Zhi Road Huangdu, Jiading District, Shanghai, 201804, China
Tel.: (86) 2139123800
Sales Range: $25-49.9 Million
Rotary Drilling Rigs Mfr
N.A.I.C.S.: 333132

BAUER Mietpool GmbH. (1)
Bauer Strasse 1, 86529, Schrobenhausen, Germany
Tel.: (49) 8252970
Web Site: http://www.bauer.be
Sales Range: $25-49.9 Million
Emp.: 50
Construction Machinery Mfr
N.A.I.C.S.: 333120
Hartmut Beutler (Mgr)

BAUER Resources Canada Ltd. (1)
8003 102 St NW Ste 202, Edmonton, T6E 4A2, AB, Canada
Tel.: (780) 433-3448
Sales Range: $75-99.9 Million
Emp.: 2
Coal & Diamond Mining Services
N.A.I.C.S.: 212115

BAUER SPEZIALTIEFBAU Gesellschaft m.b.H. (1)
Warneckestrasse 1-3, 1110, Vienna, Austria
Tel.: (43) 1760220
Web Site: http://www.bauer-spezialtiefbau.at
Foundation Work Contract Services
N.A.I.C.S.: 238910

BAUER Services Singapore Pte. Ltd. (1)
51 Goldhill Plaza 08-06/07, 308900, Singapore, Singapore
Tel.: (65) 62585113
Sales Range: $25-49.9 Million
Emp.: 5
Foundation Work Contract Services
N.A.I.C.S.: 238910

BAUER Special Foundations Cambodia Co., Ltd. (1)
10 Oknha Pich Avenue Street 242, Sangkat Chaktamuk Khan Daun Penh, Phnom Penh, Cambodia
Tel.: (855) 23963777
Web Site: https://www.bauercambodia.com
Civil Engineering Services
N.A.I.C.S.: 541330

BAUER Spezialtiefbau GmbH. (1)
Tel.: (49) 8252970
Sales Range: $100-124.9 Million
Emp.: 500
Foundation Engineering Services
N.A.I.C.S.: 238910

Subsidiary (Non-US):

BAUER BULGARIA EOOD. (2)
11A Samokov Street, 1113, Sofia, Bulgaria
Tel.: (359) 29746169
Web Site: http://www.bauer.bg
Sales Range: $25-49.9 Million
Emp.: 50
Foundation Work Contract Services
N.A.I.C.S.: 321114

BAUER FUNDACIONES PANAMA S.A. (2)
Building 319 D, PO Box 0819-03827, Ancon, Panama, Panama
Tel.: (507) 3176078
Web Site: http://www.bauerpanama.com.pa
Sales Range: $25-49.9 Million
Emp.: 100
Civil Engineering Services
N.A.I.C.S.: 541330

BAUER Fondations Speciales S.A.S. (2)
5 rue La Fayette, 67100, Strasbourg, Bas-Rhin, France
Tel.: (33) 390409850
Web Site: http://www.bauer-france.fr
Sales Range: $25-49.9 Million
Emp.: 2
Foundation Work Contract Services
N.A.I.C.S.: 238910

BAUER ROMANIA S.R.L. (2)
10 Constantin Disescu Str 1st Floor Sector 1, 011087, Bucharest, Romania
Tel.: (40) 213150020
Web Site: http://wwwbauer.ro
Sales Range: $25-49.9 Million
Emp.: 46
Foundation Work Contract Services
N.A.I.C.S.: 238910
Qvidiu Constantinescu (Mng Dir)

BAUER Spezialtiefbau Schweiz AG. (2)
Im Langacker 20a, Dattwil, 5405, Baden, Switzerland
Tel.: (41) 562039050
Web Site: http://www.bauer-schweiz.ch
Emp.: 30
Civil Engineering Services
N.A.I.C.S.: 541330

BAUER Technologies Limited (2)
10 Ducketts Wharf South Street, Bishop's

Stortford, CM23 3AR, Hertfordshire, United Kingdom
Tel.: (44) 1279653108
Sales Range: $25-49.9 Million
Emp.: 20
Piling Works Contract Services
N.A.I.C.S.: 238910

BAUER Technologies South Africa (PTY) Ltd. (1)
First Floor Unit 215 Palms Office Park Nupen Crescent, Midrand, 1685, Gauteng, South Africa
Tel.: (27) 118053307
Web Site: http://www.bauersa.co.za
Sales Range: $50-74.9 Million
Emp.: 10
Mineral Exploration & Drilling Services
N.A.I.C.S.: 213115
Alexander Dittmar (Member-Mgmt Bd)

BAUER Umwelt GmbH. (1)
In der Scherau 1, 86529, Schrobenhausen, Germany
Tel.: (49) 8252970
Web Site: http://www.bauerenvironment.com
Sales Range: $25-49.9 Million
Emp.: 80
Environmental Services
N.A.I.C.S.: 541330

BAUER Vietnam Inc. (1)
6th Floor No 9 Dinh Tien Hoang Street, Da Kao Ward District 1, Ho Chi Minh City, Vietnam
Tel.: (84) 2838206137
Web Site: http://www.bauervietnam.com
Sales Range: $25-49.9 Million
Emp.: 229
Foundation Engineering Services
N.A.I.C.S.: 238190

BAUER-Pileco Inc. (1)
100 N FM 3083 E, Conroe, TX 77303
Tel.: (713) 691-3000
Web Site: http://www.bauerpileco.com
Sales Range: $10-24.9 Million
Emp.: 35
General Construction Machinery & Equipment Mfr
N.A.I.C.S.: 423810
Rene Gudjons (Chm)

BRK Specialis Melyepito Kft. (1)
Budapest 2 4 str 10, 1093, Budapest, Hungary
Tel.: (36) 12163053
Web Site: http://www.brk.hu
Sales Range: $25-49.9 Million.
Emp.: 50
Underground Work Contract Services
N.A.I.C.S.: 541330

Bauer Ambiente S.r.l. (1)
Via Trento 7/F, 22074, Lomazzo, CO, Italy
Tel.: (39) 0296370237
Resource & Environment Services
N.A.I.C.S.: 813312

Bauer Angola Lda. (1)
Rua Comandante Cheriff Km 25 da Via Expressa, Cacuaco Viana, Luanda, Angola
Tel.: (244) 942583583
Web Site: http://www.bauer-angola.com
Construction Equipment Mfr
N.A.I.C.S.: 333120
Daniela Gloria (Mng Dir)

Bauer Casings Makina Sanayi ve Ticaret Limited Sirketi (1)
Ahi Evran OSB Mahallesi Buyuk Timur Cad No 5, Sincan, 06935, Ankara, Turkiye
Tel.: (90) 3122674501
Web Site: https://bauer.com.tr
Pile Pipe & Parts Mfr
N.A.I.C.S.: 326122
Hayati Emiroglu (Gen Mgr)

Bauer Engineering Ghana Lmtd. (1)
PMB L12 Legon Cotton Street No 6, East Legon, Accra, Ghana
Tel.: (233) 302544113
Web Site: http://bauer-ghana.com
Construction Equipment Mfr
N.A.I.C.S.: 333120
Giuseppe Canducci (Mng Dir)

Bauer Equipamientos De Panama S.A. (1)
Boulevard Panama Pacifico International

Busines Park, Edificio 3845 Oficina 201,
Panama, Panama
Tel.: (507) 3963982
Web Site:
http://www.bauerequipamientos.com.pa
Construction Equipment Mfr
N.A.I.C.S.: 333120

Bauer Equipment America Inc. **(1)**
680 Conroe Park W Dr, Conroe, TX 77303
Tel.: (713) 691-3000
Web Site: https://www.bauer-equipment.com
Construction Equipment Mfr
N.A.I.C.S.: 333120
Daniel Dragone *(Chief Sls Officer)*

Bauer Equipment Australia Pty.
Ltd. **(1)**
36 Bearing Road, Seven Hills, 2147, NSW,
Australia
Tel.: (61) 296749691
Web Site:
https://www.bauerequipment.com.au
Construction Equipment Mfr
N.A.I.C.S.: 333120
Michael Minsky *(Gen Mgr)*

Bauer Equipment India Private
Limited **(1)**
1102 Tower 'B' Millennium Plaza 'B' Block
Sushant Lok - I, Gurgaon, 122002, Hary-
ana, India
Tel.: (91) 1244300450
Web Site: http://www.bauer-equipment.in
Construction Equipment Mfr
N.A.I.C.S.: 333120
Jagpal Singh *(Mng Dir)*

Bauer Equipment UK Limited **(1)**
Rotary Drive, Wath Upon Dearne, Rother-
ham, S63 7FD, South Yorkshire, United
Kingdom
Tel.: (44) 1709874555
Web Site: https://www.bauer-
equipment.co.uk
Construction Equipment Mfr
N.A.I.C.S.: 333120
Graeme McWhirter *(Mng Dir)*

Bauer Fondations Speciales Eurl **(1)**
BAUER-Strasse 1, 86529, Schroben-
hausen, Germany
Tel.: (49) 8252972164
Web Site: http://www.bauer-algerie.com
Construction Equipment Mfr
N.A.I.C.S.: 333120

Bauer Georgia Foundation Specialists
LCC **(1)**
27 Mitskevich Str Floor 6, 0194, Tbilisi,
Georgia
Tel.: (995) 322251466
Web Site: http://www.bauer.ge
Construction Equipment Mfr
N.A.I.C.S.: 333120
Fatih Catalbas *(Gen Mgr)*

Bauer Geotechnical Specialized
Foundation LLC **(1)**
Office No 304 Al Ain Tower Hamdan Street,
PO Box 43673, Abu Dhabi, United Arab
Emirates
Tel.: (971) 26721405
Emp.: 1,500
Construction Equipment Mfr
N.A.I.C.S.: 333120

Bauer Geoteknoloji Insaat Anonim
Sirketi **(1)**
POL Center Esentepe Mahallesi Buyukere
Caddesi Ecza Sokagi D, No 4/1 34394 Sisli,
34394, Istanbul, Turkiye
Tel.: (90) 2129428228
Web Site: http://bauerturkiye.com
Ground Foundation Services
N.A.I.C.S.: 238110

Bauer International FZE **(1)**
Office No 304 Al Ain Tower Hamdan Street,
PO Box 43673, Abu Dhabi, United Arab
Emirates
Tel.: (971) 26721405
Web Site: https://www.baueruae.ae
Construction Equipment Mfr
N.A.I.C.S.: 333120
Ulrich Emmer *(Gen Mgr)*

Bauer Lebanon Foundation Special-
ists S.a.r.l. **(1)**

Chalet Suisse Street 457 Michel Cortbawi
Building 4th floor, PO Box 90467, Jdeidet El
Metn, Beirut, Lebanon
Tel.: (961) 1875707
Web Site: http://www.bauerlebanon.com
Construction Equipment Mfr
N.A.I.C.S.: 333120
Georges Assaf Abdo *(Gen Mgr)*

Bauer Macchine Italia Srl **(1)**
Strada Statale 610 Selice 10/C, 40027,
Mordano, BO, Italy
Tel.: (39) 05421895011
Web Site: http://bauer-italia.it
Construction Equipment Mfr
N.A.I.C.S.: 333120
Alberto Dalle Coste *(Mng Dir)*

Bauer Magyarorszag Specialis Mely-
epito Kft. **(1)**
Mariassy utca 7, 1095, Budapest, Hungary
Tel.: (36) 12163053
Web Site: https://www.bauerhungary.hu
Construction Equipment Mfr
N.A.I.C.S.: 333120
Kristof Nagy *(Mng Dir)*

Bauer Maszyny Polska Sp.z.o.o. **(1)**
Krolowej Marysienki 9/11 Street, 02-954,
Warsaw, Poland
Tel.: (48) 226426486
Web Site: https://www.bauermaszyny.pl
Construction Equipment Mfr
N.A.I.C.S.: 333120
Dariusz Mikulski *(Mng Dir)*

Bauer Nimr LLC **(1)**
PC 114 Al Mina, PO Box 1186, Muscat,
Oman
Tel.: (968) 22009560
Web Site: https://bauer-nimr.de
Hazardous & Waste Management Services
N.A.I.C.S.: 562211
Peter Hingott *(Chm)*

Bauer Renewables Limited **(1)**
Regus Stirling Lomond Court Castle Busi-
ness Park, Stirling, FK9 4TU, United King-
dom
Tel.: (44) 1786431709
Web Site: https://www.bauer-
renewables.co.uk
Construction Equipment Mfr
N.A.I.C.S.: 333120
Bill Shaw *(Comml Dir)*

Bauer Training Center GmbH **(1)**
BAUER-Strasse 1, 86529, Schroben-
hausen, Germany
Tel.: (49) 8252971804
Web Site: http://bauer-trainingcenter.de
Education Training Services
N.A.I.C.S.: 611710

Brasbauer Equipamentos De Perfura-
cao Ltda. **(1)**
Rua Olimpiadas 194-13 Andar Vila Olimpia,
Guarulhos, 04551-000, Sao Paulo, Brazil
Tel.: (55) 1130289800
Web Site: https://www.brasbauer.com.br
Oil & Gas Equipment Mfr
N.A.I.C.S.: 333132
Rolf Pickert *(Gen Mgr)*

EURODRILL GmbH. **(1)**
Industriestr 5, 57489, Drolshagen, Germany
Tel.: (49) 2763212280
Web Site: https://eurodrill.de
Sales Range: $25-49.9 Million
Emp.: 39
Rotary Drill Heads & Drifters Mfr
N.A.I.C.S.: 333131
Ralf Sonnecken *(Mng Dir & Member-Mgmt
Bd)*

FORALITH Equipment AG. **(1)**
Bionstrasse 4, Saint Gallen, 9015, Switzer-
land
Tel.: (41) 713137050
Sales Range: $25-49.9 Million
Emp.: 20
Industrial Machinery & Equipment Whslr
N.A.I.C.S.: 423830

Fielddata.io GmbH **(1)**
Konrad-Zuse-Platz 8, 81829, Munich, Ger-
many
Tel.: (49) 8999742870
Web Site: http://www.fielddata.io
Construction Engineering Services

N.A.I.C.S.: 541330
Jochen Maurer *(CEO)*

GF-Tec GmbH. **(1)**
Kronberger Strasse 4, 63110, Rodgau, Ger-
many
Tel.: (49) 61062668880
Web Site: http://www.gf-tec.com
Sales Range: $25-49.9 Million
Emp.: 6
Plastics & Metal Components Development
& Mfr
N.A.I.C.S.: 333511

GWE Budafilter Kft. **(1)**
Paskom ret 1, 2422, Mezofalva, Hungary
Web Site: http://www.gwe-budafilter.com
Water Pump Mfr & Distr
N.A.I.C.S.: 333914

GWE France S.A.S. **(1)**
ZI Les pins 19 bis Avenue de la Gare,
34800, Aspiran, France
Tel.: (33) 467442153
Web Site: https://www.gwefrance.fr
Geothermal Energy Services
N.A.I.C.S.: 213112

GWE Pol-Bud Sp.z.o.o **(1)**
ul Demokratyczna 89/93, 93-430, Lodz,
Poland
Tel.: (48) 6388930
Web Site: https://www.gwe-polbud.pl
PVC Pipe Mfr
N.A.I.C.S.: 326122

GWE Tubomin S.A. **(1)**
Los Arrayanes 450, Colina, Santiago, Chile
Tel.: (56) 227387294
Web Site: https://www.gwe-tubomin.com
PVC & Steel Mfr
N.A.I.C.S.: 331210

GWE pumpenboese GmbH. **(1)**
Moorbeerenweg 1, 31228, Peine, Germany
Tel.: (49) 51712940
Web Site: http://www.gwe-gruppe.de
Sales Range: $50-74.9 Million
Emp.: 50
Well Casings & Screening Services
N.A.I.C.S.: 213112

KLEMM Bohrtechnik GmbH. **(1)**
Wintersohler Strasse 5, 57489, Drolshagen,
Germany
Tel.: (49) 27617050
Web Site: https://klemm.de
Sales Range: $50-74.9 Million
Emp.: 230
Drilling Rigs & Accessories Mfr
N.A.I.C.S.: 333132
Thorsten Marquard *(Reg Dir-Sls-Continental
Asia, Japan, Taiwan & Singapore)*

MAT Mischanlagentechnik
GmbH. **(1)**
Illerstrasse 6, 87509, Immenstadt, Germany
Tel.: (49) 832396410
Web Site: http://www.mat-oa.de
Sales Range: $25-49.9 Million
Emp.: 80
Industrial Machinery & Pumps Mfr
N.A.I.C.S.: 333248

MMG Mitteldeutsche MONTAN
GmbH. **(1)**
Geseniusstrasse 18 b, 99734, Nordhausen,
Germany
Tel.: (49) 3631468990
Web Site: https://www.mdt-montan.de
Emp.: 200
Consturction & Mining Machinery Mfr
N.A.I.C.S.: 333120

Nippon Bauer Y.K. **(1)**
1-36-16 Uehara, Shibuya-ku, Tokyo, 151-
0064, Japan
Tel.: (81) 357616424
Web Site: https://www.nippon-bauer.com
Emp.: 14
Construction Equipment Mfr
N.A.I.C.S.: 333120

OOO Bauer Maschinen
Russland **(1)**
Kalanchevskaya- Str 6/2 billd 2, Moscow,
107078, Russia
Tel.: (7) 4957716920
Web Site: https://www.bauer-rus.ru
Construction Equipment Mfr

N.A.I.C.S.: 333120

Olbersdorfer GuB GmbH. **(1)**
An Der Stadtgrenze, 02785, Olbersdorf,
Germany
Tel.: (49) 358357620
Web Site: http://www.olbersdorfer-guss.de
Sales Range: $50-74.9 Million
Emp.: 128
Ductile Iron Castings Mfr
N.A.I.C.S.: 331511
Lamine El-Robrini *(Mng Dir)*

Olbersdorfer Guss GmbH **(1)**
An der Stadtgrenze 4, 02785, Olbersdorf,
Germany
Tel.: (49) 358357620
Web Site: https://www.olbersdorfer-guss.de
Steel Casting Mfr
N.A.I.C.S.: 331513

P.T. BAUER Pratama Indonesia **(1)**
Alamanda Tower 19th Floor Jl TB Simatu-
pang Kav 23-24, Cilandak Barat, Jakarta,
12430, Indonesia
Tel.: (62) 2129661988
Web Site: http://www.bauer.co.id
Sales Range: $25-49.9 Million
Emp.: 25
Foundation Equipments Mfr & Contract Ser-
vices
N.A.I.C.S.: 238910
Hemanth Poothata Narayanan *(Dir)*

PESA ENGINEERING, S.A. **(1)**
Calle de la Electricidad 25, Pol Ind San
Jose de Valderas Leganes, 28918, Madrid,
Spain
Tel.: (34) 917920330
Web Site:
http://www.pesawellengineering.es
Water Distribution Services
N.A.I.C.S.: 221310

PRAKLA Bohrtechnik GmbH. **(1)**
Moorbeerenweg 3, 31228, Peine, Germany
Tel.: (49) 517190550
Web Site: http://www.prakla-bohrtechnik.de
Sales Range: $25-49.9 Million
Emp.: 70
Drilling Rigs Mfr
N.A.I.C.S.: 333132
Wulf Flos *(Mng Dir)*

Pol-Bud Technologia Wody
Sp.z.o.o **(1)**
Demokratyczna 8993, 92-142, Lodz, Poland
Tel.: (48) 426388930
Web Site: http://www.gwe-polbud.pl
Sales Range: $25-49.9 Million
Emp.: 50
Stainless Steel & Plastic Pipes & Tubes Mfr
N.A.I.C.S.: 326122

RTG Rammtechnik GmbH. **(1)**
Bauer Strasse 1, 86529, Schrobenhausen,
Germany
Tel.: (49) 8252970
Web Site: http://rtg-rammtechnik.de
Sales Range: $25-49.9 Million
Emp.: 83
Pilings & Drilling Rigs Mfr & Sales
N.A.I.C.S.: 331110
Bernhard Lindermair *(Mng Dir)*

SBF-Hagusta GmbH. **(1)**
Schwarzwaldstrasse 7, 77871, Renchen,
Baden-Wurttemberg, Germany
Tel.: (49) 78437020
Web Site: http://www.gwe-gruppe.com
Sales Range: $25-49.9 Million
Emp.: 35
Corrosion Protected Steel Processing Ser-
vices
N.A.I.C.S.: 332111

SCHACHTBAU NORDHAUSEN
GmbH - Mechanical Engineering
Division **(1)**
Industrieweg 2a, 99734, Nordhausen, Ger-
many
Tel.: (49) 3631632450
Web Site: http://www.schachtbau.de
Sales Range: $100-124.9 Million
Emp.: 300
Rotary Drilling Rigs & Pilings Mfr
N.A.I.C.S.: 333132

SCHACHTBAU NORDHAUSEN
GmbH. **(1)**

BAUER Aktiengesellschaft—(Continued)

Industrieweg 2a, 99734, Nordhausen, Germany
Tel.: (49) 36316320
Web Site: https://www.schachtbau.de
Sales Range: $75-99.9 Million
Emp.: 400
Mining Engineering Services
N.A.I.C.S.: 541330

Division (Domestic):

SCHACHTBAU NORDHAUSEN GmbH - Civil Engineering Division **(2)**
Industrieweg 2a, 99734, Nordhausen, Germany
Tel.: (49) 3631632214
Web Site: http://www.schachtbau.de
Civil Engineering Services
N.A.I.C.S.: 541330
Michael Seifert *(Mng Dir)*

SCHACHTBAU NORDHAUSEN GmbH - Environmental Technology Division **(2)**
Industrieweg 2a, 99734, Nordhausen, Germany
Tel.: (49) 3631632355
Web Site: http://www.schachtbau.de
Water Resources Management Construction & Installation Services
N.A.I.C.S.: 237110

SCHACHTBAU NORDHAUSEN GmbH - Reconstruction Division **(2)**
Industrieweg 2a, 99734, Nordhausen, Thuringia, Germany
Tel.: (49) 3631632215
Sales Range: $50-74.9 Million
Emp.: 200
Civil Engineering Services
N.A.I.C.S.: 237310

SCHACHTBAU NORDHAUSEN GmbH - Underground Construction Division **(2)**
Industrieweg 2A, Nordhausen, 99734, Thuringia, Germany
Tel.: (49) 3631632571
Web Site: http://www.schachtbau.de
Underground Engineering & Mining Services
N.A.I.C.S.: 541330

SPESA Spezialbau und Sanierung GmbH. **(1)**
Munchener Strasse 16, 86529, Schrobenhausen, Germany
Tel.: (49) 8252971300
Web Site: http://www.spesa.de
Sales Range: $25-49.9 Million
Emp.: 150
Civil Engineering Services
N.A.I.C.S.: 541330

Saudi BAUER Foundation Contractors Ltd. **(1)**
Sixth Floor Office No 64 - 65, PO Box 10740, Bagdadiyah Dist, Jeddah, 21443, Makkah, Saudi Arabia
Tel.: (966) 126441727
Web Site: http://www.saudibauer.com
Sales Range: $25-49.9 Million
Emp.: 60
Foundation Work Contract Services
N.A.I.C.S.: 238910

Schachtbau Nordhausen Bau GmbH **(1)**
Industrieweg 2a, 99734, Nordhausen, Germany
Tel.: (49) 3631632214
Site Preparation Contractor Services
N.A.I.C.S.: 238910

Schachtbau Nordhausen Stahlbau GmbH **(1)**
Industrieweg 2a, 99734, Nordhausen, Germany
Tel.: (49) 3631632537
Civil Engineering Services
N.A.I.C.S.: 541330

Thai BAUER Co.Ltd. **(1)**
Two Pacific Place 17th floor 142 Sukhumvit Road, Bangkok, 10110, Thailand
Tel.: (66) 2653207682

Web Site: https://www.thaibauer.com
Sales Range: $25-49.9 Million
Emp.: 300
Foundation Work Equipment & Supplies
N.A.I.C.S.: 238910
Mike Sinkinson *(Mng Dir)*

TracMec Srl **(1)**
SP 610 Selice n 10/C, 40027, Mordano, BO, Italy
Tel.: (39) 054258911
Web Site: https://www.sottocarri.it
Construction Equipment Mfr
N.A.I.C.S.: 333120
Maurizio Venara *(Co-CEO)*

BAUER COMP HOLDING AG
Sollner Strasse 43B, 81479, Munich, Germany
Tel.: (49) 897450100
Web Site: http://www.bauergroup.de
Year Founded: 1946
Rev.: $132,804,100
Emp.: 1,000
Holding Company
N.A.I.C.S.: 551112
Heinz Bauer *(Founder & CEO)*

Subsidiaries:

BAUER COMPRESSEURS S.A.R.L. **(1)**
60 Avenue Franklin D Roosevelt, 73100, Aix-les-Bains, France
Tel.: (33) 479882100
Web Site: http://www.bauer-compresseurs.com
Sales Range: $25-49.9 Million
Emp.: 25
Air Compressors
N.A.I.C.S.: 333912

BAUER COMPRESSORI s.r.l. unipersonale **(1)**
Via Galileo Galilei 9, 36057, Vicenza, Italy
Tel.: (39) 0444 653653
Air & Gas Compressor Mfr
N.A.I.C.S.: 333912

BAUER COMPRESSORS ASIA PTE LTD **(1)**
25 Pandan Crescent 01-10 Tic Tech Centre, 01-05 Penjuru Tech Hub, Singapore, 128477, Singapore
Tel.: (65) 62716271
Web Site: http://www.bauer-kompressoren.de
Air & Gas Compressor Mfr
N.A.I.C.S.: 333912

BAUER COMPRESSORS Co. Ltd. **(1)**
10-36 Ryutsu-Ctr , Kitakami-shi, 024 0014, Iwate, Japan
Tel.: (81) 197682251
Web Site: http://www.bauer.co.jp
Sales Range: $25-49.9 Million
Emp.: 15
Air & Gas Compressor Mfr
N.A.I.C.S.: 333912
Teruki Oitome *(Mng Dir)*

BAUER COMPRESSORS Inc. **(1)**
1328 Azalea Garden Rd, Norfolk, VA 23502
Tel.: (757) 855-6006
Web Site: http://www.bauercomp.com
Rev.: $24,380,954
Emp.: 135
Air & Gas Compressors Including Vacuum Pumps
N.A.I.C.S.: 333912
Bob Straddeck *(Mgr-Sls-Parts)*

BAUER KOMPRESSOREN AUSTRALIA PTY LTD **(1)**
2/35 Hallstrom Place, Wetherill Park, Sydney, 2164, Australia
Tel.: (61) 297562700
Web Site: http://www.bauer-kompressoren.com.au
Sales Range: $25-49.9 Million
Emp.: 14
Air & Gas Compressor Mfr
N.A.I.C.S.: 333912
Neno Padjen *(Gen Mgr)*

BAUER KOMPRESSOREN Beijing Ltd. **(1)**

4-1211 Purple International 2 Yinhe South Str, Shijingshan, Beijing, 100040, China
Tel.: (86) 10 6870 5035
Compressor Distr
N.A.I.C.S.: 423830

BAUER KOMPRESSOREN China Ltd. **(1)**
Unit 1802 Seaview Centre 139-141 Hoi Bun Road Kwun Tong, Kowloon, China (Hong Kong)
Tel.: (852) 25951898
Web Site: http://www.bauerchina.com
Air & Gas Compressor Mfr
N.A.I.C.S.: 333912

BAUER KOMPRESSOREN Egypt Ltd. **(1)**
Nasser Street, Suez, Hurghada, Egypt
Tel.: (20) 65 335 2747
Air & Gas Compressor Mfr
N.A.I.C.S.: 333912

BAUER KOMPRESSOREN GCC FZE **(1)**
Jebel Ali Free Zone, PO Box 261413, Dubai, United Arab Emirates
Tel.: (971) 4 8860259
Web Site: http://www.bauer-kompressoren.de
Air & Gas Compressor Mfr
N.A.I.C.S.: 333912

BAUER KOMPRESSOREN GmbH **(1)**
Stablistr 8, 81477, Munich, 81477, Germany
Tel.: (49) 89780490
Web Site: http://www.bauer-kompressoren.de
Air Compressor Mfr
N.A.I.C.S.: 333912

BAUER KOMPRESSOREN India Pvt. Ltd. **(1)**
T 128 T-Block MIDC Bhosari, 411 018. Pune, India
Tel.: (91) 2067308100
Web Site: http://www.bauerkompressoren.in
Emp.: 56
Air & Gas Compressor Mfr
N.A.I.C.S.: 333912
Anand Pradhan *(Mng Dir)*

BAUER KOMPRESSOREN Russia Ltd. **(1)**
22/25 B Strochenovskiy per Office 509, Moscow, 115054, Russia
Tel.: (7) 495 755 58 60
Compressor Distr
N.A.I.C.S.: 423830
Anton Riabov *(Mgr-Sls-High Pressure Compressors)*

BAUER KOMPRESSOREN SERVICE, S.L.U. **(1)**
Pol Ind La Clota C/ Josep Ros i Ros 45B, 08740, Sant Andreu de la Barca, Spain
Tel.: (34) 93 6726036
Compressor Distr
N.A.I.C.S.: 423830
Toni Perez Garzon *(Mgr-Sls-Breathing Air)*

BAUER KOMPRESSOREN Shanghai Ltd. **(1)**
878 Jianchuan Road, Minhang, Shanghai, 200240, China
Tel.: (86) 2154713598
Web Site: http://www.bauerchina.com
Air & Gas Compressor Mfr
N.A.I.C.S.: 333912

BAUER KOMPRESSOREN Turkiye **(1)**
Yeni Soganlik Mah Balikesir Cd Uprise Elite Residence No K 8 D 84, Istanbul, Turkiye
Tel.: (90) 216 290 11 15
Compressor Distr
N.A.I.C.S.: 423830

BAUER KOMPRESSOREN UK Ltd. **(1)**
North Florida Road Haydock Industrial Estate, Saint Helens, WA11 9TN, Merseyside, United Kingdom
Tel.: (44) 1942 724248
Compressor Distr
N.A.I.C.S.: 423830
Steve Duffy *(Dir-Sls)*

BAUER-POSEIDON KOMPRESSOREN Ges.m.b.H. **(1)**
Strasse 3 Objekt 26, 2355, Wiener Neudorf, Austria
Tel.: (43) 2236636250
Web Site: http://www.bauer-kompressoren.de
Emp.: 15
Air & Gas Compressor Mfr
N.A.I.C.S.: 000012
Stephen Hacker *(Gen Mgr)*

Bauer Kompressoren Korea Limited **(1)**
607 KolonTechnoValley 56 Digital-ro 9-gil, Geumcheon-gu, Seoul, 153-770, Korea (South)
Tel.: (82) 2 868 9974
Web Site: http://www.bauercomp.co.kr
Emp.: 302
Compressor Distr
N.A.I.C.S.: 423830
D. Y. Lee *(Mgr)*

ROTORCOMP VERDICHTER GmbH **(1)**
Industriestr 9, 82110, Germering, Germany
Tel.: (49) 897240967
Web Site: http://www.rotorcomp.de
Emp.: 40
Air & Gas Compressor Mfr
N.A.I.C.S.: 333912
Stephan Zettl *(Mng Dir)*

UNICCOMP GmbH **(1)**
Bayerwaldstr. 6, 82538, Geretsried, Germany
Tel.: (49) 81713440
Web Site: http://www.uniccomp.de
Air & Gas Compressor Mfr
N.A.I.C.S.: 333912

BAUER HOLZBAU GMBH
Rotstrasse 11, Groningen, 74589, Satteldorf, Germany
Tel.: (49) 79553850
Web Site: https://www.bauer-holzbau.de
Construction Services
N.A.I.C.S.: 236210

BAUER-WALSER AG
Bunsenstrasse 4-6, 75210, Pforzheim, Germany
Tel.: (49) 72367040
Web Site: http://www.bauer-walser.de
Year Founded: 2004
Sales Range: $75-99.9 Million
Emp.: 124
Jewellery & Watches Mfr
N.A.I.C.S.: 423940
Bernd Augenstein *(Mgr-Production)*

BAUHAUS INTERNATIONAL (HOLDINGS) LIMITED
Room 501 Sino Industrial Plaza 9 Kai Cheung Road, Kowloon Bay, Kowloon, China (Hong Kong)
Tel.: (852) 3 513 9700
Web Site:
http://www.bauhaus.com.hk
0483—(HKG)
Rev.: $32,155,230
Assets: $32,434,472
Liabilities: $8,161,210
Net Worth: $24,273,262
Earnings: $18,393,967
Emp.: 188
Fiscal Year-end: 03/31/22
Garments & Accessories Mfr
N.A.I.C.S.: 315250
Kin Cheong Li *(Sec, Controller-Fin & Accountant)*

BAULOISE AUTOMOBILES S.A.
Route De La Baule, 44350, Guerande, Loire Atlantique, France
Tel.: (33) 240111213

Web Site:
   http://www.baulautos.peugeot.fr
Rev.: $19,500,000
Emp.: 49
Peugeot Automobile Dealer
N.A.I.C.S.: 441110
Franck Guillet *(Mgr)*

BAUMANN FEDERN AG
Fabrikstrasse, 8734, Ermenswil, Switzerland
Tel.: (41) 552868111
Web Site: http://www.baumann-group.com
Year Founded: 1886
Sales Range: $25-49.9 Million
Emp.: 1,200
Mfr of Springs, Wire Forms & Couplings
N.A.I.C.S.: 334519
Uwe Brauning *(CTO)*

Subsidiaries:

BAUMANN SPRINGS & COATING
PVT. LTD **(1)**
703 Ideal Towers Ideal Colony Paud Road,
Kothrud, Pune, India
Tel.: (91) 20 25422077
Spring & Stamp Product Mfr
N.A.I.C.S.: 332613
Thomas Rugg *(CEO)*

Bamatec AG **(1)**
Fabrikstrasse, Ermenswil, 8734,
Switzerland **(100%)**
Tel.: (41) 552868585
Web Site: http://www.bamatec.ch
Sales Range: $10-24.9 Million
Emp.: 300
Measuring & Controlling Device Mfr
N.A.I.C.S.: 334519
Rolf Meier *(CEO)*

Baumann GmbH **(1)**
Friedrich List Str 131, 72805, Lichtenstein,
Germany **(100%)**
Tel.: (49) 71296970
Web Site: http://www.baumanngroup.com
Sales Range: $50-74.9 Million
Emp.: 190
Mfr of Springs, Wire Forms, Couplings &
Automotive Parts
N.A.I.C.S.: 332613

Baumann Muelles S.A. **(1)**
Poligono Industrial Gojain c/ Padurea s/n,
1170, Legutiano, Alava, Spain
Tel.: (34) 945 46 55 10
Web Site: http://www.baumann-springs.com
Sales Range: $25-49.9 Million
Emp.: 15
Mfr of Annular Springs & Torsion Springs for
Automotive Industry
N.A.I.C.S.: 332613
Ricardo Omaechevarria *(Mng Dir)*

Baumann Ressorts S.A. **(1)**
727 Rte les Tattes de Borly, BP 3, 74380,
Cranves Sales, France
Tel.: (33) 4 50 31 67 00
Emp.: 6
Compression & Torsion Springs Mfr
N.A.I.C.S.: 332618
Gaime Belarve *(Mng Dir)*

Baumann Spring Co. (S) Pte.
Ltd. **(1)**
33 Gul Lane, Singapore, 629427, Singapore
Tel.: (65) 6268 5222
Web Site: http://www.baumann-springs.com
Sales Range: $25-49.9 Million
Emp.: 75
Mfr of Technical Springs & Stampings
N.A.I.C.S.: 332613
Cecilia Wong *(Mgr-Pur)*

Baumann Springs & Pressings (UK)
Ltd. **(1)**
E Mill Ln, Sherborne, DT9 3DR, Dorset,
United Kingdom **(100%)**
Tel.: (44) 935818100
Web Site: http://www.baumann-springs.com
Sales Range: $1-9.9 Million
Emp.: 50
Mfr of Springs & Pressings

N.A.I.C.S.: 332722

Baumann Springs (Shanghai) Co.
Ltd. **(1)**
No 358-2 Shen Xia Road, Forward High
Tech Zone, Shanghai, 201818, China
Tel.: (86) 21 5990 0606
Emp.: 20
Spring Mfr
N.A.I.C.S.: 332613
R. Tan *(Mng Dir)*

Baumann Springs Leon S. de R.L.
Dec. V. **(1)**
Kappa 310 y 312 Frac Industrial Delta,
37545, Leon, Guanajuato, Mexico
Tel.: (52) 477 152 1400
Web Site: http://www.baumann-springs.com
Emp.: 95
Spring & Stamping Mfr
N.A.I.C.S.: 336390

Baumann Springs Texas Holdings
LLC **(1)**
3075 N Great SW Pkwy 10, Grand Prairie,
TX 75050
Tel.: (972) 641-7272
Web Site: http://www.baumann-springs.com
Sales Range: $25-49.9 Million
Emp.: 39
Spring (Light Gauge) Mfr
N.A.I.C.S.: 332613

Baumann Springs Texas Ltd. **(1)**
3075 N Great SW Pkwy Ste 100, Grand
Prairie, TX 75050-7823
Tel.: (972) 641-7272
Web Site: http://www.baumann-springs.com
Sales Range: $25-49.9 Million
Emp.: 60
Mfr of Wire Springs
N.A.I.C.S.: 332613
Pedro Sainz *(Pres)*

Baumann Springs USA, Inc. **(1)**
3075 No Great SW Pkwy Ste 100, Grand
Prairie, TX 75050 **(100%)**
Tel.: (972) 641-7272
Web Site: http://www.baumann-springs.com
Sales Range: $25-49.9 Million
Emp.: 65
Springs & Retaining Ring for Wheel Cover
Mfr
N.A.I.C.S.: 332613
Pedro Sainz *(Pres)*

Baumann Springs s.r.o. **(1)**
Na Novem poli 384/6, 733 01, Karvina,
Czech Republic
Tel.: (420) 595 390 010
Web Site: http://www.baumann-springs.com
Spring Mfr
N.A.I.C.S.: 332613
M. Vrla *(Mng Dir)*

Prodotti Baumann SpA **(1)**
Via Brescia 261, I 25075, Cortine di Nave,
Brescia, Italy **(100%)**
Tel.: (39) 0302534221
Web Site: http://www.baumann-springs.com
Sales Range: $25-49.9 Million
Emp.: 70
Valve Springs & Compression Springs Mfr
N.A.I.C.S.: 332613
Jaroslava Hudecova *(Mgr-Sls)*

BAUMART HOLDINGS LIMITED
15 McCabe St, North Fremantle,
Perth, 6159, WA, Australia
Tel.: (61) 865580814
Web Site:
   https://www.baumart.com.au
BMH—(ASX)
Rev.: $163,975
Assets: $6,102,787
Liabilities: $1,940,967
Net Worth: $4,161,820
Earnings: $268,767
Fiscal Year-end: 06/30/22
Building Products Supplier
N.A.I.C.S.: 444180
Natalie Teo *(Sec)*

BAUMEISTER DOO
Maksima Gorkog 117, Vozdovac,

11010, Belgrade, Serbia
Tel.: (381) 11 783 8238   RS
Web Site: http://baumeister.ls.rs
Year Founded: 2013
Road Construction & Engineering
Services
N.A.I.C.S.: 237310
Lazo Pribisic *(Owner)*

Subsidiaries:

Vojvodinaput Backaput a.d. **(1)**
Jovana Dordevica 2, 21 000, Novi Sad,
Serbia **(95.77%)**
Tel.: (381) 21 557 095
Web Site: http://www.backaput.co.rs
Sales Range: $1-9.9 Million
Road Construction Management Services
N.A.I.C.S.: 237310
Dragan Jakovljevic *(Dir Gen)*

BAUMER BOURDON-HAENNI S.A.S.
125 Rue De La Marre, BP 70214,
41103, Orleans, Vendome, France
Tel.: (33) 254737475
Web Site: http://www.baumer.com
Rev.: $22,000,000
Emp.: 278
Instruments To Measure Electricity
N.A.I.C.S.: 334515
Oliver Vietze *(Chm & CEO)*

BAUMER HOLDING AG
Hummelstrasse 17, 8501, Frauenfeld,
Switzerland
Tel.: (41) 527281155
Web Site: https://www.baumer.com
Year Founded: 1991
Holding Company
N.A.I.C.S.: 551112

BAUMER S.A.
Av Prefeito Antonio Tavares Leite
181, Mogi Mirim, 13830-330, SP, Brazil
Tel.: (55) 1938057665
Web Site: https://www.baumer.com.br
Year Founded: 1952
BALM4—(BRAZ)
Rev.: $30,380,221
Assets: $44,676,533
Liabilities: $18,649,291
Net Worth: $26,027,242
Earnings: $1,598,291
Fiscal Year-end: 12/31/23
Medical Equipment Mfr
N.A.I.C.S.: 339112
Monica Salvari Baumer *(Dir-IR)*

Subsidiaries:

Baumer S.A. - Mogi Mirim
Factory **(1)**
Av Pref Antonio Tavares Leite, 181 - Distrito
Industrial Jose Marangoni, Mogi Mirim,
13803-330, SP, Brazil
Tel.: (55) 1938057655
Medicinal Product Mfr
N.A.I.C.S.: 339112

BAUMGARTNER & LAMPERSTORFER INSTRUMENTS GMBH.
Friedrich-Schule Str 9, D-85622,
Feldkirchen, Germany
Tel.: (49) 8966072922
Web Site: https://www.bnli.de
Precision Instrument Mfr
N.A.I.C.S.: 332721

BAUMOT GROUP AG
Eduard-Rhein-Strasse 21-23,
D-53639, Konigswinter, Germany
Tel.: (49) 224491800
Web Site: http://www.twintec.de
TIN—(DEU)
Rev.: $16,909,886
Assets: $11,086,614
Liabilities: $7,615,048

Net Worth: $3,471,566
Earnings: $111,986
Emp.: 59
Fiscal Year-end: 12/31/19
Particle Filters Mfr
N.A.I.C.S.: 336390

Subsidiaries:

Baumot Ag **(1)**
Thurgauerstrasse 105 Glattpark, 8152,
Opfikon, Switzerland
Tel.: (41) 449548070
Automobile Exhaust Parts Distr
N.A.I.C.S.: 441330

Baumot UK Ltd. **(1)**
Silverstone Park Unit 1118 Buckingham
Road, Silverstone, Towcester, NN12 8FU,
United Kingdom
Tel.: (44) 1327226930
Web Site: http://www.baumot.co.uk
Automobile Exhaust Parts Distr
N.A.I.C.S.: 441330
Della Howard *(Acct Mgr)*

INTERKAT Katalysatoren GmbH **(1)**
Eduard Rhein Strasse 21-23, 53639,
Konigswinter, 53639, Nordrhein-Westfalen,
Germany
Tel.: (49) 2244 87 88 0
Web Site: http://www.interkat.com
Emp.: 25
Catalytic Converters Mfr & Sales
N.A.I.C.S.: 336390

TWINTEC Technologie GmbH **(1)**
Eduard Rhein Strasse 21, 53639,
Konigswinter, Nordrhein-Westfalen, Germany
Tel.: (49) 2244 918040
Web Site: http://www.twintec.de
Automobile Equipment Mfr
N.A.I.C.S.: 336390

BAUSCH HEALTH COMPANIES INC.
2150 St Elzear Blvd West, Laval, H7L
4A8, QC, Canada
Tel.: (514) 744-6792   Ca
Web Site:
   https://www.bauschhealth.com
Year Founded: 1994
BHC—(NYSE)
Rev.: $8,757,000,000
Assets: $27,350,000,000
Liabilities: $27,432,000,000
Net Worth: ($82,000,000)
Earnings: ($592,000,000)
Emp.: 20,270
Fiscal Year-end: 12/31/23
Holding Company; Pharmaceuticals &
Drug Delivery Systems Mfr
N.A.I.C.S.: 551112
Thomas J. Appio *(CEO)*

Subsidiaries:

AGMS Inc. **(1)**
PO Box 5686, Kent, WA 98064
Tel.: (253) 249-4542
Web Site: http://www.agmsservices.com
Residential Contract Services
N.A.I.C.S.: 236118

Bausch + Lomb Corporation **(1)**
520 Applewood Crescent, Vaughan, L4K
4B4, ON, Canada **(88.7%)**
Tel.: (905) 695-7700
Web Site: http://www.bausch.com
Holding Company; Ophthalmic Surgical
Products Mfr
N.A.I.C.S.: 551112
Sam Eldessouky *(CFO & Exec VP)*

Subsidiary (US):

AcuFocus, Inc. **(2)**
32 Discovery Ste 200, Irvine, CA 92618-3161
Tel.: (949) 585-9511
Web Site: https://acufocus.com
Freestanding Ambulatory Surgical & Emergency Centers
N.A.I.C.S.: 621493
Olga Conseko *(Mgr)*

Bausch Health Companies Inc.—(Continued)

Alden Optical Laboratories, Inc. (2)
6 Lancaster Pkwy, Lancaster, NY 14086
Tel.: (716) 937-9181
Web Site: http://www.aldenoptical.com
Contact Lense Mfr & Distr
N.A.I.C.S.: 339115

Subsidiary (Non-US):

B.L.J. Company Ltd. (2)
Omori Bellport Building B 6-26-2 Minamioi,
Shinagawa-ku, Tokyo, 140-0013, Japan
Tel.: (81) 120132490
Web Site: https://www.bausch.co.jp
Sales Range: Less than $1 Million
Emp.: 153
Optical & Ophthalmic Equipment & Supplies
Mfr & Distr
N.A.I.C.S.: 339113

BL Industria Otica, Ltda. (2)
Web Site: http://www.bausch.com.br
Mfr of Optical Products
N.A.I.C.S.: 339113

BLEP Holding GmbH
Brunsbutteler Damm 165/173, 13581, Berlin, Germany
Tel.: (49) 30330930
Holding Company
N.A.I.C.S.: 551112

Bausch & Lomb (HK) Ltd. (2)
Rooms 3901 and 3912-14 39/F Tower 6
Gateway Tower 9 Canton Road, Tsim Sha
Tsui, Hong Kong, Kowloon, China (Hong Kong)
Tel.: (852) 2133309
Web Site: https://www.ultraoneday.com
Sales Range: $25-49.9 Million
Emp.: 80
Distribution & Manufacturing of Optical
Products & Pharmaceuticals
N.A.I.C.S.: 423460
Thomas Appio (Pres-Asia Pacific & Exec VP)

Bausch & Lomb (M) Sdn Bhd (2)
Sales Range: $25-49.9 Million
Emp.: 50
Mfr & Developer of Eye Care Products, Precision Optical Devices for Scientific Use &
Specialized Biomedical Products & Services, Contact Lenses, Contact Lens Solution
N.A.I.C.S.: 333310

Division (Domestic):

**Bausch & Lomb Malaysia Sdn Bhd -
Surgical Division** (3)
Suite 17-01 & 17-02 Level 17 the Pinnacle
Persiaran Lagoon, Bandar Sunway, 46150,
Petaling Jaya, Selangor Darul Ehsan, Malaysia
Tel.: (60) 3 7680 8828
Web Site: http://www.bauschhealth.com
Ophthalmic Surgical Instruments Mfr
N.A.I.C.S.: 339115

Subsidiary (Non-US):

**Bausch & Lomb (Singapore) Private
Limited** (2)
151 Lorong Chuan #04-03A, Singapore,
556741, Singapore
Tel.: (65) 68349112
Web Site: http://www.bausch.com.sg
Distribution of Medical & Ophthalmic Equipment
N.A.I.C.S.: 423460

**Bausch & Lomb Australia Pty.
Ltd.** (2)
Sales Range: $25-49.9 Million
Emp.: 80
Mfr of Optical Products & Instruments
N.A.I.C.S.: 339113
Dan Spira (Mng Dir-Australasia & VP-N America)

Bausch & Lomb B.V. (2)
Koolhovenlaan 110, 1119 NH, Schiphol-Rijk,
Netherlands
Tel.: (31) 206554500
Web Site: http://www.bausch.com
Mfr of Optical Products
N.A.I.C.S.: 339113

Bausch & Lomb B.V.B.A. (2)
Regent Building, Uitbreidingsstraat 46,
B-2600, Antwerp, Belgium
Tel.: (32) 32808220
Sales Range: $25-49.9 Million
Emp.: 47
Eye Care Products Whslr
N.A.I.C.S.: 423460

Bausch & Lomb Espana S.A. (2)
Avenida Valdelaparra 4, 28108, Alcobendas, Spain
Tel.: (34) 916576300
Web Site: http://www.bausch.com
Sales Range: $25-49.9 Million
Emp.: 70
Mfr of Optical Products
N.A.I.C.S.: 339113

**Bausch & Lomb Eyecare (India) Pvt
Ltd.** (2)
Plot No 13 Sector-34, Gurgaon, 122001,
Haryana, India
Tel.: (91) 18002677707
Web Site: https://www.bauschandlomb.in
Emp.: 50
Mfr of Optical & Ophthalmic Products
N.A.I.C.S.: 423460

Bausch & Lomb France SAS (2)
416 rue Samuel Morse, CS 99535, 34967,
Montpellier, France
Tel.: (33) 467123030
Web Site: https://www.bausch.fr
Sales Range: $125-149.9 Million
Emp.: 380
Distribution of Ophthalmic Goods & Pharmaceuticals & Camera Equipment & Supplies
N.A.I.C.S.: 423410

Bausch & Lomb Greece (2)
53 Pentelis St, Vilissia, 15235, Athens,
Greece
Tel.: (30) 2108108460
Web Site: https://www.bausch.gr
Distr of Ophthalmic Products & Pharmaceuticals & Photographic Equipment
N.A.I.C.S.: 423460

Bausch & Lomb IOM S.p.A. (2)
Viale Martesana 12, 20090, Vimodrone, MI,
Italy
Tel.: (39) 0227407300
Web Site: http://www.bausch.it
Sales Range: $50-74.9 Million
Mfr of Optical, Ophthalmic & Photographic
Products
N.A.I.C.S.: 339113

Subsidiary (US):

Bausch & Lomb Incorporated (2)
400 Somerset Corporate Blvd, Bridgewater,
NJ 08807
Web Site: http://www.bausch.com
Sales Range: $1-4.9 Billion
Emp.: 10,001
Pharmaceutical & Ophthalmic Equipment
Mfr
N.A.I.C.S.: 339115
John Ferris (Gen Mgr-Vision Care)

Subsidiary (Domestic):

Bausch & Lomb (3)
15272 Alton Pkwy Ste 200, Irvine, CA
92618-2315
Tel.: (949) 788-6000
Emp.: 330
Drug Products for Eye Diseases & Conditions Developer & Marketer
N.A.I.C.S.: 424210

Subsidiary (Non-US):

Bausch & Lomb Canada, Inc. (3)
520 Applewood Crescent, Vaughan, L4K
4B4, ON, Canada
Web Site: http://www.bausch.ca
Sales Range: $100-124.9 Million
Emp.: 500
Distr, Marketer & Laboratory Research of
Health & Vision Care Products
N.A.I.C.S.: 333310

Subsidiary (Domestic):

Bausch & Lomb Instruments (3)
50 Technology Dr, Irvine, CA 92618
Web Site: http://www.bausch.com

Design, Development & Sales of Intraocular
Lenses for Vision Correction
N.A.I.C.S.: 339115

Unit (Non-US):

Bausch & Lomb (S) Pte Ltd. (4)
Tel.: (65) 68349112
Web Site: http://www.bausch.com.sg
Sales Range: $25-49.9 Million
Emp.: 70
Surgical Products
N.A.I.C.S.: 339113
Thomas Appio (Pres-Asia Pacific & Exec VP)

Bausch & Lomb (Thailand) Ltd. (4)
No 98 Sathorn Square Office Tower 19th
Floor Unit 1909-12, North Sathorn Road
Silom Subdistrict Bang Rak District, Bangkok, 10500, Bangrak, Thailand
Tel.: (66) 26437888
Web Site: https://www.bausch.co.th
Sales Range: $25-49.9 Million
Emp.: 15
Ophthalmic Surgical Instruments Mfr
N.A.I.C.S.: 339112

**Bausch & Lomb Saglik ve Optik
Urunleritic A.S.** (4)
Buyukdere Cad Kirgulu St No4 Metrocity Is
Merkezi K3, Esentepe, 34394, Istanbul,
Turkiye **(100%)**
Tel.: (90) 2123718200
Web Site: https://www.bausch.com.tr
Sales Range: $25-49.9 Million
Emp.: 40
Ophthalmic Surgical Instruments Mfr
N.A.I.C.S.: 339112

Bausch & Lomb Surgical Corp. (4)
106 London Road, Kingston upon Thames,
KT2 6TN, Surrey, United Kingdom
Tel.: (44) 2087812900
Web Site: http://www.bausch.co.uk
Sales Range: $50-74.9 Million
Surgical & Pharmaceutical Products Mfr
N.A.I.C.S.: 339113

Bausch & Lomb Surgical Korea (4)
13F KT&G Cosmo Daechi Tower #945-10
Daechi-Dong Gangnam-Gu, Seoul, 135-280, Korea (South)
Tel.: (82) 2 558 2988
Web Site: http://www.bausch.kr
Ophthalmic Surgical Instruments Mfr
N.A.I.C.S.: 339112
Andrew Chang (Sr VP & Gen Mgr)

Subsidiary (Non-US):

**Bausch & Lomb Mexico S.A. de
C.V.** (3)
Web Site: http://www.bausch.com
Sales Range: $25-49.9 Million
Emp.: 70
Mfr of Optical Products
N.A.I.C.S.: 339113

Subsidiary (Domestic):

**Bausch & Lomb Pharmaceuticals,
Inc.** (3)
8500 Hidden River Pkwy, Tampa, FL
33637-1014
Tel.: (813) 975-7700
Web Site: http://www.bausch.com
Sales Range: $100-124.9 Million
Emp.: 750
Mfr of Ophthalmic Pharmaceuticals & Products
N.A.I.C.S.: 325412

Bausch & Lomb Puerto Rico Inc. (3)
1738 Amarillo St BBV Plz Ste 210 Corner
Lomas Verdes Ave, Rio Piedras, PR 00926
Tel.: (787) 758-4330
Web Site: http://www.bausch.com
Sales Range: $25-49.9 Million
Emp.: 36
Mfr & Developer of Eye Care Products, Precision Optical Devices for Scientific Use &
Specialized Biomedical Products & Services, Contact Lenses & Contact Lens Solution
N.A.I.C.S.: 423460

Subsidiary (Non-US):

**Bausch & Lomb India Private
Limited** (2)

4th Floor Tower B Unitech Business Park
South City - 1, Gurgaon, 122 001, Haryana,
India
Tel.: (91) 1244152100
Web Site: http://www.bausch.in
Contact Lens Mfr
N.A.I.C.S.: 339115

Bausch & Lomb Korea, Co. Ltd. (2)
8 Teheran-ro 98-gil 13 Fl KT G Kosmo
Daechi Tower, Gangnam-Gu, Seoul, 06181,
Korea (South)
Tel.: (82) 25582988
Web Site: http://www.bausch.com
Sales & Marketing of Optical, Ophthalmic &
Photographic Supplies
N.A.I.C.S.: 423460

Bausch & Lomb Nordic AB (2)
Soder Malarstrand 45, PO Box 15070, 118
25, Stockholm, Sweden
Tel.: (46) 86169570
Web Site: https://www.bausch.se
Sales Range: $25-49.9 Million
Emp.: 40
Sales & Marketing of Optical, Ophthalmic &
Photographic Equipment
N.A.I.C.S.: 423460

**Bausch & Lomb Nordic
Aktiebolag** (2)
Soder Malarstrand 45, Box 15070, 104 60,
Stockholm, Sweden
Tel.: (46) 80010440
Contact Lens Mfr
N.A.I.C.S.: 339115

Bausch & Lomb Philippines, Inc. (2)
1806 The Finance Centre 26th Street Corner 9th Avenue, Bonifacio Global City,
Taguig, 1634, Philippines
Tel.: (63) 283967470
Web Site: https://www.bausch.com.ph
Emp.: 110
Ophthalmic Products & Pharmaceuticals &
Camera Equipment Distr
N.A.I.C.S.: 423460

**Bausch & Lomb Polska Sp.
z.o.o.** (2)
Tel.: (48) 178655100
Web Site: http://www.bausch.com.pl
Ophthalmic & Pharmaceutical Mfr & Distr
N.A.I.C.S.: 339115

**Bausch & Lomb Polska Sp.
z.o.o.** (2)
ul Marynarska 15, 02-674, Warsaw, Poland
Tel.: (48) 226272888
Web Site: https://bauschlombpolska.com
Ophthalmic Product Distr
N.A.I.C.S.: 456130

**Bausch & Lomb Scotland
Limited** (2)
6-8 Cochrene Sq Brucefields Indstl Est, Livingston, EH54 9DR, United Kingdom
Tel.: (44) 1506404500
Ophthalmic Product Distr
N.A.I.C.S.: 456130

**Bausch & Lomb South Africa Pty.
Ltd.** (2)
Sales Range: $25-49.9 Million
Emp.: 45
Eye Care Products & Surgical Intrument Mfr
N.A.I.C.S.: 333310

Bausch & Lomb Taiwan Ltd. (2)
Web Site: http://www.bausch.com
Ophthalmic & Optical Products
N.A.I.C.S.: 339113

Bausch & Lomb U.K. Limited (2)
106 London Road, Kingston upon Thames,
KT2 6TN, Surrey, United Kingdom
Tel.: (44) 2087812900
Web Site: http://www.bausch.co.uk
Sales Range: $25-49.9 Million
Emp.: 150
Ophthalmic & Pharmaceutical Products
Whslr
N.A.I.C.S.: 423460

Bausch & Lomb Venezuela S.A. (2)
Ave Francisco Solano Lo pez Edificio Galerias Bolivar, Torre A Floor 3 Officina 31-A
Sector Sabana Grande, Caracas, Venezuela
Tel.: (58) 2761 6920

Web Site: http://www.bausch.com
Mfr & Developer of Eye Care Products, Precision Optical Devices for Scientific Use & Specialized Biomedical Products & Services Contact Lenses, Contact Lens Solution
N.A.I.C.S.: 333310

Bausch Health Hellas Single-Member Pharmaceuticals SA (2)
53 Pentelis Avenue, 152 35, Vrilissia, Greece
Tel.: (30) 2108108460
Web Site: http://www.bauschhealth.gr
Pharmaceuticals Product Mfr
N.A.I.C.S.: 325412

Bausch Health LLC (2)
Office 22 Olshevskogo str 22, Minsk, 220073, Belarus
Tel.: (375) 173974422
Pharmaceuticals Product Mfr
N.A.I.C.S.: 325412

Bausch Health LLP (2)
22/5 Khadzhi Mukan street Business Center Khan-Tengri 6th floor, A26T9GO, Almaty, Kazakhstan
Tel.: (7) 7273111516
Pharmaceuticals Product Mfr
N.A.I.C.S.: 325412

Bausch Health Limited Liability Company (2)
Shabolovka Str 31 bldg 5, 115162, Moscow, Russia
Tel.: (7) 4955102879
Web Site: http://www.bausch.ru
Pharmaceuticals Product Mfr
N.A.I.C.S.: 325412

Bausch Health Limited Liability Company (2)
6V Pidvisotskogo Str Floor 2, 01103, Kiev, Ukraine
Tel.: (380) 444590484
Pharmaceuticals Product Mfr
N.A.I.C.S.: 325412

Bausch Health Peru S.R.L. (2)
Calle German Schreiber 276, San Isidro, Lima, Peru
Tel.: (51) 16521756
Pharmaceuticals Product Mfr
N.A.I.C.S.: 325412

Bausch Health Romania SRL (2)
No 6 Maria Rosetti Av 7B Floor, District 2, 020485, Bucharest, Romania
Tel.: (40) 374102600
Pharmaceuticals Product Mfr
N.A.I.C.S.: 325412

Bausch Health Trading DWC-LLC (2)
14th Floor Rolex Tower Sheikh Zayed road, PO Box 9767, Dubai; United Arab Emirates
Tel.: (971) 47065900
Pharmaceuticals Product Mfr
N.A.I.C.S.: 325412

Bausch Health Ukraine LLC (2)
Vasylya Tiutiunnyka Street Building 58/1 suite 9, 03150, Kiev, Ukraine
Tel.: (380) 444590484
Pharmaceutical Product Mfr & Distr
N.A.I.C.S.: 325412

Beijing Bausch & Lomb Eyecare Company, Ltd. (2)
No 37 Xingfu Street, Chong Wen District, Beijing, 100061, China
Tel.: (86) 1067768585
Ophthalmic Products Mfr & Whslr
N.A.I.C.S.: 339115

Dr. Gerhard Mann chem.-pharm. Fabrik GmbH (2)
Brunsbuetteler Damm 165-173, 13581, Berlin, Germany
Tel.: (49) 30330930
Sales Range: $125-149.9 Million
Mfr of Ophthalmic Pharmaceuticals & Non-Prescription Medications, Analgesics, Sedatives, Sleep Aids, Over-the-Counter Medicines
N.A.I.C.S.: 325412
Gaelle Waltinger *(Mng Dir & VP-Western Europe)*

Subsidiary (Non-US):

Bausch & Lomb Gesellschaft m.b.H. (3)

Office Park I Top B02, 1300, Vienna, Austria
Tel.: (43) 810001238
Sales Range: $10-24.9 Million
Ophthalmic Goods & Pharmaceuticals Whslr
N.A.I.C.S.: 423460
Gaelle Waltinger *(Mng Dir & VP-Western Europe)*

Bausch & Lomb Swiss AG (3)
Sales Range: $25-49.9 Million
Emp.: 2
Surgical Supplies Mfr
N.A.I.C.S.: 339113

Subsidiary (Domestic):

Dr. Gerhard Mann chem.-pharm. Fabrik Gesellschaft mit beschrankter Haftung (3)
Brunsbuetteler Damm 165-173, 13581, Berlin, Germany
Tel.: (49) 30330930
Web Site: https://www.bausch-lomb.de
Pharmaceutical Drug & Supplement Whslr
N.A.I.C.S.: 424210

Subsidiary (Non-US):

Limited Liability Company Bausch & Lomb (2)
3rd Floor d 31 p 5 Shabolovka Str; Moscow, 115162, Russia
Tel.: (7) 4959692130
Web Site: http://www.bausch.ru
Sales Range: $25-49.9 Million
Emp.: 15
Mfr & Developer of Eye Care Products, Precision Optical Devices for Scientific Use & Specialized Biomedical Products & Services, Contact Lenses, Contact Lens Solution
N.A.I.C.S.: 333310

PT Bausch & Lomb Indonesia (2)
Web Site: http://www.valeant.com
Mfr & Distr of Ophthalmic Preparations
N.A.I.C.S.: 339115

PharmaSwiss drustvo s ogranicenom odgovornoscu za trgovinu i usluge (2)
D T Gavrana 11, Zagreb, Croatia
Tel.: (385) 16311833
Pharmaceuticals Product Mfr
N.A.I.C.S.: 325412

Sterimedix Limited
26 Thornhill Road North Moons Moat, Redditch, B98 9ND, Worcestershire, United Kingdom
Tel.: (44) 1527501480
Web Site: https://www.sterimedix.com
Surgical Instrument Mfr
N.A.I.C.S.: 339112

Subsidiary (US):

Synergetics, Inc. (2)
3365 Tree Ct Industrial Blvd, Saint Louis, MO 63122
Web Site: http://www.bauschretina.com
Rev.: $75,019,000
Assets: $95,621,000
Liabilities: $27,179,000
Net Worth: $68,442,000
Earnings: $4,478,000
Emp.: 418
Fiscal Year-end: 07/31/2015
Microsurgery Instruments & Electrosurgery Systems Mfr
N.A.I.C.S.: 334510
Debbie Jorgenson *(Dir-Finance)*

Unilens Vision Inc. (2)
10431 72nd St N, Largo, FL 33777-1511
Tel.: (727) 544-2531
Web Site: http://www.unilens.com
Emp.: 45
Contact Lens Developer, Mfr, Distr & Licensor
N.A.I.C.S.: 339115

Subsidiary (Non-US):

Valeant Med Sp. z o.o. (2)
Ul Ryzowa 31, 02-495, Warsaw, Poland
Tel.: (48) 225781600
Pharmaceutical Mfr & Distr
N.A.I.C.S.: 325412

Bausch Health Magyarorszag Kft (1)
Vaci str 33 / B 7th floor, 1134, Budapest, Hungary
Tel.: (36) 13455900
Pharmaceuticals Product Mfr
N.A.I.C.S.: 325412

Bausch Health Slovakia s.r.o. (1)
Galvaniho 7/B, 821 04, Bratislava, Slovakia
Tel.: (421) 232334900
Pharmaceuticals Product Mfr
N.A.I.C.S.: 325412

Bausch Health, Canada Inc. (1)
2150 St Elzear Blvd West, Laval, H7L 4A8, QC, Canada
Tel.: (514) 744-6792
Web Site: https://www.bauschhealth.ca
Pharmaceuticals Product Mfr
N.A.I.C.S.: 325412
Richard Lajoie *(Pres & Gen Mgr)*

Bausch Pharma Kazakhstan LLP (1)
22/5 Khadzhi Mukan Street Business Center KhanTengri 6th floor A26T9GO, Almaty, Kazakhstan
Tel.: (7) 273111516
Pharmaceutical Product Mfr & Distr
N.A.I.C.S.: 325412

Bausch Rumo LLC (1)
Shabolovka St 31 Bld 5, Floor/room 3/1, Moscow, 115162, Russia
Tel.: (7) 4955102879
Pharmaceutical Product Mfr & Distr
N.A.I.C.S.: 325412

Bunker Industria Farmaceutica Ltda. (1)
Rua Anibal dos Anjos Carvalho 212 Cidade Dutra, Sao Paulo, 04810, Brazil
Tel.: (55) 1156660266
Web Site: http://www.bunker.com.br
Pharmaceuticals Product Mfr
N.A.I.C.S.: 325412

Croma Pharma SL (1)
C Juan Gris 10-18 9 A, 08014, Barcelona, Spain
Tel.: (34) 936455117
Pharmaceutical Products Distr
N.A.I.C.S.: 424210

Croma Pharmaceuticals Inc. (1)
100 NE 3rd Ave, Fort Lauderdale, FL 33301
Tel.: (954) 334-3800
Drugs Whslr
N.A.I.C.S.: 424210

Dendreon Pharmaceuticals LLC (1)
1700 Saturn Way, Seal Beach, CA 90740
Tel.: (206) 256-4545
Web Site: https://www.dendreon.com
Biotechnology Mfr & Researcher
N.A.I.C.S.: 325412
Fang Xu *(Chm)*

Emo-Farm Ltd. (1)
Ul Lodzka 52, Ksawerow, 95-054, Warsaw, Poland
Tel.: (48) 422128085
Web Site: https://www.emo-farm.pl
Pharmaceuticals Mfr
N.A.I.C.S.: 325412

Humax Pharmaceutical S.A. (1)
Calle 97B Sur No 50 - 95, Antioquia, Colombia
Tel.: (57) 6044448629
Web Site: https://www.humax.com.co
Pharmaceutical Products Distr
N.A.I.C.S.: 424210

ICN Polfa Rzeszow S.A. (1)
street Przemyslowa 2, 35-959, Rzeszow, Poland   **(100%)**
Tel.: (48) 178655100
Web Site: https://www.icnpolfa.pl
Sales Range: $10-24.9 Million
Pharmaceuticals Product Mfr
N.A.I.C.S.: 325412

Laboratorios Grossman, S.A. (1)
Calz de Tlalpan 2021, Coyoacan, 04040, Mexico
Tel.: (52) 5550624800
Pharmaceuticals Product Mfr
N.A.I.C.S.: 325412

M.I.S.S. Ophthalmics Limited (1)
3 Ryder Court Saxon Way East Oakley Hay

Industrial Estate, Corby, NN18 9NX, Northamptonshire, United Kingdom
Tel.: (44) 1536741139
Web Site: http://www.miss-ophth.com
Contact Lens Mfr
N.A.I.C.S.: 339115

OPO, Inc. (1)
5379 E Mountain St, Stone Mountain, GA 30083
Tel.: (770) 465-4318
Ammunition Product Whslr
N.A.I.C.S.: 423990

OrphaMed Inc. (1)
14875 SW 72nd Ave, Tigard, OR 97224
Tel.: (503) 234-9691
Web Site: https://www.orthomedinc.com
Surgical & Medical Product Mfr & Distr
N.A.I.C.S.: 339112

PT Armoxindo Farma (1)
Jl Arjuna 28 Tanjung Duren, Jakarta, 11470, Indonesia
Tel.: (62) 215685973
Pharmaceutical Products Distr
N.A.I.C.S.: 424210

PharmaSwiss BH d.o.o. (1)
Fra Andela Zvizdovica 1 B/7, 71000, Sarajevo, Bosnia & Herzegovina
Tel.: (387) 33295195
Pharmaceutical Product Mfr & Distr
N.A.I.C.S.: 325412

PharmaSwiss Ceska republika s.r.o. (1)
Jankovcova 1569/2c Lighthouse, 170 00, Prague, Czech Republic
Tel.: (420) 234719600
Web Site: https://www.pharmaswiss.cz
Pharmaceuticals Product Mfr
N.A.I.C.S.: 325412

PharmaSwiss Hellas S.A. (1)
Pentelis Avenue 53 Vrilissia, 15235, Athens, Greece
Tel.: (30) 2108108460
Web Site: http://www.valeant.com
Emp.: 60
Pharmaceuticals Product Mfr
N.A.I.C.S.: 325412

PharmaSwiss S.A. (1)
Baarerstrasse 94, CH-6300, Zug, Switzerland
Tel.: (41) 417295800
Web Site: http://www.pharmaswiss.lt
Sales Range: $200-249.9 Million
Emp.: 760
Generic Pharmaceutical Mfr
N.A.I.C.S.: 325412

PharmaSwiss d.o.o. (1)
Brodisce 32, 1236, Trzin, Slovenia
Tel.: (386) 12364700
Pharmaceuticals Product Mfr
N.A.I.C.S.: 325412

PharmaSwiss doo (1)
Batajnicki drum 5a, Zemun, 11080, Belgrade, Serbia
Tel.: (381) 113093900
Pharmaceuticals Product Mfr
N.A.I.C.S.: 325412

ProSkin LLC (1)
1101 E 78th St, Minneapolis, MN 55420
Tel.: (651) 207-8031
Personal Care Services
N.A.I.C.S.: 812199

Probiotica Laboratories Ltda. (1)
Av Joao Paulo I - n 1795 Jd Sta Barbara, Embu das Artes, Sao Paulo, 06817-000, Brazil
Tel.: (55) 1147853322
Web Site: http://www.probiotica.com.br
Sales Range: $50-74.9 Million
Emp.: 200
Food Supplements & Sports Nutrition Product Mfr
N.A.I.C.S.: 456191

Probiotica Laboratorios Ltda. (1)
Av Joao Paulo 1 N 1795 - Jd Sta Barbara, Sao Paulo, 06817-000, Brazil
Tel.: (55) 800105242
Web Site: http://www.probiotica.com.br
Nutritional Product Mfr & Distr
N.A.I.C.S.: 325412

Bausch Health Companies Inc.—(Continued)

Przedsiebiorstwo Farmaceutyczne Jelfa SA (1)
ul Wincentego Pola 21, 58-500, Jelenia Gora, Poland
Tel.: (48) 756433100
Web Site: https://www.jelfa.com.pl
Pharmaceutical Products Distr
N.A.I.C.S.: 424210

Rapid Diagnostics, Inc. (1)
1429 Rollins Rd, Burlingame, CA 94010
Tel.: (650) 558-0395
Pharmaceutical Drug & Supplement Whslr
N.A.I.C.S.: 424210

S.C. Croma Romania Srl (1)
Str Al Vlahuta 21 bl C1 ap 45, Cluj-Napoca, Romania
Tel.: (40) 264585866
Pharmaceutical Products Distr
N.A.I.C.S.: 424210

Salix Pharmaceuticals, Inc. (1)
400 Somerset Corporate Blvd, Bridgewater, NJ 08807
Tel.: (908) 927-1400
Web Site: https://www.salix.com
Pharmaceutical Drug & Supplement Whslr
N.A.I.C.S.: 424210
Mark McKenna (Sr VP & Gen Mgr)

Solta Medical, Inc. (1)
7031 Koll Ctr Pkwy St 260, Pleasanton, CA 94566
Tel.: (510) 782-2286
Web Site: http://www.solta.com
Sales Range: $125-149.9 Million
Emp.: 375
Medical Device Mfr
N.A.I.C.S.: 334510

Synergy Pharmaceuticals, Inc. (1)
420 Lexington Ave Ste 2012, New York, NY 10170
Tel.: (212) 297-0020
Web Site: http://www.synergypharma.com
Rev.: $16,820,000
Assets: $166,606,000
Liabilities: $172,124,000
Net Worth: ($5,518,000)
Earnings: ($224,338,000)
Emp.: 313
Fiscal Year-end: 12/31/2017
Biopharmaceutical Mfr
N.A.I.C.S.: 325412

Tecnofarma, S.A. de C.V. (1)
Azafran 123 Colonia Granjas Delegacion Iztacalco, Mexico, 08400, DF, Mexico
Tel.: (52) 5556543000
Pharmaceuticals Product Mfr
N.A.I.C.S.: 325412

UAB PharmaSwiss (1)
Seimyniskiu Str 21b, 09200, Vilnius, Lithuania
Tel.: (370) 52078000
Sales Range: $25-49.9 Million
Emp.: 24
Pharmaceuticals Product Mfr
N.A.I.C.S.: 325412
Tomas Lisis (Gen Mgr)

Valeant Canada Ltd. (1)
2150 boul St-Elzear Ouest, Laval, H7L 4A8, QC, Canada (100%)
Tel.: (514) 744-6792
Web Site: http://www.valeantcanada.com
Sales Range: $50-74.9 Million
Emp.: 400
Pharmaceuticals Product Mfr
N.A.I.C.S.: 325412

Subsidiary (Domestic):

Biovail Pharmaceuticals Canada (2)
7150 Mississauga Rd, Mississauga, L5N 8M5, ON, Canada
Tel.: (905) 286-3100
Pharmaceutical Preparation Mfr
N.A.I.C.S.: 325412

Laboratorie Dr Renaud Inc. (2)
2805 Place Louis-R Renaud, Laval, H7V0A3, QC, Canada
Tel.: (450) 688-8241
Web Site: http://www.ldrenaud.com
Skin Care Product Mfr
N.A.I.C.S.: 325620

Valeant Canada Holdings Limited (2)
2150 St Elzear Blvd West, Laval, H7L 4A8, QC, Canada
Tel.: (514) 744-6792
Investment Management Service
N.A.I.C.S.: 523940

Vital Science Corp. (1)
6299 Airport Road Suite 601, Mississauga, L4V 1N3, ON, Canada
Tel.: (905) 264-7393
Web Site: http://www.VitalScienceCorp.com
Skin Care Product Mfr
N.A.I.C.S.: 325620

Valeant Canada S.E.C./Valeant Canada LP (1)
2150 boul St-Elzear Ouest, Laval, H7L 4A8, QC, Canada
Tel.: (514) 744-6792
Pharmaceutical Product Mfr & Distr
N.A.I.C.S.: 325412

Valeant Czech Pharma s.r.o. (1)
Jankovcova 1569/2c, 170 00, Prague, Czech Republic
Tel.: (420) 234719600
Web Site: http://www.pharmaswiss.cz
Sales Range: $10-24.9 Million
Emp.: 40
Pharmaceutical Products
N.A.I.C.S.: 325412

Valeant Farmaceutica do Brasil Ltda. (1)
Rua Surubim 577 11th Floor, 04571-050, Sao Paulo, Brazil
Tel.: (55) 1132382900
Web Site: http://valeant.com.br
Pharmaceuticals Product Mfr
N.A.I.C.S.: 325412

Valeant Farmaceutica, S.A. de C.V. (1)
Calzada de Tlalpan 2021 Colonia Parque San Andres, Mexico, 04040, Mexico
Tel.: (52) 55 50624800
Web Site: http://www.valeant.com
Sales Range: $150-199.9 Million
Pharmaceuticals Product Mfr
N.A.I.C.S.: 325412

Valeant Farmacuetica Panama S.A. (1)
Calle 51 & Ricardo Arias, Panama, 0819-03772, Panama
Tel.: (507) 2125511
Pharmaceuticals Product Mfr
N.A.I.C.S.: 325412

Valeant Groupe Cosmoderme Inc. (1)
2805 Place Louis-R-Renaud, Laval, H7V 0A3, QC, Canada
Tel.: (450) 688-8241
Emp.: 50
Toilet Product Mfr
N.A.I.C.S.: 325611

Valeant LLC (1)
Ul Korovy Val d 7 Str 1 Pom I Komn 9, 115162, Moscow, Russia
Tel.: (7) 4955102879
Web Site: http://valeant.com.ru
Healthcare Product Distr
N.A.I.C.S.: 424210

Valeant Pharma Hungary Commercial LLC (1)
Csatarka u 82 84, 1025, Budapest, Hungary
Tel.: (36) 13257696
Web Site: http://www.valeant.com
Sales Range: $150-199.9 Million
Emp.: 11
Pharmaceutical Product Mfr
N.A.I.C.S.: 325412

Valeant Pharmaceuticals International Corporation (1)
400 Somerset Corporate Blvd, Bridgewater, NJ 08807
Tel.: (908) 927-1400
Sales Range: $25-49.9 Million
Emp.: 100
Pharmaceutical Products
N.A.I.C.S.: 325412

Subsidiary (Domestic):

Aton Pharma, Inc. (2)

3150 Brunswick Pike Ste 230, Lawrenceville, NJ 08648
Tel.: (609) 671-9010
Sales Range: $75-99.9 Million
Specialty Pharmaceutical Mfr
N.A.I.C.S.: 325412

Biovail Technologies Ltd. (2)
14555 Avion Pkwy, Chantilly, VA 20151
Tel.: (703) 803-3260
Web Site: http://www.valeant.com
Emp.: 435
Surgical & Medical Instrument Mfr
N.A.I.C.S.: 339112

Dow Pharmaceutical Sciences, Inc. (2)
1330 Redwood Way, Petaluma, CA 94954-1169
Tel.: (707) 793-2600
Sales Range: $25-49.9 Million
Emp.: 53
Pharmaceutical Product Mfr
N.A.I.C.S.: 325412
Simon Yeh (Dir-Analytical Science)

Eyetech Inc. (2)
700 US Rte 202/206 N, Bridgewater, NJ 08807
Tel.: (973) 539-6009
Retinal Disease Treatment Biopharmaceutical Developer
N.A.I.C.S.: 541715
Howard Bradley Schiller (CFO & Treas)

Medicis Pharmaceutical Corporation (2)
7720 N Dobson Rd, Scottsdale, AZ 85256-2740
Tel.: (602) 808-8800
Web Site: http://www.medicis.com
Sales Range: $700-749.9 Million
Emp.: 646
Holding Company; Dermatological Pharmaceutical Developer, Mfr & Distr
N.A.I.C.S.: 551112

Subsidiary (Domestic):

Dermavest, Inc. (3)
101 Convention Ctr Dr, Las Vegas, NV 89109 (100%)
Tel.: (702) 380-4931
Security Brokers
N.A.I.C.S.: 523150
Howard Bradley Schiller (Treas)

Subsidiary (Non-US):

Medicis Aesthetics Canada, Ltd. (3)
543 Richmond St W Suite 226, PO Box 102, Toronto, M5V 1Y6, ON, Canada (100%)
Tel.: (416) 306-9850
Web Site: http://www.restylane.ca
Sales Range: $50-74.9 Million
Emp.: 13
Pharmaceuticals Whslr
N.A.I.C.S.: 424210

Subsidiary (Domestic):

Medicis Aesthetics Inc. (3)
7720 N Dobson Rd, Scottsdale, AZ 85256
Tel.: (866) 222-1480
Pharmaceuticals Product Mfr
N.A.I.C.S.: 325412

Medicis Global Services Corporation (3)
7720 N Dobson Rd, Scottsdale, AZ 85256
Tel.: (602) 808-8800
Emp.: 88
Pharmaceuticals Product Mfr
N.A.I.C.S.: 325412

Ucyclyd Pharma, Inc. (3)
8125 N Hayden Rd, Scottsdale, AZ 85258 (100%)
Tel.: (602) 808-8800
Web Site: http://www.medicis.com
Rev.: $2,700,000
Emp.: 4
Pharmaceuticals Whslr
N.A.I.C.S.: 424210

Subsidiary (Domestic):

OraPharma, Inc. (2)
5 Walnut Grove Dr Ste 300, Horsham, PA 19044 (100%)

Tel.: (215) 956-2200
Web Site: http://www.orapharma.com
Sales Range: $50-74.9 Million
Oral Healthcare Products Mfr
N.A.I.C.S.: 325412

Subsidiary (Non-US):

Valeant Pharmaceuticals International (2)
Pharmaceutical Products Mfr & Distr
N.A.I.C.S.: 325412
Thomas J. Appio (CEO)

Subsidiary (Domestic):

Valeant Pharmaceuticals North America LLC (2)
400 Somerset Corporate Blvd, Bridgewater, NJ 08807
Tel.: (908) 927-1400
Specialty Pharmaceutical Mfr
N.A.I.C.S.: 325412

BAUUNTERNEHMAN ECHTER-HOFF GMBH & CO. KG
Industriestr 9, 49492, Westerkappeln, Germany
Tel.: (49) 5456810
Web Site: http://www.echterhoff.de
Year Founded: 1968
Emp.: 500
Holding Company; Civil Engineering & Industrial Construction Services
N.A.I.C.S.: 551112

Subsidiaries:

Bauunternehmung Gebr. Echterhoff GmbH & Co. KG (1)
Industriestrasse 9, Westerkappeln, Germany
Tel.: (49) 5456 81 0
Web Site: http://www.echterhoff.de
Civil Engineering & Industrial Construction Services
N.A.I.C.S.: 237990

domoplan Baugesellschaft mbh (1)
Europaplatz 14, 44575, Castrop-Rauxel, Germany
Tel.: (49) 2305 69 889 00
Web Site: http://www.domoplan.net
Residential Housing Concrete Structure Repair Services
N.A.I.C.S.: 238110
Klaus-Dieter Schindler (Mgr-Technical)

BAUVAL INC.
210 Montarville Blvd bureau 2006, Boucherville, J4B 6T3, QC, Canada
Tel.: (514) 875-4270
Web Site: http://www.bauval.com
Year Founded: 1954
Sales Range: $25-49.9 Million
Emp.: 40
Building Contractor & Industrial Work Services
N.A.I.C.S.: 236220
Luc Lachapelle (Pres)

Subsidiaries:

BAUVAL inc. - Bauval Sainte-Sophie Division (1)
1128 Abercrombie St, Sainte-Sophie, J5J 2R8, QC, Canada
Tel.: (450) 530-7776
Mineral Exploration & Mining Services
N.A.I.C.S.: 212312

BAUVAL inc. - Carriere L'Ange-Gardien Division (1)
368 rue Saint-Georges, L'Ange-Gardien, J0E 1E0, QC, Canada
Tel.: (450) 293-6368
Mineral Exploration & Mining Services
N.A.I.C.S.: 212312

BAUVAL inc. - Les Carrieres Regionales Division (1)
355 Mgr Langlois Blvd, Salaberry-de-Valleyfield, J6S 0G5, QC, Canada
Tel.: (450) 377-4544
Mineral Exploration & Mining Services
N.A.I.C.S.: 212312

BAUVAL inc. - Sables L.G.
Division   **(1)**
435 chemin de la Carriere, Saint-Hippolyte,
J8A 1E9, QC, Canada
Tel.: (450) 436-8767
Mineral Exploration & Mining Services
N.A.I.C.S.: 212312

Les Pavages Dorval inc.   **(1)**
2282 Montee Saint-Remi, Pointe-Claire,
H9P 1L1, QC, Canada
Tel.: (514) 636-4400
Highway Construction Services
N.A.I.C.S.: 237310

BAVARIA FILM GMBH
Bavariafilmplatz 7, Geiselgasteig,
82031, Munich, Germany
Tel.: (49) 89 64990
Web Site: http://www.bavaria-film.de
Year Founded: 1919
Sales Range: $250-299.9 Million
Emp.: 740
TV & Film Production
N.A.I.C.S.: 512110
Matthias Esche (Mng Dir)

Subsidiaries:

Askania Media Filmproduktion
GmbH   **(1)**
Kantstrasse 13, Berlin, 10623, Germany
Tel.: (49) 30 31 99 06 0
Web Site: http://www.askania-media.de
Film & Television Program Production Ser-
vices
N.A.I.C.S.: 512110
Martin Hofmann (Mng Dir)

Bavaria Fernsehproduktion
GmbH   **(1)**
Bavariafilmplatz 7, Geiselgasteig, 82031,
Munich, Germany   **(50%)**
Tel.: (49) 8964990
Web Site: http://www.bavaria-
fernsehproduktion.de
Sales Range: $100-124.9 Million
Emp.: 300
Motion Picture & Video Production
N.A.I.C.S.: 512110
Christione Frankenstein (Mng Dir)

Bavaria Film Interactive GmbH   **(1)**
Bavariafilmplatz 7, Geiselgasteig, Munich,
82031, Germany   **(100%)**
Tel.: (49) 8964992288
Web Site: http://www.bavaria-film-
interactive.de
Sales Range: $25-49.9 Million
Emp.: 30
Motion Picture & Video Industries
N.A.I.C.S.: 512199
Lars Rechmann (Mng Dir)

Bavaria Film- und Fernsehstudios
GmbH   **(1)**
Bavariafilmplatz 7, Geiselgasteig, 82031,
Munich, Germany
Tel.: (49) 8964993110
Web Site: http://www.bavaria-studios.de
Sales Range: $25-49.9 Million
Emp.: 71
Television Broadcasting
N.A.I.C.S.: 516120
Michael Klee (Mng Dir)

Bavaria Filmverleih- und Produktions
GmbH   **(1)**
Bavariafilmplatz 7, Geiselgasteig, 82031,
Munich, Germany   **(100%)**
Tel.: (49) 8964992465
Sales Range: $25-49.9 Million
Emp.: 3
Motion Picture & Video Production
N.A.I.C.S.: 512110
Gerorg Hoess (Mng Dir)

Bavaria Media Italia S.r.l.   **(1)**
Piazza San Bernardo 108/A, 00187, Rome,
Italy   **(100%)**
Tel.: (39) 0648907856
Web Site: http://www.bavariamedia.it
Sales Range: $25-49.9 Million
Emp.: 2
Motion Picture & Video Production
N.A.I.C.S.: 512110

Bavaria Media Television GmbH **(1)**

Bavariafilmplatz 7, Geiselgasteig, 82031,
Munich, Germany   **(100%)**
Tel.: (49) 89 6499 2694
Web Site: http://www.bavaria-media.tv
Sales Range: $25-49.9 Million
Emp.: 40
Television Broadcasting
N.A.I.C.S.: 516120

Bavaria Pictures GmbH   **(1)**
Bavariafilmplatz 7, Geiselgasteig, 82031,
Munich, Germany   **(50%)**
Tel.: (49) 8964993903
Web Site: http://www.bavaria-pictures.de
Sales Range: $25-49.9 Million
Emp.: 40
Motion Picture & Video Production
N.A.I.C.S.: 512110

Bavaria Production Services
GmbH   **(1)**
Bavariafilmplatz 7, Geiselgasteig, 82031,
Munich, Germany
Tel.: (49) 8964992500
Web Site: http://www.bavaria.film.de
Sales Range: $25-49.9 Million
Emp.: 70
Motion Picture & Video Production
N.A.I.C.S.: 512110
Gunther Farrenkopf (Dir-Production & Tech)

Bavaria Sonor Musikverlag und Mer-
chandising GmbH   **(1)**
Bavariafilmplatz 7, Geiselgasteig, 82031,
Munich, Germany   **(100%)**
Tel.: (49) 8964992238
Web Site: http://www.bavaria-sonor.de
Sales Range: $25-49.9 Million
Emp.: 20
Prerecorded Compact Disc & Tape & Re-
cord Reproducing
N.A.I.C.S.: 334610
Rolf Moser (Mng Dir)

Bayerisches Filmzentrum Wirtschafts-
forderungs GmbH   **(1)**
Bavariafilmplatz 7, Geiselgasteig, 82031,
Munich, Germany
Tel.: (49) 89649810
Web Site: http://www.bavaria-film.de
Motion Picture & Video Production
N.A.I.C.S.: 512110

Bremedia Produktion GmbH   **(1)**
Grobenstrabe 2, Bremen, 28195, Germany
Tel.: (49) 4212464000
Web Site: http://www.bremedia-
produktion.de
Sales Range: $50-74.9 Million
Emp.: 200
Motion Picture & Video Production
N.A.I.C.S.: 512110
Bernd Bielefeld (Mng Dir)

EuroVideo Bildprogramm GmbH   **(1)**
Oskar-Messter-Str 15, Ismaning, 85737,
Germany
Tel.: (49) 899624440
Web Site: http://www.eurovideo.de
Sales Range: $25-49.9 Million
Emp.: 45
Prerecorded Compact Disc & Tape & Re-
cord Reproducing
N.A.I.C.S.: 334610
Ulich Raum (Gen Mgr)

FTA Film- und Theaterausstattung
GmbH   **(1)**
Bavariafilmplatz 7, Geiselgasteig, 82031,
Munich, Germany
Tel.: (49) 89649890
Web Site: http://www.fta-muenchen.de
Emp.: 60
Motion Picture & Video Industries
N.A.I.C.S.: 512199
Hubert Lackner (Mng Dir)

First Entertainment GmbH   **(1)**
Bavaria film platz 7, Munich, 82031, Ger-
many
Tel.: (49) 8964994100
Web Site: http://www.first-entertainment.de
Sales Range: $25-49.9 Million
Emp.: 50
Broadcasting Services
N.A.I.C.S.: 516120
Florian Karl Otto Bahr (Mng Dir)

Maran Film GmbH   **(1)**

Lange Str 71, 76530, Baden-Baden,
Germany   **(49%)**
Tel.: (49) 722130250
Web Site: http://www.maranfilm.de
Sales Range: $25-49.9 Million
Emp.: 5
Motion Picture & Video Industries
N.A.I.C.S.: 512199
Sabine Tettenborn (Mng Dir)

Media & Communication Systems
(MCS) GmbH   **(1)**
Konigsbrucker Strasse 88, Dresden, 1099,
Germany
Tel.: (49) 3518463508
Web Site: http://www.mcs-sachsen.de
Media Representative Services
N.A.I.C.S.: 541840

Media City Atelier (MCA) GmbH **(1)**
Altenburger Strasse 13, 04275, Leipzig,
Germany
Tel.: (49) 341 3500 2299
Web Site: http://www.mca.de
Motion Picture & Video Production
N.A.I.C.S.: 512110

MotionWorks GmbH   **(1)**
Grobe Ulrichstrabe 23 Saale, Halle, 6108,
Germany   **(51%)**
Tel.: (49) 345205690
Web Site: http://www.motionworks-halle.eu
Sales Range: $25-49.9 Million
Emp.: 60
Motion Picture & Video Production
N.A.I.C.S.: 512110
Anthony Loeser (CEO)

Noon Filmtechnik Spol.S r.o.   **(1)**
Jihlavska 610-16, 14000, Prague, Czech
Republic
Tel.: (420) 261262111
Web Site: http://www.noon.cz
Sales Range: $25-49.9 Million
Emp.: 6
Photography Studios, Portrait
N.A.I.C.S.: 541921
Jiri Ondracek (Mgr)

Ottonia Media GmbH   **(1)**
Altenburger Strasse 7, 04275, Leipzig, Ger-
many
Tel.: (49) 34135002010
Web Site: http://www.ottonia.de
Sales Range: $25-49.9 Million
Emp.: 50
Motion Picture & Video Production
N.A.I.C.S.: 512110
Frank Hofling (Mng Dir)

ProSaar Medienproduktion
GmbH   **(1)**
Funkhaus Halberg, Saarbrucken, 66121,
Germany   **(51%)**
Tel.: (49) 681 687 92 91
Web Site: http://www.prosaar-medien.de
Film & Video Production Services
N.A.I.C.S.: 512110

Satel Fernseh- und Filmproduktions
GmbH   **(1)**
Linzer Strasse 375, 1140, Vienna, Austria
Tel.: (43) 1588720
Web Site: http://www.satel.at
Sales Range: $10-24.9 Million
Emp.: 14
Film Production Company
N.A.I.C.S.: 512110
Heinrich Ambrosch (Mng Dir)

Saxonia Entertainment GmbH   **(1)**
Altenburger Strasse 9, 04275, Leipzig,
Germany   **(49%)**
Tel.: (49) 34135004100
Web Site: http://www.saxonia-
entertainment.de
Sales Range: $50-74.9 Million
Emp.: 9
Amusement & Recreation Industries
N.A.I.C.S.: 713990
Adolf Kann (Mng Dir)

Saxonia Media Filmproduktion
GmbH   **(1)**
Altenburger Strasse 7, 04275, Leipzig,
Germany   **(51%)**
Tel.: (49) 34135001200
Web Site: http://www.saxonia-media.de
Sales Range: $25-49.9 Million
Emp.: 2
Motion Picture & Video Production

N.A.I.C.S.: 512110
Sven Sund (CEO)

Vienna Cine & TV Services
GmbH   **(1)**
Bavariafilmplatz 7, D-82031, Munich, Gei-
selgasteig, Germany   **(100%)**
Tel.: (49) 89 6499 3192
Web Site: http://www.bavaria-production-
services.de
Sales Range: $25-49.9 Million
Emp.: 5
Television Broadcasting
N.A.I.C.S.: 516120
Heinz Ratzinger (Mng Dir)

BAVARIA INDUSTRIES GROUP AG
Bavariaring 24, 80336, Munich, Ger-
many
Tel.: (49) 8972989670
Web Site: https://www.baikap.de
B8A—(DEU)
Rev.: $122,883,320
Assets: $414,880,230
Liabilities: $59,708,577
Net Worth: $355,171,653
Earnings: $20,951,540
Fiscal Year-end: 12/31/23
Investment Services
N.A.I.C.S.: 523999
Reimar Scholz (CEO & Member-Exec
Bd)

Subsidiaries:

BB Government Services GmbH **(1)**
Flickerstal 5, 67657, Kaiserslautern, Ger-
many
Tel.: (49) 63134320
Web Site: https://bbgs.eu
Construction Engineering Services
N.A.I.C.S.: 541330
Michael Bayer (CEO)

Subsidiary (Non-US):

BB Government Services s.r.l.   **(2)**
Via L L Zamenhof 200, 36100, Vicenza,
Italy
Tel.: (39) 0444239526
Construction Engineering Services
N.A.I.C.S.: 541330

CARBODY S.A.S.   **(1)**
17 rue du Moulin Florent, CS 50002, 51420,
Witry-les-Reims, France
Tel.: (33) 326844800
Web Site: https://www.carbody.eu
Sales Range: $50-74.9 Million
Emp.: 500
Motor Vehicle Parts Mfr
N.A.I.C.S.: 336390
Philippe Chedru (Mng Dir)

Cobelplast NV   **(1)**
Antwerpse Steenweg 14, B-9160, Lokeren,
Belgium
Tel.: (32) 93409911
Web Site: https://www.cobelplast.be
Emp.: 100
Plastics Product Mfr
N.A.I.C.S.: 326199
Guido Vuotto (Mng Dir)

Hering AG   **(1)**
Nurnberger Str 96, 91710, Gunzenhausen,
Germany
Tel.: (49) 983180000
Web Site: https://www.hering-ag.de
Emp.: 74
Heat Exchanger Mfr & Distr
N.A.I.C.S.: 332410
Christian Rasch (CEO)

Stobart Rail Limited   **(1)**
The Terminal Aviation Way Carlisle Lake
District Airport, Carlisle, CA6 4NZ, Cumbria,
United Kingdom
Tel.: (44) 1228 518 150
Web Site: http://www.stobartrail.com
Rail Infrastructure Engineering Services
N.A.I.C.S.: 541330
David Richardson (Plant Mgr)

TriStone Flowtech Germany
GmbH   **(1)**
Unterschweinstiege 2-14, Frankfurt am

BAVARIA Industries Group AG—(Continued)

Main, Germany
Tel.: (49) 69 904 300 100
Web Site: http://www.tristone.com
Emp.: 2,700
Motor Vehicle Parts Mfr
N.A.I.C.S.: 336390
Volker Butz *(CFO)*

BAVARIAN NORDIC A/S

Tel.: (45) 33268383
Web Site: https://www.bavarian-nordic.com
Year Founded: 1994
BVNKF—(OTCIQ)
Rev.: $1,026,488,189
Assets: $2,106,880,131
Liabilities: $575,871,324
Net Worth: $1,531,008,806
Earnings: $213,317,094
Emp.: 1,379
Fiscal Year-end: 12/31/23
Novel Vaccines Mfr
N.A.I.C.S.: 325412
Gerard W. M. van Odijk *(Chm)*

Subsidiaries:

Bavarian Nordic GmbH　　　　(1)
Fraunhoferstrasse 13, 82152, Martinsried, Germany
Tel.: (49) 89255446300
Emp.: 100
Vaccines Mfr
N.A.I.C.S.: 325414
Paul Chaplin *(Gen Mgr)*

Bavarian Nordic, Inc.　　　　(1)
2425 Garcia Ave, Mountain View, CA 94043
Tel.: (650) 681-4660
Emp.: 90
Vaccines Mfr
N.A.I.C.S.: 325414
Erin Stonestreet *(Mgr-HR)*

BAVELLONI S.P.A.

via G Natta 16, 20823, Lentate sul Seveso, MB, Italy
Tel.: (39) 0362682201
Web Site: http://www.bavelloni.com
Flat Glass Grinding Equipments & Machinery Mfr
N.A.I.C.S.: 327211
Stefano Bavelloni *(Mng Dir)*

BAWAG GROUP AG

Wiedner Gurtel 11, 1100, Vienna, Austria
Tel.: (43) 59905　　　　　AT
Web Site:
　　https://www.bawaggroup.com
Year Founded: 1922
BG—(VIE)
Rev.: $1,413,123,246
Assets: $61,000,431,686
Liabilities: $56,693,287,287
Net Worth: $4,307,144,399
Earnings: $343,513,922
Emp.: 2,117
Fiscal Year-end: 12/31/22
Holding Company
N.A.I.C.S.: 551111
Andrew Wise *(Chief Investment Officer, Member-Mgmt Bd & Head-Nonretail Lending)*

Subsidiaries:

Aegon Bank N.V.　　　　(1)
Thomas R Malthusstraat 1-3, 1066JR, Amsterdam, Noord-Holland, Netherlands
Tel.: (31) 203031600
Web Site: https://www.knab.nl
Financial Services
N.A.I.C.S.: 523999

BFL Leasing GmbH　　　　(1)
Mergenthalerallee 42, 65760, Eschborn, Germany
Tel.: (49) 61965820200
Web Site: https://www.bfl-leasing.de
Investment Services

N.A.I.C.S.: 523999

Deutscher Ring Bausparkasse Aktiengesellschaft　　　　(1)
Ludwig Erhard Strasse 22, 20459, Hamburg, Germany
Tel.: (49) 40 3599 50
Web Site: http://www.drebsk.de
Emp.: 100
Commercial Banking Services
N.A.I.C.S.: 522110

Health Coevo AG　　　　(1)
Lubeckertordamm 1-3, 20099, Hamburg, Germany
Tel.: (49) 40524709000
Web Site: https://www.healthag.de
Financial Services
N.A.I.C.S.: 523999

Omnicas Management AG　　　　(1)
Seestrasse 13, 8820, Wadenswil, Switzerland
Tel.: (41) 447830566
Web Site: http://www.omnicas.ch
Financial Services
N.A.I.C.S.: 523999

dd-roadmap Unternehmensberatung GmbH　　　　(1)
Wiedner Belt 11, 1100, Vienna, Austria
Tel.: (43) 5990545500
Web Site: http://www.dd-roadmap.com
Financial Services
N.A.I.C.S.: 523999

start:bausparkasse AG　　　　(1)
Lubeckertordamm 1-3, 20099, Hamburg, Germany
Tel.: (49) 40524709700
Web Site: https://www.start-bsk.de
Financial Services
N.A.I.C.S.: 523999

start:bausparkasse AG　　　　(1)
Wiedner Gurtel 11, 1100, Vienna, Austria
Tel.: (43) 1313800
Web Site: http://www.start-bausparkasse.at
Financial Services
N.A.I.C.S.: 523999

BAWAG P.S.K. BANK FUR ARBEIT UND WIRTSCHAFT UND OSTERREICHISCHE POSTSPARKASSE AKTIENGESELLSCHAFT

Wiedner Gurtel 11, 1100, Vienna, Austria
Tel.: (43) 59905　　　　　AT
Web Site: http://www.bawagpsk.com
Sales Range: $1-4.9 Billion
Emp.: 6,300
Bank Holding Company Retail Commercial & Private Banking Services
N.A.I.C.S.: 551111
Byron Haynes *(CEO & Chm-Mgmt Bd)*

Subsidiaries:

BAWAG Leasing & Fleet s.r.o.　　　　(1)
CORSO Karlin - Krizikova 36a, 180 00, Prague, Czech Republic
Tel.: (420) 221 511 241
Fleet Leasing Services
N.A.I.C.S.: 532120
Petra Pribylova *(Head-Collection Dept)*

BAWAG Leasing & Fleet s.r.o.　　　　(1)
Trnavska cesta 50, 821 02, Bratislava, Slovakia
Tel.: (421) 2 44634 700
Fleet Leasing & Management Services
N.A.I.C.S.: 485310

BAWAG P.S.K. Datendienst Gesellschaft m.b.H.　　　　(1)
Quellenstrasse 51-55, 1100, Vienna, Austria
Tel.: (43) 1 53453 0
Banking Services52211
N.A.I.C.S.: 522110

HBV Holding und Beteiligungsverwaltung GmbH　　　　(1)
Seitzergasse 2-4, 1010, Vienna, Austria
Tel.: (43) 1534530
Holding Company

N.A.I.C.S.: 551112

easybank AG　　　　(1)
Quellenstrasse 51-55, Vienna, 1100, Austria　　　　(100%)
Tel.: (43) 1217110
Web Site: http://www.easybank.at
Direct Banking Services
N.A.I.C.S.: 522110

Subsidiary (Domestic).

easyleasing GmbH　　　　(2)
Wiedner Belt 11, 1100, Vienna, Austria　　　　(100%)
Tel.: (43) 5055779000
Web Site: https://www.easybank.at
Financial Services
N.A.I.C.S.: 522220

BAWAN COMPANY

Alsahab Bldg No 1073 King Fahad Rd, PO Box 331, Al Muhammadiyah district, Riyadh, 11371, Saudi Arabia
Tel.: (966) 112917799
Web Site: https://bawan.com.sa
Year Founded: 1980
1302—(SAU)
Rev.: $968,372,217
Assets: $608,731,103
Liabilities: $360,862,285
Net Worth: $247,868,817
Earnings: $47,490,201
Emp.: 3,050
Fiscal Year-end: 12/31/22
Building Materials Mfr & Distr
N.A.I.C.S.: 321999
Abdullahn Abdul Latif Al Fozan *(Chm)*

Subsidiaries:

Bawan Wood Industries Co.　　　　(1)
2nd Industrial City, Dammam, Saudi Arabia
Tel.: (966) 138121234
Web Site: https://www.bawanwood.com
Wood Products Mfr
N.A.I.C.S.: 321999

Bina Advanced Concrete Products Company　　　　(1)
2nd Industrial Area, Dammam, 31952, Saudi Arabia
Tel.: (966) 138125555
Web Site: https://binaprecast.com
Precast Concrete Products Mfr
N.A.I.C.S.: 327390
Ahmed Al Osaimi *(CEO)*

Bina Ready-Mix Concrete Products Company　　　　(1)
2nd Industrial Area, PO Box 1594, Riyadh, 31952, Saudi Arabia
Tel.: (966) 138125555
Web Site: http://www.binareadymix.com
Emp.: 400
Cement Mfr
N.A.I.C.S.: 327310
Fouad Fahad Al Saleh *(Chm)*

United Transformers Electric Company　　　　(1)
Al Ojaimi Area 3rd Industrial District Al Kharj Road, PO Box 458, Riyadh, 11411, Saudi Arabia
Tel.: (966) 8003034000
Web Site: https://www.utec.com.sa
Transformer Mfr
N.A.I.C.S.: 335311

BAWANG INTERNATIONAL (GROUP) HOLDING LIMITED

468 Guanghua 3rd Road Bawang Industrial Park, Baiyun District, Guangzhou, 510450, China
Tel.: (86) 2086117888
Web Site: http://www.bawang.com.cn
1338—(HKG)
Rev.: $34,586,276
Assets: $34,289,471
Liabilities: $16,596,263
Net Worth: $17,693,208
Earnings: ($2,728,112)
Emp.: 442
Fiscal Year-end: 12/31/22

N.A.I.C.S.: 551112

Home & Personal Care Products Mfr
N.A.I.C.S.: 325620
Qiyuan Chen *(Chm)*

Subsidiaries:

Bawang International Group Holding (HK) Limited　　　　(1)
Rm B 16/F Ritz Plz, Tsim Tsa Tsui, China (Hong Kong)
Tel.: (852) 35431998
Web Site: http://www.bawang.com.cn
Emp.: 1
Holding Company
N.A.I.C.S.: 551112
Bill Wong *(Gen Mgr)*

BAXENDALE ADVISORY LIMITED

Wework Offices 22 Upper Ground, London, SE1 9PD, United Kingdom
Tel.: (44) 2035989982
Web Site:
　　http://www.baxendale.co.uk
Year Founded: 1866
Business Support Services
N.A.I.C.S.: 561499
Campbell McDonald *(Founder)*

BAY AREA GOLD GROUP LIMITED

Units 5 & 6 17/F Convention Plaza Office Tower 1 Harbour Road, Wanchai, China (Hong Kong)
Tel.: (852) 25177755　　　　BM
Web Site:
　　http://www.cpm.etnet.com.hk
Year Founded: 1999
1194—(HKG)
Rev.: $187,468,819
Assets: $1,301,063,179
Liabilities: $733,368,672
Net Worth: $567,694,507
Earnings: ($375,006,126)
Emp.: 750
Fiscal Year-end: 12/31/20
Gold Mining Services
N.A.I.C.S.: 212220
Yi Shuhao *(Chm & CEO)*

Subsidiaries:

Hongkong Bay Securities Limited　(1)
Room 05-06 17/F Office Building Convention Plaza 1 Harbour Road, Wanchai, China (Hong Kong)
Tel.: (852) 2 186 8870
Web Site: https://www.hkbay.hk
Security Trading Services
N.A.I.C.S.: 523150

BAY CAPITAL PLC

28 Esplanade, Channel Islands, Saint Helier, JE2 3QA, Jersey
Tel.: (44) 1534700000　　　　JE
Web Site:
　　https://www.baycapitalplc.com
Year Founded: 2021
BAY—(LSE)
Assets: $8,029,597
Liabilities: $66,464
Net Worth: $7,963,133
Earnings: ($312,090)
Emp.: 2
Fiscal Year-end: 12/31/22
Investment Management Service
N.A.I.C.S.: 523999

BAY GROUP HOLDINGS SDN BHD

Unit 13A01 Level 13A Tropicana Gardens Office Tower No 2A, Persiaran Surian Tropicana Indah, 47810, Petaling Jaya, Selangor, Malaysia
Tel.: (60) 18282224
Web Site: http://capbay.com
Supply Chain Finance Services
N.A.I.C.S.: 525990
Mohd Mokhtar *(Chm)*

Subsidiaries:

Kenanga Capital Islamic Sdn
Bhd (1)
Level 11 Kenanga Tower 237 Jalan Tun
Razak, 50400, Kuala Lumpur,
Malaysia (49%)
Tel.: (60) 21722888
Investment Banking Services
N.A.I.C.S.: 523150
Jalia Norhanim *(Asst VP)*

BAY HILL CONTRACTING LTD.
19122 21st Avenue, Surrey, V3Z
3M3, BC, Canada
Tel.: (604) 533-3306
Web Site:
http://www.bayhillcontracting.com
Year Founded: 1986
Sales Range: $10-24.9 Million
Electrical Contractor
N.A.I.C.S.: 238210
R. C. Burns *(Gen Mgr)*

BAY KING CHRYSLER DODGE JEEP
1655 Upper James Street, Hamilton,
L9B 2J1, ON, Canada
Tel.: (905) 383-7700
Web Site: http://www.bayking.ca
Year Founded: 1968
Rev.: $31,500,460
Emp.: 85
New Car Dealers
N.A.I.C.S.: 441110
Jamie Richter *(Pres)*

BAY LEASING & INVESTMENT LIMITED
Eunoos Trade Centre Level 18 52-53
Dilkusha C/A, Dhaka, 1000, Bangla-
desh
Tel.: (880) 29592501
Web Site: https://blilbd.com
Year Founded: 1996
BAYLEASING—(CHT)
Rev.: $7,216,677
Assets: $138,984,642
Liabilities: $123,650,914
Net Worth: $15,333,728
Earnings: ($7,556,929)
Emp.: 61
Fiscal Year-end: 12/31/22
Financial Services
N.A.I.C.S.: 523999
Maswooda Ghani *(Chm)*

Subsidiaries:

BLI Capital Limited (1)
10th Floor of Rupayan Trade Centre 114
Kazi Nazrul Islam Avenue, Banglamotor,
Dhaka, 1000, Bangladesh
Tel.: (880) 4103006165
Web Site: https://www.blicapitalltd.com
Financial Banking Services
N.A.I.C.S.: 522110
Israil Hossain *(Mng Dir)*

BAY OF QUINTE MUTUAL IN-SURANCE CO.
13379 Loyalist Parkway, PO Box
6050, Picton, K0K 2T0, ON, Canada
Tel.: (613) 476-2145
Web Site:
http://www.bayofquintemutual.com
Year Founded: 1874
Rev.: $16,917,543
Emp.: 32
Insurance & Brokerage Services
N.A.I.C.S.: 524298
Jeffery D. Howell *(Pres)*

BAY TREE PRIVATE EQUITY LLP
1 Bickenhall Mansions Bickenhall
Street, London, W1U 6BP, United
Kingdom
Tel.: (44) 0207160631

Web Site: https://www.baytree.pe
Emp.: 100
Privater Equity Firm
N.A.I.C.S.: 523999
Ed Cottrell *(Partner)*

Subsidiaries:

Hawco Ltd. (1)
Lower South Street, Lower Eashing,
Godalming, GU7 1BZ, Surrey, United King-
dom
Tel.: (44) 1483869100
Web Site: https://www.hawco.co.uk
Sales Range: $25-49.9 Million
Emp.: 100
Distr of Control Devices Used in Sensing,
Measurement & Control of Temperature &
Pressure
N.A.I.C.S.: 334513
Martin Butler *(Mng Dir)*

BAYALAG NALAIKH JOINT STOCK COMPANY
2nd Khoroo, Nailaikh District, Ulaan-
baatar, Mongolia
Tel.: (976) 99098503
Building Construction Services
N.A.I.C.S.: 236220

BAYAN INVESTMENT HOLD-ING COMPANY K.S.C.C.
11th &12th Floors Al-Qibla Fahad Al-
Salem Street, Suad Commercial
Complex, Kuwait, 35151, Kuwait
Tel.: (965) 1840000
Web Site:
http://www.bayaninvest.com
BAYANINV—(KUW)
Rev.: $2,299,067
Assets: $57,541,100
Liabilities: $9,652,020
Net Worth: $47,889,080
Earnings: ($21,535,731)
Emp.: 20
Fiscal Year-end: 12/31/22
Investment & Portfolio Management
Services
N.A.I.C.S.: 523150
Faisal Ali Abdul Wahab Al-Mutawa
(Chm)

Subsidiaries:

Arkan Holding Company K.S.C. (1)
Suad Complex 11th Floor Fahad Al-Salem
Street, Kuwait, 35359, Kuwait
Tel.: (965) 1840000
Web Site: http://www.arkanholding.com
Ceramic Tile Mfr
N.A.I.C.S.: 327120

Dar Al Dhabi Holding Co. K.S.C. (1)
Sadoun Jassim Al-Yacoub Building Office
Number 36 Block 11, Fahad Al-Salem
Street Al-Qibla, 35151, Kuwait, Kuwait
Tel.: (965) 22417868
Web Site: https://www.dadholding.com
Real Estate Development Services
N.A.I.C.S.: 531390

BAYAN SULU JSC
198 Borodin Street, 110000, Ko-
stanay, Kazakhstan
Tel.: (7) 7142562952
Web Site: https://www.bayansulu.kz
BSUL—(KAZ)
Rev.: $106,353,193
Assets: $110,785,183
Liabilities: $57,425,406
Net Worth: $53,359,777
Earnings: $6,638,062
Emp.: 1,340
Fiscal Year-end: 12/31/20
Confectionery Products Mfr & Sales
N.A.I.C.S.: 311340

BAYANAT AI PLC
Al Nahyan Area Delma Street No 13,
Abu Dhabi, United Arab Emirates
Tel.: (971) 26410000

Web Site: https://www.bayanat.ai
Emp.: 100
Software Publr
N.A.I.C.S.: 513210

Subsidiaries:

Al Yah Satellite Communications
Company PJSC (1)
Al Falah City, Abu Dhabi, United Arab Emir-
ates
Tel.: (971) 2 510 0000
Web Site: http://www.yahsat.com
Satellite Communication Services
N.A.I.C.S.: 517410
Massod M. Sharif Mahmood *(CEO)*

BAYANGOL HOTEL JOINT STOCK COMPANY
Chinggis Khaan Avenue-5, Ulaanbaa-
tar, 14251, Mongolia
Tel.: (976) 11312255
Web Site:
http://www.bayangolhotel.mn
BNG—(MONG)
Rev.: $2,554,570
Assets: $12,443,268
Liabilities: $222,244
Net Worth: $12,221,024
Earnings: $804,746
Fiscal Year-end: 12/31/19
Food & Accommodation Services
N.A.I.C.S.: 722511

BAYARD-PRESSE S.A.
18 Rue Barbes, 92128, Montrouge,
Cedex, France
Tel.: (33) 174316060
Web Site:
http://www.groupebayard.com
Sales Range: $350-399.9 Million
Emp.: 1,773
Newspaper Publishers
N.A.I.C.S.: 513120

Subsidiaries:

Bayard Canada, Inc. (1)
4475 rue Frontenac, Montreal, H2H 2S2,
QC, Canada
Tel.: (514) 278-3020
Web Site: http://www.bayardcanada.ca
Emp.: 100
Book & Magazine Publisher
N.A.I.C.S.: 513120
Suzanne Spino *(Mgr)*

Bayard Presse Asia (1)
Room 8 9/F Block A Hong Kong Industrial
Centre 489 - 491, Cheung Sha Wan, Kow-
loon, (Hong Kong).
Tel.: (852) 3665 9398
Web Site: http://www.bayard.com.hk
Emp.: 21
Magazine Publisher
N.A.I.C.S.: 513120
Michael Ren *(Gen Mgr)*

Bayard Revistas S.A. (1)
261-265 Edif 4 Alcala No 1 CW, 28027, Ma-
drid, Spain
Tel.: (34) 914057010
Magazine Publisher
N.A.I.C.S.: 513120
Marta Tobella *(Mgr-Sls)*

Bayard, Inc. (1)
1 Montauk Ave Ste 200, New London, CT
06320
Tel.: (860) 437-3012
Web Site: http://www.bayard-inc.com
Sales Range: $25-49.9 Million
Emp.: 50
Magazine & Book Publisher
N.A.I.C.S.: 513130
Daniel Connors *(Editor-in-Chief)*

BAYCURRENT CONSULTING, INC.
Toranomon Hills Mori Tower 9th floor
23-1 Toranomon 1-Chome Minato-ku,
Tokyo, 105-6309, Japan
Tel.: (81) 355010151
Web Site: http://www.baycurrent.co.jp

Year Founded: 1998
6532—(TKS)
Sales Range: $25-49.9 Billion
Emp.: 2,317
Business Management Consulting
Services
N.A.I.C.S.: 541611
Yoshiyuki Abe *(Pres & CEO)*

BAYER AKTIENGESELL-SCHAFT
Kaiser-Wilhelm-Allee 1, 51373, Le-
verkusen, Germany
Tel.: (49) 214301 De
Web Site: https://www.bayer.com
Year Founded: 1863
BAYN—(MUN)
Rev.: $52,585,274,320
Assets: $128,335,357,121
Liabilities: $91,821,393,103
Net Worth: $36,513,964,019
Earnings: ($3,247,599,073)
Emp.: 99,723
Fiscal Year-end: 12/31/23
Holding Company
N.A.I.C.S.: 551112
Oliver Zuhlke *(Deputy Chm-Supervisory Bd)*

Subsidiaries:

Adverio Pharma GmbH (1)
Willy-Brandt-Platz 2, 12529, Schonefeld,
Germany
Tel.: (49) 2143056487
Pharmaceuticals Product Mfr
N.A.I.C.S.: 325412

Bayer (China) Limited (1)
34/F Jing Guang Center Hu Jia Lou, Cho-
ayang District, Beijing, 100020, China
Tel.: (86) 1065973181
Sales Range: $25-49.9 Million
Emp.: 50
Executive Office
N.A.I.C.S.: 921110

Bayer (Malaysia) Sdn. Bhd. (1)
T1-14 Jaya 33 No 3 Jalan Semangat
Seksyen 13, 46200, Petaling Jaya, Selan-
gor, Malaysia
Tel.: (60) 3 6209 3088
Pharmaceutical Products Distr
N.A.I.C.S.: 424210

Bayer (Proprietary) Limited (1)
27 Wrench Road, PO Box 143, Isando,
1600, South Africa
Tel.: (27) 119215911
Web Site: https://www.bayer.com
Emp.: 1,000
Pharmaceuticals Product Mfr
N.A.I.C.S.: 325412

Bayer (SCHWEIZ) AG (1)
Uetlibergstrasse 132, 8045, Zurich,
Switzerland (100%)
Tel.: (41) 444658111
Web Site: https://www.bayer.com
Corporate Business Services
N.A.I.C.S.: 561499

Subsidiary (Domestic):

Berlis AG (2)
Uetlibergstrasse 132, 8045, Zurich, Switzer-
land
Tel.: (41) 444658444
Web Site: https://www.berlis.ch
Sales Range: $25-49.9 Million
Emp.: 2
Pharmaceutical Drugs Mfr & Whslr
N.A.I.C.S.: 325412

Bayer (Sichuan) Animal Health Co.,
Ltd. (1)
No 189 Section 1 Changcheng Road Xinan
Airport Economic, Chengdu, 610225, Sich-
uan, China
Tel.: (86) 2885860334
Biological Product Mfr
N.A.I.C.S.: 325414

Bayer 04 Leverkusen Fussball
GmbH (1)
BayArena Bismarckstr 122 - 124, 51373,

Bayer Aktiengesellschaft—(Continued)

Leverkusen, Germany
Tel.: (49) 21450001904
Web Site: https://www.bayer04.de
Sports Club Facility Operation Services
N.A.I.C.S.: 713940
Fernando Carro de Prada (CEO)

Bayer 04 Leverkusen Sportforderung gGmbl l (1)
Bismarckstrasse 122-124, 51373, Leverkusen, Germany
Tel.: (49) 1805040404
Sport & Recreation Services
N.A.I.C.S.: 611620

Bayer A/S (1)
Arne Jacobsens Alle 13 6, 2300, Copenhagen, Denmark
Tel.: (45) 45235000
Web Site: https://www.bayer.com
Sales Range: $50-74.9 Million
Emp.: 120
Chemical & Pharmaceutical Products Mfr
N.A.I.C.S.: 325412

Bayer AB (1)
Berzelius vag 35, 171 65, Solna, Stockholm, Sweden (100%)
Tel.: (46) 858022300
Web Site: http://www.bayer.se
Rev.: $169,200,000
Emp.: 120
Pharmaceutical & Chemical Products
N.A.I.C.S.: 325412

Bayer AGCO Limited (1)
230 Cambridge Science Park Milton Road, Cambridge, CB4 0WB, United Kingdom
Tel.: (44) 1223226500
Sales Range: $25-49.9 Million
Emp.: 10
Crop Protection Chemical Mfr
N.A.I.C.S.: 325320

Bayer AS (1)
Chemical & Pharmaceutical Products Mfr
N.A.I.C.S.: 325412

Bayer Agriculture BVBA (1)
Haven 627 Scheldelaan 460, 2040, Antwerp, Belgium
Tel.: (32) 35685111
Pharmaceuticals Product Mfr
N.A.I.C.S.: 325412

Bayer Agriculture Limited (1)
230 Cambridge Science Park, Cambridge, CB4 0WB, United Kingdom
Tel.: (44) 12 23 22 65 00
Sales Range: $50-74.9 Million
Emp.: 150
Agricultural Chemical Mfr
N.A.I.C.S.: 325320

Bayer Algerie S.P.A. (1)
Lot 424-Cooperative El BouroudjAin Allah, DelyBrahim, 16047, Algiers, Algeria
Tel.: (213) 21918900
Web Site:
  http://www.algeria.cropscience.bayer.com
Pesticide Mfr
N.A.I.C.S.: 325320

Bayer Argentina S.A. (1)
Ricardo Gutierrez 3652, B1605EHD, Munro, Buenos Aires, Argentina (99.9%)
Tel.: (54) 114 762 7000
Web Site: https://www.conosur.bayer.com
Sales Range: $700-749.9 Million
Emp.: 1,200
Pharmaceuticals, Organic & Inorganic Chemicals, Dyes, Synthetic Fibers, Agrichemicals, Veterinary Products & Toiletries Mfr
N.A.I.C.S.: 325412
Richard Van der Merwe (Pres & CEO)

Bayer Australia Limited (1)
(100%)
Tel.: (61) 29 391 6000
Web Site: https://www.bayer.com.au
Sales Range: $450-499.9 Million
Emp.: 980
Mfr of Pharmaceuticals, Over-the-Counter Medicines, Diagnostic Products & Dyes
N.A.I.C.S.: 325412

Division (Domestic):

Bayer CropScience Australia Pty. Ltd. (2)

8 Redfern Rd, Hawthorn East, 3123, VIC, Australia
Tel.: (61) 39 248 6888
Web Site: https://www.crop.bayer.com.au
Sales Range: $50-74.9 Million
Emp.: 200
Crop Protection Product Mfr
N.A.I.C.S.: 325320

Bayer HealthCare Australia (2)
391-393 Tooronga Road, Hawthorn East, 3123, VIC, Australia
Tel.: (61) 392486888
Sales Range: $25-49.9 Million
Emp.: 100
Health Care Products Mfr
N.A.I.C.S.: 325412
George Ellmanns (Chm & Mng Dir)

Bayer MaterialScience Australia (2)
391-393 Tooronga Road, Hawthorn East, 3123, VIC, Australia
Tel.: (61) 95819888
Web Site: http://www.bayer.com.au
Chemicals & Compounds Mfr
N.A.I.C.S.: 325998

Bayer Austria GmbH. (1)
Herbststrasse 6-10, 1160, Vienna, Austria (100%)
Tel.: (43) 1711460
Web Site: https://www.bayer.com
Sales Range: $75-99.9 Million
Emp.: 241
Sales of Pharmaceutical & Chemical Products
N.A.I.C.S.: 424690

Bayer B.V. (1)
Energieweg 1, PO Box 80, 3641 RT, Mijdrecht, Netherlands (92%)
Tel.: (31) 297280666
Web Site: https://www.bayer.com
Sales Range: $500-549.9 Million
Emp.: 300
Pharmaceuticals & Chemicals Mfr
N.A.I.C.S.: 424690

Bayer Beteiligungsverwaltung Goslar GmbH (1)
Lilienthalstr 4, Schonefeld, Brandenburg, 12529, Germany
Tel.: (49) 214301
Investment Management Service
N.A.I.C.S.: 523940

Bayer Bitterfeld GmbH (1)
Salegaster Chaussee 1, Greppin, 06803, Bitterfeld-Wolfen, Germany
Tel.: (49) 349497812100
Web Site: https://www.bayer.com
Logistics Consulting Servies
N.A.I.C.S.: 541614

Bayer Boliviana Ltda. (1)
Edificio Tacuaral II Piso 2 Zona Centro Empresarial Equipetrol Norte, Santa Cruz, Bolivia
Tel.: (591) 33153300
Pharmaceuticals Product Mfr
N.A.I.C.S.: 325412

Bayer Bulgaria EOOD (1)
5 Rezbarska Str, 1510, Sofia, Bulgaria
Tel.: (359) 24247280
Web Site: https://www.bayer.com
Sales Range: $50-74.9 Million
Emp.: 15
Pharmaceuticals Product Mfr
N.A.I.C.S.: 325412

Bayer Business Services GmbH (1)
Bldg No151 Parkplatz Otto-Bayer-Strasse C, D-51368, Leverkusen, Germany (100%)
Tel.: (49) 214301
Web Site: http://www.bayerbbs.com
Sales Range: $1-4.9 Million
Emp.: 4,555
Information Technology & Business Management Services
N.A.I.C.S.: 541611

Subsidiary (Domestic):

Bayer Direct Services GmbH (2)
Kaiser-Wilhelm-Allee 50, 51373, Leverkusen, Germany
Tel.: (49) 214 3066 222
Business Support Services
N.A.I.C.S.: 561499

Bayer Canadian Holdings Inc. (1)
2920 Matheson Boulevard East, Mississauga, L4W5R6, ON, Canada
Tel.: (416) 248-0771
Investment Management Service
N.A.I.C.S.: 523999

Bayer Capital Corporation B.V. (1)
Energieweg 1, PO Box 80, 3641 RT, Mijdrecht, Netherlands
Tel.: (31) 297280666
Web Site: http://www.bayer.com
Security Brokerage Services
N.A.I.C.S.: 523150

Bayer Chemicals AG (1)
Chemiepark Leverkusen Gebaude K10 St Kaiser Wilhelm Allee 1, Leverkusen, 51368, Germany
Tel.: (49) 214301
Web Site: http://www.bayer.com
Emp.: 2,000
Chemical Mfr & Whslr
N.A.I.C.S.: 325998

Bayer Co. (Malaysia) Sdn. Bhd. (1)
25-03 25-04 Level 25 Imazium No 8 Jalan SS21/37, Damansara Uptown, 47400, Petaling Jaya, Selangor, Malaysia
Tel.: (60) 378013088
Web Site: https://www.bayer.com
Pharmaceutical Products Distr
N.A.I.C.S.: 424210

Bayer Consumer Care AG (1)
Peter Merian Str 84, 4002, Basel, Switzerland
Tel.: (41) 582727272
Pharmaceutical Products Distr
N.A.I.C.S.: 424210

Bayer Corporation (1)
100 Bayer Blvd, Whippany, NJ 07981 (100%)
Tel.: (862) 404-3000
Sales Range: $5-14.9 Billion
Emp.: 22,300
Science & Technology Product Mfr
N.A.I.C.S.: 541715
Jennifer Brendel (VP-Comm-Consumer Health Div)

Subsidiary (Domestic):

BAYPO Limited Partnership (2)
Hc 2 Box N, New Martinsville, WV 26155
Tel.: (304) 455-3688
Health Care Consulting Services
N.A.I.C.S.: 541690

Subsidiary (Domestic):

Baypo I LLC (3)
164 Fairview Dr, New Martinsville, WV 26155-2806
Tel.: (304) 455-3122
Chemical Products Mfr
N.A.I.C.S.: 325998

Baypo II LLC (3)
103 Foulk Rd, Wilmington, DE 19803-3742
Tel.: (302) 571-8909
Medical Laboratory Testing Services
N.A.I.C.S.: 541380

Subsidiary (Domestic):

Bayer International Trade Services Corporation (2)
100 Bayer Rd Bldg 4, Pittsburgh, PA 15205-9707
Tel.: (412) 777-2000
Plastics Material Mfr
N.A.I.C.S.: 325211

Bayer Puerto Rico, Inc. (2)
Lote 6 St 1 Km 25.2 Quebrada Arena, Rio Piedras, PR 00922-1848
Tel.: (787) 622-2937
Sales Range: $50-74.9 Million
Emp.: 20
Drugs, Proprietaries & Sundries
N.A.I.C.S.: 424210
Maria T. Musignac (Mgr-Credit)

Bayer U.S. LLC (2)
100 Bayer Rd, Pittsburgh, PA 15205-9741
Tel.: (412) 777-2000
Business Support Services
N.A.I.C.S.: 561499

Ahmad Soltani (Chief Procurement Officer & VP)

Co-Ex Corp. (2)
5 Alexander Dr, Wallingford, CT 06492-2429 (100%)
Tel.: (203) 679-0500
Web Site: https://www.co-excorp.com
Sales Range: $25-49.9 Million
Emp.: 9
Plastics Sheets & Rods Mfr
N.A.I.C.S.: 326121
Cosimo Conterno (Exec VP)

NOR-AM Agro LLC (2)
100 Bayer Rd Bldg 4, Pittsburgh, PA 15205-9707
Tel.: (412) 777-2000
Plastic Materials Mfr
N.A.I.C.S.: 325211

NippoNex Inc. (2)
100 Bayer Rd Bldg 4, Pittsburgh, PA 15205-9707
Tel.: (412) 777-2000
Plastic Materials Mfr
N.A.I.C.S.: 325211

Subsidiary (Domestic):

NippoNex Holdings LLC (3)
100 Bayer Rd Bldg 4, Pittsburgh, PA 15205-9707
Tel.: (412) 777-2000
Investment Management Service
N.A.I.C.S.: 523940

Subsidiary (Domestic):

SB Capital Corporation (2)
6701 Beryl Dr, Arlington, TX 76002-5468
Tel.: (817) 707-7305
Business Support Services
N.A.I.C.S.: 561499

STWB Inc. (2)
100 Bayer Rd Bldg 4, Pittsburgh, PA 15205-9707
Tel.: (412) 777-2000
Pharmaceutical Product Mfr & Whslr
N.A.I.C.S.: 325412

Schering Berlin Inc. (2)
340 Changebridge Rd, Pine Brook, NJ 07058
Tel.: (973) 487-2000
Pharmaceuticals Product Mfr
N.A.I.C.S.: 325998

The SDI Divestiture Corporation (2)
100 Bayer Rd Bldg 4, Pittsburgh, PA 15205-9707
Tel.: (412) 777-2000
Plastic Resin Mfr
N.A.I.C.S.: 325211

Viterion Telehealthcare LLC (2)
555 White Plains Rd, Tarrytown, NY 10591
Tel.: (914) 333-6600
Web Site: http://www.viterion.com
Sales Range: $10-24.9 Million
Emp.: 30
Healthcare Technology Services
N.A.I.C.S.: 621999

Bayer CropScience (China) Company Ltd. (1)
34th Floor Jing Guang Centre Hujialou, Chaoyang District, Beijing, 100020, China
Tel.: (86) 1065973181
N.A.I.C.S.: 325320

Bayer CropScience AG (1)
Alfred-Nobel-Strasse 50, 40789, Monheim, Germany (100%)
Tel.: (49) 2173383125
Web Site: http://www.bayercropscience.com
Sales Range: $5-14.9 Billion
Emp.: 1,800
Crop Protection, Pest Control, Seeds & Biotechnology Products Mfr
N.A.I.C.S.: 325320
Bernd Naaf (Member-Mgmt Bd, Head-Bus Affairs & Comm & Dir-Labor)

Subsidiary (Non-US):

Bayer (South East Asia) Pte Ltd. (2)
2 Tanjong Katong Road 07-01 Paya Lebar Quarter 3, Singapore, 437161, Singapore
Tel.: (65) 64961888

Web Site: https://www.bayer.com
Emp.: 360
Pharmaceutical Products Distr
N.A.I.C.S.: 424210

Subsidiary (Non-US):

Bayer CropScience (Private)
Limited **(3)**
Bahria Complex II 4th Floor M T Khan
Road, Karachi, Pakistan
Tel.: (92) 21 35646700
Crop Farming Services
N.A.I.C.S.: 111998

Bayer CropScience Holdings Pty
Ltd. **(3)**
Level 1 8 Redfern Road, Hawthorn East,
Melbourne, 3123, VIC, Australia
Tel.: (61) 392486888
Emp.: 140
Investment Management Service
N.A.I.C.S.: 523999
Jackie Applegate *(Chm)*

Bayer CropScience K.K. **(3)**
Marunouchi Kitaguchi Building 1-6-5
Marunouchi, Chiyoda-ku, Tokyo, 100-8262,
Japan
Tel.: (81) 362667007
Web Site: https://cropscience.bayer.jp
Sales Range: $125-149.9 Million
Emp.: 292
Crop Protection Chemicals Mfr & Distr
N.A.I.C.S.: 325320

Bayer CropScience Ltd. **(3)**
23 Boramae-ro 5-gil 395-62 Sindaebang-
dong Samsung Boramae Omni Tower,
Dongjak-gu, Seoul, 07071, Korea (South)
Tel.: (82) 15774644
Web Site:
   https://www.cropscience.bayer.co.kr
Sales Range: $50-74.9 Million
Emp.: 185
Crop Protection Chemicals Mfr & Distr
N.A.I.C.S.: 325320
Holger Detje *(Pres)*

Bayer CropScience Pty Limited **(3)**
391-393 Tooronga Rd, Hawthorn East, Mel-
bourne, 3123, VIC, Australia
Tel.: (61) 3 9248 6888
Web Site:
   http://www.bayercropscience.com.au
Crop Protection Services
N.A.I.C.S.: 115114

Bayer CropScience, Inc. **(3)**
Bayer House Canlubang Industrial Estate
Canlubang Calamba, Laguna, 4028, Philip-
pines
Tel.: (63) 2 450 5400
Farm Chemicals & Fertilizer Whslr
N.A.I.C.S.: 424690

Subsidiary (Non-US):

Bayer CropScience (Portugal) Produ-
tos para a Agricultura, Lda. **(2)**
Avenida Vitor Figueiredo n 4-4 piso, 2790-
255, Carnaxide, Portugal
Tel.: (351) 214172121
Web Site: https://www.bayer.com
Agricultural Fertilizer Mfr
N.A.I.C.S.: 325314
Nelson Ambrogio *(Mng Dir)*

Subsidiary (Domestic):

Bayer CropScience Deutschland
GmbH **(2)**
Alfred-Nobel-Str 50, 40789, Monheim,
Germany **(100%)**
Tel.: (49) 2173380
Web Site: https://agrar.bayer.de
Sales Range: $125-149.9 Million
Emp.: 120
Crop Protection & Pesticides Marketer &
Whslr
N.A.I.C.S.: 424590

Subsidiary (Non-US):

Bayer CropScience Holding SA **(2)**
Tel.: (33) 472854545
Web Site: http://www.bayer.com
Emp.: 700
Investment Management Service
N.A.I.C.S.: 523999

Subsidiary (US):

Bayer CropScience LP **(2)**
2 TW Alexander Dr, Research Triangle
Park, NC 27709
Tel.: (919) 549-2000
Web Site:
   http://www.bayercropscienceus.com
Rev.: $130,000,000
Emp.: 400
Mfr of Pesticides: Bifenox, Ethoprop, Mer-
phos, Bromoxynil & Bromoxynil Octanoate
N.A.I.C.S.: 325320
John Wendorf *(Mgr-Market Segment-
Environmental Science)*

Plant (Domestic):

Bayer CropScience **(3)**
8400 Hawthorne Rd, Kansas City, MO
64120-2301
Tel.: (816) 242-2000
Web Site: http://www.bayercropscience.com
Insecticides & Herbicides Distr
N.A.I.C.S.: 325320

Subsidiary (Domestic):

Bayer CropScience Holding Inc. **(3)**
100 Bayer Rd Bldg 4, Pittsburgh, PA 15205-
9707
Tel.: (412) 777-2000
Crop Farming Services
N.A.I.C.S.: 111998

Subsidiary (Non-US):

Bayer CropScience Inc. **(3)**
160 Quarry Park Blvd Suite 100, Calgary,
T2C 3G3, AB, Canada
Tel.: (403) 723-7400
Web Site: http://www.bayercropscience.ca
Sales Range: $25-49.9 Million
Emp.: 80
Crop Farming Services
N.A.I.C.S.: 111998

Subsidiary (Domestic):

Bayer CropScience Holdings Inc. **(4)**
Suite 200 160 Quarry Park Blvd SE, Cal-
gary, T2C 3G3, AB, Canada
Tel.: (403) 723-7400
Emp.: 7
Crop Farming Services
N.A.I.C.S.: 111998

Subsidiary (Domestic):

US Seeds LLC **(3)**
2528 Alexander Dr, Jonesboro, AR 72401
Tel.: (870) 336-0111
Agricultural Crop Farming Services
N.A.I.C.S.: 111998
Jamie Boone *(Gen Mgr)*

Subsidiary (Non-US):

Bayer CropScience Limited **(2)**
230 Cambridge Science Park Milton Road,
Cambridge, CB4 0WB, United Kingdom
Tel.: (44) 1223 226500
Web Site: http://www.bayergarden.co.uk
Chemical Products Mfr & Distr
N.A.I.C.S.: 325320

Bayer CropScience Limited **(2)**
Bayer House Central Avenue Hiranandani
Estate, West, Thane, 400 607, Maharash-
tra, India **(28.45%)**
Tel.: (91) 2225311234
Web Site: https://www.bayer.in
Rev.: $590,376,150
Assets: $578,664,450
Liabilities: $230,548,500
Net Worth: $348,115,950
Earnings: $67,308,150
Emp.: 1,254
Fiscal Year-end: 03/31/2021
Agricultural Seed Production
N.A.I.C.S.: 111199
Duraiswami Narain *(Vice Chm, CEO & Mng
Dir)*

Bayer CropScience Ltda. **(2)**
Rua Domingos Jorge 1100 Predio 9504,
Socorro, Sao Paulo, 04779-900, Brazil
Tel.: (55) 11 56945166
Web Site:
   http://www.bayercropscience.com.br

Sales Range: $800-899.9 Million
Emp.: 850
Seeds Mfr & Distr
N.A.I.C.S.: 424930

Bayer CropScience N.V. **(2)**
Tel.: (32) 25356311
Sales Range: $25-49.9 Million
Emp.: 150
Crop Protection Chemical Mfr
N.A.I.C.S.: 325998
Klaus Koetting *(Mng Dir)*

Subsidiary (Domestic):

Bayer CropScience Raps GmbH **(2)**
Streichmuhler Str 8, 24977, Grundhof,
Schleswig-Holstein, Germany
Tel.: (49) 46 36 89 0
Web Site: http://raps.bayer.de
Oil Seed Production Services
N.A.I.C.S.: 311224

Subsidiary (Non-US):

Bayer CropScience S.A.S. **(2)**
16 rue Jean-Marie Leclair, PO Box 310,
F-69009, Lyon, France **(100%)**
Tel.: (33) 472854321
Web Site: http://www.bayer.fr
Sales Range: $800-899.9 Million
Emp.: 700
Insecticides, Fungicides, Herbicides, Growth
Regulators, Garden & Household Products,
Cosmetics & Perfumes; Joint Venture of
Aventis S.A. (76%) & Schering AG (24%)
N.A.I.C.S.: 325620

Bayer CropScience S.r.l. **(2)**
Viale Certosa 130, 20156, Milan, Italy
Tel.: (39) 0239721
Web Site: https://www.cropscience.bayer.it
Crop Protection Chemicals Distr
N.A.I.C.S.: 424910

Subsidiary (Domestic):

Bayer CropScience Vermogensver-
waltungsgesellschaft mbH **(2)**
Alfred-Nobel-Str 50 Ambrhein, 40789, Mon-
heim, Germany
Tel.: (49) 214301
Web Site: http://www.bayercropscience.com
Crop Protection Chemicals Mfr & Distr
N.A.I.C.S.: 325320

Subsidiary (Non-US):

Bayer CropScience, S.L. **(2)**
Avinguda Comarques del Pais Valencia
267, Quart de Poblet, 46930, Valencia,
Spain
Tel.: (34) 961597930
Web Site: https://www.cropscience.bayer.es
Sales Range: $25-49.9 Million
Emp.: 55
Crop Farming & Protection Services
N.A.I.C.S.: 115112
Rolf Deege *(Dir Gen)*

Nunhems B.V. **(2)**
Napoleonsweg 152, 6083 AB, Nunhem,
Netherlands
Tel.: (31) 47 559 9222
Web Site: https://www.nunhems.com
Sales Range: $450-499.9 Million
Emp.: 1,700
Vegetable Seed Distr
N.A.I.C.S.: 424590

Subsidiary (Non-US):

Nunhems Chile S.A. **(3)**
Avenida Presidente Riesco No 5335 Oficina
2101, Las Condes, Santiago, Chile
Tel.: (56) 2 620 9700
Sales Range: $25-49.9 Million
Emp.: 55
Vegetable Seed Distr
N.A.I.C.S.: 424590
Albert Schurte *(Gen Mgr)*

Nunhems France S.A.R.L. **(3)**
8 rue Olivier de Serres, CS 10027, 49072,
Beaucouze, Cedex, France
Tel.: (33) 24 131 1280
Web Site: https://www.nunhems.com
Sales Range: $25-49.9 Million
Emp.: 40
Seed Mfr & Whslr
N.A.I.C.S.: 311911

Nunhems Hungary Kft. **(3)**
Vaci ut 96-98, 1133, Budapest, Hungary
Tel.: (36) 704234693
Sales Range: $25-49.9 Million
Emp.: 7
Crop Planting & Protection Services
Iaszlo Sarfalvi *(Gen Mgr & Country Mgr-Sls)*

Nunhems India Private Limited **(3)**
Opp Brahama Kumari Ashram Pataudi
Road Bhora Kalan, Bilaspur, Gurgaon,
122413, Haryana, India
Tel.: (91) 124 305 1300
Web Site: http://www.nunhems.com
Sales Range: $25-49.9 Million
Emp.: 6
Vegetable Seeds Mfr & Distr
N.A.I.C.S.: 311411

Nunhems Italy S.r.l. **(3)**
Via Ghiarone 2, 40019, Sant'Agata Bolog-
nese, Bologna, Italy
Tel.: (39) 051 681 7411
Web Site: https://www.nunhems.com
Vegetable Seed Distr
N.A.I.C.S.: 424590

Nunhems Mexico S.A. de C.V. **(3)**
Blvd Campestre 2502 2 Piso 201 El Refu-
gio Campestre, 37156, Leon, Guanajuato,
Mexico
Tel.: (52) 477 214 5200
Web Site: https://www.nunhems.com
Sales Range: $25-49.9 Million
Emp.: 42
Vegetable Seed Distr
N.A.I.C.S.: 424910
Ricardo Ramos Perez *(Mgr-Crop Sls)*

Subsidiary (Domestic):

Nunhems Netherlands B.V. **(3)**
Napoleonsweg 152, PO Box 4005, 6083
AB, Nunhem, Netherlands
Tel.: (31) 47 559 9222
Web Site: https://www.nunhems.com
Vegetable Seed Distr
N.A.I.C.S.: 424910

Subsidiary (Non-US):

Nunhems Poland Sp. z o.o. **(3)**
Al Jerozolimskie 142B, 02-305, Warsaw,
Poland
Tel.: (48) 51 007 9862
Web Site: https://www.nunhems.com
Sales Range: $50-74,9 Million
Emp.: 7
Vegetable Seed Distr
N.A.I.C.S.: 424590

Nunhems Spain, S.A. **(3)**
Paterna Technology Park C/ Juan de la
Cierva y Codorniu, n 27 Wellness II Build-
ing, 46980, Valencia, Spain
Tel.: (34) 950497776
Web Site: https://www.nunhems.com
Vegetable Seed Distr
N.A.I.C.S.: 424590
Paqa Arcudero *(Mgr)*

Nunhems Tohumculuk Limited
Sirketi **(3)**
Satirli Mah Merkez Sokak No 101/1, Serik,
07510, Antalya, Turkiye
Tel.: (90) 2427102244
Sales Range: $25-49.9 Million
Emp.: 68
Vegetable Seed Distr
N.A.I.C.S.: 424590

Subsidiary (US):

Nunhems USA, Inc. **(3)**
1200 Anderson Corner Rd, Parma, ID
83660
Tel.: (208) 674-4000
Web Site: http://www.nunhemsusa.com
Vegetable Seed Distr
N.A.I.C.S.: 424590

Subsidiary (Non-US):

Nunhems do Brasil Comercio de Se-
mentes Ltda. **(3)**
Rua Umbu 302 - Sala 01 - Terreo Alphaville
Campinas Empresarial, 13098-325, Campi-
nas, 13098-325, Sao Paulo, Brazil
Tel.: (55) 19 3733 9500

Bayer Aktiengesellschaft—(Continued)

Web Site: http://www.nunhems.com.br
Emp.: 16
Agricultural Seed Distr
N.A.I.C.S.: 424910
Fabricio Benatti *(Gen Dir)*

**Bayer CropScience Guatemala,
Limitada** (1)
Km 14.5 Calzada Roosevelt 2 3, 01010,
Mixco, Guatemala
Tel.: (502) 24369786
N.A.I.C.S.: 325320

Bayer CropScience Schweiz AG (1)
Rothausstrasse 61, 4132, Muttenz, Switzer-
land
Tel.: (41) 444658111
Pharmaceuticals Product Mfr
N.A.I.C.S.: 325412

Bayer East Africa Ltd. (1)
Thika Road/Outering Road Junction, 30321-
00100, Ruaraka, 00100, Nairobi, Kenya
Tel.: (254) 208600000
Pharmaceutical Products Distr
N.A.I.C.S.: 424210

Bayer Finance Ltda. (1)
Av Isidora Goyenechea 2800 Oficina 1702
Las Condes, Santiago, Chile
Tel.: (56) 25208417
Web Site: http://www.bayer.cl
Sales Range: $50-74.9 Million
Emp.: 1
Financial Management Services
N.A.I.C.S.: 523999
Kurt Solan *(Gen Mgr)*

Bayer Global Investments B.V. (1)
Energieweg 1, Mijdrecht, 3641 RT, Utrecht,
Netherlands
Tel.: (31) 297280340
Investment Management Service
N.A.I.C.S.: 523999

Bayer HealthCare AG (1)
Chemiepark Gebaude Q30, Kaiser-Wilhelm-
Allee, 51368, Leverkusen,
Germany (100%)
Tel.: (49) 2143061380
Web Site: http://www.bayerhealthcare.com
Sales Range: $15-24.9 Billion
Emp.: 55,700
Mfr of Healthcare Products
N.A.I.C.S.: 325412

Subsidiary (Domestic):

Bayer BioScience GmbH (2)
Alfred-Nobel-Str 50, Monheim am Rhein,
40789, Germany
Tel.: (49) 2173380
Web Site: http://www.bayer.com
Crop Farming Services
N.A.I.C.S.: 111998

Subsidiary (Non-US):

Bayer BioScience Pvt. Ltd. (3)
8-1-39 Qutub Shahi Tombs Road
Tolichowki, Hyderabad, 500008, India
Tel.: (91) 4023585200
Hybrid Seed Mfr & Whslr
N.A.I.C.S.: 325320

Subsidiary (Domestic):

Bayer Gastronomie GmbH (2)
Kaiser-Wilhelm-Allee 3, 51373, Leverkusen,
Germany
Tel.: (49) 2143056141
Home Management Services
N.A.I.C.S.: 721110
Sascha Witt *(Gen Mgr)*

Unit (Domestic):

**Bayer HealthCare AG - Dermatology
Unit** (2)
Max-Dohrn-Strasse 10, Berlin, 10589, Ger-
many
Tel.: (49) 30520075650
Web Site:
    http://www.dermatology.bayer.com
Rev.: $417,559,240
Emp.: 12
Pharmaceutical Products Mfr & Distr
N.A.I.C.S.: 325412

Unit (US):

**Bayer HealthCare Biological
Products** (2)
800 Dwight Way, Berkeley, CA 94710-2428
Tel.: (510) 705-5000
Web Site:
    http://www.livingwithhemophilia.com
Sales Range: $400-449.9 Million
Emp.: 1,500
Research Development & Products Facility
for Pharmaceutical Drugs
N.A.I.C.S.: 325412

Subsidiary (Non-US):

Bayer HealthCare Co. Ltd. (2)
Bldg A Jiaming Center No 27 North Dong-
shanhuan Rd, Chaoyang, Beijing, 100020,
China
Tel.: (86) 1059218282
Web Site:
    http://www.bayerhealthcare.com.cn
Pharmaceutical Products Mfr & Distr
N.A.I.C.S.: 325412

Unit (US):

**Bayer HealthCare Consumer
Care** (2)
36 Columbia Rd, Morristown, NJ 07962-
1910
Tel.: (973) 254-5000
Web Site: http://www.bayercare.com
Sales Range: $125-149.9 Million
Emp.: 500
Over-the-Counter Consumer Healthcare
Products Research, Development, Mfr &
Marketing
N.A.I.C.S.: 424210

Subsidiary (Non-US):

**Bayer HealthCare Manufacturing
S.r.l.** (2)
Via Delle Groane 126, Garbagnate Mila-
nese, 20024, Milan, Italy
Tel.: (39) 0239781
Pharmaceuticals Product Mfr
N.A.I.C.S.: 325412

Subsidiary (Domestic):

Bayer Pharma AG (2)
Mullerstrasse 178, 13353, Berlin, Germany
Tel.: (49) 304681111
Web Site: http://www.bayerpharma.com
Pharmaceutical Products Mfr & Distr
N.A.I.C.S.: 325412

Plant (Domestic):

Bayer Pharma AG - Wuppertal (3)
Friedrich-Ebert-Strasse 217, Wuppertal,
42117, Germany
Tel.: (49) 214301
Web Site: http://www.healthcare.bayer.com
Pharmaceutical Services
N.A.I.C.S.: 325412

Subsidiary (Domestic):

Bayer Schering Pharma AG (3)
Mullerstrasse 178, Berlin, 13353, Germany
Tel.: (49) 304681111
Web Site: http://www.bayerpharma.com
Sales Range: $15-24.9 Billion
Emp.: 5,500
Pharmaceuticals Researcher, Mfr & Distr
N.A.I.C.S.: 325412

Joint Venture (Domestic):

ALK-Scherax Arzneimittel GmbH (4)
PO Box 22876, Wedel, Germany
Tel.: (49) 408707070
Web Site: http://www.alkscherax.de
Sales Range: $25-49.9 Million
Emp.: 83
Allergy Treatment Sales
N.A.I.C.S.: 424210

Subsidiary (Non-US):

Bayer HealthCare Pharma (4)
92 Je 2 Gongdan 1 Miyang-myun Ansung-si
Kyunggi-do, Anseong, 456 843, Gyeonggi-
do, Korea (South)
Tel.: (82) 316708700
Web Site: http://www.bayer.co.kr

Sales Range: $75-99.9 Million
Emp.: 260
Pharmaceuticals Mfr
N.A.I.C.S.: 325412

**Bayer HealthCare Pharmaceuticals
Canada** (4)
334 Ave Avro, Pointe-Claire, H9R 5W5, QC,
Canada
Tel.: (514) 631-7400
Web Site: http://www.bayerhealth.com
Sales Range: $25-49.9 Million
Emp.: 200
Mfr of Pharmaceuticals
N.A.I.C.S.: 325412

Bayer Oy (4)
Pansiontie 47, PO Box 415, 20101, Turku,
Finland
Tel.: (358) 2078521
Web Site: http://www.bayer.fi
Sales Range: $300-349.9 Million
Emp.: 712
Pharmaceuticals Product Mfr
N.A.I.C.S.: 325412

Bayer S.p.A. (4)
Viale Certosa 130, 20156, Milan, 20156,
Italy
Tel.: (39) 0239781
Web Site: https://www.bayer.com
Sales Range: $25-49.9 Million
Emp.: 40
Pharmaceuticals Product Mfr
N.A.I.C.S.: 325412

Bayer Thai Company Limited (4)
130/1 North Sathon Road, Bangrak, 10500,
Bangkok, 10500, Thailand
Tel.: (66) 22327000
Web Site: https://www.bayer.com
Pharmaceutical Mfr & Distr
N.A.I.C.S.: 325412

Bayer s.r.o. (4)
Siemensova 2717/4, 155 80, Prague, 5,
Czech Republic
Tel.: (420) 266101111
Web Site: https://www.bayer.com
Sales Range: $25-49.9 Million
Emp.: 100
Pharmaceuticals Product Mfr
N.A.I.C.S.: 325412

BayerHealth Care (4)
33 Rue De L Industries, 74240, Gaillard,
France
Tel.: (33) 450877070
Web Site: http://www.bayer.com
Sales Range: $150-199.9 Million
Emp.: 200
Mfr & Sales of Pharmaceuticals (OTC)
N.A.I.C.S.: 325412

Berlimed, S.A. (4)
Poligono Santa Rosa Francisco Alonso
No7, 28806, Alcala de Henares, Spain
Tel.: (34) 918871400
Web Site: http://www.bayer.es
Sales Range: $75-99.9 Million
Emp.: 280
Pharmaceuticals Product Mfr
N.A.I.C.S.: 325412

**Berlimed-Productos Quimicos Farma-
ceuticos e Biologicos Ltda.** (4)
Rua Cancioneiro de Evoa 255 Santo
Amaro, CEP 04708 010, Sao Paulo, Brazil
Tel.: (55) 1130942245
Web Site: http://www.bayerpharma.com.br
Pharmaceuticals Mfr
N.A.I.C.S.: 325412

Subsidiary (Domestic):

Jenapharm GmbH & Co. KG (4)
Otto Schott Strasse 15, 07745, Jena, Ger-
many
Tel.: (49) 3641645
Web Site: http://www.jenapharm.de
Sales Range: $25-49.9 Million
Emp.: 80
Developer & Manufacturer of Fertility Con-
trol & Hormone Replacement Products
N.A.I.C.S.: 325412
Astrid Lindorfer *(Coord-Online Media)*

Subsidiary (Domestic):

**EnTec Gesellschaft fur Endokrinolo-
gische Technologie GmbH** (5)

Adolf Reichwein Strasse 22, D 07745,
Jena, Germany
Tel.: (49) 3641658430
Sales Range: $75-99.9 Million
Emp.: 18
Endocrine Therapy Research
N.A.I.C.S.: 325411

**EnTec Gesellschaft fur Endokrinolo-
gische Technologie mbH** (5)
Grandweg 64, D 22529, Hamburg, Ger-
many
Tel.: (49) 3641658430
Web Site: http://www.schering.de
Endocrine Therapy Research
N.A.I.C.S.: 325411

**Schering GmbH & Co. Produktions
KG** (5)
Dobereinerstrasse 20, 99427, Weimar, Thu-
ringia, Germany
Tel.: (49) 36434330
Web Site: http://www.bayer.de
Mfr of Pharmaceuticals
N.A.I.C.S.: 325412

Subsidiary (Non-US):

PT Schering Indonesia (4)
Jl TB Simatupang, Pasar Rebo, Jakarta,
13760, Indonesia
Tel.: (62) 2130014200
Web Site: http://www.schering.com
Sales Range: $50-74.9 Million
Emp.: 350
Provider of Pharmaceuticals
N.A.I.C.S.: 325412

Affiliate (Non-US):

Schering AG (4)
Lootsa 2, Eesti Filiaal, Tallinn, 11317, Esto-
nia
Tel.: (372) 6558565
Web Site: http://www.bayer.ee
Emp.: 25
Pharmaceuticals Product Mfr
N.A.I.C.S.: 325412
Christian Albert Meyer *(Country Mgr)*

Subsidiary (Non-US):

**Schering AG Regional Scientific Of-
fice, Malaysia** (4)
PO Box 13 4, 46200, Petaling Jaya, Malay-
sia
Tel.: (60) 379551366
Web Site: http://www.schering.de
Sales Range: $25-49.9 Million
Emp.: 100
Provider of Pharmaceutical Products
N.A.I.C.S.: 325412

Schering China Limited (4)
24 Cosco Tower, Grand Millennium Plaza,
Bayer Health Care Ltd 801 808, Central,
China (Hong Kong)
Tel.: (852) 25293078
Web Site: http://www.bayer.com.cn
Management Services
N.A.I.C.S.: 541611

Schering Norge A/S (4)
Ringsveien 3, PO Box 1 83, N 1321,
Stabekk, Norway
Tel.: (47) 67592000
Web Site: http://www.schering.no
Sales Range: $1-9.9 Million
Emp.: 19
Pharmaceuticals Product Mfr
N.A.I.C.S.: 325412

Schering Pharmaceutical Limited (4)
Youyi Economic And Tech Dist, 103 Youyi
Rd, 510730, Guangzhou, China
Tel.: (86) 82214680
Web Site: http://www.schering.com.cn
Sales Range: $25-49.9 Million
Emp.: 130
Pharmaceuticals Product Mfr
N.A.I.C.S.: 325412

**Schering Predstavnistvo u
Jugoslaviji** (4)
Omlaeskahvragea 88 B, 11 070, Belgrade,
Serbia
Tel.: (381) 113020523
Web Site: http://www.schering.com
Pharmaceuticals Product Mfr
N.A.I.C.S.: 325412

Schering Taiwan Ltd.   **(4)**
Min Sheng E Rd, PO Box 17-183, Min
Sheng E Rd, Taipei, 105, Taiwan
Tel.: (886) 287125282
Web Site: http://www.schering.com.tw
Sales Range: $25-49.9 Million
Emp.: 67
Pharmaceuticals Product Mfr
N.A.I.C.S.: 325412

Schering de Chile S.A.   **(4)**
General Del Canto No 421 Piso 6, Casilla
Postal 3926, Santiago, Chile
Tel.: (56) 25208200
Pharmaceuticals Product Mfr
N.A.I.C.S.: 325412

Schering do Brasil Ltda.   **(4)**
Rua Cancioneiro de Evora 255, Caixa
Postal 21457, CEP 04602-970, Sao Paulo,
Brazil
Tel.: (55) 1151863000
Web Site: http://www.schering.com.br
Sales Range: $150-199.9 Million
Emp.: 753
Mfr of Pharmaceuticals
N.A.I.C.S.: 325412

Subsidiary (Domestic):

Bayer Vital GmbH   **(2)**
Bldg D 162, D 51368, Leverkusen,
Germany   **(100%)**
Tel.: (49) 214301
Web Site: http://www.bayervital.de
Sales Range: $800-899.9 Million
Emp.: 5,000
Pharmaceutical & Healthcare Products Distr
N.A.I.C.S.: 325412
Werner Baumann *(Mng Dir)*

Subsidiary (US):

Conceptus, Inc.   **(2)**
331 E Evelyn, Mountain View, CA 94041
Tel.: (650) 962-4000
Web Site: http://www.conceptus.com
Sales Range: $125-149.9 Million
Emp.: 300
Minimally Invasive Devices for Reproductive
Medical Applications
N.A.I.C.S.: 339112

Subsidiary (Non-US):

Conceptus Medical Limited   **(3)**
Sloane House 2 Littleworth Avenue, Esher,
KT10 9PB, Surrey, United Kingdom
Tel.: (44) 1372849762
Web Site: http://www.essure.co.uk
Sales Range: $10-24.9 Million
Emp.: 4
Health Care Srvices
N.A.I.C.S.: 621610

Conceptus, SAS   **(3)**
50 Ave de St Cloud, 78000, Versailles,
France
Tel.: (33) 130847515
Web Site: http://www.conceptus.com
Sales Range: $10-24.9 Million
Emp.: 15
Contraceptive Device Mfr
N.A.I.C.S.: 325412

Subsidiary (Domestic):

**GP Grenzach Produktions
GmbH**   **(2)**
Emil-Barell-Strasse 7, 79639, Grenzach-
Wyhlen, Germany
Tel.: (49) 76249070
Web Site: https://www.bayer.com
Sales Range: $100-124.9 Million
Emp.: 47
Pharmaceuticals Product Mfr
N.A.I.C.S.: 325412
Dirk Oebels *(Mng Dir)*

Generics Holding GmbH   **(2)**
Kaiser-Wilhelm-Allee 10, 51373, Le-
verkusen, Germany
Tel.: (49) 214301
Investment Management Service
N.A.I.C.S.: 523999

**KVP Pharma+Veterinar Produkte
GmbH**   **(2)**
Projensdorfer Strasse 324, 24106, Kiel,
Germany

Tel.: (49) 43138200
Web Site: http://www.kiel.bayer.com
Sales Range: $100-124.9 Million
Emp.: 50
Pharmaceuticals Product Mfr
N.A.I.C.S.: 325412

Subsidiary (Non-US):

**Quimica Farmaceutica Bayer,
S.A.**   **(2)**
Ave Baix Llobregat 3-5, Sant Joan Despi,
08970, Spain   **(100%)**
Tel.: (34) 932284000
Web Site: http://www.bayer.es
Sales Range: $400-449.9 Million
Emp.: 1,200
Mfr of Pharmaceuticals
N.A.I.C.S.: 325412

Bayer Hellas AG   **(1)**
Sorou 18-20 Maroussi, Maroussi, 15125,
Athens, Greece
Tel.: (30) 2106187500
Rev.: $248,421,320
Emp.: 400
Agrochemicals Distr
N.A.I.C.S.: 424690

Bayer Hispania SL   **(1)**
Avda Baix Llobregat 3-5 Sant Joan Despi,
08970, Barcelona, Spain   **(100%)**
Tel.: (34) 932284000
Web Site: https://www.bayer.com
Rev.: $433,269,088
Emp.: 500
Mfr of Pharmaceutical, Chemical & Agricul-
tural Products
N.A.I.C.S.: 325412

**Bayer Holding (Thailand) Co.,
Ltd.**   **(1)**
130/1 North Sathon Road Silom, Bangrak,
Bangkok, 10500, Thailand
Tel.: (66) 22327000
Pharmaceuticals Product Mfr
N.A.I.C.S.: 325412

Bayer Holding Ltd.   **(1)**
1-6-5 Marunouchi, Chiyoda-ku, Tokyo, 100-
8268, Japan
Tel.: (81) 36 266 7010
Web Site: https://www.bayer.jp
Rev.: $3,091,992,940
Emp.: 339
Investment Management Service
N.A.I.C.S.: 523999
Miho Oka *(Head-Comm)*

Bayer Hungaria Kft.   **(1)**
Dombovari ut 26, 1117, Budapest, Hungary
Tel.: (36) 14874100
Web Site: https://www.bayer.com
Emp.: 475
Pharmaceutical Products Distr
N.A.I.C.S.: 424210
Kokavecz Pal *(Head-Fin & Admin)*

Bayer Inc.   **(1)**
2920 Matheson Boulevard East, Missis-
sauga, L4W 5R6, ON, Canada   **(100%)**
Tel.: (905) 282-5550
Web Site: https://www.bayer.com
Emp.: 1,400
Pharmaceutical Preparations
N.A.I.C.S.: 325412
Alok Kanti *(Pres & CEO)*

**Bayer Industry Services GmbH & Co.
OHG**   **(1)**
Chemiepark Gebaude Q26, Kaiser-Wilhelm-
Allee, D-51368, Leverkusen,
Germany   **(60%)**
Tel.: (49) 214301
Web Site: http://www.bayerindustry.com
Sales Range: $1-4.9 Billion
Emp.: 5,500
Chemical Industry Utility Supply, Waste
Management, Infrastructure, Safety, Secu-
rity & Technical Services
N.A.I.C.S.: 561210
Joachim Waldi *(Dir-Labor)*

**Bayer Intellectual Property
GmbH**   **(1)**
Alfred-Nobel-Str 10, Monheim am Rhein,
40789, Germany
Tel.: (49) 2143010
Property Rights Services
N.A.I.C.S.: 813311

Bayer Israel Ltd.   **(1)**
36 Hacharash St Neve, Neeman Industrial
area, Hod Hasharon, 45244, Israel
Tel.: (972) 97626700
Pharmaceutical Products Mfr & Distr
N.A.I.C.S.: 325412

**Bayer Jinling Polyurethane Co.,
Ltd.**   **(1)**
No 46 Taixin Road, Qixia District, Nanjing,
210038, China
Tel.: (86) 2585311682
Organic Chemical Mfr
N.A.I.C.S.: 325199

Bayer Korea Ltd.   **(1)**
24th floor Park One Tower 2 108 Yeoui-
daero, Yeongdeungpo-gu, Seoul, 07335,
Korea (South)
Tel.: (82) 28296600
Web Site: https://www.bayer.com
Emp.: 520
Crop Protection Chemicals Distr
N.A.I.C.S.: 424910

Bayer Limited   **(1)**
The Atrium Blackthorn Road, Stillorgan,
Dublin 18, Sandyford, Ireland
Tel.: (353) 12163300
Web Site: https://www.bayer.com
Pharmaceutical Products Distr
N.A.I.C.S.: 424210

Bayer Limited Egypt LLC   **(1)**
Raya Offices 2nd & 3rd Floor Plot No 133
Road 70 Banking Sector, New Cairo, Egypt
Tel.: (20) 25980666
Medicinal Product Mfr
N.A.I.C.S.: 325412

Bayer Ltd.   **(1)**
str Verhnii Val 4-b, 04071, Kiev, Ukraine
Tel.: (380) 442203300
Web Site: https://www.bayer.com
Emp.: 700
Crop Protection Chemicals Distr
N.A.I.C.S.: 424910

Bayer Medical Care B.V.   **(1)**
Avenue Ceramique 27, 6221 KV, Maas-
tricht, Netherlands
Tel.: (31) 433585600
N.A.I.C.S.: 325320

Bayer Middle East FZE   **(1)**
Dubai Science Park Tower North 13th Floor
/ 14th Floor Units 1406 1409, PO Box
500829, Dubai, United Arab Emirates
Tel.: (971) 44452700
Sales Range: $125-149.9 Million
Emp.: 700
Plastics Product Mfr
N.A.I.C.S.: 326199

Bayer Mozambique, Limitada   **(1)**
Rua 1301 Nr 97 Bairro da Sommerschield,
Maputo, Mozambique
Tel.: (258) 21499832
N.A.I.C.S.: 325320

Bayer Netherlands B.V.   **(1)**
Bright Office Building B La Guardiaweg 68,
1043 DK, Amsterdam, Netherlands
Tel.: (31) 204249000
Pharmaceuticals Product Mfr
N.A.I.C.S.: 325412

Bayer New Zealand Limited   **(1)**
72 Taharoto Rd Smales Farm, Takapuna,
Auckland, 0622, New Zealand
Tel.: (64) 94433093
Web Site: https://www.bayer.co.nz
Rev.: $891,611,280
Pharmaceuticals Product Mfr
N.A.I.C.S.: 325412

Bayer Nordic SE   **(1)**
Keilaranta 14, 2151, Espoo, Finland
Tel.: (358) 2078521
Pharmaceuticals Product Mfr
N.A.I.C.S.: 325412

Bayer OU   **(1)**
Lootsa 12, 11415, Tallinn, Estonia
Tel.: (372) 6558565
Medical Equipment Mfr
N.A.I.C.S.: 339112

Bayer Oy   **(1)**
Tel.: (358) 2078521
Web Site: https://www.bayer.com

Chemical & Pharmaceutical Products Mfr
N.A.I.C.S.: 325412

Bayer Pakistan (Private) Limited   **(1)**
Plot 23 Sector 22, Korangi Industrial Area,
Karachi, 74900, Sindh, Pakistan
Tel.: (92) 2135108000
Sales Range: $450-499.9 Million
Emp.: 700
Pharmaceuticals Product Mfr
N.A.I.C.S.: 325412
Amir Iqbal *(Mng Dir)*

Bayer Parsian AG   **(1)**
8th Floor No 3 Maadiran Bldg Aftab St
Khoddami St Vanak Sq, PO Box 11365 /
716, Tehran, 1994834594, Iran
Tel.: (98) 215 453 8000
Web Site: https://www.bayer.com
Pharmaceuticals Product Mfr
N.A.I.C.S.: 325412

Bayer Parsian P.J.S. Co.   **(1)**
8th Floor No 3 Maadiran Bldg Aftab St
Khoddami St Vanak Sq, 1994834594, Teh-
ran, Iran
Tel.: (98) 2154538000
Pharmaceuticals Product Mfr & Distr
N.A.I.C.S.: 325412

Bayer Philippines, Inc.   **(1)**
8th Flr Science Hub Tower 1 Campus Ave
Cor Turin St, Bayer House, McKinley Hill
Cyberpark Pinagsama, Taguig, 1630,
Philippines   **(100%)**
Tel.: (63) 232264888
Web Site: https://www.bayer.com
Sales Range: $25-49.9 Million
Emp.: 100
Pharmaceuticals & Chemicals Mfr
N.A.I.C.S.: 325412

Bayer Polyurethanes B.V.   **(1)**
Energieweg 1, Mijdrecht, 3641 RT, Nether-
lands
Tel.: (31) 297280340
Web Site: http://www.bayer.com
Commercial Banking Services
N.A.I.C.S.: 522110

Bayer Portugal S.A.   **(1)**
Rua Quinta do Pinheiro 5, PO Box 666,
2794-003, Carnaxide, Portugal   **(89%)**
Tel.: (351) 21 417 2121
Web Site: https://www.bayer.com
Mfr of Pharmaceuticals & Chemicals
N.A.I.C.S.: 325412

Bayer Portugal, Lda.   **(1)**
Av Vitor Figueiredo no 4 - 4 piso, 2790-255,
Carnaxide, Portugal
Tel.: (351) 214172121
Medicinal Product Mfr
N.A.I.C.S.: 325412

Bayer Real Estate GmbH   **(1)**
Hauptstr 119 Bldg 4809, Leverkusen,
51373, Germany
Tel.: (49) 214 30 57673
Web Site: http://www.bayer-realestate.com
Real Estate Management Services
N.A.I.C.S.: 531390
Bjorn Christmann *(Mng Dir)*

Bayer S.A.   **(1)**
Km 4 5 Carretera a Masaya Centro Pellas
Piso 3 Check In Office, Managua, Nicara-
gua
Tel.: (505) 83952900
Pharmaceuticals Product Mfr
N.A.I.C.S.: 325412

Bayer S.A.   **(1)**
Luxemburgo N34-359 y Portugal Edificio
Cosmopolitan Parc Pisos 6, Quito, Ecuador
Tel.: (593) 23975200
Pharmaceuticals Product Mfr
N.A.I.C.S.: 325412

Bayer S.A.   **(1)**
Tel.: (809) 8095308086
Pharmaceuticals Product Mfr
N.A.I.C.S.: 325412

Bayer S.A.   **(1)**
Bd Sidi Mohamed Ben Abdellah, 20030,
Casablanca, Morocco
Tel.: (212) 522954854
Pharmaceuticals Product Mfr
N.A.I.C.S.: 325412

Bayer Aktiengesellschaft—(Continued)

Bayer S.A. (1)
Rua Domingos Jorge 1100, Sao Paulo,
04779-900, Brazil (100%)
Tel.: (55) 1156945166
Web Site: https://www.bayer.com.br
Sales Range: $1-9.9 Million
Emp.: 100
Mfr & Marketer of Chemical Products, Pharmaceuticals, Consumer Products, Animal Health Products & Agrichemicals
N.A.I.C.S.: 325412
Theo Vanderloo *(Pres)*

Subsidiary (Non-US):

Bayer S.A. (2)
Ricardo Gutierrez 3652, Munro-Pcia,
B1605EHD, Munro, Argentina
Tel.: (54) 1147627000
Web Site: https://www.conosur.bayer.com
Pharmaceuticals Product Mfr
N.A.I.C.S.: 325412

Bayer S.A. (2)
Costanera Center Building Tower 2 Avenida Andres Bello 2457 21st floor, Metropolitan Region, Santiago, Santiago, Chile
Tel.: (56) 225208200
Web Site: https://www.bayer.cl
Pharmaceutical Products Distr
N.A.I.C.S.: 424210

Bayer S.A. (2)
AK 45 N 123 - 60 Torre Sapiencia Piso 6,
Bogota, Colombia
Tel.: (57) 6014234000
Web Site: https://www.bayer.co
Crop Farming Services
N.A.I.C.S.: 111998

Bayer S.A. (2)
Plaza Tempo Edificio A 2do Piso Autopista Prospero Fernandez, Escazu, Costa Rica
Tel.: (506) 4 100 6300
Web Site: https://www.bayer.com
Pharmaceutical Products Distr
N.A.I.C.S.: 424210

Bayer S.A. (2)
Km 14 5 Carretera Roosevelt Zona 3 de Mexico, Guatemala, 1573, Guatemala
Tel.: (502) 2 436 9090
Web Site: https://www.bayer.com
Pharmaceuticals Product Mfr
N.A.I.C.S.: 325412

Bayer S.A. (1)
Av Tamanaco Torre Bayer, El Rosal, Caracas, Venezuela (100%)
Tel.: (58) 212 905 2111
Web Site: http://andina.bayer.com
Sales Range: $125-149.9 Million
Emp.: 480
Mfr of Pharmaceuticals & Chemicals
N.A.I.C.S.: 325412

Bayer S.A. de C.V. (1)
Parque Comercial Los Proceres Noveno piso, Apartado Postal 3333, Edificio Nova 2 Oficina 143 Regus, Tegucigalpa, Honduras
Tel.: (504) 22692100
Pharmaceuticals Product Mfr
N.A.I.C.S.: 325412

Bayer S.A.S. (1)
74 rue Gorge de Loup, CS 90106, 69009,
Lyon, Cedex, France (100%)
Tel.: (33) 472854321
Web Site: https://www.bayer.com
Sales Range: $50-74.9 Million
Emp.: 160
Mfr of Pharmaceutical, Chemical & Agricultural Products
N.A.I.C.S.: 325412
Lise Lemonnier *(Dir-Publication)*

Bayer S.p.A. (1)
Viale Certosa 130, 20156, Milan,
Italy (100%)
Tel.: (39) 0239781
Web Site: https://www.bayer.com
Sales Range: $1-4.9 Billion
Emp.: 1,800
Mfr & Marketer of Chemicals, Pharmaceuticals & Agricultural Chemicals, Dyestuffs & Fibers
N.A.I.C.S.: 325998

Bayer SA (1)

Tel.: (51) 12113800
Web Site: http://www.bayer.com
Plastic Compounds Mfr
N.A.I.C.S.: 325220

Bayer SA (1)
Luis Alberto de Herrera 1248 Torre 3 Piso 20 - Unidad 2074/2075, 11300, Montevideo, Uruguay
Tel.: (598) 21922300
Pharmaceuticals Product Mfr
N.A.I.C.S.: 325412

Bayer SA-NV (1)
JE Mommaertslaan 14, 1831, Diegem, Belgium
Tel.: (32) 2 535 6311
Web Site: http://www.bayer.be
Chemicals Mfr
N.A.I.C.S.: 325998

Bayer Sante SAS (1)
Parc Eurasante 220 Ave de la Recherche, BP 60 114, Loos, 59373, France
Tel.: (33) 328163400
Pharmaceutical Products Mfr & Distr
N.A.I.C.S.: 325412

Bayer Saudi Arabia LLC (1)
Al Kamal Building 3rd Floor Plot No 10, PO Box 16207, Al Ruwaiss District, Jeddah, 21464, Saudi Arabia
Tel.: (966) 126573015
N.A.I.C.S.: 325320
Maged Elshazly *(Gen Mgr)*

Bayer South Africa (Pty.) Ltd. (1)
27 Wrench Road, PO Box 143, Isando, 1600, Gauteng, South Africa (100%)
Tel.: (27) 119215911
Web Site: https://www.bayer.com
Sales Range: $700-749.9 Million
Emp.: 600
Mfr of Pharmaceutical, Diagnostic, Agricultural & Chemical Products
N.A.I.C.S.: 325412

Bayer Sp. z o.o. (1)
Al Jerozolimskie 158, 02-326, Warsaw, Poland
Tel.: (48) 225723500
Web Site: https://www.bayer.com
Sales Range: $125-149.9 Million
Emp.: 300
Pharmaceuticals Product Mfr
N.A.I.C.S.: 325412

Bayer TPU (Shenzhen) Co. Ltd. (1)
No 1 Nan 2nd road Datianyang Songgang street, Bao'an District, Shenzhen, 518105, Guangdong, China
Tel.: (86) 75527068308
Emp.: 80
Plastic Material Distr
N.A.I.C.S.: 424610
Stefan Huber *(Gen Mgr)*

Bayer Taiwan Co., Ltd. (1)
(100%)
Tel.: (886) 281011000
Web Site: https://www.bayer.com.tw
Sales Range: $125-149.9 Million
Emp.: 300
Provider of Pharmaceutical & Chemical Products
N.A.I.C.S.: 325412

Bayer Technology Services GmbH (1)
Chemiepark Gebaude K9, Kaiser-Wilhelm-Allee, Leverkusen, 51368,
Germany (100%)
Tel.: (49) 214301
Web Site: http://www.bayertechnology.com
Sales Range: $400-449.9 Million
Emp.: 2,200
Plant Engineering, Technical Process Development & Optimization Services
N.A.I.C.S.: 541690

Branch (US):

Bayer Technology Services Americas (2)
8500 W Bay Rd, Baytown, TX 77523 (100%)
Tel.: (281) 383-6000
Web Site: http://www.btsamericas.com
Sales Range: $75-99.9 Million
Emp.: 495

(60%)
Web Site: http://www.bayer.com
Plastic Compounds Mfr
N.A.I.C.S.: 325220

Plant Engineering, Technical Process Development & Optimization Services
N.A.I.C.S.: 541690

Subsidiary (Domestic):

Ehrfeld Mikrotechnik BTS GmbH (2)
Mikroforum Ring 1, 55234, Wendelsheim, Germany
Tel.: (49) 673 491 5460
Web Site: https://www.ehrfeld.com
Micro Technology Products Research & Development Services
N.A.I.C.S.: 541715
Joachim Heck *(Mng Dir)*

Bayer Turk Kimya Sanayi Limited Sirketi (1)
Fatih Sultan Mehmet Mah Balkan Cad No 53, Umraniye, 34770, Istanbul, Turkiye
Tel.: (90) 2165283600
Sales Range: $50-74.9 Million
Emp.: 200
Chemical Products Mfr
N.A.I.C.S.: 325320

Bayer UK Limited (1)
Bayer House Strawberry Hill, Newbury, RG14 1JA, Berkshire, United Kingdom
Tel.: (44) 1635 563000
Web Site: http://www.bayer.co.uk
Pharmaceutical Products Distr
N.A.I.C.S.: 424210

Bayer Uretech Ltd. (1)
8 Chang-Pin E 6th Rd Chang Hwa Changping Industrial Park, Hsien-Hsi Hsiang, Chang-Hua, Taiwan
Tel.: (886) 4791 0099
Web Site: http://www.bayer.com.tw
Sales Range: $50-74.9 Million
Emp.: 150
Thermoplastic Polyurethane Mfr
N.A.I.C.S.: 325211

Bayer Vapi Private Limited (1)
Plot No 306/3 Phase II GIDC, Vapi, 396195, Gujarat, India
Tel.: (91) 2602407123
N.A.I.C.S.: 325320

Bayer Vietnam Ltd. (1)
118/4 Amata Industrial Zone, Long Binh Ward, Bien Hoa, Dong Nai, Vietnam
Tel.: (84) 2518877120
Pharmaceutical Products Distr
N.A.I.C.S.: 424210

Bayer WR LLC (1)
Dzerzhinskogo Avenue 57 Office 54 14th Floor, 220073, Minsk, Belarus
Tel.: (375) 172395420
Pharmaceuticals Product Mfr
N.A.I.C.S.: 325412

Bayer Weimar GmbH & Co. KG (1)
Dobereinerstr 20, 99427, Weimar, Germany
Tel.: (49) 36434330
Web Site: https://www.bayer.com
Emp.: 530
Pharmaceuticals Product Mfr
N.A.I.C.S.: 325412
Mike Eckelmann *(Gen Mgr)*

Bayer West-Central Africa S.A. (1)
Boulevard de l Aeroport Immeuble Carre Massina 2eme Etage 30, BP 461, Abidjan, Cote d'Ivoire
Tel.: (225) 778148887
N.A.I.C.S.: 325320

Bayer Yakuhin, Ltd. (1)
2-4-9 Umeda, Kita-ku, Osaka, 530-0001,
Japan (100%)
Tel.: (81) 661337000
Web Site: https://www.bayer.jp
Sales Range: $800-899.9 Million
Emp.: 1,650
Development, Import, Manufacture & Sales of Pharmaceuticals, Medical Devices & Animal Products
N.A.I.C.S.: 325412

Bayer Zambia Limited (1)
Plot 10103 Mumbwa Road, PO Box 37131, Lusaka, Zambia
Tel.: (260) 211286451
Medicinal Product Mfr
N.A.I.C.S.: 325412

Bayer Zimbabwe (Private) Limited (1)

Off Martin Road, Msasa, Harare, Zimbabwe
Tel.: (263) 242487211
N.A.I.C.S.: 325320

Bayer Zydus Pharma Private Limited (1)
Central Avenue Hiranandani Estate, Thane, 400607, Maharashtra, India
Tel.: (91) 2225311234
Web Site: https://www.bayerzyduspharma.com
N.A.I.C.S.: 622110
Shweta Rai *(Mng Dir)*

Bayer d.o.o. (1)
Beograd Airport City Omladinskih brigada 88b, 11070, Belgrade, Serbia
Tel.: (381) 11 207 0200
Web Site: https://www.bayer.com
Emp.: 70
Chemical Products Mfr & Whslr
N.A.I.C.S.: 325199

Bayer d.o.o. (1)
Bravnicarjeva 13, PO Box 2354, 1000, Ljubljana, Slovenia
Tel.: (386) 15814400
Web Site: https://www.bayer.com
Emp.: 100
Pharmaceutical Product Whslr
N.A.I.C.S.: 424210

Bayer d.o.o. (1)
Radnicka Cesta 80, 10000, Zagreb, 10000, Croatia
Tel.: (385) 16599900
Web Site: https://www.bayer.com
Emp.: 70
Pharmaceutical Product Mfr & Distr
N.A.I.C.S.: 325412

Bayer d.o.o. Sarajevo (1)
Trg solidarnosti 2A, Sarajevo, 71000, Bosnia & Herzegovina
Tel.: (387) 33941600
Chemical Products Mfr
N.A.I.C.S.: 325320

Bayer de Mexico, S.A. de C.V. (1)
Blvd M Cervantes Saavedra No 259 Col Ampl, 11520, Mexico, Granada,
Mexico (100%)
Tel.: (52) 57283000
Web Site: https://www.bayer.com
Sales Range: $600-649.9 Million
Emp.: 3,400
Mfr & Marketer of Chemical Products, Pharmaceuticals, Consumer Products, Animal Health Products & Agrichemicals
N.A.I.C.S.: 325412

Bayer plc (1)
400 South Oak Way Green Park, Reading, RG2 6AD, Berkshire, United
Kingdom (100%)
Tel.: (44) 1182063000
Web Site: https://www.bayer.co.uk
Sales Range: $200-249.9 Million
Emp.: 500
Mfr of Healthcare, Crop Science, Polymer & Chemical Products
N.A.I.C.S.: 532210

Bayer, spol. s.r.o. (1)
Karadzicova 2, 811 09, Bratislava, Slovakia
Tel.: (421) 259213321
Web Site: https://www.bayer.com
Sales Range: $50-74.9 Million
Emp.: 100
Pharmaceutical Products Distr
N.A.I.C.S.: 424210

Bayer-Handelsgesellschaft mit beschrankter Haftung (1)
Kaiser-Wilhelm-Allee 20, 51373, Leverkusen, Germany
Tel.: (49) 2143081949
Chemical Products Distr
N.A.I.C.S.: 424690

Bayer-Unterstutzungskasse GmbH (1)
Chemiepark Leverkusen Q 26, Leverkusen, 51373, Germany
Tel.: (49) 2143061354
Web Site: https://www.bayer.de
Business Management Services
N.A.I.C.S.: 561499

Bayhealth, S.L. (1)

Avenida Baix Llobregat 3 - 5, Sant Joan Despi, 8970, Barcelona, Spain
Tel.: (34) 932284331
Web Site: http://www.bayerhealthcare.es
Emp.: 900
Pharmaceuticals Product Mfr
N.A.I.C.S.: 325412
Rainer Kruse *(Gen Mgr)*

Berlimed - Especialidades Farmaceuticas Lda. (1)
Rua Quinta Do Pinheiro 5, Carnaxide, 2794-003, Oeiras, Portugal
Tel.: (351) 214172121
Web Site: http://www.bayer.com
Pharmaceutical Product Whslr
N.A.I.C.S.: 424210

Blackford Analysis Limited (1)
The Royal Observatory Blackford Hill, Edinburgh, EH9 3HJ, United Kingdom
Tel.: (44) 1316688228
Web Site: http://www.blackfordanalysis.com
Emp.: 11
Medical Software Development Services
N.A.I.C.S.: 541511
Ben Panter *(CEO)*

BlueRock Therapeutics LP (1)
238 Main St 3rd Fl, Cambridge, MA 02142
Tel.: (857) 299-7589
Web Site: https://www.bluerocktx.com
N.A.I.C.S.: 541715
Seth Ettenberg *(Pres)*

CleanTech NRW GmbH (1)
Chempark Geb K12, 51368, Leverkusen, Germany
Tel.: (49) 214 30 44006
Web Site: http://www.cleantechnrw.de
Sales Range: $25-49.9 Million
Emp.: 20
Cluster Management Services
N.A.I.C.S.: 541618
Tony Van Osselaer *(Chm-Exec Bd)*

Climate LLC (1)
201 3rd St Ste 1100, San Francisco, CA 94103
Web Site: https://climate.com
N.A.I.C.S.: 333111
Jeremy Williams *(Head)*

Cooper Land Company of New Jersey, Inc. (1)
28 Flood Cir, Atherton, CA 94027
Tel.: (650) 323-6582
Web Site: https://www.cooperlandco.com
N.A.I.C.S.: 926140

Corporacion Bonima S.A. de C.V. (1)
Carretera Panamericana Km 11 1/2 Ilopango, San Salvador, El Salvador
Tel.: (503) 22950577
Pharmaceuticals Product Mfr
N.A.I.C.S.: 325412

CoverCress Inc. (1)
10407 Baur Blvd Ste A, Saint Louis, MO 63132
Tel.: (314) 222-1403
Web Site: https://www.covercress.com
Oil Seed Mfr
N.A.I.C.S.: 311224

Covestro AG (1)
Kaiser-Wilhelm-Allee 60, 51373, Leverkusen, Germany **(53.3%)**
Tel.: (49) 21460092000
Web Site: https://www.covestro.com
Rev: $15,515,864,451
Assets: $14,717,245,845
Liabilities: $7,575,005,396
Net Worth: $7,142,240,449
Earnings: ($218,001,295)
Emp.: 17,520
Fiscal Year-end: 12/31/2023
Plastic Product Mfr & Distr
N.A.I.C.S.: 326199
Klaus Schafer *(CTO & Member-Mgmt Bd)*

Subsidiary (Non-US):

Bayer Malibu Polymers Private Limited (2)
Navdeep House 2nd Floor Ashram Road, Ahmedabad, 380 014, India
Tel.: (91) 79 2754 2266
Web Site: http://www.bayermalibu.com

Polycarbonate Sheet Mfr
N.A.I.C.S.: 325211

Bayer MaterialScience (Beijing) Company Limited (2)
20 Hong Da Beilu Beijing Development Area Yi Zhuang, Daxing County, Beijing, 100176, China
Tel.: (86) 10 67 88 33 31
Web Site: http://www.bayersheetchina.com
Sales Range: $25-49.9 Million
Emp.: 18
Polycarbonate Sheet Mfr
N.A.I.C.S.: 326113

Bayer MaterialScience (China) Company Limited (2)
18th Fl Citigroup Tower No 33 Huayuan Shiqiao Rd, Shanghai, 200120, China
Tel.: (86) 21 6146 8802
Sales Range: $200-249.9 Million
Emp.: 600
Chemical Products Mfr
N.A.I.C.S.: 325998
Patrick Sion *(VP-Procurement)*

Bayer MaterialScience (Shanghai) Management Company Limited (2)
No 82 Muhua Road Shanghai Chemical Industry Park, Shanghai, China
Tel.: (86) 21 37491000
Plastics Product Mfr
N.A.I.C.S.: 326199
Holly Lei *(Sr VP & Head-Comml Ops-APAC-Polycarbonates)*

Bayer MaterialScience B.V. (2)
Korte Groningerweg 1a, 9607 PS, Foxhol, Netherlands
Tel.: (31) 297 280 426
Web Site: http://www.materialscience.bayer.com
Emp.: 4
Polyurethane Plastic Products Mfr
N.A.I.C.S.: 325211

Subsidiary (Domestic):

Bayer MaterialScience GmbH (2)
Otto-Hesse-Strasse 19/T9, 64293, Darmstadt, Germany
Tel.: (49) 615113030
Web Site: http://www.bayersheeteurope.com
Plastic Product Mfr & Whslr
N.A.I.C.S.: 326199

Subsidiary (Non-US):

Bayer MaterialScience Ltd. (2)
Howell center 44 floor, 99 Queens Road, Wanchai, China (Hong Kong)
Tel.: (852) 28947256
Web Site: http://www.bayermaterialscience.com
Sales Range: $25-49.9 Million
Emp.: 100
Polymer & Plastic Materials Mfr
N.A.I.C.S.: 326199

Bayer MaterialScience Ltd. (2)
1-6-5 Marunouchi, Chiyoda-ku, Tokyo, 100-8261, Japan
Tel.: (81) 3 6266 7260
Polymer Plastic Materials Mfr
N.A.I.C.S.: 325211

Bayer MaterialScience Trading (Shanghai) Co. Ltd. (2)
18F Citigroup Tower No 33 Huayuan-Shiqiao Road, Pudong, Shanghai, 200120, China
Tel.: (86) 2161468282
Web Site: http://www.bayermaterialscience.de
Polymer & Plastic Materials Mfr
N.A.I.C.S.: 326199

Bayer SA (2)
Rua Domingos Jorge 1100, Bairro do Socorro, Sao Paulo, 04779-900, SP, Brazil
Tel.: (55) 8000115560
Web Site: https://www.agro.bayer.com.br
Sales Range: $400-449.9 Million
Emp.: 2,000
Polymer & Plastic Materials Mfr
N.A.I.C.S.: 326199

Covestro (2)
Apdo 76, La Canonja, 43110, Tarragona, Spain

Tel.: (34) 977358342
Sales Range: $50-74.9 Million
Emp.: 200
Pharmaceuticals Product Mfr
N.A.I.C.S.: 325412
Juan Carlos Nebot *(Head-Pur)*

Covestro (India) Private Limited (2)
Unit No SB-801 8th Floor Empire Tower, Cloud City Campus Airoli Thane - Belapur Rd, Navi Mumbai, 400 708, Maharashtra, India
Tel.: (91) 2268195555
Plastics Product Mfr
N.A.I.C.S.: 326199

Covestro A/S (2)
Kronborgvej 24, 5450, Otterup, Denmark
Tel.: (45) 63939393
Web Site: http://www.covestro.dk
Sales Range: $25-49.9 Million
Emp.: 12
Chemical Products Mfr & Whslr
N.A.I.C.S.: 325199

Division (Non-US):

Covestro A/S - Polyurethanes (3)
Siemensova 2717/4, Stodulky, 155 00, Prague, 5, Czech Republic
Tel.: (420) 266 101 111
Web Site: http://www.covestro.dk
Sales Range: $25-49.9 Million
Emp.: 16
Foam Products Mfr & Distr
N.A.I.C.S.: 326140

Subsidiary (Non-US):

Covestro Japan Ltd. (2)
1-7-6 Shibakoen KDX Hamamatsucho Place 3F, Minato-ku, Tokyo, 105-0011, Japan
Tel.: (81) 03 6403 9100
Chemical & Allied Products Merchant Whslr
N.A.I.C.S.: 424690

Subsidiary (Domestic):

Japan Fine Coatings Co., Ltd. (3)
57-1 Sawabe, Minato-ku, Tsuchiura, 300-4104, Ibaraki, Japan **(100%)**
Tel.: (81) 298625784
Web Site: http://www.jsr.co.jp
Fiber-Optic Cables Coating Materials Distr
N.A.I.C.S.: 424610
Takashi Furutani *(CEO)*

Subsidiary (US):

Covestro LLC (2)
1 Covestro Cir, Pittsburgh, PA 15205-9723
Tel.: (412) 413-2000
Web Site: http://www.covestro.us
Plastics & Polymer Products Mfr
N.A.I.C.S.: 326199
Gerald F. MacCleary *(Chm & CEO)*

Unit (Domestic):

Covestro LLC - Automotive Product Center (3)
2401 Walton Blvd, Auburn Hills, MI 48326-1957
Tel.: (248) 475-7700
Web Site: http://www.covestro.us
Sales Range: $25-49.9 Million
Emp.: 20
Sales Office of Raw Materials For Plastics
N.A.I.C.S.: 326199

Covestro LLC - Specialty Films Business (3)
8 Fairview Way, South Deerfield, MA 01373
Tel.: (413) 665-7016
Web Site: http://www.covestro.us
Thermoplastic Polyurethane Film Mfr
N.A.I.C.S.: 326113

Subsidiary (Non-US):

Covestro N.V. (2)
Haven 507 Scheldelaan 420, 2040, Antwerp, Belgium **(100%)**
Tel.: (32) 3 540 30 11
Web Site: http://www.covestro.be
Sales Range: $1-4.9 Billion
Emp.: 850
Polymer & Plastic Materials Mfr
N.A.I.C.S.: 326199

Subsidiary (Domestic):

Covestro (Tielt) N.V. (3)
Industriepark Zuid Wakkensesteenweg 47, 8700, Tielt, Belgium
Tel.: (32) 51 426 200
Web Site: http://www.covestro.be
Sales Range: $50-74.9 Million
Emp.: 13
Plastic Products Mfr & Distr
N.A.I.C.S.: 326199

Subsidiary (Domestic):

Epurex Films GmbH & Co.KG (2)
Bayershofer Weg 21, Postfach 1652, 29699, Walsrode, Germany
Tel.: (49) 5161443393
Web Site: http://www.epurex.de
Polyurethane Products Mfr
N.A.I.C.S.: 326130

Subsidiary (Domestic):

Epurex Films Geschaftsfuhrungs-GmbH (3)
Bayershofer Weg 21, 29699, Walsrode, Germany
Tel.: (49) 51617043000
Administrative Management Services
N.A.I.C.S.: 541611

Subsidiary (Domestic):

PLIXXENT GmbH & Co. KG (2)
Mittelkamp 112, 26125, Oldenburg, Germany
Tel.: (49) 44168099201
Web Site: http://www.materialscience.bayer.com
Pharmaceuticals Product Mfr
N.A.I.C.S.: 325412
Herbert Radunz *(Mng Dir)*

Subsidiary (Domestic):

Bayer MaterialScience Oldenburg Verwaltungs-GmbH (3)
Mittelkamp 112, 26125, Oldenburg, Germany
Tel.: (49) 4419317257
Web Site: http://www.covestro.com
Sales Range: $25-49.9 Million
Emp.: 90
Plastics Product Mfr
N.A.I.C.S.: 326199

Subsidiary (Non-US):

PT Covestro Polymers Indonesia (2)
World Trade Centre 2 20th Floor, Jl Jend Sudirman Kav 29-31, Jakarta, 12920, Indonesia
Tel.: (62) 2130051400
Polyether Chemicals Mfr & Whslr
N.A.I.C.S.: 325998

Currenta Geschaftsfuhrungs-GmbH (1)
Kaiser-Wilhelm-Allee 20, 51368, Leverkusen, Germany
Tel.: (49) 214 30 1
Financial Management Services
N.A.I.C.S.: 523999

Branch (Non-US):

Bayer Technology & Engineering (Shanghai) Co., Ltd. (2)
Shanghai Chemical Industrial Park, Lot F3 Muhua Rd, 201507, Shanghai, PR, China **(100%)**
Tel.: (86) 2161465100
Web Site: http://www.bayertechnology.cn
Sales Range: $200-249.9 Million
Emp.: 700
Plant Engineering, Technical Process Development & Optimization Services
N.A.I.C.S.: 541690

Erste K-W-A Beteiligungsgesellschaft mbH (1)
Kaiser-Wilhelm-Allee 20, Leverkusen, 51373, Germany
Tel.: (49) 214301
Financial Advisory Services
N.A.I.C.S.: 523940

Euroservices Bayer GmbH (1)
Building E47, Leverkusen, 51368, Germany

Bayer Aktiengesellschaft—(Continued)

Tel.: (49) 214301
Accounting Services
N.A.I.C.S.: 541219

Euroservices Bayer S.L. (1)
Avda Baix Llobregat 3 - 5, 8970, Sant Joan
Despi, 8970, Barcelona, Spain
Tel.: (34) 932284000
Business Support Services
N.A.I.C.S.: 561499

Gloryfeel GmbH (1)
Dorotheenstrasse 54, 22301, Hamburg,
Germany
Tel.: (49) 4030397997
Web Site: https://www.gloryfeel.de
Nutritional Supplement Distr
N.A.I.C.S.: 424210

Hild Samen GmbH (1)
Kirchenweinbergstr 115, 71672, Marbach
am Neckar, Germany
Tel.: (49) 7144 8473 11
Web Site: http://www.hildsamen.de
Food Products Mfr & Distr
N.A.I.C.S.: 311991

Intendis Derma, S.L. (1)
Avenida Baix Llobregat 3 - 5, Sant Joan
Despi, 08970, Barcelona, Spain
Tel.: (34) 932284331
Pharmaceutical Products Mfr & Distr
N.A.I.C.S.: 325412

Intendis Manufacturing S.p.A. (1)
Ring Via She 21, 20090, Segrate, Milan,
Italy
Tel.: (39) 0221651
Pharmaceutical Product Whslr
N.A.I.C.S.: 424210

Matys Healthy Products LLC (1)
6707 Winchester Cir Ste 500, Boulder, CO
80301
Web Site: https://matyshealthyproducts.com
N.A.I.C.S.: 325412
Sarita T. Finnie *(Gen Mgr)*

Mediterranean Seeds Ltd. (1)
Kibbutz Einat, Einat, 4880500, Israel
Tel.: (972) 3 902 7008
Web Site: http://www.nunhems.com
Sales Range: $25-49.9 Million
Emp.: 15
Vegetable Seed Distr
N.A.I.C.S.: 424910

Mediwest Norway AS (1)
Drammensveien 147B, Oslo, 0212, Norway
Tel.: (47) 22065710
Web Site: http://www.medrad.com
Pharmaceutical Products Distr
N.A.I.C.S.: 424210

Monsanto Company (1)
800 N Lindbergh Blvd, Saint Louis, MO
63167
Tel.: (314) 694-1000
Web Site: http://www.monsanto.com
Rev.: $14,640,000,000
Assets: $21,333,000,000
Liabilities: $14,875,000,000
Net Worth: $6,458,000,000
Earnings: $2,260,000,000
Emp.: 20,500
Fiscal Year-end: 08/31/2017
Crop Protection Chemicals, Herbicide Prod-
ucts & Genetically-Altered Crop Seeds Mfr
N.A.I.C.S.: 325320
Michael J. Bush *(Sec)*

Subsidiary (Domestic):

American Seeds, LLC (2)
6051 Carlton Ave, Spring Grove, PA 17362
Tel.: (717) 225-3730
Web Site: https://americanseedco.com
Emp.: 4
Agricultural Seed Retailer
N.A.I.C.S.: 424910
Michael Rishel *(CEO)*

Beeologics Inc. (2)
800 N Lindbergh Blvd, Saint Louis, MO
63167
Tel.: (314) 694-1000
Web Site: http://www.beeologics.com
Food Products Mfr
N.A.I.C.S.: 311991

Channel Bio, LLC (2)
800 N Lindbergh Blvd, Saint Louis, MO
63167
Tel.: (314) 694-1000
Web Site: http://www.channel.com
Premium Corn, Soybeans, Alfalfa & Sor-
ghum Seed Products Distr
N.A.I.C.S.: 424910

Unit (Domestic):

Jung Seed Genetics (2)
341 S High St, Randolph, WI 53956-0001
Tel.: (920) 326-5891
Web Site: http://www.jungseedgenetics.com
Sales Range: $25-49.9 Million
Emp.: 28
Feed
N.A.I.C.S.: 424910

Subsidiary (Non-US):

Mahyco Monsanto Biotech (India)
Limited (2)
Ahura Centre 5th floor, 96 Mahakali Caves
Road Andheri East, Mumbai, 400 093, India
Tel.: (91) 2228246450
Web Site: http://www.mmbindia.com
Pesticide & Agricultural Chemical Product
Mfr
N.A.I.C.S.: 325320
T. Rajmohan *(Mgr-Strategic Acct)*

Monsanto (Malaysia) Sdn Bhd (2)
Plot 211 Jalan Emas Satu Pasir Gudang
Estate, 81700, Pasir Gudang, Johor, Malay-
sia
Tel.: (60) 72523472
Web Site: http://www.monsanto.com
Sales Range: $50-74.9 Million
Emp.: 100
Agricultural Chemical Formulations Mfr
N.A.I.C.S.: 325320

Monsanto Agricoltura Italia
S.p.A. (2)
Via Spadolini 5 Palazzo A, 20141, Milan,
Italy
Tel.: (39) 02 84780 1
Agricultural Chemical Mfr
N.A.I.C.S.: 325320

Monsanto Agriculture France
SAS (2)
Eden Park 1 Rue Buster Keaton, Saint
Priest, 69800, France
Tel.: (33) 472144040
Web Site: http://www.monsanto.fr
Agricultural Seeds & Pesticide Mfr
N.A.I.C.S.: 325320

Monsanto Argentina SRL (2)
Maipu 1210 10, Capital Federal,
C1006ACT, Buenos Aires, Argentina
Tel.: (54) 1143162400
Web Site: http://www.monsantoglobal.com
Seeds & Agrochemical Mfr
N.A.I.C.S.: 325320

Monsanto Australia Ltd. (2)
12 600 St Kilda Road, PO Box 6051, Mel-
bourne, 3004, Australia
Tel.: (61) 395227122
Web Site: http://www.monsanto.com.au
Sales Range: $25-49.9 Million
Emp.: 60
Seed Treatment & Distr
N.A.I.C.S.: 325320
Tony May *(Mng Dir)*

Monsanto Canada, Inc. (2)
900-1 Research Rd, Winnipeg, R3T 6E3,
MB, Canada (100%)
Tel.: (204) 985-1000
Web Site: http://www.monsanto.ca
Sales Range: $50-74.9 Million
Emp.: 80
Seed Whslr
N.A.I.C.S.: 444240
Michiel De Jongh *(Pres & Gen Mgr)*

Unit (Domestic):

Monsanto Canada, Inc. - Tillsonburg
Corn & Soybean
Manufacturing/Distribution (3)
281 Tilson Ave, Tillsonburg, N4G 5X2, ON,
Canada
Tel.: (519) 688-9888
Web Site: http://www.monsanto.ca

Sales Range: $25-49.9 Million
Emp.: 65
Treated Corn & Soybean Seed Processor &
Whslr
N.A.I.C.S.: 325320

Subsidiary (Non-US):

Monsanto Chile S.A. (2)
Rosario Norte 555 Piso 13, Las Condes,
Santiago, Chile
Tel.: (56) 22002300
Web Site: http://www.monsanto.com
Agricultural Chemical Mfr
N.A.I.C.S.: 325320

Plant (Domestic):

Monsanto Co. - Ankeny (2)
3302 SE Convenience Rd, Ankeny, IA
50021-9424
Tel.: (515) 963-4200
Web Site: http://www.monsanto.com
Sales Range: $50-74.9 Million
Emp.: 150
Agricultural Seed Distr
N.A.I.C.S.: 424910

Monsanto Co. - Ashton (2)
1990WRte 38, Ashton, IL 61006-9526
Tel.: (815) 453-2000
Web Site: http://www.monsanto.com
Sales Range: $50-74.9 Million
Emp.: 20
Soybean Seed Whslr
N.A.I.C.S.: 424910

Monsanto Co. - Beaman (2)
410 Center St, Beaman, IA 50609
Tel.: (641) 366-2606
Web Site: http://www.monsanto.com
Sales Range: $50-74.9 Million
Emp.: 20
Treated Seed Whslr
N.A.I.C.S.: 424910

Monsanto Co. - Bloomington (2)
14018 Carole Dr, Bloomington, IL 61705
Tel.: (309) 829-6707
Web Site: http://www.monsanto.com
Agriculture & Farming Company; Soybean
Seed Distr
N.A.I.C.S.: 424910

Monsanto Co. - Davis (2)
1910 5th St, Davis, CA 95616-4018
Tel.: (530) 753-6313
Web Site: http://www.monsanto.com
Seed Treatment & Whslr
N.A.I.C.S.: 325320

Monsanto Co. - Dayton (2)
2476 370th St, Dayton, IA 50530
Tel.: (515) 547-2550
Web Site: http://www.monsanto.com
Sales Range: $1-9.9 Million
Emp.: 4
Agricultural Product Research & Develop-
ment
N.A.I.C.S.: 541715

Monsanto Co. - Farmer City (2)
14901 Asgrow Rd, Farmer City, IL 61842
Tel.: (309) 928-9445
Web Site: http://www.monsanto.com
Sales Range: $50-74.9 Million
Emp.: 58
Treated Seed Distr
N.A.I.C.S.: 424910

Monsanto Co. - Glyndon (2)
11486 12th Ave S, Glyndon, MN 56547
Tel.: (218) 498-0267
Web Site: http://www.monsanto.com
Sales Range: $10-24.9 Million
Emp.: 16
Agricultural Product Research & Develop-
ment
N.A.I.C.S.: 541715

Monsanto Co. - Grinnell (2)
721 Hwy 6 E, Grinnell, IA 50112-8004
Tel.: (641) 236-6179
Web Site: http://www.monsanto.com
Sales Range: $50-74.9 Million
Emp.: 50
Seed Whslr
N.A.I.C.S.: 424910
Al Henderson *(Plant Mgr)*

Monsanto Co. - Illiopolis (2)

4370 Mt Polasky Rd, Illiopolis, IL 62539
Tel.: (217) 486-2211
Web Site: http://www.monsanto.com
Sales Range: $25-49.9 Million
Emp.: 25
Seed Grower
N.A.I.C.S.: 111422

Monsanto Co. - Janesville (2)
5926 E US Hwy 14, Janesville, WI 53546-
8655
Tel.: (608) 755-1777
Web Site: http://www.monsanto.com
Sales Range: $25-49.9 Million
Emp.: 12
Soybean Seed Treatment & Distr
N.A.I.C.S.: 325320

Monsanto Co. - Kahaheo (2)
4556 Awa Rd, Hanapepe, HI 96716
Tel.: (808) 335-5712
Web Site: http://www.monsanto.com
Sales Range: $25-49.9 Million
Emp.: 40
Corn Seed Treatment & Whslr
N.A.I.C.S.: 325320

Monsanto Co. - Kearney (2)
2615 Antelope Ave, Kearney, NE 68847
Tel.: (308) 234-9710
Web Site: http://www.monsanto.com
Sales Range: $25-49.9 Million
Emp.: 17
Seed Treatment & Distr
N.A.I.C.S.: 325320

Monsanto Co. - Lincoln (2)
3820 N 56th St, Lincoln, NE 68504
Tel.: (402) 467-2517
Web Site: http://www.monsanto.com
Sales Range: $25-49.9 Million
Emp.: 59
Processing Corn
N.A.I.C.S.: 424510

Monsanto Co. - Loxley Agronomy
Center (2)
25920 Monsanto Rd, Loxley, AL 36551
Tel.: (314) 694-1000
Web Site: http://www.monsanto.com
Sales Range: $1-9.9 Million
Emp.: 9
Agricultural Research & Development
N.A.I.C.S.: 541715

Monsanto Co. - Marshall (2)
830 N Miami Ave, Marshall, MO 65340-
9135
Tel.: (660) 886-9645
Web Site: http://www.monsanto.com
Sales Range: $25-49.9 Million
Emp.: 23
Soybean Seed Treatment & Whslr
N.A.I.C.S.: 325320

Monsanto Co. - Matthews (2)
2992 State Hwy V, Matthews, MO 63867-
9115
Tel.: (573) 471-5606
Web Site: http://www.monsanto.com
Sales Range: $50-74.9 Million
Emp.: 45
Agricultural Seed Treatment & Distr
N.A.I.C.S.: 325320

Monsanto Co. - Maui (2)
2111 Piilani Hwy, Kihei, HI 96753
Tel.: (314) 694-1000
Web Site: http://www.monsanto.com
Sales Range: $25-49.9 Million
Emp.: 100
Agricultural Product Research & Develop-
ment
N.A.I.C.S.: 541720

Monsanto Co. - Monmouth Agronomy
Center (2)
1677 80th St, Monmouth, IL 61462
Tel.: (309) 734-2184
Web Site: http://www.monsanto.com
Agricultural Seed Research & Development
N.A.I.C.S.: 541715

Monsanto Co. - Muscatine Plant (2)
2500 Wiggins Rd, Muscatine, IA 52761
Tel.: (563) 263-0093
Web Site: http://www.monsanto.com
Sales Range: $200-249.9 Million
Emp.: 420
Agricultural Fungicides & Herbicides Mfr

N.A.I.C.S.: 325320

Monsanto Co. - Mystic (2)
62 Maritime Dr, Mystic, CT 06355-1958
Tel.: (860) 572-5200
Web Site: http://www.monsanto.com
Sales Range: $25-49.9 Million
Emp.: 84
Corn Seed Treatment & Whslr
N.A.I.C.S.: 325320

Monsanto Co. - Olivia (2)
2135 W Lincoln Ave, Olivia, MN 56277-1702
Tel.: (320) 523-2222
Web Site: http://www.monsanto.com
Sales Range: $1-9.9 Million
Emp.: 10
Agricultural Seed Research & Development
N.A.I.C.S.: 541715

Monsanto Co. - Parkersburg Foundation (2)
18739 Hwy 57, Aplington, IA 50604
Tel.: (319) 347-6633
Web Site: http://www.monsanto.com
Sales Range: $50-74.9 Million
Emp.: 4
Agricultural Seed Research & Development
N.A.I.C.S.: 541715

Monsanto Co. - Redwood Falls-Soybean Research (2)
29770 US Hwy 71, Redwood Falls, MN 56283-2401
Tel.: (507) 644-3011
Web Site: http://www.monsanto.com
Sales Range: $1-9.9 Million
Emp.: 5
Soybean Agricultural Product Research & Development
N.A.I.C.S.: 541720

Monsanto Co. - Remington (2)
15849 S US Hwy 231, Remington, IN 47977-8765
Tel.: (219) 261-2122
Web Site: http://www.monsanto.com
Sales Range: $25-49.9 Million
Emp.: 20
Seed Testing Laboratory
N.A.I.C.S.: 541380

Monsanto Co. - Soda Springs Plant (2)
1853 Hwy 34, Soda Springs, ID 83276-5227
Tel.: (208) 547-4300
Web Site: http://www.monsanto.com
Sales Range: $200-249.9 Million
Emp.: 400
Agricultural Chemical Mfr
N.A.I.C.S.: 325320

Monsanto Co. - Stonington (2)
1982 Illinois Rte 48, Stonington, IL 62567
Tel.: (217) 325-3234
Web Site: http://www.monsanto.com
Sales Range: $50-74.9 Million
Emp.: 40
Soybean Seed Treatment & Distr
N.A.I.C.S.: 325320
Joan Burns (Branch Mgr)

Monsanto Co. - Stromsburg (2)
1110 E Ninth St, Stromsburg, NE 68666
Tel.: (402) 764-8261
Web Site: http://www.monsanto.com
Sales Range: $50-74.9 Million
Emp.: 7
Agricultural Seed & Pesticide Distr
N.A.I.C.S.: 424910

Monsanto Co. - Stuttgart (2)
2476 Highway 130 E, Stuttgart, AR 72160-5550
Tel.: (870) 673-8565
Web Site: http://www.monsanto.com
Sales Range: $25-49.9 Million
Emp.: 10
Agricultural Research & Development
N.A.I.C.S.: 541715

Monsanto Co. - Washington DC (2)
1300 I St NW Ste 450 E, Washington, DC 20005-3011
Tel.: (202) 783-2460
Web Site: http://www.monsanto.com
Sales Range: $50-74.9 Million
Emp.: 20
Chemical & Agricultural Fertilizer Whslr

N.A.I.C.S.: 424910

Monsanto Co. - Waterman Seed Technology Center (2)
460 E Adams, Waterman, IL 60556
Tel.: (815) 264-8100
Web Site: http://www.monsanto.com
Sales Range: $50-74.9 Million
Emp.: 50
Agricultural Product Research & Development
N.A.I.C.S.: 541715

Monsanto Co. - West Fargo (2)
304 Center St, West Fargo, ND 58078-3134
Tel.: (701) 282-7338
Web Site: http://www.monsanto.com
Sales Range: $50-74.9 Million
Emp.: 25
Hybrid Seeds Distr
N.A.I.C.S.: 424910

Monsanto Co. - Williamsburg (2)
503 S Maplewood Ave, Williamsburg, IA 52361
Tel.: (319) 668-1100
Web Site: http://www.monsanto.com
Sales Range: $10-24.9 Million
Emp.: 100
Corn Seed Treatment & Distr
N.A.I.C.S.: 325320

Subsidiary (Non-US):

Monsanto Comercial, S de RL de CV (2)
Javier Barros Sierra No 540 Torre II Piso 1 y 2 Park Plaza, Col Santa Fe, Mexico, 01210, Mexico
Tel.: (52) 5552459600
Web Site: http://www.monsanto.com
Pesticide & Agricultural Chemical Product Mfr
N.A.I.C.S.: 325320
Pierre Courduroux (Sr VP & CFO)

Monsanto Commercial, S.A. de C.V. (2)
Av Javier Barros Sierra No 540 Tower II Floor 1 and 2 Park Plaza, Col Desarrollo Santa Fe, 01210, Mexico, D.F., Mexico
Tel.: (52) 55 52 45 96 00
Web Site: http://www.monsanto.com
Chemical & Agricultural Pesticide Mfr
N.A.I.C.S.: 325320

Monsanto Deutschland GmbH (2)
Vogelsanger Weg 91, Dusseldorf, 40470, Germany (100%)
Tel.: (49) 21136750
Web Site: http://www.monsanto.de
Sales Range: $25-49.9 Million
Emp.: 25
Synthetic Fiber Whslr
N.A.I.C.S.: 313310

Monsanto Europe S.A./N.V. (Belgium) (2)
Avenue de Tervuren 270-272, 1150, Brussels, Belgium
Tel.: (32) 27767600
Web Site: http://www.monsanto.com
Sales Range: $25-49.9 Million
Emp.: 28
Agricultural Chemical Product Mfr
N.A.I.C.S.: 325320
Leticia Goncalves (Pres)

Monsanto Far East Ltd. (2)
7/8 F Phoenix Place 5A Shuguang Xili, Chaoyang District, Beijing, 100028, China (100%)
Tel.: (86) 10 58290888
Sales Range: $150-199.9 Million
Agricultural Chemicals
N.A.I.C.S.: 325320

Monsanto Gida ve Tarim Ticaret Limited Sirketi (2)
Palladium Tower Is Merkezi Barbaros Mah Kardelen Sok No:2 Atasehir, 34746, Istanbul, Turkiye
Tel.: (90) 2165595900
Web Site: http://www.monsanto.com
Emp.: 25
Agricultural Seed Retailer
N.A.I.C.S.: 424910

Monsanto Hellas, E.p.E. (2)

29 Michalakopoulou St, Athens, 11528, Greece
Tel.: (30) 2107259435
Web Site: http://www.monsanto.com
Sales Range: $50-74.9 Million
Emp.: 3
Seed Whslr
N.A.I.C.S.: 111120

Monsanto Holdings Private Ltd. (2)
Ahura Centre 5th Floor 96 Mahakali Caves Road Andheri E, Mumbai, 400093, Maharashtra, India
Tel.: (91) 22 28246450
Web Site: http://www.monsantoindia.com
Emp.: 230
Agricultural Chemical Mfr
N.A.I.C.S.: 325320

Monsanto Holland BV (2)
2660 BB, PO Box 1050, 2660 BB, Bergschenhoek, Netherlands
Tel.: (31) 105292222
Agricultural Chemical Mfr
N.A.I.C.S.: 325320

Monsanto Hungaria Kft. (2)
Turi Istvan ut 1, 1238, Budapest, Hungary
Tel.: (36) 12893100
Emp.: 300
Agricultural Seed Retailer
N.A.I.C.S.: 424910

Monsanto International S.A.R.L (2)
Rue des Sablon 2-4, 1110, Morges, Switzerland
Tel.: (41) 218046700
Web Site: http://www.monsanto.com
Emp.: 200
Agricultural Chemical Product Mfr
N.A.I.C.S.: 325320

Monsanto Japan Ltd. (2)
Ginza Sannou Bldg 8th Fl 4-10-10 Ginza Chuo-ku, Tokyo, 104-0061, Japan
Tel.: (81) 362266080
Web Site: http://www.monsanto.com
Sales Range: $10-24.9 Million
Emp.: 18
Chemical & Agricultural Products Mfr
N.A.I.C.S.: 325199

Monsanto Korea Ltd. (2)
S Tower 12F 82 Saemunan-ro, Jongno-gu, Seoul, 03185, Korea (South)
Tel.: (82) 233933700
Web Site: http://www.seminis.kr
Agricultural Product Mfr & Distr
N.A.I.C.S.: 111199

Monsanto NL BV (2)
Leeuwenhoekweg 52, Bergschenhoek, 2661 CZ, Netherlands
Tel.: (31) 105292222
Web Site: http://www.monsanto.com
Emp.: 400
Business Support Services
N.A.I.C.S.: 561110
Rutger Dewal (Mgr-HR)

Monsanto Romania SRL (2)
O21 Building 5th Floor SOS Bucuresti - Nord no 10, 77190, Voluntari, Ilfov, Romania
Tel.: (40) 213057140
Web Site: http://www.monsanto.ro
Sales Range: $50-74.9 Million
Emp.: 16
Agricultural Chemicals Manufacturing
N.A.I.C.S.: 325320

Monsanto SAS (2)
1 Rue Buster Keaton Eden Park-Batiment B, Cedex, Saint Priest, France
Tel.: (33) 472144040
Web Site: http://www.monsanto.fr
Sales Range: $125-149.9 Million
Emp.: 30
Vegetable Seed Whslr, Research & Development
N.A.I.C.S.: 541715
Catherine Lamboley (Pres)

Monsanto Singapore Company (Pte.) Ltd. (2)
151 Lorong Chuan New Tech Park Lobby Hitch 06-08, 06 07 08 New Tech Park, Singapore, 556741, Singapore (100%)
Tel.: (65) 64885501
Sales Range: $10-24.9 Million
Emp.: 100
Chemical & Agricultural Products Mfr

N.A.I.C.S.: 325320

Monsanto Thailand Ltd. (2)
555 Paholyothin Rd 22th floor Rasa Tower 1, Chatuchack, Bangkok, 10900, Thailand
Tel.: (66) 27934888
Web Site: http://www.monsanto.com
Farm Product Raw Material Merchant Wholesalers
N.A.I.C.S.: 424590

Monsanto UK Ltd. (2)
PO Box 663, Cambourne, Cambridge, CB1 0LD, United Kingdom
Tel.: (44) 1223849200
Web Site: http://www.monsanto.com
Sales Range: $150-199.9 Million
Agricultural Chemicals Whslr
N.A.I.C.S.: 325320

Monsanto Ukraine LLC (2)
101-A Volodymyrska St, Kiev, 01033, Ukraine
Tel.: (380) 444907575
Web Site: http://www.monsanto.com
Agricultural Seed Retailer
N.A.I.C.S.: 424910
Ozerova Libya (Gen Mgr)

Monsanto do Brasil Ltda. (2)
Av Nacoes Unidas 12901 7o Andar, Sao Paulo, 04578-000, Brazil
Tel.: (55) 1155032600
Web Site: http://www.monsanto.com
Sales Range: $150-199.9 Million
Chemical Product Mfr & Whslr
N.A.I.C.S.: 325998

Subsidiary (Domestic):

Seminis Vegetable Seeds, Inc. (2)
800 N Lindbergh Blvd, Saint Louis, MO 63167
Tel.: (866) 334-1056
Web Site: http://www.seminis-us.com
Sales Range: $250-299.9 Million
Vegetable Seed Whslr
N.A.I.C.S.: 424910

The Climate Corporation (2)
201 3rd St Ste 1100, San Francisco, CA 94103
Tel.: (415) 363-0500
Web Site: https://www.climate.com
Pesticide & Agricultural Chemical Product Mfr
N.A.I.C.S.: 325320
David Friedberg (CEO)

Monsanto Pakistan (Private) Limited (1)
Plot 23 Sector 22, Korangi Industrial Area, Karachi, 74900, Sindh, Pakistan
Tel.: (92) 2135108000
Pharmaceuticals Product Mfr
N.A.I.C.S.: 325412

Monsanto Polska Sp. z o.o. (1)
Al Jerozolimskie 158, 02-326, Warsaw, Poland
Tel.: (48) 225723500
Web Site: https://www.bayer.com.pl
Farm Good Distr
N.A.I.C.S.: 424910

NoHo Health Inc. (1)
850 3rd Ave Ste 601, Brooklyn, NY 11232
Web Site: https://www.takecareof.com
N.A.I.C.S.: 325412

Orbia Argentina S.A.U. (1)
Juana Manso 205, C1107CBE, Buenos Aires, Argentina
Tel.: (54) 1120400722
Web Site: https://argentina.orbia.ag
Farm Maintenance Services
N.A.I.C.S.: 115116

P.T. Bayer Indonesia (1)
Menara Astra 33rd floor Jl Jend Sudirman Kav 5-6, Jakarta, 10220, Indonesia
Tel.: (62) 2130491111
Web Site: https://www.bayer.com
Pharmaceutical Products Mfr & Whslr
N.A.I.C.S.: 325412

P.T. Monagro Kimia (1)
Jl Industri Manis 4 No 11 RT 002/RW 007 Manis Jaya, Jatiuwung, Tangerang, 15136, Banten, Indonesia
Tel.: (62) 215918506

Bayer Aktiengesellschaft—(Continued)

N.A.I.C.S.: 325412

PGS International N.V. **(1)**
Energieweg 1, 3641 RT, Mijdrecht, Nether-
lands
Tel.: (31) 297280666
Web Site: http://www.bayer.com
Emp.: 300
Stock Broking Services
N.A.I.C.S.: 523150

Pallas Versicherung AG **(1)**
Chempark Building Q 26, 51368, Le-
verkusen, Germany
Tel.: (49) 2143061398
Web Site: https://www.pallas-
versicherung.de
General Insurance Services
N.A.I.C.S.: 524210

Pandias Re AG **(1)**
Rue de Neudorf 534, 2220, Luxembourg,
Luxembourg
Tel.: (352) 267547
General Insurance Services
N.A.I.C.S.: 524298

**Productos Quimicos Naturales, S.A.
de C.V.** **(1)**
Domicilio Conocido Ojo de Agua, Ixtaczo-
quitlan, 94450, Veracruz, Mexico
Tel.: (52) 2727425842
Web Site:
http://www.proquina.bayer.com.mx
Emp.: 400
Chemical Products Mfr
N.A.I.C.S.: 325998

Quimicas Unidas S.A. **(1)**
Calle 3ra E / 76 and 78 Edif Beijing 1st
Floor Office 101, Playa, Havana, Cuba
Tel.: (53) 72041383
Pharmaceuticals Product Mfr
N.A.I.C.S.: 325412

SC Bayer SRL **(1)**
Ploiesti No 1A Building B Floor 1 Sector 1,
13681, Bucharest, Romania
Tel.: (40) 215295900
Pharmaceuticals Product Mfr
N.A.I.C.S.: 325412

SIA Bayer **(1)**
50 Skanstes Street 2nd entrance 7th floor,
Riga, 1013, Latvia
Tel.: (371) 67845563
Web Site: https://www.bayer.com
Sales Range: $25-49.9 Million
Emp.: 20
Agricultural Chemical Mfr
N.A.I.C.S.: 325320

Seminis S de RL de CV **(1)**
Javier Barros Sierra N 540 Tower II Floor 1
and 2 Park Plaza, Col Santa Fe Del Alvaro
Obregon, 01210, Mexico, Mexico
Tel.: (52) 18005014929
Web Site: http://www.seminis.mx
Crop Protection Services
N.A.I.C.S.: 115112

Sumika Bayer Urethane Co., Ltd. **(1)**
2-4-9 Umeda, Kita-ku, Osaka, 530-0001,
Japan
Tel.: (81) 661337000
Web Site: https://www.bayer.jp
Plastic Materials Mfr
N.A.I.C.S.: 325211

**TAAV Biomanufacturing Solutions,
S.L.U.** **(1)**
Parque Cientifico y Tecnologico de
Gipuzkoa Paseo Mikeletegi 73 B, 20009,
San Sebastian, Spain
Tel.: (34) 943209060
Web Site: https://taav.com
Enzymatic Dna Mfr
N.A.I.C.S.: 325412

TECTRION GmbH **(1)**
Kaiser-Wilhelm-Allee, 51368, Leverkusen,
Germany
Tel.: (49) 21334 892 2100
Web Site: https://www.tectrion.de
Pharmaceuticals Product Mfr
N.A.I.C.S.: 325412

TecArena+ GmbH **(1)**
Bismarck Strasse 122-124, Leverkusen,

51373, Germany
Tel.: (49) 214 8660 500
Management Consulting Services
N.A.I.C.S.: 541618
Felix Burden *(Gen Mgr)*

TravelBoard GmbH **(1)**
Kaiser-Wilhelm-Allee K17 OlofPalme
Strasse, 51368, Leverkusen, Germany
Tel.: (49) 214 30 62633
Web Site: http://www.travelboard.de
Sales Range: $25-49.9 Million
Emp.: 60
Travel Arrangement Services
N.A.I.C.S.: 561599

UAB Bayer **(1)**
Sporto st 18, 09238, Vilnius, Lithuania
Tel.: (370) 5 233 6868
Web Site: https://www.bayer.com
Emp.: 59
Pharmaceuticals Product Mfr
N.A.I.C.S.: 325412

**Viralgen Commercial Therapeutic
Vector Core, S.L.** **(1)**
Paseo Mikeletegi 8 Parque Cientifico y
Tecnologico de Gipuzkoa, 20009, San Se-
bastian, Spain
Tel.: (34) 943477733
Web Site: https://viralgenvc.com
Medicinal Product Mfr
N.A.I.C.S.: 325412

Viralgen Vector Core, S.L. **(1)**
Paseo Mikeletegi 83, 20009, San Sebas-
tian, Spain
Tel.: (34) 943477733
Web Site: https://viralgenvc.com
N.A.I.C.S.: 325412
Jimmy Vanhove *(CEO)*

ZAO Bayer **(1)**
3rd Rybinskaya Str 18 build 2, 107113,
Moscow, Russia
Tel.: (7) 4952311200
Web Site: http://www.bayer.ru
Sales Range: $150-199.9 Million
Emp.: 500
Polycarbonate Products Distr
N.A.I.C.S.: 424610
Irina Yasina *(Mgr-Logistics)*

**Zweite K-W-A Beteiligungsgesell-
schaft mbH** **(1)**
Kaiser-Wilhelm-Allee 20, Leverkusen,
51373, Germany
Tel.: (49) 2141301
Business Management Consulting Services
N.A.I.C.S.: 541618

BAYERISCHE BORSE AG

Karolinenplatz 6, 80333, Munich,
Germany
Tel.: (49) 895490450　　　　　　　　De
Web Site: http://www.bayerische-
boerse.de
Sales Range: $25-49.9 Million
Emp.: 30
Stock Securities Exchange
N.A.I.C.S.: 523210
Uto Baader *(Co-CEO)*

BAYERISCHE MASINDUSTRIE A. KELLER GMBH

Rosengasse 12, 91217, Hersbruck,
Germany
Tel.: (49) 915173010
Web Site: http://www.bmi.de
Year Founded: 1993
Rev.: $21,802,935
Emp.: 150
Measuring Equipment Mfr
N.A.I.C.S.: 334519
Hans Keller *(Owner & CEO)*

BAYERISCHE MOTOREN WERKE AKTIENGESELL-SCHAFT

Petuelring 130, 80809, Munich, Germany
Tel.: (49) 893820　　　　　　　　　　De
Web Site:
https://www.bmwgroup.com

Year Founded: 1916
1BMW—(EUR)
Rev.: $171,650,292,551
Assets: $276,951,098,394
Liabilities: $174,375,758,938
Net Worth: $102,575,339,456
Earnings: $13,428,634,509
Emp.: 154,950
Fiscal Year-end: 12/31/23
Cars & Motorbikes Mfr & Whslr
N.A.I.C.S.: 336110
Kurt Bock *(Deputy Chm-Supervisory
Bd)*

Subsidiaries:

Alphabet (GB) Ltd. **(1)**
Alphabet House Summit Avenue, Farnbor-
ough, GU14 0FB, Hampshire, United King-
dom
Tel.: (44) 370 505 0100
Web Site: https://www.alphabet.com
Financial & Insurance Services
N.A.I.C.S.: 524210
Nick Brownrigg *(CEO)*

**Alphabet Austria Fuhrparkmanage-
ment GmbH** **(1)**
Siegfried-Marcus-Strasse 24, 5020,
Salzburg, Austria
Tel.: (43) 6 628 3790
Web Site: https://www.alphabet.com
Financial & Insurance Services
N.A.I.C.S.: 524210

**Alphabet France Fleet Management
S.N.C.** **(1)**
1 Avenue Edouard Belin, 92566, Rueil-
Malmaison, Cedex, France
Tel.: (33) 149049100
Web Site: http://www.alphabet.com
Financial & Insurance Services
N.A.I.C.S.: 524210

Alphabet Franco S.A.S. **(1)**
5 Rue des Herons Montigny-le-Bretonneux,
CS 40752, 78182, Saint-Quentin-en-
Yvelines, Cedex, France
Tel.: (33) 149049100
N.A.I.C.S.: 518210

**Alphabet Fuhrparkmanagement
(Schweiz) AG** **(1)**
Industriestrasse 20, 8157, Dielsdorf, Swit-
zerland
Tel.: (41) 58 269 6567
Web Site: https://www.alphabet.com
Financial & Insurance Services
N.A.I.C.S.: 524210

**Alphabet Fuhrparkmanagement
GmbH** **(1)**
Lilienthalalee 26, 80939, Munich, Germany
Tel.: (49) 8 999 8220
Web Site: https://www.alphabet.com
Passenger Car Leasing & Rental
N.A.I.C.S.: 532112
Marco Lessacher *(CEO)*

Subsidiary (Non-US):

**Alphabet Belgium Long Term Rental
N.V.** **(2)**
Ingbernhoeveweg 6, 2630, Aartselaar,
Belgium **(100%)**
Tel.: (32) 34501818
Web Site: http://www.alphabet.com
Sales Range: $75-99.9 Million
Emp.: 130
Passenger Car Rental
N.A.I.C.S.: 532111
Christel Reynaerts *(CEO)*

Branch (Domestic):

Alphabet Belgium N.V./S.A. **(3)**
Leuvensesteenweg 400, Zaventem, 1932,
Belgium
Tel.: (32) 27259090
Web Site: http://www.alphabet.be
Emp.: 4
Passenger Car Rental
N.A.I.C.S.: 532111
Jan Vanroon *(Mgr)*

Subsidiary (Non-US):

Alphabet Nederland B.V. **(2)**

Takkebijsters 59, 4817 BL, Breda,
Netherlands **(100%)**
Tel.: (31) 76 579 3200
Web Site: https://www.alphabet.com
Sales Range: $150-199.9 Million
Emp.: 500
Passenger Car Rental
N.A.I.C.S.: 532111

BMW Korea Co. Ltd. **(2)**
14F State Tower Namsan 100 Toegye-ro,
Jung-gu, Seoul, 100-052, Korea (South)
Tel.: (82) 19056831201
Automobile Parts Mfr
N.A.I.C.S.: 336110

BMW Malaysia Sdn Bhd **(2)**
3501 Jalan Teknokrat 5, 63000, Cyberjaya,
Selangor, Malaysia
Tel.: (60) 32 172 0088
Web Site: https://www.bmw.com.my
Automobile Parts Mfr
N.A.I.C.S.: 336110
Sarah Tan *(Mgr-Retail Performance Pro-
gram)*

BMW Motoren GmbH **(2)**
Hinterbergerstrasse 2, 4400, Steyr, Austria
Tel.: (43) 7 252 8880
Web Site: https://www.bmwgroup-
werke.com
Diesel & Petrol Engine Mfr
N.A.I.C.S.: 333618

BMW de Argentina S.A. **(2)**
Ruta Panamerica Ramar Pilar Km 35 5,
B1667KQT, Tortuguitas, Buenos Aires, Ar-
gentina
Tel.: (54) 1155556191
Web Site: http://www.bmw.com.ar
Automobile Parts Mfr
N.A.I.C.S.: 336110

**Alphabet Italia Fleet Management
S.p.A.** **(1)**
Via Romano Guardini 24, 38121, Trento,
Italy
Tel.: (39) 04611829729
N.A.I.C.S.: 532112

Alphabet Luxembourg S.A. **(1)**
Rue Du Chateau d'Eau 2-4, 3364, Leude-
lange, Luxembourg
Tel.: (352) 250009
Web Site: https://www.alphabet.com
Financial & Insurance Services
N.A.I.C.S.: 524210

**Alphabet Polska Fleet Management
Sp. z o.o.** **(1)**
ul Woloska 22a Mokotow Nova C building,
02-675, Warsaw, Poland
Tel.: (48) 22 820 5555
Web Site: https://www.alphabet.com
Financial & Insurance Services
N.A.I.C.S.: 524210
Helmut Hoidn *(Pres & Gen Mgr)*

Alphabet UK Ltd. **(1)**
Alphabet House Summit Avenue, Farnbor-
ough, GU14 0FB, Hampshire, United King-
dom
Tel.: (44) 3705050100
Web Site: https://www.alphabet.com
N.A.I.C.S.: 532112

Automag GmbH **(1)**
Wasserburger Landstr 81, 81827, Munich,
Germany
Tel.: (49) 8951020
Web Site: http://www.automag.de
Automobile Parts Mfr
N.A.I.C.S.: 336110

BMW (GB) Ltd. **(1)**
Summit One Summit Avenue, Farnborough,
GU14 0FB, Hampshire, United Kingdom
Tel.: (44) 3705050160
Web Site: https://www.bmw.co.uk
N.A.I.C.S.: 332510

BMW (Schweiz) AG **(1)**
Industriestrasse 20, 8157, Dielsdorf, Swit-
zerland
Tel.: (41) 84 425 0250
Web Site: https://www.bmw.ch
Emp.: 200
Automobile Mfr & Distr
N.A.I.C.S.: 336110

BMW (South Africa) Pty. Ltd. **(1)**

1 Bavaria Avenue Randjespark Ext 17, Midrand, 1685, Gauteng, South Africa **(100%)**
Tel.: (27) 12 522 3000
Web Site: https://www.bmw.co.za
Sales Range: $800-899.9 Million
Emp.: 4,000
Production & Marketing of BMW Products
N.A.I.C.S.: 336110

Plant (Domestic):

BMW (South Africa) Pty. Ltd. - Rosslyn Plant **(2)**
6 Frans Du Troit Street, Rosslyn, Pretoria, South Africa
Tel.: (27) 12 5 22 22 04
Automobile Mfr
N.A.I.C.S.: 336110

BMW (Thailand) Co. Ltd. **(1)**
CRC All Seasons Place 44th floor Witthayu Road Lumpini, Pathumwan, 10330, Bangkok, Thailand
Tel.: (66) 953708888
Web Site: http://www.bmw.co.th
Automobile Parts Mfr
N.A.I.C.S.: 336110

BMW (UK) Ltd **(1)**
Summit One Summit Avenue, Farnborough, GU14 0FB, Hampshire, United Kingdom
Tel.: (44) 800 325 6000
Web Site: https://www.bmw.co.uk
Automobile & Other Motor Vehicle Merchant Whslr
N.A.I.C.S.: 423110

Subsidiary (Domestic):

BMW (UK) Capital Plc **(2)**
Ellesfield Avenue, Bracknell, RG12 8TA, United Kingdom
Tel.: (44) 13 4442 6565
Financial Management Services
N.A.I.C.S.: 523999

Plant (Domestic):

BMW (UK) Ltd. - Hams Hall Plant **(2)**
Canton Lane Hams Hall, Coleshill, B46 1GB, North Warwickshire, United Kingdom
Tel.: (44) 16 75 4 60742
Automotive Engine Mfr
N.A.I.C.S.: 336310

BMW Australia Finance Ltd. **(1)**
783 Springvale Road, Mulgrave, 3170, VIC, Australia
Tel.: (61) 392644422
Automobile Parts Mfr
N.A.I.C.S.: 336110

BMW Australia Ltd. **(1)**
783 Springvale Road, PO Box 745, Mulgrave, 3170, VIC, Australia **(100%)**
Tel.: (61) 133269
Web Site: http://www.bmw.com.au
Sales Range: $150-199.9 Million
Emp.: 300
Marketing of BMW Products
N.A.I.C.S.: 423110
Phil Horton *(Mng Dir)*

BMW Austria Bank GmbH **(1)**
Siegfried-Marcus-Strasse 24, 5020, Salzburg, Austria
Tel.: (43) 66221910
Financial & Insurance Services
N.A.I.C.S.: 524210

BMW Austria Gesellschaft m.b.H. **(1)**
Siegfried-Marcus-Str 24, 5020, Salzburg, Austria **(100%)**
Tel.: (43) 6 628 3830
Web Site: https://www.bmw.at
Sales Range: $125-149.9 Million
Emp.: 300
Marketing of BMW Products
N.A.I.C.S.: 423110

Subsidiary (Domestic):

BMW Motoren Ges.m.b.H. **(2)**
Hinterbergerstrasse 2, 4400, Steyr, Austria **(100%)**
Tel.: (43) 72528880
Web Site: http://www.bmw.co.at
Emp.: 4,400

Development, Production & Marketing of Engines
N.A.I.C.S.: 336110

BMW Austria Leasing GmbH **(1)**
Siegfried-Marcus-Strasse 24, 5020, Salzburg, Austria
Tel.: (43) 66221910
Web Site: https://www.alphabet.com
N.A.I.C.S.: 532120

BMW Automotive (Ireland) Ltd. **(1)**
Swift Square Santry Demesne, 9, Dublin, D09 A0E4, Ireland
Tel.: (353) 18619425
Web Site: https://www.bmw.ie
N.A.I.C.S.: 332510

BMW Bank GmbH **(1)**
Lilienthalallee 26, 80939, Munich, Germany
Tel.: (49) 8 931 8403
Web Site: https://www.bmwbank.de
Automotive Financial Leasing Services
N.A.I.C.S.: 522220

BMW Brilliance Automotive Ltd. **(1)**
25th F Tower B GATEWAY No18 Xiaguangli Dongsanhuanbeilu, Chaoyang District, Beijing, 100027, China **(50%)**
Tel.: (86) 108 455 7000
Web Site: https://www.bmw-brilliance.cn
Motor Vehicle & Automotive Parts Mfr & Distr
N.A.I.C.S.: 336110
Johann Wieland *(Pres & CEO)*

BMW Car IT GmbH **(1)**
Moosacher Strasse 86, 80809, Munich, Germany
Tel.: (49) 8938217001
Automobile Parts Mfr
N.A.I.C.S.: 336110

BMW China Automotive Trading Ltd **(1)**
28th Floor Block B Jiacheng Plaza No 18 Xiaguangli, North East Third Ring Road Chaoyang, Beijing, 100027, China
Tel.: (86) 4008006666
Web Site: http://www.bmw.com.cn
Motor Vehicle Whslr
N.A.I.C.S.: 423110

BMW Danmark A/S **(1)**
Borgmester Christiansens Gade 50, 2450, Copenhagen, Denmark
Tel.: (45) 7 015 6156
Web Site: https://www.bmw.dk
Automobile Parts Mfr
N.A.I.C.S.: 336110

BMW Fahrzeugtechnik GmbH **(1)**
Stedtfelder Strasse 2, 99819, Krauthausen, Germany
Tel.: (49) 893820
Web Site: https://www.bmwgroup-werke.com
Automotive Components Mfr
N.A.I.C.S.: 336390

BMW Finance S.N.C. **(1)**
Immeuble Le Renaissance 3 Rond Point Des Saules, 78280, Guyancourt, France
Tel.: (33) 130448000
Automobile Parts Mfr
N.A.I.C.S.: 336110

BMW Financial Services (GB) Ltd **(1)**
Europa House Bartley Way, Hook, RG27 9UF, United Kingdom
Tel.: (44) 87 0505 0120
Sales Range: $200-249.9 Million
Emp.: 400
Personal Financial Services
N.A.I.C.S.: 523999

BMW Financial Services (Ireland) DAC **(1)**
Swift Square Santry Demesne, Dublin, 216410, Ireland
Tel.: (353) 1344480544
Automobile Parts Mfr
N.A.I.C.S.: 336110

BMW Financial Services (South Africa) (Pty) Ltd. **(1)**
1 Bavaria Road, Randjespark, Midrand, South Africa
Tel.: (27) 115645044
Automobile Parts Mfr

N.A.I.C.S.: 336110
Charl Barnardo *(Gen Mgr-Sls & Mktg)*

BMW Financial Services B.V. **(1)**
Madame Curielaan 1, 2289 CA, Rijswijk, Netherlands
Tel.: (31) 704147510
Web Site: http://www.bmw.nl
Financial & Insurance Services
N.A.I.C.S.: 524210

BMW Financial Services Denmark A/S **(1)**
Mayor Christiansens Gade 50, 2450, Copenhagen, Denmark
Tel.: (45) 70151542
Financial & Insurance Services
N.A.I.C.S.: 524210

BMW Financial Services GmbH **(1)**
Heidemannstrasse 164, 80787, Munich, Germany **(100%)**
Tel.: (49) 89318403
Web Site: http://www.schering.com
Sales Range: $700-749.9 Million
Emp.: 1,500
Provider of Financial Services
N.A.I.C.S.: 522320
Kathrin Frauscher *(CEO & Mng Dir)*

BMW Financial Services Korea Co. Ltd. **(1)**
12F State Tower Namsan 100 Toegye-ro, Jung-gu, Seoul, 04631, Korea (South)
Tel.: (82) 1 577 5822
Web Site: https://www.bmwfs.co.kr
Emp.: 192
Automobile Parts Mfr
N.A.I.C.S.: 336110

BMW Financial Services New Zealand Ltd. **(1)**
7 Pacific Rise, Mt Wellington, Auckland, 1060, New Zealand
Tel.: (64) 800639269
N.A.I.C.S.: 532120

BMW Financial Services Singapore Pte. Ltd. **(1)**
1 HarbourFront Avenue 15-02/07 Keppel Bay Tower, Singapore, 098632, Singapore
Tel.: (65) 6 838 9701
Web Site: https://www.bmw.com.sg
Automobile Parts Mfr
N.A.I.C.S.: 336110

BMW Financial Services de Mexico S.A. de C.V. **(1)**
Javier Barros Sierra 495 Floor 14 Office 1401, Park Plaza III Santa Fe Colony, 01376, Mexico, Alvaro Obregon, Mexico
Tel.: (52) 15591408600
Web Site: https://bmwfs.com.mx
N.A.I.C.S.: 532120

BMW Finanz Verwaltungs GmbH **(1)**
Petuelring 130, Munich, Bavaria, Germany
Tel.: (49) 893820
Web Site: http://www.bmw.de
Financial Management Services
N.A.I.C.S.: 523999
Norbert Reithofer *(Member-Mgmt Bd)*

BMW France S.A. **(1)**
3 Avenue Ampere, 78180, Montigny-le-Bretonneux, France **(100%)**
Tel.: (33) 969322039
Web Site: http://www.bmw.fr
Sales Range: $75-99.9 Million
Emp.: 150
Sales of BMW Products
N.A.I.C.S.: 423110

BMW Hams Hall Motoren GmbH **(1)**
Petuelring 130, 80809, Munich, Germany
Tel.: (49) 893820
Web Site: http://www.bmw.com
Automotive Engine Mfr
N.A.I.C.S.: 336310

BMW Holding B.V. **(1)**
Einsteinlaan 5, PO Box 5808, Rijswijk, 2289 CC, South Holland, Netherlands **(100%)**
Tel.: (31) 704133222
Web Site: http://www.bmw.nl
Sales Range: $75-99.9 Million
Emp.: 40
Holding Company
N.A.I.C.S.: 551112
Arjende Jong *(Mng Dir)*

BMW Hungary Kft. **(1)**
Lorinci u 59, Airport Business Park, 2220, Vecses, Hungary
Tel.: (36) 80990011
Car Dealer
N.A.I.C.S.: 441110

BMW Iberica S.A. **(1)**
Avenida de Burgos n 118, 28050, Madrid, Spain **(100%)**
Tel.: (34) 90 035 7902
Web Site: https://www.bmw.es
Sales Range: $50-74.9 Million
Emp.: 100
Marketing of BMW Products
N.A.I.C.S.: 423110

BMW India Financial Services Private Ltd. **(1)**
1st Floor Oberoi Centre Building No11 DLF Cyber City Phase-II, Gurgaon, 122 022, Haryana, India
Tel.: (91) 1244566600
Automobile Parts Mfr
N.A.I.C.S.: 336110
S. Sayan *(Asst Mgr-Legal)*

BMW India Private Limited **(1)**
2nd Floor Oberoi Centre Building No 11 DLF Cyber City Phase-II, Gurgaon, 122 022, Haryana, India
Tel.: (91) 1244566600
Automobile Parts Mfr
N.A.I.C.S.: 336110

BMW Ingenieur Zentrum GmbH & Co. **(1)**
PO Box 40 02 40, D-8000, Munich, Germany **(100%)**
Real Estate Management Company
N.A.I.C.S.: 531210

BMW Insurance Services Korea Co. Ltd. **(1)**
16F State Tower Namsan 100 Toegye-Ro, Jung-gu, Seoul, 04631, Korea (South)
Tel.: (82) 16617301
Web Site: https://www.bmwisk.co.kr
N.A.I.C.S.: 524210

BMW Italia S.p.A. **(1)**
Via Della Unione Europea 1, 20097, San Donato Milanese, Italy **(100%)**
Tel.: (39) 025 161 0111
Web Site: https://www.bmw.it
Sales Range: $75-99.9 Million
Emp.: 250
BMW Products Marketing
N.A.I.C.S.: 423110

BMW Japan Corp. **(1)**
1-9-2 Gran Tokyo South Tower Marunouchi, Chiyoda-ku, Tokyo, 100-6622, Japan **(100%)**
Tel.: (81) 120201438
Web Site: http://www.bmw.co.jp
Automobile Whslr
N.A.I.C.S.: 423110
Peter Kronschnabl *(Pres)*

BMW Kundenbetreuung **(1)**
Kundenbetreuung, 80788, Munich, Germany **(100%)**
Tel.: (49) 1802324252
Web Site: http://www.bmw.com
Sales Range: $200-249.9 Million
Emp.: 550
Automobile Mfr & Distr
N.A.I.C.S.: 336110

BMW Lease (Malaysia) Sdn. Bhd. **(1)**
2nd floor 3501Teknokrat 5, Cyberjaya, 63000, Selangor, Malaysia
Tel.: (60) 327 307 888
Web Site: https://www.bmwgroup.com
Leasing & Closed-End Leasing Services
N.A.I.C.S.: 522299

Subsidiary (Domestic):

BMW Credit (Malaysia) Sdn Bhd **(2)**
Suite 7-7 Level 7 Wisma UOA Damansara II No 6 Jalan Changkat Semantan, Damansara Heights, 50490, Kuala Lumpur, Malaysia
Tel.: (60) 327307888
Financial Services
N.A.I.C.S.: 522390

Bayerische Motoren Werke
Aktiengesellschaft—(Continued)

BMW Leasing GmbH (1)
Heidemannstr 164, Munich, 80787, Germany
Tel.: (49) 89 3184 2137
Web Site: http://www.bmw.de
Sales Range: $350-399.9 Million
Emp.: 700
Automotive Financial Leasing Services
N.A.I.C.S.: 522220
Hans-Juergen Cohrs (Gen Mgr)

BMW M GmbH (1)
Daimlerstr 19, Hochbruck, 85748, Garching, Germany
Tel.: (49) 89125016016
Web Site: https://www.bmw-m.com
N.A.I.C.S.: 332510

BMW M GmbH Gesellschaft fur individuelle Automobile (1)
Preussenstrasse 45, 80809, Munich, Germany
Tel.: (49) 89 329030
Automotive Distr
N.A.I.C.S.: 423110

BMW Madrid S.L. (1)
Avda Burgos 133, 28050, Madrid, Spain
Tel.: (34) 91 335 1900
Web Site: https://www.bmw.madrid
Used Vehicle Distr
N.A.I.C.S.: 441120

BMW Malta Ltd. (1)
5th Floor Development House St Anne Street, Floriana, FRN 9010, Malta
Tel.: (356) 23162000
Web Site: http://www.bmw.com.mt
Automobile Parts Mfr
N.A.I.C.S.: 336110

BMW Manufacturing (Thailand) Co., Ltd. (1)
7/201 Moo 6 Amata City Industrial Estate Mabyangporn, Pluak Daeng, Rayong, 21140, Thailand
Tel.: (66) 23058888
Automobile Parts Mfr
N.A.I.C.S.: 336110

BMW Manufacturing Industria de Motos da Amazonia Ltda. (1)
Avenida Torquato Tapajos Number 4 010 Warehouses 1 & 2, Manaus, 69093-018, AM, Brazil
Tel.: (55) 8007073578
N.A.I.C.S.: 332510

BMW Maschinenfabrik Spandau GmbH (1)
Am Juliusstrum 14, 13599, Berlin, Germany (100%)
Tel.: (49) 33962250
Web Site: http://www.bmw.ag
Mfr of BMW Automobiles
N.A.I.C.S.: 336110

BMW Nederland B.V. (1)
Einsteinlaan 5, 2289 CC, Rijswijk, Netherlands (100%)
Tel.: (31) 800 099 2234
Web Site: https://www.bmw.nl
Sales Range: $800-899.9 Million
Emp.: 140
Marketing of BMW Products
N.A.I.C.S.: 423110

BMW New Zealand Ltd. (1)
7 Pacific Rise, PO Box 9510, 1149, Auckland, Mount Wellington, New Zealand (100%)
Tel.: (64) 95736999
Web Site: http://www.bmw.co.nz
Rev.: $18,210
Emp.: 55
Marketing of BMW Products
N.A.I.C.S.: 423110
Nina Englert (Mng Dir)

BMW Norge AS (1)
Rolfsbuktveien 4A, 1364, Fornebu, Norway
Tel.: (47) 6 781 8500
Web Site: https://www.bmw.no
Automobile Parts Mfr
N.A.I.C.S.: 336110

BMW Northern Europe AB (1)
Vetenskapsvagen 10, PO Box 775, 191 38,

Sollentuna, Sweden
Tel.: (46) 84706000
Automobile Parts Mfr
N.A.I.C.S.: 336110

BMW Overseas Enterprises N. V. (1)
Einsteinlaan 5, Rijswijk, 2289 CC, Netherlands
Tel.: (31) 704133222
Web Site: http://www.bmw.nl
Emp.: 200
Financial Management Services
N.A.I.C.S.: 523999
Menno Benjert (Office Mgr)

BMW Portugal Lda (1)
Lagoas Park Ed 11 - 2nd Floor, 2740-244, Porto Salvo, Portugal
Tel.: (351) 808200807
Web Site: http://www.bmw.pt
Automobile Mfr
N.A.I.C.S.: 336110

BMW SA/NV (1)
Industriepark De Vliet Lodderstraat 16, 2880, Bornem, Belgium
Tel.: (32) 38909711
Web Site: http://www.bmw.be
Sales Range: $50-74.9 Million
Emp.: 250
Automobile Manufacturing
N.A.I.C.S.: 336110
Philipp von Sahr (Head-Branch Association-East)

BMW Slovenska Republika s.r.o. (1)
Karadzicova 8, 821 08, Bratislava, Slovakia
Tel.: (421) 26 020 2080
Web Site: https://www.bmw.sk
Automobile Parts Mfr
N.A.I.C.S.: 336110
Milan Koza (Mgr-Sls)

BMW Sverige AB (1)
Vetenskapsvagen 10, PO Box 775, 19138, Sollentuna, Sweden (100%)
Tel.: (46) 8 470 6000
Web Site: https://www.bmw.se
Emp.: 100
Automobile Mfr & Exporter
N.A.I.C.S.: 336110
Christer Stahl (Mng Dir)

BMW Sydney Pty. Ltd. (1)
65 Craigend Street, Rushcutters Bay, North Sydney, 2011, NSW, Australia
Tel.: (61) 29 334 4555
Web Site: https://www.bmwsydney.com.au
Automobile Parts Mfr
N.A.I.C.S.: 336110

BMW de Mexico, S. A. de C. V. (1)
Paseo de los Tamarindos No 100-501 Colonia Bosques de las Lomas, 05120, Mexico, Mexico
Tel.: (52) 55 9140 8700
Web Site: http://www.bmw.com.mx
Automobile Whslr
N.A.I.C.S.: 423110

BMW of North America, LLC (1)
300 Chestnut Rdg Rd, Woodcliff Lake, NJ 07675 (100%)
Tel.: (201) 307-4000
Web Site: http://www.bmwgroupna.com
Sales Range: $350-399.9 Million
Emp.: 900
BMW Automobiles, Motorcycles, Parts & Accessories Mfr & Sales
N.A.I.C.S.: 423110
Peter Miles (VP-Special Projects-Americas)

Subsidiary (Domestic):

BMW (US) Holding Corporation (2)
1100 N Market St Ste 780, Wilmington, DE 19801-1297
Tel.: (201) 307-4000
Holding Company
N.A.I.C.S.: 333310
Stefan Richmann (CFO)

Subsidiary (Domestic):

BMW of Manhattan Inc. (3)
555 W 57th St, New York, NY 10019-2925
Tel.: (212) 586-2269
Web Site: http://www.bmwnyc.com
Rev.: $25,700,000
Emp.: 204

Automobiles New & Used
N.A.I.C.S.: 441110
Jeff Falk (CFO)

Westchester BMW Inc. (3)
543 Tarrytown Rd, White Plains, NY 10607-1315 (100%)
Tel.: (914) 761-5555
Web Site: http://www.westchesterbmw.com
Emp.: 121
Car Dealership
N.A.I.C.S.: 441110
Andre Accurso (Mgr-Sls)

Subsidiary (Domestic):

BMW Bank of North America Inc. (2)
2735 E Parleys Way Ste 301, Salt Lake City, UT 84109
Tel.: (801) 461-6500
Web Site: http://www.bmwusa.com
Sales Range: $25-49.9 Million
Emp.: 35
Financial Services
N.A.I.C.S.: 522299

Subsidiary (Non-US):

BMW Canada Inc. (2)
50 Ultimate Drive, Richmond Hill, L4S 0C8, ON, Canada (100%)
Tel.: (905) 683-1200
Web Site: https://www.bmw.ca
Sales Range: $75-99.9 Million
Emp.: 250
Marketing of BMW Products
N.A.I.C.S.: 423110
Kevin Marcotte (Natl Mgr-M, i & Luxury Class Brands)

Subsidiary (Domestic):

BMW Financial Services NA, LLC (2)
300 Chestnut Rdg Rd, Woodcliff Lake, NJ 07677-7739
Tel.: (201) 307-4000
Web Site: http://www.bmwusa.com
Rev.: $83,000,000
Emp.: 400
Automobile Finance Leasing
N.A.I.C.S.: 522220

BMW Leasing Corp. (2)
PO Box 3608, Dublin, OH 43016-3606 (100%)
Web Site: http://www.fs.bmwusa.com
Finance Leasing of Automobiles
N.A.I.C.S.: 532112

BMW Manufacturing Co., LLC (2)
1400 Hwy 101 S, Greer, SC 29651-6731 (100%)
Tel.: (864) 989-6000
Web Site: http://www.bmwusfactory.com
Rev.: $348,700,000
Emp.: 5,000
Automobile Assembly Including Specialty Automobiles
N.A.I.C.S.: 336110
Barry Richardson (Mgr-Project Mgmt)

BMW US Capital, LLC (2)
300 Chestnut Ridge Rd, Woodcliff Lake, NJ 07677-1227
Tel.: (201) 307-4000
Financial Management Services
N.A.I.C.S.: 523999

Designworks USA (2)
2201 Corporate Ctr, Newbury Park, CA 91320-1421
Tel.: (805) 499-9590
Web Site: http://www.bmwgroupdesignworks.com
Sales Range: $25-49.9 Million
Emp.: 115
Designing Services For Ship Boat Machine & Product
N.A.I.C.S.: 541330
Holger Hampf (Pres)

Bavaria Wirtschaftsagentur GmbH (1)
Knorrstrasse 147, 80788, Munich, Germany (100%)
Tel.: (49) 8938226041
Insurance Broker Firm
N.A.I.C.S.: 524298

Subsidiary (Domestic):

Bavaria Lloyd Reisebuero GmbH (2)
Heidemannstr 170, 80939, Munich, Germany (51%)
Tel.: (49) 893 822 040
Web Site: https://www.bavaria-lloyd.de
Sales Range: $10-24.9 Million
Emp.: 25
Travel Agency
N.A.I.C.S.: 561510

Plant (Domestic):

Bayerische Motoren Werke Aktiengesellschaft - Berlin Plant (1)
Am Juliusturm 14-38, 13599, Berlin, Germany
Tel.: (49) 30 33 96 20 20
Automobile Mfr
N.A.I.C.S.: 336110

Bayerische Motoren Werke Aktiengesellschaft - Leipzig Plant (1)
BMW Allee 1, 04349, Leipzig, Germany
Tel.: (49) 341 445 0
Web Site: http://www.bmw-plant-leipzig.com
Automobile Mfr
N.A.I.C.S.: 336110

Bayerische Motoren Werke Aktiengesellschaft - Munich Plant (1)
Petuelring 130, 80809, Munich, Germany
Tel.: (49) 893820
Web Site: http://www.bmw-werk-muenchen.de
Automobile Mfr
N.A.I.C.S.: 336110

Bayerische Motoren Werke Aktiengesellschaft - Wackersdorf Plant (1)
Oskar-von-Miller-Strasse 21, 92442, Wackersdorf, Germany
Tel.: (49) 94316307806
Automobile Mfr
N.A.I.C.S.: 336110

Content4all B.V. (1)
Derde Morgen 11, 5233 NL, 's-Hertogenbosch, Netherlands
Tel.: (31) 51800299
Web Site: https://content4all.nl
N.A.I.C.S.: 513210

Digital Charging Solution Corp. (1)
Rosenstrasse 18-19, 10178, Berlin, Germany
Tel.: (49) 3083799779
Web Site: https://digitalchargingsolutions.com
N.A.I.C.S.: 221114
Jorg Reimann (CEO)

Digital Charging Solutions GmbH (1)
Brunnenstrasse 19-21, 10119, Berlin, Germany
Tel.: (49) 8941207773
Web Site: http://www.digitalchargingsolutions.com
Electronic Equipment Services
N.A.I.C.S.: 811310
Jorg Reimann (Mng Dir)

DriveNow Belgium S.p.r.l. (1)
Buro and Design Center Esplanade 1, PO Box 57, 1020, Brussels, Belgium
Tel.: (32) 80060163
Automobile Parts Mfr
N.A.I.C.S.: 336110
Dominique Cornut (Mgr-Comm & Mktg)

DriveNow Italy S.r.l. (1)
Via Carlo Ottavio Cornaggia 16, 20123, Milan, Italy
Tel.: (39) 0294754881
Automobile Parts Mfr
N.A.I.C.S.: 336110

IDEALworks GmbH (1)
Riesstrabe 22, 80992, Munich, Germany
Tel.: (49) 89262008381
Web Site: https://idealworks.com
Software Development Services
N.A.I.C.S.: 541511

Oy BMW Suomi AB (1)
Ayritie 8c, 01510, Vantaa, Finland
Tel.: (358) 20 734 5920
Web Site: https://www.bmw.fi
Automobile Parts Mfr
N.A.I.C.S.: 336110
Tapio Kontkanen (Dir-Aftersls)

Park Lane Ltd. (1)
Unit 9 Alton Business Centre Omega Park,
Alton, GU34 2YU, United Kingdom
Tel.: (44) 1420544300
Web Site: http://www.parklaneuk.com
Automobile Parts Mfr
N.A.I.C.S.: 336110
Roland Dane *(Mng Dir)*

ParkNow Austria GmbH (1)
Rinnbockstrasse 3, 1030, Vienna, Austria
Tel.: (43) 800656688
Web Site: http://at.park-now.com
Parking Application Services
N.A.I.C.S.: 812930

Pt Bmw Indonesia (1)
The Plaza 21st Floor Jalan M H Thamrin
Kav 28-30, Jakarta, 10350, Indonesia
Tel.: (62) 212 992 3000
Web Site: https://www.bmw.co.id
Automobile Parts Mfr
N.A.I.C.S.: 336110
Bayu Riyanto *(VP-Sls)*

Rolls-Royce Motor Cars Limited (1)
The Drive Westhampnett, Chichester, PO18
0SH, West Sussex, United Kingdom
Tel.: (44) 1243525700
Web Site: https://www.rolls-
    roycemotorcars.com
N.A.I.C.S.: 332510

Rolls-Royce Motor Cars NA LLC (1)
300 Chestnut Ridge Rd, Woodcliff Lake, NJ
07677
Tel.: (201) 307-4490
Web Site: https://www.rolls-
    roycemotorcars.com
N.A.I.C.S.: 332510

**SGL Automotive Carbon Fibers
GmbH & Co. KG** (1)
Anton-Ditt-Bogen 5, 80939, Munich,
Germany (49%)
Tel.: (49) 89 316 0568 0
Web Site: http://www.sgl-acf.com
Non-Crimp Carbon Fiber Fabrics Mfr
N.A.I.C.S.: 335991
Andreas Wullner *(Mng Dir)*

Swindon Pressings Limited (1)
Bridge End Road Stratton St Margaret,
Swindon, SN3 4PE, Wiltshire, United King-
dom
Tel.: (44) 8458466003
Automobile Parts Mfr
N.A.I.C.S.: 336110

BAYERISCHE STADTE- UND WOHNUNGSBAU GMBH & CO. KG

Lilienthalallee 25, Munich, 80939,
Germany
Tel.: (49) 8932358555
Web Site: http://www.bayerische-
    staedtebau.de
Sales Range: $25-49.9 Million
Emp.: 100
Investor
N.A.I.C.S.: 523160
Alfons Doblinger *(Mng Dir)*

Subsidiaries:

Monachia AG (1)
Nymphenburger Strasse 48, 80335, Mu-
nich, Germany
Tel.: (49) 89126910
Web Site: http://www.monachia.de
Management & Trading of Real Estate
Property & Capital Assets
N.A.I.C.S.: 531311

BAYERNLAND EG

Breslauer Str 406, 90471, Nurem-
berg, Germany
Tel.: (49) 91141400   De
Web Site: http://www.bayernland.de
Year Founded: 1972
Sales Range: $550-599.9 Million
Emp.: 419
Dairy Product Butter & Cheese Distr
N.A.I.C.S.: 424430
Gerhard M. Meier *(Mng Dir)*

Subsidiaries:

Bergland GmbH (1)
Hauptstrasse 71, 88161, Lindenberg im All-
gau, Germany (50%)
Tel.: (49) 83815050
Sales Range: $25-49.9 Million
Emp.: 150
Cheese Mfr
N.A.I.C.S.: 311513

BAYERNLB HOLDING AG

Brienner Strasse 18, 80333, Munich,
Germany
Tel.: (49) 89217101
Web Site: http://www.bayernlb.de
Year Founded: 1884
Sales Range: $1-4.9 Billion
Emp.: 7,133
Financial Management & Investment
Banking Services
N.A.I.C.S.: 523999
Edgar Zoller *(Deputy CEO &
Member-Mgmt Bd)*

Subsidiaries:

**ADEM Allgemeine Dienstleistungen
fur Engineering und Management
GmbH** (1)
Schwarzwaldstr 39, 76137, Karlsruhe, Ger-
many
Tel.: (49) 72 1921393
Financial Management Services
N.A.I.C.S.: 523999

**Aero Lloyd Flugreisen GmbH & Co.
Luftverkehrs-KG** (1)
Lessingstr 7-9, 61440, Oberursel, Germany
Tel.: (49) 6171 62500
Holding Company
N.A.I.C.S.: 551112

Bauland GmbH (1)
Elsenheimerstr 50, 80687, Munich, Ger-
many
Tel.: (49) 89 54419 0
Web Site: http://www.bauland.com
Emp.: 10
Holding Company
N.A.I.C.S.: 551112
Florean Leab *(Gen Mgr)*

**Bavaria Immobilien-Beteiligungs-
Gesellschaft mbH & Co. Objekt Furth
KG** (1)
Brienner Str 18, 80333, Munich, Germany
Tel.: (49) 89 2171 22076
Holding Company
N.A.I.C.S.: 551112
Johannes-Jorg Riegler *(CEO)*

**Bayerische Landesbank Immobilien-
Beteiligungs-Gesellschaft mbH & Co.
KG** (1)
Karlstrasse 68, 80335, Munich, Germany
Tel.: (49) 89442334000
Web Site: http://www.bayernimmo.de
Investment Banking Services
N.A.I.C.S.: 523150
Bernd Mayer *(Chm)*

**Bayern Bankett Gastronomie
GmbH** (1)
Arnulfstrasse 50, 80335, Munich, Germany
Tel.: (49) 89 2171 24600
Holding Company
N.A.I.C.S.: 551112

Bayern Card-Services GmbH (1)
Barer Strasse 24, 80333, Munich, Germany
Tel.: (49) 899040760
Web Site: http://www.bayerncard.de
Banking Credit Card Services
N.A.I.C.S.: 522210
Carsten Walter *(Head-Chargeback & Proj-
ect Mgr)*

**Bayern Corporate Services
GmbH** (1)
Arnulfstrasse 50, 80335, Munich, Germany
Tel.: (49) 89442336110
Web Site: http://www.bayerncs.de
Building Construction Services
N.A.I.C.S.: 236220

BayernInvest Luxembourg S.A. (1)
6B rue Gabriel Lippmann, 5365, Munsbach,
Luxembourg
Tel.: (352) 2826240
Web Site: http://www.bayerninvest.lu
Investment Fund Services
N.A.I.C.S.: 525910
Jan Schoener *(Mgr-Risk)*

BayernLB (1)
Brienner Strasse Str 18, Munich, 80333,
Germany
Tel.: (49) 89217101
Web Site: http://www.bayernlb.de
Sales Range: $1-4.9 Billion
Emp.: 5,000
Financial Management & Investment Bank-
ing Services
N.A.I.C.S.: 523999

Branch (Non-US):

**Bayerische Landesbank
Girozentrale** (2)
Moor House, 13/14 Appold St, London,
EC2Y 5ET, United Kingdom
Tel.: (44) 2079555100
Web Site: http://www.bayernlb.de
Sales Range: $75-99.9 Million
Emp.: 140
International Banking
N.A.I.C.S.: 522299

Subsidiary (Non-US):

**Bayerische Landesbank International
S.A.** (2)
3 Rue Jean Monnet, L 2180, Luxembourg,
Luxembourg (100%)
Tel.: (352) 2000424341
Web Site: http://www.bayernlux.lu
Sales Range: $75-99.9 Million
Emp.: 200
International Banking; Securities Trading
N.A.I.C.S.: 522299

Subsidiary (Domestic):

**Bayerische
Landesbodenkreditanstalt** (2)
Prienner Str 22, 80333, Munich,
Germany (100%)
Tel.: (49) 89217128003
Web Site: http://www.labobayern.de
Sales Range: $100-124.9 Million
Emp.: 210
Johannes-Jorg Riegler *(Mng Dir)*

**BayernInvest Kapitalanlagegesell-
schaft mbH** (2)
Karlstrasse 35, 80333, Munich, Germany
Tel.: (49) 89 54 850 0
Web Site: http://www.bayerninvest.de
Emp.: 170
Holding Company
N.A.I.C.S.: 551112

BayernLB Capital Partner GmbH (2)
Ottostr 21, 80333, Munich, Germany
Tel.: (49) 89 552563 0
Web Site: http://www.bayernlb-cp.de
Emp.: 5
Holding Company
N.A.I.C.S.: 551112
Elmer Mied *(Mng Dir)*

Deutsche Kreditbank AG (2)
Taubenstrasse 7-9, 10117, Berlin,
Germany (100%)
Tel.: (49) 3012030000
Web Site: http://www.dkb.de
Sales Range: $700-749.9 Million
Emp.: 1,200
Banking Services
N.A.I.C.S.: 523150

Subsidiary (Domestic):

DKB Finance GmbH (3)
Friedrichstrasse 60, 10117, Berlin, 10117,
Germany
Tel.: (49) 30 20155886
Web Site: http://www.dkb.de
Emp.: 10
Holding Company
N.A.I.C.S.: 551112
Axel Bublitz *(Mng Dir)*

**DKB Grundbesitzvermittlung
GmbH** (3)

Taubenstr 44-45, 10117, Berlin, Germany
Tel.: (49) 30 12030 7661
Web Site: http://www.dkb-grund.de
Holding Company
N.A.I.C.S.: 551112

Subsidiary (Domestic):

**LBS Bayerische
Landesbausparkasse** (2)
Arnulfstrasse 50, 80335, Munich,
Germany (100%)
Tel.: (49) 1803114477
Sales Range: $350-399.9 Million
Emp.: 700
N.A.I.C.S.: 522299

**Berchtesgaden International Resort
Betriebs GmbH** (1)
Hintereck 1, 83471, Berchtesgaden, Ger-
many
Tel.: (49) 8652 97 55 0
Hotel & Resort Management Services
N.A.I.C.S.: 721110

**BestLife 3 International GmbH & Co.
KG** (1)
Innere Wiener Str 17, 81667, Munich,
81667, Germany
Tel.: (49) 89 4890820
Holding Company
N.A.I.C.S.: 551112

**Cottbuser Energieverwaltungsgesell-
schaft mbH** (1)
Karl-Liebknecht-Strasse 130, 03046, Cott-
bus, Germany
Tel.: (49) 355351101
Holding Company
N.A.I.C.S.: 551112

DKB Code Factory GmbH (1)
Hardenbergstrasse 32, 10623, Berlin, Ger-
many
Tel.: (49) 30120303898
Web Site: http://www.dkbcodefactory.com
Computer Software Services
N.A.I.C.S.: 541511
Arnulf Keese *(Mng Dir)*

DKB IT-Services GmbH (1)
Herzbergstr 56-59, 10365, Berlin, Germany
Tel.: (49) 30 120 30 4301
Web Site: http://www.dkbatwin.de
Holding Company
N.A.I.C.S.: 551112

**DKB Immobilien Beteiligungs
GmbH** (1)
Jagerallee 23, Jagervorstadt, 14469, Pots-
dam, Germany
Tel.: (49) 331 2903560
Holding Company
N.A.I.C.S.: 551112

DKB Service GmbH (1)
Jagerallee 23, 14469, Potsdam, Germany
Tel.: (49) 3012030000
Web Site: http://www.dkb.de
Commercial Banking Services
N.A.I.C.S.: 522110

DKB Wohnen GmbH (1)
Kronenstrasse 8/10, 10117, Berlin, Ger-
many
Tel.: (49) 331 290 5005
Financial Investment Services
N.A.I.C.S.: 523940

**Degg's Immobilienprojektentwicklung
GmbH & Co. Einkaufspassage
KG** (1)
Klaus-Bumgerg- st 1, 45141, Dusseldorf,
Germany
Tel.: (49) 201820810
Holding Company
N.A.I.C.S.: 551112

Euro Ingatlan Center Kft. (1)
Hajogyari-sziget 307, 1033, Budapest, Hun-
gary
Tel.: (36) 6 1 430 2360
Financial Management Services
N.A.I.C.S.: 523999

**Exter-Real Ingatlanforgalmazasi Kor-
latolt Felelossegu Tarsasag** (1)
Kassak Lajos Utca 18, Budapest, Hungary
Tel.: (36) 12687175
Financial Management Services

BayernLB Holding AG—(Continued)
N.A.I.C.S.: 523999

FMP Forderungsmanagement Pots-
dam GmbH **(1)**
Jagerallee 23, 14469, Potsdam, Germany
Tel.: (49) 33188998877
Web Site: http://www.fmp-potsdam.de
Financial & Insurance Services
N.A.I.C.S.: 524210
Michael Schneider (Mng Dir)

Fischer & Funke Gesellschaft fur Per-
sonaldienstleistungen mbH **(1)**
Goethestr 4, 96450, Coburg, Germany
Tel.: (49) 9561 7424 0
Web Site: http://www.fischerundfunke.de
Temporary Help Service
N.A.I.C.S.: 561320

GDF Gesellschaft fur dentale Forsc-
hung und Innovationen GmbH **(1)**
Dieselstrasse 5-6, 61191, Rosbach vor der
Hohe, Germany
Tel.: (49) 6003 814 125
Web Site: http://www.gdfmbh.com
Dental Research & Development Services
N.A.I.C.S.: 541715
Thomas Niem Wolf Zientz (Mng Dir)

German Centre For Industry And
Trade Shanghai Co. Ltd. **(1)**
88 Ke Yuan Road, Zhang Jiang Hi-
Techpark, 201203, Shanghai, China
Tel.: (86) 2128986888
Web Site:
http://www.germancentreshanghai.com
Meeting Room Leasing Services
N.A.I.C.S.: 531120
Matthias Muller (Gen Mgr)

Global Format GmbH & Co. KG **(1)**
Brienner Strasse 24, 80333, Munich, Ger-
many
Tel.: (49) 89217126288
Web Site: http://www.global-format.de
Global Format Application & Financial Re-
port Services
N.A.I.C.S.: 518210
Lutz R. Krull (Mng Dir)

Hormannshofer Fassaden GmbH &
Co. Halle KG **(1)**
Reideburger Str 55, 06116, Halle, Germany
Tel.: (49) 345 56993 0
Financial Management Services
N.A.I.C.S.: 523999

Hormannshofer Fassaden Sud GmbH
& Co. KG **(1)**
Schwabenstrasse 114, 87616, Marktober-
dorf, Germany
Tel.: (49) 8342 96270
Web Site: http://www.hoermannshofer.de
Financial Management Services
N.A.I.C.S.: 523999

LB Immobilienbewertungsgesellschaft
mbH **(1)**
Main Tower Neue Mainzer Strasse 52-58,
60311, Frankfurt am Main, Germany
Tel.: (49) 69920345700
Web Site: http://www.lb-immowert.de
Sales Range: $50-74.9 Million
Emp.: 70
Real Estate Services
N.A.I.C.S.: 531390

MB Holding GmbH **(1)**
Dutendorfer Strasse 5-7, 91487, Vesten-
bergsgreuth, Germany
Tel.: (49) 9163 88 0
Web Site: http://www.martin-bauer-
group.com
Emp.: 1,000
Holding Company
N.A.I.C.S.: 551112

MRG Massnahmetrager Munchen-
Riem GmbH **(1)**
Paul-Henri-Spaak-Strasse 5, 81829, Mu-
nich, Germany
Tel.: (49) 89 945 500 0
Web Site: http://www.mrg-gmbh.de
Financial Management Services
N.A.I.C.S.: 523999

Mediport Venture Fonds Zwei
GmbH **(1)**

Friedrichstr 81, Berlin, 10117, Germany
Tel.: (49) 30 720 141 0
Financial Management Services
N.A.I.C.S.: 523999

RSA Entgrat- u. Trenn-Systeme
Verwaltungs-GmbH **(1)**
Adolph Kolping strasse 14, 58513, Schw-
erte, Germany **(100%)**
Tel.: (49) 23519955
Industrial Machinery Mfr
N.A.I.C.S.: 333310
Thomas Berg (Gen Mgr)

RSA Systemes Ebavurage et Tron-
connage S.A.R.L. **(1)**
8 Zone Industrielle Gutenberg, 57200, Sarreguemines, France
Tel.: (33) 3 87 87 27 21
Industrial Machinery Mfr
N.A.I.C.S.: 333310

Real I.S. AG Gesellschaft fur Immo-
bilien Assetmanagement **(1)**
Innere Wiener Str 17, 81667, Munich, Ger-
many
Tel.: (49) 894890820
Web Site: http://www.realisag.de
Property Investment Services
N.A.I.C.S.: 531390
Markus Weinert (Dir-Fund Mgmt)

Real I.S. Management Hamburg
GmbH **(1)**
Heegbarg 30, 22391, Hamburg, 22391,
Germany
Tel.: (49) 40 60606 0
Real Estate Management Services
N.A.I.C.S.: 531390

Real I.S. Management SA **(1)**
3 rue Jean Monnet, 2180, Luxembourg,
Luxembourg
Tel.: (352) 264 32 392
Financial Management Services
N.A.I.C.S.: 523999

Schutz Group GmbH & Co. KG **(1)**
Schutzstrasse 12, Selters, 56242, Hessen,
Germany
Tel.: (49) 2626770
Web Site: http://www.schuetz.net
Industrial Packaging Services
N.A.I.C.S.: 561910
Marion Dohle (Chm)

Subsidiary (US):

SCHUTZ Container Systems,
INC. **(2)**
2105 S Wilkinson Way, Perrysburg, OH
43551
Tel.: (419) 872-2477
Web Site: http://www.schuetz.net
Container Systems
N.A.I.C.S.: 321920

Sud-Fassaden GmbH **(1)**
Schafflerstrasse 10, 86343, Konigsbrunn,
Germany
Tel.: (49) 82 31 96 84 0
Web Site: http://www.sued-fassaden.de
Building Construction Services
N.A.I.C.S.: 236220

gewerbegrund Airport GmbH & Co.
Hallbergmoos KG **(1)**
Arnulfstr 39, Munich, 80636, Bavaria, Ger-
many
Tel.: (49) 811 2813
Commercial Real Estate Consulting Ser-
vices
N.A.I.C.S.: 531210

gewerbegrund Airport GmbH & Co.
Schwaig KG **(1)**
Nymphenburger Strasse 3, 80335, Munich,
Bayern, Germany
Tel.: (49) 89 55257
Real Estate Consulting Service
N.A.I.C.S.: 531390

BAYHORSE SILVER INC.
2501 4398 Buchanan Street,
Burnaby, V5C 6R7, BC, Canada
Tel.: (604) 684-3394
Web Site:
https://www.bayhorsesilver.com
BHS—(DEU)

Assets: $1,531,096
Liabilities: $2,951,364
Net Worth: ($1,420,268)
Earnings: ($2,421,364)
Fiscal Year-end: 12/31/20
Silver Mining Services
N.A.I.C.S.: 212220
Donna M. Moroney (Sec)

BAYLEYS CORPORATION LIM-
ITED
30 Gaunt Street, Auckland, New Zea-
land
Tel.: (64) 93756868
Web Site: https://www.bayleys.co.nz
Emp.: 100
Real Estate Agency
N.A.I.C.S.: 531210
Mike Bayley (Mng Dir)

Subsidiaries:

McGrath Limited **(1)**
55 Pyrmont Street, Pyrmont, 2009, NSW,
Australia
Tel.: (61) 293863333
Web Site: http://www.mcgrath.com.au
Rev.: $21,595,887
Assets: $23,287,260
Liabilities: $7,462,607
Net Worth: $15,824,653
Earnings: $879,407
Emp.: 283
Fiscal Year-end: 06/30/2024
Real Estate Agency
N.A.I.C.S.: 531210
John McGrath (Founder, CEO & Mng Dir)

Subsidiary (Domestic):

McGrath Sales Paddington Pty
Ltd **(2)**
195 Given Terrace, Paddington, Brisbane,
4064, QLD, Australia
Tel.: (61) 730881555
Real Estate Prorperty Leasing Services
N.A.I.C.S.: 531110
Charles Higgins (Sls Mgr)

BAYLIN TECHNOLOGIES INC.
503-4711 Yonge Street, North York,
M2N 6K8, ON, Canada
Tel.: (416) 805-9127 ON
Web Site: https://www.baylintech.com
Year Founded: 2013
BYL—(TSX)
Rev.: $117,328,893
Assets: $112,916,519
Liabilities: $67,858,422
Net Worth: $45,058,096
Earnings: ($15,009,417)
Emp.: 819
Fiscal Year-end: 12/31/19
Antenna Mfr
N.A.I.C.S.: 334220
Harold Morton Wolkin (Vice Chm)

Subsidiaries:

Advantech Wireless Technologies
(USA) Inc. **(1)**
4908 Golden Pkwy Ste 400, Buford, GA
30518
Tel.: (470) 210-5717
Web Site: https://advantechwireless.com
Telecommunications Equipment Mfr
N.A.I.C.S.: 334290

Baylin Technologies Do Brazil Produ-
tos De Telecommunicacoes Ltda. **(1)**
Rua Capricornio 100 Conde 1, Alphaville,
Barueri, 06473-005, Brazil
Tel.: (55) 114 326 6200
Telecommunication Servicesb
N.A.I.C.S.: 517810

Galtronics Canada Co., Ltd. **(1)**
200A Terence Matthews Crescent, Kanata,
K2M 2C6, ON, Canada
Tel.: (613) 457-5126
Web Site: https://gtottawa.com
Research & Development Services
N.A.I.C.S.: 541715

Galtronics Corporation Ltd. **(1)**

Tsivonit Street 1 Industrial Zone, PO Box
1589, Tiberias, 14115, Israel
Tel.: (972) 4 673 9777
Web Site: http://www.galtronics.com
Electronic Products Mfr
N.A.I.C.S.: 334419

Subsidiary (US):

Galtronics USA Inc **(2)**
1131 W Warner Rd Ste 109, Tempe, AZ
85284
Tel.: (480) 496-5100
Electronic Product Distr
N.A.I.C.S.: 423690
Simon Yang (Gen Mgr-Galtronics R&D Cen-
tre of Excellence)

Galtronics Electronics (Wuxi) Co.,
Ltd. **(1)**
No 1 XiShi Road, Wuxi New District, Wuxi,
214028, Jiangsu, China
Tel.: (86) 5108 866 5500
Telecommunication Servicesb
N.A.I.C.S.: 517111

BAYMOUNT INCORPORATED
130 Adelaide Street West Suite 1901,
Toronto, M5H 3P5, ON, Canada
Tel.: (416) 843-2881
Casino & Gaming Services
N.A.I.C.S.: 713210
J. Graham Simmonds (Founder, Chm
& CEO)

BAYN EUROPE AB
Hornsgatan 79, 118 49, Stockholm,
Sweden
Tel.: (46) 8 613 28 88
Web Site:
http://www.bayneurope.com
Rev.: $358,289
Assets: $1,305,197
Liabilities: $354,951
Net Worth: $950,246
Earnings: ($1,148,306)
Emp.: 11
Fiscal Year-end: 12/31/18
Natural & Healthy Sweetener Mfr
N.A.I.C.S.: 311999
Lucy Dahlgren (Founder)

BAYO
Aerodrome d'Auxerre- Branches,
89380, Appoigny, France
Tel.: (33) 386482022
Web Site: http://bayo.com
Rev.: $21,500,000
Emp.: 42
N.A.I.C.S.: 423830
Odile Rebesche (Mgr-Fin)

BAYOU HOLZWERKSTOFFE
GMBH
Siemensstrasse 2, 97855, Lengfurt,
Germany
Tel.: (49) 939587770
Web Site: http://www.bayou-holz.com
Rev.: $16,782,562
Emp.: 14
Plywood Distr
N.A.I.C.S.: 423310
Bekir Nakic (Co-CEO)

BAYPORT MANAGEMENT LIM-
ITED
3rd Floor Ebene Skies Rue de L Insti-
tut, Ebene, Mauritius
Tel.: (230) 465 1605
Web Site:
http://www.bayportfinance.com
Year Founded: 2001
Rev.: $236,827,000
Assets: $1,225,839,000
Liabilities: $995,441,000
Net Worth: $230,398,000
Earnings: $44,962,000
Fiscal Year-end: 12/31/18
Financial Services
N.A.I.C.S.: 523999

Grant Kurland *(Co-CEO)*

Subsidiaries:

Bayport Fimsa S.A.S   **(1)**
Calle 71 N 10 - 68 Piso 2, Cundinamarca,
Bogota, Colombia
Tel.: (57) 17458920
Web Site: http://www.bayportcolombia.com
Financial Management Services
N.A.I.C.S.: 523999

Bayport Financial Services (T)
Limited   **(1)**
Bayport House 3rd Floor Al Dua Tower New
Bagamoyo Road, Plot 3/12 Regent Estate,
Dar es Salaam, Tanzania
Tel.: (255) 2227714201
Web Site: http://www.bayporttanzania.com
Financial Management Services
N.A.I.C.S.: 523999
Ken Kwaku *(Chm)*

Bayport Financial Services 2010
(Proprietary) Limited   **(1)**
Bayport House 23A 10th Avenue, Rivonia,
Johannesburg, Gauteng, South Africa
Tel.: (27) 861 456 456
Web Site: http://www.bayportsa.com
Financial Management Services
N.A.I.C.S.: 523999
Alfred Ramosedi *(CEO)*

Subsidiary (Domestic):

M-Stores Proprietary Limited   **(2)**
70 Watt St, Edenvale, 1614, South Africa
Tel.: (27) 115656000
Financial Management Services
N.A.I.C.S.: 523999

Bayport Financial Services Ghana
Limited   **(1)**
71 Osu Badu Street Airport West, Accra,
Ghana
Tel.: (233) 302745454
Web Site: http://www.bayportghana.com
Financial Management Services
N.A.I.C.S.: 523999
Kwane Pianim *(Chm)*

Bayport Financial Services
Limited   **(1)**
Plot 68 Independence Avenue, Lusaka,
Zambia
Tel.: (260) 211257243
Web Site: http://www.bayportzambia.com
Financial Management Services
N.A.I.C.S.: 523999
Justin Chola *(CEO)*

Bayport Financial Services Mozam-
bique (MCB), SA   **(1)**
Rua de Franca - Esquina com Avenida
Kennet Kaunda No 19 1 Andar Coop, Ma-
puto, Mozambique
Tel.: (258) 214152601
Financial Management Services
N.A.I.C.S.: 523999
Nuno Quelhas *(Chm)*

Bayport Financial Services Uganda
Limited   **(1)**
Plot 54 Lugogo Bypass, Kampala, Uganda
Tel.: (256) 312764400
Web Site: http://www.bayportuganda.com
Financial Management Services
N.A.I.C.S.: 523999
Charles Mbire *(Chm)*

Consumer Finance Company
Limited   **(1)**
No 212 Block B Addae House Akweteyman
Off the N1 Highway, Accra, Ghana
Tel.: (233) 30 220 0902
Web Site: http://www.cfc-gh.com
Financial Management Services
N.A.I.C.S.: 523999
A. T. D. Okine *(Chm)*

Financiera Fortaleza, S.A de C.V   **(1)**
Prado Norte 550, Lomas de Chapultepec,
11000, Mexico, Mexico
Tel.: (52) 52825353
Web Site:
    http://www.financierafortaleza.com.mx
Financial Management Services
N.A.I.C.S.: 523999

BAYRAK EBT TABAN SANAYI

VE TICARET A.S.
Calislar Street No 24, Adnan Kahveci
Mahallesi, 34528, Istanbul, Turkiye
Tel.: (90) 2124172408
Web Site:
    https://www.bayrakebt.com.tr
Year Founded: 1994
BAYRK—(IST)
Information Technology Services
N.A.I.C.S.: 541512
Turgut Bayrak *(Chm, Gen Mgr &
Mgr)*

BAYRIDGE RESOURCES
CORP.
1480-885 West Georgia St, Vancou-
ver, V6C 3E3, BC, Canada
Tel.: (604) 484-3031   BC
Web Site:
    https://bayridgeresources.com
Year Founded: 2022
BYRRF—(OTCIQ)
Mineral Exploration Services
N.A.I.C.S.: 212390
Charn Deol *(Dir)*

BAYTACARE PHARMACEUTI-
CAL CO., LTD
2 3 Gaoxin District, Jilin, 132013,
China
Tel.: (86) 432 64641900   CN
Web Site: http://www.baytacare.com
Pharmaceutical Products Mfr & Distr
N.A.I.C.S.: 325412
Shaoyan Wang *(Exec Dir)*

BAYTEX ENERGY CORP.
Centennial Place East Tower 2800
520 - 3rd Avenue SW, Calgary, T2P
0R3, AB, Canada
Tel.: (587) 952-3000   AB
Web Site:
    https://www.baytexenergy.com
Year Founded: 2010
BTE—(NYSE)
Rev.: $2,260,042,123
Assets: $3,992,576,413
Liabilities: $1,621,941,803
Net Worth: $2,370,634,611
Earnings: $669,322,679
Emp.: 157
Fiscal Year-end: 12/31/22
Oil & Natural Gas Exploration & Pro-
duction
N.A.I.C.S.: 211120
Julia C. Gwaltney *(Sr VP & Gen Mgr-
Eagle Ford Ops)*

Subsidiaries:

Baytex Energy USA, Inc.   **(1)**
16285 Park Ten Pl Ste 500, Houston, TX
77084
Tel.: (713) 722-6500
Holding Company; Oil & Gas Production
Services
N.A.I.C.S.: 551112

Subsidiary (Domestic):

Ranger Oil Corporation   **(2)**
16285 Park 10 Pl Ste 500, Houston, TX
77084
Tel.: (713) 722-6500
Web Site: http://www.pennvirginia.com
Rev.: $1,145,189,000
Assets: $2,014,207,000
Liabilities: $957,185,000
Net Worth: $1,057,022,000
Earnings: $464,518,000
Emp.: 136
Fiscal Year-end: 12/31/2022
Oil & Gas Exploration & Production Ser-
vices
N.A.I.C.S.: 211120

Subsidiary (Domestic):

Lonestar Resources US Inc.   **(3)**
111 Boland St Ste 301, Fort Worth, TX
76107

Tel.: (817) 921-1889
Web Site: http://www.lonestarresources.com
Oil & Gas Support Services
N.A.I.C.S.: 213112
John Howard Pinkerton *(Chm)*

Penn Virginia MC Energy LLC   **(3)**
Four Radnor Corporate Ctr Ste 200, Tulsa,
OK 74119
Tel.: (918) 295-9800
Web Site: http://www.pennvirginia.com
Sales Range: $75-99.9 Million
Emp.: 100
Oil & Gas Exploration Services
N.A.I.C.S.: 211120

Penn Virginia Oil & Gas Corp.   **(3)**
1000 Town Centre Way Ste 210, Canons-
burg, PA 15317   **(100%)**
Tel.: (724) 743-6640
Web Site: http://www.pennvirginia.com
Sales Range: $25-49.9 Million
Emp.: 25
Oil & Gas Exploration Services
N.A.I.C.S.: 213112

Penn Virginia Oil & Gas GP LLC   **(3)**
14701 St Mary's Lane 3275 Ste 275, Hous-
ton, TX 77079-4147
Tel.: (713) 722-6500
Web Site: http://www.pennvirginia.com
Sales Range: $50-74.9 Million
Emp.: 50
Oil & Gas Exploration Services
N.A.I.C.S.: 213112

Penn Virginia Oil & Gas LP LLC   **(3)**
14701 St Mary's Lane Ste 275, Houston,
TX 77079
Tel.: (610) 687-8900
Web Site: http://www.pennvirginia.com
Emp.: 50
Oil & Gas Operations Services
N.A.I.C.S.: 213112

Penn Virginia Oil & Gas, L.P.   **(3)**
840 Gessner Rd Ste 800, Houston, TX
77024
Tel.: (713) 722-6500
Web Site: http://www.pennvirginia.com
Sales Range: $25-49.9 Million
Emp.: 40
Oil & Gas Exploration Services
N.A.I.C.S.: 211120

BAYVIEW CHRYSLER DODGE
LTD.
255 South Indian Road, Sarnia,
N7T3W5, ON, Canada
Tel.: (519) 337-7561
Web Site:
    http://www.bayview.dealers.ca
Sales Range: $25-49.9 Million
Emp.: 58
New & Used Car Dealers
N.A.I.C.S.: 441110
Al Deserrano *(Bus Mgr)*

BAYWA AG
Arabellastrasse 4, D-81925, Munich,
Germany
Tel.: (49) 8992220   De
Web Site: https://www.baywa.com
Year Founded: 1966
BYW—(MUN)
Rev.: $26,435,699,534
Assets: $13,819,017,369
Liabilities: $12,851,254,540
Net Worth: $967,762,829
Earnings: ($108,289,647)
Emp.: 23,144
Fiscal Year-end: 12/31/23
Building Materials, Farm Supplies,
Farm & Garden Machinery, Fuel &
Agricultural Products Whslr
N.A.I.C.S.: 423390
Andreas Helber *(CFO & Member-
Mgmt Bd)*

Subsidiaries:

AFS Franchise-Systeme GmbH   **(1)**
Wienerbergstrasse 3, Vienna, Austria
Tel.: (43) 1605150
Agricultural Equipment Whslr

N.A.I.C.S.: 423820

AWS Entsorgung GmbH   **(1)**
Altenoer Strasse 10, Luckau, 15926, Bran-
denburg, Germany
Tel.: (49) 35456674620
Web Site: http://www.awsboppard.de
Waste Management Services
N.A.I.C.S.: 562998

Abemec B.V.   **(1)**
Pater van den Elsenlaan 4, 5462 GG, Veg-
hel, Netherlands
Tel.: (31) 413382911
Web Site: https://www.abemec.nl
Agriculture Equipment Services
N.A.I.C.S.: 423820

Agrarproduktenhandel GmbH   **(1)**
Sudring 240, 9020, Klagenfurt, Carinthia,
Austria
Tel.: (43) 463382540
Web Site: https://aph.co.at
Emp.: 3
Agricultural Product Whslr
N.A.I.C.S.: 424910

Agro Innovation Lab GmbH   **(1)**
Raiffeisenstrasse 1, 2100, Korneuburg, Aus-
tria
Tel.: (43) 22 627 5550
Web Site:
    https://www.agroinnovationlab.com
Agricultural Consulting Services
N.A.I.C.S.: 541690
Hannes Schauer *(Mgr-Innovation)*

Agro-Property Kft.   **(1)**
Halasi Ut 29, 6000, Kecskemet, Hungary
Tel.: (36) 76481325
Web Site: https://agro-property-kft.uzleti.hu
N.A.I.C.S.: 531210

AgroMed Austria GmbH   **(1)**
Bad Haller Strasse 23, 4550, Kremsmun-
ster, Austria
Tel.: (43) 758351050
Web Site: https://www.agromed.at
Sales Range: $25-49.9 Million
Emp.: 8
Animal Feed Mfr
N.A.I.C.S.: 311119
Helmut Grabherr *(Founder & CEO)*

Agrosaat d.o.o   **(1)**
Dolenjaka cesta 250 a, 1291, Ljubljana,
Slovenia
Tel.: (386) 15140070
Web Site: http://www.agrosaat.si
Agriculture Products Mfr
N.A.I.C.S.: 424910

Ampero GmbH   **(1)**
Arabellastrasse 4, 81925, Munich, Germany
Tel.: (49) 893839320
Web Site: https://www.ampero.ai
Management Software Solution Services
N.A.I.C.S.: 513210

Aufwind Schmack Elso Biogaz Szol-
galtato Kft.   **(1)**
Mezoberenyi ut 0640 hrs, Szarvas, 5540,
Bekescsaba, Hungary
Tel.: (36) 66514400
Web Site: http://www.biogazszarvas.hu
Thermal Energy Services
N.A.I.C.S.: 221118

BOR s.r.o.   **(1)**
Na Bile 1231, 56501, Chocen, Czech
Republic   **(92.8%)**
Tel.: (420) 465461751
Web Site: http://www.bor-sro.cz
Sales Range: $25-49.9 Million
Emp.: 45
Farm Supplies Whslr
N.A.I.C.S.: 424910

Baltic Logistic Holding B.V.   **(1)**
Boompjes 40, PO Box 113, 3011 XB, Rot-
terdam, Netherlands
Tel.: (31) 637636358
Web Site: https://balticlogisticholding.com
Grain & Protein Whslr
N.A.I.C.S.: 424510

Bautechnik Gesellschaft m.b.H   **(1)**
Wienerbergstrasse 3, 1100, Vienna, Austria
Tel.: (43) 1605153810
Agricultural Related Product Mfr
N.A.I.C.S.: 325320

BayWa AG—(Continued)

BayWa Agrarhandel GmbH (1)
Kl Drakenburger Str 7b Weser, 31582,
Nienburg, Germany
Tel.: (49) 502192200
Farm Management Services
N.A.I.C.S.: 115116

BayWa Agro Polska Sp. z o.o. (1)
ul Keplinska 62, Biwinow, 05-840,
Pruszkow, Poland
Tel.: (48) 223546580
Web Site: https://www.baywa.pl
Farm Management Services
N.A.I.C.S.: 115116

**BayWa Assekuranz-Vermittlung
GmbH** (1)
Arabellastr 4, Munich, 81925, Germany
Tel.: (49) 8992220
Web Site: http://www.baywa.de
Emp.: 800
Insurance Brokerage Services
N.A.I.C.S.: 524210

BayWa Bulgaria EOOD (1)
Evlogi-Georgiev-Str 137, 1504, Sofia, Bulgaria
Tel.: (359) 2448324
Farm Supplies-Wholesale
N.A.I.C.S.: 424910

BayWa CR Spol. s.r.o. (1)
Brnenska 311, CZ66482, Ricany, Czech
Republic (100%)
Tel.: (420) 546427341
Web Site: http://www.baywa.cz
Farm Supplies
N.A.I.C.S.: 424910

BayWa CS GmbH (1)
Spitalhofstr 94, 94032, Passau, Germany
Tel.: (49) 851756340
N.A.I.C.S.: 424910

**BayWa Energie Dienstleistungs
GmbH** (1)
Arabellastrasse 4, 81925, Munich, Germany
Tel.: (49) 8992222841
Heating Contracting Services
N.A.I.C.S.: 238220

BayWa Global Produce GmbH (1)
Arabellastr 4, 81925, Munich, Germany
Tel.: (49) 92222930
Web Site: https://www.baywa-gp.com
N.A.I.C.S.: 424480
Benedikt Mangold (Mng Dir)

**BayWa Handels-Systeme-Service
GmbH** (1)
Arabellastr 4, Munich, 81925, Germany
Tel.: (49) 8992220
Web Site: http://www.baywa.de
Agricultural Equipment Whslr
N.A.I.C.S.: 423820

**BayWa InterOil Mineralolhandelsge-
sellschaft mbH** (1)
Saint Martin Strasse 76, Munich, 81541,
Bayern, Germany
Tel.: (49) 8992220
Oil & Gas Exploration Services
N.A.I.C.S.: 213112

BayWa Obst GmbH & Co. KG (1)
Raiffeisenstr 24, Kressbronn am Bodensee,
88079, Ravensburg, Germany
Tel.: (49) 754396160
Fruit Whslr
N.A.I.C.S.: 424480

BayWa Rent GmbH (1)
Arabellastrasse 4, 81925, Munich, Germany
Tel.: (49) 8006633669
Web Site: https://www.baywa-rent.de
N.A.I.C.S.: 333120
Markus Daik (Mng Dir)

BayWa Venture GmbH (1)
Arabellastrasse 4, 81925, Munich, Germany
Tel.: (49) 8992222859
Web Site: https://venture.baywa.com
N.A.I.C.S.: 311999
Kristal Golan (Mng Dir)

**BayWa Vorarlberg
HandelsGmbH** (1)
Scheibenstrasse 2, 6923, Lauterach,
Austria (51%)

Tel.: (43) 557 470 0600
Web Site: https://lagerhaus.at
N.A.I.C.S.: 444240

BayWa r.e GmbH (1)
Arabellastr 4, Munich, 81925, Bayern, Germany
Tel.: (49) 8992220
Agricultural Equipment Whslr
N.A.I.C.S.: 423820
Gordon MacDougall (Mng Dir)

BayWa r.e. (Thailand) Co., Ltd. (1)
Renewable Energy Services
N.A.I.C.S.: 221118
Daniel Gafke (Mng Dir)

BayWa r.e. AG (1)
Arabellastrasse 4, D-81925, Munich, Germany
Tel.: (49) 893839320
Web Site: https://www.baywa-re.com
Energy Production & Distribution Services
N.A.I.C.S.: 221330

BayWa r.e. Asset Holding GmbH (1)
Am Haag 10, 82166, Grafelfing, Germany
Tel.: (49) 893839320
Renewable Energy Services
N.A.I.C.S.: 221118
Holger Marg (Mng Dir)

**BayWa r.e. Asset Management
GmbH** (1)
Am Haag 10, 82166, Grafelfing, Germany
Tel.: (49) 893839320
N.A.I.C.S.: 221114
Holger Marg (Mng Dir)

BayWa r.e. Bioenergy GmbH (1)
Blumenstrasse 16, 93055, Regensburg,
Germany
Tel.: (49) 9416987300
Renewable Energy Services
N.A.I.C.S.: 221118
Christian Brachlow (Mng Dir)

BayWa r.e. Clean Energy S.r.i. (1)
Largo Augusto 3, 20122, Milan, Italy
Tel.: (39) 023211191
Renewable Energy Services
N.A.I.C.S.: 221118
Cosimo Lena (Mng Dir)

**BayWa r.e. Clean Energy Sourcing
GmbH** (1)
Katharinenstrasse 6, 04109, Leipzig, Germany
Tel.: (49) 34130860600
Renewable Energy Services
N.A.I.C.S.: 221118
Markus Burger (Mng Dir)

**BayWa r.e. Energy Ventures
GmbH** (1)
Am Haag 10, Grafelfing District, 82166, Munich, Germany
Tel.: (49) 893839320
Web Site: https://energy-ventures.baywa-re.com
N.A.I.C.S.: 221114
Greg Zavorotniy (Mng Dir)

BayWa r.e. Espana S.L.U. (1)
Tel.: (34) 936033110
Renewable Energy Services
N.A.I.C.S.: 221118

BayWa r.e. France SAS (1)
Tel.: (33) 155314980
Wind & Solar Energy Services
N.A.I.C.S.: 221118
Can Nalbantoglu (Mng Dir)

**BayWa r.e. Green Energy Products
GmbH** (1)
Arabellastrasse 4, 81925, Munich, Germany
Renewable Energy Services
N.A.I.C.S.: 221118

BayWa r.e. Hellas MEPE (1)
280 Kifissias Ave, 15232, Athens, Greece
Tel.: (30) 6984449440
N.A.I.C.S.: 221114
Nikolaos Tsiantoulas (Mng Dir)

BayWa r.e. Italia S.r.l. (1)
Largo Augusto 3, 20122, Milan, Italy
Tel.: (39) 023211191
N.A.I.C.S.: 221114
Lorenzo Palombi (Mng Dir)

BayWa r.e. Japan K.K. (1)
Tel.: (81) 364320111
Renewable Energy Services
N.A.I.C.S.: 221118
Tetsuya Oura (Mng Dir)

BayWa r.e. Nordic AB (1)
Frihamnsallen 8, 211 20, Malmo, Sweden
Tel.: (46) 406941960
N.A.I.C.S.: 221114
Maria Roske (Mng Dir)

BayWa r.e. Offshore Wind GmbH (1)
Arabellastr 4, 81925, Munich, Germany
Tel.: (49) 893839320
N.A.I.C.S.: 221114
Felipe Cornago (Mng Dir)

**BayWa r.e. Operation Services
GmbH** (1)
Arabellastrasse 4, 81925, Munich, Germany
Tel.: (49) 893839325597
Renewable Energy Services
N.A.I.C.S.: 221118
Christoph Reiners (Mng Dir)

**BayWa r.e. Operation Services
Limited** (1)
Percivals Barn Fairfield Farm Upper Weald,
Milton Keynes, MK19 6EL, United Kingdom
Tel.: (44) 1908229735
Wind & Solar Energy Services
N.A.I.C.S.: 221118

**BayWa r.e. Operation Services
S.r.l.** (1)
Via di Settebagni 390, 00139, Rome, Italy
Tel.: (39) 0687131446
N.A.I.C.S.: 221114
Max Sebastian Methe (Mng Dir)

BayWa r.e. Polska Sp. z o.o. (1)
Plac Przymierza 6 lok U8, 03-944, Warsaw,
Poland
Tel.: (48) 221150482
N.A.I.C.S.: 221114
Matthias Emminghaus (Mng Dir)

BayWa r.e. Progetti S.r.i. (1)
Largo Augusto 3, 20122, Milan, Italy.
Tel.: (39) 023211191
N.A.I.C.S.: 221114
Lorenzo Palombi (Mng Dir)

**BayWa r.e. Projects Espana
S.L.U.** (1)
C/ Sagasta 31 planta 4, 28004, Madrid,
Spain
Tel.: (34) 919158800
Agricultural Product Whslr
N.A.I.C.S.: 423390

BayWa r.e. Romania S.R.L. (1)
Calea Floreasca 246c, 14473, Bucharest,
Romania
Tel.: (40) 751110303
Web Site: https://www.baywa-re.ro
Solar Electric Power Distr
N.A.I.C.S.: 221114

BayWa r.e. Rotor Service GmbH (1)
Am Diesterkamp 63, Basdahl, 27432, Regensburg, Germany
Tel.: (49) 4766821100
Renewable Energy Services
N.A.I.C.S.: 221118

BayWa r.e. Scandinavia AB (1)
Frihamnsallen 8, 211 20, Malmo, Sweden
Renewable Energy Services
N.A.I.C.S.: 221118

**BayWa r.e. Solar Energy Systems
GmbH** (1)
Eisenbahnstrasse 150, 72072, Tubingen,
Germany
Tel.: (49) 7071989870
Renewable Energy Services
N.A.I.C.S.: 221118
Alexander Schutt (Mng Dir)

BayWa r.e. Solar Projects GmbH (1)
Arabellastrasse 4, 81925, Munich, Germany
Tel.: (49) 893839325077
Renewable Energy Services
N.A.I.C.S.: 221118
Stefanie Wimmer (Mng Dir)

BayWa r.e. Solar Projects LLC (1)
Tel.: (949) 398-3915
Renewable Energy Services

N.A.I.C.S.: 221118

BayWa r.e. Solar Pte. Ltd. (1)
109 North Bridge Road 07-22 Funan, Singapore, 179097, Singapore
Tel.: (65) 20912658
N.A.I.C.S.: 221114
Daniel Gaefke (Mng Dir)

**BayWa r.e. Solar Systems Co.,
Ltd.** (1)
Renewable Energy Services
N.A.I.C.S.: 221118
Daniel Gafke (Mng Dir)

**BayWa r.e. Solar Systems
Corporation** (1)
27/F Tower 2 The Enterprise Center Ayala
Ave cor, Paseo de Roxas, Makati, 1224,
Philippines
Tel.: (63) 9190731108
Solar Energy Distr
N.A.I.C.S.: 424490

**BayWa r.e. Solar Systems
GmbH** (1)
Wirtschaftspark 15, 9130, Pottendorf, Austria
Tel.: (43) 42243441000
Web Site: https://solar-distribution.baywa-re.at
Solar Panels Installation Services
N.A.I.C.S.: 238210

BayWa r.e. Solar Systems Inc. (1)
4703-101 Street NW, Edmonton, T6E 5C6,
AB, Canada
Web Site: https://solar-distribution.baywa-re.ca
Solar Energy Distr
N.A.I.C.S.: 424490

BayWa r.e. Solar Systems LLC (1)
1596 Pacheco St Ste 103, Santa Fe, NM
87505
Tel.: (505) 216-7834
Renewable Energy Services
N.A.I.C.S.: 221118

**BayWa r.e. Solar Systems Pty.
Ltd.** (1)
10A Thermal Chase, Bibra Lake, Perth,
6163, WA, Australia
Tel.: (61) 863243700
Web Site: https://solar-distribution.baywa-re.com.au
Renewable Energy Services
N.A.I.C.S.: 221118
Durmus Yildiz (Mng Dir)

**BayWa r.e. Solar Systems S. de R.L
de C.V.** (1)
Camino al CUCBA 1204 Int 28-29 San Juan
de Ocotan, 45019, Zapopan, Jalisco,
Mexico
Tel.: (52) 3336190695
N.A.I.C.S.: 221114
Andres Gonzalez (Mng Dir)

BayWa r.e. Solar Systems S.L.U. (1)
Calle Zamora 46-48 3 2, 08005, Barcelona,
Spain
Tel.: (34) 830830270
Web Site: https://solar-distribution.baywa-re.es
Agricultural Product Whslr
N.A.I.C.S.: 423390
Daniel Roca (Mng Dir)

**BayWa r.e. Solar Systems S.a
r.l.** (1)
15 Op der Haart, 9999, Wemperhardt, Luxembourg
Tel.: (352) 27802820
Web Site: https://solar-distribution.baywa-re.lu
Solar System & Installation Services
N.A.I.C.S.: 221114
Thomas Lechat (Mng Dir)

BayWa r.e. Solar Systems S.r.l. (1)
Anello Nord 25, 39031, Bruneck, Italy
Tel.: (39) 0474375050
Solar System & Installation Services
N.A.I.C.S.: 221114
Enrico Marin (Mng Dir)

BayWa r.e. Solar Systems SAS (1)
Tel.: (33) 556528552
Solar System & Installation Services

N.A.I.C.S.: 221114

BayWa r.e. Solar Systems s.r.o. (1)
Za Trati 206, 25219, Chrastany, Czech Republic
Tel.: (420) 555444237
Web Site: https://solar-distribution.baywa-re.cz
Solar Energy Distr
N.A.I.C.S.: 424490

BayWa r.e. Solar Systems sp. z o. o. (1)
ul Krakowska 390, 32080, Zabierzow, Poland
Tel.: (48) 123978200
Web Site: https://solar-distribution.baywa-re.pl
Solar Energy Distr
N.A.I.C.S.: 424490

BayWa r.e. Solarsysteme GmbH (1)
Eisenbahnstrasse 150, 72072, Tubingen, Germany
Tel.: (49) 707 198 9870
Web Site: http://www.baywa-re.com
Sales Range: $50-74.9 Million
Emp.: 15
Photovoltaic System Distr
N.A.I.C.S.: 423690

BayWa r.e. Solarsystemer ApS (1)
Kullinggade 31 E, 5700, Svendborg, Denmark
Tel.: (45) 62211000
Agricultural Product Whslr
N.A.I.C.S.: 423390
Henrik Borreby (Mng Dir)

BayWa r.e. UK Limited (1)
Ground Floor West Suite Prospect House 5
Thistle Street, Edinburgh, EH2 1DF, United Kingdom
Renewable Energy Services
N.A.I.C.S.: 221118

BayWa r.e. Wind GmbH (1)
Arabellastrasse 4, 81925, Munich, Germany
Tel.: (49) 8938393252
Renewable Energy Services
N.A.I.C.S.: 221118
Marie Luise Portner (Mng Dir)

BayWa r.e. Wind LLC (1)
5901 Priestly Dr Ste 300, Carlsbad, CA 92008
Tel.: (858) 450-6800
N.A.I.C.S.: 221114
Gordon MacDougall (Mng Dir)

BayWa r.e. renewable energy GmbH (1)
Arabellastrabe 4, 81925, Munich, Germany
Tel.: (49) 893839320
Renewable Energy
N.A.I.C.S.: 221114
Elisabeth Koppl (Mgr-HR)

Subsidiary (Domestic):

Clean Energy Sourcing AG (2)
Katharinenstrasse 6, 04109, Leipzig, Germany
Tel.: (49) 341 30 86 06 00
Renewable Energy Distribution Services
N.A.I.C.S.: 221122

BayWa re (Malaysia) Sdn. Bhd. (1)
A-03-07 Connection Commercial Persiaran
IRC 3 IOI Resort City, 62502, Putrajaya, Selangor, Malaysia
Tel.: (60) 386842303
N.A.I.C.S.: 221114
Niranpal Singh (Mng Dir)

BayWa-Tankstellen-GmbH (1)
Arabellastr 4, Munich, 81925, Bayern, Germany
Tel.: (49) 8992220
Agricultural Equipment Whslr
N.A.I.C.S.: 423820

Bayerische Futtersaatbau GmbH (1)
Max-von-Eyth-Strasse 2-4, 85737, Ismaning, Germany
Tel.: (49) 89 962 4350
Web Site: https://www.bsv-saaten.de
Sales Range: $50-74.9 Million
Emp.: 100
Agricultural Product Whslr
N.A.I.C.S.: 424910

BioCore B.V. (1)
Nesland 5M, 1382 MZ, Weesp, Netherlands
Tel.: (31) 29 480 5000
Web Site: https://www.biocore.nl
Farm Management Services
N.A.I.C.S.: 115116

Bolke Handel GmbH (1)
Queiser Ring 5 OT Queis, 06188, Landsberg, Germany
Tel.: (49) 34 602 6010
Web Site: https://www.boelke-handel.de
Disposal & Landscaping Services
N.A.I.C.S.: 561730

CLAAS Main-Donau GmbH & Co. KG (1)
Sudstrasse 6, Gollhofen, 97258, Bad Windsheim, Germany
Tel.: (49) 93399887140
Web Site: https://www.claas-main-donau.de
Agricultural Machinery Mfr
N.A.I.C.S.: 333111

CLAAS Nordostbayern GmbH & Co. KG (1)
Auf der Haide 8, 92665, Altenstadt, Germany
Tel.: (49) 960 294 4180
Web Site: https://www.claas-nordostbayern.de
Agricultural Equipment Whslr
N.A.I.C.S.: 423820

CLAAS Wurttemberg GmbH (1)
Magirusstrasse 17, 89129, Langenau, Germany
Tel.: (49) 73 459 3330
Web Site: https://www.claas-wuerttemberg.de
Agricultural Machinery Mfr
N.A.I.C.S.: 333111

Cefetra B.V. (1)
Boompjes 40, 3011 XB, Rotterdam, Netherlands
Tel.: (31) 104007900
Web Site: https://cefetra.nl
Grain & Protein Whslr
N.A.I.C.S.: 424510

Cefetra Dairy B.V. (1)
Helftheuvelweg 11, 5222 AV, 's-Hertogenbosch, Netherlands
Tel.: (31) 732200620
Web Site: https://cefetradairy.com
Dairy Product Whslr
N.A.I.C.S.: 424430

Cefetra Digital Services S.L. (1)
Av de Europa 19 - Building II - 2A, 28224, Pozuelo de Alarcon, Spain
Tel.: (34) 911928800
Agricultural Equipment Mfr & Distr
N.A.I.C.S.: 333111

Cefetra Feed Service B.V. (1)
Boompjes 40, South Holland, 3011 XB, Rotterdam, Netherlands
Tel.: (31) 104007970
Web Site: https://cefetrafeedservice.nl
Grain & Protein Whslr
N.A.I.C.S.: 424510

Cefetra Group B.V. (1)
Boompjes 40, 3011 XB, Rotterdam, Netherlands
Tel.: (31) 104007900
Web Site: https://cefetra.com
Agriculture Product Distr
N.A.I.C.S.: 424910

Cefetra Iberica S.L.U. (1)
Avda de Europa n 19 Edif II- 2 A, Pozuelo de Alarcon, 28224, Madrid, Spain
Tel.: (34) 911928800
Web Site: https://cefetra.es
Agricultural Raw Material Distr
N.A.I.C.S.: 424910

Cefetra Limited (1)
The Lightyear Building Glasgow Airport
Business Park, Marchburn Drive, Paisley, PA3 2SJ, United Kingdom
Tel.: (44) 1414455721
Web Site: https://cefetra.co.uk
Agricultural Raw Material Distr
N.A.I.C.S.: 424910

Cefetra Polska Sp. z o.o. (1)
ul 10 Lutego 16, 81-364, Gdynia, Poland

Tel.: (48) 586665205
Web Site: https://cefetra.pl
Agricultural Raw Material Distr
N.A.I.C.S.: 424910

Cefetra S.p.A. (1)
Via G Mercalli 21, 00197, Rome, Italy
Tel.: (39) 0689219801
Web Site: https://cefetra.it
Agricultural Raw Material Distr
N.A.I.C.S.: 424910

Centro Agricolo Friulano S.R.L. (1)
Via Ellero 7 Fr Rivolto, 33033, Codroipo, UD, Italy
Tel.: (39) 0432815240
Web Site: https://centro-agricolo.it
N.A.I.C.S.: 424910

Citygreen Gartengestaltungs GmbH (1)
Heiligenstadter Lande 11, 1190, Vienna, Austria
Tel.: (43) 150580100
Web Site: https://www.citygreen.at
Garden Maintenance Services
N.A.I.C.S.: 561730

Claas Sudostbayern GmbH (1)
Franz-Marc-Strasse 12, 84513, Toging am Inn, Germany
Tel.: (49) 863 116 7560
Web Site: https://www.claas-suedostbayern.de
Agricultural Equipment Mfr
N.A.I.C.S.: 333111

Class Nordostbayern GmbH & Co. KG (1)
Auf der Haide 8, 92665, Altenstadt, Germany
Tel.: (49) 9602944180
Web Site: https://www.claas-nordostbayern.de
Farming Equipment Whslr
N.A.I.C.S.: 423820

Class Sudostbayern GmbH (1)
Franz-Marc-Str 12, 84513, Toging am Inn, Germany
Tel.: (49) 8631167560
Web Site: https://www.claas-suedostbayern.de
Farming Equipment Whslr
N.A.I.C.S.: 423820

DTL Donau-Tanklagergesellschaft mbH & Co. KG (1)
Wallnerlande 34, 94469, Deggendorf, Bayern, Germany
Tel.: (49) 99130073
Agricultural Equipment Whslr
N.A.I.C.S.: 423820

Daipur Wind Farm Pty. Ltd. (1)
266 Diapur-Lawloit Rd, Nhill, 3418, VIC, Australia
Tel.: (61) 1800667867
Web Site: https://diapurwindfarm.com.au
N.A.I.C.S.: 221114

Danufert Handelsgesellschaft mbH (1)
Karl Mierka Strasse 7-9, 3500, Krems, Austria (60%)
Tel.: (43) 273273571
Web Site: http://www.mierka.com
Sales Range: $50-74.9 Million
Agricultural Product Whslr
N.A.I.C.S.: 424910

Danugrain Lagerei GmbH (1)
Karl-Mierka-Strasse 7-9, Krems an der Donau, Austria
Tel.: (43) 273273571
Agricultural Product Whslr
N.A.I.C.S.: 423390
Andreas Jirkowsky (Mng Dir)

Diermeier Energie GmbH (1)
Industriestr 3, 94559, Niederwinkling, Germany
Tel.: (49) 942155000
Web Site: https://www.diermeier-energie.de
Emp.: 30
High Quality Lubricant Distr
N.A.I.C.S.: 424720

E3 Energie Effizienz Experten GmbH (1)

Eugen-Bolz-Strasse 5, 74523, Schwabisch Hall, Germany
Tel.: (49) 7919 460 0300
Web Site: https://www.e3-experten.de
Emp.: 220
Photovoltaic Modules Mfr & Solar Equipment Installation Services
N.A.I.C.S.: 334419

ECOwind Handels- & Wartungs-GmbH (1)
Fohrafeld 11, Kilb, 3233, Vienna, Austria
Tel.: (43) 27 482 0310
Web Site: https://www.ecowind.at
Wind Power Installation Services
N.A.I.C.S.: 221115

ECOwind d.o.o. (1)
Ilica 1a, 10000, Zagreb, Croatia
Tel.: (385) 1 233 4012
Web Site: https://www.ecowind.hr
Wind Power Installation Services
N.A.I.C.S.: 221115

EUROGREEN CZ s.r.o., (1)
Namesti Jiriho 2, Jiretin pod Jedlovou, 407 56, Decin, Czech Republic
Tel.: (420) 41 237 9115
Web Site: https://www.eurogreen.cz
Sales Range: $25-49.9 Million
Emp.: 30
Agricultural Equipment Whslr
N.A.I.C.S.: 423820

EUROGREEN GmbH (1)
Betzdorfer Str 25-29, 57520, Rosenheim, Germany
Tel.: (49) 27 479 1680
Web Site: https://www.eurogreen.de
Agricultural Product Whslr
N.A.I.C.S.: 424910

Emera S.R.L. (1)
Via F Patrizio da Cherso 35, 00143, Rome, Italy
Tel.: (39) 03483191302
Web Site: https://www.emeracomunicazione.it
Information & Communication Technology Services
N.A.I.C.S.: 541430

Eurogreen Austria GmbH (1)
Wagnermuhle 7, 5310, Mondsee, Austria
Tel.: (43) 62326768
Web Site: https://www.eurogreen.at
Lawn Care Services
N.A.I.C.S.: 561730

Eurogreen Italia S.r.l. (1)
Via I Galvani 19, Monterotondo, 00015, Rome, Italy
Tel.: (39) 03351064152
Web Site: https://www.eurogreenroma.it
N.A.I.C.S.: 562219

Evergrain Germany GmbH & Co. KG (1)
Ballindamm 4-5, 20095, Hamburg, Germany
Tel.: (49) 4022865010
Web Site: http://www.evergrain.de
Fresh Produce Whslr
N.A.I.C.S.: 424480

FarmFacts GmbH (1)
Rennbahnstrasse 9, 84347, Pfarrkirchen, Germany
Tel.: (49) 8561300680
Web Site: https://www.nextfarming.de
Farm Management Services
N.A.I.C.S.: 115116

FarmFacts Hungary Kft (1)
Roboz I u 7, 7400, Kaposvar, Hungary
Tel.: (36) 309938998
Farm Management Services
N.A.I.C.S.: 115116

Fatent Co. Doo Laktasi (1)
Gradiska cesta 198, Aleksandrovac, 78250, Laktasi, Bosnia & Herzegovina
Tel.: (387) 51582080
Pet Food Mfr
N.A.I.C.S.: 311119

Ferguson Wind Farm Pty. Ltd. (1)
1862 Princetown Rd, Princetown, Melbourne, 3269, VIC, Australia
Tel.: (61) 800667867
Web Site: https://fergusonwindfarm.com.au
N.A.I.C.S.: 221114

BayWa AG—(Continued)

Forster GmbH (1)
Am Muhlbach 32, 87487, Wiggensbach,
Germany
Tel.: (49) 8370929782
Web Site: https://www.forster-gmbh.com
Building Carpentry Services
N.A.I.C.S.: 238350

Freshmax New Zealand Ltd. (1)
12 Hugo Johnston Drive, Penrose, Auck-
land, New Zealand
Tel.: (64) 95536374
Fresh Fruit Distr
N.A.I.C.S.: 424480

**Garant-Tiernahrung Gesellschaft
m.b.H** (1)
Raiffeisenstrasse 3, 3380, Pochlarn, Austria
Tel.: (43) 27 572 2810
Web Site: https://www.garant.co.at
Sales Range: $25-49.9 Million
Emp.: 170
Animal Feed Mfr
N.A.I.C.S.: 311119
Christoph Henockl (Mng Dir)

Genol Gesellschaft mbH (1)
Raiffeisenstrasse 1, 2100, Korneuburg, Aus-
tria
Tel.: (43) 2262755500
Web Site: https://www.genol.at
N.A.I.C.S.: 324199

Grainli GmbH & Co. KG (1)
Ballindamm 4-5, 20095, Hamburg, Germany
Tel.: (49) 4022865010
Web Site: https://www.grainli.de
Raw Food Product Mfr
N.A.I.C.S.: 311999

Grainvest B.V. (1)
Markerkant 11-11, 1316 AE, Almere, Neth-
erlands
Tel.: (31) 854839888
Wine Beverage Mfr & Distr
N.A.I.C.S.: 312130

**Graninger & Mayr Gesellschaft
m.b.H** (1)
Alberner Hafenzufahrtsstrasse 17, Vienna,
1110, Austria
Tel.: (43) 1 728 91 80
Web Site: http://www.gmreifen.at
Emp.: 10
Tire Repair & Maintenance Services
N.A.I.C.S.: 811198
Johann Oberger (Gen Mgr)

GroenLeven B.V. (1)
Lange Marktstraat 5-7, 8911 AD, Leeuwar-
den, Netherlands
Tel.: (31) 58 799 0000
Web Site: https://www.groenleven.nl
Solar System & Installation Services
N.A.I.C.S.: 221114

H2X GmbH (1)
Hohenzollernstrasse 47, 80801, Munich,
Germany
Tel.: (49) 89319017686
Web Site: https://h2x.de
Construction Materials Whslr
N.A.I.C.S.: 423390

Heinrich Bruning GmbH (1)
Stenzelring 22, 21107, Hamburg, Germany
Tel.: (49) 407510050
Web Site: https://www.bruening-suntree.de
Emp.: 20
Dry Fruit Whslr
N.A.I.C.S.: 445230

**Immobilienvermietung Gesellschaft
m.b.H.** (1)
Rubensstrasse 35, 4050, Traun, Austria
Tel.: (43) 1605162300
Agricultural Product Whslr
N.A.I.C.S.: 423390
Karl Hofbauer (Mng Dir)

Interlubes GmbH (1)
Max-von-Laue-Strasse 12, 97080,
Wurzburg, Germany
Tel.: (49) 93199172415
Web Site: https://www.interlubes.de
Engine & Transmission Oil Mfr
N.A.I.C.S.: 324191

Intersaatzucht GmbH (1)

Eichethof 6, 85411, Hohenkammer, Ger-
many
Tel.: (49) 81 379 3240
Web Site: https://www.intersaatzucht.de
Agricultural Crop Distr
N.A.I.C.S.: 424910

Karl Theis GmbH (1)
Broad Street 11, 57076, Siegen, Germany
Tel.: (49) 27 177 2850
Web Site: https://www.theis-tubes.com
Metal Pipe Mfr
N.A.I.C.S.: 332996

**LHD Landhandel Drebkau Import -
und Export GmbH** (1)
Grunstrasse 19, Drebkau, 03116, Branden-
burg, Germany
Tel.: (49) 356025720
Agricultural Raw Material Distr
N.A.I.C.S.: 424910

LTZ Chemnitz GmbH (1)
Muhlauer Strasse 11, Hartmannsdorf,
09232, Chemnitz, Germany
Tel.: (49) 372289070
Web Site: https://www.ltz-chemnitz.de
Emp.: 100
Machinery & Equipment Distr
N.A.I.C.S.: 423810

Lagerhaus Franchise GmbH (1)
Raiffeisenstrasse 1, 2100, Korneuburg, Aus-
tria
Tel.: (43) 2262755500
Warehouse Services
N.A.I.C.S.: 236220

**Lagerhaus Technik-Center
GmbH** (1)
Raiffeisenstrasse 1, 2100, Korneuburg, Aus-
tria
Tel.: (43) 2262712600
Web Site: https://www.lagerhaustc.at
Gunter Kallus (Mng Dir)

**Lagerhaus Technik-Center GmbH &
Co. KG** (1)
Raiffeisenstrasse 1, 2100, Korneuburg, Aus-
tria
Tel.: (43) 2262712600
Web Site: https://www.lagerhaustc.at
Farm Equipment Distr
N.A.I.C.S.: 423820

Lagerhaus e-Service GmbH (1)
Wienerbergstrasse 3, 1100, Vienna, Austria
Tel.: (43) 599209907962
Farm Management Services
N.A.I.C.S.: 115116
Stefan Winkler (Mgr-E-Commerce)

Landhandel Knaup GmbH (1)
Rudolf-Diesel-Strasse 8, Alfen, 33178,
Borchen, Germany
Tel.: (49) 5251690990
Agricultural Raw Material Distr
N.A.I.C.S.: 424910

MHH France S.A.S (1)
24 Ave Marcel Dassault, 31500, Toulouse,
France
Tel.: (33) 562577488
Web Site: http://www.mhh-france.fr
Sales Range: $50-74.9 Million
Emp.: 8
Photovoltaics Distr
N.A.I.C.S.: 423720

OneShore Energy GmbH (1)
Oranienburger Str 17, 10178, Berlin, Ger-
many
Tel.: (49) 30208981720
Web Site: http://www.oneshore.com
Solar System Construction Services
N.A.I.C.S.: 237130

**PARGA Park- und Gartentechnik Ge-
sellschaft m.b.H** (1)
Telefonweg 1, Aderklaa, 2232, Ganserndorf,
Austria
Tel.: (43) 22 474 0500
Web Site: https://www.parga.at
Farm Equipment Distr
N.A.I.C.S.: 423820

Patent Co. DOO (1)
Vlade Cetkovica 1a, Misicevo, Subotica,
Serbia
Tel.: (381) 244760001

Web Site: https://www.patent-co.com
Animal Feed Mfr
N.A.I.C.S.: 311111

Patent Co., Doo Laktasi (1)
Gradiska Cesta 198, Aleksandrovac, 78250,
Laktasi, Bosnia & Herzegovina
Tel.: (387) 51582080
Animal Feed Mfr & Distr
N.A.I.C.S.: 311119

Peter Frey GmbH (1)
Zur Fasanerie 1, 85456, Wartenberg, Ger-
many
Tel.: (49) 8762727720
Web Site: https://www.peter-frey-gmbh.de
Natural Stone Product Distr
N.A.I.C.S.: 423320

RENERCO GEM 2 GmbH (1)
Herzog Heinrich Strasse 9, 80336, Munich,
Germany
Tel.: (49) 893839320
Web Site: http://www.renerco.com
Sales Range: $75-99.9 Million
Emp.: 170
Agricultural Product Whslr
N.A.I.C.S.: 424910
Matthias Taft (Gen Mgr)

RI-Solution GmbH (1)
Arabellastrasse 4, 81925, Munich, Germany
Tel.: (49) 8992220
Web Site: http://ri-solution.com
IT Application & Development Services
N.A.I.C.S.: 541511

**RI-Solution GmbH Gesellschaft fur
Retail-Informationssysteme, Services
und Losungen mbH** (1)
Arabellastr 4, Munich, 81925, Germany
Tel.: (49) 8992220
Information Technology Consulting Services
N.A.I.C.S.: 541512

RI-Solution Service GmbH (1)
Kaiserstr 17, Auerbach, 08209, Germany
Tel.: (49) 374483480
Web Site: http://www.ri-solution.com
Information Technology Consulting Services
N.A.I.C.S.: 541512

**RUG Raiffeisen Umweltgesellschaft
m.b.H** (1)
Raiffeisenstrasse 1, 2100, Korneuburg, Aus-
tria
Tel.: (43) 2262755502700
Web Site: https://www.rug-ingenieurbuero.at
Environmental Consulting Services
N.A.I.C.S.: 541620

RWA Hrvatska d.o.o. (1)
Zapadno predgrade 18, 31000, Osijek,
Croatia
Tel.: (385) 31333300
Web Site: https://www.rwa.hr
Emp.: 60
Farm Management Services
N.A.I.C.S.: 115116

RWA Magyarorszag Kft (1)
Lesvar Major, Ikreny, 9141, Gyor, Hungary
Tel.: (36) 212110400
Web Site: https://www.rwa.hu
Agricultural Related Product Mfr
N.A.I.C.S.: 325320

RWA RAIFFEISEN AGRO d.o.o (1)
Buzetkki Trilaz 10, Zagreb, 10010, Croatia
Tel.: (385) 12022650
Web Site: http://www.rwa.hr
Sales Range: $25-49.9 Million
Emp.: 34
Agricultural Product Whslr
N.A.I.C.S.: 424910

**RWA Raiffeisen Agro Romania
S.r.l.** (1)
Calea Aradului no 85 A, Timis County, Timi-
soara, Romania
Tel.: (40) 744309838
Web Site: https://www.raiffeisen-agro.ro
Agricultural Related Product Mfr
N.A.I.C.S.: 325320

RWA Slovakia Spol. s.r.o. (1)
Pri trati 15, 820 14, Bratislava, Slovakia
Tel.: (421) 240201111
Web Site: https://www.rwa.sk
Agricultural Related Product Mfr
N.A.I.C.S.: 325320

RWA Slovenija d.o.o. (1)
Dolenjska cesta 250 a Lavrica, Skofljica,
1291, Ljubljana, Slovenia
Tel.: (386) 1 514 0070
Web Site: https://www.agrosaat.si
Vegetable Fertilizer Mfr
N.A.I.C.S.: 311421

RWA Srbija d.o.o. (1)
Bulevar Zorana Dindica 67/17, Novi Beo-
grad, 11070, Belgrade, Serbia
Tel.: (381) 112123035
Web Site: https://www.rwa.co.rs
Emp.: 38
Agricultural Related Product Mfr
N.A.I.C.S.: 325320

RWA Ukrajina LLC (1)
St Velika Kiltseva 7, Kyiv-Svyatoshinsky
District Village of Petropavlivska Borshcha-
givka, 08131, Vyshneve, Ukraine
Tel.: (380) 504929242
Web Site: https://www.rwa-ukraine.com.ua
N.A.I.C.S.: 423820
Vitaly Janitor (CEO)

**Raiffeisen Agro Magyarorszag
Kft.** (1)
Takarodo ut 2, H-8000, Szekesfehervar,
Hungary (100%)
Tel.: (36) 22534401
Web Site: http://www.raiffeisen-agro.hu
Farm & Garden Supplies Whslr
N.A.I.C.S.: 424910
Laszlo Bene (CEO)

Raiffeisen Agro d.o.o (1)
Bulevar Zorana Djindjica 67/17, 11070, Bel-
grade, Serbia
Tel.: (381) 112123035
Web Site: http://www.raiffeisen-agro.rs
Sales Range: $50-74.9 Million
Emp.: 28
Agricultural Product Whslr
N.A.I.C.S.: 424910
Dusan Mezulic (Gen Mgr)

Raiffeisen Trgovina d.o.o. (1)
Industrijska 8, 2230, Lenart, Slovenia
Tel.: (386) 27200560
Web Site: www.raiffeisen-trgovina.si
Agricultural Farm Product Distr
N.A.I.C.S.: 424910

Raiffeisen Waren GmbH (1)
Standeplatz 1-3, 34117, Kassel, Germany
Tel.: (49) 5 617 1220
Web Site: https://www.raiwa.net
Fuel & Gas Station Services
N.A.I.C.S.: 457210

Raiffeisen-Lagerhaus GmbH (1)
Lagerhausstrasse 3, 2460, Bruck an der
Leitha, Austria
Tel.: (43) 21622101260
Agricultural Product Whslr
N.A.I.C.S.: 424910

**Raiffeisen-Lagerhaus Investitionsh-
olding GmbH** (1)
Wienerbergstrasse 3, Vienna, 1100, Austria
Tel.: (43) 1605156390
Agricultural Equipment Whslr
N.A.I.C.S.: 423820

Renerco Plan Consult GmbH (1)
Ganghoferstr 66, 80339, Munich, Germany
Tel.: (49) 8938 393 2147
Web Site:
https://www.renercoplanconsult.com
Wind Power & Geothermal Services
N.A.I.C.S.: 221115

**Renerco Renewable Energy Con-
cepts AG** (1)
Herzog Heinrich Str 9, Munich, 80336, Ger-
many
Tel.: (49) 893839320
Web Site: http://www.renerco.de
Emp.: 120
Eletric Power Generation Services
N.A.I.C.S.: 221118

Ri-Solution Data GmbH (1)
Wienerbergstrasse 3, 1100, Vienna, Austria
Tel.: (43) 1605152150
Web Site: http://www.ri-solutions.com
Sales Range: $150-199.9 Million
Emp.: 400
Agricultural Equipment Whslr

Riveka BVBA (1)
Scherpenhoek 10, 2850, Boom, Belgium
Tel.: (32) 35021900
Web Site: https://www.riveka.com
Grain & Protein Whslr
N.A.I.C.S.: 424510

RoyBalt Ingredients S.A. de C.V (1)
Queretaro-San Luis Potosi Highway 16368,
Nave 29 Santa Rosa Jauregui, 76220, Que-
retaro, Mexico
Tel.: (52) 4421894671
Web Site: https://roybalt-ingredients.com
Starch Distr
N.A.I.C.S.: 424490

SC Puterea Verde S.r.l. (1)
Str Turnului nr 16, 550197, Sibiu, Romania
Tel.: (40) 75 642 0296
Web Site: https://putereaverde.ro
Wind Power Installation Services
N.A.I.C.S.: 221115

Saatzucht Edelhof GmbH (1)
Edelhof 1, 3910, Zwettl, Austria
Tel.: (43) 282252402116
Web Site: https://saatzucht-edelhof.at
Planting Crop Services
N.A.I.C.S.: 115112

Schradenbiogas GmbH & Co.
KG (1)
Groden-Nord 2, 04932, Groden, Germany
Tel.: (49) 35343786310
Web Site: https://www.schradenbiogas.de
Biogas Mfr
N.A.I.C.S.: 324199
Christoph von Jan *(Mng Dir)*

Sedaco DMCC (1)
Unit 1404 Tiffany Towers Cluster W Jumei-
rah Lake Towers, Dubai, United Arab Emir-
ates
Tel.: (971) 45515624
Web Site: https://sedacogroup.com
Raw Food Material Whslr
N.A.I.C.S.: 445298

Sempol spol. s r.o (1)
Pri Trati 15, Bratislava, 820 14, Slovakia
Tel.: (421) 2 4020 1111
Web Site: http://www.sempol.sk
Agricultural Product Whslr
N.A.I.C.S.: 424910

Sol in one GmbH (1)
Denissstrasse 18, 67663, Kaiserslautern,
Germany
Tel.: (49) 6315600210
Web Site: https://www.solinone.de
Solar Panels Installation Services
N.A.I.C.S.: 238210

Solar-Planit Software GmbH (1)
Eisenbahnstrasse 150, D-72072, Tubingen,
Germany
Tel.: (49) 7071989870
Web Site: https://www.solar-planit.de
Energy Production & Distribution Services
N.A.I.C.S.: 221330

Solarmarkt GmbH (1)
Neumattstrasse 2, 5000, Aarau, Switzerland
Tel.: (41) 622006200
Web Site: https://www.solarmarkt.ch
Solar Energy Supply Services
N.A.I.C.S.: 221118

Sud-Treber GmbH (1)
Zaunackerstr 1, 70771, Leinfelden-
Echterdingen, Germany
Tel.: (49) 7119528210
Web Site: https://www.suedtreber.de
Corn Glutten Mfr
N.A.I.C.S.: 311221

T&G Global Limited (1)
Building 1 Level 1 Central Park 660 Great
South Road Ellerslie, Mount Wellington,
Auckland, 1061, New Zealand **(73.1%)**
Tel.: (64) 95738700
Web Site: https://tandg.global
Rev.: $1,015,652,210
Assets: $705,153,498
Liabilities: $331,450,372
Net Worth: $373,703,126
Earnings: $11,928,210
Emp.: 1,184
Fiscal Year-end: 12/31/2020

Fresh Fruits & Vegetables Marketer, Distr &
Exporter
N.A.I.C.S.: 424480
Klaus Josef Lutz *(Chm)*

Subsidiary (Non-US):

ENZACOR Pty Limited (2)
Unit 7 9 Compark Circuit, Mulgrave, 3170,
VIC, Australia
Tel.: (61) 385613188
Web Site: http://www.fruitmark.com.au
Sales Range: $25-49.9 Million
Emp.: 11
Frozen & Processed Fruits & Vegetables
Whslr
N.A.I.C.S.: 424420

Subsidiary (Domestic):

ENZAFOODS New Zealand
Limited (2)
1223 Tomoana Rd, Hastings, 4120, Hawkes
Bay, New Zealand
Tel.: (64) 68781460
Web Site: http://www.enzafoods.co.nz
Sales Range: $25-49.9 Million
Emp.: 150
Fruits & Vegetable Juice Mfr
N.A.I.C.S.: 311411

ENZAFRUIT Marketing Limited (2)
2Anderson Rd, PO Box 279, Hastings,
4180, Hawkes Bay, New Zealand
Tel.: (64) 68781898
Web Site: http://www.enza.co.nz
Sales Range: $25-49.9 Million
Emp.: 40
Pipfruit Distr
N.A.I.C.S.: 424480

Subsidiary (Non-US):

ENZAFRUIT New Zealand (Conti-
nent) NV (2)
Tongersesteenweg 135, 3800, Saint Tru-
iden, Limburg, Belgium
Tel.: (32) 1 168 9941
Web Site: https://www.enzafruit.be
Sales Range: $25-49.9 Million
Emp.: 13
Fresh Fruit Distr
N.A.I.C.S.: 424480

Subsidiary (Domestic):

Status Produce Limited (2)
42 Favona Road, Mangere, Auckland,
2151, New Zealand
Tel.: (64) 92751819
Web Site: http://www.statusproduce.co.nz
Sales Range: $25-49.9 Million
Emp.: 250
Tomato Farming & Distr
N.A.I.C.S.: 111419

TFC Holland B.V. (1)
Transportweg 49, 2676 LM, Maasdijk, Neth-
erlands
Tel.: (31) 17 452 5700
Web Site: https://www.tfc-holland.nl
Emp.: 150
Fruit & Vegetable Mfr
N.A.I.C.S.: 311421

TechnikCenter Grimma GmbH (1)
Gewerbestrasse 1, 04668, Grimma, Ger-
many
Tel.: (49) 343855090
Web Site: https://www.tc-grimma.de
Agricultural Equipment Whslr
N.A.I.C.S.: 423820

Thenergy B.V. (1)
Bouwlingplein 34, Postbus 319, 4900 AH,
Oosterhout, Netherlands
Tel.: (31) 162437800
Web Site: https://www.thenergy.nl
Fruit & Vegetable Mfr
N.A.I.C.S.: 311421

Tjiko GmbH (1)
Riedstrasse 12, 83126, Flintsbach am Inn,
Germany
Tel.: (49) 80349087460
Web Site: https://www.tjiko.de
Emp.: 50
Wooden Construction Services
N.A.I.C.S.: 541330

Tracomex B.V. (1)

Bouwlingplein 34, 4901 KZ, Oosterhout,
Netherlands
Tel.: (31) 162437800
Web Site: https://www.tracomex.nl
Agricultural Raw Material Distr
N.A.I.C.S.: 424590
Jan Willem Pons *(Dir-Comml)*

URL Agrar GmbH (1)
Seering 7, Premstatten, 8141, Unterpremst-
atten, Austria
Tel.: (43) 31359007400
Web Site: https://www.urlagrar.at
Agricultural Raw Material Distr
N.A.I.C.S.: 424590

Unser Lagerhaus Warenhandelsge-
sellschaft m.b.H. (1)
Sudring 240-244, 9020, Klagenfurt,
Austria **(51.1%)**
Tel.: (43) 4633865570
Web Site: https://www.lagerhaus.at
Sales Range: $650-699.9 Million
Emp.: 1,100
Farm Supplies, Building Materials, Fuel &
Garden Products Whslr & Retailer
N.A.I.C.S.: 493110
Klaus Josef Lutz *(Chm-Supervisory Bd)*

Holding (Domestic):

RWA Raiffeisen Ware Austria
Aktiengesellschaft (2)
Raiffeisenstrasse 1, 2100, Korneuburg,
Austria **(50%)**
Tel.: (43) 226275550
Web Site: https://www.rwa.at
Farm Supplies, Building Materials, Fuel &
Garden Products Whslr & Warehousing
Services
N.A.I.C.S.: 493110
Reinhard Wolf *(CEO & Member-Exec Bd)*

Joint Venture (Domestic):

AUSTRIA JUICE GmbH (3)
Krollendorf 45, A- 3365, Allhartsberg,
Austria **(49.99%)**
Tel.: (43) 744823040
Web Site: https://www.austriajuice.com
Emp.: 1,000
Juice Concentrate Mfr
N.A.I.C.S.: 311421
Franz Ennser *(CEO)*

Subsidiary (Non-US):

Lukta Polska Sp. z o.o (4)
ul Plantowa 231, 96-230, Biala Rawska,
Poland
Tel.: (48) 814 60 25
Sales Range: $25-49.9 Million
Fruit Juices Mfr & Whslr
N.A.I.C.S.: 311411

Subsidiary (Domestic):

Ybbstaler Fruit Austria GmbH (4)
Kroellendorf 45, 3365, Allhartsberg, Austria
Tel.: (43) 744823040
Web Site: https://www.austriajuice.com
Sales Range: $25-49.9 Million
Emp.: 60
Beverage Compounds Mfr & Whslr
N.A.I.C.S.: 312111

Subsidiary (Non-US):

Ybbstaler Fruit Polska Sp. z o.o (4)
Ul Plantowa 231, Biala Rawska, Poland
Tel.: (48) 825622150
Web Site: http://www.ybbstaler.pl
Emp.: 200
Fruit Juices Whslr
N.A.I.C.S.: 424490
Helmut Stoger *(Gen Mgr)*

Subsidiary (Domestic):

GENOL Gesellschaft m.b.H. & Co.
KG (3)
Wienerbergstrasse 3, 1100, Vienna,
Austria **(100%)**
Tel.: (43) 1605150
Web Site: http://www.genol.at
Emp.: 100
Petroleum Product Whslr
N.A.I.C.S.: 424720

RWA International Holding
GmbH (3)

Wienerbergstrasse 3 Business Park, Vi-
enna, 1100, Austria
Tel.: (43) 1605150
Web Site: http://www.rwa.at
Emp.: 400
Agricultural Product Whslr
N.A.I.C.S.: 424910

Saatzucht Gleisdorf Gesellschaft
m.b.H (3)
Am Tieberhof 33, 8200, Gleisdorf, Austria
Tel.: (43) 311221050
Web Site: https://www.saatzuchtgleisdorf.at
Sales Range: $25-49.9 Million
Emp.: 12
Agricultural Equipment Whslr
N.A.I.C.S.: 423820

VISTA Geowissenschaftliche Ferner-
kundung GmbH (1)
Gabelsbergerstrasse 51, 80333, Munich,
Germany
Tel.: (49) 8945216140
Web Site: https://www.vista-geo.de
Smart Farming Services
N.A.I.C.S.: 115116
Silke Migdall *(Head-R&D)*

Voss GmbH & Co. KG (1)
Engelhardstr 10, 81369, Munich, Germany
Tel.: (49) 895 421 5121
Web Site: https://www.voss-gmbh.de
Real Estate Manangement Services
N.A.I.C.S.: 531390

WAV Warme Austria
VertriebsgmbH (1)
Raiffeisenstrasse 1, 2100, Korneuburg, Aus-
tria
Tel.: (43) 2262716170
Web Site: https://www.waermeaustria.com
Heating Oil & Lubricant Distr
N.A.I.C.S.: 457210

Windpark Berschweiler GmbH & Co.
KG (1)
Industriestrasse 2, 68519, Viernheim, Ger-
many
Tel.: (49) 6 204 9890
Web Site: https://www.windpark-
berschweiler.de
Wind Power Generation Services
N.A.I.C.S.: 221115

Wingenfeld Energie GmbH (1)
Zum Wolfsgraben 1, 36088, Hunfeld, Ger-
many
Tel.: (49) 66523033
Web Site: http://www.wingenfeld-energie.de
Agricultural Equipment Whslr
N.A.I.C.S.: 423820
Joseph Pfannes *(Mng Dir)*

Wohnen am Lerchenberg GmbH &
Co. KG (1)
Gewerbegebiet Eula-West Nr 14, 04552,
Borna, Germany
Tel.: (49) 3433209220
Web Site: https://www.wohnen-am-
lerchenberg.de
Construction Services
N.A.I.C.S.: 236220

Wohnen am Lerchenberg Verwal-
tungs GmbH (1)
Industrial Estate Eula West No 14, 04552,
Borna, Germany
Tel.: (49) 3433209220
Web Site: https://www.wohnen-am-
lerchenberg.de
N.A.I.C.S.: 236220
Sylvio Weise *(Mng Dir)*

biohelp - biologischer Pflanzenschutz-
Nutzlingsproduktions-, Handels- und
Beratungs GmbH (1)
Kapleigasse 16, 1110, Vienna, Austria
Tel.: (43) 17699769
Web Site: https://www.biohelp-profi.at
N.A.I.C.S.: 333111
Michael Gross *(Mng Dir)*

bs Baufachhandel Brands & Schnit-
zler GmbH & Co. KG (1)
Folradstr 11, Monchengladbach, 41065,
Germany
Tel.: (49) 2161496900
Web Site: http://www.brandsschnitzler.de
Construction Engineering Services

BayWa AG—(Continued)

N.A.I.C.S.: 541330

Subsidiary (Domestic):

bs Baufachhandel Brands & Schnitzler Verwaltungs-GmbH **(2)**
Folradstr 11, Monchengladbach, 41065, Nordrhein-Westfalen, Germany
Tel.: (49) 2101490900
Agricultural Equipment Whslr
N.A.I.C.S.: 423820
Peter Jasinski *(Mng Dir)*

BAZEL INTERNATIONAL LIMITED

II B/20 First Floor, New Delhi, 110024, Delhi, India
Tel.: (91) 1146081516
Web Site:
   https://www.bazelinternational.com
Year Founded: 1982
539946—(BOM)
Rev.: $115,257
Assets: $2,386,885
Liabilities: $450,568
Net Worth: $1,936,317
Earnings: ($46,171)
Emp.: 9
Fiscal Year-end: 03/31/21
Consumer Lending Services
N.A.I.C.S.: 522291
Preeti Puri *(Compliance Officer)*

BAZNA HEMIJA D.D.

1 drinske brigade broj 3, 73000, Gorazde, Bosnia & Herzegovina
Tel.: (387) 62937371
BHMGRK1—(SARE)
Sales Range: Less than $1 Million
Emp.: 1
Inorganic Chemical Mfr
N.A.I.C.S.: 325180

BB ELECTRONICS A/S

Ane Staunings Vej 21, 8700, Horsens, Denmark
Tel.: (45) 7625 1000   DK
Web Site:
   http://www.bbelectronics.dk
Year Founded: 1975
Emp.: 600
Electronics Mfr
N.A.I.C.S.: 334419
Susanne Schaldemose *(Chief Bus Dev Officer)*

Subsidiaries:

BB Electronics Suzhou Co. Ltd. **(1)**
Building E 58 Yangdong Road, Loufeng Suzhou Industrial Park, 215122, Suzhou, China
Tel.: (86) 512 6956 2880
Web Site: http://www.bbelectronics.dk
Electric Equipment Mfr
N.A.I.C.S.: 334419
Donna Deng *(Gen Mgr)*

BB MINAQUA AD

Number 93b Futoski put, 21000, Novi Sad, Serbia
Tel.: (381) 21 402 611
Web Site: http://www.bbminaqua.com
Emp.: 200
Mineral Water Mfr
N.A.I.C.S.: 312112
Sanja Bjelica *(Gen Mgr)*

BB TRADE A.D.

Trg Oslobodenja bb, Zitiste, Serbia
Tel.: (381) 23 821 969
Year Founded: 1956
BBTR—(BEL)
Sales Range: $25-49.9 Million
Emp.: 149
Beverage Whslr
N.A.I.C.S.: 424820
Dragoljub Bjeloglav *(Gen Mgr)*

BBC CO., LTD.

25 Munpyeongdong-Ro, Daedeok-Gu, Daejeon, Korea (South)
Tel.: (82) 429329773
Web Site:
   https://www.bestbristle.com
Year Founded: 1998
318410—(KRS)
Emp.: 96
Brush & Broom Mfr
N.A.I.C.S.: 339994
Steve Kang *(CEO)*

BBG BAUGERATE GMBH

Werk-VI-Stasse 55, 8605, Kapfenberg, Austria
Tel.: (43) 38623040   AT
Web Site: http://www.bbg-gmbh.at
Year Founded: 1919
Pneumatic Tool Mfr
N.A.I.C.S.: 334513
Josef Pagger *(Mng Dir & Head-Sls)*

Subsidiaries:

FAVRE Sarl **(1)**
Ets Favre Sarl 27 B rue Casimir Perier, 95871, Bezons, France
Tel.: (33) 139960096
Web Site: http://www.favre.eu
Machine Shops & Tool Mfr
N.A.I.C.S.: 332710

BBGI GLOBAL INFRASTRUCTURE S.A

Ebbc 6 E Route De Treves, 2633, Senningerberg, Luxembourg
Tel.: (352) 2634791   LU
Web Site: https://www.bb-gi.com
Year Founded: 2011
BBGI—(LSE)
Rev.: $63,047,741
Assets: $1,354,351,374
Liabilities: $9,185,232
Net Worth: $1,345,166,142
Earnings: $51,288,352
Emp.: 26
Fiscal Year-end: 12/31/23
Investment Management Service
N.A.I.C.S.: 523940
Duncan Ball *(Co-CEO & Member-Mgmt Bd)*

Subsidiaries:

Agder OPS Vegselskap AS **(1)**
Vestre Strandgate 23, 4611, Kristiansand, Norway
Tel.: (47) 47611800
Web Site: https://www.agderops.no
Construction Services
N.A.I.C.S.: 236220
Jan Walle *(Mng Dir)*

BBI DEVELOPMENT SA

ul Pulawska 2 Plac Unii Building A, 02-566, Warsaw, Poland
Tel.: (48) 222040040
Web Site:
   https://www.bbidevelopment.pl
BBD—(WAR)
Rev.: $6,210,366
Assets: $67,068,089
Liabilities: $24,675,051
Net Worth: $42,393,039
Earnings: $12,937,500
Fiscal Year-end: 12/31/23
Real Estate Development Services
N.A.I.C.S.: 531390
Michal Skotnicki *(Chm-Mgmt Bd)*

BBI LIFE SCIENCES CORPORATION

698 Xiangmin Road, Songjiang, Shanghai, 201611, China
Tel.: (86) 21 800 820 1016
Web Site: https://www.bbi-lifesciences.com
Rev.: $84,558,824

Assets: $148,008,765
Liabilities: $36,032,585
Net Worth: $111,976,179
Earnings: $11,041,789
Emp.: 1,472
Fiscal Year-end: 12/31/18
Life Science Researcher & Developer
N.A.I.C.S.: 541715
Qisong Wang *(Founder & Chm)*

Subsidiaries:

BBI Basic Canada INC. **(1)**
20 Konrad Crescent, Markham, L3R 8T4, ON, Canada
Tel.: (905) 474-4493
Web Site: http://www.biobasic.com
Life Science Product Mfr & Distr
N.A.I.C.S.: 325411

Bio Basic Canada Inc. **(1)**
20 Konrad Crescent, Markham, L3R 8T4, ON, Canada
Tel.: (905) 474-4493
Web Site: http://www.biobasic.com
Life Science Product Mfr
N.A.I.C.S.: 325414

NBS Biologicals Limited **(1)**
14 Tower Square, Huntingdon, PE29 7DT, Cambridgeshire, United Kingdom
Tel.: (44) 1480433875
Web Site: http://www.nbsbio.co.uk
Laboratory Equipment Mfr
N.A.I.C.S.: 334516

BBIGPLAS POLY PVT LTD.

2B Pretoria Street Kolkata,, West Bengal, 700071, India
Tel.: (91) 3322823744
Plastic Materials Mfr
N.A.I.C.S.: 325211

Subsidiaries:

Kkalpana Plastick Ltd. **(1)**
12 Dr U N Brahmachari Street Maruti Building 5th Floor Flat No 5F, Kolkata, 700017, West Bengal, India   **(72.56%)**
Tel.: (91) 3340030674
Web Site: https://www.kkalpanaplastick.com
Rev.: $56,225
Assets: $755,799
Liabilities: $7,550
Net Worth: $748,249
Earnings: ($57,374)
Emp.: 9
Fiscal Year-end: 03/31/2023
Plastic Materials Mfr
N.A.I.C.S.: 325211
Ankita Karnani *(Sec & Compliance Officer)*

BBK B.S.C.

43 Government Avenue, PO Box 597, Manama, Bahrain
Tel.: (973) 17223388
Web Site: https://www.bbkonline.com
BBK—(BAH)
Rev.: $403,968,065
Assets: $9,957,030,317
Liabilities: $8,368,213,045
Net Worth: $1,588,817,273
Earnings: $172,409,220
Emp.: 1,295
Fiscal Year-end: 12/31/22
Banking Services
N.A.I.C.S.: 522110
Murad Ali Murad *(Chm)*

Subsidiaries:

CrediMax B.S.C. **(1)**
Building 858 Road 3618 Block 436, PO Box 5350, Seef District, Manama, Bahrain
Tel.: (973) 17117117
Web Site: https://www.credimax.com.bh
Credit Card Issuing Services
N.A.I.C.S.: 522210
Ahmed A.Rahman Seyadi *(Asst Gen Mgr-Bus Dev Dept)*

Global Payment Services W.L.L. **(1)**
Building - 722 Road 3616 Block 436, PO Box 2110, Seef District, Manama, Bahrain
Tel.: (973) 17569000
Web Site: https://www.gps.com.bh

Sales Range: $50-74.9 Million
Emp.: 30
Credit Card Issuing Services
N.A.I.C.S.: 522210
Ali Arab *(Gen Mgr)*

Invita B.S.C. **(1)**
Suite 107 Bahrain Car Park Commercial Centre, Manama, 1197, Bahrain
Tel.: (973) 17 50 6000
Web Site: http://www.invita.com.bh
Emp.: 200
Business Process Outsourcing Services
N.A.I.C.S.: 561499

Invita Kuwait K.S.C.C **(1)**
Sharq Ahmed al-jaber St - Wafra Real Estate Bldg, PO Box 2294, Mezzanin Safat, Kuwait, 13023, Kuwait
Tel.: (965) 2 205 9888
Web Site: https://www.invita.com.kw
Management Consulting Services
N.A.I.C.S.: 541611

BBKO CONSULTING S.A.

Calc Dos Cravos 98, 06453-000, Barueri, SP, Brazil
Tel.: (55) 1131013234
Web Site: http://www.bbko.com.br
Year Founded: 2001
Sales Range: $10-24.9 Million
Emp.: 400
Computer Consulting Services
N.A.I.C.S.: 541690
Jose Eduardo F. Nascimento *(CEO)*

BBMG CORPORATION

22F/ Tower D Global Trade Center No 36 North 3rd Rising East Road, Dongcheng District, Beijing, 100013, China
Tel.: (86) 1066417706   CN
Web Site: https://bbmg-umb.azurewebsites.net
Year Founded: 2005
BBMPY—(OTCIQ)
Rev.: $14,236,564,313
Assets: $38,978,740,353
Liabilities: $25,839,626,138
Net Worth: $13,139,114,215
Earnings: $240,901,511
Emp.: 45,991
Fiscal Year-end: 12/31/22
Cement Product Mfr
N.A.I.C.S.: 327310
Wenyan Liu *(Deputy Gen Mgr)*

Subsidiaries:

Beijing BBMG Tiantan Furniture Co., Ltd. **(1)**
No 9 Xiaohuangzhuang Road Andingmenwai Street, Dongcheng District, Beijing, 100013, China
Tel.: (86) 1082928020
Web Site: https://ttjj.com.cn
Emp.: 2,000
Furniture Mfr & Distr
N.A.I.C.S.: 337214

Beijing Building Materials Import and Export Co., Ltd **(1)**
Rm B302 Jin Yu Mansion No 129 Jia Xuan Wu Men Xi Da Jie, Xicheng, Beijing, 100031, China
Tel.: (86) 1066414599
Web Site: http://www.bbmiec.com
Building Material Supplier
N.A.I.C.S.: 444180

Beijing Building Materials Testing Academy Co., Ltd. **(1)**
No 69 Jinding North Road, Shijingshan District, Beijing, 100041, China
Tel.: (86) 1088724984
Building Material Quality Testing Services
N.A.I.C.S.: 541350

Beijing Liulihe Cement Co., Ltd **(1)**
15 Chezhan Jie Liulihe Xiang, Fangshan, 102403, Beijing, China
Tel.: (86) 1089382980
Cement Mfr
N.A.I.C.S.: 327310

Beijing Sanchong Mirrors Co., Ltd (1)
No 2 Chengxi Road Xisanqi building, Haidian District, Beijing, 100096, China
Tel.: (86) 1082910836
Web Site: https://www.bsmirror.com
Sales Range: $25-49.9 Million
Emp.: 100
Optical Glasses Mfr
N.A.I.C.S.: 327215

Beijing Star Building Materials Co., Ltd (1)
No 2 Gaojin Chaoyang, Beijing, China
Tel.: (86) 1085767806
Web Site: http://www.bsbm.cc
Mineral Wool Mfr
N.A.I.C.S.: 327993

Beijing Tongda Refractory Engineering Technology Co., Ltd. (1)
No 1 Anningzhuang East Road, Qinghe Haidian, Beijing, 100085, China
Tel.: (86) 1082714360
Web Site: http://www.bjtd.com.cn
Building Construction Material Mfr
N.A.I.C.S.: 327120

Beijing Woodworking Factory Co., Ltd (1)
4 Dahongmen W Rd Yongwai Ave Fengtai, Beijing, 100075, China
Tel.: (86) 1067248319
Building Materials Mfr
N.A.I.C.S.: 561790

Luquan Dongfang Dingxin Cement Co., Ltd (1)
Tongge Indust Zone, Luquan, Shijiazhuang, Hebei, China
Tel.: (86) 31182213023
Cement Mfr
N.A.I.C.S.: 327310

Tangshan High Voltage Porcelain Insulator Works Co., Ltd. (1)
No 1 dianporcelain Road, modern equipment manufacturing industrial zone Kaiping District, Tangshan, 063021, Hebei, China
Tel.: (86) 3158736557
Web Site: https://en.td.com.cn
Emp.: 150
Insulator Mfr & Distr
N.A.I.C.S.: 335932

Tangshan Jidong Development Yan Dong Construction Co., Ltd. (1)
Linyin North Road, Fengrun, Tangshan, 064009, China
Tel.: (86) 3155589032
Web Site: http://tsjdjs.com
Building Construction Contracting Services
N.A.I.C.S.: 236220

BBR BANK AO
1st Nikoloschepovskiy Lane Bld 6 Block 1, 121099, Moscow, Russia
Tel.: (7) 4953639162
Web Site: http://www.bbr.ru
Year Founded: 1994
Sales Range: Less than $1 Million
Commercial Banking Services
N.A.I.C.S.: 522110
Alexey Shitov *(Chm & CEO)*

BBR HOLDINGS (S) LTD.
50 Changi South Street 1, BBR Building, Singapore, 486126, Singapore
Tel.: (65) 65462280
Web Site:
   https://bbr.listedcompany.com
Year Founded: 1944
BBR—(SES)
Rev.: $126,414,628
Assets: $235,822,953
Liabilities: $166,790,044
Net Worth: $69,032,909
Earnings: $3,685,997
Emp.: 699
Fiscal Year-end: 12/31/22
Holding Company; Structural Engineering Design & Services
N.A.I.C.S.: 551112
Andrew Kheng Hwee Tan *(CEO)*

Subsidiaries:

BBR Construction Systems (M) Sdn. Bhd. (1)
No 17 Jalan Sg Jeluh 32/191, Kawasan Perindustrian Kemuning Seksyen 32, 40460, Shah Alam, Selangor Darul Ehsan, Malaysia
Tel.: (60) 355253270
Web Site: https://bbr.com.my
Sales Range: $25-49.9 Million
Emp.: 40
Engineeering Services
N.A.I.C.S.: 541330

BBR Construction Systems Pte Ltd (1)
BBR Building 50 Changi South Street 1, Singapore, 486126, Singapore
Tel.: (65) 65462280
Sales Range: $25-49.9 Million
Emp.: 70
Engineeering Services
N.A.I.C.S.: 541330

BBR Piling Pte Ltd. (1)
BBR Building 50 Changi South Street 1, Singapore, 486126, Singapore
Tel.: (65) 65462280
Emp.: 100
Piling & Foundation Systems
N.A.I.C.S.: 237990
John Mo *(Mng Dir)*

Moderna Homes Pte. Ltd. (1)
50 Changi South Street 1 BBR Building, Singapore, 486126, Singapore
Tel.: (65) 6 345 1511
Web Site: https://www.homesmoderna.com
Construction Services
N.A.I.C.S.: 236220
Pei San Neo Dawn *(Mgr-Technical)*

Singapore Engineering & Construction Pte. Ltd. (1)
50 Changi South Street 1 BBR Building 3rd Floor, Singapore, 486126, Singapore
Tel.: (65) 6 235 6602
Web Site:
   https://www.attc.singaporepiling.com.sg
Construction Engineering Services
N.A.I.C.S.: 541330

Singapore Piling & Civil Engineering Private Limited (1)
50 Changi S St 1 BBR Bldg, Singapore, 486126, Singapore
Tel.: (65) 62355088
Web Site: http://www.singaporepiling.com.sg
Sales Range: $25-49.9 Million
Emp.: 2
Piling & Civil Engineering Services
N.A.I.C.S.: 541330
Loy Fai Lim *(Mgr-HR)*

Subsidiary (Domestic):

Singa Development Pte Ltd (2)
50 Changi S St 1, Singapore, 486126, Singapore
Tel.: (65) 65465257
Sales Range: $10-24.9 Million
Civil Engineering Services
N.A.I.C.S.: 541330

BBREAK SYSTEMS CO., LTD.
5F Higashi Gotanda Square 2-10-2 Higashi gotanda Shinagawa, Tokyo, 141-0022, Japan
Tel.: (81) 354877855
Web Site: https://www.bbreak.co.jp
Year Founded: 2002
3986—(TKS)
Sales Range: Less than $1 Million
System Integration Services
N.A.I.C.S.: 541512
Jiro Shiraiwa *(Founder, Chm, Pres & CEO)*

BBS KRAFTFAHRZEUGTECHNIK AG
Welschdorf 220, 77761, Schiltach, Germany
Tel.: (49) 7836520
Web Site: http://www.bbs.com
Year Founded: 1970

Automobile Parts Mfr
N.A.I.C.S.: 336110
Walter Doerig *(Chm-Supervisory Bd)*

Subsidiaries:

BBS of America, Inc. (1)
5320 BBS Way, Braselton, GA 30517
Tel.: (770) 967-9848
Web Site: http://www.bbs-usa.com
Motor Vehicle Parts Mfr
N.A.I.C.S.: 336390

BBS-BIOACTIVE BONE SUBSTITUTES PLC
Kiviharjunlenkki 6, 90220, Oulu, Finland
Tel.: (358) 504485132
Web Site: https://www.bbs-artebone.fi
Year Founded: 2003
Rev.: $59,102
Assets: $11,011,374
Liabilities: $7,563,103
Net Worth: $3,448,271
Earnings: ($1,834,499)
Emp.: 12
Fiscal Year-end: 12/31/19
Medical Equipment Mfr
N.A.I.C.S.: 339112
Ilkka Kangasniemi *(CEO)*

BBTV HOLDINGS INC.
1205 Melville Street,, Vancouver, V6E 0A6, BC, Canada
Tel.: (604) 900-5202
Emp.: 361
Advertising Services
N.A.I.C.S.: 541810

Subsidiaries:

15384150 Canada Inc. (1)
20 Holly St, Suite 300,, Toronto, M4S 3B1, ON, Canada
Tel.: (604) 715-9016
Financial Services
N.A.I.C.S.: 523999

Subsidiary (Domestic):

BBTV Holdings Inc. (2)
1205 Melville Street, Vancouver, V6E 0A6, BC, Canada
Tel.: (604) 900-5202
Web Site: http://www.bbtv.com
Rev.: $372,851,858
Assets: $318,676,621
Liabilities: $128,117,907
Net Worth: $190,558,714
Earnings: ($25,923,195)
Emp.: 284
Fiscal Year-end: 12/31/2021
Communication Service
N.A.I.C.S.: 517810
Todd Tappin *(CFO)*

Subsidiary (Domestic):

BroadbandTV Corporation (3)
1500 - 777 Hornby St, Vancouver, V6Z 2T3, BC, Canada
Tel.: (604) 647-2288
Web Site: http://www.bbtv.com
Television Broadcasting Services
N.A.I.C.S.: 516120
Shahrzad Rafati *(CEO)*

BBX MINERALS LIMITED
Level 1 50 Angove Street, Perth, 6006, WA, Australia
Tel.: (61) 865552955
Web Site:
   http://www.bbxminerals.com.au
BCM—(ASX)
Rev.: $18,216
Assets: $1,654,921
Liabilities: $542,618
Net Worth: $1,112,304
Earnings: ($4,038,604)
Fiscal Year-end: 06/30/24
Mineral Exploration Services
N.A.I.C.S.: 213115
Simon Robertson *(Sec)*

Subsidiaries:

BBX CHINA CO., LTD (1)
Zhaolin Mansion No 15 Ronghua Middle Rd BDA, Beijing, 100176, China
Tel.: (86) 1051078888
Barter Business Providers
N.A.I.C.S.: 561499

BBX Centroamerica La Uruca (1)
De la plz 200 mts Norte, PO Box 1298-1000, San Jose, Costa Rica
Tel.: (506) 22332839
Web Site: http://www.ebbx.co.cr
Sales Range: $25-49.9 Million
Emp.: 5
Barter Business Providers
N.A.I.C.S.: 561990
Mariamalia Jacobo *(Mgr)*

BBX MANAGEMENT PTY. LTD (1)
916 Pacific Hwy, Gordon, 2072, NSW, Australia
Tel.: (61) 294991100
Sales Range: $25-49.9 Million
Emp.: 20
Barter Business Providers
N.A.I.C.S.: 561990
Michael Touma *(Mgr)*

BBX Management Ltd (1)
1/11 Homersham Pl Burnside, Christchurch, 8053, Canterbury, New Zealand
Tel.: (64) 33721562
Web Site: http://www.ebbx.co.nz
Sales Range: $25-49.9 Million
Emp.: 2
Business Exchange Services
N.A.I.C.S.: 561990
Joyce Chen *(Mgr-South Island)*

BBYE CORPORATION
MA-SIX, 1F 6-4-5 Minamiaoyama, Minato-ku, Tokyo, 107-0062, Japan
Tel.: (81) 368046530
Web Site: https://www.bxe.co.jp
Year Founded: 2004
Cosmetic Product Mfr & Whslr
N.A.I.C.S.: 424210
Emi Sugitani *(CEO)*

BC COMERTBANK SA
Independentei st 1/1, MD-2043, Chisinau, Moldova
Tel.: (373) 22839839
Web Site: http://www.comertbank.md
Year Founded: 1990
Commercial Banking Services
N.A.I.C.S.: 522110
Serghei Cartasov *(Chm-Mgmt Bd)*

BC CRAFT SUPPLY CO., LTD.
810-789 West Pender Street, Vancouver, V6C 1H2, BC, Canada
Tel.: (604) 687-2038
Web Site: http://www.bccraftsupply.ca
CRFT—(CNSX)
Rev.: $22,527
Assets: $7,413,941
Liabilities: $14,120,465
Net Worth: ($6,706,523)
Earnings: ($27,840,632)
Fiscal Year-end: 09/30/20
Cannabis Product Mfr
N.A.I.C.S.: 325411
Matthew Watters *(CEO)*

BC INSTITUT D.D. ZAGREB
Rugvica Dugoselska 7, 10370, Dugo Selo, Croatia
Tel.: (385) 12781510
Web Site: http://www.bc-institut.hr
Year Founded: 1897
Seed Producer
N.A.I.C.S.: 111211

BC MOLDINDCONBANK S.A.
Str Armeneasca 38, MD-2012, Chisinau, Moldova
Tel.: (373) 22576782
Web Site: http://www.micb.md
Rev.: $53,434,564

BC Moldindconbank S.A.—(Continued)

Assets: $1,056,067,522
Liabilities: $869,088,361
Net Worth: $186,979,161
Earnings: $38,859,497
Fiscal Year-end: 12/31/19
Commercial Banking Services
N.A.I.C.S.: 522110
Herbert Steplc *(Chm)*

BC MOLDOVA AGROINDBANK S.A.
Str Constantin Tanase 9/1, MD-2005, Chisinau, Moldova
Tel.: (373) 22450603
Web Site: http://www.maib.md
Year Founded: 1991
Rev.: $79,345,459
Assets: $1,487,188,020
Liabilities: $1,233,838,866
Net Worth: $253,349,154
Earnings: $40,649,096
Fiscal Year-end: 12/31/19
Commercial Banking Services
N.A.I.C.S.: 522110
Victor Miculet *(Vice Chm)*

Subsidiaries:

MAIB-Leasing SA　　　　　　**(1)**
Str Tighina 49 4th Floor Mun, Chisinau, 2001, Moldova
Tel.: (373) 22844202
Web Site: http://www.leasing.md
Car Lending Services
N.A.I.C.S.: 532112

BC MOLY LTD.
3606 - 833 Seymour Street, Vancouver, V6B 3L4, BC, Canada
Tel.: (416) 301-3036
Year Founded: 1984
BM—(TSXV)
Rev.: $22,149
Assets: $559,050
Liabilities: $66,458
Net Worth: $492,592
Earnings: ($17,369)
Fiscal Year-end: 04/30/24
Mineral Exploration Services
N.A.I.C.S.: 213114
Edward Alfred Yurkowski *(Pres, CEO, CFO & Sec)*

BC PARTNERS LLP
40 Portman Square, London, W1H 6DA, United Kingdom
Tel.: (44) 2070094800　　　UK
Web Site: http://www.bcpartners.com
Year Founded: 1986
Privater Equity Firm
N.A.I.C.S.: 523999
Nikos Stathopoulos *(Partner)*

Subsidiaries:

ATI Enterprises, Inc.　　　　　**(1)**
6331 Blvd 26 Ste 275, North Richland Hills, TX 76180
Tel.: (855) 203-1599
Web Site: http://www.aticareertraining.edu
Sales Range: $200-249.9 Million
Technical & Trade Career Training Schools
N.A.I.C.S.: 611519

Accudyne Industries, LLC　　　**(1)**
2728 N Harwood St Ste 200, Dallas, TX 75201-1579
Tel.: (469) 518-4777
Sales Range: $1-4.9 Billion
Emp.: 3,000
Holding Company; Industrial Pumps & Compressors Mfr
N.A.I.C.S.: 551112
Donna Peruta *(CIO)*

Subsidiary (Non-US):

Accudyne Industries Asia Pte. Ltd.　　　　　　　　　　**(2)**
501 510 Thomson Rd 13-01, Singapore, 298135, Singapore

Tel.: (65) 64557559
Emp.: 20
High-Pressure Pumps, Gas Boosters & Valves Distr
N.A.I.C.S.: 423830
Danny Yue *(Reg Mgr)*

Subsidiary (Domestic):

Haskel International, LLC　　　**(2)**
100 E Graham Pl, Burbank, CA 91502-2027
Tel.: (818) 843-4000
Web Site: http://www.haskel.com
Sales Range: $100-124.9 Million
Emp.: 1,300
High-Pressure Pumps, Gas Boosters & Valves Mfr & Distr
N.A.I.C.S.: 333914
Pat Kealey *(Pres)*

Subsidiary (Non-US):

Haskel Europe Ltd.　　　　　　**(3)**
North Hylton Road, Sunderland, SR5 3JD, Tyne & Wear, United Kingdom
Tel.: (44) 1915491212
Web Site: http://www.haskel-europe.com
High-Pressure Pumps, Gas Boosters & Valves Mfr & Distr
N.A.I.C.S.: 333914
Stephen Learney *(Mng Dir)*

Plant (Domestic):

Haskel Europe Ltd. - Aberdeen　**(4)**
Unit 14 Airways Industrial Estate, Pitmedden Road, Dyce, AB21 0DT, Scotland, United Kingdom
Tel.: (44) 1224771784
Web Site: http://www.haskel-europe.com
High-Pressure Pumps, Gas Boosters & Valves Mfr
N.A.I.C.S.: 333914

Subsidiary (Non-US):

Haskel France SAS　　　　　　**(4)**
34 Rue Des Chateaux, 59290, Wasquehal, France
Tel.: (33) 320046600
Web Site: http://www.haskel.fr
High-Pressure Pumps, Gas Boosters & Valves Distr
N.A.I.C.S.: 423830
Alexandre Clay *(Mng Dir)*

Haskel Sistemas de Fluidos Espana, S.R.L.　　　　　　　　**(4)**
Paseo Ubarburu No 81 Edificio 5 Planta 1 Locales 1 y 2, Poligono 27 Martutene, 20115, Astigarraga, Gipuzkoa, Spain
Tel.: (34) 943474566
Web Site: http://www.haskel-es.com
Emp.: 6
High-Pressure Pumps, Gas Boosters & Valves Mfr & Distr
N.A.I.C.S.: 333914

Subsidiary (Non-US):

M2S Middle East FZE　　　　　**(2)**
LOB 16 Suite 16614, PO Box 262384, Jebel Ali, Dubai, United Arab Emirates
Tel.: (971) 48875646
Emp.: 25
High-Pressure Pumps, Gas Boosters & Valves Distr
N.A.I.C.S.: 423830
Robert Roy *(Dir-Sls)*

Subsidiary (Domestic):

Milton Roy, LLC　　　　　　　**(2)**
201 Ivyland Rd, Ivyland, PA 18974-1706
Tel.: (215) 441-0800
Web Site: http://www.miltonroy.com
Sales Range: $75-99.9 Million
Controlled Volume (Metering) Pumps & Related Equipment Mfr
N.A.I.C.S.: 333914
Kris Kimmel *(Product Mgr-YZ Sys)*

Division (Domestic):

Milton Roy - Hartell Division　**(3)**
201 Ivyland Rd, Ivyland, PA 18974
Tel.: (215) 441-0800
Web Site: http://www.hartell.com
Sales Range: $50-74.9 Million
Pumps Mfr
N.A.I.C.S.: 333914

Lisa Haines *(Mgr-Sls-Western Reg)*

Subsidiary (Non-US):

Milton Roy Europe　　　　　　**(3)**
10 Grande Rue, Pont-Saint-Pierre, 27360, France
Tel.: (33) 232683000
Web Site: http://www.miltonroy-europe.com
Sales Range: $100-124.9 Million
Emp.: 250
Pumps & Compressors Mfr
N.A.I.C.S.: 333914

Subsidiary (Domestic):

Milton Roy Liquid Metronics Incorporated　　　　　　　**(3)**
8th Post Office Sq, Acton, MA 01720-3948
Tel.: (978) 635-4999
Web Site: http://www.lmipumps.com
Sales Range: $25-49.9 Million
Measuring & Dispensing Pumps
N.A.I.C.S.: 333914

Williams Instrument Company　**(3)**
201 Ivyland Rd, Warminster, PA 18974-1706
Tel.: (215) 441-0800
Web Site: http://www.williamspumps.com
Sales Range: $1-9.9 Million
Pneumatic Metering Pumps & Chemical Injection Systems Mfr
N.A.I.C.S.: 333914

Y-Z Systems Inc.　　　　　　　**(3)**
8875 North Sam Houston Pkwy West, Houston, TX 77064
Tel.: (281) 362-6500
Web Site: http://www.yzsystems.com
Sales Range: $25-49.9 Million
Emp.: 12
Odorization Systems Mfr
N.A.I.C.S.: 334516
Kris Kimmel *(Mgr-Sls)*

Subsidiary (Domestic):

Sundyne, LLC　　　　　　　　**(2)**
14845 W 64th Ave, Arvada, CO 80007-7523
Tel.: (303) 425-0800
Web Site: http://www.sundyne.com
Sales Range: $125-149.9 Million
Emp.: 400
Pumps & Pumping Equipment Mfr
N.A.I.C.S.: 333914
Daryl Lamy *(Dir-Sls-Tactical, Worldwide)*

Aenova Holding GmbH　　　　**(1)**
Gut Kerschlach 1, 82396, Pahl, Germany
Tel.: (49) 88 08 9243 111
Web Site: http://www.aenova.de
Sales Range: $650-699.9 Million
Emp.: 2,500
Vitamins & Pharmaceuticals Mfr
N.A.I.C.S.: 325412
Frank Elsen *(CFO)*

Subsidiary (Domestic):

Dragenopharm Apotheker Puschl GmbH & Co. KG　　　　　**(2)**
Gollstr 1, 84549, Munich, Germany
Tel.: (49) 86838950
Web Site: http://www.dragenopharm.de
Sales Range: $100-124.9 Million
Mfr of Generic Pharmaceutical Products
N.A.I.C.S.: 325412

Haupt Pharma AG　　　　　　**(2)**
Moosrosenstr 7-13, D 12347, Berlin, Germany
Tel.: (49) 30 609 03 0
Web Site: http://www.haupt-pharma.de
Sales Range: $350-399.9 Million
Emp.: 2,000
Contract Pharmaceutical Mfr
N.A.I.C.S.: 325412
Otto Prange *(Chm-Supervisory Bd)*

Subsidiary (Domestic):

Haupt Pharma Amareg GmbH　**(3)**
Donaustaufer Strasse 378, D 93055, Regensburg, Germany
Tel.: (49) 941 4601 0
Web Site: http://www.haupt-pharma.de
Emp.: 250
Contract Development & Contract Manufacturing of Pharmaceuticals
N.A.I.C.S.: 325412

Oliver Schmied *(Mng Dir)*

Haupt Pharma Berlin GmbH　　**(3)**
Gradestrasse 13, 12347, Berlin, Germany
Tel.: (49) 30 60903 0
Web Site: http://www.haupt-pharma.de
Emp.: 170
Pharmaceuticals Mfr
N.A.I.C.S.: 325412
Hans-Werner Prokasky *(Mng Dir)*

Plant (Domestic):

Haupt Pharma Berlin GmbH - Brackenheim　　　　　　　**(4)**
Moosrosenstrasse 713, 12347, Berlin, Germany
Tel.: (49) 30609030
Blistering & Packaging of Pharmaceuticals
N.A.I.C.S.: 561910

Subsidiary (Domestic):

Haupt Pharma Development GmbH　　　　　　　　　　**(3)**
Pfaffenrieder Strasse 5, 82515, Wolfratshausen, Germany
Tel.: (49) 8171 414 111
Pharmaceutical Developer
N.A.I.C.S.: 541715
Markus Hinterberger *(Mng Dir)*

Subsidiary (US):

Haupt Pharma Inc.　　　　　　**(3)**
100 Chesterfield Business Pkwy Ste 279, Chesterfield, MO 63005
Tel.: (636) 681-1899
Web Site: http://www.haupt-pharma.de
Sales of Contract Manufacturing & Development of Pharmaceuticals
N.A.I.C.S.: 325412
Andrej Gasperlin *(Mng Dir)*

Subsidiary (Non-US):

Haupt Pharma Latina S.r.l.　　**(3)**
SS 156 Km 47600, Borgo San Michele, 4100, Latina, LT, Italy
Tel.: (39) 0773 4251
Web Site: http://www.haupt-pharma.de
Emp.: 430
Pharmaceuticals Mfr
N.A.I.C.S.: 325412
Giuseppe Martelli *(Mng Dir)*

Haupt Pharma Livron S.A.S.　　**(3)**
1 Rue Comte de Sinard, Livron-Sur-Drome, 26250, Paris, France
Tel.: (33) 4 75 61 02 00
Web Site: http://www.haupt-pharma.de
Emp.: 150
Pharmaceuticals Mfr
N.A.I.C.S.: 325412
Norbert Schwella *(Mng Dir)*

Subsidiary (Domestic):

Haupt Pharma Munster GmbH　**(3)**
Schleebrueggenkamp 15, 48159, Munster, Germany
Tel.: (49) 251 28 55 0
Web Site: http://www.haupt-pharma.de
Emp.: 220
Pharmaceuticals Mfr
N.A.I.C.S.: 325412
Hubert Bensmann *(Mng Dir)*

Haupt Pharma Sales GmbH　　**(3)**
Pfaffenrieder Strasse 5-7, 82515, Wolfratshausen, Germany
Tel.: (49) 8171 414 126
Web Site: http://www.haupt-pharma.de
Pharmaceutical Contract Sales
N.A.I.C.S.: 561499
Erich Scheibner *(Mng Dir)*

Subsidiary (Non-US):

Haupt Pharma Toride Co., Ltd.　**(3)**
5662 Omonma, Toride, 302 0001, Ibaraki, Japan
Tel.: (81) 297 77 8331
Web Site: http://www.haupt-pharma.de
Emp.: 20
Pharmaceuticals Mfr
N.A.I.C.S.: 325412
Keizo Yanagisawa *(Mng Dir)*

Subsidiary (Domestic):

Haupt Pharma Wolfratshausen GmbH　　　　　　　　　**(3)**

Pfaffenrieder Strasse 5, 82515, Wolfrat-
shausen, Germany
Tel.: (49) 8171 414 201
Web Site: http://www.haupt-pharma.de
Emp.: 300
Pharmaceuticals Mfr
N.A.I.C.S.: 325412
Norbert Kuebler (Mng Dir)

Haupt Pharma Wulfing GmbH (3)
Bethelner Landstrasse 18, 31028, Gronau,
Germany
Tel.: (49) 5182 585 0
Web Site: http://www.aenova-group.com
Pharmaceuticals Mfr
N.A.I.C.S.: 325412

Subsidiary (Non-US):

Swiss Caps AG (2)
Husenstrasse 35, 9533, Kirchberg, Switzer-
land
Tel.: (41) 71 93 26 262
Emp.: 210
Contract Vitamins & Pharmaceuticals Mfr
N.A.I.C.S.: 325412

Subsidiary (Domestic):

**Temmler Pharma GmbH & Co.
KG** (2)
Temmlerstrasse 2, 35039, Marburg, Ger-
many
Tel.: (49) 64214940
Emp.: 210
Pharmaceuticals Mfr
N.A.I.C.S.: 325412

Subsidiary (Domestic):

**C.P.M. ContractPharma GmbH & Co.
KG** (3)
Gutenbergstrasse 1, D 83052, Bruckmuhl,
Germany
Tel.: (49) 80629048 25
Web Site: http://www.cpm-
contractpharma.com
Sales Range: $50-74.9 Million
Emp.: 150
Pharmaceuticals Mfr
N.A.I.C.S.: 325412
Stefan Fasching (Mng Dir)

Subsidiary (Non-US):

SwissCo Services AG (3)
Bahnhofstr 14, CH 4334, Sisseln, Switzer-
land
Tel.: (41) 628664141
Web Site: http://www.temmler.eu
Sales Range: $50-74.9 Million
Pharmaceuticals Mfr
N.A.I.C.S.: 325412

Temmler Ireland Ltd. (3)
Banshagh, Killorglin, Co Kerry, Ireland
Tel.: (353) 6697926 00
Web Site: http://www.temmler.de
Sales Range: $25-49.9 Million
Pharmaceuticals Mfr
N.A.I.C.S.: 325412
Peter Quane (Mng Dir)

Temmler Italia S.r.l. (3)
Via delle Industrie 2, 20061, Carugate, Mi-
lan, Italy
Tel.: (39) 029250341
Web Site: http://www.temmler.de
Pharmaceuticals Mfr
N.A.I.C.S.: 325412
Massimiliano Del Frate (Mng Dir)

Subsidiary (Domestic):

Temmler Werke GmbH (3)
Weihenstephaner Strasse 28, 81673, Mu-
nich, Germany
Tel.: (49) 8942729901
Web Site: http://www.temmler.eu
Sales Range: $50-74.9 Million
Emp.: 200
Pharmaceuticals Mfr
N.A.I.C.S.: 325412

Allflex Europe SA (1)
35 Rue des Eaux, 35500, Vitre, France
Tel.: (33) 2 99 75 77 00
Web Site: http://www.allflex-europe.com
Emp.: 1,200
Animal Identification Tag Mfr
N.A.I.C.S.: 326199

Jacques Martin (COO)

Subsidiary (US):

Allflex USA, Inc. (2)
PO Box 612266, Dallas-Fort Worth Airport,
TX 75261
Tel.: (972) 456-3686
Web Site: http://www.allflexusa.com
Sales Range: $250-299.9 Million
Animal Identification Tag Mfr
N.A.I.C.S.: 326199
Glenn Fischer (Pres)

BC Partners, Inc. (1)
650 Madison Ave 23rd Fl, New York, NY
10022
Tel.: (212) 891-2880
Web Site: http://www.bcpartners.com
Privater Equity Firm
N.A.I.C.S.: 523999
Justin Bateman (Partner)

**Bulgarian Telecommunications Com-
pany EAD** (1)
115 I Tsarigradsko chaussee Blvd, 1784,
Sofia, Bulgaria
Tel.: (359) 2 949 43 31
Web Site: http://www.vivacom.bg
Rev.: $542,830,461
Assets: $973,114,597
Liabilities: $553,506,788
Net Worth: $419,607,809
Earnings: $73,134,498
Emp.: 5,433
Fiscal Year-end: 12/31/2018
Telecommunication Servicesb
N.A.I.C.S.: 517810
Atanas Dobrev (CEO & Member-Mgmt Bd)

CarTrawler Ltd. (1)
Classon House Dundrum Business Park
Dundrum, Dublin, Ireland
Tel.: (353) 23 8883011
Web Site: http://www.cartrawler.com
Car Rental Services
N.A.I.C.S.: 532111
Mike McGearty (CEO)

CeramTec GmbH (1)
CeramTec-Platz 1-9, 73207, Plochingen,
Germany
Tel.: (49) 7153 611 0
Web Site: http://www.ceramtec.com
Ceramic Components for Medical, Automo-
tive, Electronic Equipment & Machinery
Applications
N.A.I.C.S.: 339999
Gunter von Au (Chm-Supervisory Bd)

Subsidiary (Non-US):

CeramTec Commerciale Italiana (2)
Via Campagnola 40, Bergamo, 24126, Italy
Tel.: (39) 035 322382
Web Site: http://www.ceramtec.it
Ceramic Components Sales
N.A.I.C.S.: 423990

CeramTec Czech Republic s.r.o. (2)
Zerotinova 62, 78701, Sumperk, Czech
Republic
Tel.: (420) 583 369 111
Web Site: http://www.ceramtec.cz
Ceramic Components Mfr & Sales
N.A.I.C.S.: 339999

Branch (Non-US):

CeramTec France (2)
21 rue Clement Marot, 75008, Paris, Ce-
dex, France
Tel.: (33) 254971531
Web Site: http://www.ceramtec.fr
Ceramic Components Sales
N.A.I.C.S.: 423990

Subsidiary (Non-US):

**CeramTec Iberica, Innovative Ce-
ramic Engineering, S.L.**
Santa Marta 23-25, Vilassar de Mar, 08340,
Barcelona, Spain
Tel.: (34) 93 7 50 65 60
Web Site: http://www.ceramtec.es
Ceramic Components Mfr & Marketer
N.A.I.C.S.: 339999

**CeramTec Innovative Ceramic Engi-
neering, (M) Sdn. Bhd.** (2)
Lot 17 & 18 Lorong Bunga Tanjung 3/1,

Senawang Industrial Park, Seremban,
70400, Negeri Sembilan, Malaysia
Tel.: (60) 6 6 77 93 00
Web Site: http://www.ceramtec.my
Ceramic Components Mfr & Marketer
N.A.I.C.S.: 339999
Guruvala Ravichandran (Gen Mgr)

**CeramTec Korea Ltd., Innovative Ce-
ramic Engineering** (2)
105-15 Sinwon-ro, Yeongtong-gu, Suwon,
443 390, Gyeonggi-do, Korea (South)
Tel.: (82) 31 2 04 06 63
Web Site: http://www.ceramtec.co.kr
Ceramic Components Mfr & Marketer
N.A.I.C.S.: 339999

Branch (Non-US):

**CeramTec Medical Products Division
China**
Room 1817 Building 4 Power Land No 17
Fuxing Road, Haidian District, Beijing,
100036, China
Tel.: (86) 10 59706078
Web Site: http://www.ceramtec.cn
Ceramic Components Sales
N.A.I.C.S.: 423990

Subsidiary (US):

CeramTec North America Corp. (2)
1 Technology Pl, Laurens, SC 29360
Tel.: (864) 682-3215
Web Site: http://www.ceramtec.us
Ceramic Components Mfr & Marketer
N.A.I.C.S.: 327999

Subsidiary (Non-US):

CeramTec Suzhou Ltd. (2)
428 Zhongnan Street, Suzhou Industrial
Park, Suzhou, 215026, China
Tel.: (86) 512 62 74 07 88
Web Site: http://www.ceramtec.cn
Ceramic Components Mfr & Sales
N.A.I.C.S.: 339999

Subsidiary (Domestic):

CeramTec-ETEC GmbH (2)
An der Burg Sulz 17, 53797, Lohmar, Ger-
many
Tel.: (49) 2205 9200 0
Web Site: http://www.ceramtec.de
Emp.: 14
Protective Ceramics Mfr
N.A.I.C.S.: 339999

Emil Muller GmbH (2)
Durrnbucher Strasse 10, 91452, Wil-
hermsdorf, Germany
Tel.: (49) 9102 9935 35
Web Site: http://www.ceramtec.de
Ceramic Components Mfr
N.A.I.C.S.: 339999

Subsidiary (Non-US):

**PST Press + Sintertechnik
Sp.z.o.o.** (3)
Ul Odlewnikow 52, PL 39-432, Gorzyce,
Poland
Tel.: (48) 9102 9935 35
Web Site: http://www.ceramtec.com
Ceramic Mfr
N.A.I.C.S.: 212323

**PST Press Sintertecnica Brasil
Ltda** (3)
Rodovia Arnaldo Julio Mauerberg 3960,
Distrito Industrial 1 Predio 5, Nova Odessa,
13460-000, SP, Brazil
Tel.: (55) 19 3466 5116
Web Site: http://www.ceramtec.com.br
Ceramic Components Mfr
N.A.I.C.S.: 327999

**Press and Sinter Technics de Mexico,
S.A. de C.V.** (3)
Resurreccion Oriente 10, Parque Industrial
Resurreccion, Puebla, 72228, Mexico
Tel.: (52) 222 1689412
Web Site: http://www.ceramtec.com
Ceramic Components Mfr
N.A.I.C.S.: 339999

GFL Environmental Inc. (1)
100 New Park Place Suite 500, Vaughan,
L4K 0H9, ON, Canada
Tel.: (905) 326-0101

Web Site: https://www.gflenv.com
Rev.: $5,289,229,764
Assets: $15,463,798,128
Liabilities: $10,735,619,580
Net Worth: $4,728,178,548
Earnings: ($243,914,904)
Emp.: 19,500
Fiscal Year-end: 12/31/2022
Solid & Liquid Waste Collection, Processing
& Recycling Services
N.A.I.C.S.: 562998
Patrick Dovigi (Founder, Pres & CEO)

Subsidiary (US):

Alabama Dumpster Service, LLC (2)
804 County Rd 37 S, Hope Hull, AL 36043
Tel.: (334) 288-1500
Web Site: http://www.alabamadumpster.com
Sales Range: $1-9.9 Million
Emp.: 17
Hazardous Waste Treatment & Disposal
N.A.I.C.S.: 562211

Subsidiary (Domestic):

**Fielding Chemical Technologies
Inc.** (2)
3575 Mavis Road, Mississauga, L5C 1T7,
ON, Canada
Tel.: (905) 279-5122
Web Site:
    https://www.fieldingenvironmental.com
Rev.: $12,072,186
Emp.: 60
Chemical Recycling & Refrigerant Reclama-
tion
N.A.I.C.S.: 562920
Ellen McGregor (Pres & Co-CEO)

Joint Venture (US):

Reclamation Technologies, Inc. (3)
10005 Flanders Ct NE, Blaine, MN 55449
Tel.: (877) 407-2910
Web Site: https://www.reclamationtech.com
Emp.: 100
Refrigerants Merchant Whslr
N.A.I.C.S.: 424690

Subsidiary (Domestic):

**Reclamation Technologies USA,
LLC** (4)
10005 Flanders Ct NE, Blaine, MN 55449
Tel.: (877) 407-2910
Web Site: https://www.reclamationtech.com
Refrigerants Merchant Whslr
N.A.I.C.S.: 424690
Rodney Pierce (Pres)

Subsidiary (Domestic):

AllCool Refrigerant Reclaim, LLC (5)
8606 Hunters Dr, Frederick, MD 21701-
2614
Tel.: (301) 898-0808
Web Site: http://www.allcool.us
Plumbing, Heating & Air-Conditioning Con-
tractors
N.A.I.C.S.: 238220
Jimmy Trout (Pres)

Novent Refrigerant Services, Inc. (5)
10311 Woodberry Rd Ste 101, Tampa, FL
33619-8019
Tel.: (813) 679-9470
Web Site: http://www.noventing.com
Hazardous Waste Collection
N.A.I.C.S.: 562112
Robert P. Sheehan Sr. (Pres)

Division (Domestic):

**GFL Environmental Inc. - Liquid
Waste East Division** (2)
1070 Toy Avenue, Pickering, L1W 3P1, ON,
Canada
Tel.: (905) 509-2460
Liquid Waste Disposal Services
N.A.I.C.S.: 562219

**GFL Environmental Inc. - Liquid
Waste West Division** (2)
4208 84th Avenue NW, Edmonton, T6B
3N5, AB, Canada
Tel.: (780) 485-5000
Liquid Waste Disposal Services
N.A.I.C.S.: 562219

BC Partners LLP—(Continued)

Plant (Domestic):

**GFL Environmental Inc. - Material
Recycling Facility**
242 Cherry Street, Toronto, M5A 3L2, ON,
Canada
Tel.: (416) 406-2040
Material Recovery Services
N.A.I.C.S.: 562920

**GFL Environmental Inc. - Sault Ste
Marie Facility** **(2)**
86 Sackville Road, Sault Sainte Marie, P6B
4T6, ON, Canada
Tel.: (705) 945-7554
Material Recovery Services
N.A.I.C.S.: 562920

Division (Domestic):

**GFL Environmental Inc. - Solid Waste
Transfer Division** **(2)**
1048 Toy Avenue, Pickering, L1W 3P1, ON,
Canada
Tel.: (905) 428-2755
Solid Waste Disposal Services
N.A.I.C.S.: 562212

Subsidiary (Domestic):

M&R Environmental Ltd. **(2)**
7890 Vantage Way, Delta, V4G 1A7, BC,
Canada
Tel.: (604) 946-0506
Waste Collection Services
N.A.I.C.S.: 562119

Subsidiary (US):

**Rizzo Environmental Services,
Inc.** **(2)**
6200 Elmridge Dr, Sterling Heights, MI
48313
Tel.: (586) 772-8900
Web Site: http://www.rizzoservices.com
Emp.: 1,000
Hazardous Waste Disposal Services
N.A.I.C.S.: 562211
Michael Jansen (Dir-Fin)

Subsidiary (Domestic):

Duncan Disposal Systems LLC **(3)**
3101 Travis Ln, New Hudson, MI 48165
Tel.: (248) 437-8600
Web Site:
   http://www.duncandisposalsystems.com
Sales Range: $1-9.9 Million
Emp.: 12
Hazardous Waste Treatment & Disposal
Services
N.A.I.C.S.: 562211
Tom Duncan (Pres)

Subsidiary (Domestic):

Services Matrec Inc. **(2)**
4 Chemin Du Tremblay, Boucherville, J4B
6Z5, QC, Canada
Tel.: (450) 641-3070
Web Site: http://www.matrec.ca
Waste Management Services
N.A.I.C.S.: 221320

Subsidiary (US):

Soil Safe, Inc. **(2)**
6700 Alexander Bell Dr Ste 300, Columbia,
MD 21046
Tel.: (410) 872-3990
Web Site: http://www.soilsafe.com
Hazardous Waste Treatment & Disposal
N.A.I.C.S.: 562211
Bill Bishop (VP-Ops)

Subsidiary (Domestic):

The Garbage Company Inc. **(2)**
4315 72 AV SE, Calgary, T2C 2G5, AB,
Canada
Tel.: (403) 265-0044
Waste Collection & Disposal Services
N.A.I.C.S.: 562119

Tri-Line Disposal Inc. **(2)**
8409 - 15 Street NW, Edmonton, T6P 0B8,
AB, Canada
Tel.: (780) 444-8805
Web Site: http://www.trilinedisposal.com

Solid Waste Collection, Processing & Recy-
cling Services
N.A.I.C.S.: 562111
Keith D. Hawkins (VP & Gen Mgr)

Subsidiary (US):

WCA Waste Corporation **(2)**
1330 Post Oak Blvd 30th Fl, Houston, TX
77056
Tel.: (713) 292-2400
Web Site: http://www.wcawaste.com
Nonhazardous Waste Management Ser-
vices
N.A.I.C.S.: 562212

Subsidiary (Domestic):

Automated Waste Services LLC **(3)**
1252 Ashley Dr, Nixa, MO 65714
Tel.: (417) 725-4872
Web Site:
   https://www.automatedwasteservices.com
Sales Range: $1-9.9 Million
Hazardous Waste Treatment & Disposal
N.A.I.C.S.: 562211

Eagle Ridge Landfill, LLC **(3)**
13100 Hwy VV, Bowling Green, MO 63334
Tel.: (573) 324-5610
Web Site: http://www.wcaamerica.com
Sales Range: $200-249.9 Million
Emp.: 15
Solid Waste Landfill
N.A.I.C.S.: 562212
Ralph Fred (Gen Mgr)

Fort Bend Regional Landfill, LP **(3)**
14115 Davis Estate Rd, Needville, TX
77461
Tel.: (979) 793-4430
Web Site: http://www.wcawaste.com
Sales Range: $10-24.9 Million
Solid Waste Landfill
N.A.I.C.S.: 562212

Freedom Waste Service, LLC **(3)**
1330 Post Oak Blvd 30th Fl, Houston, TX
77056
Tel.: (502) 895-5100
Waste Collection
N.A.I.C.S.: 562119

Material Reclamation, LLC **(3)**
421 Raleigh View Rd, Raleigh, NC 27601
Tel.: (919) 838-6973
Sales Range: $200-249.9 Million
Waste Transfer Station
N.A.I.C.S.: 562219

Ruffino Hills Transfer Station, LP **(3)**
9720 Ruffino Rd, Houston, TX 77031
Tel.: (713) 988-4274
Web Site: http://wcawaste.com
Sales Range: $25-49.9 Million
Solid Waste Transfer Service
N.A.I.C.S.: 562219

Transit Waste, LLC **(3)**
203 Idaho, Bloomfield, NM 87413
Tel.: (505) 634-2510
Web Site: http://www.wcawaste.com
Sales Range: $25-49.9 Million
Solid Waste Collection Services
N.A.I.C.S.: 562111

WCA Shiloh Landfill, LLC **(3)**
40 Estes Plant Rd, Piedmont, SC 29673
Tel.: (864) 845-8355
Sales Range: $200-249.9 Million
Emp.: 35
Waste Management Services
N.A.I.C.S.: 562219

WCA of Oklahoma, LLC **(3)**
1001 S Rockwell Ave, Oklahoma City, OK
73128-2214
Tel.: (405) 677-2000
Sales Range: $200-249.9 Million
Waste Collection & Landfills
N.A.I.C.S.: 562212

Subsidiary (Domestic):

American Waste, LLC **(4)**
1001 S Rockwell, Oklahoma City, OK
73128
Tel.: (405) 495-0800
Web Site: http://www.wcawaste.com
Sales Range: $150-199.9 Million
Solid Waste Collection Services
N.A.I.C.S.: 562111

N.E. Land Fill, LLC **(4)**
2601 N Midwest Blvd, Spencer, OK 73084
Tel.: (405) 424-8000
Web Site: http://www.wcawaste.com
Sales Range: $10-24.9 Million
Landfill Operator
N.A.I.C.S.: 562212

Pauls Valley Landfill, LLC **(4)**
405 East Airport Industrial Rd, Pauls Valley,
OK 73075
Tel.: (405) 238-2012
Web Site: http://www.wcawaste.com
Sales Range: $200-249.9 Million
Solid Waste Landfill
N.A.I.C.S.: 562212

Sooner Landfill **(4)**
36339 East West 127, Wewoka, OK 74884
Tel.: (405) 257-6108
Web Site: http://www.wcawaste.com
Sales Range: $200-249.9 Million
Non-Hazardous Solid Waste Landfill Opera-
tions
N.A.I.C.S.: 562212

Subsidiary (Domestic):

**Waste Corporation of Kansas,
Inc.** **(3)**
1150 E 700 Ave, Arcadia, KS 66711
Tel.: (620) 638-4339
Sales Range: $25-49.9 Million
Emp.: 8
Solid Waste Landfill
N.A.I.C.S.: 562212
Matt Sanders (Gen Mgr)

Waste Corporation of Texas, LP **(3)**
1330 Post Oak Blvd 7th Fl, Houston, TX
77056
Tel.: (713) 670-9199
Web Site: http://www.wcawaste.com
Sales Range: $200-249.9 Million
Waste Collection & Landfills
N.A.I.C.S.: 562212

Subsidiary (US):

Waste Industries USA, LLC **(2)**
3301 Benson Dr Ste 601, Raleigh, NC
27609
Tel.: (919) 325-3000
Web Site: http://www.wasteindustries.com
Solid Waste & Recyclable Material Collec-
tion, Transfer, Processing & Disposal Ser-
vices
N.A.I.C.S.: 562211
Steve Grissom (CFO & Sr VP)

Subsidiary (Domestic):

**North Davidson Garbage Service,
Inc.** **(3)**
4157 Old Us Hwy 52, Lexington, NC 27295
Tel.: (336) 475-0657
Web Site: http://www.ndgarbage.com
Waste Treatment & Disposal
N.A.I.C.S.: 562211

Red Rock Disposal LLC **(3)**
7130 New Landfill Dr, Holly Springs, NC
27540-6921
Tel.: (919) 557-9583
Web Site: http://www.wasteindustries.com
Sales Range: $25-49.9 Million
Emp.: 5
Refuse System
N.A.I.C.S.: 562212
Don Plessinger (Mgr)

**Safeguard Landfill Management
LLC** **(3)**
6895 Roosevelt Hwy, Fairburn, GA 30259
Tel.: (770) 969-0084
Web Site: http://www.wasteindustries.com
Refuse System
N.A.I.C.S.: 562212
George Gibbons (Gen Mgr)

**Garda World Security
Corporation** **(1)**
1390 Barre Street, Montreal, H3C 5X9, QC,
Canada **(51%)**
Tel.: (514) 281-2811
Web Site: http://www.garda.com
Sales Range: $1-4.9 Billion
Risk Consulting & Security Services
N.A.I.C.S.: 561621
Guy Cote (Chief Security Officer & VP)

Subsidiary (US):

Arca.Tech Systems, L.L.C. **(2)**
1400 Dogwood Way, 27302, Mebane, NC
Tel.: (919) 442-5200
Web Site: https://www.arca.com
Professional Equipment & Supplies Mer-
chant Whslr
N.A.I.C.S.: 423490
Jim Halpin (Dir-Retail Solutions)

Garda CL Atlantic, Inc. **(2)**
4200 Governor Printz Blvd, Wilmington, DE
19802-2315
Tel.: (302) 294-2114
Web Site: http://www.garda.com
Cash Logistics Services
N.A.I.C.S.: 522320

Garda CL Great Lakes, Inc. **(2)**
2100 W 21st St, Broadview, IL 60155
Tel.: (708) 343-2200
Web Site: http://www.garda.com
Cash Logistics Services
N.A.I.C.S.: 522320

Garda CL Northwest, Inc. **(2)**
2985 Naches Ave SW, Renton, WA 98057
Tel.: (425) 873-3526
Web Site: http://www.garda.com
Cash Logistics Services; Armored Truck
Transport & Cash Vault Services
N.A.I.C.S.: 561613

Garda CL West, Inc. **(2)**
1200 W 7th St E 300 L3, Los Angeles, CA
90017
Tel.: (213) 345-2447
Web Site: http://www.garda.com
Cash Logistics Services; Armored Truck
Transport & Cash Vault Services
N.A.I.C.S.: 522320

Subsidiary (Domestic):

Garda Security Screening Inc. **(2)**
2005 Sheppard Avenue East, North York,
M2J 5B4, ON, Canada
Tel.: (416) 915-9500
Web Site: http://www.garda.com
Airport Preboarding Screening Services
N.A.I.C.S.: 561621

Subsidiary (US):

Onsolve, LLC **(2)**
780 W Granada Blvd, Ormond Beach, FL
32174
Tel.: (866) 939-0911
Web Site: http://www.ecnetwork.com
Telecommunication Servicesb
N.A.I.C.S.: 517810
Alan Epstein (VP-Ops)

Subsidiary (Domestic):

SWN Communications, Inc. **(3)**
224 W 30th St Ste 500, New York, NY
10001
Tel.: (212) 379-4900
Web Site: http://www.sendwordnow.com
Sales Range: $1-9.9 Million
Emp.: 69
Corporate Messaging Services
N.A.I.C.S.: 517810
Tony Schmitz (Pres & CEO)

Subsidiary (US):

United American Security, LLC **(2)**
7610 Falls of Neuse Rd Ste 290, Raleigh,
NC 27615
Tel.: (919) 847-8180
Security Guards & Patrol Services
N.A.I.C.S.: 561612
Rick Coker (Branch Mgr/Dir-Security)

Subsidiary (Domestic):

Top Gun Security Services **(3)**
550 North Egret Bay Blvd, League City, TX
77573
Tel.: (281) 335-3641
Web Site:
   http://www.topgunsecurityservices.com
Security Officer & K-9 Security Services
N.A.I.C.S.: 561612
Rebecca Moore (Pres)

Intelsat S.A. **(1)**
4 Rue Albert Borschette, Luxembourg,

L-1246, Luxembourg **(53.3%)**
Tel.: (352) 27841600
Web Site: http://www.intelsat.com
Rev.: $1,913,080,000
Assets: $12,797,681,000
Liabilities: $18,712,149,000
Net Worth: ($5,914,468,000)
Earnings: ($911,664,000)
Emp.: 1,774
Fiscal Year-end: 12/31/2020
Satellite Telecommunications
N.A.I.C.S.: 517410
Michelle Bryan *(Chief Admin Officer, Gen Counsel & Exec VP)*

Keter Plastic Ltd. **(1)**
2 Sapir St, PO Box 12558, Herzliyya, 46766, Israel
Tel.: (972) 99591212
Web Site: http://www.keter.com
Plastics Product Mfr
N.A.I.C.S.: 326199
Sami Sagol *(CEO)*

Subsidiary (US):

Adams Mfg Corp. **(2)**
109 W Park Rd, Portersville, PA 16051
Tel.: (800) 237-8287
Web Site: http://www.adamsmfg.com
All Other Plastics Product Mfr
N.A.I.C.S.: 326199
John Fischer *(VP-Sls & Mktg)*

Kin + Carta Plc **(1)**
The Spitfire Building 71 Collier Street, London, N1 9B3, United Kingdom
Tel.: (44) 2079288844
Web Site: http://www.kinandcarta.com
Business Consulting Services
N.A.I.C.S.: 333310

Subsidiary (US):

Spiremedia, Inc. **(2)**
940 Lincoln St, Denver, CO 80203
Tel.: (303) 620-9974
Sales Range: $1-9.9 Million
Emp.: 30
Data Processing & Preparation
N.A.I.C.S.: 518210

Migros Ticaret A.S. **(1)**
Ataturk Mah Turgut Ozal Bulvar No 7, 34758, Istanbul, Turkiye **(40.25%)**
Tel.: (90) 2165793000
Web Site: http://www.migroskurumsal.com
Rev.: $2,301,183,827
Assets: $1,125,044,185
Liabilities: $998,721,780
Net Worth: $126,322,404
Earnings: $79,684,607
Emp.: 44,520
Fiscal Year-end: 12/31/2022
Supermarket Chain Operator
N.A.I.C.S.: 445110
Omer Ozgur Tort *(CEO)*

NAVEX Global, Inc. **(1)**
5500 Meadows Rd Ste 500, Lake Oswego, OR 97035
Tel.: (971) 250-4100
Web Site: http://www.navexglobal.com
Governance, Risk & Compliance Solutions
N.A.I.C.S.: 541618
Steve Chapman *(Chief Customer Officer)*

Subsidiary (Domestic):

CSRware, Inc. **(2)**
100 Shoreline Hwy 100B, Mill Valley, CA 94941
Tel.: (855) 277-9273
Web Site: http://www.csrware.com
Electrical Contractor
N.A.I.C.S.: 238210
Robert Phocas *(Mgr-Energy & Sustainability)*

Lockpath, Inc. **(2)**
6240 Sprint Pkwy Ste 100, Overland Park, KS 66211
Tel.: (913) 601-4800
Governance, Risk & Compliance Software Applications Developer
N.A.I.C.S.: 513210

PetSmart, Inc. **(1)**
19601 N 27th Ave, Phoenix, AZ 85027
Tel.: (623) 587-2025
Web Site: https://www.petsmart.com

Sales Range: $5-14.9 Billion
Emp.: 50,000
Pet & Pet Supplies Retailers
N.A.I.C.S.: 459910
Raymond Svider *(Chm)*

Subsidiary (Domestic):

Chewy, Inc. **(2)**
7700 W Sunrise Blvd, Plantation, FL 33322
Tel.: (786) 320-7111
Web Site: https://www.chewy.com
Rev.: $11,147,720,000
Assets: $3,186,851,000
Liabilities: $2,676,607,000
Net Worth: $510,244,000
Earnings: $39,580,000
Emp.: 18,100
Fiscal Year-end: 01/28/2024
Animal Food Distr
N.A.I.C.S.: 459910
Raymond Svider *(Chm)*

Phones 4u Ltd. **(1)**
Phones 4u House Ore Close, Lymedale Business Park, Newcastle-under-Lyme, ST5 9QD, Staffordshire, United Kingdom
Tel.: (44) 844 871 2231
Web Site: http://www.phones4u.co.uk
Sales Range: $1-4.9 Billion
Retailer of Mobile Telecommunications Products & Services
N.A.I.C.S.: 517112
Tom Shorten *(Dir-Ops-Intl)*

Presidio, Inc. **(1)**
One Penn Plz Ste 2832, New York, NY 10119
Tel.: (212) 652-5700
Web Site: http://www.presidio.com
Rev.: $3,026,100,000
Assets: $2,870,900,000
Liabilities: $2,232,500,000
Net Worth: $638,400,000
Earnings: $35,200,000
Emp.: 2,900
Fiscal Year-end: 06/30/2019
Holding Company; Technology Solutions
N.A.I.C.S.: 551112
Robert Cagnazzi *(Chm & CEO)*

Subsidiary (Non-US):

Arkphire Group Ltd. **(2)**
Unit 1A Sandyford Business Centre, Sandyford, Dublin, D18 RX65, Ireland
Tel.: (353) 1 207 5700
Web Site: http://www.arkphire.com
IT Solutions
N.A.I.C.S.: 519290
Paschal Naylor *(CEO)*

Subsidiary (Domestic):

Trilogy Technologies Limited **(3)**
7 Beckett Way Park West Business Park, Dublin, Ireland
Tel.: (353) 1 4768050
Web Site: http://www.trilogytechnologies.ie
Information Technology Consulting Services
N.A.I.C.S.: 541690
Edel Creely *(Mng Dir-Grp)*

Subsidiary (Domestic):

Zinopy Limited **(4)**
Unit G1 Riverview Business Park Nangor Road, Dublin, D12 DE70, Ireland
Tel.: (353) 1 897 6750
Web Site: http://www.zinopy.ie
Cyber Security Services
N.A.I.C.S.: 541519
Aidan McEvoy *(Dir-Sls)*

Subsidiary (Domestic):

Internetwork Engineering **(2)**
13777 Ballantyne Corporate Pl Ste 305, Charlotte, NC 28277-3419
Tel.: (704) 540-5800
Web Site: http://www.ineteng.com
Sales Range: $75-99.9 Million
Emp.: 78
Information Technology Services
N.A.I.C.S.: 541512
Chuck Steiner *(Pres)*

Branch (Domestic):

Presidio - Caledonia **(2)**
6355 East Paris Ave, Caledonia, MI 49316

Tel.: (616) 871-1500
Web Site: http://www.presidio.com
Network Design Services
N.A.I.C.S.: 541512
Mark Wierenga *(Pres-North Central)*

Presidio - Lewisville **(2)**
1955 Lakeway Dr Ste 220, Lewisville, TX 75057
Tel.: (469) 549-3800
Web Site: http://www.presidio.com
IT & Related Hardware & Software Services
N.A.I.C.S.: 541512

Presidio - Norcross **(2)**
2 Sun Ct, Norcross, GA 30092
Tel.: (770) 449-6116
Web Site: http://www.presidio.com
Network Design Services
N.A.I.C.S.: 541512

Pronovias SL **(1)**
Poligono Industrial Mas Mateu s/n, El Prat de Llobregat, 08820, Barcelona, Spain
Tel.: (34) 934 799 700
Web Site: http://www.pronovias.com
Wedding & Cocktail Dress Designer, Mfr & Retailer
N.A.I.C.S.: 315250
Alberto Palatchi Ribera *(Founder)*

Subsidiary (US):

Pronovias U.S.A., Inc. **(2)**
14 E 52nd St b/w 5th & Madison, New York, NY 10022
Tel.: (212) 897-6393
Web Site: http://www.pronovias.com
Wedding & Cocktail Dress Retailer
N.A.I.C.S.: 458110

Springer Science+Business Media S.A. **(1)**
Heidelberger Platz 3, 14197, Berlin, Germany
Tel.: (49) 30827875434
Web Site: http://www.springer-sbm.com
Sales Range: $1-4.9 Billion
Emp.: 7,000
Holding Company; Scientific & Business Book & Journal Publisher
N.A.I.C.S.: 551112
Martin P. Mos *(COO)*

Co-Headquarters (Non-US):

Springer Science+Business Media B.V. **(2)**
Van Godewijckstraat 30, Dordrecht, 3311 GX, Netherlands **(100%)**
Tel.: (31) 78 657 6000
Web Site: http://www.springer.com
Emp.: 220
Scientific & Business Book & Journal Publisher
N.A.I.C.S.: 921140
Martin P. Mos *(Grp COO)*

Subsidiary (Domestic):

Springer Media B.V. **(3)**
Het Spoor 2, 3994 AK, Houten, Netherlands **(100%)**
Tel.: (31) 30 638 3838
Web Site: http://www.springermedia.nl
Trade Periodical Publisher
N.A.I.C.S.: 513120
Yvonne Campfens *(Mng Dir)*

Starkstrom-Geratebau GmbH **(1)**
Ohmstr. 10, 93055, Regensburg, Germany
Tel.: (49) 941 78 41 0
Transformer Mfr
N.A.I.C.S.: 335311

Subsidiary (Non-US):

S.C. RETRASIB S.A. Sibiu **(2)**
str Stefan cel Mare nr 156 Hermanstadt, Sibiu, 550321, Romania **(93.19%)**
Tel.: (40) 269212969
Web Site: http://www.retrasib.ro
Rev.: $51,310,528
Assets: $38,584,480
Liabilities: $38,056,846
Net Worth: $527,633
Earnings: ($785,449)
Emp.: 202
Fiscal Year-end: 12/31/2020
Power Grid & Distribution Equipment Mfr
N.A.I.C.S.: 335999

Zest Anchors LLC **(1)**
2875 Loker Ave E, Carlsbad, CA 92010
Tel.: (442) 244-4835
Web Site: http://www.zestdent.com
Dental Implant Mfr
N.A.I.C.S.: 339114
Max Zuest *(Founder)*

Subsidiary (Domestic):

Danville Materials, LLC **(2)**
2875 Loker Avenue E, Carlsbad, CA 92010 **(100%)**
Tel.: (442) 244-4890
Web Site: http://www.zestdent.com
Dental Equipment & Supplies Mfr
N.A.I.C.S.: 339114
Drew McIlveen *(Dir-Global Sls)*

BC POWER CONTROLS LTD.
7A/39 W E A Channa Market Karol Bagh, New Delhi, 110005, India
Tel.: (91) 1147532795
Web Site:
https://www.bcpowercontrols.com
Year Founded: 2008
537766—(BOM)
Rev.: $20,514,173
Assets: $8,262,078
Liabilities: $3,967,960
Net Worth: $4,294,117
Earnings: $60,154
Emp.: 27
Fiscal Year-end: 03/31/21
Wire & Cable Mfr
N.A.I.C.S.: 335929
Arun Kumar Jain *(Chm, Mng Dir & Compliance Officer)*

BC TECHNOLOGY GROUP LIMITED
Unit 1704 Shanghai Times Square No 99 Middle Hwaihai Road, Huangpu District, Shanghai, China
Tel.: (86) 21611600218054   Ky
Web Site: http://bc.group
0863—(HKG)
Rev.: $16,264,638
Assets: $353,007,580
Liabilities: $260,442,000
Net Worth: $92,565,580
Earnings: ($77,215,507)
Emp.: 209
Fiscal Year-end: 12/31/22
Marketing Consulting Services
N.A.I.C.S.: 541613
Ken Bon Lo *(Deputy Chm)*

Subsidiaries:

Shanghai Power Stream Mobile Media Co., Ltd. **(1)**
37th Floor No 500 North Chengdu Road, Shanghai, 200003, China
Tel.: (86) 2153752806
Marketing Consulting Services
N.A.I.C.S.: 541613

Shanghai SMU Warner Investment Management Co., Ltd. **(1)**
20th Floor No 45 NanChang Road, Shanghai, 200020, China
Tel.: (86) 2154653333
Marketing Consulting Services
N.A.I.C.S.: 541613

BCAL DIAGNOSTICS LIMITED
Suite 506 Level 5 50 Clarence Street, Sydney, 2000, NSW, Australia
Tel.: (61) 290787671   AU
Web Site:
https://www.bcaldiagnostics.com
Year Founded: 2010
BDX—(ASX)
Rev.: $1,860,008
Assets: $5,458,150
Liabilities: $2,058,682
Net Worth: $3,399,469
Earnings: ($3,300,355)
Fiscal Year-end: 06/30/23

BCAL Diagnostics Limited—(Continued)

Biotechnology Research & Development Services
N.A.I.C.S.: 541714
Jayne Shaw *(Chm)*

BCB BERHAD
No 4B 2nd and 3rd Floor Jalan Sentol South Wing-Kluang Parade, Kluang, 86000, Johor, Malaysia
Tel.: (60) 77760089 　　MY
Web Site:
　https://www.bcbbhd.com.my
BCB—(KLS)
Rev.: $54,359,128
Assets: $285,430,425
Liabilities: $156,897,532
Net Worth: $128,532,893
Earnings: $4,745,855
Fiscal Year-end: 06/30/22
Property Development & Hotel Operations
N.A.I.C.S.: 237310
Ashari Ayub *(Chm)*

Subsidiaries:

BCB Management Sdn. Bhd. 　(1)
F50-F55 1st Floor U-Mall No 45 Jalan Pulai 20, Taman Pulai Utama, 81110, Johor Bahru, Johor, Malaysia
Tel.: (60) 75213128
Web Site: https://www.bcbbhd.com.my
Property Development Services
N.A.I.C.S.: 531390

Johbase Development Sdn. Bhd. 　(1)
4B 2nd N 3rd Fl jalan S Wing, 86000, Keluang, Johor, Malaysia
Tel.: (60) 77722567
Property Development Services
N.A.I.C.S.: 531390

BCC FUBA INDIA LTD.
109 Wing-II Hans Bhawan Bahadurshah Zafar Marg, New Delhi, 110002, India
Tel.: (91) 1149287223
Web Site: https://www.bccfuba.com
517246—(BOM)
Rev.: $3,918,952
Assets: $3,761,016
Liabilities: $1,928,507
Net Worth: $1,832,509
Earnings: $121,618
Emp.: 128
Fiscal Year-end: 03/31/22
Industrial Machinery Mfr
N.A.I.C.S.: 333248
Amit Lohia *(CEO)*

BCD HOLDINGS N.V.
Utrechtseweg 67, 3704 HB, Zeist, Netherlands
Tel.: (31) 306976140 　　Nl
Web Site: http://www.bcdgroup.com
Year Founded: 1975
Sales Range: $25-49.9 Billion
Emp.: 12,500
Holding Company; Financial & Travel Services
N.A.I.C.S.: 551112
John A. Fentener van Vlissingen *(Founder & Chm)*

Subsidiaries:

BCD Meetings & Events LLC 　(1)
Citigroup Ctr 500 W Madison St Ste 1200, Chicago, IL 60661
Tel.: (312) 396-2000
Web Site: http://www.bcdme.com
Sales Range: $600-649.9 Million
Emp.: 700
Meetings & Events Solutions
N.A.I.C.S.: 561499
Scott Graf *(Pres)*

Subsidiary (Non-US):

BCD Meetings & Events Germany GmbH 　(2)

Prinzenallee 15, 40549, Dusseldorf, Germany
Tel.: (49) 30403652900
Employee & Customer Engagement Solutions
N.A.I.C.S.: 541910

BCD Meetings & Events Switzerland AG 　(2)
Thurgauerstrasse 39, 8050, Zurich, Switzerland
Tel.: (41) 445292426
Employee & Customer Engagement Solutions
N.A.I.C.S.: 541910

Subsidiary (Domestic):

L37 LLC 　(2)
211 N Clinton St Ste 2S, Chicago, IL 60661
Tel.: (312) 702-1217
Web Site: http://l37.com
Media Production Services
N.A.I.C.S.: 512110
Ryan Legue *(Gen Mgr)*

Plan 365, Inc. 　(2)
3201 Glenwood Ave Ste 300, Raleigh, NC 27612
Tel.: (919) 534-2200
Web Site: http://www.plan365inc.com
Emp.: 35
Marketing Logistics Services for Life Sciences Companies
N.A.I.C.S.: 541613
Carey Barnes *(Founder & Pres)*

Subsidiary (Non-US):

Zibrant Limited 　(2)
2 Prospect Place Millennium Way Pride Park, Derby, DE24 8HG, United Kingdom
Tel.: (44) 8434 79 79 79
Web Site: http://www.zibrant.com
Emp.: 200
Accommodation & Event Management Services
N.A.I.C.S.: 541618
Fay Sharpe *(Mng Dir-Sls & Mktg)*

BCD Travel Services B.V. 　(1)
Europalaan 400, PO Box 5035, 3502JA, Utrecht, Netherlands
Tel.: (31) 20562 1800
Web Site: http://www.bcdtravel.com
Travel Tour Operator
N.A.I.C.S.: 561520
Stuart Harvey *(Mng Dir)*

Subsidiary (US):

Adelman Travel Systems, Inc. 　(2)
6980 N Port Washington Rd, Milwaukee, WI 53217
Tel.: (414) 410-8300
Web Site: http://www.adelmantravel.com
Emp.: 300
Travel Agency
N.A.I.C.S.: 561510
Craig Adelman *(Founder & Chm)*

Subsidiary (Domestic):

Plaza Travel, Inc. 　(3)
13140 Coit Rd Ste 110, Dallas, TX 75240
Tel.: (972) 980-1191
Web Site: http://www.plazatravelinc.com
Emp.: 20
Travel Agencies
N.A.I.C.S.: 561510
Debbie Ford *(Office Mgr)*

Subsidiary (US):

BCD Travel 　(2)
6 Concourse Pkwy Ste 2400, Atlanta, GA 30328-6003
Tel.: (678) 441-5200
Web Site: http://www.bcdtravel.com
Sales Range: $25-49.9 Million
Travel Agencies
N.A.I.C.S.: 561510
Stephan Baars *(Global CFO)*

Branch (Domestic):

BCD Travel 　(3)
Ste 220 7 Parkway Ctr, Pittsburgh, PA 15220-3704
Tel.: (412) 928-7500
Web Site: http://www.bcdtravel.us

Sales Range: $25-49.9 Million
Travel Services
N.A.I.C.S.: 561510

Affiliate (Domestic):

Executive Travel, Inc. 　(3)
1212 O St, Lincoln, NE 68508
Tel.: (402) 435-8888
Web Site: http://www.executivetravel.com
Sales Range: $1-9.9 Million
Emp.: 34
Travel Agency Services
N.A.I.C.S.: 561510
Paul Glenn *(Pres & COO)*

Parkmobile USA, Inc. 　(1)
3200 Cobb Galleria Pkwy Ste 100, Atlanta, GA 30339
Tel.: (770) 818-9036
Web Site: http://us.parkmobile.com
Parking Garage Operator
N.A.I.C.S.: 812930
Laurens Eckelboom *(Exec VP-Bus Dev)*

BCE INC.
1 carrefour Alexander-Graham-Bell Building A 4th Floor, Verdun, H3E 3B3, QC, Canada
Tel.: (514) 870-8777 　　Ca
Web Site: https://www.bce.ca
Year Founded: 1880
BCE—(NYSE)
Rev.: $18,343,683,720
Assets: $52,228,141,920
Liabilities: $34,281,856,440
Net Worth: $17,946,285,480
Earnings: $2,262,353,760
Emp.: 49,781
Fiscal Year-end: 12/31/21
Telecommunication Servicesb
N.A.I.C.S.: 551112
Mirko Bibic *(Pres & CEO)*

Subsidiaries:

Axia NetMedia Corporation 　(1)
110 220 12th Ave SW, Calgary, T2R 0E9, AB, Canada
Tel.: (403) 538-4000
Web Site: http://www.axia.com
Fibre Optic Communication Services
N.A.I.C.S.: 334220

Bell Aliant Inc. 　(1)
1 Carrefour Alexandre-Graham-Bell, Montreal, H3E 3B3, QC, Canada
Tel.: (709) 739-2320
Web Site: http://www.aliant.bell.ca
Wireless, Internet, Data & Information Technology Services
N.A.I.C.S.: 517112

Branch (Domestic):

Bell Aliant 　(2)
69 Belevedere Avenue, Charlottetown, C1A 9K5, PE, Canada
Tel.: (902) 487-3166
Web Site: http://www.aliant.ca
Telecommunication Servicesb
N.A.I.C.S.: 517111

Subsidiary (Domestic):

Bell Aliant Preferred Equity Inc. 　(2)
4 South Maritime Centre 1505 Barrington Street, Halifax, B3J 3K5, NS, Canada
Tel.: (902) 487-3166
Investment Management Service
N.A.I.C.S.: 523940

Innovatia Inc. 　(2)
1 Germain Street, PO Box 6081, Saint John, E2L 4V1, NB, Canada
Tel.: (506) 640-4000
Web Site: http://www.innovatia.net
Sales Range: $50-74.9 Million
Emp.: 150
Employee Performance & Operational Efficiency Services & Products
N.A.I.C.S.: 541611
Roxanne Fairweather *(Co-CEO)*

NorthernTel Limited Partnership 　(2)
PO Box 1110, Timmins, P4N 7J4, ON, Canada
Tel.: (705) 360-8555
Web Site: http://www.northerntel.ca

Emp.: 250
Wired & Wireless Telecommunications & Internet Services
N.A.I.C.S.: 517111

Telebec Limited Partnership 　(2)
7151 Jean Talon E, Anjou, H1M 3N8, QC, Canada 　　(63.4%)
Tel.: (514) 493-5335
Web Site: http://www.telebec.ca
Telecommunications & Internet Services
N.A.I.C.S.: 517111

Unit (Domestic):

Xwave 　(2)
1 Brunswick Sq, Saint John, E2L 1Z4, NB, Canada
Tel.: (506) 694-4102
Sales Range: $300-349.9 Million
Emp.: 1,500
Information Technology, Website & Network Management Services
N.A.I.C.S.: 541512

Bell Canada 　(1)
1 Carrefour Alexander Graham Bell Building A 4th Fl, Verdun, H3E 3B3, QC, Canada 　　(100%)
Tel.: (514) 870-8777
Web Site: http://www.bce.ca
Telecommunications Services; Voice, Data & Image Transmissions
N.A.I.C.S.: 517111
Jeremy Wubs *(Sr VP-Mktg)*

Subsidiary (Domestic):

NorthwesTel Inc. 　(2)
301 Lambert St, PO Box 2727, Whitehorse, Y1A 4Y4, YT, Canada 　　(100%)
Tel.: (867) 668-5300
Web Site: http://www.nwtel.ca
Sales Range: $100-124.9 Million
Emp.: 650
Telephone, Telecommunications, Mobile Communications & Cable Television Services
N.A.I.C.S.: 517111
Curtis Shaw *(COO)*

The Source (Bell) Electronics Inc. 　(2)
279 Bayview Drive, Barrie, L4M 4W5, ON, Canada
Tel.: (705) 728-2262
Web Site: http://www.thesource.ca
Emp.: 250
Online Marketing Services
N.A.I.C.S.: 541613
Andy Wright *(Pres)*

Bell ExpressVu, L.P. 　(1)
100 Wynford Dr Ste 300, Toronto, M3C 4B4, ON, Canada 　　(100%)
Tel.: (416) 446-2600
Sales Range: $25-49.9 Million
Emp.: 100
N.A.I.C.S.: 517112

Branch (Domestic):

Bell ExpressVu 　(2)
100 Wynford Dr, North York, M3C 4B4, ON, Canada 　　(100%)
Tel.: (416) 383-6600
Web Site: http://www.bell.ca
Sales Range: $50-74.9 Million
N.A.I.C.S.: 517112

Bell MTS Inc. 　(1)
333 Main Street, PO Box 6666, Winnipeg, R3C 3V6, MB, Canada
Tel.: (204) 225-5687
Web Site: http://www.mts.ca
Telephone Communications
N.A.I.C.S.: 517112
Wade Oosterman *(Vice Chm & Pres)*

Bell Media Inc. 　(1)
299 Queen Street West, Toronto, M5V 2Z5, ON, Canada 　　(100%)
Tel.: (416) 384-8000
Web Site: https://www.bellmedia.ca
Sales Range: $1-4.9 Billion
Emp.: 3,000
Multi-Media Holding Company
N.A.I.C.S.: 551112
Nikki Moffat *(Sr VP-Fin)*

Subsidiary (Domestic):

Artech Digital Entertainments, Inc. (2)
6 Hamilton Ave N, Ottawa, K1Y 4R1, ON, Canada (51%)
Tel.: (613) 728-4880
Sales Range: $25-49.9 Million
Emp.: 50
Develops Media Games & Software Mfr
N.A.I.C.S.: 334610

Unit (Domestic):

Astral Out-of-Home (2)
1800 McGill College Ave Ste 1600, Montreal, H3A 3J6, QC, Canada
Tel.: (514) 939-5000
Web Site: http://www.bellmedia.ca
Emp.: 500
Outdoor Advertising Services
N.A.I.C.S.: 541850
Karine Moses (Pres)

Division (Domestic):

Bell Media Radio (2)
299 Queen Street West, Toronto, M5V 2Z5, ON, Canada
Tel.: (416) 384-8000
Web Site: http://www.bellmedia.ca
Radio Broadcasting Stations Operator
N.A.I.C.S.: 516110

Unit (Domestic):

Bell Media Radio - Calgary (3)
300-1110 Centre Street NE, Calgary, T2E 2R2, AB, Canada
Tel.: (403) 240-5800
Web Site: http://www.cjay92.com
Sales Range: $1-9.9 Million
Emp.: 60
Radio Broadcasting Stations
N.A.I.C.S.: 516110

Subsidiary (Domestic):

CTV Inc. (2)
9 Channel 9 Ct, Toronto, M1S 4B5, ON, Canada (51%)
Tel.: (416) 332-5000
Web Site: http://www.ctv.ca
Sales Range: $1-4.9 Billion
Emp.: 2,600
Holding Company; Television Broadcasting Stations Operator
N.A.I.C.S.: 551112

Subsidiary (Domestic):

Agincourt Productions, Inc. (3)
9 Channel Nine Ct, Scarborough, M1S 4B5, ON, Canada (20%)
Tel.: (416) 299-2000
Sales Range: $150-199.9 Million
Emp.: 1,053
Production & Television Programming
N.A.I.C.S.: 516120

Unit (Domestic):

CTV Atlantic, Halifax (3)
2885 Robie St, Halifax, B3K 5Z4, NS, Canada
Tel.: (902) 453-4000
Web Site: http://www.ctv.ca
Sales Range: $50-74.9 Million
Emp.: 200
Television Broadcasting Station
N.A.I.C.S.: 516120

CTV Atlantic, Moncton (3)
191 Halifax Street, E1C 9R7, Moncton, NB, Canada
Tel.: (506) 857-2600
Web Site: http://www.ctv.ca
Sales Range: $25-49.9 Million
Emp.: 15
Television Broadcasting Station
N.A.I.C.S.: 516120

CTV Atlantic, Saint John (3)
12 Smythe Street Suite 126, Saint John, E2L 5G5, NB, Canada
Tel.: (506) 658-1010
Web Site: http://www.ctv.ca
Sales Range: $1-9.9 Million
Emp.: 3
Television Broadcasting Station
N.A.I.C.S.: 516120

CTV Atlantic, Sydney (3)
1283 George St, Sydney, B1P 1N7, NS, Canada
Tel.: (902) 562-5511
Web Site: http://www.ctv.ca
Sales Range: $25-49.9 Million
Emp.: 10
Television Broadcasting Station
N.A.I.C.S.: 516120

CTV Calgary (3)
80 Patina Rise SW, Calgary, T3H 2W4, AB, Canada (100%)
Tel.: (403) 240-5600
Web Site: http://www.calgary.ctv.ca
Sales Range: $50-74.9 Million
Emp.: 130
Television Broadcasting Station
N.A.I.C.S.: 516120

CTV Edmonton (3)
18520 Stony Plain Rd, Edmonton, T5S 1A8, AB, Canada (100%)
Tel.: (780) 483-3311
Web Site: http://www.edmonton.ctv.ca
Sales Range: $50-74.9 Million
Emp.: 130
Television Broadcasting Station
N.A.I.C.S.: 516120

CTV Lethbridge (3)
640 13th St N, Lethbridge, T1H 2S8, AB, Canada
Tel.: (403) 329-3644
Web Site: http://www.ctv.ca
Sales Range: $25-49.9 Million
Emp.: 15
Television Broadcasting Station
N.A.I.C.S.: 516120

CTV Montreal (3)
1205 Papineau Ave, Montreal, H2K 4R2, QC, Canada
Tel.: (514) 273-6311
Web Site: http://www.montreal.ctv.ca
Sales Range: $50-74.9 Million
Emp.: 130
Television Broadcasting Station
N.A.I.C.S.: 516120

Subsidiary (Domestic):

CTV Newsnet (3)
9 Channel 9 Ct, Toronto, M1S 4B5, ON, Canada (100%)
Tel.: (416) 332-5000
Sales Range: $400-449.9 Million
Emp.: 2,500
Cable Television Services
N.A.I.C.S.: 516210
Wendy Freeman (Pres)

Unit (Domestic):

CTV Northern Ontario, North Bay (3)
245 Oak St E, North Bay, P1B 8P8, ON, Canada
Tel.: (705) 476-3111
Sales Range: $25-49.9 Million
Emp.: 12
Television Broadcasting Station
N.A.I.C.S.: 516120
Scott Lund (VP & Gen Mgr)

CTV Northern Ontario, Sault Saint Marie (3)
119 E St, Sault Sainte Marie, P6A 3C7, ON, Canada
Tel.: (705) 759-7788
Web Site: http://www.ctv.ca
Sales Range: $25-49.9 Million
Emp.: 13
Television Broadcasting Station
N.A.I.C.S.: 516120

CTV Northern Ontario, Sudbury (3)
699 Frood Rd, Sudbury, P3C 5A3, ON, Canada
Tel.: (705) 674-8301
Web Site: http://www.ctv.ca
Sales Range: $10-24.9 Million
Emp.: 60
Television Broadcasting Station
N.A.I.C.S.: 516120

CTV Northern Ontario, Timmins (3)
681 Pine St N, PO Box 620, Timmins, P4N 7G3, ON, Canada
Tel.: (705) 264-4211

Web Site: http://www.ctv.ca
Sales Range: $25-49.9 Million
Emp.: 11
Television Broadcasting Station
N.A.I.C.S.: 516120

CTV Ottawa (3)
87 George St, Ottawa, K1N 9H7, ON, Canada
Tel.: (613) 224-1313
Web Site: http://www.ctv.ca
Sales Range: $25-49.9 Million
Emp.: 100
Television Broadcasting Station
N.A.I.C.S.: 516120

CTV Prince Albert (3)
22 10th St W, Prince Albert, S6V 3A5, SK, Canada
Tel.: (306) 922-6066
Web Site: http://www.ctv.ca
Sales Range: $25-49.9 Million
Emp.: 4
Television Broadcasting Station
N.A.I.C.S.: 516120

CTV Regina (3)
1 Hwy E, PO Box 2000, Regina, S4P 3E5, SK, Canada (100%)
Tel.: (306) 569-2000
Web Site: http://www.ctv.ca
Sales Range: $25-49.9 Million
Emp.: 55
Television Broadcasting Station
N.A.I.C.S.: 516120

CTV Saskatoon (3)
216 1st Ave N, Saskatoon, S7K 3W3, SK, Canada (100%)
Tel.: (306) 665-8600
Web Site: http://www.ctv.ca
Sales Range: $25-49.9 Million
Emp.: 80
Television Broadcasting Station
N.A.I.C.S.: 516120

CTV Vancouver (3)
500 969 Robson Street, Vancouver, V6Z 1X5, BC, Canada
Tel.: (604) 608-2868
Web Site: http://bc.ctvnews.ca
Sales Range: $50-74.9 Million
Emp.: 250
Television Broadcasting Station
N.A.I.C.S.: 516120

CTV Winnipeg (3)
400 345 Graham Ave, Winnipeg, R3C 5S6, MB, Canada (100%)
Tel.: (204) 788-3300
Web Site: http://www.ctv.ca
Sales Range: $10-24.9 Million
Emp.: 100
Television Broadcasting Station
N.A.I.C.S.: 516120

CTV Yorkton (3)
95 E Broadway, Yorkton, S3N 0L1, SK, Canada (100%)
Tel.: (306) 786-8400
Web Site: http://www.ctv.ca
Sales Range: $25-49.9 Million
Emp.: 8
Television Broadcasting Station
N.A.I.C.S.: 516120

Subsidiary (Domestic):

The Comedy Network (3)
299 Queenstreet W, Toronto, M5V 2ZY, ON, Canada (65.1%)
Tel.: (416) 332-5000
Web Site: http://www.ctv.ca
Sales Range: $25-49.9 Million
Emp.: 34
N.A.I.C.S.: 517112

The Discovery Channel (3)
9 Channel 9 Ct, Scarborough, M1S 4B5, ON, Canada (51%)
Tel.: (416) 332-5000
Web Site: http://www.discoverychannel.ca
Sales Range: $800-899.9 Million
Television Station
N.A.I.C.S.: 516120
Mario Filice (Sls Dir)

The Sports Network Inc. (3)
299 Queen Street West, Toronto, M5V 2Z5, ON, Canada (51%)
Tel.: (416) 384-8000

Web Site: http://www.tsn.ca
Sports Television, Radio & Other Media Network
N.A.I.C.S.: 516120

Unit (Domestic):

Sympatico (2)
207 Queens St W, Toronto, M5J 1A7, ON, Canada
Tel.: (416) 353-0123
Web Site: http://www.sympatico.ca
Sales Range: $25-49.9 Million
Emp.: 40
Internet Portal
N.A.I.C.S.: 517810

Bell Mobility Inc. (1)
5099 Creekbank Rd, Mississauga, L4W 5N2, ON, Canada (100%)
Tel.: (905) 282-2000
Web Site: http://www.bell.ca
Sales Range: $800-899.9 Million
Emp.: 4,000
Mobile Telecommunications Products & Services
N.A.I.C.S.: 517112
Blaik Kirby (Pres)

Unit (Domestic):

Virgin Mobile Canada (2)
720 King St W Suite 905, M5V2T3, Toronto, ON, Canada
Tel.: (888) 999-2321
Web Site: http://www.virginmobile.ca
Mobile Telecommunications
N.A.I.C.S.: 517112

Glentel Inc. (1)
8501 Commerce Court, Burnaby, V5A 4M3, BC, Canada
Tel.: (604) 415-6500
Web Site: http://www.glentel.com
Sales Range: $1-4.9 Billion
Wireless Communication Products Distr
N.A.I.C.S.: 423690
Damon A. Jones (VP-Retail Sls & Ops)

Subsidiary (US):

Diamond Wireless LLC (2)
200 W Civic Ctr Dr Ste 202, Sandy, UT 84070
Tel.: (801) 733-6929
Web Site: http://www.diamond-wireless.com
Wireless Handset & Accessories Retailer
N.A.I.C.S.: 449210

Maple Leaf Sports & Entertainment Ltd. (1)
50 Bay St Suite 400, Toronto, M5J 2L2, ON, Canada (39.76%)
Tel.: (416) 815-5400
Web Site: http://www.mlse.com
Sales Range: $550-599.9 Million
Emp.: 900
Holding Company; Professional Sports Teams, Broadcast Media Licensing, Internet Publishing, Sports & Entertainment Venues Owner & Operator
N.A.I.C.S.: 551112
Larry Tanenbaum (Chm)

Unit (Domestic):

The Air Canada Centre (2)
40 Bay Street, Toronto, M5J 2L2, ON, Canada
Tel.: (416) 815-5982
Web Site: https://www.scotiabankarena.com
Sports & Entertainment Facility Operator
N.A.I.C.S.: 711310

Subsidiary (Domestic):

Toronto Maple Leafs Hockey Club Inc. (2)
50 Bay Street Suite 500, Toronto, M5J 2L2, ON, Canada
Tel.: (416) 815-5700
Web Site: http://www.mapleleafs.com
Professional Hockey Club
N.A.I.C.S.: 711211
Brendan Shanahan (Pres)

Toronto Raptors Basketball Club Inc. (2)
40 Bay Street Suite 400, Toronto, M5J 2X2, ON, Canada
Tel.: (416) 815-5500

BCE Inc.—(Continued)

Web Site: http://www.raptors.com
Professional Basketball Team
N.A.I.C.S.: 711211
Bobby Webster (Gen Mgr)

Q9 Networks Inc.   (1)
Suite 1100 100 Wellington Street West, PO
Box 235, Toronto, M5K 1J3, ON,
Canada   (100%)
Tel.: (877) 519-7200
Web Site: http://www.q9.com
Outsourced Information Technology Infra-
structure Design, Installation & Manage-
ment Services
N.A.I.C.S.: 541519

BCEG ENVIRONMENTAL RE-MEDIATION CO., LTD.
Building 16 Linktech Times Center No
6 Jingshun East Street, Chaoyang,
Beijing, 100015, China
Tel.: (86) 1068096688
Web Site: https://bceer.bcegc.com
Year Founded: 2007
300958—(SSE)
Rev.: $178,274,304
Assets: $418,852,512
Liabilities: $254,223,684
Net Worth: $164,628,828
Earnings: $13,729,716
Fiscal Year-end: 12/31/22
Engineeering Services
N.A.I.C.S.: 541330
Lu Gang (Chm)

BCG COMMUNICATIONS
6 Roslyn Rd Ste 100, Winnipeg, R3L
0G5, MB, Canada
Tel.: (204) 786-1964
Web Site: http://www.bcg.ca
Year Founded: 1993
Sales Range: $10-24.9 Million
Emp.: 27
Advertising, Brand Development &
Integration, Digital/Interactive, Event
Planning & Marketing, Media Plan-
ning, Public Relations
N.A.I.C.S.: 541810
Barbara Jankowski (Office Mgr)

BCI GROUP HOLDINGS LIM-ITED
Floor 14 Bupa Centre 141 Connaught
Road West, Sai Ying Pun, Hong
Kong, China (Hong Kong)
Tel.: (852) 21619009   Ky
Web Site:
    http://www.bcigroup.com.hk
Year Founded: 2013
8412—(HKG)
Rev.: $9,942,578
Assets: $7,058,783
Liabilities: $5,723,858
Net Worth: $1,334,925
Earnings: $749,700
Emp.: 47
Fiscal Year-end: 05/31/23
Restaurant Management Services
N.A.I.C.S.: 722511
Kester Shing joe Ng (Founder &
Chm)

BCI MINERALS LIMITED
Level 2 1 Altona Street, West Perth,
6005, WA, Australia
Tel.: (61) 863113400   AU
Web Site:
    https://www.bciminerals.com.au
BCI—(ASX)
Rev.: $5,800,614
Assets: $682,050,612
Liabilities: $144,376,335
Net Worth: $537,674,277
Earnings: ($32,843,216)
Fiscal Year-end: 06/30/24
Iron Ore Exploration & Mining
N.A.I.C.S.: 212210

Brian O'Donnell (Chm)

BCL ENTERPRISES LTD.
510 Arunachal Building 19 Bara-
khamba Road, New Delhi, 110 001,
India
Tel.: (91) 1143080469
Web Site:
    https://www.bclenterprisesltd.in
539621—(BOM)
Rev.: $1,047,328
Assets: $2,865,745
Liabilities: $1,834,329
Net Worth: $1,031,416
Earnings: $291,504
Emp.: 4
Fiscal Year-end: 03/31/21
Financial Support Services
N.A.I.C.S.: 523999
Mahendra Kumar Sharda (Mng Dir)

BCL INDUSTRIES LIMITED
Hazi Rattan Link Road, PO BOX 71,
Bathinda, 151005, Punjab, India
Tel.: (91) 1642240163   In
Web Site: https://www.bcl.ind.in
Year Founded: 1976
524332—(BOM)
Rev.: $273,161,930
Assets: $103,400,156
Liabilities: $51,748,692
Net Worth: $51,651,464
Earnings: $11,571,610
Emp.: 494
Fiscal Year-end: 03/31/22
Real Estate Development Services
N.A.I.C.S.: 531390
Ramesh Chander Nayyar (Chm)

BCL LIMITED
PO Box 3, Selebi-Phikwe, Botswana
Tel.: (267) 262 1200
Web Site: http://www.bcl.bw
Year Founded: 1956
Emp.: 4,200
Holding Company; Copper & Nickel
Mining & Smelting
N.A.I.C.S.: 551112
Mack William (Mgr-Corp Strategy Div)

Subsidiaries:

Tati Nickel Mining Company (Pty)
Ltd.   (1)
Matsiloje Road Phoenix Site, PO Box 1272,
Francistown, Botswana   (100%)
Tel.: (267) 2410701
Web Site: http://www.tatinickel.co.bw
Nickel & Other Metal Ore Mining
N.A.I.C.S.: 212230
Ditiro Clement Lentswe (Mng Dir)

BCM ALLIANCE BERHAD
No 73-2 Jalan Equine 10 Taman
Equine, Seri Kembangan, 43300,
Kuala Lumpur, Selangor, Malaysia
Tel.: (60) 389939139   MY
Web Site:
    https://www.bcmalliance.com.my
Year Founded: 1978
BCMALL—(KLS)
Rev.: $20,539,589
Assets: $37,077,158
Liabilities: $9,277,796
Net Worth: $27,799,363
Earnings: ($9,311,720)
Fiscal Year-end: 12/31/23
Investment Holding Services
N.A.I.C.S.: 551112
Chong Lin Liaw (Mng Dir)

Subsidiaries:

Bc Medicare Sdn. Bhd.   (1)
Level 3 Tower 11 Avenue 5 No 8 Jalan Ker-
inchi Bangsar South, 59200, Kuala Lumpur,
Malaysia
Tel.: (60) 27047622
Web Site: https://www.bcmedicare.com.my
Surgical & Medical Instrument Distr

N.A.I.C.S.: 423450

CS Laundry System Sdn. Bhd.   (1)
NO 21-1 21-2 21-3 Jalan 5/152 Batu 6
Jalan Puchong, Taman Perindustrian,
58200, Kuala Lumpur, Malaysia
Tel.: (60) 37 785 9386
Web Site: https://www.cslaundry.com.my
Commercial Laundry Equipment Distr
N.A.I.C.S.: 423850
Koh Lap Hing (Co-Founder)

Cs Laundry System Philippines
Corp.   (1)
MG Tower 2 St Mandaluyong Shaw Boule-
vard Coner L Gonzales St, 29 De Agosto
Metro Manila, Mandaluyong, 1552, Philip-
pines
Tel.: (63) 9277767892
Web Site: https://cs-laundry.com
Laundry Equipment Testing Services
N.A.I.C.S.: 812310

Cypress Medic Sdn. Bhd.   (1)
No 73-3 & 73-4 Jalan Equine 10 Taman
Equine, 43300, Seri Kembangan, Selangor,
Malaysia
Tel.: (60) 389582266
Web Site: http://www.cypressmedic.com.my
Medical Device Distr
N.A.I.C.S.: 423450

Maymedic Technology Sdn. Bhd.   (1)
No 19 Jalan 5/152 Batu 6 Jalan Puchong,
Taman Perindustrian Oug, 58200, Kuala
Lumpur, Malaysia
Tel.: (60) 37 785 9380
Web Site:
    https://www.maymedictechnology.com
Medical Equipment Distr
N.A.I.C.S.: 423450
Chung Eng Lam (Co-Founder, Mng Dir &
Head-Bus Unit)

BCM RESOURCES CORP.
2705-1328 West Pender St, Vancou-
ver, V6E 4T1, BC, Canada
Tel.: (604) 646-0144   BC
Web Site:
    https://www.bcmresources.com
Year Founded: 2005
BCMRF—(OTCIQ)
Assets: $16,905,575
Liabilities: $1,027,731
Net Worth: $15,877,844
Earnings: ($1,382,569)
Fiscal Year-end: 08/31/23
Mineral Exploration Services
N.A.I.C.S.: 213114
Dale McClanaghan (Pres & CEO)

BCNC CO., LTD.
25 Maso-ro 57beon-gil Sindun-
myeon, Icheon, Gyeonggi-do, Korea
(South)
Tel.: (82) 316388434
Web Site: https://www.bcnc.co.kr
Year Founded: 2003
146320—(KRS)
Rev.: $62,932,696
Assets: $85,007,999
Liabilities: $28,805,871
Net Worth: $56,202,127
Earnings: $7,766,429
Emp.: 225
Fiscal Year-end: 12/31/22
Semiconductor Parts Mfr & Distr
N.A.I.C.S.: 334413

Subsidiaries:

BCnC USA, Inc.   (1)
13015 Dessau Rd, Austin, TX 78754
Tel.: (512) 285-3762
Semiconductor Parts Mfr
N.A.I.C.S.: 334413

GI Co., Ltd.   (1)
253-5 Wonsi-ro, Danwon-gu, Ansan,
Gyeonggi-do, Korea (South)
Tel.: (82) 314946711
Chemical Etching Semiconductor Parts Mfr
N.A.I.C.S.: 334413

BCO BRASIL S.A.
Saun Quadra 5 - Lote B - Torre I - Ed
Bb - 1, Brasilia, 70040911, Distrito
Federal, Brazil
Tel.: (55) 6134933100
Web Site: https://www.bb.com.br
BBAS11—(BRAZ)
Sales Range: Less than $1 Million
Financial Investment Services
N.A.I.C.S.: 523999
Jose Mauricio Pereira Coelho (Dir-IR)

BCO BTG PACTUAL S.A.
Praia de Botafogo 501 - 5. 6 E 7 An-
dares, 22250040, Rio de Janeiro, RJ,
Brazil
Tel.: (55) 2132629600
Web Site: http://www.btgpactual.com
BTGP.BANCO—(BRAZ)
Rev.: $1,814,525,077
Assets: $98,736,825,207
Liabilities: $87,491,802,373
Net Worth: $11,245,022,834
Earnings: $2,045,021,438
Fiscal Year-end: 12/31/23
Investment Banking Services
N.A.I.C.S.: 523150

Subsidiaries:

BTG Pactual Argentina S.A.   (1)
Av Del Libertador 101 Piso 9, Vicente Lo-
pez, 1638, Argentina
Tel.: (54) 1137540900
Investment Bank Services
N.A.I.C.S.: 523150
Rodrigo Diaz Valdez (Assoc Dir-Investment
Banking Div)

BTG Pactual Asia Limited   (1)
3712 14 Two International Finance Center 8
Finance Street Central, Hong Kong, China
(Hong Kong)
Tel.: (852) 34134600
Investment Bank Services
N.A.I.C.S.: 523150
BTG Pactual Casa de Bolsa, S.A. de
C.V.   (1)
Paseo de Tamarindos Number 400-A Floor
23 Col, 05120, Mexico, Mexico
Tel.: (52) 5536922200
Investment Bank Services
N.A.I.C.S.: 523150
Francisco Acosta Garcia (COO)

BTG Pactual Europe LLP   (1)
Berkeley Square House 4 19 Berkeley
Square, London, W1J 6BR, United Kingdom
Tel.: (44) 2076474900
Investment Bank Services
N.A.I.C.S.: 523150

BTG Pactual NY Corporation   (1)
601 Lexington Ave - 57th Fl, New York, NY
10022
Tel.: (212) 293-4600
Financial Banking Services
N.A.I.C.S.: 522110
Roberto Schott (Mng Dir)

BCO ESTADO DO PARA S.A.
Av Presidente Vargas n 251 4th floor,
Meadow Bethlehem, Belem, 66010-
000, PA, Brazil
Tel.: (55) 33483211   BR
Web Site: http://www.banpara.b.br
Year Founded: 1960
BPAR3—(BRAZ)
Sales Range: Less than $1 Million
Financial Investment Services
N.A.I.C.S.: 523999
Helenilson Cunha Pontes (Chm)

BCO NORDESTE DO BRASIL S.A.
Tel.: (55) 8532516634
Web Site: https://www.bnb.gov.br
Year Founded: 1952
BNBR3—(BRAZ)
Rev.: $1,529,844,796
Assets: $11,750,104,262
Liabilities: $9,835,839,105

Net Worth: $1,914,265,157
Earnings: $397,761,560
Fiscal Year-end: 12/31/23
Financial Investment Services
N.A.I.C.S.: 523999

BCP LTD.
3530 St Lawrence Ste 300, Montreal,
H2X 2V1, QC, Canada
Tel.: (514) 285-0077　　　Ca
Year Founded: 1963
Emp.: 60
Advetising Agency
N.A.I.C.S.: 541810
Patrice Landry (Controller)

**BCPL RAILWAY INFRASTRUC-
TURE LIMITED**
112 Raja Ram Mohan Roy Sarani,
Kolkata, 700009, India
Tel.: (91) 913322190085
Web Site: https://www.bcril.com
Year Founded: 1984
542057—(BOM)
Rev.: $14,686,226
Assets: $13,859,391
Liabilities: $3,334,872
Net Worth: $10,524,519
Earnings: $1,011,738
Emp.: 87
Fiscal Year-end: 03/31/22
Railway Transportation Services
N.A.I.C.S.: 488210
Aparesh Nandi (Chm)

**BCT BANK INTERNATIONAL
S.A.**
BCT Bank Building Ground Floor, PO
Box 0832-1786, Panama, Panama
Tel.: (507) 297 4200
Web Site: http://www.bctbank.com.pa
Year Founded: 2002
BCTB—(PAN)
Sales Range: Less than $1 Million
Commercial Banking Services
N.A.I.C.S.: 522110

BCW GROUP HOLDING, INC.
Room 1201 Building 6 Caimanjie Fi-
nancia, Chaoyang, Beijing, 10014,
China
Tel.: (86) 1056253285　　　NV
BCWG—(OTCIQ)
Sales Range: Less than $1 Million
Data Processing Services
N.A.I.C.S.: 518210
Wei Lu (Pres)

BCWORLD PHARM CO., LTD.
22 Geumto-ro 40beon-gil, Sujeong-
gu, Seongnam, 13453, Gyeonggi-do,
Korea (South)
Tel.: (82) 3151783300
Web Site: https://www.bcwp.co.kr
Year Founded: 1980
200780—(KRS)
Rev.: $55,762,834
Assets: $140,399,901
Liabilities: $80,942,151
Net Worth: $59,457,750
Earnings: $45,848
Emp.: 296
Fiscal Year-end: 12/31/22
Pharmaceuticals Mfr
N.A.I.C.S.: 325412
Sunghan Hong (CEO)

Subsidiaries:

Bcworld Pharm Co., Ltd. - Yeoju
Factory　　　　　　　　　　　(1)
872-23 Yeojunam-ro, Ganam-eup, Yeoju,
Gyeonggi-do, Korea (South)
Tel.: (82) 318816800
Pharmaceuticals Product Mfr
N.A.I.C.S.: 325412

BD AGRO AD
Lole Ribara b b Dobanovci, 11272,
Belgrade, Serbia
Tel.: (381) 11 8465 400
Year Founded: 1947
Milk Production
N.A.I.C.S.: 112120
Ljubisa Jovanovic (Mng Dir)

BD DIESEL PERFORMANCE
33541 MacLure Road, Abbotsford,
V2S 7W2, BC, Canada
Tel.: (604) 853-6096
Web Site:
　http://www.dieselperformance.com
Year Founded: 1971
Rev.: $15,472,337
Emp.: 70
Diesel Parts Mfr
N.A.I.C.S.: 336390
Brian Roth (Pres)

BD MULTIMEDIA SA
16 Cite Joly, 75011, Paris, France
Tel.: (33) 153362424
Web Site:
　https://www.bdmultimedia.fr
Year Founded: 1986
ALBDM—(EUR)
Sales Range: $1-9.9 Million
Telecommunications & Internet Ser-
vices
N.A.I.C.S.: 517810
Daniel Dorra (Chm & CEO)

**BD THAI FOOD & BEVERAGE
LTD.**
BTA Tower 8th Floor 29 Kemal Atat-
urk Avenue Road No 18, Banani,
Dhaka, 1212, Bangladesh
Tel.: (880) 9821572
Web Site: http://www.btfbl.com
Year Founded: 2010
Food & Beverage Product Mfr & Distr
N.A.I.C.S.: 312111

**BD-CAPITAL PARTNERS LIM-
ITED**
23a Motcomb Street, London, SW1X
8LB, United Kingdom
Tel.: (44) 7881655998　　　UK
Web Site: https://bd-cap.com
Year Founded: 2019
Privater Equity Firm
N.A.I.C.S.: 523999
Richard Baker (Mng Partner)

BD-NTWK LONDON
Tea Bldg 56 Shoreditch High St, Lon-
don, E1 6PQ, United Kingdom
Tel.: (44) 20 7749 5500
Web Site: http://www.thisisbd.com
Emp.: 100
Sales Promotion
N.A.I.C.S.: 541810
Phil Latham (Dir-Project)

Subsidiaries:

BD-NTWK Scotland　　　　　(1)
Cochrane House 27-29 Cochrane Street,
Glasgow, G1 1HL, Scotland, United King-
dom
Tel.: (44) 141 567 8000
Web Site: http://www.thisisbd.com
Sales Range: $50-74.9 Million
Emp.: 20
N.A.I.C.S.: 541810
Steven Pearson (Head-Strategic Plng)

**BDC VIETNAM INVESTMENT &
CONSTRUCTION JSC**
No 15 lane 45 Hao Nam O, Cho Dua
ward Dong Da district, Hanoi, Viet-
nam
Tel.: (84) 435373241
MCO—(HNX)
Rev.: $7,228,000

Assets: $13,599,800
Liabilities: $8,332,900
Net Worth: $5,266,900
Earnings: $21,400
Fiscal Year-end: 12/31/22
Transporation Structures Construction
Services
N.A.I.C.S.: 237310
Nguyen Quoc Huong (Gen Dir &
Member-Mgmt Bd)

BDCOM ONLINE LIMITED
Rangs Nilu Square 5th Floor Sat-
mosjid Road House 75 Road 5A,
Dhanmondi RA, Dhaka, 1209, Ban-
gladesh
Tel.: (880) 9666333666
Web Site: https://www.bdcom.com
BDCOM—(CHT)
Rev.: $7,628,222
Assets: $13,996,791
Liabilities: $4,178,569
Net Worth: $9,818,223
Earnings: $696,356
Emp.: 475
Fiscal Year-end: 06/30/21
Internet Service Provider
N.A.I.C.S.: 517112
A. K. M. Kutub Uddin (Sec & Exec
Dir-Admin)

BDH INDUSTRIES LTD.
Nair Baug Akurli Road Kandivali East,
Mumbai, 400 101, India
Tel.: (91) 2261551234
Web Site: https://www.bdhind.com
Year Founded: 1935
524828—(BOM)
Rev.: $8,020,017
Assets: $9,677,181
Liabilities: $3,798,276
Net Worth: $5,878,905
Earnings: $868,058
Emp.: 128
Fiscal Year-end: 03/31/21
Pharmaceutical Preparation Mfr
N.A.I.C.S.: 325412
Jayashree Nair (Chm & Co-Mng Dir)

**BDI - BIOENERGY INTERNA-
TIONAL AG**
Parkring 18, 8074, Grambach, Austria
Tel.: (43) 316 4009 100
Web Site: http://www.bdi-
　bioenergy.com
Year Founded: 1996
Sales Range: $25-49.9 Million
Emp.: 128
Fuel Exploration Services
N.A.I.C.S.: 213112
Markus Dielacher (Mng Dir)

Subsidiaries:

Enbasys Gmbh　　　　　　　(1)
Parkring 18, Grambach, 8074, Graz, Austria
Tel.: (43) 316 4009 5600
Web Site: http://www.enbasys.com
Waste Water Treatment Services
N.A.I.C.S.: 562998

UIC Gmbh　　　　　　　　　(1)
Am Neuen Berg 4, Horstein, 63755,
Alzenau, Germany
Tel.: (49) 6023 950 0
Web Site: http://www.uic-gmbh.de
Sales Range: $25-49.9 Million
Emp.: 35
Vacuum Distilling Equipment Mfr
N.A.I.C.S.: 333248
Oliver Stoll (Mng Dir)

BDI. CO., LTD
13F Kolon Digital Tower Eston
505-14 Gasan-dong Kumcheon-gu,
Seoul, Korea (South)
Tel.: (82) 220828890
Web Site: http://www.bdh.kr
Year Founded: 1990

148140—(KRS)
Rev.: $9,931,759
Assets: $39,075,016
Liabilities: $109,404,762
Net Worth: ($70,329,746)
Earnings: ($52,849,414)
Emp.: 13
Fiscal Year-end: 12/31/22
Industrial Equipment Mfr
N.A.I.C.S.: 334513

BDL HOTEL GROUP
40 Brund St, Glasgow, G51 1DG,
United Kingdom
Tel.: (44) 1414194567
Web Site: http://www.bdlhotels.co.uk
Year Founded: 1997
Sales Range: $10-24.9 Million
Emp.: 5,000
Hotel Operator
N.A.I.C.S.: 721110
Louis Woodcock (CEO)

**BDO AG WIRTSCHAFTSPRU-
FUNGSGESELLSCHAFT**
Fuhlentwiete 12, Hamburg, 4940
30293 0, Germany
Tel.: (49) 40 30293 0　　　De
Web Site: http://www.bdo.de
Year Founded: 1920
Sales Range: $250-299.9 Million
Emp.: 1,900
Accounting, Tax, Financial Advisory &
Consulting Services
N.A.I.C.S.: 541211
Werner Jacob (Vice Chm-Exec Bd)

Subsidiaries:

BDO Dr. Lauter & Fischer GmbH
Wirtschaftsprufungs-gesellschaft　(1)
Im Zollhafen 22, 50678, Cologne,
Germany　　　　　　　　　(100%)
Tel.: (49) 221973570
Web Site: http://www.bdo.com
Sales Range: $25-49.9 Million
Emp.: 120
Other Accounting Services
N.A.I.C.S.: 541219
Guido Siepert (Gen Mgr)

BDO Schleswig-Holsteinische Treu-
handgesellschaft mbH Wirtschaftspru-
fungsgesellschaft
Steuerberatungsgesellschaft　　(1)
Dahlmannstr 1-3, 24103, Kiel,
Germany　　　　　　　　　(100%)
Tel.: (49) 431519600
Sales Range: $25-49.9 Million
Emp.: 40
Tax Preparation Services
N.A.I.C.S.: 541213

BDO Schurmann & Glashoff Steuer-
beratungsgesellschaft mbH　　(1)
Gruneburgweg 102, 60323, Frankfurt,
Germany　　　　　　　　　(100%)
Tel.: (49) 6995941356
Web Site: http://www.bdo.de
Sales Range: $25-49.9 Million
Emp.: 150
Other Accounting Services
N.A.I.C.S.: 541219

BDO Westfalen-Revision GmbH
Wirtschaftsprufungsgesellschaft　(1)
Stockholmer Allee 32 b, 44269, Dortmund,
Germany　　　　　　　　　(74.9%)
Tel.: (49) 231419040
Web Site: http://www.bdo.de
Sales Range: $25-49.9 Million
Emp.: 50
Other Accounting Services
N.A.I.C.S.: 541219

BDO DUNWOODY LLP
36 Toronto St Ste 600, Toronto, M5C
2C5, ON, Canada
Tel.: (416) 865-0111
Web Site: http://www.bdo.ca
Sales Range: $100-124.9 Million
Emp.: 1,941

BDO Dunwoody LLP—(Continued)

Accounting & Consulting Services
N.A.I.C.S.: 541211
Keith Farlinger (CEO)

BDO INTERNATIONAL LIMITED

55 Baker Street, London, W1U 7EU,
United Kingdom　　　　　　　　UK
Web Site: http://www.bdo.global
Year Founded: 1963
Holding Company; Accounting & Advisory Services Organization
N.A.I.C.S.: 551112
Keith Farlinger (CEO)

BDO KENDALLS

Level 8 85 Macquarie Street, Hobart,
7000, TAS, Australia
Tel.: (61) 362342499
Web Site: http://www.bdo.com.au
Sales Range: $25-49.9 Million
Emp.: 35
Accounting & Consulting Services
N.A.I.C.S.: 541211
Craig Stephens (Mng Dir-Hobart)

BDO UNIBANK, INC.

7899 Makati Avenue, Makati, 0726,
Philippines
Tel.: (63) 288407000
Web Site: https://www.bdo.com.ph
Year Founded: 2008
BDO—(PHI)
Rev.: $2,655,326,418
Assets: $72,502,410,989
Liabilities: $64,291,578,442
Net Worth: $8,210,832,547
Earnings: $1,018,380,456
Emp.: 39,323
Fiscal Year-end: 12/31/22
Commercial Banking Services
N.A.I.C.S.: 522110
Nestor V. Tan (Pres & CEO)

Subsidiaries:

Armstrong Securities, Inc.　　　　(1)
20th Floor South BDO Corporate Center,
7899 Makati Avenue, Makati, Philippines
Tel.: (63) 28784552
Investment Services
N.A.I.C.S.: 523999
Antonio C. Pacis (Sec)

BDO Capital & Investment
Corporation　　　　　　　　　　　(1)
17/F BDO Equitable Tower 8751 Paseo de
Roxas, Salcedo Village, Makati, 1209, Philippines
Tel.: (63) 288784700
Investment Banking Services
N.A.I.C.S.: 523999

BDO Elite Savings Bank, Inc.　　(1)
10th & 11th Floors Net Cube Bldg 30th St
cnr 3rd Ave Crescent Park W, Bonifacio
Global City, Taguig, Philippines　(99%)
Tel.: (63) 8 777 8600
Commercial Banking & Lending Services
N.A.I.C.S.: 522110

BDO Insurance Brokers, Inc.　　(1)
8th Floor JMT Condominium 27 ADB Avenue, Ortigas Center, Pasig, Philippines
Tel.: (63) 2 688 1288
Insurance Services
N.A.I.C.S.: 524210

BDO Private Bank, Inc.　　　　　(1)
Banking Services
N.A.I.C.S.: 522110
Stella L. Cabalatungan (Exec VP)

BDO Remit Limited　　　　　　　(1)
Shop 231-234 & 237 Worldwide House 19
Des Voeux Road, Central, China (Hong
Kong)
Tel.: (852) 25377148
N.A.I.C.S.: 541611

BDO Remittance (USA) Inc.　　　(1)

1559 E Amar Rd Ste U, West Covina, CA
91792
Tel.: (626) 363-9800
Web Site: http://www.bdo.com.ph
Money Transfer Services
N.A.I.C.S.: 522320
Alex Dulay (Mgr-Bus Dev)

BDO Rental, Inc.　　　　　　　　(1)
BDO Leasing Centre Corinthian Gardens,
Ortigas Avenue, Quezon City, Philippines
Tel.: (63) 2 635 6416
Rental & Leasing Services
N.A.I.C.S.: 532490
Antonio N. Cotoco (Chm)

BDO Securities Corporation　　(1)
33/F BDO Towers Valero 8741 Paseo de
Roxas, Salcedo Village, Makati, 1209, Philippines
Tel.: (63) 288407000
Investment Services
N.A.I.C.S.: 523999

BDO Strategic Holdings, Inc.　(1)
2/F BDO Towers Valero 8741 Paseo de
Roxas, Makati, 1209, Philippines
Tel.: (63) 288407000
Holding Company
N.A.I.C.S.: 551111

Banco De Oro Savings Bank Inc.　(1)
G/F ILAC Bldg Ayala Ave corner Paseo de
Roxas, Makati, 1226, Philippines
Tel.: (63) 29959999
Sales Range: $100-124.9 Million
Commercial Banking Services
N.A.I.C.S.: 522110
Cecille Fonacier (Dir-Mktg)

Dominion Holdings, Inc.　　　　(1)
BDO Leasing Centre Corinthian Gardens,
Ortigas Avenue, Quezon City, 1100,
Philippines　　　　　　　　　　(85%)
Tel.: (63) 26356416
Web Site: http://www.bdo.com.ph
Rev.: $6,206,012
Assets: $115,249,435
Liabilities: $238,151
Net Worth: $115,011,284
Earnings: $5,006,410
Fiscal Year-end: 12/31/2023
Leasing & Financial Services
N.A.I.C.S.: 522220
Jason Joseph M. Natividad (Sec)

Equimark-NFC Development
Corporation　　　　　　　　　　(1)
Room 603 EBC Building 262 Juan Luna
Street, Binondo, Manila, 1006, Philippines
Tel.: (63) 288407000
Financial Services
N.A.I.C.S.: 561499

PCIB Securities, Inc.　　　　　　(1)
BDO Equitable Tower, Paseo de Roxas,
Makati, 8751, Philippines
Tel.: (63) 27027878
Investment Services
N.A.I.C.S.: 523150

BDR BUILDCON LIMITED

21 Ring Road Third Floor, Lajpat Nagar -IV, New Delhi, 110024, India
Tel.: (91) 911126477771
Web Site:
　　https://www.bdrbuildcon.com
Year Founded: 2010
BDR—(NSE)
Rev.: $49,223
Assets: $1,290,938
Liabilities: $446
Net Worth: $1,290,492
Earnings: $40,476
Emp.: 1
Fiscal Year-end: 03/12/21
Real Estate Services
N.A.I.C.S.: 531390
Rajesh Gupta (Mng Dir)

BDR THERMEA GROUP B.V.

Marchantstraat 55, 7332 AZ, Apeldoorn, Netherlands
Tel.: (31) 555496969
Web Site:
　　http://www.bdrthermea.com

Sales Range: $1-4.9 Billion
Emp.: 6,300
Heating & Hot Water System Mfr
N.A.I.C.S.: 332410
Hubert Schwein (CFO)

Subsidiaries:

BDR THERMEA (Czech Republic)
s.r.o.　　　　　　　　　　　　　(1)
Jeseniova 2770/56, Zizkov, 13000, Prague,
Czech Republic
Tel.: (420) 271001627
Web Site: http://www.bdrthermea.cz
Water Heater Distr
N.A.I.C.S.: 423720

BDR Thermea (Tianjin) Co. Ltd　(1)
Prime Tower 1410 22 Chao Wai Da Jie,
Chaoyang District, Beijing, China
Tel.: (86) 10 65888700
Web Site: http://www.baxichina.com
Water Heater Distr
N.A.I.C.S.: 423720

Baxi AB　　　　　　　　　　　　(1)
Storgatan 50, 521 43, Falkoping, Sweden
Tel.: (46) 515 171 10
Web Site: http://www.baxi.se
Water Heater Distr
N.A.I.C.S.: 423720

Baxi Belgium SA/NV　　　　　　(1)
Koralenhoeve 10, 2160, Wommelgem, Belgium
Tel.: (32) 2 366 04 00
Web Site: http://www.baxi.be
Water Heater Distr
N.A.I.C.S.: 423720

Baxi Calefaccion, SLU　　　　　(1)
Salvador Espriu 9-11, 8908, Barcelona,
Spain
Tel.: (34) 93 263 00 09
Web Site: http://www.baxi.es
Water Heater Distr
N.A.I.C.S.: 423720

Baxi Group Ltd.　　　　　　　　(1)
Brooks House, Coventry Road, Warwick,
CV34 4LL, United Kingdom　　(100%)
Tel.: (44) 844 8711525
Web Site: http://www.baxi.co.uk
Sales Range: $1-4.9 Billion
Emp.: 400
Boiler, Heater, Shower & Related Appliance
Mfr
N.A.I.C.S.: 333414
David Pinder (Mng Dir)

Subsidiary (Non-US):

August Brotje GmbH　　　　　　(2)
August Brotje Str 17, 26180, Rastede,
Germany　　　　　　　　　　　(100%)
Tel.: (49) 4402800
Web Site: http://www.broetje.de
Emp.: 300
Commercial Boilers & Burners
N.A.I.C.S.: 333414
Sten Daugaard-Hansen (Mng Dir)

Baxi A/S　　　　　　　　　　　　(2)
Smedevej, 6880, Tarm, Denmark (100%)
Tel.: (45) 97371511
Web Site: http://www.baxi.dk
Sales Range: $1-9.9 Million
Emp.: 160
Boiler & Heater Mfr & Distr
N.A.I.C.S.: 333414

Baxi France　　　　　　　　　　(2)
157 Ave Charles Floquet, Le Blanc-Mesnil,
93150, France　　　　　　　　(100%)
Tel.: (33) 145915600
Web Site: http://www.baxifrance.com
Sales Range: $25-49.9 Million
Emp.: 100
Mfr of Plumbing Products
N.A.I.C.S.: 326199

Subsidiary (Domestic):

Baxi Potterton Ltd.　　　　　　　(2)
Brooks House Coventry Road, Warwick,
CV34 4LL, United Kingdom
Tel.: (44) 8448711560
Web Site: http://www.potterton.co.uk
Sales Range: $75-99.9 Million
Emp.: 400
Boilers & Water Heaters Mfr

N.A.I.C.S.: 333414

Subsidiary (Non-US):

Baxi S.p.A.　　　　　　　　　　(2)
Via Trozzetti 20, Bassano Del Grappa,
36061, Vicenza, Italy　　　　　(80%)
Tel.: (39) 0424517111
Web Site: http://www.baxi.it
Sales Range: $150-199.9 Million
Emp.: 800
Boiler & Heater Mfr & Distr
N.A.I.C.S.: 333414

Subsidiary (Domestic):

Heatrae Saidia Heating Ltd.　　(2)
Hurricane Way, Norwich, NR6 6EA, Norfolk,
United Kingdom　　　　　　　(100%)
Tel.: (44) 1603420100
Web Site: http://www.heatraesadia.com
Sales Range: $75-99.9 Million
Emp.: 250
Electric Water Heater Mfr
N.A.I.C.S.: 333414
Jon Cockburn (Head-Mktg)

Baxi Innotech GmbH　　　　　　(1)
Ausschlager Elbdeich 127, 20539, Hamburg, Germany
Tel.: (49) 40 7309810
Web Site: http://www.baxi-innotech.de
Emp.: 14
Water Heater Distr
N.A.I.C.S.: 423720
Sten Daugaard-Hansen (CEO)

Baxi Romania SA　　　　　　　(1)
Bd Pipera nr 1/VI Twin Towers Barba Center Et 4 Voluntari, 77190, Bucharest, Romania
Tel.: (40) 31 229 2294
Web Site: http://www.baxiromania.ro
Water Heater Distr
N.A.I.C.S.: 423720

Baxi Sistemas de Aquecimento Unipessoal LDA　　　　　　　　　(1)
Campo Grande 35-10 D, Apartado 52287,
1721-501, Lisbon, Portugal
Tel.: (351) 217 981 200
Web Site: http://www.baxi.pt
Water Heater Distr
N.A.I.C.S.: 423720

Baxi heating (Slovakia) S.R.O　(1)
Piarsticka 6836, 911 01, Trencin, Slovakia
Tel.: (421) 32 652 3532
Web Site: http://www.baxi.sk
Water Heater Distr
N.A.I.C.S.: 423720
Adam Turk (Mng Dir-Comml Bus-UK)

Baxi-senertec UK Ltd　　　　　(1)
Wood Lane, Erdington, B24 9QP, Birmingham, United Kingdom
Tel.: (44) 845 070 1055
Web Site: http://www.senertec.co.uk
Water Heater Distr
N.A.I.C.S.: 423720

Baymak Makina San.Ve Tic.A.S.　(1)
Orhanli Beldesi Orta Mahalle Akdeniz
Sokak No 8 Tepeoren Mevkii, Orhanli Tuzla,
34959, Istanbul, Turkiye
Tel.: (90) 216 581 65 00
Web Site: http://www.baymak.com.tr
Water Heater Mfr
N.A.I.C.S.: 335220

D.D. Promoterm S.R.L.　　　　(1)
Str Crinului 17 Rosu-Chiajna, Ilfov, Bucharest, 77042, Romania
Tel.: (40) 21 350 13 59
Water Heater Distr
N.A.I.C.S.: 423720

DDR Americas Inc.　　　　　　(1)
1090 Fountain St N Unit 10 & 11, Cambridge, N3E 1A3, ON, Canada
Tel.: (519) 650-0420
Web Site: http://www.dedietrichboilers.com
Water Heater Distr
N.A.I.C.S.: 423720

De Dietrich Remeha GmbH　　(1)
Rheiner Str 151, 48282, Emsdetten, Germany
Tel.: (49) 2572 230
Web Site: http://www.dedietrich-remeha.de
Water Heater Distr

N.A.I.C.S.: 423720

De Dietrich Technika Grzewcza Sp. z o.o (1)
Ul Mydlana 1, 51 502, Wroclaw, Poland
Tel.: (48) 713450051
Web Site: http://www.dedietrich.pl
Water Heater Distr
N.A.I.C.S.: 423720

De Dietrich Thermique Iberia S.L.U (1)
Salvador Espriu 11, 8908, L'Hospitalet de Llobregat, Spain
Tel.: (34) 935 475 850
Web Site: http://www.dedietrich-calefaccion.es
Water Heater Distr
N.A.I.C.S.: 423720

De Dietrich Thermique, S.A.S. (1)
57 rue de la Gare, 67580, Mertzwiller, France
Tel.: (33) 3 88 80 27 00
Web Site: http://www.dedietrich-heating.com
Water Heater Distr
N.A.I.C.S.: 423720
Eric Boulin *(Area Mgr-Export)*

Remeha B.V. (1)
Marchantstraat 55, 7332 AZ, Apeldoorn, Netherlands
Tel.: (31) 55 5496969
Web Site: http://www.remeha.nl
Water Heater Distr
N.A.I.C.S.: 423720
Niels Bonhof *(Dir-Fin)*

Remeha SRL (1)
Str Oltului Nr 4/A, Sfantu Gheorghe, Romania
Tel.: (40) 74 6170 515
Web Site: http://www.remehacazan.ro
Water Heater Distr
N.A.I.C.S.: 423720

BE GROUP AB
Krangatan 4B, 211 24, Malmo, Sweden
Tel.: (46) 40384200　　　　　SE
Web Site: http://www.begroup.com
BEGR—(OMX)
Rev.: $657,767,040
Assets: $379,058,400
Liabilities: $206,559,360
Net Worth: $172,499,040
Earnings: $60,429,600
Emp.: 621
Fiscal Year-end: 12/31/21
Stainless Steel & Aluminum Trading Services
N.A.I.C.S.: 423510
Jorgen Zahlin *(Chm)*

Subsidiaries:

BE Group AS (1)
Vana-Narva mnt 5, 74114, Maardu, Estonia
Tel.: (372) 605 1300
Web Site: http://www.begroup.ee
Stainless Steel & Aluminum Trading Services
N.A.I.C.S.: 423510

BE Group OU (1)
Vana-Narva mnt 5, 74114, Maardu, Estonia
Tel.: (372) 6051300
Web Site: https://www.begroup.ee
Steel Aluminium Product Mfr & Distr
N.A.I.C.S.: 332999

BE Group Oy Ab (1)
Laiturikatu 2, 15140, Lahti, Finland **(100%)**
Tel.: (358) 3825200
Web Site: https://www.begroup.fi
Sales Range: $10-24.9 Million
Emp.: 350
Stainless Steel & Aluminum Trading Services
N.A.I.C.S.: 423510
Seija Friman *(Sec-Sls)*

BE Group SIA (1)
Piedrujas iela 7, Riga, 1073, Latvia
Tel.: (371) 67 147371
Web Site: http://www.begroup.lv
Emp.: 11

Stainless Steel & Aluminum Trading Services
N.A.I.C.S.: 423510

BE Group Slovakia s.r.o. (1)
Tovarenska 6, 071 01, Michalovce, Slovakia
Tel.: (421) 566 889 040
Web Site: http://www.begroup.sk
Stainless Steel & Aluminum Trading Services
N.A.I.C.S.: 423510
Peter Balint *(Mng Dir)*

BE Group Sp. z o.o (1)
ul Przemyslowa 22, Trebaczew, 98-355, Lodz, Poland
Tel.: (48) 433330004
Web Site: https://www.begroup.pl
Sales Range: $25-49.9 Million
Emp.: 40
Stainless Steel & Aluminum Trading Services
N.A.I.C.S.: 423510
Mariusz Paluch *(Mng Dir)*

BE Group Sverige AB (1)
Krusegatan 19B, 212 25, Malmo, Sweden
Tel.: (46) 40384000
Web Site: https://www.begroup.se
Sales Range: $75-99.9 Million
Emp.: 50
Stainless Steel & Aluminum Trading Services
N.A.I.C.S.: 423510

BE Group UAB (1)
T Masiulio 18 B, 52459, Kaunas, Lithuania
Tel.: (370) 37370699
Web Site: http://www.begroup.lt
Sales Range: $25-49.9 Million
Emp.: 10
Stainless Steel & Aluminum Trading Services
N.A.I.C.S.: 423510
Giedrius Tumas *(Dir)*

BE Group s.r.o. (1)
Kojetinska 3109/73a, 751 52, Prerov, Czech Republic
Tel.: (420) 596 223 122
Web Site: http://www.begroup.cz
Stainless Steel & Aluminum Trading Services
N.A.I.C.S.: 423510
Peter Bellind *(Mng Dir)*

Goodtech Solutions Manufacturing AB (1)
Motterudsvagen 7, 671 34, Arvika, Varmland, Sweden
Tel.: (46) 570727700
Web Site: http://www.goodtech.se
Material Handling Machinery Mfr
N.A.I.C.S.: 333248

BE RESOURCES INC.
82 Richmond Street East Suite 200, Toronto, M5C 1P1, ON, Canada
Tel.: (416) 848-0106　　　　CO
Web Site: http://www.beresources.ca
Year Founded: 2007
BER.H—(TSXV)
Assets: $33,654
Liabilities: $352,634
Net Worth: ($318,980)
Earnings: ($24,415)
Fiscal Year-end: 12/31/23
Beryllium Exploration & Mining Services
N.A.I.C.S.: 212290
Carmelo Marrelli *(Pres & CEO)*

BE SEMICONDUCTOR INDUSTRIES N.V.
Ratio 6, 6921 RW, Duiven, Netherlands
Tel.: (31) 263194500　　　　　NI
Web Site: https://www.besi.com
BESIY—(OTCIQ)
Rev.: $638,991,059
Assets: $989,682,084
Liabilities: $524,494,977
Net Worth: $465,187,107
Earnings: $195,478,530
Emp.: 1,736

Fiscal Year-end: 12/31/23
Semiconductor Packaging, Plating & Die Handling Equipment Mfr
N.A.I.C.S.: 333242
Richard W. Blickman *(Chm-Mgmt Bd & CEO)*

Subsidiaries:

Besi (Shanghai) Trading Co., Ltd. (1)
2/F East No 32 Building No 76 Fu Te Dong San Road, Pilot Free Trade Zone Pudong, Shanghai, 200131, China
Tel.: (86) 2160930588
Semiconductor Assembly Equipment Mfr & Distr
N.A.I.C.S.: 333242

Besi (Thai) S&S Ltd. (1)
2/51 Bangna Complex Office Tower 11th Floor Soi Bangna Trad 25, Bangna Nua Bangna, Bangkok, 10260, Thailand
Tel.: (66) 21736027
Semiconductor Assembly Equipment Mfr & Distr
N.A.I.C.S.: 333242

Besi APac Sdn. Bhd. (1)
No 3 Jalan 26/7 Seksyen 26, 40400, Shah Alam, Selangor, Malaysia
Tel.: (60) 355147777
Semiconductor Assembly Equipment Mfr & Distr
N.A.I.C.S.: 333242
Henk-Jan Jonge Poerink *(Sr VP)*

Besi Austria GmbH (1)
Innstrasse 16, 6241, Radfeld, Austria
Tel.: (43) 53376000
Web Site: http://www.dceu.com
Sales Range: $100-124.9 Million
Emp.: 290
Microchip Assembly Equipment Mfr
N.A.I.C.S.: 333242

Subsidiary (Non-US):

Datacon Hungary Termelo Kft. (2)
Juharfa Utca 24, Gyor, 9027, Hungary　　　　　　　**(100%)**
Tel.: (36) 96510400
Web Site: http://www.datacon.at
Sales Range: $25-49.9 Million
Emp.: 20
Electronic Capacitor Mfr
N.A.I.C.S.: 334416

Subsidiary (US):

Datacon North America, Inc. (2)
3150 Tremont Ave, Trevose, PA 19053　　　　　　　　**(100%)**
Tel.: (215) 791-7070
Web Site: http://www.datacon.at
Sales Range: $25-49.9 Million
Emp.: 15
Marketing Consulting Services
N.A.I.C.S.: 541613

Besi Austria GmbH (1)
Innstrasse 16, 6241, Radfeld, Austria
Tel.: (43) 5 337 6000
Semiconductor Assembly Equipment Mfr & Distr
N.A.I.C.S.: 333242

Besi Japan Co. Ltd. (1)
Nakamura Building 6th Floor, 31-7 Shinbashi 4-chome Minato-, 105-0004, Tokyo, Japan　　　　　　　　**(100%)**
Tel.: (81) 334341251
Sales Range: $50-74.9 Million
Emp.: 9
Industrial Machinery & Equipment Whslr
N.A.I.C.S.: 423830

Besi Korea Ltd. (1)
2F 170 Unjoong-ro, Bundang-gu, 13467, Seongnam, 13467, Gyeonggi do, Korea (South)　　　　　　　　**(100%)**
Tel.: (82) 317189002
Space Research & Technology
N.A.I.C.S.: 927110

Besi Leshan Co., Ltd. (1)
No 8 Ying Bin Road, High Tech Zone, Leshan, 614012, Sichuan, China
Tel.: (86) 8332596385

Semiconductor Assembly Equipment Mfr & Distr
N.A.I.C.S.: 333242

Besi North America, Inc. (1)
33 E Comstock Dr Ste 4, Chandler, AZ 85225　　　　　　　　**(100%)**
Tel.: (480) 497-6404
Sales Range: $25-49.9 Million
Emp.: 30
Microelectronic Assembly Equipment Mfr
N.A.I.C.S.: 333242

Besi Philippines, Inc. (1)
Unit 2603 Entrata Urban Complex Condominium Filinvest, Alabang, Muntinlupa, 1781, Philippines
Tel.: (63) 25737230
Semiconductor Assembly Equipment Mfr & Distr
N.A.I.C.S.: 333242

Besi Singapore Pte. Ltd. (1)
No 1 Science Park Road Singapore Science Park 2 03-11, Capricorn Building, Singapore, 117528, Singapore **(100%)**
Tel.: (65) 63037000
Web Site: http://www.datacon.at
Sales Range: $25-49.9 Million
Emp.: 10
Semiconductor Machinery Mfr
N.A.I.C.S.: 333242

Besi USA, Inc. (1)
10 Tinker Ave, Londonderry, NH 03053
Tel.: (603) 626-4700
Semiconductor Device Distr
N.A.I.C.S.: 423690

Esec (Singapore) Pte. Ltd. (1)
1 Science Park Road Singapore Science Park 2 04-12 Capricorn Building, Singapore, 117528, Singapore
Tel.: (65) 6303 7000
Sales Range: $25-49.9 Million
Emp.: 7
Semiconductor Devices Mfr
N.A.I.C.S.: 334413
Soh Kianloo *(Gen Mgr)*

Esec AG (1)
Hinterbergstrasse 32, Cham, 6330, Switzerland
Tel.: (41) 7495111
Web Site: http://www.besi.com
Sales Range: $50-74.9 Million
Emp.: 180
Chip Assembly Equipment Mfr
N.A.I.C.S.: 333242

Fico B.V. (1)
Ratio 6, 6921, Duiven, Netherlands　　　　　　　　**(100%)**
Tel.: (31) 263193600
Web Site: http://www.fico.nl
Sales Range: $50-74.9 Million
Emp.: 150
Industrial Mold Mfr
N.A.I.C.S.: 333511

Subsidiary (Non-US):

Fico Asia Sdn. Bhd. (2)
3 Jalan 26-7, Shah Alam, Malaysia **(100%)**
Tel.: (60) 351911799
Sales Range: $25-49.9 Million
All Other Industrial Machinery Mfr
N.A.I.C.S.: 333248

Fico Tooling Leshan Company Ltd. (2)
Electronic Park, Leshan High Tech Zone, Leshan, 614012, Sichuan, China　**(87%)**
Tel.: (86) 8332596385
Web Site: http://www.pesi.com
Sales Range: $25-49.9 Million
Semiconductor & Related Device Mfr
N.A.I.C.S.: 334413

Fico International B.V. (1)
Ratio 6, 6921 RW, Duiven, Netherlands
Tel.: (31) 263196100
Sales Range: $50-74.9 Million
Emp.: 20
Semiconductor Devices Mfr
N.A.I.C.S.: 334413
Richard Blickman *(Gen Mgr)*

Meco Equipment Engineers B.V (1)
Het Sterrenbeeld 24, 5215 ML, s-Hertogenbosch, Netherlands　　**(100%)**

BE Semiconductor Industries N.V.—(Continued)

Tel.: (31) 416384384
Web Site: http://www.meco.nl
Sales Range: $25-49.9 Million
Emp.: 30
Plate Work Mfr
N.A.I.C.S.: 332313

BE-BE A.D.

12 September no 30, 31250, Bajina Basta, Serbia
Tel.: (381) 31865549
Web Site: https://www.fmpbebe.co.rs
Year Founded: 1978
BEBE—(BEL)
Rev.: $130,445
Assets: $230,155
Liabilities: $65,497
Net Worth: $164,658
Earnings: ($107,810)
Emp.: 15
Fiscal Year-end: 12/31/22
Hardware Mfr
N.A.I.C.S.: 332722
Slobodan Zivanovic (Dir)

BEACH ENERGY LIMITED

Level 8 80 Flinders Street, Adelaide, 5000, SA, Australia
Tel.: (61) 883382833   **AU**
Web Site:
  https://www.beachenergy.com.au
BEPTF—(OTCIQ)
Rev.: $1,357,228,966
Assets: $3,909,177,999
Liabilities: $1,196,942,018
Net Worth: $2,712,235,981
Earnings: $383,707,952
Emp.: 500
Fiscal Year-end: 06/30/22
Crude Petroleum Extraction Services
N.A.I.C.S.: 211120
Glenn Stuart Davis (Chm)

BEACH HATCHERY LIMITED

Concord Tower Apt 201 2nd Floor
113 Kazi Nazrul Islam Avenue, Bangla Motor, Dhaka, 1000, Bangladesh
Tel.: (880) 29833506
Web Site: https://www.bhlbd.net
Year Founded: 1997
BEACHHATCH—(CHT)
Rev.: $1,080,973
Assets: $4,755,651
Liabilities: $758,974
Net Worth: $3,996,677
Earnings: $349,814
Emp.: 39
Fiscal Year-end: 06/30/23
Seafood Product Mfr
N.A.I.C.S.: 311710
Mohammad Shariful Islam (Mng Dir)

BEACHCOMBER HOT TUBS

13245 Comber Way, Surrey, V3W 5V8, BC, Canada
Tel.: (604) 591-8611
Web Site:
  http://www.beachcomberhottub.com
Year Founded: 1978
Rev.: $33,718,135
Emp.: 350
Spas & Hot Tub Accessories Mfr
N.A.I.C.S.: 322219
Keith Scott (Co-Owner & Pres)

BEACON ENERGY PLC

55 Athol Street, Douglas, IM1 1LA, Isle of Man
Tel.: (44) 1624681250
Web Site:
  https://www.beaconenergyplc.com
ADV—(AIM)
Assets: $28,568,000
Liabilities: $1,138,000
Net Worth: $27,430,000
Earnings: ($2,854,000)

Emp.: 5
Fiscal Year-end: 04/30/21
Oil & Gas Production Services
N.A.I.C.S.: 211120
Larry Bottomley (Interim CEO)

BEACON INTERNATIONAL SPECIALIST CENTRE SDN. BHD.

No 1 Jalan 215 Section 51 Off Jalan Templer, 46050, Petaling Jaya, Selangor, Malaysia
Tel.: (60) 3 76207979
Web Site:
  http://www.beaconhospital.com.my
Year Founded: 2005
Sales Range: $10-24.9 Million
Emp.: 150
Hospital & Medical Diagnostic Services
N.A.I.C.S.: 622110
Joen Chua (Mgr)

BEACON LIGHTING GROUP LTD

5 Bastow Place, Mulgrave, 3170, VIC, Australia
Tel.: (61) 385611555
Web Site:
  https://www.beaconlighting.com.au
Year Founded: 1967
BLX—(ASX)
Rev.: $216,041,666
Assets: $245,108,172
Liabilities: $134,404,380
Net Worth: $110,703,792
Earnings: $20,100,160
Fiscal Year-end: 06/30/24
Lighting & Ceiling Fans Retailer
N.A.I.C.S.: 459999
Ian Robinson (Chm)

Subsidiaries:

Beacon International Limited   **(1)**
11/Fl Guzhen Lighting Building B Mid Zhongxing Road, Guzhen, Zhongshan, GuangDong, China (Hong Kong)
Tel.: (852) 76089866388
Web Site:
  https://www.beaconinternational.com
Light Emitting Diode Product Mfr & Distr
N.A.I.C.S.: 335132

Beacon Lighting Europe GmbH   **(1)**
Campus Fichtenhain 42, 47807, Krefeld, Germany
Tel.: (49) 21513258239
Web Site: https://www.beaconlighting-europe.com
Light Emitting Diode Products Distr
N.A.I.C.S.: 423610
Jack Panjer (Gen Mgr)

Light Source Solutions New Zealand Limited   **(1)**
Level 1 130 St Georges Bay Rd, Parnell, Auckland, 1052, New Zealand
Tel.: (64) 800334352
Web Site:
  http://www.lightsourcesolutions.co.nz
Light Emitting Diode Product Mfr & Distr
N.A.I.C.S.: 335132

BEACON MINERALS LTD.

144 Vivian Street, Boulder, Kalgoorlie, 6432, WA, Australia
Tel.: (61) 890932477   **AU**
Web Site:
  https://www.beaconminerals.com.au
BCN—(ASX)
Rev.: $55,675,125
Assets: $75,215,210
Liabilities: $29,949,161
Net Worth: $45,266,049
Earnings: $6,134,332
Fiscal Year-end: 06/30/24
Copper-Goldmolybdenum Mineralization
N.A.I.C.S.: 212230

Geoffrey Greenhill (Bd of Dirs & Chm)

BEACON PHARMACEUTICALS LTD.

153-154 Tejgaon I/A, Dhaka, 1208, Bangladesh
Tel.: (880) 29888176
Web Site: http://www.beacon-pharma.com
Sales Range: $300-349.9 Million
Emp.: 1,264
Pharmaceuticals Mfr
N.A.I.C.S.: 325412
Mohammad Ebadul Karim (Mng Dir)

BEACON RISE HOLDINGS PLC

Viking House Nelson Street, IM1 2AH, Douglas, Isle of Man
Tel.: (44) 1624639396   **UK**
Web Site:
  https://www.braddaheadltd.com
Year Founded: 2021
BRS—(LSE)
Assets: $708,385
Liabilities: $238,109
Net Worth: $470,276
Earnings: ($338,641)
Fiscal Year-end: 03/31/23
Holding Company
N.A.I.C.S.: 551112
Denham Eke (CFO)

BEACONSMIND AG

Seestrasse 3, Stafa, 8712, Zurich, Switzerland
Tel.: (41) 782221105
Web Site:
  https://www.beaconsmind.com
Year Founded: 2015
MLBMD—(EUR)
Rev.: $2,250,492
Assets: $6,593,356
Liabilities: $2,468,259
Net Worth: $4,125,097
Earnings: ($2,838,453)
Emp.: 10
Fiscal Year-end: 06/30/22
Software Development Services
N.A.I.C.S.: 541511
Jonathan Sauppe (CEO)

BEAGLEE, INC.

2-13-5 Kita-Aoyama, Minato-ku, Tokyo, 107-0061, Japan
Tel.: (81) 367064000
Web Site: https://www.beaglee.com
3981—(TKS)
Rev.: $135,277,200
Assets: $130,342,560
Liabilities: $81,045,790
Net Worth: $49,296,770
Earnings: $4,885,010
Emp.: 86
Fiscal Year-end: 12/31/23
Digital Media Publishing Services
N.A.I.C.S.: 513199
Jinpei Yoshida (Chm & Pres)

BEALE LIMITED

The Granville Chambers 21 Richmond Hill, Bournemouth, BH2 6BJ, United Kingdom
Tel.: (44) 1202552022   **UK**
Web Site: http://www.beales.co.uk
Year Founded: 1881
Sales Range: $150-199.9 Million
Departmental Store Operator
N.A.I.C.S.: 455110
Tony Brown (CEO)

BEAM COMMUNICATIONS PTY. LTD.

5/8 Anzed Court, Mulgrave, 3170, VIC, Australia

Tel.: (61) 385884500
Web Site:
  https://www.beamcommunication.com
Year Founded: 2002
BCC—(ASX)
Sales Range: $1-9.9 Million
Radio & Television Broadcasting & Wireless Communications Equipment Manufacturing
N.A.I.C.S.: 334220
Michael Ian Capocchi (Mng Dir)

Subsidiaries:

Beam Communications Pty Ltd.   **(1)**
Unit 5 8 Anzed Ct, Mulgrave, 3170, VIC, Australia
Tel.: (61) 385884500
Web Site:
  http://www.beamcommunications.com
Remote Satellite Communication Equipments Mfr & Distr
N.A.I.C.S.: 334220

BEAMMWAVE AB

Ideon Science Park, 223 70, Lund, Sweden
Web Site:
  https://www.beammwave.com
Year Founded: 2017
OX0—(DEU)
Semiconductor Mfr
N.A.I.C.S.: 334413
Fredrik Rosenqvist (Chm)

BEAMR IMAGING LTD.

10 Hamenofim Street, Herzliya Pituach, 66183, Israel
Tel.: (972) 6509613098
Web Site: https://beamr.com
Year Founded: 2009
BMR—(NASDAQ)
Rev.: $2,909,000
Assets: $11,523,000
Liabilities: $1,263,000
Net Worth: $10,260,000
Earnings: ($695,000)
Emp.: 28
Fiscal Year-end: 12/31/23
Software Development Services
N.A.I.C.S.: 541511
Danny Sandler (CFO)

BEAMR LTD.

23 Menachem Begin Road, 61366, Tel Aviv, Israel
Tel.: (972) 3 560 7333   II
Web Site: http://www.beamr.com
Year Founded: 2009
Media Optimization Solutions
N.A.I.C.S.: 541519
Sharon Carmel (Founder & CEO)

Subsidiaries:

Vanguard Video LLC   **(1)**
974 Commercial St Ste 200, Palo Alto, CA 94303-4929
Tel.: (650) 961-3098
Web Site: http://www.vanguardvideo.com
Video Encoding & Optimization Solutions
N.A.I.C.S.: 541519
Irena Terterov (Founder & CEO)

BEAMTREE HOLDINGS LIMITED

Suite 2 Level 10 5 Blue Street, North Sydney, 2060, NSW, Australia
Tel.: (61) 283139990   **AU**
Web Site:
  https://www.beamtree.com.au
Year Founded: 1996
BMT—(ASX)
Rev.: $14,845,146
Assets: $40,769,381
Liabilities: $9,980,439
Net Worth: $30,788,942
Earnings: ($4,504,140)
Emp.: 30
Fiscal Year-end: 06/30/23

Holding Company
N.A.I.C.S.: 551112
Cheryl McCullagh (Chief Product Officer)

BEAR CREEK MINING CORPORATION
Suite 3200 733 Seymour Street, Vancouver, V6B 0S6, BC, Canada
Tel.: (604) 685-6269
Web Site:
https://www.bearcreekmining.com
Year Founded: 1999
BCM—(TSXV)
Sales Range: Less than $1 Million
Mineral Exploration Services
N.A.I.C.S.: 213114
Andrew T. Swarthout (Co-Chm)

Subsidiaries:

Bear Creek Mining Inc. **(1)**
7761 Shaffer Pkwy, Littleton, CO 80127-3728
Tel.: (303) 390-0071
Coal Surface Mining Services
N.A.I.C.S.: 212114

Bear Creek Mining S.A.C. **(1)**
Avenida Republica de Panama 3505 Piso 6, San Isidro, Lima, 27, Peru
Tel.: (51) 12220922
Metal Mining Services
N.A.I.C.S.: 213114
Eric Caba (VP-Project Dev)

BEAR ELECTRIC APPLIANCE CO., LTD.
No 3 Fuxing Road Fu'an Industrial Zone Leliu Street, Shunde District, Foshan, 528322, Guangdong, China
Tel.: (86) 4006622580
Web Site: https://www.bears.com.cn
Year Founded: 2006
002959—(SSE)
Rev.: $578,125,080
Assets: $684,136,908
Liabilities: $351,869,076
Net Worth: $332,267,832
Earnings: $54,237,924
Fiscal Year-end: 12/31/22
Electrical Equipment Mfr & Distr
N.A.I.C.S.: 335999
Yifeng Li (Chm & Gen Mgr)

BEARCLAW CAPITAL CORP.
214 3540 West 41st Avenue, Vancouver, V6E 4H3, BC, Canada
Tel.: (604) 682-2201
Web Site:
https://www.bearclawcapital.com
Year Founded: 1999
BRL.H—(TSXV)
Rev.: $5,653
Assets: $224,718
Liabilities: $61,368
Net Worth: $163,350
Earnings: ($69,655)
Fiscal Year-end: 12/31/23
Mineral Exploration Services
N.A.I.C.S.: 212290
Arthur W. Lilly (CFO & Sec)

BEARDSELL LIMITED
47 Greams Road, Chennai, 600 006, India
Tel.: (91) 4428293296
Web Site: https://www.beardsell.co.in
539447—(BOM)
Rev.: $25,773,056
Assets: $17,421,140
Liabilities: $10,506,855
Net Worth: $6,914,285
Earnings: $383,838
Emp.: 195
Fiscal Year-end: 03/31/22
Storage & Packaging Services
N.A.I.C.S.: 493110
R. Gowri Shanker (Chm)

BEARINGPOINT HOLDINGS EUROPE B.V.
De entree 89, Amsterdam, NL-1101, BH, Netherlands
Tel.: (31) 205049000   NI
Web Site:
http://www.bearingpoint.com
Holding Company; Management & Technology Consulting Services
N.A.I.C.S.: 551112
Peter Mockler (Mng Partner)

Subsidiaries:

BearingPoint GmbH **(1)**
Speicherstrasse 1, Frankfurt, D 60327, Germany
Tel.: (49) 69130220
Web Site: http://www.bearingpoint.de
Sales Range: $200-249.9 Million
Emp.: 600
Management & Technology Consulting Services
N.A.I.C.S.: 541611

Subsidiary (Non-US):

Bearing Point Middle East Fz Llc **(2)**
Sheikh Khalifa Street, Gibca Tower, Abu Dhabi, United Arab Emirates
Tel.: (971) 2 5580 880
Business Consulting Services
N.A.I.C.S.: 541611

BearingPoint (Shanghai) Enterprise Management Consulting Co. Ltd. **(2)**
No 925 Wu Ding Road 4th Floor, Jing An District, 200040, Shanghai, China
Tel.: (86) 21 6288 7866
Management Consulting Services
N.A.I.C.S.: 541611
Jan Bernstorf (Deputy Gen Mgr)

BearingPoint Belgium s.p.r.l. **(2)**
rue de la Loi 82, 1040, Brussels, Belgium
Tel.: (32) 2 639 59 11
Management Consulting Services
N.A.I.C.S.: 541611

Subsidiary (US):

BearingPoint Consulting Inc. **(2)**
Hickory St Annex 501 S 2nd Ave Ste A-700, Dallas, TX 75226
Tel.: (214) 821-0990
Management Consulting Services
N.A.I.C.S.: 541611

Subsidiary (Non-US):

BearingPoint Denmark AS **(2)**
Islands Brygge 43, Copenhagen, 2300, S, Denmark
Tel.: (45) 32888888
Web Site: http://www.bearingpoint.dk
Sales Range: $25-49.9 Million
Emp.: 30
Management & Technology Consulting Services
N.A.I.C.S.: 541611

BearingPoint Finland Oy **(2)**
Kluuvikatu 3, 00100, Helsinki, Finland
Tel.: (358) 10802288
Sales Range: $25-49.9 Million
Emp.: 60
Management & Technology Consulting Services
N.A.I.C.S.: 541611
Riku Sanpala (Mng Dir)

BearingPoint France SAS **(2)**
51 Esplanade du General de Gaulle, 20 Pl De La Defense, 92050, Paris, Cedex, France
Tel.: (33) 158863000
Web Site: http://www.bearingpoint.fr
Sales Range: $150-199.9 Million
Management & Technology Consulting Services
N.A.I.C.S.: 541611

BearingPoint GmbH **(2)**
Schwartzenbergplatz 5, Vienna, A 1010, Austria
Tel.: (43) 1506320
Sales Range: $25-49.9 Million
Emp.: 50

Management & Technology Consulting Services
N.A.I.C.S.: 541611
Klaus Kalthoff (Gen Mgr)

BearingPoint INFONOVA GmbH **(2)**
Seering 6 Block D, 8141, Graz, Unterpremstatten, Austria
Tel.: (43) 31680030
Sales Range: $25-49.9 Million
Emp.: 200
Management & Technology Consulting Services
N.A.I.C.S.: 541611
Gerhard Greiner (Mng Dir)

BearingPoint Ireland Limited **(2)**
Montague House Adelaide Road, Dublin, D02 K039, Ireland
Tel.: (353) 14181111
Sales Range: $25-49.9 Million
Emp.: 120
Management & Technology Consulting Services
N.A.I.C.S.: 541611

BearingPoint Italy Srl. **(2)**
Corso Italia 1, 20122, Milan, Italy
Tel.: (39) 02 45476804
Business Consulting Services
N.A.I.C.S.: 541611

BearingPoint Limited **(2)**
16 Great Queen Street, London, WC2B 5DG, United Kingdom
Tel.: (44) 203 206 96 00
Sales Range: $25-49.9 Million
Emp.: 100
Management & Technology Consulting Services
N.A.I.C.S.: 541611
Kevin O'Reilly (Head-Fin)

BearingPoint Norway A/S **(2)**
Tjuvholmen Alle 1, 0252, Oslo, Norway
Tel.: (47) 24069000
Web Site: http://www.bearingpoint.no
Sales Range: $25-49.9 Million
Emp.: 100
Management & Technology Consulting Services
N.A.I.C.S.: 541611

BearingPoint Sweden AB **(2)**
Sveavagen 21, PO Box 3033, 103 61, Stockholm, Sweden
Tel.: (46) 841011600
Web Site: http://www.bearingpoint.se
Sales Range: $25-49.9 Million
Emp.: 68
Management & Technology Consulting Services
N.A.I.C.S.: 541611
Patrick Talmgren (VP)

BearingPoint Switzerland AG **(2)**
West-Park, Pfingstweidstrasse 60, Zurich, 8005, Switzerland
Tel.: (41) 432996464
Sales Range: $25-49.9 Million
Emp.: 120
Management & Technology Consulting Services
N.A.I.C.S.: 541611
Patrick Mader (Partner-Insurance)

Bearingpoint Maroc **(2)**
16 Boulevard Abdellatif Ben Kaddour, 20050, Casablanca, Morocco
Tel.: (212) 522 269 721
Management Consulting Services
N.A.I.C.S.: 541611

BEATTIE COMMUNICATIONS GROUP
118 N Main St, Carronshore, Falkirk, FK2 8HU, United Kingdom
Tel.: (44) 1324 602 550
Web Site:
http://www.beattiegroup.com
Year Founded: 1986
Emp.: 120
N.A.I.C.S.: 541810
Laurna O'Donnell (Grp Mng Dir)

Subsidiaries:

Beattie Communications Group **(1)**
18 Glasgow Rd, Uddingston, Glasgow, G71

7AS, United Kingdom
Tel.: (44) 1698 787 878
Emp.: 100
N.A.I.C.S.: 541820
Chris Gilmour (Mng Dir)

Beattie Communications Group **(1)**
46 The Calls, Leeds, LS2 7EY, Yorkshire, United Kingdom
Tel.: (44) 113 213 0300
Emp.: 10
N.A.I.C.S.: 541820
Victoria Walker (Dir)

Beattie Communications Group **(1)**
4 Great James St, Holborn, London, WC1N 3DB, United Kingdom
Tel.: (44) 207 053 6000
Web Site: http://www.beattiegroup.com
Emp.: 20
N.A.I.C.S.: 541820
Jacquie Boyd (Dir)

Beattie Communications Group **(1)**
3 Brindley Place 2nd Fl, Birmingham, B1 2JB, United Kingdom
Tel.: (44) 12 1698 8625
N.A.I.C.S.: 541810
Gordon Beattie (Chm)

Beattie Communications Group **(1)**
Royal Mills Business Ctr, 17 Redhill St, Ancoats Urban Vlg, Manchester, M4 5BA, United Kingdom
Tel.: (44) 161 932 1026
Emp.: 5
N.A.I.C.S.: 541810
Victoria Walker (Dir)

BEATTIE DODGE CHRYSLER LTD.
8 Chase Street, Brockville, K6V 5V7, ON, Canada
Tel.: (613) 342-4404
Web Site:
http://www.beattiedodge.com
Year Founded: 1978
New & Used Cars Dealers
N.A.I.C.S.: 441110

BEATTIE HOMES LTD
3165 114th Ave SE, Calgary, T2Z 3X2, AB, Canada
Tel.: (403) 252-0995
Web Site:
http://www.beattiehomes.com
Sales Range: $75-99.9 Million
Emp.: 77
Construction Services
N.A.I.C.S.: 236115
Bruce Taylor (Mgr-Sls-Coopers Crossing)

BEATTIE MCGUINNESS BUNGAY
16 Short's Gardens, Covent Garden, London, WC2H 9AU, United Kingdom
Tel.: (44) 207 632 0400
Web Site:
http://www.bmbagency.com
Year Founded: 2005
Rev.: $20,000,000
Emp.: 90
N.A.I.C.S.: 541810
Trevor Beattie (Founder & Chm)

BEATTIES BASICS
399 Vansickle Road, Saint Catharines, L2S 3T4, ON, Canada
Tel.: (905) 688-4040
Web Site: http://www.beatties.com
Year Founded: 1900
Sales Range: $10-24.9 Million
Emp.: 130
Office Furniture Distr
N.A.I.C.S.: 337214
Rob Caruso (Mgr-Pur)

Subsidiaries:

Beatties Basics Office Products **(1)**
399 Vansickle Road, Saint Catharines, L2S 3T4, ON, Canada

Beatties Basics—(Continued)

Tel.: (905) 688-4040
Web Site: http://www.beatties.com
Rev.: $20,002,830
Emp.: 100
Office Furniture Distr
N.A.I.C.S.: 337214
Edward Hoxie (Pres)

BEATTY FLOORS LIMITED

1840 Pandora Street, Vancouver,
V5L1M7, BC, Canada
Tel.: (604) 254-9571
Web Site:
    http://www.beattyfloors.com
Year Founded: 1929
Rev.: $13,650,357
Emp.: 85
Floor Coverings & Installation Carpet
& Rug Dealers
N.A.I.C.S.: 449121
Don Brletic (Pres)

BEAUCE GOLD FIELDS, INC.

3000 Rue Omer Lavallee 306, Mon-
treal, H1Y 3R8, QC, Canada
Tel.: (514) 846-3271
Web Site:
    https://www.beaucegold.com
BGF—(TSXV)
Assets: $3,067,060
Liabilities: $344,586
Net Worth: $2,722,474
Earnings: ($661,805)
Fiscal Year-end: 07/31/21
Gold Exploration & Mining Services
N.A.I.C.S.: 212220
Bernard J. Tourillon (CEO)

BEAUFORT CAPITAL GMBH

Alsterarkaden 20, 20354, Hamburg,
Germany
Tel.: (49) 40 34 99 99 6   De
Web Site: http://www.bo4.de
Privater Equity Firm
N.A.I.C.S.: 523999

Subsidiaries:

Nordseewerke Emden Shipyard
GmbH   (1)
Zum Zungenkai, 26725, Emden, Germany
Tel.: (49) 4921 85 0
Web Site: www.nordseewerke.com
Sales Range: $50-74.9 Million
Emp.: 240
Shipbuilding & Other Steel Structural Engi-
neering Services
N.A.I.C.S.: 336611
Thierry Putters (Mng Dir)

BEAULIEU INTERNATIONAL GROUP NV

Kalkhoevestraat 16, PO Box 01,
Waregem, 8790, Belgium
Tel.: (32) 56625900   BE
Web Site: http://www.bintg.com
Year Founded: 2005
Sales Range: $1-4.9 Billion
Emp.: 5,000
Holding Company; Mfr of Floor Cov-
erings & Fabrics & Production of Raw
Materials, Semi-Finished & Finished
Products
N.A.I.C.S.: 551112
Geert Roelens (CEO)

Subsidiaries:

Act Global Americas Inc.   (1)
4201 West Parmer Ln Ste B 175, Austin,
TX 78727
Tel.: (512) 733-5300
Web Site: https://www.actglobal.com
Sales Range: $1-9.9 Million
Emp.: 11
Specialty Trade Contractors
N.A.I.C.S.: 238990
John T. Baize (CEO)

Alloc AS   (1)

Svardvagen 27, 182 33, Danderyd, Sweden
Tel.: (46) 4 218 2890
Floor Covering Mfr
N.A.I.C.S.: 321918

BIG Floorcoverings NV   (1)
Rijksweg 442, 8710, Wielsbeke, Belgium
Tel.: (32) 5 667 6611
Web Site: https://www.beauflor.com
Floor Covering Mfr
N.A.I.C.S.: 321918

Beauflor USA, LLC   (1)
1 Beauflor Way, White, GA 30184
Web Site: https://www.beauflor.us
Textile Mfr & Distr
N.A.I.C.S.: 325220
Richard Runkel (Gen Mgr)

Beaulieu Fibres International Terni
SRL   (1)
Ple Piazzale Donegani 4, 05100, Terni, Italy
Tel.: (39) 0744 3991
Web Site: https://www.beaulieufibres.com
Emp.: 240
Floor Covering Mfr
N.A.I.C.S.: 321918

Beaulieu International Group NV
Berry Yarns Plant   (1)
Route des Ecluses 52-54, 7780, Comines-
Warneton, Belgium
Tel.: (32) 56560811
Fabric Distr
N.A.I.C.S.: 424310

Beaulieu International Group NV Dis-
triplast Plant   (1)
Z I de Petite Synthe, BP 20106, 59944,
Dunkerque, Cedex, France
Tel.: (33) 328292480
Web Site: http://www.distriplast.com
Polypropylene Mfr
N.A.I.C.S.: 325211

Beaulieu International Group NV Her-
mosa Plant   (1)
Rijksweg 442, 8710, Wielsbeke, Belgium
Tel.: (32) 56676611
Web Site: http://www.beauflor.com
Flooring Installation Services
N.A.I.C.S.: 238330

Beaulieu International Group NV
Juteks Ru Plant   (1)
Dorozhnaja street 10, Kameshkovo,
601301, Vladimir, Russia
Tel.: (7) 4924825006
Web Site: http://www.en.juteks.ru
Flooring Installation Services
N.A.I.C.S.: 238330

Beaulieu International Group NV Ko-
men Plant   (1)
Boulevard Industriel 3, 7780, Comines-
Warneton, Belgium
Tel.: (32) 56560670
Web Site:
    http://www.beaulieutechnicaltextiles.com
Carpet Backing & Textile Mfr
N.A.I.C.S.: 314999

Beaulieu International Group NV
Kruishoutem Plant   (1)
Groene Dreef 15A, 9770, Kruishoutem,
Belgium
Tel.: (32) 93381211
Polymers Mfr
N.A.I.C.S.: 325991

Beaulieu International Group NV Lyn-
gdal Plant   (1)
Fiboveien 26, 4580, Lyngdal, Norway
Tel.: (47) 38342200
Web Site: http://www.berryalloc.com
Flooring Installation Services
N.A.I.C.S.: 238330

Beaulieu International Group NV Pin-
nacle Plant   (1)
1 Pinnacle Ave, Garyville, LA 70051
Tel.: (985) 535-2000
Web Site: http://www.pinnaclepolymers.com
Polypropylene Mfr
N.A.I.C.S.: 325211
Isabella Atkins (Mgr-Pur)

Beaulieu International Group NV
Terni Plant   (1)

P le Piazzale Donegani 4, 05100, Terni,
Italy
Tel.: (39) 07443991
Polypropylene Mfr
N.A.I.C.S.: 325211

Beaulieu International Group NV Wei-
hai Plant   (1)
Lingang Science and Technology Industrial
Park, Qiaotou Town, Weihai, 264212, Shan-
dong, China
Tel.: (86) 6313850210
Web Site: http://www.yarns.bintg.com
Yarn Distr
N.A.I.C.S.: 424310

Beaulieu International Group NV
Wielsbeke Plant   (1)
Ooigemstraat 2B, 8710, Wielsbeke, Belgium
Tel.: (32) 56668191
Yarn Distr
N.A.I.C.S.: 424310

Beaulieu Rizhao Floorcoverings Co.
Ltd.   (1)
189 Weifang Rd, 276800, Rizhao, Shan-
dong, China
Tel.: (86) 6338688598
Polypropylene Mfr
N.A.I.C.S.: 325211

Beaulieu Technical Textiles nv   (1)
Groene Dreef 19, 9770, Kruishoutem, Bel-
gium
Tel.: (32) 93381500
Textile Products Distr
N.A.I.C.S.: 424310

Beaulieu of Australia Pty Ltd   (1)
PO Box 6160, Yatala, 4207, QLD, Australia
Tel.: (61) 75 540 6600
Web Site: https://www.beaulieu.com.au
Carpet Mfr
N.A.I.C.S.: 314110
Allan Russell (CEO)

Berryalloc NV   (1)
Industrielaan 100, 8930, Menen, Belgium
Tel.: (32) 5 652 8480
Web Site: https://www.berryalloc.com
Engineered Wood Products Mfr
N.A.I.C.S.: 321211

Distriplast SAS   (1)
Z I de Petite Synthe, BP 20106, 59944,
Dunkerque, Cedex, France
Tel.: (33) 32 829 2480
Web Site: https://www.distriplast.com
Emp.: 54
Polypropylene Resin Mfr
N.A.I.C.S.: 325211

Domenech Hermanos S.A.U   (1)
Apdo Correos 23, Muro De Alcoy, Alicante,
Spain
Tel.: (34) 965530151
Web Site: http://www.bydomenech.com
Carpet Product Mfr
N.A.I.C.S.: 337910
Antonio Domenech (Mgr)

Ideal Fibres & Fabrics Comines
SAS   (1)
Rue de l'Energie, BP 139, 59560, Comines,
France
Tel.: (33) 32 838 8770
Yarn Mfr
N.A.I.C.S.: 313110

Ideal Fibres & Fabrics Wielsbeke
NV   (1)
Ooigemstraat 2B, 8710, Wielsbeke, Belgium
Tel.: (32) 5 666 8191
Web Site: https://www.beaulieuyarns.com
Fabric & Textile Mfr
N.A.I.C.S.: 325220

Ideal Floorcoverings NV   (1)
Boffonstraat 3, 8710, Wielsbeke, Belgium
Tel.: (32) 56674211
Web Site: http://www.ideal-bintg.com
Flooring Installation Services
N.A.I.C.S.: 238330
Lieven Opsomer (Coord-Environmental)

Juteks d.d.   (1)
Lodge 53a, 3310, Zalec, Slovenia (52,42%)
Tel.: (386) 3 71 20 700
Web Site: http://www.juteks.si
Sales Range: $50-74.9 Million
Emp.: 290
PVC Floor Coverings Mfr

N.A.I.C.S.: 326199
Dusan Stiherl (Gen Mgr)

Orotex Belgium NV   (1)
Ingelmunstersteenweg 162, 8780, Oostro-
zebeke, Belgium
Tel.: (32) 56672211
Web Site: http://www.orotex.com
Carpet Product Mfr
N.A.I.C.S.: 337910

Polychim Industrie SAS   (1)
4810 Route d'Artois, 59279, Loon-Plage,
France
Tel.: (33) 328580270
Web Site: http://www.polychim-industrie.com
Polypropylene Mfr
N.A.I.C.S.: 325211
Gerald Monnaux (Mgr-Site)

Tessutica NV   (1)
Kalkhoevestraat 30, Box 0 1, 8790, Ware-
gem, Belgium
Tel.: (32) 9 338 1361
Web Site: https://www.tessutica.com
Fabric & Textile Mfr
N.A.I.C.S.: 325220

BEAUMONT AUTOMOBILES

Bd Fernand Darchicourt, 62110,
Henin-Beaumont, Pas De Calais,
France
Tel.: (33) 321132050
Web Site:
    http://www.beaumontautomobile.com
Rev.: $18,000,000
Emp.: 33
N.A.I.C.S.: 441110
Bernard Wantiez (VP)

BEAUMONT CAPITAL LLP

37 Shenley Pavilions Chalkdell Drive,
Shenley Wood, Milton Keynes, MK5
6LB, United Kingdom
Tel.: (44) 8456000103
Web Site:
    http://www.beaumontllp.co.uk
Investment Services
N.A.I.C.S.: 523999
Andrew Johnson (Partner)

BEAUMONT SELECT CORPO-RATIONS INC.

915 42nd Avenue SE, Calgary, T2G
1Z1, AB, Canada
Tel.: (403) 250-8757   AB
Web Site: https://www.bsci.ca
Year Founded: 1985
Sales Range: $10-24.9 Million
Investment Management Service
N.A.I.C.S.: 523999
Bernadette Churchill (Dir-Res & Port-
folio Mgmt)

Subsidiaries:

Naleway Foods Ltd.   (1)
233 Hutchings Street, Winnipeg, R2X 2R4,
MB, Canada
Tel.: (204) 633-6535
Web Site: http://www.naleway.com
Sales Range: $25-49.9 Million
Emp.: 100
Frozen Food Mfr
N.A.I.C.S.: 311412
Richard Lyles (Gen Mgr)

BEAUTIFUL CHINA HOLDINGS COMPANY LIMITED

Units 2003 & 2005 20/F Great Eagle
Center, 23 Harbour Road, Wanchai,
China (Hong Kong)
Tel.: (852) 22349723
Web Site:
    http://www.beautifulchina.com.hk
Rev.: $6,179,941
Assets: $85,494,329
Liabilities: $20,383,027
Net Worth: $65,111,302
Earnings: ($17,554,949)
Emp.: 158
Fiscal Year-end: 12/31/18

ATM & Payment Processing Operations & Services
N.A.I.C.S.: 522320
Marco Wai Sze *(Chm)*

BEAUTY COMMUNITY PUBLIC COMPANY LIMITED
50/1-3 Nuan Chan 34 Alley, Chan Sub-district Buengkum District, Bangkok, 10230, Thailand
Tel.: (66) 29460700
Web Site:
http://www.beautycommunity.co.th
Year Founded: 2000
BEAUTY—(THA)
Rev.: $12,658,793
Assets: $24,508,965
Liabilities: $5,234,800
Net Worth: $19,274,164
Earnings: ($1,333,315)
Emp.: 184
Fiscal Year-end: 12/31/23
Cosmetics & Beauty Products Retailer
N.A.I.C.S.: 456120
Norarit Keetanon *(Dir-IT)*

BEAUTY FARM MEDICAL & HEALTH INDUSTRY INC.
Unit 1206 12th Floor No 1089 Dongdaming Road, Hongkou District, Shanghai, China
Tel.: (86) 2160953299   Ky
Web Site:
https://ir.beautyfarm.com.cn
Year Founded: 1993
2373—(HKG)
Rev.: $250,561,779
Assets: $382,318,549
Liabilities: $351,200,219
Net Worth: $31,118,330
Earnings: $16,934,608
Emp.: 3,707
Fiscal Year-end: 12/31/22
Health Care Srvices
N.A.I.C.S.: 621610
Songyong Lian *(Vice Chm)*

BEAUTY GARAGE INC.
1-34-25 Sakura-Shinmachi, Setagaya, Tokyo, 154-0015, Japan
Tel.: (81) 357523880
Web Site:
https://www.beautygarage.co.jp
Year Founded: 2003
3180—(TKS)
Rev.: $174,621,738
Assets: $79,702,676
Liabilities: $38,447,308
Net Worth: $41,255,368
Earnings: $5,715,230
Emp.: 542
Fiscal Year-end: 04/30/23
Hair & Nail Salon Owner
N.A.I.C.S.: 812112
Hideki Nomura *(CEO)*

Subsidiaries:

Adachi Factory Inc.   (1)
613 Fushibe, Nishikan-ku, Niigata, 953-0026, Niigata, Japan
Tel.: (81) 256720117
Web Site: https://adachi-factory.com
Emp.: 50
Beauty Product Distr
N.A.I.C.S.: 456120

BG Partners Inc.   (1)
5th floor Kaleido Shibuya Miyamasuzaka Building 1-12-1 Shibuya, Shibuya-ku, Tokyo, 150-0002, Japan
Tel.: (81) 354683280
Web Site: https://www.bgpartners.jp
Cosmetic Product Distr
N.A.I.C.S.: 456120

BG Ventures Inc.   (1)
1-34-25 Sakurashinmachi, Setagaya-ku, Tokyo, 154-0015, Japan

Tel.: (81) 357521175
Web Site: https://www.bgventures.jp
Cosmetic Product Distr
N.A.I.C.S.: 456120

Beauty Garage Singapore Pte. Ltd.   (1)
Block 1093 Lower Delta Road 03-10, Singapore, 169204, Singapore
Tel.: (65) 65570909
Web Site: https://www.beautygarage.sg
Cosmetic Product Distr
N.A.I.C.S.: 456120

Beauty Garage Taiwan Inc.   (1)
4th Floor No 104 Minquan West Road Minde Building, Datong District, Taipei, 10361, Taiwan
Tel.: (886) 22 553 6179
Web Site: https://www.beautygarage.tw
Cosmetic Product Distr
N.A.I.C.S.: 456120

Japan Eyelash Products Institute Inc.   (1)
19F OMM Building 1-7-31 Otemae, Chuo-ku, Osaka, 540-6591, Japan
Tel.: (81) 663359692
Beauty Product Distr
N.A.I.C.S.: 456120

BEAUTY HEALTH GROUP LIMITED
Level 2 230 Church Street, Richmond, 3121, VIC, Australia
Tel.: (61) 394292888
Sales Range: Less than $1 Million
Beauty & Healthcare Services
N.A.I.C.S.: 812199
Con Scrinis *(Chm & Sec)*

BEAUTY KADAN CO., LTD.
1-46 Ryutsudanchi, Minami-ku, Kumamoto, 8620967, Japan
Tel.: (81) 963700004   JP
Web Site: https://www.beauty-kadan.co.jp
Year Founded: 1997
3041—(TKS)
Rev.: $43,428,040
Assets: $16,899,740
Liabilities: $13,516,060
Net Worth: $3,383,680
Earnings: $174,160
Emp.: 238
Fiscal Year-end: 06/30/24
Flower Whslr
N.A.I.C.S.: 424930

Subsidiaries:

CROWN Gardenex Co., Ltd.   (1)
7-11-52 Chikami, Kumamoto, 861-4101, Japan   (100%)
Tel.: (81) 962238783
Web Site: http://www.crown-g.co.jp
Bridal Bouquet Whslr
N.A.I.C.S.: 424930

SHF Co., Ltd.   (1)
353 Koaza Koaza, Fukuchiyama, 620-0017, Kyoto, Japan
Tel.: (81) 77 323 8117
Web Site: https://www.shfweb.com
Emp.: 40
Cad System Distr
N.A.I.C.S.: 423430

BEAUTY SKIN CO., LTD.
JS Global Building 598 Olympic-ro, Gangdong-gu, Seoul, Korea (South)
Tel.: (82) 234363650
Web Site:
https://www.beautyskincorp.co.kr
Year Founded: 2011
406820—(KRS)
Rev.: $33,249,450
Assets: $49,456,160
Liabilities: $24,367,590
Net Worth: $25,088,570
Earnings: $2,293,330
Fiscal Year-end: 12/31/22
Cosmetics Products Mfr

N.A.I.C.S.: 325620

BEAVER ELECTRICAL MACHINERY LTD.
7440 Lowland Dr, Burnaby, V5J 5A4, BC, Canada
Tel.: (604) 431-5000
Web Site:
https://www.beaverelectrical.com
Year Founded: 1955
Rev.: $10,684,764
Emp.: 65
Electrical Products Sales & Services
N.A.I.C.S.: 238210
Serg Nosella *(Chm & CEO)*

BEAVER ENTECH LIMITED
No 6 Jalan TP 3/1 Taman Perindustrian SIME UEP, Subang Jaya, 47600, Selangor, Malaysia
Tel.: (60) 3 8011 9792
Web Site: http://www.beaver-entech.com
Year Founded: 2015
Investment Holding Company; Environmental Coatings & Chemicals
N.A.I.C.S.: 551112
Ghauth Jasmon *(Chm)*

BEAVER GROUP (HOLDING) COMPANY LIMITED
Room 1204 12/F Block 2 Golden Industrial Building, 16-26 Kwai Tak Street, Kwai Chung, NT, China (Hong Kong)
Tel.: (852) 2 776 9577   Ky
Web Site:
http://www.beavergroup.com.hk
Year Founded: 2008
8275—(HKG)
Rev.: $18,288,203
Assets: $17,114,872
Liabilities: $10,051,153
Net Worth: $7,063,719
Earnings: ($1,897,812)
Emp.: 102
Fiscal Year-end: 03/31/21
Construction Management Services
N.A.I.C.S.: 238910
Stanley Kwai Leung Tang *(Co-Founder & Chm)*

Subsidiaries:

Triangular Force Construction Engineering Limited   (1)
Rm 1815 220-248 Texaco Road, Tsuen Wan Industrial Centre, Tsuen Wan, China (Hong Kong)
Tel.: (852) 27769578
Web Site: http://www.tfcel.com.hk
Engineeering Services
N.A.I.C.S.: 541330
Tang Kwai Leung Stanley *(Chm & Exec Dir)*

BEAVER MACHINE CORPORATION
1341 Kerrisdale Boulevard, Newmarket, ON, Canada
Tel.: (905) 836-4700
Web Site:
http://www.beavervending.com
Year Founded: 1963
Rev.: $17,002,568
Emp.: 33
Automatic Vending Machine Mfr
N.A.I.C.S.: 333310
Bernie Schwarzli *(Pres)*

BEAZLEY PLC
Plantation Place South 60 Great Tower Street, London, EC3R 5AD, United Kingdom
Tel.: (44) 2076670623
Web Site: http://www.beazley.com
Year Founded: 1986
BEZ—(LSE)
Rev.: $4,618,900,000

Assets: $12,807,400,000
Liabilities: $10,676,600,000
Net Worth: $2,130,800,000
Earnings: $308,700,000
Emp.: 1,617
Fiscal Year-end: 12/31/21
Insurance Services
N.A.I.C.S.: 524298
Adrian Peter Cox *(CEO)*

Subsidiaries:

Beazley Dedicated Ltd.   (1)
60 Great Tower Street, London, EC3R 5AD, United Kingdom
Tel.: (44) 2076670623
Insurance Underwriting Services
N.A.I.C.S.: 524298

Beazley Dedicated No.2 Limited   (1)
One Aldgate, London, EC3N 1AA, United Kingdom
Tel.: (44) 2076670623
Insurance Underwriting Services
N.A.I.C.S.: 524298

Beazley Furlonge Holdings Limited   (1)
Plantation Place South 60 Great Tower Street, London, EC3R 5AD, United Kingdom
Tel.: (44) 2076670623
Web Site: http://www.beazley.com
Emp.: 700
Insurance Underwriting Services
N.A.I.C.S.: 524298

Beazley Furlonge Limited   (1)
22 Bishopsgate, 60 Great Tower Street, London, EC2N 4BQ, United Kingdom
Tel.: (44) 2076670623
Sales Range: $200-249.9 Million
Emp.: 300
Insurance Services
N.A.I.C.S.: 524298
Andrew Horton *(CEO)*

Beazley Group Limited   (1)
22 Bishopsgate, London, EC2N 4BQ, United Kingdom
Tel.: (44) 2076670623
Sales Range: $200-249.9 Million
Emp.: 400
Underwriting Services
N.A.I.C.S.: 523150

Beazley Holdings, Inc.   (1)
1209 Orange St, Wilmington, DE 19801
Tel.: (860) 677-0400
Sales Range: $100-124.9 Million
Emp.: 120
Insurance Brokerage Services
N.A.I.C.S.: 524210
Elizabeth Benet *(Head-Bus Dev-Partners Solutions Grp)*

Beazley Insurance dac   (1)
2 Northwood Avenue Northwood Park Santry Demesne Santry, Dublin, D09 X5N9, Ireland
Tel.: (353) 18544700
Insurance Services
N.A.I.C.S.: 524210
Emma Leonard *(Chief Risk Officer)*

Beazley Investments Limited   (1)
Plantation Pl S 60 Great Tower St, London, EC3R 5AD, United Kingdom
Tel.: (44) 2076670623
Sales Range: $350-399.9 Million
Emp.: 600
Investment Management Service
N.A.I.C.S.: 523999

Beazley Limited   (1)
Suite 1703 Central Plaza 18 Harbour Road, Wanchai, China (Hong Kong)
Tel.: (852) 25225033
Web Site: http://www.beazley.com
General Insurance Services
N.A.I.C.S.: 524210

Beazley Pte. Limited   (1)
138 Market Street 03-04 Capita Green, Singapore, 048946, Singapore
Tel.: (65) 65766288
Sales Range: $50-74.9 Million
Emp.: 7
General Insurance Services

BEAZLEY PLC

Beazley plc—(Continued)
N.A.I.C.S.: 524210

Beazley USA Services, Inc. **(1)**
1209 Orange St, Wilmington, DE 19801
Tel.: (860) 677-3700
Sales Range: $50-74.9 Million
Emp.: 130
Management Services
N.A.I.C.S.: 541011

Beazley Underwriting Pty Ltd **(1)**
Level 22 215 Adelaide Street, Brisbane,
4000, QLD, Australia
Tel.: (61) 73 228 1600
Web Site: http://www.beazley.com
Sales Range: $50-74.9 Million
Emp.: 14
General Insurance Services
N.A.I.C.S.: 524210

Beazley Underwriting Services Ltd. **(1)**
22 Bishopsgate, London, EC2N 4BQ,
United Kingdom
Tel.: (44) 2073983250
Insurance Underwriting Services
N.A.I.C.S.: 524298

BEBO HEALTH SA
1 Rue de la Cite, 1204, Geneva,
Switzerland
Tel.: (41) 786457800
Web Site: https://bebo-health.com
Year Founded: 2019
MLBBO—(EUR)
Medical Device Mfr
N.A.I.C.S.: 339112
Cyril Baechler *(CEO)*

BEC WORLD PUBLIC COMPANY LIMITED
3199 Maleenont Tower Floor 2 3 4 9
10 3034 Rama 4 Rd Klongton, Klong-
toey, Bangkok, 10110, Thailand
Tel.: (66) 22623333
Web Site: https://www.becworld.com
BECVY—(OTCIQ)
Rev.: $136,148,716
Assets: $275,606,011
Liabilities: $96,175,734
Net Worth: $179,430,276
Earnings: $6,130,513
Emp.: 992
Fiscal Year-end: 12/31/23
Television & Radio Broadcasting Services
N.A.I.C.S.: 516120
Ratchanee Nipatakusol *(Exec Dir)*

Subsidiaries:

BEC Asset Co., Ltd. **(1)**
3rd Floor Maleenont Tower, 3199 Rama IV
Rd Klongton Klong, Bangkok, 3199,
Thailand **(100%)**
Tel.: (66) 22623333
Web Site: http://www.thaitv3.com
Sales Range: $550-599.9 Million
Emp.: 2,000
Holding Company
N.A.I.C.S.: 551112

BEC Broadcasting Center Co., Ltd. **(1)**
2nd Floor Maleenont Tower, 3199 Rama IV
Rd Klongton Klong, 10110, Bangkok,
Thailand **(100%)**
Tel.: (66) 22623333
Sales Range: $200-249.9 Million
Emp.: 1,000
Satellite Telecommunications
N.A.I.C.S.: 517410

BEC Multimedia Co., Ltd. **(1)**
No 3199 Maleenont Tower Rama 4 Road,
Khlong Tan Sub-District Khlong Toei, 10110,
Bangkok, Thailand **(100%)**
Tel.: (66) 22623333
Web Site: http://www.becmultimedia.com
Sales Range: $700-749.9 Million
Emp.: 2,000
Financial Investment Activities
N.A.I.C.S.: 523999

BEC News Bureau Co., Ltd. **(1)**
2nd Fl Maleenont Tower, 3199 Rama IV Rd
Klongton Klong, 10110, Bangkok,
Thailand **(100%)**
Tel.: (66) 22623333
Web Site: http://www.becnews.com
Sales Range: $25-49.9 Million
Emp.: 100
Television Broadcasting
N.A.I.C.S.: 516120

BEC Studio Co., Ltd. **(1)**
2nd Floor Maleenont Tower, 3199 Rama IV
Rd Klongton Klong, 10110, Bangkok,
Thailand **(100%)**
Tel.: (66) 22623333
Web Site: http://www.thaitv3.com
Sales Range: $25-49.9 Million
Emp.: 100
Radio Television & Electronics Stores
N.A.I.C.S.: 449210

BEC-Tero Entertainment Public Company Limited **(1)**
998/3 Building 7 Floor 4-5 7 Phahon Yothin
Road, Chom Phon Chatuchak, Bangkok,
10900, Thailand **(60%)**
Tel.: (66) 24958936
Web Site: https://corporate.teroasia.com
Television Broadcasting
N.A.I.C.S.: 517410

Subsidiary (Domestic):

BEC-Tero Entertainment Co., Ltd. **(2)**
3199 Maleenont Tower 25th - 28th floor
Rama IV Road, Khlongton Khlongtoey,
10110, Bangkok, Thailand
Tel.: (66) 22623800
Web Site: https://corporate.teroasia.com
Audio & Video Equipment Mfr
N.A.I.C.S.: 334310
Prasan Maleenont *(Chm)*

BEC-TERO Sasana Co., Ltd. **(2)**
199 Maleenont Tower 26th Floor Rama IV
Road Klongton, Klongtoey, Bangkok, 10110,
Thailand
Tel.: (66) 2 262 3919
Web Site: http://www.becterosasana.in.th
Sports Club Operating Services
N.A.I.C.S.: 711211

BEC-Tero Arsenal Co., Ltd. **(2)**
26th Floor Maleenont Twr, 3199 Rama IV
Rd Klongton Klong, 10110, Bangkok,
Thailand **(100%)**
Tel.: (66) 22623333
Sports Teams & Clubs
N.A.I.C.S.: 711211
Sunny Pattiyawongse *(Brand Mgr)*

Affiliate (Domestic):

BEC-Tero Exhibitions Co., Ltd. **(2)**
27th Floor Maleenont Twr, 3199 Rama IV
Rd Klongton Klong, 10110, Bangkok,
Thailand **(60%)**
Tel.: (66) 22623333
Convention & Trade Show Organizers
N.A.I.C.S.: 561920

SMBT Publishing (Thailand) Co., Ltd. **(2)**
22nd Floor Maleenont Twr, 3199 Rama IV
Rd Klongton Klong, 10110, Bangkok,
Thailand **(40%)**
Tel.: (66) 22623333
Audio & Video Equipment Mfr
N.A.I.C.S.: 334310

Subsidiary (Domestic):

Thai Ticket Major Co., Ltd. **(2)**
3199 Maleenont Tower 7th Floor Rama 4
Road, Khlong Tan Subdistrict Khlong Toei
District, Bangkok, 10110, Thailand
Tel.: (66) 2 262 3456
Web Site: https://www.thaiticketmajor.com
Ticketing Services
N.A.I.C.S.: 561599

Virgin BEC-Tero Radio (Thailand) Co., Ltd. **(1)**
24th Floor Maleenont Twr, 3199 Rama IV
Rd Klongton Klong, 10110, Bangkok,
Thailand **(49%)**
Tel.: (66) 22623333
Radio Stations

N.A.I.C.S.: 516110

BECi Corporation Co., Ltd. **(1)**
3199 Maleenont Tower 4th Floor Rama
4Rd, Klongton Klongtoey, Bangkok, 10110,
Thailand **(100%)**
Tel.: (66) 26835070
Sales Range: $50-74.9 Million
Emp.: 30
Financial Investment Services
N.A.I.C.S.: 523999

Subsidiary (Domestic):

Digital Factory Co., Ltd. **(2)**
4th Floor Maleenont Tower, 3199 Rama IV
Rd Klongton Klong, 10110, Bangkok,
Thailand **(51%)**
Tel.: (66) 22623333
Satellite Telecommunications
N.A.I.C.S.: 517410

Mobi (Thai) Co., Ltd. **(2)**
3199 Maleenont Tower Floors 2 3 8 9 30-
34, Rama 4 Rd Klongton Klongtoey, 10110,
Bangkok, Thailand **(60%)**
Tel.: (66) 22623333
Satellite Telecommunications
N.A.I.C.S.: 517410

Bangkok Satellites & Telecommunication Co., Ltd. **(1)**
2nd Fl Maleenont Tower, 3199 Rama IV Rd
Klongton Klong, 10110, Bangkok,
Thailand **(100%)**
Tel.: (66) 22623333
Web Site: http://www.becworld.com
Satellite Telecommunications
N.A.I.C.S.: 517410

Bec-Tero Radio Co., Ltd. **(1)**
23rd - 24th Fl Maleena Tower 3199 Rama
IV Road Klongton, Klongtoey, Bangkok,
10110, Thailand
Tel.: (66) 22043500
Television & Radio Broadcasting Services
N.A.I.C.S.: 516120

New World Production Co, Ltd. **(1)**
2nd Floor Maleenont Tower, 3199 Rama IV
Rd Klongton Klong, 10110, Bangkok,
Thailand **(100%)**
Tel.: (66) 22623333
Web Site: http://www.becworld.com
Sales Range: $100-124.9 Million
Emp.: 500
Television Broadcasting
N.A.I.C.S.: 516120

Rungsirojvanit Co., Ltd. **(1)**
2nd Floor Maleenont Tower, 3199 Rama IV
Rd Klongton Klong, 10110, Bangkok, Thai-
land
Tel.: (66) 22623333
Sales Range: $400-449.9 Million
Emp.: 1,200
Television Broadcasting
N.A.I.C.S.: 516120
Vichai Maleenont *(Chm)*

TVB 3 Network Co., Ltd. **(1)**
9th Floor Maleenont Tower, 3199 Rama IV
Rd Klongton Klong, 10110, Bangkok,
Thailand **(60%)**
Tel.: (66) 22623333
Television Broadcasting
N.A.I.C.S.: 516120

The Bangkok Entertainment Co., Ltd. **(1)**
2nd Floor Maleenont Tower, 3199 Rama IV
Rd Klongton Klong, 10110, Bangkok,
Thailand **(100%)**
Tel.: (66) 22623333
Web Site: http://www.becworld.com
Sales Range: $25-49.9 Million
Emp.: 100
Television Broadcasting
N.A.I.C.S.: 516120
Prasan Maleenont *(Vice Chm & Mng Dir)*

BECA GROUP LIMITED
21 Pitt Street, Auckland, 1010, New
Zealand
Tel.: (64) 93009000
Web Site: http://www.beca.com
Sales Range: $200-249.9 Million
Emp.: 4,000

Provider of Engineering & Manage-
ment Services
N.A.I.C.S.: 541330
Greg Lowe *(Grp CEO)*

Subsidiaries:

Beca Applied Technologies Ltd **(1)**
21 Pitt Street, PO Box 6345, Auckland,
1010, New Zealand
Tel.: (64) 9 300 9000
Web Site: http://www.beca.com
Emp.: 1,200
Engineering Consultancy Services
N.A.I.C.S.: 541330
Don Lyon *(Mng Dir)*

Beca Carter Hollings & Ferner Ltd **(1)**
Harrington St, PO Box 903, Tauranga, New
Zealand **(100%)**
Tel.: (64) 75780896
Web Site: http://www.becagroup.com
Emp.: 150
N.A.I.C.S.: 541330
John Revington *(Reg Mgr)*

Beca Pty. Ltd. **(1)**
Level 4 5 Queens Rd, Melbourne, 3004,
VIC, Australia **(100%)**
Tel.: (61) 392721400
Web Site: http://www.beca.com.au
Sales Range: $75-99.9 Million
Emp.: 300
Provider of Engineering Design & Project,
Management Services
N.A.I.C.S.: 541330
Grag Lowa *(CEO)*

PT Bimatekno Karyatama Konsultan **(1)**
Level 2 Graha Mustika Ratu Centre Jl Jend
Gatot Subroto Kav 74-75, Jakarta, 12870,
Indonesia
Tel.: (62) 21 830 7403
Engineering Consultancy Services
N.A.I.C.S.: 541330

BECEJSKA PEKARA A.D.
Novosadska br 157, 21220, Becej,
Serbia
Tel.: (381) 216912044
Web Site:
http://www.becejskapekara.com
Year Founded: 1946
PMLI—(BEL)
Rev.: $623,704
Assets: $1,936,644
Liabilities: $923,913
Net Worth: $1,012,731
Earnings: $5,693
Emp.: 10
Fiscal Year-end: 12/31/23
Bakery Products Mfr
N.A.I.C.S.: 311812
Maja Konta *(Gen Dir)*

BECHTLE AG
Bechtle Platz 1, 74172, Neckarsulm,
Germany
Tel.: (49) 71329810 De
Web Site: https://www.bechtle.com
Year Founded: 1983
BC8—(STU)
Rev.: $7,089,870,004
Assets: $4,198,227,345
Liabilities: $2,274,612,445
Net Worth: $1,923,614,901
Earnings: $293,088,524
Emp.: 14,649
Fiscal Year-end: 12/31/23
Computer Peripheral Equipment &
Software Merchant Whslr
N.A.I.C.S.: 423430
Thomas Olemotz *(CEO & Chm-Exec Bd)*

Subsidiaries:

ACS Systems UK Limited **(1)**
ACS House Oxwich Close Brackmills,
Northampton, NN4 7BH, United Kingdom
Tel.: (44) 1604700400
Web Site: https://www.acs365.co.uk

Information Technology Consulting Services
N.A.I.C.S.: 541512

ARP Europe AG   **(1)**
Birkenstrasse 43b, 6343, Rotkreuz, Switzerland
Tel.: (41) 417990909
Web Site: http://www.arp.com
Hardware & Software Services
N.A.I.C.S.: 541512
Stefan Sagowski *(Mng Dir)*

ARP GmbH   **(1)**
Lise-Meitner-Strasse 1, 63128, Dietzenbach, Germany
Tel.: (49) 6074 491 100
Web Site: http://www.arp.de
Information Technology Consulting Services
N.A.I.C.S.: 541512

ARP NV   **(1)**
Peerderbaan 207, 3910, Neerpelt, Belgium
Tel.: (32) 1 139 8460
Web Site: https://www.arp.be
Hardware & Software Services
N.A.I.C.S.: 541512
Jan Prinsen *(Mng Dir)*

ARP Nederland B.V.   **(1)**
Withuisveld 30, 6226 NV, Maastricht, Netherlands
Tel.: (31) 43 855 0000
Web Site: https://www.arp.nl
Emp.: 70
Information Technology Consulting Services
N.A.I.C.S.: 541512

ARP SAS   **(1)**
3 Avenue du Quebec, 91951, Villebon-sur-Yvette, France
Tel.: (33) 160923090
Information Technology Consulting Services
N.A.I.C.S.: 541512

ARP Schweiz AG   **(1)**
Birkenstrasse 43b, 6343, Rotkreuz, Switzerland
Tel.: (41) 41 79909 09
Web Site: http://www.arp.ch
Emp.: 150
Information Technology Consulting Services
N.A.I.C.S.: 541512

Acommit AG   **(1)**
Seestrasse 202, 8810, Horgen, Switzerland
Tel.: (41) 582116100
Web Site: http://www.acommit.ch
Software Development Services
N.A.I.C.S.: 541511
Robert Zanzerl *(CEO)*

Alpha Solutions AG   **(1)**
Schuppisstrasse 7, 9016, Saint Gallen, Switzerland
Tel.: (41) 582001414
Web Site: http://www.alpha-solutions.ch
ERP & CRM System Services
N.A.I.C.S.: 811210
Daniel Metzger *(Head-Dev)*

Amaras AG   **(1)**
Rheinpromenade 9, 40789, Monheim am Rhein, Germany
Tel.: (49) 21739377690
Web Site: http://www.amaras.de
Client Support Services
N.A.I.C.S.: 561499

Bechtle Brussels NV   **(1)**
Square de Meeus 35, 1000, Brussels, Belgium
Web Site: http://www.bechtle.com
Emp.: 60
Information Technology Consulting Services
N.A.I.C.S.: 541512

Bechtle Clouds GmbH   **(1)**
Bechtle Platz 1, 74172, Neckarsulm, Germany
Tel.: (49) 71329816200
Web Site: https://www.bechtle-clouds.com
Information Technology & Services
N.A.I.C.S.: 541511

Bechtle Comsoft SAS   **(1)**
216/218 Avenue Jean Jaures, 75019, Paris, France
Tel.: (33) 153382050
Web Site: https://www.bechtle-comsoft.fr
Asset Management Services
N.A.I.C.S.: 523940

Bechtle Direct GmbH   **(1)**
Johann Roithner-Strasse 131, 4050, Traun, Austria
Tel.: (43) 7229641100
Information Technology Services
N.A.I.C.S.: 541512

Bechtle Direct NV   **(1)**
Peerderbaan 207, Pelt, 3910, Neerpelt, Belgium
Tel.: (32) 11397900
Computer Peripheral Equipment Whslr
N.A.I.C.S.: 423430
Raf Wellens *(Mgr-Mktg)*

Bechtle Direct S.L.U.   **(1)**
C/ Via de los Poblados 3, 28033, Madrid, Spain
Tel.: (34) 913640234
Computer Peripheral Equipment Whslr
N.A.I.C.S.: 423430
Juan Jose Moneo *(Mng Dir)*

Bechtle Financial Services AG   **(1)**
Gutenbergstr 15, 10587, Berlin, Germany
Tel.: (49) 30398856210
Computer Peripheral Equipment Whslr
N.A.I.C.S.: 423430

Bechtle Finanz- & Marketingservices GmbH   **(1)**
Kanzleistr 17, 74405, Gaildorf, Germany
Tel.: (49) 797195020
Information Technology Consulting Services
N.A.I.C.S.: 541512

Bechtle GmbH   **(1)**
Kaiserin-Augusta-Allee 14, 10553, Berlin, Germany
Tel.: (49) 303640680
Web Site: http://www.bechtle.com
Emp.: 43
Information Technology Consulting Services
N.A.I.C.S.: 541512

Bechtle GmbH   **(1)**
Technologiestrasse 8D, 1120, Vienna, Austria
Tel.: (43) 570040
Web Site: http://www.bechtle.com
Emp.: 250
Information Technology Consulting Services
N.A.I.C.S.: 541512

Bechtle GmbH & Co. KG   **(1)**
Industriestrasse 33, 33689, Bielefeld, Germany
Tel.: (49) 5205998870
Web Site: http://www.bechtle.com
Emp.: 150
Information Technology Consulting Services
N.A.I.C.S.: 541512
Michael Tappe *(Mng Dir)*

Bechtle GmbH & Co. KG   **(1)**
Usinger Strasse 114, 61239, Obermorlen, Germany
Tel.: (49) 6002 9131 00
Web Site: http://www.bechtle.com
Sales Range: $25-49.9 Million
Emp.: 22
Information Technology Consulting Services
N.A.I.C.S.: 541512
Joachim Dieth *(Mng Dir)*

Bechtle Hosting & Operations GmbH & Co. KG   **(1)**
Bechtle Platz 1, 74172, Neckarsulm, Germany
Tel.: (49) 71329815400
Computer Peripheral Equipment Whslr
N.A.I.C.S.: 423430
Gunther Frauenknecht *(Mng Dir)*

Bechtle IT-Systemhaus GmbH   **(1)**
Parkstrasse 2-8, 47829, Krefeld, Germany
Tel.: (49) 21514550
Information Technology Consulting Services
N.A.I.C.S.: 541512

Bechtle Network & Security Solutions GmbH   **(1)**
Elisabeth-Schiemann-Bogen 3, 85716, Unterschleissheim, Germany
Tel.: (49) 891472764100
Web Site: https://www.bechtle-network.com
Emp.: 100
Network & Security Services
N.A.I.C.S.: 561612

Bechtle Onsite Services GmbH   **(1)**

Bechtle Platz 1, 74172, Neckarsulm, Germany
Tel.: (49) 71329815300
Computer Peripheral Equipment Whslr
N.A.I.C.S.: 423430
Marcus Schonberg *(Mgr-Service Line)*

Bechtle Printing Solutions AG   **(1)**
Ringstrasse 15a, 8600, Dubendorf, Switzerland
Tel.: (41) 44 956 66 99
Information Technology Consulting Services
N.A.I.C.S.: 541512
Daniel Schlumpf *(Mng Dir)*

Bechtle Regensdorf AG   **(1)**
Bahnstrasse 58/60, 8105, Regensdorf, Switzerland
Tel.: (41) 43 388 72 00
Emp.: 60
Information Technology Consulting Services
N.A.I.C.S.: 541512
Roger Muller *(Mng Dir)*

Bechtle Remarketing GmbH   **(1)**
Am Schornacker 18 a, 46485, Wesel, Germany
Tel.: (49) 28120 675 0102
Web Site: https://www.remarketing-bechtle.com
Information Technology Consulting Services
N.A.I.C.S.: 541512

Bechtle St. Gallen AG   **(1)**
Gaiserwaldstrasse 6, 9015, Saint Gallen, Switzerland
Tel.: (41) 71272 6262
Information Technology Consulting Services
N.A.I.C.S.: 541512
Valentino Osta *(Mng Dir)*

Bechtle Steffen Schweiz AG   **(1)**
Feldstrasse 4, 5506, Magenwil, Switzerland
Tel.: (41) 564183333
Web Site: http://www.bechtle-steffen.ch
Software Development Services
N.A.I.C.S.: 541511

Bechtle direct AG   **(1)**
Ringstrasse 15a, 8600, Dubendorf, Switzerland
Tel.: (41) 84 881 0410
Web Site: http://www.bechtle-direct.ch
Information Technology Consulting Services
N.A.I.C.S.: 541512

Bechtle direct B.V.   **(1)**
Meerenakkerplein 27, 5652 BJ, Eindhoven, Netherlands
Web Site: http://www.bechtle.com
Emp.: 150
Information Technology Consulting Services
N.A.I.C.S.: 541512
Jean-Paul Bierens *(Mng Dir)*

Bechtle direct GmbH   **(1)**
Bechtle Platz 1, 74172, Neckarsulm, Germany
Tel.: (49) 71329811600
Web Site: http://www.bechtle.de
Information Technology Consulting Services
N.A.I.C.S.: 541512

Bechtle direct Kft.   **(1)**
Montevideo utca 16/B, 1037, Budapest, Hungary
Tel.: (36) 18827391
Web Site: http://www.bechtle.com
Information Technology Consulting Services
N.A.I.C.S.: 541512
Orban Barnabas *(Mng Dir)*

Bechtle direct Limited   **(1)**
Ground Floor Corrig Court Corrig Road, Sandyford Business Park, Dublin, D18 C6K1, Ireland
Tel.: (353) 14266700
Web Site: http://www.bechtle.com
Information Technology Consulting Services
N.A.I.C.S.: 541512

Bechtle direct Ltd.   **(1)**
Village Green Methuen Park, Chippenham, SN14 0GF, Wiltshire, United Kingdom
Tel.: (44) 1249467900
Web Site: https://www.bechtle.com
Information Technology Consulting Services
N.A.I.C.S.: 541512
James Napp *(Mng Dir)*

Bechtle direct Polska Sp.z.oo.   **(1)**

ul Krakowska 29, 50-424, Wroclaw, Poland
Tel.: (48) 713479947
Web Site: http://www.bechtle.com
Information Technology Consulting Services
N.A.I.C.S.: 541512
Karolina Romanczuk *(Mng Dir & Dir-Comml)*

Bechtle direct Portugal Unipessoal Lda   **(1)**
Av Congr Opos Democr 65 Lt 6l, 3800-365, Aveiro, Portugal
Tel.: (351) 234100640
Web Site: http://www.bechtle.com
Information Technology Consulting Services
N.A.I.C.S.: 541512

Bechtle direct S.L.   **(1)**
C/ Via de los Poblados 3, 28033, Madrid, Spain
Tel.: (34) 91 364 0234
Web Site: http://www.bechtle.com
Information Technology Consulting Services
N.A.I.C.S.: 541512

Bechtle direct SAS   **(1)**
Rue Geiler de Kaysersberg, 67400, Illkirch-Graffenstaden, France
Tel.: (33) 390404545
Web Site: https://www.bechtle.com
Information Technology Consulting Services
N.A.I.C.S.: 541512

Bechtle direct Srl-GmbH   **(1)**
Via Luigi Negrelli 13, 39100, Bolzano, Italy
Tel.: (39) 047 154 8548
Web Site: http://www.bechtle.com
Information Technology Consulting Services
N.A.I.C.S.: 541512
Davide Mamma *(Mng Dir)*

Bechtle direct s.r.o.   **(1)**
U Dubu 1875/38a, Branik, 14700, Prague, Czech Republic
Tel.: (420) 725455205
Web Site: https://www.bechtle.com
Information Technology Consulting Services
N.A.I.C.S.: 541512
Petr Polak *(Mng Dir)*

Buyitdirect.com N.V.   **(1)**
Kruisweg 661, 2132 NC, Hoofddorp, Netherlands
Tel.: (31) 88 707 7800
Web Site: https://www.buyitdirect.com
Emp.: 50
Online Electronic Retailer
N.A.I.C.S.: 449210

Cadmes France S.A.S.   **(1)**
125 Avenue du Bois de la Pie, 95700, Roissy-en-France, France
Tel.: (33) 159031020
Emp.: 100
Professional Training Services
N.A.I.C.S.: 611430

Coffee GmbH   **(1)**
In der Werr 11, Angelburg, 35719, Biedenkopf, Germany
Tel.: (49) 27 778 1180
Web Site: https://www.coffee.de
Emp.: 70
Solidcam & 3D Printer Mfr
N.A.I.C.S.: 323111

Coma Services AG   **(1)**
Oberebenstrasse 45, 5620, Bremgarten, Switzerland
Tel.: (41) 56 6488181
Web Site: http://www.coma-services.ch
Emp.: 70
Information Technology Consulting Services
N.A.I.C.S.: 541512

Comsoft Direct AG   **(1)**
Birkenstrasse 43b, 6343, Rotkreuz, Switzerland
Tel.: (41) 848820420
Web Site: http://www.comsoft-direct.ch
Software Development Services
N.A.I.C.S.: 541511
Roger Suter *(Chm)*

Comsoft SOS Developers SAS   **(1)**
400 Avenue de Roumanille Green Side 1 Bat 2, BP 265, 06905, Valbonne, Cedex, France
Tel.: (33) 825070607
Web Site: http://www.comsoft-direct.fr
Emp.: 50

Bechtle AG—(Continued)

Information Technology Consulting Services
N.A.I.C.S.: 541512
Alphonse Dupierre *(Dir-Sls)*

Comsoft direct B.V **(1)**
De Corridor 5 1e etage, 3621 ZA, Breuke-
len, Netherlands
Tel.: (31) 20 2065390
Web Site: http://www.comsoft-direct.nl
Information Technology Consulting Services
N.A.I.C.S.: 541512

Comsoft direct GmbH **(1)**
Triester Strasse 14, 2355, Wiener Neudorf,
Austria
Tel.: (43) 0205293 10
Web Site: http://www.comsoft-direct.at
Information Technology Consulting Services
N.A.I.C.S.: 541512

Comsoft direct NV **(1)**
Heerstraat 73, 3910, Neerpelt, Belgium
Tel.: (32) 3 206 86 30
Web Site: http://www.comsoft-direct.be
Emp.: 5
Software Licensing & Asset Management
Services
N.A.I.C.S.: 541519

Comsoft direct S.L.U. **(1)**
Paseo Imperial 8, 28005, Madrid, Spain
Tel.: (34) 913644327
Web Site: http://www.comsoft-direct.es
Information Technology Consulting Services
N.A.I.C.S.: 541512

Comsoft direct S.r.l **(1)**
Via del Vigneto 35, 39100, Bolzano, Italy
Tel.: (39) 0471 548575
Web Site: http://www.comsoft-direct.it
Information Technology Consulting Services
N.A.I.C.S.: 541512

Cordsen Engineering GmbH **(1)**
Am Klinggraben 1a, 63500, Seligenstadt,
Germany
Tel.: (49) 618292940
Web Site: https://cordsen.com
Computer Hardware Mfr & Distr
N.A.I.C.S.: 332510

Data Store 365 Limited **(1)**
Bechtle House Oxwich Close, Northampton,
NN4 7BH, United Kingdom
Tel.: (44) 8000481848
Web Site: https://www.datastore365.co.uk
Data Processing & Cloud Services
N.A.I.C.S.: 518210

Evolusys SA **(1)**
Avenue de la Gottaz 28a, 1110, Morges,
Switzerland
Tel.: (41) 798973383
Web Site: http://www.evolusys.ch
IT Consulting Services
N.A.I.C.S.: 541618

Gate Informatic AG **(1)**
Route de la Pierre 22, 1024, Ecublens,
1024, Switzerland
Tel.: (41) 21 695 21 21
Web Site: http://www.gate.ch
Information Technology Consulting Services
N.A.I.C.S.: 541512
Alexandra Lochner *(Acct Mgr)*

HCV Data Management GmbH **(1)**
Am Eichelgarten 1, 65396, Walluf, Germany
Tel.: (49) 61239950310
Web Site: https://www.hcv.de
Information Technology Consulting Services
N.A.I.C.S.: 541512

HanseVision GmbH **(1)**
Atlantic Haus Bernhard-Nocht-Str 113,
20359, Hamburg, Germany
Tel.: (49) 40288075900
Web Site: https://www.hansevision.com
Emp.: 80
Information Technology Consulting Services
N.A.I.C.S.: 541512

ITZ Informationstechnologie
GmbH **(1)**
Heinrich-Held-Strasse 16, 45133, Essen,
Germany
Tel.: (49) 201247140
Web Site: https://www.itz-essen.de
Emp.: 111

Information Technology Consulting Services
N.A.I.C.S.: 541512
Peter Heinrichs *(Mng Dir)*

MODUS Consult GmbH **(1)**
James-Watt-Strasse 6, 33334, Gutersloh,
Germany
Tel.: (49) 524192170
Web Site: https://www.modusconsult.de
Emp.: 300
Information Technology Consulting Services
N.A.I.C.S.: 541512

Modus Consult AG **(1)**
James-Watt-Strasse 6, 33334, Gutersloh,
Germany
Tel.: (49) 52 419 2170
Web Site: https://www.modusconsult.de
Emp.: 300
System Consulting & Engineering Services
N.A.I.C.S.: 541330
Thomas Olemotz *(Chm)*

PP 2000 Business Integration
AG **(1)**
Schwieberdinger Strasse 60, Zuffenhausen,
70435, Stuttgart, Germany
Tel.: (49) 711 820 56 0
Web Site: http://www.pp2000.com
Emp.: 150
Information Technology Consulting Services
N.A.I.C.S.: 541512
Michael Guschlbauer *(Deputy Chm-*
Supervisory Bd)

PQR B.V. **(1)**
Papendorpseweg 91, 3528 BJ, Utrecht,
Netherlands
Tel.: (31) 306629729
Web Site: https://www.pqr.com
Emp.: 300
Information Technology Management Ser-
vices
N.A.I.C.S.: 541512

PQR Holding B.V. **(1)**
Papendorpseweg 91, 3528, Utrecht, Neth-
erlands
Tel.: (31) 306629729
Web Site: https://pqr.com/
Software Development Services
N.A.I.C.S.: 541511

PSB GmbH **(1)**
Max-Planck-Strasse 20, 63303, Dreieich,
Germany
Tel.: (49) 610380970
Emp.: 15
Information Technology Consulting Services
N.A.I.C.S.: 541512

Planetsoftware GmbH **(1)**
EURO PLAZA 2D/2nd floor Technologi-
estrasse 8, 1120, Vienna, Austria
Tel.: (43) 50246
Web Site: https://www.cad.at
Emp.: 60
Information Technology & Services
N.A.I.C.S.: 541511

Redmond Integrators GmbH **(1)**
Lise-Meitner-Allee 10, 44801, Bochum, Ger-
many
Tel.: (49) 234 54182 00
Web Site:
    http://www.redmondintegrators.com
Emp.: 10
Information Technology Consulting Services
N.A.I.C.S.: 541512
Mirco Kappe *(Mng Dir)*

Smartpoint IT Consulting GmbH **(1)**
Strasserau 6, 4020, Linz, Austria
Tel.: (43) 570047700
Web Site: https://www.smartpoint.at
IT Consulting Services
N.A.I.C.S.: 541618
Michael Pachlatko *(CEO & Mng Dir)*

Solid Line AG **(1)**
Am Eichelgarten 1, 65396, Walluf, Germany
Tel.: (49) 612399500
Web Site: http://www.solidline.de
Emp.: 190
Software Development Services
N.A.I.C.S.: 541511

Subsidiary (Domestic):

C-CAM GmbH **(2)**
Otto-Schmerbach-Strasse 19, 09117,

Chemnitz, Germany
Tel.: (49) 3712780730
Web Site: http://www.c-cam.de
Data Management & Computer Services
N.A.I.C.S.: 541512

Solid Solutions AG **(1)**
Hohlstrasse 534, 8048, Zurich, Switzerland
Tel.: (41) 444342121
Web Site: https://www.solidsolutions.ch
Emp.: 40
Information Technology Consulting Services
N.A.I.C.S.: 541512
Hanspeter Lampert *(Mng Dir)*

SolidPro Informationssysteme
GmbH **(1)**
Benzstrasse 15, 89129, Langenau, Ger-
many
Tel.: (49) 734596170
Web Site: https://www.solidpro.de
Emp.: 200
Information Technology Consulting Services
N.A.I.C.S.: 541512

Stemmer GmbH **(1)**
Peter-Henlein-Strasse 2, 82140, Olching,
Germany
Tel.: (49) 81 424 5860
Web Site: https://www.stemmer.de
IT Security Services
N.A.I.C.S.: 541512
Oliver Hermann *(Mgr-Bus Dev)*

BECKER & K LLP
95 Rozybakiev str, 050046, Almaty,
Kazakhstan
Tel.: (7) 701 715 98 68
Web Site: http://www.becker.kz
Restaurant Operators
N.A.I.C.S.: 722511

BECLE, S.A.B. DE C.V.
Guillermo Gonzalez Camarena No
800-4, Alvaro Obregon Santa Fe, CP
01210, Mexico, Mexico
Tel.: (52) 5552587000   **MX**
Web Site:
    https://www.cuervo.com.mx
Year Founded: 1758
CUERVO—(MEX)
Sales Range: $1-9.9 Million
Emp.: 6,836
Alcoholic Beverage Mfr & Distr
N.A.I.C.S.: 312130
Juan Francisco Beckmann Vidal
(Chm)

BECO PETROLEUM PROD-
UCTS PLC.
No 4 Gabaro Close Off Ahmodu Oji-
kutu Street, Victoria Island, Lagos,
Nigeria
Tel.: (234) 1 737 4284
Web Site:
    http://www.becopetroleum.com
Year Founded: 1986
Sales Range: $1-9.9 Million
Petroleum Product Whslr
N.A.I.C.S.: 424720
Eugene C. Mojekwu *(Vice Chm &*
CEO)

BECO STEEL LIMITED
79 - Peco Road Badami Bagh, Mul-
tan Cantt, Lahore, Pakistan
Tel.: (92) 42111112326
Web Site: https://becosteel.com
Year Founded: 1984
BECO—(PSX)
Rev.: $13,498,232
Assets: $21,060,055
Liabilities: $9,628,658
Net Worth: $11,431,396
Earnings: ($734,342)
Emp.: 34
Fiscal Year-end: 06/30/23
Yarn Product Mfr
N.A.I.C.S.: 313110
Muhammad Waseem-ur-Rehman
(CEO)

BECRYPT LIMITED
90 Long Acre, Covent Garden, Lon-
don, WC2E 9RA, United Kingdom
Tel.: (44) 8458382050
Web Site: http://www.becrypt.com
Year Founded: 2001
Sales Range: $10-24.9 Million
Emp.: 68
Data Security & Protection Solutions
N.A.I.C.S.: 513210
Steve Bellamy *(Chm)*

BECUAI INC.
Jun Tower 9th Floor 385 Toegye-ro,
Jung-gu, Seoul, Korea (South)
Tel.: (82) 234870215
Web Site: https://becuai.com
Year Founded: 1998
Software Development Services
N.A.I.C.S.: 513210
Im Kyung-Hwan *(CEO)*

BEDELL CRISTIN
26 New Street, Saint Helier, JE2
3RA, Jersey
Tel.: (44) 1534 814814
Web Site:
    http://www.bedellcristin.com
Year Founded: 1939
Legal & Fiduciary Services
N.A.I.C.S.: 523991
David Cadin *(Mng Partner)*

BEDFORD CAPITAL LTD.
130 Adelaide Street West Suite 2900,
Toronto, M5H 3P5, ON, Canada
Tel.: (416) 947-1492
Web Site:
    http://www.bedfordcapital.ca
Year Founded: 1982
Private Investment Firm
N.A.I.C.S.: 523999
Tim Bowman *(Mng Dir)*

BEDFORD METALS CORP.
2200 - 885 West Georgia Street,
Vancouver, V6C 3E8, BC, Canada
Tel.: (647) 725-3888   **Ca**
Web Site: https://acadmetals.com
Year Founded: 2006
O8D—(DEU)
Assets: $302,482
Liabilities: $570,048
Net Worth: ($267,566)
Earnings: ($453,508)
Fiscal Year-end: 03/31/23
Metal Exploration Services
N.A.I.C.S.: 213114
Richard Ko *(CFO)*

BEDMUTHA INDUSTRIES LIM-
ITED
Plot No A - 70 71 72 STICE Sinnar-
Shirdi Road Musalgaon, Sinnar,
Nasik, 422 103, Maharashtra, India
Tel.: (91) 2551240481
Web Site: https://www.bedmutha.com
533270—(BOM)
Rev.: $98,077,803
Assets: $66,933,485
Liabilities: $55,124,952
Net Worth: $11,808,533
Earnings: $1,279,892
Emp.: 529
Fiscal Year-end: 03/31/22
Steel Products Mfr & Distr
N.A.I.C.S.: 331110
Vijay Kachardas Vedmutha *(Chm &*
Mng Dir)

BEE ELECTRONIC MACHINES
LTD.
266 Dr Annie Besant Road Worli,
Mumbai, 400030, Maharashtra, India
Tel.: (91) 2224301873

Web Site:
http://www.beeelectronic.com
Year Founded: 1981
Electronic Components Mfr
N.A.I.C.S.: 334419

**BEE VECTORING TECHNOLO-
GIES INTERNATIONAL INC.**
7 - 4160 Sladeview Crescent, Missis-
sauga, L5L 0A1, ON, Canada
Tel.: (647) 660-5119   BC
Web Site: https://www.beevt.com
Year Founded: 2011
BEVVF—(OTCQB)
Rev.: $454,316
Assets: $2,731,948
Liabilities: $1,710,823
Net Worth: $1,021,125
Earnings: ($3,529,989)
Emp.: 10
Fiscal Year-end: 09/30/23
Organic Pesticide Developer & Mfr
N.A.I.C.S.: 325320
Michael Collinson *(Chm)*

**BEECHCROFT DEVELOP-
MENTS LTD.**
1 Church Ln, Wallingford, OX10 0DX,
Oxon, United Kingdom
Tel.: (44) 1491834975
Web Site:
http://www.beachcroft.co.uk
Sales Range: $50-74.9 Million
Emp.: 25
Retirement Homes
N.A.I.C.S.: 624229
Christopher R. Thompson *(Mng Dir)*

BEEDIE CAPITAL PARTNERS
Suite 900 1111 West Georgia Street,
Vancouver, V6E 4M3, BC, Canada
Tel.: (604) 436-7888
Web Site: https://beediecapital.com
Emp.: 100
Private Equity
N.A.I.C.S.: 523940

Subsidiaries:

Beedie Investments Ltd.   (1)
3030 Gilmore Diversion, Burnaby, V5G
3B4, BC, Canada
Tel.: (604) 435-3321
Web Site: https://www.beedie.ca
Real Estate
N.A.I.C.S.: 531390

Holding (Domestic):

Think Research Corporation   (2)
199 Bay Street 4000, Toronto, M5L 1A9,
ON, Canada
Tel.: (416) 977-1955
Web Site: https://www.thinkresearch.com
Clinical Content & Technology Company
N.A.I.C.S.: 541511
Sachin Aggarwal *(CEO)*

Subsidiary (Non-US):

Pharmapod Ltd.   (3)
151-156 Thomas Street Ushers Island,
Dublin, D08 PY5E, Ireland
Tel.: (353) 1 685 2242
Web Site: http://www.pharmapodhq.com
Pharmaceuticals Product Mfr
N.A.I.C.S.: 325412
Leonora O'Brien *(Founder & CEO)*

BEEHIVE COILS LTD
Studlands Park Avenue, Newmarket,
CB8 7AU, Suffolk, United Kingdom
Tel.: (44) 1638664134
Web Site:
http://www.beehivecoils.co.uk
Year Founded: 1968
Rev.: $18,251,677
Emp.: 87
Coil Mfr
N.A.I.C.S.: 334416
Eddy Copeman *(Mgr-Sls)*

BEEIO HONEY LTD
Oppenheimer 4 St, Rehovot,
7670104, Israel
Tel.: (972) 86131198   II
Web Site: https://bee-io.com
BHNY—(TAE)
Assets: $2,515,817
Liabilities: $1,782,843
Net Worth: $732,974
Earnings: ($2,132,891)
Fiscal Year-end: 12/31/23
All Other Specialty Food Retailers
N.A.I.C.S.: 445298
David Gerbi *(CEO)*

BEEKAY NIRYAT LTD.
9 Hungerford Street, Kolkata, 700
017, India
Tel.: (91) 3332619344   In
Web Site:
http://www.beekayniryat.co.in
539546—(BOM)
Rev.: $134,302
Assets: $2,949,369
Liabilities: $679,961
Net Worth: $2,269,408
Earnings: $213,814
Emp.: 5
Fiscal Year-end: 03/31/22
Jute Product Trading Services
N.A.I.C.S.: 523160
Sree Gopal Bjaoria *(Chm & Mng Dir)*

**BEEKAY STEEL INDUSTRIES
LTD.**
Lansdowne Towers 4th Floor 2/1A
Sarat Bose Road, Kolkata, 700 020,
India
Tel.: (91) 3330514444
Web Site:
https://www.beekaysteel.com
539018—(BOM)
Rev.: $179,405,049
Assets: $143,784,650
Liabilities: $47,258,798
Net Worth: $96,525,852
Earnings: $21,401,480
Emp.: 600
Fiscal Year-end: 03/31/22
Steel Products Mfr
N.A.I.C.S.: 331110
Suresh Chand Bansal *(Chm)*

**BEEKS FINANCIAL CLOUD
GROUP PLC**
Riverside Building 2 Kings Inch Way,
Braehead, Renfrew, PA4 8YU, Ren-
frewshire, United Kingdom
Tel.: (44) 1505800771   UK
Web Site:
https://www.beeksfinancialcloud.com
Year Founded: 2011
Low Latency Hosting, Co-location &
Cloud Services
N.A.I.C.S.: 518210
Gordon McArthur *(CEO)*

Subsidiaries:

Commercial Network Services   (1)
11622 El Camino Real 1st Fl, San Diego,
CA 92130
Tel.: (619) 225-7882
Web Site:
http://www.commercialservices.com
Virtual Private Server
N.A.I.C.S.: 423430

BEELK HOLDING AG
Arbachstrasse 2, 6340, Baar, Swit-
zerland
Tel.: (41) 41 748 14 14
Web Site: http://www.beelk.com
Real Estate Services
N.A.I.C.S.: 531390
Andreas Kleeb *(Chm)*

Subsidiaries:

Kinetic Worldwide Ltd   (1)
121-141 Westbourne Terrace, London,
W26JR, United Kingdom
Tel.: (44) 20 7544 4600
Web Site: http://www.kineticww.com
Emp.: 40
Media Agencies
N.A.I.C.S.: 541840
Lucy Catchpole *(Grp Acct Dir)*

**BEEMA-PAKISTAN COMPANY
LIMITED**
412-427 4th Floor Muhammadi
House I I Chundrigar Road, PO Box
5626, Karachi, Pakistan
Tel.: (92) 21 2429530
Web Site:
http://www.beemapakistan.com
General Insurance Services
N.A.I.C.S.: 524298

BEENOS INC.
Gotenyama Trust Tower 7F 4-7-35
Kita-shinagawa, Shinagawa-ku, To-
kyo, 1400001, Japan
Tel.: (81) 357393350
Web Site: https://www.beenos.com
Year Founded: 1999
3328—(TKS)
Rev.: $230,481,720
Assets: $197,888,990
Liabilities: $105,648,090
Net Worth: $92,240,900
Earnings: $15,583,820
Emp.: 438
Fiscal Year-end: 09/30/23
Mail-Order Services
N.A.I.C.S.: 459999
Shota Naoi *(Pres & Grp CEO)*

Subsidiaries:

Beecruise Inc.   (1)
6F Gotenyama Trust Tower 4-7-35 Kitashi-
nagawa, Shinagawa-ku, Tokyo, 140-0001,
Japan
Tel.: (81) 357393366
Web Site: https://beecruise.co.jp
Electronic Commerce Services
N.A.I.C.S.: 532210

Defactostandard, Ltd.   (1)
Sankyu Heiwajima Logistics Center 5F Hei-
wajima 3-3-8, Ota-ku, Tokyo, 143-0006,
Japan   (100%)
Tel.: (81) 3 4405 8177
Web Site: http://www.defactostandard.co.jp
Emp.: 66
Online Auction Services
N.A.I.C.S.: 541611
Katsura Sato *(Auditor)*

Fasbee Inc.   (1)
Gotenyama Trust Tower 6F 4-7-35 Kita-
shinagawa, Shinagawa-ku, Tokyo, 140-
0001, Japan
Tel.: (81) 357393350
Web Site: https://fas-bee.com
Fashion Apparel Online Services
N.A.I.C.S.: 541490

Joylab, Inc.   (1)
7-16 Matsuyamachi, Chuo-ku, Osaka, 542-
0067, Japan
Tel.: (81) 667675620
Web Site: https://joylab.jp
Alcoholic Beverage Distr
N.A.I.C.S.: 424820

BEEYU OVERSEAS LIMITED
15 Chittaranjan Avenue Ground
Floor, Kolkata, 700 072, India
Tel.: (91) 22484787
Web Site:
https://www.beeyuoverseas.in
Year Founded: 1993
532645—(BOM)
Rev.: $21,349
Assets: $454,472
Liabilities: $420,429
Net Worth: $34,043

Earnings: $2,134
Fiscal Year-end: 03/31/21
Cultivation Services
N.A.I.C.S.: 111998
Shouvik Kundu *(CFO)*

BEFAR GROUP CO., LTD.
No 869 Huanghe 5th Road, Bincheng
District, Binzhou, 256600, Shandong,
China
Tel.: (86) 4008696888
Web Site: https://www.befar.com
Year Founded: 1968
601678—(SHG)
Rev.: $1,248,445,982
Assets: $2,537,815,293
Liabilities: $933,314,405
Net Worth: $1,604,500,888
Earnings: $165,451,263
Emp.: 2,600
Fiscal Year-end: 12/31/22
Chemical Products Mfr & Distr
N.A.I.C.S.: 325998
Yu Jiang *(Chm)*

BEFESA S.A.
68-70 Boulevard de la Petrusse,
2320, Luxembourg, Luxembourg
Tel.: (352) 210210010   LU
Web Site: https://www.befesa.com
Year Founded: 2013
BFSA—(DEU)
Rev.: $1,303,228,922
Assets: $2,147,777,782
Liabilities: $1,238,707,720
Net Worth: $909,070,061
Earnings: $63,991,344
Emp.: 1,790
Fiscal Year-end: 12/31/23
Waste Recycling Services
N.A.I.C.S.: 562920
Javier Molina Montes *(Chm & CEO)*

Subsidiaries:

American Zinc Recycling Corp.   (1)
3000 GSK Dr Ste 201 Moon Township,
Pittsburgh, PA 15108
Tel.: (724) 774-1020
Web Site: http://www.azr.com
Sales Range: $400-449.9 Million
Holding Company; Zinc Products Recycler
& Mfr
N.A.I.C.S.: 551112
Greg Belland *(Sr VP)*

Plant (Domestic):

Horsehead Corp.   (2)
900 Delaware Ave, Palmerton, PA 18071
Tel.: (610) 826-2111
Web Site: http://www.horsehead.net
Sales Range: $50-74.9 Million
Emp.: 161
Zinc Recycling & Production Services
N.A.I.C.S.: 331492
Greg Belland *(Sr VP)*

Subsidiary (Domestic):

Horsehead Metals Development,
LLC   (2)
4955 Steubenville Pike Ste 405, Pittsburgh,
PA 15205
Tel.: (724) 774-1020
Web Site: http://www.horsehead.net
Zinc & Related Products Mfr
N.A.I.C.S.: 331491

The International Metals Reclamation
Company, Inc.   (2)
1 Inmetco Dr, Ellwood City, PA 16117
Tel.: (724) 758-5515
Web Site: https://www.inmetco.com
Sales Range: $25-49.9 Million
Emp.: 100
Metal-Bearing Waste Recycling Services
N.A.I.C.S.: 562920
Mark Tomaszewski *(Pres)*

Befesa (China) Investment Co.,
Ltd.   (1)
2006 Room of Deji Plaza No18 Zhongshan

Befesa S.A.—(Continued)

Road, Xuanwu District, Nanjing, 21005, China
Tel.: (86) 2585590300
Recycling Services
N.A.I.C.S.: 562920

Befesa Aluminium Germany GmbH (1)
Claude-Breda-Str 6, 06406, Bernburg, Germany
Tel.: (49) 3471628790
Recycling Services
N.A.I.C.S.: 562920

Befesa Management Services GmbH (1)
Balcke- Durr Allee 1, 40882, Ratingen, Germany
Tel.: (49) 210210010
Emp.: 14
Steel Dust Recycling Services
N.A.I.C.S.: 562920

Befesa Medio Ambiente, S.L. (1)
Ctra Bilbao-Plentzia n 21, 48950, Erandio, Spain
Tel.: (34) 955404896
Steel Dust Recycling Services
N.A.I.C.S.: 562920

Befesa Salt Slags, Ltd. (1)
Fenns Bank, Whitchurch, SY13 3PA, Shropshire, United Kingdom
Tel.: (44) 1948780441
Recycling Services
N.A.I.C.S.: 562920

Befesa ScanDust AB (1)
Box 204, 261 23, Landskrona, Sweden
Tel.: (46) 418437800
Web Site: https://www.scandust.se
Emp.: 80
Recycling Services
N.A.I.C.S.: 562920

Befesa Silvermet Iskenderun Celik Tozu Geri Donusumu, A.S. (1)
Organize Sanayi Bolgesi, Noksel Boru Fab Arkasi, Iskenderun, Hatay, Turkiye
Tel.: (90) 3266562525
Recycling Services
N.A.I.C.S.: 562920

Befesa Steel Services GmbH (1)
Balcke- Durr- Allee 1, 40882, Ratingen, Germany
Tel.: (49) 210210010
Recycling Services
N.A.I.C.S.: 562920

Befesa Valera, S.A.S. (1)
Route Duvigneau, 59820, Gravelines, France
Tel.: (33) 328519191
Recycling Services
N.A.I.C.S.: 562920

Befesa Zinc Comercial, S.A. (1)
Ctra Bilbao-Plencia 21, Asua, 48950, Erandio, Vizcaya, Spain
Tel.: (34) 944535030
Recycling Services
N.A.I.C.S.: 562920

Befesa Zinc Duisburg GmbH (1)
Richard-Seiffert-Strasse 1, 47249, Duisburg, Germany
Tel.: (49) 203758160
Recycling Services
N.A.I.C.S.: 562920

Befesa Zinc Freiberg GmbH & Co. KG (1)
Alfred-Lange-Strasse 10, 09599, Freiberg, Germany
Tel.: (49) 373138990
Recycling Services
N.A.I.C.S.: 562920

Befesa Zinc Korea Ltd. (1)
265-15 Cheonbuksandan-ro, Cheonbuk-myeon, Gyeongju, Korea (South)
Tel.: (82) 547773111
Recycling Services
N.A.I.C.S.: 562920

Befesa Zinc Oxido, S.A. (1)
Sangroniz Bidea 24, 48150, Sondika, Vizcaya, Spain

Tel.: (34) 944711445
Recycling Services
N.A.I.C.S.: 562920

Befesa Zinc US, Inc. (1)
3000 GSK Dr Ste 201, Moon Township, PA 15108
Tel.: (724) 774-1020
Emp.: 39
Environmental Management Services
N.A.I.C.S.: 541620

BEFIMMO SCA

Chaussee de Wavre 1945, B-1160, Brussels, Belgium
Tel.: (32) 26793860
Web Site: http://www.befimmo.be
BEFB—(EUR)
Rev.: $143,533,348
Assets: $3,327,514,569
Liabilities: $1,549,533,779
Net Worth: $1,777,980,790
Earnings: $36,536,801
Emp.: 77
Fiscal Year-end: 12/31/22
Property Asset Management Services
N.A.I.C.S.: 531390
Aminata Kake *(Gen Counsel & Sec)*

Subsidiaries:

Fedimmo S.A. (1)
Cantersteen 47, 1000, Brussels, Belgium
Tel.: (32) 26793860
Web Site: https://www.befimmo.be
Sales Range: $50-74.9 Million
Emp.: 15
Real Estate Agencies
N.A.I.C.S.: 531210
Benoit De Blieck *(Mng Dir)*

BEFOREPAY GROUP LIMITED

Suite 2 Level 6 50 Carrington Street, Sydney, 2000, NSW, Australia
Tel.: (61) 1300870711   AU
Web Site:
https://www.beforepay.com.au
Year Founded: 2019
B4P—(ASX)
Rev.: $20,022,913
Assets: $42,494,144
Liabilities: $25,002,180
Net Worth: $17,491,963
Earnings: ($4,326,441)
Emp.: 30
Fiscal Year-end: 06/30/23
Software Development Services
N.A.I.C.S.: 541511
James Twiss *(CEO)*

BEFUT GLOBAL, INC.

27th Floor Liangjiu International Tower, 5 Heyi Street Xigang District, Dalian, 116011, Liaoning, China
Tel.: (86) 411 83678755   NV
Web Site: http://www.befut.com
Sales Range: $50-74.9 Million
Emp.: 291
Cable & Wire Mfr & Distr
N.A.I.C.S.: 335921
Hongbo Cao *(Chm)*

BEGA CHEESE LTD.

23-45 Ridge St, PO Box 123, Bega, 2550, NSW, Australia
Tel.: (61) 264917777   AU
Web Site:
https://www.begacheese.com.au
BGA—(ASX)
Rev.: $2,351,495,717
Assets: $1,428,151,704
Liabilities: $750,534,185
Net Worth: $677,617,519
Earnings: $20,365,919
Fiscal Year-end: 06/30/24
Cheese Mfr
N.A.I.C.S.: 311513
Barry Irvin *(Chm)*

Subsidiaries:

Bega Cheese Ltd. - Strathmerton Process and Packaging Plant (1)
Murray Valley Highway, PO Box 100, Strathmerton, 3641, VIC, Australia
Tel.: (61) 358758111
Cheese Mfr
N.A.I.C.S.: 311513

Bega Dairy and Drinks Pty. Ltd. (1)
Level 4 737 Bourke St, Docklands, 3008, VIC, Australia
Tel.: (61) 1800677852
Dairy Product Mfr & Distr
N.A.I.C.S.: 311514

Capitol Chilled Foods (Australia) Pty. Limited (1)
2-8 Mildura Street, Griffith, 2603, ACT, Australia
Tel.: (61) 262609111
Web Site: https://www.ccfa.com.au
Sales Range: $50-74.9 Million
Emp.: 70
Dairy Product Whslr; Joint Venture of Australian Co-Operative Foods Limited & Bega Cheese Ltd.
N.A.I.C.S.: 424430
David Tyack *(Mng Dir & Member-Exec Bd)*

LD&D Australia Pty. Ltd. (1)
737 Bourke Street, Docklands, Melbourne, 3008, VIC, Australia   (100%)
Tel.: (61) 1800677852
Web Site: http://www.lionco.com
Sales Range: $1-4.9 Billion
Emp.: 700
Dairy Products Mfr
N.A.I.C.S.: 551112

Subsidiary (Non-US):

Lactalis Singapore Pte. Ltd. (2)
10 Raeburn Park 01-19, 2 A No 05-12 AMK Tech 1, Singapore, 088702, Singapore   (66.2%)
Tel.: (65) 64846090
Web Site: http://www.qbb.com.sg
Sales Range: $50-74.9 Million
Emp.: 20
Dairy Product Whslr
N.A.I.C.S.: 424430

Plant (Domestic):

Lion Dairy & Drinks Pty. Ltd. - Chelsea Heights Plant (2)
150 Wells Rd, Chelsea Heights, 3196, VIC, Australia
Tel.: (61) 392133700
Web Site: http://www.natfoods.com.au
Sales Range: $75-99.9 Million
Emp.: 500
Milk Production
N.A.I.C.S.: 112120

Lion Dairy & Drinks Pty. Ltd. - Penrith Plant (2)
Castlereagh Rd, Penrith, 2750, NSW, Australia
Tel.: (61) 247210241
Sales Range: $25-49.9 Million
Emp.: 200
Milk Production
N.A.I.C.S.: 112120

Lion Dairy & Drinks Pty. Ltd. - Salisbury Plant (2)
167 Cross Keys Rd, Salisbury, 5108, SA, Australia
Tel.: (61) 882825678
Web Site: http://www.lionco.com
Sales Range: $25-49.9 Million
Emp.: 130
Milk Production
N.A.I.C.S.: 112120
Gabrielle Liston *(Gen Mgr)*

Lion Dairy & Drinks Pty. Ltd. - Thebarton Plant (2)
Unit 3 31-35 George Street, Thebarton, 5031, SA, Australia
Tel.: (61) 883549600
Sales Range: $25-49.9 Million
Emp.: 6
Producer of Dairy Products
N.A.I.C.S.: 311514

Subsidiary (Domestic):

Malanda Dairyfoods Pty. Limited (2)
737 Bourke Street, Malanda, Docklands, 3008, VIC, Australia   (100%)
Tel.: (61) 800677852
Web Site: https://www.dairyfarmers.com.au
Dry Condensed & Evaporated Dairy Product Mfr
N.A.I.C.S.: 311514

Joint Venture (Domestic):

Vitasoy Australia Products Pty. Ltd. (2)
737 Bourke Street Docklands, PO Box 6089, Melbourne, 3008, VIC, Australia
Tel.: (61) 800001029
Web Site: http://www.vitasoy.com.au
Sales Range: $25-49.9 Million
Emp.: 200
Soy Milk Mfr & Whslr
N.A.I.C.S.: 311224

Tatura Milk Industries Pty Ltd (1)
236 Hogan Street, PO Box 213, Tatura, 3616, VIC, Australia   (70%)
Tel.: (61) 358246200
Web Site: https://www.tatura.com.au
Sales Range: $125-149.9 Million
Emp.: 361
Dairy Products Mfr
N.A.I.C.S.: 311512
Tony Kilmartin *(Bus Mgr-Dairy Ingredients)*

BEGA ELECTROMOTOR SA

Republicii Bv no 21, Timisoara, 300159, Timis, Romania
Tel.: (40) 256492004
Year Founded: 1900
Sales Range: $1-9.9 Million
Emp.: 61
Electric Motor Mfr
N.A.I.C.S.: 333996
Vaieriu Riscuta *(Pres & Gen Mgr)*

BEGBIES TRAYNOR GROUP PLC

340 Deansgate, Manchester, M3 4LY, United Kingdom
Tel.: (44) 1618371700   UK
Web Site: https://www.begbiestraynorgroup.com
BEG—(AIM)
Rev.: $172,595,646
Assets: $199,230,387
Liabilities: $100,240,037
Net Worth: $98,990,350
Earnings: $1,830,350
Fiscal Year-end: 04/30/24
Holding Company; Corporate Finance, Investigation, Forensic Accounting & Security Risk Consulting Services
N.A.I.C.S.: 551112
Andrew Dick *(Partner-Manchester)*

Subsidiaries:

BTG Global Advisory Limited (1)
31st Floor 40 Bank Street Canary Wharf, London, E14 5NR, United Kingdom
Tel.: (44) 207 412 8371
Web Site: https://www.btgga.com
Investment Banking Services
N.A.I.C.S.: 523999

BTG Intelligence Limited (1)
340 Deansgate, Manchester, M3 4LY, Greater Manchester, United Kingdom
Tel.: (44) 1618371700
Web Site: http://www.begbiestraynorgroup.com
Sales Range: $50-74.9 Million
Emp.: 150
Financial Investigation & Advisory Services
N.A.I.C.S.: 523999

Ernest Wilsons & Co Limited (1)
The Business Centre Deanhurst Park Gelderd Road, Gildersome, Leeds, LS27 7LG, West Yorkshire, United Kingdom
Tel.: (44) 113 238 2900
Web Site: https://www.ernest-wilson.co.uk
Property Consultancy Services

N.A.I.C.S.: 531311
Paul Williamson *(Mng Dir)*

Pugh & Company Limited (1)
Toronto Square Toronto Street, Leeds, LS1 2HJ, United Kingdom
Tel.: (44) 113 283 2487
Web Site: https://www.pugh-auctions.com
Real Estate Services
N.A.I.C.S.: 531390
Paul Thompson *(Mng Dir)*

Springboard Corporate Finance LLP (1)
340 Deansgate, Manchester, M3 4LY, United Kingdom
Tel.: (44) 845 838 1680
Web Site: https://springboardcf.com
Investment Banking Services
N.A.I.C.S.: 523999
Siobhan Lloyd *(Mgr-Business Development)*

BEGHELLI S.P.A.
Via Mozzeghine 13 15, Monteveglio, 40050, Bologna, Italy
Tel.: (39) 0519660411
Web Site: https://www.beghelli.it
BE—(ITA)
Sales Range: $75-99.9 Million
Emp.: 1,908
Home Security Systems, Lamps & Other Various Lighting Systems Mfr
N.A.I.C.S.: 561621
Luca Beghelli *(Dir-Mktg)*

Subsidiaries:

Becar Srl (1)
1 Via Della Pace, Bologna, 40050, Bologna, Italy
Tel.: (39) 0516702242
Other Electronic Component Mfr
N.A.I.C.S.: 334419

Beghelli Asia Pacific Ltd. (1)
2605 S Twr Concordia Plz Museum Rd, Kowloon, China (Hong Kong) (60%)
Tel.: (852) 26205522
Web Site: http://www.beghelliasia.com
Sales Range: $50-74.9 Million
Emp.: 10
Other Electronic Parts & Equipment Whslr
N.A.I.C.S.: 423690
Spes Stanley Wai-Nam Ku *(Gen Mgr)*

Beghelli Canada Inc. (1)
3900 14th Ave Unit 1, Markham, L3R 4R3, ON, Canada (75%)
Tel.: (905) 948-9500
Web Site: https://www.beluce.com
Sales Range: $25-49.9 Million
Emp.: 100
Electric Lamp Bulb & Part Mfr
N.A.I.C.S.: 335139

Beghelli China Co., Ltd. (1)
199 Daqing Road North, BGI Industrial Park, Yizheng, 211400, Jiangsu, China
Tel.: (86) 5148 358 0268
Web Site: https://www.beghellichina.com
Lighting Equipment Mfr & Distr
N.A.I.C.S.: 335139

Beghelli De Mexico, S.A. De C.V. (1)
Av El Marques No 70 Int 4, Parque Industrial Bernardo Quintana, 76246, Santiago de Queretaro, Mexico
Tel.: (52) 442 221 6215
Web Site: https://beghelli.com.mx
Lighting Equipment Mfr
N.A.I.C.S.: 335139

Beghelli Elplast A.S. (1)
Porici 3a, Brno, 60316, Czech Republic (92.19%)
Tel.: (420) 531014111
Web Site: http://www.beghelli.cz
Emp.: 100
Commercial Industrial & Institutional Electric Lighting Fixture Mfr
N.A.I.C.S.: 335132
Radim Linka *(CEO)*

Beghelli Hungary Kft. (1)
Tinodi u 1-3 C/4/9, 1095, Budapest, Hungary
Tel.: (36) 1 951 3194

Web Site: https://www.beghelli.it
Lighting Equipment Mfr
N.A.I.C.S.: 335139

Beghelli Inc. (1)
3250 Corporate Way, Miramar, FL 33025 (90%)
Tel.: (954) 442-6600
Web Site: http://www.beghelliusa.com
Sales Range: $25-49.9 Million
Emp.: 50
All Other Miscellaneous Electrical Equipment & Component Mfr
N.A.I.C.S.: 335999
Derek Schimming *(Mng Dir)*

Beghelli Polska Sp. z o.o. (1)
ul Suburban 95, 44-207, Rybnik, Poland
Tel.: (48) 32 422 5579
Web Site: https://www.beghelli.it
Lighting Equipment Mfr
N.A.I.C.S.: 335139

Beghelli Praezisa GmbH (1)
Lanterstrasse 34, 46539, Dinslaken, Germany
Tel.: (49) 20 649 7010
Web Site: https://www.beghelli.it
Lighting Equipment Mfr
N.A.I.C.S.: 335139
Thomas Buhren *(Mng Dir)*

Elettronica Cimone Srl (1)
1 Via Comunale Per Casoni, 41027, Pievepelago, Modena, Italy (100%)
Tel.: (39) 053671108
Sales Range: $50-74.9 Million
Emp.: 150
Electric Lamp Bulb & Part Mfr
N.A.I.C.S.: 335139

BEGISTICS PUBLIC COMPANY LIMITED
52 Thaniya Plaza Building 28th Floor Silom Road Suriyawong, Bangrak, Bangkok, 10500, Thailand
Tel.: (66) 23673570
Web Site: https://www.btc.co.th
Year Founded: 1999
B—(THA)
Rev.: $26,304,265
Assets: $199,937,350
Liabilities: $72,713,853
Net Worth: $127,223,498
Earnings: $5,973,928
Emp.: 135
Fiscal Year-end: 12/31/23
Marine & Cargo Handling Services, Port Facilities & Truck Dealership
N.A.I.C.S.: 488320
Somkid Boonthanom *(Chm)*

BEGLES DISTRIBUTION SA
4 Rue Maurice Martin, 33130, Begles, Gironde, France
Tel.: (33) 556 85 1055
Rev.: $18,600,000
Emp.: 15
Distribution of Products to Supermarkets
N.A.I.C.S.: 445110
Francois Mortel *(Pres)*

BEHAVIOR TECH COMPUTER CORPORATION
20F-B No 98 Sec 1 Sintai 5th Rd Sijhih City, Taipei, 22102, Taiwan
Tel.: (886) 226961888
Web Site: http://www.btc.com.tw
Year Founded: 1982
Sales Range: $50-74.9 Million
Emp.: 300
Computer Keyboards, CD-Rom Drives & Sound Cards Mfr
N.A.I.C.S.: 334118
Julia Yi *(Sls Mgr)*

Subsidiaries:

Behavior Tech Computer (US) Corporation (1)
412 Emerson St, Fremont, CA 94539-5224
Tel.: (510) 657-3956

Sales Range: $25-49.9 Million
Emp.: 20
Mfr & Sales of Personal Computer Peripherals, Keyboards, Optical Devices & Sound Cards
N.A.I.C.S.: 423430

Behavior Tech Computer Corporation (1)
10 Rue Marcel Sallnave, 94200, Ivry-sur-Seine, France (100%)
Tel.: (33) 241438757
Sales Range: $75-99.9 Million
Emp.: 12
N.A.I.C.S.: 334118

Behavior Tech Computer Corporation - Chung Li Factory (1)
14 Chi Chang First Rd Industrial Park, Chung-li, Taiwan
Tel.: (886) 3 452 6374
Keyboard Mfr
N.A.I.C.S.: 334118

Behavior Tech Computer Europe B.V. (1)
Cypresbaan 38, 2908LT, Capelle aan de IJssel, Igsel, Netherlands (100%)
Tel.: (31) 0102642444
Web Site: http://www.btceurope.nl
Emp.: 25
N.A.I.C.S.: 334118
Taki Petridis *(Gen Mgr)*

Top Glory Electronics CO., Ltd. (1)
Jing Xing Industrial City, Xianj District Qing Xi Town, Dongguan, Guangdong, China
Tel.: (86) 769 3889 8579
Keyboard Mfr
N.A.I.C.S.: 334118

BEHBAHAN CEMENT COMPANY
No 36 Kordestan Highway Near Hemmat Highway Akikhani St In, Front Of Vanak Park Complex, Tehran, Iran
Tel.: (98) 2188215626
Web Site: https://behcco.ir
Year Founded: 1972
Emp.: 350
Cement Mfr
N.A.I.C.S.: 327310

BEHCERAM COMPANY
No 421-420 Floor Second-Trade Central-Chahar Bagh-Si o Se Pol, PO Box 8173696854, Isfahan, Iran
Tel.: (98) 311 6204801
Web Site: http://www.behceramtile.com
Year Founded: 1996
Granite Ceramic Product Mfr
N.A.I.C.S.: 327120

BEHN MEYER (D) HOLDING AG & CO.
Ballindamm 1, 20095, Hamburg, Germany
Tel.: (49) 40302990 De
Web Site: http://www.behnmeyer.com
Year Founded: 1857
Sales Range: $150-199.9 Million
Emp.: 800
Holding Company; Manufacturer of Specialty Chemicals
N.A.I.C.S.: 551112

Subsidiaries:

Behn Meyer Agricare, PT. (1)
Taman Tekno BSD Blok B No 1 Sektor XI, Tangerang, 15314, Indonesia
Tel.: (62) 21 756 1000
Chemical Fertilizer Distr
N.A.I.C.S.: 424910
Secian Brilianto *(Area Mgr)*

Behn Meyer Chemicals (Philippines) Inc. (1)
No 17 San Miguel Avenue 1808 Hanston Square Ortigas Center, Pasig, 1605, Manila, Philippines
Tel.: (63) 2 477 6819

Chemical Products Distr
N.A.I.C.S.: 424690
Gene Medallo *(Mgr-Sls-Rubber & Coatings)*

Behn Meyer Chemicals (Qingdao) Co., Ltd (1)
No 36 Miaoling Road Room 2511 International Development Center, Laoshan, Qingdao, 266061, China
Tel.: (86) 532 6872 1811
Chemical Products Distr
N.A.I.C.S.: 424690

Behn Meyer Chemicals (T) Co., Ltd (1)
No 628 Moo 1 Front of Soi Foknang Sukhumvit Road K M 34, Amphur Muang, Samut Prakan, Thailand
Tel.: (66) 2709 1584
Chemical Products Distr
N.A.I.C.S.: 424690
Ekkawit Saenkham *(Reg Mgr-Sls)*

Behn Meyer Chemicals Taiwan Co., Ltd (1)
No 461 Nanking East Road Section 6 9th Floor, Neihu, 11469, Taipei, Taiwan
Tel.: (886) 2 2793 6715
Chemical Products Distr
N.A.I.C.S.: 424690
Piasonk Hung *(Gen Mgr)*

Behn Meyer Group Malaysia (1)
No 5 Jalan TP2 Taman Perindustrian Sime UEP, 47600, Subang Jaya, Selangor, Malaysia
Tel.: (60) 3 8026 3333
Chemical Products Distr
N.A.I.C.S.: 424690

Behn Meyer Group Singapore (1)
2 Boon Leat Terrace #06-01 Harbour Side Industrial Bldg 2, Singapore, 119844, Singapore (100%)
Tel.: (65) 6511 6666
Web Site: http://www.behnmeyer.com
Chemical Distr
N.A.I.C.S.: 424690

Behn Meyer Group Vietnam (1)
No 36 Street 6 VSIP 1, Thuan An, Binh Duong, Vietnam
Tel.: (84) 650 376 6030
Chemical Products Distr
N.A.I.C.S.: 424690

Myanmar Behn Meyer Co. Ltd. (1)
No 12 Inlay-Yeiktha 7 1/2 Miles Pyay Road, Mayangon Township, Yangon, Myanmar
Tel.: (95) 1 664 049
Chemical Products Distr
N.A.I.C.S.: 424690

Performance Additives of America, LLC (1)
906 Cookson Ave SE, New Philadelphia, OH 44663
Tel.: (330) 365-9256
Chemical Products Mfr
N.A.I.C.S.: 325199

BEHRINGER GMBH
Industriestrasse 23, 74912, Heilbronn, Germany
Tel.: (49) 72662070
Web Site: http://www.behringer.net
Year Founded: 1919
Rev.: $51,036,310
Emp.: 383
Bandsaw Machines Mfr
N.A.I.C.S.: 333243
Christian Behringer *(Mng Partner-Sls & Mktg Div)*

Subsidiaries:

Behringer Anlagenbau GmbH (1)
Industriestrasse 23, 74912, Berlin, Germany
Tel.: (49) 72662070
Industrial Equipment Mfr
N.A.I.C.S.: 333243

Behringer Eisele GmbH (1)
Austrasse 29, 73235, Weilheim, Germany
Tel.: (49) 7023957570
Industrial Equipment Mfr
N.A.I.C.S.: 333243
Manfred Gruninger *(Mgr-Sls)*

Behringer GmbH—(Continued)

Behringer Ltd. (1)
1 Quarry Court, Pitstone Green Business Park, Pitstone, LU7 9GW, United Kingdom
Tel.: (44) 1296668259
Industrial Equipment Distr
N.A.I.C.S.: 423830

Vernet Behringer SA (1)
13 rue de la Brot, ZAE Cap Nord, 21074, Dijon, France
Tel.: (33) 380732163
Industrial Equipment Distr
N.A.I.C.S.: 423830
Philippe Bourdier (Project Mgr)

BEHSHAHR INDUSTRIAL DEVELOPMENT CORP.
No 8 24th Street Ghaem Magham Avenue, Hafte Tir Square, Tehran, Iran
Web Site: http://www.bidc.ir
Sales Range: $1-4.9 Billion
Investment Services
N.A.I.C.S.: 523940

Subsidiaries:

Behpak Industrial Company Limited (1)
1st Floor Behshahr Group No 28/1 Crossing 7th Street, Ahmad Ghasir Avenue, Tehran, 1513736611, Iran
Tel.: (98) 2188706429
Web Site: http://www.behpak.com
Oil Extraction Services
N.A.I.C.S.: 311710

Paxan Yeravan Co. (1)
8th Km Fath Highway, Tehran, Iran
Tel.: (98) 2164562395
Web Site: http://www.paxando.com
Toiletries Products Mfr & Distr
N.A.I.C.S.: 325620

BEHSHAHR INDUSTRIAL GROUP INVESTMENT COMPANY
Park Haqshen Alley No 10 3rd floor Valiasr St in front of Mellat, Khalili Chhanqi Street, 19677-43465, Tehran, Iran
Tel.: (98) 22655607
Web Site: https://www.behshahrinvest.ir
Year Founded: 1996
Financial Services
N.A.I.C.S.: 525990
Amir Shafii (Chm)

BEIBU GULF PORT CO., LTD.
Floor 9-10 South Building Beibu Gulf Shipping Center, Liangqing District No 12 Tiqiang Road, Nanning, 530201, Guangxi, China
Tel.: (86) 7712519801
Web Site: https://www.bbwport.cn
Year Founded: 1988
000582—(SSE)
Rev.: $895,451,544
Assets: $4,137,072,732
Liabilities: $2,026,956,204
Net Worth: $2,110,116,528
Earnings: $145,892,448
Emp.: 3,119
Fiscal Year-end: 12/31/22
Cargo Transportation Services
N.A.I.C.S.: 483111
Zhou Shaobo (Chm)

BEIGENE, LTD.
94 Solaris Avenue, Grand Cayman, Camana Bay, KY1-1108, Cayman Islands
Tel.: (345) 9494123　　Ky
Web Site: https://www.beigene.com
Year Founded: 2010
BGNE—(NASDAQ)
Rev.: $2,458,779,000
Assets: $5,805,275,000

Liabilities: $2,267,948,000
Net Worth: $3,537,327,000
Earnings: ($881,708,000)
Emp.: 10,600
Fiscal Year-end: 12/31/23
Biotechnology Research & Development Services
N.A.I.C.S.: 541714
John V. Oyler (Co-Founder & CEO)

Subsidiaries:

BeiGene (Beijing) Co., Limited (1)
No 30 Science Park Road, Zhongguancun Life Science Park Changping District, Beijing, 102206, China
Tel.: (86) 1085148500
Web Site: https://www.beigene.com.cn
N.A.I.C.S.: 325412
John V. Oyler (Co-Founder)

BeiGene (Shanghai) Co., Limited (1)
1228 Middle Yanan Road Jingan Kerry Centre 21F Tower 3, Shanghai, 200020, China
Tel.: (86) 1085148500
N.A.I.C.S.: 325412

BeiGene (Suzhou) Co., Limited (1)
218 Sangtian Street 4F Building 6, Biological Industries Park 218 Industrial Park, Suzhou, 215025, China
Tel.: (86) 1085148500
N.A.I.C.S.: 325412

BeiGene AUS PTY LTD. (1)
Level 4 275 George Street, Sydney, 2000, NSW, Australia
Tel.: (61) 290636400
Web Site: https://www.beigene.com.au
N.A.I.C.S.: 325412

BeiGene Switzerland GmbH (1)
Aeschengraben 27 21st Floor, 4051, Basel, Switzerland
Tel.: (41) 616851900
N.A.I.C.S.: 325412

BEIH-PROPERTY CO., LTD.
Unit 2 Building 4 No 2 Auto Museum East Road, Fengtai District, Beijing, 100070, China
Tel.: (86) 1062690958
Web Site: http://www.beih-zy.com
Year Founded: 1993
600791—(SHG)
Rev.: $867,516,198
Assets: $2,829,754,053
Liabilities: $2,024,501,605
Net Worth: $805,252,449
Earnings: $2,382,658
Fiscal Year-end: 12/31/22
Real Estate Property Development Services
N.A.I.C.S.: 531110
Zan Rongshi (Chm & Sec-Party Committee)

BEIHAI GOFAR CHUANSHAN BIOLOGICAL CO., LTD.
No 3 Beibu Gulf Middle Road, Beihai, 536000, Guangxi, China
Tel.: (86) 7793200619
Web Site: http://www.gofar.com.cn
Year Founded: 1993
600538—(SHG)
Rev.: $64,539,634
Assets: $160,357,144
Liabilities: $25,576,022
Net Worth: $134,781,122
Earnings: $4,894,512
Fiscal Year-end: 12/31/22
Agriculture Chemical Product Mfr & Distr
N.A.I.C.S.: 325320
Pan Libin (Chm & Pres)

BEIJER ALMA AB
Dragarbrunnsgatan 45, Box 1747, Forumgallerian, 751 47, Uppsala, Sweden
Tel.: (46) 18157160

Web Site: https://beijeralma.se
Year Founded: 1983
BEIA—(OMX)
Rev.: $549,401,969
Assets: $763,859,620
Liabilities: $423,014,602
Net Worth: $340,845,018
Earnings: $91,123,662
Emp.: 3,307
Fiscal Year-end: 12/31/22
Industrial Product & Component Producer
N.A.I.C.S.: 333248
Jan Blomen (CFO)

Subsidiaries:

A/S Preben Z Jensen (1)
Guldalderen 11, 2640, Hedehusene, Denmark
Tel.: (45) 46563666
Web Site: https://prebenz.dk
Grinding & Polishing Machines Distr
N.A.I.C.S.: 423830

AB Tebeco (1)
Box 40, 301 02, Halmstad, Sweden
Tel.: (46) 35 15 32 00
Core Adhesive Mfr
N.A.I.C.S.: 325520

Alma Uppsala AB (1)
Dragarbrunnsgatan 45, PO Box 1747, 75147, Uppsala, Sweden
Tel.: (46) 18157160
Web Site: http://www.beijer.se
Industrial Spring Mfr
N.A.I.C.S.: 332613

Beijer AS (1)
Lerpeveien 25, 3036, Drammen, Norway
Tel.: (47) 32 20 24 00
Aluminum Treatment Services
N.A.I.C.S.: 331314

Beijer Industri AB (1)
Jagershillgatan 16, 213 75, Malmo, Sweden
Tel.: (46) 40358300
Web Site: https://www.beijerind.com
Sales Range: $25-49.9 Million
Emp.: 35
Industrial Machinery Distr
N.A.I.C.S.: 423830
Henrik Kristensen (Mgr-IT)

Beijer OY (1)
Elannontie 5, 01510, Vantaa, Finland
Tel.: (358) 961520550
Web Site: https://beijeroy.com
Sales Range: $50-74.9 Million
Emp.: 1
Industrial Supplies Distr
N.A.I.C.S.: 423840

Beijer Tech AB (1)
Studiovagen 3, 135 48, Tyreso, Sweden
Tel.: (46) 40358380
Web Site: http://www.beijertech.com
Industrial Rubber Product Mfr
N.A.I.C.S.: 326299

Encitech Connectors AB (1)
Rorkullsvagen 4, 302 41, Halmstad, Sweden
Tel.: (46) 35151390
Web Site: https://encitech.com
Electronic Components Mfr & Distr
N.A.I.C.S.: 334419

Ernst W. Velleuer GmbH & Co. KG (1)
Heidestrasse 115, 42549, Velbert, Germany
Tel.: (49) 20512900
Web Site: https://velleuer.de
Spring Equipment Mfr & Distr
N.A.I.C.S.: 332613

Habia Cable AB (1)
Kanalvagen 16, Box 5076, 194 05, Upplands Vasby, Sweden
Tel.: (46) 8 630 7440
Web Site: https://www.habia.com
Sales Range: $50-74.9 Million
Emp.: 100
Other Holding Companies Offices of Holding Companies
N.A.I.C.S.: 551112

Subsidiary (Non-US):

Habia Benelux BV (2)

Voorerf 33, Breda, 4824 GM, Netherlands (100%)
Tel.: (31) 765416400
Web Site: http://www.habia.com
Sales Range: $25-49.9 Million
Emp.: 5
Electrical Apparatus & Equipment Wiring Supplies & Construction Material Whslr
N.A.I.C.S.: 423610

Habia Cable AB (2)
Jukolansuora 3 C5, FI-043 40, Tuusula, Finland (100%)
Tel.:) (358) 201552530
Fiber Optic Cable Mfr
N.A.I.C.S.: 335921

Habia Cable Asia Ltd (2)
Flat 1109 11th Floor Fast Industrial Building, 658 Castle Peak Rd Lai Chi Kok, Kowloon, China (Hong Kong) (100%)
Tel.: (852) 25911375
Web Site: http://www.habia.com
Sales Range: $25-49.9 Million
Emp.: 4
Fiber Optic Cable Mfr
N.A.I.C.S.: 335921

Subsidiary (Domestic):

Habia Cable CS Technology AB (2)
Dalenum 27, SE-181 70, Lidingo, Sweden
Tel.: (46) 854481340
Web Site: http://www.habia.com
Sales Range: $25-49.9 Million
Emp.: 7
Fiber Optic Cable Mfr
N.A.I.C.S.: 335921

Subsidiary (Non-US):

Habia Cable China Ltd (2)
No 16 Changjiang Middle Road, New District, Changzhou, 213022, Jiangsu, China (100%)
Tel.: (86) 51985118010
Web Site: http://www.habia.com
Sales Range: $25-49.9 Million
Emp.: 70
Fiber Optic Cable Mfr
N.A.I.C.S.: 423610

Habia Cable India Ltd (2)
1/1 Sai Towers First Floor R V Road, Bengaluru, 560 004, India
Tel.: (91) 8041214707
Web Site: http://www.habia.com
Emp.: 1
Fiber Optic Cable Mfr
N.A.I.C.S.: 335921

Habia Cable Ltd (2)
Oak House Southwell Road West, Ransom Wood Business Park, Mansfield, NG21 0HJ, Notts, United Kingdom (100%)
Tel.: (44) 145 441 2522
Web Site: https://www.habia.com
Sales Range: $25-49.9 Million
Emp.: 10
Electrical Apparatus & Equipment Wiring Supplies & Construction Material Whslr
N.A.I.C.S.: 423610

Subsidiary (Domestic):

Habia Cable Nordic AB (2)
Element Vagen 8, 81504, Soderfors, Sweden (100%)
Tel.: (46) 86307480
Web Site: http://www.habia.com
Sales Range: $25-49.9 Million
Emp.: 15
Fiber Optic Cable Mfr
N.A.I.C.S.: 335921

Habia Cable Production AB (2)
Box 5076, 19405, Upplands Vasby, Sweden (100%)
Tel.: (46) 29322000
Web Site: http://www.habia.se
Sales Range: $25-49.9 Million
Emp.: 200
Fiber Optic Cable Mfr
N.A.I.C.S.: 335921

Subsidiary (Non-US):

Habia Cable SA (2)
23 Rue Antigna, 45000, Orleans, France (100%)
Tel.: (33) 23 822 1570

Web Site: https://www.habia.com
Sales Range: $25-49.9 Million
Emp.: 5
Structural Steel Erection Contractors
N.A.I.C.S.: 238120

Habia Cable SP.Z.O.O (2)
Lubieszyn 8C, Doluje, 72-002, Szczecin,
Poland
Tel.: (48) 532725985
Web Site: http://www.habia.com
Sales Range: $25-49.9 Million
Emp.: 60
Fiber Optic Cable Mfr
N.A.I.C.S.: 335921

**Habia Kabel Produktions GmbH &
Co.KG** (2)
Oststrasse 91, 22844, Norderstedt,
Germany (100%)
Tel.: (49) 405353500
Web Site: http://www.habia.com
Sales Range: $25-49.9 Million
Emp.: 50
Current-Carrying Wiring Device Mfr
N.A.I.C.S.: 335931

**John While Springs (Shanghai) Co.,
Ltd.** (1)
Building A-3 No 38 Dongsheng Road, East
Region of Zhangjiang High-Tech Park Pu-
dong New District, Shanghai, 201201,
China
Tel.: (86) 2150326638
Gas Spring Product Distr
N.A.I.C.S.: 423840

Lesjofors A/S (1)
Professor Birkelandsvei 24A, 1081, Oslo,
Norway
Tel.: (47) 22 90 57 00
Spring Mfr
N.A.I.C.S.: 332613

Lesjofors AB (1)
Lagergrens gata 2, 65 226, Karlstad,
Sweden (100%)
Tel.: (46) 5 419 9900
Web Site: https://www.lesjoforsab.com
Sales Range: $50-74.9 Million
Emp.: 10
Other Holding Companies Offices of Hold-
ing Companies
N.A.I.C.S.: 551112

Subsidiary (Non-US):

**European Springs & Pressings
Ltd.** (2)
Chaffinch Business Park Croydon Road,
Beckenham, BR3 4DW, Kent, United
Kingdom (100%)
Tel.: (44) 2086631800
Web Site: https://www.europeansprings.com
Sales Range: $25-49.9 Million
Heavy Gauge Spring Mfr
N.A.I.C.S.: 332613

Division (Domestic):

**European Springs & Pressings
Ltd** (3)
Chaffinch Business Park Croydon Road,
Beckenham, BR3 4DW, Kent, United
Kingdom (100%)
Tel.: (44) 208 663 1800
Web Site: https://www.europeansprings.com
Sales Range: $25-49.9 Million
Emp.: 3
Bolt Screw Rivet & Washer Mfr
N.A.I.C.S.: 332722

Subsidiary (Non-US):

Lesjofors A/S (2)
Ringager 9-11, Postboks 362, 2605,
Brondby, Denmark (100%)
Tel.: (45) 46956100
Web Site: https://www.lesjoforsab.com
Sales Range: $25-49.9 Million
Structural Steel Erection Contractors
N.A.I.C.S.: 238120

Subsidiary (Domestic):

Lesjofors Automotive AB (2)
Radjursvagen 8, 352 45, Vaxjo,
Sweden (100%)
Tel.: (46) 470707280

Sales Range: $25-49.9 Million
Emp.: 30
Spring (Heavy Gauge) Mfr
N.A.I.C.S.: 332613

Subsidiary (Non-US):

Lesjofors Automotive Ltd (2)
Lowfields Way Lowfields Business Park,
Elland, HX5 9DA, United Kingdom (100%)
Tel.: (44) 1422370770
Web Site: http://www.lesjofors.com
Sales Range: $25-49.9 Million
Emp.: 20
All Other Motor Vehicle Parts Mfr
N.A.I.C.S.: 336390

Subsidiary (Domestic):

Lesjofors Banddetaljer AB (2)
Expovagen 7, 331 42, Varnamo,
Sweden (100%)
Tel.: (46) 370694500
Sales Range: $10-24.9 Million
Engineeering Services
N.A.I.C.S.: 541330
Marcus Hartvigsson (Mng Dir)

Subsidiary (Non-US):

Lesjofors China Ltd (2)
No 22 TianShan Road, New district of
Changzhou, Changzhou, 213032,
China (100%)
Tel.: (86) 51985138912
Radio & Television Broadcasting & Wireless
Communication Equipment Mfr
N.A.I.C.S.: 334220

Subsidiary (Domestic):

Lesjofors Fjadrar AB (2)
Fjadervagen 4, 682 60, Lesjofors,
Sweden (100%)
Tel.: (46) 590608100
Sales Range: $25-49.9 Million
Emp.: 85
Other Fabricated Wire Product Mfr
N.A.I.C.S.: 332618
Bjorn Persson (Mng Dir)

Lesjofors Industrifjadrar AB (2)
Hudene, 524 92, Herrljunga,
Sweden (100%)
Tel.: (46) 51322000
Sales Range: $25-49.9 Million
Bolt Nut Screw Rivet & Washer Mfg
N.A.I.C.S.: 332722

Subsidiary (Non-US):

Lesjofors Springs GmbH (2)
Spannstiftstr 10, Hohenlimburg, 58119, Ha-
gen, Germany (100%)
Tel.: (49) 233450170
Web Site: https://www.lesjofors-
automotive.com
Sales Range: $25-49.9 Million
Emp.: 17
Spring (Heavy Gauge) Mfr
N.A.I.C.S.: 332613

Lesjofors Springs LV (2)
Dunu street 4, Liepaja, 3401,
Latvia (100%)
Tel.: (371) 25784100
Web Site: http://www.lesjofors.lv
Sales Range: $25-49.9 Million
Emp.: 25
Spring (Heavy Gauge) Mfr
N.A.I.C.S.: 332613

Lesjofors Springs Oy (2)
Hallimestarinkatu 7, 20780, Kaarina,
Finland (100%)
Tel.: (358) 207649340
Web Site: https://www.lesjofors.fi
Sales Range: $25-49.9 Million
Emp.: 7
Spring (Heavy Gauge) Mfr
N.A.I.C.S.: 332613

Subsidiary (Domestic):

Lesjofors Stockholms Fjader AB (2)
Jamtlandsgatan 62, 162 60, Vallingby,
Sweden (100%)
Tel.: (46) 84458870
Sales Range: $25-49.9 Million
Bolt Nut Screw Rivet & Washer Mfg
N.A.I.C.S.: 332722

Subsidiary (Non-US):

Oy Lesjofors AB (2)
Valsverksvagen 115, 10410, Aminnefors,
Finland (100%)
Tel.: (358) 192766200
Web Site: http://www.lesjofors.fi
Sales Range: $25-49.9 Million
Emp.: 20
Spring (Heavy Gauge) Mfr
N.A.I.C.S.: 332613

Subsidiary (US):

Plymouth Spring Company, Inc. (2)
281 Lk Ave, Bristol, CT 06010
Tel.: (860) 584-0594
Web Site: http://www.plymouthspring.com
Sales Range: $10-24.9 Million
Emp.: 55
Steel & Wire Spring Mfr
N.A.I.C.S.: 332613
Richard Rubenstein (Pres)

Lesjofors Gas Springs LV (1)
Kapsedes Iela 2b, Liepaja, 3414, Latvia
Tel.: (371) 63401840
Web Site: http://www.lesjoforsab.com
Sales Range: $25-49.9 Million
Emp.: 60
Industrial Spring Mfr
N.A.I.C.S.: 332613

Lesjofors Heavy Springs UK Ltd. (1)
Unit 3 Parkengue Kernick Industrial Estate,
Penryn, TR10 9EP, Cornwall, United King-
dom
Tel.: (44) 1726861444
Spring Equipment Mfr
N.A.I.C.S.: 332613

**Lesjofors Industrial Springs & Press-
ings GmbH** (1)
Spannstiftstr 10, 58119, Hagen-
Hohenlimburg, Germany
Tel.: (49) 2334501722
Spring Equipment Mfr
N.A.I.C.S.: 332613

**Lesjofors Springs & Pressings
AB** (1)
Jamtlandsgatan 62, 162 60, Vallingby, Swe-
den
Tel.: (46) 8870250
Web Site: https://www.lesjoforsab.com
Spring Mfr & Distr
N.A.I.C.S.: 332613

Lesjofors Springs Slovakia s.r.o. (1)
Tehelna 655/25, 907 01, Myjava, Slovakia
Tel.: (421) 346212975
Emp.: 60
Spring Equipment Mfr
N.A.I.C.S.: 332613

Lesjofors Stock Spring AB (1)
Jamtlandsgatan 62, 162 60, Vallingby, Swe-
den
Tel.: (46) 84458890
Spring Equipment Mfr
N.A.I.C.S.: 332613

Lundgrens Norge AS (1)
Karihaugveien 102, 1086, Oslo, Norway
Tel.: (47) 22906550
Web Site: https://www.lundgrensnorge.no
Injection Equipment Distr
N.A.I.C.S.: 423840

Lundgrens Sverige AB (1)
Datavagen 27, Box 9114, 400 93, Gothen-
burg, Sweden
Tel.: (46) 3 184 0390
Web Site: https://www.lundgrenssverige.se
Emp.: 120
Plastic Pipe Mfr & Distr
N.A.I.C.S.: 326122

Metrol Springs Ltd. (1)
5 Clayfield Close Moulton Park Industrial
Estate, Northampton, NN3 6QF, United
Kingdom
Tel.: (44) 1604499332
Web Site: https://www.metrol.com
Gas Spring Mfr & Distr
N.A.I.C.S.: 332613

Mountpac AB (1)
Storgatan 42, 335 73, Hillerstorp, Sweden
Tel.: (46) 370375070
Web Site: https://mountpac.se

Sheet Metal Products Mfr
N.A.I.C.S.: 332322

Noxon AB (1)
Fjaras Industrivag 19, Box 53, 439 03, Fja-
ras, Sweden
Tel.: (46) 30055440
Web Site: https://noxon.com
Centrifuges Mfr & Distr
N.A.I.C.S.: 333998

Preben Z. Jensen A/S (1)
Guldalderen 11, 2640, Hedehusene, Den-
mark
Tel.: (45) 46 56 36 66
Web Site: http://www.prebenz.dk
Deburring Grinding & Polishing Equipment
Distr
N.A.I.C.S.: 423840

Stece Fjadrar AB (1)
Lillgatan, PO Box 75, 383 25, Monsteras,
Sweden
Tel.: (46) 49916260
Web Site: https://www.stecefjadrar.com
Industrial Spring Mfr
N.A.I.C.S.: 332613

Stumpp+Schule GmbH (1)
Linsenhofer Str 61, 72660, Blaubeuren,
Germany
Tel.: (49) 702591220
Web Site: https://www.stumpp-schuele.de
Emp.: 150
Spring Equipment Mfr
N.A.I.C.S.: 332613

Swedish Microwave AB (1)
Dynamovagen 5, 591 61, Motala, Sweden
Tel.: (46) 141216135
Web Site: https://www.smw.se
Low Noise Block Down Converter Mfr &
Distr
N.A.I.C.S.: 334413

Tribelt B.V. (1)
Metaalstraat 9, 7483, Haaksbergen, Nether-
lands
Tel.: (31) 742501877
Web Site: https://metal-conveyor-belts.com
Metal Conveyor Belts Mfr
N.A.I.C.S.: 333922

BEIJER REF AB
Stortorget 8 211 34 Malmo, SE-211
34, Malmo, Sweden
Tel.: (46) 40358900 SE
Web Site: https://www.beijerref.com
BEIJ.B—(OMX)
Rev.: $2,069,565,839
Assets: $1,867,819,971
Liabilities: $1,225,007,243
Net Worth: $642,812,728
Earnings: $120,863,595
Emp.: 4,200
Fiscal Year-end: 12/31/21
Refrigeration Equipment & Industrial
Machinery Mfr
N.A.I.C.S.: 333415
Per Bertland (Pres & CEO)

Subsidiaries:

Airconditioning Direct Pty. Ltd. (1)
46 Flinders Parade, North Lakes, 4509,
QLD, Australia
Tel.: (61) 734919926
Refrigeration Equipment Mfr & Distr
N.A.I.C.S.: 333415

Armcor Air Solutions Pty. Ltd. (1)
109-111 Northcorp Blvd, Broadmeadows,
3047, VIC, Australia
Tel.: (61) 383019200
Web Site: https://armcor.com.au
Air Conditioning Equipment Mfr & Distr
N.A.I.C.S.: 333415

**Australian Airconditioning Distributors
Pty. Ltd.** (1)
57-63 McNaughton Road, Clayton, 3168,
VIC, Australia
Tel.: (61) 1300223223
Web Site: https://www.aad.net.au
Air Conditioning Equipment Mfr & Distr
N.A.I.C.S.: 333415

Beijer ECR Iberica S.L. (1)

Beijer Ref AB—(Continued)

Calle San Dalmacio 18, Pl Villaverde Alto,
28021, Madrid, Spain
Tel.: (34) 917230802
Web Site: https://www.beijer.es
Sales Range: $25-49.9 Million
Emp.: 120
Refrigeration Products Whslr
N.A.I.C.S.: 423740

Beijer Ref (Mauritius) Ltd. (1)
31 Ternay St, Port Louis, Mauritius
Tel.: (230) 2126695
Air Conditioning Accessories Whlsr
N.A.I.C.S.: 423730

Beijer Ref Academy Ltd. (1)
Unit 609 Street 3 Chapel Wood Thorp Arch
Trading Estate, Wetherby, LS23 7FS,
United Kingdom
Tel.: (44) 8000778436
Web Site:
   https://www.beijerrefacademy.co.uk
Job Training Services
N.A.I.C.S.: 611430

Beijer Ref Belgium B.V. (1)
Prins Boudewijnlaan 7D, 2550, Kontich,
Belgium
Tel.: (32) 34579132
Web Site: https://www.beijerref.com
Refrigeration Equipment Mfr & Distr
N.A.I.C.S.: 333415

Beijer Ref Czech s.r.o. (1)
Obchodni 107, 251 01, Cestlice, Czech
Republic
Tel.: (420) 379302111
Web Site: https://www.beijerref.cz
Emp.: 10
Refrigeration Products Whslr
N.A.I.C.S.: 423740
Martin Sejvl (Mng Dir)

Beijer Ref India Pvt. Ltd. (1)
Khasra No 304/2 100 Feet Road Ghitorni,
New Delhi, 110030, Delhi, India
Tel.: (91) 9266706670
Web Site: https://www.refshoppe.com
Refrigeration Equipment Distr
N.A.I.C.S.: 423740

Beijer Ref Latvia SIA (1)
K Ulmana Gatve 2, Riga, 1004, Latvia
Tel.: (371) 67395757
Web Site: https://www.beijerref.lv
Refrigeration Equipment Distr
N.A.I.C.S.: 423740

Beijer Ref Lithuania UAB (1)
Savanoriu pr 189, LT-02300, Vilnius, Lithu-
ania
Tel.: (370) 52311762
Web Site: https://www.refrigeration.lt
Refrigeration Equipment Mfr & Distr
N.A.I.C.S.: 333415

Beijer Ref Polska Sp.z.o.o. (1)
Al Krakowska 22 Sekocin Nowy, 05-090,
Raszyn, Masovian, Poland
Tel.: (48) 227155858
Web Site: https://www.beijer.pl
Air Conditioner & Refrigeration Products
Whslr
N.A.I.C.S.: 423740

Beijer Ref Support Norway AS (1)
PB 168, Holmlia, NO-1203, Oslo, Norway
Tel.: (47) 23169400
Refrigeration Equipment Mfr & Distr
N.A.I.C.S.: 333415

Charles Hasler AG (1)
Althardstrasse 238, 8105, Regensdorf,
Switzerland
Tel.: (41) 448439393
Web Site: https://shop.charles-hasler.ch
Sales Range: $10-24.9 Million
Air Conditioning System Mfr
N.A.I.C.S.: 333415

Clima Sverige AB (1)
Box 8213, 163 08, Spanga, Sweden
Tel.: (46) 858007400
Web Site: https://www.clima.se
Air Conditioning & Heat Pump Distr
N.A.I.C.S.: 423730

Cofriset S.A.S. (1)
1063 rue Nicephore Niepce, CS 90073,

ZAC de la Fouillouse Saint Priest, 69800,
Lyon, France
Tel.: (33) 472236160
Web Site: https://www.cofriset.fr
Refrigeration Equipment Distr
N.A.I.C.S.: 423740

Complete Air Supply Pty. Ltd. (1)
2-4 Alex Fisher Drive, PO Box 2656, Bur-
leigh, 4220, QLD, Australia
Tel.: (61) 755220033
Web Site:
   https://www.completeairsupply.com.au
Refrigeration Equipment Distr
N.A.I.C.S.: 423740

Coolair Klimasysteme GmbH (1)
Lise-Meitner-Str 14, 48529, Nordhorn, Ger-
many
Tel.: (49) 592171040
Web Site: https://coolair.de
Refrigeration Equipment Distr
N.A.I.C.S.: 423740

Coolmark bv (1)
Zweth 24, 2991 LH, Barendrecht, Nether-
lands
Tel.: (31) 180751300
Web Site: https://www.coolmark.nl
Sales Range: $50-74.9 Million
Emp.: 70
Refrigeration & Air Conditioning Compo-
nents Distr
N.A.I.C.S.: 423730

DEM Production AB (1)
Olvagen 17, 342 50, Vislanda, Smaland,
Sweden
Tel.: (46) 47235010
Web Site: http://www.dem.se
Sales Range: $25-49.9 Million
Emp.: 19
Refrigeration Components Mfr
N.A.I.C.S.: 333415

Dean & Wood Ltd. (1)
15 Bruntcliffe Avenue Leeds 27 Industrial
Estate, Morley, Leeds, LS27 0LL, United
Kingdom
Tel.: (44) 1132052917
Web Site: https://www.dean-wood.co.uk
Refrigeration & Air Conditioning Equipment
Sales
N.A.I.C.S.: 423740

Delmo SA (1)
70 Rue Ambroise Croizat, Saint Denis,
93200, Seine-Saint-Denis, France
Tel.: (33) 155844400
Web Site: http://www.delmo.fr
Sales Range: $25-49.9 Million
Emp.: 50
Refrigeration Products Whslr
N.A.I.C.S.: 423740

ECR Belgium BVBA (1)
Ingberthoeveweg 3B, 2630, Aartselaar, Ant-
werp, Belgium
Tel.: (32) 34579132
Web Site: http://www.ecr-belgium.be
Sales Range: $25-49.9 Million
Emp.: 30
Refrigeration Products Whslr
N.A.I.C.S.: 423740
Udo van der Meer (Mng Dir)

ECR Italy SpA (1)
Via Socrate 32/34, 20128, Milan, Italy
Tel.: (39) 022520081
Web Site: http://www.ecritaly.it
Sales Range: $50-74.9 Million
Emp.: 75
Refrigeration Products Whslr
N.A.I.C.S.: 423740

ECR Nederland B.V. (1)
Westfields 1210, PO Box 16, 5688 HA,
Oirschot, Netherlands
Tel.: (31) 882990600
Web Site: https://www.ecr-nederland.nl
Sales Range: $50-74.9 Million
Emp.: 60
Refrigeration Products Whslr
N.A.I.C.S.: 423740
Udo van der Meer (Mng Dir)

EID S.A.S. (1)
481 rue du petit mas Zl Courtine, 84000,
Avignon, France
Tel.: (33) 490012285
Web Site: https://www.eid-distribution.com

Emp.: 20
Air Conditioning Accessories Mfr
N.A.I.C.S.: 333415

**Easyairconditioning Group
Limited** (1)
262-264 Baldwins Lane Hall Green, Bir-
mingham, B28 0XB, United Kingdom
Tel.: (44) 1217463500
Web Site:
   https://www.easyairconditioninggroup.com
Refrigeration Equipment Distr
N.A.I.C.S.: 423740

Equinoxe Kft Cg (1)
Gubacsi ut 32, 1097, Budapest, Hungary
Tel.: (36) 1 273 3200
Web Site: https://www.equinoxe.hu
Sales Range: $25-49.9 Million
Emp.: 28
Refrigeration & Air Conditioning Compo-
nents Distr
N.A.I.C.S.: 423730

G & L Beijer A/S (1)
Tempovej 18-22, 2750, Ballerup, Denmark
Tel.: (45) 7026 5666
Holding Company; Refrigeration Products
Whslr
N.A.I.C.S.: 551112
Claus Bo Jacobsen (Mng Dir)

Subsidiary (Domestic):

Aircon Teknik A/S (2)
Johann Gutenbergsvej 11-13, 8200, Arhus,
Denmark
Tel.: (45) 86345111
Web Site: http://www.aircon.dk
Sales Range: $50-74.9 Million
Emp.: 7
Refrigeration & Ventilation Products Whslr
N.A.I.C.S.: 423740
Claus Bo Jacobsen (Mng Dir)

Armadan A/S (2)
Tempovej 18-22, 2750, Ballerup, Hovedsta-
den, Denmark
Tel.: (45) 70260636
Web Site: https://www.armadan.dk
Sales Range: $50-74.9 Million
Emp.: 10
Heat Insulation Materials Whslr
N.A.I.C.S.: 423330
Claus Bo Jacobsen (Mng Dir)

BKF-Klima A/S (2)
Tempovej 18 22, 2750, Ballerup, Denmark
Tel.: (45) 70265666
Web Site: https://www.daikin.dk
Sales Range: $50-74.9 Million
Emp.: 8
Refrigeration Products Whslr
N.A.I.C.S.: 423740
Claus Bo Jacobsen (Mng Dir)

H. Jessen Jurgensen A/S (2)
Tempovej 18-22, 2750, Ballerup, Hovedsta-
den, Denmark
Tel.: (45) 7 027 0607
Web Site: https://www.hjj.dk
Sales Range: $50-74.9 Million
Emp.: 60
Refrigeration Products Whslr
N.A.I.C.S.: 423740
Claus Bo Jacobsen (Mng Dir)

G & L Beijer Forvaltning AB (1)
Norra Vallgatan 70, 211 22, Malmo, Scania,
Sweden
Tel.: (46) 40358900
Web Site: http://www.beijers.com
Sales Range: $50-74.9 Million
Emp.: 8
Refrigeration Products Whslr
N.A.I.C.S.: 423740

GFF SA (1)
12 rue des Freres Lumiere, BP 166, 69720,
Saint-Bonnet-de-Mure, France
Tel.: (33) 472483000
Web Site: https://www.lagff.com
Sales Range: $75-99.9 Million
Emp.: 250
Refrigeration Products Whslr
N.A.I.C.S.: 423740

H. Jessen Jurgensen AB (1)
Arods Industrivag 70, 422 43, Hisings
Backa, Sweden
Tel.: (46) 3 151 4546

Web Site: https://hjj.se
Sales Range: $25-49.9 Million
Emp.: 5
Refrigerant Repackaging Services
N.A.I.C.S.: 811310

HRP Limited (1)
15 Bruntcliffe Avenue Leeds 27 Industrial
Estate, Morley, Leeds, LS27 0LL, United
Kingdom
Tel.: (44) 1132052930
Web Site: https://www.hrponline.co.uk
Refrigerator & Air Conditioner Distr
N.A.I.C.S.: 423730

HVAC Consolidated Pty. Ltd. (1)
1535 Centre Rd, Clayton, 3168, VIC, Aus-
tralia
Tel.: (61) 1300223223
Web Site:
   https://www.hvacconsolidated.com.au
Havc Installation Services
N.A.I.C.S.: 561730

Heritage Distribution Holdings (1)
10 Glenlake Pkwy NE, S Tower, Ste 445,
Atlanta, GA 30328   (98%)
Tel.: (205) 251-8500
Holding Company
N.A.I.C.S.: 551112
Alex Averitt (CEO)

Subsidiary (Domestic):

Coastal Supply Company Inc. (2)
1031 Lee St, Knoxville, TN 37917
Tel.: (865) 637-9262
Sales Range: $10-24.9 Million
Emp.: 50
Air Conditioning Equipment
N.A.I.C.S.: 423730
Ronald E. Kennedy (Pres)

Inventor A.G.S.A. (1)
2 Thoukididou str, Ag Stefanos, 14565, Ath-
ens, Greece
Tel.: (30) 2113003326
Web Site:
   https://www.inventorairconditioner.com
Air Conditioning Equipment Mfr & Distr
N.A.I.C.S.: 333415

Inventor Concept S.R.L. (1)
Splaiul Independentei nr 17 bl 101 izvor sc
4 et 5 ap 68 sector 5, 050093, Bucharest,
Romania
Tel.: (40) 3142522002
Web Site:
   https://www.inventoraerconditionat.ro
Air Conditioning Equipment Mfr & Distr
N.A.I.C.S.: 333415

Kulmakomponentide OU (1)
Kadaka Tee 1, Tallinn, 10621, Harju, Esto-
nia
Tel.: (372) 6518060
Web Site: http://www.kylm.ee
Sales Range: $50-74.9 Million
Emp.: 8
Refrigeration Products Whslr
N.A.I.C.S.: 423740

Kylma AB (1)
Fagerstagatan 29, PO Box 8213, 163 53,
Spanga, Stockholm, Sweden
Tel.: (46) 85 989 0800
Web Site: https://www.kylma.se
Sales Range: $50-74.9 Million
Emp.: 80
Refrigeration Products Whslr
N.A.I.C.S.: 423740
Bjoern Gryding (Head-Pur, IT & Product)

**Metraclark South Africa Propriety
Ltd.** (1)
2 Afteron Road, PO Box 57115, Denver,
Johannesburg, 2137, Gauteng, South Africa
Tel.: (27) 11 620 0500
Web Site: https://www.metraclark.co.za
Refrigeration Products Whslr
N.A.I.C.S.: 423740

Metraclark Tanzania (Pty.) Ltd. (1)
Rex Building Plot No 49 - 55 At
Makamba/Sikukuu Street, Gerezani Area
Ilala, Dar es Salaam, Tanzania
Tel.: (255) 713046665
Web Site: https://www.metraclark.co.za
Refrigeration Equipment Distr
N.A.I.C.S.: 423740

OY Combi Cool AB (1)
Pakkalantie 19, 01510, Vantaa, Uusimaa, Finland
Tel.: (358) 97771230
Web Site: https://www.combicool.fi
Sales Range: $25-49.9 Million
Emp.: 27
Refrigeration Products Whslr
N.A.I.C.S.: 423740

RK Slovakia s.r.o. (1)
Vlcany 1588, 925 84, Vlcany, Slovakia
Tel.: (421) 317794187
Web Site: http://www.rkslovakia.sk
Sales Range: $50-74.9 Million
Emp.: 8
Refrigeration & Air Conditioning Equipments Whslr
N.A.I.C.S.: 423740

Realcold New Zealand Ltd. (1)
7 Lockhart Place, Mt Wellington, Auckland, 1060, New Zealand
Tel.: (64) 95265700
Web Site: http://www.realcold.co.nz
Air Conditioner Mfr
N.A.I.C.S.: 333415

SCM Ref AB (1)
Olvagen 17, 342 50, Vislanda, Sweden
Tel.: (46) 47235010
Web Site: https://www.scmref.se
Emp.: 20
Refrigeration Equipment Mfr & Distr
N.A.I.C.S.: 333415

Schlosser Moller Kulde AS (1)
Ole Deviks Vei 18, PO Box 65, Bryn, 0611, Oslo, Norway
Tel.: (47) 2 337 9300
Web Site: https://www.smk.as
Sales Range: $25-49.9 Million
Emp.: 29
Refrigeration Products Whslr
N.A.I.C.S.: 423740
Tanja Saetaberget *(Accountant)*

Sinclair Global Group s.r.o. (1)
Purkynova 45, 612 00, Brno, Czech Republic
Tel.: (420) 800100285
Web Site: https://www.sinclair-solutions.com
Air Conditioning Equipment Mfr & Distr
N.A.I.C.S.: 333415

Sinclair Slovakia s.r.o. (1)
Technicka 2, 821 04, Bratislava, Slovakia
Tel.: (421) 232605050
Refrigeration Equipment Distr
N.A.I.C.S.: 423740

TT Coil Ltd. (1)
Unit A Imperial Park Randalls Way, Leatherhead, KT22 7 TA, Surrey, United Kingdom
Tel.: (44) 1372 378 788
Refrigeration Coils Whslr
N.A.I.C.S.: 423740

TT-Coil A/S (1)
Svanningevej 2, 9220, Aalborg, Denmark
Tel.: (45) 98159500
Web Site: https://tt-coil.com
Sales Range: $25-49.9 Million
Emp.: 5
Air Conditioners & Heat Exchangers Distr
N.A.I.C.S.: 333415

TT-Coil Norge AS (1)
Stabburveien 10, 1859, Eidsberg, Slitu, Norway
Tel.: (47) 6 984 5100
Web Site: https://www.ttc.no
Sales Range: $25-49.9 Million
Emp.: 45
Refrigeration Components Mfr
N.A.I.C.S.: 333415
Tore Grefslie *(Mng Dir)*

TTC Norge AS (1)
Stabburveien 10, 1859, Slitu, Norway
Tel.: (47) 69845100
Web Site: https://www.ttc.no
Heat Exchanger Mfr
N.A.I.C.S.: 332410

UAB Beijer Ref (1)
Savanoriu Pr 189, Vilnius, 02300, Lithuania
Tel.: (370) 5 231 1762
Web Site: https://www.refrigeration.lt
Sales Range: $50-74.9 Million
Emp.: 8
Refrigeration Products Whslr

Uniechemie B.V. (1)
Aruba 21, Postbus 426, 7332 BJ, Apeldoorn, Netherlands
Tel.: (31) 555334529
Web Site: http://www.uniechemie.nl
Sales Range: $25-49.9 Million
Emp.: 46
Refrigeration Products Whslr
N.A.I.C.S.: 423740
Richard Droop *(Mng Dir)*

Werner Kuster AG (1)
Parkstrasse 6, 4402, Frenkendorf, Switzerland
Tel.: (41) 619061414
Web Site: https://www.wernerkuster.ch
Sales Range: $25-49.9 Million
Emp.: 40
Refrigeration Equipment Whslr
N.A.I.C.S.: 423740

BEIJING ABT NETWORKS CO., LTD.
Room 301 Block A Building 15 East District No 10 Xibeiwang East Road, Haidian District, Beijing, 100095, China
Tel.: (86) 1057649050
Web Site: http://www.abtnetworks.com
Year Founded: 2007
688168—(SHG)
Rev.: $64,084,415
Assets: $201,950,897
Liabilities: $32,549,437
Net Worth: $169,401,459
Earnings: ($1,188,065)
Fiscal Year-end: 12/31/22
Software Development Services
N.A.I.C.S.: 541511
Xia Zhenfu *(CFO)*

BEIJING AEROSPACE CHANGFENG CO., LTD.
Aerospace Changfeng Building No 51 Yongding Road, Haidian District, Beijing, 100854, China
Tel.: (86) 1068385399
Web Site: https://www.ascf.com.cn
Year Founded: 1986
600855—(SHG)
Rev.: $253,002,653
Assets: $564,617,350
Liabilities: $299,057,897
Net Worth: $265,559,454
Earnings: $769,083
Fiscal Year-end: 12/31/22
Security System Mfr
N.A.I.C.S.: 334419
Su Zihua *(Pres)*

Subsidiaries:

Beijing Changfeng Kewei Photoelectric Co., Ltd. (1)
Building 4 No 1 insititution No 3 Minzhuang Road, Haidian District, Beijing, China
Tel.: (86) 10 88845916
Security System Mfr
N.A.I.C.S.: 334419

BEIJING AEROSPACE SHEN-ZHOU INTELLIGENT EQUIP-MENT TECHNOLOGY CO., LTD.
No 16 Zhongguancun South Third Street, Haidian District, Beijing, 100190, China
Tel.: (86) 1068378620
Web Site: https://www.asiet.net
Year Founded: 2007
300455—(CHIN)
Rev.: $189,264,816
Assets: $495,575,496
Liabilities: $255,796,164
Net Worth: $239,779,332
Earnings: $12,116,520
Emp.: 200

Fiscal Year-end: 12/31/22
Railway & Locomotive Vehicle Safety Inspection & Maintenance Equipment Mfr
N.A.I.C.S.: 334515
Li Yong *(Chm)*

BEIJING AIRDOC TECHNOL-OGY CO., LTD.
Room 21 4/F Deputy Building Building 2 No 2 A North Xisanhuan Road, Haidian, Beijing, 100089, China
Tel.: (86) 4001003999   CN
Web Site: https://www.airdoc.com
Year Founded: 2015
2251—(HKG)
Rev.: $17,413,389
Assets: $266,578,506
Liabilities: $10,509,134
Net Worth: $256,069,372
Earnings: ($27,997,595)
Emp.: 275
Fiscal Year-end: 12/31/22
Information Technology Services
N.A.I.C.S.: 541512
Dalei Zhang *(Founder, Chm, Gen Mgr & Exec Dir)*

BEIJING AIRPORT HIGH-TECH PARK CO., LTD.
No 6 Yumin Street Zone B Beijing Airport Economic Development Zone, Shunyi District, Beijing, 101318, China
Tel.: (86) 1080489277
Web Site: https://www.600463.com.cn
Year Founded: 2000
600463—(SHG)
Rev.: $91,664,773
Assets: $359,563,530
Liabilities: $192,726,448
Net Worth: $166,837,081
Earnings: ($4,480,164)
Fiscal Year-end: 12/31/22
Real Estate Manangement Services
N.A.I.C.S.: 531390
Xia Zijing *(Chm)*

BEIJING ANDAWELL SCIENCE & TECHNOLOGY CO., LTD.
No 19 Duyang North Street Renhe District Shunyi, Beijing, 101300, China
Tel.: (86) 61089401998   CN
Web Site: https://www.andawell.com
Year Founded: 2001
300719—(CHIN)
Rev.: $119,843,758
Assets: $223,894,428
Liabilities: $70,311,503
Net Worth: $153,582,925
Earnings: $15,983,602
Fiscal Year-end: 12/31/23
Aircraft Parts Equipment Mfr & Distr
N.A.I.C.S.: 336413
Zian Zhao *(Chm & Pres)*

BEIJING AOSAIKANG PHAR-MACEUTICAL CO., LTD.
No 699 Kejian Road Jiangning Science Park, Fengtai District, Nanjing, 211112, Jiangsu, China
Tel.: (86) 2552292222
Web Site: http://www.bnec.cn
Year Founded: 1996
002755—(SSE)
Rev.: $262,908,828
Assets: $479,377,548
Liabilities: $56,304,612
Net Worth: $423,072,936
Earnings: ($31,706,532)
Emp.: 420
Fiscal Year-end: 12/31/22
Survey & Geotechnical Engineering Construction Services

N.A.I.C.S.: 237990
Qingcai Chen *(Chm & Gen Mgr)*

BEIJING ARITIME INTELLI-GENT CONTROL CO., LTD.
No 6 Fufeng Road Science City, Fengtai District, Beijing, 100070, China
Tel.: (86) 1083671666
Web Site: http://www.aritime.com
Year Founded: 1999
600560—(SHG)
Rev.: $103,222,698
Assets: $275,762,757
Liabilities: $148,936,811
Net Worth: $126,825,945
Earnings: $6,180,576
Fiscal Year-end: 12/31/22
Industrial Automation Products Mfr
N.A.I.C.S.: 334513
Hao Xiaodong *(Chm)*

BEIJING ASIACOM INFORMA-TION TECHNOLOGY CO., LTD.
Room 805 No 18 Danling Street, Haidian District, Beijing, 100080, China
Tel.: (86) 1058834063
Web Site: https://www.asiacom.net.cn
Year Founded: 2007
301085—(CHIN)
Rev.: $215,834,901
Assets: $297,063,140
Liabilities: $141,411,000
Net Worth: $155,652,140
Earnings: $10,966,394
Fiscal Year-end: 12/31/23
Information Technology Services
N.A.I.C.S.: 541512
Jiang Xu *(Chm)*

BEIJING AUTELAN TECHNOL-OGY CO. LTD.
1/F 3rd Area 9# Building Zhongguancun Software Park 8 DongbeRoad, Haidian District, Beijing, 100193, China
Tel.: (86) 10 5691 7000
Web Site: http://www.autelan.com
Emp.: 600
Wireless Broadband Solutions
N.A.I.C.S.: 334220
Lin Chen *(Pres)*

Subsidiaries:

AUTELAN Technology International Limited (1)
Unit 2203 22th Floor Mega Trade Centre 1-6 Mei Wan Street, Tsuen Wan, New Territories, China (Hong Kong)
Tel.: (852) 31628360
Communication Equipment Mfr
N.A.I.C.S.: 334220

BEIJING AUTOMOTIVE INDUS-TRY HOLDING CO., LTD.
25 E. Third Ring Rd S, Beijing, 100021, China
Web Site: http://www.baihc.com
Sales Range: $25-49.9 Billion
Emp.: 83,000
Automobile Mfr
N.A.I.C.S.: 336110
Heyi Xu *(Chm)*

Subsidiaries:

BAIC Motor Corporation Ltd. (1)
99 Shuanghe Avenue, Shunyi District, Beijing, 101300, China **(42.63%)**
Tel.: (86) 1056635500
Web Site: https://www.baicmotor.com
Rev.: $26,740,947,074
Assets: $24,341,912,057
Liabilities: $13,259,142,515
Net Worth: $11,082,769,542
Earnings: $2,293,476,401
Emp.: 19,491

Beijing Automotive Industry Holding Co.,
Ltd.—(Continued)

Fiscal Year-end: 12/31/2022
Passenger Automobile Mfr
N.A.I.C.S.: 336110
Heyi Xu *(Chm)*

BEIJING BAINATION PICTURES CO., LTD.
Room 5365 Building 3 No 3 Xijing
Road Badachu High-tech Park, Shijingshan District, Beijing, 100107,
China
Tel.: (86) 1067788998
Web Site:
https://www.bainaqiancheng.com
Year Founded: 2002
300291—(CHIN)
Rev.: $65,819,520
Assets: $591,649,812
Liabilities: $41,559,804
Net Worth: $550,090,008
Earnings: $2,920,320
Emp.: 40
Fiscal Year-end: 12/31/22
Television & Film Production & Distribution
N.A.I.C.S.: 512110
Li Qian *(Sec)*

BEIJING BALANCE MEDICAL TECHNOLOGY CO., LTD,
Tel.: (86) 1060735920
Web Site:
https://www.balancemed.cn
Year Founded: 2005
688198—(SHG)
Rev.: $41,441,405
Assets: $165,624,292
Liabilities: $11,256,359
Net Worth: $154,367,933
Earnings: $13,357,445
Fiscal Year-end: 12/31/22
Medical Product Mfr & Distr
N.A.I.C.S.: 339112
Lei Jin *(Chm, Sec & Gen Mgr)*

BEIJING BAOLANDE SOFTWARE CORP.
28th Floor Maotai Building Building 3
No 29 North Third Ring Road,
Xicheng District, Beijing, 100088,
China
Tel.: (86) 1057592666
Web Site: http://www.bessystem.com
Year Founded: 2008
688058—(SHG)
Rev.: $34,772,854
Assets: $126,083,328
Liabilities: $7,569,203
Net Worth: $118,514,125
Earnings: ($4,865,702)
Fiscal Year-end: 12/31/22
Software Development Services
N.A.I.C.S.: 541511
Na Zhonghong *(CFO)*

BEIJING BASHI MEDIA CO., LTD.
No 32 Zizhuyuan Road, Haidian District, Beijing, 100048, China
Tel.: (86) 1068429295
Web Site: https://www.bbcm.com.cn
Year Founded: 1999
600386—(SHG)
Rev.: $498,774,566
Assets: $660,099,600
Liabilities: $379,545,637
Net Worth: $280,553,963
Earnings: $12,150,019
Fiscal Year-end: 12/31/22
Automobile & Transportation Advertising Services
N.A.I.C.S.: 441110
Yan Guangxing *(Chm)*

BEIJING BAYI SPACE LCD TECHNOLOGY CO., LTD.
No 20 dongliushui Road, Yanshan
Fangshan District, Beijing, 102502,
China
Tel.: (86) 1069765588
Web Site: https://www.bayi.com.cn
Year Founded: 2004
688181—(SHG)
Rev.: $131,170,834
Assets: $340,730,414
Liabilities: $61,112,933
Net Worth: $279,617,481
Earnings: $28,627,686
Fiscal Year-end: 12/31/22
Electronic Materials Mfr
N.A.I.C.S.: 334414
Lei Zhao *(Chm & Gen Mgr)*

BEIJING BDSTAR NAVIGATION CO., LTD.
No 7 Fengxian East Road Yongfeng
Industrial Base, Haidian district, Beijing, 100094, China
Tel.: (86) 1069939966
Web Site: https://www.bdstar.com
Year Founded: 2000
002151—(SSE)
Rev.: $535,777,632
Assets: $1,068,240,420
Liabilities: $392,370,264
Net Worth: $675,870,156
Earnings: $20,388,888
Emp.: 4,000
Fiscal Year-end: 12/31/22
Satellite Navigation Positioning Product Mfr
N.A.I.C.S.: 334511
Zhou Ruxin *(Chm & Gen Mgr)*

Subsidiaries:

BDStar Information Service Co., **(1)**
Ltd.
F4 No 7 Fengxian East Road Yongfeng Industrial Base, Haidian District, Beijing,
100094, China
Tel.: (86) 1069939700
Satellite Navigation & Positioning Product
Mfr
N.A.I.C.S.: 334511

ICOE (Shanghai) Technologies Co., **(1)**
Ltd.
8th Floor Bldg 1 Lane 500 Shengxia Road,
Pudong New District, Shanghai, China
Tel.: (86) 2158213950
Web Site: https://www.icoe-tech.com
Wireless Communication Equipment Mfr
N.A.I.C.S.: 334220

Jiaxing Glead Electronics Co., **(1)**
Ltd.
No 66 Zhengyuan Road in Tanghui Industrial Garden, Jiaxing Economic Development Zone, Jiaxing, 314003, Zhejiang,
China
Tel.: (86) 573 83651818
Web Site: http://www.glead.com.cn
Navigation Component Mfr & Distr
N.A.I.C.S.: 334419
Elina Zhang *(Mgr-Customer Svc)*

TruePoint Technology Co., Ltd. **(1)**
First Floor North Building No 7 Fengxian
East Road, Haidian District, Beijing, China
Tel.: (86) 1069939988
Web Site: https://www.true-point.com
Satellite Navigation & Positioning Product
Mfr
N.A.I.C.S.: 334511

BEIJING BEETCH INC.
6-7th Floor Building 2 Huizhong
Building No 1 Shangdi 7th Street,
Haidian District, Beijing, 100085,
China
Tel.: (86) 1082783640
Web Site: https://www.beetech.cn
Year Founded: 2005
300667—(CHIN)
Rev.: $125,886,392

Assets: $226,409,516
Liabilities: $45,511,959
Net Worth: $180,897,557
Earnings: $5,111,179
Fiscal Year-end: 12/31/23
Electrical Component Mfr & Distr
N.A.I.C.S.: 335999
Dai Xiaoning *(Chm & Gen Mgr)*

BEIJING BEIDA JADE BIRD UNIVERSAL SCI-TECH LIMITED
3rd Floor Beida Jade Bird Building
207 Chengfu Road, Haidian District,
Beijing, 100871, China
Tel.: (86) 1082615888   CN
Web Site: https://www.jbu.com.cn
Year Founded: 2000
8095—(HKG)
Rev.: $38,774,830
Assets: $704,931,412
Liabilities: $181,455,066
Net Worth: $523,476,346
Earnings: $44,881,528
Emp.: 584
Fiscal Year-end: 12/31/22
Embedded System Products Including Network Security, Wireless Fire
Alarm Systems & Related Products
Developer, Marketer & Mfr
N.A.I.C.S.: 541512
Jinlei Ni *(Chm & Exec Dir)*

BEIJING BEILU PHARMACEUTICAL CO., LTD.
No 32 Xizhimen North Street 7/F
Tower A Maples International Center,
Haidian District, Beijing, 100082,
China
Tel.: (86) 1062622266
Web Site: https://www.beilu.com.cn
Year Founded: 1992
300016—(CHIN)
Rev.: $125,457,644
Assets: $397,115,870
Liabilities: $145,513,797
Net Worth: $251,602,073
Earnings: ($10,106,988)
Fiscal Year-end: 12/31/23
Pharmaceutical Product Mfr & Distr
N.A.I.C.S.: 325412

BEIJING BEIMO HIGH-TECH FRICTIONAL MATERIAL CO., LTD.
Shahe Industrial Park, Changping,
Beijing, 102206, China
Tel.: (86) 1080725919
Web Site: https://www.bjgk.com
Year Founded: 2003
002985—(SSE)
Rev.: $140,098,140
Assets: $588,278,808
Liabilities: $87,278,256
Net Worth: $501,000,552
Earnings: $44,077,176
Fiscal Year-end: 12/31/22
Brake Product Mfr & Distr
N.A.I.C.S.: 336340
Shumin Wang *(Chm & Gen Mgr)*

BEIJING BEWINNER COMMUNICATIONS CO., LTD.
5F and 26F Guoxing Building No 22
Shouti South Road, Haidian District,
Beijing, 100044, China
Tel.: (86) 1088356661   CN
Web Site: http://www.bisp.com
Year Founded: 1997
002148—(SSE)
Rev.: $36,732,540
Assets: $188,023,094
Liabilities: $18,494,794
Net Worth: $169,528,301
Earnings: $3,167,991
Fiscal Year-end: 12/31/23

Telecommunication Servicesb
N.A.I.C.S.: 517810
Lemin Fu *(CEO)*

BEIJING BOHUI INNOVATION BIOTECHNOLOGY GROUP CO., LTD.
No 9 Shengmingyuan Road, Changping District, Beijing, 102200, China
Tel.: (86) 1088850168
Web Site: https://www.bohui-tech.com
Year Founded: 2001
300318—(CHIN)
Rev.: $111,748,572
Assets: $548,683,200
Liabilities: $222,410,448
Net Worth: $326,272,752
Earnings: ($10,997,532)
Emp.: 185
Fiscal Year-end: 12/31/22
Medical Testing Equipment Mfr
N.A.I.C.S.: 339112
Shen Zhiwei *(Chm & Gen Mgr)*

Subsidiaries:

Advion, Inc. **(1)**
61 Brown Rd Ste 100, Ithaca, NY 14850
Tel.: (607) 266-9162
Web Site: https://www.advion.com
Emp.: 25
Bioanalytical Contract Services
N.A.I.C.S.: 541720
Jamey Jones *(Pres)*

BEIJING BOHUI SCIENCE & TECHNOLOGY CO., LTD.
Building 1 No 8 Linglan Road, Haidian, Beijing, 100095, China
Tel.: (86) 1057682700
Web Site: https://www.bohui.com.cn
Year Founded: 1993
688004—(SHG)
Rev.: $23,027,720
Assets: $115,601,204
Liabilities: $15,253,267
Net Worth: $100,347,938
Earnings: ($3,989,901)
Fiscal Year-end: 12/31/22
Software Development Services
N.A.I.C.S.: 541511
Chuanming Sun *(Chm)*

BEIJING CAPITAL AGRIBUSINESS GROUP CO., LTD.
No 4 Yuminzhonglu, Xicheng District,
Beijing, 100029, China
Tel.: (86) 1062003652   CN
Holding Company; Livestock Production & Food Processing; Biopharmaceutical Mfr; Real Estate Investment
& Development
N.A.I.C.S.: 551112
Jiantong Liu *(Vice Chm & Gen Mgr)*

Subsidiaries:

Beijing Sanyuan Foods Co., Ltd. **(1)**
No 8 Yuchang Street, Ouhai District, Beijing, China
Tel.: (86) 1056306666
Web Site: http://www.sanyuan.com.cn
Rev.: $1,123,556,658
Assets: $1,972,386,880
Liabilities: $1,114,357,566
Net Worth: $858,029,314
Earnings: $5,125,077
Fiscal Year-end: 12/31/2022
Milk Product Mfr
N.A.I.C.S.: 311511
Yi Chang *(Chm)*

Joint Venture (Non-US):

St. Hubert SAS **(2)**
13-15 rue du Pont des Halles, 94150, Rungis, Cedex, France
Tel.: (33) 969326600
Web Site: https://www.sthubert.fr
Food Spreads Mfr & Marketer
N.A.I.C.S.: 311999

Patrick Cahuzac *(CEO)*

Cherry Valley Farms Ltd. (1)
Cherry Valle House Laceby Business Park
Grimsby Road, Grimsby, DN37 7DP, United
Kingdom
Tel.: (44) 1472808400
Web Site: http://www.cherryvalley.co.uk
Duck Meat Production
N.A.I.C.S.: 112390
Richard Bird *(Mng Dir)*

BEIJING CAPITAL DEVELOPMENT HOLDING GROUP CO., LTD

No 22 Shatanhoujie, Dongcheng District, Beijing, China
Tel.: (86) 1064053987
Web Site: https://en.bcdh.com.cn
Year Founded: 2005
Rev.: $6,635,032,468
Assets: $38,532,288,187
Liabilities: $29,251,183,443
Net Worth: $9,281,104,744
Earnings: ($63,821,791)
Fiscal Year-end: 12/31/22
Holding Company
N.A.I.C.S.: 551112

Subsidiaries:

Beijing Capital Development Group
Co., Ltd. (1)
Room 103B 1st Floor No 189 Andingmenwai Street, Dongcheng District, Beijing,
100031, China
Tel.: (86) 1059090981
Web Site: https://en.bcdh.com.cn
Rev.: $6,613,166,039
Assets: $35,061,350,811
Liabilities: $26,773,880,040
Net Worth: $8,287,470,771
Earnings: ($877,620,126)
Fiscal Year-end: 12/31/2023
Real Estate Manangement Services
N.A.I.C.S.: 531390
Yan Li *(Chm)*

BEIJING CAPITAL GRAND LIMITED

Suites 4602-05 One Exchange
Square, Central, China (Hong Kong)
Tel.: (852) 28699098   Ky
Web Site: http://www.bcgrand.com
1329—(HKG)
Rev.: $205,462,117
Assets: $2,916,608,517
Liabilities: $2,182,724,497
Net Worth: $733,884,020
Earnings: ($34,310,920)
Emp.: 1,181
Fiscal Year-end: 12/31/21
Holding Company
N.A.I.C.S.: 551112
Beichen Zhong *(Chm)*

BEIJING CAPITAL GROUP CO., LTD.

15/F Capital Group Plaza, No.6 Chaoyangmen North Street, Dongcheng,
Beijing, China
Tel.: (86) 1058385566
Web Site: https://www.bjcapital.com
Holding Company; Financial Services
& Investments, Urban Infrastructure
Development & Real Estate Investment & Development
N.A.I.C.S.: 551112
Songping Li *(Gen Mgr)*

Subsidiaries:

Beijing Capital Eco-Environment Protection Group Co., Ltd. (1)
Building 2 New Metropolis Hotel No 21
Chegongzhuang Street, Xicheng District,
Beijing, 100044, China
Tel.: (86) 1068356169
Web Site: https://www.capitaleco-pro.com
Rev.: $3,110,888,472
Assets: $14,725,606,882
Liabilities: $9,320,383,084

Net Worth: $5,405,223,798
Earnings: $442,789,926
Emp.: 36,000
Fiscal Year-end: 12/31/2022
Waste Water Treatment Services
N.A.I.C.S.: 562211
Liu Yongzhang *(Chm)*

Capital Securities Co., Ltd. (1)
Beijing Deshengmen Wai Avenue No 115
Ruby Shang City Block E, Xicheng District,
Beijing, 100088, China
Tel.: (86) 1059366000
Web Site: http://www.sczq.com.cn
Securities Brokerage Services
N.A.I.C.S.: 523150

BEIJING CAPITAL INTERNATIONAL AIRPORT COMPANY LIMITED

Capital Airport, Beijing, 100621,
China
Tel.: (86) 1064507700
Web Site: http://www.bcia.com.cn
Year Founded: 1999
BJCHF—(OTCIQ)
Rev.: $512,442,866
Assets: $5,384,923,349
Liabilities: $2,293,941,015
Net Worth: $3,090,982,334
Earnings: ($324,274,634)
Emp.: 1,567
Fiscal Year-end: 12/31/21
Airport
N.A.I.C.S.: 488119
Qiang Du *(Deputy Gen Mgr)*

BEIJING CAPITAL JIAYE PROPERTY SERVICES CO., LIMITED

11/F Building B Chengjian Plaza 18
North Taipingzhuang Road, Haidian
District, Beijing, China
Tel.: (86) 1062091607   CN
Web Site: https://www.bcjps.com
Year Founded: 1991
2210—(HKG)
Rev.: $253,292,673
Assets: $327,789,239
Liabilities: $209,378,323
Net Worth: $118,410,916
Earnings: $16,017,944
Emp.: 1,865
Fiscal Year-end: 12/31/23
Property Management Services
N.A.I.C.S.: 531311
Suyan Ma *(Gen Counsel)*

BEIJING CAPITAL LAND LTD.

Block A Fucheng Building 98A Beilishi
Road, Xicheng District, Beijing,
100037, China
Tel.: (86) 10 66523000   CN
Web Site:
   http://www.bjcapitalland.com
Rev.: $2,974,513,091
Assets: $26,512,039,406
Liabilities: $20,495,957,137
Net Worth: $6,016,082,269
Earnings: $367,604,152
Emp.: 3,768
Fiscal Year-end: 12/31/19
Property Development
N.A.I.C.S.: 524126
Weimin Hu *(VP)*

BEIJING CAPITAL RETAILING GROUP CO., LTD.

No 23 North 3rd Ring Middle Road,
Xicheng District, Beijing, 100029,
China
Tel.: (86) 1082270256
Web Site: http://www.xdsc.com.cn
600723—(SHG)
Rev.: $1,422,989,591
Assets: $998,228,237
Liabilities: $341,392,826
Net Worth: $656,835,411

Earnings: $70,795,319
Fiscal Year-end: 12/31/19
Departmental Store Operator
N.A.I.C.S.: 455110
Zhang Yuejin *(Pres)*

BEIJING CAREER INTERNATIONAL CO., LTD.

5F Tower A Zhaotai International
Center No 10 Chaoyangmen Nandajie, Chaoyang District, Beijing,
100020, China
Tel.: (86) 1059271212
Web Site: https://en.careerintlinc.com
Year Founded: 2005
300662—(CHIN)
Rev.: $1,377,301,697
Assets: $527,956,436
Liabilities: $267,065,924
Net Worth: $260,890,511
Earnings: $28,240,594
Emp.: 3,000
Fiscal Year-end: 12/31/23
Human Resource Consulting Services
N.A.I.C.S.: 541612
Yong Gao *(Chm & Pres)*

BEIJING CENTERGATE TECHNOLOGIES (HOLDING) CO., LTD.

2208 22nd Floor Building B Pengrun
Building No 26 Xiaoyun Road, Chaoyang District, Beijing, 100016, China
Tel.: (86) 1057768899
Web Site: https://www.centek.com.cn
Year Founded: 1999
000931—(SSE)
Rev.: $289,263,312
Assets: $497,378,232
Liabilities: $262,608,372
Net Worth: $234,769,860
Earnings: ($6,016,140)
Fiscal Year-end: 12/31/22
Holding Company
N.A.I.C.S.: 551112
Xu Zhongmin *(Chm)*

BEIJING CENTURY GSR VENTURES MANAGEMENT CO., LTD.

Room 5620 Block III China World
Tower No 1 Jianguomenwai Street,
Chaoyang District, Beijing, 100004,
China
Tel.: (86) 1057069898   CN
Web Site: http://www.gsrventures.cn
Year Founded: 2004
Venture Capital Investment Firm
N.A.I.C.S.: 523999
James Ding *(Mng Dir)*

Subsidiaries:

Golden Sand River (Hong Kong)
Limited (1)
Suite 4801 48/F Central Plaza 18 Harbour
Road, Wanchai, China (Hong Kong)
Tel.: (852) 2201 6300
Web Site: http://www.gsrventures.cn
Venture Capital Investment Firm
N.A.I.C.S.: 523999

Golden Sand River California
Corp. (1)
245 Lytton Ave Ste 350, Palo Alto, CA
94301-1638
Tel.: (650) 331-7300
Web Site: http://www.gsrventures.com
Venture Capital Investment Firm
N.A.I.C.S.: 523999
Richard Lim *(Exec Dir)*

BEIJING CENTURY TECHNOLOGY CO., LTD.

Floor 9 & 10 Building B Shichuang
Technology Complex, No 22 Shangdi

Xinxi Road Haidian District, Beijing,
100085, Shangdi, China
Tel.: (86) 1062970877
Web Site: https://www.c-real.com.cn
Year Founded: 1999
300150—(CHIN)
Rev.: $119,079,408
Assets: $348,021,111
Liabilities: $56,399,665
Net Worth: $291,621,446
Earnings: ($13,902,275)
Fiscal Year-end: 12/31/20
Software Publisher
N.A.I.C.S.: 513210
Junjie Niu *(Chm & Gen Mgr)*

BEIJING CERTIFICATE AUTHORITY CO., LTD.

Unit 1501 No 68 Beisihuan West
Road, Haidian District, Beijing,
100080, China
Tel.: (86) 1058045600
Web Site: https://www.bjca.cn
Year Founded: 2001
300579—(CHIN)
Rev.: $136,972,667
Assets: $212,767,827
Liabilities: $84,020,884
Net Worth: $128,746,943
Earnings: ($6,648,458)
Fiscal Year-end: 12/31/23
Security Consulting Services
N.A.I.C.S.: 541690
Xueyan Lin *(Gen Mgr)*

BEIJING CHANGJIU LOGISTICS CORP

No 99 Shigezhuang Road, Chaoyang
District, Beijing, 101101, China
Tel.: (86) 1057355999
Web Site:
   https://changjiulogistics.com
603569—(SHG)
Rev.: $555,647,840
Assets: $761,634,437
Liabilities: $398,966,663
Net Worth: $362,667,774
Earnings: $2,522,581
Emp.: 1,900
Fiscal Year-end: 12/31/22
Vehicle Logistics Services
N.A.I.C.S.: 541614
Yan Chao *(Sec & Gen Mgr)*

BEIJING CHIEFTAIN CONTROL ENGINEERING TECHNOLOGY CO., LTD.

No 27 Qingfeng West Road Biomedicine Industry Base, Daxing District,
Beijing, 102600, China
Tel.: (86) 1089287888
Web Site: https://www.ctntech.com
Year Founded: 2003
300430—(CHIN)
Rev.: $136,812,780
Assets: $439,919,532
Liabilities: $159,999,840
Net Worth: $279,919,692
Earnings: $17,510,688
Emp.: 1,300
Fiscal Year-end: 12/31/22
Process Automation Control Systems
Mfr
N.A.I.C.S.: 334513
Kai Liang *(Chm & Gen Mgr)*

BEIJING CHUNLIZHENGDA MEDICAL INSTRUMENTS CO., LTD.

10/F Deyuanjiuhe Plaza 10 Hongyan
Road, Chaoyang District, Beijing,
100021, China
Tel.: (86) 1058611761   CN
Web Site: https://www.clzd.com
Year Founded: 1998

Beijing Chunlizhengda Medical Instruments Co., Ltd.—(Continued)

1858—(HKG)
Rev.: $168,705,237
Assets: $478,731,243
Liabilities: $96,885,394
Net Worth: $381,845,849
Earnings: $43,203,768
Emp.: 1,303
Fiscal Year-end: 12/31/22
Medical Instrument Mfr
N.A.I.C.S.: 339112
Chunbao Shi *(Chm, Gen Mgr, Exec Dir, Dir-Mktg & Chief Engr)*

BEIJING COMENS NEW MATE-RIALS CO., LTD.

No 8 Dongliushui Industrial Zone Yanshan, Fangshan District, Beijing, 102502, China
Tel.: (86) 1081334710
Web Site: https://www.co-mens.com
Year Founded: 1999
300200—(CHIN)
Rev.: $142,630,956
Assets: $325,344,708
Liabilities: $48,461,868
Net Worth: $276,882,840
Earnings: $19,764,108
Emp.: 340
Fiscal Year-end: 12/31/22
Adhesive Mfr
N.A.I.C.S.: 325520
Wang Ziping *(Chm)*

BEIJING CONST INSTRU-MENTS TECHNOLOGY INC.

Building 5 Yard 3 Fengxiu Middle Road, Haidian District, Beijing, 100094, China
Tel.: (86) 1056973355
Web Site: http://www.constgroup.com
Year Founded: 2004
300445—(CHIN)
Rev.: $58,124,196
Assets: $164,392,956
Liabilities: $22,145,292
Net Worth: $142,247,664
Earnings: $10,594,584
Emp.: 220
Fiscal Year-end: 12/31/22
Digital Pressure Detection & Temperature Calibration Instruments Mfr
N.A.I.C.S.: 334514
Weili Jiang *(Chm)*

BEIJING CONSTRUCTION EN-GINEERING (GROUP) CO., LTD.

16th Floor No 1 Guanglian Road Xuanwu District, Beijing, China
Tel.: (86) 10 63927209
Web Site: http://www.bcegc.com
Sales Range: $1-4.9 Billion
Emp.: 20,000
Construction Services
N.A.I.C.S.: 237990
Weilin Sun *(Pres)*

Subsidiaries:

Beijing Chang Cheng Bilfinger Berger Construction Engineering Corp., Ltd. **(1)**
16th Fl Golden Tower 1 Xibahe S Rd, Chaoyang Dt, Beijing, 100028, China
Tel.: (86) 1064402721
Web Site: http://www.bcbb.com.cn
Transportation Infrastructure Engineering & Construction Services
N.A.I.C.S.: 237310

BEIJING CREATIVE DISTRIBU-TION AUTOMATION CO., LTD.

No 4 East District No 10 Xibeiwang East Road, Haidian District, Beijing, 100193, China

Tel.: (86) 1062981321
Web Site: https://www.creat-da.com.cn
002350—(SSE)
Rev.: $305,605,872
Assets: $470,928,276
Liabilities: $197,131,428
Net Worth: $273,796,848
Earnings: $2,195,856
Fiscal Year-end: 12/31/22
Power Distribution & Control Equipment Mfr
N.A.I.C.S.: 335311

BEIJING CTJ INFORMATION TECHNO CO., LTD.

Room 1710 Building 8 No 68 Wanquanhe Road, Haidian, Beijing, 100086, China
Tel.: (86) 1082650616
Web Site: https://www.ctjsoft.com
Year Founded: 2011
301153—(SSE)
Rev.: $128,164,407
Assets: $312,578,431
Liabilities: $94,451,629
Net Worth: $218,126,802
Earnings: $36,299,999
Fiscal Year-end: 12/31/22
Information Technology Services
N.A.I.C.S.: 541512
Luo Panfeng *(Chm)*

BEIJING CUIWEI TOWER CO.,LTD.

No 33 Fuxing Road, Haidian District, Beijing, 100036, China
Tel.: (86) 1068241688
Web Site: http://www.cwjt.com
Year Founded: 2003
603123—(SHG)
Rev.: $556,893,371
Assets: $1,121,702,129
Liabilities: $639,883,965
Net Worth: $481,818,163
Earnings: ($61,648,924)
Fiscal Year-end: 12/31/22
Departmental Store Operator
N.A.I.C.S.: 455110
Kuang Zhenxing *(Chm)*

BEIJING CULTURAL INVEST-MENT HOLDINGS CO., LTD.

No 22 Baisong Road, Sujiatun District, Shenyang, 110101, Liaoning, China
Tel.: (86) 24 31387078
Construction Material & Automobile Parts Distr
N.A.I.C.S.: 423320
Maofei Zhou *(Chm)*

BEIJING DABEINONG TECH-NOLOGY GROUP CO., LTD.

1 No 19 Chengwan Street, Haidian District, Beijing, 100194, China
Tel.: (86) 1082856450
Web Site: https://www.dbn.com.cn
Year Founded: 1993
002385—(SSE)
Rev.: $4,548,503,700
Assets: $4,376,889,972
Liabilities: $2,550,719,808
Net Worth: $1,826,170,164
Earnings: $7,806,240
Fiscal Year-end: 12/31/22
Feed & Seed Products
N.A.I.C.S.: 111191
Shao Genhuo *(Chm)*

BEIJING DAHAO TECHNOL-OGY CORPORATION LIMITED

No 1 Jiuxianqiao East Road, Chaoyang District, Beijing, 100015, China
Tel.: (86) 1059248888
Web Site: https://en.dahaobj.com

Year Founded: 2000
603025—(SHG)
Rev.: $224,306,410
Assets: $438,964,349
Liabilities: $135,117,506
Net Worth: $303,846,843
Earnings: $61,102,333
Fiscal Year-end: 12/31/22
Electronic Component Mfr & Distr
N.A.I.C.S.: 334419
Jianjun Zheng *(Chm)*

Subsidiaries:

Taiyuan Dahao Yida Electronic Co., Ltd. **(1)**
No 403 Tiyu Road High-tech Zone, Taiyuan, Shanxi, China
Tel.: (86) 3512202707
Control Equipment Mfr & Distr
N.A.I.C.S.: 334519

Zhejiang Dahao Technology Co., Ltd. **(1)**
No 511 Jidong Road Huandong Street, Zhuji, Zhejiang, China
Tel.: (86) 57587279015
Control Equipment Mfr & Distr
N.A.I.C.S.: 334519

BEIJING DALONG WEIYE REAL ESTATE DEVELOPMENT CO., LTD.

No 2 Fuqian East Street, Shunyi District, Beijing, 101300, China
Tel.: (86) 1069446339
Web Site: http://www.dldc.com.cn
Year Founded: 1998
600159—(SHG)
Rev.: $121,831,988
Assets: $584,397,267
Liabilities: $256,975,019
Net Worth: $327,422,249
Earnings: ($24,204,637)
Emp.: 2,235
Fiscal Year-end: 12/31/22
Real Estate Management & Construction Services
N.A.I.C.S.: 531390
Li Wenjiang *(Chm)*

BEIJING DATAWAY HORIZON CO., LTD.

8th Floor East District Building 1 878 No 24 Jiuxianqiao Middle Road, Chaoyang District, Beijing, 100015, China
Tel.: (86) 1053896000
Web Site: https://www.idataway.com
Year Founded: 2012
301169—(CHIN)
Rev.: $45,569,628
Assets: $118,181,700
Liabilities: $24,491,376
Net Worth: $93,690,324
Earnings: ($1,485,432)
Fiscal Year-end: 12/31/22
Information Technology Services
N.A.I.C.S.: 541512
Yue Yuan *(Chm)*

BEIJING DIGITAL TELECOM CO., LTD.

Room 2460X 46th Floor-4 to 45th Floor 101 Bldg 1 No 20 Courtyard, Fengtai District, Beijing, China
Tel.: (86) 1088516752   CN
Web Site: http://www.dixintong.com
Year Founded: 2001
Rev.: $2,196,721,374
Assets: $1,565,693,877
Liabilities: $968,036,011
Net Worth: $597,657,866
Earnings: $37,270,681
Emp.: 5,997
Fiscal Year-end: 12/31/19
Communications Terminals & Related Products Distr
N.A.I.C.S.: 423430
Songshan Liu *(Exec Dir & Dir)*

BEIJING DINGHAN TECHNOL-OGY GROUP CO., LTD.

Building 2 No 18 District No 188 Nansihuan Xi Road, Fengtai District, Beijing, China
Tel.: (86) 1083683366
Web Site: https://www.dinghantech.com
Year Founded: 2002
300011—(CHIN)
Rev.: $178,191,468
Assets: $482,637,636
Liabilities: $299,287,872
Net Worth: $183,349,764
Earnings: ($27,577,368)
Emp.: 1,900
Fiscal Year-end: 12/31/22
Rail Transit Power Supply System Mfr
N.A.I.C.S.: 335999

Subsidiaries:

SMA Railway Technology GmbH **(1)**
Miramstr 87, 34123, Kassel, Germany
Tel.: (49) 561506346000
Sales Range: $25-49.9 Million
Emp.: 165
Railways Power Electronic Component Mfr
N.A.I.C.S.: 334290
Dirk Wimmer *(Gen Mgr)*

BEIJING DYNAMIC POWER CO., LTD.

No 8 Xinghuo Road Science City, Fengtai District, Beijing, 100070, China
Tel.: (86) 1083682266
Web Site: https://en.dpc.com.cn
Year Founded: 1995
600405—(SHG)
Rev.: $190,406,591
Assets: $364,617,031
Liabilities: $238,965,967
Net Worth: $125,651,064
Earnings: ($2,267,994)
Emp.: 2,000
Fiscal Year-end: 12/31/22
Power Supply Equipment Mfr & Whslr
N.A.I.C.S.: 335999
Zhenya He *(Chm & Gen Mgr)*

BEIJING E-HUALU INFORMA-TION TECHNOLOGY CO., LTD.

China Hualu Building No 165 Fushi Road, Shijingshan District, Beijing, 100043, China
Tel.: (86) 1052281111
Web Site: https://www.ehualu.com
Year Founded: 2001
300212—(CHIN)
Rev.: $107,746,250
Assets: $1,874,886,168
Liabilities: $1,296,189,168
Net Worth: $578,697,000
Earnings: ($266,204,796)
Fiscal Year-end: 12/31/23
Information Technology & Services Company; Traffic Management Systems & Software
N.A.I.C.S.: 336999
Ou Li *(Chm)*

Subsidiaries:

Beijing Gaocheng Science & Technology Development Co., Ltd. **(1)**
Room 805 Tower C China Hualu Building 165 Fushi Road, Shijingshan District, Beijing, China
Tel.: (86) 1052281264
Information Technology Services
N.A.I.C.S.: 541511

Beijing Sunrising Technology Co., Ltd. **(1)**
8/F China Hualu Building 165 Fushi Road, Shijingshan District, Beijing, China
Tel.: (86) 1052281000
Information Technology Services

N.A.I.C.S.: 541511

Cross-strait Information Consumption Institute (Xiamen) Co., Ltd. (1)
Room 905 Haitou Building 8 Zhonglin Road, Xiamen, China
Tel.: (86) 5926892821
Information Technology Services
N.A.I.C.S.: 541511

E-Hualu (Fujian) Information Technology Co., Ltd. (1)
Room 402 57 Wanghai Road Software Park Phase II, Xiamen, China
Tel.: (86) 5922529380
Information Technology Services
N.A.I.C.S.: 541511

E-Hualu (Jilin) Information Technology Co., Ltd. (1)
Room 403 Tower A Pearl Square 8688 Renmin Street, Nanguan District, Changchun, China
Tel.: (86) 43181812057
Information Technology Services
N.A.I.C.S.: 541511

E-Hualu (Leshan) Investment Development Co., Ltd. (1)
15/F World Trade Center, Leshan, Sichuan, China
Tel.: (86) 8332427189
Information Technology Services
N.A.I.C.S.: 541511

E-Hualu (Quanzhou) Investment Development Co., Ltd. (1)
11/F Former Bureau of Ocean and Fishery, Quanzhou, Fujian, China
Tel.: (86) 59528288890
Information Technology Services
N.A.I.C.S.: 541511

E-Hualu (Shandong) Information Technology Co., Ltd. (1)
786 Xinluo Street 9/F South Building, Gaoxin District, Jinan, Shandong, China
Tel.: (86) 53155721999
Information Technology Services
N.A.I.C.S.: 541511

E-Hualu (Tianjin) Information Technology Co., Ltd. (1)
3/F China Hualu Building 1 Tianhua Road, Balitai Industrial Park Jinnan District, Tianjin, China
Tel.: (86) 2259781555
Information Technology Services
N.A.I.C.S.: 541511

E-Hualu (Tianjin) International Trade Company (1)
9/F China Hualu Building 165 Fushi Road, Shijingshan District, Beijing, China
Tel.: (86) 1052281364
Information Technology Services
N.A.I.C.S.: 541511

E-Hualu Integration Technology Co., Ltd. (1)
China Hualu Building 165 Fushi Road, Shijingshan District, Beijing, China
Tel.: (86) 1052281398
Information Technology Services
N.A.I.C.S.: 541511

Hualu Optical Storage Institute (Dalian) Co., Ltd. (1)
10/F Hualu Building 717, Huangpu Road Gaoxin District, Dalian, Liaoning, China
Tel.: (86) 41165801888
Information Technology Services
N.A.I.C.S.: 541511

Hualu Senior Care & Health Development Co., Ltd. (1)
4/F Meiji Building 195 Andingmenwai Street, Beijing, China
Tel.: (86) 1064295900
Information Technology Services
N.A.I.C.S.: 541511

Infologic Pte Ltd (1)
5 Harper Road 06-01, Singapore, 369673, Singapore
Tel.: (65) 64119500
Web Site: https://www.infologic.sg
Software Services
N.A.I.C.S.: 541511

Tianjin Huayi Zhicheng Technology Development Co., Ltd. (1)
China Hualu Building Tianhua Road, Balitai Industrial Park Jinnan District, Tianjin, China
Tel.: (86) 2228669111
Information Technology Services
N.A.I.C.S.: 541511

BEIJING E-TECHSTAR CO LTD
Floor 9-11 Building 1 No 39 Linfeng 2nd Road, Haidian District, Beijing, 100194, China
Tel.: (86) 1062670506
Web Site: http://www.techstar.com.cn
Year Founded: 2000
300513—(CHIN)
Rev.: $189,705,485
Assets: $648,940,980
Liabilities: $300,842,205
Net Worth: $348,098,775
Earnings: $5,842,317
Fiscal Year-end: 12/31/23
Information Technology Services
N.A.I.C.S.: 541511
Sujin Qian (Chm & Gen Mgr)

BEIJING E-TOWN INTERNATIONAL INVESTMENT & DEVELOPMENT CO., LTD.
23rd-25th Floor Tower A Yicheng Fortune Center 22 Ronghua Middle Road, Beijing Economic-Technological Development Area, Beijing, China
Tel.: (86) 400 832 5066   CN
Web Site:
http://www.en.etowncapital.com
Year Founded: 2009
Privater Equity Firm
N.A.I.C.S.: 523999
Zhao Guangyi (Chm & Gen Mgr)

Subsidiaries:

Mattson Technology, Inc. (1)
47131 Bayside Pkwy, Fremont, CA 94538
Tel.: (510) 657-5900
Web Site: http://www.mattson.com
Semiconductor Fabrication Equipment Designer, Mfr & Marketer
N.A.I.C.S.: 333242
Allen Lu (Pres & CEO)

Subsidiary (Non-US):

Mattson Technology Singapore Pte. Ltd. (2)
159 Kampong Ampat #05-01A, KA Place, 368328, Singapore, Singapore
Tel.: (65) 62865600
Web Site: http://www.mattson.com
Semiconductor Fabrication Equipment Designer, Mfr & Marketer
N.A.I.C.S.: 333242

Mattson Thermal Products GmbH (2)
Daimlerstrasse 10, Dornstadt, 89160, Germany
Tel.: (49) 73489810
Web Site: http://www.mattson.com
Developer of Dry Strip & Rapid Thermal Processing Products & Services
N.A.I.C.S.: 334413
Andreas Toennis (VP & Gen Mgr-Thermal Products)

Mattson Trading (Shanghai) Co., Ltd. (2)
Suite 3201 Xin Jin Qiao Building 28 Xin Jin Qiao Road, Pudong New Area, Shanghai, 201206, China
Tel.: (86) 2150325701
Web Site: http://www.mattson.com
Semiconductor Fabrication Equipment Designer, Mfr & Marketer
N.A.I.C.S.: 333242
David Yang (Country Mgr-China)

BEIJING EASPRING MATERIAL TECHNOLOGY CO., LTD.
No 21 Block 18 Headquarters Base
No 188 South Fourth Ring Road

West, Fengtai District, Beijing, 100160, China
Tel.: (86) 1052269718
Web Site:
http://www.easpring.com.cn
Year Founded: 1998
300073—(CHIN)
Rev.: $2,985,485,256
Assets: $3,026,389,392
Liabilities: $1,413,172,332
Net Worth: $1,613,217,060
Earnings: $317,107,440
Fiscal Year-end: 12/31/22
Lithium Batteries & Power Supply Products Mfr
N.A.I.C.S.: 335910
Chen Yanbin (Chm)

Subsidiaries:

Beijing Zodngoc Automatic Technology Co., Ltd. (1)
2H Liandong U Gu 15 jingsheng 4th South Road, Majuqiao, Tongzhou, '101102, China
Tel.: (86) 1061057635
Automation Equipment Mfr
N.A.I.C.S.: 333248

BEIJING EGOVA CO., LTD.
International Software Building Building 9, Zhongguancun Software Park No 8 Dongbeiwang West Road Haidian District, Beijing, 100193, China
Tel.: (86) 1056161666
Web Site: https://www.egova.com.cn
300075—(CHIN)
Rev.: $214,198,452
Assets: $666,669,744
Liabilities: $129,808,224
Net Worth: $536,861,520
Earnings: $35,745,840
Fiscal Year-end: 12/31/22
Electronic Data Management Products Mfr
N.A.I.C.S.: 334112
Qianghua Wu (Chm)

BEIJING ELECTRONIC ZONE HIGH-TECH GROUP CO., LTD.
Room 1508 15F Building No 5 Yard No 6 Jiuxianqiao Road, Chaoyang District, Beijing, 100015, China
Tel.: (86) 1058833515
Web Site: http://www.bez.com.cn
Year Founded: 1986
600658—(SHG)
Rev.: $723,014,300
Assets: $2,960,591,578
Liabilities: $1,855,540,075
Net Worth: $1,105,051,503
Earnings: $83,097,846
Fiscal Year-end: 12/31/22
Real Estate Investment & Property Management Services
N.A.I.C.S.: 523999
Qi Zhanyong (Chm)

BEIJING EMERGING EASTERN AVIATION EQUIPMENT CO., LTD.
Building 4 Zone 4 Xishan Creative Park, Haidian District, Beijing, 100195, China
Tel.: (86) 1063861683
Web Site: http://www.eeae.com.cn
Year Founded: 1997
002933—(SSE)
Rev.: $26,784,108
Assets: $245,427,624
Liabilities: $42,994,692
Net Worth: $202,432,932
Earnings: ($8,110,908)
Fiscal Year-end: 12/31/22
Aircraft Parts Mfr & Distr
N.A.I.C.S.: 336411
Li Weifeng (Chm)

BEIJING ENERGY INTERNA-

TIONAL HOLDING CO., LTD.
Unit 1012 10/F West Tower Shun Tak Centre, 168-200 Connaught Road, Central, China (Hong Kong)
Tel.: (852) 31128461   BM
Web Site: http://www.bjei.com
0686—(HKG)
Rev.: $577,746,000
Assets: $8,470,051,200
Liabilities: $7,040,358,000
Net Worth: $1,429,693,200
Earnings: $66,268,800
Emp.: 1,011
Fiscal Year-end: 12/31/22
Solar Silicon Cell Mfr
N.A.I.C.S.: 334413
Zhenwei Lu (Exec Dir)

Subsidiaries:

Wollar Solar Holding Pty Ltd (1)
Suite 3, Level 21, 1 York Street,, Sydney, 2000, NSW, Australia
Tel.: (61) 1800700743
Web Site: https://wollarsolar.com.au
Electric Power Energy
N.A.I.C.S.: 221114

BEIJING ENLIGHT MEDIA CO., LTD.
3rd Floor Building 3 No 11 Hepingli East Street, Dongcheng District, Beijing, 100013, China
Tel.: (86) 1064516000
Web Site: https://www.ewang.com
Year Founded: 1998
300251—(CHIN)
Rev.: $105,989,364
Assets: $1,273,116,312
Liabilities: $112,824,036
Net Worth: $1,160,292,276
Earnings: ($100,089,756)
Emp.: 460
Fiscal Year-end: 12/31/22
Television Program Production
N.A.I.C.S.: 512110
Changtian Wang (Chm & Gen Mgr)

BEIJING ENTERPRISES HOLDINGS LIMITED
66th Floor Central Plaza 18 Harbour Road, Wanchai, Hong Kong, China (Hong Kong)
Tel.: (852) 29152898   HK
Web Site: https://www.behl.com.hk
Year Founded: 1997
0392—(OTCIQ)
Rev.: $11,795,538,870
Assets: $28,253,015,068
Liabilities: $15,084,625,609
Net Worth: $13,168,389,459
Earnings: $1,056,145,411
Emp.: 33,000
Fiscal Year-end: 12/31/22
Holding Company
N.A.I.C.S.: 551112
Xinhao Jiang (VP)

Subsidiaries:

Beijing Enterprises Environment Group Limited (1)
66/F Central Plaza 18 Harbour Road, Wanchai, China (Hong Kong)
Tel.: (852) 28611880
Web Site: https://www.beegl.com.hk
Rev.: $326,956,793
Assets: $1,551,321,315
Liabilities: $1,027,322,325
Net Worth: $523,998,990
Earnings: $41,742,990
Emp.: 1,324
Fiscal Year-end: 12/31/2022
Network Infrastructure Facility Construction, Network System Integration & Internet Support Services
N.A.I.C.S.: 517810
Robin Kwok Wai Wong (Sec & Controller-Fin)

Beijing Enterprises Holdings Limited—(Continued)

Subsidiary (Domestic):

China Information Technology Development Limited (2)
Unit 3308 33/F Millennium City 6 392 Kwun Tong Road, Kwun Tong, Hong Kong, China (Hong Kong)
Tel.: (852) 25440330
Web Site: http://www.citd.com.hk
Rev.: $8,027,018
Assets: $59,769,960
Liabilities: $24,555,608
Net Worth: $35,214,353
Earnings: ($10,915,530)
Emp.: 59
Fiscal Year-end: 12/31/2022
Software Development Services
N.A.I.C.S.: 541511
Chi Wai Tse (CFO & Sec)

Beijing Yanjing Brewery Co., Ltd. (1)
No 9 Shuanghe Road, Shunyi District, Beijing, 101300, China
Tel.: (86) 1089495588
Web Site: https://www.yanjing.com.cn
Rev.: $1,853,570,628
Assets: $2,905,514,820
Liabilities: $902,575,440
Net Worth: $2,002,939,380
Earnings: $49,461,516
Fiscal Year-end: 12/31/2022
Beer Mfr
N.A.I.C.S.: 312140
Geng Chao (Chm)

EEW Energy from Waste GmbH (1)
Schoninger Strasse 2 - 3, 38350, Helmstedt, Germany (100%)
Tel.: (49) 535 1180
Web Site: https://www.eew-energyfromwaste.com
Emp.: 1,150
Holding Company; Waste-to-Energy Power Generation Services
N.A.I.C.S.: 551112
Bernard M. Kemper (Chm & Mng Dir)

Subsidiary (Non-US):

EEW Energy from Waste Delfzijl B.V. (2)
Oosterhorn 38, 9936, Farmsum, Netherlands (100%)
Tel.: (31) 59 667 4000
Web Site: http://www.eew-energyfromwaste.com
Waste-to-Energy Power Generation Services
N.A.I.C.S.: 221117

Subsidiary (Domestic):

EEW Energy from Waste Goppingen GmbH (2)
Iltishofweg 40, 73037, Goppingen, Germany (100%)
Tel.: (49) 71 616 7160
Web Site: https://www.eew-energyfromwaste.com
Waste-to-Energy Power Generation Services
N.A.I.C.S.: 221117

EEW Energy from Waste Grossraschen GmbH (2)
Bergmannstrasse 29, 01983, Grossraschen, Germany (100%)
Tel.: (49) 357 533 7750
Web Site: https://www.eew-energyfromwaste.com
Waste-to-Energy Power Generation Services
N.A.I.C.S.: 221117

EEW Energy from Waste Hannover GmbH (2)
Moorwaldweg 310, 30659, Hannover, Germany (85%)
Tel.: (49) 511 336 3970
Web Site: https://www.eew-energyfromwaste.com
Waste-to-Energy Power Generation Services
N.A.I.C.S.: 221117

EEW Energy from Waste Helmstedt GmbH (2)
Am Kraftwerk 2, Buddenstedt, 38372, Helm-stedt, Germany (100%)
Tel.: (49) 53529 684 1308
Web Site: https://www.eew-energyfromwaste.com
Waste-to-Energy Power Generation Services
N.A.I.C.S.: 221117

EEW Energy from Waste Heringen GmbH (2)
In der Aue 3 Werra, 36266, Heringen, Germany (100%)
Tel.: (49) 662 454 2100
Web Site: https://www.eew-energyfromwaste.com
Waste-to-Energy Power Generation Services
N.A.I.C.S.: 221117

EEW Energy from Waste Premnitz GmbH (2)
Dr-Herbert-Rein-Strasse 1, 14727, Premnitz, Germany (100%)
Tel.: (49) 338621 387 3370
Web Site: https://www.eew-energyfromwaste.com
Waste-to-Energy Power Generation Services
N.A.I.C.S.: 221117

EEW Energy from Waste Saarbrucken GmbH (2)
Am Blucherfloz 12, Neunkirchen, 66538, Saarbrucken, Germany (100%)
Tel.: (49) 68 218 6980
Web Site: http://www.eew-energyfromwaste.com
Waste-to-Energy Power Generation Services
N.A.I.C.S.: 221117

EEW Energy from Waste Stapelfeld GmbH (2)
Ahrensburger Weg 4, 22145, Stapelfeld, Germany (100%)
Tel.: (49) 4 067 5760
Web Site: http://www.eew-energyfromwaste.com
Waste-to-Energy Power Generation Services
N.A.I.C.S.: 221117

Kraftwerk Schwedt GmbH & Co. KG (2)
Kuhheide 34, 16303, Schwedt an der Oder, Germany (99%)
Tel.: (49) 3332 581 4120
Web Site: https://www.eew-energyfromwaste.com
Eletric Power Generation Services
N.A.I.C.S.: 221118

MHKW Rothensee GmbH (2)
Kraftwerk-Privatweg 07, 39126, Magdeburg, Germany (51%)
Tel.: (49) 391 587 2534
Web Site: https://www.mhkw-rothensee.de
Electric Power Generation & Distribution Services
N.A.I.C.S.: 221118
Rolf Oesterhoff (Dir-Comml)

EEW Holding GmbH (1)
Im Grunewald 2, Erndtebruck, 57339, Siegen, Germany
Tel.: (49) 27536090
Web Site: https://eew-group.com
N.A.I.C.S.: 332420
Christoph Schorge (Chm)

BEIJING ENTERPRISES URBAN RESOURCES GROUP LIMITED
Rooms 6706-07 67/F Central Plaza 18 Harbour Road, Wanchai, China (Hong Kong)　　　Ky
Web Site: https://en.beur.net.cn
Year Founded: 2013
3718—(HKG)
Rev.: $637,911,606
Assets: $1,127,742,305
Liabilities: $604,324,311
Net Worth: $523,417,994
Earnings: $40,755,358
Emp.: 51,367
Fiscal Year-end: 12/31/22

Waste Management Services
N.A.I.C.S.: 562998
Kexi Zhao (Pres)

BEIJING ENTERPRISES WATER GROUP LIMITED
Rooms 6706-07 67th Floor Central Plaza 18 Harbour Road, Wanchai, China (Hong Kong)
Tel.: (852) 21050800　　　BM
Web Site: https://www.bewg.net
BJWTF—(OTCIQ)
Rev.: $3,595,981,360
Assets: $23,683,718,530
Liabilities: $15,487,200,239
Net Worth: $8,196,518,291
Earnings: $705,252,451
Emp.: 17,888
Fiscal Year-end: 12/31/21
Waste Treatment Services
N.A.I.C.S.: 221310
Yongcheng Cheng Li (Chm)

Subsidiaries:

BEWG (M) Sdn Bhd (1)
Tropicana City Office Tower Level 8 No 3 Jalan SS20/27, Petaling Jaya, 47400, Selangor, Malaysia
Tel.: (60) 377108828
Waste Management Services
N.A.I.C.S.: 924110

Be Water S.A. (1)
Avenida Conde Valbom n 30- 3, 1050-068, Lisbon, Portugal
Tel.: (351) 211552700
Emp.: 250
Canal Services
N.A.I.C.S.: 221310

Shandong Hi-Speed New Energy Group Limited (1)
Rooms 6706-07 Central Plaza 67th Floor 18 Harbour Road, Wanchai, China (Hong Kong)
Tel.: (852) 21050860
Web Site: http://www.bece.com.hk
Rev.: $675,265,118
Assets: $6,633,603,788
Liabilities: $4,709,408,978
Net Worth: $1,924,194,810
Earnings: $28,790,903
Emp.: 1,953
Fiscal Year-end: 12/31/2022
Investment Services
N.A.I.C.S.: 523999
Xiaoyong Hu (Chm)

BEIJING FOREVER TECHNOLOGY COMPANY LIMITED
12th Floor Building A Imperial City International Center, No 138 Andingmenwai Street Dongcheng District, Beijing, 100011, China
Tel.: (86) 1062078588
Web Site: http://www.ieforever.com
Year Founded: 2000
300365—(CHIN)
Rev.: $85,271,940
Assets: $336,930,516
Liabilities: $52,085,592
Net Worth: $284,844,924
Earnings: ($30,795,336)
Emp.: 540
Fiscal Year-end: 12/31/22
Software & Hardware Producer & Distr
N.A.I.C.S.: 513210
Jiang Chunhua (Chm)

BEIJING GALLOPING HORSE FILM & TV PRODUCTION CO., LTD.
11/F Easyhome Tower No 3A Dongzhimen South Street, Dongcheng District, Beijing, 100007, China
Tel.: (86) 10 84990264
Sales Range: $75-99.9 Million
Emp.: 300

Motion Picture & Television Program Production Services
N.A.I.C.S.: 512110
Ivy Zhong (Vice Chm & Mng Dir)

Subsidiaries:

Instant Karma Films, LLC (1)
212 Marine St, Santa Monica, CA 90405
Tel.: (310) 526-7703
Web Site: http://www.instantkarmafilms.tv
Motion Picture & Video Production Services
N.A.I.C.S.: 512110

BEIJING GAS BLUE SKY HOLDINGS LIMITED
Room 1411 14th Floor New World Tower No 16-18 Queens Road, Central, China (Hong Kong)
Tel.: (852) 3425 4538　　　BM
Web Site: http://www.bgbluesky.com
Rev.: $343,641,725
Assets: $1,111,688,516
Liabilities: $524,716,518
Net Worth: $586,971,998
Earnings: $9,485,647
Emp.: 1,008
Fiscal Year-end: 12/31/19
Natural Gas Services
N.A.I.C.S.: 221210
Weiqi Li (CEO)

BEIJING GEHUA CATV NETWORK CO., LTD.
No 35 East Gate Huayuan North Road, Haidian District, Beijing, 100007, China
Tel.: (86) 1062035573
Web Site: http://www.bgctv.com.cn
Year Founded: 1999
600037—(SHG)
Rev.: $342,812,307
Assets: $2,268,458,370
Liabilities: $429,120,975
Net Worth: $1,839,337,395
Earnings: $46,940,381
Fiscal Year-end: 12/31/22
Television Broadcasting Services
N.A.I.C.S.: 516120
Guo Zhangpeng (Chm)

BEIJING GEHUA CULTURAL DEVELOPMENT GROUP CO., LTD.
A 14F Gehua Tower No 1 Qinglong Bystreet, Dongcheng District, Beijing, 100007, China
Tel.: (86) 8418 6060
Web Site: http://www.gehua.com
Year Founded: 1997
Holding Company Services
N.A.I.C.S.: 551112

Subsidiaries:

Beijing Gehua Culture Center Co., Ltd. (1)
The China Millennium Monument No 9 Fuxing Road, Haidian District, Beijing, 100038, China
Tel.: (86) 10 5980 2288
Web Site: http://www.gehua.com
Cultural & Entertainment Events Organizer & Hosting Facilities Operator
N.A.I.C.S.: 711310
Chenghu Pei (Chm)

Beijing Gehua Media Center Co., Ltd. (1)
Gehua Kaiyuan Hotel No 19 Golou Wai Street, Chaoyang District, Beijing, 100011, China
Tel.: (86) 10 6236 9978
Web Site: http://www.gehua.com
Media Industry Events Organizer & Hosting Facilities Operator
N.A.I.C.S.: 561920
Lizhi Ge (Chm)

Beijing Gehua Science & Technology Center Co., Ltd. (1)

Gehua Tower No 1 Qinglong Hutong, Dongcheng District, Beijing, 100007, China
Tel.: (86) 10 8418 6800
Web Site: http://www.gehua.com
Science & Technology Industry Events Organizer & Hosting Facilities Operator
N.A.I.C.S.: 561920
Guangxian Huang *(Chm)*

BEIJING GEOENVIRON ENGINEERING & TECHNOLOGY, INC.
Building 1 High Energy Environment Building, No 36 Qiufeng Road Haidian District, Beijing, China
Tel.: (86) 1062490000
Web Site: https://www.bgechina.cn
Year Founded: 1992
603588—(SHG)
Rev.: $1,231,902,496
Assets: $3,181,482,266
Liabilities: $1,821,401,731
Net Worth: $1,360,080,535
Earnings: $97,223,953
Fiscal Year-end: 12/31/22
Solid Waste Management Solution Provider
N.A.I.C.S.: 541618

BEIJING GS TECHNOLOGY CO., LTD
Building 1 Yard 3 Fengxiu Middle Road, Haidian District, Beijing, 100094, China
Tel.: (86) 1057930999
Web Site: https://www.gsafety.com
Year Founded: 2005
300523—(CHIN)
Rev.: $317,873,759
Assets: $601,093,122
Liabilities: $346,520,663
Net Worth: $254,572,459
Earnings: $11,217,533
Emp.: 2,300
Fiscal Year-end: 12/31/23
Public Safety Software Solution Services
N.A.I.C.S.: 541511
Zheng Jiasheng *(Chm)*

BEIJING HAIXIN ENERGY TECHNOLOGY CO., LTD.
9/F Dahang Jiye Building Tower 1 No 33 Renda North Road, Haidian, Beijing, 100080, China
Tel.: (86) 1050911296   CN
Web Site: https://www.hxnk.com
Year Founded: 1997
300072—(SSE)
Rev.: $1,053,198,344
Assets: $1,497,690,479
Liabilities: $536,427,451
Net Worth: $961,263,028
Earnings: ($11,579,886)
Emp.: 180
Fiscal Year-end: 12/31/23
Chemical Mfr & Distr
N.A.I.C.S.: 325998
Yu Zhiwei *(Chm)*

BEIJING HANBANG TECHNOLOGY CORP.
11-4 Changchun Road, Haidian District, Beijing, 100089, China
Tel.: (86) 10 5798 5798
Web Site: http://www.hbgk.net
Sales Range: $75-99.9 Million
Emp.: 750
Digital Video Surveillance Products & Systems Mfr
N.A.I.C.S.: 334310
Liqun Wang *(Chm & Pres)*

Subsidiaries:

SZ Hanbang Technology Co., Ltd.   **(1)**

4/F Tefa Information & Industrial Building NO 3 Qiongyu Rd, Hi-tech Park Nanshan District, Shenzhen, Guangdong, China
Tel.: (86) 75586017248
Audio & Video Equipment Mfr
N.A.I.C.S.: 334310
Cherry Tong *(Reg Mgr)*

BEIJING HANJIAN HESHAN PIPELINE CO.,LTD.
building 6 No 6 Yard Zhuoxiu North Street, Fangshan District, Beijing, 102488, China
Tel.: (86) 1069362150
Web Site: https://www.bjhs.cn
Year Founded: 2004
603616—(SHG)
Rev.: $78,251,505
Assets: $287,003,237
Liabilities: $184,395,590
Net Worth: $102,607,647
Earnings: ($50,830,528)
Emp.: 1,000
Fiscal Year-end: 12/31/22
Concrete Product Mfr & Distr
N.A.I.C.S.: 327332
Tian Yubo *(Chm & Pres)*

Subsidiaries:

Anhui Jianhuai Pipeline Engineering Co., Ltd.   **(1)**
Liugang Town, Shou County, Lu'an, Anhui, China
Tel.: (86) 5644916600
Steel Cylinder Concrete Pipe Mfr & Distr
N.A.I.C.S.: 327332

Beijing Hanjian Heshan Technology Co., Ltd.   **(1)**
Liangxiang Village, Fangshan District, Beijing, China
Tel.: (86) 1061353741
Steel Cylinder Concrete Pipe Mfr & Distr
N.A.I.C.S.: 327332

Hebei Hezhong Building Materials Co., Ltd.   **(1)**
Furao Road No 52 Longhe Tech Industrial Park, Langfang, Hebei, China
Tel.: (86) 3162577918
Web Site: https://www.hezhongjc.com
Chemical Building Material Mfr & Distr
N.A.I.C.S.: 325998

Qingqing Environmental Protection Equipment Co., Ltd.   **(1)**
558 Haiyang Road, Haigang District, Qinhuangdao, China
Tel.: (86) 3358889885
Chemical Building Material Mfr & Distr
N.A.I.C.S.: 325998

BEIJING HANYI INNOVATION TECHNOLOGY CO., LTD.
2F A tower China Printing SciTech Institute No 2 Cuiwei Road, Haidian District, Beijing, 100036, China
Tel.: (86) 13810951118
Web Site: https://www.hanyi.com.cn
Year Founded: 1993
301270—(CHIN)
Rev.: $29,895,372
Assets: $160,331,184
Liabilities: $7,804,836
Net Worth: $152,526,348
Earnings: $7,771,140
Fiscal Year-end: 12/31/22
Software Development Services
N.A.I.C.S.: 541511
Liqun Xie *(Chm & Gen Mgr)*

BEIJING HAOHUA ENERGY RESOURCE CO., LTD.
No 2 Xinqiao South Street, Mentougou District, Beijing, 102300, China
Tel.: (86) 1069839418
Web Site: https://www.bjhhny.com
Year Founded: 2002
601101—(SHG)
Rev.: $1,303,860,205
Assets: $4,184,609,125

Liabilities: $2,257,833,937
Net Worth: $1,926,775,188
Earnings: $188,641,075
Emp.: 12,400
Fiscal Year-end: 12/31/22
Coal Mining Services
N.A.I.C.S.: 212115
Dong Yongzhan *(Chm)*

BEIJING HEALTH (HOLDINGS) LIMITED
Unit 2704 27/F 909 Cheung Sha Wan Road Cheung Sha Wan, Kowloon, China (Hong Kong)
Tel.: (852) 26013633   Ky
Web Site: http://www.bemh.com.hk
Year Founded: 1995
2389—(HKG)
Rev.: $21,226,710
Assets: $307,967,453
Liabilities: $34,650,803
Net Worth: $273,316,650
Earnings: ($12,597,638)
Emp.: 166
Fiscal Year-end: 12/31/22
Geriatric, Medical & Health Care Investment Services
N.A.I.C.S.: 523999
Zheng Chun Wang *(Exec Dir)*

Subsidiaries:

Gerrards (Comercial Offshore De Macau) Ltd   **(1)**
Av Marciano Baptista 26 3 Floor Flat F Ed Chong Fok Comm Centre, Macau, China (Macau)
Tel.: (853) 2872 8202
Web Site: http://www.genvon.com
Power Tool Distr
N.A.I.C.S.: 423710

BEIJING HENGYU DATACOM AVIATION EQUIPMENT CO., LTD.
Building 5 East District CCCC Technology City Wei 26th Road, Chang'an District, Xi'an, 710077, Shaanxi, China
Tel.: (86) 2963389916
Web Site: https://www.bjhyxt.cn
Year Founded: 2002
300965—(SSE)
Rev.: $25,802,712
Assets: $221,407,992
Liabilities: $27,639,144
Net Worth: $193,768,848
Earnings: $4,650,048
Fiscal Year-end: 12/31/22
Aircraft Parts Mfr & Distr
N.A.I.C.S.: 336413
Liubin Wu *(Chm)*

BEIJING HEZONG SCIENCE & TECHNOLOGY CO., LTD.
D1211 1212 Jiahua Building No 9 Shangdi Third Street, Haidian District, Beijing, 100085, China
Tel.: (86) 1062978271
Web Site: http://www.hezong-tech.com
Year Founded: 1997
300477—(CHIN)
Rev.: $415,845,144
Assets: $1,020,900,348
Liabilities: $601,142,256
Net Worth: $419,758,092
Earnings: $1,015,092
Fiscal Year-end: 12/31/22
Power Distribution Equipment Mfr
N.A.I.C.S.: 335311
Liu Zegang *(Chm)*

BEIJING HIGHLANDER DIGITAL TECHNOLOGY CO., LTD.
Building 10 Yard 7 Dijin Road, Haidian District, Beijing, 100095, China

Tel.: (86) 1059738989
Web Site: http://www.highlander.com.cn
Year Founded: 2001
300065—(CHIN)
Rev.: $101,707,164
Assets: $365,546,844
Liabilities: $93,512,016
Net Worth: $272,034,828
Earnings: ($110,753,136)
Emp.: 150
Fiscal Year-end: 12/31/22
Marine Electronic Technology Products Mfr
N.A.I.C.S.: 334511
Wanqiu Shen *(Co-Founder)*

Subsidiaries:

Laurel Technologies Co. Ltd.   **(1)**
2F Lisichen Building Building 25 No 8 Dongbeiwang West Road, Haidian District, Beijing, 100193, China
Tel.: (86) 1082550789
Web Site: http://www.laureltechnologies.com
Geophysical Exploration Services
N.A.I.C.S.: 541360

BEIJING HOMYEAR CAPITAL HOLDINGS CO., LTD.
16F Tower A Huaye International Mansion, No 39 East 4th Ring Middle Road Chaoyang District, Beijing, 100025, China
Tel.: (86) 10 85710735
Web Site: http://www.huayedc.com
Sales Range: $400-449.9 Million
Property Leasing Services
N.A.I.C.S.: 531120
Hong Xu *(Chm)*

BEIJING HONGGAO CREATIVE CONSTRUCTION DESIGN CO., LTD.
No 7 Building Chlai Hi-tech Industrial Park Laiguangying West Road, Chaoyang District, Beijing, 100012, China
Tel.: (86) 1057963201
002504—(SSE)
Rev.: $26,454,771
Assets: $444,092,974
Liabilities: $415,271,109
Net Worth: $28,821,865
Earnings: ($56,794,947)
Fiscal Year-end: 12/31/21
Electronic Component Mfr & Distr
N.A.I.C.S.: 335999
Ning He *(Chm & Gen Mgr)*

BEIJING HOTGEN BIOTECH CO., LTD.
9 building No 9 Tianfu Street, Daxing District, Beijing, 102600, China
Tel.: (86) 1050973600
Web Site: https://www.hotgen.com.cn
Year Founded: 2005
688068—(SHG)
Rev.: $499,339,845
Assets: $547,457,761
Liabilities: $76,600,710
Net Worth: $470,857,051
Earnings: $132,641,019
Fiscal Year-end: 12/31/22
Medical Product Mfr & Distr
N.A.I.C.S.: 339112
Changqing Lin *(Chm & Gen Mgr)*

BEIJING HUAFENG TEST & CONTROL TECHNOLOGY CO., LTD.
7/F 2 Bldg 1 Haiying Rd, Fengtai, Beijing, 100070, China
Tel.: (86) 63725600
Web Site: https://www.accotest.com
Year Founded: 1999
688200—(SHG)
Rev.: $150,306,399
Assets: $473,338,453

Beijing Huafeng Test & Control Technology Co.,
Ltd.—(Continued)

Liabilities: $32,629,690
Net Worth: $440,708,763
Earnings: $73,891,172
Fiscal Year-end: 12/31/22
Semiconductor Product Mfr
N.A.I.C.S.: 334413
Xi Sun (Chm)

Subsidiaries:

AccoTEST Technology (Malaysia)
Sdn. Bhd.   (1)
PT 9742 No 20-1 Jalan Seri Bayan 7, Ta-
man Seri Bayan Durian Tunggal Hang Tuah
Jaya, 76100, Melaka, Malaysia
Tel.: (60) 124551643
Electric Equipment Mfr
N.A.I.C.S.: 335999

Beijing Huafeng Electronic Equipment
Co., Ltd.   (1)
10th Floor Building 2 No 1 Haiying Road
Science City, Fengtai District, Beijing,
100070, China
Tel.: (86) 1063725600
Web Site: https://www.hfee.com.cn
Electronic Equipment Services
N.A.I.C.S.: 611519

Huafeng Test & Control Technology
(Tianjin) Co., Ltd.   (1)
1201 Chuanbo Road Zhongxin Ecological
City Binhai, Tianjin, 300480, China
Tel.: (86) 2267253518
Semiconductor Testing Equipment Mfr &
Distr
N.A.I.C.S.: 334515

**BEIJING HUALIAN DEPART-
MENT STORE CO., LTD.**
No 208 Building No 2 Innovation
Center North Fourth Strip, Xiangyun
Road Qingyundian Town Daxing Dis-
trict, Beijing, 102605, China
Tel.: (86) 1057391734
Web Site: http://www.beijing-
    hualian.com
Year Founded: 1998
000882—(SSE)
Rev.: $157,308,372
Assets: $1,737,232,380
Liabilities: $761,679,828
Net Worth: $975,552,552
Earnings: ($26,537,004)
Fiscal Year-end: 12/31/22
Commercial Property Leasing & Man-
agement Services
N.A.I.C.S.: 531120
Wang Rui (Chm)

**BEIJING HUALIAN HYPER-
MARKET CO., LTD.**
No 208 Beisitiao Xiangyun Road,
Qingyundian Town Daxing District,
Beijing, 100037, China
Tel.: (86) 1068364982
Web Site: http://zc.beijing-
    hualian.com
600361—(SHG)
Rev.: $9,732,430,183
Assets: $2,369,381,021
Liabilities: $1,257,345,826
Net Worth: $1,112,035,195
Earnings: $152,892,399
Fiscal Year-end: 12/31/22
Supermarket Operator
N.A.I.C.S.: 445110

**BEIJING HUARU TECHNOL-
OGY CO., LTD.**
Block B Junzheng Building No 14,
East District Yard No 10 Xibeiwang
East Road Haidian District, Beijing,
100193, China
Tel.: (86) 1056380866
Web Site: https://www.huaru.com.cn
Year Founded: 2011

301302—(CHIN)
Rev.: $50,125,762
Assets: $326,915,997
Liabilities: $30,162,079
Net Worth: $296,753,918
Earnings: ($30,687,154)
Fiscal Year-end: 12/31/23
Software Development Services
N.A.I.C.S.: 541511
Chao Han (Chm)

**BEIJING INFOSEC TECH-
NOLOGIES CO., LTD.**
Xin'an Building Building 2 Xisanqi
Science and Technology Park, No 6
Jianfeng Road South Extension Haid-
ian District, Beijing, 100096, China
Tel.: (86) 1068025518
Web Site: https://www.infosec.com.cn
Year Founded: 2001
688201—(SHG)
Rev.: $92,393,884
Assets: $186,559,364
Liabilities: $24,703,197
Net Worth: $161,856,167
Earnings: $23,015,000
Fiscal Year-end: 12/31/22
Software Development Services
N.A.I.C.S.: 541511
Wei Li (Chm & Gen Mgr)

**BEIJING INFRASTRUCTURE
INVESTMENT CO., LTD.**
9th Floor Building 2 No 6 Xiaoying
North Road, Chaoyang District, Bei-
jing, China
Tel.: (86) 10 8468 6060   CN
Web Site: http://www.bii.com.cn
Infrastructure Investment Holding
Company
N.A.I.C.S.: 551112
Weiya Hao (Gen Mgr)

Subsidiaries:

BII Railway Transportation Technol-
ogy Holdings Company Limited   (1)
Room 4407 44/F Cosco Tower 183 Queen
s Road, Central, Sheung Wan, China (Hong
Kong)   (55%)
Tel.: (852) 28052588
Web Site: https://www.biitt.cn
Rev.: $209,458,254
Assets: $562,802,408
Liabilities: $224,157,731
Net Worth: $338,644,676
Earnings: $23,642,951
Emp.: 744
Fiscal Year-end: 12/31/2022
Holding Company; Urban Railway Technolo-
gies & Software Development Services
N.A.I.C.S.: 551112
Wei Cao (Vice Chm)

**BEIJING INHAND NETWORKS
TECHNOLOGY CO., LTD.**
Room 501 5th Floor Building 3 No 18
Ziyue Road, Chaoyang District, Bei-
jing, 100102, China
Tel.: (86) 1084170010
Web Site: http://www.inhand.com.cn
Year Founded: 2001
688080—(SHG)
Rev.: $54,328,229
Assets: $126,652,888
Liabilities: $11,215,854
Net Worth: $115,437,034
Earnings: $9,877,126
Fiscal Year-end: 12/31/22
Communication Product Mfr
N.A.I.C.S.: 334290
Ming Li (Chm)

**BEIJING INTERACT TECH-
NOLOGY CO., LTD.**
19th Floor Zhongxiu Building Building
1 No 10 Guanghua Road, Chaoyang
District, Beijing, 100020, China
Tel.: (86) 1088878800

Web Site: https://www.interact.net.cn
Year Founded: 2005
300419—(SSE)
Rev.: $148,738,356
Assets: $158,244,840
Liabilities: $72,332,676
Net Worth: $85,912,164
Earnings: $5,600,556
Emp.: 190
Fiscal Year-end: 12/31/22
Information Solutions
N.A.I.C.S.: 541511
Wang Jian (Chm)

**BEIJING JETSEN TECHNOL-
OGY CO., LTD.**
No 9 Banbi Street Village, Baishan
Town Haidian District, Beijing,
102211, China
Tel.: (86) 1061733068
Web Site: http://www.jetsen.com.cn
Year Founded: 2006
300182—(CHIN)
Rev.: $548,563,860
Assets: $1,410,532,812
Liabilities: $373,746,204
Net Worth: $1,036,786,608
Earnings: $73,089,432
Emp.: 480
Fiscal Year-end: 12/31/22
Audio & Video Equipment Mfr
N.A.I.C.S.: 334310
Ziquan Xu (Chm)

**BEIJING JIAMAN DRESS CO.,
LTD.**
8F-801 Building 1 Courtyard 26 Gu-
cheng West Street, Shijingshan, Bei-
jing, 100043, China
Tel.: (86) 1068149600
Web Site: https://www.shuihaier.com
Year Founded: 1992
301276—(SSE)
Rev.: $160,489,836
Assets: $333,303,984
Liabilities: $71,671,392
Net Worth: $261,632,592
Earnings: $23,302,188
Fiscal Year-end: 12/31/22
Apparel Product Mfr & Distr
N.A.I.C.S.: 315990
Cao Shengkui (Chm)

**BEIJING JIAODA SIGNAL
TECHNOLOGY CO., LTD.**
No 3 Liye Road Huilongguan Interna-
tional Information Industry Base,
Changping District, Beijing, 102206,
China
Tel.: (86) 1062119891
Web Site: https://www.jd-signal.com
Year Founded: 2001
300851—(SSE)
Rev.: $41,113,332
Assets: $190,931,364
Liabilities: $16,975,764
Net Worth: $173,955,600
Earnings: $5,193,396
Fiscal Year-end: 12/31/22
Software Development Services
N.A.I.C.S.: 541511
Wei Li (Chm)

**BEIJING JIAXUN FEIHONG
ELECTRICAL CO., LTD.**
No 1 Building Jiaxun Feihong Build-
ing No 88 Jindai Road, Zhongguan-
cun Environmental Protection Tech-
nology Demonstration Park, Beijing,
100095, China
Tel.: (86) 1062460088
Web Site: https://www.jiaxun.com
Year Founded: 1995
300213—(CHIN)
Rev.: $160,750,980
Assets: $426,084,516

Liabilities: $112,054,644
Net Worth: $314,029,872
Earnings: $8,749,728
Emp.: 290
Fiscal Year-end: 12/31/22
Dispatching & Other Traffic Equip-
ment Mfr
N.A.I.C.S.: 336999

**BEIJING JINGCHENG MA-
CHINERY ELECTRIC CO., LTD.**
No 2 Nansan Street, Cao County
Tongzhou District, Beijing, 101109,
China
Tel.: (86) 1067365383   CN
Web Site: https://www.jingchenggf.com
600860—(SHG)
Rev.: $192,665,472
Assets: $341,816,310
Liabilities: $144,346,307
Net Worth: $197,470,003
Earnings: $2,569,657
Emp.: 1,374
Fiscal Year-end: 12/31/22
Industrial Equipment Mfr & Distr
N.A.I.C.S.: 333248
Li Junjie (Chm)

Subsidiaries:

Beijing Jinggheng Compressor Co.,
Ltd   (1)
No 1 Guangming East Road Dongcheng
District, Beijing, China
Tel.: (86) 1067142237
Compressor Mfr
N.A.I.C.S.: 333912

Beijing Tianhai Industry Co., Ltd   (1)
No 1 South Fourth Street, Miao County
Miao County Town Tongzhou District, Bei-
jing, 101109, China
Tel.: (86) 1067383444
Web Site: https://www.btic.cn
Gas Cylinder Mfr & Distr
N.A.I.C.S.: 332420

Subsidiary (Domestic):

Beijing Tianhai Cryogenic Equipment
Co., Ltd.   (2)
No 4 Huoxing 3 street, Huoxian Town
Tongzhou District, Beijing, 101109, China
Tel.: (86) 13671324672
Web Site: https://www.btce-intl.com
Gas Cylinder Mfr
N.A.I.C.S.: 332420

Subsidiary (US):

Btic America Corporation   (2)
6200 Savoy Dr Ste 868, Houston, TX
77036
Tel.: (713) 779-8882
Web Site: https://www.btic-america.com
Gas Cylinder Mfr & Distr
N.A.I.C.S.: 332420

Shandong Tianhai High Pressure
Container Co., Ltd.   (1)
Hedong Industrial Park Hedong District,
Linyi, 276034, Shandong, China
Tel.: (86) 5398080656
Seamless Steel Gas Cylinder Mfr
N.A.I.C.S.: 332420

**BEIJING JINGCHENG MA-
CHINERY ELECTRIC HOLDING
CO., LTD.**
59 Dongsanhuan Zhonglu, Chaoyang
District, Beijing, 100022, China
Tel.: (86) 1067702828   CN
Web Site: http://www.jcmeh.com
Sales Range: $1-4.9 Billion
Emp.: 20,000
Holding Company; Industrial Machin-
ery Mfr
N.A.I.C.S.: 551112
Daniel Legault (VP-Building Ottawa
Reg)

Subsidiaries:

Beijing B. J. Electric Motor Co.,
Ltd.   (1)

7 Jiuxianqiaobeilu, Chaoyang District, Beijing, 100015, China
Tel.: (86) 10 64362131
Industrial Motor Mfr & Distr
N.A.I.C.S.: 335312
Hou xiaokun *(Chm)*

Beijing B.J. Electric Motor Co., Ltd. (1)
7 Jiuxianqiaobeilu, Chaoyang District, Beijing, 100015, China
Tel.: (86) 10 6436 2131
Web Site: http://www.chinabjem.com
Electric Motor Mfr
N.A.I.C.S.: 335312
Xiaokun Hou *(Chm)*

Beijing BEIZHONG Steam Turbine Generator Co., Ltd. (1)
No 57 Wujiacun, Shijingshan District, Beijing, 100040, China
Tel.: (86) 1051792435
Web Site: http://www.bzd.com.cn
Sales Range: $400-449.9 Million
Emp.: 1,867
Steam Turbine Mfr
N.A.I.C.S.: 333611

Subsidiary (Domestic):

Beijing Jingcheng New Energy Co., Ltd. (2)
No 57 Wujiacun, Shijingshan District, Beijing, 100040, China
Tel.: (86) 10 5179 2570
Web Site: http://www.jcnewenergy.com
Wind Power Generation Equipment Mfr
N.A.I.C.S.: 333611

Beijing Huade Hydraulic Industrial Group Co., Ltd. (1)
No 5 Tongji North Road Economic And Technological Development Zone, Beijing E&T Development Zone, Beijing, 100176, China
Tel.: (86) 10 6787 2595
Web Site: http://www.huade-hyd.com.cn
Emp.: 500
Hydraulic Components Mfr
N.A.I.C.S.: 333996
Xiansheng Liao *(Gen Mgr)*

Beijing Jingcheng Environmental Protection Development Co., Ltd. (1)
No 1 Guangming East Road, Chongwen District, Beijing, 100061, China
Tel.: (86) 10 6711 8725
Web Site: http://www.jcep.com.cn
Sales Range: $100-124.9 Million
Emp.: 275
Industrial Compressor Mfr
N.A.I.C.S.: 333912

Beijing Jingcheng Heavy Industry Co., Ltd. (1)
Xinghu Industrial Garden, Tongzhou District, Beijing, China
Tel.: (86) 10 6153 9210
Web Site: http://www.jchic.com
Sales Range: $200-249.9 Million
Emp.: 700
Crane & Hoist Machinery Mfr
N.A.I.C.S.: 333923

Beijing No. 1 Machine Tool Plant (1)
No 16 Shuanghe Street Linhe Industrial Development Dist, Beijing, 101300, ShunYi, China
Tel.: (86) 105869024
Web Site: http://www.byjc.com.cn
Sales Range: $50-74.9 Million
Machine Tools Mfr
N.A.I.C.S.: 333517

Subsidiary (Non-US):

Waldrich Coburg Werkzeugmaschinenfabrik GmbH (2)
Hahnweg 116, Coburg, 96450, Germany
Tel.: (49) 9561650
Web Site: http://www.waldrich-coburg.de
Machine Tools Mfr
N.A.I.C.S.: 333517
Hubert Becker *(CEO)*

Beijing No.2 Machine Tool Works Co., Ltd. (1)
No 4 Nanli Lugou Bridge, Fengtai District, Beijing, 100165, China

Tel.: (86) 1083216622
Grinding Machine Mfr & Distr
N.A.I.C.S.: 333248

Beiren Group Corporation (1)
No 6 Rongchang Dongjie BDA, Beijing, 100176, China   **(47.78%)**
Tel.: (86) 10 6780 2109
Web Site: http://www.beirengf.com
Sales Range: $100-124.9 Million
Emp.: 3,043
Holding Company; Printing Machinery Mfr & Distr
N.A.I.C.S.: 551112
Bangshe Chen *(Gen Mgr)*

Subsidiary (Domestic):

Beijing Beiren Fuji Printing Machinery Co., Ltd. (2)
6 Rongchang east St Yizhunge Busoness Developement Area, Chaoyang District, Beijing, 100176, China   **(70%)**
Tel.: (86) 10 6736 5831
Printing Machinery Mfr
N.A.I.C.S.: 333248

Beijing Yanlong Import & Export Co., Ltd. (2)
44 Dong San Huan Nan Lu, Chaoyang District, Beijing, 100022, China
Tel.: (86) 10 6771 8827
Printing Machinery Wholesale Trade Broker
N.A.I.C.S.: 425120

Shaanxi Beiren Printing Machinery Co., Ltd. (2)
West Dongfeng Street, Gaoxin District, Weinan, 714000, Shaanxi, China **(86.24%)**
Tel.: (86) 91 3218 8615
Web Site: http://www.shaanxibeiren.com
Soft Packaging Printing Machinery Mfr & Distr
N.A.I.C.S.: 333248

Shenzhen Beiren Printing Co., Ltd. (2)
Building 702 Liantang Pengji Industry Zone, Luohu, Shenzhen, 51800, China
Tel.: (86) 75 5570 8272
Sales Range: $25-49.9 Million
Emp.: 60
Offset Press Printing Machinery Mfr
N.A.I.C.S.: 333248

BEIJING JINGKELONG COMPANY LIMITED
Block No 45 Xinyuan Street, Chaoyang District, Beijing, China
Tel.: (86) 1064688238
Web Site: https://www.jkl.com.cn
0814—(HKG)
Rev.: $1,693,974,841
Assets: $641,834,895
Liabilities: $402,021,477
Net Worth: $239,813,417
Earnings: ($3,443,276)
Emp.: 4,781
Fiscal Year-end: 12/31/21
General Merchandise Retailer & Wholesale Distr
N.A.I.C.S.: 455219
Jianwen Li *(Bd of Dirs & Chm)*

Subsidiaries:

Beijing Xinyang Tongli Commercial Facilities Company Limited (1)
Beijing Liu-fang S Ln A on the 1st, Beijing, China
Tel.: (86) 1064672168
Web Site: http://www.xytl2002.com
Plastic Packing Materials & Commercial Equipments Mfr
N.A.I.C.S.: 326112

BEIJING JINGNENG CLEAN ENERGY CO., LTD.
No 6 Xibahe Road, Chaoyang District, Beijing, 100028, China
Tel.: (86) 1087407188   CN
Web Site: https://www.jncec.com
Year Founded: 2010
0579—(HKG)
Rev.: $2,812,251,452

Assets: $12,354,437,066
Liabilities: $7,800,748,535
Net Worth: $4,553,688,532
Earnings: $425,218,810
Emp.: 3,190
Fiscal Year-end: 12/31/22
Electric Power
N.A.I.C.S.: 221122
Chen Dayu *(Chm & Sec-Party)*

BEIJING JINGNENG POWER CO., LTD.
Building G HuaTeng Century Park Headquarters, Chaoyang District, Beijing, 100025, China
Tel.: (86) 1085218686
Web Site:
    https://www.jingnengpower.com
Year Founded: 2000
600578—(SHG)
Rev.: $4,280,152,224
Assets: $11,890,916,421
Liabilities: $7,761,315,356
Net Worth: $4,129,601,065
Earnings: $112,770,249
Fiscal Year-end: 12/31/22
Electric Power Generation & Distribution Services
N.A.I.C.S.: 221116

BEIJING JINGNENG THERMAL CO., LTD
908 9F Building No 3 Yard No 8 Auto Museum East Road, Fengtai District, Beijing, 100160, China
Tel.: (86) 1083934888
Web Site: http://www.huatongreli.com
Year Founded: 2002
002893—(SSE)
Rev.: $144,409,824
Assets: $290,841,408
Liabilities: $196,835,184
Net Worth: $94,006,224
Earnings: $4,334,148
Fiscal Year-end: 12/31/22
Heat Supply Management Services
N.A.I.C.S.: 221330
Fu Qiang *(Chm)*

BEIJING JINGXI CULTURE & TOURISM CO., LTD.
Block C Beijing Digital Cultural Industry Park No 1 Wangjing Street, Chaoyang District, Beijing, 100016, China
Tel.: (86) 1057807777
Web Site: http://www.bjwhmedia.com
Year Founded: 1997
000802—(SSE)
Rev.: $15,161,796
Assets: $483,859,116
Liabilities: $271,028,160
Net Worth: $212,830,956
Earnings: ($8,606,520)
Fiscal Year-end: 12/31/22
Tour Operating Services
N.A.I.C.S.: 561520
Zhang Li *(Dir)*

Subsidiaries:

Wumart Stores, Inc. (1)
Wuamrt Commercial Building 158-1 West 4th Ring North Road, Haidian District, Beijing, China   **(95%)**
Tel.: (86) 10 882599488
Web Site: http://www.wumart.com
Sales Range: $1-4.9 Billion
Emp.: 28,578
Superstore Retail Chain Owner & Operator
N.A.I.C.S.: 455211
Ying Xu *(Pres)*

BEIJING JINGYEDA TECHNOLOGY CO., LTD.
Building 6 No 60 Yinhua Road, Haidian District, Beijing, 100095, China
Tel.: (86) 1052168888
Web Site: https://www.jyd.com.cn

Year Founded: 1997
003005—(SSE)
Rev.: $61,806,888
Assets: $260,437,788
Liabilities: $52,655,616
Net Worth: $207,782,172
Earnings: $7,057,908
Fiscal Year-end: 12/31/22
Educational Support Services
N.A.I.C.S.: 611710
Rui Qian *(Chm)*

BEIJING JINGYUNTONG TECHNOLOGY CO., LTD.
No158 Jinghai 4th Rd Beijing Economic & Technological Development Zone, Beijing, 100176, China
Tel.: (86) 1080803016
Web Site:
    https://www.jingyuntong.com
Year Founded: 2002
601908—(SHG)
Rev.: $1,712,769,449
Assets: $3,128,430,961
Liabilities: $1,551,210,481
Net Worth: $1,577,220,480
Earnings: $59,456,845
Emp.: 5,033
Fiscal Year-end: 12/31/22
Solar & Semiconductor Equipment Mfr
N.A.I.C.S.: 334413
Feng Huanpei *(Chm)*

BEIJING JOIN-CHEER SOFTWARE CO., LTD.
No 26 Liangshuihe Road, Economic and Technological Development Zone, Beijing, 100176, China
Tel.: (86) 1088551199
Web Site: https://www.jiuqi.com.cn
Year Founded: 1999
002279—(SSE)
Rev.: $406,855,332
Assets: $388,380,096
Liabilities: $131,587,092
Net Worth: $256,793,004
Earnings: $7,224,984
Fiscal Year-end: 12/31/22
Software Development Services
N.A.I.C.S.: 541511
Zhao Fujun *(Chm)*

BEIJING JWGB SCI. & TECH. CO., LTD.
Dewei Science Park 2F Bldg 5 12 Kechuang 13th Street, Economic & Tech Dev Zone Daxing, Beijing, 100018, China
Tel.: (86) 1068949825
Web Site: http://www.cjwgb.com
Emp.: 50
Specialty Chemicals Mfr
N.A.I.C.S.: 325199

BEIJING KAWIN TECHNOLOGY SHARE-HOLDING CO., LTD.
6 Rongjing East Street BDA, Beijing, 100176, China
Tel.: (86) 1087120888
Web Site: https://www.kawin-bio.com
Year Founded: 2008
688687—(SHG)
Rev.: $162,860,293
Assets: $310,245,390
Liabilities: $74,122,046
Net Worth: $236,123,344
Earnings: $11,710,455
Fiscal Year-end: 12/31/22
Holding Company
N.A.I.C.S.: 551112
Desheng Zhou *(Chm, Pres & Gen Mgr)*

Beijing Kawin Technology Share-Holding Co., Ltd.—(Continued)

Subsidiaries:

Etinpro (Beijing) Co., Ltd.　　　　(1)
Beijing Economic Development Zone
Branch Chong Sixth Street No 88, 2207
Business Center, Beijing, China
Tel.: (86) 1056317076
Web Site: https://www.etinpro.com
Drug Substance Mfr & Distr
N.A.I.C.S.: 325414

**BEIJING KINGFORE HV & EN-
ERGY CONSERVATION TECH-
NOLOGY CO., LTD.**
Room 1201-12 Building 1 Yard 23
Huangsi Street, Xicheng, Beijing,
100120, China
Tel.: (86) 1067711118
Year Founded: 1992
001210—(SSE)
Rev.: $122,291,208
Assets: $275,779,296
Liabilities: $90,315,108
Net Worth: $185,464,188
Earnings: $13,495,248
Fiscal Year-end: 12/31/22
Eletric Power Generation Services
N.A.I.C.S.: 221116
Jianxun Yang *(Chm)*

**BEIJING KINGSOFT OFFICE
SOFTWARE, INC.**
Bldg D Xiaomi Science & Technology
Park Yard 33 Xi Erqi Middle Road,
Haidian, Beijing, 100085, China
Tel.: (86) 1062927777
Web Site: http://www.kingsoft.com
Year Founded: 2011
688111—(SHG)
Rev.: $630,810,852
Assets: $1,934,816,861
Liabilities: $547,520,921
Net Worth: $1,387,295,940
Earnings: $182,451,401
Fiscal Year-end: 12/31/23
Software Development Services
N.A.I.C.S.: 541511
Tao Zou *(CEO)*

**BEIJING KONRUNS PHARMA-
CEUTICAL CO., LTD.**
Building 3 No 7 Science Park Road
Zhongguancun Life Science Park,
Changping District, Beijing, 102206,
China
Tel.: (86) 1082898888
Web Site: https://www.konruns.cn
Year Founded: 2003
603590—(SHG)
Rev.: $124,066,394
Assets: $516,519,937
Liabilities: $36,883,775
Net Worth: $479,636,162
Earnings: $22,673,548
Fiscal Year-end: 12/31/21
Drugs Product Mfr & Distr
N.A.I.C.S.: 325412
Jianhua Liu *(Chm & Pres)*

**BEIJING LABTECH INSTRU-
MENTS CO., LTD.**
No 6 Anqing Street, Area B Tianzhu
Airport Industrial Zone Shunyi District,
Beijing, 101312, China
Tel.: (86) 1080492709
Web Site: http://www.power-zyt.com
Year Founded: 2002
688056—(SHG)
Rev.: $49,842,674
Assets: $134,998,728
Liabilities: $18,933,263
Net Worth: $116,065,465
Earnings: $6,265,280
Fiscal Year-end: 12/31/22
Analytical Instrument Mfr & Distr

N.A.I.C.S.: 334516
Yu Hao *(CFO & Sec)*

**BEIJING LEADMAN BIOCHEM-
ISTRY CO., LTD.**
No 5 Xinghai Road Beijing Economic
and Technological Development
Zone, Beijing, 100176, China
Tel.: (86) 1067855500
Web Site:
　https://www.leadmanbio.com
Year Founded: 1997
300289—(CHIN)
Rev.: $99,119,592
Assets: $280,397,052
Liabilities: $30,419,064
Net Worth: $249,977,988
Earnings: $7,900,308)
Emp.: 270
Fiscal Year-end: 12/31/22
In-Vitro Diagnosis Products & Bio-
chemical Raw Materials Mfr, Devel-
oper & Researcher
N.A.I.C.S.: 325413

**BEIJING LIER HIGH-
TEMPERATURE MATERIALS
CO., LTD.**
Xiaotangshan Industrial Park Chang-
ping District, Beijing, 102211, China
Tel.: (86) 1061712828
Web Site: http://www.bjlirr.com.cn
002392—(SSE)
Rev.: $662,598,144
Assets: $1,063,802,376
Liabilities: $365,353,092
Net Worth: $698,449,284
Earnings: $35,977,500
Fiscal Year-end: 12/31/22
Fireproof Materials Mfr & Distr
N.A.I.C.S.: 339999

**BEIJING LIVEN TECHNOLOGY
CO., LTD.**
4-5th Floor Jingrun Building No 28
Fuwai Street, Xicheng District, Bei-
jing, 100037, China
Tel.: (86) 1068042018
Web Site: https://www.l-ren.com.cn
Year Founded: 1998
001259—(SSE)
Rev.: $92,223,144
Assets: $124,471,620
Liabilities: $20,489,976
Net Worth: $103,981,644
Earnings: $7,233,408
Fiscal Year-end: 12/31/22
Household Appliance Mfr & Distr
N.A.I.C.S.: 335220
Laoliang Song *(Chm & Gen Mgr)*

**BEIJING LONGRUAN TECH-
NOLOGIES, INC.**
Room 1008 Tianchuang Technology
Building No 8 Caihefang Road, Haid-
ian District, Beijing, 100190, China
Tel.: (86) 1062670727
Web Site: https://www.longruan.com
Year Founded: 2002
688030—(SHG)
Rev.: $51,229,447
Assets: $112,125,532
Liabilities: $21,413,050
Net Worth: $90,712,482
Earnings: $11,238,276
Fiscal Year-end: 12/31/22
Software Development Services
N.A.I.C.S.: 541511
Shanjun Mao *(Chm)*

**BEIJING LUZHU BIOTECH-
NOLOGY CO., LTD.**
No 3 Guangtong Street Industrial De-
velopment Zone, Tongzhou District,
Beijing, China
Tel.: (86) 61568561　　　　　CN

Web Site:
　https://www.luzhubiotech.com
Year Founded: 2001
2480—(HKG)
Information Technology Services
N.A.I.C.S.: 541512
Jian Kong *(Chm)*

**BEIJING MEDIA CORPORA-
TION LIMITED**
Building A No 23 Baijiazhuang Dongli,
Chaoyang District, Beijing, 100026,
China
Tel.: (86) 1065902806
Web Site:
　https://www.bjmedia.com.cn
Year Founded: 2001
1000—(HKG)
Rev.: $22,238,939
Assets: $98,997,304
Liabilities: $10,873,699
Net Worth: $88,123,604
Earnings: ($3,955,630)
Emp.: 329
Fiscal Year-end: 12/31/22
Advertising Space Providers & News-
papers Producers
N.A.I.C.S.: 424920
Chuanpai Ji *(Chm)*

**BEIJING NEW SPACE TECH-
NOLOGY CO., LTD.**
No 15 Building 8 Area A No1 Jinghai
5th Road, Tongzhou District, Beijing,
101111, China
Tel.: (86) 1087217171
Web Site: https://www.nnlighting.com
Year Founded: 2004
605178—(SHG)
Rev.: $46,316,514
Assets: $325,960,278
Liabilities: $72,250,472
Net Worth: $253,709,806
Earnings: ($29,357,233)
Fiscal Year-end: 12/31/22
Information Technology Services
N.A.I.C.S.: 541512
Palace Sea *(Chm)*

**BEIJING NEW UNIVERSAL
SCIENCE AND TECHNOLOGY
CO., LTD.**
12th Floor Building B Technology For-
tune Center No 8 Xueqing Road,
Haidian District, Beijing, 100192,
China
Tel.: (86) 1062665166
Web Site: https://www.newu.com.cn
Year Founded: 2003
300472—(CHIN)
Rev.: $79,657,344
Assets: $245,194,560
Liabilities: $133,431,948
Net Worth: $111,762,612
Earnings: ($10,638,108)
Fiscal Year-end: 12/31/22
Industrial Machinery Mfr
N.A.I.C.S.: 333248
Zhu Yesheng *(Chm)*

Subsidiaries:

Beijing New Universal Environmental
Engineering & Technology Co.,
Ltd.　　　　　　　　　　　(1)
New land plaza 58 Fucheng Rd, Haidian
District, Beijing, China
Tel.: (86) 105167633
Intelligent Equipment Mfr
N.A.I.C.S.: 333248

Beijing Sifang Tongxing Mechanical
Technology Development Co.,
Ltd.　　　　　　　　　　　(1)
No 3 Development Zone Nankouzhen,
Changping District, Beijing, China
Tel.: (86) 1089790925
Intelligent Equipment Mfr
N.A.I.C.S.: 333248

Beijing Tianzhongfang Environmental
Protection Science & Technology Co.,
Ltd.　　　　　　　　　　　(1)
631 No 2 Building Chuangxin Road 11,
Changping District, Beijing, China
Tel.: (86) 1069716656
Intelligent Equipment Mfr
N.A.I.C.S.: 333248

Tianjin New Universal Science &
Technology Co., Ltd.　　　　(1)
North of Baozhong Road and West of Tian-
zhong Road, Industry Park Baodi District,
Tianjin, China
Tel.: (86) 2222520698
Intelligent Transport Services
N.A.I.C.S.: 485999

Wuhu New Universal Environmental
Science & Technology Co., Ltd.　(1)
Guandoumen Road No 258 Economic
Zone, Jiujiang District, Wuhu, Anhui, China
Tel.: (86) 5538298639
Intelligent Equipment Mfr
N.A.I.C.S.: 333248

**BEIJING NORTH STAR COM-
PANY LIMITED**
No 8 Beichen East Road, Chao Yang
District, Beijing, 100101, China
Tel.: (86) 1064991284　　　　CN
Web Site:
　http://www.beijingnorthstar.com
Year Founded: 1997
601588—(SHG)
Rev.: $1,823,647,134
Assets: $9,446,142,972
Liabilities: $7,205,400,460
Net Worth: $2,240,742,512
Earnings: ($221,202,474)
Emp.: 5,387
Fiscal Year-end: 12/31/22
Property Investment & Development
Services
N.A.I.C.S.: 523940
Chuan Guo *(Deputy Gen Mgr)*

**BEIJING ORIENT LANDSCAPE
& ENVIRONMENT CO., LTD.**
Floor 104 IT Industrial Park, No 10
Jiuxianqiao North Road Chaoyang
District, Beijing, 100015, China
Tel.: (86) 1059388888
Web Site:
　https://www.orientscape.com
002310—(SSE)
Rev.: $473,591,664
Assets: $5,724,466,020
Liabilities: $4,874,411,412
Net Worth: $850,054,608
Earnings: ($821,686,788)
Emp.: 3,925
Fiscal Year-end: 12/31/22
Landscaping Services
N.A.I.C.S.: 541320
Dong Zhao *(Pres)*

**BEIJING ORIENT NATIONAL
COMMUNICATION SCIENCE &
TECHNOLOGY CO., LTD.**
Wangjing Road 9 D Block 1108, Cha-
oyang District, Beijing, 100102, China
Tel.: (86) 1064392089
Web Site: http://www.bonc.com.cn
300166—(CHIN)
Rev.: $321,337,692
Assets: $1,133,374,788
Liabilities: $214,637,904
Net Worth: $918,736,884
Earnings: ($50,704,056)
Fiscal Year-end: 12/31/22
Computer Programming Services
N.A.I.C.S.: 541511
Guan Lianping *(Chm & Pres)*

**BEIJING ORIENTAL JICHENG
CO.,.LTD**
12th Floor Yindu Building No 67

Fucheng Road, Haidian District, Beijing, 100142, China
Tel.: (86) 1068715566
Web Site: https://www.dfzk.com
Year Founded: 2000
002819—(SSE)
Rev.: $424,402,524
Assets: $723,627,216
Liabilities: $185,294,304
Net Worth: $538,332,912
Earnings: $124,793,136
Fiscal Year-end: 12/31/22
Electronic Instrument Distr
N.A.I.C.S.: 423860
Ge Wang *(Board of Directors & Chm)*

BEIJING ORIENTAL YUHONG WATERPROOF TECHNOLOGY CO., LTD.

Courtyard 19 9th Kechuang Street, Beijing Economic-technological Development Area E-town, Beijing, China
Tel.: (86) 4007791975
Web Site: https://en.yuhong.com.cn
Year Founded: 1995
002271—(SSE)
Rev.: $4,382,423,136
Assets: $7,098,031,512
Liabilities: $3,280,767,516
Net Worth: $3,817,263,996
Earnings: $297,690,120
Emp.: 1,120
Fiscal Year-end: 12/31/22
Waterproofing Material Supplier
N.A.I.C.S.: 325510

BEIJING ORIGIN WATER TECHNOLOGY CO., LTD.

OriginWater Building No 23-2 Life Science Park Road, Haidan District, Beijing, 102206, China
Tel.: (86) 1088465890
Web Site:
http://www.en.originwater.com
Year Founded: 2001
300070—(CHIN)
Rev.: $1,220,042,304
Assets: $10,199,974,356
Liabilities: $6,065,802,288
Net Worth: $4,134,172,068
Earnings: $99,471,996
Fiscal Year-end: 12/31/22
Industrial Sewage Treatment & Water Recycling Services
N.A.I.C.S.: 221320
Huang Jianglong *(Chm & Pres)*

Subsidiaries:

Beijing Jiuan Construction Investment Group Co., Ltd. **(1)**
23-2 Bishuiyuan Building Life Science Park Beiging Road, Haidian District, Beijing, 102206, China
Tel.: (86) 1061779577
Web Site: http://www.j-j-a.com
Water Conservancy Services
N.A.I.C.S.: 237110

Beijing OriginWater Membrane Technology Co., Ltd. **(1)**
No 4 Leyuan South 2nd Street Yanxi Economic Area C Block, Huairou District, Beijing, 102206, China
Tel.: (86) 1060689256
Water Conservancy Services
N.A.I.C.S.: 237110

Beijing OriginWater PureTech Co., Ltd. **(1)**
23-2 BOW Building Life Science Park Road, Haidian District, Beijing, 102206, China
Tel.: (86) 1080180742
Water Conservancy Services
N.A.I.C.S.: 237110

Guangdong O'Water Environmental Protective Technology Co., Ltd. **(1)**
No 4 Building Mengyong Industrial Zone Dashi Shinan Rd Panyu District,

Guangzhou, 511430, China
Tel.: (86) 2066208087
Web Site: http://www.en.gzqwell.com
Water Conservancy Services
N.A.I.C.S.: 237110

Wuxi Rayon Membrane Technology Co.,Ltd. **(1)**
No 26 Xinjin Road, Wuxi New District, Wuxi, China
Tel.: (86) 5181103557
Chemical Product Mfr & Distr
N.A.I.C.S.: 325998

BEIJING OUTSELL HEALTH PRODUCT DEVELOPMENT CO., LTD.

No 9 West Road Beisihuan, Beijing, China
Tel.: (86) 1062800800
Web Site: http://www.outsell.com.cn
Year Founded: 1998
Sales Range: $25-49.9 Million
Tea Producer
N.A.I.C.S.: 311920
Yihong Zhao *(CEO)*

BEIJING PHILISENSE TECHNOLOGY CO., LTD.

Room 1001 10th Floor No 2 Courtyard Zhixin Village, Haidian District, Beijing, 100191, China
Tel.: (86) 1062358383
Web Site: http://www.philisense.com
Year Founded: 1997
300287—(CHIN)
Rev.: $160,471,584
Assets: $430,334,424
Liabilities: $197,203,032
Net Worth: $233,131,392
Earnings: ($65,822,328)
Emp.: 340
Fiscal Year-end: 12/31/22
Electronic & Communications Products Mfr
N.A.I.C.S.: 334419
Yang Zhenhua *(Chm & Gen Mgr)*

BEIJING PROPERTIES (HOLDINGS) LIMITED

66/F Central Plaza 18 Harbour Road, Wanchai, China (Hong Kong)
Tel.: (852) 25116016 **BM**
Web Site: http://www.bphl.com.hk
0925—(HKG)
Rev.: $167,424,713
Assets: $2,262,250,095
Liabilities: $1,654,729,935
Net Worth: $607,520,160
Earnings: $6,925,163
Emp.: 525
Fiscal Year-end: 12/31/22
Investment Management Service
N.A.I.C.S.: 523940
Kin Wai Siu *(CEO)*

Subsidiaries:

Beijing Inland Port International Logistics Co. Ltd. **(1)**
No A1 Dongsihuan Nanlu, Chaoyang, Beijing, 100023, China
Tel.: (86) 10 8769 4546
Logistics Consulting Servies
N.A.I.C.S.: 541614

Holiday Inn Downtown Beijing Company Limited **(1)**
98 Beilishilu Xichengqu, Beijing, 100037, China
Tel.: (86) 1068338822
Web Site: http://www.holidayinn.com
Restaurant Operators
N.A.I.C.S.: 722511

Tianjin Transwell International Logistics Co., Ltd. **(1)**
No 19 The Third Avenue Tianjin Airport International Logistics Zone, Tianjin, 300300, China
Tel.: (86) 22 8488 9990

Logistics Consulting Servies
N.A.I.C.S.: 541614

BEIJING QIANJING LANDSCAPE CO., LTD.

Block 2 No 2 East Landianchan, Haidian District, Beijing, 100097, China
Tel.: (86) 1088862070
Web Site:
http://www.qianjingyuanlin.com
603778—(SHG)
Rev.: $27,778,238
Assets: $335,201,350
Liabilities: $160,509,520
Net Worth: $174,691,830
Earnings: ($22,770,086)
Fiscal Year-end: 12/31/22
Landscape Architectural Services
N.A.I.C.S.: 541320
Quanfu Hui *(Chm & Gen Mgr)*

BEIJING QUANSHI WORLD ONLINE NETWORK INFORMATION CO., LTD.

No 1 Wuliqiao 1st Street, Chaoyang District, Beijing, 100024, China
Tel.: (86) 1053565333
Web Site: https://www.372163.com
Year Founded: 2005
002995—(SSE)
Rev.: $427,468,860
Assets: $200,708,820
Liabilities: $53,952,912
Net Worth: $146,755,908
Earnings: $446,472
Fiscal Year-end: 12/31/22
Information Technology Services
N.A.I.C.S.: 541512
Yian Xin *(Chm & Gen Mgr)*

BEIJING ROBOROCK TECHNOLOGY CO., LTD.

Building 3 Yard 17 Anju Road, ChangPing District, Beijing, 102206, China
Tel.: (86) 1053241660
Web Site: https://global.roborock.com
Year Founded: 2014
688169—(SHG)
Rev.: $930,671,783
Assets: $1,520,960,768
Liabilities: $179,106,314
Net Worth: $1,341,854,453
Earnings: $166,160,157
Fiscal Year-end: 12/31/22
Application Development Services
N.A.I.C.S.: 541511
Jing Chang *(Chm & Gen Mgr)*

BEIJING SANFO OUTDOOR PRODUCTS CO., LTD

Building 23 No 3 Chenjiaying West Road, Changping District, Beijing, 100192, China
Tel.: (86) 1087409280
Web Site: http://www.sanfo.com
Year Founded: 1997
002780—(SSE)
Rev.: $78,956,748
Assets: $150,315,048
Liabilities: $54,330,588
Net Worth: $95,984,460
Earnings: ($4,658,472)
Emp.: 1,000
Fiscal Year-end: 12/31/22
Outdoor Product Distr
N.A.I.C.S.: 459110
Zhang Heng *(Chm & Gen Mgr)*

BEIJING SCIENCE SUN PHARMACEUTICAL CO., LTD.

No 8 Xingsheng Street, Beijing Economic and Technological Development Zone, Beijing, 100176, China
Tel.: (86) 1067877178

Web Site: https://www.ssyy.com.cn
Year Founded: 1999
300485—(CHIN)
Rev.: $67,124,828
Assets: $510,187,109
Liabilities: $21,776,875
Net Worth: $488,410,235
Earnings: $14,495,972
Fiscal Year-end: 12/31/23
Pharmaceuticals Product Mfr
N.A.I.C.S.: 325412

BEIJING SCITOP BIO-TECH CO., LTD.

No 1-2 No 31 Niuhe Road Yanqi Economic Development Zone, Huairou District, Beijing, 101407, China
Tel.: (86) 1069667389
Web Site: http://www.scitop.cn
Year Founded: 2003
300858—(SSE)
Rev.: $51,831,468
Assets: $251,394,624
Liabilities: $13,196,196
Net Worth: $238,198,428
Earnings: $15,428,556
Fiscal Year-end: 12/31/22
Biotechnology Products Mfr
N.A.I.C.S.: 325199
Tiansong Sun *(Chm)*

BEIJING SDL TECHNOLOGY CO., LTD.

No 3 Gaoxin 3rd Street, Changping, Beijing, 102206, China
Tel.: (86) 1080735600
Web Site: https://www.chsdl.com
002658—(SSE)
Rev.: $211,269,708
Assets: $485,327,700
Liabilities: $111,373,704
Net Worth: $373,953,996
Earnings: $39,832,884
Emp.: 2,000
Fiscal Year-end: 12/31/22
Analysis Instruments, Environmental Monitoring, Industrial Process Analysis Systems Mfr
N.A.I.C.S.: 334513
Xiaoqiang Ao *(Chm & Gen Mgr)*

BEIJING SEEYON INTERNET SOFTWARE CORP.

Block N Jingxinyuan No 25 Beiwucun Road, Haidian District, Beijing, 100195, China
Tel.: (86) 1088850901
Web Site: http://www.seeyon.com
Year Founded: 2002
688369—(SHG)
Rev.: $144,953,144
Assets: $273,844,261
Liabilities: $67,903,983
Net Worth: $205,940,278
Earnings: $13,208,916
Fiscal Year-end: 12/31/22
Software Development Services
N.A.I.C.S.: 541511
Shi Xu *(Chm & Gen Mgr)*

BEIJING SHENGTONG PRINTING CO., LTD.

No 18 Jinghai 3rd Road Economic and Technological Development Zone, Beijing, 100176, China
Tel.: (86) 1052249888
Web Site:
https://www.shengtongprint.com
Year Founded: 2000
002599—(SSE)
Rev.: $314,324,712
Assets: $382,084,560
Liabilities: $178,111,440
Net Worth: $203,973,120
Earnings: $679,536
Emp.: 1,000

Beijing Shengtong Printing Co., Ltd.—(Continued)

Fiscal Year-end: 12/31/22
Printing Services
N.A.I.C.S.: 323111
Chunlin Jia *(Chm)*

BEIJING SHIJI INFORMATION TECHNOLOGY CO., LTD.

Fuxing Road Jia No 65, Haidian District, Beijing, 100036, China
Tel.: (86) 1058672266
Web Site: http://www.shijigroup.com
Year Founded: 1995
002153—(SSE)
Rev.: $364,387,140
Assets: $1,346,589,036
Liabilities: $198,307,980
Net Worth: $1,148,281,056
Earnings: ($109,382,832)
Emp.: 5,000
Fiscal Year-end: 12/31/22
Software Development Services
N.A.I.C.S.: 513210
Li Zhongchu *(Founder, Chm & Pres)*

Subsidiaries:

Baoku Online Technology Ltd. **(1)**
No 1 Jiuxianqiao East Road, Chaoyang District, Beijing, China
Tel.: (86) 4000010066
Software Services
N.A.I.C.S.: 541511

Beijing Changyi Information Technologies Co., Ltd. **(1)**
No 5-303 3/F Building 5 Tian Chang Yuan Media Village, Chao Yang District, Beijing, China
Tel.: (86) 1084982277
Web Site: http://www.changyi.com
Information Technology Consulting Services
N.A.I.C.S.: 541512

Beijing Shiji Kunlun Software Co., Ltd. **(1)**
Floor 15 Beijing INN No 5 Dongshuijing Hutong, Dongcheng District, Beijing, 100010, China
Tel.: (86) 1059325388
Web Site: https://www.shijinet.cn
Software Services
N.A.I.C.S.: 541511

China National Electronic Devices Corp. **(1)**
6F Yanbao Building No 59 Yuquan Road, PO Box 160, Shijingshan District, Beijing, 100036, China
Tel.: (86) 1068211166
Electronic Device Mfr & Distr
N.A.I.C.S.: 334419

Galasys Global (Suzhou) Co. Ltd. **(1)**
Unit 203 204 Tower F Plaza Jia Hua No 9 Shangdi 3rd Street, Haidian District, Beijing, 10085, China
Tel.: (86) 1062986912
Software Services
N.A.I.C.S.: 541511

GuangZhou Armitage Technologies Ltd. **(1)**
Room 3203 A - 3205 32F Zhujiang International Building, No 112 Yuehua Road Yuexiu District, Guangzhou, Guangdong, China
Tel.: (86) 2028826288
Web Site: http://www.armitage.com.cn
Hotel Management Software Development Services
N.A.I.C.S.: 541511

Guangzhou Armitage Computer Software Co., Ltd. **(1)**
6-4F No.3 Affiliated Building of Guangzhou Venture Capital Town, No 1601 South Guangzhou Avenue Haizhu District, Guangzhou, China
Tel.: (86) 2028826288
Software Services
N.A.I.C.S.: 541511

Horwath HTL Limited **(1)**
Unit 903-904 Tower E3 Oriental Plaza No 1

East Chang-An Ave, Beijing, 100738, China
Tel.: (86) 1085181833
Web Site: http://www.horwathhtl.com
Hospitality Services
N.A.I.C.S.: 561720
Dorothy Dowling *(Mng Dir)*

ICE Portal, Inc. **(1)**
4601 Sheridan St Ste 600, Hollywood, FL 33021
Tel.: (954) 893-6778
Web Site: http://iceportal.shijigroup.com
Computer System Design Services
N.A.I.C.S.: 541512
Henry Woodman *(Pres)*

Infrasys International Limited **(1)**
6/F Aitken Vanson Centre 61 Hoi Yuen Road, Kwun Tong, Kowloon, China (Hong Kong)
Tel.: (852) 27501682
Software Development Services
N.A.I.C.S.: 541511

Subsidiary (Non-US):

Infrasys (Beijing) Ltd. **(2)**
15F Beijing INN No 5 East Shui Jing Hu Tong Chao Yang Men Nei, Dongcheng District, Beijing, 100022, China
Tel.: (86) 1059325388
Software Development Services
N.A.I.C.S.: 541511

Infrasys Malaysia Sdn. Bhd. **(2)**
B-3A-01 Block B Arena Mentari 1 Jalan PJS8/15 Dataran Mentari, 46150, Petaling Jaya, Selangor, Malaysia
Tel.: (60) 356211122
Software Development Services
N.A.I.C.S.: 541511
Eric Hong *(Country Mgr)*

NanJing SilverStone Computer System Co., Ltd. **(1)**
5F Building 4 Nanjing BigData Industrial Park 180 Software Ave, Yuhua District, Nanjing, 210012, China
Tel.: (86) 2552806888
Web Site: http://www.ss-soft.com
Hotel Management Software Development Services
N.A.I.C.S.: 541511

Quick Check Limited **(1)**
24 Raul Wallenberg Street Ziv tower C, Tel Aviv, 6971923, Israel
Tel.: (972) 773447510
Software Services
N.A.I.C.S.: 541511

Review Rank S.A. **(1)**
Aribau 240 6-M, Barcelona, 08006, Spain
Tel.: (34) 93 452 0069
Hospitality Services
N.A.I.C.S.: 561720
Guille Garcia *(Mgr-Product)*

Subsidiary (Non-US):

ReviewPro Asia Pacific Pte Ltd **(2)**
152 Beach Road 06-03 Gateway East, Singapore, 189721, Singapore
Hospitality Services
N.A.I.C.S.: 561720
Michael Chin *(Reg VP)*

Subsidiary (US):

ReviewPro, Inc **(2)**
149 Madison Ave Ste 1173, New York, NY 10016
Tel.: (888) 743-8827
Hospitality Services
N.A.I.C.S.: 541511
Josiah Mackenzie *(VP-Bus Dev)*

SHIJI (US) INC. **(1)**
303 Perimeter Ctr N Ste 300, Atlanta, GA 30346
Tel.: (678) 502-1066
Hotel Management Software Development Services
N.A.I.C.S.: 541511

Shanghai Bestech Software Co., Ltd. **(1)**
Room 102 Building 4 396 Guilin Road, Zhonghe Puyuan Science and Technology Park Xuhui District, Shanghai, China
Tel.: (86) 2152360316

Software Development Services
N.A.I.C.S.: 541511

Shenzhen Solusoft Software Co., Ltd. **(1)**
13F Block 2C Shenzhen Software Industry Base, District Branch Garden Road 1003 Nanshan, Shenzhen, 518057, China
Tel.: (86) 75526520714
Web Site: http://www.siss.com.cn
Hotel Management Software Development Services
N.A.I.C.S.: 541511

Shiji (Australia) Pty Ltd **(1)**
Suite 10 04 Tower 1 475 Victoria Avenue, Chatswood, 2067, NSW, Australia
Tel.: (61) 288805102
Software Services
N.A.I.C.S.: 541511

Shiji (Hong Kong) Ltd. **(1)**
Rm 1802 18/F Great Eagle Centre 23 Harbour Road, Wanchai, China (Hong Kong)
Tel.: (852) 23328520
Software Services
N.A.I.C.S.: 541511

Shiji (UK) Limited **(1)**
The Kinetic Centre Theobald Street, Elstree, WD6 4PJ, Hertfordshire, United Kingdom
Tel.: (44) 775 440 6104
Software Services
N.A.I.C.S.: 541511

Shiji Deutschland GmbH **(1)**
Tempelhofer Ufer 1, 10961, Berlin, Germany
Tel.: (49) 3058849515
Software Services
N.A.I.C.S.: 541511

Shiji GmbH **(1)**
Auerspergstrasse 8, 5700, Zell am See, Austria
Tel.: (43) 720116300
Software Services
N.A.I.C.S.: 541511
Kevin Patrick King *(Mng Dir)*

Shiji Information Technology (Hong Kong) Limited **(1)**
Unit A 3/F KOHO 73-75 Hung To Road, Kwun Tong, Kowloon, China (Hong Kong)
Tel.: (852) 27501682
Software Services
N.A.I.C.S.: 541511

Shiji Information Technology (Philippines), Inc. **(1)**
Unit 1206 Trade Financial Tower 7th Avenue 32nd St, Bonifacio Global City, Taguig, 1634, Metro Manila, Philippines
Tel.: (63) 285409595
Software Services
N.A.I.C.S.: 541511

Shiji Information Technology Spain, S.A. **(1)**
Passeig de Gracia 17 planta 6, 08007, Barcelona, Spain
Tel.: (34) 981225366
Hospital Services
N.A.I.C.S.: 622110
Michael Levie *(CEO & Partner)*

Shiji Japan Co., Ltd. **(1)**
Ueno TH Building 3F B 3-39-10 Yushima, Bunkyo-Ku, Tokyo, 113-0034, Japan
Tel.: (81) 5031961025
Software Services
N.A.I.C.S.: 541511

Shiji Malaysia Sdn. Bhd. **(1)**
Unit 3A-1 Tower 9 UOA Business Park 1 Jalan Pengaturcara U1/51A, Seksyen U1, 40150, Shah Alam, Selangor, Malaysia
Tel.: (60) 37 662 1121
Software Services
N.A.I.C.S.: 541511

Shiji Middle East FZ-LLC **(1)**
Dubai Internet City Building 11 Office G08, PO Box 73000, 7300, Dubai, United Arab Emirates
Tel.: (971) 586507202
Software Services
N.A.I.C.S.: 541511

Shiji Poland Sp. z o.o. **(1)**

ul Chorzowska 148, 40-101, Katowice, Poland
Tel.: (48) 324117000
Software Services
N.A.I.C.S.: 541511

Shiji Portugal - Conceptek Sistemas de Informacao S.A. **(1)**
Edificio Shiji Sitio da Igreja Caminho do Cerro do Galo, 8135-028, Almancil, Portugal
Tel.: (351) 28 935 1200
Software Services
N.A.I.C.S.: 541511

Shiji Singapore Pte. Ltd. **(1)**
152 Beach Road 06-01 Gateway East Building, Singapore, 189721, Singapore
Tel.: (65) 63374543
Software Services
N.A.I.C.S.: 541511

Shiji Slovakia s.r.o. **(1)**
Marianske Namestie 191/14, 010 01, Zilina, Slovakia
Tel.: (421) 412302924
Software Services
N.A.I.C.S.: 541511

Shiji Thailand Limited **(1)**
152 Chartered Square Building 30/F Room 30-01 Unit, 3039 North Sathorn Road Silom Bangrak, Bangkok, 10500, Thailand
Tel.: (66) 25440088
Software Services
N.A.I.C.S.: 541511

Snapshot GmbH **(1)**
Auerspergstrasse 8, Zell am See, Austria
Tel.: (43) 69910109327
Web Site: http://www.snapshot.travel
Hotel Management Software Development Services
N.A.I.C.S.: 541511
David Turnbull *(Co-Founder & Chief Comml Officer)*

eFuture Holding Inc. **(1)**
/F Topnew Tower 15 Guanghua Road Chaoyang District, Beijing, 100026, China
Tel.: (86) 10 5165 0988
Web Site: http://www.e-future.com.cn
Sales Range: $200-249.9 Million
Holding Company
N.A.I.C.S.: 551112
Dong Cheng *(Chm)*

hetras Deutschland GmbH **(1)**
Tassiloplatz 27 RGB, 81541, Munich, Germany
Tel.: (49) 8941207171
Hotel Management Software Development Services
N.A.I.C.S.: 541511

BEIJING SHOUGANG CO., LTD.

No 99 Shijingshan Road, Shijingshan District, Beijing, China
Tel.: (86) 1088293727
Web Site: https://www.sggf.com.cn
Year Founded: 1999
000959—(SSE)
Rev.: $16,587,162,072
Assets: $20,101,552,380
Liabilities: $13,071,432,348
Net Worth: $7,030,120,032
Earnings: $157,885,416
Fiscal Year-end: 12/31/22
Iron & Steel Product Smelting Services
N.A.I.C.S.: 331410
Zhao Min'ge *(Chm)*

BEIJING SHUNXIN AGRICULTURE CO., LTD.

12F Shunxin International Business Center Building No 1, No 1 Yard of Zhanqian Street Shunyi District, Beijing, 101300, China
Tel.: (86) 1069420860
Web Site: http://www.000860.com
Year Founded: 1998
000860—(SSE)
Rev.: $1,639,638,936

Assets: $2,843,873,604
Liabilities: $1,849,126,968
Net Worth: $994,746,636
Earnings: ($94,521,492)
Fiscal Year-end: 12/31/22
Meat Mfr & Distr
N.A.I.C.S.: 311615

**BEIJING SHUZHI TECHNOL-
OGY CO., LTD.**
Suite 302 Major Building No 28 Outer
New Street, Xicheng District, Beijing,
100060, China
Tel.: (86) 1082055588
Web Site: http://www.shuzhi.ai
300038—(CHIN)
Rev.: $690,079,289
Assets: $840,436,519
Liabilities: $410,610,461
Net Worth: $429,826,059
Earnings: ($1,223,268,475)
Emp.: 2,000
Fiscal Year-end: 12/31/20
Communication Tower Mfr
N.A.I.C.S.: 237130

**BEIJING SIFANG AUTOMA-
TION CO., LTD.**
No 9 Shangdi 4th street, Haidian Dis-
trict, Beijing, 100085, China
Tel.: (86) 1082181545
Web Site: https://www.sifang-
electric.com
Year Founded: 1994
601126—(SHG)
Rev.: $713,020,642
Assets: $1,186,611,828
Liabilities: $618,283,889
Net Worth: $568,327,940
Earnings: $76,267,288
Fiscal Year-end: 12/31/22
Power Plant Automation Product Mfr
& Whslr
N.A.I.C.S.: 335311
Gao Xiuhuan *(Chm)*

Subsidiaries:

ABB Sifang Power System Co.,
Ltd.　　　　　　　　　　　　　**(1)**
Jia 3 Anxiang Avenue District B Tianzhu
Airport Industrial Area, Shunyi District, Bei-
jing, 101300, China
Tel.: (86) 1080475588
Converter Valve Mfr
N.A.I.C.S.: 332912

Baoding Sifang Sanyi Electric Co.,
Ltd.　　　　　　　　　　　　　**(1)**
NO 5999 North 3rd Ring, High-Tech New
Development Zone, Baoding, 071051,
China
Tel.: (86) 312 627 1618
Web Site: https://www.sanyii.com
Power & Electronics Product Mfr
N.A.I.C.S.: 335311

**BEIJING SINNET TECHNOL-
OGY COMPANY LIMITED**
2 floor block A east ring Plaza No 9
Dongzhong Street, Dongcheng Dis-
trict, Beijing, 100011, China
Tel.: (86) 1064181150
Web Site: https://www.sinnet.com.cn
Year Founded: 1999
300383—(CHIN)
Rev.: $1,009,620,612
Assets: $2,711,204,028
Liabilities: $934,941,852
Net Worth: $1,776,262,176
Earnings: ($123,540,768)
Fiscal Year-end: 12/31/22
Broadband Access Services, Internet
Data Center, Value-Added Services &
Other Internet Integrated Services
N.A.I.C.S.: 517810

**BEIJING SINODATA TECH CO.,
LTD.**

Guangzhou Avenue North 1421 St
Building 601 Baiyun District,
Guangzhou, 510510, China
Tel.: (86) 2038858687
Web Site: http://www.gddaan.com
Rev.: $72,113,440
Assets: $145,390,000
Liabilities: $47,542,530
Net Worth: $97,847,470
Earnings: $9,450,350
Fiscal Year-end: 12/31/18
Engineering Construction Services
N.A.I.C.S.: 541330
Yedong Zhu *(Chm & Pres)*

**BEIJING SINOHYTEC CO.,
LTD.**
7th Floor Building B-6 Block B No 66,
Xixiaokou Road, Beijing, 100192,
China
Tel.: (86) 1062796418
Web Site: https://www.sinohytec.com
Year Founded: 2012
688339—(SHG)
Rev.: $103,631,571
Assets: $530,568,315
Liabilities: $145,232,779
Net Worth: $385,335,536
Earnings: ($23,370,184)
Fiscal Year-end: 12/31/22
Application Development Services
N.A.I.C.S.: 541511
Guoqiang Zhang *(Chm & Gen Mgr)*

**BEIJING SL PHARMACEUTI-
CAL CO., LTD.**
Building 1 Bitongyuan No 69 Fushi
Road, Haidian District, Beijing,
100143, China
Tel.: (86) 1088799370
Web Site: http://www.slpharm.com.cn
Year Founded: 1994
002038—(SSE)
Rev.: $147,443,868
Assets: $824,967,936
Liabilities: $55,682,640
Net Worth: $769,285,296
Earnings: $32,909,760
Fiscal Year-end: 12/31/22
Pharmaceuticals Mfr
N.A.I.C.S.: 325412
Xu Mingbo *(Chm & Gen Mgr)*

**BEIJING SNLN HP NEW
SYNTC FBR SER CO LTD**
No 1 Building No 68 Beiqing Road,
Haidian District, Beijing, 100094,
China
Tel.: (86) 1064390678
Web Site: https://www.slhpcn.com
300384—(CHIN)
Rev.: $176,078,402
Assets: $551,143,318
Liabilities: $183,705,824
Net Worth: $367,437,494
Earnings: $40,889,530
Fiscal Year-end: 12/31/23
Engineeering Services
N.A.I.C.S.: 541330

**BEIJING SOJO ELECTRIC
COMPANY LIMITED**
Room 1111 Block D Jiahua Plaza
Shangdi 3rd Street, Haidian District,
Beijing, 100085, China
Tel.: (86) 1062983386
Web Site: https://en.sojoline.com
Year Founded: 2002
300444—(CHIN)
Rev.: $264,259,476
Assets: $550,244,448
Liabilities: $382,111,236
Net Worth: $168,133,212
Earnings: ($24,190,920)
Emp.: 600
Fiscal Year-end: 12/31/22

Power Distribution & Automation
Equipment Mfr
N.A.I.C.S.: 335313
Zhihong Zhao *(Chm)*

Subsidiaries:

Joyo Electric Co., Ltd.　　　　**(1)**
Unit D 13/F World Tech Centre 95 How
Ming Street, Kwun Tong, Kowloon, China
(Hong Kong)
Tel.: (852) 2 790 3889
Web Site: https://www.joyo-ind.com.hk
Baby Monitor Equipment Mfr
N.A.I.C.S.: 334310

Sojo Electric Co., Ltd.　　　　**(1)**
Room 1111 Block D Jiahua Plaza Shangdi
3rd Street, Haidian District, Beijing, China
Tel.: (86) 1062983386
Web Site: https://en.sojoline.com
Emp.: 500
Power Distribution Equipment Mfr
N.A.I.C.S.: 335311

**BEIJING SPC ENVIRONMENT
PROTECTION TECH CO., LTD.**
10th Floor CPPCC News Building No
69 Xibalizhuang Road, Haidian Dis-
trict, Beijing, 100142, China
Tel.: (86) 1088111168
Web Site: https://www.qingxin.com.cn
Year Founded: 2001
002573—(SSE)
Rev.: $1,127,733,516
Assets: $3,323,743,956
Liabilities: $2,253,530,916
Net Worth: $1,070,213,040
Earnings: $62,678,772
Emp.: 2,000
Fiscal Year-end: 12/31/22
Gas Equipment Mfr
N.A.I.C.S.: 333132
Zou Aiai *(Chm)*

Subsidiaries:

Sichuan Development Guorun Water
Supply Investment Co Ltd　　　**(1)**
17/F, Development Building No. 151, Tianfu
2nd Street High-tech Zone Chengdu,, Sich-
uan, 610095, China
Tel.: (86) 2885328315
Industrial Services
N.A.I.C.S.: 236210

**BEIJING SPORTS & ENTER-
TAINMENT INDUSTRY GROUP
LIMITED**
Room 101 5/F Greatmany Centre 111
Queen's Road East, Wanchai, China
(Hong Kong)
Tel.: (852) 22378206　　　　**Ky**
Web Site: http://www.bsehk.com
1803—(HKG)
Rev.: $8,742,803
Assets: $49,281,810
Liabilities: $16,691,918
Net Worth: $32,589,893
Earnings: ($11,260,673)
Emp.: 141
Fiscal Year-end: 12/31/22
Investment Services
N.A.I.C.S.: 523999
Xue Heng Liu *(Chm & CEO)*

Subsidiaries:

AOE Freight (HK) Ltd.　　　　**(1)**
Units 1106-1112 11th Floor Lu Plaza, 2
Wing Yip Street, Kowloon, China (Hong
Kong)
Tel.: (852) 2331 3022
Web Site: http://www.asrholdings.com.hk
Freight Forwarding
N.A.I.C.S.: 488510
Tom Lee *(Gen Mgr)*

Subsidiary (Non-US):

AOE Freight (ShenZhen) Ltd.　　**(2)**
Unit 9Q Taiyangdao Building Dongmen
South Road, Luohu District, Shenzhen,
China

Tel.: (86) 755 8207 5085
Freight Forwarding
N.A.I.C.S.: 488510

Subsidiary (Domestic):

AOE Freight (ShenZhen) Ltd.　　**(3)**
Units 1009-1010 Holdround Plaza 2 Danan
Road, Yue Xiu District, Guangzhou, China
Tel.: (86) 20 8372 0085
Freight Forwarding
N.A.I.C.S.: 488510

AOE Freight (ShenZhen) Ltd.　　**(3)**
Unit 2213 Level 22 Block 1 Lan Tian Jun
Hotel Apartment, Qingyunpu District, Nan-
chang, China
Tel.: (86) 791 6497 627
Freight Forwarding
N.A.I.C.S.: 488510

AOE Freight (ShenZhen) Ltd.　　**(3)**
Room 709 Level 7 Yizhong Building 48
Zhongshan Second Road, Shiqi District,
Zhongshan, China
Tel.: (86) 760 8881 6281
Web Site: http://www.aoecargo.com.cn
Freight Forwarding
N.A.I.C.S.: 488510
K. K. Liu *(Gen Mgr)*

AOE Freight (ShenZhen) Ltd.　　**(3)**
Unit A Level 12 Dongjian Building, 121
Fenjiang Middle Road, Foshan, China
Tel.: (86) 757 8801 8261
Freight Forwarding
N.A.I.C.S.: 488510

AOE Freight (ShenZhen) Ltd.　　**(3)**
Unit 9Q Taiyangdao Building Dongmen
South Road, Luohu District, Shenzhen,
China　　　　　　　　　　　　**(100%)**
Tel.: (86) 755 8207 5085
Web Site: http://www.aoecargo.com
Freight Forwarding Services
N.A.I.C.S.: 488510

ASR Europe Logistics Ltd.　　**(1)**
Units 1106-12 11th Floor Lu Plaza, 2 Wing
Yip Street, Kowloon, China (Hong Kong)
Tel.: (852) 2331 3022
Web Site: http://www.asreu.com
Emp.: 100
Logistics
N.A.I.C.S.: 541614
Jouni Ritola *(Dir-Sls)*

ASR Logistics Ltd.　　　　　　**(1)**
Units 1106-12 11th Floor Lu Plaza, 2 Wing
Yip Street, Kowloon, China (Hong Kong)
Tel.: (852) 2331 3022
Logistics
N.A.I.C.S.: 541614

ASRCO Logistics Ltd.　　　　　**(1)**
Units 1106-1112 11th Floor Lu Plaza, 2
Wing Yip Street, Kowloon, China (Hong
Kong)
Tel.: (852) 3518 7300
Web Site: http://www.asr.com.hk
Emp.: 5
Logistics
N.A.I.C.S.: 541614
Marc Groenewoud *(Dir-Grp Mgmt Perfor-
mance)*

MetaSpace (Beijing) Air Dome
Corp.　　　　　　　　　　　　**(1)**
East Side of Tennis Center, Chaoyang Park
Chaoyang District, Beijing, China
Tel.: (86) 4006502050
Web Site: https://metaspacedome.com
Dome Installation Services
N.A.I.C.S.: 238210

Star Pacific Logistics Ltd.　　**(1)**
Units 1106-1112 11th Floor Lu Plaza, 2
Wing Yip Street, Kowloon, China (Hong
Kong)
Tel.: (852) 27853822
Logistics
N.A.I.C.S.: 541614

**BEIJING STARNETO TECH-
NOLOGY CO.,LTD**
Yard No 6 Kegu 2nd Street, Beijing
Economic and Technological Devel-
opment Zone, Beijing, 100176, China
Tel.: (86) 1087838888

Beijing StarNeto Technology
Co.,Ltd—(Continued)

Web Site: http://www.starneto.com
Year Founded: 2005
002829—(SSE)
Rev.: $150,842,952
Assets: $328,300,128
Liabilities: $122,306,652
Net Worth: $205,993,176
Earnings: $30,251,988
Fiscal Year-end: 12/31/22
Measurement Product Mfr & Distr
N.A.I.C.S.: 334513
Chi Jiasheng *(Chm & Gen Mgr)*

BEIJING STRONG BIOTECH-NOLOGIES, INC.

5/F Kuang Yi Building No 15 Hua
Yuan Dong Lu, Haidian District, Bei-
jing, 100191, China
Tel.: (86) 1082012486
Web Site: https://en.bsbe.com.cn
Year Founded: 2001
300406—(CHIN)
Rev.: $212,126,148
Assets: $647,648,352
Liabilities: $188,713,044
Net Worth: $458,935,308
Earnings: $54,633,852
Emp.: 230
Fiscal Year-end: 12/31/22
In-Vitro Diagnostic Reagents Mfr
N.A.I.C.S.: 325413
Zuojun Zou *(Chm)*

BEIJING SUCCEEDER TECH-NOLOGY, INC.

8th Floor Building 1 No 7 Science
Park Road, Changping District, Bei-
jing, 102200, China
Tel.: (86) 1089281810
Web Site:
    https://www.succeeder.com.cn
Year Founded: 2003
688338—(SHG)
Rev.: $32,125,331
Assets: $226,325,853
Liabilities: $15,085,095
Net Worth: $211,240,758
Earnings: $14,617,634
Fiscal Year-end: 12/31/22
Medical Product Mfr & Distr
N.A.I.C.S.: 339112
Shiming Wu *(Chm)*

BEIJING SUPLET POWER CO., LTD

Tianliao Subdistrict Guangming,
Shenzhen, Guangdong, China
Tel.: (86) 75586001502
Web Site: http://www.suplet.com
Year Founded: 1997
300593—(CHIN)
Rev.: $206,587,427
Assets: $647,366,826
Liabilities: $176,867,486
Net Worth: $470,499,340
Earnings: $13,638,590
Fiscal Year-end: 12/31/23
Power Supply Product Mfr & Distr
N.A.I.C.S.: 333613

BEIJING SWT COMMUNICA-TIONS CO., LTD.

Yanjiao Economic & Technical Devel-
opment Zone, Yingbinbei Road Hei-
bei, Beijing, 065201, China
Tel.: (86) 1061597788
Web Site: http://www.swt-oc.com
Sales Range: $50-74.9 Million
Emp.: 300
Holding Company; Optoelectronic
Products Mfr
N.A.I.C.S.: 551112
Wang Gong *(Gen Mgr)*

Subsidiaries:

Beijing SWT Optical Communications
Technologies, Co., Ltd.   **(1)**
10th Floor Tower C2 Oriental Plaza No1
East Chang An Avenue, Dong Cheng Dis-
trict, Beijing, 100738, China
Tel.: (86) 1085180588
Web Site: http://www.swt-oc.com
Sales Range: $1-9.9 Million
Optoelectronic Products Mfr; Owned 50%
by Beijing SWT Communications Co., Ltd.
& 50% by Polaray Optoelectronics Ltd.
N.A.I.C.S.: 334413

BEIJING TEAMSUN TECHNOL-OGY CO., LTD.

Building 23 East District No 10 North-
west Wang East Road, Haidian Dis-
trict, Beijing, 100193, China
Tel.: (86) 1080986698   **CN**
Web Site:
    https://www.teamsun.com.cn
Year Founded: 1998
600410—(SHG)
Rev.: $571,398,432
Assets: $1,201,434,755
Liabilities: $486,435,891
Net Worth: $714,998,864
Earnings: ($45,429,916)
Emp.: 5,500
Fiscal Year-end: 12/31/22
Computer System Integration Ser-
vices; Software Products
N.A.I.C.S.: 541512
Weihang Wang *(Chm)*

Subsidiaries:

Automated Systems Holdings
Limited   **(1)**
15/F Topsail Plaza No 11 On Sum Street,
Sha Tin, China (Hong Kong)   **(68.43%)**
Tel.: (852) 26016998
Web Site: https://www1.asl.com.hk
Rev.: $282,474,465
Assets: $386,616,083
Liabilities: $123,989,160
Net Worth: $262,626,923
Earnings: $12,952,088
Emp.: 1,146
Fiscal Year-end: 12/31/2022
Computer Services; Communications Sys-
tems Engineering; Facilities Management;
Business Data Processing Services; Sys-
tems Integration
N.A.I.C.S.: 518210
Weihang Wang *(Chm)*

Subsidiary (Non-US):

ASL Automated (Thailand) Ltd.   **(2)**
283/42 Home Place Office Building Unit
0901 9th Fl, Soi Sukhumvit 55 Thonglor 13
Sukhumvit Road Klongtan Nua Vadhana,
Bangkok, 10110, Thailand   **(100%)**
Tel.: (66) 21853206
Web Site: http://www.aslth.co.th
Emp.: 35
Computer Services; Communications Sys-
tems Engineering; Facilities Management;
Business Data Processing Services; Sys-
tems Integration
N.A.I.C.S.: 518210

Subsidiary (Domestic)

ELM Computer Technologies
Limited   **(2)**
16/F Topsail Plaza 11 On Sum Street, Sha
Tin, China (Hong Kong)   **(100%)**
Tel.: (852) 25419900
Web Site: http://www.elm.com.hk
Sales Range: $25-49.9 Million
Emp.: 60
Computer Services; Communications Sys-
tems Engineering; Facilities Management;
Business Data Processing Services; Sys-
tems Integration
N.A.I.C.S.: 518210

Subsidiary (Non-US):

Guangzhou Automated Systems
Limited   **(2)**

Unit 1402A 1403A Chuangju Commercial
Bldg No 185 Yuexiu South Road, Yuexiu
District, Guangzhou, 510100, China
Tel.: (86) 2022038111
Web Site: http://www2.asl.com.hk
Computer Services; Communications Sys-
tems Engineering; Facilities Management;
Business Data Processing Services; Sys-
tems Integration
N.A.I.C.S.: 518210

Taiwan Automated Systems Ltd.   **(2)**
9F No 19 Ruihu St, Neihu Dist, Taipei, Tai-
wan
Tel.: (886) 226598598
Web Site: http://asl.com.hk
Computer Services; Communications Sys-
tems Engineering; Facilities Management;
Business Data Processing Services; Sys-
tems Integration
N.A.I.C.S.: 518210

BEIJING TELESOUND ELEC-TRONICS CO., LTD.

Building 11 Yard 9 Fenghao East
Road, Haidian District, Beijing,
100094, China
Tel.: (86) 1062988833
Web Site:
    https://en.telesound.com.cn
Year Founded: 1994
003004—(SSE)
Rev.: $44,543,304
Assets: $126,900,540
Liabilities: $24,171,264
Net Worth: $102,729,276
Earnings: $5,126,004
Fiscal Year-end: 12/31/22
Software Development Services
N.A.I.C.S.: 541511
Zheng Tan *(Chm & Gen Mgr)*

BEIJING THUNISOFT CORPO-RATION LIMITED

25th Floor Block C Science & Tech-
nology Building, Tsinghua Science
Park No 1 Zhongguancun East Road
Haidian District, Beijing, 100084,
China
Tel.: (86) 1082150085
Web Site: http://www.thunisoft.com
Year Founded: 2001
300271—(CHIN)
Rev.: $311,918,256
Assets: $1,027,493,532
Liabilities: $212,377,464
Net Worth: $815,116,068
Earnings: ($138,132,540)
Fiscal Year-end: 12/31/22
Software Publisher
N.A.I.C.S.: 513210
Guo Ying *(Chm)*

BEIJING TIANYISHANGJIA NEW MATERIAL CORP., LTD.

No 7 Yingbin South Street, Fangshan
District, Beijing, 102433, China
Tel.: (86) 1082470775
Web Site: https://www.bjtysj.com
Year Founded: 2009
688033—(SHG)
Rev.: $138,591,339
Assets: $962,663,130
Liabilities: $236,482,754
Net Worth: $726,180,376
Earnings: $25,154,443
Fiscal Year-end: 12/31/22
Railroad Equipment Mfr
N.A.I.C.S.: 336510
Peifang Wu *(Chm & Gen Mgr)*

BEIJING TIEKE SHOUGANG RAILWAY-TECHNOLOGY CO., LTD.

No 11 Fusheng Road, Changping
District, Beijing, 102206, China
Tel.: (86) 1051529898
Web Site: https://www.bjtkgd.com

Year Founded: 2006
688569—(SHG)
Rev.: $188,156,414
Assets: $488,666,974
Liabilities: $87,813,180
Net Worth: $400,853,794
Earnings: $33,263,063
Fiscal Year-end: 12/31/22
Railroad Equipment Mfr
N.A.I.C.S.: 336510
Li Wei *(Chm)*

BEIJING TINAVI MEDICAL TECHNOLOGIES CO., LTD.

Bldg 2 Sec 8 Jianfeng South Ext Rd
Xisanqi Jinyu Science Park II, Zhong-
guancun Haidian District, Beijing,
100096, China
Tel.: (86) 1082156660
Web Site: https://en.tinavi.com
Year Founded: 2010
688277—(SHG)
Rev.: $20,822,771
Assets: $171,484,889
Liabilities: $14,207,163
Net Worth: $157,277,726
Earnings: ($8,345,349)
Fiscal Year-end: 12/31/20
Medical Product Mfr & Distr
N.A.I.C.S.: 339112
Songgen Zhang *(Chm)*

BEIJING TONG REN TANG CHINESE MEDICINE COM-PANY LIMITED

Tel.: (852) 28817989   **CN**
Web Site:
    https://cm.tongrentang.com
Year Founded: 1669
3613—(HKG)
Rev.: $220,714,613
Assets: $538,723,073
Liabilities: $62,026,965
Net Worth: $476,696,108
Earnings: $88,139,858
Emp.: 762
Fiscal Year-end: 12/31/22
Chinese Medicine Retailer, Distr &
Mfr
N.A.I.C.S.: 456110
Yong Ling Ding *(Chm)*

Subsidiaries:

Beijing Tong Ren Tang (Auckland)
Company Limited   **(1)**
Unit 8 6 Ormiston Road, Flat Bush, Auck-
land, New Zealand
Tel.: (64) 99729897
Pharmaceutical Products Distr
N.A.I.C.S.: 424210

Beijing Tong Ren Tang Australia Pty.
Ltd.   **(1)**
18 Fisher St, Silverwater, 2128, NSW, Aus-
tralia
Tel.: (61) 280143872
Pharmaceutical Product Mfr & Distr
N.A.I.C.S.: 325412
Anyang Ma *(Founder & Mng Dir)*

Beijing Tong Ren Tang Canada Co.
Ltd.   **(1)**
103-1277 Marine Drive, North Vancouver,
V7P 1T3, BC, Canada
Tel.: (604) 770-3400
Web Site: https://beijingtrt.janeapp.com
Pharmaceutical Products Distr
N.A.I.C.S.: 424210

Beijing Tong Ren Tang Gulf
FZ-LLC   **(1)**
Dubai Health Care city building 49 unit 9
ground floor, PO Box 333339, Dubai,
United Arab Emirates
Tel.: (971) 44356905
Pharmaceutical Products Distr
N.A.I.C.S.: 424210

Beijing Tong Ren Tang Poland
sp.zo.o.   **(1)**

ul Grzybowska 2 lok 5, 00-131, Warsaw, Poland
Tel.: (48) 221263330
Web Site: http://tongrentang.pl
Pharmaceutical Products Distr
N.A.I.C.S.: 424210

Beijing Tong Ren Tang Science Arts (Singapore) Co. Pte. Ltd.   (1)
209 South Bridge Road, Singapore, 058758, Singapore
Tel.: (65) 62239513
Pharmaceutical Products Distr
N.A.I.C.S.: 424210

Beijing Tong Ren Tang Vancouver Healthcare Center Co., Ltd.   (1)
103- 1277 Marine Dr, North Vancouver, V7P 1T3, BC, Canada
Tel.: (604) 770-3400
Web Site: https://beijingtrt.ca
Acupuncture Services
N.A.I.C.S.: 621399

Beijing TongRenTang Gulf Medical Clinic LLC   (1)
Shop Number GD-56 Ground Floor, Dubai, United Arab Emirates
Tel.: (971) 45148428
Pharmaceutical Products Distr
N.A.I.C.S.: 424210

Peking Tongrentang (M) Sdn. Bhd   (1)
Ground Floor Sun Complex Jalan Bukit Bintang, 55100, Kuala Lumpur, Malaysia
Tel.: (60) 321417958
Emp.: 10
Pharmaceutical Products Distr
N.A.I.C.S.: 424210

BEIJING TONGRENTANG CO., LTD.
No 42 Chongwai Street, Dongcheng District, Beijing, 100062, China
Tel.: (86) 1067179780
Web Site: https://gf.tongrentang.com
Year Founded: 1997
600085—(SHG)
Rev.: $2,158,288,245
Assets: $3,797,046,663
Liabilities: $1,206,095,473
Net Worth: $2,590,951,189
Earnings: $200,183,963
Fiscal Year-end: 12/31/22
Pharmaceutical Product Mfr & Distr
N.A.I.C.S.: 325412
Di Shubing *(Chm)*

BEIJING TONGTECH COM-PANY LIMITED
Room 311 No 139 Main building Fengtai Road Crossing, Fengtai District, Beijing, 100080, China
Tel.: (86) 1082652228
Web Site: https://www.tongtech.com
Year Founded: 1992
300379—(CHIN)
Rev.: $127,460,736
Assets: $414,094,356
Liabilities: $73,457,280
Net Worth: $340,637,076
Earnings: $8,313,084
Emp.: 430
Fiscal Year-end: 12/31/22
Software Publisher
N.A.I.C.S.: 513210

Subsidiaries:

Beijing Microvision Technology Co., Ltd.   (1)
3/F 1 1 building 10 Caihefang Road, Haidian District, Beijing, China
Tel.: (86) 1064135099
Pharmaceutical & Medicine Mfr
N.A.I.C.S.: 325412

Beijing Testor Technology Co., Ltd.   (1)
Room 1003 Block B Shuma Building No 2 Zhongguancun South Street, Zhongguancun South Street Haidian District, Beijing, 100086, China

Tel.: (86) 1082856116
Web Site: https://www.testor.com.cn
Software Development Services
N.A.I.C.S.: 541511

Chengdu Tongtech Co., Ltd.   (1)
No 6-7 11 / Floor Block E1 Tianfu Software Park building 1 No 1268, Middle Section of Tianfu Avenue Chengdu Hightech Zone, Chengdu, 610041, China
Tel.: (86) 2885333077
Pharmaceutical & Medicine Mfr
N.A.I.C.S.: 325412

Shanghai Tongtech Software Co., Ltd.   (1)
Room 303 No 26 28 Jiangchang Third Road, Zhabei District, Shanghai, 200436, China
Tel.: (86) 2136321800
Pharmaceutical & Medicine Mfr
N.A.I.C.S.: 325412

BEIJING TOPNEW INFORMA-TION & TECHNOLOGY CO., LTD.
Tongniu Information Building No 31 Tiantan East Road, Dongcheng District, Beijing, 100061, China
Tel.: (86) 1052186999
Web Site: http://www.topnewinfo.cn
Year Founded: 2005
300895—(SSE)
Rev.: $61,958,520
Assets: $179,320,284
Liabilities: $21,106,332
Net Worth: $158,213,952
Earnings: ($9,177,948)
Fiscal Year-end: 12/31/22
Information Technology Services
N.A.I.C.S.: 541512
Liu Yi *(Sec)*

BEIJING TRANSTRUE TECH-NOLOGY INC.
11F Tower B China international science & Tec Convention center 12, Yumin Road Madian Intersection Dist Chaoyang, Beijing, 100029, China
Tel.: (86) 1059220168
Web Site: https://www.bjzst.cn
Year Founded: 2000
002771—(SSE)
Rev.: $90,866,880
Assets: $152,707,464
Liabilities: $51,195,456
Net Worth: $101,512,008
Earnings: $1,434,888
Fiscal Year-end: 12/31/22
Software Development Services
N.A.I.C.S.: 541511
Wang Guohong *(Chm)*

BEIJING TRICOLOR TECH-NOLOGY CO., LTD.
Building 1 No 39 Linfeng 2nd Road Green Central Plaza, Haidian District, Beijing, 100095, China
Tel.: (86) 1053563888
Web Site: https://www.tricolortechnology.com
Year Founded: 2011
603516—(SHG)
Rev.: $53,465,527
Assets: $197,402,344
Liabilities: $52,966,658
Net Worth: $144,435,686
Earnings: $4,116,626
Fiscal Year-end: 12/31/22
Surveillance Product Mfr & Distr
N.A.I.C.S.: 334290

BEIJING TRS INFORMATION TECHNOLOGY CO., LTD.
Building 3 Jinyuxisanqi Science & Technology Park, Haidian District No 6 Jianfeng Road South Extension, Beijing, 100096, China
Tel.: (86) 1064848899

Web Site: http://www.trs.com.cn
Year Founded: 1993
300229—(CHIN)
Rev.: $127,380,708
Assets: $545,278,500
Liabilities: $166,549,500
Net Worth: $378,729,000
Earnings: $17,929,080
Emp.: 430
Fiscal Year-end: 12/31/22
Software Publisher; Search, Content Management & Text Mining Services
N.A.I.C.S.: 513210
Yuqin Li *(Chm)*

BEIJING TRUSTFAR TECH-NOLOGY CO., LTD.
8th Floor Anhua Development Building No 35 Anding Road, Chaoyang District, Beijing, 100029, China
Tel.: (86) 1082629666
Web Site: https://www.trustfar.cn
300231—(CHIN)
Rev.: $278,385,250
Assets: $353,840,497
Liabilities: $127,315,090
Net Worth: $226,525,407
Earnings: $14,945,875
Fiscal Year-end: 12/31/23
Software Development Services
N.A.I.C.S.: 541511
Lixiong Zhan *(Chm & Pres)*

BEIJING ULTRAPOWER SOFT-WARE CO., LTD.
22/F Building 1 Jia No13 Yard Beiyuan Road, Chaoyang District, Beijing, 100107, China
Tel.: (86) 1084927606
Web Site:
   http://www.ultrapower.com.cn
Year Founded: 2001
300002—(CHIN)
Rev.: $839,782,138
Assets: $958,170,450
Liabilities: $143,105,023
Net Worth: $815,065,428
Earnings: $124,959,345
Fiscal Year-end: 12/31/23
Information Management Services
N.A.I.C.S.: 519290
Mao Dawei *(Chm & Pres)*

BEIJING UNISTRONG SCI-ENCE & TECHNOLOGY CO., LTD.
No8 Kechuang 12 Street Economy & Technology Zone, Beijing, 100176, China
Tel.: (86) 2151727616   CN
Web Site: http://www.unistrong.com
Year Founded: 1994
002383—(SSE)
Rev.: $270,079,056
Assets: $637,898,976
Liabilities: $434,611,008
Net Worth: $203,287,968
Earnings: ($33,760,584)
Emp.: 2,000
Fiscal Year-end: 12/31/22
GPS, Receivers, Multi-System Navigation, Surveying, GNSS Data Post-Processing & System Integration Products Mfr
N.A.I.C.S.: 334511

Subsidiaries:

UniStrong Technology (S) Pte. Ltd.   (1)
51 Ubi Ave 1 Unit 01-22 Paya Ubi Industrial Park, Singapore, Singapore
Tel.: (65) 62968238
Global Positioning System Devices Mfr
N.A.I.C.S.: 334220
Edward Teo *(Gen Mgr)*

BEIJING UNITED INFORMA-

TION TECHNOLOGY CO., LTD.
Building 3 Area 6 Headquarters Base No 188 South Fourth Ring Road West, Fengtai District, Beijing, 100070, China
Tel.: (86) 1063701497
Web Site: https://www.ueiibi.com
Year Founded: 2002
603613—(SHG)
Rev.: $5,653,764,076
Assets: $1,801,623,948
Liabilities: $976,394,320
Net Worth: $825,229,628
Earnings: $158,061,169
Fiscal Year-end: 12/31/22
Information Technology Services
N.A.I.C.S.: 541512
Quan Liu *(Chm)*

BEIJING URBAN CONSTRUC-TION DESIGN & DEVELOP-MENT GROUP CO., LTD.
No 5 Fuchengmen Street North, Xicheng District, Beijing, 100037, China
Tel.: (86) 1088336666   CN
Web Site: https://www.bjucd.com
Year Founded: 1958
1599—(HKG)
Rev.: $1,488,218,238
Assets: $3,361,764,838
Liabilities: $2,379,323,138
Net Worth: $982,441,699
Earnings: $127,871,827
Emp.: 4,946
Fiscal Year-end: 12/31/22
Rail Transit-Related Designing, Surveying & Consulting
N.A.I.C.S.: 237990
Wenchang Xuan *(Co-Sec)*

Subsidiaries:

Beijing Urban Construction Exploration & Surveying Design Research Institute Co., Ltd.   (1)
No 6 District 5, Anhuili Chaoyang District, Beijing, 100101, China
Tel.: (86) 1064922389
Web Site: https://www.cki.com.cn
Underground Railway Construction Surveying Services
N.A.I.C.S.: 541360
Ma Haizhi *(Chm)*

BEIJING URBAN CONSTRUC-TION INVESTMENT & DEVEL-OPMENT CO., LTD.
Chengjian Development Building No 11 Beitucheng West Road, Chaoyang District, Beijing, 100029, China
Tel.: (86) 1082275566
Web Site: https://www.bucid.com
Year Founded: 1998
600266—(SHG)
Rev.: $3,448,487,896
Assets: $19,482,736,993
Liabilities: $15,624,684,761
Net Worth: $3,858,052,232
Earnings: ($130,035,546)
Fiscal Year-end: 12/31/22
Real Estate Support Services
N.A.I.C.S.: 531390
Chu Zhaowu *(Chm, Pres & Sec-Party Committee)*

BEIJING VASTDATA TECH-NOLOGY CO., LTD.
6th Floor Block B Tiangong Building Keda No 30 Xueyuan Road, Haidian District, Beijing, 100083, China
Tel.: (86) 1082838118
Web Site:
   https://www.vastdata.com.cn
Year Founded: 2007
603138—(SHG)
Rev.: $42,533,141
Assets: $143,848,449

Beijing Vastdata Technology Co., Ltd.—(Continued)

Liabilities: $21,903,748
Net Worth: $121,944,701
Earnings: ($8,954,038)
Fiscal Year-end: 12/31/22
Data Processing Services
N.A.I.C.S.: 518210
Zhongwen Yan (Chm)

BEIJING VRV SOFTWARE CORPORATION LIMITED

3rd Floor Building 3 Phase 2 Yuquan
Huigu Minzhuang Road, Haidian District, Beijing, 100081, China
Tel.: (86) 1062140485
Web Site: https://www.vrv.com.cn
Year Founded: 1996
300352—(CHIN)
Rev.: $76,217,544
Assets: $378,514,188
Liabilities: $162,112,860
Net Worth: $216,401,328
Earnings: ($26,340,444)
Emp.: 630
Fiscal Year-end: 12/31/22
Security Software Publisher
N.A.I.C.S.: 513210
Wang Xiaona (Sec)

BEIJING WALUER INFORMATION TECHNOLOGY CO., LTD.

Room 408 Building 1 No 51 Zhichun
Road, Haidian District, Beijing,
100029, China
Tel.: (86) 1062986992
Year Founded: 2011
301380—(CHIN)
Rev.: $118,288,201
Assets: $165,272,652
Liabilities: $43,772,264
Net Worth: $121,500,388
Earnings: $8,178,417
Fiscal Year-end: 12/31/23
Information Technology Services
N.A.I.C.S.: 541512

BEIJING WANDONG MEDICAL TECHNOLOGY CO., LTD.

Building 3 No 9 Jiuxianqiadong Road,
Chaoyang District, Beijing, 100015,
China
Tel.: (86) 1084569688
Web Site:
  https://www.wandong.com.cn
Year Founded: 1997
600055—(SHG)
Rev.: $157,416,971
Assets: $738,868,928
Liabilities: $77,498,203
Net Worth: $661,370,725
Earnings: $24,621,822
Emp.: 930
Fiscal Year-end: 12/31/22
Medical Equipment Mfr
N.A.I.C.S.: 339112
Ou Yunbin (Sec)

BEIJING WANTAI BIOLOGICAL PHARMACY ENTERPRISE CO., LTD.

No 31 Kexueyuan Rd, Changping,
Beijing, 102206, China
Tel.: (86) 1059528888
Web Site: http://www.ystwt.cn
Year Founded: 1991
603392—(SHG)
Rev.: $763,012,641
Assets: $2,175,869,226
Liabilities: $392,022,126
Net Worth: $1,783,847,101
Earnings: $172,751,398
Emp.: 4,000
Fiscal Year-end: 12/31/23
Pharmaceutical Product Mfr & Distr
N.A.I.C.S.: 325412

Zixin Qiu (Chm & Gen Mgr)

Subsidiaries:

Xiamen Innovax Biotech Co., Ltd.   **(1)**
No 50 Shanbianhong East Road, Haicang
District, Xiamen, 361022, Fujian, China
Tel.: (86) 5926536555
Web Site: https://www.innovax.cn
Biological Product Mfr
N.A.I.C.S.: 325414

BEIJING WATER BUSINESS DOCTOR CO., LTD.

Building 22 Zhonghong International
Business Garden, No 1 Wuliqiao 1st
Street Chaoyang District, Beijing,
100024, China
Tel.: (86) 1059621877
Web Site: http://www.waterbd.cn
Year Founded: 1998
300055—(CHIN)
Rev.: $381,562,272
Assets: $1,066,100,724
Liabilities: $325,240,812
Net Worth: $740,859,912
Earnings: $11,014,380
Emp.: 300
Fiscal Year-end: 12/31/22
Water Treatment Systems Mfr
N.A.I.C.S.: 562211
Wang Piaoyang (Chm & Gen Mgr)

BEIJING WATERTEK INFORMATION TECHNOLOGY CO., LTD.

Building 12 No 3 Fengxiu Middle
Road, Haidian District, Beijing,
100094, China
Tel.: (86) 1082883933
Web Site: https://www.watertek.com
Year Founded: 1997
300324—(CHIN)
Rev.: $344,401,200
Assets: $860,715,180
Liabilities: $344,455,956
Net Worth: $516,259,224
Earnings: ($82,831,788)
Emp.: 300
Fiscal Year-end: 12/31/22
Computer Related Services
N.A.I.C.S.: 541519
Chen Weiqun (Chm & Gen Mgr)

Subsidiaries:

Baiwang Holding Co., Ltd.   **(1)**
7F Yicheng International Center No 59
Shangdi Malianwa North Street, Haidian
District, Beijing, 100085, China
Tel.: (86) 1084782665
Software Development Services
N.A.I.C.S.: 513210

Beijing Acoinfo Information Technology Co. Ltd   **(1)**
3F Building Huashengtiancheng Zhongguancun Software Park Phase ii, Haidian
District, Beijing, 100193, China
Tel.: (86) 1056082456
Software Development Services
N.A.I.C.S.: 513210

Beijing Cloudnet Technology Co., Ltd.   **(1)**
8F Building C Zhonghui Square Dongzhimen South Street, Dongcheng District, Beijing, 100007, China
Tel.: (86) 1059786576
Software Development Services
N.A.I.C.S.: 513210

Beijing Handrun Technology Co., Ltd.   **(1)**
Building No 12 Compound No 3 Fengxiu
Middle Street, Haidian District, Beijing,
100094, China
Tel.: (86) 1082695000
Software Development Services
N.A.I.C.S.: 513210

Beijing Navistar Cloud Science & Technology Co., Ltd.   **(1)**
No 11 Hepingli East Street, Dongcheng District, Beijing, 100013, China
Tel.: (86) 1088103260
Software Development Services
N.A.I.C.S.: 513210

Beijing Tellhow Intelligent Engineering Co., Ltd   **(1)**
11F Tellhow Intelligent Building A No 2
Yuncheng Street, economic and Technological Development Zone, Beijing, 100176,
China
Tel.: (86) 1058380808
Software Development Services
N.A.I.C.S.: 513210

Beijing Watertek Fuxi Big Data Technology Co., Ltd.   **(1)**
16F No 6 Building Defense Technology
Compound No A2, The Third Ring North
Street Haidian District, Beijing, 100081,
China
Tel.: (86) 1068269900
Software Development Services
N.A.I.C.S.: 513210

Beijing Watertek Sinda Technology Co., Ltd   **(1)**
No 5 Haiying Street Science City, Fengtai
District, Beijing, 100070, China
Tel.: (86) 1083602282
Software Development Services
N.A.I.C.S.: 513210

Beijing Zhongruan Jinka Information Technology Co., Ltd.   **(1)**
15F Design Building No 8 Huixin East
Street, Chaoyang District, Beijing, 100029,
China
Tel.: (86) 1084126600
Software Development Services
N.A.I.C.S.: 513210

Best Wonders Science & Technology Co., Ltd   **(1)**
21F No 1Building No 99 CompoundThe
Third Ring North Street, Haidian District,
Beijing, 100089, China
Tel.: (86) 1082208388
Software Development Services
N.A.I.C.S.: 513210

Chengdu Water Star-Source Information Technology Co., Ltd.   **(1)**
A402-406 Fuhe electric incubator industrial
base No 12 Gaopeng Avenue, Gaoxin District, Chengdu, 610041, China
Tel.: (86) 2886028176
Software Development Services
N.A.I.C.S.: 513210

Chengdu Watertek Information Technology Co., Ltd.   **(1)**
RM 1302 Building No 2 Federal Wealth
Center Wuke East Road No 18, Wuhou
District, Chengdu, 610041, China
Tel.: (86) 2886618108
Software Development Services
N.A.I.C.S.: 513210

Shanghai Watertek Information Technology Co., Ltd.   **(1)**
A3 2F No 1528 Gumei Road, XuHui District, Shanghai, 200233, China
Tel.: (86) 2164326688
Software Development Services
N.A.I.C.S.: 513210

Shenzhen Watertek Information Technology Co., Ltd.   **(1)**
F5 Building No 38, Dayun Software Town
Longgang District, Shenzhen, 518173,
China
Tel.: (86) 75526727208
Software Development Services
N.A.I.C.S.: 513210

Watertek International (Hong Kong) Limited   **(1)**
Flat G 12/F Wong King Industrial Bldg No 2
Tai Yau Street, Kowloon, China (Hong
Kong)
Tel.: (852) 21922969
Software Development Services
N.A.I.C.S.: 513210

Xi'an Xigu Microelectronics Co., Ltd.   **(1)**

Xian Modern Business Center East Zone
No 2-10402 Zone A pioneer park, No 69
Jinye Street Gaoxin District, Xi'an, 710077,
Shanxi, China
Tel.: (86) 2968590621
Software Development Services
N.A.I.C.S.: 513210

BEIJING WKW AUTOMOTIVE PARTS CO., LTD.

Room 101 4th Floor Building 35 No 2
Wailangying Village North, Tongzhou
District, Beijing, 101116, China
Tel.: (86) 1060276313
Web Site: https://www.beijing-wkw.com
Year Founded: 2002
002662—(SSE)
Rev.: $502,410,168
Assets: $687,312,756
Liabilities: $167,102,676
Net Worth: $520,210,080
Earnings: $61,349,184
Emp.: 8,000
Fiscal Year-end: 12/31/22
Automobile Parts Mfr
N.A.I.C.S.: 336390
Jingyu Li (Chm & Pres)

Subsidiaries:

Ningbo Fuerda Smartech Co., Ltd.   **(1)**
Xiaolin Avenue, Xiaolin Town, Cixi, 315321,
Zhejiang, China
Tel.: (86) 574 63511308
Web Site: http://www.fuerda-china.com
Motor Vehicle Parts Mfr
N.A.I.C.S.: 336390

Branch (US):

Ningbo Fuerda Smartech Co., Ltd. -
Melvindale Branch   **(2)**
No 18765 Seaway Dr, Melvindale, MI
48122
Tel.: (519) 250-8893
Motor Vehicle Parts Mfr
N.A.I.C.S.: 336390

Subsidiary (Domestic):

Shanghai Futailong Auto Tech Co., Ltd.   **(2)**
No 55 Yuanyao Road, Anting Town Jiading
District, Shanghai, 201814, China
Tel.: (86) 2169573749
Motor Vehicle Parts Mfr
N.A.I.C.S.: 336390

Shanghai Fuyulong Auto Tech Co., Ltd.   **(2)**
No 999 Yuanqi Road, Anting Town Jiading
District, Shanghai, 201814, China
Tel.: (86) 2159581843
Motor Vehicle Parts Mfr
N.A.I.C.S.: 336390

BEIJING WORLDIA DIAMOND TOOLS CO., LTD.

Tel.: (86) 1058411388
Web Site: https://www.worldia-tools.com
Year Founded: 2006
688028—(SHG)
Rev.: $58,169,980
Assets: $289,507,411
Liabilities: $25,430,133
Net Worth: $264,077,279
Earnings: $8,820,153
Fiscal Year-end: 12/31/22
Cutting Tool Mfr
N.A.I.C.S.: 333515
Jifeng Chen (Founder)

Subsidiaries:

Worldia Europe GmbH   **(1)**
Benzstr 38, D-71083, Herrenberg, Germany
Tel.: (49) 70322890690
Web Site: https://www.worldia-europe.com
Super Hard Cutting Tool Mfr & Distr
N.A.I.C.S.: 333515

Worldia Nice Nova Diamond Technology (Jiaxing) Co., Ltd. **(1)**
Plant 5 No 1136 Bazi Road Gaozhao Street, Xiuzhou District, Jiaxing, Zhejiang, China
Tel.: (86) 57383772713
Web Site: https://www.nicenova-diamond.com
Diamond Material Mfr & Distr
N.A.I.C.S.: 333514

BEIJING XIAOCHENG TECHNOLOGY STOCK CO., LTD
Room 503 Block D IFEC blog No 87 Xisanhuan Beilu, Haidian District, Beijing, 100089, China
Tel.: (86) 1068459012
Web Site:
https://www.xiaocheng.com
Year Founded: 2000
300139—(SSE)
Rev.: $30,680,208
Assets: $168,825,384
Liabilities: $19,780,956
Net Worth: $149,044,428
Earnings: ($11,637,756)
Fiscal Year-end: 12/31/22
Integrated Circuits Mfr
N.A.I.C.S.: 334419
Cheng Yi *(Chm & Gen Mgr)*

BEIJING XINWEI TECHNOLOGY GROUP CO., LTD.
1F Xinwei Building No 7 Zhongguancun Software Park, No 8 Dongbeiwang West Road Haidian District, Beijing, China
Tel.: (86) 106 280 2288
Web Site:
http://www.xinweigroup.com.cn
Year Founded: 1995
Rev.: $39,086,506
Assets: $347,028,132
Liabilities: $1,971,395,542
Net Worth: ($1,624,367,410)
Earnings: ($2,638,208,629)
Fiscal Year-end: 12/31/19
Electric Equipment Mfr
N.A.I.C.S.: 334419
Jing Wang *(Chm)*

Subsidiaries:

Beijing Zhongchuang Telecom Test Co., Ltd. **(1)**
12-14F Block C Beijing International Building 18 ZhongGuanCun South, Beijing, 100081, China
Tel.: (86) 1062100110
Web Site: http://www.zctt.com
Testing Equipment Mfr & Distr
N.A.I.C.S.: 334515
Huibin Wang *(Mgr-Sls)*

Chongqing Xinwei Telecom Technology Co., Ltd. **(1)**
Xinwei Building No 60 Starlight Avenue Hi-Tech Development Park, Northern New District, Chongqing, 401121, China
Tel.: (86) 2386076800
Wireless Communication Product Mfr
N.A.I.C.S.: 334210

Shenzhen Xinwei Telecom Technology Co., Ltd. **(1)**
Room 803 Tower A Hengyu Center Dengliang Road Nanhai Avenue, Nanshan District, Shenzhen, 518054, China
Tel.: (86) 75533189800
Wireless Communication Product Mfr
N.A.I.C.S.: 334210

BEIJING YJK BUILDING SOFTWARE CO., LTD.
18th Floor Building C Global Trade Center No 36 North Third Ring Road, East Dongcheng District, Beijing, 100013, China
Tel.: (86) 1059575867
Web Site: https://www.yjk.cn
Year Founded: 2010

300935—(SSE)
Rev.: $23,497,344
Assets: $137,455,812
Liabilities: $7,790,796
Net Worth: $129,665,016
Earnings: ($3,922,776)
Fiscal Year-end: 12/31/22
Software Development Services
N.A.I.C.S.: 541511
Dailin Chen *(Chm)*

BEIJING YUANLIU HONGYUAN ELECTRONIC TECHNOLOGY CO., LTD.
No 1 Tiangui Street Daxing Biomedical Industry Base, Zhongguancun Science & Technology Park Daxing District, Beijing, 102600, China
Tel.: (86) 1089237777
Web Site: http://www.yldz.com.cn
Year Founded: 2001
603267—(SHG)
Rev.: $351,308,978
Assets: $750,006,186
Liabilities: $185,987,431
Net Worth: $564,018,755
Earnings: $112,966,233
Fiscal Year-end: 12/31/22
Electronic Product Mfr & Distr
N.A.I.C.S.: 334419
Hong Zheng *(Chm)*

BEIJING YUANLONG YATO CULTURE DISSEMINATION CO., LTD.
Room 1218 12F No 338 Guanganmennei Avenue, Xicheng District, Beijing, 100053, China
Tel.: (86) 1083528822
Web Site: http://www.ylyato.com
Year Founded: 1998
002878—(SSE)
Rev.: $461,980,584
Assets: $252,085,392
Liabilities: $106,553,772
Net Worth: $145,531,620
Earnings: $23,495,940
Emp.: 1,100
Fiscal Year-end: 12/31/22
General Marketing Services
N.A.I.C.S.: 541870
Sun Zhen *(Founder, Chm, Pres & Gen Mgr)*

BEIJING ZHIDEMAI TECHNOLOGY CO., LTD.
38th Floor Building 11 Phase II Nord Center, Fengtai Science and Technology Park, Beijing, 100160, China
Tel.: (86) 1056640704
Web Site: https://www.zhidemai.com
Year Founded: 2011
300785—(SSE)
Rev.: $172,470,168
Assets: $318,522,672
Liabilities: $64,758,096
Net Worth: $253,764,576
Earnings: $11,918,556
Fiscal Year-end: 12/31/22
E Commerce Site Operator
N.A.I.C.S.: 518210
Guodong Sui *(Founder, Chm & CEO)*

BEIJING ZHONG KE SAN HUAN HIGH-TECH CO., LTD.
27th Floor Building 1 No 66 Zhongguancun East Road, Haidian District, Beijing, 100190, China
Tel.: (86) 1082649988
Web Site: https://www.san-huan.com.cn
000970—(SSE)
Rev.: $1,364,099,724
Assets: $1,644,496,776
Liabilities: $574,843,932
Net Worth: $1,069,652,844

Earnings: $119,039,544
Fiscal Year-end: 12/31/22
Magnet & Application Device Mfr
N.A.I.C.S.: 332999
Zhenxi Wang *(Chm)*

Subsidiaries:

Beijing Zhong Ke San Huan International Trading Company **(1)**
No 38 Weisan Rd Jiangnan Exporting Process & Trade Zone, Ningbo, 315801, Zhejiang, China
Tel.: (86) 57486150890
Magnet Distr
N.A.I.C.S.: 423510

Jiangxi South Rare-Earth High-Tech Co., Ltd. **(1)**
No 36 Qingnian Road, Ganzhou, 341000, Jiangxi, China
Tel.: (86) 7978463339
Metals Mfr
N.A.I.C.S.: 331529

Nanjing Daluge High-Tech Co., Ltd **(1)**
No 99 Guangli Road Dongshan Bridge Industrial Zone Guli Street, Jiangning District, Nanjing, 211153, Jiangsu, China
Tel.: (86) 2566616516
Electric Automobile Mfr
N.A.I.C.S.: 336110

Ningbo Konit Industrial Inc. Ltd. **(1)**
No 18 28 Keyuan Road Beilun District, Ningbo, 315803, Zhejiang, China
Tel.: (86) 57486221333
Magnet Mfr
N.A.I.C.S.: 327110

SANVAC (Beijing) Magnetics Co., Ltd. **(1)**
No 23 Chuangxin Road Changping District, Beijing, 102200, China
Tel.: (86) 1080111940
Magnet Mfr
N.A.I.C.S.: 327110

Tianjin Sanhuan Lucky New Material Inc. **(1)**
No 22 Hongze Road Tianjin Economic Development Area, Tianjin, 300457, China
Tel.: (86) 2259829118
Web Site: http://www.shlucky.com
Magnet Mfr
N.A.I.C.S.: 327110

Zhaoqing San Huan Jingyue Magnetic Materials Inc. Ltd **(1)**
No 201 Zhaoqing Avenue Duanzhou District, Zhaoqing, 526020, Guangdong, China
Tel.: (86) 7582829278
Magnet Mfr
N.A.I.C.S.: 327110

Zhong Ke San Huan Yu Xian Jingxiu Magnetic Materials Inc., Ltd **(1)**
Xiguanping Xiushui Town, Yangquan, Yu County Shanxi, China
Tel.: (86) 3538062703
Magnet Mfr
N.A.I.C.S.: 327110

BEIJING ZHONGKE TONGRONG PRIVATE EQUITY INVESTMENT FUND CO., LTD
Room 315 3/F Building 2 1 Wenxing Street Xicheng, Beijing, 10044, China
Tel.: (86) 1083326287
Privater Equity Firm
N.A.I.C.S.: 523999
Duan Xuefeng *(Exec Dir)*

BEIJING ZHONGKEHAIXUN DIGITAL S & T CO., LTD.
No 15 building 9 Jin Jin Road, Haidian, Beijing, 100095, China
Tel.: (86) 1082492472
Web Site:
https://en.zhongkehaixun.com
Year Founded: 2005
300810—(SSE)
Rev.: $30,612,816

Assets: $163,363,824
Liabilities: $18,551,052
Net Worth: $144,812,772
Earnings: $1,778,868
Fiscal Year-end: 12/31/22
Digital Marketing Services
N.A.I.C.S.: 541870

BEIJING ZODI INVESTMENT CO., LTD.
5th Floor Building 6 No 1 Haiying Road, Science City Fengtai District, Beijing, 100005, China
Tel.: (86) 1065278816
000609—(SSE)
Rev.: $60,063,120
Assets: $324,058,644
Liabilities: $243,777,924
Net Worth: $80,280,720
Earnings: ($41,111,928)
Fiscal Year-end: 12/31/22
Real Estate Property Development Services
N.A.I.C.S.: 531110

BEIJING ZOHETEC CO., LTD
Rongyu Building Sidaokou North Street, Haidian, Beijing, China
Tel.: (86) 1082467949
Web Site: https://www.zohetec.com
Electronic Products Mfr
N.A.I.C.S.: 334417

BEIJING ZUOJIANG TECHNOLOGY CO., LTD.
Room 101 1st Floor Room 201 2nd Floor Building 9 Yard 3, Gaolizhang Road Haidian District, Beijing, 100095, China
Tel.: (86) 1088112303
Year Founded: 2007
300799—(SSE)
Rev.: $8,277,984
Assets: $106,330,536
Liabilities: $13,898,196
Net Worth: $92,432,340
Earnings: ($20,624,760)
Fiscal Year-end: 12/31/22
Electronic Product Mfr & Distr
N.A.I.C.S.: 334419

BEIJING ZZNODE TECHNOLOGIES CO., LTD.
Room 1101 11th Floor Tower A Raycom Wangjing Center Building 523, Wangjing East Park Chaoyang District, Beijing, 100102, China
Tel.: (86) 1062800055
Web Site: https://www.zznode.com
Year Founded: 2008
003007—(SSE)
Rev.: $68,978,520
Assets: $142,114,284
Liabilities: $25,829,388
Net Worth: $116,284,896
Earnings: $5,409,612
Fiscal Year-end: 12/31/22
Software Development Services
N.A.I.C.S.: 541511
Juan Yuan *(Chm)*

BEIJING-SHANGHAI HIGH SPEED RAILWAY CO., LTD.
3rd and 4th floors Office Building 1 No 5 Beifengwo Road, Haidian District, Beijing, 100038, China
Tel.: (86) 1051896399
Web Site: https://www.cr-jh.cn
Year Founded: 2008
601816—(SHG)
Rev.: $2,714,726,973
Assets: $40,511,724,613
Liabilities: $11,409,653,722
Net Worth: $29,102,070,891
Earnings: $80,892,962)
Fiscal Year-end: 12/31/22

Beijing-Shanghai High Speed Railway Co., Ltd.—(Continued)

Rail Road Construction Services
N.A.I.C.S.: 236220
Hongrun Liu *(Chm)*

BEIJINGWEST INDUSTRIES INTERNATIONAL LIMITED

Room 1005-1006 10/F Harcourt House 39 Gloucester Road, Wanchai, China (Hong Kong)
Tel.: (852) 26258699   Ky
Web Site: http://www.bwi-intl.com.hk
2339—(HKG)
Rev.: $298,199,696
Assets: $289,855,077
Liabilities: $169,426,322
Net Worth: $120,428,755
Earnings: ($6,648,145)
Emp.: 950
Fiscal Year-end: 12/31/20
Automobile Parts Mfr & Whslr
N.A.I.C.S.: 336110
Yunan Jiang *(Chm)*

Subsidiaries:

BWI Czech Republic s.r.o.   (1)
K Hradisti 168/4 Hradiste, 35002, Cheb, Czech Republic
Tel.: (420) 351016000
Automotive Parts Mfr & Distr
N.A.I.C.S.: 336390

BEING CO., LTD.

1-312 Sakurabashi, Tsu, 514-0003, Mie, Japan
Tel.: (81) 592272932
Web Site: http://www.beingcorp.co.jp
Year Founded: 1975
47340—(TKS)
Rev.: $59,485,790
Assets: $72,919,840
Liabilities: $36,945,930
Net Worth: $35,973,910
Earnings: $3,622,150
Emp.: 239
Fiscal Year-end: 03/31/20
Software Developing Services
N.A.I.C.S.: 513210
Yoshishige Tsuda *(Chm & CEO)*

BEING HOLDING CO., LTD.

3-18 Senkojimachi, Kanazawa, 920-0356, Japan
Tel.: (81) 762681110
Web Site: http://www.being-group.jp
Year Founded: 1986
9145—(TKS)
Rev.: $186,622,980
Assets: $119,431,050
Liabilities: $75,409,240
Net Worth: $44,021,810
Earnings: $7,962,070
Emp.: 3,328
Fiscal Year-end: 12/31/23
Holding Company
N.A.I.C.S.: 551112
Shigekazu Kita *(Founder, Chm & Pres)*

BEINGMATE CO., LTD.

Building 10 No 1 Weiye Road, Binjiang District, Hangzhou, 310053, Zhejiang, China
Tel.: (86) 57128038959
Web Site: http://www.beingmate.com
Year Founded: 1999
002570—(SSE)
Rev.: $372,708,648
Assets: $544,346,244
Liabilities: $320,954,400
Net Worth: $223,391,844
Earnings: ($24,710,400)
Emp.: 3,500
Fiscal Year-end: 12/31/22
Infant Food Products, Beds & Toys Mfr

N.A.I.C.S.: 311999
Xie Hong *(Chm & Gen Mgr)*

BEIQI FOTON MOTOR COMPANY LTD.

Shayang Road, Shahe Town Changping District, Beijing, 102206, China
Tel.: (86) 1080762999
Web Site: https://www.foton.com.cn
Year Founded: 1996
600166—(SHG)
Rev.: $6,521,122,858
Assets: $6,811,458,980
Liabilities: $4,882,770,688
Net Worth: $1,928,688,292
Earnings: $9,141,318
Emp.: 32,000
Fiscal Year-end: 12/31/22
Motor Vehicles & Trucks Mfr
N.A.I.C.S.: 336110
Chang Rui *(Chm)*

BEISEN HOLDING LTD.

40th Floor Dah Sing Financial Centre No 248 Queen's Road East, Wanchai, China (Hong Kong)   Ky
Year Founded: 2005
9669—(HKG)
Holding Company
N.A.I.C.S.: 551112
Zhaohui Wang *(Chm)*

BEJO ZADEN B.V.

Trambaan 1, PO Box 50, Warmenhuizen, 1749 CZ, Netherlands
Tel.: (31) 226396162
Web Site: http://www.bejo.com
Year Founded: 1963
Sales Range: $25-49.9 Million
Emp.: 600
Vegetable Seeds Breeding, Production, Processing & Sales
N.A.I.C.S.: 111998
Ger Beemsterboer *(Pres)*

Subsidiaries:

Bejo Andes Ltda.   (1)
Ebro 2740 Oficina 301 Las Condes, Santiago, Chile
Tel.: (56) 2 2335 1897
Web Site: http://www.bejoandes.cl
Emp.: 5
Seed Production Services
N.A.I.C.S.: 111219
Johannes Dekker *(Gen Mgr)*

Bejo Bohemia, s.r.o.   (1)
Podulsany 49, Opatovice nad Labem, Czech Republic
Tel.: (420) 466 981 140
Web Site: http://www.bejo.cz
Seed Production Services
N.A.I.C.S.: 111219

Bejo Graines France S.A.R.L.   (1)
Beauchene, Beaufort-en-Vallee, 49250, France
Tel.: (33) 241572458
Web Site: http://www.bejo.fr
Emp.: 90
Seed Production Services
N.A.I.C.S.: 111219
Sake Boersma *(Mgr)*

Bejo Iberica, S.L.   (1)
Calle del Hervidero 15 28750 San Agustin de Guadalix, Madrid, 28750, Spain
Tel.: (34) 91 658 70 72
Web Site: http://www.bejo.es
Emp.: 24
Seed Production Services
N.A.I.C.S.: 111219

Bejo Italia s.r.l.   (1)
Via Cervara Vecchia n 13, Cervia, 48015, Italy
Tel.: (39) 0544 959011
Web Site: http://www.bejoitalia.it
Emp.: 14
Seed Production Services
N.A.I.C.S.: 111219
Leonarde Cassi *(Mgr)*

Bejo Romania SRL   (1)
Str Intrarea Sulfinei nr 96B, Ilfov, Magurele, Romania
Tel.: (40) 21 3328666
Web Site: http://www.bejo.ro
Seed Production Services
N.A.I.C.S.: 111219

Bejo Samen GmbH   (1)
Danziger Strasse 29, 47665, Sonsbeck, Nordrhein-Westfalen, Germany
Tel.: (49) 28 38 9 89 89 0
Web Site: http://www.bejosamen.de
Seed Production Services
N.A.I.C.S.: 111219

Bejo Seeds Inc.   (1)
1972 Silver Spur Pl, Oceano, CA 93445
Tel.: (805) 473-2199
Web Site: http://www.bejoseeds.com
Sales Range: $10-24.9 Million
Emp.: 57
Wholesale Vegetable Seeds
N.A.I.C.S.: 424910

Bejo Seeds Pty Ltd   (1)
460 Hall Road Skye, PO Box 5627, Cranbourne, Casey, 3977, VIC, Australia
Tel.: (61) 3 9782 2811
Web Site: http://www.bejo.com.au
Seed Production Services
N.A.I.C.S.: 111219

Bejo Sementes do Brasil Ltda   (1)
Roda Alkindar Monteiro Junqueira, Caixa Postal 56, Paulista, Braganca, Brazil
Tel.: (55) 11 4894 8027
Web Site: http://www.bejo.com.br
Seed Production Services
N.A.I.C.S.: 111219

Bejo Semillas Argentina S.A.   (1)
Ruiz Huidobro 1647 piso 1 B 1429 - Nunez, Buenos Aires, Ciudad Autonoma, Argentina
Tel.: (54) 11 4701 5877
Web Site: http://www.bejosemillas.com.ar
Seed Production Services
N.A.I.C.S.: 111219

Bejo Zaden Belgium b.v.b.a.   (1)
Berkenhoekstraat 6, Onze-Lieve-Vrouw-Waver, 2861, Belgium
Tel.: (32) 15 207771
Web Site: http://www.bejo.com
Emp.: 5
Seed Production Services
N.A.I.C.S.: 111219
Enge Smith *(Mgr)*

Bejo Zaden Poland Sp. z o.o.   (1)
ul Rajdowa 40, Ozarow Mazowiecki, 05-850, Konotopa, Poland
Tel.: (48) 22 721 25 30
Web Site: http://www.bejo.pl
Seed Production Services
N.A.I.C.S.: 111219

Bejo Zaden d.o.o.   (1)
Soblinecka 14a, Sesvete, Hrvatska, Croatia
Tel.: (385) 1 6150 155
Web Site: http://www.bejo.hr
Seed Production Services
N.A.I.C.S.: 111219

Bejo, S.A.   (1)
Km 30 Carretera Interamericana Lote No 51 San Lucas, San Lucas, Guatemala, Sacatepequez, Guatemala
Tel.: (502) 7830 7212
Seed Production Services
N.A.I.C.S.: 111219

BEKASI ASRI PEMULA TBK

Gedung Tomang Tol Lantai 2 Jl Arjuna No 1, Tanjung Duren, Jakarta, 11470, Indonesia
Tel.: (62) 2129181028
Web Site:
https://www.bekasiasripemula.co.id
Year Founded: 1993
BAPA—(INDO)
Rev.: $527,306
Assets: $8,757,959
Liabilities: $588,504
Net Worth: $8,169,455
Earnings: ($185,555)
Emp.: 22
Fiscal Year-end: 12/31/23

Commercial Property Development Services
N.A.I.C.S.: 531311
Warinton Simanjuntak *(Chm & Dir)*

BEKEM METALS, INC.

Sankibai Batyr Ave 14D, 030000, Aktobe, Kazakhstan
Tel.: (7) 7132667664   UT
BKMM—(OTCIQ)
Sales Range: Less than $1 Million
Nickel Mining Services
N.A.I.C.S.: 212230
Adam Cook *(Sec)*

BEKEN CORPORATION

Building 41 Capital of Tech Leaders 1387 Zhangdong Road, Zhangjiang High-Tech Park Pudong New District, Shanghai, 201203, China
Tel.: (86) 2151086811
Web Site:
https://www.bekencorp.com
Year Founded: 2005
603068—(SHG)
Rev.: $100,136,285
Assets: $283,559,815
Liabilities: $31,188,695
Net Worth: $252,371,120
Earnings: ($33,423,708)
Fiscal Year-end: 12/31/22
Wireless Connection Chip Product Mfr
N.A.I.C.S.: 334220
Pengfei Zhang *(Chm & Gen Mgr)*

BEKUPLAST GMBH

Industriestrasse 1, Ringe, 49824, Germany
Tel.: (49) 594493330
Web Site: http://www.bekuplast.com
Year Founded: 1985
Rev.: $22,011,880
Emp.: 160
Transport & Storage Container Mfr
N.A.I.C.S.: 332439
Wilhelm Roelofs *(Mng Dir)*

Subsidiaries:

bekuplast Benelux B.V.   (1)
Solingenstraat 41, Deventer, Netherlands
Tel.: (31) 683264796
Packaging Services
N.A.I.C.S.: 561910

bekuplast Polska Sp. z o.o   (1)
Ul Lutoslawskiego 18, Slupsk, Poland
Tel.: (48) 598481400
Packaging Services
N.A.I.C.S.: 561910

BEKY A.S.

Podrybnicka 1, 069 01, Snina, Slovakia
Tel.: (421) 577685446
Web Site: http://www.beky.sk
Year Founded: 1992
Sales Range: $125-149.9 Million
Emp.: 450
Hardwood Mfr
N.A.I.C.S.: 321912
Dusan Breeka *(CEO)*

BEL AIR INDUSTRIES

15 Rue De Paris, 69170, Tarare, Rhone, France
Tel.: (33) 474053060
Web Site:
http://www.belairindustries.com
Rev.: $39,200,000
Emp.: 40
N.A.I.C.S.: 313110
Philippe Gonzalvez *(Dir)*

BEL GLOBAL RESOURCES HOLDINGS LIMITED

Unit 1011 10th Floor Heng Ngai Jewelry Centre 4 Hok Yuen Street East,

Hung Hom, Kowloon, China (Hong Kong)
Tel.: (852) 3618 5100
Web Site: http://www.bgr.com.hk
Sales Range: $25-49.9 Million
Emp.: 350
Coal & Nickel Mining Services
N.A.I.C.S.: 213113
Danielle Char *(Mgr-Apparel Mktg)*

Subsidiaries:

Bel Nickel Resources Limited　　**(1)**
10 F Haleson Bldg 1 Jubilee Stch, Central, China (Hong Kong)
Tel.: (852) 36185100
Sales Range: $25-49.9 Million
Emp.: 20
Minerals Whslr
N.A.I.C.S.: 423520

BELA AUTOMOTIVES LIMITED
Plot No 1-3 Mouza Pathra, Baluchistan, Hub Chowki, Pakistan
Tel.: (92) 20232455　　　　　　PK
Web Site:
　https://belaautomotivesltd.com
Year Founded: 1983
BELA—(PSX)
Assets: $886,601
Liabilities: $475,405
Net Worth: $411,196
Earnings: ($13,234)
Fiscal Year-end: 06/30/23
Fastener Product Mfr
N.A.I.C.S.: 332722
Omer Mateen Allahwala *(Sec)*

BELAGROPROMBANK JSC
3 Zhukov Ave, 220036, Minsk, Belarus
Tel.: (375) 172185777
Web Site: http://www.belapb.by
Year Founded: 1991
Sales Range: Less than $1 Million
Commercial Banking Services
N.A.I.C.S.: 522110
Tatsiana Itrafanava *(Deputy Chm-Mgmt Bd)*

BELAPUR INDUSTRIES LTD.
PO Harigaon Tal, Shrirampur, Ahmednagar, 413718, Maharashtra, India
Tel.: (91) 2222453141
Sugar Cane Mfr
N.A.I.C.S.: 311314
Avinash G. Adik *(Mng Dir)*

BELARAROX LIMITED
Level 11 12-14 The Esplanade, Perth, 6000, WA, Australia
Tel.: (61) 417934998　　　　　AU
Web Site:
　https://www.belararox.com.au
Year Founded: 2021
BRX—(ASX)
Rev.: $8,547
Assets: $9,772,605
Liabilities: $2,359,126
Net Worth: $7,413,479
Earnings: ($1,294,107)
Fiscal Year-end: 06/30/23
Mineral Exploration Services
N.A.I.C.S.: 212390
Arvind Misra *(Mng Dir)*

BELARUSBANK
Dzerzhinski Ave 18, 220089, Minsk, Belarus
Tel.: (375) 17 218 84 31
Web Site: http://www.belarusbank.by
Year Founded: 1922
Rev.: $1,003,751,725
Assets: $12,538,524,909
Liabilities: $11,225,924,266
Net Worth: $1,312,600,643
Earnings: $79,762,426

Fiscal Year-end: 12/31/20
Securities Brokerage Services
N.A.I.C.S.: 523150
Viktar Ananich *(Chm-Mgmt Bd)*

Subsidiaries:

ASB Consult LLC　　　　　　　　**(1)**
st Myasnikova 32 office 301, 220030, Minsk, Belarus
Tel.: (375) 172188226
Web Site: http://asbconsult.by
Management Consulting Services
N.A.I.C.S.: 541618

ASB Leasing LLC　　　　　　　　**(1)**
32-404 Myasnikova str, 220050, Minsk, Belarus
Tel.: (375) 172001153
Web Site: http://www.asbleasing.com
Financial Lending Services
N.A.I.C.S.: 522220
Pavel Karotkih *(Head-Individual Leasing Dept & Deputy Dir)*

ASB Sanatoriy Solnechny UE　　**(1)**
Mukhavetsky s / s 46, Brest district, 225041, Brest, Belarus
Tel.: (375) 162510446
Web Site: http://solnechny.by
Medical Therapy Services
N.A.I.C.S.: 621340

BELAVIA NATSIONALYNAYA VIAKOMPANIYA R.U.P.
14 Nemiga Str, 220004, Minsk, Belarus
Tel.: (375) 1722025555
Web Site: http://www.belavia.by
Year Founded: 1996
Sales Range: $300-349.9 Million
Emp.: 1,500
Airline Services
N.A.I.C.S.: 481111
Anatoly Nikolayevich Gusarov *(Dir Gen)*

BELC CO., LTD.
1646 Ashioori, Tsurugashima, 350-2282, Saitama, Japan
Tel.: (81) 120299332
Web Site: https://www.belc.jp
Year Founded: 1959
9974—(TKS)
Rev.: $2,494,659,040
Assets: $1,307,133,670
Liabilities: $598,381,820
Net Worth: $708,751,850
Earnings: $75,699,930
Emp.: 2,590
Fiscal Year-end: 02/29/24
Food Supermarkets, Grocery Stores & Restaurants Owner & Operator
N.A.I.C.S.: 445110
Tamotsu Harashima *(Chm)*

BELEAVE, INC.
2030 Bristol Circle 115, Oakville, L6H 0H2, ON, Canada　　　　　ON
Web Site: http://www.beleave.com
Year Founded: 1964
BE—(CNSX)
Rev.: $1,865,996
Assets: $17,304,805
Liabilities: $9,691,539
Net Worth: $7,613,266
Earnings: ($24,763,187)
Fiscal Year-end: 03/31/19
Medical Cannabis Company
N.A.I.C.S.: 325412
Roger Ferreira *(Chief Science Officer)*

BELFIUS BANK SA/NV
11 Karel Rogierplein, 1210, Brussels, Belgium
Tel.: (32) 22221111　　　　　　BE
Web Site: http://www.belfius.be
Sales Range: $1-4.9 Billion
Emp.: 7,600

Banking Services
N.A.I.C.S.: 522110
Dirk Gyselinck *(Member-Mgmt Bd)*

Subsidiaries:

Belfius Commercial Finance　　**(1)**
Dexia Tower Rogierplein 11, Brussels, B 1210, Belgium　　　　　　**(100%)**
Tel.: (32) 22852611
Sales Range: $1-9.9 Million
Emp.: 41
Short-Term Business Credit Institution
N.A.I.C.S.: 522299
Ivan DeCoen *(Mng Dir)*

Belfius Insurance　　　　　　　**(1)**
Avenue Galilee 5, Brussels, B-1210, Belgium　　　　　　　　　　**(100%)**
Tel.: (32) 22866111
Sales Range: $250-299.9 Million
Emp.: 1,000
Insurance Services
N.A.I.C.S.: 524298
Eric Kleijnen *(CEO)*

Belfius Ireland　　　　　　　　**(1)**
6 Georges Dock IFSC, Dublin, 1, Ireland　　　　　　　　　　　**(100%)**
Tel.: (353) 16455000
Sales Range: $50-74.9 Million
Emp.: 50
Investment Services
N.A.I.C.S.: 523940

Belfius Lease　　　　　　　　　**(1)**
Boulevard Pacheco 44, B 1000, Brussels, Belgium　　　　　　　　**(100%)**
Tel.: (32) 22223708
Web Site: http://www.dexia.be
Sales Range: $50-74.9 Million
Emp.: 40
Business Credit Services
N.A.I.C.S.: 522299

Unit (Domestic):

Belfius Auto Lease SA/NV　　　**(2)**
RogierTower Rogierplein 11, 1210, Brussels, Belgium　　　　　　**(99%)**
Tel.: (32) 2 285 35 94
Web Site: http://www.belfius-autolease.be
Sales Range: $25-49.9 Million
Emp.: 30
Vehicle Leasing Services
N.A.I.C.S.: 532112

Belfius Lease Services SA/NV　**(2)**
Avenue Livingstone Rueeas 6 place Rogaer, B 1210, Brussels, Belgium **(100%)**
Tel.: (32) 22223836
Sales Range: $75-99.9 Million
N.A.I.C.S.: 522210

Colin Buchanan & Partners Ltd.　**(1)**
20 Eastbourne Ter, W2 6LG, London, United Kingdom - England　　**(100%)**
Tel.: (44) 2070531300
Web Site: http://www.cbuchanan.co.uk
Sales Range: $25-49.9 Million
Emp.: 150
N.A.I.C.S.: 522210

Eurco Ltd.　　　　　　　　　　**(1)**
6 Georges Dock IFSC, Dublin, 1, Ireland　　　　　　　　　　　**(100%)**
Tel.: (353) 18515200
Sales Range: $25-49.9 Million
Emp.: 9
N.A.I.C.S.: 522210

Eurco Re Ltd.　　　　　　　　　**(1)**
6 Georges Dock, Dublin, 1, IFSC, Ireland　　　　　　　　　　　**(100%)**
Tel.: (353) 018515200
Sales Range: $250-299.9 Million
Emp.: 9
Insurance Agents, Brokers & Service
N.A.I.C.S.: 524298
Carmel O'Brien *(Mgr)*

Eurco SA　　　　　　　　　　　**(1)**
2 Rue Nicolas Bove, L 1253, Luxembourg, Luxembourg　　　　　**(100%)**
Tel.: (352) 227343
Sales Range: $50-74.9 Million
Emp.: 9
Insurance Agents, Brokers & Service
N.A.I.C.S.: 524298

Parfipar SA　　　　　　　　　　**(1)**

Boulevard Royal 10A, Luxembourg, L-2093, Luxembourg　　　　**(100%)**
Provider of Financial Services
N.A.I.C.S.: 522320

Reagra SA　　　　　　　　　　**(1)**
Rue de la gare 65, Luxembourg, Luxembourg　　　　　　　　　**(33%)**
Personal Credit Institutions
N.A.I.C.S.: 522210

Securenta Conseil　　　　　　　**(1)**
10 A Boulevard Royal, Luxembourg, L-2449, Luxembourg　　　　**(100%)**
Personal Credit Institutions
N.A.I.C.S.: 522210

Securifund NV　　　　　　　　　**(1)**
Polarisweg 35, PB 767, Willemstad, Curacao　　　　　　　　　**(100%)**
Personal Credit Institutions
N.A.I.C.S.: 522210

BELGRAVIA HARTFORD CAPITAL INC.
1410-120 Adelaide Street W, Toronto, M5H 1T1, ON, Canada
Tel.: (250) 763-5533　　　　　Ca
Web Site:
　https://belgraviahartford.com
Year Founded: 2002
ECA—(DEU)
Rev.: $44,323
Assets: $916,720
Liabilities: $638,387
Net Worth: $278,333
Earnings: ($1,638,907)
Fiscal Year-end: 12/31/23
Potash Mining Services
N.A.I.C.S.: 212390
Paul Kania *(CFO)*

BELHASA GROUP OF COMPANIES
El Ettehad St, PO Box 1286, Dubai, 1286, United Arab Emirates
Tel.: (971) 42662319
Web Site: http://www.belhasa.com
Year Founded: 1960
Sales Range: $800-899.9 Million
Emp.: 4,600
Holding Company
N.A.I.C.S.: 551112
Ahmed Saif Belhasa *(Chm)*

Subsidiaries:

Al Tatweer Contracting L.L.C　　**(1)**
Al Ittihad Rd, PO Box 55308, Dubai, United Arab Emirates
Tel.: (971) 4 297 2591
Residential & Commercial Construction Services
N.A.I.C.S.: 236220

Amaal Commercial Broker LLC　**(1)**
Floor Suite 01 Belhasa BioTek Solutions Building, Al Quoz, Dubai, United Arab Emirates
Tel.: (971) 4 347 7275
Insurance & Brokerage Services
N.A.I.C.S.: 524210

Belhasa Actioncrete International　**(1)**
PO Box 1286, Dubai, United Arab Emirates
Tel.: (971) 42662319
Web Site: http://www.belhasa.com
Emp.: 100
Provider of Maintenance & Repair Services
N.A.I.C.S.: 811412
Ahmed Belhasa *(Chm)*

Belhasa Anthony Pools
Contracting　　　　　　　　　**(1)**
PO Box 5120, Dubai, United Arab Emirates
Tel.: (971) 42 668440
Mfr of Swimming Pools; Provider of Landscaping Services
N.A.I.C.S.: 541320

Belhasa Automotive Service Center & Spare Parts　　　　　　　**(1)**
AlquozIndustrial 3, PO Box 61627, Dubai, 61627, United Arab Emirates　**(100%)**
Tel.: (971) 43472050

Belhasa Group of Companies—(Continued)
Web Site: http://www.belhasamotors.com
Sales Range: $25-49.9 Million
Emp.: 100
Provider of Automotive Maintenance & Repair
N.A.I.C.S.: 811198
Amar Ahmed Belhasa (Mng Dir)

Belhasa Diotek Solutions LLC (1)
Industrial 3rd Al Quoz Area, PO Box
282948, Dubai, United Arab Emirates
Tel.: (971) 4 347 6017
Cleaning Product Mfr
N.A.I.C.S.: 325620

Belhasa Engineering & Contracting
Company (1)
Belhasa Bldg Hor Al Anz Area Mezzanine
Fl, PO Box 5450, Dubai, United Arab Emirates
Tel.: (971) 42663925
Sales Range: $700-749.9 Million
Emp.: 4,000
Provider of Engineering & Construction Services
N.A.I.C.S.: 541330
Altaf Kazi (Gen Mgr)

Belhasa For Quarries & Crushers
Management L.L.C (1)
PO Box 2644, Fujairah, United Arab Emirates
Tel.: (971) 7 258 4115
Readymix Concrete Mfr
N.A.I.C.S.: 327320

Belhasa International Company (1)
Dubai Sharjah Rd Balhasa Bldg M Fl, PO
Box 1286, Dubai, 1286, United Arab Emirates
Tel.: (971) 42662319
Sales Range: $25-49.9 Million
Emp.: 100
Designer of Interior Decorations
N.A.I.C.S.: 541410
Ahmed Sais Belhasa (Chm)

Belhasa Joinery & Decoration Company LLC (1)
Al Qusais Industrial 5 Amman Street, PO
Box 84918, Dubai, PO box 84918, United
Arab Emirates
Tel.: (971) 42677252
Web Site: http://www.belhasajoinery.com
Sales Range: $50-74.9 Million
Emp.: 200
Interior Design & Decoration Services
N.A.I.C.S.: 541410
Mohammed Asif (Gen Mgr)

Belhasa Motors Company (1)
Alquoz 4 Interchange Shakih Rd, PO Box
61627, Dubai, United Arab Emirates
Tel.: (971) 43472050
Web Site: http://www.belhasamotors.com
Importer, Promoter, Marketer & Sales of
Automotive Parts & Equipment
N.A.I.C.S.: 336340

Belhasa Projects LLC (1)
Ras Al Khor street 13 ETISALAT warehouse, PO Box 5102, Dubai, 5102, United
Arab Emirates
Tel.: (971) 4 3331445
Web Site: http://www.belhasaprojects.com
Emp.: 2,500
Residential & Commercial Construction
Services
N.A.I.C.S.: 236220
Suleyman Busbuy (CEO)

Belhasa Real Estate (1)
PO Box 1286, Dubai, United Arab Emirates
Tel.: (971) 42683144
Provider of Investment & Securities Services
N.A.I.C.S.: 523940

Belhasa Real Estate (1)
PO Box 1286, Dubai, United Arab Emirates
Tel.: (971) 42662319
Provider of Real Estate Investment Services
N.A.I.C.S.: 525990

Belhasa Six Construction
Company (1)
Al Quoz Industrial Area 3, PO Box 13055,
Dubai, United Arab Emirates

Tel.: (971) 43472777
Web Site: http://www.bsix.com
Emp.: 15,000
Provider of Construction Services
N.A.I.C.S.: 236220
Bechara Sousso (Exec Dir)

Belhasa Trading & Development
Company (1)
Belhasa Compound Al Quoz Industrial 3,
PO Box 61627, Dubai, 61627, United Arab
Emirates
Tel.: (971) 43472050
Web Site: http://www.belhasamotors.com
Bus, Truck & Automobile Marketing, Sales
& Maintenence
Shrikumar Nair (Gen Mgr)

Belhasa, Tourism, Travel & Cargo
Co., L.L.C. (1)
Al Makhtoum Street, PO Box 20968, Dubai,
United Arab Emirates (100%)
Tel.: (971) 42957474
Web Site: http://www.belhasatravel.com
Sales Range: $25-49.9 Million
Emp.: 50
Travel, Tourism & Transportation Services
N.A.I.C.S.: 561520
Narous Sarkies (Gen Mgr)

Emirates Driving Institute (1)
Behind Al Bustan Ctr, PO Box 20948, Qusais, Dubai, 20948, United Arab Emirates
Tel.: (971) 42631100
Web Site: http://www.edi.ae
Sales Range: $75-99.9 Million
Emp.: 900
Provider of Driver Training Services
N.A.I.C.S.: 611710

INAYA Facilities Management
Services (1)
NAM Building No 3, PO Box 87074, Jebel
Ali, United Arab Emirates
Tel.: (971) 4 882 7001
Web Site: http://www.inaya.ae
Project Management & Civil Maintenance
Services
N.A.I.C.S.: 561790
Annie Sharma (Mgr-Customer Svc)

Silver Seas Shipping LLC (1)
PO Box 29242, Dubai, United Arab Emirates
Tel.: (971) 4 696923
Developer of Port & Shipping Infrastructures
N.A.I.C.S.: 339999

Union Trading Company (1)
PO Box 85983, Dubai, United Arab Emirates
Tel.: (971) 42662319
Web Site: http://www.belhasa.com
Sales Range: $25-49.9 Million
Emp.: 40
Constructor of Power Generation Plants
N.A.I.C.S.: 335311
Haitham Ahmed Belhasa (Mng Dir)

BELIEVE SAS
41 Avenue Bosquet, 75007, Paris,
France
Tel.: (33) 1 53 09 34 00
Web Site: http://www.believe.fr
Year Founded: 2004
Emp.: 100
Music Distribution Services
N.A.I.C.S.: 512230
Jean-Christophe Mercier (Dir-
Distributed Labels)

Subsidiaries:

TuneCore, Inc. (1)
63 Pearl St, Brooklyn, NY 11201
Tel.: (646) 651-1060
Web Site: http://www.tunecore.com
Emp.: 150
Online Music Sales
N.A.I.C.S.: 513210
Matt Barrington (COO)

BELIMO HOLDING AG
Brunnenbachstrasse 1, 8340, Hinwil,
Switzerland
Tel.: (41) 438436111

Web Site: https://www.belimo.com
Year Founded: 1975
BEAN—(SWX)
Rev.: $158,898,265
Assets: $378,444,261
Liabilities: $1,386,974
Net Worth: $377,057,287
Earnings: $143,147,136
Fiscal Year-end: 12/31/23
Air-Conditioning & Warm Air Heating
Equipment & Commercial & Industrial
Refrigeration Equipment Manufacturing
N.A.I.C.S.: 333415
Peter Schmidlin (Chief Innovation
Officer)

Subsidiaries:

BELIMO A/S (1)
Thomas Helsteds vej 7A, 8660, Skanderborg, Denmark
Tel.: (45) 86524400
Web Site: http://www.belimo.dk
Sales Range: $50-74.9 Million
Emp.: 10
Motors & Valves Sales
N.A.I.C.S.: 423610

BELIMO AB (1)
Stubbsundsvagen 15, 131 41, Nacka, Sweden
Tel.: (46) 84640700
Web Site: https://www.belimo.com
Air Conditioning Equipment Mfr
N.A.I.C.S.: 333415
Fredrik Moberg (Natl Sls Mgr)

BELIMO Actuators (India) Pvt
Ltd. (1)
204 Jaisingh Bus Ctr Parsiwada 104 Sahar
Rd, Andheri E, Mumbai, 400099, Maharashtra, India
Tel.: (91) 22 2822 2559
Sales Range: $25-49.9 Million
Emp.: 20
Actuators & Valves Distr
N.A.I.C.S.: 423610

BELIMO Actuators (Shanghai) Trading Ltd. (1)
450 North Hengshahe Road Building 1,
Minhang District, Shanghai, 201108, China
Tel.: (86) 2154832929
Web Site: http://www.belimo.com
Actuators & Valves Distr
N.A.I.C.S.: 423610

BELIMO Actuators Ltd. (1)
7th Fl Honjo-Azumabashi DJ Bldg 4-19-3
Honjo, Sumida-ku, Tokyo, 130-0001, Japan
Tel.: (81) 368236961
Sales Range: $50-74.9 Million
Emp.: 4
Actuators & Valves Distr
N.A.I.C.S.: 423610

BELIMO Actuators Ltd. (1)
S-13-12 1st Subang Jalan SS15/4G, 47500,
Subang Jaya, Selangor, Malaysia
Tel.: (60) 356125833
Web Site: http://www.belimo.com
Sales Range: $50-74.9 Million
Emp.: 3
Actuators & Valves Distr
N.A.I.C.S.: 423610

BELIMO Actuators Ltd. (1)
Room 1601-08 16/F New Commerce Centre 19 On Sum Street, Sha Tin, New Teritories, China (Hong Kong)
Tel.: (852) 2687 17 16
Web Site: http://www.belimo.com.hk
Sales Range: $25-49.9 Million
Emp.: 20
Actuators & Valves Distr
N.A.I.C.S.: 423610

BELIMO Actuators Ltd. (1)
90 2 Pensiri Pl Soi Phaholyothin 32 Phaholyothin Rd Chandrakasem, Jatujak, Bangkok, 10900, Thailand
Tel.: (66) 29415582
Web Site: http://www.belimo.com
Sales Range: $50-74.9 Million
Emp.: 3
Actuators & Valves Distr
N.A.I.C.S.: 423610

BELIMO Actuators Ltd. (1)
7F 343 Jhonghe Rd, Yonghe, Taipei, 234,
Taiwan
Tel.: (886) 229228805
Sales Range: $50-74.9 Million
Emp.: 2
Actuators & Valves Distr
N.A.I.C.S.: 423610

BELIMO Actuators Pty Ltd (1)
12 Enterprise Court Mulgrave Business
Park, Mulgrave, 3170, VIC, Australia
Tel.: (61) 385857800
Web Site: http://www.belimo.com.au
Sales Range: $25-49.9 Million
Emp.: 17
Actuators & Valves Distr
N.A.I.C.S.: 423610

BELIMO Aircontrols (CAN), Inc. (1)
2495 Meadowpine Boulevard, Mississauga,
L5N 6C3, ON, Canada
Tel.: (905) 712-3118
Web Site: https://www.belimo.com
Sales Range: $25-49.9 Million
Emp.: 12
Actuators & Valves Distr
N.A.I.C.S.: 423840

BELIMO Aircontrols (USA), Inc. (1)
33 Turner Rd, Danbury, CT 06810
Web Site: https://www.belimo.com
Air Conditioning Equipment Mfr
N.A.I.C.S.: 333415

BELIMO Automation AG (1)
Brunnenbachstrasse 1, 8340, Hinwil, Switzerland
Tel.: (41) 438436111
Web Site: https://www.belimo.com
Sales Range: $150-199.9 Million
Emp.: 600
Actuators & Valves Distr
N.A.I.C.S.: 423610
Lars van der Haegen (CEO)

BELIMO Automation Deutschland
GmbH (1)
Schucostrasse 8, 01900, Grossrohrsdorf,
Germany
Tel.: (49) 35952139000
Air Conditioning Equipment Mfr
N.A.I.C.S.: 333415

BELIMO Automation FZE (1)
LIU K17 Al Twar 2, PO Box 293644, Dubai
Airport Free Zone, Dubai, 219644, United
Arab Emirates
Tel.: (971) 42998050
Web Site: https://www.belimo.com
Sales Range: $25-49.9 Million
Emp.: 15
Actuators & Valves Distr
N.A.I.C.S.: 423610

BELIMO Automation Handelsgesellschaft m.b.H. (1)
Brunner Strasse 63/20, 1230, Vienna, Austria
Tel.: (43) 174903610
Web Site: https://www.belimo.com
Sales Range: $25-49.9 Million
Emp.: 15
Actuators & Valves Distr
N.A.I.C.S.: 423840

BELIMO Automation Malaysia Sdn.
Bhd. (1)
No 15 Jalan Wawasan 2C/ KU7 Sungai
Kapar Indah, 42200, Klang, Selangor, Malaysia
Tel.: (60) 333962988
Web Site: https://www.belimo.com
Air Conditioning Equipment Mfr
N.A.I.C.S.: 333415
Phang Khai Siang (Sls Mgr)

BELIMO Automation Norge A / S (1)
Nils Hansensvei 13, 0667, Oslo, 0667, Norway
Tel.: (47) 22707171
Web Site: https://www.belimo.com
Sales Range: $50-74.9 Million
Emp.: 6
Heating & Cooling System Controls Distr
N.A.I.C.S.: 423730

BELIMO Automation UK Ltd. (1)
Shepperton Business Park Govett Avenue,

Shepperton, TW17 8BA, Middlesex, United Kingdom
Tel.: (44) 1932260460
Web Site: https://www.belimo.com
Sales Range: $25-49.9 Million
Emp.: 15
Actuators & Valves Distr
N.A.I.C.S.: 423610

BELIMO Brasil Comercio de Automacao Ltda. (1)
Rua Barbalha 251 Alto da Lapa, Sao Paulo, 05083-020, Brazil
Tel.: (55) 1136435656
Web Site: http://www.belimo.com.br
Sales Range: $50-74.9 Million
Emp.: 10
Actuators & Valves Distr
N.A.I.C.S.: 423610

BELIMO Bulgaria Ltd. (1)
Balchik 6 Street Office 1-2, 1612, Sofia, Bulgaria
Tel.: (359) 2 9523470
Web Site: http://www.belimo-bg.com
Electric Actuators & Valves Distr
N.A.I.C.S.: 423610

BELIMO CZ spol. s r.o. (1)
Severni 277, Jinocany, 25225, Prague, Czech Republic
Tel.: (420) 271740311
Web Site: http://www.belimo.cz
Sales Range: $50-74.9 Million
Emp.: 10
Actuators & Valves Distr
N.A.I.C.S.: 423610

BELIMO Customization (USA), Inc. (1)
33 Turner Rd, Danbury, CT 06810-5113
Tel.: (203) 791-9915
Web Site: http://www.belimo.us
Emp.: 250
Actuators & Valves Mfr
N.A.I.C.S.: 333995
Lars Can Der Haegh (Pres)

BELIMO Finland Oy (1)
Robert Huberin tie 16 C, 01510, Vantaa, Finland
Tel.: (358) 207639500
Web Site: https://www.belimo.com
Air Conditioning Equipment Mfr
N.A.I.C.S.: 333415
Tero Mehtala (Mng Dir)

BELIMO Iberica de Servomotores S.A. (1)
C/San Romualdo 12-14, 28037, Madrid, Spain
Tel.: (34) 913041111
Web Site: https://www.belimo.com
Sales Range: $50-74.9 Million
Emp.: 7
Actuators & Valves Distr
N.A.I.C.S.: 423610

BELIMO Italia S.r.l. (1)
Via Zanica 19H, 24050, Grassobbio, Bergamo, Italy
Tel.: (39) 0355788700
Web Site: https://www.belimo.com
Air Conditioning Equipment Mfr
N.A.I.C.S.: 333415
Marco Mafessoni (Sls Mgr)

BELIMO S.R.L. (1)
Av Olazabal 5584, Villa Urquiza Capital Federal, C1431CGY, Buenos Aires, Argentina
Tel.: (54) 1145221504
Web Site: http://www.belimo.com.ar
Sales Range: $25-49.9 Million
Emp.: 15
Actuators & Valves Distr
N.A.I.C.S.: 423610

BELIMO Servomotoren BV (1)
Riezebosweg 5, 8171 MG, Vaassen, Netherlands
Tel.: (31) 578576836
Web Site: https://www.belimo.com
Sales Range: $50-74.9 Million
Emp.: 15
Heating & Cooling System Controls Distr
N.A.I.C.S.: 423730

BELIMO Servomotori S.r.l. (1)
Via Stezzano 5, 24050, Zanica, Bergamo, Italy

Tel.: (39) 035672682
Web Site: http://www.belimo.it
Actuators & Valves Distr
N.A.I.C.S.: 423610

BELIMO Siłowniki S.A. (1)
Ul Jutrzenki 98, 02-230, Warsaw, Poland
Tel.: (48) 228865305
Web Site: https://www.belimo.com
Actuators & Valves Distr
N.A.I.C.S.: 423610

BELIMO Stellantriebe Vertriebs GmbH (1)
Welfenstrasse 27, Postfach 720230, 70599, Stuttgart, Germany
Tel.: (49) 711167830
Web Site: http://www.belimo.de
Sales Range: $25-49.9 Million
Emp.: 36
Heating & Cooling System Controls Distr
N.A.I.C.S.: 423730

BELIMO Technology (USA), Inc. (1)
43 Old Ridgebury Rd, Danbury, CT 06813
Tel.: (203) 791-9915
Heating & Cooling System Controls Mfr
N.A.I.C.S.: 333415

BELIMO Turkey Otomasyon A.S. (1)
Serifali Mah Beyit Sk No 52/1, Umraniye, 34775, Istanbul, Turkiye
Tel.: (90) 2162663200
Web Site: https://www.belimo.com
Air Conditioning Equipment Mfr
N.A.I.C.S.: 333415

BEREVA S.r.l. (1)
Via Vecchia 18/C, Auer, 39040, Bolzano, Italy
Tel.: (39) 0495012161
Web Site: https://bereva.it
Air Conditioning Equipment Mfr
N.A.I.C.S.: 333415

Belimo Automation (Shanghai) Co., Ltd. (1)
Building 1 No 450 North Hengshahe Road, Minhang District, Shanghai, China
Tel.: (86) 2153299299
Web Site: https://www.belimo.com.cn
Air Conditioning System Mfr & Distr
N.A.I.C.S.: 333415

Belimo Automation India Private Limited (1)
Belimo Cesim House Plot No R -12 Rabale Ttc Industrial Area, Thane, Navi Mumbai, 400701, India
Tel.: (91) 2268516400
Web Site: https://www.belimo.com
Air Conditioning System Mfr & Distr
N.A.I.C.S.: 333415

Belimo Belgium B.V. (1)
Cokeriestraat 3A, 1850, Grimbergen, Belgium
Tel.: (32) 22105686
Web Site: https://www.belimo.com
Air Conditioning System Mfr & Distr
N.A.I.C.S.: 333415

ENYE Ltd. Corporation (1)
LOFICE I Business Center 82 Scout Ojeda St Brgy Obrero, Diliman, Quezon City, Philippines
Tel.: (63) 4108840
Web Site: http://www.enye.com.ph
Industrial Controls
N.A.I.C.S.: 423610

Hanmo Corporation (1)
1116 Kolon Digital Tower Billant Guro-3dong Guro-gu 222-7, Seoul, Korea (South)
Tel.: (82) 221035901
Web Site: http://www.hanmo.co.kr
Sales Range: $25-49.9 Million
Emp.: 21
Actuators & Valves Distr
N.A.I.C.S.: 423610

Nosters (Pvt) Ltd. (1)
72 Davidson Road, Colombo, 4, Western Province, Sri Lanka
Tel.: (94) 11 420 9152
Web Site: http://www.nostersworld.com
Sales Range: $25-49.9 Million
Emp.: 25
Automated Controllers & Valves Distr
N.A.I.C.S.: 423610

Overseas Enterprises (1)
RS-7 ST-13 Sector 31-B K D A Employers Society Korangi, 74000, Karachi, Pakistan
Tel.: (92) 213515901115
Web Site: http://www.oe.com.pk
Actuators & Valves Distr
N.A.I.C.S.: 423610

Piping System Indonesia Pt. (1)
Jl Jembatan Dua Raya No 16-06, Jakarta, 14450, Indonesia
Tel.: (62) 216618888
Web Site: http://www.pipingsystem.com
Pipes, Fittings & Valves Distr
N.A.I.C.S.: 423720

Rite Products Incorporated (1)
Rm 702 Jocfer Bldg Commonwealth Ave, Capitol Dist, Quezon City, 1121, Metro Manila, Philippines
Tel.: (63) 289327944
Web Site: http://www.riteproducts.com.ph
Sales Range: $25-49.9 Million
Emp.: 12
Actuators & Valves Distr
N.A.I.C.S.: 423610

BELIZE TELECOMMUNICATIONS LIMITED

Esquivel Telecom Ctr St Thomas St, PO Box 603, Belize, Belize
Tel.: (501) 2232868
Web Site:
http://www.belizetelemedia.net
Year Founded: 1987
Sales Range: $50-74.9 Million
Emp.: 480
Telecommunication Services Supplier
N.A.I.C.S.: 517111
Karen Bevans (COO)

Subsidiaries:

International Communication Services Limited (1)
13 1/2 miles Northern Hwy, Belize, Belize
Tel.: (501) 2280022
Web Site: http://www.icslbelize.com
Telecommunication Servicesb
N.A.I.C.S.: 517112

Telemedia Free Zone Limited (1)
Corozal Free Zone Santa Elena Border, PO Box 358, Corozal District, Belize, Belize
Tel.: (501) 4237393
Web Site: http://www.telemediafreezone.bz
Telecommunication Servicesb
N.A.I.C.S.: 517111

Total Business Solutions Limited (1)
5856 Corner Manatee Drive/Independence L/F, PO Box 1885, Belize, Belize
Tel.: (501) 2236807
Web Site: http://www.tbslcaribbean.com.bz
Information Technology Consulting Services
N.A.I.C.S.: 541512
John Doe (Founder & Pres)

BELIZE WATER SERVICES LIMITED

7 Central American Blvd, PO Box 150, Belize, Belize
Tel.: (501) 2224757
Web Site: http://www.bws.bz
Year Founded: 2001
Sales Range: $10-24.9 Million
Water Sewerage & Treatment Services
N.A.I.C.S.: 237110
Alvan Haynes (CEO)

Subsidiaries:

Consolidated Water (Belize) Limited (1)
South Coconut Drive, PO Box 146, San Pedro, Ambergris Caye, Belize
Tel.: (501) 5012263846
Water Purification Equipment Whslr
N.A.I.C.S.: 423720
Dee Dillon (Gen Mgr)

BELKORP INDUSTRIES, INC.

Suite 900 1508 West Broadway, Vancouver, V6J 1W8, BC, Canada

Tel.: (604) 688-8533 Ca
Web Site: https://www.belkorp.com
Sales Range: $10-24.9 Million
Emp.: 27
Real Estate Manangement Services
N.A.I.C.S.: 531210
Stuart Belkin (Chm & CEO)

Subsidiaries:

Belkorp Ag, LLC (1)
2413 Crowslanding Rd, Modesto, CA 95363
Tel.: (209) 538-3831
Web Site: http://www.belkorpag.com
Farm Equipment Distr
N.A.I.C.S.: 423820

Big Sky Golf and Country Club (1)
1690 Airport Rd, Pemberton, V0N 2L3, BC, Canada (100%)
Tel.: (604) 894-6106
Web Site: http://www.bigskygolf.com
Golf Club Services
N.A.I.C.S.: 713910
Woody Bishop (Gen Mgr)

Wastech Services Ltd. (1)
1200 United Blvd, Coquitlam, V3K 6T4, BC, Canada (50%)
Tel.: (604) 521-1715
Web Site: http://www.wastech.ca
Provider of Waste & Recycling Management Services
N.A.I.C.S.: 562998
Angus Gardner (Gen Mgr)

BELL & BAIN LTD.

303 Burnfield Rd, Thornliebank, Glasgow, G46 7UQ, United Kingdom
Tel.: (44) 1416495697
Web Site: http://www.bell-bain.com
Printing & Binding Services
N.A.I.C.S.: 323120
Carole McGregor (Mgr-Customer Svc)

Subsidiaries:

J. Thomson Colour Printers Ltd. (1)
14 Carnoustie Place, Glasgow, G5 8PB, United Kingdom
Tel.: (44) 1414291094
Web Site: http://www.jtcp.co.uk
Sales Range: $10-24.9 Million
Printing Services
N.A.I.C.S.: 323113
Kevin Creechan (Mng Dir)

BELL COPPER CORPORATION

Suite 900 - 885 West Georgia Street, PO Box 27, Vancouver, V6C 3H1, BC, Canada
Tel.: (480) 570-7077 BC
Web Site: https://www.bellcopper.net
Year Founded: 2005
BCU—(OTCIQ)
Assets: $4,206,388
Liabilities: $2,494,800
Net Worth: $1,711,588
Earnings: ($1,188,181)
Emp.: 14
Fiscal Year-end: 12/31/20
Copper Exploration & Development Services
N.A.I.C.S.: 212230
Timothy M. Marsh (Pres & CEO)

BELL EQUIPMENT LIMITED

13-19 Carbonode Cell Road Alton, Richards Bay, 3900, South Africa
Tel.: (27) 359079111
Web Site:
http://www.bellequipment.com
Year Founded: 1954
BEL—(JSE)
Rev.: $456,477,600
Assets: $453,043,038
Liabilities: $213,980,265
Net Worth: $239,062,773
Earnings: ($3,899,959)
Emp.: 2,969

Bell Equipment Limited—(Continued)

Fiscal Year-end: 12/31/20
Heavy Duty Equipment & Articulated Vehicle Supplier
N.A.I.C.S.: 423830
Karen van Haght *(Dir-Fin)*

Subsidiaries:

Bell Equipment (Deutschland) GmbH **(1)**
Oberste Elpersweide 4, 36304, Alsfeld, Germany **(100%)**
Tel.: (49) 663191130
Web Site: http://www.bellequipment.com
Sales Range: $50-74.9 Million
Emp.: 90
Heavy Duty Equipment & Articulated Vehicle Supplier
N.A.I.C.S.: 423810
Andre Krings *(Mng Dir)*

Bell Equipment (SEA) PTE Limited **(1)**
10 Anson Road, 14-12 International Plaza, Singapore, 079903, Singapore **(100%)**
Tel.: (65) 62208004
Heavy Duty Equipment & Articulated Vehicle Supplier
N.A.I.C.S.: 423610

Bell Equipment (Zambia) Limited **(1)**
Plot 4095/96 Chingola Road, Box 20367, Kitwe, Zambia
Tel.: (260) 977770678
Sales Range: $50-74.9 Million
Emp.: 100
Construction Machinery Distr
N.A.I.C.S.: 423810
Fred Castle *(Mgr-Sls)*

Bell Equipment Australia (Pty) Limited **(1)**
Unit 5/27 Tamara Drive, Cockburn Central, Perth, 6164, WA, Australia **(100%)**
Tel.: (61) 893552442
Web Site: http://www.bellequipment.com
Sales Range: $50-74.9 Million
Emp.: 3
Heavy Duty Equipment & Articulated Vehicle Supplier
N.A.I.C.S.: 423610

Bell Equipment Company SA (Pty) Limited **(1)**
12 Hendrick Van Eck Street Kimdustria, PO Box 2927, Kimberley, 8300, South Africa
Tel.: (27) 53 841 0710
Construction Machinery Mfr
N.A.I.C.S.: 333120

Bell Equipment Mozambique Limitada **(1)**
Avenida Samora Machel Nó 238, Matola, 70, Maputo, Mozambique
Tel.: (258) 21 722 031
Construction Machinery Mfr
N.A.I.C.S.: 333120
Nicholas Kyriacos *(Gen Mgr)*

Bell Equipment Russland LLC **(1)**
1-ya Novaya Str 7, Salaryevo Village Moskovsky Settlement, Moscow, 108811, Russia
Tel.: (7) 4952878002
Material Handling Equipment Mfr & Distr
N.A.I.C.S.: 333922

Bell Equipment Sales South Africa Limited **(1)**
Griffiths Road, PO Box 25391, Boksburg, 1459, Gauteng, South Africa
Tel.: (27) 11 928 9846
Web Site: https://www.bellequipment.com
Construction Equipment Distr
N.A.I.C.S.: 423810

Subsidiary (Non-US):

Bell Equipment Co Swaziland (Proprietary) Limited **(2)**
Tabankulu Street Plot 686, PO Box 1754, Matsapha, M202, Eswatini
Tel.: (268) 25187496
Sales Range: $25-49.9 Million
Emp.: 12
Construction Machinery Mfr
N.A.I.C.S.: 333120
Charlie Boucher *(Gen Mgr)*

IA Bell Equipment Co Namibia (Proprietary) Limited **(2)**
37 Lazaret Street Southern Industrial, Windhoek, Namibia
Tel.: (264) 61 22 60 21
Web Site: http://www.bellequipment.com
Construction Machinery Mfr
N.A.I.C.S.: 333120

Bell Equipment UK Limited **(1)**
Graycar Business Park Barton Turns, Barton Under Needwood, Burton-on-Trent, DE13 8EN, Staffordshire, United Kingdom **(100%)**
Tel.: (44) 128 371 2862
Web Site: https://www.bellequipment.com
Sales Range: $25-49.9 Million
Emp.: 30
Heavy Duty Equipment & Articulated Vehicle Supplier
N.A.I.C.S.: 423810
Andy Pearce *(Mgr-Technical & After Sls)*

Bell France SARL **(1)**
35 Avenue du Berry, Dun Le Palestel, 23800, Gueret, France **(100%)**
Tel.: (33) 555892356
Web Site: http://www.bellequipment.com
Sales Range: $50-74.9 Million
Emp.: 20
Heavy Duty Equipment & Articulated Vehicle Supplier
N.A.I.C.S.: 423810

BELL FINANCIAL GROUP LIMITED

Level 29 101 Collins Street, Melbourne, 3000, VIC, Australia
Tel.: (61) 392568700
Web Site: http://www.bellfg.com.au
BFG—(ASX)
Rev.: $168,246,032
Assets: $782,510,728
Liabilities: $622,138,138
Net Worth: $160,372,590
Earnings: $16,568,354
Emp.: 750
Fiscal Year-end: 12/31/23
Financial Advisory Services
N.A.I.C.S.: 523940
Dean Davenport *(CFO & COO)*

Subsidiaries:

Bell Potter (US) Holdings Inc. **(1)**
Level 39 444 Madison Ave, New York, NY 10022
Tel.: (212) 301-2455
Financial Services
N.A.I.C.S.: 523999

Bell Potter Capital Limited **(1)**
Level 29 101 Collins St, Melbourne, 3000, VIC, Australia
Tel.: (61) 800787233
Web Site: https://bellpottercapital.com.au
Investment Advisory Services
N.A.I.C.S.: 523940

Bell Potter Securities (HK) Limited **(1)**
Room 1601 16/F Prosperity Tower 39 Queens Road, Central, China (Hong Kong)
Tel.: (852) 3 750 8400
Financial Services
N.A.I.C.S.: 523999

Third Party Platform Pty Ltd **(1)**
GPO Box 1630, Sydney, 2001, NSW, Australia
Tel.: (61) 38 663 2700
Web Site: https://www.belldirect.com.au
Financial Brokerage Services
N.A.I.C.S.: 523150

BELL IXL INVESTMENTS PTY. LTD.

Level 2 651-653 Doncaster Road, Doncaster, 3108, VIC, Australia
Tel.: (61) 3 9840 8788
Web Site: http://www.bellixl.com
Year Founded: 2005
Sales Range: $1-9.9 Million
Investment Services
N.A.I.C.S.: 523999

Massimo Livio Cellante *(Chm & Mng Dir)*

BELL-PARK CO., LTD.

3F 6F 7F 8F 9F Sanshin Hirakawacho Center Bldg 1 4 12 Hirakawacho, Chiyoda-ku, Tokyo, 102 0093, Japan
Tel.: (81) 332885211
Web Site: https://www.bellpark.co.jp
Year Founded: 1993
9441—(TKS)
Rev.: $818,788,650
Assets: $337,023,150
Liabilities: $110,689,080
Net Worth: $226,334,070
Earnings: $16,881,290
Emp.: 1,897
Fiscal Year-end: 12/31/23
Mobile Communications Equipment & Services
N.A.I.C.S.: 334220
Takeru Nishikawa *(Pres & CEO)*

Subsidiaries:

Japan Pro Staff Co., Ltd **(1)**
5th floor Meiji Yasuda Seimei Gotanda Building 2-27-4 Nishigotanda, Shinagawaku, Tokyo, 141-0031, Japan
Tel.: (81) 35 719 7111
Web Site: https://www.japanprostaff.jp
Help Supply Services
N.A.I.C.S.: 561320

Nikka Co., Ltd. **(1)**
1-1-11 Kozaika, Wakayama, 641-0007, Japan
Tel.: (81) 73 422 3111
Web Site: https://www.nikka-c.co.jp
Sales Range: $50-74.9 Million
Emp.: 17
Other Chemical & Allied Products Merchant Whslr
N.A.I.C.S.: 424690

BELLA CASA FASHION & RETAIL LTD.

E-102 103 EPIP Sitapura Industrial Area, Jaipur, 302022, Rajasthan, India
Tel.: (91) 9352267466
Web Site: https://www.bellacasa.in
Year Founded: 1996
539399—(BOM)
Rev.: $17,664,929
Assets: $20,726,269
Liabilities: $12,541,033
Net Worth: $8,185,236
Earnings: $737,359
Emp.: 1,242
Fiscal Year-end: 03/31/21
Textile Products Mfr
N.A.I.C.S.: 314999
Harish Kumar Gupta *(Chm)*

BELLA COOLA FISHERIES LTD.

9829 River Road, Delta, BC, Canada
Tel.: (604) 583-3474
Web Site: http://www.belcofish.com
Year Founded: 1977
Rev.: $21,513,360
Emp.: 154
Seafood Product Distr
N.A.I.C.S.: 424460
Jack Groven *(Mgr-Production)*

BELLAIR VENTURES INC.

10 Bellair Street Suite 509, Toronto, M5R 3T8, ON, Canada
Tel.: (416) 840-5002
Year Founded: 2008
Venture Capital Firm
N.A.I.C.S.: 523999

BELLAVISTA RESOURCES LTD.

Ground Floor 24 Outram Street, West Perth, 6005, WA, Australia

Tel.: (61) 863837556 AU
Web Site: https://www.bellavistaresources.com
Year Founded: 2021
BVR—(ASX)
Rev.: $52,068
Assets: $4,347,612
Liabilities: $609,266
Net Worth: $3,738,346
Earnings: ($824,715)
Emp.: 10
Fiscal Year-end: 06/30/23
Mineral Exploration Services
N.A.I.C.S.: 212390
Carl Travaglini *(CFO)*

BELLE CORPORATION

5/F Tower A Two E-Com Center Palm Coast Ave, Mall of Asia Complex CBP 1-A, Pasay, 1300, Philippines
Tel.: (63) 286628888
Web Site: https://www.bellecorp.com
BEL—(PHI)
Rev.: $42,237,699
Assets: $1,005,881,547
Liabilities: $294,207,237
Net Worth: $711,674,309
Earnings: $43,751,647
Fiscal Year-end: 12/31/23
Holding Company; Property Development
N.A.I.C.S.: 551112
Manuel A. Gana *(Pres, CEO & CIO)*

Subsidiaries:

Premium Leisure Corp. **(1)**
5th Floor Tower A 2 E-Com Center Palm Coast Avenue, Mall of Asia Complex, Pasig, 1300, Philippines **(78.1%)**
Tel.: (63) 286628803
Web Site: https://www.premiumleisurecorp.com
Rev.: $53,099,007
Assets: $330,789,024
Liabilities: $22,975,498
Net Worth: $307,813,527
Earnings: $41,959,355
Fiscal Year-end: 12/31/2023
Investment Holding Company
N.A.I.C.S.: 551112
Willy N. Ocier *(Chm)*

Subsidiary (Domestic):

Pacific Online Systems Corporation **(2)**
28/F East Tower Tektite Towers Exchange Road, Ortigas Center, Pasig, 1605, Philippines **(50.1%)**
Tel.: (63) 85841700
Web Site: https://www.loto.com.ph
Online Lottery Systems
N.A.I.C.S.: 713290
Willy N. Ocier *(Chm & Pres)*

Tagaytay Highlands International Golf Club, Inc. **(1)**
Brgy Calabuso, Tagaytay, 4120, Cavite, Philippines
Tel.: (63) 9178600918
Web Site: https://www.tagaytayhighlands.com
Golf Club Management Services
N.A.I.C.S.: 713910

Tagaytay Midlands Golf Club, Inc. **(1)**
Talisay, 6115, Batangas, Philippines
Tel.: (63) 464833808
Web Site: http://www.tagaytayhighlands.com
Golf Club Management Services
N.A.I.C.S.: 713910

The Country Club at Tagaytay Highlands, Inc. **(1)**
4120 Brgy Calabuso, Tagaytay, Cavite, Philippines
Tel.: (63) 917 822 6284
Web Site: https://www.tagaytayhighlands.com
Hotel & Resort Operator
N.A.I.C.S.: 721110

BELLECAPITAL AG

Bellvueplatz 5, 8001, Zurich, Switzerland
Tel.: (41) 442681100
Web Site: http://www.bellecapital.ch
Emp.: 37
Investment Services
N.A.I.C.S.: 523940
Beat Bass *(Co-Founder & Head-Strategy, Fin & IT)*

BELLEEK POTTERY LTD.
3 Main St, Belleek, BT93 3FY, Fermanagh, United Kingdom
Tel.: (44) 2868658501
Web Site: http://www.belleek.ie
Year Founded: 1849
Sales Range: $25-49.9 Million
Emp.: 214
Parian China Giftware Mfr
N.A.I.C.S.: 327110
George Moore *(Chm)*

BELLEVUE GOLD LIMITED
Ground Floor 24 Outram Street, West Perth, 6005, WA, Australia
Tel.: (61) 863739000
Web Site:
  https://www.bellevuegold.com.au
BGL—(ASX)
Rev.: $199,256,142
Assets: $624,163,325
Liabilities: $250,472,088
Net Worth: $373,691,238
Earnings: $50,357,906
Fiscal Year-end: 06/30/24
Gold Mining Services
N.A.I.C.S.: 212220
Stephen Parsons *(Mng Dir)*

BELLEVUE GROUP AG
Seestrasse 16, 8700, Kusnacht, Switzerland
Tel.: (41) 442676777
Web Site: https://www.bellevue.ch
BBN—(SWX)
Rev.: $115,723,947
Assets: $205,333,703
Liabilities: $56,900,222
Net Worth: $148,433,481
Earnings: $28,048,780
Emp.: 104
Fiscal Year-end: 12/31/22
Investment Banking & Asset Management Services
N.A.I.C.S.: 523150
Andre Ruegg *(CEO-Grp & Member-Exec Bd)*

Subsidiaries:

Bank am Bellevue AG (1)
Seestrasse 16, 8700, Kusnacht, Switzerland
Tel.: (41) 442676767
Web Site: http://www.bellevue.ch
Sales Range: $50-74.9 Million
Emp.: 50
Commericial Banking
N.A.I.C.S.: 522110
Martin Gubler *(CFO)*

Bellevue Asset Management AG (1)
Seestrasse 16, 8700, Kusnacht, Switzerland
Tel.: (41) 442676700
Web Site: https://www.bellevue.ch
Sales Range: $50-74.9 Million
Holding & Investments
N.A.I.C.S.: 525910
Martin C. Muenchbach *(Mgr-Investment)*

Subsidiary (Domestic):

BB Biotech AG (2)
Schwertstrasse 6, 8200, Schaffhausen, Switzerland
Tel.: (41) 526240845
Web Site: http://www.bbbiotech.ch
Rev.: $840,048,126
Assets: $4,488,131,493
Liabilities: $85,601,142
Net Worth: $4,402,530,351

Earnings: $782,733,820
Fiscal Year-end: 12/31/2020
Investment Holding Company
N.A.I.C.S.: 523999
Clive A. Meanwell *(Vice Chm)*

StarCapital AG (1)
Kronberger Str 45, 61440, Oberursel, Germany
Tel.: (49) 617 169 4190
Web Site: https://www.starcapital.de
Asset Management Services
N.A.I.C.S.: 523940

adbodmer AG (1)
Seestrasse 227, 8810, Horgen, Switzerland
Tel.: (41) 43 344 9424
Web Site: https://www.adbodmer.ch
Investment Advisory Services
N.A.I.C.S.: 523940
Jan Kollros *(CEO & Mng Partner)*

BELLEVUE HEALTHCARE TRUST PLC
46-48 James Street 4th Floor, London, W1U 1EZ, United Kingdom
Tel.: (44) 2033262981 UK
Web Site:
  https://www.bbhealthcaretrust.com
Year Founded: 2016
BBH—(LSE)
Rev.: $3,143,221
Assets: $1,028,647,999
Liabilities: $181,369,829
Net Worth: $847,278,170
Earnings: ($154,090,389)
Emp.: 6
Fiscal Year-end: 11/30/23
Investment Trust Management Services
N.A.I.C.S.: 523991
Randeep Grewal *(Chm)*

BELLIARD MATERIAUX
Route Du Fief Sauvin 18 Rue Des Cedres, 49600, Nantes, France
Tel.: (33) 241630888
Web Site: http://belliard-materiaux.fr
Rev.: $11,400,000
Emp.: 15
N.A.I.C.S.: 423720
Philippe Belliard *(Mng Partner)*

BELLINI NAUTICA S.P.A.
Via Carlo Lanza 28, Clusane d'Iseo, 25049, Iseo, BS, Italy
Tel.: (39) 0309829170
Web Site: https://www.bellininautica.it
Year Founded: 1967
BELL—(ITA)
Recreational Vehicle Dealer Services
N.A.I.C.S.: 441210
Romano Bellini *(Pres)*

BELLSYSTEM24 HOLDINGS, INC.
6F Kamiyacho Trust Tower 4-1-1 Toranomon, Minato-ku, Tokyo, 105-6906, Japan
Tel.: (81) 368939827 JP
Web Site: http://www.bell24hd.co.jp
Year Founded: 1982
6183—(TKS)
Rev.: $1,054,403,530
Assets: $1,244,046,850
Liabilities: $763,777,340
Net Worth: $480,269,510
Earnings: $53,494,050
Emp.: 266
Fiscal Year-end: 02/29/24
Administrative Management Services
N.A.I.C.S.: 541611
Masaaki Obayashi *(CFO)*

Subsidiaries:

BI Medical, Inc. (1)
Bunkyo Green Court Center Office 10 F 2-28-8 Honkomagome, Bunkyo-ku, Tokyo, 113-0021, Japan (100%)
Tel.: (81) 362194400

Web Site: http://www.bi-medical.co.jp
Pharmaceutical Product Mfr & Distr
N.A.I.C.S.: 325412

BELLUNA CO. LTD.
4-2 Miyamoto-cho, Ageo, 362-8688, Saitama, Japan
Tel.: (81) 120229299
Web Site: https://www.belluna.co.jp
Year Founded: 1968
9997—(TKS)
Rev.: $1,376,849,780
Assets: $1,987,567,510
Liabilities: $1,087,404,490
Net Worth: $900,163,020
Earnings: $38,595,790
Emp.: 3,825
Fiscal Year-end: 03/31/24
Property, Finance,Catalog & Mail Order Business
N.A.I.C.S.: 455219
Yuichiro Yasuno *(Exec Officer)*

Subsidiaries:

Icnet Co., Ltd. (1)
27th floor Meiji Yasuda Life Saitama Shintoshin Building, 11-2 Shintoshin Chuo-ku, Saitama, 330-6027, Japan
Tel.: (81) 486002500
Emp.: 202
Management Consulting Services
N.A.I.C.S.: 541618
Toshiyasu Kato *(Exec VP)*

Jobstudio Pte. Ltd. (1)
1 Coleman Street 06-07 The Adelphi, Singapore, 179803, Singapore
Tel.: (65) 64221390
Human Resouce Services
N.A.I.C.S.: 541612
Mabel Wong *(Founder)*

Maimu Co., Ltd. (1)
5-18-7 Ogikubo, Suginami-ku, Tokyo, Japan
Tel.: (81) 353970123
Emp.: 183
Salon Services
N.A.I.C.S.: 812112

Sagami Group Holdings Co., Ltd. (1)
4 N&F Building 1 4F 87 Kawakami-cho, Totsuka-ku, Yokohama, 244-0805, Kanagawa, Japan
Tel.: (81) 458287011
Web Site: http://www.sagami-ghd.co.jp
Emp.: 959
Group Management Strategies & Apparel Store Operator
N.A.I.C.S.: 458110
Yukihiro Katabe *(Pres)*

Sunstage Co., Ltd. (1)
1-7-28 Nakamachi Berna Annex Building 6F, Ageo, 362-0035, Saitama, Japan
Tel.: (81) 487792411
Web Site: http://www.b-loan.jp
Emp.: 124
Consumer Finance & Consulting Services
N.A.I.C.S.: 921130
Yuki Tokutome *(Pres)*

BELLUSCURA PLC
15 Fetter Lane, Holborn, London, EC4A 1BW, United Kingdom UK
Web Site: https://belluscura.com
Year Founded: 2015
BELL—(AIM)
Rev.: $1,542,948
Assets: $23,598,342
Liabilities: $3,246,220
Net Worth: $20,352,122
Earnings: ($8,152,985)
Emp.: 24
Fiscal Year-end: 12/31/22
Medical Device Mfr
N.A.I.C.S.: 339112
Adam Reynolds *(Chm)*

BELLWAY PLC
Woolsington House Woolsington, Newcastle upon Tyne, NE13 8BF, United Kingdom
Tel.: (44) 1912170717 UK

Web Site: https://www.bellway.co.uk
Year Founded: 1946
BWY—(LSE)
Rev.: $4,230,315,880
Assets: $6,350,689,380
Liabilities: $2,052,074,500
Net Worth: $4,298,614,880
Earnings: $454,995,520
Fiscal Year-end: 07/31/23
House Builder & Property Developer
N.A.I.C.S.: 236117
Keith D. Adey *(Dir-Fin)*

Subsidiaries:

Aspen Walk (Eight Ash Green) Management Company Limited (1)
Vantage Point 23 Mark Road, Hemel Hempstead, HP2 7DN, Hertfordshire, United Kingdom
Tel.: (44) 1206688174
Apartment Building Construction Services
N.A.I.C.S.: 624229

Bellway (Services) Limited (1)
Seaton Burn House Dudley La, Newcastle upon Tyne, NE13 6BE, United Kingdom
Tel.: (44) 1912170717
Web Site: http://www.bellway.co.uk
Property Management Services
N.A.I.C.S.: 531311

Bellway Financial Services Limited (1)
Seaton Burn House Dudley Ln Seaton Burn, Newcastle, NE13 6BE, Newcastle Tyne Wear, United Kingdom (100%)
Tel.: (44) 1912172111
Sales Range: $25-49.9 Million
Emp.: 35
N.A.I.C.S.: 236118
Evan Hall *(Dir-Fin Svcs)*

Bellway Homes Limited (1)
Bellway House Bury Street, Ruislip, HA4 7SD, Middlesex, United Kingdom
Tel.: (44) 1895671100
Web Site: https://www.bellway.co.uk
Emp.: 3,042
Home Building Industry Services
N.A.I.C.S.: 541330

Bellway Homes Limited East Midlands (1)
Romulus Court Meridian East, Meridian Business Park, Leicester, LE19 1YG, Leicestershire, United Kingdom (100%)
Tel.: (44) 116 282 0400
Web Site: https://www.bellway.co.uk
Sales Range: $25-49.9 Million
Emp.: 35
House Builder
N.A.I.C.S.: 236117
Gary Mills *(Mng Dir)*

Bellway Homes Limited Essex (1)
Bellway House, 1 Cunard Square Townfield Street, Chelmsford, CM1 1AQ, Essex, United Kingdom (100%)
Tel.: (44) 1245259989
Web Site: https://www.bellway.co.uk
Sales Range: $25-49.9 Million
Emp.: 40
House Builder
N.A.I.C.S.: 236117

Bellway Homes Limited Manchester (1)
304 Bridgewater Place, Birchwood, Warrington, WA3 6XG, Cheshire, United Kingdom (100%)
Tel.: (44) 925846700
Web Site: https://www.bellway.co.uk
Sales Range: $25-49.9 Million
Emp.: 50
House Builder
N.A.I.C.S.: 236117

Bellway Homes Limited North East (1)
Bellway House Kings Park Kingsway North, Tyne and Wear, Gateshead, NE11 0JH, United Kingdom (100%)
Tel.: (44) 191 482 8800
Web Site: https://www.bellway.co.uk
Sales Range: $25-49.9 Million
Emp.: 50
House Builder

Bellway plc—(Continued)

N.A.I.C.S.: 236117
Michael Drummond *(Dir-Fin)*

Bellway Homes Limited North London (1)
Bellway House Bury Street, Ruislip, HA4 7SD, Middlesex, United Kingdom **(100%)**
Tel.: (44) 189 567 1100
Web Site: https://www.bellway.co.uk
Sales Range: $25-49.9 Million
Emp.: 50
House Builder
N.A.I.C.S.: 236117
Peter Knights *(Mng Dir)*

Bellway Homes Limited North West (1)
2 Alderman Road, Liverpool, L24 9LR, Merseyside, United Kingdom **(100%)**
Tel.: (44) 151 486 2900
Web Site: https://www.bellway.co.uk
Sales Range: $25-49.9 Million
Emp.: 50
House Builder
N.A.I.C.S.: 236117
David Williams *(Mng Dir)*

Bellway Homes Limited Northern Home Counties (1)
Building 5 Caldecotte Lake Drive, Caldecotte, Milton Keynes, MK7 8LE, Buckinghamshire, United Kingdom **(100%)**
Tel.: (44) 1908364200
Web Site: https://www.bellway.co.uk
Sales Range: $25-49.9 Million
Emp.: 30
House Builder
N.A.I.C.S.: 236117

Bellway Homes Limited Scotland (1)
Bothwell House Hamilton Business Park Caird Street, Caird St, Hamilton, ML3 0QA, South Lanarkshire, United Kingdom **(100%)**
Tel.: (44) 169 847 7440
Web Site: https://www.bellway.co.uk
Sales Range: $25-49.9 Million
Emp.: 70
House Builder
N.A.I.C.S.: 236117

Bellway Homes Limited South East (1)
Bellway House London Rd N, Merstham, RH1 3YU, United Kingdom **(100%)**
Tel.: (44) 1737644911
Web Site: http://www.bellway.co.uk
Sales Range: $25-49.9 Million
Emp.: 50
House Builder
N.A.I.C.S.: 236117
Nathan Stevenson *(Mng Dir)*

Bellway Homes Limited Thames Gateway (1)
Bellway House Anchor Boulevard, Crossways Business Park, Dartford, DA2 6QH, Kent, United Kingdom **(100%)**
Tel.: (44) 168 988 6400
Web Site: https://www.bellway.co.uk
Sales Range: $25-49.9 Million
Emp.: 40
House Builder
N.A.I.C.S.: 236117

Bellway Homes Limited Wales (1)
Building 1 Eastern Business Park, St Mellons, Cardiff, CF3 5EA, United Kingdom **(100%)**
Tel.: (44) 2920774600
Web Site: https://www.bellway.co.uk
Sales Range: $25-49.9 Million
Emp.: 40
House Builder
N.A.I.C.S.: 236117
Paul Minnis *(Mng Dir)*

Bellway Homes Limited Wessex (1)
Embankment Way Castleman Business Centre, Castleman Bus Centre, Ringwood, BH24 1EU, Hampshire, United Kingdom **(100%)**
Tel.: (44) 142 547 7666
Web Site: https://www.bellway.co.uk
Sales Range: $25-49.9 Million
Emp.: 40
House Builder
N.A.I.C.S.: 236117

Ian Beal *(Mng Dir)*

Bellway Homes Limited West Midlands (1)
1 Centurion Court Centurion Way, Wilnecote, Tamworth, B77 5PN, Staffordshire, United Kingdom **(100%)**
Tel.: (44) 182 725 5755
Web Site: https://www.bellway.co.uk
Sales Range: $25-49.9 Million
Emp.: 45
House Builder
N.A.I.C.S.: 236117
Ben Wright *(Mng Dir)*

Bellway Homes Limited Yorkshire (1)
First Floor Unit 2150 Century Way, Leeds, LS15 8ZB, West Yorkshire, United Kingdom **(100%)**
Tel.: (44) 113 390 0800
Web Site: http://www.bellway.co.uk
Sales Range: $25-49.9 Million
Emp.: 40
House Builder
N.A.I.C.S.: 236117
John Carter *(Mng Dir)*

Bellway Housing Trust Limited (1)
Seaton Burn House Dudley Lane, Newcastle upon Tyne, NE13 6BE, United Kingdom
Tel.: (44) 1912170717
Web Site: http://www.bellwayhousingtrust.bellway.co.uk
New Housing Agency Services
N.A.I.C.S.: 624229

Copperhouse Green Management Company Limited (1)
Woodland Place Wickford Business Park Hurricane Way, Wickford, SS11 8YB, Essex, United Kingdom
Tel.: (44) 1322788708
Apartment Building Construction Services
N.A.I.C.S.: 624229

Hazel Fold Residents Management Company Limited (1)
Fisher House 84 Fisherton Street, Salisbury, SP2 7QY, Wiltshire, United Kingdom
Tel.: (44) 1204208614
Apartment Building Construction Services
N.A.I.C.S.: 624229

Hinxhill Park (Ashford) Management Company Limited (1)
Woodland Place Hurricane Way, Wickford, SS11 8YB, Essex, United Kingdom
Tel.: (44) 1233234071
Apartment Building Construction Services
N.A.I.C.S.: 624229

Long Acre (Shinfield) Management Company Limited (1)
Vantage Point 23 Mark Road, Hemel Hempstead, HP2 7DN, Hertfordshire, United Kingdom
Tel.: (44) 1183150841
Apartment Building Construction Services
N.A.I.C.S.: 624229

Rolleston Manor Management Company Limited (1)
Cumberland Court 80 Mount Street, Nottingham, NG1 6HH, Nottinghamshire, United Kingdom
Tel.: (44) 1283893597
Apartment Building Construction Services
N.A.I.C.S.: 624229

Stilton Gate Management Company Limited (1)
Premier House Elstree Way, Borehamwood, WD6 1JH, United Kingdom
Tel.: (44) 1733910887
Apartment Building Construction Services
N.A.I.C.S.: 624229

Woodgreen (Blyth) Residents Management Company Limited (1)
Cheviot House Beaminster way East, Newcastle upon Tyne, NE3 2ER, United Kingdom
Property Management Services
N.A.I.C.S.: 531311

BELLWYCK PACKAGING SOLUTIONS LTD.

21 Finchdene Square, Toronto, M1X 1A7, ON, Canada
Tel.: (416) 752-1210
Web Site: http://www.bellwyck.com
Sales Range: $50-74.9 Million
Emp.: 425
Folding Cartons Mfr
N.A.I.C.S.: 322212
Jeff Sziklai *(Co-CEO)*

BELLZONE MINING PLC
3rd Floor 47-49 La Motte Street, Standard Bank House, Saint Helier, JE2 4SZ, Jersey
Tel.: (44) 1534 834 600   JE
Web Site: http://www.bellzone.com
Rev.: $8,000
Assets: $20,283,000
Liabilities: $25,860,000
Net Worth: ($5,577,000)
Earnings: ($5,748,000)
Emp.: 149
Fiscal Year-end: 12/31/17
Iron Ore Mining Services
N.A.I.C.S.: 212210
Julian Hong Lum Cheong *(CEO & CFO)*

BELMONT RESOURCES INC.
Suite 615 - 800 West Pender Street, Vancouver, V6C 2V6, BC, Canada
Tel.: (604) 505-4061   BC
Web Site: https://www.belmontresources.com
Year Founded: 1978
BEA—(DEU)
Assets: $2,088,890
Liabilities: $350,170
Net Worth: $1,738,721
Earnings: ($256,553)
Fiscal Year-end: 01/31/22
Mineral Exploration Services
N.A.I.C.S.: 213114
Gary Musil *(CFO & Sec)*

BELO SUN MINING CORP.
198 Davenport Road, PO Box 75, Toronto, M5R 1J2, ON, Canada
Tel.: (416) 309-4395
Web Site: https://www.belosun.com
VE7—(DEU)
Rev.: $800,608
Assets: $20,243,493
Liabilities: $1,298,874
Net Worth: $18,944,619
Earnings: ($8,092,756)
Emp.: 39
Fiscal Year-end: 12/31/23
Mineral Exploration Services
N.A.I.C.S.: 213114
Mark P. Eaton *(Chm)*

Subsidiaries:

Belo Sun Mining (Barbados) Corp (1)
Braemar Crt Deighton Rd, Saint Michael, BB14017, Barbados
Tel.: (246) 4676674
Mineral Mining Services
N.A.I.C.S.: 212390
Ceri Sue *(Mgr)*

Intergemas Mineracao e Industrializacao Ltda (1)
SCS Q 1 Bl I S/N S 206, Brasilia, 70304-900, Brazil
Tel.: (55) 61 3322 3682
Mineral Mining Services
N.A.I.C.S.: 212390

BELOVO PAPER MILL S.A.
1A Dabravsko shosse Str, Belovo, 4470, Bulgaria
Tel.: (359) 3581 2105
Web Site: http://www.belana.bg
Tissue Household Products Mfr
N.A.I.C.S.: 339999

BELPHAR LTD.
333 Waterfront Drive, PO Box 3175, Road Town, Tortola, Virgin Islands (British)
Tel.: (284) 203 131 0046
Web Site: http://www.belphar.com
Investment Holding Company
N.A.I.C.S.: 551112
Khofiz Shakhidi *(Founder)*

Subsidiaries:

Pan European Terminals Limited (1)
1-6 Yarmouth Place Mayfair, London, W1J 7BU, United Kingdom **(29.9%)**
Tel.: (44) 203 0059892
Web Site: http://www.peterminals.com
Sales Range: $10-24.9 Million
Emp.: 126
Oil Transhipment Infrastructure Developer
N.A.I.C.S.: 237120

BELSHIPS ASA
Lilleakerveien 4A 6th Floor, 0283, Oslo, Norway
Tel.: (47) 22527600
Web Site: https://www.belships.com
Transportation Services
N.A.I.C.S.: 484110
Asbjarn Larsen *(CEO)*

BELUGA NV
Groeneweg 17, Erembodegem, 9320, Belgium
Tel.: (32) 496 12 13 69
Web Site: http://www.belugainvest.com
BELU—(EUR)
Financial Investment Services
N.A.I.C.S.: 523940
Philippe L. Weill *(Chm)*

BEMAC CORPORATION
105 Noma, Imabari, 94-8582, Ehime, Japan
Tel.: (81) 898258282
Web Site: https://www.bemac-jp.com
Emp.: 100
Power Distribution, Communications & Land-based Ship Equipment Mfr & Sales
N.A.I.C.S.: 333618

BEMAP, INC.
Uchiyama Bldg 4F/5F 2-12-5 Uchikanda, Chiyoda-ku, Tokyo, 101-0047, Japan
Tel.: (81) 352972180
Web Site: https://www.bemap.co.jp
Year Founded: 1998
4316—(TKS)
Rev.: $10,558,306
Assets: $7,723,817
Liabilities: $3,085,562
Net Worth: $4,638,254
Earnings: $1,024,116
Emp.: 107
Fiscal Year-end: 03/31/24
Software Development Services
N.A.I.C.S.: 513210
Fuminori Sugino *(CEO & COO)*

BEMCO HYDRAULICS LTD
Udyambag, Belgaum, 590 008, Karnataka, India
Tel.: (91) 8312441980
Web Site: https://www.bemcohydraulics.net
522650—(BOM)
Rev.: $5,862,622
Assets: $11,307,667
Liabilities: $5,648,882
Net Worth: $5,658,785
Earnings: $466,866
Emp.: 296
Fiscal Year-end: 03/31/23
Hydraulic Equipment Mfr
N.A.I.C.S.: 333998

Madan Mohan Mohta *(Chm)*

Subsidiaries:

BEMCO Fulidtechnik LLP   (1)
Khanapur Road, Udyambag, Belgaum,
590008, Karnataka, India
Tel.: (91) 8312440270
Web Site: http://www.fluidik.co
Hydraulic Components Mfr
N.A.I.C.S.: 332912

Bemco Fluidtechnik LLP   (1)
Khanapur Road Udyambag, Belgaum,
590008, Karnataka, India
Tel.: (91) 8312440270
Web Site: https://www.fluidik.co
Hydraulic Components Mfr
N.A.I.C.S.: 333611

BEMETALS CORP.
Suite 3400 - 666 Burrard Street, PO
Box 49139, Vancouver British Colum-
bia, Vancouver, V6C 2X8, BC,
Canada
Tel.: (604) 928-2797   BC
Web Site: https://bemetalscorp.com
Year Founded: 2008
BMET—(OTCIQ)
Rev.: $9,984
Assets: $12,778,354
Liabilities: $63,778
Net Worth: $12,714,576
Earnings: ($1,037,970)
Fiscal Year-end: 12/31/20
Investment Services; Base Metal
Projects
N.A.I.C.S.: 523999
Kristen Reinertson *(CFO & Sec)*

BEMIND A.D.
Karadjordjeva 2, 78000, Banja Luka,
Bosnia & Herzegovina
Tel.: (387) 51316709
Web Site: https://www.bemindbl.com
BMND—(BANJ)
Sales Range: Less than $1 Million
Emp.: 2
Industrial Process Control Equipment
Mfr
N.A.I.C.S.: 334513
Drago Durovic *(Chm)*

BEML LIMITED
Beml Soudha 23/1 4th Main SR Na-
gar, Bengaluru, 560 027, Karnataka,
India
Tel.: (91) 8022963142
Web Site: https://www.bemlindia.in
500048—(BOM)
Rev.: $592,844,821
Assets: $779,282,977
Liabilities: $457,645,406
Net Worth: $321,637,571
Earnings: $17,552,317
Emp.: 5,573
Fiscal Year-end: 03/30/22
Rail Coaches Mfr
N.A.I.C.S.: 237990
Suresh S. Vastrad *(Exec Dir-Rail &
Metro Bus)*

Subsidiaries:

BEML (Malaysia) Sdn.Bhd.   (1)
Jalan Tanjung Pelepas Warehouse No
81560, Johor Bahru, Johor, Malaysia
Tel.: (60) 127011393
Web Site: http://www.bemlindia.nic.in
Sales Range: $25-49.9 Million
Emp.: 5
Rail Coaches Mfr
N.A.I.C.S.: 541330

BEML Brasil Industrial Ltda   (1)
Sala 1201 Ed Vitoria Center 629 Avenue
Princesa Isabela Centro, Vitoria, Espirito
Santo, Brazil
Tel.: (55) 27 3025 2559
Web Site: http://www.bemlindia.com
Rail Coaches & Spare Parts Mfr
N.A.I.C.S.: 336350

BEML Limited - Aerospace Manufac-
turing Division   (1)
Belavadi Post, Mysore, 570 018, Karnataka,
India
Tel.: (91) 8212400248
Web Site: http://www.bemlindia.nic.in
Sales Range: $25-49.9 Million
Emp.: 40
Aerospace Engineering Services
N.A.I.C.S.: 541330

BEML Limited - Bangalore
Complex   (1)
New Thippasandra Post, Bengaluru, 560
075, Karnataka, India
Tel.: (91) 8025242414
Rail Coaches Mfr
N.A.I.C.S.: 541330

BEML Limited - Earth Moving
Division   (1)
Marketing Division-Service BEML Nagar
Kolar Gold Fields, Bengaluru, 563 115, Kar-
nataka, India
Tel.: (91) 8153 269085
Rail Coaches & Spare Parts Mfr
N.A.I.C.S.: 336510

BEML Limited - Engine Division   (1)
Belavadi Post, Mysore, 570 018, Karnataka,
India
Tel.: (91) 8212402447
Web Site: http://www.bemlindia.com
Rail Coaches & Spare Parts Mfr
N.A.I.C.S.: 336510

BEML Limited - Hydraulics & Power-
line (H&P) Division   (1)
KGF Complex BEML Nagar, Kolar Gold
Fields, Bengaluru, 563 115, Karnataka, In-
dia
Tel.: (91) 8153263192
Transmission Equipment Mfr
N.A.I.C.S.: 336350

BEML Limited - International Busi-
ness Division   (1)
Flat no E F G H Vandana Building 11th
Floor Tolstoy Marg, New Delhi, 110 001,
India
Tel.: (91) 1123443500
Sales Range: $25-49.9 Million
Emp.: 22
Rail Coaches Mfr
N.A.I.C.S.: 488210

BEML Limited - Technology
Division   (1)
BEML Soudha 23 1 4th Main SR Nagar,
Bengaluru, 560027, Karnataka, India
Tel.: (91) 8022963100
Web Site: http://www.bemltech.com
Engineeering Services
N.A.I.C.S.: 541330

BEML Limited - Trading Division   (1)
4th Fl Unity Bldg JC Rd, Bengaluru, Karna-
taka, India
Tel.: (91) 8022963522
Sales Range: $25-49.9 Million
Emp.: 7
Steel Billets & Steam Coal Distr
N.A.I.C.S.: 331110
Deepak Kumar Hota *(Mng Dir)*

BEML Limited - Truck Division   (1)
Belavadi Post, Mysore, 570 018, Karnataka,
India
Tel.: (91) 821 2402422
Engineeering Services
N.A.I.C.S.: 541330

Vignyan Industries Limited   (1)
B H Road, PO Box 4, Chikmagalur,
Tarikere, 577 228, Karnataka, India
Tel.: (91) 8261222734
Sales Range: $50-74.9 Million
Emp.: 175
Steel Casting Mfr
N.A.I.C.S.: 331513

BEN BURGESS & COMPANY
Windmill Hill Exning, Newmarket,
CB8 7NP, Suffolk, United Kingdom
Tel.: (44) 1638577877
Web Site:
    http://www.benburgess.co.uk
Sales Range: $50-74.9 Million

Emp.: 27
Horticultural Machines Supplier
N.A.I.C.S.: 423820
David Fairman *(Mgr-Grp Sls)*

**BEN FORTUNE PASTRY
MANUFACTURING (M) SDN
BHD**
No 23 & 25 Jalan PJS 11/16 Sunway
Technology Park, Bandar Sunway,
46150, Petaling Jaya, Selangor, Ma-
laysia
Tel.: (60) 356351120
Web Site: http://www.benfortune.com
Year Founded: 1993
Frozen Bun & Dessert Mfr
N.A.I.C.S.: 311412
Eugene Lee *(Mgr-Bus Dev)*

**BEN THANH RUBBER JOINT
STOCK COMPANY**
Lot B3-1 Cu Chi Northwest Industrial
Zone, Ho Chi Minh City, Vietnam
Tel.: (84) 2837907619
Web Site:
    https://www.berubco.com.vn
Year Founded: 1976
BRC—(HOSE)
Rev.: $13,688,412
Assets: $11,973,132
Liabilities: $3,328,960
Net Worth: $8,644,172
Earnings: $800,104
Fiscal Year-end: 12/31/23
Conveyor Belts Mfr
N.A.I.C.S.: 326220

BEN THANH SERVICE JSC
390 Nguyen Cong Tru Street Cau
Ong Lanh Ward, District 1, Ho Chi
Minh City, Vietnam
Tel.: (84) 839140933
Web Site: https://www.btsc.com.vn
BSC—(HNX)
Rev.: $770,600
Assets: $4,179,200
Liabilities: $303,100
Net Worth: $3,876,100
Earnings: $266,500
Fiscal Year-end: 12/31/23
Holding Company; Motorcycle Distr;
Logistics & Warehousing Services;
Restaurant & Hotel Owner & Opera-
tor; Real Estate Rental Services
N.A.I.C.S.: 551112

**BEN THANH TRADING & SER-
VICE JOINT STOCK COMPANY**
186 - 188 Le Thanh Ton Street Ben
Thanh ward, District 1, Ho Chi Minh
City, Vietnam
Tel.: (84) 838223390
Web Site:
    http://www.benthanhtsc.com.vn
Year Founded: 2004
BTT—(HOSE)
Rev.: $9,576,240
Assets: $20,944,844
Liabilities: $4,965,712
Net Worth: $15,979,132
Earnings: $2,036,145
Fiscal Year-end: 12/31/23
Textile Product Trading Services
N.A.I.C.S.: 313310
Phan Van Quang *(CEO & Member-
Mgmt Bd)*

**BEN TRE BUILDING MATE-
RIAL JOINT STOCK COMPANY**
207D Nguyen Dinh Chieu Phu Hung,
Ben Tre, Ben Tre Province, Vietnam
Tel.: (84) 2753822315
Web Site:
    https://www.vlxdbentre.com
VXB—(HNX)
Rev.: $496,301

Assets: $4,044,705
Liabilities: $4,962,296
Net Worth: ($917,591)
Earnings: ($678,104)
Fiscal Year-end: 12/31/22
Building Materials Mfr; Sand Mining
N.A.I.C.S.: 327331

**BEN TRE PHARMACEUTICAL
JSC**
6A3 60 National Highway Phu Tan
Ward, Ben Tre, Ben Tre, Vietnam
Tel.: (84) 3900059
Web Site: https://www.bepharco.com
Year Founded: 1963
DBT—(HNX)
Rev.: $75,461,800
Assets: $84,072,000
Liabilities: $61,642,700
Net Worth: $22,429,300
Earnings: $3,799,100
Emp.: 401
Fiscal Year-end: 12/31/22
Pharmaceutical Preparation Mfr
N.A.I.C.S.: 325412

Subsidiaries:

Nha Trang Vaccines & Biological
Products Joint-Stock Company   (1)
26 Han Thuyen, Nha Trang, Khanh Hoa,
Vietnam
Tel.: (84) 583813067
Web Site: http://www.biopharco2.com.vn
Pharmaceuticals Product Mfr
N.A.I.C.S.: 325412

**BENALEC HOLDINGS BER-
HAD**
No 23 Jalan Perintis U1/52 Glenma-
rie Temasya Seksyen U1, 40150,
Shah Alam, Selangor Darul Ehsan,
Malaysia
Tel.: (60) 355697366   MY
Web Site:
    https://www.benalec.com.my
Year Founded: 2005
BENALEC—(KLS)
Rev.: $16,224,553
Assets: $146,013,577
Liabilities: $56,852,791
Net Worth: $89,160,786
Earnings: ($10,831,467)
Emp.: 94
Fiscal Year-end: 12/31/22
Marine & Civil Engineering Services
N.A.I.C.S.: 237990
Vincent Seng Hai Leaw *(CEO & Mng
Dir)*

Subsidiaries:

Benalec Sdn Bhd   (1)
No 23 Jalan Perintis U1/52 Temasya Glen-
marie Seksyen U1, 40150, Shah Alam, Se-
langor, Malaysia
Tel.: (60) 3 5569 7366
Web Site: http://en.benalec.com.my
Sales Range: $25-49.9 Million
Emp.: 50
Marine Engineering Services
N.A.I.C.S.: 541330

Ocaenline (Labuan) Ltd.   (1)
Lot A020 Level 1 Podium Level Financial
Park Labuan, Jalan Merdeka, Labuan,
87000, Federal Territory, Malaysia
Tel.: (60) 87427745
Web Site: http://www.hansworldwide.com
Marine Construction Engineering Services
N.A.I.C.S.: 237990

**BENARA BEARINGS & PIS-
TONS LTD.**
A-3 and 4 Site-B, UPSIDC Industrial
Area Sikandra, Agra, 282007, India
Tel.: (91) 5622970158
Web Site: https://www.benara-
phb.com
541178—(BOM)
Rev.: $3,562,063

BENARA BEARINGS & PISTONS LTD.

Benara Bearings & Pistons Ltd.—(Continued)

Assets: $13,868,182
Liabilities: $9,687,992
Net Worth: $4,180,190
Earnings: ($1,906,946)
Fiscal Year-end: 03/31/22
Fabricated Metal Products Mfr
N.A.I.C.S.: 332312
Vivek Benara (Founder & Mng Dir)

BENCHMARK HOLDINGS PLC

Benchmark House 8 Smithy Wood
Dr, Sheffield, S35 1QN, United King-
dom
Tel.: (44) 114 240 9939
Web Site:
　http://www.benchmarkplc.com
BMK—(AIM)
Rev.: $169,799,179
Assets: $654,407,463
Liabilities: $274,790,309
Net Worth: $379,617,154
Earnings: ($15,716,967)
Emp.: 1,042
Fiscal Year-end: 09/30/21
Animal Health Products Mfr; Techni-
cal Publishing
N.A.I.C.S.: 325412
Athene Blakeman (Head-Advanced
Nutrition)

Subsidiaries:

Benchmark Genetics Norway AS　(1)
Web Site: http://www.bmkgenetics.com
Technical Genetic Services
N.A.I.C.S.: 541714

FAI do Brasil Criacao Animal
Ltda　(1)
Fazenda Santa Terezinha S/N Bairro Rural,
Jaboticabal, SP, Brazil
Tel.: (55) 16997827786
Technical Genetic Services
N.A.I.C.S.: 541714

INVE (Thailand) Ltd.　(1)
79/1 Moo 1 Nakhon Sawan-Phitsanulok
Road Tambon Nong Lum Amphoe, Wachi-
rabarami, Phichit, 66220, Thailand
Tel.: (66) 56609800
Technical Genetic Services
N.A.I.C.S.: 541714

INVE Aquaculture, Inc.　(1)
3528 W 500 S, Salt Lake City, UT 84104
Tel.: (801) 956-0203
Web Site: https://www.inveaquaculture.com
Technical Genetic Services
N.A.I.C.S.: 541714

INVE Asia Services Ltd.　(1)
471 Bond Street, Tambon Bangpood Am-
phur Pakkred, Nonthaburi, 11120, Thailand
Tel.: (66) 29600200
Technical Genetic Services
N.A.I.C.S.: 541714

Inve Aquaculture Mexico, S.A. de
C.V.　(1)
Av Camaron Sabalo 51 L-1, Zona Dorada,
82110, Mazatlan, Sinaloa, Mexico
Tel.: (52) 6699901003
Technical Genetic Services
N.A.I.C.S.: 541714

Inve Eurasia SA　(1)
Karacaoglan Mah 6170 Sk No 17/B, Isik-
kent, 35070, Izmir, Turkiye
Tel.: (90) 2328772010
Technical Genetic Services
N.A.I.C.S.: 541714

Inve Hellas S.A.　(1)
93 Kyprou Str, 16451, Argyroupolis, Greece
Tel.: (30) 2109958380
Technical Genetic Services
N.A.I.C.S.: 541714

Inve Technologies NV　(1)
Hoogveld 93, 9200, Dendermonde, Belgium
Tel.: (32) 52409595
Technical Genetic Services
N.A.I.C.S.: 541714

Inve Vietnam Company Ltd.　(1)

8th Floor 19 Tan Canh Street, Ward 1 Tan
Binh District, Ho Chi Minh City, Vietnam
Tel.: (84) 839919864
Technical Genetic Services
N.A.I.C.S.: 541714

Inve do Brasil Ltda.　(1)
Rua Augusto Calheiros 226, Messejana,
Fortaleza, 60863-290, Brazil
Tel.: (55) 8532764222
Technical Genetic Services
N.A.I.C.S.: 541714

PT. Inve Indonesia　(1)
Jln Jalur Sutera Ruko Prominence Blok 38E
No 7, Alam Sutera, Tangerang, Indonesia
Tel.: (62) 2129407239
Technical Genetic Services
N.A.I.C.S.: 541714

SalmoBreed Salten AS　(1)
Kobbelv Sorfjordmoen, Engan, 8264, Trond-
heim, Norway
Tel.: (47) 91895511
Web Site: http://www.salmobreed.no
Technical Genetic Services
N.A.I.C.S.: 541714
Petter-Johan Hauknes (Sls Mgr)

Salt Creek, Inc.　(1)
3528 W 500 S, Salt Lake City, UT 84104
Tel.: (801) 956-2866
Animal Food Product Mfr
N.A.I.C.S.: 311119

Stofnfiskur hf.　(1)
Baejarhraun 14, 220, Hafnarfjordur, Iceland
Tel.: (354) 5646300
Web Site: http://www.stofnfiskur.is
Technical Genetic Services
N.A.I.C.S.: 541714
Omar Bjarnason (CFO)

Tianjin INVE Aquaculture Co.,
Ltd.　(1)
Room 605-607 Bulding 10 Binhai No 399
Huixiang Road, Tanggy Ocean Science and
Technology Park Binhai High - Tech Zone,
Tianjin, 300451, China
Tel.: (86) 2224992624
Technical Genetic Services
N.A.I.C.S.: 541714

BENCHMARK METALS INC.

10545 - 45 Avenue NW 250 South-
ridge Suite 300, Edmonton, T6H
4M9, AB, Canada
Tel.: (780) 437-6624　　BC
Web Site:
　https://www.benchmarkmetals.com
Year Founded: 2010
BNCHF—(OTCQX)
Rev.: $117,248
Assets: $94,309,968
Liabilities: $16,027,530
Net Worth: $78,282,437
Earnings: ($9,662,208)
Fiscal Year-end: 02/28/22
Mineral Exploration Services
N.A.I.C.S.: 212390
Jim Greig (Pres)

BENCHMARK TELECAST IN-
TEGRATION PTE LTD

12 Tannery Road #09-5/6/7, Singa-
pore, 347722, Singapore
Tel.: (65) 6749 3372　　SG
Web Site:
　http://www.benchmarktelecast.com
Year Founded: 2012
Emp.: 80
Holding Company
N.A.I.C.S.: 551112
Ashish Mukherjee (CEO)

Subsidiaries:

Benchmark Broadcast Systems (S)
Pte Ltd　(1)
12 Tannery Road #09-05/06/07 HB Center
I, Singapore, 347722, Singapore
Tel.: (65) 67493372
Web Site:
　http://www.benchmarkbroadcast.com

Sales Range: $10-24.9 Million
Emp.: 15
Video Management Software Publisher
N.A.I.C.S.: 513210
Ashish Mukherjee (CEO)

Subsidiary (Non-US):

Benchmark Broadcast Systems (P)
Limited　(2)
2nd Floor Polyhose Towers SPIC Annex NO
86 Mount Road, Guindy, Chennai, 600032,
Tamil Nadu, India
Tel.: (91) 4442154614
Web Site:
　http://www.benchmarkbroadcast.com
Sales Range: $10-24.9 Million
Emp.: 60
Digital Media Services
N.A.I.C.S.: 513199
Ashish Mukerjee (Mng Dir)

BENCIS CAPITAL PARTNERS
B.V.

World Trade Center Amsterdam
Zuidplein 76, 1077 XV, Amsterdam,
Netherlands
Tel.: (31) 205400940　　NI
Web Site: http://www.bencis.com
Year Founded: 1999
Sales Range: $25-49.9 Million
Emp.: 15
Privater Equity Firm
N.A.I.C.S.: 523999
Zoran van Gessel (Co-Founder &
Mng Partner)

Subsidiaries:

Nooteboom Bidco B.V.　(1)
Kranenberg 6, 5047 TR, Tilburg, Nether-
lands
Tel.: (31) 135711212
Investment Services
N.A.I.C.S.: 523999

Subsidiary (Non-US):

Hemmers-Itex Textil Import Export
GmbH　(2)
Twentestrasse 1, 48527, Nordhorn, Ger-
many
Tel.: (49) 59218832100
Web Site: http://www.textilhemmers.de
Textile Clothing Distr
N.A.I.C.S.: 424310

Pressure Thermal Dynamics B.V.　(1)
Komeetweg 4, 4782 SG, Moerdijk, Nether-
lands
Tel.: (31) 88 00 67 400
Holding Company
N.A.I.C.S.: 551112
Juul IJzermans (CEO)

Subsidiary (Domestic):

Schelde Exotech B.V.　(2)
Koningsweg 2, 4381 NA, Vlissingen, Neth-
erlands
Tel.: (31) 118 48 59 90
Web Site: http://www.exotech.nl
Heat Exchanger Mfr
N.A.I.C.S.: 332410
Jos Mols (Mng Dir)

Verolme Special Equipment B.V.　(2)
Komeetweg 4, 4782 SG, Moerdijk, Nether-
lands
Tel.: (31) 88 00 67 400
Web Site: http://www.verolme.com
Pressure Vessels & Heat Exchangers Mfr
N.A.I.C.S.: 332410
Juul IJzermans (CEO)

BENDA SUNKWANG IND. CO.,
LTD.

163 Seohae daero, Jung gu, Incheon,
22342, Korea (South)
Tel.: (82) 328118424　　KR
Year Founded: 1986
Emp.: 313
Motor Vehicle Parts Mfr
N.A.I.C.S.: 336390

BENDIGO & ADELAIDE BANK
LTD.

The Bendigo Centre, Bendigo, 3550,
VIC, Australia
Tel.: (61) 300236344　　AU
Web Site:
　https://www.bendigoadelaide.com
Year Founded: 1858
DXRDF—(OTCIQ)
Rev.: $1,920,300,000
Assets: $98,479,700,000
Liabilities: $91,629,000,000
Net Worth: $6,850,700,000
Earnings: $497,000,000
Emp.: 4,726
Fiscal Year-end: 06/30/23
Commercial Banking Services
N.A.I.C.S.: 522110
Marnie A. Baker (Mng Dir)

Subsidiaries:

Adelaide Bank Limited　(1)
80 Grenfell Street, Adelaide, 5000, SA, Aus-
tralia
Tel.: (61) 883006000
Web Site: https://www.adelaidebank.com.au
Sales Range: $1-4.9 Billion
Emp.: 1,185
Commercial Banking Services
N.A.I.C.S.: 522320

Subsidiary (Domestic):

Leveraged Equities Limited　(2)
Level 12 175 Pitt St, Sydney, 2000, NSW,
Australia
Tel.: (61) 1300307807
Web Site: http://www.leveraged.com.au
Sales Range: $50-74.9 Million
Emp.: 70
Financial Management Services
N.A.I.C.S.: 523940
Claire Starr (Mgr-Bus Dev-NSW & QLD)

Pirie Street Custodian Ltd.　(2)
GPO Box 5388, Sydney, 2001, NSW, Aus-
tralia
Tel.: (61) 282828282
Web Site: http://www.leveraged.com.au
Sales Range: $50-74.9 Million
Emp.: 100
Nondepository Credit Intermediation
N.A.I.C.S.: 522299

Bank of Cyprus Australia Pty Ltd　(1)
Rialto Towers Level 41, 525 Collins Street,
Melbourne, 3000, VIC, Australia
Tel.: (61) 386272727
Web Site: http://www.bankofcyprus.com.au
Sales Range: $50-74.9 Million
Emp.: 150
Commericial Banking
N.A.I.C.S.: 522110
Jim Sarris (Head-Corp Banking)

Bellarine Peninsula Community
Branch Limited　(1)
44 Newcombe Street, Portarlington, 3223,
VIC, Australia
Tel.: (61) 3 5259 3266
Banking Services
N.A.I.C.S.: 522110
Russell Enders (Chm)

Bendigo Financial Planning
Limited　(1)
L 5 120 Harbour Esplanade, Docklands,
Melbourne, 3008, VIC, Australia
Tel.: (61) 384147982
Web Site: http://www.bendigobank.com.au
Emp.: 150
Financial Management Services
N.A.I.C.S.: 523999
Mike Hurst (CEO)

Bendigo Investment Services
Limited　(1)
Level 5 120 Harbour Esplanade, Dock-
lands, Melbourne, 3008, VIC, Australia
Tel.: (61) 384147982
Web Site: http://www.bendigobank.com.au
Financial Investment Services
N.A.I.C.S.: 523940

Clifroy Limited　(1)
101 Queens Parade Clifton Hill, Melbourne,

3068, VIC, Australia
Tel.: (61) 3 9482 9040
Web Site: http://www.bendigobank.com.au
Rev.: $962,069
Assets: $699,868
Liabilities: $142,784
Net Worth: $557,084
Earnings: $67,909
Fiscal Year-end: 06/30/2017
Banking Services
N.A.I.C.S.: 522110
Peter Raymond Hille (Deputy Chm)

Community Energy Australia Pty
Ltd (1)
PO Box 480, Bendigo, 3552, VIC, Australia
Tel.: (61) 1300304543
Financial Management Services
N.A.I.C.S.: 523999

East Gosford & Districts Financial
Services Ltd. (1)
101 Victoria Street, PO Box 4021, Gosford,
2250, NSW, Australia
Tel.: (61) 243234559
Web Site: http://www.bendigobank.com.au
Rev.: $1,459,141
Assets: $1,734,827
Liabilities: $1,152,236
Net Worth: $582,591
Earnings: ($37,380)
Fiscal Year-end: 06/30/2022
Banking Services
N.A.I.C.S.: 522110
Garry Samuel Morris (Chm)

Fremantle Community Financial Ser-
vices Limited (1)
Fremantle Community Bank Oval William St
& Parry St, Fremantle, 6160, WA, Australia
Tel.: (61) 894334969
Web Site: http://www.bendigobank.com.au
Rev.: $553,490
Assets: $602,757
Liabilities: $107,304
Net Worth: $495,453
Earnings: ($29,457)
Emp.: 6
Fiscal Year-end: 06/30/2022
Banking Services
N.A.I.C.S.: 522110
John Alexander Bird (Treas)

Heidelberg District Community Enter-
prise Limited (1)
164 Burgundy Street, Heidelberg, 3084,
VIC, Australia
Tel.: (61) 394572055
Web Site: http://www.bendigobank.com.au
Rev.: $1,377,805
Assets: $2,199,804
Liabilities: $405,469
Net Worth: $1,794,335
Earnings: $52,558
Fiscal Year-end: 06/30/2022
Banking Services
N.A.I.C.S.: 522110
Nancy Louise Caple (Chm)

Inverloch & District Financial Enter-
prises Limited (1)
16C Williams Street, Inverloch, 3996, VIC,
Australia
Tel.: (61) 356742800
Web Site: http://www.bendigobank.com.au
Rev.: $400,711
Assets: $589,676
Liabilities: $38,668
Net Worth: $551,008
Earnings: ($27,102)
Fiscal Year-end: 06/30/2020
Banking Services
N.A.I.C.S.: 522110
Tristan Andrew Creed (Treas & Accountant)

Logan Community Financial Services
Limited (1)
Unit 1 54 Bryants Road, Shailer Park, Lo-
gan, 4128, QLD, Australia
Tel.: (61) 738064000
Web Site: http://www.bendigobank.com.au
Rev.: $2,531,294
Assets: $2,750,044
Liabilities: $699,752
Net Worth: $2,050,291
Earnings: $213,165
Fiscal Year-end: 06/30/2022
Banking Services
N.A.I.C.S.: 522110

Elvio John DiZane (Sls Mgr)
Manningham Community Enterprises
Limited (1)
900 Doncaster Road, Doncaster, 3109,
VIC, Australia
Tel.: (61) 398402028
Web Site: http://www.bendigobank.com.au
Rev.: $2,029,422
Assets: $2,616,209
Liabilities: $1,683,243
Net Worth: $932,967
Earnings: $159,800
Fiscal Year-end: 06/30/2022
Banking Services
N.A.I.C.S.: 522110
Geoffrey Bruce Roberts (Vice Chm)

Mooroolbark & District Financial Ser-
vices Limited (1)
Shop 19 Mooroolbark Terrace, 66-74 Brice
Ave, Mooroolbark, 3138, VIC, Australia
Tel.: (61) 3 9726 5388
Web Site: http://www.bendigobank.com.au
Rev.: $867,379
Assets: $1,419,533
Liabilities: $172,998
Net Worth: $1,246,535
Earnings: $48,580
Fiscal Year-end: 06/30/2019
Banking Services
N.A.I.C.S.: 522110
Rowan Alexander (Branch Mgr)

National Mortgage Market Corpora-
tion Pty Ltd (1)
Level 3 120 Harbour Esplanade, Dock-
lands, 3008, VIC, Australia
Tel.: (61) 384147986
Web Site: https://www.nmmc.com.au
Mortgage Origination, Management & Secu-
ritisation
N.A.I.C.S.: 522310

North Ryde Community Finance
Limited (1)
Shop 14 Cox s Road Mall, 203-213 Cox s
Road, North Ryde, 2113, NSW, Australia
Tel.: (61) 2 9878 5559
Web Site: http://www.bendigobank.com.au
Rev.: $654,815
Assets: $1,595,964
Liabilities: $94,565
Net Worth: $1,501,399
Earnings: $147,165
Fiscal Year-end: 06/30/2017
Banking Services
N.A.I.C.S.: 522110
Ian Greentree (Sec)

Pritchard Equity Limited (1)
10 Murray Street, PO Box 413, Hamilton,
2303, NSW, Australia
Tel.: (61) 249202877
Web Site: https://www.peq.com.au
Rev.: $564,580
Assets: $83,344,453
Liabilities: $79,958,892
Net Worth: $3,385,561
Earnings: $299,281
Fiscal Year-end: 06/30/2024
Financial Investment Services
N.A.I.C.S.: 523999
Steven Pritchard (Exec Chm & Chm)

Rural Bank Limited (1)
6/80 Grenfell St, 5000, Adelaide, Australia,
Australia (100%)
Tel.: (61) 871099207
Web Site: https://www.ruralbank.com.au
Banking Services
N.A.I.C.S.: 522110
Malcolm Renney (Gen Mgr-Credit & Lend-
ing)

Rural Finance Corporation of
Victoria (1)
PO Box 1313, Bendigo, 3552, VIC, Austra-
lia
Tel.: (61) 800260425
Web Site: http://www.ruralfinance.com.au
Sales Range: $100-124.9 Million
Emp.: 1
Rural Development & Government Relief
Administration Organization
N.A.I.C.S.: 925120

Rye & District Community Financial
Services Limited (1)
2271 Point Nepean Road, Rye, Canberra,

3941, Victoria, Australia
Tel.: (61) 3 5985 9755
Web Site: http://www.bendigobank.com.au
Rev.: $2,920,744
Assets: $4,213,840
Liabilities: $1,555,509
Net Worth: $2,658,332
Earnings: $215,426
Fiscal Year-end: 06/30/2017
Banking Services
N.A.I.C.S.: 522110
Gary Sanford (Sr Mgr)

San Remo District Financial Services
Ltd (1)
103A Marine Parade, San Remo, 3925,
VIC, Australia
Tel.: (61) 3 5678 5833
Web Site: http://www.bendigobank.com.au
Banking Services
N.A.I.C.S.: 522110

Sandhurst Trustees Limited (1)
Level 5 120 Harbour Esplanade, Dock-
lands, 3008, VIC, Australia
Tel.: (61) 384147859
Web Site:
https://www.sandhursttrustees.com.au
Emp.: 50
Funds Management & Financial Services
N.A.I.C.S.: 523999
Paul Rohan (Exec Dir)

Sandringham Community Financial
Services Limited (1)
75 Station Street, Sandringham, 3191, VIC,
Australia
Tel.: (61) 395216488
Web Site: http://www.bendigobank.com.au
Rev.: $662,810
Assets: $682,309
Liabilities: $93,918
Net Worth: $588,391
Earnings: $28,285
Fiscal Year-end: 06/30/2017
Banking Services
N.A.I.C.S.: 522110
Graham Manson Ludecke (Chm)

Sarina & District Community Financial
Services Limited (1)
37 Broad St, Sarina, 4737, QLD, Australia
Tel.: (61) 749432634
Web Site: http://www.bendigobank.com.au
Rev.: $887,148
Assets: $632,380
Liabilities: $37,992
Net Worth: $594,388
Earnings: $30,350
Fiscal Year-end: 06/30/2017
Banking Services
N.A.I.C.S.: 522110
Charmaine Matsen (Branch Mgr)

South Burnett Community Enterprises
Limited (1)
23 Toomey Street, Yarraman, 4614, QLD,
Australia
Tel.: (61) 7 4163 8162
Web Site: http://www.bendigobank.com.au
Rev.: $983,411
Assets: $653,270
Liabilities: $420,111
Net Worth: $233,159
Earnings: $30,039
Fiscal Year-end: 06/30/2019
Banking Services
N.A.I.C.S.: 522110

Sunshine Coast Community Financial
Services Limited (1)
114 Poinciana Avenue, PO Box 815, Te-
wantin, 4565, QLD, Australia
Tel.: (61) 754477131
Web Site: http://sccfsl.com.au
Rev.: $2,414,719
Assets: $3,297,853
Liabilities: $1,503,387
Net Worth: $1,794,466
Earnings: $119,881
Fiscal Year-end: 06/30/2022
Banking Services
N.A.I.C.S.: 522110
Rick Cooper (Bd of Dirs & Chm)

Tasmanian Banking Services
Limited (1)
45 Murray Street, Hobart, 7018, TAS, Australia
Tel.: (61) 362113700

Web Site:
http://www.tasmanianbankingservice.com
Commercial Banking Services
N.A.I.C.S.: 522110

Tongala & District Financial Services
Limited (1)
35 Mangan Street, Tongala, 3621, VIC,
Australia
Tel.: (61) 358591401
Web Site: https://www.bendigobank.com.au
Rev.: $636,179
Assets: $481,456
Liabilities: $117,341
Net Worth: $364,115
Earnings: $108,558
Fiscal Year-end: 06/30/2017
Banking Services
N.A.I.C.S.: 522110

Victorian Securities (1)
6 Chancery Lane, Ballarat, 3350, VIC, Aus-
tralia
Tel.: (61) 353044444
Web Site: http://www.vsc.com.au
Sales Range: $50-74.9 Million
Emp.: 20
Financial Products & Services
N.A.I.C.S.: 523999

BENDIGO TELCO LIMITED
23 McLaren Street, Bendigo, 3550,
VIC, Australia
Tel.: (61) 1300228123
Web Site:
https://www.bendigotelco.com.au
BCT—(NSXA)
Rev.: $22,769,707
Assets: $13,096,378
Liabilities: $6,980,566
Net Worth: $6,115,812
Earnings: $794,351
Fiscal Year-end: 06/30/21
Telecommunication Servicesb
N.A.I.C.S.: 517810
Jeffery Jordan (CEO)

BENDING SPOONS S.P.A.
Corso Como 15, 20154, Milan, Italy
Web Site: https://bendingspoons.com
Year Founded: 2013
Emp.: 100
Technology, Information & Internet
Services
N.A.I.C.S.: 518210
Luca Ferrari (Co-Founder & CEO)

Subsidiaries:

Hopin Ltd. (1)
Seedcamp Office 5 Bonhill Street Shored-
itch, London, EC2A 4BX, United Kingdom
Web Site: http://hopin.com
Virtual Event Management Services
N.A.I.C.S.: 518210
Johnny Boufarhat (Founder & CEO)

Subsidiary (US):

Boomset, Inc. (2)
305 Broadway Ste 1101, New York, NY
10007
Tel.: (860) 266-6738
Web Site: http://www.boomset.com
Sales Range: $1-9.9 Million
Emp.: 32
Software Development Services
N.A.I.C.S.: 541511
Kerem Baran (Founder & CEO)

Issuu, Inc. (1)
1370 Willow Rd, Menlo Park, CA 94025
Tel.: (650) 515-3609
Web Site: http://www.issuu.com
Digital Publishing Software
N.A.I.C.S.: 513210
Joe Hyrkin (CEO)

Meetup, Inc. (1)
632 Broadway 10th Fl, New York, NY
10012
Tel.: (212) 255-7327
Web Site: http://www.meetup.com
Internet Service Provider
N.A.I.C.S.: 517810
David Siegel (CEO)

Bending Spoons S.p.A.—(Continued)

BENDON LIMITED

8 Airpark Dr, Airport Oaks, Auckland,
New Zealand
Tel.: (64) 9 275 0000　　　　　　NZ
Web Site:
　http://www.bendonlingerie.co.nz
Women's Lingerie Mfr & Designer
N.A.I.C.S.: 458110
Justin Davis-Rice *(Chm)*

Subsidiaries:

Bendon USA Inc.　　　　　　　　　(1)
180 Madison Ave Ste 2305, New York, NY
10016
Tel.: (212) 696-4570
Web Site: http://www.bendongroup.com
Clothing Distr
N.A.I.C.S.: 458110

BENE GMBH

Schwarzwiesenstrasse 3, 3340,
Waidhofen, Austria
Tel.: (43) 7442 500 0
Web Site: http://www.bene.com
Sales Range: $200-249.9 Million
Emp.: 1,271
Office Furniture Mfr
N.A.I.C.S.: 337214
Michael Fried *(Mng Dir-Sls, Mktg &
Innovation)*

Subsidiaries:

Bene Belgium BVBA　　　　　　　(1)
Corporate Village Da Vincilaan 2 Bus 7
Business Centre-1, 1935, Zaventem, Flem-
ish Brabant, Belgium
Tel.: (32) 24214180
Web Site: http://www.bene-belgium.be
Sales Range: $50-74.9 Million
Emp.: 6
Office Furniture Whslr
N.A.I.C.S.: 423210
Stefan Geerkens *(Mgr)*

Bene Bratislava spol.s.r.o,　　　　(1)
Zilinska 7-9, 811 05, Bratislava, Slovakia
Tel.: (421) 257104311
Web Site: http://www.bene.sk
Sales Range: $50-74.9 Million
Emp.: 6
Office Furniture Sales
N.A.I.C.S.: 423210

Bene Budapest Kft.,　　　　　　　(1)
Aliz utca 1, 1117, Budapest, Hungary
Tel.: (36) 14113411
Office Furniture Mfr
N.A.I.C.S.: 423210

Bene Deutschland GmbH　　　　　(1)
The Squaire 13Am Flughafen, 60549,
Frankfurt am Main, Germany
Tel.: (49) 697104040
Web Site: http://www.bene.com
Office Furniture Sales
N.A.I.C.S.: 423210

Bene GmbH　　　　　　　　　　(1)
Magnolienweg 12, 63741, Aschaffenburg,
Bavaria, Germany
Tel.: (49) 602184090
Web Site: http://www.bene-buero.de
Sales Range: $25-49.9 Million
Emp.: 14
Office Furniture Sales
N.A.I.C.S.: 423210

Bene Kyiv TOV　　　　　　　　　(1)
Kubik-2 BC Office 314 Sholudenko Street 3,
04116, Kiev, Ukraine
Tel.: (380) 44 49 940 51
Web Site: http://www.bene.ua
Office Furniture Sales
N.A.I.C.S.: 423210

Bene Ljubljana d.o.o.,　　　　　　(1)
Dunajska cesta 151, 1000, Ljubljana, Slove-
nia
Tel.: (386) 15680970
Web Site: http://www.bene-slovenija.si
Sales Range: $50-74.9 Million
Emp.: 3
Office Furniture Sales
N.A.I.C.S.: 423210

Bene Office Furniture Ireland
Ltd.　　　　　　　　　　　　　　(1)
50 City Quay, Dublin, 2, Ireland
Tel.: (353) 17079110
Web Site: http://bene-ireland.ie
Sales Range: $50-74.9 Million
Emp.: 4
Office Furniture Sales
N.A.I.C.S.: 423210
Gerhard Grabnor *(Mgr)*

Bene PLC
47-53 Saint John St, London, EC1M 4AN,
United Kingdom
Tel.: (44) 2076891234
Web Site: http://www.bene.co.uk
Sales Range: $25-49.9 Million
Emp.: 40
Office Furniture Sales
N.A.I.C.S.: 423210
Stephen Block *(Mgr-Mktg)*

Bene Praha spol.s.r.o,　　　　　　(1)
The Park-Building 2 V Parku 2294/4,
Chodov, 14800, Prague, Czech Republic
Tel.: (420) 221507511
Web Site: http://www.bene-praha.com.cz
Office Furniture Sales
N.A.I.C.S.: 423210

Bene Romania S.R.L.　　　　　　(1)
Str Tipografilor No 11-15 S-Park Aripa A
1-2, Parter Sector 1, 013714, Bucharest,
Romania
Tel.: (40) 312253200
Web Site: http://www.bene.com.ro
Sales Range: $50-74.9 Million
Emp.: 4
Office Furniture Sales
N.A.I.C.S.: 423210

Bene Rus OOO　　　　　　　　　(1)
Petrovka str 27 2nd floor area I room 49,
107031, Moscow, Russia
Tel.: (7) 4957923200
Web Site: http://www.bene.ru
Sales Range: $50-74.9 Million
Emp.: 40
Office Furniture Retailer
N.A.I.C.S.: 423210
Michel Ftockford *(Dir Gen)*

Bene Warszawa Sp. z o.o.　　　　(1)
ul Al Armii Ludowej nr 26, 00-609, Warsaw,
Poland
Tel.: (48) 225793480
Web Site: http://www.bene.com
Office Furniture Sales
N.A.I.C.S.: 423210

BENEFEX LIMITED

Mountbatten House Grosvenor
Square, Southampton, SO15 2JU,
United Kingdom
Tel.: (44) 8451298636
Web Site: http://www.benefex.co.uk
Year Founded: 2003
Reward & Employee Benefit Services
N.A.I.C.S.: 541618
Steve Bellamy *(Chm)*

BENEFIT JAPAN CO., LTD.

2nd floor Asahi Life Doshomachi
Building 1518 Doshomachi, Chuo-ku,
Osaka, 541-0045, Japan
Tel.: (81) 662239888
Web Site: https://benefitjapan-co
　jp.prm-ssl.jp
3934—(TKS)
Rev.: $86,359,650
Assets: $74,045,220
Liabilities: $26,142,550
Net Worth: $47,902,670
Earnings: $4,851,740
Emp.: 327
Fiscal Year-end: 03/31/24
Communication Service
N.A.I.C.S.: 517810
Yutaka Sakuma *(Pres)*

BENEFIT SYSTEMS SA

Plac Europejski 2, 00-844, Warsaw,
Poland
Tel.: (48) 222424242

Web Site:
　https://www.benefitsystems.pl
Year Founded: 2000
BFT—(WAR)
Rev.: $479,606,090
Assets: $561,227,202
Liabilities: $378,989,348
Net Worth: $182,237,854
Earnings: $34,938,703
Emp.: 1,487
Fiscal Year-end: 12/31/22
Benefit Systems
N.A.I.C.S.: 513210
James van Bergh *(Chm-Supervisory
Bd)*

Subsidiaries:

Benefit IP Spolka z ograniczona od-
powiedzialnoscia sp.k.　　　　　(1)
Plac Europejski 2, 00-844, Warsaw, Poland
Tel.: (48) 508563626
Business Support Services
N.A.I.C.S.: 561499

Benefit Systems International Sp. z
o.o.　　　　　　　　　　　　　　(1)
Mlynarska 8/12, 01-194, Warsaw, Poland
Tel.: (48) 222424242
Business Support Services
N.A.I.C.S.: 561499

Subsidiary (Non-US):

Benefit Systems Bulgaria eood　　(2)
11-13 Yunak Str floor 1, 1612, Sofia, Bul-
garia
Tel.: (359) 28205770
Web Site: https://www.benefitsystems.bg
Sports & Physical Fitness Center Operator
N.A.I.C.S.: 713940
Tzvetan Ivanov *(Mng Dir)*

Benefit Systems Greece MIKE　　(2)
12 Agias Fotinis Str, Nea Smyrni, Athens,
Greece
Tel.: (30) 2111100111
Web Site: http://www.benefitsystems.gr
Sports & Physical Fitness Center Operator
N.A.I.C.S.: 713940

Benefit Systems Slovakia s.r.o.　　(2)
Prievozska 14, 821 09, Bratislava, Slovakia
Tel.: (421) 949516152
Web Site: https://www.multi-sport.sk
Sports & Physical Fitness Center Operator
N.A.I.C.S.: 713940
Marian Skripecky *(Mng Partner)*

Benefit Systems d. o. o.　　　　　(2)
Heinzelova 44, 10000, Zagreb, Croatia
Tel.: (385) 15544581
Web Site: http://www.benefitsystems.hr
Sports & Physical Fitness Center Operator
N.A.I.C.S.: 713940

Fit Fabric Sp. z o.o.　　　　　　　(1)
Zielona al 1 Maja 119/121, 90-766, Lodz,
Poland
Tel.: (48) 224878133
Web Site: https://www.fitfabric.pl
Sports & Physical Fitness Center Operator
N.A.I.C.S.: 713940

MyBenefit Sp. z o.o.　　　　　　　(1)
ul Powstancow Slaskich 28/30, 53-333,
Wroclaw, Poland
Tel.: (48) 717766480
Web Site: https://www.mybenefit.pl
Business Support Services
N.A.I.C.S.: 561499
Andrzej Stasiak *(Dir-IT)*

VanityStyle Sp. z o.o.　　　　　　(1)
ul Skierniewicka 16/20, 01-230, Warsaw,
Poland
Tel.: (48) 227463097
Web Site: https://www.vanitystyle.pl
Sports Card Services
N.A.I.C.S.: 522210
Robert Skawinski *(Mgr-Trade Mktg)*

BENETEAU S.A

16 boulevard de la Mer, 85800, Saint-
Gilles-Croix-de-Vie, France
Tel.: (33) 251268850

Web Site: https://www.beneteau-
　group.com
Year Founded: 1884
BEN—(EUR)
Rev.: $1,627,555,580
Assets: $1,862,216,706
Liabilities: $1,099,769,048
Net Worth: $762,447,658
Earnings: $111,323,117
Emp.: 7,884
Fiscal Year-end: 12/31/22
Recreational Boat Building & Sales
N.A.I.C.S.: 336612
Louis-Claude Roux *(Vice Chm)*

Subsidiaries:

Bio Habitat SAS　　　　　　　　　(1)
ZI de la Folie Sud Rue Charles Tellier, CS
50001, La Chaize le Vicomte, 85036, La
Roche-sur-Yon, Cedex, France
Tel.: (33) 251262028
Web Site: http://www.case-mobili-bhi.com
Mobile Home Mfr
N.A.I.C.S.: 321991
Florence Bugeon *(Dir-Publ)*

Chantiers Jeanneau SA　　　　　(1)
Route de La Roche Sur Yon, 85500, Les
Herbiers, France
Tel.: (33) 251642020
Sailing Boat Mfr
N.A.I.C.S.: 336611

Construction Navale Bordeaux
SA　　　　　　　　　　　　　　　(1)
162 quai de Brazza, 33072, Bordeaux,
France
Tel.: (33) 557 80 85 50
Web Site: http://www.construction-navale-
　bordeaux.com
Emp.: 1,000
Sailing Yacht Construction Services
N.A.I.C.S.: 336612

Digital Nautic SAS　　　　　　　　(1)
6 rue Rene Viviani, 44200, Nantes, France
Tel.: (33) 972166306
Web Site: http://www.digital-nautic.com
Application Software Development Services
N.A.I.C.S.: 513210

Fonderie Vrignaud SA　　　　　　(1)
124 rue du Moulin des Oranges ZI La Ribo-
tiere, 85170, Le Poire-sur-Vie, France
Tel.: (33) 2 51 34 13 64
Cast Iron Mfr
N.A.I.C.S.: 331511

Jeanneau America Inc.　　　　　　(1)
105 Eastern Ave Ste 203, Annapolis, MD
21403
Tel.: (410) 280-9400
Web Site: http://www.jeanneauamerica.com
Sailing & Power Boats Whslr
N.A.I.C.S.: 423910

Monte Carlo Yacht SPA　　　　　(1)
Via Consiglio d'Europa 90, 34074, Monfal-
cone, GO, Italy
Tel.: (39) 0481283111
Web Site: http://www.montecarloyachts.it
Sailing Boat Mfr
N.A.I.C.S.: 336611
Carla Demaria *(Pres)*

O'Hara Vacances SAS　　　　　　(1)
Parc D Activits Soleil Levant BP 656,
85806, Saint-Gilles-Croix-de-Vie, France
Tel.: (33) 2 51 26 20 28
Web Site: http://www.ohara.com
Emp.: 850
Mobile Home Mfr
N.A.I.C.S.: 321991

Ostroda Yacht Sp. z o.o.　　　　　(1)
ul Spokojna 1, 14-100, Ostroda, Poland
Tel.: (48) 896460700
Web Site: http://ostroda-yacht.com.pl
Recreational Boat Construction Services
N.A.I.C.S.: 336612

Rec Boat Holdings, LLC　　　　　(1)
925 Frisbie St, Cadillac, MI 49601
Tel.: (231) 775-1351
Sales Range: $150-199.9 Million
Emp.: 475
Recreational Boat Mfr
N.A.I.C.S.: 336612

Julie Johnson *(Dir-Mktg)*

Subsidiary (Domestic):

Four Winns, LLC (2)
925 Frisbie St, Cadillac, MI
49601-9259 (100%)
Tel.: (231) 775-1343
Web Site: http://www.fourwinns.com
Sales Range: $25-49.9 Million
Emp.: 200
Fiberglass Boats, Outboard & Inboard Mfr
N.A.I.C.S.: 336612
Andy Lindsay *(VP-Sls)*

Glastron, LLC (2)
925 Frisbie St, Cadillac, MI 49601
Tel.: (231) 775-1351
Web Site: http://www.glastronboats.com
Sales Range: $150-199.9 Million
Emp.: 450
Fiberglass Boat Mfr
N.A.I.C.S.: 336612

Wellcraft, LLC (2)
925 Frisbie St, Cadillac, MI 49601
Tel.: (231) 775-1351
Web Site: http://www.wellcraft.com
Sales Range: $10-24.9 Million
Emp.: 50
Fiberglass Boat Mfr
N.A.I.C.S.: 336612

S. J. Delphia sp z.o.o. (1)
ul Kosciuszki 63, Olecko, 19-400, Suwalki,
Poland
Tel.: (48) 875207400
Web Site: http://www.boat-delphia.com
Sailing Boat Mfr
N.A.I.C.S.: 336611
Wojciech Kot *(Founder)*

BENEVOLENTAI SA
4-8 Maple Street, London, W1T 5HD,
United Kingdom
Tel.: (44) 2037819360
Web Site:
    https://www.benevolent.com
Year Founded: 2013
BAI—(EUR)
Rev.: $9,253,976
Assets: $156,312,800
Liabilities: $37,313,810
Net Worth: $118,998,990
Earnings: ($79,925,524)
Emp.: 343
Fiscal Year-end: 12/31/23
Software Development Services
N.A.I.C.S.: 541511
Daniel Neil *(CTO)*

**BENG KUANG MARINE LIM-
ITED**
2 Venture Drive 1415Vision Ex-
change, Singapore, 628141, Singa-
pore
Tel.: (65) 62660010
Web Site:
    https://www.bkmgroup.com.sg
Year Founded: 1990
BEZ—(SES)
Rev.: $59,957,603
Assets: $47,716,836
Liabilities: $38,740,395
Net Worth: $8,976,441
Earnings: $5,996,636
Emp.: 492
Fiscal Year-end: 12/31/23
Ship Maintenance & Supplies Ser-
vices
N.A.I.C.S.: 336611
Beng Kuang Chua *(Co-Founder &
Chm)*

Subsidiaries:

Asian Sealand Offshore & Marine
Pte. Ltd. (1)
8 Boon Lay Way 09-16 8 TradeHub 21, Sin-
gapore, 609964, Singapore
Tel.: (65) 6 966 6027
Web Site: https://www.asiansealand.com
Offshore & Marine Equipment Repair &
Maintenance Services

N.A.I.C.S.: 336611
Low Kok Chiang *(Asst Gen Mgr-Comml)*

Subsidiary (Non-US):

ASIC Engineering Sdn Bhd (2)
No 28 Jalan Cenderai 25 Taman Perindus-
trian Kota Puteri, 81750, Masai, Johar, Ma-
laysia
Tel.: (60) 3873551
Ship Construction & Repair Services
N.A.I.C.S.: 336611

B & J Marine Pte. Ltd. (1)
55 Shipyard Road, Singapore, 628141,
Singapore
Tel.: (65) 62660010
Emp.: 20
Marine Tank Cleaning Services
N.A.I.C.S.: 488390
Chua Wing Keung *(Gen Mgr)*

**Beng Kuang Marine (B&Y) Pte.
Ltd.** (1)
55 Shipyard Rd, Singapore, 628141, Singa-
pore
Tel.: (65) 62660010
Sales Range: $25-49.9 Million
Emp.: 20
Corrosion Prevention Services
N.A.I.C.S.: 237120
Lee Choon Hwee *(Gen Mgr)*

Cattle Line Two Pte. Ltd. (1)
55 Shipyard Road, Singapore, 628141,
Singapore
Tel.: (65) 62660010
Ship Construction & Repair Services
N.A.I.C.S.: 336611

MTM Engineering Pte. Ltd. (1)
2 Venture Drive 09-22 Vision Exchange,
Singapore, 608526, Singapore
Tel.: (65) 62660010
Maritime Solution Services
N.A.I.C.S.: 488390

Nexus Sealand Trading Pte. Ltd. (1)
164 Gul Circle 01-08, Singapore, 629621,
Singapore
Tel.: (65) 6 898 2345
Web Site: https://www.bkmgroup.com.sg
Sales Range: $25-49.9 Million
Emp.: 100
Marine Freight Forwarding Services
N.A.I.C.S.: 488510

Subsidiary (Domestic):

**BT Asia Marketing & Engineering Pte
LtdBT Asia Marketing & Engineering
Pte Ltd** (2)
2 Venture Drive 09-22 Vision Exchange,
Singapore, 608526, Singapore
Tel.: (65) 62660010
Marine Engineering Services
N.A.I.C.S.: 541330

PT Berger Batam (1)
Jl Re Martadinata Kompleks Shangri-La
Gardens Blok A No 5/6, Sekupang, Pulau
Batam, 29422, Indonesia
Tel.: (62) 7785119994
Web Site: http://www.bergerbatam.com
Sales Range: $25-49.9 Million
Emp.: 75
Corrosion Prevention Services
N.A.I.C.S.: 237120

PT Master Indonesia (1)
Jl Brigjen Katamso Km 20 Tanjung Uncang,
Batam, 29422, Indonesia
Tel.: (62) 778 392 899
Marine Engineering Services
N.A.I.C.S.: 541330

PT. Nexelite CP Indonesia (1)
Jl Brigjen Katamso Kampung Taroka RT04
RW15, Kamp Torka-Tanjung Uncang,
Batam, 29424, Indonesia
Tel.: (62) 778392168
Ship Construction & Repair Services
N.A.I.C.S.: 336611
Suresh Ganapathy *(Mgr-Comml)*

**PT. Nexus Engineering
Indonesia** (1)
Jl Pattimura RT 01 RW 04 Kamp Panau
Kabil, Batam, 29467, Indonesia
Tel.: (62) 7782100958
Ship Construction & Repair Services

N.A.I.C.S.: 336611
Azman Hassan *(Project Mgr)*

Picco Enterprise Pte. Ltd. (1)
2 Venture Drive 09-22 Vision Exchange,
Singapore, 608526, Singapore
Tel.: (65) 6252379192
Maritime Solution Services
N.A.I.C.S.: 488390

**Venture Automation & Engineering
Pte. Ltd.** (1)
55 Shipyard Rd, Singapore, 628141, Singa-
pore
Tel.: (65) 62660010
Sales Range: $25-49.9 Million
Emp.: 20
Marine Automation Systems Mfr & Related
Services
N.A.I.C.S.: 541330
Lee Choon Hwee *(Gen Mgr)*

**BENG SOON MACHINERY
HOLDINGS LIMITED**
21 Tuas South Street 7, Singapore,
637111, Singapore
Tel.: (65) 62881280 Ky
Web Site: https://www.bsm.com.sg
Year Founded: 1979
1987—(HKG)
Rev.: $22,231,468
Assets: $40,370,419
Liabilities: $10,002,264
Net Worth: $30,368,155
Earnings: $18,400
Emp.: 121
Fiscal Year-end: 12/31/23
Holding Company
N.A.I.C.S.: 551112
Chee Beng Tan *(Founder, Chm &
CEO)*

**BENGAL & ASSAM COMPANY
LTD.**
Gulab Bhawan 3rd Floor Rear Wing
6A Bahadur Shah Zafar Marg, New
Delhi, 110002, India
Tel.: (91) 68201888
Web Site:
    https://www.bengalassam.com
Year Founded: 1947
533095—(BOM)
Rev.: $1,860,644,590
Assets: $2,229,396,242
Liabilities: $1,392,155,460
Net Worth: $837,240,782
Earnings: $99,779,876
Emp.: 10
Fiscal Year-end: 03/31/22
Financial Investment Services
N.A.I.C.S.: 523999
Bharat Hari Singhania *(Chm)*

Subsidiaries:

J.K. Fenner (India) Ltd. (1)
Khivraj Complex II V Floor 480 Anna Salai,
Nandanam, Chennai, 600 035, India
Tel.: (91) 4443994666
Web Site: https://jkfenner.com
Power Transmission Equipment Mfr & Distr
N.A.I.C.S.: 333612

JKF Americas Inc. (1)
960 Holmdel Rd Ste 2-02, Holmdel, NJ
07733
Tel.: (919) 922-8794
Web Site: https://jkfamericas.com
Power Transmission Equipment Mfr & Distr
N.A.I.C.S.: 333612

**Modern Cotton Yarn Spinners
Ltd.** (1)
Manavasi Post Krishnarayapuram Taluk,
Karur, 639 108, India
Tel.: (91) 4323243363
Sales Range: $25-49.9 Million
Emp.: 250
Cotton Yarn Mfr
N.A.I.C.S.: 313110

Panchmahal Properties Ltd. (1)
1st Floor Divya Enclave 6th Cross MG
Road, Mangalore, 575 003, India

Tel.: (91) 8244268043
Web Site:
    https://www.panchmalproperties.com
Property Management Services
N.A.I.C.S.: 531311

Umang Dairies Ltd. (1)
4th Floor Patriot House 3 Bahadur Shah
Zafar Marg, Vikram Nagar, New Delhi, 110
002, India (55.3%)
Tel.: (91) 1168201770
Web Site: https://www.umangdairies.com
Rev.: $35,350,291
Assets: $19,806,870
Liabilities: $14,546,970
Net Worth: $5,259,900
Earnings: ($390,816)
Emp.: 322
Fiscal Year-end: 03/31/2023
Dairy Products Mfr & Distr
N.A.I.C.S.: 311514

BENGAL ENERGY LTD.
Suite 640 630 6th Avenue S W, Cal-
gary, T2P 0S8, AB, Canada
Tel.: (403) 205-2526 AB
Web Site:
    https://www.bengalenergy.ca
Year Founded: 2007
BNG—(TSX)
Rev.: $5,625,375
Assets: $38,000,816
Liabilities: $5,208,420
Net Worth: $32,792,395
Earnings: ($292,573)
Emp.: 6
Fiscal Year-end: 03/31/22
Oil & Gas Exploration Services
N.A.I.C.S.: 213111
Ian James Towers *(Chm)*

BENGAL GROUP
Bengal House 75 Gulshan Avenue
Gulshan 1, Dhaka, 1212, Bangladesh
Tel.: (880) 29888248
Web Site:
    http://www.bengalgroup.com
Rev.: $5,770,548
Assets: $28,380,499
Liabilities: $2,501,013
Net Worth: $25,879,486
Earnings: $126,700
Fiscal Year-end: 06/30/20
Holding & Trading Company; Plastics,
Adhesives, Metal, Paper, Real Estate,
Agriculture, Food, Banking, Insurance
& Energy Products & Services
N.A.I.C.S.: 551112
Morshed Alam *(Chm)*

Subsidiaries:

**Bengal Windsor Thermoplastics
Limited** (1)
Bengal House 75 Gulshan Avenue Gulshan
1, Dhaka, 1212, Bangladesh
Tel.: (880) 2222288248
Web Site:
    https://www.windsor.bengalgroup.com
Rev.: $8,709,735
Assets: $29,998,661
Liabilities: $3,095,226
Net Worth: $26,903,435
Earnings: $552,039
Emp.: 322
Fiscal Year-end: 06/30/2022
Hanger Mfr
N.A.I.C.S.: 326199
Morshed Alam *(Chm)*

**BENGAL STEEL INDUSTRIES
LTD.**
84/1A Topsia Road South Trinity
Plaza 3rd Floor, Kolkata, 700046,
India
Tel.: (91) 3340556800
Web Site:
    https://www.bengalsteel.co.in
Year Founded: 1947
512404—(BOM)
Rev.: $86,096
Assets: $1,392,489

Bengal Steel Industries Ltd.—(Continued)

Liabilities: $95,456
Net Worth: $1,297,033
Earnings: $51,280
Fiscal Year-end: 03/31/21
Fabricated Metal Products Mfr
N.A.I.C.S.: 332312
Neha Mehra (Chief Compliance Officer & Sec)

BENGAL TEA & FABRICS LTD
Century Towers 4th Floor 45 Shakespeare Sarani, Kolkata, 700017,
West Bengal, India
Tel.: (91) 3322836416
Web Site: https://www.bengaltea.com
532230—(BOM)
Rev.: $7,712,141
Assets: $17,087,398
Liabilities: $1,386,212
Net Worth: $15,701,186
Earnings: $2,495,903
Emp.: 1,527
Fiscal Year-end: 03/31/22
Tea & Fabrics
N.A.I.C.S.: 311920
Adarsh Kanoria (Chm & Mng Dir)

BENGANG STEEL PLATES COMPANY LTD.
No 16 Renmin Road, Pingshan District, Benxi, 117000, Liaoning, China
Tel.: (86) 247828360   CA
Year Founded: 1997
200761—(SSE)
Rev.: $8,791,373,448
Assets: $6,193,696,860
Liabilities: $3,473,623,764
Net Worth: $2,720,073,096
Earnings: ($173,110,392)
Emp.: 26,000
Fiscal Year-end: 12/31/22
Metal Smelting & Mfr
N.A.I.C.S.: 331110

BENGO4.COM, INC.
Kurosaki Building 1-4 Roppongi
4-chome, Minato-ku, Tokyo, 106-0032, Japan
Tel.: (81) 355492555
Web Site: https://www.bengo4.com
6027—(TKS)
Rev.: $74,845,030
Assets: $67,184,040
Liabilities: $39,706,270
Net Worth: $27,447,770
Earnings: $5,532,570
Emp.: 576
Fiscal Year-end: 03/31/24
Online Legal Services
N.A.I.C.S.: 541199
Taichiro Motoe (Pres)

Subsidiaries:

LIC Co., Ltd.   (1)
465-4 Shimonakano, Okayama, 700-0973,
Japan
Tel.: (81) 862456700
Web Site: http://www.lic.jp
Home Improvement & Pet Stores Operator
N.A.I.C.S.: 444110
Yasuo Sanu (Founder & Pres)

BENGUET CORPORATION
7th Floor Universal Re Building, 106
Paseo de Roxas, Makati, 1226, Philippines
Tel.: (63) 288121380   PH
Web Site:
  https://www.benguetcorp.com
Year Founded: 1903
BC—(PHI)
Rev.: $33,690,280
Assets: $153,489,066
Liabilities: $54,064,192
Net Worth: $99,424,874

Earnings: $7,932,808
Emp.: 411
Fiscal Year-end: 12/31/20
Gold, Chromite, Copper & Natural
Resource Exploration, Mining, Development & Marketing Services
N.A.I.C.S.: 212220
Reynaldo P. Mendoza (Sr VP-Legal
Svcs & Asst Sec)

Subsidiaries:

BEREC Land Resources Inc.   (1)
7th Floor Universal Re Building 106 Paseo
De Roxas, Makati, 1226, Philippines
Tel.: (63) 28121380
Mineral Exploration Services
N.A.I.C.S.: 213115
Benjamin Romualdez (Pres)

BMC Forestry Corporation   (1)
4103 Woodkilton Road, Woodlawn, Toronto,
K0A 3M0, ON, Canada
Tel.: (613) 832-3617
Web Site: https://bmcforestry.ca
Wood Product Distr
N.A.I.C.S.: 423310

Benguet Management
Corporation   (1)
Universal Re Bldg, 106 Paseo de Roxas,
Makati, Philippines   (100%)
Tel.: (63) 28121359
Rev.: $17,325,000
Emp.: 2
Mfrs. Castings, Production of Mango Fruits,
Real Estate Development
N.A.I.C.S.: 111339

Subsidiary (Domestic):

Agua de Oro Ventures
Corporation   (2)
Bago Antamok, Itogon, 2604, Benguet, Philippines
Tel.: (63) 28121380
Water Purification Services
N.A.I.C.S.: 221310

Arrow Freight Corporation   (1)
368 F San Diego Street Veinte Reales Malanday, Valenzuela, 1444, Metro Manila,
Philippines
Tel.: (63) 22929149
Logistic Services
N.A.I.C.S.: 541614

Joint Venture (Domestic):

Benguet Ebara Real Estate
Corp.   (2)
Canlubang Industrial Estate, Cebuyao, Laguna, 4025, Philippines
Tel.: (63) 495491806
Web Site: http://www.ebaraphilippines.com
Real Estate; Joint Venture of Benguet Corporation (60%) & Ebara Corporation (40%)
N.A.I.C.S.: 531210

Subsidiary (Domestic):

Benguetrade, Inc   (2)
106 Paseo De Roxas, Makati, 1226, Metro
Manila, Philippines
Tel.: (63) 28121380
Gold & Copper Products Distr
N.A.I.C.S.: 423520

Benguetcorp Nickel Mines, Inc. (1)
Monsalud Building Lipay, Santa Cruz, 2213,
Zambales, Philippines
Tel.: (63) 28121380
Web Site: http://www.benguetcorp.com
Nickel Mining Services
N.A.I.C.S.: 212230
Glenn Buka (Gen Mgr)

Ebara-Benguet, Inc.   (1)
Canlubang Industrial Estate, Cabugao,
4025, Laguna, Philippines   (10.6%)
Tel.: (63) 495491806
Web Site: http://www.ebaraphilippines.com
Sales Range: $1-9.9 Million
Emp.: 100
Casting Mfr
N.A.I.C.S.: 331523

BENIN TELECOMS SA

PO Box 5959, Cotonou, Benin
Tel.: (229) 21312045
Web Site:
  http://www.benintelecoms.bj
Sales Range: $350-399.9 Million
Emp.: 1,500
Telecommunication Servicesb
N.A.I.C.S.: 517111
Jalil Assouma (Gen Dir)

BENITEC BIOPHARMA INC.
14/114 William Street, Melbourne,
3000, VIC, Australia
Tel.: (61) 295556986
Web Site: http://www.benitec.com
BNTC—(NASDAQ)
Rev.: $12,312,679
Assets: $19,286,512
Liabilities: $2,648,327
Net Worth: $16,638,185
Earnings: $2,878,983
Emp.: 21
Fiscal Year-end: 06/30/19
Biotechnology Research & Development Services
N.A.I.C.S.: 541714
Megan Joan Boston (Head-Ops-Australia)

BENIX & CO INC.
98 Orfus Road, Toronto, M6A 1L9,
ON, Canada
Tel.: (416) 784-0732
Web Site: http://www.benix.ca
Year Founded: 1991
Rev.: $50,912,400
Emp.: 500
House Ware Retail Stores
N.A.I.C.S.: 449129
Fred Benitah (Pres)

BENJAMIN HORNIGOLD LTD.
Level 17 25 Bligh Street, Sydney,
2000, NSW, Australia
Tel.: (61) 281178123
BHD—(ASX)
Rev.: $273,931
Assets: $4,876,958
Liabilities: $312,314
Net Worth: $4,564,644
Earnings: ($378,556)
Fiscal Year-end: 06/30/24
Investment Management Service
N.A.I.C.S.: 525990
Stuart Mcauliffe (Mgr-Fund)

BENJAMIN TOYS LTD.
Unit 2 The Bridge Business Centre
Bridge Rd, Southall, UB2 4AY, Mddx,
United Kingdom
Tel.: (44) 208 843 0578
Web Site: http://www.benjamin-toys.com
Sales Range: $1-9.9 Million
Emp.: 9
Mfr, Designer, Developer & Marketer
of Electronic Learning Aids, Electronic
Games, Activity Books, Science &
Nature Products, Board Games &
Other Products for Use in Both
Schools & Homes
N.A.I.C.S.: 339930
Raj Samarani (CEO)

Subsidiaries:

Benjamin Toys (HK) Ltd.   (1)
Flat B 12/F Gee Luen Factory Building 316-318 Kwun Tong Road, Hong Kong, China
(Hong Kong)
Tel.: (852) 27538636
Web Site: http://www.benjamin-toys.com
Toy Mfr & Distr
N.A.I.C.S.: 339930

BENJI INVEST KFT.
Kossuth L ut 12, Magyarorszag, H
2251, Tapioszecso, Hungary

Tel.: (36) 309491195
Real Estate Manangement Services
N.A.I.C.S.: 531390
Attila Juhasz (Owner)

Subsidiaries:

FCI Composite Insulator Ltd.   (1)
Kesmark Str 28A, 1158, Budapest, Hungary
Tel.: (36) 1 4196620
Web Site: http://www.fcifurukawa.hu
Sales Range: $25-49.9 Million
Emp.: 60
Silicon Insulator Mfr
N.A.I.C.S.: 335929
Attila Juhasz (Mng Dir)

BENKALA MINING COMPANY JSC
Mangilik El 7b, Astana district Aktobe
region, D05A5T5, Aktobe, Kazakhstan
Tel.: (7) 132908002
BENK—(KAZ)
Rev.: $6,558,892
Assets: $19,864,136
Liabilities: $5,384,337
Net Worth: $14,479,799
Earnings: $1,522,486
Fiscal Year-end: 12/31/20
Gold & Copper Mining Services
N.A.I.C.S.: 212220
Akzholov Bekbolat (CEO & Gen Mgr)

BENNER HOLDING GMBH
Adolfsallee 21, 65185, Wiesbaden,
Germany
Tel.: (49) 6192902870   De
Web Site: https://benner-holding.com
Holding Company
N.A.I.C.S.: 551112
Dominik Benner (CEO)

Subsidiaries:

The Platform Group AG   (1)
Schloss Elbroich Am Falder 4, 40589, Dusseldorf, Germany   (79.81%)
Tel.: (49) 8002404430
Web Site: https://corporate.the-platform-group.com
Software Development Services
N.A.I.C.S.: 513210
Dominik Benner (Chm-Mgmt Bd)

BENNETT CHEVROLET OLDS-MOBILE CADILLAC LTD
445 Hespeler Road, Cambridge, N1R
6J2, ON, Canada
Tel.: (519) 621-1250
Year Founded: 1931
Rev.: $34,000,000
Emp.: 60
New & Used Car Dealers
N.A.I.C.S.: 441110
Jim Ross (Gen Mgr)

BENNETT DUNLOP FORD
770 Broad Street, Regina, S4R 8H7,
SK, Canada
Tel.: (306) 522-6612
Web Site:
  http://www.bennettdunlopford.com
Year Founded: 1975
New & Used Car Dealers
N.A.I.C.S.: 441110
Dave Kohonick (VP-Sls)

BENNETT, COLEMAN & CO. LTD.
Times of India 7 Bahadur Shah Zafar
Marg, New Delhi, 110103, India
Tel.: (91) 1123302000   In
Web Site: http://www.timesgroup.com
Year Founded: 1838
Holding Company
N.A.I.C.S.: 551112

Subsidiaries:

Entertainment Network (India) Limited (1)
14th Floor Trade World D wing Kamala Mills Compound, Senapati Bapat Marg Lower Parel West, Mumbai, 400 013, India
Tel.: (91) 2267536983
Web Site: https://www.enil.co.in
Rev.: $39,745,415
Assets: $151,835,652
Liabilities: $42,326,589
Net Worth: $109,509,063
Earnings: ($15,083,673)
Emp.: 910
Fiscal Year-end: 03/31/2021
Radio Broadcasting Services
N.A.I.C.S.: 516210
Prashant Panday (CEO & Mng Dir)

The Times of India (1)
1 World Tower DLF City Phase V Opp DLF Golf Course, Gurgaon, 122002, Haryana, India
Tel.: (91) 1123302000
Web Site: http://www.in.indiatimes.com
Emp.: 500
Newspaper Publishers
N.A.I.C.S.: 513110
Ajay Vaishnavi (Dir-Telecom)

Holding (Non-US):

TIML Radio Ltd. (2)
1 Golden Square, London, W1F 9DJ, United Kingdom
Tel.: (44) 2074341215
Web Site: http://www.absoluteradio.co.uk
Sales Range: $25-49.9 Million
Emp.: 100
Holding Company
N.A.I.C.S.: 551112
Richard Huntingford (Chm)

BENO TNR, INC.
5F Creas Yeoksam Bldg 322 Nonhyeon-ro, Gangnam-gu, Seoul, Korea (South)
Tel.: (82) 234612150
Web Site: http://www.entermate.com
Year Founded: 2014
206400—(KRS)
Rev.: $16,718,197
Assets: $77,684,846
Liabilities: $23,993,615
Net Worth: $53,691,230
Earnings: ($16,763,898)
Emp.: 28
Fiscal Year-end: 12/31/22
Software Publishing Services
N.A.I.C.S.: 513210
Jeong Jip-Hun (Dir-Rep)

BENOIT OILFIELD CONSTRUCTION (1997) LTD.
302 Rupert St, PO Box 277, Chauvin, T0B 0V0, AB, Canada
Tel.: (780) 858-3794
Web Site:
   https://www.benoitoilfield.ca
Year Founded: 1976
Rev.: $16,519,541
Emp.: 100
Oil & Natural Gas Distr
N.A.I.C.S.: 221210
Calvin Winterholt (Pres)

BENQ CORPORATION
16 Jihu Road, Neihu, Taipei, 114, Taiwan
Tel.: (886) 227278899
Web Site: http://www.benq.com
Year Founded: 1884
Sales Range: $1-4.9 Billion
Emp.: 19,000
Color CRT/LCD Monitors, Digital Projectors, CD-ROM Drives, CD-ReWrite, DVD-ROM Drives, Scanners, Photo Printers & GSM/CDMA Mobile Phones
N.A.I.C.S.: 334118
Kuen-Yao Lee (Chm)

Subsidiaries:

BenQ America Corp. (1)
15375 Barranca Pkwy Ste A205, Irvine, CA 92618
Tel.: (949) 255-9500
Web Site: http://www.benq.us
Sales Range: $25-49.9 Million
Emp.: 50
Marketing & Sales of Brand Peripheral Products
N.A.I.C.S.: 423430
Lars Yoder (Pres)

BenQ Benelux (1)
Ekkersryt 4130, 5692 DC, Son, Netherlands
Tel.: (31) 499750500
Web Site: http://www.benq.com
Sales Range: $25-49.9 Million
Emp.: 25
Marketer & Retailer of Brand Peripheral Products
N.A.I.C.S.: 423430

BenQ Europe B.V. (1)
Meerenakkerweg 1-17, 5652 AR, Eindhoven, Netherlands
Tel.: (31) 88 888 9200
Web Site: http://www.benq.eu
Emp.: 68
Electronic Components Distr
N.A.I.C.S.: 423690
Pete Wang (Pres)

BenQ Latin America Corp. (1)
8200 NW 33 St Ste 301, Miami, FL 33122
Tel.: (305) 421-1200
Electronic Components Distr
N.A.I.C.S.: 423690
Peter Tan (Pres)

Darfon Electronics Corporation (1)
No 167-1 Shanying Rd, Guishan District, Taoyuan, 333, Taiwan (58.3%)
Tel.: (886) 32508800
Web Site: https://www.darfon.com.tw
Rev.: $843,438,995
Assets: $1,140,704,166
Liabilities: $625,020,252
Net Worth: $515,683,914
Earnings: $62,039,338
Emp.: 10,000
Fiscal Year-end: 12/31/2023
Mfr & Design of Keyboards, Fly Back Transformers, Chip Transformers, Motors & Ceramic
N.A.I.C.S.: 334118
Kai-Chien Su (Chm)

BENQ MATERIALS CORP.
29 Jianguo E Rd Guishan, Taoyuan, 33341, Taiwan
Tel.: (886) 33748800
Web Site:
   https://www.benqmaterials.com
Year Founded: 1998
8215—(TAI)
Rev.: $560,107,340
Assets: $672,284,157
Liabilities: $385,942,135
Net Worth: $286,342,021
Earnings: $16,475,064
Emp.: 944
Fiscal Year-end: 12/31/23
Optical Storage Devices Mfr
N.A.I.C.S.: 334112
Zhien-Chi Chen (Chm)

Subsidiaries:

BenQ Material (Wuhu) Co. Ltd. (1)
NO 106 Huajin South Rd Yijiang High-tech Development Zone, Wuhu, China
Tel.: (86) 5535938800
Medical Equipment Mfr & Distr
N.A.I.C.S.: 339112

Cenefom Corporation Limited (1)
3F No 50-3 Keyan Rd, Miaoli County Hsinchu Science Park, Zhunan, 35053, Taiwan
Tel.: (886) 37580058
Web Site: https://www.cenefom.com
Medical Equipment Mfr & Distr
N.A.I.C.S.: 334510

Genejet Biotech Co., Ltd. (1)
3F No 56 Ln77 Xingai Rd, Neihu Dist, Taipei, 11494, Taiwan

Tel.: (886) 287929762
Web Site: https://www.tissueaid.com
Medical Product Mfr & Distr
N.A.I.C.S.: 339112

BENQ MEDICAL TECHNOLOGY CORP.
7th Floor No 46 Zhou-Z St, Nei-hu, Taipei, 114, Taiwan
Tel.: (886) 287975533
Web Site:
   https://www.benqmedicaltech.com
Year Founded: 1989
4116—(TAI)
Medical Equipment Mfr
N.A.I.C.S.: 339112
Peter Chen (Chm)

BENSON STEEL LIMITED
72 Commercial Road, Bolton, L7E 1K4, ON, Canada
Tel.: (905) 857-0684
Web Site:
   http://www.bensonsteel.com
Year Founded: 1980
Rev.: $13,355,955
Emp.: 40
Steel Industry
N.A.I.C.S.: 331513
Robert Morrison (VP-Sls & Tech)

BENTALL KENNEDY LP
1 York Street Suite 1100, Toronto, M5J 0B6, ON, Canada
Tel.: (416) 681-3400
Web Site:
   http://www.bentallkennedy.com
Sales Range: $75-99.9 Million
Emp.: 1,000
Holding Company; Real Estate & Investment Management Services
N.A.I.C.S.: 551112
Richard Crofts (Chief Corp & Fin Officer)

Subsidiaries:

Bentall Kennedy (Canada) Limited Partnership (1)
Four Bentall Centre 1055 Dunsmuir Street Suite 1800, Vancouver, V7X 1B1, BC, Canada (100%)
Tel.: (604) 661-5000
Web Site: http://www.bentallkennedy.com
Real Estate Investment & Management Services
N.A.I.C.S.: 531390
David Barry (Exec VP & Mgr-Portfolio)

Subsidiary (Domestic):

Bentall Kennedy Real Estate Services LP (2)
55 University Avenue Suite 300, Toronto, M5J 2H7, ON, Canada
Tel.: (416) 681-6250
Web Site: http://www.bentallkennedy.com
Sales Range: $75-99.9 Million
Residential & Commercial Real Estate Development, Property Management & Leasing Services
N.A.I.C.S.: 531210

Bentall Kennedy Retail Services LP (2)
55 University Ave Ste 300, Toronto, M5J 2H7, ON, Canada
Tel.: (416) 681-3400
Web Site: http://www.bentallkennedy.com
Emp.: 200
Retail Property Management & Leasing Services
N.A.I.C.S.: 531120
Andy Clydesdale (Pres & COO)

BENTELER INTERNATIONAL AG
Schillerstrasse 25-27, 5020, Salzburg, Austria
Tel.: (43) 662 2283 0
Web Site: http://www.benteler.com

Year Founded: 1876
Rev.: $9,232,234,808
Assets: $6,098,745,470
Liabilities: $4,788,496,279
Net Worth: $1,310,249,190
Earnings: $29,655,043
Emp.: 28,578
Fiscal Year-end: 12/31/18
Automotive & Steel Pipe Parts Distr
N.A.I.C.S.: 331210
Ulrich Dohle (Chm-Supervisory Bd)

Subsidiaries:

BENTELER Automobiltechnik Nowgorod GmbH (1)
Ul Welikaja 20, 173003, Velikiy Novgorod, Russia
Tel.: (7) 8162731087
Automobile Component Distr
N.A.I.C.S.: 441330

BENTELER Automotive South Africa (PTY) Ltd. (1)
No 13 Bentonite Street Alrode Extension 7, 1450, Alberton, South Africa
Tel.: (27) 116178600
Automotive Components Mfr
N.A.I.C.S.: 336110

BENTELER Automotive Thailand Limited (1)
Unit 0831 8th Floor Zuellig House Building No 1-7 Silom Road, Bang Rak, 10500, Bangkok, Thailand
Tel.: (66) 22318303
Automobile Component Distr
N.A.I.C.S.: 441330

BENTELER Automotive Vigo, S.L. (1)
Parcelas 13 14 y 17 01 Valladeres, 36314, Vigo, Spain
Tel.: (34) 986268800
Automobile Component Distr
N.A.I.C.S.: 441330

BENTELER Distribucion Iberica S.L. (1)
C/ Progres 6-14, Abrera, 08630, Barcelona, Spain
Tel.: (34) 938190414
Automobile Component Distr
N.A.I.C.S.: 441330

BENTELER Distribution (Thailand) Company Limited (1)
Unit 184/142 24th Floor Forum Tower Ratchadapisek Road, Huai Khwang, Bangkok, 10310, Thailand
Tel.: (66) 22481530
Automobile Component Distr
N.A.I.C.S.: 441330

BENTELER Distribution Boru San. Tic. Ltd. Sti (1)
1 Cadde 15 Sokak No 12, Sekerpinar Cayirova, 41420, Kocaeli, Turkiye
Tel.: (90) 26272302000
Web Site: http://www.benteler-distribution.com
Automobile Component Distr
N.A.I.C.S.: 441330

BENTELER Distribution Cso-es Acelkereskedelmi Kft. (1)
Lorinci ut 139, Vecses, Hungary
Tel.: (36) 29889190
Web Site: http://www.benteler-distribution.hu
Automobile Component Distr
N.A.I.C.S.: 441330

BENTELER Distribution Romania SRL (1)
32 Soseaua Draganesti, 230119, Slatina, Romania
Tel.: (40) 372499300
Web Site: http://www.benteler-distribution.com
Automobile Component Distr
N.A.I.C.S.: 441330

BENTELER France S.A.S (1)
4 avenue Laurent Cely, 92606, Asnieres-sur-Seine, Cedex, France
Tel.: (33) 140864337
Steel Pole Mfr
N.A.I.C.S.: 331210

Benteler International AG—(Continued)

BENTELER J.I.T. Douai S.A.S. (1)
Usine RSA Georges Besse PIF - Batiment
L, 59553, Cuincy, France
Tel.: (33) 327081650
Web Site: http://www.benteler.com
Emp.: 50
Automotive Components Mfr
N.A.I.C.S.: 336110

**BENTELER JIT Pamplona,
S.L.U.** (1)
Pol Ind Arazuri - Orcoyen Calle E 2-4, Na-
varra, 31170, Arazuri, Spain
Tel.: (34) 948355215
Automotive Components Mfr
N.A.I.C.S.: 336110

BENTELER JIT Vitoria, S.L.U. (1)
Parque proveedores Mercedes-Benz C/Las
Arenas 1 - Puerta 4, 01015, Vitoria, Spain
Tel.: (34) 945188450
Automotive Components Mfr
N.A.I.C.S.: 336110

**BENTELER Steel/Tube (Nantong)
Co. Ltd.** (1)
Jianghai Road No 168, 226017, Nantong,
Jiangsu, China
Tel.: (86) 2139761061
Steel Pole Mfr
N.A.I.C.S.: 331210

BENTELER Trgovina d.o.o. (1)
Stjepana Radica 5, 49247, Zlatar, Croatia
Tel.: (385) 49461353
Automobile Component Distr
N.A.I.C.S.: 441330

**BLV Versicherungsmanagement
GmbH** (1)
Höhenzollernstr 2, 44135, Dortmund, Ger-
many
Tel.: (49) 23154040
General Insurance Services
N.A.I.C.S.: 524210

BMB Ocel s.r.o. (1)
Daliborova 432/3, Marianske Hory, 70900,
Ostrava, Czech Republic
Tel.: (420) 596622461
Web Site: http://www.bmbocel.cz
Steel Pipe Distr
N.A.I.C.S.: 423510
Eva Horvathova (Head-Acct)

Benteler (U.K.) Ltd. (1)
Sitka Drive Shrewsbury Business Park,
Shrewsbury, SY2 6LG, United Kingdom
Tel.: (44) 1743235235
Emp.: 2
Automobile Component Distr
N.A.I.C.S.: 441330

**Benteler Aluminium Systems Den-
mark AS** (1)
Kaergardsvej 5, 6270, Tonder, Denmark
Tel.: (45) 73926600
Automobile Component Distr
N.A.I.C.S.: 441330

**Benteler Aluminium Systems France
SNC** (1)
Parc Industriel d Incarville Voie de Iouvrage,
BP 613, 27406, Louviers, Cedex, France
Tel.: (33) 232093209
Automobile Component Distr
N.A.I.C.S.: 441330

**Benteler Aluminium Systems Korea
Ltd.** (1)
804 Gwell Tower 356 Seocho-daero,
Seocho-gu, 137-881, Seoul, Korea (South)
Tel.: (82) 25813209
Automobile Component Distr
N.A.I.C.S.: 441330

**Benteler Aluminium Systems Michi-
gan, Inc** (1)
533 Ottawa Ave, Holland, MI 49423
Tel.: (616) 396-6591
Automobile Component Distr
N.A.I.C.S.: 441330

**Benteler Aluminium Systems Norway
AS** (1)
Fabrikkveien 2, 2830, Raufoss, Norway
Tel.: (47) 61156000
Automobile Component Distr

N.A.I.C.S.: 441330

**Benteler Aluminium Systems Sweden
AB** (1)
Ostra Verken, Box 84, 726 20, Skultuna,
Vastmanland, Sweden
Tel.: (46) 2123400
Automotive Components Mfr
N.A.I.C.S.: 331318

**Benteler Automobiltechnik Eisenach
GmbH** (1)
Adam-Opel-Strasse 99, 99817, Eisenach,
Germany
Tel.: (49) 5254810
Automobile Component Distr
N.A.I.C.S.: 441330

**Benteler Automotive (Changshu)
Company Limited** (1)
No 3 Dongzhou Road Economic and tech-
nology zone, Changshu, 215513, Suzhou,
Jiangsu, China
Tel.: (86) 51252023019
Automotive Components Mfr
N.A.I.C.S.: 336110

**Benteler Automotive (China) Invest-
ment Co. Ltd.** (1)
10 F No 126 Jiang Chang No 3 Road,
Shanghai, 200436, China
Tel.: (86) 13918984239
Glass Processing Equipment Mfr
N.A.I.C.S.: 333248
Lei Zhang (Mgr-Treasury)

**Benteler Automotive (Chongqing) Co.
Ltd.** (1)
No 886 HaiEr Road, Jiang Bei, 400026,
Chongqing, China
Tel.: (86) 2367768100
Automotive Components Mfr
N.A.I.C.S.: 336110
Juliet Chen (Mgr-HR)

**Benteler Automotive (Fuzhou) Co.,
Ltd.** (1)
Xincheng Road, Qingkou Investment Dis-
trict, 350119, Fuzhou, China
Tel.: (86) 59122796969
Automobile Component Distr
N.A.I.C.S.: 441330

**Benteler Automotive (Shanghai) Co.,
Ltd.** (1)
No 1688 HuaLong Road, Qing Pu, 201708,
Shanghai, China
Tel.: (86) 2139761088
Automotive Components Mfr
N.A.I.C.S.: 336110
Sam Wang (Mgr-Production)

**Benteler Automotive Belgium
N.V.** (1)
Mai Zetterlingstraat 70, Desteldonk, 9042,
Gent, Belgium
Tel.: (32) 92180511
Automotive Components Mfr
N.A.I.C.S.: 336110
Olivier Biebaut (Mgr-Supply Chain)

**Benteler Automotive India Private
Limited** (1)
Plot No A3 Chakan MIDC Area Phase II
Chakan Talegaon Road, Village Khalumbre
Taluka Khed Chakan, Pune, 410 501, India
Tel.: (91) 2135612251
Industrial Machinery Mfr
N.A.I.C.S.: 333248
Ganesh Mane (Mng Dir)

**Benteler Automotive International
GmbH** (1)
An der Talle 27-31, 33102, Paderborn, Ger-
many
Tel.: (49) 5254810
Automobile Component Distr
N.A.I.C.S.: 441330

Benteler Automotive K.K. (1)
Yaesu Dai Bldg 9F 1-1-1 Kyobashi, Chuo-
ku, Tokyo, 104-0031, Japan
Tel.: (81) 352013881
Automobile Component Distr
N.A.I.C.S.: 441330

**Benteler Automotive Rumburk
s.r.o.** (1)
Bentelerova 460/2, 40801, Rumburk, Czech
Republic

Tel.: (420) 482358111
Automotive Components Mfr
N.A.I.C.S.: 336110

Benteler Automotive SAS (1)
Z A parc de Bourgogne 1 Rue Raymond
Poincare, 89400, Migennes, France
Tel.: (33) 386929810
Automotive Components Mfr
N.A.I.C.S.: 336110

Benteler Automotive SK s.r.o. (1)
Priemyselna 5471, 90101, Malacky, Slova-
kia
Tel.: (421) 912323111
Automotive Components Mfr
N.A.I.C.S.: 336110

Benteler Automotive UK Ltd. (1)
Willowbrook North, Corby, NN 17 5BB,
Northamptonshire, United Kingdom
Tel.: (44) 1536272802
Web Site: http://www.benteler.com
Automotive Components Mfr
N.A.I.C.S.: 336110

Benteler Autotechnika Kft (1)
Akai u 5, PF 76, 8061, Mor, Hungary
Tel.: (36) 22881200
Automotive Components Mfr
N.A.I.C.S.: 336110

Benteler Benelux B.V (1)
Paardeweide 3E, 4824 EH, Breda, Nether-
lands
Tel.: (31) 765421700
Automobile Component Distr
N.A.I.C.S.: 441330
Remko Silvertand (Mgr-Sls)

**Benteler CAPP Automotive System
(Changchun) Co., Ltd.** (1)
No 588 Yumin Road, 130103, Changchun,
Jilin, China
Tel.: (86) 43185858418
Automotive Components Mfr
N.A.I.C.S.: 336110
Thomas Bunke (Gen Mgr)

Benteler CR s.r.o. (1)
Skolni 713, 46331, Chrastava, Czech Re-
public
Tel.: (420) 482357111
Automotive Components Mfr
N.A.I.C.S.: 336110

**Benteler Componentes Automotivos
Ltda.** (1)
Av Marginal Sul 802 Distrito Industrial,
Campinas, 13054-750, Sao Paulo, Brazil
Tel.: (55) 1921223154
Automobile Component Distr
N.A.I.C.S.: 441330
Joao Martinez (Mgr-Pur)

Benteler Defense GmbH (1)
Frachtstrasse 10-16, 33602, Bielefeld, Ger-
many
Tel.: (49) 521542600
Web Site: http://www.benteler-defense.com
Automobile Detection System Mfr
N.A.I.C.S.: 334511

**Benteler Distribution Austria
GmbH** (1)
Siegfried-Marcus-Strasse 8, 2362, Bieder-
mannsdorf, Austria
Tel.: (43) 161530000
Web Site: http://www.benteler-distribution.at
Automobile Component Distr
N.A.I.C.S.: 441330

**Benteler Distribution Bulgaria
S.R.L.** (1)
65 Lyben Karavelov Str floor 3 office 4,
6000, Stara Zagora, Bulgaria
Tel.: (359) 42660760
Web Site: http://www.benteler-distribution.bg
Automobile Component Distr
N.A.I.C.S.: 441330

**Benteler Distribution Czech Republic
spof. s.r.o.** (1)
Prumyslova 1666, 26301, Dobris, Czech
Republic
Tel.: (420) 318533420
Web Site: http://www.benteler-
distribution.com
Automobile Component Distr
N.A.I.C.S.: 441330

**Benteler Distribution Deutschland
GmbH & Co. KG** (1)
Am Schlutershof 30, 47059, Duisburg, Ger-
many
Tel.: (49) 20399340
Automotive Components Distr
N.A.I.C.S.: 441330
Oliver Rechtsprecher (Mng Dir)

Benteler Distribution Estonia OU (1)
Tule 25, 76505, Saue, Estonia
Tel.: (372) 6709608
Web Site: http://www.helensbaltic.com
Automobile Component Distr
N.A.I.C.S.: 441330

**Benteler Distribution France
S.a.r.l.** (1)
15 route de Merville RN 12, PO Box 30,
Nonancourt, 27320, La Madeleine, France
Tel.: (33) 232580154
Web Site: http://www.benteler-
distribution.com
Automobile Component Distr
N.A.I.C.S.: 441330

**Benteler Distribution India Private
Limited** (1)
Plot No 679/2/3, Village - Kuruli Chakan
Taluka - Khed, Pune, 410 501, India
Tel.: (91) 2135670900
Web Site: http://www.benteler-distribution.in
Automobile Component Distr
N.A.I.C.S.: 441330

**Benteler Distribution International
GmbH** (1)
Heltorfer Strasse 1, 40472, Dusseldorf, Ger-
many
Tel.: (49) 211311140
Web Site: http://www.benteler-distribution.de
Automobile Component Distr
N.A.I.C.S.: 441330

Benteler Distribution Limited (1)
Crompton Way, Bolton, BL1 8TY, Lan-
cashire, United Kingdom
Tel.: (44) 8453306727
Web Site: http://www.benteler-
distribution.co.uk
Automobile Component Distr
N.A.I.C.S.: 441330

**Benteler Distribution Poland Sp.
z.o.o.** (1)
ul Rozdzienskiego 17, 41-303, Dabrowa
Gornicza, Poland
Tel.: (48) 327653600
Web Site: http://www.benteler-
distribution.com
Automobile Component Distr
N.A.I.C.S.: 441330

**Benteler Distribution Singapore Pte
Ltd** (1)
No 43 Tuas Avenue 13, Singapore, 639001,
Singapore
Tel.: (65) 68616388
Web Site: http://www.benteler-
distribution.com.sg
Automobile Component Distr
N.A.I.C.S.: 441330

**Benteler Distribution Slovakia
s.r.o.** (1)
Jurajov Dvor 523, Puste Ulany, 925 28,
Galanta, Slovakia
Tel.: (421) 317711500
Web Site: http://www.benteler-distribution.sk
Automobile Component Distr
N.A.I.C.S.: 441330

**Benteler Distribution Ukraine
LLC** (1)
5 Mlynova Str, 79020, Lviv, Ukraine
Tel.: (380) 50374789
Automobile Component Distr
N.A.I.C.S.: 441330

**Benteler Distribuzione Italia
S.p.A.** (1)
Via Leonardo da Vinci 97, Trezzano Sul
Naviglio, 20090, Milan, Italy
Tel.: (39) 02484271
Web Site: http://www.benteler-
distribution.com
Automobile Component Distr
N.A.I.C.S.: 441330

**Benteler Engineering Chennai Private
Limited** (1)

3rd Floor Apex Plaza No 3 Nungambakkam
High Road, 600 034, Chennai, India
Tel.: (91) 4445984455
Engineeering Services
N.A.I.C.S.: 541330
Amal Kumar *(Engr-Design)*

Benteler Espana S.A. (1)
P l de Villalonquejar c/ Lopez Bravo s/n,
09080, Burgos, Spain
Tel.: (34) 947477000
Automotive Components Mfr
N.A.I.C.S.: 336110

**Benteler Glass Processing
GmbH** (1)
Frachtstrasse 10-16, 33602, Bielefeld, Germany
Tel.: (49) 5215420
Grinding Machine Mfr
N.A.I.C.S.: 333517

Benteler Goshen, Inc. (1)
910 Eisenhower Dr S, Goshen, IN 46526
Tel.: (574) 537-2803
Automotive Components Mfr
N.A.I.C.S.: 336110

**Benteler JIT Dusseldorf GmbH & Co.
KG** (1)
Rather Strasse 49a, 40476, Dusseldorf,
Germany
Tel.: (49) 211699330
Automotive Components Mfr
N.A.I.C.S.: 336110

**Benteler Management Consulting
(Shanghai) Co., Ltd.** (1)
Rm 2311 Maxdo Centre Building No 8
Xingyi Road, 200336, Shanghai, China
Tel.: (86) 2152082666
Business Management Consulting Services
N.A.I.C.S.: 541611

**Benteler Netherlands Holding
B.V.** (1)
Steenovenweg 1, Helmond, 5708 HN, Netherlands
Tel.: (31) 492566111
Holding Company
N.A.I.C.S.: 551112

Benteler Palencia S.L. (1)
c/ Tren Expreso s/n, Venta de Banos,
34200, Palencia, Spain
Tel.: (34) 979761144
Automotive Components Mfr
N.A.I.C.S.: 336110

Benteler Rothrist AG (1)
Neue Industriestrasse 14, 4852, Rothrist,
Switzerland
Tel.: (41) 627855111
Steel Pole Mfr
N.A.I.C.S.: 331210

**Benteler Sistemas Automotivos
Ltda.** (1)
Rua Via Fornecedores n 401 Sala C, Roseira de Sao Sebastiao, 83070-147, Sao
Jose dos Pinhais, Brazil
Tel.: (55) 4121064886
Automotive Components Mfr
N.A.I.C.S.: 336110

**Benteler Steel & Tube
Corporation** (1)
3050 Post Oak Blvd Ste 1130, Houston, TX
77056
Tel.: (713) 629-9111
Web Site: http://www.benteler.com
Emp.: 20
Steel Pole Mfr
N.A.I.C.S.: 331210
Dean Rougas *(Exec VP)*

**Benteler Steel/Tube Manufacturing
Corporation** (1)
1 Benteler Dr, Shreveport, LA 71115
Tel.: (318) 216-4200
Steel Pole Mfr
N.A.I.C.S.: 331210
Bernd Brinkmann *(CFO)*

**Benteler Trading (Shanghai) Co.,
Ltd.** (1)
1207 Finance Square No 333 Jiu Jiang
Road, Shanghai, 200001, China
Tel.: (86) 2163507568

Web Site: http://www.benteler-
distribution.com.cn
Automobile Component Distr
N.A.I.C.S.: 441330

**Benteler Trading International
GmbH** (1)
Heltorfer Str 1a, 40472, Dusseldorf, Germany
Tel.: (49) 21131114400
Web Site: http://www.benteler-trading.com
Automobile Component Distr
N.A.I.C.S.: 441330

Benteler Trgovina d.o.o. (1)
Otiski Vrh 25A, Dravogradu, 2373,
Sentjanz, Slovenia
Tel.: (386) 28787852
Web Site: http://www.benteler-trgovina.si
Automobile Component Distr
N.A.I.C.S.: 441330

**Benteler Tubos y Maquinaria
S.A.** (1)
C/ Progreso n 6 nave 11 planta 1 oficinas,
Abrera, 08630, Barcelona, Spain
Tel.: (34) 938190416
Steel Pole Mfr
N.A.I.C.S.: 331210

**Benteler-IndUstria de Componentes
para AutomOveis Lda.** (1)
Parque Industrial de AutoEuropa Quinta da
Marqueza Lote 13, 2950-678, Palmela,
Portugal
Tel.: (351) 34934796900
Automotive Components Mfr
N.A.I.C.S.: 336110

Helens Ror A/S (1)
Hvamstubben 17, 2013, Skjetten, Norway
Tel.: (47) 64840830
Web Site: http://www.helens.no
Steel Product Distr
N.A.I.C.S.: 423510

Helens Ror AB (1)
Vastergardsvagen 16, PO Box 101, Halmstad, Sweden
Tel.: (46) 35149000
Web Site: http://www.helens.se
Emp.: 230
Steel Product Distr
N.A.I.C.S.: 423510
Stig Rex *(Gen Mgr-Sls)*

Kindlimann AG (1)
Glarnischstrasse 33, CH-9501, Wil, Switzerland
Tel.: (41) 71 929 93 93
Web Site: http://www.kindlimann.ch
Steel Distr
N.A.I.C.S.: 331110

Kindlimann SA (1)
Mochettaz 2, 1030, Bussigny-pres-
Lausanne, Switzerland
Tel.: (41) 217066060
Steel Product Distr
N.A.I.C.S.: 423510

**Noord-Nederlandse Schrootverwerk-
ing B.V.** (1)
Oostelijke Industrieweg 23, 8801 JW,
Franeker, Netherlands
Tel.: (31) 517393341
Web Site: http://www.schrootverwerking.nl
Steel Product Distr
N.A.I.C.S.: 423510

OOO Benteler Automotive (1)
1st Avtomobilniy proezd 5, 248926, Kaluga,
Russia
Tel.: (7) 4842211168
Automotive Components Mfr
N.A.I.C.S.: 336110

**OOO Benteler Distribution
Russia** (1)
Engels Av 163-A Industrial Zone Parnas,
Saint Petersburg, Russia
Tel.: (7) 8123260511
Automobile Component Distr
N.A.I.C.S.: 441330

**PT Benteler Distribution
Indonesia** (1)
Jalan Haryono Kav 15, 12810, Jakarta,
Indonesia
Tel.: (62) 2183793770

Web Site: http://www.benteler-
distribution.co.id
Steel Product Distr
N.A.I.C.S.: 423350

**Shanghai BENTELER Huizhong Au-
tomotive Company Ltd.** (1)
No 251 Wen Shui Road, 200072, Shanghai,
China
Tel.: (86) 2156037771
Automotive Components Mfr
N.A.I.C.S.: 336110
Nick Borislavski *(Gen Mgr)*

**UAB Benteler Distribution
Lithuania** (1)
Rodunios kelias 11, 002189, Vilnius, Lithuania
Tel.: (370) 52329472
Web Site: http://www.benteler-distribution.lt
Automobile Component Distr
N.A.I.C.S.: 441330

**Wuhu BENTELER-POSCO Automo-
tive Co., Ltd.** (1)
NO 6-8 Hongqi Road Wuhu
Economy&Technology Development,
241009, Wuhu, Anhui, China
Tel.: (86) 5535666999
Automotive Components Mfr
N.A.I.C.S.: 336110
Jin Fang *(Gen Mgr)*

BENTLEY CAPITAL LTD.
Tel.: (61) 892149757   AU
Web Site: https://www.bel.com.au
BEL—(ASX)
Rev.: $3,271
Assets: $1,698,485
Liabilities: $783,109
Net Worth: $915,376
Earnings: ($1,361,235)
Fiscal Year-end: 06/30/24
Investment Management Service
N.A.I.C.S.: 523150
Farooq Khan *(Chm)*

Subsidiaries:

**Scarborough Equities Pty.
Limited** (1)
Suite 202 Angela House 30-36 Bay Street,
Double Bay, 2028, NSW, Australia
Tel.: (61) 293635088
Web Site:
   http://www.scarboroughequities.com.au
Sales Range: $50-74.9 Million
Emp.: 5
Investment Fund Management Services
N.A.I.C.S.: 525910

**BENTLEY COMMERCIAL EN-
TERPRISES LIMITED**
Bhansali House A-5 Veera Desai
Road, Andheri West, Mumbai, 400
053, India
Tel.: (91) 22 26731779
Web Site:
   http://www.bentleycommercial.net
Year Founded: 1985
Sales Range: Less than $1 Million
Financial Services
N.A.I.C.S.: 523999
Arun Kinjawadekar *(CFO)*

BENTLEY GROUP
6125 Chemin de la Cote de Liesse,
Saint Laurent, H4T 1C8, QC, Canada
Tel.: (514) 341-9333
Web Site: http://www.onlinebags.com
Year Founded: 1987
Sales Range: $50-74.9 Million
Emp.: 5,000
Retailer of Handbags & Luggage
N.A.I.C.S.: 458320

**BENTLEY REID (HOLDINGS)
LIMITED**
24th Floor Diamond Exchange Build-
ing 8-10 Duddell Street, Central,
China (Hong Kong)
Tel.: (852) 2810 1233

Web Site: http://www.bentleyreid.com
Year Founded: 1979
Financial Services Holding Company
N.A.I.C.S.: 551112
Nic Bentley *(Chm)*

Subsidiaries:

Bentley Reid & Company Limited (1)
24th Floor Diamond Exchange Building
8-10 Duddell Street, Central, China (Hong
Kong)
Tel.: (852) 2810 1233
Web Site: http://www.bentleyreid.com
Tax & Financial Advice; Investment Man-
agement
N.A.I.C.S.: 523940
Jeanette Chiu *(Dir-Hong Kong)*

Bentley Trust (Malta) Limited (1)
Level 7 Portomaso Business Tower, Saint
Julian's, STJ 4011, Malta
Tel.: (356) 21378828
Web Site: http://www.bentleyreid.com
Emp.: 15
Trust & Fiduciary Services
N.A.I.C.S.: 523991
David Magri *(Mgr)*

BENTON RESOURCES INC.
176 1100 Memorial Avenue, Thunder
Bay, P7B 4A8, ON, Canada
Tel.: (807) 475-7474
Web Site:
   https://www.bentonresources.ca
Year Founded: 2003
BEX—(TSXV)
Rev.: $56,433
Assets: $12,167,805
Liabilities: $508,610
Net Worth: $11,659,195
Earnings: ($830,787)
Fiscal Year-end: 06/30/21
Mineral Exploration Services
N.A.I.C.S.: 213114
Gordon Fretwell *(Sec)*

Subsidiaries:

**Rio Tinto Exploration Canada
Inc.** (1)
400-1190 Av Des-Canadiens-De-Montreal,
Montreal, H3B 0E3, QC, Canada
Tel.: (514) 848-8000
Web Site: https://www.riotinto.com
Metal Exploration Services
N.A.I.C.S.: 213114

BENTONIT A.D.
Gavrila Principa Bb, 70270, Sipovo,
Bosnia & Herzegovina
Tel.: (387) 50 371 328
BENT—(BANJ)
Sales Range: Less than $1 Million
Emp.: 5
Clay Mining Services
N.A.I.C.S.: 212323
Stevica Stojanovic *(Chm-Mgmt Bd)*

**BENTRE AQUAPRODUCT IM-
PORT & EXPORT JOINT
STOCK COMPANY**
Tanthach village, Chauthanh district,
Ho Chi Minh City, Bentre, Vietnam
Tel.: (84) 75 3 860 265
Web Site:
   http://www.aquatexbentre.com
Year Founded: 1977
Rev.: $18,966,843
Assets: $23,386,239
Liabilities: $7,086,556
Net Worth: $16,299,683
Earnings: $2,755,400
Emp.: 1,200
Fiscal Year-end: 12/31/15
Fisheries Product Sales & Services
N.A.I.C.S.: 423990

BENZ MINING CORP.
401 Bay Street Suite 2100, PO Box
55, Toronto, M5H 2Y4, ON, Canada

Benz Mining Corp.—(Continued)

Tel.: (416) 356-8165   BC
Web Site:
   https://www.benzmining.com
Year Founded: 2011
BENZF—(OTCIQ)
Rev.: $87,921
Assets: $9,657,975
Liabilities: $3,102,555
Net Worth: $6,475,420
Earnings: ($3,528,819)
Fiscal Year-end: 04/30/23
Investment Services
N.A.I.C.S.: 523999
Miloje Vicentijevic *(Pres & Co-CEO)*

BEOCIN A.D.
Desanke Maksimovic 5, Beocin, Serbia
Tel.: (381) 64 240 31 64
Year Founded: 1968
Sales Range: Less than $1 Million
Hardware Product Whslr
N.A.I.C.S.: 444140

BEOENTERIJER A.D.
Kneza Mutimira 6, Belgrade, Serbia
Tel.: (381) 11 288 1933
Year Founded: 2001
Sales Range: Less than $1 Million
Office Furniture Mfr
N.A.I.C.S.: 337214

BEOGRAD A.D.
Svetozara Markovica-baraka f, 78000, Banja Luka, Bosnia & Herzegovina
Tel.: (387) 51319538
BEOG-R-A—(BANJ)
Bar Operator
N.A.I.C.S.: 722410
Bosa Marinkovic *(Chm-Mgmt Bd)*

BEOGRAD PROMET A.D.
Pregrevica 4, Zemun, Belgrade, Serbia
Tel.: (381) 2618057
Year Founded: 2001
BPRZ—(BEL)
Sales Range: Less than $1 Million
Emp.: 3
Meat Product Whslr
N.A.I.C.S.: 424470
Mira Rakazov *(Exec Dir)*

BEOGRADMONTAZA A.D.
Kosovska 39/III, 11000, Belgrade, Serbia
Tel.: (381) 112466778
Web Site:
   https://www.beogradmontaza.co.rs
Year Founded: 1990
BGMN—(BEL)
Sales Range: Less than $1 Million
Emp.: 101
Electric Equipment Mfr
N.A.I.C.S.: 335999
Damir Lamza *(Mng Dir)*

BEOGRADSKA AUTOBUSKA STANICA A.D.
Zeleznicka 4, 11000, Belgrade, Serbia
Tel.: (381) 117621457
Web Site: https://www.bas.rs
Year Founded: 1965
BASB—(BEL)
Rev.: $12,355,957
Assets: $24,875,354
Liabilities: $19,541,243
Net Worth: $5,334,110
Earnings: $1,686,976
Emp.: 569
Fiscal Year-end: 12/31/22
Passenger Transportation Services
N.A.I.C.S.: 485999

Andelko Mucibabic *(Exec Dir)*

BEOGRADSKA INDUSTRIJA PIVA A.D.
Bulevar vojvode Putnika 5, 11000, Belgrade, Serbia
Tel.: (381) 11 2652322
Web Site: http://www.bip.rs
Year Founded: 1899
Sales Range: $10-24.9 Million
Beer Mfr
N.A.I.C.S.: 312120

BEOPAN A.D.
Prvomajska 10a, Pancevo, Serbia
Tel.: (381) 13 312 346
Year Founded: 2002
BPNP—(BEL)
Sales Range: Less than $1 Million
Painting & Glazing Services
N.A.I.C.S.: 238320
Bojat Novica *(Exec Dir)*

BEOTRANS A.D.
Karadordeva 11, Belgrade, Serbia
Tel.: (381) 11 2629599
Web Site: http://www.beotrans.co.rs
Year Founded: 1980
Sales Range: Less than $1 Million
Emp.: 3
Food Transportation Services
N.A.I.C.S.: 484121

BEOWULF MINING PLC
201 Temple Chambers 3-7 Temple Avenue, London, EC4Y 0DT, United Kingdom
Tel.: (44) 2037716993   UK
Web Site:
   https://www.beowulfmining.com
Year Founded: 1988
BEM—(AIM)
Rev.: $105,301
Assets: $18,817,769
Liabilities: $3,093,391
Net Worth: $15,724,378
Earnings: ($2,535,075)
Emp.: 3
Fiscal Year-end: 12/31/22
Mineral Exploration Services
N.A.I.C.S.: 213115
Rasmus Blomqvist *(Mgr-Exploration)*

Subsidiaries:

Grafintec Oy   **(1)**
Yrittajankatu 17 Futura 1 3rd Floor, 65380, Vaasa, Finland
Tel.: (358) 505877246
Web Site: https://www.grafintec.fi
Mineral Geological Exploration Services
N.A.I.C.S.: 213114

Oy Fennoscandian Resources AB   **(1)**
Laivurintie 11, 21100, Naantali, Finland
Tel.: (358) 505877246
Web Site: http://www.fennoscandian.com
Mineral Exploration Services
N.A.I.C.S.: 213114

BEOZASTITA A.D.
Dimitrija Tucovica 115, Belgrade, Serbia
Tel.: (381) 112750774
Web Site:
   https://www.beozastita.co.rs
Year Founded: 2001
BEOZ—(BEL)
Rev.: $9,061
Assets: $36,336
Liabilities: $1,831
Net Worth: $34,506
Earnings: $567
Emp.: 120
Fiscal Year-end: 12/31/23
Security System Services
N.A.I.C.S.: 561621
Radivoje Kisa *(CEO)*

BERA HOLDING A.S.
Nisantas Mah Dr M Hulusi Baybal St Bera Business Center No12, Seluklu, Konya, Turkiye
Tel.: (90) 3322212000
Web Site:
   https://www.beraholding.com.tr
Year Founded: 1988
BERA   (IST)
Rev.: $265,518,541
Assets: $400,505,974
Liabilities: $114,438,136
Net Worth: $286,067,838
Earnings: $73,131,225
Emp.: 6,000
Fiscal Year-end: 12/31/22
Holding Company
N.A.I.C.S.: 551112
Ali Riza Alaboyun *(Chm)*

Subsidiaries:

Golda Gida Ihtiyac Maddeler San. And Trade Inc.   **(1)**
Eminettin Mahallesi Sanayi Bolgesi Kume Evler No 1, Kazimkarabekir, Karaman, Turkiye
Tel.: (90) 3383112901
Web Site: https://golda.com.tr
Emp.: 5,000
Grocery Product Mfr & Distr
N.A.I.C.S.: 311999

Hisar Maden A.S.   **(1)**
Konya Yolu 15 km, 68500, Aksaray, Turkiye
Tel.: (90) 3822373200
Web Site: https://www.hisarmaden.net
Stainless Steel Mfr & Distr
N.A.I.C.S.: 331110

Komyapi Insaat A.S.   **(1)**
Nisantas Dr Mehmet Hulusi Baybal Cd, No 12 Bera is Merkezi Kat 1, 42060, Konya, Turkiye
Tel.: (90) 3322364466
Web Site: https://www.komyapi.com.tr
Real Estate Manangement Services
N.A.I.C.S.: 531390

Kongaz A.S.   **(1)**
Karatepe Sk No 84 Karahuyuk Mah, Meram, 42140, Konya, Turkiye
Tel.: (90) 3323272027
Web Site: https://www.kongaz.com.tr
Auto Gas Cylinder Mfr & Distr
N.A.I.C.S.: 333995

Konya Kagit San. ve Tic. A.S.   **(1)**
Buyukkayacik mah O S B Vezirkoy Caddesi No 1, Selcuklu, 42250, Konya, Turkiye
Tel.: (90) 3322390054
Web Site: https://konyakagit.com.tr
Newspaper Publishers
N.A.I.C.S.: 513110

Konya Petrol A.S.   **(1)**
Yeni Istanbul Caddesi No 28B, Selcuklu, 42285, Konya, Turkiye
Tel.: (90) 3322355540
Web Site: https://www.konyapetrol.com.tr
Petroleum Refineries Mfr
N.A.I.C.S.: 324110

Rulmenti S.A.   **(1)**
Republicii Street No 320, PO 731108, County Vaslui, Barlad, Romania
Tel.: (40) 235412120
Web Site: https://www.urbgroup.com
Emp.: 1,400
Bearing Machinery Mfr & Distr
N.A.I.C.S.: 332991

BERCHTESGADENER BERGBAHN AG
Tel.: (49) 865295810
Web Site: https://www.jennerbahn.de
Year Founded: 1953
Transportation Services
N.A.I.C.S.: 485112
Stefan Kurz *(Member-Mgmt Bd)*

BEREKET VARLIK KIRALAMA A.S.
Saray Mahallesi Dr Adnan Buyukdeniz Caddesi No 6, Umraniye,

34768, Istanbul, Turkiye
Tel.: (90) 2166660303
Web Site:
   http://www.bereketvarlik.com
BRKT—(IST)
Sales Range: Less than $1 Million
Asset Leasing Services
N.A.I.C.S.: 531390
Meliksah Utku *(Chm)*

BERENDSEN FLUID POWER PTY LIMITED
31 Powers Road, Seven Hills, 2147, NSW, Australia
Tel.: (61) 298385800
Web Site:
   http://www.berendsen.com.au
Year Founded: 1993
Sales Range: $25-49.9 Million
Emp.: 300
Hydraulic Services
N.A.I.C.S.: 333120
James Leach *(CEO)*

BERENTZEN-GRUPPE AG
Ritterstrasse 7, 49740, Haselunne, Germany
Tel.: (49) 59615020   De
Web Site: http://www.berentzen-gruppe.de
Year Founded: 1858
Sales Range: $600-649.9 Million
Emp.: 700
Alcoholic Beverage Producer Mfr
N.A.I.C.S.: 312140
Ralf Bruhofner *(Member-Exec Bd)*

Subsidiaries:

Die Stonsdorferei W. Koerner GmbH & Co. KG   **(1)**
Ritterstr 7, Haselunne, 49740, Germany
Tel.: (49) 5961502386
Web Site: http://www.berentzen-gruppe.de
Alcoholic Beverage Distr
N.A.I.C.S.: 424820

Kornbrennerei Berentzen GmbH   **(1)**
Ritterstr 7, Haselunne, 49740, Germany
Tel.: (49) 59615020
Beverages Mfr
N.A.I.C.S.: 312120

LANDWIRTH'S GmbH   **(1)**
Sollingweg 41, Minden, 32427, Germany
Tel.: (49) 5961502386
Sales Range: $25-49.9 Million
Emp.: 10
Beverages Mfr
N.A.I.C.S.: 312120
Schmidt Frank *(Gen Mgr)*

Pabst & Richarz Vertriebs GmbH   **(1)**
Sollingweg 41, Minden, 32427, Germany
Tel.: (49) 571 4040400
Web Site: http://www.pabst-richarz.de
Alcoholic Beverages Mfr
N.A.I.C.S.: 312120
Frank Schmidt *(Mng Dir)*

Strothmann Spirituosen Verwaltung GmbH   **(1)**
Ritterstr 7, Haselunne, 49740, Germany
Tel.: (49) 59615020
Investment Management Service
N.A.I.C.S.: 523999

Vivaris Getranke GmbH & Co. KG   **(1)**
Neuer Grund 24, 49740, Haselunne, Germany
Tel.: (49) 5961 502 865
Web Site: http://www.vivaris.net
Sales Range: $25-49.9 Million
Emp.: 80
Beverages Mfr
N.A.I.C.S.: 312111
Bernhard Brinkmann *(Gen Mgr)*

Vivaris Getranke Verwaltung GmbH   **(1)**
Neuer Grund 24, 49740, Haselunne, Germany
Tel.: (49) 5961502865
Web Site: http://www.vivaris.net

Emp.: 70
Beverages Mfr
N.A.I.C.S.: 312111
Johan Bosch (CEO)

BERESFORD BOX COMPANY INC.
607 Kumpf Drive, Waterloo, N2V
1K8, ON, Canada
Tel.: (519) 885-4580
Web Site:
   http://www.beresfordbox.com
Year Founded: 1964
Sales Range: $10-24.9 Million
Emp.: 100
Carton & Packaging Products Mfr
N.A.I.C.S.: 322212
Natalia Storozhilov (Graphic Designer)

BERETTA VENTURES LTD.
515 - 701 West Georgia Street, PO
Box 10068, Pacific Centre, Vancouver, V7Y 1C6, BC, Canada
Tel.: (778) 331-8505   BC
Year Founded: 2013
BRTA.H—(TSXV)
Assets: $3,907
Liabilities: $133,157
Net Worth: ($129,250)
Earnings: ($53,451)
Fiscal Year-end: 05/31/24
Capital Pool Company
N.A.I.C.S.: 523999
Scott Ackerman (CEO & CFO)

BERG EARTH CO., LTD.
88-1 Kitanada, Tsushima-cho, Uwajima, 798-3361, Ehime, Japan
Tel.: (81) 895208231
Web Site: https://www.bergearth.co.jp
Year Founded: 2001
1383—(TKS)
Rev.: $50,062,490
Assets: $40,214,480
Liabilities: $25,453,100
Net Worth: $14,761,380
Earnings: $553,020
Emp.: 261
Fiscal Year-end: 10/31/23
Grafted Nursery Plants Production &
Sales
N.A.I.C.S.: 113210
Kazuhiko Yamaguchi (Pres & CEO)

BERGBAHNEN ENGELBERG-TRUBSEE-TITLIS AG
Poststrasse 3, 6390, Engelberg, Switzerland
Tel.: (41) 416395050
Web Site: https://www.titlis.ch
TIBN—(SWX)
Sales Range: Less than $1 Million
Tourism Services
N.A.I.C.S.: 561499
Norbert Patt (CEO)

BERGE Y CIA SA
Calle Barroeta Aldamar 2, 48001, Bilbao, Spain
Tel.: (34) 91 420 02 28
Web Site: http://www.bergeycia.es
Holding Company
N.A.I.C.S.: 551112
Jorge Navea (Mng Dir)

Subsidiaries:

Berge Automocion, SL   (1)
C/ Alcala 65, 28014, Madrid, Spain
Tel.: (34) 915 320 609
Web Site: http://www.bergeauto.es
Automotive Distr
N.A.I.C.S.: 423110
Eduardo Zavala (Dir-Bus Dev)

Subsidiary (Non-US):

RECAMBIA   (2)

C/Rayo 7 Pol Ind La Quinta R2, Cabanillas
del Campo, 19171, Guadalajara, Mexico
Tel.: (52) 949329908
Web Site: http://www.recambia.es
Automotive Distr
N.A.I.C.S.: 423110

MMC Automoviles Espana, S.A.   (1)
Calle Francisco Gervas 4, 28108, Alcobendas, Spain   (76%)
Tel.: (34) 91 387 74 43
Web Site: http://www.mitsubishi-motors.es
Automobiles Distr & Retailer
N.A.I.C.S.: 423110

BERGEN CARBON SOLUTIONS AS
Fleslandsveien 70E, Blomsterdalen,
5258, Bergen, Norway
Tel.: (47) 56123777
Web Site:
   https://www.bergensolutions.com
Year Founded: 2016
BCS—(OSL)
Rev.: $27,342
Assets: $25,353,408
Liabilities: $2,510,807
Net Worth: $22,842,601
Earnings: ($5,996,120)
Emp.: 34
Fiscal Year-end: 12/31/23
Chemical Products Mfr
N.A.I.C.S.: 335991
Finn Blydt-Svendsen (COO)

BERGENBIO ASA
Mollendalsbakken 9, PO Box 2324,
5009, Bergen, Norway
Tel.: (47) 55961159
Web Site: https://www.bergenbio.com
Year Founded: 2007
BGBIO—(OSL)
Rev.: $35,932
Assets: $15,398,670
Liabilities: $7,224,090
Net Worth: $8,174,580
Earnings: ($27,907,076)
Emp.: 29
Fiscal Year-end: 12/31/22
Pharmaceuticals Product Mfr
N.A.I.C.S.: 325412
Sveinung Hole (Chm)

Subsidiaries:

BerGenBio Limited   (1)
Magdalen Centre Robert Robinson Avenue
The Oxford Science Park, Oxford, OX4
4GA, United Kingdom
Tel.: (44) 1865784588
Pharmaceutical Drug Mfr
N.A.I.C.S.: 325412

BERGER HOLDING GMBH
Aussere Spitalhofstrasse 19, 94036,
Passau, Germany
Tel.: (49) 8518060   De
Web Site:
   http://www.bergerholding.eu
Holding Company; Construction Services
N.A.I.C.S.: 551112
Hermann Bock (Member-Mgmt Bd)

Subsidiaries:

BERGER BAU GmbH   (1)
Aussere Spitalhofstrasse 19, D-94036, Passau, Germany   (100%)
Tel.: (49) 8518060
Web Site: http://www.bergerbau.eu
Commercial, Industrial & Civil Engineering
Construction Services
N.A.I.C.S.: 236220

Subsidiary (Domestic):

Flugplatz Werneuchen GmbH   (2)
Alte Hirschfelder Str 6, 16356, Werneuchen,
Germany
Tel.: (49) 177 300 500 2
Web Site: http://www.flugplatz-werneuchen.de

Construction Engineering Services
N.A.I.C.S.: 541330

autobahnplus Services GmbH   (2)
Neulwirth 1, 86453, Dasing, Germany
Tel.: (49) 8205 96350 200
Web Site: http://www.autobahnplus.de
Construction Engineering Services
N.A.I.C.S.: 541330

BERGER BAU POLSKA Sp. z
o.o.   (1)
ul Szczecinska 11, 54-517, Wroclaw, Poland
Tel.: (48) 71 356 68 00
Construction Engineering Services
N.A.I.C.S.: 541330
Maciej Gala (Mgr-Site)

BERGER BETON GmbH   (1)
Aussere Spitalhofstrasse 19, Passau,
94036, Germany   (100%)
Tel.: (49) 8518060
Web Site: http://www.bergerbeton.eu
Sales Range: $150-199.9 Million
Emp.: 500
Ready-Mix Concrete, Asphalt, Mortar, Cement & Other Related Products Mfr & Contractor Services
N.A.I.C.S.: 327320

Subsidiary (Non-US):

Die Alpenpumpe GmbH   (2)
Stampfergasse 15, 5541, Altenmarkt, Austria
Tel.: (43) 810 810411
Web Site: http://www.die-alpenpumpe.at
Readymix Concrete Mfr
N.A.I.C.S.: 327320

Subsidiary (Domestic):

Donau-Mortel GmbH & Co. KG   (2)
Gewerbering Furstdobl 21, 94127, Neuburg
am Inn, Germany
Tel.: (49) 8507 217
Web Site: http://www.donau-moertel.de
Readymix Concrete Mfr
N.A.I.C.S.: 327320

Geirhos-Beton GmbH   (2)
Unterfeldweg 2, 86517, Wehringen, Germany
Tel.: (49) 8234 904 9544
Readymix Concrete Mfr
N.A.I.C.S.: 327320

Isar-Donau-Mortel GmbH & Co.
KG   (2)
Robert - Bosch - Strasse 8, 94447, Plattling, Germany
Tel.: (49) 99 31 20 26
Readymix Concrete Mfr
N.A.I.C.S.: 327320

Munchner Mortel GmbH & Co.
KG   (2)
Gerner Str 50, 80638, Munich, Germany
Tel.: (49) 89 456012 80
Web Site: http://www.muenchnermoertel.de
Readymix Concrete Mfr
N.A.I.C.S.: 327320

Regensburger Frischmortel GmbH &
Co.KG   (2)
Bahnhofstrasse 24a, 93087, Alteglofsheim,
Germany
Tel.: (49) 94 06 34 63
Readymix Concrete Mfr
N.A.I.C.S.: 327320

COMAIR Reise und Charter
GmbH   (1)
Am Flugplatz, 94474, Vilshofen an der
Donau, Germany
Tel.: (49) 851 8061170
Aircraft Charter Services
N.A.I.C.S.: 481212

EUROKONTOR s.r.o.   (1)
Torvarenska 3/B, 901 01, Malacky, Slovakia
Tel.: (421) 34 773 16 99
Web Site: http://www.eurokontor.sk
Automobile Spare Parts Mfr
N.A.I.C.S.: 336390

Eurosond GmbH   (1)
Pressather Strasse 95, 92637, Weiden,
Germany
Tel.: (49) 961 38 158 0

Web Site: http://www.eurosand.de
Construction Engineering Services
N.A.I.C.S.: 541330

Ladce Beton s.r.o.   (1)
Dolnozemska 13, 850 07, Bratislava, Slovakia
Tel.: (421) 42 4603 107
Web Site: http://www.ladcebeton.sk
Readymix Concrete Mfr
N.A.I.C.S.: 327320

Povazska Cementaren a.s.   (1)
Ul Janka Krala, 018 63, Ladce, Slovakia
Tel.: (421) 42 4603 111
Web Site: http://www.pcla.sk
Cement Mfr
N.A.I.C.S.: 327310

BERGER KAROSSERIE- UND FAHRZEUGBAU GMBH
Schmidtstrasse 49, 60326, Frankfurt,
Germany
Tel.: (49) 69759030
Web Site: http://www.berger-frankfurt.de
Rev.: $13,750,559
Emp.: 112
Vehicle Bodies Mfr
N.A.I.C.S.: 336390
Dierk Conrad (Mng Dir-Vehicle Sls)

BERGER PAINTS BANGLADESH LIMITED
Berger House House 8 Road 2 Sector 3, Uttara Model Town, Dhaka,
1230, Bangladesh
Tel.: (880) 28953665   BD
Web Site: https://www.bergerbd.com
Year Founded: 1973
BERGERPBL—(CHT)
Rev.: $239,452,510
Assets: $228,978,818
Liabilities: $98,035,775
Net Worth: $130,943,042
Earnings: $29,580,459
Fiscal Year-end: 03/31/24
Paints Mfr
N.A.I.C.S.: 325510
Rupali Chowdhury (Mng Dir)

Subsidiaries:

Jenson & Nicholson (Bangladesh)
Limited   (1)
House- 8 Road- 2 Sector- 3, Uttara Model
Town, Dhaka, Bangladesh
Tel.: (880) 1844147401
Web Site: http://www.jnbl.com.bd
Metal Container Mfr
N.A.I.C.S.: 332439
Gerald K. Adams (Chm)

BERGER PAINTS INDIA LIMITED
Berger House 129 Park Street, Kolkata, 700017, India
Tel.: (91) 3322299724
Web Site:
   http://www.bergerpaints.com
Year Founded: 1760
012529—(KOL)
Rev.: $1,204,799,505
Assets: $984,528,090
Liabilities: $447,515,250
Net Worth: $537,012,840
Earnings: $113,697,675
Emp.: 3,931
Fiscal Year-end: 03/30/22
Paints Mfr & Marketer
N.A.I.C.S.: 325510
Kuldip Singh Dhingra (Chm)

Subsidiaries:

Berger Jenson & Nicholson (Nepal)
Private Limited   (1)
Berger House 492 Tinkune Koteshwor,
Kathmandu, Nepal
Tel.: (977) 15199463
Web Site: https://www.bergernepal.com
Paint Product Mfr

Berger Paints India Limited—(Continued)
N.A.I.C.S.: 325510

Bolix S.A. (1)
ul Stolarska 8, 34-300, Zywiec, Poland
Tel.: (48) 334750600
Web Site: https://bolix.pl
Sales Range: $50-74.9 Million
Paints Mfr
N.A.I.O.U.: 325510
Maciej Korbasiewicz (CEO)

Bolix Ukraina Sp. z o.o. (1)
Street Industrial 10, Vyshneve, Ukraine
Tel.: (380) 50 417 7766
Web Site: https://www.bolix.ua
Paint Product Mfr
N.A.I.C.S.: 325510

SBL Specialty Coatings Private Limited (1)
Unit-1, Haibatpur Road, Dera Bassi, 140 507, Punjab, India
Tel.: (91) 1762522101
Web Site: https://www.sblcoatings.com
Paint Coating Mfr & Distr
N.A.I.C.S.: 325510
Anil Kumar Mehrotra (Mng Dir)

Soltherm External Insulations Limited (1)
Challenge House Sherwood Drive, Bletchley, Milton Keynes, MK3 6DP, United Kingdom
Tel.: (44) 1908533444
Web Site: https://soltherm.webflow.io
Building Material Mfr & Distr
N.A.I.C.S.: 327120
Stephen Gapik (Mng Dir)

Surefire Management Services Ltd. (1)
Unit 1 Denbigh Hall, Denbigh Industrial Estate, Bletchley, MK3 7QT, United Kingdom
Tel.: (44) 1908803776
Web Site: https://www.surefirems.co.uk
Construction Services
N.A.I.C.S.: 236220

BERGER PAINTS NIGERIA PLC.
102 Oba Akran Avenue, PMB 21052, Ikeja Industrial Estate Ikeja, Lagos, Nigeria
Tel.: (234) 012805167
Web Site:
  https://www.bergerpaintsnig.com
Year Founded: 1959
BERGER—(NIGE)
Rev.: $4,686,662
Assets: $4,092,205
Liabilities: $1,632,198
Net Worth: $2,460,007
Earnings: $154,457
Emp.: 127
Fiscal Year-end: 12/31/22
Paint Mfr & Distr
N.A.I.C.S.: 325510
Abi Allison Ayida (Chm)

BERGER PAINTS PAKISTAN LIMITED
36 Industrial Estate Kot Lakhpat, Lahore, Pakistan
Tel.: (92) 4235151545
Web Site: https://www.berger.com.pk
BERG—(KAR)
Rev.: $36,764,788
Assets: $31,211,324
Liabilities: $19,864,992
Net Worth: $11,346,331
Earnings: $723,924
Emp.: 737
Fiscal Year-end: 06/30/19
Paints Mfr
N.A.I.C.S.: 339940
Maqbool H. H. Rahimtoola (Chm)

BERGER PAINTS SINGAPORE PTE LTD
22 Benoi Sector, Singapore, 629854, Singapore

Tel.: (65) 62615224
Web Site:
  http://www.bergeronline.com
Year Founded: 1939
Sales Range: $50-74.9 Million
Emp.: 150
Paint Varnish & Supplies Whslr
N.A.I.C.S.: 424950
Jaideep Nandi (CEO)

BERGMAN & BEVING AB
Cardellgatan 1, 114 36, Stockholm, Sweden
Tel.: (46) 104547700   SE
Web Site:
  https://www.bergmanbeving.com
Year Founded: 1906
BERG-B—(OMX)
Rev.: $558,393,920
Assets: $646,413,600
Liabilities: $412,630,400
Net Worth: $233,783,200
Earnings: $24,416,000
Emp.: 1,245
Fiscal Year-end: 03/31/22
Industrial & Construction Tools Distr
N.A.I.C.S.: 423830
Pontus Boman (Exec VP & Head-Building Materials Div)

Subsidiaries:

BSafe Systems AS (1)
Bekkeveien 9, 3236, Sandefjord, Norway
Tel.: (47) 33426200
Web Site: https://bsafe.no
Marking Machine Mfr & Distr
N.A.I.C.S.: 333248

Bergman & Beving Development AB (1)
Box 10024, 100 55, Stockholm, Sweden
Tel.: (46) 8 623 61 00
Business Development Services
N.A.I.C.S.: 561499

Bergman & Beving Fastigheter AB (1)
Box 10024, 100 55, Stockholm, Sweden
Tel.: (46) 86601030
Real Estate Investment, Development & Property Management
N.A.I.C.S.: 531390

Bergman & Beving Invest AB (1)
Box 10024, 100 55, Stockholm, Sweden
Tel.: (46) 104547700
Investment Activities
N.A.I.C.S.: 523999
Ulf Lilius (Mgr)

Bergman & Beving Safety AB (1)
Karlsnas Industriomrade Vistaforsvagen 3, 523 37, Ulricehamn, Sweden
Tel.: (46) 321677300
Web Site: http://www.skydda.com
Holding Company; Personal Protection Products Distr
N.A.I.C.S.: 551112
Lars Jonas Peterson (Mng Dir)

Subsidiary (Domestic):

Skydda i Sverige AB (2)
Vistaforsvagen 3, 523 85, Ulricehamn, Sweden
Tel.: (46) 321677300
Personal Protection Products Distr
N.A.I.C.S.: 423990

DigiPrint AS (1)
Bekkeveien 9, 3236, Sandefjord, Norway
Tel.: (47) 40006325
Web Site: https://digiprint.no
Industrial Marking Product Mfr & Distr
N.A.I.C.S.: 333248

Essve Produkter AB (1)
Sidensvansvagen 10, PO Box 770, 191 27, Sollentuna, Stockholm, Sweden
Tel.: (46) 86236100
Web Site: http://www.essve.com
Sales Range: $50-74.9 Million
Emp.: 52
Industrial Tools & Fire Seals Distr
N.A.I.C.S.: 423840

Per Lind (Mgr-Export)

Luna AB (1)
Sandbergsvagen 3, 441 39, Alingsas, Vastra Gotaland, Sweden
Tel.: (46) 322606260
Web Site: http://www.luna.se
Sales Range: $50-74.9 Million
Emp.: 250
Industrial Tools Mfr
N.A.I.C.S.: 333517

Outreach Organisation Ltd. (1)
Tan-y-Bwlch Centre, Llanllechid, Bangor, LL57 3HY, Gwynedd, United Kingdom
Tel.: (44) 1248601546
Web Site: https://www.outreachrescue.com
Rescue Training Services
N.A.I.C.S.: 611699

Safe Time, Spol. s.r.o. (1)
Partizanska cesta 89, 974 01, Banska Bystrica, Slovakia
Tel.: (421) 484147074
Web Site: https://www.crestosafety.sk
Fall Protection Equipment Mfr & Distr
N.A.I.C.S.: 332999

Screen Tryck AB (1)
Skrittgatan 10, 213 77, Malmo, Sweden
Tel.: (46) 406714780
Web Site: https://3screen.nu
Graphic Product Mfr & Distr
N.A.I.C.S.: 323113

BERGOS AG
Kreuzstrasse 5, 8008, Zurich, Switzerland
Tel.: (41) 44 284 2120
Web Site: http://www.bergos.ch
Sales Range: $1-9.9 Million
Emp.: 30
Banking Services
N.A.I.C.S.: 522110
Markus Zwyssig (Mng Partner)

BERICAP GMBH & CO. KG
Kirchstr 5, 55257, Budenheim, Germany
Tel.: (49) 6139 2902 0   De
Web Site: http://www.bericap.com
Sales Range: $800-899.9 Million
Emp.: 3,535
Plastic Bottle Cap & Other Closure Mfr & Distr
N.A.I.C.S.: 326199
Jorg Thiels (Mng Dir)

Subsidiaries:

Al Kawthar Company (1)
PO Box 7771, Jeddah, 21472, Saudi Arabia
Tel.: (966) 126364337
Web Site: http://www.alkawther.com
Water Treatment Equipment & Services
N.A.I.C.S.: 333310

Almer Ltd. (1)
Vrajdebna 15 Chelopeshko Shose str, Industrial District, Sofia, 1839, Bulgaria
Tel.: (359) 24512020
Web Site: http://www.almer-bg.com
Food Process Ingredient Packing Mfr
N.A.I.C.S.: 311999
Dimitrina Shuleva (COO)

Amir Semel Packaging & Chemicals Ltd. (1)
10 Elimelech St, PO Box 2549, 52124, Ramat Gan, Israel
Tel.: (972) 36731127
Chemical & Mineral Product Mfr
N.A.I.C.S.: 325998
Amir Semel (Mgr)

Amwaal Trade & Engineering Co., Ltd. (1)
Alshaar Building-Ground Glour Khartoum East-2l October St, Khartoum, Sudan
Tel.: (249) 183769078
Plastic Closure Mfr
N.A.I.C.S.: 326199

BEKOMOLD Werkzeugbau GmbH (1)
Bojtar u 74, 1037, Budapest, Hungary
Tel.: (36) 14392460

Plastic Closure Mfr
N.A.I.C.S.: 326199
Gabor Goz (Engr-Mechanical)

BERICAP (Kunshan) Co. Ltd (1)
298 South Qing Yang Road Kunshan Economic Technical Development Zone, Kunshan, 215 300, Jiangsu, China
Tel.: (86) 512 5771 6868
Plastic Cap & Closure Mfr
N.A.I.C.S.: 326199

BERICAP Asia Pte. Ltd. (1)
73 Kim Yam Road 01-01, Singapore, 239370, Singapore
Tel.: (65) 62227666
Plastic Closure Mfr
N.A.I.C.S.: 326199

BERICAP Asia Pte. Ltd. (1)
Unit 16 No 23 Phung Khac Khoan Street, Da Kao Ward District 1, Ho Chi Minh City, Vietnam
Tel.: (84) 2838224666
Plastic Closure Mfr
N.A.I.C.S.: 326199

BERICAP Benelux B.V. (1)
Minervum 7006, 4817 ZL, Breda, Netherlands
Tel.: (31) 76 7920020
Plastic Cap & Closure Mfr
N.A.I.C.S.: 326199

BERICAP East Africa Ltd. (1)
Swastik Business Park Warehouse Number 1, Nairobi, Kenya
Tel.: (254) 720604413
Plastic Closure Mfr
N.A.I.C.S.: 326199

BERICAP Egypt JSC (1)
Plot 66 Extension of Industrial Zone 6th, PO Box 48, 12573, Cairo, Egypt
Tel.: (20) 3824 3171
Plastic Cap & Closure Mfr
N.A.I.C.S.: 326199
Tarek Sultan (Gen Mgr)

BERICAP India Pvt. Ltd. (1)
Plot No A-6 Talegaon MIDC Navlak Umbre, Maval Dist, Pune, 410507, Maharashtra, India
Tel.: (91) 2114 661100
Plastic Cap & Closure Mfr
N.A.I.C.S.: 326199
Rajendra Mahadik (Dir-Mfg)

BERICAP Kapak Sanayi A.S. (1)
Celikoglu C No 153, Gebze, 41 700, Kocaeli, Turkiye
Tel.: (90) 262 653 25 90
Plastic Cap & Closure Mfr
N.A.I.C.S.: 326199
Cuneyt Bayraktar (Mgr-Sls)

BERICAP Kazakhstan Ltd. (1)
Zhansugurov street 3 B Otegen Batyr Village, Ili district, 040700, Almaty, Kazakhstan
Tel.: (7) 727 387 9271
Plastic Cap & Closure Mfr
N.A.I.C.S.: 326199

BERICAP Malaysia Sdn. Bhd. (1)
59 Jalan i-Park Kawasan Jaya, Perindustrian i-Park Bandar Indahpura, 81000, Kulai, Johor, Malaysia
Tel.: (60) 76607666
Plastic Closure Mfr
N.A.I.C.S.: 326199

BERICAP Mexico, S. de R.L. de C.V. (1)
Av Tlaloc S/N Edificio 2 Colonia Axotlan, Parque Industrial O'Donnell Puente Mexico, Cuautitlan Izcalli, 54719, Estado de Mexico, Mexico
Tel.: (52) 5586258900
Plastic Closure Mfr
N.A.I.C.S.: 326199
Jose Leonardo Serrano (Ops Mgr)

BERICAP Middle East FZE (1)
Mr Erden Ayalp Jebel Ali Free Zone South 1 No FZ 31AA02, PO Box 262497, Dubai, United Arab Emirates
Tel.: (971) 4 880 7022
Plastic Cap & Closure Mfr
N.A.I.C.S.: 326199

BERICAP North America, Inc. (1)

835 Syscon Court, Burlington, L7L 6C5,
ON, Canada
Tel.: (905) 634-2248
Sales Range: $50-74.9 Million
Emp.: 140
Plastic Bottle Cap & Other Packaging En-
closure Products Mfr & Distr
N.A.I.C.S.: 326199

Subsidiary (US):

BERICAP, LLC   (2)
1671 Champagne Ave Ste B, Ontario, CA
91761-3650
Tel.: (909) 390-5518
Web Site: http://www.bericap.com
Plastic Bottle Cap & Other Packaging En-
closure Products Mfr & Distr
N.A.I.C.S.: 326199

Subsidiary (Domestic):

BERICAP SC LLC   (3)
1300 Mount Olive Rd, Cowpens, SC 29330
Tel.: (864) 463-1967
Emp.: 100
Plastic Cap & Closure Mfr
N.A.I.C.S.: 326199

BERICAP Polska Sp. z o.o.   (1)
Ul Struzanska 12, Stanislawow Pierwszy,
05-126, Nieporet, Poland
Tel.: (48) 22 774 70 50
Plastic Cap & Closure Mfr
N.A.I.C.S.: 326199

BERICAP Romania S.R.L.   (1)
Str Sferei nr 2 Parcul Industrial Ploiesti SA,
100213, Ploiesti, jud Prahova, Romania
Tel.: (40) 244 338 030
Plastic Cap & Closure Mfr
N.A.I.C.S.: 326199
Tiberiu Bako (Mng Dir)

BERICAP S.A.   (1)
Ruta 5 km 75, Jauregui, B6706XAA, Bue-
nos Aires, Argentina
Tel.: (54) 2323 497596
Plastic Cap & Closure Mfr
N.A.I.C.S.: 326199

BERICAP S.A.U.   (1)
Pol Ind Can Font c/ Isaac Peral s/n, La
Roca del Valles, 08430, Barcelona, Spain
Tel.: (34) 938424722
Plastic Closure Mfr
N.A.I.C.S.: 326199

BERICAP S.R.L.   (1)
Via C Colombo 6/C, 20066, Melzo, Milano,
Italy
Tel.: (39) 02 95 73 12 80
Web Site: http://www.bericap.com
Emp.: 5
Plastic Cap & Closure Mfr
N.A.I.C.S.: 326199
Antonio De Rochis (Gen Mgr)

BERICAP Sarl   (1)
1 Bd Eiffel ZI Dijon Longvic, BP 96, 21603,
Longvic, Cedex, France
Tel.: (33) 3 80 63 29 31
Plastic Cap & Closure Mfr
N.A.I.C.S.: 326199

BERICAP Singapore Pte Ltd   (1)
14 Ang Mo Kio Street 63 Block B, Singa-
pore, 569116, Singapore
Tel.: (65) 6222 76 66
Plastic Cap & Closure Mfr
N.A.I.C.S.: 326199

BERICAP UK Ltd.   (1)
Oslo Road Sutton Fields Industrial Estate,
Hull, HU7 0YN, United Kingdom
Tel.: (44) 1482 82 66 66
Emp.: 200
Plastic Cap & Closure Mfr
N.A.I.C.S.: 326199

BERICAP ZARODASTECHNIKAI
B.T.   (1)
Aszalvolgyi u 13, 8000, Szekesfehervar,
Hungary
Tel.: (36) 22 887 500
Plastic Closure Distr
N.A.I.C.S.: 326199

BERICAP Zhuhai Co., Ltd.   (1)
No 9 QingNian Road, HongQi Town Jinwan
District, Zhuhai, China

Tel.: (86) 7567686599
Plastic Closure Mfr
N.A.I.C.S.: 326199

BERICAP d.o.o.   (1)
Bulevar Cara Lazara 44/IV lokal 4 5, 21000,
Novi Sad, Serbia
Tel.: (381) 21 4750 909
Plastic Cap & Closure Mfr
N.A.I.C.S.: 326199

BERICAP do Brasil Ltda.   (1)
Av Parana 2870 B Cajuru do Sul, Soro-
caba, 18105-000, Sao Paulo, Brazil
Tel.: (55) 15 3235 4500
Plastic Closure Mfr & Distr
N.A.I.C.S.: 326199
Fernando Seabra (Plant Mgr)

Bericap S.A. - Buenos Aires
Plant   (1)
Fondo de la Legua 1111 - Floor 2 A Marti-
nez, San Isidro, B1607BJD, Buenos Aires,
Argentina
Tel.: (54) 11524533878
Plastic Closure Mfr
N.A.I.C.S.: 326199

Bevpac Company Limited   (1)
123 Central Hotel Annexe, Karachi, Paki-
stan
Tel.: (92) 214556817
Plastic Closure Mfr
N.A.I.C.S.: 326199

Borealmagic Unipessoal, Lda.   (1)
Rua do Capelo 63, Perosinho, 4415-015,
Vila Nova de Gaia, Portugal
Tel.: (351) 917504996
Plastic Closure Mfr
N.A.I.C.S.: 326199

Caribbean Caps & Containers
Ltd.   (1)
1-3 Golden Grove Road, Piarco, Trinidad &
Tobago
Tel.: (868) 6692225
Plastic Closure Mfr
N.A.I.C.S.: 326199
Philippe Bruchet (Owner)

Dwewang International Corp.   (1)
Seoul IT Valley 207 Sungsu-dong 1 ga 13-
164, Sungdong-gu, Seoul, Korea (South)
Tel.: (82) 25113440
Plastic Closure Mfr
N.A.I.C.S.: 326199

E. Callsen & Co. A.S.   (1)
Strandvejen 130, 2900, Hellerup, Denmark
Tel.: (45) 33369090
Web Site: http://www.callsen.dk
Packaging Material Whslr
N.A.I.C.S.: 424130

Interpak SN SA   (1)
Cite Hamo II Villa N S-65 Rond Point Case
Bi, BP 23424, Dakar, Senegal
Tel.: (221) 338558008
Plastic Closure Mfr
N.A.I.C.S.: 326199

Marina for Industrial Solutions
Co.   (1)
Alsalameh Street Building 11, Amman, Jor-
dan
Tel.: (962) 64200940
Plastic Closure Mfr
N.A.I.C.S.: 326199

Modern Trading & Services
SARL   (1)
Zouk Michael Centre Khoury and Bitar-2nd
Floor, Beirut, Lebanon
Tel.: (961) 9222118
Web Site: http://www.mts-leb.com
Plastic Closure Mfr
N.A.I.C.S.: 326199
Maroun Chaccour (Ops Mgr)

O.O.O BERICAP   (1)
ul Koltsova 71, 606440, Bor, Russia
Tel.: (7) 83159 67727
Web Site: http://www.bericap.com
Emp.: 130
Plastic Cap & Closure Mfr
N.A.I.C.S.: 326199
Serge Litskevitch (Gen Mgr)

O.O.O. BERICAP   (1)
ul Smolnaya 9B 3rd floor office 6 7, 03680,

Kiev, Ukraine
Tel.: (380) 44 257 8166
Plastic Cap & Closure Mfr
N.A.I.C.S.: 326199

Peter Henningsen S.A.C.   (1)
Av Del Pinar 152 Oficina 405 Urb Chacarilla
del Estanque, Santiago de Surco, Lima,
Peru
Tel.: (51) 17178686
Web Site: http://www.phperu.com
Industrial Packing Machinery & Equipment
Distr
N.A.I.C.S.: 423830

Polydakis Ltd.   (1)
17 Filikis Eterias Str, 152 32, Halandri, Ath-
ens, Greece
Tel.: (30) 2105200575
Plastic Closure Mfr
N.A.I.C.S.: 326199
Emmanuel Polydakis (Mgr)

Polyprint Ltd.   (1)
Opposite New Ash Foam, North Industrial
Area, Accra, Ghana
Tel.: (233) 302253200
Plastic Closure Mfr
N.A.I.C.S.: 326199

Sealcoat Technologies LLC   (1)
2730 SW 3rd Ave Ste 601, Miami, FL
33129
Tel.: (305) 858-8774
Ingredient Packaging & Equipment Mfr
N.A.I.C.S.: 333993
Alexander Meyer (Pres)

TCL Hofmann Pty. Ltd.   (1)
150 Woodlands Drive, Braeside, 3195, VIC,
Australia
Tel.: (61) 385862900
Web Site: http://www.tclhofmann.com.au
Plastic Closure Mfr & Distr
N.A.I.C.S.: 326199
Ryan Naylor (Mgr-Sls, Pkg & Industrial)

TCL Hunt Limited   (1)
7-9 Fisher Crescent, Mount Wellington,
Auckland, 1060, New Zealand
Tel.: (64) 95262700
Web Site: http://www.tclhunt.co.nz
Nondurable Goods Merchant Whslr
N.A.I.C.S.: 424990
Robin Mckay (Bus Mgr)

Tradcorp S.A.   (1)
Av Dagoberto Godoy 182, Cerrillos, Chile
Tel.: (56) 229374922
Web Site: http://www.tradcorp.com
Packaging Material Distr
N.A.I.C.S.: 424130

Vitis d.o.o.   (1)
Jalkovec B Radic 52c, 42000, Varazdin,
Croatia
Tel.: (385) 42211035
Plastic Closure Mfr
N.A.I.C.S.: 326199
Mladen Misak (Owner)

Young's Corporation   (1)
3rd Floor YoungJoo B/D 242-8 Yangjae-
dong, Seocho-gu, Seoul, 137-130, Korea
(South)
Tel.: (82) 25551040
Plastic Closure Mfr
N.A.I.C.S.: 326199

BERINGER CAPITAL

141 Adelaide Street West Suite 750,
Toronto, M5H 3L5, ON, Canada
Tel.: (416) 928-2166
Web Site:
http://www.beringercapital.com
Year Founded: 1990
Privater Equity Firm
N.A.I.C.S.: 523999
Lu Cacioppo (Mng Partner)

Subsidiaries:

Blue Acorn, LLC   (1)
145 Williman St, Charleston, SC 29403
Tel.: (877) 944-2583
Web Site: http://www.blueacorn.com
ECommerce Agency
N.A.I.C.S.: 541890

Inman Group, LLC   (1)

1400 Vlg Sq Blvd Ste 3-80368, Tallahassee,
FL 32312
Tel.: (510) 658-9252
Web Site: http://www.inman.com
Sales Range: $1-9.9 Million
Emp.: 22
Real Estate Brokerage Services
N.A.I.C.S.: 531210
Bradley Inman (Chm)

BERJAYA ASSETS BERHAD

Lot 08-16 Level 8 Berjaya Times
Square No 1 Jalan Imbi, PO Box 08-
23, 55100, Kuala Lumpur, Malaysia
Tel.: (60) 351022999
Web Site: https://www.berjaya.com
Year Founded: 1960
BJASSET—(KLS)
Rev.: $43,078,860
Assets: $768,657,533
Liabilities: $305,218,485
Net Worth: $463,439,048
Earnings: ($13,829,805)
Fiscal Year-end: 06/30/22
Lottery Consultancy & Forecasting
Services
N.A.I.C.S.: 713290
Wira Ek seang Lye (Exec Dir)

Subsidiaries:

Berjaya Times Square Sdn. Bhd.   (1)
Lot 08-20 Level 8 Berjaya Time Square, PO
Box 08-33, No 1 Jalan Imbi, 55100, Kuala
Lumpur, Malaysia   (100%)
Tel.: (60) 321449821
Web Site: https://berjayatimessquarekl.com
Emp.: 50
Shopping Center Rental Services
N.A.I.C.S.: 531120

Subsidiary (Domestic):

Berjaya Times Square Theme Park
Sdn Bhd   (2)
No 09 103 9th Floor Berjaya Times Square
No 1 Jalan Imbi, 55100, Kuala Lumpur,
Federal Territory, Malaysia
Tel.: (60) 321173118
Web Site:
    https://berjayatimessquarethemeparkkl.com
Sales Range: $50-74.9 Million
Theme Park & Cinema Theatre Operation
Services
N.A.I.C.S.: 713110
Tian Keng Swee (Gen Mgr)

Berjaya Waterfront Sdn. Bhd.   (1)
88 Jalan Ibrahim Sultan, Johor Darul
Takzim, 80300, Johor Bahru, Malaysia
Tel.: (60) 72218000
Web Site:
    https://www.berjayawaterfront.com.my
Hotel & Resort Operator
N.A.I.C.S.: 721120

Natural Avenue Sdn. Bhd.   (1)
No 273 - 274 Lot 2545 - 2546 Central Park
Commercial Centre, Off Jalan Rock, 93250,
Kuching, Sarawak, Malaysia
Tel.: (60) 82233466
Web Site: https://www.cashsweep.com.my
Sales Range: $50-74.9 Million
Emp.: 84
Lottery Operating Services
N.A.I.C.S.: 713290

Natural Avenue Sdn. Bhd.   (1)
No 273 - 274 Lot 2545 - 2546 Central Park
Commercial Centre, Off Jalan Rock, 93250,
Kuching, Sarawak, Malaysia
Tel.: (60) 82233466
Web Site: https://www.cashsweep.com.my
Sales Range: $50-74.9 Million
Emp.: 84
Lottery Operating Services
N.A.I.C.S.: 713290

Natural Avenue Sdn. Bhd.   (1)
No 273 - 274 Lot 2545 - 2546 Central Park
Commercial Centre, Off Jalan Rock, 93250,
Kuching, Sarawak, Malaysia
Tel.: (60) 82233466
Web Site: https://www.cashsweep.com.my
Sales Range: $50-74.9 Million
Emp.: 84
Lottery Operating Services

Berjaya Assets Berhad—(Continued)

N.A.I.C.S.: 713290

Natural Avenue Sdn. Bhd. (1)
No 273 - 274 Lot 2545 - 2546 Central Park
Commercial Centre, Off Jalan Rock, 93250,
Kuching, Sarawak, Malaysia
Tel.: (60) 82233466
Web Site: https://www.cashsweep.com.my
Sales Range: $50-74.9 Million
Emp.: 84
Lottery Operating Services
N.A.I.C.S.: 713290

Oriental Assemblers Sdn. Bhd. (1)
99 & 99A-C Jalan Tampoi, Johor Bahru,
Johor, 81200, Malaysia
Tel.: (60) 72361400
Automobile Mfr
N.A.I.C.S.: 336390

BERJAYA CORPORATION BERHAD

Level 12 East Wing Berjaya Times
Square No 1 Jalan Imbi, 55100,
Kuala Lumpur, Malaysia
Tel.: (60) 321491999   MY
Web Site: https://www.berjaya.com
Year Founded: 1967
BJCORP—(KLS)
Rev.: $2,018,396,903
Assets: $5,061,515,580
Liabilities: $2,863,940,558
Net Worth: $2,197,575,023
Earnings: $5,814,518
Emp.: 11,089
Fiscal Year-end: 06/30/22
Property Development, Entertainment
Management & Financial Services
N.A.I.C.S.: 721110
Robin Tan Yeong Ching (CEO)

Subsidiaries:

ANSA Hotel KL Sdn Bhd (1)
No 101 Jalan Bukit Bintang, 55100, Kuala
Lumpur, Malaysia
Tel.: (60) 321465000
Web Site: http://www.ansahotels.com
Hotel Services
N.A.I.C.S.: 721110

**Asia Jet Partners Malaysia Sdn
Bhd** (1)
Lot AM 1 Skypark Subang Terminal Lapan-
gan Terbang, Sultan Abdul Aziz Shah,
47200, Subang Jaya, Selangor, Malaysia
Tel.: (60) 378451888
Web Site: http://www.asiajet.com.my
Aircraft Management Services
N.A.I.C.S.: 488190
Stutijn Van Till (CEO)

Asia Jet Sdn. Bhd. (1)
Lot M6 & M7 Mezzanine Floor Skypark Ter-
minal, Sultan Abdul Aziz Shah Airport,
47200, Subang Jaya, Malaysia
Tel.: (60) 378451888
Web Site: https://www.asiajet.com.my
Oil Transportation Services
N.A.I.C.S.: 532411

**Berjaya Beau Vallon Bay Beach Re-
sort Limited** (1)
PO Box 550, Victoria, Mahe, Seychelles
Tel.: (248) 4287287
Web Site: https://www.berjayahotel.com
Hotel Services
N.A.I.C.S.: 721110

Berjaya Books Sdn Bhd (1)
Lot 16 Ground Floor The Curve No 6 Jalan
PJU 7/4, Mutiara Damansara, 47810, Petal-
ing Jaya, Malaysia
Tel.: (60) 377258412
Web Site: https://www.borders.net.my
Book Store Services
N.A.I.C.S.: 459210

Berjaya China Motor Sdn Bhd (1)
Lot 3 Jalan 225 Section 51A, 46100, Petal-
ing Jaya, Selangor, Malaysia
Tel.: (60) 379541188
Web Site: https://www.bcmgroup.com.my
Motor Vehicle Mfr & Distr
N.A.I.C.S.: 336110

Berjaya Food Supreme Sdn Bhd (1)
Tel.: (673) 60320525888
Restaurant Services
N.A.I.C.S.: 722511

Berjaya Food Trading Sdn Bhd (1)
Level 10 Berjaya Times Square No 1 Jalan
Imbi, 55100 KL, Kuala Lumpur, Malaysia
Tel.: (60) 1300808989
Web Site: https://berjayafood.com
Restaurant Services
N.A.I.C.S.: 722511

Berjaya Group Berhad (1)
Lot 13-01a Level 13 East Wing Berjaya
Times Square No 1 Jalan Imbi, Kuala Lum-
pur, 55100, Malaysia
Tel.: (60) 321491999
Web Site: http://www.berjaya.com.my
Holding Company
N.A.I.C.S.: 551112
Dato Robin Tan (Chm)

Subsidiary (Domestic):

**Academy of Nursing (M) Sdn
Bhd** (2)
10th Floor Berjaya Times Square Jln Imbi,
55100, Kuala Lumpur, Wilayah Persekutu-
an, Malaysia
Tel.: (60) 3 2148 8068
Emp.: 10
Nursing Educational Services
N.A.I.C.S.: 611710
Kanandran Arulrajah (CEO)

BLoyalty Sdn Bhd (2)
16th Floor Menara Cosway 12 Jalan Imbi,
55100, Kuala Lumpur, Malaysia
Tel.: (60) 321418080
Web Site: http://www.binfinite.com.my
Loyalty Program Operation Services
N.A.I.C.S.: 541618

**Berjaya 2nd Homes (MM2H) Sdn
Bhd** (2)
02-20 Level 2 West Wing Berjaya Times
Square No1 Jln Imbi, Kuala Lumpur, 55100,
Malaysia
Tel.: (60) 321428028
Web Site:
    http://www.berjayaproperties.com.my
Sales Range: $50-74.9 Million
Emp.: 1
Property Development Services
N.A.I.C.S.: 531390
Mah Siew Wan (Sr Gen Mgr)

Berjaya Capital Berhad (2)
Berjaya Times Square, 1 Jalan Imbi, Kuala
Lumpur, 55100, Malaysia
Tel.: (60) 321491999
Web Site: http://www.berjaya.com
Sales Range: $50-74.9 Million
Emp.: 700
Investment Holding Company
N.A.I.C.S.: 551112
Swee Hong Su (Sec)

Subsidiary (Domestic):

Inter-Pacific Capital Sdn Bhd (3)
West Wing Level 13 Berjaya Times Square
No 1 Jalan Imbi, Kuala Lumpur, 55100,
Malaysia
Tel.: (60) 321211888
Web Site: http://www.interpac.com.my
Sales Range: $25-49.9 Million
Emp.: 50
Online Trading Services
N.A.I.C.S.: 541613
Tan Mun Choy (Exec Dir)

Subsidiary (Domestic):

Inter-Pacific Research Sdn Bhd (4)
West Wing Level 13 Berjaya Times Square
No 1 Jalan Imbi, Kuala Lumpur,
Malaysia
Tel.: (60) 321171888
Web Site: http://www.paconline.com.my
Marketing Research Service
N.A.I.C.S.: 541910

Inter-Pacific Securities Sdn Bhd (4)
West Wing Level 13 Berjaya Times Square
No 1 Jalan Imbi, Kuala Lumpur,
Malaysia
Tel.: (60) 321171888
Web Site: http://www.paconline.com.my

Securities Brokerage Services
N.A.I.C.S.: 523150

Subsidiary (Domestic):

**Inter-Pacific Asset Management Sdn
Bhd** (5)
West Wing Level 13 Berjaya Times Square
No1 Jalan Imbi, Kuala Lumpur, Ma-
laysia
Tel.: (60) 321171889
Web Site: https://www.interpac-
asset.com.my
Asset Management Services
N.A.I.C.S.: 523940

Subsidiary (Domestic):

Inter-Pacific Trading Sdn Bhd (4)
Lot 1-35A 1st Floor Podium Block Plaza
Berjaya 12 Jalan Imbi, Kuala Lumpur,
55100, Malaysia
Tel.: (60) 3 21444507
Sales Range: $50-74.9 Million
Emp.: 6
Commodity Trading Services
N.A.I.C.S.: 523160
Tan Chin Bock (Gen Mgr)

Subsidiary (Non-US):

Berjaya Corporation (S) Pte.Ltd (2)
680 Upper Thomson Road 01-13, Singa-
pore, 787103, Singapore
Tel.: (65) 60262273688
Sales Range: $50-74.9 Million
Emp.: 20
Real Estate Development Services
N.A.I.C.S.: 531390

Subsidiary (Domestic):

Berjaya Food Berhad (2)
Level 12 East Wing Berjaya Times Square
No 1 Jalan Imbi, Kuala Lumpur,
Malaysia
Tel.: (60) 321491999
Web Site: https://www.berjaya.com
Rev.: $236,183,280
Assets: $306,062,011
Liabilities: $202,851,640
Net Worth: $103,210,370
Earnings: $21,397,249
Emp.: 4,458
Fiscal Year-end: 06/30/2023
Holding Company; Fast Food Restaurants
Operator
N.A.I.C.S.: 551112
Michelle Lai Heng Tham (Co-Sec)

Subsidiary (Domestic):

**Berjaya Pizza Company Sdn
Bhd** (3)
Lot 09-23 9th Floor Berjaya Times Square
No1 Jalan Imbi, Kuala Lumpur, Ma-
laysia
Tel.: (60) 3 2119 7272
Web Site: http://www.papajohns.com.my
Pizza Restaurant Operating Services
N.A.I.C.S.: 722513
Marry Goh (Gen Mgr)

Joint Venture (Domestic):

**Berjaya Starbucks Coffee Company
Sdn. Bhd.** (3)
Lot 10-04 Level 10 West Wing Berjaya
Times Square No 1 Jalan Imbi, Federal Ter-
ritory, 55100, Kuala Lumpur,
Malaysia   (50%)
Tel.: (60) 300808989
Web Site: http://www.starbucks.com.my
Cafeteria Operator
N.A.I.C.S.: 722515

Subsidiary (Non-US):

**Berjaya Higher Education Sdn
Bhd** (2)
Tel.: (60) 326877000
Educational Support Services
N.A.I.C.S.: 611710

Subsidiary (Domestic):

Berjaya Hills Berhad (2)
KM48 Persimpangan Bertingkat Lebuhraya
Karak, Bukit Tinggi, 28750, Bentung, Pah-
ang, Malaysia
Tel.: (60) 9 288 8888

Home Management Services
N.A.I.C.S.: 721110

Berjaya Land Berhad (2)
Level 12 East Wing Berjaya Times Square
No 1 Jalan Imbi, 55100, Kuala Lumpur,
Malaysia
Tel.: (60) 321491999
Web Site: http://www.berjaya.com
Rev.: $1,538,550,688
Assets: $3,071,248,677
Liabilities: $1,804,859,048
Net Worth: $1,266,389,630
Earnings: $50,213,333
Emp.: 2,944
Fiscal Year-end: 06/30/2023
Resort, Hotel & Casino Management Ser-
vices
N.A.I.C.S.: 721110
Thiam Chai Tan (Exec Dir)

Subsidiary (Domestic):

Amat Muhibah Sdn Bhd (3)
Taman Danau Desa Waterpark, Kuala Lum-
pur, 58100, Wilayah Persekutuan, Malaysia
Tel.: (60) 3 7118 8338
Web Site:
    http://www.desawaterpark.com.my
Emp.: 30
Theme Park Operating Services
N.A.I.C.S.: 713110
Gunaseelan Manickam (Mgr)

Subsidiary (Non-US):

**Berjaya (China) Great Mall Co.
Ltd** (3)
38 Xing Gong West Street Yanjiao Develop-
ment Zone, 065201, Sanhe, China
Tel.: (86) 316 332 0309
Real Estate Development Services
N.A.I.C.S.: 531390

Subsidiary (Domestic):

Berjaya Air Sdn Bhd (3)
Lot AM 1 SkyPark Terminal Sultan Abdul
Aziz Shah Airport, 47200, Subang Jaya,
Selangor, Malaysia
Tel.: (60) 378471338
Web Site: https://www.berjaya-air.com
Airline Reservation Services
N.A.I.C.S.: 561599

**Berjaya Hotels & Resorts Vietnam
Sdn Bhd** (3)
12B-West Wing Level 15 Berjaya Times
Square 1 Jalan Imbi, Kuala Lumpur, 55100,
Malaysia
Tel.: (60) 321429611
Restaurant Operating Services
N.A.I.C.S.: 722511

**Berjaya Land Development Sdn
Bhd** (3)
74 & 75 Jalan Gemilang Taman Banang
Jaya, Batu Pahat, 83000, Johor, Johor
Darul Takzim, Malaysia
Tel.: (60) 74288678
Web Site:
    http://www.berjayaproperty.com.my
Property Development Services
N.A.I.C.S.: 531390

Subsidiary (Domestic):

Indra Ehsan Sdn Bhd (4)
Level 12 East Wing Berjaya Times Square
No 1, Jalan Imbi, 55100, Kuala Lumpur,
Malaysia
Tel.: (60) 3 2142 8028
Emp.: 2,000
Real Estate Development Services
N.A.I.C.S.: 531390

Sri Panglima Sdn Bhd (4)
Level 12 East Wing Berjaya Times Square
No 1, Jalan Imbi, 55100, Kuala Lumpur,
Malaysia
Tel.: (60) 321428028
Web Site: http://www.berjaya.com.my
Real Estate Development Services
N.A.I.C.S.: 531390
Tamsri Vincent (Founder)

Subsidiary (Non-US):

**Berjaya Mount Royal Beach Hotel
Limited** (3)

36 College Avenue, Mount Lavinia, Sri
Lanka
Tel.: (94) 112739610
Web Site: https://www.berjayahotel.com
Restaurant Operating Services
N.A.I.C.S.: 722511
Kirthi Wickramasinghe (Gen Mgr-Sri Lanka)

Subsidiary (Domestic):

Berjaya Vacation Club Berhad (3)
Lot 5-04 Level 5 Fahrenheit 88 179 Jalan
Bukit Bintang, 55100, Kuala Lumpur, Malay-
sia
Tel.: (60) 321169999
Web Site:
https://www.berjayavacation.com.my
Vacation Club Operating Services
N.A.I.C.S.: 721214

Subsidiary (Domestic):

Berjaya Golf Resort Berhad (4)
Jalan Jalil Perkasa 3, Bukit Jalil, 57000,
Kuala Lumpur, Malaysia
Tel.: (60) 389941600
Web Site: http://www.berjayaclubs.com
Sales Range: $150-199.9 Million
Golf Club Operating Services
N.A.I.C.S.: 713910

**Berjaya Hospitality Services Sdn
Bhd** (4)
14th Floor Times Square Blok B 1 Jln Imbi,
Kuala Lumpur, 55100, Malaysia
Tel.: (60) 326877000
Hospitality Services
N.A.I.C.S.: 622110

**Berjaya Langkawi Beach Resort Sdn
Bhd** (4)
Karung Berkunci 200 Burau Bay, Langkawi,
07000, Kuah, Kedah, Malaysia
Tel.: (60) 49591888
Sales Range: $100-124.9 Million
Resort Operating Services
N.A.I.C.S.: 721110

Berjaya Penang Hotel Sdn Bhd. (4)
1-Stop Midlands Park Burmah Road,
10350, George Town, Penang, Malaysia
Tel.: (60) 42277111
Home Management Services
N.A.I.C.S.: 721110
Tan Yew Jin (Gen Mgr)

**Berjaya Resort Management Services
Sdn Bhd** (4)
Level 15 West Wing Berjaya Times Square
No 1 Jalan Imbi, Kuala Lumpur, 55100,
Malaysia
Tel.: (60) 321429611
Web Site: http://www.berjayahotel.com
Emp.: 100
Resort Operating Services
N.A.I.C.S.: 721110
Foo Toon Kee (COO)

Bukit Kiara Resort Berhad (4)
Jalan Bukit Kiara Off Jalan Damansara,
60000, Kuala Lumpur, Malaysia
Tel.: (60) 320931222
Emp.: 300
Horse Riding Club Operating Services
N.A.I.C.S.: 713910
Mazne Shaffe (Asst Mgr-Sports & Recre-
ation)

Indah Corporation Berhad (4)
74 & 75 Jalan Gemilang Taman Banang
Jaya, 83000, Batu Pahat, Johor, Malaysia
Tel.: (60) 74286001
Golf Club Operating Services
N.A.I.C.S.: 713910
Steven Seo (Mgr-Ops)

KDE Recreation Berhad (4)
Taman Tun Abdul Razak Jalan Kerja Air
Lama, Ampang Jaya, 68000, Ampang, Se-
langor Darul Ehsan, Malaysia
Tel.: (60) 342572333
Web Site: https://www.berjayaclubs.com
Sales Range: $75-99.9 Million
Emp.: 20
Golf Club Operating Services
N.A.I.C.S.: 713910

Subsidiary (Domestic):

Budi Impian Sdn Bhd (3)
LG Berjaya Times Square Jln Imbi, 55100,

Kuala Lumpur, Wilayah Persekutuan, Ma-
laysia
Tel.: (60) 321417601
Restaurant Operating Services
N.A.I.C.S.: 722511

Cerah Bakti Sdn Bhd (3)
18th Floor Blok 488A One Stop Centre Jln
Burma, George Town, 10350, Pulau Pinang,
Malaysia
Tel.: (60) 42274188
Property Development Services
N.A.I.C.S.: 531390

Subsidiary (Non-US):

Icelandair Hotels ehf. (3)
Nautholsvegur 52, 102, Reykjavik,
Iceland (75%)
Tel.: (354) 4444000
Web Site: http://www.icelandairhotels.com
Hotel Operator
N.A.I.C.S.: 713210
Arny Hilmarsdottir (Dir-Fin & Admin)

Subsidiary (Domestic):

**Kota Raya Development Sdn
Bhd** (3)
Lot 5 0A-1 Level 5 Kota Raya Complex
Jalan Tun Tan Cheng Lock, 50000, Kuala
Lumpur, Wilayah Persekutuan, Malaysia
Tel.: (60) 320722562
Web Site: http://www.berjaya.com.my
Sales Range: $25-49.9 Million
Real Estate Development Services
N.A.I.C.S.: 531390

Subsidiary (Non-US):

Mahameru Consultancy d.o.o. (3)
Zanatski Centar-carsijska BB, Visoko, Bos-
nia & Herzegovina
Tel.: (387) 61792186
Real Estate Manangement Services
N.A.I.C.S.: 531390

Subsidiary (Domestic):

Nural Enterprise Sdn Bhd (3)
Lot 2 05 Second Floor Podium Block Plaza
Berjaya 12 Jalan Imbi, Kuala Lumpur,
55100, Malaysia
Tel.: (60) 321412818
Sales Range: $50-74.9 Million
Emp.: 25
Financial Management Services
N.A.I.C.S.: 523999

Pakar Angsana Sdn Bhd (3)
Level 12 East Wing Berjaya Times Square
No 1, Jalan Imbi, Kuala Lumpur, 55100,
Malaysia
Tel.: (60) 321428028
Web Site:
http://www.berjayaproperties.com.my
Emp.: 2,000
Property Management Services
N.A.I.C.S.: 531311
Wan Siew Mah (Gen Mgr)

SPORTS TOTO BERHAD (3)
Lot 13-01A Level 13 East Wing Berjaya
Times Square No 1 Jalan Imbi, 55100,
Kuala Lumpur, Malaysia
Tel.: (60) 321491999
Web Site: http://www.berjaya.com
Rev.: $1,290,933,333
Assets: $833,046,984
Liabilities: $591,135,026
Net Worth: $241,911,958
Earnings: $48,956,190
Emp.: 1,310
Fiscal Year-end: 06/30/2023
Gambling Services
N.A.I.C.S.: 713290
Swee Pin Seow (Exec Dir)

Subsidiary (Non-US):

**Berjaya Lottery Management (HK)
Ltd.** (4)
5/F Manulife Place 348 Kwun Tong Road,
Kowloon, China (Hong Kong) (100%)
Tel.: (852) 29801981
Web Site: http://www.berjaya.com
Sales Range: $10-24.9 Million
Emp.: 50
Operator of Gambling Establishments &
Casinos
N.A.I.C.S.: 721120

Subsidiary (Non-US):

Berjaya Philippines, Inc. (5)
9/F Rufino Pacific Tower 6784 Ayala Av-
enue Corner VA Rufino Street, Legaspi Vil-
lage, Makati, 1200, Philippines (68%)
Tel.: (63) 28110668
Web Site: https://berjaya.com.ph
Rev.: $685,276,636
Assets: $518,922,532
Liabilities: $324,681,627
Net Worth: $194,240,905
Earnings: $10,981,371
Emp.: 493
Fiscal Year-end: 06/30/2023
Amusement & Recreation Gaming Services
N.A.I.C.S.: 713290
Seow Swee Pin (Chm)

Subsidiary (Domestic):

**Philippine Gaming Management
Corporation.** (6)
9th Floor Rufino Pacific Tower 6784 Ayala
Avenue, San Lorenzo Village, Makati, 1229,
Philippines
Tel.: (63) 28110668
Lottery Equipment Leasing Services
N.A.I.C.S.: 532490

Subsidiary (US):

**International Lottery & Totalizator
Systems, Inc.** (5)
2310 Cousteau Ct, Vista, CA
92081-8346 (100%)
Tel.: (760) 598-1655
Web Site: https://ilts.com
Sales Range: $10-24.9 Million
Computer-Based Ticket Processing Sys-
tems & Terminals for Pari-Mutual Wagering
& On-Line Lotteries
N.A.I.C.S.: 333310
Theodore A. Johnson (Chm)

Subsidiary (Domestic):

Unisyn Voting Solutions, Inc. (6)
2310 Cousteau Ct, Vista, CA 92081-8346
Tel.: (760) 734-3233
Web Site: https://unisynvoting.com
Voting Machinery Mfr
N.A.I.C.S.: 333310

Subsidiary (Non-US):

H.R. Owen plc (4)
Melton Court 25-27 Old Brompton Road,
London, SW7 3TD, United Kingdom
Tel.: (44) 2072451122
Web Site: https://www.hrowen.co.uk
Sales Range: $400-449.9 Million
Emp.: 360
Luxury Automobile Sales
N.A.I.C.S.: 441110

Subsidiary (Domestic):

Broughtons of Cheltenham Ltd (5)
Rutherford Way, Cheltenham, GL51 9TU,
Gloucestershire, United Kingdom
Tel.: (44) 1242509635
Car Dealership
N.A.I.C.S.: 441110

Heathrow Limited (5)
Berry Heathrow Stone Close, West Drayton,
UB7 8JU, Middlesex, United Kingdom
Tel.: (44) 1895433999
Sales Range: $25-49.9 Million
Emp.: 65
Used Car Dealers
N.A.I.C.S.: 441120
Steve Kerbey (Mgr)

Holland Park Limited (5)
5-9 School North Acton, London, NW 10
6TD, United Kingdom (100%)
Tel.: (44) 2089684444
Web Site: http://www.bmw-net.co.uk
Sales Range: $25-49.9 Million
Emp.: 60
Motor Vehicle Dealers
N.A.I.C.S.: 441227

Jack Barclay Limited (5)
18 Berkeley Square, Mayfair, London, W1J
6AE, United Kingdom (100%)
Tel.: (44) 2031990333
Web Site: https://www.jackbarclay.co.uk

Sales Range: $25-49.9 Million
Emp.: 30
Motor Vehicle Dealers
N.A.I.C.S.: 441227
John Walden (CEO)

Subsidiary (Domestic):

Securiservices Sdn Bhd (3)
Level 12 East Wing Berjaya Times Square
No1, Jalan Imbi, Kuala Lumpur, 55100,
Malaysia
Tel.: (60) 321428028
Web Site: http://www.berjayaproperties.com
Sales Range: $25-49.9 Million
Emp.: 30
Property Management Services
N.A.I.C.S.: 531311

Selat Makmur Sdn Bhd (3)
Level 12 East Wing Berjaya Times Square
No 1, Jalan Imbi, Kuala Lumpur, 55100,
Malaysia
Tel.: (60) 321428028
Real Estate Development Services
N.A.I.C.S.: 531390

Semangat Cergas Sdn Bhd (3)
Level 12 East Wing Berjaya Times Square
No 1, Jalan Imbi, 55100, Kuala Lumpur,
Malaysia
Tel.: (60) 321428028
Property Development Services
N.A.I.C.S.: 531390

Tioman Island Resort Berhad (3)
PO Box 4, 86807, Mersing, Johor, Malaysia
Tel.: (60) 94191000
Web Site: https://tioman.berjayahotel.com
Emp.: 300
Resort Operating Services
N.A.I.C.S.: 721110

Subsidiary (Non-US):

**Berjaya Hotels & Resorts (Singapore)
Pte Ltd** (4)
67 Tanjong Pagar Road, Singapore,
088488, Singapore
Tel.: (65) 62273688
Web Site: http://www.berjayahotel.com
Sales Range: $10-24.9 Million
Emp.: 18
Home Management Services
N.A.I.C.S.: 721110
Jocelyn Gwee (Dir-Sls)

Subsidiary (Domestic):

Tiram Jaya Sdn Bhd (3)
Level 12 East Wing Berjaya Times Square
No 1, Jalan Imbi, 55100, Kuala Lumpur,
Malaysia
Tel.: (60) 321428028
Property Management Services
N.A.I.C.S.: 531311

Subsidiary (Domestic):

Berjaya Media Berhad (2)
Lot 13-01A Level 13 East Wing Berjaya
Times Square, No 1 Jalan Imbi, 55100,
Kuala Lumpur, Malaysia
Tel.: (60) 321491999
Web Site: https://www.berjaya.com
Rev.: $6,173,619
Assets: $5,393,705
Liabilities: $5,450,255
Net Worth: ($56,550)
Earnings: ($4,089,917)
Emp.: 14,000
Fiscal Year-end: 04/30/2019
Newspaper Publishing Services
N.A.I.C.S.: 513110
Robin Tan Yeong Ching (Chm)

Affiliate (Domestic):

Bermaz Auto Berhad (2)
no 7 Jalan Pelukis U1/46, Temasya Indus-
trial Park Seksyen U1, 40150, Shah Alam,
Selangor Darul Ehsan, Malaysia (60%)
Tel.: (60) 376278888
Web Site: http://www.bauto.com.my
Rev.: $749,334,603
Assets: $378,430,053
Liabilities: $200,342,011
Net Worth: $178,088,042
Earnings: $69,698,201
Emp.: 944
Fiscal Year-end: 04/30/2023

Berjaya Corporation Berhad—(Continued)

Automobile Distr & Sales
N.A.I.C.S.: 423110
Choon San Yeoh (Chm & Exec Dir)

Subsidiary (Domestic):

Bermaz Motor Sdn Bhd (3)
Lot 5 Jalan Pelukis U1/46 Temasysa Indu-
trial Park U1, 40150, Shah Alam, Selangor
Darul Ehsan, Malaysia
Tel.: (60) 3 76278888
Web Site: http://www.mazda.com.my
Sales Range: $100-124.9 Million
Emp.: 30
New Car Dealers
N.A.I.C.S.: 441110

Subsidiary (Domestic):

Changan Berjaya Auto Sdn Bhd (2)
Lot 3 Jalan 225 Section 51A, Petaling Jaya,
46100, Selangor Darul Ehsan, Malaysia
Tel.: (60) 379541188
Web Site: http://www.brilliance-auto.com.my
Automotive Distr
N.A.I.C.S.: 423110
Eddie Tiew (Mgr-Sls)

Subsidiary (Domestic):

Berjaya Brilliance Auto Sdn Bhd (3)
Lot 3 Jalan 225 Section 51A, Petaling Jaya,
46100, Selangor Darul Ehsan, Malaysia
Tel.: (60) 379541188
Web Site: http://www.brilliance-auto.com.my
Automotive Distr
N.A.I.C.S.: 423110
Mahamud Mohd Nor (Branch Mgr)

Subsidiary (Domestic):

Cosway Corporation Berhad (2)
Berjaya Times Square, 1 Jalan Imbi, Kuala
Lumpur, 55100, Malaysia
Tel.: (60) 321491999
Sales Range: $250-299.9 Million
Emp.: 3,100
Mfg & Commercial Retail Services
N.A.I.C.S.: 459999
Ismail Bin Osman (Exec Dir)

Subsidiary (Non-US):

Berjaya Holdings (HK) Limited (3)
2301 Wing On House 71 Des Voeux Road,
Central, China (Hong Kong) (100%)
Tel.: (852) 28776616
Web Site: http://www.berjaya.com
Sales Range: $50-74.9 Million
Emp.: 100
Investor in Real Estate
N.A.I.C.S.: 523160

Cosway (China) Co. Ltd (3)
Huaqiang North, Shenzhen, China
Tel.: (86) 755 28153049
Web Site: http://www.ecosway.com.cn
Cosmetic Product Distr
N.A.I.C.S.: 424210

Subsidiary (Domestic):

Cosway (M) Sdn Bhd (3)
18-01-01B Menara Cosway Plaza Berjaya
12 Jalan Imbi, 55100, Kuala Lumpur, Ma-
laysia
Tel.: (60) 321130813
Web Site: https://shop.cosway.com.my
Healthcare Product Distr
N.A.I.C.S.: 424210

Subsidiary (Domestic):

Kimia Suchi Marketing Sdn Bhd (4)
21 Jalan Tudm Kampung Baru Subang,
Shah Alam, 40000, Selangor, Malaysia
Tel.: (60) 378476268
Emp.: 60
Personal Care Product Distr
N.A.I.C.S.: 424210
Mohammed Naeem Rathor (Mng Dir)

Stephens Properties Sdn Bhd (4)
8 08 8th Floor Wisma Cosway Jln Raja Cu-
lan, Kuala Lumpur, 50200, Malaysia
Tel.: (60) 321482722
Property Management Services
N.A.I.C.S.: 531311

Subsidiary (Non-US):

eCosway Korea, Inc. (3)
PMK Building 3rd Floor 746 Yeoksam Dong,
Gangnam-Gu, Seoul, 135925, Korea
(South)
Tel.: (82) 25689575
Web Site: http://www.ecosway.co.kr
Personal Care Product Distr
N.A.I.C.S.: 424210

Subsidiary (Domestic):

Dunham-Bush (Malaysia) Berhad (2)
Berjaya Times Square, 1 Jalan Imbi, Kuala
Lumpur, 55100, Malaysia
Tel.: (60) 321491999
Web Site: http://www.dunham-bush.com.my
Sales Range: $100-124.9 Million
Refrigeration & Air Conditioning Mfg & Re-
tail Services
N.A.I.C.S.: 333415

Subsidiary (US):

Dunham-Bush, Inc. (3)
175 South St, West Hartford, CT 06110
Tel.: (860) 956-8500
Web Site: http://www.dunham-bush.com
Refrigeration & Air Conditioning Services
N.A.I.C.S.: 333415

Subsidiary (Domestic):

Hartford Compressors Inc. (4)
179 South St, West Hartford, CT 06110
Tel.: (860) 249-8671
Refrigeration Components Mfr
N.A.I.C.S.: 333415

Subsidiary (Domestic):

Graphic Press Group Sdn Bhd (2)
No 3 Jalan PJS 3/2 Jalan Medan 3 Taman
Medan PJS 3, Petaling Jaya, 46000, Malay-
sia
Tel.: (60) 3 7783 9988
Emp.: 200
Printing & Packaging Services
N.A.I.C.S.: 323111
Kenny Wong (Mng Dir)

REDtone Digital Berhad (2)
Suites 22-30 5th Floor IOI Business Park,
47100, Puchong, Selangor,
Malaysia (51.34%)
Tel.: (60) 380848888
Web Site: https://www.redtone.com
Rev.: $45,429,418
Assets: $90,182,434
Liabilities: $35,844,021
Net Worth: $54,338,413
Earnings: $11,678,095
Emp.: 350
Fiscal Year-end: 06/30/2023
Telecommunication Servicesb
N.A.I.C.S.: 517111
Bik Soon Lau (CEO-Grp)

Securexpress Services Sdn Bhd (3)
No 16 Jln Kecapi 33/2, Shah Alam, 40400,
Selangor, Malaysia
Tel.: (60) 355661999
Courier Service
N.A.I.C.S.: 492110

VRS (Malaysia) Sdn Bhd (2)
Directorate 2 Level 12 Berjaya Times
Square No 1, Jalan Imbi, 55100, Kuala
Lumpur, Malaysia
Tel.: (60) 321491527
Property Development Services
N.A.I.C.S.: 531390
Francis N. G. (Gen Mgr)

Wangsa Tegap Sdn Bhd (2)
Level 12 East Wing Berjaya Times Square
No 1, Jalan Imbi, Kuala Lumpur, 55100,
Malaysia
Tel.: (60) 3 2142 8028
Web Site:
  http://www.berjayaproperties.com.my
Emp.: 2,000
Property Management Services
N.A.I.C.S.: 531311

**Berjaya Hotels & Resorts (M) Sdn
Bhd** (1)
Level 15 West Berjaya Times Square Hotel
Kuala Lumpur 1 Jalan Imbi, 55100, Kuala
Lumpur, Malaysia

Tel.: (60) 321429611
Web Site: http://www.berjayahotel.com
Hotel Services
N.A.I.C.S.: 721110

**Berjaya Krispy Kreme Doughnuts Ma-
laysiaSdn Bhd** (1)
Lot 07-33 Level 7 West Wing Berjaya Times
Square No 1 Jalan Imbi, 55100, Kuala Lum-
pur, Malaysia
Tel.: (60) 321412699
Web Site: http://www.krispykreme.com.my
Restaurant Services
N.A.I.C.S.: 722511

**Berjaya Pharmacy Distribution Sdn
Bhd** (1)
Lot 15 C D Level 15 Office Block Plaza
Berjaya 12 Jalan Imbi, 12 Jalan Imbi Bukit
Bintang, 55100, Kuala Lumpur, Malaysia
Tel.: (60) 321106688
Web Site: http://www.soberupcandy.com
Pharmaceutical Products Distr
N.A.I.C.S.: 424210

Berjaya Pharmacy Sdn Bhd (1)
Lot 15 C and D Level 15 Plaza Berjaya
Jalan Imbi, 55100, Kuala Lumpur, Malaysia
Tel.: (60) 321106688
Pharmacy & Drug Retailer
N.A.I.C.S.: 456110

Berjaya Praslin Limited (1)
Anse Volbert, Praslin, Victoria, Seychelles
Tel.: (248) 4286286
Hotel Services
N.A.I.C.S.: 721110

Berjaya Roasters (M) Sdn Bhd (1)
Lot 9-16 Level 9 East Wing Berjaya Times
Square No 1 Jalan Imbi, 55100, Kuala Lum-
pur, Malaysia
Tel.: (60) 321199888
Web Site: http://www.krr.com.my
Restaurant Services
N.A.I.C.S.: 722511

Bodytechnics Limited (1)
381 Sykes Road, Slough, SL1,4SP, United
Kingdom
Tel.: (44) 1753505900
Motor Vehicle Maintenance & Repair Ser-
vices
N.A.I.C.S.: 811111

Country Farms Sdn Bhd (1)
Lot 9 Unit C2 Natco Industrial Park Lorong
Keluli 1B, Kawasan Perindustrian Bukit
Raja Selatan Seksyen 7, 40000, Shah
Alam, Selangor, Malaysia
Tel.: (60) 333424401
Web Site:
  https://www.countryfarmorganics.com
Organic Food Retailer
N.A.I.C.S.: 445298

**Inter-Pacific Equity Nominees (Asing)
Sdn Bhd** (1)
West Wing Level 13 Berjaya Times Square
No 1 Jalan Imbi, 55100, Kuala Lumpur,
Malaysia
Tel.: (60) 321171888
Financial Institution Services
N.A.I.C.S.: 522110

JL Morison (Malaya) Sdn Bhd (1)
Lot 18-01-01C Level 18 Menara Cosway
Plaza Berjaya No 12 Jalan Imbi, 55100,
Kuala Lumpur, Malaysia
Tel.: (60) 321422311
Web Site: http://www.jlmorison.com.my
Food Distr
N.A.I.C.S.: 424420

JannaFarm Sdn. Bhd. (1)
Unit No 201 Blok 1 Laman Seri Business
Park Seksyen 13, 40100, Shah Alam, Se-
langor Darul Ehsan, Malaysia
Tel.: (60) 350370901
Web Site: https://www.jannafarm.com.my
Black Ginger Farming Services
N.A.I.C.S.: 115116

Jollibean Foods Pte Ltd. (1)
6 Woodlands Woods Square Tower 2 10-
06A, Singapore, 737737, Singapore
Tel.: (65) 67463877
Web Site: https://www.jollibean.com.sg
Restaurant Services
N.A.I.C.S.: 722511

Mantra Design Sdn. Bhd. (1)
Lot 920 & 921 Level 9 Berjaya Times
Square No 1 Jalan Imbi, 55100, Kuala Lum-
pur, Malaysia
Tel.: (60) 321491542
Web Site: https://mantradesign.com.my
Project Management Consultancy Services
N.A.I.C.S.: 541618

PT Berjaya Cosway Indonesia (1)
Gedung Kencana Tower Ruko Business
Park Blok B20 Jl Meruya Ilir No 88, Jakarta
Barat, 11620, Indonesia
Tel.: (62) 2158901465
Web Site: http://www.ecosway.co.id
Personal Care Product Distr
N.A.I.C.S.: 456199

Prime Credit Leasing Berhad (1)
Level 13 West Wing Berjaya Times Square
No 1 Jalan Imbi, 55100, Kuala Lumpur,
Malaysia
Tel.: (60) 321481009
Web Site:
  http://www.primecreditleasing.com
Credit Leasing Services
N.A.I.C.S.: 522220

Proton Therapy Pte. Ltd. (1)
1 Biopolis Drive B1 Amnios, Singapore,
138622, Singapore
Tel.: (65) 67087890
Web Site: http://www.advancedmedicine.sg
Therapy Treatment Services
N.A.I.C.S.: 621420

**Roasters Asia Pacific (M) Sdn
Bhd** (1)
Lot 7-33 Level 7 West Wing Berjaya Times
Square No 1 Jalan Imbi, 55100, Kuala Lum-
pur, Malaysia
Tel.: (60) 321453259
Web Site:
  https://www.kennyrogersroasters.com
Restaurant Services
N.A.I.C.S.: 722511

STM Lottery Sdn. Bhd. (1)
Level 13-01 Berjaya Times Square No 1
Jalan Imbi, 55100, Kuala Lumpur, Malaysia
Tel.: (60) 321489779
Web Site: https://www.sportstoto.com.my
Emp.: 2,800
Sports Club Facility Operation Services
N.A.I.C.S.: 213112

Ser Vegano Sdn. Bhd. (1)
Lot 07-33 Level 7 Berjaya Times Square No
1 Jalan Imbi, 55100, Kuala Lumpur, Malay-
sia
Tel.: (60) 321453259
Web Site: https://sala.com.my
Vegan Restaurant Operator
N.A.I.C.S.: 722511

**Singapore Institute of Advanced
Medicine Holdings Pte Ltd** (1)
1 Biopolis Dr 02-01 Amnios, Singapore,
138622, Singapore
Tel.: (65) 67087890
Web Site: http://www.advancedmedicine.sg
Hospital & Health Care Services
N.A.I.C.S.: 622110

Staffield Country Resort Berhad (1)
13th Mile Seremban-Kuala Lumpur Country
Road, 71700, Mantin, Negeri Sembilan,
Malaysia
Tel.: (60) 182221919
Web Site: http://www.berjayaclubs.com
Golf Operator
N.A.I.C.S.: 713910

**Sweet Spot Digital (Malaysia) Sdn
Bhd** (1)
Suite B and E 18th Floor Office Block Plaza
Berjaya 12 Jalan Imbi, 55100, Kuala Lum-
pur, Malaysia
Tel.: (60) 321427288
Web Site: https://www.mysweetspot.com.my
Consumer Marketing Services
N.A.I.C.S.: 541613

**True Healthcare (Thailand) Co.,
Ltd.** (1)
15 Floor Capital Tower All Seasons Place
87/1 Wireless Road Lumpini, Prathumwan,
Bangkok, 10330, Thailand
Tel.: (66) 661152202

Web Site:
https://www.truehealthcarethailand.com
Medical Equipment Mfr & Distr
N.A.I.C.S.: 339112

True Healthcare India Pvt. Ltd. (1)
101 Veritas Business Suites Sector 53, Gurgaon, 122002, Haryana, India
Tel.: (91) 8800132150
Medical Equipment Distr
N.A.I.C.S.: 423450

eCosway Mexico, S.A. de C.V. (1)
Av Insurgentes Sur 1605 Piso 8 Col San Jose Insurgentes, 03900, Mexico, Mexico
Tel.: (52) 5562847474
Personal Care Product Distr
N.A.I.C.S.: 456199

eCosway Rus LLC (1)
Marksistskaya St 3 Building 4, Moscow, Russia
Tel.: (7) 4957392738
Web Site: http://www.ecosway.com
Personal Care Product Distr
N.A.I.C.S.: 456199

BERKELEY ENERGIA LIMITED
Level 9 28 The Esplanade, Perth, 6000, WA, Australia
Tel.: (61) 893226322   AU
Web Site:
https://www.berkeleyenergia.com
BKY—(AIM)
Assets: $59,656,736
Liabilities: $1,361,904
Net Worth: $58,294,832
Earnings: ($914,612)
Fiscal Year-end: 06/30/23
Other Metal Ore Mining
N.A.I.C.S.: 212290
Ian Peter Middlemas (Chm)

Subsidiaries:

Berkeley Exploration Espana
S.L.U. (1)
Carretera SA-322 Km 30, Retortillo, 37495, Salamanca, Spain
Tel.: (34) 923193903
Web Site: https://www.berkeleyenergia.com
Metal Mining Support Services
N.A.I.C.S.: 213114

Berkeley Minera Espana, S.A. (1)
Carretera SA-322 Km 30, Retortillo, 37495, Salamanca, Spain
Tel.: (34) 923193903
Web Site:
http://www.berkeleyresources.com.au
Sales Range: $50-74.9 Million
Uranium Mining Services
N.A.I.C.S.: 212290

Minera de Rio Alagon, S.L. (1)
Carretera SA-322 Km 30 Retortillo, Salamanca, 37495, Spain
Tel.: (34) 923193903
Uranium Exploration & Development Services
N.A.I.C.S.: 212290
Ian Middleman (Gen Mgr)

BERKH UUL JOINT STOCK COMPANY
Berkh Uul JSC office building, Berkh town Batnorov sum, Ulaanbaatar, Khentii, Mongolia
Tel.: (976) 1810002001
BEU—(MONG)
Rev.: $520,626
Assets: $5,576,813
Liabilities: $18,098,808
Net Worth: ($12,521,995)
Earnings: ($1,455,753)
Fiscal Year-end: 12/31/20
Mineral Mining Services
N.A.I.C.S.: 212390

BERKIM CONSTRUCTION INC.
120 Willowdale Ave, Toronto, M2N 4Y2, ON, Canada
Tel.: (416) 224-2550
Web Site: http://www.berkim.com

Year Founded: 1966
Rev.: $27,108,683
Emp.: 30
Construction Services
N.A.I.C.S.: 236220
David Kimmerle (Pres)

BERKLEY RENEWABLES INC.
Suite 900 570 Granville St, Vancouver, V6C 3P1, BC, Canada
Tel.: (604) 682-3701   BC
Web Site:
http://www.berkleyresources.com
Rev.: $1,373,931
Assets: $5,116,794
Liabilities: $6,179,693
Net Worth: ($1,062,899)
Earnings: ($953,583)
Fiscal Year-end: 12/31/17
Oil & Gas Resource Development
N.A.I.C.S.: 211120
Matt Wayrynen (Pres & CEO)

BERKOSAN YALITIM VE TECRIT MADDELERI URETIM VE TICARET A.S.
Seba Office Boulevard Ayazaga Mh Mimarsinan Sk No 21 K 6 D41, Sariyer, 34485, Istanbul, Turkiye
Tel.: (90) 2128304455
Web Site: https://www.berkosan.com
Year Founded: 1993
BRKSN—(IST)
Rev.: $19,062,098
Assets: $17,442,848
Liabilities: $4,443,388
Net Worth: $12,999,460
Earnings: $2,541,698
Emp.: 250
Fiscal Year-end: 12/31/23
Packaging Products Mfr
N.A.I.C.S.: 326112
Memet Aldikacti (Chm)

BERLI JUCKER PUBLIC CO. LTD.
Berli Jucker House 99 Soi Rubia Sukhumvit 42 Road, Phrakanong Klongtoey, Bangkok, 10110, Thailand
Tel.: (66) 23671111
Web Site: https://www.bjc.co.th
Year Founded: 1882
BLJZY—(OTCIQ)
Rev.: $4,905,117,144
Assets: $9,895,196,554
Liabilities: $6,220,058,807
Net Worth: $3,675,137,747
Earnings: $166,730,958
Emp.: 45,373
Fiscal Year-end: 12/31/23
Industrial, Glass, Engineering, Hospital, Photographic, Pharmaceutical, Consumer & Confectionary Products Mfr & Distr
N.A.I.C.S.: 327212
Prasert Maekwatana (Vice Chm-Exec Bd)

Subsidiaries:

BJC Engineering Company
Limited (1)
99 Berli Jucker Ho 10th Fl, Soi Rubia Sukhumvit 42 Rd, Bangkok, 10110, Thailand (100%)
Tel.: (66) 23671111
Web Site: http://www.bjcengineering.co.th
Sales Range: $25-49.9 Million
Emp.: 100
Engineeering Services
N.A.I.C.S.: 541330

BJC Foods (Malaysia) Sdn. Bhd. (1)
Lot 1 Jalan Pelabur 23/1 Seksyen 23, 40300, Shah Alam, Selangor, Malaysia
Tel.: (60) 355423566
Web Site: https://www.bjcfoods.com
Potato Chips & Snack Food Mfr
N.A.I.C.S.: 311919

BJC Industrial and Trading Co.,
Ltd. (1)
99 Soi Rubia Sukhumvit 42 Road, Phrakanong Sub-district Klongtoey District, Bangkok, Thailand
Tel.: (66) 23671111
Imaging Product & Stationery Distr
N.A.I.C.S.: 424120

BJC International Co., Ltd. (1)
31/F Tower Two Times Square 1 Matheson Street, Causeway Bay, China (Hong Kong)
Tel.: (852) 31888333
Glass Container Mfr
N.A.I.C.S.: 327213

BJC International Holding Pte.
Ltd. (1)
80 Robinson Road Ste 02-00, Singapore, Singapore
Tel.: (65) 68898
Glass Container Mfr
N.A.I.C.S.: 327213

BJC Marketing Company Limited (1)
99 Berli Jucker Ho 10th Floor, Soi Rubia Sukhumvit 42 Road, 10110, Bangkok, Thailand (100%)
Tel.: (66) 23671111
Web Site: http://www.bjchealthcare.co.th
Sales Range: $25-49.9 Million
Emp.: 100
Marketing Consulting Services
N.A.I.C.S.: 541613

BJC Specialties Co., Ltd. (1)
10th Floor Berli Jucker House 99 Soi Rubia Sukhumvit 42 Road, Kwaeng Phrakanong Khet Klongtoey, Bangkok, Thailand
Tel.: (66) 21465999
Foods & Beverage Distr
N.A.I.C.S.: 423740

BJC Trading Company Limited (1)
99 Berli Jucker Ho 10th Floor, Soi Rubia Sukhumvit 42 Rd, 10110, Bangkok, Thailand (100%)
Tel.: (66) 23671111
Web Site: http://www.bjc.co.th
Sales Range: $200-249.9 Million
Emp.: 1,000
Specialty Trade Contractors
N.A.I.C.S.: 238990

Berli Jucker Cellox Limited (1)
330 Moo 9 Bangna - Trad Road, Bangchalong Bangplee, Samut Prakan, 10540, Thailand (100%)
Tel.: (66) 2 312 6115
Web Site: http://www.bjc.co.th
Sales Range: $25-49.9 Million
Emp.: 100
Paper Mills
N.A.I.C.S.: 322120

Berli Jucker Foods Limited (1)
Berli Jucker House 99 Soi Rubia Sukhumvit 42 Road, Phrakanong Klongtoey, Bangkok, 10110, Thailand (100%)
Tel.: (66) 23132003
Web Site: http://www.bjc.co.th
Sales Range: $100-124.9 Million
Food Service Contractors
N.A.I.C.S.: 722310

Berli Jucker Logistics Limited (1)
Berli Jucker House 4th Floor 99 Soi Rubia Sukhumvit 42 Road, Phrakanong Klongtoey, Bangkok, 10110, Thailand (100%)
Tel.: (66) 23671234
Web Site: https://www.bjc.co.th
Sales Range: $25-49.9 Million
Emp.: 200
Engineeering Services
N.A.I.C.S.: 541330

Berli Jucker Specialties Ltd. (1)
99 Berli Jucker Ho 10th Floor, Soi Rubia Sukhumvit 42 Road, 10110, Bangkok, Thailand (99.15%)
Tel.: (66) 23671111
Web Site: http://www.bjc.co.th
Sales Range: $25-49.9 Million
Emp.: 20
Basic Organic Chemical Mfr
N.A.I.C.S.: 325199

Subsidiary (Domestic):

White Group Public Company
Limited (2)

75 Soi Rubia Sukhumvit 42 Road, Phrakanong Klongtoey, Bangkok, 10110, Thailand (93.09%)
Tel.: (66) 23902445
Web Site: http://www.whitegroup.co.th
Rev.: $35,435,443
Assets: $70,133,366
Liabilities: $7,001,437
Net Worth: $63,131,929
Earnings: $5,602,922
Emp.: 143
Fiscal Year-end: 12/31/2019
Petroleum & Petrochemical Distr
N.A.I.C.S.: 424720
Somchai Chaisuparakul (Exec Dir)

Big C Fairy Limited (1)
88/9 Samannachan - Barbos Alley, Phrakanong Sub-district Klongtoey District, Bangkok, Thailand
Tel.: (66) 26550666
Glass Container Mfr
N.A.I.C.S.: 327213

Big C Supercenter Public Company
Limited (1)
6th Floor 97/11 Rajdamri Road Lumpini, Pathumwan, Bangkok, 10330, Thailand
Tel.: (66) 2 655 0666
Web Site: https://www.bigc.co.th
Food & Non-Food Products Distr
N.A.I.C.S.: 455211
Hoang Linh (Mgr-HRPB-Reg)

C Smart Solution Company
Limited (1)
88/9 Samannachan - Barbos Alley, Phrakanong Sub-district Klongtoey District, Bangkok, Thailand
Tel.: (66) 26550666
Glass Container Mfr
N.A.I.C.S.: 327213

Myanmar Indo Best Co., Ltd. (1)
BB1A No 2 Corner of Laydaungkan Rd and Bayint Naung Rd, Ward No 26 South Dagon Township, Yangon, Myanmar
Tel.: (95) 181003347
Web Site:
https://www.myanmarindobest.com
Camera & Mobile Distr
N.A.I.C.S.: 423410

Rubia Industries Limited (1)
70 Moo13 Poochaosamingprai Rd, Bangyapraek Prapadaeng, Bangkok, 10130, Samutprakarn, Thailand (99.7%)
Tel.: (66) 2 385 9024
Web Site: https://www.rubia.co.th
Sales Range: $125-149.9 Million
Emp.: 700
Soap & Detergent Mfr
N.A.I.C.S.: 325611

Thai Corp International (Vietnam) Co.
Ltd. (1)
Lot 5-4 M14 Str Kcn Tan Binh morong, Binh Hung Hoa Ward Binh Tan District, Ho Chi Minh City, Vietnam
Tel.: (84) 2862960000
Web Site: https://tcivn.com
Chill Product & Snack Food Distr
N.A.I.C.S.: 424450

Thai Corp International Co., Ltd. (1)
31/F Tower Two Times Square 1 Matheson Street, Causeway Bay, China (Hong Kong)
Tel.: (852) 31888333
Vehicle Investment Services
N.A.I.C.S.: 525990

Thai Malaya Glass Co., Ltd. (1)
28 Moo 1 Sil Industrial Land, Bualoy Subdistrict Nongkae District, Saraburi, Thailand
Tel.: (66) 363738217
Glass Packaging Containers Mfr & Distr
N.A.I.C.S.: 327213

Thai-Scandic Steel Company
Limited (1)
7 I-5 Road, Mabtaphut Industrial Estate T Mabtaphut A Muang, Rayong, 21150, Thailand
Tel.: (66) 3 868 3070
Web Site: https://www.thaiscandic.com
Sales Range: $50-74.9 Million
Emp.: 250
Steel Wire Drawing
N.A.I.C.S.: 331222

Berli Jucker Public Co. Ltd.—(Continued)

BERLINER EFFEKTENG-ESELLSCHAFT AG

Kurfurstendamm 119, 10711, Berlin, Germany
Tel.: (49) 3089021100
Web Site:
　https://www.effektengesellschaft.de
Year Founded: 1986
BFV—(DEU)
Assets: $404,586,661
Liabilities: $263,393,050
Net Worth: $141,193,611
Earnings: $10,446,795
Emp.: 163
Fiscal Year-end: 12/31/23
Financial Investment Services
N.A.I.C.S.: 523940
Holger Timm *(Chm-Mgmt Bd)*

BERLINER VOLKSBANK EG

Budapester Strasse 35, 10787, Ber-lin, Germany
Tel.: (49) 3030630
Web Site: http://www.berliner-volksbank.de
Sales Range: $400-449.9 Million
Emp.: 1,987
Banking Services
N.A.I.C.S.: 522110
Stefan Gerdsmeier *(Member-Mgmt Bd)*

BERLING S.A.

Al Krakowska 80A, 05-552, Ste-fanowo, Poland
Tel.: (48) 22 727 84 97
Web Site: http://www.berling.pl
Year Founded: 1993
BRG—(WAR)
Sales Range: $25-49.9 Million
Emp.: 30
Refrigeration Equipment Whslr
N.A.I.C.S.: 423740
Lukasz Janik *(Mgr-Sls)*

Subsidiaries:

Arkton sp. z o.o.　　　　　　　**(1)**
Wilkowice ul Morkowska 36, 64-100, Leszno, Poland
Tel.: (48) 65 525 28 42
Web Site: http://www.arkton.pl
Sales Range: $25-49.9 Million
Refrigerator Equipment Mfr
N.A.I.C.S.: 333415

BERLINOVO IMMOBILIEN GE-SELLSCHAFT MBH

Hallesches Ufer 74-76, 10963, Berlin, Germany
Tel.: (49) 30 25441 0　　　　　De
Web Site: http://www.berlinovo.de
Year Founded: 2006
Emp.: 350
Real Estate Asset & Property Man-agement Services
N.A.I.C.S.: 531390
Roland J. Stauber *(CEO)*

BERMAS SA

Str Humorului nr 61, Scheia, Roma-nia
Tel.: (40) 230526543
Web Site: https://www.bermas.ro
Year Founded: 1974
BRM—(BUC)
Rev.: $9,056,294
Assets: $8,569,369
Liabilities: $3,464,272
Net Worth: $5,105,098
Earnings: $318,740
Emp.: 204
Fiscal Year-end: 12/31/22
Beer Mfr
N.A.I.C.S.: 312120
Elena Anisoi *(Chm & Gen Mgr)*

BERMAX CONSTRUCTION

267 Rte de Saint Jean d'Angely, 16710, Saint-Yrieix-sur-Charente, France
Tel.: (33) 5 4595 1005
Web Site: http://www.bermax.com
Rev.: $10,400,000
Emp.: 13
Residential Construction Services
N.A.I.C.S.: 236115
Damien Kohler *(Pres)*

BERMELE PLC

6th Floor 60 Gracechurch Street, London, EC3V 0HR, United Kingdom
Tel.: (44) 2034759760　　　　　UK
Web Site: http://www.bermele.com
Year Founded: 2017
Assets: $664,314
Liabilities: $85,680
Net Worth: $578,633
Earnings: ($837,531)
Emp.: 5
Fiscal Year-end: 01/31/20
Pharmaceutical Product Mfr & Distr
N.A.I.C.S.: 325412

BERMONT DEVELOPMENT SDN. BHD

Wisma 1 Alliance Unit 3A-B 4th Floor No 1, Lorong Kasawari 4B Taman Eng Ann, Kelang, 41150, Malaysia
Tel.: (60) 67635100
Property Development Services
N.A.I.C.S.: 531190
Wong Kiew *(Mng Dir)*

BERMUDA MONETARY AU-THORITY

BMA House 43 Victoria Street, Hamil-ton, HM 12, Bermuda
Tel.: (441) 2955278
Web Site: http://www.bma.bm
Sales Range: $10-24.9 Million
Emp.: 170
Banking Services
N.A.I.C.S.: 521110
Marcia Woolridge-Allwood *(Mng Dir-Banking, Trust, Corp Svcs & Invest-ment)*

BERMULLER & CO. GMBH

Rotterdamer Strasse 7, 90451, Nuremberg, Germany
Tel.: (49) 911642000　　　　　De
Web Site: http://www.beco-bermueller.de
Year Founded: 1960
Sales Range: $10-24.9 Million
Emp.: 45
Construction Materials Distr
N.A.I.C.S.: 423390
Rudolf Bermuller *(Mng Dir)*

Subsidiaries:

REGUM GmbH　　　　　　　　**(1)**
Heinrich-Diehl-Strasse 2, Rothenbach, 90552, Pegnitz, Germany
Tel.: (49) 9119533540
Rail Product Mfr
N.A.I.C.S.: 331110
Rudolf Bermuller *(Mng Dir)*

BERNABE COTE D'IVOIRE

Bd de Marseille Km 4 01, BP 1867, Abidjan, 01, Cote d'Ivoire
Tel.: (225) 21212020
Year Founded: 1951
BNBC—(BRVM)
Sales Range: Less than $1 Million
Industrial Material Distr
N.A.I.C.S.: 423840

BERNARD ATHLETIC KNIT LTD.

2 Scarlett Road, Toronto, M6N 4J6, ON, Canada
Tel.: (416) 766-6151
Web Site: http://www.athleticknit.com
Year Founded: 1962
Rev.: $14,513,471
Emp.: 250
Sportswear & Accessories Mfr
N.A.I.C.S.: 339920
David Sliwin *(Co-Pres)*

BERNARD KRIEF CONSUL-TANTS SA

112 Avenue Kleber, 75116, Paris, France
Tel.: (33) 1 53 05 80 00
Web Site: http://www.krief-group.com
Financial Restructuring & Consulting Services
N.A.I.C.S.: 523999
Jean-Claude Dutoit *(CEO)*

Subsidiaries:

Dollfus Mieg & Cie, S.A.　　　**(1)**
13 rue de Pfastatt, 68200, Mulhouse, France
Tel.: (33) 3 89 32 4444
Web Site: http://www.dmc.com
Sales Range: $1-4.9 Billion
Emp.: 7,600
Mfr of Fashion Apparel Fabrics & Leisure Crafts
N.A.I.C.S.: 314999
Dominique Poile *(Chm & CEO)*

Subsidiary (US):

The DMC Corporation　　　　　**(2)**
Port Kearny Bldg 10F 77 S Hackensack Ave, Kearny, NJ 07032
Tel.: (973) 589-0606
Web Site: http://www.dmc-usa.com
Sales Range: $25-49.9 Million
Emp.: 25
Art Needlework, Threads, Accessories & Craft Products
N.A.I.C.S.: 459130
Joseph McCade *(CEO)*

BERNARD LOISEAU SA

2 avenue Bernard Loiseau, Saulieu, 21210, Cote-d'Or, France
Tel.: (33) 380905353
Web Site: https://www.bernard-loiseau.com
ALDBL—(EUR)
Sales Range: $1-9.9 Million
Emp.: 110
Restaurant & Hotel Owner & Opera-tor
N.A.I.C.S.: 722511

Subsidiaries:

SA Loiseau Rive Gauche　　　**(1)**
5 rue de Bourgogne, 75007, Paris, France
Tel.: (33) 145517942
Hotel & Spa Services
N.A.I.C.S.: 721110

SA Loiseau des Vignes　　　　**(1)**
31 rue Maufoux Bourgogne, 21200, Beaune, France
Tel.: (33) 380241206
Hotel & Spa Services
N.A.I.C.S.: 721110

SARL Loiseau des Ducs　　　　**(1)**
3 rue Vauban Bourgogne, 21000, Dijon, France
Tel.: (33) 380302809
Hotel & Spa Services
N.A.I.C.S.: 721110

SAS Loiseau des Sens　　　　**(1)**
4 Avenue de la Gare, Saulieu, 21210, Bour-gogne, France
Tel.: (33) 345447000
Hotel & Spa Services
N.A.I.C.S.: 721110

BERNARDAUD S.A.

27 Rue Ave Albert Thomas, 87050, Limoges, France

Tel.: (33) 555105550
Web Site: http://www.bernardaud.fr
Year Founded: 1863
Porcelain Mfr
N.A.I.C.S.: 327110
Michel Bernardaud *(Chm)*

Subsidiaries:

Bernardaud　　　　　　　　　**(1)**
32, rue de Paradis, 75010, Paris, France
Tel.: (33) 523 00 03
N.A.I.C.S.: 332119

BERNDORF AG

Leobersdorfer Strasse 26, 2560, Berndorf, Austria
Tel.: (43) 267282900　　　　　AT
Web Site: http://www.berndorf.at
Year Founded: 1843
Rev.: $571,047,970
Assets: $625,606,429
Liabilities: $425,605,033
Net Worth: $200,001,397
Earnings: $6,046,124
Emp.: 2,274
Fiscal Year-end: 12/31/19
Tool & Equipment Mfr; Metal Pro-cessing Services
N.A.I.C.S.: 333515
Franz Viehboeck *(Chm-Mgmt Bd & CEO-Tech & HR)*

Subsidiaries:

Aichelin GmbH　　　　　　　　**(1)**
Fabriksgasse 3, 2340, Modling, Austria
Tel.: (43) 2236236460
Web Site: http://www.aichelin.at
Heat Treatment Products Mfr
N.A.I.C.S.: 332811

Aichelin Heat Treatment Systems (Beijing) Co., Ltd.　　　　　　　**(1)**
Shahe Industrial Park, Changping District, Beijing, 102206, China
Tel.: (86) 1050815998
Web Site: http://www.aichelin.com.cn
Heat Treatment Equipment Mfr
N.A.I.C.S.: 333414

Aichelin Heat Treatment Systems Inc.　　　　　　　　　　　　　**(1)**
44160 Plymouth Oaks Blvd, Plymouth, MI 48170
Tel.: (734) 459-9850
Web Site: http://www.aichelinusa.com
Heat Tracing Equipment Mfr
N.A.I.C.S.: 333414

Aichelin Service GmbH　　　　**(1)**
Schultheiss-Kohle-Str 7, 71636, Ludwigs-burg, Germany
Tel.: (49) 7141 6437 0
Web Site: http://www.aichelin-service.com
Heat Tracing Equipment Mfr
N.A.I.C.S.: 333414
Thomas Peinkofer *(CEO)*

Berndorf Baderbau Deutschland GmbH　　　　　　　　　　　　**(1)**
Siegweg 1, 35767, Breitscheid, Germany
Tel.: (49) 2777 81 28 23 0
Web Site: http://www.berndorf-baederbau.com
Heat Tracing Equipment Mfr
N.A.I.C.S.: 333414

Berndorf Baderbau Schweiz AG　**(1)**
Gewerbestrasse 8, 8212, Neuhausen am Rheinfall, Switzerland
Tel.: (41) 52 674 05 70
Pool Construction Services
N.A.I.C.S.: 236220

Berndorf Band GmbH　　　　　**(1)**
Leobersdorfer Strasse 26, 2560, Berndorf, Austria
Tel.: (43) 2672 8000
Web Site: http://www.berndorfband-group.com
Process & Surface Technology
N.A.I.C.S.: 325613

Subsidiary (Non-US):

Beijing Berndorf Technology Develop-ment Co., Ltd.　　　　　　　　**(2)**

No 17 Xinggu West RD Xinggu Economic & Development Zone, Pinggu, Beijing, 101200, China
Tel.: (86) 1080723901
Web Site: http://www.berndorf.com.cn
Process & Surface Technology
N.A.I.C.S.: 325613

Subsidiary (Domestic):

Berndorf Band Engineering GmbH (2)
Leobersdorfer Strasse 26, 2560, Berndorf, Austria
Tel.: (43) 26728000
Web Site: http://www.berndorf-engineering.at
Process & Surface Technology
N.A.I.C.S.: 325613

Subsidiary (US):

Berndorf Belt Technology Inc. (2)
2525 Bath Rd, Elgin, IL 60124
Tel.: (847) 931-5264
Web Site: http://www.berndorf-usa.com
Steel Belts & Continuous Steel Belt Conveyor Systems Mfr
N.A.I.C.S.: 332111

Berndorf Band Latinoamerica S.A.S. (1)
Cra 46 62 sur 33, Medellin, Antioquia, Colombia
Tel.: (57) 42040517
Web Site: http://www.berndorf-lat.com
Steel Belt Mfr
N.A.I.C.S.: 332999

Berndorf Metall- und Baderbau GmbH (1)
Leobersdorfer Str 26, 2560, Berndorf, Austria
Tel.: (43) 2672836400
Web Site: http://www.berndorf-baederbau.com
Pool Construction Services
N.A.I.C.S.: 541330

Subsidiary (Non-US):

Berndorf Baderbau SK s.r.o. (2)
Bystricka 1571, 966 81, Zarnovica, Slovakia
Tel.: (421) 45 6844780
Web Site: http://www.berndorf-baederbau.sk
Stainless Steel Pool Mfr
N.A.I.C.S.: 332111

Berndorf Baderbau Sp. z o.o (2)
ul Zdrojowa 78, 43-384, Jaworze, Poland
Tel.: (48) 3382 89700
Web Site: http://www.berndorf.pl
Stainless Steel Pool Mfr
N.A.I.C.S.: 332111
Marek Wrzal (Chm)

Berndorf Baderbau s.r.o. (2)
Bystrice 1312, Bystrice, 73995, Czech Republic
Tel.: (420) 558 362389
Stainless Steel Pool Mfr
N.A.I.C.S.: 332111
Rudolf Cieslar (CEO)

Berndorf Baderbau srl (2)
Str 22 Decembrie nr 28, RO-430314, Baia Mare, Romania
Tel.: (40) 268 418298
Stainless Steel Pool Mfr
N.A.I.C.S.: 332111

Berndorf Metall- und Baderbau AG (2)
Gewerbestrasse 8, CH-8212, Neuhausen, Switzerland
Tel.: (41) 52674 0570
Stainless Steel Pool Mfr
N.A.I.C.S.: 332111

Berndorf Metallwaren GmbH (2)
Wittestrasse 24, D-13509, Berlin, Germany
Tel.: (49) 30 432 2072
Stainless Steel Products & Swimming Pools Mfr
N.A.I.C.S.: 332111

Berndorf Steel Belt Systems Co. Ltd. (1)
15 bodeum 2-ro, Seo-gu, Incheon, Korea (South)
Tel.: (82) 32 816 0432

Web Site: http://www.berndorf.co.kr
Steel Belt Mfr
N.A.I.C.S.: 332999

Bosio d.o.o. (1)
Bukovzlak 109, 3000, Celje, Slovenia
Tel.: (386) 3 780 25 10
Web Site: http://www.bosio.si
Industrial Process Furhace Mfr
N.A.I.C.S.: 333994
Hugo Bosio (Founder & CEO)

FerRobotics Compliant Robot Technology GmbH (1)
Altenberger Strasse 66c Science Park 4, 4040, Linz, Austria
Tel.: (43) 72010810701
Web Site: https://www.ferrobotics.com
Industrial Machinery Mfr & Distr
N.A.I.C.S.: 314999
Harald Gschnaidtner (Acct Mgr)

HASCO America Inc. (1)
270 Rutledge Road Unit B, Fletcher, NC 28732
Tel.: (828) 650-2600
Plastic Product Whslr
N.A.I.C.S.: 424610
Brenda Clark (Mgr-Engrg)

HASCO Austria Gesellschaft m.b.H (1)
Industriestrasse 21, 2353, Guntramsdorf, Austria
Tel.: (43) 2236 202 300
Machine Tools Mfr
N.A.I.C.S.: 333517

HASCO Canada Inc. (1)
60 Ironside Crescent Unit 5, Scarborough, M1X 1G4, ON, Canada
Tel.: (416) 293-5044
Machine Tools Mfr
N.A.I.C.S.: 333517
Louis Hebert (Mgr)

HASCO Encounter Ltd. (1)
Unit 2B 2/F Wah Shing Centre No 11-13 Shing Yip Street, Kwun Tong, Kowloon, China (Hong Kong)
Tel.: (852) 2511 2002
Machine Tools Mfr
N.A.I.C.S.: 333517
Billykam Hasco (Mgr-Sls)

HASCO France S.A.R.L. (1)
9 allee des Tulipiers, 69673, Bron, Cedex, France
Tel.: (33) 4 7222 4444
Web Site: http://www.hasco.com
Industrial Mold Mfr
N.A.I.C.S.: 333511

HASCO Hasenclever GmbH & Co. KG (1)
Romerweg 4, 58513, Ludenscheid, Germany
Tel.: (49) 2351 9570
Web Site: http://www.hasco.com
Tool & Mould Mfr
N.A.I.C.S.: 333517

HASCO Iberica S.L.U. (1)
Ctra de Sant Cugat 63 A 1 Planta 2 - 3, Trade Center Porta Rubi, 8191, Barcelona, Spain
Tel.: (34) 93 719 2440
Machine Tools Mfr
N.A.I.C.S.: 333517

HASCO India Pvt. Ltd. (1)
2C-413 Ombr Layout Banaswadi MS Nagar PO, 560 033, Bengaluru, India
Tel.: (91) 80 2545 7113
Machine Tools Mfr
N.A.I.C.S.: 333517
P. V. Sonichen (Mng Dir)

HASCO Internorm Ltd. (1)
HASCO House London Road, Daventry, NN11 4SE, United Kingdom
Tel.: (44) 1327 87 60 18
Machine Tool Distr
N.A.I.C.S.: 332710
Wade Hopewell (Reg Mgr-Sls)

HASCO Normalien Mexico S.A. De C.V. (1)
Blvd Prolongacion Bernardo Quintana 2481, Int 29-30 Col San Pedro Martir, 76117, Queretaro, Mexico

Tel.: (52) 442 441 8022
Web Site: http://www.hasco.com
Machine Tool Distr
N.A.I.C.S.: 332710

HASCO Polska SP zo.o. (1)
ul Leczycka 53, 85-737, Bydgoszcz, Poland
Tel.: (48) 52 325 47 00
Web Site: http://www.hasco.com
Machine Tool Distr
N.A.I.C.S.: 332710

HASCO Portuguesa Lda. (1)
Estrada Nacional 242 Km 9 2, 2430-091, Marinha Grande, Portugal
Tel.: (351) 244 572 570
Machine Tool Distr
N.A.I.C.S.: 332710

HASCO Singapore (PTE) LTD. (1)
48 Toh Guan Road East 07-108, Enterprise Hub, Singapore, 608586, Singapore
Tel.: (65) 6861 1585
Web Site: http://www.hasco.com
Machine Tool Distr
N.A.I.C.S.: 332710

HASCO Suisse AG (1)
Huhnerhubelstrasse 64, Postfach 95, 3123, Belp, Switzerland
Tel.: (41) 31 924 39 00
Web Site: http://www.hasco-suisse.ch
Machine Parts Whslr
N.A.I.C.S.: 332710

HASCO Trading (Shenzhen) Co., Ltd. (1)
Room 505 Liantai Building Shennan Road, Futian District, Shenzhen, 518040, China
Tel.: (86) 755 8831 5112
Machine Parts Whslr
N.A.I.C.S.: 332710
Alex Zeng (Asst Mgr-Mktg)

HASCO form-service AB (1)
Mastunga 102, Hokerum, 52398, Ulricehamn, Sweden
Tel.: (46) 321 288 00
Emp.: 25
Industrial Mold Mfr
N.A.I.C.S.: 333511
Carl-Johan Holmberg (Mng Dir)

Hueck Rheinische GmbH (1)
Helmholtzstrasse 9, 41747, Viersen, Germany
Tel.: (49) 2162 946940
Web Site: http://www.hueck-rheinische.com
Process & Surface Technology
N.A.I.C.S.: 325613

Joh. Pengg AG (1)
Nr 35, Thorl, 8621, Leoben, Austria (50%)
Tel.: (43) 38615090
Web Site: http://www.wire-pengg.com
Sales Range: $50-74.9 Million
Emp.: 200
Other Communication & Energy Wire Mfr
N.A.I.C.S.: 335929
Alexander Phillipp (CEO)

Joint Venture (Non-US):

Peng Usha Martin Pvt. Ltd. (2)
Tatisilwai, Ranchi, 835103, India
Tel.: (91) 651 3053900
Wire Product Mfr
N.A.I.C.S.: 332618

Subsidiary (Non-US):

Pengg Drat s.r.o. (2)
Beethovenova 1269, 43013, Chomutov, Czech Republic
Tel.: (420) 474 332 050
Wire Product Mfr
N.A.I.C.S.: 332618

Subsidiary (Domestic):

Penng Austria GmbH (2)
A-8621, Thorl, 8621, Austria
Tel.: (43) 3861 5090
Web Site: http://www.wire-pengg.com
Steel Products Mfr
N.A.I.C.S.: 332111
Alexander Phillipp (Mng Dir)

Lumpi-Berndorf Draht- und Seilwerk GmbH (1)

Binderlandweg 7, 4030, Linz, Austria
Tel.: (43) 7323838480
Web Site: http://www.lumpi-berndorf.at
Wire & Cable Mfr
N.A.I.C.S.: 332618

OOO HASCO RU (1)
Khoroshevskoye shosse 32 A, 123007, Moscow, Russia
Tel.: (7) 4952870357
Web Site: https://www.hasco.com
Emp.: 5
Machine Parts Whslr
N.A.I.C.S.: 332710

Online Media Communications Design GmbH (1)
W A Mozartgasse 5, 2353, Guntramsdorf, Austria
Tel.: (43) 6641759997
Web Site: https://www.online-media.at
Marketing Consulting Services
N.A.I.C.S.: 541613

PC Electric GmbH (1)
Diesseits 145, 4973, Saint Martin, Austria
Tel.: (43) 7751 61220
Web Site: http://www.pcelectric.at
Electronic Products Mfr
N.A.I.C.S.: 335999

PC&S Technologies GmbH (1)
Am Bleichanger 48, 87600, Kaufbeuren, Germany
Tel.: (49) 8341960150
Web Site: https://pcs-tech.de
Mechatronic Component Mfr
N.A.I.C.S.: 334419

Plasmo Industrietechnik GmbH (1)
Dresdner Strasse 81-85 Stiege 2 6 OG, 1200, Vienna, Austria
Tel.: (43) 18901366
Web Site: https://www.plasmo.eu
Additive Mfr
N.A.I.C.S.: 325998
Juergen Mueller-Borhanian (Mng Dir)

SAFED Industrieofen GmbH (1)
Robert-Bosch-Strasse 4, 73463, Westhausen, Germany
Tel.: (49) 7363 50 71
Industrial Furnace Mfr
N.A.I.C.S.: 333994

SAFED Suisse S.A. (1)
9 Rue du 24-Septembre, 2800, Delemont, Switzerland
Tel.: (41) 32 421 44 60
Web Site: http://www.safed.ch
Heat Tracing Equipment Mfr
N.A.I.C.S.: 333414

Silica Verfahrenstechnik GmbH (1)
Wittestrasse 24, 13509, Berlin, Germany
Tel.: (49) 30 435 735
Web Site: http://silica.berlin
Sales Range: $10-24.9 Million
Engineeering Services
N.A.I.C.S.: 541330

Venturetec Rotating Systems GmbH (1)
Johann-Georg-Weinhart-Strasse 2, 87600, Kaufbeuren, Germany
Tel.: (49) 834190050
Web Site: https://venturetec.de
Slip Ring Mfr
N.A.I.C.S.: 335312
Rainer Fasel (Sls Mgr)

stoba Prazisionstechnik GmbH & Co. KG (1)
Lange Acker 8, 71522, Backnang, Germany
Tel.: (49) 7 191 8060
Web Site: http://www.stoba.de
Metal Component Mfr
N.A.I.C.S.: 332312
Christoph Bode (Mng Dir)

stoba Prazisionstechnik UK Ltd. (1)
Unit Z1 The Old Sawmill Mackleys Industrial Estate Henfield Road, Small Dole, Horsham, BN5 9XR, West Sussex, United Kingdom
Tel.: (44) 1273 494379
Metal Component Mfr
N.A.I.C.S.: 332312
Lee Christian (Mgr-Quality)

stoba Sondermaschinen GmbH (1)

Berndorf AG—(Continued)

Mittereschweg 1, 87700, Memmingen, Germany
Tel.: (49) 83 31 98487 120
Web Site: http://www.stoba-memmingen.de
Metal Component Mfr
N.A.I.C.S.: 332999
Oliver Gunther (Mng Dir)

BERNER KANTONALBANK AG

Bundesplatz 8, PO Box 3001, 3001, Bern, Switzerland
Tel.: (41) 316661111
Web Site: http://www.bekb.ch
BEKN—(SWX)
Sales Range: $500-549.9 Million
Emp.: 1,450
Banking Services
N.A.I.C.S.: 522110
Jurg Rieben (Chm)

BERNER OY

Hitsaajankatu 24, 00810, Helsinki, Finland
Tel.: (358) 2079100   FI
Web Site: http://www.berner.fi
Year Founded: 1883
Rev.: $340,302,639
Assets: $210,888,416
Liabilities: $52,878,697
Net Worth: $158,009,718
Earnings: $13,808,469
Emp.: 510
Fiscal Year-end: 12/31/19
Chemical Specialties, Lubricating Oils, Car Care Chemicals, Crop Protection Products & Household Chemicals Importer, Mfr & Exporter
N.A.I.C.S.: 324191
Hannes Berner (Chm)

Subsidiaries:

Auto-Berner   **(1)**
Toikansuontie 11, 53500, Lappeenranta, Finland   **(100%)**
Tel.: (358) 54515215
Web Site: http://www.autoberner.fi
Sales Range: $25-49.9 Million
Emp.: 32
Automobiles
N.A.I.C.S.: 336110

Auto-Berner Kouvola   **(1)**
Kymenlaaksontie 1, 45100, Kouvola, Finland   **(100%)**
Tel.: (358) 20791011
Web Site: http://www.autoberner.fi
Sales Range: $25-49.9 Million
Emp.: 30
Automobile Dealers
N.A.I.C.S.: 336110

Berner Eesti Oy   **(1)**
Kadaka tee 133, 12915, Tallinn, Estonia   **(100%)**
Tel.: (372) 53333198
Web Site: http://www.berner.ee
Sales Range: $25-49.9 Million
Mfr & Distr of Pesticides & Pest Repellents
N.A.I.C.S.: 325320

Berner Oy - Heinavesi Plant   **(1)**
Yrittajatie 5 Karpalotie 6, 79700, Heinavesi, Finland
Tel.: (358) 20 791 4800
Emp.: 50
Detergent & Shampoo Mfr
N.A.I.C.S.: 325620
Jari Puustinen (Dir-Plant)

Broderna Berner Handels AB   **(1)**
Hemsogatan 10 B, Box 50132, 202 11, Malmo, Sweden
Tel.: (46) 406806840
Web Site: http://www.gullviks.se
Pesticide Distr
N.A.I.C.S.: 424910

UAB Kruzas Nordic Cosmetics Distribution   **(1)**
Lakunu st 30, 09131, Vilnius, Lithuania
Tel.: (370) 61840000
Web Site: http://www.kruzas.lt
Cosmetic Product Distr

N.A.I.C.S.: 424210

BERNER SE

Bernerstrasse 6, 74653, Kunzelsau, Germany
Tel.: (49) 7940 121 0
Web Site: http://www.berner-group.com
Sales Range: $1-4.9 Billion
Emp.: 9,050
Holding Company
N.A.I.C.S.: 551112
Christian A. W. Berner (CEO & Member-Exec Bd)

Subsidiaries:

Albert Berner Deutschland GmbH   **(1)**
Bernerstrasse 4, D-74653, Kunzelsau, Germany
Tel.: (49) 79 40 12 10
Web Site: http://www.berner.de
Door Distr
N.A.I.C.S.: 423710

BTI Befestigungstechnik GmbH & Co. KG   **(1)**
Salzstrasse 51, D-74653, Ingelfingen, Germany
Tel.: (49) 79 40 14 10
Web Site: http://www.bti.de
Sales Range: $250-299.9 Million
Construction Equipment Distr
N.A.I.C.S.: 423390
Jurgen Dietz (Mng Dir)

Caramba Bremen GmbH   **(1)**
Bergedorfer Strasse 6-8, 28219, Bremen, Germany
Tel.: (49) 421389970
Car Wash & Cleaning Services
N.A.I.C.S.: 811192

Caramba Holding GmbH   **(1)**
Wanheimer Strasse 343, 47055, Duisburg, Germany
Tel.: (49) 79 40 12 16 91
Web Site: http://www.caramba.eu
Sales Range: $150-199.9 Million
Chemicals Mfr
N.A.I.C.S.: 325998

Subsidiary (Domestic):

Caramba Chemie GmbH & Co. KG   **(2)**
Wanheimer Str 334 - 336, 47055, Duisburg, Germany
Tel.: (49) 20377860
Web Site: http://www.caramba.eu
Chemicals Mfr
N.A.I.C.S.: 325998

Subsidiary (Domestic):

Ambratec GmbH   **(3)**
Carl-Zeiss-Strasse 43, Mainz, 55129, Germany
Tel.: (49) 6131583930
Web Site: http://www.ambratec.de
Sales Range: $50-74.9 Million
Emp.: 100
Chemical & Allied Product Merchant Distr
N.A.I.C.S.: 424690
Wolfgang Schiller (Mng Dir)

Subsidiary (Non-US):

Automotive Cleaning Chemicals Ltd.   **(3)**
Showground Road, Bridgwater, TA6 6AJ, United Kingdom
Tel.: (44) 1278431310
Web Site: http://www.acc-limited.co.uk
Sales Range: $25-49.9 Million
Emp.: 21
Inorganic Chemical Mfr
N.A.I.C.S.: 325180
Chris Waller (Mng Dir)

Subsidiary (Domestic):

Matecra GmbH   **(3)**
Daimlerstrasse 29, D-89564, Nattheim, Germany
Tel.: (49) 73 21 97 770
Web Site: http://www.matecra.de

Chemicals Mfr
N.A.I.C.S.: 325998

Caramba Nederlands B.V.   **(1)**
Borgstee 3A, 9403 TS, Assen, Netherlands
Tel.: (31) 592345161
Car Wash & Cleaning Services
N.A.I.C.S.: 811192
Romke Kiestra (Mng Dir)

Firmann-Berner AS   **(1)**
Holmaveien 25, 1339, Voyenenga, Norway
Tel.: (47) 67174900
Web Site: http://www.shop.berner.no
Industrial Machinery & Equipment Whslr
N.A.I.C.S.: 423830
Erling Bruun (Mng Dir)

Kent France SAS   **(1)**
29 rue Charles Edouard Jeanneret Technoparc, CS 7001, 78306, Poissy, Cedex, France
Tel.: (33) 182030215
Automotive Repair & Maintenance Services
N.A.I.C.S.: 811111
Christophe Pichon (Mng Dir)

Kent Industri Danmark ApS   **(1)**
Bjergvangen 5D, 3060, Espergaerde, Denmark
Tel.: (45) 49177888
Automotive Repair & Maintenance Services
N.A.I.C.S.: 811111
Marianne Kongsgaard Pedersen (Office Mgr)

Kent Italia s.r.l.   **(1)**
Via Vittime di Piazza della Loggia 6, 10024, Moncalieri, TO, Italy
Tel.: (39) 0800011780
Automotive Repair & Maintenance Services
N.A.I.C.S.: 811111
Marco Molinari (Mng Dir)

Kent Nederland B.V.   **(1)**
Claudius Prinsenlaan 128, 4818 CP, Breda, Netherlands
Tel.: (31) 854868360
Automotive Repair & Maintenance Services
N.A.I.C.S.: 811111

Kent UK Ltd.   **(1)**
Forsyth House Pitreavie Drive Pitreavie Business Park, Dunfermline, KY11 8US, Fife, United Kingdom
Tel.: (44) 1383737172
Automotive Repair & Maintenance Services
N.A.I.C.S.: 811111

WIGO Chemie GmbH   **(1)**
Sandweg 7-13, 55543, Bad Kreuznach, Germany
Tel.: (49) 67189200888
Web Site: http://www.wigo.de
Chemical Product Mfr & Distr
N.A.I.C.S.: 325199

BERNHARD SCHULTE SHIP-MANAGEMENT (CYPRUS) LTD.

Hanseatic House 111 Spyrou Araouzou St, 3036, Limassol, Cyprus
Tel.: (357) 25846400
Web Site: http://www.bs-shipmanagement.com
Year Founded: 1972
Sales Range: $25-49.9 Million
Emp.: 17,000
Ship Management Services
N.A.I.C.S.: 488330
Norbert Aschmann (CEO & Member-Mgmt Bd)

Subsidiaries:

BSM Crew Service Centre (Croatia) Ltd.   **(1)**
Velebitska 36, 21000, Split, Croatia
Tel.: (385) 21 322860
Human Resource Consulting Services
N.A.I.C.S.: 541612

BSM Crew Service Centre (Estonia) Ltd.   **(1)**
53 - 6 Narva Road, 10152, Tallinn, Estonia
Tel.: (372) 6659861
Ship Management Services
N.A.I.C.S.: 488330

BSM Crew Service Centre (Latvia) Ltd.   **(1)**
103-1 Brivibas Str, Riga, 1001, Latvia
Tel.: (371) 6 7501360
Human Resource Consulting Services
N.A.I.C.S.: 541612

BSM Crew Service Centre (Myanmar) Ltd.   **(1)**
F/6 1 Shwe Malar Yeilmon Bayin Naung Road, Kamaryut Township, Yangon, Myanmar
Tel.: (95) 1 536805
Human Resource Consulting Services
N.A.I.C.S.: 541612

BSM Crew Service Centre (Romania) SRL   **(1)**
6th Petru Rares Street, Constanta, 900745, Romania
Tel.: (40) 241 54 59 50
Web Site: http://www.bs-shipmanagement.com
Emp.: 10
Human Resource Consulting Services
N.A.I.C.S.: 541612

BSM Crew Service Centre (Venezuela) C.A.   **(1)**
Centro Banaven Cubo Negro Torre B Oficina B-61 al lado del CCCT, Caracas, Edo Miranda, Venezuela
Tel.: (58) 212 959 0959
Human Resource Consulting Services
N.A.I.C.S.: 541612

Bernhard Schulte Shipmanagement (China) Company Limited   **(1)**
1-3F Block No 7 1690 Cai Lun Road, Zhang Jiang, 201203, Shanghai, China
Tel.: (86) 21 61061333
Ship Management Services
N.A.I.C.S.: 488330
Mingfa Liu (Mng Dir)

Bernhard Schulte Shipmanagement (Deutschland) GmbH & Co. KG   **(1)**
Vorsetzen 54, 20459, Hamburg, Germany
Tel.: (49) 40 822265 0
Ship Management Services
N.A.I.C.S.: 488330
Jan Warmke (Mng Dir)

Bernhard Schulte Shipmanagement (Hellas) SPLLC.   **(1)**
Kifisias Avenue 6-8, Marousi, 15125, Athens, Greece
Tel.: (30) 210 6930 330
Ship Management Services
N.A.I.C.S.: 488330

Bernhard Schulte Shipmanagement (Hong Kong) Ltd.   **(1)**
2602 K Wah Centre 191 Java Road, North Point, Hong Kong, China (Hong Kong)
Tel.: (852) 2561 8838
Ship Management Services
N.A.I.C.S.: 488330

Bernhard Schulte Shipmanagement (India) Pvt. Limited   **(1)**
401 Olympia Hiranandani Gardens, Powai, Mumbai, 400 076, India
Tel.: (91) 22 400173 00
Web Site: http://www.bs-shipmanagement.com
Emp.: 200
Ship Management Services
N.A.I.C.S.: 488330
Sanjeev Sharma (Mng Dir)

Bernhard Schulte Shipmanagement (Isle of Man) Ltd.   **(1)**
Dorchester House Belmont Hill, London, IM1 4RE, Isle of Man, United Kingdom
Tel.: (44) 1624 631800
Web Site: http://www.bs-shipmanagement.com
Emp.: 45
Ship Management Services
N.A.I.C.S.: 488330
Neil McNeil (Mng Dir)

Bernhard Schulte Shipmanagement (Poland) Ltd.   **(1)**
27 Jana z Kolna Str, 81 354, Gdynia, Poland
Tel.: (48) 58 66 11 661

Human Resource Consulting Services
N.A.I.C.S.: 541612

Bernhard Schulte Shipmanagement (Singapore) Pte. Ltd., (1)
152 Beach Rd #32-00 Gateway East, Singapore, 189721, Singapore
Tel.: (65) 62722220
Web Site: http://www.bs-shipmanagement.com
Sales Range: $10-24.9 Million
Emp.: 29
Ship Management, Logistics & Customer Services Operations
N.A.I.C.S.: 561110
Sandip Mirchandani *(Gen Mgr)*

Bernhard Schulte Shipmanagement (UK) Ltd. (1)
3 Hedley Court Orion Way Orion Business Park, Newcastle upon Tyne, NE29 7ST, United Kingdom
Tel.: (44) 191 29318 20
Web Site:
　　http://www.bernhardschultenewcastle.com
Emp.: 36
Ship Management Services
N.A.I.C.S.: 488330
Norbert Aschmann *(Pres)*

PT. BSM Crew Service Centre Indonesia (1)
Sentra Pemuda Kav 5-6 Jalan Pemuda No 61, Jakarta, 13220, Indonesia
Tel.: (62) 21 2961 7300
Human Resource Consulting Services
N.A.I.C.S.: 541612

BERNINA SCHWEIZ AG
Gubelstrasse 39 Oerlikon, 8050, Zurich, Oerlikon, Switzerland
Tel.: (41) 442861060
Web Site: http://www.bernina.com
Sales Range: $150-199.9 Million
Emp.: 1,000
Mfr of Household Sewing Machines, Quilting Machines & Embroidery Machines
N.A.I.C.S.: 335220
Rols Hugelshofer *(CFO)*

Subsidiaries:

Bernina International AG (1)
Seestrasse 161, CH 8266, Steckborn, Switzerland (100%)
Tel.: (41) 527621111
Web Site: http://www.bernina.com
Sales Range: $100-124.9 Million
Emp.: 340
Mfr of Sewing Machines
N.A.I.C.S.: 339999
Claude Dreyer *(CEO)*

Bernina of America Inc. (1)
3702 Prairie Lake Ct, Aurora, IL 60504
Tel.: (630) 978-2500
Web Site: http://www.berninausa.com
Sales Range: $100-124.9 Million
Emp.: 150
Sewing Machines & Related Items
N.A.I.C.S.: 321999
Paul Ashworth *(Pres)*

BERONI GROUP LIMITED
Level 16 175 Pitt Street, Sydney, 2000, NSW, Australia
Tel.: (61) 291591827　　　　AU
Web Site:
　　https://www.beronigroup.com
BTG—(NSXA)
Rev.: $1,683,140
Assets: $9,124,851
Liabilities: $2,760,150
Net Worth: $6,364,701
Earnings: ($2,208,888)
Fiscal Year-end: 12/31/21
Medicinal & Botanical Manufacturing
N.A.I.C.S.: 325411
Boqing Zhang *(Founder)*

Subsidiaries:

Beroni Biotech Inc. (1)

1 - 144 6 Ginza, Tyuo-ku, Tokyo, 104-0061, Japan
Tel.: (81) 338638998
Pharmaceutical Mfr & Distr
N.A.I.C.S.: 325412

Beroni Japan Inc. (1)
1 - 144 6 Ginz, Tyuo-ku, Tokyo, 104-0061, Japan
Tel.: (81) 338638998
Pharmaceutical Preparation Mfr
N.A.I.C.S.: 325412

Beroni USA Corporation (1)
2083 Center Ave Ste 3A, Fort Lee, NJ 07024
Tel.: (214) 762-2888
Pharmaceutical Preparation Mfr
N.A.I.C.S.: 325412

Tianjin Beroni Biotechnology Co., Limited (1)
Level 10/ Building 11, Zhong Bei High Technology Industry Park XiQing District, Tianjin, China
Tel.: (86) 2259955753
Pharmaceutical Preparation Mfr
N.A.I.C.S.: 325412

BERRY BROS. & RUDD LIMITED
3 St James's Street, London, SW1A 1EG, United Kingdom
Tel.: (44) 2070228973
Web Site: http://www.bbr.com
Year Founded: 1698
Sales Range: $300-349.9 Million
Emp.: 200
Wine & Spirits Retailer
N.A.I.C.S.: 445320
Jasper Morris *(Dir-Burgundy)*

Subsidiaries:

Berry Bros & Rudd Singapore Pte. Ltd. (1)
88B Amoy Street, Singapore, 69907, Singapore
Tel.: (65) 67090100
Wine Distr
N.A.I.C.S.: 445320

BERRY GENOMICS CO., LTD.
Building 5 No 4 Life Garden Road Science Park, Changping District, Beijing, China
Tel.: (86) 1053259188
Web Site:
　　http://www.berrygenomics.com
Year Founded: 2010
710—(SSE)
Sales Range: $25-49.9 Million
Biotechnology Company; Prenatal Genetic Testing
N.A.I.C.S.: 541714
Gao Yang *(Chm & Gen Mgr)*

Subsidiaries:

Xcelom Limited (1)
10/F Metropole Square No 2 On Yiu Street, Sha Tin, NT, China (Hong Kong)
Tel.: (852) 39900880
Web Site: https://www.xcelom.com
Testing Laboratory Services
N.A.I.C.S.: 541380

BERTAM ALLIANCE BERHAD
Lot 10 8th Floor Wisma Damai Point Luyang, Sabah, 88300, Kota Kinabalu, Malaysia
Tel.: (60) 88201832　　　　MY
Web Site:
　　https://www.bertamalliance.com
Year Founded: 1994
BERTAM—(KLS)
Rev.: $4,949,852
Assets: $35,085,826,963
Liabilities: $6,386,190,290
Net Worth: $28,699,636,672
Earnings: $123,501,742
Emp.: 40
Fiscal Year-end: 12/31/23

Property Development Services
N.A.I.C.S.: 531311
Chiew Boon Chin *(Exec Dir)*

Subsidiaries:

Bertam Development Sdn. Bhd. (1)
Brem House Level 3A Crystal Crown Hotel No 12, Lorong Utara A Off Jalan Utara, Petaling Jaya, 46200, Selangor, Malaysia
Tel.: (60) 379587288
Sales Range: $50-74.9 Million
Emp.: 15
Property Development Services
N.A.I.C.S.: 531312

Subsidiary (Domestic):

Antara Megah Sdn. Bhd. (2)
3rd Floor Brem House Crystal Crown Hotel No 12 Lorong Utara A, Off Jalan Utara, Petaling Jaya, 46200, Selangor, Malaysia
Tel.: (60) 3 79587288
Property Development Services
N.A.I.C.S.: 531312

UH Industries & Development Sdn. Bhd. (1)
Brem House Level 3A Crystal Crown Hotel No 12, Lorong Utara A Off Jalan Utara, Petaling Jaya, 46200, Selangor, Malaysia
Tel.: (60) 379587288
Sales Range: $25-49.9 Million
Emp.: 30
Property Development Services
N.A.I.C.S.: 531312

BERTEL O. STEEN AS
Solheimveien 7, 1473, Lorenskog, Norway
Tel.: (47) 67 92 60 00
Web Site: http://www.bos.no
Sales Range: $1-4.9 Billion
Emp.: 2,000
Holding Company
N.A.I.C.S.: 551112
Inge Ketil Hansen *(Chm)*

Subsidiaries:

Viking Fottoy A/S (1)
Luhrtoppen 2, PO Box 143, N-1471, Lorenskog, Norway
Tel.: (47) 22072400
Web Site: http://www.vikingfootwear.com
Sales Range: $25-49.9 Million
Emp.: 77
Outdoor Footwear Mfr
N.A.I.C.S.: 316210
Hakom Migard *(Mng Dir)*

Subsidiary (Non-US):

Viking Footwear A/S (2)
Langebjergvaenget 2, 4000, Roskilde, Denmark (100%)
Tel.: (45) 72118180
Web Site: http://www.vikingfootwear.com
Sales Range: $25-49.9 Million
Emp.: 6
Outdoor Footwear Mfr
N.A.I.C.S.: 316210

Viking Footwear AB (2)
Gamla Almedalsvagen 6, Gothenburg, 41263, Sweden (100%)
Tel.: (46) 31985090
Web Site: http://www.vikingfootwear.com
Sales Range: $25-49.9 Million
Emp.: 7
Outdoor Footwear Mfr
N.A.I.C.S.: 316210
Michael Frederiksson *(Gen Mgr)*

Viking Jalkineet Oy (2)
Pakkalankuja 6, SF-01510, Vantaa, Finland (100%)
Tel.: (358) 98386180
Web Site: http://www.vikingfootwear.com
Sales Range: $25-49.9 Million
Emp.: 8
Outdoor Footwear Mfr
N.A.I.C.S.: 316210
Tapio Valkonen *(Mng Dir)*

BERTELSMANN SE & CO. KGAA
Carl-Bertelsmann-Strasse 270,

33311, Gutersloh, Germany
Tel.: (49) 5241800　　　　De
Web Site: http://www.bertelsmann.de
Year Founded: 1835
Rev.: $20,183,236,780
Assets: $30,591,215,620
Liabilities: $18,894,277,920
Net Worth: $11,696,937,700
Earnings: $1,221,767,260
Emp.: 126,447
Fiscal Year-end: 12/31/19
Holding Company; Magazine, Book & Newspaper Publisher; Television Broadcasting; Film Production; Direct Marketing Services
N.A.I.C.S.: 551112
Christoph Mohn *(Chm-Supervisory Bd)*

Subsidiaries:

3 C Deutschland GmbH (1)
Edisonstrasse 19, 74076, Heilbronn, Germany
Tel.: (49) 7131797866700
Web Site: https://www.3c-d.de
Digital Services
N.A.I.C.S.: 518210

8ball Music B.V. (1)
Graaf Florislaan 38, 1217 KM, Hilversum, Netherlands
Tel.: (31) 352050820
Web Site: http://www.8ballmusic.nl
Music Publishing Services
N.A.I.C.S.: 711130
Ronald De Bas *(Head-Promo & Mgr-Artist)*

99 Pro Media GmbH (1)
Plagwitzer Hofe Zschochersche Strasse 80a, 04229, Leipzig, Germany
Tel.: (49) 3412134160
Web Site: https://www.99pro.de
Emp.: 120
Media Production Services
N.A.I.C.S.: 512110

AFS IT Services Estonia OU (1)
Telliskivi 60-2 I hoone, 10412, Tallinn, Estonia
Tel.: (372) 51917882
Web Site: http://www.itarvato.com
Emp.: 130
Information Technology Development Services
N.A.I.C.S.: 541611
Ants Konga *(Mgr-Dev)*

AZ Direct AG (1)
Lorzenparkstrasse 10, 6330, Cham, Switzerland
Tel.: (41) 412484444
Web Site: http://www.az-direct.ch
Internet Marketing Services
N.A.I.C.S.: 541613
Rene Schaad *(Mgr-Sls & Bus Dev)*

AZ Direct Osterreich GmbH (1)
Donau City Strasse 6 Andromeda Tower, 1220, Vienna, Austria
Tel.: (43) 125965050
Marketing Consulting Services
N.A.I.C.S.: 541613
Markus Duft *(Head-Digital Mktg)*

Ad Alliance GmbH (1)
Picassoplatz 1, 50679, Cologne, Germany
Tel.: (49) 22145620
Web Site: https://www.ad-alliance.de
Advertisement & Media Agency Services
N.A.I.C.S.: 541810

Affero Lab Participacoes S.A. (1)
Praca Pio X 99 8th Floor, Downtown, Rio de Janeiro, 20040-020, Brazil
Tel.: (55) 1133726100
Web Site: http://www.afferolab.com.br
Software Services
N.A.I.C.S.: 541511

Albrecht Knaus Verlag (1)
Neumarkter Strasse 28, Munich, 81673, Germany (100%)
Tel.: (49) 8941360
Web Site: http://www.bertelsmann.com
Sales Range: $50-74.9 Million
Emp.: 250
Publisher of Fiction, Memoirs, History, Art, Politics

Bertelsmann SE & Co. KGaA—(Continued)

N.A.I.C.S.: 513130

Alliant International University, Inc. (1)
2030 W El Camino Ave, Sacramento, CA 95833
Tel.: (916) 565-2955
Web Site: http://www.alliant.edu
Educational Support Services
N.A.I.C.S.: 611710
Marion Chiurazzi (Program Dir)

Alliant International University-Campus Mexico, S.C. (1)
Amberes, 06600, Mexico, Mexico
Tel.: (52) 5591300590
Web Site: http://www.alliantmexico.com.mx
College Campus Services
N.A.I.C.S.: 611310

AppLike Group GmbH (1)
An der Alster 42, 20099, Hamburg, Germany
Tel.: (49) 4037035440
Web Site: https://www.applike-group.com
Software Development Services
N.A.I.C.S.: 541511

Arvato Digital Services Limited (1)
9 Dai Hei Street, Tai Po Industrial Estate
New Territories, Tai Po, China (Hong Kong)
Tel.: (852) 26661792
Digital Services
N.A.I.C.S.: 518210
Jeff Wong (Dir-Bus Unit & Sourcing Svcs)

Arvato SE (1)
Reinhard-Mohn-Strasse 22, 33333, Gutersloh, Germany
Tel.: (49) 511899955650
Web Site: https://arvato.com
Logistic Services
N.A.I.C.S.: 541614

Arvato Services k.s. (1)
Plaska 622/3, 150 00, Prague, Czech Republic
Tel.: (420) 602200121
Web Site: http://www.arvato-services.cz
Electronic Product Repairing Services
N.A.I.C.S.: 811210
Barbora Pesalova (Controller-Fin)

Arvato Supply Chain Solutions SE (1)
Reinhard-Mohn-Strasse 22, 33333, Gutersloh, Germany
Tel.: (49) 52419090174
Web Site: http://www.arvato-supply-chain.com
Emp.: 15,000
Logistic Services
N.A.I.C.S.: 541614
Andreas Barth (Mng Dir)

Arvato de Mexico, S.A. de C.V. (1)
Av Cuitlahuac 2519 Col San Salvador
Xochimanca, Azcapotzalco, 02870, Mexico, Mexico
Tel.: (52) 5553428014
Phonograph Services
N.A.I.C.S.: 512250
Arvato Tatiana (Mgr-Facilities)

Ausbildung.de GmbH (1)
Wittener Str 87, D-44789, Bochum, Germany
Tel.: (49) 23441560000
Web Site: https://www.ausbildung.de
Internet Provider Services
N.A.I.C.S.: 516210

BCE France SAS (1)
18 rue Bela Bartok, 79000, Niort, France
Tel.: (33) 649157748
Web Site: http://www.bcefrance.fr
Information Technology Security Services
N.A.I.C.S.: 561621
Eric Boutillon (Pres)

BCS Broadcast Sachsen GmbH & Co. KG (1)
Ammonstrasse 35, 01067, Dresden, Germany
Tel.: (49) 351500110
Web Site: http://www.bcs-sachsen.de
Advertising Services
N.A.I.C.S.: 541810

BMG Production Music (France) SAS (1)
5 rue de Castiglione, 75008, Paris, France
Tel.: (33) 140727890
Web Site: http://www.bmgproductionmusic.fr
Music Publishing Services
N.A.I.C.S.: 512230
Jerome Keff (Mng Dir)

BMG Production Music (Germany) GmbH (1)
Charlottenstrasse 59, 10117, Berlin, Germany
Tel.: (49) 30300133277
Web Site: http://www.bmgproductionmusic.de
Music Program Services
N.A.I.C.S.: 512230

BMG Production Music, Inc. (1)
1 Park Ave, New York, NY 10016
Tel.: (323) 248-9527
Web Site: http://www.bmgproductionmusic.com
Film Production Services
N.A.I.C.S.: 512110
Darrel Shirk (VP-Ops)

BMG Rights Management GmbH (1)
Tel.: (49) 30300133300
Web Site: https://www.bmg.com
Sales Range: $100-124.9 Million
Emp.: 150
Music Intellectual Property Management Services
N.A.I.C.S.: 533110
Maximilian Kolb (Exec VP)

Subsidiary (US):

BMG Rights Management (US) LLC (2)
1 Park Ave, New York, NY 10016
Tel.: (212) 561-3000
Web Site: http://www.bmg.com
Sales Range: $25-49.9 Million
Emp.: 85
Music Patent Owner & Publisher
N.A.I.C.S.: 512230
Joe Gillen (CFO-North America & Exec VP)

Subsidiary (Domestic):

Verse Music Group LLC (3)
134 W 25th St 5th Fl, New York, NY 10001
Tel.: (212) 494-0078
Web Site: http://www.versemusicgroup.com
Music Publishing
N.A.I.C.S.: 512230
Curt Frasca (Co-Founder & CEO)

Subsidiary (Non-US):

Chrysalis Group PLC (2)
33 Wigmore St, London, W1U 1QX, United Kingdom
Tel.: (44) 2072212213
Web Site: http://www.chrysalis.com
Sales Range: $75-99.9 Million
Emp.: 50
Music, Radio, Television & Media Products
N.A.I.C.S.: 516110

Lasgo Chrysalis (2)
Unit 1 Falcon Park Neasden Lane, Neasden, London, NW10 1RZ, United Kingdom
Tel.: (44) 2084598800
Web Site: http://www.lasgo.com
Sales Range: $25-49.9 Million
Emp.: 12
CD, DVD & Book Distr
N.A.I.C.S.: 423990
Garry Elwood (Mng Dir)

Union Square Music Ltd. (2)
8th Floor 5 Merchant Square Paddington, London, W2 1AS, United Kingdom
Tel.: (44) 20 3214 1200
Web Site: http://www.unionsquaremusic.co.uk
Sales Range: $10-24.9 Million
Digital CD & DVD Mfr
N.A.I.C.S.: 334112

BMG Rights Management Services (UK) Limited (1)
5 Merchant Square, London, W2 1AS, United Kingdom
Tel.: (44) 2032141200
Music Publishing Services

N.A.I.C.S.: 512230

Bertelsmann Corporate Services India Private Limited (1)
Windsor IT Park Tower B 9th Floor A-1 Sector 125, Noida, 201301, India
Tel.: (91) 1204517413
Web Site: http://www.bertelsmann.in
Media Services
N.A.I.C.S.: 541840

Bertelsmann Data Services GmbH (1)
Carl-Bertelsmann-Strasse 270, 33311, Gutersloh, Germany
Tel.: (49) 5241800
Web Site: https://dataservices.bertelsmann.de
Information Technology Services
N.A.I.C.S.: 518210

Bertelsmann Global Business Services GmbH (1)
Ringstrasse 16-20, 33378, Rheda-Wiedenbruck, Germany
Tel.: (49) 52418044000
Web Site: https://www.invoice.bertelsmann.com
Online Shopping Services
N.A.I.C.S.: 812990

Bertelsmann Inc. (1)
1745 Broadway, New York, NY 10019 (100%)
Tel.: (212) 782-1000
Web Site: http://www.bertelsmann.com
Sales Range: $350-399.9 Million
Emp.: 800
Publishing Holding Company
N.A.I.C.S.: 551112

Subsidiary (Domestic):

OnCourse Learning Corporation (2)
20225 Water Tower Blvd, Brookfield, WI 53045
Tel.: (262) 754-3744
Web Site: http://www.oncourselearning.com
Sales Range: $25-49.9 Million
Emp.: 110
Online Professional Training Services
N.A.I.C.S.: 611420
Michael McNulty (VP-Client Svcs)

Subsidiary (Domestic):

Gannett Healthcare Group (3)
1721 Moon Lake Blvd Ste 540, Hoffman Estates, IL 60169-2170
Tel.: (847) 839-1700
Web Site: http://www.nurse.com
Sales Range: $25-49.9 Million
Emp.: 60
Healthcare Magazine & Website Publisher
N.A.I.C.S.: 513120
Melyni Serpa (CEO)

Subsidiary (Domestic):

Penguin Random House LLC (2)
1745 Broadway, New York, NY 10019 (75%)
Tel.: (212) 366-2652
Web Site: http://www.penguinrandomhouse.com
Book Publisher & Distr
N.A.I.C.S.: 513130
Annette Danek-Akey (Exec VP-Supply Chain)

Subsidiary (Domestic):

Hay House, LLC (3)
2776 Loker Ave W, Carlsbad, CA 92010
Web Site: http://www.hayhouse.com
Book Publishers
N.A.I.C.S.: 513130
Stacey Smith (Mgr-Contracts)

Division (Domestic):

Random House LLC (3)
1745 Broadway, New York, NY 10019
Tel.: (212) 782-9000
Web Site: http://www.randomhouse.com
Sales Range: $1-4.9 Billion
Emp.: 5,264
Book Publishers
N.A.I.C.S.: 513130
Gina Centrello (Pres & Publr)

Group (Domestic):

Bantam Dell Publishing Group (4)
1745 Broadway, New York, NY 10019 (100%)
Tel.: (212) 782-9000
Web Site: http://www.randomhouse.com
Sales Range: $50-74.9 Million
Emp.: 200
Publisher of Hardcover, Mass Market & Trade Paperback Books, General Fiction & Non-Fiction for Adults & Young Readers
N.A.I.C.S.: 513130
Sanyu Dillon (VP & Dir-Creative Mktg & Bantam Dell)

Subsidiary (Domestic):

Arvato Digital (5)
108 Monticello Rd, Weaverville, NC 28787-9442
Tel.: (828) 658-2000
Web Site: http://www.arvatodigitalservices.com
Production of VCDs & CDs
N.A.I.C.S.: 334610

Subsidiary (Non-US):

Bantam Dell Canada (5)
320 Front Street West, Toronto, M5C 2V6, ON, Canada (100%)
Tel.: (416) 364-4449
Web Site: http://www.randomhouse.ca
Sales Range: $25-49.9 Million
Emp.: 60
Wholesale & Direct Book Supplier
N.A.I.C.S.: 459210

Subsidiary (Domestic):

Berryville Graphics Inc. (5)
25 Jack Enders Blvd, Berryville, VA 22613 (100%)
Tel.: (540) 955-2750
Web Site: http://www.bpg-usa.com
Book Manufacturer-Letterpress, Web & Sheetfed Offset Printing, Binding
N.A.I.C.S.: 323117

Dell Publishing (5)
1745 Broadway, New York, NY 10036-4039 (100%)
Tel.: (212) 782-9000
Web Site: http://www.bdd.com
Books Publishing Services
N.A.I.C.S.: 513130

Doubleday (5)
1745 Broadway, New York, NY 10019
Tel.: (212) 782-9000
Web Site: http://www.doubleday.com
Sales Range: $25-49.9 Million
Emp.: 100
Book Publishers; Mail Order Book Club
N.A.I.C.S.: 513130

Division (Domestic):

Alfred A. Knopf, Inc. (6)
1745 Broadway, New York, NY 10019
Tel.: (212) 782-9000
Sales Range: $25-49.9 Million
Emp.: 85
Publishers of Fiction, Nonfiction, Juvenile Books
N.A.I.C.S.: 513130
Gabrielle Brooks (VP-Dir-Promo)

Subsidiary (Domestic):

Dynamic Graphics Inc. (5)
945 Horsham Rd, Horsham, PA 19044-1238
Tel.: (215) 441-8880
Web Site: http://www.dgs.com
Sales Range: $25-49.9 Million
Emp.: 60
Book Cover Decorating
N.A.I.C.S.: 323111
Jack O'Donnell (Exec VP)

Offset Paperback Mfrs., Inc. (BPMC) (5)
2211 Memorial Hwy, Dallas, PA 18612
Tel.: (570) 675-5261
Web Site: http://www.bpg-usa.com
Mfr of Offset Paperbacks
N.A.I.C.S.: 513130
Bob Scheifflee (Mgr-Production)

Subsidiary (Non-US):

Transworld Publishers **(5)**
61-63 Uxbridge Road, London, W5 5SA,
United Kingdom **(100%)**
Tel.: (44) 2085792652
Web Site: http://www.transworld-
publishers.co.uk
Sales Range: $50-74.9 Million
Emp.: 207
Publishers of Fiction & Non-Fiction Books
N.A.I.C.S.: 513120
Larry Snilay (Mng Dir)

Subsidiary (Domestic):

Bantam Books Ltd. **(6)**
Century House 61 63 Uxbridge Road, Eal-
ing, London, W5 5SA, United
Kingdom **(100%)**
Tel.: (44) 2085792652
Web Site:
http://www.booksattransworld.co.uk
Sales Range: $25-49.9 Million
Emp.: 200
Book Publishers
N.A.I.C.S.: 513130

Bantam Paperbacks UK **(6)**
Century House 61 63 Uxbridge Rd Ealing,
London, W5 5SA, United Kingdom **(100%)**
Tel.: (44) 2085792652
Web Site:
http://www.booksattransworld.co.uk
Sales Range: $25-49.9 Million
Emp.: 200
Paperback Books
N.A.I.C.S.: 513120

Bantam Press UK **(6)**
61 63 Uxbridge Rd Ealing, London, W5
5SA, United Kingdom **(100%)**
Tel.: (44) 2085792652
Web Site:
http://www.booksattransworld.co.uk
Emp.: 200
Fiction & Non-Fiction Book Publisher
N.A.I.C.S.: 513120
Larry Finlay (Mng Dir)

Corgi Books Ltd. **(6)**
61 63 Uxbridge Rd Ealing, London, W5
5SA, United Kingdom **(100%)**
Tel.: (44) 2085792652
Web Site:
http://www.booksattransworld.co.uk
Sales Range: $25-49.9 Million
Publisher of Mass-Market & Trade Paper-
backs in all General Fiction & Non-Fiction
Areas
N.A.I.C.S.: 513120

Subsidiary (Domestic):

Books on Tape, Inc. **(4)**
400 Hahn Rd, Westminster, MD 21157
Tel.: (410) 848-1900
Web Site: http://www.booksontape.com
Sales Range: $100-124.9 Million
Emp.: 500
Books on Tape Operations & Distribution
Center
N.A.I.C.S.: 334610
Frank Steinert (Sr VP-HR)

Fodor's Travel Publications, Inc. **(4)**
1745 Broadway, New York, NY 10019
Tel.: (212) 751-2600
Web Site: http://www.fodors.com
Sales Range: $25-49.9 Million
Emp.: 40
Travel Guides Publisher
N.A.I.C.S.: 513130

Subsidiary (Non-US):

Penguin Books Ltd **(4)**
80 Strand, London, WC2R 0RL, United
Kingdom
Tel.: (44) 2071393000
Web Site: http://www.penguin.co.uk
Book Publishers
N.A.I.C.S.: 513130

Subsidiary (Non-US):

Penguin Australia Pty Ltd **(5)**
707 Collins St, PO Box 23360, Melbourne,
3008, VIC, Australia
Tel.: (61) 385374599

Web Site: http://www.penguin.com.au
Sales Range: $125-149.9 Million
Emp.: 345
Book Publishers
N.A.I.C.S.: 513130
Julie Burland (CEO-Australia & New Zea-
land)

Penguin Books Benelux BV **(5)**
Herengracht 418 II, Amsterdam, 1017 BZ,
Netherlands
Tel.: (31) 20 625 9566
Book Publishers
N.A.I.C.S.: 513130

**Penguin Books Deutschland
GmbH** **(5)**
Justinianstr 4, 60322, Frankfurt am Main,
Germany
Tel.: (49) 69628081
Books Publishing Services
N.A.I.C.S.: 513130

Penguin Books South Africa **(5)**
Rosebank Office Park Block D 181 Jan
Smuts Avenue, Parktown, 2193, South Af-
rica
Tel.: (27) 11 327 3550
Web Site: http://www.penguinbooks.co.za
Sales Range: $25-49.9 Million
Emp.: 68
Book Distr
N.A.I.C.S.: 424920
Steve Connolly (Mng Dir)

Penguin Books, S.A. **(5)**
Glorieta de Quevedo 9, 28015, Madrid,
Spain
Tel.: (34) 91 593 1306
Web Site: http://www.penguinspain.com
Sales Range: $50-74.9 Million
Book Distr
N.A.I.C.S.: 424920
Javier Riveira (Mng Dir)

Penguin Ireland **(5)**
Suites 47-51 Morrison Chambers 32 Nas-
sau Street, Dublin, Ireland
Tel.: (353) 15314150
Web Site: http://www.penguin.ie
Sales Range: $25-49.9 Million
Book Publishers
N.A.I.C.S.: 513130
Michael McLoughlin (Publr)

Subsidiary (Domestic):

Penguin Random House Ltd. **(5)**
80 Strand, London, WC2R 0RL, United
Kingdom **(100%)**
Tel.: (44) 2071393000
Web Site: http://www.penguin.co.uk
Holding Company; Book Publisher
N.A.I.C.S.: 551112
Nigel Portwood (Exec VP-Global Ops)

Subsidiary (US):

Penguin Group (USA) Inc. **(6)**
375 Hudson St, New York, NY
10014-3658 **(100%)**
Tel.: (212) 366-2000
Web Site: http://www.us.penguingroup.com
Sales Range: $1-4.9 Billion
Emp.: 1,200
Book Publishers
N.A.I.C.S.: 513130
Frank Autunnale (VP-Fin)

Unit (Domestic):

DK Publishing **(7)**
1450 Broadway Ste 801, New York, NY
10018 **(100%)**
Tel.: (646) 674-4047
Web Site: http://www.dk.com
Sales Range: $100-124.9 Million
Nonfiction Books, CD-ROMs & Videos Pub-
lisher
N.A.I.C.S.: 513130
Ian Hudson (CEO)

Division (Domestic):

Penguin Group UK **(6)**
80 Strand, London, WC2R 0RL, United
Kingdom **(100%)**
Tel.: (44) 2070103000
Web Site: http://www.penguin.co.uk

Sales Range: $150-199.9 Million
Emp.: 950
Book Publishers
N.A.I.C.S.: 513130
Helena Peacock (Sec & Dir-Legal)

Subsidiary (Domestic):

Dorling Kindersley Ltd. **(7)**
80 Strand, London, WC2R 0RL, United
Kingdom **(100%)**
Tel.: (44) 1206255678
Web Site: http://www.dk.com
Nonfiction & Reference Books Publisher
N.A.I.C.S.: 513130

Ladybird Books Ltd. **(7)**
80 Strand, London, WC2R 0RL, United
Kingdom **(100%)**
Tel.: (44) 2071393000
Web Site: http://www.penguin.co.uk
Sales Range: $200-249.9 Million
Emp.: 500
Children's Book & Educational Material Pub-
lisher
N.A.I.C.S.: 513130
Sally Folyer (Mng Dir)

Subsidiary (Non-US):

**Penguin Random House Grupo
Editorial** **(4)**
Travessera de Gracia 47-49, 8021, Barce-
lona, Spain **(100%)**
Tel.: (34) 933660300
Web Site:
http://www.penguinrandomhouse.com
Sales Range: $50-74.9 Million
Book Publishers
N.A.I.C.S.: 513130
Nuria Cabuti Brull (CEO)

**Penguin Random House LLC -
Canada** **(4)**
320 Front Street West Suite 1400, Toronto,
M5V 3B6, ON, Canada
Tel.: (416) 364-4449
Web Site:
http://www.penguinrandomhouse.ca
Book Publishing & Printing
N.A.I.C.S.: 513130
Kristin Cochrane (CEO)

Subsidiary (Domestic):

Tundra Books Inc. **(5)**
320 Front Street West, Toronto, M5C 2V6,
ON, Canada **(100%)**
Tel.: (416) 364-4449
Web Site: http://www.tundrabooks.com
Sales Range: $10-24.9 Million
Emp.: 35
Children's Book Publishers
N.A.I.C.S.: 513130
Tara Walker (Publr)

Group (Domestic):

**Random House Adult Trade
Group** **(4)**
1745 Broadway, New York, NY 10019-0002
Tel.: (212) 751-2600
Web Site: http://www.randomhouse.com
Sales Range: $200-249.9 Million
Emp.: 1,000
Book Publishers
N.A.I.C.S.: 513130

Unit (Domestic):

**Random House Trade Publishing
Group** **(5)**
1745 Broadway, New York, NY 10019
Tel.: (212) 751-2600
Web Site: http://www.randomhouse.com
Rev.: $100,000,000
Emp.: 150
Trade Paperback Book Publishers
N.A.I.C.S.: 513130

Subsidiary (Domestic):

Random House Children's Books **(4)**
1745 Broadway, New York, NY 10019
Tel.: (212) 366-2652
Web Site:
http://www.penguinrandomhouse.com
Children's Book Publishers
N.A.I.C.S.: 513130
Barbara Marcus (Pres & Publr)

Schocken Books **(4)**
1745 Broadway, New York, NY 10019
Tel.: (212) 751-2600
Web Site: http://www.randomhouse.com
Books Publishing Services
N.A.I.C.S.: 513130

Smashing Ideas, Inc. **(4)**
2211 Elliott Ave Ste 110, Seattle, WA 98121
Tel.: (206) 378-0100
Web Site: http://smashingideas.com
Sales Range: $1-9.9 Million
Emp.: 30
Motion Picture & Video Production Services
N.A.I.C.S.: 512110
Lisa Forsyth (Program Dir)

Group (Domestic):

The Ballantine Publishing Group **(4)**
1745 Broadway, New York, NY 10019
Tel.: (212) 782-9000
Web Site: http://www.randomhouse.com
Sales Range: $25-49.9 Million
Emp.: 100
Mass Market Books, Trade Paperbacks
N.A.I.C.S.: 513130

The Crown Publishing Group **(4)**
1745 Broadway, New York, NY 10019
Tel.: (212) 782-9000
Web Site: http://www.crownpublishing.com
Sales Range: $100-124.9 Million
Emp.: 400
Book Publishers
N.A.I.C.S.: 513130
Tammy Blake (VP & Dir-Publicity Crown
Archetype, Harmony Books & Rodale)

Subsidiary (Domestic):

Relias Learning LLC **(2)**
111 Corning Rd Ste 205, Cary, NC 27518
Tel.: (877) 200-0020
Web Site: http://www.reliaslearning.com
Sales Range: $50-74.9 Million
Online Training to Senior Care, Health &
Human Services, Corrections & Intellectual
& Developmental Disabilities Organizations
N.A.I.C.S.: 611430
Bjoern Bauer (CFO)

Subsidiary (Domestic):

AHC Media LLC **(3)**
950 E Paces Ferry Rd NE, Atlanta, GA
30326
Tel.: (404) 262-5476
Web Site: http://ahcmedia.com
Healthcare Newsletter Publisher
N.A.I.C.S.: 513120
Tria Kreutzer (Sr Acct Mgr)

**Advanced Practice Strategies,
Inc.** **(3)**
470 Atlantic Ave 14th Fl, Boston, MA 02210
Tel.: (617) 275-7300
Web Site: http://www.aps-web.com
Medical Education Solutions Provider
N.A.I.C.S.: 923110

Subsidiary (Domestic):

StyleHaul, Inc. **(2)**
1149 Gower St, Los Angeles, CA
90038-1801 **(93.6%)**
Tel.: (323) 785-2412
Web Site: http://www.stylehaul.com
Emp.: 200
Fashion, Beauty & Branded Content Multi-
Channel Network on YOUtube
N.A.I.C.S.: 513199
Olivier Delfosse (COO)

**Bertelsmann Lexikothek Verlag
GmbH** **(1)**
Carl Bertelsmann Strasse 161, 33310, Gut-
ersloh, Germany **(100%)**
Tel.: (49) 5241800
Web Site: http://www.lexikothek.de
Encyclopedias, Dictionaries, Reference
Books
N.A.I.C.S.: 513130

Big Break Productions, Inc. **(1)**
952 W Webster Ave, Chicago, IL 60614
Tel.: (608) 909-1321
Web Site:
http://www.bigbreakproductions.net
Art Services

Bertelsmann SE & Co. KGaA—(Continued)

N.A.I.C.S.: 711320

Blanvalet Verlag GmbH **(1)**
Neumarkter Strasse 28, Munich, 81673,
Germany **(100%)**
Tel.: (49) 8941360
Web Site: http://www.randomhouse.de
Sales Range: $200-249.9 Million
Emp.: 000
Book Publishers
N.A.I.C.S.: 513130
Silvia Kuttny-Walser (Dir-Pub)

Bookspan, LLC **(1)**
34 W 27th St 10th Fl, New York, NY 10001
Tel.: (516) 490-4561
Web Site: http://www.bookspan.com
Mail Order Book Club Operator
N.A.I.C.S.: 459210

Subsidiary (Domestic):

Book-of-the-Month Club, Inc. **(2)**
501 Franklin Ave, Garden City, NY 11530
Tel.: (516) 490-4561
Web Site: http://www.bomc.com
Rev.: $200,000,000
Emp.: 850
Book Publishing & Production
N.A.I.C.S.: 459210

Unit (Domestic):

Doubleday Book Club **(2)**
401 Franklin Ave, Garden City, NY 11530-
5943
Tel.: (212) 901-0700
Web Site:
http://www.doubledaybookclub.com
Sales Range: $100-124.9 Million
Emp.: 2,000
Book Club
N.A.I.C.S.: 459210

History Book Club **(2)**
501 Franklin Ave, Garden City, NY 11530
Tel.: (516) 490-4561
Web Site: http://www.historybookclub.com
Book Club
N.A.I.C.S.: 459210

Military Book Club **(2)**
501 Franklin Ave, Garden City, NY 11530-
5943
Tel.: (516) 490-4561
Web Site: http://www.militarybookclub.com
Sales Range: $100-124.9 Million
Emp.: 2,000
Book Club
N.A.I.C.S.: 459210

Mystery Guild **(2)**
501 Franklin Ave, Garden City, NY 11530-
5943
Tel.: (516) 490-4561
Web Site: http://www.mysteryguild.com
Sales Range: $10-24.9 Million
Emp.: 20
Book Club
N.A.I.C.S.: 541110

Buchgemeinschaft Donauland
Kremayr & Scheriau KG **(1)**
Biberstrasse 9, 1010, Vienna,
Austria **(100%)**
Tel.: (43) 15123107
Web Site: http://www.donauland-
stiftungsfonds.at
Sales Range: $25-49.9 Million
Book Publishing, Book Clubs, Book Store
N.A.I.C.S.: 513130

Checkout Charlie GmbH **(1)**
Salzufer 15, 10587, Berlin, Germany
Tel.: (49) 309210640
Web Site: https://www.checkout-charlie.com
Emp.: 86
Online Shopping Services
N.A.I.C.S.: 812990

Cometz SARL **(1)**
130 route de Thionville, 57050, Metz,
France
Tel.: (33) 440323426
Web Site: http://cometz.spotskills.fr
Telecommunication Servicesb
N.A.I.C.S.: 517810

Credify Informationsdienstleistungen
GmbH **(1)**

Gumpendorfer Strasse 21, 1060, Vienna,
Austria
Tel.: (43) 13913003
Web Site: http://www.credify.at
Credit Agency Services
N.A.I.C.S.: 522299

DPV Deutscher Pressevertrieb
GmbH **(1)**
Am Baumwall 11, 20459, Hamburg, Ger-
many
Tel.: (49) 40378450
Web Site: https://www.dpv.de
Magazine & Digital Product Mfr
N.A.I.C.S.: 323120

Die Mehrwertmacher GmbH **(1)**
Grune Str 16 a, 01067, Dresden, Germany
Tel.: (49) 35148643000
Web Site: http://www.diemehrwertmacher.de
Media Services
N.A.I.C.S.: 541840

Digital Media Hub GmbH **(1)**
Kurfurstendamm 208, 10719, Berlin, Ger-
many
Tel.: (49) 3088484150
Web Site: https://www.dmhub.de
Digital Marketing Services
N.A.I.C.S.: 541810

Direct Analytics GmbH **(1)**
Carl Bertelsmann Strasse 270, 33311, Gut-
ersloh, Germany
Tel.: (49) 52418075620
Web Site: https://www.direct-analytics.de
Data Processing Services
N.A.I.C.S.: 518210
Peter Lipp (Head-Analytics)

Direct Services Gutersloh GmbH **(1)**
Tel.: (49) 52418040865
Web Site: https://www.campaign-services.de
Internet Marketing Services
N.A.I.C.S.: 541613
Tessa Strathoff (Mktg Mgr)

DirectGroup Bertelsmann **(1)**
Carl-Bertelsmann-Strasse, 33311, Gut-
ersloh, Germany
Tel.: (49) 5241800
Web Site: http://www.directgroup-
bertelsmann.com
Sales Range: $1-4.9 Billion
Emp.: 8,485
Direct Marketing Services
N.A.I.C.S.: 541860
Gerd Buhrig (Exec VP)

Subsidiary (Non-US):

Book Club Associates Ltd. **(2)**
Hargreaves Rd Groundwell Industrial Es-
tate, Swindon, SN25 5BG, Wiltshire, United
Kingdom **(100%)**
Tel.: (44) 1793723547
Web Site: http://www.bca.co.uk
Rev.: $165,200,000
Emp.: 1,000
Mail Order Book Retailer
N.A.I.C.S.: 459210

Circulo de Lectores S.A. **(2)**
Avenida Diagonal 662-664, 08034, Barce-
lona, Catalunya, Spain **(50%)**
Tel.: (34) 902221022
Web Site: http://www.circulo.es
Sales Range: $100-124.9 Million
Emp.: 500
Book Club
N.A.I.C.S.: 459210

Subsidiary (Domestic):

Der Club GmbH **(2)**
Carl-Bertelsmann-Strasse, Gutersloh,
33300, Germany **(100%)**
Tel.: (49) 1805415233
Web Site: http://www.derclub.de
Book & Media Mail-Order Services
N.A.I.C.S.: 459210
Bernd Schroder (Mng Dir)

Subsidiary (Non-US):

Doubleday Australia Pty Ltd **(2)**
Unit F33 16 Mars Road, Lane Cove, 2066,
NSW, Australia **(100%)**
Tel.: (61) 299111400
Web Site: http://www.doubleday.com.au

Sales Range: $100-124.9 Million
Emp.: 300
Book Club Publications
N.A.I.C.S.: 513130

Subsidiary (Non-US):

Doubleday New Zealand Ltd. **(3)**
1 Parkway Dr, Mairangi Bay, Industrial Es-
tate, Auckland, 9, New Zealand **(100%)**
Tel.: (64) 9 479 4846
Web Site: http://www.doubleday.co.nz
Book Club Publishing
N.A.I.C.S.: 513130

Subsidiary (Non-US):

France Loisirs SAS **(2)**
31 rue du Val de Marne, 75013, Paris,
France **(50%)**
Tel.: (33) 320177542
Web Site: http://www.franceloisirs.com
Book Club
N.A.I.C.S.: 459210

Joint Venture (Non-US):

Mondolibri S.p.A. **(2)**
Via Lampedusa 13, 20141, Milan, Italy
Tel.: (39) 02844011
Web Site: http://www.mondolibri.it
Sales Range: $50-74.9 Million
Emp.: 130
Book Publisher, Marketer & Distr; Owned
50% by Bertelsmann AG & 50% by Finin-
vest S.p.A.
N.A.I.C.S.: 513130

Dorling Kindersley Publishing Private
Limited **(1)**
3rd Floor Mindmill Corporate Tower Plot No
24A Sector 16A Film City, Noida, 201 301,
Uttar Pradesh, India
Tel.: (91) 1204689600
Books Publishing Services
N.A.I.C.S.: 513130
Monica Saigal (Mng Editor)

Dresdner Chauffeur Service 8x8
GmbH **(1)**
Ostra Allee 18 20, 01067, Dresden, Ger-
many
Tel.: (49) 3518888860
Web Site: http://www.8mal8.de
Cab Services
N.A.I.C.S.: 485310

Easy Tiger Productions Pty Ltd. **(1)**
Suite 2 07 75 Mary Street, Saint Peters,
2044, NSW, Australia
Tel.: (61) 295575051
Web Site: http://www.easytiger.tv
Film Production Services
N.A.I.C.S.: 512110
Ian Collie (Founder)

Embrace GmbH **(1)**
Carl-Bertelsmann-Str 29, 33332, Gutersloh,
Germany
Tel.: (49) 52418070500
Web Site: https://embrace.agency
Emp.: 120
Advertising Agency Services
N.A.I.C.S.: 541810

Euston Films Limited **(1)**
1 Stephen Street, London, W1T 1AL,
United Kingdom
Tel.: (44) 2076916000
Web Site: http://www.eustonfilms.tv
Film Production Services
N.A.I.C.S.: 512110
Kate Harwood (Mng Dir)

FT Studios GmbH **(1)**
Kiefholzstrasse 402, 12435, Berlin, Ger-
many
Tel.: (49) 3029779167
Web Site: https://www.studioft.com
Transportation Design Services
N.A.I.C.S.: 541420

Frechverlag GmbH **(1)**
Dieselstrasse 5, 70839, Gerlingen, Ger-
many
Tel.: (49) 711830860
Web Site: https://topp-kreativ.de
Book Publishers
N.A.I.C.S.: 513130

Fremantle Productions Asia Pte.
Ltd. **(1)**
3 Fusionopolis Way 06-21 Symbiosis, Sin-
gapore, 138633, Singapore
Tel.: (65) 62238771
Television Programming Services
N.A.I.C.S.: 512110
Ganesh Rajaram (Exec VP & Gen Mgr)

G+J International Sales Italy
S.r.l. **(1)**
Via Benedetto Marcello 4, 20124, Milan,
Italy
Tel.: (39) 022052671
Media Advertising Services
N.A.I.C.S.: 541840
Delphine Majoie (Acct Mgr-Intl)

G+J iMS BVBA **(1)**
Coupure rechts 64B, 9000, Gent, Belgium
Tel.: (32) 92350213
Advertising Services
N.A.I.C.S.: 541810

GJ International Media Sales
Ltd. **(1)**
Silver House 31 Beak Street, London, W1F
9SX, United Kingdom
Tel.: (44) 2074374377
Media Advertising Services
N.A.I.C.S.: 541840

Grantham Book Services Limited **(1)**
Trent Road, Grantham, NG31 7XQ, Lincoln-
shire, United Kingdom
Tel.: (44) 1476541000
Books Publishing Services
N.A.I.C.S.: 513130

Gruner + Jahr GmbH **(1)**
Am Baumwall 11, PO Box 20080, 20459,
Hamburg, Germany **(100%)**
Tel.: (49) 4037030
Web Site: http://www.guj.de
Sales Range: $1-4.9 Billion
Magazine Publisher
N.A.I.C.S.: 513120

Subsidiary (Domestic):

G+J Electronic Media Sales
GmbH **(2)**
Am Baumwall 11, 20459, Hamburg, Ger-
many
Tel.: (49) 4037030
Web Site: http://www.gujmedia.de
Sales Range: $25-49.9 Million
Mobile Advertising Network
N.A.I.C.S.: 541890

Subsidiary (Non-US):

G+J Espana S.A. **(2)**
Calle Ancora 40, 28045, Madrid,
Spain **(74.9%)**
Tel.: (34) 913470100
Web Site: http://www.gyj.es
Magazine Printing & Publishing
N.A.I.C.S.: 513120

Gruner + Jahr AG (Schweiz) **(2)**
Zeltweg 15, PO Box 1672, 8032, Zurich,
Switzerland **(100%)**
Tel.: (41) 442697070
Web Site: http://www.guj.de
Sales Range: $25-49.9 Million
Emp.: 5
Magazine Advertising & Publishing
N.A.I.C.S.: 513120
Jorinde Gersina (Member-Exec Bd)

IP Belgium S.A. **(1)**
Avenue Jacques Georgin 2, 1030, Brussels,
Belgium
Tel.: (32) 23376211
Web Site: http://www.ipb.be
Media Advertising Services
N.A.I.C.S.: 541810
Edouard De Witte (Head-Digital MDI)

Infoscore Nederland B.V. **(1)**
KR Poststraat 90-5, 8441 ER, Heerenveen,
Netherlands
Tel.: (31) 850220101
Web Site: http://www.infoscore.nl
Financial Consulting Services
N.A.I.C.S.: 541611

JustDice GmbH **(1)**

An der Alster 42, 20099, Hamburg, Germany
Tel.: (49) 4037035440
Web Site: https://www.justdice.io
Software Development Services
N.A.I.C.S.: 541511

Justtrack GmbH (1)
An der Alster 42, 20099, Hamburg, Germany
Tel.: (49) 4037035440
Web Site: https://justtrack.io
Software Development Services
N.A.I.C.S.: 541511

KURIER Direktservice Dresden GmbH (1)
Ostra-Allee 18, 01067, Dresden, Germany
Tel.: (49) 35148644000
Web Site: http://www.kds-dresden.de
Advertising Material Distribution Services
N.A.I.C.S.: 541870

LiquidM Technology GmbH (1)
Invalidenstr 74, 10557, Berlin, Germany
Tel.: (49) 3028040667
Web Site: http://www.liquidm.com
Software Services
N.A.I.C.S.: 541519
Arnaud Creput (Mng Dir)

M6 Publicite SAS (1)
89 Avenue Charles de Gaulle, 92575, Neuilly-sur-Seine, Cedex, France
Tel.: (33) 141926666
Web Site: http://www.m6pub.fr
Marketing & Advertising Services
N.A.I.C.S.: 541613

MSP Medien-Service und Promotion GmbH (1)
Am Baumall 11, 20459, Hamburg, Germany
Tel.: (49) 4087709376
Web Site: https://www.meinabo.de
Online Shopping Services
N.A.I.C.S.: 541890

MVD Medien Vertrieb Dresden GmbH (1)
Ostra-Allee 20, 01067, Dresden, Germany
Tel.: (49) 35148642079
Web Site: http://www.medienvertrieb-dresden.de
Magazine Delivery Services
N.A.I.C.S.: 459210

Majorel Berlin GmbH (1)
Wohlrabedamm 32, 13629, Berlin, Germany
Tel.: (49) 52418075121
Web Site: http://www.berlin-majorel.career.softgarden.de
Emp.: 1,000
Telecommunication Servicesb
N.A.I.C.S.: 517410
Pierre Stahn (Mgr-IT Project Mgmt)

Majorel Dortmund GmbH (1)
Schleefstrasse 1, 44287, Dortmund, Germany
Tel.: (49) 52418049734
Web Site: http://www.dortmund-majorel.career.softgarden.de
Telecommunication Servicesb
N.A.I.C.S.: 517410
Wilma Maria Ryjkin (Ops Mgr)

Majorel Neubrandenburg GmbH (1)
Flurstrasse 2, 17034, Neubrandenburg, Germany
Tel.: (49) 39537903808
Web Site: http://www.neubrandenburg-majorel.career.softgarden.de
Telecommunication Servicesb
N.A.I.C.S.: 517410

Majorel Rostock I GmbH (1)
Deutsche Med Platz 1, 18057, Rostock, Germany
Tel.: (49) 38180086158
Web Site: http://www.rostock1-majorel.career.softgarden.de
Emp.: 330
Telecommunication Servicesb
N.A.I.C.S.: 517410

Mambo-Plak GmbH (1)
Leipziger Str 31, 01097, Dresden, Germany
Tel.: (49) 3514244267
Web Site: http://www.mambo-plak.de
Outdoor & Indoor Advertising Services

N.A.I.C.S.: 541810

Market Self Chile SpA (1)
Merced 280 10th Floor Centro, Santiago, Chile
Tel.: (56) 228695923
Web Site: http://www.marketself.cl
Book Distr
N.A.I.C.S.: 424920

Market Self S.A. (1)
Humberto Primo 555 Caba, C1103ACK, Buenos Aires, Argentina
Tel.: (54) 1152633373
Web Site: http://www.marketself.com.ar
Books Publishing Services
N.A.I.C.S.: 513130
Guillermo Romano (Dir Gen)

Media Assurances S.A. (1)
Boulevard Pierre Frieden 43, 1543, Luxembourg, Luxembourg
Tel.: (352) 2635595805
Web Site: http://www.media-assurances.com
Insurance Services
N.A.I.C.S.: 524210
Pierrot Gieres (CEO)

Media Logistik GmbH (1)
Meinholdstrasse 2, 01129, Dresden, Germany
Tel.: (49) 35148642508
Web Site: http://www.post-modern.de
Courier Service
N.A.I.C.S.: 492110

NOW GmbH (1)
Fasanenstr 5, 10623, Berlin, Germany
Tel.: (49) 303116116100
Web Site: http://www.now-gmbh.de
Media Advertising Services
N.A.I.C.S.: 541840
Wolfgang Axthammer (Mng Dir)

No Pictures Please Productions B.V. (1)
Pieter Braaijweg 1, 1114 AJ, Amsterdam, Netherlands
Tel.: (31) 202365151
Web Site: http://www.nopicturesplease.nl
Media Production Services
N.A.I.C.S.: 512110
Nienke Kroon (Production Mgr)

ORTEC Messe und Kongress GmbH (1)
Bertolt-Brecht-Allee 24, 01309, Dresden, Germany
Tel.: (49) 351315330
Web Site: http://www.ortec.de
Event Management Services
N.A.I.C.S.: 561990

Oberuber Karger Kommunikation-sagentur GmbH (1)
Devrientstrasse 11, 01067, Dresden, Germany
Tel.: (49) 351829680
Web Site: http://www.oberueber-karger.de
Advertising Agency Services
N.A.I.C.S.: 541810
Sylvia Wirkner (Head-Agency)

Penguin Random House Grupo Editorial S.A. (1)
Humberto Primo 555, C1103ACK, Buenos Aires, Argentina
Tel.: (54) 1152354400
Books Publishing Services
N.A.I.C.S.: 513130

Penguin Random House Grupo Editorial S.A.S. (1)
Carrera 775-51 Piso 7, Bogota, Colombia
Tel.: (57) 17430700
Book Distr
N.A.I.C.S.: 424920
Lina Maria Ortega Martinez (Acct Mgr)

Penguin Random House Grupo Editorial, S.A. (1)
Merced 280 Piso 6, Santiago, Chile
Tel.: (56) 27828200
Book Distr
N.A.I.C.S.: 424920

Penguin Random House Grupo Editorial, S.A. de C.V. (1)

Boulevard Miguel de Cervantes Saavedra 301 Floor 1 Delegation, Colonia Ampliacion Granada Miguel Hidalgo, Mexico, 11520, Mexico
Tel.: (52) 5530678400
Book Distr
N.A.I.C.S.: 424920
Roberto Banchik (Dir Gen)

Penguin Random House South Africa (Pty) Ltd. (1)
Rosebank Office Park Block D 181 Jan Smuts Ave, Parktown North, Johannesburg, 2193, South Africa
Tel.: (27) 113273550
Web Site:
    http://www.penguinrandomhouse.co.za
Books Publishing Services
N.A.I.C.S.: 513130

Penguin Random House Verlags-gruppe GmbH (1)
Neumarkter Str 28, D-81673, Munich, Germany
Tel.: (49) 8005003322
Web Site: https://www.penguin.de
Book Publishers
N.A.I.C.S.: 513130

Prestel Publishing Limited (1)
16-18 Berners Street, London, W1T 3LN, United Kingdom
Tel.: (44) 2073235004
Web Site: http://www.prestelpublishing.de
Books Publishing Services
N.A.I.C.S.: 513130
Andrew Hansen (VP)

Prinovis UK Limited (1)
Liverpool International Business Park 4 Dakota Drive, Liverpool, L24 8RJ, United Kingdom
Tel.: (44) 1514945200
Web Site: http://www.prinovis.co.uk
Emp.: 491
Commercial Printing & Publishing Services
N.A.I.C.S.: 323111
Richard Gray (Mng Dir)

Prisma Verlag GmbH & Co. KG (1)
Zulpicher Strasse 10, 40549, Dusseldorf, Germany
Tel.: (49) 2115052850
Web Site: http://www.prisma-verlag.de
Sales Range: $25-49.9 Million
Publisher of Magazine Supplement
N.A.I.C.S.: 513120

Subsidiary (Non-US):

Prisma Presse & Cie (2)
6 Rue Daru, 75008, Paris, France (100%)
Tel.: (33) 144153000
Magazine Publisher
N.A.I.C.S.: 513120

RTL AdConnect S.r.l. (1)
Corso Italia 50, 20122, Milan, Italy
Tel.: (39) 0236752900
Broadcasting Media Services
N.A.I.C.S.: 516120
Mattia Badino (Sls Mgr-Intl)

RTL AdConnect UK Ltd. (1)
4 Tenderten Street 4th Floor, London, W1S 1TE, United Kingdom
Tel.: (44) 2075505652
Broadcasting Media Services
N.A.I.C.S.: 516120
Ajay Misra (Head-Digital Ad Ops)

RTL Audio Center Berlin GmbH (1)
Kurfurstendamm 208, 10719, Berlin, Germany
Tel.: (49) 30884840
Web Site: https://www.rtl-audiocenter.de
Audio Production Services
N.A.I.C.S.: 512230

RTL Audio Vermarktung GmbH (1)
Kurfurstendamm 208, 10719, Berlin, Germany
Tel.: (49) 3088484310
Web Site: https://www.rtl-audiovermarktung.de
Radio Broadcasting Services
N.A.I.C.S.: 516110

RTL Group S.A. (1)
43 Bd Pierre Frieden, L-1543, Luxembourg, Luxembourg (76.28%)

Tel.: (352) 24861
Web Site: https://www.company.rtl.com
Rev.: $6,727,822,145
Assets: $10,432,764,947
Liabilities: $4,928,771,854
Net Worth: $5,503,993,093
Earnings: $645,370,171
Emp.: 17,732
Fiscal Year-end: 12/31/2023
Advertising Media Services
N.A.I.C.S.: 551112
Thomas Rabe (CEO)

Subsidiary (Non-US):

104.6 RTL (2)
Kurfurstendamm 208, 10719, Berlin, Germany (100%)
Tel.: (49) 30884840
Web Site: http://www.104.6rtl.com
Sales Range: $25-49.9 Million
Radio Broadcasting Services
N.A.I.C.S.: 516110
Stephan Schmitter (Mng Dir)

11 Freunde Verlag GmbH & Co. KG (2)
Gubener Str 47, 10243, Berlin, Germany
Tel.: (49) 304039360
Web Site: http://www.11freunde.de
Television Broadcasting Services
N.A.I.C.S.: 516120

AVE Gesellschaft fur Horfunkbeteili-gungen mbH (2)
Kurfurstendamm 207 208, 10719, Berlin, Germany (100%)
Tel.: (49) 3088484130
Web Site: http://www.ave-hoerfunk.de
TV & Broadcasting-Music & Art
N.A.I.C.S.: 516120

AZ Direct GmbH (2)
Carl-Bertelsmann-Strasse 161S, 33311, Gutersloh, Germany
Tel.: (49) 52418070800
Web Site: https://www.az-direct.com
General Marketing Services
N.A.I.C.S.: 541613
Dirk Kemmerer (Mng Dir)

Subsidiary (US):

Allied Communications Inc (2)
708 Werne Dr, Lexington, KY 40504-1009
Tel.: (859) 255-3058
Web Site: http://alliedlex.com
Electrical Contractor
N.A.I.C.S.: 238210

Subsidiary (Non-US):

Antenne Niedersachsen GmbH & Co. KG (2)
Goseriede 9, 30159, Hannover, Germany
Tel.: (49) 51191180
Web Site: https://www.antenne.com
Television Broadcasting Services
N.A.I.C.S.: 516120

Asia Sports Ventures Pte Ltd (2)
63 Market Street 04-05 Bank of Singapore Centre, Singapore, 048942, Singapore
Tel.: (65) 8845013
Web Site: http://www.asvworld.com
Television Broadcasting Services
N.A.I.C.S.: 516120
Chee Beng Goh (Mgr-Intl Mktg & Events)

BFS finance GmbH (2)
Gutersloher Str 123, 33415, Verl, Germany
Tel.: (49) 52418043199
Web Site: http://www.bfs-finance.de
Financial Management Services
N.A.I.C.S.: 541611
Stefan Kessling (Mgr-Credit)

BFS finance Munster GmbH (2)
Holtenweg 35, 48155, Munster, Germany
Tel.: (49) 251500447070
Financial Management Services
N.A.I.C.S.: 541611

BFS health finance GmbH (2)
Hulshof 24, 44369, Dortmund, Germany
Tel.: (49) 231945362600
Web Site: http://meinebfs.de
Television Broadcasting Services
N.A.I.C.S.: 516120

Bertelsmann SE & Co. KGaA—(Continued)

BMG RIGHTS MANAGEMENT (Europe) GmbH (2)
Charlottenstrasse 59, 10117, Berlin, Germany
Tel.: (49) 300133300
Web Site: https://www.bmg.com
Television Broadcasting Services
N.A.I.C.S.: 516120

Berliner Presse Vertrieb GmbH & Co. KG (2)
Ullsteinstr 89, 12109, Berlin, Germany
Tel.: (49) 30701880
Web Site: http://www.bpv-berlin.de
Emp.: 34
Magazine Publisher
N.A.I.C.S.: 513120

Berliner Rundfunk (2)
Grunewaldstrasse 3, 12165, Berlin, Germany (100%)
Tel.: (49) 3091425914
Web Site: http://www.berliner-rundfunk.de
Sales Range: $25-49.9 Million
Radio Broadcasting
N.A.I.C.S.: 516110

Bertelsmann Aviation GmbH (2)
Flughafenstrasse 33 Hangar 2 a, Ahden, 33142, Buren, Germany
Tel.: (49) 29557472444
Web Site: https://www.bertelsmann-aviation.de
Television Broadcasting Services
N.A.I.C.S.: 516120

Blu A/S (2)
Skolegade 19 C, 2500, Valby, Denmark
Tel.: (45) 32648200
Web Site: http://www.blu.dk
Television Broadcasting Services
N.A.I.C.S.: 516120

Blue Circle BV (2)
Pieter Braaijweg 1, 1114 AJ, Amsterdam, Netherlands
Tel.: (31) 202365000
Web Site: http://www.bluecircle.nl
Television Broadcasting Services
N.A.I.C.S.: 516120

Subsidiary (Domestic):

Broadcasting Center Europe SA (2)
43 Boulevard Pierre Frieden, 1543, Luxembourg, Luxembourg
Tel.: (352) 24801
Web Site: http://www.bce.lu
Emp.: 200
Television Broadcasting Services
N.A.I.C.S.: 516120
Frederic Lemaire *(CEO)*

Subsidiary (Non-US):

CCM Communication-Center Mitteldeutschland GmbH (2)
Maximilianallee 4, 04129, Leipzig, Germany
Tel.: (49) 3414431999
Web Site: http://www.ccm-leipzig.de
Telecommunication Servicesb
N.A.I.C.S.: 517111

COUNTDOWN MEDIA GmbH (2)
Wichmannstr 4 Haus 10 Sud, 22607, Hamburg, Germany
Tel.: (49) 408229860
Web Site: https://www.countdownmedia.com
Emp.: 13
Television Broadcasting Services
N.A.I.C.S.: 516120
Helge Jurgens *(Mng Dir)*

Cologne Broadcasting Center (2)
Picassoplatz 1, 50679, Cologne, Germany (100%)
Tel.: (49) 22145640
Web Site: http://www.cbc.de
Sales Range: $50-74.9 Million
Emp.: 850
Provider of Television Production Services
N.A.I.C.S.: 512110

Delta Advertising GmbH (2)
Balanstr 73 Haus 31 E, 81541, Munich, Germany
Tel.: (49) 8918941390
Web Site: http://www.delta-advertising.com
Television Broadcasting Services

N.A.I.C.S.: 516120

Divimove GmbH (2)
Munzstrasse 19, 10178, Berlin, Germany (100%)
Tel.: (49) 3056838074
Web Site: http://www.divimove.com
Television Broadcasting Services
N.A.I.C.S.: 516120
Brian Ruhe *(Co-Founder)*

Dresdner Druck- und Verlagshaus GmbH & Co. KG (2)
Meinholdstr 2, 01129, Dresden, Saxony, Germany
Tel.: (49) 35148642801
Television Broadcasting Services
N.A.I.C.S.: 516120

Subsidiary (Domestic):

European News Exchange (2)
43 Boulevard Pierre Frieden, 1543, Luxembourg, Luxembourg (100%)
Tel.: (352) 421423101
Web Site: http://www.enex.lu
Sales Range: $25-49.9 Million
Television Broadcasting
N.A.I.C.S.: 516120

Subsidiary (Non-US):

FremantleMedia Ltd (2)
1 Stephen Street, London, W1T 1AL, United Kingdom
Tel.: (44) 2076916000
Web Site: http://www.fremantle.com
Sales Range: $350-399.9 Million
Emp.: 1,200
Independent Producer of Television Programs
N.A.I.C.S.: 512110
Rob Clark *(Dir-Global Entertainment)*

Subsidiary (Non-US):

Beach House Pictures Pte Limited (2)
1 Boon Leat Terrace Harbourside 1 07-03, Singapore, 119843, Singapore
Tel.: (65) 69217878
Web Site: https://www.beachhousepictures.com
Media & Entertainment Services
N.A.I.C.S.: 512199

Fremantle India TV Productions Pvt Ltd (3)
406 Morya Landmark II Plot B-17 Off New Link Road, Oshiwara Andheri, Mumbai, 400053, India
Tel.: (91) 2242769000
Television Broadcasting Services
N.A.I.C.S.: 516120

Fremantle Licensing Germany GmbH (3)
Dianastrasse 21, 14482, Potsdam, Germany
Tel.: (49) 3317060117
Television Broadcasting Services
N.A.I.C.S.: 516120
Michael Unger *(Sr Mgr-Interactive)*

Fremantle Productions SA (3)
10 Ziridi, 15124, Maroussi, Greece
Tel.: (30) 2106196970
Television Broadcasting Services
N.A.I.C.S.: 516120

FremantleMedia Asia Pte Ltd (3)
10 Raeburn Park Block A 03-01, Singapore, 088702, Singapore
Tel.: (65) 62238771
Television Broadcasting Services
N.A.I.C.S.: 516120

FremantleMedia Australia Pty Ltd (3)
110-112 Christie Street, Saint Leonards, 2065, NSW, Australia
Tel.: (61) 294340666
Web Site: http://www.fremantlemedia.com.au
Television Broadcasting Services
N.A.I.C.S.: 516120
Simon Rabbitt *(COO)*

FremantleMedia Belgium NV (3)
J B Vandendrieschstraat 12, 1082, Sint-Agatha-Berchem, Belgium
Tel.: (32) 27023080

Television Broadcasting Services
N.A.I.C.S.: 516120
Stefan De Keyser *(Mng Dir)*

FremantleMedia Brazil Producao de Televisao Ltda (3)
Av Professor Manuel Jose Chaves 300 Alto de, Pinheiros, Sao Paulo, Brazil
Tel.: (55) 1130267700
Television Broadcasting Services
N.A.I.C.S.: 516120
Paula Cavalcanti *(CEO)*

FremantleMedia Finland Oy (3)
Televisiokatu 4, 00240, Helsinki, Finland
Tel.: (358) 207567800
Television Broadcasting Services
N.A.I.C.S.: 516120
Eerika Vermila *(Mng Dir)*

FremantleMedia France SAS (3)
51 Rue Vivienne, 75002, Paris, France
Tel.: (33) 146623800
Television Broadcasting Services
N.A.I.C.S.: 516120
Bruno Fallot *(Pres)*

FremantleMedia Hrvatska d.o.o. (3)
Brezovicka 1, Zagreb, 10020, Croatia
Tel.: (385) 13863976
Television Broadcasting Services
N.A.I.C.S.: 516120

FremantleMedia Italia Spa (3)
Via Monte Zebio 24, 0195, Rome, Italy
Tel.: (39) 06372761
Television Broadcasting Services
N.A.I.C.S.: 516120
Lorenzo Mieli *(Mng Dir)*

FremantleMedia Mexico SA de CV (3)
Calle Boulevard Picacho Ajusco 124 Colonia Jardines En La Montana, Tlalpan, Mexico, 14210, Mexico
Tel.: (52) 5554494370
Television Broadcasting Services
N.A.I.C.S.: 516120
Coty Cagliolo *(Dir-Creative)*

FremantleMedia Norge AS (3)
Ivan Bjorndals Gate 9, 0472, Oslo, Norway
Tel.: (47) 40000624
Television Broadcasting Services
N.A.I.C.S.: 516120
Petter Testmann-Koch *(Mng Dir)*

Subsidiary (US):

FremantleMedia North America Inc. (3)
28 E 28th St, New York, NY 10016 (100%)
Tel.: (212) 541-2800
Sales Range: $25-49.9 Million
Emp.: 15
Production & Distribution of Motion Pictures & Television Programs; Marketing of Commercial Time to National Television Advertisers
N.A.I.C.S.: 512120
Keith Hindle *(CEO-Digital & Branded Entertainment)*

Subsidiary (Domestic):

Fremantle Productions North America Inc (4)
2900 W Alameda Ave Ste 800, Burbank, CA 91505
Tel.: (818) 748-1100
Television Broadcasting Services
N.A.I.C.S.: 516120

FremantleMedia Latin America Inc (4)
5200 Blue Lagoon Dr Ste 200, Miami, FL 33126
Tel.: (305) 267-0821
Television Broadcasting Services
N.A.I.C.S.: 516120

Original Productions LLC (4)
308 W Verdugo Ave, Burbank, CA 91502
Tel.: (818) 295-6966
Web Site: http://www.origprod.com
Emp.: 50
Television Commercial & Progam Producer
N.A.I.C.S.: 512110
Ernie Avila *(COO/Exec VP-Bus Affairs)*

Subsidiary (Non-US):

FremantleMedia Polska Sp.Zo.o. (3)
ul Wolodyjowskiego 63, Warsaw, Poland
Tel.: (48) 228538111
Television Broadcasting Services
N.A.I.C.S.: 516120
Piotr Radzyminski *(Gen Mgr)*

FremantleMedia Portugal SA (3)
Avendina Quinta Grande no 53-5B, Alfragide, 2614521, Amadora, Portugal
Tel.: (351) 214254627
Television Broadcasting Services
N.A.I.C.S.: 516120

FremantleMedia Sverige AB (3)
TegeluddsvAgen 76, 115 28, Stockholm, Sweden
Tel.: (46) 857844500
Web Site: http://www.fremantlemedia.se
Television Broadcasting Services
N.A.I.C.S.: 516120
Tomas Akerstedt *(Head-Dev & Sls)*

Subsidiary (Domestic):

TalkBack Thames (3)
1 Stephen Street, London, W1T 1AL, United Kingdom
Tel.: (44) 20 7691 6000
Web Site: http://www.talkbackthames.tv
Television Broadcasting
N.A.I.C.S.: 516120
Leon Wilson *(Mng Dir)*

Subsidiary (Non-US):

Funkhaus Halle GmbH & Co. KG (2)
City Center Escalator Grosse Ulrichstrasse 60 D, Saale, 06108, Halle, Germany
Tel.: (49) 3455258222
Web Site: http://www.funkhaus-halle.de
Television Broadcasting Services
N.A.I.C.S.: 516120

G+J / Klambt Style-Verlag GmbH & Co. KG (2)
Gansemarkt 21-23, 20354, Hamburg, Germany
Tel.: (49) 4118825800
Web Site: http://www.grazia-magazin.de
Magazine Publisher
N.A.I.C.S.: 513120

GGP Media GmbH (2)
Karl-Marx-Str 24, 07381, Possneck, Germany
Tel.: (49) 36474300
Web Site: https://www.ggp-media.de
Emp.: 1,000
Television Broadcasting Services
N.A.I.C.S.: 516120

Hit Radio Veronica (2)
Bergweg 70, 1217 SC, Hilversum, Netherlands
Tel.: (31) 356252727
Web Site: http://www.veronica.nl
Radio Broadcasting
N.A.I.C.S.: 516110

Hitradio RTL Sachsen GmbH (2)
Ammonstrasse 35, 01067, Dresden, Germany
Tel.: (49) 351500110
Web Site: http://www.hitradio-rtl.de
Television Broadcasting Services
N.A.I.C.S.: 516120

I 2 I Musikproduktions- und Musikverlagsgesellschaft mbH (2)
Picassoplatz 1, 50679, Cologne, Germany
Tel.: (49) 22145676100
Web Site: http://www.i2i.de
Television Broadcasting Services
N.A.I.C.S.: 516120
Lutz Fassbender *(Mng Dir)*

IP Plurimedia SA (2)
J Georginlaan 2, 1030, Brussels, Belgium
Tel.: (32) 23376211
Web Site: http://www.iloveradioadvertising.be
Media Advertising Services
N.A.I.C.S.: 541810

Inadi S.A. (2)
Avenue Jacques Georgin 2, 1030, Brussels, Belgium (43%)
Tel.: (32) 23376911

Web Site: http://www.belrtl.be
Sales Range: $100-124.9 Million
Emp.: 500
Radio Broadcasting
N.A.I.C.S.: 516110

Klassik Radio GmbH & Co. KG   (2)
Planckstrasse 15, 22765, Hamburg, Germany
Tel.: (49) 403005050
Web Site: http://www.klassikradio.de
Radio Broadcasting
N.A.I.C.S.: 516110

Subsidiary (US):

LBS Communications Inc   (2)
1325 Ave Of The Americas, New York, NY 10019
Tel.: (212) 541-2800
Motion Picture Distr
N.A.I.C.S.: 512120

Subsidiary (Non-US):

MEDIASCORE Gesellschaft fur Medien- und Kommunikationsforschung mbH   (2)
Hildeboldplatz 23-25, 50672, Cologne, Germany
Tel.: (49) 2213468810
Web Site: http://www.mediascore.de
Market Research Services
N.A.I.C.S.: 541910

Medienfabrik Gutersloh GmbH   (2)
Carl-Bertelsmann-Strasse 33, 33311, Gutersloh, Germany
Tel.: (49) 52412348050
Web Site: http://www.medienfabrik.de
Magazine Publisher
N.A.I.C.S.: 513120

Miso Film ApS   (2)
Ryesgade 3E, 2200, Copenhagen, Denmark
Tel.: (45) 33337337
Web Site: http://www.misofilm.dk
Motion Picture & Film Production Services
N.A.I.C.S.: 512110
Morten Gerner *(Head-Fin)*

Miso Film Norge AS   (2)
Ivan Bjorndalsgate 9 Bygg A4, 0472, Oslo, Norway
Tel.: (47) 40008878
Motion Picture & Film Production Services
N.A.I.C.S.: 512110
Brede Hovland *(Mng Dir)*

Miso Film Sverige AB   (2)
Hokens gata 10, 116 46, Stockholm, Sweden
Tel.: (46) 87520804
Motion Picture & Film Production Services
N.A.I.C.S.: 512110
Sandra Harms *(Mng Dir)*

NIONEX GmbH   (2)
Ringstrasse 16-20, 33378, Rheda-Wiedenbruck, Germany
Tel.: (49) 5242914444
Web Site: http://www.nionex.de
Mobile Application Development Services
N.A.I.C.S.: 541511

NORDDEICH TV Produktionsgesellschaft mbH   (2)
Claudius-Dornier-Str 1, 50829, Cologne, Germany
Tel.: (49) 221331000
Web Site: http://www.norddeich.tv
Television Broadcasting Services
N.A.I.C.S.: 516120

PRINOVIS GmbH & Co. KG   (2)
Friedensallee 271, 22763, Hamburg, Germany
Tel.: (49) 91180030
Web Site: http://www.prinovis.com
Emp.: 2,200
Commercial Printing Services
N.A.I.C.S.: 323111

Plant (Domestic):

Prinovis GmbH & Co. KG   (3)
Breslauer Strasse 300, 90471, Nuremberg, Germany
Tel.: (49) 911 8003 0
Web Site: http://www.prinovis.com

Emp.: 2,200
Commercial Printing & Related Services
N.A.I.C.S.: 323111

Subsidiary (Non-US):

PSC Print Service Center GmbH   (2)
Saalfelder Str 41-43, Possneck, 07381, Germany
Tel.: (49) 3647430500
Book Printing Services
N.A.I.C.S.: 513130

PT Dunia Visitama   (2)
Jl Barito II 3 Kramat Pela, Kebayoran Baru, Jakarta, 12130, Indonesia
Tel.: (62) 2172801001
Motion Picture & Film Production Services
N.A.I.C.S.: 512110

Joint Venture (Non-US):

RTL Disney Fernsehen GmbH & Co. KG   (2)
Picassoplatz 1, 50679, Cologne, Germany
Tel.: (49) 22145654565
Web Site: http://www.superrtl.de
Television Broadcasting
N.A.I.C.S.: 516120

Subsidiary (Non-US):

RTL Group Cable & Satellite GmbH   (2)
Picasso-Platz 1, 50679, Cologne, Germany
Tel.: (49) 2214560
Television Broadcasting Services
N.A.I.C.S.: 516120

RTL Hessen GmbH   (2)
Solmsstr 4, 60486, Frankfurt, Germany
Tel.: (49) 69716780
Web Site: https://www.rtl.de
Television Broadcasting Services
N.A.I.C.S.: 516120

RTL Hessen Programmfenster GmbH   (2)
Ffh-Platz 1, 61118, Bad Vilbel, Hessen, Germany
Tel.: (49) 6971678200
Television Broadcasting Services
N.A.I.C.S.: 516120

RTL Klub   (2)
Nagytetenyi ut 29, 1222, Budapest, Hungary   (48.8%)
Tel.: (36) 13828283
Web Site: http://www.rtl.hu
Sales Range: $50-74.9 Million
Broadcast Television Station Operations
N.A.I.C.S.: 516120

RTL Nederland BV   (2)
Barend en Van Dorpweg 2, 1217 WP, Hilversum, Netherlands
Tel.: (31) 356718711
Web Site: http://www.rtl.nl
Television Broadcasting Services
N.A.I.C.S.: 516120
Sven Sauve *(CEO)*

Subsidiary (Domestic):

BrandDeli C.V.   (3)
Toetsenbordweg 26, 1033 MZ, Amsterdam, Netherlands
Tel.: (31) 207054705
Web Site: http://www.branddeli.nl
Television Broadcasting Services
N.A.I.C.S.: 516120

Subsidiary (Non-US):

RTL Nederland Interactief BV   (2)
Postbus 15016, 1200 TV, Hilversum, Netherlands
Tel.: (31) 356718718
Television Broadcasting Services
N.A.I.C.S.: 516120

RTL Nederland Productions BV   (2)
Sumatralaan 47, Hilversum, 1217 GP, Netherlands
Tel.: (31) 356718711
Television Broadcasting Services
N.A.I.C.S.: 516120

RTL Nord GmbH   (2)
Strassenbahnring 18, 20251, Hamburg, Germany

Tel.: (49) 1805442040
Web Site: https://www.rtl.de
Television Broadcasting Services
N.A.I.C.S.: 516120

Subsidiary (Domestic):

RTL Radio   (2)
43 bd Pierre Frieden, 1543, Luxembourg, Luxembourg   (100%)
Tel.: (352) 421423442
Web Site: http://www.rtl.lu
Sales Range: $25-49.9 Million
Radio Broadcasting
N.A.I.C.S.: 516110

Subsidiary (Domestic):

RTL Radio Letzeburg   (3)
43 bd Pierre Frieden, 1543, Luxembourg, Luxembourg   (100%)
Tel.: (352) 421423405
Web Site: http://www.rtl.lu
Radio Broadcasting
N.A.I.C.S.: 516110

Subsidiary (Non-US):

RTL Radio   (2)
Kurfurstendamm 207-208, 10719, Berlin, Germany
Tel.: (49) 30884840
Web Site: http://rtlradiodeutschland.de
Sales Range: $50-74.9 Million
Radio Broadcasting
N.A.I.C.S.: 516110
Stephan Schmitter *(Mng Dir)*

Subsidiary (Domestic):

RTL Tele Letzeburg   (2)
43 bd Pierre Frieden, 1543, Luxembourg, Luxembourg
Tel.: (352) 421421
Web Site: http://www.rtl.lu
Television Services
N.A.I.C.S.: 516120
Alain Rousseau *(Editor-In-Chief & Dir-News)*

Subsidiary (Non-US):

RTL Television GmbH   (2)
Picassopplatz 1, 50679, Cologne, Germany   (99.7%)
Tel.: (49) 22145670
Web Site: http://www.mediengruppe-rtl.de
Sales Range: $150-199.9 Million
Operator of a Television Station
N.A.I.C.S.: 516120

Subsidiary (Domestic):

RTL4 Holding SA   (2)
43 Bd Pierre Frieden, 1543, Luxembourg, Luxembourg   (99.7%)
Tel.: (352) 421421
Web Site: http://www.rtl.lu
Sales Range: $150-199.9 Million
Operator of a Broadcast Television Station
N.A.I.C.S.: 516120

Subsidiary (Non-US):

Radio City 93.7 FM   (2)
Belehradska 132, 120 00, Prague, Czech Republic   (100%)
Tel.: (420) 224409719
Web Site: http://www.radiocity.cz
Radio Broadcasting
N.A.I.C.S.: 516110

Radio Contact   (2)
Avenue Jacques Georgin 2, 1030, Brussels, Belgium   (100%)
Tel.: (32) 23376680
Web Site: http://www.radiocontact.be
Sales Range: $50-74.9 Million
Radio Broadcasting
N.A.I.C.S.: 516110

Radio Hamburg GmbH & Co KG   (2)
Spitalerstrasse 10 / Semperhaus A, 20095, Hamburg, Germany
Tel.: (49) 403397140
Web Site: http://www.radiohamburg.de
Sales Range: $25-49.9 Million
Radio Broadcasting
N.A.I.C.S.: 516110
Marzel Becker *(Exec Dir & Dir-Program)*

Radio NRW   (2)

Essener Str 55, 46047, Oberhausen, Germany
Tel.: (49) 20885870
Web Site: http://www.radionrw.de
Sales Range: $25-49.9 Million
Radio Broadcasting
N.A.I.C.S.: 516110

SSB Software Service und Beratung GmbH   (2)
Thomas-Dehler-Str 9, 81737, Munich, Germany
Tel.: (49) 896389870
Web Site: http://www.ssb-diso.de
Emp.: 10
Television Broadcasting Services
N.A.I.C.S.: 516120

Sellwell GmbH & Co. KG   (2)
Am Baumwall 11, 20459, Hamburg, Germany
Tel.: (49) 40378453137
Web Site: http://www.sellwell.de
Television Broadcasting Services
N.A.I.C.S.: 516120

Subsidiary (US):

SpotXchange Inc   (2)
11030 Circle Point Rd Ste 350, Westminster, CO 80020   (65%)
Tel.: (303) 345-6650
Television Broadcasting Services
N.A.I.C.S.: 516120
Mike Shehan *(Co-Founder & CEO)*

Style Haul Inc   (2)
1149 N Gower St, Los Angeles, CA 90038
Tel.: (323) 510-3829
Television Broadcasting Services
N.A.I.C.S.: 516120

Subsidiary (Non-US):

TVI SA   (2)
Avenue Jacques Georgin 2, 1030, Brussels, Belgium   (65.8%)
Tel.: (32) 23376811
Web Site: http://www.rtlbelgium.be
Sales Range: $150-199.9 Million
Operator of a Broadcast Television Station
N.A.I.C.S.: 516120

UFA Cinema GmbH   (2)
Dianastrasse 21, 14482, Potsdam, Germany
Tel.: (49) 33170600
Television Broadcasting Services
N.A.I.C.S.: 516120

UFA Show GmbH   (2)
Siegburger Strasse 215, 50679, Cologne, Germany
Tel.: (49) 22199551000
Entertainment Program Production Services
N.A.I.C.S.: 512110
Ute Biernat *(CEO)*

UFA Sports Asia Pte LTD   (2)
9 Raffles Place Level 18 Republic Plaza 2, Singapore, 048619, Singapore
Tel.: (65) 68236861
Sports Club Facility Operation Services
N.A.I.C.S.: 713940

UFA Sports GmbH   (2)
Grosse Elbstrasse 59, 22767, Hamburg, Germany
Tel.: (49) 40380371710
Sports Management Services
N.A.I.C.S.: 711310

UFA Sports Slovakia s.r.o   (2)
Cintorinska 9, Bratislava, 811 08, Slovakia
Tel.: (421) 249103051
Sports Club Facility Operation Services
N.A.I.C.S.: 713940
Karsten Mahlmann *(Chm & Mng Dir)*

Ufa Radio-Programmgesellschaft in Bayern mbH   (2)
Munchener Str 101, 85737, Ismaning, Germany
Tel.: (49) 89992770
Commercial Radio Broadcasting Services
N.A.I.C.S.: 516210

VIVENO Group GmbH   (2)
Kirchstrasse 27, 33330, Gutersloh, Germany
Tel.: (49) 52418770

Bertelsmann SE & Co. KGaA—(Continued)

Web Site: https://www.viveno.de
Restaurant Operators
N.A.I.C.S.: 492210

Verlegerdienst Munchen GmbH (2)
Gutenbergstrasse 1, 82205, Gilching, Germany
Tel.: (49) 81053880
Magazine Publisher
N.A.I.C.S.: 513120

**Video Communication France
S.A.** (2)
48 Quai Carnot, F 92210, Saint-Claud,
France (100%)
Tel.: (33) 141121212
Sales Range: $25-49.9 Million
Emp.: 100
N.A.I.C.S.: 334310

**Vogel Druck und Medienservice
GmbH** (2)
Leibnizstr 5, 97204, Hochberg, Germany
Tel.: (49) 931460002
Web Site: http://www.vogel-druck.de
Media Advertising Services
N.A.I.C.S.: 541840

**Vox Film & Fernseh GmbH & Co.
KG** (2)
Richard Byrd Strasse 6, D 50829, Cologne,
Germany (100%)
Tel.: (49) 22195340
Web Site: http://www.vox.de
Sales Range: $50-74.9 Million
Emp.: 120
Operator of a Television Station
N.A.I.C.S.: 516120
Frank Hoffman (Pres)

arvato SCM Ireland Limited (2)
Ida Industrial Estate, Balbriggan, County
Dublin, Ireland
Tel.: (353) 18409000
Television Broadcasting Services
N.A.I.C.S.: 516120
Roger Byrne (Dir-Comml)

maul + co - Chr. Belser GmbH (2)
Breslauer Str 300, 90471, Nuremberg, Germany
Tel.: (49) 91180030
Media Advertising Services
N.A.I.C.S.: 541810

rewards arvato services GmbH (2)
Neumarkter Str 22, 81673, Munich, Germany
Tel.: (49) 8941367264
Web Site: http://www.arvato-rewards.com
Media Advertising Services
N.A.I.C.S.: 541810
Robert Holm (VP)

rtv media group GmbH (2)
Breslauer Strasse 300, 90471, Nuremberg,
Germany
Tel.: (49) 911892010
Web Site: http://www.rtv-mediagroup.de
Television Broadcasting Services
N.A.I.C.S.: 516120

RTL Journalistenschule GmbH (1)
Picassoplatz 1, 50679, Cologne, Germany
Tel.: (49) 22145676400
Web Site: https://www.rtl-
journalistenschule.de
Educational Support Services
N.A.I.C.S.: 611710
Jutta Lindemann (Office Mgr)

RTL Music Publishing GmbH (1)
Picassoplatz 1, 50679, Cologne, Germany
Tel.: (49) 22145676100
Web Site: https://www.rtl-musicpublishing.de
Music Publishers
N.A.I.C.S.: 512230

RTL Studios GmbH (1)
Picassoplatz 1, D-50679, Cologne, Germany
Tel.: (49) 221456580
Web Site: https://www.rtlstudios.de
Online Shopping Services
N.A.I.C.S.: 812990

Relias LLC (1)
1010 Sync St, Morrisville, NC 27560
Tel.: (919) 655-7934

Web Site: http://www.relias.com
Health Care Srvices
N.A.I.C.S.: 621999
Kay Krafft (CEO)

Riverty Group GmbH (1)
Rheinstrasse 99, 76532, Baden-Baden,
Germany
Tel.: (49) 722150400
Web Site: https://www.riverty.com
Emp.: 5,000
Financial Services
N.A.I.C.S.: 523999

SHOC Media Agency AB (1)
Norrlandsgatan 12, 11143, Stockholm, Sweden
Tel.: (46) 85322211
Web Site: http://www.shocmedia.com
Media Marketing Services
N.A.I.C.S.: 541613

SZ-Reisen GmbH (1)
Ostra-Allee 20, 01067, Dresden, Germany
Tel.: (49) 35148642814
Web Site: http://www.sz-reisen.de
Tour Arrangement Services
N.A.I.C.S.: 561520

Sasquatch Books LLC (1)
1904 3 Ave Ste 710, Seattle, WA 98101
Web Site: http://www.sasquatchbooks.com
Books Publishing Services
N.A.I.C.S.: 513130
Nicole Sprinkle (Mktg Dir)

Saxo-Phon GmbH (1)
Ostra-Allee 20, 01067, Dresden, Germany
Tel.: (49) 35148642257
Web Site: http://www.saxo-phon.de
Advertising & Marketing Services
N.A.I.C.S.: 541810

Smartclip Europe GmbH (1)
Uberseeallee 10, 20457, Hamburg, Germany
Tel.: (49) 40286686122
Web Site: https://smartclip.tv
Advertising Agency Services
N.A.I.C.S.: 541810
Thomas Servatius (Co-CEO & Mng Dir)

Smartclip Nordics AB (1)
Drottninggatan 71C 4 tr, 111 36, Stockholm,
Sweden
Tel.: (46) 702587675
Metal Products Mfr
N.A.I.C.S.: 332999
Jonas Rundgren (Mng Dir)

Sonopress GmbH (1)
Carl-Bertelsmann-Str 161 F, 33332, Gutersloh, Germany
Tel.: (49) 5241803074
Web Site: https://www.sonopress.de
Digital Entertainment Services
N.A.I.C.S.: 541330
Sven Deutschmann (CEO)

Studyflix GmbH (1)
Kirchbergstr 23, 86157, Augsburg, Germany
Tel.: (49) 82156733431
Web Site: https://www.studyflix.de
Digital Educational Services
N.A.I.C.S.: 611513

Sunday GmbH (1)
An der Alster 42, 20099, Hamburg, Germany
Tel.: (49) 4037035440
Web Site: https://sunday.gg
Video Game Publisher
N.A.I.C.S.: 513210

TERRITORY EMBRACE GmbH (1)
Kortumstr 16, 44787, Bochum, Germany
Tel.: (49) 23441560000
Web Site:
http://www.recruiting.ausbildung.de
Internet Provider Services
N.A.I.C.S.: 517810

Tabbler GmbH (1)
An der Alster 42, 20099, Hamburg, Germany
Tel.: (49) 40468953738
Web Site: https://www.tabbler.io
Mobile Game Publisher
N.A.I.C.S.: 513210

**Telamo Musik & Unterhaltung
GmbH** (1)

Lucile-Grahn-Strasse 41, 81675, Munich,
Germany
Tel.: (49) 8945554930
Web Site: https://www.telamo.de
Music Publishers
N.A.I.C.S.: 512230

Territory GmbH (1)
Am Baumwall 11, 20459, Hamburg, Germany
Tel.: (49) 40809046100
Web Site: https://territory.de
Emp.: 850
Communication Service
N.A.I.C.S.: 517122

Territory Influence GmbH (1)
Neumarkter Str 26, 81673, Munich, Germany
Tel.: (49) 89437210000
Web Site: https://www.territory-
influence.com
Marketing Consulting Services
N.A.I.C.S.: 541613

The Book Service Limited (1)
Distribution Centre Colchester Road, Frating Green, Colchester, CO7 7DW, Essex,
United Kingdom
Tel.: (44) 1206256000
Web Site: http://www.thebookservice.co.uk
Books Publishing Services
N.A.I.C.S.: 513130

Ufa Film und Fernseh GmbH (1)
Dianastr 21, 14482, Potsdam, Germany
Tel.: (49) 33170600
Web Site: https://www.ufa.de
Emp.: 215
Motion Picture Production for Television
N.A.I.C.S.: 512110

**Verlag Automobil Wirtschaft (Pty)
Ltd.** (1)
104 Algoa Road, Uitenhage, 6229, South
Africa
Tel.: (27) 419955200
Web Site: http://www.arvato.com
Business Development Services
N.A.I.C.S.: 561499

Vidispine AB (1)
Kista Allevag 3, 164 55, Kista, Sweden
Tel.: (46) 763134592
Web Site: http://www.vidispine.com
Metal Products Mfr
N.A.I.C.S.: 332999
Erik Ahlin (CEO)

We are era GmbH (1)
Kalckreuthstrasse 1-2, 10777, Berlin, Germany
Tel.: (49) 304036180
Web Site: https://www.weareera.com
Emp.: 250
Radio Broadcasting Services
N.A.I.C.S.: 516110

Wildside S.r.l. (1)
Viale Giuseppe Mazzini 9 Scala B int 4,
00195, Rome, Italy
Tel.: (39) 0694516900
Web Site: http://www.wildside.it
Media Production Services
N.A.I.C.S.: 512110
Martina Borg (Mgr-Corp Ops & Dev)

Wilhelm Goldmann Verlag GmbH (1)
Neumarkter Strasse 28, 81673, Munich,
Germany (100%)
Tel.: (49) 8941360
Web Site: http://www.randomhouse.de
Sales Range: $100-124.9 Million
Emp.: 500
Book Publishing
N.A.I.C.S.: 513130
Joerg Pfuhl (CEO)

Yospace Technologies Limited (1)
18-20 Church Street, Staines-upon-
Thames, TW18 4EP, Surrey, United Kingdom
Tel.: (44) 1784466388
Web Site: http://www.yospace.com
Interactive Mobile Application Development
Services
N.A.I.C.S.: 541511

arvato AG (1)
Carl Bertelsmann Strasse 270, D 33311,
Gutersloh, Germany

Tel.: (49) 5241800
Web Site: http://www.arvato.com
Sales Range: $5-14.9 Billion
Emp.: 63,985
Media & Communications Services
N.A.I.C.S.: 561499
Debra Maxwell (CEO-CRM Solutions-UK &
Ireland)

Subsidiary (Domestic):

arvato CRM Nordhorn GmbH (2)
Bentheimer Strasse 118a, 48529, Nordhorn,
Lower Saxony, Germany
Tel.: (49) 52418082597
Television Broadcasting Services
N.A.I.C.S.: 516120

arvato CrossMarketing GmbH (2)
Neumarkter Strasse 22, 81673, Munich,
Germany
Tel.: (49) 8941367100
Web Site: http://www.crossmarketing.de
Television Broadcasting Services
N.A.I.C.S.: 516120
Frederik Schott (Deputy Mng Dir)

Subsidiary (Non-US):

arvato Finance AS (2)
Kongens gate 6, 0101, Oslo, Norway
Tel.: (47) 22 87 89 00
Web Site: http://www.finance.arvato.com
Sales Range: $150-199.9 Million
Holding Company; Credit, Sales Financing
& Debt Collection Services
N.A.I.C.S.: 551112
Karl Otto Aam (Sr VP-Norway & Denmark)

Subsidiary (Non-US):

Gothia Financial Group AB (3)
Jarngatan 2, SE-432 31, Varberg, Sweden
Tel.: (46) 340664440
Web Site: http://www.gothiagroup.com
Holding Company; Credit & Debt Collection
Services
N.A.I.C.S.: 551112

Subsidiary (Non-US):

Gothia A/S (4)
Ostbanegade 55 2 Tv, 2100, Copenhagen,
Denmark
Tel.: (45) 38418000
Web Site: http://www.gothiagroup.com
Credit & Debt Collection Services
N.A.I.C.S.: 522299

Gothia AS (4)
PO Box 115, 7901, Rorvik, Norway
Tel.: (47) 74366800
Web Site: http://www.gothiagroup.com
Credit & Debt Collection Services
N.A.I.C.S.: 522299

Gothia Deutschland GmbH (4)
Wilhelm-Theodor-Romheld-Strasse 26,
D-55130, Mainz, Germany
Tel.: (49) 6131 9075 0
Web Site: http://www.gothiagroup.com
Credit & Debt Collection Services
N.A.I.C.S.: 522299
Fred Fegel (CFO)

Gothia Oy (4)
PL 722, 20101, Turku, Finland
Tel.: (358) 22792000
Web Site: http://www.gothiagroup.com
Credit & Debt Collection Services
N.A.I.C.S.: 522299

Subsidiary (Non-US):

**arvato Financial Solutions
Limited** (3)
24 George Square, Glasgow, G2 1EG,
Scotland, United Kingdom
Tel.: (44) 1412214567
Web Site: http://finance.arvato.com
Sales Range: $25-49.9 Million
Credit Management, Debt Collection & Consultancy Services
N.A.I.C.S.: 522390
Craig McKechnie (Head-Infrastructure &
Architechture)

Subsidiary (Domestic):

BCW Group (Gothia) Limited (4)
Ground Floor Ridgeworth House, Liverpool

Gardens, Worthing, BN11 1RS, W Sussex,
United Kingdom
Tel.: (44) 844 248 0300
Emp.: 80
Credit & Debt Collection Services
N.A.I.C.S.: 522299
Emma Frost *(Acct Dir-Key Accts)*

Subsidiary (Domestic):

arvato Systems S4M GmbH (2)
Am Coloneum 3, 50829, Cologne, Germany
Tel.: (49) 221285550
Web Site: http://www.s4m.arvato-
systems.de
Software Development Services
N.A.I.C.S.: 541511
Ralf Schurmann *(Chm-Exec Bd)*

arvato Systems perdata GmbH (2)
Martin-Luther-Ring 7-9, 04109, Leipzig,
Germany
Tel.: (49) 341355220
Web Site: http://www.utilities.arvato-
systems.de
Software Development Services
N.A.I.C.S.: 541511
Percy Dahm *(Member-Exec Bd)*

**arvato direct services Brandenburg
GmbH** (2)
Wilhelmsdorfer Landstrasse 43, Branden-
burg an der Havel, 14776, Brandenburg,
Germany
Tel.: (49) 33817982100
Web Site: http://www.majorel.com
Television Broadcasting Services
N.A.I.C.S.: 516120
Oliver Carlsen *(Gen Mgr)*

**arvato direct services Cottbus
GmbH** (2)
Am Seegraben 21, 03051, Cottbus, Ger-
many
Tel.: (49) 8001115201
Web Site: http://www.cottbus.arvato-
customer-services.de
Television Broadcasting Services
N.A.I.C.S.: 516120

**arvato direct services Dortmund
GmbH** (2)
Personalabteilung Schleefstr 1, 44287,
Dortmund, Germany
Tel.: (49) 2314441657
Television Broadcasting Services
N.A.I.C.S.: 516120

**arvato direct services Frankfurt
GmbH** (2)
Schumannstrasse 164, 63069, Offenbach,
Hessen, Germany
Tel.: (49) 6942693520
Telecommunication Servicesb
N.A.I.C.S.: 517111

**arvato direct services Munster
GmbH** (2)
Holtenweg 33, 48155, Munster, Germany
Tel.: (49) 25150040
Web Site: http://www.muenster.arvato-
customer-services.de
Emp.: 500
Telecommunication Servicesb
N.A.I.C.S.: 517111
Natascha Melanie Reichart *(Mgr-
Integration)*

**arvato direct services Neckarsulm
GmbH** (2)
Kanalstr 15, 74172, Neckarsulm, Germany
Tel.: (49) 71329790
Telecommunication Servicesb
N.A.I.C.S.: 517111

**arvato direct services Neubranden-
burg GmbH** (2)
Flurstrasse 2, 17034, Neubrandenburg,
Germany
Tel.: (49) 39537903808
Web Site:
http://www.neubrandenburg.arvato-
customer-services.de
Telecommunication Servicesb
N.A.I.C.S.: 517111

**arvato direct services Potsdam
GmbH** (2)
Behlertstrasse 3a, 14467, Potsdam, Ger-
many

Tel.: (49) 33158174306
Web Site: http://www.potsdam.arvato-
customer-services.de
Emp.: 500
Telecommunication Servicesb
N.A.I.C.S.: 517111
Andreas Krohn *(Mng Dir & Member-Exec
Bd)*

**arvato direct services Schwerin
GmbH** (2)
Marienplatz 12, 19053, Schwerin, Germany
Tel.: (49) 38559239104
Web Site: http://www.schwerin.arvato-
customer-services.de
Telecommunication Servicesb
N.A.I.C.S.: 517111

**arvato direct services Stralsund
GmbH** (2)
Grosse Parower Strasse 133, 18435,
Stralsund, Germany
Tel.: (49) 38313568502
Web Site: http://www.stralsund.arvato-
customer-services.de
Telecommunication Servicesb
N.A.I.C.S.: 517111

**arvato direct services Wilhelmshaven
GmbH** (2)
Personalabteilung Olympiastrasse 1,
Schortens, 26419, Wilhelmshaven, Ger-
many
Tel.: (49) 4421760
Web Site: http://www.arvato-customer-
services.de
Telecommunication Servicesb
N.A.I.C.S.: 517111
Christian Buschmeier *(Member-Exec Bd)*

**arvato direct services eiweiler
GmbH** (2)
Lebacher Strasse 60, Eiweiler, 66265, Heu-
sweiler, Germany
Tel.: (49) 800664870102
Web Site: http://www.eiweiler.arvato-
customer-services.de
Telecommunication Servicesb
N.A.I.C.S.: 517111

arvato infoscore GmbH (2)
Rheinstrasse 99, 76532, Baden-Baden,
Germany
Tel.: (49) 722150400
Web Site: http://www.finance.arvato.com
Television Broadcasting Services
N.A.I.C.S.: 516120

arvato media GmbH (2)
An der Autobahn 100, 33333, Gutersloh,
Germany
Tel.: (49) 5241801820
Web Site: http://www.vva-online.net
Television Broadcasting Services
N.A.I.C.S.: 516120

arvato p.s. GmbH (2)
Gutersloher Strasse 123, 33415, Verl, Ger-
many
Tel.: (49) 5241800
Television Broadcasting Services
N.A.I.C.S.: 516120

arvato services Chemnitz GmbH (2)
Rathausstrasse 7, 09111, Chemnitz, Ger-
many
Tel.: (49) 3713558146315
Web Site: http://www.chemnitz-zieht-an.de
Television Broadcasting Services
N.A.I.C.S.: 516120

arvato services Dresden GmbH (2)
Personalabteilung Frau Anne-Christin Dor-
ing Ammonstr 74, 01067, Dresden, Ger-
many
Tel.: (49) 35186265117
Television Broadcasting Services
N.A.I.C.S.: 516120

arvato services Duisburg GmbH (2)
Keniastrasse 33, 47269, Duisburg, Ger-
many
Tel.: (49) 20393459345
Web Site: http://www.duisburg.arvato-
customer-services.de
Telecommunication Servicesb
N.A.I.C.S.: 517111
Herr Ulrich Geissler *(Mng Dir)*

arvato services Essen GmbH (2)

Hollestr 7 a, 45127, Essen, Nordrhein-
Westfalen, Germany
Tel.: (49) 52415276000
Telecommunication Servicesb
N.A.I.C.S.: 517111
Benjamin de Bruin *(Acct Mgr)*

**arvato services technical information
GmbH** (2)
Gottlieb-Daimler-Str 1, 33428, Harsewinkel,
Germany
Tel.: (49) 2845949800
Web Site: http://ti.arvato-cim.com
Television Broadcasting Services
N.A.I.C.S.: 516120

**arvato telco services Erfurt
GmbH** (2)
Camburger Strasse 4, 99091, Erfurt, Ger-
many
Tel.: (49) 36155597463
Television Broadcasting Services
N.A.I.C.S.: 516120

informa HIS GmbH (1)
Kreuzberger Ring 68, 65205, Wiesbaden,
Germany
Tel.: (49) 6118808700
Web Site: https://www.informa-his.de
Insurance Services
N.A.I.C.S.: 524210

infoscore AG (1)
Ifangstrasse 8, 8952, Schlieren, Switzerland
Tel.: (41) 447386888
Credit Management Services
N.A.I.C.S.: 522299

mbs Nurnberg GmbH (1)
Breslauer Strasse 300, 90471, Nuremberg,
Germany
Tel.: (49) 911893193420
Web Site: https://www.mbs-team.de
Advertising Agency Services
N.A.I.C.S.: 541810
Andrea Altvater *(Head-Photography Dept)*

scoyo GmbH (1)
Grosser Burstah 50-52, 20457, Hamburg,
Germany
Tel.: (49) 4035777357
Web Site: http://www.scoyo.de
Online Learning Services
N.A.I.C.S.: 611710
Daniel Bialecki *(CEO)*

stern.de GmbH (1)
Am Baumenall 11, 20459, Hamburg, Ger-
many
Tel.: (49) 4037030
Web Site: http://www.stern.de
News Publishing Services
N.A.I.C.S.: 711510

topac GmbH (1)
Carl-Miele-Strasse 202-204, 33332, Gut-
ersloh, Germany
Tel.: (49) 52418089600
Web Site: http://www.topac.de
Cardboard Packaging Mfr
N.A.I.C.S.: 322211
Sven Deutschmann *(CEO)*

trnd SARL (1)
3 Rue de Liege, 75009, Paris, France
Tel.: (33) 146224866
Marketing Consulting Services
N.A.I.C.S.: 541613

BERTHOLD TECHNOLOGIES GMBH & CO. KG

Calmbacher Str 22, Bad Wilbad,
75323, Germany
Tel.: (49) 70811770
Web Site: http://www.berthold.com
Year Founded: 1949
Rev.: $62,744,314
Emp.: 300
Detection Instruments Mfr
N.A.I.C.S.: 334513

Subsidiaries:

BERTHOLD FRANCE SAS (1)
Parc Technologique des Bruyeres 8 Route
des Bruyeres, 78770, Thoiry, France
Tel.: (33) 134947900
Web Site: http://www.berthold.fr
Measuring Device Distr

N.A.I.C.S.: 423830

BERTHOLD ITALIA S.r.l (1)
Viale Europa 35, 20047, Brugherio, Monza
and Brianza, Italy
Tel.: (39) 0392873064
Web Site: http://www.berthold-italia.com
Measuring Device Distr
N.A.I.C.S.: 423830
Anna Bedini *(Mgr-Sls)*

**BERTHOLD TECHNOLOGIES (Bel-
gium) NV/SA** (1)
Vaartdijk 22, 1800, Vilvoorde, Belgium
Tel.: (32) 22516010
Measuring Device Distr
N.A.I.C.S.: 423830

**BERTHOLD TECHNOLOGIES (U.K.)
Ltd.** (1)
Allied Business Centre Coldharbour Lane,
Harpenden, AL5 4UT, Herts, United King-
dom
Tel.: (44) 1582761477
Measuring Device Distr
N.A.I.C.S.: 423830

**BERTHOLD TECHNOLOGIES
GmbH** (1)
Goldschlagstrasse 182, 1140, Vienna, Aus-
tria
Tel.: (43) 191422510
Measuring Device Distr
N.A.I.C.S.: 423830

**Berthold Technologies (Schweiz)
GmbH** (1)
Chollerstrasse 37, 6300, Zug, Switzerland
Tel.: (41) 448712500
Measuring Device Distr
N.A.I.C.S.: 423830

**Berthold Technologies U.S.A.
LLC** (1)
99 Midway Ln, Oak Ridge, TN 37830
Tel.: (865) 483-1488
Web Site: http://www.berthold-us.com
Measuring Device Distr
N.A.I.C.S.: 423830
Jon Buchanan *(Gen Mgr)*

BERTRANDT AG

Birkensee 1, 71139, Ehningen, Ger-
many
Tel.: (49) 70346560
Web Site: https://www.bertrandt.com
BDT—(MUN)
Rev.: $1,276,967,855
Assets: $1,055,432,184
Liabilities: $553,579,766
Net Worth: $501,852,418
Earnings: $33,601,803
Emp.: 13,406
Fiscal Year-end: 09/30/23
Automotive & Aviation Equipment De-
sign & Engineering Services
N.A.I.C.S.: 541330
Dietmar Bichler *(Chm-Supervisory
Bd)*

Subsidiaries:

**Bertrandt Ceska Republika Engineer-
ing Technologies s.r.o.** (1)
Mlada Boleslav I, 293 01, Mlada Boleslav,
Czech Republic
Tel.: (420) 70346560
Engineering Services
N.A.I.C.S.: 541330

**Bertrandt Engineering Shanghai Co.,
Ltd.** (1)
Kaidabeijie 1777, Jiading District, Changc-
hun, 130013, China
Tel.: (86) 81507599
Web Site: https://www.bertrandt.com
Engineering Services
N.A.I.C.S.: 541330

**Bertrandt Fahrerprobung Sud
GmbH** (1)
Ferdinand-Porsche-Str 12, 71154, Nufrin-
gen, Germany
Tel.: (49) 70346560
Web Site: https://www.bertrandt.com
Engineering Services
N.A.I.C.S.: 541330

Bertrandt AG—(Continued)

Bertrandt Projektgesellschaft mbH (1)
Birkensee 1, Ehningen Near Stuttgart, 71139, Ehningen, Germany
Tel.: (49) 70346560
Engineeering Services
N.A.I.C.S.: 541330

Bertrandt S.A.S. (1)
35-37 Avenue Louis Breguet, BP 35, 78140, Velizy-Villacoublay, France
Tel.: (33) 1 6935 1505
Web Site: http://www.bertrandt.com
Emp.: 600
Automotive & Aviation Equipment Design & Engineering Services
N.A.I.C.S.: 541330

Bertrandt SAS Betriebsstatte (1)
Val Parc, 25200, Montbeliard, France
Tel.: (33) 381993500
Web Site: https://www.bertrandt.com
Engineeering Services
N.A.I.C.S.: 541330

Bertrandt UK Ltd. (1)
Jubilee House 3 The Drive, Warley, CM13 3FR, United Kingdom
Tel.: (44) 1268564300
Web Site: https://www.bertrandt.com
Emp.: 2
Automotive & Aviation Equipment Design & Engineering Services
N.A.I.C.S.: 541330

Bertrandt US Inc. (1)
1273 Reamwood Ave, Sunnyvale, CA 94089
Tel.: (248) 598-5100
Web Site: http://www.bertrandt.com
Emp.: 200
Automotive & Aviation Equipment Design & Engineering Services
N.A.I.C.S.: 541330

Bertrandt Verwaltungs GmbH (1)
Am Dieb 2, Monsheim Near Weissach, 71297, Weissach, Germany
Tel.: (49) 70346560
Web Site: https://www.bertrandt.com
Engineeering Services
N.A.I.C.S.: 541330

Concept AG (1)
Zettachring 6, 70567, Stuttgart, Germany
Tel.: (49) 711132740
Web Site: https://concept.ag
Emp.: 29
Economic Consulting Services
N.A.I.C.S.: 541690

Jobfair GmbH (1)
Augustaanlage 18, 68165, Mannheim, Germany
Tel.: (49) 62140047333
Web Site: https://www.bertrandt.com
Engineeering Services
N.A.I.C.S.: 541330

Philotech France S.A.S. (1)
1 rond-point du General Eisenhower Golf Park Pavillion 2a, 31100, Toulouse, France
Tel.: (33) 581761830
Engineering Consultancy Services
N.A.I.C.S.: 541330

Philotech Iberica Sistemas y Logistica S.L. (1)
Avenida Leonardo da Vinci 15, 28906, Madrid, Spain
Tel.: (34) 914912788
Engineering Consultancy Services
N.A.I.C.S.: 541330

digital result GmbH (1)
Viktualienmarkt 8, Im Mindspace, 80331, Munich, Germany
Tel.: (49) 89954577820
Web Site: https://digital-result.com
Software Development Services
N.A.I.C.S.: 541511

BERVIN INVESTMENT & LEASING LIMITED
607 Rohit House 3 Tolstoy Marg, New Delhi, 110 001, India
Tel.: (91) 1123353697

Web Site: https://www.bervin.com
Year Founded: 1990
531340—(BOM)
Rev.: $1,482,490
Assets: $4,784,625
Liabilities: $1,520,693
Net Worth: $3,263,932
Earnings: $472,614
Emp.: 1
Fiscal Year-end: 03/31/21
Investment Services
N.A.I.C.S.: 523910
Kalpana Umakanth (Sec)

BERYL DRUGS LTD.
133 Ground Floor Kanchan Bagh, Indore, 452001, Madhya Pradesh, India
Tel.: (91) 7312517677
Web Site:
   https://www.beryldrugs.com
Year Founded: 1993
524606—(BOM)
Rev.: $2,015,914
Assets: $2,432,949
Liabilities: $1,437,372
Net Worth: $995,576
Earnings: ($89,954)
Fiscal Year-end: 03/31/22
Pharmaceutical Product Mfr & Distr
N.A.I.C.S.: 325412
Ashish Baraskar (CFO)

BERYL SECURITIES LIMITED
133 Kanchan Bagh, Indore, 452 001, Madhya Pradesh, India
Tel.: (91) 7312517677
Web Site: https://berylsecurities.com
531582—(BOM)
Rev.: $108,736
Assets: $1,318,126
Liabilities: $33,183
Net Worth: $1,284,943
Earnings: $47,120
Fiscal Year-end: 03/31/22
Investment Management Service
N.A.I.C.S.: 523940
Sudhir Sethi (Mng Dir)

BES ENGINEERING CORPORATION
6th Floor No 12 Dongxing Road, Songshan District, Taipei, Taiwan
Tel.: (886) 287876687
Web Site: https://www.bes.com.tw
Year Founded: 1950
2515—(TAI)
Rev.: $620,011,717
Assets: $1,832,931,714
Liabilities: $1,071,012,746
Net Worth: $761,918,968
Earnings: $20,459,694
Emp.: 1,160
Fiscal Year-end: 12/31/23
Civil Engineering Services
N.A.I.C.S.: 541330
Chih-Ming Chou (Chm)

Subsidiaries:

Core Asia Human Resources Management Co., Ltd. (1)
2F No 12 Dongxing Rd, Songshan District, Taipei, 105, Taiwan
Tel.: (886) 277061288
Web Site: https://www.coreasia.com.tw
Emp.: 1,000
Human Resource Consulting Services
N.A.I.C.S.: 541612

Corporacion de Inversion y Desarrollo BES, S.A. (1)
Juan Santamaria International Airport, Alajuela, 21005, Costa Rica
Tel.: (506) 24381111
Industrial Park Operation Services
N.A.I.C.S.: 561210

Elite Human Resource Management Co., Ltd. (1)

No 12 Dongxing Road 2nd Fl, Songshan District, Taipei, 105, Taiwan
Tel.: (886) 287873547
Web Site: http://www.ehrmc.com.tw
Sales Range: $25-49.9 Million
Emp.: 40
Human Resource Consulting Services
N.A.I.C.S.: 541612

Xiamen Bonded Area Airport Logistics Park Construction Co., Ltd. (1)
Room 420-2 4F Xiangyu Complex, Xiandai Logistics Park, Xiamen, 361006, Fujian, China
Tel.: (86) 5925745718
Warehousing & Logistics Services
N.A.I.C.S.: 493110

BESALCO S.A.
Ebro 2705, PO Box 14754 C-21, Las Condes, Santiago, Chile
Tel.: (56) 223380800
Web Site: https://www.besalco.cl
BESALCO—(SGO)
Sales Range: Less than $1 Million
Real Estate Development Services
N.A.I.C.S.: 531390
Victor Manuel Bezanilla Saavedra (Chm)

BESANA UK LIMITED
Randall Rd Rissington Business Park, Bourton on the Water, Cheltenham, GL54 2QB, Gloucestershire, United Kingdom
Tel.: (44) 1451810023
Web Site:
   http://www.besanagroup.com
Sales Range: $50-74.9 Million
Emp.: 15
Production & Processing of Nuts & Dried Fruit
N.A.I.C.S.: 311423
Giuseppe Calcagni (Pres)

BESIKTAS FUTBOL YATIRIMLARI SANAYI VE TICARET AS
Tupras Stadium 1 Kadirgalar Street Visnezade, 34357, Besiktas, Istanbul, Turkiye
Tel.: (90) 2129481903
Web Site: https://www.bjk.com.tr
Year Founded: 1995
BJKAS—(IST)
Rev.: $40,135,855
Assets: $121,287,048
Liabilities: $225,583,576
Net Worth: ($104,296,528)
Earnings: ($14,192,998)
Fiscal Year-end: 06/30/23
Professional Soccer Club Operator
N.A.I.C.S.: 711211

BESQAB AB
Hamngatan 13, 111 47, Stockholm, Sweden
Tel.: (46) 86786640
Web Site: http://www.arosbostad.se
BESQ—(OMX)
Sales Range: Less than $1 Million
Emp.: 29
Real Estate Services
N.A.I.C.S.: 531390
Ken Wendelin (Deputy CEO & CFO)

BESRA GOLD INC.
4-158 240 Richmond St West, Toronto, M5C 1C3, ON, Canada
Tel.: (416) 572-2525
Web Site: http://www.besra.com
Sales Range: $75-99.9 Million
Emp.: 1,681
Gold Mining Services
N.A.I.C.S.: 212220
David Alexander Seton (Chm)

BESSOR MINERALS INC.

PO Box 37033, Country Club PO, Nanaimo, V9T 6N4, BC, Canada
Tel.: (250) 729-0453   AB
Web Site: http://www.troymet.com
Year Founded: 2007
BST.H—(TSXV)
Rev.: $1,993
Assets: $815,708
Liabilities: $47,076
Net Worth: $768,632
Earnings: ($119,414)
Fiscal Year-end: 10/31/22
Natural Resource Mining Services
N.A.I.C.S.: 212390
Kieran M. J. Downes (Pres & CEO)

BEST & CROMPTON ENGG. LTD.
No 96/97 Greenways Road Extension, RA Puram, Chennai, 600 028, India
Tel.: (91) 4445066410
Web Site:
   http://www.bestcrompton.com
Sales Range: $10-24.9 Million
Electrical Component Mfr
N.A.I.C.S.: 335999
K. Sai Prasad (VP-Ops)

BEST AGROLIFE LTD.
B4 Bhagwan Das Nagar, East Punjabi Bagh, New Delhi, 110026, India
Tel.: (91) 1145803300   In
Web Site:
   https://www.bestagrolife.com
539660—(BOM)
Rev.: $124,589,092
Assets: $50,734,757
Liabilities: $33,033,969
Net Worth: $17,700,788
Earnings: $5,060,847
Emp.: 160
Fiscal Year-end: 03/31/21
Financial Support Services
N.A.I.C.S.: 523999
Vimal Kumar (Mng Dir)

Subsidiaries:

Seedlings India Private Limited (1)
Block no 6 Tribhuvan Complex Ishwar Nagar, Delhi, New Delhi, 110065, India
Tel.: (91) 9650004154
Web Site: https://seedlingsindia.com
Agricultural Services
N.A.I.C.S.: 115112

BEST CAST IT LTD
Plot No 58 SP SF No 184 & 185 3rd Cross Road, Ambattur Industrial Estate Ambattur, Chennai, 600 058, India
Tel.: (91) 4443233215
Web Site: http://www.bcil.net
Year Founded: 1974
Sales Range: $10-24.9 Million
Emp.: 270
Aluminum Die-Casting Services
N.A.I.C.S.: 331523
Murali Kabirdass (Dir-Comml)

Subsidiaries:

Kabirdass Motor Company Ltd (1)
Best Cast House 16 Poonamallee High Road, Vellappan Chavadi, Chennai, 600077, India
Tel.: (91) 4426800988
Web Site: http://www.kabirdass.com
Electric Bike Mfr
N.A.I.C.S.: 336991

BEST CHIPS CO., LTD.
3-15-2 Nakanishi Kumagaya, Saitama, 3600013, Japan
Tel.: (81) 5055327594
Web Site: https://www.bestchips.jp
Electronic Products Mfr
N.A.I.C.S.: 334417

BEST CUT LIMITED
12 Fifth Street, PO Box 128, Empangeni, 3880, South Africa
Tel.: (27) 35 787 1960   ZA
Web Site: http://www.bestcut.co.za
Year Founded: 1989
Meat Product Whslr
N.A.I.C.S.: 424470
A. H. Steenkamp (CEO)

BEST DEAL PROPERTIES HOLDING PLC
Number 63 J L Building Luqa Road, Paola, PLA 9045, Malta
Tel.: (356) 79094686
Web Site:
https://www.bestdealmalta.com
Year Founded: 2011
BD24A—(MAL)
Sales Range: Less than $1 Million
Real Estate Agency Services
N.A.I.C.S.: 531210
Christopher Attard (Board of Directors & Co-Founder)

BEST EASTERN HOTELS LTD.
401 Chartered House 293/299 Dr C H Street Near Marine Lines Church, Mumbai, 400 002, India
Tel.: (91) 2222078292
Web Site:
https://www.ushaascot.com
508664—(BOM)
Rev.: $726,000
Assets: $751,382
Liabilities: $445,537
Net Worth: $305,845
Earnings: $70,104
Fiscal Year-end: 03/31/23
Home Management Services
N.A.I.C.S.: 721110
Vinaychand Yadavsingh Kothari (Chm & Co-Mng Dir)

BEST EFFORTS BANK PJSC
Dolgorukovskaya house 38 Moscow street, Moscow, 127006, Russia
Tel.: (7) 4957059031
Web Site:
http://www.besteffortsbank.ru
ALBK—(RUS)
Sales Range: $1-9.9 Million
Banking & Financial Services
N.A.I.C.S.: 522320
Irina Ionova (Chm-Mgmt Bd)

BEST FENCING GROUP B.V.
Zandstraat 15, Best, 5683 CC, Netherlands
Tel.: (31) 499363666
Web Site:
http://www.bestfencinggroup.com
Sales Range: $50-74.9 Million
Emp.: 100
Fencing & Security System Mfr
N.A.I.C.S.: 561621
Arthur Van Del Graas (CEO)

BEST FINANCE COMPANY LIMITED
Kamaladi, Kathmandu, Nepal
Tel.: (977) 14542461
Web Site:
https://www.bestfinance.com.np
BFC—(NEP)
Rev.: $4,483,385
Assets: $43,595,891
Liabilities: $34,649,663
Net Worth: $8,946,228
Earnings: $65,395
Fiscal Year-end: 07/16/23
Financial Services
N.A.I.C.S.: 523999
Shailendra Bade Shrestha (Head-Compliance, AML & CFT & Asst Gen Mgr)

BEST FOOD HOLDING COMPANY LIMITED
Suite 2701 One Exchange Square, Central, China (Hong Kong)
Tel.: (852) 39619700   Ky
1488—(HKG)
Rev.: $75,466,404
Assets: $188,607,182
Liabilities: $159,037,819
Net Worth: $29,569,363
Earnings: ($23,405,803)
Emp.: 2,162
Fiscal Year-end: 12/31/22
Holding Company; Investment Services
N.A.I.C.S.: 551112

Subsidiaries:

Lee & Man Company Limited   (1)
8/F Liven House 61-63 King Yip Street, Kwun Tong, Kowloon, China (Hong Kong)   (100%)
Tel.: (852) 23199888
Sales Range: $25-49.9 Million
Emp.: 100
Handbag Mfr
N.A.I.C.S.: 316990

Lee & Man Handbag Manufacturing Co. Ltd.   (1)
8/F Liven House 61-63 King Yip Street, Kwun Tong, Kowloon, China (Hong Kong)   (100%)
Tel.: (852) 23199888
Handbag Mfr
N.A.I.C.S.: 316990

Lee & Man Management Co. Ltd.   (1)
8th Floor Liven House Kwun Tong, Kowloon, China (Hong Kong)   (100%)
Tel.: (852) 23199888
Web Site: http://www.leeman.com.hk
Sales Range: $25-49.9 Million
Emp.: 45
Other Management Consulting Services
N.A.I.C.S.: 541618

BEST HOTEL PROPERTIES A.S.
Hodzovo Namestie 2, Bratislava, 811 06, Slovakia
Tel.: (421) 259348152
Web Site: http://www.bhp.sk
Real Estate Investment Services
N.A.I.C.S.: 531210
Branislav Babik (Chm-Mgmt Bd)

BEST INC.
2nd Floor Block A Huaxing Modern Industry Park No 18th Tangmiao Road, Xihu District, Hangzhou, 310013, Zhejiang, China
Tel.: (86) 57188995656   Ky
Web Site: https://www.best-inc.com
Year Founded: 2007
BEST—(NYSE)
Rev.: $1,186,469,271
Assets: $1,193,543,436
Liabilities: $1,099,797,148
Net Worth: $93,746,288
Earnings: ($224,193,878)
Emp.: 3,628
Fiscal Year-end: 12/31/22
Online & Offline Retail Services
N.A.I.C.S.: 459999
Shao-Ning Johnny Chou (Founder, Chm & CEO)

Subsidiaries:

BEST Logistics Technologies (China) Co., Ltd.   (1)
Block A Huaxing Modern Industrial Park No 18 Tangmiao Road, Xihu District, Hangzhou, 310013, China
Tel.: (86) 57188995656
Logistic & Supply Chain Services
N.A.I.C.S.: 541614

BEST LINKING GROUP HOLDINGS LIMITED
Unit 1226B 12/F Star House No 3 Salisbury Road, Kowloon, China (Hong Kong)
Tel.: (852) 23819300   Ky
Web Site: http://www.blg.hk
Year Founded: 2007
8617—(HKG)
Rev.: $16,285,575
Assets: $19,021,470
Liabilities: $716,933
Net Worth: $18,304,538
Earnings: $4,453,448
Emp.: 82
Fiscal Year-end: 12/31/22
Holding Company
N.A.I.C.S.: 551112
Yuk Pan Chan (Founder, Chm & CEO)

BEST MART 360 HOLDINGS LIMITED
11/F C-BONS International Center 108 Wai Yip Street, Kwun Tong, Kowloon, China (Hong Kong)
Tel.: (852) 39161888   Ky
Web Site:
https://www.bestmart360.com
Year Founded: 2013
2360—(HKG)
Rev.: $255,835,183
Assets: $116,101,734
Liabilities: $59,602,948
Net Worth: $56,498,786
Earnings: $14,162,520
Emp.: 778
Fiscal Year-end: 12/31/22
Holding Company
N.A.I.C.S.: 551112
Tsz Fung Lin (Chm)

BEST MOUNTAIN DEUTSCHLAND HOLZWIRTSCHAFT GMBH
Pivitsheider Strasse 22, Detmold, 32758, Germany
Tel.: (49) 523298100
Web Site: http://www.best-mount.de
Rev.: $21,025,576
Emp.: 240
Plywood, Model Making Boards, Bamboo, Beech & Veneer Mfr
N.A.I.C.S.: 321211
Yu Zhao (Mng Dir)

BEST N.V.
Research Park Hassrode, Romeinse Straat 20, 3001, Leuven, Belgium
Tel.: (32) 16396396   BE
Web Site: http://www.tomra.com
Year Founded: 1996
Sales Range: $100-124.9 Million
Emp.: 250
Sorting Equipment Mfr for Food Industry
N.A.I.C.S.: 333241
Ashley Hunter (Gen Mgr)

Subsidiaries:

BEST Eindhoven BV   (1)
J.F. Kennedylaan 3, 5612, Eindhoven, Netherlands   (100%)
Tel.: (31) 402472896
Sales Range: $25-49.9 Million
Emp.: 40
Food Industry Sorting Equipment Mfr
N.A.I.C.S.: 333241

BEST OF THE BEST PLC
2 Plato Place 72-74 St Dionis Road, London, SW6 4TU, United Kingdom
Tel.: (44) 207 371 8866
Web Site: http://www.botb.com
BOTB—(LSE)
Rev.: $62,022,007
Assets: $18,122,847

Liabilities: $5,952,244
Net Worth: $12,170,602
Earnings: $15,605,634
Emp.: 21
Fiscal Year-end: 04/30/21
Travel & Leisure
N.A.I.C.S.: 713290
William S. Hindmarch (Founder & CEO)

BEST PACIFIC INTERNATIONAL HOLDINGS LIMITED
8th Floor West Gate Tower No 7 Wing Hong Street Lai Chi Kok, Kowloon, China (Hong Kong)
Tel.: (852) 31853187   Ky
Web Site: http://www.bestpacific.com
2111—(HKG)
Rev.: $618,157,416
Assets: $903,094,486
Liabilities: $468,013,217
Net Worth: $435,081,269
Earnings: $51,765,607
Emp.: 8,957
Fiscal Year-end: 12/31/21
Holding Company
N.A.I.C.S.: 551112
Yuguang Lu (Chm)

BEST S.A.
ul Luzycka 8A, 81-537, Gdynia, Poland
Tel.: (48) 587699299
Web Site: https://www.best.com.pl
Year Founded: 1994
BST—(WAR)
Rev.: $89,896,595
Assets: $392,561,483
Liabilities: $202,007,367
Net Worth: $190,554,115
Earnings: $12,976,372
Emp.: 653
Fiscal Year-end: 12/31/23
Financial Debit Collection Services
N.A.I.C.S.: 561440
Hubert Janiszewski (Deputy Chm-Supervisory Bd)

Subsidiaries:

Best Capital Italy S.r.l.   (1)
Via Vittorio Betteloni 2, 20131, Milan, Italy
Tel.: (39) 0282762406
Credit Management Services
N.A.I.C.S.: 522390

Best Italia S.r.l.   (1)
Via Larga 31, 20122, Milan, Italy
Tel.: (39) 0282762406
Web Site: https://bestsa.it
Credit Management Services
N.A.I.C.S.: 522390

Best TFI S.A.   (1)
ul Luzycka 8A, 81-537, Gdynia, Poland
Tel.: (48) 587699299
Web Site: https://tfi.best.com.pl
Fund Management Services
N.A.I.C.S.: 541611
Witold Orlowski (Pres)

BEST WESTERN VILLAGE PARK INN
1804 Crowchild Trail Northwest, Calgary, T2M 3Y7, AB, Canada
Tel.: (403) 289-0241
Web Site:
https://www.villageparkinn.com
Sales Range: $10-24.9 Million
Emp.: 120
Hotel Operations
N.A.I.C.S.: 721110
Emad Khalilah (Gen Mgr)

BEST WORLD INTERNATIONAL LTD.
20W Pasir Panjang Road 0828 Mapletree, Singapore, 534057, Singapore

Best World International Ltd.—(Continued)

Tel.: (65) 68990088   SG
Web Site:
  https://www.bestworld.com.sg
Year Founded: 1990
CGN—(SES)
Rev.: $389,691,737
Assets: $655,054,154
Liabilities: $207,901,009
Net Worth: $447,093,085
Earnings: $91,248,201
Fiscal Year-end: 12/31/23
Health & Wellness Products Developer & Mfr
N.A.I.C.S.: 325411
Ban Chin Huang (COO)

Subsidiaries:

BWL Health & Sciences, Inc.   (1)
32nd Floor Units 3205-3206 Robinsons Equitable Tower, ADB Avenue corner Poveda Road Ortigas Center, Pasig, 1605, Philippines
Tel.: (63) 23971700
Web Site: http://ph.bwlgroup.com
Cosmetics Products Mfr
N.A.I.C.S.: 325620

BWL Korea Co., Ltd.   (1)
13-101 373 Gangnam-daero, Seocho-gu, Seoul, 06621, Korea (South)
Tel.: (82) 236759190
Web Site: https://kr.bwlgroup.com
Cosmetics Products Mfr
N.A.I.C.S.: 325620

Best World Lifestyle (HK) Company Limited   (1)
Rm 1402-03 14F Causeway Bay Plz 1, 489 Hennessy Rd, Causeway Bay, China (Hong Kong)
Tel.: (852) 35831838
Personal Care Product Distr
N.A.I.C.S.: 456199

Best World Lifestyle Pte Ltd   (1)
51 Cuppage Road 05-11, No 15-00 HDB Hub E Wing, Singapore, 229469, Singapore
Tel.: (65) 63420888
Web Site: http://www.bestworld.com.sg
Sales Range: $50-74.9 Million
Emp.: 100
Personal Care Products & Health Care Equipments Distr
N.A.I.C.S.: 423440

Best World Lifestyle Sdn. Bhd.   (1)
Suite 29 05 Level 29 Menara Exchange 106 Lingkaran TRX, Tun Razak Exchange, 55188, Kuala Lumpur, Federal Territory, Malaysia
Tel.: (60) 321198829
Web Site: http://www.bwl.com.my
Sales Range: $25-49.9 Million
Emp.: 30
Personal Care Product Distr
N.A.I.C.S.: 456199

Best World Vietnam Company Limited   (1)
152 150/4 Vo Thi Sau St W 8 D 3, District 3, Ho Chi Minh City, Vietnam
Tel.: (84) 839331030
Web Site: http://vn.bwlgroup.com
Cosmetics Products Mfr
N.A.I.C.S.: 325620

PT BWL Indonesia   (1)
ASG Tower 12th Floor Unit A and C Jalan Pantai Indah Kapuk Boulevard, Jakarta Utara, 14470, Indonesia
Tel.: (62) 2150111120
Web Site: http://id.bwlgroup.com
Cosmetics Products Mfr
N.A.I.C.S.: 325620
Frengky Frederick (Mgr)

PT Best World Indonesia   (1)
Mayapada Tower 8th Fl Ste 0802A, Jalan Jendral Sudirman Kav 28, Jakarta, 12920, Indonesia
Tel.: (62) 215213566
Web Site: http://www.bwl.co.id
Sales Range: $25-49.9 Million
Emp.: 100
Personal Care Product Distr

N.A.I.C.S.: 456199

BESTEC POWER ELECTRONICS CO., LTD.
No 69 Keji 1st Rd, Guishan Township, Taoyuan, 333, Taiwan
Tel.: (886) 33286800
Web Site: https://www.bestec.com.tw
Year Founded: 1988
3308—(TAI)
Rev.: $17,618,855
Assets: $67,387,453
Liabilities: $31,284,148
Net Worth: $36,103,305
Earnings: $14,496,190
Emp.: 4,000
Fiscal Year-end: 12/31/23
Power Products Mfr & Supplier
N.A.I.C.S.: 335910
Mike Chen (Founder)

Subsidiaries:

Bestec Electronics USA   (1)
18221 E Railroad St, City of Industry, CA 91748
Tel.: (626) 581-4348
Electronic Goods Mfr
N.A.I.C.S.: 334419

BESTECHNIC SHANGHAI CO., LTD.
Room 201 Building B Chamtime Plaza No 2889 Jinke Road, Pudong, Shanghai, 201203, China
Tel.: (86) 2168771788
Web Site:
  https://www.bestechnic.com
Year Founded: 2015
688608—(SHG)
Rev.: $208,465,695
Assets: $900,422,350
Liabilities: $63,250,242
Net Worth: $837,172,108
Earnings: $17,187,684
Fiscal Year-end: 12/31/22
Audio Equipment Mfr & Distr
N.A.I.C.S.: 334310
Zhang Liang (Chm & Gen Mgr)

BESTERRA CO., LTD.
4-24-3 Koto Bridge Sumida-ku, Tokyo, 130-0022, Japan
Tel.: (81) 3 3630 5555
Web Site: http://www.besterra.co.jp
Year Founded: 1974
Emp.: 63
Wrecking & Demolition
N.A.I.C.S.: 238990
Yoshihide Yoshino (Pres)

BESTODECK LTD.
331 Long Ln, Hillingdon, London, UB10 9JU, Middlesex, United Kingdom
Tel.: (44) 1895209700
Web Site: http://www.smc-cars.com
Sales Range: $75-99.9 Million
Emp.: 250
Car Dealerships Owner & Operator
N.A.I.C.S.: 441110
Michael Warnes (Chm)

Subsidiaries:

SMC Rover   (1)
Unit 1 Perrite St Iron Bridge Rd S, UB7 8HY, West Drayton, United Kingdom - England   (100%)
Tel.: (44) 01494520531
Web Site: http://www.smc-cars.com
Sales Range: $25-49.9 Million
Emp.: 35
Vehicle Motor Retailing
N.A.I.C.S.: 441110

BESTON GLOBAL FOOD COMPANY LIMITED

Ground Floor 84 Greenhill Road, Wayville, 5034, SA, Australia
Tel.: (61) 884706500
Web Site:
  https://www.bestonglobalfoods.com
Year Founded: 2014
BFC—(ASX)
Rev.: $113,208,270
Assets: $69,601,306
Liabilities: $47,314,147
Net Worth: $22,287,158
Earnings: ($27,662,006)
Emp.: 300
Fiscal Year-end: 06/30/23
Food & Beverage Investors
N.A.I.C.S.: 523999
Roger Sexton (Chm)

Subsidiaries:

AQUAessence Pty Ltd   (1)
PO Box 155, Findon, 5023, SA, Australia
Tel.: (61) 884434455
Web Site: https://www.aquaessence.com.au
Bottled Water Mfr & Distr
N.A.I.C.S.: 312112

Beston Technologies Pty Ltd   (1)
Level 9 420 King William Street, Adelaide, 5000, SA, Australia
Tel.: (61) 13000237866
Web Site:
  https://www.bestontechnologies.com.au
Dairy Products Mfr
N.A.I.C.S.: 311514

BESTONE.COM CO., LTD.
2nd floor Nishikura LK Building 16-6 Tomihisacho, Shinjuku-Ku, Tokyo, 162-0067, Japan
Tel.: (81) 353126247
Web Site:
  https://www.best1cruise.com
Year Founded: 2005
6577—(TKS)
Rev.: $19,512,140
Assets: $17,845,180
Liabilities: $10,685,960
Net Worth: $7,159,220
Earnings: $1,542,560
Emp.: 36
Fiscal Year-end: 07/31/24
Travel Agency Services
N.A.I.C.S.: 561510
Hidetaka Sawada (Chm & Pres)

BESTORE CO., LTD.
No 8 Zoumaling Gexin Avenue, Dongxihu, Wuhan, 430000, Hubei, China
Tel.: (86) 2785793003
Web Site: https://www.517lppz.com
Year Founded: 2010
603719—(SHG)
Rev.: $1,325,321,806
Assets: $707,034,716
Liabilities: $370,379,356
Net Worth: $336,655,360
Earnings: $47,100,830
Emp.: 200
Fiscal Year-end: 12/31/22
Snack Product Mfr
N.A.I.C.S.: 311919
Hongchun Yang (Board of Directors & Chm)

BESTPARK INTERNATIONAL LIMITED
Lloyds Chambers 1 Portsoken St, London, E1 8BT, United Kingdom
Tel.: (44) 2077672700
Sales Range: $50-74.9 Million
Emp.: 20
Insurance Brokerage, Reinsurance & Underwriting Services
N.A.I.C.S.: 524210
Steven Charles Gowland (Co-Owner)

BESTSELLER A/S

Fredskovvej 5, 7330, Brande, Denmark
Tel.: (45) 99423200
Web Site: http://www.bestseller.com
Year Founded: 1975
Clothing Retailer
N.A.I.C.S.: 458110
Anders Holch Povlsen (Owner & CFO)

Subsidiaries:

M & M Direct Limited   (1)
Clinton Road, Leominster, HR6 0SP, Hertfordshire, United Kingdom
Tel.: (44) 1568619521
Web Site: http://www.mandmdirect.com
Sales Range: $200-249.9 Million
Emp.: 500
Clothing Mail Order & Electronic Retailer
N.A.I.C.S.: 424350
Ryan Morris (Dir-Ops)

Toast (Mail Order) Limited   (1)
3rd Floor Matrix Beta, Matrix Bus Park, Swansea, SA6 8RE, United Kingdom
Tel.: (44) 334005200
Web Site: http://www.toast.co.uk
Online Clothing Retailer
N.A.I.C.S.: 458110
Jessica Seaton (Co-Founder)

BESTSUN ENERGY CO., LTD.
2301 Building A Lize Ping An Financial Center No 2 Jinze West Road, Fengtai District, Beijing, 430000, Hubei, China
Tel.: (86) 1085670030
Web Site:
  https://www.bestsungas.com
600681—(SHG)
Rev.: $703,345,608
Assets: $1,098,719,238
Liabilities: $561,220,190
Net Worth: $537,499,048
Earnings: $54,923,511
Fiscal Year-end: 12/31/22
Investment Services
N.A.I.C.S.: 523999

BESTTECHNICA TM - RADOMIR
Industrial zone, 2400, Radomir, Bulgaria
Tel.: (359) 777 82185
Web Site: http://www.besttechnica.bg
Engineering Services
N.A.I.C.S.: 541330
Penka Nikolova (Mgr-Sls)

Subsidiaries:

Besttechnica EOOD   (1)
168 Tzar Boris III Bul Andromeda Business Center floor 1 office 12, Sofia, 1000, Bulgaria
Tel.: (359) 2 9309919
Emp.: 20
Industrial Supplies Whslr
N.A.I.C.S.: 423840
Maxim Kleytman (Gen Mgr)

BESTWAY (HOLDINGS) LIMITED
2 Abbey Road, Park Royal, London, NW10 7BW, United Kingdom
Tel.: (44) 20 8453 1234   UK
Web Site:
  http://www.bestwaygroup.co.uk
Year Founded: 1956
Sales Range: $1-4.9 Billion
Investment Holding Company
N.A.I.C.S.: 551112
Anwar Pervez (Chm)

Subsidiaries:

Bellevue Cash & Carry Ltd.   (1)
30 McDonald Place, Edinburgh, EH7 4NH, United Kingdom
Tel.: (44) 13 1557 5350
Food Products Distr
N.A.I.C.S.: 424490

Bestway Cement Limited (1)
Bestway Building 19-A College Road F-7
Markaz, Islamabad, 44000, Pakistan
Tel.: (92) 512654856
Web Site: https://www.bestway.com.pk
Rev.: $432,352,768
Assets: $630,065,694
Liabilities: $407,575,840
Net Worth: $222,489,854
Earnings: $42,780,432
Emp.: 2,128
Fiscal Year-end: 06/30/2023
Cement Mfr
N.A.I.C.S.: 325520
Muhammad A. Irfan (CFO & Dir-Fin)

Subsidiary (Domestic):

Pakcem Limited (2)
Bestway Building 19-A College Road F-8
Markaz, Islamabad, Pakistan **(88.37%)**
Tel.: (92) 512654856
Web Site: http://www.pakcem.com.pk
Sales Range: $100-124.9 Million
Cement Mfr & Whslr
N.A.I.C.S.: 327310
Rizwan Jamil (Dir-Mktg)

Bestway Panacea Holdings Ltd (1)
Merchants Warehouse Castle Street,
Castlefield, Manchester, M3 4LZ, United
Kingdom
Tel.: (44) 161 259 9100
Web Site: http://www.pharmacy.co.uk
Holding Company; Pharmacies
N.A.I.C.S.: 551112
Janice Perkins (Superintendent-Pharmacy)

Bestway Wholesale Limited (1)
2 Abbey Road Park Royal, London, NW10
7BW, United Kingdom
Tel.: (44) 20 8453 1234
Food Service Contractors
N.A.I.C.S.: 722110
Dawood Pervez (Mng Dir)

Subsidiary (Domestic):

**Costcutter Supermarkets Group
Limited** (2)
Harvest Mills Common Road, Dunnington,
York, YO19 5RY, United Kingdom
Tel.: (44) 1904 488663
Web Site: http://www.costcutter.com
Grocery Stores
N.A.I.C.S.: 445110
Angela Barber (Dir-Trading)

Karsons Pharmacy Limited (1)
35 Wellington Road South, Stockport, SK1
3RP, Cheshire, United Kingdom
Tel.: (44) 161 355 0990
Health Care Srvices
N.A.I.C.S.: 621999

Red Hall Pharmacy Limited (1)
Red Hall Precinct Connah's Quay, Deeside,
CH5 4TS, Clwyd, United Kingdom
Tel.: (44) 1244 818 434
Pharmaceutical Products Distr
N.A.I.C.S.: 424210

UBL Bank (Tanzania) Limited (1)
26 Mkwepu/Kaluta Street, PO Box 5887,
Dar es Salaam, Tanzania
Tel.: (255) 22 5510200
Web Site: http://www.ubldirect.com
Commercial Banking Services
N.A.I.C.S.: 522110
Muhammad Tanveer (CEO)

United Bank Limited (1)
UBL City Building 1st Floor, I I Chundrigar
Road, Karachi, 74000, Pakistan
Tel.: (92) 21111825888
Web Site: http://www.ubldigital.com
Rev.: $559,628,916
Assets: $13,032,874,807
Liabilities: $11,803,659,957
Net Worth: $1,229,214,849
Earnings: $122,671,039
Emp.: 13,248
Fiscal Year-end: 12/31/2019
Commercial Banking Services
N.A.I.C.S.: 522110
Aameer M. Karachiwalla (CFO)

Subsidiary (Domestic):

UBL Fund Managers Limited (2)
4th Floor STSM Building Beaumont Road

Civil Lines, Karachi, 74200, Sindh, Pakistan
Tel.: (92) 21111825262
Web Site: http://www.ublfunds.com
Emp.: 250
Asset Management & Investment Advisory
Services
N.A.I.C.S.: 523940
Hasnain Raza Nensey (COO & CFO)

Subsidiary (Non-US):

United Bank AG (2)
Feldeggstrasse 55, PO Box 1176, Zurich,
8008, Switzerland
Tel.: (41) 434991920
Web Site: http://www.ubl.com.pk
Sales Range: $50-74.9 Million
Emp.: 8
Commercial Banking Services
N.A.I.C.S.: 522110

Joint Venture (Non-US):

United National Bank Limited (2)
2 Brook Street, London, W1S 1BQ, United
Kingdom
Tel.: (44) 2072908000
Web Site: http://www.unbankltd.com
Sales Range: $600-649.9 Million
Emp.: 1,500
Commercial Banking & Treasury Services;
Owned 55% by United Bank Limited & 45%
by National Bank of Pakistan
N.A.I.C.S.: 522110
Mansoor Khan (CEO)

**BESTWAY GLOBAL HOLDING
INC.**
No 3065 Cao An Road, Shanghai,
201812, China
Tel.: (86) 2169135588   Ky
Web Site:
http://www.bestwaycorp.com
Year Founded: 1994
Rev.: $934,626,618
Assets: $967,534,266
Liabilities: $532,016,145
Net Worth: $435,518,121
Earnings: $47,575,906
Emp.: 11,700
Fiscal Year-end: 12/31/19
Leisure Product Mfr & Distr
N.A.I.C.S.: 326299
Qiang Zhu (Founder, Chm & CEO)

Subsidiaries:

Bestway (Europe) S.R.L. (1)
Via Resistenza 5, 20098, San Giuliano
Milanese, Italy
Tel.: (39) 029884881
Swim Product Distr
N.A.I.C.S.: 423910
Marco Villa (Mgr-Product)

**Bestway (Hong Kong) International
Limited** (1)
7th Floor East Wing Tsim Sha Tsui Centre
66 Mody Road, Kowloon, China (Hong
Kong)
Tel.: (852) 29977169
Swim Product Mfr
N.A.I.C.S.: 339920

Bestway (USA), Inc. (1)
3411 E Harbour Dr, Phoenix, AZ 85034
Swim Product Distr
N.A.I.C.S.: 423910

Bestway Australia Pty. Ltd. (1)
100 Carnarvon St, Silverwater, 2128, NSW,
Australia
Tel.: (61) 290371388
Swim Product Mfr & Distr
N.A.I.C.S.: 339920

**Bestway Central & South America
Ltda.** (1)
Salar Ascotan 1282 Parque Enea, Puda-
huel, Santiago, Chile
Tel.: (56) 232036438
Swim Product Mfr & Distr
N.A.I.C.S.: 339920

Bestway Deutschland GmbH (1)
Parkstrasse 11, 24534, Neumunster, Ger-
many
Tel.: (49) 4321555050

Swim Product Mfr & Distr
N.A.I.C.S.: 339920

**Bestway Eastern Europe Sp. z
o.o.** (1)
Ulica Stanislawa Moniuszki n 1A, 00-014,
Warsaw, Poland
Tel.: (48) 226022508
Swim Product Mfr & Distr
N.A.I.C.S.: 339920

Bestway France S.R.L. (1)
1681 Route Des Dolines Les Taissounieres
HB1, 06560, Valbonne, France
Tel.: (33) 497049299
Swim Product Mfr & Distr
N.A.I.C.S.: 339920

Bestway Italy S.R.L. (1)
Via Bergamo 35, 23807, Merate, LC, Italy
Tel.: (39) 0236265687
Web Site: http://www.bestway-europe.eu
Swim Product Mfr & Distr
N.A.I.C.S.: 339920

**BESUNYEN HOLDINGS COM-
PANY LIMITED**
Units 2005C-2006A 20/F Exchange
Tower No 33 Wang Chiu Road, Kow-
loon Bay, Kowloon, China (Hong
Kong)
Tel.: (852) 23248000
Web Site: http://www.besunyen.com
0926—(HKG)
Rev.: $132,436,933
Assets: $215,814,175
Liabilities: $68,055,811
Net Worth: $147,758,364
Earnings: ($14,656,216)
Emp.: 1,317
Fiscal Year-end: 12/31/22
Tea Mfr
N.A.I.C.S.: 311920
Yihong Zhao (Co-Founder, Chm &
CEO)

**BET SHEMESH ENGINES
HOLDINGS (1997) LTD.**
Virginia 1, Beit Shemesh, 9905529,
Israel
Tel.: (972) 29911661   II
Web Site: https://bsel.co.il
Year Founded: 1997
BSEN—(TAE)
Rev.: $209,687,000
Assets: $288,938,000
Liabilities: $134,618,000
Net Worth: $154,320,000
Earnings: $59,954,000
Emp.: 1,000
Fiscal Year-end: 12/31/23
Offices of Other Holding Companies
N.A.I.C.S.: 551112
Ariel Madmoni (VP-Production)

Subsidiaries:

Bet Shemesh Engines Ltd. (1)
Virginia 1, Beit Shemesh, 9905529,
Israel **(99.97%)**
Tel.: (972) 2 991 1661
Web Site: https://www.bsel.co.il
Jet Engine Parts Mfr, Maintenance, Repair
& Overhaul Services
N.A.I.C.S.: 336412

Carmel Forge Ltd. (1)
PO Box 30, Tirat Karmel, 3900001, Israel
Tel.: (972) 4 850 6203
Web Site: https://www.carmel-forge.com
Metal Alloy Component Mfr
N.A.I.C.S.: 332312
Nir Sadeh (Mgr-Engrg)

**Livnica Preciznih Odlivaka
D.O.O.** (1)
29 Novembra BB, 24430, Ada, Serbia
Tel.: (381) 24851807
Web Site: http://www.lpo.rs
Emp.: 200
Vacuum & Air Casting Mfr
N.A.I.C.S.: 333912
Marija Mitrovic (Mgr-Fin)

BET-AT-HOME.COM AG
Tersteegenstrasse 30, 40474, Dussel-
dorf, Germany
Tel.: (49) 211384240
Web Site: https://www.bet-at-
home.ag
ACX—(MUN)
Rev.: $390,328,432
Assets: $62,677,739
Liabilities: $32,387,546
Net Worth: $30,290,193
Earnings: ($1,655,805)
Emp.: 101
Fiscal Year-end: 12/31/23
Gambling Services
N.A.I.C.S.: 713210
Veronique Giraudon (Deputy Chm-
Supervisory Bd)

Subsidiaries:

**bet-at-home.com Entertainment
GmbH** (1)
Hafenstr 47-51, 4020, Linz, Austria
Online Sport Betting Services
N.A.I.C.S.: 713290
Franz Omer (Gen Mgr)

**bet-at-home.com Entertainment
Ltd.** (1)
Portomaso Business Tower Level 12, STJ
4011, San Giljan, Malta
Tel.: (356) 21314833
Online Sport Betting Services
N.A.I.C.S.: 713290

BET365 GROUP LIMITED
Hillside Festival Way, Stoke-on-Trent,
ST1 5SH, United Kingdom
Tel.: (44) 1782 684 757
Web Site: http://www.bet365.com
Year Founded: 1974
Sales Range: $750-799.9 Million
Emp.: 1,900
Online Gambling Services
N.A.I.C.S.: 713290
Denise Coates (Joint CEO)

BETA DRUGS LIMITED
SCO 184 Sector - 5, Andheri West,
Panchkula, 134114, Haryana, India
Tel.: (91) 7225854813
Web Site:
https://www.betadrugslimited.com
BETA—(NSE)
Rev.: $31,103,861
Assets: $27,084,531
Liabilities: $10,310,838
Net Worth: $16,773,693
Earnings: $4,193,105
Emp.: 243
Fiscal Year-end: 03/30/23
Pharmaceuticals Product Mfr
N.A.I.C.S.: 325412
Vijay Kumar Batra (Chm & Mng Dir)

Subsidiaries:

**Adley Formulations Private
Limited** (1)
SCO-915 2nd Floor NAC ManiMajra, Chan-
digarh, 160101, India
Tel.: (91) 1725017242
Web Site:
https://www.adleyformulations.tradeindia.com
Emp.: 400
Pharmaceuticals Mfr
N.A.I.C.S.: 325412
Vijay Batra (CEO)

BETA SA BUZAU
39 Santierului Street, 120226, Buzau,
Romania
Tel.: (40) 238 725 500
Web Site: http://www.betabuzau.ro
Year Founded: 1925
Sales Range: $10-24.9 Million
Emp.: 250
Oil & Gas Refinery Industry Services
N.A.I.C.S.: 213112
Varriale Gennaro (Gen Mgr)

BETA SA BUZAU—(Continued)

BETA SECURITIZADORA S.A.
R Minas de Prata 30-15 Andar,
4552080, Sao Paulo, Brazil
Tel.: (55) 1131652000
Financial Investment Services
N.A.I.C.S.: 523999
Rodrigo Capato de Alencar *(Dir-IR)*

BETACOM S.A.
ul Polczynska 31 A, 01-377, Warsaw,
Poland
Tel.: (48) 225339888
Web Site:
https://www.betacom.com.pl
BCM—(WAR)
Rev.: $44,952,744
Assets: $12,509,909
Liabilities: $7,393,801
Net Worth: $5,116,108
Earnings: $295,224
Fiscal Year-end: 12/31/23
Information Technology Consulting
Services
N.A.I.C.S.: 541512
Zbigniew Wierzbicki *(Chm-Supervisory Bd)*

BETAGRO PUBLIC COMPANY LIMITED
Betagro Tower North Park 323 Vibhavadi Rangsit Road, Bangkok, 10210,
Laksi, Thailand
Tel.: (66) 2 833 8000   TH
Web Site: http://www.betagro.com
Year Founded: 1967
Animal Feed Mfr & Distr
N.A.I.C.S.: 311119
Chaivat Taepaisitphongse *(Chm)*

Subsidiaries:

Ajinomoto Betagro Frozen Foods   (1)
(Thailand) Co., Ltd.
Betagro Twr N Pk 323 Vibhavadi Rangsit
Rd, Bangkok, 10210, Thailand   **(50%)**
Tel.: (66) 29550555
Web Site: http://www.betagro.com
Sales Range: $25-49.9 Million
Frozen Process Chicken Production
N.A.I.C.S.: 311412

Ajinomoto Betagro Specialty Foods   (1)
(Thailand) Co., Ltd.
323 Moo 6, Lak si, Bangkok, 10210,
Thailand   **(49%)**
Tel.: (66) 28338000
Frozen Food Products Mfr & Distr
N.A.I.C.S.: 311412

Betagro Science Center Company   (1)
Limited
136 Moo 9, Klong Nueng, Pathumthani,
12120, Thailand
Tel.: (66) 2564793240
Laboratory Testing Services
N.A.I.C.S.: 621511

BETAMEK BERHAD
Lingkaran Taman Industri Integrasi
Taman Industri Integrasi Lot 137
Rawang, 48000, Selangor, Malaysia
Tel.: (60) 36094299
Web Site:
https://www.betamek.com.my
Year Founded: 1989
BETA—(KLS)
Electronics Mfr
N.A.I.C.S.: 334419

BETAPART PARTICIPACOES S/A
Av Presidente Wilson 231 - 28
Andar/parte, 20030905, Rio de Janeiro, Brazil
Tel.: (55) 2138043700
Web Site: http://www.betapart.com.br
Year Founded: 1998
BETP3—(BRAZ)

Assets: $99,926,706
Liabilities: $99,926,706
Earnings: $9,831,787
Fiscal Year-end: 12/31/23
Investment Management Service
N.A.I.C.S.: 523999
Norberto Aguiar Tomaz *(CEO & Dir-IR)*

BETBULL HOLDING SE
Mariahilfer Strasse 116, 1070, Vienna, Austria
Tel.: (43) 21494443
Web Site: http://www.betbullplc.com
Year Founded: 2003
BET—(VIE)
Sales Range: $10-24.9 Million
Emp.: 180
Holding Company
N.A.I.C.S.: 551112

BETER BED HOLDING N.V.
Linie 27 7689, NL-5405 AR, Uden,
Netherlands
Tel.: (31) 413338811   NI
Web Site:
http://www.beterbedholding.com
BBED—(EUR)
Rev.: $228,960,474
Assets: $151,695,853
Liabilities: $117,986,970
Net Worth: $33,708,883
Earnings: $14,853,114
Emp.: 937
Fiscal Year-end: 12/31/21
Holding Company; Mattresses, Bedsprings & Other Bedroom Furniture
Sales
N.A.I.C.S.: 551112
B. E. Karis *(Chm-Supervisory Bd)*

Subsidiaries:

Bedden & Matrassen B.V.   (1)
Linie 27, 5405 AR, Uden, Netherlands
Tel.: (31) 413 338902
Mattress Retailer
N.A.I.C.S.: 459999

Beter Bed B.V.   (1)
Industrielaan 15, 5405 AA, Uden, Netherlands
Tel.: (31) 413330336
Web Site: http://www.beterbed.nl
Mattress Mfr & Whslr
N.A.I.C.S.: 423210

Beter Beheer B.V.   (1)
Linie 27, 5405 AR, Uden, Netherlands
Tel.: (31) 413338819
Web Site: http://www.beterbedholding.com
Mattress Retailer
N.A.I.C.S.: 459999

DBC Deutschland GmbH   (1)
Bullermannshof 15, 47441, Moers, Germany
Tel.: (49) 2841 88 44 9 0
Web Site: http://www.dbc-deutschland.de
Sales Range: $50-74.9 Million
Emp.: 3
Mattress Mfr & Whslr
N.A.I.C.S.: 423210

DBC International B.V.   (1)
Linie 27, 5405 AR, Uden, Netherlands
Tel.: (31) 413338811
Web Site: http://www.dbcinternational.nl
Sales Range: $25-49.9 Million
Mattress Mfr & Whslr
N.A.I.C.S.: 337910

Dormael Slaapkamers B.V.   (1)
Linie 27, 5405 AR, Uden, Netherlands
Tel.: (31) 413 243005
Mattress Mfr & Whslr
N.A.I.C.S.: 337910

Sangjatten Sverige AB   (1)
Lona Knapes gata 5, 421 32, Vastra Frolunda, Sweden
Tel.: (46) 3 165 6660
Web Site: https://www.sangjatten.se
Bed Whslr
N.A.I.C.S.: 423210

Slaapgenoten   (1)
Postbus 148, 5400 AC, Uden, Netherlands
Tel.: (31) 413 245205
Web Site: http://www.slaapgenoten.nl
Mattress Retailer
N.A.I.C.S.: 459999

BETEX INDIA LIMITED
504 Trividh Chambers, 5th Floor Opp
Fire Station Ring Road, Surat, 395
002, Gujarat, India
Tel.: (91) 2612328902
Web Site:
https://www.betexindia.com
Year Founded: 1987
512477—(BOM)
Rev.: $6,663,267
Assets: $6,912,601
Liabilities: $3,466,045
Net Worth: $3,446,556
Earnings: $281,780
Emp.: 690
Fiscal Year-end: 03/31/21
Textile Products Mfr
N.A.I.C.S.: 314999
Manish Kumar Somani *(CFO)*

BETHEL AUTOMOTIVE SAFETY SYSTEMS CO., LTD.
19 Taishan Road, Economic & Technological Development Zone, Wuhu,
241009, China
Tel.: (86) 18626220725
Web Site: https://www.btl-auto.com
Year Founded: 2004
603596—(SHG)
Rev.: $777,696,463
Assets: $1,213,675,852
Liabilities: $572,536,275
Net Worth: $641,139,576
Earnings: $98,099,530
Emp.: 2,900
Fiscal Year-end: 12/31/22
Automotive Parts Mfr & Distr
N.A.I.C.S.: 336510
Yuan Yongbin *(Chm & Gen Mgr)*

BETI D.D.
Tovarniska 2, 8330, Metlika, Slovenia
Tel.: (386) 73638100
Web Site: http://www.beti.si
Year Founded: 1956
Sales Range: $25-49.9 Million
Emp.: 150
Apparel & Accessory Mfr
N.A.I.C.S.: 315990
Maja Cibej *(CEO)*

Subsidiaries:

Beti Preja d.o.o.   (1)
2 Tovarniska Cesta, Metlika, 8330, Slovenia
Tel.: (386) 73638100
Web Site: http://www.beti.eu
Sales Range: $25-49.9 Million
Emp.: 176
Textile Mill
N.A.I.C.S.: 314999

BETLAN DOS S.A.
Isidora Goyenechea 2800 piso 50,
Las Condes, Santiago, Chile
Tel.: (56) 3695400
Web Site: https://www.betlandos.cl
BETLAN.DOS—(SGO)
Sales Range: Less than $1 Million
Investment Services
N.A.I.C.S.: 523999
Ana Soledad Bull Zuniga *(CEO)*

BETMAKERS TECHNOLOGY GROUP LTD.
Tel.: (61) 0249574704
Web Site:
https://www.betmakers.com
BET—(ASX)
Rev.: $63,570,851
Assets: $100,597,034

Liabilities: $26,107,966
Net Worth: $74,489,068
Earnings: ($25,819,503)
Emp.: 376
Fiscal Year-end: 06/30/24
Online Gaming
N.A.I.C.S.: 713290
Oliver Shanahan *(CIO)*

BETON 6 CORPORATION
Hung Binh Building Fl 6 406 Ung Van
Khiem St, Ward 25 Binh Tranh District, Ho Chi Minh City, Vietnam
Tel.: (84) 8 6682 6555
Web Site: http://www.beton6.com
Year Founded: 1958
Sales Range: $25-49.9 Million
Precast Concrete Products Mfr
N.A.I.C.S.: 327331

BETON A.D.
Str Mile Pop Jordanov 32a, 1000,
Skopje, North Macedonia
Tel.: (389) 25513700
Web Site: http://www.beton.com.mk
Year Founded: 1947
BESK—(MAC)
Rev.: $23,318,783
Assets: $66,007,638
Liabilities: $27,811,262
Net Worth: $38,196,376
Earnings: $254,592
Fiscal Year-end: 12/31/19
Civil Engineering Construction
N.A.I.C.S.: 236220

BETON PROVINCIAL LTEE
1825 Avenue Du Phare Oust, Matane, G4W 3M6, QC, Canada
Tel.: (418) 562-0074
Web Site:
http://www.betonprovincial.com
Year Founded: 1960
Sales Range: $25-49.9 Million
Emp.: 2,000
Concrete, Asphalt, Crushed Stone &
Aggregate Mfr
N.A.I.C.S.: 327390
Andre Belanger *(Pres)*

Subsidiaries:

Beton Belanger inc.   (1)
12231 Sherbrooke St East, Pointe-aux-
Trembles, H1B 5L4, QC, Canada
Tel.: (514) 640-9194
Concrete Product Distr
N.A.I.C.S.: 423320
Sylvain Veronneau *(Mng Dir)*

Beton Brunswick ltee   (1)
49 Alford Drive, Tide Head, E3N 4M9, NB,
Canada
Tel.: (506) 753-5133
Concrete Product Distr
N.A.I.C.S.: 423320

Beton Hi-Tech inc.   (1)
8080 A boul Cavendish, Ville St-Laurent,
Montreal, H4T 1T1, QC, Canada
Tel.: (514) 734-0088
Concrete Product Distr
N.A.I.C.S.: 423320

Beton Mistral ltee   (1)
28 rue de la Riviere, La Tuque, G9X 3N6,
QC, Canada
Tel.: (819) 523-4545
Concrete Product Distr
N.A.I.C.S.: 423320
Rene Larochelle *(Mgr)*

Beton Regional inc.   (1)
850 Ave Sicard, Alma, G8B 6Y8, QC,
Canada
Tel.: (418) 668-3379
Concrete Product Distr
N.A.I.C.S.: 423320
Rene Larochelle *(Mgr)*

Beton Rive-Nord inc.   (1)
501 Gilles Moreau, Saint-Lin-Laurentides,
J5M 1Y2, QC, Canada

Tel.: (450) 439-2589
Concrete Product Distr
N.A.I.C.S.: 423320

Betons Trio inc. (1)
3979 boul Fiset, Sorel-Tracy, J3P 5J3, QC,
Canada
Tel.: (450) 742-9451
Concrete Product Distr
N.A.I.C.S.: 423320

BETON-STIP
Vanco Prke St 119, Stip, 2000, North
Macedonia
Tel.: (389) 92 390466
Web Site: http://betonstip.com.mk
Emp.: 205
Construction Services
N.A.I.C.S.: 237310

BETONJERKA A.D
Apatinski put bb, 25000, Sombor,
Serbia
Tel.: (381) 25 421 362
Web Site: http://www.betonjerka-
sombor.co.rs
Year Founded: 1961
BTSO—(BEL)
Sales Range: $1-9.9 Million
Emp.: 50
Concrete Products Mfr
N.A.I.C.S.: 327390
Dragan Durdev *(Gen Mgr)*

BETONJERKA A.D.
Centrala br 6, 25000, Sombor, Serbia
Tel.: (381) 25421362
Web Site: https://www.betonjerka-
sombor.co.rs
Year Founded: 1992
Sales Range: $1-9.9 Million
Reinforced Concrete Pipe Mfr
N.A.I.C.S.: 327332
Aleksandar Stankovic *(Head-Fin &
Comml Sectors)*

BETONSKI PROIZVODI A.D.
Nenada Kostica 20, Zaluzani, 78000,
Banja Luka, Bosnia & Herzegovina
Tel.: (387) 51385507
Year Founded: 1971
BTPR-R-A—(BANJ)
Sales Range: $1-9.9 Million
Emp.: 31
Concrete Products Mfr
N.A.I.C.S.: 327390
Brane Miloseviae *(Chm-Mgmt Bd)*

BETONSTAHL LEIPZIG GMBH
Am Glaschen 6, Markranstadt,
04420, Grosslehna, Germany
Tel.: (49) 34205940   De
Web Site: http://www.betonstahl-
leipzig.de
Year Founded: 1990
Sales Range: $25-49.9 Million
Emp.: 80
Welded Steel Mfr
N.A.I.C.S.: 332111

**BETONUT SZOLGALTATO ES
EPITO RT.**
Pannonia utca 59-61, 1133, Buda-
pest, Hungary
Tel.: (36) 14511700
Year Founded: 1950
Sales Range: $150-199.9 Million
Emp.: 650
Highway Construction Services
N.A.I.C.S.: 237310
Laszlo Szerencses *(CEO)*

Subsidiaries:

Betonut Constructii S.R.L. (1)
Intr Domnesti 4 Bucuresti Sectorul 2, Bu-
charest, Romania
Tel.: (40) 21 2115291
Building Construction Services

N.A.I.C.S.: 236210

Kotiviep 'B Kft. (1)
Gaz Utca 1, Szolnok, Hungary
Tel.: (36) 56425142
Web Site: http://www.kotiviepb.hu
Building Construction Services
N.A.I.C.S.: 236210

SZAM-ERT Kft. (1)
Gogol Utca 13, 1133, Budapest, Hungary
Tel.: (36) 14511600
Highway & Street Construction Services
N.A.I.C.S.: 237310

BETREND CORPORATION
2F Okamura Akasaka Building 2-13-1
Nagatacho, Chiyoda-Ku, Tokyo, 100-
0014, Japan
Tel.: (81) 362057981
Web Site: https://www.betrend.com
Year Founded: 2000
4020—(TKS)
Software Development Services
N.A.I.C.S.: 541511
Hideaki Inoue *(Chm & Pres)*

BETSSON AB
Regeringsgatan 28, SE-111 53,
Stockholm, Sweden
Tel.: (46) 850640300
Web Site:
https://www.betssonab.com
Year Founded: 1963
BETS.B—(OMX)
Rev.: $94,129,094
Assets: $119,135,547
Liabilities: $42,696,608
Net Worth: $76,438,940
Earnings: $17,600,810
Emp.: 2,192
Fiscal Year-end: 12/31/23
Gaming Software Development Ser-
vices
N.A.I.C.S.: 541511
Pontus Lindwall *(Pres & CEO)*

Subsidiaries:

Europebet LLC (1)
29 I Chavchavadze Ave 5th Fl, 0179, Tbilisi,
Georgia
Tel.: (995) 322194000
Web Site: http://www.europebet.com
Online Gambling Services
N.A.I.C.S.: 713290

**Racebets International Gaming
Ltd.** (1)
Dragonara Business Centre Dragonara
Road, Saint Julian's, STJ 3141, Malta
Tel.: (356) 8082380022
Web Site: http://www.racebets.com
Online Gambling Services
N.A.I.C.S.: 713290

**BETTA PHARMACEUTICALS
CO., LTD.**
No 355 Xingzhong Road Economic
and Technological Development
Zone, Yuhang, Hangzhou, 311100,
Zhejiang, China
Tel.: (86) 57189265665
Web Site:
http://www.bettapharma.com
Year Founded: 2003
300558—(CHIN)
Rev.: $345,955,277
Assets: $1,288,342,048
Liabilities: $534,586,977
Net Worth: $753,755,071
Earnings: $49,020,378
Emp.: 1,900
Fiscal Year-end: 12/31/23
Drug Mfr & Distr
N.A.I.C.S.: 325411
Jianxun Fan *(CFO & VP)*

**BETTER BATHROOMS UK
LIMITED**

Horizon Park Greenfold Way, Leigh,
WN7 3XH, Lancashire, United King-
dom
Tel.: (44) 844 484 7678
Web Site:
http://www.betterbathrooms.com
Year Founded: 2003
Sales Range: $25-49.9 Million
Emp.: 77
Bathroom Product & Tile Whslr
N.A.I.C.S.: 423220
Colin Stevens *(Founder)*

**BETTER CAPITAL PCC LIM-
ITED**
Floor 2 Trafalgar Court Les Banques,
PO Box 286, Saint Peter Port, GY1
4LY, Guernsey
Tel.: (44) 1481716000   GY
Web Site: http://www.bettercapital.gg
Year Founded: 2009
Assets: $106,078,651
Liabilities: $234,769
Net Worth: $105,843,882
Earnings: ($53,308,992)
Investment Management Service
N.A.I.C.S.: 523940

BETTER COLLECTIVE A/S
Sankt Annae Plads 28, 1250, Copen-
hagen, K, Denmark
Tel.: (45) 29919965
Web Site: https://bettercollective.com
BETCO—(OMX)
Rev.: $290,629,182
Assets: $847,430,391
Liabilities: $401,804,446
Net Worth: $445,625,944
Earnings: $51,883,229
Emp.: 949
Fiscal Year-end: 12/31/22
Online Gaming
N.A.I.C.S.: 512199
Jesper Sogaard *(Co-Founder & CEO)*

Subsidiaries:

Action Network Inc. (1)
9009461 W 23rd St 2nd Fl, New York, NY
10010
Web Site: https://www.actionnetwork.com
Sports Network Services
N.A.I.C.S.: 713990

Better Collective D.o.o. (1)
Trg kralja Milana 2, 18000, Nis, Serbia
Tel.: (381) 66246444
Online Gambling Services
N.A.I.C.S.: 713290

Better Collective Greece P.C. (1)
Tel.: (30) 2310220554
Online Gambling Services
N.A.I.C.S.: 713290

Better Collective SAS (1)
6 passage Lathuille, Paris-8E-
Arrondissement, 75018, Paris, France
Tel.: (33) 776060227
Online Gambling Services
N.A.I.C.S.: 713290

Bola Webinformation GmbH (1)
Goldmarkplatz 10, 1130, Vienna, Austria
Tel.: (43) 6769057752
Web Site: https://www.bola-
webinformation.com
Online Marketing Services
N.A.I.C.S.: 541613

Mindway ApS (1)
Aabogade 15, 8200, Aarhus, Denmark
Tel.: (45) 40632099
Web Site: https://mindway.ai
Software Development Services
N.A.I.C.S.: 541511

Playmaker Capital Inc. (1)
365 Bay Street Suite 800, Toronto, M5H
2V1, ON, Canada
Tel.: (416) 361-4783
Rev.: $1,684
Assets: $374,974
Liabilities: $52,099

Net Worth: $322,875
Earnings: ($70,779)
Fiscal Year-end: 12/31/2019
Business Consulting Services
N.A.I.C.S.: 522299

**BETTER LIFE COMMERCIAL
CHAIN SHARE CO., LTD.**
Better Life Building No 309 West
Shaoshan Road, Yuhu District, Xi-
angtan, 411100, Hunan, China
Tel.: (86) 73152339880   CN
Web Site: https://www.bbg.com.cn
Year Founded: 2004
002251—(SSE)
Rev.: $1,227,776,940
Assets: $3,917,947,644
Liabilities: $3,189,873,960
Net Worth: $728,073,684
Earnings: ($357,122,844)
Fiscal Year-end: 12/31/22
Retail Store Operator
N.A.I.C.S.: 459999
Wang Tian *(Founder & Chm)*

**BETTER PLANT SCIENCES
INC.**
107 1489 Marine Drive, Vancouver,
V7T 1B8, BC, Canada
Tel.: (604) 632-1700
Web Site:
http://betterplantsciences.com
PLNT.X—(CNSX)
Rev.: $411,608
Assets: $1,127,015
Liabilities: $1,761,949
Net Worth: ($634,934)
Earnings: ($1,832,201)
Fiscal Year-end: 11/30/22
Cannabis Product Distr
N.A.I.C.S.: 445110

**BETTER WORLD GREEN PUB-
LIC COMPANY LIMITED**
No 488 Soiladprao 130 Mahatthai 2,
Klongchan Bangkapi, Bangkok,
10240, Thailand
Tel.: (66) 20127888
Web Site:
http://www.betterworldgreen.com
BWG—(THA)
Rev.: $71,416,036
Assets: $290,324,428
Liabilities: $126,721,036
Net Worth: $163,603,391
Earnings: ($3,956,768)
Emp.: 98
Fiscal Year-end: 12/31/23
Waste Management Services
N.A.I.C.S.: 562000
Suwat Leungviriya *(CEO & Mng Dir)*

Subsidiaries:

**Earth Tech Environment Public Com-
pany Limited** (1)
88 88/1 Village No 1, Kaeng Khoi District,
Saraburi, 18110, Thailand
Tel.: (66) 36200294
Web Site: https://www.etcenvi.com
Rev.: $20,679,165
Assets: $148,938,725
Liabilities: $63,360,505
Net Worth: $85,578,220,
Earnings: $1,005,380
Emp.: 211
Fiscal Year-end: 12/31/2023
Electric Power Distribution Services
N.A.I.C.S.: 221122
Anusorn Nuangpolmak *(Chm)*

**BETTERLIFE HOLDING LIM-
ITED**
BetterLife Auto Park No 143 West 4th
Ring Road, Haidian, Beijing, China
Tel.: (86) 58739000   Ky
Web Site: https://www.blchina.com
Year Founded: 1998

BetterLife Holding Limited—(Continued)

6909—(HKG)
Rev.: $1,485,442,512
Assets: $652,493,908
Liabilities: $251,911,276
Net Worth: $400,582,632
Earnings: $11,683,512
Emp.: 1,440
Fiscal Year-end: 12/31/23
Holding Company
N.A.I.C.S.: 551112
Kwok Keung Chau (CFO)

BETTERLIFE PHARMA INC.
1275 West 6th Avenue 300, Vancouver, V6H 1A6, BC, Canada
Tel.: (514) 943-1899   BC
Web Site:
https://www.abetterlifepharma.com
Year Founded: 2002
BETRF—(OTCQB)
Assets: $908,511
Liabilities: $3,944,429
Net Worth: ($3,035,918)
Earnings: ($9,511,879)
Emp.: 4
Fiscal Year-end: 01/31/22
Biopharmaceutical Researcher & Developer
N.A.I.C.S.: 325412
Moira Ong (CFO)

BETTERMOO(D) FOOD CORPORATION
800 1199 West Hastings Street, Vancouver, V6E 3T5, BC, Canada   ON
Web Site: https://www.bettermoo.com
Year Founded: 2019
MOOOF—(OTCQB)
Food Product Mfr & Distr
N.A.I.C.S.: 311813

BETTERWARE DE MEXICO S.A.P.I. DE C.V.
Luis Enrique Williams 549 Colonia Belenes Norte, 45145, Zapopan, Jalisco, Mexico
Tel.: (52) 3338360500   MX
Web Site:
https://www.betterware.com.mx
Year Founded: 1995
BWMX—(NASDAQ)
Rev.: $504,694,111
Assets: $266,659,277
Liabilities: $200,956,437
Net Worth: $65,702,840
Earnings: $90,530,439
Emp.: 1,272
Fiscal Year-end: 12/31/21
Direct-to-Consumer Solutions Services
N.A.I.C.S.: 541860
Luis G. Campos (Chm)

Subsidiaries:

Jafra Cosmetics International, Inc.   (1)
2451 Townsgate Rd, Westlake Village, CA 91361
Tel.: (805) 449-3000
Web Site: http://www.jafra.com
Sales Range: $350-399.9 Million
Emp.: 200
Cosmetics Direct Sales
N.A.I.C.S.: 456120

BETTS GROUP PTY. LTD.
32 Millrose Dr, Malaga, 6090, WA, Australia
Tel.: (61) 892097777
Web Site: http://www.betts.com.au
Year Founded: 1892
Shoe Distr
N.A.I.C.S.: 424340
Danny Breckler (Chm & Mng Dir)

BETTY BARCLAY KLEIDER-FABRIK GMBH
Heidelberger Strasse 9 11, 69226, Nussloch, Germany
Tel.: (49) 62249000
Web Site:
http://www.bettybarclay.com
Year Founded: 1955
Sales Range: $000-049.9 Million
Emp.: 1,000
Mfr of Womens Clothing
N.A.I.C.S.: 315210
Jurgen Winter (Mng Partner)

BETTZEIT GMBH
Wilhelm-Leuschner-Str 78, 60329, Frankfurt am Main, Germany
Tel.: (49) 69 989 723 300
Web Site: http://www.bettzeit.com
Mattress, Pillows & Boxspring Beds Mfr
N.A.I.C.S.: 337910
Dennis Schmoltzi (Mng Dir)

Subsidiaries:

Dunlopillo Deutschland GmbH   (1)
Wilhelm-Leuschner-Strasse 78, 60329, Frankfurt am Main, Germany
Tel.: (49) 69989723300
Web Site: http://www.dunlopillo.de
Mattress Mfr & Distr
N.A.I.C.S.: 337910
Manuel Muller (Mng Dir)

BEUTLER & LANG SCHALUNGS- UND BEHALTER-BAU GMBH
Mainleite 35, 97340, Kitzingen, Germany
Tel.: (49) 933250550
Web Site: http://www.sbb-beutler-lang.de
Year Founded: 1974
Sales Range: $10-24.9 Million
Emp.: 70
Engineeering Services
N.A.I.C.S.: 541330
Michael Beutler (Mng Dir)

Subsidiaries:

SBB Beutler & Lang GmbH & Co (1)
Am Piperfenn 16, 14776, Brandenburg, Germany
Tel.: (49) 3381212153
Construction Engineering Services
N.A.I.C.S.: 541330

BEUTTER PRAZISIONS-KOMPONENTEN GMBH & CO. KG
Butzensteigleweg 4-6, 72348, Rosenfeld, Germany
Tel.: (49) 74289330
Web Site: http://www.beutter.de
Year Founded: 1909
Rev.: $12,276,660
Emp.: 124
Mechanical Components Supplier
N.A.I.C.S.: 423830
W. D. Kiessling (Mng Dir)

BEVCANNA ENTERPRISES, INC.
1672 West 2nd Avenue, Vancouver, V6J 1H4, BC, Canada
Tel.: (604) 569-1414
Web Site: http://www.bevcanna.com
7BC—(DEU)
Rev.: $4,310,086
Assets: $16,103,471
Liabilities: $11,347,585
Net Worth: $4,755,886
Earnings: ($12,544,492)
Fiscal Year-end: 12/31/22
Beverages Mfr
N.A.I.C.S.: 312140
Marcello Leone (Founder)

BEVERLEY BUILDING SOCI-ETY
57 Market Place, Beverley, HU17 8AA, East Yorkshire, United Kingdom
Tel.: (44) 1482 881510
Web Site:
http://www.beverleybs.co.uk
Year Founded: 1866
Rev.: $5,552,003
Assets: $251,917,700
Liabilities: $237,135,968
Net Worth: $14,781,732
Earnings: $187,559
Emp.: 26
Fiscal Year-end: 12/31/19
Mortgage Lending
N.A.I.C.S.: 522310
Janet E. Bedford (Deputy CEO & Dir-Fin)

BEWHERE HOLDINGS INC.
3264 Lakeshore Boulevard West, Etobicoke, M8V 1M4, ON, Canada
Tel.: (844) 229-4373   BC
Web Site: http://www.bewhere.com
Year Founded: 1994
BEWFF—(OTCQB)
Rev.: $5,505,128
Assets: $4,412,212
Liabilities: $1,251,545
Net Worth: $3,160,667
Earnings: ($1,542,565)
Fiscal Year-end: 12/31/20
Logistic Services
N.A.I.C.S.: 541614
Owen Moore (Pres & CEO)

BEWI ASA
Dyre halses gate 1A, PO Box 3009, 7042, Trondheim, Norway
Tel.: (47) 72448888
Web Site: https://www.bewi.com
Year Founded: 1980
BEWI—(OSL)
Rev.: $1,221,768,407
Assets: $1,383,596,424
Liabilities: $924,715,752
Net Worth: $458,880,671
Earnings: ($17,220,444)
Emp.: 3,216
Fiscal Year-end: 12/31/23
Packaging Components Mfr & Insulation Solutions
N.A.I.C.S.: 326130
Charlotte Knudsen (Dir-IR & Comms)

Subsidiaries:

Biobe AS   (1)
Kampenveien 5, 1618, Fredrikstad, Norway
Tel.: (47) 6 935 1020
Web Site: https://www.biobe.no
Plastic Product Mfr & Distr
N.A.I.C.S.: 326199

Eurec A/S   (1)
Ndr Fabriksvej 1 G, 8722, Hedensted, Denmark
Tel.: (45) 7 674 9001
Web Site: https://www.eurec.dk
Recycling Services
N.A.I.C.S.: 562111

IZOBLOK SA   (1)
ul Legnicka 15, 41-503, Chorzow, Poland   (54.66%)
Tel.: (48) 327725701
Web Site: https://izoblok.pl
Rev.: $109,115,345
Assets: $52,849,847
Liabilities: $30,206,047
Net Worth: $22,643,801
Earnings: $4,778,963
Emp.: 500
Fiscal Year-end: 12/31/2023
Plastics Product Mfr
N.A.I.C.S.: 326199
Przemyslaw Skrzydlak (CEO & Member-Mgmt Bd)

Subsidiary (Non-US):

Izoblok GmbH   (2)

Herrenhofer Landstrasse 6, Ohrdruf, 99885, Gotha, Germany
Tel.: (49) 362433990
EPP Component Mfr
N.A.I.C.S.: 334419

IsoBouw Systems BV   (1)
Canal Street 107, 5711 EC, Someren, Netherlands
Tel.: (31) 49 349 8111
Web Site: https://www.isobouw.nl
Construction Materials Mfr
N.A.I.C.S.: 327120

NOKK ehf.   (1)
Vikurhvarfi 5, 203, Kopavogur, Iceland
Tel.: (354) 533 5555
Web Site: http://www.nokk.is
Non-Durable Goods Whslr
N.A.I.C.S.: 424990

Synprodo BV   (1)
Nieuweweg 235, 6603 BM, Wijchen, Netherlands
Tel.: (31) 24 649 1911
Web Site: https://www.synprodo.nl
Packaging Services
N.A.I.C.S.: 561910

BEWI PRODUKTER AS
Hamarvikringen 64, 7263, Froya, Norway
Tel.: (47) 72 44 88 88
Web Site: http://www.bewi.no
Plastics Product Mfr
N.A.I.C.S.: 326199
Rune Kvilvang (Mng Dir)

Subsidiaries:

Bewi Norplasta AS   (1)
Havnegata 20B, N-7503, Stjordal, Norway
Tel.: (47) 992 38 900
Web Site: http://www.norplasta.com
Sales Range: $10-24.9 Million
Emp.: 80
Plastics Product Mfr
N.A.I.C.S.: 326199
Svenn Bekken (CEO)

BEWITAL GMBH & CO. KG
Industriestr 10, Sudlohn-Oeding, 46354, Borken, Germany
Tel.: (49) 2862581600
Web Site: http://www.bewital-agrar.de
Year Founded: 1963
Rev.: $89,313,543
Emp.: 160
Health & Nutrition Products Distr
N.A.I.C.S.: 456191
Jurgen Petershagen (Gen Mgr)

Subsidiaries:

Palital GmbH & Co. KG.   (1)
De Tweede Geerden 13, 5334LH, Velddriel, Netherlands
Tel.: (31) 418840017
Web Site: http://www.palital.com
Feed Additive Distr
N.A.I.C.S.: 424910
Jurgen Petershagen (Mng Dir)

BEXAR VENTURES, INC.
207 W Hastings Street Suite 1116, Vancouver, V6B 1H7, BC, Canada
Tel.: (778) 327-8179
BXV—(CNSX)
Rev.: $238,904
Assets: $39,310
Liabilities: $223,071
Net Worth: ($183,761)
Earnings: ($231,112)
Fiscal Year-end: 09/30/19
Information Technology Management Services
N.A.I.C.S.: 541512

BEXCELLENT GROUP HOLD-INGS LIMITED
Unit 01-03 05-06 12/F CDW Building 388 Castle Peak Road, New Territories, Tsuen Wan, China (Hong Kong)
Tel.: (852) 39031748

Web Site:
http://www.bexcellentgroup.com
Year Founded: 2014
1775—(HKG)
Rev.: $25,406,093
Assets: $23,644,743
Liabilities: $7,394,036
Net Worth: $16,250,706
Earnings: ($3,554,044)
Emp.: 228
Fiscal Year-end: 07/31/21
Educational Support Services
N.A.I.C.S.: 611699
Tam-Wai Lung *(CEO)*

Subsidiaries:

Ascent Prep International Education
Limited　　　　　　　　　　　　(1)
5/F Siu On Plaza 482 Jaffe Road, Cause-
way Bay, Hong Kong, China (Hong Kong)
Tel.: (852) 59909930
Web Site: https://www.ascent-prep.com
Internet Service Provider
N.A.I.C.S.: 561730

Glocal Education Services
Limited　　　　　　　　　　　　(1)
Shop 3019 L3 D PARK 398 Castle Peak
Road, Tsuen Wan, China (Hong Kong)
Tel.: (852) 31506060
Web Site: https://ges.glocalgroup.cc
School Education Services
N.A.I.C.S.: 611710

New Creation Advertising Agency
Limited　　　　　　　　　　　　(1)
Unit 8 12/F Shiu Fat Industrial Building 139-
141 Wai Yip Street, Kwun Tong, Kowloon,
China (Hong Kong)
Tel.: (852) 31882986
Web Site: https://www.creativeadv.com
Multimedia Advertising Services
N.A.I.C.S.: 541810

Vioo Company Limited　　　　　(1)
Unit 2 3/F Tower 3 Enterprise Square
Phase I 9 Sheung Yuet Road, Kowloon
Bay, Kowloon, China (Hong Kong)
Tel.: (852) 35210280
Web Site: https://www.vioo.com.hk
Custom Software Development Services
N.A.I.C.S.: 541511

**BEXIMCO PHARMACEUTI-
CALS LIMITED**
19 Dhanmondi R/A Road No 7,
Dhaka, 1205, Bangladesh
Tel.: (880) 258611001
Web Site:
https://www.beximcopharma.com
BXPHARMA—(DHA)
Rev.: $402,162,396
Assets: $767,317,215
Liabilities: $249,539,563
Net Worth: $517,777,652
Earnings: $57,984,087
Emp.: 7,000
Fiscal Year-end: 06/30/22
Pharmaceuticals Mfr
N.A.I.C.S.: 325412
Nazmul Hassan *(Mng Dir)*

Subsidiaries:

Synovia Pharma PLC.　　　　　(1)
6/2/A Segun Bagicha, Dhaka, 1000, Ban-
gladesh
Tel.: (880) 9678000777
Web Site: https://synoviapharma.com
Emp.: 1,000
Pharmaceutical Product Mfr & Distr
N.A.I.C.S.: 325412

**BEXIMCO SYNTHETICS LIM-
ITED**
17 Dhanmondi R/A Road No 2,
Dhaka, 1205, Bangladesh
Tel.: (880) 28618220　　　　　BD
Web Site:
http://www.beximcosynthetics.com
Year Founded: 1990
BXSYNTH—(CHT)

Assets: $13,946,342
Liabilities: $16,738,834
Net Worth: ($2,792,492)
Earnings: ($1,387,012)
Emp.: 408
Fiscal Year-end: 06/30/21
Yarn Mfr
N.A.I.C.S.: 313110
A. S. F. Rahman *(Chm & Mng Dir)*

**BEYAZ FILO OTO KIRALAMA
A.S.**
Birlik Mahallesi Sehit Kurbani Akboga
Sokak No 24, Ankara, 6610, Turkiye
Tel.: (90) 312 454 20 00
Web Site: http://www.beyazfilo.com
Sales Range: $50-74.9 Million
Emp.: 130
Passenger Car Rental
N.A.I.C.S.: 532111
Gurkan Gencler *(Chm)*

**BEYERDYNAMIC GMBH & CO
KG**
Theresienstrasse 8, Heilbronn,
74072, Germany
Tel.: (49) 71316170
Web Site:
http://www.beyerdynamic.de
Year Founded: 1924
Rev.: $47,589,300
Emp.: 300
Audio Equipment Mfr
N.A.I.C.S.: 334310
Wolfgang Luckhardt *(Co-Mng Dir)*

BEYON3D LTD.
Maskit 6, Herzliya Pituach, Israel
Tel.: (972) 98877633
Web Site: https://beyon3d.com
Year Founded: 2011
BYON—(TAE)
Rev.: $2,582,401
Assets: $2,963,116
Liabilities: $1,948,888
Net Worth: $1,014,228
Earnings: ($3,848,322)
Fiscal Year-end: 12/31/23
Building Technology Services
N.A.I.C.S.: 236220
Daniel Pierre Ivesha *(Chm)*

**BEYOND FRAMES ENTER-
TAINMENT AB**
Bondegatan 21, 116 33, Stockholm,
Sweden
Tel.: (46) 791002290
Web Site:
https://www.beyondframes.com
Year Founded: 2018
Entertainment Services
N.A.I.C.S.: 711130
Johan Larsson *(CEO)*

BEYOND LITHIUM INC.
30th Floor-360 Main Street, Winni-
peg, R3C 4G1, MB, Canada
Tel.: (204) 957-4668　　　　　Ca
Web Site: https://beyondlithium.ca
Year Founded: 2019
BY—(CNSX)
Assets: $408,734
Liabilities: $26,985
Net Worth: $381,750
Earnings: ($205,794)
Fiscal Year-end: 12/31/21
Mineral Exploration Services
N.A.I.C.S.: 212220
Craig Gibson *(Pres & CEO)*

**BEYOND MEDICAL TECH-
NOLOGIES INC.**
Suite 915-700 West Pender Street,
Vancouver, V6C 1G8, BC, Canada
Tel.: (604) 805-4602　　　　　BC
Web Site: http://www.beyondmd.ca

Year Founded: 2015
DOCT—(DEU)
Rev.: $738,023
Assets: $1,527,651
Liabilities: $323,299
Net Worth: $1,204,352
Earnings: ($2,278,592)
Fiscal Year-end: 12/31/21
Waste Technology Solutions
N.A.I.C.S.: 562998

BEYONDSOFT CORPORATION
Bldg 7 East Zone Courtyard 10 Xibei-
wang East Road, Haidian District,
Beijing, 100193, China
Tel.: (86) 1050965888
Web Site:
https://www.beyondsoft.com
Year Founded: 1995
002649—(SSE)
Rev.: $909,660,024
Assets: $735,482,592
Liabilities: $185,554,044
Net Worth: $549,928,548
Earnings: $43,418,700
Emp.: 29,000
Fiscal Year-end: 12/31/22
IT Services
N.A.I.C.S.: 541519
Wang Bin *(Chm & CEO)*

Subsidiaries:

Beyondexpect S.L.　　　　　　(1)
Av Can Fatjo dels Aurons No3, Sant Cugat
del Valles, Barcelona, Spain
Tel.: (34) 931597788
Web Site: http://www.beyondexpect.com
IT Services
N.A.I.C.S.: 541519

Beyondsoft Consulting Inc.　　(1)
3025 112th Ave NE Ste 200, Bellevue, WA
98004
Tel.: (425) 242-5419
Web Site: http://www.beyondsoft.com
IT Consulting Services
N.A.I.C.S.: 541690

Subsidiary (Domestic):

The Portal Group Consulting
LLC　　　　　　　　　　　　　(2)
65 Pine Ave Ste 344, Long Beach, CA
90802
Tel.: (949) 682-9735
Web Site: http://www.theportalgrp.com
Sales Range: $10-24.9 Million
Emp.: 59
Business Technology Solutions Consulting
Services
N.A.I.C.S.: 541690
Jordan Fisher *(Mng Dir)*

Beyondsoft Corporation　　　　(1)
Boyan Technology Building Building 7 East
Building No 10 West, Wangdong Road
Haidian District, Beijing, China
Tel.: (86) 1050965888
Web Site: http://www.beyondsoft.com
IT Services
N.A.I.C.S.: 541519

Beyondsoft Corporation　　　　(1)
Unit A Zone 3 Building 9 Zhongguancun
Software Park, Haidian District, Beijing,
100193, China
Tel.: (86) 10 8282 6100
IT Services
N.A.I.C.S.: 541519

Beyondsoft Corporation　　　　(1)
3F 1Building 500 Lane Zhangheng Road
Zhangjiang High Tech Park, Pudong Dis-
trict, Shanghai, 201203, China
Tel.: (86) 21 6165 6766
IT Services
N.A.I.C.S.: 541519

Beyondsoft Corporation　　　　(1)
4th Floor Building 2 Optical Valley Software
Park, Eastlake Developing Zone, Wuhan,
430073, China
Tel.: (86) 27 8758 8009
IT Services
N.A.I.C.S.: 541519

Beyondsoft Corporation　　　　(1)
F2 Tianda Technologies Garden 88 the 4th
Street, Economic & Tech Devel Area, Tian-
jin, 300384, China
Tel.: (86) 22 2532 1029
IT Services
N.A.I.C.S.: 541519

Beyondsoft Corporation　　　　(1)
IT Services
N.A.I.C.S.: 541519

Beyondsoft Corporation　　　　(1)
23/F Bldg T2 Shenye Shangcheng 5001
Huanggang Road, Futian District, Shen-
zhen, 518026, Guangdong, China
Tel.: (86) 75526030128
IT Services
N.A.I.C.S.: 541519

Beyondsoft Corporation　　　　(1)
11F 12F Baode Yungu International Jinye
Road Xi 'an High-tech Zone, Hi-tech Indus-
trial Devel Zone, Xi'an, 710065, Shanxi,
China
Tel.: (86) 2981105576
IT Services
N.A.I.C.S.: 541519
Ma Qiang *(Gen Mgr)*

Beyondsoft Corporation　　　　(1)
3/F Bldg 11 Saiyin International Plaza 665
Gaojiao Road, Binxing Road, Hangzhou,
310012, Zhejiang, China
Tel.: (86) 57187696000
IT Services
N.A.I.C.S.: 541519

Beyondsoft Corporation　　　　(1)
Unit D Delphini Wuxi National Software
Park, 18 Zhenze Road, New District, Wuxi,
214135, China
Tel.: (86) 51085382368
IT Services
N.A.I.C.S.: 541519

Beyondsoft Corporation　　　　(1)
6F KDX-Akihabara Bldg 1-14
Kandaiwamoto-cho, Chiyoda-ku, Tokyo,
101-0033, Japan
Tel.: (81) 352078005
IT Services
N.A.I.C.S.: 541519

Beyondsoft Corporation　　　　(1)
38 Beach Road 04-12 South Beach Tower,
Singapore, 189767, Singapore
Tel.: (65) 62684401
IT Services
N.A.I.C.S.: 541519

Beyondsoft Japan Co., Ltd.　　(1)
6F KDX-Akihabara Bldg 1-14
Kandaiwamoto-cho, Chiyoda-ku, Tokyo,
101-0033, Japan
Tel.: (81) 352078005
Software Development Services
N.A.I.C.S.: 541511

Beyondsoft Jizhi Tech Co., Ltd.　(1)
No 18 Building No 106 West Section of
Jinkai Avenue, Yubei District, Chongqing,
China
Tel.: (86) 2367778746
IT Services
N.A.I.C.S.: 541519

Beyondsoft Solutions Corp　　(1)
220 Duncan Mill Road Suite 505, Toronto,
M3B 3J5, ON, Canada
Tel.: (416) 383-1818
Software Development Services
N.A.I.C.S.: 541511
Steven Kiss *(VP-Sls & Mktg)*

Chongqiong Yibohutong Tech Co.,
Ltd.　　　　　　　　　　　　　(1)
2-3/F Bldg 7 Zone C Software Park 801
Heshun Avenue, Yongchuan District,
Chongqing, China
Tel.: (86) 2385360299
IT Services
N.A.I.C.S.: 541519

Eastern Software Systems Pvt.
Ltd.　　　　　　　　　　　　　(1)
B-65 Sector 63, Noida, 201 307, India
Tel.: (91) 120 4212931
Web Site: http://www.essindia.com
IT Services
N.A.I.C.S.: 541519

Beyondsoft Corporation—(Continued)

Sanjay Agarwala *(Founder & Mng Dir)*

Division (Domestic):

Eastern Software Systems Pvt.
Ltd. **(2)**
301 Arvind Chambers Above Sai Service
Western Express Highway, Adheri E, Mumbai, 400 060, India
Tel.: (91) 22 66945190
IT Services
N.A.I.C.S.: 541519

Eastern Software Systems Pvt.
Ltd. **(2)**
S&S Business Center #224, 1st Main Road
Domlur 2nd Stage, Indiranagar, Bengaluru,
560 071, India
Tel.: (91) 8041538463
IT Services
N.A.I.C.S.: 541519

Eastern Software Systems Pvt.
Ltd. **(2)**
9-1-159/3 Gomez Building Sebastian Road,
Secunderabad, 500 003, India
Tel.: (91) 4030626992
IT Services
N.A.I.C.S.: 541519

Hongzhi Technology Co., Ltd. **(1)**
Unit 607 and 608 Bldg 3 968 Jinzhong
Road, Changning District, Shanghai,
200335, China
Tel.: (86) 2162917138
IT Services
N.A.I.C.S.: 541519

BEZANT RESOURCES PLC

Floor 6 Quadrant House 4 Thomas
More Square, London, E1W 1YW,
United Kingdom
Tel.: (44) 893681566
Web Site:
    https://www.bezantresources.com
BZT—(AIM)
Assets: $13,402,747
Liabilities: $1,348,595
Net Worth: $12,054,153
Earnings: $1,783,225
Emp.: 5
Fiscal Year-end: 12/31/22
Mineral Exploration Services
N.A.I.C.S.: 213115
Colin Bird *(Chm & CEO)*

BEZDAN POLJOPRIVREDNO PREDUZECE A.D.

ul Somborski put bb, Bezdan, 25270,
Serbia
Tel.: (381) 25 810 320
Web Site: http://www.ppbezdan.rs
Year Founded: 1991
Sales Range: $1-9.9 Million
Cereal Crop Farming Services
N.A.I.C.S.: 111998

BEZEQ - THE ISRAEL TELECOMMUNICATION CORP. LIMITED

132 Menachem Begin Avenue 27th
Floor Azrieli Center, Tel Aviv, Israel
Tel.: (972) 36262201
Web Site: https://www.bezeq.co.il
Year Founded: 1984
BZQIY—(OTCIQ)
Rev.: $2,468,141,641
Assets: $3,762,811,127
Liabilities: $3,167,127,596
Net Worth: $595,683,531
Earnings: $322,379,481
Emp.: 5,432
Fiscal Year-end: 12/31/23
Holding Company; Telecommunications Products & Services
N.A.I.C.S.: 551112

Subsidiaries:

Pelephone Communications, Ltd. **(1)**

33 Yitzhak Rabin Street, Givatayim, 53489,
Israel **(100%)**
Tel.: (972) 35728881
Web Site: http://www.pelephone.co.il
Sales Range: $800-899.9 Million
Mobile Telecommunications Services
N.A.I.C.S.: 517112
Gil Sharon *(CEO)*

BF INVESTMENT LIMITED

Mundhwa Pune Cantonment, Pune,
411036, Maharashtra, India
Tel.: (91) 7719005777
Web Site: https://www.bfilpune.com
BFINVEST—(NSE)
Sales Range: $1-9.9 Million
Emp.: 2
Investment & Real Estate Management Services
N.A.I.C.S.: 523999
S. R. Kshirsagar *(Officer-Compliance & Sec)*

BF SPA

Via Cavicchini 2, Jolanda di Savoia,
44037, Ferrara, Italy
Tel.: (39) 0532836102
Web Site: https://www.bfspa.it
Agriculture Product Distr
N.A.I.C.S.: 484220
Federico Vecchioni *(CEO)*

BF UTILITIES LTD.

Mundhwa, Pune, 411036, Maharashtra, India
Tel.: (91) 7719004777
Web Site: https://www.bfutilities.com
Year Founded: 2000
532430—(BOM)
Rev.: $72,919,529
Assets: $293,676,338
Liabilities: $283,859,940
Net Worth: $9,816,398
Earnings: $12,713,064
Emp.: 8
Fiscal Year-end: 03/31/22
Eletric Power Generation Services
N.A.I.C.S.: 221118
Bhalchandra S. Mitkari *(CEO, Compliance Officer & Sec)*

Subsidiaries:

Nandi Infrastructure Corridor Enterprises Ltd. **(1)**
Office 1 Midford House Midford Garden Off
M G Road, Bengaluru, 560 001, India
Tel.: (91) 8025559819
Web Site: http://www.nicelimited.com
Infrastructure Corridor Services
N.A.I.C.S.: 541330

BF&M LIMITED

BF&M Insurance Building 112 Pitts
Bay Road, Pembroke, HM08, Bermuda
Tel.: (441) 2955566
Web Site: https://www.bfm.bm
Year Founded: 1991
BFM—(BERM)
Rev.: $363,050,000
Assets: $2,167,194,000
Liabilities: $1,863,927,000
Net Worth: $303,267,000
Earnings: ($8,764,000)
Emp.: 248
Fiscal Year-end: 12/31/22
Insurance Services
N.A.I.C.S.: 524298
R. John Wight *(Chm & CEO)*

Subsidiaries:

BF&M (Canada) Limited **(1)**
36 Solutions Drive Suite 410, Halifax, B3S
1N2, NS, Canada
Tel.: (902) 482-8924
Sales Range: $25-49.9 Million
Emp.: 25
Investment Management Service
N.A.I.C.S.: 541618

Paul Mathews *(Gen Mgr)*

BF1 MOTORSPORT HOLDINGS LTD.

Technical Centre, Owen Road, Diss,
IP22 4ER, Norfolk, United Kingdom
Tel.: (44) 1379 646 200
Web Site: http://www.f1systems.com
Sales Range: $25-49.9 Million
Emp.: 76
Holding Company
N.A.I.C.S.: 551112
John Bailey *(Mng Dir)*

Subsidiaries:

bf1systems Ltd. **(1)**
Technical Centre, Owen Road, Diss, IP22
4ER, Norfolk, United Kingdom
Tel.: (44) 1379646200
Web Site: http://www.bf1systems.com
Sales Range: $10-24.9 Million
Automotive Ignition, Electronics & Sensor
Technology
N.A.I.C.S.: 336390
John Bailey *(Owner & Mng Dir)*

BFA TENEDORA DE ACCIONES, S.A.U.

Avenida General Peron 38 Masters II
Building 16th Floor, 28020, Madrid,
Spain
Tel.: (34) 902 460 460 **ES**
Web Site:
    http://www.bfatenedora.com
Year Founded: 2010
Sales Range: $1-4.9 Billion
Emp.: 13,572
Bank Holding Company
N.A.I.C.S.: 551111
Jose Ignacio Goirigolzarri Tellaeche
(Chm)

BFFI GROUP INC.

No 230 Waihuan West Road, Panyu
District, Guangzhou, Guangdong,
China
Tel.: (86) 13392064846 **DE**
Year Founded: 2019
Law firm
N.A.I.C.S.: 541199
Hongbin Chen *(CEO, Co-Founder & Chm)*

BFL ASSET FINVEST LIMITED

1 Tara Nagar Ajmer Road, Jaipur,
302 006, Rajasthan, India
Tel.: (91) 9214018877
Web Site: http://www.bflfin.com
Year Founded: 1995
539662—(BOM)
Rev.: $181,901
Assets: $1,954,231
Liabilities: $443,983
Net Worth: $1,510,248
Earnings: $1,935
Emp.: 6
Fiscal Year-end: 03/31/21
Financial Support Services
N.A.I.C.S.: 523999
Mahendra Kumar Baid *(Mng Dir)*

BFLABS CO.,LTD.

3rd floor 153-32 Yesulgongwon-ro,
Manan-gu, Anyang, 13911, Gyeonggi-do, Korea (South)
Tel.: (82) 314704800
Web Site: https://www.bflabs.co.kr
Year Founded: 2006
139050—(KRS)
Rev.: $21,748,604
Assets: $51,767,262
Liabilities: $24,566,116
Net Worth: $27,201,145
Earnings: ($14,807,538)
Emp.: 122
Fiscal Year-end: 12/31/22
Transport Information Systems

N.A.I.C.S.: 488490
Yeong Jung Cho *(CEO)*

BFP WHOLESALE LTD.

Unit 8 Connections Indus Ctr Vestry
Rd, Sevenoaks, TN14 5DF, Kent,
United Kingdom
Tel.: (44) 1732228400 **UK**
Web Site:
    http://www.bfpwholesale.com
Year Founded: 1992
Sales Range: $125-149.9 Million
Emp.: 13
Bakery Ingredient Whslr
N.A.I.C.S.: 424490
Bill Thurston *(CEO)*

BFW LIEGENSCHAFTEN AG

Bahnhofstrasse 92, 8500, Frauenfeld,
Switzerland
Tel.: (41) 848 820 410
Web Site:
    http://www.bfwliegenschaften.ch
Year Founded: 2002
Real Estate Development Services
N.A.I.C.S.: 531390

BG AGRO JSC

12 Gen Kolev Str, 9000, Varna, Bulgaria
Tel.: (359) 52601656
Web Site: http://www.bgagro.bg
BGAG—(BUL)
Sales Range: Less than $1 Million
Chemical & Fertilizer Distr
N.A.I.C.S.: 424690
Nenko Nenkov *(Chm)*

BG CONTAINER GLASS PUBLIC COMPANY LIMITED

47/1 Moo 2 Rangsit-Nakhon Nayok
Rd Bueng Yitho, Thanyaburi, Pathumthani, 12130, Thailand
Tel.: (66) 28347000 **TH**
Web Site: https://www.bgc.co.th
Year Founded: 1974
BGC—(THA)
Rev.: $438,036,866
Assets: $558,727,796
Liabilities: $406,679,552
Net Worth: $152,048,244
Earnings: $10,219,350
Fiscal Year-end: 12/31/23
Packaging Product Mfr & Distr
N.A.I.C.S.: 333993
Sirikul Mangkornkanok *(CFO)*

Subsidiaries:

Ayutthaya Glass Industry Co.,
Ltd. **(1)**
55 Moo 3 Sambundit Uthai, Rojana Industrial Park Uthai, Ayutthaya, 13210, Thailand
Tel.: (66) 35334100
Glass Bottle Mfr
N.A.I.C.S.: 327213

BGC Glass Solution Co., Ltd. **(1)**
111 Moo 19 208 Rd Khon Kaen-Maha Sarakham Tapra, Tha Phra Subdistrict Muang
Khon Kaen District, Khon Kaen, 40260,
Thailand
Tel.: (66) 43349900
Glass Bottle Mfr
N.A.I.C.S.: 327213

BGC Packaging Co., Ltd. **(1)**
47/1 Moo 2 Rangsit-Nakornnayok Rd Km 7,
Bueng Yitho, Thanyaburi, 12130, Pathum
Thani, Thailand
Tel.: (66) 28347000
Glass Packaging Container Mfr & Distr
N.A.I.C.S.: 327213

Pathumthani Glass Industry Co.,
Ltd. **(1)**
47/1 Moo 2 Rangsit-Nakornnayok Rd Km 7
Buengyeetho, Thanyaburi, 12130, Pathumthani, Thailand
Tel.: (66) 28347000
Glass Bottle Mfr

N.A.I.C.S.: 327213

Prachinburi Glass Industry Co., Ltd. (1)
63 Moo 9 Bangkanak-Bansrang, Prachin Buri, 25150, Ban Tan, Thailand
Tel.: (66) 37415100
Glass Bottle Mfr
N.A.I.C.S.: 327213

Ratchaburi Glass Industry Co., Ltd. (1)
155/111 Moo 4 Chet Samian, Ratchaburi Industrial Estate Photharam, Ratchaburi, 70120, Thailand
Tel.: (66) 32925560
Glass Bottle Mfr
N.A.I.C.S.: 327213

Solar Power Management (Thailand) Company Limited (1)
333/22 16F United Tower Sukhumvit 55 Sukhumvit Road, Klongton-Nua Wattana, Bangkok, 10110, Thailand
Tel.: (66) 2 712 7374 6
Environmental Engineering Services
N.A.I.C.S.: 541330
Wandee Khunchornyakong *(Chm, Pres & Mng Dir)*

BG T&A CO.
5 6F L&C Tower 153-18 LS Road 1026-52 Sanbon-dong, Gunpo, Gyeonggi, Korea (South)
Tel.: (82) 314887900
Web Site: https://www.bgtna.com
Year Founded: 1996
046310—(KRS)
Rev.: $113,211,642
Assets: $91,311,604
Liabilities: $29,180,480
Net Worth: $62,131,125
Earnings: $8,639,107
Emp.: 60
Fiscal Year-end: 12/31/22
Nautical System & Instrument Mfr
N.A.I.C.S.: 334511
Hak-Gyu Lim *(CEO)*

Subsidiaries:

Point Mobile Co., Ltd. (1)
9F Gabeul Great Valley 32 Digital-ro-9gil, Geumcheon-gu, Seoul, 08512, Korea (South)
Tel.: (82) 233977870
Web Site: https://pointmobile.com
Radar Detector Mfr
N.A.I.C.S.: 334511

BGC (AUSTRALIA) PTY. LTD.
6th Floor 22 Mount St, Perth, 6000, WA, Australia
Tel.: (61) 862204800
Web Site: http://www.bgc.com.au
Year Founded: 1960
Building Construction Services
N.A.I.C.S.: 236116
Alan Tate *(CEO & CFO)*

BGE ELEKTROTECHNIK GMBH
Auf der Aue 3, 99834, Gerstungen, Germany
Tel.: (49) 369279400
Web Site: http://www.bge-elektrotechnik.de
Year Founded: 1978
Sales Range: $10-24.9 Million
Emp.: 76
Automotive Wiring Systems Mfr
N.A.I.C.S.: 336390
Gerald Bicking *(Mng Dir)*

BGF CO., LTD.
405 Teheran-ro, Gangnam-gu, Seoul, 06162, Korea (South)
Tel.: (82) 15773663
Web Site: https://www.bgf.co.kr
Year Founded: 2012
027410—(KRS)
Convenience Store Operator

N.A.I.C.S.: 445131
Jeong-Kook Hong *(CEO)*

Subsidiaries:

BGF Ecomaterials, Co. Ltd. (1)
142, Sangduwon-gil, Jangan-myeon, Hwaseong-si, Gyeonggi-do, 18586, Korea (South)
Tel.: (82) 27081372
Web Site: https://www.bgf.co.kr
Plastics Materials Wholesale Mfg.
N.A.I.C.S.: 326199
Jung-Hyuk Hong *(CEO)*

BGF GROUP PLC
13-15 York Buildings, London, WC2N 6JU, United Kingdom
Tel.: (44) 2073400600
Web Site: https://www.bgf.co.uk
Emp.: 100
Investment Services
N.A.I.C.S.: 523999

Subsidiaries:

Business Growth Fund Limited (1)
13-15 York Buildings, London, WC2N 6JU, United Kingdom
Tel.: (44) 2073400600
Web Site: https://www.businessgrowthfund.co.uk
Emp.: 50
Investment Management Service
N.A.I.C.S.: 523940
Alistair Brew *(Dir-Investment)*

Branch (Domestic):

Business Growth Fund PLC - Midlands (2)
45 Church Street, Birmingham, B3 2RT, United Kingdom
Tel.: (44) 8452668862
Web Site: http://www.bgf.co.uk
Emp.: 35
Privater Equity Firm
N.A.I.C.S.: 523999
Catherine Clarke *(Head-Legal)*

Business Growth Fund PLC - North, Northeast & Ireland (2)
1 City Square, Leeds, LS1 2ES, United Kingdom
Tel.: (44) 8456000142
Privater Equity Firm
N.A.I.C.S.: 523999
John Swarbrick *(Head-Portfolio)*

Business Growth Fund PLC - Scotland (2)
Atholl Exchange 6 Canning Street, Edinburgh, United Kingdom
Tel.: (44) 8452668863
Privater Equity Firm
N.A.I.C.S.: 523999
Mark Bryant *(Head-Mfr)*

Holding (Domestic):

Invenio Business Solutions Limited (2)
125 Wharfedale Road IQ Winnersh, Reading, RG41 5RB, Berkshire, United Kingdom
Tel.: (44) 3304401800
Web Site: http://www.invenio-solutions.com
Sales Range: $10-24.9 Million
Emp.: 700
Information Technology Consultancy Services
N.A.I.C.S.: 541512
Partho Bhattacharya *(Mng Dir & Pres-Ops-US)*

Subsidiary (Non-US):

Invenio Business Solutions DWC LLC (3)
Office 113 SADA Business Center Wadi Awal Street King Fahad Road, PO Box 69806, Opp Al-Muhaidib Hotel, Riyadh, 11557, Saudi Arabia
Tel.: (966) 114628000
Information Technology Consulting Services
N.A.I.C.S.: 541512

Invenio Business Solutions GMBH (3)

Kurfuerstendamm 21, Berlin, 10719, Germany
Tel.: (49) 30887061203
Information Technology Consulting Services
N.A.I.C.S.: 541512

Subsidiary (US):

Invenio Business Solutions Inc. (3)
Ste 1043 6303 Owensmouth Ave, Woodland Hills, CA 91367
Tel.: (818) 917-8298
Information Technology Consulting Services
N.A.I.C.S.: 541512

Subsidiary (Non-US):

Invenio Business Solutions Ltd (3)
Suite 1C First Floor Ebene Mews, CyberCity, Ebene, Mauritius
Tel.: (230) 4642237
Information Technology Consulting Services
N.A.I.C.S.: 541512

Invenio Business Solutions Pvt Ltd (3)
3rd Floor B Wing Madhu Corporate Park Ltd, Pandurang Budhkar Marg Worli, Mumbai, 400 013, India
Tel.: (91) 2266044999
Information Technology Consulting Services
N.A.I.C.S.: 541512

Subsidiary (US):

Labyrinth Solutions Inc. (3)
303 Wyman St Ste 300, Waltham, MA 02451
Tel.: (978) 261-6100
Web Site: http://www.lsiconsulting.com
Rev.: $3,500,000
Emp.: 30
Data Processing, Hosting & Related Services
N.A.I.C.S.: 518210
Katy Quilter *(Dir-HR)*

Holding (Domestic):

Kick ICT Group Ltd. (2)
Solais House 19 Phoenix Crescent Strathclyde Business Park, Bellshill, ML4 3NJ, United Kingdom
Tel.: (44) 3450349600
Web Site: http://www.kickict.com
Rev.: $17,360,251
Assets: $13,375,212
Liabilities: $4,051,088
Net Worth: $9,324,124
Earnings: $1,623,550
Fiscal Year-end: 12/31/2019
Holding Company; Information Technology Support & Consultancy Services
N.A.I.C.S.: 551112
Geoff Neville *(Chm)*

Subsidiary (Domestic):

C2 Software Limited (3)
Unit 2 Valentine Court Kinnoull Road, Dundee, DD2 3QB, United Kingdom
Tel.: (44) 1382723040
Web Site: http://www.c2software.com
Emp.: 20
Software Development Services
N.A.I.C.S.: 541512
Richard Tindall *(Dir-Sls & Mktg)*

Castle Computer Services Ltd. (3)
Stewart House Pochard Way Strathclyde Business Park, Bellshill, ML4 3HB, United Kingdom
Tel.: (44) 8452301314
Web Site: http://www.castle-cs.com
Information Technology Support Services
N.A.I.C.S.: 541512

BGF RETAIL CO. LTD.
BGF Building 405 Teheran-ro Samsung-dong, Gangnam-gu, Seoul, 135-876, Korea (South)
Web Site: http://www.bgfretail.com
027410—(KRS)
Sales Range: $100-124.9 Million
Emp.: 1,876
Convenience Store Owner & Operator
N.A.I.C.S.: 445131
Suk-Jo Hong *(Chm & Co-CEO)*

BGFECOMATERIALS CO., LTD.
142 Sangduwon-gil Jangan-myeon, Jangan-myeon, Hwaseong, Gyeonggi-do, Korea (South)
Tel.: (82) 314992195
Web Site: https://www.bgfecomaterials.com
Year Founded: 1997
126600—(KRS)
Rev.: $201,952,320
Assets: $270,094,243
Liabilities: $115,202,373
Net Worth: $154,891,870
Earnings: $22,150,639
Emp.: 150
Fiscal Year-end: 12/31/22
Plastic Resin Mfr
N.A.I.C.S.: 325211

Subsidiaries:

KOPLA America Inc. (1)
371 Progress Blvd, West Point, GA 31833
Tel.: (706) 663-3900
Web Site: https://eng.kopla.com
Plastic Product Distr
N.A.I.C.S.: 424990

BGH CAPITAL PTY LTD
Level 26 101 Collins Street, Melbourne, 3000, VIC, Australia
Tel.: (61) 391338800   AU
Web Site: http://www.bghcapital.com
Year Founded: 2017
Privater Equity Firm
N.A.I.C.S.: 523999
Robin Bishop *(Founder)*

Subsidiaries:

Abano Healthcare Group Limited (1)
Level 11 AMP Centre 29 Customs Street West, Auckland, 1010, New Zealand
Tel.: (64) 93001410
Web Site: http://www.abano.co.nz
Rev.: $187,084,877
Assets: $231,012,159
Liabilities: $127,358,165
Net Worth: $103,653,994
Earnings: $5,132,487
Emp.: 1,700
Fiscal Year-end: 05/31/2019
Healthcare & Medical Services
N.A.I.C.S.: 621410
Richard G. Keys *(CEO)*

Subsidiary (Non-US):

1300 Smiles Limited (2)
Ground Floor 105 Denham Street, Townsville, 4810, QLD, Australia   (84%)
Tel.: (61) 747201300
Web Site: http://www.1300smiles.com.au
Rev.: $34,436,410
Assets: $55,755,646
Liabilities: $21,762,861
Net Worth: $33,992,786
Earnings: $7,375,345
Emp.: 338
Fiscal Year-end: 06/30/2021
Dentistry Services
N.A.I.C.S.: 621210
Daryl Shane Holmes *(Mng Dir)*

Subsidiary (Domestic):

Plaza Central Dentists Pty. Ltd. (3)
Shop 7 Plaza Central 31-33 Plaza Parade, Maroochydore, Sunshine Coast, 4558, QLD, Australia
Tel.: (61) 754794499
Web Site: http://www.plazacentraldentists.com.au
Dental Care Services
N.A.I.C.S.: 621210
David Mcfall *(Principal)*

Subsidiary (Domestic):

Aotea Pathology Limited (2)
Level 6 CMC Building 89 Courtenay Place, Wellington, 6011, New Zealand
Tel.: (64) 43815900
Web Site: http://www.apath.co.nz

BGH Capital Pty Ltd—(Continued)

Sales Range: $25-49.9 Million
Emp.: 230
Pathological Laboratory Services
N.A.I.C.S.: 621511

Auckland Dental Group (2)
134 Remuera Road, Remuera, Auckland,
New Zealand
Tel.: (04) 95200009
Web Site: http://www.akldental.co.nz
Sales Range: $10-24.9 Million
Emp.: 25
Dental Services
N.A.I.C.S.: 621210

Subsidiary (Non-US):

Dental Partners Pty Limited (2)
Suite 30901 Southport Central 3 Level 9/9
Lawson St, Southport, 4215, QLD, Australia
Tel.: (61) 755917772
Web Site: http://www.dentalpartners.com.au
Sales Range: $10-24.9 Million
Emp.: 40
Dental Care Services
N.A.I.C.S.: 621491
Alan Clarke (Chm)

Subsidiary (Domestic):

Greenlane Imaging Ltd
Ascot Central Bldg Ground Fl, 7 Ellerslie
Racecourse Dr, Auckland, 1051, Remuera,
New Zealand
Tel.: (64) 9 555 9556
Web Site: http://www.ascotrad.co.nz
Sales Range: $10-24.9 Million
Emp.: 8
Health Care Srvices
N.A.I.C.S.: 621999
David Milne (Dir-Clinical)

Insight Radiology Limited (2)
20 Titoki Street, Parnell, 1052, Auckland,
New Zealand
Tel.: (64) 93735988
Web Site: http://www.insightrad.co.nz
Sales Range: $10-24.9 Million
Emp.: 15
Diagnostic Radiology Services
N.A.I.C.S.: 621512

Kidz Teeth Limited (2)
21 St Johns Rd, Meadowbank, Auckland,
1072, New Zealand
Tel.: (64) 95219003
Web Site: http://www.kidz-teeth.com
Dental Care Services
N.A.I.C.S.: 621999

Lumino Care Dental (2)
AMP Tower 29 Customs St West, PO Box
106514, Auckland, 1010, New Zealand
Tel.: (64) 93617100
Web Site: http://www.lumino.co.nz
Sales Range: $50-74.9 Million
Emp.: 400
Dental Services
N.A.I.C.S.: 621210
Andrew Tappar (Mng Dir)

Lumino Dental Limited (2)
40 Panama St Wellington Central, Welling-
ton, 6011, New Zealand
Tel.: (64) 4 384 8481
Web Site: http://www.lumino.co.nz
Emp.: 15
Dental Care Services
N.A.I.C.S.: 339116

Medical Laboratory Wellington (2)
CMC Building, 89 Courtenay Place, Wel-
lington, New Zealand
Tel.: (64) 48015111
Pathology Laboratory Diagnostics
N.A.I.C.S.: 621511

Nelson Diagnostic Laboratory (2)
1 Harley Street, Nelson, New Zealand
Tel.: (64) 35487395
Pathology Laboratory Diagnostics
N.A.I.C.S.: 621511

Pushpay Holdings Limited (1)
Vero Centre Level 19 48 Shortland Street,
Auckland, 1010, New Zealand
Tel.: (64) 800995045
Web Site: https://www.pushpay.com
Rev.: $202,841,000

Assets: $261,338,000
Liabilities: $99,093,000
Net Worth: $162,245,000
Earnings: $33,403,000
Emp.: 564
Fiscal Year-end: 03/31/2022
Software Development Services
N.A.I.C.S.: 541511
Aaron Senneff (CTO)

Subsidiary (US):

Resi Media LLC (2)
3409 N Central Expwy Ste 201, Plano, TX
75023
Web Site: https://resi.io
Video Streaming Platform Developer & Mar-
keter
N.A.I.C.S.: 541511
Collin Jones (Pres)

ZipZap Processing Incorporated (2)
18300 Redmond Way Ste 130, Redmond,
WA 98052-3937
Tel.: (844) 947-9277
Web Site: http://zipzapprocessing.com
Credit Card Processing Services
N.A.I.C.S.: 522320

BGI GENOMICS CO., LTD.
7F-14F Block 7 Huada Comprehen-
sive Park No 21 Hong'an 3rd Street,
Yantian District, Shenzhen, 518083,
Guangdong, China
Tel.: (86) 75536307065
Web Site: http://www.bgi.com
Year Founded: 1999
300676—(CHIN)
Rev.: $612,646,414
Assets: $1,917,392,163
Liabilities: $508,325,903
Net Worth: $1,409,066,259
Earnings: $13,085,021
Emp.: 5,000
Fiscal Year-end: 12/31/23
Healthcare Research Services
N.A.I.C.S.: 541714
Jian Wang (Chm)

BGI GROUP AD
ul Dobrudzha 6 et 3, Sofia, 1000,
Bulgaria
Tel.: (359) 29210510
BOHB—(BUL)
Sales Range: Less than $1 Million
Real Estate Rental Services
N.A.I.C.S.: 531110
Nadezhda Asenova (Dir-IR)

**BGI INVESTMENTS (1961)
LTD.**
44 Israel Pollack Road, Kiryat Gat,
82101, Israel
Tel.: (972) 86873917
Clothing Apparel Mfr
N.A.I.C.S.: 315120
Haim Shalom (CEO)

BGI-SHENZHEN
Build 11 Beishan Industrial Zone,
Yantian District, Shenzhen, 518083,
China
Web Site: http://www.genomics.cn
Year Founded: 1999
Genomics Research & Development
N.A.I.C.S.: 541715
Jian Wang (Pres)

Subsidiaries:

BGI Americas Corporation (1)
1 Broadway 3rd Floor, Cambridge, MA
02142
Tel.: (617) 500-2741
Web Site: http://www.bgiamericas.com
Genomics Research & Development
N.A.I.C.S.: 541715
Yuqing Jiang (Acct Mgr)

Subsidiary (Domestic):

Complete Genomics, Inc. (2)

2071 Stierlin Ct, Mountain View, CA 94043
Tel.: (650) 943-2800
Web Site:
http://www.completegenomics.com
Emp.: 255
DNA Sequencing Services
N.A.I.C.S.: 541715

BGI China (1)
No 389 Haiyuan Road High-tech Develop-
ment Zone, Kunming, Yunnan, Yunnan,
China
Tel.: (86) 27 50161515
Genomics Research & Development Ser-
vices
N.A.I.C.S.: 541715

BGI Hong Kong Co. Limited (1)
16th Dai Fu Street Tai Po Industrial Estate,
Tai Po, China (Hong Kong)
Tel.: (852) 3610 3510
Genomics Research & Development Ser-
vices
N.A.I.C.S.: 541715
Grover Cheung Wai Fung (Reg Mgr)

BGI Japan (1)
Kobe KIMEC Center BLDG 8F 1-5-2
Minatojima-minamimachi, chuo-ku, Kobe,
650-0047, Japan
Tel.: (81) 78 599 6108
Web Site: http://www.bgisequence.com
Genomics Research & Development Ser-
vices
N.A.I.C.S.: 541715

**BGIL FILMS & TECHNOLO-
GIES LTD.**
44 Backery Portion 2nd Floor Regal
Building Connaught Place, New
Delhi, 110001, India
Tel.: (91) 1140765562
Web Site: https://www.bgilfilms.com
Rev.: $4,347,402
Assets: $7,429,853
Liabilities: $4,163,934
Net Worth: $3,265,920
Earnings: $1,338
Fiscal Year-end: 03/31/18
Post Production Services
N.A.I.C.S.: 512191
Umesh Kumar Singh (Exec Dir)

BGL GROUP LIMITED
Pegasus House Bakewell Road, Or-
ton Southgate, Peterborough, PE2
6YS, United Kingdom
Tel.: (44) 1733374444 UK
Year Founded: 1992
Sales Range: $800-899.9 Million
Emp.: 2,270
Holding Company; Insurance Inter-
mediary & Brokerage Services
N.A.I.C.S.: 551112
Peter Winslow (Chm)

Subsidiaries:

**Budget Insurance Company
Limited** (1)
Pegasus House Bakewell Road, Orton
Southgate, Peterborough, PE2 6YS, United
Kingdom
Tel.: (44) 1733374444
Insurance Intermediary & Brokerage Ser-
vices
N.A.I.C.S.: 524210

Subsidiary (Non-US):

**Auto & General Insurance Company
Limited** (2)
Level 13 Sherwood Road, Toowong, 4066,
QLD, Australia
Tel.: (61) 733778804
Web Site: http://www.agic.com.au
Sales Range: $25-49.9 Million
Emp.: 400
Insurance Services
N.A.I.C.S.: 524210
Donald Campbell (Chm)

**BGMC INTERNATIONAL LIM-
ITED**

A-3A-02 Block A Level 3A Sky Park
One City Jalan USJ 25/1, Subang
Jaya, 47650, Selangor, Malaysia
Tel.: (60) 351151128 Ky
Web Site: http://www.bgmc.asia
Year Founded: 1996
Rev.: $126,820,611
Assets: $220,108,972
Liabilities: $137,548,437
Net Worth: $82,560,535
Earnings: ($77,410)
Emp.: 428
Fiscal Year-end: 09/30/18
Civil Engineering Services
N.A.I.C.S.: 236220
Mohammed Arifin Mohammed Arif
(Vice Chm)

**BGR ENERGY SYSTEMS LIM-
ITED**
443 Anna Salai, Teynampet, Chennai,
600018, India
Tel.: (91) 4424301000
Web Site: https://www.bgrcorp.com
Year Founded: 1985
532930—(BOM)
Rev.: $116,932,725
Assets: $676,417,560
Liabilities: $669,718,140
Net Worth: $6,699,420
Earnings: ($66,584,700)
Emp.: 1,689
Fiscal Year-end: 03/31/23
Industrial Machinery Mfr
N.A.I.C.S.: 811310
R. Ramesh Kumar (Pres, Compliance
Officer & Sec)

Subsidiaries:

BGR Boilers Private Limited (1)
443 Anna Salai, Teynampet, Chennai, 600
018, India
Tel.: (91) 4424334940
Steam Turbine & Generator Mfr & Distr
N.A.I.C.S.: 333611

**BGR Energy Systems Limited - Air
Fin Cooler Division** (1)
Ist Floor SKCL - 'Triton Square' C-3 to C-7,
Thiru-Vi-Ka Industrial Estate Guindy, Chen-
nai, 600 032, Tamil Nadu, India
Tel.: (91) 4422504300
Air Cooler Mfr
N.A.I.C.S.: 333415

**BGR Energy Systems Limited - Cap-
tive Power Division** (1)
443 Anna Salai, Teynampet, Chennai,
600018, Tamil Nadu, India
Tel.: (91) 4424334826
Web Site: http://www.bgrenergy.com
Power Plant Construction Services
N.A.I.C.S.: 237130

**BGR Energy Systems Limited - Elec-
trical Projects Division** (1)
No 443 Anna Salai, Teynampet, Chennai,
600 018, India
Tel.: (91) 4424301000
Sales Range: $25-49.9 Million
Emp.: 200
Electrical Contracting Services
N.A.I.C.S.: 541330

**BGR Energy Systems Limited - Envi-
ronment Engineering Division** (1)
443 Anna Salai, Teynampet, Chennai,
60018, Tamil Nadu, India
Tel.: (91) 4424354105
Web Site:
http://www.bgrenergysystems.com
Sales Range: $500-549.9 Million
Emp.: 1,000
Waste Treatment Services
N.A.I.C.S.: 221310

**BGR Energy Systems Limited - Infra-
structure Division** (1)
443 Anna Salai, Teynampet, Chennai,
600018, Tamil Nadu, India
Tel.: (91) 4424301000
Sales Range: $350-399.9 Million
Emp.: 1,005
Civil Engineering Services

N.A.I.C.S.: 541330

**BGR Energy Systems Limited - Oil &
Gas Equipment Division**   (1)
443 Anna Salai, Teynampet, Chennai,
600018, Tamil Nadu, India
Tel.: (91) 4424301000
Sales Range: $450-499.9 Million
Oil & Gas Equipments Mfr
N.A.I.C.S.: 333912

**BGR Energy Systems Limited -
Power Projects Division**   (1)
No 443 Anna Salai 7th Floor Guna Building,
Teynampet, Chennai, 600 018, Tamilnadu,
India
Tel.: (91) 4424352436
Power Plant Construction & Engineering
Services
N.A.I.C.S.: 237130

**BGR Turbines Company Private
Limited**   (1)
443 Anna Salai, Teynampet, Chennai, 600
018, India
Tel.: (91) 4424326171
Steam Turbine & Generator Mfr & Distr
N.A.I.C.S.: 333611

**Progen Systems and Technologies
Limited**   (1)
New No 443 Old No 304-305 Guna Bldg
3rd Fl Anna Salai, Teynampet, Chennai,
600018, Tamil Nadu, India   **(30.33%)**
Tel.: (91) 4424301000
Sales Range: $400-449.9 Million
Heat Exchanger Mfr
N.A.I.C.S.: 332410

**SCHMITZ Reinigungskugeln
GmbH**   (1)
Bahnhofstrasse 45A, 31188, Holle, Ger-
many
Tel.: (49) 50622626
Web Site: http://www.schmitz-
    cleaningballs.de
Sponge Cleaning Ball Mfr
N.A.I.C.S.: 326140
Anke Leder (Mgr-Dept)

**BGRIMM SCIENCE & TECH-
NOLOGY CO., LTD.**
4F Building 23 No 18 Zone No 188
Nansihuan West Road, Fengtai Dis-
trict, Beijing, 100160, China
Tel.: (86) 1067537184
Web Site: http://www.magmat.com
600980—(SHG)
Rev.: $122,177,765
Assets: $256,567,241
Liabilities: $85,210,782
Net Worth: $171,356,459
Earnings: $11,719,862
Emp.: 600
Fiscal Year-end: 12/31/22
Magnetic Material Mfr & Distr
N.A.I.C.S.: 327992
Xiaoou Xia (Chm)

BGS ACQUISITION CORP.
Olazbal 1150, 1428, Buenos Aires,
Argentina
Tel.: (54) 11 47868600   VG
Year Founded: 2011
Emp.: 5
Investment Services
N.A.I.C.S.: 523999
Julio Gutierrez (Chm)

**BGT CORPORATION PUBLIC
COMPANY LIMITED**
188 Suwinthawong Road, Minburi
Subdistrict Minburi District, Bangkok,
10510, Thailand
Tel.: (66) 25402888
Web Site:
    https://www.bodyglove.co.th
Year Founded: 1988
BGT—(THA)
Rev.: $14,238,928
Assets: $22,131,033
Liabilities: $12,313,539

Net Worth: $9,817,495
Earnings: ($1,444,097)
Emp.: 389
Fiscal Year-end: 12/31/23
Mens Apparel Retailer
N.A.I.C.S.: 315210
Nopdol Tumwattana (Chm & CEO)

Subsidiaries:

Body Glove(M) Sdn. Bhd.   (1)
115 Lebuh Victoria, Kawasan Perindustriah
Bayan Lepas, 10300, George Town, Pen-
ang, Malaysia
Tel.: (60) 4 250 0888
Web Site: https://www.bodyglove.com.my
Apparel Retailer
N.A.I.C.S.: 458110
Herbert Goh (CEO)

BGT GROUP CO., LTD.
Room 501 Building 8 No 8 Ronghua
Middle Road, Beijing Economic &
Technological Development Zone,
Beijing, 100176, China
Tel.: (86) 1067986889
Web Site: https://www.bgtwater.com
Year Founded: 2004
300774—(CHIN)
Rev.: $117,791,388
Assets: $352,819,584
Liabilities: $139,021,272
Net Worth: $213,798,312
Earnings: $4,626,180
Fiscal Year-end: 12/31/22
Waste Management Services
N.A.I.C.S.: 221310
Qiuhong Quan (Chm)

BH BOTSWANA (PTY) LTD.
Plot 69500 Lejara Road Broadhurst
Industrial, Gaborone, Botswana
Tel.: (267) 391 2811   BW
Web Site: http://www.bh.co.bw
Year Founded: 1973
Emp.: 70
Construction & Industrial Equipment
Distr
N.A.I.C.S.: 423810
G. R. Keevil (Mng Dir)

Subsidiaries:

Kemach Equipment (Pty) Ltd.   (1)
Portion 6 Aero Star Park Jet Park Road,
Witfield, 1469, South Africa
Tel.: (27) 11 826 6710
Web Site: http://www.kemachjcb.co.za
Mining Construction Quarrying & Building
Equipment Distr
N.A.I.C.S.: 423810

BH CO., LTD.
25 Pyeongcheon-ro 199beon-gil,
Bupyeong-gu, Incheon, Korea (South)
Tel.: (82) 325102000
Web Site: https://www.bhe.co.kr
Year Founded: 1999
090460—(KRS)
Rev.: $1,289,368,356
Assets: $772,610,886
Liabilities: $329,303,885
Net Worth: $443,307,001
Earnings: $107,889,840
Emp.: 1,494
Fiscal Year-end: 12/31/22
Printed Circuit Board Mfr
N.A.I.C.S.: 334412
Choi Yeong-Sik (Dir-Rep)

**BH GLOBAL CORPORATION
LIMITED**
8 Penjuru Lane, Singapore, 609189,
Singapore
Tel.: (65) 62914444
Web Site:
    https://www.bhglobal.com.sg
Year Founded: 1963
BQN—(SES)
Rev.: $44,803,454

Assets: $66,925,699
Liabilities: $24,960,994
Net Worth: $41,964,705
Earnings: $2,020,753
Emp.: 172
Fiscal Year-end: 12/31/23
Marine & Offshore Oil & Gas Supply
Chain Management, Design, Manu-
facturing & Engineering Solutions
N.A.I.C.S.: 237990
Johnny Huay Hua Lim (Dir-Logistics
& Mobility-Global)

Subsidiaries:

Athena Dynamics Pte. Ltd.   (1)
8 Penjuru Lane, Singapore, 609189, Singa-
pore
Tel.: (65) 84311778
Web Site: https://www.athenadynamics.com
Software Technology Development Services
N.A.I.C.S.: 541511
Patrick Hui Peng Lim (COO)

Beng Hui Marine Electrical Pte
Ltd   (1)
8 Penjuru Lane, Singapore, 609189, Singa-
pore
Tel.: (65) 62914444
Web Site: https://www.benghui.com
Offshore Electrical Product Distr
N.A.I.C.S.: 423610

Oil & Gas Solutions Pte Ltd   (1)
101 Cecil Street 19-01A Tong Eng Building,
Singapore, 069533, Singapore
Tel.: (65) 62220889
Web Site: http://www.oilgassol.com
Offshore Engineering Services
N.A.I.C.S.: 541330
Jason Antunovich (CEO)

Omnisense Systems Private
Limited   (1)
8 Penjuru Lane, Singapore, 609189, Singa-
pore
Tel.: (65) 68443191
Web Site: https://www.omnisense-
    systems.com
Night Vision Optical Device Mfr
N.A.I.C.S.: 333310

SASA APAC Pte. Ltd.   (1)
8 Penjuru Lane, Singapore, 609189, Singa-
pore
Tel.: (65) 91370722
Software Development Services
N.A.I.C.S.: 541511

Sea Forrest Technologies Pte.
Ltd.   (1)
8 Penjuru Lane, Singapore, 609189, Singa-
pore
Tel.: (65) 62914444
Web Site: https://www.seaforrest.com
Marine & Offshore Project Management
Services
N.A.I.C.S.: 541330

BH MACRO LTD.
Trafalgar Court Les Banques, PO
Box 255, Saint Peter Port, GY1 3QL,
Guernsey
Tel.: (44) 1481745413
Web Site: https://www.bhmacro.com
Year Founded: 2007
BHMG—(LSE)
Rev.: $14,309,000
Assets: $1,707,130,000
Liabilities: $66,682,000
Net Worth: $1,640,448,000
Earnings: ($242,433,000)
Fiscal Year-end: 12/31/22
Asset Management Services
N.A.I.C.S.: 523940
Richard Horlick (Chm)

BH TELECOM D.D.
Franca Lehara 7, 71 000, Sarajevo,
Bosnia & Herzegovina
Tel.: (387) 33255140
Web Site: http://www.bhtelecom.ba
BHTSR—(SARE)
Rev.: $262,266,213

Assets: $695,103,195
Liabilities: $123,530,782
Net Worth: $571,572,412
Earnings: $27,113,718
Emp.: 2,944
Fiscal Year-end: 12/31/21
Telecommunication Servicesb
N.A.I.C.S.: 517810
Muamer Hadzovic (Member-Mgmt Bd
& Mgr-Bus Dev)

**BHAGAWATI OXYGEN LIM-
ITED**
Plot-5 Sector-25, Ballabgarh, 121
004, Haryana, India
Tel.: (91) 3322296257
Web Site: https://www.globalbol.com
Year Founded: 1972
509449—(BOM)
Rev.: $228,445
Assets: $2,145,701
Liabilities: $1,236,909
Net Worth: $908,792
Earnings: ($384,778)
Emp.: 22
Fiscal Year-end: 03/31/22
Oxygen Gas Mfr
N.A.I.C.S.: 325120
Suresh Kumar Sharma (Chm)

**BHAGERIA INDUSTRIES LIM-
ITED**
1002 10th Floor Topiwala Center
Near Railway Station, Goregaon
West, Mumbai, 400062, Maharashtra,
India
Tel.: (91) 2240436666
Web Site:
    https://www.bhageriagroup.com
Year Founded: 1989
BHAGERIA—(NSE)
Rev.: $83,344,361
Assets: $88,151,482
Liabilities: $18,941,750
Net Worth: $69,209,732
Earnings: $9,636,491
Emp.: 345
Fiscal Year-end: 03/31/22
Dye Mfr & Whslr
N.A.I.C.S.: 325130
Suresh Bhageria (Chm)

**BHAGIRADHA CHEMICALS &
INDUSTRIES LTD.**
Plot No 3 Sagar Society Road No 2
Banjara Hills, Hyderabad, 500 034,
Telangana, India
Tel.: (91) 4042221212
Web Site: https://www.bhagirad.com
531719—(BOM)
Rev.: $43,480,143
Assets: $37,288,173
Liabilities: $16,036,949
Net Worth: $21,251,224
Earnings: $3,183,016
Emp.: 385
Fiscal Year-end: 03/31/21
Pesticide Mfr
N.A.I.C.S.: 325320
Boddu Naga Suvarchala (Compliance
Officer & Sec)

BHAGWAN MARINE
Level 3 / 251 St Georges Tce, Perth,
6000, WA, Australia
Tel.: (61) 894242300
Web Site:
    https://www.bhagwanmarine.com
Year Founded: 2000
BWN—(ASX)
Emp.: 830
Marine Engineering Services
N.A.I.C.S.: 541330
Loui Kannikoski (Founder & Mng Dir)

Bhagwati Syndicate Pvt. Ltd.—(Continued)

BHAGWATI SYNDICATE PVT. LTD.
Vishwakrama South West Block 86C Topsia Road South 2nd Floor, Kolkata, 700046, West Bengal, India
Tel.: (91) 3340049801
Steel Works Services
N.A.I.C.S.: 212290
Ramesh Kumar Jhunjhunwala *(Dir)*

Subsidiaries:

Maithan Alloys Ltd **(1)**
PO Kalyaneshwari Vill Debipur, Burdwan, 713369, West Bengal, India **(55.6%)**
Tel.: (91) 8170018296
Web Site: https://www.maithanalloys.com
Rev.: $224,371,875
Assets: $259,060,620
Liabilities: $51,397,710
Net Worth: $207,662,910
Earnings: $31,399,095
Emp.: 548
Fiscal Year-end: 03/31/2021
Alloy Mfr
N.A.I.C.S.: 332999
Subhas Chandra Agarwalla *(Chm & Mng Dir)*

Subsidiary (Domestic):

Anjaney Alloys Ltd. **(2)**
Kalyaneshwari, Burdwan, 713 369, West Bengal, India
Tel.: (91) 3416464693
Sales Range: $50-74.9 Million
Emp.: 20
Ferro Alloy Mfr
N.A.I.C.S.: 331110
Pramod Chowdhury *(Gen Mgr)*

BHAGYANAGAR INDIA LIMITED
5th Floor Surya Towers Sardar Patel Road, Secunderabad, 500 003, Telangana, India
Tel.: (91) 4027845119
Web Site:
    https://www.bhagyanagarindia.com
512296—(BOM)
Rev.: $214,906,924
Assets: $47,966,428
Liabilities: $29,196,313
Net Worth: $18,770,115
Earnings: $1,512,679
Emp.: 154
Fiscal Year-end: 03/31/22
Copper Mfr
N.A.I.C.S.: 212230
Surendra Bhutoria *(CFO)*

BHAGYANAGAR PROPERTIES LIMITED
2nd 3rd & 5th Floors Surya Towers S P Road, Secunderabad, 500 003, Andhra Pradesh, India
Tel.: (91) 4027845119
Web Site:
    http://www.bhagyanagar.com
Year Founded: 2006
BHAGYAPROP—(NSE)
Rev.: $1,049,760
Assets: $18,991,736
Liabilities: $2,691,287
Net Worth: $16,300,448
Earnings: $289,796
Emp.: 19
Fiscal Year-end: 03/31/21
Real Estate Development Services
N.A.I.C.S.: 531390
Devendra Surana *(Exec Dir)*

Subsidiaries:

Masanto Containers Private Limited **(1)**
5th Floor Surya Towers SP Road, Secunderabad, 500003, India
Tel.: (91) 4027845119
Property Development Services

N.A.I.C.S.: 531390

BHAKTI GEMS & JEWELLERY LIMITED
209 Balaji Paragon Besides Axis Bank Swagat Char Rasta Off C G Road, Ahmedabad, 380009, India
Tel.: (91) 7926421701
Web Site:
    https://www.bhaktijewellery.com
540545—(BOM)
Rev.: $9,274,858
Assets: $3,088,094
Liabilities: $1,032,351
Net Worth: $2,055,744
Earnings: $35,856
Emp.: 15
Fiscal Year-end: 03/31/21
Jewellery Product Mfr & Distr
N.A.I.C.S.: 339910
Akshay Sevantilal Mehta *(Mng Dir)*

BHALCHANDRAM CLOTHING LIMITED
307 Arun Chambers Tardeo Road, Mumbai, 400034, India
Tel.: (91) 2240500100
Web Site:
    http://www.bhalchandram.com
BHALCHANDRA—(NSE)
Rev.: $30,508
Assets: $842,983
Liabilities: $736,404
Net Worth: $106,579
Earnings: ($415,738)
Emp.: 2
Fiscal Year-end: 03/30/22
Clothing Product Mfr
N.A.I.C.S.: 315990
Ujwal Rambilas Lahoti *(Mng Dir)*

BHANDARI HOSIERY EXPORTS LTD.
Village Meharban Rahon Road, Ludhiana, 141007, Punjab, India
Tel.: (91) 8872016419
Web Site:
    https://www.bhandariexport.com
BHANDARI—(NSE)
Rev.: $38,689,041
Assets: $29,733,768
Liabilities: $18,601,619
Net Worth: $11,132,148
Earnings: $855,869
Emp.: 426
Fiscal Year-end: 03/31/22
Textile Garment Mfr
N.A.I.C.S.: 315250
Nitin Bhandari *(Chm & Mng Dir)*

BHANDERI INFRACON LIMITED
B/12 Jabuka Complex Near Bajrang Ashram Below Vikas School, NH 8 Post Thakkarbapanagar, Ahmedabad, 382350, Gujarat, India
Tel.: (91) 7900941000
Web Site:
    https://www.bhanderiinfracon.com
538576—(BOM)
Rev.: $914,550
Assets: $5,784,870
Liabilities: $2,497,950
Net Worth: $3,286,920
Earnings: $47,775
Emp.: 19
Fiscal Year-end: 03/31/22
Real Estate Developers
N.A.I.C.S.: 237210
Sunil Patel *(Mng Dir)*

BHANERO TEXTILE MILLS LIMITED
Umer House Plot 23 Sector 23/1 S M

Farooq Road Korangi Industrial Area, Karachi, Pakistan
Tel.: (92) 2135115177
Web Site:
    https://www.umergroup.com
BHAT—(PSX)
Rev.: $66,716,101
Assets: $94,339,844
Liabilities: $55,718,891
Net Worth: $38,620,953
Earnings: $5,052,121
Emp.: 1,636
Fiscal Year-end: 06/30/23
Textile Products Mfr
N.A.I.C.S.: 313110
Anwar Hussain *(CFO)*

BHANG INC.
40 King Street West Suite 5800, Toronto, M5H 3S1, ON, Canada
Tel.: (416) 368-7224
Web Site:
    https://www.bhangnation.com
Year Founded: 1997
BHNGF—(OTCEM)
Rev.: $1,266,456
Assets: $1,719,361
Liabilities: $1,976,868
Net Worth: ($257,507)
Earnings: ($3,298,022)
Emp.: 6
Fiscal Year-end: 12/31/21
Gold & Uranium Mining Services
N.A.I.C.S.: 212220
Stephen Gledhill *(CFO)*

Subsidiaries:

Pele Diamond Corporation **(1)**
2200 Yonge St Ste 905, Toronto, M4S 2C6, ON, Canada
Tel.: (416) 368-7224
Web Site: http://www.pelemountain.com
Sales Range: $50-74.9 Million
Emp.: 4
Diamond Mining Services
N.A.I.C.S.: 212390

BHANSALI ENGINEERING POLYMERS LIMITED
301 & 302 3rd Floor Peninsula Heights C D Barfiwala Road, Andheri West, Mumbai, 400058, Maharashtra, India
Tel.: (91) 2226216060
Web Site:
    https://www.bhansaliabs.com
Year Founded: 1986
BEPL—(NSE)
Rev.: $189,935,573
Assets: $159,306,666
Liabilities: $13,522,277
Net Worth: $145,784,389
Earnings: $18,667,508
Emp.: 446
Fiscal Year-end: 03/31/23
Plastic Materials Mfr
N.A.I.C.S.: 325211
M. C. Gupta *(Chm)*

BHARAT AGRI FERT & REALTY LIMITED
301 Hubtown Solaris N S Phadke Marg, Andheri E, Mumbai, 400 069, India
Tel.: (91) 2261980100
Web Site:
    https://www.bharatrealty.co.in
531862—(BOM)
Rev.: $3,601,498
Assets: $13,560,552
Liabilities: $5,281,513
Net Worth: $8,279,039
Earnings: $58,941
Emp.: 40
Fiscal Year-end: 03/31/22
Fertilizer Mfr & Whslr; Real Estate Services

N.A.I.C.S.: 325314
Arvind Jaykumar Chakote *(Compliance Officer & Sec)*

BHARAT BHUSHAN FINANCE & COMMODITY BROKERS LTD.
304 404 503 3 Tolstoy Marg, New Delhi, 110001, India
Tel.: (91) 1149800900
Web Site:
    https://www.bbinvestments.in
Year Founded: 1954
511501—(BOM)
Rev.: $67,390
Assets: $2,750,844
Liabilities: $147,966
Net Worth: $2,602,878
Earnings: $13,350
Emp.: 5
Fiscal Year-end: 03/31/22
Financial Services
N.A.I.C.S.: 523999
Sathish Agarwal *(CFO)*

BHARAT BIJLEE LTD
Electric Mansion 6th Floor Appasaheb Marathe Marg Prabhadevi, Mumbai, 400 025, India
Tel.: (91) 2246141414
Web Site:
    https://www.bharatbijlee.com
BBL—(NSE)
Rev.: $197,591,940
Assets: $280,032,480
Liabilities: $91,976,430
Net Worth: $188,056,050
Earnings: $11,359,530
Emp.: 1,400
Fiscal Year-end: 03/30/23
Electrical Engineering Services
N.A.I.C.S.: 541330
Durgesh N. Nagarkar *(Compliance Officer, Sec & Sr Gen Mgr-Legal)*

Subsidiaries:

Bharat Bijlee Ltd - Drives Division **(1)**
No 2 MIDC Thane-Belapur Road, Airoli, Navi Mumbai, 400 708, Maharastra, India
Tel.: (91) 2227637200
Web Site: http://www.bharatbijlee.com
Sales Range: $400-449.9 Million
Electrical Products Mfr
N.A.I.C.S.: 335999

BHARAT DYNAMICS LIMITED
Plot No 38-39 TSFC Building Near ICICI Towers, Financial District Gachibowli Nanakramguda, Hyderabad, 500 032, Telangana, India
Tel.: (91) 4023456173
Web Site: https://bdl-india.in
Year Founded: 1970
Allied Defence Equipment Mfr
N.A.I.C.S.: 336992
P. V. Raja Ram *(Dir)*

BHARAT ELECTRONICS LIMITED
Outer Ring Road Nagavara, Bengaluru, 560045, India
Tel.: (91) 8025039300
Web Site: https://www.bel-india.in
Year Founded: 1954
500049—(BOM)
Rev.: $2,159,971,225
Assets: $4,255,280,858
Liabilities: $2,591,186,380
Net Worth: $1,664,094,479
Earnings: $358,040,885
Emp.: 8,832
Fiscal Year-end: 03/31/23
Defense Electronics Mfr
N.A.I.C.S.: 334220
Koshy Alexander *(Dir-Fin)*

Subsidiaries:

BEL Optronic Devices Ltd.　　　(1)
EL-30 J Block, Bhosari Industrial Area,
Pune, 411026, India
Tel.: (91) 2027130981
Web Site: https://belop-india.in
Sales Range: $50-74.9 Million
Emp.: 200
Other Lighting Equipment Mfr
N.A.I.C.S.: 335139

BHARAT GEARS LIMITED
20 KM Mathura Road Amar Nagar
PO Opp Sarai Khwaja, Faridabad,
121 003, Haryana, India
Tel.: (91) 911294288888
Web Site:
　　https://www.bharatgears.com
Year Founded: 1971
505688—(BOM)
Rev.: $100,050,651
Assets: $55,085,053
Liabilities: $40,316,817
Net Worth: $14,768,235
Earnings: $3,527,092
Emp.: 1,281
Fiscal Year-end: 03/31/22
Automotive Gear Mfr & Distr
N.A.I.C.S.: 336350
Surinder P. Kanwar (Chm & Co-Mng Dir)

BHARAT HEAVY ELECTRI-CALS LIMITED
BHEL House Siri Fort, New Delhi,
110049, India
Tel.: (91) 1166337598
Web Site: https://www.bhel.com
500103—(BOM)
Rev.: $3,256,012,305
Assets: $8,103,976,335
Liabilities: $4,441,950,240
Net Worth: $3,662,026,095
Earnings: $65,163,735
Emp.: 30,000
Fiscal Year-end: 03/31/23
Engineering & Manufacturing Ser-vices
N.A.I.C.S.: 237990
D. Bandyopadhyay (Dir-HR)

Subsidiaries:

BHEL Electrical Machines
Limited　　　(1)
Bedradka Post, Kasaragod, Kerala, 671124,
India
Tel.: (91) 499 423 2316
Web Site: https://www.bheleml.com
Electrical Machinery Mfr & Distr
N.A.I.C.S.: 335311
Kamalesh Das (Chm)

Bharat Heavy Plates & Vessels
Limited　　　(1)
Near Mindi, Visakhapatnam, 530 012,
Andhra Pradesh, India　　　(100%)
Tel.: (91) 8916681280
Web Site: http://hpvp.bhel.com
Sales Range: $450-499.9 Million
Emp.: 1,100
Mfr of Industrial Boilers, Process Equipment
& Allied Products & Cryogenic Equipment
for Petrochemical, Refinery & Fertilizer In-dustries
N.A.I.C.S.: 332410

BHARAT HIGHWAYS INVIT.
2nd floor, Novus Tower, Plot No. 18,
Sector 18,, Gurugram, 122015, India
Tel.: (91) 1246435000
Web Site:
　　https://www.bharatinvit.com
Emp.: 100
Infrastructure Investment
N.A.I.C.S.: 523999

BHARAT IMMUNOLOGICALS AND BIOLOGICALS CORPO-RATION LIMITED

Village Chola OPV Plant, Buland-shahr, 203203, Uttar Pradesh, India
Tel.: (91) 7500241125
Web Site: http://www.bibcol.com
Year Founded: 1989
524663—(BOM)
Rev.: $11,877,261
Assets: $14,194,062
Liabilities: $9,547,452
Net Worth: $4,646,610
Earnings: ($2,472,384)
Fiscal Year-end: 03/31/21
Pharmaceuticals Product Mfr
N.A.I.C.S.: 325412
Chandra Prakash Goyal (Mng Dir)

BHARAT PARENTERALS LIM-ITED
Survey No 144 A At Haripura Jarod
Samlaya Road, Taluka Savli District,
Vadodara, 391520, India
Tel.: (91) 9909928332
Web Site: https://www.bplindia.in
Year Founded: 1992
541096—(BOM)
Rev.: $30,001,704
Assets: $30,856,699
Liabilities: $7,632,343
Net Worth: $23,224,356
Earnings: $2,840,811
Emp.: 241
Fiscal Year-end: 03/31/22
Pharmaceuticals Product Mfr
N.A.I.C.S.: 325412
Bharat R. Desai (Mng Dir)

BHARAT PETROLEUM COR-PORATION LIMITED
Bharat Bhawan P B No 688 4 and 6
Currimbhoy Road, Ballard Estate,
Mumbai, 400001, India
Tel.: (91) 2222713000
Web Site:
　　https://www.bharatpetroleum.in
Year Founded: 1952
BPCL—(BOM)
Rev.: $41,839,887,180
Assets: $21,975,412,095
Liabilities: $14,665,143,675
Net Worth: $7,310,268,420
Earnings: $2,364,156,795
Emp.: 9,251
Fiscal Year-end: 03/31/21
Petroleum Products Sales
N.A.I.C.S.: 324110
Dipti Sanzgiri (Exec Dir)

Subsidiaries:

BPCL-KIAL Fuel Farm Private
Limited　　　(1)
C/o Kannur International Airport Ltd Anjara-kandy Road, Mattanur Mattanur Distt, Kan-nur, 670702, kerala, India
Tel.: (91) 4902997444
Web Site: https://www.bkffpl.com
Aircraft Maintenance Services
N.A.I.C.S.: 561720

BPRL Ventures BV　　　(1)
Strawinskylaan 1143, 1077 XX, Amsterdam,
Netherlands　　　(100%)
Tel.: (31) 205788388
Web Site: https://www.bharatpetroleum.com
Petroleum Products Mfr & Whslr
N.A.I.C.S.: 324110

Bharat Oman Refineries Limited　　(1)
Mahul Chembur, Mumbai, 400 074, Maha-rashtra, India　　　(63.38%)
Tel.: (91) 2225533888
Web Site: http://www.borl.in
Joint Venture of Bharat Petroleum Corpora-tion Ltd. & Oman Oil Company Limited
N.A.I.C.S.: 324110
S. S. Sundararajan (Mng Dir)

Bharat Petro Resources Ltd.　　(1)
Bharat Bhavan 4 and 6 Currimbhoy Road,
Ballard Estate, Mumbai, 400001, India
Tel.: (91) 2222713000
Web Site: http://bharatpetroresources.in

Gas Distribution Services
N.A.I.C.S.: 221210
S. Ramesh (Mng Dir)

Bharat Petroleum Corporation Limited
- Kochi Refinery　　　(1)
Ambalamugal Ernakulam District, PO Box
2, Kochi, 682 302, India
Tel.: (91) 4842722061
Web Site: http://www.kochirefineries.com
Sales Range: $1-4.9 Billion
Emp.: 1,900
Petroleum Refiner
N.A.I.C.S.: 324110
John Minu Mathew (Exec Dir)

Bharat Shell Limited　　　(1)
3rd Floor 1 Tower A B 37 Sector 1, Gautam
Budh Nagar, Noida, 201301, India
Tel.: (91) 202445001
Web Site: http://www.shell.com
Sales Range: $25-49.9 Million
Emp.: 30
Petroluem Refining; Owned 49% by Bharat
Petroleum Corporation Ltd. & 51% by Shell
International Petroleum Company
N.A.I.C.S.: 324110

BHARAT RASAYAN LIMITED
1501 Vikram Tower Rajendra Place,
New Delhi, 110008, India
Tel.: (91) 1143661111
Web Site:
　　https://www.bharatgroup.co.in
590021—(BOM)
Rev.: $179,742,941
Assets: $148,759,939
Liabilities: $43,652,454
Net Worth: $105,107,484
Earnings: $24,021,871
Emp.: 646
Fiscal Year-end: 03/30/22
Pesticide Mfr
N.A.I.C.S.: 325320
Sat Narain Gupta (Founder, Chm & Mng Dir)

BHARAT ROAD NETWORK LTD.
Plot No X1-2 and 3 Ground Floor
Block EP Sector V, Saltlake, Kolkata,
700091, West Bengal, India
Tel.: (91) 3366662700
Web Site: https://www.brnl.in
Year Founded: 2006
BRNL—(NSE)
Rev.: $30,948,003
Assets: $388,524,741
Liabilities: $306,373,554
Net Worth: $82,151,187
Earnings: ($53,053,168)
Emp.: 12
Fiscal Year-end: 03/31/22
Road Highway Construction Services
N.A.I.C.S.: 237310
Naresh Mathur (Chief Compliance Officer & Sec)

BHARAT SEATS LIMITED
Plot No 1 Maruti Udyog Joint Venture
Complex Phase IV Sector 18, Hary-ana, Gurgaon, 122015, India
Tel.: (91) 9643339870
Web Site:
　　https://www.bharatseats.com
523229—(BOM)
Rev.: $112,325,891
Assets: $46,029,779
Liabilities: $28,675,565
Net Worth: $17,354,214
Earnings: $1,626,179
Emp.: 376
Fiscal Year-end: 03/31/22
Automotive Seating System Mfr
N.A.I.C.S.: 336360
Rohit Relan (Chm & Mng Dir)

BHARAT TELECOM LTD.
6th floor 57 Ebene Mews, Cyber City,
Ebene, Mauritius

Tel.: (230) 404 6400　　　MU
Web Site: http://www.btl.mu
Year Founded: 2010
Sales Range: Less than $1 Million
Telecommunication Servicesb
N.A.I.C.S.: 517810

BHARAT WIRE ROPES LIM-ITED
A - 701 Trade World Building Kamala
Mills Senapati Bapat Marg, Lower
Parel W, Mumbai, 400013, India
Tel.: (91) 2266824600
Web Site:
　　https://www.bharatwireropes.com
Year Founded: 1986
539799—(BOM)
Rev.: $80,498,664
Assets: $106,629,268
Liabilities: $30,168,643
Net Worth: $76,460,625
Earnings: $8,494,996
Emp.: 504
Fiscal Year-end: 03/30/23
Wire Rope Mfr & Distr
N.A.I.C.S.: 332618
Murarilal Mittal (Co-Mng Dir)

BHARATI DEFENCE AND IN-FRASTRUCTURE LIMITED
Oberoi Chambers-II Ground Floor
Link Road, Near Lakshmi Industrial
Estate Andheri West, Mumbai,
400053, Maharashtra, India
Tel.: (91) 2239506800
Web Site: https://bdil.co.in
Year Founded: 1976
532609—(BOM)
Ship Building & Repairing Services
N.A.I.C.S.: 336611

BHARATIYA GLOBAL INFOME-DIA LTD.
44 Backery Portion 2nd Floor Regal
Building, Connaught Place, New
Delhi, 110001, India
Tel.: (91) 1140765562
Web Site: https://www.bgil.in
Rev.: $4,896,514
Assets: $24,570,594
Liabilities: $10,161,271
Net Worth: $14,409,322
Earnings: $10,098
Emp.: 50
Fiscal Year-end: 03/31/18
IT & Entertainment Services
N.A.I.C.S.: 541519
Rakesh Bhhatia (Chm & Mng Dir)

BHARGAV BIKASH BANK LIM-ITED
Surkhet Road, PO Box 85, Nepal-gunj, Nepal
Tel.: (977) 521027
Web Site:
　　http://www.bhargavbank.com.np
Commercial Banking Services
N.A.I.C.S.: 522110
Dambar Bahadur Thapa (Chm)

BHARTI ENTERPRISES LIM-ITED
1 Nelson Mandela Rd Bharti Cres-cent Vasant Kunj Phase 2, New
Delhi, 110 070, India
Tel.: (91) 1146661100
Web Site: http://www.bharti.com
Holding Company; Telecom, Agri-Business, Insurance & Retail
N.A.I.C.S.: 551112
Sunil Bharti Mittal (Chm)

Subsidiaries:

Airtel Networks Kenya Limited　　(1)
Parkside Towers Mombasa Road, PO Box
73146-00200, 140223, Nairobi, Kenya

Bharti Enterprises Limited—(Continued)

Tel.: (254) 733100100
Web Site: https://www.airtelkenya.com
Mobile Communications Services Provider
N.A.I.C.S.: 517810
Ashish Malhotra *(CEO)*

Bharti Airtel Limited **(1)**
Bharti Crescent 1 Nelson Mandela Road
Phase II, Vasant Kunj, New Delhi, 110 070,
India **(65.23%)**
Tel.: (91) 1146666100
Web Site: https://www.airtel.in
Rev.: $16,795,324,021
Assets: $53,549,931,059
Liabilities: $40,787,590,672
Net Worth: $12,762,340,387
Earnings: $1,473,221,030
Emp.: 13,708
Fiscal Year-end: 03/31/2023
Telecommunication Servicesb
N.A.I.C.S.: 517112
Sunil Bharti Mittal *(Chm)*

Subsidiary (Non-US):

Airtel (Seychelles) Limited **(2)**
Airtel House Josephine Cafrine Road, PO
Box 1358, Providence, Mahe, Seychelles
Tel.: (248) 4600600
Web Site: https://www.airtel.sc
Telecommunication Servicesb
N.A.I.C.S.: 517410
Amadou Dina *(Mng Dir)*

Joint Venture (Non-US):

Airtel Ghana Limited **(2)**
AT Ghana Barnes Road PMB-TUC, Accra,
Ghana **(49.95%)**
Tel.: (233) 260000100
Web Site: https://www.at.com.gh
Telecommunication Servicesb
N.A.I.C.S.: 517410
Rosy Fynn *(Mktg Dir)*

Subsidiary (Domestic):

**Airtel M Commerce Services
Limited** **(2)**
Airtel Center Plot no 16 Udyog Vihar
Phase-IV, Gurgaon, 122015, India
Tel.: (91) 124 4222222
Telecommunication Servicesb
N.A.I.C.S.: 517410
Rohan Bhandari *(Mgr-Legal, Regulatory &
Compliance)*

Subsidiary (Non-US):

Airtel Malawi Limited **(2)**
airtel Complex City Centre Behind Bis-
nowaty, PO Box 57, Lilongwe, Malawi
Tel.: (265) 999 901 300
Telecommunication Servicesb
N.A.I.C.S.: 517410
Alick Sikelo *(Dir-HR)*

**Airtel Mobile Commerce Holdings
B.V.** **(2)**
Keizersgracht 62 - 64, 1015 CS, Amster-
dam, Noord-Holland, Netherlands
Tel.: (31) 205207430
Telecommunication Servicesb
N.A.I.C.S.: 517410

Airtel Networks Limited **(2)**
Plot L2 Banana Island Foreshore Estate,
Ikoyi, Lagos, Nigeria
Tel.: (234) 8021500111
Telecommunication Servicesb
N.A.I.C.S.: 517410
Okey Igwegbe *(Head-New Products Dev)*

Airtel Networks Zambia Plc **(2)**
Airtel House Stand No 2375 Cnr Addis Ab-
baba Drive and Great East Road, Lusaka,
Zambia
Tel.: (260) 977770097
Web Site: https://www.airtel.co.zm
Telecommunication Servicesb
N.A.I.C.S.: 517410
Bavo Emmanuel Mzee *(Dir-IT)*

Airtel Rwanda Limited **(2)**
Remera- airtel near Amahoro National Sta-
dium UTC Building City Town, Kigali,
Rwanda
Tel.: (250) 730 000 456
Alex

N.A.I.C.S.: 517410
Alex Mugisha *(Dir-Customer Svc)*

Airtel Tanzania Limited **(2)**
Airtel House Corner of A H Mwinyi Road &
Kawawa Road, PO Box 9623, Kinondoni,
Dar es Salaam, Tanzania
Tel.: (255) 784 103 001
Telecommunication Servicesb
N.A.I.C.S.: 517410
Patrick Foya *(Dir-HR)*

Airtel Tchad S.A. **(2)**
Avenue Charles de Gaulle, BP 5665,
N'djamena, Chad
Tel.: (235) 63000000
Web Site: https://www.airtel.td
Telecommunication Servicesb
N.A.I.C.S.: 517410
Abderamane Salah *(Mgr-Fin Sys)*

Subsidiary (Non-US):

Amanco Mexico **(3)**
Rio San Javier No 10 Fraccionamiento
Viveros del Rio, Tlalnepantla, 54060,
Mexico
Tel.: (52) 55 5366 4000
Web Site: http://www.amanco.com.mx
Plastic Pipe & Pipe Fittings Mfr
N.A.I.C.S.: 326122

Wavin N.V. **(3)**
Stationsplein 3, PO Box 173, 8000 AD,
Zwolle, Netherlands
Tel.: (31) 384294911
Web Site: http://www.wavin.com
Emp.: 5,000
Plastic Tubes & Conduits Mfr
N.A.I.C.S.: 326122
Maarten Roef *(CEO)*

Subsidiary (Non-US):

AB Svenska Wavin **(4)**
Kjulamon 6, 635 06, Eskilstuna, Sweden
Tel.: (46) 165410000
Web Site: http://www.wavin.com
Sales Range: $25-49.9 Million
Emp.: 70
Plastic Pipes Distr
N.A.I.C.S.: 424610

Arot Polska Sp.z.o.o. **(4)**
ul Dobiezynska 43, 64-320, Buk, Greater
Poland, Poland
Tel.: (48) 655252525
Web Site: http://www.arot.pl
Plastic Tank Mfr
N.A.I.C.S.: 326122

Chemidro S.p.A. **(4)**
Via Giovanni Paolo II -Terminal Nord,
33100, Udine, Italy
Tel.: (39) 0432626562
Web Site: http://www.chemidro.com
Sales Range: $10-24.9 Million
Emp.: 30
Radiators Mfr
N.A.I.C.S.: 333414

**Foshan Hepworth Pipe Company
Ltd.** **(4)**
Datong Road Dwarf 1 Fu Gang Industrial
District, Zhangcha Town, Foshan, Guang-
dong, China
Tel.: (86) 757 82516490
Plumbing Accessories Whslr
N.A.I.C.S.: 423720

**Hepworth Building Products
Limited** **(4)**
Hazlehead, Crow Edge, Sheffield, S36
4HG, United Kingdom **(100%)**
Tel.: (44) 226763561
Web Site: http://www.hepworthbp.co.uk
Sales Range: $75-99.9 Million
Emp.: 400
Mfr of Vitrified Clay Plastic & Concrete
Drainage Systems
N.A.I.C.S.: 327120

MPC Sp.z.o.o. **(4)**
Pecz 59, 57-100, Strzelin, Lower Silesian,
Poland
Tel.: (48) 713957000
Web Site: https://www.mpc.pl
Sales Range: $25-49.9 Million
Emp.: 140
Plastic Tank Mfr
N.A.I.C.S.: 326122

Joanna Karsznia *(Sec)*

Nordisk Wavin A/S **(4)**
Wavinvej 1, Hammel, 8450, Denmark
Tel.: (45) 86962000
Web Site: http://www.wavin.com
Plastic Tank Mfr
N.A.I.C.S.: 326122

Norsk Wavin A/S **(4)**
Post Box 55, N-1472, Fjellhamar, Akershus,
Norway
Tel.: (47) 67979334
Web Site: http://www.wavin.no
Plastic Tank Mfr
N.A.I.C.S.: 326122
Tor Martin Garsjo *(Mng Dir)*

OOO Wavin Rus **(4)**
vil Bikovo Ul Verhnyaya 18/2 Ramenskij
Dist, Bykovo village Ramensky district,
140153, Moscow, Russia
Tel.: (7) 4959267970
Web Site: http://www.wavin.ru
Plastic Pipes Distr
N.A.I.C.S.: 424610

UAB Wavin Baltic **(4)**
Ugniagesiu g 4, LT-02244, Vilnius, Lithuania
Tel.: (370) 52691800
Web Site: http://www.wavin.com
Sales Range: $25-49.9 Million
Emp.: 100
Plastic Pipes Whslr
N.A.I.C.S.: 424610
Virginijus Ramanauskas *(Mgr)*

Warmafloor (GB) Ltd. **(4)**
Concorde House Concorde Way, Segens-
worth North, Fareham, PO15 5RL, Hamp-
shire, United Kingdom
Tel.: (44) 1489581787
Web Site: http://www.warmafloor.co.uk
Sales Range: $25-49.9 Million
Emp.: 60
Underfloor Heating & Cooling Systems Mfr
N.A.I.C.S.: 333415
Mike Lamb *(Mng Dir)*

Subsidiary (Domestic):

Wavin B.V. **(4)**
Station Splein 3, Zwolle, 8011 3W, Overijs-
sel, Netherlands
Tel.: (31) 384294911,
Sales Range: $25-49.9 Million
Emp.: 110
Civil Engineering Services
N.A.I.C.S.: 541330

Subsidiary (Domestic):

Wavin Assurantie B.V. **(5)**
Stationsplein 3, Zwolle, 8011, Netherlands
Tel.: (31) 384294333
Sales Range: $125-149.9 Million
General Insurance Services
N.A.I.C.S.: 524210
H. J. Meijrink *(Dir-Fin)*

Wavin Diensten B.V. **(5)**
Bruchterweg 88, Hardenberg, 7770 AA,
Overijssel, Netherlands
Tel.: (31) 523 288911
Web Site: http://www.wavin.com
Sales Range: $75-99.9 Million
Emp.: 80
Plastic Tank Mfr
N.A.I.C.S.: 326122
Harm Dries *(Mng Dir)*

Wavin Nederland B.V. **(5)**
J C Kellerlaan 8, Postbus 5, 7772 SG,
Hardenberg, Netherlands
Tel.: (31) 523288165
Web Site: http://www.wavin.com
Sales Range: $100-124.9 Million
Emp.: 100
Plastic Pipes Distr
N.A.I.C.S.: 424990
Tom Lentfert *(Acct Mgr)*

Wavin Overseas B.V. **(5)**
Stationsplein 3, PO Box 173, 8000 AD,
Zwolle, Netherlands
Tel.: (31) 523624911
Web Site: http://www.wavin.com
Plumbing Accessories Whslr
N.A.I.C.S.: 423720

**Wavin Technology & Innovation
B.V.** **(5)**

Rollepaal 20, PO Box 110, Dedemsvaart,
7701BS, Netherlands **(100%)**
Tel.: (31) 523624911
Web Site: http://www.wavin.com
Sales Range: $75-99.9 Million
Emp.: 60
Pipes & Plumbing Systems Mfr
N.A.I.C.S.: 326191
Henk Olsmrn *(Mgr-Fin)*

Subsidiary (Non-US):

Wavin Balkan d-o.o. **(4)**
Justina Popovica 3, Zemun, 11283, Bel-
grade, Serbia
Tel.: (381) 11 316 91 96
Web Site: http://www.rs.wavin.com
Plastic Tank Mfr
N.A.I.C.S.: 326122
Igor Solovjev *(Mgr)*

Wavin Belgium N.V. **(4)**
Industriepark Lakeland L Bekaertlaan 30,
9880, Aalter, East Flanders, Belgium
Tel.: (32) 93259511
Web Site: http://www.wavin.be
Sales Range: $50-74.9 Million
Emp.: 190
Plumbing Fixture Whslr
N.A.I.C.S.: 423720

Wavin Ekoplastik s.r.o. **(4)**
Rudec 848, 277 13, Kostelec nad Labem,
Czech Republic
Tel.: (420) 326983460
Web Site: http://www.wavin.cz
Plastic Tank Mfr
N.A.I.C.S.: 326122
Morten Vollan *(Mng Dir & CEO)*

Wavin Estonia OU **(4)**
Parnasalu 29 PK5827, 76501, Saue, Harju-
maa, Estonia
Tel.: (372) 6506840
Web Site: http://www.wavin.ee
Plumbing Fixture Mfr
N.A.I.C.S.: 332913

Wavin France S.A.S. **(4)**
ZI la Feuillouse, BP 5, 3150, Varennes-sur-
Allier, France
Tel.: (33) 470484848
Web Site: http://www.wavin.fr
Drainage System Installation Services
N.A.I.C.S.: 237110
Didier Prouteau *(Pres)*

Subsidiary (Domestic):

Climasol S.A. **(5)**
Z I de la Louee, Rue Denis Papin, 44115,
Haute-Goulaine, France
Tel.: (33) 2 40 06 29 00
Pipeline Rehabilitation Services
N.A.I.C.S.: 237120

Subsidiary (Non-US):

Wavin GmbH **(4)**
Industriestrasse 20, 49767, Twist, Germany
Tel.: (49) 5936120
Web Site: http://www.wavin.com
Sales Range: $100-124.9 Million
Emp.: 400
Plastic Pipes Distr
N.A.I.C.S.: 424610
Frank Schellhoeh *(Mgr)*

Wavin Ireland Ltd. **(4)**
Dublin Road, Balbriggan, Dublin, Ireland
Tel.: (353) 18020200
Web Site: http://www.wavin.ie
Sales Range: $25-49.9 Million
Emp.: 80
Plastic Pipe & Fitting Mfr
N.A.I.C.S.: 326122
Celine Wogan *(Product Mgr)*

Wavin Italia S.p.A. **(4)**
Via Boccalara 24, Santa Maria Maddalena,
45030, Occhiobello, Rovigo, Italy
Tel.: (39) 0425758811
Web Site: http://www.wavin.it
Sales Range: $50-74.9 Million
Emp.: 250
Plastic Pipes Distr
N.A.I.C.S.: 424610

Wavin Latvia SIA **(4)**
Sipolini 1 Tiraine, Marupes Pag, Riga, 2167,
Latvia

Tel.: (371) 671 46400
Web Site: http://www.wavin.lv
Water Treatment Equipment Mfr
N.A.I.C.S.: 333310

Wavin Metalplast-BUK Sp.z.o.o. (4)
Ul Dobiezynska 43, 64-320, Buk, Poland
Tel.: (48) 618911000
Web Site: http://www.wavin.pl
Sales Range: $25-49.9 Million
Emp.: 200
Plumbing Fixture Mfr
N.A.I.C.S.: 326191

Wavin Novotech S.A.S. (4)
ZI de Motz-Serrieres, 73310, Motz, Savoie, France
Tel.: (33) 479 63 79 00
Web Site: http://www.telecom.wavin.com
Plastic Pipes Retailer
N.A.I.C.S.: 424990

Wavin Plastics Ltd. (4)
Hazlehead Crow Edge, Sheffield, S36 4HG, S Yorkshire, United Kingdom
Tel.: (44) 1249766600
Plastic Tank Mfr
N.A.I.C.S.: 326122
Callum Forsyth (Mng Dir)

Wavin Polyfemos AS (4)
Betongveien 12, 9515, Alta, Finnmark, Norway
Tel.: (47) 78456300
Web Site: http://www.wavin.no
Sales Range: $25-49.9 Million
Emp.: 25
Thermoplastic Product Mfr
N.A.I.C.S.: 325211

Wavin Portugal-Plasticos S.A. (4)
Brejinha - Beduido, 3860-210, Estarreja, Portugal
Tel.: (351) 234840490
Web Site: http://www.wavin.pt
Plastic Tank Mfr
N.A.I.C.S.: 326122

Wavin Romania s.r.l. (4)
37 Sos De Centura, Popesti-Leordeni, 077160, Ilfov, Romania
Tel.: (40) 213 519 376
Web Site: http://ro.wavin.com
Plastic Pipes Distr
N.A.I.C.S.: 423390
Dragos Ularu (Mgr)

Wavin Slovakia spol s.r.o. (4)
Partizanska 73/916, 957 01, Banovce nad Bebravou, Trencin, Slovakia
Tel.: (421) 387605895
Web Site: http://www.wavin.sk
Emp.: 17
Plastic Tank Mfr
N.A.I.C.S.: 326122
Ludmila Minarikova (Mgr)

Wavin Swisspipe AG (4)
C/o Engel Copera Ag Waldeggstrasse 37, 3097, Liebefeld, Bern, Switzerland
Tel.: (41) 81 253 62 83
Web Site: http://www.wavin.ch
Plastic Pipes & Tubes Mfr
N.A.I.C.S.: 326122

Wavin Ukrain O.O.O.T.O.V. (4)
Smt Shepherds St, Machine Builders 1, Kiev, Ukraine
Tel.: (380) 444992610
Web Site: http://www.wavin.com.ua
Sales Range: $25-49.9 Million
Emp.: 24
Plastic Pipes Retailer
N.A.I.C.S.: 424610

Wavin-Labko Oy (4)
Visiokatu 1, 33720, Tampere, Finland
Tel.: (358) 201285200
Web Site: http://www.wavin.com
Sales Range: $25-49.9 Million
Emp.: 65
Water Treatment Equipment Mfr
N.A.I.C.S.: 333310
Milla Rantanen (Mgr-Quality & Environment)

Plant (Domestic):

Wavin-Labko Oy - PE Factory (5)
Makirinteentie 38 40, 36220, Kangasala, Pirkanmaa, Finland
Tel.: (358) 201285430

Web Site: http://www.wavin-labko.fi
Plumbing Fixture Mfr
N.A.I.C.S.: 332913
Tony Aijo (Mgr-Production & Pur)

Subsidiary (Non-US):

Airtel Uganda Limited (2)
Airtel Towers Plot 16A Clement Hill, PO Box 6771, Kampala, Uganda
Tel.: (256) 705100100
Web Site: https://www.airtel.co.ug
Mobile Telecommunications Services
N.A.I.C.S.: 517112
V. G. Somasekhar (Mng Dir)

Bharti Airtel (France) SAS (2)
88 T Avenue du General Leclerc, 92100, Boulogne-Billancourt, France
Tel.: (33) 8 99 37 79 11
Telecommunication Servicesb
N.A.I.C.S.: 517810

Bharti Airtel (UK) Limited (2)
Fairfax House 15 Fulwood Place, London, WC1V 6AY, United Kingdom
Tel.: (44) 8049010200
Telecommunication Servicesb
N.A.I.C.S.: 517810

Bharti Airtel International (Netherlands) B.V. (2)
Keizersgracht 62-64, Amsterdam, 1015 CS, Netherlands
Tel.: (31) 235689310
Telecommunication Servicesb
N.A.I.C.S.: 517810

Bharti Airtel Lanka (Private) Limited (2)
Level 10 & 11 West Tower World Trade Centre Echelon Square, Colombo, Sri Lanka
Tel.: (94) 755 555 555
Emp.: 220
Telecommunication Servicesb
N.A.I.C.S.: 517410
Feroz Ahamed (Mgr-Network Quality)

Subsidiary (Domestic):

Bharti Airtel Services Limited (2)
Tonk Road SB-115A, Jaipur, India
Tel.: (91) 7523077392
Telecommunication Servicesb
N.A.I.C.S.: 517410
Rajiv Mathrani (Chief Brand Officer)

Subsidiary (Non-US):

Bharti International (Singapore) Pte. Ltd (2)
150 Orchard Road 08-01 Orchard Plaza, Singapore, 238841, Singapore
Tel.: (65) 68228578
Telecommunication Servicesb
N.A.I.C.S.: 517410

Jersey Airtel Limited (2)
26 Queen Street St, Saint Helier, JE2 4WD, Jersey
Tel.: (44) 7839 700121
Telecommunication Servicesb
N.A.I.C.S.: 517410

Uganda Towers Limited (2)
Airtel House Plot no 40 Jinja Road, PO Box 6771, Kampala, Uganda
Tel.: (256) 752 230110
Telecommunication Servicesb
N.A.I.C.S.: 517410

Bharti Realty Limited (1)
3rd floor Worldmark 2 Asset 8, Aerocity, New Delhi, 110 037, India
Tel.: (91) 1141384000
Web Site: http://www.bhartirealty.com
Real Estate Development Services
N.A.I.C.S.: 531390

Bharti Resources Ltd. (1)
Neelagagan Mandi Rd, Sultanpur Mehrauli, New Delhi, 110 030, India (100%)
Tel.: (91) 1146001100
Web Site: http://www.centumlearning.com
Sales Range: $25-49.9 Million
Emp.: 150
Learning & Development Solutions for Improved Business Performance
N.A.I.C.S.: 611430

Centum Learning Limited (1)
127 Neelagagan Mandi Road, Sultanpur Mehrauli, New Delhi, 110030, India
Tel.: (91) 1145881000
Web Site: http://www.centumlearning.com
Softskill Training Services
N.A.I.C.S.: 611430
Sanjay Bahl (CEO & Mng Dir)

FieldFresh Foods Pvt. Ltd. (1)
ower C-2 First Floor Plot No 16 Udyog Vihar Phase IV, Gurgaon, 122 015, India
Tel.: (91) 1244109400
Web Site: http://www.fieldfreshfoods.in
Sales Range: $75-99.9 Million
Emp.: 200
Fresh & Processed Fruits & Vegetable Bharti Enterprise & Del Monte Food Joint Venture Distr
N.A.I.C.S.: 424480
Yogesh Billani (CEO)

Gourmet Investments Pvt Ltd (1)
301/302/303/304 3rd Floor CentrePoint Above Standard Chartered Bank, SV Road Santacruz West, Mumbai, India
Tel.: (91) 22 66862900
Financial Investment Services
N.A.I.C.S.: 523940
Sunil Kuttan (Head-Supply Chain Mgmt)

Indus Towers Limited (1)
Building No 10 Tower-A 4th Floor, DLF Cyber City, Gurgaon, 122 002, Haryana, India
Tel.: (91) 1244296766
Web Site: https://www.industowers.com
Rev.: $3,446,208,261
Assets: $5,583,885,858
Liabilities: $3,052,922,487
Net Worth: $2,530,963,372
Earnings: $244,589,653
Emp.: 3,249
Fiscal Year-end: 03/31/2023
Telecom Structures
N.A.I.C.S.: 237130
Akhil Kumar Gupta (Chm)

BHARTIA BACHAT LIMITED
2 Barretto Lane, Kolkata, 700069, West Bengal, India
Tel.: (91) 7016141083
Web Site:
http://www.bhartiabachat.ltd
Year Founded: 1982
543208—(BOM)
Rev.: $45,797
Assets: $2,416,675
Liabilities: $6,072
Net Worth: $2,410,604
Earnings: $(16,408)
Fiscal Year-end: 03/31/21
Non-Banking Financial Services
N.A.I.C.S.: 522299
Chandrakant Govindbhai Parmar (Compliance Officer & Sec)

BHARTIYA INTERNATIONAL LTD.
38 Sector 44 Gurgaon, 122 002, New Delhi, 122 002, India
Tel.: (91) 1244888555
Web Site: https://www.bhartiya.com
526666—(BOM)
Rev.: $73,094,330
Assets: $115,316,893
Liabilities: $73,875,998
Net Worth: $41,440,895
Earnings: $1,631,039
Emp.: 310
Fiscal Year-end: 03/30/22
Textile Apparel Mfr
N.A.I.C.S.: 315250

Subsidiaries:

Ultima Italia S.R.L. (1)
Via Dei Tigli 4, Casaletto Vaprio, 26010, Cremona, Italy
Tel.: (39) 0373273411
Web Site: https://www.bhartiyafashion.com
Sales Range: $25-49.9 Million
Solar Power Park Development Services
N.A.I.C.S.: 237130
Nikhil Aggarwal (Mng Dir)

BHASKAR AGROCHEMICALS LTD.
D No-1-90/C Office Unit - 608 1T06 6th Floor Gowra Fountain, Head SY No-83P and 84P Madhapur Hitech City, Hyderabad, 500081, Telangana, India
Tel.: (91) 4045474617
Web Site:
https://www.bhaskaragro.com
Year Founded: 1978
524534—(BOM)
Rev.: $8,920,366
Assets: $6,010,691
Liabilities: $4,399,372
Net Worth: $1,611,319
Earnings: $148,474
Emp.: 78
Fiscal Year-end: 03/31/22
Chemical Products Mfr
N.A.I.C.S.: 325998
P. Pattabhi Rama Rao (Chm & Mng Dir)

BHATIA BROTHERS GROUP
PO Box 1275, Dubai, United Arab Emirates
Tel.: (971) 42137777
Web Site: http://www.bhatia.com
Sales Range: $150-199.9 Million
Emp.: 1,100
Diverse Holding Company Industrial Machinery Distr & Engineering Services
N.A.I.C.S.: 551112
Ajay B. Bhatia (Chm)

Subsidiaries:

Bhatia Brothers & Partners L.L.C (1)
Warehouse No 2 Building No 1628 Near Holiday Inn, PO Box 934, Ghallah, Oman
Tel.: (968) 24501109
Web Site: http://www.bhatia.com
Electronic Product Distr
N.A.I.C.S.: 423610
Ashok Shetty (Gen Mgr-Automotive)

Bhatia Brothers Group - Bhatia Brothers-Automotive Division (1)
Khan Saheb Building Green Belt Road Industrial Area-2, PO Box 40687, Sharjah, United Arab Emirates
Tel.: (971) 6 5337166
Automobile Parts Mfr
N.A.I.C.S.: 336390

Bhatia Brothers LLC - Automotive & Industrial Chemicals (1)
PO Box 1275, Dubai, United Arab Emirates
Tel.: (971) 42137750
Web Site: http://www.bbisd.com
Distr of Car Care Products, including Accessories, Lubricants, Spare Parts, Batteries & Maintenance Chemicals
N.A.I.C.S.: 441330

Bhatia Brothers LLC - Industrial Supplies Division (1)
PO Box 1275, Dubai, United Arab Emirates
Tel.: (971) 42137715
Web Site: http://www.bhatia.com
Sales Range: $150-199.9 Million
N.A.I.C.S.: 541330

Bhatia Cold Storage & Trading Co., LLC (1)
PO Box 322, Dubai, 332, United Arab Emirates
Tel.: (971) 42850618
Frozen & Chilled Food Warehousing
N.A.I.C.S.: 493120
A.B. Bhatia (Mng Dir)

C & J Gulf Pipe Coating Est. (1)
PO Box 7702, Abu Dhabi, United Arab Emirates
Tel.: (971) 2 5553 453
Web Site: http://www.cjengg.com
Emp.: 200
Steel Fabrication Services
N.A.I.C.S.: 332312
Khan Immran Moideen (Sr Engr-Procurement)

Bhatia Brothers Group—(Continued)

Emirates Cold Storage Company (1)
PO Box 337, Abu Dhabi, United Arab Emirates
Tel.: (971) 5553455
Cold Storage
N.A.I.C.S.: 493120

Gulfdetection LLC (1)
Airport Rd T1, PO Box 52495, Dubai, United Arab Emirates
Tel.: (971) 4 2137777
Web Site: http://www.gulfdtn.com
Security System Installation Services
N.A.I.C.S.: 238210

Oilfields Supply Centre LLC (1)
PO Box 2855, Ruwi, 112, Oman
Tel.: (968) 247 05077
Web Site: http://www.ofsc.co
Oil & Gas Field Engineering Services
N.A.I.C.S.: 541330

Petrogulf WLL (1)
11th-Flr Almana Business Tower C-Ring Road, PO Box 9841, Doha, Qatar
Tel.: (974) 44350151
Web Site: http://www.pgulf.net
Emp.: 30
Petroleum Product Distr
N.A.I.C.S.: 424720
Amit Khanna (Mgr-Mktg & Sls)

Super General Trading Co, LLC (1)
Al Owais Building Behind HSBC Bank, PO Box 322, Nasser Square Deira, Dubai, United Arab Emirates
Tel.: (971) 42219495
Web Site: http://www.bhatiabrothers.com
Sales Range: $50-74.9 Million
Emp.: 12
Retailer, Whslr & Exporter of Branded Consumer Electronics, Office Automation Products, Home Appliances & Internet Technology Products
N.A.I.C.S.: 423990

TPC FZE (1)
PO Box 1275, Jebel Ali, United Arab Emirates
Tel.: (971) 4 8132 761
Web Site: http://www.tpcfze.com
Industrial Supplies Whslr
N.A.I.C.S.: 423840

Division (Domestic):

TPC FZE - Process Package Division (2)
Jebel Ali, Dubai, United Arab Emirates
Tel.: (971) 4 8132750
Packaging Products Mfr
N.A.I.C.S.: 326112

Technical Parts Company India Pvt Ltd. (1)
601 Cosmos Court SV Road Vile Parle, Mumbai, 400 056, India
Tel.: (91) 22 2613 4570
Engineeering Services
N.A.I.C.S.: 541330

Technical Parts Company LLC (1)
PO Box 5071, Dubai, United Arab Emirates
Tel.: (971) 42823414
Sales Range: $25-49.9 Million
Emp.: 50
Engineering Products, Services & Solutions
N.A.I.C.S.: 541330

Technical Parts Establishment (1)
PO Box 337, Abu Dhabi, United Arab Emirates
Tel.: (971) 2 6732200
Web Site: http://www.bhatia.com
Industrial Supplies Whslr
N.A.I.C.S.: 423840
Ravi Vadivelu (Mgr-Sls)

V.V. & Sons LLC (1)
Al Fahidi Street, PO Box 105, Dubai, United Arab Emirates
Tel.: (971) 4 3532444
Web Site: http://www.vvsons.com
Electronic Components Distr
N.A.I.C.S.: 423690

BHATIA COLOUR CHEM LIMITED

Plot No A/2/12 Road No 1 Udhna Udhyog Nagar, Sangh Udhna, Surat, 394210, Gujarat, India
Tel.: (91) 9104294564
Web Site: https://www.bccl.info
Year Founded: 1975
543497—(BOM)
Chemical Products Mfr
N.A.I.C.S.: 325199
Bharat Bhatia (Mng Dir)

BHATIA COMMUNICATION & RETAIL (INDIA) LIMITED

132 Dr Ambedkar Shopping Centre Ring Road, Surat, 395 002, Gujarat, India
Tel.: (91) 9227610000
Web Site:
  https://www.bhatiamobile.com
540956—(BOM)
Rev.: $41,333,769
Assets: $11,381,896
Liabilities: $4,840,417
Net Worth: $6,541,478
Earnings: $1,017,481
Emp.: 92
Fiscal Year-end: 03/31/23
Wireless Telecommunication Services
N.A.I.C.S.: 517112
Sanjeev Bhatia (Mng Dir)

BHB BRAUHOLDING BAYERN-MITTE AG

Manchinger Str 95, 85053, Ingolstadt, Germany
Tel.: (49) 8416310
Web Site: https://www.bhb-ag.de
Year Founded: 1882
B9B—(DEU)
Rev.: $20,079,479
Assets: $16,149,685
Liabilities: $3,863,561
Net Worth: $12,286,124
Earnings: $264,930
Fiscal Year-end: 12/31/23
Alcoholic Beverage Mfr & Distr
N.A.I.C.S.: 312140

BHCC HOLDING LIMITED

No1 Tampines North Drive 3 08-01 BHCC Space, Singapore, 528499, Singapore
Tel.: (65) 66594666   Ky
Web Site: https://www.bhcc.com.sg
Year Founded: 2003
1552—(HKG)
Rev.: $234,174,281
Assets: $100,360,763
Liabilities: $70,674,041
Net Worth: $29,686,721
Earnings: $1,357,684
Emp.: 360
Fiscal Year-end: 12/31/23
Construction Management Services
N.A.I.C.S.: 236220
Xinping Yang (Chm)

Subsidiaries:

BHCC Construction Pte. Ltd. (1)
No 1 Tampines North Drive 3 08-01 BHCC SPACE, Singapore, 528499, Singapore
Tel.: (65) 66594666
Web Site: https://www.bhcc.com.sg
Building Construction Services
N.A.I.C.S.: 236220

BHEEMA CEMENTS LTD.

No 6-3-652/C/A Flat 5a Kautilya Amrutha Estates Somajiguda, Hyderabad, 500082, India
Tel.: (91) 40 23423270
Web Site:
  http://www.bheemacements.net
Cement Mfr
N.A.I.C.S.: 327310
Sikakollu Kishore Chandra (Mng Dir)

BHG GROUP AB

Hans Michelsensgatan 9, 211 20, Malmo, Sweden
Tel.: (46) 706056334
Web Site: https://www.wearebhg.com
Year Founded: 2012
BHG—(OMX)
Rev.: $1,259,818,109
Assets: $1,337,623,048
Liabilities: $619,255,013
Net Worth: $718,368,035
Earnings: $4,280,349
Emp.: 2,759
Fiscal Year-end: 12/31/22
Online Shopping Site Operator
N.A.I.C.S.: 455219
Adam Schatz (Pres, CEO & Head-Home Furnishing Segment)

Subsidiaries:

AH-Trading GmbH (1)
Luttinger Str 25, 46509, Xanten, Germany
Tel.: (49) 28013713333
Web Site: https://www.ah-trading.de
Garden Furniture Store Services
N.A.I.C.S.: 712130

Baldai1 UAB (1)
Plunges g 4, 03205, Vilnius, Lithuania
Tel.: (370) 62020111
Web Site: https://www.baldai1.lt
Furniture Whslr
N.A.I.C.S.: 444180
Arturas Sabaliauskas (Project Mgr)

Bygghemma Sverige AB (1)
Hans Michelsensgatan 9, 211 42, Malmo, Sweden
Tel.: (46) 101400100
Web Site: https://www.bygghemma.se
Home Construction & Garden Product E-Retailer
N.A.I.C.S.: 449210
Fredrik Lind (Mgr-HR)

Subsidiary (Domestic):

Arc E-commerce AB (2)
Box 3124, 13603, Haninge, Sweden
Tel.: (46) 841021005
Web Site: https://www.arcecommerce.se
Ecommerce Services
N.A.I.C.S.: 423620
Lina Eckardt (Mgr-Content)

Bygghemma Butik i Sthlm AB (2)
Jarlsgatan 62, 114 29, Stockholm, Sweden
Tel.: (46) 852211990
Building Materials Distr
N.A.I.C.S.: 449210

Subsidiary (Non-US):

Bygghjemme Norge AS (2)
Stalsbergveien 3, 3128, Notteroy, Norway
Tel.: (47) 21601818
Web Site: https://www.bygghjemme.no
Household Product Distr
N.A.I.C.S.: 449210
Petter Engo (Country Mgr)

Byghjemme.dk ApS (2)
Nordensvej 2, 7000, Fredericia, Denmark
Tel.: (45) 2 066 5321
Web Site: https://www.byghjemme.dk
Building Material & Product Distr
N.A.I.C.S.: 444180

Camola ApS (2)
Nordensvej 2, 7000, Fredericia, Denmark
Tel.: (45) 72207212
Web Site: https://www.frishop.dk
Building Material & Product Distr
N.A.I.C.S.: 444180
Carsten Mortensen (Owner)

Subsidiary (Domestic):

Linoleumkompaniet AB (2)
Radmansgatan 27, Box 5891, 102 40, Stockholm, Sweden
Tel.: (46) 85 223 2100
Web Site: https://www.linoleumkompaniet.se
Flooring Services
N.A.I.C.S.: 238330

Nordiska Fonster i Angelholm AB (2)
Lagegatan 24, 262 71, Angelholm, Sweden

Tel.: (46) 431371400
Web Site: https://www.nordiskafonster.se
Housing Furniture Whslr
N.A.I.C.S.: 444180
Jimmy Sandberg (CEO)

Polarpumpen AB (2)
Stora Avagen 19B, Askim, 436 34, Gothenburg, Sweden
Tel.: (46) 770777600
Web Site: https://www.polarpumpen.se
Emp.: 30
Heat Pump Distr
N.A.I.C.S.: 423730
Martin Gerre (CEO)

Subsidiary (Domestic):

Svensk Installationspartner AB (3)
Datavagen 14A, Askim, 436 32, Gothenburg, Sweden
Tel.: (46) 770220300
Web Site: http://www.installationspartner.se
Installation Services
N.A.I.C.S.: 238210
Carl Palsson (CEO)

Subsidiary (Domestic):

Vitvaruexperten.com Nordic AB (2)
Glimmervagen 10-12, 191 62, Sollentuna, Sweden
Tel.: (46) 20121340
Web Site: https://www.vitvaruexperten.com
Household Appliance Distr
N.A.I.C.S.: 449210

Dogger AB (1)
Stockholmsvagen 49, 761 43, Norrtalje, Sweden
Tel.: (46) 17614889
Web Site: https://www.dogger.se
Fishing Equipment Mfr & Distr
N.A.I.C.S.: 311710

ETR1 Group OU (1)
Lootsa 12. Tallinn. Estonia
Tel.: (372) 6346288
Web Site: https://www.moobel1.ee
Furniture Whslr
N.A.I.C.S.: 444180

Edututor Oy (1)
Kannistontie 5, 36620, Kangasala, Finland
Tel.: (358) 103226944
Web Site: https://www.edututor.fi
Emp.: 15
Online Marketing Services
N.A.I.C.S.: 541613
Ossi Jaaskelainen (Founder, CEO & Sls Mgr)

Eurotrade1 SIA (1)
Maskavas iela 497, Stopinu pagasts Ropazu novads Rumbula, Riga, 2121, Latvia
Tel.: (371) 22722280
Web Site: https://www.mebeles1.lv
Furniture Whslr
N.A.I.C.S.: 444180

Eurotrade1 d.o.o. (1)
Toplarniska ulica 1B, 1000, Ljubljana, Slovenia
Tel.: (386) 40675275
Web Site: https://www.pohistvo.si
Furniture Whslr
N.A.I.C.S.: 444180

Furniture1 Kft (1)
Hutyra Ferenc utca 11-15, 1074, Budapest, Hungary
Tel.: (36) 15507624
Web Site: https://www.butor1.hu
Furniture Whslr
N.A.I.C.S.: 444180

Furniture1 UAB (1)
Konstitucijos 21A, Vilnius, Lithuania
Tel.: (370) 68701110
Web Site: https://www.furniture1.eu
Emp.: 300
Housing Furniture Whslr
N.A.I.C.S.: 444180
Pijus Makarevicius (CEO)

Furniture1 d.o.o. (1)
Prosinacka ulica 3, Kerestinec, Zagreb, Croatia
Tel.: (385) 18000383
Web Site: https://www.namjestaj.hr
Furniture Whslr

N.A.I.C.S.: 444180

Golvpoolen Helsingborg AB　(1)
Garnisonsgatan 18, 254 66, Helsingborg,
Sweden
Tel.: (46) 424507770
Bathroom & Tile Product Distr
N.A.I.C.S.: 444180

Hemmy AB　(1)
Lagervagen 7, 136 50, Jordbro, Sweden
Tel.: (46) 103302012
Web Site: https://hemmy.se
Online Household Appliance Distr
N.A.I.C.S.: 423620

Hylte Jakt & Lantman AB　(1)
Hantverksgatan 15, 314 34, Hyltebruk,
Sweden
Tel.: (46) 34540000
Web Site: https://www.hylte-lantman.com
Fishing Goods Store Services
N.A.I.C.S.: 711211

IP-Agency Finland Oy　(1)
Honkanummentie 13, 01380, Vantaa, Fin-
land
Tel.: (358) 103229330
Web Site: https://ip-agency.fi
Sports Store Operator
N.A.I.C.S.: 711211

Lampgallerian i Vaxjo AB　(1)
Harlovsvagen 21, 352 50, Vaxjo, Sweden
Tel.: (46) 47060935
Web Site: https://www.lampgallerian.se
Electrical Light Whslr
N.A.I.C.S.: 423610

Lindstrom & Sonden AB　(1)
Haysbadvagen 1, 262 63, Angelholm, Swe-
den
Tel.: (46) 101011656
Web Site:
　　https://lindstromsondenab.teamtailor.com
Emp.: 40
Ecommerce Services
N.A.I.C.S.: 322291

M & M Visions Oy　(1)
Junailijankatu 15, 11100, Riihimaki, Finland
Tel.: (358) 405574070
Web Site: https://www.talotarvike.com
Household Appliance Distr
N.A.I.C.S.: 449210

Maskinklippet AB　(1)
Byggesvagen 4, 375 32, Morrum, Sweden
Tel.: (46) 45450590
Web Site: https://www.maskinklippet.se
Emp.: 16
Online Shopping Services
N.A.I.C.S.: 531120

Mebeli24 OOD　(1)
Henrik Ibsen 17, Sofia, Bulgaria
Tel.: (359) 896709455
Furniture Whslr
N.A.I.C.S.: 444180

Navitek Oy　(1)
Vaunusepantie 4, 68660, Pietarsaari, Fin-
land
Tel.: (358) 445123744
Web Site: https://www.navitek.fi
Department Store Services
N.A.I.C.S.: 517122

Netrauta Finland Oy　(1)
Junailijankatu 15, Lempaala, 11100, Riihi-
maki, Finland
Tel.: (358) 291800220
Web Site: https://www.netrauta.fi
Emp.: 200
Home Construction Product Distr
N.A.I.C.S.: 444180

Nordic Nest AB　(1)
Stampelvagen 3, 394 70, Kalmar, Sweden
Tel.: (46) 480449920
Web Site: https://www.nordicnest.com
Home Decor Product Worldwide Whslr
N.A.I.C.S.: 423220

Noro AB　(1)
Box 525, 301 80, Halmstad, Sweden
Tel.: (46) 35166430
Web Site: https://www.noro.se
Bathroom Furniture Mfr & Distr
N.A.I.C.S.: 326199

Taloon Yhtiot Oy　(1)

Junailijankatu 15, 11100, Riihimaki, Finland
Tel.: (358) 104409200
Web Site: https://www.taloon.com
Building Materials Distr
N.A.I.C.S.: 444180

**BHG RETAIL TRUST MANAGE-
MENT PTE. LTD.**
250 North Bridge Road Raffles City
Tower No 32-01, Singapore, 179101,
Singapore
Tel.: (65) 68058288　　　　　　SG
Web Site: https://www.bhgreit.com
Year Founded: 2015
Retail Property Owner & Operator
N.A.I.C.S.: 459999
Jeff Tan *(Mgr-Compliance)*

BHI CO., LTD.
122 Jangbaek-ro Gunbuk-myeon, Ha-
man, 52063, Gyeongsangnam-do,
Korea (South)
Tel.: (82) 555853800
Web Site: https://www.bhi.co.kr
Year Founded: 1998
083650—(KRS)
Rev.: $253,261,183
Assets: $344,670,114
Liabilities: $306,674,045
Net Worth: $37,996,069
Earnings: ($14,663,319)
Emp.: 412
Fiscal Year-end: 12/31/22
Boiler & Heat Exchanger Mfr
N.A.I.C.S.: 332410
Woo Jong-In *(Dir-Rep)*

BHI HOLDINGS INC.
22nd Floor The Pearlbank Center
146 Valero Street Salcedo Village,
Makati, 1227, Philippines
Tel.: (63) 8171406　　　　　　　PH
Web Site: http://www.bhi-
　　holdings.com
Year Founded: 1963
BH—(PHI)
Rev.: $65,358
Assets: $2,145,165
Liabilities: $110,059
Net Worth: $2,035,106
Earnings: ($8,797)
Fiscal Year-end: 12/31/20
Investment Services
N.A.I.C.S.: 523940
Manuel N. Tankiansee *(Chm)*

**BHILAI ENGINEERING CORP
LTD.**
Industrial Area, Hathkhoj Village Durg
Dist, Bhilai, 490026, Chhattisgarh,
India
Tel.: (91) 7884088100
Web Site: http://www.bec-group.com
Year Founded: 1960
Engineering & Construction Services
N.A.I.C.S.: 541330
Veenu Jain *(Mng Dir)*

**BHILWARA SPINNERS LIM-
ITED**
26 Industrial Area, Post Box No 6,
Gandhi Nagar, Bhilwara, 311001, Ra-
jasthan, India
Tel.: (91) 1482246600
514272—(BOM)
Rev.: $500,559
Assets: $3,317,377
Liabilities: $188,237
Net Worth: $3,129,140
Earnings: $147,783
Emp.: 2
Fiscal Year-end: 03/31/21
Yarn Mfr
N.A.I.C.S.: 313110
Bhopal Singh Choudhary *(CFO)*

**BHILWARA TECHNICAL TEX-
TILES LIMITED**
LNJ Nagar Mordi, Banswara, 327001,
Rajasthan, India
Tel.: (91) 2961231251
Web Site: https://www.bttl.co.in
533108—(BOM)
Sales Range: Less than $1 Million
Textile Products Mfr & Distr
N.A.I.C.S.: 314999
Shekhar Agarwal *(Chm, CEO & Mng
Dir)*

**BHIRAJ OFFICE LEASEHOLD
REIT**
591 United Business Center II Build-
ing 7th floor Sukhumvit Road, Klong-
ton Nuea Vadhana, Bangkok, 10110,
Thailand
Tel.: (66) 22610170
Web Site: https://www.bofficereit.com
BOFFICE—(THA)
Rev.: $26,314,155
Assets: $284,047,627
Liabilities: $74,362,297
Net Worth: $209,685,331
Earnings: ($4,358,912)
Emp.: 16
Fiscal Year-end: 12/31/23
Real Estate Investment Services
N.A.I.C.S.: 531390
Prapee Buri *(Chm)*

**BHM CAPITAL FINANCIAL
SERVICES PSC**
49th Floor Vision Tower Business
Bay, PO Box 26730, Dubai, United
Arab Emirates
Tel.: (971) 45247555　　　　　AE
Web Site: https://www.bhmuae.ae
Year Founded: 2006
BHMCAPITAL—(DFM)
Rev.: $37,227,021
Assets: $332,336,853
Liabilities: $270,688,478
Net Worth: $61,648,375
Earnings: $9,623,301
Fiscal Year-end: 12/31/23
Securities Brokerage Services
N.A.I.C.S.: 523150
Al Hurr Mohammad Al Suwaidi *(Chm)*

BHORUKA ALUMINIUM LTD.
427E 2nd Floor Hebbal Industrial
Area, Mysore, 570016, Karnataka,
India
Tel.: (91) 821 2510351　　　　　In
Web Site:
　　http://www.bhorukaaluminium.com
Year Founded: 1979
Rev.: $294
Assets: $4,027,398
Liabilities: $2,331,832
Net Worth: $1,695,566
Earnings: ($119,837)
Fiscal Year-end: 03/31/19
Aluminium Products Mfr
N.A.I.C.S.: 331410
Raj Kumar Aggarwal *(Chm & Mng
Dir)*

Subsidiaries:

Bhoruka Fabcons Private Limited　(1)
427E Hebbal Industrial Area, Mysore,
570016, Karnataka, India
Tel.: (91) 8212510351
Web Site: http://www.bhorukafabcons.com
Sales Range: $25-49.9 Million
Emp.: 40
Aluminium Products Mfr
N.A.I.C.S.: 331318
Prakash Chandra *(Mgr)*

Maverick Infotec　(1)
1 K R S Rd, Metagalli, Mysore, 570016,
Karnataka, India
Tel.: (91) 8212582625

Sales Range: $25-49.9 Million
Emp.: 30
SAP Project Management Services
N.A.I.C.S.: 541618
A. Raj Kumar *(Exec Dir)*

BHP GROUP LIMITED
171 Collins Street, Melbourne, 3000,
VIC, Australia
Tel.: (61) 396093333　　　　　　AU
Web Site: https://www.bhp.com
Year Founded: 1851
BHP—(NYSE)
Rev.: $55,658,000,000
Assets: $102,362,000,000
Liabilities: $53,242,000,000
Net Worth: $49,120,000,000
Earnings: $9,601,000,000
Emp.: 38,962
Fiscal Year-end: 06/30/24
Holding Company; Petroleum, Coal,
Diamond, Ferrous & Non-Ferrous
Metals Exploring, Drilling, Mining &
Processing Operations
N.A.I.C.S.: 551112
Athalie Williams *(Chief People Offi-
cer)*

Subsidiaries:

**BHP Billiton International Trading
(Shanghai) Co. Ltd.**　(1)
Level 12 Link Square 1 222 Hubin Road,
Shanghai, 200021, China
Tel.: (86) 2161227000
Mining Services
N.A.I.C.S.: 213113

BHP Group Plc　(1)
Nova South 160 Victoria Street, London,
SW1E 5LB, United Kingdom
Tel.: (44) 2078024000
Web Site: http://www.bhpbilliton.com
Rev.: $61,326,999,999
Assets: $108,926,999,999
Liabilities: $53,321,999,999
Net Worth: $55,604,999,999
Earnings: $11,303,999,999
Emp.: 79,999
Fiscal Year-end: 06/30/2021
Petroleum, Coal, Diamond, Ferrous & Non-
Ferrous Metals Exploring, Drilling, Mining &
Processing Operations
N.A.I.C.S.: 211120
Athalie Williams *(Chief People Officer)*

Subsidiary (Non-US):

BHP Billiton China　(2)
One Corporate Ave 222 Hubin Rd, Level
12, Shanghai, 200021, China
Tel.: (86) 2161227000
Web Site: http://www.bhpbilliton.com
Sales Range: $50-74.9 Million
Emp.: 70
Petroleum, Coal, Diamond, Ferrous & Non-
Ferrous Metals Exploring, Drilling, Mining &
Processing Marketing Operations
N.A.I.C.S.: 212210

Division (Non-US):

BHP Billiton Petroleum Pty. Ltd.　(2)
Level 34 120 Collins Street, Melbourne,
3000, VIC, Australia　　　　(100%)
Tel.: (61) 448098943
Sales Range: $75-99.9 Million
Emp.: 200
N.A.I.C.S.: 212210

Subsidiary (Non-US):

BHP Billiton (Bolivia), Inc.　(3)
Km 3 5 Antigua Carretera A Cochabamba,
Casilla, 3568, Santa Cruz, Bolivia　(100%)
Tel.: (591) 133546404
N.A.I.C.S.: 212210

Subsidiary (US):

**BHP Billiton Petroleum (Americas)
Inc.**　(3)
BHP Twr 1360 Post Oak Blvd Ste 150,
Houston, TX 77056　　　　　(100%)
Tel.: (713) 961-8500
Web Site: http://www.bhpbilliton.com

BHP Group Limited—(Continued)

Oil & Gas Exploration, Development & Production
N.A.I.C.S.: 213112

Division (Non-US):

BHP Minerals (2)
171 Collins Street, Melbourne, 3000, VIC, Australia (100%)
Tel.: (61) 396093333
Sales Range: $150-199.9 Million
Emp.: 350
N.A.I.C.S.: 212210

Subsidiary (Domestic):

BHP Billiton Iron Ore Pty. Ltd. (3)
125 St Georges Terrace, Perth, 6000, WA, Australia
Tel.: (61) 863210000
Sales Range: $700-749.9 Million
Iron Ore Mining
N.A.I.C.S.: 212210
Edgar Basto (Pres)

BHP Billiton Nickel West Pty. Ltd. (3)
BHP Billiton Centre 180 Lonsdale Street, Melbourne, 3000, VIC, Australia (100%)
Tel.: (61) 1300554757
Web Site: http://www.bhpbilliton.com
Nickel, Uranium Oxide, Copper & Gold Miner; Fertilizer Mfr
N.A.I.C.S.: 212230

Subsidiary (Domestic):

Olympic Dam Corporation Pty Ltd. (4)
Roxby, PO Box 150, Downs, 5725, SA, Australia
Tel.: (61) 886718888
Web Site: http://www.bhpbilliton.com
Sales Range: $1-4.9 Billion
Emp.: 2,880
Copper, Uranium Oxide, Gold & Silver Miner
N.A.I.C.S.: 212230

Subsidiary (Domestic):

BHP Coal Pty. Ltd. (3)
180 Lonsdale Street, Melbourne, 3000, VIC, Australia
Tel.: (61) 396093333
Web Site: http://www.bhpbilliton.com
Sales Range: $350-399.9 Million
Emp.: 650
Coal Mining
N.A.I.C.S.: 212115

BHP Titanium Minerals (3)
180 Lonsdale St, Melbourne, 3000, VIC, Australia (100%)
Tel.: (61) 396093333
Sales Range: $200-249.9 Million
Emp.: 300
N.A.I.C.S.: 212210

Delta End Australia Pty. Ltd. (3)
Steel River Industrial Estate Lot 16 Mcintosh Dr, PO Box 249, Mayfield, 2304, NSW, Australia
Tel.: (61) 249411500
Web Site: http://www.deltaplc.com
Sales Range: $50-74.9 Million
Emp.: 95
N.A.I.C.S.: 212210

Division (Non-US):

Billiton Base Metals (2)
120 Adelaide St W Ste 2600, Toronto, M5H 1W5, ON, Canada
Tel.: (416) 367-4000
Web Site: http://www.rioalgom.com
Sales Range: $700-749.9 Million
Emp.: 2,774
Mining & Metals Distribution Company
N.A.I.C.S.: 333131

Subsidiary (Non-US):

Compania Minera Cerro Colorado Limitada (3)
Avenida Americo Vespucio Sur No 100 Piso 10, Las Condes, 7580 154, Santiago, Chile (100%)
Tel.: (56) 23305851

Web Site: http://www.bhp.com
Sales Range: $50-74.9 Million
Emp.: 4
N.A.I.C.S.: 212210

Subsidiary (Domestic):

Metaux Billiton Canada Incorporated (2)
Les Mines Selbaie, Villebois, J0Z 3V0, QC, Canada (100%)
Tel.: (819) 756-2491
Sales Range: $75-99.9 Million
Emp.: 125
Copper Ores Mining Company
N.A.I.C.S.: 212230

Rio Algom Inc. (3)
PO Box 38, Elliot Lake, PSA 256, ON, Canada
Tel.: (705) 848-0111
Web Site: http://www.rioalgom.com
Sales Range: $50-74.9 Million
Emp.: 1
Minerals Exploration
N.A.I.C.S.: 213113

Subsidiary (Non-US):

P.T. BHP Indonesia (2)
Midplaza Bldg 3rd Fl JL Jend Sudirman Kav 11, Jakarta, 12910, Indonesia (55%)
Tel.: (62) 215706281
Web Site: http://www.bhpbilliton.com
Sales Range: $50-74.9 Million
Emp.: 15
N.A.I.C.S.: 212210

BHP Shared Services Malaysia Sdn. Bhd. (3)
Level 35 Menara Southpoint Mid Valley City Medan Syed Putra Selatan, 59200, Kuala Lumpur, Malaysia
Tel.: (60) 320376188
N.A.I.C.S.: 213114

BHP Shared Services Philippines Inc. (1)
Levels 23 - 27 Arthaland Century Pacific Tower 5th Avenue Corner, 30th Street Corner 4th Avenue Bonifacio Global City Metro Manila, Taguig, Philippines
Tel.: (63) 289670010
N.A.I.C.S.: 213114

OZ Minerals Limited (1)
2 Hamra Drive, PO Box 248, Adelaide, 5950, SA, Australia
Tel.: (61) 882296600
Web Site: http://www.ozminerals.com
Rev.: $1,028,456,837
Assets: $3,643,999,640
Liabilities: $1,183,457,074
Net Worth: $2,460,542,566
Earnings: $162,891,994
Emp.: 785
Fiscal Year-end: 12/31/2020
Zinc, Lead & Silver Mining, Smelting & Refining
N.A.I.C.S.: 212230
Rebecca Joy McGrath (Chm)

Subsidiary (Domestic):

Cassini Resources Limited (2)
Ground Floor 16 Ord Street, West Perth, 6005, WA, Australia
Tel.: (61) 861648900
Web Site:
   http://www.cassiniresources.com.au
Rev.: $302,125
Assets: $16,331,225
Liabilities: $3,612,025
Net Worth: $12,719,200
Earnings: ($2,656,315)
Fiscal Year-end: 06/30/2019
Metal Mining
N.A.I.C.S.: 212290
Gregory James Miles (COO)

Subsidiary (US):

Lynx Resources (US) Inc. (3)
40 W Main St Ct Ste 250C, Alpine, UT 84004
Tel.: (801) 642-2254
Gold Exploration Services
N.A.I.C.S.: 213114

Subsidiary (Non-US):

OZ Minerals Insurance Pte. Ltd. (2)

Marsh & McLennan Ctr, 18 Cross St No 04-00, Singapore, 048423, Singapore
Tel.: (65) 62208141
Gold Mining & Exploration Services
N.A.I.C.S.: 212220

Subsidiary (Domestic):

OZ Minerals Prominent Hill Pty Ltd (2)
Ground Fl, 170 Greenhill Rd, Parkside, 5063, South Australia, Australia
Tel.: (61) 882296600
Web Site: http://www.ozminerals.com
Sales Range: $50-74.9 Million
Emp.: 60
Gold Mining Services
N.A.I.C.S.: 212220

BHUDEVI INFRA PROJECTS LTD.
1 8 303/48/13 Arya One 3rd Floor Prenderghast Road Sardar Patel Rd, Hyderabad, 500003, India
Tel.: (91) 4046031001
Web Site:
   https://www.bhudeviprojects.com
Year Founded: 1992
526488—(BOM)
Rev.: $38,548
Assets: $601
Liabilities: $77,873
Net Worth: ($77,273)
Earnings: $27,314
Fiscal Year-end: 03/31/22
Yarn Mfr
N.A.I.C.S.: 313110
Anitha Sakuru (Mng Dir)

BHUTAN NATIONAL BANK LIMITED
Nordzin Lam II, PO Box 439, Thimphu, Bhutan
Tel.: (975) 2322767
Web Site: http://www.bnb.bt
BNBL—(BHU)
Rev.: $50,761,506
Assets: $721,650,164
Liabilities: $636,285,117
Net Worth: $85,365,047
Earnings: $15,202,780
Emp.: 563
Fiscal Year-end: 12/31/22
Banking Services
N.A.I.C.S.: 522110
Sonam Lhundrup Tobgay (CEO & Head-OSM & Strategy Mgmt Dept)

BI PURE WATER INC.
Unit 2 9790 190th Street, Surrey, V4N 3M9, BC, Canada
Tel.: (604) 882-6650
Web Site:
   https://www.bipurewater.com
Year Founded: 1995
Water Purification Services
N.A.I.C.S.: 221310
Scott Foster (Pres)

BI-INVEST ADVISORS S.A.
51 Avenue J F Kennedy, 1855, Luxembourg, Luxembourg
Tel.: (352) 260 9531   LU
Web Site: http://www.bi-invest.com
Investment & Financial Advisory Services
N.A.I.C.S.: 523999
Kader Derrouiche (Controller-Fin)

Subsidiaries:

InvestIndustrial S.A. (1)
23 Avenue Monterey, Luxembourg, L-2163, Luxembourg
Tel.: (352) 260 9531
Web Site: http://www.investindustrial.com
Private Equity Investment & Asset Management Firm
N.A.I.C.S.: 523999

Holding (Non-US):

Artsana S.p.A. (2)
Via Saldarini Catelli 1, 22070, Grandate, Italy (60%)
Tel.: (39) 0800188898
Web Site: http://www.artsana.com
Sales Range: $1-9.9 Million
Health & Beauty Care Products & Baby Products Mfr
N.A.I.C.S.: 325620
Michele Catelli (Chm)

Subsidiary (Non-US):

ARTSANA FRANCE S.A.S. (3)
17/19 avenue de la Metallurgie, 93210, Saint Denis, La Plaine, France
Tel.: (33) 0155932640
Web Site: http://www.chicco.fr
Health & Infant Product Distr
N.A.I.C.S.: 456191

Artsana Argentina S.A. (3)
Uruguay 4501, Victoria, Buenos Aires, Argentina
Tel.: (54) 8108882442
Web Site: http://www.chicco.com.ar
Health & Infant Product Distr
N.A.I.C.S.: 456191
Carlos Melatini (Gen Mgr)

Artsana Belgium SA (3)
Temselaan 5, 1853, Strombeek-Bever, Belgium
Tel.: (32) 2 300 82 40
Web Site: http://www.chicco.be
Health & Infant Product Distr
N.A.I.C.S.: 456191

Artsana Germany GmbH (3)
Borsigstrasse 1-3, D-63128, Dietzenbach, Germany
Tel.: (49) 1805 780005
Web Site: http://www.chicco.de
Health & Infant Product Distr
N.A.I.C.S.: 456191
Caroline Eva Meissner (Sr Product Mgr)

Artsana Portugal, S.A. (3)
Rua humberto Madeira 9, Queluz de Baixo, 2730-097, Barcarena, Portugal
Tel.: (351) 800201977
Web Site: http://www.chicco.pt
Health & Infant Product Distr
N.A.I.C.S.: 456191
Vera Vieira (Area Mgr)

Artsana Spain S.A.U. (3)
C/industria 10 Poligono industrial urtinsa, Alcorcon, 28923, Madrid, Spain
Tel.: (34) 902 117093
Web Site: http://www.chicco.es
Health & Infant Product Distr
N.A.I.C.S.: 456191

Artsana Suisse S.A. (3)
Via Cantonale 2b, 6928, Manno, Switzerland
Tel.: (41) 91935 50 80
Web Site: http://www.chicco.ch
Health & Infant Product Distr
N.A.I.C.S.: 456191

Artsana Turkey Bebek ve Saglik Urunleri A.S. (3)
Sok Kat 12 No 4/1 Icerenkoy, Istanbul, Turkiye
Tel.: (90) 2165703030
Web Site: http://www.chicco.com.tr
Health & Infant Product Distr
N.A.I.C.S.: 456191

Subsidiary (US):

Artsana USA, Inc. (3)
1826 William Penn Way, Lancaster, PA 17601
Web Site: http://www.chiccousa.com
Health & Infant Product Distr
N.A.I.C.S.: 456191
Dan Kilgore (Mktg Dir-Soft Goods)

Subsidiary (Domestic):

Prenatal Retail Group S.p.A. (3)
Via delle Primule n 5, 20815, Cogliate, Italy (100%)
Tel.: (39) 02964621
Web Site: https://prenatalretailgroup.com

Children & Infants Clothing Store; Baby
Products & Toys Whslr
N.A.I.C.S.: 458110

Subsidiary (US):

The Boppy Company, LLC.   **(3)**
560 Golden Ridge Rd Ste 150, Golden, CO
80401
Tel.: (720) 746-3820
Web Site: http://www.boppy.com
Baby Products Mfr & Distr
N.A.I.C.S.: 424350
Nancy Bartley *(CEO)*

Holding (Non-US):

Benvic Europe S.A.S.   **(2)**
57 Avenue de Tavaux, 21800, Chevigny-
Saint-Sauveur, France   **(100%)**
Tel.: (33) 3 8046 7300
Web Site: http://www.benvic.com
Thermoplastics Mfr
N.A.I.C.S.: 326199
Philippe Gressier *(Comml Dir)*

Subsidiary (Non-US):

Benvic Europe IBE SL   **(3)**
Carretera La Roca Besos 4-6, 08170, Mon-
tornes del Valles, Barcelona,
Spain   **(100%)**
Tel.: (34) 935444212
Web Site: http://www.benvic.com
Thermoplastics Mfr
N.A.I.C.S.: 326199

Benvic Europe S.p.A.   **(3)**
Via Marconi 73, 44122, Ferrara,
Italy   **(100%)**
Tel.: (39) 05321910300
Web Site: http://www.benvic.com
Thermoplastics Mfr
N.A.I.C.S.: 326199

Holding (Non-US):

Perfume Holding S.p.A.   **(2)**
Strada Maretto 13, Roncopascolo, 43126,
Parma, Italy
Tel.: (39) 0521 662 111
Web Site: http://www.perfumeholding.com
Perfume Mfr & Distr
N.A.I.C.S.: 325199

Subsidiary (Non-US):

MSB Perfume Holding Diffusion
GmbH   **(3)**
Kormorangweg 1, 65201, Wiesbaden, Ger-
many
Tel.: (49) 611 9 28 56 0
Perfume Distr
N.A.I.C.S.: 424210

MSB Perfume Holdings Ltd.   **(3)**
Albion House Office 11 1st Floor Chertsey
Road, Woking, GU21 6BD, Surrey, United
Kingdom
Tel.: (44) 1483 755 772
Perfume Distr
N.A.I.C.S.: 424210

Perfume Holding Asia Pte Ltd   **(3)**
Tai Seng Street 12 05-01 Luxasia Bld,
534118, Singapore, Singapore
Tel.: (65) 6 280 9559
Perfume Distr
N.A.I.C.S.: 424210

Subsidiary (US):

Perfume Holding Corp.   **(3)**
60 Broad St Ste 3502, New York, NY 10004
Tel.: (646) 356-0479
Perfume Distr
N.A.I.C.S.: 424210

Subsidiary (Non-US):

Perfume Holding LLC   **(3)**
17 Neglinnaya street bld 2 office 301, Mos-
cow, Russia
Tel.: (7) 495 5310965
Perfume Distr
N.A.I.C.S.: 424210

Perfume Holding SAS   **(3)**
Rue d Astorg 12, 75008, Paris, France
Tel.: (33) 143 120 750
Perfume Distr
N.A.I.C.S.: 424210

Holding (Non-US):

Port Aventura Entertainment,
S.A.U.   **(2)**
Avda Alcalde Pere Molas km 2, 43480,
Tarragona, Spain
Tel.: (34) 977 779 000
Web Site: http://www.portaventura.co.uk
Resort Operator
N.A.I.C.S.: 721120

Sergio Rossi S.p.A.   **(2)**
Via Montenapoleone 27, Milan, Italy
Tel.: (39) 0276006140
Web Site: http://www.sergiorossi.com
Adult Footwear & Handbag Designer Distr
& Retailer
N.A.I.C.S.: 458210
Dimitri Ferroni *(Dir-Retail)*

BIA OVERSEAS S.A.

200 Rue du Cerf 200, 1332, Genval,
Belgium, Belgium
Tel.: (32) 26892811
Web Site: http://www.biagroup.com
Sales Range: $250-299.9 Million
Emp.: 3,000
Mining & Quarrying Equipment Distr
N.A.I.C.S.: 423810
Vincent Bia *(CEO)*

Subsidiaries:

BIA Burkina sarl   **(1)**
01 Voie B N 259 ZAD Secteur 15, BP 5620,
Ouagadougou, Burkina Faso
Tel.: (226) 50377440
Construction Equipment Distr
N.A.I.C.S.: 423810
Eric Perben nomme *(Gen Mgr)*

BIA Cameroon   **(1)**
Z I de Bassa Ex base Sumoca Rue du
complexe CCC, BP 1935, Douala, Camer-
oon
Tel.: (237) 33397620
Construction Equipment Distr
N.A.I.C.S.: 423810
Remi Auge *(Dir-Comml)*

BIA Cote d'Ivoire   **(1)**
Rue Louis Lumieres Zone 4, Abidjan, Cote
d'Ivoire
Tel.: (225) 21358541
Construction Equipment Distr
N.A.I.C.S.: 423810
Bia Romain *(Country-Mgr)*

BIA Guinee s.a.   **(1)**
BP 732, Kipe Ratoma, 030, Conakry,
Guinea
Tel.: (224) 621356635
Construction Equipment Distr
N.A.I.C.S.: 423810

BIA Pointe Noire   **(1)**
KM4 Route Aeroport, BP 5429, Pointe
Noire, Congo, Republic of
Tel.: (242) 69385352
Construction Equipment Distr
N.A.I.C.S.: 423810
Eric Perben nomme *(Gen Mgr)*

BIA Togo   **(1)**
Siege Social 13 rue du commerce, BP 346,
Lome, Togo
Tel.: (228) 2213286
Web Site: http://www.biat.tg
Commercial Banking Services
N.A.I.C.S.: 522110

BIA Zambia   **(1)**
Karibu Business Park Plot 2335, PO Box
28054, Kitwe, 10101, Ndola, Zambia
Tel.: (260) 68347476
Construction Equipment Distr
N.A.I.C.S.: 423810
Eric Perben nomme *(Gen Mgr)*

BIA b.v./s.a.   **(1)**
Skagerrakstraat 6, 7202, Zutphen, Nether-
lands
Tel.: (31) 883032200
Web Site:
   http://www.netherlands.biagroup.com
Construction Equipment Distr
N.A.I.C.S.: 423810

BIA n.v./s.a.   **(1)**

Rameistraat 123, 3090, Overijse, Belgium
Tel.: (32) 26892811
Web Site: http://www.belgium.biagroup.com
Construction Equipment Distr
N.A.I.C.S.: 423810
Quentin Scouflaire *(Gen Mgr)*

Equipements & Service Mauritanie
sarl   **(1)**
Ilot B 151 Nord, Tevragh Zeina, Nouakchott,
Mauritania
Tel.: (222) 45252394
Construction Equipment Distr
N.A.I.C.S.: 423810

Equipements & Services BIA   **(1)**
Level 2 Nexteracom Tower 1 Cybercity,
Ebene, Mauritius
Tel.: (230) 4026700
Construction Equipment Distr
N.A.I.C.S.: 423810

Equipements & Services Niamey   **(1)**
675 Rue IB-42 Yantala, BP 559, Niamey,
Niger
Tel.: (227) 23900379
Construction Equipment Distr
N.A.I.C.S.: 811310
Eric Perben nomme *(Gen Mgr)*

Metalubia   **(1)**
Boulevard du 1er Novembre, BP 3028, Bu-
jumbura, Burundi
Tel.: (257) 22213775
Construction Equipment Distr
N.A.I.C.S.: 423810
Eric Perben nomme *(Gen Mgr)*

BIAFO INDUSTRIES LIMITED

1st Floor Biafo House Plot No 23 St
No 38-40, I&T Centre G-10/4, Islam-
abad, Pakistan
Tel.: (92) 512353450
Web Site: https://www.biafo.com
BIFO—(KAR)
Rev.: $10,120,773
Assets: $16,314,981
Liabilities: $6,225,360
Net Worth: $10,089,621
Earnings: $2,584,025
Emp.: 210
Fiscal Year-end: 06/30/19
Industrial & Commercial Explosives
Mfr
N.A.I.C.S.: 325920
M. Humayun Khan *(Chm)*

BIALETTI INDUSTRIE S.P.A.

Via Fogliano 1 Coccaglio, 25030,
Brescia, Italy
Tel.: (39) 0307720011   IT
Web Site: https://bialetti.com
Year Founded: 1919
BIA—(ITA)
Sales Range: Less than $1 Million
Housewares Mfr & Sales
N.A.I.C.S.: 335210

BIANCAMANO S.P.A.

Strada 4 Palazzo Q6 Milanofiori,
20089, Rozzano, MI, Italy
Tel.: (39) 02528682225
Web Site:
   http://www.gruppobiancamano.it
Year Founded: 2004
BCM—(ITA)
Sales Range: Less than $1 Million
Emp.: 2,000
Holding Company; Environmental
Services
N.A.I.C.S.: 551112
Giovanni Battista Pizzimbone *(Pres &
Mng Dir)*

Subsidiaries:

Aimeri Ambiente Srl   **(1)**
Strada 4 - Palazzo Q6, Milanofiori, 20089,
Rozzano, Italy   **(99.95%)**
Tel.: (39) 025286821
Web Site: http://www.aimeriambiente.it

Sales Range: $25-49.9 Million
Emp.: 80
Solid Waste Collection
N.A.I.C.S.: 562111

Ponticelli S.R.L.   **(1)**
Via Don Abbo il Santo 12/15, 18100, Impe-
ria, Italy
Tel.: (39) 0183720205
Solid Waste Disposal Services
N.A.I.C.S.: 562219

BIANOR HOLDING AD

Syergy Tower 15th Floor Tsarigradsko
Shose Blvd, 1784, Sofia, Bulgaria
Tel.: (359) 889255075
Web Site: https://www.bianor-
   holding.bg
Year Founded: 1998
BNR—(BUL)
Sales Range: Less than $1 Million
Mobile Application Development Ser-
vices
N.A.I.C.S.: 541511
Metodi Filipov *(Mng Dir-Bianor Inc-
US)*

BIAO-COTE D'IVOIRE

8-10 Avenue Joseph Anoma, BP
1274, Abidjan, 01, Cote d'Ivoire
Tel.: (225) 20200702   CI
Web Site: http://www.biao.co.ci
Year Founded: 1980
Sales Range: $10-24.9 Million
Emp.: 650
Commercial Banking Services
N.A.I.C.S.: 522110
Deajou Jean *(Pres)*

BIBBINSTRUMENTS AB

Scheeletorget 1 building 405, Medi-
con Village, 223 81, Lund, Sweden
Tel.: (46) 708999486
Web Site:
   https://www.bibbinstruments.com
Year Founded: 2013
V0R—(DEU)
Medical Equipment Distr
N.A.I.C.S.: 423450
Charles Walther *(Founder)*

BIBBY LINE GROUP LIMITED

105 Duke Street, Liverpool, L1 5JQ,
United Kingdom
Tel.: (44) 151 708 8000
Web Site:
   http://www.bibbylinegroup.co.uk
Year Founded: 2007
Sales Range: $1-4.9 Billion
Emp.: 4,000
Holding Company; Financial, Logis-
tics & Shipping
N.A.I.C.S.: 551112
Paul Drechsler *(Chm)*

Subsidiaries:

Bibby Financial Services Limited   **(1)**
105 Duke Street, Liverpool, L1 5JQ, United
Kingdom
Tel.: (44) 151 708 8000
Financial Services
N.A.I.C.S.: 525990
Blake Kennedy *(Head-Sls-South)*

Subsidiary (Non-US):

Bibby Factor France S.A.   **(2)**
158 Avenue Thiers CS 70033, 69454, Lyon,
Cedex, France
Tel.: (33) 472131857
Web Site:
   http://www.bibbyfinancialservices.fr
Financial, Logistics & Shipping Services
N.A.I.C.S.: 523940

Bibby Factoring Services (Malaysia)
Sdn Bhd   **(2)**
Lot 1B Podium 1 Menara Ansar 65 Jalan
Trus, Johor Bahru, 8000, Johor, Malaysia
Tel.: (60) 607 2185 168
Web Site: http://www.bibbyfs.my

Bibby Line Group Limited—(Continued)

Financial Lending Services
N.A.I.C.S.: 525990

Bibby Factoring Slovakia a.s. (2)
Prievozska 4D, 821 09, Bratislava, Slovakia
Tel.: (421) 2 32 780 056
Web Site:
http://www.bibbyfinancialservices.sk
Financial Lending Services
N.A.I.C.S.: 525990

Bibby Financial Services (Asia)
Limited (2)
Unit 2302 23/F Jubilee Centre 18 Fenwick
Street, Wanchai, China (Hong Kong)
Tel.: (852) 3759 0333
Web Site:
http://www.bibbyfinancialservices.hk
Financial Lending Services
N.A.I.C.S.: 525990

Subsidiary (US):

Bibby Financial Services (CA),
Inc (2)
2945 Townsgate Rd Ste 140, Westlake Vil-
lage, CA 91361-5868
Tel.: (805) 446-6111
Financial Advisory Services
N.A.I.C.S.: 523940

Subsidiary (Non-US):

Bibby Financial Services (Canada),
Inc (2)
4 Robert Speck Parkway Ste 310, Missis-
sauga, L4Z 1S1, ON, Canada
Tel.: (866) 502-4229
Web Site: http://www.bibbycanada.ca
Financial Lending Services
N.A.I.C.S.: 525990
Dan Millar (VP & Mgr-Portfolio)

Bibby Financial Services (India) Pvt
Limited (2)
First Floor Plot No 121 Institutional Area
Sector 44, Gurgaon, 122003, India
Tel.: (91) 124 4675300
Web Site:
http://www.bibbyfinancialservices.in
Financial Lending Services
N.A.I.C.S.: 525990
Vikas Nanda (Mng Dir)

Bibby Financial Services (Ireland)
Limited (2)
Fourth Floor Heather House Heather Road
Sandyford, Dublin, Ireland
Tel.: (353) 1 297 4911
Web Site:
http://www.bibbyfinancialservices.ie
Financial Lending Services
N.A.I.C.S.: 525990
Bernard O'Hare (Mng Dir)

Bibby Financial Services (Singapore)
Pte Limited (2)
6 Shenton Way OUE Downtown 2 18-08A,
Singapore, 068809, Singapore
Tel.: (65) 6922 5030
Web Site:
http://www.bibbyfinancialservices.sg
Financial Lending Services
N.A.I.C.S.: 525990

Bibby Financial Services AB (2)
Sveavagen 31, Stockholm, 111 31, Sweden
Tel.: (46) 8 402 36 30
Web Site:
http://www.bibbyfinancialservices.se
Financial, Logistics & Shipping Services
N.A.I.C.S.: 523940

Bibby Financial Services GmbH (2)
Hansaallee 249, 40549, Dusseldorf, Ger-
many
Tel.: (49) 211 520653 60
Web Site:
http://www.bibbyfinancialservices.de
Financial Lending Services
N.A.I.C.S.: 525990

Bibby Financial Services S.p. (2)
z.o.o.
ul Woloska 9a, 02-583, Warsaw, Poland
Tel.: (48) 22 545 61 23
Web Site:
http://www.bibbyfinancialservices.pl

Financial Lending Services
N.A.I.C.S.: 525990

Bibby Financial Services a.s. (2)
Hlinky 505/118, Brno, 603 00, Czech Re-
public
Tel.: (420) 228882376
Web Site:
http://www.bibbyfinancialservices.cz
Emp.: 23
Financial Lending Services
N.A.I.C.S.: 525990
Michal Gabriel (Mng Dir)

Bibby Holdings Limited (1)
105 Duke Street, Liverpool, L1 5JQ, United
Kingdom
Tel.: (44) 151 708 8000
Web Site: http://www.bibbyholdings.com
Investment Holding Company
N.A.I.C.S.: 551112

Bibby Line Limited (1)
105 Duke Street, Liverpool, L1 5JQ, United
Kingdom
Tel.: (44) 151 708 8000
Web Site: http://www.bibbyline.co.uk
Emp.: 3
Shipping Services
N.A.I.C.S.: 488510

Division (Domestic):

Bibby Line Limited (2)
The Baltic Exchange Saint Mary Axe, Lon-
don, EC3A 8BH, United Kingdom
Tel.: (44) 20 7621 1567
Shipping Services
N.A.I.C.S.: 488510

Bibby Marine Limited (1)
3rd Floor Walker House Exchange Flags,
Liverpool, L2 3YL, United Kingdom
Tel.: (44) 151 708 8000
Web Site: https://www.bibbymarine.com
Maritime Services
N.A.I.C.S.: 488390

Bibby Maritime Limited (1)
105 Duke Street, Liverpool, L1 5JQ, United
Kingdom
Tel.: (44) 151 708 8000
Web Site: http://www.bibbymaritime.com
Emp.: 25
Water Transportation Services
N.A.I.C.S.: 483111
Jon Osbourne (Mng Dir)

Bibby Maritime Limited (1)
72 Elder Place, Fremantle, 6160, WA, Aus-
tralia
Tel.: (61) 8 9239 0300
Web Site: http://www.bibbymaritime.com
Marine Shipping Services
N.A.I.C.S.: 488510

Garic Limited (1)
Kingfisher Park Aviation Road, Pilsworth,
Bury, BL9 8GD, Lancashire, United King-
dom
Tel.: (44) 161 766 8808
Web Site: http://www.garic.co.uk
Emp.: 15
Plant, Welfare & Servicing Equipment Mfr
N.A.I.C.S.: 333248

Woodland Burial Parks Group
Ltd. (1)
105 Duke Street, Liverpool, L1 5JQ, United
Kingdom
Tel.: (44) 151 708 8000
Web Site:
http://www.woodlandburialparks.co.uk
Funeral Parks
N.A.I.C.S.: 812210
Andrew Paling (Mng Dir)

BIBENDUM WINE LIMITED
113 Regents Park Road, London,
NW1 8UR, United Kingdom
Tel.: (44) 20 7449 4120
Web Site: http://www.bibendum-
wine.co.uk
Year Founded: 1982
Sales Range: $250-299.9 Million
Emp.: 256
Wine Whslr
N.A.I.C.S.: 424820
Simon Farr (Founder)

BIBLIU LTD.
All Saints Church Hall Carnegie St,
London, N1 9QW, United Kingdom
Tel.: (44) 2033221903   UK
Web Site: https://bibliu.com
Digital Content & Electronic Learning
Services
N.A.I.C.S.: 611710
David Sherwood (Founder & CEO)

Subsidiaries:

Texas Book Company Inc. (1)
8501 Tech Cir, Greenville, TX 75402
Tel.: (903) 455-6937
Web Site: http://www.texasbook.com
Sales Range: $10-24.9 Million
Emp.: 150
Book Stores
N.A.I.C.S.: 459210
Brent Dyer (CEO)

BIBOJEE SERVICES PRIVATE
LIMITED
Ghandhara House 109/2, Clifton, Ka-
rachi, Pakistan
Tel.: (92) 21 35830251 57
Web Site: http://www.bibojee.com.pk
Year Founded: 1981
Holding Company Services
N.A.I.C.S.: 551112
Raza Kuli Khan Khattak (Chm)

Subsidiaries:

Babri Cotton Mills Limited (1)
Deans Trade Center 145 & 146 3rd Floor
Saddar Road, Peshawar, Pakistan
Tel.: (92) 915286764
Web Site: http://www.bcm.com.pk
Rev.: $1,396,199
Assets: $6,617,260
Liabilities: $4,390,984
Net Worth: $2,226,276
Earnings: ($979,039)
Emp.: 3
Fiscal Year-end: 06/30/2021
Yarn Mfr
N.A.I.C.S.: 313110
Raza Kuli Khan Khattak (CEO)

Ghanadhara Industries Ltd. (1)
F-3 Hub Chauki Road SITE, Karachi,
75730, Pakistan
Tel.: (92) 2138709000
Web Site: https://www.gil.com.pk
Rev.: $52,316,983
Assets: $59,341,531
Liabilities: $29,762,367
Net Worth: $29,579,164
Earnings: $645,479
Emp.: 664
Fiscal Year-end: 06/30/2023
Motor Vehicle Chassis & Load Bodies Mfr
N.A.I.C.S.: 336390
Ahmed Kuli Khan Khattak (CEO)

Ghandhara Automobiles Limited (1)
F-3 Hub Chowki Road Site, Karachi, Paki-
stan
Tel.: (92) 2132556901
Web Site:
https://ghandharaautomobiles.com.pk
Rev.: $47,143,718
Assets: $45,410,596
Liabilities: $16,914,295
Net Worth: $28,496,301
Earnings: $624,264
Emp.: 1,060
Fiscal Year-end: 06/30/2023
Automotive Mfr & Distr
N.A.I.C.S.: 336110
Ali Kuli Khan Khattak (Pres)

The Universal Insurance Company
Limited (1)
63- Shahrah-e- Quaid-e- Azam, Lahore,
Pakistan
Tel.: (92) 4237353315
Web Site: https://uic.com.pk
Rev.: $160,004
Assets: $3,051,930
Liabilities: $679,480
Net Worth: $2,372,451
Earnings: ($550,183)
Emp.: 33
Fiscal Year-end: 12/31/2023

Insurance Management Services
N.A.I.C.S.: 524298
Raza Kuli Khan Khattak (Chm)

BIC CAMERA INC.
3-23-23 Takada, Toshima-ku, Tokyo,
171 0033, Japan
Tel.: (81) 339878785
Web Site:
https://www.biccamera.co.jp
Year Founded: 1978
3048—(TKS)
Rev.: $5,738,397,840
Assets: $2,974,702,560
Liabilities: $1,773,129,180
Net Worth: $1,201,573,380
Earnings: $86,507,760
Emp.: 10,200
Fiscal Year-end: 08/31/24
Audiovisual Products, Electrical
Home Appliances & Information Com-
munications Equipment Retailer
N.A.I.C.S.: 449210
Akiho Tetsu (Pres)

Subsidiaries:

Nippon BS Broadcasting
Corporation (1)
2-5 Kanda Surugadai, Chiyoda-ku, Tokyo,
101-0062, Japan
Tel.: (81) 335181800
Web Site: https://www.bs11.jp
Rev.: $76,139,020
Assets: $161,060,680
Liabilities: $14,281,120
Net Worth: $146,779,560
Earnings: $9,050,100
Emp.: 132
Fiscal Year-end: 08/31/2024.
Cable Television Broadcasting Services
N.A.I.C.S.: 516120
Toru Onodera (Pres & COO)

BICAPITAL CORPORATION
Federico Boyd Avenue No 18 & 51st
Street, Scotia Plaza 11th Floor,
Panama, Panama
Tel.: (507) 396 9872   Pa
Web Site:
http://www.corporationbi.com
Year Founded: 2006
Emp.: 11,941
Holding Company; Financial Services
N.A.I.C.S.: 551112
Julio Ramiro Castillo Arevalo (Vice
Chm)

BICECORP SA
Av Apoquindo n 3846 Piso 17, Las
Condes, Chile
Tel.: (56) 226922000   CL
Web Site: https://www.bicecorp.com
Year Founded: 1978
BICECORP—(SGO)
Assets: $20,305,361,649
Liabilities: $18,714,358,765
Net Worth: $1,591,002,884
Earnings: $258,150,626
Emp.: 3,021
Fiscal Year-end: 12/31/23
Commercial Banking Services
N.A.I.C.S.: 522110
L. Bernardo Matte (Pres)

BICHAMP CUTTING TECH-
NOLOGY (HUNAN) CO., LTD
No 68 Taijia Road Wangcheng,
Wangcheng Economic and Techno-
logical Development Zone, Chang-
sha, 410023, Hunan, China
Tel.: (86) 73188059666
Web Site: https://www.bichamp.com
Year Founded: 2003
002843—(SSE)
Rev.: $137,276,100
Assets: $276,474,276
Liabilities: $167,331,528
Net Worth: $109,142,748

Earnings: $18,322,200
Fiscal Year-end: 12/31/22
Hacksaw Blade Mfr & Distr
N.A.I.C.S.: 332216
Fang Hong *(Chm & Pres)*

BICO GROUP AB
Langfilsgatan 9, 412 77, Gothenburg, Sweden
Tel.: (46) 709918604
Web Site: https://www.bico.com
Year Founded: 2016
BICO—(OMX)
Rev.: $209,755,823
Assets: $955,051,655
Liabilities: $305,768,636
Net Worth: $649,283,018
Earnings: ($78,273,249)
Emp.: 1,200
Fiscal Year-end: 12/31/22
Printing Device Mfr
N.A.I.C.S.: 333248
Rolf A. Classon *(Chm)*

Subsidiaries:

Advanced BioMatrix Inc.   (1)
5930 Sea Lion Pl, Carlsbad, CA 92010
Tel.: (760) 929-0755
Web Site: https://advancedbiomatrix.com
Biotechnology Research Services
N.A.I.C.S.: 541714

Cellink Bioprinting AB   (1)
Langfilsgatan 1, 412 77, Gothenburg, Sweden
Tel.: (46) 31128700
3D Printing & Art Services
N.A.I.C.S.: 513140

Cellink KK   (1)
302 Creation Core Kyoto Mikuruma 448-5 Kajii-cho Imadegawa-Sagaru, Kawaramachi-dori Kamigyo-ku, Kyoto, 602-0841, Kyoto, Japan
Tel.: (81) 757463032
3D Printing & Art Services
N.A.I.C.S.: 513140

Cytena GmbH   (1)
Zollhallenstr 5, 79106, Freiburg, Germany
Tel.: (49) 76121632000
Web Site: https://www.cytena.com
Biotechnology Products Mfr
N.A.I.C.S.: 325414
Jonas Schondube *(CEO)*

Discover Echo Inc.   (1)
9530 Padgett St Ste 101, San Diego, CA 92126
Tel.: (858) 429-9565
Web Site: https://discover-echo.com
Biotechnology Research Services
N.A.I.C.S.: 541714

Dispendix GmbH   (1)
Ruppmannstrasse 28, 70565, Stuttgart, Germany
Tel.: (49) 71149054400
Web Site: https://www.dispendix.com
Nanoliter Dispensing Equipment Mfr
N.A.I.C.S.: 333914

MatTek Corporation   (1)
200 Homer Ave, Ashland, MA 01721
Tel.: (508) 881-6771
Web Site: http://www.mattek.com
Sales Range: $1-9.9 Million
Emp.: 80
Biotechnology Research & Development
N.A.I.C.S.: 541714
Mitchell Klausner *(Pres)*

Nanoscribe GmbH   (1)
Hermann-von-Helmholtz-Platz 6, 76344, Eggenstein, Germany
Tel.: (49) 7219819800
Web Site: https://www.nanoscribe.com
High Precision Additive Mfr
N.A.I.C.S.: 332721

Qinstruments GmbH   (1)
Loebstedter Str 101, 07749, Jena, Germany
Tel.: (49) 364155430
Web Site: https://www.qinstruments.com
Emp.: 30
Biotechnology Research Services
N.A.I.C.S.: 541714

Scienion GmbH   (1)
Wagner-Regeny-Strasse 15, 12489, Berlin, Germany
Tel.: (49) 3063921700
Web Site: https://www.scienion.com
Life Science Product Mfr & Distr
N.A.I.C.S.: 325412

Visikol, Inc.   (1)
53 Frontage Rd Ste 120 Shelbourne Bldg, Hampton, NJ 08827
Tel.: (800) 615-8474
Web Site: http://www.visikol.com
Contract Research Services Company
N.A.I.C.S.: 541714
Michael Johnson *(CEO)*

BICYCLE THERAPEUTICS PLC
Blocks A & B Portway Building Granta Park Great Abington, Cambridge, CB216GS, United Kingdom
Tel.: (44) 1223261503   **UK**
Web Site:
https://www.bicycletherapeutics.com
Year Founded: 2009
BCYC—(NASDAQ)
Rev.: $26,976,000
Assets: $595,344,000
Liabilities: $224,412,000
Net Worth: $370,932,000
Earnings: ($180,664,000)
Emp.: 284
Fiscal Year-end: 12/31/23
Biotechnology Research & Development Services
N.A.I.C.S.: 541714
Kevin Lee *(CEO)*

BID GROUP LTD
Unit C Elland Close, Wingates Industrial Park, Westhoughton, BL5 3XE, United Kingdom
Tel.: (44) 870 607 5050
Web Site: http://bidgroup1.bpweb.net
Forestry Services
N.A.I.C.S.: 115310
John Thompson *(Mng Dir)*

Subsidiaries:

Lowland Doors Limited   (1)
9 Netherton Road, Wishaw, ML2 0EQ, Lanarkshire, United Kingdom
Tel.: (44) 1698376444
Web Site: http://www.lowlanddoors.co.uk
Sales Range: $25-49.9 Million
Emp.: 25
Industrial Door Mfr
N.A.I.C.S.: 332321
Stuart West *(Mng Dir)*

BIDCO OIL REFINERIES LIMITED
PO Box 239, 01000, Thika, Kenya
Tel.: (254) 6730102
Web Site: http://www.bidco-oil.com
Sales Range: $650-699.9 Million
Emp.: 3,000
Vegetable Oils, Fats, Margarine, Soaps & Protein Concentrates Mfr
N.A.I.C.S.: 311225
Vimal Shah *(CEO)*

BIDSTACK GROUP PLC
201 Temple Chambers 3-7 Temple Avenue, London, EC4Y 0DT, United Kingdom
Tel.: (44) 2074491000   **UK**
Web Site:
http://www.bidstackgroup.com
BIDS—(AIM)
Rev.: $6,648,769
Assets: $23,741,358
Liabilities: $10,338,908
Net Worth: $13,402,450
Earnings: ($9,702,330)
Emp.: 86
Fiscal Year-end: 12/31/22
Online Health & Wellness Coaching Services

N.A.I.C.S.: 519290
Donald John Stewart *(Chm)*

BIDV INSURANCE CORPORATION
11/F 263 Cau Giay St, Hanoi, Vietnam
Tel.: (84) 2422200282
Web Site: https://bic.vn
Year Founded: 1999
BIC—(HOSE)
Rev.: $265,450,700
Assets: $665,645,600
Liabilities: $405,808,700
Net Worth: $259,836,900
Earnings: $31,151,700
Emp.: 1,236
Fiscal Year-end: 12/31/22
Insurance Services
N.A.I.C.S.: 524298
Tran Trung Tinh *(Deputy Gen Dir)*

Subsidiaries:

BIDV Bac Bo Insurance
Company   (1)
5th Floor BIDV Tower No 92C Hung Vuong, Vi Xuyen Ward, Nam Dinh, Vietnam
Tel.: (84) 2283630397
Non-Life Insurance Services
N.A.I.C.S.: 524128

BIDV Bac Tay Nguyen Insurance
Company   (1)
6th floor Duc Long Gia Lai Tower No 117 Tran Phu, Dien Hong Ward, Pleiku, Vietnam
Tel.: (84) 2623957351
Non-Life Insurance Services
N.A.I.C.S.: 524128

BIDV Bac Trung Bo Insurance
Company   (1)
8th Floor BIDV Tower No 08 Le Nin Boulevard, Hung Dung Ward, Vinh, Nghe An, Vietnam
Tel.: (84) 2383592877
Non-Life Insurance Services
N.A.I.C.S.: 524128

BIDV Binh Dinh Insurance
Company   (1)
No 72 Le Duan, Quy Nhon, Binh Dinh, Vietnam
Tel.: (84) 2563520080
Non-Life Insurance Services
N.A.I.C.S.: 524128

BIDV Binh Duong Insurance
Company   (1)
12A Floor Becamex Tower No 230 Binh Duong Boulevard, Phu Hoa Ward, Thu Dau Mot, Binh Duong, Vietnam
Tel.: (84) 2743848509
Non-Life Insurance Services
N.A.I.C.S.: 524128

BIDV Da Nang Insurance
Company   (1)
No 40-42 Hung Vuong, Hai Chau District, Da Nang, Vietnam
Tel.: (84) 2363865803
Non-Life Insurance Services
N.A.I.C.S.: 524128

BIDV Dong Bac Insurance
Company   (1)
4th floor Trung Thanh Plaza building 10 Nguyen Dang Dao, Tien An Ward, Bac Ninh, Bac Ninh, Vietnam
Tel.: (84) 2223875899
Non-Life Insurance Services
N.A.I.C.S.: 524128

BIDV Ha Noi Insurance
Company   (1)
No 46-48 Ba Trieu, Hang Bai Ward Hoan Kiem District, Hanoi, Vietnam
Tel.: (84) 2439328888
Non-Life Insurance Services
N.A.I.C.S.: 524128

BIDV Hai Duong Insurance
Company   (1)
No 115 Tran Hung Dao Street, Tran Hung Dao Ward, Hai Duong, Vietnam
Tel.: (84) 2203837779

Non-Life Insurance Services
N.A.I.C.S.: 524128

BIDV Hai Phong Insurance
Company   (1)
7th Floor BIDV Dong Hai Phong Tower No 12 Lot 30A Le Hong Phong Str, Dong Khe Ward Ngo Quyen Dist, Haiphong, Vietnam
Tel.: (84) 2253747373
Non-Life Insurance Services
N.A.I.C.S.: 524128

BIDV Ho Chi Minh Insurance
Company   (1)
5th Floor C Section Waseco Building No 10 Pho Quang Street, Tan Binh District, Ho Chi Minh City, Vietnam
Tel.: (84) 2839973999
Non-Life Insurance Services
N.A.I.C.S.: 524128

BIDV Mien Dong BIDV Insurance
Company   (1)
No 4-5 Unit 23 Street 3, Tam Hoa Ward, Bien Hoa, Dong Nai, Vietnam
Tel.: (84) 2518823111
Non-Life Insurance Services
N.A.I.C.S.: 524128

BIDV Mien Tay Insurance
Company   (1)
11th floor No 16-18 Hoa Binh Boulevard, Tan An Ward Ninh Kieu District, Can Tho, Vietnam
Tel.: (84) 2923816367
Non-Life Insurance Services
N.A.I.C.S.: 524128

BIDV Quang Ninh Insurance
Company   (1)
No 88 Le Thanh Tong, Hong Gai Ward, Ha Long, Quang Ninh, Vietnam
Tel.: (84) 2033518338
Non-Life Insurance Services
N.A.I.C.S.: 524128

BIDV Sai Gon Insurance
Company   (1)
08th Floor No 472 Nguyen Thi Minh Khai, District 3, Ho Chi Minh City, Vietnam
Tel.: (84) 2838303000
Non-Life Insurance Services
N.A.I.C.S.: 524128

BIDV Tay Bac Insurance
Company   (1)
4th Floor Viettel Son La Tower No 1 Chu Van Thinh, Son La, Vietnam
Tel.: (84) 2126268888
Non-Life Insurance Services
N.A.I.C.S.: 524128

BIDV Tay Nguyen Insurance
Company   (1)
No 389 Phan Chu Trinh Street, Tan Loi Ward, Buon Ma Thuot, Daklak, Vietnam
Tel.: (84) 2623957351
Non-Life Insurance Services
N.A.I.C.S.: 524128

BIDV Thai Nguyen Insurance
Company   (1)
7th Floor No 653 Luong Ngoc Quyen, Thai Nguyen, Vietnam
Tel.: (84) 2803841122
Non-Life Insurance Services
N.A.I.C.S.: 524128

BIDV Thang Long Insurance
Company   (1)
3rd Floor Golden Palace Me Tri Street, Nam Tu Liem District, Hanoi, Vietnam
Tel.: (84) 2466641188
Non-Life Insurance Services
N.A.I.C.S.: 524128

BIDV Vung Tau Insurance
Company   (1)
No 24 Tran Hung Dao, Ward 1, Vung Tau, Ba Ria-Vung Tau, Vietnam
Tel.: (84) 2546253218
Non-Life Insurance Services
N.A.I.C.S.: 524128

BIDV SECURITIES JOINT STOCK COMPANY
8th 9th floor ThaiHoldings Tower 210 Tran Quang Khai street, Ly Thai To

BIDV Securities Joint Stock Company—(Continued)

Ward Hoan Kiem District, Hanoi, Vietnam
Tel.: (84) 2439352722
Web Site: https://www.bsc.com.vn
Year Founded: 1999
BSI—(HOSE)
Rev.: $51,870,718
Assets: $343,040,815
Liabilities: $150,048,917
Net Worth: $192,997,898
Earnings: $16,820,312
Fiscal Year-end: 12/31/23
Investment Management Service
N.A.I.C.S.: 523999
Anh Sang Doan (Chm)

BIEGELAAR BV
Nijverheidsweg 15, 3606AH, Maarssen, Netherlands
Tel.: (31) 346599199
Web Site: http://www.biegelaar.nl
Sales Range: $50-74.9 Million
Emp.: 200
Commercial Printing Services
N.A.I.C.S.: 323111

BIEM.L .FDLKK GARMENT CO., LTD.
No 608 Xingye Avenue East Nancun Town, Panyu District, Guangzhou, 511442, Guangdong, China
Tel.: (86) 2039952666
Web Site: http://www.biemlf.com
Year Founded: 2003
002832—(SSE)
Rev.: $405,031,536
Assets: $783,276,156
Liabilities: $203,216,364
Net Worth: $580,059,792
Earnings: $102,155,040
Fiscal Year-end: 12/31/22
Golf Apparel Mfr & Distr
N.A.I.C.S.: 339920
Xie Bingzheng (Chm)

BIEN HOA PACKAGING COMPANY
Road 7 Bien Hoa 1 Industrial Parl, Bien Hoa, Dong Nai, Vietnam
Tel.: (84) 2513836121
Web Site: https://www.sovi.com.vn
Year Founded: 1968
Packaging Products Mfr
N.A.I.C.S.: 326112
Ekarach Sinnarong (Gen Dir)

BIEN HOA SUGAR JSC
Bien Hoa Industrial Zone 1, An Binh, Bien Hoa, Dong Nai, Vietnam
Tel.: (84) 61 3836199
Web Site: http://www.bhs.vn
Sales Range: $50-74.9 Million
Sugar Mfr
N.A.I.C.S.: 311314

BIEN SPAREBANK A.S.A.
Dronning Mauds gate 11, 0250, Oslo, Norway
Tel.: (47) 91502436
Web Site: https://www.bien.no
Year Founded: 1885
BIEN—(EUR)
Investment Banking Services
N.A.I.C.S.: 523150
Bendik Falch-Koslung (Chm)

BIERHAKE GMBH & CO. KG
Eikesberg 56, 49076, Osnabruck, Germany
Tel.: (49) 541912030
Web Site: http://www.bierhake.de
Year Founded: 1885
Rev.: $18,194,286
Emp.: 100
Automotive Part Whslr

N.A.I.C.S.: 423120
Jorg Matuschewski (Mgr-CV Spare Parts)

BIESSE S.P.A.
Via Della Meccanica 16, 61122, Pesaro, Italy
Tel.: (39) 0721439100   IT
Web Site: http://www.biocco.com
BSS—(ITA)
Rev.: $866,543,769
Assets: $717,303,234
Liabilities: $428,697,428
Net Worth: $288,605,806
Earnings: $13,779,667
Emp.: 3,924
Fiscal Year-end: 12/31/23
Mfr of Woodworking Machinery.
N.A.I.C.S.: 333998
Roberto Selci (Co-CEO)

Subsidiaries:

BSoft S.r.l.   (1)
Via Carlo Cattaneo 24 c a p, Portomaggiore, 44015, Ferrara, Italy
Tel.: (39) 03405289949
Web Site: http://bsoftsrl.it
Software Development Services
N.A.I.C.S.: 541511

Biesse America, Inc.   (1)
4110 Meadow Oak Dr, Charlotte, NC 28208
Tel.: (704) 357-3131
Web Site: https://biesse.com
Sales Range: $25-49.9 Million
Emp.: 55
Mfr of Woodworking Machinery.
N.A.I.C.S.: 333998

Biesse Asia Pte Ltd.   (1)
12 Woodlands Square Woods Square Tower 1, Singapore, 737715, Singapore   (100%)
Tel.: (65) 63682632
Web Site: https://biesse.com
Sales Range: $25-49.9 Million
Emp.: 2
All Other Industrial Machinery Mfr
N.A.I.C.S.: 333248

Biesse Canada Inc.   (1)
18005 Rue Lapointe, Mirabel, J7J 0G2, QC, Canada   (100%)
Tel.: (450) 437-5534
Web Site: https://biesse.com
Sales Range: $25-49.9 Million
Emp.: 40
Industrial Machinery & Equipment Whslr
N.A.I.C.S.: 423830

Biesse Group Australia Pty Ltd.   (1)
473 Victoria St Wetherill Park, Sydney, 2164, NSW, Australia   (100%)
Tel.: (61) 1300243773
Web Site: https://biesse.com
Industrial Machinery & Equipment Whslr
N.A.I.C.S.: 423830

Biesse Group Deutschland GmbH   (1)
An der Leibi 10, 89278, Nersingen, Germany   (100%)
Tel.: (49) 730896060
Web Site: https://biesse.com
Sales Range: $25-49.9 Million
Emp.: 50
Industrial Machinery & Equipment Whslr
N.A.I.C.S.: 423830

Biesse Group France Sarl   (1)
4 Chemin de Moninsadle, 69530, Lyon, France   (100%)
Tel.: (33) 478967329
Web Site: http://www.biessefrance.fr
Sales Range: $25-49.9 Million
Emp.: 50
Industrial Machinery & Equipment Whslr
N.A.I.C.S.: 423830

Biesse Group UK Ltd.   (1)
4 Lamport Dr, Heartlands Business Park, Daventry, NN11 8YZ, Northamptonshire, United Kingdom   (100%)

Tel.: (44) 1327300366
Web Site: https://biesse.com
Sales Range: $25-49.9 Million
Emp.: 30
Industrial Machinery & Equipment Merchant Whslr
N.A.I.C.S.: 423830
Steve Bulmer (CEO)

Biesse Manufacturing Co. Pvt. Ltd.   (1)
Survey No 32 No 46, Jakkasandra Village Nelamangala Bangalore Rural District, Bengaluru, 562 123, India
Tel.: (91) 8049489800
Woodworking Mfr
N.A.I.C.S.: 337212

Biesservice Scandinavia AB   (1)
Betavagen 11, 55652, Jonkoping, Sweden   (60%)
Tel.: (46) 36150380
Web Site: http://www.biesse.it
Sales Range: $50-74.9 Million
Emp.: 3
Industrial Machinery & Equipment Merchant Whslr
N.A.I.C.S.: 423830

Cabi S.r.l.   (1)
2 Perceptumbero, Porto, 63018, Rome, Italy   (100%)
Tel.: (39) 0734992352
Web Site: http://www.cabi.it
Sales Range: $50-74.9 Million
Emp.: 2
Industrial Machinery & Equipment Merchant Whslr
N.A.I.C.S.: 423830

HSD S.p.A.   (1)
Via della Meccanica 16, 61122, Pesaro, PU, Italy   (100%)
Tel.: (39) 0541979001
Web Site: https://www.hsdmechatronics.com
Industrial Machinery & Equipment Merchant Whslr
N.A.I.C.S.: 423830

HSD USA, Inc.   (1)
4060 SW 30th Ave, Fort Lauderdale, FL 33312   (100%)
Tel.: (954) 587-1991
Web Site: http://www.hsdusa.com
Sales Range: $50-74.9 Million
Emp.: 10
Industrial Machinery & Equipment Merchant Whslr
N.A.I.C.S.: 423830
Giuseppe Benelli (CEO)

Intermac do Brasil Comercio de Maquinas e Equipamentos Ltda.   (1)
Coronel Antonio Marcelo 220, Sao Paulo, 03054-040, Brazil
Tel.: (55) 11941101919
Web Site:
   http://www.intermaqdobrasil.com.br
Machinery Equipment Mfr
N.A.I.C.S.: 333248

Montresor & Co. S.r.l.   (1)
Via Francia 13, 37069, Villafranca di Verona, VR, Italy
Tel.: (39) 0456300690
Web Site: http://www.montresor.net
Edge Polishing Machine Mfr
N.A.I.C.S.: 333517

Movetro S.r.l.   (1)
Via della Maeccanica 16, 61122, Pesaro, Italy
Tel.: (39) 0429695098
Web Site: http://www.movetro.eu
Glass Sheet Mfr
N.A.I.C.S.: 327211

Sandymac S.r.l.   (1)
Via Case Nuove Snc, San Giovanni In Marignano, Rimini, Italy   (80%)
Tel.: (39) 0541828511
Other Business Service Centers (including Copy Shops)
N.A.I.C.S.: 561439

Viet Italia S.r.l.   (1)
Via della Meccanica No 16, 61122, Pesaro, PU, Italy
Tel.: (39) 0721401997
Web Site: http://www.viet.it

Edge Polishing Machine Mfr
N.A.I.C.S.: 333517

BIFFA GROUP LIMITED
Coronation Road, Cressex, High Wycombe, HP12 3TZ, Bucks, United Kingdom
Tel.: (44) 1494521221   UK
Web Site: http://www.biffa.co.uk
Sales Range: $1-4.9 Billion
Emp.: 6,000
Holding Company; Waste Management Services
N.A.I.C.S.: 551112
Michael Topham (CEO)

Subsidiaries:

Biffa Leicester Limited   (1)
Coronation Road Cressex, High Wycombe, HP12 3TZ, Buckinghamshire, United Kingdom
Tel.: (44) 149 452 1221
Web Site: https://www.biffa.co.uk
Renewable Energy Semiconductor Mfr
N.A.I.C.S.: 334413

Biffa Waste Services Limited   (1)
Coronation Road, Cressex, High Wycombe, HP12 3TZ, Bucks, United Kingdom
Tel.: (44) 1494521221
Web Site: http://www.biffa.co.uk
Emp.: 300
Waste Management Services
N.A.I.C.S.: 562998
Matt Humphreys (Head-Health, Safety & Quality)

Company Shop Limited   (1)
Wentworth Way Wentworth Industrial Estate, Tankersley, Barnsley, S75 3DH, South Yorkshire, United Kingdom
Tel.: (44) 122 674 7121
Web Site:
   https://www.companyshopgroup.co.uk
Household Product Retailer
N.A.I.C.S.: 423620

BIFIDO CO., LTD.
23-16 Nonggongdanji-gil Hongcheoneup, Hongcheon, 25117, Gangwon-do, Korea (South)
Tel.: (82) 334354962
Web Site: https://www.bifido.com
Year Founded: 1999
238200—(KRS)
Rev.: $11,181,782
Assets: $42,136,660
Liabilities: $1,877,427
Net Worth: $40,259,233
Earnings: $1,185,558
Emp.: 81
Fiscal Year-end: 12/31/22
Probiotic Product Mfr
N.A.I.C.S.: 325411
Hee Suk Lee (Mng Dir)

BIFIRE S.P.A.
Via Lavoratori dell 'Autobianchi 1, 20832, Desio, MB, Italy
Tel.: (39) 0362364570
Web Site: https://www.bifire.it
Year Founded: 2002
FIRE—(ITA)
Thermal Insulation Mfr & Distr
N.A.I.C.S.: 326140
Alberto Abbo (CEO & Chm)

BIG 8 SPLIT, INC.
25 Price Street, Toronto, M4W 1Z1, ON, Canada
Tel.: (416) 923-9967
Web Site:
   http://www.timbercreek.com
Rev.: $2,079,998
Assets: $20,479,252
Liabilities: $7,208,641
Net Worth: $13,270,611
Earnings: $1,427,890
Fiscal Year-end: 12/15/17
Investment Services

N.A.I.C.S.: 523999
Corrado Russo *(Sr Mng Dir & Head-Global Real Estate Securities)*

BIG BANC SPLIT CORP.

130 Adelaide Street West Suite 3100,
PO Box 109, Toronto, M5H 3P5, ON,
Canada
Tel.: (416) 583-2271   ON
Year Founded: 2020
BNK—(TSX)
Rev.: $10,740,360
Assets: $35,126,515
Liabilities: $12,826,843
Net Worth: $22,299,672
Earnings: $9,542,067
Fiscal Year-end: 12/31/21
Commercial Banking Services
N.A.I.C.S.: 522110

BIG BLOCKCHAIN INTELLI-GENCE GROUP INC.

#200 8338 120 Street, Surrey, V3W
3N4, BC, Canada
Tel.: (604) 592-6881   BC
Year Founded: 2014
Real Estate Services
N.A.I.C.S.: 531390
Lucky Janda *(CEO)*

BIG CAMERA CORPORATION PCL

115 115/1 Sawatdikan 1 Rd Khwaeng
Nong Khaem, Khet Nong Khaem,
Bangkok, 10160, Thailand
Tel.: (66) 2809995665
Year Founded: 1974
Sales Range: $10-24.9 Million
Teak Furniture Mfr
N.A.I.C.S.: 337211
Thavisak Wayakornvichit *(CEO)*

Subsidiaries:

Gardenside Ltd.   **(1)**
808 Anthony St, Berkeley, CA 94710
Tel.: (415) 455-4500
Web Site: http://www.gardenside.com
Furniture Whslr
N.A.I.C.S.: 423210
Leo Krashanoff *(Mgr-Bus Dev)*

BIG GOLD INC.

9th Floor-1021 West Hastings Street,
Vancouver, V6E 0C3, BC, Canada
Tel.: (647) 367-6201   BC
Web Site: https://www.biggold.ca
Year Founded: 2018
BG—(CNSX)
Assets: $271,744
Liabilities: $74,532
Net Worth: $197,212
Earnings: ($437,878)
Fiscal Year-end: 12/31/23
Gold Exploration Services
N.A.I.C.S.: 212220
Scott Walters *(Pres)*

BIG M FORD LINCOLN LTD.

1312 Trans Canada Way SE, Medi-cine Hat, T1A 7G8, AB, Canada
Tel.: (403) 527-4406
Web Site:
    http://www.bigmfordloln.dealer.com
Rev.: $17,215,100
Emp.: 37
New & Used Car Dealer
N.A.I.C.S.: 441110
Barry Hagemeister *(Mgr-Sls)*

BIG PHARMA SPLIT CORP.

610 Chartwell Rd Suite 204, Oakville,
L6J 4A5, ON, Canada
Tel.: (416) 649-4541   ON
Year Founded: 2017
PRM—(TSX)
Rev.: $617,339
Assets: $17,939,735

Liabilities: $7,625,165
Net Worth: $10,314,570
Earnings: ($170,058)
Fiscal Year-end: 12/31/20
Investment Management Service
N.A.I.C.S.: 525990

BIG PHARMACY HEALTH-CARE SDN. BHD

No 19 Jalan 15/23 Taman Perindus-trian Tiong Nam Section 15, Shah
Alam, 40200, Selangor, Malaysia
Tel.: (60) 125215809
Web Site:
    https://www.bigpharmacy.com.my
Pharmacies & Drug Stores
N.A.I.C.S.: 456110

Subsidiaries:

Caring Pharmacy Group Bhd   **(1)**
No 1 Jalan 51/203A Kawasan Perindustrian
Tiong Nam, Seksyen 51 Selangor Darul
Ehsan, 46050, Petaling Jaya,
Malaysia   **(75%)**
Tel.: (60) 374531988
Web Site: http://www.caring2u.com.my
Rev.: $144,199,789
Assets: $69,169,864
Liabilities: $31,052,192
Net Worth: $38,117,672
Earnings: $6,172,448
Emp.: 1,332
Fiscal Year-end: 05/31/2019
Pharmacies
N.A.I.C.S.: 456110
Yeow Siang Chong *(Mng Dir)*

BIG RED MINING CORPORA-TION

101-17565 58 Avenue, Surrey, V3S
4E3, BC, Canada
Tel.: (778) 218-9638   BC
Web Site:
    https://www.bigredmining.com
Year Founded: 2020
RED—(CNSX)
Rev.: $12,675
Assets: $942,822
Liabilities: $52,220
Net Worth: $890,602
Earnings: ($525,535)
Fiscal Year-end: 08/31/22
Mineral Mining Services
N.A.I.C.S.: 213115
Jag Sandhu *(CEO)*

BIG RIDGE GOLD CORP.

18 King St EastSuite 1400, Toronto,
M5C 1C4, ON, Canada
Tel.: (604) 689-2599
Web Site: https://bigridgegold.com
Year Founded: 1987
ALVLF—(OTCQB)
Rev.: $15,572
Assets: $4,735,322
Liabilities: $375,029
Net Worth: $4,360,293
Earnings: ($3,513,514)
Emp.: 2
Fiscal Year-end: 06/30/24
Gold Exploration Services
N.A.I.C.S.: 212220
Marian Koziol *(Pres)*

Subsidiaries:

Empress Resources Corp.   **(1)**
Suite 3123 595 Burrard Street, Vancouver,
V7X 1J1, BC, Canada
Tel.: (604) 331-2080
Web Site: https://www.empressroyalty.com
Rev.: $21,552
Assets: $1,278,292
Liabilities: $50,688
Net Worth: $1,227,604
Earnings: ($780,589)
Fiscal Year-end: 03/31/2020
Mineral Exploration Services
N.A.I.C.S.: 213114

BIG RIVER INDUSTRIES LIM-ITED

Trenayr Road, Junction Hill, 2460,
NSW, Australia
Tel.: (61) 1300554474   AU
Web Site:
    https://www.bigriverindustries.com
Year Founded: 2015
BRI—(ASX)
Rev.: $293,050,140
Assets: $179,694,204
Liabilities: $100,988,459
Net Worth: $78,705,744
Earnings: $14,459,151
Fiscal Year-end: 06/30/23
Hardwood Veneer & Plywood Mfr
N.A.I.C.S.: 321211
James Bernard Bindon *(CEO)*

Subsidiaries:

Plytech International Limited   **(1)**
26 Business Parade North, PO Box 204-070, Highbrook, Auckland, 2161, New Zea-land
Tel.: (64) 95735016
Web Site: https://www.plytech.co.nz
Plywood Panel Mfr & Distr
N.A.I.C.S.: 321211

BIG ROCK BREWERY INC.

5555 76th Ave SE, Calgary, T2C 4L8,
AB, Canada
Tel.: (403) 720-3239   AB
Web Site:
    https://www.bigrockbeer.com
Year Founded: 1984
BR—(OTCIQ)
Rev.: $34,407,804
Assets: $40,643,357
Liabilities: $13,402,803
Net Worth: $27,240,554
Earnings: ($520,998)
Emp.: 124
Fiscal Year-end: 12/30/20
Beer Brewer & Marketer
N.A.I.C.S.: 312120
Kathleen McNally-Leitch *(Vice Chm)*

Subsidiaries:

Pine Creek Brewing Company
Ltd   **(1)**
5555 76th Ave SE, Calgary, T2C 4L8, AB,
Canada
Tel.: (403) 279-2337
Beer Mfr
N.A.I.C.S.: 312120

BIG ROCK RESOURCES INC.

703 938 Howe Street, Vancouver,
V4Z 1N4, BC, Canada
Tel.: (604) 800-2955
Web Site:
    http://www.bigrockresources.com
Year Founded: 2005
Gold Mining Services
N.A.I.C.S.: 212220
Ken Van Boeyen *(Pres & Sec)*

BIG SHOPPING CENTERS LTD.

Sapir 1 Floor 8 AMPA Building Indus-trial Zone, Herzliya Pituach, 12683,
Israel
Tel.: (972) 732600400
Web Site: https://www.bigcenters.co.il
Year Founded: 1994
BIG—(TAE)
Rev.: $645,709,618
Assets: $10,120,508,476
Liabilities: $6,755,277,143
Net Worth: $3,365,231,333
Earnings: $268,758,664
Emp.: 342
Fiscal Year-end: 12/31/23
Lessors of Nonresidential Buildings
(except Miniwarehouses)
N.A.I.C.S.: 531120

Eitan Bar Zeev *(Chm)*

Subsidiaries:

Afi Properties Ltd.   **(1)**
4 Derech Hahoresh, Yehud, 5647003, Israel
Tel.: (972) 35393540
Web Site: https://afi-properties.com
Real Estate Manangement Services
N.A.I.C.S.: 531390

BIG SOFA TECHNOLOGIES GROUP PLC

Unit 106 Metal Box Factory 30 Great
Guildford Street, London, SE1 0HS,
United Kingdom
Tel.: (44) 2073570033
Web Site:
    http://www.bigsofatech.com
Management Consulting Services
N.A.I.C.S.: 541618
Daniel Barry *(Dir-Accts)*

BIG SUNSHINE CO., LTD.

No 16 Gongye 3rd Rd, Pingzhen
Dist, Taoyuan, 324, Taiwan
Tel.: (886) 34193881
Web Site: http://www.sumagh.com.tw
1475—(TAI)
Rev.: $42,061,609
Assets: $52,772,195
Liabilities: $11,495,241
Net Worth: $41,276,953
Earnings: $9,087,086
Fiscal Year-end: 12/31/23
Textile Products Mfr
N.A.I.C.S.: 314999

BIG TECHNOLOGIES PLC

Talbot House 17 Church Street, Rick-mansworth, WD3 1DE, United King-dom
Tel.: (44) 800978800   UK
Web Site:
    https://www.bigtechnologies.co.uk
Year Founded: 2005
BIG—(AIM)
Rev.: $62,293,655
Assets: $140,534,506
Liabilities: $13,283,535
Net Worth: $127,250,971
Earnings: $24,788,812
Emp.: 300
Fiscal Year-end: 12/31/22
Custom Computer Programming Ser-vices
N.A.I.C.S.: 541511

Subsidiaries:

Buddi Limited   **(1)**
Talbot House 17 Church St, Rickmans-worth, WD3 1DE, United Kingdom
Tel.: (44) 1923601909
Web Site: https://www.buddi.co.uk
Electronic Monitoring Services
N.A.I.C.S.: 561621

Buddi US LLC   **(1)**
1964 Bayshore Blvd Ste B, Dunedin, FL
34698
Web Site: https://buddi.us
Electronic Monitoring Services
N.A.I.C.S.: 561621

BIG TREE CARBON INC.

22 Adelaide St W Suite 3600, To-ronto, M5H 4E3, ON, Canada
Tel.: (807) 737-5353
Web Site: https://bigtreecarbon.ca
TBMIF—(OTCIQ)
Assets: $625,334
Liabilities: $848,268
Net Worth: ($222,934)
Earnings: $478,230
Fiscal Year-end: 12/31/22
Mineral Mining Exploration Service
N.A.I.C.S.: 213114
William R. Johnstone *(Sec)*

Big Tree Carbon Inc.—(Continued)

BIG TREE CLOUD HOLDINGS LIMITED
Room 3303 Building 1 Zhongliang Yunjing Plaza Heshuikou Community, Matian Street Guangming District, Shenzhen, 518083, China
Tel.: (86) 75527595623　　Ky
Web Site: https://ir.bigtreeclouds.com
Year Founded: 2020
DSY—(NASDAQ)
Rev.: $7,323,356
Assets: $8,967,937
Liabilities: $13,546,734
Net Worth: ($4,578,797)
Earnings: $640,485
Emp.: 50
Fiscal Year-end: 06/30/24
Holding Company
N.A.I.C.S.: 551112

BIG TREE GROUP INC.
South Part 1-101 Nanshe Area Pennan Indus Pk North Yingbinbei Road, Waisha Town Longhu, Shantou, 515023, Guangdong, China
Tel.: (86) 7548323888　　CO
Web Site:
　http://www.bigtreegroup.net
Year Founded: 1987
Sales Range: $25-49.9 Million
Emp.: 145
Toy Sourcing & Contract Manufacturing Services
N.A.I.C.S.: 423920
Jiale Cai (CFO & Dir-Acctg)

BIG YELLOW GROUP PLC
1 The Deans Bridge Road, Bagshot, GU19 5AT, Surrey, United Kingdom
Tel.: (44) 1276470190　　UK
Web Site:
　https://www.bigyellow.co.uk
BYG—(LSE)
Rev.: $169,606,931
Assets: $2,119,966,624
Liabilities: $593,426,862
Net Worth: $1,526,539,762
Earnings: $121,422,682
Emp.: 405
Fiscal Year-end: 03/31/20
Self Storage Services
N.A.I.C.S.: 531130
Nicholas Vetch (Co-Founder & Chm)

Subsidiaries:

BYSSCo Limited　　　　　　　(1)
Unit 2 The Deans Bridge Road, Bagshot, GU19 5AT, United Kingdom
Tel.: (44) 12 76 47 01 90
Web Site: http://www.bigyellow.co.uk
Emp.: 50
Self Storage Services
N.A.I.C.S.: 493190
James Gibson (CEO)

Big Yellow (Battersea) Limited　(1)
55 Lombard Road, Battersea, London, SW11 3RX, United Kingdom
Tel.: (44) 207 801 0280
General Storage Services
N.A.I.C.S.: 493110

Big Yellow Self Storage (GP) Limited　　　　　　　　　(1)
1-2 The Deans Bridge Road, Bagshot, GU19 5AT, Surrey, United Kingdom
Tel.: (44) 1276 470190
Self Storage Services
N.A.I.C.S.: 493190

Big Yellow Self Storage Company 6 Limited　　　　　　　(1)
2 The Deans Bridge Rd, Bagshot, GU19 5AT, Surrey, United Kingdom
Tel.: (44) 1276470190
Web Site: http://www.bigyellow.co.uk
Sales Range: $10-24.9 Million
Emp.: 50
Self Storage Services

N.A.I.C.S.: 493190

Big Yellow Self Storage Company 8 Limited　　　　　　　(1)
2 The Deans Bridge Road, Bagshot, GU19 5AT, Surrey, United Kingdom
Tel.: (44) 8001300170
Self Storage Services
N.A.I.C.S.: 493190

Big Yellow Self Storage Company Limited　　　　　　　(1)
1 The Deans Bridge Road, Bagshot, GU19 5AT, Surrey, United Kingdom
Tel.: (44) 1276477177
Web Site: http://www.bigyellow.co.uk
Sales Range: $25-49.9 Million
Self Storage Services
N.A.I.C.S.: 493190

BIGBEN INTERACTIVE SA
396 Rue de la Voyette CRT 2 Fretin CS 90414, 59814, Lesquin, Cedex, France
Tel.: (33) 320907200
Web Site: http://www.bigben-group.com
Year Founded: 1981
Emp.: 300
Game Software Publishing Services
N.A.I.C.S.: 513210
Alain Falc (Chm & CEO)

BIGBLOC CONSTRUCTION LIMITED
908 9th Rajhans Montessa Dumas Road, Surat, 395007, Gujarat, India
Tel.: (91) 2612463262　　In
Web Site: https://www.nxtbloc.in
Year Founded: 2015
540061—(BOM)
Rev.: $23,994,298
Assets: $15,565,095
Liabilities: $9,146,155
Net Worth: $6,418,940
Earnings: $2,195,507
Emp.: 250
Fiscal Year-end: 03/30/22
Construction Material Mfr & Distr
N.A.I.C.S.: 327331
Narayan Sitaram Saboo (Chm)

BIGBLU BROADBAND GROUP PLC
The Old Bakery Broadband House Victoria Road, Bicester, OX26 6PB, Oxon, United Kingdom
Tel.: (44) 1869222900
Web Site: https://www.bbb-plc.com
Year Founded: 2008
BBB—(AIM)
Rev.: $42,388,018
Assets: $32,746,849
Liabilities: $14,566,978
Net Worth: $18,179,871
Earnings: ($3,983,550)
Emp.: 141
Fiscal Year-end: 11/30/22
Satellite Services
N.A.I.C.S.: 517410
Andrew Walwyn (CEO)

Subsidiaries:

Quickline Communications Limited　　　　　　　　　(1)
3 Priory Court Saxon Way, Hessle, HU13 9PB, United Kingdom
Tel.: (44) 1482247365
Web Site: https://www.quickline.co.uk
Internet Providing Services
N.A.I.C.S.: 517111

SkyMesh Pty. Ltd.　　　　　　(1)
Level 5/51 Alfred Street, Fortitude Valley, 4006, QLD, Australia
Tel.: (61) 731235800
Web Site: https://www.skymesh.net.au
Emp.: 50
Telecommunication Servicesb
N.A.I.C.S.: 517810

BIGEON CORP.
Manesova 345/13 Ceske Budejovice 6, 37001, Ceske Budejovice, Czech Republic
Tel.: (420) 234768135　　NV
Year Founded: 2018
BIGN—(OTCIQ)
Assets: $849
Liabilities: $59,594
Net Worth: ($58,745)
Earnings: ($46,053)
Emp.: 1
Fiscal Year-end: 07/31/21
Messaging Software Development Services
N.A.I.C.S.: 541511
Olegas Tunevicius (Pres, CEO, CFO, Treas & Sec)

BIGZ PUBLISHING A.D.
Pozeska 60, 11000, Belgrade, Serbia
Tel.: (381) 113690181
Web Site: http://www.bigz-publishing.co.rs
Year Founded: 2002
BGZP—(BEL)
Sales Range: Less than $1 Million
Emp.: 12
Books Publishing Services
N.A.I.C.S.: 513130
Sanja Jovicic (CEO)

BIHACKA PIVOVARA D.D.
Vinicka bb, 77 000, Bihac, Bosnia & Herzegovina
Tel.: (387) 37318500
Web Site: http://www.preminger.ba
BIPVR—(SARE)
Rev.: $5,090,350
Assets: $23,902,145
Liabilities: $23,902,145
Earnings: $6,352
Emp.: 77
Fiscal Year-end: 12/31/21
Beverage Mfr & Distr
N.A.I.C.S.: 312120

BIHAR SPONGE IRON LIMITED
Umesh Nagar, Saraikela-Kharsawan, Chandil, 832401, Jharkhand, India
Tel.: (91) 9955542302
Web Site: https://www.bsil.org.in
500058—(BOM)
Rev.: $3,316,472
Assets: $8,821,927
Liabilities: $20,232,822
Net Worth: ($11,410,895)
Earnings: $540,731
Emp.: 271
Fiscal Year-end: 03/31/21
Iron Product Mfr
N.A.I.C.S.: 331110
Umesh Kumar Modi (Chm)

BIJLEE TEXTILES LIMITED
Garden House Dr Amichand Shahs Wadi Rampura Tunki, Surat, 395003, Gujarat, India
Tel.: (91) 261 2419019
Web Site: http://www.bijleetex.com
Year Founded: 1985
Textile Products Mfr
N.A.I.C.S.: 314999
Jayendra S. Shah (Sec)

BIJOU BRIGITTE MODISCHE ACCESSOIRES AG
Poppenbutteler Bogen 1, 22399, Hamburg, Germany
Tel.: (49) 40606090
Web Site: https://www.group.bijou-brigitte.com
Year Founded: 1963
BIJ—(DEU)
Rev.: $361,942,065

Assets: $449,748,129
Liabilities: $185,208,030
Net Worth: $264,540,099
Earnings: $26,576,072
Emp.: 2,353
Fiscal Year-end: 12/31/23
Jewelry Mfr & Distr
N.A.I.C.S.: 339910
Friedhelm Steinberg (Chm-Supervisory Bd)

Subsidiaries:

Rubin GmbH　　　　　　　　(1)
Patschenweg 10, 01979, Lauchhammer, Germany
Tel.: (49) 3574789020
Web Site: https://www.rubin-lauchhammer.de
Container & Transport Services
N.A.I.C.S.: 484110

BIJOUTERIE ADLER SA
23 rue du Rone, 1204, Geneva, Switzerland
Tel.: (41) 228198007
Web Site: http://www.adler.ch
Year Founded: 1886
Sales Range: $10-24.9 Million
Emp.: 30
Jewelry & Watch Mfr & Retailer
N.A.I.C.S.: 458310
Carlo Adler (Mng Dir)

BIKAJI FOODS INTERNATIONAL LIMITED
Plot No E-558-561 C-569-572 E-573-577 F-585-592 Karni Extension, RIICO Industrial Area Bikaner, Jaipur, 334004, Rajasthan, India
Tel.: (91) 18001029046　　In
Web Site: https://www.bikaji.com
Year Founded: 1986
543653—(BOM)
Rev.: $221,328,062
Assets: $150,440,595
Liabilities: $38,417,283
Net Worth: $112,023,311
Earnings: $10,377,836
Emp.: 2,698
Fiscal Year-end: 03/31/22
Snack Food Product Mfr
N.A.I.C.S.: 311919

BIKE O & COMPANY LTD.
3-15-4 Wakabayasi, Setagaya-Ward, Tokyo, 154-0023, Japan
Tel.: (81) 368038811
Web Site: https://www.8190.co.jp
Year Founded: 1998
3377—(TKS)
Rev.: $324,086,400
Assets: $116,324,560
Liabilities: $49,290,560
Net Worth: $67,034,000
Earnings: $15,004,000
Fiscal Year-end: 11/30/22
Used Motorcycle Dealers
N.A.I.C.S.: 441227
Yoshihiro Kato (Chm)

BIKE24 HOLDING AG
Breitscheidstr 40, 1237, Dresden, Germany
Tel.: (49) 35141749779　　De
Web Site: https://ir.bike24.com
Year Founded: 2019
BIKE—(DEU)
Rev.: $244,466,868
Assets: $266,139,650
Liabilities: $117,114,181
Net Worth: $149,025,469
Earnings: ($86,772,070)
Emp.: 524
Fiscal Year-end: 12/31/23
Holding Company
N.A.I.C.S.: 551112
Andres Martin-Birner (Founder)

Subsidiaries:

Bike24 GmbH (1)
Breitscheidstr 40, 01237, Dresden, Germany
Tel.: (49) 35141749750
Bike Pedal & Functional Jacket Distr
N.A.I.C.S.: 423120

BIKEEXCHANGE LIMITED
Level 5 126 Phillip Street, Sydney, 2000, NSW, Australia
Tel.: (61) 280721400 AU
Web Site:
https://www.bikeexchange.com
Year Founded: 2007
BEX—(ASX)
Rev.: $4,380,090
Assets: $3,266,438
Liabilities: $4,302,731
Net Worth: ($1,036,293)
Earnings: ($10,766,597)
Fiscal Year-end: 06/30/23
Sporting Goods Distr
N.A.I.C.S.: 459110
Kathy Kotsiopoulos (CFO)

Subsidiaries:

BikeExchange Australia Pty. Ltd. (1)
101 Moray Street, South Melbourne, 3205, VIC, Australia
Tel.: (61) 1300471320
Web Site: https://www.bikeexchange.com.au
Bike Accessories Distr
N.A.I.C.S.: 423120

BikeExchange Colombia S.A.S. (1)
Carrera 65 No 50-12 Edificio Everfit barrio Carlos E Restrepo, Medellin, Antioqua, Colombia
Tel.: (57) 3053668258
Web Site: https://www.bikeexchange.com.co
Bike Accessories Distr
N.A.I.C.S.: 423120

BikeExchange DE Vertriebs GmbH (1)
Leightonstrasse 3, 97074, Wurzburg, Germany
Tel.: (49) 93161423011
Web Site: https://www.bikeexchange.de
Bike Accessories Distr
N.A.I.C.S.: 423120

BIKEN TECHNO CORPORATION LTD.
2-12-1 Minamikanaden, Suita, 564-0044, Osaka, Japan
Tel.: (81) 663802141
Web Site:
https://www.bikentechno.co.jp
Year Founded: 1963
9791—(TKS)
Rev.: $253,632,310
Assets: $272,213,020
Liabilities: $134,685,360
Net Worth: $137,527,660
Earnings: $8,659,100
Emp.: 2,089
Fiscal Year-end: 03/31/24
Building Maintenance Services
N.A.I.C.S.: 561790
Kajiyama Takashi (Chm)

Subsidiaries:

Best Property Co., Ltd. (1)
Sakaisuji Best Building 1F 1-16-13 Minamisenba, Chuo-ku, Osaka, Japan
Tel.: (81) 662610110
Emp.: 92
Real Estate Manangement Services
N.A.I.C.S.: 531210

Care Hotel Management Co., Ltd. (1)
Tennoz First Tower 3F 2-2-4 Higashishinagawa Shinagawa-ku, Tokyo, 140-0002, Japan
Tel.: (81) 368647109
Web Site: http://www.mercilife.co.jp
Home Nursing Care Services
N.A.I.C.S.: 621610

Kokura Enterprise Co., Ltd. (1)
2-14-1 Asano, Kokura Kita Ward, Kitakyushu, 802-8543, Fukuoka, Japan
Tel.: (81) 935114101
Emp.: 77
Real Estate Manangement Services
N.A.I.C.S.: 531210

Mym Community Co., Ltd. (1)
7th floor Fukuya Nikka Kyodo Building 2-2-16 Higashigotanda, Shinagawa-ku, Tokyo, 141-0022, Japan
Tel.: (81) 344121020
Emp.: 56
Real Estate Manangement Services
N.A.I.C.S.: 531210

Singapore Biken Pte. Ltd. (1)
38 Jalan Pemimpin 02-07 M38, Singapore, 577178, Singapore
Tel.: (65) 63486177
Real Estate Manangement Services
N.A.I.C.S.: 531210
Hideto Nakamura (Mng Dir)

VIETNAM BIKEN COMPANY LIMITED (1)
Sky City Tower B No 88 Lang Ha Street Dong Da District, Hanoi, Vietnam
Tel.: (84) 437767036
Web Site: http://www.vnbiken.com
Real Estate Manangement Services
N.A.I.C.S.: 531210
Yuji Koyama (Mng Dir)

BIKUREY HASADE HOLDINGS LTD
Leon Schriber St 1, Kiryat Malachi, 8310902, Israel
Tel.: (972) 89559300
Web Site: https://www.bikurey.co.il
Year Founded: 1950
BKRY—(TAE)
Rev.: $481,880,592
Assets: $311,072,339
Liabilities: $214,304,539
Net Worth: $96,767,800
Earnings: $10,788,732
Fiscal Year-end: 09/30/23
Fresh Fruit & Vegetable Distr
N.A.I.C.S.: 424480
Ilan Sheva (Chm & CEO)

BIL ENERGY SYSTEMS LIMITED
S-105 1st Floor Rajiv Gandhi Commercial Complex, Ekta Nagar Kandivali (West), Mumbai, 400067, India
Tel.: (91) 02228670603 In
Web Site: http://www.bilenergy.com
Year Founded: 2010
Rev.: $3,291,747
Assets: $15,717,802
Liabilities: $12,651,508
Net Worth: $3,066,294
Earnings: $1,310,002
Fiscal Year-end: 03/31/19
Rotating Machine Stamping Mfr
N.A.I.C.S.: 322299
Rajendra Kumar Anandilal Choudhary (CFO)

BILAL FIBRES LIMITED
109-A Street No 3 Cavalry Ground, Lahore, Pakistan
Tel.: (92) 4236672423
Web Site: https://www.bilalfibres.com
Year Founded: 1987
BILF—(PSX)
Rev.: $76,457
Assets: $8,025,422
Liabilities: $7,036,257
Net Worth: $989,165
Earnings: ($62,334)
Emp.: 4
Fiscal Year-end: 06/30/19
Yarn Mfr
N.A.I.C.S.: 313110
Naeem Omer (CEO)

BILCARE LIMITED

601 ICC Trade Tower, Pune, 411 016, India
Tel.: (91) 2067490100 In
Web Site: https://www.bilcare.com
Year Founded: 1995
526853—(BOM)
Rev.: $117,292,007
Assets: $153,809,647
Liabilities: $131,791,105
Net Worth: $22,018,542
Earnings: ($595,317)
Emp.: 288
Fiscal Year-end: 03/31/22
Holding Company; Pharmaceutical & Healthcare Product Research & Development, Packaging Innovation & Brand Authentication Technology Services
N.A.I.C.S.: 551112
Mohan H. Bhandari (Chm & Mng Dir)

Subsidiaries:

Bilcare Ltd. (1)
1028 Shiroli, Rajgurunagar, Pune, 411016, India
Tel.: (91) 2135304200
Web Site: http://www.bilcare.com
Sales Range: $50-74.9 Million
Emp.: 200
Pharmaceutical & Healthcare Product Research & Development, Packaging Innovation & Brand Authentication Technology Services
N.A.I.C.S.: 621511
Mohan H. Bhandari (Chm & Mng Dir)

Bilcare Marketing America Latina Ltda. (1)
Alameda Campinas 834 Apto 111, Jardim Paulista, 01404-001, Sao Paulo, Brazil
Tel.: (55) 11 32669064
Pharmaceutical & Healthcare Product Research & Development, Packaging Innovation & Brand Authentication Technology Services
N.A.I.C.S.: 621511

Bilcare Research GmbH (1)
Schlossmattenstr 2, 79268, Botzingen, Germany
Tel.: (49) 7663 630
Web Site: http://www.bilcaresolutions.com
Emp.: 200
Pharmaceutical & Healthcare Product Research & Development, Packaging Innovation & Brand Authentication Technology Services
N.A.I.C.S.: 621511
Heinz Gartner (Chm)

Subsidiary (Non-US):

Caprihans India Limited (2)
1028 Shiroli Rajgurunagar, Pune, 410505, India (51%)
Tel.: (91) 2135647300
Web Site: https://www.caprihansindia.com
Rev.: $41,545,823
Assets: $27,827,040
Liabilities: $6,129,560
Net Worth: $21,697,480
Earnings: $2,760,644
Emp.: 361
Fiscal Year-end: 03/31/2021
PVC Films Products Mfr
N.A.I.C.S.: 326199
Robin Banerjee (Mng Dir & CEO)

Bilcare Singapore Pte. Ltd. (1)
52 Changi South Street 1, Singapore, 486161, Singapore
Tel.: (65) 63954130
Web Site: http://www.belcare.com
Sales Range: $25-49.9 Million
Emp.: 75
Pharmaceutical & Healthcare Product Research & Development, Packaging Innovation & Brand Authentication Technology Services
N.A.I.C.S.: 621511
Rahul Bharadia (Exec Dir)

Subsidiary (Domestic):

Bilcare Technologies Singapore Pte. Ltd. (2)

52 Changi S St 1, Singapore, 486161, Singapore
Tel.: (65) 63954130
Web Site: http://www.bilcare.com
Sales Range: $50-74.9 Million
Pharmaceutical Preparation Products Mfr
N.A.I.C.S.: 325412
Srinidhi Rao (Mgr-HR)

BILENDI SA
4 Rue de Ventadour, 75001, Paris, France
Tel.: (33) 144886030
Web Site: https://www.bilendi.co.uk
Year Founded: 1999
ALBLD—(EUR)
Sales Range: $25-49.9 Million
Information Technology Services
N.A.I.C.S.: 541512
Thierry Hollocou (Dir-Admin & Fin)

Subsidiaries:

Bilendi A/S (1)
Londongade 4, 5000, Odense, Denmark
Tel.: (45) 70701718
Marketing Research Service
N.A.I.C.S.: 541910
Mona Chrestensen (Sr Project Mgr)

Bilendi AB (1)
Birger Jarlsgatan 18 4th Floor, 114 34, Stockholm, Sweden
Tel.: (46) 723109422
Marketing Research Service
N.A.I.C.S.: 541910
Per Johansson (Country Mgr)

Bilendi GmbH (1)
Uhlandstr 47, 10719, Berlin, Germany
Tel.: (49) 30880013949
Marketing Research Service
N.A.I.C.S.: 541910
Julie Petrone (Mktg Mgr)

Bilendi Limited (1)
8 Holyrood Street, London, SE1 2EL, United Kingdom
Tel.: (44) 2078192820
Internet Services
N.A.I.C.S.: 517121
Stephen Boardman (Dir-Svcs for Customer Engagement & Loyalty)

Bilendi Oy (1)
Lonnrotinkatu 5 3rd Floor, 00120, Helsinki, Finland
Tel.: (358) 503497543
Marketing Research Service
N.A.I.C.S.: 541910
Janne Auma-aho (Country Mgr)

Bilendi SA (1)
San Bernardo 20-1, 28015, Madrid, Spain
Tel.: (34) 674911452
Marketing & Consulting Services
N.A.I.C.S.: 541613

BILFINGER SE
Oskar-Meixner-Strabe 1, 68163, Mannheim, Germany
Tel.: (49) 6214590 De
Web Site: https://www.bilfinger.com
Year Founded: 1880
GBF—(STU)
Rev.: $4,951,539,906
Assets: $3,706,148,582
Liabilities: $2,401,920,742
Net Worth: $1,304,227,840
Earnings: $200,463,627
Emp.: 28,650
Fiscal Year-end: 12/31/23
Civil, Commercial & Industrial Construction & Engineering Services
N.A.I.C.S.: 237990
Stephan Bruckner (Deputy Chm-Supervisory Bd)

Subsidiaries:

ALPHA Mess-Steuer-Regeltechnik GmbH (1)
Dr Julius-Leber-Strasse 12, Neustadt, 67433, Germany
Tel.: (49) 632140050
Software Development Services

Bilfinger SE—(Continued)

N.A.I.C.S.: 541511

Abbakus GmbH & Co. KG (1)
Einsteinstrasse 30, 85520, Ottobrunn, Munich, Germany
Tel.: (49) 89 44 49 17604
Web Site: http://www.abbakus.net
Business Management Consulting Services
N.A.I.C.S.: 541018

Achatz Service GmbH (1)
Bergiusstrasse 19-21, 68219, Mannheim, Germany
Tel.: (49) 621898040
Web Site: https://www.achatz-bau.de
Emp.: 200
Construction Engineering Services
N.A.I.C.S.: 541330
Thomas Schroeder (Gen Mgr)

Apleona R&M Ausbau Berlin GmbH (1)
Oberlandstrasse 89, 12099, Berlin, Germany
Tel.: (49) 3062602206
Web Site:
    http://www.rumausbau.bilfinger.com
Construction Engineering Services
N.A.I.C.S.: 541330

Apleona R&M Ausbau Frankfurt GmbH (1)
Carl-Zeiss-Strasse 10/3, 63322, Rodermark, Germany
Tel.: (49) 607492000
Web Site:
    http://www.rumausbau.bilfinger.com
Interior Design Services
N.A.I.C.S.: 541410

Apleona R&M Ausbau GmbH (1)
Gneisenaustrasse 15, 80992, Munich, Germany
Tel.: (49) 89558901101
Web Site: http://www.rum-ausbau.de
Emp.: 5
Interior Design Services
N.A.I.C.S.: 541410
Joachim Mosch (Gen Mgr)

Apleona R&M Ausbau Mannheim GmbH (1)
Kreisstrasse 96, 66127, Saarbrucken, Germany
Tel.: (49) 68985690420
Construction Engineering Services
N.A.I.C.S.: 541330

Apleona R&M Ausbau Munchen GmbH (1)
Gneisenaustrasse 15, 80992, Munich, Germany
Tel.: (49) 895589010
Sales Range: $25-49.9 Million
Emp.: 50
Interior Design Services
N.A.I.C.S.: 541410
Michael Ferchland (Mng Dir)

Apleona R&M Ausbau Stuttgart GmbH (1)
Steinbeisstr 9, 71101, Schonaich, Germany
Tel.: (49) 7031491960
Web Site:
    http://www.rumausbau.bilfinger.com
Construction Engineering Services
N.A.I.C.S.: 541330

Apleona Real Estate GmbH (1)
An der Gehespitz 50, 63263, Neu-Isenburg, Germany
Tel.: (49) 6102453400
Web Site: https://realestate.apleona.com
Emp.: 3,000
Real Estate Management Services
N.A.I.C.S.: 531390
Joachim Ott (CEO)

BAR Industrieservice GmbH (1)
Kuferstr 5, Brunsbuttel, 25541, Germany
Tel.: (49) 485254050
Emp.: 90
Air-Conditioning & Heating Equipment Mfr
N.A.I.C.S.: 333415
Gunter Ahlf (Mgr)

BB Gamma PPP-Projektgesellschaft mbH (1)

Herriotstr 1, 60528, Frankfurt, Hessen, Germany
Tel.: (49) 69 47891 0
Financial Management Services
N.A.I.C.S.: 523999

BB Grundbesitz GmbH (1)
Ludwig-Erhard-Str 30, 28197, Bremen, Germany
Tel.: (49) 421549940
Investment Management Service
N.A.I.C.S.: 523940

BB Infrastructure Services GmbH (1)
Diffenestr 14, 68169, Mannheim, Germany
Tel.: (49) 62170014355
Construction Engineering Services
N.A.I.C.S.: 541330

BBFS Alpha Verwaltungs GmbH (1)
Carl-Reiß-Platz 1-5, Mannheim, 68165, Germany
Tel.: (49) 6214590
Investment Management Service
N.A.I.C.S.: 523940

BBPI seNTinel Pty Ltd (1)
Level 22 111 Pacific Highway, North Sydney, 2060, NSW, Australia
Tel.: (61) 299233300
Construction Engineering Services
N.A.I.C.S.: 541330

BBS Schalungsbau GmbH (1)
Industriestrasse 21, 67240, Bobenheim-Roxheim, Germany
Tel.: (49) 623999820
Construction Engineering Services
N.A.I.C.S.: 541330

BBV Systems GmbH (1)
Industriestrasse 98, 67240, Bobenheim-Roxheim, Germany
Tel.: (49) 623999810
Web Site: https://www.bbv-systems.com
Emp.: 50
Engineering Consulting Services
N.A.I.C.S.: 541330
Guido Mertens (Chm-Exec Bd)

BBV Systems Sp. z o.o. (1)
Siennicka Street 25, Gdansk, 40758, Poland
Tel.: (48) 58 30067 93
Web Site: http://www.bbv-systems.pl
Sales Range: $25-49.9 Million
Emp.: 30
Construction Engineering Services
N.A.I.C.S.: 237990
Krzysztof Lewandowski (Pres)

BEDFORD EDUCATION PARTNERSHIP LIMITED (1)
3rd Floor Braywick Gate, Maidenhead, SL6 1DA, United Kingdom
Tel.: (44) 1628503400
Financial Management Services
N.A.I.C.S.: 523999

BILFINGER BERGER AMBIENTE S.r.l. (1)
Via Fermi Enrico 13/A, 37135, Verona, Italy
Tel.: (39) 0458230715
Construction Engineering Services
N.A.I.C.S.: 541330

Babcock Borsig Power Usluge d.o.o. (1)
Skadarska 15, 11108, Belgrade, Serbia
Tel.: (381) 11 3033 344
Consulting Engineering Services
N.A.I.C.S.: 541330

Babcock Borsig Service Arabia Ltd. (1)
Tel.: (966) 138688833
Web Site: http://www.babcock.bilfinger.com
Eletric Power Generation Services
N.A.I.C.S.: 221118
Souhad Zebian (Mng Dir)

Babcock Borsig Steinmuller GmbH (1)
Duisburger Strasse 375, 46049, Oberhausen, Germany
Tel.: (49) 208 4575 9
Web Site: http://www.bbs.bilfinger.com
Rev: $330,347,500
Emp.: 1,000

Power Plant Engineering Services
N.A.I.C.S.: 541330
Bernhard Kothgasser (Mng Dir)

Subsidiary (Domestic):

Babcock Kraftwerkservice GmbH (2)
Teichlandstrasse 1, Teichland, 3185, Peitz, Germany
Tel.: (49) 35601830
Web Site: https://www.kls-industrieservice.de
Eletric Power Generation Services
N.A.I.C.S.: 221118

Bau-Union Potsdam GmbH (1)
Walter-Kohn-Str 4A, 04356, Leipzig, Germany
Tel.: (49) 341 35130
Construction Engineering Services
N.A.I.C.S.: 541330

BfP Beteiligungsgesellschaft fur Projekte mbH (1)
Volklinger Strasse 4, 40219, Dusseldorf, Germany
Tel.: (49) 211 90101 03
Investment Management Service
N.A.I.C.S.: 523940

Bilfinger Berger (Canada) Inc. (1)
1140 Pender St W Suite 1210, Vancouver, V6E 4G1, BC, Canada
Tel.: (778) 329-4404
Construction Management Services
N.A.I.C.S.: 237990

Bilfinger Berger A1 mobil GmbH (1)
Gustav-Stresemann-Ring 1, 65189, Wiesbaden, Germany
Tel.: (49) 611334800
Investment Management Service
N.A.I.C.S.: 523940

Bilfinger Berger AG-Civil (1)
Gustav-Nachtigal-Strasse 3, D-65189, Wiesbaden, Germany (100%)
Tel.: (49) 61170800
Web Site: http://www.civil.bilfinger.com
Sales Range: $150-199.9 Million
Emp.: 500
Civil Engineering & Construction Services
N.A.I.C.S.: 237990
Jochen Keysberg (Sec)

Subsidiary (Domestic):

BBV Systems GmbH (2)
Industriestrasse 98, 67240, Bobenheim-Roxheim, Germany (100%)
Tel.: (49) 623999810
Web Site: https://www.bbv-systems.com
Sales Range: $25-49.9 Million
Emp.: 100
Pre-Stressed Concrete Construction & Maintenance Contracting Services
N.A.I.C.S.: 238990
Thomas Heubel (Mng Dir)

Subsidiary (Non-US):

Bilfinger Berger (Thai) Construction Co., Ltd. (2)
587 55 Sutthisarnvinijchai Rd 10th Fl Viriyathavorn Bldg, Binbaeng District, Bangkok, 10400, Thailand (100%)
Tel.: (66) 26919449
Web Site: http://www.bilfinger-berger.com
Sales Range: $25-49.9 Million
Emp.: 70
Civil Engineering & Construction Services
N.A.I.C.S.: 237990
Uwe Neidhardt (Mng Dir)

Bilfinger Berger Construction, LLC (2)
Massionan Office 2 Bldg 129 4th St, PO Box 41967, Abu Dhabi, United Arab Emirates (100%)
Tel.: (971) 26324005
Web Site: http://www.bilfingerberger.com
Civil Engineering & Construction Services
N.A.I.C.S.: 237990

Subsidiary (Domestic):

Bilfinger Berger Instandsetzung GmbH (2)
Zielstattstrasse 19, 81379, Munich, Germany (100%)
Tel.: (49) 8972018870

Web Site:
    http://www.instandsetzung.bilfinger.de
Sales Range: $25-49.9 Million
Emp.: 40
Civil Engineering Repair & Maintenance Services
N.A.I.C.S.: 237990

Subsidiary (Non-US):

Bilfinger Berger UK Limited (2)
7400 Daresbury Park, Daresbury, Warrington, WA4 4BS, United Kingdom
Tel.: (44) 1928737500
Sales Range: $50-74.9 Million
Emp.: 200
Civil Engineering & Construction Services
N.A.I.C.S.: 237990

Companhia de Construcao e Engenharia Kin Sun (Macau), Limitada (2)
Nos 60-64 Avenida Infante D Henrique 5 Andar, Edf Centro Comercial Central, Macau, Kin Sun, China (Macau)
Tel.: (853) 28556281
Civil Engineering & Construction Services
N.A.I.C.S.: 237990
Vong Kock Kei (Gen Mgr)

Subsidiary (Domestic):

F+Z Baugesellschaft mbH (2)
Kanalstrasse 44, D-22085, Hamburg, Germany (100%)
Tel.: (49) 402272470
Web Site: http://www.fz-bau.de
Sales Range: $25-49.9 Million
Emp.: 218
Marine & Port Engineering Contractor
N.A.I.C.S.: 238990

Bilfinger Berger AG-Hochbau (1)
Herriotstrasse 1, 60528, Frankfurt, Germany (100%)
Tel.: (49) 69478910
Web Site:
    http://www.hochbau.bilfingerberger.de
Sales Range: $500-549.9 Million
Emp.: 1,800
Commercial Construction Services
N.A.I.C.S.: 236220

Subsidiary (Domestic):

Bilfinger Berger Parking GmbH (2)
Herreiot Strasse 1, D-60528, Frankfurt, Germany (100%)
Tel.: (49) 696688170
Web Site: http://www.parking.bilfinger.de
Multilevel Parking Facility Construction Contracting Services
N.A.I.C.S.: 238190

Implenia Tesch GmbH (2)
Schnabelstrasse 1, 45134, Essen, Germany (100%)
Tel.: (49) 2011707512
Web Site: http://www.tesch-bau.de
Sales Range: $10-24.9 Million
Construction Finance Services
N.A.I.C.S.: 525990

Modernbau GmbH (2)
Eschberger Weg 59, D-66121, Saarbrucken, Germany (100%)
Tel.: (49) 68181990
Web Site: http://www.modernbau.de
Sales Range: $25-49.9 Million
Emp.: 100
Civil Engineering & Commercial Construction Services
N.A.I.C.S.: 237990

bauperformance GmbH (2)
Goldsteinstrasse 114, D-60528, Frankfurt am Main, Germany (100%)
Tel.: (49) 696688440
Web Site: http://www.bauperformance.de
Commercial Building Design & Functionality Advisory Services
N.A.I.C.S.: 541690

Bilfinger Berger Baugesellschaft mbH (1)
Diefenbachgasse 5, A-1150, Vienna, Austria (100%)
Tel.: (43) 1899370
Web Site: http://www.bilfingerberger.at
Sales Range: $25-49.9 Million
Emp.: 70

Private & Public Sector Construction Services
N.A.I.C.S.: 237990
Rudolph Kraft *(Gen Mgr-Structural Engrg)*

Bilfinger Berger Belgium S.A. **(1)**
Interleuvenlaan 64, B-3001, Leuven, Belgium
Tel.: (32) 1640 0305
Construction Services
N.A.I.C.S.: 237990

Bilfinger Berger Budownictwo S.A. **(1)**
ul Domaniewska 50A, 02-672, Warsaw, Poland
Tel.: (48) 22 24 43 400
Web Site: http://www.bilfinger.pl
Construction Engineering Services
N.A.I.C.S.: 541330

Bilfinger Berger Building Polska Sp. z o.o. **(1)**
Domaniewska 50a, 02-672, Warsaw, Poland
Tel.: (48) 22 854 03 20
Construction Engineering Services
N.A.I.C.S.: 541330

Bilfinger Berger Emirates Construction B.V. **(1)**
Werfplein 5, 3238 BH, Zwartewaal, Netherlands
Tel.: (31) 0458230715
Building Construction Services
N.A.I.C.S.: 236210

Bilfinger Berger Entsorgung GmbH **(1)**
Passavant-Geiger-Str 1, Aarbergen, 65326, Hessen, Germany
Tel.: (49) 6120280
Web Site: http://www.bilfinger.com
Emp.: 250
Environmental Consulting Services
N.A.I.C.S.: 541620
Joachim Foerderer *(Gen Mgr)*

Bilfinger Berger Industrial Services GmbH **(1)**
Gneisenaustrasse 15, D-80992, Munich, Germany **(100%)**
Tel.: (49) 89149980
Web Site: http://www.bis.bilfinger.com
Sales Range: $1-4.9 Billion
Emp.: 21,000
Industrial Facility & Equipment Maintenance, Repair & Modernization Services
N.A.I.C.S.: 236210
Hans-Michael Gopfert *(Head-Fin & Controlling)*

Subsidiary (Non-US):

BIS Beteiligungsverwaltungs GmbH **(2)**
Lunzerstrasse 64, Linz, 4031, Austria
Tel.: (43) 73269879798
Web Site: http://www.bilfinger.com
Emp.: 2,000
Investment Management Service
N.A.I.C.S.: 523999
Hans-Michael Goepfert *(CEO)*

BIS Brabant Mobiel B.V. **(2)**
Gooikensdam 4, Postbus 612, 4900 AP, Oosterhout, North Brabant, Netherlands
Tel.: (31) 162428160
Construction Engineering Services
N.A.I.C.S.: 541330
Eric Adal *(Gen Mgr)*

BIS Czech s.r.o. **(2)**
Vaclava Rezace 313, c p 2600, 434 01, Most, Czech Republic **(51%)**
Tel.: (420) 47 645 6602
Web Site: https://www.bisczech.cz
Emp.: 700
Industrial Facility & Equipment Maintenance, Repair & Modernization Contracting Services
N.A.I.C.S.: 811310
Martin Krbec *(CEO)*

Subsidiary (Domestic):

BIS EnTech GmbH **(2)**
Gneisenaustr 15, Munich, 80992, Bavaria, Germany
Tel.: (49) 20997650

Construction Engineering Services
N.A.I.C.S.: 541330

BIS Geratetechnik Deutschland GmbH **(2)**
Hallesche Str 18, 06749, Bitterfeld, Germany
Tel.: (49) 349360558522
Web Site: https://de.geraete.com
Construction Equipment Rental Services
N.A.I.C.S.: 532412
Gerhard Hunger *(CEO)*

Subsidiary (Non-US):

BIS Geratetechnik GmbH **(2)**
Boschstrasse 48, 4600, Wels, Austria
Tel.: (43) 7242 78101 0
Web Site: http://www.gta.bis.bilfinger.com
Construction Machinery Rental Services
N.A.I.C.S.: 532412
Gerhard Hunger *(Mgr)*

BIS Hungary Kft. **(2)**
Akna u 2-4, 1106, Budapest, Hungary **(96.63%)**
Tel.: (36) 1 433 3666
Web Site: https://www.bishungary.hu
Sales Range: $200-249.9 Million
Emp.: 1,000
Industrial Facility & Equipment Maintenance, Repair & Other Specialty Contracting Services
N.A.I.C.S.: 811310

Subsidiary (Domestic):

BIS IKF GmbH **(2)**
Meessen 9, 22113, Oststeinbek, Germany
Tel.: (49) 407139020
Web Site: http://www.ikf.bis.bilfinger.com
Construction Engineering Services
N.A.I.C.S.: 541330

Subsidiary (Non-US):

BIS Industrial Services Belgie N.V. **(2)**
Oude Brug 10, Schoten, 2900, Antwerpen, Belgium
Tel.: (32) 3 3280 010
Web Site: http://www.bilfinger.com
Emp.: 450
Insulation Installation Services
N.A.I.C.S.: 238310
Ruud van Doorn *(Gen Mgr)*

BIS Industrial Services Nederland B.V. **(2)**
Werfplein 5, 3238 BH, Zwartewaal, Netherlands
Tel.: (31) 181 66 73 00
Web Site: http://www.bis-is.com
Emp.: 1,400
Construction Engineering Services
N.A.I.C.S.: 541330
Ruud Van-Dorn *(Mng Dir)*

BIS Industrial Services Osterreich GmbH **(2)**
Lunzer Strasse 64, 4031, Linz, Austria
Tel.: (43) 732 69874588
Web Site: http://www.bilfinger.com
Emp.: 500
Construction Engineering Services
N.A.I.C.S.: 541330
Manfred Handshue *(CIO)*

BIS Industrial Services Sweden AB **(2)**
Frogatan 1, 65343, Karlstad, Sweden **(100%)**
Tel.: (46) 54570970
Web Site: http://www.bis.bilfinger.se
Sales Range: $300-349.9 Million
Emp.: 650
Holding Company; Industrial Equipment Maintenance & Facility Support Services
N.A.I.C.S.: 551112

Subsidiary (Domestic):

BIS Isenta AB **(3)**
Frogatan 1, SE-65343, Karlstad, Sweden **(100%)**
Tel.: (46) 54570970
Industrial Facility Heat, Cold & Acoustical Insulation Contracting Services
N.A.I.C.S.: 238310

Division (Domestic):

BIS Isenta Norr AB **(4)**
Angermanlandsg 28 A, PO Box 259, SE-89126, Ornskoldsvik, Sweden
Tel.: (46) 66010850
Web Site: http://www.bis.bilfinger.se
Sales Range: $25-49.9 Million
Emp.: 5
Industrial Facility Heat, Cold & Acoustical Insulation Contracting Services
N.A.I.C.S.: 238310

Subsidiary (Domestic):

BIS Mixab AB **(3)**
Enekasvagen 4, SE-45155, Uddevalla, Sweden **(90.08%)**
Tel.: (46) 522261170
Sales Range: $50-74.9 Million
Emp.: 160
Scaffolding Construction Services
N.A.I.C.S.: 238990

BIS Nyhammar Vast AB **(3)**
Slattna Basteviksholmen 601, SE-45392, Lysekil, Sweden
Tel.: (46) 52315505
Web Site: http://www.bis.bilfinger.se
Industrial Pipelines, Steel Structures, Heating & Process Equipment Contracting Services
N.A.I.C.S.: 238220

Subsidiary (Non-US):

BIS Industrier AS **(2)**
Luramyrveien 51, NO-4313, Sandnes, Norway **(88.82%)**
Tel.: (47) 51637600
Industrial Contracting Services
N.A.I.C.S.: 238990
Bjorn Harald Celius *(Dir-Sls & Mktg)*

BIS Industrier Danmark A/S **(2)**
Flakagervej 36, 4400, Kalundborg, Denmark
Tel.: (45) 25324671
Nonmetallic Mineral Mining Services
N.A.I.C.S.: 213115

BIS Insulation B.V. **(2)**
Werfplein 5, 3238 BH, Zwartewaal, Netherlands
Tel.: (31) 181667300
Insulation Installation Services
N.A.I.C.S.: 238310

BIS International Construction and Trading N.V. **(2)**
Oude Brug 10, 2900, Schoten, Belgium
Tel.: (32) 33 28 00 10
Industrial Building Construction Services
N.A.I.C.S.: 236210
Wil de Geus *(Gen Mgr)*

Subsidiary (Domestic):

BIS Isoliertechnik Nord GmbH **(2)**
Am Haupttor Bau 3030, Leuna, 6237, Germany
Tel.: (49) 34 61 43 24 95
Web Site: http://www.bilfinger.com
Emp.: 500
Engineering Consulting Services
N.A.I.C.S.: 541330
Michael Dossert *(CEO)*

Subsidiary (Non-US):

BIS Izomar Sp. z o.o. **(2)**
Ul Augustowka 24, PL-02 981, Warsaw, Poland **(100%)**
Tel.: (48) 226516083
Web Site: http://www.izomar.com
Sales Range: $75-99.9 Million
Emp.: 500
Industrial Heating & Insulation Contracting Services
N.A.I.C.S.: 541330

BIS MainServ Sp. z o.o. **(2)**
Ul Augustowka 30, 02-981, Warsaw, Poland
Tel.: (48) 22 587 78 93
Web Site: http://www.bbis.pl
Construction Engineering Services
N.A.I.C.S.: 541330

Subsidiary (Domestic):

BIS Maintenance Nord GmbH **(2)**

In den Leuna-Werken Gebaude 8642, 06237, Leuna, Germany
Tel.: (49) 3461432991
Web Site: http://www.mn.bis.bilfinger.com
Emp.: 300
Construction Engineering Services
N.A.I.C.S.: 541330
Hermann Holme *(Mng Dir)*

BIS Maintenance Sudwest GmbH **(2)**
An der Bundesstr 3, Leimen, 69181, Germany
Tel.: (49) 6224 701 701
Web Site: http://www.msw.bis.bilfinger.com
Emp.: 480
Industrial Plant Construction Services
N.A.I.C.S.: 236210
Franz Braun *(Gen Mgr)*

Subsidiary (Non-US):

BIS Multiserwis Sp. z o.o. **(2)**
ul Prudnicka 40, 47-300, Krapkowice, Poland
Tel.: (48) 774009100
Web Site: https://multiserwis.com.pl
Sales Range: $400-449.9 Million
Emp.: 1,500
Insulation Installation Services
N.A.I.C.S.: 238310
Pawel Zielinski *(Dir-Fin)*

BIS Prefal - Isolamentos Termicos Lda. **(2)**
Rua de Marvila n 121, 1950-197, Lisbon, Portugal
Tel.: (351) 21 861 0550
Web Site: https://www.prefal.com.pt
Emp.: 50
Insulation Installation Services
N.A.I.C.S.: 238310
Armando Mendes *(Gen Mgr)*

BIS Production Partner AB **(2)**
Gesallgatan 5, 444 32, Stenungsund, Sweden
Tel.: (46) 770 110 411
Web Site: http://www.se.productionpartner.com
Sales Range: $150-199.9 Million
Emp.: 330
Industrial Machinery Sales & Maintenance Services
N.A.I.C.S.: 423830

BIS Production Partner Ipec AS **(2)**
Sagmyra 25, Kristiansand, 4624, Norway
Tel.: (47) 38 11 11 50
Engineering Consulting Services
N.A.I.C.S.: 541330

Subsidiary (Domestic):

BIS Prozesstechnik GmbH **(2)**
Industriepark Hochst Geb C619, 65926, Frankfurt am Main, Germany
Tel.: (49) 6930513734
Web Site: http://www.pte.bis.bilfinger.com
Technical Consulting Services
N.A.I.C.S.: 541690

Subsidiary (Non-US):

BIS ROB Zeeland B.V. **(2)**
Ambachtstraat 15, 4538 AV, Terneuzen, Netherlands
Tel.: (31) 115 648 754
Web Site: http://www.bisrob.be
Industrial Machinery Maintenance Services
N.A.I.C.S.: 811310

Subsidiary (Domestic):

BIS Rohrbau Grenzach GmbH **(2)**
Gewerbestr 5, 79639, Grenzach-Wyhlen, Germany
Tel.: (49) 762491650
Pipeline Construction Engineering Services
N.A.I.C.S.: 237120

BIS Rohrleitungsbau GmbH **(2)**
Hallesche Strasse 18, 06749, Bitterfeld, Germany
Tel.: (49) 3493 6099 0
Web Site: http://www.bis-rohrleitungsbau.de
Sales Range: $100-124.9 Million
Emp.: 400
Pipeline Construction Engineering Services
N.A.I.C.S.: 237120
Berd Koanig *(Gen Mgr)*

Bilfinger SE—(Continued)

Subsidiary (Non-US):

BIS Salamis International Limited **(2)**
4 Greenhole Place Bridge Don, Aberdeen,
AB23 8EU, United Kingdom
Tel.: (44) 12 24 24 60 00
Web Site: http://www.bilfinger.com
Sales Range: $50-74.9 Million
Emp.: 200
Industrial Coating Services
N.A.I.C.S.: 238990
Steve Waugh *(CEO)*

BIS Shared Services B.V. **(2)**
Werfplein 5, 3238 BH, Zwartewaal, Netherlands
Tel.: (31) 181667300
Human Resource Consulting Services
N.A.I.C.S.: 541612

**BIS Shared Services Osterreich
GmbH** **(2)**
Lunzerstrasse 64, 4031, Linz, Austria
Tel.: (43) 73269870
Human Resource Consulting Services
N.A.I.C.S.: 541612

Subsidiary (Domestic):

BIS TSG Industrieservice GmbH **(2)**
Ludwig-Hermann-Strasse 100, Gersthofen,
86368, Germany
Tel.: (49) 8214792500
Industrial Machinery Repair & Maintenance
Services
N.A.I.C.S.: 811310

Subsidiary (Non-US):

BIS VAM Anlagentechnik GmbH **(2)**
Dieselstrasse 2, A-4600, Wels, Austria
Tel.: (43) 72424060
Web Site: http://www.vam.at
Sales Range: $250-299.9 Million
Emp.: 900
Industrial Plant, Pipework & Vessel Engineering & Construction Services
N.A.I.C.S.: 236210
Christian Hoefurthner *(CEO)*

BIS Willich GmbH **(2)**
Alxingergasse 31, Vienna, 1230, Austria
Tel.: (43) 1 3300125 0
Emp.: 40
Construction Engineering Services
N.A.I.C.S.: 541330

BIS plettac Sp. z o.o. **(2)**
ul Kosciuszki 19, 63-500, Ostrzeszow,
Poland **(80%)**
Tel.: (48) 625870100
Web Site: http://www.plettac.pl
Sales Range: $10-24.9 Million
Emp.: 500
Scaffolding Construction Services
N.A.I.C.S.: 238990
Boleslaw Janik *(Pres)*

**Bilfinger Berger Industrial Services
Spain S.A.** **(2)**
Calle Monasterio de Suso Y Yuso n 34 -
Planta 3 - Puerta 4, Madrid, 28049, Spain
Tel.: (34) 915 358 760
Web Site: http://www.bis-bilfinger.es
Sales Range: $100-124.9 Million
Emp.: 450
Insulation Installation Services
N.A.I.C.S.: 238310
Victor Oviano *(Reg Mgr)*

Bilfinger Chemserv GmbH **(2)**
St-Peter-Strasse 25, 4021, Linz, Austria
Tel.: (43) 73269870
Web Site: http://www.chemserv.at
Sales Range: $250-299.9 Million
Emp.: 540
Industrial Engineering, Maintenance & Repair Services
N.A.I.C.S.: 333248
Johann Mandl *(Co-CEO & Mgr-HR)*

Subsidiary (Domestic):

Bilfinger EMS GmbH **(2)**
Hohe Tannen 11, 49661, Cloppenburg, Germany
Tel.: (49) 4 471 1820
Web Site: https://www.ems.bilfinger.com
Construction Engineering Services

N.A.I.C.S.: 541330
Karsten Hoffhaus *(Mng Dir & Head-Sls)*

Subsidiary (Non-US):

Bilfinger Industrial Automation Services Ltd. **(2)**
Prospect House Kilbuck Lane, Haydock,
Saint Helens, WA11 9UX, United Kingdom
Tel.: (44) 1942 868 900
Web Site: http://www.bis-atg.cu.uk
Emp.: 200
Design, Manufacturing, Installation, Maintenance of Control & Instrumentation Systems, Electrical Power Systems & Data
Communications Systems
N.A.I.C.S.: 541330
Duncan Hall *(Mng Dir)*

Subsidiary (US):

Bilfinger Industrial Services Inc. **(2)**
15933 Clayton Rd Ste 305, Ballwin, MO
63011
Tel.: (636) 391-4500
Web Site: http://www.is-usa.bilfinger.com
Construction Engineering Services
N.A.I.C.S.: 541330
Boudewijn van Lent *(Pres & CEO)*

Subsidiary (Domestic):

**BIS Frucon Industrial Services
Inc.** **(3)**
15933 Clayton Rd Ste 220, Ballwin, MO
63011-2146 **(100%)**
Tel.: (636) 391-4500
Web Site: http://www.bisfrucon.com
Sales Range: $550-599.9 Million
Industrial Construction, Maintenance & Support Services
N.A.I.C.S.: 236210

Subsidiary (Non-US):

Fru-Con Mexico S.A. de C.V. **(4)**
Bondojito No 340 Col Las Americas, Deleg
Alvaro Obregon, C P 01120, Mexico, D F,
Mexico
Tel.: (52) 5 277 8311
N.A.I.C.S.: 425120

Subsidiary (Domestic):

BIS Salamis Inc. **(3)**
510 Laflamme Rd, Broussard, LA 70518
Tel.: (337) 289-0092
Web Site: http://www.bissalamis.com
Industrial Machinery Maintenance Services
N.A.I.C.S.: 811310
David Hebert *(Pres)*

BIS Tepsco Inc. **(3)**
2909 Aaron St, Deer Park, TX 77536
Tel.: (281) 604-0309
Web Site: http://www.tepsco.com
Emp.: 50
Civil Engineering Construction Services
N.A.I.C.S.: 237990
Chris Nordberg *(CEO)*

Westcon, Inc. **(3)**
7401 Yukone Dr, Bismarck, ND 58503
Tel.: (701) 222-0076
Web Site: http://www.westconindustries.com
Sales Range: $150-199.9 Million
Emp.: 1,000
Construction Contracting Services Specializing in Industrial Buildings & Warehouses
N.A.I.C.S.: 236220
Mark C. Peterson *(Founder & Pres)*

Subsidiary (Non-US):

**Bilfinger Industrial Services Norway
AS** **(2)**
Hydroveien 55 Heroya Industripark, Porsgrunn, 3936, Norway
Tel.: (47) 3592 3000
Web Site: http://www.is-norway.bilfinger.com
Emp.: 1,300
Industrial Maintenance & Project Management Consulting Services
N.A.I.C.S.: 541618
Paul Rune Aasrum *(Mng Dir)*

**Bilfinger Industrial Services Schweiz
AG** **(2)**
Untere Bruhlstrasse 4, 4800, Zofingen,
Switzerland
Tel.: (41) 627467111

Web Site: https://www.bilfinger.com
Emp.: 220
Industrial Machinery Maintenance Services
N.A.I.C.S.: 811310
Stefan Frefel *(Branch Mgr)*

Bilfinger Life Science GmbH **(2)**
Urstein Nord 31, 5412, Salzburg, Austria
Tel.: (43) 66286950
Web Site: https://lifescience.bilfinger.com
Pipeline Construction Engineering Services
N.A.I.C.S.: 237120

Bilfinger Salamis UK Limited **(2)**
4 Greenhole Place Bridge of Don, Aberdeen, AB23 8EU, United Kingdom
Tel.: (44) 1224246000
Web Site: http://www.salamis.bilfinger.com
Industrial Insulation & Coating Services
N.A.I.C.S.: 238310
Sandy Onner *(COO)*

Subsidiary (Domestic):

Bilfinger Scheven GmbH **(2)**
Max-Planck-Strasse 77, D-40699, Erkrath,
Germany **(80%)**
Tel.: (49) 210449050
Web Site: http://www.scheven.bilfinger.com
Sales Range: $50-74.9 Million
Emp.: 200
Industrial Pipeline Construction Contracting
Services
N.A.I.C.S.: 332919
Alexander Klocker *(CEO)*

Subsidiary (Non-US):

Bilfinger Tebodin **(2)**
Laan van Nieuw Oost-Indie 25, PO Box
16029, 2593 BJ, Hague, **(100%)**
Netherlands
Tel.: (31) 889967000
Web Site: https://www.tebodin.bilfinger.com
Sales Range: $200-249.9 Million
Emp.: 3,200
Engineering & Consulting Services
N.A.I.C.S.: 541330

Bilfinger UK Limited **(2)**
Wilson House Kelburn Court Daten Park
Birchwood, Warrington, WA3 6UT, Cheshire, United Kingdom
Tel.: (44) 1615375555
Web Site: https://www.uk.bilfinger.com
Emp.: 110
Engineering Consulting Services
N.A.I.C.S.: 541330

Subsidiary (Domestic):

Bilfinger arnholdt GmbH **(2)**
Dorstener Strasse 19 - 26, 44651, Herne,
Germany
Tel.: (49) 20960571000
Web Site: https://www.arnholdt.bilfinger.com
Sales Range: $150-199.9 Million
Emp.: 1,500
Scaffolding Construction Services
N.A.I.C.S.: 238990

Peters Engineering AG **(2)**
Karl-Rader-Str 3-5, 67069, Ludwigshafen,
Germany
Tel.: (49) 621 6506 0
Web Site: http://www.pegmbh.com
Emp.: 200
Construction Engineering Services
N.A.I.C.S.: 541330
Bernd Bodeit *(Mng Dir)*

**Bilfinger Berger Ingenieurbau
GmbH** **(1)**
Am Rohrenwerk 50, 47259, Duisburg, Germany
Tel.: (49) 203 7586 341
Construction Engineering Services
N.A.I.C.S.: 541330

Bilfinger Berger PI Corporate Services GmbH **(1)**
Gustav-Stresemann-Ring 1, Wiesbaden,
65189, Hessen, Germany
Tel.: (49) 611334800
Construction Engineering Services
N.A.I.C.S.: 541330

Bilfinger Berger PI International Holding GmbH **(1)**
Gustav-Stresemann-Ring 1, 65189, Wiesbaden, Germany

Tel.: (49) 611334800
Investment Management Service
N.A.I.C.S.: 523999

Bilfinger Berger Polska S.A. **(1)**
Domaniewska 50 A, PL-02 672, Warsaw,
Poland **(100%)**
Tel.: (48) 222010233
Web Site: http://www.bilfinger.pl
Sales Range: $300-349.9 Million
Emp.: 1,328
Holding Company; Civil Engineering & Facility Construction Services
N.A.I.C.S.: 551112

Subsidiary (Domestic):

Hydrobudowa-6 S.A. **(2)**
ul Domaniewska 50A, PL-02 672, Warsaw,
Poland **(100%)**
Tel.: (48) 224949000
Web Site: http://www.hb6.pl
Sales Range: $500-549.9 Million
Emp.: 1,300
Civil Engineering & Facility Construction
Services
N.A.I.C.S.: 237990

**Bilfinger Berger Power Holdings (pty)
Ltd.** **(1)**
45 Delaruy road, Rivonia, 2191, South Africa
Tel.: (27) 11 806 3000
Web Site:
http://www.powerafrica.bilfinger.com
Power Plant Construction Services
N.A.I.C.S.: 237130

Bilfinger Berger Projects S.a.r.l. **(1)**
Aerogolf Center Heienhaff 1A, 1736, Senningerberg, Luxembourg **(100%)**
Tel.: (352) 621273100
Sales Range: $25-49.9 Million
Emp.: 6
Public Building & Transportation Infrastructure Construction Services
N.A.I.C.S.: 236220

Subsidiary (Non-US):

**Bilfinger Berger Project Investments
GmbH** **(2)**
Gustav-Stresemann-Ring 1, Wiesbaden,
65189, Germany **(100%)**
Tel.: (49) 611334800
Web Site: http://www.bilfinger.com
Sales Range: $25-49.9 Million
Public Building & Transportation Infrastructure Construction Services
N.A.I.C.S.: 236220
Herbert Bodner *(Chm)*

**Bilfinger Berger Project Investments
Inc.** **(2)**
675 Cochrane Drive, West Tower Suite 630,
Markham, L3R 0B8, ON, Canada **(100%)**
Tel.: (905) 530-2114
Web Site: http://www.pi.bilfinger.com
Sales Range: $25-49.9 Million
Public Building & Transportation Infrastructure Construction Services
N.A.I.C.S.: 236220
Damian Joy *(Pres)*

Bilfinger Berger Regiobau GmbH **(1)**
Hans-Bunte-Str 12, 79108, Freiburg, Germany
Tel.: (49) 761510490
Web Site: http://www.regiobau.bilfinger.com
Construction Engineering Services
N.A.I.C.S.: 541330

**Bilfinger Berger Spezialtiefbau
GmbH** **(1)**
Goldsteinstrasse 114, 60528, Frankfurt am
Main, Germany
Tel.: (49) 696688345
Web Site:
http://www.spezialtiefbau.bilfinger.com
Construction Engineering Services
N.A.I.C.S.: 541330

**Bilfinger Berger Umwelttechnik
GmbH** **(1)**
Passavant-Roediger-Strasse 1, D-65326,
Aarbergen, Germany **(100%)**
Tel.: (49) 6120280
Web Site: http://www.passavant-roediger.de
Sales Range: $300-349.9 Million
Emp.: 368

Holding Company; Water & Waste Management Facility Construction & Engineering Services
N.A.I.C.S.: 551112

Bilfinger Berger stavebni Praha, s.r.o. (1)
Pekarska 603/12, CZ-155 00, Prague, Czech Republic
Tel.: (420) 257013612
Construction Services
N.A.I.C.S.: 237990

Bilfinger Bohr- und Rohrtechnik GmbH (1)
Adelheid Popp-Strasse 8, 1210, Wolkersdorf im Weinviertel, Austria
Tel.: (43) 2245211030
Web Site: http://www.bur.at
Pipeline System Installation Services
N.A.I.C.S.: 237990
Christian Strondl (Mng Dir)

Bilfinger Brabant Mobiel B.V. (1)
Waalhaven East side 123, 3087 BM, Rotterdam, Netherlands
Tel.: (31) 102034000
Industrial Construction Services
N.A.I.C.S.: 541330

Bilfinger Danmark A/S (1)
Vesterhavsgade 147, 6700, Esbjerg, Denmark
Tel.: (45) 88638861
Web Site: https://www.bilfinger.com
Industrial Maintenance & Engineering Services
N.A.I.C.S.: 811310

Bilfinger EMV B.V. (1)
Boereveldseweg 4 - Haven 1062, B-2070, Zwijndrecht, Belgium
Tel.: (32) 35751414
Piping & Mechanical Project Maintenance Services
N.A.I.C.S.: 811310

Bilfinger Engineering & Maintenance GmbH (1)
Europaallee 1, 46047, Oberhausen, Germany
Tel.: (49) 6102452740
Web Site: https://bem.bilfinger.com
Emp.: 3,000
Industrial Maintenance & Engineering Services
N.A.I.C.S.: 811310

Bilfinger Engineering & Maintenance Nordics AB (1)
Rattgatan 4, 44240, Kungalv, Sweden
Tel.: (46) 200770900
Engineering Services
N.A.I.C.S.: 541330

Bilfinger Engineering & Maintenance Nordics AS (1)
Hydroveien 55, 3936, Porsgrunn, Norway
Tel.: (47) 35923000
Engineering Services
N.A.I.C.S.: 541330

Bilfinger Engineering & Maintenance Nordics Oy (1)
Rihkamakatu 2, 06100, Porvoo, Finland
Tel.: (358) 503163732
Engineering Services
N.A.I.C.S.: 541330

Bilfinger Gerber GmbH (1)
Revierstr 3, 44379, Dortmund, Germany
Tel.: (49) 231 9952 0
Web Site: http://www.gerber.bilfinger.com
Emp.: 30
Mfr of Customized Noise Control & Air Intake Systems
N.A.I.C.S.: 334519
Thomas Meyer (Gen Mgr)

Bilfinger Height Specialists B.V. (1)
Weg en Land 48, 2661 KR, Bergschenhoek, Netherlands
Tel.: (31) 152565662
Web Site: https://heightspecialists.com
Industrial Rope Access Services
N.A.I.C.S.: 561990

Bilfinger Industrial Automation Services Ltd. (1)
Redwood House Woodlands Park Ashton

Road, Newton-le-Willows, WA12 0HF, United Kingdom
Tel.: (44) 1942 868900
Web Site: http://www.ias.bilfinger.com
Automation & Control Solutions Mfr & Services
N.A.I.C.S.: 334513
Dave Pickles (Mng Dir)

Bilfinger Industrial Services Austria GmbH (1)
Lunzerstrasse 64, 4030, Linz, Austria
Tel.: (43) 7322724040
Web Site: https://bis-austria.bilfinger.com
Emp.: 2,000
Industrial Maintenance Services
N.A.I.C.S.: 811310

Bilfinger Industrial Services Belgie N.V. (1)
Boereveldseweg 4, B-2070, Zwijndrecht, Belgium
Tel.: (32) 33280010
Industrial Construction Services
N.A.I.C.S.: 541330

Bilfinger Industrial Services Beteiligungs GmbH (1)
Lunzerstrasse 64, 4030, Linz, Austria
Tel.: (43) 7322724040
Web Site: https://bis-austria.bilfinger.com
Hydropower Energy Storage Services
N.A.I.C.S.: 926130

Bilfinger Industrial Services Germany GmbH (1)
Gewerbestrasse 5, D-79639, Grenzach-Wyhlen, Germany
Tel.: (49) 762491650
Industrial Pipeline Construction Services
N.A.I.C.S.: 541990

Bilfinger Industrial Services Nederland B.V. (1)
Waalhaven Oostzijde 123, 3087 BM, Rotterdam, Netherlands
Tel.: (31) 102034000
Web Site: https://www.bilfinger.com
Industrial Construction Services
N.A.I.C.S.: 541330

Bilfinger Industrial Services Polska Sp. z o.o (1)
Ul Pozarowa 6, 03-309, Warsaw, Poland
Tel.: (48) 223409100
Web Site: https://www.bilfinger.com
Industrial Maintenance & Repair Services
N.A.I.C.S.: 811310

Bilfinger Industrial Services Switzerland AG (1)
Untere Bruhlstrasse 4, 4800, Zofingen, Switzerland
Tel.: (41) 627467101
Web Site: https://ch.bilfinger.com
Pipe & Plant Construction Services
N.A.I.C.S.: 541990

Bilfinger LTM Industrie SAS (1)
114 Rue Pasteur, 69780, Toussieu, France
Tel.: (33) 472045354
Web Site: https://www.bilfinger.com
Civil Engineering Construction Services
N.A.I.C.S.: 541330

Bilfinger Life Science Automation GmbH (1)
Conrad-Rontgen-str 1, 24941, Flensburg, Germany
Tel.: (49) 4615054870
Web Site: https://life-science.bilfinger.com
Emp.: 500
Electrical Engineering Services
N.A.I.C.S.: 541330

Bilfinger Maschinenbau GmbH & Co KG (1)
Wahringerstrasse 34, Postfach 35, 4031, Linz, Austria
Tel.: (43) 732 6987 3365
Web Site:
http://www.maschinenbau.bilfinger.com
Rev.: $66,069,500
Emp.: 350
Turbine Mfr
N.A.I.C.S.: 333611
Juergen Winkler (Chm)

Bilfinger Nordics AS (1)
Kanalarmen 8, 4033, Stavanger, Norway

Tel.: (47) 48024444
Web Site: https://nordics.bilfinger.com
Emp.: 3,600
Industrial Maintenance & Engineering Services
N.A.I.C.S.: 811310

Bilfinger North America Inc. (1)
2909 Aaron St, Deer Park, TX 77536
Tel.: (281) 604-0309
Web Site: https://northamerica.bilfinger.com
Emp.: 25
Construction & Maintenance Services
N.A.I.C.S.: 811310

Bilfinger Nuclear & Energy Transition GmbH (1)
Europaallee 1, 46047, Oberhausen, Germany
Tel.: (49) 9319030
Web Site: https://www.bilfinger.com
Nuclear & Magnet Technology Services
N.A.I.C.S.: 541690
Andreas Hilpert (Executives)

Bilfinger Personalservice Osterreich GmbH (1)
Lunzerstrasse 64, Linz, A-4031, Austria
Tel.: (43) 732 6987 6299
Web Site: http://www.ps-a.bilfinger.com
Emp.: 15
Temporary Staffing Services
N.A.I.C.S.: 561320
Manfred Handschuh (Mng Dir)

Bilfinger Peters Engineering SAS (1)
155 Bis Avenue Pierre Brossolette, 92120, Montrouge, France
Tel.: (33) 173791199
Web Site: https://www.peters.bilfinger.com
Emp.: 200
Industrial Engineering Services
N.A.I.C.S.: 541330

Bilfinger Power Systems GmbH (1)
Europaallee 1, D-46047, Oberhausen, Germany **(100%)**
Tel.: (49) 20845759
Web Site:
http://www.powerservices.bilfinger.de
Sales Range: $1-4.9 Billion
Emp.: 4,000
Holding Company; Power Station & Industrial Plant Technology & Engineering Services
N.A.I.C.S.: 551112

Subsidiary (Domestic):

BHR Hochdruck-Rohrleitungsbau GmbH (2)
Wolbeckstrasse 25, D-45329, Essen, Germany
Tel.: (49) 20136450
Web Site: http://www.bhr.bilfinger.de
Sales Range: $200-249.9 Million
Emp.: 950
Industrial Pipe Mfr & Installation Services
N.A.I.C.S.: 332996

Subsidiary (Non-US):

BHR Piping Systems (Pty) Ltd. (3)
Block D Homestead Park 37 Homestead Road, Rivonia, 2191, South Africa
Tel.: (27) 118063911
Web Site: http://www.bhr-p.bilfinger.com
Sales Range: $50-74.9 Million
Emp.: 130
Construction Piping System Mfr
N.A.I.C.S.: 331210

Subsidiary (Domestic):

Babcock Borsig Service GmbH (2)
Duisburger Strasse 375, D-46049, Oberhausen, Germany
Tel.: (49) 20845759
Web Site: http://www.babcock-borsig-service.de
Sales Range: $800-899.9 Million
Emp.: 2,946
Power Station & Industrial Plant Technology & Engineering Services
N.A.I.C.S.: 561210

Subsidiary (Non-US):

Babcock Borsig Steinmuller CZ s.r.o. (2)

Krizikova 72, Brno, 612 00, Czech Republic
Tel.: (420) 545104040
Web Site: http://www.babcock-cz.bilfinger.com
Electric Equipment Mfr
N.A.I.C.S.: 335999
Michal Enzl (CEO)

Steinmuller Africa (pty) Ltd. (2)
45 De La Rey Road, PO Box 1537, Rivonia, Johannesburg, 2128, South Africa
Tel.: (27) 118063000
Web Site:
https://www.steinmuller.bilfinger.com
Eletric Power Generation Services
N.A.I.C.S.: 221118
Juergen Koerner (Mng Dir)

Bilfinger ROB N.V. (1)
Boereveldseweg 4 - Haven 1062, 2070, Zwijndrecht, Belgium
Tel.: (32) 35751414
Web Site: https://rob.bilfinger.com
Emp.: 600
Manufacture & Assembly of Piping & Furnaces for Petro-Chemical & Energy Industries
N.A.I.C.S.: 237120
Thierry Burki (Mng Dir)

Bilfinger Real Estate GmbH (1)
Berner Strasse 35, D-60437, Frankfurt am Main, Germany
Tel.: (49) 6939001600
Web Site: http://www.realestate.bilfinger.de
Sales Range: $250-299.9 Million
Emp.: 460
Portfolio Asset & Real Estate Management Services
N.A.I.C.S.: 531190
Aydin Karaduman (Mng Dir)

Subsidiary (Non-US):

Bilfinger Real Estate BV (2)
Euclideslaan 135, 3584 BR, Utrecht, Netherlands
Tel.: (31) 302565165
Web Site: http://www.realestate.bilfinger.nl
Real Estate Development Services
N.A.I.C.S.: 531390
Paul Blijham (CEO)

Subsidiary (Domestic):

Bilfinger Real Estate GeServ GmbH (2)
Olof-Palme-Strasse 17, 60439, Frankfurt am Main, Germany
Tel.: (49) 21187632206
Real Estate Advisory Services
N.A.I.C.S.: 531390

Bilfinger Real Estate InServ GmbH (2)
Aarstrasse 1, Wiesbaden, 65195, Germany
Tel.: (49) 8954095498
Real Estate Development Services
N.A.I.C.S.: 531390

VIVANIUM GmbH (2)
Hildebrandtstrasse 24C, 40215, Dusseldorf, Germany
Tel.: (49) 21130131380
Logistics Consulting Servies
N.A.I.C.S.: 541614

Bilfinger Rotring Engineering GmbH (1)
Rudolf-Diesel-Str 2c, Buxtehude, 21614, Germany
Tel.: (49) 4161 7409 0
Web Site: http://www.rotring.bilfinger.com
Sales Range: $25-49.9 Million
Emp.: 40
Fuel Gas System Installation Services
N.A.I.C.S.: 238220
Andreas Hilpert (CFO)

Bilfinger Shared Services GmbH (1)
Oskar-Meixner-Strasse 1, 68163, Mannheim, Germany
Tel.: (49) 81415278447
Industrial Engineering Services
N.A.I.C.S.: 541330

Bilfinger Tebodin Belgium NV (1)
Boereveldseweg 4 Harbor 1062, Zwijndrecht, 2070, Antwerp, Belgium
Tel.: (32) 32502801

Bilfinger SE—(Continued)

Construction Management Services
N.A.I.C.S.: 541330

Bilfinger Tebodin Hungary Kft. (1)
Lomb Utca 37-39, 1139, Budapest, Hungary
Tel.: (36) 302301124
Construction Management Services
N.A.I.C.S.: 541330

**Bilfinger Tebodin Netherlands
B.V.** (1)
Laan van Nieuw Oost-Indie 25, 2593 BJ,
Hague, Netherlands
Tel.: (31) 889967000
Web Site: https://www.tebodin.bilfinger.com
Asset Management Services
N.A.I.C.S.: 531390

Bilfinger Tebodin Romania S.R.L. (1)
Str Eminescu No 108-112 020074 Emi-
nescu Offices Sector 2, Bucharest, Roma-
nia
Tel.: (40) 372727440
Construction Management Services
N.A.I.C.S.: 541330

**Bilfinger Wolfferts Gebaudetechnik
GmbH** (1)
Hansestrasse 1, 51149, Cologne, Germany
Tel.: (49) 220330020
Web Site:
　http://www.gebaeudetechnik.bilfinger.com
Sales Range: $50-74.9 Million
Emp.: 150
Construction Engineering Services
N.A.I.C.S.: 237990
Horst Kever (Chm-Mgmt Bd)

Subsidiary (Domestic):

**Wolfferts Haus- und Warmetechnik
GmbH** (2)
Hansestrasse 1, 51149, Cologne,
Nordrhein-Westfalen, Germany
Tel.: (49) 220330020
Plumbing & Heating Equipment Installation
Services
N.A.I.C.S.: 238220

**CEC Construction Engineering +
Contracting GmbH** (1)
Gustav-Nachtigal-Str 5, Wiesbaden, 65189,
Hessen, Germany
Tel.: (49) 611708587
Emp.: 2
Construction Engineering Services
N.A.I.C.S.: 541330
Hartwig Ruckert (Mng Dir)

**COVENTRY EDUCATION PART-
NERSHIP HOLDINGS LIMITED** (1)
3rd Floor Braywick Gate Braywick Road,
Maidenhead, SL6 1DA, Berkshire, United
Kingdom
Tel.: (44) 1628503400
Investment Management Service
N.A.I.C.S.: 523999

**Centennial Contractors Enterprises,
Inc.** (1)
11111 Sunset Hills Rd Ste 350, Reston, VA
20190
Tel.: (703) 885-4600
Web Site: https://cce-inc.com
Sales Range: $25-49.9 Million
Emp.: 30
Commercial & Institutional Facility Engineer-
ing & Construction Services
N.A.I.C.S.: 541330
Mark Bailey (Pres & CEO)

**Clackmannanshire Schools Education
Partnership (Holdings) Ltd.** (1)
3rd Floor Braywick Gate Braywick Road,
Maidenhead, SL6 1DA, United Kingdom
Tel.: (44) 1628503400
Emp.: 20
Investment Management Service
N.A.I.C.S.: 523999
Tim Sharpe (Mng Dir)

**Deutsche Babcock Middle East
FZE** (1)
PO Box 46698, Abu Dhabi, United Arab
Emirates
Tel.: (971) 2 49959 99
Web Site: http://www.babcock.bilfinger.com

Industrial Machinery Repair & Maintenance
Services
N.A.I.C.S.: 811310
Thomas Suckut (CEO & Mng Dir)

Djuro Djakovic Montage GmbH (1)
Max-Planck-Ring 13, 46049, Oberhausen,
Germany
Tel.: (49) 208 85 79 70
Web Site: http://www.ddm.bilfinger.com
Construction Engineering Services
N.A.I.C.S.: 237990

Duro Dakovic Montaza d.d. (1)
Dr Mile Budaka 1, 35000, Slavonski Brod,
Croatia
Tel.: (385) 35218119
Web Site: https://www.ddmontaza.hr
Emp.: 1,100
Construction Engineering Services
N.A.I.C.S.: 237990
Darko Katic (CFO)

**EPM Swiss Property Management
AG** (1)
Industriestrasse 21, 8304, Wallisellen, Swit-
zerland
Tel.: (41) 44 878 78 78
Web Site: http://www.epm-swiss.ch
Real Estate Manangement Services
N.A.I.C.S.: 531390

Euro Ressurs AS (1)
Luramyrveien 51, 4391, Sandnes, Norway
Tel.: (47) 51 63 76 00
Textile Machinery Distr
N.A.I.C.S.: 423830

FCC Corporation (1)
15933 Clayton Rd, Ballwin, MO 63011
Tel.: (636) 391-4433
Real Estate Manangement Services
N.A.I.C.S.: 531390

**Fire Support (SSFR) Holdings
Ltd.** (1)
3rd Floor Braywick Gate, Maidenhead, SL6
1DA, Berkshire, United Kingdom
Tel.: (44) 1628503400
Web Site: http://www.bilfinger.com
Emp.: 20
Investment Management Service
N.A.I.C.S.: 523999
Tim Sharpe (Gen Mgr)

Fondsmanagement Berlin GmbH (1)
Friedrichstr 194-199, 10117, Berlin, Ger-
many
Tel.: (49) 3022663076
Fund Management Services
N.A.I.C.S.: 523940

**Fondsmanagement Dusseldorf
GmbH** (1)
Moskauer Strasse 27, 40227, Dusseldorf,
Nordrhein-Westfalen, Germany
Tel.: (49) 21138059661
Investment Management Service
N.A.I.C.S.: 523999

Franz Kassecker GmbH (1)
Egerer Strasse 36, 95652, Waldsassen,
Germany (60%)
Tel.: (49) 9 632 5010
Web Site: https://www.kassecker.de
Sales Range: $100-124.9 Million
Emp.: 500
Commercial, Industrial & Civil Engineering
& Construction Contracting Services
N.A.I.C.S.: 237990
Walter Arnold (Mng Dir)

Friedrich Eisen GmbH (1)
August-Borsig-Strasse 4, 68199, Mann-
heim, Germany
Tel.: (49) 621853051
Pipeline Repair & Maintenance Services
N.A.I.C.S.: 811310

Huser & Co GmbH (1)
Carl-Reiss-Platz 1-5, 68165, Mannheim,
Baden-Wurttemberg, Germany
Tel.: (49) 621 4590
Real Estate Manangement Services
N.A.I.C.S.: 531390

Inselko AS (1)
Heroya Naeringspark, 3908, Porsgrunn,
Norway
Tel.: (47) 32 92 28 10
Electrical Engineering Services

N.A.I.C.S.: 541330

Julius Berger Nigeria PLC (1)
10 Shettima A Munguno Crescent, Utako,
900 108, Abuja, Nigeria (49%)
Tel.: (234) 8039067000
Web Site: http://www.julius-berger.com
Rev.: $884,285,743
Assets: $1,245,592,605
Liabilities: $1,106,968,265
Net Worth: $138,624,340
Earnings: $21,778,649
Emp.: 13,358
Fiscal Year-end: 12/31/2021
Civil, Industrial & Commercial Engineering,
Construction & Contracting Services
N.A.I.C.S.: 237990
George Marks (Vice Chm)

L.T.M. Industrie SAS (1)
114 Rue Pasteur, 69780, Toussieu, France
Tel.: (33) 472045354
Web Site: http://wwwltm-france.com
Emp.: 250
Pipeline Construction Engineering Services
N.A.I.C.S.: 237120
Iacovella Daniel (Mgr)

Lauing Heatec Co., Ltd. (1)
49/21 Moo 5 Laemchabang Industrial Es-
tate Export Zone 2 Tungsukla, Sriracha,
Chon Buri, 20230, Thailand
Tel.: (66) 384916207
Web Site: https://lauing-heatec.com
Industrial Machinery & Equipment Mainte-
nance Services
N.A.I.C.S.: 811310

**Millennium Risk Management
LLC** (1)
2236 Cahaba Valley Dr Ste 101, Birming-
ham, AL 35242-2677
Tel.: (205) 451-0812
Business Management Consulting Services
N.A.I.C.S.: 541611
Amy Enman (Supvr)

Noggerath France EURL (1)
11 Rue Du General De Gaulle, 45650,
Saint-Jean-le-blanc, France
Tel.: (33) 238224054
Waste Water Treatment Services
N.A.I.C.S.: 221310

P.T. Bilfinger Berger Indonesia (1)
JI Tol Cakung Cilincing Km 11 725, Bintara,
Bekasi, 17136, Indonesia (100%)
Tel.: (62) 218894232
Construction Services
N.A.I.C.S.: 237990

PJB Beteiligungs-GmbH (1)
Gustav-Stresemann-Ring 1, 65189, Wies-
baden, Germany
Tel.: (49) 611334800
Construction Engineering Services
N.A.I.C.S.: 541330

PJB Management-GmbH (1)
Gustav-Stresemann-Ring 1, Wiesbaden,
65189, Germany
Tel.: (49) 611 33480 0
Real Estate Manangement Services
N.A.I.C.S.: 531390

**PPP Schloss Sonnenstein
GmbH** (1)
Herriotstrasse 1, 60528, Frankfurt am Main,
Germany
Tel.: (49) 69478910
Property Development Services
N.A.I.C.S.: 531312

PPP Schulen Halle GmbH (1)
Grosse Brauhausstrasse 17, 06108, Halle,
Germany
Tel.: (49) 341 3513 0
Construction Engineering Services
N.A.I.C.S.: 541330

**PPP Schulen Landkreis Hof
GmbH** (1)
Herriotstr 1, 60528, Frankfurt am Main,
Hessen, Germany
Tel.: (49) 69668800
Construction Engineering Services
N.A.I.C.S.: 541330

**Projekt- und Betriebsgesllschaft
Justizzentrum Chemnitz GmbH** (1)
An Der Gehespitz 50, 63263, Neu-Isenburg,

Hessen, Germany
Tel.: (49) 6102 453400
Construction Engineering Services
N.A.I.C.S.: 541330

**Projektgesellschaft Justizvollzug Burg
GmbH & Co. KG** (1)
c/o Bilfinger RE Asset Management GmbH
An der Gehespitze 50, 63263, Neu-
Isenburg, Germany
Tel.: (49) 6102450
Web Site: http://www.jva-brg.sachsen-
　anhalt.de
Construction Engineering Services
N.A.I.C.S.: 541330

R&M Ausbau Leipzig GmbH (1)
Walter-Kohn-Strasse 4, 04365, Leipzig,
Germany
Tel.: (49) 341649690
Construction Engineering Services
N.A.I.C.S.: 541330

R&M Baudienstleistungen GmbH (1)
Gneisenaustr 15, 80992, Munich, Germany
Tel.: (49) 89 149980
Construction Engineering Services
N.A.I.C.S.: 541330

**R&M Fassadentechnik Sudwest
GmbH** (1)
Gneisenaustr 15, 80992, Munich, Bavaria,
Germany
Tel.: (49) 8914998121
Industrial Machinery Repair & Maintenance
Services
N.A.I.C.S.: 811310

**R&M Kuhllagerbau Bielefeld
GmbH** (1)
Sudbrackstrasse 17, 33611, Bielefeld, Ger-
many
Tel.: (49) 521 98250 0
Web Site: http://www.rum-kuehllagerbau.de
Construction Engineering Services
N.A.I.C.S.: 541330

**R&M Kuhllagerbau Holding
GmbH** (1)
Sudbrackstrasse 17, Bielefeld, 33611, Ger-
many
Tel.: (49) 521 98250 0
Web Site: http://www.rum-kuehllagerbau.de
Emp.: 20
Cold Storage Plant Construction Services
N.A.I.C.S.: 236220

Roediger Gebaudetechnik GmbH (1)
Kinzigheimer Weg 104-106, 63450, Hanau,
Germany
Tel.: (49) 618 1309 0
Web Site: http://www.roediger-gt.de
Heating & Plumbing Equipment Installation
Services
N.A.I.C.S.: 238220

Roediger Grundbesitz GmbH (1)
Kinzigheimer Weg 104-106, 63450, Hanau,
Hessen, Germany
Tel.: (49) 61813090
Real Estate Manangement Services
N.A.I.C.S.: 531390

**SVA Verkehrssicherungs-Anlagen Ge-
sellschaft mit beschrankter
Haftung** (1)
Kreissstr 96, 66127, Saarbrucken, Germany
Tel.: (49) 6898933800
Web Site: http://www.sva-verkehr.com
Traffic Safety Equipment Installation Ser-
vices
N.A.I.C.S.: 238990

**Scottish Borders Education Partner-
ship Holdings Ltd.** (1)
3rd Floor Braywick Gate Braywick Road,
Maidenhead, SL6 1DA, Berkshire, United
Kingdom
Tel.: (44) 1628503400
Investment Management Service
N.A.I.C.S.: 523999

**Scottish Borders Education Partner-
ship Ltd.** (1)
3rd Floor Braywick Gate, Maidenhead, SL6
1DA, Berkshire, United Kingdom
Tel.: (44) 1628503400
Educational Consulting Services611710
N.A.I.C.S.: 611710
Tim Sharpe (Mng Dir)

Steinmuller Engineering Services (pty) Ltd. (1)
45 Delarey Road, Rivonia, 2128, South Africa
Tel.: (27) 11 806 3000
Engineeering Services
N.A.I.C.S.: 541330

Tebodin Peters Engineering GmbH (1)
Karl Rader Str 3-5, 67069, Ludwigshafen, Germany
Tel.: (49) 62165060
Web Site: http://www.pe-france.com
Engineeering Services
N.A.I.C.S.: 541330
Bernd Bodelt *(Mng Dir)*

Subsidiary (Non-US):

Tebodin Peters Engineering France SARL (2)
53-55 bd Romain Rolland, 92120, Montrouge, France
Tel.: (33) 147351380
Web Site: http://www.pe-france.com
Construction Engineering Services
N.A.I.C.S.: 541330
Gilles Maes *(Gen Mgr)*

The Stoke On Trent & Staffordshire Safer Communities Community Interest Company (1)
3rd Floor Braywick Gate Braywick Road, Maidenhead, SL6 1DA, Berkshire, United Kingdom
Tel.: (44) 1628 503 400
Emp.: 7
Construction Engineering Services
N.A.I.C.S.: 541330
Nick Harris *(Gen Mgr)*

Victorian Correctional Infrastructure Partnership Pty. Ltd. (1)
Level 51 525 Collins Street, Melbourne, 3000, VIC, Australia
Tel.: (61) 299233300
Web Site: http://www.bilfinger.com
Emp.: 20
Real Estate Manangement Services
N.A.I.C.S.: 531390
Graham Whitson *(Gen Mgr)*

Willich Beteiligungen GmbH (1)
Gneisenaustr 15, 80992, Munich, Bavaria, Germany
Tel.: (49) 51153520
Investment Management Service
N.A.I.C.S.: 523999

Women's College Partnership (1)
790 Bay St Suite 750, Toronto, M5G 1N8, ON, Canada
Tel.: (416) 351-2535
Investment Management Service
N.A.I.C.S.: 523999

bebit Informationstechnik GmbH (100%)
Dynamostrasse 17, D-68165, Mannheim, Germany
Tel.: (49) 62140010
Web Site: http://www.bebit.de
Sales Range: $25-49.9 Million
Emp.: 140
Enterprise Solutions, Human Resource & Information Technology Support Services
N.A.I.C.S.: 561499
Christian Thum *(Mng Dir-Sls & Mktg)*

projekt-partner-online GmbH (1)
Dynamostrasse 17, 68165, Mannheim, Germany
Tel.: (49) 621 4001 0
Web Site: http://www.p-p-o.de
Software Development Services
N.A.I.C.S.: 541511

BILGIN ENERJI YATIRIM HOLDING A.S.
Kazim Ozalp Mahallesi Kuleli Sokagi No 87, Cankaya, 06700, Ankara, Turkiye
Tel.: (90) 312 446 30 23
Holding Company
N.A.I.C.S.: 551112

Subsidiaries:

Yapisan Elektrik Uretim AS (1)

Kazim Ozalp Mahallesi Kuleli Sokagi No 87, Cankaya, 06700, Ankara, Turkiye
Tel.: (90) 312 446 30 23
Power Generation
N.A.I.C.S.: 221115

Subsidiary (Domestic):

OMV Samsun Elektrik Uretim Sanayi ve Ticaret A.S. (2)
33 Eski Buyukdere Caddesi, Istanbul, 34398, Turkiye
Tel.: (90) 2123291000
Sales Range: $75-99.9 Million
Emp.: 1
Eletric Power Generation Services
N.A.I.C.S.: 221118
Korkut Ozturkmen *(Gen Mgr)*

BILIA AB
Norra Langebergsgatan 3 Vastra Frolunda, PO Box 9003, SE-400 91, Gothenburg, Sweden
Tel.: (46) 104977000   SE
Web Site: https://www.bilia.com
Year Founded: 1967
BILI—(OMX)
Rev.: $3,310,479,830
Assets: $1,873,331,647
Liabilities: $1,415,605,946
Net Worth: $457,725,702
Earnings: $151,919,601
Emp.: 5,110
Fiscal Year-end: 12/31/22
Automobile Sales & Services
N.A.I.C.S.: 441227
Mats Qviberg *(Chm)*

Subsidiaries:

AS Insignia (1)
Konows gate 67B, 0196, Oslo, Norway
Tel.: (47) 23233300
Web Site: https://insignia.no
Car Dealership Operator
N.A.I.C.S.: 441110

Allbildelar i Huddinge AB (1)
Hokarrsvagen 125 Glado Industriomrade, 141 91, Huddinge, Sweden
Tel.: (46) 104974200
Web Site: https://www.allbildelar.se
Emp.: 28
Automotive Repair Services
N.A.I.C.S.: 811111
Annika Hemlen *(Fin Mgr)*

Autohaus Bilia GmbH & Co. KG (1)
Raun 97-99, 63667, Nidda, Germany
Tel.: (49) 6043404140
Web Site: http://www.bmw-bilia.de
Used Car Retailer
N.A.I.C.S.: 441120

Bilia BMU AB (1)
Stromledningsgatan 11, 721 37, Vasteras, Sweden
Tel.: (46) 771400000
Automotive Parts Mfr & Distr
N.A.I.C.S.: 332119

Bilia Emond Luxembourg SA (1)
184 Route de Thionville, 2610, Luxembourg, Luxembourg
Tel.: (352) 4919411
Web Site: http://www.bilia-emond.bmw.lu
Car Retailer
N.A.I.C.S.: 441110

Bilia Fordon AB (1)
Jolengatan 15, Box 9260, Goteborg, 400 96, Gothenburg, Sweden
Tel.: (46) 317517500
Web Site: http://www.bilia.se
Sales Range: $25-49.9 Million
Emp.: 100
Automobile Sales & Service
N.A.I.C.S.: 441227

Bilia Group Goteborg AB (1)
Goteborgsvägen 92, 431 37, Molndal, Sweden
Tel.: (46) 104978500
Web Site: http://www.biliagroup.se
Sales Range: $25-49.9 Million
Emp.: 80
New Car Dealers
N.A.I.C.S.: 441110

Bilia Personbil as (1)
Okernveien 121, Okern, 579, Oslo, Norway
Tel.: (47) 91508555
Web Site: http://www.bilia.no
Sales Range: $50-74.9 Million
Emp.: 180
Automobile Sales & Service
N.A.I.C.S.: 441227

Bilia Personbilar AB (1)
Norra Langebergsgatan 3, PO Box 9003, 400 97, Gothenburg, Sweden
Tel.: (46) 317095500
Web Site: http://www.bilia.se
Sales Range: $25-49.9 Million
Emp.: 100
Automobile Sales & Service
N.A.I.C.S.: 441227

Bilia Verstraeten NV (1)
Antwerpsesteenweg 81, 9080, Lochristi, Belgium
Tel.: (32) 93450688
Web Site: http://www.bilia-verstraeten.bmw.be
Automotive Repair Services
N.A.I.C.S.: 811111

Bilsalongen AS (1)
Bilia Skien Ostre Buktenveg 8, 3736, Skien, Norway
Tel.: (47) 53024040
General Automotive Repair Services
N.A.I.C.S.: 811111

Felgteknikk Norge AS (1)
Myrveien 8, 1640, Rade, Norway
Tel.: (47) 69323510
Web Site: https://www.felgteknikk.no
Tire Distr
N.A.I.C.S.: 423130

Gent Store by Bilia Verstraeten BVBA (1)
Kortrijksesteenweg 1228, Sint-Denijs-Westrem, 9051, Sint-Martens-Latem, Belgium
Tel.: (32) 93352700
Car Retailer
N.A.I.C.S.: 441110

Haglund & Hellberg Bil i Haninge AB (1)
Dantorpsvagen 3, SE-136 50, Haninge, Sweden
Tel.: (46) 850410300
Web Site: http://www.bilia.se
Sales Range: $25-49.9 Million
Emp.: 50
Automobile Sales & Service
N.A.I.C.S.: 441227

Hedbergs Bilskrot AB (1)
Bastborregatan 3, 721 34, Vasteras, Sweden
Tel.: (46) 104974230
Web Site: http://www.hedbergsbilskrot.se
Used Car Parts & Tire Retailer
N.A.I.C.S.: 441330

Holmgrens Truck-Motor AB (1)
Triangelvagen 4, 982 38, Gallivare, Sweden
Tel.: (46) 97074540
Web Site: https://www.htmab.se
Emp.: 15
Forklift Repair Services
N.A.I.C.S.: 811310

Jensen & Scheele Bil AS (1)
Vestgardveien 1 - 3, Pb 1080, Sorlie, 1787, Halden, Norway
Tel.: (47) 69213500
Web Site: https://www.jensen-scheele.no
Emp.: 50
Used Car Retailer
N.A.I.C.S.: 441120

M Bilar Group AB (1)
Transformatorgatan 11, 721 37, Vasteras, Sweden
Tel.: (46) 21171180
Web Site: https://mbilargroup.nu
Automotive Parts Mfr & Distr
N.A.I.C.S.: 336211

Motoria Bil AB (1)
Danmarksgatan 52, SE-164 40, Kista, Sweden
Tel.: (46) 850162480
Automobile Sales & Service

N.A.I.C.S.: 441227

Motorit AB (1)
Norra Langebergsgatan 3, 421 32, Vastra Frolunda, Sweden
Tel.: (46) 104979000
Web Site: https://www.motorit.se
Automotive IT Development Services
N.A.I.C.S.: 541511

Netbil i Skandinavien AB (1)
Faktorvagen 2, SE-434 37, Kungsbacka, Sweden
Tel.: (46) 300430330
Web Site: http://www.netbil.se
Sales Range: $25-49.9 Million
Emp.: 12
Automobile Sales & Service
N.A.I.C.S.: 441227

S.A. Bilia Emond Belgium (1)
Route de Bastogne 394, 6700, Arlon, Belgium
Tel.: (32) 63230560
Web Site: https://bilia.bmw.be
Car Retailer
N.A.I.C.S.: 441110

Toyota Bilia AS (1)
Leangen Alle 4, 7044, Trondheim, Norway
Tel.: (47) 98294900
Web Site: https://www.toyota.bilia.no
Car Retailer
N.A.I.C.S.: 441110

BILIBILI INC.
Building 3 Guozheng Center No 485 Zhengli Road, Yangpu District, Shanghai, 200433, China
Tel.: (86) 2125099255   Ky
Web Site: https://bilibili.com
Year Founded: 2013
BILI—(NASDAQ)
Rev.: $3,119,182,959
Assets: $4,591,142,418
Liabilities: $2,596,754,541
Net Worth: $1,994,387,877
Earnings: $(667,689,549)
Emp.: 8,801
Fiscal Year-end: 12/31/23
Advertising Media Services
N.A.I.C.S.: 516210
Yi Xu *(Pres)*

Subsidiaries:

Bilibili Co., Ltd. (1)
Sumitomo Real Estate Roppongi Dori Building 9th Floor 12th Floor, 7-18-18 Roppongi Minato-ku, Tokyo, 106-0032, Japan
Tel.: (81) 356430189
Web Site: https://bilibili.co.jp
N.A.I.C.S.: 713290

BILICI YATIRIM SANAYI VE TICARET A.S.
AcidereOSB Mah Ataturk Boulevard No 7 A, Saricam, 01350, Adana, Turkiye
Tel.: (90) 3223944646
Web Site:
https://www.biliciyatirim.com
Year Founded: 1950
BLCYT—(IST)
Rev.: $17,446,369
Assets: $107,599,141
Liabilities: $7,294,129
Net Worth: $100,305,012
Earnings: $10,197,889
Fiscal Year-end: 12/31/23
Textile Fabric Mfr
N.A.I.C.S.: 313210
Mehmet Ali Bilici *(Chm)*

Subsidiaries:

Bilgun Tekstil A.S (1)
Haci Sabanci Atatrk Bulvari No 5/B, Organized Industrial Zone Yakapinar, 01350, Adana, Turkiye
Tel.: (90) 3223943637
Web Site: http://www.bilguntekstil.com
Fabrics Mfr
N.A.I.C.S.: 314999

Bilici Yatirim Sanayi ve Ticaret A.S.—(Continued)

Biteks Iplik A.S. (1)
Macka Caddesi Azize Palas No 24 K1 D1,
Tesvikiye, Istanbul, Turkiye
Tel.: (90) 2123439740
Web Site: http://www.biteksiplik.com
Textile Product Retailer
N.A.I.C.S.: 424310
Mehmet Ali Bilici (Pres)

BILL HOUSTON FORD LTD.
5786 Main St, PO Box 1589, Stn
Main, Stouffville, L4A 8A4, ON,
Canada
Tel.: (905) 640-4541
Web Site:
http://www.billhoustonford.com
Year Founded: 1985
New & Used Car Dealers
N.A.I.C.S.: 441110
Craig Lill (Mgr-Parts)

BILL HOWICH CHRYSLER LTD.
2777 North Island Hwy, Campbell
River, V9W 2H4, BC, Canada
Tel.: (250) 287-9514
Web Site: http://billhowich.com
New & Used Car Dealers
N.A.I.C.S.: 441110
Bill Howich (Pres)

BILLBOARD JSC
1 Bulgaria Square NDK ent Al4,
1463, Sofia, 1463, Bulgaria
Tel.: (359) 29166500
Web Site: https://www.bilbord.bg
Year Founded: 2001
BBRD—(BUL)
Rev.: $17,064,893
Assets: $22,445,094
Liabilities: $11,110,805
Net Worth: $11,334,290
Earnings: $285,840
Fiscal Year-end: 12/31/21
Digital Printing Services
N.A.I.C.S.: 323111
Kalin Vasilev Genchev (Chm)

Subsidiaries:

Dedrax AD (1)
1 Bulgaria Sq NPC- Dedrax Printing House,
1463, Sofia, Bulgaria
Tel.: (359) 888499689
Web Site: https://dedrax.com
Emp.: 300
Book Binding Services
N.A.I.C.S.: 513199

BILLERUD AB
Evenemangsgatan 17, PO Box 703,
169 79, Solna, Sweden
Tel.: (46) 855333500
Web Site: https://www.billerud.com
Year Founded: 1883
BILL—(OMX)
Rev.: $3,224,987,360
Assets: $4,636,354,240
Liabilities: $2,189,748,960
Net Worth: $2,446,605,280
Earnings: $181,288,800
Emp.: 4,370
Fiscal Year-end: 12/31/21
Packaging Materials Mfr
N.A.I.C.S.: 322211
Michael M. F. Kaufmann (Vice Chm & Vice Chm)

Subsidiaries:

Billerud Americas Corporation (1)
8540 Gander Creek Dr, Miamisburg, OH
45342
Tel.: (901) 369-4100
Web Site: http://www.versoco.com
Rev.: $1,278,000,000
Assets: $1,055,000,000
Liabilities: $356,000,000
Net Worth: $699,000,000

Earnings: ($3,000,000)
Emp.: 1,600
Fiscal Year-end: 12/31/2021
Holding Company; Producer of Printing Papers, Specialty Papers & Pulp
N.A.I.C.S.: 551112
Tonie Meyers (CFO, Sr VP-Sheeting Ops & Gen Mgr)

Subsidiary (Domestic):

Verso Bucksport LLC (2)
2 River Rd, Bucksport, ME 04416
Tel.: (207) 469-1700
Web Site: http://www.versopaper.com
Sales Range: $250-299.9 Million
Emp.: 795
Coated Groundwood Paper Mill
N.A.I.C.S.: 322120

Plant (Domestic):

Verso Corporation - Escanaba Mill (2)
7100 County 426 M 5 Rd, Escanaba, MI
49829
Tel.: (906) 786-0135
Web Site: http://www.versoco.com
Emp.: 940
Paper Mfr
N.A.I.C.S.: 322120

Verso Corporation - Luke Mill (2)
300 Pratt St, Luke, MD 21540
Tel.: (301) 359-3311
Web Site: http://www.versoco.com
Emp.: 800
Paper Mfr
N.A.I.C.S.: 322120

Verso Corporation - Wisconsin Rapids Mill (2)
700 Dura Beauty Ln, Wisconsin Rapids, WI
54495
Tel.: (715) 422-3471
Web Site: http://www.versoco.com
Emp.: 980
Paper Mfr
N.A.I.C.S.: 322120

Subsidiary (Domestic):

Verso Maine Energy LLC (2)
6775 Lenox Ct Park Bldg E, Memphis, TN
38115
Tel.: (901) 419-7130
Coated Paper Production & Distr
N.A.I.C.S.: 322120

Verso Paper Holdings LLC (2)
6775 Lenox Ctr Ct Ste 400, Memphis, TN
38115-4436
Tel.: (901) 369-4100
Web Site: http://www.versoco.com
Rev.: $3,121,000,000
Assets: $2,733,000,000
Liabilities: $3,912,000,000
Net Worth: ($1,179,000,000)
Earnings: ($421,000,000)
Fiscal Year-end: 12/31/2015
Investment Management Service
N.A.I.C.S.: 551112

Verso Paper LLC (2)
60 E 42nd St Ste 1942, New York, NY
10165
Tel.: (212) 599-2700
Coated Paper Production & Distr
N.A.I.C.S.: 322120

Verso Quinnesec LLC (2)
W6791 US Hwy 2, Quinnesec, MI 49876
Tel.: (877) 447-2737
Coated Paper Production & Distr
N.A.I.C.S.: 322120

Verso Quinnesec REP LLC (2)
W 6791 US Hwy 2, Quinnesec, MI 49876
Tel.: (906) 779-3200
Web Site: http://www.versopaper.com
Emp.: 420
Coated Paper Production & Distr
N.A.I.C.S.: 322120

nexTier Solutions Corporation (2)
6775 Lenox Ct Park Bldg E Ste 400, Memphis, TN 38115
Tel.: (901) 369-4140
Web Site: http://www.nextiersolutions.com
Paper Mfr & Distr
N.A.I.C.S.: 322120

Billerud Beetham Ltd (1)
Waterhouse Mills Beetham Milnthorpe,
Cumbria, Lancaster, LA7 7AR, United
Kingdom (100%)
Tel.: (44) 1539565000
Sales Range: $50-74.9 Million
Emp.: 180
Paperboard Mills
N.A.I.C.S.: 322130
Ying Sou (Gen Mgr)

Billerud France S.A (1)
16 Rue d'Athenes, 75009, Paris,
France (100%)
Tel.: (33) 14 469 9440
Web Site: http://www.billerudkorsnas.com
Paper Mills
N.A.I.C.S.: 322120

Billerud Gulf (1)
Jebel Ali Free Zone, LOB 16 Unit 128,
Dubai, United Arab Emirates (100%)
Tel.: (971) 48814663
Web Site: http://www.billerud.com
Sales Range: $50-74.9 Million
Emp.: 4
Paper Sales
N.A.I.C.S.: 424130

Billerud Iberica S.L (1)
Calle de la Constitucion No 3 5o-5a, 08960,
Sant Just Desvern, Barcelona, Spain
Tel.: (34) 93 470 0556
Web Site: https://www.billerudkorsnas.com
Emp.: 12
Packaging Paper Products Mfr
N.A.I.C.S.: 322220

Billerud Karlsborg AB (1)
Karlsborgsverken, Karlskoga, 95283,
Sweden (100%)
Tel.: (46) 92366000
Web Site: http://www.billerud.se
Sales Range: $125-149.9 Million
Emp.: 410
Paperboard Mills
N.A.I.C.S.: 322130

Billerud S.r.l. (1)
Via Pisa 250, 20099, Sesto San Giovanni,
Italy
Tel.: (39) 022 483 9085
Web Site: http://www.billerudkorsnas.com
Sales Range: $25-49.9 Million
Emp.: 10
Paper Mills
N.A.I.C.S.: 322120
Arnaldo Ferrari (Mng Dir)

Billerud Scandinavia (1)
Frosundaleden 2 b, 169 70, Solna, Stockholm, Sweden
Tel.: (46) 8 553 337 00
Web Site: http://www.billerudskog.se
Lumber Product Whslr
N.A.I.C.S.: 423990

Billerud Skarblacka AB (1)
Bergslagsvagen 45, Skarblacka, 617 10,
Norrkoping, Sweden (100%)
Tel.: (46) 11245300
Web Site: http://www.billerudkorsnas.se
Sales Range: $200-249.9 Million
Emp.: 740
Paperboard Mills
N.A.I.C.S.: 322130

Billerud Skog AB (1)
Frosundaleden 2 B, 169 27, Solna, Sweden
Tel.: (46) 855333600
Web Site: http://www.billerudkorsnas.se
Emp.: 700
Timber Logging Services
N.A.I.C.S.: 113310

Billerud Tenova Bioplastics AB (1)
Torshagshuset, 616 33, Aby, Sweden
Tel.: (46) 11 10 52 75
Web Site: http://www.tenova.com
Sales Range: $25-49.9 Million
Emp.: 15
Bioplastic Materials Distr
N.A.I.C.S.: 424610

**Billerud Trading (Shanghai) Co,
Ltd** (1)
300 Huaihai Middle Road Unit 4109,
200021, Shanghai, China
Tel.: (86) 2153510622
Sales Range: $50-74.9 Million
Emp.: 11
Printing & Writing Paper Whslr

N.A.I.C.S.: 424110

BillerudKorsnas Finland OY (1)
Larsmovagen 149 PL 13, 68601, Pietarsaari, Finland
Tel.: (358) 624138000
Packaging Materials Mfr
N.A.I.C.S.: 322211
Risto Hovi (Mng Dir)

BillerudKorsnas Latvia SIA (1)
Meza iela 4, Jaunjelgava, 5134, Latvia
Tel.: (371) 6 515 2800
Web Site: https://www.billerudkorsnas.lv
Forest Management Services
N.A.I.C.S.: 115310

BillerudKorsnas Managed Packaging AB (1)
PO Box 703, 169 27, Solna, Sweden
Tel.: (46) 855333500
Packaging Material Distr
N.A.I.C.S.: 423840

BillerudKorsnas Skarblacka AB (1)
Bergslagsvagen 45, Skarblacka, 617 10,
Norrkoping, Sweden
Tel.: (46) 771141411
Packaging Materials Mfr
N.A.I.C.S.: 322211
Monica Lundgren (Mgr-Comm)

Korsnas AB (1)
E4 Industrie Pl, S 801 81, Gavle,
Sweden (100%)
Tel.: (46) 26151000
Web Site: http://www.korsnas.com
Sales Range: $1-4.9 Billion
Emp.: 1,900
Fluff Pulp, Paper, Sack & Kraft Paper, Paperboard; Timber
N.A.I.C.S.: 322130

Subsidiary (Domestic):

Korsnas AB - Frovi (2)
Frovifors, 718 80, Frovi, Sweden
Tel.: (46) 58137000
Web Site: http://www.korsnas.com
Sales Range: Less than $1 Million
Emp.: 685
Cartonboard
N.A.I.C.S.: 322299

Subsidiary (Non-US):

Korsnas GmbH (2)
Haubachstrasse 74, DE-22765, Hamburg,
Germany (100%)
Tel.: (49) 40 85 35 26 41
Paper Product Distr
N.A.I.C.S.: 322220

Subsidiary (Domestic):

Korsnas Rockhammar AB (2)
Rockhammar, 718 91, Frovi, Sweden
Tel.: (46) 581 370 00
Chemical Pulp Mfr
N.A.I.C.S.: 325998

Subsidiary (Non-US):

Korsnas Shanghai Trading Ltd. (2)
Unit 2008 20th Floor Maxdo Centre No 8
Xing Yi Road, Chang Ning District, Shanghai, China
Tel.: (86) 21 5208 0186
Packaging Materials Mfr
N.A.I.C.S.: 322220

ScandFibre Logistics AB (1)
Aspholmsvagen 12A, 702 27, Orebro, Sweden
Tel.: (46) 1 920 8080
Web Site: https://www.scandfibre.se
Emp.: 25
Transport & Logistics Services
N.A.I.C.S.: 488510
Patrik Leylin (Dir-Bus)

BILLET SAS
Zac De Volvic, 63530, Volvic, Puy De
Dome, France
Tel.: (33) 473387983
Rev.: $14,100,000
Emp.: 100
N.A.I.C.S.: 237310
Bernard Billet (Pres)

BILLING SYSTEM CORP.
13th Floor Hibiya Daibiru 1-2-2 Uchi-saiwaicho, Chiyoda-ku, Tokyo, 100-0011, Japan
Tel.: (81) 355014402
Web Site:
https://www.billingsystem.co.jp
Year Founded: 2000
3623—(TKS)
Rev.: $26,814,380
Assets: $150,953,190
Liabilities: $132,427,020
Net Worth: $18,526,170
Earnings: $2,127,000
Emp.: 28
Fiscal Year-end: 12/31/23
Online Transaction Settlement Services
N.A.I.C.S.: 522320
Toshihiko Eda (Pres & CEO)

BILLINGTON CARTMELL
The Blue Bldg Fulham Island 40 Vanston Pl, London, SW6 1AX, United Kingdom
Tel.: (44) 207 471 1900
Year Founded: 1990
Emp.: 130
N.A.I.C.S.: 541810
Robin Shelley (Sr Acct Mgr)

BILLINGTON HOLDINGS PLC
Steel House Barnsley Road, Wombwell, Barnsley, S73 8DS, South Yorkshire, United Kingdom
Tel.: (44) 1226340666   UK
Web Site: https://www.billington-holdings.plc.uk
Year Founded: 1970
BILN—(AIM)
Rev.: $109,333,502
Assets: $76,591,770
Liabilities: $33,235,294
Net Worth: $43,356,476
Earnings: $5,975,764
Emp.: 415
Fiscal Year-end: 12/31/22
Structural Steel & Engineering Services
N.A.I.C.S.: 237990
Trevor Michael Taylor (CFO)

Subsidiaries:

Billington Structures Limited   (1)
Barnsley Road Wombwell, Barnsley, S73 8DS, South Yorkshire, United Kingdom   (100%)
Tel.: (44) 1226340666
Web Site: https://www.billington-structures.co.uk
Sales Range: $50-74.9 Million
Emp.: 250
Structural Steel Erection Contractors
N.A.I.C.S.: 238120

Hoard-it Limited   (1)
Netherwood House Mitchell's Industrial Park Bradberry Balk Lane, Barnsley, S73 8HR, United Kingdom
Tel.: (44) 1226752143
Web Site: https://hoard-it.co.uk
Steel Stair Installation Services
N.A.I.C.S.: 238120

Peter Marshall Steel Stairs
Limited   (1)
Lincoln House Gelderd Road, Gildersome, Leeds, LS27 7LL, United Kingdom
Tel.: (44) 1133076730
Web Site: https://marshallstairs.com
Steel Stair Installation Services
N.A.I.C.S.: 238120

Specialist Protective Coatings
Limited   (1)
Unit 22 Newton Chambers Road, Thorncliffe Park Estate Chapeltown, Sheffield, S35 2PH, United Kingdom
Tel.: (44) 1143212651
Web Site:
https://www.specialistprotectivecoatings.co.uk

Coating Mfr
N.A.I.C.S.: 332812

easi-edge Limited   (1)
Ollerton Road, Tuxford, Tuxford, NG22 0PQ, Nottinghamshire, United Kingdom
Tel.: (44) 177 787 0901
Web Site: https://easi-edge.co.uk
Sales Range: $25-49.9 Million
Emp.: 50
Fabricated Metal Products Mfr
N.A.I.C.S.: 332312

BILLION ELECTRIC CO., LTD.
8F No 192 Sec 2 Zhongxing Rd, Xindian Dist, New Taipei City, 23146, Taiwan
Tel.: (886) 229145665
Web Site: https://www.billion.com
Year Founded: 1973
3027—(TAI)
Rev.: $59,804,144
Assets: $118,669,703
Liabilities: $41,296,411
Net Worth: $77,373,292
Earnings: $3,670,918
Emp.: 124
Fiscal Year-end: 12/31/23
Network Equipment & Power Supply Products Mfr
N.A.I.C.S.: 334210
Felix Cheng (COO)

Subsidiaries:

BEC Technologies Inc.   (1)
3301 Matrix Dr Ste 200, Richardson, TX 75082
Tel.: (972) 422-0877
Web Site: https://bectechnologies.net
Internet Service Provider
N.A.I.C.S.: 517112

Billion Watts Technologies Co.,
Ltd.   (1)
7F No 190 Sec 2 Zhongxing Rd, Xindian Dist, New Taipei City, 231, Taiwan
Tel.: (886) 908810876
Web Site: https://www.billionwatts.com.tw
Grid Storage Device Mfr & Distr
N.A.I.C.S.: 335999

VGwatt Energy Co., Ltd.   (1)
10F No 200 Sec 2 Gaotie S Rd, Zhongli Dist, Taoyuan, 320, Taiwan
Tel.: (886) 34250170
Web Site: https://www.vgwatt.com
Switching Power Inverter Mfr & Distr
N.A.I.C.S.: 335312

BILLION HOLDING INC.
11 Shanzhuang Rd Xikeng Henggang, Longgang, Shenzhen, 518000, China
Tel.: (86) 755 2555 3140   DE
Year Founded: 2017
Holding Company
N.A.I.C.S.: 551112
Ming Sang Chan (Pres, CFO & Sec)

BILLION INDUSTRIAL HOLDINGS LIMITED
Fenglin Industrial Zone, Longhu Town, Jinjiang, 362241, Fujian, China
Tel.: (86) 59588299999   Ky
Web Site: http://www.baihong.com
2299—(HKG)
Rev.: $2,185,324,315
Assets: $3,716,985,823
Liabilities: $2,337,292,292
Net Worth: $1,379,693,531
Earnings: $92,076,847
Emp.: 8,197
Fiscal Year-end: 12/31/22
Polyester Filament Yarn Mfr
N.A.I.C.S.: 313110
Tin Yau Sze (Co-Chm)

BILLIONS CO., LTD.
648 Samseong-ro 3rd floor Fantagio Building, Gangnam-gu, Seoul, Korea (South)

Tel.: (82) 222033830   KR
Web Site: https://www.bladeent.com
Year Founded: 1973
Rev.: $13,815,163
Assets: $46,111,409
Liabilities: $19,949,882
Net Worth: $26,161,527
Earnings: ($6,463,077)
Emp.: 89
Fiscal Year-end: 12/31/18
Clinical Latex Products Mfr
N.A.I.C.S.: 326299
Gun Woo Bae (CEO)

Subsidiaries:

BioGenetics Co.,Ltd. - China
Factory   (1)
Xizhang Zhenbei Road, Fenghuang Town, Zhangjiagang, 215614, Jiangsu, China
Tel.: (86) 51258458985
Medicinal Product Mfr
N.A.I.C.S.: 339112

BioGenetics Co.,Ltd. - Jeungpyoung
Factory   (1)
473-3 Gwangjang-ro Jeungpyoung-eup, Jeungpyoung-gun, Chuncheon, Chungbuk, Korea (South)
Tel.: (82) 438360025
Medicinal Product Mfr
N.A.I.C.S.: 339112

BILLIONTON SYSTEMS INC.
No 21 Sui-Lih Rd, Hsinchuang, 300, Taiwan
Tel.: (886) 35729399
Web Site:
http://www.billionton.com.tw
6172—(TAI)
Rev.: $18,442,227
Assets: $29,169,712
Liabilities: $17,615,971
Net Worth: $11,553,741
Earnings: $430,219
Fiscal Year-end: 12/31/20
Personal Digital Assistant & Data Storage Device Mfr
N.A.I.C.S.: 518210

Subsidiaries:

TURANLI ELEKTRONIK LTD.   (1)
Selahattin Pinar cad No 4/2, Mecidiyekoy, Istanbul, 80310, Turkiye
Tel.: (90) 212 216 0520
Web Site: https://www.turanli.com.tr
Sales Range: $25-49.9 Million
Emp.: 30
Computer Accessories Distr
N.A.I.C.S.: 423430
Omer Turanli (Owner)

BILLSAVE UK LIMITED
Unit 3-4 St Georges House Gaddesby Lane Rearsby, Leicester, LE7 4YH, United Kingdom
Tel.: (44) 800616302
Web Site: http://www.billsaveuk.com
Emp.: 40
Electrical Insulation & Energy Storage Contracting Services
N.A.I.C.S.: 238210
Julian Cummins (CFO)

BILLWIN INDUSTRIES LIMITED
79 Vishal Industrial Estate Village Road, Nahur W, Mumbai, 400078, India
Tel.: (91) 2225668112
Web Site:
https://www.billwinindustries.com
Year Founded: 2014
543209—(BOM)
Rev.: $599,208
Assets: $1,405,909
Liabilities: $728,678
Net Worth: $677,231
Earnings: $29,825
Fiscal Year-end: 03/31/22
Apparels Mfr

N.A.I.C.S.: 315250
Subrata Dey (Compliance Officer & Sec)

BILPOWER LIMITED
B-11 Viral Shopping Center, Mantriwadi Sainath Road Malad-West, Mumbai, 400064, Maharashtra, India
Tel.: (91) 2867 060304
Web Site: http://www.bilpower.com
Rev.: $2,535,004
Assets: $12,024,737
Liabilities: $30,558,953
Net Worth: ($18,534,216)
Earnings: $479,170
Emp.: 500
Fiscal Year-end: 03/31/18
Power Engineering Solutions
N.A.I.C.S.: 335311
Sureshkumar Anandilal Choudhary (Exec Dir)

Subsidiaries:

Bilpower Limited - Baroda Unit   (1)
440-441-446 GIDC Industrial Estate POR, Ramangamdi, Baroda, 391 243, India
Tel.: (91) 265 2830 824
Transformers Lamination Mfr
N.A.I.C.S.: 334416

Bilpower Ltd - Kanchad Plant   (1)
Kanchad Vlg Taluka Wada, Thane, 421 303, Maharastra, India
Tel.: (91) 2526235772
Web Site: http://www.bilpower.com
Sales Range: $25-49.9 Million
Emp.: 100
Transformers Lamination Mfr
N.A.I.C.S.: 334416

Bilpower Ltd - Uttranchal Plant   (1)
Unit D 10 11 Raipur Notified Area Bhagwanpur, Haridwar, 247667, Roorkee, Uttarakhand, India
Tel.: (91) 1332235070
Web Site: http://www.bilpower.com
Sales Range: $25-49.9 Million
Emp.: 20
Transformers Lamination Mfr
N.A.I.C.S.: 334416

Tarapur Transformers Limited   (1)
S-105 Rajiv Commercial Complex 1st Floor Ekta Nagar, Kandivali West, Mumbai, 400067, India
Tel.: (91) 2228670603
Web Site:
https://www.tarapurtransformers.com
Rev.: $415,929
Assets: $7,098,956
Liabilities: $6,777,976
Net Worth: $320,980
Earnings: ($3,636,319)
Emp.: 7
Fiscal Year-end: 03/31/2021
Transformer Mfr
N.A.I.C.S.: 335311
Kanji Dayabhai Chavda (CFO)

BIM AD
Ul Zeleznicka br 164, Sveti Nikole, Makedonija, North Macedonia
Tel.: (389) 32455177
Web Site: https://www.bim.com.mk
Year Founded: 1957
BIM—(MAC)
Rev.: $10,509,577
Assets: $9,095,638
Liabilities: $210,112
Net Worth: $8,885,526
Earnings: $933,129
Fiscal Year-end: 12/31/21
Bitumen Product Mfr
N.A.I.C.S.: 324122
Stojanche Stojanov (Chm)

BIM BIRLESIK MAGAZALAR A.S.
Ebubekir Cad No 73 Sancaktepe, 34887, Istanbul, Turkiye
Tel.: (90) 2165640303   TR
Web Site: https://www.bim.com.tr

BIM Birlesik Magazalar A.S.—(Continued)

Year Founded: 1995
BIMAS—(IST)
Rev.: $9,561,301,872
Assets: $4,122,971,380
Liabilities: $1,058,675,891
Net Worth: $3,064,295,489
Earnings: $400,027,755
Emp.: 70,197
Fiscal Year-end: 12/31/21
Grocery Store Operator
N.A.I.C.S.: 445110
Haluk Dortluoglu *(CEO)*

Subsidiaries:

Gida Paketleme ve Sanayi ve Ticaret
A.S. **(1)**
Turgut Ozal Bulvari No 2 AD 1, Akova Hendek, 54300, Sakarya, Turkiye
Tel.: (90) 264 614 3614
Web Site: https://gdpgida.com.tr
Chemical Product & Preparation Mfr
N.A.I.C.S.: 325998

BIMAL D.D.
Bijeljinska br 9, 76100, Brcko, Bosnia
& Herzegovina
Tel.: (387) 4 923 3311
Web Site: http://www.bimaldd.com
Year Founded: 1943
BBR9R—(SARE)
Rev.: $108,853,268
Assets: $116,388,631
Liabilities: $65,004,765
Net Worth: $51,383,866
Earnings: $2,798,500
Emp.: 283
Fiscal Year-end: 12/31/20
Edible Oil Mfr
N.A.I.C.S.: 311225

**BIMAN BANGLADESH AIR-
LINES**
Kurmitola, Dhaka, 1229, Bangladesh
Tel.: (880) 28901600
Web Site: http://www.biman-
airlines.com
Year Founded: 1972
Sales Range: $250-299.9 Million
Emp.: 2,400
Oil Transportation Services
N.A.I.C.S.: 481111
A. M. Mosaddique Ahmed *(CEO &
Mng Dir)*

Subsidiaries:

Biman Flight Catering Centre Ltd **(1)**
Biman Bangladesh Airlines Balaka bhaban,
Baba Hotels, kurmitola, Zia, Dhaka, Bangladesh
Tel.: (880) 289147004
Web Site: http://www.bfcc-bd.com
Sales Range: $50-74.9 Million
Emp.: 500
Caterers
N.A.I.C.S.: 722320

Biman Poultry Complex Ltd **(1)**
Biman Press Bldg Compound, Ganakbari,
Savar, Dhaka, Bangladesh
Tel.: (880) 2 9560151 10
Poultry Hatcheries
N.A.I.C.S.: 112340

**BIMECO GARNHANDEL GMBH
& CO. KG**
Hemdener Weg 109, Bocholt, 46399,
Germany
Tel.: (49) 287127020
Web Site: http://www.bimeco.de
Year Founded: 1985
Rev.: $44,830,500
Emp.: 32
Industrial Yarns & Spuns Supply Services
N.A.I.C.S.: 424990
Dirk Ciborski *(Mng Dir)*

**BIMEKS BILGI ISLEM VE DIS
TICARET A.S.**
Sutcuyolu Cad No 62, Yenisahra
Atasehir, 34746, Istanbul, Turkiye
Tel.: (90) 216 542 62 92
Web Site: http://www.bimeks.com.tr
Year Founded: 1989
Sales Range: $300-349.9 Million
Emp.: 450
Electronic Product Whslr
N.A.I.C.S.: 423620
Mehmet Murat Akgiray *(Chm)*

**BIMI INTERNATIONAL MEDI-
CAL INC.**
Room 3601 Building A Harbour View
Place No 2 Wuwu Road, Zhongshan
District, Dalian, 116000, Liaoning,
China
Tel.: (86) 1182209211
Web Site: http://www.bimihc.com
BIMI—(NASDAQ)
Rev.: $11,830,379
Assets: $35,714,490
Liabilities: $30,497,257
Net Worth: $5,217,233
Earnings: ($22,393,259)
Emp.: 298
Fiscal Year-end: 12/31/22
Energy Equipment Mfr & Distr
N.A.I.C.S.: 333415
Tiewei Song *(Pres & CEO)*

BIMOBJECT AB
Nordenskioldsgatan 24, 211 19,
Malmo, Sweden
Tel.: (46) 406852900
Web Site: http://www.bimobject.com
Year Founded: 2011
Data Management
N.A.I.C.S.: 518210
Stefan Larrson *(Founder & CEO)*

**BIMSON CEMENT JOINT
STOCK COMPANY**
Ba Dinh Ward, Bim Son, Thanh Hoa,
Vietnam
Tel.: (84) 2373824242
Web Site:
https://ximangbimson.com.vn
BCC—(HNX)
Rev.: $173,202,050
Assets: $155,055,770
Liabilities: $70,309,762
Net Worth: $84,746,007
Earnings: $3,119,767
Fiscal Year-end: 12/31/21
Cement Mfr
N.A.I.C.S.: 327310
Nguyen Van Hoanh *(Member-Mgmt
Bd & Gen Dir)*

**BIN CHUAN ENTERPRISE
CORP.**
No 2 Xingye Rd, Daliao Dist, Kaohsiung, 831, Taiwan
Tel.: (886) 77871521
Web Site:
https://www.hamagawa.com.tw
1569—(TPE)
Rev.: $156,463,496
Assets: $225,737,955
Liabilities: $110,718,413
Net Worth: $115,019,542
Earnings: $12,737,829
Fiscal Year-end: 12/31/22
Computer Peripheral Equipment Mfr
N.A.I.C.S.: 334118
Chin-Ming Hsiao *(Chm)*

BINA DARULAMAN BERHAD
Level 910 Menara BDB 88 Lebuhraya
Darulaman, 05100, Alor Setar, Kedah, Malaysia
Tel.: (60) 47300303
Web Site: https://www.bdb.com.my

BDB—(KLS)
Rev.: $475,088
Assets: $3,087,252
Liabilities: $4,675,768
Net Worth: ($1,588,515)
Earnings: ($228,596)
Fiscal Year-end: 12/31/22
Property Development & General
Construction Services
N.A.I.C.S.: 236116
Fakhruzi Ahmad *(CFO)*

Subsidiaries:

BDB Hotels Sdn. Bhd. **(1)**
Darulaman Suites Lot 888 Bandar Darulaman, 06007, Jitra, Kedah, Malaysia
Tel.: (60) 49172008
Web Site:
http://www.darulamangolf.bdb.com.my
Hotel Accommodation Services
N.A.I.C.S.: 721110
Akhtar Ahmad Darwis *(Head-Fin)*

BDB Infra Sdn. Bhd. **(1)**
Level 9 Menara Bina Darulaman Berhad No
88 Lebuhraya Darulaman, 05100, Alor
Setar, Kedah Darul Amam, Malaysia
Tel.: (60) 47300303
Web Site: http://www.infra.bdb.com.my
Road Construction Project & Maintenance
Road Services
N.A.I.C.S.: 237310
Yusuf Hasim *(Mgr-Contact)*

BDB Land Sdn. Bhd. **(1)**
Lot 1 Bandar Darulaman, P/O Box 12,
Kubang Pasu, 06700, Jitra, Kedah Darul
Aman, Malaysia
Tel.: (60) 4 919 9080
Web Site: https://bandardarulaman.my
Sales Range: $25-49.9 Million
Emp.: 47
Property Development & Construction Services
N.A.I.C.S.: 236116
Nor Hayati Zainuddin *(Head-Fin, Accounts
& IT)*

BDB Synergy Sdn. Bhd. **(1)**
Level 8 Menara BDB 88 Lebuhraya Darulaman, 05100, Alor Setar, Kedah Darul
Amam, Malaysia
Tel.: (60) 47318322
Web Site: http://www.synergy.bdb.com.my
Engineering & Construction Services
N.A.I.C.S.: 541330
Safrizuan Saad *(Mgr-Fin)*

Darulaman Aset Sdn. Bhd. **(1)**
Lot 2156 A B & C Jalan Tunku Abdul Halim,
05100, Alor Setar, Kedah Darul Aman, Malaysia
Tel.: (60) 4 730 6468
Web Site: https://www.dasb.my
Property Development & General Construction Services
N.A.I.C.S.: 531311

Darulaman Golf Resort Behard **(1)**
Bandar Darulaman, 06000, Jitra, Kedah,
Malaysia
Tel.: (60) 4 917 0001
Web Site:
http://www.darulamangolf.bdb.com.my
Sales Range: $50-74.9 Million
Emp.: 90
Golf Club Management Services
N.A.I.C.S.: 713910
Tunku Aziz Bendahara *(Chm)*

Kedah Holdings Sdn. Bhd. **(1)**
Lot 1 Bandar Darulaman, PO Box 12,
06007, Jitra, Kedah, Malaysia
Tel.: (60) 49178080
Web Site:
http://www.kedahholdings.bdb.com.my
Real Estate Developer Services
N.A.I.C.S.: 531390

BINA PURI HOLDINGS BHD
Wisma Bina Puri 88 Jalan Bukit Idaman 8/1, Bukit Idaman, 68100, Selayang, Selangor Darul Ehsan, Malaysia
Tel.: (60) 361363333
Web Site:
https://www.binapuri.com.my

BPURI—(KLS)
Rev.: $20,072,593
Assets: $217,248,677
Liabilities: $173,119,788
Net Worth: $44,128,889
Earnings: ($26,696,931)
Fiscal Year-end: 06/30/23
Property Development & Construction
Serviooo
N.A.I.C.S.: 237310
Matthew Kai Woon Tee *(Exec Dir-
Grp)*

Subsidiaries:

Bina Puri (B) Sdn Bhd **(1)**
Level 1 Block 1C Jalan Ong Sum Ping, BA
1311, Bandar Seri Begawan, Brunei Darussalam
Tel.: (673) 2232373
Web Site: http://www.binapuri.com
Sales Range: $25-49.9 Million
Emp.: 20
Building Construction Services
N.A.I.C.S.: 236116

Bina Puri Construction Sdn Bhd. **(1)**
Wisma Bina Puri 88 Jalan Bukit Idaman
8/1, Bukit Idaman, 68100, Selayang, Selangor, Malaysia
Tel.: (60) 361363333
Building Construction Services
N.A.I.C.S.: 236116

Bina Puri Pakistan (Private) Ltd. **(1)**
No 84 HH Phase IV, Defence Housing Authority, Lahore, Punjab, Pakistan
Tel.: (92) 425747888
Web Site: http://www.binapuri.com.my
Sales Range: $25-49.9 Million
Emp.: 55
Building Construction Services
N.A.I.C.S.: 236210

Bina Puri Properties Sdn Bhd **(1)**
Wisma Bina Puri 88 Jalan Bukit Idaman 8/1
Bukit Idaman, Sulaman Coastal Highway,
68100, Selayang, Selangor Darul Ehsan,
Malaysia **(100%)**
Tel.: (60) 361363333
Web Site: http://www.binapuri.com.my
Property Development Services
N.A.I.C.S.: 531390

Bina Puri Sdn Bhd **(1)**
Wisma Bina Puri 88 Jalan Bukit Idaman
8/1, Bukit Idaman, 68100, Selayang, Selangor Darul Ehsan, Malaysia
Tel.: (60) 361363333
Building Construction Services
N.A.I.C.S.: 236116

Easy Mix Sdn. Bhd. **(1)**
Batu 11 3/4 Jalan, Hulu Langat, Selangor,
Malaysia
Tel.: (60) 390215851
Civil & Building Construction Services
N.A.I.C.S.: 541330

Ideal Heights Properties Sdn.
Bhd. **(1)**
No 1 and 2 Jalan Bukit Idaman 8/1, PO Box
20, 68100, Selayang, Selangor, Malaysia
Tel.: (60) 361386102
Civil & Building Construction Services
N.A.I.C.S.: 541330

Karak Land Sdn. Bhd. **(1)**
BHPetrol Lot 63 Jalan Lama Bentong-
Karak, Karak Daerah Bentong, 28600, Pahang, Malaysia
Tel.: (60) 92318008
Web Site: https://www.thevalley.com.my
Civil & Building Construction Services
N.A.I.C.S.: 541330

Maskimi Polyol Sdn. Bhd. **(1)**
Lot 5815 Unit 1-8 Jalan Reko, Kajang,
43000, Selangor Darul Ehsan, Malaysia
Tel.: (60) 387332078
Web Site: http://www.maskimi.com.my
Sales Range: $25-49.9 Million
Emp.: 21
Natural Oil Mfr & Distr
N.A.I.C.S.: 111120
Andrew Chan *(Mgr-Technical Sls)*

Sungai Long Industries Sdn Bhd **(1)**
Jalan Hulu Langat Batu 11 3/4, Hulu Lan-

gat, 43100, Selangor, Malaysia
Tel.: (60) 390212400
Web Site: http://www.sglong-ind.com
Rev.: $27,519,300
Emp.: 150
Granites & Bricks Mfr & Distr
N.A.I.C.S.: 212313
Tee Hock Seng (Mng Dir)

BINA WAREHOUSE SDN. BHD.
7A Jalan 51/215 Seksyen 51, 46050,
Petaling Jaya, Selangor, Malaysia
Tel.: (60) 3 7781 5269   MY
Web Site:
http://www.binawarehouse.com
Kitchen Cabinet Mfr
N.A.I.C.S.: 337110
Henry Kok (Exec Dir)

BINAS D.D.
Armije BiH 171, Bugojno, 70230,
Bosnia & Herzegovina
Tel.: (387) 30251148
Web Site: http://www.binas.com.ba
UBNSRK2—(SARE)
Rev.: $3,707,131
Assets: $20,180,587
Liabilities: $4,912,803
Net Worth: $15,267,785
Earnings: ($2,318,657)
Emp.: 340
Fiscal Year-end: 12/31/20
Military Equipment Mfr & Distr
N.A.I.C.S.: 336992

**BINASAT COMMUNICATIONS
BERHAD**
Menara Binasat Lot PT 13824 Jalan
Teknologi 4 Technology Park Malay-
sia, Bukit Jalil, 57000, Kuala Lumpur,
Malaysia
Tel.: (60) 395461881
Web Site:
https://www.binacom.com.my
Year Founded: 2017
BINACOM—(KLS)
Rev.: $27,980,524
Assets: $36,026,989
Liabilities: $10,836,134
Net Worth: $25,190,855
Earnings: ($2,642,184)
Emp.: 402
Fiscal Year-end: 12/31/23
Telecommunication Servicesb
N.A.I.C.S.: 517112
Na Boon Aik (Mng Dir)

**BINATONE ELECTRONICS IN-
TERNATIONAL LTD.**
Floor 23A 9 Des Voeux Road West,
Hong Kong, China (Hong Kong)
Tel.: (852) 28027388   HK
Web Site:
http://www.binatoneglobal.com
Year Founded: 1958
Sales Range: $1-9.9 Million
Emp.: 30
Electronics & Telecommunications
Products Mfr
N.A.I.C.S.: 334220
Dino Lalvani (Chm & CEO)

Subsidiaries:

Binatone Communications
Europe   (1)
Europark 2056, 3530, Houthalen, Belgium
Tel.: (32) 11 510953
Telecommunication Product Distr
N.A.I.C.S.: 423690
Neil Scanlon (Mng Dir-Reg Ops)

Binatone Global Electronics (Shen-
zhen) Co. Limited   (1)
Flat H 14/F Tower B World Trade Plaza
Fuhong Road, Shenzhen, China
Tel.: (86) 755 8375 7088
Telecommunication Product Distr
N.A.I.C.S.: 423690

Binatone North America Inc.   (1)
11550 N Meridian St Ste 525, Carmel, IN
46032-6956
Tel.: (317) 436-8383
Telecommunication Product Distr
N.A.I.C.S.: 423690

Binatone Telecom Plc   (1)
1 Absley Way, London, NW2 7HF, United
Kingdom
Tel.: (44) 208955270
Web Site: http://www.binatonetelecom.com
Electronic Products Mfr
N.A.I.C.S.: 335220
Dino Lavani (Chm)

Binatone Telecommunication Pvt
Limited   (1)
A-36 Lower Ground Floor Sector - 4, Noida,
201301, Uttar Pradesh, India
Tel.: (91) 120 4381381
Telecommunication Product Distr
N.A.I.C.S.: 423690
Surendra Pratap Singh (Gen Mgr)

**BINAYAK TEX PROCESSORS
LIMITED**
384-m Dabholkarwadi 5th Floor Kal-
badevi Road, Mumbai, 400 002, Ma-
harashtra, India
Tel.: (91) 2240542222
Web Site: https://binayaktex.in
Year Founded: 1971
523054—(BOM)
Rev.: $27,393,861
Assets: $24,785,898
Liabilities: $14,226,977
Net Worth: $10,558,921
Earnings: $609,770
Fiscal Year-end: 03/31/21
Textile Fabric Mfr & Distr
N.A.I.C.S.: 313310
Pradipkumar Pacheriwala (Mng Dir)

BINDAL EXPORTS LIMITED
Bindal House Kumbharia Surat Kado-
dara Road, Surat, 395 010, Gujarat,
India
Tel.: (91) 2612640700
Web Site:
https://www.bindalexports.com
Year Founded: 1980
540148—(BOM)
Rev.: $3,179,380
Assets: $1,822,391
Liabilities: $609,818
Net Worth: $1,212,573
Earnings: $28,919
Emp.: 72
Fiscal Year-end: 03/31/21
Textile Product Mfr & Distr
N.A.I.C.S.: 315210
Ravindrakumar K. Arya (Chm & Mng
Dir)

**BINDAR TRADING & INVEST-
MENT CO. PLC**
Al Madinah Al Munawara Street, PO
Box 1921, Amman, 11821, Jordan
Tel.: (962) 65518916
Web Site: https://www.bindar-jo.com
Year Founded: 2000
BIND—(AMM)
Rev.: $11,818,262
Assets: $103,339,296
Liabilities: $57,625,655
Net Worth: $45,713,641
Earnings: $4,804,073
Emp.: 58
Fiscal Year-end: 12/31/21
Financial Services
N.A.I.C.S.: 523999
Walid Mohammed Syrian (Fin Dir &
Dir-Administration)

**BINDAREE BEEF PTY. LIM-
ITED**
7307 Gwydir Highway, Inverell, 2360,
NSW, Australia

Tel.: (61) 267211411
Web Site:
http://www.bindareebeef.com.au
Sales Range: $150-199.9 Million
Emp.: 600
Beef Slaughtering Services
N.A.I.C.S.: 311611
John Newton (Dir-Livestock)

Subsidiaries:

Sanger Australia Pty Ltd   (1)
Level 16 1 York Street, Sydney, 2000,
NSW, Australia
Tel.: (61) 292588333
Web Site: http://www.sanger.com.au
Meat Distr
N.A.I.C.S.: 424470
Richard Rains (CEO)

BINDER+CO AG
Grazer Strasse 19-25, 8200, Gleis-
dorf, Austria
Tel.: (43) 31128000
Web Site: http://www.binder-co.com
Year Founded: 1894
Rev.: $131,163,603
Assets: $97,683,148
Liabilities: $67,285,668
Net Worth: $30,397,480
Earnings: $1,739,143
Emp.: 383
Fiscal Year-end: 12/31/19
Bulk Material Separation & Sorting
Services
N.A.I.C.S.: 562920
Martin Pfeffer (CFO & Member-Mgmt
Bd)

BINDERHOLZ GMBH
Zillertalstrasse 39, 6263, Zillertal,
Austria
Tel.: (43) 5288 601   AT
Web Site: http://www.binderholz.com
Year Founded: 1950
Sawmills Operator & Wood Products
Whslr
N.A.I.C.S.: 321113
Reinhard Binder (CEO)

Subsidiaries:

Binderholz Nordic Oy   (1)
Joensuun Tiedepuisto Bldg 4A Office 533
Lansikatu 15, 80110, Joensuu, Finland
Tel.: (358) 20 7871 780
Web Site: http://www.binderholz.com
Sawmills Operator & Wood Products Whslr
N.A.I.C.S.: 321113

BINDI METALS LIMITED
Level 8 London House 216 St
Georges Terrace, Perth, 6000, WA,
Australia
Tel.: (61) 894810389   AU
Web Site:
https://www.bindimetals.com.au
Year Founded: 2021
BIM—(ASX)
Rev.: $32,431
Assets: $1,936,373
Liabilities: $272,123
Net Worth: $1,664,251
Earnings: ($1,348,489)
Fiscal Year-end: 06/30/23
Metal Exploration Services
N.A.I.C.S.: 213114
Eddie King (Chm)

BINEX CO., LTD.
368-3 Dadae-ro, Saha-Gu, Busan,
49496, Korea (South)
Tel.: (82) 328503000
Web Site: https://www.bi-nex.com
Year Founded: 1985
053030—(KRS)
Rev.: $120,171,278
Assets: $228,880,423
Liabilities: $81,399,552
Net Worth: $147,480,871

Earnings: $9,544,954
Emp.: 587
Fiscal Year-end: 12/31/22
Pharmaceutical & Medicinal Products
Mfr
N.A.I.C.S.: 325412
Lee Hyuk-Jong (CEO)

**BING POWER SYSTEMS
GMBH**
Dorfaeckerstrasse 16, 90427, Nurem-
berg, Germany
Tel.: (49) 91132670
Web Site: http://www.bingpower.de
Year Founded: 1926
Emp.: 140
Carburetor & Industrial Engines Mfr
N.A.I.C.S.: 423110
Martin Fischer (Mng Dir)

Subsidiaries:

BING Power Origin Kft.   (1)
Gyari ut 72, 2310, Szigetszentmiklos, Hun-
gary
Tel.: (36) 24444128
Web Site: http://www.origin.hu
Automobile Parts Distr
N.A.I.C.S.: 423110

BINGGRAE CO., LTD.
45 Dasansunhwan-ro, Jung-Gu,
Namyangju, Gyeonggi-do, Korea
(South)
Tel.: (82) 800220056
Web Site: https://www.bing.co.kr
Year Founded: 1967
005180—(KRS)
Rev.: $972,315,026
Assets: $590,027,473
Liabilities: $148,412,669
Net Worth: $441,614,804
Earnings: $19,700,792
Emp.: 1,816
Fiscal Year-end: 12/31/22
Dairy Products Mfr
N.A.I.C.S.: 311514
Won Jeon Chang (CEO)

**BINGO GROUP HOLDINGS
LIMITED**
Unit 202 2/F Chinaweal Centre 414-
424 Jaffe Road, Hong Kong, China
(Hong Kong)
Tel.: (852) 21190333   Ky
Web Site: https://www.irasia.com
8220—(HKG)
Rev.: $1,095,556
Assets: $4,566,795
Liabilities: $3,967,425
Net Worth: $599,370
Earnings: ($1,892,266)
Emp.: 44
Fiscal Year-end: 03/31/22
Film Production Services
N.A.I.C.S.: 512110
Sing Chi Chiau (Exec Dir)

**BINGSHAN REFRIGERATION
& HEAT TECHNOLOGIES CO.,
LTD.**
No 106 Liaohe East Road Economic
and Technological Development
Zone, Dalian, 116630, Liaoning,
China
Tel.: (86) 41187968130
Web Site: http://en.daleng.cn
Year Founded: 1993
000530—(SSE)
Rev.: $406,189,836
Assets: $1,067,312,376
Liabilities: $637,650,468
Net Worth: $429,661,908
Earnings: $2,563,704
Emp.: 1,832
Fiscal Year-end: 12/31/22
Refrigeration Equipment Mfr & Whslr
N.A.I.C.S.: 333415

Binh Chanh Construction Investment Joint Stock Company—(Continued)

BINH CHANH CONSTRUCTION INVESTMENT JOINT STOCK COMPANY

550 Kinh Duong Vuong An Lac Binh Tan, Ho Chi Minh City, Vietnam
Tel.: (84) 838753021
Web Site: http://bcci.com.vn
Sales Range: $1-9.9 Million
Real Estate Manangement Services
N.A.I.C.S.: 531390

BINH DINH BOOK & EQUIPMENT JOINT STOCK COMPANY

219 Nguyen Lu, Quy Nhon, Binh Dinh, Vietnam
Tel.: (84) 563522645
Web Site:
  http://www.sachthietbibinhdinh.com
Year Founded: 2007
BDB—(HNX)
Rev.: $6,446,100
Assets: $1,966,200
Liabilities: $591,800
Net Worth: $1,374,400
Earnings: $94,300
Fiscal Year-end: 12/31/23
Book Whslr
N.A.I.C.S.: 459210
Ho Van Linh (Chm-Mgmt Bd)

BINH DINH MINERALS JOINT STOCK COMPANY

11 Ha Huy Tap, Quy Nhon, Binh Dinh, Vietnam
Tel.: (84) 2562240025
Web Site: https://www.bimico.vn
BMC—(HOSE)
Rev.: $7,413,610
Assets: $10,332,012
Liabilities: $925,640
Net Worth: $9,406,372
Earnings: $996,916
Emp.: 196
Fiscal Year-end: 12/31/23
Mining Services
N.A.I.C.S.: 212323
Tran Ho Toai Nguyen (Gen Dir)

BINH DUONG MINERAL & CONSTRUCTION JSC

Binh Duong Avenue Hoa Lan I Quarter, Thuan Giao, Thuan An, Binh Duong, Vietnam
Tel.: (84) 2743822602
Web Site: http://www.bimico.com.vn
Year Founded: 1993
Mineral Exploration Services
N.A.I.C.S.: 213115

BINH DUONG WATER ENVIRONMENT JSC

11 Ngo Van Tri street, Phu Loi ward, Thu Dau Mot, Binh Duong, Vietnam
Tel.: (84) 2743838333
Web Site: https://www.biwase.com.vn
Year Founded: 1975
BWE—(HNX)
Electric Power Distribution Services
N.A.I.C.S.: 221310
Tran Chien Cong (Gen Dir)

BINH MINH PLASTICS JOINT STOCK COMPANY

240 Hau Giang Phuong 9, Quan 6, Ho Chi Minh City, Vietnam
Tel.: (84) 839690973
Web Site:
  https://ww.binhminhplastic.com.vn
Year Founded: 1977
BMP—(HOSE)
Rev.: $582,483,326
Assets: $304,479,199

Liabilities: $42,347,339
Net Worth: $262,131,860
Earnings: $69,426,877
Emp.: 1,358
Fiscal Year-end: 12/31/22
Plastic Tank Mfr
N.A.I.C.S.: 326122

BINH THANH IMPORT EXPORT PRODUCTION & TRADE JSC

334A Phan Van Tri Street, Ward 11 Binh Thanh District, Ho Chi Minh City, Vietnam
Tel.: (84) 2871008888
Web Site: https://www.gilimex.com
Year Founded: 1982
GIL—(HOSE)
Rev.: $38,579,515
Assets: $138,314,951
Liabilities: $33,519,784
Net Worth: $104,795,166
Earnings: $1,189,897
Emp.: 5,000
Fiscal Year-end: 12/31/23
Food Product Mfr & Whslr
N.A.I.C.S.: 311710
Nguyen Bang Tam (Chm-Mgmt Bd)

BINH THUAN BOOK & EQUIPMENT JOINT STOCK COMPANY

70 Nguyen Van Troi, Phan Thiet, Binh Thuan, Vietnam
Tel.: (84) 523816118
Web Site: https://www.stbbt.com.vn
Year Founded: 1982
BST—(HNX)
Rev.: $2,747,792
Assets: $845,939
Liabilities: $272,148
Net Worth: $573,792
Earnings: $60,764
Fiscal Year-end: 12/31/21
Stationery Product Whslr
N.A.I.C.S.: 459410

BINH TIEN IMEX CORP. PTE. LTD.

22 Ly Chieu Hoang Phuong 10 Quan 6, Ward 10 District 6, Ho Chi Minh City, Vietnam
Tel.: (84) 2838753443
Web Site: http://www.bitis-vn.com
Sales Range: $25-49.9 Million
Emp.: 7,500
Footwear Mfr
N.A.I.C.S.: 316210

Subsidiaries:

Binh Tien Dong Nai Imex Corp., Pte., Ltd (1)
1/1 Pham Van Thuan Street Tam Hiep Ward, Bien Hoa, Dong Nai, Vietnam
Tel.: (84) 61 3813887
Footwear Mfr
N.A.I.C.S.: 316210

BINHAI INVESTMENT COMPANY LIMITED

Suite 3205-07 32/F Tower 2 Times Square 1 Matheson Street, Causeway Bay, Hong Kong, China (Hong Kong)
Tel.: (852) 25729228 BM
Web Site: http://www.binhalinv.com
2886—(DEU)
Rev.: $471,275,637
Assets: $915,095,559
Liabilities: $657,164,579
Net Worth: $257,930,980
Earnings: $46,543,594
Emp.: 1,718
Fiscal Year-end: 12/31/20
Oil & Gas Pipeline Construction Services

N.A.I.C.S.: 237120
Liang Gao (Gen Mgr)

BINJIANG SERVICE GROUP CO., LTD.

Room 1201-1 Block 1 New Town Times Square, Shangcheng, Hangzhou, China Ky
Web Site: https://www.hzbjwy.com
Year Founded: 1995
3316—(HKG)
Rev.: $388,957,410
Assets: $561,434,149
Liabilities: $347,989,449
Net Worth: $213,444,700
Earnings: $69,648,732
Emp.: 11,674
Fiscal Year-end: 12/31/23
Property Management Services
N.A.I.C.S.: 531311
Lidong Zhu (CEO)

BINNY LIMITED

No 1 Cooks Road, Perambur, Chennai, 600 012, Tamilnadu, India
Tel.: (91) 4426621053
Web Site: https://www.binnyltd.in
Year Founded: 1799
514215—(BOM)
Rev.: $9,744,353
Assets: $160,074,806
Liabilities: $114,655,878
Net Worth: $45,418,928
Earnings: $2,767,729
Emp.: 16
Fiscal Year-end: 03/31/21
Warehousing Services
N.A.I.C.S.: 493110
M. Nandagopal (Chm)

BINNY MILLS LIMITED

Sapthagiri Bhavan New No 4 Old.No 10 Karpagamabal Nagar, Mylapore, Chennai, 600 004, Tamilnadu, India
Tel.: (91) 4424991518
Web Site: https://www.bmlindia.com
Year Founded: 2007
535620—(BOM)
Rev.: $1,178,882
Assets: $24,002,570
Liabilities: $45,359,141
Net Worth: ($21,356,572)
Earnings: ($1,533,277)
Emp.: 9
Fiscal Year-end: 03/31/22
Textile Product Whslr
N.A.I.C.S.: 424990
V. R. Venkataachalam (Chm)

BINOVI TECHNOLOGIES CORP.

574 Chartwell Rd, Oakville, L6J 4A8, ON, Canada
Tel.: (416) 943-6271
Web Site: http://www.binovi.com
BNVIF—(OTCEM)
Rev.: $146,206
Assets: $850,500
Liabilities: $2,673,311
Net Worth: ($1,822,811)
Earnings: ($12,851,815)
Fiscal Year-end: 02/28/22
Software Development Services
N.A.I.C.S.: 541511
Jatinder Dhaliwal (CEO)

BINTER CANARIAS, S.A.

Gran Canaria Tenerife Norte Lanzarote Fuerteventura, Parcela 9 Del Zima, 35230, Las Palmas, Gran Canaria, Spain
Tel.: (34) 902875787 ES
Web Site:
  http://www.bintercanarias.com
Year Founded: 1989
Sales Range: $75-99.9 Million

Emp.: 400
Air Passenger Service
N.A.I.C.S.: 481111
Pedro Agustin del Castillo Machado (Pres & CEO)

Subsidiaries:

Atlantica de Handling (1)
Carretera General Del Norte C 820 Ed Star, San Cristobal de La Laguna, 38206, Spain
Tel.: (34) 922 568000
Air Freight Transportation Services
N.A.I.C.S.: 481112

BInterSwift (1)
C Canon Del Ambar Autovia GC-1km 11 600 SN, Gran Canaria, 35200, Telde, Spain
Tel.: (34) 928 305 635
Web Site: http://www.binterswift.com
Sales Range: $25-49.9 Million
Emp.: 3
Air Freight Transportation Services
N.A.I.C.S.: 481112
Jose-Luis Becerra (Gen Mgr)

BInterTechnic (1)
Aeropuerto de Gran Canaria Parcela 9 Del Zima, 35230, Telde, Las Palmas, Spain
Tel.: (34) 649503460
Web Site: http://www.bintertechnic.com
Aircraft Maintenance Services
N.A.I.C.S.: 488190
Rafael Lopez (Dir Gen)

BinterSistemas (1)
Calle Canon Del Ambar SN GC-1 Salinetas, Telde, 35219, Spain
Tel.: (34) 928 30 56 25
Sales Range: $25-49.9 Million
Emp.: 30
Software Development Services
N.A.I.C.S.: 541512
Hector Reboso (Mng Dir)

Servicious Aerotecnicos insulares SL (1)
41th Beneficiado Jose Estupinan Industrial Park of El Goro, Gran Canaria, 35219, Telde, Las Palmas, Spain
Tel.: (34) 928 70 13 07
Web Site: http://www.satiaero.com
Sales Range: $25-49.9 Million
Emp.: 50
Aircraft Maintenance Services
N.A.I.C.S.: 488190
Eduardo Serradilla (Gen Mgr)

BINTULU PORT HOLDINGS BERHAD

Lot 15 Block 20 Kemena Land District 12th Mile Tanjung Kidurong Road, PO Box 996, 97008, Bintulu, Sarawak, Malaysia
Tel.: (60) 86291001 MY
Web Site:
  https://www.bintuluport.com.my
Year Founded: 1983
5032—(KLS)
Rev.: $167,849,101
Assets: $656,141,587
Liabilities: $284,867,725
Net Worth: $371,273,862
Earnings: $27,031,534
Emp.: 1,555
Fiscal Year-end: 12/31/22
Investment Holding Company
N.A.I.C.S.: 551114
Abu Bakar Husaini (COO-Biport Bulkers Sdn. Bhd.)

Subsidiaries:

Bintulu Port Sdn. Bhd. (1)
Lot 15 Block 20 12th Mile Tanjung Kidurong Road, PO Box 996, Kemena Land District, 97008, Bintulu, Sarawak, Malaysia
Tel.: (60) 86291001
Investment Holding Company Services
N.A.I.C.S.: 551112

Biport Bulkers Sdn. Bhd. (1)
Lot 15 Block 20 12th Mile Tanjung Kidurong Road, PO Box 996, Kemena Land District, 97008, Bintulu, Sarawak, Malaysia

Tel.: (60) 86255101
Refining & Blending Vegetable Oil Mfr
N.A.I.C.S.: 311225

Samalaju Industrial Port Sdn.
Bhd.   **(1)**
Lot 82 Samalaju Industrial Park Block 1,
Kemena Land District, 97300, Bintulu, Sara-
wak, Malaysia
Tel.: (60) 86296825
Port Services
N.A.I.C.S.: 488330

BINZAGR COMPANY
PO Box 54, Jeddah, 21411, Saudi
Arabia
Tel.: (966) 122168000   **SA**
Web Site: http://www.binzagr.com.sa
Year Founded: 1925
Sales Range: $100-124.9 Million
Emp.: 1,700
Holding Company; Industrial & Manu-
facturing Services
N.A.I.C.S.: 532281
Wahib Said Binzagr *(CEO & Exec
Partner)*

Subsidiaries:

Abdullah & Said M.O. Binzagr
Company   **(1)**
9th floor Mahmal tower, PO Box 209, Jed-
dah, 21411, Saudi Arabia
Tel.: (966) 26438235
Web Site: http://www.binzagr.com.sa
Sales Range: $25-49.9 Million
Emp.: 40
Holding Company
N.A.I.C.S.: 551112
Paul Sutcliffe *(Mgr)*

Division (Domestic):

Binzagr Industrial Cleaning
Services   **(2)**
PO Box 54, Jeddah, 21411, Saudi Arabia
Tel.: (966) 26470000
Industrial Cleaning Services
N.A.I.C.S.: 541420

Binzagr Factory for Insulation Materi-
als Ltd.   **(1)**
PO Box 96, Al Khobar, 31952, Saudi
Arabia   **(100%)**
Tel.: (966) 38640980
Web Site: http://www.binzagr-
insulation.com
Oil & Other Industrial Services
N.A.I.C.S.: 213112
Anil Vig *(VP)*

BIO FD&C CO., LTD.
509 512 B07 A-dong Smartvalley 30
Songdomirae-ro, Yeonsu-gu, Incheon,
Korea (South)
Tel.: (82) 328112027
Web Site: https://www.biofdnc.com
Year Founded: 2005
251120—(KRS)
Rev.: $12,161,032
Assets: $45,280,467
Liabilities: $4,646,816
Net Worth: $40,633,651
Earnings: $3,325,148
Emp.: 54
Fiscal Year-end: 12/31/22
Biotechnology Research & Develop-
ment Services
N.A.I.C.S.: 541714

BIO GREEN ENERGY TECH PUBLIC COMPANY
Mano Tower 153 Soi Sukhumvit 39
Sukhumvit Road, Phra Khanong,
Bangkok, 10110, Thailand
Tel.: (66) 22600050
Web Site: https://www.biogreen-
energytech.com
Year Founded: 1976
BIOTEC—(THA)
Rev.: $133,906,194
Assets: $88,686,956

Liabilities: $54,228,755
Net Worth: $34,458,201
Earnings: ($3,538,943)
Fiscal Year-end: 12/31/23
Marine Transport Services
N.A.I.C.S.: 488320
Chano Phenjati *(Chm)*

Subsidiaries:

Thaiden Maritime Co., Ltd.   **(1)**
Mano Tower 153 Sukhumvit 39 Klongton-
Nua, Wattana, Bangkok, 10110, Thailand
Tel.: (66) 22600050
Marine Transportation Services
N.A.I.C.S.: 488390

BIO GREEN PAPERS LIMITED
Sy no 66/2, Street No 03 2nd floor
Rai Durgam Prashanth Hills Nav
Khalsa Gachi Bowli, Rangareddi,
Hyderabad, 500034, Telangana, India
Tel.: (91) 8019998603
Web Site:
   https://www.biogreenpapers.com
Rev.: $1,428,768
Assets: $7,922,592
Liabilities: $940,326
Net Worth: $6,982,266
Earnings: $66,630
Emp.: 6
Fiscal Year-end: 03/31/19
Kraft Paper & Duplex Board Mfr
N.A.I.C.S.: 322120
Velamala Jagadish *(Mng Dir)*

Subsidiaries:

Bio Green Papers Limited - Srikaku-
lam Facility   **(1)**
Sy No 256 Akkurada Village Jalumuru Man-
dal, Srikakulam, Andhra Pradesh, India
Tel.: (91) 9912213949
Paper & Paperboard Mfr
N.A.I.C.S.: 322130

BIO METHANOL CHEMIE NED-ERLAND BV
Oosterhorn 10 - Gate 3, 9936 HD,
Delfzijl, Netherlands
Tel.: (31) 88 6647700   **NI**
Web Site: http://www.biomcn.eu
Sales Range: $50-74.9 Million
Emp.: 100
Methanol Mfr
N.A.I.C.S.: 325194
Rob Voncken *(CEO)*

BIO MILK LTD.
Rehov Prof Hillel Vhanan Oppen-
heimer 2, 7670102, Rehovot, Israel
Tel.: (972) 3 374 2282
Web Site: http://www.biomilk.com
Year Founded: 2018
BMLK—(TAE)
Cultured Milk Production Services
N.A.I.C.S.: 424430
Tomer Aizen *(CEO)*

BIO PAPPEL, S.A.B. DE C.V.
Ejercito Nacional 1130 Col Los Mor-
ales Polanco, Miguel Hidalgo,
Mexico, CP 11510, Mexico
Tel.: (52) 5591266000   **MX**
Web Site: http://www.biopappel.com
Year Founded: 1982
PAPPEL—(MEX)
Sales Range: Less than $1 Million
Recycled Paper & Paper Products
Mfr
N.A.I.C.S.: 322120
Miguel Rincon Arredondo *(Chm &
CEO)*

Subsidiaries:

Bio Pappel Scribe, S.A. de C.V.   **(1)**
Ejercito Nacional 1130 Col Los Morales Po-
lanco, Delegacion Miguel Hidalgo, Mexico,
CP 11510, DF, Mexico

Tel.: (52) 55 91 26 6000
Web Site: http://www.biopappel.com
Recycled Writing Paper & Paper Products
Mfr
N.A.I.C.S.: 322120

U.S. Corrugated, Inc.   **(1)**
95 W Beau St Ste 430, Washington, PA
15301   **(55%)**
Tel.: (724) 345-2050
Web Site: http://www.uscorr.com
Emp.: 10
Packaging & Corrugated Products Mfr
N.A.I.C.S.: 322211
Dennis Mehiel *(Chm)*

Plant (Domestic):

U.S. Corrugated, Inc. - Cleveland
Sheet Plant   **(2)**
16645 Granite Rd, Cleveland, OH 44137
Tel.: (216) 663-3344
Sales Range: $1-9.9 Million
Emp.: 70
Corrugated & Solid Fiber Box Mfr
N.A.I.C.S.: 322211
Harry Oshell *(Gen Mgr)*

U.S. Corrugated, Inc. - Coal Center
Corrugator Plant   **(2)**
400 Technology Dr, Coal Center, PA 15423
Tel.: (724) 938-3020
Web Site: http://www.uscorr.com
Sales Range: $25-49.9 Million
Emp.: 150
Corrugated & Solid Fiber Boxes
N.A.I.C.S.: 322211
Aron Dentino *(Mgr-Customer Svc)*

U.S. Corrugated, Inc. - Milwaukee
Sheet Plant   **(2)**
3832 N Third St, Milwaukee, WI 53212-
1109
Tel.: (414) 264-8100
Web Site: http://www.uscorr.com
Sales Range: $25-49.9 Million
Emp.: 50
Corrugated Cardboard Sheet Mfr
N.A.I.C.S.: 322211
Dennis Bartlein *(Plant Mgr)*

BIO VIEW LTD.
3 Pekeris St, Rehovot, 7670203, Is-
rael
Tel.: (972) 732271025
Web Site: http://www.bioview.co.il
BIOV—(TAE)
Rev.: $9,605,470
Assets: $11,591,380
Liabilities: $4,047,520
Net Worth: $7,543,860
Earnings: $105,816
Emp.: 31
Fiscal Year-end: 12/31/23
Analytical Laboratory Instrument
Manufacturing
N.A.I.C.S.: 334516
Yuval Harari *(Exec VP)*

BIO-AMD, INC.
Daresbury Innovation Center Kick-
wick Lane, Daresbury, WA4 4FS,
United Kingdom
Tel.: (44) 8445861910   **NV**
Web Site: http://www.bioamd.com
Year Founded: 2006
BIAD—(OTCIQ)
Sales Range: Less than $1 Million
Emp.: 2
Holding Company; Medical Devices
N.A.I.C.S.: 551112
Thomas Barr *(CEO)*

BIO-AMERICA, INC.
497 Soudan Ave, Toronto, M4S 1X1,
ON, Canada
Tel.: (416) 951-0270
BOAA—(OTCIQ)
Sales Range: Less than $1 Million
Pharmaceuticals Product Mfr
N.A.I.C.S.: 325412

BIO-GATE AG

Neumeyerstrasse 28-34, 90411,
Nuremberg, Germany
Tel.: (49) 911477523100
Web Site: https://www.bio-gate.de
BIG1—(MUN)
Rev.: $8,003,057
Assets: $5,806,356
Liabilities: $2,086,314
Net Worth: $3,720,042
Earnings: ($1,788,269)
Emp.: 42
Fiscal Year-end: 12/31/23
Antimicrobial Coatings Mfr
N.A.I.C.S.: 325998
Marc Lloret-Grau *(CEO & Member-
Exec Bd)*

Subsidiaries:

BioEpiderm GmBH   **(1)**
Neumeyerstrasse 28 - 34, Nuremberg, 90
411, Germany   **(100%)**
Tel.: (49) 911 2526 350
Web Site: http://www.bioepiderm.de
Cosmetics Products Mfr
N.A.I.C.S.: 456120
Kai Martin *(Dir-Mktg & Sls)*

QualityLabs BT GmBH   **(1)**
Neumeyerstrasse 22, 90411, Nuremberg,
Germany
Tel.: (49) 9112526210
Web Site: https://www.qualitylabs-bt.de
Biomaterial Testing Services
N.A.I.C.S.: 541380

BIO-GENE TECHNOLOGY LIM-ITED
Level 6 400 Collins Street, Mel-
bourne, 3000, VIC, Australia
Tel.: (61) 390681062   **AU**
Web Site: https://www.bio-
gene.com.au
Year Founded: 1995
BGT—(ASX)
Rev.: $474,083
Assets: $2,109,769
Liabilities: $246,024
Net Worth: $1,863,745
Earnings: ($1,608,693)
Fiscal Year-end: 06/30/24
Research & Development in Biotech-
nology (except Nanobiotechnology)
N.A.I.C.S.: 541714
Richard Jagger *(CEO & Mng Dir)*

BIO-PROTECH INC
151-3 Donghwagongdan-ro, Munmak-
eup, Wonju, 26365, Gangwon, Korea
(South)
Tel.: (82) 337357720
Web Site:
   https://www.protechsite.com
Year Founded: 2000
Electrode Mfr
N.A.I.C.S.: 334513
Ik-ro Park *(Co-Pres)*

BIO-SYNECTICS
708 Byucksan Digital Valley II 184
Gasandigital 2-ro, Geumchun-gu,
Seoul, Korea (South)
Tel.: (82) 221131285
Web Site: http://www.bio-
synectics.com
Year Founded: 2004
Prototype Development Services
N.A.I.C.S.: 541713
Jason Lee *(VP-Mktg)*

BIO-THERA SOLUTIONS LTD.
Floor 5 Building A6 11 Kai-Yuan Blvd,
Huangpu District, Guangzhou,
510530, Guangdong, China
Tel.: (86) 2032203220
Web Site: https://www.bio-thera.com
Year Founded: 2003
688177—(SHG)
Rev.: $63,900,533

Bio-Thera Solutions Ltd.—(Continued)

Assets: $306,035,061
Liabilities: $80,376,431
Net Worth: $225,658,630
Earnings: ($67,448,006)
Emp.: 4,200
Fiscal Year-end: 12/31/22
Pharmaceutical Product Mfr & Distr
N.A.I.C.S.: 325412
Shengfeng Li (Founder & CEO)

BIO-UV GROUP

Tel.: (33) 499133911
Web Site: https://www.bio-uv.com
ALTUV—(EUR)
Sales Range: Less than $1 Million
Water Treatment Equipment Mfr
N.A.I.C.S.: 333310
Laurent-Emmanuel Migeon (COO)

BIO-WORKS TECHNOLOGIES AB

Virdings alle 18, 754 50, Uppsala, Sweden
Tel.: (46) 856267430
Web Site: https://www.bio-works.com
Year Founded: 2006
BIOWKS—(OMX)
Rev.: $3,947,859
Assets: $8,408,237
Liabilities: $2,183,096
Net Worth: $6,225,142
Earnings: ($4,114,751)
Emp.: 50
Fiscal Year-end: 12/31/22
Biotechnology Research & Development Services
N.A.I.C.S.: 541714
Anna Lindqvist (CMO)

BIOALPHA HOLDINGS BERHAD

No 10 Jalan P/9A Seksyen 13, 43650, Bandar Baru Bangi, Selangor Darul Ehsan, Malaysia
Tel.: (60) 389251222   MY
Web Site: https://www.bioa.com.my
Year Founded: 2005
BIOHLDG—(KLS)
Rev.: $10,031,957
Assets: $35,530,164
Liabilities: $7,312,468
Net Worth: $28,217,696
Earnings: ($9,502,344)
Fiscal Year-end: 12/31/23
Health Supplement Product Mfr & Distr
N.A.I.C.S.: 325411
Tian Kok Hon (Founder, CEO & Mng Dir)

Subsidiaries:

Mediconstant Holding Sdn. Bhd.   (1)
80-81 Blk I Jalan Tek 3/9 Bestari DKota Kota Damansara, Petaling Jaya, 47810, Malaysia
Tel.: (60) 3 6140 8638
Holding Company
N.A.I.C.S.: 551112

Subsidiary (Domestic):

Mediconstant Pharmacy (Ampang) Sdn. Bhd.   (2)
No 18 Jalan Ruang U8/109, Bukit Jelutong, 40150, Shah Alam, Selangor, Malaysia
Tel.: (60) 37 832 3018
Web Site: https://www.constant.com.my
Drug Product Distr
N.A.I.C.S.: 424210

Mediconstant Pharmacy (Klang) Sdn. Bhd.   (2)
No 145 Ground Floor Jln Meru Kaw 19, 41050, Klang, Selangor, Malaysia
Tel.: (60) 333436579
Drug Product Distr
N.A.I.C.S.: 424210
Sally Chuah (Mgr)

BIOAMBER INC.

1250 Rene Levesque West Suite 4310, Montreal, H3B 4W8, QC, Canada
Tel.: (514) 844-8000   DE
Web Site: http://www.bio-amber.com
Year Founded: 2008
Rev.: $8,272,497
Assets: $161,330,465
Liabilities: $112,839,565
Net Worth: $48,490,900
Earnings: ($22,478,081)
Emp.: 86
Fiscal Year-end: 12/31/16
Chemical Products Mfr
N.A.I.C.S.: 325110

BIOARCTIC AB

Warfvinges Vag 35, 112 51, Stockholm, Sweden
Tel.: (46) 86956930
Web Site: https://www.bioarctic.se
Year Founded: 2003
BIOA.B—(OMX)
Rev.: $3,258,071
Assets: $109,594,878
Liabilities: $13,313,312
Net Worth: $96,281,566
Earnings: ($14,623,841)
Emp.: 49
Fiscal Year-end: 12/31/21
Biotechnology Research & Development Services
N.A.I.C.S.: 541714
Wenche Rolfsen (Chm)

BIOCARTIS GROUP NV

Generaal De Wittelaan 11 B, B-2800, Mechelen, Belgium
Tel.: (32) 15632600
Web Site: https://www.biocartis.com
BCART—(EUR)
Rev.: $67,427,920
Assets: $174,999,635
Liabilities: $216,633,286
Net Worth: ($41,633,651)
Earnings: ($87,784,769)
Emp.: 407
Fiscal Year-end: 12/31/21
Molecular Diagnostic Systems
N.A.I.C.S.: 325413
Benoit Devogelare (CTO)

Subsidiaries:

Biocartis US Inc.   (1)
30 Montgomery St 9th Fl Ste 970, Jersey City, NJ 07302
Diagnostic Imaging Equipment Mfr
N.A.I.C.S.: 339112

BIOCELTIX S.A.

Bierutowska 57-59 bud III, 51-317, Wroclaw, Poland
Tel.: (48) 718808771   PL
Web Site: https://www.bioceltix.com
Year Founded: 2018
BCX—(WAR)
Assets: $3,235,595
Liabilities: $576,367
Net Worth: $2,659,228
Earnings: ($3,477,528)
Fiscal Year-end: 12/31/23
Biotechnology Research & Development Services
N.A.I.C.S.: 541714
Andrij Wlach (CFO)

BIOCERES S.A.

Ocampo 210 bis Predio CCT Rosario, Santa Fe, 2000, Argentina
Tel.: (54) 341 486 1100   Ar
Web Site: http://www.bioceres.com.ar
Year Founded: 2001
Emp.: 500
Crop Farming Services
N.A.I.C.S.: 111219
Federico Trucco (CEO)

Subsidiaries:

Bioceres Crop Solutions Corp.   (1)
Ocampo 210 bis Predio CCT, Rosario, 2000, Santa Fe, 2000, Argentina
Tel.: (54) 3414861122
Web Site: https://www.biocerescrops.com
Rev.: $464,828,548
Assets: $850,628,347
Liabilities: $501,063,986
Net Worth: $349,564,361
Earnings: $6,256,656
Emp.: 983
Fiscal Year-end: 06/30/2024
Software Development Services
N.A.I.C.S.: 541511
Federico Trucco (CEO)

Subsidiary (US):

Pro Farm Group, Inc.   (2)
7780-420 Brier Creek Pkwy, Raleigh, NC 27617-7882
Tel.: (530) 750-2800
Web Site: http://www.marronebioinnovations.com
Rev.: $44,310,000
Assets: $87,056,000
Liabilities: $57,403,000
Net Worth: $29,653,000
Earnings: ($16,554,000)
Emp.: 51
Fiscal Year-end: 12/31/2021
Biological Pest Management & Plant Health Products
N.A.I.C.S.: 325320
Federico Trucco (CEO)

Subsidiary (Non-US):

Pro Farm OU   (3)
Keevise str 10, 11415, Tallinn, Estonia
Tel.: (372) 6622291
Fertilizer Mfr
N.A.I.C.S.: 325311

Pro Farm Technologies Comercio de Insumos Agricolas do Braisil Ltda   (3)
Alameda Lorena 1304 CJ 30501, Jardim Paulista, 01424-004, Sao Paulo, Brazil
Tel.: (55) 11961677227
Fertilizer Mfr
N.A.I.C.S.: 325311

Pro Farm Technologies Oy   (3)
Vantaankoskentie 14 a, 01670, Vantaa, Finland
Tel.: (358) 981711630
Web Site: http://www.profarm.org
Fertilizer Mfr
N.A.I.C.S.: 325311
Toni Murtoniemi (Fin Dir)

BIOCODEX SA

7 avenue Gallieni, 94257, Gentilly, Cedex, France
Tel.: (33) 1 41 24 30 00
Web Site: http://www.biocodex.com
Year Founded: 1953
Emp.: 1,000
Pharmaceuticals Mfr
N.A.I.C.S.: 325412
Jean-Marie Lefevre (Chm & CEO)

Subsidiaries:

Biocodex Oy   (1)
Karapellontie 6, FI-02610, Espoo, Finland
Tel.: (358) 9 5099 1
Web Site: http://www.biocodexnordics.fi
Sales & Support Services for Healthcare Industry
N.A.I.C.S.: 424210
Tessa Ahosalmi (Gen Mgr)

Subsidiary (Non-US):

Biocodex AB   (2)
Isafjordsgatan 36, SE-164 40, Kista, Sweden
Tel.: (46) 8 615 2760
Web Site: http://www.biocodexnordics.fi
Pharmaceutical Product Whslr
N.A.I.C.S.: 424210

Biocodex SIA   (2)
Kalnini A, Marupe District, 2167, Marupe, Latvia

Tel.: (371) 6761 9365
Web Site: http://www.biocodexnordics.fi
Pharmaceutical Product Whslr
N.A.I.C.S.: 424210

Biocodex UAB   (2)
9-ojo Forto 70, LT-48179, Kaunas, Lithuania
Tel.: (370) 37 408 681
Web Site: http://www.biocodexnordics.fi
Pharmaceutical Product Whslr
N.A.I.C.S.: 424210

Biocodex, Inc.   (1)
255 Shoreline Dr Ste 450, Redwood City, CA 94065
Tel.: (877) 356-7787
Web Site: http://www.biocodexusa.com
Pharmaceuticals Mfr
N.A.I.C.S.: 325412
Diana Weitzel (Product Mgr)

BIOCON LTD.

20th KM Hosur Road Electronic City, Bengaluru, 560 100, India
Tel.: (91) 8028082808
Web Site: https://www.biocon.com
532523—(BOM)
Rev.: $1,384,821,054
Assets: $6,239,769,798
Liabilities: $3,543,432,648
Net Worth: $2,696,337,150
Earnings: $77,093,699
Emp.: 9,698
Fiscal Year-end: 03/31/23
Biopharmaceutical Research, Development & Manufacturing Services
N.A.I.C.S.: 325412
Kiran Mazumdar-Shaw (Chm)

Subsidiaries:

Biocon Academy Pvt. Ltd.   (1)
3rd Floor PB Soft Tech Electronic City Phase II, Bengaluru, 560100, Karnataka, India
Tel.: (91) 8951775283
Web Site: https://www.bioconacademy.com
Biosciences Education Services
N.A.I.C.S.: 541715

Biocon Biopharmaceuticals Private Limited   (1)
20th KM Hosur Rd, Electronics City, Bengaluru, India
Tel.: (91) 8028082808
Clinical Research Services
N.A.I.C.S.: 541715

Biocon Sdn. Bhd.   (1)
No 1 Jalan Bioteknologi 1 Kawasan Perindustrian SILC, 79200, Iskandar Puteri, Johor, Malaysia
Tel.: (60) 75600000
Biopharmaceutical Mfr
N.A.I.C.S.: 325412

Clinigene International Limited   (1)
Clinigene House Tower 1 Semicon Park Electronic City, Phase II Hosur Rd, Bengaluru, 560100, India
Tel.: (91) 8028082780
Web Site: http://www.clinigeneintl.com
Sales Range: $25-49.9 Million
Emp.: 160
Clinical Research Services
N.A.I.C.S.: 541715

Syngene International Limited   (1)
Biocon SEZ Biocon Park Plot No 2 3 Bommasandra Industrial Area, IV Phase Jigani Link Road, Bengaluru, 560 099, India
Tel.: (91) 8068919191
Web Site: https://www.syngeneintl.com
Clinical Research Services
N.A.I.C.S.: 541715
Jonathan Hunt (CEO)

BIOCRATES LIFE SCIENCES AG

Eduard-Bodem-Gasse 8, 6020, Innsbruck, Austria
Tel.: (43) 512 57 98 23
Web Site: http://www.biocrates.com
Year Founded: 2002
Bio Technology Services
N.A.I.C.S.: 541714

Moritz Seuster *(Co-CEO & CFO)*

Subsidiaries:

Metanomics Health GmbH **(1)**
Tegeler Weg 33, 10589, Berlin, Germany
Tel.: (49) 30319840400.
Health Care Research & Drug Development
Services
N.A.I.C.S.: 621999

BIOCRUDE TECHNOLOGIES INC.
1255 Phillips Square Suite 605, Montreal, H3B 3G5, QC, Canada
Tel.: (514) 840-9719   NV
Web Site:
    http://www.biocrudetech.com
Year Founded: 2015
Assets: $24,057
Liabilities: $384,177
Net Worth: ($360,120)
Earnings: ($289,627)
Fiscal Year-end: 12/31/19
Industrial Waste Collection & Recycling Services
N.A.I.C.S.: 562111
John Moukas *(Chm, Pres & CEO)*

BIOCRUDE TECHNOLOGIES USA, INC.
605-1255 Phillips Square, Montreal, H3B 3G5, QC, Canada
Tel.: (514) 840-9719   NV
Web Site:
    http://www.biocrudetech.com
Year Founded: 2015
Assets: $22,681
Liabilities: $173,066
Net Worth: ($150,385)
Earnings: ($181,526)
Emp.: 1
Fiscal Year-end: 12/31/22
Solid Waste Management & Recycling Services
N.A.I.C.S.: 562212
John Moukas *(Chm, Pres & CEO)*

BIOCYTOGEN PHARMACEUTI-CALS (BEIJING) CO., LTD.
12 Baoshen South Street, Daxing District, Beijing, China
Tel.: (86) 1056967680   CN
Web Site:
    https://www.biocytogen.com.cn
Year Founded: 2009
2315—(HKG)
Rev.: $81,795,908
Assets: $428,962,261
Liabilities: $252,645,741
Net Worth: $176,316,519
Earnings: ($92,256,474)
Emp.: 1,348
Fiscal Year-end: 12/31/22
Biotechnology Research & Development Services
N.A.I.C.S.: 541714
Bin Liu *(CFO)*

Subsidiaries:

Biocytogen Boston Corp. **(1)**
6th Fl 300 3rd Ave, Waltham, MA 02451
Tel.: (781) 587-3558
Web Site: https://biocytogen.com
Biopharmaceutical Product Research & Development Services
N.A.I.C.S.: 541714

Xadcera Biopharmaceutical (Suzhou) Co., Ltd. **(1)**
3F C29 Building Biomedical Industrial Park No 218 Xinghu Street, Suzhou, Jiangsu, China
Tel.: (86) 51285889070
Biopharmaceutical Product Research & Development Services
N.A.I.C.S.: 541714

BIODEXA PHARMACEUTI-CALS PLC
1 Caspian Point Caspian Way, Cardiff, CF10 4DQ, United Kingdom
Tel.: (44) 1235888300   UK
Web Site: https://biodexapharma.com
BDRX—(NASDAQ)
Rev.: $480,939
Assets: $13,307,246
Liabilities: $7,402,171
Net Worth: $5,905,074
Earnings: ($8,935,875)
Emp.: 21
Fiscal Year-end: 12/31/23
Nanomedicines Developer & Mfr
N.A.I.C.S.: 325412
Stephen Stamp *(CEO & CFO)*

BIODIEM LIMITED
Level 4 100 Albert Road, South Melbourne, 3205, VIC, Australia
Tel.: (61) 3 9692 7240   AU
Web Site: http://www.biodiem.com
Rev.: $130,747
Assets: $689,164
Liabilities: $224,298
Net Worth: $464,866
Earnings: ($303,858)
Fiscal Year-end: 06/30/19
Biopharmaceutical Research Services
N.A.I.C.S.: 541715
Julie Phillips *(CEO & Exec Dir)*

BIODUE S.P.A
Via ALorenzetti 3/A Loc Sambuca Val di Pesa, Tavarnelle Val Di Pesa, 50028, Florence, Italy
Tel.: (39) 0558071140
Web Site: http://www.biodue.com
Year Founded: 1986
Sales Range: $25-49.9 Million
Emp.: 130
Pharmaceutical Products, Nutritional & Herbal Supplements, Medical Devices & Cosmetics Mfr
N.A.I.C.S.: 325412
Vanni Benedetti *(Chm & CEO)*

BIODYNE CO., LTD.
24-4 Achasan-Ro 5-Gil, Seongdong-Gu, Seoul, 04793, Korea (South)
Tel.: (82) 15224811
Web Site: https://www.biodyne.asia
Year Founded: 2009
314930—(KRS)
Rev.: $9,365,397
Assets: $34,832,682
Liabilities: $962,891
Net Worth: $33,869,791
Earnings: $4,303,883
Emp.: 30
Fiscal Year-end: 12/31/22
Medical & Surgical Equipment Mfr
N.A.I.C.S.: 339112
Woo-Suk Cho *(COO & Gen Mgr)*

BIOENZYMES PTY LTD.
Unit 1C 424 Bilsen Rd, Geebung, Brisbane, 4034, QLD, Australia
Tel.: (61) 410797713
Web Site:
    http://www.bioenzymes.com.au
Biological Product Mfr & Distr
N.A.I.C.S.: 325414
James Page *(Mng Dir)*

BIOERA S.P.A.
Via della Repubblica 82, 42025, Cavriago, Italy
Tel.: (39) 0522 373177   IT
Web Site: http://www.bioera.it
Year Founded: 2004
Sales Range: $125-149.9 Million
Organic Food Product, Natural Cosmetics & Nutritional Supplement Mfr & Distr

N.A.I.C.S.: 456191
Canio Giovanni Mazzaro *(CEO & Gen Mgr)*

Subsidiaries:

CDD SpA **(1)**
Via Bosco 99 A, 42019, Scandiano, Italy
Tel.: (39) 0522915401
Web Site: http://www.cdd.it
Sales Range: $25-49.9 Million
Emp.: 30
Food Retailer
N.A.I.C.S.: 445131

ERBORISTERIE D'ITALIA Srl **(1)**
Via Sandro Pertini 8/12, Bibbona, 57020, Italy
Tel.: (39) 0586679101
Natural & Organic Products Mfr
N.A.I.C.S.: 311411

KI Group S.p.A **(1)**
Strada Settimo 399 11, 10156, Turin, Italy
Tel.: (39) 0117176700
Web Site: http://www.kigroup.com
Sales Range: Less than $1 Million
Variety Health Food Mfr & Whslr
N.A.I.C.S.: 424490
Giuseppe Dossena *(Mng Dir)*

Subsidiary (Domestic):

LA FONTE DELLA VITA Srl **(2)**
Via Monviso 18, Cuneo, 12030, Italy
Tel.: (39) 0172652003
Diet Food Mfr & Whslr
N.A.I.C.S.: 311999

Natfood S.R.L. **(1)**
Via Bosco 99/A, 42019, Scandiano, RE, Italy
Tel.: (39) 0522300259
Web Site: http://www.natfood.it
Sales Range: $25-49.9 Million
Emp.: 30
Food & Beverage Mfr & Distr
N.A.I.C.S.: 312111

Subsidiary (Non-US):

Natfood Iberica S.L. **(2)**
Can Diners 1-11 Nave 5, 08310, Argentona, Spain
Tel.: (34) 93 741 18 63
Web Site: http://www.natfoodiberica.com
Emp.: 10
Food & Beverage Mfr & Whslr
N.A.I.C.S.: 424490
Josef Daron *(Gen Mgr)*

Subsidiary (Non-US):

Natfood Portugal Lda **(3)**
Travessa Fidonio Pais 29, Maia, 4475 299, Portugal
Tel.: (351) 229605155
Web Site: http://www.natfood.pt
Sales Range: $25-49.9 Million
Emp.: 8
Food Products Mfr & Distr
N.A.I.C.S.: 311999
Francisco Pereira *(Mgr)*

Organic Oils S.p.A. **(1)**
Str Montebuono 12 b, 06132, Perugia, Italy
Tel.: (39) 075529991
Web Site: http://www.organicoils.it
Sales Range: $25-49.9 Million
Emp.: 20
Organic Health Foods Mfr & Whslr
N.A.I.C.S.: 311999
Thomas Rossi *(Mgr-Export)*

BIOEXTRAX AB
Skiffervagen 76, 224 78, Lund, Sweden
Tel.: (46) 736267643
Web Site: https://www.bioextrax.com
Year Founded: 2014
BIOEX—(NASDAQ)
Biotechnology Research & Development Services
N.A.I.C.S.: 541714
Mats Persson *(Chm)*

BIOFIL CHEMICALS & PHAR-MACEUTICALS LIMITED

1112 Sector E Sanwer Road, Indore, 452 015, Madhya Pradesh, India
Tel.: (91) 7312426700
Web Site: https://www.biofilgroup.net
BIOFILCHEM—(NSE)
Rev.: $3,075,700
Assets: $2,556,945
Liabilities: $258,599
Net Worth: $2,298,346
Earnings: $95,332
Emp.: 47
Fiscal Year-end: 03/31/22
Pharmaceuticals Product Mfr
N.A.I.C.S.: 325412
Ramesh S. Shah *(Mng Dir & Chm)*

BIOFISH HOLDING AS
Tangavegen 19, Torvikbygd, 5620, Hordaland, Norway
Tel.: (47) 48381546
Web Site: https://www.biofish.no
Year Founded: 2016
BFISH—(OSL)
Rev.: $4,687,586
Assets: $25,486,513
Liabilities: $6,353,171
Net Worth: $19,133,342
Earnings: ($1,752,487)
Emp.: 11
Fiscal Year-end: 12/31/23
Holding Company
N.A.I.C.S.: 551112
Torbjorn Gjelsvik *(Chm)*

BIOFRONTERA AG
Hemmelrather Weg 201, 51377, Leverkusen, Germany
Tel.: (49) 214876320
Web Site:
    https://www.biofrontera.com
BFFTF—(OTCIQ)
Rev.: $35,357,345
Assets: $94,204,780
Liabilities: $22,970,544
Net Worth: $71,234,235
Earnings: $41,584,522
Emp.: 76
Fiscal Year-end: 12/31/21
Pharmaceuticals Product Mfr
N.A.I.C.S.: 325412
Hermann Lubbert *(CEO, Founder & Chm-Exec Bd)*

Subsidiaries:

Cutanea Life Sciences, Inc. **(1)**
1500 Liberty Ridge Dr Ste 3000, Wayne, PA 19087   **(100%)**
Tel.: (484) 588-2036
Web Site: http://www.cutanealife.com
Pharmaceuticals Mfr
N.A.I.C.S.: 325412
Robert L. Ferrara *(Co-CFO)*

BIOGAIA AB
Kungsbroplan 3, 112 27, Stockholm, Sweden
Tel.: (46) 855529300
Web Site: https://www.biogaia.com
Year Founded: 1990
BGLA—(DEU)
Rev.: $95,846,229
Assets: $259,792,832
Liabilities: $30,603,869
Net Worth: $229,188,963
Earnings: $23,961,008
Emp.: 167
Fiscal Year-end: 12/31/21
Foods, Beverages & Healthcare Products
N.A.I.C.S.: 624210
David E. R. Dangoor *(Vice Chm)*

Subsidiaries:

BioGaia Japan Inc. **(1)**
1-10-3-901 Roppongi, Minato-ku, Tokyo, 106-0032, Japan
Tel.: (81) 57 008 1055
Web Site: https://www.biogaia.jp

Biogaia AB—(Continued)

Emp.: 28
Biotechnology Development Services
N.A.I.C.S.: 541714

BioGaia Pharma AB (1)
Bryggargatan 10, 111 21, Stockholm, Sweden
Tel.: (46) 5591148191
Web Site: https://biogaiapharma.com
Pharmaceutical Drug Mfr
N.A.I.C.S.: 325412
Peter Rothschild (Chm)

BIOGAS NORD AG
Werningshof 2-4, 33719, Bielefeld, Germany
Tel.: (49) 49 52196330
Year Founded: 2000
Sales Range: $100-124.9 Million
Emp.: 147
Engineering & Construction Services
N.A.I.C.S.: 541330

Subsidiaries:

BIOGAS NORD Anlagenbau GmbH (1)
Werningshof 2-4, 33719, Bielefeld, Germany
Tel.: (49) 521 9633 0
Biogas Plant Construction Services
N.A.I.C.S.: 237120

BIOGAS NORD Polska Sp.z o.o. (1)
ul Pulawska 182, Warsaw, 02-670, Poland
Tel.: (48) 22 6202921
Biogas Plant Construction Services
N.A.I.C.S.: 237120

BIOGAS NORD UK Ltd. (1)
2 Temple Back East Temple Quay, Bristol, BS1 6EG, United Kingdom
Tel.: (44) 1258 475300
Biogas Plant Construction Services
N.A.I.C.S.: 237120

Bio.S Biogas Verwaltungs GmbH (1)
Werningshof 2-4, 33719, Bielefeld, Germany
Tel.: (49) 52 15 57 50 70
Biogas Plant Construction Services
N.A.I.C.S.: 237120

Bioenergie Ahlen GmbH & Co. KG (1)
Borbeiner 28 Aussenbereich, 59227, Ahlen, Germany
Tel.: (49) 521 96330
Sales Range: $25-49.9 Million
Emp.: 1
Biogas Plant Construction Services
N.A.I.C.S.: 237120

BIOGASPARK NV
Kruisdonk 66, 6222 PH, Maastricht, Netherlands
Tel.: (31) 43 631 269
Web Site: http://www.biogaspark.de
Year Founded: 2008
Investment Services
N.A.I.C.S.: 523999
Joachim Haedke (Chm-Mgmt Bd)

BIOGEN LIMITED
Level 11 225 St Georges Terr, Perth, 6000, WA, Australia
Tel.: (61) 8 9226 4033
Web Site: http://www.biogen.com.au
Renewable Electricity Generation
N.A.I.C.S.: 221118
Susan H. Alexander (Sec & Exec VP)

BIOGEND THERAPEUTICS CO., LTD.
F4 No 3-2 Park Street, Nangang District, Taipei, 115, Taiwan
Tel.: (886) 226558366
Web Site: https://www.biogend.com
Year Founded: 2016
6733—(TPE)
Rev.: $983,210
Assets: $25,695,588

Liabilities: $2,831,379
Net Worth: $22,864,209
Earnings: ($6,425,257)
Fiscal Year-end: 12/31/22
Biomedical Research & Development Services
N.A.I.C.S.: 541715
Rongjin Lin (Chm)

BIOHARVEST SCIENCES INC.
1140-625 Howe Street, Vancouver, V6C 2T6, BC, Canada
Tel.: (604) 622-1186   BC
Web Site:
    https://www.bioharvest.com
Year Founded: 2013
8MV—(DEU)
Rev.: $5,498,000
Assets: $9,393,000
Liabilities: $15,322,000
Net Worth: ($5,929,000)
Earnings: ($11,236,000)
Fiscal Year-end: 12/31/22
Bio Technology Services
N.A.I.C.S.: 541714
Zaki Rakib (Chm & Pres)

BIOIASIS JSC
70 Ralevitsa Str Atelier 1, 1618, Sofia, Bulgaria
Tel.: (359) 24807788
Web Site: https://www.bioiasis.com
Year Founded: 2005
BIOA—(BUL)
Sales Range: Less than $1 Million
Medical Devices Trading Services
N.A.I.C.S.: 423450

BIOINFRA LIFE SCIENCE INC.
Daehak-ro 49 7F, Jongno-gu, Seoul, 03127, Korea (South)
Tel.: (82) 16447160
Web Site: https://www.bioinfra.co.kr
Year Founded: 2001
266470—(KRS)
Biotechnology Research & Development Services
N.A.I.C.S.: 541714
Dukyun Lee (CEO)

BIOINGENIERIA DEHNER S.R.L.
Ing Guillermo Fuchs 6148 Ph1, Cordoba, X5021DPB, Argentina
Tel.: (54) 3543444955   Ar
Web Site: http://www.bio-ingenieria.com
Microscopy Equipment Mfr
N.A.I.C.S.: 333310

BIOINVENT INTERNATIONAL AB
The Gamma Building Ideongatan 1, Lund, Sweden
Tel.: (46) 462868550
Web Site: https://www.bioinvent.com
BINV—(OMX)
Rev.: $30,545,581
Assets: $160,362,215
Liabilities: $9,936,778
Net Worth: $150,432,437
Earnings: ($3,980,912)
Emp.: 94
Fiscal Year-end: 12/31/22
Pharmaceuticals
N.A.I.C.S.: 325412
Stefan Ericsson (CFO)

BIOKARPET S.A.
Tel.: (30) 2410688688
Web Site: https://www.biokarpet.gr
Year Founded: 1950
BIOKA—(ATH)
Sales Range: $100-124.9 Million
Emp.: 578

Holding Company; Textiles, Metallurgy & Information Technology
N.A.I.C.S.: 551112
Georgios Vasilios Papageorgiou (Dir-Fin Svcs)

Subsidiaries:

Albio Data S.A. (1)
8 km Larissa -Thessaloniki, 41100, Larissa, Greece (80%)
Tel.: (30) 2410661168
Web Site: http://www.albiodata.gr
Sales Range: $25-49.9 Million
Emp.: 15
Other Management Consulting Services
N.A.I.C.S.: 541618
Barboutis Vasilios (Mng Dir)

Biokarpet Bulgaria E.O.O.D. (1)
348 Botevgradsko Shose Blvd, 1839, Sofia, Bulgaria (100%)
Tel.: (359) 29898894
Web Site: http://www.biokarpet.bg
Emp.: 6
Carpet & Upholstery Cleaning Services
N.A.I.C.S.: 561740
Sarry Cacadouos (Gen Mgr)

Biokarpet Romania S.R.L. (1)
B-Dul Unirii Nr 69 Bloc G2B, Bucharest, Romania (95%)
Tel.: (40) 213212065
Web Site: http://www.biokarpet.ro
Sales Range: $25-49.9 Million
Blankets, Carpet & Rug Mills
N.A.I.C.S.: 314110

Exalco Bulgaria A.D. (1)
348 Blvd Botevgradsko Rd & Ring Rd, PO Box 10, Sofia, 1839, Bulgaria (95%)
Tel.: (359) 29452233
Web Site: http://www.exalco.bg
Emp.: 20
Aluminum Extruded Product Mfr
N.A.I.C.S.: 331318
Aris Tseledis (Gen Mgr)

Exalco Romania srl (1)
Sos Centurii Nr 11, Bragadiru, 077025, Bucharest, Ilfov, Romania (75%)
Tel.: (40) 213693275
Other Aluminum Rolling & Drawing
N.A.I.C.S.: 331318
Dimitris Michailidis (Gen Mgr)

Exalco S.A. (1)
5th Km Larissa - Athens National Rd, PO Box 1129, Larissa, 411 10, Greece (98.39%)
Tel.: (30) 2410688688
Web Site: http://www.exalco.gr
Sales Range: $100-124.9 Million
Emp.: 350
Aluminum Extruded Product Mfr
N.A.I.C.S.: 331318
John Kantonias (Pres)

Persika SA (1)
5 Km National Road, 41110, Larissa, Athens, Greece
Tel.: (30) 2410688688
Web Site: http://www.persika.gr
Carpet Mfr
N.A.I.C.S.: 314110

BIOKRAFT INTERNATIONAL AB
Kungsbron 1 Staircase C, 111 22, Stockholm, Sweden
Tel.: (46) 850387220
Web Site: https://www.biokraft.com
Year Founded: 2004
3JE—(DEU)
Rev.: $50,028,005
Assets: $183,728,961
Liabilities: $128,949,488
Net Worth: $54,779,473
Earnings: ($14,909,850)
Emp.: 122
Fiscal Year-end: 12/31/23
Biotechnology Research & Development Services
N.A.I.C.S.: 541714
Matti Vikkula (CEO)

BIOLASCO TAIWAN CO., LTD.
3F No 316 Chongyang Rd, Nangang Dist, Taipei, 115, Taiwan
Tel.: (886) 226518669
Web Site:
    https://www.biolasco.com.tw
6662—(TPE)
Rev.: $7,376,169
Assets: $17,812,244
Liabilities: $3,597,255
Net Worth: $14,214,989
Earnings: $1,322,922
Fiscal Year-end: 12/31/22
Pharmaceuticals Product Mfr
N.A.I.C.S.: 325412
Chen Chung-Chen (Chm & Pres)

Subsidiaries:

BMN MSI Co., Ltd. (1)
Lot 32 Block 2 Dai Thanh Urban, Thanh Tri Dist, Hanoi, Vietnam
Tel.: (84) 2473099661
Web Site: http://www.bmnmed.com
Pharmaceuticals Product Mfr
N.A.I.C.S.: 325412

BioRIVER Co., Ltd. (1)
39 Chaophaya Jewelry Building 4th Fl Room no 410 Phayathai Rd, Thanonphayathai Ratchathewi, Bangkok, 10400, Thailand
Tel.: (66) 21054775
Web Site: http://www.bio-river.com
Animal Laboratory Equipment Distr
N.A.I.C.S.: 423490

PT. Elo Karsa Utama (1)
Jl Raya Kebayoran Lama 34E, Jakarta, 12220, Indonesia
Tel.: (62) 217392856
Web Site: https://www.elokarsa.com
Medical Product Distr
N.A.I.C.S.: 423450
Hans Suwandi (Mng Dir)

SciGate Technology Corp. (1)
Unit 1C of A L Building 126 N Domingo Street at Brgy Pedro Cruz, San Juan, 1500, Philippines
Tel.: (63) 28703190203
Web Site: https://www.scigate.com.ph
Life Science Equipment Mfr
N.A.I.C.S.: 325412
Maria Issandra Pineda (Accountant)

i-DNA Biotechnology (M) Sdn Bhd (1)
A-1-6 Pusat Perdagangan Kuchai No 2 Jalan 1/127 Off Jalan Kuchai Lama, 58200, Kuala Lumpur, Malaysia
Tel.: (60) 379820322
Web Site: https://www.i-dna.com.my
Laboratory Testing Services
N.A.I.C.S.: 541380
Joni Tan (Sls Mgr)

BIOLEADERS CORPORATION
A-7 767 Sinsu-ro, Suji-gu, Yongin, 16827, Gyeonggi-do, Korea (South)
Tel.: (82) 312809650
Web Site:
    https://www.bioleaders.co.kr
Year Founded: 2000
142760—(KRS)
Rev.: $77,016,757
Assets: $113,835,579
Liabilities: $62,200,456
Net Worth: $51,635,123
Earnings: ($17,746,303)
Emp.: 50
Fiscal Year-end: 12/31/22
Biological Products Including Pharmaceuticals & Cosmetics
N.A.I.C.S.: 325414
Young-chul Park (Chm & CEO)

BIOLIDICS LIMITED
18 Howard Road 11-09 Novelty Biz Centre, Singapore, 369585, Singapore
Tel.: (65) 64820668   SG
Web Site: https://www.biolidics.com

Year Founded: 2009
8YY—(SES)
Rev.: $1,747,179
Assets: $8,624,664
Liabilities: $6,863,763
Net Worth: $1,760,901
Earnings: ($4,518,038)
Emp.: 34
Fiscal Year-end: 12/31/21
Medical Device Mfr
N.A.I.C.S.: 334515
Qing-Yin Wang (COO)

BIOLIFE REMEDIES, INC.
675 W Hastings St Ste 501, Vancouver, V6B 1N2, BC, Canada
Tel.: (604) 630-8881
Year Founded: 2004
Health Care Srvices
N.A.I.C.S.: 621999
Jack J. Guo (Pres & CEO)

BIOLIGHT LIFE SCIENCES LTD.
Aba Hillel Silver 12 11 floor Ramat Gan Israel 5250606, Tel Aviv, 5250606, Israel
Tel.: (972) 732753400
Web Site: https://www.bio-light.co.il
BOLT—(TAE)
Rev.: $32,601
Assets: $9,242,160
Liabilities: $870,562
Net Worth: $8,371,598
Earnings: ($7,594,143)
Emp.: 200
Fiscal Year-end: 12/31/23
Research & Development in the Physical, Engineering & Life Sciences (except Nanotechnology & Biotechnology)
N.A.I.C.S.: 541715
Suzana Nahum-Zilberberg (CEO)

BIOLINERX LTD.
2 HaMa ayan Street, Modi'in-Maccabim-Re'ut, 7177871, Israel
Tel.: (972) 86429100   II
Web Site: https://www.biolinerx.com
Year Founded: 2003
BLRX—(NASDAQ)
Rev.: $694,000
Assets: $76,384,000
Liabilities: $25,543,000
Net Worth: $50,841,000
Earnings: ($24,951,000)
Emp.: 49
Fiscal Year-end: 12/31/22
Pharmaceutical Developer & Mfr
N.A.I.C.S.: 325412
Aharon Schwartz (Chm)

Subsidiaries:

BioLine Innovations Jerusalem   (1)
19 Hartum St, PO Box 45158, Jerusalem, 91450, Israel
Tel.: (972) 25489100
Web Site: http://www.biojerusalem.org.il
Sales Range: $25-49.9 Million
Biopharmaceutical Research & Development Services
N.A.I.C.S.: 541715

BIOLITEC AG
Untere Viaduktgasse 6/9, A-1030, Vienna, Austria
Tel.: (43) 1361990950
Web Site: http://www.biolitec.com
Year Founded: 1999
Sales Range: $50-74.9 Million
Emp.: 231
Photosensitizers, Lasers & Optical Fibers Mfr
N.A.I.C.S.: 334510
Wolfgang Neuberger (Chm & CEO)

Subsidiaries:

CeramOptec GmbH   (1)
Siemensstrabe 44, Bonn, 53121, Germany
Tel.: (49) 228979670
Web Site: http://www.ceramoptec.de
Sales Range: $25-49.9 Million
Emp.: 60
Optical Fiber & Laser Mfr
N.A.I.C.S.: 334510

biolitec (M) Sdn. Bhd.   (1)
No 18 Jalan PJS 7 21, Bandar Sunway, Petaling Jaya, 46150, Selangor Darul Ehsan, Malaysia
Tel.: (60) 356327128
Web Site: http://www.biolitec.com
Sales Range: $25-49.9 Million
Emp.: 10
Medical Laser Systems Mfr
N.A.I.C.S.: 334510

biolitec Italia SRL   (1)
Viale Monza 133, 20123, Milan, Italy
Tel.: (39) 0228172400
Sales Range: $25-49.9 Million
Emp.: 3
Medical Laser Systems Mfr
N.A.I.C.S.: 334510

biolitec Pharma (Ireland) Ltd.   (1)
United Drug House, Magna Dr, Dublin, Ireland
Tel.: (353) 14637415
Web Site: http://www.biolitecpharma.com
Sales Range: $25-49.9 Million
Emp.: 10
Medical Laser Systems Mfr
N.A.I.C.S.: 334510

BIOLOG DEVICE CO., LTD
64-10 Dongtangiheung-ro, Hwaseong, Gyeonggi-do, Korea (South)
Tel.: (82) 318313696
Web Site: https://www.biologdevice.com
Year Founded: 2012
208710—(KRS)
Rev.: $81,676,257
Assets: $66,004,107
Liabilities: $26,658,764
Net Worth: $39,345,343
Earnings: $197,411
Emp.: 33
Fiscal Year-end: 12/31/22
Electronic Components Mfr
N.A.I.C.S.: 334419
Hwang Hoon (CEO)

BIOLOGICAL E. LIMITED
18/1&3 Azamabad, Hyderabad, 500 020, Telangana, India
Tel.: (91) 40 3021 3999   In
Web Site: http://www.biologicale.com
Year Founded: 1953
Biopharmaceutical Products Developer, Mfr & Whslr
N.A.I.C.S.: 325414
Mahima Datla (Chm & Mng Dir)

Subsidiaries:

BE Vaccines SAS   (1)
Campus Bio-Ouest 6 Rue Alain Bombard, 44821, Saint-Herblain, Cedex, France
Tel.: (33) 2 2807 3710
Sales Range: $25-49.9 Million
Emp.: 80
Biopharmaceutical Research & Development
N.A.I.C.S.: 541715

BIOMARK DIAGNOSTICS INC.
130 - 3851 Shell Road, Richmond, V6X 2W2, BC, Canada
Tel.: (604) 370-0779   BC
Web Site: https://www.biomarkdiagnostics.com
Year Founded: 2014
20B—(DEU)
Rev.: $2,771
Assets: $745,465

Liabilities: $807,339
Net Worth: ($61,874)
Earnings: ($855,963)
Fiscal Year-end: 03/31/21
Cancer Diagnostic Products Mfr
N.A.I.C.S.: 339112
Brian Cheng (CTO)

BIOMASS HEATING SOLUTIONS LTD.
Kantoher Business Park, Killeedy Ballagh, Limerick, Ireland
Tel.: (353) 6985926
Web Site: http://www.bhslhydro.com
Agricultural Product Mfr
N.A.I.C.S.: 325320
Nicolas Faure (Dir-Reg Sls)

Subsidiaries:

Glanua UK Limited   (1)
268 Bath Road, Slough, SL1 4DX, United Kingdom
Tel.: (44) 2031142135
Web Site: https://glanua.com
Emp.: 219
Water System Construction Services
N.A.I.C.S.: 237110
Paul Gardner (Dir-UK Ops)

BIOMASS SECURE POWER INC.
40218 Wellsline Road, PO Box 21098, Abbotsford, V3G 2K7, BC, Canada
Tel.: (604) 807-4957
Web Site: https://www.biomasssecure.com
Year Founded: 2002
BMSPF—(OTCIQ)
Assets: $127,000
Liabilities: $2,841,000
Net Worth: ($2,714,000)
Earnings: ($258,000)
Emp.: 3
Fiscal Year-end: 06/30/22
Power Distr
N.A.I.C.S.: 221122
James Carroll (Pres & CEO)

BIOMAX RUBBER INDUSTRIES LIMITED
B2-3A-8 Solaris Dutamas No 1 Jalan Dutamas 1, Kuala Lumpur, 50480, Malaysia
Tel.: (60) 3 6211 4651
Web Site: http://www.biomaxcorporation.com
Rubber Glove Mfr
N.A.I.C.S.: 326299

BIOME AUSTRALIA LIMITED
192/194 Johnston Street, Collingwood, 3066, WA, Australia
Tel.: (61) 390175800   AU
Web Site: https://www.biomeaustralia.com
Year Founded: 2018
BIO—(ASX)
Rev.: $4,717,749
Assets: $4,928,788
Liabilities: $2,590,479
Net Worth: $2,338,309
Earnings: ($2,007,255)
Emp.: 30
Fiscal Year-end: 06/30/23
Biotechnology Research & Development Services
N.A.I.C.S.: 541714
Douglas Loh (CFO)

BIOME GROW INC.
600 535 Howe Street, Vancouver, V6C 2Z4, BC, Canada
Tel.: (604) 727-1295   BC
Year Founded: 2013
6OTA—(DEU)
Assets: $340,795

Liabilities: $3,597,610
Net Worth: ($3,256,815)
Earnings: ($8,019,593)
Emp.: 1
Fiscal Year-end: 12/31/22
Touchscreen Monitors & Panels Mfr
N.A.I.C.S.: 334118

BIOME GROW, INC.
480 University Avenue, Toronto, M5G 1V2, ON, Canada
Tel.: (416) 875-8395
Web Site: http://www.biomegrow.com
BIOIF—(OTCIQ)
Assets: $8,662,668
Liabilities: $3,633,596
Net Worth: $5,029,072
Earnings: ($109,464)
Fiscal Year-end: 12/31/21
Cannabis Product Mfr
N.A.I.C.S.: 325411
Khurram Malik (CEO)

Subsidiaries:

Great Lake Cannabis Co.   (1)
4000 S Calhoun Rd, New Berlin, WI 53151
Tel.: (262) 894-7466
Web Site: http://www.greatlakescannabisco.com
Cannabis Product Whslr
N.A.I.C.S.: 424590

BIOME TECHNOLOGIES PLC
North Road, Marchwood, Southampton, SO40 4BL, United Kingdom
Tel.: (44) 2380867100   UK
Web Site: https://www.biometechnology.com
BIOM—(AIM)
Rev.: $7,785,166
Assets: $6,245,512
Liabilities: $2,306,766
Net Worth: $3,938,746
Earnings: ($1,547,801)
Emp.: 29
Fiscal Year-end: 12/31/21
Bioplastics Products & Radio Frequency Technologies & Equipment Mfr
N.A.I.C.S.: 326199
Paul R. Mines (CEO)

Subsidiaries:

Biome Bioplastics Limited   (1)
North Road, Fairhills Industrial Estate, Marchwood, Southampton, SO40 4BL, United Kingdom
Tel.: (44) 2380867100
Web Site: https://biomebioplastics.com
Biodegradable Plastics Mfr
N.A.I.C.S.: 326199

Stanelco RF Technologies Limited   (1)
Starpol Technology Centre, Marchwood, Southampton, SO40 4BL, United Kingdom
Tel.: (44) 238 086 7100
Web Site: https://www.stanelcorftechnologies.com
Electric Equipment Mfr
N.A.I.C.S.: 335999

BIOMED-LUBLIN WYTWORNIA SUROWIC I SZCZEPIONEK S.A.
ul Uniwersytecka 10, Lublin, 20-029, Poland
Tel.: (48) 815338221
Web Site: http://www.biomed.lublin.pl
SVE—(WAR)
Rev.: $14,889,990
Assets: $67,556,656
Liabilities: $38,939,024
Net Worth: $28,617,632
Earnings: $1,208,841
Emp.: 230
Fiscal Year-end: 12/31/23

Biomed-Lublin Wytwornia Surowic I Szczepionek S.A.—(Continued)

Pharmaceuticals Mfr
N.A.I.C.S.: 325412
Waldemar Sierocki *(Pres & Member-Mgmt Bd)*

BIOMIND LABS INC.
181 Bay Street Brookfield Place, Toronto, M5J 2T9, ON, Canada   **AB**
Web Site: https://biomindlabs.com
Year Founded: 2005
CRSWF—(OTCIQ)
Assets: $2,527,965
Liabilities: $334,954
Net Worth: $2,193,011
Earnings: ($4,332,360)
Emp.: 9
Fiscal Year-end: 12/31/21
Merchant Banking & Alternative Asset Management Services
N.A.I.C.S.: 523150
J. Roy Pottle *(Chm)*

BIOMM S. A.
Avenida Regent n 705 Lote 15 ao 21, Alphaville, Nova Lima, 34018-000, MG, Brazil
Tel.: (55) 32991000
Web Site: http://www.biomm.com
Year Founded: 1975
BIOM3—(BRAZ)
Rev.: $24,357,342
Assets: $71,035,136
Liabilities: $45,699,742
Net Worth: $25,335,394
Earnings: ($16,721,484)
Fiscal Year-end: 12/31/23
Drug Mfr
N.A.I.C.S.: 325412
Renato Arroyo Barbeiro *(Dir-Investor Relations)*

BIOMX INC.
7 Pinhas Sapir St Floor 2, Ness Ziona, 7414002, Israel
Tel.: (972) 723942377   **DE**
Web Site: https://www.biomx.com
Year Founded: 2017
PHGE—(NYSEAMEX)
Rev.: $134,000
Assets: $45,531,000
Liabilities: $24,492,000
Net Worth: $21,039,000
Earnings: ($28,317,000)
Emp.: 54
Fiscal Year-end: 12/31/22
Investment Services
N.A.I.C.S.: 523999
Jonathan Eitan Solomon *(CEO)*

BIONEER CORPORATION
8-11 Munpyeongseo-ro, Daedeok-gu, Daejeon, 34302, Korea (South)
Tel.: (82) 15889788
Web Site: https://www.bioneer.co.kr
Year Founded: 1992
064550—(KRS)
Rev.: $167,508,546
Assets: $229,131,544
Liabilities: $42,336,656
Net Worth: $186,794,887
Earnings: $11,598,586
Emp.: 625
Fiscal Year-end: 12/31/22
Bio Technology Services
N.A.I.C.S.: 541714
Park Han-Oh *(Chm & CEO)*

Subsidiaries:

Bioneer, Inc.   **(1)**
155 Filbert St Ste 216, Oakland, CA 94607
Tel.: (510) 865-0330
Web Site: https://us.bioneer.com
Biotechnology Research & Development Services
N.A.I.C.S.: 541720

BIONET CORP.
No 28 Ln 36 Xinhu 1st Rd, Nei-Hu Dist, Taipei, 11494, Taiwan
Tel.: (886) 800800018
Web Site:
   https://www.bionetcorp.com
Year Founded: 1999
1784—(TPE)
Rev.: $30,653,066
Assets: $57,489,604
Liabilities: $16,069,943
Net Worth: $41,419,660
Earnings: $1,675,609
Fiscal Year-end: 12/31/22
Biotechnology Research & Development Services
N.A.I.C.S.: 541714
Christopher Tsai *(Chm)*

BIONEUTRA GLOBAL CORPORATION
1101 - 1030 West Georgia St, Vancouver, V6E 2Y3, BC, Canada
Tel.: (604) 210-5669   **AB**
Web Site: https://www.bioneutra.ca
Year Founded: 1996
BGA—(TSXV)
Rev.: $18,865,255
Assets: $18,522,748
Liabilities: $17,974,432
Net Worth: $548,316
Earnings: ($2,899,896)
Fiscal Year-end: 12/31/20
Breakfast Cereal Mfr
N.A.I.C.S.: 311230
Jianhua Zhu *(Founder, Pres & CEO)*

Subsidiaries:

Bioneutra North America Inc.   **(1)**
9608 25 Avenue NW, Edmonton, T6N 1J4, AB, Canada
Tel.: (780) 466-1481
Web Site: https://www.bioneutra.ca
Food Products Mfr
N.A.I.C.S.: 311230
Lei Ling *(VP-Product Dev & Compliance)*

BIONEXUS GENE LAB CORP.
Unit 02 Level 10 Tower B Avenue 3 The Vertical Business Suite II, Bangar South No 8 Jalan Kerinchi, 59200, Kuala Lumpur, Malaysia
Tel.: (60) 122126512   **WY**
Web Site:
   http://www.bionexusgenelab.com
Year Founded: 2017
BGLC—(OTCIQ)
Rev.: $10,928,707
Assets: $8,740,162
Liabilities: $2,075,149
Net Worth: $6,665,013
Earnings: ($355,966)
Emp.: 27
Fiscal Year-end: 12/31/22
Healtcare Services
N.A.I.C.S.: 621610
Chi Yuen Leong *(CEO)*

BIONI CS GMBH
Lessingstr 21, Oberhausen, 46149, Germany
Tel.: (49) 208 621 75 53
Web Site: http://www.bioni.de
Coating Mfr
N.A.I.C.S.: 325510
Sven Knoll *(CEO)*

Subsidiaries:

BIONI CS GmbH FZE   **(1)**
PO Box 31291, Al-Jazeera Al-Hamra, Ras al Khaimah, United Arab Emirates
Tel.: (971) 504591001
Paint & Coating Mfr
N.A.I.C.S.: 325510
Bjorn Fischer *(Project Mgr)*

BIONI SYSTEM GmbH   **(1)**

Lessingstr 21, 46149, Oberhausen, Germany
Tel.: (49) 2086217554
Web Site: http://www.bioni-system.de
Paint & Coating Mfr
N.A.I.C.S.: 325510

Bioni USA and Americas LLC.   **(1)**
1343 Main St Ste 204, Sarasota, FL 34236
Tel.: (941) 926-5881
Web Site: http://www.bioni-america.com
Paint & Coating Mfr
N.A.I.C.S.: 325510

BIONIK LABORATORIES CORP.
483 Bay Street N105, Toronto, M5G 2C9, ON, Canada
Tel.: (416) 640-7887   **DE**
Web Site: https://www.bioniklabs.com
Year Founded: 2010
BNKL—(OTCIQ)
Rev.: $1,805,202
Assets: $3,362,127
Liabilities: $5,002,715
Net Worth: ($1,640,588)
Earnings: ($4,946,024)
Emp.: 12
Fiscal Year-end: 03/31/23
Medical Device Mfr
N.A.I.C.S.: 339112
Michael Prywata *(Co-Founder)*

Subsidiaries:

Interactive Motion Technologies, Inc.   **(1)**
80 Coolidge Hill Rd, Watertown, MA 02472
Tel.: (617) 926-4800
Web Site: http://www.interactive-motion.com
Electromedical & Electrotherapeutic Apparatus Mfr
N.A.I.C.S.: 334510

BIONIME CORPORATION
No 100 Sec 2 Daqing St, South Dist, Taichung, 40242, Taiwan
Tel.: (886) 423692388
Web Site: https://www.bionime.com
Year Founded: 2003
4737—(TAI)
Rev.: $57,410,868
Assets: $173,340,358
Liabilities: $108,158,307
Net Worth: $65,182,051
Earnings: $213,578
Emp.: 1,040
Fiscal Year-end: 12/31/23
Self Monitoring Blood Glucose System Mfr
N.A.I.C.S.: 339112

Subsidiaries:

BIONIME (Malaysia) SDN. BHD.   **(1)**
C-05-11 ITech Tower Jalan Impact Cyber 6, 63000, Cyberjaya, Selangor, Malaysia
Tel.: (60) 383228213
Web Site: https://www.bionime.com.my
Medical Testing Equipment Mfr & Distr
N.A.I.C.S.: 339112

Bionime (Pingtan) Co., Ltd.   **(1)**
Taiwan Pioneer Park Pingtan Comprehensive Experimental Area, Pingtan County, Fuzhou, Fujian, China
Tel.: (86) 59162523167
Testing & Measuring Equipment Distr
N.A.I.C.S.: 423830

Bionime Australia Pty Limited   **(1)**
Level 7 60 York Street, Sydney, 2000, NSW, Australia
Tel.: (61) 292626900
Web Site: http://www.bionime.com
Electromedical Equipment Mfr
N.A.I.C.S.: 325413

Bionime GmbH   **(1)**
Tramstrasse 16, 9442, Berneck, Switzerland
Tel.: (41) 717229840
Web Site: http://www.bionime.com

Sales Range: $50-74.9 Million
Emp.: 3
Blood Glucose Monitoring Systems Mfr
N.A.I.C.S.: 325413

Bionime USA Corporation   **(1)**
1450 E Spruce St Bldg B, Ontario, CA 91761-8314
Tel.: (909) 781-6969
Web Site: https://bionimeusa.com
Emp.: 7
Blood Glucose Monitoring Systems Mfr & Distr
N.A.I.C.S.: 325413

BIONOMICS LIMITED
200 Greenhill Road, Eastwood, 5063, SA, Australia
Tel.: (61) 881507400
Web Site:
   https://www.bionomics.com.au
BNOX—(NASDAQ)
Rev.: $2,312,890
Assets: $27,649,093
Liabilities: $10,158,721
Net Worth: $17,490,372
Earnings: ($15,492,166)
Emp.: 8
Fiscal Year-end: 06/30/24
Pharmaceutical Preparation Manufacturing
N.A.I.C.S.: 325412
Timothy M. Cunningham *(CFO)*

Subsidiaries:

Bionomics Inc   **(1)**
PO Box 817, Kingston, TN 37763
Tel.: (865) 220-8501
Radioactive Waste Disposal Services
N.A.I.C.S.: 562211
Karen McCormick *(Pres)*

Neurofit SAS   **(1)**
850 Blvd S Brant - Bioparc 1, Parc d Innovation, 67400, Illkirch-Graffenstaden, France
Tel.: (33) 388651606
Sales Range: $25-49.9 Million
Emp.: 12
Pre Clinical Research Services
N.A.I.C.S.: 541715
Deborah Rathjen *(Pres)*

BIONOR HOLDING AS
Karenslysts Alle 6, 0278, Oslo, Norway
Tel.: (47) 2301 0960   **NO**
Web Site:
   http://www.bionorholding.com
Year Founded: 1985
Sales Range: Less than $1 Million
Emp.: 18
Holding Company; Vaccine Developer & Mfr
N.A.I.C.S.: 551112
Birger Sorensen *(Chm & CEO)*

Subsidiaries:

Bionor Immuno AS   **(1)**
Karenslysts Alle 6, 0278, Oslo, Norway
Tel.: (47) 2301 0960
Vaccine Developer & Mfr
N.A.I.C.S.: 325414

BIONTECH SE
An der Goldgrube 12, D-55131, Mainz, D-55131, Germany
Tel.: (49) 61319084   **De**
Web Site: https://pro.biontech.de
Year Founded: 2008
BNTX—(NASDAQ)
Rev.: $21,261,571,344
Assets: $28,592,321,784
Liabilities: $3,959,231,640
Net Worth: $24,633,090,144
Earnings: $11,587,707,456
Emp.: 4,530
Fiscal Year-end: 12/31/22
Biotechnology Research & Development Services
N.A.I.C.S.: 541714

Ugur Sahin *(Co-Founder & CEO)*

Subsidiaries:

BioNTech Delivery Technologies GmbH **(1)**
Weinbergweg 23, 06120, Halle, Germany
Tel.: (49) 34513142903
Bio Technology Services
N.A.I.C.S.: 541714

BioNTech Europe GmbH **(1)**
An der Goldgrube 12, D-55131, Mainz, Germany
Tel.: (49) 613190840
Biotechnology Research & Development Services
N.A.I.C.S.: 541714

BioNTech Innovative Manufacturing Services GmbH **(1)**
Vollmersbachstr 66, 55743, Idar-Oberstein, Germany
Tel.: (49) 678198550
Web Site: https://www.biontech-imfs.de
Cell & Gene Therapy Mfr
N.A.I.C.S.: 325414

BioNTech Manufacturing Marburg GmbH **(1)**
Emil-von-Behring-Str 76, 35041, Marburg, Germany
Tel.: (49) 642138744111
Immunotherapy Development Services
N.A.I.C.S.: 541714

BioNTech US Inc. **(1)**
40 Erie St Ste 110, Cambridge, MA 02139
Tel.: (617) 337-4701
Web Site: http://www.neontherapeutics.com
Rev.: $1,401,000
Assets: $46,372,000
Liabilities: $16,955,000
Net Worth: $29,417,000
Earnings: ($79,776,000)
Emp.: 71
Fiscal Year-end: 12/31/2019
Immunotherapy Research & Development Services
N.A.I.C.S.: 541714
Kelledy Manson *(VP-Product Dev)*

JPT Peptide Technologies GmbH **(1)**
Volmerstrasse 5, 12489, Berlin, Germany
Tel.: (49) 3063925500
Web Site: https://www.jpt.com
Cell & Gene Therapy Mfr
N.A.I.C.S.: 325414

BIONXT SOLUTIONS INC.
Suite 270-1820 Fir Street, Vancouver, V7Y 1G5, BC, Canada
Tel.: (780) 818-6422
Web Site: https://bionxt.com
BXT—(DEU)
Rev.: $219,725
Assets: $1,191,246
Liabilities: $4,240,958
Net Worth: ($3,049,712)
Earnings: ($9,142,403)
Emp.: 1
Fiscal Year-end: 12/31/22
Biotechnology Research & Development Services
N.A.I.C.S.: 541714
Hugh Rogers *(Pres & CEO)*

BIOPHARMA CREDIT PLC
51 New North Road, Exeter, EX4 4EP, United Kingdom
Tel.: (44) 3031231113
Web Site: http://www.bpcruk.com
BPCR—(LSE)
Rev.: $218,140,000
Assets: $1,364,020,000
Liabilities: $23,160,000
Net Worth: $1,340,860,000
Earnings: $182,310,000
Fiscal Year-end: 12/31/22
Pharmaceuticals Product Mfr
N.A.I.C.S.: 325412
Harry Hyman *(Chm)*

BIOPHYTIS SA

4 place Jussieu Batiment A 4 eme etage Sorbonne University, Paris, 75252, France
Tel.: (33) 144272300   FR
Web Site: http://www.biophytis.com
Year Founded: 2006
BPTS—(NASDAQ)
Rev.: $1,207,360
Assets: $27,005,313
Liabilities: $29,352,480
Net Worth: ($2,347,167)
Earnings: ($29,743,060)
Emp.: 25
Fiscal Year-end: 12/31/22
Biotechnology Research & Development Services
N.A.I.C.S.: 541714
Stanislas Veillet *(Co-Founder, Chm & CEO)*

BIOPLUS CO., LTD.
Seongnam Woolim Lions Valley 2 cha A dong 1801 & 1802 ho, Sagimakgol-ro 45th Street 14 Jungwon-gu, Seongnam, Gyeonggi-do, Korea (South)
Tel.: (82) 317421898
Web Site: https://www.ubioplus.com
Year Founded: 2003
099430—(KRS)
Emp.: 70
Pharmaceutical Preparation Mfr
N.A.I.C.S.: 325412
Hyun Kyu Jung *(CEO)*

BIOPLUS LIFE CORP.
No 9 & 10 Jalan P4/8B Bandar Teknologi Kajang, 43500, Semenyih, Selangor, Malaysia
Tel.: (60) 387032020   NV
Year Founded: 2017
Rev.: $3,549,313
Assets: $3,769,186
Liabilities: $1,787,790
Net Worth: $1,981,396
Earnings: $214,194
Emp.: 30
Fiscal Year-end: 12/31/20
Holding Company
N.A.I.C.S.: 551112
Khooi You Chong *(Pres, CEO, CFO, Chief Acctg Officer, Treas & Sec)*

BIOPORTO A/S
Tuborg Havnevej 15 st, DK-2900, Hellerup, Denmark
Tel.: (45) 45290000
Web Site: https://www.bioporto.com
Year Founded: 2000
BIOPOR—(CSE)
Rev.: $4,191,663
Assets: $15,719,639
Liabilities: $5,559,028
Net Worth: $10,160,611
Earnings: ($10,985,661)
Emp.: 32
Fiscal Year-end: 12/31/22
Pharmaceuticals Product Mfr
N.A.I.C.S.: 325412
Thomas Magnussen *(Chm)*

Subsidiaries:

BioPorto Diagnostics Inc. **(1)**
117 Kendrick St Ste 300, Needham, MA 02494
Clinical Testing Services
N.A.I.C.S.: 541380

BIOPREMIER - INOVACAO E SERVICOS EM BIOTECNOLO-GIA S.A.
Ed ICAT Campus da Fac de Ciencias da Univ de Lisboa Campo Grande, 1749-016, Lisbon, Portugal
Tel.: (351) 217500218
Web Site: http://www.biopremier.com

Year Founded: 2003
Sales Range: Less than $1 Million
Biological Product Mfr
N.A.I.C.S.: 325414
Manuel Jose Gomes Rodrigues *(Chm)*

BIOPTIK TECHNOLOGY, INC.
No 188 Zhonghua S Rd, Miaoli, Zhunan, 35057, Taiwan
Tel.: (886) 37626699
Web Site: https://www.bioptik.com.tw
Year Founded: 1999
4161—(TPE)
Rev.: $24,005,034
Assets: $47,376,137
Liabilities: $24,932,120
Net Worth: $22,444,017
Earnings: $1,470,406
Fiscal Year-end: 12/31/22
Medical Device Mfr
N.A.I.C.S.: 334510
Chin-Chang Yang *(Chm)*

BIOQUANTA SA
5 rue de l'Abbe de l Epee, 75005, Paris, France
Tel.: (33) 146331424
Biotechnology Pharmaceutical Researcher, Developer & Mfr
N.A.I.C.S.: 325412
Flavio Toma *(Chief Scientific Officer)*

BIORETEC LTD.
Yrittajankulma 5, 33710, Tampere, Finland
Tel.: (358) 207789500
Web Site: https://www.bioretec.com
Year Founded: 1998
BRETEC—(HEL)
Rev.: $4,215,599
Assets: $11,501,377
Liabilities: $2,619,535
Net Worth: $8,881,842
Earnings: ($4,088,722)
Emp.: 37
Fiscal Year-end: 12/31/23
Biotechnology Research & Development Services
N.A.I.C.S.: 541714
Kimmo Lahteenkorva *(CTO)*

BIOS S.P.A.
Via Domenico Chelini 39, 00197, Rome, Italy
Tel.: (39) 06809641
Web Site: http://www.bios-spa.it
Year Founded: 1974
Sales Range: $10-24.9 Million
Emp.: 90
Health Services
N.A.I.C.S.: 621999
Maria Grazia Tambroni *(Dir-Health Admin)*

Subsidiaries:

FISIOBIOS S.R.L. **(1)**
Via Francesco Denza 27, 00197, Rome, Italy
Tel.: (39) 068082536
Web Site: http://www.fisiobios.it
Medical Equipment Mfr & Whslr
N.A.I.C.S.: 334510

LABORATORIO ANALISI CLINICHE MEDICHE IANNACCONE S.R.L. **(1)**
Via del Fornaccio 1-3, Bracciano, 00062, Italy
Tel.: (39) 06 99805073
Web Site: http://www.bios-bracciano.it
Medical Equipment Mfr
N.A.I.C.S.: 334510

BIOSCIENCE BRANDS LIMITED
4 Brewery Street, Isando, 1609, South Africa
Tel.: (27) 877401300   ZA

Web Site:
http://www.bioscience.co.za
Year Founded: 2005
Sales Range: $1-9.9 Million
Pharmaceutical Product Mfr & Whslr
N.A.I.C.S.: 325412
Jonathan Julius Fenster *(Chm & CEO)*

BIOSENSORS INTERNATIONAL GROUP, LTD.
36 Jalan Tukang, Singapore, 619266, Singapore
Tel.: (65) 6213 5777
Web Site: http://www.biosensors.com
Sales Range: $200-249.9 Million
Medical Device Mfr
N.A.I.C.S.: 339112
Yoh-Chie Lu *(Founder & Chm)*

Subsidiaries:

Biosensors International Pte Ltd **(1)**
36 Jalan Tukang Singapore, Singapore, 619266, Singapore **(100%)**
Tel.: (65) 62938066
Web Site: http://www.biosensors.com
Mfr, Marketer & Distr of Medical Devices for Critical Care
N.A.I.C.S.: 339112
Jose Calle Gordo *(CEO)*

Subsidiary (Non-US):

Biosensors B.V. **(2)**
Arnoudstraat 8, 2182 DZ, Hillegom, Netherlands **(100%)**
Tel.: (31) 252517676
Web Site: http://www.biosensors.com
Sales Range: $25-49.9 Million
Emp.: 12
Medical Devices Sales & Marketing
N.A.I.C.S.: 423450
Bram Raetsma *(Mgr-Sls)*

JW ICU Medical Limited **(2)**
328 Shichang Ave, High-Tech Industry Development Zone, Weihai, 264209, Shandong, China **(100%)**
Tel.: (86) 6313651906
Sales Range: $25-49.9 Million
Emp.: 200
Medical Device Mfr
N.A.I.C.S.: 339112

Biosensors Interventional Technologies Pte Ltd **(1)**
36 Jalan Tukang, Kampong Ubi Industrial Estate, Singapore, 619266, Singapore **(100%)**
Tel.: (65) 62135777
Medical Devices Mfr, Marketer & Distr
N.A.I.C.S.: 339112

Subsidiary (Non-US):

Biosensors Europe SA **(2)**
Rue de Lausanne 29, Morges, 1110, Switzerland **(100%)**
Tel.: (41) 218048000
Sales Range: $25-49.9 Million
Emp.: 80
Medical Devices Sales & Marketing
N.A.I.C.S.: 423450

Subsidiary (US):

Biosensors International USA **(3)**
20250 Sw Acacia St Ste 200, Newport Beach, CA 92660-1737 **(100%)**
Tel.: (949) 553-8300
Sales Range: $25-49.9 Million
Emp.: 52
Medical Device Mfr
N.A.I.C.S.: 339112

Subsidiary (Domestic):

Devax, Inc. **(4)**
13900 Alton Pkwy Ste 125, Irvine, CA 92618-1621
Tel.: (949) 334-2333
Web Site: http://www.devax.net
Sales Range: $10-24.9 Million
Emp.: 33
Medical Device Mfr
N.A.I.C.S.: 339112

Biosensors International Group, Ltd.—(Continued)

Subsidiary (Non-US):

Biosensors Japan Co., Ltd. **(3)**
Bellebs Nagayama 501 1-5 Nagayama,
Tama-shi, Tokyo, 260 0025, Japan **(100%)**
Tel.: (81) 423553311
Medical Devices Sales & Marketing
N.A.I.C.S.: 423450

BIOSERGEN AB
Fogdevreten 2, 171 65, Solna, Sweden
Tel.: (46) 20802470
Web Site: https://www.biosergen.net
Year Founded: 2004
BIOSGN—(OMX)
Rev.: $475,799
Assets: $3,101,922
Liabilities: $1,009,525
Net Worth: $2,092,397
Earnings: ($3,125,606)
Emp.: 3
Fiscal Year-end: 12/31/22
Biotechnology Research & Development Services
N.A.I.C.S.: 541714
Niels Laursen (CFO)

BIOSIGN TECHNOLOGIES INC.
14-3715 Laird Rd, Mississauga, L5L
0A3, ON, Canada
Tel.: (416) 218-9800   ON
Web Site: https://www.biosign.com
Year Founded: 2006
BITKF—(TSXV)
Sales Range: Less than $1 Million
Emp.: 12
Health Care Monitoring Products Mfr
N.A.I.C.S.: 339112
Michael Gross (Chm & Interim CEO)

BIOSINO BIO-TECHNOLOGY & SCIENCE INC.
27 Chaoqian Road, Changping District, Beijing, 102200, China
Tel.: (86) 1069722840   CN
Web Site: https://www.sinobio.com.cn
Year Founded: 1988
Rev.: $44,085,737
Assets: $112,823,803
Liabilities: $59,834,528
Net Worth: $52,989,276
Earnings: ($2,432,520)
Emp.: 479
Fiscal Year-end: 12/31/18
Diagnostic Reagent Mfr & Distr
N.A.I.C.S.: 325412
Lebin Wu (Chm)

Subsidiaries:

Beijing BIOSINO-AGIACCU Biotechnology CO., LTD **(1)**
Science & Technology Park ahead of Road
No 27 Building 1 Layer 3, Changping Business Hotel opposite Changping, Beijing,
102200, China
Tel.: (86) 1069722940
Web Site: http://www.langjiebio.net
Biochemical Product Mfr & Distr
N.A.I.C.S.: 325412

BIOSMART CO. LTD.
172 Gwangnaru-ro, Seondong-gu,
Seoul, Korea (South)
Tel.: (82) 232189000
Web Site: https://www.bio-smart.com
Year Founded: 1971
038460—(KRS)
Rev.: $300,527,298
Assets: $181,919,520
Liabilities: $111,121,384
Net Worth: $70,798,136
Earnings: $553,247
Emp.: 163
Fiscal Year-end: 12/31/22

Credit Card Services
N.A.I.C.S.: 522210
YoonHo Kwon (CEO)

BIOSOLUTION CO., LTD.
5F Seoul Technopark Gongneung-Ro
232, Nowon-Gu, Seoul, 01811, Korea
(South)
Tel.: (82) 234168884
Web Site:
    https://www.biosolutions.co.kr
Year Founded: 2000
086820—(KRS)
Rev.: $7,747,960
Assets: $70,357,332
Liabilities: $36,781,831
Net Worth: $33,575,501
Earnings: ($6,202,907)
Emp.: 96
Fiscal Year-end: 12/31/22
Cell Therapy Product Mfr
N.A.I.C.S.: 325414
Eun Kyung Yun (Gen Mgr)

BIOSTAR MICROTECH INTERNATIONAL CORP.
2F No 108-2 Minquan Road, Xindian
District, New Taipei City, 231, Taiwan
Tel.: (886) 222180150
Web Site: https://www.biostar.com.tw
Year Founded: 1986
2399—(TAI)
Rev.: $76,668,135
Assets: $91,214,000
Liabilities: $21,050,197
Net Worth: $70,163,803
Earnings: ($3,707,119)
Fiscal Year-end: 12/31/23
Hardware Parts Mfr & Distr
N.A.I.C.S.: 332510
Wang Mingyi (Chm)

Subsidiaries:

Biostar Microtech (U.S.A) Corp. **(1)**
18343 E Gale Ave, City of Industry, CA
91748
Computer Peripheral Equipment Mfr
N.A.I.C.S.: 334118
Chung M. Wang (Pres)

BIOSTAR PHARMACEUTICALS, INC.
No 588 Shiji Avenue, Xiangyang,
712046, Shaanxi, China
Tel.: (86) 2933686638   MD
Web Site:
    http://www.biostarpharma.com
Year Founded: 2007
BSPM—(OTCEM)
Sales Range: $1-9.9 Million
Emp.: 200
Pharmaceuticals Mfr
N.A.I.C.S.: 325412
Ronghua Wang (Chm & CEO)

BIOSYENT INC.
2476 Argentia Rd Suite 402, Mississauga, L5N 6M1, ON, Canada
Tel.: (905) 206-0013   Ca
Web Site: https://www.biosyent.com
Year Founded: 1947
RX—(OTCIQ)
Rev.: $17,470,008
Assets: $26,262,089
Liabilities: $5,300,149
Net Worth: $20,961,940
Earnings: $2,969,015
Fiscal Year-end: 12/31/20
Pharmaceuticals Product Mfr
N.A.I.C.S.: 325412
Rene C. Goehrum (Chm, Pres & CEO)

Subsidiaries:

Hedley Technologies (USA) Inc. **(1)**
102-202 N Ave, Grand Junction, CO 81501
Tel.: (888) 476-4473

Web Site: http://www.hedleytech.com
Insecticides Mfr & Distr
N.A.I.C.S.: 325320

Hedley Technologies Ltd. **(1)**
2476 Argentia Road Suite 402, Mississauga, L5N 6M1, ON, Canada
Tel.: (905) 206-0013
Web Site: https://www.hedleytech.com
Pest Control Services
N.A.I.C.S.: 561710

BIOSYN ARZNEIMITTEL GMBH
Schorndorfer Strasse 32, 70734, Fellbach, Germany
Tel.: (49) 7115753200
Web Site: http://www.biosyn.de
Year Founded: 1984
Sales Range: $10-24.9 Million
Emp.: 70
Pharmaceuticals Mfr
N.A.I.C.S.: 325412
Thomas Stiefel (Co-Founder & Mng Dir)

Subsidiaries:

biosyn Corporation **(1)**
5939 Darwin Ct Ste 114, Carlsbad, CA
92008
Tel.: (760) 431-0590
Web Site: http://www.biosyncorp.com
Pharmaceutical Mfr & Whslr
N.A.I.C.S.: 325412
S. N. Muddukrishna (Pres)

BIOSYNEX SA
22 Boulevard Sebastien Brant,
Illkirch-Graffenstaden, 67400, Strasbourg, France
Tel.: (33) 88787887
Web Site: https://www.biosynex.com
ALBIO—(EUR)
Sales Range: $150-199.9 Million
Emp.: 20
Diagnostic Testing Kits Mfr
N.A.I.C.S.: 325413
Thierry Paper (Co-Founder & Deputy Mng Dir)

Subsidiaries:

Chembio Diagnostics, Inc. **(1)**
3661 Horseblock Rd, Medford, NY 11763
Tel.: (631) 924-1135
Web Site: https://www.chembio.com
Rev.: $49,521,923
Assets: $62,611,405
Liabilities: $44,813,048
Net Worth: $17,798,357
Earnings: ($23,290,657)
Emp.: 188
Fiscal Year-end: 12/31/2022
Diagnostic Testing Kits
N.A.I.C.S.: 339112
Larry Abensur (Pres)

Subsidiary (Domestic):

Chembio Diagnostic Systems,
Inc. **(2)**
3661 Horseblock Rd, Medford, NY 11763
Tel.: (631) 924-1135
Web Site: http://www.chembio.com
Emp.: 100
Surgical & Medical Instrument Mfr
N.A.I.C.S.: 339112
Robert Passas (Chief Comml Officer & Sr VP)

Subsidiary (Non-US):

Chembio Diagnostics GmbH **(2)**
Schwarzschildstrasse 1, 12489, Berlin, Germany
Tel.: (49) 3063922032
Web Site: http://www.chembiogermany.de
Medical Device Mfr
N.A.I.C.S.: 339112
Lutz Melchior (Mng Dir)

opTricon GmbH **(2)**
Schwarzschildstrasse 1, 12489, Berlin, Germany
Tel.: (49) 3063922032
Web Site: http://www.optricon.de

Testing Equipment Mfr
N.A.I.C.S.: 334515
Volker Plickert (Co-Founder & Mng Dir)

BIOTAGE AB
Vimpelgatan 5, 75318, Uppsala, Sweden
Tel.: (46) 18565900
Web Site: https://www.biotage.com
Year Founded: 1999
BIOT—(OMX)
Rev.: $146,674,534
Assets: $219,075,182
Liabilities: $65,750,653
Net Worth: $153,324,529
Earnings: $25,101,389
Emp.: 517
Fiscal Year-end: 12/31/22
Medicinal Chemistry Research & Applied Genetic Analysis Solution Supplier
N.A.I.C.S.: 541715
Torben Jorgensen (Chm)

Subsidiaries:

Biotage **(1)**
Oberer Moosweg 11, Grellingen, Basel,
Switzerland **(100%)**
Tel.: (41) 617439015
Chemical & Allied Products Whslr
N.A.I.C.S.: 424690

Biotage GB Ltd. **(1)**
Distribution Way, Dyffryn Business Park
Ystrad Mynach Hengoed, Hengoed, CF82
7TS, United Kingdom **(100%)**
Tel.: (44) 1443811811
Web Site: http://www.biotage.com
Sales Range: $25-49.9 Million
Emp.: 100
Medicinal Chemistry Research & Development Services
N.A.I.C.S.: 541715

Biotage Korea Co., Ltd. **(1)**
Korea Design Center Rm 803 322
Yanghyeon-ro, Bundang-gu, Seongnam,
13496, Kyeonggi, Korea (South)
Tel.: (82) 317068500
Environmental Testing Services
N.A.I.C.S.: 541380

Biotage LLC **(1)**
10430 Harris Oak Blvd Ste C, Charlotte, NC
28269 **(100%)**
Sales Range: $25-49.9 Million
Emp.: 20
Medicinal Chemistry Research & Development Services
N.A.I.C.S.: 541715

Biotage Singapore PTE. Ltd. **(1)**
2 Venture Drive 24-01, Singapore, 608526,
Singapore
Tel.: (65) 9149351
Medical Analytical Testing & Consulting
Services
N.A.I.C.S.: 621511

Biotage Sweden AB **(1)**
Vimpelgatan 5, 753 18, Uppsala,
Sweden **(100%)**
Tel.: (46) 18565900
Web Site: https://www.biotage.com
Sales Range: $25-49.9 Million
Emp.: 50
Medicinal Chemistry Research & Development Services
N.A.I.C.S.: 541715

Biotage Trading (Shanghai) Co.,
Ltd. **(1)**
7F-B Building C5 No 2555 Xiu Pu Road, Pu
Dong, Shanghai, China
Tel.: (86) 2168162810
Environmental Testing Services
N.A.I.C.S.: 541380

Horizon Technology, Inc. **(1)**
16 Northwestern Dr, Salem, NH 03079
Tel.: (603) 893-3663
Automated Sample Preparation System Mfr
N.A.I.C.S.: 333248

Pyrosequencing, Inc. **(1)**
16 Northwestern Dr, Salem, NH 03079
Tel.: (603) 893-3663

Drug Research & Testing Services
N.A.I.C.S.: 541380

Separtis Holdings AG　　　　　　(1)
Oberer Moosweg 11, Grellingen, 4203, Basel, Switzerland　　　　**(100%)**
Tel.: (41) 617439015
Management Consulting Services
N.A.I.C.S.: 541618

BIOTALYS NV

Buchtenstraat 11, 9051, Gent, Belgium
Tel.: (32) 92745400
Web Site: https://www.biotalys.com
Year Founded: 2013
BTLS—(EUR)
Rev.: $2,817,829
Assets: $39,479,819
Liabilities: $11,885,387
Net Worth: $27,594,431
Earnings: ($22,134,686)
Emp.: 65
Fiscal Year-end: 12/31/23
Biotechnology Research & Development Services
N.A.I.C.S.: 541714
Carlo Boutton *(Chief Scientific Officer)*

BIOTECHPROGRESS SCIENTIFIC RESEARCH & PRODUCTION CO. ZAO

Enthuziastov Shosse 6, Kirishi, 187110, Leningrad Region, Russia
Tel.: (7) 81368 255 07
Web Site: http://biotechprogress.ru
Waste Treatment Services
N.A.I.C.S.: 924110

BIOTEKNO

K Bakkalkoy Mah Kaysdagi Cad Kayaoglu Plaza No 119, 34750, Atasehir, Istanbul, Turkiye
Tel.: (90) 2165763848
Web Site: http://www.biotekno.biz
Sales Range: $50-74.9 Million
Emp.: 100
Mobile Business Solutions
N.A.I.C.S.: 513210
Ahmet Ilhan Oney *(CEO)*

BIOTER S.A.

45 Eftychidou, 11634, Athens, Greece
Tel.: (30) 2107248762
Web Site: https://bioter.gr
Year Founded: 1961
BIOT—(ATH)
Sales Range: Less than $1 Million
Emp.: 4
Civil Engineering Construction Services
N.A.I.C.S.: 237990
Georgios Andreas Mavroskotis *(Chm, Mng Dir & Gen Mgr)*

BIOTEST AG

Landsteinerstr 5, D-63303, Dreieich, Germany
Tel.: (49) 61038010　　　　　De
Web Site: http://www.biotest.com
BIO—(STU)
Rev.: $755,709,402
Assets: $1,557,450,183
Liabilities: $1,006,729,440
Net Worth: $550,720,743
Earnings: $140,191,490
Emp.: 2,426
Fiscal Year-end: 12/31/23
Pharmaceutical, Biotherapeutic & Diagnostic Products
N.A.I.C.S.: 325412
Monika Buttkereit *(Head-IR)*

Subsidiaries:

Bio-Rad Medical Diagnostics
GmbH　　　　　　　　　　(1)

Industriestrasse 1, 63303, Dreieich, Germany
Tel.: (49) 610331300
Web Site: http://www.medizinische-diagnostik-dreieich.de
Immunology Instruments & Reagents Mfr
N.A.I.C.S.: 334516
Roland Michael Klug *(Mng Dir)*

Biotest (Schweiz) AG　　　　(1)
Schutzenstrasse 17, 5102, Rupperswil, Aargau, Switzerland
Tel.: (41) 628890000
Web Site: http://www.biotest.com
Emp.: 10
Pharmaceutical Products Distr
N.A.I.C.S.: 424210

Biotest (UK) Ltd.　　　　　　(1)
First Floor Park Point 17 High Street, Longbridge, Birmingham, B31 2UQ, West Midlands, United Kingdom
Tel.: (44) 1217333393
Web Site: http://www.biotest.com
Sales Range: $25-49.9 Million
Emp.: 18
Pharmaceutical Products Distr
N.A.I.C.S.: 424210

Biotest Austria GmbH　　　　(1)
Einsiedlergasse 58, 1050, Vienna, Austria
Tel.: (43) 15451561
Pharmaceuticals Product Mfr
N.A.I.C.S.: 325412

Biotest Farmaceutica Ltda.　　(1)
Pharmaceuticals Product Mfr
N.A.I.C.S.: 325412

Biotest France SARL　　　　(1)
45-47 Rue d Hauteville, 75010, Paris, France
Tel.: (33) 184175620
Web Site: http://www.biotest.com
Pharmaceutical Products Distr
N.A.I.C.S.: 424210

Biotest Grundstucksverwaltungs GmbH　　　　　　　　　　(1)
Landsteiner Strasse 5, 63303, Dreieich, Germany
Tel.: (49) 61038010
Sales Range: $200-249.9 Million
Emp.: 800
Pharmaceuticals Product Mfr
N.A.I.C.S.: 325412

Biotest Hellas M.E.P.E.　　　(1)
25 Kiprion Agoniston St, Maroussi, Athens, Greece
Tel.: (30) 2108043437
Web Site: http://www.biotest.gr
Sales Range: $25-49.9 Million
Emp.: 20
Medical Equipment Whslr
N.A.I.C.S.: 423450

Biotest Hungaria Kft.　　　　(1)
Torbagy u 15/A, 2045, Torokbalint, Pest, Hungary
Tel.: (36) 23511311
Web Site: https://www.biotest.com
Sales Range: $25-49.9 Million
Emp.: 24
Pharmaceutical Preparation Mfr
N.A.I.C.S.: 325412
Borbas Gyula *(Comml Dir)*

Biotest Italia S.R.L.　　　　(1)
Via Leonardo da Vinci 43, 20090, Trezzano sul Naviglio, Italy
Tel.: (39) 024844291
Pharmaceuticals Product Mfr
N.A.I.C.S.: 325412

Biotest K.K.　　　　　　　　(1)
Daini Yasuda Building 2F 3-32-13 Tsuruya-cho, Kanagawa-ku, Yokohama, 221-0835, Kanagawa, Japan
Tel.: (81) 453175111
Web Site: http://www.biotest.co.jp
Sales Range: $50-74.9 Million
Emp.: 10
Pharmaceutical Products Distr
N.A.I.C.S.: 424210

Biotest Medical, S.L.U.　　　(1)
C/ Frederic Mompou n 5-6 3 A, Sant Just Desvern, 08960, Barcelona, Spain
Tel.: (34) 935952661
Pharmaceutical Products Distr

N.A.I.C.S.: 424210

Biotest Pharma GmbH　　　　(1)
Landsteiner Strasse 5, 63303, Dreieich, Germany
Tel.: (49) 61038010
Web Site: http://www.biotest.com
Sales Range: $250-299.9 Million
Emp.: 800
Medical Diagnostic Equipments & Supplies Distr
N.A.I.C.S.: 423450
Gregor Schulz *(CEO)*

Biotest Pharmaceuticals Corporation　　　　　　　　(1)
5800 Park of Commerce Blvd NW, Boca Raton, FL 33487-8222
Tel.: (561) 569-3100
Web Site: http://www.biotestpharma.com
Sales Range: $250-299.9 Million
Emp.: 600
Biological Product Mfr
N.A.I.C.S.: 325414
Ileana Carlisle *(CEO)*

Plasma Service Europe GmbH　(1)
Landsteinerstrasse 5, 63303, Dreieich, Germany
Tel.: (49) 3816665470
Web Site: http://www.plasmaservice.de
Sales Range: $25-49.9 Million
Emp.: 250
Blood Plasma Collection Services
N.A.I.C.S.: 621991
Martin Reinecke *(Mng Dir)*

Plasmadienst Tirol GmbH　　(1)
Innrain 6-8, 6020, Innsbruck, Tyrol, Austria
Tel.: (43) 5125847230
Web Site: http://www.plasma-tirol.at
Plasmapheresis Services
N.A.I.C.S.: 621991

Plazmaszolgalat Kft.　　　　(1)
Czuczor u 10, 1093, Budapest, Hungary
Tel.: (36) 680111120
Web Site: http://plazmaadas.hu
Sales Range: $25-49.9 Million
Emp.: 25
Pharmaceutical Preparation Mfr
N.A.I.C.S.: 325412

BIOTIKA BOHEMIA SPOL. S R.O.

Durychova 101/66, 142 00, Prague, Czech Republic
Tel.: (420) 244464454
Web Site: http://www.biotika.net
Sales Range: $25-49.9 Million
Emp.: 14
Pharmaceuticals Mfr
N.A.I.C.S.: 325412
Vladimir Jirout *(Mng Dir)*

BIOTON S.A.

Macierzysz ul Poznanska 12, 05-850, Ozarow Mazowiecki, Poland
Tel.: (48) 227214000
Web Site: https://bioton.com
Year Founded: 1989
BIO—(WAR)
Rev.: $58,937,833
Assets: $203,568,809
Liabilities: $51,315,380
Net Worth: $152,253,429
Earnings: $356,981
Emp.: 400
Fiscal Year-end: 12/31/22
Biopharmaceutical Mfr
N.A.I.C.S.: 325412
Adam Polonek *(Member-Mgmt Bd)*

Subsidiaries:

Fisiopharma S.r.l.　　　　　(1)
Nucleo Industriale, PO Box 84020, Palomonte, 84020, Salerno, Italy
Tel.: (39) 0828997491
Web Site: http://www.fisiopharma.com
Drug Mfr
N.A.I.C.S.: 424210

MJ BioPharm Pvt Ltd　　　　(1)
113 Jolly Makers Chambers - II, Nariman

Point, Mumbai, 400 021, Maharashtra, India
　　　　　　　　　　　　(50%)
Tel.: (91) 2222020644
Web Site: http://mjgroup.co.in
Sales Range: $25-49.9 Million
Emp.: 100
Pharmaceuticals Product Mfr
N.A.I.C.S.: 325412

Subsidiary (Domestic):

SciGen Biopharma Pvt Ltd　　(2)
Plot 18 International Biotech Park, Hinjewadi Phase II, Pune, 411 057, Maharastra, India
　　　　　　　　　　　　(50.01%)
Tel.: (91) 20 3980 3220
Web Site: http://www.scigenltd.com
Sales Range: $25-49.9 Million
Emp.: 52
Therapeutic Proteins Mfr
N.A.I.C.S.: 325411

Medipolis GMP Oy　　　　　(1)
Kiviharjunlenkki 2, PO Box 90220, Oulu, Finland
Tel.: (358) 207545880
Web Site: http://www.medipolisgmp.com
Sales Range: $25-49.9 Million
Emp.: 15
Pharmaceuticals Product Mfr
N.A.I.C.S.: 325412

BIOTOXTECH CO., LTD.

53 Yeongudanji-ro Ochang-eup, Cheongwon-gu, Cheongju, 28115, Chungcheongbuk-do, Korea (South)
Tel.: (82) 432107777
Web Site:
　　https://www.biotoxtech.com
Year Founded: 2000
086040—(KRS)
Rev.: $28,602,766
Assets: $96,412,189
Liabilities: $62,382,802
Net Worth: $34,029,387
Earnings: $2,090,227
Emp.: 253
Fiscal Year-end: 12/31/22
Bio Technology Services
N.A.I.C.S.: 541714
Jong-Koo Kang *(CEO)*

BIOTREND CEVRE VE ENERJI YATIRIMLARI A.S.

Ekinciler Caddesi Erturk Sokak 3, Kavacik Beykoz, 34810, Istanbul, Turkiye
Tel.: (90) 2166800000
Web Site:
　　https://www.biotrendenerji.com.tr
Year Founded: 2017
BIOEN—(IST)
Rev.: $75,624,109
Assets: $225,826,438
Liabilities: $129,264,006
Net Worth: $96,562,432
Earnings: $32,176,708
Fiscal Year-end: 12/31/23
Electrical Products Mfr
N.A.I.C.S.: 334515
Ilhan Dogan *(Chm)*

BIOTRON LIMITED

Level 2 66 Hunter Street, Sydney, 2000, NSW, Australia
Tel.: (61) 293003344
Web Site: https://www.biotron.com.au
BITRF—(OTCIQ)
Rev.: $1,194,126
Assets: $1,460,405
Liabilities: $623,345
Net Worth: $837,060
Earnings: ($2,130,838)
Emp.: 3
Fiscal Year-end: 06/30/22
Regulation, Licensing & Inspection of Miscellaneous Commercial Sectors
N.A.I.C.S.: 926150
Peter J. Nightingale *(Sec)*

Biotron Limited—(Continued)

BIOTRONIK GMBH & CO.
Woermannkehre 1, Berlin, 12359,
Germany
Tel.: (49) 30689050
Web Site: http://www.biotronik.com
Year Founded: 1969
Sales Range: $300-349.9 Million
Emp.: 3,000
Implantable Cardiac Devices Mfr &
Sales
N.A.I.C.S.: 334510
Max Schaldach (Pres)

Subsidiaries:

Arlab S.A. (1)
Ensign Royal 1380 Region Metropolitana,
Providencia, Santiago, Chile
Tel.: (56) 222041949
Web Site: http://www.arlab.cl
Medical Device Mfr
N.A.I.C.S.: 339112

BIOMEDICA Argentina S.A. (1)
Peru 345-Piso 6 RA-1067, Buenos Aires,
Argentina
Tel.: (54) 11 434 39 197
Medical Device Distr
N.A.I.C.S.: 423450

BIOTRONIK (Beijing) Medical Devices Ltd. (1)
1122 Interchina Commercial Building 33
Dengshikou Street, Dongcheng District, Beijing, 100006, China
Tel.: (86) 10 65223851
Web Site: http://www.biotronik.com
Medical Device Distr
N.A.I.C.S.: 423450

BIOTRONIK AG (1)
Ackerstrasse 6, 8180, Bulach, Switzerland
Tel.: (41) 44 864 51 11
Medical Device Distr
N.A.I.C.S.: 423450

BIOTRONIK ApS (1)
Lyngso Alle 3A Bygning 16 2 Sal, 2970,
Horsholm, Denmark
Tel.: (45) 45 860886
Medical Device Distr
N.A.I.C.S.: 423450

BIOTRONIK Asia Pacific Pte Ltd. (1)
30 Raffles Place Suite 12-04 Chevron
House, Singapore, 48622, Singapore
Tel.: (65) 6632 5990
Medical Device DistrMedical Device Distr
N.A.I.C.S.: 423450

BIOTRONIK Australia Pty. Ltd. (1)
Suite 2 Level 4 Building 2 20 Bridge Street,
Pymble, 2073, NSW, Australia
Tel.: (61) 2 94973700
Medical Device Distr
N.A.I.C.S.: 423450

BIOTRONIK BALTIJA SIA (1)
Kalnciema Street 37-4, 1046, Riga, Latvia
Tel.: (371) 676 13071
Medical Device Distr
N.A.I.C.S.: 423450

BIOTRONIK BELGIUM S.A. (1)
Telecom Gardens Medialaan 36, 1800, Vilvoorde, Belgium
Tel.: (32) 2 7710435
Web Site: http://www.biotronik.com
Emp.: 50
Medical Device Distr
N.A.I.C.S.: 423450
Ivo Vanderick (Gen Mgr)

BIOTRONIK Biyomedikal Teknolojiler Ltd. Sti. (1)
29 Ekim Cad Vizyonpark D Blok Ofis B1
Apt No 5 D 610, Yenibosna, 34197, Istanbul, Turkiye
Tel.: (90) 212 217 57 51
Web Site: http://biotronikbiyomedikal.com
Medical Device Distr
N.A.I.C.S.: 423450

BIOTRONIK Bulgaria Ltd (1)
Manastirski Livadi Iztok 81B Bulgaria Blvd
6th Floor Office II-B-2, 1404, Sofia, Bulgaria
Tel.: (359) 2 428 16 70

Medical Device Distr
N.A.I.C.S.: 423450

BIOTRONIK Canada Inc. (1)
185 The West Mall Suite 1000, Toronto,
M9C 5L5, ON, Canada
Tel.: (416) 620-0069
Medical Device Distr
N.A.I.C.S.: 423450

BIOTRONIK Comercial Medica Ltda. (1)
Rua Leoncio de Carvalho 234, 04003-010,
Sao Paulo, Brazil
Tel.: (55) 11 5694 7755
Medical Device Distr
N.A.I.C.S.: 423450

BIOTRONIK D.O.O. (1)
Nad Lipom 12B, 10000, Zagreb, Croatia
Tel.: (385) 91 6131 820
Medical Device Distr
N.A.I.C.S.: 423450

BIOTRONIK France S.A.S. (1)
Parc D'affaires Silic 2 Rue Nicolas Ledoux,
70231, Rungis, France
Tel.: (33) 1 46759660
Medical Device Distr
N.A.I.C.S.: 423450

BIOTRONIK HUNGARIA Kft (1)
Fajd U 2/b Magyarorszag 2, 1025, Budapest, Hungary
Tel.: (36) 1 3264941
Medical Device Distr
N.A.I.C.S.: 423450

BIOTRONIK Hellas Single Member Ltd. (1)
2-4 Mesogeion Avenue, 11527, Athens,
Greece
Tel.: (30) 210 7777147
Medical Device Distr
N.A.I.C.S.: 423450

BIOTRONIK Hong Kong Limited (1)
Unit 2106 Infinitus Plaza 199 Des Voeux
Road, Central, China (Hong Kong)
Tel.: (852) 3190 4500
Medical Device Distr
N.A.I.C.S.: 423450

BIOTRONIK ITALIA S.p.A. (1)
Via delle Industrie 11, 20090, Vimodrone,
MI, Italy
Tel.: (39) 02 274394200
Medical Device Distr
N.A.I.C.S.: 423450

BIOTRONIK Japan, Inc. (1)
Ebisu Business Tower 13F 1-19-19 Ebisu,
Shibuya-ku, Tokyo, 150-0013, Japan
Tel.: (81) 3 3473 7471
Web Site: http://www.biotronik.com
Medical Device Distr
N.A.I.C.S.: 423450

BIOTRONIK Korea Co., Ltd. (1)
3rd Floor Shindo Building 6 Hyoryeong-ro,
61-gil, Seocho, Seoul, Korea (South)
Tel.: (82) 2 598 4555
Medical Device Distr
N.A.I.C.S.: 423450

BIOTRONIK Medical Devices (Malaysia) SDN BHD (1)
Unit 1304A Level 13A Uptown 1 Jalan
SS21/58 Damansara Uptown, 47400, Petaling Jaya, Selangor, Malaysia
Tel.: (60) 12 217 7
Medical Device Distr
N.A.I.C.S.: 423450

BIOTRONIK Medical Devices India Private Limited. (1)
Unit No-805-807 DLF Tower-B District Centre Jasola, 110044, New Delhi, India
Tel.: (91) 11 40587850 54
Web Site: http://www.biotronik.com
Medical Device Distr
N.A.I.C.S.: 423450

BIOTRONIK OY (1)
Hirsalantie 11, 02420, Jorvas, Finland
Tel.: (358) 9 425 79 216
Medical Device Distr
N.A.I.C.S.: 423450

BIOTRONIK Polska Sp. z.o.o (1)
Ul Murawa 12-18, 61-655, Poznan, Poland

Tel.: (48) 61 8681465
Medical Device Distr
N.A.I.C.S.: 423450

BIOTRONIK Praha spol. s.r.o. (1)
Polygon House Doudlebska 1699/5, 140
00, Prague, Czech Republic
Tel.: (420) 267 913 962
Medical Device Distr
N.A.I.C.S.: 423450

BIOTRONIK SA (Pty) Ltd. (1)
56 Regency Road Route 21 Office Park,
0047, Centurion, South Africa
Tel.: (27) 12 941 4955
Medical Device Distr
N.A.I.C.S.: 423450

BIOTRONIK Schweiz AG (1)
Neuhofstrasse 4, 6341, Baar, Switzerland
Tel.: (41) 41 560 36 60
Web Site: http://www.biotronik.com
Emp.: 20
Medical Device Distr
N.A.I.C.S.: 423450
Marcel Ackermann (Mng Dir)

BIOTRONIK Slovensko, s.r.o. (1)
Pri Suchom Mlyne C 34, 811 04, Bratislava,
Slovakia
Tel.: (421) 2 5479 3230
Medical Device Distr
N.A.I.C.S.: 423450

BIOTRONIK UK Ltd. (1)
Avonbury Business Park, Bicester, OX26
2UA, OX26 2UA, United Kingdom
Tel.: (44) 1869 362100
Web Site: http://www.biotronik.com
Emp.: 20
Medical Device Distr
N.A.I.C.S.: 423450

BIOTRONIK Vertriebs-GmbH (1)
Euro Plaza Gebaude G Am Euro Platz
2/Stiege 2, 1120, Vienna, Austria
Tel.: (43) 1 6154450
Medical Device Distr
N.A.I.C.S.: 423450

Biotronik (Thailand) Co., Ltd. (1)
No 428 Ari Hills Building 17th Floor Room
17A Soi Phahonyothin 10, Phahonyothin
Road Samsen Nai Phayathai, 10400, Bangkok, Thailand
Tel.: (66) 20267099
Medical Device Mfr
N.A.I.C.S.: 339112

Biotronik Argentina S.R.L. (1)
Peru 345 Piso 6 RA, 1067, Buenos Aires,
Argentina
Tel.: (54) 1143439197
Medical Device Mfr
N.A.I.C.S.: 339112
Osvaldo Camurri (Acct Mgr)

Biotronik GmbH & Co. (1)
Hartmann Strasse 65, PO Box 1369,
91052, Erlangen, Bavaria,
Germany **(100%)**
Tel.: (49) 913189240
Web Site: http://www.biotronik.com
Sales Range: $50-74.9 Million
Emp.: 140
Mfr & Sales of Implantable Cardiac Devices
N.A.I.C.S.: 339113

Biotronik GmbH & Co. Vertriebs KG (1)
Woermannkehre 1, 12359, Berlin, Germany
Tel.: (49) 30689050
Web Site: http://www.biotronik.com
Sales Range: $25-49.9 Million
Emp.: 2,500
Mfr & Sales of Implantable Cardiac Devices
N.A.I.C.S.: 339113

Biotronik Inc. (1)
6024 Jean Rd, Lake Oswego, OR 97035-
5308
Tel.: (503) 635-3594
Web Site: http://www.biotronik.com
Sales Range: $150-199.9 Million
Emp.: 150
Implantable Cardiac Device Distr
N.A.I.C.S.: 423450
Ryan Walters (Pres)

Biotronik Kazakhstan GmbH (1)
Bukhar Zyrau 26 1 Office 41, 050013, Al-

maty, Kazakhstan
Tel.: (7) 7273394813
Medical Device Mfr
N.A.I.C.S.: 339112

Biotronik Nederland B.V. (1)
Takenhofplein 3, 6538 SZ, Nijmegen, Netherlands
Tel.: (31) 24 3555975
Medical Device Distr
N.A.I.C.S.: 423450
Gert Van Alst (Mng Dir)

Biotronik Portugal Unipessoal Lda. (1)
R S Francisco de Sales 17 B, 1250-230,
Lisbon, Portugal
Tel.: (351) 211305507
Medical Device Mfr
N.A.I.C.S.: 339112

C.E.M. BIOTRONIK S.A. (1)
Circunvalacion 29, 28224, Madrid, Spain
Tel.: (34) 91 7994670
Medical Device Distr
N.A.I.C.S.: 423450

Gilmedica. S.A. (1)
Calle 13 No 32 418 Acopi Valle del Cauca,
Yumbo, Colombia
Tel.: (57) 26903999
Web Site: http://www.gilmedica.com
Medical Device & Equipment Distr
N.A.I.C.S.: 423450
Luis Fernando Gil (CEO)

Manning Jaya Trading (B) Sdn. Bhd. (1)
Unit 17 2nd Floor Block B Simpang 68
Complex Warisan P H N Delima Satu, Kampong Serusop Jalan Muara, Bandar Seri
Begawan, BB4713, Brunei Darussalam
Tel.: (673) 2342332
Web Site:
http://www.manningjayabrunei.wixsite.com
Medical Equipment Distr
N.A.I.C.S.: 423450

Medsoll Cyprus Ltd (1)
Evagoras Ste 51 31 Evagorou Ave, Nicosia,
1066, Cyprus **(100%)**
Tel.: (357) 22671638
Web Site: http://www.medsoll.com
Sales Range: $25-49.9 Million
Emp.: 10
Mfr & Sales of Implantable Cardiac Devices
N.A.I.C.S.: 339113
Christos Vasiliadis (Gen Mgr)

OOO BIOTRONIK (1)
Building 1A floor 2 room 6 street
Nikoloyamskaya 26, 109240, Moscow, Russia
Tel.: (7) 4957896831
Web Site: http://www.biotronik.ru
Medical Device Distr
N.A.I.C.S.: 423450

OOO BIOTRONIK URAL (1)
Belinskogo Str Bldg 83 Office 1906,
620026, Ekaterinburg, Russia
Tel.: (7) 3433457017
Web Site: https://www.biotronik.com
Medical Device Distr
N.A.I.C.S.: 423450

World Medical S.A.S. (1)
Cra 7 156-68 piso 28 Torre North Point III,
Bogota, Colombia
Tel.: (57) 17433292
Web Site: http://www.worldmedical.com
Healtcare Services
N.A.I.C.S.: 621491

BIOVAXYS TECHNOLOGY CORP.
146 Thirtieth Street Suite 100, Toronto, M8W 3C4, ON, Canada
Tel.: (604) 262-8835
Web Site: https://www.biovaxys.com
Year Founded: 2018
BVAXF—(OTCQB)
Rev.: $12,337
Assets: $677,113
Liabilities: $1,282,232
Net Worth: ($605,119)
Earnings: ($9,174,145)
Fiscal Year-end: 10/31/22

Biotechnology Research & Development Services
N.A.I.C.S.: 541714
David Berd (*Co-Founder & Chief Medical Officer*)

BIOVENTIX PLC
7 Romans Business Park East Street, Farnham, GU9 7SX, Surrey, United Kingdom
Tel.: (44) 1252728001
Web Site: https://www.bioventix.com
Year Founded: 2003
BVXP—(AIM)
Rev.: $15,919,876
Assets: $16,491,104
Liabilities: $1,514,996
Net Worth: $14,976,108
Earnings: $10,393,866
Emp.: 16
Fiscal Year-end: 06/30/23
Biotechnology Specializing in High-Affinity Sheep Monoclonal Antibodies
N.A.I.C.S.: 541714
Peter John Harrison (*CEO*)

BIOVICA INTERNATIONAL AB
Dag Hammarskjolds Vag 54B Uppsala Science Park, 752 37, Uppsala, Sweden
Tel.: (46) 184444830
Web Site: https://www.biovica.com
Year Founded: 2009
BIOVIC.B—(OMX)
Rev.: $768,616
Assets: $18,511,112
Liabilities: $3,362,449
Net Worth: $15,148,663
Earnings: ($7,325,166)
Emp.: 25
Fiscal Year-end: 04/30/22
Pharmaceuticals Product Mfr
N.A.I.C.S.: 325412
Lars Holmqvist (*Chm*)

Subsidiaries:

Biovica Inc. (1)
303 Wyman St Ste 300, Waltham, MA 02451
Tel.: (617) 631-0234
Medical Device Mfr
N.A.I.C.S.: 339112

BIOVILL CO., LTD.
94 Dujeon Street, Yangsan, 626-220, Kyungnam, Korea (South)
Tel.: (82) 55 385 1500
Web Site: http://www.kscbys.co.kr
Year Founded: 1986
Sales Range: $25-49.9 Million
Emp.: 75
Chemical Products Mfr
N.A.I.C.S.: 325130

BIOWIND GROUP S.A.
58 rue Pottier, 78150, Le Chesnay, France
Tel.: (33) 1 39 02 25 42
Web Site:
　http://www.biowindgroup.com
Year Founded: 2001
Sales Range: Less than $1 Million
Emp.: 4
Industrial Air, Surface Cleaning & Decontamination Equipment Mfr
N.A.I.C.S.: 333413
Valery Bonnet (*Chm & Mng Dir*)

Subsidiaries:

Biowind Group S.A. - Manufacturing Plant (1)
58 Rue Pottier, 78150, Le Chesnay, France
Tel.: (33) 1 39 02 25 42
Air Purification Equipment Mfr
N.A.I.C.S.: 333413

BIOXYNE LIMITED
Suite 506 Level 5 50 Clarence Street, Sydney, 2000, NSW, Australia
Tel.: (61) 290788180
Web Site: https://www.bioxyne.com
BXN—(ASX)
Rev.: $6,226,643
Assets: $4,472,245
Liabilities: $2,269,016
Net Worth: $2,203,229
Earnings: ($8,663,629)
Fiscal Year-end: 06/30/24
Biotechnology Products Mfr
N.A.I.C.S.: 325412
N. H. Chua (*CEO & Mng Dir*)

Subsidiaries:

Bioxyne International Malaysia Sdn Bhd (1)
D-27-03 Menara Suezcap1 No 2 Jalan Kerinchi, Gerbang Kerinchi Lestari, 59200, Kuala Lumpur, Malaysia
Tel.: (60) 37 931 9892
Web Site: https://www.bioxyne.com.my
Supplement Product Mfr
N.A.I.C.S.: 325411

P.T. Gamata Utama (1)
Jl Gunung Sahari Raya Ruko Marinatama Blok A No 5, Mangga Dua, Jakarta, 14420, Indonesia
Tel.: (62) 2164719757
Web Site: http://www.bioxyne.co.id
Skin Care Product Mfr & Retailer
N.A.I.C.S.: 325620
A. Uun Achmad (*Pres*)

BIP INVESTMENT PARTNERS S.A.
1 Rue Des Coquelicots, 1356, Luxembourg, Luxembourg
Tel.: (352) 2600261　　　　　LU
Web Site: http://www.bip.lu
Year Founded: 2000
Sales Range: $10-24.9 Million
Emp.: 10
Investment Management Service
N.A.I.C.S.: 523940
Natalia Sutugina (*Dir-Investments*)

BIPADOSA SA
Ctra de Castilla 802-820, 15570, Naron, Spain
Tel.: (34) 981 399 000
Web Site: http://www.megasa.es
Year Founded: 1953
Emp.: 1,000
Holding Company
N.A.I.C.S.: 551112
Alberto Carreira Miguez (*Controller*)

Subsidiaries:

Megasa Siderurgica S.L. (1)
Ctra de Castilla 802-820, 15570, Naron, Spain
Tel.: (34) 981 399 000
Web Site: http://www.megasa.es
Steel Rebar, Coils & Spools Mfr
N.A.I.C.S.: 331110
Carlos Gil Robles (*Gen Mgr*)

Subsidiary (Domestic):

Megasider Zaragoza S.A.U. (2)
Parque Tecnologico de Reciclado Lopez Soriano, Av de Jose Lopez Soriano 100, 50720, Zaragoza, Spain
Tel.: (34) 976 46 61 71
Rolled Steel Products Mfr
N.A.I.C.S.: 331221

BIPL SECURITIES LTD.
Suite 602 6th Floor Continental Trade Center Block 8 Clifton, Karachi, 75600, Pakistan
Tel.: (92) 21111222000
Web Site: http://www.biplsec.com
Year Founded: 1991
AKDSL—(PSX)
Rev.: $2,320,334
Assets: $39,339,817
Liabilities: $10,005,479

Net Worth: $29,334,339
Earnings: $1,463,305
Emp.: 244
Fiscal Year-end: 06/30/23
Security Brokerage Services
N.A.I.C.S.: 523150
Kamal Uddin Tipu (*Chm*)

BIPROGY INC.
1-1-1 Toyosu, Koto-ku, Tokyo, 1358560, Japan
Tel.: (81) 355464111　　　　　JP
Web Site: https://biprogy.com
Year Founded: 1958
8056—(TKS)
Rev.: $2,446,638,620
Assets: $2,076,987,590
Liabilities: $964,432,050
Net Worth: $1,112,555,540
Earnings: $166,876,060
Emp.: 8,218
Fiscal Year-end: 03/31/24
Computers & Related Products
N.A.I.C.S.: 334111
Akiyoshi Hiraoka (*Pres, CEO & Chief Health Officer*)

Subsidiaries:

AFAS Inc. (1)
1-1-1 Toyosu, Koto-ku, Tokyo, 135-8560, Japan
Tel.: (81) 345791670
Web Site: http://www.afasinc.co.jp
Emp.: 32
Software Development Services
N.A.I.C.S.: 541511

Axxis Consulting (S) Pte. Ltd. (1)
10 Ubi Crescent Lobby B 02-26 Ubi Techpark, Singapore, 408564, Singapore
Tel.: (65) 67497069
Web Site: http://www.axxis-consulting.com
IT Management Consulting Services
N.A.I.C.S.: 541618
Tan Woan San (*Mgr-Fin & Admin*)

Cambridge Technology Partners, Ltd. (1)
Akasaka 2-14 Plaza Building 4F 2-14-32 Akasaka, Minato-ku, Tokyo, 107-0052, Japan
Tel.: (81) 335604061
Web Site: https://www.ctp.co.jp
Emp.: 188
Software Development Services
N.A.I.C.S.: 541511

Canal Globe, Ltd. (1)
1-1-1 Toyosu, Koto-ku, Tokyo, 135-8560, Japan
Tel.: (81) 345792098
Web Site: https://en.canalglobe.com
Software Development Services
N.A.I.C.S.: 541511

Canal Payment Service, Ltd. (1)
1-1-1 Toyosu, Koto Ward, Tokyo, 135-8560, Japan
Tel.: (81) 345792336
Web Site: https://www.canalpayment.co.jp
Software Development Services
N.A.I.C.S.: 541511

Canal Ventures, Ltd. (1)
1-1-1 Toyosu, Koto-ku, Tokyo, 135-8560, Japan
Tel.: (81) 345792457
Web Site: https://www.canal-v.com
Digital Transformation Services
N.A.I.C.S.: 518210

G&U System Service, Ltd. (1)
3-14-24 Fukushima Osaka Fukushima Hanshin Building 8th floor, Fukushima-ku, Osaka, 553-0003, Japan　　(51%)
Tel.: (81) 664584658
Web Site: https://www.guss.co.jp
Sales Range: $10-24.9 Million
Emp.: 74
Information Technology Services
N.A.I.C.S.: 541512

Intechstra Co., Ltd. (1)
1-1-1 Toyosu, Koto-ku, Tokyo, 135-8560, Japan
Tel.: (81) 355467100

Web Site: http://www.intechstra.com
Intellectual Property Management, Technology & Strategies
N.A.I.C.S.: 541690

International Systems Development Co., Ltd. (1)
Okinawa Cellular Forest Building 11F 4-1 Higashimachi, Naha, 900-0034, Okinawa, Japan
Tel.: (81) 988548352
Web Site: https://www.isd.co.jp
Emp.: 172
Software Development Services
N.A.I.C.S.: 541511

NUL Accessibility, Ltd. (1)
1-1-1 Toyosu, Koto-ku, Tokyo, 135-8560, Japan
Tel.: (81) 345792071
Web Site: http://nul-acc.co.jp
Emp.: 7
Web Accessibility Services
N.A.I.C.S.: 541511

NUL System Services Corporation (1)
3945 Freedom Cir Ste 430, Santa Clara, CA 95054
Tel.: (408) 824-8408
Web Site: http://www.nulssc.com
Information Technology Management Services
N.A.I.C.S.: 541512
Waka Minagawa (*Pres & CEO*)

S&I Co., Ltd. (1)
Keihanshin Toranomon Building 1-7-14 Nishi-Shimbashi, Minato-ku, Tokyo, 105-0003, Japan
Tel.: (81) 368228080
Web Site: https://www.sandi.jp
Emp.: 241
ICT Infrastructure Solution Services
N.A.I.C.S.: 541511

Trade Vision, Ltd. (1)
1-1-1 Toyosu, Koto-ku, Tokyo, 135-8560, Japan
Tel.: (81) 345791160
Web Site: https://www.tradevision.co.jp
Telecommunication Servicesb
N.A.I.C.S.: 517810

UEL Corporation (1)
1-1-1 Toyosu, Koto-ku, Tokyo, 135-8560, Japan
Tel.: (81) 355466600
Web Site: https://www.biprogy-uel.co.jp
Emp.: 175
CAD & CAM Integrated System Design Services
N.A.I.C.S.: 541512

UNIAID Co., Ltd. (1)
4-28 Echocho, Naka-ku, Hiroshima, 730-0021, Hiroshima Prefecture, Japan
Tel.: (81) 822415788
Web Site: https://www.uniaid.co.jp
Emp.: 38
Software Development Services
N.A.I.C.S.: 541511

USOL Vietnam Co., Ltd. (1)
14th 20th Floor Hoa Binh Tower 106 Hoang Quoc Viet Street, Cau Giay District, Hanoi, Vietnam
Tel.: (84) 2437556500
Web Site: https://www.usol-v.com.vn
Emp.: 275
Software Development Services
N.A.I.C.S.: 541511

Uniadex, Ltd. (1)
1-1-1 Toyosu, Koto-ku, Tokyo, 135-8560, Japan
Tel.: (81) 355464900
Web Site: https://www.uniadex.co.jp
Emp.: 2,512
IT Outsourcing Services
N.A.I.C.S.: 541511

BIR FINANCIAL LIMITED
Level 2 350 Kent Street, Sydney, 2000, WA, Australia
Tel.: (61) 292992289
Web Site:
　http://www.birfinancial.com.au

BIR Financial Limited—(Continued)

ICU—(ASX)
Rev.: $319,087
Assets: $422,610
Liabilities: $1,967,141
Net Worth: ($1,544,532)
Earnings: ($1,293,126)
Emp.: 10
Fiscal Year-end: 06/30/24
Property & Infrastructure Development Services
N.A.I.C.S.: 531390
Daniel Johannes Bredenkamp *(CFO & Sec)*

Subsidiaries:

Pulse Markets Pty. Ltd. **(1)**
Level 19 10 Eagle Street, Brisbane, 4000, QLD, Australia
Tel.: (61) 400094848
Web Site: https://www.pulsemarkets.com.au
Capital Raising Financial Services
N.A.I.C.S.: 522320

BIRCH BRANCH ACQUISITION CORP.
c/o Henan Shuncheng Group Coal Coke Co Ltd New Building, Cai Cun Road Intersection, Anyang, 455141, Henan, China
Tel.: (86) 372 323 7890
Year Founded: 1989
Sales Range: $350-399.9 Million
Emp.: 1,625
Coke & Refined Coal Mfr
N.A.I.C.S.: 331110
Xinshun Wang *(Chm)*

BIRCH HILL EQUITY PARTNERS MANAGEMENT INC.
100 Wellington Street Suite 2300 West TD West Tower, PO Box 22, Toronto, M5K 1A1, ON, Canada
Tel.: (416) 775-3800
Web Site:
http://www.birchhillequity.com
Rev.: $3,000,000,000
Emp.: 34,000
Privater Equity Firm
N.A.I.C.S.: 523999
Peter Zissis *(CFO)*

Subsidiaries:

Citron Hygiene Ltd **(1)**
555 Alden Road, Markham, L3R 3L5, ON, Canada
Tel.: (905) 946-1711
Web Site: http://www.citronhygiene.com
Janitorial Services
N.A.I.C.S.: 561720
Phil Mason *(CEO)*

Cozzini Bros., Inc. **(1)**
350 Howard Ave, Des Plaines, IL 60018
Tel.: (224) 217-6100
Web Site: http://www.cozzinibros.com
Commercial Cutlery Sharpening Services
N.A.I.C.S.: 811490
Edward Finnegan *(Chm)*

Subsidiary (Domestic):

Ambrosi Cutlery Ltd. **(2)**
55 Fields Ln, North Salem, NY 10560
Tel.: (914) 617-8444
Web Site: http://www.ambrosicutlery.com
Leading Cutlery & Sharpening Services Company
N.A.I.C.S.: 332215

Diamond Sharp Services, Inc. **(2)**
513 Mercury Ln, Brea, CA 92821
Tel.: (714) 990-9402
Web Site: http://www.diamondsharp.net
Sales Range: $1-9.9 Million
Emp.: 20
Consumer Goods Rental
N.A.I.C.S.: 532289
Bryan Hampton *(Pres)*

ERCO Worldwide, Inc. **(1)**
335 Carlingview Drive Unit 1, Etobicoke,

M9W 5G8, ON, Canada
Tel.: (416) 239-7111
Web Site: http://www.ercoworldwide.com
Sales Range: $100-124.9 Million
Sodium Chlorate & Sodium Chlorite Mfr;
Chlorine Dioxide Generation Systems Supplier
N.A.I.C.S.: 325998

Subsidiary (US):

ERCO Worldwide **(2)**
5700 Hunt Rd, Valdosta, GA 31606
Tel.: (229) 244-6780
Organic Chemical Mfr
N.A.I.C.S.: 325199

ERCO Worldwide (USA) Inc. **(2)**
101 Hwy 73 S, Nekoosa, WI 54457
Tel.: (715) 887-4000
Organic Chemical Mfr
N.A.I.C.S.: 325199

HomeQ Corporation **(1)**
1881 Yonge St Ste 300, Toronto, M4V 1K9, ON, Canada
Tel.: (416) 925-4757
Web Site: http://www.homeq.ca
Mortgage Administration Services
N.A.I.C.S.: 522310
Steven K. Ranson *(Pres & CEO)*

Park Lawn Corporation **(1)**
2 St Clair Ave E Suite 705, Toronto, M4T 2T5, ON, Canada
Tel.: (416) 231-1462
Web Site: https://www.parklawncorp.com
Rev.: $289,083,933
Assets: $1,394,782,625
Liabilities: $859,191,176
Net Worth: $535,591,450
Earnings: $241,829,198
Fiscal Year-end: 12/31/2021
Funeral Services
N.A.I.C.S.: 812210
Jim Price *(Sr VP-Industry Rels)*

Subsidiary (US):

Callaway Jones Funeral Home **(2)**
3001 S College Ave, Bryan, TX 77801-2512
Tel.: (979) 822-3717
Web Site: http://www.callawayjones.com
Funeral Homes & Funeral Services
N.A.I.C.S.: 812210
Cody Jones *(Owner)*

Christy Smith Funeral Homes, Inc. **(2)**
1801 Morningside Ave, Sioux City, IA 51106-2402
Tel.: (712) 276-7319
Web Site: http://www.christysmith.com
Sales Range: $1-9.9 Million
Emp.: 10
Funeral Homes & Funeral Services
N.A.I.C.S.: 812210

Farris Funeral Service, Inc. **(2)**
427 E Main, Abingdon, VA 24210-3407
Tel.: (276) 628-3394
Web Site:
http://www.farrisfuneralservice.com
Funeral Homes & Funeral Services
N.A.I.C.S.: 812210

Integrity Funeral Care **(2)**
3915 Dacoma St Ste E, Houston, TX 77092
Tel.: (713) 344-0764
Web Site: https://www.integrityfuneral.com
Funeral Homes & Funeral Services
N.A.I.C.S.: 812210
David Pena *(Founder & Pres)*

Memorial Park Cemetery Association of Missouri, Inc. **(2)**
8251 Hillcrest Rd, Kansas City, MO 64138
Tel.: (816) 523-2053
Web Site: http://www.parklawnfunerals.com
Sales Range: $1-9.9 Million
Emp.: 25
Funeral Homes & Funeral Services
N.A.I.C.S.: 812210
Henry W. De Vry *(Pres)*

Speaks Chapels LLC **(2)**
1501 W Lexington Ave, Independence, MO 64052
Tel.: (816) 252-7900
Web Site: http://www.speakschapel.com

Sales Range: $1-9.9 Million
Emp.: 40
Funeral Homes & Funeral Services
N.A.I.C.S.: 812210
Robert Speaks *(Chm)*

The Baue Funeral Home Co. **(2)**
620 Jefferson St, Saint Charles, MO 63301-4419
Tel.: (636) 940-1000
Web Site: http://www.baue.com
Funeral Services
N.A.I.C.S.: 812210
Lisa Bowley *(Pres & CEO)*

WFH, Inc **(2)**
3715 Asheville Highway, Canton, NC 28716
Tel.: (828) 648-2371
Web Site: http://www.wellsfuneralhome.com
Funeral Homes & Funeral Services
N.A.I.C.S.: 812210
J. Wells Greeley *(Dir-Emeritus and Funeral Service)*

Revolution Environmental Solutions Acquisition GP Inc. **(1)**
1100 Burloak Drive Suite 500, Burlington, L7L 6B2, ON, Canada
Tel.: (905) 561-0305
Web Site: http://www.terrapureenv.com
Industry-Focused Environmental Consulting & Support Services
N.A.I.C.S.: 561499

Sleep Country Canada Income Fund **(1)**
140 Wendell Ave Unit 2, Toronto, M9N 3R2, ON, Canada
Tel.: (416) 242-4774
Web Site: http://www.sleepcountry.ca
Sales Range: $350-399.9 Million
Emp.: 900
Holding Company; Owned by Birch Hill Equity Partners Management Inc. & Westerkirk Capital Inc.
N.A.I.C.S.: 551112
Christine A. Magee *(Pres)*

Softchoice Corporation **(1)**
20 Mowat Avenue, Toronto, M6K 3E8, ON, Canada
Tel.: (416) 588-9000
Web Site: http://www.softchoice.com
Sales Range: $1-4.9 Billion
Information Technology Products & Services
N.A.I.C.S.: 541512
Vince De Palma *(CEO)*

Sport Maska Inc. **(1)**
3400 Raymond-Lasnier Street, Montreal, H4R 3L3, QC, Canada
Tel.: (800) 644-1677
Web Site: http://www.ccmhockey.com
Sporting & Athletic Goods Mfr & Distr
N.A.I.C.S.: 339920

BIRCHCLIFF ENERGY LTD
Suite 1000 600 - 3rd Avenue S W, Calgary, T2P 0G5, AB, Canada
Tel.: (403) 261-6401
Web Site:
https://www.birchcliffenergy.com
BIR—(OTCIQ)
Rev.: $736,774,772
Assets: $2,315,522,985
Liabilities: $815,420,510
Net Worth: $1,500,102,475
Earnings: $246,164,741
Emp.: 204
Fiscal Year-end: 12/31/21
Oil & Gas Developer & Producer
N.A.I.C.S.: 213112
A. Jeffery Tonken *(Chm, Pres & CEO)*

BIRCHLAND PLYWOOD-VENEER LIMITED
Hwy 17, PO Box 430, Thessalon, P0R 1L0, ON, Canada
Tel.: (705) 842-2430
Web Site:
http://www.birchlandplywood.com
Year Founded: 1958
Rev.: $10,626,605
Emp.: 85

Hardwood Plywood Distr
N.A.I.C.S.: 423310
Lou Vanoyen *(VP-Ops)*

BIRCHTREE INVESTMENTS LTD.
1133 Melville St Suite 2700, Vancouver, V6E 4E5, BC, Canada
Tel.: (416) 369-5265
Year Founded: 2021
BRCH—(CNSX)
Rev.: $44,838
Assets: $1,652,461
Liabilities: $89,568
Net Worth: $1,562,892
Earnings: ($623,562)
Fiscal Year-end: 08/31/23
Investment Management Service
N.A.I.C.S.: 523999

BIRD & BIRD LLP
15 Fetter Lane, London, EC4A 1JP, United Kingdom
Tel.: (44) 20 7415 6000
Web Site: http://www.twobirds.com
Year Founded: 1846
Emp.: 698
Law firm
N.A.I.C.S.: 541110
Chris Barrett *(Partner)*

BIRD CONSTRUCTION INC.
5700 Explorer Drive Suite 400, Mississauga, L4W 0C6, ON, Canada
Tel.: (905) 602-4122
Web Site: https://www.bird.ca
Year Founded: 1920
BDT—(TSX)
Rev.: $1,176,887,065
Assets: $830,621,775
Liabilities: $664,301,224
Net Worth: $166,320,551
Earnings: $28,242,655
Emp.: 1,509
Fiscal Year-end: 12/31/20
Construction Services
N.A.I.C.S.: 236220
Paul R. Raboud *(Co-Chm)*

Subsidiaries:

BFL Fabricators Ltd. **(1)**
706-25 Ave, Nisku, T9E 0C2, AB, Canada
Tel.: (780) 955-3465
Web Site: https://www.bflfabricators.ca
Steel Product Distr
N.A.I.C.S.: 423510

Canadian Consulting Group Limited **(1)**
102 17007 107 Avenue, Edmonton, T5S 1G3, AB, Canada
Tel.: (780) 470-7126
Web Site:
https://canadianconsultinggroup.com
Sewage Treatment Facility Services
N.A.I.C.S.: 221320

Nason Contracting Group Ltd. **(1)**
Suite 205 18304 105 Ave NW, Edmonton, T5S 0C6, AB, Canada
Tel.: (780) 229-3502
Web Site: http://www.nason.ca
Construction Engineering Services
N.A.I.C.S.: 541330
Marian Bratu *(Specialist-Water & Wastewater Automation)*

Stuart Olson Inc. **(1)**
600 4820 Richard Road SW, Calgary, T3E 6L1, AB, Canada
Tel.: (780) 481-9600
Web Site: https://www.stuartolson.com
Sales Range: $700-749.9 Million
Emp.: 5,000
Commercial & Industrial Construction Services
N.A.I.C.S.: 236220
David LeMay *(Pres & CEO)*

Subsidiary (Domestic):

Broda Construction Inc. **(2)**

4271 5th Avenue East, PO Box 5800, Prince Albert, S6V 7V6, SK, Canada
Tel.: (306) 764-5337
Web Site: http://www.brodagroup.com
Sales Range: $50-74.9 Million
Emp.: 150
Construction Engineering Services
N.A.I.C.S.: 237990

Canem Holdings Ltd.　　　　　**(2)**
Business Bldg, Richmond, V6V 2X7, BC, Canada
Tel.: (604) 214-8650
Emp.: 20
Investment Management Service
N.A.I.C.S.: 523999
Al Miller *(Pres)*

Fuller Austin Inc.　　　　　　　**(2)**
15505-137 Avenue, Edmonton, T5V 1R9, AB, Canada　　　　　　　**(100%)**
Tel.: (780) 481-9600
Web Site: http://www.fulleraustin.com
Sales Range: $25-49.9 Million
Emp.: 30
Insulation Services
N.A.I.C.S.: 238310

Insulation Holdings Inc.　　　　　**(2)**
11825-149 St, Edmonton, T5L 2J1, AB, Canada
Tel.: (780) 481-9600
Web Site:
　http://www.churchillcorporation.com
Construction Engineering Services
N.A.I.C.S.: 236210

Kam-Crete Ltd.　　　　　　　　**(2)**
529 Park St West, Kamsack, S0A 1S0, SK, Canada
Tel.: (306) 542-2060
Web Site: http://www.brodaconstruction.com
Sales Range: $25-49.9 Million
Emp.: 15
Precast Concrete Products Mfr
N.A.I.C.S.: 327390

Laird Electric Inc.　　　　　　　**(2)**
15505-137 Avenue, Edmonton, T5V 1R9, AB, Canada
Tel.: (780) 481-9600
Web Site: http://www.lairdelectric.com
Electrical Contractor
N.A.I.C.S.: 238210

Northern Industrial Insulation Contractors, Inc.　　　　　　　　**(2)**
15505-137 Avenue, Edmonton, T5V 1R9, AB, Canada　　　　　　　**(100%)**
Tel.: (780) 481-9600
Web Site: http://www.northern-insulation.ca
Sales Range: $50-74.9 Million
Emp.: 150
Provider of Commercial & Industrial Construction Services
N.A.I.C.S.: 236220

Stuart Olson Dominion Construction Ltd.　　　　　　　　　　**(2)**
Ste 400 4954 Richard Rd SW, Calgary, T3E 6L1, AB, Canada　　　**(100%)**
Tel.: (403) 520-2767
Web Site: http://www.sodcl.com
Sales Range: $25-49.9 Million
Emp.: 60
Commercial & Industrial Construction Services
N.A.I.C.S.: 236220

BIRD PACKAGING LIMITED
670 Southgate Dr, PO Box 1506, Guelph, N1H 6N9, ON, Canada
Tel.: (519) 836-3470
Web Site:
　http://www.birdpackaging.com
Year Founded: 1975
Rev.: $27,200,000
Emp.: 170
Packaging Materials & Corrugated Boxes Mfr
N.A.I.C.S.: 322211
Mike Dienst *(Pres & Gen Mgr)*

BIRD RIVER RESOURCES INC.
5204 Roblin Blvd, Winnipeg, R3R 0H1, MB, Canada
Tel.: (587) 896-7020　　　　MB

Web Site: https://www.birdriver.net
Year Founded: 1958
BDR—(CNSX)
Assets: $112,227
Liabilities: $66,395
Net Worth: $45,831
Earnings: ($417,602)
Fiscal Year-end: 07/31/23
Precious Metals, Base Metals & Industrial Minerals Mining & Exploration Services
N.A.I.C.S.: 212220
Edward Thompson *(Treas & Sec)*

BIRDDOG TECHNOLOGY LIMITED
Level 21 459 Collins Street, Melbourne, 3000, VIC, Australia
Tel.: (61) 386303321　　　　AU
Web Site: https://www.birddog.tv
Year Founded: 2016
BDT—(ASX)
Rev.: $29,677,603
Assets: $38,447,414
Liabilities: $3,333,693
Net Worth: $35,113,722
Earnings: ($1,562,261)
Fiscal Year-end: 06/30/22
Software Development Services
N.A.I.C.S.: 541511
Barry Calnon *(CFO)*

BIRDHI CHAND PANNALAL AGENCIES LIMITED
27 Biplabi Trailokya Maharaj Sarani Narayani Building 7th Floor, Room No-703, Kolkata, 700001, West Bengal, India
Tel.: (91) 33 32978096
Web Site: http://www.birdhichand.in
Year Founded: 1985
Sales Range: Less than $1 Million
Security Brokerage Services
N.A.I.C.S.: 523150
Aindrila Banerjee *(Mng Dir & CFO)*

BIRDIE WIN CORPORATION
D109 Level 1 Block D Kelana Square Jalan SS 7/26, 47301, Petaling Jaya, Selangor, Malaysia
Tel.: (60) 327764841　　　NV
Web Site: https://ethin31.wixsite.com
Year Founded: 2021
BRWC—(OTCIQ)
Rev.: $25,000
Assets: $12,894
Liabilities: $13,190
Net Worth: ($296)
Earnings: ($24,082)
Emp.: 1
Fiscal Year-end: 07/31/24
Financial Investment Services
N.A.I.C.S.: 523999
Zonghan Wu *(Chm, Pres, CEO, Treas & Sec)*

BIRDMAN, INC.
1-5-3 Shoto, Shibuya-Ku, Tokyo, 150-0046, Japan
Tel.: (81) 368651320
Web Site: https://birdman.tokyo
Year Founded: 2012
7063—(TKS)
Rev.: $29,626,693
Assets: $19,240,172
Liabilities: $15,857,284
Net Worth: $3,382,887
Earnings: ($46,250)
Fiscal Year-end: 06/30/23
Digital Marketing Services
N.A.I.C.S.: 541870
Akihiro Date *(Founder, Chm, Pres & CEO)*

BIRIKIM VARLIK YONETIM A.S.

Buyukdere Cad ozsezen Is Merkezi A Blok No 122 Kat 5 Esentepe, Sisli, 34394, Istanbul, Turkiye
Tel.: (90) 2123551900
Web Site:
　https://www.birikimvarlik.com.tr
BRKVY—(IST)
Sales Range: Less than $1 Million
Asset Management Services
N.A.I.C.S.: 531390
Inan Altinbas *(Chm)*

BIRKENSTOCK HOLDING PLC.
1-2 Berkeley Square, London, W1J 6EA, United Kingdom
Tel.: (44) 1534835600　　　JE
Web Site: https://www.birkenstock-holding.com
Year Founded: 2021
BIRK—(NYSE)
Rev.: $2,412,690,061
Assets: $6,530,674,949
Liabilities: $3,021,287,048
Net Worth: $3,509,387,901
Earnings: $256,152,714
Emp.: 6,200
Fiscal Year-end: 09/30/24
Holding Company
N.A.I.C.S.: 551112
Erik Massmann *(CFO)*

BIRKO BIRLESIK KOYUNLU-LULAR MENSUCATTICARET VE SANAYI AS
Sancak Mah 1 Cad No 8/2, Cankaya, Ankara, 06550, Turkiye
Tel.: (90) 2162180092
Web Site: http://www.birko.com.tr
BRKO—(IST)
Rev.: $1,527,555
Assets: $29,042,313
Liabilities: $2,396,135
Net Worth: $26,646,178
Earnings: ($10,121,934)
Fiscal Year-end: 12/31/23
Textile Products Mfr
N.A.I.C.S.: 314999
Izzet Okaline *(Chm)*

BIRKS GROUP INC.
2020 Robert Bourassa Blvd Suite 200, Montreal, H3A 2A5, QC, Canada
Tel.: (514) 397-2501　　　　Ca
Web Site:
　https://www.birksgroup.com
Year Founded: 1879
BGI—(NYSEAMEX)
Rev.: $185,275,000
Assets: $203,268,000
Liabilities: $208,417,000
Net Worth: ($5,149,000)
Earnings: ($4,631,000)
Emp.: 290
Fiscal Year-end: 03/31/24
Silverware & Jewelry Retailer & Mfr
N.A.I.C.S.: 339910
Miranda Melfi *(Chief Legal Officer, Sec & VP-HR)*

BIRLA CORPORATION LTD.
Birla Building 3rd and 4th Floors 9/1 R N Mukherjee Road, Kolkata, 700 001, India
Tel.: (91) 3366166745
Web Site:
　https://www.birlacorporation.com
500335—(BOM)
Rev.: $939,851,640
Assets: $1,760,248,035
Liabilities: $1,011,404,940
Net Worth: $748,843,095
Earnings: $86,014,110
Emp.: 7,212
Fiscal Year-end: 03/31/21
Cement Mfr
N.A.I.C.S.: 325520

Aditya Saraogi *(CFO)*

Subsidiaries:

Birla Cable Ltd.　　　　　　　**(1)**
Udyog Vihar, PO Chorhata, Chorhata, Rewa, 486006, Madhya Pradesh, India
Tel.: (91) 7662400580
Web Site: https://www.birlacable.com
Rev.: $95,523,230
Assets: $55,239,746
Liabilities: $27,733,481
Net Worth: $27,506,265
Earnings: $3,949,392
Emp.: 285
Fiscal Year-end: 03/31/2023
Fiber Optic Cable Mfr
N.A.I.C.S.: 335921
Somesh Laddha *(Officer-Compliance, Sec & Gen Mgr-Accts)*

Birla Corporation Ltd. - AutoTrim Division I　　　　　　　　　　**(1)**
24 Parganas S, Birlapur, 743 318, West Bengal, India
Tel.: (91) 3324209821
Automotive Interiors Mfr
N.A.I.C.S.: 336360

Birla Corporation Ltd. - Durgapur Cement Works　　　　　　　**(1)**
Near DSP Slag Bank, Paschim Bardhaman, 713 203, West Bengal, India
Tel.: (91) 7477799614
Sales Range: $125-149.9 Million
Emp.: 400
Cement Mfr
N.A.I.C.S.: 327310

Birla Corporation Ltd. - Jute Division　　　　　　　　　　**(1)**
9 1 R N Mukherjee Rd, Kolkata, 700 001, West Bengal, India
Tel.: (91) 33 2213 0380
Sales Range: $75-99.9 Million
Emp.: 250
Cement & Jute Mfr
N.A.I.C.S.: 327310

Birla Corporation Ltd. - Raebareli Cement Works　　　　　　**(1)**
Plot No D/9 to D/15 UPSIDC Industrial Area Phase II Amawan Road, Rae Bareli, 229 001, Uttar Pradesh, India
Tel.: (91) 7052049444
Cement Mfr
N.A.I.C.S.: 327310

Birla Corporation Ltd. - Satna Cement Works　　　　　　　　**(1)**
PO Birla Vikas, Satna, 485 005, Madhya Pradesh, India
Tel.: (91) 7672412000
Cement Mfr
N.A.I.C.S.: 327310

Birla Corporation Ltd. - Vindhyachal Steel Foundry　　　　　　**(1)**
PO Birla Vikas, Satna, 485 005, Madhya Pradesh, India
Tel.: (91) 7672412000
Cement Plant Castings Mfr
N.A.I.C.S.: 331511

Birla Vikas Cement　　　　　　**(1)**
PO Birla Vikas, Satna, 485 005, Madhya Pradesh, India
Tel.: (91) 7672412000
Sales Range: $450-499.9 Million
Emp.: 1,501
Cement Mfr
N.A.I.C.S.: 327310
Bhaskar Bhattacharya *(Pres)*

Budge Budge Floorcoverings Limited　　　　　　　　　　**(1)**
9 1 R N Mukherjee Rd, Kolkata, 700001, West Bengal, India
Tel.: (91) 3322489101
Floor Covering Mfr
N.A.I.C.S.: 238330

BIRLA SUN LIFE INSURANCE COMPANY LIMITED
2nd Floor Ahura Center Mahakali Caves Road, Near MIDC Andheri-East, 400093, Mumbai, India
Tel.: (91) 2228307081

Birla Sun Life Insurance Company
Limited—(Continued)

Web Site: http://www.birlasunlife.com
Financial Services
N.A.I.C.S.: 523999

BIRLA TYRES LIMITED

9/1 R N Mukherjee Road Birla Build-
ing 0th Floor, Kolkata, 700 001, West
Bengal, India
Tel.: (91) 3322624355   In
Web Site: https://www.birlatyre.com
Year Founded: 1991
542932—(BOM)
Rev.: $3,063,442
Assets: $137,548,921
Liabilities: $304,265,748
Net Worth: ($166,716,828)
Earnings: ($89,499,010)
Emp.: 1,373
Fiscal Year-end: 03/31/22
Tire Mfr & Whslr
N.A.I.C.S.: 326211
Manjushree Khaitan *(Chm)*

BIRLASOFT LTD.

Plot No 35 & 36 Midc Phase I Rajiv
Gandhi Infotech Park, Hinjawadi,
Pune, 411 057, India
Tel.: (91) 2066525000
Web Site: https://www.birlasoft.com
Year Founded: 1990
532400—(BOM)
Rev.: $572,829,348
Assets: $461,826,047
Liabilities: $109,239,722
Net Worth: $352,586,325
Earnings: $63,286,587
Emp.: 10,122
Fiscal Year-end: 03/30/22
Software Development Services
N.A.I.C.S.: 541511
Dharmender Kapoor *(CEO & Mng
Dir)*

Subsidiaries:

Birlasoft Solutions France SAS   **(1)**
19 Boulevard Malesherbes, 75008, Paris,
France
Tel.: (33) 147178190
Information Technology Services
N.A.I.C.S.: 541511

Birlasoft Solutions GmbH   **(1)**
Meisenstr 96, 33607, Bielefeld, Germany
Tel.: (49) 5213056650
Information Technology Services
N.A.I.C.S.: 541511

Birlasoft Solutions Limited   **(1)**
4th Floor 53-54 Grosvenor Street, London,
W1K 3HU, United Kingdom
Tel.: (44) 2073195700
Information Technology Services
N.A.I.C.S.: 541511

Birlasoft Solutions Ltda.   **(1)**
Alameda Santos 1165 - 10 Andar, Cer-
queira Cesar, Sao Paulo, 01419-002, Brazil
Tel.: (55) 1140813010
Information Technology Services
N.A.I.C.S.: 541511

Birlasoft Solutions ME FZE   **(1)**
West Wing 2 Office 2W113, PO Box 54931,
Dubai Airport Free Zone Area, Dubai,
United Arab Emirates
Tel.: (971) 42998842
Information Technology Services
N.A.I.C.S.: 541511

BIRLIK MENSUCAT TICARET VE SANAYI ISLETMESI A.S.

Osman Kavuncu Mah Mensucat Cad
No 22, Melikgazi, Kayseri, Turkiye
Tel.: (90) 3523221270
Web Site:
   https://www.birlikmensucat.com.tr
Year Founded: 1953
BRMEN—(IST)
Rev.: $1,111,083

Assets: $2,023,080
Liabilities: $1,251,431
Net Worth: $771,649
Earnings: ($133,947)
Fiscal Year-end: 12/31/23
Cotton Yarn Mfr
N.A.I.C.S.: 313110
Yasar Kucukcalik *(Chm)*

BIRMAN WOOD & HARDWARE LTD.

A T Galil front Galil bottom P O 102,
Tiberias, 14100, Israel
Tel.: (972) 46768000
Web Site: https://www.birman.co.il
Year Founded: 1932
BIRM—(TAE)
Rev.: $101,513,743
Assets: $113,142,974
Liabilities: $86,404,751
Net Worth: $26,738,223
Earnings: ($1,012,571)
Emp.: 270
Fiscal Year-end: 12/31/23
All Other Miscellaneous Wood Prod-
uct Manufacturing
N.A.I.C.S.: 321999

BIRMINGHAM SPORTS HOLDINGS LIMITED

31/F Vertical Sq No 28 Heung Yip
Road, Wong Chuk Hang, Hong Kong,
China (Hong Kong)
Tel.: (852) 25482928   Ky
2309—(HKG)
Rev.: $28,496,712
Assets: $131,276,360
Liabilities: $102,537,939
Net Worth: $28,738,421
Earnings: $13,899,788
Emp.: 270
Fiscal Year-end: 06/30/22
Investment Holding Company
N.A.I.C.S.: 551112
Wenqing Zhao *(Chm)*

Subsidiaries:

Birmingham City Football Club
plc   **(1)**
St Andrew's Trillion Trophy Stadium, Bir-
mingham, B9 4RL, Midlands, United King-
dom
Tel.: (44) 1217720101
Web Site: http://www.bcfc.com
Sales Range: $50-74.9 Million
Emp.: 250
Fiscal Year-end: 12/31/2014
Football Team Operations
N.A.I.C.S.: 711211
Garry Monk *(Mgr-First Team)*

Medi Hub Co., Ltd.   **(1)**
7F 4-chome-7-3 Ayase, Adachi, Tokyo, 120-
0005, Japan
Tel.: (81) 358495886
Web Site: https://www.aimmeditech.co.jp
Medical Tourism Agency Operator
N.A.I.C.S.: 621491

BIRN SERBIA

Kosovska 17, 11000, Belgrade, Ser-
bia
Tel.: (381) 114030316
Web Site: https://www.birn.eu.com
Year Founded: 2004
Investigation Services
N.A.I.C.S.: 561611

BIRZEIT PHARMACEUTICAL COMPANY

Betunia Industrial Area 20 Shatella
Street, PO Box 79, Ramallah, Pales-
tine
Tel.: (970) 22987573
Web Site: https://www.bpc.ps
Year Founded: 1974
BPC—(PAL)
Rev.: $43,126,283

Assets: $125,146,969
Liabilities: $20,122,207
Net Worth: $105,024,762
Earnings: $6,153,724
Emp.: 370
Fiscal Year-end: 12/31/23
Generic Medicine Mfr
N.A.I.C.S.: 325412
Talal Kathem Abdullah Nasereddin
*(Chm, Chm, CEO, Gen Mgr & Gen
Mgr)*

BISALLOY STEEL GROUP LTD.

18 Resolution Drive, PO Box 1246,
Unanderra, 2526, NSW, Australia
Tel.: (61) 42720400   AU
Web Site:
   https://www.bisalloy.com.au
BIS—(ASX)
Rev.: $102,068,643
Assets: $79,176,682
Liabilities: $27,584,135
Net Worth: $51,592,548
Earnings: $10,828,659
Fiscal Year-end: 06/30/24
Distribution Of Metal Products
N.A.I.C.S.: 331221
Willy Pang *(Mgr-Technical-Armour)*

Subsidiaries:

Bisalloy (Thailand) Co Limited   **(1)**
16th Floor Bangna Complex Office Tower
2/81 Soi Bangna Trad 25, Bangna, Bang-
kok, 10260, Thailand
Tel.: (66) 2 744 1913
Web Site: https://www.bisalloy-thailand.com
Sales Range: $25-49.9 Million
Emp.: 22
Steels & Metals Distr
N.A.I.C.S.: 423510

Bisalloy Steels Pty Limited   **(1)**
18 Resolution Drive, PO Box 1246,
Unanderra, 2526, NSW, Australia
Tel.: (61) 242720444
Web Site: http://www.bisalloy.com.au
Sales Range: $25-49.9 Million
Steel Plate Mfr
N.A.I.C.S.: 331221
Shane Gleeson *(Grp Gen Mgr-Sls & Mktg)*

Subsidiary (Non-US):

P.T. Bima Bisalloy   **(2)**
MM2100 Industrial Town Jl Sumbawa Kav
C7 No 1 Desa Mekarwangi, Kecamatan
Cikarang Barat - Kabupaten, Bekasi,
17520, West Java, Indonesia
Tel.: (62) 218 998 1540
Web Site: https://bimabisalloy.com
Sales Range: $25-49.9 Million
Emp.: 25
Steel Plate Mfr
N.A.I.C.S.: 331221

BISCA MATERIAUX SARL

Zone Commerciale de Pastebuch,
40600, Biscarrosse, France
Tel.: (33) 5 58 83 10 40
Building Materials Whslr
N.A.I.C.S.: 444180
Joel Villenave *(Mng Dir)*

Subsidiaries:

Valdeyron Materiaux SAS   **(1)**
443 Rue Emile Zola, 30600, Vauvert, Gard,
France
Tel.: (33) 466882160
Web Site: http://www.valdeyron-
materiaux.com
Construction Materials Dealer
N.A.I.C.S.: 444180

BISCHOF + KLEIN GMBH & CO. KG

Rahestrasse 47, 49525, Lengerich,
Germany
Tel.: (49) 54819200
Web Site: http://www.bk-
international.com

Year Founded: 1922
Sales Range: $500-549.9 Million
Emp.: 1,300
Flexible Plastic & Paper Packaging
Mfr & Distr
N.A.I.C.S.: 322220
Volker Pfennig *(Member-Exec Bd)*

Subsidiaries:

B+K BETEILIGUNGEN GMBH   **(1)**
Str Rahova nr 12 ap 27 11 Florin Margin-
ean, 550340, Sibiu, Romania
Tel.: (40) 371 075385
Packaging Material Distr
N.A.I.C.S.: 423840

B+K POLSKA GMBH SP.K.   **(1)**
Eichendorffa 3, 47-344, Walce, Poland
Tel.: (48) 77 4076 310
Web Site: http://www.bk-international.com
Emp.: 180
Packaging Material Distr
N.A.I.C.S.: 423840
Ginter Miecer *(Gen Mgr)*

BERKEMPLAST SAN. VE TIC. LTD.
STI.   **(1)**
Yenidogan Mah Akin Cad 39, Sancaktepe,
34791, Istanbul, Turkiye
Tel.: (90) 216 429 99 91
Web Site: http://www.berkemplast.com
Protective Film Mfr
N.A.I.C.S.: 326113
Semiha Berkem *(Mgr-Import & Export)*

BISCHOF + KLEIN (SHANGHAI)
TRADING CO. LTD.   **(1)**
XiZang Middle Road 168, 25/F The Head-
quarters Building, 200001, Shanghai, China
Tel.: (86) 21 51798313
Packaging Material Distr
N.A.I.C.S.: 423840

BISCHOF + KLEIN ASIA PTE.
LTD.   **(1)**
Henderson Road 205 02-01, 159549, Sin-
gapore, Singapore
Tel.: (65) 63 777555
Packaging Material Distr
N.A.I.C.S.: 423840
Jack Ho *(Gen Mgr)*

BISCHOF + KLEIN FRANCE
SAS   **(1)**
rue des Papetiers 15, PO Box 232, 27500,
Pont Audemer, France
Tel.: (33) 2 32 56 79 14
Web Site: http://www.bk-international.com
Packaging Material Distr
N.A.I.C.S.: 423840

BISCHOF + KLEIN MIDDLE EAST
CO.   **(1)**
PO Box 1176, 31952, Al Khobar, Saudi
Arabia
Tel.: (966) 3 8124443
Packaging Material Distr
N.A.I.C.S.: 423840

Bischof & Klein (U.K.) Ltd.   **(1)**
Hortonwood 2, Telford, TF1 7XX, Shrop-
shire, United Kingdom   **(100%)**
Tel.: (44) 1952606848
Web Site: http://www.bk-international.co.uk
Sales Range: $50-74.9 Million
Emp.: 150
Plastic Flexible Packaging Materials Mfr
N.A.I.C.S.: 326199
Niall Keating *(Dir-Sls)*

MARKET QUEST, INC.   **(1)**
Anderson St 2, Monmouth Beach, NJ
07750
Tel.: (732) 229-8127
Packaging Material Distr
N.A.I.C.S.: 423840

MODCHEM LTD. AGENCIES   **(1)**
Mobile Post, Misgav, 20182, Hararit, Israel
Tel.: (972) 4 67827 77
Web Site: http://www.modchem.com
Packaging Material Distr
N.A.I.C.S.: 423840
Nachum Paran *(Gen Mgr)*

PROSIM KIMYA SANAYI VE TI-
CARET LTD. STI.   **(1)**
Kaleagasi Sokak No 5B 34470 Rumeli-

hisari, Sariyer, Istanbul, Türkiye
Tel.: (90) 212 263 78 21
Web Site: http://www.prosim.com.tr
Emp.: 20
Chemical Products Distr
N.A.I.C.S.: 424690
Gozde Sasmaz (Engr-Sls)

SOBRA D.O.O. (1)
Banatska 29, 10040, Zagreb, Croatia
Tel.: (385) 1 2910060
Packaging Material Distr
N.A.I.C.S.: 423840

STARMER PACKAGING PTY. LTD. (1)
Gilda Street 29, PO Box 63 25, North Ryde, 2113, NSW, Australia
Tel.: (61) 2 94823986
Packaging Material Distr
N.A.I.C.S.: 423840

STEFAN TAGESSON (1)
Hokhult 34 93, 28792, Traryd, Sweden
Tel.: (46) 433 26050
Packaging Material Distr
N.A.I.C.S.: 423840

THE BOXBORO GROUP (1)
86 Davidson Rd, Boxboro, MA 01719
Tel.: (617) 970-2959
Web Site: http://www.boxborogroup.com
Protective Film Mfr
N.A.I.C.S.: 326130
John Mosher (Pres)

TREZOS & ASSOCIATES S.A. (1)
E Lampsa 1, 115 24, Athens, Greece
Tel.: (30) 210 6993700
Web Site: http://www.trezos.com
Emp.: 5
Industrial Equipment Distr
N.A.I.C.S.: 423830
Maro Trezou (Chm & Co-Mng Dir)

The Overby Group Inc. (1)
13807 Village Mill Dr Ste 201, Midlothian, VA 23114
Tel.: (804) 897-0110
Packaging Material Distr
N.A.I.C.S.: 423840

BISCUITS LECLERC LTD.
91 de Rotterdam Francois-Leclerc Industrial Park, Saint-Augustin-de-Desmaures, G3A 1T1, QC, Canada
Tel.: (418) 878-2601
Web Site: http://www.leclerc.ca
Year Founded: 1905
Rev.: $163,920,000
Emp.: 650
Cookie Mfr
N.A.I.C.S.: 311821
Jean-Robert Leclerc (Pres-Admin Counsel)

BISHRELT INDUSTRIAL JOINT STOCK COMPANY
Peace Avenue 48 Bishrelt Building, Ulaanbaatar, Mongolia
Tel.: (976) 11 314185
Apparels Mfr
N.A.I.C.S.: 315990

BISICHI PLC
12 Little Portland Street 2nd Floor, London, W1W 8BJ, United Kingdom
Tel.: (44) 2074155030
Web Site: https://www.bisichi.co.uk
BISI—(LSE)
Rev.: $40,466,845
Assets: $52,475,878
Liabilities: $30,495,749
Net Worth: $21,980,129
Earnings: ($5,151,190)
Emp.: 236
Fiscal Year-end: 12/31/20
Coal Mining
N.A.I.C.S.: 212115
Michael A. Heller (Chm)

BISIL PLAST LIMITED
Silver Oaks Commercial Complex

406, Opp Arun Society Paldi, Ahmedabad, 380007, Gujarat, India
Tel.: (91) 7926588065
Web Site: https://bisilplast.com
Year Founded: 1986
Assets: $138,155
Net Worth: $138,155
Earnings: ($12,759)
Plastic Beverage Bottle Mfr
N.A.I.C.S.: 326160
Khushbu Shah (Officer & Sec)

BISLEY & COMPANY PTY. LTD.
Level 12 Tower B Citadel Towers 799 Pacific Highway, Chatswood, 2067, NSW, Australia
Tel.: (61) 289054200
Web Site: http://www.bisley.biz
Year Founded: 1955
Industrial Chemical Distr
N.A.I.C.S.: 424690
Nick Granville (CEO)

BISON BANK, S.A
Rua Barata Salgueiro n 33 Floor 0, 1250-042, Lisbon, Portugal
Tel.: (351) 213816200
Web Site: http://www.bisonbank.com
Rev.: $2,953,917
Assets: $135,562,077
Liabilities: $59,687,551
Net Worth: $75,874,526
Earnings: ($8,557,148)
Emp.: 58
Fiscal Year-end: 12/31/20
Investment & Wealth Management Services
N.A.I.C.S.: 523150
Bian Fang (CEO)

BISON ENERGY SERVICES PLC
9a West Halkin Street, London, SW1X 8JL, United Kingdom
Tel.: (44) 20 7135 2250
Web Site: http://www.bison-energy.com
Oil Exploration
N.A.I.C.S.: 211120
Graham Dransfield (Chm)

BISTOS CO., LTD.
7th Fl A Bldg 302 Galmachi-ro, Jungwon-gu, Seongnam, 13201, Gyeonggi-do, Korea (South)
Tel.: (82) 317500340
Web Site: https://www.bistos.co.kr
Year Founded: 2001
419540—(KRS)
Medical Device Mfr
N.A.I.C.S.: 339112

BIT BROTHER LIMITED
Room 910 Building 1 Huitong Building No 168 Hehua Road, Hehuayuan Street Furong District, Changsha, Hunan, China
Tel.: (86) 73185133570   VG
Web Site: http://www.h-n-myt.com
BETS—(NASDAQ)
Rev.: $2,883,418
Assets: $32,264,250
Liabilities: $3,365,261
Net Worth: $28,898,989
Earnings: ($92,158,726)
Emp.: 106
Fiscal Year-end: 06/30/23
Holding Company; Chemical Mfr
N.A.I.C.S.: 551112
Xianlong Wu (Chm & CEO)

BIT COMPUTER CO., LTD.
33 Seocho-daero 74-gil Seocho-dong Beat Building, Seocho-gu, Seoul, 6621, Korea (South)

Tel.: (82) 234861234   KR
Web Site: https://www.bit.kr
Year Founded: 1983
032850—(KRS)
Rev.: $26,948,288
Assets: $56,976,094
Liabilities: $8,558,123
Net Worth: $48,417,971
Earnings: $3,777,523
Emp.: 119
Fiscal Year-end: 12/31/22
Software Developer
N.A.I.C.S.: 513210
Hyeon-jeong Jo (Founder, Chm & Co-CEO)

Subsidiaries:

BITNIX, Inc. (1)
118/75 Floor 3 Youngplace Building Soi Sukhumvit 23 Sukhumvit Rd, Klongtan Nue Wattana, Bangkok, 10110, Thailand
Tel.: (66) 26622767
Software Developer Services
N.A.I.C.S.: 513210

Goodgene Inc. (1)
11F Mario Digital Tower 222-12, Guro-dong Guro-gu, Seoul, 152-050, Korea (South)
Tel.: (82) 2208800558
Web Site: http://www.goodgene.co.kr
Diagnostic Services
N.A.I.C.S.: 621511

BIT MINING LTD.
14F West Side Block B Building No 7 Shenzhen Bay Eco-Technology Park, Nanshan District, Shenzhen, 518115, China
Tel.: (86) 75588352500   Ky
Web Site: http://www.500.com
BTCM—(NYSE)
Rev.: $43,101,000
Assets: $72,596,000
Liabilities: $47,464,000
Net Worth: $25,132,000
Earnings: ($28,710,000)
Emp.: 75
Fiscal Year-end: 12/31/23
Holding Company; Online Sports Lottery Services
N.A.I.C.S.: 551112
Bo Yu (COO)

BITAUTO HOLDINGS LIMITED
New Century Hotel Office Tower 10/F No 6 South Capital Stadium Road, Beijing, 100044, China
Tel.: (86) 1068492345   Ky
Web Site: http://www.bitauto.com
Year Founded: 2005
BITA—(NYSE)
Rev.: $1,538,742,423
Assets: $6,922,754,996
Liabilities: $4,151,511,306
Net Worth: $2,771,243,690
Earnings: ($171,736,886)
Emp.: 7,935
Fiscal Year-end: 12/31/19
Automotive Internet Content & Marketing Services
N.A.I.C.S.: 541613
William Bin Li (Founder & Chm)

BITBURGER BRAUGRUPPE GMBH
Roemermauer 3, Bitburg, 54634, Germany
Tel.: (49) 6561140
Web Site: http://www.bitburger-braugruppe.de
Year Founded: 1817
Sales Range: $100-124.9 Million
Emp.: 1,000
Brewery Operator Services
N.A.I.C.S.: 312120
Jan Niewodniczanski (Chm-Tech Production Parts)

Subsidiaries:

Bitburger Brauerei Th. Simon GmbH (1)
Romermauer 3, 54634, Bitburg, Germany (100%)
Tel.: (49) 6561 140
Web Site: http://www.bitburgerbrauerei.com
Alcoholic Beverage Brewing Services
N.A.I.C.S.: 312120

Kostritzer Schwarzbierbrauerei GmbH & Co. (1)
Hemrich Schuetz St 16, 7586, Bad Kostritz, Germany (100%)
Tel.: (49) 36605830
Web Site: http://www.koestritzer.de
Sales Range: $25-49.9 Million
Emp.: 150
Malt Beverages
N.A.I.C.S.: 312120

trinkkontor Bitburger Bier GmbH (1)
Getrankefachgrosshandel, Kirschbaumweg 19, 50996, Cologne, Germany
Tel.: (49) 223639060
Web Site: http://www.bitburgerbier.trinkkontor.de
Malt Beverages
N.A.I.C.S.: 312120
Thomas Nuhn (Mng Dir)

BITBURGER HOLDING GMBH
Römermauer 3, 54634, Bitburg, Germany
Tel.: (49) 0656114224
Web Site: https://www.bitburger-holding.de
Food & Beverage Service
N.A.I.C.S.: 722410

BITCOIN GROUP SE
Luisenstrasse 4, 32052, Herford, Germany
Tel.: (49) 52216943520
Web Site: https://www.bitcoingroup.com
Year Founded: 2008
ADE—(MUN)
Rev.: $8,554,992
Assets: $203,741,286
Liabilities: $51,506,574
Net Worth: $152,234,712
Earnings: $2,141,508
Emp.: 32
Fiscal Year-end: 12/31/23
Financial Investment Services
N.A.I.C.S.: 523910
Michael Nowak (Mng Dir)

Subsidiaries:

Futurum Bank AG (1)
Hochstrasse 35-37, 60313, Frankfurt am Main, Germany
Tel.: (49) 6994515980
Web Site: https://futurumbank.hanteras.com
Operation Commercial Bank Services
N.A.I.C.S.: 522110

BITDEFENDER S.R.L.
24 Delea Veche Street, Bucharest, 024102, Romania
Tel.: (40) 21 206 3470
Web Site: http://pan.bitdefender.com
Year Founded: 2001
Sales Range: $75-99.9 Million
Emp.: 300
Security Software Developer
N.A.I.C.S.: 513210
Florin Talpes (Founder & CEO)

Subsidiaries:

BitDefender LLC (1)
6301 Nw 5th Way, Fort Lauderdale, FL 33309
Tel.: (954) 776-6262
Sales Range: $25-49.9 Million
Emp.: 18
Security Software Developer
N.A.I.C.S.: 513210

BitDefender S.R.L.—(Continued)

BITEBACK PUBLISHING LTD.

Westminster Tower 3 Albert Embankment, London, SE1 7SP, United Kingdom
Tel.: (44) 20 7091 1260
Web Site:
http://www.bitebackpublishing.com
Emp.: 12
Publishing Services
N.A.I.C.S.: 513130

Subsidiaries:

Holyrood Communications Ltd.　　(1)
14-16 Holyrood Road, Edinburgh, EH8 8AF, United Kingdom
Tel.: (44) 131 2722113
Publishing Services
N.A.I.C.S.: 513120
Mandy Rhodes (Head-Ops)

BITEK PTY LTD.

6/8 Victoria Avenue, Castle Hill, NSW, Australia
Tel.: (61) 29) 659 2272
Web Site: http://www.bitek.com.au
Year Founded: 1998
Television Product Mfr
N.A.I.C.S.: 334220
George Vildos (Mgr-Sls-Natl)

BITFUFU INC.

111 North Bridge Road 15-01 Peninsula Plaza, Singapore, 179098, Singapore
Tel.: (65) 62524595　　　　　　**Ky**
Web Site: https://www.bitfufu.com
Year Founded: 2021
FUFU—(NASDAQ)
Rev.: $284,106,012
Assets: $210,032,651
Liabilities: $192,698,978
Net Worth: $17,333,673
Earnings: $10,494,462
Emp.: 29
Fiscal Year-end: 12/31/23
Digital Asset Mining Services
N.A.I.C.S.: 518210

BITHEADS, INC.

1309 Carling Ave, Ottawa, K1Z 7L3, ON, Canada
Tel.: (613) 722-3232
Web Site: http://www.bitheads.com
Sales Range: $10-24.9 Million
Emp.: 55
Software Development Services
N.A.I.C.S.: 541512
Scott Simpson (Co-Founder, Pres & CEO)

BITMIS CORP.

Unit No 5784 152 Chartered Square Building 212/19, Bangkok, 10500, Thailand
Tel.: (66) 7026050123　　　　　**NV**
Year Founded: 2016
BIMT—(OTCIQ)
Rev.: $463,000
Assets: $893,000
Liabilities: $3,909,000
Net Worth: ($3,016,000)
Earnings: ($1,095,000)
Emp.: 1
Fiscal Year-end: 06/30/23
Business Consulting Services
N.A.I.C.S.: 541611

BITROS HOLDING S.A.

100 Nato Avenue, 19300, Aspropyrgos, Attiki, Greece
Tel.: (30) 2105509450
Web Site: https://www.bitros.gr
Year Founded: 1945
MPITR—(ATH)
Sales Range: $150-199.9 Million

Emp.: 355
Steel & Real Estate Development Services
N.A.I.C.S.: 331110
Ioannis P. Bitros (CEO)

Subsidiaries:

BITROS CONSTRUCTION S.A.　(1)
100 Nato Ave, 193 00, Aspropyrgos, Greece
Tel.: (30) 2105509155
Residential Building Construction Services
N.A.I.C.S.: 236220

BITROS REBAR CENTER S.A.　(1)
100 Nato Avenue, Aspropyrgos, 193 00, Markopoulon, Greece
Tel.: (30) 2105509450
Sales Range: $50-74.9 Million
Emp.: 200
Steel Products Mfr
N.A.I.C.S.: 331110
Stavros Gatopoulos (CEO)

BITROS STEEL S.A.　　　　　　(1)
100 Nato Avenue, Aspropyrgos, 193 00, Athens, Greece
Tel.: (30) 2105509000
Steel Processing & Distr
N.A.I.C.S.: 331110
Ioannis P. Bitros (Mng Dir)

BITRUSH CORP.

100 King Street West 56th Floor, Toronto, M5X 1C9, ON, Canada
Tel.: (416) 847-1831
Year Founded: 1999
Investment Services
N.A.I.C.S.: 523999
Karsten Arend (CEO)

BITS LTD.

711 7th Floor New Delhi House 27, Barakhamba Road Cannaught Place, New Delhi, 110 001, India
Tel.: (91) 1143656567　　　　　**In**
Web Site: http://www.bits.net.in
Year Founded: 1992
Computer Education Services
N.A.I.C.S.: 611420
Sonam Gupta (Compliance Officer & Sec)

BITS PRIVATE LIMITED

Nandadeep 1st floor 1238/5 apte road Deccan Gymkhana, Pune, 411004, India
Tel.: (91) 20 2553 0241
Web Site: http://www.bitsindia.co.in
Sales Range: $25-49.9 Million
Emp.: 200
Translation Services
N.A.I.C.S.: 541930
Sandeep Nulkar (Chm & Mng Dir)

BITTERROOT RESOURCES LTD.

West Vancouver STN, PO Box 91878, West Vancouver, V7V4S4, BC, Canada
Tel.: (604) 922-1351　　　　　　**Ca**
Web Site:
https://www.bitterrootresources.com
BITTF—(OTCIQ)
Assets: $4,235,042
Liabilities: $74,639
Net Worth: $4,160,403
Earnings: ($1,401,706)
Fiscal Year-end: 10/31/22
Mineral Exploration Services
N.A.I.C.S.: 213114
George Walter Sanders (CFO)

BITTIUM OYJ

Ritaharjuntie 1, FI 90590, Oulu, Finland
Tel.: (358) 403442000　　　　　　**FI**
Web Site: https://www.bittium.com

BITTI—(HEL)
Rev.: $109,880,807
Assets: $204,072,076
Liabilities: $60,595,220
Net Worth: $143,476,856
Earnings: $4,082,670
Emp.: 653
Fiscal Year-end: 12/31/21
Holding Company: Wireless Technology Embedded Hardware & Software Solutions
N.A.I.C.S.: 551112
Pekka Kunnari (CFO)

Subsidiaries:

Bittium Biosignals Ltd.　　　　　(1)
Pioneerikatu 6, 70800, Kuopio, Finland
Tel.: (358) 17 581 7700
Medical Technology Services
N.A.I.C.S.: 423450

Bittium Germany GmbH　　　　　(1)
Alte Landstr 21a, 85521, Ottobrunn, Germany
Tel.: (49) 16090633833
Telecommunication Servicesb
N.A.I.C.S.: 517810

Bittium Mexico S.A. de C.V　　　(1)
Av Rio Mixcoac 274 y 276 5 Piso Col Acacias Del, Benito Juarez, Mexico, Mexico
Tel.: (52) 5584362888
Telecommunication Servicesb
N.A.I.C.S.: 517810

Bittium Safemove Oy　　　　　　(1)
Hatsinanpuisto 8, 2600, Espoo, Finland
Tel.: (358) 403442000
Telecommunication Servicesb
N.A.I.C.S.: 517810

Bittium Singapore Pte. Ltd.　　　(1)
9 Battery Road 15-01 Straits Trading Building, Singapore, 49910, Singapore
Tel.: (65) 90614099
Telecommunication Servicesb
N.A.I.C.S.: 517810

Bittium USA, Inc.　　　　　　　(1)
22722 29th Dr SE Ste 100, Bothell, WA 98021
Tel.: (425) 780-4480
Telecommunication Servicesb
N.A.I.C.S.: 517810

Bittium Wireless Oy　　　　　　(1)
Ritaharjuntie 1, 90590, Oulu, Finland
Tel.: (358) 403442000
Telecommunication Servicesb
N.A.I.C.S.: 517810

Elektrobit Technologies Oy　　　(1)
Automaatiotie 1, PO Box 45, 90570, Oulunsalo, Finland　　　　　　　　(100%)
Tel.: (358) 403442000
Web Site: http://www.elektrobit.com
Sales Range: $150-199.9 Million
Emp.: 500
Wireless Technology Components Mfr & Programming Services
N.A.I.C.S.: 335999

BITTNET SYSTEMS SA BUCURESTI

One Cotroceni Park Office Corp B Strada Progresului Nr 1, 52034, Bucharest, Romania
Tel.: (40) 215271600
Web Site: https://www.bittnet.ro
Year Founded: 2007
BNET—(BUC)
Rev.: $4,524,004
Assets: $28,318,582
Liabilities: $11,130,361
Net Worth: $17,188,221
Earnings: ($1,903,449)
Fiscal Year-end: 12/31/23
Business Support Services
N.A.I.C.S.: 561499
Cristian Logofatu (Founder & CFO)

Subsidiaries:

Dendrio Solutions SRL　　　　　(1)
Bd Timisoara nr 26 Etaj 1 Cladirea Plaza

Romania Offices, Sector 6, 061331, Bucharest, Romania
Tel.: (40) 213032070
Web Site: https://www.dendrio.com
Management Consulting Services
N.A.I.C.S.: 541611

Elian Solutions SRL　　　　　　(1)
Strada Progresului No 1 One Cotroceni Park Office building B floor 4, Sector 5, 0507602, Bucharest, Romania
Tel.: (40) 737512579
Web Site: https://www.elian-solutions.ro
IT Services
N.A.I.C.S.: 541511

BITTUBE INTERNATIONAL SE

Am Borsigturm 56, 13507, Berlin, Germany
Tel.: (49) 3043598788
Software Services
N.A.I.C.S.: 513210
Peter Becker (Chm)

BITUMENKA D.D.

ul Aleja Bosne srebrene br 2, 71000, Sarajevo, Bosnia & Herzegovina
Tel.: (387) 33460568
BITMR—(SARE)
Rev.: $22,653
Assets: $5,352,508
Liabilities: $647,323
Net Worth: $4,705,186
Earnings: $2,932,695
Emp.: 4
Fiscal Year-end: 12/31/21
Building Materials Distr
N.A.I.C.S.: 444180

BITUMINA INDUSTRIES LTD.

The Broadgate Tower Third Floor 20 Primrose Street, London, EC2A 2RS, United Kingdom
Web Site: http://www.bitumina.com
Year Founded: 2019
Construction Services & Petroleum Products
N.A.I.C.S.: 236210
Bernd Schmidt (Chm)

Subsidiaries:

Nynas AB　　　　　　　　　　(1)
Lindetorpsvagen 7, PO Box 10700, 121 29, Stockholm, Sweden　　　　　(100%)
Tel.: (46) 86021200
Web Site: http://www.nynas.com
Sales Range: $1-4.9 Billion
Emp.: 800
Specialty Oil Product Mfr
N.A.I.C.S.: 324199
Hans Ostlin (Dir-Comm)

Subsidiary (Non-US):

Nynas (Australia) Pty Ltd　　　(2)
Unit 4a 40 Rivergate Place, Murarrie, 4172, QLD, Australia
Tel.: (61) 733906155
Oil Product Distr
N.A.I.C.S.: 424720
Philippe Raeboul (Gen Mgr)

Nynas (South Africa) (Pty) Ltd　(2)
4th Fl Block E The Pivot Monte C, Johannesburg, 2055, South Africa
Tel.: (27) 105901052
Oil Product Distr
N.A.I.C.S.: 424720
Melissa Hill (Coord-Customer Svc)

Nynas A/S　　　　　　　　　　(2)
Lyngbyvej 20, Copenhagen, 2100, Denmark
Tel.: (45) 39158080
Oil Product Distr
N.A.I.C.S.: 424720

Nynas Argentina SA　　　　　　(2)
Cd de la Paz 3252, Buenos Aires, Argentina
Tel.: (54) 1145441440
Oil Product Distr
N.A.I.C.S.: 424720

Nynas Belgium AB　　　　　　　(2)
Excelsiorlaan 87, 1930, Zaventem, Belgium

Tel.: (32) 27251818
Oil Product Distr
N.A.I.C.S.: 424720

Nynas Canada Inc **(2)**
201 City Centre Dr Suite 610, Mississauga,
L5B 2T4, ON, Canada
Tel.: (905) 804-8540
Oil Product Distr
N.A.I.C.S.: 424720

Nynas Mexico SA **(2)**
Av Paseo De La Reforma No 350 Pis
Juarez, Cuauhtemoc, Mexico, 6600, Mexico
Tel.: (52) 5555363088
Oil Product Distr
N.A.I.C.S.: 424720
Roberto Ortiz Guzman *(Gen Mgr)*

Nynas Naphthenics Ltd **(2)**
Wallis House 76 North Street, Guildford,
GU1 4AW, Surrey, United Kingdom
Tel.: (44) 1483506953
Oil Product Distr
N.A.I.C.S.: 424720
Rafael Renaudeau *(Office Mgr)*

Nynas OY **(2)**
Orevagen 12, Vantaa, 1510, Finland
Tel.: (358) 207433313
Oil Product Distr
N.A.I.C.S.: 424720
Marko Sallinen *(Mng Dir)*

Nynas PTE, Ltd **(2)**
3 Fusionopolis Link 02-12 Nexus one-north,
Singapore, 138543, Singapore
Tel.: (65) 65920168
Oil Product Distr
N.A.I.C.S.: 424720

Nynas Petroleo SA **(2)**
Calle Garcia de Paredes 86, Madrid, 28010,
Spain
Tel.: (34) 917021875
Oil Product Distr
N.A.I.C.S.: 424720

Nynas SA **(2)**
54 r de Paradis, 75010, Paris, France
Tel.: (33) 153349901
Oil Product Distr
N.A.I.C.S.: 424720
Jacquet Bruno *(Gen Mgr)*

Nynas Servicios SA **(2)**
Emerson 150 Piso 8 Int 802, Mexico,
11560, Mexico
Tel.: (52) 5555453870
Oil Product Distr
N.A.I.C.S.: 424720

Nynas Sp. z o.o. **(2)**
ul Gornoslaska 17/18, Szczecin, 70-664,
Poland
Tel.: (48) 914623121
Oil Product Distr
N.A.I.C.S.: 424720
Rafal Pajak *(Mgr-Sls)*

Nynas Srl **(2)**
51 Viale Jenner Edoardo, 20159, Milan,
Italy
Tel.: (39) 026070187
Oil Product Distr
N.A.I.C.S.: 424720

Nynas Technol handels Gmbh **(2)**
Grieskai 16, 8020, Graz, Austria
Tel.: (43) 316734600
Oil Product Distr
N.A.I.C.S.: 424720
Klauds Cichock *(Gen Mgr)*

Subsidiary (Domestic):

Nynas UK AB **(2)**
PO Box 10700, Stockholm, 121 29, Swe-
den
Tel.: (46) 86021200
Oil Products Mfr
N.A.I.C.S.: 324199

Subsidiary (US):

Nynas USA, Inc **(2)**
1800 W Loop S Ste 1150, Houston, TX
77027-3291
Tel.: (713) 586-3832
Oil Product Distr
N.A.I.C.S.: 424720

Subsidiary (Non-US):

Nynas Verwaltungs Gmbh **(2)**
Am Kaiserkai 1, 20457, Hamburg, Germany
Tel.: (49) 40808074526
Oil Product Distr
N.A.I.C.S.: 424720
Frank Walenta *(Gen Mgr)*

BITZER SE
Eschenbruennlestrasse 15, 71065,
Sindelfingen, Germany
Tel.: (49) 7031 932 0 De
Web Site: http://www.bitzer.de
Year Founded: 1934
Emp.: 3,400
Holding Company; Refrigeration & Air
Conditioning Compressors Mfr & Distr
N.A.I.C.S.: 551112
Rainer Grosse-Kracht *(CTO)*

Subsidiaries:

Armaturenwerk Altenburg GmbH **(1)**
Am Weissen Berg 30, 4600, Altenburg, Ger-
many
Tel.: (49) 3447 89 30
Web Site: http://www.awa-armaturenwerk.de
Sales Range: $25-49.9 Million
Emp.: 200
Refrigerant Systems Mfr
N.A.I.C.S.: 333415
Diana Schubert *(Mng Dir)*

Subsidiary (US):

Awa Americas LLC **(2)**
PO Box 1887, Oakwood, GA 30566
Tel.: (678) 267-7622
Air Conditioning System Distr
N.A.I.C.S.: 423730
Mathias Layher *(Mgr-Bus)*

**BITZER (Portugal) Compressores
para Frio, S.A.** **(1)**
Zona Industrial Rua G, 6000-459, Castelo
Branco, Portugal
Tel.: (351) 272348550
Air Conditioning System Distr
N.A.I.C.S.: 423730

**BITZER (South East Asia) Sdn.
Bhd.** **(1)**
No 201 Block A Kelana Business Centre 97
Jalan Ss 7/2, 47301, Petaling Jaya, Selan-
gor, Malaysia
Tel.: (60) 378061220
Air Conditioning System Distr
N.A.I.C.S.: 423730
Chee Wei Kwan *(Gen Mgr)*

BITZER Andina SpA **(1)**
Carlos Alberto Fuentealba Avalos Camino
Lo Echevers 891 Modulo A5, Quilicura,
8730591, Santiago, Chile
Tel.: (56) 232627538
Refrigeration & Air Conditioning Mfr
N.A.I.C.S.: 333415

BITZER Australia Pty Limited **(1)**
134-136 Dunheved Circuit, Saint Mary,
2760, NSW, Australia
Tel.: (61) 288019300
Web Site: http://www.bitzeravp.com.au
Air Conditioning System Mfr
N.A.I.C.S.: 333415
Simon Wood *(Mng Dir)*

BITZER Austria GmbH **(1)**
Asperngasse 4, 8020, Graz, Austria
Tel.: (43) 3165827670
Air Conditioning System Distr
N.A.I.C.S.: 423730
Martin Grebien *(Mgr-Technical)*

BITZER Benelux BVBA **(1)**
Diepenbekerweg 30 bus 1, 3500, Hasselt,
Belgium
Tel.: (32) 11325353
Air Conditioning System Distr
N.A.I.C.S.: 423730

BITZER CIS LTD. **(1)**
Leninsky Avenue 15A 9th floor premises 1
office 1, 119071, Moscow, Russia
Tel.: (7) 4959338831
Web Site: http://www.bitzer.de
Air Conditioning System Distr
N.A.I.C.S.: 423730

**BITZER COMPRESSORES
LTDA** **(1)**
Av Joao Paulo Ablas 777 - Jd da Gloria,
06711-250, Cotia, Brazil
Tel.: (55) 1146179100
Air Conditioning System Distr
N.A.I.C.S.: 423730
Fernando Bueno *(Dir Gen)*

BITZER Canada Inc. **(1)**
21125 Daoust Street, Sainte-Anne-de-
Beaupre, H9X 0A3, QC, Canada
Tel.: (514) 697-3363
Web Site: https://www.bitzer.de
Air Conditioning System Distr
N.A.I.C.S.: 423730

BITZER Compressores S.A. **(1)**
Giribone 745 Avellaneda 1870, Buenos Ai-
res, Argentina
Tel.: (54) 1141395855
Air Conditioning System Distr
N.A.I.C.S.: 423730

**BITZER Compressors (Beijing)
Ltd.** **(1)**
Gon Yuan Dong Street Tongzhou Industrial
Development Zone, Beijing, 101113, China
Tel.: (86) 1067819000
Air Conditioning System Distr
N.A.I.C.S.: 423730

BITZER Electronics A/S **(1)**
Kaervej 77, 6400, Sonderborg, Denmark
Tel.: (45) 73423730
Refrigeration & Air Conditioning Mfr
N.A.I.C.S.: 333415
Michael Antoniussen *(Sls Mgr)*

BITZER France s.a.r.l. **(1)**
Parc Technologique de Lyon 6 place Berthe
Morisot - Bat B4, 69800, Saint Priest,
France
Tel.: (33) 472148686
Air Conditioning System Distr
N.A.I.C.S.: 423730

BITZER India Private Limited **(1)**
R-708/1 TTC Industrial Area Rabale, 400
701, Navi Mumbai, India
Tel.: (91) 2227601730
Air Conditioning System Distr
N.A.I.C.S.: 423730
Harvinder Bhatia *(Gen Mgr)*

**BITZER Industrial Equipment (Bei-
jing) Co., Ltd.** **(1)**
No 7 Kechuang 2nd Street, Economic and
Technological Development Area, Beijing,
101111, China
Tel.: (86) 1067818600
Refrigeration & Air Conditioning Mfr
N.A.I.C.S.: 333415
Iris Liu *(Asst Gen Mgr)*

**BITZER Invertertechnologie
GmbH** **(1)**
Eschenbrunnlestrasse 15, 71065, Sindelfin-
gen, Germany
Tel.: (49) 70319320
Air Conditioning System Mfr
N.A.I.C.S.: 333415

BITZER Italia S.r.l. **(1)**
Viale del Mercato Nuovo 44G, 36100, Vice-
nza, Italy
Tel.: (39) 0444962020
Air Conditioning System Distr
N.A.I.C.S.: 423730
Andrea Zocche *(Mng Dir)*

BITZER Japan K.K. **(1)**
Senri Life Science Center Bldg 14F 1-4-2
Shinsenri-higashimachi, Toyonaka, 560-
0082, Japan
Tel.: (81) 668738555
Air Conditioning System Distr
N.A.I.C.S.: 423730

BITZER Kenya Ltd. **(1)**
Landmark Offices 4th Floor Cavendish
Block, 14 Riverside Business Park River-
side Drive, Nairobi, Kenya
Tel.: (254) 204231248
Refrigeration & Air Conditioning Mfr
N.A.I.C.S.: 333415
Tariq Zaffar *(Gen Mgr)*

BITZER Korea Co., Ltd. **(1)**
101 26 Jeonpa-ro 104beon-gil, Dongan-gu,

Anyang, 431-836, Gyeonggi, Korea (South)
Tel.: (82) 314523931
Air Conditioning System Distr
N.A.I.C.S.: 423730
Jong Hwan Byun *(Mng Dir)*

**BITZER Kuhlmaschinenbau (S.A.)
(Proprietary) Ltd.** **(1)**
Unit 1 Marine Park 18 Marine Drive
Paarden Eiland, PO Box 119, 7420, Cape
Town, South Africa
Tel.: (27) 215104680
Air Conditioning System Distr
N.A.I.C.S.: 423730

**BITZER Kuhlmaschinenbau
GmbH** **(1)**
Eschenbrunnlestrasse 15, Sindelfingen,
71065, Germany **(100%)**
Tel.: (49) 7031 932 0
Web Site: http://www.bitzer.de
Refrigeration & Air Conditioning Compres-
sors Mfr & Distr
N.A.I.C.S.: 333415
Christian Wehle *(CEO)*

**BITZER Kuhlmaschinenbau Schkeud-
itz GmbH** **(1)**
Industriestrasse 48, 04435, Schkeuditz,
Germany
Tel.: (49) 342047020
Air Conditioning System Mfr
N.A.I.C.S.: 333415

**BITZER Mexico, S. de R.L. de
C.V.** **(1)**
Av Adolfo Lopez Mateos 221 Bodega 9 Col
Victoria, 67110, Guadalupe, Mexico
Tel.: (52) 8115224500
Air Conditioning System Distr
N.A.I.C.S.: 423730

BITZER New Zealand Pty. Ltd. **(1)**
Unit 5 5 7 Henry Rose Place, Albany, Auck-
land, 0632, New Zealand
Tel.: (64) 94152030
Refrigeration & Air Conditioning Mfr
N.A.I.C.S.: 333415

**BITZER Refrigeration Asia
Limited** **(1)**
Unit 1503 Tai Tung Building 8 Fleming
Road, Wan Chai, Hong Kong, China (Hong
Kong)
Tel.: (852) 28680206
Air Conditioning System Distr
N.A.I.C.S.: 423730
Wai Yin Cheng *(Mgr-Sls)*

**BITZER Refrigeration Asia PTE.
LTD** **(1)**
Unit 007 Level 4 Centec Tower 72-74
Nguyen Thi Minh Khai St District 3, Ho Chi
Minh City, Vietnam
Tel.: (84) 838227024
Air Conditioning System Distr
N.A.I.C.S.: 423730
Ngo Quang Truong *(Gen Mgr)*

**BITZER Refrigeration Asia Pte
Ltd** **(1)**
33/4 Tower A 35th floor Rama 9 road, Huai
Khwang, 10310, Bangkok, Thailand
Tel.: (66) 21180425
Air Conditioning System Distr
N.A.I.C.S.: 423730

**BITZER Refrigeration Asia Pte.,
Ltd.** **(1)**
112 Robinson Road 07-02, Singapore,
068902, Singapore
Tel.: (65) 62204942
Air Conditioning System Distr
N.A.I.C.S.: 423730
Chin Leong Ang *(Mgr-Fin)*

**BITZER Refrigeration Technology
(China) Co. Ltd.** **(1)**
No 20 Fourth Jing Hai Road Beijing Eco-
nomic Technological Development, Beijing,
100176, China
Tel.: (86) 1067819000
Air Conditioning System Distr
N.A.I.C.S.: 423730

BITZER SA **(1)**
Lot No 5 Route de l'aeroport, Dakar,
29783, Senegal
Tel.: (221) 771005797
Refrigeration & Air Conditioning Mfr

BITZER SE—(Continued)

N.A.I.C.S.: 333415

BITZER SE (1)
1703 Twin Towers Baniyas Street Deira, PO Box 82571, Dubai, United Arab Emirates
Tel.: (971) 42218780
Refrigeration & Air Conditioning Mfr
N.A.I.C.S.: 333415
Franca Jatzlau (Mgr-Admin)

BITZER SL (1)
Calle Andarella N 1 Blq 2 Plta 3a Puerta 4, 46014, Valencia, Spain
Tel.: (34) 649588654
Refrigeration & Air Conditioning Mfr
N.A.I.C.S.: 333415

BITZER Scroll, Inc. (1)
6055 Center St Rd, Syracuse, NY 13206
Tel.: (315) 463-2101
Air Conditioning System Distr
N.A.I.C.S.: 423730
James Cullen (Dir-Product Mgmt)

BITZER UK Limited (1)
Advantage One Third Avenue, Denbigh, Milton Keynes, MK1 1DR, United Kingdom
Tel.: (44) 8452303007
Air Conditioning System Distr
N.A.I.C.S.: 423730
Kevin Glass F Inst R (Mng Dir)

BITZER US, Inc. (1)
4080 Enterprise Way, Flowery Branch, GA 30542
Tel.: (770) 503-9226
Web Site: http://www.bitzerus.com
Refrigeration & Air Conditioning Compressors Mfr & Distr
N.A.I.C.S.: 333415
Dave Sylves (VP-Sls & Mktg)

Subsidiary (Domestic):

Electratherm, Inc. (2)
1575 Delucchi Ln Ste 116B, Reno, NV 89502
Tel.: (775) 398-4680
Web Site: http://electratherm.com
Waste Heat Recovery Services
N.A.I.C.S.: 221122
John Fox (Mng Dir)

Green Point Asia Pacific Pte. Ltd. (1)
23 Neythal Road 01-01D Block B, Singapore, 628585, Singapore
Tel.: (65) 62674834
Air Conditioning System Distr
N.A.I.C.S.: 423730
Marco Candotti (Mng Dir)

Green Point Korea Co. Ltd. (1)
101 26 Jeonpa-ro 104beon-gil, Dongan-gu, Anyang, 431-836, Gyeonggi, Korea (South)
Tel.: (82) 314770262
Air Conditioning System Distr
N.A.I.C.S.: 423730

Green Point Pty. Ltd. (1)
Unit 3 City Deep Mini Units Corner Heidelberg and Outspan Road, City Deep, Johannesburg, 2092, South Africa
Tel.: (27) 118376975
Refrigeration & Air Conditioning Mfr
N.A.I.C.S.: 333415
Rudelee Merks (Founder)

Green Point UK Limited (1)
Advantage One Third Avenue, Bletchley, Milton Keynes, MK1 1DR, United Kingdom
Tel.: (44) 1908622125
Refrigeration & Air Conditioning Whslr
N.A.I.C.S.: 423730
Will Pribyl (Gen Mgr)

GreenPoint US, LLC (1)
4080 Enterprise Way, Flowery Branch, GA 30542
Tel.: (770) 718-2900
Air Conditioning System Distr
N.A.I.C.S.: 423730

KIMO RHVAC Controls GmbH (1)
Huttendorfer Weg 60, 90768, Furth, Germany
Tel.: (49) 9118018778
Refrigeration & Air Conditioning Mfr
N.A.I.C.S.: 333415

Lodam Electronics a/s (1)
Kaervej 77, 6400, Sonderborg, Denmark
Tel.: (45) 73423737
Air Conditioning System Distr
N.A.I.C.S.: 423730
Claus Henningsen Jensen (Mgr-Production)

Lumikko Technologies Oy (1)
Pl 304 Kylmatie 1, 60101, Seinajoki, Finland
Tel.: (358) 108355450
Web Site: http://www.lumikko.com
Transportation Services
N.A.I.C.S.: 484121
Jani Leppanen (Dir-Sls & Mktg)

PT. BITZER Compressors Indonesia (1)
Jl Raya Tlajung Udik No 2 Gunung Putri, 16962, Bogor, Indonesia
Tel.: (62) 218671041
Air Conditioning System Distr
N.A.I.C.S.: 423730
Joao Vitorio (Mgr-Factory)

S.R.S. BITZER s.a.r.l. (1)
2 Boulevard Jean Monnet ZAC Parisud IV, 77380, Combs-la-Ville, France
Tel.: (33) 174591010
Air Conditioning System Distr
N.A.I.C.S.: 423730

VaCom Technologies LLC (1)
1747 Wright Ave, La Verne, CA 91750
Tel.: (909) 392-6704
Web Site: http://www.vacomtech.com
Refrigeration Equipment Maintenance Services
N.A.I.C.S.: 811310

BIURO INWESTYCJI KAPITALOWYCH S.A.

Albatrosow 2, 30-716, Krakow, Poland
Tel.: (48) 126518280
Web Site: http://www.bik.com.pl
Year Founded: 1996
BIK—(WAR)
Sales Range: Less than $1 Million
Real Estate Development Services
N.A.I.C.S.: 531390
Miroslaw Koszany (Pres-Mgmt Bd)

BIVICTRIX THERAPEUTICS PLC

Mereside, Alderley Park, Alderley Edge, SK10 4TG, Cheshire, United Kingdom   UK
Web Site: https://www.bivictrix.com
Year Founded: 2016
BVX—(AIM)
Rev.: $4,967
Assets: $5,632,805
Liabilities: $719,002
Net Worth: $4,913,803
Earnings: ($3,100,775)
Emp.: 17
Fiscal Year-end: 12/31/22
Biotechnology Research & Development Services
N.A.I.C.S.: 541714

BIWATER HOLDINGS LIMITED

Biwater House Station Apprach, Dorking, RH4 1TZ, Surrey, United Kingdom   UK
Tel.: (44) 1306740740
Web Site: http://www.biwater.com
Year Founded: 1968
Sales Range: $400-449.9 Million
Emp.: 200
Water Treatment & Distribution Facilities Design, Construction & Maintenance Services
N.A.I.C.S.: 221310
Adrian E. White (Chm)

Subsidiaries:

BIWATER Maroc SA (1)
28 rue Galicia Secteur 19, Hay Riad, Rabat, Morocco
Tel.: (212) 537570486

Waste Water Treatment Services
N.A.I.C.S.: 221320

Biwater (Malaysia) Sdn Bhd (1)
Wisma Biwater Plaza Damansara 9 Medan Setia 1, Bukit Damansara, 50490, Kuala Lumpur, Malaysia
Tel.: (60) 320954366
Waste Water Treatment Services
N.A.I.C.S.: 221320
Stanley Mgr-Contracts & Proposal (Mgr-Contracts & Proposal)

Biwater (Nigeria) Limited (1)
Plot 12B Kaduna/Abuja Expressway PMB 1140, Beijing, Niger, China
Tel.: (86) 7031667849
Waste Water Treatment Services
N.A.I.C.S.: 221320

Biwater (Pty) Limited (1)
Fourways North, PO Box 59, Johannesburg, 2086, South Africa
Tel.: (27) 11 510 0360
Web Site: http://www.biwater.com
Water Treatment & Distribution Facilities Design, Construction & Maintenance Services
N.A.I.C.S.: 221310
Justin Edwards (CEO)

Biwater AEWT, Inc. (1)
136 E Lemon Ave, Monrovia, CA 91016
Tel.: (626) 358-7707
Web Site: http://www.biwater-aewt.com
Sales Range: $75-99.9 Million
Emp.: 15
Water Treatment Equipment Mfr
N.A.I.C.S.: 221310

Biwater Algérie SPA (1)
126 Rue Didouche, Mourad, 1650, Algiers, Algeria
Tel.: (213) 21646546
Waste Water Treatment Services
N.A.I.C.S.: 221320
Mohammad Alloue (Dir-Fin)

Biwater Construction Limited (1)
Almenshi Street, Bin Ashour, Tripoli, Libya
Tel.: (218) 913833825
Waste Water Treatment Services
N.A.I.C.S.: 221320

Biwater Contracting B.V. (1)
Herikerbergweg 178, 1101 CM, Amsterdam, Netherlands
Tel.: (31) 205755600
Waste Water Treatment Services
N.A.I.C.S.: 221320

Biwater International Limited (1)
Planta de Tratamiento de Aguas Servidas de Managua Del Cafe Soluble, 1200 mts al Noreste, Managua, Nicaragua
Tel.: (505) 22520707
Waste Water Treatment Services
N.A.I.C.S.: 221320

Biwater International Limited (1)
36 Nii Kwabena Crescent, Dzorwulu, Accra, Ghana
Tel.: (233) 302782399
Waste Water Treatment Services
N.A.I.C.S.: 221320

Biwater International Limited (1)
Nispetiye Cad Seher Yildizi Sok 23/3, Etiler, 34337, Istanbul, Turkiye
Tel.: (90) 2123526520
Web Site: http://www.biwater.com
Waste Water Treatment Services
N.A.I.C.S.: 221320
Burak Bashkal (Mgr)

Biwater International Limited (Panama) (1)
C C Camino de Cruces Nivel 4, Boulevard El Dorado, Panama, El Dorado, Panama   (100%)
Tel.: (507) 3602160
Sales Range: $75-99.9 Million
Emp.: 60
Water Treatment & Distribution Facilities
N.A.I.C.S.: 221310

Biwater Leisure Plc (1)
Biwater House Station Approach, Dorking, London, RH4 1TZ, United Kingdom
Tel.: (44) 1306740740
Waste Water Treatment Services

N.A.I.C.S.: 221320

Biwater Philippines Inc. (1)
Unit 1603 Antel Global Corporate Center Julia Vargas Avenue, Ortigas Centre, Pasig, Philippines
Tel.: (63) 26673493
Waste Water Treatment Services
N.A.I.C.S.: 221320

Biwater S.A. (1)
15 Rue des Draperies Batiment A, 69450, Saint-Cyr-au-Mont-D'or, France
Tel.: (33) 4 78 43 86 96
Web Site: http://www.biwater.com
Emp.: 10
Water Treatment & Distribution Facilities Design, Construction & Maintenance Services
N.A.I.C.S.: 221310

Biwater USA Inc. (1)
4000 Hollywood Blvd, Hollywood, FL 33021
Tel.: (954) 987-6676
Web Site: http://www.biwater.com
Sales Range: $25-49.9 Million
Emp.: 8
Engineeering Services
N.A.I.C.S.: 541330

REI-Biwater Consortium Sdn Bhd (1)
2nd Floor Administration Building Yen So Sewage Treatment Plant KU2, Bridge opposite house number 739 Tam Trinh Street Hoang Mai, Hanoi, Vietnam
Tel.: (84) 485875811
Waste Water Treatment Services
N.A.I.C.S.: 221320

BIXOLON CO LTD

5F 344 Pangyo-ro, Bundang-gu, Seongnam, 13494, Gyeonggi-do, Korea (South)
Tel.: (82) 312185500
Web Site: https://www.bixolon.com
Year Founded: 2002
093190—(KRS)
Rev.: $103,463,673
Assets: $186,851,896
Liabilities: $29,106,025
Net Worth: $157,745,872
Earnings: $8,290,941
Emp.: 112
Fiscal Year-end: 12/31/22
Printer Mfr
N.A.I.C.S.: 325992
Hyoun Chall Roh (Pres & CEO)

Subsidiaries:

BIXOLON America Inc. (1)
2575 W 237th St, Torrance, CA 90505
Tel.: (858) 355-9615
Web Site: https://bixolonusa.com
Sales Range: $25-49.9 Million
Emp.: 10
Computer Printers Mfr
N.A.I.C.S.: 334118

BIXOLON Europe GmbH (1)
Tiefenbroicher Weg 35, 40472, Dusseldorf, Germany
Tel.: (49) 211 687 8540
Web Site: https://bixoloneu.com
Sales Range: $25-49.9 Million
Emp.: 11
Computer Printer Whslr
N.A.I.C.S.: 423430
Jay Kim (Mng Dir)

Bixolon Middle East & Africa Co., Ltd. (1)
Jafza view 18 Jebel Ali Free Zone, Dubai, United Arab Emirates
Tel.: (971) 509749698
Printer Mfr
N.A.I.C.S.: 314999

BIZCONF TELECOM CO., LTD.

17/F South Building China Merchants Plaza 333 North Chengdu Road, Jin-gan District, Shanghai, 200041, China
Tel.: (86) 2161321868
Web Site: https://www.bizconf.cn

Year Founded: 2006
300578—(SSE)
Rev.: $94,032,900
Assets: $278,883,540
Liabilities: $45,179,316
Net Worth: $233,704,224
Earnings: $2,371,356
Fiscal Year-end: 12/31/22
Tele Conferencing Services
N.A.I.C.S.: 561499
He Qijin *(Chm)*

BIZERBA CANADA INC.
2810 Argentia Road Unit 9, Mississauga, L5N 8L2, ON, Canada
Tel.: (905) 816-0498
Web Site: http://bizerbausa.com
Rev.: $12,636,000
Emp.: 35
Weight Scale Equipment Mfr
N.A.I.C.S.: 423850
Robert Slykhuis *(Pres)*

BIZIM TOPTAN SATIS MAGA-ZALARI A.S.
Kusbakisi Caddesi No 19 Altunizade Uskudar, 34662, Istanbul, Turkiye
Tel.: (90) 2164744280
Web Site:
https://www.bizimtoptan.com.tr
Year Founded: 2001
BIZIM—(IST)
Rev.: $433,625,240
Assets: $123,932,648
Liabilities: $108,784,443
Net Worth: $15,148,205
Earnings: $8,598,379
Emp.: 2,213
Fiscal Year-end: 12/31/22
Supermarket Operator
N.A.I.C.S.: 445110

BIZLINK HOLDING INC.
3F No 186 Jian 1st Road, Zhonghe District, New Taipei City, 23553, Taiwan
Tel.: (886) 282261000
Web Site:
https://www.bizlinktech.com
3665—(TAI)
Rev.: $1,669,504,859
Assets: $1,788,250,954
Liabilities: $983,863,431
Net Worth: $804,387,523
Earnings: $75,567,445
Emp.: 14,520
Fiscal Year-end: 12/31/23
Wires, Connectors & Optical Components Mfr
N.A.I.C.S.: 332618
Roger Liang *(Co-Chm)*

Subsidiaries:

BizConn Int'l Corp. (1)
Offshore Chambers, PO Box 217, Apia, Samoa (Western)
Tel.: (685) 282261000
Industrial Machinery Equipment Mfr & Distr
N.A.I.C.S.: 332312

BizLink Industry Czech s.r.o. (1)
Ostrov u Stribra 20, Kostelec, 349 01, Tachov, Czech Republic
Tel.: (420) 373340940
Fibber Optic Components Mfr
N.A.I.C.S.: 335921

BizLink Industry Slovakia Spol. S.r.o. (1)
Trencianska 401/81, 019 01, Ilava, Slovakia
Tel.: (421) 914363226
Information Technology Services
N.A.I.C.S.: 541519

BizLink Inti Corp. (1)
3F No 186 Jian 1st Rd, Zhonghe Dist, New Taipei City, 235603, Taiwan
Tel.: (886) 282261000
Information Technology Services
N.A.I.C.S.: 541519

BizLink Robotic Solutions Germany GmbH (1)
Brusseler Strasse 12, 30539, Hannover, Germany
Tel.: (49) 51112357630
Information Technology Services
N.A.I.C.S.: 541519

BizLink Silitherm S.R.L. (1)
SS 10 Via Breda 134, 29010, Monticelli d'Ongina, PC, Italy
Tel.: (39) 0523815711
Fibber Optic Components Mfr
N.A.I.C.S.: 335921

BizLink Special Cables (Changzhou) Co., Ltd. (1)
No 21 Taihu West Road, Xinbei District, Changzhou, 213022, Jiangsu, China
Tel.: (86) 2162375569101
Information Technology Services
N.A.I.C.S.: 541519

BizLink Special Cables Germany GmbH (1)
Eschstrasse 1, 26169, Friesoythe, Germany
Tel.: (49) 44912910
Fibber Optic Components Mfr
N.A.I.C.S.: 335921

BizLink elocab GmbH (1)
Obere Lerch 34, 91166, Georgensgmund, Germany
Tel.: (49) 917269800
Information Technology Services
N.A.I.C.S.: 541519

BizLink elocab Ltd. (1)
258 McBrine Drive, Kitchener, N2R 1H8, ON, Canada
Fibber Optic Components Mfr
N.A.I.C.S.: 335921

Bizlink Technology (Slovakia) S.R.O. (1)
Trencianska Tepla 1356, Trencianska Tepla, 914 01, Trencin, Slovakia
Tel.: (421) 326570200
Connector & Power Cord Mfr & Distr
N.A.I.C.S.: 335931

EA Cable Assemblies (HongKong) Co., Limited (1)
Tel.: (852) 282261000
Wire Connector & Optical Component Mfr
N.A.I.C.S.: 332618

Excel de Mexico S de R.L. de C.V. (1)
Blvd Independencia 2550-1 Parque Industrial Independencia 1, Chihuahua, 32575, Ciudad Juarez, Mexico
Tel.: (52) 6562570010
Information Technology Services
N.A.I.C.S.: 541519

Jo Yeh Company Limited (1)
Tel.: (852) 26872002
Wire Connector & Optical Component Mfr
N.A.I.C.S.: 332618

NanHai Jo Yeh Electronics Co., Ltd. (1)
Dungenduan Industrial Park Longgao Rd, Jiujiang Township Nanhai Dist, Foshan, Guangdong, China
Tel.: (86) 75786503111
Information Technology Services
N.A.I.C.S.: 541519

OptiWork, Inc. (1)
47211 Bayside pkwy, Fremont, CA 94538
Tel.: (510) 438-4560
Web Site: https://www.optiworks.com
Emp.: 100
Fibber Optic Components Mfr
N.A.I.C.S.: 335921
Roger Ling *(Owner)*

OptiWorks, Inc. (1)
47211 Bayside Pkwy, Fremont, CA 94538
Tel.: (510) 438-4560
Web Site: https://www.optiworks.co
Fibber Optic Component Mfr & Distr
N.A.I.C.S.: 335921

SIS Speedy Industrial Supplies Sdn. Bhd.
PTD 8738 & 8739 Jalan Perindustrian 3, Kawasan Perindustrian Pontian Pontian,

82000, Johor, Malaysia
Tel.: (60) 76870158
Fibber Optic Components Mfr
N.A.I.C.S.: 335921

Silitherm Immobiliare S.R.L. (1)
S S 10 Via Breda 134 PC, 29010, Monticelli d'Ongina, Italy
Tel.: (39) 0523815711
Information Technology Services
N.A.I.C.S.: 541519

Speedy Industrial Supplies Pte. Ltd. (1)
3 Kallang Sector 07-06, Singapore, 349278, Singapore
Tel.: (65) 67434116
Industrial Machinery Equipment Mfr & Distr
N.A.I.C.S.: 332312

Zellwood Int'l Corp. (1)
OMC Chambers Wickhams Cay 1, Tortola, Road Town, Virgin Islands (British)
Tel.: (284) 282261000
Industrial Machinery Equipment Mfr & Distr
N.A.I.C.S.: 332312

BIZMATES, INC.
11th Floor Daiwa Akihabara Building 2-19-23 Kanda Sudacho, Chiyoda-ku, Tokyo, 101-0041, Japan
Tel.: (81) 358607565
Web Site: https://www.bizmates.co.jp
Year Founded: 2012
9345—(TKS)
Rev.: $22,227,150
Assets: $14,569,950
Liabilities: $3,899,500
Net Worth: $10,670,450
Earnings: $1,410,910
Fiscal Year-end: 12/31/23
Recruitment Services
N.A.I.C.S.: 561311
Nobuaki Suzuki *(Pres & CEO)*

BIZOTIC COMMERCIAL LIM-ITED
15 Ashwamegh Warhouse b/h Ujala Hotel Ujala Circle, Sarkhe, Ahmedabad, 382210, India
Tel.: (91) 6358859971
Web Site: https://www.urbanunited.in
Year Founded: 2016
543926—(BOM)
Rev.: $6,451,835
Assets: $4,353,699
Liabilities: $4,203,720
Net Worth: $149,979
Earnings: $76,244
Fiscal Year-end: 03/31/23
Garment Product Mfr & Distr
N.A.I.C.S.: 325612
Inderpreet Kaur Gulati *(CFO)*

BJB CAREER EDUCATION COMPANY, LIMITED
Beida Jade Bird Building 3/F 207 Chengfu Road, Haidian District, Beijing, 100871, China
Tel.: (86) 1062760088 Ky
Web Site: http://www.jbit.cn
Sales Range: $25-49.9 Million
Emp.: 1,160
Vocational IT Education Services
N.A.I.C.S.: 611710
Yongli Zhang *(Chm)*

BJB GMBH & CO. KG
Werler Str 1, 59755, Arnsberg, Germany
Tel.: (49) 29329820
Web Site: http://www.bjb.com
Year Founded: 1867
Sales Range: $100-124.9 Million
Lamp Components Mfr
N.A.I.C.S.: 335139
Dieter Henrici *(Co-Mng Dir)*

Subsidiaries:

BJB (UK) Ltd. (1)

5 Axis Centre Cleeve Road, Leatherhead, KT22 7RD, United Kingdom
Tel.: (44) 1372380850
Lighting Fixture Distr
N.A.I.C.S.: 423610

BJB Co., Ltd. (1)
2-5-9 Nakagawa-chuo, Tsuzuki-ku, Yokohama, 224-0003, Japan
Tel.: (81) 455951239
Lighting Fixture Distr
N.A.I.C.S.: 423610

BJB Electric Dongguan Ltd. (1)
Guancheng High-Tech Park Five Road North, Eastern Industrial Zone JiangNan-DaDao Qishi Town, Dongguan, China
Tel.: (86) 76922766891
Lighting Fixture Distr
N.A.I.C.S.: 423610

BJB Electric L.P. (1)
6375 Alabama Hwy, Ringgold, GA 30736
Tel.: (706) 965-2526
Emp.: 40
Lighting Fixture Distr
N.A.I.C.S.: 423610
Joe Laufer *(Pres)*

BJB Electric Taiwan Corporation (1)
4/F No 108 Chow-Tze Street, Nei-Hu District, 114, Taipei, Taiwan
Tel.: (886) 226277722
Lighting Fixture Distr
N.A.I.C.S.: 423610

BJB Procesa S.A. (1)
C-155 De Sabadell a Granollers km 14 2, Apartado de Correos 8, Llica de Vall, 8185, Barcelona, Spain
Tel.: (34) 938445170
Lighting Fixture Distr
N.A.I.C.S.: 423610
Joaquin Bruned *(Mng Dir)*

BJB S.p.A. (1)
Viale Famagosta 61, 20142, Milano, Italy
Tel.: (39) 0289150276
Lighting Fixture Distr
N.A.I.C.S.: 423610

BJC HEAVY INDUSTRIES PUB-LIC COMPANY LIMITED
594 Moo4 Makham Khu Nikhom Phatthana, Rayong, 21180, Thailand
Tel.: (66) 33017345
Web Site: https://www.bjc1994.com
Year Founded: 1994
BJCHI—(THA)
Rev.: $67,800,630
Assets: $127,221,199
Liabilities: $18,404,656
Net Worth: $108,816,543
Earnings: ($6,461,491)
Emp.: 941
Fiscal Year-end: 12/31/20
Heavy Construction
N.A.I.C.S.: 237990
Young Kyu Lee *(Pres)*

BJORN BORG AB
Frosundaviks Alle 1, 16970, Solna, Sweden
Tel.: (46) 850633700
Web Site: https://www.bjornborg.com
BORG—(OMX)
Rev.: $80,643,645
Assets: $61,198,123
Liabilities: $30,775,895
Net Worth: $30,422,228
Earnings: $4,764,862
Emp.: 151
Fiscal Year-end: 12/31/22
Apparel, Footwear, Handbags, Eyewear & Fragrances Mfr & Sales
N.A.I.C.S.: 315250
Henrik Bunge *(CEO)*

Subsidiaries:

Bjorn Borg Brands AB (1)
Tulegatan 11, Stockholm, 11353, Sweden
Tel.: (46) 850633700
Web Site: http://www.bjornborg.com

Bjorn Borg AB—(Continued)

Sales Range: $25-49.9 Million
Emp.: 65
Apparel & Accessories Mfr & Whslr
N.A.I.C.S.: 315990

Subsidiary (Domestic):

Anteros Lagerhantering AB (2)
Alvsjo Angsvag 6, Alvsjo, 12530, Stockholm, Sweden
Tel.: (46) 86471860
Warehouse Storage Services
N.A.I.C.S.: 455211

Bjorn Borg Clothing AB (2)
Tulegatan 11, Stockholm, 113 53, Sweden
Tel.: (46) 850633700
Web Site: http://www.bjornborg.net
Sales Range: $25-49.9 Million
Emp.: 60
Apparels & Accessories Mfr & Whslr
N.A.I.C.S.: 315990

Bjorn Borg Retail AB (2)
Culegatan 11, 118 30, Stockholm, Sweden
Tel.: (46) 850633700
Sales Range: $10-24.9 Million
Emp.: 50
Apparels & Accessories Mfr & Retailer
N.A.I.C.S.: 315990
Arthur Engel (Gen Mgr)

Bjorn Borg Sweden AB (2)
Frosundaviks Alle 1, 16970, Solna, Sweden
Tel.: (46) 85 063 3700
Web Site: https://corporate.bjornborg.com
Sales Range: $25-49.9 Million
Emp.: 80
Apparels & Accessories Whslr
N.A.I.C.S.: 315210

Bjorn Borg Finland OY (1)
Vilhonvuorenkatu 11 C 6, 00500, Helsinki, Finland
Tel.: (358) 9644233
Sports Cloth Distr
N.A.I.C.S.: 424350

Bjorn Borg Footwear AB (1)
Backgatan 36, PO Box 223, 43225, Varberg, Sweden
Tel.: (46) 340646530
Web Site: http://www.bjornborgfootwear.se
Sales Range: $25-49.9 Million
Emp.: 9
Footwear Design & Mfr
N.A.I.C.S.: 316210

Bjorn Borg UK Limited (1)
Golderbrock House 19 Great Titchfield Street, London, W1W 8AZ, United Kingdom
Tel.: (44) 2035820173
Sports Cloth Distr
N.A.I.C.S.: 424350

Dutch Brand Management BV (1)
Pedro de Medinalaan 11-2, 1086 XK, Amsterdam, Netherlands
Tel.: (31) 203657848
Sports Cloth Distr
N.A.I.C.S.: 424350

BJORNSEN BERATENDE INGENIEURE GMBH
Maria Trost 3, 56070, Koblenz, Germany
Tel.: (49) 26188510
Web Site: http://www.bjoernsen.de
Year Founded: 1960
Rev.: $19,989,750
Emp.: 180
Engineering Consulting Services
N.A.I.C.S.: 541690
Gerhard Bjornsen (Founder, Mng Dir & Engr-Consulting)

Subsidiaries:

BCE Krakow Sp. z o.o. (1)
Ul Wladyslawa Syrokomli 23/3, 30-102, Krakow, Poland
Tel.: (48) 124279020
Engineering Consulting Services
N.A.I.C.S.: 541330
B. Slizewski (Mgr)

Bjornsen Consulting Engineering Erfurt GmbH (1)
Bruhler Herrenberg 2a, 99092, Erfurt, Germany
Tel.: (49) 36122490
Engineering Consulting Services
N.A.I.C.S.: 541330
J. Kretzschmar (Mgr)

BK HOLDINGS CO., LTD
3F 1-dong Golden Plaza 23 Sindang 2-ro, Sandong-eup, Gumi, 39171, Gyeongsangbuk-do, Korea (South)
Tel.: (82) 544730886
Web Site: http://www.phoenixmaterials.kr
Year Founded: 1983
050090—(KRS)
Rev.: $13,260,986
Assets: $22,210,113
Liabilities: $5,148,161
Net Worth: $17,061,952
Earnings: ($2,344,766)
Emp.: 65
Fiscal Year-end: 12/31/22
Display Component Mfr & Distr
N.A.I.C.S.: 334419
Hong Seok-Gyu (Dir-Rep)

BKI INVESTMENT COMPANY LIMITED
Level 12 680 George Street, Sydney, 2000, NSW, Australia
Tel.: (61) 1300853816
Web Site: https://www.bkilimited.com.au
BKI—(ASX)
Rev.: $45,635,684
Assets: $990,525,503
Liabilities: $75,551,549
Net Worth: $914,973,955
Earnings: $42,996,795
Emp.: 2
Fiscal Year-end: 06/30/24
Investment Services
N.A.I.C.S.: 523999
Thomas L. Millner (Portfolio Mgr)

Subsidiaries:

Pacific Strategic Investments Pty Limited (1)
Level 2 160 Pitt St, Sydney, 2000, NSW, Australia
Tel.: (61) 292107000
Web Site: http://www.pcap.com.au
Sales Range: $50-74.9 Million
Emp.: 14
Securities Brokerage Services
N.A.I.C.S.: 523150
Robert Millner (Chm)

BKM MANAGEMENT LIMITED
Suite 1 1233 High Street, PO Box 8694, Armadale, 3143, VIC, Australia
Tel.: (61) 3 9824 5254 AU
Web Site: http://www.bkmmanagement.com
International Model Management
N.A.I.C.S.: 541611

Subsidiaries:

Scene Model Management Pty Ltd. (1)
Level 1 872-876 Hay St, Perth, 6000, WA, Australia (100%)
Tel.: (61) 894869994
Web Site: http://www.scenemodels.com
Emp.: 7
Model Management Agency
N.A.I.C.S.: 711410

Scene Model Management Pty Ltd. (1)
Level 1 5 Cubitt St Richmond, PO Box 6072, South Yarra, Melbourne, 3141, VIC, Australia (100%)
Tel.: (61) 398265233
Web Site: http://www.scenemodels.com

Sales Range: $50-74.9 Million
Emp.: 2
Modeling Agency
N.A.I.C.S.: 711410

Scene Model Management Pty Ltd. (1)
Level 2 181 Riley St, Darlinghurst, NSW 2010, Sydney, Australia (100%)
Tel.: (61) 283357293
Web Site: http://www.scenemodels.com
Modeling Agency Management
N.A.I.C.S.: 711410

BKN BIOSTROM AG
Graf von Galen Strasse 17, D-49377, Vechta, Germany
Tel.: (49) 4441909660
Year Founded: 2006
Emp.: 30
Holding Company; Biogas Plant Operations & Renewable Energy Resource Research
N.A.I.C.S.: 551112
Gunter Schlotmann (COO & Chm-Exec Bd)

BKW AG
Viktoriaplatz 2, 3013, Bern, Switzerland
Tel.: (41) 584775356
Web Site: https://www.bkw.ch
Year Founded: 1898
BKW—(SWX)
Rev.: $5,763,636,364
Assets: $13,176,496,674
Liabilities: $8,321,064,302
Net Worth: $4,855,432,373
Earnings: $636,917,960
Emp.: 7,997
Fiscal Year-end: 12/31/22
Eletric Power Generation Services
N.A.I.C.S.: 221111
Suzanne Thoma (Chm-Mgmt Bd & CEO)

Subsidiaries:

A. Dietrich Kalte Klima Luftung AG (1)
Steinwiesenstr 8, 8222, Beringen, Switzerland
Tel.: (41) 526813939
Web Site: https://www.dietrich-klima.ch
Air Conditioning Product Distr
N.A.I.C.S.: 423730

A1 Elektro AG (1)
In der Luberzen 42, 8902, Urdorf, Switzerland
Tel.: (41) 447354040
Web Site: https://www.a1-elektro.ch
Engineeering Services
N.A.I.C.S.: 541330

AEK Build Tec AG (1)
Industriestrasse West 24, 4613, Rickenbach, Switzerland
Tel.: (41) 622091010
Web Site: http://www.aekbuildtec.ch
Building Automation Services
N.A.I.C.S.: 236220

AEK Elektro AG (1)
Dammstrasse 12, 4500, Solothurn, Switzerland
Tel.: (41) 326248686
Web Site: http://www.aekelektro.ch
Building Automation Services
N.A.I.C.S.: 236220

AEK Energie AG (1)
Westbahnhofstrasse 3, 4502, Solothurn, Switzerland
Tel.: (41) 326248888
Web Site: http://www.aek.ch
Facility Services
N.A.I.C.S.: 561210

AEK Pellet AG (1)
Industriegebiet Klus, Balsthal, 4710, Solothurn, Switzerland
Tel.: (41) 584778082
Web Site: https://www.aekpellets.ch
Electric Power Distr

N.A.I.C.S.: 221122

AEP Planung und Beratung Gesellschaft mbH (1)
Munchner Strasse 22, 6130, Schwaz, Austria
Tel.: (43) 524271455
Web Site: https://www.aep.co.at
Building Services
N.A.I.C.S.: 561790

ASAG Air System AG (1)
Dennliweg 33, 4900, Langenthal, Switzerland
Tel.: (41) 629220055
Web Site: https://www.asag-air.ch
Air Conditioning Product Distr
N.A.I.C.S.: 423730

Ahochn AG (1)
Lagerstrasse 14, 8600, Dubendorf, Switzerland
Tel.: (41) 84779090
Web Site: https://www.ahochn.ch
Renewable Energy Services
N.A.I.C.S.: 221111

Aicher, De Martin, Zweng AG (1)
Wurzenbachstrasse 56, 6006, Lucerne, Switzerland
Tel.: (41) 587217000
Web Site: https://www.adz.ch
Emp.: 59
Construction Services
N.A.I.C.S.: 236220

Arpe AG (1)
Hauptstrasse 1, Buckten, 4446, Sissach, Switzerland
Tel.: (41) 614662000
Web Site: https://www.arpe.ch
Construction Services
N.A.I.C.S.: 236220

BEBAG Bioenergie Batterkinden AG (1)
Industriestrasse 30, Batterkinden, 3315, Bern, Switzerland
Tel.: (41) 326654428
Web Site: https://www.bebag-bioenergie.ch
Biogas Energy Generation Services
N.A.I.C.S.: 221117

BKW AEK Contracting AG (1)
Westbahnhofstrasse 3, 4502, Solothurn, Switzerland
Tel.: (41) 584775656
Web Site: https://www.bac.ch
Air Conditioning Product Distr
N.A.I.C.S.: 423730

BKW Energie AG (1)
Viktoriaplatz 2, 3013, Bern, Switzerland
Tel.: (41) 844121113
Renewable Energy Services
N.A.I.C.S.: 221111

BKW Italia S.p.A. (1)
Via Gustavo Fara 26, 20124, Milan, Italy
Tel.: (39) 0237011750
Web Site: https://www.bkw-italia.it
Renewable Energy Services
N.A.I.C.S.: 221114
Marco Ortu (CEO & Country Mgr)

BKW Smart Energy & Mobility AG (1)
Westbahnhofstrasse 3, 4500, Solothurn, Switzerland
Tel.: (41) 584774919
Web Site: https://www.smart-mobility.ch
Other Electronic Parts Distr
N.A.I.C.S.: 423690

BPU Ingenieurunternehmung AG (1)
Bernstrasse 21, 3400, Burgdorf, Switzerland
Tel.: (41) 344451145
Web Site: https://bpu-ingenieure.ch
Engineeering Services
N.A.I.C.S.: 541330

Bajuenergy Wind GmbH (1)
Marie-Curie-Strasse 5, 16225, Eberswalde, Germany
Tel.: (49) 3334380998
Web Site: http://www.bajuenergy.de
Wind Turbine Mfr & Distr
N.A.I.C.S.: 333611

Balzer Ingenieure AG (1)

La-Nicca-Strasse 6, 7000, Chur, Switzerland
Tel.: (41) 584776060
Web Site: https://balzer-ingenieure.ch
Engineeering Services
N.A.I.C.S.: 541330

Baumeler Leitungsbau AG (1)
Dorfstrasse 43, 6035, Perlen, Switzerland
Tel.: (41) 4103347
Web Site: https://www.baumeler-leitungsbau.ch
Construction Services
N.A.I.C.S.: 236220

CC Energie SA (1)
Irisweg 12, 3280, Morat, Switzerland
Tel.: (41) 264676666
Web Site: https://www.ccenergie.ch
Electric Power Distr
N.A.I.C.S.: 221122

Curea Elektro AG (1)
Muhlestrasse 5, 7302, Landquart, Switzerland
Tel.: (41) 813006969
Web Site: https://www.curea.ch
Construction Services
N.A.I.C.S.: 236220

Daninger + Partner Engineering GmbH (1)
Reininghausstrasse 78, 8020, Graz, Austria
Tel.: (43) 509785000
Web Site: https://www.daninger.at
Building Services
N.A.I.C.S.: 561790

Darnuzer Ingenieure AG (1)
Bramabuelstrasse 15 Platz, 7270, Davos, Switzerland
Tel.: (41) 814153100
Web Site: https://www.darnuzer.ch
Engineeering Services
N.A.I.C.S.: 541330

E3 HLK AG (1)
Horwerstrasse 62, 6010, Kriens, Switzerland
Tel.: (41) 413292040
Web Site: https://www.e3-hlk.ch
Renewable Energy Services
N.A.I.C.S.: 221111

Electricite G. Bugnard SA (1)
Rue de l Etang 8, 1630, Bulle, Switzerland
Tel.: (41) 269273035
Web Site: http://www.bugnard-electricite.ch
Electrical Installation Services
N.A.I.C.S.: 238210

Elektro Feuz AG (1)
Spillstattstrasse 8, 3818, Grindelwald, Switzerland
Tel.: (41) 338532133
Web Site: https://www.feuzag.ch
Electrical Installation Services
N.A.I.C.S.: 238210

Elektro Naegelin AG (1)
Guterstrasse 10, 4402, Frenkendorf, Switzerland
Tel.: (41) 619012626
Web Site: https://www.elektro-naegelin.ch
Construction Services
N.A.I.C.S.: 236220

Elektro Winter AG (1)
Eichfeldstrasse 3, Rapperswil-Jona, 8645, Saint Gallen, Switzerland
Tel.: (41) 552206220
Web Site: https://www.winter-gruppe.ch
Construction Services
N.A.I.C.S.: 236220

Enerpeak AG (1)
Stettbachstrasse 7, 8600, Dubendorf, Switzerland
Tel.: (41) 584778900
Web Site: https://www.enerpeak.ch
Engineeering Services
N.A.I.C.S.: 541330

Flotron AG (1)
Gemeindemattenstrasse 4, Meiringen, 3860, Bern, Switzerland
Tel.: (41) 339723030
Web Site: https://www.flotron.ch
Engineeering Services
N.A.I.C.S.: 541330

Frey + Gnehm Ingenieure AG (1)
Solothurnerstrasse 257, 4600, Olten, Switzerland
Tel.: (41) 622062424
Web Site: https://www.frey-gnehm.ch
Real Estate Services
N.A.I.C.S.: 531210

Grunder Ingenieure AG (1)
Bernstrasse 19, 3400, Burgdorf, Switzerland
Tel.: (41) 344601010
Web Site: https://grunder.ch
Emp.: 60
Engineeering Services
N.A.I.C.S.: 541330

Guggisberg Kurz AG (1)
Zentweg 46, 3072, Ostermundigen, Switzerland
Tel.: (41) 313306565
Web Site: https://www.guggisbergkurz.ch
Other Electronic Parts Distr
N.A.I.C.S.: 423690

Hensel AG Elektrotechnische Unternehmungen (1)
Berninastrasse 46, 8057, Zurich, Switzerland
Tel.: (41) 443640404
Web Site: http://www.hensel.ch
Engineeering Services
N.A.I.C.S.: 541330

Hertig Haustechnik AG (1)
Schutzenmattweg 35, 5610, Wohlen, Switzerland
Tel.: (41) 566211111
Web Site: https://www.hhertig.ch
Electrical Mfr
N.A.I.C.S.: 335210

Hertli & Bertschy AG, elektrische Anlagen (1)
Schwarzseestrasse 12, 1712, Tafers, Switzerland
Tel.: (41) 264941010
Web Site: https://www.hertlibertschy.ch
Electrical Mfr
N.A.I.C.S.: 335210

Hinni AG (1)
Gewerbestrasse 18, Biel-Benken, 4105, Arlesheim, Switzerland
Tel.: (41) 617266600
Web Site: https://www.hinni.ch
Water Supply Services
N.A.I.C.S.: 561320

Holzwarme Grindelwald AG (1)
Endweg 75, 3818, Grindelwald, Switzerland
Tel.: (41) 584775656
Web Site: http://www.holzwaerme-grindelwald.ch
Wood Waste Services
N.A.I.C.S.: 562111

Hydroconsult GmbH (1)
Reininghausstrasse 78, 8020, Graz, Austria
Tel.: (43) 509780
Web Site: https://www.hydroconsult.net
Engineeering Services
N.A.I.C.S.: 541330

Hydronext SAS (1)
14 rue Ybry, 92200, Neuilly-sur-Seine, France
Tel.: (33) 184200236
Web Site: https://www.hydronext.fr
Electrical Engineering Services
N.A.I.C.S.: 541330

IKK Engineering GmbH (1)
Reininghausstrasse 78, 8020, Graz, Austria
Tel.: (43) 509782000
Web Site: http://www.ikk.at
Building Construction & Civil Engineering Services
N.A.I.C.S.: 541330
Bernhard Kaufmann *(Engr-Civil)*

ISP Electro Solutions AG (1)
Zentweg 46, 3072, Ostermundigen, Switzerland
Tel.: (41) 319304646
Web Site: https://www.ispag.ch
Electrical Mfr
N.A.I.C.S.: 335210

ITS Ingenieurgesellschaft mbH (1)
Parkallee 1-Marstall, 99867, Gotha, Germany
Tel.: (49) 3621302660
Web Site: https://www.its-gotha.de
Engineeering Services
N.A.I.C.S.: 541330

IWM AG (1)
Route de Pre-Berard 26, 1870, Monthey, Switzerland
Tel.: (41) 244723003
Web Site: https://www.iwm.ch
Electrical Mfr
N.A.I.C.S.: 335210

Inag-Nievergelt AG (1)
Hohlstrasse 536, 8048, Zurich, Switzerland
Tel.: (41) 444323232
Web Site: https://www.inag.ch
Plumbing Equipment Services
N.A.I.C.S.: 532490

Inelectro SA (1)
Route de Coeuve 13, 2900, Porrentruy, Switzerland
Tel.: (41) 324651150
Web Site: https://www.inelectro.ch
Electrical Mfr
N.A.I.C.S.: 335210

Ingenhoven Architects International GmbH & Co. KG (1)
Plange Muhle 1, 40221, Dusseldorf, Germany
Tel.: (49) 2113010101
Web Site: http://www.ingenhovenarchitects.com
Emp.: 100
Architecture & Planning Services
N.A.I.C.S.: 541310
Christoph Ingenhoven *(Founder & Principal)*

Ingenieurburo Prof. Dr.-Ing. Vogt Planungsgesellschaft mbH (1)
Schonbachstrasse 2, 04299, Leipzig, Germany
Tel.: (49) 3412330559
Web Site: https://www.ib-prof-vogt-leipzig.de
Emp.: 37
Architecture & Planning Services
N.A.I.C.S.: 541310

Institut Dr.-Ing. Gauer Ingenieurgesellschaft mbH (1)
Gutenbergstrasse 9, 93128, Regenstauf, Germany
Tel.: (49) 940293000
Web Site: https://www.ifbgauer.de
Road Construction Services
N.A.I.C.S.: 237310

Institut Gauer GmbH (1)
Gutenbergstrasse 9, 93128, Regenstauf, Germany
Tel.: (49) 94029300900
Web Site: https://www.gauergmbh.de
Surveyor Services
N.A.I.C.S.: 541370

Jermann Ingenieure und Geometer AG (1)
Altenmatteweg 1, 4144, Arlesheim, Switzerland
Tel.: (41) 617069393
Web Site: https://www.jermann-ag.ch
Engineeering Services
N.A.I.C.S.: 541330

KAE Kraftwerks- & Anlagen-Engineering GmbH (1)
Pilatusring 12 Hausen, 91353, Miltenberg, Germany
Tel.: (49) 91917169180
Web Site: https://www.kae-gmbh.de
Hardware Product Mfr
N.A.I.C.S.: 332510

KFP Ingenieure GmbH (1)
Luneburger Schanze 9, 21614, Buxtehude, Germany
Tel.: (49) 416174010
Web Site: https://www.kfp-ingenieure.de
Engineeering Services
N.A.I.C.S.: 541330

KMT Planungsgesellschaft mbH (1)
Erdkampsweg 49, 22335, Hamburg, Germany
Tel.: (49) 405005730
Web Site: https://www.kmt-ai.de

Engineeering Services
N.A.I.C.S.: 541330

Karl Waechter AG (1)
Eidmattstrasse 14, 8032, Zurich, Switzerland
Tel.: (41) 447128080
Web Site: https://www.karlwaechter.ch
Emp.: 50
Building Services
N.A.I.C.S.: 561790

LTB Leitungsbau GmbH (1)
Friedrich-List-Str 27, 01445, Radebeul, Germany
Tel.: (49) 3518450
Web Site: https://www.ltb-leitungsbau.de
Building Construction Services
N.A.I.C.S.: 236220

Lindschulte + GGL Ingenieurgesellschaft mbH (1)
Neuer Weg 24, 47803, Krefeld, Germany
Tel.: (49) 2151479900
Engineeering Services
N.A.I.C.S.: 541330

Lindschulte Ingenieurgesellschaft mbH (1)
Nino-Allee 30, 48529, Nordhorn, Germany
Tel.: (49) 592188440
Web Site: https://www.lindschulte.de
Engineeering Services
N.A.I.C.S.: 541330

Lindschulte Planungsgesellschaft mbH (1)
Ofener Str 4, 26121, Oldenburg, Germany
Tel.: (49) 4413506680
Web Site: https://www.lindschulte-khp.de
Architecture & Planning Services
N.A.I.C.S.: 541310

Lindschulte Thillmann GmbH (1)
Mainzer Street 93, 56068, Koblenz, Germany
Tel.: (49) 2619883890
Web Site: http://www.thillmann-architekten.de
Building Construction Services
N.A.I.C.S.: 236220

Lutz Bodenmuller AG (1)
Steinwiesenstrasse 10, 8222, Beringen, Switzerland
Tel.: (41) 526851821
Web Site: https://www.solarlutz.ch
Building Services
N.A.I.C.S.: 561790

Marcel Rieben Ingenieure AG (1)
Waldeggstrasse 41, 3097, Liebefeld, Switzerland
Tel.: (41) 584774949
Web Site: https://www.mri.ch
Engineeering Services
N.A.I.C.S.: 541330

Marzolo & Partner AG (1)
Industriepark 3, 8610, Uster, Switzerland
Tel.: (41) 449056080
Web Site: http://www.marzolo.ch
Building Services
N.A.I.C.S.: 561790

Michel Rime SA (1)
Chemin de la Clopette 7, Echallens, 1040, Lausanne, Switzerland
Tel.: (41) 218811170
Web Site: https://www.michelrimesa.ch
Engineeering Services
N.A.I.C.S.: 541330

Neukom Installationen AG (1)
Lachewag 2, 8197, Rafz, Switzerland
Tel.: (41) 448791414
Web Site: http://www.neukom.com
Building Services
N.A.I.C.S.: 561790

Osd GmbH (1)
Hamburger Allee 26-28, 60486, Frankfurt am Main, Germany
Tel.: (49) 692722170
Web Site: https://www.o-s-d.com
Structural Design Services
N.A.I.C.S.: 541330

PALATIA Ingenieur- und Stadtebau GmbH (1)

BKW AG—(Continued)

Luitpoldstrasse 60a, 67806, Rockenhausen, Germany
Tel.: (49) 63615001
Web Site: https://www.palatia.com
Building Construction Services
N.A.I.C.S.: 236220

Podufal-Wiehofsky Generalplanung GmbH (1)
Hartsieker Weg 150, 32584, Lohne, Germany
Tel.: (49) 5732686800
Web Site: https://www.wiehofsky.de
Engineering Services
N.A.I.C.S.: 541330

Propertunities Immobilien Consulting GmbH (1)
Graf-Adolf-Platz 6, 40213, Dusseldorf, Germany
Tel.: (49) 2118681310
Web Site: https://www.propertunities.de
Real Estate Consulting Service
N.A.I.C.S.: 531390

Proxima Scandinavia AS (1)
Maridalsveien 91, 0461, Oslo, Norway
Tel.: (47) 95218549
Web Site: http://www.proxima-scandinavia.com
Construction Development Services
N.A.I.C.S.: 236220
Tormod Nyberg (CEO)

Proxima Solutions GmbH (1)
Hauptstrase 65, 12159, Berlin, Germany
Tel.: (49) 30240006014
Web Site: http://www.proximasolutions.eu
Software Development Services
N.A.I.C.S.: 541511
Giuseppe Madia (Mng Dir)

R. Monnet & Cie SA (1)
Avenue du Rumine 20, 1005, Lausanne, Switzerland
Tel.: (41) 213214455
Web Site: https://www.rmonnet.ch
Building Services
N.A.I.C.S.: 561790

Raboud Energie SA (1)
Rue de l'Etang 8, 1630, Bulle, Switzerland
Tel.: (41) 263471010
Web Site: https://www.raboud-energie.ch
Building Services
N.A.I.C.S.: 561790

Ruefer Ingenieure AG (1)
Bernstrasse 14, 3550, Langnau, Switzerland
Tel.: (41) 344084848
Web Site: https://ruefer-ing.ch
Building Services
N.A.I.C.S.: 561790

Securon AG (1)
Westbahnhofstrasse 3, 4502, Solothurn, Switzerland
Tel.: (41) 326248383
Web Site: https://www.securon.ch
Engineering Services
N.A.I.C.S.: 541330

Societe des Forces Electriques de la Goule SA (1)
Route de Tramelan 16, 2610, Saint Imier, Switzerland
Tel.: (41) 329424111
Web Site: https://www.lagoule.ch
Building Services
N.A.I.C.S.: 561790

Solar-Log GmbH (1)
Fuhrmannstrasse 9, Binsdorf, 72351, Geislingen, Germany
Tel.: (49) 74284089300
Web Site: https://www.solar-log.com
Renewable Energy Services
N.A.I.C.S.: 221114

TBH Ingenieur GmbH (1)
Reininghausstrasse 78, 8020, Graz, Austria
Tel.: (43) 509784000
Web Site: https://www.tbh.at
Energy Consulting Services
N.A.I.C.S.: 541690
Robert Pichler (Exec Dir & Mgr-Energy-Europe)

TID Technische Informationen & Dienstleistungen P. Tschannen GmbH (1)
Dahlenweg 3, Schupfen, 3054, Bern, Switzerland
Tel.: (41) 318692491
Web Site: https://www.tid-cad.ch
Building Services
N.A.I.C.S.: 561790

Traital S.r.l. (1)
Viale Toscana 13 / B, 20136, Milan, Italy
Tel.: (39) 025695402
Web Site: https://www.traital.it
Network Infrastructure Services
N.A.I.C.S.: 518210

UMB Communication AG (1)
In der Luberzen 1, 8902, Urdorf, Switzerland
Tel.: (41) 582632111
Web Site: http://www.swisspro.ch
Engineering Services
N.A.I.C.S.: 541330
Bernard Frossard (CEO)

WAB Technique S.A.R.L. (1)
Route de Chesalles 13, 1723, Marly, Switzerland
Tel.: (41) 264365800
Web Site: https://www.wab-technique.ch
Engineering Services
N.A.I.C.S.: 541330

Wald + Corbe Consulting GmbH (1)
Am Hecklehamm 18, Hugelsheim, 76549, Karlsruhe, Germany
Tel.: (49) 7229187600
Web Site: https://www.wald-corbe.de
Engineering Services
N.A.I.C.S.: 541330

Weber AG (1)
Industriestrasse 9, 8712, Stafa, Switzerland
Tel.: (41) 434772233
Web Site: https://www.weber-staefa.ch
Building Services
N.A.I.C.S.: 561790

Werner Electro AG (1)
Weidenweg 235, PO Box 288, 3902, Brig, Switzerland
Tel.: (41) 279224050
Web Site: https://www.wernerag.ch
Building Services
N.A.I.C.S.: 561790

Wind Energy Trading WET AG (1)
Avenue Mon-Repos 14, Vaud, 1005, Lausanne, Switzerland
Tel.: (41) 217910533
Web Site: https://www.wet-ag.ch
Engineering Services
N.A.I.C.S.: 541330

Winkelmann Elektro AG (1)
Vordere Gasse 16, Kerzers, 3210, Fribourg, Switzerland
Tel.: (41) 317558414
Web Site: https://www.winkelmann-elektro.ch
Building Services
N.A.I.C.S.: 561790

Wiserock AG (1)
Gemeindemattenstrasse 4, Meiringen, 3860, Bern, Switzerland
Tel.: (41) 339723032
Web Site: https://wiserock.ch
Engineering Services
N.A.I.C.S.: 541330

b+s Elektro Telematik AG (1)
Hauptstrasse 183, 4466, Ormalingen, Switzerland
Tel.: (41) 619859797
Web Site: https://www.bs-elektro.ch
Construction Services
N.A.I.C.S.: 236220

pi-System GmbH (1)
Langgasse 3, Oberkirch, 6208, Sursee, Switzerland
Tel.: (41) 412293000
Web Site: https://www.pi-system.ch
Construction Services
N.A.I.C.S.: 532412

BL PHARMTECH CORP

7F 767 Sinsu-ro, Suji-gu, Yongin, Gyeonggi-do, Korea (South)
Tel.: (82) 0234014490
Web Site: http://www.nextbt.co.kr
Year Founded: 1995
065170—(KRS)
Rev.: $61,814,764
Assets: $79,527,552
Liabilities: $48,017,572
Net Worth: $31,509,980
Earnings: ($10,469,102)
Emp.: 21
Fiscal Year-end: 12/31/22
Food Products Mfr
N.A.I.C.S.: 311421
Park Yeong-Cheol (Dir-Rep)

Subsidiaries:

TCM Biosciences, Inc. (1)
Bldg 3 3rd fl Pangyo-ro 228 beon-gil 15, Bundang-gu, Seongnam, 13487, Gyeonggi-do, Korea (South) (100%)
Tel.: (82) 316983041
Web Site: http://www.tcmbiosciences.com
Medical Device Mfr
N.A.I.C.S.: 339112
Kim Sung-Mok (Exec Dir)

BLAACANKA A.D.

Kosancic Ivana 35, Prokuplje, Serbia
Tel.: (381) 27321826
Year Founded: 2003
BLCN—(BEL)
Sales Range: Less than $1 Million
Apparels Mfr
N.A.I.C.S.: 315120
Ivana Dikic (Exec Dir)

BLACK & DECKER HOLDINGS GMBH

Black-&-Decker-Str 40, Idstein, 65510, Germany
Tel.: (49) 6126210
Power-Driven Handtool Mfr
N.A.I.C.S.: 333991

BLACK & MCDONALD LIMITED

Suite 2100-2 Bloor Street East, Toronto, M4W 1A8, ON, Canada
Tel.: (416) 920-5100
Web Site:
http://www.blackandmcdonald.com
Year Founded: 1920
Sales Range: $600-649.9 Million
Emp.: 3,000
Electrical Contractor Services
N.A.I.C.S.: 238210
J. Bruce McDonald (Co-Pres & Co-CEO)

Subsidiaries:

Black & McDonald Bermuda Limited (1)
KEMH Re-Development Site 9 Point Finger Road, Paget, DV 04, Bermuda
Tel.: (441) 232 0234
Industrial Building Construction Services
N.A.I.C.S.: 236210
Leonard Fearon (Sr Mgr-Facility)

Land & Sea Instrumentation Ltd (1)
25 Estates Rd Woodside Industrial Park, Dartmouth, B2Y 4K3, NS, Canada
Tel.: (902) 461-2009
Web Site:
http://www.landandseainstruments.com
Industrial Machinery Repair & Maintenance Services
N.A.I.C.S.: 811310
Charles Callaghan (Mgr-Quality Assurance & Safety)

Roberts Onsite Inc. (1)
209 Manitou Drive, Kitchener, N2C 1L4, ON, Canada
Tel.: (519) 578-2230
Web Site: http://www.robertsonsite.ca
Emp.: 70
Building Maintenance Services
N.A.I.C.S.: 561790

BLACK BOX LIMITED

501 5th Floor Building No 9 Airoli Knowledge Park, MIDC Industrial Area, Mumbai, 400708, Maharashtra, India
Tel.: (91) 2266617272 In
Web Site: https://www.blackbox.com
Year Founded: 1986
BBOX (NSE)
Rev.: $639,522,975
Assets: $314,374,515
Liabilities: $286,159,965
Net Worth: $28,214,550
Earnings: $10,659,285
Emp.: 381
Fiscal Year-end: 03/31/21
Communications Systems, Applications & Services
N.A.I.C.S.: 517810
Sanjeev Shekhar Verma (Exec Dir)

Subsidiaries:

AGC Networks & Cyber Solutions Limited (1)
The Oval Office 2-3 2nd Fl Off Ring Road Westlands, PO Box 45742-00100, Nairobi, Kenya
Tel.: (254) 708803803
Software Development Services
N.A.I.C.S.: 541511

AGC Networks Pte. Limited (1)
50 Raffles Place #32-01 Singapore Land Tower, Singapore, 048623, Singapore
Tel.: (65) 663 128 78
IT Services
N.A.I.C.S.: 513210
Sanjeev Verma (Pres)

Subsidiary (US):

Black Box Corporation (2)
1000 Park Dr, Lawrence, PA 15055-1018
Tel.: (724) 746-5500
Web Site: http://www.blackbox.com
Rev.: $774,637,000
Assets: $376,335,000
Liabilities: $325,993,000
Net Worth: $50,342,000
Earnings: ($100,095,000)
Emp.: 3,264
Fiscal Year-end: 03/31/2018
Computer Network Infrastructure Services
N.A.I.C.S.: 334118
Josh Whitney (Sr VP-Technical Products Solutions)

Subsidiary (Domestic):

ACS Dataline, LP (3)
2535 Brockton Dr Ste 400, Austin, TX 78758
Tel.: (512) 837-4400
Information Technology Consulting Services
N.A.I.C.S.: 541512

Subsidiary (Non-US):

Black Box A/S (3)
Stoberivej 14 2 sal, Koge, 4600, Denmark (100%)
Tel.: (45) 56633010
Web Site: http://www.blackbox.dk
Sales Range: $25-49.9 Million
Emp.: 10
Network Infrastructure Services
N.A.I.C.S.: 541519
Pia Dyrberg (Gen Mgr)

Black Box AB (3)
Maltesholmsvagen 138, PO BOX 4490, 165 16, Stockholm, Sweden
Tel.: (46) 84455880
Web Site: http://www.blackboxab.se
Communication Equipment Installation Services
N.A.I.C.S.: 238210

Black Box Chile S.A. (3)
Calle Nueva 1661 Modulo E, Huechuraba, Santiago, Chile
Tel.: (56) 224891210
Web Site: https://www.blackbox.cl
Network Infrastructure Services
N.A.I.C.S.: 541519
Jorge Navarrete (Country Mgr)

Black Box Comunicaciones, S.A. (3)
Avenida de la Industria 32, Alcobendas, 28108, Madrid, Spain
Tel.: (34) 916590191
Web Site: https://www.blackbox.es
Communication Equipment Distr
N.A.I.C.S.: 423690

Black Box Datacom B.V. (3)
Zonnebaan 39, 3542 EB, Utrecht, Netherlands
Tel.: (31) 302417700
Web Site: http://www.blackbox.nl
Sales Range: $25-49.9 Million
Emp.: 25
Electronic Parts & Equipment Whslr
N.A.I.C.S.: 423690
Sean Kirby (Country Mgr)

Black Box Deutschland GmbH (3)
Ludwigstrasse 45 B, 85399, Hallbergmoos, Germany
Tel.: (49) 81155410
Web Site: http://www.black-box.com
Sales Range: $900-999.9 Million
Emp.: 25
Network Infrastructure Services
N.A.I.C.S.: 541519
Peter Obermeir (Mng Dir)

Black Box Finland Oy (3)
Vaisalantie 6, Espoo, 02130, Finland
Tel.: (358) 201888888
Web Site: http://www.blackbox.fi
Sales Range: $25-49.9 Million
Emp.: 10
Network Infrastructure Services
N.A.I.C.S.: 541519

Black Box France (3)
46 Rue de la Couture, 94150, Rungis, Cedex, France (100%)
Tel.: (33) 145606717
Web Site: https://www.blackbox.fr
Sales Range: $25-49.9 Million
Emp.: 40
Network Infrastructure Services
N.A.I.C.S.: 541519

Black Box GmbH (3)
Hegelgasse 8/22, 1010, Vienna, Austria
Tel.: (43) 12569856
Web Site: https://www.black-box.at
Telecommunication Product Distr
N.A.I.C.S.: 423690

Black Box International B.V. (3)
Zonnebaan 39, 3542 EB, Utrecht, Netherlands
Tel.: (31) 302417700
Web Site: https://www.blackbox.nl
Telecommunication Product Distr
N.A.I.C.S.: 423690

Black Box Italia S.r.l. (3)
Viale Delle Industrie 11, 20090, Vimodrone, Italy (100%)
Tel.: (39) 02274041
Web Site: http://www.blackbox.it
Sales Range: $25-49.9 Million
Emp.: 16
Network Infrastructure Services
N.A.I.C.S.: 541519

Black Box Network Products NV (3)
Ikaroslaan 69, 1930, Zaventem, Flemish Brabant, Belgium
Tel.: (32) 27258550
Web Site: http://www.blackbox.be
Emp.: 17
Network Providing Services
N.A.I.C.S.: 541512
Josh Witney (CEO)

Branch (Domestic):

Black Box Network Services (3)
2100 Riverchase Ctr Ste 214, Birmingham, AL 35244-1852
Tel.: (205) 444-2200
Web Site: http://www.blackbox.com
Sales Range: $10-24.9 Million
Emp.: 25
Telecommunication Servicesb
N.A.I.C.S.: 517810

Black Box Network Services (3)
6800 Lake Dr Ste 240, West Des Moines, IA 50309-6704
Tel.: (515) 698-5000
Web Site: http://www.blackbox.com

Sales Range: $10-24.9 Million
Emp.: 25
Telecommunication Servicesb
N.A.I.C.S.: 517112
Robert Plate (Gen Mgr)

Black Box Network Services (3)
10503 Timberwood Cir Ste 202, Louisville, KY 40223
Tel.: (502) 423-4200
Web Site: http://www.blackbox.com
Sales Range: $25-49.9 Million
Emp.: 2
Telecommunication Servicesb
N.A.I.C.S.: 517810
Sharon Colbin (Office Mgr)

Black Box Network Services (3)
6650 W Snowville Rd, Brecksville, OH 44141
Tel.: (440) 526-4350
Web Site: http://www.blackbox.com
Sales Range: $50-74.9 Million
Emp.: 80
Telecommunication Servicesb
N.A.I.C.S.: 517810

Black Box Network Services (3)
8023 E 63rd Pl Ste 225, Tulsa, OK 74133
Tel.: (918) 488-7700
Web Site: http://www.blackbox.com
Sales Range: $25-49.9 Million
Emp.: 10
Communication Service
N.A.I.C.S.: 423610

Black Box Network Services (3)
5959 Corporate Dr Ste 250, Houston, TX 77036
Tel.: (713) 307-4743
Web Site: http://www.blackbox.com
Sales Range: $200-249.9 Million
Fully Integrated Enterprise Communications Services & Voice & Data Conveyence Operations
N.A.I.C.S.: 517810

Black Box Network Services (3)
148 Park S Ct, Nashville, TN 37210-4823 (100%)
Tel.: (615) 256-8951
Web Site: http://www.blackbox.com
Sales Range: $50-74.9 Million
Emp.: 100
Network Infrastructure Services
N.A.I.C.S.: 541519
Trish Harris (VP-Admin)

Black Box Network Services (3)
255 Enterprise Dr, Lewis Center, OH 43035-9418
Tel.: (614) 825-7428
Web Site: http://www.blackbox.com
Sales Range: $25-49.9 Million
Emp.: 40
Network Infrastructure Services
N.A.I.C.S.: 541519

Black Box Network Services (3)
3708 Davis Ave, Cincinnati, OH 45211
Tel.: (513) 662-3800
Web Site: http://www.blackbox.com
Sales Range: $100-124.9 Million
Emp.: 220
Network Infrastructure Services
N.A.I.C.S.: 541519

Black Box Network Services (3)
2707 Main St, Duluth, GA 30096-2741 (100%)
Tel.: (678) 475-5500
Web Site: http://www.blackbox.com
Sales Range: $50-74.9 Million
Emp.: 30
Network Infrastructure Services
N.A.I.C.S.: 541519

Black Box Network Services (3)
7950 Cherry Ave Ste 107, Fontana, CA 92336
Tel.: (909) 428-9030
Web Site: http://www.blackbox.com
Rev.: $14,000,000
Emp.: 100
Network Infrastructure Services
N.A.I.C.S.: 541519
Dave Berry (Mgr-Ops)

Black Box Network Services (3)
3247 Tech Dr N, Saint Petersburg, FL 33716 (100%)

Tel.: (727) 571-4144
Web Site: http://www.blackbox.com
Sales Range: $25-49.9 Million
Emp.: 10
Network Infrastructure Services
N.A.I.C.S.: 541519
Patrick Chouinard (Mgr-Ops)

Black Box Network Services (3)
1701 Lomond St, Winston Salem, NC 27127-2730 (100%)
Tel.: (336) 748-0500
Web Site: http://www.blackbox.com
Sales Range: $25-49.9 Million
Emp.: 20
Network Infrastructure Services
N.A.I.C.S.: 541519
Bradley Foster (Acct Mgr)

Black Box Network Services (3)
6000 New Horizons Blvd, Amityville, NY 11701 (100%)
Tel.: (631) 232-8300
Web Site: http://www.blackbox.com
Sales Range: $10-24.9 Million
Emp.: 150
Local & Long Distance Telephone Communications
N.A.I.C.S.: 517121
James McKenna (Gen Mgr)

Black Box Network Services (3)
1550 NE Loop 410 Ste 121, San Antonio, TX 78209
Tel.: (210) 828-4966
Web Site: http://www.blackbox.com
Sales Range: $25-49.9 Million
Emp.: 11
Networking Services
N.A.I.C.S.: 335921

Black Box Network Services (3)
800 SW 34th St A, Renton, WA 98057
Tel.: (206) 575-1363
Web Site: http://www.blackbox.com
Sales Range: $25-49.9 Million
Emp.: 20
Network Infrastructure Services
N.A.I.C.S.: 541519
Rob Tate (Gen Mgr)

Black Box Network Services (3)
1930 Junction Ave, San Jose, CA 95131
Tel.: (408) 432-6100
Web Site: http://www.blackbox.com
Sales Range: $50-74.9 Million
Emp.: 28
Network Infrastructure Services
N.A.I.C.S.: 541519

Black Box Network Services (3)
6675 S Kenton St Ste 116, Englewood, CO 80111-6823
Tel.: (303) 623-2631
Web Site: http://www.blackbox.com
Sales Range: $25-49.9 Million
Emp.: 5
Network Infrastructure Services
N.A.I.C.S.: 541519

Black Box Network Services (3)
851 Busse Rd, Elk Grove Village, IL 60007
Tel.: (847) 439-5000
Web Site: http://www.blackbox.com
Sales Range: $25-49.9 Million
Emp.: 35
Network Infrastructure Services
N.A.I.C.S.: 541519
Anita Fletcher (Gen Mgr)

Black Box Network Services (3)
I-75 Tech Park 1391 Wheaton Dr Ste 200, Troy, MI 48083
Tel.: (248) 743-1320
Web Site: http://www.blackbox.com
Sales Range: $25-49.9 Million
Emp.: 30
Network Infrastructure Services
N.A.I.C.S.: 541519

Black Box Network Services (3)
1520 Platt Springs Rd, West Columbia, SC 29169
Tel.: (803) 791-1094
Web Site: http://www.blackbox.com
Sales Range: $25-49.9 Million
Emp.: 20
Network Infrastructure Services
N.A.I.C.S.: 541519
Kenny Parker (Project Mgr)

Black Box Network Services (3)
44873 Falcon Pl Ste 118, Sterling, VA 20166
Tel.: (703) 404-8885
Web Site: http://www.blackbox.com
Sales Range: $25-49.9 Million
Emp.: 35
Network Infrastructure Services
N.A.I.C.S.: 541519

Black Box Network Services (3)
629 1st St, Huntington, WV 25701
Tel.: (304) 525-2651
Web Site: http://www.blackbox.com
Network Infrastructure Services
N.A.I.C.S.: 541519

Black Box Network Services (3)
426 N 44th St Ste 470, Phoenix, AZ 85008-7614
Tel.: (602) 273-6400
Web Site: http://www.blackbox.com
Sales Range: $50-74.9 Million
Emp.: 20
Network Infrastructure Services
N.A.I.C.S.: 541519
Linda Bauerle (Branch Mgr)

Black Box Network Services (3)
1421 Champion Dr Ste 312, Carrollton, TX 75006
Tel.: (214) 261-3269
Web Site: http://www.blackbox.com
Sales Range: $25-49.9 Million
Emp.: 20
Network Infrastructure Services
N.A.I.C.S.: 541519
Tim D'Antonio (Gen Mgr)

Subsidiary (Non-US):

Black Box Network Services (3)
Avenida de la Industria 32, Alcobendas, 28108, Madrid, Spain
Tel.: (34) 916590191
Web Site: http://www.blackbox.es
Sales Range: $900-999.9 Million
Emp.: 10
Network Infrastructure Services
N.A.I.C.S.: 541519
Francisco Fernandez (Dir-Supervision)

Black Box Network Services (3)
Aventem Bus Pk, Ikaroslaan 57, 1930, Zaventem, Belgium
Tel.: (32) 27258550
Web Site: http://www.blackbox.be
Sales Range: $25-49.9 Million
Emp.: 30
Network Infrastructure Services
N.A.I.C.S.: 541519

Black Box Network Services (UK) Ltd. (3)
Blake House Manor Farm Road, Reading, RG2 0NA, Berkshire, United Kingdom (100%)
Tel.: (44) 1189655100
Sales Range: $50-74.9 Million
Emp.: 100
Network Infrastructure Services
N.A.I.C.S.: 541519
Leslie Fernandes (Grp Mng Dir)

Black Box Network Services AB (3)
Maltesholms Vagen 138, Hasselby, 16566, Sweden
Tel.: (46) 87390140
Web Site: http://www.blackbox.com
Sales Range: $25-49.9 Million
Emp.: 20
Network Infrastructure Services
N.A.I.C.S.: 541519
Marcel Huesman (Mng Dir)

Black Box Network Services AG (3)
Leuholz 10A, 8855, Wangen, Switzerland
Tel.: (41) 554517070
Web Site: https://www.black-box.ch
Sales Range: $25-49.9 Million
Emp.: 10
Network Infrastructure Services
N.A.I.C.S.: 541519
Angelo Stirnemann (Dir-Fin)

Black Box Network Services Australia Pty Ltd (3)
15-17 Jellico Drive, Scoresby, 3179, Australia (100%)
Tel.: (61) 1300734455

Black Box Limited—(Continued)

Web Site: https://www.blackbox.com.au
Sales Range: $25-49.9 Million
Emp.: 25
Network Infrastructure Services
N.A.I.C.S.: 541519
Denzil Stephenson (Gen Mgr)

Black Box Network Services B.V. (3)
Zonnebaan 30, PO Box 1615, 3542 EB,
Utrecht, Netherlands
Tel.: (31) 302417700
Web Site: http://www.blackbox.nl
Sales Range: $25-49.9 Million
Emp.: 25
Network Infrastructure Services
N.A.I.C.S.: 541519

**Black Box Network Services
Corporation** (3)
Nei-Hu District 2F No 24 Lane 13 Sec6
Min-Quan E Road, Taipei, 114, Taiwan
Tel.: (886) 287925789
Web Site: https://www.black-box.com.tw
Communication Equipment Distr
N.A.I.C.S.: 423690

**Black Box Network Services India
Private Limited** (3)
A-407 Neelkanth Business Park Nathani
Road, Vidyavihar, Mumbai, 400 086, Maha-
rashtra, India
Tel.: (91) 7718843838
Web Site: http://www.blackbox.com
Emp.: 3
Communication Equipment Distr
N.A.I.C.S.: 423690

Black Box Network Services NV (3)
Tel.: (32) 27258550
Web Site: https://www.blackbox.be
Emp.: 17
Communication Equipment Distr
N.A.I.C.S.: 423690
Igor Demesmaeker (Mgr-Sls)

**Black Box Network Services New
Zealand Limited** (3)
Wellesley Street, PO Box 7341, Auckland,
1036, New Zealand
Tel.: (64) 800653219
Web Site: https://www.blackboxnz.co.nz
Network Providing Services
N.A.I.C.S.: 541512

**Black Box Network Services
S.r.l.** (3)
Via Fiume Giallo 3, 00144, Rome, Italy
Tel.: (39) 065750350
Web Site: https://www.blackbox.it
Emp.: 30
Communication Equipment Installation Ser-
vices
N.A.I.C.S.: 238210

**Black Box Network Services SDN.
BHD.** (3)
Unit 19A-LGF-15 UOA Centre 19 Jalan
Pinang, 50450, Kuala Lumpur, Selangor,
Malaysia
Tel.: (60) 321631166
Web Site: https://www.blackbox.com
Emp.: 5
Communication Equipment Installation Ser-
vices
N.A.I.C.S.: 238210

**Black Box Network Services Singa-
pore Pte Ltd** (3)
151 Lorong Chuan 02-01A, New Tech Park,
Singapore, 556741, Singapore
Tel.: (65) 66717320
Web Site:
https://www.blackboxnetwork.com.sg
Sales Range: $25-49.9 Million
Emp.: 29
Network Infrastructure Services
N.A.I.C.S.: 541519
Ronnie Thien (Mng Dir)

Subsidiary (Domestic):

**Black Box Network Services, Inc. -
Government Solutions** (3)
1010 Haley Rd, Murfreesboro, TN 37129
Tel.: (615) 890-3505
Web Site: http://www.bbns-gov.com
Sales Range: $50-74.9 Million
Emp.: 100
Network Infrastructure Services

N.A.I.C.S.: 541519

Branch (Domestic):

**Black Box Network Services - Gov-
ernment Solutions** (4)
519 Oliver Rd, Montgomery, AL 36117
Tel.: (334) 409-5901
Web Site: http://www.bbns-gov.com
Sales Range: $100-124.9 Million
Emp.: 10
Network Infrastructure Services
N.A.I.C.S.: 541519

Subsidiary (Non-US):

Black Box Norge AS (3)
Damsgardsveien 131, Laksevag, 5160, Ber-
gen, Norway
Tel.: (47) 55300700
Web Site: https://www.blackboxas.no
Sales Range: $900-999.9 Million
Emp.: 10
Network Infrastructure Services
N.A.I.C.S.: 541519
Ingrid Jakobsen (Reg Mgr)

Subsidiary (Domestic):

Black Box P.R. Corp. (3)
125 Eleanor Roosevelt St, San Juan, PR
00918
Tel.: (787) 767-3500
Web Site: https://www.pr.blackbox.com
Sales Range: $25-49.9 Million
Emp.: 8
Network Infrastructure Services
N.A.I.C.S.: 541519
Myrna Suarez (Gen Mgr)

Branch (Domestic):

Black Box Philadelphia (3)
540 Township Line Rd, Blue Bell, PA 19422-
2719
Tel.: (215) 654-9226
Web Site: http://www.blackbox.com
Sales Range: $50-74.9 Million
Emp.: 120
Network Infrastructure Services
N.A.I.C.S.: 541519
Natalie Linder (Mgr-Reg)

Subsidiary (Non-US):

**Black Box Services Reseaux
Mediterranee** (3)
46 Rue De La Couture Silic 195, 94563,
Rungis, France
Tel.: (33) 820086086
Web Site: http://www.blackbox.fr.com
Emp.: 25
Communication Equipment Installation Ser-
vices
N.A.I.C.S.: 238210
Catherine Nadaud (Mgr-Sls)

**Black Box de Mexico S.A. de
C.V.** (3)
Montes Urales 755 Floor 5 Col Lomas de
Chapultepec, 11000, Mexico, DF, Mexico
Tel.: (52) 5554200100
Web Site: https://www.blackbox.com.mx
Sales Range: $25-49.9 Million
Emp.: 15
Network Infrastructure Services
N.A.I.C.S.: 541519

**Black Box do Brasil Industria e Com-
ercio Ltda** (3)
Avenida Ceci 06 Tambore, Barueri, 06460-
120, SP, Brazil
Tel.: (55) 1141344000
Web Site: https://www.blackbox.com.br
Sales Range: $25-49.9 Million
Emp.: 40
Network Infrastructure Services
N.A.I.C.S.: 541519
Wilson Donavete (Gen Mgr)

Subsidiary (Domestic):

FBS Communications, L.P. (3)
1550 NE Loop 410 Ste 121, San Antonio,
TX 78209
Tel.: (210) 828-4966
Communication Equipment Installation Ser-
vices
N.A.I.C.S.: 238210

InnerWireless, Inc. (3)

N.A.I.C.S.: 541519

Branch (Domestic):

1155 Kas Dr Ste 200, Richardson, TX
75081
Tel.: (972) 479-9898
Web Site: http://www.innerwireless.com
Wireless Telecommunication Services
N.A.I.C.S.: 517112
William Holman (Sr VP-Sls)

LOGOS Communications, Inc. (3)
26100 1st St, Westlake, OH 44145 **(100%)**
Tel.: (440) 871-0777
Web Site: http://www.logosinc.com
Sales Range: $25-49.9 Million
Emp.: 40
Communication Equipment Mfr & Distr
N.A.I.C.S.: 334290
Christopher A. Tjotjos (Pres & CEO)

Michael Electric, Inc. (3)
91 Avis Dr, Brick, NJ 08724
Tel.: (732) 892-3433
Electronic Parts & Equipment Whslr
N.A.I.C.S.: 423690

Mutual Telecom Services Inc. (3)
250 1st Ave Ste 301 1st Needham Pl,
Needham, MA 02494
Tel.: (800) 687-2848
Web Site: http://www.blackbox.com
Emp.: 10
Network Providing Services
N.A.I.C.S.: 541512
James Meade (VP-Network Ops)

Norstan, Inc. (3)
5101 Shady Oak Rd, Minnetonka, MN
55343-4100
Tel.: (952) 352-4000
Web Site: http://www.blackbox.com
Sales Range: $200-249.9 Million
Holding Company; A Full-Service Provider
of Communications Solutions that Include
Business Telephone Systems, Videoconfer-
encing Equipment, Voice Processing Prod-
ucts & Network Integration Services
N.A.I.C.S.: 561421

Subsidiary (Non-US):

Black Box Canada Corp. (4)
2225 Sheppard Ave E 16th Fl, Toronto, M2J
5C2, ON, Canada
Tel.: (416) 490-7100
Web Site: http://www.blackboxcanada.ca
Sales Range: $10-24.9 Million
Emp.: 45
Telecommunication Network Services
N.A.I.C.S.: 517810

Branch (Domestic):

Black Box Network Services (5)
Unit 1158 St 13351 Commerce Pkwy, Rich-
mond, V6V 2X7, BC, Canada **(100%)**
Tel.: (604) 276-9433
Sales Range: $10-24.9 Million
Emp.: 8
Telecommunication Servicesb
N.A.I.C.S.: 517810
John Talerico (Mgr-Sls)

Division (Domestic):

**Black Box Network Services-Voice
Services Canada** (5)
214 King St West, Toronto, M5H 3S6, ON,
Canada
Tel.: (416) 490-9500
Web Site: http://www.blackbox-vs.com
Sales Range: $10-24.9 Million
Telecommunication Servicesb
N.A.I.C.S.: 517810

Subsidiary (Domestic):

Black Box Resale Services (4)
9155 Cottonwood Ln N, Maple Grove, MN
55369
Tel.: (763) 971-6260
Web Site: http://www.blackboxresale.com
Sales Range: $25-49.9 Million
Emp.: 100
Refurbishes & Repairs Telecommunications
Equipment
N.A.I.C.S.: 541690
Linda J. Ethen (Controller)

NextiraOne (4)
1290 Silas Deane Hwy, Wethersfield, CT
06109

Tel.: (860) 258-2800
Rev.: $76,700,000
Emp.: 40
Telephone & Communication Equipment
N.A.I.C.S.: 424120

Subsidiary (Domestic):

PS Technologies, LLC (3)
2555 S Dixie Dr Ste 270, Kettering, OH
45409
Tel.: (937) 242-6422
Web Site: http://www.pst24.com
Communication Equipment Mfr
N.A.I.C.S.: 334290

Quanta Systems, LLC (3)
510 Spring St Ste 200, Herndon, VA
20170-5148 **(100%)**
Tel.: (301) 590-3300
Web Site: http://www.quantasystem.com
Sales Range: $10-24.9 Million
Emp.: 15
Government & Industrial Security Systems
N.A.I.C.S.: 561621

Scottel Voice & Data, Inc. (3)
11261 Washington Blvd, Culver City, CA
90230
Tel.: (310) 737-7300
Web Site: http://www.scottel.com
Communication Equipment Mfr
N.A.I.C.S.: 334290

UCI Communications LLC (3)
500 St Michael St, Mobile, AL 36602
Tel.: (251) 457-1404
Web Site: http://www.ucicom.com
Telephone Equipment Distr
N.A.I.C.S.: 423430

Vibes Technologies, Inc. (3)
9155 Cottonwood Ln N, Maple Grove, MN
55369
Tel.: (877) 415-3379
Web Site: http://www.blackboxresale.com
Communication Equipment Mfr
N.A.I.C.S.: 334290

AGC Networks, Inc. (1)
222 W Las Colinas Blvd Ste 200 N Tower,
Irving, TX 75039
Tel.: (972) 443-9000
Web Site: https://www.agcnetworks.com
Telecommunication Network Integration
Services
N.A.I.C.S.: 541512
Mike D. Carney (Founder, Officer-Ethics,
Sec & Sr VP)

Subsidiary (Domestic):

Ensource, Inc. (2)
7970 Bayberry Rd Ste 5, Jacksonville, FL
32256
Tel.: (904) 448-6901
Web Site: http://www.ensource.net
Telecommunication Servicesb
N.A.I.C.S.: 517810

**Transcend United Technologies
LLC** (2)
460 E Swedesford Rd Ste 1080, Wayne,
PA 19087
Tel.: (484) 654-1500
Web Site: http://www.transcendunited.com
Technical Consulting
N.A.I.C.S.: 541990
Stephen Benson (Sr VP-Managed Svcs)

**Black Box Network Services Hong
Kong Limited** (1)
14th Fl One Taikoo Place 979 Kings Road,
Quarry Bay, China (Hong Kong)
Tel.: (852) 886287925789
Information Technology Services
N.A.I.C.S.: 541512

COPC Inc. (1)
941 W Morse Blvd Ste 100, Winter Park, FL
32789
Tel.: (407) 304-9032
Web Site: https://www.copc.com
Business Consulting Services
N.A.I.C.S.: 541611

Dragonfly Technologies Pty. Ltd. (1)
Level 4 165-167 Phillip Street, Sydney,
2000, NSW, Australia
Tel.: (61) 1300663220
Web Site:
https://www.dragonflytechnologies.com

Computer Security Services
N.A.I.C.S.: 541512

BLACK CANYON LIMITED

283 Rokeby Road, Subiaco, 6008,
WA, Australia
Tel.: (61) 894260666   AU
Web Site:
   https://www.blackcanyon.com.au
Year Founded: 2011
BCA—(ASX)
Rev.: $26,488
Assets: $4,006,344
Liabilities: $352,437
Net Worth: $3,653,908
Earnings: ($1,318,295)
Fiscal Year-end: 06/30/23
Mineral Exploration Services
N.A.I.C.S.: 212390
Jay Stephenson *(Sec)*

BLACK CAT BLADES LTD.

5604-59 Street, Edmonton, T6B 3C3,
AB, Canada
Tel.: (780) 465-6666   Ca
Web Site:
   http://www.blackcatblades.com
Year Founded: 1968
Construction Machinery Parts Mfr
N.A.I.C.S.: 333120
Teresa Popowicz *(Mgr-IT)*

Subsidiaries:

AMSCO Cast Products (Canada)
Inc.   (1)
35 Mercy Street, Selkirk, R1A 1N5, MB,
Canada
Tel.: (204) 482-4442
Web Site: http://www.amscocast.com
Stainless Steel Cast Products Mfr
N.A.I.C.S.: 331513
Glenna Kells *(Sls Mgr)*

BLACK CAT SYNDICATE LIMITED

Tel.: (61) 458007713   AU
Web Site:
   https://www.blackcatsyndicate.com
Year Founded: 2017
BC8—(ASX)
Rev.: $3,188,458
Assets: $105,367,369
Liabilities: $27,245,795
Net Worth: $78,121,574
Earnings: ($2,542,086)
Fiscal Year-end: 06/30/24
Mineral Exploration Services
N.A.I.C.S.: 213114
Gareth Solly *(Mng Dir)*

BLACK DIAMOND GROUP LIMITED

1000 - 440 2nd Avenue SW, Calgary,
T2P 5E9, AB, Canada
Tel.: (403) 206-4747   AB
Web Site:
   https://www.blackdiamond.com
Year Founded: 2009
8B8—(DEU)
Rev.: $297,143,496
Assets: $489,045,162
Liabilities: $267,068,576
Net Worth: $221,976,585
Earnings: $22,923,933
Emp.: 485
Fiscal Year-end: 12/31/23
Holding Company; Commercial
Modular Building Construction, Logistics & Energy Support Services
N.A.I.C.S.: 551112
Trevor Haynes *(Chm, Pres & CEO)*

Subsidiaries:

Australian Portable Buildings Pty
Limited   (1)
21 Cox Place, Glendenning, 2761, NSW,
Australia

Tel.: (61) 2 8602 8000
Emp.: 20
Modular House Construction Services
N.A.I.C.S.: 236117

BOXX Modular Inc.   (1)
Suite 1000 440-2nd Avenue Sw, Calgary,
T2P 5E9, AB, Canada
Tel.: (403) 206-4747
Web Site: https://www.boxxmodular.ca
Emp.: 8
Commercial Modular Building Construction
N.A.I.C.S.: 236115

Branch (US):

BOXX Modular Inc. - Denver
Office   (2)
1675 Larimer St Ste 740, Denver, CO
80202
Tel.: (303) 623-0324
Web Site: http://www.blackdiamondus.com
Regional Managing Office; Commercial
Modular Building Construction & Leasing
Services
N.A.I.C.S.: 551114

Subsidiary (US):

MPA Systems, LLC   (2)
3475 High River Rd, Fort Worth, TX 76155
Tel.: (972) 492-4040
Web Site:
   http://www.blackdiamondgroup.com
High-Security Modular Buildings Leasing
Services
N.A.I.C.S.: 236220
Kimberly Shaw *(Pres)*

Spectrum Building Systems, Inc.   (2)
1716 Candler Rd, Gainesville, GA 30507
Tel.: (770) 503-1011
Web Site: http://www.spectrummodular.com
New Housing Operative Builders
N.A.I.C.S.: 236117

Black Diamond Energy Services
Inc.   (1)
1000-440 2nd Avenue Sw, Calgary, T2P
5E9, AB, Canada
Tel.: (403) 206-4747
Web Site:
   http://www.blackdiamondgroup.com
Emp.: 300
Energy Equipment Leasing & Support Services
N.A.I.C.S.: 532412

Black Diamond Limited
Partnership   (1)
Suite 2000 715 5th Avenue SW, Calgary,
T2P 2X6, AB, Canada
Tel.: (403) 206-4747
Web Site:
   http://www.blackdiamondlimited.com
Commercial Modular Building Construction
N.A.I.C.S.: 236115

BLACK DRAGON GOLD CORP.

Ground Floor Regent House Rodney
Road, Cheltenham, GL50 1HX,
United Kingdom
Tel.: (44) 2079930066   BC
Web Site:
   https://www.blackdragongold.com
Year Founded: 2007
BDG—(ASX)
Rev.: $3,721
Assets: $405,943
Liabilities: $91,918
Net Worth: $314,024
Earnings: ($1,133,583)
Fiscal Year-end: 12/31/23
Gold Mining Services
N.A.I.C.S.: 212220
Paul Cronin *(Exec Dir)*

BLACK IRON INC.

198 Davenport Rd, Toronto, M5R
1J2, ON, Canada
Tel.: (416) 309-2138   ON
Web Site: https://www.blackiron.com
Year Founded: 2010
BKIRF—(OTCIQ)
Rev.: $3,681
Assets: $1,391,705

Liabilities: $3,123,029
Net Worth: ($1,731,324)
Earnings: ($2,898,038)
Emp.: 4
Fiscal Year-end: 12/31/19
Iron Ore Mining Services
N.A.I.C.S.: 212210
Matthew Simpson *(CEO)*

BLACK ISLE RESOURCES CORP.

Suite 810 789 West Pender St, Vancouver, V6C 1H2, BC, Canada
Tel.: (604) 687-2038
Year Founded: 1987
Assets: $29,336
Liabilities: $187,259
Net Worth: ($157,923)
Earnings: ($71,159)
Fiscal Year-end: 12/31/19
Mineral Exploration Services
N.A.I.C.S.: 212290
Eugene Beukman *(CEO)*

BLACK MAMMOTH METALS CORPORATION

1710 1177 West Hastings Street,
Vancouver, V6E 2L3, BC, Canada
Tel.: (604) 347-9101   BC
Web Site:
   http://www.blackmammoth.com
Year Founded: 2004
3618—(HKG)
Assets: $565,112
Liabilities: $505,920
Net Worth: $59,192
Earnings: $157,710
Fiscal Year-end: 12/31/21
Gold, Silver, Copper & Zinc Mining
N.A.I.C.S.: 212220
Dustin Henderson *(Pres, CEO & Sec)*

BLACK MOUNTAIN RESOURCES LIMITED

Suite 5 531 Hay Street, Subiaco,
6008, WA, Australia
Tel.: (61) 9 9280 8300
Web Site:
   http://www.blackmountain.com.au
Year Founded: 2010
Sales Range: Less than $1 Million
Metal Mining Services
N.A.I.C.S.: 212290
John Ryan *(Exec Dir)*

BLACK PEARL S.A.

15 Zygmunta Slominskiego Str, 00-
195, Warsaw, Poland
Tel.: (48) 224154146
Web Site:
   https://www.blackpearlcapital.pl
Year Founded: 2009
BPC—(WAR)
Rev.: $62,163,587
Assets: $278,166,277
Liabilities: $78,999,175
Net Worth: $199,167,102
Earnings: ($163,212,555)
Emp.: 1
Fiscal Year-end: 12/31/23
Investment Management Service
N.A.I.C.S.: 523999
Arkadiusz Trela *(Pres)*

BLACK PEONY (GROUP) CO., LTD.

No 47 QingYang North Road,
Changzhou, 213017, China
Tel.: (86) 51968866958
Web Site: http://www.blackpeony.com
Year Founded: 1940
600510—(SHG)
Rev.: $1,620,976,140
Assets: $4,421,753,641
Liabilities: $2,891,236,393
Net Worth: $1,530,517,248

Earnings: $85,769,321
Emp.: 3,000
Fiscal Year-end: 12/31/22
Construction Engineering Services
N.A.I.C.S.: 541330
Feng Xiaoyu *(Chm)*

BLACK PRESS GROUP LTD.

5460 - 152 St #309, Victoria, V3S
5J9, BC, Canada
Tel.: (604) 575-2744
Web Site: http://www.blackpress.ca
Year Founded: 1975
Newspaper Publishers
N.A.I.C.S.: 513110
David Black *(Chm)*

Subsidiaries:

Cranbrook Daily Townsman   (1)
42-12th Avenue South, Cranbrook, V1C
2R7, BC, Canada
Tel.: (250) 426-5201
Web Site:
   https://www.cranbrooktownsman.com
Sales Range: $25-49.9 Million
Emp.: 40
Newspaper Publishing
N.A.I.C.S.: 513110
Jenny Leiman *(Mgr-Acctg)*

Grand Forks Gazette   (1)
7330 2 St, Grand Forks, V0H 1H0, BC,
Canada
Tel.: (250) 442-2191
Web Site: http://www.grandforksgazette.ca
Emp.: 6
Newspaper Publishers
N.A.I.C.S.: 513110
Eric Lawson *(Publr)*

Oahu Publications Inc.   (1)
500 Ala Moana Blvd Ste 7 500, Honolulu,
HI 96813
Tel.: (808) 529-4700
Web Site: http://www.oahupublications.com
Newspaper & Magazine Publisher
N.A.I.C.S.: 513110
Dennis Francis *(Pres & Publr)*

Unit (Domestic):

Honolulu Star-Advertiser   (2)
500 Ala Moana Blvd, Honolulu, HI 96813
Tel.: (808) 529-4747
Web Site: http://www.staradvertiser.com
Newspaper Publishers
N.A.I.C.S.: 513110
Dennis Francis *(Pres & Publr)*

Sound Publishing, Inc.   (1)
19351 8th Ave NE Ste 106, Poulsbo, WA
98370
Tel.: (360) 394-5800
Web Site: http://www.soundpublishing.com
Sales Range: $10-24.9 Million
Emp.: 50
Newspaper Publishers
N.A.I.C.S.: 513110
David Theobald *(Controller)*

Subsidiary (Domestic):

The Daily Herald Company   (2)
1213 California St, Everett, WA
98201   **(100%)**
Tel.: (425) 339-3000
Web Site: http://www.heraldnet.com
Newspaper Publishers
N.A.I.C.S.: 513110
Tom McLaughlin *(Acct Exec-Automotive)*

Unit (Domestic):

The Tukwila Reporter   (2)
19426 68th Ave S Ste A, Kent, WA 98032
Tel.: (253) 872-6600
Web Site: http://www.pnwlocalnews.com
Newspaper Publishers
N.A.I.C.S.: 513110
Polly Shepherd *(Reg Mgr-S Div)*

BLACK RED WHITE SA

ul Krzeszowska 63, Bilgoraj, Lublin,
23400, Poland
Tel.: (48) 846850202
Web Site: http://www.brw.com.pl

Black Red White SA—(Continued)

Sales Range: $400-449.9 Million
Emp.: 890
Household Furniture Mfr
N.A.I.C.S.: 337122
Zbigigniew Andrzejewski (Pres)

BLACK ROCK MINING LIMITED

Level 1 1 Walker Ave, West Perth,
6005, WA, Australia
Tel.: (61) 893894415　　　　　**AU**
Web Site:
　https://www.blackrockmining.com
BKT—(ASX)
Rev.: $70,009
Assets: $42,138,359
Liabilities: $2,395,425
Net Worth: $39,742,935
Earnings: ($7,080,902)
Fiscal Year-end: 06/30/24
Graphite Mining
N.A.I.C.S.: 212290
Gabriel Chiappini (Sec)

BLACK ROSE INDUSTRIES LTD.

145/A Mittal Towers Nariman Point,
Mumbai, 400 021, India
Tel.: (91) 2243337200
Web Site:
　https://www.blackrosechemical.com
Year Founded: 1990
514183—(BOM)
Rev.: $66,744,309
Assets: $23,985,521
Liabilities: $7,284,978
Net Worth: $16,700,543
Earnings: $4,353,941
Emp.: 104
Fiscal Year-end: 03/31/22
Chemical Products Mfr & Distr
N.A.I.C.S.: 325998
Anup Jatia (Exec Dir)

Subsidiaries:

B.R. Chemicals Co., Ltd.　　　**(1)**
5-5-801 Nihonbashitomizawa-cho, Chuo-ku,
Tokyo, 103-0006, Japan
Tel.: (81) 362062715
Chemical Products Mfr
N.A.I.C.S.: 325199

BLACK SEA PROPERTY AS

Sagveien 23 A, 0459, Oslo, Norway
Tel.: (47) 90770976
Web Site:
　https://www.blackseaproperty.no
Year Founded: 2015
BSP—(EUR)
Real Estate Investment Services
N.A.I.C.S.: 531190
Egil Melkevik (Chm)

BLACK SPADE ACQUISITION CO.

Suite 2902 29/F The Centrium 60
Wyndham Street, Central, China
(Hong Kong)
Tel.: (852) 39551316　　　　**Ky**
Web Site:
　http://www.blackspade.com
Year Founded: 2021
BSAQ—(NYSE)
Rev.: $15,309,647
Assets: $171,735,496
Liabilities: $180,739,556
Net Worth: ($9,004,060)
Earnings: $12,018,933
Emp.: 3
Fiscal Year-end: 12/31/22
Investment Services
N.A.I.C.S.: 523999
Dennis Tam (Chm & Co-CEO)

BLACK STAR PETROLEUM LIMITED

Suite 12 177 Rokeby Road, Subiaco,
6008, WA, Australia
Tel.: (61) 86 558 1859　　　　**AU**
Web Site:
　http://www.blackstarpetroleum.com
Year Founded: 2011
ВЗР　(ЛƐX)
Sales Range: $1-9.9 Million
Oil & Gas Mining Services
N.A.I.C.S.: 211120
Ian Gregory (Sec)

BLACK TUSK RESOURCES, INC.

Suite 500- 666 Burrard St, Vancouver, V6C 3P6, BC, Canada
Tel.: (778) 384-8923
Web Site:
　https://www.qmetalscorp.com
BTKRF—(OTCIQ)
Assets: $3,385,220
Liabilities: $119,452
Net Worth: $3,265,769
Earnings: ($2,562,138)
Fiscal Year-end: 04/30/21
Metal Exploration Services
N.A.I.C.S.: 213114
Richard Penn (CEO)

BLACKBERRY LIMITED

2200 University Ave East, Waterloo,
N2K 0A7, ON, Canada
Tel.: (519) 888-7465　　　　　**ON**
Web Site:
　https://www.blackberry.com
Year Founded: 1984
BB—(NYSE)
Rev.: $656,000,000
Assets: $1,679,000,000
Liabilities: $822,000,000
Net Worth: $857,000,000
Earnings: ($734,000,000)
Emp.: 3,181
Fiscal Year-end: 02/28/23
Designer, Mfr & Marketer of Wireless
Solutions
N.A.I.C.S.: 334210
John J. Giamatteo (CEO & Pres-Cyber Security Bus Unit)

Subsidiaries:

BlackBerry Australia Pty Limited　**(1)**
Level 6 100 Pacific Highway, North Sydney,
2060, NSW, Australia
Tel.: (61) 294637600
Web Site: http://au.blackberry.com
Emp.: 5
Wireless Telecommunication Services
N.A.I.C.S.: 517112

BlackBerry Austria GmbH　　　**(1)**
Parkring 10, 1010, Vienna, Austria
Tel.: (43) 1 51633 0
Sales Range: $25-49.9 Million
Emp.: 6
Wireless Telecommunication Services
N.A.I.C.S.: 517112

BlackBerry Corporation　　　　**(1)**
Tel.: (972) 650-6126
Web Site: http://www.rim.com
Sales Range: $25-49.9 Million
Emp.: 50
Licensing of Telecommunications Products
N.A.I.C.S.: 517810

Subsidiary (Domestic):

AtHoc, Inc.　　　　　　　　　**(2)**
2988 Campus Dr Ste 100, San Mateo, CA
94403
Tel.: (650) 685-3000
Web Site: http://www.athoc.com
Software Publisher
N.A.I.C.S.: 513210
Ramon J. Pinero (VP-Svcs)

WatchDox, Inc.　　　　　　　　**(2)**

299 S California Ave Ste 300, Palo Alto, CA
94306
Web Site: http://www.watchdox.com
Data Security Software
N.A.I.C.S.: 513210

BlackBerry Ltd. - Waterloo Manufacturing Facility　　　　　　　　**(1)**
2200 University Aenue E, Waterloo, N2k
0A7, ON, Canada
Tel.: (519) 888-7465
Mobile Phone Mfr
N.A.I.C.S.: 334220

BlackBerry Mobile South Africa (Proprietary) Limited　　　　　　　**(1)**
Palazzo Towers West Monte Casino William
Nicol Drive, Fourways, Johannesburg,
2086, South Africa
Tel.: (27) 116536583
Emp.: 3
Wireless Telecommunication Services
N.A.I.C.S.: 517112

BlackBerry Singapore Pte.
Limited　　　　　　　　　　　**(1)**
1 International Business Park The Synergy
02-12, Singapore, 609917, Singapore
Tel.: (65) 68798700
Emp.: 100
Wireless Telecommunication Services
N.A.I.C.S.: 517112

Blackberry UK Limited　　　　　**(1)**
200 Bath Road, Slough, SL1 3XE, Berkshire, United Kingdom　　　**(100%)**
Tel.: (44) 1753667000
Web Site: http://www.blackberry.com
Sales Range: $50-74.9 Million
Emp.: 120
Designer, Mfr & Marketer of Wireless Solutions for Mobile Communications Market
N.A.I.C.S.: 334210

Certicom Corp.　　　　　　　　**(1)**
4701 Tahoe Blvd 5th Floor, Mississauga,
L4W 0B5, ON, Canada
Tel.: (905) 507-4220
Web Site: http://www.certicom.com
Sales Range: $10-24.9 Million
Emp.: 112
Hardware & Software Cryptography
N.A.I.C.S.: 541512

Cylance, Inc.　　　　　　　　　**(1)**
2618 San Miguel Dr Ste 223, Newport
Beach, CA 92660
Tel.: (914) 295-2623
Web Site: http://www.cylance.com
Software Publisher
N.A.I.C.S.: 513210
Stuart McClure (Co-Founder)

Scoreloop AG　　　　　　　　　**(1)**
Landsbergerstr 110, 80339, Munich, Germany
Tel.: (49) 89 203044600
Web Site: http://www.scoreloop.com
Sales Range: $25-49.9 Million
Emp.: 30
Mobile Game Publishing Services
N.A.I.C.S.: 513210

BLACKBIRD PLC

LABS House 15-19 Bloomsbury Way,
London, WC1A 2TH, United Kingdom
Tel.: (44) 3303801130　　　　**UK**
Web Site: https://www.blackbird.video
Year Founded: 1998
BIRD—(LSE)
Rev.: $2,127,695
Assets: $11,260,984
Liabilities: $1,567,835
Net Worth: $9,693,149
Earnings: ($2,553,334)
Emp.: 23
Fiscal Year-end: 12/31/20
Video Compression Technology Developer
N.A.I.C.S.: 541519
Stephen B. Streater (Dir-R&D)

BLACKBURN RADIO INC

700 Richmond St Unit 102, London,
N6A 5C7, ON, Canada
Tel.: (519) 679-8680

Web Site:
　http://www.blacburnradio.com
Sales Range: $50-74.9 Million
Emp.: 200
Broadcasting Holding Company
N.A.I.C.S.: 551112
James K. Knowles (VP-Fin)

Subsidiaries:

CFCO Radio AM　　　　　　　　**(1)**
117 Keil Dr, PO Box 100, Chatham, N7M
5K1, ON, Canada
Tel.: (519) 351-2326
Web Site: http://www.630cfco.com
Sales Range: $25-49.9 Million
Emp.: 10
Radio Stations
N.A.I.C.S.: 516110

BLACKFIN CAPITAL PARTNERS SAS

15 Rue De Laborde, 75008, Paris,
France
Tel.: (33) 1 75 00 02 30
Web Site: http://www.blackfincp.com
Year Founded: 2009
Sales Range: $25-49.9 Million
Emp.: 75
Investment Management Service
N.A.I.C.S.: 523940
Laurent Bouyoux (Co-Founder & Mng Partner)

Subsidiaries:

Hestis SAS　　　　　　　　　　**(1)**
10 Quai Leon Blum, 92150, Suresnes,
France
Tel.: (33) 1 71 11 32 03
Web Site: http://www.hyperassur.com
Insurance Services
N.A.I.C.S.: 524298

BLACKFINCH SPRING VCT PLC

1350-1360 Montpellier Court Gloucester Business Park, Brockworth,
Gloucester, GL3 4AH, United Kingdom
Tel.: (44) 1452717070　　　　**UK**
Web Site:
　https://www.blackfinch.ventures
Year Founded: 2019
BFSP—(LSE)
Assets: $24,578,389
Liabilities: $257,511
Net Worth: $24,320,879
Earnings: ($411,512)
Fiscal Year-end: 12/31/22
Investment Management Service
N.A.I.C.S.: 523999

BLACKFISH CAPITAL MANAGEMENT LTD.

5 Savile Row, London, W1S 3PD,
United Kingdom
Tel.: (44) 2070877970　　　　**UK**
Web Site:
　http://www.blackfishcapital.com
Year Founded: 2006
Rev.: $1,000,000,000
Emp.: 2
Privater Equity Firm
N.A.I.C.S.: 523999
David Rowland (Co-Owner)

Subsidiaries:

Banque Havilland S.A.　　　　　**(1)**
35 A JK Kennedy, Luxembourg, 1855, Luxembourg
Tel.: (352) 463131
Web Site: http://www.banquehavilland.com
Sales Range: $50-74.9 Million
Emp.: 70
Banking Services
N.A.I.C.S.: 522110
Jean-Francois Willems (CEO)

BLACKFOOT MOTORCYCLES LTD.
6 Highfield Circle SE, Calgary, T2G 5N5, AB, Canada
Tel.: (403) 243-2636
Web Site:
  https://www.blackfootonline.com
Year Founded: 1970
Rev.: $14,094,020
Emp.: 65
Motorcycle Dealers
N.A.I.C.S.: 441227
Doug MacRae (Pres)

BLACKGOLD NATURAL RE-SOURCES LTD.
7 Temasek Boulevard Suntec Tower One No 08-07, Singapore, 038987, Singapore
Tel.: (65) 68844418   SG
Web Site: http://www.blackgold-group.com
Year Founded: 1997
41H—(SES)
Rev.: $9,648,646
Assets: $5,568,893
Liabilities: $15,423,138
Net Worth: ($9,854,245)
Earnings: ($4,039,537)
Fiscal Year-end: 12/31/20
Coal Mining Operations
N.A.I.C.S.: 212115
Suherman Budiono (CFO)

Subsidiaries:

NH Enterprises (2008) Pte. Ltd.   (1)
No 2 Tuas S Ave 2 Ste 02-00, Singapore, 637601, Singapore
Tel.: (65) 68612626
Property Rental & Investment Services
N.A.I.C.S.: 531210

Nam Hong Properties Pte. Ltd.   (1)
50 Bukit Batok St 23 Midview Bldg 06-04, Singapore, 659578, Singapore
Tel.: (65) 68612626
Property Management Services
N.A.I.C.S.: 531311
Ricky Paul Moh Chye Goh (Mng Dir)

BLACKHAWK CAPITAL LLP
Lynton House 7-12 Tavistock Square, London, WC1H 9BQ, United Kingdom
Tel.: (44) 1252913636   UK
Web Site:
  http://www.blackhawkcapital.co.uk
Year Founded: 2010
Privater Equity Firm
N.A.I.C.S.: 523999
Alan Watkins (Co-Founder, Chm & Sr Partner)

Subsidiaries:

Computer Systems Integration Limited   (1)
Newstead House Lake View Drive, Sherwood Business Park, Annesley, NG15 0DT, Notts, United Kingdom
Tel.: (44) 1623 726 300
Web Site: http://www.csiltd.co.uk
Sales Range: $50-74.9 Million
Emp.: 130
Information Technology Systems Integration Services
N.A.I.C.S.: 541519
Richard Mitchley (Dir-Managed Svcs)

BLACKHAWK GROWTH CORP.
303-750 West Pender Street, Vancouver, V6C 2T7, BC, Canada
Tel.: (403) 991-7737
Web Site:
  https://www.blackhawkgrowth.com
QD6—(DEU)
Assets: $266
Liabilities: $1,467,800
Net Worth: ($1,467,533)
Earnings: ($1,218,713)
Fiscal Year-end: 06/30/24

Oil & Gas Exploration Services
N.A.I.C.S.: 213112
David Michael Antony (CEO)

BLACKHEATH & BROMLEY HARRIERS AC
The Sydney Wooderson Ctr, 56 Bourne Way Hayes, Bromley, BR2 7EY, Kent, United Kingdom
Tel.: (44) 2084623115
Web Site:
  http://www.bandbhac.org.uk
Sales Range: $50-74.9 Million
Emp.: 700
Sports Clubs & Associations
N.A.I.C.S.: 711211
Stephen Hollingdale (Head-Fin)

BLACKICE ENTERPRISE RISK MANAGEMENT INC.
310 - 207 W Hastings Street, Vancouver, V6B 1H7, BC, Canada
Tel.: (604) 336-0107   Ca
Web Site: http://www.blackiceinc.com
Year Founded: 2007
Risk Management Software
N.A.I.C.S.: 513210
David Taylor (COO)

BLACKLINE SAFETY CORP.
Unit 100 803 24 Avenue SE, Calgary, T2G 1P5, AB, Canada
Tel.: (403) 451-0327   AB
Web Site:
  https://www.blacklinesafety.com
Year Founded: 2006
BLN—(TSX)
Rev.: $57,052,463
Assets: $84,524,572
Liabilities: $43,562,826
Net Worth: $40,961,745
Earnings: ($41,966,193)
Emp.: 477
Fiscal Year-end: 10/31/22
Safety Monitoring Technology Developer
N.A.I.C.S.: 334220
Kevin Meyers (COO)

Subsidiaries:

Blackline Safety Europe Ltd.   (1)
12 De Grey Square De Grey Road, Colchester, CO4 5YQ, Essex, United Kingdom
Tel.: (44) 1787222684
Monitoring Device Mfr
N.A.I.C.S.: 334519

BLACKMAGIC DESIGN PTY. LTD.
11 Gateway Court, Port Melbourne, 3207, VIC, Australia
Tel.: (61) 396824770
Web Site: http://www.blackmagic-design.com
Year Founded: 2001
Emp.: 200
Video Editing Equipment Mfr
N.A.I.C.S.: 334310
Grant Petty (CEO)

Subsidiaries:

Ultimatte Corporation   (1)
20945 Plummer St, Chatsworth, CA 91311   (100%)
Tel.: (818) 993-8007
Web Site: http://www.ultimatte.com
Sales Range: $1-9.9 Million
Emp.: 30
Mfr of Broadcast Quality Realtime Blue & Green Screen Removal Hardware for Broadcast Television, Commercial & Feature Film Industries
N.A.I.C.S.: 334220
Paul E. Vlahos (Pres)

eyeon Software, Inc.   (1)
2175 Queen Street East Suite 301, Toronto, M4E 1E5, ON, Canada

Tel.: (416) 686-8411
Software Development Services
N.A.I.C.S.: 541511

BLACKMORES LIMITED
20 Jubilee Avenue, Warriewood, 2102, NSW, Australia
Tel.: (61) 299105000   AU
Web Site:
  http://www.blackmores.com.au
Year Founded: 1930
BKL—(ASX)
Rev.: $497,656,495
Assets: $452,684,207
Liabilities: $139,556,145
Net Worth: $313,128,062
Earnings: $29,540,455
Emp.: 1,200
Fiscal Year-end: 06/30/22
Health Product Mfr & Whslr
N.A.I.C.S.: 325411
Marcus C. Blackmore (Exec Dir)

Subsidiaries:

Blackmores (Malaysia) Sdn Bhd   (1)
UOA Business Park Shah Alam Unit No 7-05-01 Level 5 Tower 7, UOA Business Park No 1 Jalan Pengaturcara U1/51A Seksyen U1, 40150, Shah Alam, Selangor, Malaysia
Tel.: (60) 350228238
Web Site: https://www.blackmores.com.my
Emp.: 25
Health Care Product Whslr
N.A.I.C.S.: 424210

Blackmores (New Zealand) Limited   (1)
Building 10 Level 4 Central Park Corporate Centre 666 Great South Road, Greenlane, Auckland, 1051, New Zealand
Tel.: (64) 95267431
Web Site: http://www.blackmoresnz.co.nz
Health Care Product Whslr
N.A.I.C.S.: 424210

Blackmores (Singapore) Pte Limited   (1)
160 Robinson Road 08-02 SBF Centre, Singapore, 068914, Singapore
Tel.: (65) 62253933
Web Site: http://www.blackmores.com.sg
Health Care Product Whslr
N.A.I.C.S.: 424210

Blackmores (Taiwan) Limited   (1)
26F No 456 Sec 4 Xinyi Road, XinYi District, Taipei, 11052, Taiwan
Tel.: (886) 223450138
Web Site: http://www.blackmores.com.tw
Health Care Product Whslr
N.A.I.C.S.: 424210

Blackmores (Thailand) Limited   (1)
21 A Mahanakorn Gypsum Bldg 539/2 Sri-Ayuddhaya Road Thanon Phayathai, Ratchathewi, Bangkok, 10400, Thailand
Tel.: (66) 224882902
Web Site: https://www.blackmores.co.th
Health Care Product Whslr
N.A.I.C.S.: 424210

Blackmores China Co. Limited   (1)
6F Tower B One ITC plaza No 1901 Huashan Road, Xuhui District, Shanghai, China
Tel.: (86) 216 229 1788
Natural Health Product Distr
N.A.I.C.S.: 424490
Kitty Liu (Mng Dir)

Blackmores India Private Limited   (1)
335 Udyog Vihar Phase IV, Gurgaon, 122015, Haryana, India
Tel.: (91) 12 443 0812
Web Site: https://www.blackmores.in
Natural Health Product Distr
N.A.I.C.S.: 424490

Blackmores International Pte. Limited   (1)
160 Robinson Road 08-02 SBF Centre, Singapore, 068914, Singapore
Tel.: (65) 68051733
Pharmaceutical Mfr & Distr
N.A.I.C.S.: 325412

Blackmores Korea Limited   (1)
11th Floor Hanmaru Building 81 Yeouinaruro, Yeongdeungpo-gu, Seoul, Korea (South)
Tel.: (82) 1 600 5446
Web Site: https://www.blackmores.co.kr
Natural Health Product Distr
N.A.I.C.S.: 424490

Blackmores Vietnam Co. Limited   (1)
Level 6 202 Ly Chinh Thang Street, Ward 9 District 3, Ho Chi Minh City, Vietnam
Tel.: (84) 283 526 1265
Natural Health Product Distr
N.A.I.C.S.: 424490

FIT-BioCeuticals Limited   (1)
Level 4 64 Kippax Street, Surry Hills, 2010, NSW, Australia
Tel.: (61) 1300650455
Web Site: https://www.bioceuticals.com.au
Health Care Product Whslr
N.A.I.C.S.: 424210
Adrian Sturrock (Dir-Fin)

PharmaFoods Pty Ltd   (1)
Unit 16 37-41 O'Riordan St, Alexandria, 2015, NSW, Australia
Tel.: (61) 2 9080 0900
Web Site:
  http://www.pharmafoodsprofessional.com
Health Care Product Whslr
N.A.I.C.S.: 424210

BLACKOUT MEDIA CORP.
2-3 Soi Jadsansoonthon 5 Sukhumvitt 103 Road, Norgborn, Bangkok, 10250, Thailand
Tel.: (66) 26614322
Year Founded: 2005
Holding Company
N.A.I.C.S.: 551112
Samai Singjan (Pres)

BLACKPOOL PLEASURE BEACH LTD.
Ocean Blvd Promenade S Shore, Blackpool, FY4 1EZ, Lancashire, United Kingdom
Tel.: (44) 1253341033
Web Site:
  http://www.blackpoolpleasure.com
Sales Range: $50-74.9 Million
Emp.: 1,187
Amusement Park Operator
N.A.I.C.S.: 713110
Amanda Thompson (Mng Dir)

BLACKROCK FRONTIERS INVESTMENT TRUST PLC
12 Throgmorton Avenue, London, EC2N 2DL, United Kingdom
Tel.: (44) 2077433000   UK
Web Site: http://www.blackrock.com
Year Founded: 2010
BRFI—(LSE)
Rev.: $159,340,000
Assets: $372,490,000
Liabilities: $19,710,000
Net Worth: $352,780,000
Earnings: $149,470,000
Fiscal Year-end: 09/30/21
Investment Management Service
N.A.I.C.S.: 525990
Samuel Vecht (Mgr)

BLACKROCK GREATER EUROPE INVESTMENT TRUST PLC
12 Throgmorton Avenue, London, EC2N 2DL, United Kingdom
Tel.: (44) 2077433000   UK
Web Site: http://www.blackrock.com
Year Founded: 2004
BRGE—(LSE)
Assets: $608,247,860
Liabilities: $4,368,700
Net Worth: $603,879,160
Earnings: ($251,350,034)
Fiscal Year-end: 08/31/22
Investment Management Service

BlackRock Greater Europe Investment Trust plc—(Continued)

N.A.I.C.S.: 523940
Eric Sanderson (Chm)

BLACKROCK INCOME & GROWTH INVESTMENT TRUST PLC

12 Throgmorton Avenue, London, EC2N 2DL, United Kingdom
Tel.: (44) 2077433000　　UK
Web Site: http://www.blackrock.com
BRIG—(NYSE)
Rev.: $3,732,641
Assets: $55,243,600
Liabilities: $4,122,201
Net Worth: $51,121,399
Earnings: $2,737,100
Emp.: 3,953
Fiscal Year-end: 10/31/23
Investment Management Service
N.A.I.C.S.: 523940
Graeme Proudfoot (Chm)

BLACKROCK LATIN AMERICAN INVESTMENT TRUST PLC

12 Throgmorton Avenue, London, EC2N 2DL, United Kingdom
Tel.: (44) 2077433000　　UK
Web Site: http://www.blackrock.com
Year Founded: 1990
BRLA—(LSE)
Rev.: $16,530,000
Assets: $159,880,000
Liabilities: $11,770,000
Net Worth: $148,110,000
Earnings: $13,670,000
Fiscal Year-end: 12/31/22
Investment Management Service
N.A.I.C.S.: 523940
Carolan Dobson (Chm)

BLACKROCK OIL CORPORATION

255 Duncan Mill Road, Toronto, M3B 3H9, ON, Canada
Tel.: (416) 510-2991
Year Founded: 2009
Oil & Energy Services
N.A.I.C.S.: 213112
Oliver Xing (Pres, CEO & CFO)

BLACKROCK SILVER CORP.

Suite 2300-1177 West Hastings St, Vancouver, V6E 2K3, BC, Canada
Tel.: (604) 817-6044　　BC
Web Site: http://blackrockgold.ca
Year Founded: 1999
BKRRF—(OTCQX)
Rev.: $446,114
Assets: $6,608,880
Liabilities: $806,259
Net Worth: $5,802,621
Earnings: ($13,696,958)
Emp.: 2
Fiscal Year-end: 10/31/22
Mineral Exploration Services
N.A.I.C.S.: 213114
William Howald (Chm)

BLACKROCK SMALLER COMPANIES TRUST PLC

12 Throgmorton Avenue, London, EC2N 2DL, United Kingdom
Tel.: (44) 2077433000　　UK
Web Site: http://www.blackrock.com
Year Founded: 1906
BRSC—(LSE)
Rev.: $98,035,530
Assets: $1,406,141,726
Liabilities: $161,006,584
Net Worth: $1,245,135,142
Earnings: $84,368,721
Fiscal Year-end: 02/28/22
Investment Management Service

N.A.I.C.S.: 523940
Ronald Gould (Chm)

BLACKROCK SUSTAINABLE AMERICAN INCOME TRUST PLC

12 Throgmorton Avenue, London, EC2N 2DL, United Kingdom
Tel.: (44) 2077433000　　UK
Year Founded: 2012
BRNA—(LSE)
Sales Range: $1-9.9 Million
Investment Management Service
N.A.I.C.S.: 523940
Tony DeSpirito (Portfolio Mgr)

BLACKROCK THROGMORTON TRUST PLC

12 Throgmorton Avenue, London, EC2N 2DL, United Kingdom
Tel.: (44) 2077433000　　UK
Web Site: http://www.blackrock.com
THRG—(LSE)
Rev.: $79,680,514
Assets: $832,036,613
Liabilities: $22,543,583
Net Worth: $809,493,030
Earnings: $68,965,387
Fiscal Year-end: 11/30/20
Investment Management Service
N.A.I.C.S.: 523940
Christopher Samuel (Chm)

BLACKROCK WORLD MINING TRUST PLC

12 Throgmorton Avenue, London, EC2N 2DL, United Kingdom
Tel.: (44) 2077433000　　UK
Year Founded: 1993
BRWM—(LSE)
Rev.: $119,039,459
Assets: $1,750,110,584
Liabilities: $198,407,697
Net Worth: $1,551,702,887
Earnings: $261,320,368
Fiscal Year-end: 12/31/21
Investment Management Trust Services
N.A.I.C.S.: 523940
Evy Hambro (Portfolio Mgr)

BLACKSTEEL ENERGY INC.

1220 717 - 7th Avenue SW, Calgary, T2P 3H6, AB, Canada
Tel.: (403) 540-2408　　Ca
Web Site: http://www.blacksteelenergy.ca
Year Founded: 2009
BEY—(TSXV)
Rev.: $68,428
Assets: $545,861
Liabilities: $2,284,770
Net Worth: ($1,738,909)
Earnings: ($187,964)
Fiscal Year-end: 04/30/21
Oil & Gas Exploration Services
N.A.I.C.S.: 211120
Les Treitz (Pres-Interim & CEO)

BLACKSTONE MINERALS LIMITED

Level 5 600 Murray Street, West Perth, 6005, WA, Australia
Tel.: (61) 894255217　　AU
Web Site: https://www.blackstoneminerals.com
Year Founded: 2016
BLSTF—(OTCQX)
Rev.: $1,027,576
Assets: $53,732,669
Liabilities: $5,069,871
Net Worth: $48,662,798
Earnings: ($27,232,359)
Fiscal Year-end: 06/30/22
Support Activities for Metal Mining
N.A.I.C.S.: 213114

Andrew Radonjic (Dir-Technical)

BLACKSTONE RESOURCES AG

Blegistrasse 5, 6340, Baar, Switzerland
Tel.: (41) 414496163　　CH
Web Site: http://www.blackstoneresources.ch
Year Founded: 1995
BLS—(SWX)
Rev.: $25,399,555
Assets: $118,411,202
Liabilities: $24,433,976
Net Worth: $93,977,227
Earnings: $19,149,953
Fiscal Year-end: 12/31/20
Financial Investment Services
N.A.I.C.S.: 523999
Ulrich Ernst (Pres & CEO)

Subsidiaries:

Blackstone Resources Management AG　　　　　　　　　　　(1)
Steinhaldenring 8b, 8954, Geroldswil, Switzerland
Tel.: (41) 414496163
Web Site: http://www.blackstoneresourcesmgt.ch
Metal Mining Services
N.A.I.C.S.: 213114

BLACKWALL LIMITED

50 Yeo Street, PO Box 612, Neutral Bay, 2089, NSW, Australia
Tel.: (61) 290338611　　AU
Web Site: https://www.blackwall.com.au
BWF—(ASX)
Rev.: $1,312,767
Assets: $48,705,262
Liabilities: $1,917,735
Net Worth: $46,787,527
Earnings: ($474,092)
Emp.: 21
Fiscal Year-end: 06/30/24
Property Funds Management Services
N.A.I.C.S.: 523940
Timothy Brown (Co-Mng Dir & CFO)

Subsidiaries:

Armada Holdings Pty Ltd　　　　(1)
2/19 Harley Cres, Condell Park, Sydney, 2200, NSW, Australia
Tel.: (61) 297070111
Web Site: https://www.amarda.com.au
Pool Table & Jukebox Distr
N.A.I.C.S.: 423990

BlackWall Fund Services Limited　(1)
50 Yeo Street, PO Box 612, Neutral Bay, 2089, NSW, Australia
Tel.: (61) 290338611
Web Site: https://blackwall.com.au
Property Development Services
N.A.I.C.S.: 531190

Blackwall Management Services Pty Ltd　　　　　　　　　　(1)
Level 1 50 Yeo St, Neutral Bay, 2089, NSW, Australia
Tel.: (61) 290338622
Web Site: http://www.blackwallfunds.com.au
Real Estate Manangement Services
N.A.I.C.S.: 531390

TFML Limited　　　　　　　　(1)
L 3 50 Yeo St, Neutral Bay, 2089, NSW, Australia
Tel.: (61) 2 9033 8614
Real Estate Management Services
N.A.I.C.S.: 531390
Clare Simmons (Gen Mgr)

BLACKWOOD BUILDING CENTRE LTD.

33050 South Fraser Way, Abbotsford, V2S 2A9, BC, Canada
Tel.: (604) 853-6471

Web Site:
https://www.homehardware.ca
Year Founded: 1971
Building Materials Distr
N.A.I.C.S.: 444180

BLACKWOOD SEVEN A/S

Livjgergade 17B 2nd Floor, 2100, Copenhagen, Denmark
Tel.: (45) 53660777
Web Site: http://www.blackwoodseven.com
Year Founded: 2013
Automated Media Allocation Services
N.A.I.C.S.: 541519

Subsidiaries:

Booming GmbH　　　　　　　(1)
Adelgundenstrasse 7, 80538, Munich, Germany
Tel.: (49) 89 2000 452 0
Web Site: http://www.blackwoodseven.de
Sales Range: $50-74.9 Million
Emp.: 50
Digital Marketing Services
N.A.I.C.S.: 541810
Andreas Schwabe (CEO)

BLADERANGER LTD.

1 Hayasmin St, Ramat Efal, Ramat Gan, Israel
Tel.: (972) 36792121
Web Site: https://bladeranger.com
Year Founded: 2015
BLRN—(TAE)
Rev.: $225,169
Assets: $164,940
Liabilities: $479,072
Net Worth: ($314,132)
Earnings: ($2,925,542)
Fiscal Year-end: 12/31/23
Solar Panel Mfr
N.A.I.C.S.: 335999
Ety Zohar (VP-R&D)

BLAKE HOLDINGS LIMITED

46/50 Kensington Place, Saint Helier, JE1 1ET, Jersey
Tel.: (44) 1534 719 761　　JE
Web Site: http://www.blake.je
Holding Company; Investment Services
N.A.I.C.S.: 551112
Richard Griffiths (Chm)

Subsidiaries:

Hardy Oil and Gas plc　　　　(1)
16 North Silver Street, Aberdeen, AB10 1RL, United Kingdom　　(86.16%)
Tel.: (44) 1224612900
Web Site: http://www.hardyoil.com
Rev.: $456,691
Assets: $14,761,588
Liabilities: $13,201,249
Net Worth: $1,560,339
Earnings: ($56,299,750)
Emp.: 12
Fiscal Year-end: 03/31/2019
Oil & Gas Exploration Services
N.A.I.C.S.: 213112
Richard Galvin (Exec Dir)

BLAMMO WORLDWIDE

154 Pearl Street, Toronto, M5H 1L3, ON, Canada
Tel.: (416) 979-7999　　ON
Web Site: http://www.gipadvertising.com
Year Founded: 1991
Sales Range: $75-99.9 Million
Emp.: 80
Advertising Services
N.A.I.C.S.: 541810
Alan Gee (Chm)

BLANCO Y NEGRO SA

Av Marathon 5300, Macul, Santiago, 5300, Santiago, Chile
Tel.: (56) 4602600

Web Site: http://www.colocolo.cl
COLO.COLO—(SGO)
Sales Range: Less than $1 Million
Sports Club Facility Operator
N.A.I.C.S.: 713940
Alejandro Paul Gonzalez (CEO)

BLAST RESOURCES INC.
380 580 Hornby Street, Vancouver,
V6C 3B6, BC, Canada
Tel.: (778) 688-1799 BC
Web Site: https://blastresources.com
Year Founded: 2021
BLST—(CNSX)
Assets: $134,470
Liabilities: $128,956
Net Worth: $5,514
Earnings: ($298,681)
Fiscal Year-end: 01/31/24
Mineral Mining Services
N.A.I.C.S.: 212290
Derek Tam (Pres, CEO & CFO)

BLAUWHOED HOLDING B.V.
Lichtenauerlaan 80, Rotterdam,
3062ME, Netherlands
Tel.: (31) 104535311
Web Site: http://www.blauwhoed.nl
Sales Range: $200-249.9 Million
Emp.: 88
Real Estate Development Services
N.A.I.C.S.: 531390
Philip Smith (Gen Mgr)

BLAZE MINERALS LIMITED
Level 3 88 William Street, Perth,
6000, WA, Australia
Tel.: (61) 894632463
Web Site:
  https://www.blazelimited.com.au
BLZ—(ASX)
Rev.: $10,600
Assets: $2,846,365
Liabilities: $49,595
Net Worth: $2,796,770
Earnings: ($1,957,804)
Fiscal Year-end: 06/30/24
Minerals Exploration
N.A.I.C.S.: 213115
Loren King (Sec)

BLB LTD
H No 4760-61/23 3rd Floor Ansari
Road Daryaganj, New Delhi, 110002,
India
Tel.: (91) 1149325600
Web Site:
  http://www.blbcommodities.com
BLBLIMITED—(NSE)
Rev.: $48,492,621
Assets: $12,773,684
Liabilities: $812,844
Net Worth: $11,960,840
Earnings: $1,285,298
Emp.: 24
Fiscal Year-end: 03/30/22
Finance Investments
N.A.I.C.S.: 522291
Brij Rattan Bagri (Chm)

BLC BANK SAL
BLC Building Adlieh Intersection, Bei-
rut, 2064-5809, Lebanon
Tel.: (961) 1429000
Web Site: http://www.blcbank.com
Year Founded: 1950
Sales Range: $50-74.9 Million
Emp.: 150
Banking Services
N.A.I.C.S.: 522110
Rida Mroueh (CFO)

Subsidiaries:

BLC Finance SAL (1)
BLC Bank building Adlieh square, 2064-
5809, Beirut, Lebanon
Tel.: (961) 1387000

Financial Management Consulting Services
N.A.I.C.S.: 541611

BLC Invest SAL (1)
Royal Tower Building- 3rd Floor Nicolas
Turk Street- Medawar, Achrafieh, Beirut,
2064-5809, Lebanon
Tel.: (961) 566207
Financial Management Consulting Services
N.A.I.C.S.: 541611

USB Bank Plc (1)
83 Digeni Akrita Ave 5th floor, 1070, Nico-
sia, Cyprus (98.83%)
Tel.: (357) 22883333
Web Site: http://www.usbbank.com.cy
Rev.: $5,693,000,000
Assets: $10,230,000,000
Liabilities: $5,741,000,000
Net Worth: $4,489,000,000
Earnings: $1,175,000,000
Emp.: 237
Fiscal Year-end: 12/31/2017
Commercial Banking Services
N.A.I.C.S.: 522110
Michalis Kokkinos (Mgr-Risk & Legal Svcs)

BLD PLANTATION BHD
Level 6 Crown Towers 88 Jalan
Pending, 93450, Kuching, Sarawak,
Malaysia
Tel.: (60) 82335311
Web Site: https://www.bldpb.com.my
BLDPLNT—(KLS)
Rev.: $361,752,472
Assets: $228,492,346
Liabilities: $67,114,697
Net Worth: $161,377,649
Earnings: $6,138,115
Emp.: 441
Fiscal Year-end: 03/31/24
Oil Palm Cultivation Services
N.A.I.C.S.: 115112
Cheak Chai Seng (Controller-Fin)

BLE KEDROS REAL ESTATE INVESTMENT COMPANY SA
4 Palaia Tatoiou str, Kifissia, 14 671,
Athens, Greece
Tel.: (30) 2106204194
Web Site: https://www.blekedros.com
Year Founded: 2014
N67—(DEU)
Real Estate Development Services
N.A.I.C.S.: 531190

BLEACH INC.
21F Nakameguro GT Tower 2-1-1
Kamimeguro, Meguro-ku, Tokyo, 153-
0051, Japan
Tel.: (81) 362658346
Web Site: https://www.bleach.co.jp
Year Founded: 2010
9162—(TKS)
Advertising Agency Services
N.A.I.C.S.: 541840
Takuya Matsumoto (CFO)

BLEECKER SA
39 avenue George V, 75008, Paris,
France
Tel.: (33) 3315856244
Web Site: https://www.bleecker.fr
BLEE—(EUR)
Sales Range: $125-149.9 Million
Real Estate Investment & Manage-
ment Services
N.A.I.C.S.: 523999
Muriel Marcilhacy-Giraud (Chm-Exec Bd)

BLENCOWE RESOURCES PLC
167-169 Great Portland Street Fifth
Floor, London, W1W 5PF, Warwick-
shire, United Kingdom
Tel.: (44) 1624681250 UK
Web Site:
  https://www.blencoweresource.com
Year Founded: 2017
BRES—(LSE)

Assets: $7,982,010
Liabilities: $1,302,030
Net Worth: $6,679,980
Earnings: ($1,585,080)
Fiscal Year-end: 09/30/22
Natural Gas Exploration Service
N.A.I.C.S.: 213112
Cameron Pearce (Chm)

BLENDE SILVER CORP.
1100 - 1111 Melville St, Vancouver,
V6E 3V6, BC, Canada
Tel.: (604) 669-6463 BC
Web Site: https://blendesilver.com
BCW1—(DEU)
Assets: $2,607,961
Liabilities: $382,062
Net Worth: $2,225,899
Earnings: ($259,945)
Emp.: 1
Fiscal Year-end: 11/30/22
Metal Mining Services
N.A.I.C.S.: 212290
Thomas John Kennedy (CEO)

BLENDER FINANCIAL TECH-NOLOGIES LTD.
Jabotinsky 7, Ramat Gan, 5252007,
Israel
Tel.: (972) 722779906 II
Web Site: https://blender.global
Year Founded: 2014
BLND—(TAE)
Rev.: $9,702,998
Assets: $56,965,878
Liabilities: $42,608,094
Net Worth: $14,357,784
Earnings: ($4,517,751)
Fiscal Year-end: 12/31/23
Miscellaneous Financial Investment
Activities
N.A.I.C.S.: 523999

BLESSED TEXTILES LIMITED
Umer House 23/1 Sector 23 SM Fa-
rooq Road Korangi Industrial Area,
Karachi, Pakistan
Tel.: (92) 2135115177
Web Site:
  https://www.umergroup.com
BTL—(LAH)
Rev.: $88,645,535
Assets: $65,543,001
Liabilities: $38,581,464
Net Worth: $26,961,537
Earnings: $4,562,350
Emp.: 1,344
Fiscal Year-end: 06/30/19
Yarn & Woven Fabric Mfr
N.A.I.C.S.: 313110
Mohammad Amin (CEO)

BLEU OCEANE
Route De La Roche Sur Yon, 85230,
Challans, Vendee, France
Tel.: (33) 251687165
Web Site: http://www.bleu-oceane.com
Rev.: $13,400,000
Emp.: 91
N.A.I.C.S.: 315250
Andre Dugast (Pres)

BLEVINS FRANKS FINANCIAL MANAGEMENT LIMITED
28 St James Square, London, SW1Y
4JH, United Kingdom
Tel.: (44) 2073898133 UK
Web Site:
  http://www.blevinsfranks.com
Year Founded: 1975
Sales Range: $10-24.9 Million
Financial Management & Tax Ser-
vices
N.A.I.C.S.: 523150
John Stone (Chm)

Subsidiaries:

Blevins Franks Tax Limited (1)
4 Fenchurch Avenue, London, EC3M 5BS,
United Kingdom
Tel.: (44) 20 7336 1000
Tax Services
N.A.I.C.S.: 541213

BLH SAS
Lotissement 16 Zac Du Pilon, 06460,
Saint-Vallier-de-Thiey, Alpes Mari-
times, France
Tel.: (33) 492603560
Web Site: https://www.blhsas.com
Rev.: $17,000,000
Emp.: 14
All Other Basic Organic Chemical Mfr
N.A.I.C.S.: 325199

BLIS TECHNOLOGIES LIM-ITED
Tel.: (64) 34740988
BLT—(NZX)
Rev.: $6,273,923
Assets: $7,660,885
Liabilities: $1,180,024
Net Worth: $6,480,861
Earnings: ($807,416)
Emp.: 4
Fiscal Year-end: 03/31/23
Health Care Products Mfr
N.A.I.C.S.: 325412
Anthony P. Offen (Chm)

BLISS GVS PHARMA LTD.
102 Hyde Park Sakivihar Road And-
heri East, Mumbai, 400 072, India
Tel.: (91) 2242160000
Web Site: https://www.blissgvs.com
BLISSGVS—(BOM)
Rev.: $92,245,537
Assets: $138,703,027
Liabilities: $28,706,804
Net Worth: $109,996,223
Earnings: $9,200,264
Emp.: 763
Fiscal Year-end: 03/31/23
Pharmaceuticals Product Mfr
N.A.I.C.S.: 325412
Shibroor N. Kamath (Mng Dir)

Subsidiaries:

Kremoint Pharma Private Limited (1)
C 1904-1910 Bldg No 2 19th Floor Kailash
Business Park, Veer Savarkar Marg Vikhroli
Powai Link Road Vikhroli West, Mumbai,
400079, Maharashtra, India
Tel.: (91) 2220852045
Web Site: https://www.kremointpharma.com
Pharmacy Product Mfr
N.A.I.C.S.: 325412

Subsidiary (Domestic):

Eipii Exports Pvt Ltd. (2)
D59/60 Additional Ambernath M I D C Opp
Anand Nagar Police Check Post, Amber-
nath East Dist, Thane, 421506, Maharash-
tra, India
Tel.: (91) 9820191597
Web Site: https://www.eipii.in
Health Care Products Mfr
N.A.I.C.S.: 311999
Bhadresh Thakkar (Founder)

BLISS INTELLIGENCE PUBLIC COMPANY LIMITED
96 Chaloem Phrakiat Rama 9 Rd
Nong Bon Prawet, Bangkok, 10250,
Thailand
Tel.: (66) 20263245 TH
Web Site: http://www.blisstel.co.th
Year Founded: 1989
BLISS—(THA)
Rev.: $31,056,689
Assets: $64,315,561
Liabilities: $46,492,284
Net Worth: $17,823,277
Earnings: ($30,127,415)

Bliss Intelligence Public Company
Limited—(Continued)

Fiscal Year-end: 12/31/20
Information Technology Communica-
tions & Telecommunications
N.A.I.C.S.: 541511
Thanaboon Thongtang (*Deputy Mng
Dir*)

Subsidiaries:

Information Technology Group Com-
pany Limited **(1)**
200 Moo 4 18th Floor Unit 1801A and 25th
Floor, Jasmine International Tower Chaeng-
wattana Road, Pak Kret, 11120, Nonthaburi,
Thailand
Tel.: (66) 28325500
Web Site: http://www.itg.co.th
Information Technology Services
N.A.I.C.S.: 541511

Subsidiary (Domestic):

IT Management Company
Limited **(2)**
562 Bejaravudh Building 7th Floor Din
Daeng Road, Din Daeng, Bangkok, 10400,
Thailand
Tel.: (66) 224575989
Web Site: http://www.itmanagement.co.th
IT Management Consulting Services
N.A.I.C.S.: 541618

BLITZWAY CO., LTD.
638 Gukhoe-daero, Yeongdeungpo-
gu, Seoul, Korea (South)
Tel.: (82) 25127692
Web Site: https://www.blitzway.com
Year Founded: 2010
369370—(KRS)
Rev.: $14,686,707
Assets: $38,285,770
Liabilities: $8,932,456
Net Worth: $29,353,315
Earnings: ($2,688,523)
Emp.: 46
Fiscal Year-end: 12/31/22
Toy Mfr & Distr
N.A.I.C.S.: 339930

**BLIVEX ENERGY TECHNOL-
OGY CO., LTD.**
Room 4602 Shimao Financial Center
Building Phase II, Xinghai Avenue No
3040 Nanshan Street, Shenzhen,
710075, Shaanxi, China
Tel.: (86) 75586069330
Web Site: https://www.blivex.com
Year Founded: 2005
300116—(CHIN)
Rev.: $26,868,348
Assets: $97,405,308
Liabilities: $54,845,856
Net Worth: $42,559,452
Earnings: ($26,190,216)
Fiscal Year-end: 12/31/22
Fire Extinguishing Systems Mfr
N.A.I.C.S.: 922160

BLIXT GROUP LIMITED
10 Ledbury Mews North, London,
W11 2AF, United Kingdom
Tel.: (44) 2045996031 UK
Web Site: https://www.blixtgroup.com
Year Founded: 2020
Investment Management Service
N.A.I.C.S.: 523999
Carl Harring (*CEO*)

Subsidiaries:

Lawfront Group Limited **(1)**
10 Ledbury Mews North, London, W11 2AF,
United Kingdom
Tel.: (44) 1206835300
Web Site: https://www.lawfront.com
Law firm
N.A.I.C.S.: 541199
Neil Lloyd (*CEO*)

Subsidiary (Domestic):

Nelsons Solicitors Limited **(2)**
8 Stanford St Pennine House, Nottingham,
NG1 7BQ, United Kingdom
Tel.: (44) 1159586262
Web Site: http://www.nelsonslaw.co.uk
Emp.: 73
Law firm
N.A.I.C.S.: 541110
Stewart Vandermark (*CEO*)

BLME HOLDINGS PLC
Cannon Place 78 Cannon Street,
London, EC4N 6HL, United Kingdom
Tel.: (44) 2076180000
Web Site: http://www.blme.com
Rev.: $65,057,579
Assets: $1,623,010,591
Liabilities: $1,323,910,191
Net Worth: $299,100,400
Earnings: $14,266,323
Emp.: 121
Fiscal Year-end: 12/31/18
Holding Company
N.A.I.C.S.: 551112
Chris Power (*CFO*)

BLOCK ENERGY PLC
33 Cavendish Square, London, W1G
0PW, United Kingdom
Tel.: (44) 2034689891 UK
Web Site:
https://www.blockenergy.co.uk
BLOE—(AIM)
Rev.: $6,114,000
Assets: $30,926,000
Liabilities: $3,861,000
Net Worth: $27,065,000
Earnings: ($4,581,000)
Emp.: 37
Fiscal Year-end: 12/31/21
Oil & Gas Exploration Services
N.A.I.C.S.: 213111
Paul Haywood (*CEO*)

BLOCK SOLUTIONS LTD.
14 Shepherdess Walk, London, N1
7LB, United Kingdom
Tel.: (44) 84 4967 1646
Web Site: http://www.block-
solutions.net
Year Founded: 2006
Sales Range: $10-24.9 Million
Emp.: 100
IT Consulting Services
N.A.I.C.S.: 541512
Jon Pickering (*Co-Founder & Mng
Dir*)

**BLOCKCHAIN GROUP COM-
PANY LIMITED**
Room 3505 35th Floor West Block
Shun Tak Centre, 200 Connaught
Road Sheung Wan, Central, China
(Hong Kong)
Tel.: (852) 25490669 Ky
Web Site:
http://www.blockchaingroup.com.hk
Rev.: $36,051,320
Assets: $616,640,695
Liabilities: $337,505,998
Net Worth: $279,134,696
Earnings: ($18,672,383)
Emp.: 193
Fiscal Year-end: 12/31/17
Investment Holding Company
N.A.I.C.S.: 551112
Zhenyao Cai (*Fin Dir*)

Subsidiaries:

Huafeng Trading Macao Commercial
Offshore Limited **(1)**
Rua S Domingos No 16F-16L Edif Hin Lei
Comml Ctr 2 Andar E-34, Macau, China
(Macau)
Tel.: (853) 28323861
Fabrics Processing Services

N.A.I.C.S.: 313210

**BLOCKCHAIN VENTURE
CAPITAL INC.**
130 King St. West Suite 1800, To-
ronto, M5X 1E3, ON, Canada
Tel.: (647) 404-8966
Web Site: http://www.bvcadt.com
BVCI (CNSX)
Assets: $23,979
Liabilities: $2,006,584
Net Worth: ($1,982,604)
Earnings: ($3,343,634)
Fiscal Year-end: 12/31/23
Financial Services
N.A.I.C.S.: 523999

BLOCKCHAINK2 CORP.
400 - 837 West Hastings Street, Van-
couver, V6C3N6, BC, Canada
Tel.: (604) 630-8746 BC
Web Site: https://blockchaink2.com
Year Founded: 1983
BIDCF—(OTCQB)
Rev.: $89,842
Assets: $1,463,881
Liabilities: $283,379
Net Worth: $1,180,503
Earnings: ($1,737,485)
Emp.: 6
Fiscal Year-end: 09/30/21
Oil & Gas Extraction Services
N.A.I.C.S.: 211120
Sergei Stetsenko (*CEO*)

BLOCKMATE VENTURES, INC.
505 Kootenay Street, Nelson, V1L
1K9, BC, Canada
Tel.: (416) 214-9910 BC
Web Site: http://www.midpoint.com
Year Founded: 2010
MATE—(TSXV)
Assets: $955,671
Liabilities: $2,711,768
Net Worth: ($1,756,097)
Earnings: ($2,137,606)
Fiscal Year-end: 06/30/24
Foreign Exchange & International
Payments Platform
N.A.I.C.S.: 525990
Corbin Comishin (*CFO*)

**BLOCKMINT TECHNOLOGIES,
INC.**
595 Burrard Street, Vancouver, V7X
1J5, BC, Canada
Tel.: (503) 961-4022
Web Site: https://getminter.com
BKMT—(TSXV)
Assets: $2,605,417
Liabilities: $61,889
Net Worth: $2,543,528
Earnings: ($425,833)
Fiscal Year-end: 12/31/20
Information Technology Services
N.A.I.C.S.: 541512
Nelson Ijih (*CEO & CTO*)

BLOK TECHNOLOGIES, INC.
310-221 West Esplanade Ave North,
Vancouver, V7M 3J3, BC, Canada
Web Site: http://www.bloktechinc.com
Investment Management Service
N.A.I.C.S.: 525990
Jamie Hyland (*Pres*)

BLOM BANK, S.A.L.
Verdun Rachid Karami St BLOM
BANK Bldg, Riad El Solh, PO Box
11-1540, 1107 2807, Beirut, Lebanon
Tel.: (961) 1743300 LB
Web Site: https://www.blom.com.lb
Year Founded: 1951
BLOM—(BEY)
Rev.: $27,116,292
Assets: $434,250,751

Liabilities: $381,544,771
Net Worth: $52,705,980
Earnings: $80,223
Emp.: 3,122
Fiscal Year-end: 12/31/22
Banking Services
N.A.I.C.S.: 522110
Pierre Abou Ezze (*Asst Gen Mgr-HR*)

Subsidiaries:

Arope Insurance SAL **(1)**
Zalka Michel El-Murr Str Arope Bldg, PO
Box 113-5686, Beirut, Lebanon **(88.56%)**
Tel.: (961) 1905777
Web Site: https://www.arope.com
Direct Property & Casualty Insurance Carri-
ers
N.A.I.C.S.: 524126

Subsidiary (Non-US):

Syria International Insurance
Company **(2)**
Al Taghez Facing Omaia Hotel First Floor,
PO Box 33015, Damascus, Syria
Tel.: (963) 11 9279
Insurance Management Services
N.A.I.C.S.: 524298

Banque Banorient (Switzerland)
SA **(1)**
1 Rue Rodolphe-Toepffer, PO Box 3040,
1211, Geneva, Switzerland **(100%)**
Tel.: (41) 228177100
Web Site: https://www.banorientsuisse.ch
Sales Range: $50-74.9 Million
Emp.: 21
Commercial Banking
N.A.I.C.S.: 522110
Michel Chikhani (*CEO*)

Banque Banorient France **(1)**
21 Avenue George V, 75008, Paris,
France **(99.99%)**
Tel.: (33) 144950606
Web Site: https://www.banorientfrance.com
Sales Range: $50-74.9 Million
Emp.: 40
Commercial Banking
N.A.I.C.S.: 522110
Samer Azhari (*Chm & Gen Mgr*)

Blom Asset Management Company
S.A.L. **(1)**
Mina El Hosn Facing Saint George BLOM
Bank Building 5th Floor, PO Box 11-1912,
Riad El Solh, Beirut, Lebanon
Tel.: (961) 1760033
Web Site:
http://www.blomassetmanagement.com
Financial Investment Services
N.A.I.C.S.: 523999
Fadi Osseiran (*Chm & Gen Mgr*)

Blom Bank Egypt S.A.E. **(1)**
61 Ninety St-El Tagamo El Khames, PO
Box 410, New Cairo, Egypt
Tel.: (20) 233322778
Web Site: http://www.blombankegypt.com
Sales Range: $1-9.9 Million
Emp.: 452
Banking Services
N.A.I.C.S.: 522110
Saad Azhari (*Chm*)

Blom Bank Qatar LLC **(1)**
West Bay Area Al Qassar Region 61 Al
Wahda St, PO Box 27700, NBK Amwal
Tower 11th Flr Suite 1110, Doha, Qatar
Tel.: (974) 44992999
Financial Investment Services
N.A.I.C.S.: 523999
Saad Azhari (*Chm*)

Blom Development Bank S.A.L. **(1)**
Abdel Aziz Street Daher Bldg 7th Floor, Bei-
rut, Lebanon
Tel.: (961) 1751091
Web Site:
https://www.blomdevelopment.com
Financial Investment Services
N.A.I.C.S.: 523999
Saad N. Azhari (*Chm & Gen Mgr*)

BlomInvest Bank SAL **(1)**
Mena El Hosn Zaytouna Facing Saint
Georges Blom Bldg, 2nd Fl Blk A Blom
Banks Bldg, Beirut, Lebanon **(99.88%)**

Tel.: (961) 1983225
Web Site: http://www.blominvestement.com
Commericial Banking
N.A.I.C.S.: 522110

Subsidiary (Non-US):

Blom Egypt Investment S.A.E. **(2)**
Mossadek St 30 Bldg, Giza Dokki, Cairo, Egypt
Tel.: (20) 233360948
Financial Investment Services
N.A.I.C.S.: 523999
Fadi Osseiran *(Chm)*

Blom Egypt Securities S.A.E. **(2)**
Address Bldg 8 - Gezerat El Arab - 1st floor, Mohandesein, Giza, Egypt
Tel.: (20) 237617682
Web Site:
https://www.blomegyptsecurities.com
Financial Investment Services
N.A.I.C.S.: 523999
Rabih Halabi *(Chm)*

Blominvest Bank Saudi Arabia Company **(1)**
Tel.: (966) 114949555
Web Site: https://www.blominvest.sa
Financial Investment Services
N.A.I.C.S.: 523999
Fadi Al Khalaf *(VP-Real Estate Investments & Funds)*

BLOMQUIST ANNONSBYRA AB
Upplandsgatan 7 2 tr, 111 23, Stockholm, Sweden
Tel.: (46) 854525000
Web Site: http://www.blomquist.se
Year Founded: 1932
Sales Range: $10-24.9 Million
Emp.: 20
N.A.I.C.S.: 541810
Anders Wistrom *(Owner)*

BLOOM & WAKE LTD
130 Wisbech Road Outwell, Wisbech, PE14 8PF, Cambs, United Kingdom
Tel.: (44) 1945772578   UK
Web Site:
http://www.bloomandwake.co.uk
Year Founded: 1969
Electrical Contracting Services
N.A.I.C.S.: 238210
John Bloom *(Co-Founder)*

BLOOM DEKOR LIMITED
2/F Sumel SG Highway, Thaltej, Ahmedabad, 380054, Gujarat, India
Tel.: (91) 7926841916
Web Site:
https://www.bloomdekor.com
Year Founded: 1994
526225—(BOM)
Rev.: $4,330,258
Assets: $7,443,277
Liabilities: $8,267,655
Net Worth: ($824,378)
Earnings: ($1,051,350)
Emp.: 66
Fiscal Year-end: 03/31/21
Decorative Laminates Mfr & Distr
N.A.I.C.S.: 326130
Sunil Sitaram Gupta *(Mng Dir)*

BLOOM INDUSTRIES LIMITED
Plot No P 25 Civil Township, Sundergarh, Rourkela, 769004, Odisha, India
Tel.: (91) 9937040828   In
Web Site: https://www.bloom-industries.com
Year Founded: 1989
513422—(BOM)
Rev.: $1,855,772
Assets: $1,716,979
Liabilities: $597,720
Net Worth: $1,119,259
Earnings: $60,975
Fiscal Year-end: 03/31/22

Iron & Steel Whslr
N.A.I.C.S.: 423510

BLOOM INVESTMENT COUNSEL, INC.
150 York Street Suite 1710, Toronto, M5H 3S5, ON, Canada
Tel.: (416) 861-9941   ON
Web Site: http://www.bloomfunds.ca
Year Founded: 1985
Investment Management Service
N.A.I.C.S.: 523940
M. Paul Bloom *(Pres, Sec & Portfolio Mgr)*

Subsidiaries:

Bloom Select Income Fund **(1)**
150 York Street Suite 1710, Toronto, M5H 3S5, ON, Canada
Tel.: (416) 861-9941
Web Site: http://www.bloomfunds.ca
Rev.: $319,895
Assets: $7,165,917
Liabilities: $90,745
Net Worth: $7,075,172
Earnings: $56,290
Fiscal Year-end: 12/31/2023
Closed-End Investment Fund
N.A.I.C.S.: 525990

BLOOMAGE BIOTECHNOLOGY CORPORATION LIMITED
No 678 Tianchen St High -Tech Development Zone, Jinan, 250101, China
Tel.: (86) 53182685998   Ky
Web Site:
https://www.bloomagebioactive.com
Year Founded: 2000
688363—(CHIN)
Biotechnology Research & Development Services
N.A.I.C.S.: 541714

BLOOMBERRY RESORTS CORPORATION
The Executive Offices Solaire Resort and Casino Asean Ave, Entertainment City Tambo, Paranaque, 1701, Philippines
Tel.: (63) 88838920   PH
Web Site: https://bloomberry.ph
Year Founded: 1999
BLOOM—(PHI)
Rev.: $864,756,843
Assets: $2,891,935,987
Liabilities: $2,020,647,644
Net Worth: $871,288,343
Earnings: $171,913,520
Emp.: 6,772
Fiscal Year-end: 12/31/23
Holding Company; Printed Circuit Boards & Other Electronic Components Mfr & Distr
N.A.I.C.S.: 551112
Jose Eduardo J. Alarilla *(Vice Chm)*

BLOOMSBURY PUBLISHING PLC
50 Bedford Square, London, WC1B 3DP, United Kingdom
Tel.: (44) 2076315000
Web Site:
https://www.bloomsbury.com
Year Founded: 1986
BMY—(LSE)
Rev.: $312,424,949
Assets: $392,702,860
Liabilities: $163,290,269
Net Worth: $229,412,591
Earnings: $22,931,891
Emp.: 818
Fiscal Year-end: 02/28/22
Magazine & Book Publisher
N.A.I.C.S.: 513130
Nigel Newton *(Founder & CEO)*

Subsidiaries:

A&C Black Publishers Ltd. **(1)**
Alderman House 36 Soho Sq, London, W1D 3QY, United Kingdom   **(100%)**
Tel.: (44) 2077580200
Book Publishers
N.A.I.C.S.: 513130

Berg Fashion Library Limited **(1)**
Oxford University Press Great Clarendon Street, Oxford, OX2 6DP, United Kingdom
Tel.: (44) 1865 353705
Web Site: http://www.bergfashionlibrary.com
Sales Range: $800-899.9 Million
Online Portal Services
N.A.I.C.S.: 519290
Valerie Cumming *(Chm)*

Bloomsbury Book Publishing Company Limited **(1)**
36 Soho Sq, W1D 3QY, London, United Kingdom - England   **(100%)**
Tel.: (44) 2074942111
Web Site: http://www.bloomsbury-ir.co.uk
Book Publishers
N.A.I.C.S.: 513130

Bloomsbury India UK Limited **(1)**
50 Bedford Square, London, WC1B 3DP, United Kingdom
Tel.: (44) 207 631 5600
Book Publishers
N.A.I.C.S.: 513130

Bloomsbury Information Limited **(1)**
36 Soho Square, London, W1D 3QY, United Kingdom
Tel.: (44) 2074942111
Web Site: http://www.qfinancebooks.com
Books Publishing Services
N.A.I.C.S.: 513130

Bloomsbury Professional Limited **(1)**
9/10 St Andrew Square, Edinburgh, EH2 2AF, West Sussex, United Kingdom
Tel.: (44) 131 718 6073
Web Site:
https://www.bloomsburyprofessional.com
Emp.: 25
Books Publishing Services
N.A.I.C.S.: 513130

Bloomsbury Publishing Inc. **(1)**
1385 Broadway 5th Floor, New York, NY 10018
Tel.: (212) 419-5300
Books Publishing Services
N.A.I.C.S.: 513130
George Gibson *(Dir-Publ)*

Bloomsbury Publishing India Pvt Limited **(1)**
Vishrut Building no 3 DDA Complex Ground Floor, Pocket C 6&7 Vasant Kunj, New Delhi, 110070, India
Tel.: (91) 11 4057 4957
Book & Magazine Publishing Services
N.A.I.C.S.: 513130
Rajiv Beri *(Mng Dir)*

Bloomsbury Publishing Pty Ltd. **(1)**
Level 6 387 George St, Sydney, 2000, NSW, Australia
Tel.: (61) 28 820 4900
Web Site: https://www.bloomsbury.com
Sales Range: $1-9.9 Million
Books Publishing Services
N.A.I.C.S.: 513130

Osprey Publishing Limited **(1)**
Kemp House Chawley Park, Cumnor Hill, Oxford, OX2 9PH, United Kingdom
Tel.: (44) 186 572 7022
Web Site: https://ospreypublishing.com
Book Publishers
N.A.I.C.S.: 513130

Peter Collin Publishing Limited **(1)**
36 Soho Square, London, W1D 3QY, United Kingdom   **(100%)**
Tel.: (44) 2074942111
Sales Range: $25-49.9 Million
Emp.: 60
Book Publishers
N.A.I.C.S.: 513130

Reeds Nautical Almanac **(1)**
Adlard Coles Nautical 36 Soho Square, London, W1D 3QY, United Kingdom   **(100%)**

Tel.: (44) 2074942111
Web Site:
http://www.reedsnauticalalmanac.co.uk
Book Publishers of Navigational Information
N.A.I.C.S.: 513130

BLOWTHERM S.P.A.
Via Guido Reni 5, 35134, Padua, Italy
Tel.: (39) 049601600
Web Site: http://www.blowtherm.it
Year Founded: 1956
Sales Range: $10-24.9 Million
Emp.: 100
Spray Booth for Automotive Refinishing & Heating System Mfr
N.A.I.C.S.: 333517

BLP TRAINING & SERVICES PTY. LTD.
Building 9 The Construction Training Centre, 460-492 Beaudesert Road, Salisbury, 4107, QLD, Australia
Tel.: (61) 732768947   AU
Web Site: http://www.blpts.com.au
Sales Range: $10-24.9 Million
Emp.: 5
Security Training & Equipment Supply Services
N.A.I.C.S.: 611430
Darren McDonald *(Gen Mgr & Mgr-Munitions)*

BLRT GRUPP AS
Kopli 103, 11712, Tallinn, Estonia
Tel.: (372) 6102408
Web Site: http://www.blrt.ee
Year Founded: 1912
Sales Range: $350-399.9 Million
Emp.: 4,000
Ship Building Services
N.A.I.C.S.: 336611
Veronika Ivanovskaja *(Chm)*

Subsidiaries:

Elme Metall Finland Oy **(1)**
Rannikontie 4, PO Box 11, 13721, Parola, Finland
Tel.: (358) 3 630 070
Web Site: http://www.elmemetall.fi
Emp.: 21
Steel Product Distr
N.A.I.C.S.: 423510
Markus Kosk *(Dir-Bus Segment)*

Elme Metall Latvia SIA **(1)**
Katlakalna 9, 1073, Riga, Latvia
Tel.: (371) 671 39051
Emp.: 47
Steel Product Distr
N.A.I.C.S.: 423510
Marina Demidova *(Sec)*

Elme Metall Lithuania, UAB **(1)**
Granito 10, 02241, Vilnius, Lithuania
Tel.: (370) 526 44441
Emp.: 153
Steel Product Distr
N.A.I.C.S.: 423510
Kristina Bubeleviciene *(Sec)*

Elme Metall OU **(1)**
Vana-Narva mnt 24a, 74114, Maardu, Estonia
Tel.: (372) 610 2554
Web Site: http://www.elmemetall.eu
Emp.: 143
Steel Product Mfr & Distr
N.A.I.C.S.: 331221
Igor Novosselov *(Member-Mgmt Bd)*

Elme Metall Poland Sp. z o.o. **(1)**
Ul Struga 61, 70-784, Szczecin, Poland
Tel.: (48) 508 173 276
Emp.: 7
Steel Product Distr
N.A.I.C.S.: 423510
Agata Czekin *(Sec)*

Elme Metall Russia **(1)**
Kamskaja 49, 236005, Kaliningrad, Russia
Tel.: (7) 40 126 504 15
Emp.: 18

BLRT Grupp AS—(Continued)

Steel Product Distr
N.A.I.C.S.: 423510
Margarita Yurasova *(Sec)*

MacGregor BLRT Baltic OU (1)
103 Kopli Str, 11712, Tallinn, Estonia
Tel.: (372) 6102200
Cargo Handling Services
N.A.I.C.S.: 488320

OOO Elme Trans Ukraine (1)
Avtogennaya 10, 61046, Kharkiv, Ukraine
Tel.: (380) 577280 118
Construction Equipment Rental Services
N.A.I.C.S.: 532412

OOO Elmeta (1)
Sudostroitelnaya 75, 236011, Kaliningrad, Russia
Tel.: (7) 90 621 71 538
Construction Equipment Rental Services
N.A.I.C.S.: 532412

SC Western Shipyard (1)
Minijos str 180, 93269, Klaipeda, Lithuania
Tel.: (370) 46 48 36 00
Web Site: http://www.wsy.lt
Emp.: 1,900
Ship Building & Repair Services
N.A.I.C.S.: 336611

Subsidiary (Domestic):

UAB Western Baltija Shipbuilding (2)
Pilies str 8, 91503, Klaipeda, Lithuania
Tel.: (370) 46 398 249
Emp.: 450
Ship Building Services
N.A.I.C.S.: 336611
Jelena Fiodorova *(Sr Mgr-Cost)*

SIA ELME MESSER L (1)
Aplokciema 3, Riga, 1034, Latvia
Tel.: (371) 67355445
Web Site: http://www.elmemesser.lv
Industrial Gas Distr
N.A.I.C.S.: 424690
Janis Bardulis *(Mgr-Sls)*

SIA Elme Trans L (1)
Katlakalna iela 9, 1073, Riga, Latvia
Tel.: (371) 673 96 410
Web Site: http://www.elmetrans.ee
Emp.: 6
Construction Equipment Rental Services
N.A.I.C.S.: 532412
Svetlana Tokmanceva *(CEO)*

SIA REFONDA (1)
Katlakalna 9, Riga, 1073, Latvia
Tel.: (371) 25 4444 22
Web Site: http://www.refonda.lv
Scrap Metal Distr
N.A.I.C.S.: 423930

Turku Repair Yard Ltd (1)
Navirentie, 21100, Naantali, Finland
Tel.: (358) 2 44 511
Web Site: http://www.turkurepairyard.com
Emp.: 100
Ship Repair Services
N.A.I.C.S.: 336611
Kim Kangas *(Mng Dir)*

UAB ELME MESSER LIT (1)
Ateities g 10, 08303, Vilnius, Lithuania
Tel.: (370) 5 271 5605
Web Site: http://www.elmemesser.lt
Industrial Gas Distr
N.A.I.C.S.: 424690

BLS INFOTECH LIMITED
1 / 1A Upper Wood Street, Kolkata, 700017, West Bengal, India
Tel.: (91) 3322814418
Web Site: http://www.blsinfotech.com
Year Founded: 1985
Rev.: $29,953
Assets: $6,370,420
Liabilities: $14,128
Net Worth: $6,356,291
Earnings: ($36,395)
Fiscal Year-end: 03/31/18
Software Development Services
N.A.I.C.S.: 541511
Sushil K. Saraogi *(Chm)*

BLS INTERNATIONAL SERVICES LIMITED
912 Indra Prakash Building 21 Barakhamba Road, Mathura Road, New Delhi, 110001, India
Tel.: (91) 1143750006
Web Site:
https://www.blsinternational.com
Year Founded: 2005
540073—(BOM)
Rev.: $209,860,396
Assets: $129,043,769
Liabilities: $14,774,733
Net Worth: $114,269,037
Earnings: $27,882,282
Emp.: 20,000
Fiscal Year-end: 03/31/23
Passport Issuing Services
N.A.I.C.S.: 928120
Nikhil Gupta *(Co-Mng Dir)*

Subsidiaries:

BLS International (Thailand) Ltd. (1)
399 Interchange Building B2 Floor Unit A/1 Sukhumvit Road, Klongtoey-Nua Wattana, Bangkok, 10110, Thailand
Tel.: (66) 22583524
Passport Issuing Services
N.A.I.C.S.: 928120

BLS International Services Belarus Inc. (1)
Spain Visa Application Centre 8-2 2nd Floor St Tolstoy, 220007, Minsk, Belarus
Tel.: (375) 291389454
Passport Issuing Services
N.A.I.C.S.: 928120

BLS International Services Canada Inc. (1)
1-91 Oxford Street, Toronto, M5T 1P2, ON, Canada
Tel.: (647) 846-4077
Web Site: https://www.blsindia-canada.com
Passport Issuing Services
N.A.I.C.S.: 928120

BLS International Services China Inc. (1)
5th Floor Block A Gateway Plaza No 18 East Third Ring North Road, Chao Yang District, Beijing, China
Tel.: (86) 13335978935
Passport Issuing Services
N.A.I.C.S.: 928120

BLS International Services Dominican Republic Inc. (1)
Ave 27 de Febrero Unicentro Plaza Suite No 46II 3rd Level, Piantini, Santo Domingo, Dominican Republic
Tel.: (809) 8295451159
Web Site: https://do.blsspainvisa.com
Passport Issuing Services
N.A.I.C.S.: 928120

BLS International Services Egypt Inc. (1)
20 Geziret Al-Arab St, Mohandeseen, Giza, Egypt
Tel.: (20) 233020783
Passport Issuing Services
N.A.I.C.S.: 928120

BLS International Services Ghana Inc. (1)
6th Floor GNAT heights 30 Independence Avenue, Ridge, Accra, Ghana
Tel.: (233) 302961521
Passport Issuing Services
N.A.I.C.S.: 928120

BLS International Services Indonesia Inc, (1)
Unit 1001 Level 10 Palma One Building Jl H R Rasuna Said Kav X-2 No 4, Jakarta Selatan, 12950, Indonesia
Tel.: (62) 2129023407
Passport Issuing Services
N.A.I.C.S.: 928120

BLS International Services Jordan Inc, (1)
Building Name Housing bank complex First floor, Near Ministry of Interior circle, Amman, 11821, Jordan

Tel.: (962) 65626066
Passport Issuing Services
N.A.I.C.S.: 928120

BLS International Services Kazakhstan Inc. (1)
14 Beibitshilik Street BC Marden Office 404 4th Floor, 010000, Astana, Kazakhstan
Tel.: (7) 7292781375
Passport Issuing Services
N.A.I.C.S.: 928120

BLS International Services Lebanon Inc. (1)
2nd Floor Kalot Center Badaro Sami El Solh Boulevard, Beirut, Lebanon
Tel.: (961) 1390383
Passport Issuing Services
N.A.I.C.S.: 928120

BLS International Services Limited (1)
Room 2302 23/Floor Olympia Plaza 255 King's Road, Nearest Metro station is Fortress Hill Exit-B, North Point, China (Hong Kong)
Tel.: (852) 58195329
Web Site: https://www.blsinternational.com
Passport Issuing Services
N.A.I.C.S.: 928120

BLS International Services Limited (1)
No 344/9 Dashrath Chand Marg Baluwatar, PO Box 5657, Kathmandu, Nepal
Tel.: (977) 124 455 6710
Web Site: https://india.blsspainvisa.com
Passport Issuing Services
N.A.I.C.S.: 928120

BLS International Services Limited (1)
55 W 39th St 18th Fl, New York, NY 10018
Tel.: (516) 888-1169
Web Site: https://usa.blsspainvisa.com
Passport Issuing Services
N.A.I.C.S.: 928120

BLS International Services Ltd. (1)
Unit 5 12th Floor No 1 Artemis Complex 4th Narenjestan St Pasdaran St, Kolahdouz Dowlat Street, Tehran, Iran
Tel.: (98) 2126253136
Web Site: https://spainvisa-iran.com
Passport Issuing Services
N.A.I.C.S.: 928120

BLS International Services Mauritania Inc. (1)
Al Khaima City Center 10 Rue Mamadou Konate, BP 5219, Nouakchott, Mauritania
Tel.: (222) 25057372
Passport Issuing Services
N.A.I.C.S.: 928120

BLS International Services Nigeria Inc. (1)
3rd Floor Amazing Grace Plaza 2E-4E Ligali Ayorinde St, Victoria Island, Lagos, Nigeria
Tel.: (234) 7056645455
Passport Issuing Services
N.A.I.C.S.: 928120

BLS International Services Norway AS (1)
Gronland Basar 2 Floor Toyengata 2, 0190, Oslo, Norway
Tel.: (47) 22555544
Web Site: https://www.blsindia-norway.com
Passport Issuing Services
N.A.I.C.S.: 928120

BLS International Services Oman Inc. (1)
Al Tamimah Building B Block 4th Floor Al Wattaya, Near Sultan qaboos Street, Muscat, Oman
Tel.: (968) 24568065
Passport Issuing Services
N.A.I.C.S.: 928120

BLS International Services Pakistan Inc. (1)
TCS Visatronix Shakeel Chamber Khayaban-E- Suharwardy G-6, Islamabad, Pakistan
Tel.: (92) 512607123
Passport Issuing Services

N.A.I.C.S.: 928120

BLS International Services Philippines Inc. (1)
Unit 1903 19th Floor Philippine AXA Life Centre, Sen Gil Puyat Ave, Makati, Philippines
Tel.: (63) 282712196
Passport Issuing Services
N.A.I.C.S.: 928120

BLS International Services Qatar Inc. (1)
Office No 22 5th Floor Al Reem Tower Opposite Intercontinental Hotel, Al Wahda Street, Doha, Qatar
Tel.: (974) 40000705
Passport Issuing Services
N.A.I.C.S.: 928120

BLS International Services Republic of Cote d'Ivoire Inc. (1)
B1 Residence IBD Riviera ANONO Lot 470, Abidjan, Cote d'Ivoire
Tel.: (225) 160242361
Passport Issuing Services
N.A.I.C.S.: 928120

BLS International Services Russia Inc. (1)
Kaluzhskaya square 1 Build 2, 119049, Moscow, Russia
Tel.: (7) 4951890061
Web Site: https://blsspain-russia.com
Passport Issuing Services
N.A.I.C.S.: 928120

BLS International Services Saudiarabia Inc. (1)
Room No 201-203 2nd Floor Building Abi Al Abbas Al Harbi, Prince Mashal Ibn Abdulaziz Irqah, Riyadh, 12532, Saudi Arabia
Tel.: (966) 114831162
Web Site: https://saudi.blsspainvisa.com
Passport Issuing Services
N.A.I.C.S.: 928120

BLS International Services Senegal Inc. (1)
133 Avenue Lamine Gueye Jules Ferry Immeuble Alyama 4th floor, Dakar, Senegal
Tel.: (221) 338223303
Passport Issuing Services
N.A.I.C.S.: 928120

BLS International Services Singapore Pte Ltd (1)
Unit 14 - 02/04/05 Sim Lim Tower 10 Jalan Basar, Singapore, 208787, Singapore
Tel.: (65) 31635611
Web Site: https://www.blsinternational.com
Passport Issuing Services
N.A.I.C.S.: 928120

BLS International Services South Africa Inc. (1)
10th Floor The Tower Building 2 Hertzog Boulevard, Foreshore, Cape Town, 8000, South Africa
Tel.: (27) 10 745 4657
Web Site: https://sa.blsspainvisa.com
Passport Issuing Services
N.A.I.C.S.: 928120

BLS International Services Turkey Inc. (1)
Yesilce Mah Diken Sk No 2, Kagithane, 34418, Istanbul, Turkiye
Tel.: (90) 212 279 3831
Web Site: https://turkey.blsspainvisa.com
Passport Issuing Services
N.A.I.C.S.: 928120

BLS International Services UAE Inc. (1)
507 Habib Bank AG Zurich Al Jawarah Building Bank Street, Next to ADCB Bank, Dubai, United Arab Emirates
Tel.: (971) 43875777
Passport Issuing Services
N.A.I.C.S.: 928120

BLS International Services Ukraine Inc. (1)
Obolonska Str 29 Building B 2-nd floor Office 203, Kiev, 04071, Ukraine
Tel.: (380) 443907690
Web Site: http://blsspain-ukraine.com
Passport Issuing Services

N.A.I.C.S.: 928120

BLS International Services United Kingdom Inc. (1)
Spain Visa Application Centre Lower Ground Floor Cromwell House, 14 Fulwood Place, London, WC1V 6HZ, United Kingdom
Tel.: (44) 2038070750
Web Site: https://uk.blsspainvisa.com
Passport Issuing Services
N.A.I.C.S.: 928120

BLS International Services Vietnam Inc. (1)
13th Floor Hoa Binh Office Towers 106 Hoang Quoc Viet, Cau Giay, Hanoi, Vietnam
Tel.: (84) 243 219 1755
Web Site: https://vietnam.blsspainvisa.com
Passport Issuing Services
N.A.I.C.S.: 928120

BLS International Services kuwait Inc. (1)
Office No 224 22nd Floor Baitak Tower Ahmed Al Jaber Street, Kuwait, Kuwait
Tel.: (965) 22240677
Passport Issuing Services
N.A.I.C.S.: 928120

BLUE ANT MEDIA NZ LIMITED
5 Melville Street, 9016, Dunedin, New Zealand
Tel.: (64) 34799799
Web Site: http://www.nhnz.tv
Television Broadcasting Services
N.A.I.C.S.: 516120
Craig Meade *(Head-Production)*

BLUE ANT MEDIA, INC.
130 Merton Street Suite 200, Toronto, M4S 1A4, ON, Canada
Tel.: (416) 646-4434
Web Site: http://blueantmedia.com
Year Founded: 2011
Television Broadcasting
N.A.I.C.S.: 516120
Michael MacMillan *(Founder & CEO)*

BLUE BLENDS (INDIA) LIMITED
2nd Floor JBF House Old Post Office Lane Kalbadevi Road, Mumbai, 400 002, India
Tel.: (91) 2222088736
Web Site: https://www.bseindia.com
Year Founded: 1995
Rev.: $8,230,405
Assets: $12,796,370
Liabilities: $15,677,211
Net Worth: ($2,880,841)
Earnings: ($6,521,731)
Emp.: 127
Fiscal Year-end: 03/31/19
Yarn & Denim Fabric Mfr
N.A.I.C.S.: 313210
Anand Arya *(Chm & Mng Dir)*

Subsidiaries:

Blue Blends (India) Limited - Denim Division (1)
603 Sahajanand Shaibaug Road, Ahmedabad, 380 004, Gujarat, India
Tel.: (91) 79 25622141
Denim Fabric Mfr
N.A.I.C.S.: 313210

BLUE CAP AG
Ludwigstrasse 11, 80539, Munich, Germany
Tel.: (49) 89288909   De
Web Site: https://www.blue-cap.de
B7E—(BER)
Rev.: $301,709,748
Assets: $269,233,893
Liabilities: $176,751,664
Net Worth: $92,482,229
Earnings: ($19,670,963)
Emp.: 1,279
Fiscal Year-end: 12/31/23

Privater Equity Firm
N.A.I.C.S.: 523999
Matthias Kosch *(CFO & Member-Mgmt Bd)*

Subsidiaries:

Carl Schaefer Gold- und Silberscheideanstalt GmbH (1)
Altstadter Kirchenweg 23, 75175, Pforzheim, Germany
Tel.: (49) 723115760
Precious Metal Jewellery Distr
N.A.I.C.S.: 423940

Filmolux Benelux B.V. (1)
Gotlandstraat 44, 7418 AX, Deventer, Netherlands
Tel.: (31) 572346000
Web Site: https://www.filmolux.nl
Media Advertising Services
N.A.I.C.S.: 541840

Filmolux Deutschland GmbH (1)
Marienstrasse 108a, 32425, Minden, Germany
Tel.: (49) 5716456560
Web Site: https://www.filmolux.de
Graphic Design Services
N.A.I.C.S.: 541430

Filmolux Italia S.R.L. (1)
Via Libero Grassi 9/11, 26010, Bagnolo Cremasco, CR, Italy
Tel.: (39) 0373237911
Web Site: https://filmolux.it
Consultancy Services
N.A.I.C.S.: 541611

Filmolux Swiss AG (1)
Oberhofstrasse 2, 6020, Emmenbrucke, Switzerland
Tel.: (41) 2673300
Web Site: https://www.filmolux.ch
Graphic Design Services
N.A.I.C.S.: 541430

Gammerler GmbH (1)
Leitenstr 26, Gelting, 82538, Geretsried, Germany
Tel.: (49) 81714040
Web Site: https://gammerler.de
Machinery Maintenance & Repair Services
N.A.I.C.S.: 811310

HY-LINE Communication Products Vertriebs GmbH (1)
Inselkammerstr 10, 82008, Unterhaching, Germany
Tel.: (49) 8961450360
Electronic Components Mfr & Distr
N.A.I.C.S.: 334413

HY-LINE Computer Components Vertriebs GmbH (1)
Inselkammerstr 10, 82008, Unterhaching, Germany
Tel.: (49) 8961450340
Electronic Components Mfr & Distr
N.A.I.C.S.: 334413

HY-LINE Holding GmbH (1)
Inselkammerstr 10, 82008, Unterhaching, Germany
Tel.: (49) 896145030
Electronic Components Mfr & Distr
N.A.I.C.S.: 334413

HY-LINE Power Components Vertriebs GmbH (1)
Inselkammerstr 10, 82008, Unterhaching, Germany
Tel.: (49) 8961450310
Electronic Components Mfr & Distr
N.A.I.C.S.: 334413

Hy-Line AG (1)
Hochstrasse 355, 8200, Schaffhausen, Switzerland
Tel.: (41) 526474200
Electronic Components Mfr & Distr
N.A.I.C.S.: 334413

Neschen AG (1)
Hans-Neschen-Strasse 1, 31675, Buckeburg, Germany
Tel.: (49) 57222070
Web Site: https://www.neschen.de

Sales Range: $75-99.9 Million
Emp.: 300
Holding Company; Coated Self-Adhesive & Digital Print Media Developer, Mfr & Marketer
N.A.I.C.S.: 551112
Phuan Chua *(Reg Sls Mgr-Bus Unit Graphics)*

Subsidiary (Non-US):

Filmolux Sarl (2)
14 Ave Du Professuer A Lemiere, Paris, 75020, France (100%)
Tel.: (33) 149206789
Web Site: http://www.filmolux.com.fr
Sales Range: $25-49.9 Million
Emp.: 70
Book Restoration & Self Adhesive Book Protection & Book Care
N.A.I.C.S.: 323120
Joceline Allia *(Gen Mgr)*

Affiliate (Non-US):

Filmolux Co., Ltd. (3)
130-16 Yamabuki-ch Espoir 21 Building 6th Floor, Shinjuku Ku, Tokyo, 162-0801, Japan (24%)
Tel.: (81) 332690491
Web Site: http://www.filmolux.co.jp
Sales Range: $25-49.9 Million
Emp.: 32
Book Restoration & Self Adhesive Book Protection & Book Care
N.A.I.C.S.: 323120

PLANATOL System GmbH (1)
Fabrikstrasse 30-32, 83101, Rohrdorf, Germany
Tel.: (49) 80317200
Adhesive Film Distr
N.A.I.C.S.: 424690

Planatol GmbH (1)
Fabrikstrasse 30-32, 83101, Rohrdorf, Germany
Tel.: (49) 80317200
Web Site: https://www.planatol.de
Adhesive Film Distr
N.A.I.C.S.: 424690

Uniplast Knauer Verwaltungs GmbH (1)
Im Handelsteich 18, 72581, Dettingen an der Erms, Germany
Tel.: (49) 71237250
Web Site: https://www.uniplast.de
Printing & Packaging Product Mfr & Distr
N.A.I.C.S.: 326112

con-pearl North America Inc. (1)
6400 Augusta Rd Ste 101, Greenville, SC 29605-3752
Tel.: (864) 365-0674
Lightweight Plastic Product Mfr & Distr
N.A.I.C.S.: 326199

BLUE CHIP INDIA LTD.
10 Princep Street 2nd Floor, Kolkata, 700 072, India
Tel.: (91) 3340022880
Web Site:
https://www.bluechipind.net
531936—(BOM)
Rev.: $1,461
Assets: $1,368,808
Liabilities: $840,212
Net Worth: $528,596
Earnings: ($33,961)
Emp.: 5
Fiscal Year-end: 03/31/22
Financial Fund Management Services
N.A.I.C.S.: 523940
Arihant Jain *(Mng Dir & Compliance Officer)*

BLUE CHIP TEX INDUSTRIES LTD.
15-17 Maker Chamber III 1st Floor Jamnalal Bajaj Road Nariman Point, Mumbai, 400 021, India
Tel.: (91) 2243530400
Web Site:
https://www.bluechiptexindustry.com

506981—(BOM)
Rev.: $33,271,971
Assets: $6,627,184
Liabilities: $2,888,477
Net Worth: $3,738,708
Earnings: $439,189
Emp.: 130
Fiscal Year-end: 03/31/22
Textile Products Mfr
N.A.I.C.S.: 313310
Rahul A. Khemani *(CFO)*

BLUE CIRCLE SERVICES LIMITED
Unit No 324 3rd Floor Building No 9 Laxmi Plaza, New Link Road Andheri West, Mumbai, 400 053, India
Tel.: (91) 2269969555
Web Site:
http://www.bluecircleservices.com
Year Founded: 1983
508939—(BOM)
Assets: $1,349,945
Liabilities: $963,412
Net Worth: $386,532
Earnings: ($148,567)
Emp.: 3
Fiscal Year-end: 03/31/20
Financial Advisory Services
N.A.I.C.S.: 523940
Anil Kumar Purohit *(Chm & Mng Dir)*

BLUE CLOUD SOFTECH SOLUTIONS LTD.
Plot No 38 5th Floor Software Units Layout HITEC City, Hyderabad, 500029, India
Tel.: (91) 8466022022
Web Site:
https://www.bluecloudsoftech.com
539607—(BOM)
Rev.: $14,988
Assets: $647,310
Liabilities: $3,286
Net Worth: $644,024
Earnings: $1,207
Fiscal Year-end: 03/31/21
Software Publishing Services
N.A.I.C.S.: 513210
B. Ravi Kumar *(Mng Dir)*

BLUE COAST HOTELS LIMITED
415-417 Antriksh Bhawan 22 Kasturba Gandhi Marg, New Delhi, 110001, India
Tel.: (91) 1123358774
Web Site: https://www.bluecoast.in
Rev.: $7,918,820
Assets: $6,764,852
Liabilities: $16,829,266
Net Worth: ($10,064,414)
Earnings: ($27,790,475)
Emp.: 5
Fiscal Year-end: 03/31/19
Home Management Services
N.A.I.C.S.: 721110
Kushal Suri *(Exec Dir)*

BLUE COLIBRI AG
Lenbachplatz 5, 80333, Munich, Germany
Tel.: (49) 89 3090 9690   De
Web Site: http://www.bluecolibri.de
Year Founded: 2006
Commercial Real Estate Investment & Portfolio Management
N.A.I.C.S.: 531390
Andreas Reinert *(CEO)*

BLUE DART EXPRESS LIMITED
Blue Dart Center Sahar Airport Road Andheri East, Mumbai, 400099, India
Tel.: (91) 2262601234
Web Site: https://www.bluedart.com

Blue Dart Express Limited—(Continued)

526612—(BOM)
Rev.: $606,234,720
Assets: $386,125,740
Liabilities: $267,099,105
Net Worth: $119,026,635
Earnings: $52,171,665
Emp.: 12,288
Fiscal Year-end: 03/31/22
Trucking & Courier Services
N.A.I.C.S.: 488510
Sharad Upasani *(Chm)*

BLUE ENERGY LIMITED
Level 10 26 Wharf Street, PO Box
10261, Brisbane, 4000, QLD, Austra-
lia
Tel.: (61) 732708800   AU
Web Site:
  https://www.blueenergy.com.au
BLU—(ASX)
Rev.: $110,176
Assets: $50,447,382
Liabilities: $1,171,875
Net Worth: $49,275,507
Earnings: ($9,113,916)
Fiscal Year-end: 06/30/24
Oil & Gas Exploration
N.A.I.C.S.: 211120
John Phillips *(Mng Dir)*

BLUE ENSIGN TECHNOLO-
GIES LIMITED
Ste 202 Angela House 30-36 Bay
Street, Double Bay, 2028, NSW, Aus-
tralia
Tel.: (61) 2 9363 5088
Web Site:
  http://www.blueensigntech.com.au
Oil & Minerals Producer
N.A.I.C.S.: 211120
John Blumer *(Chm)*

Subsidiaries:

Queensland Shale Oil Pty. Ltd.   (1)
Ste 202 Angela House 30-36 Bay St,
Double Bay, 2028, NSW, Australia
Tel.: (61) 2 93635088
Web Site:
  http://www.blueensigntech.com.au
Sales Range: $50-74.9 Million
Emp.: 2
Oil Shale Mining Services
N.A.I.C.S.: 213112

BLUE FALLS MANUFACTUR-
ING LTD.
4549-52 Street, Thorsby, T0C 2P0,
AB, Canada
Tel.: (780) 789-2626
Web Site: http://www.goarctic.com
Year Founded: 1994
Sales Range: $75-99.9 Million
Emp.: 130
Hot Tub Mfr
N.A.I.C.S.: 339920
Darcy Amendt *(Pres & CEO)*

BLUE FINANCIAL COMMUNI-
CATION S.P.A.
Via Melchiorre Gioia 55, 20124, Mi-
lan, Italy
Tel.: (39) 023032111
Web Site:
  http://www.bluefinancial.com
Year Founded: 1995
Investment Management Service
N.A.I.C.S.: 523940
Denis Masetti *(Pres & Publr)*

BLUE HAT INTERACTIVE EN-
TERTAINMENT TECHNOLOGY
7th Floor Building C No 1010 Anling
Road, Huli District, Xiamen,, 361009,
China
Tel.: (86) 5922280081   Ky

Web Site:
  http://www.bluehatgroup.com
Year Founded: 2010
BHAT—(NASDAQ)
Rev.: $15,155,074
Assets: $36,511,577
Liabilities: $18,861,371
Net Worth: $17,650,206
Earnings: ($57,135,940)
Emp.: 80
Fiscal Year-end: 12/31/21
Interactive Mobile Application Devel-
opment Services
N.A.I.C.S.: 541511
Xiaodong Chen *(CEO)*

BLUE INC.
13 Uplands Business Park Black-
horse Lane, London, E17 5QN,
United Kingdom
Tel.: (44) 208 531 7651
Web Site: http://www.blueinc.co.uk
Year Founded: 1912
Emp.: 2,236
Clothing Store Operator
N.A.I.C.S.: 458110
Steven William Guy Cohen *(CEO)*

BLUE INNOVATION CO., LTD.
4F Ichigo Hongo Building 5-33-10,
Hongo Bunkyo-ku, Tokyo, Japan
Tel.: (81) 368018781
Web Site: https://www.blue-i.co.jp
Year Founded: 1999
5597—(TKS)
Emp.: 67
Software Development Services
N.A.I.C.S.: 541511

BLUE ISLAND PLC
10 Polyfimou Street Strovolos Indus-
trial Area 2033, PO Box 26073, 1666,
Nicosia, Cyprus
Tel.: (357) 22516555
Web Site: https://blue-island.com
Year Founded: 1993
BLUE—(CYP)
Sales Range: Less than $1 Million
Fish Farming Services
N.A.I.C.S.: 112511
Stavros Kremmos *(Chm)*

BLUE JET HEALTHCARE LIM-
ITED
701 702 7th Floor Plot No 1 & 2 Bhu-
miraj Costarica Sector 18 Sanpada,
Mumbai, 400705, India
Tel.: (91) 2222075307
Web Site:
  https://www.bluejethealthcare.com
Year Founded: 1968
544000—(BOM)
Rev.: $90,286,486
Assets: $104,482,278
Liabilities: $21,886,175
Net Worth: $82,596,103
Earnings: $19,395,272
Fiscal Year-end: 03/31/23
Pharmaceutical Product Mfr & Distr
N.A.I.C.S.: 325412

BLUE LABEL TELECOMS LIM-
ITED
75 Grayston Drive Corner Benmore
Drive, Morningside Extension 05,
Sandton, 2196, South Africa   ZA
Web Site:
  http://www.bluelabeltelecoms.co.za
BLU—(JSE)
Rev.: $770,944,120
Assets: $799,403,175
Liabilities: $529,430,960
Net Worth: $269,972,216
Earnings: $34,832,697
Emp.: 1,150
Fiscal Year-end: 03/31/24

Prepaid Secure Electronic Tokens
Distr
N.A.I.C.S.: 522320
Mark S. Levy *(Co-CEO)*

Subsidiaries:

Activi Deployment Services (Propri-
etary) Limited   (1)
Unit L 7 Enterprise Bldg The Innovation
Hub, Pretoria, 0087, Gauteng, South Africa
Tel.: (27) 128440072
Web Site: http://www.bluelabeltelecom.com
Sales Range: $50-74.9 Million
Emp.: 25
Electronic Financial Transaction Processing
Services
N.A.I.C.S.: 522320

Africa Prepaid Services (Mozam-
bique) Limitada   (1)
Times Sq Block 3 Ground Fl 25 Septembro
Ave, Maputo, Mozambique
Tel.: (258) 21315551
Web Site: http://www.oxigen.co.mz
Prepaid Cards & Starter Packs Distr
N.A.I.C.S.: 424990

Blue Label Distribution Proprietary
Limited   (1)
75 Grayston Drive Morningside ext 5, Sand-
ton, 2196, South Africa
Tel.: (27) 115233030
Financial Services
N.A.I.C.S.: 524210

Cellfind (Proprietary) Limited   (1)
300 Witch-Hazel Avenue Eco Fusion 4 Of-
fice Park, Centurion, 0169, Gauteng, South
Africa
Tel.: (27) 10 442 3100
Web Site: https://www.cellfind.net.za
Sales Range: $25-49.9 Million
Emp.: 52
Cellular Phone Users Tracking Services
N.A.I.C.S.: 517810
Victor Probert *(Head-Intl Sls-Cellfind)*

Comm Express Services SA (Propri-
etary) Limited   (1)
Ste 13-19 1st Fl Coldstream Ofc Park Cor-
ner Hendrik Potgieter Ave, Van Staden Rd
Little Falls, Roodepoort, 1175, Gauteng,
South Africa
Tel.: (27) 112228666
Web Site: http://www.commexpress.co.za
Sales Range: $50-74.9 Million
Emp.: 81
Cellular Airtime & Prepaid Cards Distr
N.A.I.C.S.: 424990

Content Connect Africa (Proprietary)
Limited   (1)
1st Floor Block 3 Riviera Office Park 66 Ox-
ford Road Riviera, Johannesburg, 2021,
Gauteng, South Africa
Tel.: (27) 116466048
Web Site: http://www.contentca.co.za
Sales Range: $25-49.9 Million
Emp.: 7
Mobile Entertainment Application Develop-
ment Services
N.A.I.C.S.: 541511

SharedPhone International (Propri-
etary) Limited   (1)
Sharedphone House Kempground Rd,
Cape Town, 7700, Western Cape, South
Africa
Tel.: (27) 216774620
Web Site: http://www.sharedphone.co.za
Sim Card Operated Payphone Service Pro-
viders
N.A.I.C.S.: 517810

Transaction Junction (Proprietary)
Limited   (1)
No 1 Waterhouse Place Block 3 Second
Floor, Century City, Cape Town, 7441,
Western Cape, South Africa
Tel.: (27) 215253100
Web Site:
  https://www.transactionjunction.co.za
Sales Range: $50-74.9 Million
Emp.: 15
Transaction Processing Software Solutions
N.A.I.C.S.: 522320

Velociti (Proprietary) Limited   (1)

67 KE Masinga Rd, Durban, 4001,
Kwazulu-Natal, South Africa
Tel.: (27) 31 327 8200
Web Site: https://www.velociti.biz
Sales Range: $150-199.9 Million
Emp.: 1,000
Call Center Operation Services
N.A.I.C.S.: 561422

Virtual Voucher (Proprietary)
Limited   (1)
113-11th St, PO Box 73789, Fairland, Jo-
hannesburg, 2030, Gauteng, South Africa
Tel.: (27) 114789874
Web Site: http://www.virtualvoucher.co.za
Sales Range: $25-49.9 Million
Emp.: 5
Cellular Airtime & Prepaid Cards Distr
N.A.I.C.S.: 517121
Klaus Johanson *(Gen Mgr)*

BLUE LAGOON RESOURCES,
INC.
1200 750 West Pender St, Vancou-
ver, V6C 2T8, BC, Canada
Tel.: (604) 218-4766
Web Site:
  https://www.bluelagoon.com
7BL—(DEU)
Rev.: $68,986
Assets: $17,460,492
Liabilities: $3,370,802
Net Worth: $14,089,690
Earnings: ($9,111,384)
Fiscal Year-end: 03/31/23
Mining Services
N.A.I.C.S.: 212290
Carmelo Marrelli *(CFO)*

BLUE LOTUS COMMUNICA-
TIONS CONSULTANCY
2/33 Kamal Mansion 2nd Fl Arthur
Blunder Road, Near Radio Club Co-
laba, Mumbai, 400005, India
Tel.: (91) 22 6652 2800
Web Site: http://www.bluelotuspr.com
Year Founded: 2002
Sales Range: Less than $1 Million
Emp.: 115
N.A.I.C.S.: 541820
N. Chandramouli *(CEO)*

Subsidiaries:

Blue Lotus Communications
(Bangalore)   (1)
No 117 2nd Fl 18th Main Hal 2nd Stage,
Indiranagar, Bengaluru, 560008, India
Tel.: (91) 80 41526656
Emp.: 28
N.A.I.C.S.: 541810
Dhananjay Kulkarni *(Head-South India)*

Blue Lotus Communications
(Chennai)   (1)
82 3rd Fl Hardevi Chambers Pantheon Rd,
Egmore, Chennai, 600008, India
Tel.: (91) 44 421 46123
Emp.: 15
N.A.I.C.S.: 541810
Gopu Ramamoorthi *(Mgr)*

Blue Lotus Communications
(Hyderabad)   (1)
RO 1 1 256B Plot No 107, Bhagwanthpur
Begumpet, Hyderabad, 500016, India
Tel.: (91) 40 40041957
Emp.: 10
N.A.I.C.S.: 541810
Yves Gougoux *(Chm & CEO)*

Blue Lotus Communications
(Kolkata)   (1)
11A Ground Floor Bompas Road, Opp
CESC Office, Kolkata, 700 029, India
Tel.: (91) 33 645 30865
N.A.I.C.S.: 541810

Blue Lotus Communications (New
Delhi)   (1)
C-10 2nd Fl Amar Colony Market, Lajpat
Nagar IV, New Delhi, 110 024, India
Tel.: (91) 11 46517241
Emp.: 20

N.A.I.C.S.: 541810
Archana Tomar *(Co-Founder & VP)*

Blue Lotus Communications
(Pune)   (1)
Flat No 3A 1st and 2nd Fl A Wing, Mastani
Baug Apartments, Pune, 411009, India
Tel.: (91) 20 56027869
N.A.I.C.S.: 541810
Chitra Shripad *(Pub Rel Mgr)*

BLUE MAX BANNER LIMITED
Unit 5 Kennet Way, Trowbridge,
BA14 8BL, Wilts, United Kingdom
Tel.: (44) 1225 715070   UK
Web Site:
    http://www.bluemaxbanner.co.uk
Year Founded: 2010
Emp.: 100
Children's Uniforms & Apparel Mfr &
Distr
N.A.I.C.S.: 315250
Glenn Leech *(CEO)*

**BLUE MOON GROUP HOLD-
INGS LIMITED**
No 36 Punan Road, Yunpu Industrial
Park Huangpu, Guangzhou, Guang-
dong, China
Tel.: (86) 4001111118   Ky
Web Site:
    http://www.bluemoon.com.cn
Year Founded: 1992
6993—(HKG)
Holding Company
N.A.I.C.S.: 551112
Pan Dong *(Chm & CTO)*

BLUE MOON METALS INC.
1040 West Georgia 15th Floor, Van-
couver, V6E 4H1, BC, Canada
Tel.: (832) 499-6009   BC
Web Site:
    http://www.bluemoonmining.com
Year Founded: 2007
MOON—(OTCIQ)
Assets: $772,940
Liabilities: $437,401
Net Worth: $335,539
Earnings: ($206,003)
Fiscal Year-end: 12/31/20
Mineral Exploration Services
N.A.I.C.S.: 212290
Patrick McGrath *(CEO)*

BLUE MOUNTAIN CHRYSLER
9950 Hwy 26 E, Collingwood, L9Y
3Z1, ON, Canada
Tel.: (705) 445-2740
Web Site:
    http://www.bluemountain.com
Year Founded: 1974
New & Used Car Dealers
N.A.I.C.S.: 441110
Warren Sly *(Gen Mgr)*

**BLUE MOUNTAIN ECO TOURS
INC.**
11 Rocky Road, Queensborough,
Kingston, Jamaica
Tel.: (876) 310 7166   NV
Web Site:
    http://bluemountainecotours.net
Year Founded: 2010
Tour Operator
N.A.I.C.S.: 561520
Donald Lindo *(Pres, CEO, CFO,
Chief Acctg Officer, Treas & Sec)*

**BLUE MOUNTAIN WALLCOV-
ERINGS, INC.**
15 Akron Road, Toronto, M8W 1T3,
ON, Canada
Tel.: (416) 251-1678
Web Site: http://www.ihdg.com
Rev.: $84,231,556
Emp.: 200

Residential Wall Coverings Distr &
Mfr
N.A.I.C.S.: 238320
Christopher M. Wood *(Chm)*

BLUE NILE MAHSREG BANK
Elnagoumi Street, Khartoum, Sudan
Tel.: (249) 183 764490
Web Site:
    http://www.bluemashreg.com
Rev.: $81,936,313
Assets: $420,322,726
Liabilities: $293,930,520
Net Worth: $126,392,207
Earnings: $47,088,160
Fiscal Year-end: 12/31/15
Banking Services
N.A.I.C.S.: 522110
Mohamed Ismail Mohamed *(Chm)*

**BLUE PLANET INVESTMENT
TRUST PLC**
17 Grosvenor Crescent, Edinburgh,
EH12 5EL, United Kingdom
Tel.: (44) 131 466 6666   UK
Web Site: http://www.blueplanet.eu
Year Founded: 1998
BLP—(LSE)
Rev.: $3,140,402
Assets: $20,510,135
Liabilities: $630,163
Net Worth: $19,879,972
Earnings: ($8,606,210)
Fiscal Year-end: 04/30/20
Investment Trust Management Ser-
vices
N.A.I.C.S.: 523940

**BLUE PLANET WORLDWIDE
FINANCIALS INVESTMENT
TRUST PLC**
Greenside House 25 Greenside
Place, Edinburgh, EH1 3AA, United
Kingdom
Tel.: (44) 1314666666
Web Site: http://www.blueplanet.eu
Investment Services
N.A.I.C.S.: 523999
Philip Court *(Chm)*

BLUE RIBBON INCOME FUND
407 2nd St. S W Ste 1120, Calgary,
T2P 2Y3, AB, Canada
Tel.: (403) 261-9674
BLUBF—(OTCIQ)
Sales Range: Less than $1 Million
Investment Management Service
N.A.I.C.S.: 525990
M. Paul Bloom *(Portfolio Mgr-Fund)*

BLUE RIDGE CHINA
3701 Tower A Beijing Fortune Centre
No 7 Dongsanhuan Rd, Beijing,
100020, China
Tel.: (86) 10 65309900
Web Site:
    http://www.blueridgechina.com
Year Founded: 2006
Privater Equity Firm
N.A.I.C.S.: 621999
Justin Yue Tang *(CEO)*

**BLUE RIVER RESOURCES
LTD.**
Suite 2607 - 1128 Alberni Street,
Vancouver, V6E 4R6, BC, Canada
Tel.: (604) 682-7339   BC
Web Site: https://www.blueriv.com
Year Founded: 2008
BXR—(OTCIQ)
Assets: $294,133
Liabilities: $1,233,733
Net Worth: ($939,600)
Earnings: ($214,680)
Fiscal Year-end: 10/31/21
Copper Mining

N.A.I.C.S.: 212230
Griffin Jones *(Pres & CEO)*

**BLUE SAFARI GROUP ACQUI-
SITION CORP.**
Cheung Kong Center 58 Floor Unit
5801 2 Queens Road, Central, China
(Hong Kong)
Tel.: (852) 92589728   VG
Year Founded: 2021
BSGA—(NASDAQ)
Rev.: $742,433
Assets: $18,885,035
Liabilities: $27,499,792
Net Worth: ($8,614,757)
Earnings: ($3,917,800)
Emp.: 2
Fiscal Year-end: 12/31/22
Investment Services
N.A.I.C.S.: 523999
Alan Yamashita *(Chm)*

**BLUE SAIL MEDICAL CO.,
LTD.**
No 48 Yinuo Road Jixia Street, Linzi
District, Zibo, 255400, Shandong,
China
Tel.: (86) 5337871008
Web Site: http://www.bluesail.cn
Year Founded: 1989
002382—(SSE)
Rev.: $688,027,392
Assets: $2,228,504,616
Liabilities: $747,013,644
Net Worth: $1,481,490,972
Earnings: ($52,273,728)
Emp.: 5,000
Fiscal Year-end: 12/31/22
PVC Gloves Mfr & Sales
N.A.I.C.S.: 326299
Wenjing Liu *(Chm)*

**BLUE SALON ESTABLISH-
MENT**
Suhaim Bin Hamad St, PO Box 6255,
Doha, Qatar
Tel.: (974) 44466111
Web Site: http://www.bluesalon.com
Year Founded: 1981
Sales Range: $10-24.9 Million
Emp.: 700
Department Stores
N.A.I.C.S.: 455110
Ashraf Abu Issa *(Chm & CEO)*

**BLUE SKY ALTERNATIVE IN-
VESTMENTS LIMITED**
Level 46 111 Eagle Street, Brisbane,
4000, QLD, Australia
Tel.: (61) 7 3270 7500
Web Site:
    http://www.blueskyfunds.com.au
Rev.: $23,529,432
Assets: $253,344,713
Liabilities: $127,933,238
Net Worth: $125,411,475
Earnings: ($52,760,344)
Emp.: 24
Fiscal Year-end: 06/30/18
Investment Management
N.A.I.C.S.: 523150
Andrew Werro *(COO)*

BLUE SKY ENERGY INC.
65 Queen Street West 8th floor Suite
805, Toronto, M5H 2M5, ON, Canada
Tel.: (416) 309-2963
Web Site:
    http://brookwaterventures.com
BSI.H—(TSXV)
Assets: $13,168
Liabilities: $1,896,079
Net Worth: ($1,882,911)
Earnings: ($492,784)
Fiscal Year-end: 07/31/21
Oil & Gas Exploration Services

N.A.I.C.S.: 213112

BLUE SKY HOSTING LTD
14 Great College Street Westminster,
London, SW1P 3RX, United Kingdom
Tel.: (44) 2071835854
Web Site: http://www.bluesky.co.uk
Year Founded: 1997
Web Hosting Services
N.A.I.C.S.: 518210
Matthew McCloskey *(Dir-Sls & Mktg)*

BLUE SKY URANIUM CORP.
Suite 411837 West Hastings Street,
Vancouver, V6C 3N6, BC, Canada
Tel.: (604) 687-1828   BC
Web Site:
    https://www.blueskyuranium.com
Year Founded: 2005
BKUCF—(OTCQB)
Rev.: $250,754
Assets: $1,042,847
Liabilities: $1,580,922
Net Worth: ($538,075)
Earnings: ($1,508,954)
Fiscal Year-end: 12/31/20
Uranium Exploration Services
N.A.I.C.S.: 212290
Nikolaos Cacos *(Pres & CEO)*

BLUE SOLUTIONS LIMITED
12b Oklands Business Centre Oak-
lands Park, Wokingham, RG41 2FD,
Berkshire, United Kingdom
Tel.: (44) 118 9898 222
Web Site:
    http://www.bluesolutions.co.uk
Sales Range: $1-9.9 Million
Emp.: 18
Software & Other Computer Products
Distr
N.A.I.C.S.: 423430

BLUE STAR CAPITAL PLC
Griffin House 135 High Street, Craw-
ley, RH10 1DQ, W Sussex, United
Kingdom
Tel.: (44) 7771782434   UK
Web Site:
    https://www.bluestarcapital.co.uk
BLU—(AIM)
Assets: $12,997,656
Liabilities: $79,254
Net Worth: $12,918,402
Earnings: ($1,471,860)
Fiscal Year-end: 09/30/22
Venture Capital Funding Services
N.A.I.C.S.: 523999
Anthony Fabrizi *(CEO)*

**BLUE STAR FORD LINCOLN
SALES LTD**
115 Queensway East, Simcoe,
N3Y4M5, ON, Canada
Tel.: (519) 426-3673
Web Site:
    http://www.bluestarford.com
Year Founded: 1985
Rev.: $16,832,542
Emp.: 37
New & Used Car Dealers
N.A.I.C.S.: 441110
Robert Kowtaluk *(Founder)*

BLUE STAR GOLD CORP.
507-700 W Pender Street, Vancou-
ver, V6C 1G8, BC, Canada
Tel.: (778) 379-1433   BC
Web Site:
    https://www.bluestargold.ca
Year Founded: 2007
BAUFF—(OTCQB)
Assets: $21,831,149
Liabilities: $2,234,428
Net Worth: $19,596,721
Earnings: ($1,146,597)

Blue Star Gold Corp.—(Continued)

Emp.: 8
Fiscal Year-end: 11/30/22
Natural Resource Mining Services
N.A.I.C.S.: 212390
Grant Ewing (CEO)

BLUE STAR HELIUM LTD.
Level 8 London House 216 St
Georges Terrace, Perth, 6000, WA,
Australia
Tel.: (61) 894810389   **AU**
Web Site:
   https://www.bluestarhelium.com
BNL—(ASX)
Rev.: $77,286
Assets: $15,327,929
Liabilities: $397,238
Net Worth: $14,930,691
Earnings: ($2,129,050)
Emp.: 6
Fiscal Year-end: 12/31/23
Oil & Gas Exploration Services
N.A.I.C.S.: 213112
James Andrew Cruickshank (Chm &
CEO)

BLUE STAR LIMITED
Band Box House 4th Floor 254 D Dr
Annie Besant Road Worli, Mumbai,
400 030, India
Tel.: (91) 2266544000   **In**
Web Site:
   https://www.bluestarindia.com
Year Founded: 1943
BLUESTARCO—(NSE)
Rev.: $830,097,450
Assets: $588,675,360
Liabilities: $449,371,650
Net Worth: $139,303,710
Earnings: $22,932,000
Emp.: 2,533
Fiscal Year-end: 03/30/22
Air Conditioning & Refrigeration Systems & Products Mfr
N.A.I.C.S.: 333415
B. Thiagarajan (Mng Dir)

Subsidiaries:

Blue Star Design & Engineering
Ltd.   (1)
Mirchandani Business Park 4th Floor Off
Ghatkopar Link Road, Mumbai, 400 072,
Maharashtra, India
Tel.: (91) 2267774000
Web Site: http://www.bluestar-de.com
Sales Range: $50-74.9 Million
Emp.: 200
Computer Aided Designing Services
N.A.I.C.S.: 541330

Blue Star Engineering & Electronics
Ltd.   (1)
Band Box House 4th Floor 254D Dr Annie
Besant Road, Worli, Mumbai, 400 030, India
Tel.: (91) 2266544000
Web Site: https://bluestar-ee.com
Electronic Equipment Mfr & Distr
N.A.I.C.S.: 334419

Blue Star International FZCO   (1)
Building E3 Side Office 520, Dubai Airport
Free Zone, Dubai, 293723, United Arab
Emirates
Tel.: (971) 42306900
HVAC Equipment Distr
N.A.I.C.S.: 423730

Blue Star Limited - Thane
Facility   (1)
II nd Pokhran Road Near Bethany Hospital
Majiwada, Thane, 400 601, Maharashtra,
India
Tel.: (91) 2267154500
Web Site: http://www.bluestarindia.com
Air Conditioning & Refrigeration Systems
Mfr
N.A.I.C.S.: 333415

Blue Star Ltd.   (1)

Blue Star House 9A Ghatkopar Link Road,
Sakinaka, Mumbai, 400 072, India   **(100%)**
Tel.: (91) 2266684000
Sales Range: $50-74.9 Million
Provider of Air Conditioning & Heating Services
N.A.I.C.S.: 333415

Blue Star Ltd.   (1)
7 Hare Street, Kolkata, 700 001,
India   **(100%)**
Tel.: (91) 3322134000
Sales Range: $50-74.9 Million
Emp.: 250
Provider of Air Conditioning & Heating Services
N.A.I.C.S.: 333415

Blue Star Ltd.   (1)
6th Floor Vatika Atrium Golf Course Road
Sector 53, Gurgaon, 122 002, Haryana,
India
Tel.: (91) 1244044000
Sales Range: $50-74.9 Million
Air Conditioning & Heating Services
N.A.I.C.S.: 333415

Blue Star Ltd.   (1)
KRM Plaza No 2 Harrington Road, Chetpet,
Chennai, 600 031, Tamil Nadu,
India   **(100%)**
Tel.: (91) 4442444000
Sales Range: $50-74.9 Million
Emp.: 125
Commercial, Industrial & Institutional Heating, Ventilating, Air-Conditioning, Filtration &
Air Pollution Control Products, Systems &
Controls
N.A.I.C.S.: 333415

Blue Star North America Inc.   (1)
4851 Tamiami Trl N Ste 200, Naples, FL
34103
Tel.: (469) 847-3183
Web Site: https://www.bluestarindia.com
Air Conditioning Product Mfr & Distr
N.A.I.C.S.: 333415

Blue Star Qatar WLL   (1)
Building No-349 Zone No Area-52 Street
No-990 Office No 1 Al Rayyan, PO Box
47242, Al Qadeem Street Near Al Rayyan
Park, Doha, Qatar
Tel.: (974) 44582271
Web Site: http://www.bluestarqatar.com
HVAC Equipment Distr
N.A.I.C.S.: 423730

BLUE THUNDER MINING, INC.
2300 Rue Tupper Suite 2901, Montreal, H3H 0B9, ON, Canada
Tel.: (647) 848-1009   **Ca**
Web Site:
   https://www.bluethundermining.com
Year Founded: 2017
BLUE—(TSXV)
Assets: $883,045
Liabilities: $533,847
Net Worth: $349,199
Earnings: ($226,536)
Fiscal Year-end: 12/31/23
Mineral Exploration Services
N.A.I.C.S.: 213115
Chad Williams (Chm & CEO-Interim)

BLUE VISION A/S
Vester Farimagsgade 1 2, 1606, Copenhagen, Denmark
Tel.: (45) 36944417
Web Site: http://www.blue-vision.dk
Year Founded: 2002
PEG—(CSE)
Rev.: $2,073
Assets: $12,043,385
Liabilities: $6,278,818
Net Worth: $5,764,567
Earnings: ($3,643,888)
Emp.: 6
Fiscal Year-end: 12/31/23
Real Estate Support Services
N.A.I.C.S.: 531210

BLUE WATER ENERGY LLP

17 Connaught Place, London, W2
2ES, United Kingdom
Tel.: (44) 20 7290 5090   **UK**
Web Site:
   http://www.bluewaterenergy.com
Privater Equity Firm
N.A.I.C.S.: 523999
Jerker Johansson (Chm & Partner)

Subsidiaries:

IMServ Europe Limited   (1)
Cygnus House Sunrise Parkway, Linford
Wood, Milton Keynes, MK14 6LS, United
Kingdom
Tel.: (44) 1908 696000
Web Site: http://www.imserv.com
Energy Consulting Services
N.A.I.C.S.: 541690
Steve Brown (Mng Dir)

Pipeline Technique Ltd.   (1)
Midmill Business Park Tofthills Avenue Kintore, Aberdeenshire, AB51 0QP, Scotland ,
United Kingdom
Tel.: (44) 1466795888
Web Site: https://www.pipeline-technique.com
Emp.: 157
Oil & Gas Services
N.A.I.C.S.: 237120
Frederic Castrec (CEO)

Subsidiary (Domestic):

Global Project (services) Ltd   (2)
Supply Base Shore Road, Invergordon,
IV18 0EX, United Kingdom
Tel.: (44) 1349 855135
Web Site:
   http://www.globalprojectservicesuk.com
Engineeering Services
N.A.I.C.S.: 541330

Varel International Energy Services,
Inc.   (1)
1625 W Crosby Rd Ste 124, Carrollton, TX
75006
Tel.: (972) 242-1160
Web Site: http://www.varelintl.com
Oil & Gas Well Drill Bits Mfr
N.A.I.C.S.: 333132
Jim Nixon (Chm)

BLUE WATER GLOBAL GROUP, INC.
7070 E Farrell Rd SE Ste 1019, Calgary, T2H 0T2, AB, Canada
Tel.: (954) 837-6833   **NV**
Year Founded: 2011
BLUU—(OTCEM)
Holding Company; Casual Dining
Restaurant Operator
N.A.I.C.S.: 551112

BLUE ZEN MEMORIAL PARKS INC.
c/o Dentons Canada LLP 77 King
Street West Suite 400, Toronto,
M5K0A1, ON, Canada
Tel.: (514) 288-0900   **Ca**
Year Founded: 1994
Sales Range: $1-9.9 Million
Copper & Mineral Exploration & Development
N.A.I.C.S.: 212230
Xian Ming Kong (Chm & CEO)

BLUE-CON CONSTRUCTION
1915 Crumlin Side Road, London,
N5V 3B8, ON, Canada
Tel.: (519) 659-2400
Web Site: http://www.bluecon.on.ca
Year Founded: 1976
Rev.: $10,607,284
Emp.: 60
Construction Services
N.A.I.C.S.: 237990
Joe Haasen (CEO)

BLUEBAND FINANCING LIMITED

33 Kurmangazy Street Apt 33, Medeu
District, Almaty, Kazakhstan
Tel.: (7) 35722023000
Financial Management Services
N.A.I.C.S.: 541611

BLUEBERRIES MEDICAL CORP.
Warehouse 0 Trafalgar Industrial
Park Km 1 via Briceno Zipaquira, Tocancipa, Cundinamarca, Colombia
Tel.: (57) 316170133
Web Site:
   https://www.blueberriesmed.com
BBM—(OTCIQ)
Rev.: $1,834
Assets: $7,488,981
Liabilities: $1,309,352
Net Worth: $6,179,628
Earnings: ($8,255,314)
Fiscal Year-end: 12/31/19
Medical Product Distr
N.A.I.C.S.: 459999
Facundo Garreton (Chm-Interim &
CEO)

BLUEBET HOLDINGS LTD.
Level 9 8 Spring Street, PO Box
R1316, Sydney, 2000, NSW, Australia
Tel.: (61) 295710033   **AU**
Web Site:
   https://www.bluebet.com.au
Year Founded: 2015
BBT—(ASX)
Rev.: $38,962,340
Assets: $25,046,074
Liabilities: $22,757,078
Net Worth: $2,288,996
Earnings: ($31,328,793)
Fiscal Year-end: 06/30/24
Holding Company
N.A.I.C.S.: 551112
Michael David Sullivan (Chm)

BLUEBLOOD VENTURES LIMITED
P-27 Malviya Nagar, New Delhi,
110017, India
Tel.: (91) 1126671594
Web Site:
   https://www.bluebloodventure.com
Year Founded: 2007
539637—(BOM)
Rev.: $63,385
Assets: $13,367,487
Liabilities: $12,986,032
Net Worth: $381,454
Earnings: ($90,466)
Emp.: 6
Fiscal Year-end: 03/31/21
Securities Trading
N.A.I.C.S.: 523150
Suresh Bohra (Mng Dir & CFO)

BLUECHIIP LIMITED
1 Dalmore Drive Caribbean Business
Park, Scoresby, 3179, VIC, Australia
Tel.: (61) 397639763
Web Site: https://www.bluechiip.com
Year Founded: 2003
BCT—(ASX)
Rev.: $610,878
Assets: $4,208,620
Liabilities: $2,630,214
Net Worth: $1,578,406
Earnings: ($3,365,388)
Emp.: 24
Fiscal Year-end: 06/30/23
RFID Memory & Temperature Sensing Devices
N.A.I.C.S.: 334413
Lee D. Mitchell (Sec)

BLUECHIP STOCKSPIN LIMITED

A/301 Wall Street-II Opp Orient Club
Gujarat College Road Ellisbridge, Nr
Gujarat College Railway Crossing
Ellisbridge, Ahmedabad, 380006, Gu-
jarat, India
Tel.: (91) 79 28015419
Web Site:
　http://www.bluechipstockspin.com
Year Founded: 1994
Assets: $1,057,862
Liabilities: $561,343
Net Worth: $496,520
Earnings: ($8,620)
Emp.: 3
Fiscal Year-end: 03/31/18
Medical Consulting Services
N.A.I.C.S.: 541690
Karan P. Shah *(Mng Dir)*

BLUECOM CO., LTD.
116 Venture-ro 11-80 Songdo-dong,
Yeonsu-gu, Incheon, Korea (South)
Tel.: (82) 328100500
Web Site: https://www.bluec.co.kr
Year Founded: 1990
033560—(KRS)
Rev.: $44,960,042
Assets: $134,495,740
Liabilities: $11,501,235
Net Worth: $122,994,505
Earnings: ($203,017)
Emp.: 67
Fiscal Year-end: 12/31/22
Wireless Communication Product Mfr
N.A.I.C.S.: 334220
Jong Kyu Kim *(CEO)*

Subsidiaries:

Blucom Vina Co., Ltd. 　　　　　**(1)**
Area C5-4 Trang Due IZ, AnDuong Dist,
Haiphong, Vietnam
Tel.: (84) 318830681
Electronic Products Mfr
N.A.I.C.S.: 334419

BLUEDON INFORMATION SE-CURITY TECHNOLOGIES CO., LTD.
20th Information Harbor Building A
No 16 Keyun Road, Tianhe District,
Guangzhou, 510665, China
Tel.: (86) 2085526663
Web Site: http://www.bluedon.com
300297—(CHIN)
Rev.: $13,781,664
Assets: $683,333,820
Liabilities: $774,042,048
Net Worth: ($90,708,228)
Earnings: ($246,647,700)
Emp.: 390
Fiscal Year-end: 12/31/22
Information Security Software
N.A.I.C.S.: 513210

BLUEFIELD SOLAR INCOME FUND
6 New Street Square, London, EC4A
3BF, United Kingdom
Tel.: (44) 2070780020　　　　　UK
Web Site: https://bluefieldsif.com
Year Founded: 2013
BSIF—(LSE)
Rev.: $1,169,110
Assets: $988,650,150
Liabilities: $837,968
Net Worth: $987,812,182
Earnings: ($12,134,732)
Fiscal Year-end: 06/30/24
Investment Advisory Services
N.A.I.C.S.: 523940
James Armstrong *(Mng Partner)*

BLUEFOCUS INTELLIGENT COMMUNICATIONS GROUP CO., LTD.
C9c Universal Creative Park Jiuxi-
anqiao North Road, Chaoyang Dis-
trict, Beijing, 100015, China
Tel.: (86) 1056478800
Web Site:
　https://www.bluefocusgroup.com
Year Founded: 1996
300058—(CHIN)
Rev.: $5,150,235,636
Assets: $2,550,985,164
Liabilities: $1,509,656,616
Net Worth: $1,041,328,548
Earnings: ($305,392,464)
Emp.: 5,000
Fiscal Year-end: 12/31/22
Holding Company; Marketing & Brand
Management Services
N.A.I.C.S.: 551112
Oscar Zhao *(Co-Founder, Chm & CEO)*

Subsidiaries:

BlueFocus International Limited　**(1)**
1451 Grant Rd Ste 200, Mountain View, CA
94040　　　　　　　　　**(100%)**
Tel.: (650) 772-6800
Emp.: 1,500
Holding Company; Marketing & Brand Man-
agement Services
N.A.I.C.S.: 551112
Oscar Zhao *(Founder)*

Subsidiary (Domestic):

Fuse Project, LLC　　　　　　　**(2)**
1401 16th St, San Francisco, CA
94103　　　　　　　　　　**(75%)**
Tel.: (415) 908-1492
Web Site: http://www.fuseproject.com
Design & Branding Services
N.A.I.C.S.: 541618
Yves Behar *(Founder & CEO)*

Subsidiary (Non-US):

Vision 7 International ULC　　　　**(2)**
300 St Paul Street Suite 300, Quebec, G1K
7R1, QC, Canada
Tel.: (418) 647-2727
Web Site:
　http://www.vision7international.com
Emp.: 1,000
Holding Company; Advertising, Public Rela-
tions & Marketing Consulting Services
N.A.I.C.S.: 551112
Claude Lessard *(Chm-Cossette)*

Subsidiary (US):

Citizen Relations LLC　　　　　　**(3)**
5510 Lincoln Blvd Ste 110, Los Angeles,
CA 90094
Tel.: (213) 996-3800
Web Site: http://www.us.citizenrelations.com
Emp.: 200
Public Relations & Communications Agency
N.A.I.C.S.: 541820
Daryl McCullough *(Chm & CEO-Global)*

Subsidiary (Non-US):

Citizen Brando Limited　　　　　　**(4)**
Alphabeta Bldg 2 Worship Street, London,
EC2A 2BH, United Kingdom
Tel.: (44) 2031953400
Web Site: http://uk.citizenrelations.com
Public Relations Agency
N.A.I.C.S.: 541820
Mark John Cater *(Mng Dir & Grp Head-
EMEA & Asia Pacific)*

Branch (Domestic):

Citizen Relations LLC - Irvine　　**(4)**
19100 Von Karman Ave Ste 650, Irvine, CA
92612
Tel.: (949) 809-6700
Web Site: http://us.citizenrelations.com
Public Relations & Communications Agency
N.A.I.C.S.: 541820
Erin Oliver-Georgieff *(Exec VP-West Coast
Ops)*

Citizen Relations LLC - New
York　　　　　　　　　　　　**(4)**
600 Lexington Ave 6th Fl, New York, NY
10022

Tel.: (212) 613-4900
Web Site: http://us.citizenrelations.com
Public Relations & Communications Agency
N.A.I.C.S.: 541820

Subsidiary (Non-US):

Citoyen Relations Inc.　　　　　　**(4)**
2100 rue Drummond 2nd floor, Montreal,
H3G 1X1, QC, Canada
Tel.: (514) 865-6772
Web Site: http://citoyen.com
Public Relations Agency
N.A.I.C.S.: 541820
François Vaque *(Sr VP)*

Branch (Domestic):

Citizen Relations Inc. - Toronto　**(5)**
33 Jefferson Avenue, Toronto, M6K 1Y3,
ON, Canada
Tel.: (416) 934-8011
Web Site: http://ca.citizenrelations.com
Public Relations Agency
N.A.I.C.S.: 541820
Jenn Duggan *(Pres)*

Citizen Relations Inc. -
Vancouver　　　　　　　　　　**(5)**
1085 Homer Street Suite 500, Vancouver,
V6B 1J4, BC, Canada
Tel.: (778) 331-8342
Web Site: http://ca.citizenrelations.com
Public Relations Agency
N.A.I.C.S.: 541820
Jenn Duggan *(Pres)*

Citoyen Relations Inc. - Quebec
City　　　　　　　　　　　　**(5)**
300 rue Saint-Paul, Quebec, G1K 7R1, QC,
Canada
Tel.: (418) 521-3744
Web Site: http://www.citoyenoptimum.com
Public Relations Agency
N.A.I.C.S.: 541820

Subsidiary (Domestic):

The Narrative Group LLC　　　　　**(4)**
250 Hudson St 2nd Fl, New York, NY
10013
Tel.: (646) 435-9810
Web Site: https://thenarrativegroup.com
Lifestyle Communications Agency
N.A.I.C.S.: 541830

Subsidiary (Domestic):

Cossette Communication Inc.　　**(3)**
300 St-Paul 3rd floor, Quebec, G1K 7R1,
QC, Canada
Tel.: (418) 647-2727
Web Site: http://www.cossette.com
Advetising Agency
N.A.I.C.S.: 541810

Branch (Domestic):

Cossette Communication Inc. -
Toronto　　　　　　　　　　　**(4)**
32 Atlantic Avenue, Toronto, M6K 1X8, ON,
Canada
Tel.: (416) 922-2727
Web Site: http://www.cossette.com
Advetising Agency
N.A.I.C.S.: 541810
Cat Wiles *(Chief Strategy Officer)*

Cossette Communication Inc. -
Vancouver　　　　　　　　　　**(4)**
1085 Homer Street Suite 400, Vancouver,
V6B 1J4, BC, Canada
Tel.: (604) 669-2727
Web Site: http://www.cossette.com
Advetising Agency
N.A.I.C.S.: 541810

Subsidiary (Domestic):

Cossette Communication-Marketing
(Montreal) Inc.　　　　　　　　**(4)**
2100 Drummond Street, Montreal, H3G
1X1, QC, Canada
Tel.: (514) 845-2727
Web Site: http://www.cossette.com
Advetising Agency
N.A.I.C.S.: 541810

Unit (Domestic):

Impact Recherche　　　　　　　　**(5)**

2100 Rue Drummond, Montreal, H3G 1X1,
QC, Canada
Tel.: (514) 973-4845
Web Site: http://www.impactrecherche.com
Marketing Research Service
N.A.I.C.S.: 541910

Subsidiary (US):

Eleven Inc.　　　　　　　　　　**(3)**
500 Sansome St, San Francisco, CA 94108
Tel.: (415) 707-1111
Web Site: http://www.eleveninc.com
Advetising Agency
N.A.I.C.S.: 541810
Dodie Martz *(Dir-Revenue & Ops & Assoc
Partner)*

Subsidiary (Non-US):

We Are Social Ltd.　　　　　　　**(2)**
Alphabeta Floor 5 14-18 Finsbury Square,
London, EC2A 1AH, United Kingdom
Tel.: (44) 2031951700
Web Site: https://www.wearesocial.com
Marketing Consulting & Advertising Support
Services
N.A.I.C.S.: 541613
Gerry Cyron *(Head-Strategy)*

BLUEGEM CAPITAL PART-NERS LLP
16 Berkeley Street, London, W1J
8DZ, United Kingdom
Tel.: (44) 20 7647 9710　　　　UK
Web Site: http://www.bluegemcp.com
Year Founded: 2007
Private Equity Investment Manage-
ment Services
N.A.I.C.S.: 523940
Marco Capello *(Founder & Mng Part-
ner)*

Subsidiaries:

Enotria Group Limited　　　　　　**(1)**
4-8 Chandos Park Estate Chandos Road,
London, NW10 6NF, United
Kingdom　　　　　　　　**(88.2%)**
Tel.: (44) 20 8961 4411
Web Site: http://www.enotria.co.uk
Wine Importer & Distr
N.A.I.C.S.: 424820
Alison Levett *(CEO)*

Liberty Ltd　　　　　　　　　　**(1)**
Regent Street, London, W1B 5AH, United
Kingdom
Tel.: (44) 2077341234
Web Site: http://www.liberty.co.uk
Sales Range: $125-149.9 Million
Women's Fashions, Gifts & Housewares
Mfr & Distr
N.A.I.C.S.: 458110
G.K. Nandwana *(CFO)*

Subsidiary (Domestic):

Liberty Retail Limited　　　　　　**(2)**
210-220 Regent St, London, W1B 5AH,
United Kingdom　　　　　　**(100%)**
Tel.: (44) 2077341234
Web Site: http://www.liberty.co.uk
Sales Range: $50-74.9 Million
Emp.: 200
Management of Retail Operations
N.A.I.C.S.: 455110

BLUEHONE SECURED AS-SETS LIMITED
107 Cannon Street, London, EC4N
5AF, United Kingdom
Tel.: (44) 2032067335
Web Site: http://www.bluehone.com
Sales Range: $25-49.9 Million
Loan Services
N.A.I.C.S.: 522310
Bill Brown *(Partner)*

BLUEJAY MINING PLC
6 Heddon Street, London, W1B 4BT,
United Kingdom
Tel.: (44) 2079079326　　　　　UK
Web Site:
　https://www.bluejaymining.com

Bluejay Mining plc—(Continued)

BLLYF—(OTCQB)
Rev.: $2,237,027
Assets: $50,952,716
Liabilities: $1,267,047
Net Worth: $49,685,668
Earnings: $2,067,027
Emp.: 11
Fiscal Year-end: 12/31/22
Copper, Nickel, Lead & Zinc Mining
N.A.I.C.S.: 212230
Roderick McIllree *(CEO)*

BLUELAKE MINERAL AB
Brahegatan 29, 114 37, Stockholm,
Sweden
Tel.: (46) 725382525
Web Site:
  https://www.bluelakemineral.com
Year Founded: 1994
5KG0—(DEU)
Assets: $5,342,475
Liabilities: $1,688,162
Net Worth: $3,654,313
Earnings: ($1,894,312)
Emp.: 2
Fiscal Year-end: 12/31/23
Mineral Mining Services
N.A.I.C.S.: 213115
Thomas Haggqvist *(CFO)*

BLUELIFE LTD.
Azuri Ocean & Golf Village, 31201,
Riviere du Rempart, Mauritius
Tel.: (230) 2606868
Web Site: https://www.bluelife.mu
BLL—(MAU)
Rev.: $21,718,638
Assets: $79,212,101
Liabilities: $29,157,284
Net Worth: $50,054,817
Earnings: $1,206,861
Emp.: 351
Fiscal Year-end: 06/30/23
Real Estate Management Services
N.A.I.C.S.: 531390
Kishore Sunil Banymandhub *(Chm)*

BLUELINEA SA
2-12 parvis du Colonel Arnaud Bel-
trame, 78000, Versailles, France
Tel.: (33) 176217060
Web Site: http://www.bluelinea.com
ALBLU—(EUR)
Sales Range: Less than $1 Million
Electronic Surveillance & Medical Te-
leassistance Systems
N.A.I.C.S.: 334310
Laurent Levasseur *(Deputy CEO)*

BLUENORD ASA
Nedre Vollgate 3, 158, Oslo, Norway
Tel.: (47) 22336000
Web Site: https://www.bluenord.com
0HTF—(LSE)
Rev.: $966,900,000
Assets: $3,244,000,000
Liabilities: $2,641,500,000
Net Worth: $602,500,000
Earnings: ($30,500,000)
Emp.: 33
Fiscal Year-end: 12/31/22
Oil Production Services
N.A.I.C.S.: 211120
Riulf Rustad *(Chm)*

Subsidiaries:

Altinex Oil Denmark A/S   **(1)**
Parallelvej 14, PO Box 110, Kongens Lyn-
gby, 2800, Denmark
Tel.: (45) 45469500
Web Site: http://www.noreco.com
Sales Range: $50-74.9 Million
Emp.: 30
Oil & Gas Extraction Services
N.A.I.C.S.: 211130
Svein Arild Killingland *(VP)*

Shell Olie - OG Gasudvinding Dan-
mark B.V.   **(1)**
Rued Langgaards Vej 6-8, Copenhagen,
2300, Denmark
Tel.: (45) 33372000
Oil & Gas Exploration Services
N.A.I.C.S.: 213112

BLUENRGY GROUP LIMITED
Level 32 200 George Street, Sydney,
2000, NSW, Australia
Tel.: (61) 282774111   **AU**
CBDEF—(OTCBB)
Sales Range: $10-24.9 Million
Emp.: 90
Holding Company; Renewable En-
ergy Investment, Development &
Support Services
N.A.I.C.S.: 551112
Richard Pillinger *(CFO & Sec)*

Subsidiaries:

BlueNRGY, LLC   **(1)**
110 E Broward Blvd 19th Fl, Fort Lauder-
dale, FL 33301
Tel.: (954) 892-6658
Web Site: http://www.bluenrgy.com
Energy Monitoring & Consulting Services
N.A.I.C.S.: 541990
Emmanuel Cotrel *(Co-Founder & CEO)*

Parmac Air Conditioning & Mechani-
cal Services Pty. Ltd.   **(1)**
15 Terra Cotta Drive, Blackburn, 3130, VIC,
Australia
Tel.: (61) 398532477
Web Site: http://www.parmac.com.au
Sales Range: $25-49.9 Million
Emp.: 45
Air Conditioning System Installation & Me-
chanical Services
N.A.I.C.S.: 238220

**BLUEPLANET ENVIRONMEN-
TAL INC.**
16431 Kennedy Road, Stouffville,
L3Y 4W1, ON, Canada
Tel.: (905) 830-5555
Web Site:
  https://www.blueplanetenviro.com
Year Founded: 2005
Clean Water Products & Solutions
N.A.I.C.S.: 541620
Richard Lonetto *(Pres)*

BLUEPOOL GMBH
Schelmenwasenstrabe 16-20, 70567,
Stuttgart, Germany
Tel.: (49) 711902140
Web Site: https://www.bluepool.de
BPU—(STU)
Sales Range: Less than $1 Million
Exhibition & Trade Fair Platform Ser-
vices
N.A.I.C.S.: 561920

BLUEROCK DIAMONDS PLC
4th Floor Reading Bridge House
George Street, Reading, RG1 8LS,
Berkshire, United Kingdom
Tel.: (44) 2072361177
Web Site:
  http://www.bluerockdiamonds.co.uk
Year Founded: 2012
BRD—(AIM)
Rev.: $10,665,244
Assets: $11,651,128
Liabilities: $7,934,425
Net Worth: $3,716,703
Earnings: ($1,831,424)
Emp.: 107
Fiscal Year-end: 12/31/21
Diamond Mining
N.A.I.C.S.: 212311
David Facey *(Fin Dir & Sec)*

Subsidiaries:

Kareevlei Mining Proprietory
Limited   **(1)**
Wesselton Village off Old Boshoff Road,
Kimberley, South Africa
Tel.: (27) 87 808 6116
Diamond Mining Services
N.A.I.C.S.: 212390

BLUEROCK VENTURES CORP.
1055 West Georgia Street Suite
2050, Vancouver, V6E 3P3, BC,
Canada
Tel.: (604) 684-2181   **BC**
Year Founded: 2011
BCR—(TSXV)
Assets: $197,247
Liabilities: $213,766
Net Worth: ($16,519)
Earnings: ($22,011)
Fiscal Year-end: 02/28/19
Investment Services
N.A.I.C.S.: 523999
Praveen Varshney *(CEO & CFO)*

BLUERUSH INC.
4711 Yonge Street 10th Floor, To-
ronto, M2N 6K8, ON, Canada
Tel.: (416) 203-0618   **ON**
Web Site: https://www.bluerush.com
Year Founded: 2004
BTVRF—(OTCIQ)
Rev.: $3,432,903
Assets: $2,145,356
Liabilities: $5,335,530
Net Worth: ($3,190,174)
Earnings: ($1,723,914)
Fiscal Year-end: 07/31/23
Digital Video Marketing Services
N.A.I.C.S.: 541613
Larry Lubin *(Chm & Pres)*

Subsidiaries:

BlueRush Digital Media Corp   **(1)**
366 Adelaide St E Suite 433, Toronto, M5A
3X9, ON, Canada
Tel.: (416) 203-0618
Sales Range: $25-49.9 Million
Emp.: 50
Digital Marketing Services
N.A.I.C.S.: 541613

BLUESCOPE STEEL LIMITED
Level 24 181 William St, Melbourne,
3000, VIC, Australia
Tel.: (61) 396664000   **AU**
Web Site: http://www.bluescope.com
Year Founded: 2002
BSL—(ASX)
Rev.: $14,580,519,081
Assets: $12,726,798,995
Liabilities: $4,721,569,256
Net Worth: $8,005,229,739
Earnings: $2,285,544,770
Emp.: 15,000
Fiscal Year-end: 06/30/22
Steel Plate, Slab & Coil Mfr
N.A.I.C.S.: 331110
Charlie S. R. Elias *(CEO)*

Subsidiaries:

BlueScope Acier Nouvelle Caledonie
SA   **(1)**
238 Route de la Baie des Dames Numbo,
BP 3424, 98846, Noumea, New Caledonia
Tel.: (687) 282944
Emp.: 50
Steel Products Mfr
N.A.I.C.S.: 331110
Denis Etournaud *(Gen Mgr)*

BlueScope Building Systems (Xi'an)
Co., Ltd.   **(1)**
No 1 Dingkunchi Second Road, Western
Hi-Tech Industrial Zone, Xi'an, 710119,
Shaanxi, China
Tel.: (86) 2965651717
Steel Products Mfr
N.A.I.C.S.: 331110

BlueScope Buildings (Guangzhou)
Ltd.   **(1)**
No 98 Pubei Road, East District Yunpu In-
dustrial Zone Huangpu, Guangzhou,
510530, Guangdong, China
Tel.: (86) 2082251717
Web Site: http://www.bluescopesteel.com
Emp.: 200
Steel Products Mfr
N.A.I.C.S.: 331110

BlueScope Buildings (Vietnam)
Limited   **(1)**
No 3 9A St Bien Hoa 2 Industrial Zone,
Bien Hoa, 810000, Dong Nai, Vietnam
Tel.: (84) 613836245
Web Site: http://www.bluescopesteel.com
Steel Products Mfr
N.A.I.C.S.: 331110
Vo Minh Nhut *(Mng Dir)*

BlueScope Buildings North America
Engineering (Michigan) LLC   **(1)**
1540 Genessee St Ste 100, Kansas City,
MO 64102
Tel.: (816) 968-3001
Web Site: https://bluescopebuildings.com
Emp.: 2,000
Steel Building Mfr
N.A.I.C.S.: 332311

BlueScope Coated Products LLC   **(1)**
530 N 2nd St, Cambridge, OH 43725
Tel.: (740) 432-7351
Web Site:
  https://www.bluescopecoatedproducts.com
Metal Coil Mfr & Distr
N.A.I.C.S.: 334416

BlueScope Distribution Pty Ltd.   **(1)**
88 Ricketts Road, Mount Waverley, 3149,
VIC, Australia
Tel.: (61) 385408600
Web Site:
  https://www.bluescopedistribution.com.au
Sales Range: $50-74.9 Million
Emp.: 170
Steel Products Mfr
N.A.I.C.S.: 331110

BlueScope Lysaght (Thailand)
Ltd.   **(1)**
16 Soi Paholyothin 96 Prachatipat, Th-
anyaburi, Pathumthani, 12130, Thailand
Tel.: (66) 25249800
Web Site: http://www.bluescopelysaght.co.th
Sales Range: $100-124.9 Million
Emp.: 400
Steel Products Mfr
N.A.I.C.S.: 331110

BlueScope Lysaght (Brunei) Sdn
Bhd   **(1)**
Industrial Complex Beribi Phase 1 6Km Jln
Gadong, Bandar Seri Begawan, BE 1118,
Brunei Darussalam
Tel.: (673) 2447155
Emp.: 27
Roofing & Walling Material Distr
N.A.I.C.S.: 423330
Judith Fong *(Pres)*

BlueScope Lysaght (Chengdu)
Ltd.   **(1)**
West Avenue of Chengdu Economic And
Technological Development Zone,
Longquanyi District, Chengdu, 610100, Si-
chuan, China
Tel.: (86) 2884848686
Web Site:
  http://www.bluescopesteelasia.com
Steel Products Mfr
N.A.I.C.S.: 331110

BlueScope Lysaght (Sabah) Sdn
Bhd   **(1)**
Lorong Kurma Off Jalan Kolombong, 88450,
Kota Kinabalu, Sabah, Malaysia
Tel.: (60) 88445161
Sales Range: $25-49.9 Million
Emp.: 45
Steel Products Mfr
N.A.I.C.S.: 331110

BlueScope Lysaght (Shanghai)
Ltd.   **(1)**
7F Building 5 of Source Innovation Valley
Lane 88 Shengrong Rd, Zhangjiang Pu-
dong New District, Shanghai, 201302,
China

Tel.: (86) 2158120138
Steel Products Mfr
N.A.I.C.S.: 331110

BlueScope Lysaght (Singapore) Pte. Ltd. (1)
18 Benoi Sector, Jurong Town, Singapore, 629851, Singapore
Tel.: (65) 6264 1577
Web Site: http://www.lysaght.com.sg
Emp.: 100
Steel Building & Rollformer Products Mfr
N.A.I.C.S.: 236220
Tarun Sinha *(Pres)*

BlueScope Lysaght (Vanuatu) Ltd. (1)
Route de Tagabe, PO Box 453, Port-Vila, Vanuatu
Tel.: (678) 23261
Steel Mfrs
N.A.I.C.S.: 331110

BlueScope Lysaght Fiji Ltd. (1)
169-171 Lakeba Street, Samabula, Suva, Fiji
Tel.: (679) 3382388
Emp.: 42
Steel Products Mfr
N.A.I.C.S.: 331110

BlueScope Lysaght Taiwan Ltd. (1)
A6 12F No 6 Su Wei 3rd Road, Kaohsiung, 802, Taiwan
Tel.: (886) 73336900
Steel Products Mfr
N.A.I.C.S.: 331110

BlueScope Properties Group LLC (1)
1540 Genessee St, Kansas City, MO 64102
Tel.: (816) 245-6970
Web Site: https://bluescopepropertiesgroup.com
Building Construction Services
N.A.I.C.S.: 236220
Denise Holt *(Project Mgr)*

BlueScope Pty Ltd. (1)
Level 11 120 Collins Street, Melbourne, 3000, VIC, Australia
Tel.: (61) 396664000
Steel Mfrs
N.A.I.C.S.: 331110

BlueScope Recycling and Materials LLC (1)
295 S Commerce Dr, Waterloo, IN 46793
Tel.: (419) 540-4355
Web Site: https://www.bluescoperecycling.com
Scrap Metal Recycling Services
N.A.I.C.S.: 562920

BlueScope Steel (AIS) Pty Ltd (1)
L 11 120 Collins St, Melbourne, 3000, VIC, Australia
Tel.: (61) 396664000
Web Site: http://www.bluescope.com
Steel Products Mfr
N.A.I.C.S.: 331110

BlueScope Steel (Finance) Ltd. (1)
L 11 120 Collins St, Melbourne, 3000, VIC, Australia
Tel.: (61) 396664000
Web Site: http://www.bluescopesteel.com
Emp.: 80
Steel Mfrs
N.A.I.C.S.: 331110

BlueScope Steel (Suzhou) Ltd (1)
12th Floor Hang Seng Bank Tower 1000, Lujiazui Ring Road, Shanghai, 200120, China
Tel.: (86) 2120591616
Web Site: https://www.bluescope.com
Steel Products Mfr
N.A.I.C.S.: 331110

BlueScope Steel (Thailand) Ltd. (1)
Soi G9 Pakornsongkrohrad Road, Map Ta Phut A Muang, Rayong, 21150, Thailand
Tel.: (66) 38918300
Web Site: http://www.bluescopesteel.co.th
Steel Products Mfr
N.A.I.C.S.: 331110
Jason Ellis *(Pres)*

BlueScope Steel Americas LLC (1)

111 W Ocean Blvd Ste 1370, Long Beach, CA 90802
Tel.: (562) 491-1441
Sales Range: $25-49.9 Million
Emp.: 10
Rolled Steel Shape Manufacturing
N.A.I.C.S.: 331221

BlueScope Steel Asia Holdings Pty Ltd. (1)
L 11 120 Collins St, Melbourne, 3000, VIC, Australia
Tel.: (61) 396664000
Web Site: http://www.bluescopesteel.com.au
Steel Products Mfr
N.A.I.C.S.: 331110

BlueScope Steel Asia Pte Ltd. (1)
20 Anson Road 09-01 Twenty Anson, Singapore, 079912, Singapore
Tel.: (65) 63333378
Web Site: http://www.bluescope.com
Sales Range: $25-49.9 Million
Emp.: 35
Steel Products Mfr
N.A.I.C.S.: 331110

BlueScope Steel International Trading (Shanghai) Co.,Ltd. (1)
12 f Hsbc Tower No 1000 Lujiazui Ring Rd, Pudong New Dist, Shanghai, 200120, China
Tel.: (86) 2168411898
Steel Mfrs
N.A.I.C.S.: 331110

BlueScope Steel Investment Management (Shanghai) Ltd. (1)
12th Floor Hang Seng Bank Tower 1000 Lujiazui Ring Road, Pudong New Dist, Shanghai, 200120, China
Tel.: (86) 2168411898
Web Site: http://www.bluescopeco.com
Steel Mfrs
N.A.I.C.S.: 331110

BlueScope Steel Logistics Co Pty Ltd. (1)
L 11 120 Collins St, Melbourne, 3000, VIC, Australia
Tel.: (61) 396664000
Metal Products Logistics Services
N.A.I.C.S.: 541614

BlueScope Steel North America Corporation (1)
1540 Genessee St, Kansas City, MO 64102
Tel.: (816) 968-3000
Web Site: http://www.butlermfg.com
Sales Range: $50-74.9 Million
Emp.: 200
Steel Construction Products & Prefabricated Steel Building Mfr
N.A.I.C.S.: 332311
Mark Vassella *(Pres-Australia)*

Subsidiary (Domestic):

ASC Profiles Inc. (2)
2110 Enterprise Blvd, West Sacramento, CA 95691-3428
Tel.: (916) 372-0933
Web Site: https://www.ascprofiles.com
Sales Range: $25-49.9 Million
Emp.: 50
Steel Construction Materials & Building Mfr
N.A.I.C.S.: 332311
John Cross *(Pres)*

BlueScope Buildings North America Inc. (2)
273 Water St, Evansville, WI 53536-1433
Tel.: (608) 882-5000
Construction Engineering Services
N.A.I.C.S.: 541330

BlueScope Construction Inc. (2)
1540 Genessee St, Kansas City, MO 64102
Tel.: (816) 245-6000
Web Site: https://www.bluescopeconstruction.com
Sales Range: $25-49.9 Million
Emp.: 150
Construction Engineering Services
N.A.I.C.S.: 541330
Kenny G. Strope *(Exec VP-Construction)*

Butler Manufacturing Company (2)
1540 Genessee St, Kansas City, MO 64102
Tel.: (816) 968-3000

Web Site: http://www.butlermfg.com
Mfr of Pre-Engineered Buildings, Agricultural Buildings; Aluminum Extrusion & Finishing; Skylights & General Contracting
N.A.I.C.S.: 332311
Mike McQuillen *(Mgr-Buildings HR Grp)*

Subsidiary (Non-US):

BHP New Zealand Steel Ltd. (3)
Mission Bush Road, Private Bag 92121, Auckland, 1142, New Zealand
Tel.: (64) 93758999
Web Site: http://www.nzsteel.co.nz
Sales Range: $700-749.9 Million
Emp.: 1,500
N.A.I.C.S.: 212210
Andrew Garey *(Gen Mgr)*

Butler (Shanghai), Inc. (3)
No 1506 Rongle Road E Songjiang Industrial Zone, Shanghai, 201613, Songjiang, China
Tel.: (86) 2157741717
Web Site: http://www.butlerchina.com
Sales Range: $25-49.9 Million
Emp.: 30
Mfr of Pre-Engineered Buildings, Agricultural Buildings; Aluminum Extrusion & Finishing; Skylights & General Contracting
N.A.I.C.S.: 331318

Affiliate (Non-US):

Saudi Building Systems, Ltd. (3)
Industrial City 1 Phase 3 Corner of Road 44 and Street 75, PO Box 8648, Mahjar District, Jeddah, 21492, Saudi Arabia
Tel.: (966) 126370036
Web Site: http://www.saudibuilding.site
Sales Range: $25-49.9 Million
Emp.: 60
Mfr of Pre-Engineered Metal Buildings
N.A.I.C.S.: 332311

Subsidiary (Domestic):

Steelscape Inc. (2)
222 W Kalama River Rd, Kalama, WA 98625-9420
Tel.: (360) 673-8200
Web Site: https://www.steelscape.com
Sales Range: $25-49.9 Million
Coated Steel Coil Mfr
N.A.I.C.S.: 331221
Penny Shepherd *(Mgr-Customer Svc)*

VSMA Inc (2)
1540 Genessee St, Kansas City, MO 64102-1069
Tel.: (816) 968-3000
Steel Products Mfr
N.A.I.C.S.: 331110

Varco Pruden Buildings, Inc. (2)
3200 Players Club Cir, Memphis, TN 38125-8843
Tel.: (901) 748-8000
Web Site: https://varcopruden.com
Prefabricated Metal Building Mfr
N.A.I.C.S.: 332311
Jim Peckham *(Mgr)*

BlueScope Steel North Asia Ltd (1)
A6 12F No 6 Su Wei 3rd Road, Kaohsiung, 802, Taiwan
Tel.: (886) 7 333 6900
Web Site: http://www.bluescopesteel.com
Sales Range: $25-49.9 Million
Emp.: 3
Steel Products Mfr
N.A.I.C.S.: 331110

BlueScope Steel Philippines Inc (1)
603 SEDCCO 1 Building 120 Rada St, Legaspi Village, Makati, 1229, Philippines
Tel.: (63) 28170121
Sales Range: $25-49.9 Million
Emp.: 3
Steel Products Mfr
N.A.I.C.S.: 331110

BlueScope Steel Southern Africa (Pty) Ltd. (1)
No1 Bridgeway Bridgeways Precinct Office 335, Fir Road Observatory, Cape Town, 7441, South Africa
Tel.: (27) 214425420
Steel Product Distr
N.A.I.C.S.: 423510

BlueScope Steel Trading NZ Ltd. (1)
Mission Bush Road, PO Box 92121, Glenbrook, Auckland, 1142, New Zealand
Tel.: (64) 93758999
Steel Products Mfr
N.A.I.C.S.: 331110

BlueScope Steel Vietnam Limited. (1)
9th Floor Vincom Center 72 Le Thanh Ton Street, District 1, Ho Chi Minh City, Vietnam
Tel.: (84) 838210066
Steel Products Mfr
N.A.I.C.S.: 331110

BlueScope Water Pty Ltd. (1)
113 Dunheved Circuit, Saint Marys, 2760, NSW, Australia
Tel.: (61) 2 8801 9200
Web Site: http://www.bluescopewater.com
Water Tank Mfr
N.A.I.C.S.: 332420

Bluescope Lysaght Singapore Pte. Ltd. (1)
18 Benoi Sector, Jurong Town, Singapore, 629851, Singapore
Tel.: (65) 62641577
Web Site: http://www.bluescopesteel.com
Sales Range: $25-49.9 Million
Emp.: 80
Steel Producer
N.A.I.C.S.: 331110
Tarun Sinht *(Pres)*

Bluescope Steel (1)
5 Islands Rd, Port Kembla, 2505, NSW, Australia **(100%)**
Tel.: (61) 242757522
Web Site: http://www.bluescope.com
Sales Range: $1-4.9 Billion
Emp.: 6,000
N.A.I.C.S.: 212210

Butler (Tianjin) Inc. (1)
No 151 Beihai Road, TEDA Industrial Zone, Tianjin, 300457, China
Tel.: (86) 2225321717
Steel Products Mfr
N.A.I.C.S.: 331110

Fielders Australia Pty. Ltd. (1)
169 James Melrose Road, Novar Gardens, 5040, SA, Australia **(100%)**
Tel.: (61) 882923611
Web Site: https://fielders.com.au
Sales Range: $25-49.9 Million
Emp.: 100
Steel Roofing & Flooring Mfr
N.A.I.C.S.: 238120

Fielders Manufacturing Pty. Ltd. (1)
35 Prestige Parade, Wangara, 6065, WA, Australia
Tel.: (61) 893031400
Web Site: https://fielders.com.au
Building & Construction Product Mfr
N.A.I.C.S.: 333120

Fulton County Properties LLC (1)
141 Pryor St Sw, Atlanta, GA 30303
Tel.: (404) 612-4000
Web Site: https://www.fultoncountyga.gov
Real Estate Property Management & Development Services
N.A.I.C.S.: 531311

Laser Dynamics Australia Pty Ltd. (1)
920 Nudgee Road, Northgate, Brisbane, 4013, QLD, Australia
Tel.: (61) 732679666
Web Site: http://www.laserdynamics.com.au
Sales Range: $25-49.9 Million
Emp.: 20
Steel Mfrs
N.A.I.C.S.: 331110
Rod Hammel *(Mgr)*

NS BlueScope (Malaysia) Sdn Bhd (1)
Lot 1551 Jalan Bukit Kapar 42200, Kapar, Selangor Darul Ehsan, Malaysia
Tel.: (60) 333616888
Web Site: https://www.nsbluescope.com
Steel Products Mfr
N.A.I.C.S.: 331110

Subsidiary (Domestic):

Star Shine Marketing Sdn. Bhd. (2)

BlueScope Steel Limited—(Continued)

Wisma Star Shine Lot 6472 Lorong Sungai
Puluh KU06 Kawasan, Perindustrian Sungai
Puloh, 42100, Kelang, Selangor, Malaysia
Tel.: (60) 332975555
Web Site: http://www.starshinegroup.com
Emp.: 40
Galvanized Iron Sheets & Coils Distr
N.A.I.C.S.: 332812

Subsidiary (Domestic):

Star Shine Global Trading Sdn.
Bhd.   **(3)**
Lot 6472 Lorong Sg Puluh Batu 6 Jalan
Kapar, Perindustrian Sungai Puloh, 42100,
Kelang, Selangor, Malaysia
Tel.: (60) 332975555
Web Site: http://www.starshinegroup.com
Flat Steel Products Whslr
N.A.I.C.S.: 423510

Star Shine Industries Sdn. Bhd.   **(3)**
Lot 6472 Lorong Sungai Puloh/KU 06 Ka-
wasan Perindustrian Sungai Buloh, Perin-
dustrian Ringan Silibin, Klang, 42100, Se-
langor, Malaysia
Tel.: (60) 332975555
Web Site: http://www.starshinegroup.com
Metal Drawer Slides Mfr
N.A.I.C.S.: 332999

Star Shine Steel Products Sdn.
Bhd.   **(3)**
Wisma Star Shine Lot 6472 Lorong Sungai
Puluh KU06 Kawasan, Perindustrian Sungai
Puloh, 42100, Kelang, Selangor, Malaysia
Tel.: (60) 332975555
Emp.: 200
Building Materials & Steel Products Distr
N.A.I.C.S.: 444180
Soh Thian Lai (Mng Dir)

New Zealand Steel (Aust) Pty
Ltd.   **(1)**
20 Council St, Hawthorn East, 3123, VIC,
Australia
Tel.: (61) 398040788
Steel Products Mfr
N.A.I.C.S.: 331110

New Zealand Steel Development
Ltd.   **(1)**
Mission Bush Road, PO Box 92121, Auck-
land, 1142, New Zealand
Tel.: (64) 93758999
Web Site: http://www.newzealandsteel.co.nz
Emp.: 1,300
Steel Products Mfr
N.A.I.C.S.: 331110
Andrew Garry (Gen Mgr)

New Zealand Steel Holdings Ltd. **(1)**
131 Mission Bush Road Glenbrook, Auck-
land, 1852, New Zealand
Tel.: (64) 93758999
Steel Products Mfr
N.A.I.C.S.: 331110
Simon Linge (Pres)

New Zealand Steel Limited   **(1)**
Mission Bush Road, Private Bag 92121,
Auckland, 1142, New Zealand   **(100%)**
Tel.: (64) 93758999
Web Site: http://www.bluescopesteel.com
Rolled Steel Shape Mfr
N.A.I.C.S.: 331221

North Star Bluescope Steel LLC   **(1)**
6767 County Rd 9, Delta, OH
43515   **(100%)**
Tel.: (419) 822-2200
Web Site: https://nsbsl.com
Smelting, Refining & Alloying of Nonferrous
Metal
N.A.I.C.S.: 331492
Ashley Kotowski (VP)

Orrcon Operations Pty. Ltd.   **(1)**
121 Evans Road Bldg 7, Salisbury, 4107,
QLD, Australia   **(100%)**
Tel.: (61) 732740660
Web Site: http://www.orrcon.com.au
Sales Range: $50-74.9 Million
Emp.: 200
Steel, Tube & Pipe Mfr & Distr
N.A.I.C.S.: 331210
Leon Andrewartha (Mng Dir)

PT BlueScope Lysaght Indonesia **(1)**
Jl Irian Blok DD2/2 Kawasan Industri MM -
1200, Cibitung, Bekasi, 17152, West Java,
Indonesia
Tel.: (62) 2189982965
Sales Range: $50-74.9 Million
Emp.: 150
Steel Products Mfr
N.A.I.C.S.: 331110

Pacific Steel (NZ) Limited   **(1)**
21 Beach Road, Otahuhu, Auckland, 22041,
New Zealand
Tel.: (64) 92761849
Web Site: https://www.pacificsteel.co.nz
Reinforcing Bar Mfr & Distr
N.A.I.C.S.: 332312

Pioneer Water Tanks (Australia) Pty
Ltd.   **(1)**
23 Clayton St, Bellevue, Perth, 6056, WA,
Australia
Tel.: (61) 892744577
Sales Range: $25-49.9 Million
Emp.: 10
Water Tanks Mfr & Distr
N.A.I.C.S.: 332420
Daniel Wyatt (Gen Mgr)

Steltech Structural Ltd.   **(1)**
17-19 Gladding Place, Manukau, Auckland,
2105, New Zealand
Tel.: (64) 92673875
Web Site: https://www.steltech.co.nz
Building Maintenance Services
N.A.I.C.S.: 561790
Chris Cussen (Sls Mgr)

The Roofing Centre (Tasmania) Pty
Ltd.   **(1)**
Lower Level unit 3/4 Yamada Place, Morn-
ington, Hobart, 7018, TAS, Australia
Tel.: (61) 362451500
Web Site:
   https://www.roofingcentretas.com.au
Residential & Industrial Roofing Services
N.A.I.C.S.: 238160

BLUESKY DIGITAL ASSETS CORP.

First Canadian Place 100 King Street
West Suite 5700, Toronto, M5X 1C9,
ON, Canada
Tel.: (416) 363-3833
Web Site:
   https://www.blueskydigitalasset.com
Year Founded: 2006
BTCWF—(OTCQB)
Rev.: $1,045,434
Assets: $1,452,034
Liabilities: $1,040,628
Net Worth: $411,406
Earnings: ($5,464,889)
Fiscal Year-end: 12/31/22
Investment Services
N.A.I.C.S.: 523999
Frank Kordy (Sec)

BLUESKY HOTELS & RE-SORTS INC.

Suite 5300 TD Bank Tower 66 Wel-
lington Street West, Toronto, M5K
1E6, ON, Canada
Tel.: (416) 270-9158
Web Site:
   http://www.blueskyhotels.ca
Year Founded: 2016
Holding Company; Hotel, Real Estate
& Hospitality Services Investment,
Development & Operation
N.A.I.C.S.: 551112
Li Chen (Pres & CEO)

BLUESKY INTERNATIONAL LTD.

The Station Station Road, Ashby de
la Zouch, LE65 2AS, United Kingdom
Tel.: (44) 1530 518518
Web Site: http://www.bluesky-
world.com
Emp.: 32
Aerial & Mapping Services

N.A.I.C.S.: 541360
Rachel Tidmarsh (Mng Dir)

Subsidiaries:

Col-East, Inc.   **(1)**
PO Box 347 Harriman & West Airport, North
Adams, MA 01247-0347
Tel.: (800) 359-8676
Web Site: http://www.col-east.com
Aerial Surveying & Mapping Services
N.A.I.C.S.: 541370
Mark L. Thaisz (Gen Mgr)

BLUESKY SECURITIES JOINT STOCK COMPANY

Suit 207 Taiwan Culture Center Tour-
ist Street 3th Horoo, Chingeltei dis-
trict, Ulaanbaatar, Mongolia
Tel.: (976) 70129060
BSKY—(MONG)
Sales Range: Less than $1 Million
Food & Beverage Stores
N.A.I.C.S.: 445298

BLUESKY.ENERGY GMBH

Fornacher Strasse 12, 4870, Vockla-
markt, Austria
Tel.: (43) 720 01 01 88
Web Site: http://www.bluesky-
energy.eu
Energy Storage Solutions Develop-
ment, Mfr & Sales
N.A.I.C.S.: 335910
Helmut Mayer (CEO)

Subsidiaries:

Aquion Energy LLC   **(1)**
32 39th St, Pittsburgh, PA 15201
Tel.: (412) 392-7270
Web Site: http://www.aquionenergy.com
Energy Storage System Mfr
N.A.I.C.S.: 335999

BLUESOURCE LTD.

122 Tooley Street, London, SE1 2TU,
United Kingdom
Tel.: (44) 845 319 2100
Web Site:
   http://www.bluesource.co.uk
Year Founded: 2001
Sales Range: $10-24.9 Million
Emp.: 65
IT Services
N.A.I.C.S.: 541512
Andy Ward (Co-Founder & CEO)

BLUESTAR ADISSEO COM-PANY LIMITED

9 West Beitucheng Road, Chaoyang
District, Beijing, 100029, China
Tel.: (86) 1061958710
Web Site: http://www.bluestar-
adisseo.com
Year Founded: 1999
Chemical Products Mfr
N.A.I.C.S.: 325998
Zhigang Hao (Chm)

Subsidiaries:

Bluestar (Beijing) Chemical Machin-
ery Co., Ltd.   **(1)**
No 5 Xingye Street Beijing Economic Tech-
nological Development Area, Beijing,
100176, China
Tel.: (86) 10 58082189
Web Site: http://www.bcmc.chemchina.com
Chemical Products Mfr
N.A.I.C.S.: 325998
Pan Jeff (Dir-Oversea Sls Dept)

Bluestar Harbin Petrochemical
Corporation   **(1)**
Huagong Road No 182, Xiangfang District,
Harbin, 150038, China
Tel.: (86) 451 82406347
Web Site: http://www.lxhsh.chemchina.com
Chemical Products Mfr
N.A.I.C.S.: 325998

Bluestar Silicon Material Co. Ltd. **(1)**

Zhongpu, Yongdeng town, Lanzhou,
730301, Gansu, China
Tel.: (86) 6477918
Web Site: http://www.lxgc.chemchina.com
Chemical Products Mfr
N.A.I.C.S.: 325998

Bluestar Wuxi Petrochemical Co
Ltd   **(1)**
No 311 East Renmin Road, Wuxi, 214007,
Jiangsu, China
Tel.: (86) 510 82401334
Web Site: http://www.lxwx.chemchina.com
Chemical Product Mfr & Distr
N.A.I.C.S.: 325998

China BlueStar International Chemi-
cal Corporation   **(1)**
No 9 West Road Beituchengxi, ChaoYang
District, Beijing, 100029, China
Tel.: (86) 10 61958500
Chemical Products Mfr
N.A.I.C.S.: 325998
Kong Deliang (CFO)

China BlueStar Lehigh Engineering
Corp   **(1)**
No 51 West Chaoyang Road, Lianyungang,
222004, Jiangsu, China
Tel.: (86) 518 85520192
Web Site: http://www.lxlhy.chemchina.com
Emp.: 600
Civil Engineering Services
N.A.I.C.S.: 541330
Jiang Quanwei (Deputy Dir-Science & Tech)

China Bluestar Changsha Chemical
Engineering Co Ltd   **(1)**
6 Dongzhu Rd Dongjingpu, Yuhua District,
Changsha, 410116, Hunan, China
Tel.: (86) 731 8563 7200
Web Site: http://www.lxcsy.chemchina.com
Chemical Research & Development Ser-
vices
N.A.I.C.S.: 541715
Wei Yeqiu (Pres & Member-Mgmt Bd)

Nantong Xingchen Synthetic Material
Co., Ltd.   **(1)**
118 Jianggang Rd, Nantong Economic De-
velopment Zone, Nantong, 226017, Ji-
angsu, China
Tel.: (86) 513 8599 7818
Web Site: http://www.lxnt.chemchina.com
Chemical Product Mfr & Distr
N.A.I.C.S.: 325998
Lily Zhao (Dir-Export)

Shanxi Synthetic Rubber Group Co
Ltd   **(1)**
No 1 North Yongjun Road, Datong, 037005,
Shanxi, China
Tel.: (86) 352 2894852
Web Site: http://www.lxsx.chemchina.com
Synthetic Rubber Mfr
N.A.I.C.S.: 325212

BLUESTAR SECUTECH INC.

14th Floor Tower A Chengjian Plaza,
18 Beitaipingzhuang Road Haidian
District, Beijing, 100088, China
Tel.: (86) 10 8225 5855
Web Site: http://www.bstar.com.cn
Year Founded: 2006
Sales Range: $25-49.9 Million
Emp.: 505
Surveillance Equipment Mfr & Distr
N.A.I.C.S.: 335999
Gang Xiao (CEO)

BLUESTONE GLOBAL LIM-ITED

Level 2 420 St Kilda Road, Mel-
bourne, 3004, VIC, Australia
Tel.: (61) 396854400
Web Site:
   http://www.bglcorporate.com
Sales Range: $250-299.9 Million
Emp.: 203
Recruitment, Professional Placement
& Labor Hiring Services
N.A.I.C.S.: 561311
Jason Sweeney (Mng Dir-Resco
Svcs)

Subsidiaries:

Westaff (Australia) Pty. Ltd. **(1)**
Level 3 100 Albert Road 4th Floor, Melbourne, 3205, VIC, Australia
Tel.: (61) 396965451
Web Site: http://www.westaff.com.au
Sales Range: $100-124.9 Million
Emp.: 27
Temporary Help Service
N.A.I.C.S.: 561320

Subsidiary (Non-US):

Westaff NZ Limited **(2)**
Level 1 14 Oimietion Road, PO Box 21, 7034 Potiny Junction, Auckland, New Zealand
Tel.: (64) 95255990
Web Site: http://www.westaff.co.nz
Sales Range: $1-9.9 Million
Emp.: 15
Temporary Help Service
N.A.I.C.S.: 561320

BLUESTONE RESOURCES INC.

Suite 2800 Four Bentall Centre 1055 Dunsmuir Street, PO Box 49225, Vancouver, V7X 1L2, BC, Canada
Tel.: (604) 757-4715
Web Site:
https://www.bluestoneresources.ca
Year Founded: 2004
BBSRF—(OTCQB)
Rev.: $447,486
Assets: $87,019,390
Liabilities: $13,364,417
Net Worth: $73,654,973
Earnings: ($30,682,962)
Emp.: 121
Fiscal Year-end: 12/31/20
Gold Exploration & Geothermal Well Drilling Services
N.A.I.C.S.: 213114
John Robins (Chm)

BLUESWORD INTELLIGENT TECHNOLOGY CO., LTD.

17-19F Tower A 909 North Longao Road, High-Tech Zone, Jinan, 250101, Shandong, China
Tel.: (86) 53188876633
Web Site:
https://www.bluesword.com
Year Founded: 2001
688557—(SHG)
Rev.: $128,528,661
Assets: $213,226,463
Liabilities: $73,538,951
Net Worth: $139,687,512
Earnings: $12,709,542
Fiscal Year-end: 12/31/22
Logistics Consulting Servies
N.A.I.C.S.: 541614
Yaohua Wu (Chm)

BLUEWATER AB

Danderydsgatan 11, 114 26, Stockholm, Sweden
Tel.: (46) 856 473 800
Web Site:
https://www.bluewatergroup.com
Year Founded: 2013
Emp.: 100
Water Purification Services
N.A.I.C.S.: 423720
Bengt Rittri (Founder & CEO)

Subsidiaries:

FloWater, Inc. **(1)**
4045 Pecos St, Denver, CO 80211
Web Site: http://www.drinkflowater.com
Sales Range: $1-9.9 Million
Emp.: 200
Water Purification Product Distr
N.A.I.C.S.: 423720

BLUEWATER ACQUISITION CORP.

1400 350 - 7th Ave SW, Calgary, T2P 3N9, AB, Canada
Tel.: (416) 414-9916
Year Founded: 2018
BAQ.P—(TSXV)
Assets: $29,808
Liabilities: $11,906
Net Worth: $17,902
Earnings: ($119,819)
Fiscal Year-end: 05/31/21
Business Consulting Services
N.A.I.C.S.: 522299

BLUEWATER POWER DISTRIBUTION CORPORATION

855 Confederation St, PO Box 2140, Sarnia, N7T 7L6, ON, Canada
Tel.: (519) 337-8201
Web Site:
http://www.bluewaterpower.com
Year Founded: 1917
Rev.: $47,700,000
Emp.: 73
Electrical Contractor
N.A.I.C.S.: 238210
G. Firman Bentley (Chm)

BLUGLASS LIMITED

74 Asquith Street, Silverwater, 2128, NSW, Australia
Tel.: (61) 293342300
Web Site: https://bluglass.com
BLG—(ASX)
Rev.: $6,735,425
Assets: $15,451,460
Liabilities: $5,511,507
Net Worth: $9,939,953
Earnings: ($6,770,076)
Emp.: 50
Fiscal Year-end: 06/30/24
Semiconductor & Related Device Manufacturing
N.A.I.C.S.: 334413
Emmanuel Correia (Sec)

Subsidiaries:

BluSolar Pty Ltd **(1)**
18B Mareno Road, Tullamarine, 3043, VIC, Australia
Tel.: (61) 394920953
Web Site: http://www.bluesolar.com.au
Solar Energy Services
N.A.I.C.S.: 221114

BLUMAR S. A.

Magdalena 181 piso 13 oficina 1301 sur, Las Condes, Santiago, Chile
Tel.: (56) 227825400
Web Site: https://www.blumar.com
Year Founded: 1948
BLUMAR—(SGO)
Sales Range: Less than $1 Million
Sea Product Mfr
N.A.I.C.S.: 311710
Rodrigo Sarquis Said (Pres)

BLUMETRIC ENVIRONMENTAL INC.

1682 Woodward Drive, PO Box 430, Ottawa, K2C 3R8, ON, Canada
Tel.: (613) 839-3053
Web Site: https://www.blumetric.ca
Year Founded: 1985
BLMWF—(OTCQX)
Rev.: $26,172,991
Assets: $27,755,771
Liabilities: $18,659,007
Net Worth: $9,096,764
Earnings: $378,013
Emp.: 175
Fiscal Year-end: 06/30/23
Water & Wastewater Treatment Solutions
N.A.I.C.S.: 924110
Vivian Karaiskos (CFO)

Subsidiaries:

Seprotech **(1)**
2378 Holly Lane, Ottawa, K1V 7P1, ON, Canada
Tel.: (613) 523-1641
Web Site: http://www.seprotech.com
Waste Water Treatment Services
N.A.I.C.S.: 221310

WESAtech **(1)**
3108 Carp Road, PO Box 430, Ottawa, K0A 1L0, ON, Canada
Tel.: (613) 839-3053
Web Site: http://www.wesa.ca
Water & Wastewater Treatment Projects Developer
N.A.I.C.S.: 237110

BLUNDELL SEAFOODS LTD.

11351 River Road, Richmond, V6X 1Z6, BC, Canada
Tel.: (604) 270-3300
Web Site:
http://www.blundellseafoods.com
Year Founded: 1975
Emp.: 120
Seafood Product Whslr
N.A.I.C.S.: 424460
Anita Law (Sec)

BLUNDEN CONSTRUCTION LTD.

519 Herring Cove Rd, PO Box 280, Halifax, B3J 2P3, NS, Canada
Tel.: (902) 477-2531
Web Site: https://www.blunden.com
Year Founded: 1949
Rev.: $11,082,640
Emp.: 50
Construction Services
N.A.I.C.S.: 236210

BLUO SICAV-SIF

2 rue Heinrich Heine, L 1720, Luxembourg, Luxembourg
Tel.: (352) 26302605 **LU**
Web Site: http://www.blu-o.lu
Privater Equity Firm
N.A.I.C.S.: 523999
Lothar Rafalski (Chm)

Subsidiaries:

AlzChem Holding GmbH **(1)**
Chemiepark Trostberg Dr Albert Frank Str 32, Trostberg, 83308, Germany
Tel.: (49) 8621860
Web Site: http://www.alzchem.com
Sales Range: $450-499.9 Million
Emp.: 1,300
Specialty Chemicals Mfr
N.A.I.C.S.: 325998
Ulli Seibel (CEO)

Subsidiary (Domestic):

AlzChem Trostberg GmbH **(2)**
Dr Albert Frank Strasse 32, 83308, Trostberg, Germany
Tel.: (49) 8621860
Web Site: http://www.alzchem.com
Sales Range: $200-249.9 Million
Emp.: 1,000
Chemicals Mfr
N.A.I.C.S.: 325998
Stefan Greger (Mng Dir-Comml)

NIGU Chemie GmbH **(2)**
Beuthener Strasse 2, Waldkraiburg, 84478, Germany
Tel.: (49) 86389620
Web Site: http://www.nigu.de
Sales Range: $25-49.9 Million
Emp.: 60
Mfr of Guanidine Salts
N.A.I.C.S.: 325998
Sigmund Walz (Product Mgr)

Pit-Stop Auto Service GmbH **(1)**
Seligenstadter Grund 11, D-63150, Heusenstamm, Germany **(100%)**
Tel.: (49) 610496170
Web Site: http://www.pit-stop.de

Sales Range: $500-549.9 Million
Emp.: 1,500
Automotive Tires, Parts & Repair Shops Operator
N.A.I.C.S.: 811111

BLUTIP POWER TECHNOLOGIES LTD.

6705 Millcreek Drive Unit 4, Mississauga, L5N 5M4, ON, Canada
Tel.: (905) 363-3634 **ON**
Web Site: http://www.blutipower.com
Year Founded: 1996
Sales Range: Less than $1 Million
Diesel-Powered Engine Control Solutions Developer & Mfr
N.A.I.C.S.: 333618
Andrew H. Lindsay (VP-Engrg & Tech Dev)

BM CARPENTERIE OIL & GAS S.R.L.

Via Dogana 3, 20123, Milan, Italy
Tel.: (39) 0963544910 **IT**
Web Site:
http://bmcarpenteriesrl.com
Steel Structural Mfr
N.A.I.C.S.: 238120

BM GREENTECH BHD

Lot 875 Jalan Subang 8 Taman Perindustrian Subang, 47620, Subang Jaya, Selangor Darul Ehsan, Malaysia
Tel.: (60) 380239137
Web Site:
https://www.boilermech.com
BMGREEN—(KLS)
Rev.: $93,185,883
Assets: $88,803,155
Liabilities: $30,238,649
Net Worth: $58,564,506
Earnings: $7,521,580
Emp.: 543
Fiscal Year-end: 03/31/24
Boiler Mfr
N.A.I.C.S.: 332410
Yew Cheong Leong (Mng Dir)

Subsidiaries:

Boilermech Sdn Bhd **(1)**
Lot 875 Jalan Subang 8 Taman Perindustrian Subang, 47620, Subang Jaya, Selangor, Malaysia
Tel.: (60) 380239137
Power Boiler Mfr
N.A.I.C.S.: 332410

PT Boilermech Manufacturing Indonesia **(1)**
Jalan Pantai Indah Selatan Elang Laut Boulevard Blok C No 52, Pantai Indah Kapuk - Kamal Muara, Jakarta Utara, 14470, Indonesia
Tel.: (62) 2129678052
Boiler Mfr & Distr
N.A.I.C.S.: 332410

BM MOBILITY LTD.

10 Anson Road No 18-15 International Plaza, Singapore, 079903, Singapore
Tel.: (65) 69095780 **SG**
Web Site: http://bmm.com.sg
Year Founded: 2008
Rev.: $540,851
Assets: $5,336,540
Liabilities: $5,983,380
Net Worth: ($646,840)
Earnings: ($1,943,428)
Fiscal Year-end: 03/31/19
Investment Holding Company
N.A.I.C.S.: 551112
Wee Kwang Tay (CEO)

BM POLYCO LTD.

Crown Road, Enfield, EN1 1TX, Middlesex, United Kingdom

BM Polyco Ltd.—(Continued)

Tel.: (44) 20 8443 9010
Web Site: http://www.polyco.co.uk
Year Founded: 1979
Sales Range: $75-99.9 Million
Emp.: 132
Glove Mfr
N.A.I.C.S.: 326199
Mark Holdaway (Mng Dir)

BMB MUSIC & MAGNETICS LIMITED

G-2 IInd Floor Nandpuri Extension
Swej Farm New Sanganer Road,
Sodala, Jaipur, 302019, Rajasthan,
India
Tel.: (91) 141 3018919
Sales Range: Less than $1 Million
Motion Picture Production Services
N.A.I.C.S.: 512110
K. C. Bokadia (Mng Dir)

BMC BOLSA MERCANTIL DE COLOMBIA SA

Calle 113 7-21 Torre A Piso 15 Edif
Teleporto BusinessPark, Bogota, Colombia
Tel.: (57) 6292529
Web Site:
https://www.bolsamercantil.com.co
Year Founded: 1979
BMC—(COLO)
Sales Range: Less than $1 Million
Farm Management Services
N.A.I.C.S.: 115116
Rafael Mejia Lopez (Pres)

BMC MEDICAL CO., LTD.

Room 110 Tower A Fengyu Building
No 115 Fucheng Road, Haidian, Beijing, 100036, China
Tel.: (86) 18622933511
Web Site: https://www.bmc-medical.com
Year Founded: 2001
301367—(CHIN)
Rev.: $158,087,338
Assets: $411,062,618
Liabilities: $18,537,352
Net Worth: $392,525,266
Earnings: $41,878,831
Emp.: 800
Fiscal Year-end: 12/31/23
Medical Equipment Mfr & Distr
N.A.I.C.S.: 339112
Zhi Zhuang (Chm)

BMEX GOLD, INC.

Suite 904-409 Granville Street, Vancouver, V6C 1T2, BC, Canada
Tel.: (604) 808-5282   Ca
Web Site: https://www.bmexgold.com
Year Founded: 2017
BMEX—(TSXV)
Rev.: $305,891
Assets: $11,126,045
Liabilities: $462,275
Net Worth: $10,663,771
Earnings: ($85,531)
Fiscal Year-end: 08/31/23
Gold Mining Services
N.A.I.C.S.: 212220
Mickey Goldstein (CFO)

BMG RESOURCES LIMITED

13th Floor 37 St Georges Terrace,
Perth, 6000, WA, Australia
Tel.: (61) 93215922
Web Site: https://www.bmgl.com.au
BMG—(ASX)
Rev.: $9,149
Assets: $10,060,957
Liabilities: $114,646
Net Worth: $9,946,311
Earnings: ($4,799,444)
Fiscal Year-end: 06/30/24

Metal Mining Services
N.A.I.C.S.: 212290
Bruce Alexander McCracken (Mng Dir)

BMGB CAPITAL CORP.

1090 West Georgia Street Suite 600,
Vancouver, V6E 3V7, BC, Canada
Tel.: (770) 549-0714   Ca
Year Founded: 2018
BMGB.P—(TSXV)
Rev.: $4,271
Assets: $90,766
Liabilities: $14,766
Net Worth: $76,000
Earnings: ($57,953)
Fiscal Year-end: 06/30/21
Business Consulting Services
N.A.I.C.S.: 522299
Lucas Birdsall (CEO & Sec)

BMH LTD.

BMH Ltd La Maison 1794 Constance,
Centre de Flacq, 40609, Port Louis,
Mauritius
Tel.: (230) 4608600
Web Site: https://www.bmhmu.com
BMHL—(MAU)
Rev.: $135,390,225
Assets: $524,642,658
Liabilities: $266,850,608
Net Worth: $257,792,050
Earnings: $11,881,576
Emp.: 45
Fiscal Year-end: 12/31/23
Holding Company
N.A.I.C.S.: 551112

BMH TECHNOLOGY OY

Sinkokatu 11, PO Box 32, 26101,
Rauma, Finland
Tel.: (358) 204866800
Web Site: http://www.bmh.fi
Year Founded: 1929
Sales Range: $25-49.9 Million
Emp.: 120
Mfr of Biomass Fuel & Ash Handling
Systems, Waste Processing Plants &
Chip & Bark Handling Systems
N.A.I.C.S.: 333243
Peter Wallenius (Sr VP-Sls, Tech &
Mktg)

Subsidiaries:

BMH Technology AB   (1)
Tallbacksvagen 11, 745 42, Enkoping, Sweden
Tel.: (46) 104992700
Industrial Machinery Distr
N.A.I.C.S.: 423830

BMH Technology Oy   (1)
Zhang Jiang High Tech Park Bibo Road 690
Office 401-11, Shanghai, 201203, China
Tel.: (86) 2161042236
Industrial Machinery Distr
N.A.I.C.S.: 423830

BMH Technology Sp. z o.o.   (1)
ul Godlewskiego 7a/1, 54-609, Wroclaw,
Poland
Tel.: (48) 713505949
Web Site: http://www.bmhtechnology.pl
Industrial Machinery Distr
N.A.I.C.S.: 423830

BMH Wood Technology AB   (1)
Kaptensgatan 23, PO Box 12, 745 21, Enkoping, Sweden
Tel.: (46) 17124374
Web Site: http://www.bmh.fi
Spare Parts & Repair Services
N.A.I.C.S.: 423690

BMK & ZANATPRODUKT A.D.

Svetosavska 9, Stara Pazova, Serbia
Tel.: (381) 22 311 330
Year Founded: 1989
Sales Range: Less than $1 Million
Emp.: 2

Wholesale Trade Management Services
N.A.I.C.S.: 425120

BML, INC.

21-3 5-chome Sendagaya, Shibuya-ku, Tokyo, 151-0051, Japan
Tel.: (81) 333500111
Web Site: https://www.bml.co.jp
Year Founded: 1955
4694—(TKS)
Rev.: $911,942,040
Assets: $1,130,250,510
Liabilities: $270,025,110
Net Worth: $860,225,400
Earnings: $39,884,740
Emp.: 4,415
Fiscal Year-end: 03/31/24
Laboratory Testing Services
N.A.I.C.S.: 541380
Masato Chikira (Exec Officer)

Subsidiaries:

BML Food Science Solutions,
Inc.   (1)
2-12-14 Nishiochiai, Shinjuku-Ku, Tokyo,
161-0031, Japan
Tel.: (81) 359880211
Web Site: https://www.bfss.co.jp
Emp.: 396
All Other Miscellaneous Ambulatory Health
Care Services
N.A.I.C.S.: 621999

BML Fukushima, Inc.   (1)
29-1 Azaippongi Oyama, Fukushima, 960-
8252, Japan
Tel.: (81) 245330806
Clinical Laboratory Testing Services
N.A.I.C.S.: 541380

BML Life Science Holdings, Inc.   (1)
5-21-3 Sendagaya, Shibuya-ku, Tokyo, 151
0051, Japan
Tel.: (81) 333500259
Investment Management Service
N.A.I.C.S.: 523940

BML Medical Works, Inc.   (1)
1361-1 Matoba, Kawagoe, 350-1101, Saitama, Japan
Tel.: (81) 492320010
Web Site: http://www.bml.co.jp
Sales Range: $25-49.9 Million
Emp.: 20
Medical Instruments & Materials Distr
N.A.I.C.S.: 423450
Shmizu Tatsuo (Pres)

Daiichi Clinical Laboratories, Inc.   (1)
3-5-10 7Jo Fushiko, Higashi-ku, Sapporo,
007-0867, Hokkaido, Japan
Tel.: (81) 117872111
Clinical Laboratory Testing Services
N.A.I.C.S.: 621511

Japan Clinical Service, Inc.   (1)
1-34-5 Koenjiminami, Suginami-Ku, Tokyo,
166-0003, Japan
Tel.: (81) 333165223
Specimen Receiving Services
N.A.I.C.S.: 541380

Kyodo Igaku Laboratories, Inc.   (1)
5-20-25 Matsushima, Higashi-Ku, Fukuoka,
Japan
Tel.: (81) 926221319
All Other Miscellaneous Ambulatory Health
Care Services
N.A.I.C.S.: 621999

Labotec, Inc.   (1)
166-1 Shiratake, Sasebo, 857-1164, Nagasaki, Japan
Tel.: (81) 956 34 0015
Web Site: http://www.labo-tech.co.jp
Clinical Laboratory Testing Services
N.A.I.C.S.: 621511
Kenji Matsumura (Pres)

Matsudo Medical Laboratories,
Inc.   (1)
23-16 Matsudoshinden, Matsudo, 270-2241,
Chiba, Japan
Tel.: (81) 333500111
Clinical Laboratory Testing Services
N.A.I.C.S.: 621511

Nikken Igaku, Inc.   (1)
110-25 Wadanakacho, Fukui, 918-8235,
Japan
Tel.: (81) 776303702
Sales Range: $10-24.9 Million
Emp.: 60
Clinical Laboratory Testing Services
N.A.I.C.S.: 621511

PCL Japan, Inc.   (1)
1-32-3 Koenjiminami, Suginami-Ku, 166-
003, Tokyo, Japan
Tel.: (81) 333142824
Web Site: http://www.pcljapan.co.jp
Sales Range: $25-49.9 Million
Emp.: 236
Medical Laboratories
N.A.I.C.S.: 621511
Kondo Kenji (Dir)

Tokyo Koshueisei Laboratories,
Inc.   (1)
5-7-3 Koenjiminami, Suginami-ku, Tokyo,
166-0003, Japan
Tel.: (81) 353053570
Web Site: http://www.tokyo-koken.co.jp
Diagnostic Testing Services
N.A.I.C.S.: 621511

BMMI B.S.C.

812 Shaikh Jaber Al Ahmed Al Subah
Highway, PO Box 828, Sitra, Bahrain
Tel.: (973) 17739444
Web Site:
https://www.bmmigroup.com
Year Founded: 1883
BMMI—(BAH)
Rev.: $349,454,304
Assets: $310,189,319
Liabilities: $132,201,944
Net Worth: $177,987,374
Earnings: $15,997,504
Emp.: 601
Fiscal Year-end: 12/31/22
Food & Beverages Retailer, Whslr &
Distr
N.A.I.C.S.: 424420
Shawki Ali Fakhroo (Vice Chm)

Subsidiaries:

Alosra Supermarket W.L.L.   (1)
PO Box 828, Manama, Bahrain
Tel.: (973) 17697558
Supermarket Operator
N.A.I.C.S.: 445110

BMMI Djibouti   (1)
Warehouse No 1 Djibouti Free Zone, PO
Box 795, Djibouti, Djibouti
Tel.: (253) 21 320 600
Emp.: 25
Logistics Consulting Servies
N.A.I.C.S.: 541614
Gordon Boyle (CEO)

BMP BETEILIGUNGSMANAGE-MENT AG

Schluterstrasse 38, D-10629, Berlin,
Germany
Tel.: (49) 30 20 30 5 0
Web Site: http://www.bmp.com
Year Founded: 2005
Venture Capital & Private Equity
N.A.I.C.S.: 523999
Christof Nesemeier (Chm-Supervisory
Bd)

BMP METALS INC.

18 Chelsea Ln, Brampton, L6T 3Y4,
ON, Canada
Tel.: (905) 799-2002
Web Site: http://www.bmpmetals.com
Rev.: $22,866,522
Emp.: 175
Fabricated Metal Mfr
N.A.I.C.S.: 332999
Robert Bedard (Pres)

BMP PHARMA TRADING AG

Bornbarch 16, 22848, Norderstedt,
Germany

Tel.: (49) 406455680
Web Site: https://www.bmp.ag
Year Founded: 1979
BMP—(BER)
Sales Range: Less than $1 Million
Pharmaceutical Raw Material Distr
N.A.I.C.S.: 424690
Bernd Michael Joerss *(Chm-Mgmt Bd)*

BMS GROUP LTD.
1 America Square, London, EC3N
2LS, United Kingdom
Tel.: (44) 2074807288　　　　　UK
Web Site: http://www.bmsgroup.com
Year Founded: 1980
Sales Range: $50-74.9 Million
Emp.: 220
Reinsurance Broker
N.A.I.C.S.: 524130
David Spiegler *(Chief Actuary)*

Subsidiaries:

BMS Asia Inter-mediaries Pte.,
Ltd.　　　　　　　　　　　　　(1)
20 Raffles Place, 11-01 Raffles Towers, Singapore, Singapore
Tel.: (65) 63233326
Insurance Services
N.A.I.C.S.: 524298

BMS Asia Intermediaries Ltd.　(1)
Wisma UOA II, 21 Jalan Pinang, Kuala Lumpur, Malaysia
Tel.: (60) 321643326
Insurance Services
N.A.I.C.S.: 524298

BMS Associates Ltd.　　　　　(1)
1 America Sq, 17 Crosswall Rd Tower Hill, EC3N2LS, London, United Kingdom
Tel.: (44) 2074807288
Sales Range: $100-124.9 Million
Emp.: 215
Insurance Services
N.A.I.C.S.: 524298
John Hills *(Sec)*

BMS Bermuda Ltd.　　　　　　(1)
PO Box Number 2953, HMMX, Hamilton, Bermuda
Tel.: (441) 232 3784
Insurance Services
N.A.I.C.S.: 524298
Dean Carberry *(CEO)*

BMS Facultative Ltd.　　　　　(1)
1 America Sqare, London, EC3N 2LS, United Kingdom
Tel.: (44) 2074800306
Web Site: http://www.bmsgroup.com
Sales Range: $100-124.9 Million
Emp.: 150
Insurance Services
N.A.I.C.S.: 524298
Darren Doherty *(Mng Dir)*

BMS Harris & Dixon Ltd.　　　(1)
1 America Square, London, EC3N 2LS, United Kingdom
Tel.: (44) 2074800350
Sales Range: $50-74.9 Million
Emp.: 20
Insurance Services
N.A.I.C.S.: 524298

BMS Harris & Dixon Marine Ltd.　(1)
1 America Sq, London, EC3 N2LS, United Kingdom
Tel.: (44) 2074800366
Web Site: http://www.bmsgroup.com
Sales Range: $100-124.9 Million
Insurance Services
N.A.I.C.S.: 524298
Tony Pryce *(Chm)*

BMS Harris & Dixon Reinsurance
Brokers Ltd.　　　　　　　　　(1)
Latham House, 6 Minories, London, EC3N 1AX, United Kingdom
Tel.: (44) 20 7480 0346
Insurance Services
N.A.I.C.S.: 524298

BMS International Intermediaries
Ltd.　　　　　　　　　　　　　(1)

Latham House, Latham House, London, EC3N 1AX, United Kingdom
Tel.: (44) 20 7480 0346
Insurance Services
N.A.I.C.S.: 524298

BMS Management Services Ltd.　(1)
No 1 America Sq, London, EC3N 2LS, United Kingdom
Tel.: (44) 2073745159
Web Site: http://www.bmsgroup.co.uk
Sales Range: $25-49.9 Million
Emp.: 200
Centralized Group Support Services
N.A.I.C.S.: 561499
Adam Dixey *(Dir-Div & Mgr-Broking Svcs)*

BMS Re Ltd.　　　　　　　　　(1)
One America Sq, London, EC3N 2LS, United Kingdom
Tel.: (44) 2074807288
Web Site: http://www.bmsgroup.co.uk
Sales Range: $100-124.9 Million
Emp.: 217
Non-Marine, Property & Casualty Reinsurance
N.A.I.C.S.: 524130
Adam Mullan *(Chm-Bermuda)*

BMS Special Risk Services Ltd.　(1)
1 America Sq, London, EC3N 2LS, United Kingdom
Tel.: (44) 2074807288
Sales Range: $100-124.9 Million
Insurance Services
N.A.I.C.S.: 524298
Paul Daly *(Mng Dir)*

BMS Vision Re Ltd.　　　　　　(1)
1101 Perimeter Dr Ste 875, Chicago, IL 60173
Tel.: (847) 277-0201
Web Site: http://www.bmsgroup.co.uk
Sales Range: $50-74.9 Million
Emp.: 3
Insurance Services
N.A.I.C.S.: 524298

Ballantyne McKean & Sullivan
Ltd.　　　　　　　　　　　　　(1)
1 America Sq, London, EC3N 2LS, United Kingdom
Tel.: (44) 2073745936
Web Site: http://www.bmsgroup.com
Reinsurance Broker
N.A.I.C.S.: 524130
Simon Clutterbuck *(Dir-Property & Casualty)*

BankServe Insurance Services
Ltd.　　　　　　　　　　　　　(1)
1 America Sq, London, EC3N2LS, United Kingdom
Tel.: (44) 2074800274
Sales Range: $100-124.9 Million
Emp.: 200
Insurance Services
N.A.I.C.S.: 524210

BMT CO., LTD.
43 Seokgyesandan 2-gil Sangbukmyeon, Yangsan, 50561, Gyeongsangnam-do, Korea (South)
Tel.: (82) 557831200
Web Site: https://www.superlok.com
Year Founded: 2000
086670—(KRS)
Rev.: $108,982,786
Assets: $182,471,096
Liabilities: $100,890,306
Net Worth: $81,580,790
Earnings: $11,503,124
Emp.: 358
Fiscal Year-end: 12/31/22
Hose Fittings & Valve Mfr
N.A.I.C.S.: 332912
Jong-chan Yoon *(CEO)*

Subsidiaries:

BMT Co., Ltd. - Yangsan Factory　(1)
43 Seokgyesandan 2-gil, Yangsan, 50568, Gyeongsangnam-do, Korea (South)
Tel.: (82) 557831200
Valve Mfr
N.A.I.C.S.: 332911

BMT GROUP LIMITED

1 Park Road, Teddington, TW11 0AP, United Kingdom
Tel.: (44) 20 8943 5544　　　UK
Web Site: http://www.bmt.org
Year Founded: 1985
Rev.: $222,942,703
Assets: $84,413,941
Liabilities: $49,882,638
Net Worth: $34,531,303
Earnings: $321,062
Emp.: 1,500
Fiscal Year-end: 09/30/18
Holding Company; Multi-Disciplinary Engineering, Science & Technology Consultancy Services
N.A.I.C.S.: 551112
Anne Segall *(Dir-HR)*

Subsidiaries:

BMT Argoss B.V.　　　　　　　(1)
Voorsterweg 28, Marknesse, 8316 PT, Netherlands
Tel.: (31) 527 242 299
Web Site: http://www.bmtargoss.com
Emp.: 22
Weather Forecasting Services
N.A.I.C.S.: 541990
David Hurdle *(Sr Project Mgr)*

BMT Argoss Limited　　　　　(1)
Broadfold House Broadfold Road, Bridge of Don, Aberdeen, AB23 8EE, United Kingdom
Tel.: (44) 1224 414200
Web Site: http://www.bmtargoss.com
Weather Forecasting Services
N.A.I.C.S.: 541990
Shane Amaratunga *(Dir-Internal Affairs)*

BMT Asia Pacific Pte., Ltd.　　(1)
03-01 Harbour Front Tower Two, 3 Harbour-Front Place, Singapore, 99254, Singapore
Tel.: (65) 17 6800
Web Site: http://www.bmtasia.com.sg
Sales Range: $25-49.9 Million
Emp.: 50
Maritime Transport Services
N.A.I.C.S.: 488999
Anil Thapar *(Deputy Mng Dir)*

Division (Non-US):

BMT Asia Pacific Ltd.　　　　(2)
5th Fl ING Tower, 308 Des Voeux Road, Central, China (Hong Kong)
Tel.: (852) 28152221
Web Site: http://www.bmtasiapacific.com
Emp.: 50
Maritime Transport Services
N.A.I.C.S.: 488999

BMT Consultants (India) Pvt.
Ltd.　　　　　　　　　　　　　(1)
310 Sarthik Square SG Highway, Ahmedabad, 380 054, Gujarat, India
Tel.: (91) 7940028708
Web Site: http://www.bmtindia.org
Sales Range: $25-49.9 Million
Emp.: 30
Maritime Transport Services
N.A.I.C.S.: 488999

BMT De Beer bv　　　　　　　(1)
Guldenwaard 141, 3078 AJ, Rotterdam, Netherlands
Tel.: (31) 0104790311
Web Site: http://www.bmtdebeer.com
Sales Range: $25-49.9 Million
Emp.: 15
Nautical, Cargo & Technical Surveying & Consulting Services
N.A.I.C.S.: 488320
Jeroen J. De Haas *(Mng Dir)*

BMT Defence Services Ltd.　　(1)
Maritime House, 210 Lower Bristol Rd, Bath, BA2 3DQ, United Kingdom
Tel.: (44) 1225473600
Web Site: http://www.bmtdsl.co.uk
Sales Range: $50-74.9 Million
Emp.: 160
Naval Defence Design, Engineering & Management Support Services
N.A.I.C.S.: 541611
Roy Quilliam *(Dir-Bus Dev)*

Subsidiary (Non-US):

BMT Defence Services (Australia)
Pty. Ltd.　　　　　　　　　　　(2)

99 King St Level 5, Melbourne, 3000, VIC, Australia
Tel.: (61) 386206180
Web Site:
　http://www.bmtdesigntechnology.com.au
Sales Range: $25-49.9 Million
Emp.: 21
Naval Defence Engineering & Technology Services
N.A.I.C.S.: 541330
Gordon MacDonald *(Mng Dir)*

Oceanica AG　　　　　　　　　(2)
Hohe Bleichen 12, Hamburg, 20354, Germany
Tel.: (49) 4030082522
Web Site: http://www.oceanica.de
Financial Investment Services
N.A.I.C.S.: 523940
Felix Von Buchwaldt *(Member-Mgmt Bd)*

BMT Design & Technology Pty
Ltd　　　　　　　　　　　　　(1)
Level 5 99 King Street, Melbourne, 3000, VIC, Australia
Tel.: (61) 3 8620 6180
Web Site:
　http://www.bmtdesigntechnology.com.au
Emp.: 30
Marine Engineering Services
N.A.I.C.S.: 541330
Heidi Garth *(Mgr-Canberra)*

BMT Designers & Planners, Inc.　(1)
4401 Ford Ave Ste 1000, Alexandria, VA 22302
Tel.: (703) 920-7070
Web Site: http://www.dandp.com
Sales Range: $25-49.9 Million
Emp.: 30
Engineering Consulting Services
N.A.I.C.S.: 541330
Mike Hicks *(Dir-Environmental & Energy)*

BMT Energy and Environment　(1)
Broadfold House Broadfold Road Bridge of Don, Bridge of Don, Aberdeen, AB23 8HG, United Kingdom
Tel.: (44) 1224414200
Web Site: http://www.bmtcordah.com
Emp.: 25
Engineeering Services
N.A.I.C.S.: 541330

Subsidiary (Domestic):

BMT Cordah Limited　　　　　(2)
Broadfold Rd Bridge of Don, Aberdeen, AB23 8EE, United Kingdom
Tel.: (44) 1224414200
Web Site: http://www.bmtcordah.com
Sales Range: $25-49.9 Million
Emp.: 25
Environmental Consulting Services
N.A.I.C.S.: 541620
Andrew Glass *(Mng Dir)*

Division (US):

BMT Energy　　　　　　　　　(2)
11505 W littlerack, Houston, TX 77041
Tel.: (281) 858-8090
Web Site: http://www.scimar.com
Sales Range: $25-49.9 Million
Emp.: 19
Engineeering Services
N.A.I.C.S.: 541330

BMT Fleet Technology Limited　(1)
311 Legget Drive, Kanata, K2K 1Z8, ON, Canada
Tel.: (613) 592-2830
Web Site: http://www.fleetech.com
Sales Range: $25-49.9 Million
Emp.: 100
Maritime Transport Services
N.A.I.C.S.: 488999
Darcy Byrtus *(Pres)*

Branch (Domestic):

BMT Fleet Technology Limited　(2)
611 Alexander St Ste 412, Vancouver, V6A 1E1, BC, Canada
Tel.: (604) 253-0955
Web Site: http://www.fleettech.com
Sales Range: $25-49.9 Million
Emp.: 11
Maritime Transport Services
N.A.I.C.S.: 488999

BMT Group Limited—(Continued)

BMT Fleet Technology Limited (2)
Shoal Point, 101-19 Dallas Road, Victoria,
V8V 5A6, BC, Canada
Tel.: (250) 598-5150
Web Site: http://www.fleetech.com
Sales Range: $25-49.9 Million
Emp.: 5
Maritime Transport Services
N.A.I.C.S.: 488999

BMT Fleet Technology Limited (2)
25 Kenmount Rd, Saint John's, A1D 1W1,
NL, Canada
Tel.: (709) 753-5690
Web Site: http://www.fleettech.com
Sales Range: $25-49.9 Million
Emp.: 14
Maritime Transport Services
N.A.I.C.S.: 488999

BMT Fluid Mechanics Limited (1)
67 Stanton Avenue, Teddington, TW11 0JY,
Middlesex, United Kingdom
Tel.: (44) 2089435544
Web Site: http://www.bmtfm.com
Sales Range: $25-49.9 Million
Emp.: 30
Wind Engineering & Offshore Marine Consultancy
N.A.I.C.S.: 541330
Chris Craddock (Dir-Consultancy)

BMT Hi-Q Sigma Ltd (1)
Berkeley House The Square, Bath, BA2
3BH, United Kingdom
Tel.: (44) 1225 820 980
Web Site: http://www.bmt-hqs.com
Emp.: 100
Management Consulting Services
N.A.I.C.S.: 541611
Simon Gould (Mng Dir)

BMT Isis Ltd (1)
First Floor Berkeley House The Square
Lower Bristol Road, Bath, BA2 3BH, United
Kingdom
Tel.: (44) 1225 473 727
Web Site: http://www.bmt-isis.com
Emp.: 60
Environmental Management Services
N.A.I.C.S.: 541620
Lee Rhodes (Mgr-Bus Dev-Wind Energy)

BMT JFA Consultants Pty Ltd (1)
Level 3 20 Parkland Rd, Osborne Park,
Perth, 6017, WA, Australia
Tel.: (61) 8 6163 4900
Web Site: http://www.bmtjfaconsultants.com
Emp.: 15
Engineeering Services
N.A.I.C.S.: 541330
Jesz Fleming (Founder)

BMT Nigel Gee Ltd (1)
Building 14 Shamrock Quay William Street,
Southampton, SO14 5QL, United Kingdom
Tel.: (44) 23 8022 6655
Web Site: http://www.bmtng.com
Emp.: 50
Ship Design Services
N.A.I.C.S.: 541990
John Bonafoux (Mng Dir)

BMT Oceanica Pty Ltd. (1)
353 Cambridge St, Wembley, Perth, 6014,
WA, Australia
Tel.: (61) 8 6272 0000
Web Site: http://www.bmtoceanica.com.au
Emp.: 35
Environmental Consulting Services
N.A.I.C.S.: 541620
Mark Bailey (Mng Dir)

BMT Reliability Consultants Ltd. (1)
12 Little Park Farm Road, Fareham, PO15
5SU, Hampshire, United Kingdom
Tel.: (44) 1489553100
Web Site: http://www.bmtrcl.com
Sales Range: $25-49.9 Million
Emp.: 45
Engineering Consultancy Services
N.A.I.C.S.: 541330
Andrew Cooper (Mng Dir)

BMT SMART Ltd (1)
Spectrum Building 1600 Parkway, Whiteley
Solent Business Park, Fareham, PO15
7AH, Hampshire, United Kingdom

Tel.: (44) 1489 889260
Web Site: http://www.bmtsmart.bmthq.com
Emp.: 40
Business Support Services
N.A.I.C.S.: 561499

**BMT Scientific Marine Services
Inc** (1)
955 Borra Pl Ste 100, Escondido, CA
92029
Tel.: (760) 737-3505
Web Site: http://www.scimar.com
Marine Engineering Services
N.A.I.C.S.: 541330
Kevin A Hearn (VP-Technical)

**BMT Scientific Marine Services
Ltda** (1)
Ed Manhattan Tower 26th Floor Avenida
Rio Branco 89, Rio de Janeiro, 20040-004,
Brazil
Tel.: (55) 21 2516 5923
Web Site: http://www.scimar.com
Marine Engineering Services
N.A.I.C.S.: 541330

BMT Surveys (Amsterdam) B.V. (1)
Zekeringstraat 36D, Amsterdam, 1014 BS,
Netherlands
Tel.: (31) 20 584 0800
Marine Engineering Services
N.A.I.C.S.: 541330

BMT Surveys (Antwerp) NV (1)
Kapelsesteenweg 286, Brasschaat, 2930,
Antwerp, Belgium
Tel.: (32) 3664 0279
Marine Engineering Services
N.A.I.C.S.: 541330
Carlos Maenhout (Mng Dir)

BMT Surveys (London) Limited (1)
1st Floor International House Saint Katharine's Way, London, E1W 1UN, United
Kingdom
Tel.: (44) 207 101 2114
Web Site: http://www.bmtsurveys.com
Emp.: 3
Marine Engineering Services
N.A.I.C.S.: 541330
Andy Morris (Dir)

BMT Surveys (Rotterdam) B.V. (1)
Guldenwaard 141, Rotterdam, 3078 AJ,
Netherlands
Tel.: (31) 10 479 0311
Web Site: http://www.bmtsurveys.com
Emp.: 30
Marine Engineering Services
N.A.I.C.S.: 541330
Jeroen de Haas (Mng Dir)

BMT Syntek Technologies, Inc. (1)
2120 Washington Blvd Ste 110, Arlington,
VA 22204-1627
Tel.: (703) 525-3403
Web Site: http://www.BMTsyntek.com
Sales Range: $25-49.9 Million
Emp.: 30
Professional Services for Transportation,
Telecommunications, Information Technology, Energy, Defense, Intelligence, Maritime, Electronics & Space Industries
N.A.I.C.S.: 541715
James C. Davis (Pres)

BMT WBM Pty. Ltd. (1)
Level 8 200 Creek Street, Brisbane, 4000,
QLD, Australia
Tel.: (61) 7 3831 6744
Web Site: http://www.bmtwbm.com.au
Environmental Engineering Services
N.A.I.C.S.: 541330
Tony McAlister (Mng Dir-Water & Environment Grp)

Subsidiary (US):

BMT WBM Inc. (1)
8200 S Akron St Ste 120, Centennial, CO
80112
Tel.: (303) 792-9814
Web Site: http://www.bmtwbm.com
Emp.: 7
Environmental Engineering Services
N.A.I.C.S.: 541330
Ryan Sharp (Mgr)

Gee Ltd. (1)
Plot No E-1 Road No 7 Wagle Industrial

Estate, Thane, 400 604, Maharashtra, India
Tel.: (91) 8308840280
Web Site: https://www.geelimited.com
Rev.: $34,688,894
Assets: $35,983,764
Liabilities: $12,674,604
Net Worth: $23,309,161
Earnings: $1,728,333
Emp.: 322
Fiscal Year-end: 03/31/2021
Welding Electrode Mfr
N.A.I.C.S.: 333992
Ramkishan Agarwal (Founder)

WBM Pty. Ltd. (1)
490 Upper Edward Street, Brisbane, 4000,
QLD, Australia
Tel.: (61) 738316744
Web Site: http://www.wbmpl.com.au
Rev.: $25,000,000
Emp.: 150
Engineeering Services
N.A.I.C.S.: 541330

Branch (Domestic):

WBM - Sydney (2)
256-258 Level 1 Norton Street, PO Box
194, Leichhardt, 2040, NSW, Australia
Tel.: (61) 297134836
Web Site: http://www.wbmpl.com.au
Sales Range: $25-49.9 Million
Emp.: 10
Engineeering Services
N.A.I.C.S.: 541330
Rob Widders (Mng Dir)

BMTC GROUP INC.
8500 Place Marien, Montreal, H1B
5W8, QC, Canada
Tel.: (514) 648-5757
Web Site: https://www.bmtc.ca
Year Founded: 1989
GBT—(TSX)
Rev.: $641,035,435
Assets: $430,196,111
Liabilities: $126,776,297
Net Worth: $303,419,814
Earnings: $64,092,983
Emp.: 1,251
Fiscal Year-end: 01/31/22
Financial Management Services
N.A.I.C.S.: 523940

Subsidiaries:

Ameublements Tanguay Inc. (1)
7200 rue Armand-Viau, Quebec, G2C 2A7,
QC, Canada
Tel.: (418) 871-4411
Web Site: http://www.tanguay.ca
Home Furnishing Product Distr
N.A.I.C.S.: 423220

BMW INDUSTRIES LIMITED
119 Park Street White House 3Rd
Floor, Kolkata, 700016, India
Tel.: (91) 3340071704
Web Site: https://www.bmwil.co.in
542669—(BOM)
Rev.: $78,005,641
Assets: $131,132,233
Liabilities: $48,722,610
Net Worth: $82,409,623
Earnings: $7,436,752
Emp.: 378
Fiscal Year-end: 03/31/23
Steel Products Mfr
N.A.I.C.S.: 332999
Abhishek Agarwal (CFO)

BMW TORONTO
11 Sunlight Park Rd, Toronto, M4M
1B5, ON, Canada
Tel.: (416) 623-4269
Web Site: http://www.bmwtoronto.ca
Rev.: $37,396,674
Emp.: 120
New & Used Car Dealers
N.A.I.C.S.: 441110
Antonio Masciangelo (Mgr-Sls)

BNC COMPANY CO., LTD.

405-406 Sahoi Gongdan, Jungwang-
dong 1268-4-5, Siheung, 429849,
Korea (South)
Tel.: (82) 31 4889471
Web Site: http://www.techgs.net
Sales Range: $10-24.9 Million
Emp.: 18
Electronic Scrap Recyclable Services
N.A.I.C.S.: 331314
Ju-Hyung Park (CEO)

BNC KOREA CO., LTD.
405 Structure 1 Daegu Techno Park
Venture Factor, 62
Seongseogongdan-ro 11-gil Dalseo-
gu, Daegu, Korea (South)
Tel.: (82) 7071160059
Web Site: https://www.bnckorea.co.kr
Year Founded: 2007
256840—(KRS)
Rev.: $32,446,691
Assets: $178,343,911
Liabilities: $32,538,647
Net Worth: $145,805,264
Earnings: ($34,163,579)
Emp.: 125
Fiscal Year-end: 12/31/22
Medical Substances & Pharmaceutical Mfr
N.A.I.C.S.: 325412
Wan-gyu Choi (CEO)

BNDES PARTICIPACOES SA
Avenida Republica do Chile 100, Rio
de Janeiro, 20031-917, Brazil
Tel.: (55) 21 2052 7447   BR
Web Site: http://www.bndes.gov.br
Year Founded: 1952
Rev.: $16,100,289,083
Assets: $206,690,806,186
Liabilities: $186,201,088,590
Net Worth: $20,489,717,596
Earnings: $1,728,360,616
Emp.: 2,711
Fiscal Year-end: 12/31/18
Financial Investment Services
N.A.I.C.S.: 523999
Marcelo Serfaty (Co-Pres)

BNG BANK N.V.
Koninginnegracht 2, 2514 AA, Hague,
Netherlands
Tel.: (31) 703750750
Web Site: http://www.bngbank.nl
Year Founded: 1914
Rev.: $6,184,986,780
Assets: $167,630,723,540
Liabilities: $162,157,967,720
Net Worth: $5,472,755,820
Earnings: $182,537,180
Emp.: 314
Fiscal Year-end: 12/31/19
Financial Services
N.A.I.C.S.: 522320
Olivier J. Labe (CFO)

Subsidiaries:

BNG Capital Management B.V. (1)
Koninginnetracht 2, Hague, 2514 AA,
Netherlands (100%)
Tel.: (31) 703750245
Web Site: http://www.bcmnet.nl
Sales Range: $50-74.9 Million
Emp.: 14
Miscellaneous Financial Investment Activities
N.A.I.C.S.: 523999
Jof Da Wit (Mng Dir)

BNG Consultancy Services B.V. (1)
Koninginnegracht 2, 2514 AA, Hague,
Netherlands (100%)
Tel.: (31) 703750750
Web Site: http://www.bngbank.nl
Sales Range: $25-49.9 Million
Emp.: 10
Management Consulting Services
N.A.I.C.S.: 541618

BNG Gebiedsontwikkeling BV (1)

Dr Kuyperstraat 12, Hague, 2514 BB,
Netherlands **(100%)**
Tel.: (31) 70 3119 900
Emp.: 16
Venture Capital & Investment Services
N.A.I.C.S.: 523999
C. C. A. Rodewijk *(Mng Dir)*

BNG Management Services B.V. **(1)**
Koninginnegracht 2, PO Box 30305, Hague,
2500GH, Netherlands **(100%)**
Tel.: (31) 703750884
Web Site: http://www.bngadvies.nl
Sales Range: $50-74.9 Million
Miscellaneous Financial Investment Activities
N.A.I.C.S.: 523999

BNG Vastgoedontwikkeling B.V. **(1)**
PO Box 16075, 2500BB, Hague,
Netherlands **(100%)**
Tel.: (31) 703750750
Web Site: http://www.bngbank.no
Sales Range: $100-124.9 Million
Emp.: 220
Investment Advice
N.A.I.C.S.: 523940
Van Eigkelenburg *(Pres)*

BNG Vermogensbeheer BV **(1)**
Koninginnegracht 2, Hague, 2514 AA,
Netherlands **(100%)**
Tel.: (31) 70 3750 245
Investment Fund Management Services
N.A.I.C.S.: 523999
J. J.M. De Wit *(Member-Mgmt Bd)*

Dataland B.V. **(1)**
Noothoven van Goorstraat 11d, PO Box
210, 2806 RA, Gouda,
Netherlands **(42%)**
Tel.: (31) 883282000
Web Site: http://www.dataland.nl
Sales Range: $25-49.9 Million
Emp.: 10
All Other Information Services
N.A.I.C.S.: 519290

Hypotheekfonds voor Overheidspersoneel B.V. **(1)**
30305, 2500GH, Hague,
Netherlands **(100%)**
Tel.: (31) 703750580
Securities Brokerage
N.A.I.C.S.: 523150

BNK BANKING CORPORATION LIMITED

Lvl 14 191 St Georges Terrace,
Perth, 6000, WA, Australia
Tel.: (61) 894388888
Web Site:
https://www.goldfieldsmoney.com.au
BBC—(ASX)
Rev.: $64,043,803
Assets: $1,151,782,848
Liabilities: $1,070,908,783
Net Worth: $80,874,065
Earnings: $4,474,493
Fiscal Year-end: 06/30/24
Banking & Financial Services
N.A.I.C.S.: 522110
Jon Sutton *(Chm)*

Subsidiaries:

1300 Home Loan Holdings Pty
Ltd **(1)**
Level 24 52 Martin Place, Sydney, 2000,
NSW, Australia
Tel.: (61) 1300466356
Web Site: http://www.1300homeloan.com.au
Home Loan Services
N.A.I.C.S.: 522310
John Kolenda *(Co-Founder & Mng Dir)*

Australian Asset Aggregation Pty
Ltd **(1)**
175 Melbourne Street South, Brisbane,
4101, QLD, Australia
Tel.: (61) 1300859123
Web Site:
https://www.australianaggregation.com
Financial Services
N.A.I.C.S.: 523999

Australian Capital Home Loans Pty
Ltd **(1)**

PO Box 1275, Slacks Creek, Logan, 4127,
QLD, Australia
Tel.: (61) 1300797338
Web Site: http://www.achl.com.au
Financial Services
N.A.I.C.S.: 523999

Better Choice Home Loans Pty
Ltd **(1)**
Level 5 50 Cavill Avenue, PO Box 845,
Surfers Paradise, 4217, QLD, Australia
Tel.: (61) 1300334336
Web Site: https://www.betterchoice.com.au
Home Loan Services
N.A.I.C.S.: 522310
Kathryn Whitney *(Mgr-Relationship)*

Finsure Finance & Insurance Pty
Ltd **(1)**
27/10 Carrington St, Sydney, 2000, NSW,
Australia
Tel.: (61) 1300346787
Web Site: https://www.finsure.com.au
Finance & Insurance Services
N.A.I.C.S.: 524210

BNK FINANCIAL GROUP INC.

30 Munhyeongeumyung-ro, Nam-gu,
Busan, 48400, Korea (South)
Tel.: (82) 516203000   KR
Web Site: https://www.bnkfg.com
Year Founded: 2011
138930—(KRS)
Rev.: $4,966,911,346
Assets: $108,207,498,103
Liabilities: $100,284,972,324
Net Worth: $7,922,525,779
Earnings: $474,875,091
Emp.: 129
Fiscal Year-end: 12/31/23
Financial Investment Services
N.A.I.C.S.: 551111
Dae-In Bin *(Chm & CEO)*

Subsidiaries:

BNK Asset Management Co.,
Ltd. **(1)**
21st floor 32 Gukjegeumyung-ro 2-gil,
Yeongdeungpo-gu, Seoul, Korea (South)
Tel.: (82) 269101100
Web Site: https://www.bnkasset.co.kr
Asset Management Services
N.A.I.C.S.: 523150
Yun-Hak Lee *(CEO)*

BNK Capital Co., Ltd. **(1)**
8th Fl of Busan Bank Bujeondong Branch
Bldg 1 Saessak-ro, Busanjin-gu, Busan,
47256, Korea (South)
Tel.: (82) 220590304
Web Site: https://www.bnkcapital.co.kr
Financial Services
N.A.I.C.S.: 522320
Lee Doo Ho *(CEO)*

BNK Credit Information Co., Ltd. **(1)**
92 Beomil-ro 5th floor of Beamildong
Branch of Busan Bank, Dong-gu, Busan,
Korea (South)
Tel.: (82) 518905000
Web Site: https://www.bnkci.co.kr
Investment & Security Services
N.A.I.C.S.: 523150
Seang-Ju Kim *(CEO)*

BNK Savings Bank Co., Ltd. **(1)**
92 Beomil-ro 2nd 3rd Floor, Dong-gu, Busan, Korea (South)
Tel.: (82) 16449988
Investment & Security Services
N.A.I.C.S.: 523150
Hyoung-Guk Myoung *(CEO)*

BNK Securities Co., Ltd. **(1)**
Busan Bank Bujeondong Annex 3 4F
Bujeon 1-Dong 259-4, Busanjin-gu, Busan,
Korea (South)
Tel.: (82) 516698000
Web Site: https://www.bnkfn.co.kr
Securities Exchange Services
N.A.I.C.S.: 523210
Byung Young-Kim *(CEO)*

BNK System Co., Ltd. **(1)**
8th Floor BNK Financial Group IT Center
Development Building, 21 Mieumsandan-ro

127beon-gil Gangseo-gu, Busan, 46744,
Korea (South)
Tel.: (82) 516021700
Web Site: https://www.bnksys.co.kr
Information Technology Services
N.A.I.C.S.: 518210
Young-Moon Kim *(CEO)*

BNK Venture Capital Co., Ltd. **(1)**
12th Floor BNK Digital Tower 398 Seochodaero, Seocho-gu, Seoul, 06619, Korea
(South)
Tel.: (82) 25088187
Web Site: https://www.bnkvc.co.kr
Investment Services
N.A.I.C.S.: 523150
Sang-Yun Kim *(CEO)*

BNKC (Cambodia) MFI PLC **(1)**
Ground and first Floor of B-Ray Tower
Preah Norodom Blvd, Sangkat Tonle Bassac Khan Chamkamorn, Phnom Penh,
Cambodia
Tel.: (855) 23213900
Web Site: https://bnkcmfi.com
Financial Services
N.A.I.C.S.: 921130
Kim Soonjo *(CEO)*

BS Capital Co., Ltd. **(1)**
259-4 Bujeon 1 dong lin-gu 9th Floor, Busan, Korea (South)
Tel.: (82) 51 665 1000
Web Site: http://www.bscapital.co.kr
Mortgage Loan Services
N.A.I.C.S.: 522310
Sang-Chun Lee *(CEO)*

BS Savings Bank Co., Ltd. **(1)**
1466-1 Jwa-dong, Haeundae-gu, Busan,
Korea (South)
Tel.: (82) 51 713 1000
Web Site: http://www.bnksv.com
Commercial Banking Services
N.A.I.C.S.: 522110
Chung Jae-Young *(CEO)*

BS Securities Co., Ltd. **(1)**
Busan Bank Bujeondong 3 4F Bujeon
1-Dong 259-4, Busanjin-Gu, Busan, Korea
(South) **(100%)**
Tel.: (82) 51 669 8000
Web Site: http://www.bsfn.co.kr
Emp.: 180
Security Brokerage Services
N.A.I.C.S.: 523150
Hyo-joon An *(CEO)*

BS System Information Co., Ltd. **(1)**
Sinchang-dong 9-2 1 4th Floor, Jung-gu,
Busan, 600061, Korea (South)
Tel.: (82) 51 602 1700
Web Site: http://www.bsisys.co.kr
Information Technology Consulting Services
N.A.I.C.S.: 541512
Yeong-Woo Lee *(CEO)*

Busan Bank, Ltd. **(1)**
830-38 Bomil-dong, Busan, 601-060, Dong-gu, Korea (South)
Tel.: (82) 516423300
Web Site: http://www.busanbank.co.kr
Sales Range: $1-4.9 Billion
Emp.: 3,398
Banking Services
N.A.I.C.S.: 522110

Busan Credit & Information Co.,
Ltd. **(1)**
378-11 Gaya 1-Dong, Busanjin-Gu, Busan,
614-011, Korea (South) **(100%)**
Tel.: (82) 518905000
Sales Range: $50-74.9 Million
Emp.: 15
Credit Services
N.A.I.C.S.: 522299

Kyongnam Bank Co., Ltd. **(1)**
642 3 15 Daero Masan Hoewon-gu,
Changwon, Geyongsangnam, Korea
(South) **(100%)**
Tel.: (82) 55 290 8000
Web Site: http://www.knbank.co.kr
Sales Range: $100-124.9 Million
Emp.: 2,686
Commercial Bank
N.A.I.C.S.: 522110
Gyo-Duk Son *(CEO)*

BNN TECHNOLOGY PLC

First Floor Mallory House Goosetrey
Way, Knutsford, WA16 7GY, Cheshire, United Kingdom
Tel.: (44) 156 587 2990
Web Site:
http://www.bnntechnology.com
Sales Range: $1-9.9 Million
Gambling Software
N.A.I.C.S.: 513210

BNP PARIBAS SA

16 boulevard des Italiens, 75009,
Paris, France
Tel.: (33) 142981234   FR
Web Site: https://group.bnpparibas
Year Founded: 2000
BNPQF—(OTCQX)
Rev.: $58,502,299,440
Assets: $3,274,949,658,240
Liabilities: $3,119,509,745,040
Net Worth: $155,439,913,200
Earnings: $13,015,659,280
Fiscal Year-end: 12/31/22
Financial Investment Services
N.A.I.C.S.: 551111
Yann Gerardin *(COO-Institutional
Banking & Corp)*

Subsidiaries:

Ace Leasing BV **(1)**
Hambakenwetering 4, 's-Hertogenbosch,
5231 DC, Netherlands
Tel.: (31) 73 5118667
Securities Brokerage Services
N.A.I.C.S.: 523150

Agrilease BV **(1)**
Hambakenwetering 4, 's-Hertogenbosch,
5231 DC, Netherlands
Tel.: (31) 73 6399437
Web Site:
http://www.leasingsolutions.bnpparibas.nl
Sales Range: $50-74.9 Million
Emp.: 70
Consumer Lending Services
N.A.I.C.S.: 522291
Raf Ramaekers *(Gen Mgr)*

Albury Asset Rentals Ltd. **(1)**
Northern Cross, Basingstoke, RG21 4HL,
Hampshire, United Kingdom
Tel.: (44) 1256 377176
Financial Planning Services
N.A.I.C.S.: 523940

All In One Vermietung GmbH **(1)**
Vordere Zollamtsstrasse 13, 1030, Vienna,
Austria
Tel.: (43) 127158000
Web Site: http://www.bnpparibas.at
Financial Lending Services
N.A.I.C.S.: 522220

Amanda Storesenter AS **(1)**
Longhammarveien AS 5536, Haugesund,
Norway
Tel.: (47) 52 71 97 00
Web Site: http://www.amanda.no
Shopping Mall Operator
N.A.I.C.S.: 531120

Arius SA **(1)**
12 Rue du Port, 92000, Nanterre, France
Tel.: (33) 155697000
Web Site:
http://www.technology.rentalsolutions.fr
Software Development Services
N.A.I.C.S.: 541511

Artegy Ltd. **(1)**
5 Ohio Avenue Central Park Salford Quays,
M50 2GT, Manchester, United Kingdom -
England
Tel.: (44) 8452 666010
Web Site: http://www.artegy.co.uk
Truck Rental & Leasing Services
N.A.I.C.S.: 532120

Artegy SAS **(1)**
46 Rue Arago, 92800, Puteaux, France
Tel.: (33) 1 30 14 94 00
Truck Rental & Leasing Services
N.A.I.C.S.: 532120

Artigiancassa Spa **(1)**
Via Cristoforo Colombo 283/A, 00147,

BNP Paribas SA—(Continued)

Rome, Italy
Tel.: (39) 0658451
Web Site: http://www.artigiancassa.it
Financial Institution
N.A.I.C.S.: 522110

Arval AB **(1)**
Vendevagen 89, 182 32, Danderyd, Sweden
Tel.: (46) 87998890
Web Site: http://www.arval.se
Vehicle Leasing Services
N.A.I.C.S.: 532112

Arval AS **(1)**
Gjerdrums Vei 4, 0484, Oslo, Norway
Tel.: (47) 23007070
Web Site: https://www.arval.no
N.A.I.C.S.: 532112

Arval Brasil Ltda **(1)**
Rua Joaquim Floriano 960 9 andar Bibi,
04534-004, Itaim, Brazil
Tel.: (55) 1122468080
Web Site: http://www.arvalbrasil.com.br
Emp.: 170
Vehicle Leasing Services
N.A.I.C.S.: 532112

Arval OY **(1)**
Karhumaentie 3, 1530, Vantaa, Finland
Tel.: (358) 982541234
Vehicle Leasing Services
N.A.I.C.S.: 532112

Arval Service Lease Aluger Operational Automoveis SA
Rua Dr Antonio Loureiro Borges Edificio 5
Piso 4 Miraflores, 1495-131, Alges, Portugal
Tel.: (351) 214709400
Vehicle Leasing Services
N.A.I.C.S.: 532112

Arval Service Lease Romania SRL **(1)**
Gheorghe Titeica Nr 212-214 Sector 2,
020305, Bucharest, Romania
Tel.: (40) 212060300
Vehicle Leasing Services
N.A.I.C.S.: 532112
Bogdan Carp (Dir-Ops)

Arval Service Lease SA **(1)**
1 Boulevard Haussmann, Paris, 75009,
France
Tel.: (33) 1 57 69 50 00
Web Site: http://www.arval.fr
Passenger Car Leasing Services
N.A.I.C.S.: 532112

Subsidiary (Non-US):

Arval Austria GmbH **(2)**
Austria Campus Am Tabor 44 Top 3 02 C,
1020, Vienna, Austria **(100%)**
Tel.: (43) 170698200
Web Site: http://www.arval.at
Sales Range: $50-74.9 Million
Emp.: 35
Long Term Vehicle Rental Company for
Businesses
N.A.I.C.S.: 532120
Kalman Tekse (Gen Mgr)

Arval Benelux BV **(2)**
Duwboot 10, Houten, 3991 CD, Netherlands
Tel.: (31) 306 02 44 44
Web Site: http://www.arval.nl
Sales Range: $75-99.9 Million
Emp.: 200
Car Lending Services
N.A.I.C.S.: 532112

Subsidiary (Domestic):

Arval B.V. **(3)**
Duwboot 10, 3991 CD, Houten, Netherlands
(100%)
Tel.: (31) 306024444
Web Site: http://www.arval.nl
Sales Range: $75-99.9 Million
Emp.: 190
Long Term Vehicle Rental Company for
Businesses
N.A.I.C.S.: 532120

Subsidiary (Non-US):

Arval Belgium **(3)**

Ikaroslaan 99, 1930, Zaventem,
Belgium **(100%)**
Tel.: (32) 22400199
Web Site: http://www.arval.be
Sales Range: $75-99.9 Million
Emp.: 240
Long Term Vehicle Rental Company for
Businesses
N.A.I.C.S.: 532120

Arval Luxembourg **(3)**
2 Rue Nicolas Bove, 1253, Luxembourg,
Luxembourg **(100%)**
Tel.: (352) 4491801
Web Site: http://www.arval.lu
Sales Range: $25-49.9 Million
Emp.: 20
Long Term Vehicle Rental Company for
Businesses
N.A.I.C.S.: 532120

Subsidiary (Non-US):

Arval CZ s.r.o. **(2)**
Milevska 2095/5, 140 00, Prague, Czech
Republic
Tel.: (420) 261109109
Web Site: http://www.arval.cz
Car Leasing & Fleet Management Services
N.A.I.C.S.: 532112

Arval Deutschland GmbH **(2)**
Bajuwarenring 5, 82041, Oberhaching,
Germany **(100%)**
Tel.: (49) 89 74423 0
Web Site: http://www.arval.de
Sales Range: $300-349.9 Million
Emp.: 150
Automotive Sales Financing & Leasing Services
N.A.I.C.S.: 522220

Subsidiary (Domestic):

Arval Service GmbH **(3)**
Kuhnehofe 3, Hamburg, 22761, Germany
Tel.: (49) 40853500
Passenger Car Rental Services
N.A.I.C.S.: 532111

Subsidiary (Domestic):

Arval ECL SAS **(2)**
119/121 Grand Rue, 92318, Sevres, France
Tel.: (33) 141141818
Automobile Rental Services
N.A.I.C.S.: 532120

Arval France **(2)**
119 121 Grande Rue, F 92320, Sevres,
France **(100%)**
Tel.: (33) 141145728
Web Site: http://www.arvalphh.fr
Sales Range: $75-99.9 Million
Emp.: 250
Long Term Vehicle Rental Company for
Businesses
N.A.I.C.S.: 532120

Subsidiary (Non-US):

Arval India Private Ltd. **(2)**
BNP Paribas House 1 North Avenue Maker
Maxity Bandra Kurla Complex, Bandra East,
Mumbai, 400 051, India
Tel.: (91) 22 6196 4100
Web Site: http://www.arval.in
Sales Range: $50-74.9 Million
Emp.: 60
Commercial Car Leasing Services
N.A.I.C.S.: 532112

Arval Magyarorszag Kft. **(2)**
Bocskai ut 134-146, 1113, Budapest, Hungary
Tel.: (36) 1 279 3300
Web Site: http://www.arval.hu
Sales Range: $25-49.9 Million
Emp.: 35
Automobile Leasing Services
N.A.I.C.S.: 532120

Arval Maroc **(2)**
Zenith Millenium Sidi Maarouf Lotissement
Taoufik - Imm 3/4, 20190, Casablanca, Morocco
Tel.: (212) 522879800
Web Site: http://www.arval.ma
Emp.: 70
Automotive Financial Leasing Services
N.A.I.C.S.: 522220

Arval OOO **(2)**
Leninskaya Sloboda 26 BC Simonov Plaza
5th Floor, 115280, Moscow, Russia
Tel.: (7) 4956442270
Web Site: http://www.arval.ru
Vehicle Leasing Services
N.A.I.C.S.: 532120

**Arval PHH Service Lease CZ
s.r.o** **(2)**
Na Pankraci 1683/127, Prague, 140 00,
Czech Republic
Tel.: (420) 261109011
Sales Range: $50-74.9 Million
Emp.: 85
Automobile Leasing Services
N.A.I.C.S.: 532112
Arnault Leglay (Mng Dir)

Branch (Non-US):

Arval Portugal **(2)**
Rua Dr Antonio Loureiro Borges Edificio 5
Piso 4, Miraflores, 1495-131, Alges,
Portugal **(100%)**
Tel.: (351) 214709400
Web Site: http://www.arval.pt
Sales Range: $50-74.9 Million
Emp.: 60
Long Term Vehicle Rental Services for Businesses & Fleet Services
N.A.I.C.S.: 532120

Subsidiary (Non-US):

Arval Schweiz AG **(2)**
Suurstoffi 22, 6343, Rotkreuz,
Switzerland **(100%)**
Tel.: (41) 7483700
Web Site: http://www.arval.ch
Sales Range: $50-74.9 Million
Emp.: 60
Long Term Vehicle Rental Company for
Businesses
N.A.I.C.S.: 532120

Arval Service Lease Italia S.p.A. **(2)**
Via Sette Regole 21, 50018, Scandicci,
Firenze, Italy **(100%)**
Tel.: (39) 05573701
Web Site: http://www.arval.it
Provider of Corporate Long Term Vehicle
Rental Services
N.A.I.C.S.: 532120

**Arval Service Lease Polska Sp. z
o.o.** **(2)**
ul Woloska 24, 02-675, Warsaw, Poland
Tel.: (48) 224545500
Web Site: http://www.arval.pl
Sales Range: $50-74.9 Million
Emp.: 120
Long Term Vehicle Rental Company for
Businesses
N.A.I.C.S.: 532120

Arval Service Lease, S.A. **(2)**
Edificio Louis Pasteur Avenida del Juncal
22-24 PI 9, 28703, San Sebastian de los
Reyes, Madrid, Spain **(100%)**
Tel.: (34) 919100744
Web Site: http://www.arval.es
Sales Range: $75-99.9 Million
Emp.: 240
Long Term Vehicle Rental Company for
Businesses
N.A.I.C.S.: 532120

Arval Slovakia, s.r.o. **(2)**
Pribinova 19, 811 09, Bratislava, Slovakia
Tel.: (421) 2 5710 8000
Web Site: http://www.arval.sk
Sales Range: $50-74.9 Million
Emp.: 55
Passenger Car Leasing Services
N.A.I.C.S.: 532112

Subsidiary (Domestic):

Arval Trading SAS **(2)**
La Ravoire, 74370, Metz-Tessy, France
Tel.: (33) 4 78 66 51 85
Web Site: http://www.arvaltrading.com
Sales Range: $25-49.9 Million
Emp.: 35
New & Used Car Dealer
N.A.I.C.S.: 441110

Subsidiary (Non-US):

Arval UK Ltd. **(2)**

Whitehill House Windmill Hill Business Park
Whitehill Way, Swindon, SN5 6PE, United
Kingdom **(100%)**
Tel.: (44) 370 419 7000
Web Site: http://www.arval.co.uk
Long Term Vehicle Rental Company for
Businesses
N.A.I.C.S.: 532120

Atelier Services **(1)**
1 Boulevard Haussmann, 75009, Paris,
France **(98.5%)**
Web Site: http://www.atelier.fr
Minority Holdings Manager for Quoted
Companies on the French Stock Exchange
N.A.I.C.S.: 551112
Xavier Parizot (Project Mgr)

Auguste Thouard Expertise, SAS **(1)**
28/32 Rue Jacques Ibert, Levallois-Perret,
92300, France
Tel.: (33) 1 47 59 20 00
Web Site: http://www.auguste-thouard.fr
Real Estate Manangement Services
N.A.I.C.S.: 531390

Autovalley, SAS **(1)**
1 Rue des Bordes, Bondoufle, 91070,
Paris, France
Tel.: (33) 969397059
Web Site: http://www.autovalley.fr
New & Used Car Dealer
N.A.I.C.S.: 441110

B*capital **(1)**
16 Rue De Hanovre, 75009, Paris,
France **(100%)**
Tel.: (33) 140175000
Web Site: http://www.b-capital.com
Sales Range: $100-124.9 Million
Emp.: 214
Stock Brokerage
N.A.I.C.S.: 523150
Biraud Frederic (Mgr)

Subsidiary (Domestic):

**Portzamparc societe de Bourse
S.A.** **(2)**
13 Rue De La Brasserie, Nantes, 44100,
France
Tel.: (33) 240449400
Web Site: http://www.portzamparc.fr
Securities Brokerage Services
N.A.I.C.S.: 523150

BCI Mer Rouge **(1)**
Place lagarde, BP 2122, Djibouti,
Djibouti **(51%)**
Tel.: (253) 21350857
Web Site: http://www.bcimr.dj
Sales Range: $100-124.9 Million
Emp.: 235
Commericial Banking
N.A.I.C.S.: 522110

**BGZ BNPP Faktoring Spolka z
o.o.** **(1)**
ul M Kasprzaka 2, 01-211, Warsaw, Poland
Tel.: (48) 223477766
Web Site: http://faktoring.bnpparibas.pl
Banking Services
N.A.I.C.S.: 522110

BICI-BAIL de Cote d'Ivoire **(1)**
Avenue Franchet d'Esperey, BP 01, 1298,
Abidjan, Cote d'Ivoire
Tel.: (225) 2720242424
Web Site: http://www.bicici.com
Sales Range: $25-49.9 Million
Emp.: 24
Provider of Leasing Services
N.A.I.C.S.: 561330

BNL Finance SPA **(1)**
Viale Altiero Spinelli 30, 00157, Rome, RM,
Italy
Tel.: (39) 0803373910
Web Site: http://www.bnlfinance.it
Financial Services
N.A.I.C.S.: 522320
Erminio Di Iorio (Gen Mgr)

BNP Factor - Portugal **(1)**
Edificio Urbo Rua Henrique Pousao n 900
5, Snehora Hora, 4460-191, Porto,
Portugal **(95%)**
Tel.: (351) 226191600
Web Site: http://factor.bnpparibas.pt
Sales Range: $50-74.9 Million
Emp.: 30
Factoring Services

N.A.I.C.S.: 522299

BNP Jersey Trust Corp. Limited (1)
BNP House Anley Street, PO Box 158,
Saint Helier, JE4 8RD, Jersey (100%)
Tel.: (44) 1534815200
Trust Services
N.A.I.C.S.: 523991

BNP Pacific (Australia) Ltd. (1)
60 Castlereagh St, Sydney, 2000, NSW,
Australia
Tel.: (61) 2 9216 8633
Commercial Banking Services
N.A.I.C.S.: 522110

BNP Paribas (Canada) (1)
2001 Robert-Bourassa boulevard, Montreal,
H3A 2A6, QC, Canada
Tel.: (514) 285-6000
Web Site: http://www.bnpparibas.ca
Sales Range: $100-124.9 Million
Emp.: 1,200
Provider of Banking Services
N.A.I.C.S.: 522320

BNP Paribas (Canada) Inc. (1)
2001 Robert-Bourassa Avenue, Montreal,
H3A 2W8, QC, Canada
Tel.: (514) 285-6000
Web Site: http://www.bnpparibas.ca
Sales Range: $200-249.9 Million
Emp.: 275
Banking Services
N.A.I.C.S.: 522299
Michel Allen (Mng Dir)

BNP Paribas (China) Ltd. (1)
25F Shanghai World Financial Center 100
Century Avenue, Pudong New Area, Shang-
hai, 200120, China
Tel.: (86) 2128962666
Web Site: http://china.bnpparibas.com
Commercial Banking & Financial Advisory
Services
N.A.I.C.S.: 522110

BNP Paribas (Suisse) SA (1)
Place de Hollande 2, Case Postale, 1211,
Geneva, Switzerland (99%)
Tel.: (41) 582122111
Web Site: http://www.bnpparibas.ch
Sales Range: $700-749.9 Million
Emp.: 1,500
International Banking Services
N.A.I.C.S.: 523150
Jean Clamon (Chm)

Branch (Non-US):

BNP Paribas Suisse S.A. (2)
Trafalgar Court Admiral Park, PO Box 224,
Saint Peter Port, GY1 3NU,
Guernsey (100%)
Tel.: (44) 1481712171
Web Site: http://www.bnpparibas.ch
Sales Range: $50-74.9 Million
Emp.: 4
International & Offshore Banking Services
N.A.I.C.S.: 522299

**BNP Paribas - Mexico Representative
Office** (1)
Av Paseo de las Palmas 425 piso 14 Col,
Lomas de Chapultepec, 11000, Mexico, DF,
Mexico
Tel.: (52) 55 5003 9400
Web Site: http://www.bnpparibas.com.mx
Corporate & Investment Banking
N.A.I.C.S.: 522110
Edith Aviles (Head-Country-Mexico & Head-
Regional-Hispanic Latin America)

BNP Paribas - South East Asia (1)
20 Collyer Quay 01-01, Singapore, 049319,
Singapore (100%)
Tel.: (65) 62101288
Web Site: http://www.bnpparibas.com.sg
Sales Range: $700-749.9 Million
Emp.: 2,000
Full Service & International Banking Ser-
vices
N.A.I.C.S.: 522320

Subsidiary (Non-US):

BNP Paribas (Japan) Limited (2)
GranTokyo North Tower 1-9-1 Marunouchi,
Chiyoda-ku, Tokyo, 100-6741, Japan
Tel.: (81) 363771000
Web Site: http://www.bnpparibas.jp

Corporate, Institutional & International
Banking Services
N.A.I.C.S.: 522110

Subsidiary (Domestic):

**BNP Paribas Securities (Japan)
Limited** (3)
GranTokyo North Tower 1-9-1 Marunouchi,
Chiyoda-ku, Tokyo, 100-6740, Japan
Tel.: (81) 363772000
Web Site: http://www.bnpparibas.jp
Sales Range: $50-74.9 Million
Emp.: 700
Investment Banking Services
N.A.I.C.S.: 523150

Subsidiary (Domestic):

**BNP Paribas (Singapore) Pte.
Ltd.** (2)
20 Collyer Quay 01-01, Singapore, 049319,
Singapore (100%)
Tel.: (65) 62101288
Web Site: http://www.bnpparibas.com.sg
Sales Range: $300-349.9 Million
Emp.: 2,000
Provider of Banking Services
N.A.I.C.S.: 522320
Pierre Veyres (CEO)

**BNP Paribas Asia Private
Banking** (2)
Level 35 Ocean Financial Centre, Singa-
pore, 049315, Singapore (100%)
Tel.: (65) 62103888
Web Site: http://www.bnpparibas.com.sg
Sales Range: $50-74.9 Million
Emp.: 100
Private Banking Services
N.A.I.C.S.: 522180

Subsidiary (Non-US):

BNP Paribas Bangkok (2)
990 Abdulrahim Place 29th Floor Rama 4
Road, Silom, Bangkok, 10500,
Thailand (100%)
Tel.: (66) 26598900
Web Site: http://www.bnpparibas.co.th
Sales Range: $50-74.9 Million
Emp.: 75
Offshore & Commercial Banking Services
N.A.I.C.S.: 522110

Subsidiary (Domestic):

BNP Paribas Peregrine Thailand (3)
29th Fl Abdulrahim Pl, Bangkok, 10500,
Thailand (100%)
Tel.: (66) 26361900
Web Site: http://www.bnpparibas.co.th
Sales Range: $50-74.9 Million
Emp.: 75
Investment Banking Services
N.A.I.C.S.: 523150
Richard Andre (Gen Mgr)

Subsidiary (Non-US):

BNP Paribas China Group (2)
2001 20/F China World Tower A 1 Jian-
guomenwai Avenue, Beijing, 100004,
China (100%)
Tel.: (86) 1065350888
Web Site: http://china.bnpparibas.com
Banking Services
N.A.I.C.S.: 522320

Subsidiary (Domestic):

BNP Paribas Beijing (3)
2001 20/F China World Tower A 1 Jian-
guomenwai Avenue, Beijing, 100004,
China (100%)
Tel.: (86) 1065350888
Web Site: http://china.bnpparibas.com
Sales Range: $50-74.9 Million
Emp.: 50
Provider of Banking Services; Joint Venture
of BNP Paribas (50%) & Industrial & Com-
mercial Bank of China (50%)
N.A.I.C.S.: 522320

BNP Paribas Guangzhou (3)
RM10-11 48F CTF Finance Centre No 6
Zhujiang East Roa, Tianhe District,
Guangzhou, 510623, Guangdong, China
Tel.: (86) 2038139233
Web Site: http://www.bnpparibas.com.cn

Retail & International Banking Services
N.A.I.C.S.: 522299

Subsidiary (Non-US):

BNP Paribas Hong Kong (3)
63/F Two IFC 8 Finance Street, Central,
China (Hong Kong) (100%)
Tel.: (852) 29098888
Web Site: http://www.bnpparibas.com.hk
Sales Range: $700-749.9 Million
Emp.: 1,500
Retail & International Banking Services
N.A.I.C.S.: 522320

BNP Paribas Macau (3)
61 Avda Almeida Ribeiro Central Plaza 5
andar C, Macau, China (Macau) (100%)
Tel.: (853) 28562777
Web Site: http://bank.bnpparibas.com
Sales Range: $1-9.9 Million
Emp.: 100
Retail & International Banking Services
N.A.I.C.S.: 522110
Sanco Sze (Branch Mgr)

BNP Paribas Peregrine (3)
63rd Fl 2 Intl Fin Ctr 8 Finance St, Central,
China (Hong Kong) (100%)
Tel.: (852) 29098888
Web Site: http://www.bnpparibas.com.hk
Sales Range: $700-749.9 Million
Emp.: 1,200
Fund Management & Investment Advice
N.A.I.C.S.: 523940

Subsidiary (Domestic):

BNP Paribas Shanghai (3)
25F Shanghai World Financial Center 100
Century Avenue, Pudong New Area, Shang-
hai, 200120, China (100%)
Tel.: (86) 2128962666
Web Site: http://www.bnpparibas.com.cn
Retail & International Banking Services
N.A.I.C.S.: 522299

Subsidiary (Non-US):

BNP Paribas South Korea (2)
24F and 25F State Tower Namsan 100
Toegye-ro Hoehyeon-dong 2-ga, Jung-gu,
Seoul, 04631, Korea (South) (100%)
Tel.: (82) 23171700
Web Site: http://www.bnpparibas.co.kr
Sales Range: $50-74.9 Million
Emp.: 100
Banking Services
N.A.I.C.S.: 522320

BNP Paribas Sydney (2)
60 Castlereagh Street, Sydney, 2000,
NSW, Australia (100%)
Tel.: (61) 292168633
Web Site: http://www.bnpparibas.com.au
Sales Range: $300-349.9 Million
Emp.: 750
Corporate, Institutional & Retail Banking
Services
N.A.I.C.S.: 522320

BNP Paribas Taiwan (2)
71-72/F Taipei 101 Tower 7 Xin Yi Road
Sec 5, Taipei, 110, Taiwan (100%)
Tel.: (886) 287583101
Web Site: http://www.bnpparibas.com.tw
Emp.: 200
Retail & International Banking Services
N.A.I.C.S.: 522110

**BNP Paribas-Manila Offshore
Branch** (2)
30th Fl Philamlife Tower, PO Box 2265
MCPO, 8767 Paseo De Roxas, 1262,
Makati, 1262, Philippines
Tel.: (63) 28148730
Web Site: http://www.bnpparibas.com.ph
Sales Range: $50-74.9 Million
Emp.: 12
Offshore Banking Services
N.A.I.C.S.: 522299
Peter Labrie (Head-Territory)

Subsidiary (Domestic):

**BNP Prime Peregrine (Securities)
PTE Ltd.** (2)
20 Collyer Quay 01 01 Tung Centre, 49319,
Singapore, Singapore (100%)
Tel.: (65) 62101288
Web Site: http://www.bnpparibas.com.sg

Sales Range: $50-74.9 Million
Emp.: 100
International Security & Investment Services
N.A.I.C.S.: 523940

Subsidiary (Non-US):

Cardif Societe Vie Taiwan (2)
18th Floor No 270, Chung Hsiao East
Road, 2nd Floor, 106, Taipei,
Taiwan (100%)
Tel.: (886) 266363456
Web Site: http://www.tw.cardif.com
Sales Range: $50-74.9 Million
Emp.: 100
Insurance & Finance Services
N.A.I.C.S.: 524298

PT Bank BNP Paribas Indonesia (2)
Sequis Tower Level 28 Jl Jendral Sudirman
Kav 71 SCBD Lot 11B, Jakarta, 12190,
Indonesia (100%)
Tel.: (62) 2150814789
Web Site: http://www.bnpparibas.co.id
Sales Range: $25-49.9 Million
Emp.: 50
Commercial Banking Services for Large In-
donesian Companies & Multinationals
N.A.I.C.S.: 522110

Subsidiary (Domestic):

BNP Paribas Peregrine (3)
Menara Batavia 20th Floor, Jl KH Mas Man-
syur Kav 126, Jakarta, 10220,
Indonesia (100%)
Tel.: (62) 2157900500
Web Site: http://www.bnpparibas.co.id
Sales Range: $50-74.9 Million
Emp.: 25
Capital Markets Products
N.A.I.C.S.: 523910

Bank BNP Lippo Utama Leasing (3)
Menara Batavia 20th Fl, PO Box 1655, Jl
KH Mas Mansyur Kav 126, Jakarta, 10220,
Indonesia (100%)
Tel.: (62) 215722288
Web Site: http://www.bnpparibas.co.id
Long Term Finance Facilities
N.A.I.C.S.: 522299

BNP Paribas Abu Dhabi (1)
Etihad Tower-3 Level 12 Unit 1201 & 1206,
PO Box 2742, Abu Dhabi, United Arab
Emirates (100%)
Tel.: (971) 26938888
Web Site: http://mea.bnpparibas.com
Retail, Commercial & Corporate Banking
Services
N.A.I.C.S.: 522110

BNP Paribas Andes (1)
Avenida Caraval y Moreyra 380 Piso 11,
San Isidro, 27, Lima, Peru (99.99%)
Tel.: (51) 1 215 1700
Sales Range: $50-74.9 Million
Emp.: 28
Retail & International Banking Services
N.A.I.C.S.: 522320

BNP Paribas Antilles Guyane SA (1)
72 Avenue des Caraibes, Fort-de-France,
Martinique
Tel.: (596) 808800301
Banking Services
N.A.I.C.S.: 522110

BNP Paribas Arbitrage (1)
8 Rue De Sofia, 75018, Paris,
France (100%)
Tel.: (33) 140142299
Web Site: http://www.bnp.com
Sales Range: $350-399.9 Million
Emp.: 700
Arbitrage
N.A.I.C.S.: 523999

BNP Paribas Argentina (1)
Bouchard 547 piso 26, 1106, Buenos Aires,
Argentina (100%)
Tel.: (54) 1148754300
Web Site: http://www.bnpparibas.com.ar
Sales Range: $200-249.9 Million
Emp.: 280
Corporate & International Banking Services
N.A.I.C.S.: 522320

**BNP Paribas Asset Management
Holding SA** (1)

BNP Paribas SA—(Continued)

1 Boulevard Haussmann, 75009, Paris,
France
Tel.: (33) 158972525
Asset Management Services
N.A.I.C.S.: 523940

BNP Paribas Asset Management Luxembourg S.A. (1)
10 Rue Edward Steichen, 2540, Luxembourg, Luxembourg
Tel.: (352) 26463121
Asset Management Services
N.A.I.C.S.: 523940

BNP Paribas Asset Management S.A.S. (1)
1 Boulevard Haussmann, 75009, Paris,
France (100%)
Tel.: (33) 158972525
Web Site: http://www.bnpparibas-am.com
Sales Range: $1-4.9 Billion
Emp.: 3,000
Financial Services
N.A.I.C.S.: 522320
Sophie Lugiez (Head-Trading-Global)

Subsidiary (Non-US):

Alfred Berg Asset Management AB (2)
Nybrokajen 5, Po Box 70447, 107 25,
Stockholm, Sweden
Tel.: (46) 856234700
Web Site: http://www.alfredberg.com
Asset Management Services
N.A.I.C.S.: 523940
Vincent Marie Den Trouillard-Perrot (Mgr)

Subsidiary (Domestic):

Alfred Berg Fonder AB (3)
Nybrokajen 5, Po Box 70447, 107 25,
Stockholm, Sweden
Tel.: (46) 856234700
Web Site: http://www.alfredberg.se
Investment Management Service
N.A.I.C.S.: 523940

Subsidiary (Non-US):

Alfred Berg Forvaltning AS (3)
Olav V's gate 5, Oslo, 0161, Norway
Tel.: (47) 22005100
Web Site: http://www.alfredberg.no
Emp.: 40
Asset Management Services
N.A.I.C.S.: 523940

Subsidiary (Domestic):

Alfred Berg Kapitalforvaltning AB (3)
Nybrokajen 5, Po Box 70447, 107 25,
Stockholm, Sweden
Tel.: (46) 856234700
Web Site: http://www.alfredberg.com
Sales Range: $50-74.9 Million
Emp.: 70
Financial Investment Services
N.A.I.C.S.: 523999

Subsidiary (Non-US):

Alfred Berg Kapitalforvaltning AS (3)
Munkedamsveien 35 4 Etg, Po Box 1294,
Vika, 0250, Oslo, Norway
Tel.: (47) 22 00 51 00
Web Site: http://www.alfredberg.no
Investment Management Service
N.A.I.C.S.: 523940

Alfred Berg Kapitalforvaltning Finland AB (3)
Keskuskatu 1 B, Helsinki, 100, Finland
Tel.: (358) 9228321
Web Site: http://www.alfredberg.com
Emp.: 22
Investment Management Service
N.A.I.C.S.: 523940
Sami Vartiainen (Gen Mgr)

Subsidiary (Non-US):

BNP Paribas Asset Management (2)
Level 6 60 Castlereagh Street, Sydney,
2000, NSW, Australia (100%)
Tel.: (61) 296196291
Web Site: http://www.bnpparibas.com.au

Sales Range: $50-74.9 Million
Emp.: 9
Fund Management
N.A.I.C.S.: 523940
Sandro Pierri (Head-Client Grp-Global)

Subsidiary (US):

BNP Paribas Asset Management Inc. (2)
200 Park Ave, New York, NY 10166
Tel.: (212) 681-3180
Web Site: http://www.am.bnpparibas.com
Rev.: $720,000
Emp.: 120
Investment & Asset Management Services
N.A.I.C.S.: 523940
Philip Dawes (Head-Institutional Sls-UK &
Ireland)

Subsidiary (Non-US):

BNP Paribas Investment Partners (Hong Kong) Limited (3)
17/F Lincoln House Taikoo Place 979 King's
Road, Quarry Bay, China (Hong Kong)
Tel.: (852) 2533 0000
Web Site: http://www.bnpparibas.com.hk
Emp.: 100
Asset Management & Investment Banking
Services
N.A.I.C.S.: 523940

Subsidiary (Domestic):

BNP Paribas Investment Partners - Boston (3)
75 State St 6th Fl, Boston, MA 02109
Tel.: (617) 478-7200
Web Site: http://www.bnpparibas-ip.com
Sales Range: $75-99.9 Million
Emp.: 60
Asset Management & Investment Banking
Services
N.A.I.C.S.: 523940

Fischer, Francis, Trees & Watts, Inc. (3)
200 Park Ave 46th Fl, New York, NY
10166 (100%)
Tel.: (212) 681-3000
Web Site: http://www.fftw.com
Sales Range: $75-99.9 Million
Emp.: 120
Fixed Income Investment Portfolio Management Services
N.A.I.C.S.: 523940
Dominick DeAlto (Head-Global Multi Sector
Fixed Income)

Subsidiary (Non-US):

BNP Paribas Asset Management India Private Ltd (2)
BNP Paribas House 1 North Avenue Maker
Maxity Bandra Kurla Complex, Bandra E,
Mumbai, 400 051, India
Tel.: (91) 22 3370 4000
Web Site: http://www.bnpparibasmf.in
Asset Management Services
N.A.I.C.S.: 523940
Anand Shah (CIO)

BNP Paribas Investment Partners Asia Limited (2)
30/F Three Exchange Square, 8 Connaught
Place, Central, China (Hong Kong)
Tel.: (852) 2533 0000
Web Site: http://www.bnpparibas-ip.com.hk
Fund Management & Investment Advice
N.A.I.C.S.: 523940
Tan Feng Cheng (Mng Dir & Head-Greater
China Bus)

Subsidiary (Non-US):

BNP Paribas Asset Management Singapore Limited (3)
20 Collyer Quay Ste 01-01 Tung Ctr, Singapore, 049319, Singapore
Tel.: (65) 62101288
Investment & Asset Management Services
N.A.I.C.S.: 523940
Mark Speciale (Head-Institutional Sls-Asia
Pacific)

Affiliate (Non-US):

Fortis Haitong Investment Management Co., Ltd. (3)

36-37 Floor Bank of East Asia Tower 66
Hua Yuan Shi Qiao Road, Pudong, Shanghai, 200120, China (49%)
Tel.: (86) 21 3865 0999
Web Site: http://www.hftfund.com
Investment Fund Management Services
N.A.I.C.S.: 523940

Subsidiary (Non-US):

PT BNP Paribas Investment Partners (3)
World Trade Center Building 5th Floor, Jl
Jend Sudirman Kav 29-31, Jakarta, 12920,
Indonesia
Tel.: (62) 212521574
Web Site: http://www.bnpparibas-ip.co.id
Sales Range: $50-74.9 Million
Emp.: 55
Investment Fund Asset Management Services
N.A.I.C.S.: 523940
Vivian Secakusuma (Dir-Mktg)

Subsidiary (Domestic):

PT ABN AMRO Manajemen Investasi (4)
Jakarta Stock Exchange Building Tower 2
11th Floor, Jl Jend Sudirman Kav 52-53,
Jakarta, 12190, Indonesia
Tel.: (62) 215156000
Asset Management & Investment Banking
Services
N.A.I.C.S.: 523940

Subsidiary (Non-US):

BNP Paribas Investment Partners Japan Ltd. (2)
Grand Tokyo North Tower 1-9-1
Marunouchi, Chiyoda-ku, Tokyo, 100-6742,
Japan (100%)
Tel.: (81) 3 6377 2800
Web Site: http://www.bnpparibas.jp
Sales Range: $25-49.9 Million
Emp.: 39
Establishment & Management of Mutual
Funds
N.A.I.C.S.: 523940
Daisuke Toki (CEO)

Division (Domestic):

BNP Paribas Private Equity (2)
14 rue Bergere, 75009, Paris,
France (100%)
Tel.: (33) 1 5897 2525
Web Site: http://www.bnppe.com
Privater Equity Firm
N.A.I.C.S.: 523999
Jean-Marc Rivet-Fusil (Head-Funds Mgmt)

Subsidiary (Non-US):

Roadchef Motorways Ltd (2)
Roadchef House Norton Canes MSA Bettys
Lane, Norton Canes, Cannock, WS11 9UX,
Staffordshire, United Kingdom
Tel.: (44) 1543 272540
Web Site: http://www.roadchef.com
Sales Range: $350-399.9 Million
Emp.: 3,200
Motorway Restaurant Operating Services
N.A.I.C.S.: 722511
Simon Turl (CEO)

Joint Venture (Non-US):

SAIB BNP Paribas Asset Management Co., Ltd. (2)
PO Box 5556, Riyadh, 11432, Saudi Arabia
Tel.: (966) 14742121
Web Site: http://www.saibbnpp.com
Asset Management & Investment Services;
Owned by Saudi Investment Bank & by
BNP Paribas S.A.
N.A.I.C.S.: 523940

Shinhan BNP Paribas Asset Management Co., Ltd. (2)
GoodmorningShinhan-Tower 18th Floor
23-2 Yeouido-Dong, Yeongdeunpo-gu,
Seoul, Korea (South) (35%)
Tel.: (82) 2 767 5777
Web Site: http://www.shbnppam.com
Asset Management & Commercial Banking
Services
N.A.I.C.S.: 522110
Lee Chang-Goo (CEO)

TKB BNP Paribas Investment Partners JSC (2)
69/71 lit A Marata Street, 191119, Saint Petersburg, Russia (50%)
Tel.: (7) 8123327332
Web Site: http://www.tkbip.com
Emp.: 90
Investment Fund Asset Management Services
N.A.I.C.G.: 520040
Tanya Landwehr (CFO & Head-Comml Dev
& Intl Sls)

BNP Paribas Athens Branch (1)
Lampsakou 2, 115 28, Athens, Greece
Tel.: (30) 2107468500
Web Site: http://www.bnpparibas.gr
Sales Range: $50-74.9 Million
Emp.: 100
International Banking Services
N.A.I.C.S.: 522299

BNP Paribas BDDI Participations (1)
1 Boulevard Haussmann, 75009, Paris,
France
Tel.: (33) 8 20 82 00 01
Financial Planning Services
N.A.I.C.S.: 523940

BNP Paribas Bank JSC (1)
5 Lesnaya str building B, 125047, Moscow,
Russia
Tel.: (7) 4957856000
Web Site: http://www.bnpparibas.ru
Representative Office
N.A.I.C.S.: 522299

BNP Paribas Bank Polska SA (1)
ul Kasprzaka 10/16, 01-211, Warsaw,
Poland (88.33%)
Tel.: (48) 228604400
Web Site: http://www.bnpparibas.pl
Rev.: $2,496,763,205
Assets: $40,911,012,853
Liabilities: $37,643,412,505
Net Worth: $3,267,600,347
Earnings: $257,252,540
Emp.: 8,101
Fiscal Year-end: 12/31/2023
Commercial Banking
N.A.I.C.S.: 522110
Jean-Paul Sabet (Vice Chm-Supervisory
Bd)

BNP Paribas Bulgaria EAD (1)
2 Tzar Osvoboditel Blvd, PO Box 11, 1000,
Sofia, Bulgaria (100%)
Tel.: (359) 70011004
Web Site: http://www.bnpparibas.bg
Sales Range: $50-74.9 Million
Emp.: 100
Banking Services
N.A.I.C.S.: 522299

BNP Paribas CMG Ltd. (1)
10 Harewood Avenue, London, NW1 6AA,
United Kingdom
Tel.: (44) 20 7595 2000
Web Site: http://www.bnpparibas.co.uk
Emp.: 1,000
Financial Management Services
N.A.I.C.S.: 523999

BNP Paribas Canada (1)
155 Wellington Street West Suite 3110, Toronto, M5V 3H1, ON, Canada (100%)
Tel.: (514) 285-6000
Web Site: http://www.bnpparibas.ca
Sales Range: $50-74.9 Million
Emp.: 1,200
International Banking Services
N.A.I.C.S.: 522299
Abhoy Vaidya (Mng Dir)

BNP Paribas Canada-Quebec (1)
925 Chemin St Louis Ste 350, Quebec,
G1S 1C1, QC, Canada (100%)
Tel.: (418) 684-7575
Web Site: http://www.bnpparibas.ca
Sales Range: $50-74.9 Million
Emp.: 3
Provider of Banking Services
N.A.I.C.S.: 523320

BNP Paribas Canada-Toronto (1)
155 Wellington Street West Suite 3110, Box
149, Toronto, M5V 3H1, ON,
Canada (100%)
Tel.: (514) 285-6000
Web Site: http://www.bnpparibas.ca

Sales Range: $50-74.9 Million
Emp.: 20
International Banking Services
N.A.I.C.S.: 522320
Anne Marie Verstraeten *(CEO)*

**BNP Paribas Capital (Asia Pacific)
Ltd.** **(1)**
63 F Two International Finance Centre,
Central, China (Hong Kong)
Tel.: (852) 28251888
Venture Capital Funding Services
N.A.I.C.S.: 523910
Christophe Cerisier *(Head-Loan Capital
Markets)*

**BNP Paribas Capital (Singapore)
Ltd.** **(1)**
20 Collyer Quay 01-01, Singapore, 049319,
Singapore
Tel.: (65) 6210 1288
Commercial Banking & Financial Services
N.A.I.C.S.: 522110

**BNP Paribas Capital Investments
Ltd.** **(1)**
33 Wigmore St, London, W1U 1QX, United
Kingdom
Tel.: (44) 2075954267
Capital Investment Services
N.A.I.C.S.: 523910

BNP Paribas Cardif SA **(1)**
8 rue du Port, 92728, Nanterre, Cedex,
France
Tel.: (33) 141428300
Web Site: http://www.bnpparibascardif.com
Rev.: $20,000,000,000
Emp.: 8,000
Holding Company; Insurance Products &
Services
N.A.I.C.S.: 551112
Jean-Bertrand Laroche *(Deputy COO-Intl
Markets)*

Branch (Non-US):

BNP Paribas Cardif - Portugal **(2)**
Torre Ocidente Rua Galileu Galilei N2 10B,
1500-392, Lisbon, Portugal
Tel.: (351) 213825540
Web Site: http://bnpparibascardif.pt
Sales Range: $50-74.9 Million
Emp.: 40
Personal insurance services
N.A.I.C.S.: 524113

Subsidiary (Non-US):

**BNP Paribas Cardif Emeklilik Anonim
Sirketi** **(2)**
Askerocagi Cad Suzer Plaza Kat 15 El-
madag, Sisli, 34367, Istanbul, Turkiye
Tel.: (90) 212 393 3000
Web Site: http://www.cardif.com.tr
Financial Management Services
N.A.I.C.S.: 523999

Branch (Non-US):

Cardif **(2)**
Hoevestein 28, 4903 SC, Oosterhout,
Netherlands **(100%)**
Tel.: (31) 162486000
Web Site: http://www.bnpparibascardif.nl
Sales Range: $300-349.9 Million
Emp.: 125
Insurance & Financing Services
N.A.I.C.S.: 524298

Cardif **(2)**
Rotenturmstrasse 16-18, 1010, Vienna,
Austria **(100%)**
Tel.: (43) 1533987883
Web Site: http://bnpparibascardif.at
Sales Range: $50-74.9 Million
Emp.: 15
Insurance & Finance Services
N.A.I.C.S.: 524298

Subsidiary (Non-US):

**Cardif Biztosito Magyarorszag
Zrt** **(2)**
Korhaz utca 6-12, 1033, Budapest, Hungary
Tel.: (36) 15012300
Web Site: http://www.bnpparibascardif.hu
General Insurance Services
N.A.I.C.S.: 524210

**Cardif Colombia Seguros Generales
S.A.** **(2)**
Calle 113 No 7-80, Bogota, Colombia
Tel.: (57) 1744 4040
General Insurance Services
N.A.I.C.S.: 524210

Cardif El Djazair, SPA **(2)**
Quartier D Affaires D Alger Lot 1 N I 03,
16024, Algiers, Algeria
Tel.: (213) 21995822
Insurance Services
N.A.I.C.S.: 327910

Branch (Non-US):

Cardif Germany **(2)**
Friolzheimer Str 6, 70499, Stuttgart,
Germany **(100%)**
Tel.: (49) 711820550
Web Site: http://www.cardif.de
Sales Range: $50-74.9 Million
Emp.: 100
Insurance & Financing Services
N.A.I.C.S.: 524298
Pierre-Olivier Brassart *(CEO)*

Subsidiary (Domestic):

Cardif I-Services **(2)**
1 Boulevard Haussmann, 75009, Paris,
France
Tel.: (33) 1 45 25 25 25
General Insurance Services
N.A.I.C.S.: 524210

Subsidiary (Non-US):

Cardif Lux Vie SA **(2)**
23-25 avenue de la Porte-Neuve, 2227,
Luxembourg, Luxembourg
Tel.: (352) 262141
Web Site: http://cardifluxvie.com
Insurance Services
N.A.I.C.S.: 524210

**Cardif Mexico Seguros de Vida SA
de CV** **(2)**
Avenida Paseo de las Palmas 425 Piso 5
Colonia, Lomas de Chapultepec, Mexico,
11000, Mexico
Tel.: (52) 55 2282 2000
Web Site:
http://www.bnpparibascardif.com.mx
General Insurance Services
N.A.I.C.S.: 524210

Cardif Polska S.A. **(2)**
Pl Pilsudskiego 2, 00-073, Warsaw,
Poland **(100%)**
Tel.: (48) 225290123
Web Site: http://cardif.pl
Sales Range: $50-74.9 Million
Emp.: 100
Insurance & Finance Services
N.A.I.C.S.: 524298

Branch (Non-US):

Cardif Spain **(2)**
C / Emilio Vargas n 4 Floor 3, 28043, Ma-
drid, Spain **(100%)**
Tel.: (34) 915903005
Web Site: http://bnpparibascardif.es
Sales Range: $50-74.9 Million
Emp.: 60
Insurance & Finance Services
N.A.I.C.S.: 524298

Cardif Vie & Cardif RD **(2)**
Chaussee de Mons 1424, Anderlecht, 1170,
Brussels, Belgium **(100%)**
Tel.: (32) 25280000
Web Site: http://www.cardif.be
Sales Range: $50-74.9 Million
Emp.: 16
Crop Insurance
N.A.I.C.S.: 524114

Subsidiary (Non-US):

Cardif Vita S.p.A. **(2)**
Piazza Lina Bo Bardi 3, 20124, Milan,
Italy **(100%)**
Tel.: (39) 02772241
Web Site: http://bnpparibascardif.it
Fire Insurance Services
N.A.I.C.S.: 524113

**Cardif del Peru Sa Compania de
Seguros** **(2)**

Av Enrique Canaval y Moreyra 380 Of
1101, Lima, Peru
Tel.: (51) 1 6151700
General Insurance Services
N.A.I.C.S.: 524210

Subsidiary (Domestic):

**Cardif-Assurances Risques Divers
S.A.** **(2)**
41 Ave Friedland, PO Box 366, 75367,
Paris, Cedex, France **(100%)**
Tel.: (33) 153538888
Web Site: http://www.cardif.fr
Sales Range: $600-649.9 Million
Emp.: 2,000
Wealth Management & Insurance Products
& Services
N.A.I.C.S.: 523991
Pierre de Villeneuve *(Chm & CEO)*

Branch (Non-US):

**Cardif-Assurances Risques Divers -
Italy** **(3)**
Piazza Lina Bo Bardi 3, 20124, Milan, Italy
Tel.: (39) 02772241
Web Site: http://bnpparibascardif.it
Insurance & Credit Services
N.A.I.C.S.: 812990

Subsidiary (Domestic):

GIE BNP Paribas Cardif S.A. **(2)**
1 Boulevard Haussmann, 75009, Paris,
France
Tel.: (33) 141428300
Web Site: http://www.bnpparibascardif.com
Emp.: 8,000
Creditor Insurance Products & Services
N.A.I.C.S.: 524128
Renaud Dumora *(Chm)*

Icare S.A. **(2)**
93 Rue Nationale, 92100, Boulogne-
Billancourt, France
Tel.: (33) 141101930
Web Site: http://www.icare-service.com
Sales Range: $75-99.9 Million
Emp.: 130
Holding Company; Automobile Insurance
Products & Services
N.A.I.C.S.: 551112
Pascal Briodin *(CEO & Mng Dir)*

Subsidiary (Domestic):

Icare Assurance S.A. **(3)**
93 rue Nationale, 92100, Boulogne-
Billancourt, France
Tel.: (33) 141101900
Web Site: http://www.icare-service.com
Automobile Insurance Products & Services
N.A.I.C.S.: 524126

BNP Paribas Columbia **(1)**
Carrera 7 No 77 07 Edificio Torre Siete 77
Piso 11, Bogota, Colombia
Tel.: (57) 12184097
Web Site: http://www.bnpparibas.com.co
Sales Range: $50-74.9 Million
Emp.: 7
Global Banking & Financial Services
N.A.I.C.S.: 522180

**BNP Paribas Commodity Futures
Ltd.** **(1)**
10 Harewood Avenue, London, NW1 6AA,
United Kingdom
Tel.: (44) 20 7595 2000
Investment Management Service
N.A.I.C.S.: 523940

BNP Paribas Developpement SA **(1)**
20 Rue Chauchat, 75009, Paris, France
Tel.: (33) 1 40 14 55 78
Private Equity Investment Services
N.A.I.C.S.: 523999
Delphine Larrandaburu *(Dir-Investments)*

Holding (Domestic):

Faure Herman SAS **(2)**
Route de Bonnetable, BP 20154, 72406, La
Ferte-Bernard, France
Tel.: (33) 243602860
Web Site: http://www.faureherman.com
Precision Flowmeters Measuring Liquid &
Gas Flows Mfr & Designer
N.A.I.C.S.: 334514

Subsidiary (US):

Faure Herman Meter, Inc. **(3)**
8280 Willow Pl Dr N Ste 150, Houston, TX
77040
Tel.: (713) 623-0808
Web Site: http://www.faureherman.com
Precision Flowmeters Measuring Liquid &
Gas Flows Mfr & Designer
N.A.I.C.S.: 423830

Joint Venture (Domestic):

Fondasol SA **(2)**
290 rue des Galoubets, 84035, Avignon,
Cedex, France
Tel.: (33) 490312396
Web Site: http://www.fondasol.fr
Sales Range: $50-74.9 Million
Emp.: 520
Environmental & Geotechnical Consulting
Services
N.A.I.C.S.: 541620
Hocine Akir *(Dir-Resource)*

BNP Paribas Dubai **(1)**
Twin Towers 19th Fl Beniyas Rd, PO Box
7233, Deira, Dubai, United Arab
Emirates **(100%)**
Tel.: (971) 42106767
Sales Range: $100-124.9 Million
Emp.: 120
Provider of Retail, Commercial & Corporate
Banking Services
N.A.I.C.S.: 522110

BNP Paribas Dublin **(1)**
5 George's Dock IFSC, Dublin, D01 X8N7,
Ireland **(100%)**
Tel.: (353) 16125000
Web Site: http://www.bnpparibas.ie
Sales Range: $100-124.9 Million
Emp.: 630
Retail & International Banking Services
N.A.I.C.S.: 522299
Derek Kehoe *(CEO & Head-Country)*

BNP Paribas E & B Ltd. **(1)**
10 Harewood Avenue, London, NW1 6AA,
United Kingdom
Tel.: (44) 2075952000
Financial Planning Services
N.A.I.C.S.: 523940

BNP Paribas El Djazair S.P.A. **(1)**
13 Rue Djamila, 16035, Hydra, Algeria
Tel.: (213) 21981366
Web Site: http://www.bnpparibas.dz
Commercial Banking Services
N.A.I.C.S.: 522110

**BNP Paribas Energy Trading Canada
Corp** **(1)**
335 8th Ave Sw Suite 1230, Calgary, T2P
1C9, AB, Canada
Tel.: (403) 691-8800
Sales Range: $25-49.9 Million
Emp.: 7
Natural Gas Transmission Services
N.A.I.C.S.: 486210

**BNP Paribas Equity Strategies
S.N.C.** **(1)**
41 Avenue de l'Opera, 75002, Paris, France
Tel.: (33) 8 20 82 00 01
Securities Brokerage Services
N.A.I.C.S.: 523150

BNP Paribas Espana S.A. **(1)**
c/ Hermanos Becquer 3, 28006, Madrid,
Spain **(99%)**
Tel.: (34) 913888900
Web Site: http://www.bnpparibas.es
Sales Range: $700-749.9 Million
Emp.: 4,300
Investment Banking
N.A.I.C.S.: 523150

BNP Paribas Factor **(1)**
Seine Way 12/14 rue Louis Bleriot, PO Box
10096, 92506, Rueil-Malmaison, Cedex,
France **(100%)**
Tel.: (33) 491396381
Web Site: http://factor.bnpparibas.com
Sales Range: $1-4.9 Billion
Emp.: 400
Factoring
N.A.I.C.S.: 522299
Patrick De Villepin *(Chm & Pres)*

BNP Paribas SA—(Continued)

BNP Paribas Fin AMS (1)
1 Boulevard Haussmann, 75009, Paris, France
Tel.: (33) 825334335
Financial Planning Services
N.A.I.C.S.: 523940

BNP Paribas Finance (Hong-Kong) Ltd. (1)
59-63/F Two Intl Finance Ctr, Central, China (Hong Kong)
Tel.: (852) 29098888
Investment Management Service
N.A.I.C.S.: 523940

BNP Paribas Finance PLC (1)
10 Harewood Ave, London, NW1 6AA, United Kingdom
Tel.: (44) 20 75952000
Financial Management Services
N.A.I.C.S.: 523999

BNP Paribas Fleet Holdings Ltd. (1)
Arval Centre, Swindon, SN5 6PE, Wiltshire, United Kingdom
Tel.: (44) 1793 887000
Investment Management Service
N.A.I.C.S.: 523940

BNP Paribas Fortis Funding SA (1)
Eugene Ruppert 19, Luxembourg, 2453, Luxembourg
Tel.: (352) 264 49 416
Web Site: http://www.bp2fu.lu
Emp.: 6
Commercial Banking Services
N.A.I.C.S.: 522110
Didier Giblet (Chm)

BNP Paribas Fortis SA/NV (1)
Montagne du Parc 3 / 1KB1D, B-1000, Brussels, Belgium (74.93%)
Tel.: (32) 25651111
Web Site: http://www.bnpparibasfortis.com
Rev.: $43,279,229,420
Assets: $350,734,552,700
Liabilities: $319,204,894,400
Net Worth: $31,529,658,300
Earnings: $2,931,793,480
Emp.: 13,443
Fiscal Year-end: 12/31/2019
Banking, Investment & Insurance Services
N.A.I.C.S.: 522110
Maxime Jadot (CEO & Chm-Exec Bd)

Subsidiary (Domestic):

Alpha Credit SA/NV (2)
Rue Ravenstein 60, PO Box 15, B-1000, Brussels, Belgium
Tel.: (32) 25080223
Web Site: http://www.acred.be
Sales Range: $50-74.9 Million
Emp.: 100
Consumer Credit Services
N.A.I.C.S.: 522390
Bart Vervenne (CEO)

Subsidiary (Non-US):

BGL BNP Paribas S.A. (2)
50 avenue JF Kennedy, 2951, Luxembourg, Luxembourg (65.96%)
Tel.: (352) 42421
Web Site: https://www.bnpparibas.lu
Personal, Commercial, Investment & Private Banking & Other Financial Services
N.A.I.C.S.: 522110

Subsidiary (Domestic):

ABN AMRO Bank (Luxembourg) S.A. (3)
46 Ave J F Kennedy, Luxembourg, 1855, Luxembourg (100%)
Tel.: (352) 26071
Private Banking
N.A.I.C.S.: 522299

Division (Domestic):

BGL Luxembourg (3)
10A Boulevard Royal, L-2093, Luxembourg, Luxembourg
Tel.: (352) 46461
Web Site: http://www.bgl.lu
Wealth Management & Private Banking Services
N.A.I.C.S.: 523991

Subsidiary (Non-US):

Societe Alsacienne de Developpement et d'Expansion S.A. (3)
4 allee de la Robertsau, F-67084, Strasbourg, Cedex, France (100%)
Tel.: (33) 388455151
Web Site: http://www.sade-financement.com
Sales Range: $50-74.9 Million
Emp.: 20
Real Estate Investment & Financing Services
N.A.I.C.S.: 531390
Antoine Gilliot (Gen Dir)

Subsidiary (Non-US):

BNP Paribas Commercial Finance Ltd. (2)
Brockbourne House 77 Mount Ephraim, Tunbridge Wells, TN4 8BS, Kent, United Kingdom
Tel.: (44) 845 693 1433
Web Site:
http://commercialfinance.bnpparibas.co.uk
Commercial Finance, Factoring, Credit Management, Debt Administration & Other Financial Services
N.A.I.C.S.: 522299

BNP Paribas Factor A/S (2)
Stationsparken 21 1, Albertslund, 2600, Glostrup, Denmark
Tel.: (45) 43 30 88 00
Web Site: http://www.factor.bnpparibas.dk
Commercial Finance, Factoring, Credit Management, Debt Administration & Other Financial Services
N.A.I.C.S.: 522299
Geraud Billaudel (Mng Dir)

BNP Paribas Factor Asia Ltd. (2)
25/F Three Exchange Square, 8 Connaught Place, Central, China (Hong Kong)
Tel.: (852) 31 97 39 70
Web Site: http://factoring.bnpparibas.com
Commercial Finance, Factoring, Credit Management, Debt Administration & Other Financial Services
N.A.I.C.S.: 522299

BNP Paribas Factor GmbH (2)
Hansaallee 299, 40549, Dusseldorf, Germany
Tel.: (49) 21153840
Web Site: http://factor.bnpparibas.de
Commercial Finance, Factoring, Credit Management, Debt Administration & Other Financial Services
N.A.I.C.S.: 522299
Wolfgang Reiser (Mng Dir & Member-Mgmt Bd)

BNP Paribas Factor, SA Sucursal en Espana (2)
Calle de Emilio Vargas 4 6 planta, 28043, Madrid, Spain
Tel.: (34) 917625694
Web Site: http://www.factor.bnpparibas.es
Commercial Finance, Factoring, Credit Management, Debt Administration & Other Financial Services
N.A.I.C.S.: 522299

Subsidiary (Domestic):

BNP Paribas Fortis Factor NV/SA (2)
PJ Brepolsplein 41, 2300, Turnhout, Antwerpen, Belgium (100%)
Tel.: (32) 14405411
Web Site:
http://www.factor.bnpparibasfortis.be
Factoring & Brokerage Credit Insurance Services
N.A.I.C.S.: 522299

Division (Domestic):

BNP Paribas Fortis Merchant Banking (2)
Montagne du Parc 3, 1000, Brussels, Belgium
Tel.: (32) 22287218
Sales Range: $1-4.9 Billion
Emp.: 3,000
Commercial & Investment Banking, Trade Financing, Clearing, Custody & Fund Services

N.A.I.C.S.: 522110

Joint Venture (Domestic):

Banque de La Poste S.A./Bank van De Post N.V. (2)
Boulevard Anspach 1, 1000, Brussels, Belgium
Tel.: (32) 25456211
Web Site: http://www.bpo.be
Sales Range: $100-124.9 Million
Emp.: 170
Retail Banking Services; Owned 50% by La Poste S.A./De Post N.V. & 50% by Fortis Bank SA/NV
N.A.I.C.S.: 522180

Subsidiary (Non-US):

Fortis Bank Polska S.A. (2)
ul Suwak 3, PL-02 676, Warsaw, Poland (99.29%)
Tel.: (48) 225669000
Web Site: http://www.bnpparibasfortis.pl
Sales Range: $300-349.9 Million
Emp.: 1,000
Personal & Commercial Banking Services
N.A.I.C.S.: 522110

Subsidiary (Domestic):

TFI BNP Paribas Polska SA (3)
Spektrum Tower ul Twarda 18, 00-105, Warsaw, Poland (100%)
Tel.: (48) 225669898
Web Site: http://www.tfi.bnpparibas.pl
Securities Brokerage & Investment Management Services
N.A.I.C.S.: 523150
Rafal Lerski (Member-Mgmt Bd)

Subsidiary (Non-US):

Fortis Banque S.A. (2)
29-30 Quai de Dion Bouton, F-92824, Puteaux, Cedex, France
Tel.: (33) 155678900
Web Site: http://www.fr.fortisbank.com
Sales Range: $100-124.9 Million
Emp.: 250
Retail, Merchant & Investment Banking & Wealth Management Services
N.A.I.C.S.: 522110
Francois Villeroy de Galhau (Chm-Supervisory Bd)

Subsidiary (US):

Fortis Capital Corp. (2)
275 Madison Ave Ste 2218, New York, NY 10016-1101
Tel.: (212) 418-8700
Web Site: http://www.fortisbank.com
Sales Range: $50-74.9 Million
Emp.: 75
Securities & Commodities Investment Services
N.A.I.C.S.: 523150

Subsidiary (Non-US):

Fortis Commercial Finance S.A.S. (2)
8/10 rue Godefroy Hall B, 92819, Puteaux, France
Tel.: (33) 155677400
Web Site: http://www.fortiscomfin.com
Commercial Finance, Factoring, Credit Management, Debt Administration & Other Financial Services
N.A.I.C.S.: 522299

Fortis Commercial Finance S.p.A. (2)
Viale Fulvio Testi 124, 20092, Cinisello Balsamo, MI, Italy
Tel.: (39) 0230 4181
Web Site: http://www.fortiscomfin.com
Commercial Finance, Factoring, Credit Management, Debt Administration & Other Financial Services
N.A.I.C.S.: 522299

Fortis Commercial Finance Sp. z o.o. (2)
ul Cybernetyki 19 B, 02 677, Warsaw, Poland
Tel.: (48) 22 431 69 30
Web Site: http://www.fortiscomfin.com

Commercial Finance, Factoring, Credit Management, Debt Administration & Other Financial Services
N.A.I.C.S.: 522299

Subsidiary (Domestic):

Fortis Finance Belgium S.C.R.L. (2)
Rue Montagne du Parc 3, 1000, Brussels, Belgium
Tel.: (32) 2 228 61 11
Investment Management Service
N.A.I.C.S.: 523940

Subsidiary (Non-US):

Fortis Investment Management Chile SA (2)
Mariano Sanchez Fontecilla 310 Piso 16, Las Condes, Chile
Tel.: (56) 27873302
Investment Management Service
N.A.I.C.S.: 523940

Subsidiary (Domestic):

Fortis Private Banking - Brussels (2)
Tervurenlaan 270, 1150, Brussels, Belgium
Tel.: (32) 25659271
Sales Range: $100-124.9 Million
Emp.: 136
Private Banking Services
N.A.I.C.S.: 523991

Fortis Private Equity Belgium NV (2)
Warandeberg 3 1KA0C, Brussels, 1000, Belgium
Tel.: (32) 2 565 97 69
Emp.: 20
Investment Banking Services
N.A.I.C.S.: 523150
Luc Weverbergh (Gen Mgr)

Fortis Private Equity Expansion Belgium NV (2)
Warandeberg 3, Brussels, 1000, Belgium
Tel.: (32) 24334032
Management Consulting Services
N.A.I.C.S.: 541611

Subsidiary (Non-US):

Fortis Private Investment Management Limited (2)
5 Aldermanbury Square, London, EC2V 7HR, United Kingdom (100%)
Tel.: (44) 2073694800
Web Site: http://www.bnpparibasfortis.com
Private Banking & Wealth Management Services
N.A.I.C.S.: 523991

Von Essen GmbH & Co. KG Bankgesellschaft (2)
Huyssenallee 86-88, 45128, Essen, 45128, Germany (100%)
Tel.: (49) 20181180
Web Site: http://www.vonessenbank.de
Personal & Commercial Banking Services
N.A.I.C.S.: 522110
Ralf Dreher (Chm-Mgmt Bd)

BNP Paribas Fortis Yatirimlar Holding A.S. (1)
Gayrettepe Mahallesi Yener Sokak No 1 Kat 10, Besiktas, Istanbul, Turkiye
Tel.: (90) 2123183330
Web Site:
http://www.bnppfortisyatirimlarholding.com
Bank Holding Company
N.A.I.C.S.: 551111

BNP Paribas Frankfurt Branch (1)
Europa-Allee 12, 60327, Frankfurt am Main, Germany (100%)
Tel.: (49) 6971930
Web Site: http://www.bnpparibas.de
Sales Range: $200-249.9 Million
Emp.: 300
Retail, Commercial & International Banking Services
N.A.I.C.S.: 522299

BNP Paribas Fund Services Australasia Ltd. (1)
Level 6 60 Castlereagh Street, Sydney, 2000, NSW, Australia
Tel.: (61) 292168633
Web Site:
http://www.securities.bnpparibas.com

Investment Advisory Services
N.A.I.C.S.: 523940

BNP Paribas Fund Services Dublin Ltd. (1)
Trinity Point 10-11 Leinster Street, Dublin, D02 EF85, Ireland
Tel.: (353) 1 612 6400
Web Site: http://www.bnpparibas.ie
Portfolio Management Services
N.A.I.C.S.: 523940

BNP Paribas Guyane (1)
2 Place Victor Schoelcher, 97300, Cayenne, French Guiana (100%)
Tel.: (594) 808800301
Sales Range: $50-74.9 Million
Emp.: 35
Provider of Banking Services
N.A.I.C.S.: 522320

BNP Paribas Home Loan SFH (1)
1 Boulevard Haussmann, Paris, 75009, France
Tel.: (33) 1 40 14 85 75
Mortgage Loan Brokerage Services
N.A.I.C.S.: 522310
Jean Clamon (Head-Compliance & Internal Control)

BNP Paribas Hungaria Bank RT (1)
Terez korut 55-57, 1062, Budapest, Hungary (100%)
Tel.: (36) 13746300
Web Site: http://www.bnpparibas.hu
Sales Range: $100-124.9 Million
Emp.: 120
Retail & International Banking Services
N.A.I.C.S.: 522299
Gyorgy Takacs (Exec Dir)

BNP Paribas Immobilier Promotion Immobilier d'Entreprise (1)
167 Quai de la Bataille de Stalingrad, 92867, Issy-les-Moulineaux, France
Tel.: (33) 155652424
Web Site:
http://www.realestate.bnpparibas.fr
Property Development Services
N.A.I.C.S.: 531312

BNP Paribas Immobilier Residentiel Promotion Mediterranee (1)
Azurea-Immeuble Le Phoenix 455 Promenade Des Anglais, Nice, 06000, France
Tel.: (33) 4 92 29 25 30
Real Estate Management & Development Services
N.A.I.C.S.: 531390
Frederique Combes (Mgr-Sls)

BNP Paribas Immobilier Residentiel Residences Services BSA (1)
7 Avenue de la Gare, BP 35157, 26958, Valence, France
Tel.: (33) 4 75 40 80 25
Real Estate Manangement Services
N.A.I.C.S.: 531390

BNP Paribas Immobilier Residentiel Residences Services Sofiane (1)
1 Rue Lesage, 26000, Valence, France
Tel.: (33) 8 99 96 36 39
Real Estate Manangement Services
N.A.I.C.S.: 531390

BNP Paribas Immobilier Residentiel S.A.S. (1)
1 Place Occitane, Toulouse, 31000, France
Tel.: (33) 561111600
Real Estate Development Services
N.A.I.C.S.: 531390

BNP Paribas Immobilier Residentiel Transaction & Conseil (1)
13 Boulevard du Fort de Vaux13 Boulevard du Fort de Vaux, Paris, 75017, France
Tel.: (33) 1 55 65 29 30
Real Estate Development Services
N.A.I.C.S.: 531390

BNP Paribas India Solutions Private Ltd. (1)
Infinity Building No 4 Unit No 601 6th Floor Off Film City Road, Malad East, Mumbai, 400097, India
Tel.: (91) 2262710000
Web Site:
http://www.indiasolutions.bnpparibas.co.in
Corporate & Investment Banking Services

N.A.I.C.S.: 523150

BNP Paribas Investment Partners (Australia) Ltd (1)
60 Castlereagh Street, Sydney, 2000, NSW, Australia
Tel.: (61) 292168633
Web Site: http://www.bnpparibas.com.au
Commercial Banking Services
N.A.I.C.S.: 522110

BNP Paribas Investment Partners Asia Ltd (1)
8 Connaught Place 30/F Three Exchange Square, Central, China (Hong Kong)
Tel.: (852) 2533 0000
Web Site: http://www.bnpparibas-ip.com.hk
Investment Management Service
N.A.I.C.S.: 523940

BNP Paribas Investment Partners BSC (1)
Bahrain Financial Harbour 4th Floor West Tower Financial Centre, PO Box 5253, Manama, Bahrain
Tel.: (973) 17 866160
Investment Management Service
N.A.I.C.S.: 523940

BNP Paribas Investment Partners Belgium SA (1)
Rue du Progres 55, 1210, Brussels, Belgium
Tel.: (32) 2274 83 11
Web Site: http://www.bnpparibas.be
Investment Management Service
N.A.I.C.S.: 523999

BNP Paribas Investment Partners Luxembourg SA (1)
33 Rue de Gasperich H2O Building Bloc B, 5826, Hesperange, Luxembourg
Tel.: (352) 26 46 30 01
Web Site: http://www.bnpparibas-ip.lu
Asset Management Services
N.A.I.C.S.: 523940

BNP Paribas Investment Partners NL Holding NV (1)
Oval Tower De Entree 99-197, Amsterdam, 1101 HE, Netherlands
Tel.: (31) 206 28 93 93
Web Site: http://www.bnpparibas-ip.nl
Investment Management Service
N.A.I.C.S.: 523940

BNP Paribas Investment Partners Netherlands NV (1)
Burgerweeshuispad 201 Tripolis Building, 1076 GR, Amsterdam, Netherlands
Tel.: (31) 20 527 52 75
Web Site: http://www.bnpparibas-ip.nl
Sales Range: $100-124.9 Million
Emp.: 200
Investment Management Service
N.A.I.C.S.: 523940
Graham Miller (Controller-Fin)

BNP Paribas Investment Partners Singapore Limited (1)
20 Collyer Quay 08-01 Tung Centre, Singapore, 049319, Singapore
Tel.: (65) 6210 3976
Web Site: http://www.bnpparibas-ip.com.sg
Sales Range: $50-74.9 Million
Emp.: 30
Investment Management Service
N.A.I.C.S.: 523940
Christian Bucaro (Head-Distr-Asia-Pacific)

BNP Paribas Investment Partners UK Ltd (1)
5 Aldermanbury Square, London, EC2V7HR, United Kingdom
Tel.: (44) 207 595 2000
Web Site: http://www.bnpparibas-ip.co.uk
Investment Management Service
N.A.I.C.S.: 523999
Colin Graham (Chief Investment Officer & Head-Tactical Asset Allocation & Res)

BNP Paribas Islamic Issuance BV (1)
Reguliersdwarsstraat 90, Amsterdam, 1017 BN, Netherlands
Tel.: (31) 205215645
Financial Management Services
N.A.I.C.S.: 523999

BNP Paribas Issuance B.V. (1)
Reguliersdwarsstraat 90, Amsterdam, 1017BN, Netherlands
Tel.: (31) 14 0149615
Web Site: http://www.bnpparibas.nl
Financial Services
N.A.I.C.S.: 523999

BNP Paribas Istanbul (1)
Mete Caddesi 16 3, Istanbul, 34437, Turkiye (100%)
Tel.: (90) 2122930032
Web Site: http://www.turkey.bnpparibas.com
Sales Range: $50-74.9 Million
Emp.: 5
Representative Office
N.A.I.C.S.: 522180

BNP Paribas Le Caire (1)
3 Latin America Street, Garden City, Cairo, Egypt
Tel.: (20) 27948323
Corporate & International Banking Services
N.A.I.C.S.: 522110

BNP Paribas Lease Group (Rentals) Ltd. (1)
St James Court St James Parade, Bristol, BS1 3LH, United Kingdom
Tel.: (44) 845 345 0915
Financial Planning Services
N.A.I.C.S.: 523940

BNP Paribas Lease Group Belgium SA (1)
Chaussee de Gand 1440, 1082, Brussels, Belgium
Tel.: (32) 25060211
Banking Services
N.A.I.C.S.: 522110

BNP Paribas Lease Group GmbH & Co KG (1)
Vordere Zollamtsstrasse 13, 1030, Vienna, Austria
Tel.: (43) 12724312
Web Site:
http://leasingsolutions.bnpparibas.at
Sales Range: $50-74.9 Million
Emp.: 26
Equipment Leasing Services
N.A.I.C.S.: 532490

BNP Paribas Lease Group Lizing RT (1)
Honved U 20/A, 1055, Budapest, Hungary
Tel.: (36) 1 3019000
Sales Range: $50-74.9 Million
Emp.: 40
Asset Management Services
N.A.I.C.S.: 523940

BNP Paribas Lease Group Luxembourg SA (1)
16 Rue Edward Steichen, 2540, Luxembourg, Luxembourg
Tel.: (352) 47 99 85 05
Sales Range: $50-74.9 Million
Emp.: 20
Financial Lending Services
N.A.I.C.S.: 523999
Christelle Bouichou (Acct Mgr)

BNP Paribas Lease Group S.A. (1)
51 Boulevard des Dames, 13002, Marseille, Cedex, France (100%)
Tel.: (33) 141972000
Web Site:
http://www.leasingsolutions.bnpparibas.com
Sales Range: $650-699.9 Million
Emp.: 1,500
Holding Company; Leasing Equipment & Vehicles
N.A.I.C.S.: 532420
Didier Chappet (Dir Gen)

Subsidiary (Non-US):

BNP Paribas Lease Group IFN S.A. (2)
Str Banul Antonache 40-44 Etaj 1 Sector 1, Bucharest, 011665, Romania (100%)
Tel.: (40) 31 425 4950
Web Site: http://www.romania-leasingsolutions.bnpparibas.com
Sales Range: $50-74.9 Million
Emp.: 20
Commercial Leasing & Factoring Services
N.A.I.C.S.: 522180

BNP Paribas Lease Group SA EFC (2)
Torre Ejesur Calle Retama 3 Planta 9, 28045, Madrid, Spain (100%)
Tel.: (34) 914682048
Web Site: http://www.bnpparibas-leasegroup.es
Sales Range: $50-74.9 Million
Emp.: 60
Financial Services; Lease & Rental Services
N.A.I.C.S.: 523940

BNP Paribas Lease Group Sp. z o.o. (2)
ul Grzybowska 78, 00-844, Warsaw, Poland (100%)
Tel.: (48) 225669688
Web Site: http://www.leasegroup.pl
Sales Range: $10-24.9 Million
Emp.: 40
Leasing Services
N.A.I.C.S.: 561330

BNP Paribas Leasing Solutions (2)
10 Rue Edward Steichen, 2540, Luxembourg, Luxembourg (100%)
Tel.: (352) 42428505
Web Site: http://www.bnpparibas.lu
Sales Range: $25-49.9 Million
Emp.: 25
Commercial Leasing & Rental Solutions for Professional Equipment & Real Estate Assets
N.A.I.C.S.: 532490

BNP Paribas Leasing Solutions (Belgium) S.A. (2)
Gentsesteenweg Chaussee de Gand 1440, 1082, Brussels, Belgium
Tel.: (32) 25060211
Web Site:
http://www.leasingsolutions.bnpparibas.be
Sales Range: $10-24.9 Million
Emp.: 150
Commercial Leasing & Factoring Services
N.A.I.C.S.: 522180

Subsidiary (Domestic):

Fortis Lease Car & Truck S.A. (3)
Chaussee de Gand 1440, Brussels, 1082, Belgium
Tel.: (32) 25060211
Commercial Equipment & Vehicle Leasing Services
N.A.I.C.S.: 532120

Fortis Lease Group Services S.A. (3)
Chaussee de Gand 1440, Brussels, 1082, Belgium
Tel.: (32) 25060211
Commercial Equipment Leasing Services
N.A.I.C.S.: 532490

Subsidiary (Non-US):

BNP Paribas Leasing Solutions Limited (2)
Northern Cross Basing View, Basingstoke, RG21 4HL, Hampshire, United Kingdom (100%)
Tel.: (44) 845 226 7367
Web Site:
http://leasingsolutions.bnpparibas.co.uk
Sales Range: $200-249.9 Million
Emp.: 337
Equipment Leasing, Long Term Rental Solutions & IT Asset Management Services
N.A.I.C.S.: 522320
Charlotte Dennery (CEO)

BNP Paribas Leasing Solutions N.V. (2)
Hambakenwetering 4, 5231 DC, 's-Hertogenbosch, Netherlands
Tel.: (31) 736399400
Web Site:
http://leasingsolutions.bnpparibas.nl
Sales Range: $50-74.9 Million
Emp.: 65
Commercial Leasing & Factoring Services
N.A.I.C.S.: 522180

BNP Paribas Leasing Solutions Sp. z o.o. (2)
ul Grzybowska 78, 00-844, Warsaw, Poland (100%)

BNP Paribas SA—(Continued)

Tel.: (48) 225669688
Web Site:
http://www.leasingsolutions.bnpparibas.pl
Commercial Leasing & Factoring Services
N.A.I.C.S.: 522180

BNP Paribas Leasing Solutions NV (1)
Hambakenwetering 4, 5231 DC, 's-Hertogenbosch, Netherlands
Tel.: (31) 73 63 99 400
Web Site: http://www.bnpparibas.nl
Financial Lending Services
N.A.I.C.S.: 523999

BNP Paribas Leasing Solutions SpA (1)
Piazza Lina Bo Bardi 3, 20124, Milan, Italy
Tel.: (39) 02 67 3331
Web Site: http://www.bnpparibas.it
Leasing Solutions
N.A.I.C.S.: 525990

BNP Paribas Leasing Solutions Zrt (1)
Dunavirag U 2, 1138, Budapest, Hungary
Tel.: (36) 1 577 6700
Web Site:
http://www.leasingsolutions.bnpparibas.hu
Sales Range: $50-74.9 Million
Emp.: 34
Financial Lending Services
N.A.I.C.S.: 522220
Andras Pfeningberger (Mng Dir)

BNP Paribas Martinique (1)
72 Avenue des Caraibes, 97200, Fort-de-France, Martinique
Tel.: (596) 596 59 4600
Web Site: http://www.bnpparibas.mq
Full Banking Services
N.A.I.C.S.: 522320

BNP Paribas Mumbai Branch (1)
1 North Avenue Maker Maxity Bandra Kurla Complex, Bandra E, Mumbai, 400 051, India (100%)
Tel.: (91) 2261964000
Web Site: http://www.bnpparibas.co.in
Sales Range: $100-124.9 Million
Emp.: 200
Retail & International Banking Services
N.A.I.C.S.: 522299

BNP Paribas Netherlands (1)
Herengracht 595, 1017 CE, Amsterdam, Netherlands (100%)
Tel.: (31) 205501212
Web Site: http://www.bnpparibas.nl
Sales Range: $50-74.9 Million
Emp.: 100
Corporate & International Banking Services
N.A.I.C.S.: 522320

Subsidiary (Domestic):

BNP Paribas Bank N.V. (2)
Herengracht 595, 1017 CE, Amsterdam, Netherlands (100%)
Tel.: (31) 20 550 1212
Web Site: https://www.bnpparibas.nl
Sales Range: $50-74.9 Million
Cross Border Financing Services
N.A.I.C.S.: 522299

BNP Paribas New Delhi Branch (1)
8th & 9th Floor East Towers Sood Towers 25 Barakhamba Road, New Delhi, 110 001, India
Tel.: (91) 1141796600
Web Site: http://www.bnpparibas.co.in
Retail & International Banking Services
N.A.I.C.S.: 522010

BNP Paribas Nouvelle Caledonie (1)
37 Ave Henri Lafleur, BP K3, 98849, Noumea, New Caledonia (100%)
Tel.: (687) 258400
Web Site: http://www.bnpparibas.nc
Sales Range: $100-124.9 Million
Emp.: 165
Retail Banking Services
N.A.I.C.S.: 522299

BNP Paribas Panama (1)
Edificio Omanco No 200 Via Espana, Panama Zona 1, Panama, 1, Panama (100%)
Tel.: (507) 2648555

Web Site: http://www.bnpparibas.pa
Sales Range: $100-124.9 Million
Emp.: 130
Full Banking Services
N.A.I.C.S.: 522320

BNP Paribas Personal Finance BV (1)
Marten Meesweg 97, Rotterdam, 3068 AV, Netherlands
Tel.: (31) 10 286 58 00
Web Site: http://www.bnpparibas-pf.nl
Sales Range: $50-74.9 Million
Emp.: 26
Mortgage Loan Brokerage Services
N.A.I.C.S.: 522310
Alexander Paklons (Pres)

BNP Paribas Personal Finance SPA (1)
Via Gustavo Fara 39, Milan, 20124, Italy
Tel.: (39) 0267602332
Web Site: http://www.bnpparibas.it
Financial Management Services
N.A.I.C.S.: 523999

BNP Paribas Portugal (1)
Torre Ocidente Rua Galileu Galilei 2 13, 1500-392, Lisbon, Portugal
Tel.: (351) 217910200
Web Site: http://www.bnpparibas.pt
Sales Range: $100-124.9 Million
Emp.: 150
Commercial Bank
N.A.I.C.S.: 522110

BNP Paribas Principal Investments Japan Ltd. (1)
GranTokyo North Tower 1-9-1 Marunouchi, Chiyoda-ku, Tokyo, 100-6742, Japan
Tel.: (81) 3 6377 2000
Web Site: http://www.bnpparibas.jp
Investment Management Service
N.A.I.C.S.: 523999
Philippe Avril (Gen Mgr)

BNP Paribas Private Bank Plc (1)
10 Harewood Ave, London, NW1 6AA, United Kingdom
Tel.: (44) 2075952000
Sales Range: $50-74.9 Million
Emp.: 100
Provider of Private Banking Services
N.A.I.C.S.: 522180

BNP Paribas Private Bank Switzerland S.A. (1)
Place de Hollande 2, PO Box 5060, 1204, Basel, Geneve, Switzerland (100%)
Tel.: (41) 582122111
Web Site: http://www.bnpparibas.ch
Sales Range: $100-124.9 Million
Emp.: 110
International Banking Services
N.A.I.C.S.: 522320
Pascal Boris (CEO)

BNP Paribas Qatar (1)
Al Fardan Office Tower 6th Floor 61 Al Funduq Street, Diplomatic District West Bay, Doha, Qatar (100%)
Tel.: (974) 44537115
Web Site: http://mea.bnpparibas.com
Sales Range: $100-124.9 Million
Emp.: 140
Retail & International Banking Services
N.A.I.C.S.: 522299

BNP Paribas Real Estate (1)
57 Adelaide Road, Dublin, D02 Y3C6, Ireland (50%)
Tel.: (353) 16611233
Web Site:
http://www.realestate.bnpparibas.ie
Sales Range: $100-124.9 Million
Emp.: 200
Property Management Services
N.A.I.C.S.: 531312
Sylvie Lemaire (Gen Counsel)

BNP Paribas Real Estate Advisory & Property Management Luxembourg SA (1)
10 Rue Edward Steichen, Luxembourg, 2540, Luxembourg
Tel.: (352) 34 94 84
Web Site:
http://www.realestate.bnpparibas.co.in
Sales Range: $50-74.9 Million
Emp.: 20
Property Management Services

N.A.I.C.S.: 531311
Marylene Graff (Head-Property Mgmt)

BNP Paribas Real Estate Advisory Belgium SA (1)
Boulevard Louis Schmidtlaan 2 B3, 1040, Brussels, Belgium
Tel.: (32) 2 646 49 49
Web Site:
http://www.realestate.bnpparibas.be
Sales Range: $50-74.9 Million
Emp.: 60
Real Estate Development Services
N.A.I.C.S.: 531390

BNP Paribas Real Estate Advisory Italy SPA (1)
Via Carlo Bo 6, Milan, 20143, Italy
Tel.: (39) 02 3211 5310
Web Site:
http://www.realestate.bnpparibas.it
Sales Range: $75-99.9 Million
Emp.: 220
Real Estate Management Services
N.A.I.C.S.: 531390
Roberto Nicosia (Mng Dir)

BNP Paribas Real Estate Advisory Spain SA (1)
C/ Emilio Vargas 4, 28043, Madrid, Spain
Tel.: (34) 914549600
Web Site:
http://www.realestate.bnpparibas.es
Real Estate Property Management Services
N.A.I.C.S.: 531390

BNP Paribas Real Estate Consult France (1)
167 Quai de la Bataille de Stalingrad, Issy-les-Moulineaux, 92867, France
Tel.: (33) 1 55 65 28 02
Real Estate Management Services
N.A.I.C.S.: 531390
Thierry Laroue-Pont (Chm)

BNP Paribas Real Estate Consult GmbH (1)
Schleusenbrucke 1 Neuer Wall 25, Hamburg, 20354, Germany
Tel.: (49) 40 348 48 101
Sales Range: $50-74.9 Million
Emp.: 9
Real Estate Advisory Services
N.A.I.C.S.: 531390
Wolfgang Schneider (Mng Dir)

BNP Paribas Real Estate Facilities Management Ltd. (1)
5 Aldermanbury Square, London, EC2V 7BP, United Kingdom
Tel.: (44) 20 7338 4400
Real Estate Management Services
N.A.I.C.S.: 531390

BNP Paribas Real Estate Financial Partner (1)
167 Quai De La Bataille De Stalingrad, Issy-les-Moulineaux, France
Tel.: (33) 155652424
Real Estate Investment Services
N.A.I.C.S.: 531390

BNP Paribas Real Estate GmbH (1)
Goetheplatz 4, Frankfurt, 60311, Germany
Tel.: (49) 69 2 98 99 0
Web Site:
http://www.realestate.bnpparibas.de
Real Estate Development Services
N.A.I.C.S.: 531390

BNP Paribas Real Estate Holding GmbH (1)
Fritz-Vomfelde-Strasse 26, Dusseldorf, 40547, Germany
Tel.: (49) 211 301 82.00
Emp.: 150
Real Estate Brokerage Services
N.A.I.C.S.: 531210
Loic Niederberger (COO)

BNP Paribas Real Estate Investment Management (1)
167 Quai de la bataille de Stalingrad, 92867, Issy-les-Moulineaux, France
Tel.: (33) 173257786
Web Site: http://www.reim.bnpparibas.fr
Emp.: 150
Real Estate Development Services
N.A.I.C.S.: 531390

Sigrid Duhamel (CEO & Member-Mgmt Bd)

Subsidiary (Non-US):

BNP Paribas Real Estate Investment Management Germany GmbH (2)
Lilli-Palmer-Strasse 2, 80636, Munich, Germany
Tel.: (49) 89121730
Web Site: http://www.reim.bnpparibas.de
Commercial Real Estate Investment Company
N.A.I.C.S.: 525990
Claus P. Thomas (CEO)

BNP Paribas Real Estate Investment Management Ltd. (1)
5 Aldermanbury Square, London, EC2V 7BP, United Kingdom
Tel.: (44) 20 7338 4000
Web Site: http://www.reim.bnpparibas.co.uk
Sales Range: $75-99.9 Million
Emp.: 185
Real Estate Management Services
N.A.I.C.S.: 531390

BNP Paribas Real Estate Investment Management Luxembourg SA (1)
Axento Building Avenue J F Kennedy 44, Luxembourg, 1855, Luxembourg
Tel.: (352) 26 26 06 41
Web Site:
http://www.realestate.bnpparibas.lu
Sales Range: $50-74.9 Million
Emp.: 15
Real Estate Management Services
N.A.I.C.S.: 531390
Laurent Ternisien (CEO)

BNP Paribas Real Estate Jersey Ltd. (1)
3rd Floor Dialogue House 2-6 Anley Street, Saint Helier, JE2 3QE, Jersey
Tel.: (44) 1534 629001
Web Site:
http://www.realestate.bnpparibas.je
Emp.: 8
Real Estate Management Services
N.A.I.C.S.: 531390

BNP Paribas Real Estate Property Developpement UK Ltd. (1)
5 Aldermanbury Square, London, EC2V 7HR, United Kingdom
Tel.: (44) 20 7338 4000
Real Estate Property Management Services
N.A.I.C.S.: 531390

BNP Paribas Real Estate Property Management Belgium SA (1)
Boulevard Louis Schmidtlaan 87, 1040, Brussels, Belgium
Tel.: (32) 26464949
Web Site:
http://www.realestate.bnpparibas.be
Sales Range: $50-74.9 Million
Emp.: 70
Real Estate Management Services
N.A.I.C.S.: 531312
Bert Leerschool (Acct Mgr)

BNP Paribas Real Estate Property Management GmbH (1)
Fritz-Vomfelde-Str 34, Dusseldorf, 40547, Nordrhein-Westfalen, Germany
Tel.: (49) 211301820
Real Estate Development Services
N.A.I.C.S.: 531390

BNP Paribas Real Estate Transaction France S.A. (1)
167 Quai de la Bataille de Stalingrad, 92867, Issy-les-Moulineaux, France
Tel.: (33) 173329220
Web Site: http://www.bnppre.fr
Real Estate Management Services
N.A.I.C.S.: 531390

BNP Paribas Real Estate, S.A. (1)
167 quai de la Bataille de Stalingrad, 92867, Issy-les-Moulineaux, France
Tel.: (33) 1 55 65 20 04
Web Site:
http://www.realestate.bnpparibas.com
Real Estate Development Services
N.A.I.C.S.: 531390
Barbara Antonia Knoflach (Deputy CEO-Investment Mgmt & Member-Exec Bd)

BNP Paribas Reunion (1)

67 Rue Juliette Dodu, Saint-Denis, 97463, Reunion
Tel.: (262) 820840830
Web Site: http://www.bnpparibas.re
Full Banking Services
N.A.I.C.S.: 522110

BNP Paribas SAE (1)
Plot 85 - Block G 90th Street Fifth Settlement City Centre Sector A, Cairo, Egypt
Tel.: (20) 2 19267
Commercial Banking & Financial Services
N.A.I.C.S.: 522110
Shahinaz Foda (Deputy Mng Dir & Head-Treas & Wealth Mgmt)

BNP Paribas Securities (Asia) Ltd. (1)
63/F Two International Finance Centre 8 Finance Street, Central, China (Hong Kong)
Tel.: (852) 2909 8888
Securities Brokerage Services
N.A.I.C.S.: 523150

BNP Paribas Securities (Singapore) Pte Ltd. (1)
20 Collyer Quay 04-00, Singapore, 049319, Singapore
Tel.: (65) 62101288
Web Site: http://www.bnpparibas.com.sg
Securities Brokerage Services
N.A.I.C.S.: 523150

BNP Paribas Securities (Taiwan) Co Ltd. (1)
3/F 52 Min Sheng East Road Sec 4, Taipei, Taiwan
Tel.: (886) 2 2719 8530
Securities Brokerage Services
N.A.I.C.S.: 523150

BNP Paribas Securities Korea Company Ltd. (1)
25th Floor State Tower Mamsan, Jung-gu, Seoul, 100-052, Korea (South)
Tel.: (82) 2 2125 0500
Securities Brokerage Services
N.A.I.C.S.: 523150
Hyungho Choi (CEO)

BNP Paribas Securities Services (1)
Trinity Point 10-11 Leinster Street, Dublin, Ireland (100%)
Tel.: (353) 1 612 6400
Web Site: http://www.bnpparibas.ie
Sales Range: $50-74.9 Million
Emp.: 70
Investment Management Service
N.A.I.C.S.: 523999
Diarmuid Ryan (Head-Hedge Fund & Liquid Alternative Svcs-Global)

BNP Paribas Securities Services (Holdings) Ltd. (1)
Liberte House 19-23 La Motte Street, PO Box 451, Saint Helier, JE4 5RL, Jersey
Tel.: (44) 1534 813800
Sales Range: $100-124.9 Million
Emp.: 200
Investment Management Service
N.A.I.C.S.: 523999
Alexandra Ricciardi (Head-Product Dev-Collateral Svcs-North America)

BNP Paribas Services (Hong Kong) Ltd. (1)
23/F Two Ifc, Central, China (Hong Kong)
Tel.: (852) 28251888
Financial Planning Services
N.A.I.C.S.: 523940

BNP Paribas Succursale Italia (1)
Piazza Lina Bo Bardi 3, 20124, Milan, Italy
Tel.: (39) 0272471
Web Site: http://www.bnpparibas.it
Retail & International Banking Services
N.A.I.C.S.: 522299

Subsidiary (Domestic):

BNP Lease Group S.p.A. (2)
Via Le Della Liberazione 16-18, Milan, 20320, Italy (100%)
Tel.: (39) 02673331
Web Site: http://www.leasegroup.it
Emp.: 300
Leasing Services
N.A.I.C.S.: 525990
Thierry Bonetto (Mng Dir)

BNP Paribas Asset Management SGR SpA (2)
Via Ansperto 5, 20123, Milan, Italy (100%)
Tel.: (39) 0272475101
Sales Range: $25-49.9 Million
Emp.: 30
Asset Management Services
N.A.I.C.S.: 531390

BNP Paribas-Succursale Italia (2)
Piazza San Fedele 2, 20121, Milan, Italy
Tel.: (39) 02 7247 1
Web Site: http://www.bnpparibas.it
Financial Services
N.A.I.C.S.: 522320

Banca UCB S.p.A. (2)
Via G Fara 39, 20124, Milan, Italy (100%)
Tel.: (39) 02676021
Web Site: http://www.bancaucb.com
Sales Range: $50-74.9 Million
Emp.: 18
Provider of Banking & Home Finance Services
N.A.I.C.S.: 522320

BNP Paribas Tel-Aviv (1)
Museum Tower 4 Berkowitz Street 5th floor, 64238, Tel Aviv, Israel (100%)
Tel.: (972) 36970500
Web Site: http://www.bnpparibas.co.il
Sales Range: $50-74.9 Million
Emp.: 50
Representative Office
N.A.I.C.S.: 522180

BNP Paribas Trust Company (Guernesey) Ltd. (1)
BNP Paribas House St Julians Avenue, Saint Peter Port, GY1 3WE, Guernsey
Tel.: (44) 1481750800
Financial Planning Services
N.A.I.C.S.: 523940

BNP Paribas UK Treasury Ltd. (1)
10 Harewood Avenue, Camden Town, London, NW1 6AA, United Kingdom
Tel.: (44) 2075952000
Financial Management Services
N.A.I.C.S.: 523999

BNP Paribas USA, Inc. (1)
787 7th Ave The Equitable Tower, New York, NY 10019
Tel.: (212) 841-3000
Web Site: http://www.usa.bnpparibas.com
Sales Range: $700-749.9 Million
Emp.: 2,000
Holding Company; Regional Managing Office; Banking & Financial Services
N.A.I.C.S.: 551112
Nandita Bakhshi (Co-CEO)

Subsidiary (Domestic):

1897 Services Corporation (2)
180 Montgomery St, San Francisco, CA 94104
Tel.: (415) 765-4800
Financial Planning Services
N.A.I.C.S.: 523940

BNP Commodity Futures Inc. (2)
787 7th Ave, New York, NY 10019-6018
Tel.: (212) 841-3366
Web Site: http://www.cfi.bnpparibas.com
Sales Range: $25-49.9 Million
Emp.: 40
Commodity Futures Brokers
N.A.I.C.S.: 523160
Tom Walsh (VP-Ops)

Group (Domestic):

BNP Cooper-Neff Group (2)
555 Croton Rd ste 100, King of Prussia, PA 19406
Tel.: (610) 491-1400
Web Site: http://www.cooperneff.com
Sales Range: $100-124.9 Million
Emp.: 150
Provider of Banking Services
N.A.I.C.S.: 523150

Subsidiary (Domestic):

BNP Paribas Brokerage Services, Inc (2)
555 Croton Rd Fl 4, King of Prussia, PA 19406 (100%)

Tel.: (212) 841-3101
Sales Range: $100-124.9 Million
Emp.: 150
Brokerage Services
N.A.I.C.S.: 523150

BNP Paribas Capstar Partners Inc. (2)
2711 Centerville Rd Ste 400, Wilmington, DE 19808
Tel.: (302) 636-5401
Capital Investment Services
N.A.I.C.S.: 523910

BNP Paribas Financial Services LLC (2)
555 Croton Rd Fl 4 Ste 100, King of Prussia, PA 19406
Tel.: (610) 491-1400
Financial Management Services
N.A.I.C.S.: 523999

BNP Paribas Leasing Corporation (2)
100 Crescent Ct 500, Dallas, TX 75201
Tel.: (972) 788-9191
Commercial Equipment Leasing Services
N.A.I.C.S.: 532490

BNP Paribas Mortgage Corporation (2)
787 7th Ave Fl 27, New York, NY 10019
Tel.: (212) 841-2000
Mortgage Loan Brokerage Services
N.A.I.C.S.: 522310
Catherine Flax (Mng Dir & Head-Commodities-America)

BNP Paribas Prime Brokerage Inc. (2)
787 7th Ave The Equitable Tower, New York, NY 10019
Tel.: (212) 841-3000
Web Site: http://www.primebroker.com
Securities Brokerage Services
N.A.I.C.S.: 523150

BNP Paribas RCC, Inc. (2)
525 Washington Blvd, Jersey City, NJ 07310
Tel.: (201) 850-4000
Web Site: http://cib.bnpparibas.com
Corporate & Institutional Banking
N.A.I.C.S.: 522110

BNP Paribas Securities Corp. (2)
787 7th Ave 31st Fl, New York, NY 10019-6018
Tel.: (212) 841-3000
Web Site: http://www.usa.bnpparibas.com
Rev.: $311,901,000
Emp.: 2,000
Security Brokers
N.A.I.C.S.: 523150
Florent Thiry (Head-Product Mgmt-Clearing & Custody Svcs)

Branch (Domestic):

BNP Paribas-Chicago (2)
155 N Wacker Dr, Chicago, IL 60606
Tel.: (312) 977-2200
Web Site: http://www.bnpparibas.com
Sales Range: $25-49.9 Million
Emp.: 50
International Bankers
N.A.I.C.S.: 522110

BNP Paribas-Dallas (2)
2021 McKinney Ave Ste 240, Dallas, TX 75201
Tel.: (214) 953-9739
Web Site: http://www.bnpparibas.com
Sales Range: $50-74.9 Million
Emp.: 15
International Bankers
N.A.I.C.S.: 532490

BNP Paribas-Houston (2)
1200 Smith St Ste 3100, Houston, TX 77002-4308
Tel.: (713) 982-1100
Web Site: http://www.bnpparibas.com
Sales Range: $50-74.9 Million
Emp.: 55
International Bankers
N.A.I.C.S.: 522299

BNP Paribas-New York (2)

The Equitable Tower 787 7th Ave, New York, NY 10019
Tel.: (212) 841-3000
Web Site: http://usa.bnpparibas.com
Sales Range: $700-749.9 Million
Emp.: 1,400
Financial Services
N.A.I.C.S.: 523150
John Gallo (Head-Global Markets)

BNP Paribas-San Francisco (2)
180 Montgomery St 14th Fl, San Francisco, CA 94104
Tel.: (415) 772-1300
Web Site: http://www.usa.bnpparibas.com
Sales Range: $25-49.9 Million
Emp.: 50
International Bankers
N.A.I.C.S.: 522110

Subsidiary (Domestic):

BNPP Asset Management USA Inc. (2)
200 Park Ave 11th Fl, New York, NY 10166
Tel.: (212) 681-3181
Banking Services
N.A.I.C.S.: 522110
Daniel Klein (CEO)

Center Club, Inc. (2)
100 Light St 16th Fl, Baltimore, MD 21202
Tel.: (410) 727-7788
Web Site: http://www.centerclub.org
Pub Operator
N.A.I.C.S.: 813410
Nancy Sloane (Dir-Membership & Mktg)

Claas Financial Services Inc. (2)
1209 Orange St, Wilmington, DE 19801
Tel.: (302) 658-7581
Financial Planning Services
N.A.I.C.S.: 523940

Community Service, Inc. (2)
100 S Cherokee St, Morrilton, AR 72110
Tel.: (501) 354-4589
Web Site: http://csiyouth.com
Sales Range: $25-49.9 Million
Emp.: 30
Social Development Program Administrative Services
N.A.I.C.S.: 923130
John Gibson (Chm)

Fauchier Partners Corporation (2)
444 Madison Ave 29th Fl, New York, NY 10022
Tel.: (212) 319-8002
Web Site: http://www.fauchierpartners.com
Investment Advisory Services
N.A.I.C.S.: 523940

First Hawaiian, Inc. (2)
999 Bishop St 29th Fl, Honolulu, HI 96813
Tel.: (808) 525-7000
Web Site: https://www.fhb.com
Rev.: $1,124,394,000
Assets: $24,926,474,000
Liabilities: $22,440,408,000
Net Worth: $2,486,066,000
Earnings: $234,983,000
Emp.: 2,000
Fiscal Year-end: 12/31/2023
Financial Services
N.A.I.C.S.: 522110
Lea M. Nakamura (Chief Risk Officer-Risk Mgmt Grp & Exec VP)

Subsidiary (Domestic):

Bancwest Investment Services. Inc. (3)
13505 California Street Plz W, Omaha, NE 68154
Tel.: (402) 918-4063
Commercial Banking Services
N.A.I.C.S.: 522110

Bank of the West (3)
180 Montgomery St, San Francisco, CA 94104 (100%)
Web Site: http://www.bankofthewest.com
Sales Range: $1-4.9 Billion
Emp.: 9,000
Banking Services
N.A.I.C.S.: 522110
Nandita Bakhshi (Pres & CEO)

Subsidiary (Domestic):

Essex Credit Corporation (4)

BNP Paribas SA—(Continued)

12677 Alcosta Blvd Ste 200, San Ramon,
CA 94583-4407
Tel.: (866) 377-3907
Web Site: http://www.essexcredit.com
Credit Services for the Pleasure Boating &
Recreational Vehicle Market
N.A.I.C.S.: 522299

Subsidiary (Domestic):

**Bishop Street Capital Management
Corporation**   **(3)**
1st Hawaiian Ctr 999 Bishop St Ste 2806,
Honolulu, HI 96813
Tel.: (808) 525-6246
Emp.: 10
Investment Management Service
N.A.I.C.S.: 523999
Michael Hirai (Pres & Chief Investment Officer)

First Hawaiian Bank   **(3)**
999 Bishop St, Honolulu, HI
96813-4423   **(100%)**
Tel.: (808) 525-7000
Web Site: http://www.fhb.com
Sales Range: $600-649.9 Million
Emp.: 2,100
Bank Holding Company
N.A.I.C.S.: 522110
Lea M. Nakamura (Chief Risk Officer-Risk
Mgmt Grp & Exec VP)

Subsidiary (Domestic):

FH Center, Inc.   **(4)**
999 Bishop St, Honolulu, HI
96813-4423   **(100%)**
Tel.: (808) 525-7000
Web Site: http://www.fhb.com
Real Estate Holding & Development
N.A.I.C.S.: 522299

FHB Properties, Inc.   **(4)**
999 Bishop St, Honolulu, HI
96813-4423   **(100%)**
Tel.: (808) 525-7000
Web Site: http://www.fhb.com
Sales Range: $300-349.9 Million
Emp.: 20
Bank Properties Company
N.A.I.C.S.: 531120
Donald G. Horner (Chm, Pres & CEO)

First Hawaiian Capital 1   **(4)**
1188 Bishop St Ste 3403, Honolulu, HI
96813
Tel.: (808) 524-5738
Business Trust
N.A.I.C.S.: 525920

First Hawaiian Leasing, Inc.   **(4)**
1580 Kapiolani Blvd 3rd Fl, Honolulu, HI
96814   **(100%)**
Tel.: (808) 943-4905
Emp.: 16
Commercial Equipment & Vehicle Sales Financing & Leasing Services
N.A.I.C.S.: 522220
Jeffrey K. Inouye (Sr VP)

Subsidiary (Domestic):

**FHL Lease Holding Company
Inc.**   **(5)**
1580 Kapiolani Blvd 3rd Fl, Honolulu, HI
96814
Tel.: (808) 943-4905
Emp.: 14
Investment Management Service
N.A.I.C.S.: 523999
Manny Valbuena (VP)

Subsidiary (Domestic):

Real Estate Delivery, Inc.   **(4)**
999 Bishop St, Honolulu, HI
96813-4423   **(100%)**
Tel.: (808) 525-7000
Real Property Acquired by Bank
N.A.I.C.S.: 531210

Subsidiary (Domestic):

The Bankers Club, Inc.   **(3)**
999 Bishop St, Honolulu, HI 96813
Tel.: (808) 525-6171
Web Site: http://www.fhb.com
Emp.: 12

Financial Management Services
N.A.I.C.S.: 523999
Bob Harrison (CEO)

Subsidiary (Domestic):

French American Banking Corp.   **(2)**
787 7th Ave, New York, NY 10019
Tel.: (212) 841-3000
Web Site: http://www.bnpparibas.com
Sales Range: $200-249.9 Million
Emp.: 400
Commercial Banks, Nec
N.A.I.C.S.: 522110

**Harewood Asset Management (US)
Inc.**   **(2)**
555 Croton Rd 4th Fl, King of Prussia, PA
19406
Tel.: (610) 491-1400
Asset Management Services
N.A.I.C.S.: 523940

Margaret Inc.   **(2)**
3350 Lower Honoapiilani Rd, Lahaina, HI
96761
Tel.: (808) 572-0028
Investment Management Service
N.A.I.C.S.: 523940

BNP Paribas Uruguay S.A.   **(1)**
Casilla De Correo 6729, Correo Central,
Montevideo, 11000, Uruguay   **(100%)**
Tel.: (598) 29162768
Sales Range: $50-74.9 Million
Emp.: 3
Trade Finance; International Private Banking
N.A.I.C.S.: 522299

**BNP Paribas Wealth
Management**   **(1)**
33 rue du Quatre Septembre, 75078, Paris,
France
Tel.: (33) 1 40 14 40 02
Web Site:
  http://www.wealthmanagement.com
Asset Management Services
N.A.I.C.S.: 523940
Mignonne Cheng (Chm-Asian Markets-Global)

**BNP Paribas Wealth
Management**   **(1)**
63/F Two International Finance Centre 8
Finance Street, Central, China (Hong Kong)
Tel.: (852) 29098888
Web Site: http://www.bnpparibas.com.hk
Emp.: 700
Private Banking & Wealth Management
Services
N.A.I.C.S.: 525990
Prashant Bhayani (Chief Investment Officer)

**BNP Paribas Wealth Management
Monaco**   **(1)**
15-17 Avenue dOstende, 98000, Monaco,
Monaco
Tel.: (377) 93 15 68 00
Web Site:
  http://www.wealthmanagement.mc
Wealth Management Services
N.A.I.C.S.: 523940

BNP Paribas ZAO   **(1)**
5 Lesnaya str building B, 125047, Moscow,
Russia
Tel.: (7) 4957856000
Web Site: http://www.bnpparibas.ru
Commercial Banking Services
N.A.I.C.S.: 522110

BNP Paribas-Brussels Branch   **(1)**
489 Ave Louise, 1050, Brussels,
Belgium   **(100%)**
Tel.: (32) 25180811
Web Site: http://www.bnpparibas.be
Sales Range: $50-74.9 Million
Emp.: 100
Private & Corporate Banking & International
Services
N.A.I.C.S.: 522180

BNP Paribas-Manama Branch   **(1)**
Bahrain Financial Harbour West Tower King
Faisal Highway, PO Box 5241, Manama,
Bahrain
Tel.: (973) 17866205
Web Site:
  http://www.bahrain.bnpparibas.com

Sales Range: $200-249.9 Million
Emp.: 400
Offshore Banking Services
N.A.I.C.S.: 522299

**BNPP Asset Management Asia
Ltd.**   **(1)**
17/F Lincoln House Taikoo Place 979 King's
Road, Quarry Bay, China (Hong Kong)
Tel.: (852) 25330000
Web Site: http://www.bnpparibas-am.hk
Asset Management Services
N.A.I.C.S.: 523940
Ligia Torres (CEO-Asia-Pacific)

**BNPP Asset Management Brasil
Ltda**   **(1)**
Av Presidente Juscelino Kubitschek 1 909
Torre Sul 10 andar, Vila Olimpia, Sao
Paulo, 04543-906, Brazil
Tel.: (55) 1130492820
Financial Services
N.A.I.C.S.: 522320

**BNPP Asset Management Japan
Ltd.**   **(1)**
Grant Tokyo North Tower 1-9-1, Marunouchi
Chiyoda-ku, Tokyo, 100-6742, Japan
Tel.: (81) 363772800
Web Site: http://www.bnpparibas.jp
Asset Management Services
N.A.I.C.S.: 523940

**BNPP Asset Management Nederland
NV**   **(1)**
Herengracht 595, 1017 CE, Amsterdam,
Netherlands
Tel.: (31) 205275275
Web Site: http://www.bnpparibas-am.nl
Asset Management Services
N.A.I.C.S.: 523940
Joost Hoppener (Head-Sls)

**BNPP Cardif Compania de Seguros y
Reaseguros SA**   **(1)**
Av Canaval y Moreyra n 380 piso 11,
15047, San Isidro, Lima, Peru
Tel.: (51) 6155700
Web Site: http://bnpparibascardif.com.pe
Financial Services
N.A.I.C.S.: 522320

**BNPP Cardif General Insurance Co.,
Ltd.**   **(1)**
7F 358 Samil-daero, Jung-guSeoul, Seoul,
4542, Korea (South)
Tel.: (82) 15442580
Insurance Services
N.A.I.C.S.: 524210
Olivier Calandreau (CEO)

BNPP Cardif Pojistovna AS   **(1)**
Plzenska 3217/16, 150 00, Prague, Czech
Republic
Tel.: (420) 234240234
Banking Services
N.A.I.C.S.: 522110
Zdenek Jaros (Chm & CEO)

**BNPP Cardif Seguros de Vida
SA**   **(1)**
Av Vitacura 2670 Floor 10, Las Condes,
Chile
Tel.: (56) 223704800
Web Site: http://www.bnpparibascardif.cl
Insurance Services
N.A.I.C.S.: 524210

BNPP Colombia Corporacion Financiera SA   **(1)**
Carrera 7 No 77 07 Edificio Torre Siete 77
Piso 11, Bogota, Colombia
Tel.: (57) 16516420
Web Site: http://www.bnpparibas.com.co
Financial Services
N.A.I.C.S.: 522320
Omar Duque (CEO & Head-Global Markets)

BNPP Factor NV   **(1)**
Hoevestein 28, 4903 SC, Oosterhout, Netherlands
Tel.: (31) 162447250
Web Site: http://factor.bnpparibas.nl
Financial Services
N.A.I.C.S.: 522320

BNPP Finansal Kiralama AS   **(1)**
Gayrettepe Mahallesi Yener Sokak No 1
Kat 2-3, 34349, Istanbul, Turkey
Tel.: (90) 2123184200

Banking Services
N.A.I.C.S.: 522110

**BNPP Global Securities Operations
Private Ltd.**   **(1)**
1 North Avenue Bkc Rd Bandra East, 400
051, Mumbai, India
Tel.: (91) 2261964000
Financial Investment Services
N.A.I.C.S.: 523999

**BNPP Leasing Services Sp. z
o.o.**   **(1)**
Street Grzybowska 78, 00-844, Warsaw,
Poland
Tel.: (48) 228299767
Web Site:
  https://portalklienta.leasingsolutions.pl
N.A.I.C.S.: 532112

**BNPP Leasing Solutions Suisse
SA**   **(1)**
World Trade Center Avenue Gratta-Paille 2,
1018, Lausanne, Switzerland
Tel.: (41) 216420000
Vehicle Leasing Services
N.A.I.C.S.: 532112

BNPP Malaysia Berhad   **(1)**
Vista Tower Level 48A The Intermark 348
Jalan Tun Razak, 50400, Kuala Lumpur,
Malaysia
Tel.: (60) 321798383
Banking Services
N.A.I.C.S.: 522110

BNPP Personal Finance SA   **(1)**
1 Boulevard Haussmann, 75009, Paris,
France
Tel.: (33) 146399939
Financial Services
N.A.I.C.S.: 522320
Laurent David (CEO)

BNPP Real Estate APM CR Sro   **(1)**
Ovocny trh 1096/8 3rd floor, 110 00,
Prague, Czech Republic
Tel.: (420) 224835000
Property Management Services
N.A.I.C.S.: 327910

BNPP Real Estate Advisory & Property Management Ireland Ltd.   **(1)**
20 Merrion Road, Ballsbridge, Dublin, D04
C9E2, Ireland
Tel.: (353) 16611233
Property Management Services
N.A.I.C.S.: 531311

BNPP Real Estate Advisory Netherlands BV   **(1)**
Antonio Vivaldistraat 54, 1083 HP, Amsterdam, Netherlands
Tel.: (31) 203059720
Property Management Services
N.A.I.C.S.: 327910

**BNPP Real Estate Poland Sp. z
o.o.**   **(1)**
Al Jana Pawla II 25, 00-854, Warsaw, Poland
Tel.: (48) 226534400
Property Management Services
N.A.I.C.S.: 531311
Justyna Magrzyk-Flemming (Head-Mktg, PR
& CEE)

BNPP Rental Solutions Ltd.   **(1)**
Northern Cross Basing View, Basingstoke,
RG21 4HL, Hampshire, United Kingdom
Tel.: (44) 3452666160
Web Site:
  http://rentalsolutions.bnpparibas.co.uk
Vehicle Leasing Services
N.A.I.C.S.: 327910

**BNPP Securities India Private
Ltd.**   **(1)**
8th Floor BNP Paribas House 1 North AvenueMaker Maxity Bandra Kurla, Complex
Bandra East, Mumbai, 400051, India
Tel.: (91) 226196400
Banking Services
N.A.I.C.S.: 522110
Samit Shah (CEO)

BNPP Yatirimlar Holding AS   **(1)**
Gayrettepe Mahallesi Yener Sokak No 1
Floor, Besiktas, Istanbul, Turkey   **(99.99%)**
Tel.: (90) 2123183330

Web Site:
http://www.bnppyatirimlarholding.com
Bank Holding Company
N.A.I.C.S.: 551111

Banca Nazionale del Lavoro S.p.A. **(1)**
Viale Altiero Spinelli 30, 00157, Rome, Italy **(99.14%)**
Tel.: (39) 0647021
Web Site: http://www.bnl.it
Sales Range: $1-4.9 Billion
Emp.: 16,000
Commercial Banking Services
N.A.I.C.S.: 522110
Elena Patrizia Goitini *(CEO)*

Subsidiary (Non-US):

Lavoro Bank AG **(2)**
Lowenstr 56, CH 8001, Zurich, Switzerland
Tel.: (41) 442179595
Web Site: http://www.bnpparibas.ch
Sales Range: $1-9.9 Million
Emp.: 6
Commercial Banking Services
N.A.I.C.S.: 522110

Banco BNP Paribas Brasil **(1)**
Av Pres Juscelino Kubitschek 1909 9 ao 11 andar Torre Sul do Edificio, Sao Paulo, 04543-907, Brazil **(100%)**
Tel.: (55) 1138413100
Web Site: http://www.bnpparibas.com.br
Sales Range: $50-74.9 Million
Emp.: 200
Retail & International Banking Services
N.A.I.C.S.: 522299
Louis Bazire *(Pres)*

Banco BNP Paribas Personal Finance SA **(1)**
Rua Tomas da Fonseca Torres de Lisboa Torre G - 15, 1600-209, Lisbon, Portugal
Tel.: (351) 21 721 58 00
Web Site: http://www.cetelem.pt
Sales Range: $350-399.9 Million
Emp.: 600
Financial Management Services
N.A.I.C.S.: 523999

Banco Cetelem Argentina SA **(1)**
Av del Libertador 767 2 piso CP 1638, Vicente Lopez, Buenos Aires, Argentina
Tel.: (54) 8101228787
Web Site: http://www.cetelem.com.ar
Financial Services
N.A.I.C.S.: 522320

Banexi Ventures Partners **(1)**
13-15 rue Taitbout, 75009, Paris, France
Tel.: (33) 1 73 02 89 69
Web Site: http://www.banexiventures.com
Sales Range: $50-74.9 Million
Investing & Company Restructuring Services
N.A.I.C.S.: 523999
Michel Dahan *(Chm & Gen Partner)*

Subsidiary (Non-US):

Aleva Neurotherapeutics SA **(2)**
EPFL Innovation Park Building D, CH-1015, Lausanne, Switzerland
Tel.: (41) 21 639 87 64
Web Site: http://www.aleva-neuro.com
Emp.: 14
Microfabricated Implantable Deep Brain Stimulator Devices Developer & Mfr
N.A.I.C.S.: 334510
Alain Jordan *(COO)*

ELMARCO s.r.o. **(2)**
Svarovska 621, 460 01, Liberec, Czech Republic
Tel.: (420) 489 209 200
Web Site: http://www.elmarco.com
Industrial Equipment Mfr & Whslr
N.A.I.C.S.: 423830
Miloslav Masopust *(Mng Dir)*

Subsidiary (Domestic):

EYE TECH CARE **(2)**
2871 Av de l'Europe, 69140, Rillieux-la-Pape, France
Tel.: (33) 478 88 09 00
Web Site: http://eyetechcare.com
Medical Devices Developer & Marketer
N.A.I.C.S.: 423450

Dietrich Wolf *(CEO)*

IFOTEC SA **(2)**
Zac de Champfeuillet Ouest - 8 route des Bois, PO Box 247, 38507, Voiron, Cedex, France
Tel.: (33) 476 67 53 53
Web Site: http://www.ifotec.com
Fiber Optic Equipment Designer & Mfr
N.A.I.C.S.: 334220
Gilles Billet *(CEO & Dir-Publication)*

IROC Technologies **(2)**
2 Square Roger Genin 5th floor, 38000, Grenoble, France
Tel.: (33) 438 120 763
Web Site: http://www.iroctech.com
Software Publisher
N.A.I.C.S.: 513210
Dan Alexandrescu *(CEO)*

Oxxiius SA **(2)**
4 Rue Louis de Broglie, 22300, Lannion, France
Tel.: (33) 296 48 70 28
Web Site: http://www.oxxius.com
Laser Design & Mfr
N.A.I.C.S.: 335139
Thierry Georges *(CEO)*

ScreenCell **(2)**
10 avenue Charles Peguy, 95200, Sarcelles, France
Tel.: (33) 182 32 31 30
Web Site: http://www.screencell.com
Biomedical Research Services
N.A.I.C.S.: 541715
Claude Chemla *(Member-Mgmt Bd & Sec)*

Subsidiary (Non-US):

SpineteX AG **(2)**
Sonnenbergstrasse 9, 6052, Hergiswil, Switzerland
Tel.: (41) 21 341 15 50
Web Site: http://www.spinetix.com
Digital Signage Mfr
N.A.I.C.S.: 541519
Francesco Ziliani *(CEO)*

Subsidiary (Domestic):

Webdyn **(2)**
26 Rue Gaudines, Saint-Germain-en-Laye, 78100, Paris, France
Tel.: (33) 139 04 29 40
Web Site: http://www.webdyn.com
Sales Range: $1-9.9 Million
Hardware & Software Designer & Mfr
N.A.I.C.S.: 334118
Philippe Faugeras *(Founder)*

Bank BNP Paribas Luxembourg **(1)**
33 Rue De Gasperich, 20085, Luxembourg, Luxembourg **(100%)**
Tel.: (352) 2696000
Web Site: http://www.bnpparibas.lu
Sales Range: $350-399.9 Million
Emp.: 600
Retail Banking Services
N.A.I.C.S.: 522299

Bank Insinger de Beaufort Safe Custody NV **(1)**
Herengracht 537, Amsterdam, 1017 BV, Netherlands
Tel.: (31) 20 5215000
Web Site: http://www.insinger.com
Financial Management Services
N.A.I.C.S.: 523999

Banque Internationale pour le Commerce et l'Industrie au Mali **(1)**
Quartier du Fleuve Boulevard Abdelaziz Bouteflika, PO Box 72, Bamako, Mali
Tel.: (223) 20700700
Web Site: http://www.bicimali.org
Sales Range: $25-49.9 Million
Emp.: 71
Full Banking Services
N.A.I.C.S.: 522320

Banque Internationale pour le Commerce et l'Industrie de la Cote d'Ivoire, S.A. **(1)**
Avenue Franchet d Esperey, BP 01, 1298, Abidjan, Cote d'Ivoire
Tel.: (225) 20242424
Banking Services
N.A.I.C.S.: 522110

Banque Internationale pour le Commerce et l'Industrie de la Guinee **(1)**
Ave de la Republique, BP 1484, Conakry, Papua New Guinea
Tel.: (675) 41 45 15
Web Site: http://www.biciguinet.net
Full Banking Services
N.A.I.C.S.: 522320

Banque Internationale pour le Commerce et l'Industrie du Gabon **(1)**
Avenue du Colonel Parant, PO Box 2241, Libreville, Gabon
Tel.: (241) 762613
Web Site: http://www.bicig-gabon.com
Commercial & Institutional Banking Services
N.A.I.C.S.: 522110

Banque Internationale pour le Commerce et l'Industrie du Mali SA **(1)**
Avenue Cheick zayed Immeuble Balde, BP E 4373, Hamdallaye, Bamako, Mali
Tel.: (223) 20295957
Web Site: http://www.bci-banque.com
Banking Services
N.A.I.C.S.: 522110
Haidara Zeinabou Koureichy *(Gen Mgr)*

Banque Internationale pour le Commerce et l'Industrie du Senegal SA **(1)**
2 Avenue Leopold Sedar Senghor, BP 392, Dakar, Senegal
Tel.: (221) 818040606
Banking Services
N.A.I.C.S.: 522110

Banque Internationale pour le Commerce, l'Industrie et l'Agriculture du Burkina **(1)**
479 Avenue Kwame N Krumah 01, PO Box 08, Ouagadougou, 01, Burkina Faso **(100%)**
Tel.: (226) 25325600
Web Site: http://www.biciab.bf
Full Banking Services
N.A.I.C.S.: 522320

Banque Marocaine du Commerce et de l'Industrie Offshore **(1)**
26 Place Des Nations Unies, Casablanca, Morocco
Tel.: (212) 522461000
Commercial Banking Services
N.A.I.C.S.: 522110

Banque Marocaine pour le Commerce et l'Industrie S.A. **(1)**
26 Place des Nations Unies, 20000, Casablanca, Morocco **(66.21%)**
Tel.: (212) 522461000
Web Site: http://www.bmci.ma
Sales Range: $400-449.9 Million
Emp.: 1,909
Personal, Commercial & Investment Banking Services
N.A.I.C.S.: 522110
Rachid Marrakchi *(CEO, Member-Mgmt Bd & Gen Mgr)*

Banque de Bretagne **(1)**
18 Quai Dugay Trouin, 35084, Rennes, Cedex, France **(100%)**
Tel.: (33) 299017777
Web Site: http://www.bdbretagne.com
Sales Range: $200-249.9 Million
Emp.: 500
Private Banking Services
N.A.I.C.S.: 522320

Banque de Wallis et Futuna **(1)**
Tel.: (681) 72 21 24
Commercial Banking Services
N.A.I.C.S.: 522110

Beau Sevran Invest SCI **(1)**
21 Avenue Kleber, 75116, Paris, France
Tel.: (33) 899967762
Investment Management Service
N.A.I.C.S.: 523940

Belgolaise SA **(1)**
Cantersteen 1, 1000, Brussels, Belgium
Tel.: (32) 2 312 26 86
Web Site: http://www.belgolaise.com
Commercial Banking Services
N.A.I.C.S.: 522110
Llemeiyre Beuduyn *(Mng Dir)*

Bruun s Galleri AS **(1)**

Arne Jacobsens Alle 20, 2300, Copenhagen, Denmark
Tel.: (45) 87419805
Real Estate Prorperty Leasing Services
N.A.I.C.S.: 531190

Bryggen Vejle AS **(1)**
Arne Jacobsens Alle 20, 2300, Copenhagen, Denmark
Tel.: (45) 97404666
Real Estate Manangement Services
N.A.I.C.S.: 531390

CMV Mediforce S.A. **(1)**
1 Boulevard Haussmann, 75009, Paris, Cedex, France **(100%)**
Tel.: (33) 156769922
Web Site: http://www.cmvmediforce.fr
Financial Management Services
N.A.I.C.S.: 523999
Ariane Govignon *(CEO)*

CNH Capital Europe BV **(1)**
Hambakenwetering 4, 's-Hertogenbosch, 5231 DC, Netherlands
Tel.: (31) 736399400
Consumer Credit Services
N.A.I.C.S.: 522291

CNH Capital Europe S.A.S. **(1)**
52 Rue Arago, 92800, Puteaux, France
Tel.: (33) 8 10 81 06 60
Financial & Consumer Credit Services
N.A.I.C.S.: 523999

CamGestion **(1)**
14 Rue Bergere, 75009, Paris, France
Tel.: (33) 1 58 97 60 00
Web Site: http://www.camgestion.fr
Sales Range: $50-74.9 Million
Emp.: 45
Asset Management Services
N.A.I.C.S.: 523940
Christian Dargnat *(Chm)*

Cargeas Assicurazioni SPA **(1)**
Via Tolmezzo 15, 20132, Milan, Italy
Tel.: (39) 02499801
Web Site: http://www.cargeas.it
Insurance Services
N.A.I.C.S.: 524210

Cecoville SAS **(1)**
21 Avenue Kleber, 75116, Paris, France
Tel.: (33) 140675398
Financial Planning Services
N.A.I.C.S.: 523940

Centre Jaude Clermont SAS **(1)**
21 Avenue Kleber, 75116, Paris, France
Tel.: (33) 1 45 25 25.25
Sales Range: $50-74.9 Million
Emp.: 100
Financial Management Services
N.A.I.C.S.: 523999

Cetelem **(1)**
20 Avenue Georges Pompidou, 92595, Levallois-Perret, Cedex, France
Tel.: (33) 969327502
Web Site: http://www.cetelem.fr
Sales Range: $1-4.9 Billion
Emp.: 10,000
Provider of Financial Services
N.A.I.C.S.: 522299
Bruno Salmon *(COO)*

Subsidiary (Non-US):

Banco Cetelem S.A. **(2)**
C/ Retama 3, 28045, Madrid, Spain **(100%)**
Tel.: (34) 913370700
Web Site: http://www.cetelem.es
Sales Range: $150-199.9 Million
Emp.: 300
Consumer Credit Banking Services
N.A.I.C.S.: 522299

Cetelem Belgium **(2)**
Sint-Lazaruslaan 4-10/3, 1210, Brussels, Belgium **(60%)**
Tel.: (32) 25080201
Web Site: http://www.cetelem.be
Sales Range: $75-99.9 Million
Emp.: 220
Consumer Financing; Trade & Credit Cards

Cetelem SFAC **(2)**
Rue Tomas Fonseca Torrede, Lisboa Twr

BNP Paribas SA—(Continued)

G, 1600, Lisbon, Portugal **(100%)**
Tel.: (351) 217215894
Web Site: http://www.cetelem.pt
Sales Range: $300-349.9 Million
Emp.: 700
Consumer Finance Services
N.A.I.C.S.: 522291

Cotelem Taiwan **(2)**
13 Fl 130 Sect 3 Nanking, Meng Shen East
Rd Sec 3, Taipei, 104, Taiwan **(100%)**
Tel.: (886) 227776020
Web Site: http://www.cetelem.com.tw
Consumer Finance Services
N.A.I.C.S.: 522291

Findomestic Banca S.p.A **(2)**
Via Jacopo Da Diacceto 48, 50129, Flor-
ence, Italy
Tel.: (39) 05527011
Web Site: http://www.infofindomestic.it
Sales Range: $600-649.9 Million
Emp.: 2,000
Business Banking Services
N.A.I.C.S.: 522320

Magyar Cetelem Bank Zrt. **(2)**
Terez Korut 55-57, 1062, Budapest,
Hungary **(100%)**
Tel.: (36) 61 458 6070
Web Site: http://www.cetelem.hu
Sales Range: $100-124.9 Million
Emp.: 250
Consumer Finance Services
N.A.I.C.S.: 522291

Cetelem Algerie SPA **(1)**
92 Chemin Gacem Mohamed, 16209, El
Mouradia, Algeria
Tel.: (213) 21 69 64 14
Web Site: http://dz.cetelem.com
Consumer Financial Services
N.A.I.C.S.: 522291

Cetelem IFN SA **(1)**
Calea Victoriei Nr 155 Bl D1 tronson 5 Etaj
8 Sector 1, Bucharest, 010073, Romania
Tel.: (40) 21 312 0220
Web Site: http://www.cetelem.ro
Consumer Credit Services
N.A.I.C.S.: 522291

Cetelem Servicios SA de CV **(1)**
Paseo De La Reforma 115 Piso 5, Mexico,
11000, Mexico
Tel.: (52) 5511000300
Management Consulting Services
N.A.I.C.S.: 541611

Cetelem Slovensko A.S. **(1)**
Panenska 7, Bratislava, 812 36, Slovakia
Tel.: (421) 259342100
Web Site: http://www.cetelem.sk
Consumer Credit Services
N.A.I.C.S.: 522291

Cobema SA **(1)**
Rue de Champles 61-63, 1301, Wavre,
Belgium
Tel.: (32) 10 24 37 68
Emp.: 20
Financial Planning Services
N.A.I.C.S.: 523940
Fabio Sorny (Mgr)

Cofhylux SA **(1)**
Avenue J F Kennedy 50, 2951, Luxem-
bourg, Luxembourg
Tel.: (352) 47 99 24 57
Real Estate Development Services
N.A.I.C.S.: 531390

Cofiparc SNC **(1)**
1 Boulevard Haussmann, 75009, Paris,
France
Tel.: (33) 1 47 56 38 60
Web Site: http://www.cofiparc.fr
Financial Planning Services
N.A.I.C.S.: 523940

Commerz Finanz GmbH **(1)**
Schwanthalerstr 31, Munich, 80336, Ger-
many
Tel.: (49) 89551130
Web Site: http://www.commerzfinanz.com
Commercial Banking Services
N.A.I.C.S.: 522110

**Compagnie Financiere Ottomane
SA** **(1)**

44 Avenue J-F Kennedy, 1855, Luxem-
bourg, Luxembourg
Tel.: (352) 22 18 54
Financial Planning Services
N.A.I.C.S.: 523940

**Compagnie Financiere de la Cote
d'Ivoire** **(1)**
Rue Gourgas 15 F Tour BICICI, 01 LP
1566, Abidian, 1, Cote d'Ivoire
Tel.: (225) 20 21 27 32
Investment Banking Services
N.A.I.C.S.: 523110

**Compagnie d Investsements de
Paris C.I.P** **(1)**
1 Boulevard Haussmann, 75009, Paris,
France
Tel.: (33) 140147342
Investment Management Service
N.A.I.C.S.: 523940

**Compagnie pour le Financement des
Loisirs - Cofi loisirs** **(1)**
9 Rue Jean Mermoz, 75008, Paris, France
Tel.: (33) 1 53 65 73 30
Sales Range: $50-74.9 Million
Emp.: 30
Financial Management Services
N.A.I.C.S.: 523999

Cooperleasing SpA **(1)**
Via Marconi 1, 40122, Bologna, Italy
Tel.: (39) 051 276411
Web Site: http://www.cooperleasing.it
Commercial Banking Services
N.A.I.C.S.: 522110

Cortal Consors **(1)**
24 Rue Des Deux Gares, 92855, Rueil-
Malmaison, France
Tel.: (33) 147380909
Web Site: http://www.cortalconsors.fr
Sales Range: $200-249.9 Million
Emp.: 500
Savings & Investments for Private Clients
N.A.I.C.S.: 522180

Subsidiary (Non-US):

BNP Paribas Personal Investors **(2)**
27 Avenue, 27 Monterey, 2163, Monterey,
Luxembourg **(100%)**
Tel.: (352) 25372537
Web Site: http://www.bnpparibas-
personalinvestors.lu
Sales Range: $1-9.9 Million
Emp.: 20
Savings & Investments for Private Investors
N.A.I.C.S.: 523150
Awada Philip (Gen Mgr)

Cortal Consors Belgium **(2)**
Rue Royale 145, B 1000, Brussels,
Belgium **(100%)**
Tel.: (32) 22251919
Web Site: http://www.cortal.be
Sales Range: $25-49.9 Million
Emp.: 50
Saving & Investment Services for Private
Investors
N.A.I.C.S.: 523940

Cortal Consors S.A. **(2)**
Pahnof Strasse 55, PO Box 1743, 90006,
Nuremberg, Germany
Tel.: (49) 9113690
Web Site: http://www.cortalconsors.de
Sales Range: $300-349.9 Million
Online Brokerage Service
N.A.I.C.S.: 523160

Creation Consumer Finance Ltd. **(1)**
4th-6th floor Wellington Buildings 2-4 Wel-
lington Street, Belfast, BT1 6HT, United
Kingdom
Tel.: (44) 3713769214
Web Site: http://www.creation.co.uk
Financial Services
N.A.I.C.S.: 522320

Creation Financial Services Ltd. **(1)**
Chadwick House Blenheim Court, Solihull,
B91 2AA, West Midlands, United Kingdom
Tel.: (44) 1217126952
Financial Services
N.A.I.C.S.: 522320

Credirama SPA **(1)**
Viale Belfiore 26, Florence, 50144, Italy
Tel.: (39) 0553374820

Commercial Banking Services
N.A.I.C.S.: 522110

Credissimo SA **(1)**
Rue des Premontres 4, 4000, Liege, Bel-
gium
Tel.: (32) 43375053
Web Site: http://www.credissimo.be
Litigation Services
N.A.I.C.S.: 541110

**Credit Moderne Antilles Guyane
SA** **(1)**
Immeuble Le Semaphore-rue Rene Rabat
ZAC de Houelbourg Sud II, ZI de Jarry
Baie-Mahault, 97112, La Bassee, France
Tel.: (33) 590326062
Web Site: http://www.credit-moderne.com
Loan Agency Services
N.A.I.C.S.: 522390
Emmanuel Bourg (Dir-Publ)

**Credit Moderne Ocean Indien
SA** **(1)**
22 Rue Pierre Aubert Saint Clotilde, 97495,
Paris, France
Tel.: (33) 262923924
Loan Agency Services
N.A.I.C.S.: 522390

Credit pour Habitations Sociales **(1)**
Jagersveld 4, 1170, Brussels, Belgium
Tel.: (32) 2 673 33 00
Financial Management Services
N.A.I.C.S.: 523999

DAB Bank AG **(1)**
Landsberger Str 300, 80687, Munich,
Germany **(100%)**
Tel.: (49) 89500680
Web Site: http://b2b.dab-bank.de
Securities Brokerage Services
N.A.I.C.S.: 523150
Camille Fohl (Chm)

Detaljhandelshuset i Hyllinge AB **(1)**
Kyrktorget 19, Partille, 433 33, Sweden
Tel.: (46) 850899900
Real Estate Prorperty Leasing Services
N.A.I.C.S.: 531190

Domofinance SA **(1)**
5 Avenue Kleber, 75116, Paris, France,
Tel.: (33) 1 46 39 99 39
Web Site: http://www.domofinance.com
Financial Management Services
N.A.I.C.S.: 523999

Duna Plaza Zrt **(1)**
Vaci ut 178 Duna Office 5 emelet, 1138,
Budapest, Hungary
Tel.: (36) 1 465 1600
Web Site: http://www.dunaplaza.hu
Shopping Center Operator
N.A.I.C.S.: 531120

ERBE SA **(1)**
Rue De La Blanche Borne 12, 6280, Lover-
val, Belgium **(47%)**
Tel.: (32) 71606060
Web Site: http://www.cnp.be
Emp.: 20
Holding Company
N.A.I.C.S.: 551112

Subsidiary (Domestic):

**Compagnie Nationale a Portefeuille
S.A.** **(2)**
Rue de la Blanche Borne 12, 6280, Lover-
val, Belgium
Tel.: (32) 71606060
Web Site: http://www.cnp.be
Holding Company
N.A.I.C.S.: 551112

Subsidiary (Non-US):

Agesca Nederland NV **(3)**
Veerkade 5, 3016 DE, Rotterdam,
Netherlands **(100%)**
Tel.: (31) 102183703
Holding Company
N.A.I.C.S.: 551112
Patricia Ottervanger (Acct Mgr)

Joint Venture (Domestic):

Parjointco N.V. **(4)**
Veerkade 5, Rotterdam, 3016DE, Netherlands

Tel.: (31) 4139154
Holding Company; Joint Venture Between
Power Financial Europe BV & Agesca Neth-
erland NV
N.A.I.C.S.: 551112

Holding (Non-US):

Pargesa Holding S.A. **(5)**
11 Grand-Rue, CH-1204, Geneva, Switzer-
land
Tel.: (41) 228177777
Web Site: http://www.pargesa.ch
Rev.: $5,770,980,992
Assets: $35,020,798,912
Liabilities: $11,115,023,488
Net Worth: $23,905,775,424
Earnings: $866,543,040
Emp.: 94,000
Fiscal Year-end: 12/31/2019
Holding Company
N.A.I.C.S.: 551112
Gerald Frere (Deputy Chm & Deputy Chm)

Subsidiary (Non-US):

Entremont S.A. **(3)**
25 Faubourg des Balmettes, PO Box
50029, 74001, Annecy, Cedex,
France **(75%)**
Tel.: (33) 9 69 32 09 91
Web Site: http://www.entremont.com
Producer of Cheese
N.A.I.C.S.: 311513
Olivier Brys (Dir-HR)

Joint Venture (Domestic):

TRASYS S.A **(3)**
Tarhulpsestaanveg No C 1660, B 1200,
Hoeilaart, Belgium
Tel.: (32) 27737111
Web Site: http://www.trasys.be
Sales Range: $200-249.9 Million
Emp.: 600
IT & Software Business Support Services
N.A.I.C.S.: 541511

Subsidiary (Domestic):

TRASYS Charleroi **(4)**
Terhulp Sesteenwg 6C, 1560, Hoeilaart,
Belgium
Tel.: (32) 71378211
Web Site: http://www.trasys.be
Sales Range: $50-74.9 Million
Emp.: 130
IT & Software Business Support Services
N.A.I.C.S.: 541511

Subsidiary (Non-US):

TRASYS Greece **(4)**
3 Arkadias St, Athens, 11526, Attica,
Greece
Tel.: (30) 2107769800
Web Site: http://www.trasys.gr
Sales Range: $25-49.9 Million
Emp.: 30
IT & Software Business Support Services
N.A.I.C.S.: 541511

TRASYS Luxembourg **(4)**
Route d'Arlon 283, 8011, Strassen, Luxem-
bourg
Tel.: (352) 2611101
Web Site:
　http://www.trasysinternational.com
Sales Range: $25-49.9 Million
Emp.: 43
IT & Software Business Support Services
N.A.I.C.S.: 541511

Effico Portugal **(1)**
Rua Tomas da Fonseca Centro Empresarial
Torres de Lisboa, Torre G-9 Andar, 1600-
209, Lisbon, Portugal
Tel.: (351) 21 780 60 00
Web Site: http://www.effico.pt
Asset Management Services
N.A.I.C.S.: 523999

Ejesur S.A. **(1)**
Calle Retama 3, Madrid, 28045, Spain
Tel.: (34) 914368500
Real Estate Manangement Services
N.A.I.C.S.: 531390

Ekspres Bank AS **(1)**
Oldenburg Alle 3, 2630, Taastrup, Denmark
Tel.: (45) 70235800

Web Site: http://www.expressbank.dk
Banking Services
N.A.I.C.S.: 522110

Esomet SAS (1)
37 Place du Marche Saint-Honore, 75001,
Paris, France
Tel.: (33) 173793999
Financial Investment Services
N.A.I.C.S.: 523999

**F G Ingenierie et Promotion
Immobiliere** (1)
506 Av Du Prado, 13008, Camblanes-et-
Meynac, France
Tel.: (33) 4 91 22 23 42
Real Estate Management Services
N.A.I.C.S.: 531390

Farmandstredet ANS (1)
Stoperigata 1, 0250, Oslo, Norway
Tel.: (47) 23213500
Real Estate Prorperty Leasing Services
N.A.I.C.S.: 531190

Farmandstredet Eiendom AS (1)
Stoperigata 1, Oslo, 0250, Norway
Tel.: (47) 23213500
Real Estate Prorperty Leasing Services
N.A.I.C.S.: 531190

Fastighets AB Allum (1)
Kyrktorget 19, Partille, 433 33, Sweden
Tel.: (46) 850899900
Real Estate Prorperty Leasing Services
N.A.I.C.S.: 531190

**Fastighets AB Borlange
Kopcentrum** (1)
Kyrktorget 19, Partille, 433 33, Sweden
Tel.: (46) 243248111
Real Estate Prorperty Leasing Services
N.A.I.C.S.: 531190

Fastighets AB Centrum Vasterort (1)
Kyrktorget 19, Partille, 433 33, Sweden
Tel.: (46) 850899900
Real Estate Management & Development
Services
N.A.I.C.S.: 531390

Fastighets AB CentrumInvest (1)
PO Box 200, Partille, 433 33, Sweden
Tel.: (46) 850899900
Real Estate Prorperty Leasing Services
N.A.I.C.S.: 531190

**Fastighets AB Marieberg
Centrum** (1)
Kyrktorget 19, 433 33, Partille, Sweden
Tel.: (46) 850899900
Real Estate Prorperty Leasing Services
N.A.I.C.S.: 531190

**Fastighets AB Overby
Kopcentrum** (1)
Ladugardsvagen 14, Trollhattan, 461 70,
Sweden
Tel.: (46) 520472550
Real Estate Prorperty Leasing Services
N.A.I.C.S.: 531190

**Fastighets AB Sollentuna
Centrum** (1)
Sollentunavagen 163 C, 191 47, Sollen-
tuna, Sweden
Tel.: (46) 86233370
Web Site: http://www.sollentunacentrum.se
Real Estate Prorperty Leasing Services
N.A.I.C.S.: 531190

Fimapierre (1)
23 Rue L Amiral D Estaing, 75116, Paris,
France
Tel.: (33) 1 53 67 29 00
Sales Range: $50-74.9 Million
Emp.: 100
Financial Management Services
N.A.I.C.S.: 523999

Fimestic Expansion SA (1)
Calle Retama 3, Madrid, 28045, Spain
Tel.: (34) 913370700
Financial Planning Services
N.A.I.C.S.: 523940

**Financial Telemarketing Services
Ltd.** (1)
Pinnacle House A1 Barnet Way, Boreham-
wood, WD6 2XX, Hertfordshire, United
Kingdom

Tel.: (44) 20 8324 3300
Web Site: http://www.fts-ltd.com
Debt Collection & Telemarketing Services
N.A.I.C.S.: 561440

Financiere BNP Paribas SAS (1)
1 Boulevard Haussmann, 75009, Paris,
France
Tel.: (33) 8 20 82 00 01
Financial Planning Services
N.A.I.C.S.: 523940

Financiere Paris Haussmann (1)
1 Boulevard Haussmann, 75009, Paris,
France
Tel.: (33) 8 99 96 26 48
Financial Planning Services
N.A.I.C.S.: 523940

**Friedland Participation et Gestion
S.A.** (1)
30 Quai de Dion Bouton, 92800, Puteaux,
France
Tel.: (33) 8 99 96 77 60
Financial Planning Services
N.A.I.C.S.: 523940

FundQuest MM Ltd. (1)
5 Aldermanbury Square, London, EC2V
7BP, United Kingdom
Tel.: (44) 20 7595 2000
Web Site: http://www.fundquest.com
Investment Management Service
N.A.I.C.S.: 523940

FundQuest UK Ltd. (1)
5 Aldermanbury Square, London, EC2V
7BP, United Kingdom
Tel.: (44) 20 7595 2000
Web Site: http://www.fundquest.com
Asset Management Services
N.A.I.C.S.: 523940

**Fundamentum Asset Management
S.A.** (1)
8 Rue Du Fort Rheinsheim, 2419, Luxem-
bourg, Luxembourg
Tel.: (352) 26 44 40 40
Asset Management Services
N.A.I.C.S.: 523940

Fundquest Advisor SASU (1)
1 boulevard Haussmann, 75009, Paris,
France
Tel.: (33) 158976100
Web Site: http://www.fundquestadvisor.com
Investment Advisory Services
N.A.I.C.S.: 523940

**GCC Consumo Establecimiento Fi-
nanciero de Credito SA** (1)
Paseo de los Melancolicos 14A, 28005, Ma-
drid, Spain
Tel.: (34) 910483030
Web Site: http://www.cajamarconsumo.es
Financial Services
N.A.I.C.S.: 522320

Gambit Financial Solutions SA (1)
Pole Image-36 rue de Mulhouse, 4020,
Liege, Belgium
Tel.: (32) 42798800
Web Site: http://www.gambit-finance.com
Investment Advisory Services
N.A.I.C.S.: 523940
Geoffroy De Schrevel (CEO)

Geneve Credit & Leasing SA (1)
Boulevard Du Pont-D'arve 28, Geneva,
1205, Switzerland
Tel.: (41) 223166600
Web Site: http://www.gcl-sa.ch
Financial Planning Services
N.A.I.C.S.: 523940

**Gestion et Location Holding
S.A.S.** (1)
41 Avenue de l'Opera, 75002, Paris, France
Tel.: (33) 1 41 14 18 18
Investment Management Service
N.A.I.C.S.: 523940

Greenval Insurance DAC (1)
Trinity Point 10-11 Leinster Street South,
Dublin, DO2 EF85, Ireland
Tel.: (353) 16125600
Web Site: http://www.greenval-
insurance.com
Fleet Motor Insurance Services
N.A.I.C.S.: 524128

**Gulskogen Prosjekt & Eiendom
AS** (1)
Stoperigata 1, Oslo, 250, Norway
Tel.: (47) 23 21 35 00
Emp.: 50
Real Estate Manangement Services
N.A.I.C.S.: 531390

Hamar Storsenter AS (1)
Stoperigata 1, Oslo, 0250, Norway
Tel.: (47) 23 21 35 00
Real Estate Prorperty Leasing Services
N.A.I.C.S.: 531190

Holding Gondomar 3 SAS (1)
21 Avenue Kleber, 75116, Paris, France
Tel.: (33) 1 46 08 28 19
Real Estate Management Services
N.A.I.C.S.: 531390

Horti Milano SRL (1)
Via Orti 25, 20122, Milan, Italy
Tel.: (39) 0236582730
Web Site: http://www.hortiportaromana.com
Real Estate Services
N.A.I.C.S.: 531311

**Humberclyde Commercial Invest-
ments Ltd.** (1)
Northern Cross, Basingstoke, RG21 4HL,
Hampshire, United Kingdom
Tel.: (44) 1256 377 377
Emp.: 250
Financial Management Services
N.A.I.C.S.: 523999
Jean-Michel Boyer (Gen Mgr)

Immoparibas Royale-Neuve SA (1)
Ave de la Porte-Neuve 21, 2227, Luxem-
bourg, Luxembourg
Tel.: (352) 26962000
Investment Management Service
N.A.I.C.S.: 523940

**Insinger de Beaufort Asset Manage-
ment NV** (1)
Herengracht 537, 1017 BV, Amsterdam,
Netherlands
Tel.: (31) 20 5215 000
Asset Management Services
N.A.I.C.S.: 523940

**Insinger de Beaufort Associates
BV** (1)
Parklaan 60, Eindhoven, 5613 BH, Nether-
lands
Tel.: (31) 402655255
Investment Management Service
N.A.I.C.S.: 523940

Insinger de Beaufort BV (1)
Herengracht 537, Amsterdam, 1017 BV,
Netherlands
Tel.: (31) 205215450
Web Site: http://www.insinger.com
Investment Management Service
N.A.I.C.S.: 523940

International Factors Italia SPA (1)
Via Deruta 19, PO Box 10732-20111,
20132, Milan, MI, Italy
Tel.: (39) 0267781
Web Site: http://ifitalia.it
Financial Services
N.A.I.C.S.: 522320

JCB Finance SAS (1)
3 rue du Vignolle, Sarcelles, 95842, France
Tel.: (33) 1 34 29 20 60
Sales Range: $50-74.9 Million
Emp.: 6
Financial Management Services
N.A.I.C.S.: 523999

KS Markedet (1)
Stoperigata 1, Oslo, 0250, Norway
Tel.: (47) 23123500
Real Estate Prorperty Leasing Services
N.A.I.C.S.: 531190

Kanizsa 2002 Kft. (1)
Europa Tanacs Utca 2, Nagykanizsa, 8800,
Hungary
Tel.: (36) 93537700
Real Estate Manangement Services
N.A.I.C.S.: 531390

Kle Projet 1 SAS (1)
Place St-Clair Centre Commercial B, 14200,
Herouville-Saint-Clair, France
Tel.: (33) 231237512

Real Estate Prorperty Leasing Services
N.A.I.C.S.: 531190

Kleber la Perouse SNC (1)
21 Av Kleber, 75116, Paris, France
Tel.: (33) 1 45 53 62 82
Real Estate Manangement Services
N.A.I.C.S.: 531390

Klecar Europe Sud SCS (1)
21 Avenue Kleber, Paris, 75116, France
Tel.: (33) 1 40 67 53 85
Sales Range: $300-349.9 Million
Emp.: 540
Real Estate Lending Services
N.A.I.C.S.: 531190
Laurent Morel (Pres)

Klecar Foncier Espana SA (1)
Avenida de La Vega 1 - Ed 1 Plt P Arroyo
Vega, Alcobendas, 28108, Spain
Tel.: (34) 914532308
Real Estate Development Services
N.A.I.C.S.: 531390

Klecar France SNC (1)
26 Boulevard des Capucines, 75009, Paris,
France
Tel.: (33) 140675740
Web Site: http://www.klecar.com
Emp.: 500
Real Estate Manangement Services
N.A.I.C.S.: 531390
Laurent Morin (Gen Mgr)

**Klepierre Management Magyarorszag
Kft.** (1)
Vaci Ut 178, 1138, Budapest, Hungary
Tel.: (36) 1 577 11 00
Emp.: 71
Shopping Mall Management Services
N.A.I.C.S.: 531110
Zsolt Kertai (Country Mgr)

Lafayette Services LaSer (1)
66 Rue Des Archives, 75003, Paris,
France (50%)
Tel.: (33) 44544700
Consumer Credit & Loyalty Card Schemes
N.A.I.C.S.: 522210

Subsidiary (Domestic):

Cofinoga S.A. (2)
66 Rue Des Archives, 75003, Paris, France
Tel.: (33) 556554750
Web Site: http://www.cofinoga.fr
Sales Range: $600-649.9 Million
Emp.: 2,500
Consumer Credit Services
N.A.I.C.S.: 522210

Subsidiary (Non-US):

LaSer Polska (2)
ul Suwak 3, 02 676, Warsaw, Poland
Tel.: (48) 22 591 45 45
Web Site: http://www.laserpolska.com
Consumer Finance Services
N.A.I.C.S.: 522210

**Le Sphinx Assurances Luxembourg
SA** (1)
Rue de Merl 74, 2146, Luxembourg, Lux-
embourg
Tel.: (352) 26 89 03 21
General Insurance Services
N.A.I.C.S.: 524210

Liberty Leasing Co. (1)
Liberty House Brook Avenue, Warsash,
Southampton, SO31 9HP, United Kingdom
Tel.: (44) 2380456565
Web Site: https://libertyleasing.co.uk
N.A.I.C.S.: 561990
Allan Clegg (Mng Dir)

Locatrice Italiana SPA (1)
Viale Della Liberazione 16/18, Milan, 20124,
Italy
Tel.: (39) 02 67 33 31
Passenger Car Rental Services
N.A.I.C.S.: 532111

Manitou Finance Ltd. (1)
34 Blackmoor Road, Verwood, BH31 6BB,
Dorset, United Kingdom
Tel.: (44) 1202 825331
Emp.: 50
Financial Planning Services
N.A.I.C.S.: 523940

BNP Paribas SA—(Continued)

Ivor Binns *(Gen Mgr)*

Meunier Promotion (1)
13 Blvd Fort De Vua, 75017, Paris, France (100%)
Tel.: (33) 155652004
Web Site: http://www.meunier-promotion.fr
Sales Range: $75-99.9 Million
Emp.: 250
Real Estate Developer & Housing Project Manager
N.A.I.C.S.: 531390

Microstart SCRL (1)
Rue de Fiennes 77, 1070, Brussels, Belgium
Tel.: (32) 28886100
Web Site: http://microstart.be
Banking Services
N.A.I.C.S.: 522110
Emmanuelle Decleve *(Branch Mgr)*

Miskolc 2002 Kft. (1)
Szentpali u 2-6, 3525, Miskolc, Hungary
Tel.: (36) 46503000
Web Site: http://www.miskolcplaza.hu
Commercial Building Leasing Services
N.A.I.C.S.: 531120

Natio Assurance, SA (1)
10 Rue Louis Bleriot, 92858, Rueil-Malmaison, France
Tel.: (33) 970809093
Insurance Services
N.A.I.C.S.: 524210

Natiobail 2 S.A. (1)
46 A 52 Rue Arago, Puteaux, 92800, France
Tel.: (33) 141972000
Financial Credit Services
N.A.I.C.S.: 522299

Natiocredibail SA (1)
Imm Le Metropole 46-52 46 Rue Arago, Puteaux, 92823, France
Tel.: (33) 1 41 97 20 00
Web Site: http://www.bnpparibas.com
Financial Planning Services
N.A.I.C.S.: 523940

Natiocredimurs SNC (1)
Imm Le Metropole 46-52 46 Rue Arago, Puteaux, 92800, Hauts-de-Seine, France
Tel.: (33) 1 41 97 20 00
Financial Management Services
N.A.I.C.S.: 523999

Nerstranda AS (1)
Stoperigata 1, Oslo, 0250, Norway
Tel.: (47) 23213500
Real Estate Prorperty Leasing Services
N.A.I.C.S.: 531190

Nordbyen Senter AS (1)
Stoperigata 1, Oslo, 0250, Norway
Tel.: (47) 90 89 59 00
Real Estate Prorperty Leasing Services
N.A.I.C.S.: 531190

Norrsken Finance SA (1)
1 Boulevard Haussmann, 75009, Paris, Cedex, France
Tel.: (33) 969320497
Web Site: http://www.norrsken.fr
Investment Advisory Services
N.A.I.C.S.: 523940

Norsk Kjopesenterforvaltning AS (1)
Stoperigata 1, 0250, Oslo, Norway
Tel.: (47) 23 21 35 00
Real Estate Property Management Services
N.A.I.C.S.: 531390

North Man Sverige AB (1)
Kyrktorget 19, Partille, 433 33, Sweden
Tel.: (46) 850899900
Real Estate Prorperty Leasing Services
N.A.I.C.S.: 531190

Omega Capital Europe PLC (1)
4th Floor 25-28 Adelaide Road, Dublin, Ireland
Tel.: (353) 1 605 3000
Securities Brokerage Services
N.A.I.C.S.: 523150
Brendan Roche *(Mgr)*

Omega Capital Investments Plc (1)
4th Floor 25-28 Adelaide Road, Dublin, D02

RY98, Ireland
Tel.: (353) 1 605 3000
Securities Brokerage Services
N.A.I.C.S.: 523150
Adrian John Masterson *(Dir)*

Opera Rendement SCPI (1)
4 Avenue Pablo Picasso, 92000, Nanterre, France
Tel.: (33) 1 47 24 34 25
Real Estate Manangement Services
N.A.I.C.S.: 531390

Os Alle 3 AS (1)
Stoperigata 1, Oslo, 0250, Norway
Tel.: (47) 23213500
Real Estate Prorperty Leasing Services
N.A.I.C.S.: 531190

PT BNP Paribas Securities Indonesia (1)
Sequis Tower Level 28 Jl Jendral Sudirman Kav 71 SEBC Lot 11B, Jakarta, 12190, Indonesia
Tel.: (62) 2150814700
Web Site: http://www.bnpparibas.co.id
Investment Banking Services
N.A.I.C.S.: 523150

Paribas Asia Equity Ltd. (1)
Rm 63 1/F lfc Two, Central, China (Hong Kong)
Tel.: (852) 21085600
Securities Brokerage Services
N.A.I.C.S.: 523150

Paricomi 2 (ex-Paricomi) (1)
46 52 Rue Arago, Puteaux, France
Tel.: (33) 141972000
Financial Management Services
N.A.I.C.S.: 523999

Parilease SAS (1)
41 Avenue de L Opera, Paris, 75002, France
Tel.: (33) 142980761
Financial Management Services
N.A.I.C.S.: 523999

Penne International NV (1)
Wijngaardveld 32, 9300, Aalst, Belgium
Tel.: (32) 53214419
Web Site: https://www.penne.be
N.A.I.C.S.: 332322

Phedina Hypotheken 2010 BV (1)
Reguliersdwarsstraat 90, Amsterdam, 1017 BN, Netherlands
Tel.: (31) 205215629
Securities Brokerage Services
N.A.I.C.S.: 523150

PinnAfrica Insurance (1)
Pinnafrica Life Ltd Bldg B Curzon Pl Turnberry Ofc Pk No 48, PO Box 98758, Bryanston, 2021, South Africa (100%)
Tel.: (27) 112441300
Web Site: http://www.cardifpinnacle.co.za
Sales Range: $50-74.9 Million
Emp.: 30
Consumer Credits Insurance Services
N.A.I.C.S.: 522299

Pinnacle Insurance plc (1)
Pinnacle House A1 Barnet Way, Borehamwood, WD6 2XX, Hertfordshire, United Kingdom (100%)
Tel.: (44) 20 8207 9000
Web Site: http://www.cardifpinnacle.com
Sales Range: $350-399.9 Million
Emp.: 300
Insurance & Pension Funds
N.A.I.C.S.: 524292
Gerard Binet *(Chm)*

Pinnacle Underwriting Limited (1)
Pinnacle House A1 Barnet Way, Borehamwood, WD6 2XX, Hertfordshire, United Kingdom
Tel.: (44) 2082079250
Insurance Underwriting Services
N.A.I.C.S.: 524298

Poistovna Cardif Slovakia AS (1)
Plynarenska 7/C, 821 09, Bratislava, Slovakia
Tel.: (421) 258240011
Financial Services
N.A.I.C.S.: 522320

Pommeraie Parc SC (1)

21 Avenue Kleber, 75116, Paris, France
Tel.: (33) 899963545
Real Estate Managment Services
N.A.I.C.S.: 531390

Portzamparc Gestion (1)
10 rue Meurisboite, Nantes, 44100, France
Tel.: (33) 240449400
Web Site: http://www.portzamparc.fr
Emp.: 75
Real Estate Development Services
N.A.I.C.S.: 531390

Protection 24 SACA (1)
628 avenue du Grain d'Or, 41354, Vineuil, Cedex, France
Tel.: (33) 254505697
Web Site: http://www.protection24.com
Security System Services
N.A.I.C.S.: 561621

Pyrotex SARL (1)
AV J-F Kennedy 44, 1855, Luxembourg, Luxembourg
Tel.: (352) 27848877
Web Site: http://www.legilux.lu
Investment Management Service
N.A.I.C.S.: 523940

Reconfiguration BV (1)
Herengracht 450, Amsterdam, 1017 CA, Netherlands
Tel.: (31) 205554466
Asset Management Services
N.A.I.C.S.: 523940

S.C BNP Paribas Real Estate Advisory S.A (1)
11 Ion Campineanu Street 6th floor 1st District, 010031, Bucharest, Romania
Web Site: http://realestate.bnpparibas.com.ro
Sales Range: $50-74.9 Million
Emp.: 20
Real Estate Advisory Services
N.A.I.C.S.: 531390
Philippe Mer *(Pres)*

SCI Champvernier (1)
30 Quai de Dion Bouton, 92800, Puteaux, France
Tel.: (33) 8 99 96 77 56
Financial Planning Services
N.A.I.C.S.: 523940

SCI FLIF Chateau Landon (1)
30 Quai de Dion Bouton, 92800, Puteaux, France
Tel.: (33) 8 99 96 77 60
Real Estate Management Services
N.A.I.C.S.: 531390

SCI FLIF Evry 2 (1)
30 Quai de Dion Bouton, 92800, Puteaux, France
Tel.: (33) 8 99 96 77 60
Real Estate Management Services
N.A.I.C.S.: 531390

SCI FLIF Le Gallo (1)
30 Quai de Dion Bouton, 92800, Puteaux, France
Tel.: (33) 8 99 96 77 60
Real Estate Management Services
N.A.I.C.S.: 531390

Sadyba Best Mall Sp zoo (1)
Ul Powsinska 31, 02-903, Warsaw, Poland
Tel.: (48) 223103000
Web Site: https://www.sadyba.pl
Emp.: 2
Shopping Mall Operator
N.A.I.C.S.: 531120
Elzbieta Werner *(Gen Mgr)*

Same Deutz-Fahr Finance SAS (1)
46 A 52 Rue Arago, Puteaux, 92800, France
Tel.: (33) 141972000
Financial Management Services
N.A.I.C.S.: 523999

Segece Ceska Republica SRO (1)
Plzenska 16/3217, Smichov, 150 00, Prague, Czech Republic
Tel.: (420) 257 090 600
Web Site: http://www.segece.cz
Sales Range: $25-49.9 Million
Emp.: 40
Real Estate Prorperty Leasing Services

N.A.I.C.S.: 531190

Segece Espana SLU (1)
Avenida de la Vega 1 Edificio 1 3 planta, 28108, Alcobendas, Spain
Tel.: (34) 914532370
Web Site: http://www.kaef.com
Emp.: 50
Commercial Building Leasing Services
N.A.I.C.S.: 531120

Segece Hellas Real Estate Management SA (1)
94 Vassilissis Sofias Avenue & 1 Kerasountos Str, 115 28, Athens, Greece
Tel.: (30) 210 74 68 061
Real Estate Development Services
N.A.I.C.S.: 531390

Segece Polska SP. z.o.o. (1)
Al Armii Ludowej 26/9 C, Warsaw, 609, Poland
Tel.: (48) 22 35 66 950
Web Site: http://www.segece.pl
Emp.: 30
Shopping Center Operator
N.A.I.C.S.: 531120
Homeo Michael *(Gen Mgr)*

Services Logiciels d'Integration Boursiere SA (1)
1 boulevard Haussmann, 75009, Paris, France
Tel.: (33) 170369700
Web Site: http://www.slib.com
Financial Investment Services
N.A.I.C.S.: 523999
Philippe Cognet *(Mng Dir)*

Sesame Conseil SAS (1)
13 Boulevard du Fort de Vaux, 75017, Paris, France
Tel.: (33) 1 53 59 32 32
Web Site: http://www.sesameconseil.fr
Real Estate Manangement Services
N.A.I.C.S.: 531390

Sharekhan Ltd. (1)
10th Floor Beta Building Lodha ithink Techno Campus Off jvlr, Opp Kanjurmarg Railway Station Kanjurmarg East, Mumbai, 400042, Maharashtra, India
Tel.: (91) 2261150000
Web Site: http://www.sharekhan.com
Online Security Brokerage Services
N.A.I.C.S.: 523150

Societe Orbaisienne de Participations (1)
1 Boulevard Haussmann, 75009, Paris, France
Tel.: (33) 8 99 96 77 63
Investment Management Service
N.A.I.C.S.: 523940

Societe des Centres d'Oc et d'Oil - SCOO SC (1)
Centre Commercial Les Arcades, 93160, Noisy-le-Grand, France
Tel.: (33) 1 49 31 01 72
Real Estate Management Services
N.A.I.C.S.: 531390

Stavanger Storsenter AS (1)
Stoperigata 1, 0250, Oslo, Norway
Tel.: (47) 23 21 35 00
Real Estate Prorperty Leasing Services
N.A.I.C.S.: 531190

Steen & Strom Holding AB (1)
Lastmakargatan 20, 111 44, Stockholm, Sweden
Tel.: (46) 850899900
Web Site: http://www.steenstrom.com
Sales Range: $200-249.9 Million
Emp.: 350
Investment Management Service
N.A.I.C.S.: 523940

Storm Holding Norway AS (1)
Stoperigata 1, 0250, Oslo, Norway
Tel.: (47) 23213500
Investment Management Service
N.A.I.C.S.: 523940

Stovner Senter AS (1)
Stoperigata 1, 0250, Oslo, Norway
Tel.: (47) 23 21 35 00
Real Estate Prorperty Leasing Services
N.A.I.C.S.: 531190

Symag SASU (1)
9 rue Saint Petersbourg, 75008, Paris,
France
Tel.: (33) 178682000
Web Site: http://www.symag.com
Emp.: 200
On-site Maintenance Services
N.A.I.C.S.: 561210
Philippe Gherardi (Mgr)

Szeged Plaza Kft. (1)
Kossuth Lajos sgrt 119, 6724, Szeged,
Hungary
Tel.: (36) 62789049
Web Site: http://www.szegedplaza.hu
Commercial Building Leasing Services
N.A.I.C.S.: 531120

Szolnok Plaza Kft. (1)
Ady Endre ut 28 / A, 5000, Szolnok, Hungary
Tel.: (36) 56785011
Web Site: http://www.szolnokplaza.hu
Sales Range: $50-74.9 Million
Emp.: 100
Shopping Mall Operator
N.A.I.C.S.: 531120

TEB Holding Anonim Sirketi (1)
TEB Kampus C Blok Saray Mahallesi
Sokullu Caddesi 7A Umraniye, 34768, Istanbul, Turkiye (50%)
Tel.: (90) 216 635 3535
Web Site: http://www.tebholding.com
Bank Holding Company
N.A.I.C.S.: 551111

Subsidiary (Domestic):

TEB Arval Arac Filo Kiralama AS (2)
Gayrette Mah Yener Sok No 1 Kat 5-6, Besiktas, 34349, Istanbul, Turkiye
Tel.: (90) 3375500
Web Site: https://www.teb.com.tr
N.A.I.C.S.: 532111

Turk Ekonomi Bankasi A.S. (2)
TEB Kampus C ve D Blok Saray Mah
Sokullu Cad No 7A - 7B, Umraniye, Istanbul, 34768, Turkiye (55%)
Tel.: (90) 2166353535
Web Site: http://www.teb.com.tr
Rev.: $957,963,649
Assets: $26,958,652,777
Liabilities: $25,053,044,253
Net Worth: $1,905,608,524
Earnings: $280,997,024
Emp.: 8,954
Fiscal Year-end: 12/31/2021
Banking Services
N.A.I.C.S.: 522110
Umit Leblebici (Gen Mgr)

Subsidiary (Domestic):

Fortis Faktoring A.S. (3)
Buyukdere Cad No 100-102 Maya Akar
Center B Blok, 2 nci Zemin Kat No 7-8,
Esentepe, 34394, Istanbul, Turkiye
Tel.: (90) 212 337 68 00
Web Site: http://www.fortiscomfin.com
Commercial Finance, Factoring, Credit
Management, Debt Administration & Other
Financial Services
N.A.I.C.S.: 522299

**TEB Cetelem Tuketici Finansmani
A.S.** (3)
Gayrettepe Mahallesi Yener Sokak No 1
Kat 3-4, Istanbul, 34349, Besiktas,
Turkiye (100%)
Tel.: (90) 212 355 2000
Web Site: http://www.tebcetelem.com.tr
Sales Range: $50-74.9 Million
Emp.: 77
Consumer Finance Services
N.A.I.C.S.: 522291

TEB Faktoring Inc. (3)
Yener Sokak No 1 Kat 7-8, Gayrettepe Besiktas, 34349, Istanbul, Turkiye
Tel.: (90) 2123704500
Web Site: http://www.tebfaktoring.com.tr
International & Domestic Factoring Service
Provider
N.A.I.C.S.: 522299

TEB Investment Securities, Inc (3)
TEB Kampus D Blok Saray Mah Sokullu

Cad No 7A - 7B, Umraniye, 34768, Istanbul,
Turkiye
Tel.: (90) 2166364444
Web Site: http://www.teb.com.tr
Capital markets activities
N.A.I.C.S.: 523150

TEB Leasing Inc (3)
No 103 3 Mecidiyekoy, Buyukdere Cad Sarli
Merkezi, Istanbul, Turkiye
Tel.: (90) 212 393 69 00
Web Site: http://www.tebleasing.com
Financial Services
N.A.I.C.S.: 522320

TEB Tuketici Finansman AS (3)
Gayrettepe Mahallesi Yener Sokak No 1
Kat 3-4, Besiktas, 34349, Istanbul, Turkiye
Tel.: (90) 212 355 20 00
Web Site: http://www.tebcetelem.com.tr
Emp.: 80
Financial Management Services
N.A.I.C.S.: 523999

TEB Yatirim Menkul Degerler AS (3)
TEB Kampus D Blok Saray Mahallesi
Sokullu Caddesi No7B, Umraniye, 34768,
Istanbul, Turkiye
Tel.: (90) 2166364444
Web Site: http://www.tebyatirim.com.tr
Financial Services
N.A.I.C.S.: 522320

Subsidiary (Non-US):

The Economy Bank N V (3)
Prof W H Keesomlaan 5, Park Plaza K 5,
80670, Amstelveen, North Holland, Netherlands
Tel.: (31) 205039010
Web Site: http://www.tebnv.nl
Sales Range: $25-49.9 Million
Emp.: 50
International services to the Dutch Bank
N.A.I.C.S.: 522110

Taitbout Participation 3 Snc (1)
1 Boulevard Haussmann, 75009, Paris,
France
Tel.: (33) 8 99 96 77 55
Investment Management Service
N.A.I.C.S.: 523940

Tasaciones Hipotecarias SA (1)
Calle Maria De Molina 54, Madrid, 28006,
Spain
Tel.: (34) 914549700
Web Site: http://www.tasacionesh.es
Agriculture Financing & Leasing Services
N.A.I.C.S.: 523999

Textainer Marine Containers Ltd. (1)
Century House 16 Par-la-Ville Road, Hamilton, HM HX, Bermuda
Tel.: (441) 296 2500
Marine Cargo Container Leasing & Management Services
N.A.I.C.S.: 488320
Phil Bwer (Pres)

Thunderbird Investments PLC (1)
4th Floor 25-28 Adelaide Road, Dublin, Ireland
Tel.: (353) 1 605 3000
Securities Brokerage Services
N.A.I.C.S.: 523150

Torvbyen Senter AS (1)
Stoperigata 1, Oslo, 0250, Norway
Tel.: (47) 23213500
Real Estate Prorperty Leasing Services
N.A.I.C.S.: 531190

Torvbyen Utvikling AS (1)
Stoperigata 1, 0250, Oslo, Norway
Tel.: (47) 23213500
Real Estate Prorperty Leasing Services
N.A.I.C.S.: 531190

Torvhjornet Lillestrom ANS (1)
Stoperigata 1, 0250, Oslo, Norway
Tel.: (47) 23213500
Real Estate Prorperty Leasing Services
N.A.I.C.S.: 531190

Tour El Ghazal-BNPI (1)
Ring Fouad Chehab, Place Tabaris, Beirut,
1608, Lebanon (100%)
Tel.: (961) 1200600
Web Site: http://www.bnpi-liban.bnpparibas.com

Commercial Banking Services
N.A.I.C.S.: 522110

UCB Ingatlanhitel RT (1)
Terez Krt 55-57 II Emelet, Budapest, 1062,
Hungary
Tel.: (36) 1 238 9800
Web Site: http://www.ingatlanhitel.hu
Mortgage Loan Brokerage Services
N.A.I.C.S.: 522310

UCB Locabail immobilier 2 (1)
46 Rue Aragola Defense, 92800, Puteaux,
France
Tel.: (33) 141424142
Financial Credit Services
N.A.I.C.S.: 522299

UCI (1)
C / Retama 3, Torre Ejesur, 28045, Madrid,
Spain (100%)
Tel.: (34) 913373737
Web Site: http://www.uci.com
Sales Range: $350-399.9 Million
Emp.: 700
Mortgage Services
N.A.I.C.S.: 522310

**UCI Union de Creditos
Imobiliarios** (1)
Av Engenheiro Duarte Pacheco Torre 1 14
Andar Amoreiras, 1070-101, Lisbon,
Portugal (50%)
Tel.: (351) 213835000
Web Site: http://www.uci.pt
Sales Range: $50-74.9 Million
Emp.: 60
Real Estate Credit & Finance Services
N.A.I.C.S.: 522292

UEB (Switzerland) (1)
15 17 Quai Des Bergues, PO Box 1211,
1211, Geneva, Switzerland (100%)
Tel.: (41) 229063002
Sales Range: $350-399.9 Million
Emp.: 600
Private Banking Services
N.A.I.C.S.: 522180

UkrSibbank (1)
2/12 Andriivska Str, Kiev, 04070, Ukraine
Tel.: (380) 44 590 06 90
Web Site: http://www.ukrsibbank.com
Commercial Banking Services
N.A.I.C.S.: 522110
Philippe Dumel (Chm-Mgmt Bd)

Subsidiary (Domestic):

JSC Ukrsib Asset Management (2)
8 Illinska Str, Kiev, 04070, Ukraine
Tel.: (380) 445375056
Web Site: http://www.usb.adprodev.com
Sales Range: $50-74.9 Million
Emp.: 20
Asset Management Services
N.A.I.C.S.: 523940

Ukrainian Leasing Company (1)
Blvd Vaclav Havel 18 2nd floor office 32,
04070, Kiev, Ukraine
Tel.: (380) 959040495
Web Site: http://www.ulc.com.ua
Financial Lending Services
N.A.I.C.S.: 522220

United European Bank & Trust (Nassau) Ltd. (1)
Scotia Bank Building 3rd Floor Bay Street,
PO Box N-4883, Nassau, Bahamas
Tel.: (242) 3265935
Sales Range: $50-74.9 Million
Emp.: 9
Offshore Private & Commercial Banking &
Trust Services
N.A.I.C.S.: 522110

Utexam Logistics Ltd. (1)
5 George's Dock IFSC, Dublin, 1, Ireland
Tel.: (353) 1 612 5000
Logistics Consulting Servies
N.A.I.C.S.: 541614

Vastra Torp Mark AB (1)
PO Box 200, Partille, 433 24, Sweden
Tel.: (46) 850899900
Real Estate Prorperty Leasing Services
N.A.I.C.S.: 531190

Vela ABS S.r.l (1)
Via Vittorio Alfieri 1, Conegliano, 31015,

Treviso, Italy
Tel.: (39) 0438360926
Investment Banking Services
N.A.I.C.S.: 523999

Vela Home SRL (1)
Via Vittorio Alfieri 1, Conegliano, 31015,
Italy
Tel.: (39) 0438360926
Real Estate Manangement Services
N.A.I.C.S.: 531390

Viola Finanza SRL (1)
Via Vittorio Alfieri 1, Conegliano, 31015,
Treviso, Italy
Tel.: (39) 0438360926
Financial Management Services
N.A.I.C.S.: 523999

Warranty Direct Ltd (1)
Quadrant House 20 Broad Street Mall,
Reading, RG1 7QE, United Kingdom
Tel.: (44) 8450 521 175
Web Site: http://www.warrantydirect.co.uk
Automotive Insurance Coverage Services
N.A.I.C.S.: 524298
Duncan McClure Fisher (Mng Dir)

amedes Holding GmbH (1)
Haferweg 40, 22769, Hamburg, Germany
Tel.: (49) 800 5891 669
Web Site: http://www.amedes-group.com
Medical Diagnostic Services
N.A.I.C.S.: 621511
Patrick Finzer (Mng Dir)

BNR UDYOG LTD.
6-3-650 2nd Floor 218 Maheshwari
Chambers, Somajiguda, Hyderabad,
500082, India
Tel.: (91) 4023375791
Web Site: https://www.bnrul.com
530809—(BOM)
Rev.: $283,256
Assets: $755,934
Liabilities: $129,235
Net Worth: $626,699
Earnings: $86,787
Emp.: 11
Fiscal Year-end: 03/31/22
Medical Transcription Services
N.A.I.C.S.: 621999
Kamal Narayan Rathi (Mng Dir)

BNS SPLIT CORP II
40 King Street West Scotia Plaza
26th Floor, PO Box 4085, Toronto,
M5W 2X6, ON, Canada
Tel.: (416) 862-3191
BSC.PR.C—(TSX)
Rev.: $43,059
Assets: $20,904,324
Liabilities: $6,238,446
Net Worth: $14,665,878
Earnings: ($445,079)
Fiscal Year-end: 09/22/19
Investment Fund Management Services
N.A.I.C.S.: 523940
Brian D. Mcchesney (Mgr-Fund)

**BNT HIDRAULIKA D.D. NOVI
TRAVNIK**
Mehmeda Spahe1, 72290, Novi
Travnik, Bosnia & Herzegovina
Tel.: (387) 30 525 025
Web Site: http://www.bnt-hidraulika.com.ba
Year Founded: 1949
Rev.: $223,989
Assets: $3,218,485
Liabilities: $2,521,718
Net Worth: $696,767
Earnings: ($166,085)
Emp.: 74
Fiscal Year-end: 12/31/17
Hydraulic Component & Equipment
Mfr
N.A.I.C.S.: 333995

BNT HOLDING D.D.

BNT Holding d.d.—(Continued)

Ul Mehmeda Spahe br1, Novi
Travnik, 72290, Bosnia & Herze-
govina
Tel.: (387) 30525028
Web Site: http://www.bnt-
holding.com.ba
Year Founded: 1949
BHOLRK1—(SARE)
Rev.: $1,090,410
Assets: $5,982,424
Liabilities: $2,959,175
Net Worth: $3,023,248
Earnings: ($168,266)
Emp.: 5
Fiscal Year-end: 12/31/21
Holding Company
N.A.I.C.S.: 551112

BNT POSLOVNI SUSTAV D.D.
Kralja Tvrtka 7, 72290, Novi Travnik,
Bosnia & Herzegovina
Tel.: (387) 30793812
BPSTR—(SARE)
Rev.: $18,096
Assets: $543,940
Liabilities: $308
Net Worth: $543,631
Earnings: ($20,244)
Fiscal Year-end: 12/31/20
Kitchen Product Mfr & Distr
N.A.I.C.S.: 332215

BOA CONCEPT SA
22 Rue de Meons, 42000, Saint-
Etienne, France
Tel.: (33) 477502124
Web Site: https://www.boa-
concept.com
Year Founded: 2012
ALBOA—(EUR)
Emp.: 54
Conveyor Logistic Services
N.A.I.C.S.: 238290
Jean-Lucien Rascle (CEO)

BOA GROUP S.A.
Avenue Cheick Zayed Hamdallaye
Immeuble Tomota, BP E 3291, Ba-
mako, Mali
Tel.: (223) 229 4829
Web Site: http://www.boaholding.com
Year Founded: 1988
Sales Range: $400-449.9 Million
Emp.: 4,000
Bank Holding Company
N.A.I.C.S.: 551111
Mohamed Bennani (Chm & Mng Dir)

Subsidiaries:

Bank of Africa - Benin   (1)
Avenue Jean-Paul II 08, PO Box 0879, Co-
tonou, Benin   (14.43%)
Tel.: (229) 2131 3228
Web Site: http://www.boabenin.com
Emp.: 531
Retail & Commercial Banking Services
N.A.I.C.S.: 522110
Paulin Laurent Cossi (Chm)

Bank of Africa - Burkina Faso   (1)
770 Avenue du President Aboubacar San-
goule Lamizana 01, BP 1319, Ouagadou-
gou, 01, Burkina Faso
Tel.: (226) 50308870
Web Site: http://www.boaburkinafaso.com
Sales Range: $25-49.9 Million
Emp.: 195
Retail & Commercial Banking
N.A.I.C.S.: 522110

Bank of Africa - Cote d'Ivoire   (1)
Abidjan Plateau Angle Avenue Terrasson de
Fougeres Rue Gourgas 01, PO Box 4132,
Abidjan, 01, Cote d'Ivoire   (7.19%)
Tel.: (225) 2030 3400
Web Site: http://www.boacoteivoire.com
Sales Range: $25-49.9 Million
Emp.: 206
Retail & Commercial Banking

N.A.I.C.S.: 522110

Bank of Africa - Kenya Ltd.   (1)
BOA House Karuna Close Off Waiyaki Way
Westlands, PO Box 69562, 00400, Nairobi,
Kenya   (10%)
Tel.: (254) 20 3 275 273
Web Site: http://www.boakenya.com
Rev.: $39,602,390
Assets: $520,236,394
Liabilities: $438,946,426
Net Worth: $81,289,968
Earnings: $649,133
Emp.: 6,000
Fiscal Year-end: 12/31/2017
Retail & Commercial Banking
N.A.I.C.S.: 522110
Anne Wanjiru Gitau (Sec)

Affiliate (Non-US):

Bank of Africa - Tanzania Limited   (2)
NDC Development House Ohio
Street/Kivukoni Front, PO Box 3054, Dar es
Salaam, Tanzania   (34.14%)
Tel.: (255) 222110104
Web Site: http://www.boatanzania.com
Sales Range: $10-24.9 Million
Emp.: 201
Retail & Commercial Banking
N.A.I.C.S.: 522110
Fulgence Kazaura (Chm)

Bank of Africa - Uganda Ltd.   (2)
Bank of Africa House Plot 45 Jinja Road,
PO Box 2750, Kampala, Uganda (50.01%)
Tel.: (256) 414230436
Web Site: http://www.boa-uganda.com
Emp.: 287
Retail & Commercial Banking
N.A.I.C.S.: 522110
Arthur Isiko (Exec Dir)

Bank of Africa - Madagascar   (1)
2 Place de l'Independance, BP 183, Anta-
nanarivo, 101, Madagascar
Tel.: (261) 2022 391 00
Web Site: http://www.boa.mg
Sales Range: $50-74.9 Million
Emp.: 874
Retail & Commercial Banking
N.A.I.C.S.: 522110

Bank of Africa - Mali   (1)
418 Avenue de la Marne, BP 2249, Bozola,
Bamako, Mali   (20.43%)
Tel.: (223) 2070 0500
Web Site: http://www.boamali.com
Sales Range: $25-49.9 Million
Emp.: 300
Retail & Commercial Banking Services
N.A.I.C.S.: 522110

BOAB METALS LIMITED
Level 1 105 St Georges Terrace,
Perth, 6000, WA, Australia
Tel.: (61) 862680449
Web Site:
https://www.pacificominerals.com.au
BML—(ASX)
Rev.: $158,777
Assets: $8,518,618
Liabilities: $445,692
Net Worth: $8,072,927
Earnings: ($2,218,198)
Fiscal Year-end: 06/30/24
Metal Mining
N.A.I.C.S.: 212290
Simon Noon (Mng Dir)

**BOADICEA RESOURCES LIM-
ITED**
Level 6 99 William Street, PO Box
245, Melbourne, 3000, VIC, Australia
Tel.: (61) 370477804
Web Site: https://boaresources.com
BOA—(ASX)
Rev.: $172,811
Assets: $5,002,268
Liabilities: $57,137
Net Worth: $4,945,131
Earnings: ($529,024)
Emp.: 4,628
Fiscal Year-end: 06/30/24
Gold Exploration

N.A.I.C.S.: 212220
Domenic De Marco (Chm)

**BOAI NKY MEDICAL HOLD-
INGS LTD.**
No 1888 Wenhua Road East Section,
Jiaozuo, 454450, Henan, China
Tel.: (86) 3918610680   CN
Web Site: http://eng.boai-nky.com
Year Founded: 2003
300109—(CHIN)
Rev.: $208,590,876
Assets: $521,378,208
Liabilities: $83,717,712
Net Worth: $437,660,496
Earnings: $40,920,984
Fiscal Year-end: 12/31/22
Polymers for Pharmaceuticals & Per-
sonal Care Products Mfr
N.A.I.C.S.: 325998
Zhang Junzheng (Chm & Gen Mgr)

Subsidiaries:

Tianjin Boai NKY International
Ltd   (1)
Suites 1808-9 Guohua Building 857 Dagu-
Nan Road, Hexi District, Tianjin, 300200,
China
Tel.: (86) 22 58316066
Web Site: http://www.china-pvp.com
Polymers Mfr
N.A.I.C.S.: 326113

**BOARDWALK REAL ESTATE
INVESTMENT TRUST**
200 1501 - 1 Street SW, Calgary,
T2R 0W1, AB, Canada
Tel.: (403) 531-9255   AB
Web Site: https://www.bwalk.com
Year Founded: 1984
BEI.UN—(TSX)
Rev.: $348,423,720
Assets: $4,802,940,092
Liabilities: $2,416,879,684
Net Worth: $2,386,060,408
Earnings: $26,615,812
Emp.: 1,700
Fiscal Year-end: 12/31/19
Real Estate Investment Trust
N.A.I.C.S.: 525990
Samantha Kolias (CEO)

**BOARDWARE INTELLIGENCE
TECHNOLOGY LIMITED**
Alameda Dr Carlos D Assumpcao no
335-341 Hotline Centre 15/F I-Q & X,
Macau, China (Macau)
Tel.: (853) 82916000   Ky
Web Site:
https://www.boardware.com
Year Founded: 2010
1204—(HKG)
Rev.: $91,863,921
Assets: $74,685,146
Liabilities: $31,668,054
Net Worth: $43,017,091
Earnings: $576,330
Emp.: 277
Fiscal Year-end: 12/31/23
Information Technology Services
N.A.I.C.S.: 541512
Ka Chon Chao (Founder)

Subsidiaries:

BoardWare Information System
Limited   (1)
Alameda Dr Carlos D Assumpcao No 335-
341 Hotline Centre 15/F I-Q & X, Macau,
China (Macau)
Tel.: (853) 28229801
Information Technology Services
N.A.I.C.S.: 541519

Synergy Computers & Communica-
tions Limited   (1)
Unit 1201 - 1202 12/F Tower 1 Enterprise
Square 9 Sheung Yuet Road, Kowloon bay,
Kowloon, China (Hong Kong)

Tel.: (852) 38963221
Web Site: https://www.synergy-
distribution.com
Cyber Security Services
N.A.I.C.S.: 541519

BOART LONGYEAR LTD.
26 Butler Boulevard Burbridge Busi-
ness Park Adelaide Airport, Adelaide,
5950, SA, Australia
Tel.: (61) 883758375
Web Site:
http://www.boartlongyear.com
BLY—(ASX)
Rev.: $1,038,887,000
Assets: $774,855,000
Liabilities: $493,919,000
Net Worth: $280,936,000
Earnings: $11,855,000
Emp.: 5,894
Fiscal Year-end: 12/31/22
Drilling Equipment Mfr
N.A.I.C.S.: 333131
Jeffrey Olsen (Pres & CEO)

Subsidiaries:

Boart Longyear International Holdings
Inc.   (1)
10808 S River Front Pkwy Ste 600, South
Jordan, UT 84095
Tel.: (801) 972-6430
Emp.: 300
Mfr & Supplier of Tools & Equipment for
Exploration & Mining
N.A.I.C.S.: 213115

Subsidiary (Non-US):

Boart Longyear Alberta Limited   (2)
2442 South Sheridan Way, Mississauga,
L5J 2M7, ON, Canada
Tel.: (905) 822-7922
Mineral Mining & Drilling Services
N.A.I.C.S.: 212390

Boart Longyear Australia Pty Ltd   (2)
26 Burbridge Business Park, Adelaide,
5950, SA, Australia
Tel.: (61) 883758375
Sales Range: $50-74.9 Million
Emp.: 100
Mineral Exploration Services
N.A.I.C.S.: 213115

Boart Longyear BV   (2)
Columbusweg 8, Venlo, 5928 LC, Nether-
lands
Tel.: (31) 778505850
Sales Range: $50-74.9 Million
Emp.: 15
Mineral Exploration Services
N.A.I.C.S.: 213115

Subsidiary (Domestic):

Boart Longyear EMEA Cooperatief
U.A   (3)
Columbusweg 8, 5928 LC, Venlo, Limburg,
Netherlands
Tel.: (31) 778505850
Mineral Exploration Services
N.A.I.C.S.: 213115

Boart Longyear International BV   (3)
Columbusweg 8, Venlo, 5928 LC, Limburg,
Netherlands
Tel.: (31) 778505850
Mineral Exploration Services
N.A.I.C.S.: 213115

Subsidiary (Non-US):

BLI Zambia Ltd   (4)
Ndola PO BOX 70300 Zambia Way Heavy
Industrial Area Skyways, PO Box 703000,
Ndola, Zambia
Tel.: (260) 212 65 0953
Mineral Exploration Services
N.A.I.C.S.: 212390

Boart Longyear GmbH & Co. KG   (4)
Meininger Weg 14, Eiterfeld, 36132, Hes-
sen, Germany
Tel.: (49) 6672868500
Mineral Exploration Services
N.A.I.C.S.: 213115

Boart Longyear S.A. (4)
Avda De Los Metales No 7, Leganes,
28914, Madrid, Spain
Tel.: (34) 916940011
Diamond Core Mining Drills Mfr
N.A.I.C.S.: 333131

Longyear South Africa (Pty) Ltd (4)
1067 Katrol Ave, Robertville Roodepoort,
Johannesburg, 1709, South Africa
Tel.: (27) 117679300
Mineral Drilling Services
N.A.I.C.S.: 213115

Subsidiary (Domestic):

Boart Longyear Netherlands BV (3)
Columbusweg 8, Venlo, 5928 LC, Limburg,
Netherlands
Tel.: (31) 778505850
Mineral Exploration Services
N.A.I.C.S.: 213115

Subsidiary (Non-US):

Boart Longyear Canada (2)
2442 South Sheridan Way, Mississauga,
L5J 2M7, ON, Canada
Tel.: (905) 822-7922
Drilling Product Mfr
N.A.I.C.S.: 333132

Subsidiary (Domestic):

Boart Longyear Company Inc. (2)
2455 S 3600 W, Salt Lake City, UT 84119
Tel.: (801) 972-6430
Nonmetallic Mineral Services
N.A.I.C.S.: 213115
Richard T. O'Brien *(Pres & CEO)*

Division (Domestic):

Boart Longyear Drilling Services (3)
605 Union Pacific Way, Elko, NV 89801
Tel.: (775) 738-1980
Web Site: http://www.boartlongyear.com
Emp.: 170
Drilling Services
N.A.I.C.S.: 213111

Subsidiary (Non-US):

**Boart Longyear Drilling Products
Company (Wuxi) Ltd** (2)
Inside Of Baode Industrial Park No 55 Xin-
mei Road, New District, Wuxi, 214028,
China
Tel.: (86) 51085342766
Mineral Exploration Services
N.A.I.C.S.: 213115

Boart Longyear Inc. (2)
2442 South Sheridan Way, Mississauga,
L5J 2M7, ON, Canada
Tel.: (905) 822-7922
Web Site: http://www.boartlongyear.com
Sales Range: $25-49.9 Million
Emp.: 250
Third Party Contract Drilling; Diamond Core
Drilling Equipment Mfr
N.A.I.C.S.: 333517

Boart Longyear Limited (2)
49 Changlor Road Hai Ya, Mueang Chiang
Mai, Chiang Mai, 50100, Thailand
Tel.: (66) 53203871
Sales Range: $50-74.9 Million
Emp.: 20
Mineral Exploration Services
N.A.I.C.S.: 213115

Boart Longyear Ltda. (2)
Av Los Libertadores 16 500 - Sitio 1- A-2,
Complejo Industrial Los Libertadores
Colina, Santiago, Chile
Tel.: (56) 225953300
Sales Range: $25-49.9 Million
Emp.: 30
Diamond Core Drilling Equipment Mfr
N.A.I.C.S.: 333131

**Boart Longyear SAC - Lima,
PERU** (2)
Av El Derby 055 Office 601 Centro de Ne-
gocios Cronos, Santiago de Surco, Lima,
Peru
Tel.: (51) 12034200
Web Site: http://www.boartlongyear.com
Mineral Drilling Services
N.A.I.C.S.: 213115

P.T. Boart Longyear (2)
Jl Suci No 12 B Rt 001 Rw 03 Kel Susukan
Ciracas, Jakarta, Indonesia
Tel.: (62) 2187798007
Sales Range: $50-74.9 Million
Emp.: 100
Oil & Gas Drilling Services
N.A.I.C.S.: 213111

**Boart Longyear Investments Pty
Ltd** (1)
26 Butler Blvd Burbridge Buisness Pk, Ad-
elaide, 5950, AirFort, Australia
Tel.: (61) 883758375
Mineral Exploration Services
N.A.I.C.S.: 213115

**Boart Longyear Management Pty
Ltd** (1)
26 Butler Boulevard Burbridge Business
Park, Adelaide Airport, Adelaide, 5950, SA,
Australia
Tel.: (61) 883758375
Emp.: 90
Mineral Exploration Services
N.A.I.C.S.: 213115

Globaltech Corporation Pty Ltd (1)
883 Abernethy Road, Forrestfield, 6058,
WA, Australia
Tel.: (61) 864541200
Web Site: http://www.globaltech.com.au
Mining & Metal Mfr
N.A.I.C.S.: 333131

BOAT ROCKER MEDIA
595 Adelaide Street East, Toronto,
M5A 1N8, ON, Canada
Tel.: (416) 591-0065
Web Site: http://www.boatrocker.com
Year Founded: 2014
Media Production & Distr
N.A.I.C.S.: 512110
John Young *(CEO)*

Subsidiaries:

Jam Filled Entertainment, Inc. (1)
65 Auriga Drive Suite 102, Ottawa, K2E
7W6, ON, Canada
Tel.: (613) 366-2550
Web Site: http://www.jamfilled.com
Emp.: 150
Digital Animation Solution Service
N.A.I.C.S.: 541519
Jamie Leclaire *(Co-Founder)*

BOBIJA A.D.
Karadordeva 4, Ljubovija, Serbia
Tel.: (381) 15 661 444.
Year Founded: 2004
Sales Range: Less than $1 Million
Lead & Zinc Ore Mining Services
N.A.I.C.S.: 212230

BOBSHELL ELECTRODES
LIMITED
802 Swagat Building Near Lal Bunga-
low CG Road, Ahmedabad, 380006,
Gujarat, India
Tel.: (91) 7926441025
Web Site: http://www.bobshell.net
Year Founded: 1994
526925—(BOM)
Rev.: $454,136
Assets: $607,242
Liabilities: $42,350
Net Worth: $564,892
Earnings: ($10,043)
Fiscal Year-end: 03/31/14
Welding Electrode Mfr
N.A.I.C.S.: 333992
Shailesh M. Joshi *(Chm & Mng Dir)*

BOBST GROUP S.A.
Tel.: (41) 216212111
Web Site: https://www.bobst.com
Year Founded: 1890
BOBNN—(SWX)
Rev.: $2,329,807,474
Assets: $2,102,210,610
Liabilities: $1,561,920,615

Net Worth: $540,289,995
Earnings: $141,787,498
Emp.: 6,363
Fiscal Year-end: 12/31/23
Holding Company; Packaging & Print-
ing Machines & Equipment Mfr &
Distr
N.A.I.C.S.: 551112
Thierry de Kalbermatten *(Vice Chm)*

Subsidiaries:

Bobst (Africa & Middle East) Ltd. (1)
Immeuble LLyod B11 Angle avenue Hedi
Karray et avenue, Tahar Gharssa Centre
Urbain Nord, 1001, Tunis, Tunisia (100%)
Tel.: (216) 7 180 8128
Web Site: http://www.bobst.com
Sales Range: $25-49.9 Million
Emp.: 45
Sale of Printing & Packaging Machinery
N.A.I.C.S.: 423830

Bobst (Changzhou) Ltd. (1)
26 Jinghu West Road, Wujin Zone,
Changzhou, 213164, China
Tel.: (86) 51983021888
Printing & Converting Equipment Mfr
N.A.I.C.S.: 333248
Yanqing Zou *(Mgr-Quality)*

**Bobst (Latinoamerica Norte y Caribe)
S.A. de C.V.** (1)
San Francisco 624 col. Del Valle, 03100,
Mexico, Mezzanine, Mexico
Tel.: (52) 5553400970
Sales Range: $25-49.9 Million
Emp.: 30
N.A.I.C.S.: 333517

Bobst (SEA) Pte Ltd (1)
28 Canberra Dr, 12 Fl Unit 20, Singapore,
768429, Singapore (100%)
Tel.: (65) 63538028
Sales Range: $50-74.9 Million
Emp.: 6
Sales & Service of Printing & Packaging
Machinery
N.A.I.C.S.: 423830

Bobst (Shanghai) Ltd (1)
Unit 2502 Shanghai Square 138 Middle
Huaihai Road, 200021, Shanghai, China
Tel.: (86) 21 5774 3366
Corrugated Board & Packaging Material
Distr
N.A.I.C.S.: 423840

Bobst (Taiwan) Ltd. (1)
1st Floor No 12 Lane 361 Fu-Hsing N
Road, Taipei, 105, Taiwan (100%)
Tel.: (886) 225147928
Web Site: http://www.bobstgroup.com.tw
Sales Range: Less than $1 Million
Emp.: 3
Sales & Service of Printing & Packaging
Machinery
N.A.I.C.S.: 423830

Bobst Benelux NV (1)
Kantorenpark Den Helder Potvlietlaan 3,
2600, Berchem, Belgium
Tel.: (32) 32700450
Printing & Converting Equipment Mfr
N.A.I.C.S.: 333248
Fons Marien *(Mgr-Svcs)*

Bobst Bielefeld GmbH (1)
Hakenort 47, 33609, Bielefeld, Germany
Tel.: (49) 52130480
Printing & Converting Equipment Mfr
N.A.I.C.S.: 333248
Mark Mc Inulty *(Mng Dir)*

Bobst Brasil Ltda. (1)
Av Henri Bobst 401 Barrio da Ponte, CP
22, 13250-000, Itatiba, Brazil (100%)
Tel.: (55) 145349300
Web Site: http://www.bobst.com
Sales Range: $50-74.9 Million
Emp.: 9
Printing & Packaging Machines & Equip-
ment Sales
N.A.I.C.S.: 423830

Bobst CIS LLC (1)
Golovinskoe Shosse 5 Build 1 Office 7018,
125212, Moscow, Russia
Tel.: (7) 4995515522

Printing & Converting Equipment Mfr
N.A.I.C.S.: 333248

Bobst Central Europe Limited (1)
Technicka 15, 61600, Brno, Czech
Republic (100%)
Tel.: (420) 54 738 7100
Web Site: https://www.bobst.com
Emp.: 40
N.A.I.C.S.: 333517

Bobst Firenze S.r.l. (1)
Via Fratelli Cervi 76, Campi Bisenzio,
50013, Florence, Italy
Tel.: (39) 0558830400
Printing & Converting Equipment Mfr
N.A.I.C.S.: 333248
Stefano Lascialfari *(Mgr-Production)*

Bobst Grenchen AG (1)
Niklaus-Wengi-Strasse 109, 2540,
Grenchen, Solothurn, Switzerland (100%)
Tel.: (41) 326442500
Web Site: http://www.bobs.com
Sales Range: $25-49.9 Million
Emp.: 80
Mfr of Machines for the Production of
Single-Face Microflute Board & Laminators
N.A.I.C.S.: 333998

Bobst Grenchen AG (1)
Niklaus-Wengi-Strasse 109, 2540,
Grenchen, Switzerland
Tel.: (41) 326442500
Printing & Converting Equipment Mfr
N.A.I.C.S.: 333248
Ad Jongmans *(Dir-Mktg & Sls)*

Bobst Group Benelux N.V. (1)
Kantorenpark Den Helder, Potvlietlaan 3,
2600, Berchem, Belgium (100%)
Tel.: (32) 32700450
Web Site: http://www.bobstgroup.be
Sales Range: $25-49.9 Million
Emp.: 35
Sales of Printing & Packaging Machinery
N.A.I.C.S.: 423830

**Bobst Group Central Europe spol. s
r.o.** (1)
Technicka 15, 616 00, Brno, Czech Repub-
lic
Tel.: (420) 547387100
Web Site: http://www.bobst.com
Emp.: 33
Corrugated Paper Board Distr
N.A.I.C.S.: 423840

Bobst Group Deutschland GmbH (1)
Mollsfeld 21, PO Box 40644, 40670, Meer-
busch, Germany (100%)
Tel.: (49) 21599190
Web Site: http://www.bobstgroup.de
Sales Range: $25-49.9 Million
Emp.: 100
Sales & Service of Printing & Packaging
Machinery
N.A.I.C.S.: 333248

Bobst Group Iberica, S.L. (1)
Avda Diagonal 210 5 Floor, 08018, Barce-
lona, Spain
Tel.: (34) 90 209 0538
Web Site: http://www.bobstgroup.es
Emp.: 50
Corrugated Board & Flexible Materials Distr
N.A.I.C.S.: 423840

Bobst Group Italia S.p.A. (1)
Via Pisa 250, 20099, Milan, Sesto San Gio-
vanni, Italy (100%)
Tel.: (39) 02262381
Web Site: http://www.bobstgroup.com
Sales Range: $50-74.9 Million
Emp.: 60
Sales of Printing & Packaging Machines &
Equipment
N.A.I.C.S.: 423830

**Bobst Group Latinoamerica Norte
S.A. de CV,** (1)
San Francisco 632, Col Del Valle, 3100,
Mexico, Mexico
Tel.: (52) 55 5340 0970
Web Site: http://www.bobst.com
Emp.: 3
Corrugated Board & Paper Products Distr
N.A.I.C.S.: 423840

Bobst Group North America, Inc. (1)

Bobst Group S.A.—(Continued)

10 Waterview Blvd Ste 100, Parsippany, NJ
07054 **(100%)**
Tel.: (973) 226-8000
Web Site: http://www.bobstgroup.us
Sales Range: $50-74.9 Million
Emp.: 100
Printing Presses & Electronic Equipment
Mfr
N.A.I.C.S.: 423830

Bobst Group Polska Sp. Z o.o. **(1)**
ul Niciarniana 2/6, 92-208, Lodz, Poland
Tel.: (48) 42 616 26 00
Web Site: http://www.bobstgroup.pl
Sales Range: $25-49.9 Million
Emp.: 2
Corrugated Board & Packaging Material
Distr
N.A.I.C.S.: 423840

Bobst Group Singapore Pte Ltd **(1)**
Yishun Post Office, PO Box 194, Singapore,
917607, Singapore
Tel.: (65) 6353 8028
Web Site: http://www.bobstgroup.sg
Corrugated Board & Packaging Materials
Distr
N.A.I.C.S.: 423840

Bobst Group Thailand Ltd **(1)**
123 Suntowers Building A Floor 12-01
Vibhavadee-Rangsit Rd, Jomphon Jatujak,
10900, Bangkok, Thailand
Tel.: (66) 2 617 7851
Web Site: http://www.bobst.com
Corrugated Board & Packaging Materials
Distr
N.A.I.C.S.: 423840

Bobst Group Vostok LLC **(1)**
1st Kozhevnichesky Per House 6 Build 1 of
405, Moscow, 115114, Russia
Tel.: (7) 495 933 01 01
Sales Range: $25-49.9 Million
Emp.: 27
Corrugated Board & Packaging Materials
Distr
N.A.I.C.S.: 423840
Gleb Gazelkin *(Gen Dir)*

Bobst Iberica, S.L. **(1)**
Avda Diagonal 210 5 Planta, 08018, Barce-
lona, Spain
Tel.: (34) 902090538
Printing & Converting Equipment Mfr
N.A.I.C.S.: 333248
Odalis Carmenaty *(Project Mgr)*

Bobst India Private Ltd. **(1)**
Plot No 82 Vill Kasar Amboli, Post Ambad-
vet Taluka-Mulshi, Pune, 412 108, India
Tel.: (91) 206 677 6100
Web Site: http://www.bobstgroup.com
Sales Range: $125-149.9 Million
Emp.: 300
Equipment & Services for Packaging Manu-
facturers
N.A.I.C.S.: 333248

Bobst Istanbul Ambalaj A.S. **(1)**
Kasap Sokak Gamze Apt No 19/A
Esentepe, 34394, Istanbul, Türkiye
Tel.: (90) 2122627800
Printing & Converting Equipment Mfr
N.A.I.C.S.: 333248
Yusuf Sahin *(Sls Mgr-Svcs & Parts)*

Bobst Italia SpA **(1)**
Strada Della Bosella 14/16, 29121,
Piacenza, Italy
Tel.: (39) 0523493111
Web Site: https://www.bobst.com
Machinery for Flexible Packaging Mfr &
Sales
N.A.I.C.S.: 383993

Bobst Italia SpA **(1)**
S P Casale Asti 70, 15020, San Giorgio,
Monferrato, Italy
Tel.: (39) 0142 4071
Web Site: https://www.bobst.com
Laminating, Rotogravure Printing & Coating
Machines Mfr
N.A.I.C.S.: 333243

Bobst Japan Ltd. **(1)**
6-1-1 Heiwajima TRC Center Bldg 8F, Ota-
ku, Tokyo, 143-0006, Japan
Tel.: (81) 36 404 2090

Web Site: https://www.bobst.com
Printing, Packaging Machines & Equipment
Whslr
N.A.I.C.S.: 423830

Bobst Lagos Ltd. **(1)**
227 Ikorodu Road, Ilupeju, Lagos, Nigeria
Tel.: (234) 8095103888
Printing & Converting Equipment Mfr
N.A.I.C.S.: 333248

Bobst Latinoamerica do Sul Ltda **(1)**
Rodovia Dom Pedro I SP65 - Km 97 - Area
B, Bairro da Ponte Nova, Itatiba, 13252-
350, Sao Paulo, Brazil
Tel.: (55) 114 534 9300
Web Site: https://www.bobst.com
Emp.: 170
Corrugated Box Mfr & Distr
N.A.I.C.S.: 322211

Bobst Lyon SAS **(1)**
35 Rue du 35eme Regiment d Aviation,
69500, Bron, France
Tel.: (33) 472147474
Printing & Converting Equipment Mfr
N.A.I.C.S.: 333248
David Arnaud *(Dir-Product Mktg)*

Bobst Malaysia Sdn. Bhd. **(1)**
Unit 23-3 Level 3 Block D1 Jalan PJU 1/41
Dataran Prima, 47301, Petaling Jaya, Se-
langor Darul Ehsan, Malaysia
Tel.: (60) 37 804 9281
Web Site: http://www.bobst.com
Sales, Printing & Packaging Machinery Ser-
vices
N.A.I.C.S.: 423830

Bobst Manchester Ltd **(1)**
Pilsworth Road, Pennine Business Park,
Heywood, OL10 2TL, Lancashire, United
Kingdom
Tel.: (44) 1706622442
Emp.: 100
Vacuum Web Coating Distr
N.A.I.C.S.: 424610

Bobst Manchester Ltd. **(1)**
Pilsworth Road, Pennine Business Park,
Heywood, OL10 2TL, United Kingdom
Tel.: (44) 1706622442
Printing & Converting Equipment Mfr
N.A.I.C.S.: 333248
Nick Copeland *(Dir-R&D)*

Bobst Meerbusch GmbH **(1)**
Mollsfeld 21, 40670, Meerbusch, Germany
Tel.: (49) 21599190
Printing & Converting Equipment Mfr
N.A.I.C.S.: 333248

Bobst Mex SA **(1)**
Route de Faraz 3, Mex, 1031, Lausanne,
Switzerland
Tel.: (41) 216212111
Printing & Converting Equipment Mfr
N.A.I.C.S.: 333248
Beat Burke *(CFO)*

Bobst Paris SAS **(1)**
22 Rue Decomberousse, 69628, Villeur-
banne, Cedex, France
Tel.: (33) 469855100
Printing & Converting Equipment Mfr
N.A.I.C.S.: 333248
Olivier Lange *(Mgr-Fin & Admin)*

Bobst Polska Sp. z o.o. **(1)**
Al Kosciuszki 103/105, 90-441, Lodz, Po-
land
Tel.: (48) 426162600
Printing & Converting Equipment Mfr
N.A.I.C.S.: 333248

Bobst S.A. **(1)**
Case Postale, 1001, Lausanne,
Switzerland **(100%)**
Tel.: (41) 216212111
Web Site: https://www.bobst.com
Sales Range: $400-449.9 Million
Emp.: 2,000
Internal Subcontractor
N.A.I.C.S.: 333248

Bobst Scandinavia ApS **(1)**
Park Alle 289 P, 2605, Brondby, Denmark
Tel.: (45) 36362050
Web Site: http://www.bobstgroup.dk
Corrugated Board Distr
N.A.I.C.S.: 423840

Bobst Scandinavia ApS **(1)**
Park Alle 289 P, 2605, Brondby, Denmark
Tel.: (45) 36362050
Printing & Converting Equipment Mfr
N.A.I.C.S.: 333248

Bobst Stuttgart GmbH **(1)**
Schurwaldstrasse 15, 73765, Neuhausen
auf den Fildern, Germany
Tel.: (49) 715898700
Corrugated Board Mfr
N.A.I.C.S.: 322211
Declef Hellenthal *(Gen Mgr)*

Bobst UK & Ireland Ltd **(1)**
Ravensbank House Ravensbank Drive,
Lakeside, Redditch, B98 9NA, United King-
dom
Tel.: (44) 1527519700
Web Site: http://www.bobstgroup.co.uk
Emp.: 45
Corrugated Board & Packaging Products
Distr
N.A.I.C.S.: 423840
Kearon Scarrott *(Area Sls Mgr-CI Flexo)*

Bobst UK & Ireland Ltd. **(1)**
Ravensbank House Ravensbank Drive,
Redditch, B98 9NA, United Kingdom
Tel.: (44) 1527519700
Printing & Converting Equipment Mfr
N.A.I.C.S.: 333248

Bobst UK Holdings Ltd **(1)**
Ravensbank House Ravensbank Drive,
Moons Moat North Industrial Estate, Red-
ditch, B98 9NA, Worcestershire, United
Kingdom
Tel.: (44) 1527519700
Web Site: http://www.bobst.com
Sales Range: $50-74.9 Million
Emp.: 6
Investment Management Service
N.A.I.C.S.: 523999

Bobst Vietnam Co. Ltd. **(1)**
TGA Building 15 Tran Khanh Du Str, Dist 1,
Ho Chi Minh City, Vietnam
Tel.: (84) 2835268091
Printing & Converting Equipment Mfr
N.A.I.C.S.: 333248
Minh Nguyen *(Mgr-Sls)*

Boxplan GmbH & Co. KG **(1)**
Daimler-Strasse 8, Steisslingen, 78256,
Konstanz, Germany
Tel.: (49) 7738 802 4250
Web Site: https://www.boxplan.de
Die Cutting & Stripping Mfr
N.A.I.C.S.: 333519

Brausse Europe BV **(1)**
Weerdskampweg 15, 5222 BA,
s-Hertogenbosch, Netherlands
Tel.: (31) 736277711
Web Site: http://www.brausse-europe.com
Packaging Industry Machine Mfr
N.A.I.C.S.: 333993

Martin S.A. **(1)**
22 Rue Decomberousse, 69628, Villeur-
banne, France **(100%)**
Tel.: (33) 472147474
Web Site: http://www.martin-corrugated.com
Sales Range: $200-249.9 Million
Emp.: 650
Mfr & Distr of Machines & Equipment in
Packaging & Printing
N.A.I.C.S.: 333248

Mouvent AG **(1)**
Lowengasse 8, 4500, Solothurn, Switzer-
land
Tel.: (41) 582552550
Web Site: http://www.mouvent.com
Printing Machinery Mfr
N.A.I.C.S.: 333248
Piero Pierantozzi *(Founder & CTO)*

Novaflex SAS **(1)**
Cra 69 25B-44 Of 604 Fontibon Bogota,
Cundinamarca, Colombia
Tel.: (57) 4299004
Web Site: https://novaflex.com.co
Industrial Packaging Equipment Mfr
N.A.I.C.S.: 333993

PT Bobst Group Indonesia **(1)**
Jl Panjang No 5 5Th Floor Suite 501,
Wisma AKR, 11530, Jakarta, Indonesia
Tel.: (62) 21 531 1050

Corrugated Board & Flexible Materials Distr
N.A.I.C.S.: 423840

PT. Bobst Jakarta **(1)**
The Vida Building Lt 3A Unit 10, JL Raya
Pejuangan N 8 RT001/RW007 Kebon Je-
ruk, 11530, Jakarta, Indonesia
Tel.: (62) 2129510240
Printing & Converting Equipment Mfr
N.A.I.C.S.: 333248
Hengki Oei *(Sls Mgr-Area)*

**BOC INFORMATION TECH-
NOLOGIES CONSULTING AG**
Operngasse 20b, 1040, Vienna, Aus-
tria
Tel.: (43) 1 905 10 71 0 **AT**
Web Site: http://www.uk.boc-
group.com
Year Founded: 1995
Sales Range: $25-49.9 Million
Emp.: 170
Information Technology Consulting
Services
N.A.I.C.S.: 541512
Robert Strobl *(Member-Mgmt Bd)*

Subsidiaries:

**BOC Business Objectives Consulting
Iberica S.L.U.** **(1)**
Velazquez 71, 28006, Madrid, Spain
Tel.: (34) 91 781 18 80
Sales Range: $25-49.9 Million
Emp.: 1
Information Technology Consulting Services
N.A.I.C.S.: 541512
David Orensanz *(Gen Mgr)*

BOC Information Systems GmbH **(1)**
Operngasse 20b, 1040, Vienna, Austria
Tel.: (43) 1 905 10 81 0
Sales Range: $25-49.9 Million
Emp.: 6
Information Technology Consulting Services
N.A.I.C.S.: 541512

**BOC Information Technologies Con-
sulting GmbH** **(1)**
Vossstrasse 22, 10117, Berlin, Germany
Tel.: (49) 30 22 69 25 10
Emp.: 55
Information Technology Consulting Services
N.A.I.C.S.: 541512
Martin Petersen *(Gen Mgr)*

**BOC Information Technologies Con-
sulting Ltd.** **(1)**
Unit 311 Capel Bldg Marys Abbey, Dublin,
7, Ireland
Tel.: (353) 1 63 75 240
Emp.: 2
Information Technology Consulting Services
N.A.I.C.S.: 541512
Christian Kuplich *(Gen Mgr)*

**BOC Information Technologies Con-
sulting Sp. z o.o.** **(1)**
Al Jerozolimskie 109/26, 02-011, Warsaw,
Poland
Tel.: (48) 22 628 00 15
Web Site: http://www.boc-group.com
Sales Range: $25-49.9 Million
Emp.: 10
Information Technology Consulting Services
N.A.I.C.S.: 541512
Jowita Sykus *(Office Mgr)*

**BOC Unternehmensberatung
GmbH** **(1)**
Rabensteig 2, 1010, Vienna, Austria
Tel.: (43) 1 513 27 36 0
Sales Range: $25-49.9 Million
Emp.: 25
Information Technology Consulting Services
N.A.I.C.S.: 541512
Robert Strobl *(Mng Dir)*

**BOC INTERNATIONAL CHINA
CO., LTD.**
39F Bank of China Tower No 200
Yincheng Middle Road, Pudong New
District, Shanghai, 200120, China
Tel.: (86) 2120328000
Web Site: http://www.bocichina.com
Year Founded: 2002

601696—(SHG)
Rev.: $415,481,859
Assets: $9,032,121,301
Liabilities: $6,727,897,449
Net Worth: $2,304,223,852
Earnings: $113,404,604
Fiscal Year-end: 12/31/22
Investment Banking Services
N.A.I.C.S.: 523150
Ning Min (Chm)

BOCHUMER VEREIN VERKEH-RSTECHNIK GMBH
Alleestrasse 70, 44793, Bochum, Germany
Tel.: (49) 23468910
Web Site: http://www.bochumer-verein.de
Metal Wheels Mfr
N.A.I.C.S.: 332999
Christine Mertz (Mgr-Sls)

BOCKSTAEL CONSTRUCTION LIMITED
1505 Dugald Rd, Winnipeg, R2J 0H3, MB, Canada
Tel.: (204) 233-7135
Web Site: http://www.bockstael.com
Year Founded: 1912
Rev.: $29,215,682
Emp.: 50
Construction Services
N.A.I.C.S.: 236220
John Bockstael (CEO)

BOCS BREMEN OVERSEAS CHARTERING AND SHIPPING GMBH
Martinistrasse 29, Bremen, 28195, Germany
Tel.: (49) 421369115
Web Site: http://www.bocs.de
Year Founded: 1990
Rev.: $98,737,452
Emp.: 1
Water Transportation Services
N.A.I.C.S.: 483211
Ilse Fliege (Pres)

BOD SCIENCE LIMITED
Level 1 377 New South Head Road, Double Bay, 2028, NSW, Australia
Tel.: (61) 291995018
Web Site: https://bodscience.com
Year Founded: 2014
BOD—(ASX)
Rev.: $1,994,064
Assets: $1,540,378
Liabilities: $5,091,492
Net Worth: ($3,551,114)
Earnings: ($4,282,145)
Fiscal Year-end: 06/30/24
Skin Care Product Mfr & Distr
N.A.I.C.S.: 325620
Joanne Patterson (CEO & Exec Dir)

BODAL CHEMICALS LTD.
Behind Venetian Villa Near Anand Niketan School, Shilaj Ring Road Circle Shilaj Thaltej, Ahmedabad, 380059, Gujarat, India
Tel.: (91) 7968160100
Web Site: https://www.bodal.com
Year Founded: 1986
524370—(BOM)
Rev.: $282,277,223
Assets: $289,695,452
Liabilities: $146,049,540
Net Worth: $143,645,912
Earnings: $13,467,500
Emp.: 2,025
Fiscal Year-end: 03/31/22
Dyes Mfr & Distr
N.A.I.C.S.: 325130
Suresh Jayantibhai Patel (Chm & Mng Dir)

Subsidiaries:

Trion Chemicals Pvt. Ltd.   (1)
Plot No 123-124 Phase-I GIDC, Vatva, Ahmedabad, 382445, Gujarat, India
Tel.: (91) 7925835437
Web Site: http://www.trioncpl.com
Specialty Chemicals Mfr
N.A.I.C.S.: 325998

BODARD CONSTRUCTION MODULAIRE
ZA Sud BP 24, 85150, La Mothe Achard, France
Tel.: (33) 251062222
Web Site: http://www.bodard-construction.com
Sales Range: $10-24.9 Million
Emp.: 87
Modular Construction Products Mfr
N.A.I.C.S.: 332312
Pascal Boutet (Dir-Mktg)

BODE ENERGY EQUIPMENT CO., LTD.
Floor 6th No A Pioneering Plaza 48 Keji Road, Hi-tech Zone, Xi'an, 710075, China
Tel.: (86) 2989010611
Web Site: http://www.bode-e.com
300023—(CHIN)
Rev.: $5,000,774
Assets: $79,505,265
Liabilities: $5,080,444
Net Worth: $74,424,822
Earnings: ($277,310)
Fiscal Year-end: 12/31/20
Electrical Equipment Mfr & Distr
N.A.I.C.S.: 335999

BODEGAS RIOJANAS, S.A.
Avda Dr Ricardo Ruiz Azcarraga 1, Cenicero, 26350, La Rioja, Spain
Tel.: (34) 941454050
Web Site: https://www.bodegasriojanas.com
Year Founded: 1890
RIO—(MAD)
Sales Range: Less than $1 Million
Wine Mfr
N.A.I.C.S.: 312130
Santiago Frias Monje (Chm)

BODHI TREE MULTIMEDIA LIMITED
507 Reliable Business Centre Jogeshwari West, Mumbai, 400102, Maharashtra, India
Tel.: (91) 2235129058
Web Site: https://www.bodhitreemedia.com
543767—(BOM)
Rev.: $8,105,988
Assets: $2,890,819
Liabilities: $1,588,638
Net Worth: $1,302,180
Earnings: $404,095
Emp.: 11
Fiscal Year-end: 03/30/22
Film Production Services
N.A.I.C.S.: 512110
Ravi Bhavani Shankar Bhatt (CFO)

BODHTREE CONSULTING LTD.
Level 2 Wing A Melange Towers, Hitech City Madhapur, Hyderabad, 500081, India
Tel.: (91) 8121041553
Web Site: https://www.bodhtree.com
Year Founded: 1998
539122—(BOM)
Rev.: $21,080,458
Assets: $19,225,849
Liabilities: $10,011,030
Net Worth: $9,214,819
Earnings: $1,736,589

Emp.: 53
Fiscal Year-end: 03/31/21
Information Technology Services
N.A.I.C.S.: 541512
L. N. Rama Krishna (Mng Dir)

BODITECH MED, INC.
43 Geodudanji 1-gil Dongnae-myeon, Chuncheon, 24398, Gangwon-do, Korea (South)
Tel.: (82) 332431400
Web Site: https://www.boditech.co.kr
Year Founded: 1998
206640—(KRS)
Rev.: $90,564,938
Assets: $150,068,082
Liabilities: $15,972,897
Net Worth: $134,095,184
Earnings: $18,524,227
Emp.: 465
Fiscal Year-end: 12/31/22
Medical Supply & Equipment Mfr
N.A.I.C.S.: 339112
Euiyul Choi (CEO)

Subsidiaries:

Immunostics, Inc.   (1)
38 Industrial Way Ste 1, Eatontown, NJ 07724
Tel.: (732) 918-0770
Web Site: https://www.immunostics.com
Sales Range: $1-9.9 Million
Emp.: 30
Medical Diagnostic Kits Mfr & Distr
N.A.I.C.S.: 339112

BODY ACTION ENTERPRISE CO., LTD.
No 595-597 Sec 3 Yatan Rd, Daya Dist, Taichung, 428, Taiwan
Tel.: (886) 425679000
Web Site: https://www.bodyaction.com
Year Founded: 1993
Fitness Equipment Mfr
N.A.I.C.S.: 339920

BODY AND MIND INC.
1095 West Pender Street Suite 750, Vancouver, V6E 2M6, BC, Canada   NV
Web Site: https://bodyandmind.com
Year Founded: 2010
BMMJ—(OTCQB)
Rev.: $22,819,983
Assets: $21,209,780
Liabilities: $30,549,389
Net Worth: ($9,339,609)
Earnings: ($20,566,354)
Emp.: 142
Fiscal Year-end: 07/31/23
Fleet Data Management & Weighing Solutions
N.A.I.C.S.: 513210
Dong H. Shim (CFO)

Subsidiaries:

NMG San Diego, LLC   (1)
7027 Friars Rd, San Diego, CA 92108
Tel.: (619) 692-9100
Crop Farming Services
N.A.I.C.S.: 111998

BODY ONE S.A.
47-49 Rue Cartier Bresson, 93500, Pantin, 93500, France
Tel.: (33) 141581717   FR
Year Founded: 2004
MLONE—(EUR)
Sales Range: Less than $1 Million
Clothing Store Operator
N.A.I.C.S.: 424350
Ariel Amsellem (Chm & CEO)

BODYCOTE PLC
Springwood Court Springwood Close

Tytherington Business Park, Macclesfield, SK10 2XF, Cheshire, United Kingdom
Tel.: (44) 1625505300
Web Site: https://www.bodycote.com
Year Founded: 1953
BOY—(LSE)
Rev.: $836,083,976
Assets: $1,452,488,856
Liabilities: $521,907,568
Net Worth: $930,581,288
Earnings: $81,463,200
Emp.: 4,757
Fiscal Year-end: 12/31/21
Heat Treatment, Hot Isostatic Pressing, Metallurgical Coatings & Material Testing Services
N.A.I.C.S.: 332811
Stephen C. Harris (CEO/CEO-Grp)

Subsidiaries:

Bodycote (Ningbo) Heat Treatment Co. Limited   (1)
94 Xiayu Rd Jiangnan Community Industrial Zone Jiangdong North Road, Jiangdong District, Ningbo, Zhejiang, China
Tel.: (86) 574 87781519
Web Site: http://www.bodycote.cn
Metal Heat Treatment Services
N.A.I.C.S.: 332811

Bodycote Argentina SA   (1)
Hipolito Yrigoyen Ruta 202 3288, San Fernando, Buenos Aires, Argentina
Tel.: (54) 1147460053
Metal Heat Treatment Services
N.A.I.C.S.: 332811

Bodycote Brasimet Processamento Termico S.A.   (1)
Av Das Nacoes Unidas 11633 - Cj 163 - 16o Floor, 04578-000, Sao Paulo, Brazil
Tel.: (55) 11 2755 7200
Web Site: http://brazil.bodycote.com
Metal Heat Treatment Services
N.A.I.C.S.: 332811

Bodycote Coating Centrum BV   (1)
Groethofstraat 27, 5916 PA, Venlo, Netherlands   (100%)
Tel.: (31) 77 355 9292
Web Site: http://www.mc.bodycote.com
Sales Range: $50-74.9 Million
Emp.: 120
Metal Coating & Electroplating
N.A.I.C.S.: 332813

Bodycote France   (1)
Parc Technologique de Lyon, 69800, Saint Priest, France   (100%)
Tel.: (33) 437238200
Web Site: http://www.fbi.bodycote.com
Sales Range: $25-49.9 Million
Emp.: 600
Heat Treatment & Coating of Metals
N.A.I.C.S.: 332811
Jean Luc Bion (Dir-Ops)

Bodycote H.I.P. Ltd.   (1)
Carlisle Close Sheffield Road Sheepsbridge, Chesterfield, S41 9ED, United Kingdom   (100%)
Tel.: (44) 1246260888
Web Site: http://www.hip.bodycote.com
Sales Range: $25-49.9 Million
Emp.: 60
Hot Isostatic Pressing
N.A.I.C.S.: 332811

Bodycote HIP GmbH   (1)
Kolbinger Str 7, Haag Winden, D 83527, Munich, Germany   (100%)
Tel.: (49) 807237540
Web Site: http://www.hip.bodycote.com
Sales Range: $25-49.9 Million
Emp.: 50
Hot Isostatic Pressing
N.A.I.C.S.: 332811

Bodycote HIP N.V.   (1)
Industriepark Noord 7, 9100, Saint-Niklaas, East Flanders, Belgium
Tel.: (32) 3 780 6800
Web Site: https://www.bodycote.com
Metal Heat Treatment Services
N.A.I.C.S.: 332811

Bodycote plc—(Continued)

Bodycote HT S.r.o **(1)**
CTPark Brno Turanka 112, Slatina, 627 00, Brno, Czech Republic
Tel.: (420) 516102424
Web Site: http://www.bodycote.dz
Emp.: 40
Metal Treatment Services
N.A.I.C.S.: 332811

Bodycote Hardiff B.V. **(1)**
Paramariboweg 45, 7333 PA, Apeldoorn, Netherlands **(100%)**
Tel.: (31) 555426392
Web Site: http://www.plc.bodycote.com
Sales Range: $25-49.9 Million
Emp.: 25
Heat Treatment of Metals
N.A.I.C.S.: 332811

Bodycote Hardiff GmbH **(1)**
Max-Planck-Str 9, 86899, Landsberg, Germany
Tel.: (49) 8191 9179 0
Emp.: 25
Metal Heat Treatment Services
N.A.I.C.S.: 332811
Christoph Berndes (Plant Mgr)

Bodycote Hardingscentrum BV **(1)**
Groethofstraat 27, 5916 PA, Venlo, Netherlands
Tel.: (31) 773559292
Metal Heat Treatment Services
N.A.I.C.S.: 332811

Bodycote Heat Treatments Ltd. **(1)**
Springwood Court Tytherington Business Park, Macclesfield, SK10 2XF, Cheshire, United Kingdom **(100%)**
Tel.: (44) 1625505300
Sales Range: $25-49.9 Million
Emp.: 100
Heat Treatment of Metals
N.A.I.C.S.: 332811
Simon Blantern (VP-Sls)

Bodycote Heiss-Isostatisches Pressen GmbH **(1)**
Kolbinger Str 7, Greater Munich Area, 83527, Haag, Germany
Tel.: (49) 8072 3754 0
Web Site: http://www.bodycote.com
Sales Range: $25-49.9 Million
Emp.: 45
Powder Metallurgical Component Mfr
N.A.I.C.S.: 332117

Bodycote Hokezelo KFT **(1)**
Orczy Ut 46, 1089, Budapest, Hungary
Tel.: (36) 13138680
Web Site: http://www.bodycote.com
Emp.: 15
Metal Heat Treatment Services
N.A.I.C.S.: 332811

Bodycote Hot Isostatic Pressing AB **(1)**
Stalvagen 15, Box 209, 735 23, Surahammar, Sweden **(100%)**
Tel.: (46) 2 203 4800
Web Site: http://www.bodycote.se
Sales Range: $25-49.9 Million
Emp.: 47
Hot Isostatic Pressing
N.A.I.C.S.: 332811

Bodycote IMT Inc. **(1)**
155 River St, Andover, MA 01810-5923
Tel.: (978) 470-1620
Metal Heat Treating Services
N.A.I.C.S.: 332811
Thomas Mazzola (Gen Mgr)

Bodycote International Inc. **(1)**
155 River St, Andover, MA 01810
Tel.: (978) 470-1620
Web Site: http://www.bodycote.com
Emp.: 1,000
Metal Heat Treating
N.A.I.C.S.: 332811

Unit (Domestic):

Bodycote Hot Isostatic Pressing **(2)**
155 River St, Andover, MA 01810-5923 **(100%)**
Tel.: (978) 470-1620
Web Site: http://www.na.bodycote.com

Sales Range: $25-49.9 Million
Emp.: 70
Hot Isostatic Pressing
N.A.I.C.S.: 332811

Subsidiary (Domestic):

Bodycote K-Tech, Inc. **(2)**
111 K-Tech Ln, Hot Springs, AR 71913
Tel.: (501) 760-1696
Web Site: http://www.bodycote.com
Sales Range: $25-49.9 Million
Emp.: 22
Metal Coatings Mfr
N.A.I.C.S.: 325510

Bodycote Thermal Processing **(2)**
12750 Merit Dr Ste 1400, Dallas, TX 75251-1518 **(100%)**
Tel.: (214) 904-2420
Web Site: http://www.htna.bodycote.com
Sales Range: $350-399.9 Million
Heat Treatment of Metals
N.A.I.C.S.: 332811

Bodycote Thermal Processing **(2)**
1975 N Ruby St, Melrose Park, IL 60160-1109
Tel.: (708) 344-4080
Web Site: http://www.bodycote.com
Sales Range: $350-399.9 Million
Heat Treating of Metal
N.A.I.C.S.: 332811

Bodycote Istas Isil Islem Sanayi ve Ticaret AS **(1)**
Kemalpasa OSB Mah Izmir Kemalpasa Asfalti No 17/1, Kemalpasa, Izmir, 35730, Turkiye
Tel.: (90) 232 8770300
Web Site: http://www.bodycote.com
Metal Heat Treatment Services
N.A.I.C.S.: 332811

Bodycote Italia Srl **(1)**
Via Parini, Gorgonzola, 20064, Milan, Italy **(100%)**
Tel.: (39) 029 530 4218
Web Site: http://www.fbi.bodycote.com
Sales Range: $25-49.9 Million
Emp.: 15
Heat Treating & Coating of Metals
N.A.I.C.S.: 332811

Bodycote Japan K.K. **(1)**
Nagoya Lucent Tower 40F 6-1 Ushijimacho, Nishi-ku, Nagoya, 451-6040, Aichi, Japan
Tel.: (81) 52 912 5518
Web Site: http://www.bodycote.co.jp
Metal Heat Treatment & Joining Services
N.A.I.C.S.: 332811

Bodycote Lampokasittely Oy **(1)**
Hyllilankatu 17, Tampere, 33730, Finland
Tel.: (358) 207 466 360
Sales Range: $25-49.9 Million
Emp.: 15
Metal Heat Treatment Services
N.A.I.C.S.: 332811
Toni Saarenmaa (Gen Mgr)

Bodycote Metallurgical Coatings Ltd. **(1)**
Shakespeare St, Wolverhampton, WV1 3LR, West Midlands, United Kingdom **(100%)**
Tel.: (44) 1902452915
Web Site: http://www.mc.bodycote.com
Sales Range: $25-49.9 Million
Emp.: 25
Metal Coating & Electroplating
N.A.I.C.S.: 332813

Bodycote Polska Sp z.o.o **(1)**
Ul Handlowa 2, 41-807, Zabrze, Poland
Tel.: (48) 32 273 8274
Web Site: http://internet.bodycote.org
Metal Heat Treatment Services
N.A.I.C.S.: 332811

Bodycote Rheintal Warmebehandlung AG **(1)**
Im Alten Riet 123, 9494, Schaan, Liechtenstein **(100%)**
Tel.: (423) 2392100
Web Site: http://www.bodycote.com
Sales Range: $25-49.9 Million
Emp.: 60

Vacuum Hardening, Vacuum Brazing, Carbonotriding & Carburizing
N.A.I.C.S.: 332811

Bodycote SAS **(1)**
10 rue Gustave Eiffel, 87240, Ambazac, France
Tel.: (33) 555568513
Web Site: http://www.bodycote.com
Sales Range: $25-49.9 Million
Emp.: 25
Metal Heat Treatment Services
N.A.I.C.S.: 332811

Bodycote Schweiz Warmebehandlung AG **(1)**
Steinackerstrasse 39, 8902, Urdorf, Switzerland
Tel.: (41) 44 735 60 35
Web Site: http://internet.bodycote.org
Emp.: 15
Metal Heat Treatment Services
N.A.I.C.S.: 332811

Bodycote Singapore Pte Ltd **(1)**
7 Tuas Avenue 8, Singapore, 639222, Singapore
Tel.: (65) 6576 9888
Web Site: http://www.bodycote.com.sg
Thermal Spray Coating Services
N.A.I.C.S.: 332812

Bodycote Slovakia s.r.o. **(1)**
Matuskova 48, Vlkanova, Banska Bystrica, Slovakia
Tel.: (421) 482297623
Thermal Power Services
N.A.I.C.S.: 541380

Bodycote Surface Technology Wartburg, Inc. **(1)**
1237 Knoxville Hwy, Wartburg, TN 37887
Tel.: (423) 346-3092
Thermal Power Services
N.A.I.C.S.: 541380

Bodycote Thermal Processing Canada, Inc. **(1)**
9 Shirley Ave, Kitchener, N2B2E6, ON, Canada
Tel.: (519) 744-6301
Emp.: 25
Aerospace Equipment Mfr
N.A.I.C.S.: 336413
Gary Practice (Gen Mgr)

Bodycote Tratamente Termice SRL **(1)**
Zizinului 119 Parc Industrial Carfil, Brasov, 500407, Romania
Tel.: (40) 268 330 910
Web Site: http://www.plc.bodycote.com
Emp.: 24
Metal Heat Treatment Services
N.A.I.C.S.: 332811

Bodycote Trattamenti Termici SPA **(1)**
Via Carso 89, 24040, Madone, Bergamo, Italy
Tel.: (39) 035 9956 11
Sales Range: $25-49.9 Million
Emp.: 5
Metal Heat Treatment Services
N.A.I.C.S.: 332811
Genesio Tresoldi (Plant Mgr)

Bodycote Varmebehandling A/S **(1)**
Herlev Hovedgade 15 A, 2730, Herlev, Denmark **(100%)**
Tel.: (45) 70150600
Web Site: http://www.bodycote.com
Sales Range: $25-49.9 Million
Emp.: 16
Metal Heat Treatment & Coating
N.A.I.C.S.: 332811

Bodycote Varmebehandling AB **(1)**
Spadegatan 23, PO Box 124, Gothenburg, 424 23, Angered, Sweden **(100%)**
Tel.: (46) 313321900
Web Site: http://www.bodycote.com
Sales Range: $50-74.9 Million
Emp.: 50
Heat Treatment of Metals
N.A.I.C.S.: 332811

Bodycote Warmebehandlung GmbH **(1)**

Buchwiesen 6, Stuttgart, 73061, Ebersbach, Germany **(100%)**
Tel.: (49) 71631030
Web Site: http://www.ceg.bodycote.org
Sales Range: $100-124.9 Million
Emp.: 50
Heat Treatment of Metals
N.A.I.C.S.: 332811
Peter Selbach (Gen Mgr)

Bodycote Warmebehandlung GmbH **(1)**
Georg-Hardt-Strasse 8-10, Munich, 83624, Otterfing, Germany
Tel.: (49) 80 24 47 70 0
Web Site: http://www.bodycote.com
Sales Range: $25-49.9 Million
Emp.: 35
Metal Heat Treating Services
N.A.I.C.S.: 332811

Bodycote Warmebehandlung Marchtrenk GmbH **(1)**
Linzer Strasse 108, 4614, Marchtrenk, Austria **(100%)**
Tel.: (43) 724 353 3150
Web Site: http://www.bodycote.at
Sales Range: $25-49.9 Million
Emp.: 20
Metal Heat Treatment & Coating
N.A.I.C.S.: 332811
Gerald Gerhartiter (Gen Mgr)

Bodycote Warmebehandlung Wien GmbH **(1)**
Hosnedlgasse 20, 1220, Vienna, Austria
Tel.: (43) 1 25 83 54 1
Web Site: http://internet.bodycote.org
Metal Heat Treating Services
N.A.I.C.S.: 332811

Bodycote Wuxi Technology Co. Limited **(1)**
No 6 Xiqin Road, National High-Tech Industrial Development Zone, Wuxi, 214028, Jiangsu, China
Tel.: (86) 5108 815 6388
Web Site: http://www.bodycote.cn
Heat Treatment Services
N.A.I.C.S.: 332811

Bodycote Ytbehandling AB **(1)**
Mossvagen 4, 641 21, Katrineholm, Sweden **(100%)**
Tel.: (46) 1 507 7808
Web Site: http://www.bodycote.se
Sales Range: $25-49.9 Million
Emp.: 35
Heat Treatment of Metals
N.A.I.C.S.: 332811

Ellison Surface Technologies, Inc. **(1)**
106 Innovation Dr, North Clarendon, VT 05759
Tel.: (802) 775-9300
Web Site: http://www.ellisongroup.com
Emp.: 50
Metal Coating, Engraving, except Jewelry & Silverware & Allied Services to Manufacturers
N.A.I.C.S.: 332812

Lake City Heat Treating Corp. **(1)**
2427 North Boeing Road, Warsaw, IN 46580
Tel.: (574) 269-9484
Web Site: http://www.lakecityheattreating.com
Rev.: $3,000,000
Emp.: 16
Metal Heat Treating
N.A.I.C.S.: 332811
William Davis (Pres & Mgr-Quality Assurance)

Nitruvid SAS **(1)**
ZI du Val 9 rue Jean Poulmarch, 95100, Argenteuil, France
Tel.: (33) 130259515
Web Site: http://www.nitruvid.com
Emp.: 35
Metal Heat Treatment Services
N.A.I.C.S.: 332811
Romain Lacan (Plant Mgr)

Techmeta SA **(1)**
141 route des Machurettes, Epagny, 74370, Metz-Tessy, France
Tel.: (33) 45 027 2090

Web Site: https://techmeta-engineering.com
Sales Range: $25-49.9 Million
Emp.: 70
Electron Beam Equipment Mfr
N.A.I.C.S.: 333992

BODYPOWER SPORTS PLC

13 Gate Lodge Close, Round
Spinney, Northampton, NN3 8RJ,
United Kingdom
Tel.: (44) 1604 673000
Web Site: http://www.fitness-
superstore.co.uk
Year Founded: 1994
Sales Range: $25-49.9 Million
Fitness Equipment Retailer
N.A.I.C.S.: 459110
Paul D. Walker *(CEO)*

BOE TECHNOLOGY GROUP CO., LTD.

No 12 Xihuan Middle Road Economic
and Technological Development
Zone, Beijing, 100176, China
Tel.: (86) 1064366264   CN
Web Site: https://www.boe.com
Year Founded: 1993
000725—(SSE)
Rev.: $24,166,959,169
Assets: $58,039,862,068
Liabilities: $30,653,025,795
Net Worth: $27,386,836,273
Earnings: $352,713,142
Emp.: 88,343
Fiscal Year-end: 12/31/23
Electric Equipment Mfr
N.A.I.C.S.: 335999
Yanshun Chen *(Chm)*

Subsidiaries:

BOE (Hebei) Mobile Technology Co.,
Ltd.   **(1)**
Gu an Industrial Zone, Langfang, 065500,
Hebei, China
Tel.: (86) 1064316698
Flat Screen Products Mfr
N.A.I.C.S.: 334419

BOE (Korea) Co., Ltd.   **(1)**
Room 301 3F HUMAX Village 216
Hwangsaeul-ro, Bundang-gu, Seongnam,
13595, Gyeonggi, Korea (South)
Tel.: (82) 317788063
Web Site: http://www.boe.com.cn
Sales Range: $25-49.9 Million
Emp.: 25
LCD Products Mfr
N.A.I.C.S.: 334419

BOE Healthcare Investment & Man-
agement Co., Ltd.   **(1)**
No 12 Xihuan Middle Road, Beijing Eco-
nomic & Technological Development Zone,
Beijing, 100176, China
Tel.: (86) 1060964612
N.A.I.C.S.: 334118

BOE Hyundai LCD (Beijing) Display
Technology Co., Ltd.   **(1)**
No 10 Jiuxianqiao Rd, Chaoyang, Beijing,
100015, China
Tel.: (86) 1064316698
Web Site: http://www.boe.com.cn
Sales Range: $50-74.9 Million
Emp.: 200
LCD Products Mfr
N.A.I.C.S.: 334419

BOE Land Co., Ltd.   **(1)**
No 10 Jiuxianqiao Rd, Chaoyang, Beijing,
100015, China
Tel.: (86) 1059756288
Web Site: http://www.boe.com.cn
Sales Range: $150-199.9 Million
Emp.: 300
Commercial Facilities Leasing Services
N.A.I.C.S.: 531120

BOE Optical Science & Technology
Co., Ltd.   **(1)**
No 2 Haitang Street, Suzhou Industrial Park
Zone, Suzhou, 215021, Jiangsu, China
Tel.: (86) 51287180800
Software Development Services

N.A.I.C.S.: 541511

BOE Semi-conductor Co., Ltd.   **(1)**
No 10 Jiuxianqiao Road, Chaoyang, Beijing,
100015, China
Tel.: (86) 1064365195
Semiconductor Product Mfr
N.A.I.C.S.: 334413

BOE Smart Technology Co., Ltd.   **(1)**
No 12 Xihuan Middle Road, Beijing Eco-
nomic & Technological Development Zone,
Beijing, 100176, China
Tel.: (86) 1064318888
N.A.I.C.S.: 334118

BOE Varitronix Limited   **(1)**
Unit A-F 35/F Legend Tower No 7 Shing Yip
Street, Kwun Tong, China (Hong Kong)
Tel.: (852) 21976000
Web Site: http://www.boevx.com
Rev.: $1,367,101,028
Assets: $1,056,095,250
Liabilities: $531,334,193
Net Worth: $524,761,058
Earnings: $71,345,175
Emp.: 5,730
Fiscal Year-end: 12/31/2022
Holding Company
N.A.I.C.S.: 551112
Samantha Ko Wing Yan *(Co-CEO)*

Beijing BOE Chatani Electronics Co.,
Ltd.   **(1)**
No 8 Xihuanzhong Rd, BDA, Beijing,
100176, China
Tel.: (86) 1067855825
Flat Screen Products Mfr
N.A.I.C.S.: 334419

Beijing BOE Display Technology Co.,
Ltd.   **(1)**
No 118 Jinghaiyi Rd BDA, Beijing, 100176,
China
Tel.: (86) 1057676800
Electronic Component Mfr & Distr
N.A.I.C.S.: 334419

Beijing BOE Energy Technology Co.,
Ltd.   **(1)**
No 12 Xihuan Middle Roa, Beijing, 100176,
China
Tel.: (86) 1064318888
Software Development Services
N.A.I.C.S.: 541511

Beijing BOE Marketing Co., Ltd.   **(1)**
No 12 Xihuan Middle Road, Beijing Eco-
nomic & Technological Development Zone,
Beijing, 100176, China
Tel.: (86) 1060965867
N.A.I.C.S.: 334118

Beijing BOE Optoelectronics Technol-
ogy Co., Ltd.   **(1)**
No 8 Xihuanzhong Rd, Bda, Beijing,
100176, China
Tel.: (86) 1067855688
Web Site: http://www.boe.com.cn
TFT Products Mfr
N.A.I.C.S.: 334419

Beijing BOE Real Estate Co.,
Ltd.   **(1)**
Block B6A No 10 Jiuxianqiao Road, Chaoy-
ang District, Beijing, 100015, China
Tel.: (86) 1059756288
N.A.I.C.S.: 334118

Beijing BOE Sensing Technology Co.,
Ltd.   **(1)**
No 8 Xihuan Middle Road, Beijing Eco-
nomic & Technological Development Zone,
Beijing, 100176, China
Tel.: (86) 1067855688
N.A.I.C.S.: 334118

Beijing BOE Special Display Technol-
ogy Co., Ltd.   **(1)**
No 11 Dize Road, Bda, Beijing, 100176,
China
Tel.: (86) 1081056200
Network Research & Development Services
N.A.I.C.S.: 541715

Beijing BOE Vacuum Electronics Co.,
Ltd.   **(1)**
No 15 Huitong Street Miyun Economic Development Zone, Miyun District, Beijing,
101500, China

Tel.: (86) 1061095837
N.A.I.C.S.: 334118

Beijing BOE Vacuum Technology Co.,
Ltd.   **(1)**
Tel.: (86) 1084567146
Sales Range: $100-124.9 Million
Emp.: 380
Vacuum Electronic Products Mfr
N.A.I.C.S.: 334419

Beijing BOE Video Technology Co.,
Ltd.   **(1)**
Building 3 No 118 Jinghai 1st Road, Beijing
Economic & Technological Development
Zone, Beijing, 100176, China
Tel.: (86) 1057676732
N.A.I.C.S.: 334118

Beijing Yinghe Century Co., Ltd.   **(1)**
Block B6A No 10 Jiuxianqiao Road, Chaoy-
ang District, Beijing, 100015, China
Tel.: (86) 1059756288
N.A.I.C.S.: 334118

Chengdu BOE Optoelectronics Tech-
nology Co., Ltd.   **(1)**
No 1188 Cooperation Rd, Hi-tech Zone
West Area, Chengdu, 611731, Sichuan,
China
Tel.: (86) 2861771188
Electronic Component Mfr & Distr
N.A.I.C.S.: 334419

Chongqing BOE Optoelectronics
Technology Co., Ltd.   **(1)**
No 7 Yunhan Avenue Soil, Shuitu Hi-tech
Industrial Park Beibei District, Chongqing,
400714, China
Tel.: (86) 2388935888
Semiconductor Distr
N.A.I.C.S.: 423690

Fuzhou BOE Optoelectronics Tech-
nology Co., Ltd.   **(1)**
No 99 Fuju Rd Yinxi St, Fuqing, 350300,
Fujian, China
Tel.: (86) 59138771722
N.A.I.C.S.: 334118

Hefei BOE Optoelectronics Technol-
ogy Co., Ltd.   **(1)**
No 2177 Tongling North Road, Xinzhan
General Pilot Zone, Hefei, 230012, Anhui,
China
Tel.: (86) 55165755666
Electronic Components Distr
N.A.I.C.S.: 423690

Hefei Xinsheng Optoelectronics Tech-
nology Co., Ltd.   **(1)**
No 668 Longzihu Rd, Xinzhan General Pilot
Zone, Hefei, 230012, Anhui, China
Tel.: (86) 55166229998
Electronic Component Mfr & Distr
N.A.I.C.S.: 334419

K-Tronics (Suzhou) Technology Co.,
Ltd.   **(1)**
No 1700 Zhongshan North RD Economic
and Technological Development Zone, Wuji-
ang District, Suzhou, 518000, Jiangsu,
China
Tel.: (86) 51263456336
Web Site: http://www.boe.com
Liquid Crystal Display Mfr
N.A.I.C.S.: 334419

Ordos Yuansheng Optoelectronics
Co., Ltd.   **(1)**
No 37 Science Rd Equipment Manufactur-
ing Base, Dongsheng District, Ordos,
017020, Inner Mongolia, China
Tel.: (86) 1057847777
Liquid Crystal Display Mfr & Distr
N.A.I.C.S.: 334419

Suzhou BOE Chatani Electronics Co.,
Ltd.   **(1)**
No 2 Haitang St, Suzhou Industrial Park
Zone, Suzhou, 215021, China
Tel.: (86) 51287180800
Web Site: http://www.boe.com.cn
Flat Screen Products Mfr
N.A.I.C.S.: 334419

VusionGroup   **(1)**
55 place Nelson Mandela CS 60106,
92024, Nanterre, Cedex, France **(74.39%)**
Tel.: (33) 134346161

Web Site: https://www.vusion.com
Rev.: $670,041,010
Assets: $579,188,431
Liabilities: $370,550,399
Net Worth: $208,638,032
Earnings: $20,044,248
Emp.: 608
Fiscal Year-end: 12/31/2022
Electronic Labeling Systems Mfr & Marketer
N.A.I.C.S.: 333993
Pierre Demoures *(COO-Global Sls & Cus-
tomer Svcs & Sr Exec VP)*

Xiamen BOE Electronics Co.,
Ltd.   **(1)**
No 1 Xianghong St, Torch High tech Zone,
Xiamen, 361101, China
Tel.: (86) 51287180800
Web Site: http://www.boe.com.cn
LCD Products Mfr
N.A.I.C.S.: 334419

Zhejiang BOE Display Technology
Co., Ltd.   **(1)**
No 698 Shunjiang Road, C 1 Bridge, Sha-
oxing, 312000, Zhejiang, China
Tel.: (86) 57589105548
Web Site: http://www.zboe.cn
Monitor & Related Parts Mfr
N.A.I.C.S.: 334118

BOELS TOPHOLDING B.V.

Dr Nolenslaan 140, 6136 GV, Sittard,
Netherlands
Tel.: (31) 900 0551
Web Site: http://www.boels.co.uk
Year Founded: 1977
Holding Company
N.A.I.C.S.: 551112

BOER POWER HOLDINGS LIMITED

Unit D 6th Floor Neich Tower 128
Gloucester Road, Hong Kong, China
(Hong Kong)
Tel.: (852) 25422191   Ky
Web Site: http://www.boerpower.com
Year Founded: 1985
1685—(HKG)
Rev.: $87,978,010
Assets: $193,066,988
Liabilities: $152,455,727
Net Worth: $40,611,262
Earnings: $4,224,776
Emp.: 659
Fiscal Year-end: 12/31/22
Electric Switchgear Mfr
N.A.I.C.S.: 335313
Yixiang Qian *(Chm & CEO)*

Subsidiaries:

Boer (Shanghai) Switch Apparatus
Co., Ltd.   **(1)**
1908 Caoan Road, Shanghai, 201803,
China
Tel.: (86) 2159147230
Web Site: http://sksd.seari.com.cn
Electrical Component Mfr
N.A.I.C.S.: 335313

Shanghai Electrical Apparatus Re-
search Institute Switch Apparatus
Co., Ltd.   **(1)**
1908 Caoan Road, Shanghai, 201803,
China
Tel.: (86) 2159147230
Web Site: http://www.sksd.seari.com.cn
Electric Device Mfr
N.A.I.C.S.: 335999

Temper Energy International, Socie-
dad Limitada   **(1)**
Pol Ind de Granda Nave 18, Granda,
33199, Siero, Asturias, Spain
Tel.: (34) 985793204
Web Site: https://www.grupotemper.com
Electrical Equipment Mfr & Distr
N.A.I.C.S.: 334515

BOERLIND GESELLSCHAFT FUER ERZEUGNISSE MBH

Lindenstrasse 15, 75365, Calw, Germany

Boerlind Gesellschaft fuer Erzeugnisse mbH—(Continued)

Tel.: (49) 705160000
Web Site: http://www.boerlind.com
Year Founded: 1959
Sales Range: $25-49.9 Million
Emp.: 158
Cosmetics Mfr
N.A.I.C.S.: 326620
Michael Lindner (Mng Partner)

Subsidiaries:

Annemarie Borlind SA   (1)
2 rue Thomas Edison, 67450, Mundolsheim, France
Tel.: (33) 88818228
Cosmetic Product Distr
N.A.I.C.S.: 456120

BOERO BARTOLOMEO S.P.A.
Via Macaggi 19, 16121, Genoa, Italy
Tel.: (39) 01055001
Web Site: http://www.gruppoboero.it
Sales Range: $150-199.9 Million
Emp.: 364
Paints & Resins Mfr
N.A.I.C.S.: 325510
Gabriele Tievoli (Dir-HR & TOM)

Subsidiaries:

BOAT S.p.A.,   (1)
Via Macaggi 19, 16121, Genoa, Italy
Tel.: (39) 01055005
Web Site: http://www.boat.it
Sales Range: $25-49.9 Million
Emp.: 10
Marine Protective Coatings Mfr & Whslr
N.A.I.C.S.: 325510
Massimo Zanone (Mng Dir)

Boero Colori France S.a.r.l   (1)
Park Activity Gambe Torte Lot No 1-2855, Route de la Feneri, 06580, Pegomas, Alpes Maritimes, France
Tel.: (33) 492389088
Web Site: http://www.boero-france.com
Sales Range: $25-49.9 Million
Emp.: 15
Marine Yacht Paints
N.A.I.C.S.: 325510
Eonazza Massino (Mgr)

Yacht Systems S.r.l   (1)
Piazza Niccolo, Tommaseo 4, 34121, Trieste, Italy
Tel.: (39) 0403783911
Web Site: http://www.venezianiyacht.it
Marine Paints Mfr
N.A.I.C.S.: 325510

BOG'ART S.R.L.
27 Brezoianu Av, 010131, Bucharest, Romania
Tel.: (40) 213103238
Web Site: http://www.bogart.ro
Year Founded: 1991
Sales Range: $25-49.9 Million
Emp.: 2,100
Engineeering Services
N.A.I.C.S.: 541330
Raul Doicescu (Pres)

Subsidiaries:

ALUSYSTEM SRL   (1)
Str Armoniei nr 27/A, 300291, Timisoara, Timis, Romania
Tel.: (40) 256 309 760
Web Site: http://www.alusystem.ro
Sales Range: $25-49.9 Million
Emp.: 50
Facade Construction Services
N.A.I.C.S.: 237990

BOG'ART FASHION SRL   (1)
Str Stefan Mihaileanu 36, Bucharest, 021068, Muntenia, Romania
Tel.: (40) 21 320 4733
Sales Range: $25-49.9 Million
Emp.: 40
Fashion Designing Services
N.A.I.C.S.: 541490
Mihaela Doicescuo (Gen Mgr)

Bog'Art Building Management SRL   (1)
Str Key No 55 Sector 3, Bucharest, Romania
Tel.: (40) 730280406
Web Site: https://www.bbm.ro
Property Management Services
N.A.I.C.S.: 523150

Bog'Art Steel SRl   (1)
Str Nicolae Teclu nr 55 Sector 3, 032368, Bucharest, Romania
Tel.: (40) 311020584
Web Site: https://www.bogartsteel.ro
Metal Structure Mfr
N.A.I.C.S.: 332311
George Stuparu (Gen Dir)

CONS CONSTRUCT SRL   (1)
Brezoianu 27 Sector 1, Bucharest, Romania
Tel.: (40) 21 307 12 77
Web Site: http://www.consconstruct.ro
Emp.: 6
Building Construction Services
N.A.I.C.S.: 236210

S.C. BOG'ART STEEL S.R.L.   (1)
Str Nicolae Teclu nr 55 Sector 3, Bucharest, 032368, Romania
Tel.: (40) 31 102 05 84
Web Site: http://www.bogartsteel.ro
Emp.: 35
Structured Steel Products Mfr
N.A.I.C.S.: 331110
Soren Suceu (Gen Mgr)

S.C.BOG'ART BUILDING MANAGEMENT S.R.L.   (1)
Sector 3 Calea Dudesti nr 124, Bucharest, 104-124, Romania
Tel.: (40) 213267979
Web Site: http://www.bogartfacility.ro
Building Management Services
N.A.I.C.S.: 561790

S.C.BOG'ART VEST s.r.l.   (1)
Str Armoniei nr 27A, Timisoara, 300291, Romania
Tel.: (40) 256 435 929
Web Site: http://www.bogartvest.ro
Sales Range: $25-49.9 Million
Emp.: 67
Building Construction Services
N.A.I.C.S.: 236210

TONI TRADING SRL   (1)
46 Tomis Blvd, Constanta, Romania
Tel.: (40) 755 743 432
Web Site: http://www.tonis.ro
Online Shopping Services
N.A.I.C.S.: 333241

BOGAWANTALAWA TEA ESTATES PLC
Tel.: (94) 112510100
Web Site:
    https://www.bogawantalawa.com
BOPL—(COL)
Rev.: $18,065,745
Assets: $24,655,440
Liabilities: $15,057,465
Net Worth: $9,597,974
Earnings: $4,087,022
Emp.: 14,853
Fiscal Year-end: 03/31/23
Tea Mfr & Distr
N.A.I.C.S.: 311920
Lalithkumar Jamnadas Ambani (Co-Chm)

Subsidiaries:

Bogawantalawa Tea Ceylon (Pvt) Ltd.   (1)
Tel.: (94) 112369845
Web Site: http://www.bogawantalawa.com
Tea Mfr
N.A.I.C.S.: 311920

BOGAZICI VARLIK YONETIM A.S.
Buyukdere Cad Metrocity Is Merkezi A Blok No 171 Kat 22, Levent, 34330, Istanbul, Turkiye
Tel.: (90) 2123440700

Web Site:
    http://www.bogazicivarlik.com.tr
BOGVY—(IST)
Investment Management Service
N.A.I.C.S.: 523940
Cevdet Erkanli (Chm)

Subsidiaries:

Vera Varlik Yonotim A.S.   (1)
Buyukdere Cad Metrocity is Merkezi A-blok No 171 Kat 22, Levent Sisli, 34330, Istanbul, Turkiye
Tel.: (90) 2123440700
Web Site: http://www.bogazicivarlik.com.tr
Financial Management Services
N.A.I.C.S.: 551112

BOGDAN CORPORATION
Ul Elektrikov 29A, 04176, Kiev, Ukraine
Tel.: (380) 443527496
Web Site: http://www.bogdan.ua
Sales Range: $1-4.9 Billion
Motor Vehicles Mfr
N.A.I.C.S.: 336211
Oleg Svinarchuk (Pres)

BOGO-MEDELLIN MILLING COMPANY, INC.
Barangay Luy-a, Medellin, Cebu, 6012, Philippines
Tel.: (63) 324362178
Year Founded: 1928
BMM—(PHI)
Rev.: $4,519,536
Assets: $5,405,182
Liabilities: $1,530,949
Net Worth: $3,874,233
Earnings: ($706,536)
Emp.: 248
Fiscal Year-end: 09/30/21
Sugar Mfr
N.A.I.C.S.: 311313
Melbert Mepieza (Gen Mgr)

BOHAE BREWERY CO., LTD.
36 Honam-ro 68-gil, Mokpo, 58728, Jeollanam-do, Korea (South)
Tel.: (82) 612433141
Web Site: https://www.bohae.co.kr
Year Founded: 1950
000890—(KRS)
Rev.: $69,688,685
Assets: $113,050,048
Liabilities: $49,806,081
Net Worth: $63,243,967
Earnings: ($2,169,677)
Emp.: 252
Fiscal Year-end: 12/31/22
Liquor Mfr
N.A.I.C.S.: 312130
Won-Hee Jung (Vice Chm)

BOHAI AUTOMOTIVE SYSTEMS CO., LTD.
No 569 Bohai 21st Road, Binzhou, 256602, Shandong, China
Tel.: (86) 5433288868   CN
Web Site: http://www.bhpiston.com
600960—(SHG)
Rev.: $575,961,404
Assets: $1,037,579,784
Liabilities: $391,205,548
Net Worth: $646,374,236
Earnings: ($8,741,079)
Fiscal Year-end: 12/31/22
Piston Mfr
N.A.I.C.S.: 336310
Huang Wenbing (Chm)

BOHAI FERRY GROUP CO., LTD.
No 2 Huanhai Road, Zhifu District, Yantai, 264000, Shandong, China
Tel.: (86) 5356291223
Web Site: http://www.bohailundu.cn
Year Founded: 1998

603167—(SHG)
Rev.: $183,497,437
Assets: $719,167,466
Liabilities: $174,620,338
Net Worth: $544,547,128
Earnings: $22,765,649
Fiscal Year-end: 12/31/22
Transportation Services
N.A.I.C.S.: 483111
Yu Xinjian (Pres & Gen Mgr)

Subsidiaries:

Bohai Ferry (Qingdao) International Travel Service Co., Ltd.   (1)
Zhongshan Road No 44-60 Parkson Plaza 3408 34 / F, Qingdao, China
Tel.: (86) 53282828686
Passenger Transportation Services
N.A.I.C.S.: 483112

BOHAI INDUSTRIAL INVESTMENT FUND MANAGEMENT COMPANY LTD.
26F Tower B ICTC No 59 Machang Road, Tianjin, 300203, Hexi, China
Tel.: (86) 2283867800   CN
Web Site:
    http://www.bohaicapital.com
Year Founded: 2006
Private Equity Investments
N.A.I.C.S.: 523999
Zhu Hui (CFO)

BOHAI PHARMACEUTICALS GROUP, INC.
No 9 Daxin Road, Zhifu District, Yantai, 264000, Shangdong, China
Tel.: (86) 5356857928   NV
Web Site:
    http://www.bohaipharma.com
Sales Range: $150-199.9 Million
Emp.: 660
Herbal Pharmaceutical Mfr & Distr
N.A.I.C.S.: 325412
Hongwei Qu (Chm, Pres & CEO)

BOHAI STEEL GROUP CO., LTD.
No 74 MaChang Road, Heping District, Tianjin, 300050, China
Tel.: (86) 22 58320249
Web Site: http://www.bohaisteel.com
Steel Mfrs
N.A.I.C.S.: 331110
Lv Chunfeng (Chm)

BOHAI WATER INDUSTRY CO., LTD.
No 1 Linkong 2nd Road Shunyiyuan Zhongguancun Technology Park, Shunyi District, Beijing, 101300, China
Tel.: (86) 1089586598
Web Site: http://www.bohaiwater.com
Year Founded: 1996
000605—(SSE)
Rev.: $246,168,936
Assets: $1,134,121,716
Liabilities: $765,533,808
Net Worth: $368,587,908
Earnings: $2,190,240
Fiscal Year-end: 12/31/22
Tap Water Supply Services
N.A.I.C.S.: 221310
Wang Xinling (Chm)

BOHEMIA FAKTORING, A.S.
Letenska 121/8, 118 00, Prague, 1, Czech Republic
Tel.: (420) 257199404   CZ
Web Site: https://bohemiafaktoring.cz
Financial Services
N.A.I.C.S.: 523999

BOHLE AG

Dieselstrasse 10, D-42781, Haan, Germany
Tel.: (49) 212955680
Web Site: http://www.bohle-group.com
Year Founded: 1923
Rev.: $74,156,770
Emp.: 226
Glass Processing Tools Machinery & Accessories Mfr
N.A.I.C.S.: 327215

BOHRA INDUSTRIES LTD.

301 Anand Plaza University Road, Udaipur, 313001, Rajasthan, India
Tel.: (91) 2942429513
Web Site: http://www.bohraindustries.com
Year Founded: 1996
BOHRA—(NSE)
Rev.: $2,894
Assets: $12,535,491
Liabilities: $14,530,957
Net Worth: ($1,995,466)
Earnings: ($375,116)
Fiscal Year-end: 03/31/21
Phosphate Fertilizer Product Mfr
N.A.I.C.S.: 325312
Hemant Kumar Bohra *(Chm & Mng Dir)*

BOILL HEALTHCARE HOLDINGS LIMITED

Room 2101 21/F Wing On Centre, No 111 Connaught Road, Central, China (Hong Kong)
Tel.: (852) 2796 2511
Web Site: http://www.boillhealthcare.com.hk
Year Founded: 1983
1246—(HKG)
Rev.: $27,951,256
Assets: $486,042,944
Liabilities: $363,122,037
Net Worth: $122,920,907
Earnings: ($22,634,700)
Emp.: 136
Fiscal Year-end: 03/31/21
Investment Holding Company
N.A.I.C.S.: 551112
Xing Dong Dai *(Chm)*

Subsidiaries:

Ngai Shun Construction & Drilling Company Limited **(1)**
Flat A 15/F 2-4 Tai Yau Street, Wong King Industrial Building San Po Kong, Kowloon, China (Hong Kong)
Tel.: (852) 23290268
Web Site: http://www.ngaishun.com.hk
Construction Services
N.A.I.C.S.: 236220

BOIRON GROUP

2 Avenue de l Ouest Lyonnais, FR-69510, Paris, France
Tel.: (33) 437418400
Web Site: https://www.boiron.com
BOI—(EUR)
Sales Range: $700-749.9 Million
Emp.: 3,672
Homeopathic Medical Product Mfr
N.A.I.C.S.: 325411
Thierry Boiron *(Chm)*

Subsidiaries:

BOIRON Asia Limited **(1)**
Room 3804 38/F Singga Commercial Center 144-151 Connaught Road West, Hong Kong, China (Hong Kong)
Tel.: (852) 39054671
Web Site: https://boironasia.com
Health Care Product Mfr & Distr
N.A.I.C.S.: 325620

Boiron (Hangzhou) Trading Co., Ltd. **(1)**
Office 4072 Level 40 One Museum Place No 669 Xinzha Road, Jing An District,

Shanghai, China
Tel.: (86) 2160776545
Health Care Product Mfr & Distr
N.A.I.C.S.: 325620

Boiron Bg Eood **(1)**
Bul Shipka Pass 9 Grand Rent Business Building 5th Floor Office 11 Zhk, Geo Milev, 1111, Sofia, Bulgaria
Tel.: (359) 29632091
Web Site: http://www.boiron.bg
Pharmaceutical Drug Mfr
N.A.I.C.S.: 325412
Maria Popova *(Mktg Mgr)*

Boiron CZ S.r.o **(1)**
Coastal 3/620, 186 00, Prague, Czech Republic
Tel.: (420) 224835090
Web Site: http://www.boiron.cz
Sales Range: $25-49.9 Million
Emp.: 27
Homeopathic Medicine Mfr
N.A.I.C.S.: 325412

Boiron Canada Inc. **(1)**
1300 Rene-Descartes, Saint-Bruno-de-Montarville, J3V 0B7, QC, Canada
Tel.: (450) 723-2066
Web Site: http://www.boiron.ca
Pharmaceutical Drug Mfr
N.A.I.C.S.: 325412

Boiron Hungaria Kft **(1)**
Marvany utca 18, 1012, Budapest, Hungary
Tel.: (36) 12111560
Web Site: http://www.boiron.hu
Pharmaceutical Preparations Mfr & Distr
N.A.I.C.S.: 325412

Boiron Medicamentos Homeopaticos Ltda **(1)**
Av Nove de Julho 3789, Jardim Paulista, Sao Paulo, 01407-000, Brazil
Tel.: (55) 30871050
Web Site: https://www.farmaciaboiron.com.br
Emp.: 30
Pharmaceutical Preparations Mfr & Distr
N.A.I.C.S.: 325412

Boiron Portugal Ltda **(1)**
Edif Mar do Oriente Fraccao 2 4 Lote1 07 1Y, Alameda dos Oceanos, Lisbon, Portugal
Tel.: (351) 21 193 2091
Pharmaceutical Preparations Mfr & Distr
N.A.I.C.S.: 325412
Fernando Vitorino *(Gen Mgr)*

Boiron RO Srl **(1)**
Rue Dr No 40 Etage 1 Sector 5, Bucharest, 050454, Romania
Tel.: (40) 21 410 0546
Web Site: http://www.boiron.ro
Sales Range: $25-49.9 Million
Emp.: 15
Pharmaceuticals Whslr
N.A.I.C.S.: 424210
Silvia Mainescu *(Gen Mgr)*

Boiron Russie o.o.o **(1)**
Dolgorukovskaya Building 7, 103050, Moscow, Russia
Tel.: (7) 4959560810
Web Site: http://www.boiron.ru
Emp.: 50
Pharmaceutical Preparartions Mfr & Distr
N.A.I.C.S.: 325412

Boiron SK S.r.o **(1)**
Lamacska cesta 3/A, 841 04, Bratislava, Slovakia
Tel.: (421) 259201811
Web Site: http://www.boiron.sk
Homeopathic Medicine Mfr
N.A.I.C.S.: 325412

Boiron SP z.o.o **(1)**
Ul Poleczki 21, 02-822, Warsaw, Poland
Tel.: (48) 227026670
Web Site: https://www.boiron.pl
Homeopathic Medicine Mfr
N.A.I.C.S.: 325412
Jacek Sroczynski *(Pres & Gen Dir)*

Boiron Sa **(1)**
Neufeldstrasse 1, 3076, Worb, Switzerland
Tel.: (41) 319595588
Web Site: http://www.boiron-swiss.ch
Pharmaceutical Drug Mfr
N.A.I.C.S.: 325412

Boiron Sociedad Iberica de Homeopatia **(1)**
Calle Lanzarote 2, 28703, San Sebastian de los Reyes, Madrid, Spain
Tel.: (34) 914840438
Web Site: http://www.boiron.es
Sales Range: $25-49.9 Million
Emp.: 100
Pharmaceutical Preparation Mfr
N.A.I.C.S.: 325412

Boiron Srl **(1)**
Via Cassanese 100, 20054, Segrate, Milan, Italy
Tel.: (39) 0226990382
Web Site: http://www.boiron.it
Pharmaceutical Preparation Mfr
N.A.I.C.S.: 325412

Boiron Suisse SA **(1)**
Route De La Galaise 32 Plan Les Ouates, Plan-les-Ouates, 1228, Geneva, Switzerland
Tel.: (41) 22 884 1414
Pharmaceutical Preparations Mfr & Distr
N.A.I.C.S.: 325412

Boiron TN SARL **(1)**
1 Rue du Laurier Cite Taieb M hiri, Aouina, Tunis, Tunisia
Tel.: (216) 70727161
Pharmaceuticals Mfr & Distr
N.A.I.C.S.: 325412

Boiron USA Inc. **(1)**
4 Campus Blvd, Newtown Square, PA 19073-3267
Tel.: (610) 325-7464
Web Site: http://www.boironusa.com
Sales Range: $25-49.9 Million
Emp.: 90
Homeopathic Medical Products
N.A.I.C.S.: 325411

Subsidiary (Domestic):

Boiron Inc **(2)**
4 Campus Blvd, Newtown Square, PA 19073-3267
Tel.: (610) 325-7464
Web Site: http://www.boironusa.com
Sales Range: $25-49.9 Million
Emp.: 60
Pharmaceutical Preparartions Mfr & Distr
N.A.I.C.S.: 325412

Centre D Enseignement Et de Developpement de L'Homeopathie LLC **(1)**
85 rue de Bercy, 75012, Paris, France
Tel.: (33) 140211860
Web Site: http://www.cedh.org
Homeopathy Training Center Operator
N.A.I.C.S.: 611420

Centre de Formation En Homeopathie LLC **(1)**
20 rue de la Liberation, 69110, Sainte-Foy-les-Lyon, France
Tel.: (33) 478456194
Web Site: https://www.cdfh.fr
Homeopathy Training Center Operator
N.A.I.C.S.: 611420

Laboratoires Boiron Srl **(1)**
Via U Visconti di Modrone 33, 20122, Milan, Italy
Tel.: (39) 02269901
Web Site: http://www.boiron.it
Pharmaceutical Drug Mfr
N.A.I.C.S.: 325412

SBL Pvt. Ltd **(1)**
SBL House 2 Commercial complex Shrestha Vihar, East Delhi, Delhi, 110092, India
Tel.: (91) 1122162353
Web Site: https://sblglobal.com
Pharmaceutical Drug Mfr
N.A.I.C.S.: 325412
Prashant Surana *(Mng Dir)*

UNDA S.A **(1)**
Rue de Lorce 45, Harze, 4920, Liege, Belgium
Tel.: (32) 43844309
Web Site: https://www.unda.be
Homeopathic Medicine Preparations Mfr
N.A.I.C.S.: 325412

BOIS ET CHIFFONS INTERNATIONAL SA

ZI Paris Est 13 boulevard de Beaubourg, 77183, Croissy-Beaubourg, France
Tel.: (33) 160930202
Web Site: http://www.bois-et-chiffons.fr
Home Furnishing Merchant Whslr
N.A.I.C.S.: 423220
Julien Ayache *(Chm & CEO)*

BOISERIES RAYMOND INC

11 880 56e avenue, Montreal, H1E 2L6, QC, Canada
Tel.: (514) 494-1141
Web Site: http://www.boiseriesraymond.com
Year Founded: 1958
Rev.: $36,238,655
Emp.: 175
Interior Finishing Items Mfr & Supplier
N.A.I.C.S.: 337212
Raymond Waechter *(Founder)*

BOISSET, LA FAMILLE DES GRANDS VINS

5 chemin des plateaux, 21700, Nuits-St-Georges, France
Tel.: (33) 380626100   FR
Web Site: http://www.boisset.fr
Year Founded: 1961
Sales Range: $150-199.9 Million
Emp.: 700
Holding Company Vineyard Winery & Distillery Operator Wine & Distilled Alcoholic Beverage Distr
N.A.I.C.S.: 551112

Subsidiaries:

Buena Vista Carneros Winery Inc. **(1)**
27000 Ramal Rd, Sonoma, CA 95476-9791
Tel.: (707) 252-7117
Web Site: http://www.buenavistawinery.com
Sales Range: $50-74.9 Million
Emp.: 102
Wine Producer
N.A.I.C.S.: 312130

Jean-Claude Boisset Wines U.S.A., Inc. **(1)**
849 Zinfandel Ln, Saint Helena, CA 94574
Tel.: (415) 289-4500
Web Site: http://www.boissetfamilyestates.com
Sales Range: $50-74.9 Million
Emp.: 40
Holding Company; Vineyards, Wineries & Wine Distr
N.A.I.C.S.: 551112
Lisa Heisinger *(VP-Ops)*

Unit (Domestic):

DeLoach Vineyards **(2)**
1791 Olivet Rd, Santa Rosa, CA 95401
Tel.: (707) 526-9111
Web Site: http://www.deloachvineyards.com
Sales Range: $10-24.9 Million
Vineyard & Winery
N.A.I.C.S.: 312130
Lisa Heisinger *(Grp VP-Ops & Gen Mgr)*

BOISSY

Route Du Puy, 43150, Laussonne, Haute Loire, France
Tel.: (33) 471051184
Web Site: http://boissychaussures.fr
Rev.: $10,900,000
Emp.: 159
N.A.I.C.S.: 316990
Albert Boissy *(Chm)*

BOJI MEDICAL TECHNOLOGY CO., LTD.

Room 701 No 1933 Huaguan Road, Tianhe District, Guangzhou, 510640, Guangdong, China
Tel.: (86) 4000020628

Boji Medical Technology Co.,
Ltd.—(Continued)

Web Site: https://www.bojicro.com
Year Founded: 1998
300404—(CHIN)
Rev.: $78,288,994
Assets: $201,264,382
Liabilities: $63,216,283
Net Worth: $138,048,000
Earnings: $3,428,204
Emp.: 700
Fiscal Year-end: 12/31/23
Pharmaceutical Product Research &
Development Services
N.A.I.C.S.: 621511
Tingchun Wang *(Founder, Chm &
Gen Mgr)*

BOJUN AGRICULTURE HOLD-INGS LIMITED

Level 27 50 Bridge Street, Sydney,
2000, NSW, Australia
Tel.: (61) 390098818   AU
Web Site:
   http://www.bojunagriculture.com
Year Founded: 2017
Rev.: $58,486,695
Assets: $40,171,370
Liabilities: $1,274,170
Net Worth: $38,897,200
Earnings: $8,161,372
Fiscal Year-end: 09/30/17
Food & Beverage Mfr & Distr
N.A.I.C.S.: 311423
Bo Zhu *(Exec Dir)*

BOJUN EDUCATION COM-PANY LIMITED

No 288 Jingan Road, Jinjiang District,
Chengdu, Sichuan, China
Tel.: (86) 288 600 2115   Ky
Web Site:
   http://www.bojuneducation.com
Year Founded: 2001
Rev.: $48,370,519
Assets: $258,777,175
Liabilities: $138,634,708
Net Worth: $120,142,467
Earnings: $4,141,457
Emp.: 1,709
Fiscal Year-end: 08/31/19
Educational Support Services
N.A.I.C.S.: 611710

BOKSIT A.D.

Lukic Polje bb, 75446, Milici, Bosnia
& Herzegovina
Tel.: (387) 56 745 140
Web Site: http://www.ad-boksit.com
Year Founded: 1959
BOKS—(BANJ)
Sales Range: $25-49.9 Million
Emp.: 635
Metal Ore Mining Services
N.A.I.C.S.: 212290
Rajko Dukic *(Chm-Mgmt Bd)*

BOKSIT A.D.

Trg rudara no 1, 75446, Milici, Bosnia
& Herzegovina
Tel.: (387) 56745140
Web Site: https://ad-boksit.com
Year Founded: 1959
BNEL—(BANJ)
Sales Range: $1-9.9 Million
Emp.: 90
Footwear Whslr
N.A.I.C.S.: 424340
Rajko Dukic *(Pres)*

BOKWANG INDUSTRY CO.,LTD

40 Yutongdanji-ro 3-gil, Buk-gu,
Daegu, Korea (South)
Tel.: (82) 533840881

Web Site:
   https://www.bokwangindustry.co.kr
Year Founded: 2004
225530—(KRS)
Rev.: $67,090,432
Assets: $111,966,937
Liabilities: $43,761,658
Net Worth: $68,205,280
Earnings: $9,261,326
Emp.: 104
Fiscal Year-end: 12/31/22
Civil Engineering Services
N.A.I.C.S.: 237990
Kim Yun-Su *(Dir-Rep)*

BOKWANG TS CO.

408-1 Jung-ri Seokjeok-myeon
Chilgok-gun, Seoul, Gyeongsangbuk-
do, Korea (South)
Tel.: (82) 544712354
Web Site: http://www.bksa.co.kr
Mobile Phone Metal Parts Services
N.A.I.C.S.: 334220
Sung-wook Son *(Pres)*

Subsidiaries:

Bokwang Hi-Tech Co., Ltd   (1)
1108 Woram-dong, Dalseo-gu, Daegu, Ko-
rea (South)
Tel.: (82) 53 583 2354
Web Site: http://www.bkts.co.kr
Mobile Accessories Mfr
N.A.I.C.S.: 334220

BOLAK COMPANY LIMITED

Chorokro 720-37 Yanggam-Myeon,
Hwaseong, Gyeonggi, Korea (South)
Tel.: (82) 313526455
Web Site: https://bola.inpiad.net
Year Founded: 1959
002760—(KRS)
Rev.: $37,149,427
Assets: $46,719,697
Liabilities: $9,609,363
Net Worth: $37,110,334
Earnings: $2,354,004
Emp.: 143
Fiscal Year-end: 12/31/22
Pharmaceuticals Product Mfr
N.A.I.C.S.: 325412
Kie-Ryun Chung *(CEO)*

BOLAN CASTINGS LIMITED

Main RCD Highway, District Lasbella,
Hub Chowki, Balochistan, Pakistan
Tel.: (92) 853364033
Web Site:
   https://www.bolancastings.com
Year Founded: 1982
BCL—(KAR)
Rev.: $10,867,908
Assets: $8,488,673
Liabilities: $5,747,338
Net Worth: $2,741,335
Earnings: ($1,716,016)
Emp.: 172
Fiscal Year-end: 06/30/19
Automotive Castings & Foundry
N.A.I.C.S.: 332999
Laeeq Uddin Ansari *(Exec Dir)*

BOLD INVESTMENT CO., LTD.

17th floor 2-23-1 Ark Hills Front
Tower, Akasaka Minato Ward, Tokyo,
107-0052, Japan
Tel.: (81) 3 6277 6260   JP
Web Site: http://www.bold-
   investment.com
Year Founded: 2015
Investment Services
N.A.I.C.S.: 523999
Yuichi Yanagida *(Pres)*

BOLD STROKE VENTURES INC.

Suite 414 2906 West Broadway, Vancouver, V6K 2G8, BC, Canada

Tel.: (604) 719-5258   BC
Year Founded: 2011
Investment Services
N.A.I.C.S.: 523999
Nickolaos S. Tsimidis *(CFO)*

BOLD VENTURES INC.

22 Adelaide Street West Suite 3600,
Toronto, M5H 4E3, ON, Canada
Tel.: (416) 864-1456   ON
Web Site:
   https://www.boldventuresinc.com
BVLDF—(OTCIQ)
Rev.: $22,276
Assets: $1,354,277
Liabilities: $300,655
Net Worth: $1,053,622
Earnings: ($158,377)
Fiscal Year-end: 10/31/23
Holding Company; Mineral Explora-
tion
N.A.I.C.S.: 551112
William R. Johnstone *(Sec)*

BOLDUC LEROUX INC.

3365 Boul des Enterprises, Terre-
bonne, J6X 4J9, QC, Canada
Tel.: (450) 477-3413
Web Site: http://www.bolducleroux.ca
Sales Range: $25-49.9 Million
Emp.: 25
Metal Tool Services
N.A.I.C.S.: 333517
Richard Laferriere *(Pres)*

BOLDYN NETWORKS GLOBAL LTD.

2nd Floor 2 Kingdom Street, London,
W2 6BD, United Kingdom
Tel.: (44) 2039349311
Web Site: https://www.boldyn.com
Emp.: 100
Communications & Network Provider
N.A.I.C.S.: 516210

BOLIDEN AB

Klarabergsviadukten 90, PO Box 44,
SE-101 20, Stockholm, Sweden
Tel.: (46) 86101500   SE
Web Site: https://www.boliden.com
BOL—(OTCIQ)
Rev.: $6,875,667,680
Assets: $8,849,823,360
Liabilities: $3,278,336,320
Net Worth: $5,571,487,040
Earnings: $830,266,080
Emp.: 6,071
Fiscal Year-end: 12/31/20
Copper, Zinc, Lead & Precious Met-
als Mining & Smelting
N.A.I.C.S.: 212230
Karl-Henrik Sundstrom *(Vice Chm)*

Subsidiaries:

Boliden Bergsoe AS   (1)
Hvissingevej 116, 2600, Glostrup, Denmark
Tel.: (45) 43268300
Web Site: https://boliden.dk
N.A.I.C.S.: 423510
Torben Bruun *(CEO)*

Boliden Commercial AB   (1)
Klarabergsviadukten 90, PO Box 750, 101
35, Stockholm, Sweden
Tel.: (46) 86101500
N.A.I.C.S.: 423510

Boliden Harjavalta Oy   (1)
Teollisuuskatu 1, 29200, Harjavalta, Finland
Tel.: (358) 25358111
Web Site: http://www.boliden.com
Sales Range: $300-349.9 Million
Emp.: 550
Copper & Nickel Smelting & Refining
N.A.I.C.S.: 331410

Plant (Domestic):

Boliden Harjavalta Oy - Copper
Refinery   (2)

Kuparitie 5, 28330, Pori, Finland
Tel.: (358) 2 5358 111
Web Site: http://www.boliden.com
Copper Refinery
N.A.I.C.S.: 331410

Boliden Kokkola Oy   (1)
Outokummuntie 8, Kokkola, 67200,
Finland   (100%)
Tel.: (358) 68286111
Sales Range: $200-249.9 Million
Emp.: 522
Zinc Smelting
N.A.I.C.S.: 331529
Manu Myllymaki *(Mgr)*

Boliden Tara Mines Limited   (1)
Knockumber House Knockumber Rd, Na-
van, Co Meath, Ireland   (100%)
Tel.: (353) 469079800
Sales Range: $350-399.9 Million
Emp.: 680
Zinc Mining
N.A.I.C.S.: 212230
Stefan Romedahl *(Gen Mgr)*

BOLIGA GRUPPEN A/S

Per Henrik Lings Alle 4 5, 2100, Co-
penhagen, Denmark
Tel.: (45) 43 58 3000
Web Site: http://boligagruppen.dk
Year Founded: 2007
BOLIGA—(CSE)
Rev.: $7,402,556
Assets: $31,311,702
Liabilities: $8,105,634
Net Worth: $23,206,068
Earnings: $1,056,866
Emp.: 35
Fiscal Year-end: 12/31/19
Holding Company
N.A.I.C.S.: 551112
Bo Oland *(Chm)*

BOLINA HOLDING CO., LTD.

North Longwen Road, Longwen Dis-
trict, Zhangzhou, Fujian, China
Tel.: (86) 4008826400   Ky
Web Site: http://www.bolina.cc
Year Founded: 2002
Sales Range: $50-74.9 Million
Holding Company
N.A.I.C.S.: 551112
Zhiqiang Chen *(Deputy Gen Mgr)*

BOLKAN PROPERTY INSTRU-MENTS REIT

21 Yakubitsa Street 5th floor office
501, Lozenets District, 1164, Sofia,
Bulgaria
Tel.: (359) 896113006
Web Site: https://bpireit.com
Year Founded: 2007
BPI—(BUL)
Sales Range: Less than $1 Million
Real Estate Investment Services
N.A.I.C.S.: 531210
Evelina Kostova Nikolova *(Dir-
Investor Relations)*

BOLLIN GROUP LTD.

Suite 3 Bailey Court Green Street,
Macclesfield, SK10 1JQ, United King-
dom
Tel.: (44) 1625 869754
Web Site: http://www.bollingroup.com
Year Founded: 1989
Sales Range: $75-99.9 Million
Emp.: 316
Consumer Products Whslr
N.A.I.C.S.: 445110
Stephen Cann *(CEO)*

Subsidiaries:

Bridgedale Outdoor Ltd   (1)
Unit B Kiltonga Industrial Estate, New-
townards, BT23 4YL, Northern Ireland,
United Kingdom
Tel.: (44) 2891813461
Web Site: http://www.bridgedale.com

Socks Mfr
N.A.I.C.S.: 315120

Burton McCall Limited (1)
163 Parker Drive, Leicester, LE4 0JP,
United Kingdom
Tel.: (44) 1162344600
Web Site: http://www.burton-mccall.co.uk
Marketing Consulting Services
N.A.I.C.S.: 541613

**Outdoor & Sports Company (Hold-
ings) Limited** (1)
Redfern House Dawson Street, Hyde, SK20
2LA, United Kingdom
Tel.: (44) 1613665020
Holding Company
N.A.I.C.S.: 551112

**BOLOGNESI EMPREENDIMEN-
TOS LTDA.**
Av Carlos Gomes 111-7th Floor,
Porto Alegre, 90520-002, Rio Grande
do Sul, Brazil
Tel.: (55) 5130258080   BR
Web Site:
  http://www.bolognesi.com.br
Year Founded: 1973
Residential Construction Services
N.A.I.C.S.: 236117
Ronaldo Bolognesi (Engr-Civil)

Subsidiaries:

Multiner S.A. (1)
Avenida Almirante Barroso 52 19th andar,
CEP 20031-918, Rio de Janeiro, RJ,
Brazil   (55%)
Tel.: (55) 21 2272 5500
Web Site: http://www.multiner.com.br
Holding Company; Electric Power Genera-
tion Plants Operator
N.A.I.C.S.: 551112
Paulo Cesar Rutzen (Chm & CEO)

**BOLSA DE COMERCIO DE
BUENOS AIRES**
Domingo Faustino Sarmiento 299,
C1041AAE, Buenos Aires, Argentina
Tel.: (54) 11 4316 7000
Web Site:
  http://www.bcba.sba.com.ar
Year Founded: 1854
Securities & Commodity Exchanges
N.A.I.C.S.: 523210
Adelmo J.J. Gabbi (Pres)

Subsidiaries:

Bolsas y Mercados Argentinos S.A.
(BYMA)   (1)
Autopista 25 de Mayo 359, C1002, Buenos
Aires, C1002, Argentina
Tel.: (54) 1143166000
Web Site: https://www.byma.com.ar
Securities & Commodity Exchanges; Finan-
cial Services
N.A.I.C.S.: 523210
Gabriela Terminielli (Dir)

**BOLSA DE COMERCIO DE
SANTIAGO, BOLSA DE VA-
LORES**
La Bolsa 64, Santiago, Chile
Tel.: (56) 223993000   CL
Web Site:
  https://www.bolsadesantiago.com
Year Founded: 1893
Emp.: 120
Stock Exchange Operator
N.A.I.C.S.: 523210
Eduardo Munoz Vivaldi (Vice Chm)

**BOLSA DE VALORES DE CA-
RACAS**
Calle Sorocaima entre Ave Venezuela
y Tamanaco, Caracas, 1060, Venezu-
ela
Tel.: (58) 2129055511
Web Site:
  http://www.bolsadecaracas.com
Sales Range: $25-49.9 Million

Emp.: 65
Stock Exchange Services
N.A.I.C.S.: 523210
Juan Carlos Da Silva (Mgr-Admin &
Fin)

**BOLSA DE VALORES DE LIMA
S.A.**
Pasaje Acuna 106, Lima, 100, Peru
Tel.: (51) 16193333
Web Site: http://www.bvl.com.pe
Year Founded: 1860
Sales Range: $10-24.9 Million
Stock Exchange Services
N.A.I.C.S.: 523210
Tulio Freire Ganoza (Mgr)

**BOLSA DE VALORES DE
PANAMA S.A.**
Ave Federico Boyd y Calle 49,
Panama, 0823-00963, Panama
Tel.: (507) 2691966
Web Site: http://www.panabolsa.com
Sales Range: $25-49.9 Million
Emp.: 17
Stock Exchange Services
N.A.I.C.S.: 523210
Fernando Aramburu (Treas)

**BOLSA MEXICANA DE VA-
LORES, S.A.B. DE C.V.**
Paseo de la Reforma 255, Cuauh-
temoc, 06500, Mexico, Mexico
Tel.: (52) 555342900
Web Site: https://www.bmv.com.mx
BOLSA—(MEX)
Rev.: $231,645,023
Assets: $519,292,938
Liabilities: $67,608,007
Net Worth: $451,684,931
Earnings: $99,137,116
Emp.: 503
Fiscal Year-end: 12/31/23
Stock Exchange Services
N.A.I.C.S.: 523210
Ramon Guemez Sarre (Dir-Admin)

Subsidiaries:

SIF ICAP S.A. de C.V.   (1)
Paseo de La Reforma No 255 Piso 7, Col
Cuauhtemoc, Cuauhtemoc, 6500, Mexico
Tel.: (52) 55512820
Web Site: http://www.sif.com.mx
Emp.: 35
Securities & Commodity Exchanges
N.A.I.C.S.: 523210
Gabriel Rodriguez (Gen Mgr)

**BOLSA NACIONAL DE VA-
LORES, S.A.**
Santa Forum, Apartado Postal 03-
6155, Santa Ana, Costa Rica
Tel.: (506) 22044848
Web Site: http://www.bolsacr.com
Sales Range: $25-49.9 Million
Emp.: 90
Stock Exchange Services
N.A.I.C.S.: 523210
Thomas Alberto (VP)

BOLT METALS CORP.
Suite 300 Bellevue Centre, West
Vancouver, V7T2X1, BC, Canada
Tel.: (604) 922-8272
Web Site:
  https://www.boltmetals.com
Year Founded: 1996
PCRCF—(OTCQB)
Assets: $283,095
Liabilities: $991,394
Net Worth: ($708,299)
Earnings: ($559,618)
Fiscal Year-end: 12/31/22
Metal Exploration Services
N.A.I.C.S.: 213115
Ranjeet Sundher (Pres & CEO)

BOLTEK HOLDINGS LIMITED
5/F Winning Commercial Building
46-48 Hillwood Road, Tsim Sha Tsui,
Hong Kong, China (Hong Kong)
Tel.: (852) 31682028   Ky
Web Site:
  https://www.boltekholdings.com
Year Founded: 2005
8601—(HKG)
Rev.: $19,255,682
Assets: $28,381,275
Liabilities: $3,700,436
Net Worth: $24,680,839
Earnings: $2,574,312
Emp.: 147
Fiscal Year-end: 12/31/22
Holding Company
N.A.I.C.S.: 551112
Chui Ping Chiu (Chief Admin Officer)

Subsidiaries:

Mannings (Asia) Consultants
Limited   (1)
5/F Winning Commercial Building 46-48
Hillwood Road, Tsim Sha Tsui, Kowloon,
China (Hong Kong)
Tel.: (852) 31682028
Web Site: https://manningsasia.com
Emp.: 300
Engineering Design & Consultancy Services
N.A.I.C.S.: 541330

**BOLTON FOOTWEAR (PTY)
LTD.**
12 Malherbe Street Elsies River,
Cape Town, South Africa
Tel.: (27) 215907000
Web Site: http://www.bolwear.co.za
Year Founded: 1859
Footwear Mfr
N.A.I.C.S.: 316210
Noel Whitehead (CEO)

Subsidiaries:

Feltex Holdings (Pty) Ltd. - United
Fram Footwear   (1)
18 Sprinz Ave Vlg Main, Johannesburg,
2001, Gauteng, South Africa
Tel.: (27) 113321500
Web Site: http://www.frams.co.za
Industrial & Safety Footwear Mfr
N.A.I.C.S.: 316210
Kenny Lazarus (Gen Mgr)

Feltex Holdings (Pty) Ltd. - Wayne
Plastics   (1)
No 3 Domkrag St Roberts Ville, PO Box
1525, Florida, Johannesburg, 1710, Gau-
teng, South Africa
Tel.: (27) 114721580
Web Site: http://www.wayneplastics.co.za
Sales Range: $25-49.9 Million
Emp.: 140
Plastic Boots Mfr
N.A.I.C.S.: 316210

Mossop Western Leathers (Pty)
Ltd   (1)
Blignaut St, Wellington, 7654, Western
Cape, South Africa
Tel.: (27) 218649300
Web Site: http://www.mossops.co.za
Emp.: 175
Leather Mfr
N.A.I.C.S.: 316110
Gert Kruger (CEO & Mng Dir)

BOLU CIMENTO SANAYII A.S.
Yuva Koyu Cimento Fabrikasi yani
Sokak No 1, Bolu, Turkiye
Tel.: (90) 3742264770
Web Site:
  http://www.bolucimento.com.tr
Year Founded: 1967
BOLUC—(IST)
Rev.: $54,709,321
Assets: $135,572,085
Liabilities: $72,630,350
Net Worth: $62,941,735
Earnings: ($8,097,634)
Fiscal Year-end: 09/30/19

Cement Mfr
N.A.I.C.S.: 327310
Calbiyik Suat (Chm)

BOMBARDIER INC.
400 Cote-Vertu Road West, Dorval,
H4S 1Y9, QC, Canada
Tel.: (514) 861-9481   Ca
Web Site: https://bombardier.com
Year Founded: 1902
BDRAF—(OTCQX)
Rev.: $8,046,000,000
Assets: $12,458,000,000
Liabilities: $14,862,000,000
Net Worth: ($2,404,000,000)
Earnings: $445,000,000
Emp.: 17,100
Fiscal Year-end: 12/31/23
Aircraft Mfr
N.A.I.C.S.: 336411
Pierre Beaudoin (Chm)

Subsidiaries:

Bombardier (Mauritius) Ltd   (1)
5th Floor Ebene Esplanade 24 CyberCity,
Ebene, 72201, Mauritius
Tel.: (230) 210 9000
Web Site:
  http://www.bombardiermauritius.com
Emp.: 1
Transportation Services
N.A.I.C.S.: 488999

Bombardier Aerospace   (1)
400 Chemin De La Cote Vertu W, Dorval,
H4S 1Y9, QC, Canada   (100%)
Tel.: (514) 855-5000
Web Site:
  http://www.aerospace.bombardier.com
Rev.: $6,972,768,256
Emp.: 57,000
Mfr of Civil Aircraft
N.A.I.C.S.: 336411
Doug Cai (Pres-China)

Plant (US):

Bombardier - Learjet   (2)
1 Learjet Way, Wichita, KS 67209-2924
Tel.: (316) 946-2000
Sales Range: $400-449.9 Million
Emp.: 2,500
Mfr of Business Jet Aircraft; Modification,
Maintenance & Sub-Contracting for Major
Aerospace Manufacturers
N.A.I.C.S.: 336411
Tonya Sudduth (VP-Ops)

Bombardier - Learjet   (2)
1919 14th St Ste 800, Boulder, CO 80302-
5327
Tel.: (303) 546-0017
Web Site: http://www.learjet.com
Sales Range: $25-49.9 Million
Emp.: 2
Aircraft Dealers
N.A.I.C.S.: 441227

Plant (Domestic):

Bombardier Aerospace   (2)
123 Garratt Blvd, Toronto, M3K 1Y5, ON,
Canada
Tel.: (416) 633-7310
Web Site: http://www.bombardier.com
Sales Range: $800-899.9 Million
Emp.: 2,600
Aerospace Mfr
N.A.I.C.S.: 336411

Plant (US):

Bombardier Aerospace   (2)
2400 Aviation Way, Bridgeport, WV
26330-9729   (100%)
Tel.: (304) 842-6300
Web Site: http://www.bombardier.com
Sales Range: $100-124.9 Million
Emp.: 330
Aircraft Servicing & Repairing
N.A.I.C.S.: 488190
Brant Dahlfors (VP-Sls)

Subsidiary (Non-US):

Bombardier Aerospace Belfast   (2)

Bombardier Inc.—(Continued)

Airport Rd, Belfast, BT3 9DZ, United
Kingdom   **(100%)**
Tel.: (44) 2890458444
Web Site: http://www.aero.bombardier.com
Sales Range: $800-899.9 Million
Emp.: 5,000
Aircraft Mfr
N.A.I.C.S.: 333618

Bombardier Capital Incorporated   **(1)**
261 Mountain View Dr, Colchester, VT
05446   **(100%)**
Tel.: (904) 288-1000
Web Site: http://www.bombardier.com
Sales Range: $700-749.9 Million
Emp.: 1,100
Lending, Leasing & Asset Management
Services to A Customer Base In Retail,
Mortgage, Inventory, Commercial & Indus-
trial Financing Markets
N.A.I.C.S.: 522220

Subsidiary (Non-US):

Bombardier Capital International
B.V.   **(2)**
Deboelelaan 7, Amsterdam, HJ 1083, Neth-
erlands
Tel.: (31) 206239263
Sales Range: $25-49.9 Million
Emp.: 2
N.A.I.C.S.: 333618

Subsidiary (Domestic):

Bombardier Credit Receivables
Corporation   **(2)**
261 Mountain View Dr, Colchester, VT
05446-5823
Tel.: (802) 764-5232
Web Site: http://www.bombardier.com
N.A.I.C.S.: 333618

RJ Finance Corp. One   **(2)**
261 Mountain View Dr, Colchester, VT
05446-5823
Tel.: (802) 764-5232
Web Site: http://www.bombardier.com
Finance Agency
N.A.I.C.S.: 522310

Bombardier Corp.   **(1)**
3400 Waterview Pkwy Ste 400, Richardson,
TX 75080
Tel.: (972) 720-2400
Web Site: http://www.bombardier.com
Sales Range: $1-9.9 Million
Emp.: 800
Aircraft & Parts
N.A.I.C.S.: 423860
Jeff Cole *(Sls Dir-Northeast)*

Bombardier European Holdings,
S.L.U.   **(1)**
Rambla de Catalunya 43-30 Izq, 08007,
Barcelona, Spain
Tel.: (34) 93 487 4187
Web Site: http://www.bombardier.com
Sales Range: $25-49.9 Million
Emp.: 15
Railway Signal Equipment Mfr
N.A.I.C.S.: 327910

Bombardier European Investments,
S.L.   **(1)**
Edif Louis Pasteur-Avda Del Juncal 22-24 4
Plta, San Sebastian de los Reyes, 28703,
Madrid, Spain
Tel.: (34) 916579100
Sales Range: $50-74.9 Million
Emp.: 15
Railway Transportation Equipment Mfr
N.A.I.C.S.: 336999

Bombardier Inc. - Real Estate
Services   **(1)**
2505 Rue Des Nations Ste 200, Saint Lau-
rent, H4R 3C8, QC, Canada
Tel.: (514) 335-9511
Web Site: http://www.boisfranc.com
Sales Range: $10-24.9 Million
Emp.: 5
Real Estate Lot Seller
N.A.I.C.S.: 531390

Lufthansa Bombardier Aviation Services GmbH   **(1)**
Flughafen BER ZKS 13 West Walter-

Rieseler-Strasse 1, 12529, Schonefeld,
Germany
Tel.: (49) 3088754600
Web Site: http://www.lbas.de
Aircraft Mfr
N.A.I.C.S.: 336411
Sascha Leitner *(Mgr-Accountable)*

BOMBAY CYCLE & MOTOR AGENCY LIMITED
534 SVP Road Opera House, Mum-
bai, 400 007, Maharashtra, India
Tel.: (91) 2223612195
Web Site: https://www.bcma.in
501430—(BOM)
Rev.: $973,040
Assets: $3,942,461
Liabilities: $821,962
Net Worth: $3,120,499
Earnings: $254,163
Emp.: 44
Fiscal Year-end: 03/31/22
Automobile Sales & Maintenance
Services
N.A.I.C.S.: 423110
Arun R. Mathkar *(Mgr-HR & Admin-
Auto Div & Personnel)*

BOMBAY METRICS SUPPLY CHAIN LIMITED
201/Quantum Towers Ram Baug lane
Near Chincholi Petrol Pump S V
Road, Malad West, Mumbai, 400064,
India
Tel.: (91) 2240120561
Web Site:
    https://www.bombaymetrics.com
Year Founded: 2015
BMETRICS—(NSE)
Rev.: $8,467,040
Assets: $4,879,616
Liabilities: $3,617,755
Net Worth: $1,261,861
Earnings: $169,929
Emp.: 30
Fiscal Year-end: 03/31/22
Management Consulting Services
N.A.I.C.S.: 541614

BOMBAY OXYGEN INVEST-MENTS LTD.
22/B Mittal Tower 210, Nariman
Point, Mumbai, 400021, India
Tel.: (91) 2266107503
Web Site: https://www.bomoxy.com
Year Founded: 1960
509470—(BOM)
Rev.: $939,147
Assets: $47,252,109
Liabilities: $1,834,437
Net Worth: $45,417,672
Earnings: $672,208
Emp.: 10
Fiscal Year-end: 03/31/23
Industrial Gas Mfr
N.A.I.C.S.: 325120
Bhupesh P. Mehta *(CFO)*

BOMBAY POTTERIES & TILES LIMITED
11 Happy Home 244 Waterfield
Road, Bandra West, Mumbai,
400050, Maharashtra, India
Tel.: (91) 2246092152
Web Site:
    https://bombaypotteries.com
Year Founded: 1933
502216—(BOM)
Sales Range: Less than $1 Million
Real Estate Development Services
N.A.I.C.S.: 531390
Vijay V. Wadhwa *(Co-Founder)*

BOMBAY RAYON FASHIONS LIMITED

Raheja Platinum Office Space Num-
ber -06B123 Sag Baug Road, Off
Andheri Kurla Road Marol Andheri
East, Mumbai, 400059, India
Tel.: (91) 2261068800
Web Site:
    https://www.bombayrayon.com
Year Founded: 1986
BRFL—(BOM)
Rev.: $68,334,630
Assets: $905,115,120
Liabilities: $791,487,060
Net Worth: $113,628,060
Earnings: ($249,691,260)
Emp.: 3,645
Fiscal Year-end: 03/31/20
Textile Garments Mfr & Distr
N.A.I.C.S.: 313310
Aman Agrawal *(Chm)*

Subsidiaries:

DPJ Clothing Ltd.   **(1)**
Unit 4 Wadsworth Business Centre, Green-
ford, London, UB6 7LQ, United Kingdom
Tel.: (44) 20 8998 0777
Emp.: 1
Apparel & Accessories Distr
N.A.I.C.S.: 424350

STI India Limited   **(1)**
Rau-Pithampur Link Road Tehsil Mhow, In-
dore, 453 332, MP, India
Tel.: (91) 7314014400
Web Site: http://www.stitextile.net
Rev.: $6,967,089
Assets: $15,645,657
Liabilities: $18,697,295
Net Worth: ($3,051,638)
Earnings: ($835,520)
Emp.: 591
Fiscal Year-end: 03/31/2019
Cotton Yarn Mfr
N.A.I.C.S.: 313110
Deepesh Kumar Nayak *(Officer-Compliance
& Sec)*

BOMBAY STOCK EXCHANGE LIMITED
Phiroze Jeejeebhoy Towers Dalal St,
Mumbai, 400001, India
Tel.: (91) 2222721233
Web Site: https://www.bseindia.com
Year Founded: 1875
Sales Range: $25-49.9 Million
Stock Exchange Services
N.A.I.C.S.: 523210
C. Vasudevan *(Gen Mgr)*

Subsidiaries:

Central Depository Services (India)
Limited   **(1)**
17th floor P J Towers Dalal Street, Mumbai,
400001, India
Tel.: (91) 22 2272 3333
Web Site: http://www.cdslindia.com
Depository Services
N.A.I.C.S.: 522180
N. Rangachary *(Chm)*

Marketplace Technologies Pvt
Ltd.   **(1)**
3rd floor B-wing Aggarwal Trade Centre Plot
62 Sector 11 Belapur CBD, Mumbai, 400
614, India
Tel.: (91) 22 61484250
Web Site: http://www.mkttech.in
Emp.: 200
Information Technology Consulting Services
N.A.I.C.S.: 541512
Pranav Trivedi *(Head-Comml, Bus Dev &
Exchange Solutions)*

BOMBAY SUPER HYBRID SEEDS LTD.
Plot No 8 9 10 11 Shreenathji Indus-
trial Estate Near Kuvadva GIDC, NH
8-B Kuvadva, Rajkot, 360023, India
Tel.: (91) 9638962396
Web Site:
    https://www.bombaysuperseeds.com

BSHSL—(NSE)
Rev.: $27,409,048
Assets: $15,931,635
Liabilities: $9,177,175
Net Worth: $6,754,460
Earnings: $2,012,048
Emp.: 49
Fiscal Year-end: 03/31/23
Agricultural Chemical Mfr
N.A.I.C.S.: 325320
Pintubhai Patel *(CEO & Mng Dir)*

BOMBAY WIRE ROPES LIM-ITED
401/405 Jolly Bhavan No 1 10 New
Marine Lines, Mumbai, 400 020, Ma-
harashtra, India
Tel.: (91) 2222003231
Web Site:
    https://www.bombaywireropes.com
Year Founded: 1961
504648—(BOM)
Rev.: $61,013
Assets: $960,389
Liabilities: $27,861
Net Worth: $932,528
Earnings: $20,018
Fiscal Year-end: 03/31/21
Steel Product Mfr & Distr
N.A.I.C.S.: 331110
Rajkumar Jhunjhunwala *(Exec Dir)*

BOMBRIL S.A.
Via Anchieta Km 14 S/N - Bairro
Rudge Ramos, Distrito Industrial, Sao
Bernardo do Campo, 09696-000, Sao
Paulo, Brazil
Tel.: (55) 1143661001
Web Site: https://www.bombril.com.br
Year Founded: 1948
BOBR4—(BRAZ)
Rev.: $292,773,415
Assets: $170,315,301
Liabilities: $181,753,941
Net Worth: ($11,438,640)
Earnings: $20,642,143
Emp.: 2,400
Fiscal Year-end: 12/31/23
Household Products Mfr
N.A.I.C.S.: 325611
Wagner Brilhante de Albuquerque
(Dir-Investor Relations)

BOMESC OFFSHORE ENGI-NEERING COMPANY LIMITED
No 14 the 4th Ave TEDA, Tianjin,
300457, China
Tel.: (86) 2266299900
Web Site: https://www.bomesc.com
Year Founded: 1996
603727—(SHG)
Rev.: $451,648,927
Assets: $723,289,371
Liabilities: $255,949,495
Net Worth: $467,339,877
Earnings: $9,072,269
Emp.: 1,400
Fiscal Year-end: 12/31/22
Offshore Engineering Services
N.A.I.C.S.: 541330

BOMIN ELECTRONICS CO., LTD.
Tower C Zhuoyue Qianhai Times
Square Bao hua Road, Baoan Dis-
trict, Shenzhen, China
Tel.: (86) 75527885600
Web Site:
    https://www.bominelec.com
Year Founded: 1994
603936—(SHG)
Rev.: $408,899,233
Assets: $971,357,653
Liabilities: $454,366,832
Net Worth: $516,990,820
Earnings: $11,033,278

Emp.: 2,500
Fiscal Year-end: 12/31/22
Printed Circuit Board Mfr & Distr
N.A.I.C.S.: 334412
Huan Xu *(Chm & Pres)*

Subsidiaries:

Jiangsu Bomin Electronics Co.,
Ltd. (1)
Dafeng Development Zone, Jiangsu, China
Tel.: (86) 51583890708
Printed Circuit Board Mfr
N.A.I.C.S.: 334412

Shenzhen Bomin Electronic Co.,
Ltd. (1)
Unit 21 to 23 Fuyong Rd, Longwangmiao
Industrial Park Bao' an District, Shenzhen,
China
Tel.: (86) 75527308088
Printed Circuit Board Mfr
N.A.I.C.S.: 334412

Shenzhen Juntian Hengxun Technol-
ogy Co., Ltd. (1)
East 19th Floor Desai Technology Building
South District, Nanshan District, Shenzhen,
China
Tel.: (86) 75582922364
Web Site: http://www.jthx-sz.com
Electronic Components Mfr
N.A.I.C.S.: 334419

BOMSOWA CO. LTD.
Gyeonggi-do Hwangsaeul-ro
360beongil 19 Geumhwa Building 7th
floor, Bundang-gu, Seongnam,
13591, Korea (South)
Tel.: (82) 16005893
Web Site: https://bomsowa.co.kr
Year Founded: 1992
Beverage Product Mfr & Distr
N.A.I.C.S.: 333241

BON FAME CO., LTD.
5F No 17 Ln 360 Sec 1 Neihu Rd,
Neihu Dist, Taipei, Taiwan
Tel.: (886) 287972000
Web Site: https://www.bonfame.com
Year Founded: 1985
8433—(TPE)
Rev.: $98,218,585
Assets: $122,394,272
Liabilities: $62,387,112
Net Worth: $60,007,160
Earnings: $15,743,551
Fiscal Year-end: 12/31/22
Clothing Products Distr
N.A.I.C.S.: 458110

Subsidiaries:

Limited Edition Inc. (1)
Chaussee d'Aalbeke 284 b, 7700, Mous-
cron, Belgium
Tel.: (32) 56852795
Web Site: https://www.le.be
Emp.: 200
Fabric Product Mfr
N.A.I.C.S.: 314110
Nathalie Provoost *(Sls Mgr)*

BON NATURAL LIFE LIMITED
C601 Gazelle Valley No 69 Jinye
Road Xi 'an Hi-tech Zone, Xi'an,
China
Tel.: (86) 2988318908 Ky
Web Site: https://www.bnlus.com
Year Founded: 2019
BON—(NASDAQ)
Rev.: $29,522,353
Assets: $46,556,136
Liabilities: $10,574,303
Net Worth: $35,981,833
Earnings: $4,595,982
Emp.: 96
Fiscal Year-end: 09/30/23
Holding Company
N.A.I.C.S.: 551112
Yingchun Xue *(COO)*

BONA FILM GROUP LIMITED
18/F Tower A U-town Office Building
#1 San Feng Bei Li, Chaoyang Dis-
trict, Beijing, 100020, China
Tel.: (86) 10 5631 0700 Ky
Web Site: http://www.bonafilm.cn
Year Founded: 2003
Sales Range: $250-299.9 Million
Emp.: 1,163
Motion Picture Distr & Production
N.A.I.C.S.: 512120
Dong Yu *(Founder, Chm & CEO)*

**BONANZA MINING CORPORA-
TION**
Suite 2201-8 Smithe Mews, Vancou-
ver, V6B 0A5, BC, Canada
Tel.: (604) 619-0225 Ca
Web Site: https://bonanzamining.com
Year Founded: 2016
BNZ—(TSXV)
Rev.: $1,956
Assets: $651,064
Liabilities: $104,815
Net Worth: $546,250
Earnings: ($166,554)
Fiscal Year-end: 02/28/21
Business Consulting Services
N.A.I.C.S.: 522299
Alfredo De Lucrezia *(Pres & CEO)*

**BONANZA RESOURCES
CORP.**
14727 129th Street, Edmonton, T6V
1C4, AB, Canada
Tel.: (780) 887-4998 NV
Year Founded: 2012
Quartz & Other Mineral Mining
N.A.I.C.S.: 327999
Wayne Cadence *(Pres, CEO, CFO,
Treas & Sec)*

BONASUDDEN HOLDING AB
c/o Pareto Business Management
AB, Box 7415, 103 91, Stockholm,
Sweden
Tel.: (46) 84925394
Web Site:
 https://www.bonasudden.se
BONAS—(OMX)
Rev.: $3,614,636
Assets: $77,385,332
Liabilities: $44,430,100
Net Worth: $32,955,232
Earnings: ($1,751,392)
Emp.: 1
Fiscal Year-end: 12/31/22
Real Estate Management & Invest-
ment
N.A.I.C.S.: 531312
Asa Ohlstrom *(CEO)*

**BONATLA PROPERTY HOLD-
INGS LIMITED**
31 8th Street Houghton, Johannes-
burg, 2198, South Africa
Tel.: (27) 11 442 4944
Web Site: http://www.bonatla.com
Sales Range: Less than $1 Million
Investment Management Service
N.A.I.C.S.: 523999
Niki G. Vontas *(CEO)*

Subsidiaries:

The Heights Pty Ltd (1)
99 Jan Heukelman Street Phillip Nel Park,
Pretoria, South Africa
Tel.: (27) 114424944
Web Site: http://www.tutheights.co.za
Accommodation Services
N.A.I.C.S.: 721199

BONATRANS GROUP A.S.
Revolucni 1234, 735-94, Bohumin,
Czech Republic
Tel.: (420) 597 083 112 CZ

Web Site: http://www.bonatrans.cz
Year Founded: 1999
Sales Range: $250-299.9 Million
Emp.: 1,310
Railway Rolling Stock Mfr & Whslr
N.A.I.C.S.: 336510
Jakub Weimann *(Mng Dir)*

Subsidiaries:

Gutehoffnungshutte Radsatz
GmbH (1)
Gartenstrasse 40, 46145, Oberhausen,
Germany
Tel.: (49) 208 7400 0
Web Site: http://www.ghh-radsatz.com
Sales Range: $100-124.9 Million
Emp.: 260
Railway Rolling Stock Mfr & Whslr
N.A.I.C.S.: 336510
Raimund Abele *(Mng Dir)*

BONAVA AB
Lindhagensgatan 72, 112 18, Stock-
holm, Sweden
Tel.: (46) 840954400 SE
Web Site: https://www.bonava.com
Year Founded: 2013
BONAV.B—(OMX)
Rev.: $1,317,231,543
Assets: $1,895,784,971
Liabilities: $1,240,494,790
Net Worth: $655,290,181
Earnings: ($113,467,153)
Emp.: 1,259
Fiscal Year-end: 12/31/23
Residential Property Development
Services
N.A.I.C.S.: 531311
Sofia Rudbeck *(Sr VP-Mktg & Sls)*

Subsidiaries:

Bonava Danmark A/S (1)
Gyngemose Parkvej 50, 2860, Soborg,
Denmark
Tel.: (45) 70400030
Web Site: https://www.bonava.dk
Real Estate Services
N.A.I.C.S.: 531390

Bonava Eesti OU (1)
Toompuiestee 35, Tallinn, Estonia
Tel.: (372) 6274855
Web Site: https://www.bonava.ee
Real Estate Services
N.A.I.C.S.: 531390

Bonava Latvija SIA (1)
Brivibas gatve 275, Riga, 1006, Latvia
Tel.: (371) 67567841
Web Site: https://www.bonava.lv
Real Estate Services
N.A.I.C.S.: 531390

Bonava Norge AS (1)
Minde Alle 10, 5063, Bergen, Norway
Tel.: (47) 55940600
Web Site: http://www.bonava.no
Real Estate Services
N.A.I.C.S.: 531390

Bonava Suomi Oy (1)
Toolonlahdenkatu 2, 00100, Helsinki, Fin-
land
Tel.: (358) 104002000
Web Site: https://www.bonava.fi
Real Estate Services
N.A.I.C.S.: 531390

LLC Bonava Saint-Petersburg (1)
Nevsky Pr 114-116 letter A BC Nevsky Cen-
ter 9th Floor Entrance Street, Uprisings,
191025, Saint Petersburg, Russia
Tel.: (7) 8123299225
Web Site: http://www.bonava.ru
Real Estate Services
N.A.I.C.S.: 531390

BOND BRAND LOYALTY INC.
6900 Maritz Drive, Toronto, L5W1L8,
ON, Canada
Tel.: (905) 696-9400
Web Site:
 https://www.bondbrandloyalty.com
Marketing Consulting Services

N.A.I.C.S.: 541613
Bob Macdonald *(CEO)*

BOND RESOURCES, INC.
Suite 750-580 Hornby Street, Van-
couver, V6C 3B6, BC, Canada
Tel.: (604) 602-4935
Web Site:
 https://www.bondresources.ca
BJB—(CNSX)
Assets: $1,814,552
Liabilities: $946,386
Net Worth: $868,166
Earnings: ($2,752,364)
Fiscal Year-end: 06/30/22
Mineral Exploration & Mining Ser-
vices
N.A.I.C.S.: 213115
Joseph A. Carrabba *(Pres & CEO)*

**BONDEX SUPPLY CHAIN
MANAGEMENT CO., LTD.**
10th Floor Tower B China Resources
Building No 6 Shandong Road,
Qingdao, 266071, Shandong, China
Tel.: (86) 53280978888
Web Site:
 https://www.bondex.com.cn
Year Founded: 2009
603836—(SHG)
Rev.: $1,723,924,398
Assets: $558,518,810
Liabilities: $305,746,033
Net Worth: $252,772,776
Earnings: $39,299,196
Emp.: 2,000
Fiscal Year-end: 12/31/22
Logistic Services
N.A.I.C.S.: 541614
Hai Tang *(Chm & Gen Mgr)*

**BONDFIELD CONSTRUCTION
COMPANY LIMITED**
407 Basaltic Road, Concord, L4K
4W8, ON, Canada
Tel.: (416) 667-8422
Web Site: http://www.bondfield.com
Rev.: $37,900,000
Emp.: 1,000
Construction Services
N.A.I.C.S.: 236220
Ralph Aquino *(Pres)*

BONDIOLI & PAVESI S.P.A.
Via 23 Aprile 35 A, 46029, Suzzara,
Italy
Tel.: (39) 03765141
Web Site: http://www.bypy.it
Year Founded: 1950
Sales Range: $125-149.9 Million
Emp.: 800
Motion Transmission Components
Designer, Mfr & Sales
N.A.I.C.S.: 336350
Edy Bondioli *(Pres)*

Subsidiaries:

BONDIOLI & PAVESI HYDRAULIC
AND MECHANICAL COMPONENT
(HANGZHOU) CO., LTD (1)
N 420 of Beitang East Road, Xinjie Town
Xiaoshan District, Hangzhou, Zhejiang,
China
Tel.: (86) 57183508180
Motor Distr
N.A.I.C.S.: 423610

BONDIOLI & PAVESI INDIA PVT.
LTD. (1)
D 510 TTC Industrial Area MIDC Opposite
Everest Nivara Infotech Park, Turbhe, Mum-
bai, 400703, Maharashtra, India
Tel.: (91) 2232250355
Motor Distr
N.A.I.C.S.: 423610

BONDIOLI & PAVESI LTD. (1)
Poselok Berezovyy 48 office 211, Berezovyy Krasnodarskiy kray, 350031, Kras-

Bondioli & Pavesi S.p.A.—(Continued)

nodar, Russia
Tel.: (7) 8612055427
Motor Distr
N.A.I.C.S.: 423610

BONDIOLI & PAVESI Sp.zo.o. (1)
ul Poznanska 71, 76-200, Slupsk, Poland
Tel.: (48) 598427269
Motor Distr
N.A.I.C.S.: 423610

**BONDIOLI I PAVESI UKRAINE
L.L.C.** (1)
Grushevskogo street 134B, Velyky Birky,
47470, Ternopil, Ukraine
Tel.: (380) 352492125
Motor Distr
N.A.I.C.S.: 423610

**BP COMPONENTES HIDRAULICOS
E MECANICOS Ltda.** (1)
Rua Domenico Martins Mezzomo 184 -
CEP, 95030-230, Caxias do Sul, Brazil
Tel.: (55) 5432118900
Motor Distr
N.A.I.C.S.: 423610

BPN TRANSMISSOES Ltda. (1)
Estrada dos Romeiros 42501, Portao,
06501-001, Santana de Parnaiba, Brazil
Tel.: (55) 1141549037
Motor Distr
N.A.I.C.S.: 423610

Bondioli & Pavesi GS.M.B.H (1)
Siebenhirtenstrasse 13A, A1235, Vienna,
Austria **(100%)**
Tel.: (43) 18692260
Farm Machinery
N.A.I.C.S.: 333111

**Bondioli & Pavesi GmbH
Deutschland** (1)
Im Neugrund 8, 64521, Gross-Gerau,
Germany **(100%)**
Tel.: (49) 615298160
Web Site: http://www.bypy.de
Sales Range: $25-49.9 Million
Emp.: 40
Trade of P.T.O. Drive Shafts, Gear Boxes,
Hydraulic Components & Other Implements
N.A.I.C.S.: 336350

Bondioli & Pavesi Inc. (1)
10252 Sycamore Dr, Ashland, VA
23005-8137 **(100%)**
Tel.: (804) 550-2224
Web Site: http://www.bondioliepavesi.com
Sales Range: $25-49.9 Million
Emp.: 30
Sales of P.T.O. Drive Shafts for Agricultural
Machinery & Gear Boxes & Hydraulic Com-
ponents
N.A.I.C.S.: 423820
Wayne Helton (Controller)

Bondioli & Pavesi-France S.A. (1)
1 Rue Panhard, PO Box 1, 91830, Le
Coudray-Montceaux, France **(100%)**
Tel.: (33) 164938463
Web Site: http://www.bondioli-pavesi.com
Sales Range: $25-49.9 Million
Emp.: 25
Trade of P.T.O. Drive Shafts, Gear Boxes,
Hydraulic Components & Other Implements
N.A.I.C.S.: 336350
Pascal Moreliere (Mgr)

Bondioli y Pavesi Iberica S.A. (1)
Poligono De Malpica II Calle F, PO Box
5062, 50057, Zaragoza, Espagna,
Spain **(100%)**
Tel.: (34) 976588150
Web Site: http://www.bypy-iberica.com
Sales Range: $25-49.9 Million
Emp.: 28
Trade of P.T.O. Drive Shafts, Gear Boxes,
Hydraulic Components & Other Implements
N.A.I.C.S.: 336350

BONDPARTNERS SA
Av de l'Elysee 22-24, Case Postale
174, 1001, Lausanne, Switzerland
Tel.: (41) 216134343
Web Site: http://www.bpl-
bondpartners.ch
Year Founded: 1972

Sales Range: $1-9.9 Million
Emp.: 30
Financial & Brokerage Services
N.A.I.C.S.: 523150
Pascal Kaeslin (VP-Trading)

BONDUELLE SAS
rue Nicolas Appert, BP 30173 59653,
Villeneuve d'Ascq, CEDEX, France
Tel.: (33) 320436060
Web Site: https://www.bonduelle.com
Year Founded: 1853
BON—(EUR)
Rev.: $2,354,152,774
Assets: $2,258,198,048
Liabilities: $1,347,146,515
Net Worth: $911,051,533
Earnings: $37,866,515
Emp.: 11,038
Fiscal Year-end: 06/30/23
Fresh, Frozen & Canned Vegetable
Products
N.A.I.C.S.: 311421
Christophe Bonduelle (Chm)

Subsidiaries:

BFP GmbH (1)
Industriestrasse 6-8, Erzhausen, 64390,
Hessen, Germany
Tel.: (49) 61 509 7370
Web Site: https://www.bfp.de
Worship Services
N.A.I.C.S.: 813110

Bonduelle Deutschland GmbH (1)
Am Heilbrunnen 136/138, 72766, Reutlin-
gen, Germany
Tel.: (49) 71 211 4940
Web Site: https://www.bonduelle.de
Frozen Food Product Mfr
N.A.I.C.S.: 311412

Bonduelle Europe Long Life SAS (1)
La Woestyne, Renescure, 59173, Dunker-
que, France
Tel.: (33) 320436060
Web Site: https://www.bonduelle.fr
Food Production Services
N.A.I.C.S.: 624210

Bonduelle Iberica SAU (1)
Av Isla Graciosa 1 - 2nd floor, San Sebas-
tian de los Reyes, 28703, Madrid, Spain
Tel.: (34) 916586051
Web Site: https://www.bonduelle.es
Frozen Food Product Mfr
N.A.I.C.S.: 311412

Bonduelle Northern Europe NV (1)
Amersveldestraat 21A, 8610, Lier, Belgium
Tel.: (32) 402618833
Web Site: https://www.bonduelle.be
Food Production Services
N.A.I.C.S.: 624210

Bonduelle Polska S.A. (1)
ul Szturmowa 2, 02-678, Warsaw, Poland
Tel.: (48) 222323400
Web Site: https://www.bonduelle.pl
Frozen Food Product Distr
N.A.I.C.S.: 424420

Bonduelle USA Inc. (1)
180 State St, Brockport, NY 14420
Tel.: (585) 637-3154
Food Production Services
N.A.I.C.S.: 624210

Lebanon Valley Cold Storage,
LP (1)
2750 Hanford Dr, Lebanon, PA 17046
Tel.: (717) 202-3555
Web Site: http://lvcold.com
Frozen Fruits & Vegetables Distr; Cold Stor-
age Facility
N.A.I.C.S.: 424420
David Brooks (Mgr-Warehouse)

Ready Pac Foods, Inc. (1)
4401 Foxdale Ave, Irwindale, CA
91706 **(100%)**
Tel.: (800) 800-4088
Web Site: http://www.readypac.com
Processor of Fresh-Cut Produce
N.A.I.C.S.: 311991
Scott McGuire (Chief Supply Chain Officer)

BONE THERAPEUTICS SA
rue Auguste Piccard 37, 6041, Gos-
selies, Belgium
Tel.: (32) 3225295990
Web Site: https://www.biosenic.com
BOTHE—(EUR)
Rev.: $4,502,728
Assets: $30,503,340
Liabilities: $26,419,442
Net Worth: $4,083,898
Earnings: ($19,445,496)
Emp.: 30
Fiscal Year-end: 12/31/20
Cell Therapy Products
N.A.I.C.S.: 325413
Jean-Luc Vandebroekas (Exec Mng
Dir)

**BONEI HATICHON CIVIL ENGI-
NEERING & INFRASTRUC-
TURES LTD.**
Harokmim 26 st Building B floor 5 P
O S 613, Holon, 8122504, Israel
Tel.: (972) 39064607
Web Site: https://www.boh.co.il
Year Founded: 1985
BOTI—(TAE)
Rev.: $80,721,645
Assets: $314,514,983
Liabilities: $253,565,406
Net Worth: $60,949,578
Earnings: $1,617,627
Emp.: 92
Fiscal Year-end: 12/31/23
New Multifamily Housing Construction
(except For-Sale Builders)
N.A.I.C.S.: 236116
Amram Peretz (Owner & CEO)

BONESUPPORT HOLDING AB
Scheelevagen 19, 223 70, Lund,
Sweden
Tel.: (46) 462865370
Web Site:
https://www.bonesupport.com
Year Founded: 1999
BONEX—(OMX)
Rev.: $22,079,389
Assets: $56,793,813
Liabilities: $8,096,224
Net Worth: $48,697,590
Earnings: ($12,380,377)
Emp.: 86
Fiscal Year-end: 12/31/20
Biopharmaceutical Product Mfr
N.A.I.C.S.: 325412
Emil Billback (CEO)

**BONFIGLIOLI RIDUTTORI
S.P.A.**
Via Giovanni XXIII 7/A, Lippo, 40012,
Calderara di Reno, Bologna, Italy
Tel.: (39) 051 647 3111
Web Site: http://www.bonfiglioli.com
Year Founded: 1956
Industrial Gear Reducer & Inverter
Mfr
N.A.I.C.S.: 333612
Sonia Bonfiglioli (Chm)

Subsidiaries:

Bonfiglioli France SA (1)
14 Rue Eugene Pottier, Zi de Moinont II,
95670, Marly-la-Ville, France
Tel.: (33) 134474510
Web Site: http://www.bonfiglioli.fr
Industrial Gear Reducers, Drive Systems &
Inverters Distr
N.A.I.C.S.: 423830

Bonfiglioli Italia S.p.A. (1)
Via Sandro Pertini lotto 7b, Carpiano,
20080, Milan, Italy
Tel.: (39) 02 98508 1
Web Site: http://www.bonfiglioli.it
Industrial Gear Reducers, Drive Systems &
Inverters Mfr & Distr
N.A.I.C.S.: 333612

Bonfiglioli USA, Inc. (1)
3541 Hargrave Dr, Hebron, KY 41048
Tel.: (859) 334-3333
Web Site: http://www.bonfiglioliusa.com
Sales Range: $125-149.9 Million
Emp.: 75
Industrial Gearbox Mfr
N.A.I.C.S.: 333612
Jennifer Panepinto-Sullivan (Dir-Mktg)

O&K Antriebstechnik GmbH (1)
Nierenhofer Strasse 10, 45525, Hattingen,
Germany **(100%)**
Tel.: (49) 2324 20501
Web Site: http://www.oundka.com
Emp.: 150
Industrial Gearbox Designer & Mfr
N.A.I.C.S.: 333612
Georgio Gucchi (Mng Dir)

BONG AB
Bredbandsvagen 4, Box 516, S-291
25, Kristianstad, Sweden
Tel.: (46) 44207000
Web Site: https://www.bong.com
Year Founded: 1737
BONG—(OMX)
Rev.: $202,750,288
Assets: $157,897,197
Liabilities: $104,337,857
Net Worth: $53,559,339
Earnings: $4,003,578
Emp.: 1,100
Fiscal Year-end: 12/31/22
Light Packaging & Envelope Mfr
N.A.I.C.S.: 322230
Christian Paulsson (Chm)

Subsidiaries:

BONG GmbH (1)
Piepersberg 30, 42653, Solingen, Germany
Tel.: (49) 21223391201
Web Site: http://www.bong.de
Sales Range: $50-74.9 Million
Emp.: 220
Stationery Tablet & Related Product Mfr
N.A.I.C.S.: 322230

Bong Belgium S.A. (1)
Bergensesteenweg 93, 7060, Brussels,
Belgium
Tel.: (32) 67347650
Web Site: http://www.bong.com
Sales Range: $25-49.9 Million
Emp.: 100
Stationery Tablet & Related Product Mfr
N.A.I.C.S.: 322230

Bong Caly Swiat Kopert Sp z
o.o. (1)
ul Ustronna 14, 60-012, Poznan, Poland
Tel.: (48) 61 899 3910
Web Site: http://www.bong.pl
Envelope Mfr
N.A.I.C.S.: 322230

Bong Danmark A/S (1)
Langebjergvaenget 18B, 4000, Roskilde,
Denmark **(100%)**
Tel.: (45) 46565555
Web Site: http://www.bong.dk
Sales Range: $25-49.9 Million
Emp.: 40
Stationery & Office Supplies Merchant
Whslr
N.A.I.C.S.: 424120
Mogens Hallager (Dir-Sls-Nordics & Baltics)

Bong Denmark A/S (1)
Langebjergvaenget 18B, 4000, Roskilde,
Denmark
Tel.: (45) 46565555
Web Site: https://www.bong.dk
Packaging & Envelope Distr
N.A.I.C.S.: 424120

Bong Eesti Ou (1)
Joe tn 17, EE-79801, Kohila,
Estonia **(100%)**
Tel.: (372) 4890140
Sales Range: $25-49.9 Million
Emp.: 55
Stationery Tablet & Related Product Mfr
N.A.I.C.S.: 322230

Bong Envelo SRL (1)
Strada Preciziei Nr 3W Corpul C2 - Hala

Alice de Sablaj Hala Nr 1, Sector 6, Bucharest, Romania
Tel.: (40) 312288299
Packaging & Envelope Product Distr
N.A.I.C.S.: 424120

Bong GmbH (1)
Piepersberg 30, 42653, Solingen, Germany
Tel.: (49) 21 223 3910
Web Site: https://www.bong.de
Mail Handling Machinery Mfr
N.A.I.C.S.: 333248
Kai Steigleder (CEO)

Bong Latvija SIA (1)
Krasta iela 97a, 1019, Riga, Latvia (100%)
Tel.: (371) 7241339
Web Site: http://www.bong.com
Sales Range: $50-74.9 Million
Emp.: 2
Stationery & Office Supplies Merchant Whslr
N.A.I.C.S.: 424120

Bong Ljungdahl Sverige AB (1)
Hans Michelsensgatan 9, 21120, Malmo, Sweden (100%)
Tel.: (46) 703507992
Web Site: http://www.bong.se
Sales Range: $50-74.9 Million
Emp.: 150
Stationery Tablet & Related Product Mfr
N.A.I.C.S.: 322230

Bong Netherlands BV (1)
Rivium 1e Straat 68, 2909 LE, Capelle aan den IJssel, Netherlands
Tel.: (31) 102881408
Envelope Mfr
N.A.I.C.S.: 322299

Bong Norge AS (1)
Hvamveien 4, 2013, Skjetten, Norway
Tel.: (47) 64831250
Web Site: http://www.bong.no
Sales Range: $50-74.9 Million
Emp.: 250
Stationery & Related Products Mfr
N.A.I.C.S.: 322230

Bong Norge AS (1)
Bekkeveien 161, 3173, Vear, Norway
Tel.: (47) 33 30 54 00
Web Site: http://www.bong.no
Envelope & Stationery Mfr
N.A.I.C.S.: 322230

Bong Packaging S.R.L. (1)
Via Angelo Masini 12/14, 40126, Bologna, Italy
Tel.: (39) 03347898571
Packaging & Envelope Product Distr
N.A.I.C.S.: 424120

Bong Polska S.P. z o.o. (1)
ul Kolejowa 362-364, 05-092, Dzikow Nowy, Poland
Tel.: (48) 227516652
Web Site: http://www.bong.pl
Sales Range: $25-49.9 Million
Emp.: 60
Stationery Tablet & Related Product Mfr
N.A.I.C.S.: 322230

Bong Retail Solutions AB (1)
Uddevagen 3, 291 25, Kristianstad, Sweden
Tel.: (46) 44207000
Packaging Material Distr
N.A.I.C.S.: 423840

Bong Retail Solutions N.V. (1)
Stasegemsestraat 133b, 8500, Kortrijk, Belgium
Tel.: (32) 56745510
Web Site: https://www.bongretail.com
Packaging Products Mfr
N.A.I.C.S.: 322220

Bong S.A.S. (1)
1 rue Eugene Hermann, 27180, Saint Sebastien, France
Tel.: (33) 970262171
Web Site: https://www.bongpackaging.fr
Emp.: 230
Packaging Products Mfr
N.A.I.C.S.: 322220

Bong Schweiz AG (1)
Haldenstrasse 27, 9200, Gossau, Switzerland
Tel.: (41) 713887970

Packaging & Envelope Product Distr
N.A.I.C.S.: 424120

Bong Security Solutions S.A. (1)
Zone Industrielle Rolach Halle 5, 5280, Sandweiler, Luxembourg
Tel.: (352) 35 75 04 1
Web Site: http://www.bong.lu
Envelope Mfr
N.A.I.C.S.: 322230
Mark Peterson (Mng Dir)

Bong Suomi OY (1)
Jasperintie 270 C, 33960, Pirkkala, Finland
Tel.: (358) 32418111
Web Site: http://www.bongsuomi.fi
Sales Range: $25-49.9 Million
Emp.: 50
Stationery Tablet & Related Product Mfr
N.A.I.C.S.: 322230

Bong Sverige AB (1)
Bredbandsvagen 4, Box 516, 291 25, Kristianstad, Sweden
Tel.: (46) 44207000
Web Site: https://www.bong.se
Sales Range: $50-74.9 Million
Emp.: 100
Paperboard Mfr
N.A.I.C.S.: 322130

Curtis 1000 France Sarl (1)
23 Avenue du Val de Beaute, 94736, Nogent-sur-Marne, France
Tel.: (33) 1 48 73 49 55
Web Site: http://www.curtis.fr
Envelope Mfr
N.A.I.C.S.: 322299

ENVEL EUROPA S.A (1)
Placa De Gal la Placidia 5-7 Esc d 8 1, 08006, Barcelona, Spain
Tel.: (34) 93 241 8850
Web Site: https://www.enveleuropa.com
Envelope Mfr
N.A.I.C.S.: 322230

Egaa Offset A/S (1)
Skejby Nordlandsvej 305, 8200, Arhus, Denmark
Tel.: (45) 87434282
Web Site: http://www.egaa-offset.dk
Envelope Mfr
N.A.I.C.S.: 322299

Excelsior Enveloppen BV (1)
Galileistraat 63, Heerhugowaard, 1704SE, Netherlands
Tel.: (31) 72 56 78 900
Web Site: http://www.excelsiorenveloppen.nl
Envelope Mfr
N.A.I.C.S.: 322299

Lober Druck und Kuvert GmbH (1)
Beethovenstrasse 24-26, 86368, Gersthofen, Germany
Tel.: (49) 821297880
Web Site: http://www.lopa.eu
Sales Range: $25-49.9 Million
Emp.: 100
Other Commercial Printing
N.A.I.C.S.: 323111

PK Koperty Sp. z o. o (1)
ul Zawila 56, 30-390, Krakow, Poland
Tel.: (48) 12 252 02 00
Web Site: http://www.pfluger-koperty.pl
Sales Range: $50-74.9 Million
Emp.: 270
Envelope Mfr
N.A.I.C.S.: 322230
Krzysztof Kubasiak (Gen Mgr)

Packaging First Ltd. (1)
Unit 12 Nash Hall The Street, High Ongar, Ongar, CM59NL, Essex, United Kingdom
Tel.: (44) 1277363656
Web Site: https://www.packagingfirst.co.uk
Packaging Material Mfr & Distr
N.A.I.C.S.: 326112

Pflueger Koperty Sp z o o. (1)
Ul Zawila 56, 30-390, Krakow, Poland
Tel.: (48) 122520203
Web Site: https://www.pfluger-koperty.pl
Packaging & Envelope Product Mfr & Distr
N.A.I.C.S.: 326112

Postac LLC (1)
Domostroiteley pr 17, 248915, Kaluga, Russia

Tel.: (7) 84842764468
Web Site: http://bong.ru
Emp.: 100
Envelope Mfr
N.A.I.C.S.: 322230
Alexey Artizov (Gen Dir)

ProPac International AB (1)
Hans Michelsensgatan 9, 211 20, Malmo, Sweden
Tel.: (46) 40 17 60 00
Sales Range: $25-49.9 Million
Emp.: 22
Packaging Product Distr
N.A.I.C.S.: 423840

SE (Envelope Manufacturing) Ltd (1)
Anglers Business Centre Nottingham Road, Spondon, Derby, DE21 7NJ, United Kingdom
Tel.: (44) 1332667790
Sales Range: $25-49.9 Million
Emp.: 7
Envelope Mfr
N.A.I.C.S.: 322299
Tomy Larkin (Mgr)

Surrey Envelopes Ltd (1)
Unit 7 Nelson Trading Estate Morden Road, London, SW19 3BL, United Kingdom
Tel.: (44) 2085450099
Web Site: http://www.surrey-envelopes.com
Emp.: 60
Envelope Mfr
N.A.I.C.S.: 322299

Venlop B.V. (1)
Rudolf Dieselweg 3, 5928 RA, Venlo, Netherlands
Tel.: (31) 77 382 60 35
Web Site: http://www.venlop.nl
Envelope Mfr
N.A.I.C.S.: 322299

BONHILL GROUP PLC

Fleet House 59-61 Clerkenwell Road, London, EC1M 5LA, United Kingdom
Tel.: (44) 207 250 7010　　　UK
Web Site: http://www.bonhillplc.com
Year Founded: 1991
BONH—(LSE)
Rev.: $22,212,299
Assets: $25,292,966
Liabilities: $8,309,246
Net Worth: $16,983,719
Earnings: ($10,970,378)
Emp.: 133
Fiscal Year-end: 12/31/21
Magazine & Website Publisher; Event Management Services
N.A.I.C.S.: 513120
Simon Leslie Stilwell (CEO)

Subsidiaries:

Growth Company Investor Ltd (1)
50 Banner St, London, EC1Y 8ST, United Kingdom
Tel.: (44) 2072507055
Web Site: http://www.growthcompany.co.uk
Sales Range: $50-74.9 Million
Emp.: 45
Financial Investment Services
N.A.I.C.S.: 523999
Niki Baker (Mng Dir)

InvestmentNews LLC (1)
685 3rd Ave, New York, NY 10017
Web Site: http://www.investmentnews.com
Newspaper Publishers
N.A.I.C.S.: 513110

BONIA CORPORATION BERHAD

Level 6 Ikon Connaught Lot 160 Jalan Cergas, Taman Connaught Cheras, 56000, Kuala Lumpur, Malaysia
Tel.: (60) 391089000　　　MY
Web Site: https://www.bonia.com
Year Founded: 1974
BONIA—(KLS)
Rev.: $89,766,772
Assets: $146,874,497
Liabilities: $50,450,370

Net Worth: $96,424,127
Earnings: $13,247,619
Emp.: 787
Fiscal Year-end: 06/30/23
Apparel Product Mfr & Whslr
N.A.I.C.S.: 315990
Sang Sem Chiang (Founder & CEO-Grp)

BONIFICHE FERRARESI S.P.A

Via Cavicchini 2, 44037, Ferrara, Italy
Tel.: (39) 0532836102
Web Site:
　　http://www.bonificheferraresi.it
Year Founded: 1871
Agriculture Product Distr
N.A.I.C.S.: 325320

BONJOUR HOLDINGS LIMITED

12/F Bonjour Tower 36-50 Wang Wo Tsai Street Tsuen Wan, Hong Kong, China (Hong Kong)
Tel.: (852) 28722872
Web Site: http://www.bonjourhk.com
0653—(HKG)
Rev.: $23,671,905
Assets: $64,439,393
Liabilities: $44,627,423
Net Worth: $19,811,970
Earnings: $21,320,678
Emp.: 194
Fiscal Year-end: 12/31/22
Cosmetics Whslr
N.A.I.C.S.: 456120
Ka Fai Cheung (CFO)

BONLON INDUSTRIES LIMITED

7A/39 12- First Floor Wea Channa Market, Karol Bagh, New Delhi, 110005, India
Tel.: (91) 911147532792
Web Site:
　　https://www.bonlonindustries.com
Year Founded: 1997
543211—(BOM)
Rev.: $22,011,721
Assets: $15,534,394
Liabilities: $5,643,568
Net Worth: $9,890,827
Earnings: $268,228
Emp.: 10
Fiscal Year-end: 03/31/21
Copper Mfr
N.A.I.C.S.: 331420
Raj Jain (Chm & Mng Dir)

BONMARCHE HOLDINGS PLC

Jubilee Way Grange Moor, Wakefield, WF4 4SJ, West Yorkshire, United Kingdom
Tel.: (44) 1924700100
Web Site:
　　http://www.bonmarcheplc.co.uk
Year Founded: 1982
Women's Clothing Store
N.A.I.C.S.: 458110
Geraldine Higgins (Product Dir)

BONNE CO., LTD.

Tel.: (82) 264234111　　　KR
Web Site: https://www.bonne.co.kr
Year Founded: 2015
226340—(KRS)
Rev.: $47,969,039
Assets: $66,832,044
Liabilities: $42,615,721
Net Worth: $24,216,323
Earnings: $836,003
Emp.: 61
Fiscal Year-end: 12/31/22
Personal Care Product Mfr & Distr
N.A.I.C.S.: 456199
Tae Soon Kwak (CFO)

Bonne Co., Ltd.—(Continued)

BONNIER AB
Torsgatan 21, 113 90, Stockholm, Sweden
Tel.: (46) 87364000   SE
Web Site: https://www.bonnier.com
Year Founded: 1804
Emp.: 9,226
Holding Company Multimedia & Production Services
N.A.I.C.S.: 551112
Erik Haegerstrand *(CEO)*

Subsidiaries:

Bonnier Annons AB   **(1)**
Kungsgatan 34, 111 35, Stockholm, Sweden
Tel.: (46) 8 7365300
Marketing & Advertising Services
N.A.I.C.S.: 541613

Bonnier Books AB   **(1)**
Sveavagen 56, Box 3159, SE-103 63, Stockholm, Sweden   **(100%)**
Tel.: (46) 86968000
Web Site: http://www.bok.bonnier.se
Sales Range: $800-899.9 Million
Emp.: 250
Holding Company; Book Publisher
N.A.I.C.S.: 551112

Unit (Non-US):

Akateeminen Kirjakauppa   **(2)**
Keskuskatu 1, 00100, Helsinki, Finland
Tel.: (358) 20 760 8999
Web Site: http://www.akateeminen.com
Academic Bookstores
N.A.I.C.S.: 459210
Inka Ylapelto *(Mgr-Tampere)*

Subsidiary (Non-US):

Bonnier Media Deutschland GmbH   **(2)**
Georgenstrasse 4, 80799, Munich, Germany
Tel.: (49) 89 38 18 01 0
Book Publishing
N.A.I.C.S.: 513130
Hartmut Jedicke *(CEO)*

Subsidiary (Domestic):

Aladin Verlag GmbH   **(3)**
Erdmannstrasse 10-12, 22765, Hamburg, Germany
Tel.: (49) 40 558 91 56
Web Site: http://www.aladin-verlag.de
Book Publishers
N.A.I.C.S.: 513130

BuchVertrieb Blank GmbH   **(3)**
Rohrmooser Str 16-20, 85256, Vierkirchen, Germany
Tel.: (49) 81 39 8 02 91 0
Web Site: http://www.buchvertrieb-blank.de
Book Publishers
N.A.I.C.S.: 513130

Carlsen Verlag GmbH   **(3)**
Volckersstrasse 14 - 20, 22765, Hamburg, Germany
Tel.: (49) 71178992199
Web Site: http://www.carlsen.de
Book Publishers
N.A.I.C.S.: 513130
Daniela Steiner *(Head-Rights)*

Horbuch Hamburg HHV GmbH   **(3)**
Paul-Nevermann-Platz 5, 22765, Hamburg, Germany
Tel.: (49) 40 897 207 80
Web Site: http://www.hoerbuch-hamburg.de
Internet Publisher
N.A.I.C.S.: 513199

Subsidiary (Non-US):

R. Piper & Co Verlag GmbH   **(3)**
Bleicherweg 58, 8002, Zurich, Switzerland
Tel.: (41) 44 204 12 12
Book Publishers
N.A.I.C.S.: 513130

Subsidiary (Domestic):

Thienemann Verlag GmbH   **(3)**

Blumenstr 36, 70182, Stuttgart, Germany
Tel.: (49) 711 210 55 0
Web Site: http://www.thienemann-esslinger.de
Internet Publisher
N.A.I.C.S.: 513130

Ullstein Buchverlage Gmbh   **(3)**
Friedrichstrasse 126, Berlin, 10117, Germany   **(100%)**
Tel.: (49) 30 23456 300
Web Site: http://www.ullstein-buchverlage.de
Sales Range: $25-49.9 Million
Emp.: 100
Book Publishing
N.A.I.C.S.: 513130
Alexander Lorbeer *(Mng Dir)*

arsEdition GmbH   **(3)**
Friedrichstrasse 9, 80801, Munich, Germany
Tel.: (49) 89 38 10 06 0
Web Site: http://www.arsedition.de
Newspaper & Magazine Publisher
N.A.I.C.S.: 513110
Angela Schaaf de Lavado *(Dir-Rights)*

Division (Domestic):

Bonnierforlagen AB   **(2)**
Sveavagen 56, PO Box 3159, Stockholm, 103 63, Sweden   **(100%)**
Tel.: (46) 86968000
Web Site: http://www.bonnierforlagen.se
Sales Range: $50-74.9 Million
Emp.: 200
Book Publishers
N.A.I.C.S.: 513130

Subsidiary (Domestic):

Albert Bonniers Forlag AB   **(3)**
Sveavagen 56, Stockholm, 10363, Sweden   **(100%)**
Tel.: (46) 86968620
Web Site: http://www.albertbonniersforlag.se
Emp.: 600
Book Publishers
N.A.I.C.S.: 513130
Jesper Monthan *(Deputy Mng Dir)*

Subsidiary (Non-US):

Sanoma Pro Oy   **(2)**
Annankatu 15, 00121, Helsinki, Finland
Tel.: (358) 20 11611
Web Site: http://www.sanomapro.fi
Educational Book Publisher
N.A.I.C.S.: 513130
Kirsi Harra-Vauhkonen *(Mng Dir)*

Werner Soderstrom Osakeyhtion   **(2)**
Korkeavuorenkatu 37, 00130, Helsinki, Finland
Tel.: (358) 10 5060 200
Web Site: http://www.wsoy.fi
Emp.: 100
Literature & Educational Books Publishing Services
N.A.I.C.S.: 513130
Timo Julkunen *(CEO)*

Bonnier Business Media Sweden AB   **(1)**
Gjorwellsgatan 30, 112 60, Stockholm, Sweden
Tel.: (46) 840932030
Web Site: https://www.bonniernews.se
Emp.: 8,000
Online Media & Newspaper Publishing Services
N.A.I.C.S.: 513110

Subsidiary (Domestic):

Dagens Media Sverige AB   **(2)**
Gjörwellsgatan 30, 105 16, Stockholm, Sweden
Tel.: (46) 0840932005
Web Site: https://www.dagensmedia.se
Magazine Publisher
N.A.I.C.S.: 513120

Bonnier Business Press AB   **(1)**
Torsgatan 21, SE-113 90, Stockholm, Sweden   **(100%)**
Tel.: (46) 761122399
Web Site: http://www.bonnierbusinesspress.com

Holding Company; Business Newspaper, Magazine & Internet Publisher
N.A.I.C.S.: 551112
Anders Eriksson *(Pres & CEO)*

Subsidiary (Non-US):

Aripaev, AS   **(2)**
Parnu mnt 105, 19094, Tallinn, Estonia
Tel.: (372) 667 0111
Web Site: http://www.aripaev.ee
Newspaper Publishers
N.A.I.C.S.: 513110

Bonnier Business Forum Oy   **(2)**
Korkeavuorenkatu 37, 00130, Helsinki, Finland
Tel.: (358) 30 422 8808
Web Site: http://www.bonnierbusiness.fi
Emp.: 9
Newspaper & Magazine Publisher
N.A.I.C.S.: 513110
Jami Sjoblom *(Key Acct Mgr)*

Bonnier Business Press, ZAO   **(2)**
5 ul Akademika Pavlova, 197022, Saint Petersburg, Russia
Tel.: (7) 812 3282 828
Web Site: http://www.bonnierbusinesspress.com
Newspaper & Magazine Publisher
N.A.I.C.S.: 513110
Andrus Vaher *(CEO)*

Casnik Finance, d.o.o.   **(2)**
Bleiweisova 30, Ljubljana, Slovenia
Tel.: (386) 1 3091 540
Web Site: http://www.finance.si
Newspaper Publishers
N.A.I.C.S.: 513110
Grega Gmajnar *(Project Mgr)*

Dagbladet Borsen A/S   **(2)**
Montergade 19, 1140, Copenhagen, K, Denmark   **(100%)**
Tel.: (45) 33320102
Web Site: http://www.borsen.dk
Sales Range: $25-49.9 Million
Emp.: 250
Business Newspaper Publisher
N.A.I.C.S.: 513110
Anders Krap Johansen *(CEO)*

Subsidiary (Domestic):

Dagens Industri AB   **(2)**
Gjorwellsgatan 30, 105 16, Stockholm, Sweden   **(100%)**
Tel.: (46) 857365000
Web Site: http://www.di.se
Sales Range: $50-74.9 Million
Emp.: 300
Business Newspaper & Internet Publisher
N.A.I.C.S.: 513110
Peter Fellman *(Deputy Editor-in-Chief)*

Subsidiary (Non-US):

Dagens Medicin A/S   **(2)**
Montergade 19, 1140, Copenhagen, Denmark
Tel.: (45) 33 324400
Newspaper Publishers
N.A.I.C.S.: 513110

Dagens Medisin AS   **(2)**
PO Box 2068, Vika, 0125, Oslo, Norway
Tel.: (47) 934 30 200
Web Site: http://www.dagensmedisin.no
Newspaper Publishers
N.A.I.C.S.: 513110
Lise Hjertaas *(CEO)*

Medicine Today Poland Sp. z o.o.   **(2)**
ul Kijowska 1, 03-738, Warsaw, Poland
Tel.: (48) 22 333 99 91
Newspaper & Magazine Publisher
N.A.I.C.S.: 513110

Norsk Helseinformatikk AS   **(2)**
Granasveien 9, 7048, Trondheim, Norway
Tel.: (47) 73 89 47 50
Web Site: http://www.nhi.no
Newspaper & Magazine Publisher
N.A.I.C.S.: 513110
Tone Sitouze *(CFO)*

Verslo Zinios, UAB   **(2)**
J Jasinskio g 16A, 03163, Vilnius, Lithuania
Tel.: (370) 8 5 252 6300

Web Site: http://www.vz.lt
Newspaper Publishers
N.A.I.C.S.: 513110

Bonnier Magazine Group AB   **(1)**
Kungsgatan 49, SE-113 90, Stockholm, Sweden   **(100%)**
Tel.: (46) 87364000
Web Site: http://www.bonnier.se
Sales Range: $650-699.9 Million
Holding Company; Magazine & Internet Publisher
N.A.I.C.S.: 551112
Jonas Bonnier *(CEO)*

Subsidiary (US):

Bonnier Corporation   **(2)**
460 N Orlando Ave Ste 200, Winter Park, FL 32789
Tel.: (407) 628-4802
Web Site: http://www.bonniercorp.com
Sales Range: $350-399.9 Million
Emp.: 1,200
Magazine Publisher
N.A.I.C.S.: 513120
Lisa Earlywine *(VP-Production Ops)*

Division (Domestic):

Bonnier Active Media, Inc.   **(3)**
2 Park Ave 9th Fl, New York, NY 10016-5675
Tel.: (212) 779-5000
Web Site: http://www.bonniercorp.com
Sales Range: $200-249.9 Million
Emp.: 700
Magazine & Internet Publisher
N.A.I.C.S.: 513120
Eric Zinczenko *(CEO)*

Unit (Domestic):

Field & Stream Magazine   **(4)**
2 Park Ave 9th Fl, New York, NY 10016
Tel.: (212) 779-5316
Web Site: http://www.fieldandstream.com
Outdoors Magazine & Internet Publisher
N.A.I.C.S.: 513120
Anthony Licata *(Editor)*

Popular Science Magazine   **(4)**
2 Park Ave 9th Fl, New York, NY 10016
Tel.: (212) 779-5000
Web Site: http://www.popsci.com
Sales Range: $25-49.9 Million
Emp.: 30
Science Magazine & Internet Publisher
N.A.I.C.S.: 513120
Mark Jannot *(Editor-in-Chief)*

Subsidiary (Domestic):

Warren Miller Entertainment   **(4)**
5720 Flatiron Pkwy, Boulder, CO 80301
Tel.: (303) 253-6300
Web Site: http://www.warrenmillertv.com
Multimedia Production Services
N.A.I.C.S.: 512110
Ginger Sheehy *(Mgr-Dev)*

Unit (Domestic):

Islands Magazine   **(3)**
460 N Orlando Ave Ste 200, Winter Park, FL 32789
Tel.: (407) 628-4802
Web Site: http://www.islands.com
Sales Range: $125-149.9 Million
Emp.: 500
Travel Magazine & Internet Publisher
N.A.I.C.S.: 513120
Michael Bessire *(Dir-Art)*

Subsidiary (Domestic):

Magplus Inc.   **(3)**
2 Park Ave 10th Fl, New York, NY 10016
Tel.: (855) 624-7587
Application Software Development Services
N.A.I.C.S.: 541511

Unit (Domestic):

MotorBoating   **(3)**
460 N Orlando Ave Ste 200, Winter Park, FL 32789
Tel.: (407) 628-4802
Web Site: http://www.motorboating.com

Sales Range: $100-124.9 Million
Motor Boating Digital Magazine Publisher
N.A.I.C.S.: 323111
Jeanne Craig *(Exec Editor)*

Division (Domestic):

The Parenting Group, Inc. **(3)**
2 Park Ave 10th Fl, New York, NY 10016
Tel.: (212) 779-5000
Web Site: http://www.parenting.com
Magazine & Internet Publisher
N.A.I.C.S.: 513120
Greg Schumann *(VP & Grp Publr)*

Working Mother Media, Inc. **(3)**
2 Park Ave Fl 10, New York, NY 10016-
5604
Tel.: (212) 351-6400
Web Site: http://www.workingmother.com
Sales Range: $50-74.9 Million
Emp.: 150
Business Association, Conferences Orga-
nizer, Magazine Publisher & Internet Portal
N.A.I.C.S.: 513120
Carol Evans *(Pres)*

Division (Domestic):

The National Association for Female
Executives **(4)**
2 Park Ave, New York, NY 10016 **(100%)**
Tel.: (212) 351-6451
Web Site: http://www.nafe.com
Sales Range: $10-24.9 Million
Emp.: 19
Female Executives Association & Magazine
Publisher
N.A.I.C.S.: 813910
Betty Spence *(Pres)*

Bonnier Newspapers **(1)**
Torsgatan 21, 113 90, Stockholm, Sweden
Tel.: (46) 87364000
Web Site: http://www.bonnier.se
Sales Range: $800-899.9 Million
Newspaper Publishers
N.A.I.C.S.: 513110
Jonas Bonnier *(CEO)*

MTV Oy **(1)**
Ilmalankatu 2, 00033, Helsinki, Finland
Tel.: (358) 10300300
Web Site: http://www.mtv.fi
Sales Range: $200-249.9 Million
Emp.: 600
Media Holding Company
N.A.I.C.S.: 551112
Jani Koskinen *(CFO & Interim CEO)*

Subsidiary (Domestic):

MTV Sisallot Oy **(2)**
Ilmalankatu 2, PO Box 604, 00033, Hel-
sinki, Finland
Tel.: (358) 10300300
Web Site: http://www.mtvuutiset.fi
Sales Range: $100-124.9 Million
Emp.: 450
Television Broadcasting Station Services
N.A.I.C.S.: 516120
Jani Koskinen *(CFO & Interim CEO)*

Mag+ AB **(1)**
Sveavagen 53, 113 90, Stockholm, Sweden
Tel.: (46) 8 736 53 00
Web Site: http://www.magplus.com
Magazine Related Mobile Media Platform
N.A.I.C.S.: 513210
Gregg Hano *(CEO)*

Mediafy AB **(1)**
Linnegatan 2, 114 47, Stockholm, Sweden
Tel.: (46) 8 517 502 00
Magazine Publisher
N.A.I.C.S.: 513120

Mediafy Magazines AS **(1)**
Hegdehaugsveien 21B, 0352, Oslo, Norway
Tel.: (47) 21 67 61 15
Magazine Publisher
N.A.I.C.S.: 513120

Nyhetsbolaget Sverige AB **(1)**
Tegeluddsvagen 3, 115 79, Stockholm,
Sweden
Tel.: (46) 8 459 47 00
Web Site: http://www.nyhetsbolaget.se
Multimedia Production Services
N.A.I.C.S.: 512110

Porvoon Kirjakeskus Oy **(1)**
Teollisuustie 4, 06150, Porvoo, Finland
Tel.: (358) 20 16 620
Web Site: http://www.kirjakeskus.fi
Logistics Consulting Servies
N.A.I.C.S.: 541614
Pasi Heiskanen *(Mgr-Svc)*

Scandinavian Studios AB **(1)**
Kungsbron 2, 111 22, Stockholm, Sweden
Tel.: (46) 87364019
Web Site:
     http://www.scandinavianstudios.se
Multimedia Production Services
N.A.I.C.S.: 512110
Fredrik Lybeck *(Mgr-Creative)*

Spoon Publishing AB **(1)**
Rosenlundsgatan 40, 118 53, Stockholm,
Sweden
Tel.: (46) 8 442 96 20
Web Site: http://www.spoon.se
Marketing & Advertising Services
N.A.I.C.S.: 541613
Anders Ribba *(CEO)*

Subsidiary (Non-US):

Spoon AS **(2)**
Fredensborgveien 24 D, 0177, Oslo, Nor-
way
Tel.: (47) 941 60 162
Web Site: http://www.spoonagency.com
Marketing & Advertising Services
N.A.I.C.S.: 541613
Fredrik Ostbye *(Gen Mgr)*

Weldon Owen Publishing, Inc. **(1)**
415 Jackson St Ste 200, San Francisco, CA
94111
Tel.: (415) 291-0100
Web Site: http://www.weldonowen.com
Book Publishers
N.A.I.C.S.: 513130
Kelly Booth *(Dir-Creative)*

World Entertainment Services,
LLC **(1)**
460 N Orlando Ave Ste 200, Winter Park,
FL 32789
Tel.: (407) 571-4726
Web Site: http://www.world-ent.com
Multimedia Production Services
N.A.I.C.S.: 512110
Tom Weber *(Pres)*

BONNY INTERNATIONAL
HOLDING LTD.
No 129 Chunhan Road Beiyuan
Street, Yiwu, Zhejiang, China   Ky
Web Site:
     https://www.bonnychina.com
Year Founded: 2017
1906—(HKG)
Rev.: $24,599,994
Assets: $81,424,734
Liabilities: $38,132,061
Net Worth: $43,292,673
Earnings: ($6,259,692)
Emp.: 607
Fiscal Year-end: 12/31/23
Holding Company
N.A.I.C.S.: 551112
Guojun Jin *(Chm)*

BONNY WORLDWIDE LIMITED
No 15 Lane 64 Minsheng Street,
Tanzi District, Taichung, Taiwan
Tel.: (886) 425376022
Web Site:
     https://www.bonnyworldwide.com
Year Founded: 1982
8467—(TAI)
Rev.: $65,013,831
Assets: $111,607,177
Liabilities: $45,118,609
Net Worth: $66,488,568
Earnings: $12,583,995
Fiscal Year-end: 12/31/23
Sporting Goods Manufacturing
N.A.I.C.S.: 339920
Fang-Lan Hong *(Chm)*

BONREE DATA TECHNOLOGY
CO., LTD.
4th Floor Hongji Building No 46
Dongzhong Street, Dongcheng Dis-
trict, Beijing, 100027, China
Tel.: (86) 4006808085
Web Site: https://www.bonree.com
Year Founded: 2008
688229—(SHG)
Rev.: $16,340,735
Assets: $100,218,222
Liabilities: $7,994,292
Net Worth: $92,223,930
Earnings: ($11,405,324)
Fiscal Year-end: 12/31/22
Application Development Services
N.A.I.C.S.: 541511
Kai Li *(Chm)*

BONSO ELECTRONICS INTER-
NATIONAL INC.
Unit 1404 14/F Cheuk Nang Centre 9
Hillwood Road, Tsimshatsui, Kow-
loon, China (Hong Kong)
Tel.: (852) 2 605 5822   VG
Web Site: http://www.bonso.com
Year Founded: 1980
BNSO—(NASDAQ)
Rev.: $14,801,000
Assets: $23,750,000
Liabilities: $8,407,000
Net Worth: $15,343,000
Earnings: ($2,760,000)
Emp.: 208
Fiscal Year-end: 03/31/22
Electronic Weighing Scales & Bal-
ances Mfr & Exporter
N.A.I.C.S.: 333998
Anthony So *(Founder & Chm)*

Subsidiaries:

Bonso Electronics Limited **(1)**
Unit 1404 14/F Cheuk Nang Centre 9 Hill-
wood Road, Tsim Tsa Tsui, Kowloon, China
(Hong Kong)
Tel.: (852) 2605 5822
Web Site: http://www.bonso.com
Sales Range: $400-449.9 Million
Communication Equipment Mfr
N.A.I.C.S.: 334290
Andrew So *(Deputy Chm & Dir-Ops)*

Subsidiary (Non-US):

Bonso Electronics (Shenzhen) Co.
Limited **(2)**
10 FL Commercial Building No 2 Zheng
Feng North Rd FuYong BaoAn, Shenzhen,
518103, GuangDong, China
Tel.: (86) 755 27311888
Web Site: http://www.bonso.com
Sales Range: $350-399.9 Million
Emp.: 2,500
Design, Develop & Manufacture Electronic
Scales, Weighing Instruments & Health
Care Products
N.A.I.C.S.: 333998

BONSOIR OF LONDON LTD.
Unit 3 Northern Way Cropmead,
Crewkerne, TA18 7HJ, United King-
dom
Tel.: (44) 8450712331
Web Site:
     http://www.bonsoirdirect.com
Sales Range: $50-74.9 Million
Emp.: 186
Online Nightwear & Linens Shop
N.A.I.C.S.: 315250

BONTERRA ENERGY CORP.
Suite 901 1015 - 4th Street SW, Cal-
gary, T2R 1J4, AB, Canada
Tel.: (403) 262-5307   Ca
Web Site:
     https://www.bonterraenergy.com
Year Founded: 1981
QNC1—(DEU)
Rev.: $210,710,195

Assets: $730,857,994
Liabilities: $331,959,813
Net Worth: $398,898,181
Earnings: $33,937,358
Emp.: 38
Fiscal Year-end: 12/31/23
Oil & Gas Exploration Services
N.A.I.C.S.: 211120
George F. Fink *(Chm & Co-CEO)*

BONTERRA RESOURCES INC.
2872 Sullivan Road Suite No 2, Val
d'Or, J9P 0B9, QC, Canada
Tel.: (819) 825-8678
Web Site: https://www.btrgold.com
9BR2—(DEU)
Rev.: $123,180
Assets: $20,277,444
Liabilities: $13,658,250
Net Worth: $6,619,194
Earnings: ($5,741,555)
Fiscal Year-end: 12/31/23
Precious & Base Metals Mining &
Exploration Services
N.A.I.C.S.: 212290
Allan J. Folk *(VP-Investor Relations-*
Business Development)

BONUS BIOGROUP LTD.
Matam Advanced Technology Park,
PO Box 15143, Haifa, 31905, Israel
Tel.: (972) 732067104
Web Site:
     https://www.bonusbiogroup.com
Year Founded: 1981
BONS—(TAE)
Assets: $12,401,989
Liabilities: $4,305,567
Net Worth: $8,096,422
Earnings: ($7,882,028)
Emp.: 24
Fiscal Year-end: 12/31/23
Biological Product (except Diagnostic)
Manufacturing
N.A.I.C.S.: 325414
Shai Meretzki *(Pres & CEO)*

BONVER AB
Gashaga brygga 1, 181 85, Lidingo,
Sweden
Tel.: (46) 087667800
Web Site: https://bonver.se
Emp.: 100
Transportation, Logictics & Supply
Chain Services
N.A.I.C.S.: 541614

Subsidiaries:

Apotekstjanst Sweden AB **(1)**
Gashaga brygga 1, 181 85, Lidingo, Swe-
den
Tel.: (46) 102216970
Web Site: https://apotekstjanst.se
Pharmacy Operator
N.A.I.C.S.: 456110

BONVESTS HOLDINGS LIM-
ITED
541 Orchard Road 16-00 Liat Towers,
Singapore, 238881, Singapore
Tel.: (65) 67325533
Web Site:
     https://www.bonvests.com.sg
B28—(SES)
Rev.: $164,173,294
Assets: $983,408,316
Liabilities: $348,822,995
Net Worth: $634,585,321
Earnings: $5,307,127
Emp.: 2,106
Fiscal Year-end: 12/31/23
Holding Company; Property Develop-
ment & Investment; Food & Beverage
Ownership & Management; Hotel
Ownership & Management & Waste
Management & Contract Cleaning of
Buildings

Bonvests Holdings Limited—(Continued)

N.A.I.C.S.: 551112
Henry Ngo *(Chm & Mng Dir)*

Subsidiaries:

Bon-Food Pte Ltd **(1)**
541 Orchard Rd 04 01-02 Liat Twr, 238881,
Singapore, Singapore
Tel.: (65) 67385555
Web Site: http://www.bon-food.com.sg
Sales Range: $10-24.9 Million
Emp.: 40
Food Service Contractors
N.A.I.C.S.: 722310

Bonfresh Pte Ltd **(1)**
541 Orchard Rd # 05-04 Liat Twr, 238881,
Singapore, Singapore
Tel.: (65) 67385555
Web Site: http://www.bonfresh.com.sg
Sales Range: $10-24.9 Million
Emp.: 40
Food Service Contractors
N.A.I.C.S.: 722310

Colex Environmental Pte Ltd **(1)**
8 Tuas South Street 13, Singapore,
637083, Singapore
Tel.: (65) 62687711
Waste Disposal Services
N.A.I.C.S.: 562119
Lionel Chee *(Sr Mgr)*

Colex Holdings Limited **(1)**
8 Tuas South Street 13, Singapore,
637083, Singapore
Tel.: (65) 62687711
Web Site: http://www.colex.com.sg
Rev.: $39,503,462
Assets: $32,080,360
Liabilities: $8,707,222
Net Worth: $23,373,139
Earnings: $1,333,529
Emp.: 150
Fiscal Year-end: 12/31/2020
Waste Management Services
N.A.I.C.S.: 562998
Henry Ngo *(Chm)*

Integrated Property Management Pte
Ltd **(1)**
18 Boon Lay Way 02-146/147 TradeHub
21, Singapore, 609966, Singapore
Tel.: (65) 62687333
Web Site: https://ipm.com.sg
Emp.: 1,000
Cleaning Service
N.A.I.C.S.: 561720

Sheraton Towers Singapore **(1)**
39 Scotts Road, Singapore, 228230, Singa-
pore
Tel.: (65) 6 737 6888
Web Site:
http://www.sheratonsingapore.com
Sales Range: $50-74.9 Million
Emp.: 300
Hotels & Motels
N.A.I.C.S.: 721110

The Residence Mauritius **(1)**
Coastal Road Belle Mare, Port Louis, Mau-
ritius
Tel.: (230) 401 8888
Web Site: http://www.theresidence.com
Sales Range: $50-74.9 Million
Emp.: 400
Hotels & Motels
N.A.I.C.S.: 721110

BONYAD PP FIBER PROD CO.
3rd Floor No 3 Ghobadiyan Street
Next To The Eskan Valiasr Avenue,
Tehran, 19676, Iran
Tel.: (98) 21 88779873
Year Founded: 1994
Polypropylene Fiber Mfr
N.A.I.C.S.: 313110

BOOHOO GROUP PLC
49-51 Dale Street, Manchester, M1
2HF, United Kingdom
Tel.: (44) 1612365640
Web Site:
https://www.boohooplc.com
Year Founded: 2006

BOO—(AIM)
Rev.: $2,401,399,364
Assets: $1,664,157,404
Liabilities: $1,121,069,404
Net Worth: $543,088,000
Earnings: ($102,643,632)
Emp.: 5,350
Fiscal Year-end: 02/28/23
Holding Company; Online Apparel &
Accessories Retailer
N.A.I.C.S.: 459999
Neil James Catto *(CFO)*

Subsidiaries:

boohoo.com UK Limited **(1)**
49/51 Dale Street, Manchester, M1 2HF,
United Kingdom
Tel.: (44) 161 236 5640
Web Site: http://www.boohoo.com
Online Apparel & Accessories Retailer
N.A.I.C.S.: 455110
Mahmud Abdullah Kamani *(Co-CEO)*

**BOOKOFF GROUP HOLDINGS
LTD.**
2-14-20 Furubuchi, Minami-ku, Sagamihara, 252-0344, Kanagawa, Japan
Tel.: (81) 427508588
Web Site:
https://www.bookoffgroup.co.jp
Year Founded: 1991

9278—(TKS)
Rev.: $738,052,770
Assets: $360,522,620
Liabilities: $224,971,350
Net Worth: $135,551,270
Earnings: $11,270,050
Emp.: 1,403
Fiscal Year-end: 05/31/24
Book Store Retailer
N.A.I.C.S.: 459210
Yasutaka Horiuchi *(Pres & CEO)*

Subsidiaries:

B-Assist, Inc. **(1)**
2-14-20 Kobuchi, Minami-ku, Sagamihara,
252-0344, Kanagawa, Japan
Tel.: (81) 427046610
Business Consulting Services
N.A.I.C.S.: 541611

Bookoff With Co., Ltd. **(1)**
2709-1 Kitamachi, Takamatsu, 760-0080,
Kagawa, Japan
Tel.: (81) 878123770
Web Site: https://www.bookoff-with.jp
Emp.: 270
Electronic Product Retailer
N.A.I.C.S.: 449210

Jewelry Asset Managers Inc. **(1)**
7-22-17 Nishigotanda TOC Building 6F-16
Nishigotanda, Shinagawa-ku, Tokyo, 141-
0031, Japan
Tel.: (81) 369104725
Web Site: http://www.aidect.jp
Emp.: 114
Jewelry Retailer
N.A.I.C.S.: 458310

**BOOKOOK SECURITIES CO.,
LTD.**
Yeouido-dong, Yeongdeungpo-gu,
Seoul, Korea (South)
Tel.: (82) 15887744
Web Site: https://www.bookook.co.kr
Year Founded: 1954

001270—(KRS)
Rev.: $776,891,746
Assets: $1,170,329,608
Liabilities: $621,393,741
Net Worth: $548,935,868
Earnings: $33,427,827
Fiscal Year-end: 12/31/22
Securities Brokerage Services
N.A.I.C.S.: 523150
Sung-Woon Shin *(Exec Dir)*

BOOKOOK STEEL CO., LTD.

90 Hanamsandan 9beon-ro,
Gwangsan-gu, Gwangju, 62213, Ko-
rea (South)
Tel.: (82) 629543806
Web Site: http://www.bks.co.kr
Year Founded: 1976

026940—(KRS)
Rev.: $160,860,867
Assets: $117,828,077
Liabilities: $21,179,987
Net Worth: $96,648,090
Earnings: $5,447,737
Emp.: 53
Fiscal Year-end: 12/31/22
Steel Products Mfr
N.A.I.C.S.: 331110
Nam Sang-Gyu *(Dir-Rep)*

BOOKTOPIA PTY. LTD.
Unit E1 3-29 Birnie Avenue, Lid-
combe, 2141, NSW, Australia
Tel.: (61) 290454394
Web Site:
http://www.booktopia.com.au
Year Founded: 2004
Book & Magazine Distr
N.A.I.C.S.: 424920
Simon Nash *(Co-Founder)*

BOOM LOGISTICS LIMITED
Suite 3 137 Kewdale Road, Kewdale,
6105, WA, Australia
Tel.: (61) 800073234
Web Site:
https://www.boomlogistics.com.au
BOL—(ASX)
Rev.: $173,097,622
Assets: $161,980,501
Liabilities: $87,845,886
Net Worth: $74,134,615
Earnings: $4,413,061
Emp.: 450
Fiscal Year-end: 06/30/24
Lifting Solutions & Crane Sales &
Services
N.A.I.C.S.: 532412
Tony Spassopoulos *(CEO & Mng Dir)*

Subsidiaries:

Sherrin Hire Pty Ltd **(1)**
184 Curtin Ave W, Eagle Farm, Brisbane,
4009, QLD, Australia
Tel.: (61) 738681555
Web Site: http://www.boomsherrin.com.au
Sales Range: $25-49.9 Million
Emp.: 40
Travel Towers & Access Equipments Provid-
ing Services
N.A.I.C.S.: 238290

BOOMBIT S. A.
Zacna 2, 80-283, Gdansk, Poland
Tel.: (48) 504210022
Web Site: https://www.boombit.com
BBT—(WAR)
Rev.: $73,868,261
Assets: $35,181,631
Liabilities: $16,690,700
Net Worth: $18,490,931
Earnings: $2,320,504
Emp.: 79
Fiscal Year-end: 12/31/22
Mobile Game Development Services
N.A.I.C.S.: 541511
Marcin Olejarz *(Co-Founder, Co-CEO
& Member-Mgmt Bd)*

BOOMERANG PLUS PLC
Gloworks Heol Porth Teigr, Cardiff,
CF10 4GA, United Kingdom
Tel.: (44) 2920 671500
Web Site:
http://www.boomerang.co.uk
Sales Range: $25-49.9 Million
Emp.: 188
Broadcasting & Cable TV Services
N.A.I.C.S.: 512110
Matt Pritchard *(Mng Dir)*

Subsidiaries:

Boom Extreme Publishing
Limited **(1)**
25 allee du Moura lot 8B, 64200, Biarritz,
France
Tel.: (33) 559412145
Television Program Production Services
N.A.I.C.S.: 512110

Boom Films Limited **(1)**
218 Penarth Rd, Cardiff, CF11 8NN, South
Glamorgan, United Kingdom
Tel.: (44) 2920550550
Web Site: http://www.boomerang.tv
Sales Range: $50-74.9 Million
Emp.: 150
Movie Production Services
N.A.I.C.S.: 512110
Huw Davies *(Mng Dir)*

Boom Freesports Limited **(1)**
218 Penarth Rd, Cardiff, CF11 8NN, South
Glamorgan, United Kingdom
Tel.: (44) 2920550550
Web Site: http://www.boomerang.tv
Sales Range: $25-49.9 Million
Emp.: 100
Rights Management Services
N.A.I.C.S.: 541611
Gareth Rees *(Mng Dir)*

Boom Talent Limited **(1)**
218 Penarth Rd, Cardiff, CF11 8NN, South
Glamorgan, United Kingdom
Tel.: (44) 2920550565
Web Site: http://www.boomtalent.co.uk
Actors Casting Services
N.A.I.C.S.: 561311

Cynhyrchiadau Alfresco Productions
Cyfyngedig **(1)**
The Media Centre, Culverhouse Cross, Car-
diff, CF5 6XJ, South Glamorgan, United
Kingdom
Tel.: (44) 2920550550
Web Site: http://www.alfrescotv.co.uk
Television Program Production Services
N.A.I.C.S.: 512110

Fflic Cyfyngedig **(1)**
59 Mount Stuart Sq, Cardiff, CF10 5LR,
South Glamorgan, United Kingdom
Tel.: (44) 29 20 409 000
Sales Range: $25-49.9 Million
Emp.: 15
Lifestyle & Children Programme Production
Services
N.A.I.C.S.: 512110

Gorilla Group Ltd. **(1)**
20 Cathedral Road, Pontcanna, Cardiff,
CF11 9LJ, South Glamorgan, United King-
dom
Tel.: (44) 2920399800
Web Site: http://www.gorillagroup.tv
Sales Range: $25-49.9 Million
Emp.: 60
Television Program Post Production Ser-
vices
N.A.I.C.S.: 512191
Richard Moss *(Mng Dir)*

Indus Films Limited **(1)**
17 Cathedral Rd, Cardiff, CF11 9LJ, South
Glamorgan, United Kingdom
Tel.: (44) 2920399555
Web Site: http://www.indusfilms.com
Sales Range: $25-49.9 Million
Emp.: 20
Adventure & Environmental Program Pro-
duction Services
N.A.I.C.S.: 512109
Steve Robinson *(Dir-Creative)*

Teledu Apollo Cyfyngedig **(1)**
21a Allensbank Rd, Cardiff, CF14 3PN,
South Glamorgan, United Kingdom
Tel.: (44) 29 20 251 811
Sales Range: $25-49.9 Million
Emp.: 5
Television Program Production Services
N.A.I.C.S.: 512110

BOOMI INTERNATIONAL OY
Sinikalliontie 10, FI-02630, Espoo,
Finland
Tel.: (358) 975115000
Web Site: http://www.mobileavenue.fi

Sales Range: $1-9.9 Million
Mobile Content Services
N.A.I.C.S.: 518210
Frank Bahrke *(CTO)*

BOOMSENSE TECHNOLOGY CO., LTD.

No 4 building A District Yiyuan cultural and creative industry center, 80 middle of apricot Road Haidian District, Beijing, 100195, China
Tel.: (86) 1065800000
Web Site:
http://www.boomsense.com
300312—(CHIN)
Rev.: $2,958,485
Assets: $55,860,366
Liabilities: $83,822,723
Net Worth: ($27,962,357)
Earnings: ($37,168,746)
Emp.: 1,540
Fiscal Year-end: 12/31/20
Wireless Network Optimization System & Equipment
N.A.I.C.S.: 334220

BOOMWORKS PTY, LTD.

34 Denison St, Camperdown, NSW 2050, Australia
Tel.: (61) 295579710
Web Site:
http://www.boomworks.com.au
Sales Range: $10-24.9 Million
Emp.: 21
Brand Development & Integration, E-Commerce, Graphic Design, Internet/Web Design, Logo & Package Design, Media Relations, New Technologies, Print, Strategic Planning/Research
N.A.I.C.S.: 541810
Fred Randell *(Founder)*

BOON EDAM B.V.

Ambachtstraat 4, PO Box 40, Edam, 1135 GG, Netherlands
Tel.: (31) 299380808   NI
Web Site: http://www.boonedam.com
Year Founded: 1903
Sales Range: $50-74.9 Million
Emp.: 1,000
Revolving Door Mfr
N.A.I.C.S.: 332321
Niels Huber *(Owner & CEO)*

Subsidiaries:

Boon Edam Thompson Inc   **(1)**
402 McKinney Pkwy, Lillington, NC 27546   **(100%)**
Tel.: (910) 814-3800
Web Site: http://www.boonedam.us
Sales Range: $25-49.9 Million
Emp.: 80
Revolving Door Mfr
N.A.I.C.S.: 332321
Dan Camp *(CFO)*

BOOSH PLANT-BASED BRANDS INC.

205 18428 53rd Ave, Surrey, V3S 7A4, BC, Canada
Tel.: (604) 999-5554   BC
Year Founded: 2017
VEGI—(CNSX)
Rev.: $510,297
Assets: $8,316,794
Liabilities: $2,361,628
Net Worth: $5,955,166
Earnings: ($6,015,437)
Emp.: 9
Fiscal Year-end: 03/31/22
Food Products Mfr
N.A.I.C.S.: 311813
Robert Hall *(Pres & CEO)*

BOOSTER CO., LTD.

18 Iwol-myeon, Jincheon, Chungcheongbuk-do, Korea (South)
Tel.: (82) 435362005
Web Site:
https://boostareng.imweb.me
Year Founded: 1973
008470—(KRS)
Rev.: $70,463,922
Assets: $73,811,545
Liabilities: $13,438,479
Net Worth: $60,373,066
Earnings: ($948,009)
Emp.: 381
Fiscal Year-end: 12/31/22
Boilers Mfr & Marketing
N.A.I.C.S.: 332410
Dong-Keun Yoo *(Chm)*

BOOSTHEAT SAS

41-47 Boulevard Marcel Sembat, 69200, Venissieux, France
Tel.: (33) 685655964
Web Site: https://www.boostheat.fr
Year Founded: 2011
BOOST—(EUR)
Sales Range: Less than $1 Million
Carbon & Graphite Product Mfr
N.A.I.C.S.: 335991
Luc Jacquet *(Co-Founder)*

BOOTH SECURITIES LTD.

Garden Works Charleywood Road, Knowsley, Liverpool, L33 7SG, United Kingdom
Tel.: (44) 151 549 1910
Web Site:
http://www.boothmech.co.uk
Rev.: $55,458,760
Emp.: 452
Investment Holding Company
N.A.I.C.S.: 551112
Shaun Maclean *(CEO)*

Subsidiaries:

Gas Maintenance and Training Limited   **(1)**
19 Rotherham Rd, Swallownest, Sheffield, S26 4UR, South Yorkshire, United Kingdom
Tel.: (44) 114 294 2040
Web Site: http://www.gasmaint.com
Sales Range: $25-49.9 Million
Emp.: 50
Gas Maintenance, Repair & Installation Services
N.A.I.C.S.: 238220

BOOZT AB

Hyllie Boulevard 35, 215 37, Malmo, Sweden
Tel.: (46) 30504402
Web Site:
https://www.booztgroup.com
Year Founded: 2007
BOOZT—(CSE)
Rev.: $632,021,130
Assets: $561,240,833
Liabilities: $326,842,564
Net Worth: $234,398,269
Earnings: $17,430,479
Emp.: 919
Fiscal Year-end: 12/31/22
Online Apparel Retailer
N.A.I.C.S.: 458110
Hermann Haraldsson *(Co-Founder & CEO)*

Subsidiaries:

Boozt Baltics UAB   **(1)**
Paupio St 50 Zemupys, 11341, Vilnius, Lithuania
Tel.: (370) 61210766
Web Site:
https://www.boozttechnologybaltics.com
Information Technology Services
N.A.I.C.S.: 541511

Boozt Fashion AB   **(1)**
Hyllie Boulevard 35, 215 37, Malmo, Sweden

Tel.: (46) 101388988
Online Access Services
N.A.I.C.S.: 517111

Boozt Technology Baltics UAB   **(1)**
Paupio st 50, 11341, Vilnius, Lithuania
Tel.: (370) 61210766
Web Site:
https://www.boozttechnologybaltics.com
Online Access Services
N.A.I.C.S.: 517111

Rosemunde ApS   **(1)**
Staktoften 2, 2950, Vedbaek, Denmark
Tel.: (45) 39640190
Web Site: https://rosemunde.com
Women's Clothing Retailer
N.A.I.C.S.: 458110

BOPARAN HOLDINGS LIMITED

Unit 3 Bevan Way, Alpha Business Park, Smethwick, B66 1AW, W Midlands, United Kingdom
Tel.: (44) 1215550202   UK
Year Founded: 1998
Investment Holding Company
N.A.I.C.S.: 551112
Steve Henderson *(Fin Dir)*

Subsidiaries:

2 Sisters Food Group Limited   **(1)**
Dial Lane, West Bromwich, Birmingham, B70 0EB, W Midlands, United Kingdom
Tel.: (44) 1215556661
Web Site: http://www.2sfg.com
Holding Company; Poultry, Chilled, Frozen & Bakery Foods Mfr & Distr
N.A.I.C.S.: 311615
Mranjith Takur *(Co-Founder & Owner)*

Subsidiary (Domestic):

Avana Bakeries Ltd.   **(2)**
Unit 8/9 Wern Trading Estate, Rogerstone, Newport, NP10 9YB, United Kingdom   **(100%)**
Tel.: (44) 1633 466400
Sales Range: $150-199.9 Million
Emp.: 900
Flour Confectionery, Cakes, Puddings, Puff Pastry, Chilled Desserts & Frozen Confectionery Mfr
N.A.I.C.S.: 311812

Subsidiary (Non-US):

Green Isle Brands Limited   **(2)**
Ground Floor 101-102 Beech House Naas Business Park, Naas, W91 RC85, Ireland
Tel.: (353) 45 574574
Web Site: http://www.greenislefoods.ie
Frozen Food Mfr
N.A.I.C.S.: 311412
Maurice Hickey *(Chm)*

Subsidiary (Domestic):

Northern Foods Limited   **(2)**
2180 Century Way Thorpe Park, Leeds, LS15 8ZB, United Kingdom
Tel.: (44) 1133900110
Web Site: http://www.northernfoods.com
Sales Range: $1-4.9 Billion
Emp.: 9,472
Holding Company; Frozen, Chilled & Bakery Foods Mfr & Whslr
N.A.I.C.S.: 551112

Subsidiary (Domestic):

Cavaghan & Gray Carlisle   **(3)**
Brunel House, Brunel Way, Carlisle, CA1 3NQ, Cumbria, United Kingdom   **(100%)**
Tel.: (44) 1228518200
Web Site: http://www.2sfg.com
Sales Range: $150-199.9 Million
Emp.: 900
Production of Chilled Ready Meals & Meal Accompaniments
N.A.I.C.S.: 311999
Willie Agnew *(Mgr-Ops)*

Dalepak Foods   **(3)**
Dale House, Leeming Bar, Northallerton, DL7 9UL, United Kingdom   **(100%)**
Tel.: (44) 1677424111
Web Site: http://www.dalepak.co.uk

Sales Range: $50-74.9 Million
Emp.: 200
Mfr of Meat Products
N.A.I.C.S.: 311612
Alan Harris *(Gen Mgr)*

Fox's Biscuits Ltd.   **(3)**
Wellington St, Batley, WF17 5JA, W Yorkshire, United Kingdom   **(100%)**
Tel.: (44) 924444333
Web Site: http://www.foxs-biscuits.co.uk
Rev.: $78,367,500
Emp.: 2,492
Mfr of Biscuits
N.A.I.C.S.: 311821

Branch (Domestic):

Fox's Biscuits - Preston   **(4)**
Whitworth St Wesham, Kirkham, PR4 3AX, Lancs, United Kingdom   **(100%)**
Tel.: (44) 1772683501
Web Site: http://www.sfg.com
Sales Range: $550-599.9 Million
Emp.: 3,500
Mfr of Biscuits
N.A.I.C.S.: 311821

Fox's Biscuits - Staffordshire   **(4)**
Dove Valley Bakeries, Cheadle Road, Uttoxeter, ST14 7BT, United Kingdom   **(100%)**
Tel.: (44) 1889563131
Web Site: http://www.foxsbiscuits.com
Sales Range: $150-199.9 Million
Emp.: 700
Production of Sweet & Semi-Sweet Biscuits
N.A.I.C.S.: 311821
Kevin Hand *(Gen Mgr)*

Subsidiary (Domestic):

Gunstones Bakery   **(3)**
Stubley Lane, Dronfield, S18 1PF, Sheffield, United Kingdom   **(100%)**
Tel.: (44) 1246414651
Sales Range: $400-449.9 Million
Emp.: 1,300
Sandwiches & Specialty Bakery Products Mfr
N.A.I.C.S.: 311812

Northern Foods plc-Technical Services   **(3)**
Farnsworth House, Lenton Ln, Nottingham, NG7 2NS, Nottinghamshire, United Kingdom   **(100%)**
Tel.: (44) 159868231
Web Site: http://www.northernfoods.co.uk
Sales Range: $25-49.9 Million
Emp.: 80
Provider of Auditing, Buying, Engineering & Testing Services for Food Manufacturing
N.A.I.C.S.: 541380

Pennine Foods   **(3)**
Drakehouse Crescent, Sheffield, S20 7JG, United Kingdom   **(100%)**
Tel.: (44) 142476864
Sales Range: $150-199.9 Million
Emp.: 700
Mfr of Ready Made Meals
N.A.I.C.S.: 311211

The Pizza Factory   **(3)**
Gateside Rd, PO Box 102, Nottingham, NG7 2NN, United Kingdom   **(100%)**
Tel.: (44) 1159868204
Web Site: http://www.northern-foods.com
Sales Range: $75-99.9 Million
Emp.: 400
Produces Pizzas & Quiches
N.A.I.C.S.: 311991

Walter Hollands   **(3)**
Baxenden, 523 Manchester Road, Accrington, BB5 2SA, Lancashire, United Kingdom   **(100%)**
Tel.: (44) 1706213591
Sales Range: $75-99.9 Million
Emp.: 460
Mfr of Pies, Pasties & Puddings
N.A.I.C.S.: 311999

Bernard Matthews Foods Ltd.   **(1)**
Great Witchingham Hall, Norwich, NR9 5QD, Norfolk, United Kingdom
Tel.: (44) 1603872611
Web Site: http://www.bernardmatthews.com
Poultry Processor
N.A.I.C.S.: 311615

Boparan Holdings Limited—(Continued)

David M. Reger (Sec)

Subsidiary (Non-US):

Saga Foods Zrt   (2)
Soproni utca 15, H-9600, Sarvar, Hungary
Tel.: (36) 95336108
Web Site: http://www.saga.hu
Poultry Processor
N.A.I.C.S.: 311615

BOQII HOLDING LIMITED

Building 9 No 388 Shengrong Road,
Pudong New District, Shanghai,
201210, China
Tel.: (86) 2161096226   Ky
Web Site: https://ir.boqii.com
Year Founded: 2012
BQ—(NYSE)
Rev.: $98,244,000
Assets: $53,077,000
Liabilities: $18,046,000
Net Worth: $35,031,000
Earnings: ($9,541,000)
Emp.: 241
Fiscal Year-end: 03/31/24
Holding Company
N.A.I.C.S.: 551112
Hao Liang (Founder, Chm & Co-
CEO)

BORA BORA RESOURCES LIMITED

Suite 1002 Level 10 131 Macquarie
Street, Sydney, 2000, NSW, Australia
Tel.: (61) 2 9247 3203
Web Site:
   http://www.boraboraresources.com
Sales Range: Less than $1 Million
Gold & Other Metal Mining
N.A.I.C.S.: 212220
Patrick Ford (Founder)

BORA CORPORATION

10F-6 No 2 Fuhsing North Road, Tai-
pei, 104, Taiwan
Tel.: (886) 2 8772 5598   TW
Web Site: http://www.bora-corp.com
Year Founded: 2009
Holding Company; Pharmaceutical
Research, Development, Mfr & Distr
N.A.I.C.S.: 551112
Simon Chen (VP)

Subsidiaries:

Hoan Pharmaceuticals   (1)
6F No 164 Fuxing North Road, Zhongshan
District, Taipei, 10487, Taiwan
Tel.: (886) 2 2713 3260
Web Site: http://www.hoanpharma.com
Pharmaceutical Developer, Mfr & Distr
N.A.I.C.S.: 325412

BORA KECIC ATP A.D.

Milosa Obrenovica 2 a, Obrenovac,
Serbia
Tel.: (381) 11 872 60 07
Web Site: http://www.borakecic.com
Year Founded: 2001
Sales Range: $1-9.9 Million
Emp.: 3
Food Transportation Services
N.A.I.C.S.: 484121

BORA PHARMACEUTICALS CO., LTD.

6F No 2 Alley 36 Lane 26 Ruiguang
Road, Neihu District, Taipei, 114, Tai-
wan
Tel.: (886) 227901555   TW
Web Site: https://www.bora-corp.com
Year Founded: 2007
6472—(TAI)
Rev.: $328,126,505
Assets: $711,666,041
Liabilities: $550,941,406
Net Worth: $160,724,635

Earnings: $43,820,936
Emp.: 391
Fiscal Year-end: 12/31/22
Pharmaceutical Product Mfr & Distr
N.A.I.C.S.: 325412
Bobby Sheng (CEO)

Subsidiaries:

Glaxo Smith Kline Inc.   (1)
7333 Mississauga Rd, Mississauga, L5N
6L4, ON, Canada   (100%)
Tel.: (905) 819-3000
Web Site: http://www.ca.gsk.com
Emp.: 2,600
Pharmaceuticals Mfr & Distr
N.A.I.C.S.: 325412

Division (Domestic):

GlaxoSmithKline   (2)
100 Milverton Drive Suite 800, Mississauga,
L5R 4H1, ON, Canada   (100%)
Tel.: (905) 819-3000
Web Site: https://ca.gsk.com
Sales Range: $25-49.9 Million
Emp.: 15
Distr of Medical & Hospital Equipment
N.A.I.C.S.: 423450

GlaxoSmithKline   (2)
245 Blvd Armand-Frappier, Laval, H7V 4A7,
QC, Canada   (100%)
Tel.: (450) 978-4599
Web Site: http://ca.gsk.com
Sales Range: $50-74.9 Million
Emp.: 200
Pharmaceutical Preparations
N.A.I.C.S.: 325412

TWi Pharmaceuticals USA, Inc.   (1)
115 W Century Rd Ste 135, Paramus, NJ
07652
Tel.: (201) 762-1410
Pharmaceutical Mfr & Distr
N.A.I.C.S.: 325412

Union Chemical & Pharmaceutical
Co., Ltd.   (1)
No 113 Eunos Ave 3 06-06/10, Gordon In-
dustrial Building, Singapore, 409838, Singa-
pore
Tel.: (65) 67471681
Web Site: https://www.union.com.sg
Pharmaceutical Mfr & Distr
N.A.I.C.S.: 325412

Upsher-Smith Laboratories LLC   (1)
6701 Evenstad Dr, Maple Grove, MN 55369
Tel.: (763) 315-2000
Web Site: https://www.upsher-smith.com
Pharmaceuticals Mfr
N.A.I.C.S.: 325412
Bobby Sheng (Chm)

BORA TIAL CO., LTD.

518 Gangnam-daero Nonhyeon-dong
White 518 10th floor, Gangnam-gu,
Seoul, Korea (South)
Tel.: (82) 25383373
Web Site: https://www.boratr.co.kr
Year Founded: 2015
250000—(KRS)
Rev.: $53,285,235
Assets: $79,383,816
Liabilities: $20,777,635
Net Worth: $58,606,181
Earnings: $13,281,294
Emp.: 41
Fiscal Year-end: 12/31/22
Processed Food Distr
N.A.I.C.S.: 424490
Yun-Ju Jang (Deputy Gen Mgr)

BORAC A.D.

Ive Lole Ribara 8, Surjan, Serbia
Tel.: (381) 23855020
Web Site: http://www.borac.co.rs
Year Founded: 1998
BRCS—(BEL)
Sales Range: $1-9.9 Million
Emp.: 32
Cereal Crop Farming Services
N.A.I.C.S.: 111998
Jovan Veselinovic (Dir)

BORAC EXPORT-IMPORT D.D.

Vezirska bb, 72270, Travnik, Bosnia
& Herzegovina
Tel.: (387) 30511491
BRCTR—(SARE)
Rev.: $21,040
Assets: $455,435
Liabilities: $22,329
Net Worth: $433,105
Earnings: ($113,955)
Emp.: 1
Fiscal Year-end: 12/31/21
Plastic Component Mfr & Distr
N.A.I.C.S.: 326199

BORAC H & H A.D.

Lenjinova 9, Kula, Serbia
Tel.: (381) 25 722 124
Year Founded: 1999
Sales Range: Less than $1 Million
Emp.: 12
Printing Services
N.A.I.C.S.: 323111

BORALEX INC.

36 rue Lajeunesse, Kingsey Falls,
J0A 1B0, QC, Canada
Tel.: (819) 363-6363
Web Site: https://www.boralex.com
Year Founded: 1982
B3H—(DEU)
Rev.: $771,732,640
Assets: $4,964,158,880
Liabilities: $3,435,796,000
Net Worth: $1,528,362,880
Earnings: $86,838,800
Emp.: 753
Fiscal Year-end: 12/31/23
Electricity Production
N.A.I.C.S.: 221111
Patrick Decostre (Pres & CEO)

Subsidiaries:

Boralex Power Inc.   (1)
36 rue Lajeunesse, Kingsey Falls, J0A 1B0,
QC, Canada
Tel.: (819) 363-6363
Sales Range: $50-74.9 Million
Emp.: 100
Electricity Producer
N.A.I.C.S.: 221122

Subsidiary (Domestic):

Kingsey Cogeneration   (2)
36 Lagaunesse St, Kingsey Falls, J0A 1B0,
QC, Canada
Tel.: (819) 363-5860
Web Site: http://www.boralex.com
Sales Range: $25-49.9 Million
Emp.: 30
Electricity Producer
N.A.I.C.S.: 322130

Boralex S.A.S.   (1)
8 rue Anatole France, 59 000, Lille, France
Tel.: (33) 328365495
Web Site: http://www.boralex.com
Sales Range: $50-74.9 Million
Emp.: 5
Eletric Power Generation Services
N.A.I.C.S.: 221118

BORAX ARGENTINA S.A.

Huaytiquina 227, Campo Quijano,
Salta, A4407AVE, Argentina
Tel.: (54) 3874268000
Web Site: http://www.borax.com
Lithium Mining Services
N.A.I.C.S.: 212390

BORAX MORARJI LIMITED

Prospect Chamber 317/21 Dr DN
Road, Mumbai, 400001, Maharashtra,
India
Tel.: (91) 22 22048881   In
Web Site:
   http://www.boraxmorarji.com
Year Founded: 1963
506315—(BOM)

Sales Range: $1-9.9 Million
Emp.: 42
Boron Product Mfr & Wind Power
Generation Services
N.A.I.C.S.: 212390
Dilip S. Nagle (Compliance Officer &
Sec)

Subsidiaries:

Borax Morarji (Europe) GmbH   (1)
Fehrbelliner Platz 1, 48249, Dulmen,
Nordrhein-Westfalen, Germany
Tel.: (49) 2594 7831400
Wind Power Generation Services
N.A.I.C.S.: 221115

BORBET GMBH

Hauptstr 5, Hallenberg, 59969, Ger-
many
Tel.: (49) 29843010
Web Site: http://www.borbet.de
Year Founded: 1881
Sales Range: $800-899.9 Million
Emp.: 4,000
Aluminium Wheel Mfr
N.A.I.C.S.: 336390
Peter Wilhelm Borbet (Mng Dir)

Subsidiaries:

BORBET Alabama Inc.   (1)
979 W Veterans Blvd, Auburn, AL 36832
Tel.: (334) 502-9400
Web Site: http://www.borbet.de
Sales Range: $50-74.9 Million
Emp.: 300
Aluminium Wheel Mfr
N.A.I.C.S.: 336390
Kazimierz Zurad (Coord-IT)

BORBET Austria GmbH   (1)
Lamprechtshausener Str 77, 5282, Brau-
nau, Austria
Tel.: (43) 7722 884 0
Web Site: http://www.borbet-austria.at
Automobile Parts Mfr
N.A.I.C.S.: 336390

BORBET Solingen GmbH   (1)
Weyerstrasse 112-114, 42697, Solingen,
Germany
Tel.: (49) 2 12 22 67 6
Web Site: http://www.borbet.com
Emp.: 600
Aluminum Wheel Distr
N.A.I.C.S.: 423120
Holder Maag (Gen Mgr)

BORBET South Africa (PTY) Ltd.   (1)
11 Kohler Rd Perseverance, Port Elizabeth,
6000, South Africa
Tel.: (27) 41 404 1500
Web Site: http://www.borbet.de
Aluminum Wheel Distr
N.A.I.C.S.: 423120

BORBET Thuringen GmbH   (1)
Am Fliegerhorst 17, 99947, Bad Langen-
salza, Germany
Tel.: (49) 36 03 89 46 55 00
Aluminum Wheel Distr
N.A.I.C.S.: 423120

BORBET Vertriebs GmbH   (1)
Tratmoos 5, 85467, Neuching, Germany
Tel.: (49) 81 23 93 03 0
Aluminum Wheel Distr
N.A.I.C.S.: 423120

Borbet Sachsen GmbH   (1)
Industriestrasse 3, Kodersdorf, 02923, Gor-
litz, Germany
Tel.: (49) 358256290
Alloy Steel Mfr
N.A.I.C.S.: 331110

BORBONESE SPA

Via Nazionale 99, Pianoro, 40065,
Bologna, Italy
Tel.: (39) 051770111
Web Site: http://www.borbonese.com
Sales Range: $25-49.9 Million
Emp.: 100
Women's Clothing & Accessories De-
signer, Mfr & Retailer

N.A.I.C.S.: 315990
Carlo Morsini *(CEO)*

BORCH TEXTILE GROUP A/S
Strudsbergsvej 4, Slagelse, 4200,
Denmark
Tel.: (45) 58524550
Web Site: http://www.borchtextile.dk
Sales Range: $10-24.9 Million
Emp.: 150
Clothing Mfr
N.A.I.C.S.: 315250
Ulrich Mosegaard *(CEO)*

BORD NA MONA PLC
Main Street, Newbridge, W12 XR59,
Co Kildare, Ireland
Tel.: (353) 45439000
Web Site: http://www.bordnamona.ie
Rev.: $435,145,755
Assets: $542,938,812
Liabilities: $358,518,688
Net Worth: $184,420,124
Earnings: ($57,080,840)
Emp.: 2,188
Fiscal Year-end: 03/27/19
Peat Production & Power Generation
Services
N.A.I.C.S.: 221112
Geoff Meagher *(Chm)*

Subsidiaries:

AES (Ireland) Limited   **(1)**
1 Monread Commercial Park, Monread
Road, Naas, Co Kildare, Ireland
Tel.: (353) 45 843800
Web Site: http://www.aesirl.ie
Energy Generation Services
N.A.I.C.S.: 221112

AES Portlaoise   **(1)**
Kyletalesha, Portlaoise, County Laoise,
Ireland
Tel.: (353) 578662268
Web Site: http://www.aesirl.ie
All Other Miscellaneous Waste Manage-
ment Services
N.A.I.C.S.: 562998

AES Tullamore   **(1)**
Cappincur, Offaly, Tullamore,
Ireland   **(100%)**
Tel.: (353) 579321755
Web Site: http://www.aesirl.ie
Sales Range: $10-24.9 Million
Emp.: 50
All Other Miscellaneous Waste Manage-
ment Services
N.A.I.C.S.: 562998

Acorn Environmental Systems
Limited   **(1)**
Somerset Bridge Bridgwater, TA66LL, Som-
erset, United Kingdom   **(100%)**
Tel.: (44) 1278439325
Web Site: http://www.anua.com
Sales Range: $25-49.9 Million
Emp.: 25
All Other Miscellaneous Waste Manage-
ment Services
N.A.I.C.S.: 562998

Bord na Mona Energy
Tech/Admin   **(1)**
Leabeg Boora, Tullamore, Ireland
Tel.: (353) 579345900
Web Site: http://www.bnm.ie
Sales Range: $75-99.9 Million
Emp.: 100
Other Electric Power Generation
N.A.I.C.S.: 221118
Gerry Ryan *(Sec)*

Bord na Mona Environmental
Limited   **(1)**
Main St, Newbridge, Ireland   **(100%)**
Tel.: (353) 45439000
Web Site: http://www.bnm.ie
Sales Range: $75-99.9 Million
Emp.: 260
All Other Miscellaneous Waste Manage-
ment Services
N.A.I.C.S.: 562998

Colm O'Gogain *(Head-Strategic Infrastruc-*
ture)

Bord na Mona Fuels Limited   **(1)**
Suttons Oil Centre Park Road, Cork, Ireland
Tel.: (353) 86 2440664
Fuel Mfr & Distr
N.A.I.C.S.: 325180

Bord na Mona Horticulture
Limited   **(1)**
Collnamona, Togher, Portlaoise, Laois, Ire-
land
Tel.: (353) 86 2304882
Horticulture Services
N.A.I.C.S.: 111219

Derryarkin Sand and Gravel
Limited   **(1)**
Derryarkin, Rochfortbridge, Mullingar, West-
meath, Ireland
Tel.: (353) 44 9222833
Sand & Gravel Extraction & Distr
N.A.I.C.S.: 212321

Edenderry Power Limited   **(1)**
Co Offaly Ballykilleen, Edenderry, Ireland
Tel.: (353) 469733800
Web Site: http://www.bordnamona.ie
Sales Range: $50-74.9 Million
Emp.: 75
Other Electric Power Generation
N.A.I.C.S.: 221118

Suttons Limited   **(1)**
Monahan Rd, Cork, T12 K7TV, Ireland
Tel.: (353) 214963900
Web Site: http://www.bordnamona.ie
Sales Range: $25-49.9 Million
Emp.: 12
Coal & Other Mineral & Ore Whslr
N.A.I.C.S.: 423520

Suttons Oil Limited   **(1)**
Monahan Rd, Cork, Ireland   **(100%)**
Tel.: (353) 214911700
Web Site: http://www.bordnamona.com
Sales Range: $25-49.9 Million
Emp.: 12
Petroleum & Petroleum Products Merchant
Whslr (except Bulk Stations & Terminals)
N.A.I.C.S.: 424720
Joe O'Mahony *(CEO)*

BORDEAUX DEVELOPMENTS CORPORATION
1717-9 St SW, Calgary, T2T 3C1,
AB, Canada
Tel.: (403) 215-0800   **AB**
Web Site:
https://www.bordeauxcorp.com
Year Founded: 2001
Sales Range: Less than $1 Million
Real Estate Development Services
N.A.I.C.S.: 531390

BORDEAUX INDEX LTD.
10 Hatton Garden, London, EC1N
8AH, United Kingdom
Tel.: (44) 20 7269 0703
Web Site:
http://www.bordeauxindex.com
Year Founded: 1997
Sales Range: $100-124.9 Million
Emp.: 100
Wine Merchant
N.A.I.C.S.: 424820
Gary Boom *(Mng Dir)*

Subsidiaries:

Bordeaux Index (Hong Kong)
Ltd.   **(1)**
27/F Tai Yip Building 141 Thomson Road,
Wanchai, China (Hong Kong)
Tel.: (852) 2504 1122
Web Site: http://www.bordeauxindex.com
Emp.: 8
Wine Distr
N.A.I.C.S.: 424820
Doug Rumsam *(Mng Dir)*

Bordeaux Index (Singapore) Ltd.   **(1)**
11 Collyer Quay 13-04 The Arcade, Singapore, 049317, Singapore
Tel.: (65) 6474 7310

Web Site: http://www.bordeauxindex.com
Wine Distr
N.A.I.C.S.: 424820

Bordeaux Index US Inc.   **(1)**
7083 Hollywood Blvd, Los Angeles, CA
90028
Tel.: (323) 823-9317
Wine Distr
N.A.I.C.S.: 424820

BORDER CHEMICAL CO., LTD.
2147 Portage Avenue, Winnipeg, R3J
0L4, MB, Canada
Tel.: (204) 837-1383
Year Founded: 1959
Rev.: $18,336,138
Emp.: 63
Chemical Products Distr & Mfr
N.A.I.C.S.: 325998
Patricia B. Smerchanski *(CEO)*

BORDER PETROLEUM LIM-ITED
200 407 3rd Street SW, Calgary, T2P
4Z2, AB, Canada
Tel.: (403) 538-8448
Web Site:
https://www.borderpetroleum.com
BOPFF—(OTCIQ)
Sales Range: Less than $1 Million
Oil & Gas Exploration Services
N.A.I.C.S.: 211120
Al J. Kroontje *(Chm & Interim CEO)*

BORDER TIMBERS LIMITED
1 Aberdeen Road, PO Box 458, Mu-
tare, Zimbabwe
Tel.: (263) 2064224
Web Site:
http://www.bordertimbers.com
BRDR—(ZIM)
Rev.: $15,840,384
Assets: $78,971,646
Liabilities: $26,725,549
Net Worth: $52,246,097
Earnings: ($1,526,405)
Emp.: 1,496
Fiscal Year-end: 06/30/23
Lumber Mfr
N.A.I.C.S.: 321999
M. B. Narotam *(Sec)*

BORDERS & SOUTHERN PE-TROLEUM PLC
70 Pall Mall, London, SW1Y 5ES,
United Kingdom
Tel.: (44) 2076619348   **UK**
Web Site:
https://www.borderssouthern.com
Year Founded: 2004
BOR—(AIM)
Rev.: $42,000
Assets: $296,527,000
Liabilities: $565,000
Net Worth: $295,962,000
Earnings: ($1,359,000)
Emp.: 5
Fiscal Year-end: 12/31/22
Oil & Gas Exploration Services
N.A.I.C.S.: 213112
Howard Kevin Obee *(CEO)*

BORDEX PACKAGING B.V.
Schumanpark 67, 7336 AS, Apel-
doorn, Netherlands
Tel.: (31) 55 599 65 00
Web Site:
http://www.bordexpackaging.com
Year Founded: 1977
Sales Range: $10-24.9 Million
Emp.: 15
Plastic Packaging Products Mfr
N.A.I.C.S.: 326112
Bert Hengeveld *(Owner & Mng Dir)*

BORE TECH AB
C/O GenerPro AB Terminalvagen 24,

SE-721 36, Vasteras, Sweden
Tel.: (46) 31617130
Sales Range: Less than $1 Million
Emp.: 4
Renewable Energy Investment Ser-
vices
N.A.I.C.S.: 523999
Christian Widing *(CEO)*

Subsidiaries:

Boreinvest AB   **(1)**
Little Boom 5 Ctr, 411 04, Gothenburg,
Sweden
Tel.: (46) 31617130
Sales Range: $50-74.9 Million
Investment Management Service
N.A.I.C.S.: 523940

BOREA AS
Kalfarveien 76, PO Box 2312, 5867,
Bergen, Norway
Tel.: (47) 5300 2900   **NO**
Web Site: http://www.borea.no
Investment Fund & Asset Manage-
ment Services
N.A.I.C.S.: 523940
Hilde Nodseth Bringedal *(CEO)*

Subsidiaries:

Borea Asset Management AS   **(1)**
Kalfarveien 76, PO Box 2312, 5867, Ber-
gen, Norway
Tel.: (47) 5300 2900
Web Site: http://www.borea.no
Asset Management Services
N.A.I.C.S.: 523940
Hilde Nodseth Bringedal *(CEO & Mng Dir)*

Borea Opportunity Management
AS   **(1)**
Kalfarveien 57A, 5022, Bergen, Norway
Tel.: (47) 9002 4397
Web Site: http://www.borea.no
Privater Equity Firm
N.A.I.C.S.: 523999
Harald Mowinckel Troye *(Mng Partner)*

Subsidiary (Domestic):

Sharecat Solutions AS   **(2)**
Midtunhaugen 10, Nesttun, 5224, Bergen,
Norway
Tel.: (47) 55 11 98 00
Web Site: http://www4.sharecat.com
Electronic Components Mfr
N.A.I.C.S.: 334419
Jon Gjerde *(CEO)*

BOREALIS EXPLORATION LIMITED
Suite 1 43Main Street, Gibraltar,
GX11 1AA, Gibraltar
Tel.: (350) 20059995   **GI**
Web Site: http://www.borealis.com
BOREF—(OTCIQ)
Assets: $45,476,341
Liabilities: $36,330,300
Net Worth: $9,146,041
Earnings: $531,371
Emp.: 2
Fiscal Year-end: 09/30/23
Holding Company; Technology Re-
search & Development Services for
Energy Industry
N.A.I.C.S.: 551112

Subsidiaries:

Photon Power plc   **(1)**
Suite 3-G Eurolife Building 1 Corral Road,
Gibraltar, Gibraltar
Tel.: (350) 59995
Web Site: http://www.photonpower.com
Solar Energy Equipment Services
N.A.I.C.S.: 221114

Roche Bay plc   **(1)**
43/1 Main Street, Gibraltar, Gibraltar
Tel.: (350) 20059995
Web Site: https://www.rochebay.com
Iron Ore Mining Services
N.A.I.C.S.: 212210

Borealis Exploration Limited—(Continued)

Rodney T. Cox *(Co-Chm & CEO)*

WheelTug plc   **(1)**
43/1 Main Street, Gibraltar, Gibraltar
Tel.: (350) 20066177
Web Site: http://www.wheeltug.gi
Aerospace Taxi System Services
N.A.I.C.S.: 488190

BOREALIS FOODS INC.
1540 Cornwall Rd #104, Oakville, L6J
7W5, ON, Canada
Tel.: (7) 9052782200
Web Site:
      https://www.borealisfoods.com
BRLS—(NASDAQ)
Rev.: $2,578,984
Assets: $179,449,742
Liabilities: $181,034,101
Net Worth: ($1,584,359)
Earnings: ($302,544)
Emp.: 2
Fiscal Year-end: 12/31/22
Food & Beverage Mfg
N.A.I.C.S.: 311999
Reza Soltanzadeh *(Co-Founder &
CEO)*

BOREK CONSTRUCTION, LTD.
9690 Rd 223, Box 870, Dawson
Creek, V1G 4H8, BC, Canada
Tel.: (250) 782-5561
Web Site: https://www.borekltd.com
Year Founded: 1957
Rev.: $26,170,430
Emp.: 160
Construction & Engineering Services
N.A.I.C.S.: 237990
Dean Borek *(Pres-Ops)*

Subsidiaries:

Kenn Borek Air Ltd.   **(1)**
290 MacTavish Road NE, Calgary, T2E
7G5, AB, Canada
Tel.: (403) 291-3300
Web Site: https://www.borekair.com
Aircraft Leasing & Maintenance Services
N.A.I.C.S.: 532411

BORG MANUFACTURING PTY LTD.
2 Wella Way, Somersby, 2250, NSW,
Australia
Tel.: (61) 2 4340 9800
Web Site: http://www.borgs.com.au
Emp.: 1,000
Mfr of Melanine Panels & Compo-
nents for Joinery Applications
N.A.I.C.S.: 326199
Jim Snelson *(CEO)*

BORGES AGRICULTURAL & INDUSTRIAL NUTS S.A.
Calle Flix, 29, 43205, Reus, Spain
Tel.: (34) 977309000
BAIN—(MAD)
Sales Range: Less than $1 Million
Dried Fruit Farming Services
N.A.I.C.S.: 311423
David Prats Palomo *(Exec Dir)*

Subsidiaries:

BAIN Andalucia, S.L.U.   **(1)**
Ctra Alcudia-Hernan Valle Km-7, Exfiliana
Valle del Zalabi, 18511, Granada, Spain
Tel.: (34) 958066044
Dry Fruit & Nut Distr
N.A.I.C.S.: 424490

BAIN Extremadura,S.L.U.   **(1)**
Ctra Olivenza km 10, 06011, Badajoz,
Spain
Tel.: (34) 924140559
Dry Fruit & Nut Distr
N.A.I.C.S.: 424490

BAIN-Mas Colom S.L.U.   **(1)**
C/ Mas d'en Colom s/n, 25300, Tarrega,
Lleida, Spain

Tel.: (34) 973501212
Dry Fruit & Nut Distr
N.A.I.C.S.: 424490

Borges of California, Inc.   **(1)**
1640 Hwy 45, Glenn, CA 95943
Tel.: (530) 934-8200
Dry Fruit & Nut Distr
N.A.I.C.S.: 424490

BORGESTAD ASA
Gunnar Knudsensvei 144, 3712,
Skien, Norway
Tel.: (47) 35542400
Web Site: http://borgestad.no
Sales Range: $75-99.9 Million
Emp.: 15
Property Development Services
N.A.I.C.S.: 237210
Astrid Fjeld *(Office Mgr)*

Subsidiaries:

Borgestad Poland Sp.zo.o   **(1)**
Lipowa 3, 44 100, Gliwice, Silesian, Poland
Tel.: (48) 327192628
Nursery Management Services
N.A.I.C.S.: 444240

BORGOSESIA S.P.A
Via Aldo Moro 38, 40127, Bologna,
Italy
Tel.: (39) 015405679
Web Site: https://borgosesiaspa.it
Year Founded: 1873
BO—(ITA)
Sales Range: Less than $1 Million
Real Estate Services
N.A.I.C.S.: 531390
Mauro Girardi *(Chm & Co-CEO)*

BORGUN HF
Armuli 30, 108, Reykjavik, Iceland
Tel.: (354) 560 1600   **IS**
Web Site: http://www.borgun.is
Emp.: 120
Credit Card Issuing Services
N.A.I.C.S.: 522210
Haukur Oddsson *(CEO)*

BORICI A.D.
Milorad Jovanovica 19, Sjenica, Ser-
bia
Tel.: (381) 20740268
Year Founded: 1960
BRCI—(BEL)
Sales Range: Less than $1 Million
Emp.: 22
Restaurant & Mobile Food Services
N.A.I.C.S.: 722511
Hatidza Memic *(Exec Dir)*

BORNEO OIL BERHAD
1st and 2nd Floor Victoria Point Jalan
OKK Awang Besar, 87007, Labuan,
WP, Malaysia
Tel.: (60) 87410509   **MY**
Web Site: https://www.borneo-
oil.com.my
Year Founded: 1984
BORNOIL—(KLS)
Rev.: $17,986,578
Assets: $204,315,220
Liabilities: $16,395,980
Net Worth: $187,919,240
Earnings: ($2,796,725)
Fiscal Year-end: 06/30/23
Investment Holding Company; Hotel
Management & Property Develop-
ment Services
N.A.I.C.S.: 551112
Siew Kim Chin *(Co-Sec)*

Subsidiaries:

SB Supplies & Logistics Sdn.
Bhd.   **(1)**
2nd Floor Wisma SugarBun Lot 180 Sect
19 KTLD Jalan Satok, 93400, Kuching,
Sarawak, Malaysia

Tel.: (60) 82422000
Web Site: https://www.sugarbun.com
Restaurant Services
N.A.I.C.S.: 722511

BORNEO RESOURCE INVEST-MENTS LTD.
11/F Admiralty Centre Tower 2 18
Harcourt Road, Admiralty, Hong
Kong, China (Hong Kong)
Tel.: (852) 93776536
Year Founded: 2004
BRNE—(OTCIQ)
Coal Mining Services
N.A.I.C.S.: 213113

BOROMIR PROD SA BUZAU
Nr 37 Santierului, Buzau, Romania
Tel.: (40) 238 436 646
Web Site: http://www.boromir.ro
Sales Range: $25-49.9 Million
Emp.: 492
Fresh Pastry & Cakes Mfr
N.A.I.C.S.: 311813

Subsidiaries:

Amylon S.A.   **(1)**
Sos Alba Iulia Nr 70, Sibiu, Romania
Tel.: (40) 269217722
Web Site: http://www.amylon.ro
Rev.: $20,148,036
Assets: $18,154,394
Liabilities: $10,246,497
Net Worth: $7,907,897
Earnings: $815,169
Emp.: 320
Fiscal Year-end: 12/31/2019
Starch Product Mfr
N.A.I.C.S.: 311221

BOROSIL RENEWABLES LIM-ITED
1101 Crescenzo G Block Opp MCA
Club, Worli, Mumbai, 400 051, India
Tel.: (91) 2267406300
Web Site: https://www.borosil.com
502219—(BOM)
Rev.: $124,730,738
Assets: $222,801,702
Liabilities: $94,146,712
Net Worth: $128,654,990
Earnings: $9,641,923
Emp.: 713
Fiscal Year-end: 03/31/23
Laboratory Glassware Mfr & Distr
N.A.I.C.S.: 327212
B. L. Kheruka *(Chm)*

Subsidiaries:

Klass Pack Limited   **(1)**
H-27 MIDC, Ambad, Nashik, 422010, Maha-
rashtra, India
Tel.: (91) 2532382404
Web Site: http://www.klasspack.com
Glass Ampoules Mfr
N.A.I.C.S.: 327215

BORQS TECHNOLOGIES, INC.
Suite 309 3/F Dongfeng KASO
Dongfengbeiqiao, Chaoyang District,
Beijing, 100016, China
Tel.: (86) 1064378678   **VG**
Web Site: http://www.borqs.com
BRQSF—(OTCQB)
Rev.: $32,046,000
Assets: $21,432,000
Liabilities: $35,864,000
Net Worth: ($14,432,000)
Earnings: ($26,921,000)
Emp.: 305
Fiscal Year-end: 12/31/23
Investment Services
N.A.I.C.S.: 523999
Pat Sek Yuen Chan *(Co-Founder,
Chm, Pres & CEO)*

Subsidiaries:

BORQS International Holding
Corp.   **(1)**

Building B23-A Universal Business Park No
10 Jiuxianqiao Road, Beijing, 100015, Cha-
oyang, China
Tel.: (86) 10 5975 6336
Web Site: http://www.borqs.com
Sales Range: $75-99.9 Million
Software Development Services
N.A.I.C.S.: 541511

BORR COMPANY
Elektravagen 10, 126 30, Hagersten,
Sweden
Tel.: (46) 87445065
Web Site: http://www.borrcompany.se
Sales Range: $25-49.9 Million
Emp.: 50
Construction Services
N.A.I.C.S.: 213112
Nicholas Johansson *(Pres)*

Subsidiaries:

R.A.D.i Sverige AB/ABVAC   **(1)**
Elektravagen 10, 12630, Hagersten, Swe-
den
Tel.: (46) 8178350
Web Site: http://www.radsweden.com
Sales Range: $25-49.9 Million
Power Line Construction
N.A.I.C.S.: 237130

BORR DRILLING LIMITED
S E Pearman Building 2nd Fl 9 Par-
la-Ville Road, Hamilton, HM11, Ber-
muda
Tel.: (441) 7370152   **BM**
Web Site:
      https://www.borrdrilling.com
Year Founded: 2016
BORR—(NYSE)
Rev.: $443,800,000
Assets: $3,001,700,000
Liabilities: $2,103,900,000
Net Worth: $897,800,000
Earnings: ($292,800,000)
Emp.: 1,504
Fiscal Year-end: 12/31/22
Holding Company; Oil & Gas Well
Drilling Contractor
N.A.I.C.S.: 551112
Paal Kibsgaard *(Chm)*

Subsidiaries:

Borr Drilling Management (UK)
Ltd.   **(1)**
70 Victoria Street 6th Floor The Zig Zag
Building, London, SW1E 6SQ, United King-
dom
Tel.: (44) 1224 289 200
Web Site: http://borrdrilling.com
Oil & Gas Extraction Support Services
N.A.I.C.S.: 213112
Andreas Lavik Lie *(Fin Dir)*

Subsidiary (Non-US):

Borr Drilling Management DMCC   **(2)**
STREET 28th Floor Reef Tower Cluster O,
Jumeirah Lake Towers, Dubai, United Arab
Emirates
Tel.: (971) 4 448 7501
Oil & Gas Well Drilling Contractor
N.A.I.C.S.: 213111
Svend Anton Maier *(CEO)*

Borr Drilling Management AS   **(1)**
Klingenberggata 4, 0161, Oslo, Norway
Tel.: (47) 22483000
Web Site: http://www.borrdrilling.com
Executive & Administrative Office
N.A.I.C.S.: 921140

BORRACHAS VIPAL SA
Av Severo Dullius-1395, Bairro Sao
Joao, 90200-310, Porto Alegre, Brazil
Tel.: (55) 32053000
Web Site: http://www.vipal.com.br
Rubber Mfr
N.A.I.C.S.: 326299

Subsidiaries:

Marangoni Tread N.A., Inc.   **(1)**

712 Myatt Dr, Madison, TN
37115-2168   **(100%)**
Tel.: (615) 868-4050
Web Site: http://www.ringtread.com
Sales Range: $25-49.9 Million
Emp.: 49
Distribution of Tires And Retreaded Tires
N.A.I.C.S.: 333248
Bill Sweatman *(Pres & CEO)*

BORREGAARD ASA
Hjalmar Wessels vei 6, 1721, Sarps-
borg, Norway
Tel.: (47) 69118000
Web Site: http://www.borregaard.com
BRG—(OSL)
Rev.: $635,599,483
Assets: $749,491,964
Liabilities: $338,906,337
Net Worth: $410,585,627
Earnings: $82,394,236
Emp.: 1,107
Fiscal Year-end: 12/31/22
Specialty Chemicals, Fine Chemicals;
Specialty Chemical Pulp
N.A.I.C.S.: 325998
Per Arthur Sorlie *(Pres & CEO)*

BORSA DE BARCELONA
Paseo De Gracia 19, 08007, Barce-
lona, Spain
Tel.: (34) 934013555   ES
Web Site: http://www.borsabcn.es
Year Founded: 1970
Sales Range: $10-24.9 Million
Emp.: 63
Securities Trading Services
N.A.I.C.S.: 523210
Joan Hortala Arau *(Chm)*

BORSA INSTANBUL A.S.
Resitpasa Mahallesi Tuncay Artun
Caddesi, Emirgan, 34467, Istanbul,
Turkiye
Tel.: (90) 2122982100   TR
Web Site:
   http://www.borsaistanbul.com
Year Founded: 1986
Sales Range: $100-124.9 Million
Emp.: 450
Stock Exchange Services
N.A.I.C.S.: 523210

BORSENMEDIEN AG
Am Eulenhof 14, 95326, Kulmbach,
Germany
Tel.: (49) 922190510   De
Web Site:
   http://www.boersenmedien.de
Year Founded: 1989
Media Company
N.A.I.C.S.: 541810
Bernd Fortsch *(Chm)*

Subsidiaries:

vwd NetSolutions GmbH   **(1)**
Martin-Hoffmann-Str 18, 12435, Berlin, Ger-
many
Tel.: (49) 30 200598 0
Web Site: http://www.vwd.com
Financial Portal Operator
N.A.I.C.S.: 519290
Lutz Victor Wengorz *(Head-Sls & Mktg)*

BORTEX GLOBAL LIMITED
Flat A 11/F King Palace Plaza 55
King Yip Street Kwun Tong, Kowloon,
China (Hong Kong)
Tel.: (852) 25549888   Ky
Web Site: http://www.bortex.com.cn
Year Founded: 2014
8118—(HKG)
Rev.: $8,996,655
Assets: $17,694,450
Liabilities: $5,145,900
Net Worth: $12,548,550
Earnings: ($8,916,713)
Emp.: 120

Fiscal Year-end: 04/30/23
Electronic Product Mfr & Distr
N.A.I.C.S.: 334413
X. H. Shao *(Founder & Dir-Product
Design, Procurement, Production &
Fin)*

**BORTEX GROUP FINANCE
PLC**
32 Hughes Hallet Street, Sliema,
SLM 3142, Malta
Tel.: (356) 21333565
Web Site:
   http://www.bortexgroupholdings.com
BX27A—(MAL)
Rev.: $29,305,657
Assets: $83,265,706
Liabilities: $40,853,073
Net Worth: $42,412,633
Earnings: $2,341,604
Emp.: 156
Fiscal Year-end: 10/31/22
Financial Investment Services
N.A.I.C.S.: 523940
Christine Demicoli *(CFO-Hospitality &
Property Ops)*

**BORUJERD TEXTILE CO
(PUBLIC JOINT STOCK)**
No 65 West Farzan St Afrigha Blvd,
Tehran, Iran
Tel.: (98) 21 8794431
Web Site: http://borujerdtextile.com
Year Founded: 1983
Textile Products Mfr
N.A.I.C.S.: 314999

**BORUSAN BIRLESIK BORU
FABRIKALARI SANAYI VE TI-
CARET AS**
Meclisi Mebusan Cad No 37, Sali-
pazari, 34427, Istanbul, Turkiye
Tel.: (90) 2123935800
Web Site:
   https://www.borusanmannes.com
Year Founded: 1958
BRSAN—(IST)
Rev.: $1,340,386,000
Assets: $1,475,962,000
Liabilities: $841,703,000
Net Worth: $634,259,000
Earnings: $81,485,000
Emp.: 2,095
Fiscal Year-end: 12/31/22
Line Pipe & Drilling Pipe Mfr
N.A.I.C.S.: 332996
Bedri Songul *(Mgr-Installation & In-
dustrial Applications Segment)*

**BORUSAN YATIRIM VE
PAZARLAMA AS**
Baltalimani Hisar Street No 5
Haunted Mansion Rumeli Hisari,
Findikli, 34470, Istanbul, Turkiye
Tel.: (90) 2122513410
Web Site:
   https://www.borusanyatirim.com
Year Founded: 1977
BRYAT—(IST)
Rev.: $5,619,927
Assets: $886,777,084
Liabilities: $34,426,247
Net Worth: $852,350,837
Earnings: $76,849,471
Fiscal Year-end: 12/31/23
Automobile Parts Mfr
N.A.I.C.S.: 336390
Cemil Bulent Demircioglu *(Chm)*

**BORUSSIA DORTMUND GMBH
& CO. KGAA**
Rheinlanddamm 207-209, 44137,
Dortmund, Germany
Tel.: (49) 23190200
Web Site: https://aktie.bvb.de

BVB—(BER)
Rev.: $546,488,856
Assets: $632,974,306
Liabilities: $281,955,231
Net Worth: $351,019,074
Earnings: $47,563,240
Emp.: 1,017
Fiscal Year-end: 06/30/24
Sports Club Services
N.A.I.C.S.: 711211
Gerd Pieper *(Chm-Supervisory Bd &
VP)*

Subsidiaries:

BVB Beteiligungs-GmbH   **(1)**
Rheinlanddamm 207, 44137, Dortmund,
Germany
Tel.: (49) 23190200
Investment Management Service
N.A.I.C.S.: 523940

BVB Event & Catering GmbH   **(1)**
Rheinlanddamm 207-209, 44137, Dort-
mund, Germany
Tel.: (49) 23190206600
Web Site: https://www.event.bvb.de
Food Service
N.A.I.C.S.: 722310

BVB Merchandising GmbH   **(1)**
Rheinlanddamm 207-209, 44137, Dort-
mund, Germany
Tel.: (49) 23190200
Web Site: https://www.bvbonlineshop.com
Football Club Operator
N.A.I.C.S.: 711211

BVB Stadion GmbH   **(1)**
Rheinlanddamm 207-209, Dortmund,
44137, Germany
Tel.: (49) 23190200
Football Club Operator
N.A.I.C.S.: 711211

BVB Stadion Holding GmbH   **(1)**
Mauritiuswall 35, 44263, Dortmund, Ger-
many
Tel.: (49) 231434443
Investment Management Service
N.A.I.C.S.: 523940

BVB Stadionmanagement GmbH   **(1)**
Strobelallee 50, 44139, Dortmund, Ger-
many
Tel.: (49) 23190200
Football Club Operator
N.A.I.C.S.: 711211

Sports & Bytes GmbH   **(1)**
Rheinlanddamm 207-209, 44137, Dort-
mund, Germany
Tel.: (49) 231 9020 0
Web Site: http://www.sportsandbytes.de
Online Marketing Services
N.A.I.C.S.: 541810
Carsten Cramer *(Co-CEO)*

besttravel Dortmund GmbH   **(1)**
Rheinlanddamm 207-209, 44137, Dort-
mund, Germany
Tel.: (49) 23190206920
Web Site: https://www.besttravel.bvb.de
Travel Agency Services
N.A.I.C.S.: 561510

BORUTA-ZACHEM SA
Jakoba Hechlinskiego 4 st, 85-825,
Bydgoszcz, Poland
Tel.: (48) 523748240
Web Site: https://www.boruta-
zachem.pl
Year Founded: 1894
Cosmetics Products Mfr
N.A.I.C.S.: 325620
Artur Bielski *(Pres)*

BORYSZEW S.A.
Aleje Jerozolimskie 92, 00-807, War-
saw, Poland
Tel.: (48) 226586568
Web Site:
   https://www.boryszew.com.pl
Year Founded: 1911
BRS—(WAR)
Rev.: $1,705,902,377

Assets: $1,001,274,682
Liabilities: $576,951,465
Net Worth: $424,323,218
Earnings: $28,531,628
Emp.: 8,622
Fiscal Year-end: 12/31/22
Chemical & Plastic Product Mfr
N.A.I.C.S.: 325998
Mikolaj Budzanowski *(Chief Innova-
tion Officer & Member-Mgmt Bd)*

Subsidiaries:

Hutmen S.A.   **(1)**
Grabiszynska 241 St, 53-234, Wroclaw,
Poland   **(100%)**
Tel.: (48) 713348710
Web Site: http://www.hutmen.pl
Nonferrous Metal Products Mfr
N.A.I.C.S.: 331410
Jakub Nadachewicz *(Chm-Supervisory Bd)*

Impexmetal S.A.   **(1)**
Aleje Jerozolimskie 92, 00-807, Warsaw,
Poland   **(100%)**
Tel.: (48) 22 658 65 68
Web Site: http://www.impexmetal.com.pl
Aluminium Products Mfr
N.A.I.C.S.: 331315
Malgorzata Iwanejko *(Member-Exec Bd)*

BORYUNG PHARMACEUTICAL
136 Changgyeonggung-ro, Jongno-
gu, Seoul, 03127, Korea (South)
Tel.: (82) 27088000
Web Site:
   https://pharm.boryung.co.kr
Year Founded: 1963
003850—(KRS)
Rev.: $583,284,973
Assets: $684,459,997
Liabilities: $288,368,500
Net Worth: $396,091,497
Earnings: $32,166,683
Emp.: 1,454
Fiscal Year-end: 12/31/22
Pharmaceuticals Product Mfr
N.A.I.C.S.: 325412
Daniel Chang *(CEO)*

Subsidiaries:

Boryung Pharmaceutical - Ansan
Factory   **(1)**
1122-3 Shingil-dong, Danwon-gu, Ansan,
Gyeonggi-do, Korea (South)
Tel.: (82) 31 491 5171
Pharmaceuticals Product Mfr
N.A.I.C.S.: 325412

BORZA TA' MALTA
Garrison Chapel Castille Place, Val-
letta, VLT 1063, Malta
Tel.: (356) 21244051
Web Site:
   http://www.borzamalta.com.mt
Sales Range: $1-9.9 Million
Emp.: 50
Stock Exchange Services
N.A.I.C.S.: 523210
Eileen V. Muscat *(CEO)*

BOS EQUIPEMENT HOTELIER
Z I Des Salines Royales 57 Rue Des
Acacias, 73600, Moutiers, France
Tel.: (33) 479240066   FR
Web Site: http://www.bos-
equipement.com
Emp.: 116
Commercial Hospitality Equipment &
Furnishings Distr
N.A.I.C.S.: 423440
Jean Bos *(Pres)*

**BOS GLOBAL HOLDINGS LIM-
ITED**
Suite 3 Level 3 1292 Hay Street,
West Perth, 6005, WA, Australia
Tel.: (61) 893224071
Web Site: http://www.bosglobal.com
Investment Services

BOS GLOBAL Holdings Limited—(Continued)
N.A.I.C.S.: 523999

BOSA PROPERTIES INC.
1100-838 West Hastings Street, Vancouver, V6C 0A6, BC, Canada
Tel.: (604) 299-1363
Web Site:
http://www.bosaproperties.com
Year Founded: 1961
Sales Range: $100-124.9 Million
Emp.: 400
Construction Services
N.A.I.C.S.: 236220
Robert Bosa (Founder)

BOSA TECHNOLOGY HOLDINGS LTD.
Room D 29/F King Palace Plaza 55 King Yip Street, Kwun Tong, Kowloon, China (Hong Kong)
Tel.: (852) 25055568   Ky
Web Site: http://www.bosa-tech.com
Year Founded: 2012
8140—(HKG)
Rev.: $14,050,178
Assets: $20,028,788
Liabilities: $4,100,661
Net Worth: $15,928,127
Earnings: $2,647,959
Emp.: 56
Fiscal Year-end: 06/30/22
Concrete Products Mfr
N.A.I.C.S.: 332312
Paulino Lim (COO)

BOSAL INTERNATIONAL NV
20 Dellestraat, 3560, Lummen, Belgium
Tel.: (32) 13530811
Web Site: http://www.bosal.com
Sales Range: $650-699.9 Million
Emp.: 2,500
Automotive Exhaust Systems & Parts Mfr
N.A.I.C.S.: 336390
Aag Goudriaan (CEO)

Subsidiaries:

Bosal Africa (Pty) Ltd.   (1)
Koedoespoort Industrial Sites Rooibok Avenue, Pretoria, 0186, South Africa
Tel.: (27) 123911000
Web Site: http://www.bosal.co.za
Sales Range: $25-49.9 Million
Emp.: 50
Mfr of Automotive Exhaust Systems & Accessories
N.A.I.C.S.: 336390
Norma Groenewald (Mgr-HR)

Bosal Automotive & Industrial Components Ltd   (1)
Unit 330 Four Oaks Road Walton Summit Centre Bamber Bridge, Preston, PR5 8AP, United Kingdom
Tel.: (44) 1772771000
Web Site: http://www.bosal.co.uk
Automobile Parts Distr
N.A.I.C.S.: 423120
Adrian Gill (Acct Mgr)

Bosal Germany GmbH   (1)
Metallstrasse 5, 41751, Viersen, Germany
Tel.: (49) 21629590
Web Site: http://www.bosal.com
Automobile Parts Distr
N.A.I.C.S.: 423120

Bosal International - Georgia   (1)
1 Bosal Way, Lavonia, GA 30553
Tel.: (706) 356-2889
Sales Range: $25-49.9 Million
Emp.: 50
Car Exhaust Systems Mfr
N.A.I.C.S.: 336390

Bosal International North America   (1)
1476 Seaver Way, Ypsilanti, MI 48197
Tel.: (734) 547-7000

Web Site: http://www.bosalna.com
Sales Range: $100-124.9 Million
Mfr of Car Exhaust Systems & Accessories
N.A.I.C.S.: 336390

Bosal Ireland Ltd   (1)
Unit 5 Knockmitten Lane Naas Road, Dublin, Ireland
Tel.: (353) 14565644
Web Site: http://www.bosal.ie
Automobile Parts Distr
N.A.I.C.S.: 423120
Philip Flanagan (Mng Dir)

Bosal Mexico AM   (1)
Avenida El Tepeyac #1210 Parque Industrial O'Donell Aeropuerto, CP 76240, Queretaro, El Marques, Mexico
Tel.: (52) 442 101 9900
Web Site: http://www.bosal.com
Sales Range: $50-74.9 Million
Emp.: 160
Car Exhaust Systems & Aftermarket Mfr
N.A.I.C.S.: 336390
Arturo Perez (Mng Dir)

Bosal Mimaysan A.S.   (1)
Defne Sok No 6, Pelitli Koyu, 41480, Gebze, Kocaeli, Türkiye
Tel.: (90) 2627514425
Web Site: http://www.bosal-mimaysan.com
Automobile Parts Distr
N.A.I.C.S.: 423120

Bosal Nederland BV   (1)
5 Kamerlingh Onnesweg, 4131 PK, Vianen, Netherlands
Tel.: (31) 347362911
Web Site: http://www.bosal.com
Automotive Exhaust System & Part Mfr
N.A.I.C.S.: 336390
A. Van Lopik (Mgr-Pur)

Bosal USA, Inc.   (1)
200 International Dr Ste 2, Budd Lake, NJ 07828
Tel.: (973) 428-9822
Sales Range: $25-49.9 Million
Emp.: 30
Car Exhaust Systems Mfr
N.A.I.C.S.: 336390
Jeff Berman (Mng Dir)

BOSANAC D.D.
VIII Ulica Broj 46, 76270, Orasje, Bosnia & Herzegovina
Tel.: (387) 31712104
BSNCR—(SARE)
Rev.: $287,142
Assets: $8,331,761
Liabilities: $3,291,282
Net Worth: $5,040,478
Earnings: ($250,648)
Emp.: 16
Fiscal Year-end: 12/31/20
Tobacco Product Mfr
N.A.I.C.S.: 312230

BOSCH LIMITED
Hosur Road, PO Box No 3000, Adugodi, Bengaluru, 560030, Karnataka, India
Tel.: (91) 8067521750
Web Site: https://www.bosch.in
500530—(BOM)
Rev.: $1,662,269,700
Assets: $2,102,413,950
Liabilities: $644,621,250
Net Worth: $1,457,792,700
Earnings: $166,297,950
Emp.: 6,041
Fiscal Year-end: 03/31/22
Automotive Technology
N.A.I.C.S.: 334515
Soumitra Bhattacharya (Co-Mng Dir)

BOSCUS CANADA INC
900 Ave Selkirk, Pointe-Claire, H9R 3S3, QC, Canada
Tel.: (514) 694-9805
Web Site: http://www.boscus.com
Year Founded: 1981
Rev.: $187,599,499
Emp.: 42

Lumber Distr
N.A.I.C.S.: 423310

BOSHART INDUSTRIES INC.
25 Whaley Ave, PO Box 310, Perth East, N0K 1M0, ON, Canada
Tel.: (519) 595-4444
Web Site: http://www.boshart.com
Year Founded: 1955
Sales Range: $10-24.9 Million
Industrial Valves & Plumbing Fittings Mfr & Distr
N.A.I.C.S.: 332911
Brenda Hanna (VP-Sls & Mktg)

Subsidiaries:

Flomatic Corporation   (1)
15 Pruyn's Island Dr, Glens Falls, NY 12801-4424   (100%)
Tel.: (518) 761-9797
Web Site: http://www.flomatic.com
Sales Range: $25-49.9 Million
Emp.: 50
Valve Mfr
N.A.I.C.S.: 332911
Bo Andersson (Pres)

BOSHIWA INTERNATIONAL HOLDING LIMITED
Pudong Wai Gaoqiao Free Trade Zone, No 78 Taigu Road, Shanghai, China
Tel.: (86) 21 5866 1484   Ky
Web Site: http://www.boshiwa.cn
Year Founded: 1997
Sales Range: $200-249.9 Million
Emp.: 2,097
Apparel Whslr
N.A.I.C.S.: 424350
Zheng Yong Zhong (Chm & CEO)

BOSIDENG INTERNATIONAL HOLDINGS LIMITED
Unit 5709 57/F The Center 99 Queens Road Central, Hong Kong, China (Hong Kong)
Tel.: (852) 28666918
Web Site:
https://company.bosideng.com
BSDGY—(OTCIQ)
Rev.: $2,355,100,488
Assets: $2,940,352,834
Liabilities: $1,170,699,426
Net Worth: $1,769,653,408
Earnings: $302,756,173
Emp.: 12,183
Fiscal Year-end: 03/31/23
Apparel Products Distribution & Mfr
N.A.I.C.S.: 313220
Jinsong Rui (Sr VP)

BOSIG HOLDING GMBH & CO. KG
Brunnenstr 75-77, 73333, Gingen an der Fils, Germany
Tel.: (49) 7162 40 99 0
Web Site: http://www.bosig.de
Sales Range: $10-24.9 Million
Emp.: 100
Bulding Material Mfr
N.A.I.C.S.: 325520
Oliver Schmid (Mng Dir)

Subsidiaries:

BOSIG Baukunststoffe GmbH   (1)
Roland-Schmid-Strasse 1, 04910, Elsterwerda, Germany
Tel.: (49) 35337000
Construction Materials Mfr
N.A.I.C.S.: 325520
Rene Zeidler (Project Mgr-Energy)

BOSIG GmbH   (1)
Brunnenstr 75 - 77, 73333, Berlin, Germany
Tel.: (49) 716240990
Construction Materials Mfr
N.A.I.C.S.: 325520
Markus Floruss (Asst Mgr-Company)

BOSIG Inc.   (1)
2125 Center Ave Ste 507, Fort Lee, NJ 07024
Tel.: (201) 302-6081
Construction Materials Whslr
N.A.I.C.S.: 423320

BOSIG Polska Sp. z o.o.   (1)
Ul Narutowicza 100A/19, 88-100, Inowroclaw, Poland
Tel.: (48) 523522523
Construction Material Mfr & Distr
N.A.I.C.S.: 325520

BOSKA RK A.D.
Trg Krajine 2, 78000, Banja Luka, Bosnia & Herzegovina
Tel.: (387) 51490320
Web Site: https://boska.ba
Year Founded: 1978
BOSK—(BANJ)
Sales Range: $1-9.9 Million
Emp.: 9
Grocery Store Operator
N.A.I.C.S.: 445110

BOSNA REOSIGURANJE D.D.
Zmaja od Bosne 74, 71000, Sarajevo, Bosnia & Herzegovina
Tel.: (387) 33 725 500
Web Site: http://www.bosnare.ba
Year Founded: 1978
BSRSRK2—(SARE)
Rev.: $37,981,402
Assets: $99,641,725
Liabilities: $79,828,899
Net Worth: $19,812,826
Earnings: $1,399,625
Emp.: 25
Fiscal Year-end: 12/31/20
Insurance Services
N.A.I.C.S.: 524298
Midhad Salcin (Chm-Supervisory Bd)

BOSNA TRGOVINA A.D.
Kralja Petra I Karadordevica 97, 78000, Banja Luka, Bosnia & Herzegovina
Tel.: (387) 51219576
BSNT—(BANJ)
Sales Range: Less than $1 Million
Footwear Whslr
N.A.I.C.S.: 424340
Brane Jankovic (Member-Mgmt Bd)

BOSNALIJEK D.D.
Jukiceva 53, 71000, Sarajevo, Bosnia & Herzegovina
Tel.: (387) 3 325 4400
Web Site: http://www.bosnalijek.com
Year Founded: 1951
BSNLR—(SARE)
Rev.: $87,361,815
Assets: $213,705,523
Liabilities: $94,500,833
Net Worth: $119,204,690
Earnings: $5,602,100
Emp.: 673
Fiscal Year-end: 12/31/20
Drug Mfr
N.A.I.C.S.: 325412
Nedim Uzunovic (Mgr)

BOSNAMONTAZA A.D.
Rudnicka bb, 79101, Prijedor, Bosnia & Herzegovina
Tel.: (387) 52234266
Web Site:
https://www.bosnamontaza.com
Year Founded: 1961
BMNT—(BANJ)
Sales Range: $1-9.9 Million
Emp.: 105
Structural Metal Product Mfr
N.A.I.C.S.: 332312
Sanja Tubin (Member-Mgmt Bd)

BOSNAPLAST D.O.O.

Ulica 5 Korpusa br 2, Bosanski Petro-vac, 77 250, Unsko-sanski kanton, Bosnia & Herzegovina
Tel.: (387) 37 881 039
Web Site: http://www.bosnaplast.net
Year Founded: 1960
Rev.: $2,492,292
Assets: $7,490,983
Liabilities: $3,802,298
Net Worth: $3,688,685
Earnings: $80,833
Emp.: 28
Fiscal Year-end: 12/31/17
Plastic Packaging Products Mfr
N.A.I.C.S.: 326199
Nihad Susnjar *(Mgr)*

BOSS DESIGN LTD.
Boss Drive, Dudley, DY2 8SZ, West Midlands, United Kingdom
Tel.: (44) 1384 455570
Web Site:
    http://www.bossdesign.com
Year Founded: 1983
Furniture Mfr
N.A.I.C.S.: 337214
Brian Murray *(Founder & Chm)*

Subsidiaries:

Jack Cartwright, Inc.   (1)
2014 Chestnut St, High Point, NC 27262
Tel.: (336) 889-9400
Web Site: http://www.jackcartwright.com
Sales Range: $10-24.9 Million
Emp.: 200
Upholstered Seating Mfr
N.A.I.C.S.: 337121

BOSS ENERGY LIMITED
Level 1 420 Hay Street, 234 Churchill Avenue, Subiaco, 6008, WA, Austra-lia
Tel.: (61) 862634494   **WA**
Web Site: https://bossenergy.com
Year Founded: 2005
BQSSF—(OTCQX)
Rev.: $188,327
Assets: $190,151,884
Liabilities: $8,896,669
Net Worth: $181,255,215
Earnings: $23,895,162
Fiscal Year-end: 06/30/22
Oil & Minerals Exploration Services
N.A.I.C.S.: 211120
Duncan Craib *(CEO & Mng Dir)*

BOSSA TICARET VE SANAYI ISLETMELERI TAS
Haci Sabanci Organize Sanayi Bolgesi Acidere OSB Mah, Celal Ba-yar Bul No 3 Saricam, Adana, Turkiye
Tel.: (90) 3223552000
Web Site: https://www.bossa.com.tr
Year Founded: 1951
BOSSA—(IST)
Rev.: $41,706,439
Assets: $56,938,871
Liabilities: $35,992,226
Net Worth: $20,946,646
Earnings: $10,104,810
Emp.: 1,351
Fiscal Year-end: 12/31/21
Textile & Fabric Mfr
N.A.I.C.S.: 313310
Israfil Ucurum *(Chm)*

BOSSARD HOLDING AG
Steinhauserstrasse 70, CH-6301, Zug, Switzerland
Tel.: (41) 417496611   **CH**
Web Site: https://www.bossard.com
Year Founded: 1831
BOSN—(SWX)
Rev.: $1,279,202,882
Assets: $1,008,967,849
Liabilities: $588,099,778
Net Worth: $420,868,071

Earnings: $117,054,324
Emp.: 2,604
Fiscal Year-end: 12/31/22
Holding Company; Engineering & Lo-gistic Services
N.A.I.C.S.: 551112
Thomas Schmuckli-Grob *(Chm)*

Subsidiaries:

Aero-Space Southwest Inc.   (1)
909 W Pinnacle Peak Rd Bldg A Ste 101, Phoenix, AZ 85027
Tel.: (623) 582-2779
Web Site: http://www.aerospacesw.com
Emp.: 40
Fasteners & Electronic Components Distr
N.A.I.C.S.: 423710

Bossard (Korea) Ltd.   (1)
428 Yeongok-gil, Seobuk-gu, Cheonan, Chungnam, Korea (South)
Tel.: (82) 415807000
Web Site: https://www.bossard.com
Engineering & Logistic Services
N.A.I.C.S.: 541614

Bossard Aerospace Germany GmbH   (1)
Kapellenstr 9, 85622, Feldkirchen, Germany
Tel.: (49) 894274210
Aerospace Component Mfr & Distr
N.A.I.C.S.: 334511

Bossard Aerospace Switzerland AG   (1)
Steinhauserstrasse 70, CH-6301, Zug, Swit-zerland
Tel.: (41) 417496416
Fastener Distr
N.A.I.C.S.: 423710

Bossard Aerospace, Inc.   (1)
909 W Pinnacle Peak Rd, Phoenix, AZ 85027
Tel.: (623) 582-2779
Fastener Product Distr
N.A.I.C.S.: 423710

Bossard Australia Pty Ltd   (1)
Unit 1 40-42 William Angliss Drive, Laverton North, Melbourne, 3026, VIC, Australia
Tel.: (61) 393609698
Web Site: https://www.bossard.com
Fastening & Connecting Components Distr
N.A.I.C.S.: 423990

Bossard CZ s.r.o.   (1)
Turanka 1519/115a, 627 00, Brno, Czech Republic
Tel.: (420) 547131300
Web Site: https://www.bossard.com
Engineering & Logistic Services
N.A.I.C.S.: 541614

Bossard Canada Inc.   (1)
418 Isabey, Saint Laurent, H4T 1V3, QC, Canada
Tel.: (514) 731-0817
Engineering & Logistic Services
N.A.I.C.S.: 541614

Bossard Denmark A/S   (1)
Stamholmen 150, DK-2650, Hvidovre, Den-mark
Tel.: (45) 44508888
Web Site: https://www.bossard.com
Engineering & Logistic Services
N.A.I.C.S.: 541614

Bossard Deutschland GmbH   (1)
Max-Eyth-Strasse 14, D-89186, Illerrieden, Germany
Tel.: (49) 7306782400
Web Site: https://www.bossard.com
Engineering & Logistic Services
N.A.I.C.S.: 541614

Bossard France SAS   (1)
14 rue des Tuileries, BP 84623, Suffleswey-ersheim, 67457, Mundolsheim, Cedex, France
Tel.: (33) 388207700
Web Site: https://www.bossard.com
Engineering & Logistic Services
N.A.I.C.S.: 541614

Bossard Italia S.r.l.   (1)
Via Salvatore Quasimodo 12/14, 20025, Legnano, MI, Italy

Tel.: (39) 033193701
Web Site: https://www.bossard.com
Hardware Mfr
N.A.I.C.S.: 332510

Bossard Ltd.   (1)
Tel.: (886) 424227701
Web Site: https://www.bossard.com
Engineering & Logistic Services
N.A.I.C.S.: 541614

Bossard M Sdn. Bhd.   (1)
PMT 1136 Lorong Perindustrian Bukit Min-yak 20, Taman Perindustrian Bukit Minyak, 14100, Simpang Empat, Pulau Pinang, Ma-laysia
Tel.: (60) 45042288
Web Site: https://www.bossard.com
Engineering & Logistic Services
N.A.I.C.S.: 541614

Bossard Nederland B.V.   (1)
Platinaweg 4, 1362 JL, Almere, Netherlands
Tel.: (31) 363032000
Aerospace Component Mfr & Distr
N.A.I.C.S.: 334511

Bossard North America, Inc.   (1)
6521 Production Dr, Cedar Falls, IA 50613
Tel.: (319) 277-5520
Web Site: http://www.bossard.com
Industrial Fasteners, Nuts, Bolts & Screws Distr
N.A.I.C.S.: 423840
Steen Hansen *(CEO)*

Branch (Domestic):

Bossard North America, Inc. - Milwaukee   (2)
3801 W Green Tree Rd, Milwaukee, WI 53209
Tel.: (414) 247-1100
Web Site: http://www.bossard.com
Rev.: $11,700,000
Emp.: 66
Industrial Fasteners, Nuts, Bolts & Screws Distr
N.A.I.C.S.: 423840

Bossard Norway AS   (1)
Borggaten 1, Oslo, Norway
Tel.: (47) 22681530
Fastener Distr
N.A.I.C.S.: 423710

Bossard Ontario Inc.   (1)
590 Basaltic Rd, Vaughan, L4K 5A2, ON, Canada
Fastener Distr
N.A.I.C.S.: 423710

Bossard Poland Sp. z o.o.   (1)
ul Warszawska 181, PL-26-600, Radom, Poland
Tel.: (48) 483441647
Web Site: https://www.bossard.com
Engineering & Logistic Services
N.A.I.C.S.: 541614

Bossard South Africa (Pty) Ltd.   (1)
Tel.: (27) 104923993
Web Site: https://www.bossard.com
Engineering & Logistic Services
N.A.I.C.S.: 541614

Bossard Spain SA   (1)
SC Trade Center Av de les Corts Cata-lanes, 08173, Sant Cugat del Valles, Spain
Tel.: (34) 935612890
Web Site: https://www.bossard.com
Engineering & Logistic Services
N.A.I.C.S.: 541614

Bossard Sweden AB   (1)
Tel.: (46) 40165960
Web Site: https://www.bossard.com
Engineering & Logistic Services
N.A.I.C.S.: 541614

Bossard Thailand Ltd.   (1)
103 Motorway Road Khlong Song Ton Nun, Lat Krabang, Bangkok, 10520, Thailand
Tel.: (66) 21191314
Web Site: https://www.bossard.com
Engineering & Logistic Services
N.A.I.C.S.: 541614

Bossard, Inc.   (1)
6521 Production Dr, Cedar Falls, IA 50613
Tel.: (319) 277-5520
Web Site: http://americas.bossard.com

Engineering & Logistics Services
N.A.I.C.S.: 541330

Boysen Aerospace U.S., Inc.   (1)
3050 W Story Rd, Irving, TX 75038
Tel.: (469) 629-0660
Fastener Product Distr
N.A.I.C.S.: 423710

Boysen GmbH   (1)
Stahlgruberring 49, 81829, Munich, Ger-many
Tel.: (49) 894274210
Web Site: https://www.boysen.aero
Fastener Distr
N.A.I.C.S.: 423710

Effilio AG   (1)
Steinhauserstrasse 70, 6301, Zug, Switzer-land
Tel.: (41) 417496368
Web Site: http://www.effilio.com
Inventory Management Services
N.A.I.C.S.: 561990

Interfast AG   (1)
Steinhauserstrasse 70, 6301, Zug, Switzer-land
Tel.: (41) 417496416
Web Site: https://www.interfast.ch
Emp.: 2,000
Aeronautic Product Distr
N.A.I.C.S.: 423860
Ronny Schreiter *(Gen Sls Mgr)*

Jeveka B.V.   (1)
Platinaweg 4, 1362 JL, Almere, Netherlands
Tel.: (31) 363032000
Web Site: https://jeveka.com
Fastener Distr
N.A.I.C.S.: 423710

KVT Fastening GmbH   (1)
Max-Eyth-Str 14, 89186, Illerrieden, Ger-many
Tel.: (49) 73067820
Web Site: http://www.kvt-fastening.de
Aeronautic Product Distr
N.A.I.C.S.: 423860
Frank Hilgers *(CEO)*

KVT Fastening Sp z o.o.   (1)
ul Warszawska 181, 26-600, Radom, Po-land
Tel.: (48) 587621780
Web Site: https://www.kvt-fastening.pl
Aeronautic Product Distr
N.A.I.C.S.: 423860

KVT-Fastening AG   (1)
Lagerstrasse 8, 8953, Dietikon, Switzerland
Tel.: (41) 44 743 33 33
Web Site: https://www.kvt-fastening.ch
Sales Range: $125-149.9 Million
Emp.: 230
Fastening Equipment Mfr
N.A.I.C.S.: 332999

KVT-Fastening S.R.L.   (1)
St Cobalcescu 46 Sector1, 10196, Bucha-rest, Romania
Tel.: (40) 371381155
Web Site: https://www.kvt-fastening.ro
Aeronautic Product Distr
N.A.I.C.S.: 423860

KVT-Fastening spol. s.r.o.   (1)
Pribinova 25/4195, 811 09, Bratislava, Slo-vakia
Tel.: (421) 911102510
Web Site: https://www.kvt-fastening.sk
Aeronautic Product Distr
N.A.I.C.S.: 423860

KVT-Fastening, Zweigniederlassung der Bossard AG
Lagerstrasse 8, 8953, Dietikon, Switzerland
Tel.: (41) 447433333
Web Site: https://www.kvt-fastening.com
Fastener Mfr & Distr
N.A.I.C.S.: 339993

KVT-Tehnika pritrjevanja, d.o.o.   (1)
Parmova Ulica 53, 10000, Ljubljana, Slove-nia
Tel.: (386) 12808019
Web Site: https://www.kvt-fastening.si
Self Clinching Fasteners Distr
N.A.I.C.S.: 423710

LPS Bossard Pvt. Ltd.   (1)

Bossard Holding AG—(Continued)

A-1/134 Safdarjung Enclave, New Delhi, 110029, India
Tel.: (91) 1126180086
Engineering & Logistic Services
N.A.I.C.S.: 541614

Switzerland Bossard AG **(1)**
Steinhauserstrasse 70, 6301, Zug, Switzerland
Tel.: (41) 417496611
Engineering & Logistic Services
N.A.I.C.S.: 541614

BOSSDOM DIGIINNOVATION CO., LTD.

5F No 32 Alley 18 Lane 478 Ruiguang Rd, Neihu Dist, Taipei, 11492, Taiwan
Tel.: (886) 287976799
Web Site: https://www.bossdom.com
Year Founded: 2014
6622—(TAI)
Film Production Services
N.A.I.C.S.: 512110
Cheng Hung Chang *(Chm & CEO)*

BOSTON INTERNATIONAL HOLDINGS PLC

5 Chancery Lane, London, WC2A 1LG, Surrey, United Kingdom
Tel.: (44) 7379668907   UK
Web Site: https://www.bihplc.com
Year Founded: 2015
BIH—(LSE)
Sales Range: Less than $1 Million
Financial Management Services
N.A.I.C.S.: 551112
Thomas R. DiBenedetto *(Pres)*

BOSTON LEASING & FINANCE LTD.

E-803 Titanium City Centre Near Sachin Tower Anand Nagar Road, Tower Anand Nagar Road, Ahmedabad, 80015, India
Tel.: (91) 9173178196
Web Site:
  http://www.bostonleasing.com
539274—(BOM)
Rev.: $16,482
Assets: $1,074,399
Liabilities: $95,835
Net Worth: $978,564
Earnings: $4,686
Fiscal Year-end: 03/31/20
Financial Support Services
N.A.I.C.S.: 523999
Shah Ami Namankumar *(Exec Dir)*

BOSTON PIZZA INTERNATIONAL, INC.

Unit 100 10760 Shellbridge Way, Richmond, V6X 3H1, BC, Canada
Tel.: (604) 270-1108
Web Site:
  http://www.bostonpizza.com
Sales Range: $10-24.9 Million
Emp.: 100
Pizza Restaurant Franchisor
N.A.I.C.S.: 445298
Jordan Holm *(Pres)*

BOSTON PIZZA ROYALTIES INCOME FUND

201 - 13571 Commerce Parkway, Richmond, V6V 2R2, BC, Canada
Tel.: (604) 270-1108   AB
Web Site:
  https://www.bpincomefund.com
Year Founded: 1964
BPF.UN—(TSX)
Rev.: $25,535,184
Assets: $305,718,153
Liabilities: $104,750,421
Net Worth: $200,967,732
Earnings: $7,486,420

Fiscal Year-end: 12/31/20
Investment Management Service
N.A.I.C.S.: 525990
Jordan Holm *(Pres)*

BOSTON TEKNOWSYS (INDIA) LIMITED

45 M 701 H M Tambourine Jargan Hall 6th Phase J P Nagar, Opp Metro Pillar No 82, Bengaluru, Karnataka, India
Tel.: (91) 8125191837
Web Site: http://www.btil.co.in
Textile Product Mfr & Distr
N.A.I.C.S.: 315210

BOSTONAIR LTD

1 Wood Lane Mews, Beverley, HU17 8DA, E Yorkshire, United Kingdom
Tel.: (44) 1482 679757
Web Site: http://www.bostonair.co.uk
Year Founded: 1997
Sales Range: $25-49.9 Million
Emp.: 200
Aviation Industry Recruitment Services
N.A.I.C.S.: 561311

BOSUN CO LTD

Nr 403 Yuhua East Road National High-Tech Industry Development Zone, Shijiazhuang, 050035, Hebei, China
Tel.: (86) 1185960663
Web Site:
  https://www.bosuntools.com
Year Founded: 1994
002282—(SSE)
Rev.: $204,126,156
Assets: $543,425,220
Liabilities: $54,220,500
Net Worth: $489,195,720
Earnings: $19,821,672
Emp.: 1,860
Fiscal Year-end: 12/31/22
Diamond & Small Machine Tools Mfr
N.A.I.C.S.: 333517
Chen Huairong *(Chm)*

Subsidiaries:

Bosun Tools Inc. **(1)**
425 S Turnbull Canyon Rd, City of Industry, CA 91745-1035
Tel.: (626) 968-6300
Saw Blade & Hand Tool Mfr
N.A.I.C.S.: 423710
Tony Chend *(Owner)*

BOSUNG POWER TECHNOLOGY CO., LTD.

70 Daechang-gil, Judeok-eup, Chungju, 27463, Chungcheongbuk-do, Korea (South)
Tel.: (82) 438570311
Web Site:
  https://www.bosungpower.co.kr
Year Founded: 2000
006910—(KRS)
Rev.: $41,570,424
Assets: $65,547,388
Liabilities: $3,590,491
Net Worth: $61,956,897
Earnings: ($8,524,713)
Emp.: 145
Fiscal Year-end: 12/31/22
Electrical Equipment Mfr & Distr
N.A.I.C.S.: 335311
Lim Jae-Hwang *(Dir-Rep)*

BOTA BIO CO., LTD.

641 5th floor Watergate building, Gangnam-Gu, Seoul, Korea (South)
Tel.: (82) 5466200
Web Site: http://www.idn.co.kr
026260—(KRS)
Sales Range: $10-24.9 Million
Data Processing Services

N.A.I.C.S.: 518210

BOTAI TECHNOLOGY LIMITED

Level 14 565 Bourke St, Melbourne, 3000, VIC, Australia
Tel.: (61) 75521507099   AU
Web Site: http://www.wonhe.com.au
Year Founded: 2015
Rev.: $00,447,390
Assets: $62,180,077
Liabilities: $12,429,303
Net Worth: $49,750,774
Earnings: $4,598,647
Fiscal Year-end: 12/31/17
Router Mfr & Distr
N.A.I.C.S.: 334210
Daney Xu *(Sec)*

BOTALA ENERGY LIMITED

Unit 22 22 Mounts Bay Road, Crawley, 6009, WA, Australia
Tel.: (61) 31527885   AU
Web Site:
  https://www.botalaenergy.com
Year Founded: 2018
BTE—(ASX)
Rev.: $121
Assets: $10,153,984
Liabilities: $608,832
Net Worth: $9,545,152
Earnings: ($715,766)
Fiscal Year-end: 06/30/23
Natural Gas Exploration Service
N.A.I.C.S.: 211130
Craig Basson *(CFO)*

BOTANIX PHARMACEUTICALS LIMITED

Suite 3 41 47 Colin Street, West Perth, 6005, WA, Australia
Tel.: (61) 862850083
Web Site:
  https://www.botanixpharma.com
Year Founded: 2002
BOT—(ASX)
Rev.: $1,030,574
Assets: $75,096,572
Liabilities: $2,492,039
Net Worth: $72,604,533
Earnings: ($9,261,291)
Fiscal Year-end: 06/30/24
Skin Treatment Biopharmaceutical Research & Mfr
N.A.I.C.S.: 325414
William Bosch *(Chief Scientific Officer)*

BOTHRA METALS & ALLOYS LTD

Room Number 15 Bothra House 5 AssemblyLane, Dadi Seth Agyari Lane Kalbadevi, Mumbai, 400002, Maharashtra, India
Tel.: (91) 2249785309
Web Site:
  https://www.bothrametals.com
535279—(BOM)
Rev.: $3,676,854
Assets: $4,818,680
Liabilities: $2,790,720
Net Worth: $2,027,960
Earnings: ($135,831)
Fiscal Year-end: 03/31/23
Metals & Alloys Mfr
N.A.I.C.S.: 332999
Sunderlal Likhmichand Bothra *(Mng Dir)*

BOTNIA EXPLORATION HOLDINGS AB

Cylindervagen 18 8tr, PO Box 1113, 131 26, Nacka, Sweden
Tel.: (46) 708550150
Web Site:
  https://www.botniaexploration.com
Year Founded: 2007

Mineral Exploration Services
N.A.I.C.S.: 213114
Lars Engstrom *(Chm)*

BOTSWANA DEVELOPMENT CORPORATION LIMITED

Fairscape Precinct Plot 70667 Fairgrounds, Private Bag 160, Gaborone, Botswana
Tel.: (267) 3651300   BW
Web Site: http://www.bdc.bw
Year Founded: 1970
Rev.: $15,561,841
Assets: $447,707,253
Liabilities: $175,570,931
Net Worth: $272,136,322
Earnings: $4,729,455
Fiscal Year-end: 06/30/19
Commercial & Industrial Development
N.A.I.C.S.: 925120
Blackie Marole *(Co-Chm)*

Subsidiaries:

Cresta Marakanelo (Pvt) Ltd **(1)**
Plot 50676 Fairground Office Park Phase 2 Block D Unit 2, Private Bag 00272, Gaborone, 00272, Botswana
Tel.: (267) 3912222
Web Site: http://www.crestamarakanelo.com
Emp.: 20
Hotel Owner & Operator
N.A.I.C.S.: 721110
Segomotso Banda *(Mgr-HR)*

Export Credit Insurance & Guarantee (Pty) Ltd **(1)**
Bag BO279, Gaborone, Botswana
Tel.: (267) 3188 015
Web Site: http://www.beci.co.bw
Emp.: 30
Commercial & Industrial Development Services
N.A.I.C.S.: 925120
Bonani Dube *(Mgr-Mktg)*

Fairground Holdings (Pty) Ltd **(1)**
Plot 50660, Gaborone, Botswana
Tel.: (267) 3975555
Web Site:
  http://www.fairgroundholdings.com
Event Hall Rental Services
N.A.I.C.S.: 531120
Thabo Mogomotsi *(Mgr-Sls & Mktg)*

Kwena Concrete Products (Pty) Ltd **(1)**
Plot 14404 Maakgadigau Road Gaborone West Industrial, PO Box 1029, Gaborone, Botswana
Tel.: (267) 3922850
Web Site: http://www.kwena.co.bw
Concrete Product Mfr & Distr
N.A.I.C.S.: 327331
Tutu Lenong *(Head-Sls & Mktg)*

Lobatse Clay Works (Pty) Ltd **(1)**
Woodhall Industrial Estates, Private Bag 5, Lobatse, Botswana
Tel.: (267) 5332447
Web Site: http://www.lcw.co.bw
Building Products Mfr & Distr
N.A.I.C.S.: 327331
Buzwani Manyepedza *(Gen Mgr)*

BOTSWANA DIAMONDS PLC

162 Clontarf Road, Dublin, Ireland
Tel.: (353) 18332833
Web Site:
  https://www.botswanadiamonds.com
BOD—(AIM)
Rev.: $19,226
Assets: $7,908,136
Liabilities: $983,012
Net Worth: $6,925,124
Earnings: ($4,647,174)
Emp.: 1
Fiscal Year-end: 06/30/23
Diamond Exploration Services
N.A.I.C.S.: 212311
John J. Teeling *(Chm)*

BOTSWANA STOCK EXCHANGE

Off Block 6 plot 64511 Fairgrounds, Private Bag 00417, Gaborone, Botswana
Tel.: (267) 3180201
Web Site: http://www.bse.co.bw
Sales Range: $25-49.9 Million
Emp.: 15
Stock Exchange Services
N.A.I.C.S.: 523210
Thapelo Tsheole *(CEO)*

BOTTLERS NEPAL LIMITED
Balaju Industrial District Balaju, PO Box 2253, Kathmandu, Nepal
Tel.: (977) 14352986
Web Site: https://www.bnl.com.np
Year Founded: 1979
BNL—(NEP)
Rev.: $25,335,757
Assets: $30,017,185
Liabilities: $15,171,312
Net Worth: $14,845,872
Earnings: $1,479,059
Emp.: 604
Fiscal Year-end: 07/16/22
Soft Drink Mfr & Distr
N.A.I.C.S.: 312111

Subsidiaries:

Bottlers Nepal (Terai) Limited   (1)
Gondrang, PO Box 20, Chitwan, Bharatpur, Nepal
Tel.: (977) 56420216
Soft Drink Mfr & Distr
N.A.I.C.S.: 312111

BOU KHALIL SOCIETE MODERNE SARL
Faubourg St Jean, BP 40020, Bifurc Palais Presidentiel, Baabda, Lebanon
Tel.: (961) 5454880   LB
Web Site: http://www.boukhalil.com
Year Founded: 1935
Sales Range: $75-99.9 Million
Emp.: 450
Supermarkets & Pharmacies
N.A.I.C.S.: 445110

BOUBYAN PETROCHEMICAL CO. KSC
AlSharqKhalid bin AlWaleed St KIPCO Tower 33rd Floor Office No 2, PO Box 2383, Safat, 13024, Kuwait, 13024, Kuwait
Tel.: (965) 22020111
Web Site: https://www.boubyan.com
BPCC—(KUW)
Rev.: $257,182,508
Assets: $1,946,072,898
Liabilities: $923,738,344
Net Worth: $1,022,334,554
Earnings: $136,822,929
Emp.: 20
Fiscal Year-end: 04/30/23
Petrochemical Mfr
N.A.I.C.S.: 325110
Khalid Ali Al-Ghanim *(Vice Chm)*

Subsidiaries:

Educational Holding Group K.S.C.P.   (1)
Abraj complex tower B 8th Floor Al-Othman St Hawally, PO Box 27215, Safat, Kuwait, 13133, Kuwait   **(89.1%)**
Tel.: (965) 22286770
Web Site: http://www.edu.com.kw
Rev.: $11,281,031
Assets: $128,210,611
Liabilities: $15,082,541
Net Worth: $113,128,071
Earnings: $21,782,813
Fiscal Year-end: 08/31/2020
Educational & Training Services
N.A.I.C.S.: 611710
Anas Abdulrahman Eissa Al Asousi *(Chm)*

Subsidiary (Domestic):

AFAQ Educational Services Company   (2)

Othman Street Hawally Area Abraj Complex Building 7, PO Box 27215, Kuwait, Kuwait   **(86.9%)**
Tel.: (965) 2620739
Web Site: http://www.afaq.com.kw
Educational Support Services
N.A.I.C.S.: 611710

Jubail Integrated Packaging Company Limited LLC   (1)
7846 Rd 251 Industrial Area, Jubail, 35726, Saudi Arabia
Tel.: (966) 133583272
Web Site: https://www.jubailpack.com
Stretch Films Mfr
N.A.I.C.S.: 326112

Muna Noor Manufacturing and Trading Co. L.L.C   (1)
Road 4D, Rusayl Industrial Estate, Rusayl, 114, Oman
Tel.: (968) 24442500
Web Site: http://www.munanoor.com
Petrochemical Mfr
N.A.I.C.S.: 325110

Warba Capital Holding Company K.S.C.P.   (1)
Al Sharq Khalid Bin Al-Waleed St Al-Dhow Tower Floor 28, PO Box 2383, Safat, Kuwait, 13024, Kuwait
Tel.: (965) 22064610
Web Site: https://warbacap.com
Financial Investment Services
N.A.I.C.S.: 523999

BOUCHER AND JONES FUELS
155 Roger St, Waterloo, N2J 1B1, ON, Canada
Tel.: (519) 743-3669
Web Site: http://www.boucherandjones.com
Year Founded: 1960
Rev.: $10,868,119
Emp.: 30
Fuels Whslr
N.A.I.C.S.: 424720
Kevin Jones *(Partner)*

BOUCLAIR INC.
152 Alston Avenue, Pointe-Claire, H9R 6B4, QC, Canada
Tel.: (514) 426-0115
Web Site: http://www.bouclair.com
Year Founded: 1970
Rev.: $62,000,000
Emp.: 1
Home Decorating Stores
N.A.I.C.S.: 449129
Adam Goldberg *(Pres)*

BOULD OPPORTUNITIES PLC
80 Cheapside, London, EC2V 6EE, United Kingdom
Tel.: (44) 2074690930
Web Site: http://www.bouldopportunities.com
Year Founded: 2001
Rev.: $57,106
Assets: $121,826
Liabilities: $420,046
Net Worth: ($298,220)
Earnings: ($2,610,374)
Emp.: 6
Fiscal Year-end: 12/31/18
Light Emitting Array Mfr
N.A.I.C.S.: 335132
Allan Syms *(Chm)*

Subsidiaries:

Enfis Lighting   (1)
90 Washington Valley Rd, Bedminster, NJ 07921
Tel.: (908) 719-8920
LED Design & Mfr
N.A.I.C.S.: 334413

Enfis Limited   (1)
Technium 2 Kings Rd Swansea Waterfront, Swansea, SA1 8PJ, United Kingdom
Tel.: (44) 1792485660
Web Site: http://www.enfis.com

Sales Range: $25-49.9 Million
Emp.: 18
LED Design & Mfr
N.A.I.C.S.: 334413

Enfis Ltd.   (1)
2045 20 F The Ctr 989 ChangLe Rd, Shanghai, China
Tel.: (86) 2151175422
Web Site: http://www.enfis.com
LED Design & Mfr
N.A.I.C.S.: 334413

BOULE DIAGNOSTICS AB
Domnarvsgatan 4, SE-163 53, Spanga, Sweden
Tel.: (46) 87447700
Web Site: https://www.boule.se
Year Founded: 1956
BOUL—(OMX)
Rev.: $51,334,869
Assets: $71,179,672
Liabilities: $27,860,669
Net Worth: $43,319,003
Earnings: $1,192,129
Emp.: 235
Fiscal Year-end: 12/31/22
Hematology Diagnostic Systems Mfr; Hematology Reagents & Consumables
N.A.I.C.S.: 339112
Michael Eliott *(Sr VP-R&D-OEM-CDS)*

Subsidiaries:

Boule Medical (Beijing) Co. Ltd   (1)
Development Zone, Shunyi District, 101 300, Beijing, China
Tel.: (86) 10 8945 1945
Electromedical Apparatus Mfr
N.A.I.C.S.: 334510

Boule Medical AB   (1)
Domnarvsgatan 4, 163 53, Spanga, Sweden
Tel.: (46) 8 744 77 00
Web Site: http://www.boule.com
Emp.: 100
Electromedical Apparatus Mfr
N.A.I.C.S.: 334510

Boule Medical LLC   (1)
Technopark Novoselki 13/2-4, Moscow Reg, Podolsk, 142153, Russia
Tel.: (7) 4957400671
Medical Diagnostic Equipment Mfr & Distr
N.A.I.C.S.: 339112

Clinical Diagnostics Solutions Inc.   (1)
1800 NW 65th Ave, Plantation, FL 33313
Tel.: (954) 791-1773
Web Site: https://cdsolinc.com
Chemical Products Mfr
N.A.I.C.S.: 325998

BOULEVARD HOLDINGS, INC.
1704 The Peak Tower 107 L P Leviste St, Salcedo Village, Makati, 1227, Philippines
Tel.: (63) 277531405
Web Site: https://www.boulevardholdings.com
Year Founded: 1994
BHI—(PHI)
Rev.: $1,569,776
Assets: $41,732,380
Liabilities: $7,232,195
Net Worth: $34,500,185
Earnings: ($1,506,498)
Emp.: 85
Fiscal Year-end: 05/31/20
Home Management Services
N.A.I.C.S.: 721110
Victor V. Benavidez *(Treas)*

Subsidiaries:

Fridays Holdings, Inc.   (1)
Station 1 Boracay Island, Malay, 5608, Aklan, Philippines
Tel.: (63) 362886204
Web Site: http://www.fridaysboracay.com

Sales Range: $25-49.9 Million
Emp.: 124
Resort Management Services
N.A.I.C.S.: 721110

BOUNDARY BEND LIMITED
151 Broderick Road, PO Box 92, Lara, 3212, VIC, Australia
Tel.: (61) 3 5272 9500
Web Site: http://www.boundarybend.com
Rev.: $106,706,603
Assets: $283,080,508
Liabilities: $156,666,164
Net Worth: $126,414,343
Earnings: $6,159,504
Emp.: 100
Fiscal Year-end: 06/30/19
Olive Oil Producer
N.A.I.C.S.: 111339
Robert D. McGavin *(Chm & CEO)*

Subsidiaries:

Cobram Estate Pty Ltd   (1)
Unit 14 75 Lorimer Street, Southbank, 3006, VIC, Australia
Tel.: (61) 3 9646 6081
Web Site: http://www.cobramestate.com.au
Olive Oil Mfr & Distr
N.A.I.C.S.: 311225

BOUNDARY GOLD AND COPPER MINING LTD.
250-1199 West Hastings St, Vancouver, V6E 3T5, BC, Canada
Tel.: (604) 336-1327   AB
Web Site: http://www.prizemining.com
Year Founded: 1996
PRZFF—(OTCIQ)
Assets: $716,497
Liabilities: $706,188
Net Worth: $10,310
Earnings: ($532,090)
Fiscal Year-end: 08/31/22
Gold Exploration & Mining Services
N.A.I.C.S.: 212220
Yuying Liang *(CFO)*

BOUNTY BRANDS PTY LTD.
1st Floor The Crossing Office Park 372 Main Road, Bryanston, Johannesburg, 2192, South Africa
Tel.: (27) 104429057
Web Site: http://www.bb.co.za
Brand Building Services
N.A.I.C.S.: 541611
Peter Spinks *(CFO)*

Subsidiaries:

Goldenmarc (Pty) Ltd.   (1)
Stand No 13 & 14 Angus Crescent, Longmeadow East, Edenvale, 1644, South Africa
Tel.: (27) 118423800
Sales Range: $50-74.9 Million
Emp.: 90
Home Textiles & Party Products Distr
N.A.I.C.S.: 423220

BOUNTY OIL & GAS NL
Level 7 283 George Street, Sydney, 2000, NSW, Australia
Tel.: (61) 292997200   AU
Web Site: https://www.bountyoil.com
Year Founded: 1999
BYOGF—(OTCIQ)
Rev.: $1,455,432
Assets: $9,071,007
Liabilities: $2,528,373
Net Worth: $6,542,634
Earnings: ($1,902,261)
Emp.: 2
Fiscal Year-end: 06/30/22
Crude Petroleum & Natural Gas Production, Exploration & Development
N.A.I.C.S.: 211120
Graham Charles Reveleigh *(Chm)*

Bounty Oil & Gas NL—(Continued)

BOUNTY UK LTD.
29 Broadwater Rd, Welwyn Garden
City, AL7 3BQ, Hertfordshire, United
Kingdom
Tel.: (44) 1707294000
Web Site:
http://www.bountybusiness.co.uk
Sales Range: $50-74.9 Million
Emp.: 500
N.A.I.C.S.: 541890
Zoe Tibell (Dir-Fin & Ops)

BOURBON
Avenida Paulista 287, 01311-000,
Sao Paulo, Brazil
Tel.: (55) 140138616
Web Site: http://bourbon-online.com
Sales Range: $1-4.9 Billion
Emp.: 3,000
N.A.I.C.S.: 213112
Jacques d'Armand de Chateauvieux
(Chm)

BOURBON CORPORATION
1-3-1 Ekimae, Kashiwazaki, 945-
8611, Niigata, Japan
Tel.: (81) 120285605
Web Site: https://www.bourbon.co.jp
Year Founded: 1924
2208—(TKS)
Rev.: $685,569,370
Assets: $622,880,130
Liabilities: $249,851,390
Net Worth: $373,028,740
Earnings: $20,299,310
Emp.: 5,000
Fiscal Year-end: 03/31/24
Food Product Mfr & Distr
N.A.I.C.S.: 311821
Yasushi Yoshida (Pres)

Subsidiaries:

Bourbon Foods USA Corporation (1)
1730 Rhode Island Ave NW Ste 806, Wash-
ington, DC 20036
Tel.: (202) 266-2426
Web Site:
https://www.bourbonfoodsusa.com
Food Products Distr
N.A.I.C.S.: 424420

**BOURSE DIRECT ET BOURSE
DISCOUNT SA**
374 rue Saint-Honore, 75001, Paris,
France
Tel.: (33) 156884040
Web Site: https://www.boursedirect.fr
BSD—(EUR)
Stock Broking Services
N.A.I.C.S.: 523150
Catherine Nini (CEO & Chm-Mgmt
Bd)

**BOURSE REGIONALE DES
VALEURS MOBILIERS**
18 Rue Joseph Anoma, 3802, Abi-
djan, Cote d'Ivoire
Tel.: (225) 20326685
Web Site: http://www.brvm.org
Year Founded: 1996
Stock Exchange Services
N.A.I.C.S.: 523210
Daouda Coulibaly (Co-Chm)

**BOUSSARD & GAVAUDAN
HOLDING LIMITED**
Dorey Court Ground Floor Admiral
Park, Saint Peter Port, GY1 2HT,
Guernsey
Tel.: (44) 2037515400   GY
Web Site:
https://www.bgholdingltd.com
Year Founded: 2006
BGHL—(LSE)
Rev.: $4,180,939

Assets: $380,110,325
Liabilities: $2,233,499
Net Worth: $377,876,825
Earnings: ($2,959,290)
Fiscal Year-end: 12/31/23
Investment Services
N.A.I.C.S.: 523999
Andrew Henton (Chm)

Subsidiaries:

Boussard & Gavaudan Asset Man-
agement, LP   (1)
9-10 Savile Row, London, W1S 3PF, United
Kingdom
Tel.: (44) 207 406 3250
Financial & Asset Management Services
N.A.I.C.S.: 523999

Boussard & Gavaudan Gestion
S.A.S.   (1)
69 Boulevard Haussmann, 75008, Paris,
France
Tel.: (33) 1 44 90 41 00
Emp.: 40
Holding Company
N.A.I.C.S.: 551112

**BOUSTEAD HEAVY INDUS-
TRIES CORPORATION BER-
HAD**
17th Floor Menara Boustead 69 Jalan
Raja Chulan, 50200, Kuala Lumpur,
Malaysia
Tel.: (60) 320787770
Web Site: https://www.bhic.com.my
BHIC—(KLS)
Rev.: $30,002,116
Assets: $102,622,434
Liabilities: $89,782,646
Net Worth: $12,839,788
Earnings: ($4,216,720)
Emp.: 982
Fiscal Year-end: 12/31/22
Engineeering Services
N.A.I.C.S.: 541330
Suzana Sanudin (Co-Sec)

Subsidiaries:

BHIC Bofors Asia Sdn. Bhd.   (1)
Suite 12A 03 Level 12A KH Tower 8 Jalan
P Ramlee, 50250, Kuala Lumpur, Malaysia
Tel.: (60) 320788663
Web Site: https://www.dotventures.com.my
Bofor Gun Parts Component Mfr
N.A.I.C.S.: 332994
Abdul Rahman Husain (CEO)

**BOUSTEAD SINGAPORE LIM-
ITED**
82 Ubi Avenue 4 08-01 Edward
Boustead Centre, Singapore, 408832,
Singapore
Tel.: (65) 67470016   SG
Web Site: https://www.boustead.sg
Year Founded: 1828
F9D—(SES)
Rev.: $416,459,768
Assets: $843,659,421
Liabilities: $420,415,670
Net Worth: $423,243,751
Earnings: $41,672,300
Emp.: 1,135
Fiscal Year-end: 03/31/23
Holding Company; Engineering & IT
Services
N.A.I.C.S.: 551112
Fong Fui Wong (Chm & CEO-Grp)

Subsidiaries:

BIH Heaters Malaysia Sdn Bhd   (1)
Unit 3A-1 Level 3A Tower 2A No 1 Jalan
Pengaturcara U1/51A, UOA Business Park
Seksyen U1, 40150, Shah Alam, Selangor
Darul Ehsan, Malaysia
Tel.: (60) 355673830
Web Site: http://www.bihl.com
Sales Range: $10-24.9 Million
Emp.: 50
Solid Waste Recovery Services

N.A.I.C.S.: 562213

BMEC (Malaysia) Sdn. Bhd.   (1)
B-06-01 Dataran 32 No 2 Jalan 19/1,
46300, Petaling Jaya, Selangor, Malaysia
Tel.: (60) 379566812
Healtcare Services
N.A.I.C.S.: 524114

BMEC Pte. Ltd.   (1)
82 Ubi Ave 4 08-03 Edward Boustead Cen-
tre, Singapore, 408832, Singapore
Tel.: (65) 63052525
Web Site: https://bmec.asia
Rehabilitation Staffing Services
N.A.I.C.S.: 561311

Birwelco USA Inc.   (1)
20405 State Hwy 249, Houston, TX 77070
Tel.: (832) 916-4130
Fired Heater Distr
N.A.I.C.S.: 423720

Boustead Information Technology Pte
Ltd   (1)
82 Ubi Ave 4 #02-01 Edward Boustead Ctr,
Singapore, 408832, Singapore   (100%)
Tel.: (65) 67428622
Web Site: http://www.boustead.sg
Sales Range: $25-49.9 Million
Emp.: 20
Information Technology Services
N.A.I.C.S.: 541512
Leslie Wong (Mng Dir)

Boustead Infrastructures Pte.
Ltd.   (1)
82 Ubi Avenue 4 08-01 Edward Boustead
Centre, Singapore, 408832, Singapore
Tel.: (65) 67470016
Web Site:
http://www.bousteadinfrastructures.com
Engineeering Services
N.A.I.C.S.: 541330

Boustead International Heaters
Canada Limited   (1)
Suite 200 809 Manning Road NE, Calgary,
T2E 7M9, AB, Canada
Tel.: (403) 781-7070
Solid Waste Recovery Services
N.A.I.C.S.: 562213

Boustead International Heaters
Limited   (1)
Europa House Woodlands Court Albert
Drive, Burgess Hill, RH15 9TN, West Sus-
sex, United Kingdom   (100%)
Tel.: (44) 1444237500
Web Site: http://www.bihl.com
Sales Range: $25-49.9 Million
Emp.: 60
Mfr of Heaters & Associated Products
N.A.I.C.S.: 333414

Boustead Maxitherm Energy Pte
Ltd   (1)
82 Ubi Avenue 4 #08-01 Edward Boustead,
Singapore, 408832, Singapore
Tel.: (65) 67470016
Web Site:
http://www.bousteadmaxitherm.com.sg
Solid Waste Energy Recovery Services
N.A.I.C.S.: 562998

Boustead Medical Care Holdings Pte.
Ltd.   (1)
82 Ubi Avenue 4 08-03 Edward Boustead
Centre, Singapore, 408832, Singapore
Tel.: (65) 65332237
Oil & Gas Field Engineering Services
N.A.I.C.S.: 811310

Boustead Projects Investments Pte
Ltd   (1)
82 Ubi Avenue 4 #07-01 Edward Boustead
Centre, Singapore, 408832, Singapore
Tel.: (65) 67483945
Web Site: http://www.bousteadprojects.com
Waste Water Engineering Services
N.A.I.C.S.: 541330

Boustead Projects Ltd.   (1)
82 Ubi Avenue 4 07-01 Edward Boustead
Centre, Singapore, 408832,
Singapore   (95.5%)
Tel.: (65) 67483945
Web Site: http://www.bousteadprojects.com
Sales Range: $25-49.9 Million
Emp.: 25

Project Management, Design & Construc-
tion Services & Property-Related Activities
N.A.I.C.S.: 236220
Thomas Chu (CEO)

Boustead Salcon Pte Ltd   (1)
82 Ubi Avenue 4 08-03 Edward Boustead
Centre, Singapore, 408832, Singapore
Tel.: (65) 6747 0016
Engineeering Services
N.A.I.C.S.: 541330
Ravi Subramanian (CEO)

Boustead Salcon Water Solutions Pte
Ltd   (1)
82 Ubi Avenue 4 08-03 Edward Boustead
Centre, Singapore, 408832, Singapore
Tel.: (65) 68469988
Web Site: http://www.bousteadsalcon.com
Wastewater Treatment Solutions
N.A.I.C.S.: 562998

Controls & Electric Pte. Ltd.   (1)
30 Gul Drive, Singapore, 629478,
Singapore   (100%)
Tel.: (65) 68613377
Web Site:
https://www.bousteadcontrols.com
Sales Range: $25-49.9 Million
Emp.: 40
Designer, Supplier, Installer & Commis-
sioner of Instrumentation Systems
N.A.I.C.S.: 335314
P. Chakraborty (CEO)

ESRI Australia Pty. Ltd.   (1)
Level 3 111 Elizabeth St, Brisbane, 4000,
QLD, Australia
Tel.: (61) 732184100
Web Site: https://esriaustralia.com.au
Sales Range: $50-74.9 Million
Emp.: 66
Military Services to Defense Industries
N.A.I.C.S.: 921190
Brett Sundock (Mng Dir)

ESRI Malaysia Sdn Bhd   (1)
Unit 3A-1 Level 3A Tower 2B No 1 Jalan
Pengaturcara U1/51A Seksyen U1, UOA
Business Park, 40150, Shah Alam, Selan-
gor, Malaysia
Tel.: (60) 350220122
Web Site: https://www.esrimalaysia.com.my
Sales Range: $25-49.9 Million
Emp.: 20
Geographic Information System Services
N.A.I.C.S.: 519290

ESRI South Asia Pte Ltd   (1)
82 Ubi Avenue 4 07-03 Edward Boustead
Centre, Singapore, 408832,
Singapore   (100%)
Tel.: (65) 67428622
Web Site: https://www.esrisa.com
Sales Range: $25-49.9 Million
Emp.: 20
Provides GIS-Related Solutions
N.A.I.C.S.: 541512

ESRI South Asia Sdn. Bhd.   (1)
Ste 301Block A4 Leisure Commerce Sq,
No9 Jalan PJS 8 9, 46150, Petaling Jaya,
Selangor, Malaysia   (100%)
Tel.: (60) 378749930
Web Site: http://www.esrimalaysia.com.my
Sales Range: $25-49.9 Million
Emp.: 18
Geographic Information System Technology
Whslr
N.A.I.C.S.: 423430
Daniel Boey (Country Mgr)

Esri Singapore Pte Ltd   (1)
29 Media Circle Alice Mediapolis 08-01
North Lobby, Singapore, 138565, Singapore
Tel.: (65) 67428622
Web Site: https://www.esrisingapore.com.sg
Emp.: 45
Mapping Software Development & Hosting
Services
N.A.I.C.S.: 541511

MapData Services Pty Ltd   (1)
Level 1 414 Kent Street, Sydney, 2000,
NSW, Australia
Tel.: (61) 284362800
Web Site: http://www.mapdataservices.com
Geospatial Database Development & Online
Map Hosting Services
N.A.I.C.S.: 541511

Medisolution Pte. Ltd. **(1)**
2 Kim Chuan Drive Csi Distribution Centre
06-01, Singapore, 537080, Singapore
Tel.: (65) 63052585
Web Site: http://www.medisolution.com.sg
Disaster Reconstruction Remediation Services
N.A.I.C.S.: 562910

PT Boustead Maxitherm Industries **(1)**
Graha Pratama Building 15th Floor Jalan Letjend M T Haryono Kav 15, Tebet, Jakarta, 12810, Indonesia
Tel.: (62) 2183793678
Web Site:
http://www.bousteadmaxitherm.com
Solid Waste Recovery Services
N.A.I.C.S.: 562213

PT ESRI Indonesia **(1)**
Capital Place 26th Floor Jalan Jend Gatot Subroto Kav 18, Jakarta, 12710, Selatan, Indonesia
Tel.: (62) 2127099881
Web Site: https://www.esriindonesia.co.id
Geographic Information System Services
N.A.I.C.S.: 519290

Tianjin University of Commerce-Boustead Informatics, Ltd. **(1)**
Jing Road No 28, Xiqing District, Tianjin, 300384, China
Tel.: (86) 2223799800
Web Site: http://www.boustead.edu.cn
Sales Range: $10-24.9 Million
Emp.: 100
Education Services
N.A.I.C.S.: 611310

United BMEC Pte. Ltd. **(1)**
2 Kim Chuan Drive 06-01 Csi Distribution Centre, Singapore, 537080, Singapore
Tel.: (65) 63052525
Web Site: http://www.unitedbmec.com
Software & Hardware Product Distr
N.A.I.C.S.: 423430
Don Quah *(Sr Mgr)*

Whiterock Incorporation Private Limited **(1)**
No 2 Kim Chuan Drive 06-01 CSI Distribution Centre, Singapore, 537080, Singapore
Tel.: (65) 63052573
Web Site: http://www.whiterock.com.sg
Healthcare Product Distr
N.A.I.C.S.: 423450

BOUSTEAD WAVEFRONT INC.
1 George Street 10-01, Singapore, 049145, Singapore
Tel.: (65) 6 817 3122 Ky
Year Founded: 2021
BOUW—(NASDAQ)
Rev.: $1,180,073
Assets: $1,296,650
Liabilities: $343,435
Net Worth: $953,215
Earnings: $636,696
Emp.: 4
Fiscal Year-end: 12/31/21
Investment Banking Services
N.A.I.C.S.: 523150
David U. Drake *(CEO)*

BOUTHILLETTE PARIZEAU
9825 Verville St, Montreal, H3L 3E1, QC, Canada
Tel.: (514) 383-3747
Web Site: http://www.bpa.ca
Year Founded: 1956
Rev.: $11,998,403
Emp.: 200
Engineering & Consulting Services
N.A.I.C.S.: 541330
Serge Vezina *(VP)*

BOUTIQUE CORPORATION PUBLIC COMPANY LIMITED
170/67 21st Floor Ocean Tower 1 Soi Sukhumvit 16 Ratchadaphisek Road, Klongtoey, Bangkok, 10110, Thailand
Tel.: (66) 26208777 TH

Web Site:
https://www.boutiquecorp.com
Year Founded: 2007
BC—(THA)
Rev.: $11,929,969
Assets: $112,416,361
Liabilities: $94,680,251
Net Worth: $17,736,109
Earnings: ($8,725,655)
Emp.: 336
Fiscal Year-end: 12/31/23
Real Estate Development Services
N.A.I.C.S.: 531390
Prab Thakral *(CEO)*

BOUTIQUE JACOB INC.
6125 chemin de la Cote de Liesse, Saint Laurent, H4T 1C8, QC, Canada
Tel.: (514) 731-8877
Web Site: http://www.jacob.ca
Year Founded: 1977
Rev.: $60,189,091
Emp.: 750
Women's Apparel Stores
N.A.I.C.S.: 458110
Joseph Basmaji *(Owner & Pres)*

BOUTIQUE LA VIE EN ROSE, INC.
4320 Av Pierre-de Coubertin, Montreal, H1V 1A6, QC, Canada
Tel.: (514) 729-9400
Web Site:
http://www.lavieenrose.com
Lingerie Retailer
N.A.I.C.S.: 458110
Francois Roberge *(Pres & CEO)*

BOUTIQUE NEWCITY PUBLIC COMPANY LIMITED
1112/53-75 Soi Sukhumvit 48 Phra Khanong, Khlong Toei, Bangkok, 10110, Thailand
Tel.: (66) 23913320
Web Site: https://www.btnc.co.th
Year Founded: 1974
BTNC—(THA)
Rev.: $8,450,155
Assets: $15,831,493
Liabilities: $1,546,158
Net Worth: $14,285,335
Earnings: $804,138
Emp.: 161
Fiscal Year-end: 12/31/23
Apparels Mfr
N.A.I.C.S.: 315250
Panitarn Pavarolarvidya *(Chm)*

BOUTIQUES, INC.
11th Floor Mita International Building 1-4-28 Mita, Minato-Ku, Tokyo, 108-0073, Japan
Tel.: (81) 364200721
Web Site: https://www.btix.jp
Year Founded: 2006
9272—(TKS)
Rev.: $29,176,540
Assets: $32,098,160
Liabilities: $17,516,500
Net Worth: $14,581,660
Earnings: $4,018,880
Emp.: 208
Fiscal Year-end: 03/31/24
E Commerce Site Operator
N.A.I.C.S.: 458110
Yuzo Shinmura *(Founder, Chm, Pres & CEO)*

BOUVET ASA
Sorkedalsveien 8, NO-0369, Oslo, Norway
Tel.: (47) 23406000 NO
Web Site: http://www.bouvet.no
Year Founded: 2002
0HDU—(LSE)
Rev.: $285,005,542
Assets: $133,466,931

Liabilities: $91,256,882
Net Worth: $42,210,050
Earnings: $29,218,178
Emp.: 2,041
Fiscal Year-end: 12/31/22
Information Technology Consulting Services
N.A.I.C.S.: 541519
Sverre Hurum *(CEO)*

Subsidiaries:

Bouvet Sverige AB **(1)**
Ostermalmsgatan 87 A, SE- 114 59, Stockholm, Sweden
Tel.: (46) 771611100
Web Site: https://www.bouvet.no
Information Technology & Services
N.A.I.C.S.: 541511

Subsidiary (Domestic):

Bouvet Stockholm AB **(2)**
Svetsarvagen 15 2 Tr, 17141, Solna, Stockholm, Sweden
Tel.: (46) 406366000
Web Site: http://www.bouvet.se
Information Technology Consulting Services
N.A.I.C.S.: 541690

Bouvet Syd AB **(2)**
Sodergatan 3, 211 34, Malmo, Sweden
Tel.: (46) 406366000
Software Support Services
N.A.I.C.S.: 561499

Consultants in Business Engineering and Research Sweden AB **(2)**
Drottninggatan 25, 111 51, Stockholm, Sweden
Tel.: (46) 850611100
Web Site: http://www.ciber.se
IT Solutions
N.A.I.C.S.: 541512

BOUVET LADUBAY SA
Saint-Hilaire-Saint-Florent, 49400, Saumur, France
Tel.: (33) 2 41 83 83 83 FR
Web Site:
http://www.bouvetladubay.com
Year Founded: 1851
Wine Mfr
N.A.I.C.S.: 312130
Patrice Monmousseau *(Chm & Mng Dir)*

BOUWFONDS INVESTMENT MANAGEMENT B.V.
De Beek 18, 3871 MS, Hoevelaken, Netherlands
Tel.: (31) 337504750 NI
Web Site:
http://www.bouwfondsim.com
Year Founded: 2001
Real Estate Portfolio Development, Structuring & Management Services
N.A.I.C.S.: 523940

BOUYER LEROUX SA
7 Letablere, 49280, La Seguiniere, France
Tel.: (33) 2 41 63 76 16
Web Site: http://www.bouyer-leroux.com
Sales Range: $150-199.9 Million
Emp.: 700
Building Materials Mfr
N.A.I.C.S.: 327120
Roland Besnard *(CEO)*

Subsidiaries:

Soprofen SAS **(1)**
ZA Le Bosquet, rue de la Lisiere, F-67580, Mertzwiller, France
Tel.: (33) 3 8890 5025
Web Site: http://www.soprofen.com
Emp.: 50
Roller Shutters & Garage Doors Mfr & Distr
N.A.I.C.S.: 332321
Marc Burger *(Dir Gen)*

Subsidiary (Domestic):

Soprofen Industrie SAS **(2)**
Zone Industrielle les Noyes, 70300, Froid-econche, France
Tel.: (33) 384406205
Web Site: http://www.soprofen.fr
Sales Range: $10-24.9 Million
Emp.: 49
Industrial Metal Shutters & Doors Mfr
N.A.I.C.S.: 332321

BOUYGUES S.A.
32 avenue Hoche, 75378, Paris, Cedex, France
Tel.: (33) 144201000 FR
Web Site: https://www.bouygues.com
Year Founded: 1952
EN—(LUX)
Rev.: $46,235,866,560
Assets: $54,831,090,080
Liabilities: $39,123,128,720
Net Worth: $15,707,961,360
Earnings: $1,381,770,000
Emp.: 124,600
Fiscal Year-end: 12/31/21
Construction Engineering Services
N.A.I.C.S.: 551112
Martin Bouygues *(Chm)*

Subsidiaries:

B-G Mechanical, Inc. **(1)**
6 2nd Ave, Chicopee, MA 01020
Tel.: (413) 592-5300
Web Site: https://www.equansmep.com
Heating, Ventilation & Air-Conditioning Contractors
N.A.I.C.S.: 238220

Subsidiary (Domestic):

B-G Mechanical Service, Inc. **(2)**
12 2nd Ave, Chicopee, MA 01020
Tel.: (413) 888-1500
Web Site: https://www.equansmep.com
Plumbing, Heating & Air-Conditioning Contractor
N.A.I.C.S.: 238220

Bouygues Construction **(1)**
Challenger 1 avenue Eugene Freyssinet, Guyancourt, Saint-Quentin-en-Yvelines, 78061, France **(100%)**
Tel.: (33) 130603300
Web Site:
http://www.bouygues-construction.com
Rev.: $15,001,644,560
Assets: $13,433,840,560
Liabilities: $12,345,336,640
Net Worth: $1,088,503,920
Earnings: $363,954,500
Emp.: 58,308
Fiscal Year-end: 12/31/2019
Construction & Civil Engineering
N.A.I.C.S.: 237990
Jean-Marc Kiviatkowski *(Exec VP)*

Subsidiary (Non-US):

Acieroid S.A. **(2)**
Avenida de la Granvia n 179, 08908, L'Hospitalet de Llobregat, Spain
Tel.: (34) 932616300
Web Site: http://www.acieroid.es
Emp.: 100
Engineering & Construction Services
N.A.I.C.S.: 541330

Bouygues (UK) Ltd. **(2)**
Elizabeth House 39 York Rd, London, SE1 7NQ, United Kingdom
Tel.: (44) 2074010020
Web Site: http://www.bouygues-uk.com
Sales Range: $100-124.9 Million
Emp.: 500
Construction Services
N.A.I.C.S.: 236220
Colin Whitfield *(Grp Dir-Comml)*

Subsidiary (Domestic):

Bouygues Batiment Ile-de-France **(2)**
Challenger 1 Avenue Eugene Freyssinet, Saint-Quentin-en-Yvelines, 78065, France **(100%)**
Tel.: (33) 130603400

Bouygues S.A.—(Continued)

Web Site: http://www.bouygues-
construction.com
Sales Range: $1-4.9 Billion
Emp.: 5,000
Residential & Commercial Construction
N.A.I.C.S.: 236117
Philippe Fabie (Chm & CEO)

Bouygues Batiment International (2)
1 Ave Eugene Freyssinet, Saint-Quentin-en-
Yvelines, 78280, France (100%)
Tel.: (33) 130605600
Web Site: http://www.bouygues-
construction.com
Sales Range: $1-4.9 Billion
Emp.: 4,500
Residential & Commercial Constructrion &
Development
N.A.I.C.S.: 236220

**Bouygues Entreprises
France-Europe** (2)
1 avenue Eugene Freyssinet, Saint-
Quentin-en-Yvelines, 78065,
France (100%)
Tel.: (33) 130603300
Web Site: http://www.bouygues-
construction.com
Sales Range: $1-4.9 Billion
Emp.: 9,100
Constructrion & Engineering Services
N.A.I.C.S.: 237990
Philippe Bonnave (CEO)

Bouygues Travaux Publics (2)
1 avenue Eugene Freyssinet, guyancourt,
78280, Saint-Quentin-en-Yvelines,
France (100%)
Tel.: (33) 130605700
Web Site: http://www.bouygues-
construction.com
Sales Range: $1-4.9 Billion
Emp.: 3,000
Civil Engineering Services & Construction
N.A.I.C.S.: 237990

DV Construction SA (2)
Le Seville 22 Avenue Pythagore, Merignac,
33700, France
Tel.: (33) 557532525
Web Site: http://www.dv-construction.fr
Construction Engineering Services
N.A.I.C.S.: 541330

GFC Construction SA (2)
5-7 Avenue De Poumeyrol, 69647, Caluire-
et-Cuire, France
Tel.: (33) 4 72 81 18 18
Web Site: http://www.gfc-construction.fr
Sales Range: $100-124.9 Million
Emp.: 300
Industrial Building Construction Services
N.A.I.C.S.: 236210

Subsidiary (Non-US):

Losinger Holding AG (2)
Saegestrasse 76, CP 576, 3098, Koniz,
Switzerland
Tel.: (41) 584567500
Web Site: http://www.losinger-marazzi.ch
Sales Range: $200-249.9 Million
Emp.: 800
Holding Company; Construction Services
N.A.I.C.S.: 551112
Jacky Gillmann (Mng Dir)

Subsidiary (Domestic):

Losinger Marazzi AG (3)
Wankdorfallee 5, 3014, Bern, Switzerland
Tel.: (41) 58 456 7500
Web Site: https://www.losinger-marazzi.ch
Construction Engineering Services
N.A.I.C.S.: 541330
Jacky Gillmann (Country Dir)

PraderLosinger SA (3)
Route de Vissigen 110, Case Postale 4192,
1950, Sion, Switzerland
Tel.: (41) 27 203 4361
Web Site: https://www.praderlosinger.ch
Construction Engineering Services
N.A.I.C.S.: 541330

Subsidiary (Non-US):

Plan Group Inc. (2)
2740 Steeles Avenue West, Vaughan, L4K

4T4, ON, Canada (85%)
Tel.: (416) 635-9040
Web Site: https://www.plan-group.com
Sales Range: $350-399.9 Million
Emp.: 1,700
Mechanical & Electrical Engineering Ser-
vices
N.A.I.C.S.: 541330
Paul Sheridan (CEO)

**Bouygues Energies & Services
SAS** (1)
19 Rue Stephenson, CS 20734, 78063,
Saint-Quentin-en-Yvelines, Cedex, France
Tel.: (33) 180615000
Web Site:
http://www.bouyguesenergiesservice.com
Telecommunication Networking Services
N.A.I.C.S.: 517810

Subsidiary (Non-US):

Bouygues E&S UK Ltd. (2)
Becket House 1 Lambeth Palace Road,
London, SE1.7EU, United Kingdom
Tel.: (44) 207 401 0020
Web Site: http://www.bouygues-es.co.uk
Holding Company; Contracting, Construc-
tion, Facility Management & Infrastructure
Services
N.A.I.C.S.: 551112

Subsidiary (Domestic):

**Bouygues E&S Contracting UK
Limited** (3)
88 Glasgow Road, Newbridge, EH28 8PP,
United Kingdom
Tel.: (44) 135 523 4567
Web Site: http://www.bouygues-es.co.uk
Sales Range: $25-49.9 Million
Emp.: 60
Construction, Conception, Design & Engi-
neering Services
N.A.I.C.S.: 541330
Zeb Ahmed (Deputy Mng Dir)

Bouygues E&S FM UK Limited (3)
1 Lambeth Palace Road, London, SE1
7EU, United Kingdom
Tel.: (44) 207 401 0020
Web Site: http://www.bouygues-es.co.uk
Sales Range: $75-99.9 Million
Emp.: 400
Facility Management Services
N.A.I.C.S.: 561210

**Bouygues E&S Infrastructure UK
Limited** (3)
Belgrave House Hatfield Business Park Fro-
bisher Way, Hatfield, AL10 9TQ, United
Kingdom
Tel.: (44) 170 763 0700
Web Site: http://www.bouygues-es.co.uk
Sales Range: $25-49.9 Million
Emp.: 40
Civil Infrastructure & Utilities Construction
Services
N.A.I.C.S.: 237990

Subsidiary (Non-US):

**Bouygues Energies & Services
Gabon** (2)
BP 305, Libreville, Gabon
Tel.: (241) 76 20 80
Construction Engineering Services
N.A.I.C.S.: 541330

Bouygues Immobilier (1)
3 Boulevard Gallieni, 92445, Issy-les-
Moulineaux, Cedex, France (100%)
Tel.: (33) 15 538 2525
Web Site: https://www.bouygues-
immobilier.com
Sales Range: $1-4.9 Billion
Emp.: 300
Developer of Commercial & Residential
Real Estate
N.A.I.C.S.: 236220

Subsidiary (Non-US):

Bouygues Inmobiliaria S.A. (2)
Calle Via de Los Poblados, Madrid, 28033,
Spain
Tel.: (34) 913756030
Web Site: http://www.bouygues-
inmobiliaria.com
Construction Engineering Services

N.A.I.C.S.: 541330

Bouygues Telecom SA (1)
Arcs de Seine 1 Place Abel Gance, 92640,
Boulogne-Billancourt, France (89.5%)
Tel.: (33) 139267500
Web Site: http://www.bouyguestelecom.fr
Sales Range: $1-4.9 Billion
Emp.: 6,950
Cellular Telecommunications Services
N.A.I.C.S.: 517112
Richard Viel (CEO)

Subsidiary (Domestic):

Nerim SASU (2)
1 parvis de la Defense, Paroi Nord de la
Grande Arche, 92044, Paris, France
Tel.: (33) 1 80 400 500
Web Site: http://www.nerim.fr
Broadband & Telecommunications Services
N.A.I.C.S.: 517121
Bernard Lemoine (Pres)

Subsidiary (Domestic):

Normaction SA (3)
96 Boulevard Haussmann, 75008, Paris,
France
Tel.: (33) 1 80 400 500
Web Site: http://www.normaction.com
Telecommunications & IT System Security
Services
N.A.I.C.S.: 517810

Brezillon SA (1)
8 Rue De Deportes, 60400, Noyon, France
Tel.: (33) 344932121
Industrial Building Construction Services
N.A.I.C.S.: 236210

Colas SA (1)
1 rue du Colonel Pierre Avia CS81755,
75730, Paris, Cedex, France (96.6%)
Tel.: (33) 147617500
Web Site: http://www.colas.com
Rev.: $14,327,055,400
Assets: $9,965,002,600
Liabilities: $7,020,063,400
Net Worth: $2,944,939,200
Earnings: $277,702,600
Emp.: 57,607
Fiscal Year-end: 12/31/2022
Road Construction & Infrastructure Mainte-
nance
N.A.I.C.S.: 237310
Frederic Gardes (Chm & CEO)

Subsidiary (Domestic):

Aximum (2)
8 rue Jean Mermoz, 78772, Magny-les-
Hameaux, France
Tel.: (33) 130156900
Web Site: https://www.aximum.fr
Road Construction Engineering Services
N.A.I.C.S.: 237310

Subsidiary (Non-US):

COLAS CZ, a.s. (2)
Kolbenova 259 9, 190 00, Prague, Czech
Republic
Tel.: (420) 286003511
Web Site: http://www.colas.cz
Road Construction Services
N.A.I.C.S.: 237310
Ondrej Komrska (Gen Mgr)

COLAS-HUNGARIA Zrt. (2)
Korhaz u 6-12, 1033, Budapest, Hungary
Tel.: (36) 1 883 1000
Web Site: http://www.colas.hu
Sales Range: $150-199.9 Million
Emp.: 600
Construction Engineering Services
N.A.I.C.S.: 541330

Colas Belgium SA (2)
Rue Nestor Martin 313, 1082, Brussels,
1082, Belgium
Tel.: (32) 24820630
Web Site: http://www.colas.be
Sales Range: $25-49.9 Million
Emp.: 60
Road Construction Engineering Services
N.A.I.C.S.: 237310
Megoral Pierre (Gen Mgr)

Subsidiary (Non-US):

Colas Gabon (3)

BP 3985, Libreville, Gabon
Tel.: (241) 76 15 95
Construction Engineering Services
N.A.I.C.S.: 541330

Subsidiary (Non-US):

Colas Canada Inc. (2)
4984 Place De La Savane Bureau 150,
Montreal, H4P 2M9, QC, Canada
Tel.: (514) 807-8282
Web Site: http://www.colascanada.ca
Sales Range: $25-49.9 Million
Emp.: 12
Road Construction Engineering Services
N.A.I.C.S.: 237310
Frederic Roussel (Pres & Gen Mgr)

Subsidiary (Domestic):

Miller McAsphalt Corporation (3)
505 Miller Avenue, Markham, L6G 1B2, ON,
Canada
Tel.: (905) 475-6660
Web Site: http://www.millergroup.ca
Holding Company
N.A.I.C.S.: 551112

Subsidiary (Domestic):

McAsphalt Industries Limited (4)
8800 Sheppard Avenue East, Toronto, M1B
5R4, ON, Canada
Tel.: (416) 281-8181
Web Site: https://www.mcasphalt.com
Asphalt Emulsions & Specialty Products Mfr
& Distr
N.A.I.C.S.: 324121

The Miller Group Inc. (4)
505 Miller Avenue, Markham, L6G 1B2, ON,
Canada
Tel.: (905) 475-6660
Web Site: https://www.millergroup.ca
Holding Company; Aggregates Mining;
Ready-Mix Concrete, Cement & Asphalt
Mfr; Road Paving & Maintenance Services
N.A.I.C.S.: 551112

Subsidiary (Domestic):

Miller Paving Limited (5)
505 Miller Avenue, Markham, L6G 1B2, ON,
Canada
Tel.: (905) 475-6660
Web Site: http://www.millergroup.ca
Road Paving & Construction Services
N.A.I.C.S.: 237310

Subsidiary (US):

The Miller Group, Inc. (USA) (5)
1715 Nolan Ct, Morrow, GA 30260
Tel.: (770) 968-9100
Web Site: http://www.millergroup.ca
Road Maintenance, Rehabilitation & Recon-
struction Services
N.A.I.C.S.: 237310

Subsidiary (Non-US):

Colas Danmark A/S (2)
Fabriksparken 40, Glostrup, 2600, Denmark
Tel.: (45) 989898
Web Site: https://www.colas.dk
Sales Range: $25-49.9 Million
Emp.: 25
Construction Engineering Services
N.A.I.C.S.: 541330

Subsidiary (US):

Colas Inc. (2)
163 Madison Ave Ste 500, Morristown, NJ
07960
Tel.: (973) 656-4819
Web Site: http://www.colas.com
Road Construction Engineering Services
N.A.I.C.S.: 237310
Jean Vidal (COO)

Subsidiary (Non-US):

Colas Ltd (2)
Wallage Lane, Rowfant, Crawley, RH10
4NF, West Sussex, United Kingdom
Tel.: (44) 134 271 1000
Web Site: http://www.colas.co.uk
Emp.: 120
Civil Engineering Services
N.A.I.C.S.: 237990

Jag Paddam *(Assoc Dir-Projects Bus)*

Colas Martinique (2)
BP 564 97242, Fort-de-France, cedex, Martinique
Tel.: (596) 596707070
Sales Range: $25-49.9 Million
Emp.: 100
Road & Highway Construction Engineering Services
N.A.I.C.S.: 237310

Colas Polska Sp.z.o.o (2)
Ul Nowa 49, 62070, Paledzie, Poland
Tel.: (48) 618945460
Web Site: https://www.colas.pl
Road Construction Engineering Services
N.A.I.C.S.: 237310

Subsidiary (Domestic):

Colas Rail (2)
2/3 place des Vosges, 92400, Courbevoie, France
Tel.: (33) 13 493 8300
Web Site: https://www.colasrail.com
Emp.: 5,600
Railway Track Construction Services
N.A.I.C.S.: 237990

Subsidiary (Non-US):

Bouygues E&S InTec AG (3)
Rotzmattweg 115, 4601, Olten, Switzerland (100%)
Tel.: (41) 44 247 44 44
Web Site: http://www.bouygues-es-intec.it
Power Generation, Heating & Cooling Technology, Process Automation & Energy Engineering Services
N.A.I.C.S.: 221112

Subsidiary (Domestic):

Alpiq EcoServices Ltd. (4)
Hohlstrasse 188, 8026, Zurich, Switzerland
Tel.: (41) 44 247 44 44
Web Site: http://www.alpiq-ecoservices.ch
Energy Consulting Services
N.A.I.C.S.: 541690

Alpiq InTec East Ltd. (4)
Hohlstrasse 188, Zurich, 8004, Switzerland
Tel.: (41) 442474444
Electrical Equipment Installation Services
N.A.I.C.S.: 238210
Peter Limacher *(CEO)*

Alpiq InTec Romandie SA (4)
Route des Flumeaux 45, 1008, Prilly, Switzerland
Tel.: (41) 21 632 84 44
Electrical Engineering & IT Services
N.A.I.C.S.: 519290

Subsidiary (Non-US):

Bouygues E&S InTec Italia S.p.A. (4)
Via Francia 21 / C, 37135, Verona, Italy
Tel.: (39) 045 86 28011
Web Site: http://www.bouygues-es-intec.it
Electric Power Structure Construction Services
N.A.I.C.S.: 237130

Bouygues E&S InTec Italia SpA (4)
Via Giorgio Stephenson 73, 20157, Milan, Italy
Tel.: (39) 02 33 21 101
Web Site: http://www.bouygues-es-intec.it
Electrical Engineering Services
N.A.I.C.S.: 238210
Fabio Vecchio *(Mng Dir)*

Subsidiary (Domestic):

Bouygues E&S InTec Schweiz AG (4)
Hohlstrasse 188, Zurich, 8004, Switzerland
Tel.: (41) 44 247 44 44
Web Site: http://www.bouygues-es-intec.ch
Facility Management Services
N.A.I.C.S.: 561210

Subsidiary (Domestic):

Bouygues E&S InTec Schweiz AG (5)
Buckhauserstrasse 22, 8048, Zurich, Switzerland

Tel.: (41) 44 247 44 44
Web Site: http://www.bouygues-es.ch
Electrical Installation Services
N.A.I.C.S.: 238210

Bouygues E&S Prozessautomation AG (5)
Rotzmattweg 115, 4600, Olten, Switzerland
Tel.: (41) 628348340
Web Site: http://www.bouygues-es.ch
Automation Software Development Services
N.A.I.C.S.: 541511

Subsidiary (Domestic):

Bouygues E&S InTec Schweiz AG (4)
Rotzmattweg 115, 4601, Olten, Switzerland
Tel.: (41) 62 287 67 67
Web Site: http://www.bouygues-es.ch
Electrical Equipment Installation Services
N.A.I.C.S.: 238210

Bouygues E&S InTec Switzerland Ltd (4)
Via Monte Bre 8, 6900, Lugano, Switzerland
Tel.: (41) 58 261 00 00
Web Site: http://www.bouygues-es-intec.it
Electrical Engineering Services
N.A.I.C.S.: 541330

Kummler+Matter AG (4)
Rietstrasse 14, 8108, Dallikon, Switzerland (100%)
Tel.: (41) 442474747
Web Site: http://www.kuma.ch
Transport Technology Engineering
N.A.I.C.S.: 488999

Subsidiary (Non-US):

Kraftanlagen Munchen GmbH (3)
Ridlerstrasse 31c, 80339, Munich, Germany
Tel.: (49) 89 6237 0
Web Site: http://www.kraftanlagen.com
Pipeline Construction Engineering Services
N.A.I.C.S.: 237120
Stephane Stoll *(Mng Dir)*

Joint Venture (Non-US):

Hindustan Colas Pvt. Ltd. (2)
HINCOL House B-601 6th Floor Marathon Futurex, N.M Joshi Marg Lower Parel, Mumbai, 400013, India (50%)
Tel.: (91) 222 302 3250
Web Site: https://www.hincol.com
Sales Range: $100-124.9 Million
Bitumen Emulsions Mfr & Marketer
N.A.I.C.S.: 325110
Jacques Marcel Pastor *(Chm)*

Subsidiary (Domestic):

Somaro (2)
3 Rue Des Beaunes, PO Box 76, 784 WW, Chatou, France (100%)
Tel.: (33) 130156900
Web Site: http://www.smaro.com
Sales Range: $25-49.9 Million
Emp.: 60
Installer & Maintainer of Highway Safety Equipment
N.A.I.C.S.: 423450

DTP Terrassement SA (1)
1 Avenue Eugene Freyssinet, Saint-Quentin-en-Yvelines, 78280, France
Tel.: (33) 130603851
Web Site: http://www.boygues.construction.com
Sales Range: $700-749.9 Million
Emp.: 4,500
Construction Engineering Services
N.A.I.C.S.: 541330

Exprimm IT (1)
16 Avenue Du Quebec Silic 712, 91961, Villebon-sur-Yvette, France
Tel.: (33) 160928400
Web Site: http://www.exprimm-it.fr
Telecommunication Networking Services
N.A.I.C.S.: 517810

Grands Travaux Ocean Indien (GTOI) SA (1)
Z I N 2, BP 32016, 97824, Le Port, Reunion
Tel.: (262) 2 62 42 85 85
Web Site: http://www.gtoi.fr
Road Construction Engineering Services

N.A.I.C.S.: 237310

Karmar SA (1)
6 Wyscigowa Avenue, 02-681, Warsaw, Poland
Tel.: (48) 223214400
Web Site: http://www.karmar.com.pl
Construction Engineering Services
N.A.I.C.S.: 541330
Joanna Makowiecka-Gaca *(CEO)*

Norpac SA (1)
Parc Scientifique de la Haute Borne 1 avenue de l'Horizon, 59651, Villeneuve d'Ascq, France
Tel.: (33) 357634000
Construction ServiceCivil Engineering Services
N.A.I.C.S.: 237990

Pertuy Construction SA (1)
20 Rue Blaise Pascal, 54320, Maxeville, France
Tel.: (33) 383932323
Web Site: http://www.pertuy-construction.com
Civil Engineering Services
N.A.I.C.S.: 237990

Quille SA (1)
4 Rue Saint Eloi, BP 1048, 76172, Rouen, France
Tel.: (33) 235144864
Web Site: http://www.quille.fr
Construction Engineering Services
N.A.I.C.S.: 541330

Sodearif SA (1)
1 Avenue Eugene Freyssinet, 78280, Guyancourt, France
Tel.: (33) 130604859
Web Site: http://www.sodearif.com
Sales Range: $50-74.9 Million
Emp.: 100
Real Estate Development Services
N.A.I.C.S.: 531390
Gesruelles Martial *(Gen Mgr)*

Uniservice SA (1)
Rue Du Conseil-General 3, Geneva, 1204, Switzerland
Tel.: (41) 227892421
Construction Engineering Services
N.A.I.C.S.: 541330

VSL International Ltd (1)
Saegestrasse 76, Koniz, 3098, Switzerland
Tel.: (41) 584563000
Web Site: http://www.vsl.com
Construction Engineering Services
N.A.I.C.S.: 541330

BOVA FRANCE
Zae Les Grandes Vignes 5 Rue Du Pont De La Breche, 95190, Goussainville, Val d'Oise, France
Tel.: (33) 134388940
Rev.: $18,100,000
Emp.: 26
N.A.I.C.S.: 441110
Christian Giraudon *(Dir)*

BOW CYCLE & MOTOR COMPANY LTD.
8525 Bowfort Rd NW, Calgary, T3B 2V2, AB, Canada
Tel.: (403) 288-5421
Web Site:
http://www.bowcyclecalgary.com
Year Founded: 1956
Rev.: $15,639,775
Emp.: 35
Motorcycle, Snowmobile, Lawn Mower & ATV Dealers
N.A.I.C.S.: 441227
Todd Starchuk *(Mng Partner)*

BOW PLANNING GROUP INC
5700 ch De La Cote-De-Liesse, H4T 1B1, Montreal, QC, Canada
Tel.: (514) 735-5551
Web Site: http://www.bow-group.com
Sales Range: $75-99.9 Million
Emp.: 200
Plastic Pipe & Fittings Manufacturing

N.A.I.C.S.: 326122
Pat Chiasson *(Pres)*

BOWA-ELECTRONIC GMBH & CO. KG
Heinrich Hertz Strasse 4 10, Gomaringen, 72810, Germany
Tel.: (49) 707260020
Web Site: http://www.bowa.de
Year Founded: 1977
Rev.: $41,736,564
Emp.: 188
Automobile Parts Mfr
N.A.I.C.S.: 336390
Thomas Krober *(Mng Dir)*

Subsidiaries:

Bowa International Sp. z o.o. Sp. k. (1)
Ul Obornicka 10, Suchy Las, Zlotkowo, Poland
Tel.: (48) 618926325
Surgical Equipment Distr
N.A.I.C.S.: 423450

BOWATER BUILDING PRODUCTS LTD.
Water Orton Ln Minworth, Sutton Coldfield, B76 9BW, W Midlands, United Kingdom
Tel.: (44) 1217493000
Web Site:
http://www.bowaterprojects.com
Year Founded: 1969
Sales Range: $75-99.9 Million
Emp.: 400
PVC Window & Door Mfr
N.A.I.C.S.: 326199
David Jones *(Mng Dir)*

BOWE SYSTEC AG
Werner-von-Siemens-Str 1, D-86159, Augsburg, Germany
Tel.: (49) 82157020
Web Site: http://www.boewe-systec.com
Year Founded: 1945
BSY—(DEU)
Sales Range: $550-599.9 Million
Emp.: 12,400
Cutting & Inserting Systems Mfr
N.A.I.C.S.: 333243
Jens Beutelspacher *(Member-Mgmt Bd)*

Subsidiaries:

BOWE CARDTEC GmbH (1)
Balhorner Feld 28, D-33106, Paderborn, Germany
Tel.: (49) 5251180860
Web Site: http://www.boewe-cardtec.de
Sales Range: $25-49.9 Million
Emp.: 65
Supplier of Plastic Card Personalization Systems & Products
N.A.I.C.S.: 333248

Bowe Systec, Cee, S.A. (1)
Granja Park 5, 2710-142, Sintra, Portugal
Tel.: (351) 219106610
Industrial Machinery Whslr
N.A.I.C.S.: 423830
Alfredo Calvao *(Mng Dir)*

Postrom Maskiner AS (1)
Grorudveien 55, 0976, Oslo, Norway
Tel.: (47) 23338833
Web Site: http://www.postrom.no
Industrial Machinery Whslr
N.A.I.C.S.: 423830
Tom Erik Harnes *(CEO)*

RO Systec Group Srl (1)
Sector 6 ap 28 sc 1 bl 102 Cupolei 4-8, 061157, Bucharest, Romania
Tel.: (40) 214104181
Web Site: http://www.rosystec.ro
Industrial Machinery Whslr
N.A.I.C.S.: 423830

Systec Sistem Teknolojileri A.S. (1)

BOWE SYSTEC AG—(Continued)

Barbaros Bulvari 105 B, Besiktas, Istanbul,
Turkiye
Tel.: (90) 2122591171150
Web Site: http://www.systec.com.tr
Industrial Machinery Whslr
N.A.I.C.S.: 423830
Tolga Yalniz (Asst Mgr-Technical)

BOWEN & POMEROY PTY. LTD.
48 - 52 Hallam South Road, Hallam,
3803, VIC, Australia
Tel.: (61) 397963088
Web Site: http://www.bowens.com.au
Year Founded: 1894
Emp.: 800
Timber Products Distr
N.A.I.C.S.: 423990
Jack Bowen (Owner)

BOWIM S.A.
Niwecka Street 1 E, 41-200, Sosnow-
iec, Poland
Tel.: (48) 323929300
Web Site: https://www.bowim.pl
Year Founded: 1995
BOW—(WAR)
Rev.: $526,267,783
Assets: $144,495,935
Liabilities: $61,434,959
Net Worth: $83,060,975
Earnings: $3,374,746
Emp.: 440
Fiscal Year-end: 12/31/23
Steel Product Distr
N.A.I.C.S.: 423510
Jacek Rozek (VP)

Subsidiaries:

Betstal Sp. z o.o. **(1)**
ul Mechanikow 9, 44-109, Gliwice, Poland
Tel.: (48) 32 734 55 86
Web Site: http://www.betstal.bowim.pl
Iron Rod Mfr
N.A.I.C.S.: 331511

Bowim-Podkarpacie Sp. z o.o. **(1)**
ul Cieplownicza 8a, 35-322, Rzeszow, Po-
land
Tel.: (48) 17 852 73 88
Web Site: http://www.podkarpacie.bowim.pl
Iron Rod Mfr
N.A.I.C.S.: 331511

BOWKER BLACKBURN LTD.
Trident Park, Trident Way, Blackburn,
BB1 3NU, Lancashire, United King-
dom
Tel.: (44) 12 5487 2222
Web Site:
http://www.bowkerbmw.com
Sales Range: $50-74.9 Million
Emp.: 35
New & Used Motor Vehicle Dealer
N.A.I.C.S.: 441110
Chris Eccles (Gen Mgr-Sls)

BOWLER METCALF LIMITED
15 Harris Drive Ottery, Cape Town,
7800, South Africa
Tel.: (27) 217042223 **ZA**
Web Site:
https://www.bowlermetcalf.co.za
Year Founded: 1972
BCF—(JSE)
Rev.: $37,865,419
Assets: $44,546,784
Liabilities: $6,091,583
Net Worth: $38,455,201
Earnings: $3,627,943
Emp.: 592
Fiscal Year-end: 06/30/23
Plastic Product Mfr & Whslr
N.A.I.C.S.: 326199
Paul Friedrich Sass (CEO)

Subsidiaries:

Gad-Tek Proprietary Ltd **(1)**
Mahogany Road, Mahogany Ridge
KwaZulu-Natal, 3610, Pinetown, South Af-
rica
Tel.: (27) 317001880
Soft Drinks Mfr
N.A.I.C.S.: 312111

Postal Presents Proprietary Ltd **(1)**
Benbow Avenue 10 Epping Industrial 1,
7460, Cape Town, Western Cape, South
Africa
Tel.: (27) 215348070
Soft Drinks Mfr
N.A.I.C.S.: 312111

Quality Beverages 2000 Proprietary
Ltd **(1)**
10 Benbow Avenue Epping 1, Cape Town,
7460, South Africa
Tel.: (27) 215348070
Soft Drinks Mfr
N.A.I.C.S.: 312111
Francois Agenbach (COO)

BOWLEVEN PLC
News Building 3 London Bridge
Street 3rd Floor, London, SE1 9SG,
United Kingdom
Tel.: (44) 2033270150
Web Site: https://www.bowleven.com
BLVN—(AIM)
Assets: $162,008,000
Liabilities: $668,000
Net Worth: $161,340,000
Earnings: ($2,484,000)
Emp.: 6
Fiscal Year-end: 06/30/22
Oil & Gas Exploration Services
N.A.I.C.S.: 213112
David Clarkson (COO)

Subsidiaries:

EurOil Limited **(1)**
46 Rue Foucauld 2nd Floor Next to Univer-
site de la Cote, Akwa, Douala, Littoral,
Cameroon
Tel.: (237) 233437272
Oil & Gas Exploration Services
N.A.I.C.S.: 213112

BOWMAN POWER GROUP LTD
Ocean Quay Belvidere Road, South-
ampton, SO14 5QY, Hants, United
Kingdom
Tel.: (44) 23 8023 6700
Web Site:
http://www.bowmanpower.com.uk
Year Founded: 2004
Power Generator Mfr
N.A.I.C.S.: 335312
Toby King (CEO)

BOWMARK CAPITAL LLP
One Eagle Place, London, SW1Y
6AF, United Kingdom
Tel.: (44) 207189 9000 **UK**
Web Site: http://www.bowmark.com
Year Founded: 1997
Private Equity Investment Firm
N.A.I.C.S.: 523940
David Walsh (Controller-Fin)

Subsidiaries:

Tax Systems plc **(1)**
Magna House 18-32 London Road,
Staines-upon-Thames, TW18 4BP, United
Kingdom
Tel.: (44) 1784 777700
Web Site: http://www.taxsystemsplc.co.uk
Rev.: $20,383,854
Assets: $119,229,829
Liabilities: $55,444,785
Net Worth: $63,785,044
Earnings: ($634,086)
Emp.: 90
Fiscal Year-end: 12/31/2017
Investment Services
N.A.I.C.S.: 523999

Gavin Lyons (CEO)

Subsidiary (Domestic):

KPM-UK Taxis Plc **(2)**
Hemming St, London, E1 5BL, United King-
dom
Tel.: (44) 2073772182
Web Site: http://www.kpmuktaxis.com
Sales Range: $25-49.9 Million
New & Used Taxi & Cab Dealers
N.A.I.C.S.: 441110

BOX SHIPS, INC.
15 Karamanli Ave, Voula, Athens,
Greece
Tel.: (30) 2108914600 **MH**
Year Founded: 2010
TEUFF—(OTCIQ)
Sales Range: Less than $1 Million
Shipping Services
N.A.I.C.S.: 483111
George Skrimizeas (COO)

BOX UK LIMITED
Octagon Point 5 Cheapside, London,
EC2V 6AA, United Kingdom
Tel.: (44) 20 7439 1900
Web Site: http://www.boxuk.com
Year Founded: 1998
Sales Range: $1-9.9 Million
Emp.: 66
Software Publisher
N.A.I.C.S.: 513210
Benno Wasserstein (Mng Dir)

Subsidiaries:

Box UK Limited **(1)**
Westgate Court Westgate Street, Cardiff,
CF10 1DD, United Kingdom
Tel.: (44) 29 2022 8822
Web Site: http://www.boxuk.com
Emp.: 50
Software Publisher
N.A.I.C.S.: 513210
Benno Wasserstein (Mng Dir)

BOYAA INTERACTIVE INTER-NATIONAL LTD
Room 801 Building E1 TCL Science
Park 1001 Zhongshanyuan Road,
Shuguang Community Xili Street
Nanshan District, Shenzhen, 518000,
China
Tel.: (86) 75586513574
Web Site: http://www.boyaa.com
0434—(HKG)
Rev.: $52,687,346
Assets: $250,837,236
Liabilities: $46,234,562
Net Worth: $204,602,674
Earnings: $9,013,680
Emp.: 295
Fiscal Year-end: 12/31/22
Online Game Publisher
N.A.I.C.S.: 513199
Wei Zhang (Founder)

Subsidiaries:

PT Boyaa Interactive Indonesia **(1)**
5/F Setiabudi Atrium Setiabudi One Jl HR
Rasuna Said Kav 62, Jakarta, 12920, Indo-
nesia
Tel.: (62) 215210344
Board Game Product Mfr
N.A.I.C.S.: 339930

BOYALIFE GROUP
No 800 Jiefang East Road, Wuxi,
214002, Jiangsu, China
Tel.: (86) 51081808111
Web Site:
http://www.boyalifegroup.com
Year Founded: 2009
Holding Company
N.A.I.C.S.: 551112
Chris Xu (Co-Founder & Chm)

Subsidiaries:

ThermoGenesis Holdings, Inc. **(1)**
2890 Kilgore Rd, Rancho Cordova, CA
95742
Tel.: (916) 858-5100
Web Site: https://www.thermogenesis.com
Rev.: $10,483,000
Assets: $19,386,000
Liabilities: $16,063,000
Net Worth: $3,323,000
Earnings: ($11,270,000)
Emp.: 40
Fiscal Year-end: 12/31/2022
Research & Development in the Blood Pro-
cessing & Wound Care Industries
N.A.I.C.S.: 334516
Xiaochun Xu (Pres, CEO & Chm)

Subsidiary (Non-US):

TotipotentRX Cell Therapy Pvt
Ltd. **(2)**
857 Udyog Vihar Phase V, Gurgaon,
122016, India
Tel.: (91) 124 497 6860
Web Site: http://www.totipotentrx.com
Emp.: 40
Medicinal Product Mfr
N.A.I.C.S.: 339112
Venkatesh Ponemone (Dir-Clinical & Scien-
tific Affairs)

BOYD GROUP SERVICES INC.
1745 Ellice Avenue, Winnipeg, R3H
1A6, MB, Canada
Tel.: (204) 895-1244 **MB**
Web Site:
https://www.boydgroup.com
Year Founded: 1990
BYD—(OTCIQ)
Rev.: $1,872,670,000
Assets: $2,027,127,000
Liabilities: $1,300,693,000
Net Worth: $726,434,000
Earnings: $23,540,000
Emp.: 10,151
Fiscal Year-end: 12/31/21
Unincorporated, Open-Ended Mutual
Fund Trust
N.A.I.C.S.: 525910
David G. Brown (Chm)

Subsidiaries:

The Boyd Group Inc. **(1)**
1745 Ellice Avenue, Winnipeg, R3H 1A6,
MB, Canada
Tel.: (204) 895-1244
Web Site: https://www.boydgroup.com
Sales Range: $25-49.9 Million
Emp.: 50
Collision Repair Facility Operator
N.A.I.C.S.: 811198
Brock W. Bulbuck (Pres & CEO)

Subsidiary (US):

The Boyd Group (U.S.) Inc. **(2)**
8250 N Skokie Blvd, Skokie, IL 60077
Tel.: (847) 679-0510
Automotive Repair & Maintenance Services
N.A.I.C.S.: 811111

Subsidiary (Domestic):

Collex Collision Experts, Inc. **(3)**
1998 Rochester Industrial Dr, Rochester
Hills, MI 48309
Tel.: (586) 493-9100
Web Site: http://www.collexcollision.com
Automotive Body, Paint & Interior Repair &
Maintenance
N.A.I.C.S.: 811121

Red Mountain Collision **(3)**
3145 E Main St, Mesa, AZ 85213-9503
Tel.: (480) 981-8555
Web Site: http://www.carcoa.com
Automotive Body, Paint & Interior Repair &
Maintenance
N.A.I.C.S.: 811121
Mark Smee (Pres)

The Gerber Group, Inc. **(3)**
400 W Grand Ave, Elmhurst, IL 60126
Tel.: (630) 832-0670

Holding Company; Automotive Glass & Collision Repair Services
N.A.I.C.S.: 551112

Subsidiary (Domestic):

Cars Collision Center, LLC **(4)**
8250 N Skokie Blvd, Skokie, IL 60077
Tel.: (847) 679-0510
Web Site: http://www.gerbercollision.com
Sales Range: $50-74.9 Million
Automotive Repair Services
N.A.I.C.S.: 811121

Subsidiary (Domestic):

Gerber Collision & Glass (Kansas),
Inc. **(5)**
5617 W Kellogg St, Wichita, KS 67209
Tel.: (316) 945-7007
Web Site: http://www.gerbercollision.com
Sales Range: $50-74.9 Million
Emp.: 7
Automotive Repair & Maintenance Services
N.A.I.C.S.: 811111

Gerber Collision & Glass -
Denver **(5)**
2228 S Colorado Blvd, Denver, CO 80222
Tel.: (303) 691-2639
Web Site: http://www.gerbercollision.com
Sales Range: $1-9.9 Million
Auto Body Repair Services
N.A.I.C.S.: 811121

True2Form Collision Repair Centers,
Inc. **(5)**
4853 Galaxy Pkwy Ste E, Cleveland, OH
44128
Tel.: (216) 755-1191
Web Site: http://www.true2form.com
Sales Range: $50-74.9 Million
Emp.: 12
Automobiles Collision Repair Services
N.A.I.C.S.: 811111

Subsidiary (Domestic):

True2form Collision Repair Centers,
LLC **(6)**
400 W Grand Ave, Elmhurst, IL 60126
Tel.: (630) 832-0670
Automotive Repair Services
N.A.I.C.S.: 811121

Subsidiary (Domestic):

Glass America, Inc. **(4)**
150 N Michigan Ave Ste 1580, Chicago, IL
60601
Tel.: (312) 781-6450
Web Site: http://www.glassusa.com
Sales Range: $25-49.9 Million
Automotive Glass Replacement Shops
N.A.I.C.S.: 811122

Nu-Look Collision, Inc. **(4)**
280 Monroe Ave, Rochester, NY 14607
Tel.: (585) 454-5558
Auto Body Repair/Painting
N.A.I.C.S.: 811121

**BOYNER BUYUK MAGAZACI-
LIK A.S.**
Buyukdere Caddesi Noramin Is
Merkezi No 237 E Maslak, Istanbul,
Turkiye
Tel.: (90) 2123357500
Web Site: http://www.boyner.com.tr
BOYNR—(IST)
Sales Range: $350-399.9 Million
Emp.: 2,595
Departmental Store Operator
N.A.I.C.S.: 455110
S. Arzu Sonmez *(Deputy Gen Mgr-
Fin Affairs & Info Sys)*

**BOYUAN CONSTRUCTION
GROUP, INC.**
Jinhui Plaza 500 Matang Road Jiax-
ing Economic Development Zone,
Jiaxing, 314000, Zheijiang, China
Tel.: (86) 57385581278   Ca
Web Site:
http://www.boyuangroup.com

BOY—(TSX)
Rev.: $395,171,956
Assets: $310,167,828
Liabilities: $185,026,542
Net Worth: $125,141,286
Earnings: $19,184,806
Emp.: 580
Fiscal Year-end: 06/30/19
Construction Services
N.A.I.C.S.: 236220
Cailiang Shou *(Chm, Pres & CEO)*

BOYUAN HOLDINGS LIMITED
Level 16 5 Martin Place, Sydney,
2000, NSW, Australia
Tel.: (61) 290489888   AU
Web Site:
http://www.bhlgroup.com.au
Rev.: $15,022,897
Assets: $74,205,978
Liabilities: $32,666,409
Net Worth: $41,539,570
Earnings: $1,180,570
Fiscal Year-end: 12/31/19
Property Management Services
N.A.I.C.S.: 531311
Caden Wan *(CEO)*

**BOZHON PRECISION INDUS-
TRY TECHNOLOGY CO., LTD.**
No 666 Huxin Road, Wujiang District,
Suzhou, 215222, Jiangsu, China
Tel.: (86) 51263414949
Web Site:
https://www.bozhontech.com
Year Founded: 2006
688097—(SHG)
Rev.: $675,535,765
Assets: $1,069,872,402
Liabilities: $539,272,904
Net Worth: $530,599,497
Earnings: $46,531,859
Emp.: 1,808
Fiscal Year-end: 12/31/22
Electronic Product Mfr & Distr
N.A.I.C.S.: 334419
Jie Han *(Sec)*

BOZLU HOLDING
Mongeri Binasi 19 Mayis Mahallesi Dr
Sevket Bey Sokak No 5, Sisli, Istan-
bul, 34370, Turkiye
Tel.: (90) 212 231 0303
Web Site:
http://www.bozluholding.com.tr
Holding Company
N.A.I.C.S.: 551112
Sukru Bozluolcay *(Chm & CEO)*

Subsidiaries:

Epsilon Electronics Industry and
Trade Inc. **(1)**
19 Mayis Mh Dr Sevket Bey Sk No 5,
34360, Istanbul, Turkiye
Tel.: (90) 212 219 56 57
Web Site: http://www.epsilonelektronik.com
Emp.: 20
Sale Marketing & Maintenance in Nuclear
Medicine & Radiotherapy Distr
N.A.I.C.S.: 423440
Aydin Kucuk *(Gen Mgr)*

Epsilon Landauer Dozimetri Teknolo-
jileri Sanayi ve Ticaret A.S. **(1)**
19 Mayis Mah Dr Sevket Bey Sk No 5,
Sisli, Istanbul, Turkiye **(50%)**
Tel.: (90) 2122476599
Web Site:
https://www.epsilonlandauer.com.tr
Radiation Dose Measurement & Tracking
Equipment Mfr & Services
N.A.I.C.S.: 334519

MNT Healthcare Services and Trade
Inc. **(1)**
Yucel Sk No 8 1 Levent, Nisbetiye, Besik-
tas, 34340, Turkiye
Tel.: (90) 4444668668
Web Site: http://www.mnt.com.tr
Nuclear Medicine Services

N.A.I.C.S.: 541380

Molecular Imaging Industry and Trad-
ing Co. Inc. **(1)**
Mongeri Binasi 19 Mayis Mahallesi Dr
Sevket Bey Sokak No 5, 34360, Istanbul,
Turkiye
Tel.: (90) 212 231 0303
Web Site: http://www.molimg.com
Molecular Medicine Research, Development
& Production
N.A.I.C.S.: 541715
Dilek Turhan *(Branch Mgr)*

Solar Enerji Teknolojileri Ve Metal
Sanayi Ticaret A.S. **(1)**
NOSAB Ihlamur Cd No 26, Nilufer, Bursa,
16140, Turkiye
Tel.: (90) 224 411 99 49
Web Site: http://www.solentek.com.tr
Emp.: 10
Solar Energy Technologies & Contract Ser-
vices for Metal Industry
N.A.I.C.S.: 332999
Rachel Mills *(Gen Mgr)*

Varinak Onkoloji Sistemleri Satis ve
Servis A.S. **(1)**
19 Mayis District Dr Sevket Bey Street No
5, Istanbul, Turkiye
Tel.: (90) 212 219 55 56
Web Site: http://www.varinak.com
Medical Equipment Distr
N.A.I.C.S.: 423450

BP PLASTICS HOLDING BHD.
5A Jalan Wawasan 2 Kawasan Perin-
dustrian Sri Gading, 83300, Batu Pa-
hat, Johor, Malaysia
Tel.: (60) 74557633
Web Site: https://www.bpplas.com
BPPLAS—(KLS)
Rev.: $102,220,351
Assets: $75,902,475
Liabilities: $18,521,834
Net Worth: $57,380,641
Earnings: $7,669,455
Emp.: 516
Fiscal Year-end: 12/31/23
Plastic Mfr
N.A.I.C.S.: 326112
Kim Hock Lim *(Chm)*

BP PLC
1 St James's Square, London, SW1Y
4PD, United Kingdom
Tel.: (44) 2074964000   UK
Web Site: https://www.bp.com
Year Founded: 1909
BP—(NYSE)
Rev.: $213,032,000,000
Assets: $280,294,000,000
Liabilities: $194,801,000,000
Net Worth: $85,493,000,000
Earnings: $15,880,000,000
Emp.: 88,564
Fiscal Year-end: 12/31/23
Petrochemicals Extraction Services
N.A.I.C.S.: 551112
Craig Marshall *(Sr VP & Head-IR)*

Subsidiaries:

Air BP Finland Oy **(1)**
Oljytie 4, 01530, Vantaa, Finland
Tel.: (358) 505567272
N.A.I.C.S.: 424720

Air BP Limited **(1)**
Chertsey Road, Sunbury, TW16 7LN,
Middlesex, United Kingdom
Tel.: (44) 1932762000
Sales Range: $300-349.9 Million
Aviation Fuel, Lubricants & Specialty Prod-
ucts Supplier
N.A.I.C.S.: 424720
Matt Elliott *(Chief Comml Officer)*

Subsidiary (Non-US):

AIR BP Sales Romania SRL **(2)**
Str Aurel Vlaicu nr 59 Aeroportul International Henri Coanda Bucuresti, OP 21 CP
18, Otopeni, Ilfov, Romania
Tel.: (40) 212014748

Sales Range: $25-49.9 Million
Emp.: 21
Aviation Fuel Distr
N.A.I.C.S.: 424720

Subsidiary (US):

Air BP Americas **(2)**
150 W Warrenville Rd Bldg 200, Naperville,
IL 60563
Tel.: (888) 274-3578
Aviation Fuel Distr
N.A.I.C.S.: 424720

Subsidiary (Non-US):

Air BP Argentina S.A. **(2)**
Av Alicia Moreau de Justo 140, Piso 3,
Buenos Aires, C1107AAD, Argentina
Tel.: (54) 41145000
Sales Range: $25-49.9 Million
Emp.: 11
Petroleum Product Whslr
N.A.I.C.S.: 424720

Air BP Brasil S.A. **(2)**
Av Rouxinol 55, 1206 a 1211 Moema, Sao
Paulo, 04516 000, Brazil
Tel.: (55) 1130549306
Web Site: http://www.bp.com
Emp.: 100
Storage & Distribution of Aviation Fuels &
Lubricants
N.A.I.C.S.: 424720

Air BP Canada Limited **(2)**
5915 Airport Rd Ste 820, Mississauga, L4V
1T1, ON, Canada **(100%)**
Tel.: (905) 671-4568
Web Site: http://www.airbp.com
Sales Range: $25-49.9 Million
Emp.: 5
Petroleum Fuel & Lubricant Distr
N.A.I.C.S.: 424720

Air BP China **(2)**
2101-03 21/F R F Center 10 Hua Xia Road,
Guangzhou, 510623, China
Tel.: (86) 2081136888
Web Site: http://www.bp.com
Aviation Fuel Distr
N.A.I.C.S.: 424720

Air BP Eastern Mediterranian Ltd **(2)**
41-49 Ayiou Nicolaou Street Nimeli Court
2nd Floor Office 27, Engomi, 2408, Nicosia,
Cyprus
Tel.: (357) 22362300
Web Site: http://www.bp.com
Sales Range: $25-49.9 Million
Emp.: 12
Aviation Fuels & Lubricants Supplier
N.A.I.C.S.: 424720

Air BP Italia S.p.A. **(2)**
Sede legale - Via Sardegna 38, 187, Rome,
Italy
Tel.: (39) 0642034440
Web Site: http://www.bp.com
Sales Range: $25-49.9 Million
Emp.: 15
Petroleum Product Distr
N.A.I.C.S.: 424720

Air BP Moscow **(2)**
Novinsky Blvd 8 Floor 18, 121099, Moscow,
Russia
Tel.: (7) 495 7876037
Web Site: http://www.bp.com
Emp.: 10
Aviation Fuel Distr
N.A.I.C.S.: 424720

Subsidiary (US):

Air BP Puerto Rico **(2)**
Base Muniz Area/Fuel Terminal, Carolina,
PR 00979
Tel.: (787) 253-2100
Web Site: http://www.bp.com
Sales Range: $25-49.9 Million
Emp.: 35
Petroleum Product Distr
N.A.I.C.S.: 424720

Subsidiary (Non-US):

Air BP Sweden AB **(2)**
Hemvarnsgatan 9, 171 54, Stockholm, Swe-
den
Tel.: (46) 87722320

BP plc—(Continued)

Web Site: http://www.airbp.com
Sales Range: $25-49.9 Million
Emp.: 30
Aviation Fuel, Lubricants & Specialty Products Supplier
N.A.I.C.S.: 424720

Air BP Switzerland (2)
Neuhofstrasse 12, 0040, Daar, Switzerland
Tel.: (41) 584569250
Web Site: http://www.bp.com
Aviation Fuel Distr
N.A.I.C.S.: 424720

Air BP Norway AS (1)
Tjuvholmen Alle 3, 0252, Oslo, Norway
Tel.: (47) 22511220
N.A.I.C.S.: 424720

Amoco Argentina Oil Co. (1)
Ave Leandro N Alem 1180, 1001, Buenos Aires, Argentina (100%)
Tel.: (54) 141096000
Sales Range: $200-249.9 Million
Emp.: 270
Crude Oil Exploration & Production
N.A.I.C.S.: 211120

Amoco Trinidad Gas B.V. (1)
Binckhorstlaan 410, 2516 BL, Hague, Netherlands
Tel.: (31) 703713000
Web Site: https://amocotrinidadgas.com
N.A.I.C.S.: 213112
Keon Mug Lim (Chm)

Archaea Energy Inc. (1)
500 Technology Drive 2nd Fl, Canonsburg, 15317, PA
Tel.: (713) 446-6259
Investment Services
N.A.I.C.S.: 523999
Daniel Joseph Rice IV (Chm)

Subsidiary (Domestic):

Aria Energy LLC (2)
46280 Dylan Dr Ste 200, Novi, MI 48377
Tel.: (248) 380-3920
Web Site: http://www.ariaenergy.com
Renewable Energy Power Plant Construction & Operation Services; Owned by Enpower Corp. & by EIF Management, LLC
N.A.I.C.S.: 237990
William Owen (VP-Bus Dev)

Subsidiary (Domestic):

Innovative Energy Systems, LLC (3)
2999 Judge Rd, Oakfield, NY 14125
Tel.: (585) 948-8580
Web Site: http://www.ieslfge.com
Sales Range: $10-24.9 Million
Landfill Gas Energy Conversion Facility Construction Services
N.A.I.C.S.: 237990
Peter H. Zeliff (CEO)

Aspac Lubricants (Malaysia) Sdn. Bhd. (1)
Lot No 197 II and 197 III Jalan Pelabuhan Utara, 42000, Port Klang, Malaysia
Tel.: (60) 331695300
Sales Range: $100-124.9 Million
Oil & Gas Extraction Services
N.A.I.C.S.: 213111

BP (China) Holdings Limited (1)
Unit 2001 20F West Tower World Financial Centre No 1 East 3rd Ring, Middle Road Chaoyang District, Beijing, 100020, China
Tel.: (86) 10 6589 3888
Web Site: http://www.bp.com
Investment Management Service
N.A.I.C.S.: 523940

BP - Castrol (Thailand) Limited (1)
23rd Floor Rajanakarn Building 183 South Sathon Road, Yannawa Sathon, Bangkok, 10120, Thailand
Tel.: (66) 2 684 3555
Lubricating Oil Mfr
N.A.I.C.S.: 324191

BP Algeria (1)
Lotissement No 16 Les Cretes, Hydra, 16035, Algiers, Algeria
Tel.: (213) 21481029
Web Site: http://www.bp.com

Sales Range: $75-99.9 Million
Emp.: 156
Petroleum & Petroleum Products Distr
N.A.I.C.S.: 424720

BP Alternative Energy International Ltd. (1)
Chertsey Road, Sunbury-on-Thames, TW16 7LN, United Kingdom
Tel.: (44) 1932762000
Web Site: http://www.bp.com
Eletric Power Generation Services
N.A.I.C.S.: 221118

BP America, Inc. (1)
501 Westlake Park Blvd, Houston, TX 77079-2604
Tel.: (281) 366-2000
Web Site: http://www.bp.com
Sales Range: $1-4.9 Billion
Emp.: 7,500
Oil Exploration & Production; Gas & Power & Alternative Energy Businesses
N.A.I.C.S.: 211120
David C. Lawler (Chm & Pres)

Subsidiary (Domestic):

A M P M (2)
10216 224th E, Graham, WA 98338
Tel.: (253) 853-7140
Convenience Store
N.A.I.C.S.: 445131

BP America - West (2)
6 Centerpoint Dr, La Palma, CA 90623
Tel.: (714) 670-5400
Web Site: http://www.bp.com
Sales Range: $100-124.9 Million
Emp.: 400
Petroleum Refining Services
N.A.I.C.S.: 324110

Subsidiary (Domestic):

BP Carson Refinery (3)
2350 E 200 23St, Carson, CA 90810 (100%)
Tel.: (310) 549-6204
Web Site: http://www.arco.com
Crude Oil Production
N.A.I.C.S.: 211120
Robert A. Malone (Executives)

Subsidiary (Domestic):

Arco (4)
3296 El Cajon Blvd, San Diego, CA 92104-1429 (100%)
Tel.: (619) 282-7024
Sales Range: $25-49.9 Million
Emp.: 6
Gasoline Service Stations
N.A.I.C.S.: 457120
Victor Maldonado (Gen Mgr)

Branch (Domestic):

Arco AM PM (4)
400 R St Ste 1080, Sacramento, CA 95814
Tel.: (916) 445-1254
Web Site: https://www.ampm.com
Sales Range: $25-49.9 Million
Emp.: 4
Gasoline Stations
N.A.I.C.S.: 445131

Subsidiary (Domestic):

BP West Coast Products LLC (4)
4 Centerpoint Dr, La Palma, CA 90623
Tel.: (714) 670-5400
Sales Range: $150-199.9 Million
Emp.: 400
Crude Oil Production
N.A.I.C.S.: 211120

Unit (Domestic):

BP America Production Co. (2)
509 South Boston Ave, Tulsa, OK 74103-4602
Tel.: (918) 581-3011
Sales Range: $75-99.9 Million
Emp.: 200
Oil Well Operation
N.A.I.C.S.: 211120

BP America Production Co. (2)
2225 W Oklahoma Ave, Ulysses, KS 67880-8416

Tel.: (620) 356-1237
Sales Range: $50-74.9 Million
Emp.: 100
Crude Petroleum Production & Refining
N.A.I.C.S.: 211120

BP America Production Co. (2)
369 Terrapin Neck Rd, Marshall, TX 75670
Tel.: (903) 935-1161
Sales Range: $50-74.9 Million
Emp.: 13
Oil Well Operation
N.A.I.C.S.: 211120

BP America Production Co. (2)
716 Cemetary Rd, Zachary, LA 70791-6724
Tel.: (225) 654-0782
Sales Range: $50-74.9 Million
Emp.: 2
Oil Well Operation
N.A.I.C.S.: 211120

BP America Production Co. (2)
200 Energy Ct, Farmington, NM 87401-1010
Tel.: (505) 326-9200
Sales Range: $50-74.9 Million
Emp.: 100
Oil Well Operation
N.A.I.C.S.: 211120
James Walker (Mgr)

Unit (Non-US):

BP America Production Co. (2)
Tel.: (970) 247-6900
Sales Range: $25-49.9 Million
Emp.: 40
Oil Well Operation
N.A.I.C.S.: 211120

Plant (Domestic):

BP America, Inc. - Cooper River Plant (2)
1306 Amoco Dr, Charleston, SC 29492-7879
Tel.: (843) 884-6151
Polyester Resin Mfr
N.A.I.C.S.: 325211

Subsidiary (Domestic):

BP Chemicals, Inc. (2)
150 W Warrenville Rd B6, Naperville, IL 60563-8473 (100%)
Tel.: (630) 420-4300
Web Site: http://www.bptechchoice.com
Sales Range: $200-249.9 Million
Emp.: 800
Industrial Chemical Mfr; Holding Company
N.A.I.C.S.: 325199

Subsidiary (Domestic):

BP Amoco Chemical Company (3)
610 Spring St, Atlanta, GA 30308
Tel.: (404) 876-6755
Sales Range: $25-49.9 Million
Emp.: 25
Petrochemical Mfr
N.A.I.C.S.: 325110

BP Chemicals Inc. (3)
1306 Amoco Dr, Wando, SC 29492-7879
Tel.: (843) 884-6151
Sales Range: $125-149.9 Million
Emp.: 325
Petroleum Refining
N.A.I.C.S.: 324110

Group (Domestic):

BP Corporation North America Inc. (2)
150 W Warrenville Rd, Naperville, IL 60563 (100%)
Tel.: (630) 836-5000
Web Site: http://www.bp.com
Holding Company; Regional Managing Office
N.A.I.C.S.: 551112

Division (Domestic):

BP Alternative Energy North America, Inc. (3)
700 Lousiana St Fl 33, Houston, TX 77002
Tel.: (713) 354-2166
Web Site: http://www.bp.com
Emp.: 150

Alternative Fuels & Energy Generation Technologies Research & Development
N.A.I.C.S.: 541715

Subsidiary (Domestic):

BP Biofuels North America LLC (4)
501 Westlake Park Blvd, Houston, TX 77079
Tel.: (281) 366-2000
Web Site: http://www.bp.com
Biofuel Research & Development
N.A.I.C.S.: 541715

Subsidiary (Domestic):

BP Biofuels Louisiana LLC (5)
11107 Campbell Wells Rd E Hwy 90, Jennings, LA 70546
Tel.: (337) 785-4500
Sales Range: $200-249.9 Million
Emp.: 100
Cellulosic Ethanol & Other Biofuels Developer & Mfr
N.A.I.C.S.: 325414

Subsidiary (Domestic):

BP Wind Energy North America Inc. (4)
700 N San Jacinto St, Houston, TX 77002
Tel.: (713) 354-2100
Wind Turbine Power Plant Construction, Maintenance & Operation Services
N.A.I.C.S.: 221115
Robert Baker (Reg Mgr & Mgr-O&M Facility)

Subsidiary (Non-US):

BP Canada Energy Company (3)
240 4th Ave SW, PO Box 200, Calgary, T2P 2H8, AB, Canada (100%)
Tel.: (403) 233-1313
Web Site: http://www.bp.com
Sales Range: $700-749.9 Million
Emp.: 300
Oil Exploration & Production
N.A.I.C.S.: 211120

Branch (Domestic):

BP Corporation North America Inc. (3)
501 Westlake Park Blvd, Houston, TX 77079-2604 (100%)
Tel.: (361) 983-2641
Sales Range: $50-74.9 Million
Emp.: 2
Petroleum Refining
N.A.I.C.S.: 324110

BP Corporation North America Inc. (3)
4519 Grandview Rd, Blaine, WA 98230-9640
Tel.: (360) 371-1500
Sales Range: $450-499.9 Million
Emp.: 1,100
Petroleum Refining
N.A.I.C.S.: 324110
Mike Abendhoff (Dir-Pub Affairs)

BP Corporation North America Inc. (3)
28100 Torch Pkwy, Warrenville, IL 60555-3938
Tel.: (630) 836-5001
Web Site: http://www.bp.com
Holding Company; Oil Wells, Petroleum Pipelines & Refineries Operator; Petroleum Products Distr
N.A.I.C.S.: 551112

Division (Domestic):

BP Pipelines North America Inc. (3)
28100 Torch Pkwy, Warrenville, IL 60555
Tel.: (219) 472-2323
Operation of Crude Petroleum Pipelines
N.A.I.C.S.: 324110

Branch (Domestic):

BP Pipelines North America Inc. (4)
15600 W Bruns Rd, Manhattan, IL 60442-9537 (100%)
Tel.: (815) 478-6100
Sales Range: $25-49.9 Million
Emp.: 20
Petroleum Pipeline Operation

N.A.I.C.S.: 486910
Leon Li *(Engr-Mechanical)*

BP Pipelines North America Inc. **(4)**
200 Westlake Park Blvd, Houston, TX 77079-2663
Tel.: (505) 396-2817
Sales Range: $25-49.9 Million
Emp.: 20
Crude Petroleum Pipeline Operation
N.A.I.C.S.: 486910

BP Pipelines North America Inc. **(4)**
4000 Hwy 56, Houma, LA 70363-7817 **(100%)**
Tel.: (985) 580-2424
Web Site: http://www.bppipelines.com
Sales Range: $25-49.9 Million
Emp.: 13
Crude Petroleum Pipeline Operation
N.A.I.C.S.: 486910

BP Pipelines North America Inc. **(4)**
33632 Hwy 24, Salisbury, MO 65281
Tel.: (660) 388-5445
Sales Range: $25-49.9 Million
Emp.: 3
Crude Petroleum Pipeline Operation
N.A.I.C.S.: 486910
Joe Akkos *(Supvr)*

Division (Domestic):

BP Products North America Inc. **(3)**
150 W Warrenville Rd, Naperville, IL 60563-8473
Tel.: (630) 420-4300
Sales Range: $50-74.9 Million
Emp.: 200
Petroleum Product Distr
N.A.I.C.S.: 324110

Branch (Domestic):

BP Products North America Inc. **(4)**
1636 Commerce Rd, Richmond, VA 23224-7502
Tel.: (804) 232-2347
Sales Range: $25-49.9 Million
Emp.: 4
Petroleum Product Distr
N.A.I.C.S.: 424720

BP Products North America Inc. **(4)**
28301 Ferry Rd, Warrenville, IL 60555
Tel.: (630) 420-4300
Web Site: http://www.bp.com
Sales Range: $25-49.9 Million
Emp.: 70
Petroleum Terminal
N.A.I.C.S.: 486910

BP Products North America Inc. **(4)**
100 E Standard Oil Rd, Rochelle, IL 61068 **(100%)**
Tel.: (815) 562-7023
Sales Range: $25-49.9 Million
Emp.: 4
Petroleum Product Distr
N.A.I.C.S.: 424720
Dathnen Julian *(Mgr-Terminal)*

BP Products North America Inc. **(4)**
195 NE 183rd St, Miami, FL 33179-4443
Tel.: (305) 651-0957
Sales Range: $50-74.9 Million
Emp.: 6
Natural Gas Distribution
N.A.I.C.S.: 221210

BP Products North America Inc. **(4)**
205 Marion Ave, River Rouge, MI 48218-1695
Tel.: (313) 842-2114
Sales Range: $25-49.9 Million
Emp.: 30
Petroleum Product Distr
N.A.I.C.S.: 424720

BP Products North America Inc. **(4)**
2303 S Church St, Burlington, NC 27215-5331 **(100%)**
Tel.: (336) 229-5125
Sales Range: $50-74.9 Million
Emp.: 4
Gasoline Service Station Operation
N.A.I.C.S.: 324199

BP Products North America Inc. **(4)**
28100 Torch Pkwy 4th Fl, Warrenville, IL 60555-3938

Tel.: (630) 836-5100
Sales Range: $50-74.9 Million
Emp.: 175
Petroleum Product Distr
N.A.I.C.S.: 424710

BP Whiting Refinery **(4)**
2815 Indianapolis Blvd, Whiting, IN 46394-2197
Tel.: (219) 473-3500
Web Site: http://www.bp.com
Gasoline Production & Distribution
N.A.I.C.S.: 324110

Subsidiary (Domestic):

TravelCenters of America Inc. **(4)**
24601 Center Ridge Rd, Westlake, OH 44145-5639
Tel.: (440) 808-9100
Web Site: https://www.ta-petro.com
Rev.: $10,844,990,000
Assets: $3,652,907,000
Liabilities: $2,779,701,000
Net Worth: $873,206,000
Earnings: $164,060,000
Emp.: 18,500
Fiscal Year-end: 12/31/2022
Holding Company; Full-Service Motorist Travel Centers Operator
N.A.I.C.S.: 551112
Jennifer Babbin Clark *(Sec)*

Subsidiary (Domestic):

QSL of Austintown Ohio LLC **(5)**
5800 Interstate Blvd, Austintown, OH 44515
Tel.: (330) 349-9464
Emp.: 10
Full-service Motorist Travel Center Operator
N.A.I.C.S.: 811198

Quaker Steak & Lube **(5)**
24601 Center Ridge Rd, Westlake, OH 44145
Tel.: (724) 981-3123
Web Site: http://www.thelube.com
Full-Service Restaurants
N.A.I.C.S.: 722511

Rip Griffin Truck Service Center, Inc. **(5)**
4710 4th St, Lubbock, TX 79416
Tel.: (806) 795-8785
Web Site: https://www.ripgriffin.com
Truck Refueling Stations Operator & Petroleum Products Distr
N.A.I.C.S.: 457120

Subsidiary (Domestic):

Pro Petroleum, Inc. **(6)**
4710 4th St, Lubbock, TX 79408
Tel.: (806) 795-8785
Web Site: http://www.propetroleum.com
Rev.: $85,209,337
Emp.: 40
Petroleum Product Distr
N.A.I.C.S.: 424710

Subsidiary (Domestic):

TA Operating LLC **(5)**
24601 Ctr Rdg Rd, Westlake, OH 44145
Tel.: (617) 796-8390
Web Site: http://www.ta-petro.com
Sales Range: $1-4.9 Billion
Emp.: 5,071
Full-Service Motorist Travel Centers Operator
N.A.I.C.S.: 457110

Division (Domestic):

Castrol North America Inc. **(3)**
1500 Valley Rd, Wayne, NJ 07470-2040
Tel.: (973) 633-2200
Web Site: http://www.castrolusa.com
Sales Range: $50-74.9 Million
Emp.: 300
Lubricant & Oil Mfr & Distr
N.A.I.C.S.: 324191

Subsidiary (Domestic):

BP Castrol Consumer North America Inc. **(4)**
1500 Valley Dr, Wayne, NJ 07470 **(100%)**
Tel.: (973) 633-2200
Web Site: http://www.castrolusa.com

Sales Range: $75-99.9 Million
Lubricant Mfr & Distr
N.A.I.C.S.: 324191
Peter Miller *(CFO)*

Branch (Domestic):

Castrol North America Auto **(5)**
801 Wharf St, Richmond, CA 94804-3557
Tel.: (510) 236-6312
Sales Range: $50-74.9 Million
Emp.: 35
Auto Oils & Lubricants Mfr & Distr
N.A.I.C.S.: 324191

Subsidiary (Domestic):

BP Lubricants USA Inc. **(4)**
9300 Pulaski Hwy, Baltimore, MD 21220-2418
Tel.: (410) 574-5000
Web Site: http://www.bp.com
Sales Range: $25-49.9 Million
Emp.: 95
Commercial Lubricant Mfr & Distr
N.A.I.C.S.: 324191

Branch (Domestic):

BP Lubricants USA Inc. **(5)**
1981 S Westport Dr, Port Allen, LA 70767-6128 **(100%)**
Tel.: (225) 382-8500
Web Site: http://www.castrol.com
Sales Range: $100-124.9 Million
Emp.: 83
Auto Oils & Lubricants Mfr & Distr
N.A.I.C.S.: 324191

Subsidiary (Domestic):

Castrol Industrial North America Inc. **(4)**
150 W Warrenville Rd, Naperville, IL 60563
Tel.: (630) 892-8881
Web Site: http://www.castrolindustrial.com
Sales Range: $100-124.9 Million
Industrial Lubricants & Specialist Chemicals Mfr & Distr
N.A.I.C.S.: 324191

Branch (Domestic):

Castrol Industrial North America **(5)**
775 Louis Dr, Warminster, PA 18974-2827
Tel.: (215) 443-5220
Web Site: http://www.castrol.com
Sales Range: $75-99.9 Million
Emp.: 50
Industrial Lubricants & Specialist Chemicals Mfr & Distr
N.A.I.C.S.: 324191

Subsidiary (Domestic):

LubeCon Systems, Inc. **(5)**
201 N Webster St, White Cloud, MI 49349-0824
Tel.: (231) 689-0002
Web Site: https://lubeconusa.com
Sales Range: $75-99.9 Million
Emp.: 40
Lubricating Systems Mfr
N.A.I.C.S.: 424710

Subsidiary (Domestic):

BP Energy Company **(2)**
501 W Lake Pk Blvd, Houston, TX 77079 **(100%)**
Tel.: (281) 366-2000
Web Site: http://www.bp.com
Sales Range: $250-299.9 Million
Emp.: 500
Natural Gas Production
N.A.I.C.S.: 221122

Branch (Domestic):

BP Energy Co. **(3)**
69 Winn St, Burlington, MA 01803-4870 **(100%)**
Tel.: (781) 272-9181
Sales Range: $75-99.9 Million
Emp.: 2
Natural Gas Distribution
N.A.I.C.S.: 221210

Subsidiary (Domestic):

BP Oil Co. **(2)**

150 W Warrenville Rd, Naperville, IL 60563 **(100%)**
Tel.: (630) 420-5000
Web Site: http://www.bp.com
Sales Range: $50-74.9 Million
Emp.: 150
Crude Petroleum Production & Refining; Petroleum Product Distr; Gasoline Service Stations
N.A.I.C.S.: 324110

Subsidiary (Domestic):

BP Exploration (Alaska) Inc. **(3)**
900 E Benson Blvd, Anchorage, AK 99508-4254 **(100%)**
Tel.: (907) 561-5111
Web Site: http://www.bp.com
Oil & Gas Exploration & Production
N.A.I.C.S.: 211120

Joint Venture (Domestic):

BP Husky Refinery **(3)**
4001 Cedar Point Rd, Oregon, OH 43616-1310
Tel.: (419) 698-6200
Sales Range: $125-149.9 Million
Petroleum Refining Services; Owned by BP plc & Husky Energy, Inc.
N.A.I.C.S.: 324110

Subsidiary (Domestic):

BP Oil Company **(3)**
3250 SR 133, Bethel, OH 45106-8320 **(100%)**
Tel.: (937) 378-6001
Sales Range: $50-74.9 Million
Emp.: 6
Oil Well Operation
N.A.I.C.S.: 424710
Scott Schneider *(Mgr)*

BP Pipelines (Alaska) Inc. **(3)**
900 E Benson Blvd, Anchorage, AK 99508-4254
Tel.: (907) 561-5111
Crude Petroleum Pipeline Operation
N.A.I.C.S.: 486110

Branch (Domestic):

BP Oil Pipeline **(4)**
930 Tennessee Ave, Cincinnati, OH 45229-1006 **(100%)**
Tel.: (513) 825-5250
Sales Range: $25-49.9 Million
Emp.: 25
Crude Petroleum Pipeline Operation
N.A.I.C.S.: 486110

Subsidiary (Domestic):

BP Oil Shipping Company **(2)**
4850 E 49th St, Cleveland, OH 44125
Tel.: (216) 271-8003
Rev.: $83,965,562
Emp.: 333
Oil Tanker Operation
N.A.I.C.S.: 483113

Branch (Domestic):

BP Oil Shipping Company USA **(3)**
5502 Mahoning Ave, Youngstown, OH 44515-2315 **(100%)**
Tel.: (330) 799-7961
Sales Range: $25-49.9 Million
Emp.: 7
Oil Tanker Operation
N.A.I.C.S.: 483113
Dan McCracken *(Gen Mgr)*

BP Oil Shipping Company USA **(3)**
2827 Bethel Rd, Columbus, OH 43220 **(100%)**
Tel.: (614) 326-0565
Sales Range: $25-49.9 Million
Emp.: 12
Oil Tanker Operation
N.A.I.C.S.: 483113
Paul Carsey *(Gen Mgr)*

Melzer's Fuel Service Inc. **(3)**
7669 E Derry St, Painesville, OH 44077
Tel.: (440) 354-3545
Web Site: http://www.melzersfuel.com
Sales Range: $25-49.9 Million
Emp.: 11
Bulk Shipping Services

BP plc—(Continued)
N.A.I.C.S.: 424710

Subsidiary (Domestic):

BP Oil Supply Company Inc. **(2)**
28301 Ferry Rd, Warrenville, IL
60555-3018 **(100%)**
Tel.: (630) 836-4201
Sales Range: $26 40.0 Million
Emp.: 50
Petroleum Product Distr
N.A.I.C.S.: 424720

Branch (Domestic):

BP Oil Supply Company Inc. **(3)**
2441 S Reynolds Rd, Toledo, OH 43614-1420
Tel.: (419) 381-1181
Sales Range: $50-74.9 Million
Emp.: 5
Petroleum Product Distr
N.A.I.C.S.: 424720

BP Angola **(1)**
4 February St, Towres Atlantic Bldg, Luanda, Angola
Tel.: (244) 0222637440
Web Site: http://www.angola.bp.com
Sales Range: $400-449.9 Million
Emp.: 600
Petroleum & Gas Exploration & Production
N.A.I.C.S.: 211120

BP Asia Pacific (Malaysia) **(1)**
Level 9 Tower 5 Avenue 7 The Horizon
Bangsar South City, 59200, Kuala Lumpur, Malaysia
Tel.: (60) 322818181
Web Site: http://www.bp.com
Sales Range: $150-199.9 Million
Emp.: 380
Petroleum & Petroleum Products Mfr & Whslr
N.A.I.C.S.: 424720

Joint Venture (Domestic):

BP Petronas Acetyls Sdn Bhd **(2)**
Kertih Integrated Petrochemical Complex,
24300, Terengganu, Kertih, Malaysia
Tel.: (60) 95200222
Web Site: https://www.ineos-pcg.com
Sales Range: $100-124.9 Million
Emp.: 90
Acetid Acid Mfg; Owned 70% by BP plc &
30% by Petroliam Nasional Berhad
N.A.I.C.S.: 325180

BP Australia Capital Markets Limited **(1)**
The Tower Level 29 Melbourne Central, 360
Elizabeth Street, Melbourne, 3000, VIC,
Australia
Tel.: (61) 3 9268 4111
General Insurance Services
N.A.I.C.S.: 524298

BP Australia Pty. Ltd. **(1)**
717 Bourke St, GPO Box 5222, Melbourne,
3000, VIC, Australia **(100%)**
Tel.: (61) 1300130027
Web Site: https://www.bp.com
Sales Range: $150-199.9 Million
Emp.: 490
Petroleum Additives & Synthetic Fabrics
Producer
N.A.I.C.S.: 424720

BP Austria Aktiengesellschaft **(1)**
IZ No Sud Strasse 6 Obj 17, 2355, Vienna,
2355, Austria
Tel.: (43) 223668550
Web Site: http://www.bp.com
Sales Range: $75-99.9 Million
Emp.: 137
Petroleum Product Whslr
N.A.I.C.S.: 424720

Subsidiary (Domestic):

BP Austria Marketing GmbH **(2)**
Schwarzenbergplatz 13, A 1041, Vienna,
Austria
Tel.: (43) 150161380
Web Site: http://www.bp.com
Petroleum & Petroleum Products Whslr;
Gas Service Stations
N.A.I.C.S.: 457120

Subsidiary (Domestic):

BP Gas Austria GmbH Nfg. OHG **(3)**
Ziegeleistrasse 19, 5020, Salzburg, Austria
Tel.: (43) 6628734510
Sales Range: $25-49.9 Million
Emp.: 30
Liquefied Petroleum Gas Whslr
N.A.I.C.S.: 457210
Andreas Kubek (Mng Dir)

BP Schmierstoffe GmbH Nfg. OHG **(3)**
IZ NO Sud Strasse 6, Obj 17, A 2355, Wiener Neudorf, Austria
Tel.: (43) 223668550
Web Site: http://www.bp.com
Sales Range: $25-49.9 Million
Emp.: 31
Petroleum Products & Lubricants Whslr
N.A.I.C.S.: 424720

BP Azerbaijan **(1)**
2 Neftchilar prospecti (Bailov), Villa Petrolea, AZ1003, Baku, Azerbaijan
Tel.: (994) 412979000
Sales Range: $800-899.9 Million
Emp.: 1,500
Petroleum & Natural Gas Exploration, Refining & Production
N.A.I.C.S.: 211120

BP Belgium NV/SA **(1)**
Archimedes Building 11 Rond Point R
Schuman, 1040, Brussels, Belgium
Tel.: (32) 22878080
Web Site: http://www.bp.com
Sales Range: $25-49.9 Million
Emp.: 10
Chemicals Mfr & Distr
N.A.I.C.S.: 325998

Subsidiary (Non-US):

Westbit AB **(2)**
PO Box 16, 642 21, Flen, Sweden
Tel.: (46) 15713980
Sales Range: $25-49.9 Million
Emp.: 2
Marketing of Bitumen to the Road Construction Industry
N.A.I.C.S.: 424720

BP Berau Ltd. **(1)**
JI TB Simatupang Kav 88, Jakarta, 12520,
Indonesia
Tel.: (62) 2178838000
N.A.I.C.S.: 213112

BP Brasil Ltda **(1)**
Tel.: (55) 2125174400
Sales Range: $400-449.9 Million
Emp.: 620
Oil & Gas Exploration, Production & Sales
N.A.I.C.S.: 211120

BP Capital Markets plc **(1)**
25 North Colonnade Canary Wharf, London, E14 5HZ, United Kingdom
Tel.: (44) 2036830901
Web Site: http://www.bp.com
Investment Management Service
N.A.I.C.S.: 523999

Subsidiary (Non-US):

Yangtze River Acetyls Co. Ltd. **(2)**
27F Metropolitian Plaza 68 Zourong Rd Yuzhong District, Chongqing, 400010, China
Tel.: (86) 2363810694
Web Site: http://www.bp.com
Sales Range: $50-74.9 Million
Emp.: 200
Inorganic Chemical Mfr
N.A.I.C.S.: 325180

BP Chembel N.V. **(1)**
Amocolaan 2, Geel, 20440,
Belgium **(100%)**
Tel.: (32) 14864211
Web Site: http://www.bpgeel.be
Sales Range: $125-149.9 Million
Emp.: 400
Chemicals Mfr & Distr
N.A.I.C.S.: 325998

BP Chemical Trelleborg AB **(1)**
Strandridareg 1, PO Box 302, 231 21,
Trelleborg, Sweden
Tel.: (46) 41052300
Web Site: http://www.bp.com

Sales Range: $25-49.9 Million
Emp.: 54
Polystyrene Mfr
N.A.I.C.S.: 325211

BP Chemicals Ltd. **(1)**
Saltend, Hull, HU12 8DS, East Yorkshire,
United Kingdom **(100%)**
Tel.: (44) 1482896251
Web Site: http://www.bp.com
Sales Range: $75-99.9 Million
Emp.: 200
Chemicals Mfr & Distr
N.A.I.C.S.: 424690

BP Company North America Inc. **(1)**
501 WestLake Park Blvd, Houston, TX
77079
Tel.: (281) 366-2000
Petroleum Refining Services
N.A.I.C.S.: 324110

BP Danmark A/S **(1)**
Orestads Boulevard 73, 2300, Copenhagen,
Denmark
Tel.: (45) 89487700
Web Site: http://www.bp.dk
Sales Range: $50-74.9 Million
Emp.: 65
Petroleum & Petroleum Products, Fuels,
Petrochemicals & Gas Whslr
N.A.I.C.S.: 424720

Subsidiary (Domestic):

BP Lubricants A/S **(2)**
Orestads Boulevard 73, 2300, Copenhagen,
Denmark
Tel.: (45) 80889499
Web Site: http://www.bp.com
Petroleum Products & Lubricants Whslr
N.A.I.C.S.: 424720

BP Egypt **(1)**
14 Road 252, Digla Maadi, Cairo,
Egypt **(100%)**
Tel.: (20) 25199915
Sales Range: $50-74.9 Million
Emp.: 100
Petroleum Exploration & Production
N.A.I.C.S.: 211120

Subsidiary (Domestic):

BP Exploration and Production Egypt LLC **(2)**
14 Road 252, Degla Maadi, Cairo, Egypt
Tel.: (20) 25199915
Web Site: http://www.bp.com
Sales Range: $75-99.9 Million
Petroleum & Gas Exploration & Production
N.A.I.C.S.: 211120

BP Marketing Egypt Ltd **(2)**
14 Road 252, PO Box 2409, Digla Maadi,
Cairo, Egypt
Tel.: (20) 25199915
Web Site: http://www.bp.com
Petroleum & Petroleum Products Marketing
N.A.I.C.S.: 424720

BP Energy Company-Trinidad & Tobago **(1)**
5 & 5A Queens Park West Plaza, Port of
Spain, Trinidad & Tobago **(100%)**
Tel.: (868) 6232862
Petroleum Exploration & Production
N.A.I.C.S.: 211120

BP Espana S.A.U. **(1)**
Parque Empresarial Omega Edificio D
Avenida de Barajas 30, Arroyo de la Vega,
Madrid, 28108, Alcobendas, Spain **(100%)**
Tel.: (34) 902107001
Web Site: http://www.bp.com
Sales Range: $150-199.9 Million
Emp.: 500
Petroleum Exploration & Production & Petroleum Products Whslr
N.A.I.C.S.: 211120

Subsidiary (Domestic):

BP Oil Espana S.A. **(2)**
Parque Empresarial Omega Edificio D
Avenida de Barajas 30, Alcobendas, 28108,
Madrid, Spain
Tel.: (34) 902107001
Web Site: http://www.bp.com
Sales Range: $150-199.9 Million
Emp.: 300

Petroleum Products Marketing; Gasoline
Service Stations
N.A.I.C.S.: 424720

Subsidiary (Domestic):

BP Gas Espana S.A. **(3)**
Avenida de Bruselas 36 Parque Empresarial Arroyo de la Vega, Alcobendas,
28108, Madrid, Spain
Tel.: (34) 902107001
Web Site: http://www.bpesp.com
Natural Gas Distr
N.A.I.C.S.: 213112

BP Oil Refineria de Castellon, S.A.U. **(3)**
Poligono Industrial El Serrallo s/n Codigo
Postal, El Grao, 12100, Castellon de la
Plana, Spain
Tel.: (34) 964347000
Web Site: https://www.bp.com
Sales Range: $125-149.9 Million
Petroleum Refining
N.A.I.C.S.: 324110

Subsidiary (Non-US):

BP Solar Espana, S.A.U. **(2)**
Tel.: (34) 918071600
Web Site: http://www.bp.com
Sales Range: $150-199.9 Million
Solar Cells & Modules Production
N.A.I.C.S.: 334515

BP Europa SE Oddzial w Polsce **(1)**
ul Pawia 9, 31-154, Krakow, Poland
Tel.: (48) 721020304
Web Site: http://www.bp.com
Petroleum Product Distr
N.A.I.C.S.: 424720

**BP Europa SE Zweigniederlassung
BP Austria AG** **(1)**
Am Belvedere 10, 1100, Vienna, Austria
Tel.: (43) 800223350
Web Site: https://www.bp.com
Sales Range: $75-99.9 Million
Emp.: 81
Petroleum Product Distr
N.A.I.C.S.: 424720

**BP Europa SE Zweigniederlassung
BP Gas Austria** **(1)**
Franz Broetzner Strasse 7/6, 5071,
Salzburg, Austria
Tel.: (43) 662 873451
Web Site: http://www.bp.com
Oil & Gas Exploration Services
N.A.I.C.S.: 213112

BP Exploration (Alpha) Limited **(1)**
Unit No 71 & 73 7th Floor 2nd North Avenue Maxity Bandra Kurla Complex, Bandra
E, Mumbai, 400051, India
Tel.: (91) 22 7177 7000
Web Site: http://www.bp.com
Emp.: 65
Petroleum Extraction Services
N.A.I.C.S.: 211120

BP Exploration (Caspian Sea) Ltd **(1)**
Oil & Gas Exploration Services
N.A.I.C.S.: 213112

BP Exploration Operating Co Ltd **(1)**
Tel.: (971) 24935555
Oil & Gas Exploration Services
N.A.I.C.S.: 213112

BP Exploration Operating Company Limited **(1)**
Chertsey Road, Sunbury-on-Thames, TW16
7LN, United Kingdom
Tel.: (44) 1932762000
Holding Company; Oil & Gas Exploration
N.A.I.C.S.: 551112

Subsidiary (Domestic):

BP **(2)**
124 Welhead Ave Stony Wood Park, Dyce,
Aberdeen, AB21 7PB, United
Kingdom **(100%)**
Tel.: (44) 1224832000
Web Site: http://www.bp.com
Sales Range: $300-349.9 Million
Emp.: 700
Petroleum Exploration & Production
N.A.I.C.S.: 211120

Subsidiary (Non-US):

BP Exploration (Faroes) Limited   **(2)**
Ground Floor 640 e/f, Skansavegur 1, Torshavn, Faroe Islands
Tel.: (298) 353130
Oil & Gas Exploration
N.A.I.C.S.: 211120

Subsidiary (Domestic):

BP Exploration Company Limited   **(2)**
Chertsey Rd, Sunbury-on-Thames, TW16 7LN, Mddx, United Kingdom   **(100%)**
Tel.: (44) 1932 762000
Web Site: http://www.bp.com
Sales Range: $75-99.9 Million
Emp.: 200
Exploration for & Production of Oil & Gas
N.A.I.C.S.: 211120

BP France SA   **(1)**
Campus Saint Christophe Galilee Building 3, 10 Avenue de l'Entreprise Pontoise, 95863, Cergy, France   **(100%)**
Tel.: (33) 134224000
Web Site: https://www.bp.com
Sales Range: $50-74.9 Million
Emp.: 250
Oil Refineries
N.A.I.C.S.: 324110

BP Global Investment Salalah & Co LLC   **(1)**
Raysut, PO Box 2309, 211, Salalah, Oman
Tel.: (968) 23 219156
Web Site: http://www.bp.com
Petroleum Product Distr
N.A.I.C.S.: 424720

BP Global Investments Ltd.   **(1)**
20 Canada Square, London, E14 5NJ, United Kingdom
Tel.: (44) 2079484000
Emp.: 100
Investment Management Service
N.A.I.C.S.: 523999

BP Hong Kong Limited   **(1)**
22nd Fl Devon House, 979 Kings Rd Taikoo Pl, Hong Kong, China (Hong Kong)   **(100%)**
Tel.: (852) 25868899
Web Site: http://www.bp.com
Sales Range: $25-49.9 Million
Emp.: 50
Petroleum Product Distr
N.A.I.C.S.: 424720

BP Hungary Ltd   **(1)**
Arboc utca 1-3, 1133, Budapest, Hungary
Tel.: (36) 23505350
Web Site: https://www.bp.com
Sales Range: $50-74.9 Million
Emp.: 60
Lubricants & Aviation Fuels Distr
N.A.I.C.S.: 424720

BP India Services Pvt. Ltd   **(1)**
15th Floor Dr Gopal Das Bhawan 28 Barakhamba Road, New Delhi, 110 001, India
Tel.: (91) 1143755000
Web Site: http://www.bp.com
Emp.: 10
Oil & Gas Extraction Services
N.A.I.C.S.: 213112

Subsidiary (Non-US):

BP Magyarorszag Kft   **(2)**
Puskas Tivadar u 11, 2040, Budaors, Hungary
Tel.: (36) 23505350
Web Site: http://www.bp.com
Sales Range: $25-49.9 Million
Emp.: 200
Oil & Lubricants Distr
N.A.I.C.S.: 424720

BP International Ltd.   **(1)**
20 Canada Square Canary Wharf, London, E14 5NJ, United Kingdom   **(100%)**
Tel.: (44) 2074964000
Web Site: http://www.bpintl.com
Sales Range: $100-124.9 Million
Emp.: 200
Integrated Oil Operations
N.A.I.C.S.: 211120

BP Italia SPA   **(1)**
Via G De Castillia 23, 20124, Milan, Italy
Tel.: (39) 0236012311

Web Site: https://www.bp.com
Emp.: 75
Petroleum & Lubricating Oil Mfr & Distr
N.A.I.C.S.: 324191

BP Japan KK   **(1)**
3F Petro House, 4 5 21 Kojimachi Chiyoda Ku, Tokyo, 102 0083, Japan   **(100%)**
Tel.: (81) 332387310
Petroleum Product Distr
N.A.I.C.S.: 424720

BP Kuwait Limited   **(1)**
13th floor Sahab Tower, PO Box 29335, Salhiya, 13039, Kuwait
Tel.: (965) 22403316
Web Site: https://www.bp.com
Petroleum & Petroleum Products Whslr; Oil & Gas Exploration & Production
N.A.I.C.S.: 424720

BP Luxembourg S.A.   **(1)**
Aire de Capellen, 8309, Capellen, Luxembourg
Tel.: (352) 3981991
Sales Range: $25-49.9 Million
Emp.: 22
Petroleum Products Whslr; Gasoline Service Stations
N.A.I.C.S.: 457120
Romaen Horrstmrrann (Mng Dir)

BP Malawi Limited   **(1)**
8 Independence Drive, PO Box 469, Blantyre, Malawi   **(50%)**
Tel.: (265) 1 824244
Web Site: http://www.bp.com
Petroleum Products Marketing
N.A.I.C.S.: 424720

BP Marine Limited   **(1)**
Sunbury Business Park Building D First Floor, Chertsey Road, Sunbury-on-Thames, TW16 7LN, Middlesex, United Kingdom
Tel.: (44) 1932762000
Web Site: http://www.bpmarine.com
Sales Range: $50-74.9 Million
Supplier of Fuels, Lubricants & Technical Services to the Marine Industry
N.A.I.C.S.: 424720

Unit (Non-US):

BP Marine   **(2)**
Hasselager Centervej 15, 8560, Viby, Denmark
Tel.: (45) 80889499
Supplier of Fuels, Lubricants & Technical Services to the Marine Industry
N.A.I.C.S.: 424720

BP Mexico S.A. de C.V.   **(1)**
Av Santa Fe No 505 Flr 10 Col Cruz Manca Santa Fe, 05390, Mexico, Mexico
Tel.: (52) 8006680209
Web Site: https://www.bp.com
Sales Range: $300-349.9 Million
Emp.: 900
Petroleum Refining & Petroleum Products Marketing; Petrochemicals Mfr; Convenience Stores
N.A.I.C.S.: 324110

BP Middle East Ltd.   **(1)**
8th floor Standard Chartered Tower Down Town, PO Box 1699, Burj Khalifa by Emaar Square, Dubai, United Arab Emirates
Tel.: (971) 43317999
Web Site: https://www.bp.com
Sales Range: $125-149.9 Million
Emp.: 60
Petroleum & Gas Exploration & Oil Refining; Petroleum Products Marketing; Petrochemicals Mfg
N.A.I.C.S.: 324110

BP Mozambique Limited   **(1)**
Avenida dos Martires de Inhamiga 170, 7 Andar, Maputo, Mozambique
Tel.: (258) 21325021
Web Site: http://www.bp.co.za
Sales Range: $75-99.9 Million
Emp.: 143
Petroleum & Petroleum Products Whslr; Gasoline Service Stations
N.A.I.C.S.: 424720

BP Nederland Holdings B.V.   **(1)**
Rivium Boulevard 301, PO Box 1131, Rotterdam, 2910 LK, Netherlands
Tel.: (31) 102491000

Web Site: http://www.bp.nl
Sales Range: $50-74.9 Million
Emp.: 100
Holding Company
N.A.I.C.S.: 551112

Subsidiary (Domestic):

BP Nederland B.V.   **(2)**
d'Arcyweg 76, Port number 6425, Europoort, 3198 NA, Rotterdam, Netherlands
Tel.: (31) 107133721
Web Site: http://www.bp.nl
Sales Range: $50-74.9 Million
Emp.: 2,000
Petroleum Product Whslr
N.A.I.C.S.: 424720

Subsidiary (Domestic):

BP Energy Marketing B.V.   **(3)**
Rivium Boulevard 301, 2909 LK, Capelle aan den IJssel, Netherlands
Tel.: (31) 102491000
Web Site: http://www.bp.com
Emp.: 100
Petroleum Products Research & Marketing
N.A.I.C.S.: 424720

Netherlands Refining Company B.V.   **(3)**
D'Arcyweg 76 Havennummer 6425, Haven 6425, 3198 NA, Rotterdam, Netherlands
Tel.: (31) 107133721
Petroleum Refining; Owned 69% by BP Nederland B.V. & 31% by Texaco
N.A.I.C.S.: 324110

BP Oil Australia Pty. Ltd.   **(1)**
L 17 717 Bourke St, Docklands, Melbourne, 3008, VIC, Australia
Tel.: (61) 392684111
Petroleum Product Mfr & Distr
N.A.I.C.S.: 324191

BP Oil Hellenic SA   **(1)**
26A Apostolopoulou Str, Chalandri, 15231, Athens, Greece
Tel.: (30) 2106887777
Web Site: https://www.bp.com
Sales Range: $1-4.9 Billion
Emp.: 60
Petroleum & Petroleum Products Whslr
N.A.I.C.S.: 424720

BP Oil New Zealand Limited   **(1)**
20 Customhouse Quay, Wellington, 6001, New Zealand
Tel.: (64) 4 495 5000
Web Site: http://www.bp.com
Rev.: $1,895,292,000
Emp.: 1,760
Fuel & Lubricant Distr
N.A.I.C.S.: 424720

BP Oil Thailand   **(1)**
24th Floor Rajanakarn Building 183 South Sathon Road, Bangkok, 10120, Thailand
Tel.: (66) 26843789
Web Site: http://www.castrol.com
Sales Range: $250-299.9 Million
Emp.: 450
Petroleum & Gas Exploration, Production & Sales; Petrochemical Mfg
N.A.I.C.S.: 211120

Subsidiary (Domestic):

BP Castrol (Thailand) Limited   **(2)**
3 Rajanakarn Building 23rd floor South Sathon Road, Yannawa Sathon, Bangkok, 10120, Thailand
Tel.: (66) 26843555
Web Site: https://www.bp.com
Sales Range: $50-74.9 Million
Emp.: 180
Oil & Petroleum Products Mfr
N.A.I.C.S.: 324191

BP Oil U.K.   **(1)**
Witan Gate House 500 600 Witan Gate, Milton Keynes, MK9 1ES, United Kingdom   **(100%)**
Tel.: (44) 1908853000
Web Site: http://www.bp.com
Sales Range: $550-599.9 Million
Emp.: 1,500
Refining & Marketing Services
N.A.I.C.S.: 324110

Joint Venture (Domestic):

British Pipeline Agency Ltd.   **(2)**
5-7 Alexandra Road, Hemel Hempstead, HP2 5BS, Herts, United Kingdom
Tel.: (44) 1442242200
Web Site: http://www.bpa.co.uk
Sales Range: $25-49.9 Million
Emp.: 100
Gas Pipelines Operator & Engineering Services; Owned 50% by Shell U.K. Ltd. & 50% by BP Oil U.K.
N.A.I.C.S.: 237120
Peter Davis (Gen Mgr)

BP PetroChina Jiangmen Fuels Co. Ltd.   **(1)**
Room 1101 11th Flr CTS Ctr No 219 Zhongshan Wu Rd, Guangzhou, 510030, China   **(50%)**
Tel.: (86) 2083966988
Sales Range: $75-99.9 Million
Emp.: 200
Petroleum & Petroleum Products Whslr
N.A.I.C.S.: 424720

BP Petrolleri A.S.   **(1)**
Tel.: (90) 2165712000
Sales Range: $450-499.9 Million
Emp.: 300
Petroleum & Gas Exploration & Production; Lubricants & Petroleum Products Whslr; Gasoline Service Stations
N.A.I.C.S.: 211120

BP Polska Sp. z o.o.   **(1)**
ul Pawia 9, 31-154, Krakow, Poland
Tel.: (48) 123236063
Web Site: http://www.bp.pl
Sales Range: $200-249.9 Million
Emp.: 300
Gasoline Service Stations; Petroleum Products Whslr
N.A.I.C.S.: 424720

BP Shanghai Trading Co. Ltd.   **(1)**
9th Floor Plaza 66, 1266 Nanjing West Road, Shanghai, 200040, China
Tel.: (86) 21 3227 4888
Sales Range: $25-49.9 Million
Emp.: 150
Petroleum Product Whslr
N.A.I.C.S.: 424720

BP Singapore Pte. Limited   **(1)**
7 Straits View 26-01 Marina One East Tower, Singapore, 018936, Singapore
Tel.: (65) 63353000
Web Site: https://www.bp.com
Sales Range: $1-4.9 Billion
Emp.: 650
Oil Production & Marketing of Petroleum & Petrochemical Products
N.A.I.C.S.: 424720

BP South-West Pacific Limited   **(1)**
Level 7 Vanua House, Suva, Fiji
Tel.: (679) 3311622
Sales Range: $75-99.9 Million
Emp.: 150
Petroleum & Petroleum Products Whslr
N.A.I.C.S.: 424720

BP Southeast Asia Ltd.   **(1)**
49 Hai Ba Trung Street 7th Floor Hanoi Towers, 10000, Hanoi, Vietnam
Sales Range: $75-99.9 Million
Emp.: 20
Oil & Gas Exploration, Production & Sales; Petrochemical Mfg
N.A.I.C.S.: 211120

BP Southern Africa Pty Ltd.   **(1)**
199 Oxford Road Oxford Parks, Dunkeld, Johannesburg, 2196, South Africa   **(100%)**
Tel.: (27) 860222166
Web Site: https://www.bp.com
Sales Range: $450-499.9 Million
Emp.: 1,000
Petroleum Refining & Distr; Gasoline Service Stations
N.A.I.C.S.: 324110

BP Swaziland (Pty) Limited   **(1)**
Shop No 3 Nkosingiphile Building, PO Box 1161, 8th Street, Matsapha, Eswatini
Tel.: (268) 87660
Petroleum & Petroleum Products Whslr; Gasoline Service Stations
N.A.I.C.S.: 424720

BP plc—(Continued)

BP Switzerland **(1)**
Neuhofstrasse 12, 6340, Baar, Switzerland
Tel.: (41) 584569111
Web Site: https://www.bp.com
Sales Range: $1-4.9 Billion
Emp.: 134
Petroleum Products, Fuel Oils & Petro-
chemicals Whslr; Gas Service Stations
N.A.I.C.S.: 424720

BP Taiwan Marketing Limited **(1)**
7th Floor No 71 Sec 3 Mingsheng East
Road, Taipei, 104, Taiwan
Tel.: (886) 2 8175 6800
Lubricating Oil Mfr
N.A.I.C.S.: 324191

BP Tanzania Limited **(1)**
Bandari Road, PO BOX 9043, Kurasini, Dar
es Salaam, Tanzania **(50%)**
Tel.: (255) 222112725
Sales Range: $100-124.9 Million
Emp.: 225
Petroleum & Petroleum Products Whslr;
Gasoline Service Stations; Owned 50% by
BP plc & 50% by Tanzanian Government
N.A.I.C.S.: 424720

BP Trinidad and Tobago llc **(1)**
5-5a Queen's Park West, Port of Spain,
Trinidad & Tobago
Tel.: (868) 6232862
Sales Range: $350-399.9 Million
Emp.: 700
Oil & Gas Exploration Services
N.A.I.C.S.: 213112
Giselle Thompson (VP-Corp Ops)

**BP Zhuhai Chemical Company
Limited** **(1)**
Da Ping Harbour Lin Gang Industrial Zone,
Nanshui Town, Zhuhai, 519050, Guang-
dong, China
Tel.: (86) 7567269888
Sales Range: $50-74.9 Million
Emp.: 250
Plastic Materials & Resins Mfr
N.A.I.C.S.: 325211

BP Zimbabwe (Pvt) Limited **(1)**
Block 1 Tendeseka Office Park, PO Box
982, S Machel Ave East Eastlea, Harare,
Zimbabwe
Tel.: (263) 4701572
Web Site: http://www.bp.com
Oil & Gas Distribution; Gasoline Service
Stations
N.A.I.C.S.: 457120

BPX Energy Inc. **(1)**
PO Box 941180, Houston, TX 77094
Web Site: https://ownerrelations.bpx.com
N.A.I.C.S.: 213112

**Bahia de Bizkaia Electricidad
S.L.** **(1)**
Punta Ceballos n 8, 48508, Zierbena,
Spain **(75%)**
Tel.: (34) 946366000
Web Site: https://www.bbe.es
Emp.: 49
Electricity Generation Services
N.A.I.C.S.: 221112

Bp Energy Do Brazil Ltda **(1)**
Av Atlantica n 1 130 7 andar, Copacabana,
22021-000, Rio de Janeiro, Brazil
Tel.: (55) 2121272999
Petroleum Product Distr
N.A.I.C.S.: 424720

Burmah Castrol Australia Pty ltd. **(1)**
L7 717 Bourke St, Docklands, Melbourne,
3008, VIC, Australia
Tel.: (61) 392684200
Lubricating Oil & Grease Mfr
N.A.I.C.S.: 324191

Castrol Limited **(1)**
Chertsey Road, Sunbury-on-Thames, TW16
7BP, United Kingdom
Tel.: (44) 1793512712
Web Site: https://www.castrol.com
Sales Range: $125-149.9 Million
Emp.: 400
Lubricant & Specialist Chemical Mfr & Distr
N.A.I.C.S.: 324191

Subsidiary (Non-US):

BP Castrol K.K. **(2)**

20F Gate City Osaki East Tower 1-11-2
Osaki, Shinagawa-ku, Tokyo, 141-0032,
Japan
Tel.: (81) 357196000
Web Site: http://www.bp-oil.co.jp
Sales Range: $100-124.9 Million
Automotive Lubricant Mfr
N.A.I.C.S.: 324191
Masanori Hirakawa (Pres & CEO)

**BP France Lubritiants Industriels &
Services** **(2)**
Immeuble Le Cervier 12 Avenue des Be-
guines Cergy Saint Christophe, 95688,
Cergy-Pontoise, Cedex, France
Tel.: (33) 134224000
Web Site: http://www.castrol.com
Sales Range: $125-149.9 Million
Emp.: 300
Lubricant Mfr & Distr
N.A.I.C.S.: 324191

BP Fuels & Lubricants **(2)**
Tjuvholmen alle 3, PO Box 153, 0252, Oslo,
Norway **(100%)**
Tel.: (47) 22511220
Web Site: http://www.castrol.com
Sales Range: $25-49.9 Million
Emp.: 35
Marketing of Lubricating Oils
N.A.I.C.S.: 424720

BP Korea Ltd. **(2)**
19F 302 Teheran-ro, Gangnam-gu, Seoul,
06210, Korea (South) **(100%)**
Tel.: (82) 15771904
Sales Range: $25-49.9 Million
Emp.: 50
Lubricant Distr
N.A.I.C.S.: 424720

Subsidiary (Domestic):

BP Korea Marketing Ltd **(3)**
2nd Fl Woojin Building 76-4 Jamwon Dong,
Seochu gu, Seoul, 137 909, Korea (South)
Tel.: (82) 234793800
Web Site: http://www.bp.com
Sales Range: $25-49.9 Million
Emp.: 45
Petroleum & Petroleum Products Whslr
N.A.I.C.S.: 424720

Subsidiary (Non-US):

BP Southern Africa (Pty). Ltd. **(2)**
10 Junction Ave Parktown, PO Box 1554,
Johannesburg, 2000, South Africa **(100%)**
Tel.: (27) 860222166
Web Site: https://www.bp.com
Sales Range: $50-74.9 Million
Emp.: 100
Lubricants Distr & Developer
N.A.I.C.S.: 424720

Castrol (Malaysia) Sdn. Bhd. **(2)**
Level 35 Menara Maxis, Kuala Lumpur City
Ctr, 50088, Kuala Lumpur, Malaysia
Tel.: (60) 320595555
Web Site: http://www.castrol.com
Sales Range: $125-149.9 Million
Emp.: 400
Lubricant Distr
N.A.I.C.S.: 424720

Castrol (Shenzhen) Co. Ltd. **(2)**
No 29 Mawan Road, Nanshan District,
Shenzhen, 518054, China
Tel.: (86) 7556390238
Sales Range: $25-49.9 Million
Emp.: 50
Oil & Gas Refining
N.A.I.C.S.: 324110

Castrol (Switzerland) AG **(2)**
(100%)
Lubricant Distr
N.A.I.C.S.: 425120

Subsidiary (Domestic):

Castrol (U.K.) Limited **(2)**
Whitchurch Hill, Pipers Way, Pangbourne,
RG8 7QR, Berkshire, United
Kingdom **(100%)**
Tel.: (44) 1932775644
Web Site: http://www.castrol.co.uk
Lubricant & Specialist Chemical Mfr & Distr
N.A.I.C.S.: 324191

Subsidiary (Non-US):

Castrol Australia Pty. Ltd. **(2)**
132 McCredie Road, Guildford, 2161, NSW,
Australia **(100%)**
Tel.: (61) 1300554890
Web Site: https://www.castrol.com
Sales Range: $25-49.9 Million
Emp.: 100
Lubricant Distr
N.A.I.C.S.: 424720

Castrol Austria GmbH **(2)**
IZ NOE SUED Strasse 6, Postfach 104,
2355, Wiener Neudorf, Austria **(100%)**
Tel.: (43) 22366950
Web Site: http://www.castrol.at
Emp.: 220
Lubricant Distr
N.A.I.C.S.: 424720

Castrol Brasil Limitada **(2)**
Av Dr Marcos Penteado de Ulhoa Rodri-
gues, 939- Torre Jacaranda - 7th Floor Al-
phaville, Sao Paulo, 06460-040, SP,
Brazil **(100%)**
Tel.: (55) 8007040720
Web Site: https://www.castrol.com
Emp.: 25
Lubricant Distr
N.A.I.C.S.: 424720

Castrol Chile SA **(2)**
Eliodoro Yanez 1572, Santiago, 6640659,
Chile **(100%)**
Tel.: (56) 22358444
Web Site: http://www.castrol.com
Sales Range: $25-49.9 Million
Emp.: 60
Lubricant Distr
N.A.I.C.S.: 424720

Castrol Colombia Limitada **(2)**
Calle 81 No 11 - 42 Oficina 901, Torre Su,
Bogota, Colombia
Tel.: (57) 14159288
Sales Range: $25-49.9 Million
Emp.: 70
Petroleum & Petroleum Products Whslr
N.A.I.C.S.: 424720

Castrol Croatia d.o.o. **(2)**
Kovinska 4a, 10090, Zagreb, Croatia
Tel.: (385) 16002222
Web Site: https://www.castrol.com
Sales Range: $25-49.9 Million
Emp.: 17
Motor Oil & Lubricants Sales & Distr
N.A.I.C.S.: 324191

Castrol France SA **(2)**
Campus Saint-Christophe Batiment Galilee
3 10 avenue de l'Entreprise, Pontoise,
95863, Cergy, France **(100%)**
Tel.: (33) 172009551
Web Site: http://www.castrol.com
Sales Range: $50-74.9 Million
Emp.: 200
Lubricant Distr
N.A.I.C.S.: 424720

Castrol Hellas S.A. **(2)**
26 Kifissias Ave, Maroussi, 151 25, Athens,
Greece
Tel.: (30) 2106887111
Web Site: http://www.castrol.com
Lubricant Distr
N.A.I.C.S.: 424720

Castrol Hungary Ltd **(2)**
Soroksari Road 30-34 E, 1095, Budapest,
Hungary
Tel.: (36) 1 799 0350
Web Site: http://www.castrol.hu
Sales Range: $25-49.9 Million
Emp.: 30
Lubricant Distr
N.A.I.C.S.: 424720

Castrol India Limited **(2)**
Technopolis Knowledge Park, Mahakali
Caves Road Andheri East, Mumbai,
400093, Maharashtra, India
Tel.: (91) 2266984100
Web Site: https://www.castrol.com
Rev.: $417,546,675
Assets: $326,712,750
Liabilities: $133,670,355
Net Worth: $193,042,395

Earnings: $79,571,310
Emp.: 690
Fiscal Year-end: 12/31/2020
Oil & Lubricants Mfg & Distr
N.A.I.C.S.: 324191
Jayanta Chatterjee (Dir-Supply Chain)

Castrol Industria **(2)**
Lagoas Park - Edificio 3, 2780-689, Porto
Salvo, Portugal
Tel.: (351) 21 389 10 00
Web Site: http://www.castrol.com
Petroleum & Lubricant Distr
N.A.I.C.S.: 424720

Castrol Industrie Schwitzerland **(2)**
Neuhofstrasse 12, Baar, 6340, Zug, Swit-
zerland
Tel.: (41) 800225050
Petroleum & Lubricant Distr
N.A.I.C.S.: 424720

Castrol Ireland Ltd. **(2)**
One Spencer Dock North Wall Quay, Bally-
coolin Blanchardstown, Dublin, 1,
Ireland **(100%)**
Tel.: (353) 8665100
Web Site: http://www.castrol.co.uk
Sales Range: $25-49.9 Million
Emp.: 9
Lubricant Distr
N.A.I.C.S.: 424720

Castrol K.K. **(2)**
1-11-2 Osaki, Shinagawa-ku, Tokyo, 141-
0032, Japan **(100%)**
Tel.: (81) 120059617
Web Site: https://www.castrol.com
Lubricant Distr
N.A.I.C.S.: 424720

Castrol Lubricants (CR), s.r.o. **(2)**
V Parku 2294/2, 148 00, Prague, Czech
Republic
Tel.: (420) 296770311
Lubricating Oil & Grease Mfr
N.A.I.C.S.: 324191

Castrol NZ Ltd. **(2)**
6 Monier Place Penrose, PO Box 99873,
Newmarket, Auckland, New
Zealand **(100%)**
Tel.: (64) 800227876
Web Site: https://www.castrol.com
Sales Range: $25-49.9 Million
Emp.: 60
Lubricant Distr
N.A.I.C.S.: 424720

Castrol Nederland B.V. **(2)**
d'Arcyweg 76, Europoort, 3198 NA, Rotter-
dam, Netherlands **(100%)**
Tel.: (31) 8000200355
Web Site: https://www.castrol.com
Sales Range: $25-49.9 Million
Emp.: 50
Lubricant Distr
N.A.I.C.S.: 424720

Castrol Pakistan Pvt. Ltd. **(2)**
D-67/1 Block 4 Scheme 5 Clifton, PO Box
3767, Karachi, Pakistan
Tel.: (92) 2135829000
Oil & Gas Exploration Services
N.A.I.C.S.: 213112
Hussain Zaidi (Project Mgr)

Castrol Philippines, Inc. **(2)**
32nd Floor LKG Tower 6801 Ayala Avenue,
Makati, 1226, Metro Manila, Philippines
Tel.: (63) 28841478
Web Site: https://www.castrol.com
Lubricant Distr
N.A.I.C.S.: 424720

Castrol Singapore Pte. Ltd. **(2)**
7 Straits View 26-01, Marina One East
Tower, Singapore, 018936,
Singapore **(100%)**
Tel.: (65) 63353000
Web Site: https://www.castrol.com
Sales Range: $25-49.9 Million
Emp.: 30
Lubricant Distr
N.A.I.C.S.: 424720

Castrol Slovenija d.o.o. **(2)**
Brdnikova 44, Ljubljana, Slovenia
Tel.: (386) 12425200
Sales Range: $25-49.9 Million
Emp.: 20
Motor Oil & Lubricants Whslr

N.A.I.C.S.: 324191

Castrol Slovensko, s.r.o. (2)
Roznavska 24, Bratislava, 821 04, Slovakia
Tel.: (421) 248777300
Web Site: http://www.castrol.sk
Sales Range: $25-49.9 Million
Emp.: 13
Oil & Lubricating Products Whslr
N.A.I.C.S.: 424720

Joint Venture (Non-US):

Castrol Vietnam Ltd. (2)
4th Floor Sun Wah Tower, 115 Nguyen Hue
Street District, Ho Chi Minh City,
Vietnam (60%)
Tel.: (84) 88219153
Oil & Lubricants Mfr & Distr
N.A.I.C.S.: 324191

Joint Venture (Non-US):

Castrol BP Petco Co., Ltd. (3)
Sales Range: $125-149.9 Million
Emp.: 190
Petroleum & Gas Exploration, Production &
Sales
N.A.I.C.S.: 211120

Subsidiary (Non-US):

**Deutsche Castrol Vertriebsgesell-
schaft mbH** (2)
Ubers Street Seeallee 1, Hamburg, 20457,
Germany (100%)
Tel.: (49) 40359401
Web Site: http://www.castrol.de
Sales Range: $125-149.9 Million
Emp.: 300
Lubricant Distr
N.A.I.C.S.: 424720

Enkor d.o.o. (2)
Kovinska 12, Zagreb, 10000, Croatia
Tel.: (385) 16183823
Web Site: http://www.enkor.hr
Sales Range: $25-49.9 Million
Emp.: 8
Oil & Lubricants Distr
N.A.I.C.S.: 424720

Latin Energy Argentina (2)
Guemes 4747 Floor 3 Apartment E, CP
1425, C1428DNG, Buenos Aires, Argentina
Tel.: (54) 1151993975
Web Site: https://www.lenergygroup.com
Sales Range: $25-49.9 Million
Emp.: 40
Oil & Grease Mfg
N.A.I.C.S.: 324191

Subsidiary (Domestic):

Lubricants UK Ltd (2)
Wakefield House, Pipers Way, Swindon,
SN3 1RE, Wiltshire, United
Kingdom (100%)
Tel.: (44) 1793511521
Web Site: http://www.castrol.com
Lubricant & Petroleum Product Mfr
N.A.I.C.S.: 324191

Subsidiary (Non-US):

Nordic Lubricants A/S (2)
Orestads Boulevard 73, 2300, Copenhagen,
Denmark (100%)
Tel.: (45) 70807056
Web Site: http://www.castrol.dk
Sales Range: $50-74.9 Million
Emp.: 7
Lubricants & Services Distr
N.A.I.C.S.: 424720

Nordic Lubricants AB (2)
St Goransgatan 57, PO Box 49104, Stock-
holm, 100 28, Sweden (100%)
Tel.: (46) 84411100
Web Site: http://www.castrol.com
Sales Range: $25-49.9 Million
Emp.: 95
Lubricant Distr
N.A.I.C.S.: 424720
Johan Anderssen *(Mng Dir)*

**Optimol Oelwerke Industrie GmbH &
Co. KG** (2)
Erkelenzer Str 20, 41179, Monchenglad-
bach, Germany
Tel.: (49) 21619090

Mfr of Lubricants & Greases
N.A.I.C.S.: 324191

PT Castrol Indonesia (2)
Arkadia Green Office Tower G 3rd Floor Jl
Let Jen TB, Simatupang Kav 88, Jakarta,
12520, Indonesia (100%)
Tel.: (62) 78838000
Web Site: https://www.castrol.com
Lubricant Distr
N.A.I.C.S.: 424720

Subsidiary (US):

Remet Corporation (2)
210 Commons Rd, Utica, NY 13502-6395
Tel.: (315) 797-8700
Web Site: https://www.remet.com
Sales Range: $25-49.9 Million
Emp.: 50
Mfr of Equipments for Chemicals & Heavy
Industrial
N.A.I.C.S.: 424690
John S. Paraszczak *(Chm, Pres & CEO)*

Chargemaster Limited (1)
500 Capability Green, Luton, LU1 3LS,
United Kingdom
Tel.: (44) 1582 400331
Web Site: http://www.bpchargemaster.com
Electric Vehicle Charging Solutions
N.A.I.C.S.: 335312
David Martell *(Founder & CEO)*

Chemcolor-Beta d.d. (1)
Avenija Dubrovnik 10, Zagreb, Croatia
Tel.: (385) 16520567
Sales Range: $25-49.9 Million
Emp.: 5
Lubricants Marketing Services
N.A.I.C.S.: 424720

**China American Petrochemical Co.,
Ltd.** (1)
4F 260 Tun Hua North Rd, Taipei, ROC,
Taiwan (50%)
Tel.: (886) 27156688
Web Site: http://www.capco.com.tw
Sales Range: $200-249.9 Million
Emp.: 577
Mfr & Sale of Chemical Products
N.A.I.C.S.: 325998

**Comercio de Combustiveis e Lubrifi-
cantes S.A.** (1)
Lagoa's Park Edificio 3, 2740-244, Porto
Salvo, Portugal
Tel.: (351) 213891000
Web Site: http://www.bp.pt
Sales Range: $150-199.9 Million
Emp.: 150
Petroleum & Petroleum Products Whslr
N.A.I.C.S.: 424720

Deutsche BP AG (1)
Wittener Str 45, 44789, Bochum,
Germany (100%)
Tel.: (49) 2343150
Web Site: http://www.bpdeutschland.de
Sales Range: $450-499.9 Million
Emp.: 1,200
Oil & Gas Production; Petroleum Product
Mfr & Distr
N.A.I.C.S.: 324110

Subsidiary (Domestic):

BP Europa SE (2)
Wittener Str 45, Bochum, 44789, Germany
Tel.: (49) 234 315 0
Web Site: http://www.bp.com
Petroleum Product Distr
N.A.I.C.S.: 424720
Peter Mather *(Chm-Supervisory Bd)*

Subsidiary (Non-US):

**BP Refining & Petrochemicals
GmbH** (2)
(100%)
Tel.: (49) 2343150
Web Site: http://www.bprp.de
Refinery Operator
N.A.I.C.S.: 324110

Subsidiary (Non-US):

DHC Solvent Chemie GmbH (3)
Tel.: (49) 20899400
Web Site: https://www.dhc-solvent.de

Sales Range: $25-49.9 Million
Emp.: 75
Solvents & Other Oil-Based Products Mfr
N.A.I.C.S.: 324199

Holding (Domestic):

Nord-West Oelleitung GmbH (2)
Zum Oelhafendamm 207, 26384, Wil-
helmshaven, Germany (25.64%)
Tel.: (49) 4421620
Web Site: https://nwowhv.de
Sales Range: $50-74.9 Million
Emp.: 150
Crude Petroleum Terminal Operation
N.A.I.C.S.: 424720

Empresa Petrolera Chaco S.A. (1)
Tel.: (591) 33453700
Web Site: http://www.ypfbchaco.com.bo
Sales Range: $200-249.9 Million
Emp.: 300
Oil & Gas Exploration & Production; Owned
50% by Bolivian Pension Funds, 30% by
BP plc & 20% by Bridas Corporation
N.A.I.C.S.: 211120

Finite Carbon Corporation (1)
435 Devon Park Dr 700 Bldg, Wayne, PA
19087
Web Site: http://www.finitecarbon.com
Professional, Scientific & Technical Services
N.A.I.C.S.: 541990

FreeBees B.V. (1)
D Arcyweg 76, 3198 NA, Rotterdam, Neth-
erlands
Tel.: (31) 850028405
Web Site: https://www.freebees.nl
N.A.I.C.S.: 541511

GETEC Energie AG (1)
Expo Plaza 10, 30539, Hannover, Germany
Tel.: (49) 511 51949 100
Web Site: http://www.getec-energie.de
Sales Range: $450-499.9 Million
Energy Supply & Trading Services
N.A.I.C.S.: 221122
Bernward Peters *(Chm-Mgmt Bd & CEO)*

Jovo Arco Energy Co, Ltd (1)
Huandao West Road, Gaolan'gang Zhuhai,
Zhuhai, 519050, China
Tel.: (86) 7567268222
Sales Range: $75-99.9 Million
Emp.: 116
Petroleum Product Whslr
N.A.I.C.S.: 424720

**Mach Monument Aviation Fuelling
Co. Ltd.** (1)
Naz City Building J Apartment 10, Kurdistan
Region, Erbil, Iraq
Tel.: (964) 7504458370
Web Site: https://www.mmafco.com
N.A.I.C.S.: 488190

**Net Zero Teesside Power
Limited** (1)
Chertsey Road, Sunbury-on-Thames, TW16
7BP, Middlesex, United Kingdom
Tel.: (44) 7825977265
Web Site: https://www.netzeroteesside.co.uk
N.A.I.C.S.: 221118

Pan American Energy LLC (1)
Av Leandro N Alem 1180, 1001, Buenos
Aires, Argentina (60%)
Tel.: (54) 1143104100
Web Site: http://www.pan-energy.com
Emp.: 3,000
Oil & Natural Gas Exploration & Production
N.A.I.C.S.: 211120
Jason Latkowcer *(CEO)*

Subsidiary (Domestic):

Axion Energy (2)
Carlos Maria Della Paolera 265 Piso 19,
Buenos Aires, 1001, Argentina
Tel.: (54) 8008880282
Web Site: https://www.axionenergy.com
Producing, Refining & Marketing of Petro-
leum Products & Industrial Lubricants
N.A.I.C.S.: 324110

**Peninsular Aviation Services Co.
Ltd.** (1)
Web Site: http://www.shell.com
Sales Range: $25-49.9 Million
Emp.: 90

Aviation Services; Owned 50% by Saudi
Arabian Markets Ltd., 25% by BP plc &
25% by The Shell Petroleum Co. Ltd.
N.A.I.C.S.: 488119

**Shanghai SECCO Petrochemical Co.,
Ltd.** (1)
30/31F A Building Far East International
Plaza No 319 Xian Xia Road, No 299 Xian
Xia Road, Shanghai, 200051, China
Tel.: (86) 2152574688
Web Site: https://www.secco.com.cn
Emp.: 500
Petrochemical Products Mfr
N.A.I.C.S.: 325110

Thorntons Inc (1)
10101 Linn Sta Rd Ste 200, Louisville, KY
40223-3819
Tel.: (502) 425-8022
Web Site: http://www.thorntonsinc.com
Sales Range: $1-4.9 Billion
Emp.: 950
Operator of Gasoline Service Stations &
Convenience Stores
N.A.I.C.S.: 445131
James H. Thornton *(Founder)*

BP PLC
1 St James's Square, London, SW1Y
4PD, United Kingdom
Tel.: (44) 2074964000
Web Site: https://www.bp.com
Year Founded: 1901
BP—(LSE)
Rev.: $213,032,000,000
Assets: $280,294,000,000
Liabilities: $194,801,000,000
Net Worth: $85,493,000,000
Earnings: $15,880,000,000
Emp.: 87,800
Fiscal Year-end: 12/31/23
Natural Gas Extraction Services
N.A.I.C.S.: 211130
Murray Auchincloss *(CEO)*

BPD INDUSTRIAL REAL ES-
TATE FUND REIT
137 Filip Kutev St Administrative
Building 1 Floor 2, 1407, Sofia, Bul-
garia
Tel.: (359) 28681374
Web Site: https://www.bpdreit.com
BPDW—(BUL)
Sales Range: Less than $1 Million
Real Estate Investment Trust Ser-
vices
N.A.I.C.S.: 531190

BPE UNTERNEHMENS
BETEILIGUNGEN GMBH
Schleusenbrucke 1, 20354, Hamburg,
Germany
Tel.: (49) 403615700　　　　　　De
Web Site: http://www.bpe.de
Rev.: $201,973,500
Private Equity Services
N.A.I.C.S.: 523999
Nikolai Mackscheidt *(Mgr-Investment)*

Subsidiaries:

StrikoWestofen GmbH (1)
Hohe Strasse 14, 51643, Gummersbach,
Germany
Tel.: (49) 226170910
Web Site: http://www.strikowestofen.com
Sales Range: $50-74.9 Million
Emp.: 145
Furnace Installatiosn & Die Casting Ser-
vices
N.A.I.C.S.: 541330
Altina Uwe *(Mng Dir)*

BPER BANCA S.P.A
Via San Carlo 8/20, 41121, Modena,
Italy
Tel.: (39) 0592021111
Web Site: https://www.bper.it
Year Founded: 1867
BPE—(ITA)
Rev.: $2,449,012,573

BPER BANCA S.p.A—(Continued)

Assets: $165,079,984,825
Liabilities: $156,278,197,485
Net Worth: $8,801,787,340
Earnings: $1,597,528,723
Emp.: 16,229
Fiscal Year-end: 12/31/22
Banking Services
N.A.I.C.S.: 551111
Pierpio Cerfogli *(Deputy Gen Mgr)*

Subsidiaries:

BPER Bank Luxembourg S.A. **(1)**
30 Boulevad Royal, 2449, Luxembourg,
Luxembourg
Tel.: (352) 2224301
Web Site: https://www.bperlux.lu
Investment Banking & Security Services
N.A.I.C.S.: 523150

BPER Factor S.p.A. **(1)**
Strada Maggiore 29, 40125, Bologna, Italy
Tel.: (39) 0516482111
Web Site: https://www.bperfactor.it
Financial Management Services
N.A.I.C.S.: 541611

BPER Services S.C.p.A. **(1)**
16 Via Sorrentino Andrea, 84013, Cava de
Tirreni, Italy
Tel.: (39) 0894 689.711
Information Technology Consulting Services
N.A.I.C.S.: 541512

Banca Cesare Ponti S.p.A. **(1)**
Piazza Duomo 19, Milan, Italy
Tel.: (39) 02722771
Web Site:
https://www.bperprivatecesareponti.it
Asset Management Services
N.A.I.C.S.: 531390

**Banca Popolare dell'Emilia Romagna
(Europe) International S.A.** **(1)**
Sede Sociale 30 Blvd Royal, 2012, Luxem-
bourg, Luxembourg **(99%)**
Tel.: (352) 2224301
Web Site: http://www.pt.lu
Sales Range: $50-74.9 Million
Emp.: 10
Financial Transactions Processing Reserve
& Clearinghouse Services
N.A.I.C.S.: 522320

Banca Popolare di Aprilia S.p.A. **(1)**
Piazza Roma, 04011, Aprilia, Italy
Tel.: (39) 069286251
Web Site: http://www.popaprilia.it
Sales Range: $100-124.9 Million
Emp.: 200
Savings Institutions
N.A.I.C.S.: 522180

**Banca Popolare di Crotone
S.p.A.** **(1)**
Via Panella, Crotone, 88074, Calabria, Italy
Tel.: (39) 0962933111
Web Site: http://www.bpcbank.it
Commericial Banking
N.A.I.C.S.: 522110

**Banca Popolare di Lanciano e Sul-
mona S.p.A.** **(1)**
Viale Cappuccini 76, Lanciano, 66034, Chi-
eti, Italy
Tel.: (39) 08 727041
Commercial Banking Services
N.A.I.C.S.: 522110

**Banca Popolare di Ravenna
S.p.A.** **(1)**
Via Arnaldo Guerrini 14, Ravenna,
Italy **(75%)**
Tel.: (39) 0544540111
Web Site: http://www.bpr.it
Sales Range: $200-249.9 Million
Emp.: 400
Commericial Banking
N.A.I.C.S.: 522110
Piergiorgio Giuliani *(Gen Dir)*

Banca della Campania S.p.A. **(1)**
Localita Collina Liguorini Centro Direzi-
onale, 83100, Avellino, Italy
Tel.: (39) 0825651111
Web Site: http://www.bancacampania.it

Sales Range: $350-399.9 Million
Emp.: 1,000
Commericial Banking
N.A.I.C.S.: 522110
Francesco Fornaro *(Gen Dir)*

Banca della Nuova Terra **(1)**
Via Cenisio 50, 20154, Milan, Italy
Tel.: (39) 023035251
Web Site: http://www.bntbanca.it
Financial Services
N.A.I.C.S.: 522110

Banca di Sassari S.p.A. **(1)**
Viale Mancini 2, 07100, Sassari, Italy
Tel.: (39) 079221511
Web Site: http://www.bancasassari.it
Sales Range: $50-74.9 Million
Emp.: 71
Commercial Banking
N.A.I.C.S.: 522110
Fabrizio Togni *(Gen Dir)*

Banco di Sardegna S.p.A. **(1)**
Viale Bonaria 33, 09125, Cagliari, BDS,
Italy **(100%)**
Tel.: (39) 0594242
Web Site: https://www.bancosardegna.it
Sales Range: $550-599.9 Million
Emp.: 3,739
Banking Services
N.A.I.C.S.: 522110

Subsidiary (Domestic):

**NUMERA Sistemi e Informatica
S.p.A.** **(2)**
Predda Niedda Nord - Strada 6, 7100, Sas-
sari, Italy
Tel.: (39) 079223194
Information Technology Consulting Services
N.A.I.C.S.: 541512

Sardaleasing S.p.A. **(2)**
Via IV Novembre 27, 07100, Sassari, Italy
Tel.: (39) 079289000
Web Site: https://www.bperleasing.it
Financial Services
N.A.I.C.S.: 523999

Bibanca S.p.A. **(1)**
Viale Mancini 2, 07100, Sassari, Italy
Tel.: (39) 079221511
Web Site: https://www.bibanca.it
Banking & Investment Services
N.A.I.C.S.: 523150

**Cassa di Risparmio della Provincia
dell Aquila S.p.A.** **(1)**
Via Pescara 3/4, 67100, L'Aquila, Italy
Tel.: (39) 08626491
Web Site: http://www.carispaq.it
Sales Range: $50-74.9 Million
Emp.: 48
Savings Institutions
N.A.I.C.S.: 522180

EMIL-RO LEASING S.p.A. **(1)**
Strada Maggiore 29, Bologna, 40125, Italy
Tel.: (39) 0516482111
Financial Lending Services
N.A.I.C.S.: 522220

**EMILIA ROMAGNA FACTOR
S.p.A.** **(1)**
Strada Maggiore 29, 40125, Bologna, Italy
Tel.: (39) 05 16 48 21 11
Web Site: http://bperfactor.it
Sales Range: $50-74.9 Million
Factoring Services
N.A.I.C.S.: 522299
Paolo Licciardello *(Pres)*

EMRO Finance Ireland Limited **(1)**
2 Grand Canal Square Grand Canal Har-
bour, Dublin, Ireland
Tel.: (353) 1 6700895
Web Site: http://www.emrofinance.ie
Sales Range: $50-74.9 Million
Emp.: 10
Financial Management Services
N.A.I.C.S.: 523999
Paolo Zanni *(Gen Mgr)*

Em.Ro. popolare S.p.A. **(1)**
Via San Carlo 8/20, Modena, 41100, Italy
Tel.: (39) 0592021111
Commercial Banking Services
N.A.I.C.S.: 522110

Subsidiary (Domestic):

Forum Guido Monzani s.r.l. **(2)**

Via Aristotele 33, 41126, Modena, MO, Italy
Tel.: (39) 059 2021093
Web Site: http://www.forumguidomonzani.it
Telecommunication Equipment Distr
N.A.I.C.S.: 423690

Finitalia S.p.A. **(1)**
Viale Lancetti 43, 20158, Milan, MI, Italy
Tel.: (39) 0251887829
Web Site: https://www.finitalia.it
Financial Services
N.A.I.C.S.: 523999

Melior Trust SpA **(1)**
iale Bruno Buozzi 98, Rome, 00197, Italy
Tel.: (39) 06 3211945
Fiduciary Trust Services
N.A.I.C.S.: 523991

MeliorConsulting SpA **(1)**
Via Bissolati 54, 00187, Rome, Italy
Tel.: (39) 06 68488380
Consulting Services
N.A.I.C.S.: 541618

Meliorfactor SpA **(1)**
Via Gaetano Negri 10, 20123, Milan, Italy
Tel.: (39) 02290228
Web Site: http://www.meliorbanca.it
Banking & Asset Management Services
N.A.I.C.S.: 523150

Modena Terminal S.r.l. **(1)**
Piazzale Delle Nazioni 14, 41011, Cam-
pogalliano, Modena, Italy
Tel.: (39) 059525554
Web Site: https://www.modenaterminal.it
Material Handling & Storage Services
N.A.I.C.S.: 493110

Nadia S.p.A. **(1)**
140 Via Danimarca, 41122, Modena, Italy
Tel.: (39) 0593 162 011
Commercial Banking Services
N.A.I.C.S.: 522110

Optima S.p.A. **(1)**
Via Gaggio 72, San Clemente, 47832, Ri-
mini, Italy
Tel.: (39) 0541859411
Web Site: https://www.casaoptima.com
Pastry & Gelato Mfr
N.A.I.C.S.: 311812

Optima SGR S.p.A. **(1)**
Via Camperio 8, Milan, 20123, Italy
Tel.: (39) 02 72265237
Asset Management Services
N.A.I.C.S.: 523940

Presticinque S.p.A. **(1)**
Viale Shakespeare 47, 144, Rome, Italy
Tel.: (39) 06 54 52 51 20
Investment Management Service
N.A.I.C.S.: 523999

Sant'Anna Golf S.R.L. **(1)**
Via Bellavista 1, Localita Lerca, Cogoleto,
Italy
Tel.: (39) 0109135322
Web Site: https://www.santannagolf.com
Golf Operator
N.A.I.C.S.: 713910

Sistemi Parabancari S.r.l. **(1)**
Via Anton Cechov 50/2, 20151, Milan, Italy
Tel.: (39) 02 3001101
Web Site: http://www.sistemiparabancari.it
Banking Services
N.A.I.C.S.: 522110

Unipol Banca S.p.A. **(1)**
Piazza della Costituzione 2, 40128, Bolo-
gna, Italy
Tel.: (39) 0513544111
Sales Range: $650-699.9 Million
Emp.: 1,898
Banking Services
N.A.I.C.S.: 522110

Subsidiary (Domestic):

Unipol Leasing S.p.A. **(2)**
Piazza Castelnuovo 2, 40128, Bologna,
Italy
Tel.: (39) 051 7190011
Web Site: http://www.ugfleasing.it
Sales Financing & Leasing Services
N.A.I.C.S.: 522220

Unipol Merchant S.p.A. **(2)**

Piazza Costituzione 2/2, 40128, Bologna,
Italy
Tel.: (39) 0516318211
Web Site: http://www.unipolmerchant.it
Sales Range: $50-74.9 Million
Emp.: 22
Corporate Banking Services
N.A.I.C.S.: 522110

BPH ENERGY LIMITED
Level 1 Unit 12/114 Cedric Street
Stirling, Perth, 6021, WA, Australia
Tel.: (61) 893288366 AU
Web Site:
https://www.bphenergy.com.au
BPH—(ASX)
Rev.: $563,357
Assets: $20,222,487
Liabilities: $657,598
Net Worth: $19,564,889
Earnings: $3,041,779
Fiscal Year-end: 06/30/24
Biomedical Researcher & Developer
N.A.I.C.S.: 541715
David L. Breeze *(Chm & Mng Dir)*

BPL LIMITED
System House, Palakkad, 678 007,
Kerala, India
Tel.: (91) 8025589109
Web Site: https://www.bpl.in
Year Founded: 1963
500074—(BOM)
Rev.: $6,714,681
Assets: $73,207,339
Liabilities: $32,131,117
Net Worth: $41,076,222
Earnings: $1,767,607
Emp.: 115
Fiscal Year-end: 03/30/22
Household Appliances Mfr
N.A.I.C.S.: 335220
Ajit Gopal Nambiar *(Chm & Mng Dir)*

BPLATS, INC.
15th floor Fujisoft Akihabara Building
3 Kanda Neribeicho, Chiyoda-ku, To-
kyo, Japan
Tel.: (81) 362629434
Web Site: https://www.bplats.co.jp
4381—(TKS)
Rev.: $5,929,170
Assets: $9,035,870
Liabilities: $5,321,050
Net Worth: $3,714,820
Earnings: ($647,780)
Fiscal Year-end: 03/31/24
Broadcasting Services
N.A.I.C.S.: 516210
Kenji Fujita *(Founder & Pres)*

BPLI HOLDINGS INC.
18 Prescott Street, Saint John's, A1C
3S4, NL, Canada
Tel.: (709) 739-9000 AB
Web Site: http://www.bluedrop.com
Year Founded: 1987
Rev.: $17,613,899
Assets: $13,445,765
Liabilities: $13,442,941
Net Worth: $2,824
Earnings: ($3,335,766)
Emp.: 153
Fiscal Year-end: 09/30/19
Business Course Software &
E-Learning Courses
N.A.I.C.S.: 513210
Derrick H. Rowe *(Chm)*

Subsidiaries:

Atlantis Systems Corp. **(1)**
Metropolitan Place 99 Wyse Road Suite
1100, Dartmouth, B3A 4S5, NS, Canada
Tel.: (902) 461-6600
Web Site: http://www.atlantissc.com
Sales Range: $10-24.9 Million
Emp.: 90
Aerospace & Defense Parts Mfr

N.A.I.C.S.: 334511
Bill Bartlett *(VP-Fin)*

Subsidiary (Domestic):

Atlantis Systems International
Inc.   **(2)**
1 Kenview Blvd, Brampton, L6T 5E6, ON,
Canada
Tel.: (905) 792-1981
Web Site: http://www.atlantissi.com
Flight Instruments Mfr
N.A.I.C.S.: 334511

BPM MINERALS LIMITED
Level 2 10 Outram Street, West
Perth, 6005, WA, Australia
Tel.: (61) 861497177   AU
Web Site:
  https://www.bpmminerals.com
Year Founded: 2020
BPM—(ASX)
Rev.: $41,298
Assets: $6,222,693
Liabilities: $168,450
Net Worth: $6,054,243
Earnings: ($1,210,292)
Fiscal Year-end: 06/30/23
Mineral Exploration Services
N.A.I.C.S.: 212390

BPOST NV/SA
Boulevard Anspach 1/1, 1000, Brus-
sels, Belgium
Tel.: (32) 22767643   BE
Web Site: https://www.bpost.be
Year Founded: 1830
BPOST—(OTCIQ)
Sales Range: $5-14.9 Billion
Emp.: 34,074
Physical & Electronic Postal Services
N.A.I.C.S.: 491110
Dirk Tirez *(CEO)*

Subsidiaries:

Active Ants Belgium BV   **(1)**
Molenweg 109, 2830, Willebroek, Belgium
Tel.: (32) 479924284
Web Site: http://www.activeants.be
E-Commerce Logistics Services
N.A.I.C.S.: 541614
Gert Hellemans *(Gen Mgr)*

Anthill BV   **(1)**
Rijnzathe 9, 3454 PV, De Meern, Nether-
lands
Tel.: (31) 306663093
Web Site: http://www.anthill.nl
Marketing & Communication Services
N.A.I.C.S.: 541613

Apple Express Courier Inc.   **(1)**
1715 NW 84th Ave, Miami, FL 33126
Tel.: (305) 599-0291
Courier Transportation Services
N.A.I.C.S.: 492110

Apple Express Courier Ltd.   **(1)**
5300 Satellite Drive, Mississauga, L4W 5J2,
ON, Canada
Tel.: (905) 602-9499
Web Site: http://www.appleexpress.com
Courier Transportation Services
N.A.I.C.S.: 492110

Banque de La Poste S.A./Bank van
De Post N.V.   **(1)**
Boulevard Anspach 1, 1000, Brussels, Bel-
gium
Tel.: (32) 25456211
Web Site: http://www.bpo.be
Sales Range: $100-124.9 Million
Emp.: 170
Retail Banking Services; Owned 50% by La
Poste S.A./De Post N.V. & 50% by Fortis
Bank SA/NV
N.A.I.C.S.: 522180

Belgian Post International SA/NV **(1)**
EMC Bldg 829 C, Brucargo, Zaventem,
1930, Belgium
Tel.: (32) 22762500
Web Site:
  http://www.belgianpostinternational.be

Sales Range: $75-99.9 Million
Emp.: 400
International Postal Services
N.A.I.C.S.: 491110

Certipost SA/NV   **(1)**
Ninovesteenweg 196, 9320, Erembodegem,
Belgium   **(100%)**
Tel.: (32) 53601111
Web Site: http://www.certipost.be
Sales Range: $25-49.9 Million
Emp.: 90
Electronic Document Exchange & Security
Services
N.A.I.C.S.: 519290

Deltamedia SA/NV   **(1)**
Industrielaan 24, 1740, Ternat,
Belgium   **(100%)**
Tel.: (32) 2568 0300
Web Site: http://www.deltamedia.be
Sales Range: $50-74.9 Million
Emp.: 80
Newspaper, Magazine & Other Printed Ma-
terials Distr & Sales
N.A.I.C.S.: 424920

Dynalinq BV   **(1)**
Daelderweg 21, 6361 HK, Nuth, Nether-
lands
Tel.: (31) 455245778
Web Site: http://www.dynalinq.nl
Consultancy & Management Services
N.A.I.C.S.: 541611

Euro-Sprinters SA/NV   **(1)**
Noordersingel 13, 2140, Antwerp,
Belgium   **(100%)**
Tel.: (32) 70233533
Web Site: http://www.eurosprinters.com
Sales Range: $1-9.9 Million
Emp.: 20
Courier Service
N.A.I.C.S.: 492110

Freight 4U Logistics NV-SA   **(1)**
Building 709, Box 2, 1830, Machelen, Bel-
gium
Tel.: (32) 26810490
Web Site: http://www.freight4ulogistics.com
Freight Forwarding Services
N.A.I.C.S.: 488510

Freight Distribution Management Sys-
tems Pty Ltd   **(1)**
7 Eucalyptus Place, Eastern Creek, Syd-
ney, 2766, NSW, Australia
Tel.: (61) 288820400
Web Site: http://www.fdmlogistics.com.au
Warehousing Services
N.A.I.C.S.: 493110

Imex Global Solutions LLC   **(1)**
400 Commerce Blvd Ste A2, Carlstadt, NJ
07072
Tel.: (847) 640-7776
Web Site:
  http://www.imexglobalsolutions.com
Parcel Distribution Services
N.A.I.C.S.: 492110

Leen Menken Foodservice Logistics
BV   **(1)**
Chroomstraat 155, 2718 RJ, Zoetermeer,
Netherlands
Tel.: (31) 793634160
Web Site: http://www.leenmenken.nl
Emp.: 60
Food Logistics Services
N.A.I.C.S.: 541614

Radial Italy SRL   **(1)**
Via Leonardo da Vinci 4-6-8, Cusago,
20090, Milan, Italy
Tel.: (39) 0800693035
Ecommerce Services
N.A.I.C.S.: 493110

Radial, Inc.   **(1)**
935 1st Ave, King of Prussia, PA 19406
Tel.: (610) 491-7000
Web Site: http://www.radial.com
eCommerce Products & Services
N.A.I.C.S.: 561499
Jim French *(CTO)*

SPEOS Belgium SA/NV   **(1)**
Rue Bollinckxstraat 26-32, 1070, Brussels,
Belgium   **(100%)**
Tel.: (32) 25580200
Web Site: http://www.speos.be

Sales Range: $25-49.9 Million
Emp.: 200
Document Production & Distribution Ser-
vices
N.A.I.C.S.: 561410

Taxipost SA/NV   **(1)**
Centre Monnaie/Muntcentrum 13th Floor,
1000, Brussels, Belgium   **(100%)**
Tel.: (32) 2201 2345
Sales Range: $150-199.9 Million
Emp.: 1,000
Express Mail Services
N.A.I.C.S.: 491110

Ubiway NV-SA   **(1)**
451 Route de Lennik, 1070, Anderlecht,
Belgium
Tel.: (32) 25280511
Web Site: http://www.ubiway.be
Magazine & Newspaper Distr
N.A.I.C.S.: 424920

eXbo Services International
SA/NV   **(1)**
Willebroekkaai 22, 1000, Brussels,
Belgium   **(100%)**
Tel.: (32) 2763200
Web Site: http://www.exbo.be
Sales Range: $25-49.9 Million
Emp.: 50
Document & Mailroom Solutions
N.A.I.C.S.: 561410

BPPL HOLDINGS PLC
Level 17 Access Towers 278/4 Union
Place, 2, Colombo, Sri Lanka
Tel.: (94) 112307168
Web Site:
  https://www.bpplholdings.com
Year Founded: 1991
BPPL.N0000—(COL)
Rev.: $18,290,145
Assets: $31,011,419
Liabilities: $13,768,721
Net Worth: $17,242,698
Earnings: $2,643,514
Emp.: 871
Fiscal Year-end: 03/31/21
Holding Company
N.A.I.C.S.: 551112
Sarath Dayantha Amarasinghe *(Chm)*

Subsidiaries:

Eco Spindles (Pvt) Ltd   **(1)**
No 278/4 Level 17 Access Towers Union
Place, 2, Colombo, Sri Lanka
Tel.: (94) 112307168
Web Site: https://www.ecospindles.com
Polyester Yarn Fabric Mfr
N.A.I.C.S.: 313110

BPS-SBERBANK OJSC
6 Mulyavin Boulevard, Minsk,
220005, Belarus
Tel.: (375) 5148148
Web Site: http://www.bps-
  sberbank.by
Sales Range: Less than $1 Million
Commercial Banking Services
N.A.I.C.S.: 522110
Andrey Aleksandrovich Savchenko
(Deputy Chm-Mgmt Bd)

BPTP LIMITED
BPTP Crest Plot 15 Udyog Vihar
Phase IV, Gurgaon, 122015, India
Tel.: (91) 124 385 2787
Web Site: http://www.bptp.com
Sales Range: $200-249.9 Million
Emp.: 800
Residential & Commercial Real Es-
tate Developer
N.A.I.C.S.: 236117
Kabul Chawla *(Chm & Mng Dir)*

BQE WATER INC.
uite 200 30 East 6th Avenue, Vancouver, V5T 1J4, BC, Canada
Tel.: (604) 685-1243   BC
Web Site: https://www.bqewater.com

Year Founded: 1999
BQE—(TSXV)
Rev.: $13,695,540
Assets: $14,238,572
Liabilities: $3,081,118
Net Worth: $11,157,454
Earnings: $2,003,456
Fiscal Year-end: 12/31/23
Water Treatment Processing Services
N.A.I.C.S.: 924110
David Matthew Kratochvil *(Pres &
CEO)*

Subsidiaries:

BioteQ Arizona, Inc.   **(1)**
36 W Hwy 92, Bisbee, AZ 85603
Tel.: (520) 432-3863
Web Site: http://www.bioteqwater.com
Waste Treatment Services
N.A.I.C.S.: 221310

BR INDUSTRIER AS
Forusbeen 210, 4313, Sandnes, Nor-
way
Tel.: (47) 51631711   NO
Web Site: http://www.br-industrier.no
Year Founded: 2000
Sales Range: $200-249.9 Million
Emp.: 700
Holding Company; Industrial Engi-
neering Services
N.A.I.C.S.: 551112
Bjorn Rygg *(CEO)*

**BR. HOLDINGS CORPORA-
TION**
Hikarimachi 2-6-31, Higashi-ku, Hiro-
shima, 732-0052, Japan
Tel.: (81) 822612860
Web Site: https://www.brhd.co.jp
Year Founded: 2002
1726—(TKS)
Rev.: $266,111,990
Assets: $279,940,110
Liabilities: $184,438,830
Net Worth: $95,501,280
Earnings: $8,943,330
Emp.: 617
Fiscal Year-end: 03/31/24
Holding Company
N.A.I.C.S.: 551112
Kimiyasu Fujita *(Pres & CEO)*

**BRAAS MONIER BUILDING
GROUP SERVICES GMBH**
Frankfurter Landstrasse 2-4, 61440,
Oberursel, Germany
Tel.: (49) 61 71 61 0 06
Web Site: http://www.braas-
  monier.com
Year Founded: 2017
Sales Range: $1-4.9 Billion
Emp.: 7,561
Roofing & Other Building Materials
Mfr
N.A.I.C.S.: 423330
Achim Schreck *(Dir-Comm & IR)*

BRABANK ASA
Starvhusgaten 4, Bergen, 5014, Nor-
way
Tel.: (47) 55961000
BRA-ME—(OSL)
Rev.: $46,322,723
Assets: $720,147,045
Liabilities: $634,303,699
Net Worth: $85,843,346
Earnings: ($12,831,377)
Emp.: 50
Fiscal Year-end: 12/31/19
Financial Consulting Services
N.A.I.C.S.: 541611
Bent H. Gjendem *(CEO)*

BRAC
BRAC Centre 75 Mohakhali, Dhaka,
1212, Bangladesh

BRAC—(Continued)

Tel.: (880) 2 988 1265 BD
Web Site: http://www.brac.net
Year Founded: 1972
Emp.: 115,000
Health, Education, Culture & Economic Development Services Organization
N.A.I.C.S.: 926110
Ahmed Mushtaque Raza Chowdhury
(Vice Chm)

Subsidiaries:

BRAC Bank Limited (1)
Anik Tower 220/B Tejgaon Gulshan Link
Road Tejgaon, Dhaka, 1208,
Bangladesh (44.64%)
Tel.: (880) 2 880 1301
Web Site: http://www.bracbank.com
Rev.: $7,441,120
Assets: $21,155,629
Liabilities: $9,127,734
Net Worth: $12,027,896
Earnings: $2,864,630
Emp.: 7,619
Fiscal Year-end: 12/31/2021
Banking Services
N.A.I.C.S.: 523150
M. Sarwar Ahmed (Head-Internal Control & Compliance)

BRACCO S.P.A.
Via Egidio Folli 50, 20134, Milan, Italy
Tel.: (39) 0221771 IT
Web Site:
http://www.corporate.bracco.com
Year Founded: 1927
Sales Range: $750-799.9 Million
Emp.: 2,300
Medical Imaging & Diagnostic Equipment & Pharmaceutical Mfr
N.A.I.C.S.: 325412
Diana Bracco (Pres & CEO)

Subsidiaries:

ACIST Medical Systems, Inc. (1)
7905 Fuller Rd, Eden Prairie, MN 55344
Tel.: (952) 941-3507
Web Site: http://www.acist.com
Sales Range: $25-49.9 Million
Emp.: 100
Medical Chemical Injection Systems Developer & Mfr
N.A.I.C.S.: 339112
Thomas Morizio (Pres & COO)

Bracco Imaging S.p.A. (1)
Via Caduti di Marcinelle 13, 20134, Milan,
Italy
Tel.: (39) 0221771
Web Site: http://www.imaging.bracco.com
Sales Range: $125-149.9 Million
Emp.: 300
Pharmaceuticals Mfr
N.A.I.C.S.: 325412

Subsidiary (Non-US):

BIPSO GmbH (2)
Robert-Gerwig-Str 4, 78224, Singen, Germany
Tel.: (49) 7731 7909 0
Web Site: http://www.bipso.de
Emp.: 400
Pharmaceutical Products Distr
N.A.I.C.S.: 424210
Paolo Mornata (Pres)

Subsidiary (US):

Bracco Diagnostics Inc. (2)
107 College Rd E, Princeton, NJ
08540-6612 (100%)
Tel.: (609) 514-2200
Sales Range: $50-74.9 Million
Emp.: 250
Medical Contrast Imaging Pharmaceutical
Developer & Mfr
N.A.I.C.S.: 325412
Barbara Lani (VP-Quality & Compliance)

Subsidiary (Non-US):

Bracco Far East Ltd. (2)
14/F LiFung Centre 2 On Ping Street - Siu

Lek Yuen, Sha Tin, China (Hong Kong)
Tel.: (852) 2635 5469
Pharmaceutical Products Distr
N.A.I.C.S.: 424210

Bracco Imaging Deutschland
GmbH (2)
Max Stromeyer Strasse 116, 78467, Konstanz, Germany
Tel.: (49) 75313631000
Web Site: http://www.braccoimaging.de
Sales Range: $25-49.9 Million
Emp.: 50
Pharmaceutical Development & Manufacturing
N.A.I.C.S.: 325412
Thilo Schneider (Mng Dir)

Bracco Imaging Europe BV (2)
Belgian Branch Collines de Wavre Building
H Avenue Pasteur 6, 1300, Wavre, Belgium
Tel.: (32) 10 68 63 79
Medical Equipment Distr
N.A.I.C.S.: 423450

Bracco Imaging France SA (2)
7 Place Copernic, 91080, Courcouronnes,
France
Tel.: (33) 1 60 79 82 76
Medical Equipment Distr
N.A.I.C.S.: 423450

Subsidiary (Domestic):

Bracco Imaging Italia s.r.l. (2)
Via Caduti di Marcinelle 13, 20134, Milan,
Italy
Tel.: (39) 02 21771
Medical Equipment Distr
N.A.I.C.S.: 423450

Subsidiary (Non-US):

Bracco Imaging Korea, Ltd (2)
4F Shinsung Bldg 732-27 Yoeksam-dong,
Gangnam-gu, Seoul, 135-514, Korea
(South)
Tel.: (82) 2 2222 3500
Medical Equipment Distr
N.A.I.C.S.: 423450

Bracco Imaging Polska sp.z.o.o. (2)
Horizon Plaza ul Domaniewska 39A0, 02-
672, Warsaw, Poland
Tel.: (48) 22 208 24 20
Medical Equipment Distr
N.A.I.C.S.: 423450

Bracco Imaging Scandinavia AB (2)
Salsmastaregatan 32, Hisings Backa, 422
46, Sweden
Tel.: (46) 31 760 18 80
Web Site: http://www.braccoimaging.se
Medical Equipment Distr
N.A.I.C.S.: 423450

Bracco Osterreich GmbH (2)
Floridsdorfer Hauptstrasse 1 A, 1210, Vienna, Austria
Tel.: (43) 1 489 34 95
Web Site: http://www.bracco.com
Pharmaceutical Products Distr
N.A.I.C.S.: 424210
Volkmar Leisser (Gen Mgr)

Bracco Suisse S.A. (2)
Centro Galleria 2 - Via Cantonale, Manno,
Switzerland
Tel.: (41) 91 610 87 73
Pharmaceutical Products Distr
N.A.I.C.S.: 424210
Jean-Claude Tairaire (Mgr-Mktg & Sls)

Bracco UK Ltd. (2)
Mercury Park Wycombe Lane, Wooburn
Green, High Wycombe, HP10 0HH, Bucks,
United Kingdom
Tel.: (44) 1628 851500
Web Site: http://www.bracco.com
Pharmaceutical Products Distr
N.A.I.C.S.: 424210
Steve Kennedy (Gen Mgr)

Joint Venture (Non-US):

Bracco-Eisai Co., Ltd. (2)
3-11-6 Ohtsuka, Bunkyo-ku, Tokyo, 112-
0012, Japan (51%)
Tel.: (81) 3 5319 3381
Sales Range: $1-9.9 Million
Emp.: 50

Medical Contrast Imaging Products Mfr &
Distr
N.A.I.C.S.: 325412
Neil Foust (Gen Mgr)

Bracco International B.V. (1)
Strawinskylaan 3051, 1077 ZX, Amsterdam,
Netherlands
Tel.: (31) 203012150
Web Site: http://www.bracco.com
Sales Range: $25-49.9 Million
Emp.: 2
Pharmaceutical & Medical Diagnostic
Equipment Developer & Mfr
N.A.I.C.S.: 325412
Tatjana Kabulova (Mgr)

Bracco Research USA Inc (1)
305 College Rd E, Princeton, NJ
08540-6608 (100%)
Tel.: (609) 514-2409
Web Site: http://www.bracco.com
Sales Range: $25-49.9 Million
Emp.: 48
Research & Development of Drugs
N.A.I.C.S.: 459999

Centro Diagnostico Italiano
S.p.A. (1)
Via Saint Bon 20, 20147, Milan, Italy
Tel.: (39) 0248317444
Web Site: http://www.cdi.it
Diagnostic Medical Services
N.A.I.C.S.: 621512
Elena Gavardi (Mgr-Comm)

Justesa Imagen Mexicana, S.A. (1)
Boulevard Picacho Ajusco 130- 104, Col
Jardines en la Montana Del Tlalpan, 14210,
Mexico, Mexico
Tel.: (52) 555 483 2970
Diagnostic Imaging Services
N.A.I.C.S.: 621512

Reimed, SCRL (1)
Pasaje Villaran 192-194 U-12 Urb Los
Sauces Surquillo, Lima, 15076, Peru
Tel.: (51) 1 448 1087
Diagnostic Imaging Services
N.A.I.C.S.: 621512

BRACELL
21/F China Building 29 Queen's
Road Central, Central, China (Hong
Kong)
Tel.: (852) 2864 6638 BM
Web Site:
http://www.brazilcellulose.com
Sales Range: $400-449.9 Million
Emp.: 1,379
Wood Pulp & Viscose Staple Fiber
Mfr
N.A.I.C.S.: 322110
John Jeffrey Ying (Chm)

**BRACK CAPITAL REAL ES-
TATE**
Barbara Strozzilaan 201, 1083HN,
Amsterdam, Netherlands
Tel.: (31) 205141000
Web Site: http://www.brack-
capital.com
Year Founded: 1992
Real Estate Development Services
N.A.I.C.S.: 531390
Shai Shamir (CEO-Interim)

**BRADAVERSE EDUCATION
(INT'L) INVESTMENTS GROUP
LIMITED.**
Rooms 1006-7 10/F China United
Centre 28 Marble Road, North Point,
China (Hong Kong)
Tel.: (852) 39746688
Web Site: http://www.hkeduli.com
1082—(HKG)
Rev.: $11,614,391
Assets: $21,317,170
Liabilities: $2,430,628
Net Worth: $18,886,541
Earnings: ($4,210,810)
Emp.: 81
Fiscal Year-end: 06/30/22

Tutoring Services
N.A.I.C.S.: 611691
Ka Wai Tsang (Exec Dir)

**BRADDA HEAD LITHIUM LIM-
ITED**
Viking House Nelson Street, IM1
2AH, Douglas, IM1 2AH, Isle of Man
Tel.. (44) 1024039390
Web Site:
https://www.braddaheadltd.com
Year Founded: 2009
BHLIF—(OTCIQ)
Rev.: $135,487
Assets: $15,848,063
Liabilities: $186,359
Net Worth: $15,661,704
Earnings: ($1,503,858)
Fiscal Year-end: 02/29/24
Mining Services
N.A.I.C.S.: 212390

BRADESPAR S.A.
Av Presidente Juscelino Kubitschek
1309 2 andar, Vila Nova Conceicao,
Sao Paulo, 04543-011, Brazil
Tel.: (55) 21786300
Web Site:
https://www.bradespar.com.br
XBRPO—(MAD)
Rev.: $6,479,911
Assets: $2,502,068,733
Liabilities: $134,992,252
Net Worth: $2,367,076,481
Earnings: ($99,825,989)
Emp.: 14
Fiscal Year-end: 12/31/19
Investment Company
N.A.I.C.S.: 522210

Subsidiaries:

Cia Paulista de Forca e Luz Ltda (1)
Rodovia Campinas Mogi-Mirim, Km 2 5
Jardim Santana, Campinas, 13088-900,
Brazil
Tel.: (55) 1937568704
Electric Power Distribution
N.A.I.C.S.: 221122
Wilson Pinto Ferreira Jr. (Pres & CEO)

Cia Piratininga de Forca e Luz
Ltda (1)
Rod Campinas Mogi-Mirim km 2 5, Jardim
Santana, Campinas, Brazil
Tel.: (55) 1937568704
Electric Power Distribution
N.A.I.C.S.: 221122

**BRADFORD GREENHOUSES
LTD.**
4346 County Rd 90 R R 2, Barrie,
L4M 4S4, ON, Canada
Tel.: (705) 725-9913
Web Site:
http://www.bradfordgreenhouse.com
Year Founded: 1975
Rev.: $10,433,394
Emp.: 120
Flower Shop Chemicals & Fertilizers
Distr
N.A.I.C.S.: 111422
Len Ferragine (Owner)

**BRADFORDS BUILDING SUP-
PLIES LTD.**
96 Hendford Hill, Yeovil, BA20 2QR,
Somerset, United Kingdom
Tel.: (44) 1935845245
Web Site: http://www.bradfords.co.uk
Year Founded: 1770
Sales Range: $100-124.9 Million
Emp.: 485
Building Supplies Retailer
N.A.I.C.S.: 444140
Mark Eburne (CEO)

**BRADVIN TRAILER SALES
LTD.**

10920 87 Avenue, Grande Prairie, T8V 8K4, AB, Canada
Tel.: (780) 539-6260
Web Site: http://www.bradvin.com
Year Founded: 1980
Sales Range: $10-24.9 Million
Emp.: 40
Heavy Load Truck, Trailers Sales & Repair Service
N.A.I.C.S.: 336120
Brad Willsey *(Gen Mgr)*

BRADY & MORRIS ENGINEERING CO. LTD.

Brady House 12/14 Veer Nariman Road, Fort, Mumbai, 400 001, India
Tel.: (91) 2222048361
Web Site: https://www.bradymorris.in 505690—(BOM)
Rev.: $6,464,162
Assets: $5,729,874
Liabilities: $4,379,138
Net Worth: $1,350,736
Earnings: $435,858
Emp.: 150
Fiscal Year-end: 03/31/22
Material Handling Equipment Mfr
N.A.I.C.S.: 333248
Pavan G. Morarka *(Chm)*

BRADY PLC

100 Lower Thames Street, London, EC3R 6DL, United Kingdom
Tel.: (44) 20 3301 1200   UK
Web Site: http://www.bradyplc.com
Year Founded: 1985
Rev.: $29,386,696
Assets: $47,603,478
Liabilities: $21,032,737
Net Worth: $26,570,741
Earnings: ($2,638,293)
Emp.: 180
Fiscal Year-end: 12/31/18
Holding Company; Commodity Trading Software Publisher
N.A.I.C.S.: 551112
Carmen Christine Carey *(CEO)*

Subsidiaries:

Brady Energy AG   (1)
Gubelstrasse 11, Zug, 6300, Switzerland
Tel.: (41) 417287242
Emp.: 25
Software Publishing Services
N.A.I.C.S.: 513210

Brady Energy Norway AS   (1)
Storgt 7, PO Box 154, NO 1783, Halden, Norway
Tel.: (47) 69709600
Sales Range: $25-49.9 Million
Emp.: 100
Developer of Commodity Trading Software
N.A.I.C.S.: 513210
Anette Nordskog *(Exec VP & Head-Bus Dev)*

Subsidiary (Non-US):

Brady Energy Canada, Inc.   (2)
251 Consumers Rd 12th Fl, Toronto, M2J 4R3, ON, Canada
Tel.: (416) 640-6396
Sales Range: $25-49.9 Million
Emp.: 4
Distr of Commodity Trading Software
N.A.I.C.S.: 423430

Subsidiary (US):

Brady Energy US, Inc.   (2)
199 S Los Robles Ave Ste 610, Pasadena, CA 91101
Tel.: (626) 535-9888
Sales Range: $25-49.9 Million
Emp.: 6
Distr of Commodity Trading Software
N.A.I.C.S.: 423430

Brady Switzerland SA   (1)
Rue Francois-Perreard 18, 1225, Chene-Bourg, Switzerland
Tel.: (41) 22 869 10 00

Commodity Trading Software Publishing Services
N.A.I.C.S.: 513210

Brady USA, Inc.   (1)
6555 W Good Hope Rd, Milwaukee, WI 53223-4634
Tel.: (414) 358-5148
Software Publishing Services
N.A.I.C.S.: 513210

Commodities Software (UK) Limited   (1)
281 Cambridge Science Park Milton Road, Cambridge, CB4 0WE, United Kingdom   **(100%)**
Tel.: (44) 1223 479 479
Web Site: http://www.bradyplc.com
Emp.: 50
Commodities Trading Software Publisher
N.A.I.C.S.: 513210
Gavin Lavelle *(CEO)*

Systems Alternatives International LLC   (1)
1705 Indian Wood Cir, Maumee, OH 43537
Tel.: (419) 891-1100
Web Site: http://www.bradyplc.com
Industrial Recycling Systems Software Publisher
N.A.I.C.S.: 513210

BRAEBURY HOMES

366 King Street E Suite 400, Kingston, K7K 6Y3, ON, Canada
Tel.: (613) 546-3400
Web Site:
     http://www.braeburyhomes.com
Year Founded: 1983
Rev.: $10,259,504
Emp.: 47
Residential Construction
N.A.I.C.S.: 236115
Peter Splinter *(Owner & Pres)*

BRAEMAR PLC

Tel.: (44) 2031424100
Web Site: https://www.braemar.com
BMS—(LSE)
Rev.: $151,763,226
Assets: $214,932,507
Liabilities: $128,544,856
Net Worth: $86,387,650
Earnings: $6,916,226
Emp.: 528
Fiscal Year-end: 02/28/21
Offices of Other Holding Companies
N.A.I.C.S.: 551112
James Kidwell *(CEO)*

Subsidiaries:

Braemar ACM Shipbroking (USA) Inc.   (1)
1800 W Loop S Ste 2125, Houston, TX 77027
Tel.: (832) 200-2440
Ship Broking Services
N.A.I.C.S.: 488510

Braemar ACM Shipbroking Pty Limited   (1)
Level 5 432 St Kilda Road, Melbourne, 3004, VIC, Australia
Tel.: (61) 39 867 2177
Ship Broking Services
N.A.I.C.S.: 488510

Braemar Adjusting Pte Ltd   (1)
1 Pickering Street 08-01 Great Eastern Centre, Singapore, 048659, Singapore
Tel.: (65) 62255772
Web Site: http://www.braemaradjusting.com
Marine Engineering Services
N.A.I.C.S.: 541330
John Harris *(Mng Dir)*

Braemar Falconer   (1)
1st Floor Northern Shell Building, 10 Lower Thames Street, London, EC3R 6EN, United Kingdom
Tel.: (44) 2072643250
Marine Engineering Services
N.A.I.C.S.: 541330

Braemar Falconer (Shanghai) Pte Ltd   (1)
Room 3B10 Tower B No 568 Bocheng Road, Pudong District, Shanghai, 200126, China
Tel.: (86) 2163212233
Marine Engineering Services
N.A.I.C.S.: 541330
Arthur Seah *(Area Mgr)*

Braemar Falconer Pte Limited   (1)
112 Robinson Road 09-01, Singapore, 068902, Singapore
Tel.: (65) 62249200
Sales Range: $25-49.9 Million
Emp.: 100
Marine Engineering Services
N.A.I.C.S.: 541330
Michael Yew Wah Chan *(Grp Mng Dir & Dir-Technical)*

Subsidiary (Non-US):

Braemar Falconer Vietnam Co Limited   (2)
Suite 550 Petrovietnam Towers 8 Hoang Dieu Street, Vung Tau, Vietnam
Tel.: (84) 643832178
Sales Range: $25-49.9 Million
Emp.: 17
Marine Consulting Services
N.A.I.C.S.: 541611

Braemar Technical Services (Offshore) India Pvt Ltd   (2)
801/A Malhotra Chambers Off Govandi Station Road, Mumbai, 400088, India
Tel.: (91) 2225508140
Marine Engineering Services
N.A.I.C.S.: 541330
Vishal Subhash Sharma *(Dir & Area Mgr)*

Braemar Holdings (USA) Inc.   (1)
Brookhollow Central 1 2800 N Loop W Ste 900, Houston, TX 77092
Tel.: (713) 904-5780
Ship Broking Services
N.A.I.C.S.: 488510

Braemar Naves Corporate Finance Limited   (1)
One Strand Trafalgar Square, London, WC2N 5HR, United Kingdom
Tel.: (44) 203 142 4270
Finance Services
N.A.I.C.S.: 523999

Braemar Quincannon Pte Limited   (1)
8 Cross Street 09-06 Manulife Tower, Singapore, 048424, Singapore   **(50%)**
Tel.: (65) 65330069
Web Site: http://www.braemarseascope.com
Deep Sea Freight Transportation
N.A.I.C.S.: 483111
Mark Sorgo *(Mng Dir)*

Braemar Seascope (Shanghai) Limited   (1)
Room 3B10 Tower B No 568 Bocheng Road, Pudong District, Shanghai, 200126, China
Tel.: (86) 216 321 2233
Ship Broking Services
N.A.I.C.S.: 488510

Braemar Seascope Italia SRL   (1)
Piazza Matteotti 55, 19038, Sarzana, Italy
Tel.: (39) 018 761 0173
Ship Broking Services
N.A.I.C.S.: 488510

Braemar Seascope Limited   (1)
35 Cosway St, London, NW1 5BT, United Kingdom
Tel.: (44) 2075352650
Web Site: http://www.seascope.co.uk
Ship Chartering Services
N.A.I.C.S.: 483211
James Kidwell *(Gen Mgr)*

Subsidiary (Non-US):

Braemar Seascope (Dry Cargo) Pte Limited   (2)
1 Pickering Street Singapore Land Twr, Singapore, 68898, Singapore   **(100%)**
Tel.: (65) 65330198
Sales Range: $25-49.9 Million
Emp.: 12
Marine Cargo Handling

N.A.I.C.S.: 488320

Braemar Seascope India Private Limited   (2)
405 Vyapar Bhavan 49 P D'Mello Road Carnac Bunder, Mumbai, 400 009, India
Tel.: (91) 2265292440
Ship Chartering Services
N.A.I.C.S.: 483212

Braemar Seascope Pty Limited   (2)
Level 5 432 St Kilda Road, Melbourne, 3004, VIC, Australia   **(100%)**
Tel.: (61) 398672177
Web Site:
     http://www.braemarseascope.com.au
Sales Range: $25-49.9 Million
Emp.: 50
Navigational Services to Shipping
N.A.I.C.S.: 488330

Subsidiary (Domestic):

Braemar Falconer Pty Limited   (3)
Unit 4 Churchill Court 335 Hay Street, Subiaco, 6008, WA, Australia
Tel.: (61) 893828190
Emp.: 11
Marine Engineering Services
N.A.I.C.S.: 541330
Richard Van Der Spoel *(Area Mgr)*

Subsidiary (Domestic):

Cory Brothers Shipping Agency Limited   (2)
Alpi House First Floor Miles Gray Road, Basildon, SS14 3HJ, Essex, United Kingdom   **(100%)**
Tel.: (44) 126 872 3780
Web Site: https://www.corybrothers.com
Sales Range: $25-49.9 Million
Emp.: 200
Freight Transportation Arrangement Services
N.A.I.C.S.: 488510

Subsidiary (Domestic):

Cory Brothers   (3)
4 Shore Place, Edinburgh, EH6 6SW, Leith, United Kingdom
Tel.: (44) 1315546631
Web Site: http://corybrothers.com
Sales Range: $25-49.9 Million
Emp.: 12
Logistics & Maritime Shipping Services
N.A.I.C.S.: 488330
Alan Williamson *(Mgr)*

Subsidiary (Non-US):

Cory Brothers Shipping Pte Limited   (3)
1 Pickering Street 08-02B Great Eastern Centre, Singapore, 48659, Singapore
Tel.: (65) 63393637
Freight Forwarding Services
N.A.I.C.S.: 488510

Subsidiary (Domestic):

Gorman Cory Shipping Limited   (3)
Claremont Bldg Old Clatterbridge Rd, Wirral, CH63 4JB, Bebington, United Kingdom
Tel.: (44) 1513340530
Web Site: http://www.cory.co.uk
Sales Range: $25-49.9 Million
Emp.: 8
Marine Cargo Handling
N.A.I.C.S.: 488320

Planetwide Limited   (3)
4 Capricorn Ctr, Cranes Farm Rd, Basildon, SS143JJ, Essex, United Kingdom
Tel.: (44) 1268530600
Web Site: http://www.planetwide-ltd.co.uk
Freight Transportation Arrangement
N.A.I.C.S.: 488510

Braemar Steege Pte. Ltd.   (1)
Wisma Kodel 2nd Floor Jl HR Rasuna Said Kav B-4, Jakarta, 12920, Indonesia
Tel.: (62) 21 527 6302
Web Site: http://www.braemarsteege.com
Sales Range: $25-49.9 Million
Emp.: 2
Marine Engineering Services
N.A.I.C.S.: 541330
Made Arcana *(Gen Mgr)*

Braemar PLC—(Continued)

**Braemar Technical Serviced (Off-
shore) Sdn Bhd** (1)
Level 16 Menara Genesis No 33 Jalan Sul-
tan Ismail, 50250, Kuala Lumpur, Malaysia
Tel.: (60) 321412494
Emp.: 17
Marine Engineering Services
N.A.I.C.S.: 541330
Abdul Aziz Suleiman (Mng Dir)

**Cory Brothers (The Netherlands)
B.V.** (1)
Fosfaatweg 48, Westpoort 1695, 1013 BM,
Amsterdam, Netherlands
Tel.: (31) 20 682 4456
Ship Broking Services
N.A.I.C.S.: 488510
John Snip (Mgr)

Fred. Olsen Freight Limited (1)
Cory House Haven Exchange, Felixstowe,
IP11 2QX, United Kingdom
Tel.: (44) 1394 674822
Web Site: http://www.fredolsenfreight.com
Sales Range: $25-49.9 Million
Emp.: 95
Freight Forwarding Services
N.A.I.C.S.: 488510
Kevin Gormah (Mng Dir)

**P.T. Braemar Technical Services
Offshore** (1)
Wisma Kodel 2nd Floor Jalan HR Rasuna
Said Kav B-4, Jakarta, 12920, Indonesia
Tel.: (62) 215276306
Sales Range: $25-49.9 Million
Emp.: 20
Marine Engineering Services
N.A.I.C.S.: 541330
Arthur Morgan (Area Mgr)

Wavespec Limited (1)
K85 Odhams Walk, Covent Garden, Lon-
don, WC2H 9SE, United Kingdom
Tel.: (44) 203 142 4545
Web Site: https://www.wavespec.com
Sales Range: $25-49.9 Million
Emp.: 30
Marine Engineering Consulting Services
N.A.I.C.S.: 541330
Sheila McClain (Mng Dir)

Subsidiary (US):

**BRAEMAR WAVESPEC USA
Inc.** (2)
2800 N Loop W Ste 900, Houston, TX
77092
Tel.: (713) 688-5353
Marine Engineering Services
N.A.I.C.S.: 541330

BRAGANZA AS

Froyas Gate 15, PO Box 700
Skoyen, 0273, Oslo, Norway
Tel.: (47) 22547150
Web Site: http://www.braganza.com
Year Founded: 1938
Investment Holding Company
N.A.I.C.S.: 523999
Per G. Braathen (Owner, Chm &
CEO)

Subsidiaries:

Braathens Aviation (1)
Jager Hills 18, PO Box 37, SE 201 20,
Malmo, Sweden
Tel.: (46) 406602300
Web Site: http://www.maloaviation.se
Sales Range: $200-249.9 Million
Emp.: 600
Aviation Services
N.A.I.C.S.: 481111
Oyvind Thon (CFO)

Subsidiary (Domestic):

Malmo Aviation AB (2)
Jagershillgatan 18, PO Box 37, SE 201 20,
Malmo, Sweden
Tel.: (46) 406602900
Web Site: http://www.malmoaviation.se
Sales Range: $150-199.9 Million
Emp.: 550
Oil Transportation Services

N.A.I.C.S.: 481111
Per G. Braathen (Owner & Chm)

BRAGG GAMING GROUP INC.

Exchange Tower 130 King St W Suite
1968, Toronto, M5X 1E3, ON,
Canada
Tel.: (905) 761-9200   Ca
Web Site: https://www.bragg.games
Year Founded: 2004
BRAG—(NASDAQ)
Rev.: $104,073,688
Assets: $128,213,517
Liabilities: $42,809,077
Net Worth: $85,404,440
Earnings: ($4,279,188)
Emp.: 428
Fiscal Year-end: 12/31/22
Software Development Services
N.A.I.C.S.: 541511
Yaniv Spielberg (Chief Strategy Offi-
cer)

Subsidiaries:

Devesys Technologies, Inc. (1)
802 W Broadway Ste 205, Monona, WI
53707
Tel.: (608) 223-1311
Web Site: http://www.devesys.com
Tracking & Reporting Software Develop-
ment Services
N.A.I.C.S.: 541511

BRAGG GROUP OF COMPA-
NIES

4881 Main St, Oxford, B0M 1P0, NS,
Canada
Tel.: (902) 447-2100   Ca
Holding Company
N.A.I.C.S.: 551112
John Bragg (Co-Founder & Pres)

Subsidiaries:

EastLink Cable Systems (1)
PO Box 8660 Station A, Halifax, B3K 5M3,
NS, Canada
Tel.: (902) 488-5221
Web Site: http://www.eastlink.ca
Sales Range: $150-199.9 Million
Emp.: 1,500
Cable Network; Telecommunications Ser-
vices
N.A.I.C.S.: 517810

Branch (Domestic):

EastLink (2)
17 Duffy Place, Saint John's, A1B 4L1, NL,
Canada
Tel.: (709) 754-3775
Web Site: http://www.eastlink.ca
Sales Range: $100-124.9 Million
Emp.: 50
Cable Television Services; Telecommunica-
tions
N.A.I.C.S.: 516210

Oxford Frozen Foods Limited (1)
4959 Main Street, PO Box 220, Oxford,
B0M 1P0, NS, Canada
Tel.: (902) 447-2100
Web Site:
https://www.oxfordfrozenfoods.com
Sales Range: $150-199.9 Million
Emp.: 600
Frozen Food Mfr
N.A.I.C.S.: 311411

BRAHIM'S HOLDINGS BER-
HAD

7-05 7th Floor Menara Hap Seng
Jalan P Ramlee, 50250, Kuala Lum-
pur, Wilayah Persekutuan, Malaysia
Tel.: (60) 320720730
Web Site: http://brahimsgroup.com
BRAHIMS—(KLS)
Rev.: $20,391,278
Assets: $16,063,493
Liabilities: $47,511,338
Net Worth: ($31,447,845)
Earnings: ($58,973,557)

Emp.: 298
Fiscal Year-end: 12/31/20
Holding Company
N.A.I.C.S.: 551112
Ibrahim Ahmad (Chm)

BRAHMANAND HIMGHAR LIM-
ITED

Chekuasole PO Jogerdanga PS
Goaltore Paschim, Midnapore,
721121, West Bengal, India
Tel.: (91) 33 218314
Year Founded: 1990
Sales Range: Less than $1 Million
Cold Storage Services
N.A.I.C.S.: 493120
Manoj Kumar Agarwal (Mng Dir)

BRAHMAPUTRA INFRA-
STRUCTURE LIMITED

Brahmaputra House A-7 Mahipalpur,
NH-8 Mahipalpur Crossing, New
Delhi, 110 037, India
Tel.: (91) 1142290200
Web Site:
https://www.brahmaputragroup.com
535693—(BOM)
Rev.: $22,429,680
Assets: $81,572,400
Liabilities: $59,093,580
Net Worth: $22,478,820
Earnings: $970,515
Emp.: 76
Fiscal Year-end: 03/31/22
Civil Engineering & Construction Ser-
vices
N.A.I.C.S.: 237990

BRAI-COST S.P.A.

Zona Industriale Vascigliano, I-05039,
Vascigliano di Stroncone Terni, Italy
Tel.: (39) 0744607349   IT
Web Site: http://www.brai.it
Roofing & Structure Waterproofing
Products Mfr
N.A.I.C.S.: 325211

BRAILLE ENERGY SYSTEMS
INC.

945 Princess Street, Box 117, Kings-
ton, K7L 0E9, ON, Canada
Tel.: (613) 447-8521   Ca
Web Site: https://brailleenergy.com
Year Founded: 2011
BES—(TSXV)
Rev.: $2,839,011
Assets: $2,479,744
Liabilities: $1,558,571
Net Worth: $921,173
Earnings: ($2,195,373)
Fiscal Year-end: 09/30/23
Investment Services
N.A.I.C.S.: 523999
Ivan Gissing (CTO)

Subsidiaries:

Braille Battery Inc. (1)
6935 15th St E Bldg 115, Sarasota, FL
34243
Tel.: (941) 312-5047
Web Site: https://braillebattery.com
Batteries & Related Accessories Mfr
N.A.I.C.S.: 335910

Subsidiary (Non-US):

Braille Batteries UK (2)
Unit 30 Huxley Close Park Farm Ind East,
Wellingborough, NN8 6AB, Northern Ire-
land, United Kingdom
Tel.: (44) 07738497362
Batteries & Related Accessories Mfr
N.A.I.C.S.: 335910

BRAIME GROUP PLC

Hunslet Road, Leeds, LS10 1JZ,
United Kingdom
Tel.: (44) 1132457491

Web Site:
https://www.braimegroup.com
BMTO—(AIM)
Rev.: $55,730,742
Assets: $42,655,830
Liabilities: $18,820,721
Net Worth: $23,835,109
Earnings: $3,378,938
Emp.: 186
Fiscal Year-end: 12/31/22
Metals Industry
N.A.I.C.S.: 332999
O. Nicholas A. Braime (Chm & Mng
Dir-Grp)

Subsidiaries:

**4B Africa Elevator Components (Pty)
Limited** (1)
14 Newport Business Park Mica Drive, Kya
Sand, Johannesburg, 2163, Gauteng, South
Africa
Tel.: (27) 117086114
Web Site: http://www.go4b.co.uk
Sales Range: $25-49.9 Million
Emp.: 4
Elevator & Conveyor Components Mfr
N.A.I.C.S.: 333922

4B Asia Pacific Company Limited (1)
899/1 Moo 21 Tambon Bang Phli Yai, Amphoe Bang Phli Chang Wat, Samut Prakan,
10540, Thailand
Tel.: (66) 21734339
Web Site: https://4b-asia-pacific-
coltd.business.site
Electronic Equipment Mfr & Distr
N.A.I.C.S.: 334419

**4B Braime (Changzhou) Industrial
Control Equipment Company
Limited** (1)
F1 Building 5A 8 West Lake Road, Wujin
High New Technology Development Zone,
Changzhou, 213164, Jiangsu, China
Tel.: (86) 13601609266
Bucket Elevator Component Mfr & Distr
N.A.I.C.S.: 333922

4B Braime Components Limited (1)
Hunslet Road, Leeds, LS10 1JZ, West
Yorkshire, United Kingdom
Tel.: (44) 1132461800
Web Site: https://www.go4b.co.uk
Bucket Elevator Component Mfr & Distr
N.A.I.C.S.: 333922
Nicholas Braime (Mng Dir)

4B Elevator Components Limited (1)
625 Erie Ave, Morton, IL 61550
Tel.: (309) 698-5611
Web Site: http://www.go4b.com
Emp.: 30
Elevator Components Distr
N.A.I.C.S.: 333921

**Braime Elevator Components
Limited** (1)
Hunslet Rd, Leeds, LS10 1JZ, West York-
shire, United Kingdom
Tel.: (44) 1132461800
Web Site: http://www.go4b.com
Sales Range: $25-49.9 Million
Emp.: 60
Material Handling Components Mfr
N.A.I.C.S.: 335909

Braime Pressings Limited (1)
Hunslet Road, Leeds, LS10 1JZ, West
Yorkshire, United Kingdom
Tel.: (44) 1132457491
Web Site: https://www.braimepressings.com
Sales Range: $25-49.9 Million
Emp.: 75
Metal Pressings & Sub Assemblies Mfr
N.A.I.C.S.: 321999

SETEM S.A.R.L. (1)
9 Rte de Corbie, 80800, Lamotte-Warfusee,
Somme, France
Tel.: (33) 322423226
Web Site: http://www.go4b.co.uk
Sales Range: $25-49.9 Million
Emp.: 12
Elevator Component Mfr
N.A.I.C.S.: 333921
Eric Sara (Gen Mgr)

BRAIN BIOTECH AG
Darmstadter Strasse 34-36, 64673, Zwingenberg, Germany
Tel.: (49) 625193310
Web Site: https://www.brain-biotech.com
Year Founded: 1993
BNN—(DEU)
Rev.: $61,666,307
Assets: $76,556,227
Liabilities: $51,720,268
Net Worth: $24,835,959
Earnings: ($8,756,745)
Emp.: 330
Fiscal Year-end: 09/30/23
Biotechnology Research & Development Services
N.A.I.C.S.: 541714
Georg Kellinghusen (Chm-Supervisory Bd)

Subsidiaries:

AnalytiCon Discovery GmbH   (1)
Hermannswerder Haus 17, 14473, Potsdam, Germany
Tel.: (49) 3312300300
Web Site: https://www.ac-discovery.com
Emp.: 60
Pharmaceutical Research & Development Services
N.A.I.C.S.: 327910

Subsidiary (US):

AnalytiCon Discovery LLC   (2)
15800 Crabbs Branch Way Ste 300, Rockville, MD 20855
Tel.: (240) 332-9221
Pharmaceutical Research & Development Services
N.A.I.C.S.: 541714
Dietmar Wolf (Exec VP)

BRAIN Capital GmbH   (1)
Heerstrasse 31, 56179, Vallendar, Germany
Tel.: (49) 26145093490
Web Site: https://www.braincapital.de
Emp.: 25
Financial Planning Services
N.A.I.C.S.: 523940
Rene Maier (Mng Dir)

Biocatalysts Ltd.   (1)
Unit 1 Cefn Coed Parc, Nantgarw, Cardiff, CF15 7QQ, United Kingdom   (82.2%)
Tel.: (44) 1443843712
Web Site: https://www.biocatalysts.com
Enzyme Mfr
N.A.I.C.S.: 325411

Biosun Biochemicals, Inc.   (1)
6306 Benjamin Rd Ste 600, Tampa, FL 33634
Tel.: (813) 888-9855
Web Site: https://www.biosunffi.com
Sales Range: $1-9.9 Million
Emp.: 10
Chemical & Allied Products Merchant Whslr
N.A.I.C.S.: 424690
Mark Messersmith (Founder)

Breatec B.V.   (1)
Vimmerik 2M, 5253 CB, Nieuwkuijk, Netherlands
Tel.: (31) 736571448
Web Site: https://breatec.com
Food Product Mfr & Distr
N.A.I.C.S.: 311991

Mekon Science Networks GmbH   (1)
Mergenthalerallee 10-12, Eschborn, 65760, Frankfurt, Germany
Tel.: (49) 6196400907
Web Site: http://www.myekosmetik.de
Cosmetics Products Mfr
N.A.I.C.S.: 325620

WeissBioTech GmbH   (1)
An der Hansalinie 48-50, 59387, Ascheberg, Germany   (100%)
Tel.: (49) 2593919386
Web Site: https://www.weissbiotech.com
Enzyme Mfr
N.A.I.C.S.: 325411

BRAIN LABS DIGITAL LTD.
Building 4 2 Old St Yard, London, EC1Y 8AF, United Kingdom
Tel.: (44) 203 880 8503
Web Site: http://www.brainlabsdigital.com
Year Founded: 2012
Digital Marketing Agency
N.A.I.C.S.: 541810
Daniel Gilbert (Founder & CEO)

Subsidiaries:

Hanapin Marketing, LLC   (1)
501 N Morton St Ste 212, Bloomington, IN 47404
Tel.: (812) 330-3134
Web Site: http://www.hanapinmarketing.com
Internet Marketing & Other Related Services
N.A.I.C.S.: 541613

BRAINCHIP HOLDINGS LTD.
Level 12 225 George Street, Sydney, 2000, NSW, Australia
Web Site: http://www.brainchipinc.com
Year Founded: 2006
BCHPY—(OTCQX)
Rev.: $158,030
Assets: $13,747,172
Liabilities: $2,280,432
Net Worth: $11,466,740
Earnings: ($19,672,394)
Emp.: 78
Fiscal Year-end: 12/31/23
Investment Services
N.A.I.C.S.: 523999
Ken Scarince (CFO)

Subsidiaries:

Brainchip Research Institute Pty Ltd   (1)
Level 30 Forrest Center 221 St Georges Terrace, Perth, 6000, WA, Australia
Tel.: (61) 886009662
Software Publisher Services
N.A.I.C.S.: 513210

Tanety Zina SARL   (1)
Lot A 12 Ter A, Antananarivo, 101, Madagascar
Tel.: (261) 32 0238689
Web Site: http://www.brainchipinc.com
Sales Range: $50-74.9 Million
Emp.: 7
Gold Mining Services
N.A.I.C.S.: 212220

BRAINCOOL AB
Medicon Village Scheelevagen 2, 223 81, Lund, Sweden
Tel.: (46) 733937076
Web Site: https://www.braincool.se
Year Founded: 2014
Healtcare Services
N.A.I.C.S.: 423450
Martin Waleij (CEO)

BRAINGRID LTD.
150 Bridgeland Ave Suite 100, Toronto, M6A 1Z4, ON, Canada
Tel.: (647) 360-1525
Web Site: http://www.braingrid.io
BGRDF—(OTCIQ)
Assets: $747,168
Liabilities: $1,570,455
Net Worth: ($823,287)
Earnings: ($1,420,088)
Fiscal Year-end: 01/31/24
Information Technology Services
N.A.I.C.S.: 541511
Michael Kadonoff (Founder & CEO)

BRAINHOLE TECHNOLOGY LIMITED
Office A 31/F Billion Plaza II No 10 Cheung Yue Street Cheung Sha Wan, Kowloon, China (Hong Kong)
Tel.: (852) 23253669   Ky

Web Site: http://www.brainholetechnology.com
Year Founded: 2012
2203—(HKG)
Rev.: $41,476,099
Assets: $45,611,068
Liabilities: $27,254,119
Net Worth: $18,356,950
Earnings: ($6,649,177)
Emp.: 374
Fiscal Year-end: 12/31/21
Discrete Semiconductor Product Mfr & Distr
N.A.I.C.S.: 334413
Liang Johnson Zhang (Chm)

Subsidiaries:

Top Dynamic Enterprises Limited - Dongguan Factory   (1)
No 3 Xincheng Road Songshan Lake, Dongguan, 523808, Guangdong, China
Tel.: (86) 76922897208
Semiconductor Product Mfr
N.A.I.C.S.: 334413

BRAINPAD INC.
Roppongi Tea Cube 1-1-3 Roppongi, Minato-ku, Tokyo, 1060032, Japan
Tel.: (81) 8067217002
Web Site: https://www.brainpad.co.jp
Year Founded: 2004
3655—(TKS)
Rev.: $65,689,420
Assets: $45,138,540
Liabilities: $10,717,060
Net Worth: $34,421,480
Earnings: $5,653,980
Emp.: 545
Fiscal Year-end: 06/30/24
Data Processing & Computer Programming Services
N.A.I.C.S.: 518210
Takafumi Kusano (Co-Founder & CEO)

BRAINS II INC.
165 Konrad Cres, Markham, L3R 9T9, ON, Canada
Tel.: (905) 946-8700
Web Site: http://www.brainsii.com
Sales Range: $1-9.9 Million
Emp.: 250
Computer Equipment, Training, Services & Maintenance
N.A.I.C.S.: 811210
Charles G. Hanna (Chm & CEO)

BRAINS TECHNOLOGY, INC.
3-23-17 Shinagawa Center Building 4F, Minato, Tokyo, 1080074, Japan
Tel.: (81) 364557023
Web Site: https://www.brains-tech,co.jp
Year Founded: 2008
4075—(TKS)
Software Development Services
N.A.I.C.S.: 541511

BRAINSWAY LTD.
16 Hartum St, Har Hotzvim, Jerusalem, 9777518, Israel
Tel.: (972) 25824030   II
Web Site: https://www.brainsway.com
BWAY—(NASDAQ)
Rev.: $27,177,000
Assets: $64,477,000
Liabilities: $19,080,000
Net Worth: $45,397,000
Earnings: $13,349,000
Emp.: 134
Fiscal Year-end: 12/31/22
Medical Device Mfr
N.A.I.C.S.: 339112
David Zacut (Co-Founder & Chm)

BRAINZCOMPANY CO., LTD.
87 Seongsu-iro 8th floor, Seongdong-

gu, Seoul, 04782, Korea (South)
Tel.: (82) 222056053
Web Site: https://www.brainz.co.kr
Year Founded: 2000
099390—(KRS)
Rev.: $14,000,003
Assets: $36,233,149
Liabilities: $3,146,322
Net Worth: $33,086,827
Earnings: $3,865,067
Emp.: 104
Fiscal Year-end: 12/31/22
Software Development Services
N.A.I.C.S.: 541511
Kang Seon-Geun (Dir-Rep)

BRAIT S.E.
4th Floor Avantech Building, St Julians Road, San Gwann, SGN 2805, Malta
Tel.: (356) 22486203
Web Site: http://www.brait.com
BAT—(LUX)
Assets: $849,296,000
Liabilities: $170,688,000
Net Worth: $678,608,000
Earnings: ($22,232,000)
Fiscal Year-end: 03/31/23
Investment & Financial Services
N.A.I.C.S.: 523999
Anjelica Camilleri de Marco (Sec)

Subsidiaries:

Brait International Ltd   (1)
Suite 520 5th Floor, Barkly Wharf, Port Louis, 11307, Mauritius   (100%)
Tel.: (230) 2136909
Web Site: http://www.brait.com
Miscellaneous Financial Investment Activities
N.A.I.C.S.: 523999
Dhanraj Boodhoo (CEO)

Brait Mauritius Limited   (1)
Suite 520 5th Floor Barkly Wharf, Le Caudan Waterfront, Port Louis, Mauritius
Tel.: (230) 2136909
Financial Investment Services
N.A.I.C.S.: 523999

Brait South Africa Limited   (1)
Private Bag X1 Northlands, Johannesburg, 2196, South Africa
Tel.: (27) 115071000
Miscellaneous Financial Investment Activities
N.A.I.C.S.: 523999

New Look Retail Group Limited   (1)
New Look House Mercery Road, Weymouth, DT3 5HJ, Dorset, United Kingdom   (27.6%)
Tel.: (44) 1305765000
Web Site: http://www.newlookgroup.com
Rev.: $1,572,315,780
Assets: $849,862,694
Liabilities: $2,248,830,342
Net Worth: ($1,398,967,648)
Earnings: ($701,387,354)
Emp.: 16,513
Fiscal Year-end: 03/30/2019
Holding Company; Family Fashion Retailer
N.A.I.C.S.: 551112

Subsidiary (Domestic):

New Look Group Limited   (2)
New Look House Mercery Road, Weymouth, DT3 5HJ, Dorset, United Kingdom
Tel.: (44) 3444996690
Web Site: http://www.newlook.com
Emp.: 100
Family Fashion & Accessories Retailer
N.A.I.C.S.: 458110

Virgin Active Limited   (1)
100 Aldersgate Street, London, EC1A 4LX, United Kingdom   (80%)
Tel.: (44) 207 717 9000
Web Site: http://www.virginactive.co.uk
Fitness Center Operator
N.A.I.C.S.: 713940

BRAKES AUTO (INDIA) LIMITED

Brakes Auto (India) Limited—(Continued)

1011 Embassy Centre 207 Nariman
Point, Mumbai, 400 021, India
Tel.: (91) 22 2282 3367
Year Founded: 1980
Sales Range: $10-24.9 Million
Automotive Components Mfr
N.A.I.C.S.: 336340
Suresh Sharma *(Chrm & Mng Dlr)*

BRAM INDUSTRIES LTD.
7 Lisbon St New Industrial Zone,
Sderot, Israel
Tel.: (972) 86611355
Web Site: https://www.bram.co.il
BRAM—(TAE)
Rev.: $26,930,515
Assets: $34,814,753
Liabilities: $17,190,219
Net Worth: $17,624,534
Earnings: ($915,043)
Fiscal Year-end: 12/31/23
All Other Plastics Product Manufac-
turing
N.A.I.C.S.: 326199
Shai Samai *(CFO)*

Subsidiaries:

Hai Plastic Ltd.   (1)
Lisbon 7 A New Industry, PO Box 1053,
Sderot, 80100, Israel
Web Site: https://www.hai-plastic.co.il
Plastic Box Mfr
N.A.I.C.S.: 326199

BRAMBLES LIMITED
Level 29 255 George Street, Sydney,
2000, NSW, Australia
Tel.: (61) 292565222   AU
Web Site: https://www.brambles.com
Year Founded: 1875
BMBLF—(OTCIQ)
Rev.: $6,076,800,000
Assets: $8,718,500,000
Liabilities: $5,848,500,000
Net Worth: $2,870,000,000
Earnings: $703,300,000
Emp.: 12,000
Fiscal Year-end: 06/30/23
Logistic Services
N.A.I.C.S.: 541420
Phillip Austin *(Pres-
Asia,Pacific,India,Middle East,Tur-
key,Africa)*

Subsidiaries:

Brambles Enterprises Limited   (1)
Unit 2 Weybridge Business Pk, Addlestone,
KT15 2UP, Surrey, United Kingdom
Tel.: (44) 1932 833115
Pallet Rental & Leasing Services
N.A.I.C.S.: 532490

Brambles USA Inc.   (1)
5897 Windward Pkwy, Alpharetta, GA
30005
Tel.: (770) 668-8100
Holding Company; Regional Managing Office
N.A.I.C.S.: 551112

CHEP Americas   (1)
5897 Windward Pkwy, Alpharetta, GA
30005
Tel.: (770) 668-8100
Web Site: https://www.chep.com
Regional Management Office; Pallet & Con-
tainer Collection, Reconditioning & Rental
Services
N.A.I.C.S.: 332999
Amelia Otlowski *(Gen Mgr & Sr Dir-North
America)*

Subsidiary (Non-US):

CHEP Canada, Inc.   (2)
7400 East Dandro Crescent, Mississauga,
L5N 8C6, ON, Canada   (100%)
Tel.: (905) 790-2437
Web Site: http://www.chep.com

Sales Range: $50-74.9 Million
Emp.: 100
Pallet & Container Collection, Reconditioning & Rental Services
N.A.I.C.S.: 532490
Frank Bozzo *(VP)*

CHEP Mexico SA de CV   (2)
Blvd Manuel Avila Camacho 24 Piso 22 y
23, 11000, Mexico, Mexico   (100%)
Tel.: (52) 5585031100
Web Site: https://www.chep.com
Sales Range: $75-99.9 Million
Emp.: 150
Pallet & Container Collection, Reconditioning & Rental Services
N.A.I.C.S.: 532490
Jorge Montano *(Head-Supply Chain)*

Subsidiary (Domestic):

CHEP USA   (2)
7315 Kingspointe Pkwy Ste 200, Orlando,
FL 32819-9030   (100%)
Tel.: (407) 370-2437
Sales Range: $25-49.9 Million
Emp.: 550
Pallet & Container Collection, Reconditioning & Rental Services
N.A.I.C.S.: 532490

CHEP Asia-Pacific   (1)
Level 6 Building C 11 Talavera Road, Ryde,
2113, NSW, Australia
Tel.: (61) 298562437
Web Site: http://www.chep.com
Sales Range: $50-74.9 Million
Emp.: 90
Regional Management Office; Pallet & Container Collection, Reconditioning & Rental
Services
N.A.I.C.S.: 551114

Subsidiary (Non-US):

CHEP (Malaysia) Sdn Bhd   (2)
Solok Waja 3, Taman Perindustrian Bukit
Raja, 41050, Klang, Selangor,
Malaysia   (100%)
Tel.: (60) 333433966
Web Site: http://www.chep.com
Sales Range: $50-74.9 Million
Emp.: 25
Pallet & Container Collection, Reconditioning & Rental Services
N.A.I.C.S.: 532490
Arvind Nair *(Dir-Country)*

CHEP (Shanghai) Co., Ltd.   (2)
19th Floor Xuhuiyuan Building No 1089
Zhongshan South 2nd Road, Xuhui District,
Shanghai, 200030, China   (100%)
Tel.: (86) 2161272488
Web Site: https://www.chep.com
Sales Range: $75-99.9 Million
Pallet & Container Collection, Reconditioning & Rental Services
N.A.I.C.S.: 532490

Subsidiary (Domestic):

CHEP Australia Limited   (2)
11 Talavera Road, North Ryde, 2113, NSW,
Australia   (100%)
Tel.: (61) 132437
Web Site: https://www.chep.com
Sales Range: $50-74.9 Million
Pallet & Container Collection, Reconditioning & Rental Services
N.A.I.C.S.: 532490

Subsidiary (Non-US):

CHEP Chile SA   (2)
Av Cerro Colorado 5240 Torre II Piso 15,
Las Condes, Santiago, Chile   (100%)
Tel.: (56) 223873400
Web Site: https://www.chep.com
Sales Range: $25-49.9 Million
Emp.: 33
Pallet & Container Collection, Reconditioning & Rental Services
N.A.I.C.S.: 532490
Juan Cristoval Gonzales *(Gen Mgr)*

CHEP India Pvt. Ltd.   (2)
3rd Floor Aver Plaza Opp Citi Mall New
Link Road, Andheri W, Mumbai, 400 053,
India   (100%)
Tel.: (91) 2267839400
Web Site: http://www.chep.com

Sales Range: $25-49.9 Million
Emp.: 70
Pallet & Container Collection, Reconditioning & Rental Services
N.A.I.C.S.: 532490
Stavros Kazakos *(Gen Mgr)*

CHEP New Zealand   (2)
1 - 9 Nesdale Avenue, Auckland, 2104,
New Zealand   (30%)
Tel.: (64) 92790170
Web Site: http://www.chep.com
Sales Range: $25-49.9 Million
Emp.: 50
Pallet & Container Collection, Reconditioning & Rental Services
N.A.I.C.S.: 532490

Subsidiary (Domestic):

CHEP Pallecon Solutions Pty Ltd   (2)
1/66 Christina Road, Villawood, 2163,
NSW, Australia
Tel.: (61) 287174500
Web Site: http://www.chep.com
Sales Range: $10-24.9 Million
Emp.: 50
Materials Handling Services
N.A.I.C.S.: 541614

Subsidiary (Non-US):

CHEP Singapore Pte. Ltd.   (2)
152 Beach Road Gateway East 24-01, Singapore, 189721, Singapore
Tel.: (65) 69335353
Web Site: http://www.chep.com
Sales Range: $50-74.9 Million
Emp.: 4
Pallet & Container Collection, Reconditioning & Rental Services
N.A.I.C.S.: 532490
Lars Amstrup *(Pres)*

CHEP EMEA   (1)
Rotherwick House 3 Thomas More Street,
London, E1W 1YZ, United Kingdom
Tel.: (44) 1932833089
Web Site: http://www.chep.com
Regional Management Office; Pallet & Container Collection, Reconditioning & Rental
Services
N.A.I.C.S.: 551114

Division (Domestic):

CHEP Europe   (2)
400 Dashwood Lang Road, Addlestone
Road, Weybridge, KT15 2HJ, Surrey,
United Kingdom   (100%)
Tel.: (44) 1932850085
Web Site: http://www.chep.com
Sales Range: $75-99.9 Million
Emp.: 130
Regional Managing Office; Pallet & Container Collection, Reconditioning & Rental
Services
N.A.I.C.S.: 551114
Sabrina Remedios *(Mgr-Comm)*

Subsidiary (Non-US):

CHEP Benelux N.V.   (3)
Pedro Colomalaan 15, 2880, Bornem,
Belgium   (100%)
Tel.: (32) 80039152
Web Site: http://www.chep.com
Sales Range: $50-74.9 Million
Emp.: 90
Pallet & Container Collection, Reconditioning & Rental Services
N.A.I.C.S.: 532490

CHEP Benelux Nederland BV   (3)
Bedrijvenlaan 1, 2800, Mechelen,
Belgium   (100%)
Tel.: (32) 15799700
Web Site: http://www.chep.com
Sales Range: $50-74.9 Million
Emp.: 30
Pallet & Container Collection, Reconditioning & Rental Services
N.A.I.C.S.: 532490

CHEP Denmark   (3)
Theilgaards Torv 1, 4600, Koge,
Denmark   (100%)
Tel.: (45) 70207222
Web Site: http://www.chep.com
Sales Range: $50-74.9 Million
Emp.: 7

Pallet & Container Collection, Reconditioning & Rental Services
N.A.I.C.S.: 532490
Torben Lunt *(Mgr)*

CHEP Deutschland GmbH   (3)
Siegburgirstrasse 229b, 50679, Cologne,
Germany   (100%)
Tel.: (49) 221935710
Web Site: https://www.chep.com
Sales Range: $100-124.9 Million
Pallet & Container Collection, Reconditioning & Rental Services
N.A.I.C.S.: 532490

CHEP Espana SA   (3)
Cristalia Business Park Building 2 - 5th
Floor, C/ Via de los Poblados 3, 28033, Madrid, Spain   (100%)
Tel.: (34) 915579400
Web Site: http://www.chep.com
Sales Range: $100-124.9 Million
Pallet & Container Collection, Reconditioning & Rental Services
N.A.I.C.S.: 532490

CHEP Finland   (3)
Auritia 8, 1510, Vantaa, Finland
Tel.: (358) 98256800
Web Site: https://www.chep.com
Sales Range: $50-74.9 Million
Emp.: 5
Pallet & Container Collection, Reconditioning & Rental Services
N.A.I.C.S.: 532490

CHEP France S.A.   (3)
1 Rue Mozart, PO Box 85, 92112, Clichy,
France   (100%)
Tel.: (33) 149682940
Web Site: https://www.chep.com
Sales Range: $100-124.9 Million
Pallet & Container Collection, Reconditioning & Rental Services
N.A.I.C.S.: 532490

CHEP Italia SRL   (3)
Viale Fulvio Testi 280-3, Milan, 20126,
Italy   (100%)
Tel.: (39) 0266154811
Web Site: https://www.chep.com
Sales Range: $50-74.9 Million
Emp.: 70
Pallet & Container Collection, Reconditioning & Rental Services
N.A.I.C.S.: 532490

CHEP Norway   (3)
Deliveien 5, 1540, Vestby, Norway   (100%)
Tel.: (47) 64955940
Web Site: http://www.chep.com
Sales Range: $50-74.9 Million
Emp.: 5
Pallet & Container Collection, Reconditioning & Rental Services
N.A.I.C.S.: 532490

CHEP Osterreich Gmbh   (3)
Mariahilfer Strasse 123/3, 1060, Vienna,
Austria   (100%)
Tel.: (43) 159999448
Web Site: https://www.chep.com
Sales Range: $50-74.9 Million
Emp.: 6
Pallet & Container Collection, Reconditioning & Rental Services
N.A.I.C.S.: 532490
Gernot Griess *(Gen Mgr)*

CHEP Portugal   (3)
Ave das Descobertas 59 3rd Fl Piso,
2780053, Paco d'Arcos, Oeiras,
Portugal   (100%)
Tel.: (351) 214468100
Web Site: http://www.chep.com
Sales Range: $50-74.9 Million
Emp.: 30
Pallet & Container Collection, Reconditioning & Rental Services
N.A.I.C.S.: 532490
Enrique Montanes *(Sr VP)*

CHEP Schweiz BV   (3)
Nordstrasse 3, Rheinstrasse 47, 5612, Villmergen, Switzerland
Tel.: (41) 566110044
Web Site: http://www.chep.com
Pallet & Container Collection, Reconditioning & Rental Services
N.A.I.C.S.: 532490

CHEP Sweden (3)
Danvik Center Hastholmsvagen 28, 131 30, Nacka, Sweden (100%)
Tel.: (46) 84427390
Web Site: http://www.chep.com
Sales Range: $50-74.9 Million
Emp.: 7
Pallet & Container Collection, Reconditioning & Rental Services
N.A.I.C.S.: 532490
Bo Saoecerg (Gen Mgr)

Subsidiary (Domestic):

CHEP UK Limited (3)
Weybridge Business Park Addlestone Rd Unit 2, Addlestone, KT15 2UP, Surrey, United Kingdom (100%)
Tel.: (44) 932833115
Web Site: http://www.chep.com
Sales Range: $100-124.9 Million
Emp.: 14,321
Pallet & Container Collection, Reconditioning & Rental Services
N.A.I.C.S.: 532490
Helen Lane (VP)

Subsidiary (Non-US):

CHEP South Africa (Pty) Ltd. (2)
7 Westville Rd, PO Box 1053, Westville, 3629, South Africa (100%)
Tel.: (27) 800330334
Web Site: http://www.chepsa.com
Sales Range: $25-49.9 Million
Emp.: 100
Pallet & Container Pooling
N.A.I.C.S.: 321920
Jurie Welman (Pres)

Unitpool AG (1)
Steinackerstrasse 2, 8302, Kloten, Switzerland
Tel.: (41) 43 255 4141
Web Site: http://www.unitpool.com
Sales Range: $25-49.9 Million
Emp.: 20
Aviation Pooling Services
N.A.I.C.S.: 488190
Charles Drummond (Head-Global Ops)

BRAMPTON BRICK LIMITED
225 Wanless Drive, Brampton, L7A 1E9, ON, Canada
Tel.: (905) 840-1011   ON
Web Site:
    http://www.bramptonbrick.com
BBL.A—(TSX)
Rev.: $117,277,071
Assets: $192,996,299
Liabilities: $70,203,372
Net Worth: $122,792,927
Earnings: ($978,632)
Emp.: 293
Fiscal Year-end: 12/31/20
Bricks Mfr
N.A.I.C.S.: 327331
Jeffrey G. Kerbel (Pres & CEO)

Subsidiaries:

Brampton Brick Inc (1)
1256 E County Rd 950 N, Farmersburg, IN 47850-8055
Tel.: (812) 397-2190
Web Site: http://www.bramptonbrick.com
Emp.: 35
Brick & Structural Clay Tile Mfr
N.A.I.C.S.: 327120

Oaks Concrete Products Inc (1)
51744 Pontiac Trl, Wixom, MI 48393
Tel.: (248) 684-5004
Web Site: http://www.oakspavers.com
Sales Range: $25-49.9 Million
Emp.: 10
Concrete Bricks Mfr
N.A.I.C.S.: 327120
David Carter (Pres)

Oaks Concrete Products Ltd (1)
455 Rodick Road, Markham, L6G 1B2, ON, Canada
Tel.: (905) 475-5900
Web Site: http://www.oakspavers.com
Sales Range: $25-49.9 Million
Emp.: 50
Construction Machinery Mfr

N.A.I.C.S.: 333120

BRAND ARCHITEKTS GROUP PLC
8 Waldegrave Road, TW11 8GT, Teddington, TW11 8GT, United Kingdom - England
Tel.: (44) 2031662840   UK
Web Site:
    https://www.brandarchitektsplc.com
BAR—(LSE)
Rev.: $25,353,446
Assets: $43,043,423
Liabilities: $10,727,089
Net Worth: $32,316,334
Earnings: ($8,312,295)
Emp.: 40
Fiscal Year-end: 06/30/23
Cosmetics & Skincare Product Mfr
N.A.I.C.S.: 325620
Quentin Highman (CEO)

Subsidiaries:

InnovaDerma PLC (1)
27 Old Gloucester Street, London, WC1N 3AX, United Kingdom
Tel.: (44) 8000148895
Web Site: http://www.innovaderma.com
Rev.: $18,001,925
Assets: $19,318,174
Liabilities: $5,284,945
Net Worth: $14,033,228
Earnings: ($420,036)
Emp.: 40
Fiscal Year-end: 06/30/2020
Personal Care Product Mfr & Distr
N.A.I.C.S.: 325620
Warren Dockary (CFO)

Subsidiary (US):

InnovaScience Inc. (2)
4640 Admiralty Way Ste 500, Marina Del Rey, CA 90292
Personal Care Product Mfr & Distr
N.A.I.C.S.: 325620

Subsidiary (Non-US):

Skinny Tan Pty Ltd. (2)
6/16-20 Hunter Street, Sydney, 2000, NSW, Australia
Tel.: (61) 398638030
Web Site: http://www.skinnytan.com.au
Tanning Product Mfr
N.A.I.C.S.: 316110

BRAND CONCEPTS LIMITED
4th Floor UNO Business Park By Pass Road, Opposite Sahara City Bicholi Mardana, Indore, 452016, Madhya Pradesh, India
Tel.: (91) 9752221244
Web Site:
    https://www.brandconcepts.in
Year Founded: 2007
543442—(BOM)
Rev.: $11,844,542
Assets: $10,339,479
Liabilities: $7,849,187
Net Worth: $2,490,292
Earnings: $86,009
Fiscal Year-end: 03/31/22
Fashion Accessory Distr
N.A.I.C.S.: 424350

BRAND DEVELOPMENT COMPANY LIMITED
50 Long Acre, London, WC2E 9JR, United Kingdom
Tel.: (44) 207 497 9727   UK
Year Founded: 1985
Sales Range: $10-24.9 Million
Emp.: 4
Advertising Agencies
N.A.I.C.S.: 541810
P. Morgan (Mng Dir)

BRAND LOUNGE

Immermannstr 9, 40210, Dusseldorf, Germany
Tel.: (49) 211 621 90
Web Site: http://www.brandlounge.de
Year Founded: 1986
Rev.: $28,444,500
Emp.: 20
N.A.I.C.S.: 541810
Christian Labonte (Owner)

BRAND MARVEL WORLDWIDE CONSUMER PRODUCTS CORPORATION
Suite 860 605 Robson Street, Vancouver, V6B 5J3, BC, Canada
Tel.: (604) 699-6168   Ca
Web Site:
    http://www.beijingmarvel.com
Year Founded: 1986
Sales Range: Less than $1 Million
Wet Wipe Product Mfr & Distr
N.A.I.C.S.: 313230
Yongliang Liao (Chm & CEO)

BRAND NEW VINTAGE LIMITED
Level 3 169 Fullarton Road, Dulwich, 5065, SA, Australia
Tel.: (61) 8 8330 4035
Web Site:
    http://www.brandnewvintage.com.au
Sales Range: $1-9.9 Million
Wine Mfr & Sales
N.A.I.C.S.: 312130
Sam Atkins (CEO & Mng Dir)

Subsidiaries:

Sticks Yarra Valley Pty. Ltd. (1)
179 Glenview Rd, Yarra Glen, 3775, VIC, Australia
Tel.: (61) 397301022
Web Site: http://www.sticks.com.au
Wines Mfr & Distr
N.A.I.C.S.: 312130
Sam Atkins (Mgr-Sls & Mktg)

BRAND PARTNERSHIP LTD.
Southfork Industrial Est, Dartmouth Way, Leeds, LS11 5JL, United Kingdom
Tel.: (44) 132706061
Sales Range: $50-74.9 Million
Emp.: 350
Dehydrated Food Product Mfr
N.A.I.C.S.: 311423

Subsidiaries:

Telford Foods Ltd. (1)
10 Halesfield Business Park, Telford, TF7 4LY, Shropshire, United Kingdom (100%)
Tel.: (44) 1952422000
Mfr of Muesli & Breakfast Cereals, Packet Soups & Sauce Mixes, Gravy Powder, Powdered Drinks & Desserts
N.A.I.C.S.: 311230

BRAND REALTY SERVICES LTD.
Tradex Tower Plot 15A Sector 125, Noida, 201301, India
Tel.: (91) 9999901234
Web Site: https://www.brandrealty.in
Year Founded: 2006
531203—(BOM)
Rev.: $703,517
Assets: $1,256,491
Liabilities: $658,827
Net Worth: $597,664
Earnings: ($60,775)
Fiscal Year-end: 03/31/21
Real Estate Development Services
N.A.I.C.S.: 531390
Nikita Garg (Compliance Officer & Sec)

BRAND X CO., LTD.

63 Ttukseom-ro 1-gil, Seongdong-gu, Seoul, 05835, Korea (South)
Tel.: (82) 269592362
Web Site:
    https://www.brandxcorp.com
Year Founded: 2017
337930—(KRS)
Rev.: $163,171,707
Assets: $87,609,075
Liabilities: $25,228,182
Net Worth: $62,380,893
Earnings: $7,768,567
Emp.: 209
Fiscal Year-end: 12/31/22
Apparel Product Mfr
N.A.I.C.S.: 315120
Seo Jaemin (Mgr)

BRANDALLEY UK LIMITED
3 Thomas More Square, London, E98 1XY, United Kingdom
Tel.: (44) 20 3060 1651
Web Site:
    http://www.brandalley.co.uk
Sales Range: $10-24.9 Million
Internet Retailer
N.A.I.C.S.: 458110
Rob Feldmann (CEO)

BRANDBEE HOLDING AB
Sibyllegatan 30, 114 43, Stockholm, Sweden
Tel.: (46) 724399900
Web Site: http://www.brandbee.com
Year Founded: 2014
Digital Marketing Services
N.A.I.C.S.: 541613
Magnus Clarenbring (CEO)

BRANDBUCKET MEDIA & TECHNOLOGY LIMITED
Office No 302 3rd Floor Kilfire Premises Co Op Soc Ltd C 17M, Dalia Industrial Area New Link Rd Near Fun Republic Cinema Andheri W, Mumbai, 400053, India
Tel.: (91) 8652369975
Web Site:
    https://www.brandbucketmedia.in
543439—(BOM)
Media Technology Services
N.A.I.C.S.: 541840
Nishigandha S. Keluskar (Mng Dir)

BRANDENBURG ENERGY CORP.
1100 - 789 West Pender Street, Vancouver, V6C 1H2, BC, Canada
Tel.: (604) 669-9330   BC
Web Site:
    http://www.brandenburgcorp.com
Year Founded: 2007
Investment Services
N.A.I.C.S.: 523999
Robert Menzies Findlay (Pres & CEO)

BRANDHOUSE RETAILS LTD
Marathon NextGen B2 5th Floor GK Marg Lower Parel, Mumbai, 400 013, India
Tel.: (91) 22 24824500
Web Site:
    http://www.brandhouseretails.com
Sales Range: $125-149.9 Million
Fashion Wears Retailer
N.A.I.C.S.: 458110

BRANDIA CENTRAL
Edificio Goncalves Zarco, Doca de Alcantara, 1350-352, Lisbon, Portugal
Tel.: (351) 213 923 000
Emp.: 150
N.A.I.C.S.: 541810
Tiago Viegas (Creative Dir)

Brandia Central—(Continued)

BRANDING ENGINEER CO., LTD.

28-3 Maruyamacho, Shibuya-Ku, Tokyo, 150-0044, Japan
Tel.: (81) 364160678
Web Site: http://www.b-engineer.co.jp
Year Founded: 2013
7352—(TKS)
Rev.: $88,883,800
Assets: $44,168,220
Liabilities: $26,223,520
Net Worth: $17,944,700
Earnings: $1,169,360
Fiscal Year-end: 08/31/24
Information Technology Services
N.A.I.C.S.: 541512
Yasuyuki Kawabata (Founder & CEO)

BRANDING TECHNOLOGY, INC.

15-13 Nanpeidai-cho Teito Shibuya
Building 4F & 5F, Shibuya-Ku, Tokyo,
150-0036, Japan
Tel.: (81) 354571311
Web Site: https://www.branding-t.co.jp
Year Founded: 2001
7067—(TKS)
Rev.: $30,445,660
Assets: $12,896,110
Liabilities: $4,997,160
Net Worth: $7,898,950
Earnings: $19,830
Emp.: 230
Fiscal Year-end: 03/31/24
Advertising Agency Services
N.A.I.C.S.: 541810
Yuki Kimura (Pres & CEO)

BRANDON CAPITAL PARTNERS PTY LTD.

Level 9 278 Collins Street, Melbourne, 3000, VIC, Australia
Tel.: (61) 3 9657 0700
Web Site:
http://www.brandoncapital.com.au
Venture Capital Investment Services
N.A.I.C.S.: 523999
Melissa McBurnie (Partner)

BRANDPROTECT INC.

5090 Explorer Drive Suite 203, Mississauga, L4W 4T9, ON, Canada
Tel.: (905) 271-3725
Web Site:
http://www.brandprotect.com
Year Founded: 2001
Sales Range: $1-9.9 Million
Emp.: 30
Data Protection Services
N.A.I.C.S.: 561621
Roberto Drassinower (Pres & CEO)

BRANDS EUROPEAN SHOE TRADE

Parc Des Moulins 41 Rue Albert Samain, 59650, Villeneuve d'Ascq,
Nord, France
Tel.: (33) 320050480
Rev.: $15,900,000
Emp.: 4
N.A.I.C.S.: 424340
Nicolas Dewaele (Pres)

BRANDT & WALTHER GMBH

Torneestrasse 5, D-28865, Lilienthal,
Germany
Tel.: (49) 429846620
Web Site: http://www.poliboy.de
Year Founded: 1930
Rev.: $41,382,000
Emp.: 60
Cleaning Product Mfr
N.A.I.C.S.: 339999

BRANDT INDUSTRIES LTD.

Highway #1 East, PO Box 3856, Regina, S4P 3R8, SK, Canada
Tel.: (306) 791-7777
Web Site: http://www.brandt.ca
Holding Company
N.A.I.C.S.: 551112
Shaun Semple (Pres)

Subsidiaries:

Brandt Tractor Ltd. **(1)**
Highway 1 East, PO Box 3856, Regina,
S4P 3R8, SK, Canada
Tel.: (306) 791-7777
Web Site: https://www.brandt.ca
Construction & Forestry Equipment Dealer
N.A.I.C.S.: 423810

Camex Equipment Sales & Rentals
Ltd. **(1)**
1806 2 St, Nisku, T9E 0W8, AB, Canada
Tel.: (587) 400-3750
Web Site: http://www.camex.ca
Trucks, Trailers & Heavy Equipment Sales
& Rentals
N.A.I.C.S.: 532120

Cervus Equipment Corporation **(1)**
Harvest Hills Office Park 6302-333 96 AVE
NE, Calgary, T3K 0S3, AB, Canada
Tel.: (403) 726-2426
Web Site: http://www.cervusequipment.com
Rev.: $960,551,442
Assets: $403,732,361
Liabilities: $209,173,067
Net Worth: $194,559,294
Earnings: $19,625,058
Emp.: 1,555
Fiscal Year-end: 12/31/2020
Tractors & Farming Machinery & Equipment
Dealer
N.A.I.C.S.: 423820
Adam Lowther (CFO)

Subsidiary (Domestic):

Contractors Equipment LP **(2)**
333 96 Ave Ne Ste 5201; Calgary, T3K
0S3, AB, Canada
Tel.: (403) 567-0339
Web Site: http://www.cervusequipment.com
Sales Range: $50-74.9 Million
Emp.: 100
Construction Equipment Whslr
N.A.I.C.S.: 423810
Peter Lacey (Exec Chm)

Peterbilt of Ontario Inc. **(2)**
31 Buchanan Court, London, N5Z 4P9, ON,
Canada
Tel.: (519) 686-1000
Web Site:
http://peterbilt.cervusequipment.com
Sales Range: $125-149.9 Million
Emp.: 308
Truck Dealership
N.A.I.C.S.: 423110

BRANDWELLS CONSTRUCTION

Park House Church Lane, St George,
Bristol, BS5 7AG, United Kingdom
Tel.: (44) 1179517611
Web Site:
http://www.brandwells.co.uk
Year Founded: 1973
Sales Range: $10-24.9 Million
Emp.: 100
Building Construction Services
N.A.I.C.S.: 236220
Andy Dowden (Founder & Mng Dir)

BRANKO A.S.

Novozamocka Ul 184, 949 05, Nitra,
Slovakia
Tel.: (421) 376526229
Poultry Distr
N.A.I.C.S.: 424440
Martina Horvathova (Chm-Mgmt Bd)

BRANNON STEEL

14 Tilbury Court, Brampton, L6T 3T4,
ON, Canada
Tel.: (905) 453-4730

Web Site:
http://www.brannonsteel.com
Year Founded: 1968
Rev.: $18,431,218
Emp.: 170
Carbon Steel Supplier
N.A.I.C.S.: 332811
Stephen Alfieri (Mgr-Sls)

BRASIL BROKERS PARTICIPACOES S.A.

Av Luis Carlos Prestes 230 Salas
104 A 106, 22775055, Rio de Janeiro, RJ, Brazil
Tel.: (55) 2134333001
Web Site:
http://www.brbrokers.com.br
NEXP3—(BRAZ)
Rev.: $23,778,259
Assets: $24,736,321
Liabilities: $53,071,819
Net Worth: ($28,335,497)
Earnings: ($9,893,045)
Emp.: 632
Fiscal Year-end: 12/31/23
Real Estate Brokerage Services
N.A.I.C.S.: 531390
Renato de Vicq Telles da Silva Lobo
(COO)

BRASIL PLURAL S.A. BANCO MULTIPLO

Rua Surubim 373 1 Andar, Vila Olimpia, Sao Paulo, CEP 04571-050, Brazil
Tel.: (55) 11 3206 8000 BR
Web Site: http://www.brasilplural.com
Year Founded: 2009
Sales Range: $10-24.9 Million
Emp.: 300
Investment Banking, Real Estate Investment & Asset Management Services
N.A.I.C.S.: 523150
Rodolfo Riechert (CEO)

BRASILAGRO - COMPANHIA BRASILEIRA DE PROPRIEDADES AGRICOLAS

Av Brigadeiro Faria Lima 1309 5
floor, Sao Paulo, 01452-002, Brazil
Tel.: (55) 1130355350 BR
Web Site: https://ri.brasil-agro.com
AGRO3—(NYSE)
Rev.: $137,846,299
Assets: $644,443,593
Liabilities: $254,804,698
Net Worth: $389,638,895
Earnings: $40,554,690
Emp.: 429
Fiscal Year-end: 06/30/24
Agriculture, Livestock & Property
Management Services
N.A.I.C.S.: 111998
Eduardo S. Elsztain (Chm)

BRASILAGRO-CIA BRAS DE PROP AGRICOLAS

Avenida Brigadeiro Faria Lima 1309
5 andar, Sao Paulo, 01452-002, Brazil
Tel.: (55) 1130355350
Web Site: http://www.brasil-agro.com
AGRO3—(BRAZ)
Rev.: $189,290,319
Assets: $644,443,593
Liabilities: $254,804,698
Net Worth: $389,638,895
Earnings: $40,554,690
Fiscal Year-end: 06/30/24
Real Estate Manangement Services
N.A.I.C.S.: 531390
Andre Guillaumon (CEO & COO)

BRASS AGENCY LTD.

3rd Floor 41 Spring Gardens, Manchester, M2 2BG, United Kingdom
Tel.: (44) 161 507 3900
Web Site: http://www.brassagency.com
Year Founded: 1983
Emp.: 170
N.A.I.C.S.: 541810
Katie Rand (Dir-Mktg)

BRASS CO., LTD.

4F I'm Building 2-36-20 Meieki,
Nakamura-ku, Nagoya, 450-0002,
Japan
Tel.: (81) 525713322
Web Site: https://www.brass.ne.jp
2424—(TKS)
Rev.: $79,155,720
Assets: $67,263,080
Liabilities: $43,701,720
Net Worth: $23,561,360
Earnings: $1,710,500
Emp.: 563
Fiscal Year-end: 07/31/24
Building Design & Planning Services
N.A.I.C.S.: 541310

BRASSERIE DE TAHITI SA

Place Notre Dame, BP 597, 98713,
Papeete, French Polynesia
Tel.: (689) 40467600
Web Site:
http://www.brasseriedetahiti.com
Year Founded: 1914
Sales Range: $50-74.9 Million
Emp.: 400
Alcoholic Beverage Distr
N.A.I.C.S.: 424810
Jean Pierre Fourcade (Pres)

BRASSEUR TRANSPORT INC.

1250 Rue Industrielle, La Prairie, J5R
5G4, QC, Canada
Tel.: (450) 444-7079
Web Site:
http://www.brasseurtransport.com
Year Founded: 1953
Truck Transportation Services
N.A.I.C.S.: 484110
Michel Brasseur (Pres)

BRASSO NISSAN

195 Glendeer Circle SE, Calgary,
T2H 2S8, AB, Canada
Tel.: (403) 253-5555
Web Site:
https://www.brassonissan.com
Year Founded: 1969
Rev.: $19,871,280
Emp.: 83
New & Used Car Dealers
N.A.I.C.S.: 441110
Einar Brasso (Pres)

BRASTER S.A.

Ul Cichy Ogrod 7, Szeligi, 05-850,
Ozarow Mazowiecki, Poland
Tel.: (48) 222950350
Web Site: https://www.braster.eu
BRA—(WAR)
Rev.: $81,047
Assets: $4,856,707
Liabilities: $5,981,961
Net Worth: ($1,125,254)
Earnings: ($1,206,301)
Fiscal Year-end: 12/31/23
Medical Device Mfr
N.A.I.C.S.: 339112
Dariusz Karolak (Chm-Mgmt Bd)

BRATACO, PT

Jl Cideng Barat no 78, Jakarta,
10150, Indonesia
Tel.: (62) 21 3522799
Web Site: http://www.brataco.com
Pharmaceuticals Mfr
N.A.I.C.S.: 325412

Titianus Winata *(Pres)*

Subsidiaries:

PT Distriversa Buanamas **(1)**
Jl Jati Winangun 55-A Tanjung, Purwokerto
Selatan, 53143, Purwokerto, Indonesia
Tel.: (62) 281 638191
Web Site: http://www.brataco.com
Pharmaceuticals Product Mfr
N.A.I.C.S.: 325412

PT Ikafood Putramas **(1)**
Jl Panyaungan 6 Cileunyi, Rancakek,
Bandung, 40393, Indonesia
Tel.: (62) 227797653
Web Site: http://www.ikafood.com
Sales Range: $25-49.9 Million
Emp.: 60
Food & Spice Mfr
N.A.I.C.S.: 311999
Maudy R. Winata *(Pres)*

PT Ikapharmindo Putramas **(1)**
Jl Raya Pulogadung 29, Jakarta, 13920,
Indonesia
Tel.: (62) 214614766
Web Site: http://www.ikapharmindo.com
Pharmaceuticals Product Mfr
N.A.I.C.S.: 325412

PT. Brataco Chemica **(1)**
Jl KelapaGading Bulevard Raya Blok TB 2
No 5, Jakarta, 14240, Indonesia
Tel.: (62) 21 4528542
Web Site: http://www.bratachem.com
Pharmaceutical Product Mfr & Distr
N.A.I.C.S.: 325412

BRATSTVO A.D.

Marsala Tita 31, Presevo, Serbia
Tel.: (381) 17413500
Year Founded: 1953
BRAT—(BEL)
Sales Range: Less than $1 Million
Grocery Store Operator
N.A.I.C.S.: 445110
Erdinc Agus *(Exec Dir)*

BRAUEREI FOHRENBURG GMBH & CO KG

Fohrenburgstrasse 5 Postfach 192, A
6700, Bludenz, Austria
Tel.: (43) 55526060
Web Site: http://www.fohrenburg.at
Year Founded: 1881
Sales Range: $25-49.9 Million
Emp.: 150
Beer, Alcohol-Free Beer & Soft Drinks
Mfr
N.A.I.C.S.: 312120
Wolfgang Sila *(Pres)*

BRAUEREI MAX LEIBINGER GMBH

Friedhofstrasse 20 36, 88212, Ra-
vensburg, Germany
Tel.: (49) 75136990   De
Web Site: http://www.leibinger.de
Year Founded: 1894
Sales Range: $10-24.9 Million
Beer Mfr
N.A.I.C.S.: 312120
Michael Leibinger *(Mng Partner)*

BRAUEREI ZOLLER-HOF GRAF-FLEISCHHUT GMBH & CO.KG

Leopoldstr 40, 72488, Sigmaringen,
Germany
Tel.: (49) 75717210
Web Site: http://www.zoller-hof.de
Year Founded: 1845
Rev.: $25,518,155
Emp.: 70
Beer Mfr
N.A.I.C.S.: 312120
Ralf Rakel *(Mng Dir)*

BRAVADA GOLD CORPORA-TION

Suite 1100-1199 West Hastings St,
Vancouver, V6E 3T5, BC, Canada
Tel.: (604) 641-2759   BC
Web Site:
https://www.bravadagold.com
Year Founded: 2011
BVA—(OTCIQ)
Assets: $309,392
Liabilities: $508,708
Net Worth: ($199,316)
Earnings: ($1,246,229)
Fiscal Year-end: 07/31/21
Gold Mining Services
N.A.I.C.S.: 212220
Lawrence Page *(Chm)*

BRAVE

The Blue Bldg Fulham Island, 40
Vanston Pl, London, SW6 1AX,
United Kingdom
Tel.: (44) 2074711984
Web Site: http://www.brave.co.uk
Emp.: 150
N.A.I.C.S.: 541890
Matt Crisp *(Mng Dir)*

BRAVE BISON GROUP PLC

2 Stephen St, London, W1T 1AN,
United Kingdom
Tel.: (44) 2072537000
Web Site: https://bravebison.com
BBSN—(AIM)
Rev.: $39,305,454
Assets: $25,582,322
Liabilities: $13,137,002
Net Worth: $12,445,320
Earnings: $2,582,944
Emp.: 162
Fiscal Year-end: 12/31/22
Digital & Social Media Developer
N.A.I.C.S.: 425120
Oli Green *(Chm & CEO)*

Subsidiaries:

Brave Bison Asia Pacific Pte.
Ltd. **(1)**
120 Robinson Road 08-01, Singapore,
068913, Singapore
Tel.: (65) 83281173
Digital Advertising Services
N.A.I.C.S.: 541840

Brave Bison Limited **(1)**
79-81 Borough Rd, London, SE1 1DN,
United Kingdom
Tel.: (44) 2039682475
Digital Advertising Services
N.A.I.C.S.: 541840
Oli Green *(Chm & CEO)*

Greenlight Commerce Limited **(1)**
The Varnish Works 3 Bravingtons Walk,
London, N1 9AJ, United Kingdom
Tel.: (44) 2033261900
Web Site:
https://www.greenlightcommerce.com
Digital Advertising Services
N.A.I.C.S.: 541850

Greenlight Digital Limited **(1)**
The Varnish Works 3 Bravingtons Walk
Kings Cross, London, N1 9AJ, United King-
dom
Tel.: (44) 2072537000
Web Site: https://www.greenlightdigital.com
Emp.: 170
General Marketing Services
N.A.I.C.S.: 541613

BRAVE C&H SUPPLY CO., LTD.

No 31 Ln 17 Ziqiang N Rd, Guishan,
Taoyuan, 33350, Taiwan
Tel.: (886) 33295666
Web Site: https://www.bch.com.tw
Year Founded: 1994
6538—(TPE)
Rev.: $46,517,118
Assets: $79,785,292
Liabilities: $25,163,462
Net Worth: $54,621,830

Earnings: $5,328,112
Fiscal Year-end: 12/31/22
Printing Equipment Mfr
N.A.I.C.S.: 333248

Subsidiaries:

Brave Precision Mfg. Suzhou Co.,
Ltd. **(1)**
NO 25 Zhentai Road Taiping Street, Xi-
angcheng District, Suzhou, 215137, Ji-
angsu, China
Tel.: (86) 51265992292
Screen Mfr
N.A.I.C.S.: 323113

Brave Technology (Chengdu) Co.,
Ltd. **(1)**
No 801 Siwei Road Economic Develop
Zone, Chongzhou, Chengdu, 611230, Sich-
uan, China
Tel.: (86) 2882666310
Screen Mfr
N.A.I.C.S.: 323113

BRAVEHEART INVESTMENT GROUP PLC

1 Capitol Court Capitol Business
Park, Dodworth, Barnsley, S75 3TZ,
United Kingdom
Tel.: (44) 1738587555
Web Site:
https://www.braveheartgroup.co.uk
BRH—(AIM)
Assets: $4,418,085
Liabilities: $126,231
Net Worth: $4,291,854
Earnings: ($9,151,748)
Fiscal Year-end: 03/31/24
Financial Services
N.A.I.C.S.: 523940
Trevor E. Brown *(CEO)*

Subsidiaries:

Kirkstall Limited **(1)**
York House Outgang Lane, York, YO19
5UP, North Yorkshire, United Kingdom
Tel.: (44) 170 936 1241
Web Site: https://www.kirkstall.com
Bio Technology Services
N.A.I.C.S.: 541714

Paraytec Limited **(1)**
York House Outgang Lane, Osbaldwick,
York, YO19 5UP, United Kingdom
Tel.: (44) 190 443 6620
Web Site: https://www.paraytec.com
Laboratory Instrument Mfr
N.A.I.C.S.: 334516
Professor David Goodall *(Chief Scientific
Officer)*

Strathclyde Innovation Fund LP **(1)**
Dundee Road 2, Perth, PH2 7DW, Scot-
land, United Kingdom
Tel.: (44) 1738587555
Web Site: http://www.braveheartgroup.co.uk
Sales Range: $50-74.9 Million
Emp.: 10
Investment Management Service
N.A.I.C.S.: 523999
Trevor Brown *(CEO)*

BRAVEHEART RESOURCES INC.

2520 - 16 St NW, Calgary, T2M 3R2,
AB, Canada
Tel.: (403) 512-8202   ON
Web Site:
https://canadiancriticalminerals.com
Year Founded: 2009
BHT—(OTCIQ)
Rev.: $8,611
Assets: $11,743,625
Liabilities: $6,016,942
Net Worth: $5,726,683
Earnings: ($5,677,993)
Fiscal Year-end: 05/31/21
Gold Exploration Services
N.A.I.C.S.: 212220
David W. Johnston *(Founder & Chm)*

BRAVENETMEDIA.COM

Ste 100 - 180 McCarter Str, Parks-
ville, V9P 2H5, BC, Canada
Tel.: (250) 954-3203   Ca
Web Site:
http://www.bravenetmedia.com
Year Founded: 1997
Sales Range: $10-24.9 Million
Emp.: 25
Free Webmaster Tools
N.A.I.C.S.: 541512
Melanie Peake *(Dir-Online Sls)*

BRAVERN VENTURES LTD.

515 - 701 West Georgia Street, PO
Box 10068, Pacific Centre, Vancou-
ver, V7Y 1C6, BC, Canada
Tel.: (778) 331-8505   BC
Year Founded: 1988
BAV—(TSXV)
Assets: $228
Liabilities: $10,854,325
Net Worth: ($10,854,097)
Earnings: ($1,085,541)
Emp.: 15
Fiscal Year-end: 12/31/19
Holding Company
N.A.I.C.S.: 551112
Scott Ackerman *(CEO)*

BRAVIA CAPITAL HONG KONG LIMITED

6510 13 The Center 99 Queens
Road, Hong Kong, China (Hong
Kong)
Tel.: (852) 26772104
Web Site:
http://www.braviacapital.com
Emp.: 13
Privater Equity Firm
N.A.I.C.S.: 523999
Rinarisa Coronel DeFronze *(Chief
Admin Officer)*

Subsidiaries:

Bravia Capital Partners, Inc. **(1)**
245 Park Ave 39th Fl, New York, NY 10167
Tel.: (212) 672-1844
Financial Investment Services
N.A.I.C.S.: 523999

Bravia Capital Services India Pvt.
Ltd. **(1)**
D3 Ocean Park, Dona Paula, Goa, 403004,
India
Tel.: (91) 832 2452024
Financial Investment Services
N.A.I.C.S.: 523999

Train Trailer Rentals Limited **(1)**
400 Annagem Blvd, Mississauga, L5T 3A8,
ON, Canada
Tel.: (905) 564-7247
Trailer Rental Services
N.A.I.C.S.: 532120
Anthony Nadon *(Dir-Sls-Quebec & Atlantic
Canada)*

BRAVIDA HOLDING AB

Mikrofonvagen 28, 126 81, Stock-
holm, Sweden
Tel.: (46) 86952000   SE
Web Site: https://www.bravida.se
Year Founded: 2012
BRAV—(OMX)
Rev.: $2,463,588,937
Assets: $2,104,770,201
Liabilities: $1,361,469,368
Net Worth: $743,300,833
Earnings: $120,168,217
Emp.: 13,000
Fiscal Year-end: 12/31/22
Holding Company; Heating, Ventila-
tion, Air Conditioning, Plumbing &
Electrical Installation Services
N.A.I.C.S.: 551112
Mattias Johansson *(Pres & CEO)*

Bravida Holding AB—(Continued)

Subsidiaries:

ABEKA El & Kraftanlaggningar AB (1)
Norrkopingsvagen 5A, 611 38, Nykoping, Sweden
Tel.: (46) 155291020
Web Site: https://www.abeka.se
Electricity Distribution & Renewable Energy Services
N.A.I.C.S.: 221118

AM Elektriska AB (1)
Sodra Varvindsgatan 14, 418 77, Gothenburg, Sweden
Tel.: (46) 31225515
Electrical Installation Services
N.A.I.C.S.: 238210

Ab Hango Elektriska (1)
Lahteentie 4, 10960, Hanko, Finland
Tel.: (358) 207939700
Web Site: http://www.hangonsahko.fi
Emp.: 100
Electrical & Plumbing Contracting Services
N.A.I.C.S.: 238220

Ab Hango Elektriska - Hangon Sahko Oy (1)
Lahteentie 4, 10960, Hanko, Finland
Tel.: (358) 207939700
Web Site: https://www.hangonsahko.fi
HVAC Contracting Services
N.A.I.C.S.: 238220

Bravida AB (1)
Mikrofonvagen 28, 126 81, Stockholm, Sweden
Tel.: (46) 86952000
Holding Company; Heating, Ventilation, Air Conditioning, Plumbing & Electrical Installation Services
N.A.I.C.S.: 551112

Subsidiary (Non-US):

Bravida Danmark AS (2)
Park Alle 373, 2605, Brondby, Denmark
Tel.: (45) 43221100
Web Site: https://www.bravida.dk
Sales Range: $450-499.9 Million
Heating, Ventilation, Air Conditioning, Plumbing & Electrical Installation Services
N.A.I.C.S.: 238220
Soren Frahm (Dir-East Reg)

Bravida Finland Oy (2)
Valimotie 21, 00380, Helsinki, Finland
Tel.: (358) 10 238 8000
Web Site: https://www.bravida.fi
Heating, Ventilation, Air Conditioning, Plumbing & Electrical Installation Services
N.A.I.C.S.: 238220

Bravida Norge AS (2)
Ostre Aker Vei 90, 0596, Oslo, Norway
Tel.: (47) 2 404 8000
Web Site: https://www.bravida.no
Sales Range: $450-499.9 Million
Heating, Ventilation, Air Conditioning, Plumbing & Electrical Installation Services
N.A.I.C.S.: 238220
Thomas Hveberg (Dir-Fin)

Subsidiary (Domestic):

Bravida Norge 4 AS (3)
Industrivegen 2, 2390, Moelv, Norway
Tel.: (47) 62347000
Sales Range: $10-24.9 Million
Emp.: 160
Electrical Installations Contractor
N.A.I.C.S.: 237130

Subsidiary (Domestic):

Bravida Sverige AB (2)
Mikrofonvagen 28, 126 81, Hagersten, Sweden
Tel.: (46) 86952000
Emp.: 5,000
Heating, Ventilation, Air Conditioning, Plumbing & Electrical Installation Services
N.A.I.C.S.: 238220

Division (Domestic):

Bravida Sverige AB - North Division (3)

Betonggatan 1, Box 818, 721 22, Vasteras, Sweden
Tel.: (46) 2 115 4800
Web Site: http://www.bravida.se
Regional Managing Office; Heating, Ventilation, Air Conditioning, Plumbing & Electrical Installation Services
N.A.I.C.S.: 551114
Thommy Lundmark (Head)

Bravida Sverige AB - South Division (3)
Alfagatan 8, Box 40, 431 21, Molndal, Sweden
Tel.: (46) 31 709 5100
Web Site: http://www.bravida.se
Regional Managing Office; Heating, Ventilation, Air Conditioning, Plumbing & Electrical Installation Services
N.A.I.C.S.: 551114
Anders Ahlquist (Head)

Bravida Prenad AB (1)
Muskotgatan 8 A, Box 22018, 250 22, Helsingborg, Sweden
Tel.: (46) 42167400
Web Site: http://www.prenad.se
Electrical Engineering Services
N.A.I.C.S.: 541330

E/S Styromatic AB (1)
Gradgatan 1, 931 36, Skelleftea, Sweden
Tel.: (46) 910714500
Web Site: https://www.elstyr.se
Industrial Equipment Services
N.A.I.C.S.: 811310

El-teknik i Gavle AB (1)
S Kungsgatan 59, 802 55, Gavle, Sweden
Tel.: (46) 26647200
Web Site: http://www.el-teknik.net
Electrical Contracting Services
N.A.I.C.S.: 238210

Energibygg AS (1)
Haslevangen 14, 0579, Oslo, Norway
Tel.: (47) 41544500
Web Site: http://www.energibygg.no
Building Consultancy Services
N.A.I.C.S.: 531390

Erfator Projektledning AB (1)
Soder Malarstrand 77 8 tr, 118 25, Stockholm, Sweden
Tel.: (46) 86952700
Web Site: https://www.erfator.se
Construction Services
N.A.I.C.S.: 236220

Fiberkom ApS (1)
Faaborgvej 77, 5250, Odense, Denmark
Tel.: (45) 40290047
Web Site: https://www.fiberkom.dk
Network Connection Services
N.A.I.C.S.: 517810

HNA Storkoksservice AB (1)
Farhultsvagen 396, 263 95, Farhult, Sweden
Tel.: (46) 42139777
Web Site: https://www.hna.nu
Commercial Kitchen Equipment Distr
N.A.I.C.S.: 423440

Herberts Ror AB (1)
Mejselvagen 3, 444 32, Stenungsund, Sweden
Tel.: (46) 30380109
Plumbing Installation & Bathroom Product Distr
N.A.I.C.S.: 423720

Indupipe AB (1)
Ersbogatan 13, 802 93, Gavle, Sweden
Tel.: (46) 702519890
Web Site: https://indupipe.se
Project Management Services
N.A.I.C.S.: 541611

J Beese VVS & Blik A/S (1)
Thulevej 13, 5210, Odense, Denmark
Tel.: (45) 66135503
Web Site: https://beesevvs.dk
Plumbing Services
N.A.I.C.S.: 238220

Lindstens Elektriska AB (1)
Industrigatan 1, 273 35, Tomelilla, Sweden
Tel.: (46) 41713510
Electrical Installation Services
N.A.I.C.S.: 238210

NPI Ventilation AB (1)
Hacklehemsplan 1, 681 34, Kristinehamn, Sweden
Tel.: (46) 550411154
Ventilation Installation Services
N.A.I.C.S.: 238220

Norrstyr AB (1)
Sparvagen 3, 901 31, Umea, Sweden
Tel.: (46) 90152600
Electrical Construction Services
N.A.I.C.S.: 238210

Obergs Vent Teknik AB (1)
Syrgasvagen 4, 553 02, Jonkoping, Sweden
Tel.: (46) 36342520
Electrical & Ventilation Installation Services
N.A.I.C.S.: 238210

Oras AS (1)
Ostre Aker vei 90, 0596, Oslo, Norway
Tel.: (47) 22024300
Web Site: http://www.oras.no
Plumbing Contracting Services
N.A.I.C.S.: 238220

Savon Aurinkoenergia Oy (1)
Anopintie 10, 40530, Jyvaskyla, Finland
Web Site: http://www.savonaurinkoenergia.fi
Solar Energy Services
N.A.I.C.S.: 221114

Skoglund El & Tele AB (1)
Nastagatan 6, 702 27, Orebro, Sweden
Tel.: (46) 19196200
Electrical Construction Services
N.A.I.C.S.: 238210

Solkraft EMK AB (1)
Flojelbergsgatan 18 van 2, 431 37, Molndal, Sweden
Tel.: (46) 317888399
Web Site: http://www.solkraftsverige.se
Solar Power Services
N.A.I.C.S.: 221114

Soren Anderssons El i Delsbo Aktiebolag (1)
Ullsattersvagen 21B, 824 35, Hudiksvall, Sweden
Tel.: (46) 650543412
Web Site: https://sorensel.se
Electrical Installation Services
N.A.I.C.S.: 238210

Svagstromsinstallationer i Norrkoping AB (1)
Skalles Vag 14, 605 97, Norrkoping, Sweden
Tel.: (46) 11162434
Web Site: http://www.svinab.se
Fibber Installation Services
N.A.I.C.S.: 238210

SystemHouse Solutions AB (1)
Mikrofonvagen 28, Hagersten, Sweden
Tel.: (46) 103039970
Web Site: https://systemhousesolutions.se
System Security Services
N.A.I.C.S.: 561621

Viva Energi A/S (1)
Rosbjergvej 30A, 8220, Brabrand, Denmark
Tel.: (45) 70227040
Web Site: https://www.vivaenergi.dk
Solar Energy Equipment Distr
N.A.I.C.S.: 423720

BRAVO PASSENGER SOLUTION PTE LIMITED
218 Orchard Road #06-01 Orchard Gateway Emerald, Singapore, Singapore
Tel.: (65) 6809 7631
Web Site: http://www.bravo.aero
Airline IT Solutions Services
N.A.I.C.S.: 513210
Jason Bitter (CEO)

BRAVO TANGO ADVERTISING FIRM INC.
1630B 8th Avenue, Regina, S4R 1E5, SK, Canada
Tel.: (306) 546-3799
Web Site: http://www.bravotango.ca
Year Founded: 2008

Sales Range: $10-24.9 Million
Emp.: 50
Advertising Services
N.A.I.C.S.: 541810
Stephanie Karpan (Dir-Media & Production)

BRAVOFLY RUMBO GROUP N.V.
Corso San Gottardo 30, 6830, Chiasso, Switzerland
Tel.: (41) 91 210 33 02
Web Site: http://www.bravoflyrumbogroup.com
Year Founded: 2004
Online Travel Services
N.A.I.C.S.: 561599
Fabio Cannavale (Chm)

Subsidiaries:

LMnext UK Ltd. (1)
77 Hatton Garden, London, EC1N 8JS, United Kingdom
Tel.: (44) 0800 083 4000
Web Site: http://www.lastminute.com
Holding Company; Online Travel Arrangement Services
N.A.I.C.S.: 551112
Alessandra Di Lorenzo (Chief Comml Officer-Advertising & Partnerships)

BRAWN BIOTECH LTD.
C64 Lajpat Nagar, New Delhi, 110002, India
Tel.: (91) 1132911528
Web Site: https://www.brawnbiotech.com
530207—(BOM)
Rev.: $117,720
Assets: $188,159
Liabilities: $89,601
Net Worth: $98,558
Earnings: ($22,446)
Emp.: 16
Fiscal Year-end: 03/31/22
Pharmaceuticals Product Mfr
N.A.I.C.S.: 325412
Rati Garg (CFO)

BRAXIA SCIENTIFIC CORP.
1100 Dundas St W Unit 6, Mississauga, L5C 4E7, ON, Canada
Tel.: (416) 430-9619
Web Site: https://braxiascientific.com
BRAXF—(OTCIQ)
Rev.: $1,405,592
Assets: $2,897,549
Liabilities: $1,700,421
Net Worth: $1,197,128
Earnings: ($9,803,711)
Fiscal Year-end: 03/31/23
Agricultural Product Cultivation Services
N.A.I.C.S.: 115112
Roger McIntyre (CEO)

BRAZIL FAST FOOD CORP.
Rua Voluntarios da Patria 89/901, Botafogo, 270-010, Rio de Janeiro, RJ, Brazil
Tel.: (55) 2125367500 DE
Web Site: http://www.bffc.com.br
Year Founded: 1992
Sales Range: $125-149.9 Million
Fast Food Franchise Restaurants
Owner & Operator
N.A.I.C.S.: 722513
Antonio Jose Pereira Detsi (Fin Dir)

BRAZIL PHARMA S.A.
Avenida Presidente Juscelino Kubitschek 1830, 2nd Floor Tower 4 Itaim Bibi, Sao Paulo, 04543-900, SP, Brazil
Tel.: (55) 11 2117 5200
Web Site: http://www.brasilpharma.com.br

Year Founded: 2009
Rev.: $479,242,079
Assets: $465,122,410
Liabilities: $368,060,529
Net Worth: $97,061,881
Earnings: ($202,310,376)
Fiscal Year-end: 12/31/16
Pharmaceutical Product Whslr
N.A.I.C.S.: 424210
Leonardo Leirinha Souza Campos
(CFO & Dir-IR)

Subsidiaries:

Drogaria Mais Economica S.A. **(1)**
Rua 15 De Janeiro 129 Centro, Canoas,
Brazil
Tel.: (55) 51 34271359
Pharmaceutical Products Distr
N.A.I.C.S.: 424210

Santana S.A. Drogaria
Farmacias **(1)**
Rua Minas Gerais n 762 Edificio Banbanga,
Salvador, 41830-020, Bahia, Brazil
Tel.: (55) 71 3206 3916
Web Site:
http://www.farmaciassantana.com.br
Pharmaceutical Products Distr
N.A.I.C.S.: 424210

BRAZILIAN FINANCE & REAL ESTATE S.A.

Av Paulista 1374 - 12 floor Edificio
Brazilian Financial Center, Bela Vista,
Sao Paulo, 01310-916, SP, Brazil
Tel.: (55) 11 4081 4499 **BR**
Web Site: http://www.bfre.com.br
Real Estate Financial Services
N.A.I.C.S.: 531390

BRB BANCO DE BRASILIA SA

Sbs Quadra 01 Bloco E Edificio, Federal District, 70072-900, Brasilia, Brazil
Tel.: (55) 6134128200
Web Site: http://novo.brb.com.br
BSLI4—(BRAZ)
Rev.: $766,889,738
Assets: $8,930,856,737
Liabilities: $8,517,513,940
Net Worth: $413,342,797
Earnings: $33,881,946
Fiscal Year-end: 12/31/23
Financial Consulting Services
N.A.I.C.S.: 541611
Paulo Henrique Bezerra Rodrigues
Costa *(CEO)*

BRB BCO DE BRASILIA S.A.

Sbs Q1 - Bloco E/lote 24 - Ed brasilia
- 8a, 70072900, Brasilia, DF, Brazil
Tel.: (55) 6134128092
Web Site: http://www.brb.com.br
Financial Investment Services
N.A.I.C.S.: 523999
Carlos Vinicius Raposo Machado
Costa *(Dir-IR)*

Subsidiaries:

BRB - Administradora e Corretora de
Seguros S.A. **(1)**
Sgas 902 Bloco B Lote 74 Loja 53 Ed Athenas, Brasilia, 70390-020, Brazil
Tel.: (55) 6133141279
Web Site: http://www.bancorbras.com.br
General Insurance Services
N.A.I.C.S.: 524210

BRB - Distribuidora de Titulos e Valores Mobiliarios S.A. **(1)**
SBS-Quadra I Bloco E 7th Floor South
Wing, Brasilia, 70072-900, Brazil
Tel.: (55) 6134128924
Financial Investment Services
N.A.I.C.S.: 523999

BRC ASIA LIMITED

350 Jalan Boon Lay Jurong Industrial
Estate, Singapore, 619530, Singapore

Tel.: (65) 62652333 **SG**
Web Site: https://www.brc.com.sg
Year Founded: 1938
BEC—(SES)
Rev.: $1,205,630,233
Assets: $705,713,968
Liabilities: $389,070,026
Net Worth: $316,643,942
Earnings: $56,130,419
Emp.: 751
Fiscal Year-end: 09/30/23
Prefabricated Steel Reinforcement
Mfr
N.A.I.C.S.: 331110
Chun Lee *(CFO & Co-Sec)*

Subsidiaries:

BRC Prefab Holdings Sdn. Bhd. **(1)**
PTD 103251 Jalan Idaman 3/9 Taman Perindustrian Desa Idaman, 81400, Senai, Johor, Malaysia
Tel.: (60) 75976888
Steel Products Mfr
N.A.I.C.S.: 331110
Kiin Peng Seah *(CEO-Grp)*

Lee Metal Group Ltd. **(1)**
No 7 Tuas Ave 16, Singapore, 638934, Singapore
Tel.: (65) 68622467
Web Site: https://www.leemetalgroup.com
Rev.: $253,572,666
Assets: $288,858,491
Liabilities: $152,261,086
Net Worth: $136,597,405
Earnings: $5,614,285
Emp.: 520
Fiscal Year-end: 12/31/2017
Holding Company; Structural Steel Products
Mfr & Distr
N.A.I.C.S.: 551112
Lin Poey Lee *(Founder & Chm)*

Subsidiary (Domestic):

LMG Realty Pte. Ltd. **(2)**
No 7 Tuas Avenue 16, Singapore, 638934,
Singapore **(100%)**
Tel.: (65) 68622467
Real Estate Investment, Industrial Development & Property Management Services
N.A.I.C.S.: 531390

Steel Park International Pte. Ltd. **(2)**
No 7 Tuas Avenue 16, Singapore,
Singapore **(100%)**
Tel.: (65) 68622467
Sales Range: $25-49.9 Million
International Metal & Materials Wholesale
Trade Broker
N.A.I.C.S.: 425120

Steel Park Resources Pte. Ltd. **(2)**
7 Tuas Avenue 16, Singapore, 638934,
Singapore **(100%)**
Tel.: (65) 68621898
Sales Range: $50-74.9 Million
Emp.: 50
Metal & Materials Wholesale Trade Broker
N.A.I.C.S.: 425120
Hock Seng Lee *(Gen Mgr)*

BRC SEHER A.D.

Od Zmijanja Rajka 391, 78000, Banja
Luka, Bosnia & Herzegovina
Tel.: (387) 51461225
Year Founded: 2001
SEHR-R-A—(BANJ)
Assets: $3,409,930
Liabilities: $467,981
Net Worth: $2,941,949
Earnings: ($14,229)
Fiscal Year-end: 12/31/12
Restaurant Operators
N.A.I.C.S.: 722511
Vlado Birac *(Chm-Mgmt Bd)*

BRCCA SERVICES PRIVATE LIMITED

CK-233, Sector II, Salt Lake City,
Kolkata, 700091, India
Tel.: (91) 9073626911
Web Site: https://www.brcca.in
Business Consulting Services

N.A.I.C.S.: 541618

Subsidiaries:

Aris International Limited **(1)**
129-B Ansa Industrial Estate Saki Vihar
Road Saki Naka, Andheri E, Mumbai,
400072, Maharashtra, India
Tel.: (91) 3322378520
Web Site: http://www.adityagears.in
Rev.: $42,659
Assets: $68,041
Liabilities: $13,261
Net Worth: $54,781
Earnings: $42,420
Fiscal Year-end: 03/31/2023
Automobile Parts Mfr
N.A.I.C.S.: 336350
Jayanti Pradhan *(Mng Dir)*

BRD. KLEE A/S

Gadagervej 11, DK-2620, Albertslund,
Denmark
Tel.: (45) 43868333 **DK**
Web Site: https://www.klee.dk
Year Founded: 1944
KLEE.B—(CSE)
Rev.: $34,930,764
Assets: $22,666,435
Liabilities: $7,571,877
Net Worth: $15,094,558
Earnings: $2,031,515
Emp.: 70
Fiscal Year-end: 09/30/23
Industrial Machinery Mfr & Distr
N.A.I.C.S.: 336350
Hardy Buhl Pedersen *(Chm)*

Subsidiaries:

Bonfiglioli Vectron GmbH **(1)**
Europark Fichtenhain B6, 47807, Krefeld,
Germany
Tel.: (49) 215183960
Web Site: http://www.bonfiglioli.com
Industrial Gear Motor Mfr
N.A.I.C.S.: 333612

Elbe Holding GmbH & Co. KG **(1)**
Nordfeldstrasse 22a, 27476, Cuxhaven,
Germany
Tel.: (49) 47216987900
Web Site: https://www.elbe-holding.de
Building Materials Whslr
N.A.I.C.S.: 423390

Elesa S.p.A. **(1)**
Via Pompei 29, 20900, Monza, Italy
Tel.: (39) 03928111
Web Site: http://www.elesa.com
Clamping Handle Mfr
N.A.I.C.S.: 332510

Fluro Gelenklager GmbH **(1)**
Siemensstrasse 13, 72348, Rosenfeld, Germany
Tel.: (49) 742893850
Web Site: https://www.fluro.de
Angle Joint Mfr
N.A.I.C.S.: 325520
Karl Heinz *(Head-Export)*

Muhr und Bender KG **(1)**
Postfach 360, 57427, Attendorn, Germany
Tel.: (49) 2722620
Web Site: https://www.mubea.com
Power Train Product Mfr
N.A.I.C.S.: 336350
Thomas Muhr *(CEO)*

Ortlinghaus-Werke GmbH **(1)**
Kenkhauser Str 125, 42929, Wermelskirchen, Germany
Tel.: (49) 2196850
Web Site: https://www.ortlinghaus.com
Clutch Mfr
N.A.I.C.S.: 335314

Riegler & Co. KG **(1)**
Schuetzenstrasse 27, 72574, Bad Urach,
Germany
Tel.: (49) 712594970
Hose Whslr
N.A.I.C.S.: 423840
Franz Riegler *(Founder)*

Thomas Regout International
B.V. **(1)**

Industrieweg 40, 6219 NR, Maastricht,
Netherlands
Tel.: (31) 433516666
Web Site: https://www.thomasregout-
telescopicslides.com
Heavy Duty Slide Mfr
N.A.I.C.S.: 336120

BREADTALK GROUP PTE LTD.

30 Tai Seng Street 09-01, Singapore,
534013, Singapore
Tel.: (65) 62856116 **SG**
Web Site: http://www.breadtalk.com
Year Founded: 2000
Sales Range: $400-449.9 Million
Holding Company; Bakery
N.A.I.C.S.: 551112
George Meng Tong Quek *(Founder,
Chm & CEO)*

Subsidiaries:

BreadTalk Concept Hong Kong
Limited **(1)**
Rm C 69 Ground Fl Olympian City Phase 2
Lin Cheung Rd, Mongkok, Kowloon, China
(Hong Kong)
Tel.: (852) 22734569
Baked Goods Mfr
N.A.I.C.S.: 311813

BreadTalk International Pte. Ltd. **(1)**
171 Kampong Ampat 05 05 KA Foodlink,
Singapore, Singapore
Tel.: (65) 62856116
Baked Goods Mfr
N.A.I.C.S.: 311813

BreadTalk Pte Ltd. **(1)**
30 Tai Seng Street 09-01, Singapore,
534013, Singapore
Tel.: (65) 62856116
Web Site: http://www.breadtalk.com
Sales Range: $150-199.9 Million
Emp.: 700
Bakery & Retail Servies
N.A.I.C.S.: 311811

Subsidiary (Domestic):

Taster Food Pte Ltd **(2)**
290 Orchard Road B1 03 Paragon, Singapore, 238859, Singapore
Tel.: (65) 68368336
Restaurant Operating Services
N.A.I.C.S.: 722511

Food Junction Management Pte
Ltd **(1)**
30 Tai Seng Street Breadtalk IHQ, Singapore, 534013, Singapore
Tel.: (65) 63388213
Web Site: http://www.foodjunction.com
Food Products Distr
N.A.I.C.S.: 424420
Lim Jeffrey *(CEO)*

Food Republic Pte Ltd **(1)**
30 Tai Seng Street, Singapore, 534013,
Singapore
Tel.: (65) 62760521
Restaurant Operating Services
N.A.I.C.S.: 722511

Food Republic Taiwan Co., Ltd. **(1)**
2F No 128 Xinfu Rd, Banqiao District, New
Taipei City, 22041, Taiwan
Tel.: (886) 289518551
Food Mfr
N.A.I.C.S.: 311813

ML Breadworks Sdn Bhd **(1)**
Level 6 Wisma KLIH 126 Jln Bukit Bintang,
Kuala Lumpur, 55100, Malaysia **(90%)**
Tel.: (60) 387390118
Commercial Bakeries
N.A.I.C.S.: 311812

Ramen Play Pte. Ltd. **(1)**
313 Somerset 230 Orchard Rd B3 04, Singapore, Singapore
Tel.: (65) 66340051
Web Site: http://www.ramenplay.com.sg
Sales Range: $10-24.9 Million
Emp.: 80
Restaurant Operating Services
N.A.I.C.S.: 722513

BreadTalk Group Pte Ltd.—(Continued)

Shanghai BreadTalk Co., Ltd. (1)
Floor 2 3 An Sheng Business Building No
77 Fenyang Road, Xuhui District, Shanghai,
China
Tel.: (86) 2154666565
Bakery Goods Retailer
N.A.I.C.S.: 311812

BREAKER RESOURCES NL
12 Walker Avenue, West Perth, 6005,
WA, Australia
Tel.: (61) 892263666
Web Site:
http://www.breakerresources.com
Year Founded: 2010
BRB—(ASX)
Rev.: $11,226,235
Assets: $15,769,863
Liabilities: $760,397
Net Worth: $15,009,466
Earnings: $528,873
Fiscal Year-end: 06/30/22
Gold Mining Services
N.A.I.C.S.: 212220
Thomas Stephen Sanders (Mng Dir)

BREAL CAPITAL LTD.
14th Floor 33 Cavendish Square,,
London, W1G 0PW, United Kingdom
Tel.: (44) 2071291488
Web Site: https://brealgroup.com
Year Founded: 2014
Renting Services
N.A.I.C.S.: 522291
Brent Osborne (Founder)

**BRECO ANTRIEBSTECHNIK
BREHER GMBH & CO. KG**
Kleiststr 53, Porta Westfalica, 32457,
Germany
Tel.: (49) 573176700
Web Site: http://www.breco.de
Year Founded: 1967
Rev.: $11,173,140
Emp.: 250
Timing Belts Mfr
N.A.I.C.S.: 326150
Thomas Schlinkmeier (Mng Dir)

**BREDBAND2 I SKANDINAVIEN
AB**
Box 133, 901 04, Umea, Sweden
Tel.: (46) 90149330
Web Site:
https://www.bredband2.com
Year Founded: 1989
Telecommunication Servicesb
N.A.I.C.S.: 517112
Daniel Krook (CEO & Mng Dir)

BREDERODE S.A.
4 Place Winston Churchill, L-1340,
Luxembourg, Luxembourg
Tel.: (352) 26259971
Web Site: https://www.brederode.eu
Year Founded: 1970
BREB—(LUX)
Sales Range: $350-399.9 Million
Emp.: 6
Financial Investment Services
N.A.I.C.S.: 525990
Pierre van der Mersch (Chm & Vice
Chm)

BREEDON GROUP PLC
Pinnacle House Breedon Quarry
Main Street, Breedon on the Hill,
Derby, DE73 8AP, United Kingdom
Tel.: (44) 1332694000
Web Site:
https://www.breedongroup.com
BREE—(LSE)
Rev.: $1,893,698,289
Assets: $2,384,213,886
Liabilities: $970,210,061

Net Worth: $1,414,003,825
Earnings: $134,436,665
Emp.: 4,450
Fiscal Year-end: 12/31/23
Other Concrete Product Manufactur-
ing
N.A.I.C.S.: 327390
Robert Wood (Dir-Fin)

Subsidiaries:

Alba Traffic Management Limited (1)
24 Longman Drive Longman Industrial Es-
tate, Inverness, IV1 1SU, United Kingdom
Tel.: (44) 1463259195
Web Site: https://www.traffic-management-
scotland.co.uk
Emp.: 32
Traffic Management Services
N.A.I.C.S.: 334290

BMC Enterprises, Inc (1)
8112 Maryland Ave, Ste 320, Clayton, MO
63105
Tel.: (314) 962-1234
Web Site: https://bmcenterprises.com
Distr of Ready-Mix Concrete & Mfg
N.A.I.C.S.: 327320
Andy Arnold (CEO & COO)

Subsidiary (Domestic):

Breckenridge Material Company (2)
2833 Breckenridge Indus Ct, Saint Louis,
MO 63144-2811
Tel.: (314) 962-1234
Web Site:
http://www.breckenridgematerial.com
Emp.: 100
Mfr & Distributor of Ready-Mix Concrete &
Masonry Building Materials
N.A.I.C.S.: 327320
Nathan McKean (CEO)

Eureka Materials Co (2)
2275 Highway Ff, Eureka, MO 63025
Tel.: (636) 938-6374
Rev.: $2,400,000
Emp.: 5
Brick, Stone & Related Construction Mate-
rial Merchant Whslr
N.A.I.C.S.: 423320
Bill Kopp (Owner)

Raineri Building Materials, Inc. (2)
6351 Knox Industrial Dr, Saint Louis, MO
63139
Tel.: (314) 781-1573
Web Site: http://www.raineri-materials.com
Sales Range: $10-24.9 Million
Emp.: 60
Ready Mixed Concrete
N.A.I.C.S.: 327320
Dominic Raineri (Pres)

**Blinkbonny Quarry (Borders)
Limited** (1)
Ethiebeaton Quarry, Kingennie Monifieth,
Angus, DD5 3RB, United Kingdom
Tel.: (44) 1573460200
Web Site: http://www.blinkbonnyquarry.co.uk
Ready Mix Concrete Mfr & Distr
N.A.I.C.S.: 327320

**Breedon Aggregates England
Limited** (1)
Breedon Quarry Breedon-on-the-Hill, Derby,
DE73 8AP, United Kingdom (100%)
Tel.: (44) 1332 862254
Web Site:
http://www.breedonaggregates.com
Sales Range: $200-249.9 Million
Emp.: 400
Aggregate Mining & Products Distr
N.A.I.C.S.: 212319

**Breedon Aggregates Scotland
Limited** (1)
Cupar Road, Newburgh, Dundee, KY14
6JJ, United Kingdom (100%)
Tel.: (44) 133 784 1989
Web Site:
http://www.breedonaggregates.com
Sales Range: $200-249.9 Million
Emp.: 400
Aggregate Mining & Products Distr
N.A.I.C.S.: 212319

Breedon Bow Highways Limited (1)

Pinnacle House Breedon Quarry, Breedon
On The Hill, Derby, DE73 8AP, United
Kingdom
Tel.: (44) 1332694400
Web Site:
https://www.breedonbowhighways.com
Road & Highway Construction Services
N.A.I.C.S.: 541990

Clearwell Quarries Limited (1)
Stowe St Briavels, Lydney, GL15 6QW,
Gloucestershire, United Kingdom
Tel.: (44) 1594530208
Limestone Aggregates Distr
N.A.I.C.S.: 424910

**H.V. Bowen & Sons (Quarry)
Ltd.** (1)
Dwyrhiew Mill New Mills, Powys, Newtown,
SY16 3BS, United Kingdom
Tel.: (44) 1686650242
Web Site: https://www.hvbowen.com
Natural Gas Oil Mfr & Distr
N.A.I.C.S.: 325120

RT Mycock & Sons Limited (1)
Unit 1 Hunters Way Harpur Hill Business
Park, Harpur Hill, Buxton, SK17 9JL,
Derbyshire, United Kingdom
Tel.: (44) 1298938516
Web Site: https://rtmycockandsons.com
Ready Mix Concrete Distr
N.A.I.C.S.: 423320

Severn Sands Limited (1)
Lockhead Alexandra Dock, Newport, NP20
2WZ, United Kingdom
Tel.: (44) 1633266689
Web Site: https://www.severnsands.co.uk
Ready Mix Concrete Distr
N.A.I.C.S.: 423320

Thomas Bow Limited (1)
Ashbow Court 4-12 Middleton Street, Not-
tingham, NG7 2AL, United Kingdom
Tel.: (44) 1159244555
Web Site: https://www.thomasbow.com
Civil Engineering Services
N.A.I.C.S.: 541330

UK Stone Direct Limited (1)
The Old Grainstore Bartonfields Centre,
Church, Broughton, DE65 5AP, Derbyshire,
United Kingdom
Tel.: (44) 1332492191
Web Site: https://www.stone-directuk.com
Wall & Floor Tile Distr
N.A.I.C.S.: 423320

**BREEN INTERNATIONAL PTE.
LTD.**
48 Toh Guan Road East 04 117 En-
terprise Hub, Singapore, 608586,
Singapore
Tel.: (65) 6744 3455   SG
Web Site: http://www.breenintl.com
Year Founded: 1995
Sales Range: $25-49.9 Million
Emp.: 7
Marketer, Infrastructure Industries &
Engineered Product of Distr
N.A.I.C.S.: 423840
Cheng Chai Tan (Mng Dir)

Subsidiaries:

Breen International (HK) Co Ltd (1)
Rm 1219 12/F Metro Centre II 21 Lam Hing
Street, Kowloon, China (Hong Kong)
Tel.: (852) 3421 1880
Engineeering Services
N.A.I.C.S.: 541330

Breen International Sdn Bhd (1)
No 24-1 Jalan Puteri 5/1 Bandar Puteri,
47100, Puchong, Selangor Darul Ehsan,
Malaysia
Tel.: (60) 3 8060 3027
Engineered Products Sales & Maintenance
Services
N.A.I.C.S.: 423830
Eric Yong (Gen Mgr)

BREGAL MILESTONE LLP
81 Fulham Road, London, SW3 6RD,
United Kingdom
Tel.: (44) 20 3958 3500   UK

Web Site:
http://www.bregalmilestone.com
Year Founded: 2018
Holding Company
N.A.I.C.S.: 551112
Jan Bruennler (Mng Partner)

BREGAVA D.D.
ul Brace Radica bb, 88300, Capljina,
Bosnia & Herzegovina
Tel.: (387) 36806004
BRGVRK1—(SARE)
Rev.: $441,117
Assets: $6,173,773
Liabilities: $201,221
Net Worth: $5,972,552
Earnings: $12,175
Emp.: 2
Fiscal Year-end: 12/31/20
Beverage & Food Distr
N.A.I.C.S.: 445298

BREM HOLDING BERHAD
3rd Floor Brem House Crystal Crown
Hotel No 12, Lorong Utara A Off
Jalan Utara, 46200, Petaling Jaya,
Selangor Darul Ehsan, Malaysia
Tel.: (60) 379587888
Web Site:
http://www.bremholding.com
BREM—(KLS)
Rev.: $37,851,523
Assets: $211,577,508
Liabilities: $35,117,697
Net Worth: $176,459,811
Earnings: $9,607,445
Fiscal Year-end: 03/31/21
Property Development & Investment
Services
N.A.I.C.S.: 531110
Abu Sujak Mahmud (Chm)

Subsidiaries:

Harmony Property Sdn. Bhd. (1)
G-01 Residensi Harmoni 1 No 2 Persiaran
Prima Pelangi, Bukit Prima Pelangi, 51200,
Kuala Lumpur, Malaysia
Tel.: (60) 362578621
Web Site: http://www.harmoni2.com
Real Estate Services
N.A.I.C.S.: 531390

Naga Istimewa Sdn. Bhd. (1)
Jalan Jambu Jerteh, Jinjang Selatan,
52000, Kuala Lumpur, Malaysia
Tel.: (60) 362504422
Real Estate Services
N.A.I.C.S.: 531390

BREMBO S.P.A.
Parco Scientifico Tecnologico Kilo-
metro Rosso Viale Europa 2, 24040,
Stezzano, BG, Italy
Tel.: (39) 0356052111   IT
Web Site: https://www.brembo.com
Year Founded: 1961
BRE—(ITA)
Rev.: $2,712,738,765
Assets: $3,896,893,547
Liabilities: $2,077,819,749
Net Worth: $1,819,073,798
Earnings: $167,695,292
Emp.: 11,039
Fiscal Year-end: 12/31/20
Automotive Braking Components &
Systems Mfr
N.A.I.C.S.: 336340
Alberto Bombassei (Chm)

Subsidiaries:

AP Racing Ltd. (1)
Wheler Rd Seven Stars Indust Est, Coven-
try, CV3 4LB, West Midlands, United
Kingdom (100%)
Tel.: (44) 2476639595
Web Site: https://www.apracing.com
Sales Range: $50-74.9 Million
Emp.: 120
Motor Vehicle Parts Mfr

N.A.I.C.S.: 336390

Brembo Japan Co. Ltd.   **(1)**
Tel.: (81) 337269199
Sales Range: $25-49.9 Million
Emp.: 25
Motor Vehicle Supplies & New Parts Whslr
N.A.I.C.S.: 423120

Brembo North America, Inc.   **(1)**
47765 Halyard Dr, Plymouth, MI 48170
Tel.: (734) 468-2100
Web Site: http://www.brembo.com
Sales Range: $25-49.9 Million
Emp.: 100
Motor Vehicle Brake System Mfr
N.A.I.C.S.: 336340
Daniel Sandberg *(Pres & CEO)*

Subsidiary (Domestic):

Brembo North America, Inc.   **(2)**
29991 E M 60, Homer, MI 49245-9753
Tel.: (517) 568-4398
Sales Range: $100-124.9 Million
Automotive Brake Components
N.A.I.C.S.: 336340
Jayson Wolf *(Plant Mgr)*

Subsidiary (Non-US):

Brembo Rassini S.A. de C.V.   **(3)**
Platon 100 Parque Indus Kalos, PO Box
KM17, Apodaca, CP 66600, Mexico
Tel.: (52) 8183697800
Web Site: http://www.brembo.com
Sales Range: $50-74.9 Million
Emp.: 110
Brake Rotors & Drums
N.A.I.C.S.: 336340

Brembo SGL Carbon Ceramic Brakes
S.p.A.   **(1)**
Viale Europa 2, Stezzano, 24040, Bergamo,
Italy
Tel.: (39) 0355097111
Web Site: http://www.brembo.it
Motor Vehicle & Motorbike Brake Systems
& Parts Mfr
N.A.I.C.S.: 336340

Brembo Scandinavia A.B.   **(1)**
PO Box 390, 501 13, Boras, Sweden
Tel.: (46) 707481665
Web Site: http://www.brembo.com
Sales Range: $50-74.9 Million
Emp.: 1
Motor Vehicle Supplies & New Parts Whslr
N.A.I.C.S.: 423120

Brembo do Brasil Ltda.   **(1)**
Tel.: (55) 32540990
Business Service Centers
N.A.I.C.S.: 561439

Corporacion Upwards 98 S.A.   **(1)**
Calle La Habana 17 Poligono Industrial
Centrovia, 50198, Zaragoza, Spain
Tel.: (34) 976144721
Web Site: https://www.brembo.com
Sales Range: $50-74.9 Million
Emp.: 90
Motor Vehicle Parts Whslr
N.A.I.C.S.: 423120

J.Juan S.A.U.   **(1)**
Poligono Industrial Cami Ral Miquel Servet
21-23, 08850, Gava, Barcelona, Spain
Tel.: (34) 936335959
Web Site: https://jjuan.com
Emp.: 600
Hydraulic Equipment Mfr
N.A.I.C.S.: 326220

BREMER LAGERHAUS-
GESELLSCHAFT
Prasident Kennedy Platz 1, 28203,
Bremen, 28203, Germany
Tel.: (49) 42139801
Web Site: https://www.blg-
logistics.com
BLH—(MUN)
Rev.: $1,335,726,855
Assets: $1,454,205,222
Liabilities: $1,429,975,275
Net Worth: $24,229,946
Earnings: $2,163,585
Emp.: 9,883

Fiscal Year-end: 12/31/23
Transportation & Logistic Consulting
Services
N.A.I.C.S.: 541614
Frank Dreeke *(Chm-Mgmt Bd)*

Subsidiaries:

BLG AutoTerminal Bremerhaven
GmbH & Co. KG.   **(1)**
Senator-Borttscheller-Strasse 1, 27568,
Bremerhaven, Germany
Tel.: (49) 4714844237
Logistic Services
N.A.I.C.S.: 541614

BLG AutoTerminal Gdansk Sp. z o.
o.   **(1)**
Ul Przemystowa 20, 80-542, Gdansk, Po-
land
Tel.: (48) 583436185
Web Site: https://blg.com.pl
Transportation Services
N.A.I.C.S.: 488510

BLG LOGISTICS GROUP AG & Co.
KG   **(1)**
Prasident-Kennedy-Platz 1, 28203, Bremen,
Germany
Tel.: (49) 42139801
Web Site: https://www.blg-logistics.com
Logistic Services
N.A.I.C.S.: 541614

BLG Logistics Automobile SPb   **(1)**
Gapsalskaya Ul 5 section A, 198035, Saint
Petersburg, Russia
Tel.: (7) 8126802934
Logistic Services
N.A.I.C.S.: 488510
Murat Aboev *(Mng Dir)*

BLG Logistics Inc.   **(1)**
10095 Brose Dr Ste 300, Vance, AL 35490
Tel.: (404) 586-6866
Logistic Services
N.A.I.C.S.: 488510

BLG Logistics Solutions Italia
S.r.l.   **(1)**
Via Vittor Pisani 7, 20124, Milan, Italy
Tel.: (39) 0289058876
Logistic Services
N.A.I.C.S.: 488510
Lamberto Righi *(Mng Dir)*

Hansa Marine Logistics GmbH   **(1)**
Neustadter Hafen West Zum Schuppen 22
/4 Etage, 28197, Bremen, Germany
Tel.: (49) 4215217731
Web Site: https://www.hml-bremen.de
Logistic Services
N.A.I.C.S.: 541614

BREMER STAHL SERVICE
GMBH
Ludwig von Kapff-Str 5, 28309,
Bremen, Germany
Tel.: (49) 421 59851 0
Web Site:
http://www.bremerstahlservice.de
Plate Work Mfr
N.A.I.C.S.: 331315
Bill Talayman *(Mng Dir)*

BREMWORTH LIMITED
7 Grayson Avenue, PO Box 97 040,
Parnell, 2104, Auckland, New Zea-
land
Tel.: (64) 92776000   **NZ**
Web Site: https://bremworth.co.nz
Year Founded: 1984
BRW—(NZX)
Rev.: $53,641,746
Assets: $54,507,177
Liabilities: $24,469,498
Net Worth: $30,037,679
Earnings: $6,421,053
Emp.: 413
Fiscal Year-end: 06/30/23
Carpet Mfr & Wool Processing Ser-
vices
N.A.I.C.S.: 314110
Victor Tan *(CFO & Sec)*

Subsidiaries:

Bremworth Carpets and Rugs
Limited   **(1)**
7 Grayson Ave, Papatoetoe, Auckland, New
Zealand
Tel.: (64) 800808303
Web Site: https://bremworth.co.nz
Carpet & Rugs Mfr & Distr
N.A.I.C.S.: 314110

Cavalier Bremworth Limited   **(1)**
7 Grayson Ave, PO Box 97040, Auckland,
2241, New Zealand   **(100%)**
Tel.: (64) 92776000
Web Site: http://www.cavbrem.co.nz
Sales Range: $750-799.9 Million
Carpet & Rug Mills
N.A.I.C.S.: 314110
Colin McKenzie *(Mng Dir)*

Subsidiary (Non-US):

Cavalier Bremworth (Australia)
Limited   **(2)**
165-169 Gibbes Street, Chatswood, 2067,
NSW, Australia
Tel.: (61) 299322600
Emp.: 40
Holding Company; Carpet & Rug Mills
N.A.I.C.S.: 551112
Cathy Howitd *(Gen Mgr)*

Subsidiary (Domestic):

Cavalier Bremworth Pty. Limited   **(3)**
Unit 1 165-169 Gibbes Street, 2067, Chats-
wood, Australia
Tel.: (61) 299322600
Sales Range: $25-49.9 Million
Emp.: 40
Carpet & Rug Mills
N.A.I.C.S.: 314110
Garyol Olchoway *(CFO)*

Cavalier Spinners Limited   **(1)**
Leamington St, 4540, Wanganui, New
Zealand   **(100%)**
Tel.: (64) 63445116
Web Site: http://www.cavalierbrem.co.nz
Sales Range: $25-49.9 Million
Emp.: 180
Yarn Spinning Mills
N.A.I.C.S.: 313110
Wayne Chung *(Mng Dir)*

Elco Direct Limited   **(1)**
75 Victoria Road, PO Box 665, Cambridge,
3450, New Zealand
Tel.: (64) 78275084
Web Site: https://www.elcodirect.co.nz
Sales Range: $50-74.9 Million
Emp.: 10
Wool Products Distr
N.A.I.C.S.: 424590
Shane Eades *(Gen Mgr)*

Kimberley Carpets Pty Limited   **(1)**
Unit 1 165 169 Lower Gibbes Street, Chats-
wood, 2067, NSW, Australia
Tel.: (61) 299322660
Web Site:
http://www.kimberleycarpets.com.au
Sales Range: $25-49.9 Million
Emp.: 50
Carpet Mfr
N.A.I.C.S.: 314110

Knightsbridge Carpets Limited   **(1)**
Unit 2 39 Apolloo Dr, Mairangi Bay, Auck-
land, 0745, New Zealand   **(100%)**
Tel.: (64) 6494780123
Web Site:
http://www.knightsbridgecarpets.co.nz
Sales Range: $50-74.9 Million
Emp.: 6
Home Furnishing Whslr
N.A.I.C.S.: 423220

Norman Ellison Carpets Limited   **(1)**
373 Neilson Street Onehunga, Onehunga,
Auckland, New Zealand
Tel.: (64) 96229616
Web Site: http://www.normanellison.co.nz
Sales Range: $75-99.9 Million
Emp.: 260
Wool Carpet Mfr
N.A.I.C.S.: 314110

Subsidiary (Non-US):

Norman Ellison Carpets Pty
Limited   **(2)**

13 Gassman Dr, Yatala, Gold Coast, QLD,
Australia
Tel.: (61) 733820777
Web Site:
http://www.normanellisoncarpets.com
Sales Range: $25-49.9 Million
Emp.: 15
Woolen Carpets Mfr
N.A.I.C.S.: 314110
Mark Gannon *(Mgr-Natl Contracts)*

Ontera Modular Carpets Pty.
Limited   **(1)**
7 Grayson Avenue, Papatoetoe, 1730, New
Zealand
Tel.: (64) 92776000
Web Site: http://www.cavalier.co.nz
Sales Range: $100-124.9 Million
Emp.: 300
Carpet & Rug Mills
N.A.I.C.S.: 314110
Colin McKenzie *(Mng Dir)*

BRENMILLER ENERGY LTD.
13 Amal St 4th Floor Park Afek, Rosh
Ha'Ayin, 4809249, Israel
Tel.: (972) 776935140
Web Site: https://www.bren-
energy.com
Year Founded: 2012
BNRG—(NASDAQ)
Rev.: $1,520,000
Assets: $12,383,000
Liabilities: $9,719,000
Net Worth: $2,664,000
Earnings: ($11,067,000)
Emp.: 60
Fiscal Year-end: 12/31/22
Renewable Energy Services
N.A.I.C.S.: 221116
Avi Brenmiller *(Chm & CEO)*

BRENNAN IT PTY. LIMITED
Level 14 45 Clarence Street, Sydney,
2000, NSW, Australia
Tel.: (61) 282359511
Web Site:
http://www.brennanit.com.au
Year Founded: 1997
Emp.: 100
Information Technology Services
N.A.I.C.S.: 541512
Stephen Sims *(CEO)*

Subsidiaries:

MOQ Ltd.   **(1)**
G01 3-5 West Street, North Sydney, 2060,
NSW, Australia
Tel.: (61) 280065790
Web Site: http://www.moq.com.au
Rev.: $54,502,238
Assets: $25,701,510
Liabilities: $16,652,590
Net Worth: $9,048,921
Earnings: ($774,348)
Fiscal Year-end: 06/30/2021
Software Development Services
N.A.I.C.S.: 541511
Brad Cohen *(CEO)*

Subsidiary (Domestic):

MOQdigital Pty Ltd   **(2)**
Level 2 200 Creek St, Brisbane, 4000,
QLD, Australia
Tel.: (61) 731189592
Web Site: http://www.moqdigital.com
Information Technology Services
N.A.I.C.S.: 541511
Joe D'Addio *(CEO)*

Wardy IT Solutions Pty Limited   **(2)**
164 Wharf Street, Spring Hill, 4000, QLD,
Australia
Tel.: (61) 730545300
Web Site: http://www.wardyit.com
Information Technology Services
N.A.I.C.S.: 541511

BRENNER MILLS (PTY) LTD.
Building 7 Atterbury Estate 19 Frikkie
De Beer Straat, Menlyn, Pretoria,
South Africa

Brenner Mills (Pty) Ltd—(Continued)

Tel.: (27) 124364700
Web Site: http://www.brenmill.co.za
Year Founded: 1938
Sales Range: $150-199.9 Million
Emp.: 550
Maize Products & Animal Feeds Mfr
N.A.I.C.S.: 311119
Steven Brenner (Mng Dir)

Subsidiaries:

Brenner Mills (Pty) Ltd. - Brennco
Feed Mills (1)
41 Kruger Street, Louis Trichardt, 920,
South Africa
Tel.: (27) 15 516 0133
Animal Feed Mfr
N.A.I.C.S.: 311119

Brenner Mills (Pty) Ltd. - Tswana
Mill (1)
1 Station Street, Hammanskraal, 0400,
South Africa
Tel.: (27) 12 711 8910
Animal Feed Mfr
N.A.I.C.S.: 311119

Brenner Mills (Pty) Ltd. - Warmbaths
Mill (1)
Paul Sauer Street, Bela-Bela, 0480, South
Africa
Tel.: (27) 14 736 2316
Animal Feed Mfr
N.A.I.C.S.: 311119

Brenner Mills (Pty) Ltd. - Zoutpans-
berg Mill (1)
53 Grobler Street, Louis Trichardt, 920,
South Africa
Tel.: (27) 15 516 0154
Animal Feed Mfr
N.A.I.C.S.: 311119

BRENNTAG SE

Messeallee 11, 45131, Essen, Ger-
many
Tel.: (49) 20164960 De
Year Founded: 1874
BNTGY—(OTCIQ)
Rev.: $17,665,161,800
Assets: $12,522,520,920
Liabilities: $7,615,333,648
Net Worth: $4,907,187,272
Earnings: $566,709,936
Emp.: 17,236
Fiscal Year-end: 12/31/21
Industrial & Specialty Chemical Distr
N.A.I.C.S.: 335991
Hans Nijhuis (VP-Corp Internal Audit)

Subsidiaries:

Acu Pharma und Chemie GmbH (1)
Am Tiefen Graben 6, 99510, Apolda, Ger-
many
Tel.: (49) 36 445 0580
Web Site: https://www.acu-pharma.com
Emp.: 32
Milling & Micronization Product Mfr
N.A.I.C.S.: 332721
Kristin Rudolph (Acct Mgr)

Akashi SDN. BHD. (1)
Pt 55 64 & 65 Jalan Hulu Tinggi 26/6 Sec-
tion 26, Shah Alam, 40400, Selangor, Ma-
laysia
Tel.: (60) 351918811
Chemical Products Distr
N.A.I.C.S.: 424690

Alliance Chimie Algerie SPA (1)
Tel.: (213) 770915005
Web Site: https://www.brenntag.com
Chemical Products Distr
N.A.I.C.S.: 424690

Alliance Tunisie S.A.R.L. (1)
21 Rue 8602 Zone Industriel Charguia I,
Ariana, 2035, Tunisia
Tel.: (216) 71771678
Chemical Products Distr
N.A.I.C.S.: 424690

Alphamin S.A. (1)
Avenue Pasteur 15, 1300, Wavre, Belgium

Tel.: (32) 1 023 3070
Web Site: https://www.alphamin.com
Adhesive & Sealant Distr
N.A.I.C.S.: 424690

B&M Oil Company, Inc. (1)
5731 S 49th W Ave, Tulsa, OK 74107-8818
Tel.: (918) 445-0725
Web Site: http://www.bmoil.com
Oil & Gasoline Products Distr
N.A.I.C.S.: 424710
Bobby Lee (Mgr-Div)

BRENNTAG (Holding) B.V. (1)
Donker Duyvisweg 44, 3316BM, Dordrecht,
Netherlands
Tel.: (31) 786544980
Web Site: http://www.brenntag.nl
Sales Range: $50-74.9 Million
Emp.: 10
Investment Management Service
N.A.I.C.S.: 523999

BRENNTAG HOLDING S.p.A. (1)
Palazzo A13 Str 6, Assago, 20090, Italy
Tel.: (39) 02483330
Web Site: http://www.brenntag.it
Emp.: 100
Investment Management Service
N.A.I.C.S.: 523999

BRENNTAG Hrvatska d.o.o. (1)
Tel.: (385) 12405710
Web Site: https://www.brenntag.com
Emp.: 25
Chemical Products Distr
N.A.I.C.S.: 424690

BRENNTAG International Chemicals
GmbH (1)
Stinnes-Platz 1, Mulheim an der Ruhr,
45472, Germany
Tel.: (49) 20878280
Web Site: https://www.brenntag.com
Emp.: 6
Chemical Products Distr
N.A.I.C.S.: 424690

BRENNTAG Nordic AS (1)
Kalnesveien 1, Borgenhaugen, 01712,
Gralum, Norway
Tel.: (47) 69102500
Web Site: https://www.brenntag.com
Sales Range: $25-49.9 Million
Emp.: 17
Chemical Products Distr
N.A.I.C.S.: 424690

BRENNTAG Nordic OY (1)
Ayritie 16, 01510, Vantaa, Finland
Tel.: (358) 95495640
Web Site: https://www.brenntag.com
Sales Range: $25-49.9 Million
Emp.: 2
Chemical Products Distr
N.A.I.C.S.: 424690
Minna Helkioe (Mgr-Environment & Quality)

BRENNTAG PORTUGAL-
PRODUTOS QUIMICOS Lda. (1)
Estrada de Albarraque Linho, Sintra, 2710-
297, Portugal
Tel.: (351) 219248800
Web Site: https://www.brenntag.es
Specialty Chemicals Distr
N.A.I.C.S.: 424690

BRENNTAG Polska Sp. z o.o. (1)
ul J Bema 21, 47-224, Kedzierzyn-Kozle,
Poland
Tel.: (48) 774721500
Web Site: https://www.brenntag.com
Specialty Chemicals Distr
N.A.I.C.S.: 424690
Zenon Maslona (Pres & Member-Mgmt Bd)

BRENNTAG Quimica S.A. (1)
C/ Torre de los Herberos 10 Pl La Isla,
41703, Dos Hermanas, Sevilla, Spain
Tel.: (34) 954919400
Web Site: https://www.brenntag.com
Sales Range: $75-99.9 Million
Emp.: 145
Industrial & Specialty Chemicals Distr
N.A.I.C.S.: 424690

BRENNTAG S.p.A. (1)
Milanofiori Strada 6 - Pal A/13, Assago,
I-20057, Milan, Italy
Tel.: (39) 02483330
Web Site: https://www.brenntag.com

Chemical Products Distr
N.A.I.C.S.: 424690
BRENNTAG SLOVAKIA s.r.o. (1)
Glejovka 15, 902 03, Pezinok, Slovakia
Tel.: (421) 336485111
Web Site: https://www.brenntag.com
Chemical Products Distr
N.A.I.C.S.: 424690
Marek Mikus (Co-CEO)

Bcd Polymers Sp. z o.o. (1)
Ul Obornicka 39, Suchy Las, 62-002,
Poznan, Poland
Tel.: (48) 618956580
Web Site: https://www.bcd-polymers.pl
Plastic Product Mfr & Distr
N.A.I.C.S.: 326199

Brenntag (Shanghai) Chemical Trad-
ing Co., Limited (1)
45F B M Intercontinental Business Center
100 Yutong Road, Pudong New District,
Shanghai, 200070, China
Tel.: (86) 21 5047 2500
Web Site: http://www.brenntagchina.cn
Chemical Products Distr
N.A.I.C.S.: 424690

Brenntag (Shanghai) Enterprise Man-
agement Co., Ltd. (1)
45F B M Intercontinental Business Center
100 Yutong Road, Yutong Road Jingan Dis-
trict, Shanghai, 200070, China
Tel.: (86) 2162632720
Web Site: https://www.brenntag.com
Chemical & Ingredient Distr
N.A.I.C.S.: 424690
Evelyn Shao (Mgr-Supply Chain)

Brenntag (Taiwan) Co. Ltd. (1)
4F-3 No 2 Sec 3 Minsheng E Road, Zhong-
shan Dist, Taipei, 104511, Taiwan
Tel.: (886) 225166000
Web Site: https://www.brenntag.com
Distr of Industrial & Specialty Chemicals
N.A.I.C.S.: 424690

Brenntag (Thailand) Co. Ltd. (1)
1168/98-100 Lumpini Tower 33rd Floor
Rama IV Road Thungmahamek, Bangkok,
Thailand
Tel.: (66) 2 689 5999
Emp.: 250
Industrial Chemical Product Distr
N.A.I.C.S.: 424690
Flemming Soederquist (Mng Dir)

Brenntag (UK) Ltd. (1)
Pensnett House, Kingswinford, DY6 7PP, W
Midlands, United Kingdom
Tel.: (44) 1384400222
Web Site: http://www.brenntag.co.uk
Sales Range: $50-74.9 Million
Emp.: 30
Distr of Industrial & Specialty Chemicals
N.A.I.C.S.: 424690

Brenntag Amsterdam B.V. (1)
Donker Duyvisweg 44, 3316, Dordrecht,
Netherlands
Tel.: (31) 786544944
Chemical Distr
N.A.I.C.S.: 424690

Brenntag Australia Pty. Ltd. (1)
Tel.: (61) 395598333
Web Site: https://www.brenntag.com
Logistics Consulting Servies
N.A.I.C.S.: 541614

Brenntag Austria GmbH (1)
Linke Wienzeile 152, 1060, Vienna, Austria
Tel.: (43) 599950
Chemical Products Distr
N.A.I.C.S.: 424690

Brenntag Austria Holding GmbH (1)
Tel.: (43) 599950
Web Site: https://www.brenntag-cee.com
Emp.: 30
Investment Management Service
N.A.I.C.S.: 523999

Brenntag Bangladesh Ltd. (1)
Latif Tower 6th & 7th Floors 47-Kawran Ba-
zar, Tejgaon, Dhaka, 1215, Bangladesh
Tel.: (880) 2550125313
Web Site: https://www.brenntag.com
Emp.: 50
Chemical Products Distr

N.A.I.C.S.: 424690
Azmal Hossain (Country Mgr)

Brenntag Beteiligungs GmbH (1)
Tel.: (49) 20164960
Chemical Products Distr
N.A.I.C.S.: 424690

Brenntag Bulgaria Ltd (1)
Sitnyakovo blvd 48, 1505, Sofia, Bulgaria
Tel.: (359) 29265600
Web Site: https://www.brenntag.com
Sales Range: $25-49.9 Million
Emp.: 35
Specialty & Industrial Chemical Mfr & Distr
N.A.I.C.S.: 325998

Brenntag CEE GmbH (1)
Linke Wienzeile 152, Vienna, 1060, Austria
Tel.: (43) 5 9995 0
Web Site: http://www.brenntag-cee.com
Chemical Products Distr
N.A.I.C.S.: 424690

Brenntag CR s.r.o. (1)
Mezi uvozy 1850/1, 193 00, Prague, 9,
Czech Republic
Tel.: (420) 283096111
Web Site: https://www.brenntag.com
Chemical & Ingredient Distr
N.A.I.C.S.: 424690

Brenntag Canada Inc. (1)
43 Jutland Road, Toronto, M8Z 2G6, ON,
Canada
Tel.: (416) 259-8231
Web Site: https://www.brenntag.com
Sales Range: $25-49.9 Million
Emp.: 70
Specialty & Industrial Chemical Mfr & Distr
N.A.I.C.S.: 325998

Brenntag Chemical Distribution (Ire-
land) Ltd. (1)
Unit 405 Greenogue Business Pk
Rathcoole 24, Dublin, Ireland
Tel.: (353) 1 4013500
Web Site: http://www.brenntag.ie
Sales Range: $25-49.9 Million
Emp.: 17
Chemical Products Distr
N.A.I.C.S.: 424690

Brenntag Chemicals Distribution (Ire-
land) Limited (1)
Unit 405 Greenogue Business Park, Dublin,
24, Ireland
Tel.: (353) 14013500
Chemical Products Distr
N.A.I.C.S.: 424690

Brenntag Chemicals Malaysia Sdn.
Bhd. (1)
Lot 14979 Batu 5 Jalan Nenas Jalan Kg
Jawa, 42450, Klang, Selangor Darul Ehsan,
Malaysia
Tel.: (60) 351615918
Web Site: https://www.brenntag.com
Chemical Products Distr
N.A.I.C.S.: 424690

Brenntag Chemicals Nigeria
Limited (1)
3 Block G Oshodi Industrial Layout, Lagos,
Nigeria
Tel.: (234) 9139348896
Web Site: https://www.brenntag.com
Chemical & Ingredient Distr
N.A.I.C.S.: 424690
Pieter De Koninck (Gen Mgr)

Brenntag Chile Comercial e Industrial
Ltda. (1)
Camino Lo Sierra 02966, 8060004, San-
tiago, Chile
Tel.: (56) 24402400
Web Site: https://www.brenntag.com
Emp.: 80
Chemical Products Distr
N.A.I.C.S.: 424690

Brenntag Colours Ltd. (1)
High Level Way, Halifax, HX1 4PN, United
Kingdom
Tel.: (44) 1422358431
Web Site: https://www.brenntag.co.uk
Sales Range: $25-49.9 Million
Emp.: 4
Chemical Products Distr
N.A.I.C.S.: 424690

Brenntag Cooperatief U.A. (1)
Donker Duyvisweg 44, 3316BM, Dordrecht, Netherlands
Tel.: (31) 786544944
Emp.: 75
Specialty Chemicals Distr
N.A.I.C.S.: 424690

Brenntag Dutch C.V. (1)
Industrieweg 1, Loosdrecht, 1231 KG, Netherlands
Tel.: (31) 355889300
Web Site: https://www.brenntag.nl
Sales Range: $50-74.9 Million
Emp.: 7
Chemical Products Distr
N.A.I.C.S.: 424690

Brenntag El Salvador S.A. de C.V. (1)
Boulevard del Ejercito Nacional Km 7 5, PO Box 2373, Complejo Industrial Regina Nave 9, Soyapango, San Salvador, El Salvador
Tel.: (503) 2 251 5600
Web Site: https://www.brenntag.com
Chemical Products Distr
N.A.I.C.S.: 424690

Brenntag European Services GmbH & Co. KG (1)
Bahnhofstrasse 16, 15806, Zossen, Germany
Tel.: (49) 337796910
Chemical & Ingredient Distr
N.A.I.C.S.: 424690

Brenntag Export SARL (1)
Boulevard de l Europe 21, 13741, Cedex, France
Tel.: (33) 442462242
Chemical & Ingredient Distr
N.A.I.C.S.: 424690

Brenntag Foreign Holding GmbH (1)
Stinnes-Platz 1, Mulheim an der Ruhr, 45472, Germany
Tel.: (49) 20164960
Investment Management Service
N.A.I.C.S.: 523999

Brenntag France Holding SAS (1)
Tel.: (33) 472221500
Investment Management Service
N.A.I.C.S.: 523999

Brenntag Germany Holding GmbH (1)
Tel.: (49) 20878280
Investment Management Service
N.A.I.C.S.: 523999

Branch (Domestic):

Brenntag GmbH (2)
Am Nordseekai 22, 73207, Plochingen, Germany
Tel.: (49) 715370150
Web Site: https://www.brenntag.com
Sales Range: $150-199.9 Million
Emp.: 1,100
Distr of Industrial & Specialty Chemicals
N.A.I.C.S.: 424690

Brenntag GmbH (2)
Messeallee 11, 45131, Essen, Germany
Tel.: (49) 2 016 4960
Web Site: https://www.brenntag.com
Emp.: 7,500
Chemical Preparations
N.A.I.C.S.: 325998

Brenntag GmbH (2)
Messeallee 11, 45131, Essen, Germany
Tel.: (49) 2 016 4960
Web Site: https://www.brenntag.com
Emp.: 1,200
Specialty Chemicals Distr
N.A.I.C.S.: 424690
Cosimo Alemanno *(Mng Dir)*

Brenntag GmbH (2)
Am Rohrenwerk 46, 47259, Duisburg, Germany
Tel.: (49) 20375820
Web Site: https://www.brenntag.com
Sales Range: $75-99.9 Million
Emp.: 150
Distr of Industrial & Specialty Chemicals
N.A.I.C.S.: 424690

Brenntag Holding GmbH (1)

Messeallee 11, 45131, Essen, Germany
Tel.: (49) 20164960
Chemical & Ingredient Distr
N.A.I.C.S.: 424690

Brenntag Hong Kong Limited (1)
Unit A 18th Floor Manulife Tower 169 Electric Road, North Point, China (Hong Kong)
Tel.: (852) 3752 8010
Chemical Products Distr
N.A.I.C.S.: 424690

Brenntag Hungaria Kft. (1)
Banyaleg u 45, 1225, Budapest, Hungary
Tel.: (36) 18895100
Web Site: https://www.brenntag.com
Chemical Products Distr
N.A.I.C.S.: 424690

Brenntag India Private Ltd. (1)
Ackruti Centre Point 301 3rd Floor MIDC Central Road, Andheri East, Mumbai, 400 093, India
Tel.: (91) 22 424 82 100
Sales Range: $25-49.9 Million
Emp.: 4
Chemical Products Distr
N.A.I.C.S.: 424690
Sanjay Gupta *(Dir-South Asia)*

Brenntag Ingredients (India) Private Limited (1)
6th Floor Minarch Tower Plot No 4 Sector 44, Andheri East, Gurgaon, 122002, Haryana, India
Tel.: (91) 1244525600
Web Site: https://www.brenntag.com
Sales Range: $25-49.9 Million
Emp.: 6
Specialty Chemicals Mfr
N.A.I.C.S.: 325998

Brenntag Ingredients (Thailand) Public Company Ltd. (1)
(100%)
Tel.: (66) 26895999
Web Site: https://www.brenntag.com
Sales Range: $75-99.9 Million
Emp.: 155
Chemical Distr
N.A.I.C.S.: 424690

Brenntag Ingredients Inc. (1)
16th Floor Asian Star Building 2402-2404 Asean Drive, Filinvest City Alabang, Muntinlupa, 1781, Philippines
Tel.: (63) 288129385
Web Site: https://www.brenntag.com
Sales Range: $50-74.9 Million
Emp.: 88
Chemical Products & Ingredients Distr
N.A.I.C.S.: 424690

Brenntag Inorganic Chemicals (Thetford) Ltd. (1)
Albion House Rawdon Park Green Lane, Yeadon, Leeds, LS19 7XX, West Yorkshire, United Kingdom
Tel.: (44) 1842 753662
Chemical Products Mfr & Distr
N.A.I.C.S.: 325180

Brenntag Kenya Limited (1)
Industrial Area Kampala Road GPO, PO Box 18032-00500, Nairobi, Kenya
Tel.: (254) 202458740
Emp.: 17,500
Chemical Product Mfr & Distr
N.A.I.C.S.: 325180

Brenntag Kimya Ticaret Limited Sirketi (1)
Kavacik Mh Ekinciler Cd Muhtar Sk No 1, Beykoz, 34810, Istanbul, Turkiye
Tel.: (90) 2163313966
Web Site: https://www.brenntag.com
Chemical Products Distr
N.A.I.C.S.: 424690

Brenntag Korea Co., Ltd. (1)
24-4 Chanumul-Ro, Gwacheon, 13840, Gyeonggi-do, Korea (South)
Tel.: (82) 25097900
Web Site: https://www.brenntag.com
Chemical & Ingredient Distr
N.A.I.C.S.: 424690

Brenntag Lanka (Private) Limited (1)
Shop No 527 Jana Jaya City Mall, Sri Jayawardenepura Kotte, Colombo, Sri Lanka

Tel.: (94) 117559944
Web Site: https://www.brenntag.com
Chemical & Ingredient Distr
N.A.I.C.S.: 424690

Brenntag Latin America, Inc. (1)
1500 Post Oak Blvd Ste 1300, Houston, TX 77056
Tel.: (713) 880-5400
Sales Range: $25-49.9 Million
Emp.: 60
Specialty & Industrial Chemical Distr
N.A.I.C.S.: 325998

Subsidiary (Non-US):

Brenntag Argentina S.A. (2)
Tronador 4890 Piso 6, C1430DNN, Buenos Aires, Argentina
Tel.: (54) 1148512900
Web Site: https://www.brenntag.com
Specialty & Industrial Chemical Distr
N.A.I.C.S.: 325998

Brenntag Bolivia SRL (2)
Km 10 1/2 Carretera al Norte de la Sierra, Santa Cruz, Bolivia
Tel.: (591) 33853121
Web Site: https://www.brenntag.com
Sales Range: $25-49.9 Million
Emp.: 15
Specialty & Industrial Chemical Mfr
N.A.I.C.S.: 325998

Brenntag Brasil Ltda. (2)
Rua Alexandre Dumas 1 658 9 andar, Chacara Sto Antonio, 04717 004, Sao Paulo, Brazil
Tel.: (55) 1155452100
Web Site: http://www.brenntag.com
Sales Range: $50-74.9 Million
Specialty & Industrial Chemical Distr
N.A.I.C.S.: 325998

Brenntag Caribe S.A. (2)
Ave Isabel Aguilar 209, Herrera, Santo Domingo, Dominican Republic
Tel.: (809) 5318060
Web Site: https://www.brenntag.com
Sales Range: $25-49.9 Million
Emp.: 50
Specialty & Industrial Chemical Mfr
N.A.I.C.S.: 325998

Brenntag Chile Ltda. (2)
Camino Lo Sierra 02966, Santiago, Chile
Tel.: (56) 2 440 2400
Web Site: http://www.brenntagla.com
Sales Range: $25-49.9 Million
Specialty & Industrial Chemical Distr
N.A.I.C.S.: 325998

Brenntag Colombia S. A. (2)
Carrera 15 No 93a-84 oficina 606 T, Mosquera, Bogota, Colombia
Tel.: (57) 16513600
Web Site: https://www.brenntag.com
Specialty & Industrial Chemical Distr
N.A.I.C.S.: 325998

Brenntag Ecuador S. A. (2)
Carretera a Daule Km 9 5, Guayaquil, Ecuador
Tel.: (593) 46023200
Sales Range: $50-74.9 Million
Specialty & Industrial Chemical Distr
N.A.I.C.S.: 325998

Brenntag Guatemala S. A. (2)
23 Avenida 40 19 Zona 12, Guatemala, Guatemala
Tel.: (502) 24237777
Web Site: https://www.brenntag.com
Sales Range: $25-49.9 Million
Emp.: 52
Specialty & Industrial Chemical Distr
N.A.I.C.S.: 325998

Brenntag Mexico, S. A. de C. V. (2)
Av Tejocotes Manzana 4 Lote 8 Bodega G, Parque Industrial San Martin Obispo, 9810, Cuautitlan Izcalli, Mexico
Tel.: (52) 5558996400
Web Site: https://www.brenntag.com
Specialty & Industrial Chemical Distr
N.A.I.C.S.: 325998

Brenntag Nicaragua, S.A. (2)
Km 10 a 1 Carr Nueva Leon Cd Sandino, Frente a Unilever, Managua, A P 4074, Nicaragua

Tel.: (505) 504538
Web Site: https://www.brenntag.com
Specialty & Industrial Chemical Distr
N.A.I.C.S.: 325998

Brenntag Peru A. C. (2)
Tel.: (51) 13134800
Specialty & Industrial Chemical Distr
N.A.I.C.S.: 325998

Brenntag Ljubljana d.o.o. (1)
Letaliska cesta 35, 1000, Ljubljana, Slovenia
Tel.: (386) 15483495
Web Site: https://www.brenntag.com
Emp.: 15
Chemical Products Distr
N.A.I.C.S.: 424690

Brenntag Lubricants (Thailand) Co., Ltd. (1)
10 On-Nuch Soi 88/3 On-Nuch Road, Prawet, Bangkok, 10250, Thailand
Tel.: (66) 27278000
Chemical Product Mfr & Distr
N.A.I.C.S.: 325180

Brenntag Lubricants, LLC (1)
7010 Mykawa Rd, Houston, TX 77033
Tel.: (713) 844-7788
Chemical Distr
N.A.I.C.S.: 424690

Brenntag Maghreb SAS (1)
21 Boulevard de l Europe, 13741, Vitrolles, Cedex, France
Tel.: (33) 442462206
Chemical & Ingredient Distr
N.A.I.C.S.: 424690

Brenntag Malaysia Sdn. Bhd. (1)
Lot Pt 55 64 & 65 Jalan Hulu Tinggi 26/6 Seksyen 26, 40400, Shah Alam, Selangor Darul Ehsan, Malaysia
Tel.: (60) 351012599
Web Site: https://www.brenntag.com
Chemical Products Distr
N.A.I.C.S.: 424690

Brenntag Maroc S.A.R.L. (1)
Z l de Bouskoura Lot 3 Km 18 600 Rte Ouled Salah, Bouskoura, 20180, Casablanca, Morocco
Tel.: (212) 522593460
Web Site: https://www.brenntag.com
Chemical & Ingredient Distr
N.A.I.C.S.: 424690
Mohamed Berrada *(Product Mgr)*

Brenntag N.V. (1)
Nijverheidslaan 38, B-8540, Deerlijk, Belgium
Tel.: (32) 56776944
Web Site: https://www.brenntag.com
Sales Range: $50-74.9 Million
Emp.: 200
Distr of Industrial & Specialty Chemicals
N.A.I.C.S.: 424690

Brenntag Nederland B.V. (1)
Donker Duyvisweg 44, 3316 BM, Dordrecht, Netherlands
Tel.: (31) 786544944
Web Site: https://www.brenntag.com
Sales Range: $150-199.9 Million
Emp.: 300
Distr of Specialty Chemicals
N.A.I.C.S.: 424690

Brenntag New Zealand Limited (1)
Level 2 Building C 602 Great South Road, Ellerslie, Auckland, 1051, New Zealand
Tel.: (64) 92750745
Web Site: https://www.brenntag.com
Chemical & Ingredient Distr
N.A.I.C.S.: 424690
Carmen Chapman *(Acct Mgr)*

Brenntag Nordic A/S (1)
Borupvang 5B, 2750, Ballerup, Denmark
Tel.: (45) 43292800
Web Site: https://www.brenntag.com
Sales Range: $50-74.9 Million
Emp.: 55
Chemical Products Distr
N.A.I.C.S.: 424690
Jens Henrik Meng *(Dir-Sls)*

Brenntag Nordic AB (1)
Hyllie Stationstorg 31, Box 50 121, Hyllie Boulevard 34, 215 32, Malmo, Sweden

BRENNTAG SE—(Continued)

Tel.: (46) 40287300
Web Site: https://www.brenntag.com
Sales Range: $50-74.9 Million
Emp.: 6
Specialty Chemicals Distr
N.A.I.C.S.: 424690

Brenntag North America, Inc. (1)
5083 Pottsville Pike, Reading, PA 19605
Tel.: (610) 926-6100
Web Site: https://www.brenntag.com
Industrial & Specialty Chemical Mfr & Distr
N.A.I.C.S.: 424690

Subsidiary (Domestic):

Altivia Corporation (2)
1100 Louisiana St Ste 4800, Houston, TX 77002
Tel.: (713) 658-9000
Web Site: https://www.altivia.com
Sales Range: $75-99.9 Million
Emp.: 150
Cyclic Crudes & Intermediates
N.A.I.C.S.: 325199
J. Michael Jusbasche (CEO)

Unit (Domestic):

ALTIVIA Petrochemicals, LLC (3)
1019 Haverhill Ohio Furnace Rd, Hamilton, OH 45636
Tel.: (740) 533-5252
Phenol, Acetone & Other Related Raw Products Whslr
N.A.I.C.S.: 325199

Affiliate (Domestic):

ALTIVIA Oxide Chemicals, LLC (4)
211 E 7th St Ste 620, Austin, TX 78701-3218
Tel.: (713) 658-9000
Organic Chemical Mfr
N.A.I.C.S.: 325199

Subsidiary (Domestic):

KMCO, LLC (5)
363 N Sam Houston E Ste 1040, Houston, TX 77060
Tel.: (281) 328-3501
Web Site: http://www.kmcoinc.com
Sales Range: $25-49.9 Million
Emp.: 115
Specialty Chemicals Mfr & Chemical Processing Services
N.A.I.C.S.: 325998
John C. Foley (CEO)

Subsidiary (Domestic):

KMTEX, LLC (6)
2450 S Gulfway Dr, Port Arthur, TX 77641 (100%)
Tel.: (409) 985-4200
Web Site: http://www.kmtex.com
Custom Chemical Distillation Services
N.A.I.C.S.: 325998
David Spacek (Plant Mgr)

Subsidiary (Domestic):

Brenntag Great Lakes, LLC (2)
4420 N Harley Davidson Ave Ste A, Wauwatosa, WI 53225
Tel.: (262) 252-3550
Web Site:
https://www.brenntagnorthamerica.com
Sales Range: $25-49.9 Million
Emp.: 100
Industrial & Specialty Chemical Mfr
N.A.I.C.S.: 325998

Brenntag Mid-South, Inc. (2)
1405 Hwy 136 W, Henderson, KY 42420
Tel.: (270) 827-4509
Sales Range: $100-124.9 Million
Emp.: 300
Specialty & Industrial Chemical Distr
N.A.I.C.S.: 325199
Anders Skipp (Pres)

Brenntag Northeast, Inc. (2)
81 W Huller Ln, Reading, PA 19605
Tel.: (610) 926-4151
Web Site:
https://www.brenntagnortheast.com
Emp.: 200

Specialty & Industrial Chemical Mfr & Distr
N.A.I.C.S.: 325998
Steve Lamb (VP-Ops)

Brenntag Pacific, Inc. (2)
10747 Patterson Pl, Santa Fe Springs, CA 90670-4043
Tel.: (562) 903-9626
Web Site:
https://www.brenntagnorthamerica.com
Sales Range: $25-49.9 Million
Emp.: 80
Industrial Chemical Distr
N.A.I.C.S.: 424690

Branch (Domestic):

Brenntag Pacific, Inc. - Fairbanks (3)
4199 Lathrop St, Fairbanks, AK 99701
Tel.: (907) 452-1555
Web Site: http://www.brenntag.com
Sales Range: $25-49.9 Million
Emp.: 50
Chemicals & Allied Products Whslr
N.A.I.C.S.: 424690

Brenntag Pacific, Inc. - South Gate (3)
Ardine St 4545, South Gate, CA 90280-2534
Tel.: (323) 832-5000
Web Site: https://www.brenntag.com
Sales Range: $125-149.9 Million
Industrial & Specialty Chemical Distr
N.A.I.C.S.: 424690
Debbie Thiere (Dir-HR)

Subsidiary (Domestic):

Brenntag Southeast, Inc. (2)
2000 E Pettigrew St, Durham, NC 27703
Tel.: (919) 596-0681
Web Site:
http://www.brenntagsoutheast.com
Sales Range: $50-74.9 Million
Emp.: 250
Industrial & Specialty Chemical Mfr
N.A.I.C.S.: 325998
Gil Steadman (Pres)

Brenntag Southwest, Inc. (2)
610 Fisher Rd, Longview, TX 75604
Tel.: (903) 759-7151
Web Site:
https://www.brenntagsouthwest.com
Sales Range: $25-49.9 Million
Emp.: 65
Industrial & Specialty Chemical Mfr & Distr
N.A.I.C.S.: 325998
Kevin Kessing (VP-Natl Acct)

Branch (Domestic):

Brenntag Southwest, Inc. - Borger (3)
Highway 207 S, Borger, TX 79007
Tel.: (806) 342-0163
Web Site:
http://www.brenntagsouthwest.com
Sales Range: $25-49.9 Million
Emp.: 11
Other Chemical & Allied Products Merchant Whslr
N.A.I.C.S.: 424690

Brenntag Southwest, Inc. - Lancaster (3)
704 E Wintergreen Rd, Lancaster, TX 75134
Tel.: (972) 218-3500
Web Site:
http://www.brenntagsouthwest.com
Sales Range: $25-49.9 Million
Emp.: 50
Industrial Chemical Distr
N.A.I.C.S.: 424690

Division (Domestic):

Brenntag Specialties, Inc. (2)
Coolidge St 1000, South Plainfield, NJ 07080
Tel.: (908) 561-6100
Web Site:
http://www.brenntagspecialties.com
Sales Range: $200-249.9 Million
Emp.: 400
Specialty Pigments, Coatings, Adhesives, Resins & Chemicals Mfr & Distr

N.A.I.C.S.: 325130
Robert Przybylowski (VP-Mktg Accts-Global)

Unit (Domestic):

Brenntag Specialties (3)
5700 Tacony St, Philadelphia, PA 19135
Tel.: (215) 537-1000
Web Site:
https://www.brenntagspecialties.com
Sales Range: $25-49.9 Million
Emp.: 20
Specialty Pigments, Coatings, Adhesives, Resins & Chemicals Distr
N.A.I.C.S.: 424690
Bruce L. Matta (Sr Acct Mgr-South New Jersey/Northeast Pennsylvania)

Subsidiary (Domestic):

Coastal Chemical Co., LLC (2)
3520 Veterans Memorial Dr, Abbeville, LA 70510
Tel.: (337) 898-0001
Web Site: https://www.coastalchem.com
Industrial & Specialty Chemical Distr
N.A.I.C.S.: 424690
Jim Taylor (Pres)

Brenntag PTE. LTD. (1)
9 Jalan Pesawat, Singapore, 619367, Singapore
Tel.: (65) 68634633
Web Site: https://www.brenntag.com
Emp.: 2
Chemical Products Distr
N.A.I.C.S.: 424690
Angie Ng (VP-HR)

Brenntag Panama S.A. (1)
Calle 15 Rio Abajo via Espana, Panama, Panama
Tel.: (507) 497725
Chemical & Ingredient Distr
N.A.I.C.S.: 424690

Brenntag Philippines Inc. (1)
16th Floor Asian Star Building 2402-2404 Asean Drive, Filinvest City Alabang, Muntinlupa, Philippines
Tel.: (63) 28129385
Emp.: 99
Chemical Products Distr
N.A.I.C.S.: 424690

Brenntag Portugal Lda. (1)
Rua Mourisca 26 e 32, Linho, 2710-297, Sintra, Portugal
Tel.: (351) 21 924 8800
Web Site: https://www.brenntag.com
Sales Range: $10-24.9 Million
Emp.: 11,000
Distr of Industrial & Specialty Chemicals
N.A.I.C.S.: 424690

Brenntag Pty. Ltd. (1)
Building 25 Omnico Business Park 270 Ferntree Gully Road, Notting Hill, Melbourne, 3168, VIC, Australia
Tel.: (61) 3 9501 2700
Chemical Products Distr
N.A.I.C.S.: 424690

Brenntag Puerto Rico, Inc. (1)
Rosendo Vela Acosta, Carolina, PR 00987
Tel.: (787) 286-0480
Web Site: https://www.brenntagla.com
Sales Range: $50-74.9 Million
Emp.: 10
Chemical Products Distr
N.A.I.C.S.: 424690
Samuel Cruz (Gen Mgr)

Brenntag Quimica Brasil Ltda. (1)
Rua Gomes de Carvalho 25 andar 1996, Guarulhos, Sao Paulo, 04547-006, Brazil
Tel.: (55) 1155452100
Web Site: https://www.brenntag.com
Chemical & Ingredient Distr
N.A.I.C.S.: 424690

Brenntag Real Estate GmbH (1)
Stinnes-Platz 1, Mulheim an der Ruhr, 45472, Germany
Tel.: (49) 20878280
Real Estate Development Services
N.A.I.C.S.: 531390

Brenntag S.A. (1)

Avenue du Progres 90, 69680, Chassieu, France
Tel.: (33) 42221600
Chemical Distr
N.A.I.C.S.: 424690

Brenntag S.r.l. (1)
Garii Street no 2 BIS, Jud Ilfov, 077040, Chiajna, Romania
Tel.: (40) 214360493
Web Site: https://www.brenntag.com
Chemical & Ingredient Distr
N.A.I.C.S.: 424690
Alexandru Badea (Pres)

Brenntag Schweizerhall AG (1)
Elsasserstrasse 231, CH-4002, Basel, Switzerland
Tel.: (41) 583448000
Web Site: https://www.brenntag.com
Sales Range: $75-99.9 Million
Emp.: 250
Chemical Products Distr
N.A.I.C.S.: 424690

Brenntag Singapore Pte. Ltd. (1)
9 Jalan Pesawat, Singapore, 619367, Singapore
Tel.: (65) 6 863 4633
Web Site: https://www.brenntag.com
Emp.: 30
Chemical Products Distr
N.A.I.C.S.: 424690

Brenntag Tanzania Limited (1)
Kipava Kiwalani Industrial Area Plot No 119, Dar es Salaam, Tanzania
Tel.: (255) 222864751
Chemical Transformative Supply Chain Services
N.A.I.C.S.: 541614

Brenntag Tunisie S.A.R.L. (1)
Lot No 40 ZI M Ghira 1 Fouchana, 2082, Ben Arous, Tunisia
Tel.: (216) 98314319
Chemical Transformative Supply Chain Services
N.A.I.C.S.: 541614

Brenntag UK and Ireland Limited (1)
Albion House Rawdon Park, Green Lane, Leeds, LS19 7XX, United Kingdom
Tel.: (44) 113 3879 200
Web Site: http://www.brenntag.co.uk
Sales Range: $50-74.9 Million
Emp.: 100
Chemical Products Distr
N.A.I.C.S.: 424690
Jason Woods (Mgr-Sls-Ireland & UK)

Brenntag Uganda Limited (1)
Plot 2-4 Muwesi Road, Bugolobi, Kampala, Uganda
Tel.: (256) 414254557
Chemical Transformative Supply Chain Services
N.A.I.C.S.: 541614

Brenntag Ukraine Ltd (1)
42-44 Shovkovychna Str, 01601, Kiev, Ukraine
Tel.: (380) 44 490 5860
Web Site: http://www.brenntag.com
Emp.: 3
Specialty Chemicals Mfr
N.A.I.C.S.: 325199

Brenntag Vastgoed B.V. (1)
Donker Duyvisweg 44, Dordrecht, 3316 BM, Netherlands
Tel.: (31) 786544944
Web Site: http://www.brenntag.com
Emp.: 7
Chemical Products Distr
N.A.I.C.S.: 424690

Brenntag Vietnam Company Limited (1)
120 Hoang Hoa Tham Street Ward 7, Binh Thanh District, 700000, Ho Chi Minh City, Vietnam
Tel.: (84) 2839975050
Web Site: https://www.brenntag.com
Chemical & Ingredient Distr
N.A.I.C.S.: 424690
Nguyen Thi Thu Ha (Mgr-Section)

Brenntag d.o.o. (1)
Rajka Mitica 6, 11 040, Novi Beograd, Serbia

Tel.: (381) 116550050
Chemical & Ingredient Distr
N.A.I.C.S.: 424690

CVB Albert Carl GmbH & Co. KG (1)
Oberlandstrasse 22-25, 12099, Berlin, Germany
Tel.: (49) 306289320
Emp.: 132
Chemical Products Distr
N.A.I.C.S.: 424690

CVH Chemie-Vertrieb GmbH & Co. Hannover KG (1)
Podbielskistrasse 22, 30163, Hannover, Germany
Tel.: (49) 511965350
Web Site: https://www.cvh.de
Sales Range: $25-49.9 Million
Emp.: 3
Chemical Products Distr
N.A.I.C.S.: 424690

CVH Chemie-Vertrieb Verwaltungsgesellschaft mbH (1)
Podbielskistr 22, Hannover, 30163, Germany
Tel.: (49) 511965350
Chemical Products Distr
N.A.I.C.S.: 424690

CVM Chemie-Vertrieb Magdeburg GmbH & Co. KG (1)
Geschwister-Scholl-Strasse 127, Elbe, 39218, Schonebeck, Germany
Tel.: (49) 39 28 45 64 09
Sales Range: $25-49.9 Million
Emp.: 12
Chemical Products Distr
N.A.I.C.S.: 424690

CVP Chemie-Vertrieb Berlin GmbH (1)
Tel.: (49) 306289320
Chemical Products Distr
N.A.I.C.S.: 424690

Chimab S.p.A. (1)
Via Colombo 34, Campodarsego, 35011, Padua, Italy
Tel.: (39) 0499201496
Web Site: http://www.chimab.it
Food Ingredient Distr
N.A.I.C.S.: 424490

Colony Gums LLC (1)
2626 Executive Point Dr, Monroe, NC 28110
Tel.: (704) 226-9666
Web Site: https://www.colonygums.com
Gum & Stabilizer Mfr & Distr
N.A.I.C.S.: 325998

Conquimica S.A. (1)
Cra 42 53-24, Itagui, Colombia
Tel.: (57) 403 2563
Web Site: https://www.conquimica.com
Industrial Raw Material Distr
N.A.I.C.S.: 424590

Crest Chemicals (Pty) Limited (1)
247 15th Rd Randjespark, PO Box 4280, Midrand, 1685, Gauteng, South Africa
Tel.: (27) 112543300
Sales Range: $50-74.9 Million
Emp.: 200
Chemical Distr
N.A.I.C.S.: 424690

Digib Asia Pacific Pte. Ltd. (1)
2 Bukit Merah Central 08-01, Singapore, 159835, Singapore
Tel.: (65) 65001100
Chemical & Ingredient Distr
N.A.I.C.S.: 424690

Dipol Baltija SIA (1)
Lielvarzi Ciedri, Riga, 2123, Latvia
Tel.: (371) 67803297
Specialty Chemicals Distr
N.A.I.C.S.: 424690

Eurochem Service Polska Sp. z o.o. (1)
ul Migdalowa 4/52, 02-796, Warsaw, Poland
Tel.: (48) 77 472 1548
Web Site: https://www.eurochemservice.pl
Sales Range: $50-74.9 Million
Emp.: 3
Industrial Chemical Distr

N.A.I.C.S.: 424690

Forchem Sp. z o.o. (1)
Ul Heroldow 15 B lok 1, 01-991, Warsaw, Poland
Tel.: (48) 22 896 00 51
Web Site: http://www.forchem.pl
Construction Chemicals Mfr
N.A.I.C.S.: 325998

Guangzhou Fan Ya Jia Rong Trading Co., Ltd. (1)
Room 601-605/625 Room 701/724-725 Yaozhong Plaza No 9 Linhe West Road, Tian He District, Guangzhou, China
Tel.: (86) 2038107666
Chemical & Ingredient Distr
N.A.I.C.S.: 424690

Guangzhou Saifu Chemical Co., Ltd. (1)
Room A 18F Jing An Building 300 Dongfengzhong Road, Guangzhou, China
Tel.: (86) 2083510008
Chemical Product Mfr & Distr
N.A.I.C.S.: 325180

H.C.I. Chemicals Nederland B.V. (1)
Donker Duyvisweg 44, 3316 BM, Dordrecht, Netherlands
Tel.: (31) 786544944
Chemical & Ingredient Distr
N.A.I.C.S.: 424690

HCI Central Europe Holding B.V. (1)
Donker Duyvisweg 44, 3316BM, Dordrecht, Netherlands
Tel.: (31) 786544944
Emp.: 7
Investment Management Service
N.A.I.C.S.: 523999

Holanda Venezuela C.A. (1)
Zona Industrial Carabobo 8va Transversal Parcela 15-A y 15-B, Valencia, Estado Carabobo, Venezuela
Tel.: (58) 241 200 7200
Web Site: http://www.brenntagla.com
Industrial Chemical Product Distr
N.A.I.C.S.: 424690

Inversiones Quimicas S.A. (1)
Boulevard del Norte Km 5 Frente a Sedac, Carretera a Pto Cortes, San Pedro Sula, Honduras
Tel.: (504) 551 7060
Chemical Products Distr
N.A.I.C.S.: 424690

J.A.M. Distributing Company (1)
7010 Mykawa Rd, Houston, TX 77033 **(100%)**
Tel.: (713) 844-7788
Web Site: http://www.jamdistributing.com
Engine Fuels & Oils Distr
N.A.I.C.S.: 424720

Kluman & Balter Limited (1)
Unit 8-9 I O Centre Lea Road, Waltham Abbey, EN9 1AS, Essex, United Kingdom
Tel.: (44) 199 270 4000
Web Site: https://www.klumanandbalter.com
Bakery Ingredient Distr
N.A.I.C.S.: 424490
Andy Mabbett Boon (Mgr-Ops)

Metausel SAS (1)
90 Avenue Du Progres, 69680, Chassieu, France
Tel.: (33) 388 33 44 04
Industrial Chemical Distr
N.A.I.C.S.: 424690
Bruno Mardon (Gen Mgr)

Multisol Group Limited (1)
Daresbury Park, Warrington, Daresbury, WA4 4GE, United Kingdom
Tel.: (44) 192 871 7071
Web Site: https://www.multisolgroup.com
Emp.: 150
Lubricant Additive & Specialty Chemical Distr
N.A.I.C.S.: 424690
David Hopkinson (COO)

Multisol Limited (1)
Huntsman Drive Northbank Industrial Park, Irlam, Manchester, M44 5EG, Greater Manchester, United Kingdom
Tel.: (44) 1617756028

Lubricant Additive & Specialty Chemical Distr
N.A.I.C.S.: 424690
Kevin Wright (Mng Dir)

Natural World S.r.l. (1)
Via Rambaldo Jacchia 8, 48022, Lugo, Ravenna, Italy
Tel.: (39) 0545 27100
Web Site: http://www.naturalworld.it
Food Products Ingredient Distr
N.A.I.C.S.: 424450

OOO BRENNTAG (1)
Volkonskiy 1st per 13 bldg 2 floor 6, 127473, Moscow, Russia
Tel.: (7) 4957395727
Web Site: https://www.brenntag.com
Emp.: 40
Chemical Products Distr
N.A.I.C.S.: 424690

P.T. Aik Moh Chemicals Indonesia (1)
Komplek Bintang Makmur Industri Block FG No 8-9 Batam Centre, Batam, Indonesia
Tel.: (62) 7787431208
Web Site: https://www.aikmohbatam.com
Emp.: 12
Chemical Products Distr
N.A.I.C.S.: 424690

P.T. Staris Chemicals (1)
Graha Pratama Building 20th Floor Jl MT Haryono Kav 15, Jakarta Selatan, 12810, Indonesia
Tel.: (62) 2183793823
Web Site: https://www.starischemicals.com
Oil & Gas Agrochemical Distr
N.A.I.C.S.: 424690

PHU Elmar Sp. z o.o. (1)
ul Torunska 114, Bydgoszcz, 85 123, Poland
Tel.: (48) 523704670
Logistics Consulting Servies
N.A.I.C.S.: 541614

PT Brenntag Indonesia (1)
Tel.: (62) 2183790755
Web Site: https://www.brenntag.com
Chemical Products Distr
N.A.I.C.S.: 424690

PT EAC Indonesia (1)
Graha Pratama 17th Floor Jl Letjen MT Haryono Kav 15 Pancoran, Tebet, Jakarta, 12810, Indonesia
Tel.: (62) 21 83790755
Chemical Products Mfr
N.A.I.C.S.: 325998

Pachem Distribution Inc. (1)
1800 Michelin Blvd, Laval, H7L 4R3, QC, Canada
Tel.: (450) 682-4044
Web Site:
https://www.pachemdistribution.com
Cosmetic & Pharmaceutical Natural Product Distr
N.A.I.C.S.: 424210

Pelican Chemical Traders Ltd. (1)
Building Clarendon House Street 2 Church Street, PO Box HM 1888, Hamilton, Bermuda
Tel.: (441) 292 4000
Chemical Products Distr
N.A.I.C.S.: 424690

Prime Surfactants Limited I.L. (1)
Alexandra House Redvers Close Lawnswood Business Park, Leeds, LS16 6QY, United Kingdom
Tel.: (44) 1134680000
Web Site: https://primesurfactants.com
Chemical Transformative Supply Chain Services
N.A.I.C.S.: 541614

Quimicos Holanda Costa Rica S.A. (1)
A vei 36 200 metros al Norte de la Entrada Principal de Cenada, Barreal de Heredia, San Jose, Costa Rica
Tel.: (506) 25085300
Web Site: https://www.brenntag.com
Chemical Products Distr
N.A.I.C.S.: 424690

Quimilog Transportes e Logistica Ltda. (1)

Rod Ivo Silveira Km 3 Bateas, Brusque, CEP 88355-202, SC, Brazil
Tel.: (55) 4732511058
Web Site: https://www.quimilog.com.br
Logistics & Transportation Services
N.A.I.C.S.: 541614

Raj Petro Specialities Private Limited (1)
B1/101 Boomerang Business Centre Chandivali Farm Road, Chandivali Andheri East, Mumbai, 400072, Maharashtra, India
Tel.: (91) 226 199 3333
Web Site: https://www.rajgrp.com
Emp.: 500
Petroleum & Transformer Oil Mfr
N.A.I.C.S.: 324191
Vinit Asher (Sr Dir-Sls & Mktg)

Raj Petro Specialties DMCC (1)
3L AU Tower Cluster I Jumeriah Lake Towers Sheikh Zayed Road, PO Box 309132, Dubai, United Arab Emirates
Tel.: (971) 44547059
Petroleum & Transformer Oil Mfr
N.A.I.C.S.: 324191
Mehul Nanavati (Sr Dir-Intl Bus)

Ravenswood Ingredients Pty. Ltd. (1)
2A/77-83 Bayfield Road, PO Box 585, Bayswater, 3153, VIC, Australia
Tel.: (61) 397207000
Web Site:
https://www.ravenswoodaus.com.au
Food & Beverage Distr
N.A.I.C.S.: 424490

Romana Chimici S.p.A. (1)
Localita Paduni, Anagni, 03012, Frosinone, Italy
Tel.: (39) 0775 77481
Web Site: http://www.brenntag.it
Sales Range: $25-49.9 Million
Emp.: 50
Chemical Products Distr
N.A.I.C.S.: 424690

S I A BRENNTAG LATVIA (1)
Ciedri Kekavas pag, Kekavas novads, Kekava, LV-2123, Latvia
Tel.: (371) 67803280
Web Site: https://www.brenntag.com
Emp.: 10
Chemical Products Distr
N.A.I.C.S.: 424690

Shanghai Anyijie Chemical Logistic Co., Ltd. (1)
No 133 Lane 968 Shuang Zhu Road, Hua Ting Town Jiading District, Shanghai, 201811, China
Tel.: (86) 2159975308
Chemical & Ingredient Distr
N.A.I.C.S.: 424690

Shanghai Jia Rong Trading Co., Ltd. (1)
45th Floor Baokuang Intercontinental Business Center No 100, Yutong Road Jingan District, Shanghai, China
Tel.: (86) 2164275808
Chemical & Ingredient Distr
N.A.I.C.S.: 424690

Shanghai Saifu Chemical Development Co., Ltd. (1)
20F Building 1 1628 Jinshajiang Road, Shanghai, 200333, China
Tel.: (86) 2151508000
Emp.: 100
Specialty Chemicals Distr
N.A.I.C.S.: 424690

Shanghai Yi Rong International Trading Co., Ltd. (1)
Unit 1-108 Floor 2 No 2001 Market Commercial Building, Yang Gao Road North Wai Gao Qiao, Shanghai, China
Tel.: (86) 2164275808
Chemical & Ingredient Distr
N.A.I.C.S.: 424690

Societe commerciale Tardy et Cie. S.a.r.l. (1)
21 Boulevard De L Europe, Vitrolles, 13127, France
Tel.: (33) 442462242
Web Site: http://www.brenntag.com

Sales Range: $50-74.9 Million
Emp.: 3
Chemical Products Distr
N.A.I.C.S.: 424690

Tat Petroleum Pte. Ltd. (1)
9 Jalan Pesawat, Singapore, 619367, Singapore
Tel.: (65) 6863 4633
Web Site: http://www.tatgroup-asia.com
Refined Petroleum Products Distr
N.A.I.C.S.: 424720

Subsidiary (Non-US):

Tat Petroleum (HK) Pte Limited (2)
505 - 508 Block A Vigor Industrial Building
14-20 Cheung Tat Road, Tsing Yi, New Territories, China (Hong Kong)
Tel.: (852) 35903909
Web Site: http://www.tatco.com.hk
Refined Petroleum Products Whslr
N.A.I.C.S.: 424720
Jackie Lui (Reg Dir)

Tat Petroleum (Vietnam) Co.,
Ltd. (2)
Room 201 11 Bis Nguyen Gia Thieu St
Ward 6 District 3, Ho Chi Minh City,
Vietnam (90%)
Tel.: (84) 839302686
Web Site: http://www.tatcovn.com.vn
Refined Petroleum Products Distr
N.A.I.C.S.: 424720

Tee Hai Chem Pte. Ltd. (1)
25 Greenwich Drive Teehai Tampines Logis-
Park, Singapore, 533973, Singapore
Tel.: (65) 68625655
Web Site: https://www.teehai.com
Chemical Transformative Supply Chain Services
N.A.I.C.S.: 541614

Tianjin Tai Rong Chemical Trading
Co., Ltd. (1)
19th floor Xinda Plaza 188 Jiefang North
Road, Heping District, Tianjin, China
Tel.: (86) 2223309666
Chemical & Ingredient Distr
N.A.I.C.S.: 424690

Tianjin Zhong Rong Chemical Stor-
age Co., Ltd. (1)
No 718 Hexing New Village Xinli Street,
Dongli District, Tianjin, China
Tel.: (86) 2224985006
Chemical & Ingredient Distr
N.A.I.C.S.: 424690

Tob Brenntag Ukraine LLC (1)
Leiptsyzska St 15, 01015, Kyiv, Ukraine
Tel.: (380) 444905860
Chemical Product Mfr & Distr
N.A.I.C.S.: 325180

Tride Rus OOO (1)
1st Volkonsky per 13 bld 2 floor6, Moscow,
127473, Russia
Tel.: (7) 4957395727
Web Site: http://www.brenntag.ru
Emp.: 35
Chemical Products Distr
N.A.I.C.S.: 424690

Trychem FZCO (1)
Agility Regional Office Building Jebel Ali
Free Zone South, Jebel Ali, Dubai, United
Arab Emirates
Tel.: (971) 48807059
Web Site: https://www.brenntag.com
Chemical & Ingredient Distr
N.A.I.C.S.: 424690
Jonathan Mayne (COO)

UAB Brenntag Lietuva (1)
Palemono g 171D, 52107, Kaunas, Lithu-
ania
Tel.: (370) 3730614
Web Site: https://www.brenntag.com
Specialty Chemicals Distr
N.A.I.C.S.: 424690
Tomasz Grzegorz Wronka (Gen Mgr)

Water Treatment Solution Ltd.
Boothes Lane, Sandbach, CW11 3PZ,
United Kingdom
Tel.: (44) 1270 758285
Waste Treatment Services

N.A.I.C.S.: 221310

Wellstar Enterprises (Hong Kong)
Company Limited (1)
Rm 1104 Yuen Long Trading Centre 11/F
33 Wang Yip St, West Yuen Long N T,
Hong Kong, China (Hong Kong)
Tel.: (852) 24423298
Chemical & Ingredient Distr
N.A.I.C.S.: 424690

Y.S. Ashkenazi Agencies Ltd. (1)
Kibutz Nezer Sireni, Be'er Yacov, 7039500,
Israel
Tel.: (972) 89282580
Chemical Products Distr
N.A.I.C.S.: 424690

Zhong Yung (International) Chemical
Co., Limited (1)
Flat/RM A 8/F Sun House 1818, Hong
Kong, China (Hong Kong)
Tel.: (852) 228698898
Chemical & Ingredient Distr
N.A.I.C.S.: 424690

BRENTRIDGE FORD SALES
5604 41 Ave, Wetaskiwin, T9A 3M7,
AB, Canada
Tel.: (780) 352-6048
Web Site:
http://www.brentridgeford.com
Sales Range: $10-24.9 Million
Emp.: 31
New & Used Car Dealers
N.A.I.C.S.: 441110
Rob Hardy (Mgr-Fin)

BRERA HOLDINGS PLC
One Burlington Road 4, Dublin, D04
C5Y6, Ireland
Tel.: (353) 12373700   IE
Web Site:
https://www.breraholdings.com
Year Founded: 2022
BREA—(NASDAQ)
Rev.: $1,266,687
Assets: $9,372,200
Liabilities: $6,121,852
Net Worth: $3,250,348
Earnings: ($5,421,862)
Fiscal Year-end: 12/31/23
Holding Company
N.A.I.C.S.: 551112
Daniel J. McClory (Chm)

BREUNING GMBH
Luisenstr 60, 75172, Pforzheim, Ger-
many
Tel.: (49) 72319320
Web Site: http://www.breuning.de
Year Founded: 1927
Sales Range: $75-99.9 Million
Emp.: 300
Jewelry Mfr
N.A.I.C.S.: 339910
Marcus Breuning (Mng Dir)

Subsidiaries:

Breuning Inc. (1)
PO Box 465945, Lawrenceville, GA 30042
Tel.: (678) 377-1673
Web Site: http://www.breuning.us
Sales Range: $25-49.9 Million
Emp.: 6
Mfr of Jewelry
N.A.I.C.S.: 339910
Micheal Hujara (Mgr)

BREVILLE GROUP LIMITED
Suite 2 170-180 Bourke Rd, Alexan-
dria, 2015, NSW, Australia
Tel.: (61) 293848100   AU
Web Site: https://brevillegroup.com
BRG—(ASX)
Rev.: $1,021,629,937
Assets: $895,480,098
Liabilities: $329,097,889
Net Worth: $566,382,209
Earnings: $79,131,276
Emp.: 1,079

Fiscal Year-end: 06/30/24
Kitchen Appliances
N.A.I.C.S.: 335220
Jim Clayton (CEO & Mng Dir)

Subsidiaries:

BRG Appliances Limited (1)
Studio 3 2 Power Road Studios 114 Power
Road, London, W4 5PY, United Kingdom
Tel.: (44) 8081781650
Household Appliance Retailer
N.A.I.C.S.: 449210

Breville Mexico, S.A. de C.V. (1)
Montes Urales 360 Piso 2 Col Lomas de
Chapultepec III Seccion, Miguel Hidalgo,
CP 11000, Mexico, Mexico
Tel.: (52) 8009531668
Web Site: https://www.breville.com
Electrical Kitchen Appliances Distr
N.A.I.C.S.: 423620

Breville New Zealand Limited (1)
6B Pacific Rise Mt Wellington, Private Bag
94411, Mt Wellington Botany Manukau,
2163, Auckland, New Zealand
Tel.: (64) 92713980
Household Appliance Retailer
N.A.I.C.S.: 449210

Breville Pty Limited (1)
Suite 2 170-180 Bourke Road, Locked Bag
2000, Botany, Alexandria, 2015, NSW, Aus-
tralia
Tel.: (61) 1300199798
Household Appliance Retailer
N.A.I.C.S.: 449210

Breville USA, Inc. (1)
19400 S Western Ave, Torrance, CA 90501
Tel.: (310) 755-3000
Household Appliance Retailer
N.A.I.C.S.: 449210

Sage Appliances France SaS (1)
66 avenue des Champs Elysees, 75008,
Paris, France
Tel.: (33) 800903235
Household Appliance Retailer
N.A.I.C.S.: 449210

Sage Appliances GmbH (1)
Campus Fichtenhain 48, 47807, Krefeld,
Germany
Tel.: (49) 800 505 3104
Web Site: https://www.sageappliances.com
Household Appliance Retailer
N.A.I.C.S.: 449210

BREWERS RETAIL INC.
5900 Explorer Drive, Mississauga,
L4W 5L2, ON, Canada
Tel.: (905) 361-1005
Web Site: http://www.thebeerstore.ca
Rev.: $307,763,458
Assets: $496,194,625
Liabilities: $502,339,502
Net Worth: ($6,144,877)
Earnings: ($24,809,081)
Emp.: 1,900
Fiscal Year-end: 12/31/19
Beer Retail Services
N.A.I.C.S.: 424810
Chantalle Butler (Chm)

BREWIN DOLPHIN HOLDINGS
PLC
12 Smithfield Street, London, EC1A
9BD, United Kingdom
Tel.: (44) 207 248 4400
Web Site: http://www.brewin.co.uk
BRW—(LSE)
Rev.: $551,120,272
Assets: $931,716,342
Liabilities: $460,235,852
Net Worth: $471,480,489
Earnings: $75,106,355
Emp.: 2,186
Fiscal Year-end: 09/30/21
Investment & Brokerage Services
N.A.I.C.S.: 523150
David Nicol (Co-CEO)

Subsidiaries:

Brewin Dolphin Capital & Investments
(Ireland) Limited (1)
3 Richview Office Park, Clonskeagh, Dublin,
D14 H7R0, Ireland
Tel.: (353) 12600000
Investment Advisory Services
N.A.I.C.S.: 523940

Brewin Dolphin Securities (1)
12 Smithfield St, London, EC1A 9BD,
United Kingdom
Tel.: (44) 2072484400
Web Site: http://www.brewin.co.uk
Sales Range: $200-249.9 Million
Emp.: 500
Securities Trading Services
N.A.I.C.S.: 523150

Brewin Nominees Limited (1)
12 Smithfield Street, London, EC1A 9LA,
United Kingdom (100%)
Tel.: (44) 204 502 3650
Web Site: https://www.brewin.co.uk
Securities Brokerage
N.A.I.C.S.: 523150

BRF S.A.
Av das Nacaes Unidas 14401 - Torre
Jequitiba, Chacara Santo Antonio,
Sao Paulo, 04730-090, SP, Brazil
Tel.: (55) 1123225000   BR
Web Site: https://www.brf-me.com
Year Founded: 1934
BRFS—(NYSE)
Rev.: $11,049,034,489
Assets: $11,802,594,508
Liabilities: $8,578,760,204
Net Worth: $3,223,834,304
Earnings: ($385,131,787)
Emp.: 100,000
Fiscal Year-end: 12/31/23
Holding Company; Food Products Mfr
& Distr
N.A.I.C.S.: 551112
Marcos Antonio Molina dos Santos
(Chm)

Subsidiaries:

BRF B.V. (1)
Houtwal 30, Oosterwolde, 8431 EX, Nether-
lands
Tel.: (31) 516566700
Web Site: http://www.brf-me.com
Holding Company; Poultry Processing &
Food Products Distr
N.A.I.C.S.: 551112

Subsidiary (Non-US):

BRF Germany GmbH (2)
Speditionstrass 15, 40221, Dusseldorf, Ger-
many
Tel.: (49) 21191324600
Web Site: http://www.brf-me.com
Food Products Mfr
N.A.I.C.S.: 311991

Subsidiary (Domestic):

Plusfood Holland B.V. (2)
Houtwal 30, Oosterwolde, 8431, Nether-
lands
Tel.: (31) 516566700
Web Site: http://www.plusfood.nl
Sales Range: $25-49.9 Million
Emp.: 200
Poultry Processing & Food Products Distr
N.A.I.C.S.: 311615
Hans Deboer (Mgr-Pur)

Subsidiary (Non-US):

Plusfood Hungary Trade and Service
LLC (2)
Terez krt 55-57 C intact 6th em, 1062, Bu-
dapest, Hungary
Tel.: (36) 14121236
Web Site: https://www.plusfood.hu
Meat Food Products Distr
N.A.I.C.S.: 424470

Plusfood Italy SRL (2)
Via Giardino Giusti 2, 37129, Verona, Italy
Tel.: (39) 045 8004039

Sales Range: $25-49.9 Million
Emp.: 9
Chicken Meat Mfr & Distr
N.A.I.C.S.: 311615
Giuseppe Grigolini *(Gen Mgr)*

Plusfood UK Ltd. (2)
Bell House Seebeck Place Knowlhill, Milton
Keynes, MK5 8FR, United Kingdom
Tel.: (44) 1908685000
Web Site: http://www.plusfood.co.uk
Chicken Meat Mfr & Distr
N.A.I.C.S.: 311615

Subsidiary (Domestic):

Plusfood Wrexham Ltd. (3)
Miners Road, Wrexham, LL12 0PJ, United
Kingdom
Tel.: (44) 1978 852161
Frozen Food Mfr
N.A.I.C.S.: 311412

BRF Brasil Foods PTE Ltd. (1)
350 Orchard Rd 13-01 Shaw Hse, Singa-
pore, 238868, Singapore
Tel.: (65) 67337343
Sales Range: $50-74.9 Million
Emp.: 8
Meat Product Distr
N.A.I.C.S.: 424470
Fernendo Chucid *(Country Mgr)*

Highline International Ltd. (1)
511 N 103rd St, Seattle, WA 98133-9201
Tel.: (206) 781-8736
Restaurant
N.A.I.C.S.: 722511

Perdigao Agroindustrial S.A. (1)
Av Escola Politecnica 760, Jaguare, 05350-
901, Sao Paulo, Brazil
Tel.: (55) 1137185301
Web Site: http://www.perdigao.com.br
Meat Markets
N.A.I.C.S.: 445240

Subsidiary (Non-US):

Perdigao Holland B.V. (2)
Het Sterrenbeeld 21, 5215 MK, 's-
Hertogenbosch, Netherlands
Tel.: (31) 736104501
Business Service Centers
N.A.I.C.S.: 561439

Perdigao International Ltd. (2)
City Tower 2, Dubai, United Arab Emirates
Tel.: (971) 3291155
Business Service Centers
N.A.I.C.S.: 561439

Perdigao UK Ltd. (2)
Theobald Ct Theobald Street, Boreham-
wood, WD64RN, United Kingdom
Tel.: (44) 2082362330
Business Service Centers
N.A.I.C.S.: 561439

Sadia S.A. (1)
Rua Senador Attilio Fontana 86 Centro,
Concordia, 89700-000, SC, Brazil
Tel.: (55) 494443000
Web Site: http://www.sadia.com.br
Sales Range: $5-14.9 Billion
Emp.: 60,580
Refrigerated & Frozen Foods Distr; Pork &
Poultry Producer; Meat Products Exporter
N.A.I.C.S.: 311611

Subsidiary (Non-US):

Sadia Uruguay S.A. (2)
Miraflores 1445 103, Montevideo, Uruguay
Tel.: (598) 2 601 3925
Sales Range: $25-49.9 Million
Emp.: 4
Processed Meats Distr
N.A.I.C.S.: 424470
Djalna Meme *(Mgr)*

BRG GROUP JOINT STOCK CO.
18 Ly Thuong Kiet Str, Hoan Kiem
District, Hanoi, 100000, Vietnam
Tel.: (84) 2439393691 **VN**
Web Site: http://www.brggroup.vn
Golf Resort & Commercial Banking
Services
N.A.I.C.S.: 551112

Thi Nga Nguyen *(Chm)*

BRI-CHEM CORP.
27075 Acheson Road, Acheson, T7X
6B1, AB, Canada
Tel.: (780) 962-9490 **AB**
Web Site: https://www.brichem.com
5JN—(DEU)
Rev.: $80,069,298
Assets: $51,628,927
Liabilities: $34,606,660
Net Worth: $17,022,267
Earnings: $686,714
Emp.: 6
Fiscal Year-end: 12/31/23
Drilling Fluid Chemicals & Steel Prod-
ucts Wholesale Distr
N.A.I.C.S.: 325998
Don Caron *(Chm, Pres & CEO)*

Subsidiaries:

Bri-Chem Supply Ltd. (1)
27075 Acheson Road, Acheson, T7X 6B1,
AB, Canada
Tel.: (780) 962-9490
Web Site: https://www.brichemsupply.com
Drilling Fluid Chemicals Distr
N.A.I.C.S.: 424690

Bri-Steel Corporation (1)
2125 64 Avenue, Edmonton, T6P 1Z4, AB,
Canada
Tel.: (780) 469-6603
Web Site: http://www.bri-steel.com
Sales Range: $25-49.9 Million
Emp.: 5
Steel Piping Products Mfr & Distr
N.A.I.C.S.: 331210

Sodium Solutions Inc. (1)
27075 Acheson Road, Acheson, T7X 6B1,
AB, Canada
Tel.: (780) 482-1312
Web Site: https://www.sodiumsolutions.com
Specialty Chemicals Distr
N.A.I.C.S.: 424690

BRIACELL THERAPEUTICS CORP.
Suite 300 Bellevue Centre 235 15th
Street, West Vancouver, V7T 2X1,
BC, Canada
Tel.: (604) 921-1810
Web Site: https://www.briacell.com
Year Founded: 2006
BCTX—(NASDAQ)
Rev.: $262,566
Assets: $5,872,261
Liabilities: $8,557,193
Net Worth: ($2,684,932)
Earnings: ($4,931,548)
Emp.: 17
Fiscal Year-end: 07/31/24
Investment Services
N.A.I.C.S.: 523999
Charles L. Wiseman *(Founder)*

Subsidiaries:

**BriaCell Therapeutics Corp. - Berke-
ley Branch** (1)
820 Heinz Ave, Berkeley, CA 94710
Tel.: (888) 485-6340
Biotechnology Research Services
N.A.I.C.S.: 541714

BRIAN KURTZ TRUCKING LTD.
RR 2 6960 Speedvale Avenue West,
Breslau, N0B 1M0, ON, Canada
Tel.: (519) 836-5821
Web Site:
http://www.kurtztrucking.com
Year Founded: 1980
Rev.: $13,000,000
Emp.: 100
Truck Transportation Services
N.A.I.C.S.: 484121
Trevor Kurtz *(Mgr-Sls)*

BRICKABILITY GROUP PLC

Queensgate House Cookham Rd,
Bracknell, RG12 1RB, Berkshire,
United Kingdom
Tel.: (44) 2074188900 **UK**
Web Site:
https://www.brickabilitygroupplc.com
BRCK—(AIM)
Rev.: $845,773,837
Assets: $475,128,823
Liabilities: $257,344,423
Net Worth: $217,784,400
Earnings: $34,394,135
Emp.: 725
Fiscal Year-end: 03/31/23
Concrete Product Mfr & Distr
N.A.I.C.S.: 327331
Alan Simpson *(CEO)*

Subsidiaries:

Brick Services Limited (1)
Wellington House Wellington Road, Dun-
ston, Gateshead, NE11 9JL, Tyne and
Wear, United Kingdom
Tel.: (44) 1914145030
Web Site: https://www.brickservices.com
Brick Distr
N.A.I.C.S.: 423320

Brick-Link Limited (1)
Broadgate House North Broadgate Lane,
Horsforth, Leeds, LS18 4AB, United King-
dom
Tel.: (44) 1132586600
Web Site: https://www.bricklink.co.uk
Brick Product Distr
N.A.I.C.S.: 423320
Graham Jefferey *(Mgr-Specification)*

Brick-ability Ltd. (1)
Brickability Bridgend Bridgend Industrial Es-
tate South Road, Bridgend, CF31 3XG, Mid
Glamorgan, United Kingdom
Tel.: (44) 2084400551
Web Site: https://www.brickability.co.uk
Brick Distr
N.A.I.C.S.: 423320

Brickmongers (Wessex) Ltd. (1)
Frith Farm Frith Lane, Wickham, Fareham,
PO17 5AW, Hampshire, United Kingdom
Tel.: (44) 1329830012
Web Site:
https://www.brickmongerswessex.co.uk
Building Materials Distr
N.A.I.C.S.: 423320

Crest Brick Slate & Tile Limited (1)
Howdenshire Way, Howden, DN14 7HZ,
East Yorkshire, United Kingdom
Tel.: (44) 1430432667
Web Site: https://www.crest-bst.co.uk
Building Product Distr
N.A.I.C.S.: 423320

Crown Roofing (Centres) Limited (1)
PO Box 2887, Tadley, RG26 5FF, Hamp-
shire, United Kingdom
Tel.: (44) 1256881400
Web Site: http://www.crown-roofing.co.uk
Roofing Contracting Services
N.A.I.C.S.: 238160
Michael White *(Mng Dir)*

DSH Flooring Limited (1)
Queensgate House Cookham Road, Brack-
nell, RG12 1RB, Berkshire, United Kingdom
Tel.: (44) 3334560426
Web Site: http://www.dshflooring.co.uk
Floor Covering Installation Services
N.A.I.C.S.: 238220

Excel Roofing Services Limited (1)
Unit 6 Brooklands Farm Botley Road, Bish-
ops Waltham, Southampton, SQ32 1DR,
United Kingdom
Tel.: (44) 1489896061
Web Site:
https://www.excelroofingservices.co.uk
Roofing Contracting Services
N.A.I.C.S.: 238160

FSN Doors Limited (1)
Queensgate House Cookham Road, Brack-
nell, RG12 1RB, Berkshire, United Kingdom
Tel.: (44) 3334560426
Web Site: https://www.fsndoors.co.uk
Interior Door Renovation Services

N.A.I.C.S.: 238350

Radiatorsonline.com Ltd. (1)
Cookham Rd, Binfield, Bracknell, RG12
1RB, United Kingdom
Tel.: (44) 3330094040
Web Site: https://www.radiatorsonline.com
Electric Radiator Distr
N.A.I.C.S.: 423720

**The Bespoke Brick Company
Limited** (1)
Unit 61 Riverside III Sir Thomas Longley
Road Medway City Estate, Rochester, ME2
4BH, Kent, United Kingdom
Tel.: (44) 1634707707
Web Site: http://www.bespokebrick.com
Building Material Mfr & Distr
N.A.I.C.S.: 321992

The Brick Slip Business Limited (1)
Off Sandall Lane, Kirk Sandall Industrial
Estate, Doncaster, DN3 1FB, South York-
shire, United Kingdom
Tel.: (44) 3335778831
Web Site: https://www.brickslips.co.uk
Home Decor Product Mfr
N.A.I.C.S.: 337122

BRICKS NEWCO LIMITED
First Floor 1 Cranmore Drive, Shirley,
Solihull, B90 4RZ, West Midlands,
United Kingdom
Tel.: (44) 2074665000
Web Site:
https://www.bricksnewco.co.uk
PURP—(AIM)
Rev.: $95,040,400
Assets: $96,533,892
Liabilities: $37,337,300
Net Worth: $59,196,592
Earnings: ($57,024,240)
Emp.: 873
Fiscal Year-end: 04/30/22
Lessors of Other Real Estate Prop-
erty
N.A.I.C.S.: 531190
Paul Pindar *(Chm)*

BRICKWORKS LIMITED
738-780 Wallgrove Road, Horsley
Park, 2175, NSW, Australia
Tel.: (61) 96415485
Web Site:
https://www.brickworks.com.au
Year Founded: 1934
BKW—(ASX)
Rev.: $727,439,901
Assets: $3,901,292,051
Liabilities: $1,643,164,390
Net Worth: $2,258,127,662
Earnings: ($78,281,917)
Emp.: 1,852
Fiscal Year-end: 07/31/24
Clay Products Mfr & Distr; Invest-
ments
N.A.I.C.S.: 327120
Michael J. Millner *(Deputy Chm)*

Subsidiaries:

Austral Bricks (NSW) Pty Ltd (1)
738 - 780 Wallgrove Road, Horsley Park,
2175, NSW, Australia
Tel.: (61) 291014800
Web Site: http://www.australbricks.com.au
Building Product Mfr
N.A.I.C.S.: 327390
Lindsay Partridge *(Mng Dir)*

Austral Bricks (QLD) Pty Ltd (1)
105 Gardner Road, Rochedale, Brisbane,
4123, QLD, Australia
Tel.: (61) 739053257
Bricks Mfr
N.A.I.C.S.: 327331

Austral Bricks (SA) Pty Ltd (1)
201 Greenwith Rd, Golden Grove, Adelaide,
5125, SA, Australia
Tel.: (61) 884702747
Bricks Mfr
N.A.I.C.S.: 327331

Brickworks Limited—(Continued)

Austral Bricks (Tasmania) Pty Ltd. (1)
Cressy Road, Longford, 7301, TAS, Australia (100%)
Tel.: (61) 363974500
Web Site: http://www.australbrick.com.au
Sales Range: $25-49.9 Million
Emp.: 30
Clay Refractory Mfr
N.A.I.C.S.: 327120

Austral Bricks (VIC) Pty Ltd (1)
Brick Makers Drive, Wollert, 3750, VIC, Australia
Tel.: (61) 393034004
Bricks Mfr
N.A.I.C.S.: 327331

Austral Bricks (WA) Pty Ltd (1)
Harper Street, Caversham, 6055, WA, Australia
Tel.: (61) 892619999
Web Site: http://www.australbricks.com
Construction Materials Mfr
N.A.I.C.S.: 327331
Peter Scott (Gen Mgr)

Austral Masonry (NSW) Pty Ltd (1)
4 Latitude Rd, Horsley Park, 2175, NSW, Australia
Tel.: (61) 298402333
Concrete Block & Brick Mfr
N.A.I.C.S.: 327331

Austral Masonry (QLD) Pty Ltd (1)
14 Daniel St, Brisbane, 4551, QLD, Australia
Tel.: (61) 733472111
Concrete Block & Brick Mfr
N.A.I.C.S.: 327331
Lindsay Partridge (Mng Dir)

Austral Masonry (VIC) Pty Ltd (1)
Brickmakers Drive, Wollert, 3750, VIC, Australia
Tel.: (61) 387938222
Concrete Block & Brick Mfr
N.A.I.C.S.: 327331

Austral Precast (QLD) Pty Ltd (1)
364 Fairlie Terrace, Salisbury, 4107, QLD, Australia
Tel.: (61) 737327022
Precast Concrete Building Product Mfr & Distr
N.A.I.C.S.: 327390

Austral Precast Pty Ltd (1)
33-41 Cowpasture Road North, Wetherill Park, 2164, NSW, Australia
Tel.: (61) 291014809
Web Site: http://australprecast.com.au
Emp.: 50
Concrete Products Mfr
N.A.I.C.S.: 327320

Auswest Timbers Holdings Pty Ltd (1)
455 Orrong Rd, Welshpool, 6106, WA, Australia
Tel.: (61) 897761002
Sales Range: $25-49.9 Million
Emp.: 70
Timber Product Mfr
N.A.I.C.S.: 321215
Jason Wilson (Gen Mgr)

Auswest Timbers Pty Ltd. (1)
455 Orrong Road, Welshpool, 6106, WA, Australia (100%)
Tel.: (61) 893516429
Web Site: http://www.auswesttimber.com.au
Sales Range: $25-49.9 Million
Emp.: 12
Clay Refractory Mfr
N.A.I.C.S.: 327120
Lindsay Hartley (Mng Dir)

Brickworks Building Products Pty Ltd (1)
738-780 Wallgrove Rd, Horsley Park, 2175, NSW, Australia
Tel.: (61) 298307800
Web Site: http://www.brickworks.com.au
Emp.: 100
Concrete Products Mfr
N.A.I.C.S.: 327120

Brickworks Supply LLC (1)

8995 W 95th St, Palos Hills, IL 60455
Tel.: (708) 237-5600
Web Site: https://www.brickworkssupply.com
Brick Stone Mfr & Distr
N.A.I.C.S.: 327991

Bristile Guardians Pty Ltd. (1)
Harper St, Caversham, 6055, WA, Australia (100%)
Tel.: (61) 892619999
Web Site: http://www.bristile.com.au
Structural Clay Product Mfr
N.A.I.C.S.: 327120

Bristile Ltd. (1)
Harper St, Caversham, 6055, WA, Australia
Tel.: (61) 892619999
Sales Range: $200-249.9 Million
Emp.: 920
Mfr & Distributor of Building & Other Products; General Transport
N.A.I.C.S.: 236220

Bristile Operations Pty Ltd. (1)
Harper Street, 6055, Caversham, WA, Australia (100%)
Tel.: (61) 892619999
Web Site: http://www.bristileroofing.com
Sales Range: $25-49.9 Million
Emp.: 50
Structural Clay Product Mfr
N.A.I.C.S.: 327120

Bristile Roofing (East Coast) Pty Ltd. (1)
164 Viking Drive, PO Box 3040 Darra, 4076, Wacol, QLD, Australia (100%)
Tel.: (61) 732122444
Web Site: http://www.bristileroofing.com.au
Sales Range: $25-49.9 Million
Emp.: 100
Concrete Products Mfr
N.A.I.C.S.: 327390

Bristile Roofing Pty. Ltd. (1)
Harper St, Caversham, 6055, WA, Australia (100%)
Tel.: (61) 892619999
Web Site: http://www.bristileroofing.com.au
Sales Range: $25-49.9 Million
Emp.: 50
Innovative Roofing Products Mfr, Designer & Distr
N.A.I.C.S.: 238160
Peter Scott (Gen Mgr)

Capital Battens Pty Ltd (1)
21 Geelong St, Fyshwick, 2609, ACT, Australia
Tel.: (61) 261432101
Web Site: https://capitalbattens.com.au
Sawmill Operating Services
N.A.I.C.S.: 321113

Clifton Brick Manufacturers Pty Ltd. (1)
Harper St, 6055, Caversham, WA, Australia (100%)
Tel.: (61) 892619999
Web Site: http://www.austrilbricks.com.au
Sales Range: $25-49.9 Million
Emp.: 85
Structural Clay Product Mfr
N.A.I.C.S.: 327120

Glen-Gery Corporation (1)
1166 Spring St, Wyomissing, PA 19610-6001
Tel.: (484) 334-8827
Web Site: http://www.glengery.com
Brick & Concrete Block Mfr & Sls
N.A.I.C.S.: 327120
Sarah Coburn (Dir-HR)

Hallett Roofing Services Pty Ltd (1)
Harper St, Caversham, 6055, WA, Australia
Tel.: (61) 298307800
Web Site: http://www.australbricks.com.au
Emp.: 10
Roofing Metal Sheet Work Mfr
N.A.I.C.S.: 332322

International Brick & Tile Pty Ltd (1)
738 - 780 Wallgrove Road, Horsley Park, 6090, WA, Australia
Tel.: (61) 298307800
Brick & Structural Clay Tile Mfr
N.A.I.C.S.: 327120

Metropolitan Brick Company Pty Ltd (1)

10 Bonner Dr, Malaga, 6090, WA, Australia
Tel.: (61) 298307800
Concrete Product Distr
N.A.I.C.S.: 423320

Nubrik Pty Ltd (1)
Harper St, Caversham, 6055, WA, Australia
Tel.: (61) 892619999
Concrete Products Mfr
N.A.I.C.S.: 327331

Sioux City Brick & Tile Co (1)
310 S Floyd Blvd, Sioux City, IA 51101
Tel.: (712) 258-6571
Web Site: http://www.siouxcitybrick.com
Rev.: $20,000,000
Emp.: 250
Building Tile & Clay
N.A.I.C.S.: 327120
Norman Mahoney (Chm)

Terra Timbers Pty Ltd (1)
15 Power Station Rd, Bairnsdale, 3875, VIC, Australia
Tel.: (61) 351533400
Web Site: http://www.auswesttimbers.com
Emp.: 20
Timber Products Distr
N.A.I.C.S.: 423990

The Austral Brick Company Pty. Limited (1)
738 - 780 Wallgrove Rd, Horsley Park, 2175, NSW, Australia
Tel.: (61) 298307777
Web Site: http://www.australbricks.com.au
Sales Range: $75-99.9 Million
Emp.: 250
Pavers & Brick Mfr
N.A.I.C.S.: 327331

Triffid Investments Pty Ltd. (1)
Harper St, 6055, Caversham, WA, Australia (100%)
Tel.: (61) 892619999
Structural Clay Product Mfr
N.A.I.C.S.: 327120

BRICORAMA S.A.
21a boulevard Jean Monnet, 94350, Villiers-sur-Marne, France
Tel.: (33) 177615604
Year Founded: 1975
ALBRI—(EUR)
Sales Range: $750-799.9 Million
Hardware Store Operator
N.A.I.C.S.: 444140
Bruno Deronne (Dir-Magazine)

BRIDAS CORPORATION
Leandro N Alem Av 1180, Buenos Aires, 1001, Argentina
Tel.: (54) 1143104100
Web Site: http://www.pan-energy.com
Year Founded: 1948
Sales Range: $350-399.9 Million
Emp.: 1,300
Oil & Gas Holding Company
N.A.I.C.S.: 551112
Alejandro Pedro Bulgheroni (Vice Chm & Exec VP)

Subsidiaries:

Empresa Petrolera Chaco S.A. (1)
Tel.: (591) 33453700
Web Site: http://www.ypfbchaco.com.bo
Sales Range: $200-249.9 Million
Emp.: 300
Oil & Gas Exploration & Production; Owned 50% by Bolivian Pension Funds, 30% by BP plc & 20% by Bridas Corporation
N.A.I.C.S.: 211120

Pan American Energy LLC (1)
Av Leandro N Alem 1180, 1001, Buenos Aires, Argentina (40%)
Tel.: (54) 1143104100
Web Site: http://www.pan-energy.com
Emp.: 3,000
Oil & Natural Gas Exploration & Production
N.A.I.C.S.: 211120
Jason Latkowcer (CEO)

Subsidiary (Domestic):

Axion Energy (2)

Carlos Maria Della Paglera 265 Piso 19, Buenos Aires, 1001, Argentina
Tel.: (54) 8008880282
Web Site: https://www.axionenergy.com
Producing, Refining & Marketing of Petroleum Products & Industrial Lubricants
N.A.I.C.S.: 324110

BRIDGE BIOTHERAPEUTICS, INC.
Suite 303 C'S Tower 58 Pangyo-Ro 255 Beon-Gil, Bundang-Gu, Seongnam, 13486, Gyeonggi-do, Korea (South)
Tel.: (82) 3180923280
Web Site: https://www.bridgebiorx.com
Year Founded: 2015
288330—(KRS)
Rev.: $2,319,210
Assets: $47,136,159
Liabilities: $7,355,620
Net Worth: $39,780,539
Earnings: ($31,983,675)
Emp.: 37
Fiscal Year-end: 12/31/22
Pharmaceutical Preparation Mfr
N.A.I.C.S.: 325412
Angela Yum (VP-Clinical Strategy)

BRIDGE CONSULTING GROUP INC.
Edomizaka Mori Building 7F 4-1-40 Toranomon, Minato-ku, Tokyo, 105-0001, Japan
Tel.: (81) 364579105
Web Site: https://www.bridge-group.co.jp
Year Founded: 2011
9225—(TKS)
Human Resource Consulting Services
N.A.I.C.S.: 541612
Ken Inaoka (Officer)

BRIDGE INTERNATIONAL CORP.
1-18-10 Wakabayashi, Setagaya-ku, Tokyo, 154-0023, Japan
Tel.: (81) 357873030
Web Site: https://go.bridge-g.com
Year Founded: 2002
7039—(TKS)
Rev.: $49,771,800
Assets: $36,697,840
Liabilities: $7,196,350
Net Worth: $29,501,490
Earnings: $4,565,960
Emp.: 633
Fiscal Year-end: 12/31/23
Management Consulting Services
N.A.I.C.S.: 541613
Michimasa Yoshida (Pres & CEO)

BRIDGE SAAS LIMITED
Level 15 Exchange Tower 2 The Esplanade, Perth, 6000, WA, Australia
Tel.: (61) 280909000
Web Site: https://bridge.website
Year Founded: 2008
BGE—(ASX)
Rev.: $1,055,156
Assets: $1,348,569
Liabilities: $466,440
Net Worth: $882,129
Earnings: ($3,042,579)
Emp.: 9
Fiscal Year-end: 06/30/23
Software Development Services
N.A.I.C.S.: 541511
David Low (COO)

BRIDGE SECURITIES LIMITED
17 Suhasnagar Society Ashram Road, Near Dinesh Hall, Ahmedabad, 380 009, Gujarat, India
Tel.: (91) 7926578808

Web Site: http://www.bridgesec.co.in
Year Founded: 1994
530249—(BOM)
Rev.: $291,093
Assets: $288,022
Liabilities: $21,818
Net Worth: $266,204
Earnings: $169,850
Fiscal Year-end: 03/31/21
Security Brokerage Services
N.A.I.C.S.: 523150
Pragnesh R. Shah *(Chm & Mng Dir)*

BRIDGEMARQ REAL ESTATE SERVICES INC.
39 Wynford Drive, Toronto, M3C 3K5,
ON, Canada
Tel.: (416) 380-7500   ON
Web Site:
  https://www.bridgemarq.com
Year Founded: 2010
BREUF—(OTCIQ)
Rev.: $31,556,393
Assets: $69,590,847
Liabilities: $107,483,707
Net Worth: ($37,892,861)
Earnings: $600,009
Fiscal Year-end: 12/31/20
Real Estate Broker
N.A.I.C.S.: 531210
Philip Soper *(Pres & CEO)*

BRIDGEMERE UK PLC
Bridgemere House Chester Road,
Preston Brook, WA7 3BD, Cheshire,
United Kingdom
Tel.: (44) 1928797900   UK
Web Site: http://www.bridgemere-group.co.uk
Emp.: 5
Investment Holding Company
N.A.I.C.S.: 551112
Steve P. Morgan *(Chm)*

BRIDGEPOINT GROUP PLC
5 Marble Arch, London, W1H 7EJ,
United Kingdom
Tel.: (44) 2070343500   UK
Web Site: https://www.bridgepoint.eu
Year Founded: 2018
BPT—(LSE)
Rev.: $381,729,320
Assets: $2,220,090,040
Liabilities: $1,260,551,180
Net Worth: $959,538,860
Earnings: $149,761,080
Emp.: 377
Fiscal Year-end: 12/31/22
Offices of Other Holding Companies
N.A.I.C.S.: 551112
William Jackson *(Chm)*

Subsidiaries:

Bridgepoint Advisers Group
Limited   **(1)**
5 Marble Arch, London, W1H 7EJ, United
Kingdom
Tel.: (44) 2070343500
Holding Company; Private Equity Firm
N.A.I.C.S.: 551112

Subsidiary (Domestic):

Bridgepoint Advisers Limited   **(2)**
5 Marble Arch, London, W1H 7EJ, United
Kingdom
Tel.: (44) 2070343500
Privater Equity Firm
N.A.I.C.S.: 523999
Benoit Bassi *(Sr Partner)*

Holding (Domestic):

Alpha Financial Markets Consulting
plc   **(3)**
60 Gresham Street, London, EC2V 7BB,
United Kingdom
Tel.: (44) 2077969300
Web Site: https://www.alphafmc.com
Rev.: $214,526,549

Assets: $311,353,708
Liabilities: $131,123,167
Net Worth: $180,230,541
Earnings: $11,556,913
Emp.: 646
Fiscal Year-end: 03/31/2022
Financial Consulting Services
N.A.I.C.S.: 523940
Euan Fraser *(CEO-Global)*

Subsidiary (US):

Alpha Financial Markets Consulting
Inc.   **(4)**
12 E 49th St, New York, NY 10017
Tel.: (212) 603-9307
Marketing Consultancy Services
N.A.I.C.S.: 541613

Subsidiary (Non-US):

Alpha Financial Markets Consulting
S.A.S.   **(4)**
6 Square de l Opera Louis Jouvet, 75009,
Paris, France
Tel.: (33) 140170112
Marketing Consultancy Services
N.A.I.C.S.: 541613

Alpha Financial Markets Consulting
Switzerland S.A.   **(4)**
Bleicherweg 10, 8002, Zurich, Switzerland
Tel.: (41) 445620705
Marketing Consultancy Services
N.A.I.C.S.: 541613

Axxsys Danmark ApS   **(4)**
Flaesketorvet 68, 1711, Copenhagen, Den-
mark
Tel.: (45) 78746232
Advisory Services
N.A.I.C.S.: 523940

Affiliate (Non-US):

Bridgepoint AB   **(3)**
Master Samuelsgatan 1, 111 44, Stockholm,
Sweden
Tel.: (46) 854516820
Sales Range: $50-74.9 Million
Emp.: 12
Privater Equity Firm
N.A.I.C.S.: 523999
Mikael Lovgren *(Partner-Nordic Invest-
ments)*

Holding (Domestic):

Diaverum AB   **(4)**
Gotgatan 10, 411 05, Gothenburg, Sweden
Tel.: (46) 462873000
Web Site: http://www.diaverum.com
Emp.: 10,000
Dialysis Clinic Services
N.A.I.C.S.: 621492
Dag Andersson *(CEO)*

Subsidiary (Non-US):

Diaverum S.A.   **(5)**
Carlos Pellegrini 1163 2vo Piso, 1009, Bue-
nos Aires, Argentina
Tel.: (54) 1152548300
Rev.: $25,005,400
Emp.: 1,000
Fiscal Year-end: 12/31/2004
Provider of Medical & Surgical Equipment
N.A.I.C.S.: 339113

Representative Office (Non-US):

Diaverum Spain   **(5)**
Calle Orense 4-8 izquierda, 28020, Madrid,
Spain
Tel.: (34) 916707663
Manufacture of Medical Technological
Equipment

Diaverum Uruguay   **(5)**
Mario Cassioni 1643, 11200, Montevideo,
Uruguay
Tel.: (598) 24081139
Manufacture of Medical Technological
Equipment

Holding (Non-US):

Evac Oy   **(4)**
Sinimaentie 14, Espoo, 02630, Finland
Tel.: (358) 207630200
Web Site: http://www.evac.com

Marine Vessel & Facility Solid Waste &
Wastewater Collection & Treatment Sys-
tems Designer, Mfr & Whslr
N.A.I.C.S.: 237110
Mika Karjalainen *(Gen Mgr)*

Subsidiary (Non-US):

Evac E.U.R.L.   **(5)**
21/23 rue du Petit Albi, F-95807, Cergy-
Pontoise, Cedex, France
Tel.: (33) 134219988
Web Site: http://evac.com
Water Collection & Treatment Systems Mfr
N.A.I.C.S.: 333998

Evac Germany GmbH   **(5)**
Evac Germany GmbH, D-26122, Olden-
burg, Germany
Tel.: (49) 441973570
Web Site: http://www.evac.com
Water Collection & Treatment Systems Mfr
N.A.I.C.S.: 333998

Subsidiary (US):

Evac North America Inc.   **(5)**
1445 Huntwood Dr, Cherry Valley, IL
61016-9560
Tel.: (815) 639-7725
Web Site: http://evac.com
Marine Waste & Wastewater Collection &
Treatment Systems Mfr & Whslr
N.A.I.C.S.: 335220
Ken Postle *(Pres)*

Subsidiary (Non-US):

Evac Norway AS   **(5)**
Merdeveien 1, NO-3676, Notodden, Norway
Tel.: (47) 35029700
Web Site: http://www.evac.com
Cruise Ship Waste Treatment Systems De-
signer, Mfr & Whslr
N.A.I.C.S.: 237110
Kjell Erik Reinstad *(Gen Mgr)*

Evac Vacuum Systems (Shanghai)
Co., Ltd.   **(5)**
Section A Building 27 No 500 East Fu Te Er
Road WGQ Free Trade Zone, Shanghai,
China
Tel.: (86) 2150461468
Web Site: http://evac.com
Water Collection & Treatment Systems Mfr
N.A.I.C.S.: 333998
Marjukka Lemmetti *(Gen Mgr)*

Affiliate (Domestic):

Bridgepoint Advisers UK Limited   **(3)**
5 Marble Arch, London, W1H 7EJ, United
Kingdom
Tel.: (44) 2070343500
Privater Equity Firm
N.A.I.C.S.: 523999

Subsidiary (Domestic):

Bridgepoint Development Capital
Limited   **(4)**
5 Marble Arch, London, W1H 7EJ, United
Kingdom
Tel.: (44) 2074323500
Web Site: https://www.bridgepoint.eu
Sales Range: $25-49.9 Million
Emp.: 30
Venture Capital Investment Firm
N.A.I.C.S.: 523999

Holding (Domestic):

Achilles Group Limited   **(5)**
30 Western Avenue Milton Park, Abingdon,
OX14 4SH, Oxfordshire, United Kingdom
Tel.: (44) 1235820813
Web Site: http://www.achilles.com
Supply Chain Management Services
N.A.I.C.S.: 423840
Colin Maund *(Founder & Chm)*

Subsidiary (Non-US):

Achilles Development Services
AS   **(6)**
Luramyrveien 29, 4313, Sandnes, Norway
Tel.: (47) 51969100
Business Management Consulting Services
N.A.I.C.S.: 541611

Subsidiary (Domestic):

Achilles First Point Assessment
Limited   **(6)**
7 Burnbank Business Centre Souterhead
Road, Altens, Aberdeen, AB12 3LF, United
Kingdom
Tel.: (44) 1224337500
Business Management Consulting Services
N.A.I.C.S.: 541611

Subsidiary (Non-US):

Achilles Information (Australia) Pty
Ltd   **(6)**
1/38 Redland Bay Rd, Capalaba, 4157,
QLD, Australia
Tel.: (61) 739090300
Business Management Consulting Services
N.A.I.C.S.: 541611
Carrie Riessen *(Acct Mgr)*

Achilles Information (India) Private
Limited   **(6)**
Unit 405/406 B Wing Everest Grande Ma-
hakali Caves Road, Andheri East, Mumbai,
400 093, India
Tel.: (91) 2261287900
Business Management Consulting Services
N.A.I.C.S.: 541611

Achilles Information ApS   **(6)**
Universitetsparken 7, 4000, Roskilde, Den-
mark
Tel.: (45) 46740278
Business Management Consulting Services
N.A.I.C.S.: 541611

Achilles Information Centre AS   **(6)**
Vikaveien 31, PO Box 1656, 4817, Stoa,
Norway
Tel.: (47) 37063500
Business Management Consulting Services
N.A.I.C.S.: 541611
Anja Thorsdalen *(Mgr-Ops)*

Achilles Information GmbH   **(6)**
Niederkasseler Lohweg 191, 40547, Dus-
seldorf, Germany
Tel.: (49) 2115382170
Business Management Consulting Services
N.A.I.C.S.: 541611

Achilles Information Hong Kong
Ltd   **(6)**
8/F China Minmetals Tower 79-79A
Chatham Road, South Tsim Sha Tsui, Kow-
loon, China (Hong Kong)
Tel.: (852) 39168201
Business Management Consulting Services
N.A.I.C.S.: 541611

Subsidiary (US):

Achilles Information Inc   **(6)**
14811 St Mary's Ln Ste 200, Houston, TX
77079
Tel.: (281) 809-4400
Business Management Consulting Services
N.A.I.C.S.: 541611

Subsidiary (Non-US):

Achilles Information Limited   **(6)**
Nipex Building 30 Oyinkan Abayomi Drive,
Ikoyi, Lagos, Nigeria
Tel.: (234) 14630524
Business Management Consulting Services
N.A.I.C.S.: 541611

Achilles Information Limited   **(6)**
First Steps Business Centre Building 12,
PO Box 73030, Dubai, United Arab Emir-
ates
Tel.: (971) 529610164
Business Management Consulting Services
N.A.I.C.S.: 541611

Achilles Information Slovakia
s.r.o   **(6)**
Ivanska cesta 30/B, 821 04, Bratislava,
Slovakia
Tel.: (421) 220992300
Business Management Consulting Services
N.A.I.C.S.: 541611

Achilles Procurement Services
Limited   **(6)**
1 Harmsworth Greenmount Office Park,
Harolds Cross, Dublin, Ireland

Bridgepoint Group Plc—(Continued)

Tel.: (353) 14020114
Business Management Consulting Services
N.A.I.C.S.: 541611
Jeanne Copeland *(Dir-Ops)*

Achilles South Europe S.L.U. (6)
Av 5 de Outubro 10 7, Andar, Portugal
Tel.: (351) 211203810
Business Management Consulting Services
N.A.I.C.S.: 541611

Achilles South Europe S.L.U. (6)
Via Senigallia 2 Torre A, 20161, Milan, Italy
Tel.: (39) 0240326370
Business Management Consulting Services
N.A.I.C.S.: 541611

Achilles South Europe, S.L.U. (6)
Edificio Sollube Plaza Carlos Trias Bertran
7 planta cero, 28020, Madrid, Spain
Tel.: (34) 914264935
Business Management Consulting Services
N.A.I.C.S.: 541611

Achilles do Brasil Ltda. (6)
Rua Olimpiadas 205 4 Andar-Vila Olimpia,
04551-000, Sao Paulo, Brazil
Tel.: (55) 1137289330
Web Site: http://www.achilles.com
Business Management Consulting Services
N.A.I.C.S.: 541611

Achillevs Information AB (6)
Vretenvagen 13, 171 54, Solna, Sweden
Tel.: (46) 84441700
Business Management Consulting Services
N.A.I.C.S.: 541611

Aquiles Chile SpA. (6)
Av El Bosque Norte 0110 5to piso, Las
Condes, Santiago, Chile
Tel.: (56) 25859600
Business Management Consulting Services
N.A.I.C.S.: 541611

Holding (Domestic):

Analysys Mason Limited (5)
St Giles Court 24 Castle Street, Cambridge,
CB3 0AJ, Cambridgeshire, United Kingdom
Tel.: (44) 1223460600
Web Site: http://www.analysysmason.com
Information Technology Consulting Services
N.A.I.C.S.: 541690
Chris Stanford-Beale *(Partner)*

Branch (Domestic):

Analysys Mason Limited (6)
Bush House North West Wing Aldwych,
London, WC2B 4PJ, United Kingdom
Tel.: (44) 2073959000
Telecommunication Management Consulting
Services
N.A.I.C.S.: 541618
David Abecassis *(Partner)*

Holding (Non-US):

Anaveo SAS (5)
10 rue des Rosieristes, 69410,
Champagne-au-Mont-d'Or, France
Tel.: (33) 825302312
Web Site: http://www.anaveo.com
Sales Range: $50-74.9 Million
Emp.: 280
Surveillance & Security Systems Developer,
Mfr, Sales & Support Services
N.A.I.C.S.: 561621
Gregory Louis *(CEO)*

Holding (Domestic):

Care UK plc (4)
Connaught House 850 The Crescent,
Colchester Business Park, Colchester, CO4
9QB, Essex, United Kingdom
Tel.: (44) 1206752552
Web Site: http://www.careuk.com
Sales Range: $700-749.9 Million
Emp.: 280
Specialist Care Outsourcing Services for
Nursing, Residential & Homecare to Elderly,
Mentally Ill & Adults With Learning Difficulties
N.A.I.C.S.: 623210
Karen Morrison *(Head-Svc Design)*

Subsidiary (Domestic):

Althea Park Limited (5)

10 Lansdown, Stroud, GL5 1BB, United
Kingdom
Tel.: (44) 1453767093
Web Site: http://www.careuk.com
Sales Range: $10-24.9 Million
Emp.: 75
Health Care Srvices
N.A.I.C.S.: 621610
Martin Davies *(Mgr-Ops)*

**Care UK Clinical Services
Limited** (5)
Connaught House 850 The Crescent,
Colchester Business Park, Colchester, CO4
9QB, Essex, United Kingdom
Tel.: (44) 1206752552
Web Site: http://www.careuk.com
Emp.: 280
Health & Social Care Services
N.A.I.C.S.: 621491
Mike Parish *(CEO)*

**Care UK Community Partnerships
Group Limited** (5)
Connaught Hse 850 The Crescent,
Colchester Business Park, Colchester, CO4
9QB, United Kingdom
Tel.: (44) 1206752552
Sales Range: $25-49.9 Million
Emp.: 200
Health Care Srvices
N.A.I.C.S.: 621610

**Partnership Health Group
Limited** (5)
Rosebery House, 3rd Fl 41 Springfield Rd,
Chelmsford, CM2 6QZ, United Kingdom
Tel.: (44) 1245351749
Web Site:
    http://www.partnershiphealth.co.uk
Health Care Srvices
N.A.I.C.S.: 621491

Holding (Domestic):

Qualitest Group UK Ltd. (4)
1 Appold Street, London, EC2A 2UT, United
Kingdom
Tel.: (44) 1772888344
Web Site: https://www.qualitestgroup.com
Information Technology Consulting Services
N.A.I.C.S.: 518210
Anbu Muppidathi *(CEO)*

Subsidiary (US):

Q Analysts LLC (5)
5201 Great America Pkwy Ste 238, Santa
Clara, CA 95054
Tel.: (408) 907-8500
Web Site: http://www.qanalysts.com
Sales Range: $10-24.9 Million
Emp.: 252
Information Technology Consulting Services
N.A.I.C.S.: 541512
Ross Fernandes *(CEO & Founder)*

Holding (Domestic):

The Miller Group Ltd. (4)
Miller House 2 Lochside View, Edinburgh,
EH12 9DH, United Kingdom
Tel.: (44) 8703365000
Web Site: http://www.miller.co.uk
Sales Range: $1-4.9 Billion
Emp.: 1,309
House Building, Property Development &
Construction Services
N.A.I.C.S.: 236115
Phil Miller *(CEO-Miller Developments)*

Subsidiary (Domestic):

Miller Developments Limited (5)
1 Exchange Crescent Conference Square,
Edinburgh Park, Edinburgh, EH3 8UL,
United Kingdom
Tel.: (44) 1414735770
Web Site:
    http://www.millerdevelopments.co.uk
Sales Range: $50-74.9 Million
Property Development Services
N.A.I.C.S.: 531311
Andrew Sutherland *(Co-Mng Dir)*

Miller Homes Limited (5)
First Floor Miller House 2 Lochside View,
Edinburgh, EH12 9DH, United Kingdom
Tel.: (44) 8703365000
Web Site: http://www.millerhomes.co.uk

Housing Development Management
N.A.I.C.S.: 531311
Steve Birch *(Mng Dir-North England)*

Affiliate (Non-US):

Bridgepoint GmbH (3)
Nextower Thurn-und-Taxis-Platz 6, 60313,
Frankfurt am Main, Germany
Tel.: (49) 692108770
Sales Range: $50-74.9 Million
Emp.: 10
Privater Equity Firm
N.A.I.C.S.: 523999

Holding (Non-US):

Infinitas Learning Holding B.V. (4)
Het Spoor 8-14, Houten, 3994 AK, Netherlands
Tel.: (31) 306383520
Web Site: http://www.infinitaslearning.com
Sales Range: $400-449.9 Million
Holding Company; Educational Books, CD-
ROMs & Other Materials Publisher
N.A.I.C.S.: 511112
Clice Hay-Smith *(CEO)*

Holding (Domestic):

KPS AG (4)
Beta-Strasse 10H, 85774, Munich, Germany
Tel.: (49) 89356310
Web Site: http://www.kps-consulting.com
Sales Range: $10-24.9 Million
Holding Company; Information Technology
Consultancy Software & Services
N.A.I.C.S.: 551112
Michael Tsifidaris *(Chm-Supervisory Bd)*

Branch (Domestic):

KPS Consulting (5)
Stingelstrase 10, Saarbrucken, 66117,
Germany (100%)
Tel.: (49) 681950900
Web Site: http://www.kps-consulting.com
Emp.: 40
Document Management & Data Processing
Services
N.A.I.C.S.: 518210
Wolfgang Sandmaier *(Mng Dir)*

Affiliate (Non-US):

Bridgepoint Ltd. Sti. (3)
Visnezade Mahallesi Suleyman Seba Cad-
desi BJK Plaza no 48, A blok 9 kat D 93-94
Akaretler, Istanbul, Turkiye
Tel.: (90) 2123108252
Web Site: http://www.bridgepoint.eu
Emp.: 1
Privater Equity Firm
N.A.I.C.S.: 523999
Jason McGibbon *(Partner & Head-
Consumer Sector-London)*

Bridgepoint S.A. (3)
Calle de Rafael Calvo 39A 4 andar, 28010,
Madrid, Spain
Tel.: (34) 917022490
Emp.: 7
Privater Equity Firm
N.A.I.C.S.: 523999
Jose Maria Maldonado *(Partner & Head-
Investments-Spain)*

Bridgepoint S.A.S. (3)
21 Avenue Kleber, 75116, Paris, France
Tel.: (33) 170225300
Emp.: 30
Privater Equity Firm
N.A.I.C.S.: 523999
Benoit Bassi *(Chm & Partner)*

Holding (Domestic):

Balt Extrusion SAS (4)
10 rue Croix Vigneron, 95160, Montmor-
ency, France
Tel.: (33) 1 3989 4641
Web Site: http://www.balt.fr
Sales Range: $100-124.9 Million
Interventional Neuro Radiological Device
Distr
N.A.I.C.S.: 339112
Nicolas Plowiecki *(Founder & Pres)*

Subsidiary (Domestic):

Balt International SAS (5)

10 rue Croix Vigneron, 95160, Montmor-
ency, France
Tel.: (33) 1 3989 4641
Web Site: http://www.balt.fr
Holding Company; Interventional Neuro Ra-
diological Device Distr
N.A.I.C.S.: 551112
Pascal Girin *(Pres)*

Subsidiary (US):

Blockade Medical LLC (6)
18 Technology Dr Ste 169, Irvine, CA 92618
Tel.: (949) 788-1443
Web Site: http://www.blockademedical.com
Catheter-Based Therapeutic Device Devel-
oper, Mfr & Whslr
N.A.I.C.S.: 339112
Jake Le *(Dir-R&D)*

Holding (Domestic):

**Compagnie Stephanoise de Sante
SA** (4)
9 bis rue de la Piot, 42276, Saint-Priest-en-
Jarez, France
Tel.: (33) 477915972
Web Site: http://www.groupec2s.fr
Health Care Srvices
N.A.I.C.S.: 621498

FDS Group SA (4)
250 bis rue du Faubourg Saint-Honore,
75008, Paris, France
Tel.: (33) 148888887
Web Site: http://www.flexitallicgroup.com
Sales Range: $250-299.9 Million
Holding Company; Industrial Sealing Prod-
ucts Mfr
N.A.I.C.S.: 551112
Remi Toledano *(Pres)*

Subsidiary (Non-US):

AGS Flexitallic, Inc. (5)
4340 78 Avenue, Edmonton, T6B 3J5, AB,
Canada
Tel.: (780) 466-5050
Web Site: http://www.agsflexitallic.com
Sales Range: $25-49.9 Million
Emp.: 150
Gaskets & Other Sealing Device Mfr
N.A.I.C.S.: 339991
Steve Barnes *(Reg Mgr-Sls)*

Subsidiary (US):

Custom Rubber Products, Inc. (5)
2625 Bennington St, Houston, TX 77093
Tel.: (713) 691-2211
Web Site: http://www.customrubber.com
Sales Range: $1-9.9 Million
Emp.: 63
Plastics Product Mfr
N.A.I.C.S.: 326299
John J. Jorgensen *(Pres)*

The Flexitallic Group, Inc. (5)
6915 Hwy 225, Deer Park, TX 77536
Tel.: (281) 604-2400
Web Site: http://www.flexitallic.com
Sales Range: $100-124.9 Million
Emp.: 390
Sealing Products Mfr
N.A.I.C.S.: 339991
Al Valdemar *(Reg Mgr-Sls)*

Subsidiary (Domestic):

Flexitallic LP (6)
6915 Hwy 225, Deer Park, TX
77536-2414 (100%)
Tel.: (281) 604-2400
Web Site: http://www.flexitallic.com
Sales Range: $25-49.9 Million
Emp.: 205
Mfr of Spiral Wound Gaskets, Sheet Materi-
als & Heat Exchangers
N.A.I.C.S.: 339991
Ross Simmons *(VP-Mfg)*

Subsidiary (Non-US):

Flexitallic Ltd. (6)
Scandinavia Mill Hunsworth Lane, Cleck-
heaton, BD19 4LN, W Yorkshire, United
Kingdom (100%)
Tel.: (44) 1274 851 273
Web Site: http://www.flexitallic.eu
Sales Range: $25-49.9 Million
Emp.: 110

Mfr & Marketer of Industrial Static Sealing Products for Oil & Gas, Pipeline, Refining, Petrochemical, Pulp & Paper & Energy Industries
N.A.I.C.S.: 339991
Philip Kelshaw *(Dir-Sls)*

Holding (Domestic):

Groupe Moniteur Holding **(4)**
17 rue d Uzes, Paris, 75002, France
Tel.: (33) 140133030
Web Site: http://www.groupemoniteur.fr
Holding Company; Periodical & Commercial Journal Publisher
N.A.I.C.S.: 551112
Olivier de La Chaise *(Deputy Chief Officer)*

Subsidiary (Domestic):

Group Moniteur **(5)**
17 Rue d Uzes, 75002, Paris, France
Tel.: (33) 140133030
Web Site: http://www.groupemoniteur.fr
Periodical Publishers
N.A.I.C.S.: 513120
Guillaume Prot *(Pres)*

Subsidiary (Domestic):

Editions du Moniteur **(6)**
17 Rue D'Uzes, F 75002, Paris, France
Tel.: (33) 141961550
Web Site: http://www.editionsdumoniteur.com
Publisher of Books on Architecture, Construction, Economics; Bookstores
N.A.I.C.S.: 513130

Subsidiary (Domestic):

Groupe Territorial **(5)**
BP 215, 38506, Voiron, France
Tel.: (33) 476657136
Web Site: http://www.territorial.fr
Sales Range: $25-49.9 Million
Emp.: 80
Periodical Publishers
N.A.I.C.S.: 513120
Laurent Boidi *(Dir-Comml & Mktg)*

Prosys **(5)**
23 rue du Capitaine Ferber, 92130, Issy-les-Moulineaux, France
Tel.: (33) 141232777
Web Site: http://www.prosys.fr
Construction Project Management & Document Organization Services
N.A.I.C.S.: 561499

Vecteur Plus **(5)**
1 Rue Galilee, 44341, Bouguenais, Cedex, France
Tel.: (33) 251112626
Web Site: http://wwwvecteurplus.com
Sales Range: $50-74.9 Million
Emp.: 230
Periodical Publishing
N.A.I.C.S.: 513120
Matthieu Saudubray *(Mgr)*

Holding (Domestic):

Histoire d'Or S.A.S. **(4)**
2 Rue de Valenciennes, 75010, Paris, France
Tel.: (33) 144651314
Web Site: http://www.histoiredor.fr
Sales Range: $450-499.9 Million
Jewelry Stores
N.A.I.C.S.: 458310
Eric Belmonte *(CEO)*

Affiliate (Non-US):

Bridgepoint S.p.A. **(3)**
Via Gabba Fratelli 1/A, IT-20121, Milan, MI, Italy
Tel.: (39) 02806951
Web Site: http://www.bridgepoint.eu
Sales Range: $50-74.9 Million
Emp.: 9
Privater Equity Firm
N.A.I.C.S.: 523999

Bridgepoint Sp. z o.o. **(3)**
ul Rondo ONZ 1, Warsaw, 124, Poland
Tel.: (48) 225448282
Web Site: http://www.bridgepoint.eu

Sales Range: $50-74.9 Million
Emp.: 7
Privater Equity Firm
N.A.I.C.S.: 523999
Khai Tan *(Partner & Head-Investments-Central & Eastern Europe)*

Holding (Domestic):

SMYK S.A. **(4)**
104/122 Marszakowska st, PL-00-017, Warsaw, Poland
Tel.: (48) 224610000
Web Site: http://www.smykgroup.com
Children's Toys, Apparel & School Supplies Distr
N.A.I.C.S.: 459120
Marek Lebek *(Mgr-Mktg & PR)*

Holding (US):

Kyriba Corporation **(3)**
11622 El Camino Real Ste 100, San Diego, CA 92130
Tel.: (858) 764-2458
Web Site: http://www.kyriba.com
Management Consulting Services
N.A.I.C.S.: 541611
Didier Martineau *(Chief Info Security Officer)*

Holding (Non-US):

Miya Luxemburg Holdings S.a.r.l. **(3)**
46A Avenue J F Kennedy, 1855, Luxembourg, Luxembourg
Tel.: (352) 4271713259
Web Site: http://www.miya-water.com
Water Distr
N.A.I.C.S.: 221310
Amit Horman *(CEO)*

Holding (US):

Safety Technology Holdings, Inc. **(3)**
23300 Haggerty Rd, Farmington Hills, MI 48335
Tel.: (248) 778-2000
Web Site: http://www.stholdingsinc.com
Holding Company; Safety Related Test & Measurement Systems Mfr
N.A.I.C.S.: 551112
Christopher J. O'Connor *(Pres & CEO)*

Subsidiary (Domestic):

HITEC Sensor Solutions, Inc. **(4)**
10 Elizabeth Dr, Chelmsford, MA 01824
Tel.: (978) 742-9032
Web Site: http://www.hitecorp.com
Electronic Components Mfr
N.A.I.C.S.: 334419
Chris Delling *(Sls Mgr-Western Reg)*

Humanetics Innovative Solutions, Inc. **(4)**
23300 Haggerty Rd, Farmington Hills, MI 48335
Tel.: (734) 451-7878
Web Site: http://www.humaneticsatd.com
Anthropomorphic Test Devices (Crash Test Dummies) Designer, Developer & Mfr
N.A.I.C.S.: 339999
Michael Jarouche *(VP-Sls & Mktg-Global)*

Subsidiary (Non-US):

Fibercore, Ltd. **(5)**
Fibercore House University Parkway, Southampton Science Park, Southampton, SO16 7QQ, United Kingdom
Tel.: (44) 2380769893
Web Site: http://www.fibercore.com
Optical Fiber Mfr
N.A.I.C.S.: 335921
Chris Emslie *(CEO)*

FronTone GmbH **(5)**
Teslastrasse 4, Raaba, 8074, Grambach, Austria
Tel.: (43) 316293618
Web Site: http://www.frontone.at
Vehicle Safety Test Equipment Mfr
N.A.I.C.S.: 334519
Klaus Matlschweiger *(CTO)*

Holding (Non-US):

Sapec Agro S.A. **(3)**
Av do Rio Tejo - Herdade das Prais, 2910-440, Setubal, Portugal

Tel.: (351) 265710100
Web Site: http://www.sapecagro.pt
Farm Supplies Distr
N.A.I.C.S.: 424910
Eric Van Innis *(CEO)*

Subsidiary (Non-US):

Sapec Agro Macau Ltd. **(4)**
Avenida Praia Grande 759 2, Macau, 999078, China (Macau)
Tel.: (853) 28356691
Farm Supplies Whslr
N.A.I.C.S.: 424910

Sapec Agro, S.A.U. **(4)**
Parque Empresarial TACTICA - C Botiguers n3 4th Fl, 46980, Paterna, Valencia, Spain
Tel.: (34) 961345150
Web Site: http://www.sapecagro.es
Farm Supplies Distr
N.A.I.C.S.: 424910
Andres Arevalo Fuentes *(Mgr-Iberia Area)*

Bridgepoint Investment Consultants (Shanghai) Co., Ltd. **(1)**
21F Unit 2103-2105 Shanghai One ICC 999 Huaihai Road, Shanghai, 200031, China
Tel.: (86) 2161937688
Fund Management Services
N.A.I.C.S.: 523940

Bridgepoint Netherlands B.V. **(1)**
Paulus Potterstraat 22A, 1071 DA, Amsterdam, Netherlands
Tel.: (31) 202803100
Fund Management Services
N.A.I.C.S.: 523940

Bridgepoint, LLC **(1)**
2095A Cooks Rd, Mount Juliet, TN 37122
Tel.: (615) 453-5000
Web Site: https://bridgepointtn.com
Building Construction Services
N.A.I.C.S.: 236220

Fera Science Limited **(1)**
York Biotech Campus, Sand Hutton, York, YO41 1LZ, United Kingdom **(75%)**
Tel.: (44) 3001000321
Web Site: https://www.fera.co.uk
Agriculture & Food Research Services
N.A.I.C.S.: 541714
Michael Dickinson *(Mgr-Ops)*

BRIDGEPORT CAPITAL MANAGEMENT PTY LTD
Level 14 23 Hunter St, Sydney, 2000, Australia
Tel.: (61) 2 9233 7200
Web Site:
   http://www.bridgeportcapital.com.au
Year Founded: 2015
Private Investment Firm
N.A.I.C.S.: 523999
David Plumridge *(Mng Dir)*

BRIDGES VENTURES LLP
38 Seymour Street, Marylebone, London, W1H 7BP, United Kingdom
Tel.: (44) 20 3780 8000
Web Site:
   http://www.bridgesventures.com
Investment Management Service
N.A.I.C.S.: 523999
Guy Bowden *(Partner)*

BRIDGESTONE CORPORATION
1-1 Kyobashi 3-chome, Chuo-ku, Tokyo, 104-8340, Japan
Tel.: (81) 368363333   JP
Web Site:
   https://www.bridgestone.com
Year Founded: 1931
5108—(NGO)
Rev.: $28,986,992,320
Assets: $40,552,685,360
Liabilities: $19,302,268,480
Net Worth: $21,250,416,880
Earnings: ($225,553,680)
Emp.: 138,036
Fiscal Year-end: 12/31/20
Rubber Related Product Mfr

N.A.I.C.S.: 326299
Masahiro Higashi *(COO-Global)*

Subsidiaries:

ATC Pvt. Ltd. **(1)**
336/21 Ganeshman Sing Path-2 Teku, Kathmandu, Nepal
Tel.: (977) 14261220
Web Site: http://www.atc.com.np
Tire Distr
N.A.I.C.S.: 423130

Amin Tyre Ltd. **(1)**
Olympia Business Center Jada-i-Maiwand, Kabul, Afghanistan
Tel.: (93) 202212153
Tiles Mfr
N.A.I.C.S.: 326211

Asahi Carbon Co., Ltd **(1)**
Kamomejima-cho 2, Higashi-ku, Niigata, 950 0883, Japan **(99.4%)**
Tel.: (81) 252741211
Web Site: http://www.asahicarbon.co.jp
Sales Range: $75-99.9 Million
Emp.: 161
Carbon Black Mfr & Distr
N.A.I.C.S.: 325180

BRIDGESTONE RIHGA, LTD. **(1)**
45-1 Ebisujimacho, Sakai-Ku, Sakai, 590-0985, Japan
Tel.: (81) 722241121
Emp.: 25
Automotive Tire Mfr
N.A.I.C.S.: 326211
Harold Linsschn *(Gen Mgr)*

BRIDGESTONE TYRE SALES SINGAPORE PTE. LTD. **(1)**
83 Clemenceau Avenue 08-01/08 UE Square, Singapore, 239920, Singapore
Tel.: (65) 6 540 4196
Web Site: https://www.bridgestone.com.sg
Sales Range: $25-49.9 Million
Emp.: 2
Automotive Tires Distr
N.A.I.C.S.: 423130

BRIDGESTONE TYRES (P.N.G) PTY. LTD **(1)**
Milfordhaven Road, PO Box 459, Lae, 411, Morobe, Papua New Guinea
Tel.: (675) 472 1822
Sales Range: $75-99.9 Million
Emp.: 15
Automotive Tires Distr
N.A.I.C.S.: 423130
Jon Seeto *(Gen Mgr)*

Bandag Incorporated **(1)**
2000 Bandag Dr, Muscatine, IA 52761
Tel.: (563) 262-1400
Web Site: http://www.bandag.com
Sales Range: $900-999.9 Million
Emp.: 200
Tire Treads Mfr
N.A.I.C.S.: 326212
LaTres Jarret *(Dir-Mktg)*

Binter & Co Pte. Ltd. **(1)**
24 Pandan Road, Singapore, 609275, Singapore
Tel.: (65) 63457611
Web Site: http://www.binter.com.sg
Tiles Mfr
N.A.I.C.S.: 326211
Marcus Lim *(Gen Mgr)*

Bridgestone (China) Research & Development Co., Ltd. **(1)**
No 67 Xinmei Road National High-tech Industrial Development Zone, Wuxi, 214028, Jiangsu, China
Tel.: (86) 51085322282
Tiles Mfr
N.A.I.C.S.: 326211

Bridgestone (China) Tire Assessment & Development Co., Ltd. **(1)**
No 118 Qian Da Dushan Village, Zhang Zhu Town, Yixing, 214231, Jiangsu, China
Tel.: (86) 51066510082
Tiles Mfr
N.A.I.C.S.: 326211

Bridgestone (Huizhou) Tire Co., Ltd. **(1)**
No 1 Huitai Road Huinan High-tech Indus-

Bridgestone Corporation—(Continued)

trial Park Huiao Avenue, Huizhou, 516025, Guangdong, China
Tel.: (86) 7522056688
Tiles Mfr
N.A.I.C.S.: 326211

Bridgestone (Wuxi) Tire Co., Ltd. (1)
No 67 Xinmei Road, National High-New Technical Industrial Development Zone, Wuxi, 214028, Jiangsu, China
Tel.: (86) 51085322288
Tiles Mfr
N.A.I.C.S.: 326211

Bridgestone APM Company (1)
235 Commerce Way, Upper Sandusky, OH 43351 (100%)
Tel.: (419) 294-6304
Web Site: https://www.bapm.com
Sales Range: $25-49.9 Million
Emp.: 25
Antivibration Components for Automobiles Mfr & Sales
N.A.I.C.S.: 325212
Todd Hole (Gen Mgr-HR)

Bridgestone Aircraft Tire Company (Asia) Limited (1)
22-24 Dai Wang Street, Tai Po Industry Estate, Tai Po, New Territories, China (Hong Kong) (100%)
Tel.: (852) 2 664 8303
Web Site: http://www.bridgestone.com
Sales Range: $25-49.9 Million
Emp.: 100
Aircraft Tires Distr
N.A.I.C.S.: 326211

Bridgestone Aircraft tire Company (China) Limited (1)
180 Tashan Road, Qingdao, 266500, China
Tel.: (86) 532 8098 2990
Sales Range: $25-49.9 Million
Emp.: 120
Aircraft Tire Mfr
N.A.I.C.S.: 336413

Bridgestone Americas, Inc. (1)
200 4th Ave S, Nashville, TN 37201 (100%)
Tel.: (615) 937-1000
Web Site: https://www.bridgestoneamericas.com
Sales Range: $250-299.9 Million
Emp.: 1,700
Tire Mfr & Distr
N.A.I.C.S.: 326211
Riccardo Cichi (Chief Sls Officer & Pres-Core Tire)

Subsidiary (Domestic):

BFS Diversified Products, LLC (2)
250 W 96th St, Indianapolis, IN 46260 (100%)
Tel.: (317) 575-7000
Web Site: http://www.firestonebpco.com
Sales Range: $150-199.9 Million
Emp.: 500
Roofing Materials, Synthetic Rubber & Textiles Mfr
N.A.I.C.S.: 313320

Division (Domestic):

Firestone Building Products Division (3)
250 W 96th St, Indianapolis, IN 46260 (100%)
Tel.: (317) 575-7000
Web Site: http://www.firestonebpco.com
Sales Range: $50-74.9 Million
Emp.: 200
Roofing & Insulation Mfr
N.A.I.C.S.: 326291

Plant (Domestic):

Firestone Building Products-Beech Grove (4)
3525 S Arlington Ave, Indianapolis, IN 46203-6102 (100%)
Tel.: (317) 784-1161
Web Site: http://www.bridgestone-firestone.com
Sales Range: $25-49.9 Million
Emp.: 60
Roofing Mfr

N.A.I.C.S.: 441340

Firestone Building Products-Kingstree (4)
Old Lake City Hwy, Kingstree, SC 29556-9804
Tel.: (843) 382-5040
Web Site: http://www.sharonstair.com
Sales Range: $75-99.9 Million
Rubber Roofing Mfr
N.A.I.C.S.: 441340

Firestone Building Products-Prescott (4)
1406 Hwy 371 N, Prescott, AR 71857-3903
Tel.: (870) 887-2673
Web Site: http://www.firestonebpco.com
Sales Range: $100-124.9 Million
Roofing, Flashing & Seam Tape Mfr
N.A.I.C.S.: 326299
Ray Oxley (Plant Mgr)

Division (Non-US):

Firestone Fibers & Textiles Division (3)
Tel.: (704) 734-2100
Web Site: https://www.firestonefibers.com
Sales Range: $100-124.9 Million
Emp.: 350
Tire Cord & Industrial Fabric Mfr
N.A.I.C.S.: 313110

Plant (Domestic):

Firestone Fibers & Textiles Company, LLC - Gastonia Manufacturing Facility
1101 W Second Ave, Gastonia, NC 28052
Tel.: (704) 734-2100
Web Site: http://www.bridgestone-firestone.com
Fiber Textile Products Mfr
N.A.I.C.S.: 314999

Firestone Fibers & Textiles-Kings Mountain (4)
100 Firestone Ln, Kings Mountain, NC 28086-1369
Tel.: (704) 734-2102
Sales Range: $50-74.9 Million
Emp.: 300
Tire Cord & Industrial Fabric Mfr
N.A.I.C.S.: 314994

Plant (Non-US):

Firestone Textiles-Woodstock (4)
1200 Dundas St E, PO Box 486, Woodstock, N4S 7Y9, ON, Canada
Tel.: (519) 537-6231
Web Site: http://www.firestone-textile.com
Sales Range: $50-74.9 Million
Emp.: 270
Tire Cord Fabrics & Textiles Mfr
N.A.I.C.S.: 314994
Don Bacher (Mgr-Sls & Mktg)

Division (Domestic):

Firestone Industrial Products Division (3)
250 W 96th St Ste 150, Indianapolis, IN 46260 (100%)
Tel.: (317) 818-8600
Web Site: http://www.firestoneip.com
Sales Range: $25-49.9 Million
Emp.: 100
Vehicular Suspension Systems & Industrial Air Springs Mfr
N.A.I.C.S.: 336213
Craig Schneider (Pres)

Plant (Domestic):

Firestone Industrial Products Company-Dyersburg (4)
1901 Sylvan Rd, Dyersburg, TN 38024-1703
Tel.: (731) 286-5054
Web Site: http://www.firestoneip.com
Sales Range: $25-49.9 Million
Mfr of Air Springs for Motor Vehicles & Industrial Uses
N.A.I.C.S.: 336390

Subsidiary (Non-US):

Firestone Industrial Products Poland Sp. z o.o. (4)

Berzyna 80, 64-200, Wolsztyn, Poland
Tel.: (48) 68 347 5100
Web Site: http://www.bridgestone-firestone.com
Air Spring Mfr
N.A.I.C.S.: 336413
Powell Jada (Gen Mgr)

Firestone Industrial Products de Costa Rica, S.A. (4)
500 Mts Noreste del Cruce La Suiza y Turrialba Pavones, Turrialba, Cartago, Costa Rica
Tel.: (506) 2558.4200
Sales Range: $25-49.9 Million
Emp.: 145
Air Spring Mfr
N.A.I.C.S.: 336413
Alvaro Murillo (Mgr)

Plant (Non-US):

Firestone Industrial Products, LLC - Arnhem Manufacturing Facility (4)
Delta 160, 6825 MV, Arnhem, Netherlands
Tel.: (31) 263529898
Web Site: http://www.bridgestone-firestone.com
Sales Range: $10-24.9 Million
Emp.: 25
Industrial Machinery Mfr
N.A.I.C.S.: 333248
Piotr Bogaczynski (Mng Dir)

Plant (Domestic):

Firestone Industrial Products-Williamsburg (4)
1 Firestone Blvd, Williamsburg, KY 40769-9338
Tel.: (606) 549-0528
Web Site: http://www.firestoneindustrial.com
Sales Range: $25-49.9 Million
Emp.: 100
Airsprings Mfr
N.A.I.C.S.: 315990

Subsidiary (Non-US):

Firestone Produtos Industriais Av. (4)
Queiros dos Santos 1717, 09015 311, Santo Andre, Sao Paulo, Brazil
Tel.: (55) 11 4433 1166
Industrial Machinery Mfr
N.A.I.C.S.: 333248

Plant (Domestic):

Firestone Synthetic Rubber & Latex-Orange (4)
Farm Rd 1006, Orange, TX 77630
Tel.: (409) 883-1776
Web Site: http://www.firestone.com
Sales Range: $100-124.9 Million
Synthetic Rubber Mfr
N.A.I.C.S.: 325199

Subsidiary (Non-US):

BRIDGESTONE OFF-THE-ROAD TIRE LATIN AMERICA S.A (2)
La Concepcion 322 Floor 7th Providencia, PO Box 283-T, Las Condes, Santiago, Chile
Tel.: (56) 2 264 0550
Web Site: http://www.bridgestone.com
Emp.: 35
Automotive Tire Mfr
N.A.I.C.S.: 326211

Subsidiary (Domestic):

Bridgestone Aircraft Tire (USA), Inc. (2)
802 S Ayersville Rd, Mayodan, NC 27027-1889 (100%)
Tel.: (336) 548-8100
Web Site: http://ap.bridgestone.co.jp
Sales Range: $50-74.9 Million
Emp.: 150
Aircraft Tire Retread & Sales
N.A.I.C.S.: 441340
Deron Hill (Engr-Svc Field)

Division (Domestic):

Bridgestone Americas, Inc. - Center for Research & Technology (2)
10 E Firestone Blvd, Akron, OH 44317
Tel.: (330) 379-7000

Web Site: https://www.bridgestoneamericas.com
Sales Range: $25-49.9 Million
Emp.: 60
Research & Development Services
N.A.I.C.S.: 541715

Subsidiary (Non-US):

Bridgestone Argentina S.A.I.C. (2)
Av Antartida Argentina 2715, Llavallol, 1836, Buenos Aires, Argentina (100%)
Tel.: (54) 1142393100
Web Site: http://www.bridgestone.com.ar
Sales Range: $200-249.9 Million
Tire Mfr & Distr
N.A.I.C.S.: 326211

Bridgestone Canada, Inc. (2)
5770 Hurontario St Suite 400, Mississauga, L5R 3G5, ON, Canada
Tel.: (905) 890-1990
Web Site: http://www.bridgestone-firestone.ca
Sales Range: $450-499.9 Million
Automotive Tire Mfr & Distr
N.A.I.C.S.: 326211

Bridgestone Chile, S.A. (2)
Avenida Presidente Kennedy 5735 Torre Poniente Piso 12 Oficina 1202B, Las Condes, Santiago, Chile
Tel.: (56) 2 460 7200
Web Site: http://www.bridgestone-firestone.com
Automotive Tires Distr
N.A.I.C.S.: 423130

Subsidiary (Domestic):

Bridgestone Hosepower, LLC (2)
50 Industrial Loop N, Orange Park, FL 32073
Tel.: (904) 264-1267
Web Site: https://www.hosepower.com
Hose Mfr
N.A.I.C.S.: 332912
J. Palmer Clarkson (Founder)

Subsidiary (Domestic):

Bridgestone Hosepower - Arizona (3)
2937 E Broadway Rd, Phoenix, AZ 85040
Tel.: (602) 263-8000
Web Site: http://www.hydraulichoseassembly.net
Sales Range: $10-24.9 Million
Emp.: 5
Rubber Goods Mfr
N.A.I.C.S.: 423840
Bob Traute (VP-Sls)

Cline Hose & Hydraulics, LLC (3)
601 Buncombe St, Greenville, SC 29601
Tel.: (864) 233-7104
Web Site: http://www.clinehose.com
Sales Range: $1-9.9 Million
Emp.: 30
Mfg Fluid Power Valves/Fittings Mfg Hardware Mfg Rubber/Plastic Hose/Belting
N.A.I.C.S.: 332912
Scott Cline (Principal)

Fittings, Inc. (3)
5979 4th Ave S, Seattle, WA 98108
Tel.: (206) 767-4670
Web Site: http://www.fittingsinc.com
Industrial Supplies Distr
N.A.I.C.S.: 423830

Subsidiary (Non-US):

Bridgestone Off-the-Road Tire Peru S.A.C. (2)
Avenida Jorge Chavez 263 Office 402, Miraflores, Lima, 9, Peru
Tel.: (51) 1 612 6600
Sales Range: $25-49.9 Million
Emp.: 16
Automotive Tires Distr
N.A.I.C.S.: 423130
Takumi Sadohara (Gen Mgr)

Subsidiary (Domestic):

Bridgestone Retail Operations, LLC (2)
333 E Lake St, Bloomingdale, IL 60108 (100%)
Tel.: (630) 259-9000

Web Site: http://www.bridgestone-
firestone.com
Tires & Automotive Components Sales &
Automotive Repair Services
N.A.I.C.S.: 811111
Marko Ibrahim *(Pres)*

Division (Domestic):

**Bridgestone/Firestone Credit Card
Division** (3)
6275 Eastland Rd, Brook Park, OH 44142
Tel.: (216) 362-5000
Credit Card & Collection Services
N.A.I.C.S.: 522130

Subsidiary (Domestic):

Credit First National Association (3)
6275 Eastland Rd, Brook Park, OH 44142
Tel.: (216) 362-5000
Commercial Banking Services
N.A.I.C.S.: 522110
Mary Humphrey *(Coord-Trng & Techincal)*

Unit (Domestic):

GCR Tire Centers (3)
2601 N 32nd Ave, Phoenix, AZ 85009-1505
Tel.: (602) 269-1351
Web Site: http://www.gcrtires.com
Tire Saves
N.A.I.C.S.: 423130

Subsidiary (Domestic):

Tires Plus Total Car Care (3)
2021 Sunnydale Blvd, Clearwater, FL
33765
Tel.: (321) 751-2131
Web Site: http://www.tiresplus.com
Retail Tire & Automotive Repair Facilities
N.A.I.C.S.: 811198

Subsidiary (Non-US):

**Bridgestone de Mexico, S.A.de
C.V.** (2)
Av Juan Vazquez de Mella No 481 Piso 4
Col Los Morales Polanco, Miguel Hidalgo,
11510, Mexico
Tel.: (52) 555 636 6600
Web Site: http://www.bridgestone.com
Emp.: 180
Automobile Tire Mfr & Distr
N.A.I.C.S.: 326211

Plant (Non-US):

**Bridgestone do Brasil Industria e Co-
mercio Ltda. - Sao Paulo Plant** (2)
Av Queiros dos Santos 1717, Sao Paulo,
09015-901, Brazil
Tel.: (55) 11 4433 1666
Automotive Tire Mfr
N.A.I.C.S.: 326211

Subsidiary (Non-US):

**Bridgestone/Firestone Canada,
Inc.** (2)
5770 Hurontario St Suite 400, Mississauga,
L5R 3G5, ON, Canada (100%)
Tel.: (905) 890-1990
Web Site: http://www.bridgestonetire.ca
Sales Range: $25-49.9 Million
Emp.: 90
Tires & Automotive Components Sales
N.A.I.C.S.: 326211

Bridgestone/Firestone Chile, S.A. (2)
Avenida Presidente Kennedy 5735 Torre
Poniente Piso 12 Oficina 1202B, Las Con-
des, Santiago, Chile (89.7%)
Tel.: (56) 2 460 7200
Web Site: https://www.bridgestone.cl
Sales Range: $25-49.9 Million
Emp.: 23
Tire Mfr & Distr
N.A.I.C.S.: 326211
Sergio Naqashima *(Gen Mgr)*

Division (Domestic):

**Bridgestone/Firestone Information
Services Company** (2)
1200 Ofc Main St, Akron, OH 44310-0001
Tel.: (330) 379-7000
Sales Range: $25-49.9 Million
Emp.: 100
Data Services

N.A.I.C.S.: 518210

Subsidiary (Non-US):

**Bridgestone/Firestone de Costa Rica,
S.A.** (2)
Km 11 Autopista General Canas La Ribera
de Belen, San Jose, Heredia, 4018-1000,
Costa Rica (98.6%)
Tel.: (506) 2 209 7300
Web Site: https://www.bridgestone.co.cr
Sales Range: $200-249.9 Million
Tire Mfr & DistrTire Mfr & Distr
N.A.I.C.S.: 326211
Oscar Rodriguez *(Gen Mgr)*

**Bridgestone/Firestone do Brasil In-
dustria e Comercio Ltda** (2)
Av Jornalista Roberto Marinho 85, 18 andar
Conj 181 e 182 Cond Tower Bridge Cidade
Moncoes, Sao Paulo, SP, Brazil (100%)
Tel.: (55) 1144331666
Web Site: http://www.bridgestone.com.br
Tire Mfr & Distr
N.A.I.C.S.: 326211

**Bridgestonede Mexico, S.A. de
C.V.** (2)
Av Juan Vazquez de Mella 481 4to Piso Col
Los Morales, Polanco, Mexico
Tel.: (52) 5556266600
Web Site:
http://piensaantesdeconducir.com.mx
Tire Mfr & Distr
N.A.I.C.S.: 326211

Subsidiary (Domestic):

**Firestone Building Products Com-
pany, LLC** (2)
200 4th Ave S, Nashville, TN 37201
Tel.: (317) 575-7000
Web Site: http://www.firestonebpco.com
Commercial Roofing System Mfr
N.A.I.C.S.: 332322
Michelle Lane *(Exec Dir-Mktg)*

Plant (Domestic):

**Firestone Building Products Com-
pany, LLC - Bristol Manufacturing
Facility** (3)
780 James P Casey Rd, Bristol, CT 06010
Tel.: (860) 584-9000
Web Site: http://www.bridgestone-
firestone.com
Insulation & Roofing Materials Mfr
N.A.I.C.S.: 332322

**Firestone Building Products Com-
pany, LLC - Corsicana Manufacturing
Facility** (3)
4201 E Hwy 31, Corsicana, TX 75109-9697
Tel.: (903) 874-1003
Web Site: http://www.bridgestone-
firestone.com
Insulation Material Mfr
N.A.I.C.S.: 339999

**Firestone Building Products Com-
pany, LLC - DeForest Manufacturing
Facility** (3)
612 N Stevenson Rd, De Forest, WI 53532
Tel.: (608) 846-4440
Web Site: http://www.bridgestone-
firestone.com
Insulation & Roofing Materials Mfr
N.A.I.C.S.: 332322

**Firestone Building Products Com-
pany, LLC - Florence Manufacturing
Facility** (3)
8170 Holton Dr, Florence, KY 41042
Tel.: (859) 291-4900
Web Site: http://www.bridgestone-
firestone.com
Emp.: 32
Insulation & Roofing Materials Mfr
N.A.I.C.S.: 339999
Claud Gibson *(Plant Mgr)*

**Firestone Building Products Com-
pany, LLC - Indianapolis Manufacturing Facility** (3)
3525 S Arlington Ave, Indianapolis, IN
46203
Tel.: (317) 784-1161
Web Site: http://www.bridgestone-
firestone.com

Emp.: 54
Insulation & Roofing Materials Mfr
N.A.I.C.S.: 332322
Tonecko Anderson *(Branch Mgr)*

**Firestone Building Products Com-
pany, LLC - Jacksonville Manufactur-
ing Facility** (3)
6831 Stuart Ave, Jacksonville, FL 32254
Tel.: (904) 783-3110
Web Site: http://www.bridgestone-
firestone.com
Insulation & Residential Sheeting Materials
Mfr
N.A.I.C.S.: 339999
Bruce Miller *(Plant Mgr)*

**Firestone Building Products Com-
pany, LLC - Prescott Manufacturing
Facility** (3)
1406 Hwy 371 N, Prescott, AR 71857
Tel.: (870) 887-2673
Web Site: http://www.bridgestone-
firestone.com
Building Materials Mfr
N.A.I.C.S.: 332322

**Firestone Building Products Com-
pany, LLC - Salt Lake City Manufac-
turing Facility** (3)
3790 W 2555 S, Salt Lake City, UT 84120
Tel.: (801) 972-6650
Web Site: http://www.bridgestone-
firestone.com
Sales Range: $25-49.9 Million
Emp.: 20
Insulation & Roofing Materials Mfr
N.A.I.C.S.: 339999
Jason Lakatos *(Mgr)*

**Firestone Building Products Com-
pany, LLC - Tuscumbia Manufacturing Facility** (3)
393 Denton Cir, Tuscumbia, AL 35674
Tel.: (256) 381-4001
Roofing Construction Services
N.A.I.C.S.: 238160

**Firestone Building Products Com-
pany, LLC - Wellford Manufacturing
Facility** (3)
320 Innovation Way, Wellford, SC 29385-
8900
Tel.: (864) 439-5641
Web Site: http://www.bridgestone-
firestone.com
Emp.: 100
Building Product Mfr
N.A.I.C.S.: 327331
Greg Shrrun *(Plant Mgr)*

**Firestone Building Products Com-
pany, LLC - Youngwood Manufactur-
ing Facility** (3)
Buncher Commerce Park Bldg 102 Ave A,
Youngwood, PA 15697
Tel.: (724) 755-1100
Web Site: http://www.bridgestone-
firestone.com
Sales Range: $25-49.9 Million
Emp.: 40
Insulation Materials & Metal Sheet Mfr
N.A.I.C.S.: 332322
Scott Thompson *(Mgr)*

Subsidiary (Domestic):

**Firestone Diversified Products,
LLC** (3)
250 W 96th St, Indianapolis, IN 46260
Tel.: (317) 575-7000
Extruded Rubber Product Mfr
N.A.I.C.S.: 326299

Firestone Energy Solutions (3)
250 W 96th St, Indianapolis, IN 46260
Tel.: (317) 853-4680
Solar Power Generation Services
N.A.I.C.S.: 221114

**Firestone GenFlex Roofing Systems,
LLC** (3)
250 W 96th St, Indianapolis, IN 46260
Tel.: (800) 443-4272
Web Site: http://www.genflex.com
Roofing System Mfr
N.A.I.C.S.: 332322
Tim Dunn *(Pres & CEO)*

Gaco Western Inc. (3)
200 4th Ave S, Nashville, TN 37201
Tel.: (800) 331-0196
Web Site: http://www.gaco.com
Synthetic Rubber Mfr
N.A.I.C.S.: 325212
Peter A. Davis *(Chm & CEO)*

Subsidiary (Domestic):

**Firestone Natural Rubber Company,
LLC** (2)
535 Marriott Dr, Nashville, TN 37214-0990
Tel.: (615) 937-1000
Web Site:
http://www.firestonenaturalrubber.com
Rubber Products Mfr
N.A.I.C.S.: 326291

Firestone Polymers, LLC (2)
381 W Wilbeth Rd, Akron, OH 44301
Web Site: http://www.firestonepolymers.com
Emp.: 65
Industrial Chemicals Mfr
N.A.I.C.S.: 325180
Karen Maglione *(Mgr-Product Dev)*

Plant (Domestic):

**Firestone Polymers, LLC - Lake
Charles Plant** (3)
Hwy 108 S, Lake Charles, LA 70601
Tel.: (337) 882-1211
Synthetic Rubber Mfr
N.A.I.C.S.: 325212

**Firestone Polymers, LLC - Orange
Plant** (3)
5713 Farm Rd 1006, Orange, TX 77630
Tel.: (409) 924-4500
Web Site: http://www.firestonepolymers.com
Synthetic Rubber Mfr
N.A.I.C.S.: 325212

**Bridgestone Asia Pacific Pte.
Ltd.** (1)
83 Clemenceau Avenue 08-01/ 08 UE
Square, Singapore, 239920, Singapore
Tel.: (65) 6 540 4000
Web Site: https://www.bridgestone-
asiapacific.com
Sales Range: $50-74.9 Million
Emp.: 10
Automotive Tires Distr
N.A.I.C.S.: 423130
Yoshikazu Shida *(Chm)*

Subsidiary (Non-US):

**Bridgestone (China) Investment Co.,
Ltd.** (2)
9th Floor Admiralty Plaza No 98 Huaihai
Middle Road, Huangpu, Shanghai, 200021,
China
Tel.: (86) 216 132 1888
Web Site: https://www.bridgestone.com.cn
Tire & Tube Distr
N.A.I.C.S.: 423130

**Bridgestone (Shenyang) Tire Co.,
Ltd.** (2)
No 53 Shenxiliudong Rd Shenyang Eco-
nomic & Technology Development Zone,
Shenyang, 110141, China
Tel.: (86) 2485815202
Tiles Mfr
N.A.I.C.S.: 326211

**Bridgestone (Tianjin) Tire Co.,
Ltd.** (2)
Tiedao-Dong Yinheqiao-bei, Beichen Dis-
trict, Tianjin, 300400, China
Tel.: (86) 2226881111
Tiles Mfr
N.A.I.C.S.: 326211

**Bridgestone Asia Pacific Pte. Ltd. -
Indore Plant** (1)
Plot No 12 Kheda Growth Centre Post Sag-
ore Pithampur, Dist Dhar, Indore, 454774,
Madhya Pradesh, India
Tel.: (91) 7292423333
Tiles Mfr
N.A.I.C.S.: 326211
Praveen Saxena *(Sr Gen Mgr)*

**Bridgestone Asia Pacific Technical
Center Co., Ltd.** (1)
113 Moo 18, Klong Nueng Subdistrict Klong

Bridgestone Corporation—(Continued)

Luang District, Pathumthani, 12120, Thailand
Tel.: (66) 20161200
Tiles Mfr
N.A.I.C.S.: 326211
L. Orranuch (Asst Mgr)

Bridgestone Australia Ltd.   (1)
210 Greenhill Road, Eastwood, 5063, SA, Australia   (60.3%)
Tel.: (61) 88 206 0200
Web Site: https://www.bridgestone.com.au
Sales Range: $50-74.9 Million
Emp.: 150
Tire Mfr & Distr
N.A.I.C.S.: 326211

Subsidiary (Domestic):

Bridgestone Earthmover Tyres Pty. Ltd.   (2)
223 Rookwood Road, Yagoona, 2199, NSW, Australia   (100%)
Tel.: (61) 297226111
Web Site: http://www.bridgestone-earthmover.com.au
Sales Range: $25-49.9 Million
Emp.: 60
Off-the-Road Tires Sales for Mining & Construction Vehicles
N.A.I.C.S.: 441340

Bridgestone Austria GmbH   (1)
Maria-Jacobi-Gasse 1, 1030, Vienna, Austria
Tel.: (43) 16141388
Tire & Tube Distr
N.A.I.C.S.: 423130

Bridgestone Baltics, SIA   (1)
117-303 Dzelzavas Street, Riga, 1021, Latvia
Tel.: (371) 6189250
Web Site: http://www.bridgestone.lv
Tiles Mfr
N.A.I.C.S.: 326211
Eugenijus Marcinkevicius (Mgr-Sls-Natl)

Bridgestone Belux NV/SA   (1)
Kleine Kloosterstraat 10, 1932, Zaventem, Belgium
Tel.: (32) 27190678
Tiles Mfr
N.A.I.C.S.: 326211

Bridgestone CR, s.r.o.   (1)
Klimentska 46, 110 02, Prague, Czech Republic
Tel.: (420) 226220330
Tiles Mfr
N.A.I.C.S.: 326211

Bridgestone Corporation - Amagi Plant   (1)
2011 Ota, Asakura, 838-0051, Fukuoka, Japan
Tel.: (81) 94 622 7111
Web Site: http://www.bridgestone.co.jp
Trucks, Buses & Light Trucks Radial Tires Mfr
N.A.I.C.S.: 326211

Bridgestone Corporation - Hofu Plant   (1)
100 Hamakata, Hofu, 747-0833, Yamaguchi, Japan
Tel.: (81) 83 522 8111
Web Site: https://www.bridgestone.co.jp
Automotive Tire Mfr
N.A.I.C.S.: 326211

Bridgestone Corporation - Kumamoto Plant   (1)
600 Kawasaki, Tamana, 865-0007, Kumamoto, Japan
Tel.: (81) 96 874 0111
Web Site: http://www.bridgestone.com
Emp.: 750
Automotive Tire Mfr
N.A.I.C.S.: 326211
Yasuaki Fujita (Gen Mgr)

Bridgestone Corporation - Kuroiso Plant   (1)
10 Kaminakano, Nasushiobara, 329-3154, Tochigi, Japan
Tel.: (81) 287653211
Web Site: http://www.bridgestone.co.jp

Automotive Tire Mfr
N.A.I.C.S.: 326211

Bridgestone Corporation - Kurume Plant   (1)
105 Kyomachi, Kurume, 830-0028, Japan
Tel.: (81) 942330111
Web Site: http://www.bridgestone.com
Automotive Tire Mfr
N.A.I.C.S.: 326211

Bridgestone Corporation - Nasu Plant   (1)
3-1 Higashiyamatocho, Nasushiobara, 325-0041, Tochigi, Japan
Tel.: (81) 287632311
Sales Range: $200-249.9 Million
Emp.: 847
Automotive Tire Mfr
N.A.I.C.S.: 326211

Bridgestone Corporation - Seki Plant   (1)
20 Shinhasama, Seki, 501-3923, Japan
Tel.: (81) 575234111
Automotive Tire Mfr
N.A.I.C.S.: 326211

Bridgestone Corporation - Shimonoseki Plant   (1)
3-1 Chofuminatomachi, Shimonoseki, 752-0953, Yamaguchi, Japan
Tel.: (81) 832451251
Automotive Tire Mfr
N.A.I.C.S.: 326211

Bridgestone Corporation - Tochigi Plant   (1)
800 Shimonakano, Nasushiobara, 329-3146, Tochigi, Japan
Tel.: (81) 287653111
Automotive Tire Mfr
N.A.I.C.S.: 326211

Bridgestone Corporation - Tokyo Plant   (1)
3-1-1 Ogawa Higashi-Cho, Kodaira, 187-8531, Tokyo, Japan
Tel.: (81) 423426555
Web Site: http://www.bridgestone.co.jp
Automotive Tire Mfr
N.A.I.C.S.: 326211

Bridgestone Corporation - Tosu Plant   (1)
1000 Todorokimachi, Tosu, 841-0061, Saga, Japan
Tel.: (81) 942835111
Automotive Tire Mfr
N.A.I.C.S.: 326211

Bridgestone Corporation - Yokohama Plant   (1)
1 Kashiocho, Totsuka-Ku, Yokohama, 244-0812, Kanagawa, Japan
Tel.: (81) 458241111
Automotive Tire Mfr
N.A.I.C.S.: 326211

Bridgestone Cycle Co., Ltd.   (1)
3-1-1 Nakazuma, Ageo, 362-8520, Saitama, Japan   (100%)
Tel.: (81) 12 072 1911
Web Site: https://www.bscycle.co.jp
Emp.: 872
Bicycle Mfr & Distr
N.A.I.C.S.: 336991

Plant (Domestic):

Bridgestone Cycle Co., Ltd. - Ageo Plant   (2)
3-1-1 Nakazuma, Ageo, 362-8520, Saitama, Japan
Tel.: (81) 48 773 2221
Web Site: https://www.bscycle.co.jp
Emp.: 946
Bicycle & Parts Mfr
N.A.I.C.S.: 336991

Bridgestone Cycle Co., Ltd. - Asahi Plant   (2)
1500 Saitsumachi, Tosu, Saga, Japan
Tel.: (81) 942 82 5111
Bicycle Mfr
N.A.I.C.S.: 336991

Subsidiary (Domestic):

Bridgestone Cycle East Japan Sales Co., Ltd.   (2)

2-31-6 Shimo-Shakujii, Nerima-ku, Tokyo, Japan
Tel.: (81) 3 3995 2311
Bicycles Distr
N.A.I.C.S.: 423110

Bridgestone Cycle West Japan Sales Co., Ltd.   (2)
1-4-25 Hamadera Ishizucho Nisi, Nishi-ku, Sakai, Osaka, Japan
Tel.: (81) 72 245 1111
Web Site: http://www.bscycle.co.jp
Bicycle & Parts Distr
N.A.I.C.S.: 423910

Bridgestone De Colombia, S.A.S   (1)
Calle 86 No 10-88, Bogota, Colombia
Tel.: (57) 13390120
Tiles Mfr
N.A.I.C.S.: 326211

Bridgestone De Costa Rica, S.A.   (1)
Kilometro 11 Autopista General Canas La Ribera de Belen, Heredia, 4018-1000, San Jose, Costa Rica
Tel.: (506) 22097300
Web Site: https://www.bridgestone.co.cr
N.A.I.C.S.: 326211

Bridgestone Diversified Chemical Products Co., Ltd.   (1)
3-4-4 Nihombashimuromachi Jp Bldg 4f, Tokyo, 103-0022, Japan
Tel.: (81) 332705661
Specialty Chemicals Mfr
N.A.I.C.S.: 325998

Bridgestone Diversified Products (China) Co., Ltd.   (1)
Rm 1016 Genway Bldg No 188 Wangdun Road Suzhou Industrial Park, Suzhou, 215123, Jiangsu, China
Tel.: (86) 512 6258 1088
Conveyor Belts Mfr
N.A.I.C.S.: 333922

Bridgestone Diversified Products East Co., Ltd.   (1)
1201 Ilsin Bldg 541 Dohwa-dong, Mapo-gu, Seoul, 121-701, Korea (South)
Tel.: (82) 2 565 2048
Web Site: http://www.bridgestone-dpe.co.jp
Sales Range: $25-49.9 Million
Emp.: 2
Extruded Rubber Product Mfr
N.A.I.C.S.: 326291
Yonggi Cho (Gen Mgr)

Bridgestone Diversified Products East Co., Ltd.   (1)
6F-2 No 41 Nanking W Rd, Taipei, Taiwan
Tel.: (886) 22 556 3459
Web Site: http://www.bridgestone.com
Conveyor Belts Mfr
N.A.I.C.S.: 333922

Bridgestone Diversified Products West Co., Ltd.   (1)
2-4-2 Shimmachi Nishi-Ku Nariwasujishia Bldg 13f, Osaka, 550-0013, Japan
Tel.: (81) 665348700
Automotive Tire Mfr
N.A.I.C.S.: 326211

Bridgestone Do Brasil Industria E Comercio Ltda.   (1)
Av Jornalista Roberto Marinho 85 18 Andar - Conj 181 e 182 - Cond, Tower Bridge, Cidade Moncoes, 04576-010, Sao Paulo, Brazil
Tel.: (55) 1144331666
Web Site: https://www.bridgestone.com.br
N.A.I.C.S.: 326211

Bridgestone Engineered Products of Asia, Sdn Bhd.   (1)
L1-E-3B E 4 Technology Park, Bukit Jalil, 57000, Kuala Lumpur, Malaysia
Tel.: (60) 3 8996 2670
Sales Range: $25-49.9 Million
Emp.: 50
Conveyor Belts Mfr
N.A.I.C.S.: 333922
Bukhary Yaakub (Gen Mgr)

Bridgestone Europe NV/SA   (1)
Kleine Kloosterstraat 10, 1932, Zaventem, Belgium   (100%)
Tel.: (32) 2 714 6700
Web Site: https://www.bridgestone.be

Sales Range: $150-199.9 Million
Emp.: 400
Tire Distr
N.A.I.C.S.: 441340
Paolo Ferrari (Mng Dir)

Subsidiary (Non-US):

B. GJERDE   (2)
Jerikoveien 22, 1067, Oslo, Norway
Tel.: (47) 2 230 6577
Automotive Tire Mfr
N.A.I.C.S.: 326211

BRIDGESTONE DENMARK A/S   (2)
Sigma 1 Soften, 8382, Hinnerup, Denmark
Tel.: (45) 8764 6664
Emp.: 45
Automotive Tire Mfr
N.A.I.C.S.: 326211
Martin Dahl (Gen Mgr)

BRIDGESTONE FINLAND Oy   (2)
Korpivaarantie 1, Vantaa, 01450, Finland
Tel.: (358) 9 8578 61
Web Site: http://www.bridgestone.fi
Sales Range: $25-49.9 Million
Emp.: 20
Automotive Tire Mfr
N.A.I.C.S.: 326211
Gonas Fodstad (Dir-Sls Comml)

BRIDGESTONE IRELAND Ltd.   (2)
Unit 10 Fingal Bay Business Park, Glebe North Balbriggan, Dublin, Ireland
Tel.: (353) 1 841 0000
Web Site: https://www.bridgestone.ie
Sales Range: $25-49.9 Million
Emp.: 5
Automotive Tires Distr
N.A.I.C.S.: 423130

Bridgestone (Schweiz) AG   (2)
Bodenackerstrasse 1, 8957, Spreitenbach, Switzerland   (100%)
Tel.: (41) 564187111
Tire & Tube Distr
N.A.I.C.S.: 423130

Subsidiary (Domestic):

Bridgestone Aircraft Tire (Europe) S.A.   (2)
Route de Bavay, B7080, Frameries, Belgium   (100%)
Tel.: (32) 6 561 1100
Web Site: http://www.bridgestone-eu.com
Aircraft Tires Retread & Sales
N.A.I.C.S.: 441340

Subsidiary (Non-US):

Bridgestone Benelux B.V.   (2)
Distriboulevard 15, NL 4761-RZ, Moerdijk, Netherlands   (100%)
Tel.: (31) 168385110
Web Site: http://www.bridgestone.eu
Sales Range: $25-49.9 Million
Emp.: 60
Tire Sales
N.A.I.C.S.: 441340

Bridgestone Deutschland GmbH   (2)
Justus-von-Liebig-Strasse 1, 61352, Bad Homburg, Germany   (100%)
Tel.: (49) 617240801
Web Site: http://www.bridgestone.de
Sales Range: $75-99.9 Million
Emp.: 300
Tire Mfr & Distr
N.A.I.C.S.: 441340
Des Collins (VP-Sls-Mktg)

Bridgestone France S.A.   (2)
23 Rue du Saule Trapu, 91300, Massy, France   (100%)
Tel.: (33) 169192700
Web Site: http://www.bridgestone.fr
Sales Range: $150-199.9 Million
Emp.: 50
Tire Mfr & Distr
N.A.I.C.S.: 326211

Plant (Domestic):

Bridgestone France S.A.S - Bethune Plant   (3)
575 Avenue George Washington, BP 3, 62401, Bethune, France
Tel.: (33) 3 21 64 78 60

Sales Range: $450-499.9 Million
Automotive Tire Mfr
N.A.I.C.S.: 326211

Subsidiary (Non-US):

Bridgestone Hispania S.A. **(2)**
C/ Isla Graciosa 3 1, 28703, San Sebastian
de los Reyes, Spain **(99.7%)**
Tel.: (34) 91 623 3017
Web Site: https://bridgestone.com
Tire Mfr & Sales
N.A.I.C.S.: 326211

Plant (Domestic):

Bridgestone Hispania S.A - Bilbao
Plant **(3)**
Apartado 406, Bilbao, 48970, Spain
Tel.: (34) 94 448 50 00
Automotive Tire Mfr
N.A.I.C.S.: 326211
Kepa Hernandez *(Mgr)*

Bridgestone Hispania S.A - Burgos
Plant **(3)**
Ctra. Madrid-Irun Km 243 Apartado 800,
9080, Burgos, Spain
Tel.: (34) 947479800
Web Site: http://www.bridgestone.eu
Emp.: 130
Automotive Tire Mfr
N.A.I.C.S.: 326211

Subsidiary (Non-US):

Bridgestone Industrial Ltd. **(2)**
Unit 5B Stour Valley Business Centre Brun-
don Lane, Sudbury, CO10 7GB, Suffolk,
United Kingdom **(100%)**
Tel.: (44) 178 746 4502
Sales Range: $25-49.9 Million
Emp.: 11
Engineered Rubber Products Sales
N.A.I.C.S.: 314910

Bridgestone Italia S.p.A. **(2)**
Viale Colleoni 3, Zona Industriale, 20864,
Agrate Brianza, Monza and Brianza,
Italy **(100%)**
Tel.: (39) 039656011
Web Site: http://www.bridgestone.it
Sales Range: $400-449.9 Million
Emp.: 1,060
Tire Mfr & Sales
N.A.I.C.S.: 326211

Bridgestone Nederland B.V. **(2)**
Distriboulevard 15, 4761 RZ, Moerdijk,
Netherlands
Tel.: (31) 168 38 51 10
Automotive Tire Mfr
N.A.I.C.S.: 326211

Bridgestone Portugal Lda. **(2)**
Urbanizacao do Passil Lote 96 A, 2890-118,
Alcochete, Portugal **(100%)**
Tel.: (351) 212307350
Web Site: http://www.bridgestone.eu
Sales Range: $25-49.9 Million
Emp.: 64
Tire Sales
N.A.I.C.S.: 441340

Bridgestone Poznan Sp. z.o.o. **(2)**
Ul Baltycka 65, 61-017, Poznan, Poland
Tel.: (48) 61 873 40 22
Sales Range: $400-449.9 Million
Automotive Tire Mfr
N.A.I.C.S.: 326211

Subsidiary (Domestic):

Bridgestone Stargard Sp. z.o.o **(3)**
Ul Most Kamienny 7, 73-110, Stargard Szc-
zecinski, Poland
Tel.: (48) 91 472 34 00
Sales Range: $200-249.9 Million
Emp.: 60
Automotive Tire Mfr
N.A.I.C.S.: 326211
Hiroyuki Ozaki *(Gen Mgr)*

Subsidiary (Non-US):

Bridgestone Romania S.R.L. **(2)**
Dacia Blvd No 153-155 Floor 3 Section S2,
District 2, Bucharest, 202065, Romania
Tel.: (40) 21 210 21 79

Sales Range: $25-49.9 Million
Emp.: 8
Automotive Tire Mfr
N.A.I.C.S.: 326211

Bridgestone Slovakia s.r.o. **(2)**
Michalska 9, 811 01, Bratislava, Slovakia
Tel.: (421) 220 633 218
Web Site: http://www.bridgestone.eu
Sales Range: $25-49.9 Million
Emp.: 3
Automotive Tires Distr
N.A.I.C.S.: 423130

Bridgestone Sweden AB **(2)**
Box 9074, S-850 09, Sundsvall,
Sweden **(100%)**
Tel.: (46) 60515200
Web Site: http://www.bridgestone.se
Sales Range: $25-49.9 Million
Emp.: 41
Tire Sales
N.A.I.C.S.: 441340

Bridgestone U.K. Ltd. **(2)**
Athena Drive Tachbrook Park, Warwick,
CV34 6UX, United Kingdom **(100%)**
Tel.: (44) 192 648 8500
Web Site: https://www.bridgestone.co.uk
Sales Range: $25-49.9 Million
Emp.: 150
Tire & Automotive Component Sales
N.A.I.C.S.: 441340
Andrea Manenti *(VP-North)*

Speedy France SAS **(2)**
72-78 Avenue Georges Clemenceau,
92000, Nanterre, France
Tel.: (33) 141203030
Web Site: https://www.speedy.fr
Automotive Tires, Parts & Repair Shops
Operator
N.A.I.C.S.: 811111

Bridgestone Finance Corporation **(1)**
1-7-1 Kyobashi Bridgestone Bldg 6f, Tokyo,
104-0031, Japan
Tel.: (81) 335636815
Financial Management Services
N.A.I.C.S.: 523999

Bridgestone Flowtech
Corporation **(1)**
1-3-1 Minami-shinozaki, Kazocd, Saitama,
347-0017, Japan **(100%)**
Tel.: (81) 480651121
Web Site: http://www.bsft.co.jp
Sales Range: $125-149.9 Million
Emp.: 400
Industrial Hydraulic Hoses Mfr & Sales
N.A.I.C.S.: 326220

Bridgestone India Private Limited **(1)**
Plot No 12 Kheda Growth Centre Post Sag-
ore, Pithampur, Dhar, 454 774, Madhya
Pradesh, India
Tel.: (91) 729 242 3333
Web Site: http://www.bridgestone.co.in
Sales Range: $200-249.9 Million
Emp.: 900
Automotive Tire Mfr
N.A.I.C.S.: 326211

Bridgestone Italia Sales S.r.l. **(1)**
Viale Colleoni 3, 20864, Agrate Brianza,
Monza and Brianza, Italy
Tel.: (39) 039656011
Tiles Mfr
N.A.I.C.S.: 326211

Bridgestone Magyarorszag Kft. **(1)**
Vaci Ut 135-139, 1138, Budapest, Hungary
Tel.: (36) 14302780
Web Site: https://www.bridgestone.hu
N.A.I.C.S.: 326211

Bridgestone Middle East & Africa
FZE. **(1)**
740th St Jebel Ali Free Zone Near Round
About No 7, PO Box 16813, Jebel Ali Free
Zone, Dubai, United Arab Emirates
Tel.: (971) 4 820 9333
Web Site: https://www.bridgestone-mea.com
Sales Range: $50-74.9 Million
Emp.: 90
Automotive Tires Distr
N.A.I.C.S.: 423130
Stefano Sanchini *(Dir-Sls)*

Bridgestone Mining Solutions Austra-
lia Pty. Ltd. **(1)**

223 Rookwood Road, Chullora, 2190, NSW,
Australia
Tel.: (61) 29 722 6111
Web Site:
https://www.bridgestonemining.com.au
Mining & Metals Solutions
N.A.I.C.S.: 212290
Lorenzo Gella *(Mgr-Corp Planning)*

Subsidiary (Domestic):

Otraco International Pty Limited **(2)**
130 Fauntleroy Avenue, Redcliffe, 6104,
WA, Australia
Tel.: (61) 862747200
Web Site: http://www.otraco.com
Engineeering Services
N.A.I.C.S.: 541330

Bridgestone Natural Rubber (Thai-
land) Co., Ltd. **(1)**
129/2 Moo 3, Songkhla, 90120, Thailand
Tel.: (66) 74456111
Industrial Rubber Mfr
N.A.I.C.S.: 326299

Bridgestone New Zealand Ltd. **(1)**
Level 1 Building A The Millennium Centre
602 Great South Road, Ellerslie, Auckland,
1051, New Zealand **(100%)**
Tel.: (64) 95735700
Web Site: http://www.bridgestonetyres.co.nz
Sales Range: $250-299.9 Million
Emp.: 750
Tire Mfr & Distr
N.A.I.C.S.: 326211

Bridgestone Sales Polska Sp. z
o.o. **(1)**
Ul Postepu 18b, Warsaw, 02-676, Poland
Tel.: (48) 226061820
Tiles Mfr
N.A.I.C.S.: 326211

Bridgestone Singapore Pte. Ltd. **(1)**
16 Raffles Quay Ste 32-02 Hong Leong
Bldg, Singapore, 048581,
Singapore **(100%)**
Tel.: (65) 62202811
Web Site: http://www.bridgestone.com
Sales Range: $25-49.9 Million
Emp.: 30
Natural Rubber Whslr
N.A.I.C.S.: 424990

Bridgestone South Africa (Pty)
Ltd. **(1)**
6 Ridge Road Vorna Valley, Midrand, 1685,
South Africa
Tel.: (27) 119237500
Tiles Mfr
N.A.I.C.S.: 326211

Bridgestone South Africa Holdings
(Pty) Ltd. **(1)**
6 Ridge Road, Vorna Valley, Midrand, 1685,
South Africa **(93.7%)**
Tel.: (27) 119237500
Web Site: http://www.bridgestone.co.za
Sales Range: $550-599.9 Million
Emp.: 2,000
Tire Mfr & Distr
N.A.I.C.S.: 326211

Bridgestone Sports Co., Ltd. **(1)**
Omori Bellport East Building 6-22-7 Minami-
oi, Shinagawa-ku, Tokyo, 140-0013,
Japan **(100%)**
Tel.: (81) 357632500
Web Site: http://www.bs-sports.co.jp
Sales Range: $25-49.9 Million
Emp.: 100
Sporting Goods Mfr & Sales
N.A.I.C.S.: 339920
Kawano Hisashi *(Pres)*

Subsidiary (US):

Bridgestone Golf, Inc. **(2)**
15320 Industrial Park Blvd NE, Covington,
GA 30014-6428 **(100%)**
Tel.: (770) 787-7400
Web Site: https://www.bridgestonegolf.com
Sales Range: $50-74.9 Million
Golf Equipment Mfr & Distr
N.A.I.C.S.: 339920
Angel Ilagan *(Pres & CEO)*

Bridgestone Taiwan Co., Ltd. **(1)**
No 1-1 Wenhua Rd Hsinchu Ind Park, Hu-

kou Township, Hsinchu, 30352,
Taiwan **(80%)**
Tel.: (886) 3 598 1621
Web Site: https://www.bridgestone.com.tw
Sales Range: $125-149.9 Million
Emp.: 400
Tire Mfr & Sales
N.A.I.C.S.: 326211

Bridgestone Tire Manufacturing (Thai-
land) Co., Ltd. **(1)**
700/622 Moo 4 Amata Nakorn Industrial
Estate Phan Thong, Chon Buri, 20160,
Thailand
Tel.: (66) 3821030001
Automotive Tire Mfr
N.A.I.C.S.: 326211

Bridgestone Tire Manufacturing Viet-
nam Limited Liability Company **(1)**
Land Plot CN3 6-CN4 1 Dinh Vu Industrial
Zone, Dong Hai 2 Ward Hai An District,
Haiphong, Vietnam
Tel.: (84) 882060200
Tiles Mfr
N.A.I.C.S.: 326211

Bridgestone Tire Sales Korea
Ltd. **(1)**
12F GS Tower 508 Nonhyeon-ro, Gang-
nam, Seoul, 135-985, Korea (South)
Tel.: (82) 232102480
Tiles Mfr
N.A.I.C.S.: 326211

Bridgestone Tyre Sales (Malaysia)
Sdn. Bhd. **(1)**
9th Floor West Wing & Centrelink Wisma
Consplant 2 No 7 Jalan SS 16/1, 47500,
Subang Jaya, Selangor, Malaysia
Tel.: (60) 356210270
Tiles Mfr
N.A.I.C.S.: 326211

Bridgestone Tyre Sales Vietnam
LLC **(1)**
9th Floor 233 Dong Khoi Street, Ben Nghe
Ward District 1, Ho Chi Minh City, Vietnam
Tel.: (84) 283 825 6013
Web Site: https://www.bridgestone.com.vn
Tiles Mfr
N.A.I.C.S.: 326211

Brisa Bridgestone Sabanci Lastik
Sanayi ve Ticaret A.S. **(1)**
Alikahya Fatih Mahallesi Sanayi Caddesi
No 98 Izmit, 41310, Kocaeli, Türkiye
Tel.: (90) 2623164000
Web Site: http://www.brisa.com.tr
Sales Range: $450-499.9 Million
Emp.: 1,300
Tire Mfr & Distr
N.A.I.C.S.: 326211

Buwon Motors Co., Ltd. **(1)**
3F Ju-Seong B/D 24-4 Mukejeong Dong,
Jung-gu, Seoul, Korea (South)
Tel.: (82) 222484272
N.A.I.C.S.: 326211

Eastern Motors Ltd. **(1)**
Nib House 32 Agrabad Com/Area, Chit-
tagong, 4100, Bangladesh
Tel.: (880) 31723712
Tiles Mfr
N.A.I.C.S.: 326211

Eurotred (NZ) Ltd. **(1)**
14 Karewa Place Te Rapa, PO Box 10261,
Hamilton, New Zealand
Tel.: (64) 78500785
Tiles Mfr
N.A.I.C.S.: 326211

Firestone Metal Products Company,
LLC **(1)**
1001 Lund Blvd, Anoka, MN 55303
Tel.: (800) 426-7737
Metal Products Mfr
N.A.I.C.S.: 332999

Plant (Domestic):

Firestone Metal Products Company,
LLC - Anoka Manufacturing
Facility **(2)**
1001 Lund Blvd, Anoka, MN 55303
Tel.: (800) 426-7737
Roofing Construction Services
N.A.I.C.S.: 238160

Bridgestone Corporation—(Continued)

Firestone Metal Products Company, LLC - College Park Manufacturing Facility (2)
3511 Naturally Fresh Blvd Ste 400, College Park, GA 30349
Tel.: (404) 974-3450
Web Site: http://www.bridgestone-firestone.com
Metal Sheet, Roofing & Wall Panel Mfr
N.A.I.C.S.: 332322
Jason Lakatos (Mgr)

Firestone Metal Products Company, LLC - Jackson Manufacturing Facility (2)
1085 Mendell Davis Dr, Jackson, MS 39272
Tel.: (800) 426-7737
Construction Engineering Services
N.A.I.C.S.: 237990

Firestone Metal Products Company, LLC - Las Vegas Manufacturing Facility (2)
4272 Corporate Ctr Dr, North Las Vegas, NV 89030
Tel.: (702) 880-8012
Web Site: http://www.bridgestone-firestone.com
Metal Products Mfr
N.A.I.C.S.: 332999

Firestone Metal Products Company, LLC - Warren Manufacturing Facility (2)
2050 Morrissey, Warren, MI 48091
Tel.: (888) 466-8833
Web Site: http://www.bridgestone-firestone.com
Metal Sheet Mfr
N.A.I.C.S.: 332322

First Japan Tire Services Company Limited (1)
2nd Floor Building No 9 MICT Park Thamine College Street, Hlaing Township, 11051, Yangon, Myanmar
Tel.: (95) 9797005252
Tiles Mfr
N.A.I.C.S.: 326211

Giant Tire & Service Company Limited (1)
152 Mitrphan Road, Pom Prap Subdistrict Pom Prap Sattru Phai, Bangkok, 10100, Thailand
Tel.: (66) 22260042
Web Site: https://www.gianttire.co.th
N.A.I.C.S.: 326211

Gjerde & Byhring AS (1)
Jerikoveien 22, Oslo, Norway
Tel.: (47) 23143600
Web Site: http://www.bridgestone.no
Tiles Mfr
N.A.I.C.S.: 326211
Thomas Thogersen (Mgr-Product)

Habib Gulzar Motors Ltd. (1)
Plot 3 Street 5 Near Dispechari Square Sarak-e-Naw Jalalabad Road, Kabul, Afghanistan
Tel.: (93) 788700010
Tiles Mfr
N.A.I.C.S.: 326211
Showkatullah Sultani (Mgr-Fin & Logistic)

Hock Thai Motor Co. (1)
No 13 Simpang 15 Hock Thai Building km 3 Jln Gadong, PO Box 21, BE4119, Bandar Seri Begawan, Brunei Darussalam
Tel.: (673) 8747823
Tiles Mfr
N.A.I.C.S.: 326211

Kong Nuon Group Co., Ltd. (1)
No 220 Oknha Tep Phan St 182 Sangkat Phsar Depo I, Khan Toul Kork, Phnom Penh, Cambodia
Tel.: (855) 2 388 0281
Web Site: https://www.kongnuongroup.com
Tiles Mfr
N.A.I.C.S.: 326211

Li Ang Timor, Ltda. (1)
Av Presidente Nicolau Lobato Comoro, Dili, Timor-Leste
Tel.: (670) 77021179

Tiles Mfr
N.A.I.C.S.: 326211

Masthead Industries Inc. (1)
50 Industrial Loop N, Orange Park, FL 32073
Tel.: (904) 264-1267
Emp.: 5
Hydraulic Hoses & Fttings Mfr
N.A.I.C.S.: 423840
Palmer Clarkson (Pres)

Mcleod Accessories Pty. Ltd. (1)
59 Raubers Road, Northgate, Brisbane, 4013, QLD, Australia
Tel.: (61) 736219030
Tiles Mfr
N.A.I.C.S.: 326211
Shane Musgrove (Mgr-Mdse)

P.T. Bridgestone Tire Indonesia (1)
Jl Surya Utama Kav 8-13 Kawasan Industri Suryacipta, Karawang, 41361, Jawa Barat, Indonesia **(51%)**
Tel.: (62) 26 744 0201
Web Site: https://www.bridgestone.co.id
Sales Range: $450-499.9 Million
Emp.: 1,300
Tire Mfr & Sales
N.A.I.C.S.: 326211

PT Bridgestone Tire Indonesia - Karawang Plant (1)
Kawasan Industri Surya Cipta Kav 8-13 Ci-ampel Kutanegara, Karawang, 41363, Jawa Barat, Indonesia
Tel.: (62) 2678637921
Tiles Mfr
N.A.I.C.S.: 326211
Andre Susilo (Mgr-Plant)

PT. Bridgestone Engineered Products Indonesia (1)
Wisma Slipi 12th Floor Jl Let Jend S Parman Kav 12, Jakarta, 11480, Indonesia
Tel.: (62) 21 5366 1971
Sales Range: $25-49.9 Million
Emp.: 2
Conveyor Belt Distr
N.A.I.C.S.: 423840
Herman Gunawan (Mgr-Sls)

PT. Bridgestone Tire Indonesia - Bekasi Plant (1)
Jalan Raya Bekasi Km 27 Harapan Jaya Bekasi Utara Kota Bks, Bekasi, 17124, Jawa Barat, Indonesia
Tel.: (62) 218840828
Tiles Mfr
N.A.I.C.S.: 326211

PTS S.A. (1)
Avenida Los Frutales N 945, La Molina, Lima, Peru
Tel.: (51) 12157900
All Other Rubber Product Mfr
N.A.I.C.S.: 326299

Pakistan Rahman Tyres International Pvt. Ltd. (1)
Suite C & D 11th Floor Lakson Square Bldg 1 Sarwar Shaheed Road, Karachi, Pakistan
Tel.: (92) 3070225294
Tiles Mfr
N.A.I.C.S.: 326211

Pakistan Rubber & Tyre Co. (1)
Plot No 79-C National Highway Road Ph-II Ext DHA, Karachi, Pakistan
Tel.: (92) 2135804646
Web Site: http://www.prtc.net.pk
Tiles Mfr
N.A.I.C.S.: 326211

Philippine Allied Enterprises Corporation (1)
2262 Chino Roces Avenue, Makati, Philippines
Tel.: (63) 9178367677
Tiles Mfr
N.A.I.C.S.: 326211

Quality & Winner Motors Imp Exp EIRELI (1)
Rua Bahia 383 Alphaville Empresarial, Barueri, 06465-110, Sao Paulo, Brazil
Tel.: (55) 112 134 3400
Web Site: https://www.winner-motors.com.br
Tiles Mfr
N.A.I.C.S.: 326211

RA S.A. (1)
Av Agraciada 2720, Montevideo, Uruguay
Tel.: (598) 22034449
Tiles Mfr
N.A.I.C.S.: 326211

Rm Mart Sdn. Bhd. (1)
46 Lebuh Noordin, Georgetown, 10300, Penang, Malaysia
Tel.: (60) 42285285
N.A.I.C.S.: 326211

S.A.R.L. Pacifique Pneus (1)
22 Rue Fernand Forest Ducos, PO Box 1567-98845, Noumea, New Caledonia
Tel.: (687) 772039
Tiles Mfr
N.A.I.C.S.: 326211

Servco Tire Company (1)
80 Sand Island Access Rd Bay B, Honolulu, HI 96819
Tel.: (808) 564-2600
N.A.I.C.S.: 326211

State Trading Corporation of Bhutan Ltd. (1)
PO Box 272, Babesa, Thimphu, Bhutan
Tel.: (975) 17124888
Web Site: https://www.stcb.bt
N.A.I.C.S.: 326211

Thai Bridgestone Co., Ltd. (1)
14/3 Phaholyothin Rd Klong Nueng, Khlong Luang, 12120, Pathumthaini, Thailand **(67.2%)**
Tel.: (66) 251687215
Web Site: http://www.bridgestone.co.th
Sales Range: $50-74.9 Million
Emp.: 165
Tire Mfr & Sales
N.A.I.C.S.: 326211

Thai Bridgestone Co., Ltd. - Nong Khae plant (1)
75 Moo 2 Phaholyothin Rd KM82 Tambol Paitam Amphor Nong Khae, Saraburi, 18140, Thailand
Tel.: (66) 363251016
Tiles Mfr
N.A.I.C.S.: 326211

Thai Bridgestone Co., Ltd. - Rangsit Plant (1)
14/3 Phahonyothin Rd Tambon Khlong Nueng Amphoe Khong Luang, Pathumthani, 12120, Thailand
Tel.: (66) 251687215
Tiles Mfr
N.A.I.C.S.: 326211
Vichit Lertwongpaisarn (Dir-HR)

Tires Plus Total Car Care (1)
2607 Gulf To Bay Blvd, Clearwater, FL 33759-4936 **(64.4%)**
Tel.: (727) 219-1843
Web Site: http://www.tiresplus.com
Sales Range: $1-4.9 Billion
Emp.: 6,000
Tire Dealerships Operator; Automotive Repair
N.A.I.C.S.: 441340

Tong Seng Co. Ltd. (1)
1106-7 New World Tower 16-18 Queen's Road, Central, China (Hong Kong)
Tel.: (852) 2 525 6313
Web Site: https://www.tongseng.com.hk
Tiles Mfr
N.A.I.C.S.: 326211

Wah Seng Far East Ltd. (1)
340 Pak Sha Tsuen Kung Um Road, Yuen Long, China (Hong Kong)
Tel.: (852) 65918676
Tiles Mfr
N.A.I.C.S.: 326211
Lemon Chuk Chiu (Mgr-Mktg)

BRIDGETEC CORP.
32 Gukjehang-ro 2-gil Yeouido Finance Tower 17th and 18th floor, Yeongdeungpo-gu, Seoul, Korea (South)
Tel.: (82) 234304114
Web Site: https://www.bridgetec.co.kr
Year Founded: 1999

064480—(KRS)
Rev.: $45,203,626
Assets: $53,631,076
Liabilities: $13,938,559
Net Worth: $39,692,517
Earnings: $2,593,130
Emp.: 193
Fiscal Year-end: 12/31/22
Software Development Services
N.A.I.C.S.: 541511

BRIDGETOWN 3 HOLDINGS LIMITED
38/F Champion Tower 3 Garden Road, Central, China (Hong Kong)
Tel.: (852) 2514 8888   Ky
Year Founded: 2021
BTNC—(NYSE)
Holding Company
N.A.I.C.S.: 551112
Daniel Wong (CEO & CFO)

BRIDGETOWN HOLDINGS LIMITED
3 Garden Road, Central, China (Hong Kong)
Tel.: (852) 25148888   Ky
Year Founded: 2020
BTWN—(NASDAQ)
Rev.: $24,917,061
Assets: $153,050,975
Liabilities: $178,992,149
Net Worth: ($25,941,174)
Earnings: $23,216,044
Emp.: 1
Fiscal Year-end: 12/31/22
Investment Services
N.A.I.C.S.: 523999
Daniel Wong (CEO & CFO)

BRIERTY LTD.
Ground Floor 72 Melville Parade, South Perth, 6151, WA, Australia
Tel.: (61) 8 9267 8000
Web Site: http://www.brierty.com.au
Year Founded: 1981
BYL—(ASX)
Sales Range: $125-149.9 Million
Transport Infrastructure
N.A.I.C.S.: 336214
Ray J. Bushnell (Mng Dir)

BRIGADE ENTERPRISES LTD.
29th & 30th Floors World Trade Center Brigade Gateway Campus, 26/1 Dr Rajkumar Road, Bengaluru, 560 055, India
Tel.: (91) 8041379200
Web Site: https://www.brigadegroup.com
BRIGADE—(NSE)
Rev.: $486,378,165
Assets: $2,235,516,465
Liabilities: $1,806,402,780
Net Worth: $429,113,685
Earnings: $30,326,205
Emp.: 606
Fiscal Year-end: 03/30/23
Property Development Services
N.A.I.C.S.: 531390
M. R. Jaishankar (Founder, Chm & Mng Dir)

Subsidiaries:

Brigade Hospitality Services Limited (1)
29th Floor World Trade Center Brigade Gateway Campus, 26/1 Dr Rajkumar Road, Malleshwaram West, Bengaluru, 560055, India
Tel.: (91) 8040438000
Web Site: https://brigadehospitality.com
Hotel Operator
N.A.I.C.S.: 721110

Celebration Catering & Events, LLP (1)

29th Floor World Trade Center Brigade Gateway Campus, 26/1 Dr Rajkumar Road Malleswaram West, Bengaluru, 560055, India
Tel.: (91) 8040438000
Web Site: http://www.cateringandevents.in
Catering Services
N.A.I.C.S.: 722320

Orion Mall Management Company Limited   **(1)**
Orion Mall at Brigade Gateway 26/1 Dr Rajkumar Rd, Malleshwaram, Bengaluru, 560055, India
Tel.: (91) 8067282222
Web Site: https://www.orionmalls.com
Mall Construction Services
N.A.I.C.S.: 236220

BRIGHOLME INTERIORS GROUP
4118 14th Avenue, Markham, L3R 0J3, ON, Canada
Tel.: (905) 475-0043
Web Site: https://www.brigholme.com
Year Founded: 1961
Sales Range: $10-24.9 Million
Emp.: 35
Household & Industrial Furniture Mfr
N.A.I.C.S.: 337121
Joe Williams *(Pres)*

BRIGHT BROTHERS LIMITED
Office no 91 9th Floor Jolly Maker Chambers No 2, 225 Nariman Point, Mumbai, 400021, India
Tel.: (91) 2225835158
Web Site:
   https://www.brightbrothers.co.in
526731—(BOM)
Rev.: $27,717,813
Assets: $23,476,185
Liabilities: $16,689,828
Net Worth: $6,786,357
Earnings: $778,733
Fiscal Year-end: 03/31/21
Plastic Product Mfr & Whslr
N.A.I.C.S.: 325211
Suresh Bhojwani *(Chm & Mng Dir)*

BRIGHT FOOD (GROUP) CO., LTD.
No 7 Lane 263 Huashan Road, Shanghai, China
Tel.: (86) 21 6247 4500
Web Site: http://www.brightfood.com
Year Founded: 2006
Holding Company; Diversified Food Mfr
N.A.I.C.S.: 551112
Zongnan Wang *(Chm)*

Subsidiaries:

Bright Dairy & Food Co., Ltd.   **(1)**
No 578 Wuzhong Road, Minhang District, Shanghai, 201103, China
Tel.: (86) 2154584520
Web Site: https://www.brightdairy.com
Rev.: $3,961,373,083
Assets: $3,433,108,073
Liabilities: $1,952,133,436
Net Worth: $1,480,974,637
Earnings: $50,640,623
Emp.: 2,594
Fiscal Year-end: 12/31/2022
Development, Production & Sales of Milk & Dairy Products
N.A.I.C.S.: 311511
Huang Liming *(Chm)*

Manassen Foods Australia Pty. Ltd.   **(1)**
8 Interchange Drive, Eastern Creek, 2766, NSW, Australia
Tel.: (61) 2 9421 3100
Web Site: http://www.manassen.com.au
Sales Range: $150-199.9 Million
Emp.: 100
Grocery Product Distr
N.A.I.C.S.: 424490
Fernando Arnedo *(CEO)*

Shanghai Haibo Co., Ltd.   **(1)**
829 Yishan Road, Shanghai, 200233, China
Tel.: (86) 2161132800
Web Site: http://www.hb600708.com
Sales Range: $1-4.9 Billion
Emp.: 12,768
Rental Car Services
N.A.I.C.S.: 532111
Miao Wen *(Chm)*

Shanghai Maling Aquarius Co., Ltd.   **(1)**
Shanghai City Road No. 1418, Shanghai, 200082, China
Tel.: (86) 2153891289
Web Site: http://www.shanghaimaling.com
Rev.: $3,508,217,482
Assets: $2,217,318,485
Liabilities: $1,215,598,827
Net Worth: $1,001,719,658
Earnings: $70,588,992
Fiscal Year-end: 12/31/2022
Meat, Fish, Fruits & Vegetables Processing & Distribution
N.A.I.C.S.: 311612
Junlong Li *(Pres)*

Tnuva Food Industries Ltd.   **(1)**
Rav Mecher Building Gillot Junction, Ramat HaSharon, 47100, Israel   **(76.85%)**
Tel.: (972) 36904000
Web Site: http://en.tnuva.co.il
Dairy & Meat Production
N.A.I.C.S.: 112120
Eyal Malis *(CEO)*

BRIGHT FUTURE TECHNOLOGY HOLDINGS LTD.
Rooms 201-02 & 201-03 Phase 7, Xinghai Mingcheng Community Nantou Jiedao Nanshan District, Shenzhen, China   Ky
Year Founded: 2015
1351—(HKG)
Rev.: $67,947,716
Assets: $54,880,894
Liabilities: $34,729,336
Net Worth: $20,151,558
Earnings: ($3,436,807)
Emp.: 215
Fiscal Year-end: 12/31/22
Holding Company
N.A.I.C.S.: 551112
Hui Doung *(CEO)*

BRIGHT LED ELECTRONICS CORP.
3F No 19 Heping Rd, Banqiao Dist, New Taipei City, 22061, Taiwan
Tel.: (886) 229591090
Web Site: https://www.brtled.com
Year Founded: 1981
3031—(TAI)
Rev.: $37,038,064
Assets: $116,708,129
Liabilities: $17,191,503
Net Worth: $99,516,625
Earnings: $5,822,689
Emp.: 1,000
Fiscal Year-end: 12/31/23
Light Emitting Diode Mfr
N.A.I.C.S.: 334413

Subsidiaries:

Bright Crystal Company Limited   **(1)**
East side of Electric Power Bureau North Section of Fuqiang Road, Suiping County, Henan, China
Tel.: (86) 3963222198
Semiconductor Components Mfr & Distr
N.A.I.C.S.: 334413

Bright LED Europe GmbH   **(1)**
Vogelerweg 24 A, 28355, Bremen, Germany
Tel.: (49) 4213 225 1530
Web Site: https://brightled.de
Light Emitting Diode Products Distr
N.A.I.C.S.: 423690

Bright Led Electronics Corp. - China Factory   **(1)**
No 8 Gaolong East Road, Gao Bu Town,

Dongguan, 523000, Guang Dong, China
Tel.: (86) 76988731855
Light Emitting Diode Mfr
N.A.I.C.S.: 334419

Dong Guan E-run Electronic Product Ltd.   **(1)**
Baiwang Science & Technology Park, Sanlian Village Gaobu Town, Dongguan, Guangdong, China
Tel.: (86) 76988730855
Lead Frame Mfr & Distr
N.A.I.C.S.: 331491

KoBrite DongGuan Corporation   **(1)**
Lingwu Village, Gaobu Town, Dongguan, China
Tel.: (86) 76988940123
LED Electronic Mfr
N.A.I.C.S.: 334419

KoBrite Taiwan Corporation   **(1)**
No 8 Lixing Road Hsinchu Science Park, Hsinchu, 300, Taiwan
Tel.: (886) 36117080
Web Site: https://www.kobrite.com.tw
Light Emitting Diode Light Mfr & Distr
N.A.I.C.S.: 334413

Mainbright Enterprises Ltd.   **(1)**
Unit 5 11F Hung Tai Ind Building 37-39 Hung To Road, Kwun Tong, Kowloon, China (Hong Kong)
Tel.: (852) 27979568
Light Emitting Diode Mfr & Distr
N.A.I.C.S.: 334413

BRIGHT OCEANS INTER-TELECOM CO., LTD.
10-12F Tower C and D Zhonghai Building No 1 Building No 26 Yard, Gucheng West Street Shijingshan District, Beijing, 100043, China
Tel.: (86) 45182326789
Web Site: http://www.boco.com.cn
Year Founded: 1995
600289—(SHG)
Rev.: $36,692,894
Assets: $300,108,440
Liabilities: $104,116,877
Net Worth: $195,991,563
Earnings: ($49,165,988)
Emp.: 3,000
Fiscal Year-end: 12/31/22
Software Development & Publishing Services
N.A.I.C.S.: 541511
Yuan Yixiang *(Chm)*

BRIGHT ORIENT (HOLDING) LTD.
133 Xiangnan Road, Nanshan, Shenzhen, China
Tel.: (86) 755 2640 2448
Sales Range: $50-74.9 Million
Emp.: 1,380
Garments & Textile Related Products Mfr & Distr
N.A.I.C.S.: 315990
Jian Jun Du *(Chm, Pres & Mng Dir)*

BRIGHT OUTDOOR MEDIA LIMITED
8th floor Crescent tower Near Morya House Opp VIP Plaza New Link Road, Andheri, Mumbai, 400053, India
Tel.: (91) 2267140000
Web Site:
   https://www.brightoutdoor.com
Year Founded: 2005
543831—(BOM)
Rev.: $11,023,888
Assets: $18,541,130
Liabilities: $6,649,922
Net Worth: $11,891,208
Earnings: $851,790
Emp.: 66
Fiscal Year-end: 03/31/23
Advertising Agency Services
N.A.I.C.S.: 541810

Khyati Mishra *(Sec)*

BRIGHT PACKAGING INDUSTRY BERHAD
No 23 Jalan Delima 1/3 Subang Hi-Tech Industrial Park, 40000, Shah Alam, Selangor Darul Ehsan, Malaysia
Tel.: (60) 356351949
Web Site: https://www.brightpack.net
BRIGHT—(KLS)
Rev.: $13,091,627
Assets: $28,173,124
Liabilities: $2,410,396
Net Worth: $25,762,727
Earnings: $1,144,706
Fiscal Year-end: 08/31/23
Aluminum Foil Packaging Materials Mfr
N.A.I.C.S.: 331315
Mustapha Muhamad *(Deputy Chm)*

BRIGHT SCHOLAR EDUCATION HOLDINGS LIMITED
No 1 Country Garden Road, Beijiao Town Shunde District, Foshan, 528300, Guangdong, China
Tel.: (86) 75766832507   Ky
Web Site:
   https://www.brightscholar.com
Year Founded: 2014
BEDU—(NYSE)
Rev.: $247,561,000
Assets: $429,540,000
Liabilities: $344,053,000
Net Worth: $85,487,000
Earnings: ($145,678,000)
Emp.: 2,193
Fiscal Year-end: 08/31/24
Educational Support Services
N.A.I.C.S.: 611710
Huiyan Yang *(Chm)*

Subsidiaries:

CATS Academy Boston Inc.   **(1)**
2001 Washington St, Braintree, MA 02184
Tel.: (857) 400-9700
School & College Professional Services
N.A.I.C.S.: 611310

CATS Canterbury Limited   **(1)**
68 New Dover Road, Canterbury, CT1 3LQ, United Kingdom
Tel.: (44) 1227866540
School & College Professional Services
N.A.I.C.S.: 611310

CATS College London Limited   **(1)**
43-45 Bloomsbury Square, London, WC1A 2RA, United Kingdom
Tel.: (44) 2045290844
School & College Professional Services
N.A.I.C.S.: 611310

CATS Colleges Holdings Limited   **(1)**
CATS Cambridge 1 High Street, Chesterton, Cambridge, CB4 1NQ, United Kingdom
Tel.: (44) 1223341300
Web Site: https://www.catscambridge.com
School & College Professional Services
N.A.I.C.S.: 611310

Cambridge Arts & Science Limited   **(1)**
1 High Street, Chesterton, Cambridge, CB4 1NQ, United Kingdom
Tel.: (44) 1223314431
School & College Professional Services
N.A.I.C.S.: 611310

Cambridge School of Visual & Performing Arts Limited   **(1)**
14 Round Church Street, Cambridge, CB5 8AD, United Kingdom
Tel.: (44) 1223341328
Web Site: https://www.csvpa.com
School & College Professional Services
N.A.I.C.S.: 611310
Holly Fulton *(Head-Fashion)*

Foundation Global Education Limited   **(1)**
13/F Chinachem Hollywood Centre 1 Holly-

Bright Scholar Education Holdings
Limited—(Continued)

wood Road, Central, China (Hong Kong)
Tel.: (852) 31078810
Web Site: http://www.foundationge.com
School & College Professional Services
N.A.I.C.S.: 611310
Rae Kuang (Assoc Dir)

Stafford Houoo Sohool of Englioh
Limited (1)
15 Round Church Street, Cambridge, CB5
8AD, United Kingdom
Tel.: (44) 1223341333
Web Site: http://www.staffordhouse.com
School & College Professional Services
N.A.I.C.S.: 611310

Stafford House Study Holidays
Limited (1)
19 New Dover Road, Canterbury, CT1 3AS,
Kent, United Kingdom
Tel.: (44) 1227787730
Web Site: https://www.studyholidays.com
School & College Professional Services
N.A.I.C.S.: 611310

BRIGHT SHELAND INTERNA-TIONAL CO., LTD.
10F-3 No 81 Sec 1 Xintai 5th Road,
Xizhi Dist, New Taipei City, 22101,
Taiwan
Tel.: (886) 226984989
Web Site: https://www.filtrafine.com
Year Founded: 1985
4556—(TPE)
Rev.: $21,866,116
Assets: $57,835,037
Liabilities: $31,549,980
Net Worth: $26,285,058
Earnings: $1,024,075
Fiscal Year-end: 12/31/22
Industrial Machinery Mfr & Distr
N.A.I.C.S.: 333248
Ling-Mei Wu (Chm)

Subsidiaries:

Cong TY TNHH Filtrafine Co.,
Ltd. (1)
Lo A-3E-CN KCN Bau Bang, H Bau bang T,
Lai Uyen, Binh Duong, Vietnam
Tel.: (84) 2747309968
Steel Filter Product Mfr & Distr
N.A.I.C.S.: 331110

Filtrafine Corporation (1)
1599 Monte Vista Ave, Claremont, CA
91711
Tel.: (909) 217-7043
Filter Mfr
N.A.I.C.S.: 333413

Filtrafine Japan INC. (1)
8-22-3C Ogawa-cho, Ibaraki, 567-0873,
Osaka, Japan
Tel.: (81) 726468502
Water Filter Mfr & Distr
N.A.I.C.S.: 333413

Filtrafine Pte. Ltd. (1)
750A Chai Chee Road 07-12 ESR Bizpark,
Chai Chee, Singapore, Singapore
Tel.: (65) 64495316
Industrial Filter Mfr
N.A.I.C.S.: 333248

Pride International (shanghai)Co.,
Ltd. (1)
B17 Floor 4 No 231 Fute North Road Pilot
Free Trade Zone, Shanghai, China
Tel.: (86) 18621137699
Water Filter Mfr & Distr
N.A.I.C.S.: 333413

BRIGHT SMART SECURITIES & COMMODITIES GROUP LIMITED
10/F 23/F Wing On House 71 Des
Voeux Road, Central, China (Hong
Kong)
Tel.: (852) 2 537 1371
Web Site: http://www.bsgroup.com.hk

1428—(HKG)
Rev.: $161,195,464
Assets: $1,259,942,936
Liabilities: $941,185,504
Net Worth: $318,757,432
Earnings: $72,422,528
Emp.: 262
Fiscal Year-end: 03/31/22
Securities & Commodities Brokerage
Services
N.A.I.C.S.: 523150
Peter Mow Lum Yip (Chm)

BRIGHT SOLAR LTD.
C-602 Titanium Square Thaltej Circle
S G Highway, Ahmedabad, 380059,
Gujarat, India
Tel.: (91) 9377756205
Web Site:
  https://www.brightsolarltd.com
Year Founded: 2010
BRIGHT—(NSE)
Rev.: $2,880,295
Assets: $5,678,425
Liabilities: $1,982,411
Net Worth: $3,696,013
Earnings: $6,462
Emp.: 16
Fiscal Year-end: 03/31/23
Solar Energy Generation Services
N.A.I.C.S.: 221114
Piyushkumar Babubhai Thumar (Chm
& Mng Dir)

BRIGHTCOM GROUP LTD.
Floor 5 Fairfield by Marriott Road No
2 Nanakramguda, Gachibowli,
Hyderabad, 500032, Telangana, India
Tel.: (91) 4067449910
Web Site:
  https://brightcomgroup.com
BCG—(NSE)
Rev.: $392,658,194
Assets: $503,791,331
Liabilities: $58,854,735
Net Worth: $444,936,596
Earnings: $65,930,605
Emp.: 463
Fiscal Year-end: 03/31/21
Digital Marketing Solutions
N.A.I.C.S.: 541890
M. Suresh Kumar Reddy (Co-
Founder, Chm & CEO)

Subsidiaries:

Dyomo Corporation (1)
2121 N Frontage Rd W Ste 326, Vail, CO
81657-4957
Tel.: (970) 476-7446
Web Site: https://www.dyomo.com
Digital Marketing Services
N.A.I.C.S.: 541890

Global IT, Inc. (1)
1300 W Walnut Hill Ln Ste 263, Irving, TX
75038 (100%)
Tel.: (972) 536-6063
Web Site: http://www.globalitinc.com
IT Staffing Services
N.A.I.C.S.: 561311

LIL Projects Private Limited (1)
Floor 5 Fairfield by Marriott Road No 2,
Nanakramguda Gachibowli, Hyderabad,
500032, Telangana, India
Tel.: (91) 4067449910
Web Site: https://www.lilprojects.in
Emp.: 500
Software Development Services
N.A.I.C.S.: 541511
Suresh Reddy (CEO & Chm)

Lycos, Inc. (1)
177 Huntington Ave Ste 1703 60001, Bos-
ton, MA 02115-3151
Tel.: (781) 472-2001
Web Site: http://www.lycos.com
Internet Portal & Search Services
N.A.I.C.S.: 541519
Edward Michael Philip (Founder)

Division (Domestic):

Gamesville, Inc. (2)
100 5th Ave, Waltham, MA 02451-2000
Tel.: (781) 370-2700
Web Site: http://www.gamesville.com
Emp.: 200
Online Gaming
N.A.I.C.S.: 541512

Max Interactive Pty Ltd. (1)
702.6a Glen St, Milsons Point, 2061, NSW,
Australia
Tel.: (61) 293605355
Emp.: 5
Digital Appication Developement Services
N.A.I.C.S.: 541511
Trish van Tussenbroek (Gen Mgr)

Online Media Solutions Limited (1)
HaManofim 9 floor 9, Herzliyya, 4672560,
Israel
Tel.: (972) 99609600
Web Site: https://onlinemediasolutions.com
Software Application Development Services
N.A.I.C.S.: 541511
Jacob Nizri (Pres)

Techorbit, Inc. (1)
1300 W Walnut Hill Ln Ste 260, Irving, TX
75038
Tel.: (972) 518-2200
Web Site: https://www.techorbit.com
Emp.: 5
Software Application Development Services
N.A.I.C.S.: 513210

BRIGHTEK OPTOELECTRONIC CO., LTD.
7F No 1492 Chunri Rd, Taoyuan Dist,
Taoyuan, 33051, Taiwan
Tel.: (886) 33579118
Web Site: https://www.brightek.com
Year Founded: 2001
5244—(TAI)
Emp.: 500
Electrical Contracting Services
N.A.I.C.S.: 238210
Chien-Chung Huang (Chm & Pres)

BRIGHTEN OPTIX CORPORA-TION
6F 1 No 150 Section 4 Chengde
Road, Shilin District, Taipei, Taiwan
Tel.: (886) 228801778
Web Site:
  https://www.brightenoptix.com
Year Founded: 1970
6747—(TPE)
Rev.: $23,270,738
Assets: $44,885,439
Liabilities: $6,074,571
Net Worth: $38,810,868
Earnings: $7,956,008
Fiscal Year-end: 12/31/22
Optical Lens Mfr
N.A.I.C.S.: 333310
Jason T. H. Wu (Chm)

BRIGHTGENE BIO-MEDICAL TECHNOLOGY CO., LTD.
Building C25-C28 Nano Science Park
No 218 Xinghu Street, Suzhou,
215123, Jiangsu, China
Tel.: (86) 51262620988
Web Site: http://www.bright-
gene.com
Year Founded: 2001
688166—(SHG)
Rev.: $142,833,343
Assets: $654,442,617
Liabilities: $339,710,015
Net Worth: $314,732,602
Earnings: $33,643,097
Fiscal Year-end: 12/31/22
Medical Product Mfr & Distr
N.A.I.C.S.: 339112
Jiandong Yuan (Chm & Gen Mgr)

Subsidiaries:

BrightGene Fermentation Technology
Co. Ltd. (1)

No 290 Chengnan Fengshixing Road, Bei-
bei District, Chongqing, China
Tel.: (86) 2363227399
Pharmaceuticals Product Mfr
N.A.I.C.S.: 325412

BrightGene Fine Chemical Co.
Ltd. (1)
No 22 Binjiang South Road, Taixing Eco-
nomic Development Zone, Taizhou, Ji-
angsu, China
Tel.: (86) 52367679286
Pharmaceuticals Product Mfr
N.A.I.C.S.: 325412

BrightGene Pharmaceutical Co.
Ltd. (1)
Building C25-28 No 218 Xinghu Road, Su-
zhou Industrial Park, Suzhou, Jiangsu,
China
Tel.: (86) 51262620988
Pharmaceuticals Product Mfr
N.A.I.C.S.: 325412

BRIGHTHOUSE GROUP PLC
5 Hercules Way Leavesden Park,
Watford, WD25 7GS, United Kingdom
Tel.: (44) 1923 488200
Web Site:
  http://www.brighthouse.co.uk
Year Founded: 1994
Sales Range: $400-449.9 Million
Emp.: 2,285
Household Product Whslr
N.A.I.C.S.: 423620
Hamish Paton (CEO)

BRIGHTKING HOLDINGS LIM-ITED
3F No 105 Zhongcheng Road,
Tucheng District, New Taipei City,
23674, Taiwan
Tel.: (886) 2 22685502
Web Site: http://www.brightking.com
Rev.: $91,100,746
Assets: $86,273,384
Liabilities: $33,312,087
Net Worth: $52,961,298
Earnings: $6,878,464
Fiscal Year-end: 12/31/17
Circuit Protection Components Mfr
N.A.I.C.S.: 334419

Subsidiaries:

Bestbright Electronics Co., Ltd. (1)
A Flat N 12/F Wing Hong Fty Bldg 18-26
Kwai Fung Crescent, Kwai Chung, China
(Hong Kong)
Tel.: (852) 35201056
Circuit Board Mfr
N.A.I.C.S.: 334412

Subsidiary (Non-US):

Brightking Electronics Co., Ltd. (2)
A 3F No 105 Zhongcheng Rd Tucheng Dist,
New Taipei City, 236, Taiwan
Tel.: (886) 222685502
Circuit Board Mfr
N.A.I.C.S.: 334412

Subsidiary (US):

Brightking Electronics Inc. (2)
A 17 Hammond Ste 406, Irvine, CA 92618
Tel.: (949) 305-0910
Circuit Board Mfr
N.A.I.C.S.: 334412

Subsidiary (Non-US):

Ceramate Technical (Suzhou) Co.,
Ltd. (2)
A Building D No 57 Huoju Road Suzhou
New District, Jiangsu, 215009, China
Tel.: (86) 51268410367
Circuit Board Mfr
N.A.I.C.S.: 334412

Huizhou Lien Shun Electronics Co.,
Ltd. (2)
Qiubao Road Weibu Village ZOV Industry
Park Beside Boya Kindergarten, Qiuchang
Town Huiyang District, Huizhou, Guang-
dong, China

Tel.: (86) 75583795119
Circuit Board Mfr
N.A.I.C.S.: 334412

Brightking (Shenzhen) Co., Ltd. **(1)**
A 2F Tianan Management Center Building
Tianan cyber park, Futian District, Shenzhen, China
Tel.: (86) 66 32 84 88
Circuit Board Mfr
N.A.I.C.S.: 334412

Subsidiary (Domestic):

Brightking (Beijing) Co., Ltd. **(2)**
310 Fanya Building No 128 Zhichun Road
Haidian District, Beijing, China
Tel.: (86) 1062550216
Circuit Board Mfr
N.A.I.C.S.: 334412

Brightking (Shangai) Co., Ltd. **(2)**
A Floor 23 No 465 East Beijing Road
Huangpu District, Shanghai, China
Tel.: (86) 2163221578
Circuit Board Mfr
N.A.I.C.S.: 334412

**Brightking Enterprise (H.K) Co.,
Ltd** **(1)**
A 3 Building Modern Enterprise Accelerator Park Song Shan Lake, High-tech Industrial development zone, Dongguan, Guangdong, China
Tel.: (86) 769 26626898
Circuit Board Mfr
N.A.I.C.S.: 334412

**BRIGHTLITE NOMINEES PRO-
PRIETARY LIMITED**
5 Bastow Place, Mulgrave, 3170,
VIC, Australia
Tel.: (61) 395690911
Web Site:
   http://www.beaconlighting.com.au
Sales Range: $50-74.9 Million
Emp.: 500
Outdoor Lighting Fixtures Mfr
N.A.I.C.S.: 335131
Glen Robinson *(Gen Mgr-Mdsg)*

**BRIGHTOIL PETROLEUM
HOLDINGS LIMITED**
33F 118 Connaught Road West,
Hong Kong, China (Hong Kong)
Tel.: (852) 2 834 3188
Web Site: http://www.bwoil.com
0933—(HKG)
Sales Range: $5-14.9 Billion
Fuel Station
N.A.I.C.S.: 424710
Danny Yih Lin Tan *(CFO & Sec)*

**BRIGHTON MINING GROUP
LIMITED**
Suite 1A Level 1 7 Ventnor Avenue,
West Perth, 6005, WA, Australia
Tel.: (61) 8 9368 1200
Web Site:
   http://www.brightonmininggroup.com
Gold Mining Services
N.A.I.C.S.: 212220

**BRIGHTPATH BIOTHERAPEU-
TICS CO., LTD.**
7F Kojimachi Central Building 2-2-4
Kojimachi, Chiyoda-ku, Tokyo, 102-
0083, Fukuoka, Japan
Tel.: (81) 942386550
Web Site: https://brightpathbio.com
Year Founded: 2003
4594—(TKS)
Emp.: 42
Research, Development, Manufacture
& Sales of Cancer Immunotherapeutics
N.A.I.C.S.: 325412
Kenichi Nagai *(Pres & CEO)*

**BRIGHTSTAR RESOURCES
LIMITED**

Level 2/36 Rowland Street, Subiaco,
6008, WA, Australia
Tel.: (61) 94810389
Web Site:
   https://www.brightstarresources.com
Year Founded: 2002
BTR—(ASX)
Rev.: $3,301,052
Assets: $25,645,227
Liabilities: $3,852,487
Net Worth: $21,792,740
Earnings: $1,267,762
Fiscal Year-end: 06/30/23
Gold Mining & Uranium Exploration
Services
N.A.I.C.S.: 212220

Subsidiaries:

Kingwest Resources Limited **(1)**
Level 11 London House 216 St George's
Terrace, Perth, 6000, WA, Australia
Tel.: (61) 894810389
Rev.: $9,020
Assets: $18,153,790
Liabilities: $374,866
Net Worth: $17,778,924
Earnings: ($1,361,054)
Fiscal Year-end: 06/30/2022
Gold Exploration & Mining Services
N.A.I.C.S.: 212220
Adrian Byass *(Chm)*

BRIGITTE FRANCE
Rue Ettore Bugatti, 67201, Strasbourg, France
Tel.: (33) 388770088
Rev.: $11,300,000
Emp.: 24
N.A.I.C.S.: 458110
Suzanne Kircher *(Dir)*

BRII BIOSCIENCES LIMITED
3rd Floor Building 7 Zhongguancun
No 1 North Yongtaizhuang Road,
Dongsheng International Science
Park Haidian District, Beijing, 100192,
China   Ky
Web Site: https://www.briibio.com
Year Founded: 2017
2137—(HKG)
Rev.: $85,429
Assets: $442,823,854
Liabilities: $17,427,586
Net Worth: $425,396,267
Earnings: ($25,527,525)
Emp.: 128
Fiscal Year-end: 12/31/23
Biotechnology Research & Development Services
N.A.I.C.S.: 541714
Brian Alvin Johns *(Chief Scientific
Officer)*

**BRIJLAXMI LEASING & FI-
NANCE LIMITED**
204 Sterling Centre R C Dutt Road,
Alkapuri, Vadodara, 390007, Gujarat,
India
Tel.: (91) 9879504335
Web Site: https://www.brijlaxmi.com
Year Founded: 1990
532113—(BOM)
Rev.: $51,635
Assets: $650,681
Liabilities: $271,929
Net Worth: $378,752
Earnings: $142
Fiscal Year-end: 03/31/21
Financial Investment Services
N.A.I.C.S.: 523999
H. Bhatt *(Compliance Officer)*

BRIJU S.A.
Paderewskiego 25-35 62-200, 61844,
Gniezno, Poland
Tel.: (48) 61 424 59 03
Web Site: http://www.briju.pl
Year Founded: 1920

Sales Range: $125-149.9 Million
Jewelry Mfr & Distr
N.A.I.C.S.: 339910
Przemyslaw Piotrowski *(Chm-Mgmt
Bd)*

**BRILL SHOE INDUSTRIES
LTD.**
Drive In Center 20 Friman St Ind
Zone East, Rishon le Zion, 75358,
Israel
Tel.: (972) 39501875   II
Year Founded: 1988
BRIL—(TAE)
Rev.: $143,848,319
Assets: $162,855,640
Liabilities: $125,943,360
Net Worth: $36,912,280
Earnings: ($6,537,091)
Emp.: 1,320
Fiscal Year-end: 12/31/23
Footwear Manufacturing
N.A.I.C.S.: 316210

**BRILLIANCE CHINA AUTOMO-
TIVE HOLDINGS LIMITED**
Suites 1602-1605 Chater House 8
Connaught Road, Central, China
(Hong Kong)
Tel.: (852) 25237227   BM
Web Site:
   http://www.brillianceauto.com
Year Founded: 1992
1114—(OTCIQ)
Rev.: $155,274,424
Assets: $7,636,605,560
Liabilities: $451,856,031
Net Worth: $7,184,749,529
Earnings: $1,071,174,540
Emp.: 1,200
Fiscal Year-end: 12/31/23
Holding Company
N.A.I.C.S.: 551112
Xiao An Wu *(Chm)*

Subsidiaries:

BMW Brilliance Automotive Ltd. **(1)**
25th F Tower B GATEWAY No18 Xiaguangli
Dongsanhuanbeilu, Chaoyang District, Beijing, 100027, China   **(50%)**
Tel.: (86) 108 455 7000
Web Site: https://www.bmw-brilliance.cn
Motor Vehicle & Automotive Parts Mfr &
Distr
N.A.I.C.S.: 336110
Johann Wieland *(Pres & CEO)*

**Brilliance-BEA Auto Finance Co.,
Ltd.** **(1)**
12th Floor No 8 Lane 1267 Dongfang
Road, Pudong New District, Shanghai,
200127, China
Tel.: (86) 2180237100
Web Site: https://www.brilliance-bea.com
N.A.I.C.S.: 522220

**Shenyang Brilliance JinBei Automo-
bile Co., Ltd.** **(1)**
No 39 Dongwang St, Dadong Distr, Shenyang, 110044, China   **(51%)**
Tel.: (86) 2431666631
Sales Range: $1-4.9 Billion
Emp.: 7,000
Automobile Mfr
N.A.I.C.S.: 336110
Yumin Qi *(Chm)*

**BRILLIANCE TECHNOLOGY
CO LTD**
8F Building B Block 2 Jinyuan Times
Business Center, No 2 Landian
Changdong Road Haidian District,
Beijing, 100097, China
Tel.: (86) 1088877301
Web Site:
   https://www.brilliance.com.cn
300542—(CHIN)
Rev.: $244,373,201
Assets: $229,673,982

Liabilities: $137,081,995
Net Worth: $92,591,987
Earnings: $5,121,940
Fiscal Year-end: 12/31/23
Software Development Services
N.A.I.C.S.: 513210
Lu Kang *(Chm)*

BRILLIANT FUTURE AB
Drottninggatan 26, 111, 51, Stockholm, Sweden
Tel.: (46) 86929100
Web Site:
   https://www.brilliantfuture.se
Year Founded: 1996
BRILL—(OMX)
Rev.: $8,838,128
Assets: $8,950,305
Liabilities: $5,022,138
Net Worth: $3,928,167
Earnings: ($1,109,854)
Emp.: 80
Fiscal Year-end: 12/31/23
Software Development Services
N.A.I.C.S.: 541511
Marie Rosenquist Berthold *(Chief
People Officer-Marketing)*

BRILLIANT MEDIA
1 City Sq, Leeds, LS1 2FF, United
Kingdom
Tel.: (44) 113 394 0000
Sales Range: $125-149.9 Million
Emp.: 120
Media Buying Services
N.A.I.C.S.: 541830
David Moutrie *(Mng Dir)*

Subsidiaries:

Brilliant Media **(1)**
Bauhaus, 27 Quay St, Manchester, M3
3GY, United Kingdom
Tel.: (44) 161 827 1000
Sales Range: $10-24.9 Million
Emp.: 12
N.A.I.C.S.: 541830
Chris Broadbent *(Mng Dir)*

Brilliant Media **(1)**
Innovation Centre, 1 Devon Way, Birmingham, B31 2TS, United Kingdom
Tel.: (44) 121 222 5522
Emp.: 10
N.A.I.C.S.: 541830
Paul Bramwell *(Mng Dir)*

BRILLIANT N.E.V. CORP.
2nd Floor BYD No 56 Dongsihuan
South Road, Chaoyang District, Beijing, 100023, China
Tel.: (86) 18910984577   NV
Web Site:
   https://www.corpclancy.com
Year Founded: 2016
CCYC—(OTCIQ)
Assets: $1,302
Liabilities: $6,703
Net Worth: ($5,401)
Earnings: ($292,590)
Emp.: 14
Fiscal Year-end: 07/31/23
Organic Soap Mfr
N.A.I.C.S.: 325611

**BRILLIANT PORTFOLIOS LIM-
ITED**
B-09 412 ITL Twin Tower Netaji Subhash Place, Pitampura, New Delhi,
110 088, India
Tel.: (91) 1145058963
Web Site:
   https://www.brilliantportfolios.com
539434—(BOM)
Rev.: $317,994
Assets: $4,024,356
Liabilities: $2,962,939
Net Worth: $1,061,417
Earnings: $43,510

Brilliant Portfolios Limited—(Continued)

Emp.: 2
Fiscal Year-end: 03/31/22
Financial Support Services
N.A.I.C.S.: 523999
Ravi Jain *(Mng Dir)*

BRILONER LEUCHTEN GMBH
Im Kissen 2, 59929, Brilon, Germany
Tel.: (49) 296197120
Web Site: http://www.briloner.de
Rev.: $31,726,200
Emp.: 150
Residential Lighting Product Whslr
N.A.I.C.S.: 423610
Hans-Walter Hustadt *(Founder)*

BRIMAG DIGITAL AGE LTD.
19 Shekma St, Azor, 58001, Israel
Tel.: (972) 37358000
Web Site: https://www.brimag.co.il
Year Founded: 1993
BRMG—(TAE)
Rev.: $127,903,300
Assets: $147,332,778
Liabilities: $83,210,939
Net Worth: $64,121,839
Earnings: $9,117
Emp.: 371
Fiscal Year-end: 12/31/23
Household Appliances, Electric
Housewares & Consumer Electronics
Merchant Wholesalers
N.A.I.C.S.: 423620
Shaul Silberstein *(Chm)*

BRIMSTONE INVESTMENT CORPORATION LTD.
1st Floor Slade House Boundary Terraces 1 Mariendahl Lane, Newlands, 7700, Cape Town, 7700, South Africa
Tel.: (27) 216831444   ZA
Web Site:
    https://www.brimstone.co.za
Year Founded: 1998
BRT—(JSE)
Rev.: $355,567,325
Assets: $667,445,640
Liabilities: $389,455,877
Net Worth: $277,989,763
Earnings: $22,975,258
Emp.: 4,440
Fiscal Year-end: 12/31/23
Holding Company; Financial Services, Healthcare & Industrial Services
N.A.I.C.S.: 551112
Fred Robertson *(Chm)*

Subsidiaries:

House of Monatic (Pty) Ltd.   **(1)**
364 Victoria Road, Salt River, Cape Town, 7925, Western Cape, South Africa
Tel.: (27) 214429400
Web Site: http://www.monatic.co.za
Sales Range: $200-249.9 Million
Emp.: 800
Corporate Wear Mfr
N.A.I.C.S.: 315210
Mike Maurer *(Mng Dir)*

Lion of Africa Holdings Company
(Pty) Ltd   **(1)**
Sunridge Park 62 Wierda Road East
Wierda Valley, Sandton, 2196, Gauteng, South Africa
Tel.: (27) 21 674 0450
General Insurance Services
N.A.I.C.S.: 524113

Oceana SPV (Pty) Ltd.   **(1)**
7th Floor Oceana House 25 Jan Smuts Street Foreshore, Cape Town, 8001, Western Cape, South Africa
Tel.: (27) 214101453
Fish Products Whslr
N.A.I.C.S.: 424460

Sea Harvest Corporation Limited   **(1)**
1st Floor Block C Boulevard Office Park

Searle Street, Woodstock, Cape Town, South Africa
Tel.: (27) 214687900
Web Site: http://www.seaharvest.co.za
Food Service Contractors
N.A.I.C.S.: 722310
Felix Ratheb *(CEO)*

Viking Aquaculture (Pty) Ltd.   **(1)**
West Cliff Street New Harbour, Hermanus, Cape Town, South Africa
Tel.: (27) 280085201
Web Site:
    http://www.vikingaquaculture.co.za
Aquaculture & Fish Farming Services
N.A.I.C.S.: 112512
Tim Reddell *(CEO)*

BRINDLEY ADVERTISING LTD.
Marine House Clanwilliam Place, Dublin, 2, Ireland
Tel.: (353) 17753400
Year Founded: 1956
Sales Range: $10-24.9 Million
Emp.: 15
N.A.I.C.S.: 541810
Basil Brindley *(Chm)*

BRINGSPRING SCIENCE & TECHNOLOGY CO., LTD.
No 7A3 Kaifa Road, Shenyang Economic and Technological Development Zone, Shenyang, 110027, Liaoning, China
Tel.: (86) 2422851050
Web Site: http://www.bringspring.com
Year Founded: 1996
300290—(CHIN)
Rev.: $99,001,656
Assets: $214,413,264
Liabilities: $93,497,976
Net Worth: $120,915,288
Earnings: ($31,620,888)
Emp.: 310
Fiscal Year-end: 12/31/22
IT Services
N.A.I.C.S.: 541519
Huang Liming *(Chm)*

Subsidiaries:

Liaoning Bringspring Financial Service Co., Ltd   **(1)**
F5 & F6 Ruyi Building Jinshajiang Rd, Fanhe District, Tieling, China
Tel.: (86) 24 72256409
Financial Data Management Services
N.A.I.C.S.: 518210

BRINK GROUP OF COMPANIES
2023 River Road, Prince George, V2N 5S8, BC, Canada
Tel.: (250) 564-0412
Web Site: https://www.brinkgroup.ca
Year Founded: 1965
Emp.: 400
Paper & Forest Product Mfg.
N.A.I.C.S.: 321211
John A. Brink *(Founder, Pres & CEO)*

Subsidiaries:

Brink Forest Products Ltd.   **(1)**
2023 River Road, Prince George, V2L 5S8, BC, Canada
Tel.: (250) 564-0412
Web Site: http://www.brink.bc.ca
Paper & Forest Product Mfg
N.A.I.C.S.: 423310

BRINNO, INC.
4F No 107 Zhou Zi St, Taipei, 11493, Taiwan
Tel.: (886) 287510306
Web Site: https://www.brinno.com
Year Founded: 2003
7402—(TPE)
Rev.: $19,890,473
Assets: $24,861,989
Liabilities: $12,120,939

Net Worth: $12,741,050
Earnings: $1,774,943
Fiscal Year-end: 12/31/22
Electronic Equipment Distr
N.A.I.C.S.: 423690
David Chen *(Chm & Pres)*

BRINOVA FASTIGHETER AB
Brinova Fastigheter AB Storlorget 9, 25220, Helsingborg, Sweden
Tel.: (46) 102071230
Web Site: https://www.brinova.se
BRIN.B—(OMX)
Rev.: $38,015,712
Assets: $763,549,360
Liabilities: $521,940,832
Net Worth: $241,608,528
Earnings: $19,593,840
Emp.: 48
Fiscal Year-end: 12/31/20
Real Estate Investment Services
N.A.I.C.S.: 531210
Per Johansson *(CEO-IR)*

BRIOX AB
Tel.: (46) 470322000
Web Site: https://www.briox.se
Year Founded: 2010
Software Development Services
N.A.I.C.S.: 541511
Johan Rutgersson *(Chm)*

BRIQ PROPERTIES REIC
25 Al Pantou Street, Kallithea, 17671, Athens, Greece
Tel.: (30) 2119991699
Web Site:
    https://www.briqproperties.gr
Year Founded: 2016
BRIQ—(ATH)
Rev.: $9,772,435
Assets: $167,569,773
Liabilities: $43,655,002
Net Worth: $123,914,770
Earnings: $15,704,165
Emp.: 9
Fiscal Year-end: 12/31/23
Real Estate Development Services
N.A.I.C.S.: 531390
Anna Apostolidou *(CEO)*

BRISCOE GROUP LIMITED
1 Taylors Road Morningside, PO Box 884, Auckland, 1025, New Zealand
Tel.: (64) 98153737   NZ
Web Site:
    https://www.briscoegroup.co.nz
BGP—(ASX)
Rev.: $473,656,100
Assets: $431,313,397
Liabilities: $242,397,129
Net Worth: $188,916,268
Earnings: $50,371,411
Emp.: 2,300
Fiscal Year-end: 01/28/24
Homeware & Sports Goods Retailer
N.A.I.C.S.: 459110
Geoffrey Peter Scowcroft *(CFO)*

Subsidiaries:

Briscoes (New Zealand) Limited   **(1)**
1 Taylors Road, Sandringham, Auckland, 1025, New Zealand
Tel.: (64) 95519035
Web Site: https://www.briscoes.co.nz
Household Appliances & Utensils Retailer
N.A.I.C.S.: 449210

Rebel Sport Limited   **(1)**
1 Taylors Road, Sandringham, Auckland, 1025, New Zealand
Tel.: (64) 95519036
Web Site: https://www.rebelsport.co.nz
Sporting Goods Retailer
N.A.I.C.S.: 459110

BRISSET BEER INTERNATIONAL, INC.

370 Guy Street Suite G9, Montreal, H3J 1S6, QC, Canada
Tel.: (514) 906-6851   NV
Year Founded: 2010
BBII—(OTCIQ)
Liabilities: $475,084
Net Worth: ($475,084)
Earnings: ($15,779)
Fiscal Year-end: 05/31/21
Beer Brewer, Marketer & Distr
N.A.I.C.S.: 424810
Kevin G. Malone *(Pres, CEO, Treas & Sec)*

BRISTOL GROUP
Fortis Bldg 139 Water St, PO Box 2220, Saint John's, A1C 6E6, NL, Canada
Tel.: (709) 753-7242
Year Founded: 1977
Emp.: 130
Advertising Agencies
N.A.I.C.S.: 541810
Mike Whitelaw *(Dir-Creative)*

Subsidiaries:

Bristol Group - Halifax   **(1)**
Cogswell Tower, 2000 Barrington St Suite 800, Halifax, B3J 3K1, NS, Canada
Tel.: (902) 429-0900
Advertising Agencies
N.A.I.C.S.: 541810

BRITAM HOLDINGS PLC
Britam Tower Hospital Road Upper Hill, PO Box 30375, 00100, Nairobi, Kenya
Tel.: (254) 202833000   KE
Web Site: https://www.britam.com
BRIT—(NAI)
Rev.: $276,912,882
Assets: $1,325,383,569
Liabilities: $1,130,153,314
Net Worth: $195,230,255
Earnings: $24,921,105
Emp.: 1,095
Fiscal Year-end: 12/31/23
Financial Services
N.A.I.C.S.: 523999
Benson I. Wairegi *(Mng Dir)*

Subsidiaries:

Britam - Companhia De Seguros De Mozambique S.A.   **(1)**
Marjinal Street, Maputo, Mozambique
Tel.: (258) 21492840
Web Site: https://mz.britam.com
Insurance Services
N.A.I.C.S.: 524210
Muthoga Ngera *(Chm)*

Britam Asset Managers (Kenya) Limited   **(1)**
Britam Centre Junction of Mara and Ragati Road Upper Hill, PO Box 30375, 00100, Nairobi, Kenya
Tel.: (254) 705100100
Management Consulting Services
N.A.I.C.S.: 541611
Kenneth Kaniu *(CEO)*

Britam Companhia de Seguros de Mocambique SA   **(1)**
No 1489 Caixa 3681, Maputo, Mozambique
Tel.: (258) 21 492840
Insurance Services
N.A.I.C.S.: 524298

Britam General Insurance Company (Kenya) Limited   **(1)**
Renaissance Corporate Park Elgon Road, PO Box 30375-00100, Upper Hill, Nairobi, Kenya
Tel.: (254) 202833000
Insurance Services
N.A.I.C.S.: 524298

Britam Insurance (Tanzania) Limited   **(1)**
PPF Tower 2nd Floor Garden Ohio Street, PO Bxo 75433, Dar es Salaam, Tanzania
Tel.: (255) 22 2138058

Insurance Services
N.A.I.C.S.: 524298

Britam Insurance Company (Rwanda)
Limited   **(1)**
Union Trade Centre 5th Floor, PO Box 913,
Kigali, Rwanda
Tel.: (250) 252579031
Insurance Services
N.A.I.C.S.: 524298

Britam Insurance Company (Tanza-
nia) Limited   **(1)**
Ohio Street-Ghan Avenue, Dar es Salaam,
Tanzania
Tel.: (255) 767911111
Web Site: https://tz.britam.com
Insurance Services
N.A.I.C.S.: 524210
Peter K. Munga *(Chm)*

Britam Insurance Company (Uganda)
Limited   **(1)**
Plot 24A Akii-Bua Road, PO Box 36583,
Nakasero, Kampala, Uganda
Tel.: (256) 312305600
Insurance Services
N.A.I.C.S.: 524298

Britam Insurance Company
Limited   **(1)**
The Britam Place Hai Malakai, Juba, Sudan
(South)
Tel.: (211) 91 100 6001
Web Site: https://ss.britam.com
Insurance Services
N.A.I.C.S.: 524210
Joe Muchekehu *(Chm)*

Britam Insurance Company
Limited   **(1)**
Delamere House Victoria Avenue Road, PO
Box 442, Blantyre, Malawi
Tel.: (265) 1895500
Web Site: https://mw.britam.com
Insurance Services
N.A.I.C.S.: 524210

BRITANNIA LIFE SCIENCES INC.
120 Adelaide St West Suite 2400,
Toronto, M5H 1T1, ON, Canada
Tel.: (416) 302-0779   Ca
Web Site: https://britannia.life
Year Founded: 2000
BLSIF—(OTCIQ)
Rev.: $5,591,489
Assets: $16,445,171
Liabilities: $11,517,544
Net Worth: $4,927,626
Earnings: ($3,249,231)
Fiscal Year-end: 03/31/24
Biotechnology Research & Develop-
ment Services
N.A.I.C.S.: 541714
Scott Secord *(Chm)*

BRITANNIA SUPERFINE LTD.
Chaucer Industrial Estate Dittons
Road, Lewes, BN26 6JF, East Sus-
sex, United Kingdom
Tel.: (44) 1323 485 155
Web Site: http://www.britannia-
superfine.com
Year Founded: 1953
Sales Range: $25-49.9 Million
Emp.: 106
Confectionery Mfr
N.A.I.C.S.: 311352
Colin Manser *(Mng Dir)*

BRITCON
Midland Rd, Scunthorpe, DN16 1DQ,
South Lincolnshire, United Kingdom
Tel.: (44) 1724280022
Web Site: http://www.britcon.co.uk
Sales Range: $50-74.9 Million
Emp.: 120
Engineering Services, Industrial &
Commercial Buildings Constructor
N.A.I.C.S.: 541330
John Whitmore *(Dir-Comml)*

BRITE-TECH BERHAD
Lot 14 Jalan Pendamar 27/90
Seksyen 27, 40400, Shah Alam, Se-
langor, Malaysia
Tel.: (60) 351928188   MY
Web Site: https://www.brite-tech.com
Year Founded: 2001
BTECH—(KLS)
Rev.: $6,007,622
Assets: $28,253,102
Liabilities: $10,753,280
Net Worth: $17,499,822
Earnings: $1,199,596
Fiscal Year-end: 12/31/20
Waste Water Treatment Services
N.A.I.C.S.: 221320
Wee See Pang *(Founder & Chm)*

Subsidiaries:

Akva-Tek Sdn. Bhd.   **(1)**
Lot 14 PT 5015 Jalan Pendamar 27/90
Seksyen 27, 40000, Shah Alam, Selangor,
Malaysia
Tel.: (60) 351928288
Chemical Product Wastewater Treatment
Services
N.A.I.C.S.: 221320

Brite-Tech Corporation Sdn.
Berhad   **(1)**
12 Jalan 27A Kawasan 16 Sg Rasa Indus-
trial Area, 41300, Klang, Selangor, Malaysia
Tel.: (60) 333412338
Water Treatment Chemical Distr
N.A.I.C.S.: 424690
Pang Wee See *(Founder)*

Rank Chemical Sdn. Berhad   **(1)**
5 Jalan Malinja 6 Batu 5 Jalan Mersing Ta-
man Perindustrian Matahari, 86009, Kluang,
Johor, Malaysia
Tel.: (60) 77878888
Chemical Distr
N.A.I.C.S.: 424690

Spectrum Laboratories (Johore) Sdn.
Berhad   **(1)**
18A Jalan Molek 2/5 Taman Molek, 81100,
Johor Bahru, Johor, Malaysia
Tel.: (60) 73539288
Laboratory Testing Services
N.A.I.C.S.: 541380

Spectrum Laboratories (Penang) Sdn.
Berhad   **(1)**
1904 Jalan Bukit Minyak Taman Sri Mangga
Seberang Perai Tengah, 14000, Bukit Mer-
tajam, Penang, Malaysia
Tel.: (60) 45075168
Laboratory Testing Services
N.A.I.C.S.: 541380

BRITHOL MICHCOMA MOZAM-BIQUE LIMITED
Ave Mao Tse Tung 346, Maputo, Mo-
zambique
Tel.: (258) 21493865   MZ
Web Site: http://britholmichcoma.com
Year Founded: 1990
Sales Range: $1-9.9 Million
Emp.: 400
Office Equipment, Computers & Elec-
tronics & Hotels Distr & Importer;
Printing Services
N.A.I.C.S.: 333310
Lucas Manhica *(Mgr)*

Subsidiaries:

Consulting & Banking & Administra-
tive Services, Ltd.   **(1)**
Avenida Julius Nyerere 542, Maputo, Mo-
zambique
Tel.: (258) 21485824
Web Site: http://www.coseba.co.mz
Electronic Security System Installation Ser-
vices
N.A.I.C.S.: 238210

Prodata Lda.   **(1)**
Rua de Mukumbura 151, Maputo, Mozam-
bique
Tel.: (258) 21487873
Web Site: http://prodata.co.mz

Office Equipment Distr
N.A.I.C.S.: 423420

Satellite Communication Ltd.   **(1)**
Av 25 de Setembro n 1509 1st floor, Ma-
puto, Mozambique
Tel.: (258) 21300400
Web Site: http://www.satcom.co.mz
Satellite Communication Services
N.A.I.C.S.: 517410

BRITISH & AMERICAN IN-VESTMENT TRUST PLC
1 Chesham Street, London, SW1X
8ND, United Kingdom
Tel.: (44) 2072013100
Web Site:
  https://www.baitgroup.co.uk
Year Founded: 1996
BAF—(LSE)
Rev.: $1,734,480
Assets: $16,622,100
Liabilities: $8,082,195
Net Worth: $8,539,905
Earnings: $1,180,410
Fiscal Year-end: 12/31/22
Investment Trust Management Ser-
vices
N.A.I.C.S.: 523940
David G. Seligman *(Chm)*

BRITISH & MALAYAN TRUST-EES LIMITED
1 Coleman Street 06-11 The Adelphi,
Singapore, 179803, Singapore
Tel.: (65) 65354922   SG
Web Site: https://www.bmtrust.com
Year Founded: 1924
Rev.: $1,713,187
Assets: $8,525,918
Liabilities: $521,893
Net Worth: $8,004,026
Earnings: $472,675
Fiscal Year-end: 06/30/18
Trustee & Advisory Services
N.A.I.C.S.: 523940
Angela Wei Ling Ho *(Co-Sec &
Controller-Fin)*

BRITISH AMERICAN INVEST-MENT CO. (MTIUS) LTD.
25 Pope Hennessy St, Port Louis,
Mauritius
Tel.: (230) 202 3600
Web Site:
  http://www.britishamerican.com
Sales Range: $500-549.9 Million
Investment Holding Company
N.A.I.C.S.: 551112
J. Nicholas Ashford-Hodges *(Chm)*

Subsidiaries:

Bramer Corporation Limited   **(1)**
25 Pope Hennessy Street, Port Louis, Mau-
ritius
Tel.: (230) 202 3600
Web Site:
  http://www.bramercorporation.com
Financial Services
N.A.I.C.S.: 522110

Subsidiary (Domestic):

National Commercial Bank Ltd.   **(2)**
1 Queen Street Place DArmes, Port Louis,
Mauritius
Tel.: (230) 405 4400
Web Site: http://www.ncbl.mu
Sales Range: $25-49.9 Million
Banking Services
N.A.I.C.S.: 522110
M. Ashraf Esmael *(CEO)*

Marcom Co Ltd.   **(1)**
Quality Living Centre Royal Road,
Curepipe, Mauritius
Tel.: (230) 6018700
Marketing Consulting Services
N.A.I.C.S.: 541613
Cora Korimbocus *(Gen Mgr)*

BRITISH AMERICAN TO-BACCO PLC
Globe House 4 Temple Place, Lon-
don, WC2R 2PG, United Kingdom
Tel.: (44) 2078451000   UK
Web Site: https://www.bat.com
Year Founded: 1902
BTI—(NYSE)
Rev.: $21,509,917,200
Assets: $93,595,694,400
Liabilities: $51,862,528,800
Net Worth: $41,733,165,600
Earnings: ($11,186,607,600)
Emp.: 46,000
Fiscal Year-end: 12/31/23
Holding Company; Tobacco Products
Mfr & Distr
N.A.I.C.S.: 551112
Jerome Abelman *(Member-Mgmt Bd,
Gen Counsel & Dir-Legal & External
Affairs)*

Subsidiaries:

B.A.T (U.K. and Export) Ltd.   **(1)**
Globe Ho 4 Temple Pl, London, WC2R
2PG, United Kingdom
Tel.: (44) 20 7845 1000
Web Site:
  http://www.britishamericantobacco.com
Cigarette Mfr
N.A.I.C.S.: 312230

B.A.T. (Cyprus) Ltd.   **(1)**
PO Box 21563, Nicosia, 1510,
Cyprus   **(100%)**
Tel.: (357) 22746000
Sales Range: $25-49.9 Million
Emp.: 80
Cigarette Mfr
N.A.I.C.S.: 312230

B.A.T. International Finance p.l.c.   **(1)**
Globe House 4 Temple Place, London,
WC2R 2PG, United Kingdom
Tel.: (44) 20 7845 1000
Financial Management Services
N.A.I.C.S.: 523999

B.A.T. Sucursal Costa Rica   **(1)**
225 Metros Al Este De La Firestone Flores,
Heredia, 284 3007, Costa Rica   **(100%)**
Tel.: (506) 2091717
Web Site: http://www.batcentralamerica.com
Sales Range: $25-49.9 Million
Emp.: 75
Cigarette Mfr
N.A.I.C.S.: 312230

BTomorrow Ventures Limited   **(1)**
Globe House 4 Temple Place, London,
WC2R 2PG, United Kingdom
Tel.: (44) 2078451000
Web Site: http://www.btomorrowv.com
Investment Services
N.A.I.C.S.: 523910
Lisa Smith *(Mng Dir)*

British Aamerican Tobacco Holdings
(The Netherlands) B.V.   **(1)**
Handelsweg 53A, PO Box 246, 1180 AE,
Amstelveen, North Holland,
Netherlands   **(100%)**
Tel.: (31) 205005800
Web Site: http://www.bat.nl
Sales Range: $75-99.9 Million
Emp.: 250
Holding Company; Tobacco Production
N.A.I.C.S.: 551112

Holding (Domestic):

British American Tobacco The Neth-
erlands B.V.   **(2)**
Handelsweg 53 A, 1181 ZA, Amstelveen,
Netherlands   **(100%)**
Tel.: (31) 205406911
Sales Range: $50-74.9 Million
Emp.: 250
Tobacco Product Distr
N.A.I.C.S.: 459991

Subsidiary (Domestic):

British American Tobacco Finance
BV   **(3)**

British American Tobacco plc—(Continued)

Hambelswed 53 A, Amstelveen, 1083 HJ,
Netherlands   **(100%)**
Tel.: (31) 206445366
Web Site: http://www.britishamerican.com
Sales Range: $50-74.9 Million
Emp.: 150
Tobacco Products Exporter
N.A.I.C.S.: 459991

**British American Tobacco (Algerie)
S.P.A.**   **(1)**
Bois De Cars III, Dely Ibrahim Villa 199,
Algiers, Algeria
Tel.: (213) 770325813
Cigarette Mfr
N.A.I.C.S.: 312230

**British American Tobacco (Austria)
GmbH**   **(1)**
Dr-Karl-Lueger-Platz 5, 1010, Vienna, Aus-
tria
Tel.: (43) 120512260
Web Site: http://www.bat-austria.at
Cigarette Mfr
N.A.I.C.S.: 312230

**British American Tobacco (Brands)
Ltd.**   **(1)**
Globe House 4 Temple Place, London,
WC2R 2PG, United Kingdom
Tel.: (44) 20 7845 1000
Web Site: http://www.bat.com
Cigarette Mfr
N.A.I.C.S.: 312230

**British American Tobacco (Cambodia)
Limited**   **(1)**
No 1121 National Road no 2, PO Box 2220,
Sangkat Chak Angre Leu Khan Mean Chey
Phnom Penh 3, Phnom Penh, Cambodia
Tel.: (855) 23722555
Web Site: https://www.bat-cambodia.com
Tobacco Distr
N.A.I.C.S.: 424940

**British American Tobacco (Czech Re-
public), s.r.o.**   **(1)**
Nile House Karolinska 654/2, 186 00,
Prague, Czech Republic
Tel.: (420) 730811812
Web Site: https://www.batczech.cz
Emp.: 220
Tobacco Distr
N.A.I.C.S.: 424940
Tomas Tesar (Comm Mgr)

**British American Tobacco (Fiji) Mar-
keting Pte Limited**   **(1)**
GPO Box 560, Suva, Fiji
Tel.: (679) 3381144
Cigarette Mfr
N.A.I.C.S.: 312230

**British American Tobacco (GLP)
Ltd.**   **(1)**
Globe House 4 Temple Pl, London, WC2R
2PG, United Kingdom
Tel.: (44) 2078451000
Web Site: http://www.bat.com
Tobacco Products Whslr
N.A.I.C.S.: 424940

**British American Tobacco (Hong
Kong) Ltd.**   **(1)**
Level 30 Three Pacific Place 1 Queen's
Road East, 510 Kings Road, Wanchai,
China (Hong Kong)
Tel.: (852) 29182888
Web Site: https://www.bathongkong.com
Sales Range: $50-74.9 Million
Emp.: 90
Tobacco Product Distr
N.A.I.C.S.: 424920

**British American Tobacco (Industrie)
GmbH**   **(1)**
Alsterufer 4, 20354, Hamburg, Germany
Tel.: (49) 40 4151 01
Web Site: http://www.bat.de
Tobacco Product Mfr & Whslr
N.A.I.C.S.: 312230

**British American Tobacco (Invest-
ments) Ltd.**   **(1)**
Globe House 4 Temple Place, London,
WC2R 2PG, United Kingdom
Tel.: (44) 20 7845 1000

Web Site: http://www.bat.com
Investment Management Service
N.A.I.C.S.: 523999

Subsidiary (Non-US):

**British American Tobacco (Uganda)
Ltd.**   **(2)**
Plot 69/71 Jinja Road Industrial Area, PO
Box 7100, Kampala, Uganda
Tel.: (256) 4142345678
Sales Range: $100-124.9 Million
Cigarette Mfr
N.A.I.C.S.: 312230
Jack Marie Henry David Bowles (CEO)

West Indian Tobacco Limited   **(2)**
Corner Eastern Main Road and Mount D Or
Road, Trinity, Champs Fleurs, Trinidad &
Tobago
Tel.: (868) 6622271
Web Site:
    https://www.westindiantobacco.com
Rev.: $111,623,287
Assets: $131,992,377
Liabilities: $52,446,604
Net Worth: $79,545,773
Earnings: $40,957,239
Emp.: 192
Fiscal Year-end: 12/31/2023
Tobacco Manufacturing
N.A.I.C.S.: 312230
Anthony E. Phillip (Chm)

**British American Tobacco (Malawi)
Limited**   **(1)**
PO Box 428, Blantyre, Malawi
Tel.: (265) 870033
Tobacco Mfr & Distr
N.A.I.C.S.: 312230

**British American Tobacco (Malaysia)
Berhad**   **(1)**
                                 (50%)
Web Site: http://www.batmalaysia.com
Emp.: 1,000
Cigarette Mfr & Distr
N.A.I.C.S.: 312230
C. K. Prabhakaran (Dir-Ops)

**British American Tobacco (Malta)
Limited**   **(1)**
PO Box 448, VLT 1000, Valletta, Malta
Tel.: (356) 21693503
Cigarette Mfr
N.A.I.C.S.: 312230

**British American Tobacco (New Zea-
land) Ltd.**   **(1)**
2 Watt Street Parnell, Auckland, 1052, New
Zealand
Tel.: (64) 9 357 9430
Web Site: http://www.batnz.com
Emp.: 80
Tobacco Product Mfr & Whslr
N.A.I.C.S.: 312230

**British American Tobacco (Romania)
Trading SRL**   **(1)**
1A Bucuresti - Ploiesti Road, District 1, Bu-
charest, Romania
Tel.: (40) 213115100
Cigarette Mfr
N.A.I.C.S.: 312230

**British American Tobacco (Zambia)
plc**   **(1)**
Plot F10723 Chifwema Road Off Leopards
Hill Road, PO Box 31062, Off Leopards Hill
Road, Lusaka, 10101, Zambia
Tel.: (260) 965450784
Cigarette Mfr
N.A.I.C.S.: 312230

**British American Tobacco - Albania
SH.P.K.**   **(1)**
Rr Kavajes Ish Kombinati Ushqimor, Tirana,
Albania
Tel.: (355) 42247600
Cigarette Mfr
N.A.I.C.S.: 312230

**British American Tobacco Argentina
S.A.I.C.y F.**   **(1)**
Cordoba 3201, Martinez - San Isidro,
B1640GWM, Buenos Aires, Argentina
Tel.: (54) 8008880000
Web Site: https://www.batargentina.com
Emp.: 730
Cigarette Mfr

N.A.I.C.S.: 312230

**British American Tobacco Australasia
Ltd.**   **(1)**
Level 25 210 George Street, Sydney, 2000,
NSW, Australia   **(100%)**
Tel.: (61) 293701500
Web Site: http://www.bat.com.au
Sales Range: $350-399.9 Million
Emp.: 1,500
Mfr of Cigar & Cigarette Tobacco
N.A.I.C.S.: 312230

**British American Tobacco Australia
Ltd.**   **(1)**
Locked Bag 6000, Private Bag No 1, Ma-
roubra, Sydney, 1335, NSW, Australia
Tel.: (61) 293701500
Web Site: http://www.bata.com.au
Tobacco Product Mfr
N.A.I.C.S.: 312230

**British American Tobacco Bangladesh
Co. Ltd.**   **(1)**
New DOHS Road, Mohakhali, Dhaka, 1206,
Bangladesh   **(65%)**
Tel.: (880) 48811279
Web Site: https://www.batbangladesh.com
Sales Range: $25-49.9 Million
Emp.: 130
Cigarette Mfr
N.A.I.C.S.: 312230
Shehzad Munim (Mng Dir)

**British American Tobacco Belgium
SA/NV**   **(1)**
Nieuwe Gentsesteenweg 21, B-1702,
Groot-Bijgaarden, Belgium
Tel.: (32) 24131211
Web Site: http://www.batbelgium.com
Cigarette Mfr
N.A.I.C.S.: 312230

**British American Tobacco Botswana
(Pty) Limited**   **(1)**
Portion 867 Farm Hill Forest Opposite
Kgale Hill, PO Box 21586, Next to Gabo-
rone International Commerce Park, Gabo-
rone, Botswana
Tel.: (267) 3160015
Cigarette Mfr
N.A.I.C.S.: 312230

**British American Tobacco Cameroun
S.A.**   **(1)**
620 Rue Du Gouveneur Carras Immeuble
Grass Field 9eme Etage Bonanjo, Douala,
Cameroon
Tel.: (237) 233425410
Cigarette Mfr
N.A.I.C.S.: 312230

**British American Tobacco Chile Op-
eraciones S.A.**   **(1)**
Isidora Goyenechea 3000 Piso 15, Las
Condes, Santiago, Chile
Tel.: (56) 224646141
Web Site: http://www.batchile.com
Cigarette Mfr
N.A.I.C.S.: 312230

**British American Tobacco Colombia
S.A.S.**   **(1)**
Av Carrera 72 80-94 9th Floor, Titan Busi-
ness Center, Bogota, Colombia
Tel.: (57) 17309000
Web Site: https://www.batcolombia.com
Tobacco Distr
N.A.I.C.S.: 424940

**British American Tobacco
Denmark**   **(1)**
Bernstorffgade 50, 1577, Copenhagen,
Denmark
Tel.: (45) 39556300
Web Site: https://www.batdenmark.dk
Sales Range: $1-4.9 Billion
Emp.: 1,866
Cigarette Manufacturer
N.A.I.C.S.: 312230

**British American Tobacco Egypt
LLC**   **(1)**
Downtown Mall Building S2B Area A City
Centre 5th Settlement, New Cairo, Egypt
Tel.: (20) 225996900
Cigarette Mfr
N.A.I.C.S.: 312230

**British American Tobacco Espana,
S.A.**   **(1)**

Tel.: (34) 915551904
Web Site: http://www.bat.com.es
Emp.: 100
Cigarette Mfr & Distr
N.A.I.C.S.: 312230

**British American Tobacco Estonia
AS**   **(1)**
Mustamae Tee 46, 10621, Tallinn, Estonia
Tel.: (372) 6260170
Cigarette Mfr
N.A.I.C.S.: 312230

**British American Tobacco Finland
Oy**   **(1)**
Pitk Nsillanranta 3 A 00530, 530, Helsinki,
Finland   **(100%)**
Tel.: (358) 9731311
Web Site: http://www.bat.fi
Sales Range: $25-49.9 Million
Emp.: 100
Cigarette Mfr
N.A.I.C.S.: 312230

**British American Tobacco France
SAS**   **(1)**
Tour Legende 20 place de la Defense, CS
80289, Paris La Defense, 92050, Paris, Ce-
dex, France
Tel.: (33) 155199200
Web Site: http://www.batfrance.com
Sales Range: $50-74.9 Million
Emp.: 150
Tobacco Products Mfr & Whslr
N.A.I.C.S.: 312230

**British American Tobacco Hellas
S.A.**   **(1)**
Tel.: (30) 2108198500
Cigarette Mfr
N.A.I.C.S.: 312230

**British American Tobacco Holdings
(The Netherlands) B.V.**   **(1)**
Tel.: (31) 206445366
Web Site:
    http://www.britishamericantobacco.com
Emp.: 300
Investment Management Service
N.A.I.C.S.: 523999

**British American Tobacco Holdings
South Africa (Pty) Ltd.**   **(1)**
Investment Management Service
N.A.I.C.S.: 523999

**British American Tobacco Interna-
tional Ltd.**   **(1)**
Zahlerweg 4, 6301, Zug, Switzerland
Tel.: (41) 417697676
Web Site: http://www.bati.com
Sales Range: $75-99.9 Million
Emp.: 120
Tobacco Products Whslr
N.A.I.C.S.: 424940

**British American Tobacco Italia
S.p.A.**   **(1)**
Via Amsterdam 147, 00144, Rome, Italy
Tel.: (39) 0652879101
Web Site: https://www.batitalia.com
Emp.: 400
Tobacco Products Mfr & Whslr
N.A.I.C.S.: 312230

**British American Tobacco Japan,
Ltd.**   **(1)**
                                 (100%)
Web Site: http://www.batj.com
Sales Range: $25-49.9 Million
Emp.: 100
Cigarette Manufacturing
N.A.I.C.S.: 312230

**British American Tobacco Kazakhstan
Trading LLP**   **(1)**
240G Nursultan Nazarbayev Avenue,
A26F8D4, Almaty, Kazakhstan
Tel.: (7) 7272444999
Cigarette Mfr
N.A.I.C.S.: 312230

**British American Tobacco Kenya
plc**   **(1)**
08 Likoni Road, PO Box 30000, Industrial
Area, 100, Nairobi, Kenya
Tel.: (254) 711062000
Web Site: http://www.batkenya.com
Tobacco Mfr & Distr

N.A.I.C.S.: 312230

British American Tobacco Korea Ltd. (1)
42nd Floor Star Tower 737 Yeoksam-dong, Kangnam, 135-984, Korea (South)
Tel.: (82) 2 2112 7100
Web Site: http://www.batkorea.com
Tobacco Product Mfr
N.A.I.C.S.: 312230
Tony Hayward (CEO)

British American Tobacco Korea Manufacturing Ltd. (1)
889 Yoochun-Ri Sanam-Myeon, Sacheon, 64942, Gyeongsangnam-do, Korea (South)
Tel.: (82) 558517500
Web Site: http://www.batkorea.com
Sales Range: $50-74.9 Million
Emp.: 20
Tobacco Product Mfr & Whslr
N.A.I.C.S.: 312230

British American Tobacco Kosovo SH.P.K. (1)
Lapljeselo pn, Gracanice, 10500, Pristina, Kosovo
Tel.: (383) 38556042
Cigarette Mfr
N.A.I.C.S.: 312230

British American Tobacco ME DMCC (1)
37th Floor JBC3 Building Cluster Y, PO Box 337222, Jumeriah Lake Towers, Dubai, United Arab Emirates
Tel.: (971) 43659500
Web Site: http://www.batme.com
Cigarette Mfr
N.A.I.C.S.: 312230

British American Tobacco Marketing Nigeria Limited (1)
2 Olumegbon Road Off Alfred Rewane Road, Ikoyi, Lagos, Nigeria
Tel.: (234) 7046002511
Web Site: http://www.batwca.com
Cigarette Mfr
N.A.I.C.S.: 312230

British American Tobacco Mexico (1)
Tel.: (52) 8181224000
Web Site: http://www.batmexico.com.mx
Sales Range: $25-49.9 Million
Emp.: 150
Cigarette Mfr & Distr
N.A.I.C.S.: 312230

British American Tobacco Mozambique Limitada (1)
Av De Angola, 2289, Maputo, Mozambique
Tel.: (258) 21466538
Cigarette Mfr
N.A.I.C.S.: 312230

British American Tobacco Myanmar Limited (1)
Plot No 55-56 Survey Ward No 14, Shwe Than Lwin Industrial Zone Hlaing Tharyar Township, Yangon, Myanmar
Tel.: (95) 19648151
Cigarette Mfr
N.A.I.C.S.: 312230

British American Tobacco Namibia (Pty) Limited (1)
Unit 13 Epic Park Gold Street, PO Box 9739, Prosperita, Windhoek, Namibia
Tel.: (264) 61389000
Cigarette Mfr
N.A.I.C.S.: 312230

British American Tobacco Nederland B.V. (1)
Tel.: (31) 205406911
Sales Range: $100-124.9 Million
Emp.: 300
Tobacco Product Mfr & Whslr
N.A.I.C.S.: 312230

British American Tobacco Norway AS (1)
Dronning Eufemias gate 42, 0191, Oslo, Norway
Tel.: (47) 22081000
Web Site: https://www.batnorway.no
Cigarette Mfr
N.A.I.C.S.: 312230

British American Tobacco Polska Trading Sp. z.o.o. (1)

ul Krakowiakow 48, 02-255, Warsaw, Poland
Tel.: (48) 225754300
Web Site: https://www.bat.com.pl
Tobacco Products Whslr
N.A.I.C.S.: 424940

British American Tobacco RCI SARL (1)
Rue des jardins Mezzanine de l' Immeuble SAYEG en face de Nice Cream, Cocody Deux Plateaux Vallons, Abidjan, Cote d'Ivoire
Tel.: (225) 67317182
Cigarette Mfr
N.A.I.C.S.: 312230

British American Tobacco Research & Development (1)
Regents Park Road, Millbrook, Southampton, SO15 8TL, United Kingdom (100%)
Web Site: http://www.bat.com
Sales Range: $150-199.9 Million
Emp.: 800
Tobacco Product Research & Development
N.A.I.C.S.: 541715

British American Tobacco Services Congo SARL (1)
Avenue Lukusa No 50 Immueble Horizon, Gombe, Kinshasa, Congo, Democratic Republic of
Tel.: (243) 996030200
Cigarette Mfr
N.A.I.C.S.: 312230

British American Tobacco South Africa (1)
(100%)
Tel.: (27) 218883500
Web Site: http://www.batsa.co.za
Sales Range: $400-449.9 Million
Emp.: 2,000
Tobacco Product Mfr
N.A.I.C.S.: 312230
Andre Joubert (Dir-Area-ESA)

British American Tobacco Sweden AB (1)
Vastra Tradgardsgatan 15, 111 53, Stockholm, Sweden
Tel.: (46) 854673000
Web Site: http://www.batsweden.se
Emp.: 100
Tobacco Products Whslr
N.A.I.C.S.: 424940

British American Tobacco Switzerland SA (1)
Avenue de Rhodanie 48, 1007, Lausanne, Switzerland (100%)
Tel.: (41) 216141614
Web Site: https://www.bat.ch
Sales Range: $50-74.9 Million
Emp.: 120
Tobacco & Tobacco Products Distr
N.A.I.C.S.: 459991

British American Tobacco Trading EOOD (1)
Tsarigradsko Shose Blvd 115l - 115M Building D Floor 5, 1784, Sofia, Mladost Region, Bulgaria
Tel.: (359) 29769890
Web Site: https://www.bat.bg
Cigarette Mfr
N.A.I.C.S.: 312230

British American Tobacco Tutun Mamulleri Sanayi ve Ticaret A.S. (1)
Orjin Maslak Is Merkezi Eski Buyukdere Cad No 27 K 9-10, Maslak Sariyer, 34485, Istanbul, Turkiye
Tel.: (90) 2123678000
Web Site: https://www.bat.com.tr
Tobacco Products Mfr & Distr
N.A.I.C.S.: 312230
Sabio Lima (Gen Mgr)

British American Tobacco UK Ltd. (1)
Globe House 4 Temple Place, London, WC2R 2PG, Bucks, United Kingdom
Tel.: (44) 2078451000
Web Site: http://www.bat.com
Sales Range: $250-299.9 Million
Emp.: 800
Tobacco Product Distr
N.A.I.C.S.: 424940

British American Tobacco Vietnam Ltd. (1)
Tel.: (84) 88219888
Web Site: http://www.batvietnam.com
Tobacco Production & Cigarette Manufacturing
N.A.I.C.S.: 312230

British American Tobacco Vranje a.d. (1)
Stefana Prvovencanog 209, Vranje, Serbia
Tel.: (381) 17 401 241
Sales Range: $25-49.9 Million
Emp.: 125
Tobacco Product Mfr
N.A.I.C.S.: 312230

British American Tobacco Zimbabwe (Holdings) Limited (1)
1 Manchester Road, PO Box ST98, Southerton, Harare, Zimbabwe
Tel.: (263) 7721318836
Web Site: http://www.batzimbabwe.com
Cigarette Mfr
N.A.I.C.S.: 312230

British American Tobacco del Peru Holdings S.A. (1)
Av El Derby N 055 Torre 3 Oficinas 405-406-407-408, Urb Lima Polo and Hunt Club Santiago de Surco, Lima, Peru
Tel.: (51) 13151060
Web Site: https://www.batperu.com
Cigarette Mfr
N.A.I.C.S.: 312230

British American Tobacco-B.A.T. Angola, Limitada (1)
Pavilhao n 3 Quarteirao 11 Viana Park, Polo Industrial de Viana, 1263, Luanda, Angola
Tel.: (244) 923451894
Cigarette Mfr
N.A.I.C.S.: 312230

British American Tobacco-Moldova S.R.L. (1)
65 Stefan cel Mare Avenue of 416, Chisinau, MD2001, Moldova
Tel.: (373) 22855355
Cigarette Mfr
N.A.I.C.S.: 312230

British-American Tobacco (Germany) GmbH (1)
Alsterufer 4, 20354, Hamburg, Germany (100%)
Tel.: (49) 40415101
Web Site: http://www.bat.de
Sales Range: $350-399.9 Million
Emp.: 2,200
Cigarettes & Fine-Cut Tobacco Mfr
N.A.I.C.S.: 312230

British-American Tobacco (Holdings) Ltd. (1)
Globe Ho 4 Temple Pl, London, WC2R 2PG, United Kingdom
Tel.: (44) 2078451000
Web Site: http://www.bat.com
Investment Management Service
N.A.I.C.S.: 523999

British-American Tobacco (Singapore) Pte. Ltd. (1)
15 Senoko Loop, Singapore, 758168, Singapore (100%)
Tel.: (65) 63388998
Web Site: http://www.bat.com
Sales Range: $100-124.9 Million
Emp.: 300
Cigarette Mfr & Distr
N.A.I.C.S.: 312230

British-American Tobacco Polska S.A. (1)
The Park Warsaw ul Krakowiakow 48, 02-255, Warsaw, Poland
Tel.: (48) 225754300
Web Site: http://www.bat.com.pl
Cigarette Mfr
N.A.I.C.S.: 312230

British-American Tobacco Trading Company Foreign Private Trading Unitary Enterprise (1)
Akademika Kuprevicha Str 3, Business Center Clever Park 7th Floor, 220141, Minsk, Belarus

Tel.: (375) 172698200
Cigarette Mfr
N.A.I.C.S.: 312230

C.A. Cigarrera Bigott Sucs (1)
Apartado 186, Caracas, 1010-A, Venezuela (100%)
Tel.: (58) 2122037511
Web Site: http://www.bigott.com.ve
Cigarette Mfr
N.A.I.C.S.: 312230

Carreras Limited (1)
13A Ripon Road, Kingston, 5, Jamaica
Tel.: (876) 74998000
Web Site: https://www.carrerasja.com
Rev.: $104,328,775
Assets: $35,374,735
Liabilities: $22,241,370
Net Worth: $13,133,365
Earnings: $23,377,647
Emp.: 100
Fiscal Year-end: 03/31/2023
Tobacco Product Mfr
N.A.I.C.S.: 312230
Franklin Murillo (Mng Dir)

Demerara Tobacco Co. Ltd. (1)
90 Carmichael Street, PO Box 10 262, Georgetown, South Cummingsburg, Guyana (70.25%)
Tel.: (592) 2251900
Sales Range: $10-24.9 Million
Emp.: 17
Cigars & Cigarette Mfr
N.A.I.C.S.: 312230
Maurlaine Kirton (Mng Dir)

Fiedler & Lundgren AB (1)
Stenaldersgatan 23, PO Box 9041, 200 39, Malmo, Sweden
Tel.: (46) 406303950
Web Site: http://www.fiedlerlundgren.se
Sales Range: $25-49.9 Million
Emp.: 90
Smokeless Tobacco Products Mfr
N.A.I.C.S.: 312230

Imperial Tobacco Canada Limited (1)
3711 Saint-Antoine Street, Montreal, H4C 3P6, QC, Canada (100%)
Tel.: (514) 932-6161
Web Site: http://www.imperialtobaccocanada.com
Sales Range: $100-124.9 Million
Emp.: 400
Cigarettes, Tobacco & Tobacco Products Mfr & Distr
N.A.I.C.S.: 312230

JSC JV UZBAT A.O. (1)
Tel.: (998) 781205555
Cigarette Mfr
N.A.I.C.S.: 312230
Temur Gadaybaev (Gen Mgr)

Nobleza Piccardo SAIC y F (1)
Casilla De Correo 899, 1000, Buenos Aires, Argentina (90%)
Tel.: (54) 1147248444
Sales Range: $350-399.9 Million
Emp.: 1,100
Mfr of Cigarettes
N.A.I.C.S.: 312230

P.J. Carroll & Co. Ltd. (1)
The Apex Building Blackthorn Road, Sandyford, Dublin, 18, Ireland (100%)
Tel.: (353) 12052345
Web Site: https://www.pjcarroll.ie
Sales Range: $25-49.9 Million
Emp.: 100
Cigarette & Pipe Tobacco Mfr
N.A.I.C.S.: 312230

PT Bentoel Internasional Investama Tbk (1)
Tel.: (62) 215268388
Web Site: http://www.bentoelgroup.com
Rev.: $454,201,776
Assets: $596,705,088
Liabilities: $144,101,462
Net Worth: $452,603,626
Earnings: $64,027,286
Emp.: 948
Fiscal Year-end: 12/31/2022
Cigarette Mfr
N.A.I.C.S.: 312230
Hendro Martowardojo (Pres)

British American Tobacco plc—(Continued)

Pakistan Tobacco Co. Ltd.　　　　**(1)**
Serena Business Complex Khayaban-e-
Suhrwardy, PO Box 2549, Islamabad,
44000, Pakistan　　　　　　　　　**(63%)**
Tel.: (92) 5120832000
Web Site: https://www.ptc.com.pk
Sales Range: $100-124.9 Million
Emp.: 200
Cigarette Mfr & Distr
N.A.I.C.S.: 312211
Zafar Mahmood *(Chm)*

Reynolds American Inc.　　　　**(1)**
401 N Main St, Winston Salem, NC 27101-
2990
Tel.: (336) 741-2000
Web Site:
　https://www.reynoldsamerican.com
Holding Company; Cigarettes & Other To-
bacco Products Mfr & Distr
N.A.I.C.S.: 551112
Jeff Raborn *(Gen Counsel & Exec VP-Law
& External Affairs)*

Subsidiary (Domestic):

American Snuff Company, LLC　　**(2)**
5106 Tradeport Dr, Memphis, TN 38141
Tel.: (901) 761-2050
Web Site: http://www.americansnuffco.com
Smokeless Tobacco Products Mfr
N.A.I.C.S.: 312230
Jeff Doss *(Sr Dir-Mfg-Clarksville)*

Kentucky BioProcessing, Inc.　　**(2)**
3700 Airpark Dr, Owensboro, KY
42301　　　　　　　　　　　　**(100%)**
Tel.: (270) 689-2570
Plant Made Pharmaceutical Protein Pro-
ducer
N.A.I.C.S.: 325412
Hugh Haydon *(Pres)*

Subsidiary (Non-US):

Niconovum AB　　　　　　　　**(2)**
Tel.: (46) 42199430
Web Site: http://www.niconovum.se
Smoking Cessation Product Mfr
N.A.I.C.S.: 325412
Joel Rubenstein *(CEO)*

Subsidiary (Domestic):

**Northern Brands International,
Inc.**　　　　　　　　　　　　**(2)**
401 N Main St, Winston Salem, NC 27101
Tel.: (336) 741-5000
Tobacco Products Whslr
N.A.I.C.S.: 424940

**R.J. Reynolds Tobacco
Company**　　　　　　　　　　**(2)**
401 N Main St, Winston Salem, NC 27101
Tel.: (336) 741-5000
Web Site: https://www.rjrt.com
Emp.: 4,000
Holding Company
N.A.I.C.S.: 551112
Nancy H. Hawley *(Exec VP-Ops)*

Subsidiary (Domestic):

**R.J. Reynolds Global Products,
Inc.**　　　　　　　　　　　　**(3)**
401 N Main St, Winston Salem, NC 27101-
3804
Tel.: (336) 741-5000
Tobacco Products Whslr
N.A.I.C.S.: 312230

**R.J. Reynolds Tobacco International,
Inc.**　　　　　　　　　　　　**(3)**
401 N Main St, Winston Salem, NC 27101
Tel.: (336) 741-5500
Holding Company; Cigarettes & Other To-
bacco Products International Whslr
N.A.I.C.S.: 551112

**RJR Realty Relocation Services,
Inc.**　　　　　　　　　　　　**(3)**
401 N Main St, Winston Salem, NC 27101
Tel.: (336) 741-5000
Real Estate Services
N.A.I.C.S.: 531390

Subsidiary (Domestic):

**R.J. Reynolds Tobacco Holdings,
Inc.**　　　　　　　　　　　　**(2)**

401 N Main St, Winston Salem, NC 27101
Tel.: (336) 741-5500
Holding Company
N.A.I.C.S.: 551112

**Santa Fe Natural Tobacco Company.
Inc.**　　　　　　　　　　　　**(2)**
1 Plaza La Prensa, Santa Fe, NM 87507
Tel.: (505) 982-4257
Web Site: http://www.sfntc.com
Cigarettes & Other Tobacco Products Mfr
N.A.I.C.S.: 312230

**Solomon Islands Tobacco Company
Limited**　　　　　　　　　　**(1)**
PO Box 13, Honiara, Solomon Islands
Tel.: (677) 30127
Tobacco Mfr & Distr
N.A.I.C.S.: 312230

Souza Cruz, S.A.　　　　　　**(1)**
Rua Candelaria 66, PO Box 160, 20091-
900, Rio de Janeiro, Brazil　　　**(100%)**
Tel.: (55) 2138499000
Web Site: http://www.souzacruz.com.br
Sales Range: $1-4.9 Billion
Emp.: 6,000
Holding Company; Tobacco, Pulp, Paper
N.A.I.C.S.: 551112

TDR d.o.o., Rovinj　　　　　**(1)**
Obala Vladimira Nazora 1, 52210, Rovinj,
Croatia
Web Site: http://www.tdr.hr
Sales Range: $150-199.9 Million
Emp.: 700
Cigarette Mfr
N.A.I.C.S.: 312230

Subsidiary (Non-US):

Opresa d.d.　　　　　　　　**(2)**
Trg Ivana Krndelja 11 C, 88000, Sarajevo,
Bosnia & Herzegovina
Tel.: (387) 36551125
Fish Farming Services
N.A.I.C.S.: 112511

TDR Rovita d.o.o.　　　　　　**(2)**
Dunajska Cesta 22, 1000, Ljubljana, Slove-
nia
Tel.: (386) 14305761
Web Site: http://www.tdr.hr
Sales Range: $25-49.9 Million
Emp.: 8
Tobacco Cigarette Mfr
N.A.I.C.S.: 312230

TDR Skopje DOOEL　　　　　**(2)**
Blvd 8th September No 18, 1000, Skopje,
North Macedonia
Tel.: (389) 23093737
Tobacco Mfr & Distr
N.A.I.C.S.: 312230

TDR d.o.o., Beograd　　　　　**(2)**
Milentija Popovica 5a, 11070, Belgrade,
Serbia
Tel.: (381) 116149113
Web Site: http://www.tdr.hr
Cigarette Mfr
N.A.I.C.S.: 312230

TDR d.o.o., Blazuj　　　　　**(2)**
Blazuj 78, Blazuj, Ilidza, Bosnia & Herze-
govina
Tel.: (387) 33770350
Web Site: http://www.tdr.hr
Cigarette Mfr
N.A.I.C.S.: 312230

Tabacalera Hondurena SA　　**(2)**
Zona Catao Blvd Sur S, PO Box 64, San
Pedro Sula, Honduras　　　　　**(100%)**
Tel.: (504) 25453200
Cigarette & Snuff Mfr
N.A.I.C.S.: 312230

Subsidiary (US):

Serious Cigars　　　　　　　**(2)**
2589 Eric Ln, Burlington, TX 27215
Tel.: (866) 372-4427
Web Site: http://www.seriouscigars.com
Telecommunications
N.A.I.C.S.: 517810

Tabacalera Istmena SA
Apartado A 3, Panama, 9A, Panama
Tel.: (507) 2788600
Cigarette Mfr

N.A.I.C.S.: 312230

Tabacalera Nicaraguense S.A.　**(1)**
Km 7 1/2 Carretera Norte, Managua,
Nicaragua　　　　　　　　　　**(60%)**
Web Site: http://www.batcentralamerica.com
Sales Range: $25-49.9 Million
Emp.: 100
Cigarette & Snuff Mfr
N.A.I.C.S.: 312230

**Tobacco Marketing Consultant Bur-
kina Faso SARL**　　　　　　　**(1)**
Avenue Yennega, BP 882, Ouagadougou,
Burkina Faso
Tel.: (226) 50506038
Cigarette Mfr
N.A.I.C.S.: 312230

**UAB British American Tobacco
Lietuva**　　　　　　　　　　**(1)**
JGalvydzio str 11-7, LT 08236, Vilnius,
Lithuania
Tel.: (370) 52722790
Cigarette Mfr
N.A.I.C.S.: 312230

iNovine BH d.o.o.　　　　　**(1)**
Kolodvorska 12, 71000, Sarajevo, Bosnia &
Herzegovina
Tel.: (387) 33652355
Web Site: https://inovine.ba
Corporate Services
N.A.I.C.S.: 561499

BRITISH ARAB COMMERCIAL
BANK LIMITED
8-10 Mansion House Place, London,
EC4N 8BJ, United Kingdom
Tel.: (44) 2076487777　　　　　**UK**
Web Site: http://www.bacb.co.uk
Year Founded: 1972
Sales Range: $200-249.9 Million
Emp.: 170
Banking Services
N.A.I.C.S.: 522110
Celeste Du Plessis *(CFO)*

BRITISH BROADCASTING
CORPORATION
Broadcasting House, Portland Place,
London, W1A 1AA, United Kingdom
Tel.: (44) 8700100222
Web Site: http://www.bbc.co.uk
Year Founded: 1936
Rev.: $6,204,238,780
Assets: $5,677,595,480
Liabilities: $4,190,304,040
Net Worth: $1,487,291,440
Earnings: ($87,562,380)
Emp.: 22,401
Fiscal Year-end: 03/31/19
Radio & Television Broadcasting Ser-
vices; Online Media Publishing &
Television Programming Production
Services
N.A.I.C.S.: 516210
Tim Davie *(CEO-Studios & Dir-
Global)*

Subsidiaries:

Adjacent Productions, LLC　　**(1)**
10351 Santa Monica Blvd Ste 250, Los An-
geles, CA 90025
Tel.: (310) 228-1001
Media Broadcasting Services
N.A.I.C.S.: 516120

BBC Global News Limited　　**(1)**
Woodlands 80 Wood Lane, London, W12
0ZY, United Kingdom
Tel.: (44) 20 8433 2221
Television Broadcasting Services
N.A.I.C.S.: 516120
Jim Egan *(CEO)*

BBC Property Limited　　　　**(1)**
BC2 A5 Broadcast Centre, London, W12
7TP, United Kingdom
Tel.: (44) 2087526666
Real Estate Development Services
N.A.I.C.S.: 531390

BBC Studios Africa (Pty) Limited　**(1)**

Office 003H3 Ground Floor 10 Melrose
Boulevard Melrose Arch, Melrose North,
Johannesburg, 2196, South Africa
Tel.: (27) 10 020 2115
Media Broadcasting Services
N.A.I.C.S.: 516120

BBC Studios Americas Inc.　　**(1)**
1120 Avenue of the Americas 5th Fl, New
York, NY 10036-6700
Tel.: (212) 705-9300
Media Broadcasting Services
N.A.I.C.S.: 516120

**BBC Studios Australia Holdings Pty
Limited**　　　　　　　　　　**(1)**
Level 1 35-51 Mitchell Street, McMahons
Point, 2060, NSW, Australia
Tel.: (61) 29 744 4500
Media Broadcasting Services
N.A.I.C.S.: 516120

BBC Studios Canada Limited　**(1)**
145 King St W Suite 740, Toronto, M5H
1J8, ON, Canada
Tel.: (416) 204-0500
Media Broadcasting Services
N.A.I.C.S.: 516120

BBC Studios Distribution Limited　**(1)**
1 Television Centre 101 Wood Lane, Lon-
don, W12 7FA, United Kingdom
Tel.: (44) 208 433 2000
Media Broadcasting Services
N.A.I.C.S.: 516120

BBC Studios France Sarl　　　**(1)**
18-20 Quai du Point du Jour Bat A, 92100,
Boulogne-Billancourt, France
Tel.: (33) 14 495 8400
Media Broadcasting Services
N.A.I.C.S.: 516120

BBC Studios Germany GmbH　**(1)**
Kaiser-Wilhelm-Ring 17-21, 50672, Co-
logne, Germany
Tel.: (49) 22 179 0790
Media Broadcasting Services
N.A.I.C.S.: 516120

**BBC Studios India Private
Limited**　　　　　　　　　　**(1)**
Windsor Unit no 502 Off CST Road, Kalina
Santacruz East, Mumbai, 400098, India
Tel.: (91) 226 193 4100
Media Broadcasting Services
N.A.I.C.S.: 516120

**BBC Studios Intermediadora de Pro-
gramadora Estangeira Limited**　**(1)**
Rua Ferreira de Araujo 741 Andar 1, Pin-
heiros, Sao Paulo, 05428-002, Brazil
Tel.: (55) 113 443 7482
Media Broadcasting Services
N.A.I.C.S.: 516120

BBC Studios Japan Limited　　**(1)**
Tokyo Club Building 10F 3-2-6, Kasumigas-
eki Chiyoda-ku, Tokyo, 100-0013, Japan
Tel.: (81) 35 157 3580
Media Broadcasting Services
N.A.I.C.S.: 516120

BBC Studios Polska Sp. z o.o.　**(1)**
Pl Bankowy 1, 00-139, Warsaw, Poland
Tel.: (48) 22 749 1200
Media Broadcasting Services
N.A.I.C.S.: 516120

BBC Studios Productions Limited　**(1)**
Broadcast Centre 201 Wood Lane, London,
W12 7TQ, United Kingdom
Tel.: (44) 22 749 1200
Media Broadcasting Services
N.A.I.C.S.: 516120

**BBC Studios Singapore Pte.
Limited**　　　　　　　　　　**(1)**
18 Robinson Road 18 Robinson 13-01, Sin-
gapore, 048547, Singapore
Tel.: (65) 6 849 5511
Media Broadcasting Services
N.A.I.C.S.: 516120

**BBC Studios and Post Production
Limited**　　　　　　　　　　**(1)**
Clarendon Road, Borehamwood, WD6 1JG,
Hertfordshire, United Kingdom
Tel.: (44) 20 3327 7400
Web Site:
　http://www.bbcstudiosandpostprod.com

Television Broadcasting Services
N.A.I.C.S.: 516120
Charles Tugendhat (Dir-Digital Media Svcs)

BBC Studioworks Limited **(1)**
Elstree Studios Shenley Road, Borehamwood, WD6 1JG, Hertfordshire, United Kingdom
Tel.: (44) 203 327 7400
Web Site: https://bbcstudioworks.com
Tele Production Services
N.A.I.C.S.: 512191
Rebecca Williams (Sr Mgr-Commercial)

BBC Symphony Orchestra **(1)**
BBC Maida Vale Studios, Delaware Rd, London, W9 2LG, United Kingdom
Tel.: (44) 2077652956
Sales Range: $75-99.9 Million
Emp.: 130
Symphony Orchestra Services
N.A.I.C.S.: 711130

BBC Worldwide Australia Pty Limited **(1)**
L 5 6 Eden Park Dr, Macquarie Park, 2113, NSW, Australia
Tel.: (61) 297444500
Web Site: http://www.bbcaustralia.com
Emp.: 120
Radio & Television Broadcasting Services
N.A.I.C.S.: 516120
Alistair McEwan (Sr VP-Comml Dev-BBC Adv-Asia, Australia & New Zealand)

BBC Worldwide Limited **(1)**
1 Television Centre 101 Wood Lane, London, W12 7FA, United Kingdom
Tel.: (44) 2084332000
Web Site: http://www.bbcworldwide.com
Rev.: $1,171,440,896
Assets: $1,318,764,800
Liabilities: $866,135,040
Net Worth: $452,629,760
Earnings: $115,214,848
Emp.: 1,523
Fiscal Year-end: 03/31/2018
Commercial Arm of the British Broadcasting Corporation; Magazines, Videos, Multimedia & Other Merchandise Publisher; Television Programming & Network Services
N.A.I.C.S.: 513120
Ann M. Sarnoff (Pres-Americas)

Subsidiary (US):

BBC Worldwide America Inc. **(2)**
1120 Ave Of Americas Fl 5, New York, NY 10036
Tel.: (212) 705-9300
Web Site: http://www.bbcamerica.com
Sales Range: $25-49.9 Million
Emp.: 90
Radio & TV Broadcaster
N.A.I.C.S.: 512110
Ann M. Sarnoff (Pres-North America)

Subsidiary (Domestic):

New Video Channel LLC **(3)**
1120 Ave of the Americas 5th Fl, New York, NY 10036
Tel.: (212) 705-9300
Web Site: http://www.bbcamerica.com
Sales Range: $50-74.9 Million
Cable & Satellite Broadcaster of British Television Programs in the United States
N.A.I.C.S.: 516210
Valerie Bruce (Sr VP-Bus Affairs)

Joint Venture (Domestic):

DTV Services Limited **(2)**
Broadcast Centre BC3 D5, 201 Wood Lane, London, W12 7TP, United Kingdom
Tel.: (44) 8708809980
Web Site: http://www.freeview.co.uk
Holding Company; Digital Television Services
N.A.I.C.S.: 551112

Subsidiary (Domestic):

Dovetail Services (UK) Limited **(2)**
800 Guillat Ave, Kent Science Park, Sittingbourne, ME9 8GU, Kent, United Kingdom **(100%)**
Tel.: (44) 8448150855
Web Site: http://www.dovetailservices.com
Sales Range: $25-49.9 Million
Emp.: 300

Subscription Marketing & Fulfilment Services
N.A.I.C.S.: 561499
Gill Lambert (Dir-Client Svcs)

Affiliate (Domestic):

UKTV Interactive Limited **(2)**
10 Hammersmith Grove, London, W67Ap, United Kingdom **(50%)**
Tel.: (44) 2072996200
Web Site: http://www.uktv.co.uk
Sales Range: $300-349.9 Million
Emp.: 900
Television Broadcasting; Owned 50% by British Broadcasting Corporation & 50% by NTL Incorporated
N.A.I.C.S.: 516120
Steve North (Gen Mgr-Comedy & Entertainment)

Baby Cow Productions Limited **(1)**
Unit C 8-14 Vine Hill, London, EC1R 5DX, United Kingdom
Tel.: (44) 203 696 5200
Web Site: https://babycowproductions.co.uk
Tele Production Services
N.A.I.C.S.: 512191
Steve Coogan (Creative Dir)

Lookout Point Limited **(1)**
Hammer House 1st Floor 113-117 Wardour St, London, W1F 0UN, United Kingdom
Tel.: (44) 203 640 8760
Web Site: https://www.lookoutpoint.tv
Television Drama Production Services
N.A.I.C.S.: 512191
Joanna Betts (CEO & COO)

Sid Gentle Films Limited **(1)**
40 Whitfield Street, London, W1T 2RH, United Kingdom
Tel.: (44) 207 034 2660
Web Site: https://sidgentle.com
Tele Production Services
N.A.I.C.S.: 512191
Lee Morris (Mng Dir)

UKTV Media Limited **(1)**
10 Hammersmith Grove, London, W6 7AP, United Kingdom
Tel.: (44) 144 350 8065
Web Site: https://corporate.uktv.co.uk
Media Broadcasting Services
N.A.I.C.S.: 516120
Marcus Arthur (CEO)

Worldwide Knowledge (Beijing) Business Consulting Company Ltd. **(1)**
Room 05-06 F11 Tower A Parkview Green 9 Dongdaqiao Road, Chaoyang District, Beijing, 100020, China
Tel.: (86) 106 591 6136
Media Broadcasting Services
N.A.I.C.S.: 516120

BRITISH COLUMBIA FERRY SERVICES INC

Suite 500 - 1321 Blanshard Street, Victoria, V8W 0B7, BC, Canada
Tel.: (250) 978-1187
Web Site: http://www.bcferries.com
Year Founded: 1960
Rev.: $755,176,345
Assets: $1,937,609,775
Liabilities: $1,333,443,979
Net Worth: $604,165,796
Earnings: $26,703,128
Fiscal Year-end: 03/31/22
Ferry Service
N.A.I.C.S.: 483212
Janet E. Carson (VP-Mktg & Customer Experience)

BRITISH COLUMBIA INVESTMENT MANAGEMENT CORP.

750 Pandora Ave, Victoria, V8W 0E4, BC, Canada
Tel.: (778) 410-7100
Web Site: http://www.bcimc.com
Year Founded: 1999
Rev.: $328,067,843
Assets: $216,558,918
Liabilities: $216,558,917
Net Worth: $1

Fiscal Year-end: 03/31/19
Public Funds Investment Management Services
N.A.I.C.S.: 523999
Lincoln Webb (Exec VP & Head-Infrastructure & Renewable Resources-Global)

Subsidiaries:

Compre Group Holdings Ltd. **(1)**
4th Floor Victoria Place 31 Victoria Street, Hamilton, HM 10, Bermuda
Tel.: (441) 704 0106
Web Site: https://compre-group.com
Insurance Services
N.A.I.C.S.: 524210

Corix Group **(1)**
1188 West Georgia Street Suite 1160, Vancouver, V6E 4A2, BC, Canada
Tel.: (604) 697-6700
Web Site: http://www.corix.com
Sales Range: $400-449.9 Million
Utility Infrastructure System Design, Construction & Management Services; Owned by CAI Capital Management Inc. & British Columbia Investment Management Corporation
N.A.I.C.S.: 237110
Sue Paish (Chm)

Costa Group Holdings Limited **(1)**
Tel.: (61) 383639000
Web Site: https://www.costagroup.com.au
Rev.: $885,150,942
Assets: $1,341,585,056
Liabilities: $809,824,607
Net Worth: $531,760,449
Earnings: $30,645,498
Emp.: 200
Fiscal Year-end: 01/01/2022
Holding Company
N.A.I.C.S.: 551112
David Thomas (Gen Counsel)

Hayfin Capital Management LLP **(1)**
One Eagle Place, London, SW1Y 6AF, United Kingdom
Tel.: (44) 207 074 2900
Web Site: http://www.hayfin.com
Investment Firm
N.A.I.C.S.: 523999
Tim Flynn (Co-Founder & CEO)

Subsidiary (US):

Avadim Health, Inc. **(2)**
81 Thompson St, Asheville, NC 28803
Tel.: (828) 251-7111
Web Site: http://www.avadimhealth.com
Rev.: $29,043,129
Assets: $33,448,165
Liabilities: $64,814,299
Net Worth: ($31,366,134)
Earnings: ($51,769,464)
Emp.: 226
Fiscal Year-end: 12/31/2018
Medicinal Product Mfr
N.A.I.C.S.: 325412
Stephen Woody (Founder, Chm & CEO)

Open Grid Europe GmbH **(1)**
Kallenbergstr 5, 45141, Essen, Germany
Tel.: (49) 201 3642 0
Web Site: http://www.open-grid-europe.com
Holding Company; Natural Gas Pipeline Transportation Services
N.A.I.C.S.: 551112
Jorg Bergmann (Chm-Mgmt Bd)

Joint Venture (Domestic):

MEGAL Mittel-Europaische-Gasleitungsgesellschaft mbH & Co. KG **(2)**
Kallenbergstrasse 5, D-45141, Germany
Tel.: (49) 20136420
Web Site: http://www.open-grid-europe.com
Natural Gas Pipeline Transportation Services
N.A.I.C.S.: 486210
Hans Jurgen Plattner (Mng Dir)

Subsidiary (Domestic):

Mittelrheinische Erdgastransportleitungsgesellschaft mbH **(2)**

Neuer Markt 29, 42781, Haan, Germany **(100%)**
Tel.: (49) 212993530
Sales Range: $25-49.9 Million
Emp.: 3
Natural Gas Pipeline Transportation Services
N.A.I.C.S.: 486210

PLEdoc Gesellschaft fur Dokumentationserstellung und -pflege mbH **(2)**
Gladbecker Str 404, 45326, Essen, Germany **(100%)**
Tel.: (49) 201 3659 0
Web Site: http://www.pledoc.de
Sales Range: $25-49.9 Million
Emp.: 130
Technical Consulting Services
N.A.I.C.S.: 541690
Anne-Kathrin Wirtz (Mng Dir & Member-Mgmt Bd)

Puget Energy, Inc. **(1)**
355 110th Ave NE, Bellevue, WA 98004
Tel.: (425) 454-6363
Web Site: https://www.pugetenergy.com
Rev.: $4,221,162,000
Assets: $17,187,514,000
Liabilities: $5,560,052,000
Net Worth: $11,627,462,000
Earnings: $414,345,000
Emp.: 3,250
Fiscal Year-end: 12/31/2022
Holding Company; Electric Power & Gas Distr
N.A.I.C.S.: 551112
Steven W. Hooper (Chm)

Subsidiary (Domestic):

Puget Sound Energy, Inc. **(2)**
355 110th Ave NE, Bellevue, WA 98004
Tel.: (425) 454-6363
Web Site: https://www.pse.com
Rev.: $4,216,173,000
Assets: $15,200,242,000
Liabilities: $5,542,394,000
Net Worth: $9,657,848,000
Earnings: $490,952,000
Emp.: 3,250
Fiscal Year-end: 12/31/2022
Electric Power & Natural Gas Distribution & Generation Services
N.A.I.C.S.: 221122
Steven W. Hooper (Chm)

Subsidiary (Domestic):

Puget Western, Inc. **(3)**
19515 North Creek Pkwy Ste 310, Bothell, WA 98011-8200
Tel.: (425) 487-6550
Web Site: http://www.pugetwestern.com
Sales Range: $25-49.9 Million
Emp.: 5
Real Estate Holding & Developing
N.A.I.C.S.: 237010
Joel Molander (Pres)

Reden Solar SAS **(1)**
ZAC Des Champs de Lescaze, 47310, Roquefort, France
Tel.: (33) 553772131
Web Site: http://www.reden.solar
Emp.: 100
Solar Energy Services
N.A.I.C.S.: 221118

SilverBirch Hotels & Resorts **(1)**
1640 - 1188 W Georgia Street, The Burrard Building, Vancouver, V6E 4A2, BC, Canada **(100%)**
Tel.: (604) 646-2447
Web Site: https://www.silverbirchhotels.com
Sales Range: $10-24.9 Million
Emp.: 50
Business Services
N.A.I.C.S.: 561499
Jiri Rumlena (CFO)

Springs Window Fashions LLC **(1)**
7549 Graber Rd, Middleton, WI 53562-1001
Tel.: (608) 836-1011
Web Site:
http://www.springswindowfashions.com
Drapery Rods, Window Shades, Pleated Shades, Horizontal & Vertical Blinds Mfr
N.A.I.C.S.: 337920
Frank A. Natoli Jr. (Exec VP-Integrated Supply Chain)

British Columbia Investment Management
Corp.—(Continued)

Subsidiary (Domestic):

Mariak Industries, Inc.   **(2)**
575 W Manville St, Rancho Dominguez, CA
90220
Tel.: (310) 661-4400
Web Site: http://www.mariak.com
Window Coverings Mfr
N.A.I.C.S.: 326199
Leo Elinson (Co-Founder)

Sunsetter Products, LP   **(2)**
184 Charles St, Malden, MA 02148
Tel.: (800) 876-2340
Web Site: http://www.sunsetter.com
Retractable Awnings Mfr
N.A.I.C.S.: 332323
Jonathan Hershberg (Pres)

TimberWest Forest Corp.   **(1)**
Suite 2000 1055 W Hastings St, Vancouver,
V6E 2E9, BC, Canada
Tel.: (604) 654-4600
Web Site: http://www.timberwest.com
Sales Range: $250-299.9 Million
Emp.: 80
Logging & Lumbermill Services
N.A.I.C.S.: 113310
Rick Jaccard (VP-Mktg & Sls)

Valence Surface Technologies
LLC   **(1)**
1790 Hughes Landing Blvd Ste 300, The
Woodlands, TX 77380
Tel.: (888) 540-0878
Web Site: http://valencesurfacetech.com
Aerospace & Defense Metal Finishing Ser-
vices
N.A.I.C.S.: 334511
James Mitchell (CFO)

Subsidiary (Domestic):

B & M Painting Co., Inc.   **(2)**
347 Van Buren St NE, Camden, AR 71701-
4017
Tel.: (870) 836-3388
Web Site: http://www.bandmpainting.com
Sales Range: $1-9.9 Million
Emp.: 50
Automotive Body, Paint & Interior Repair &
Maintenance Services
N.A.I.C.S.: 811121
Brian McCasland (VP)

Fountain Plating Co., Inc.   **(2)**
492 Prospect Ave, West Springfield, MA
01089-4596
Tel.: (413) 733-8217
Web Site: http://www.fountain-plating.com
Electroplating, Plating, Polishing, Anodizing
& Coloring
N.A.I.C.S.: 332813
Mark Fountain (Pres)

Triumph Processing, Inc.   **(2)**
2605 Industry Way, Lynwood, CA 90262-
4088
Tel.: (323) 563-1338
Metal Mining Services
N.A.I.C.S.: 213114
Peter J. LaBarbera (Pres)

Triumph Structures-Los Angeles,
Inc.   **(2)**
9301 Mason Ave, Chatsworth, CA 91311-
5202
Tel.: (818) 341-1314
Web Site: http://www.triumphgroup.com
Job Machine Shop For Aircraft Parts
N.A.I.C.S.: 332710

VeriFone Systems, Inc.   **(1)**
88 W Plumeria Dr, San Jose, CA 95134
Tel.: (408) 232-7800
Web Site: http://www.verifone.com
Sales Range: $1-4.9 Billion
Emp.: 5,600
Holding Company; Point-of-Sale Software &
Technologies Mfr & Distr
N.A.I.C.S.: 551112
Bulent Ozayaz (Pres-EMEA)

Subsidiary (Domestic):

2Checkout.com, Inc.   **(2)**
Versa Grandview 1201 Dublin Rd, Columbus, OH 43215

Tel.: (678) 666-2660
Web Site: http://www.2checkout.com
Emp.: 300
Payment Processing Services
N.A.I.C.S.: 459999
Alex Hart (Co-CEO)

Subsidiary (Non-US):

EFTPOS New Zealand Limited   **(2)**
Level 14 80 Boulcott Street, Wellington,
6011, New Zealand
Tel.: (64) 43857055
Web Site: http://eftpos.co.nz
Electronic Financial Payment Services
N.A.I.C.S.: 522320
Paul Galant (CEO)

Subsidiary (Domestic):

Hypercom Corporation   **(2)**
8888 E Raintree Dr Ste 300, Scottsdale, AZ
85260
Tel.: (480) 642-5000
Electronic Payment Services
N.A.I.C.S.: 522320

Subsidiary (Non-US):

Point International AS   **(2)**
Eastern Aker vei 24, 0581, Oslo, Norway
Tel.: (47) 81502200
Web Site: http://www.point.no
Secure Electronic Payment Provider
N.A.I.C.S.: 522320

VeriFone Denmark A/S   **(2)**
Knapholm 7, 2730, Herlev, Denmark
Tel.: (45) 44 53 16 10
Web Site: http://www.verifone.com
Electronic Payment Solutions
N.A.I.C.S.: 541519
Chris Lund-Hansen (Mng Dir)

VeriFone Finland Oy   **(2)**
Vantaankoskentie 14 C, 01670, Vantaa,
Finland
Tel.: (358) 9 477 4330
Web Site: http://www.verifone.fi
Electronic Payment Solutions
N.A.I.C.S.: 541519

VeriFone New Zealand   **(2)**
Unit A 525 Great South Rd Penrose, Auck-
land, 1061, New Zealand
Tel.: (64) 95820550
Web Site: http://www.verifone.co.nz
Computer Peripheral Equipment Mfr
N.A.I.C.S.: 334118

VeriFone Norway AS   **(2)**
Ostre Aker vei 24, 0581, Oslo, Norway
Tel.: (47) 23247400
Web Site: http://www.verifone.com
Electronic Payment Transaction Handling
Services
N.A.I.C.S.: 522320

VeriFone Services UK & Ireland
Ltd.   **(2)**
100 Eureka Park, Ashford, TN25 4AZ, Kent,
United Kingdom
Tel.: (44) 3333236667
Web Site: http://www.verifone.co.uk
Sales Range: $100-124.9 Million
Emp.: 200
Secure Electronic Payment Provider
N.A.I.C.S.: 522320
Douglas Adams (Acct Mgr-New Bus)

VeriFone Sweden AB   **(2)**
Ljusslingan 4, Box 92031, 120 31, Stock-
holm, Sweden
Tel.: (46) 8 566 287 00
Web Site: http://www.verifone.com
Electronic Payment Transaction Handling
Services
N.A.I.C.S.: 522320
Morgan Georg Sellen (CEO)

Subsidiary (Domestic):

Babs Paylink AB   **(3)**
Sankt Eriksgatan 117, 113 43, Stockholm,
Sweden
Tel.: (46) 8 6916900
Web Site: http://www.babspaylink.se
Payment Clearance & Settlement Services
for Card Purchases; Operator of Wireless
Payment Card Terminals
N.A.I.C.S.: 522320

Electronic Transaction Group Nordic
Holding AB   **(3)**
Karlavagen 58, 114 49, Stockholm, Sweden
Tel.: 8 56628700
Sales Range: $25-49.9 Million
Emp.: 9
Holding Company
N.A.I.C.S.: 551112

Subsidiary (Domestic):

VeriFone, Inc.   **(2)**
88 W Plumeria Dr, San Jose, CA 95134
Tel.: (408) 232-7800
Web Site: http://www.verifone.com
Sales Range: $1-4.9 Billion
Point-of-Sale Software & Technologies Mfr
& Distr
N.A.I.C.S.: 334118
Christophe Job (CTO)

Subsidiary (Non-US):

Hypercom Financial Terminals
AB   **(3)**
Drottninggatan 21 4TR, 582 25, Linkoping,
Sweden
Tel.: (46) 13367900
Computer Hardware & Related Equipments
Mfr & Distr
N.A.I.C.S.: 423430

VeriFone (U.K.) Limited   **(3)**
Symphony House 7 Cowley Business Park,
High Street Cowley, Uxbridge, UB9 2AD,
United Kingdom
Tel.: (44) 1895 275275
Web Site: http://www.verifone.co.uk
Sales Range: $25-49.9 Million
Emp.: 300
Supplier of Electronic Equipment Software
& Terminal
N.A.I.C.S.: 423430

VeriFone Africa (Pty) Ltd   **(3)**
1st Floor Block B Knightsbridge 33 Sloane
Str, Bryanston, Sandton, 2191, South Africa
Tel.: (27) 11 521 9000
Web Site: http://www.verifone.co.za
Supplies & Supports Payment Systems
N.A.I.C.S.: 541519
Jeffrey C. Dumbrell (Exec VP-EMEA)

VeriFone Asia Pacific   **(3)**
Room 2508 Ccwuo Bulding 3022308
Tenese Rd, Wan Chai, Hong Kong, China
(Hong Kong)
Tel.: (852) 28272101
Sales Range: $100-124.9 Million
Emp.: 4
Electronic Equipment, Software & Terminals
N.A.I.C.S.: 449210
Steve Aliferis (Pres)

VeriFone Australia (HAPL) Pty
Ltd   **(3)**
Level 7 213 Miller Street, North Sydney,
2060, NSW, Australia
Tel.: (61) 294640000
Web Site: http://www.verifone.com
Sales Range: $125-149.9 Million
Emp.: 80
End-to-End Electronic Payment Solutions,
Including Card Payment Systems, Peripher-
als, Network Products, Ascendent Software
& E-Commerce Payment Solutions
N.A.I.C.S.: 334118

VeriFone GmbH   **(3)**
Konrad Zuse Str 19 21, 36251, Bad Hers-
feld, Germany
Tel.: (49) 662184500
Sales Range: $50-74.9 Million
Emp.: 170
Credit & Debit Card Payment Processing
Systems
N.A.I.C.S.: 522320
Markus Hovekamp (Gen Mgr)

VeriFone Israel Ltd.   **(3)**
Labor 11 Park Afek, Rosh Ha'Ayin, 48092,
Israel
Tel.: (972) 39029740
Web Site: http://www.verifone.co.il
Sales Range: $200-249.9 Million
Emp.: 985
Engineering Services
N.A.I.C.S.: 541330

VeriFone Italia S.r.l.   **(3)**

Piazza Don Mapelli 1, 20099, Sesto San
Giovanni, Italy
Tel.: (39) 0291757623
Web Site: http://www.verifone.it
Electronic Payment Equipment Mfr
N.A.I.C.S.: 541519

Unit (Domestic):

VeriFone Latin America & the
Caribbean   **(3)**
501 Brickell Key Dri, Miami, FL 33131
Tel.: (305) 670-1820
Web Site: http://www.verifone.com
Supplier of Electronic Equipment Software
& Terminals
N.A.I.C.S.: 334118
Gennie Acosta (Office Mgr)

Subsidiary (Domestic):

VeriFone Media, LLC   **(3)**
1400 Broadway 32nd Fl, New York, NY
10018
Tel.: (800) 498-5759
Web Site: http://www.verifonemedia.com
Taxicab Advertising Services
N.A.I.C.S.: 541810

Subsidiary (Non-US):

VeriFone Singapore Pte. Ltd.   **(3)**
11 Keppel Road #11-02 ABI Plaza, Singapore, 089057, Singapore
Tel.: (65) 6390 6200
Electronic Payment Solutions Mfr & Marketer
N.A.I.C.S.: 541519

VeriFone Sp. z.o.o   **(3)**
Domaniewska 44 A, 02-672, Warsaw, Po-
land
Tel.: (48) 223801700
Sales Range: $10-24.9 Million
Emp.: 7
Supplier of Electronic Equipment, Software
& Terminals
N.A.I.C.S.: 449210
Adam Biedrzycki (Gen Mgr-Europe)

VeriFone Systems (China), Inc.   **(3)**
97 Balizhuangxili, Zhubang 2000 Business
Center Bldg 4 Room 2001, Chaoyang Dis-
trict, Beijing, China
Tel.: (86) 10 83913700
Web Site: http://www.verifone.cn
Electronic Payment Solutions Equipment
Mfr
N.A.I.C.S.: 334118
Arthur Jiang (Sr VP & Gen Mgr)

VeriFone Systems Australia Pty.
Ltd.   **(3)**
Level 7 213 Miller Street, North Sydney,
2060, NSW, Australia
Tel.: (61) 294640000
Computer Programming Services
N.A.I.C.S.: 541511
Michael Ward (Dir-Ops-Asia Pacific)

VeriFone Systems France SAS   **(3)**
10-12 rue Paul Dautier, 78140, Velizy-
Villacoublay, France
Tel.: (33) 139451210
Web Site: http://www.verifone.com
Sales Range: $10-24.9 Million
Emp.: 8
Supplier of Electronic Equipment, Software
& Terminals
N.A.I.C.S.: 423430

VeriFone Systems Spain SLU   **(3)**
Calle Via de los Poblados 1, PE Alvento
Edificio C 2 B y D, 28033, Madrid, Spain
Tel.: (34) 91 598 21 40
Web Site: http://www.verifone.es
Designs, Markets & Services Electronic
Payment Solutions
N.A.I.C.S.: 541519

VeriFone Uruguay   **(3)**
Technology & Business Park Zonamerica
Ruta 8 Km 17 500, Edificio Synergia Oficina
005, 91 600, Montevideo, Uruguay
Tel.: (598) 25182250
Web Site: http://www.verifone.com
Sales Range: $25-49.9 Million
Emp.: 100
Transaction Reconciliation & Payment Infra-
structure Software & Solutions

N.A.I.C.S.: 541511

VeriFone do Brasil Ltda. (3)
Rua Gomes de Carvalho 1507 10 Andar,
Villa Olimpia, Sao Paulo, 04547-005, SP,
Brazil
Tel.: (55) 1120789710
Web Site: http://www.verifone.com
Sales Range: $100-124.9 Million
Emp.: 500
Supplier of Electronic Equipment, Software
& Terminals
N.A.I.C.S.: 449210

VeriFone, S.A. de C.V. (3)
Boulevard Manuel Avila Camacho 40 Piso
15 Torre Esmeralda 1, Col Lomas de
Chapultepec, Mexico, 11000, DF, Mexico
Tel.: (52) 5559803300
Supplier of Electronic Equipment, Software
& Terminals
N.A.I.C.S.: 423430

BRITISH COLUMBIA TRANSIT
520 Gorge Road East, PO Box 9861,
Victoria, V8W 9T5, BC, Canada
Tel.: (250) 385-2551
Web Site: https://www.bctransit.com
Rev.: $294,255,404
Assets: $517,115,242
Liabilities: $500,807,833
Net Worth: $16,307,409
Earnings: $51,630
Fiscal Year-end: 03/31/22
Passenger Transportation System
N.A.I.C.S.: 485210
Erinn Pinkerton *(Pres & CEO)*

**BRITISH CONVERTING SOLU-
TIONS, LTD.**
Youngs Industrial Estate, Stanbridge
Road, Leighton Buzzard, LU7 4QB,
Bedfordshire, United Kingdom
Tel.: (44) 1727 866233 UK
Box Mfr
N.A.I.C.S.: 322212
Barry Tabor *(Mng Dir)*

BRITISH ENGINES LTD.
Q6 Quorum Business Park, Benton
Lane, Newcastle upon Tyne, NE12
8BT, United Kingdom
Web Site:
http://www.britishengines.co.uk
Year Founded: 1922
Emp.: 1,500
Engineeering Services
N.A.I.C.S.: 541330

Subsidiaries:

BEL Valves Ltd (1)
11 Glasshouse Street, St Peters, Newcastle
upon Tyne, NE6 1BS, United Kingdom
Tel.: (44) 1912659091
Web Site: http://www.belvalves.com
Valve Distr
N.A.I.C.S.: 423830
Neil Kirkbride *(Mng Dir)*

Bel Engineering (Uk) Ltd (1)
Unit 3 Nelson Way, Nelson Park Industrial
Estate, Cramlington, NE23 1WH, Northum-
berland, United Kingdom
Tel.: (44) 1912043680
Web Site: http://www.belengineering.co.uk
Industrial Machinery Mfr
N.A.I.C.S.: 333998

CMP Products Limited (1)
36 Nelson Way, Nelson Park East, Cram-
lington, NE23 1WH, Northumberland,
United Kingdom
Tel.: (44) 1912657411
Web Site: http://www.cmp-products.com
Cable Connector Mfr
N.A.I.C.S.: 334417
Vince Patterson *(CEO)*

Michell Bearings Ltd (1)
Waldridge Way, Simonside East Industrial
Park, South Shields, NE34 9PZ, United
Kingdom (100%)
Tel.: (44) 1912730291
Web Site: http://www.michellbearings.com

Sales Range: $1-9.9 Million
Emp.: 200
Hydrodynamic Bearing for Industrial & Ma-
rine Application Mfr
N.A.I.C.S.: 339999
Steve Dixon *(CEO)*

Rotary Power Limited (1)
Waldridge Way Simonside East Industrial
Park, South Shields, NE34 9PZ, United
Kingdom
Tel.: (44) 191 276 4444
Web Site: http://www.rotarypower.com
Hydraulic Pumps Mfr
N.A.I.C.S.: 333996
Neil Gray *(Dir-Sls & Mktg)*

Stadium Packing Services Ltd (1)
Longrigg, Swalwell, Gateshead, NE16 3AS,
United Kingdom
Tel.: (44) 1912043700
Web Site: http://www.stadiumpacking.co.uk
Wood Case Mfr
N.A.I.C.S.: 321920

Stephenson Gobin Ltd (1)
20 Longfield Road South Church Enterprise
Park, Bishop Auckland, DL14 6XB, Durham,
United Kingdom
Tel.: (44) 1388770360
Web Site: http://www.stephensongobin.com
Holding Company
N.A.I.C.S.: 551112
Martin Gamsby *(Mgr-Ops)*

BRITISH FILM INSTITUTE
21 Stephen Street, London, W1T
1LN, United Kingdom
Tel.: (44) 2072551444 UK
Web Site: http://www.bfi.org.uk
Year Founded: 1933
Sales Range: $25-49.9 Million
Emp.: 493
Film & Television Education Exhibi-
tion & Distr; National Film Archive of
the UK
N.A.I.C.S.: 512120
Amanda Nevill *(CEO)*

Subsidiaries:

BFI (Big Screen) Limited (1)
21 Stephen Street, London, W1T 1LN,
United Kingdom
Tel.: (44) 2072551444
Web Site: http://www.bfi.org.uk
Motion Picture Production & Distribution
Services
N.A.I.C.S.: 512110

BRITISH POTATO COUNCIL
4300 Nash Court John Smith Drive,
Oxford Business Park S, Oxford, OX4
2RT, United Kingdom
Tel.: (44) 1865 714455
Sales Range: $1-9.9 Million
Emp.: 60
Organization for the Promotion of
British Potatoes
N.A.I.C.S.: 813910
Jim Davies *(Mgr-Mktg)*

**BRITISH ROTOTHERM COM-
PANY LTD.**
Kenfig Industrial Estate, Margam,
Port Talbot, SA13 2PW, United King-
dom
Tel.: (44) 1656 740 551
Web Site: http://www.rototherm.co.uk
Measurement Instruments Mfr
N.A.I.C.S.: 334513
Oliver Conger *(Mng Dir)*

Subsidiaries:

Digitron Instrumentation Limited (1)
Kenfig Industrial Estate Margam, Port Tal-
bot, SA13 2PW, United Kingdom
Tel.: (44) 1656 747 575
Web Site: http://www.digitron.com
Measuring Instruments Mfr
N.A.I.C.S.: 334513

**BRITISH SMALLER COMPA-
NIES VCT PLC**
4th Floor 2 Bond Court, Leeds, LS1
2JZ, United Kingdom
Tel.: (44) 1132945002
Year Founded: 1996
Investment Trust Management Ser-
vices
N.A.I.C.S.: 523940
Rupert Cook *(Chm)*

BRITVIC PLC
Breakspear Park Breakspear Way,
Hemel Hempstead, HP2 4TZ, United
Kingdom
Tel.: (44) 1217111102 UK
Web Site: https://www.britvic.com
BVIC—(LSE)
Rev.: $1,907,732,372
Assets: $2,370,307,576
Liabilities: $1,799,657,860
Net Worth: $570,649,716
Earnings: $140,116,704
Emp.: 4,113
Fiscal Year-end: 09/30/21
Holding Company; Soft Drink Mfr
N.A.I.C.S.: 551112
Matt Barwell *(CMO)*

Subsidiaries:

Bricfruit SAS (1)
Lieu-Dit La Jaunaie, Chateau-Thebaud,
44690, France
Tel.: (33) 2 40 33 55 55
Web Site: http://www.britvic.com
Emp.: 70
Soft Drink Mfr & Distr
N.A.I.C.S.: 312111
Francois Daul *(Gen Mgr)*

Britvic Aqua Libra Co Limited (1)
1 New Street, London, EC2M 4TP, United
Kingdom
Tel.: (44) 8000806696
Web Site: https://aqualibra.com
Water Dispenser Mfr & Distr
N.A.I.C.S.: 333914

Britvic Ireland (1)
Kylemore Park, Dublin, 10, Ireland
Tel.: (353) 16161200
Web Site: http://www.britvic.ie
Sales Range: $150-199.9 Million
Emp.: 550
Bottled Water Mfr & Distr
N.A.I.C.S.: 312112

Britvic North America LLC (1)
WeWork Wynwood Garage Ste 08-127 360
NW 27th St, Miami, FL 33127
Tel.: (786) 220-0903
Soft Drink Distr
N.A.I.C.S.: 424490

Britvic Soft Drinks Ltd. (1)
Breakspear Park Breakspear Way, Hemel
Hempstead, HP2 4TZ, Hertfordshire, United
Kingdom (100%)
Tel.: (44) 1217111102
Web Site: http://www.britvic.co.uk
Soft Drink Mfr & Distr
N.A.I.C.S.: 312111

Fruite SAS (1)
Z I Les Afforets, 74800, La Roche-sur-
Foron, France
Tel.: (33) 450032146
Soft Drink Mfr & Distr
N.A.I.C.S.: 312111

Teisseire France SAS (1)
482 Avenue Ambroise Croizat, 38926,
Crolles, Cedex, France
Tel.: (33) 476436969
Web Site: https://www.teisseire.fr
Soft Drinks Mfr
N.A.I.C.S.: 312111

Teisseire SAS (1)
482 Avenue Ambroise Croizat, 38926,
Crolles, Cedex, France
Tel.: (33) 476436969
Soft Drink Mfr & Distr
N.A.I.C.S.: 312111

Unisource SAS (1)

Zi La De Mouline, Nissan-lez-Enserune,
34440, France
Tel.: (33) 467116177
Emp.: 79
Soft Drink Mfr & Distr
N.A.I.C.S.: 312111
Lauren Giroux *(Gen Mgr)*

BRIVAIS VILNIS AS
Ostas Iela 1, Salacgriva, 4033, Latvia
Tel.: (371) 64000210
Web Site: http://www.brivaisvilnis.lv
Canned Fish Product Mfr
N.A.I.C.S.: 311710
Janis Savics *(Sls Dir)*

**BRIXTON METALS CORPORA-
TION**
409 Granville St Suite 551, Vancou-
ver, V6C 1T2, BC, Canada
Tel.: (604) 630-9707
Web Site:
https://www.brixtonmetals.com
Year Founded: 2008
BBBXF—(OTCQB)
Rev.: $28,142
Assets: $10,016,117
Liabilities: $917,700
Net Worth: $9,098,416
Earnings: ($7,368,457)
Emp.: 9
Fiscal Year-end: 09/30/21
Mineral Exploration Services
N.A.I.C.S.: 213114
Gary Thompson *(Co-Founder, Chm,
Pres & CEO)*

Subsidiaries:

Brixton USA Corporation (1)
602 S Tremont St, Oceanside, CA 92054
Tel.: (760) 696-3323
Web Site: http://www.brixton.com
Menswear Cloth Retailer
N.A.I.C.S.: 458110

BRK FINANCIAL GROUP S.A.
Str Motilor Nr 119 jud CLUJ, Cluj-
Napoca, Romania
Tel.: (40) 364401709
Web Site:
https://www.brkfinancialgroup.ro
BRK—(BUC)
Rev.: $9,244,967
Assets: $50,811,108
Liabilities: $37,401,454
Net Worth: $13,409,654
Earnings: ($5,059,764)
Emp.: 39
Fiscal Year-end: 12/31/22
Financial Investment Services
N.A.I.C.S.: 523940

Subsidiaries:

Romlogic Technology S.A. (1)
Str Gramont nr 38, 77190, Bucharest, Ro-
mania
Tel.: (40) 767930930
Web Site: https://www.romlogic.eu
Software Development Services
N.A.I.C.S.: 541511

S.A.I. Broker S.A. (1)
Str Motilor No 119 Et IV, Cluj County, Cluj-
Napoca, 400370, Romania
Tel.: (40) 364260755
Web Site: http://www.saibroker.ro
Financial Investment Services
N.A.I.C.S.: 523940

BROAD-MINDED CO., LTD.
JR Ebisu Building 7F 1-5-5 Ebisu Mi-
nami, Shibuya-Ku, Tokyo, 1500022,
Japan
Tel.: (81) 368598358
Web Site: https://www.b-minded.com
Year Founded: 2002
7343—(TKS)
Rev.: $34,510,810
Assets: $33,215,250

Broad-Minded Co., Ltd.—(Continued)

Liabilities: $7,356,930
Net Worth: $25,858,320
Earnings: $264,400
Emp.: 448
Fiscal Year-end: 03/31/24
Investment Brokerage Services
N.A.I.C.S.: 524210
Kiyoshi Ito *(Founder, Chm & Pres)*

BROADBAND SECURITY, INC.
Nomura Real Estate Nishi-Shinjuku
Joint Building 4F, 8-5-1 Nishi-
Shinjuku Shinjuku-ku, Tokyo, 160-
0023, Japan
Tel.: (81) 353387430
Web Site: https://www.bbsec.co.jp
Year Founded: 2000
4398—(TKS)
Rev.: —
Emp.: 205
Internet Publishing Services
N.A.I.C.S.: 513199
Takashi Takizawa *(Pres & CEO)*

BROADBAND TOWER, INC.
Hibiya Park Front 2-1-6 Uchisaiwa-
icho, Chiyoda-Ku, Tokyo, 100-0011,
Japan
Tel.: (81) 352024800
Web Site: https://www.bbtower.co.jp
Year Founded: 2000
3776—(TKS)
Rev.: $93,892,870
Assets: $138,099,020
Liabilities: $55,387,080
Net Worth: $82,711,940
Earnings: $701,910
Emp.: 239
Fiscal Year-end: 12/31/23
Software Development Services
N.A.I.C.S.: 541511
Mieko Nakagawa *(Exec Dir-Legal &
Acctg Grp)*

Subsidiaries:

Global IoT Technology Ventures,
Inc. **(1)**
Nihon Bldg 7F 2-6-2, Ootemachi Chiyoda-
ku, Tokyo, 100-0004, Japan
Tel.: (81) 36 262 7200
Web Site: https://www.gitv.vc
Investment Services
N.A.I.C.S.: 523910
Toshihisa Adachi *(Pres & CEO)*

BROADEX TECHNOLOGIES CO., LTD.
No 306 Yatai Road, Nanhu District,
Jiaxing, 314006, Zhejiang, China
Tel.: (86) 57382585881
Web Site: https://www.broadex-
tech.com
Year Founded: 2003
300548—(CHIN)
Rev.: $235,978,414
Assets: $453,003,883
Liabilities: $152,477,745
Net Worth: $300,526,138
Earnings: $11,475,078
Fiscal Year-end: 12/31/23
Integrated Optoelectronic Device Mfr
& Distr
N.A.I.C.S.: 334413
Wei Zhu *(Founder, Chm & CEO)*

Subsidiaries:

Broadex Technologies UK ltd. **(1)**
Starlaw Business Park Starlaw Road, Liv-
ingston, EH54 8SF, United Kingdom
Tel.: (44) 1506426000
Electronic Products Mfr
N.A.I.C.S.: 334419
Matt Currie *(Head-Sls & Mktg)*

BROADGRAIN COMMODITIES INC.

18 King St East Suite 900, Toronto,
M5C 1C4, ON, Canada
Tel.: (416) 504-0070
Web Site: http://www.broadgrain.com
Year Founded: 2003
Sales Range: $600-649.9 Million
Emp.: 100
Agricultural Commodity Processing,
Storage & Marketing Service
N.A.I.C.S.: 493130
Zaid Qadoumi *(Pres & CEO)*

BROADLEAF CO., LTD.
Floor 8 Glass Cube Shinagawa
4-13-14 Higashi-Shinagawa,
Shinagawa-ku, Tokyo, 140-0002, Ja-
pan
Tel.: (81) 357813100
Web Site: https://www.broadleaf.co.jp
3673—(TKS)
Rev.: $109,079,650
Assets: $260,557,500
Liabilities: $101,124,670
Net Worth: $159,432,830
Earnings: ($10,542,830)
Emp.: 935
Fiscal Year-end: 12/31/23
Software Publisher
N.A.I.C.S.: 513210
Kenji Oyama *(Pres)*

BROADMEDIA CORPORATION
Aoyama Tower Place 6F 8-4-14 Aka-
saka, Minato-ku, Tokyo, 107-0052,
Japan
Tel.: (81) 364393725 **JP**
Web Site:
https://www.broadmedia.co.jp
Year Founded: 1996
4347—(TKS)
Rev.: $93,723,190
Assets: $78,592,900
Liabilities: $39,534,410
Net Worth: $39,058,490
Earnings: $4,494,800
Fiscal Year-end: 03/31/24
Online Content Distribution & Support
Services
N.A.I.C.S.: 518210
Taro Hashimoto *(Pres, Pres & CEO)*

Subsidiaries:

System Design Development co.,
Ltd. **(1)**
SDD Building 1-2 South 1 West 10 West,
Chuo Ward, Sapporo, 060-0061, Japan
Tel.: (81) 112816770
Web Site: https://www.sddgrp.co.jp
Emp.: 39
Software Development Services
N.A.I.C.S.: 541511

BROADSTONE ACQUISITION CORP.
7 Portman Mews South, Marylebone,
London, W1H 6AY, United Kingdom
Tel.: (44) 2077250800 **Ky**
Year Founded: 2020
BSNU—(NYSE)
Investment Services
N.A.I.C.S.: 523999
Hugh Osmond *(Chm)*

BROADVIEW PRESS INC.
815 First St SW Ste 412, Calgary,
T2P 1N3, AB, Canada
Tel.: (705) 743-8990 **AB**
Web Site:
http://www.broadviewpress.com
Year Founded: 2003
Sales Range: $1-9.9 Million
Emp.: 30
Academic Publisher
N.A.I.C.S.: 513130
Maggie Perras *(Officer-Accounts)*

BROADWAY INDUSTRIAL

GROUP LIMITED
202 Kallang Bahru 0701 Spaze, Sin-
gapore, 138633, Singapore
Tel.: (65) 62360088 **SG**
Web Site: https://www.bw-grp.com
Year Founded: 1969
B69—(SES)
Rev.: $195,919,867
Assets: $140,377,414
Liabilities: $82,073,014
Net Worth: $67,304,400
Earnings: $2,226,009
Emp.: 1,246
Fiscal Year-end: 12/31/23
Holding Company; Foam Plastics &
Packaging Products Mfr
N.A.I.C.S.: 551112
Ah Hoy Ng *(Exec Dir)*

Subsidiaries:

BIGL Technologies (Chongqing) Co.,
Ltd. **(1)**
9 Three Gorges Liange Ba, Photoelectric
Industrial Park M2 Wanzhou District,
Chongqing, China
Tel.: (86) 2385729288
Computer Storage Devices
N.A.I.C.S.: 334112
Jian Zhang *(Mgr-Quality Assurance)*

BIGL Technologies (Shenzhen) Co.,
Ltd. **(1)**
5 Luyin North Road EPZ, Big Industrial
Zone Longgang District, Shenzhen, 518118,
Guangdong, China
Tel.: (86) 75533953688
Computer Storage Devices
N.A.I.C.S.: 334112

BIGL Technologies (Thailand) Co.,
Ltd. **(1)**
135 Moo 1 T Banpo, Hi-Tech Industrial Es-
tate A Bangpa-in, Ayutthaya, 13160, Thai-
land
Tel.: (66) 35315600
Computer Storage Devices
N.A.I.C.S.: 334112
Apinya Jantakod *(Sr Mgr-HR)*

BIGL Technologies (Wuxi) Co.,
Ltd. **(1)**
No 17 District B Wuxi National, Hi-Tech In-
dustrial Dev Zone B, Wuxi, 214028, China
Tel.: (86) 5105015388
Computer Storage Devices
N.A.I.C.S.: 334112

Compart Asia Limited **(1)**
3 Fusionopolis Way 13-26/27 Symbiosis
Tower, Singapore, 138633, Singapore
Tel.: (65) 6236 0677
Web Site: http://www.compartgroup.com
Precision Metal Components Mfr
N.A.I.C.S.: 332999

BROBOT FUELS LTD.
Thorpe Road, Melton Mowbray, LE13
1SQ, Leicestershire, United Kingdom
Tel.: (44) 1664480000
Web Site:
http://www.brobotfuels.co.uk
Year Founded: 1982
Fuels Lubricants & Oil Distr
N.A.I.C.S.: 457210

BROCCOLI CO., LTD.
5F Toshin Nerima Bldg 5-14-6 Toy-
otamakita, Nerima-Ku, Tokyo, 176-
0012, Japan
Tel.: (81) 3 59462811
Web Site: http://www.broccoli.co.jp
Year Founded: 1994
27060—(JAS)
Sales Range: Less than $1 Million
Emp.: 105
Game Development Services
N.A.I.C.S.: 513210
Yoshiyuki Takahashi *(Pres, CEO &
COO)*

BROCCOLINI CONSTRUCTION INC.

16766 Transcanada Hwy 5th Floor,
Kirkland, H9H 4M7, QC, Canada
Tel.: (514) 737-0076
Web Site: http://www.broccolini.com
Year Founded: 1949
Rev.: $17,151,025
Emp.: 60
Real Estate Development & Con-
struction Services
N.A.I.C.S.: 236115
Anthony Broccolini *(COO)*

BROCK FORD SALES
4500 Drummond Rd, Niagara Falls,
L2E 6C7, ON, Canada
Tel.: (905) 357-5410
Web Site:
http://www.brockpreowned.com
Rev.: $29,735,173
Emp.: 60
New & Used Car Dealers
N.A.I.C.S.: 441110

BROCKHAUS PRIVATE EQUITY GMBH
Thurn-und-Taxis-Platz 6, 60313,
Frankfurt am Main, Germany
Tel.: (49) 69 7191 6170 **De**
Web Site: http://www.brockhaus-
pe.com
Year Founded: 2000
Rev.: $319,160,100
Privater Equity Firm
N.A.I.C.S.: 523999
Marco Brockhaus *(Chm-Mgmt Bd)*

Subsidiaries:

Brockhaus Technologies AG **(1)**
Thurn und Taxis Platz 6, 60313, Frankfurt
am Main, Germany **(3.3%)**
Tel.: (49) 6920434090
Web Site: http://www.bcm-ag.com
Rev.: $154,818,692
Assets: $707,434,708
Liabilities: $367,118,498
Net Worth: $340,316,210
Earnings: $52,902,007
Emp.: 278
Fiscal Year-end: 12/31/2022
Holding Company
N.A.I.C.S.: 551112
Marco Brockhaus *(Founder & CEO)*

Holding (Domestic):

IHSE GmbH **(2)**
Benzstrasse 1, 88094, Oberteuringen,
Germany **(100%)**
Tel.: (49) 754692480
Web Site: http://www.ihse.com
Emp.: 120
Electric Equipment Mfr
N.A.I.C.S.: 334111
Enno Littmann *(CEO)*

Subsidiary (Non-US):

IHSE GmbH Asia Pacific Pte.
Ltd. **(3)**
158 Kallang Way 07-13A, Singapore,
349245, Singapore
Tel.: (65) 68414707
Electric Equipment Mfr
N.A.I.C.S.: 334111
Robin Sim *(Reg Mgr)*

Subsidiary (US):

IHSE USA LLC **(3)**
1 Corporate Dr, Cranbury, NJ 08512
Tel.: (732) 738-8780
Electric Equipment Mfr
N.A.I.C.S.: 334111

Holding (Domestic):

Palas GmbH **(2)**
Siemensallee 84 Building 7330, 76187,
Karlsruhe, Germany
Tel.: (49) 721962130
Web Site: https://www.palas.de
Emp.: 100
Electric Equipment Mfr
N.A.I.C.S.: 335999

BROCKMAN MINING LIMITED
Level 2 679 Murray Street, West Perth, 6005, WA, Australia
Tel.: (61) 893893000   BM
Web Site:
https://www.brockmanmining.com
BCK—(ASX)
Rev.: $1,495,479
Assets: $91,352,937
Liabilities: $27,506,724
Net Worth: $63,846,213
Earnings: ($1,711,278)
Emp.: 14
Fiscal Year-end: 06/30/24
Offices of Other Holding Companies
N.A.I.C.S.: 551112
Jason Kam Kwan Chan *(Sec)*

Subsidiaries:

Brockman Iron Pty. Ltd.   (1)
Level 1 117 Stirling Hwy, Nedlands, 6009, WA, Australia
Tel.: (61) 893893000
Web Site: http://www.brockman.com.au
Sales Range: $50-74.9 Million
Emp.: 20
Iron Ore Mining Services
N.A.I.C.S.: 212210
Kevin Watpers *(Mgr-Project Dev)*

Brockman Mining (Management) Limited   (1)
3903B Far East Finance Centre 16 Harcourt Road, Admiralty, Hong Kong, China (Hong Kong)
Tel.: (852) 37661079
Investment Holding Services
N.A.I.C.S.: 525910

Guangzhou Parklane Limousine Service Ltd   (1)
Room No 16-17 16th Floor Zhong Xin Building, Baogang Haizhu, Guangzhou, 510240, Guangdong, China
Tel.: (86) 2062378441
Web Site: http://www.parklanelimochina.com
Emp.: 30
Limousine Service
N.A.I.C.S.: 485320

Parklane Limousine Service (Shanghai) Ltd   (1)
Jiang Hua Road 369 24 Room C, Shanghai, 200050, China
Tel.: (86) 2161382222
Limousine Service
N.A.I.C.S.: 485320

Parklane Limousine Service Limited   (1)
Unit 702 7/F Yue Hwa International Building No 1 Kowloon Park Drive, Kowloon, China (Hong Kong)
Tel.: (852) 2730 0662
Web Site: http://www.hongkonglimo.com
Sales Range: $50-74.9 Million
Emp.: 221
Limousine Service
N.A.I.C.S.: 485320

Subsidiary (Domestic):

Airport Shuttle Services Limited   (2)
Unit 702 7/F Yue Hwa International Building No 1 Kowloon Park Drive, Kowloon, China (Hong Kong)
Tel.: (852) 2730 0662
Web Site: http://www.hongkonglimo.com
Airport Limousine Service
N.A.I.C.S.: 485999

BRODERICK BROS. LIMITED
Cloverhill Industrial Estate Cloverhill Rd, Ballymanaggin, Dublin, Ireland
Tel.: (353) 14291500
Web Site: http://www.broderickbros.ie
Sales Range: $10-24.9 Million
Emp.: 50
Food Product Machinery Mfr
N.A.I.C.S.: 333241
Richard Kieran *(Mng Dir)*

BRODOMERKUR DD
Solinska 47, 21 000, Split, Croatia

Tel.: (385) 21301111
Web Site: http://www.brodomerkur.hr
BDMR—(ZAG)
Sales Range: Less than $1 Million
Household Appliances Mfr
N.A.I.C.S.: 335220

BRODOS AG
Erlanger Strasse 9 13, D 91083, Baiersdorf, Germany
Tel.: (49) 913377700
Web Site: http://www.brodos.com
Telecommunication Servicesb
N.A.I.C.S.: 517810
Dominik Brokelmann *(CEO)*

Subsidiaries:

STAHLGRUBER Communication Center GmbH   (1)
Kohlhauser Strasse 55, 36043, Fulda, Germany
Tel.: (49) 66148006613
Web Site: http://www.stahlgruber-com.de
Communication Equipment Mfr
N.A.I.C.S.: 334220
Gebhard Goebel *(Chm & Mng Dir)*

BRODRENE A & O JOHANSEN A/S
Roervang 3, 2620, Albertslund, Denmark
Tel.: (45) 70280000
Web Site: https://www.ao.dk
AOJ.P—(OMX)
Rev.: $676,511,333
Assets: $393,399,776
Liabilities: $223,336,409
Net Worth: $170,063,368
Earnings: $28,535,651
Emp.: 775
Fiscal Year-end: 12/31/20
Construction Materials Whslr
N.A.I.C.S.: 423610
Niels Axel Johansen *(CEO)*

Subsidiaries:

AO Sverige AB   (1)
Brodalsvagen 15, 433 38, Partille, Sweden
Tel.: (46) 104809600
Web Site: https://www.aonet.se
HVAC Material Whslr
N.A.I.C.S.: 423730

Designkupp AS   (1)
Bjornstadmyra 10, 1712, Gralum, Norway
Tel.: (47) 47057000
Web Site: https://www.vvskupp.no
Emp.: 11
Bathroom Product Whslr
N.A.I.C.S.: 444180
Hakon Tegneby *(Owner & CEO)*

Greenline A/S   (1)
Brovejen 10, 4930, Maribo, Denmark
Tel.: (45) 70222026
Web Site: http://www.greenline.dk
Plumbing Product Distr
N.A.I.C.S.: 423720

Vaga Tehnika Eesti OU   (1)
Akadeemia tee 39, 12618, Tallinn, Estonia
Tel.: (372) 6710300
Web Site: http://www.vaga.ee
Water Supply Material Retailer
N.A.I.C.S.: 423720

BROENDBYERNES IF FODBOLD A/S
Brondby Stadion 30, 2605, Brondby, Denmark
Tel.: (45) 43630810
Web Site: https://brondby.com
Year Founded: 1964
BIF—(CSE)
Rev.: $31,992,013
Assets: $51,071,465
Liabilities: $18,130,254
Net Worth: $32,941,211
Earnings: ($1,718,974)
Emp.: 168
Fiscal Year-end: 12/31/22

Professional Football Club Operator
N.A.I.C.S.: 711211
Ole Palma *(CEO)*

BROGENT TECHNOLOGIES, INC.
No 9 Fuxing 4th Rd, Qianzhen Dist, Kaohsiung, 80661, Taiwan
Tel.: (886) 75372869
Web Site: https://www.brogent.com
Year Founded: 2001
5263—(TPE)
Rev.: $25,131,038
Assets: $154,812,650
Liabilities: $54,935,434
Net Worth: $99,877,216
Earnings: ($1,950,974)
Emp.: 277
Fiscal Year-end: 12/31/22
Software Development Services
N.A.I.C.S.: 541512
Chih-Hung Ouyang *(Chm & CEO)*

BROKEN HILL OPERATIONS PTY LTD
Tel.: (61) 88 088 9111
Web Site:
http://www.cbhresources.com.au
Year Founded: 2006
Sales Range: $100-124.9 Million
Emp.: 200
Mineral Exploration Services
N.A.I.C.S.: 212230

BROKERS TRUST INSURANCE GROUP INC.
2780 Highway 7 Suite 201, Concord, L4k 3R9, ON, Canada
Tel.: (905) 760-1515
Web Site: http://www.brokerstrust.ca
Year Founded: 1963
Rev.: $27,300,714
Emp.: 50
Insurance & Risk Management Solutions
N.A.I.C.S.: 524210
Dave Bertolin *(Mng Dir)*

BROKERSCLUB AG
5 Blegistrasse Baar, 6340, Zug, Switzerland
Tel.: (41) 415880062
Web Site: http://www.brokersclub.ch
Financial Services
N.A.I.C.S.: 523160
Guido Colombo *(Chm-Exec Bd)*

BROMBERGS BOKFORLAG
Hantverkargatan 26, PO Box 12886, 112 21, Stockholm, Sweden
Tel.: (46) 856262080
Web Site: http://www.brombergs.se
Sales Range: $25-49.9 Million
Emp.: 5
Publishing House
N.A.I.C.S.: 513130
Dorothea Bromberg *(Mng Dir)*

BROME LAKE DUCKS LTD
40 Centre Road, PO Box 3430, Knowlton, J0E 1V0, QC, Canada
Tel.: (450) 242-3825
Web Site:
http://www.bromelakeducks.com
Year Founded: 1912
Rev.: $29,561,283
Emp.: 170
Duck Food Mfr
N.A.I.C.S.: 311615
Claude Trottier *(Pres & COO)*

BROMFORD INDUSTRIES LIMITED
Pegasus House 1 Bromford Gate, Birmingham, B24 8DW, United Kingdom

Tel.: (44) 1216836200
Web Site:
http://www.bromfordindustries.co.uk
Year Founded: 2009
Emp.: 100
Precision Machined Metal Component Mfr
N.A.I.C.S.: 332999
Kevin Vicha *(CEO)*

Subsidiaries:

Bromford Industries Limited - Leicester Facility   (1)
129 Scudamore Road, Leicester, LE3 1UQ, United Kingdom
Tel.: (44) 116 232 2233
Web Site:
http://www.bromfordindustries.co.uk
Engine Component Mfr
N.A.I.C.S.: 336390

Bromford Technologies - Alcester Facility   (1)
Unit 9 Kinwarton Farm Road, Arden Forest Industrial Estate, Alcester, B49 6EH, Warwickshire, United Kingdom
Tel.: (44) 1789 400 340
Web Site:
http://www.bromfordindustries.co.uk
Engine Component Mfr
N.A.I.C.S.: 336412
Gary Lowe *(CEO)*

BROMI MASKIN AB
Foretagsvagen 29 Hus 11, 23237, Arlov, Sweden
Tel.: (46) 40537550   SE
Web Site: http://www.bromi.se
Rev.: $11,706,200
Emp.: 16
Industrial Machinery & Equipment
N.A.I.C.S.: 423830
Martin Paland *(Pres)*

BROMPTON FUNDS LIMITED
Suite 2930 Bay-Wellington Tower Brookfield Place 181 Bay Street, PO Box 793, Toronto, M5J 2T3, ON, Canada
Tel.: (416) 642-9061
Web Site:
http://www.bromptongroup.com
Year Founded: 2000
Investment Fund Management Services
N.A.I.C.S.: 523940
Mark A. Caranci *(Pres & CEO)*

Subsidiaries:

Brompton Split Banc Corp.   (1)
Suite 2930 Bay-Wellington Tower Brookfield Place 181 Bay Street, PO Box 793, Toronto, M5J 2T3, ON, Canada
Tel.: (416) 642-9061
Web Site: http://www.bromptongroup.com
Rev.: $22,187,609
Assets: $150,170,464
Liabilities: $68,253,309
Net Worth: $81,917,155
Earnings: $20,604,170
Fiscal Year-end: 12/31/2019
Closed-End Investment Fund
N.A.I.C.S.: 525990
Mark A. Caranci *(Co-Founder, Pres & CEO)*

Dividend Growth Split Corp.   (1)
Bay Wellington Tower Brookfield Place 181 Bay Street Suite 2930, PO Box 793, Toronto, M5J 2T3, ON, Canada
Tel.: (416) 642-9061
Web Site: http://www.bromptongroup.com
Rev.: $86,910,032
Assets: $384,624,535
Liabilities: $254,280,420
Net Worth: $130,344,115
Earnings: $69,076,899
Fiscal Year-end: 12/31/2019
Closed-End Investment Fund
N.A.I.C.S.: 525990
Mark A. Caranci *(Pres & CEO)*

Symphony Floating Rate Senior Loan Fund   (1)

Brompton Funds Limited—(Continued)

Brookfield Place Bay Wellington Tower 181 Bay Street Suite 2930, PO Box 793, Toronto, M5J 2T3, ON, Canada
Tel.: (416) 642-9061
Web Site: http://www.bromptongroup.com
Rev.: $6,500,715
Assets: $62,949,395
Liabilities: $25,281,147
Net Worth: $37,668,248
Earnings: $4,221,045
Fiscal Year-end: 12/31/2023
Closed-End Investment Fund
N.A.I.C.S.: 525990
Mark A. Caranci (Pres & CEO)

BROMPTON LIFECO SPLIT CORP.

Wellington Tower Brookfield Place Suite 2930 181 Bay Street, PO Box 793, Toronto, M5J 2T3, ON, Canada
Tel.: (416) 642-6000　　　　　ON
Year Founded: 2007
LCS—(TSX)
Rev.: $15,110,032
Assets: $62,980,771
Liabilities: $39,162,524
Net Worth: $23,818,247
Earnings: $14,535,134
Fiscal Year-end: 12/31/21
Investment Fund Management Services
N.A.I.C.S.: 523940

BROMPTON OIL SPLIT CORP.

181 Bay Street Bay Suite 2930 Bay Wellington Tower, PO Box 793, Toronto, M5J 2T3, ON, Canada
Tel.: (416) 642-6000
Web Site:
　http://www.bromptongroup.com
7SC—(DEU)
Rev.: $350,934
Assets: $8,297,870
Liabilities: $6,391,771
Net Worth: $1,906,100
Earnings: ($980,711)
Fiscal Year-end: 12/31/23
Investment Banking Services
N.A.I.C.S.: 523150
Mark A. Caranci (Mgr-Fund)

BRONCO BILLY CO., LTD.

1-75 Heiwagaoka Meito-ku, Nagoya, 465-0097, Japan
Tel.: (81) 527758000
Web Site: http://www.bronco.co.jp
Year Founded: 1978
3091—(NGO)
Sales Range: $75-99.9 Million
Emp.: 160
Restaurant Owner & Operator
N.A.I.C.S.: 722511
Yasuhiro Takeichi (Pres)

BRONSSTADET AB

Linnegatan 18, Stockholm, 11447, Sweden
Tel.: (46) 8 120 510 00　　　　SE
Web Site: http://www.bronsstadet.se
Year Founded: 2001
Sales Range: $25-49.9 Million
Emp.: 500
Investment Holding Company
N.A.I.C.S.: 551112
Peter Gyllenhammer (Owner & Chm)

Subsidiaries:

Browallia AB　　　　　　　　　　(1)
Linnegatan 18, SE-114 38, Stockholm, Sweden　　　　　　　　　(100%)
Tel.: (46) 84428564
Web Site: http://www.browallia.se
Sales Range: $100-124.9 Million
Emp.: 1
Investment Management & Business Support Services
N.A.I.C.S.: 523940

Holding (Non-US):

Darby Glass Ltd.　　　　　　　(2)
Sunningdale Rd, Scunthorpe, DN17 2SS, North Lincolnshire, United Kingdom
Tel.: (44) 1724280044
Sales Range: $25-49.9 Million
Glass Mfr
N.A.I.C.S.: 327212

Division (Domestic):

Pro-Glass Ltd　　　　　　　　　(3)
Sunningdale Road, Scunthorpe, DN17 2SS, North Lincolnshire, United Kingdom
Tel.: (44) 1724280044
Web Site: http://www.darbyglass.co.uk
Glass Mfr
N.A.I.C.S.: 327211

Galjaden Fastigheter AB　　　　(1)
Linnegatan 18, SE-114 47, Stockholm, Sweden　　　　　　　　　(95%)
Tel.: (46) 8 120 510 00
Web Site: http://www.galjaden.se
Sales Range: $75-99.9 Million
Emp.: 10
Commercial Property Acquisition, Development & Management Services
N.A.I.C.S.: 525990
Martin Hansson (CEO)

BRONZE INFRA-TECH LIMITED

10 Phears lane 2nd Bow Bazaar under Kolkata Municipal Corporation, Kolkata, 700 012, West Bengal, India
Tel.: (91) 6291074488
Web Site: https://www.bronzeinfra-tech.com
Year Founded: 2004
534731—(BOM)
Rev.: $4,559,565
Assets: $6,467,695
Liabilities: $5,800,951
Net Worth: $666,744
Earnings: $21,619
Emp.: 6
Fiscal Year-end: 03/31/22
Land Development, Construction & Infrastructure Projects
N.A.I.C.S.: 237210
Jayashree Desai (CFO)

BROO LIMITED

20 Langtree Avenue, Mildura, 3500, VIC, Australia
Tel.: (61) 359842222　　　　　AU
Web Site: http://www.broo.com.au
Year Founded: 2009
BEE—(ASX)
Emp.: 100
Fiscal Year-end: 06/30/23
Beer Mfr & Distr
N.A.I.C.S.: 312120

BROODSTOCK CAPITAL AS

Storgata 10, 6413, Molde, Norway
Tel.: (47) 90601993
Web Site: https://broodstock.no
Privater Equity Firm
N.A.I.C.S.: 523999
Jan Erik Lovik (Mng Partner)

BROOKFIELD BUSINESS CORPORATION

1055 West Georgia Street Suite 1500, PO Box 11117, Vancouver, V6E 4N7, BC, Canada
Tel.: (416) 645-2736　　　　　BC
Year Founded: 2021
BBUC—(NYSE)
Rev.: $10,598,000,000
Assets: $27,376,000,000
Liabilities: $23,305,000,000
Net Worth: $4,071,000,000
Earnings: $1,076,000,000
Emp.: 38,000
Fiscal Year-end: 12/31/22
Asset Management Services

N.A.I.C.S.: 531390
Alan Fleming (Sr VP-Investor Relations)

BROOKFIELD CORPORATION

Brookfield Place 181 Bay Street Suite 100, PO Box 762, Bay Wellington Tower, Toronto, M5J 2T3, ON, Canada
Tel.: (416) 363-9491　　　　　BC
Web Site: https://www.brookfield.com
Year Founded: 1912
BN—(NYSE)
Rev.: $95,924,000,000
Assets: $490,095,000,000
Liabilities: $321,853,000,000
Net Worth: $168,242,000,000
Earnings: $5,105,000,000
Emp.: 240,000
Fiscal Year-end: 12/31/23
Holding Company; Natural Resources, Power Generation, Real Estate & Financial Services
N.A.I.C.S.: 551112
Brian D. Lawson (Vice Chm)

Subsidiaries:

AERC Doral West, LLC　　　　(1)
5400 NW 114th Ave, Doral, FL 33178
Residential Building Leasing Services
N.A.I.C.S.: 531110

ATC Telecom Infrastructure Private Limited　　　　　　　　　　(1)
S2 Level Block-F International Trade Tower Nehru Place, International Trade Tower Nehru Place, New Delhi, 110 019, India
Tel.: (91) 114 670 5600
Web Site: http://www.atctower.in
Wireless Telecommunication Services
N.A.I.C.S.: 517112

American National Group, Inc.　(1)
1 Moody Plz, Galveston, TX 77550-7999
Web Site: http://www.americannational.com
Rev.: $4,391,791,000
Assets: $31,320,321,000
Liabilities: $24,318,262,000
Net Worth: $7,002,059,000
Earnings: $699,325,000
Emp.: 4,545
Fiscal Year-end: 12/31/2021
Holding Company; Insurance Products & Services
N.A.I.C.S.: 551112
Timothy A. Walsh (COO)

Subsidiary (Domestic):

American National County Mutual Insurance Company　　　　　(2)
1 Moody Plz Ste 829, Galveston, TX 77550-7947
Tel.: (409) 766-6619
Web Site: http://www.anpac.com
Insurance Brokerage Services
N.A.I.C.S.: 524210

American National Insurance Company　　　　　　　　　　(2)
1 Moody Plz, Galveston, TX 77550-7999
Web Site: http://www.americannational.com
Fiscal Year-end: 12/31/2020
Individual & Group Life Insurance
N.A.I.C.S.: 524113
James Edward Pozzi (Pres & CEO)

American National Insurance Company of New York　　　　　(2)
One Moody Plaza, Galveston, TX 77550
Tel.: (409) 763-4661
Life, Accident & Health Insurance & Annuities
N.A.I.C.S.: 524113

American National Life Insurance Company of New York　　　　(2)
1 Moody Plz, Galveston, TX 77550-7947
Tel.: (866) 490-3163
Web Site: http://www.anicony.com
Insurance Brokerage Services
N.A.I.C.S.: 524210

American National Life Insurance Company of Texas　　　　　(2)

1 Moody Plz, Galveston, TX 77550-7999
Tel.: (281) 538-4800
Sales Range: $200-249.9 Million
Emp.: 1,600
Life & Health Insurance Products
N.A.I.C.S.: 524298

American National Property & Casualty Company　　　　　　(2)
1949 E Sunshine, Springfield, MO 65899-0007
Tel.: (417) 887-0220
Sales Range: $400-449.9 Million
Emp.: 850
Property & Casualty Insurance Services
N.A.I.C.S.: 524298
Ron Koch (Treas & Controller)

American National Registered Investment Advisor, Inc.　　　　(2)
1 Moody Plz, Galveston, TX 77550
Tel.: (281) 521-3438
Investment Advisory Services
N.A.I.C.S.: 523940
Anne Marie LeMire (Pres)

Farm Family Casualty Insurance Company　　　　　　　　　(2)
9 W 344 Rte 9W, Glenmont, NY 12077-2910
Tel.: (518) 431-5000
Web Site: http://www.farmfamily.com
Rev.: $3,200,000
Emp.: 600
Fire, Marine & Casualty Insurance
N.A.I.C.S.: 524126

Farm Family Life Insurance Company　　　　　　　　　　(2)
344 Rte 9 W, Glenmont, NY 12077-2910
Tel.: (518) 431-5000
Web Site: http://www.farmfamily.com
Sales Range: $200-249.9 Million
Emp.: 600
Insurance Agents, Brokers & Service
N.A.I.C.S.: 524210

Garden State Life Insurance Company　　　　　　　　　　(2)
2450 S Shore Blvd, League City, TX 77573
Tel.: (281) 538-1037
Web Site: http://www.gardenstatelife.com
Rev.: $1,600,000
Emp.: 58
Life Insurance
N.A.I.C.S.: 524210

Germann Road Land Development, LLC　　　　　　　　　　(2)
8400 E Prentice Ave Ste 910, Greenwood Village, CO 80111-2948
Tel.: (303) 843-6473
Land Development
N.A.I.C.S.: 237210

Interpark Pittsburgh, LLC　　　(2)
625 Stanwix St, Pittsburgh, PA 15222
Tel.: (412) 355-0414
Web Site: http://www.interparkonline.com
Emp.: 3
Insurance Brokerage Services
N.A.I.C.S.: 524210

Pacific Property and Casualty Company　　　　　　　　　(2)
1949 E Sunshine St, Springfield, MO 65899-0001
Tel.: (417) 887-0220
Web Site:
　http://www.pacificpropertyandcasualty.com
Sales Range: $250-299.9 Million
Emp.: 900
Insurance Services
N.A.I.C.S.: 524113

Securities Management & Research, Inc.　　　　　　　　　(2)
2450 South Shore Blvd Ste 400, League City, TX 77573
Tel.: (281) 334-2469
Web Site: http://www.smrinvest.com
Sales Range: $75-99.9 Million
Emp.: 35
Investment Advisor
N.A.I.C.S.: 523940

Affiliate (Domestic):

South Shore Harbour Development, Ltd.　　　　　　　　　　(2)

2525 S Shore Blvd Ste 207, League City, TX 77573
Tel.: (281) 334-7501
Web Site:
http://www.southshoreharbour.com
Sales Range: $10-24.9 Million
Emp.: 8
Real Estate Services
N.A.I.C.S.: 531210

Subsidiary (Domestic):

United Farm Family Insurance
Company **(2)**
Ste 344 Route 9W, Albany, NY 12201-0656
Tel.: (518) 431-5000
Insurance Brokerage Services
N.A.I.C.S.: 524210

Armtec LP **(1)**
3300 Hwy 7 West Suite 500, Concord, L4K 4M3, ON, Canada
Tel.: (519) 822-0210
Web Site: http://www.armtec.com
Sales Range: $400-449.9 Million
Emp.: 1,600
Infrastructure Concrete Products Mfr
N.A.I.C.S.: 327331
Mark D. Anderson *(Pres & CEO)*

Arteris S.A. **(1)**
Av Pres Juscelino Kubitschek 510 12th Floor Vila Nova Conceicao, Sao Paulo, 04543-906, SP, Brazil
Tel.: (55) 1130742404
Web Site: https://www.arteris.com.br
Sales Range: $1-4.9 Billion
Construction, Engineering & Infrastructure Services
N.A.I.C.S.: 237310
Andre Dorf *(CEO)*

Subsidiary (Domestic):

Centrovias Sistemas Rodoviarios, S.A. **(2)**
Rodovia Washington Luis km 216 8 Pista Sul, 13530-000, Itirapina, SP, Brazil
Tel.: (55) 1130742404
Web Site: http://www.centrovias.com.br
Sales Range: $150-199.9 Million
Road & Highway Construction Services
N.A.I.C.S.: 237310

Associated Estates Realty
Corporation **(1)**
1 AEC Pkwy, Richmond Heights, OH 44143-1550
Tel.: (216) 261-5000
Real Estate Investment Trust
N.A.I.C.S.: 525990

Subsidiary (Domestic):

AERC Arrowhead Station, Inc. **(2)**
1 Aec Pkwy, Cleveland, OH 44143
Tel.: (614) 891-8809
Residential Building Rental & Leasing Services
N.A.I.C.S.: 531110

MIG II Realty Advisors Inc. **(2)**
1655 Palm Beach Lakes Blvd Ste 810, West Palm Beach, FL 33401-5018 **(100%)**
Tel.: (561) 820-1300
Sales Range: $1-4.9 Billion
Investment Advice
N.A.I.C.S.: 523940

Merit Enterprises, Inc. **(2)**
1304 N 9th St, Sapulpa, OK 74066
Tel.: (918) 227-3794
Web Site: https://www.meritenterprises.com
N.A.I.C.S.: 423510

AusNet Services Ltd. **(1)**
Level 31 2 Southbank Boulevard, Southbank, 3006, VIC, Australia
Tel.: (61) 396956000
Web Site: http://www.ausnetservices.com.au
Rev.: $1,383,113,664
Assets: $9,990,646,272
Liabilities: $7,888,559,688
Net Worth: $2,102,086,584
Earnings: $203,312,673
Emp.: 1,700
Fiscal Year-end: 03/31/2020
Gas Distr & Electricity Transmission
N.A.I.C.S.: 221210

Geraldine Leslie *(Exec Gen Mgr-People, Safety & Corp Affairs)*

Brookfield Brasil, S.A. **(1)**
Avenida das Nacoes Unidas 14 401, Parque da Cidade - Torre Paineira 15 andar, Sao Paulo, 04794-000, SP, Brazil **(100%)**
Tel.: (55) 1125409150
Web Site: http://www.brookfieldbr.com
Emp.: 14,000
Holding Company; Real Estate, Financial & Services, Natural Resources & Agribusiness
N.A.I.C.S.: 551112

Subsidiary (Domestic):

Brookfield Incorporacoes S.A. **(2)**
Av Paisagista Jose Silva de Azevedo Neto 200, 22775056, Rio de Janeiro, Brazil
Tel.: (55) 21 3127 9200
Web Site: http://www.br.brookfield.com
Sales Range: $1-4.9 Billion
Emp.: 6,001
Real Estate Development Services
N.A.I.C.S.: 531390
Nicholas Vincent Reade *(Chm)*

Brookfield Bridge Lending Fund
Inc **(1)**
181 Bay St Ste 300, Brookfield Place, Toronto, M5J 2T3, ON, Canada
Tel.: (416) 363-9491
Investment Firm
N.A.I.C.S.: 523999

Brookfield Business Partners
L.P. **(1)**
73 Front Street, Hamilton, HM 12, Bermuda **(64%)**
Tel.: (441) 2943309
Web Site: http://www.bbu.brookfield.com
Rev.: $55,068,000,000
Assets: $82,385,000,000
Liabilities: $63,853,000,000
Net Worth: $18,532,000,000
Earnings: $3,777,000,000
Emp.: 72,000
Fiscal Year-end: 12/31/2023
Business & Industrial Investment Holding Company
N.A.I.C.S.: 551112
Jeffrey M. Blidner *(Chm)*

Subsidiary (Non-US):

Altera Infrastructure L.P. **(2)**
Altera House Unit 3 Prospect Park Arnhall Business Park, Westhill, AB32 6FJ, Aberdeenshire, United Kingdom
Tel.: (44) 122 456 8200
Web Site: http://www.alterainfra.com
Rev.: $1,151,260,000
Assets: $3,884,724,000
Liabilities: $3,784,046,000
Net Worth: $100,678,000
Earnings: ($136,450,000)
Emp.: 1,700
Fiscal Year-end: 12/31/2021
Marine Transportation & Storage Services
N.A.I.C.S.: 483111
Ingvild Saether *(Pres & CEO)*

Subsidiary (US):

CDK Global, Inc. **(2)**
1950 Hassell Rd, Hoffman Estates, IL 60169
Tel.: (847) 397-1700
Web Site: http://www.cdkglobal.com
Rev.: $1,673,200,000
Assets: $2,712,600,000
Liabilities: $2,217,700,000
Net Worth: $494,900,000
Earnings: $1,034,300,000
Emp.: 6,500
Fiscal Year-end: 06/30/2021
Digital Marketing & Advertising Services
N.A.I.C.S.: 541890
Lee J. Brunz *(Gen Counsel & Exec VP)*

Subsidiary (Non-US):

CDK Global (Canada) Limited **(3)**
1210 Sheppard Ave E Ste 600, Toronto, M2K 1E3, ON, Canada **(100%)**
Tel.: (416) 498-3700
Web Site: http://www.cdkglobal.com
Data Processing & Preparation Services
N.A.I.C.S.: 518210

CDK Global (Netherland) BV **(3)**
Industriestraat 20, 3371 XD, Hardinxveld-Giessendam, Netherlands
Tel.: (31) 184674800
Advertising Services
N.A.I.C.S.: 541890

CDK Global (UK) Limited **(3)**
The Brickworks 35-43 Greyfriars Road, Charnham Park, Reading, RG1 1NP, United Kingdom
Tel.: (44) 1488662662
Web Site: http://www.cdkglobal.co.uk
Management Consulting Services
N.A.I.C.S.: 541611

CDK Global Group BV **(3)**
Industriestraat 20, 3371 XD, Hardinxveld-Giessendam, Netherlands
Tel.: (31) 184674800
Web Site: http://www.cdkglobal.nl
IT Management Consulting Services
N.A.I.C.S.: 541611

Subsidiary (Domestic):

Roadster, Inc. **(3)**
300 De Haro St Ste 334, San Francisco, CA 94103
Web Site: https://www.roadster.com
Car Dealing Services
N.A.I.C.S.: 441110
Kevin Lorell *(VP-Customer Success)*

Subsidiary (Non-US):

CWC Energy Services Corp. **(2)**
Bow Valley Square III Suite 610 205-5th Ave SW, Calgary, T2P 2V7, AB, Canada **(56%)**
Tel.: (403) 264-2177
Web Site: http://www.cwcwellservices.com
Rev.: $58,419,888
Assets: $158,195,008
Liabilities: $34,612,761
Net Worth: $123,582,248
Earnings: $19,158,037
Emp.: 580
Fiscal Year-end: 12/31/2020
Oil & Gas Exploration Services
N.A.I.C.S.: 213112
Duncan T. Au *(Pres & CEO)*

Joint Venture (US):

Clarios Global GP LLC **(2)**
Florist Twr 5757 N Green Bay Ave, Milwaukee, WI 53201
Tel.: (414) 524-1200
Web Site: http://www.clarios.com
Holding Company; Storage Battery Mfr & Whslr
N.A.I.C.S.: 551112
Mark Wallace *(CEO)*

Subsidiary (Domestic):

Johnson Controls Battery Group,
LLC **(3)**
5757 N Green Bay Ave, Milwaukee, WI 53201
Tel.: (414) 524-1200
Web Site: http://www.johnsoncontrols.com
Sales Range: $1-4.9 Billion
Emp.: 2,000
Automotive Batteries Mfr & Whslr
N.A.I.C.S.: 335910

Subsidiary (Non-US):

Delkor Corp. Ltd. **(4)**
9th floor Korea Intellectual Property Center Building 131 Teheran-ro, Gangnam-gu, Seoul, 06133, Gyeongbuk, Korea (South)
Tel.: (82) 25298975
Web Site: https://www.delkor.com
Sales Range: $75-99.9 Million
Emp.: 400
Battery Mfr
N.A.I.C.S.: 335910

Johnson Controls Autobatterie
GmbH **(4)**
Tel.: (49) 51197502
Web Site: http://www.varta-automotive.com
Automotive Battery Mfr
N.A.I.C.S.: 335910

Subsidiary (Non-US):

Clarios VARTA Hannover GmbH **(5)**

Tel.: (49) 51179030
Web Site: http://www.varta-automotive.com
Automobile Batteries Mfr
N.A.I.C.S.: 335910

Johnson Controls Batterie AG **(5)**
Tel.: (41) 448708060
Web Site:
http://www.johnsoncontrolsbatterie.ch
Sales Range: $10-24.9 Million
Emp.: 15
Automotive Battery Mfr & Distr
N.A.I.C.S.: 335910

Johnson Controls Batteries Ltd. **(5)**
Tel.: (44) 1895838999
Sales Range: $10-24.9 Million
Emp.: 12
Automotive Battery Mfr
N.A.I.C.S.: 335910

Subsidiary (Domestic):

Optima Batteries, Inc. **(4)**
17500 E 22nd Ave, Aurora, CO 80011
Tel.: (888) 867-8462
Web Site: http://www.optimabatteries.com
Sales Range: $50-74.9 Million
Emp.: 190
Automotive Batteries
N.A.I.C.S.: 335910

Subsidiary (Non-US):

Optima Batteries AB **(5)**
Vendevagen 90, Danderyd, 182 32, Stockholm, Sweden
Tel.: (46) 858705304
Automotive Components
N.A.I.C.S.: 336390

Subsidiary (US):

DexKo Global, Inc. **(2)**
39555 Orchard Hill Pl Ste 360, Novi, MI 48375
Tel.: (248) 916-1867
Web Site: http://www.dexko.com
Tools & Hardware Mfr
N.A.I.C.S.: 333517
Fred Bentley Jr. *(Pres & CEO)*

Subsidiary (Domestic):

Dexter Axle Company **(3)**
2900 Industrial Pkwy E, Elkhart, IN 46516
Tel.: (574) 295-7888
Web Site: http://www.dexteraxle.com
Automotive Monitoring & Control Devices Mfr
N.A.I.C.S.: 336350
Adam Dexter *(Pres & CEO)*

Unit (Domestic):

Dexter Axle Division - Albion **(4)**
500 S 7th St, Albion, IN 46701
Tel.: (260) 636-2195
Sales Range: $25-49.9 Million
Automotive Monitoring & Control Devices Mfr
N.A.I.C.S.: 336350

Dexter Axle Division - El Reno **(4)**
500 SE 27th St, El Reno, OK 73036
Tel.: (405) 262-6700
Sales Range: $25-49.9 Million
Automotive Monitoring & Control Devices Mfr
N.A.I.C.S.: 336350

Dexter Axle Division - Elkhart **(4)**
2900 Industrial Pkwy E, Elkhart, IN 46516
Tel.: (574) 295-7888
Web Site: http://www.dexteraxle.com
Sales Range: $50-74.9 Million
Automotive Monitoring & Control Devices Mfr
N.A.I.C.S.: 336350
Jim Berry *(Dir-Mktg)*

Dexter Axle Division - Fremont **(4)**
301 W Pearl St, Fremont, IN 46737
Tel.: (260) 495-5100
Automotive Monitoring & Control Devices Mfr
N.A.I.C.S.: 423310

Dexter Axle Division - Monticello **(4)**
199 Perimeter Rd, Monticello, GA 31064
Tel.: (706) 468-6495
Web Site: http://www.dexteraxle.com

Brookfield Corporation—(Continued)

Emp.: 95
Automotive Monitoring & Control Devices
Mfr
N.A.I.C.S.: 336350
Martha McMichael *(Office Mgr)*

Group (Domestic):

Dexter Chassis Group **(4)**
2501 Jeanwood Dr, Elkhart, IN 46515
Tel.: (269) 483-7681
Web Site:
http://www.dexterchassisgroup.com
Sheet Metal Work Mfg
N.A.I.C.S.: 332322

Subsidiary (Domestic):

Redneck Inc. **(4)**
2100 NW Bypass, Springfield, MO 65803-2208
Tel.: (417) 864-5210
Web Site: http://www.redneck-trailer.com
Sales Range: $50-74.9 Million
Emp.: 400
Motor Vehicle Supplies & New Parts
N.A.I.C.S.: 423120
Ernest W. Giddens *(CEO)*

Silent Drive, Inc. **(4)**
1300 Arizona Pl SW, Orange City, IA 51041
Tel.: (712) 737-4865
Web Site: http://www.silentdrive.com
Rev.: $8,000,000
Emp.: 32
Motor Vehicle Body Mfr
N.A.I.C.S.: 336211
Wilbur DeJong *(Pres)*

The Expediter, LLC **(4)**
6667 White Dr, West Palm Beach, FL 33407
Tel.: (561) 863-2220
Web Site: http://www.expediter.com
Motor Vehicle Supplies And New Parts
N.A.I.C.S.: 423120
Frederick Cohen *(Principal)*

Subsidiary (Domestic):

Kodiak Products Co., Inc. **(3)**
633 NW Pkwy, Azle, TX 76020
Web Site: http://www.kodiaktrailer.com
Travel Trailer & Camper Mfr
N.A.I.C.S.: 336214

Quality/Century Holdings Corporation **(3)**
604 W Main St, Azle, TX 76020
Tel.: (817) 444-4518
Web Site: http://www.rockwellamerican.com
Trailer Components Mfr & Distr
N.A.I.C.S.: 336390
Chris Dietemann *(Pres)*

Subsidiary (Domestic):

Fenders N'More, LLC **(4)**
14420 Marquardt Ave, Santa Fe Springs, CA 90670
Tel.: (562) 921-0055
Web Site: http://www.fendersnmore.com
Rev.: $1,500,000
Emp.: 20
Fiscal Year-end: 12/31/2006
Automotive Stampings, Nsk
N.A.I.C.S.: 336370

Subsidiary (Non-US):

Healthscope Pty. Ltd. **(2)**
312 St Kilda Road, Melbourne, 3004, VIC, Australia
Tel.: (61) 3 9926 7500
Web Site: http://www.healthscope.com.au
Rev.: $1,826,970,992
Assets: $3,801,376,545
Liabilities: $1,970,659,201
Net Worth: $1,830,717,344
Earnings: $69,775,806
Emp.: 18,000
Fiscal Year-end: 06/30/2018
Holding Company; Hospital, Medical & Pathology Centers Operator
N.A.I.C.S.: 551112
Arthur Yannakou *(COO)*

Subsidiary (Domestic):

Healthscope Operations Pty. Ltd. **(3)**

Level 1 312 St Kilda Road, Melbourne, 3004, VIC, Australia
Tel.: (61) 399267500
Web Site: http://www.healthscope.com.au
Hospital, Medical & Pathology Centers Operator
N.A.I.C.S.: 622110

Subsidiary (Domestic):

Allamanda Private Hospital Pty. Ltd. **(4)**
21 Spendelove Street, Southport, 4215, QLD, Australia
Tel.: (61) 755326444
Web Site:
http://www.allamandaprivatehospital.com
General Hospital
N.A.I.C.S.: 622110
David Harper *(Gen Mgr)*

Australian Hospital Care (Como) Pty. Ltd. **(4)**
152 Como Parade West, Parkdale, Melbourne, 3194, VIC, Australia
Tel.: (61) 3 9586 3500
Web Site:
http://www.comoprivatehospital.com.au
General Hospital
N.A.I.C.S.: 622110

Australian Hospital Care (Dorset) Pty. Ltd. **(4)**
146 Derby Street, Pascoe Vale, 3044, VIC, Australia
Tel.: (61) 383719477
Web Site:
https://www.dorsetrehabilitationcentre.com
Sales Range: $25-49.9 Million
Emp.: 110
Rehabilitation Center Operator
N.A.I.C.S.: 622310

Australian Hospital Care (Knox) Pty. Ltd. **(4)**
262 Mountain Hwy, Wantirna, 3152, VIC, Australia
Tel.: (61) 392107000
Sales Range: $50-74.9 Million
Emp.: 1,000
General Hospital
N.A.I.C.S.: 622110

Brisbane Private Hospital Pty. Ltd. **(4)**
259 Wickham Terrace, Brisbane, 4000, QLD, Australia
Tel.: (61) 7 3834 6111
Web Site:
http://www.brisbaneprivatehospital.com.au
Sales Range: $25-49.9 Million
Emp.: 500
General Hospital
N.A.I.C.S.: 622110

Brisbane Waters Equities Pty. Ltd, **(4)**
21 Vidler Ave, Woy Woy, 2256, NSW, Australia
Tel.: (61) 243419522
Web Site:
https://www.brisbanewatersprivate.com.au
Sales Range: $25-49.9 Million
Emp.: 200
Surgical Hospital
N.A.I.C.S.: 622110

Subsidiary (Domestic):

Brisbane Waters Administration Pty. Ltd. **(5)**
21 Vidler Avenue, Woy Woy, 2256, NSW, Australia
Tel.: (61) 243419522
Web Site:
https://brisbanewatersprivate.com.au
Sales Range: $25-49.9 Million
Emp.: 100
Hospital Administrative Services
N.A.I.C.S.: 561110
Kathy Beverley *(CEO)*

Subsidiary (Domestic):

Darwin Private Hospital Pty. Ltd. **(4)**
Rocklands Drive, Tiwi, Darwin, 0810, NT, Australia
Tel.: (61) 889206011

Web Site:
https://www.darwinprivatehospital.com.au
General Hospital
N.A.I.C.S.: 622110

Healthscope (Tasmania) Pty. Ltd. **(4)**
Level 1 312 Saint Kilda Road, Melbourne, 3004, VIC, Australia
Tel.: (61) 399267500
Web Site: http://www.healthscope.com.au
Hospital Operator
N.A.I.C.S.: 622110

Unit (Domestic):

Hobart Private Hospital **(5)**
Corner Argyle Collins Streets, Hobart, 7000, TAS, Australia
Tel.: (61) 362143000
Web Site:
https://www.hobartprivatehospital.com.au
General Hospital
N.A.I.C.S.: 622110

St. Helens Private Hospital **(5)**
186 Macquarie Street, Hobart, 7000, TAS, Australia
Tel.: (61) 362216444
Web Site:
https://www.sthelensprivatehospital.com.au
Specialty Hospitals
N.A.I.C.S.: 622310

Subsidiary (Non-US):

Healthscope New Zealand Limited **(4)**
Tel.: (64) 95746200
Web Site: http://www.healthscope.co.nz
Holding Company; Regional Managing Office; Hospitals, Healthcare & Pathology Centers Operator
N.A.I.C.S.: 551112

Subsidiary (Non-US):

Labtests Limited **(5)**
Web Site: http://www.labtests.co.nz
Sales Range: $25-49.9 Million
Emp.: 400
Medical Pathology Laboratory Operator
N.A.I.C.S.: 621511

Northland Pathology Laboratory Limited **(5)**
Tel.: (64) 94384243
Web Site: https://www.norpath.co.nz
Emp.: 50
Medical Pathology Laboratory Operator
N.A.I.C.S.: 621511

Southern Community Laboratories Ltd. **(5)**
Tel.: (64) 34702919
Web Site: http://www.sclabs.co.nz
Medical Pathology Laboratory Operator
N.A.I.C.S.: 621511

Subsidiary (Non-US):

Quest Laboratories Pte. Ltd. **(4)**
67 Ubi Ave 1 Starhub Green N Wing 07-01 to 07 plus 09 & 10, Singapore, 408942, Singapore
Tel.: (65) 62755501
Web Site: http://www.questlabs.com.sg
Sales Range: $25-49.9 Million
Emp.: 200
Medical Pathology Laboratory Operator
N.A.I.C.S.: 621511
Cody Ng *(Head-Fin)*

Subsidiary (Domestic):

The Victorian Rehabilitation Centre Pty. Ltd. **(4)**
499 Springvale Road, Glen Waverley, 3150, VIC, Australia
Tel.: (61) 395662777
Web Site:
https://www.victorianrehabilitation.com.au
Medical Rehabilitation Hospital
N.A.I.C.S.: 622310

Subsidiary (Non-US):

Modulaire Group **(2)**
8th Floor 262 High Holborn, London, WC1V 7NA, United Kingdom
Tel.: (44) 8081082222
Web Site: https://www.modulairegroup.com

Infrastructure, Facilities & Modular Services
N.A.I.C.S.: 531120
Mark V. Higson *(CEO)*

Subsidiary (Non-US):

Algeco SAS **(3)**
Tour Pacific 11-13 cours Valmy, 92977, Paris, Cedex, France
Tel.: (33) 42919000
Web Site: http://www.algeco.fr
Mobile Buildings Leasing, Sales & Mfr
N.A.I.C.S.: 332311

Subsidiary (Non-US):

Algeco UK Limited **(4)**
Manor Drive, Peterborough, PE4 7AP, United Kingdom
Tel.: (44) 8081082222
Modular Buildings Designer, Mfr, Sales & Leasing
N.A.I.C.S.: 332311

Joint Venture (US):

Nielsen Holdings plc **(2)**
675 6th Ave, New York, NY 10010
Tel.: (646) 654-5000
Web Site: https://www.nielsen.com
Rev.: $3,500,000,000
Assets: $10,820,000,000
Liabilities: $7,324,000,000
Net Worth: $3,496,000,000
Earnings: $963,000,000
Emp.: 14,000
Fiscal Year-end: 12/31/2021
Holding Company
N.A.I.C.S.: 551112
Karthik Rao *(COO)*

Subsidiary (Non-US):

The Nielsen Company B.V. **(3)**
Diemerhof 2, 1112 XL, Diemen, Netherlands **(100%)**
Tel.: (31) 20 398 8777
Marketing, Media Rating & Business Information Services
N.A.I.C.S.: 541910

Subsidiary (US):

The Nielsen Company (US), LLC **(4)**
770 Broadway, New York, NY 10003
Tel.: (646) 654-5000
Marketing Information, Media Measurement Information & Business Information Services
N.A.I.C.S.: 541910

Subsidiary (Non-US):

A3 Distrib SAS **(5)**
2 Rue de la Fleche, PO Box 20726, 49300, Cholet, Cedex, France
Tel.: (33) 253591240
Web Site: http://www.a3distrib.fr
Customs Consulting Services
N.A.I.C.S.: 541614

Subsidiary (Domestic):

ACNielsen Corporation **(5)**
85 Broad St, New York, NY 10004
Tel.: (646) 654-5000
Sales Range: $1-4.9 Billion
Emp.: 21,000
Developer of Diagnostic, Market Measurement, Opportunity Identification & Market Analysis Products & Services
N.A.I.C.S.: 541910

Subsidiary (Domestic):

A.C. Nielsen Company, LLC **(6)**
150 N Martingale Rd, Schaumburg, IL 60173
Tel.: (847) 605-5000
Emp.: 2
Marketing Research Service
N.A.I.C.S.: 541910

Subsidiary (Domestic):

ACNielsen (US), Inc. **(7)**
150 N Martingale Rd, Schaumburg, IL 60173-2076
Tel.: (847) 605-5000
Sales Range: $25-49.9 Million
Emp.: 500

Developer of Diagnostic, Market Measurement, Opportunity Identification & Market Analysis Products & Services
N.A.I.C.S.: 541910

Branch (Domestic):

ACNielsen   **(8)**
600 Hwy 159 Ste 400, Plymouth, MN 55426
Tel.: (763) 593-2000
Sales Range: $10-24.9 Million
Emp.: 80
Developer of Diagnostic, Market Measurement, Opportunity Identification & Market Analysis Products & Services
N.A.I.C.S.: 541910

ACNielsen   **(8)**
2650 S Ashland Ave, Green Bay, WI 54304-5361
Tel.: (920) 405-7500
Rev.: $10,200,000
Emp.: 300
Developer of Diagnostic, Market Measurement, Opportunity Identification & Market Analysis Products & Services
N.A.I.C.S.: 541910

Subsidiary (Non-US):

ACNielsen Company of Canada   **(7)**
160 McNabb Street, Markham, L3R 4B8, ON, Canada
Tel.: (905) 475-3344
Web Site: https://www.nielsen.com
Sales Range: $25-49.9 Million
Emp.: 500
Developer of Diagnostic, Market Measurement, Opportunity Identification & Market Analysis Products & Services
N.A.I.C.S.: 541910

Subsidiary (Domestic):

ACNielsen Puerto Rico Inc.   **(7)**
117 Eleanor Roosevelt, Hato Rey, PR 00918
Tel.: (787) 756-0555
Emp.: 50
Developer of Diagnostic, Market Measurement, Opportunity Identification & Market Analysis Products & Services
N.A.I.C.S.: 541910

Subsidiary (Non-US):

ACNielsen Argentina S.A.   **(6)**
Av del Libertador 6350 piso 6 Ciudad Autonoma de, C1428ART, Buenos Aires, Argentina
Tel.: (54) 1168415400
Developer of Diagnostic, Market Measurement, Opportunity Identification & Market Analysis Products & Services
N.A.I.C.S.: 541910

Subsidiary (Non-US):

A.C. Nielsen Chile Limitada   **(7)**
Cerro El Plomo 5680 Piso 13, Las Condes, 8320000, Chile
Tel.: (56) 24632700
Web Site: http://www.nielsen.com
Marketing Management Consulting Services
N.A.I.C.S.: 541613

A.C. Nielsen de Colombia Ltda.   **(7)**
Calle 100 9 A-45 Torre 2 Piso 10, Bogota, Colombia
Tel.: (57) 6516500
Sales Range: $50-74.9 Million
Emp.: 600
Digital Marketing Services
N.A.I.C.S.: 541810

A.C. Nielsen de Venezuela, S.A.   **(7)**
Av Jose Maria Vargas Torre del Colegio Apdo 80008, Piso 10 Urb Santa Fe Norte, Caracas, Venezuela
Tel.: (58) 2129070100
Sales Range: $25-49.9 Million
Emp.: 300
Developer of Diagnostic, Market Measurement, Opportunity Identification & Market Analysis Products & Services
N.A.I.C.S.: 541910

A.C. Nielsen do Brasil Ltda.   **(7)**
Rua Monte Castelo 55 - Granja Viana, Cotia, Sao Paulo, 06710 675, Brazil
Tel.: (55) 1146137000

Web Site: http://www.nielsen.com
Sales Range: $25-49.9 Million
Emp.: 1,000
Marketing Research Service
N.A.I.C.S.: 541910

A.C. Nielsen, S. de RL de C.V.   **(7)**
Blvd Manuel Avila Camacho 191 Piso 8 Col Polanco, Seccion Del Miguel Hidalgo, 11510, Mexico, DF, Mexico
Tel.: (52) 5553871000
Sales Range: $50-74.9 Million
Emp.: 1,000
Developer of Diagnostic, Market Measurement, Opportunity Identification & Market Analysis Products & Services
N.A.I.C.S.: 541910

ACNielsen Ecuador S.A.   **(7)**
Kennedy Norte Av Nahim Isalas y Luis Orrantia Mz 801 No 28, 090112, Guayaquil, Ecuador
Tel.: (593) 45005402
Business Research Services
N.A.I.C.S.: 541910

Subsidiary (Non-US):

ACNielsen Cyprus Limited   **(6)**
Makariou 56 Dimofontos 1 6th floor, PO Box 26758, 1075, Nicosia, Cyprus
Tel.: (357) 22886383
Sales Range: $75-99.9 Million
Emp.: 130
Developer of Diagnostic, Market Measurement, Opportunity Identification & Market Analysis Products & Services
N.A.I.C.S.: 541910

Subsidiary (Non-US):

AC Nielsen Cote d'Ivoire Limited   **(7)**
Cocody II Plateaux Ste Cecile Rue J106 Lot 2038, PO Box 1258, Abidjan, Cote d'Ivoire
Tel.: (225) 22420044
Management Consulting & Comprehensive Market Information Solution Provider
N.A.I.C.S.: 541613

ACNielsen (Tanzania) Ltd.   **(7)**
Maktaba/Bibi Titi Mohamed Street Raha Towers 3rd floor, Dar es Salaam, 76888, Tanzania
Tel.: (255) 222117628
Web Site: http://tz.nielsen.com
Emp.: 30
Media & Marketing Consulting Services
N.A.I.C.S.: 541910

ACNielsen Cameroon Sarl   **(7)**
Bonadiwoto-Opposite Total Aeroport 4th Entrance Right, PO Box 11783, Douala, Cameroon
Tel.: (237) 33014407
Emp.: 70
Media & Marketing Research Services
N.A.I.C.S.: 541910
Brian Chung *(Mng Dir)*

ACNielsen Ghana Limited   **(7)**
4th Floor Gulf House Airport West, Tetteh Quarshie Roundabout, Accra, Ghana
Tel.: (233) 302503215
Web Site: http://www.gh.nielsen.com
Market Research & Information Solution Provider
N.A.I.C.S.: 541910

ACNielsen Kazakhstan Ltd.   **(7)**
Auezov Str 60 BC Almaty Residence 10th Floor, Bussines Center Sarkand, Almaty, 50059, Kazakhstan
Tel.: (7) 87273557750
Web Site: http://kz.nielsen.com
Market Research & Information Solution Provider
N.A.I.C.S.: 541910

ACNielsen Limited Liability Company   **(7)**
st Tushinskaya 17, 125362, Moscow, Russia
Tel.: (7) 4956465105
Web Site: http://www.nielsen.com
Sales Range: $25-49.9 Million
Marketing Research Service
N.A.I.C.S.: 541910

ACNielsen Nigeria Limited   **(7)**
1st floor Left Wing 52/54 Isaac John Street, Ikeja GRA, Lagos, Nigeria

Tel.: (234) 12702085
Sales Range: $10-24.9 Million
Emp.: 100
Marketing Research Service
N.A.I.C.S.: 541910

ACNielsen Pakistan (Private) Limited   **(7)**
Room No 716 Progressive Plaza Beaumont Rd Civil Lines, Progressive Plaza, Karachi, 75530, Pakistan
Tel.: (92) 21111111226
Web Site: http://www.pk.nielsen.com
Media & Marketing Information Services
N.A.I.C.S.: 541613

ACNielsen S.A.   **(7)**
Louise Riencourt 64, Apollon Tower, 11523, Athens, Greece
Tel.: (30) 2106999200
Sales Range: $10-24.9 Million
Marketing Research Service
N.A.I.C.S.: 541910

ACNielsen SARL   **(7)**
179 Rue Omar Riffi Imm Al Wahda Entree B 2eme Etage Appt B6, Casablanca, 20120, Morocco
Tel.: (212) 522441915
Marketing Research Service
N.A.I.C.S.: 541910

UAB ACNielsen Baltics   **(7)**
A Juozapaviciaus g 6/2, Vilnius, LT-09310, Lithuania
Tel.: (370) 52734145
Emp.: 150
Market Research & Information Solution Provider
N.A.I.C.S.: 541910

Subsidiary (Non-US):

ACNielsen Europe   **(6)**
Avenue Lavoisier 37, Avenue Einstein 6 - Bat F, 1300, Wavre, Belgium
Tel.: (32) 10454609
Market Research Services
N.A.I.C.S.: 541910

Subsidiary (Non-US):

A.C. Nielsen Company, S.L.   **(7)**
Orense 34 Torre Norte 8 Planta, 28020, Madrid, Spain
Tel.: (34) 913777200
Web Site: http://www.nielsen.com
Sales Range: $25-49.9 Million
Emp.: 350
Marketing Research & Monitoring & Documental Services
N.A.I.C.S.: 541910

A.C. Nielsen Gesellschaft m.b.H.   **(7)**
Big Biz C Dresdner Str 91, 1200, Vienna, Austria
Tel.: (43) 1981100
Web Site: http://www.nielsen.com
Sales Range: $10-24.9 Million
Emp.: 100
Marketing Research Service
N.A.I.C.S.: 541910

A.C. Nielsen GmbH   **(7)**
Sachsenstrasse 16, 20097, Hamburg, Germany
Tel.: (49) 40236420
Sales Range: $10-24.9 Million
Emp.: 150
Marketing Research Service
N.A.I.C.S.: 541910
Resto Maela *(Mng Dir)*

A.C. Nielsen Portugal   **(7)**
Rua Dona Filipa De Vilhena 38, 1049, Lisbon, Portugal
Tel.: (351) 217811200
Sales Range: $10-24.9 Million
Emp.: 100
Marketing Research Service
N.A.I.C.S.: 541910

A.C. Nielsen of Ireland Limited   **(7)**
14 Riverwalk National Digital Park Citywest Business Campus, Dublin, 24, Ireland
Tel.: (353) 14690400
Web Site: http://nielsen.com
Emp.: 70
Media & Marketing Research Services
N.A.I.C.S.: 541910

ACNielsen (Nederland) B.V.   **(7)**
Radarweg 29B- 9, 1043 NX, Amsterdam, Netherlands
Tel.: (31) 203988777
Web Site: http://www.nielsen.com
Sales Range: $10-24.9 Million
Emp.: 200
Marketing Research Service
N.A.I.C.S.: 541910

Subsidiary (Non-US):

Nielsen Admosphere, a.s   **(8)**
Ceskobratrska 2778/1, 130 00, Prague, Czech Republic
Tel.: (420) 22 271 7763
Web Site: https://www.nielsen-admosphere.eu
Emp.: 190
Media Analysis Services
N.A.I.C.S.: 541910
Michal Jordan *(Deputy Chm)*

Nielsen Arastirma Hizmetleri Limited Sirket   **(8)**
Icerenkoy Mah Umut Sok AND Plaza No 10-12 Kat 1-2, Atasehir, 34752, Istanbul, Turkiye
Tel.: (90) 2165387000
Marketing Consulting Services
N.A.I.C.S.: 541613

Subsidiary (Non-US):

ACNielsen AB   **(7)**
Gavlegatan 16, Box 6019, 102 31, Stockholm, Sweden
Tel.: (46) 2084415
Sales Range: $10-24.9 Million
Emp.: 95
Developer of Diagnostic, Market Measurement, Opportunity Identification & Market Analysis Products & Services
N.A.I.C.S.: 541910

Subsidiary (Domestic):

Nielsen Services Sweden AB   **(8)**
Gavlegatan 16, Box 6019, 102 31, Stockholm, Sweden
Tel.: (46) 2084415
Marketing Research Service
N.A.I.C.S.: 541910

Subsidiary (Non-US):

The Nielsen Company (Denmark) Aps   **(8)**
Tuborg Parkvej 3 1 sal, 2900, Hellerup, Denmark
Tel.: (45) 39400022
Web Site: http://dk.nielsen.com
Emp.: 80
Media & Marketing Research Services
N.A.I.C.S.: 541613

Subsidiary (Domestic):

ACNielsen Company (Belgium) S.A.   **(7)**
73 Avenue des Pleiades, 1200, Brussels, Belgium
Tel.: (32) 27787118
Sales Range: $10-24.9 Million
Emp.: 162
Developer of Diagnostic, Market Measurement, Opportunity Identification & Market Analysis Products & Services
N.A.I.C.S.: 541910

Subsidiary (Non-US):

ACNielsen Company Ltd.   **(7)**
Nielsen House London Rd, Headington, Oxford, OX3 9RX, Oxfordshire, United Kingdom
Tel.: (44) 1865742742
Web Site: http://www.acnielsen.co.uk
Sales Range: $25-49.9 Million
Emp.: 700
Marketing Research
N.A.I.C.S.: 541910

ACNielsen Norge AS   **(7)**
Harbitzalleen 5, 0275, Oslo, Norway
Tel.: (47) 40614240
Marketing Research Service
N.A.I.C.S.: 541910

ACNielsen S.A.   **(7)**
1 Rue Julius et Ethel Rosenberg, 95870,

Brookfield Corporation—(Continued)

Bezons, France
Tel.: (33) 134414444
Sales Range: $25-49.9 Million
Emp.: 500
Marketing Research Service
N.A.I.C.S.: 541910

ACNielsen SA (7)
Via Cassarinella 25, Ruol, 6900, Lugano,
Switzerland
Tel.: (41) 919609900
Sales Range: $10-24.9 Million
Emp.: 160
Marketing Research Service
N.A.I.C.S.: 541910

The Nielsen Company (Italy) S.r.l. (7)
Centro Direzionale Milanofiori Strada 6 Palazzo A12, 20090, Assago, MI, Italy
Tel.: (39) 02451671
Web Site: http://www.nielsen.it
Sales Range: $50-74.9 Million
Emp.: 550
Marketing Research Service
N.A.I.C.S.: 541910

Subsidiary (Domestic):

Nielsen Services Italy S.r.l. (8)
Strada 6 Palazzo A12, MilanoFiori, 20090,
Assago, MI, Italy
Tel.: (39) 027491512
Emp.: 1,400
Marketing Research Service
N.A.I.C.S.: 541910
Samantha Rovatti (Dir-Comm)

Subsidiary (Non-US):

ACNielsen Group Limited (6)
10/F Dorset House Taikoo Place 979 Kings
Road, Quarry Bay, China (Hong Kong)
Tel.: (852) 2563 9688
Web Site: http://www.hk.nielsen.com
Developer of Diagnostic, Market Measurement, Opportunity Identification & Market
Analysis Products & Services
N.A.I.C.S.: 541910

Subsidiary (Non-US):

ACNielsen (Korea) Ltd. (7)
Korea Fire Marine Insurance Bldg 51-1
Namchang-dong, Jung gu, Seoul, 004-528,
Korea (South)
Tel.: (82) 221027000
Web Site: http://www.acnielsen.co.kr
Sales Range: $25-49.9 Million
Emp.: 300
Marketing Research Service
N.A.I.C.S.: 541910

The Nielsen Company (Australia) Pty. Ltd. (7)
Level 2 Building B 11 Talavera Road, Macquarie Park, Sydney, 2113, NSW, Australia
Tel.: (61) 28 873 7000
Web Site: http://www.nielsen.com
Marketing Research & Media Measurement
Information Services
N.A.I.C.S.: 541910

Subsidiary (Non-US):

ACNielsen (N.Z.) Ltd. (8)
Level 3 Nielsen Centre 129 Hurstmere
Road, Takapuna, Auckland, 0622, New Zealand
Tel.: (64) 99704188
Web Site: http://www.nielsen.com
Sales Range: $10-24.9 Million
Emp.: 160
Marketing Research Service
N.A.I.C.S.: 541910

ACNielsen Corporation Japan (8)
Mg Shirokanedai Bldg 5-12-7 Shirokanedai,
Minato-ku, Tokyo, 108-0071, Japan
Tel.: (81) 357989300
Web Site: http://www.nielsen.com
Emp.: 50
Marketing Research Service
N.A.I.C.S.: 541910

Branch (Domestic):

ACNielsen Corporation Japan (9)
Mg Shirokanedai Bldg 5-12-7 Shirokanedai,

Minato-ku, Tokyo, 108-0071, Japan
Tel.: (81) 357989300
Web Site: http://www.acnielsen.co.jp
Sales Range: $10-24.9 Million
Emp.: 223
Marketing Research Service
N.A.I.C.S.: 541910

Subsidiary (Non-US):

The Nielsen Company Taiwan Ltd. (7)
12F No 188 Nanking E Rd Sec 5, Taipei,
105, Taiwan
Tel.: (886) 221715988
Web Site: http://www.nielsen.com
Sales Range: $25-49.9 Million
Emp.: 300
Marketing Research Service
N.A.I.C.S.: 541910

The Nielsen Nepal Pvt. Ltd. (7)
Ravi Bhawan, PO Box 1784, Kathmandu,
Nepal
Tel.: (977) 14273890
Market Research & Information Solution
Services
N.A.I.C.S.: 541910

Subsidiary (Non-US):

AGB Nielsen Media Research (Thailand) Ltd. (5)
No 323 26th Floor United Center Building
Silom Road, Silom Sub-district Bangrak District, Bangkok, 10500, Thailand
Tel.: (66) 26746000
Television Audience Measurement Services
N.A.I.C.S.: 541613

AGB Nielsen, medijske raziskave, d.o.o (5)
Litijska cesta 259, Crnuce, Ljubljana, 1261,
Slovenia
Tel.: (386) 15809000
Web Site: http://www.agbnielsen.com
Medical Research Services
N.A.I.C.S.: 541910
Mojca Celigoj (Mng Dir)

AGB Stat IPSOS sal (5)
Ipsos building, PO Box 55103, Dekwaneh,
Beirut, Lebanon
Tel.: (961) 1494136
Web Site: http://www.ipsos.com
Marketing Research Service
N.A.I.C.S.: 541910

AMER Tunisia Sarl (5)
12 Rue Echabbia Ex Rue 8003 - 4th Floor,
Montplaisir, 1073, Tunis, Tunisia
Tel.: (216) 71903549
Sales Range: $10-24.9 Million
Emp.: 30
Media & Marketing Consulting Services
N.A.I.C.S.: 541613

Admosphere, s.r.o. (5)
Ceskobratrska 2778/1, Prague, 130 00,
Czech Republic
Tel.: (420) 222717763
Web Site: http://www.nielsen-admosphere.cz
Emp.: 100
Business Research Services
N.A.I.C.S.: 541910

Subsidiary (Domestic):

Affinnova, Inc. (5)
265 Winter St Fl 4, Waltham, MA 02451
Tel.: (781) 464-4700
Web Site: http://www.affinnova.com
Software Development Services
N.A.I.C.S.: 513210

Subsidiary (Non-US):

Affinnova France Sarl (6)
9 Avenue des 3 Fontaines CS 20501,
95007, Cergy-Pontoise, Cedex, France
Tel.: (33) 134414444
Business Research Services
N.A.I.C.S.: 541910

Subsidiary (Domestic):

Baseline LLC (5)
3415 S Sepulveda Blvd Ste 200, Los Angeles, CA 90034
Tel.: (310) 482-3414

Web Site: http://studiosystem.com
Sales Range: $100-124.9 Million
Emp.: 50
Entertainment Data Analysis Services
N.A.I.C.S.: 541910
Simon Adams (Chief Product Officer)

Subsidiary (Non-US):

Brandbank Limited (5)
35B Barnard Road, Norwich, NR5 9JB,
United Kingdom
Tel.: (44) 3305553344
Software Designing Services
N.A.I.C.S.: 513210
Sean Wilkins (Grp Dir-Comml)

Subsidiary (Non-US):

Brandbank (Hungary) Kft. (6)
AC Nielsen Piackutato Kft Vaci u 81,
H-1056, Budapest, Hungary
Tel.: (36) 17940184
Web Site: http://www.brandbank.com
Marketing Research Service
N.A.I.C.S.: 541910

Brandbank (Ireland) Limited. (6)
Unit F7 Swords Enterprise Park Feltrim
Road Swords, Dublin, Ireland
Tel.: (353) 15253800
Web Site: http://www.brandbank.com
Marketing Research Service
N.A.I.C.S.: 541910

Brandbank (Netherlands) B .V. (6)
Line vest 4, 3992 DJ, Houten, Netherlands
Tel.: (31) 302040770
Web Site: http://www.brandbank.com
Marketing Research Service
N.A.I.C.S.: 541910

Brandbank (Poland) Sp. z .o.o. (6)
ul Cyfrowa 4, 71-441, Szczecin, Poland
Tel.: (48) 918522648
Web Site: http://www.brandbank.com
Marketing Research Service
N.A.I.C.S.: 541910

Brandbank (Slovakia) s.r.o. (6)
Kutlikova 17, 851 02, Bratislava, Slovakia
Tel.: (421) 1232282902
Marketing Research Service
N.A.I.C.S.: 541910
Slavomila Chovancova (Acct Mgr-Key Accts)

Subsidiary (Domestic):

Gracenote, Inc. (5)
2000 Powell St Ste 1500, Emeryville, CA
94608
Tel.: (510) 428-7200
Web Site: https://www.gracenote.com
Digital Media Identification Products & Services
N.A.I.C.S.: 541519
Karthik Rao (Pres)

Subsidiary (Non-US):

Gracenote GmbH (6)
St-Martin-Strasse 61, 81669, Munich, Germany
Tel.: (49) 89 961 1830
Web Site: http://www.gracenote.com
Television Broadcasting Services
N.A.I.C.S.: 516120

Gracenote KK (6)
Shibuya Place 8F 1-10-5 Dogenzaka,
Shibuya-ku, Tokyo, 150-0043, Japan
Tel.: (81) 334647785
Web Site: http://www.gracenote.com
Television Broadcasting Services
N.A.I.C.S.: 516120

Gracenote Korea Ltd. (6)
Seoul City Tower Building 22F 110 Huam
ro, Jung-gu, Seoul, Korea (South)
Tel.: (82) 25985857
Web Site: http://www.gracenote.com
Television Broadcasting Services
N.A.I.C.S.: 516120

Subsidiary (Non-US):

IBOPE eRatings.com Mexico (5)
Calle Bruno Traven 60, Distrito Federal,
Mexico, 03340, Mexico
Tel.: (52) 5556290620
Radio & Television Repair Services

N.A.I.C.S.: 811210

IBOPE eRatings.com do Brasil Ltda. (5)
Al Santos 2101, Sao Paulo, 01419-001,
Brazil
Tel.: (55) 1130610031
Emp.: 22
Business Research Services
N.A.I.C.S.: 541910

Informacion de Medios S.A. (5)
Urdesa Central Balsamos Norte 404,
Guayaquil, Quinta, Ecuador
Tel.: (593) 42885653
Web Site: https://www.infomedia.com.ec
N.A.I.C.S.: 516210

Landsberry & James Marketing Pty Ltd (5)
Suite 1002 Level 10 83 Mount St, North
Sydney, 2060, NSW, Australia
Tel.: (61) 288737600
Web Site: https://www.lj-oz.com
Advertising Services
N.A.I.C.S.: 541810

MEMRB Puls Panel Trgovina DOO (5)
Radnicka Cesta 47, 10000, Zagreb, Croatia
Tel.: (385) 16065500
Environmental Research Services
N.A.I.C.S.: 541715

Subsidiary (Domestic):

Marketing Analytics, Inc (5)
2306 1/2 Orrington Ave, Evanston, IL 60201
Tel.: (847) 733-8459
Web Site: http://www.marketinganalytics.com
Sales Range: $25-49.9 Million
Emp.: 5
Marketing Research & Public Opinion Polling
N.A.I.C.S.: 541910

Subsidiary (Non-US):

Media Focus Schweiz GmbH (5)
Stauffacherstrasse 28, 8004, Zurich, Switzerland
Tel.: (41) 433222750
Web Site: https://www.mediafocus.ch
Broadcast Media Rating Services
N.A.I.C.S.: 541910
Tina Fixle (Chief Analytics Officer)

Subsidiary (Domestic):

Media Solutions (5)
770 Broadway, New York, NY 10003-9522
Tel.: (646) 654-5000
Marketing Information Services
N.A.I.C.S.: 541613

Subsidiary (Non-US):

Meterology Data Private Limited (5)
Office Unit No 201-202 2nd Floor C Wing
Godrej Coliseum, Somaiya Hosp Road Sion
E, Mumbai, 400 022, India
Tel.: (91) 2241048800
Web Site: https://www.mdlindia.co.in
Household Meter Panel Mfr
N.A.I.C.S.: 335313
Sumit Singh (Head-Bus)

Milenium Espacio Soft, S.A. (5)
C/ Rafael Boti 24, 28023, Madrid, Spain
Tel.: (34) 902500921
Marketing Research Service
N.A.I.C.S.: 541910

Subsidiary (Non-US):

Nexium Portugal - Consultario e Software Lda. (6)
Praca de Alvalade 9 5 S 7, 1700-037, Lisbon, Portugal
Tel.: (351) 218484594
Marketing Research Service
N.A.I.C.S.: 541910

Subsidiary (Domestic):

NM Incite, LLC (5)
770 Bwy, New York, NY 10004
Tel.: (646) 654-5000
Web Site: http://www.nielsensocial.com
Marketing Research Service

N.A.I.C.S.: 541910

NetRatings, LLC (5)
770 Broadway, New York, NY
10003 **(100%)**
Tel.: (212) 703-5900
Web Site: http://www.nielsen-netratings.com
Sales Range: $75-99.9 Million
Emp.: 397
Internet Media & Market Research Services
N.A.I.C.S.: 541910

Division (Domestic):

AdRelevance (6)
964 N 34th St Ste 300, Seattle, WA 98103
Tel.: (206) 632-0300
Web Site: http://www.netratings.com
Tracking & Measurement of Internet Advertising Data
N.A.I.C.S.: 541810

Subsidiary (Non-US):

Netratings France SAS (5)
Le Viking 67 Rue Anatole France, 92309,
Levallois-Perret, France
Tel.: (33) 147595757
Marketing Research Service
N.A.I.C.S.: 541910

Subsidiary (Domestic):

Neurofocus, Inc. (5)
50 Green St, San Francisco, CA 94111
Tel.: (415) 262-2600
Market Research Services
N.A.I.C.S.: 541910

Subsidiary (Domestic):

Innerscope Research, Inc. (6)
98 N Washington St 2nd Fl, Boston, MA
02114
Tel.: (617) 904-0555
Web Site:
    http://www.innerscoperesearch.com
Emp.: 33
Consumer Research Services
N.A.I.C.S.: 541910

Subsidiary (Non-US):

Nexium Software Factory, S.L. (5)
Calle Juan De Quesada Pq Cientifico Y
Tecnologico 30, Las Palmas De Gran Canaria, 35001, Las Palmas, Spain
Tel.: (34) 461625531
Marketing Research Service
N.A.I.C.S.: 541910

Nielsen (India) Private Limited (5)
4B / 4th floor Raheja Platinum Sag Baug
Road off Andheri - Kurla Rd, Marol Andheri
East, Mumbai, 400059, India
Tel.: (91) 2261436400
Marketing Research Service
N.A.I.C.S.: 541910

Subsidiary (Domestic):

Indicus Analytics Private Limited (6)
2nd Floor Nehru House 4 Bahadur Shah
Zafar Marg, New Delhi, 110002, India
Tel.: (91) 1142512400
Web Site: http://www.indicus.net
Marketing Research Service
N.A.I.C.S.: 541910

Subsidiary (Non-US):

**The Nielsen Company Nepal Pvt
Ltd.** (6)
Ravi Bhawan, PO Box 1784, Kathmandu,
Nepal
Tel.: (977) 14273890
Emp.: 52
Marketing Research Service
N.A.I.C.S.: 541910

Subsidiary (Non-US):

**Nielsen Admosphere Bulgaria
JSC.** (5)
Web Site: http://www.nielsen-
    admosphere.bg
Marketing Research & Data Processing
Services
N.A.I.C.S.: 711310
Tereza Simeckova (Chm)

**Nielsen Admosphere Slovakia,
s.r.o.** (5)
Lazaretska 23, 81109, Bratislava, Slovakia
Tel.: (421) 253410254
N.A.I.C.S.: 541720

Nielsen Audience Measurement (Cyprus) Ltd. (5)
8 Skopa Str 2nd Floor The Nielsen Company Building, 1075, Nicosia, Cyprus
Tel.: (357) 2 288 6600
Sales Range: $25-49.9 Million
Emp.: 140
Media & Marketing Research Services
N.A.I.C.S.: 541910

**Nielsen Audience Measurement DOO
Beograd** (5)
Spanskih boraca 3, 11070, Belgrade, Serbia
Tel.: (381) 114141750
Marketing Research Service
N.A.I.C.S.: 541910

Subsidiary (Domestic):

Nielsen Audio, Inc. (5)
9705 Patuxent Woods Dr, Columbia, MD
21046-1572
Tel.: (410) 312-8000
Web Site: http://www.nielsen.com
Sales Range: $400-449.9 Million
Emp.: 1,292
Media & Marketing Research Services
N.A.I.C.S.: 541810

Subsidiary (Non-US):

Nielsen Consultancy LLC (5)
West Bay Reem Tower 05th Floor, PO Box
14551, Dafna, Doha, Qatar
Tel.: (974) 44121648
Marketing Research Service
N.A.I.C.S.: 541910
AlSharif AbdulAzim (Mgr-Data Aqcuisition)

Subsidiary (Domestic):

Nielsen Consumer Insights, Inc (5)
1 World Trade Ctr Fl 63, New York, NY
10007 **(100%)**
Tel.: (585) 272-8400
Web Site: http://theharrispoll.com
Internet & Traditional Market Research &
Polling Services
N.A.I.C.S.: 541910
John Gerzema (Co-CEO)

Subsidiary (Non-US):

Opinion Search Inc. (6)
1800-160 Elgin St, Ottawa, K2P 2P7, ON,
Canada
Tel.: (613) 751-5089
Web Site: http://www.opinionsearch.com
Emp.: 6
Marketing Research & Public Opinion Polling Services
N.A.I.C.S.: 541910

Subsidiary (Non-US):

Nielsen Egypt LLC (5)
8 Abdel Salam Zaki Street, Heliopolis,
Cairo, Egypt
Tel.: (20) 224178207
Marketing Services
N.A.I.C.S.: 541613
Sara Migally (Sr Mgr-Digital Center of
Excellence-Global)

Subsidiary (Domestic):

Nielsen Entertainment, LLC (5)
6255 Sunset Blvd 19th Fl Los Angeles, Hollywood, CA 90028
Information, Analytical Tools & Marketing
Services For the Global Entertainment Industry
N.A.I.C.S.: 541910

Subsidiary (Domestic):

Nielsen SoundScan (6)
770 Broadway 8th Fl, New York, NY 10003
Tel.: (813) 366-2144
Web Site: http://www.soundscan.com
Rev.: $120,000
Music Industry Information Services

Subsidiary (Non-US):

**Nielsen IBOPE Dominicana,
S.R.L.** (5)
Pedro Henriquez Urena 138, Santo Domingo, Dominican Republic
Tel.: (809) 3316500
Business Research Services
N.A.I.C.S.: 541910
Vargas Lidia (Mgr-Acctg)

Nielsen Innovate Fund, LP (5)
15 Halamish St Northern Industrial Park,
Caesarea, 30889, Israel
Tel.: (972) 722700790
Web Site: https://nif.vc
N.A.I.C.S.: 523999
Dov Yarkoni (CEO)

Nielsen Innovate Ltd. (5)
15 Halamish St, Northern Industrial Park,
Caesarea, 30889, Israel
Tel.: (972) 72 270 0790
Web Site: https://www.nif.vc
Marketing Research Service
N.A.I.C.S.: 541910
Esther Barak Landes (Founder)

Nielsen Korea Ltd. (5)
50 Central Place 13th to 16th floor,
Seosomun-ro Jung-gu, Seoul, 100-859,
Seosomun, Korea (South)
Tel.: (82) 21227000
Marketing Research Service
N.A.I.C.S.: 541910
Wonseok Choi (Dir-Pub Sector Enterprises
Industry-Consumer Insight)

Nielsen Kozonsegmeres Kft. (5)
Vaci u 81, 1056, Budapest, Hungary
Tel.: (36) 1 461 7050
Web Site: http://www.nielsen.com
Marketing Research Service
N.A.I.C.S.: 541910

**Nielsen MMRD (Myanmar) Co.,
Ltd** (5)
3rd Floor Building-18 MICT Park, Hlaing
Township, Yangon, Myanmar
Tel.: (95) 12305367
Marketing Research Service
N.A.I.C.S.: 541910
Khaing Sandar Myint (Mgr-Ops)

Nielsen Media Research AS (5)
Verkstedveien 3, PO Box 514, Skoyen,
Oslo, 0277, Norway
Tel.: (47) 22583400
Web Site: http://no.nielsen.com
Media & Marketing Information Services
N.A.I.C.S.: 541613

Subsidiary (Domestic):

Nielsen Media Research, Inc. (5)
85 Broad St, New York, NY 10004
Tel.: (646) 654-8300
Sales Range: $250-299.9 Million
Emp.: 2,100
Television Audience Measurement & Advertising Information Services
N.A.I.C.S.: 541910

Subsidiary (Non-US):

Ebiquity Associates Limited (6)
Citypoint 1 Ropemaker Street, London,
EC2Y 9AW, United Kingdom **(100%)**
Tel.: (44) 2076509600
Web Site: http://www.ebiquity.com
Technology & Media Monitoring Services
N.A.I.C.S.: 541910

Subsidiary (Non-US):

**Nielsen Music Control Nederland
B.V.** (5)
Catharina van Renneslaan 8, 1217 CX, Hilversum, Netherlands
Tel.: (31) 356254360
Television & Radio Broadcasting & Distr
N.A.I.C.S.: 516110

Division (Domestic):

Nielsen Scarborough (5)
675 6th Ave, New York, NY 10010
Tel.: (800) 753-6043
Web Site: http://www.scarborough.com
Consumer Shopping Pattern Research &
Analysis Services

N.A.I.C.S.: 541910

Subsidiary (Non-US):

**Nielsen Services Poland Sp.
z.o.o.** (5)
Ul Postepu 15b, 02-676, Warsaw, Poland
Tel.: (48) 223387300
Web Site: http://www.nielsen.com
Marketing Research Service
N.A.I.C.S.: 541910

Nielsen Services Spain, S.L. (5)
C/ Practicante Ignacio Rodriguez s/n Edificio Polivalente IV, Tercera Planta Oficinas
307 308 317 Y 318inas, Las Palmas,
35017, Gran Canaria, Spain
Tel.: (34) 928356418
Marketing Research Service
N.A.I.C.S.: 541910

Subsidiary (Domestic):

Nielsen Sports America, LLC. (5)
675 6th Ave, New York, NY 10011
Tel.: (646) 654-5000
N.A.I.C.S.: 518210

Subsidiary (Non-US):

Nielsen Sports Asia Pte. Ltd. (5)
10 Anson Road 36-01A International Plaza,
Singapore, 079903, Singapore
Tel.: (65) 62249112
Sports Analytics Services
N.A.I.C.S.: 711320

Nielsen Sports Belgium SA (5)
Avenue des Pleiades 73, 1200, Brussels,
Belgium
Tel.: (32) 27787011
Federation & Brand Analytic Services
N.A.I.C.S.: 711310
Jerome Bouchat (Mng Dir)

**Nielsen Sports Deutschland
GmbH** (5)
Scheidtweilerstr 17, 50933, Cologne, Germany
Tel.: (49) 221430730
N.A.I.C.S.: 518210

Nielsen Sports Espana S.L.U. (5)
Pl Francesc Macia 7 Planta 16, 08029, Barcelona, Spain
Tel.: (34) 933686800
Sports Analytics Services
N.A.I.C.S.: 711320
Pablo Bellido (Co-Mng Dir)

Nielsen Sports France Sarl (5)
1 rue Julius et Ethel Rosenberg, 95870,
Bezons, France
Tel.: (33) 134416262
Marketing Services
N.A.I.C.S.: 541613
Pierre-Emmanuel Davin (Mng Dir)

**Nielsen Sports India Private
Limited** (5)
Prestige Shantiniketan 1st Floor Crescent 4,
Whitefield, Bengaluru, 560048, India
Tel.: (91) 8039818000
Marketing Services
N.A.I.C.S.: 541613
R. Pradeep Kumar (Mgr)

Nielsen Sports Italia Srl. (5)
Strada 3 - Palazzo B 4, MilanoFiori, 20090,
Assago, MI, Italy
Tel.: (39) 027491512
Sports Analytics Services
N.A.I.C.S.: 711320
Gianluca Mazzardi (Dir-Comml)

Nielsen Sports Japan K.K. (5)
11F Akasaka Tameike Tower 2-17-7,
Minato-ku Akasaka, Tokyo, 107-0052, Japan
Tel.: (81) 367219436
Sports Analytics Services
N.A.I.C.S.: 711320

Nielsen Sports Korea LLC (5)
To elect 625 eonju building fifth floor 5F
Sunmin Building Eonju-ro, Gangnam-Gu,
Seoul, 135-829, Korea (South)
Tel.: (82) 25492675
Sports Analytics Services
N.A.I.C.S.: 711320

Brookfield Corporation—(Continued)

Nielsen Sports Nederland B.V. (5)
Repucom Nederland BV Diemerhof 2, 1112
XL, Diemen, Netherlands
Tel.: (31) 203988777
Sports Analytics Services
N.A.I.C.S.: 711320
Sebastiaan Westerhout (Mng Dir)

Nielsen Sports Pty. Ltd. (5)
Level 2 Building B 11 Talavera Road Mac-
quarie Park, Sydney, 2113, NSW, Australia
Tel.: (61) 288737000
N.A.I.C.S.: 518210

**Nielsen Sports UK & Ireland
Limited** (5)
66 Porchester Road, London, W2 6ET,
United Kingdom
Tel.: (44) 2072217040
Sports Analytics Services
N.A.I.C.S.: 711320
Andy Milnes (Dir-Grp Acct)

**Nielsen TV Audience Measurement
S.A.** (5)
Via Calloni 1, 6900, Lugano, Switzerland
Tel.: (41) 919609900
Media & Marketing Consulting Services
N.A.I.C.S.: 541613

**Nielsen TV Audience Measurement
S.r.l.** (5)
Viale Angelo Filippetti 37, Milan, 20122,
Italy
Tel.: (39) 02582171
Sales Range: $25-49.9 Million
Emp.: 100
Media & Marketing Information Services
N.A.I.C.S.: 541910

Nielsen Tele Medical GmbH (5)
Brenneckestr 20, 39120, Magdeburg, Ger-
many
Tel.: (49) 3916117201
Web Site: http://www.sites.nielsen.com
Medical Device Services
N.A.I.C.S.: 423450

**Nielsen Television Audience Mea-
surement Pty. Ltd.** (5)
166 Epping Rd, Lane Cove, 2066, NSW,
Australia
Tel.: (61) 294906500
Web Site: https://www.nielsentam.com.au
N.A.I.C.S.: 516120

Nielsen Tunisia Sarl (5)
12 Rue Echabbia Montplaisir, 1073, Tunis,
Tunisia
Tel.: (216) 71903549
Broadcast Media Rating Services
N.A.I.C.S.: 541910

**Nielsen for Consultancies Limited Li-
ability Company** (5)
Al Rabia 4 Abdullah Bin Rawaha str Al Ra-
bia Towers 4th floor 2354, Amman, 11181,
Jordan
Tel.: (962) 65544683
Marketing Research Service
N.A.I.C.S.: 541910

**Nielsen for Market Research
LLC** (5)
Bldg No 20 Flat No 11 First Floor Street No
1135, PO Box 436, Block No 135 Mutrah
Commercial South, 118, Muscat, Oman
Tel.: (968) 24819305
Marketing Services
N.A.I.C.S.: 541613

Nutrino Health Ltd. (5)
94 Yigal Alon Street, Tel Aviv, Israel
Tel.: (972) 722499111
Web Site: http://www.nutrinohealth.com
Nutrition Data Analytic Services
N.A.I.C.S.: 518210

Organotiki S.A. (5)
64 Louise Riencourt Street, 11523, Athens,
Greece
Tel.: (30) 2109401088
Web Site: https://organotiki.gr
N.A.I.C.S.: 541511

**PT. Nielsen Audience
Measurement** (5)
Mayapada Tower 15/F JI Jend Sudirman

Kav 28, Jakarta, 12920, Indonesia
Tel.: (62) 2129398100
Emp.: 100
Market Research & Information Solution
Provider

**PT. The Nielsen Company
Indonesia** (5)
Millennium Centennial Center 46 Floor
Jalan Jendral Sudirman Kav 25, Jakarta,
12920, Indonesia
Tel.: (62) 2129398100
N.A.I.C.S.: 541910

Subsidiary (Domestic):

PointLogic USA Inc. (5)
675 Avenue of the Americas, New York, NY
10011
Tel.: (917) 710-2068
Marketing Budget & Analytic Services
N.A.I.C.S.: 541910
Nathalie Morales (Mgr-Client Relations)

Sorenson Media (5)
703 Palomar Airport Rd Ste 310, Carlsbad,
CA 92011-1043
Web Site: http://www.sorensonmedia.com
Publisher
N.A.I.C.S.: 513199
Jim Sorenson (Founder & Chm)

The Cambridge Group, Inc. (5)
222 W Adams Ste 300, Chicago, IL 60606-
5058
Tel.: (312) 425-3600
Web Site:
   http://www.thecambridgegroup.com
Sales Range: $25-49.9 Million
Emp.: 100
Media & Marketing Consulting Services
N.A.I.C.S.: 541613
Rick Kash (Founder)

Subsidiary (Non-US):

The New Wave Research Ltd. (5)
1 Beser Towers 2 Ben Gurion St, Ramat
Gan, 52573, Israel
Tel.: (972) 35766666
Web Site: http://www.nwr.co.il
Marketing Research Service
N.A.I.C.S.: 541910
Offer Levy (Chm-Nielsen Israel Grp)

Subsidiary (Domestic):

New Sense Research Ltd. (6)
Ramat Hachayal, Tel Aviv, Israel
Tel.: (972) 35766666
Web Site: http://www.newsense.co.il
Sensory Research Services
N.A.I.C.S.: 541715

Subsidiary (Non-US):

**The Nielsen Company (Bangladesh)
Ltd.** (5)
Impetus Center 7th Floor 242/B Tejgaon-
Gulshan Link Road Tejgaon I/A, Dhaka,
1208, Bangladesh
Tel.: (880) 9609807060
Sales Range: $25-49.9 Million
Emp.: 150
Media & Marketing Research Services
N.A.I.C.S.: 541910
Anam Mahmud (Mng Dir)

**The Nielsen Company (Belgium)
SPRL** (5)
73 Ave Des Pleiades, 1200, Brussels, Bel-
gium
Tel.: (32) 27787118
Marketing Management Consulting Services
N.A.I.C.S.: 541613

Subsidiary (Non-US):

**The Nielsen Company (Philippines),
Inc.** (6)
25/F Wynsum Corporate Plaza 22 F Ortigas
Jr Road, Pasig, 1600, Philippines
Tel.: (63) 27068100
Emp.: 400
Media & Marketing Research Services
N.A.I.C.S.: 541910

Subsidiary (Non-US):

**The Nielsen Company (Germany)
GmbH** (5)

Sachsenstrasse 16, 20097, Hamburg, Ger-
many
Tel.: (49) 40236420
Market Research & Consulting Services
N.A.I.C.S.: 541613
Ludger Wibbelt (CEO-Nielsen Media)

Subsidiary (Domestic):

**Nielsen Services Germany
GmbH** (6)
Insterburger St 16, 60487, Frankfurt, Ger-
many
Tel.: (49) 6979380
Web Site: http://www.nielsen-partner.de
Marketing Consulting Services
N.A.I.C.S.: 541613

Subsidiary (Non-US):

**The Nielsen Company (Greece)
S.A.** (5)
Louise Riencourt 64 Apollon Tower, 11523,
Athens, Greece
Tel.: (30) 2106999200
Emp.: 75
Marketing Research Service
N.A.I.C.S.: 541910

**The Nielsen Company (Malaysia)
Sdn. Bhd.** (5)
Level 16 Plaza 33 Tower B No 1 Jln Kema-
juan Seksyen 13, 46100, Petaling Jaya,
Selangor Darul Ehsan, Malaysia
Tel.: (60) 379409300
Market Research & Information Solution
Provider
N.A.I.C.S.: 541910

**The Nielsen Company (Shanghai)
Ltd.** (5)
2/F East Ocean Centre Phase II 618 Yanan
East Road, Huang Pu District, Shanghai,
200001, China
Tel.: (86) 2123269200
Web Site: http://cn.nielsen.com
Management Consulting & Comprehensive
Market Information Solution Provider
N.A.I.C.S.: 541613

**The Nielsen Company (Thailand)
Limited** (5)
No 323 26th Floor United Center Building
Silom Road, Silom Sub-District Bangrak
District, Bangkok, 10500, Thailand
Tel.: (66) 26746000
N.A.I.C.S.: 541720

Division (Domestic):

**The Nielsen Company - Advisory
Services** (5)
85 Broad St, New York, NY 10004
Tel.: (646) 654-5000
Web Site: http://www.en-us.nielsen.com
Target Market Research, Analysis & Con-
sulting Services
N.A.I.C.S.: 541910

Subsidiary (Domestic):

BASES (6)
50 W River Ctr Blvd Ste 600, Covington,
KY 41011
Tel.: (859) 905-4000
Web Site: http://www.bases.com
Sales Range: $400-449.9 Million
Emp.: 650
Pre-Market Consumer Opinion Research,
New Product Sales Forecasting, Competitor
Analysis & Target Market Research Ser-
vices
N.A.I.C.S.: 541910

Claritas, Inc. (6)
8044 Montgomery Rd Ste 455, Cincinnati,
OH 45236
Tel.: (858) 622-0800
Web Site: https://www.claritas.com
Sales Range: $125-149.9 Million
Emp.: 160
Target Market Research, Analysis & Demo-
graphic Data Services
N.A.I.C.S.: 541910

Branch (Domestic):

Claritas, Inc. (7)
1525 Wilson Blvd Ste 1200, Arlington, VA
22209-2450

Tel.: (703) 812-2700
Web Site: http://www.claritas.com
Sales Range: $10-24.9 Million
Emp.: 100
Marketing Consulting Services
N.A.I.C.S.: 541910

Subsidiary (Domestic):

Spectra Marketing Systems, Inc. (6)
200 W Jackson Blvd Ste 2800, Chicago, IL
60606-6910
Tel.: (312) 583-5100
Sales Range: $75-99.9 Million
Emp.: 150
Consumer Segmentation & Targeting Ser-
vices
N.A.I.C.S.: 541910

Subsidiary (Domestic):

**Trade Dimensions International,
Inc.** (7)
40 Danbury Rd, Wilton, CT 06897-4406
Tel.: (203) 222-5750
Sales Range: $10-24.9 Million
Emp.: 105
Publisher of Print & Electronic Retail Site
Information Directories
N.A.I.C.S.: 513140

Subsidiary (Non-US):

The Nielsen Company Japan (5)
2-17-7 Akasaka Tameike Tower 11F, Aka-
saka Minato-ku, Tokyo, 107-0052, Japan
Tel.: (81) 368376600
Marketing Research Service
N.A.I.C.S.: 541910

**The Nielsen Company Lanka (Pri-
vate) Limited** (5)
98 D S Senanayake Mawatha, Colombo,
08, Sri Lanka
Tel.: (94) 1126884468
Media & Marketing Consulting Services
N.A.I.C.S.: 541613

**The Nielsen Company Medya Yayin-
cilik ve Tanitim Hizmetleri Anonim
Sirketii** (5)
Nakkastepe Gumusyolu Cad No 22 Altuni-
zade Uskudar, Istanbul, Turkiye
Tel.: (90) 2165537770
Web Site: http://www.nielsen.com
Media & Marketing Consulting Services
N.A.I.C.S.: 541613

Subsidiary (Domestic):

The Perishables Group, Inc. (5)
1700 W Irving Park Rd Ste 310, Chicago, IL
60613
Tel.: (847) 426-2665
Web Site: http://www.perishablesgroup.com
Sales Range: $10-24.9 Million
Emp.: 30
Research & Marketing Services
N.A.I.C.S.: 541613

Subsidiary (Non-US):

Toluna Group Limited. (5)
Ealing Cross 85 Uxbridge Road, London,
W5 5TH, United Kingdom
Tel.: (44) 2088321700
Web Site: http://www.toluna.com
Emp.: 70
Digital Market Research Services
N.A.I.C.S.: 541910

Subsidiary (Domestic):

Visual IQ, Inc. (5)
75 2nd Ave Ste 330, Needham, MA 02494
Tel.: (781) 657-9035
Web Site: http://www.visualiq.com
Attribution Management & Marketing Analyt-
ics
N.A.I.C.S.: 541613
Manu Mathew (Co-Founder)

Subsidiary (Non-US):

Visual IQ, Inc. (6)
25 Sackville Street, London, W1S 3AX,
United Kingdom
Tel.: (44) 2037003770
Web Site: http://www.visualiq.com
Attribution Management & Marketing Analyt-
ics

N.A.I.C.S.: 541613

Subsidiary (Domestic):

eXelate, Inc.   **(5)**
7 W 22nd St 9th Fl, New York, NY 10010
Tel.: (646) 380-4400
Web Site: http://www.exelate.com
Data Management Services
N.A.I.C.S.: 518210

Subsidiary (Non-US):

Sagen MI Canada Inc.   **(2)**
2060 Winston Park Drive Suite 300, Oak-
ville, L6H 5R7, ON, Canada   **(100%)**
Tel.: (905) 287-5300
Web Site: http://www.genworth.ca
Rev.: $551,396,175
Assets: $5,214,735,635
Liabilities: $3,075,236,772
Net Worth: $2,139,498,864
Earnings: $386,427,374
Emp.: 259
Fiscal Year-end: 12/31/2023
Mortgage Services
N.A.I.C.S.: 522310
Philip Mayers *(CFO & Sr VP)*

**Brookfield Global Relocation
Services**   **(1)**
150 Harvester DrSte201, Burr Ridge, IL
60527
Tel.: (630) 972-2250
Web Site: http://www.brookfieldgrs.com
Sales Range: $10-24.9 Million
Emp.: 70
Global Relocation & Assignment Manage-
ment Services
N.A.I.C.S.: 541618
Traci Morris *(CEO)*

**Brookfield Investment Management
Inc.**   **(1)**
4 World Financial Ctr 250 Vesey St 15th Fl,
New York, NY 10281-1010
Tel.: (212) 549-8400
Web Site: http://www.brookfieldim.com
Emp.: 70
Investment Advisory & Management Ser-
vices
N.A.I.C.S.: 523940

Subsidiary (Domestic):

**Brookfield Oaktree Holdings,
LLC**   **(2)**
333 S Grand Ave 28th Fl, Los Angeles, CA
90071
Tel.: (213) 830-6300
Web Site:
   https://www.brookfieldoaktreeholding.com
Rev.: $267,325,000
Assets: $7,555,933,000
Liabilities: $4,971,027,000
Net Worth: $2,584,906,000
Earnings: $193,861,000
Emp.: 1,183
Fiscal Year-end: 12/31/2023
Investment Holding Company
N.A.I.C.S.: 551112
Howard S. Marks *(Co-Chm)*

Subsidiary (Non-US):

Arbour CLO Limited   **(3)**
53 Merrion Sq, Dublin, Ireland
Tel.: (353) 16146240
Investment Management Service
N.A.I.C.S.: 523940

Holding (Non-US):

Banca Progetto S.p.A.   **(3)**
                      (54.21%)
Tel.: (39) 0272629911
Web Site: http://www.bancaprogetto.it
Rev.: $1,981,841
Assets: $175,493,180
Liabilities: $111,716,775
Net Worth: $63,776,405
Earnings: ($18,553,607)
Fiscal Year-end: 12/31/2016
Commercial Banking Services
N.A.I.C.S.: 522110

Fu Sheng Industrial Co., Ltd.   **(3)**
No 172 Sec 2 Nanjing E Rd, Zhongshan
Dist, Taipei, 10489, ROC, Taiwan
Tel.: (886) 225072211
Web Site: https://www.fusheng.com

Sales Range: $1-4.9 Billion
Emp.: 20,000
Industrial Air Compressors, Golf Club
Heads & Integrated Circuit Leadframes Mfr
N.A.I.C.S.: 333413

Subsidiary (US):

FS Precision Tech Co. LLC   **(4)**
3025 E Victoria St, Rancho Dominguez, CA
90221
Tel.: (310) 638-0595
Web Site: https://www.fs-precision.com
Sales Range: $25-49.9 Million
Emp.: 115
Compressors, Electronic Components &
Titanium Golf Club Heads Mfr
N.A.I.C.S.: 333413

Subsidiary (Domestic):

Curtis-Toledo, Inc.   **(5)**
1905 Kienlen Ave, Saint Louis, MO 63133
Tel.: (314) 383-1300
Web Site: http://www.fscurtis.com
Sales Range: $25-49.9 Million
Emp.: 107
Air Compressor Mfr
N.A.I.C.S.: 333912

Subsidiary (US):

Fu Sheng USA Inc   **(4)**
3025 E Victoria St, Compton, CA 90221
Tel.: (818) 291-0381
Web Site: http://www.fusheng.com
Industrial & Commercial Fan & Blower Mfr
N.A.I.C.S.: 333413

Subsidiary (Non-US):

Max Source Holding Ltd   **(4)**
Unit 908 9th Floor Lippo Sun Plaza, 28
Canton Road Tsimshatsui, Kowloon, China
(Hong Kong)
Tel.: (852) 23756786
Sporting & Recreational Goods & Supplies
Whslr
N.A.I.C.S.: 423910

Subsidiary (Domestic):

**Top Information Technologies Co.,
Ltd.**   **(4)**
172 Nanking E Rd Sec 2, Taipei, 104, Tai-
wan
Tel.: (886) 225082201
Web Site: http://www.fusheng.com
Sales Range: $50-74.9 Million
Emp.: 200
Computer System Design Services
N.A.I.C.S.: 541512
Richard Paul *(Mng Dir)*

Subsidiary (Non-US):

Worldmark Services Ltd.   **(4)**
Unit 908 9th Floor Lippo Sun Plaza 28 Can-
ton Road, Tsimshatsui, Kowloon, China
(Hong Kong)
Tel.: (852) 23756786
Web Site: http://www.fusheng.tw
Sales Range: $25-49.9 Million
Emp.: 21
Sporting & Recreational Goods & Supplies
Whslr
N.A.I.C.S.: 423910

Holding (Domestic):

GFI Energy Ventures LLC   **(3)**
11611 San Vicente Blvd Ste 700, Los Ange-
les, CA 90049
Tel.: (310) 442-0542
Web Site: http://www.oaktreecapital.com
Sales Range: $25-49.9 Million
Emp.: 15
Privater Equity Firm
N.A.I.C.S.: 523999
Ian A. Schapiro *(Co-Founder)*

Holding (Domestic):

Elgin National Industries, Inc.   **(4)**
2001 Butterfield Rd, Downers Grove, IL
60515-1050
Tel.: (630) 434-7200
Web Site: http://www.elginindustries.com
Sales Range: $25-49.9 Million
Holding Company
N.A.I.C.S.: 333248

Subsidiary (Domestic):

Centrifugal Services, Inc.   **(5)**
5595 Hwy 34 N, Raleigh, IL 62977
Tel.: (618) 268-4850
Web Site: http://www.csidryers.com
Sales Range: $25-49.9 Million
Emp.: 30
Oil & Gas Exploration & Coal Processing
Parts & Components
N.A.I.C.S.: 333132

Mining Controls, LLC   **(5)**
214 Industrial Park Rd, Beaver, WV 25813-
9306
Tel.: (304) 252-6243
Web Site: http://www.miningcontrols.com
Mining & Industrial Electrical Equipment Mfr
N.A.I.C.S.: 334419
Larry Rowley *(Mgr-Lighting)*

Tabor Machine Company   **(5)**
1176 Shelter Rd, Princeton, WV 24739
Tel.: (304) 431-4100
Web Site:
   https://elginseparationsolutions.com
Sales Range: $10-24.9 Million
Vibrating Separating Screens
N.A.I.C.S.: 333120

Holding (Domestic):

Integrated Pipeline Services, Inc.   **(4)**
952 Echo Ln Ste 130, Houston, TX 77024
Tel.: (713) 468-6500
Oil & Gas Industry Construction, Engineer-
ing, Project Management & Procurement
Services
N.A.I.C.S.: 213112

Holding (Non-US):

MediaWorks Holdings Limited   **(3)**
17 Hargreaves Street, Auckland, 1011, New
Zealand   **(77.83%)**
Tel.: (64) 99289000
Web Site: https://www.mediaworks.co.nz
Holding Company; Television, Radio & In-
teractive Stations
N.A.I.C.S.: 551112
Leon Wratt *(Dir-Content-Radio)*

Unit (Domestic):

TV3 Television Network   **(4)**
3 Flower St Eden Terrace, Auckland, New
Zealand
Tel.: (64) 99289000
Web Site: http://www.tv3.co.nz
Television Station
N.A.I.C.S.: 516120

Holding (Non-US):

Neo Performance Materials Inc.   **(3)**
Ste 1740 121 King St W, Toronto, M5H
3T9, ON, Canada
Tel.: (416) 367-8588
Web Site: https://www.neomaterials.com
Sales Range: $500-549.9 Million
Emp.: 157
Advanced Rare Earth, Zirconium & Mag-
netic Industrial Products Mfr
N.A.I.C.S.: 423840
Rahim Suleman *(Pres & CFO)*

Subsidiary (Non-US):

**Advanced Magnetic Materials (Thai-
land) Co., Ltd.**   **(4)**
202 Moo 3 Nakhonratchasima-Chokchai
Rd, Suranar Suranaree Industrial Zone,
30000, Nakhon Ratchasima, Thailand
Tel.: (66) 442182514
Web Site: http://www.amr-ltd.com
N.A.I.C.S.: 331491

Subsidiary (Domestic):

CVTech-AAB Inc.   **(4)**
3037 Boul Frontenac Est Thetford Mines,
Quebec, G6G 6P6, QC, Canada
Tel.: (418) 335-7220
Web Site: http://www.cvtech-aab.com
Sales Range: $50-74.9 Million
Emp.: 16
Engine Rebuilding Services
N.A.I.C.S.: 423120

Subsidiary (Non-US):

**Jiangyin Jia Hua Advanced Material
Resources Co., Ltd.**   **(4)**

Xili Road 103 Ligang Town, Jiangyin,
214444, Jiangsu, China   **(100%)**
Tel.: (86) 51086631888
Web Site: https://www.jamr-cn.com
Emp.: 550
Metal Production
N.A.I.C.S.: 331491

**Magnequench Neo Powders Pte.
Ltd.**   **(4)**
61 Science Park Road 01-19 The Galen,
Singapore Science Park II, Singapore,
117525, Singapore
Tel.: (65) 6415 0640
Web Site: http://www.magnequench.com
Sales Range: $25-49.9 Million
Emp.: 28
Magnets, Alloys & Powders Mfr
N.A.I.C.S.: 332999
Greg Kroll *(Sr VP)*

Subsidiary (Non-US):

Magnequench (Tianjin) Co., Ltd.   **(5)**
19 Quanzhou Road Wuqing Economic Dev
Zone, Tianjin, 301700, China
Tel.: (86) 2282125068
Web Site: http://www.magnequench.com
Sales Range: $75-99.9 Million
Rare-Earth Magnetics, Alloys & Powders
N.A.I.C.S.: 423840

Subsidiary (US):

Magnequench International, Inc.   **(5)**
237 S Pendleton Ave, Pendleton, IN 46064
Tel.: (765) 778-7809
Rare Earth Metals, Alloys & Powders Distr
N.A.I.C.S.: 423510

Subsidiary (Non-US):

**Molycorp Chemicals & Oxides (Eu-
rope) Ltd.**   **(4)**
Unit 3 the Quadrant Abingdon Science Park
Barton Ln, Abingdon, OX14 3YS, United
Kingdom
Tel.: (44) 15449349060
Advanced Rare Earth, Zirconium & Mag-
netic Industrial Products Mfr
N.A.I.C.S.: 423840
Frank Timmerman *(VP-Rare Materials)*

Subsidiary (Domestic):

Thiro Ltee.   **(4)**
489 Boul Industriel E C P 458, Victoriaville,
G6T 1S9, QC, Canada
Tel.: (819) 752-9741
Web Site: http://www.thiro.com
Sales Range: $125-149.9 Million
Emp.: 200
Power Delivery Contract Services
N.A.I.C.S.: 221122

Subsidiary (Domestic):

OCM Investments, LLC   **(3)**
333 S Grand Ave 28th Fl, Los Angeles, CA
90071
Tel.: (213) 830-6300
N.A.I.C.S.: 523940

**Oaktree Capital Management,
L.P.**   **(3)**
333 S Grand Ave 28th Fl, Los Angeles, CA
90071
Tel.: (213) 830-6300
Web Site: http://www.oaktreecapital.com
Private Equity & Investment Management
Services
N.A.I.C.S.: 523999
David M. Kirchheimer *(Partner-Advisory)*

Subsidiary (Non-US):

Aqseptence Group GmbH   **(4)**
Passavant-Geiger-Strasse 1, 65326, Aar-
bergen, Germany
Tel.: (49) 6120280
Web Site: http://www.aqseptence.com
Water & Sewage Treatment Plant Construc-
tion & Engineering Services
N.A.I.C.S.: 237110

Subsidiary (Domestic):

Aqseptence Group - Hanau   **(5)**
Kinzigheimer Weg 104, 63450, Hanau, Ger-
many
Tel.: (49) 6181309275

Brookfield Corporation—(Continued)

Web Site: http://www.aqseptence.com
Vacuum Sewer System Installation Services
N.A.I.C.S.: 237110

Subsidiary (Non-US):

Aqseptence Group Srl. (5)
Via Gessi 16, 48022, Lugo, Ravenna, Italy
Tel.: (09) 054520011
Web Site: http://www.aqseptence.com
Water Filtration Products Mfr
N.A.I.C.S.: 924110

Subsidiary (US):

Johnson Screens, Inc. (5)
1950 Old Hwy 8 NW, New Brighton, MN 55112
Tel.: (651) 636-3900
Web Site: https://johnsonscreens.com
Water Treatment Equipment Mfr
N.A.I.C.S.: 221320

Subsidiary (Non-US):

Johnson Screens (India) Private Limited (6)
E-540 GIDC Sanand-II Industrial Estate, Bol
Sanand, Ahmedabad, 382170, Gujarat, India
Tel.: (91) 2717618000
Web Site: https://johnsonscreens.com
Screening Solutions Design & Mfr
N.A.I.C.S.: 213111

M.A.IND. S.R.L. (6)
Via Pitagora 30, 41010, Soliera, MO, Italy
Tel.: (39) 059525720
Solid Separation System Mfr
N.A.I.C.S.: 333310

Joint Venture (Domestic):

City Brewing Company, LLC (4)
925 S 3rd St, La Crosse, WI 54601
Tel.: (608) 785-4200
Web Site: http://www.citybrewery.com
Rev.: $34,000,000
Emp.: 1,000
Breweries
N.A.I.C.S.: 312120
Randy Hull (VP-Sls & Bus Dev)

Holding (Domestic):

ENERCON Services, Inc. (4)
500 Townpark Ln, Kennesaw, GA 30144-5509
Tel.: (770) 919-1930
Web Site: http://www.enercon.com
Engineering & Technical Consulting Services
N.A.I.C.S.: 541330
John Richardson (CEO)

Subsidiary (Domestic):

Ardent Environmental Group, Inc. (5)
1141 Pomona Rd Ste E, Corona, CA 92882-7148
Tel.: (951) 736-5334
Web Site: http://www.ardentenv.com
Environmental Consulting Services
N.A.I.C.S.: 541620
Craig Metheny (Owner)

Talisman International, LLC (5)
1000 Potomac St NW Ste 300, Washington, DC 20007
Tel.: (202) 471-4244
Web Site: http://www.talisman-intl.com
Sales Range: $10-24.9 Million
Nuclear Facility Management Consulting Services
N.A.I.C.S.: 541690
Michael J. Hutsell (Pres)

Holding (Domestic):

Energy Systems Group, LLC (4)
9877 Eastgate Ct, Newburgh, IN 47630
Tel.: (812) 471-5000
Web Site: https://www.energysystemsgroup.com
Sales Range: $10-24.9 Million
Emp.: 50
Installation of Energy Saving Equipment & Energy Services

N.A.I.C.S.: 541330

Hartree Partners, LP (4)
1185 Ave Of The Americas, New York, NY 10036
Tel.: (212) 536-8915
Web Site: http://www.hartreepartners.com
Petroleum Wholesale Trade Agency
N.A.I.C.S.: 425120
Guy Merison (Co-Founder)

Subsidiary (Domestic):

Sprague Resources LP (5)
185 International Dr, Portsmouth, NH 03801 (100%)
Web Site: http://www.spragueenergy.com
Rev.: $3,498,160,000
Assets: $1,418,255,000
Liabilities: $1,483,837,000
Net Worth: ($65,582,000)
Earnings: ($68,916,000)
Emp.: 654
Fiscal Year-end: 12/31/2021
Holding Company; Refined Petroleum Products & Natural Gas Storage & Wholesale Distr; Material Handling Services
N.A.I.C.S.: 551112
Joseph S. Smith (VP-Refined Products)

Subsidiary (Domestic):

Sprague Energy Solutions Inc. (6)
2 International Dr Ste 200, Portsmouth, NH 03801-6813
Tel.: (603) 431-1000
Natural Gas Distr
N.A.I.C.S.: 221210

Sprague Operating Resources LLC (6)
185 International Dr, Portsmouth, NH 03801-6810
Tel.: (603) 431-1000
Web Site: https://www.spragueenergy.com
Sales Range: $150-199.9 Million
Emp.: 425
Refined Petroleum Products & Natural Gas Storage & Wholesale Distr; Material Handling Services
N.A.I.C.S.: 424710

Holding (Non-US):

IASO S.A. (4)
37 39 Kifissias Ave, Maroussi, 151 23, Athens, Greece
Tel.: (30) 2106184000
Web Site: https://www.iaso.gr
Hospital & Hospital Management Services
N.A.I.C.S.: 622310
Emmanouil Doulgerakis (CEO)

Subsidiary (Domestic):

OCM HoldCo, LLC (4)
333 S Grand Ave 28th Fl, Los Angeles, CA 90071
Tel.: (213) 830-6300
Rev.: $8,031
Assets: $88,611,426
Liabilities: $264,418
Net Worth: $88,347,008
Earnings: $11,085,078
Emp.: 2
Fiscal Year-end: 12/31/2014
Investment Holding Company; Casinos & Casino Hotels
N.A.I.C.S.: 551112
Ronald N. Beck (Chief Acctg Officer)

Subsidiary (Non-US):

Oaktree Capital (Australia) Pty. Limited (4)
Level 44 Suite 44 03 Governor Phillip Tower 1 Farrer Place, Sydney, 2000, NSW, Australia
Tel.: (61) 282789248
Financial Investment Management Services
N.A.I.C.S.: 523940

Oaktree Capital (Beijing) Ltd. (4)
Room 36 Level 28 China World Office 1 No 1 Jianguomenwai Ave, Chaoyang District, Beijing, 100004, China
Tel.: (86) 1065350208
Web Site: http://www.oaktreecapital.com
Private Equity & Investment Management Services
N.A.I.C.S.: 523999

Oaktree Capital (Hong Kong) Ltd. (4)
Suite 2001 20/F Champion Tower 3 Garden Road, Central, China (Hong Kong)
Tel.: (852) 36556800
Web Site: http://www.oaktreecapital.com
Private Equity & Investment Management Services
N.A.I.C.S.: 523999
Ralph Parks (Chm)

Oaktree Capital (Seoul) Limited (4)
Tel.: (82) 221918000
Web Site: http://www.oaktreecapital.com
Private Equity & Investment Management Services
N.A.I.C.S.: 523999

Oaktree Capital (Shanghai) Ltd. (4)
Suite 833 Level 8 Shanghai International Finance Centre Tower, 2 No 8 Century Avenue Pudong, Shanghai, 200120, China
Tel.: (86) 2160627390
Investment Management Service
N.A.I.C.S.: 523940

Oaktree Capital Management (Dubai) Limited (4)
Dubai International Financial Centre Office 5 The Gate Building, PO Box 121208, Level 15, Dubai, United Arab Emirates
Tel.: (971) 44019878
Investment Management Service
N.A.I.C.S.: 523940

Oaktree Capital Management (UK) LLP (4)
Verde 10 Bressenden Place, London, SW1E 5DH, Greater London, United Kingdom
Tel.: (44) 2072014600
Investment Management Service
N.A.I.C.S.: 523940

Oaktree Capital Management Fund (4)
26A boulevard Royal 7th Floor, 2449, Luxembourg, Luxembourg
Tel.: (352) 2663254700
Investment Management Service
N.A.I.C.S.: 523940

Oaktree Capital Management Limited (4)
10 Bressenden Place, London, SW1E 5DH, United Kingdom
Tel.: (44) 2072014600
Web Site: http://www.oaktreecapital.com
Sales Range: $50-74.9 Million
Emp.: 80
Private Equity & Investment Management Services
N.A.I.C.S.: 523999
Ashwin Ranganathan (Sr VP)

Oaktree Capital Management Pte. Ltd. (4)
80 Raffles Place, 51-03 UOB Plaza 1, Singapore, 48624, Singapore
Tel.: (65) 63056550
Web Site: http://www.oaktreecapital.com
Sales Range: $25-49.9 Million
Emp.: 8
Private Equity & Investment Management Services
N.A.I.C.S.: 523999
Bruce Karsh (Co-Chm & Chief Investment Officer)

Oaktree France S.A.S. (4)
Tel.: (33) 142991515
Web Site: http://www.oaktreecapital.com
Private Equity & Investment Management Services
N.A.I.C.S.: 523999

Oaktree GmbH (4)
Frankfurter Welle An der Welle 3 9th Floor, An der Welle 3 9th Floor, 60322, Frankfurt am Main, Germany
Tel.: (49) 692443393000
Private Equity & Investment Management Services
N.A.I.C.S.: 523999
Hermann Dambach (Mng Dir)

Oaktree Japan, GK (4)
Atago Green Hills Mori Tower 37th Floor 2-5-1 Atago, Minato-ku, Tokyo, 105-6237, Japan

Tel.: (81) 357766760
Web Site: http://www.oaktreecapital.com
Private Equity & Investment Management Services
N.A.I.C.S.: 523999
Dai Nakamura (Sr VP)

Oaktree Overseas Investment Fund Management (Shanghai) Co., Ltd. (4)
Suite 833 Level 8 Shanghai International Finance Centre, Tower 2 No 8 Century Avenue Shanghai, Pudong, 200120, China
Tel.: (86) 2160627389
Financial Investment Services
N.A.I.C.S.: 523999

Holding (Non-US):

RAFI GmbH & Co. KG (4)
Ravensburger Strasse 128-134, 88276, Ravensburg, Germany
Tel.: (49) 751890
Web Site: https://www.rafi-group.com
Appliances, Electrical & Electronics Mfr
N.A.I.C.S.: 335999
Lothar Seybold (CEO)

Subsidiary (US):

Xymox Technologies Inc. (5)
9099 W Dean Rd, Milwaukee, WI 53224
Tel.: (414) 362-9000
Web Site: http://www.xymox.com
Sales Range: $10-24.9 Million
Emp.: 85
Electronic Membrane Switch Mfr
N.A.I.C.S.: 334419
Robert Hartline (Pres)

Holding (Domestic):

Velocity Risk Underwriters, LLC (4)
20 Burton Hills Blvd Ste 350, Nashville, TN 37215
Web Site: http://www.velocityrisk.com
Insurance Services
N.A.I.C.S.: 524210
Phil Bowie (CEO)

Subsidiary (Domestic):

Oaktree Fund Advisors, LLC (3)
333 S Grand Ave 28th Fl, Los Angeles, CA 90071
Tel.: (213) 830-6300
N.A.I.C.S.: 523940

Oaktree Strategic Income Corporation (3)
333 S Grand Ave 28th Fl, Los Angeles, CA 90071 (63.73%)
Tel.: (213) 830-6300
Web Site: http://www.oaktreestrategicincome.com
Rev.: $39,534,044
Assets: $544,369,644
Liabilities: $277,688,233
Net Worth: $266,681,411
Earnings: $16,203,500
Fiscal Year-end: 09/30/2020
Investment Management Service
N.A.I.C.S.: 523940
Mathew M. Pendo (Pres & COO)

Sabal Financial Group, L.P. (3)
4675 Macarthur Ct Ste 1550, Newport Beach, CA 92660
Tel.: (949) 255-2660
Financial Investment Services
N.A.I.C.S.: 523999
Jeff Last (Mgr-Asset)

Subsidiary (Non-US):

Sabal Financial Europe Limited (4)
Verde 10 Bressenden Place 5th Floor, London, SW1E 5DH, United Kingdom
Tel.: (44) 2074292299
Web Site: http://www.sabalfin.co.uk
Financial Investment Services
N.A.I.C.S.: 523999

Holding (Domestic):

SitelogIQ Government Solutions LLC (3)
80 S 8th St IDS Ctr Ste 1850, Minneapolis, MN 55042
Web Site: https://www.sitelogiq.com

Enables Energy Consumption Reduction in Existing Buildings Through Equipment Replacement
N.A.I.C.S.: 334512
Deb Amberg *(Chief Legal Officer)*

Holding (Non-US):

Solvtrans AS   **(3)**
Skansekaia 4B, 6002, Alesund, Norway
Tel.: (47) 70128020
Web Site: http://www.solvtrans.no
Sales Range: $50-74.9 Million
Emp.: 200
Fish Transportation Services
N.A.I.C.S.: 483111
Roger Halsebakk *(CEO)*

Subsidiary (Non-US):

Solvtrans Chile S.A.   **(4)**
Av juan soler manfredini 41, Puerto Montt, Chile
Tel.: (56) 65 310198
Web Site: http://www.solvtrans.no
Transport of Salmon & Trout
N.A.I.C.S.: 483111

Subsidiary (Domestic):

Solvtrans Rederi AS   **(4)**
Korsegata 4, 6002, Alesund, Norway
Tel.: (47) 70128020
Web Site: http://www.solvtrans.no
Emp.: 40
Fish Transport Services
N.A.I.C.S.: 488510

Affiliate (Domestic):

Taylor Morrison Home Corporation   **(3)**
4900 N Scottsdale Rd Ste 2000, Scottsdale, AZ 85251   **(35.6%)**
Tel.: (480) 840-8100
Web Site: https://www.taylormorrison.com
Rev.: $7,417,831,000
Assets: $8,672,087,000
Liabilities: $3,339,801,000
Net Worth: $5,332,286,000
Earnings: $769,741,000
Emp.: 2,800
Fiscal Year-end: 12/31/2023
Holding Company; Residential Construction
N.A.I.C.S.: 551112
Sheryl D. Palmer *(Chm, Pres & CEO)*

Subsidiary (Domestic):

AV Homes, Inc.   **(4)**
8601 N Scottsdale Rd Ste 225, Scottsdale, AZ 85253
Tel.: (480) 214-7400
Web Site: http://www.taylormorrison.com
Rev.: $843,253,000
Assets: $1,010,144,000
Liabilities: $578,174,000
Net Worth: $431,970,000
Earnings: ($21,936,000)
Emp.: 367
Fiscal Year-end: 12/31/2017
Holding Company; Residential Community Development & Housing Construction Services
N.A.I.C.S.: 551112

Subsidiary (Domestic):

AV Homes of Arizona, LLC   **(5)**
8601 N Scottsdale Rd Ste 225, Scottsdale, AZ 85253
Tel.: (480) 214-7388
Real Estate Services
N.A.I.C.S.: 531210

AVH Carolinas, LLC   **(5)**
8601 N Scottsdale Rd Ste 225, Scottsdale, AZ 85253
Tel.: (480) 214-7388
Real Estate & Other Related Services
N.A.I.C.S.: 531390

AVH North Florida, LLC   **(5)**
85287 Majestic Walk Cir, Fernandina Beach, FL 32034
Tel.: (904) 875-1976
Real Estate Services
N.A.I.C.S.: 531210

Bonterra Builders, LLC   **(5)**
5615 Potter Rd, Matthews, NC 28104

Tel.: (704) 821-8020
Web Site: http://www.bonterrabuilders.com
Residential Construction Services
N.A.I.C.S.: 236117
Darren Sutton *(Owner)*

JCH Construction, LLC   **(5)**
7411 E Jackrabbit Rd, Scottsdale, AZ 85250
Tel.: (480) 306-4592
Residential Construction Services
N.A.I.C.S.: 236115

JEN Florida II, LLC   **(5)**
551 Madison Ave, New York, NY 10022-3212
Tel.: (407) 542-4909
Real Estate Manangement Services
N.A.I.C.S.: 531390

Rio Rico Properties Inc.   **(5)**
1060-8 Yavapai Dr, Rio Rico, AZ 85648
Tel.: (520) 281-8451
Sales Range: $10-24.9 Million
Emp.: 3
Retirement Communities & Housing Construction Services
N.A.I.C.S.: 623311

Royal Oak Homes, LLC   **(5)**
2420 S Lakemont Ave Ste 450, Orlando, FL 32814
Tel.: (888) 233-5159
Web Site: http://www.royaloakhomesfl.com
New Housing For Sale Builder Services
N.A.I.C.S.: 236117

Solivita at Poinciana Golf Club, Inc.   **(5)**
404 Village Dr, Kissimmee, FL 34759
Tel.: (863) 427-7150
Web Site: https://www.stonegategolf.com
Golf Club Operator
N.A.I.C.S.: 713910

Solivita at Poinciana, Inc.   **(5)**
395 Village Dr, Kissimmee, FL 34759
Tel.: (863) 427-7000
Adult Community Center Services
N.A.I.C.S.: 624120

Vitalia at Tradition, LLC   **(5)**
10051 SW Sycamore Tree Way, Port Saint Lucie, FL 34987
Tel.: (772) 800-2504
Web Site:
   https://www.vitaliaattraditionhoa.com
Adult Community Center Services
N.A.I.C.S.: 624120

Subsidiary (Domestic):

Taylor Morrison, Inc.   **(4)**
4900 N Scottsdale Rd Ste 2000, Scottsdale, AZ 85251
Tel.: (480) 344-7000
Web Site: https://www.taylormorrison.com
Sales Range: $25-49.9 Million
Emp.: 43
Housing Development Services
N.A.I.C.S.: 236115
Sheryl D. Palmer *(Chm, Pres & CEO)*

Subsidiary (Domestic):

Taylor Morrison of California, LLC   **(5)**
6440 Oak Canyon Ste 200, Irvine, CA 92618
Tel.: (949) 833-3600
Sales Range: $25-49.9 Million
Residential Construction
N.A.I.C.S.: 236115

Taylor Morrison of Florida, Inc.   **(5)**
501 N Cattlemen Rd Ste 100, Bradenton, FL 34232
Tel.: (941) 371-3008
Web Site: http://www.taylormorrison.com
Sales Range: $50-74.9 Million
Home Construction & Development Services
N.A.I.C.S.: 531390
Bob Witte *(CIO & VP)*

Subsidiary (Domestic):

Taylor Woodrow Homes - Southwest Florida Division, LLC   **(6)**
551 N Cattlemen Rd Ste 200, Sarasota, FL 34232

Tel.: (941) 371-3008
Web Site: http://www.taylormorrison.com
Sales Range: $50-74.9 Million
Emp.: 40
Residential Property Management Services
N.A.I.C.S.: 531311

Subsidiary (Domestic):

Taylor Morrison of Texas, Inc.   **(5)**
9601 Amberglen Blvs Bldg G Ste 200, Austin, TX 78729
Tel.: (512) 328-8866
Sales Range: $50-74.9 Million
Emp.: 100
Residential Development Services
N.A.I.C.S.: 531311
April Solimine *(Pres)*

Division (Domestic):

Taylor Morrison of Texas, Inc. - Houston Division   **(6)**
2929 Briarpark Dr Ste 400, Houston, TX 77042
Tel.: (281) 598-3000
Residential Construction
N.A.I.C.S.: 236117

Subsidiary (Domestic):

William Lyon Homes, Inc.   **(4)**
4695 MacArthur Ct 8th Fl, Newport Beach, CA 92660
Tel.: (949) 833-3600
Web Site: http://www.taylormorrison.com
Holding Company; Single Family Homes Designer, Construction & Sales
N.A.I.C.S.: 551112

Subsidiary (Domestic):

Duxford Financial, Inc.   **(5)**
4490 Von Karman Ave, Newport Beach, CA 92660
Tel.: (949) 833-3600
Sales Range: $25-49.9 Million
Emp.: 35
Mortgage Banking Services
N.A.I.C.S.: 522310
Mark A. Carver *(Pres)*

East Garrison Partners I, LLC   **(5)**
24571 Silver Cloud Ct, Monterey, CA 93940
Tel.: (415) 215-6800
Management Consulting Services
N.A.I.C.S.: 541618

HSP, Inc.   **(5)**
6914 Canby Ave Ste 109, Reseda, CA 91335
Web Site: https://www.hsp-inc.com
Healthcare Staffing Services
N.A.I.C.S.: 561330
Maxie Juzang *(Pres & CEO)*

PNW Cascadian Company, L.L.C.   **(5)**
11624 SE 5th St, Bellevue, WA 98005-3590
Tel.: (425) 586-7700
Building Construction Services
N.A.I.C.S.: 236115

WLH Stillwater, LLC   **(5)**
12206 Lonesome Dove, San Antonio, TX 78254
Tel.: (210) 338-8887
Building Construction & Design Services
N.A.I.C.S.: 236220

WLH Stonewall, LLC   **(5)**
79 Prospector Ln, Liberty Hill, TX 78642
Tel.: (512) 337-6336
Building Construction & Design Services
N.A.I.C.S.: 236220

WLH Trails at Leander, LLC   **(5)**
912 American Trail, Leander, TX 78641
Tel.: (512) 337-6336
Building Construction & Design Services
N.A.I.C.S.: 236220

William Lyon Homes, Inc.   **(5)**
4695 MacArthur Ct 8th Fl, Newport Beach, CA 92660
Tel.: (949) 833-3600
Web Site: http://www.lyonhomes.com
Sales Range: $25-49.9 Million
Emp.: 85
Finance, Insurance & Real Estate Developer & Subdivider

N.A.I.C.S.: 237210

Subsidiary (Domestic):

Village Homes of Colorado, Inc.   **(6)**
8480 E Orchard Rd Ste 1000, Greenwood Village, CO 80111
Tel.: (303) 795-1976
Web Site: http://www.villagehomes.com
Sales Range: $25-49.9 Million
New Construction, Single-Family Houses
N.A.I.C.S.: 236115

Holding (Domestic):

Townsquare Media, Inc.   **(3)**
1 Manhattanville Rd Ste 202, Purchase, NY 10577   **(46%)**
Tel.: (203) 861-0900
Web Site:
   https://www.townsquaremedia.com
Rev.: $463,077,000
Assets: $744,518,000
Liabilities: $675,439,000
Net Worth: $69,079,000
Earnings: $14,390,000
Emp.: 2,442
Fiscal Year-end: 12/31/2022
Holding Company; Radio Broadcasting Stations, Digital & Social Websites & Live Events
N.A.I.C.S.: 551112
Erik Hellum *(COO-Local Media)*

Subsidiary (Domestic):

Townsquare Media Broadcasting, LLC   **(4)**
240 Greenwich Ave, Greenwich, CT 06830
Tel.: (203) 861-0900
Web Site: http://www.townsquaremedia.com
Radio Broadcasting Stations Operator
N.A.I.C.S.: 516110
Steven Price *(Chm)*

Unit (Domestic):

98.7 WFGR   **(5)**
37 Ottawa Ave NW Ste 500, Grand Rapids, MI 49503
Tel.: (616) 451-4800
Web Site: https://www.wfgr.com
Radio Stations
N.A.I.C.S.: 516110
Sarah McHugh *(Dir-Sls)*

New Jersey 101.5   **(5)**
109 Walters Ave, Trenton, NJ 08638
Tel.: (609) 359-5300
Web Site: http://www.nj1015.com
Emp.: 40
Radio Stations
N.A.I.C.S.: 516110
David Kirby *(Dir-Mktg & Promo)*

Division (Domestic):

Townsquare Media - Square Division   **(5)**
12900 Preston Rd Ste 525, Dallas, TX 75230
Tel.: (214) 295-3530
Web Site: http://townsquaremedia.com
Holding Company; Radio Broadcasting Stations
N.A.I.C.S.: 551112

Subsidiary (Domestic):

Townsquare Media Abilene, LLC   **(6)**
3911 South 1st St, Abilene, TX 79605
Tel.: (915) 676-7711
Web Site: http://www.townsquaremedia.com
Sales Range: $10-24.9 Million
Emp.: 30
Radio Broadcasting Stations
N.A.I.C.S.: 516110

Townsquare Media Amarillo, LLC   **(6)**
6214 W 34th, Amarillo, TX 79109
Tel.: (806) 355-9777
Web Site: http://www.townsquaremedia.com
Sales Range: $10-24.9 Million
Emp.: 15
Radio Broadcasting Stations
N.A.I.C.S.: 516110
ReBecca Via *(Pres & Chief Revenue Officer)*

Townsquare Media Lawton, LLC   **(6)**
626 SW D Ave, Lawton, OK 73501

Brookfield Corporation—(Continued)

Tel.: (580) 581-3600
Sales Range: $10-24.9 Million
Emp.: 18
Radio Broadcasting Stations
N.A.I.C.S.: 516110

Townsquare Media Lubbock, LLC (6)
4413 82nd St Ste 300, Lubbock, TX 79424
Tel.: (806) 798-7078
Web Site: http://www.gapbroadcasting.com
Sales Range: $25-49.9 Million
Emp.: 60
Radio Broadcasting Stations
N.A.I.C.S.: 516110

Townsquare Media Lufkin, LLC (6)
1216 S 1st St, Lufkin, TX 75901
Tel.: (936) 639-4455
Web Site: http://www.townsquaremedia.com
Sales Range: $1-9.9 Million
Emp.: 25
Radio Broadcasting Stations
N.A.I.C.S.: 516110
Ishmael Johnson (Pres & Chief Revenue Officer)

Townsquare Media Texarkana, LLC (6)
2324 Arkansas Blvd, Texarkana, AR 71854
Sales Range: $1-9.9 Million
Emp.: 5
Radio Broadcasting Stations
N.A.I.C.S.: 516110

Townsquare Media Tyler, LLC (6)
3810 Brookside Dr, Tyler, TX 75701
Tel.: (903) 581-0606
Sales Range: $25-49.9 Million
Emp.: 45
Radio Broadcasting Stations
N.A.I.C.S.: 516110

Townsquare Media Victoria, LLC (6)
107 N Star Dr, Victoria, TX 77901
Tel.: (361) 573-0777
Sales Range: $10-24.9 Million
Emp.: 14
Radio Broadcasting Stations
N.A.I.C.S.: 516110

Townsquare Media Wichita Falls, LLC (6)
2525 Kell Blvd Ste 200, Wichita Falls, TX 76308
Tel.: (940) 763-1111
Sales Range: $25-49.9 Million
Emp.: 45
Radio Broadcasting Stations
N.A.I.C.S.: 516110

Division (Domestic):

Townsquare Media - Town Division (5)
4300 N Miller Rd Ste 116, Scottsdale, AZ 85251
Tel.: (480) 970-1360
Web Site: http://townsquaremedia.com
Sales Range: $25-49.9 Million
Emp.: 3
Holding Company; Radio Broadcasting Stations
N.A.I.C.S.: 551112

Subsidiary (Domestic):

Townsquare Media Billings, LLC (6)
27 N 27th St 23rd Fl, Billings, MT 59101
Tel.: (406) 248-7827
Sales Range: $10-24.9 Million
Emp.: 23
Radio Broadcasting Stations
N.A.I.C.S.: 516110
Mike Sutton (Pres-Market)

Townsquare Media Casper, LLC (6)
150 N Nichols Ave, Casper, WY 82601
Tel.: (307) 266-5252
Sales Range: $10-24.9 Million
Emp.: 30
Radio Broadcasting Stations
N.A.I.C.S.: 516110
Tom McCarthy (Pres)

Townsquare Media Twin Falls, LLC (6)

415 Park Ave, Twin Falls, ID 83301
Tel.: (208) 733-7512
Sales Range: $10-24.9 Million
Radio Broadcasting Stations
N.A.I.C.S.: 516110

Subsidiary (Domestic):

Townsquare Media Binghamton, LLC (5)
59 Court St, Binghamton, NY 13901
Tel.: (607) 772-8400
Web Site: http://www.991thewhale.com
Radio Broadcasting Stations
N.A.I.C.S.: 516110
Randy Horton (Brand Mgr)

Townsquare Media Faribault, LLC (5)
601 N Central Ave, Faribault, MN 55021
Tel.: (507) 334-0061
Radio Broadcasting Stations
N.A.I.C.S.: 516110

Townsquare Media Lansing, LLC (5)
3420 Pine Tree Rd, Lansing, MI 48911
Tel.: (517) 394-7272
Emp.: 50
Radio Broadcasting Stations
N.A.I.C.S.: 516110

Townsquare Media New Bedford, LLC (5)
22 Sconticut Neck Rd, Fairhaven, MA 02719
Tel.: (508) 999-6690
Sales Range: $1-9.9 Million
Emp.: 50
Radio Broadcasting Stations
N.A.I.C.S.: 516110

Townsquare Media Odessa-Midland II, LLC (5)
11300 State Hwy 191 Bldg Ste 2, Midland, TX 79707
Tel.: (432) 563-5636
Web Site: http://www.townsquaremediagroup.com
Emp.: 20
Radio Broadcasting Stations
N.A.I.C.S.: 516110

Townsquare Media Portsmouth, LLC (5)
292 Middle Rd, Dover, NH 03820-4901
Tel.: (603) 749-9750
Sales Range: $1-9.9 Million
Emp.: 40
Radio Broadcasting Stations
N.A.I.C.S.: 516110
Bill Wilson (CEO)

Townsquare Media of Albany, Inc. (5)
1241 Kings Rd, Schenectady, NY 12303
Tel.: (518) 881-1515
Web Site: https://www.wgna.com
Sales Range: $200-249.9 Million
Emp.: 40
Radio Broadcasting Stations
N.A.I.C.S.: 516110

Townsquare Media of Bloomington, Inc. (5)
236 Greenwood Ave, Bloomington, IL 61704
Tel.: (309) 829-1221
Web Site: http://www.radiobloomington.com
Sales Range: $10-24.9 Million
Emp.: 40
Radio Broadcasting Stations
N.A.I.C.S.: 516110

Townsquare Media of Buffalo, Inc. (5)
14 Lafayette Sq, Buffalo, NY 14203
Tel.: (716) 852-7444
Sales Range: $25-49.9 Million
Emp.: 60
Radio Broadcasting Stations
N.A.I.C.S.: 516110
Robby Bowen (Pres)

Townsquare Media of El Paso, Inc. (5)
4180 N Mesa St, El Paso, TX 79902
Tel.: (915) 544-8864
Sales Range: $10-24.9 Million
Emp.: 60
Radio Broadcasting Stations

N.A.I.C.S.: 516110

Townsquare Media of Evansville/Owensboro, Inc. (5)
20 NW 3rd St 6th Fl 5th 3rd Bank Bldg, Evansville, IN 47708
Tel.: (812) 425-4226
Sales Range: $10-24.9 Million
Emp.: 50
Radio Broadcasting Stations
N.A.I.C.S.: 516110

Unit (Domestic):

Townsquare Media of Owensboro (6)
3301 Frederica St, Owensboro, KY 42301
Tel.: (270) 683-1558
Sales Range: $10-24.9 Million
Emp.: 20
Radio Broadcasting Stations
N.A.I.C.S.: 516110

Subsidiary (Domestic):

Townsquare Media of Flint, Inc. (5)
G-3338 E Bristol Rd, Burton, MI 48529
Tel.: (810) 743-1080
Radio Broadcasting Stations
N.A.I.C.S.: 516110

Townsquare Media of Ft. Collins, Inc. (5)
600 Main St, Windsor, CO 80550
Tel.: (970) 674-2700
Sales Range: $10-24.9 Million
Emp.: 47
Radio Broadcasting Stations
N.A.I.C.S.: 516110
Wheeler Morris (Pres)

Townsquare Media of Grand Rapids, Inc. (5)
50 Monroe NW Ste 500, Grand Rapids, MI 49503
Tel.: (616) 451-4800
Sales Range: $10-24.9 Million
Emp.: 55
Radio Broadcasting Stations
N.A.I.C.S.: 516110

Townsquare Media of Killeen-Temple, Inc. (5)
608 Moody Ln, Temple, TX 76504
Tel.: (254) 773-5252
Sales Range: $25-49.9 Million
Emp.: 40
Radio Broadcasting Stations
N.A.I.C.S.: 516110
Ishmael Johnson (Pres & Chief Revenue Officer)

Townsquare Media of Lafayette, Inc. (5)
1749 Bertrand Dr, Lafayette, LA 70506
Tel.: (337) 233-6000
Sales Range: $25-49.9 Million
Emp.: 75
Radio Broadcasting Stations
N.A.I.C.S.: 516110

Townsquare Media of St. Cloud, Inc. (5)
640 SE Lincoln Ave, Saint Cloud, MN 56304
Tel.: (320) 251-4422
Radio Broadcasting Stations
N.A.I.C.S.: 516110

Townsquare Media of Utica/Rome, Inc. (5)
9418 River Rd, Marcy, NY 13403
Tel.: (315) 768-9500
Radio Broadcasting Stations
N.A.I.C.S.: 516110

Unit (Domestic):

Wxbb Fm 105.3, Inc. (5)
292 Middle Rd, Dover, NH 03820
Tel.: (603) 749-9750
Web Site: http://www.wokq.com
Radio Stations
N.A.I.C.S.: 516110
Shawn Olsten (Gen Sls Mgr)

Holding (Domestic):

Trench Plate Rental Company (3)
13217 Laureldale Ave, Downey, CA 90242

Tel.: (800) 821-4478
Web Site: http://www.tprco.com
Construction, Mining & Forestry Machinery & Equipment Rental & Leasing
N.A.I.C.S.: 532412

Subsidiary (Domestic):

National Trench Safety, LLC (4)
15955 W Hardy Rd Ste 100, Houston, TX 77060
Tel.: (832) 200-0988
Web Site: http://www.ntsafety.com
Emp.: 40
Commercial & Industrial Machinery & Equipment Rental & Leasing
N.A.I.C.S.: 532490
Ronald W. Chilton (Co-Founder & Vice Chm)

Holding (Domestic):

Triton Media, LLC (3)
15303 Ventura Blvd Ste 1500, Sherman Oaks, CA 91403
Tel.: (310) 575-9700
Web Site: http://www.tritonmedia.com
Sales Range: $25-49.9 Million
Emp.: 14
Holding Company
N.A.I.C.S.: 551112
Neal A. Schore (CEO)

Subsidiary (Domestic):

TM Studios, Inc. (4)
2002 Academy Ln, Dallas, TX 75234
Tel.: (972) 406-6800
Web Site: http://www.tmstudios.com
Sales Range: $25-49.9 Million
Music-Based Products & Services for Broadcast Media Use
N.A.I.C.S.: 512290
Greg Clancy (VP-Creative & Gen Mgr)

Affiliate (Domestic):

Brookfield Real Assets Income Fund Inc. (2)
Brookfield Place 250 Vesey Street 15th Fl, New York, NY 10281-1023
Tel.: (212) 417-7000
Web Site: http://www.brookfieldim.com
Rev.: $61,644,311
Assets: $1,092,818,830
Liabilities: $246,389,452
Net Worth: $846,429,378
Earnings: $39,973,597
Fiscal Year-end: 12/31/2019
Closed-End Investment Fund
N.A.I.C.S.: 525990
Edward A. Kuczmarski (Chm)

Subsidiary (Domestic):

IDI Logistics, LLC (2)
1197 Peachtree St NE Ste 600, Atlanta, GA 30361
Tel.: (404) 479-4000
Web Site: https://www.idilogistics.com
Industrial Real Estate Development, Property Management & Leasing Services
N.A.I.C.S.: 531390
Mark Saturno (CEO)

Division (Domestic):

IDI Services Group, LLC (3)
1100 Peachtree St NE Ste 1000, Atlanta, GA 30309 (100%)
Tel.: (404) 479-4000
Sales Range: $50-74.9 Million
Commercial Property Management & Leasing Services
N.A.I.C.S.: 531312
Bob Tardy (VP-Natl Leasing & Mktg)

Brookfield Investments Corporation (1)
Brookfield Place 181 Bay Street Suite 100, Toronto, M5J 2T3, ON, Canada
Tel.: (416) 363-9491
Web Site: https://www.brookfieldinvestmentcorp.com
Sales Range: $75-99.9 Million
Real Estate Investment Trust
N.A.I.C.S.: 525990
Edward C. Kress (Chm & Pres)

Brookfield Multiplex Group Limited (1)
Level 22 135 king st, Sydney, 2000, NSW, Australia **(100%)**
Tel.: (61) 292565000
Web Site:
http://www.brookfieldmultiplex.com
Sales Range: $1-4.9 Billion
Emp.: 2,000
Holding Company; Property Development, Facilities Management, Fund Management & Construction
N.A.I.C.S.: 551112

Subsidiary (Domestic):

Brookfield Multiplex Capital Limited (2)
Level 22 135 Kings St, Sydney, 2000, NSW, Australia
Tel.: (61) 292565000
Web Site:
http://www.brookfieldmultiplex.com
Sales Range: $150-199.9 Million
Emp.: 500
Property Fund Management
N.A.I.C.S.: 531390

Brookfield Multiplex Developments (2)
Level 22 135 King Street, Sydney, 2000, NSW, Australia
Tel.: (61) 292565000
Web Site:
http://www.brookfieldmultiplex.com
Sales Range: $75-99.9 Million
Emp.: 200
Property Developers
N.A.I.C.S.: 531390

Subsidiary (Non-US):

Nasa Multiplex LLC (2)
Level 17 Al Attar Business Tower, Sheikh Zayed Road, Dubai, United Arab Emirates
Tel.: (971) 58500
Web Site:
http://www.brookfieldmultiplex.com
Sales Range: $25-49.9 Million
Construction Management Services
N.A.I.C.S.: 236210

Brookfield Properties Retail Inc. (1)
350 N Orleans Ste 300, Chicago, IL 60654-1607
Tel.: (312) 960-5000
Retail Properties Investor, Manager & Lessor
N.A.I.C.S.: 531312

Subsidiary (Domestic):

Animas Valley Mall, LLC (2)
4601 E Main St, Farmington, NM 87402
Tel.: (505) 326-2654
Web Site:
https://www.animasvalleymall.com
Sales Range: $25-49.9 Million
Emp.: 4
Nonresidential Building Leasing Services
N.A.I.C.S.: 531120

Bay Shore Mall, LP (2)
3300 Broadway, Eureka, CA 95501
Tel.: (707) 444-3856
Web Site: https://www.bayshoremall.com
Nonresidential Building Leasing Services
N.A.I.C.S.: 531120

Birchwood Mall, LLC (2)
4350 24th Ave, Fort Gratiot, MI 48059
Tel.: (810) 294-8793
Web Site: https://www.birchwoodmall.com
N.A.I.C.S.: 722513

Boulevard Mall, LLC (2)
730 Alberta Dr, Amherst, NY 14226
Tel.: (716) 834-8600
Web Site: https://boulevard-mall.com
N.A.I.C.S.: 722513

Chula Vista Center, LP (2)
555 Broadway Ste 1019, Chula Vista, CA 91910
Tel.: (619) 427-6701
Web Site: https://www.chulavistacenter.com
Emp.: 6
Nonresidential Building Leasing Services
N.A.I.C.S.: 531120

Collin Creek Mall, LLC (2)
811 N Central Expy, Plano, TX 75075-8897
Tel.: (972) 543-0369
Web Site: https://www.collincreek.com
Nonresidential Building Leasing Services
N.A.I.C.S.: 531120

Colony Square Mall, LLC (2)
3575 Maple Ave, Zanesville, OH 43701
Tel.: (740) 454-3255
Web Site:
https://www.colonysquaremall.com
Nonresidential Building Leasing Services
N.A.I.C.S.: 531120

Unit (Domestic):

Coronado Center (2)
6600 Menaul NE Ste 1, Albuquerque, NM 87110-3428
Tel.: (505) 855-7780
Web Site: https://www.coronadocenter.com
Retail Properties Manager & Lessor
N.A.I.C.S.: 531312

Fashion Show Mall (2)
3200 Las Vegas Blvd S Ste 600, Las Vegas, NV 89109-2692
Tel.: (702) 784-7000
Web Site: https://www.fslv.com
Retail Properties Manager & Lessor
N.A.I.C.S.: 531312

Subsidiary (Domestic):

GGP-Gateway Mall L.L.C. (2)
3000 Gateway St, Springfield, OR 97477-1029
Tel.: (541) 747-6294
Web Site: http://www.gatewaymall.com
Nonresidential Building Leasing Services
N.A.I.C.S.: 531120

Grand Traverse Mall, LLC (2)
3200 S Airport Rd W, Traverse City, MI 49684
Tel.: (231) 922-2591
Web Site:
https://www.grandtraversemall.com
Nonresidential Building Leasing Services
N.A.I.C.S.: 531120

Lakeland Square Mall, LLC (2)
3800 US Hwy 98 N, Lakeland, FL 33809
Tel.: (863) 859-5414
Web Site: https://www.lakelandsquare.com
Nonresidential Building Leasing Services
N.A.I.C.S.: 531120

Lansing Mall, LLC (2)
5330 W Saginaw Hwy, Lansing, MI 48917
Tel.: (517) 321-0145
Web Site: https://www.lansingmall.com
Nonresidential Building Leasing Services
N.A.I.C.S.: 531120

Unit (Domestic):

Lynnhaven Mall (2)
701 Lynnhaven Pkwy, Virginia Beach, VA 23452-7299
Tel.: (757) 340-5636
Web Site: https://www.lynnhavenmall.com
Retail Properties Manager & Lessor
N.A.I.C.S.: 531312

Mall St. Matthews (2)
5000 Shelbyville Rd, Louisville, KY 40207-3342
Tel.: (502) 893-0312
Web Site: https://www.mallstmatthews.com
Retail Properties Manager & Lessor
N.A.I.C.S.: 531312
David Jacoby (Gen Mgr)

Subsidiary (Domestic):

Mall St. Vincent, LLC (2)
1133 St Vincent Ave Ste 200, Shreveport, LA 71104-4153
Tel.: (318) 227-9880
Web Site: https://www.mallstvincent.com
Nonresidential Buildings Rental & Leasing Services
N.A.I.C.S.: 531120

Mt. Shasta Mall (2)
900 Dana Dr, Redding, CA 96003
Tel.: (530) 223-3575

Sales Range: $1-9.9 Million
Emp.: 200
Mall Operator
N.A.I.C.S.: 459999

NewPark Mall, LP (2)
2086 NewPark Mall, Newark, CA 94560-2011
Tel.: (510) 931-5049
Web Site: https://www.newparkmall.com
Nonresidential Building Leasing Services
N.A.I.C.S.: 531120

North Plains Mall, LLC (2)
2809 N Prince St, Clovis, NM 88101
Tel.: (575) 769-2300
Web Site: https://www.northplainsmall.com
Nonresidential Building Leasing Services
N.A.I.C.S.: 531120

Unit (Domestic):

Pecanland Mall (2)
4700 Millhaven Rd Ste 2000, Monroe, LA 71203
Tel.: (318) 322-4794
Web Site: https://www.pecanlandmall.com
Retail Properties Manager & Lessor
N.A.I.C.S.: 531312

Perimeter Mall (2)
4400 Ashford Dunwoody Rd, Atlanta, GA 30346-1517
Tel.: (770) 395-5858
Web Site: https://www.perimetermall.com
Retail Properties Manager & Lessor
N.A.I.C.S.: 531312

Subsidiary (Domestic):

Pierre Bossier Mall, LLC (2)
2950 E Texas St Ste 212, Bossier City, LA 71111
Tel.: (318) 747-5701
Web Site:
https://www.pierrebossiermall.com
N.A.I.C.S.: 531120

Unit (Domestic):

Prince Kuhio Plaza (2)
111 E Puainako St, Hilo, HI 96720-5292
Tel.: (808) 959-3555
Web Site: https://www.princekuhioplaza.com
Retail Properties Manager & Lessor
N.A.I.C.S.: 531312

Subsidiary (Domestic):

Sierra Vista Mall, LLC (2)
1050 Shaw Ave, Clovis, CA 93612
Tel.: (559) 299-0660
Web Site: https://www.sierravistamall.com
N.A.I.C.S.: 531120
Daniel Delarosa (Gen Mgr)

Sikes Senter, LLC (2)
3111 Midwestern Pkwy, Wichita Falls, TX 76308
Tel.: (940) 692-5502
Web Site: https://www.sikessenter.com
N.A.I.C.S.: 531120

Silver Lake Mall, LLC (2)
200 W Hanley Ave, Coeur D'Alene, ID 83815
Tel.: (208) 762-2113
Web Site: https://silverlake.center
Sales Range: $25-49.9 Million
Emp.: 3
Property Management Services
N.A.I.C.S.: 531120

Southland Center, LLC (2)
23000 Eureka Rd, Taylor, MI 48180-5254
Tel.: (734) 374-2800
Web Site:
https://www.shopsouthlandcenter.com
Sales Range: $25-49.9 Million
Emp.: 6
Nonresidential Building Leasing Services
N.A.I.C.S.: 531120

Southland Mall, L.P. (2)
1 Southland Mall Dr, Hayward, CA 94545
Tel.: (510) 782-5050
Web Site: https://www.southlandmall.com
N.A.I.C.S.: 722513

Spring Hill Mall L.L.C. (2)
1072 Spring Hill Mall, West Dundee, IL 60118

Tel.: (847) 428-2200
Web Site: https://www.springhillmall.com
Nonresidential Building Leasing Services
N.A.I.C.S.: 531120

Three Rivers Mall, L.L.C. (2)
351 3 Rivers Dr, Kelso, WA 98626
Tel.: (360) 577-5218
Web Site: http://www.threeriversmall.com
Sales Range: $25-49.9 Million
Emp.: 5
Nonresidential Building Leasing Services
N.A.I.C.S.: 531120

Washington Park Mall, LLC (2)
2350 SE Washington Blvd Ste 315, Bartlesville, OK 74006
Tel.: (918) 335-2535
Web Site:
https://www.washingtonparkmall.com
Sales Range: $25-49.9 Million
Emp.: 3
Nonresidential Building Leasing Services
N.A.I.C.S.: 531120

Westwood Mall, LLC (2)
1850 W Michigan Ave, Jackson, MI 49202
Tel.: (517) 787-1170
Web Site:
https://www.shopwestwoodmall.com
Nonresidential Building Leasing Services
N.A.I.C.S.: 531120

White Mountain Mall, LLC (2)
2441 Foothill Blvd, Rock Springs, WY 82901
Tel.: (307) 382-9680
Web Site:
https://www.whitemountainmall.com
Emp.: 3
Nonresidential Building Leasing Services
N.A.I.C.S.: 531120

Brookfield Property Group (1)
Brookfield Place 250 Vesey St 15th Fl, New York, NY 10281-0221
Tel.: (212) 417-7000
Real Estate Services
N.A.I.C.S.: 531210

Brookfield Property Partners L.P. (1)
73 Front Street 5th Floor, Hamilton, HM 12, Bermuda **(72%)**
Tel.: (441) 2943309
Web Site: https://www.bpy.brookfield.com
Rev.: $7,365,000,000
Assets: $112,516,000,000
Liabilities: $70,779,000,000
Net Worth: $41,737,000,000
Earnings: $996,000,000
Fiscal Year-end: 12/31/2022
Real Estate Manangement Services
N.A.I.C.S.: 531390
Jane Sheere (Sec)

Subsidiary (Non-US):

Aveo Group Limited (2)
Level 5 99 Macquarie Street, Sydney, 2000, NSW, Australia
Tel.: (61) 292706100
Web Site: http://www.aveo.com.au
Rev.: $331,942,397
Assets: $5,241,458,644
Liabilities: $3,447,814,575
Net Worth: $1,793,644,069
Earnings: $284,956,899
Fiscal Year-end: 06/30/2018
Retirement Communities, Residential Communities & Apartments Development & Management
N.A.I.C.S.: 237210
Gary Kordic (Head-Dev)

Subsidiary (Domestic):

FKP Limited (3)
76 Skyring Terrace, Brisbane, 4001, Newstead, Australia
Tel.: (61) 732233888
Web Site: http://www.aveo.com.au
Sales Range: $650-699.9 Million
Emp.: 2,000
Real Estate & Investment Management Services
N.A.I.C.S.: 531390

Subsidiary (Domestic):

Australian Retirement Homes Limited (4)

Brookfield Corporation—(Continued)

Level 1 76A Skyring Terrace, Brisbane,
4006, QLD, Australia
Tel.: (61) 732233808
Web Site: http://www.aveo.com.au
Sales Range: $50-74.9 Million
Emp.: 1,000
Retirement Housing Services
N.A.I.C.S.: 624229

Aveo Healthcare Limited (4)
Level 5 99 Macquarie Street, Sydney, 2000,
NSW, Australia (86.6%)
Tel.: (61) 2 9270 6100
Web Site:
http://aveo.redpropaganda.com.au
Rev.: $15,297,604
Assets: $653,894,522
Liabilities: $475,474,508
Net Worth: $178,420,014
Earnings: ($1,404,882)
Fiscal Year-end: 06/30/2017
Retirement Services
N.A.I.C.S.: 623311

Cleveland Gardens Pty. Ltd. (4)
PO Box 2447, Brisbane, 4001, QLD, Aus-
tralia
Tel.: (61) 732233889
Web Site: http://www.fkp.com.au
Sales Range: $10-24.9 Million
Emp.: 10
Retirement Housing Services
N.A.I.C.S.: 624229

**FKP Commercial Developments Pty.
Ltd.** (4)
PO Box 2447, Brisbane, 4001, Queensland,
Australia
Tel.: (61) 732233888
Web Site: http://www.fkp.com.au
Commercial Property Development Services
N.A.I.C.S.: 236220

FKP Funds Management Limited (4)
Level 5 99 Macquarie Street, Sydney, 2000,
NSW, Australia
Tel.: (61) 292706100
Web Site: http://www.fkp.com.au
Sales Range: $550-599.9 Million
Emp.: 2,000
Real Estate & Investment Management
Services
N.A.I.C.S.: 531390
Peter Ross Brown (CEO & Mng Dir)

FKP Real Estate Pty. Ltd. (4)
Level 5 120 Edward St, Brisbane, 4001,
QLD, Australia
Tel.: (61) 732233888
Web Site: http://www.fkp.com
Sales Range: $550-599.9 Million
Emp.: 2,000
Real Estate & Investment Management
Services
N.A.I.C.S.: 531390

**FKP Residential Developments Pty.
Ltd.** (4)
PO Box 239, Peregian Beach, Brisbane,
4573, Queensland, Australia
Tel.: (61) 754482833
Web Site: http://www.fkp.com.au
Residential Real Estate Management Ser-
vices
N.A.I.C.S.: 531311

**Forest Place Management
Limited** (4)
356 Blunder Rd, Durack, Brisbane, 4077,
QLD, Australia
Tel.: (61) 73727777
Web Site: http://www.fkp.com.au
Sales Range: $10-24.9 Million
Emp.: 10
Retirement Housing Services
N.A.I.C.S.: 624229

**The Domain Retirement Country Club
Pty. Ltd.** (4)
74 Wardoo Street, Ashmore, Gold Coast,
4214, QLD, Australia
Tel.: (61) 755514469
Web Site: https://www.aveo.com.au
Sales Range: $10-24.9 Million
Emp.: 6
Retirement Homes & Aged Persons Accom-
modation Services
N.A.I.C.S.: 623312

Subsidiary (Non-US):

**Brookfield Canada Office
Properties** (2)
Brookfield Place Suite 100 181 Bay Street,
Toronto, M5J 2T3, ON, Canada (100%)
Tel.: (416) 363-9491
Web Site: http://www.brookfield.com
Real Estate Investment Trust
N.A.I.C.S.: 531300

Affiliate (Non-US):

Brookfield Office Properties Inc. (2)
Brookfield Place 181 Bay Street Suite 300,
Toronto, M5J 2T3, ON, Canada (50.7%)
Tel.: (416) 369-2300
Web Site:
http://www.brookfieldofficeproperties.com
Sales Range: $1-4.9 Billion
Emp.: 1,527
Commercial Real Estate Investment Trust
N.A.I.C.S.: 525990
Herb Mah (Sr VP-Dev & Construction)

Subsidiary (US):

**Brookfield Financial Properties,
L.P.** (3)
Brookfield Pl 250 Vesey St 15th Fl, New
York, NY 10281 (99.4%)
Tel.: (212) 417-7000
Web Site:
http://www.brookfieldofficeproperties.com
Sales Range: $50-74.9 Million
Emp.: 100
Real Estate Development & Management
N.A.I.C.S.: 531120

Subsidiary (Domestic):

33 South 6th Street LLC (4)
33 S 6th St, Minneapolis, MN 55402
Tel.: (612) 372-1234
Web Site:
http://www.brookfieldofficeproperties.com
Property Management Services
N.A.I.C.S.: 523940

BOP 1801 California Street LLC (4)
1801 California St Ste 200, Denver, CO
80202-2658
Tel.: (612) 372-1500
Real Estate Development Services
N.A.I.C.S.: 531390
Myra Napoli (Gen Mgr)

Subsidiary (US):

**Brookfield Properties Management
LLC** (3)
3 World Financial Ctr 11, New York, NY
10281-1013
Tel.: (212) 693-8150
Properties Management Services
N.A.I.C.S.: 531312

Brookfield Properties, Inc. (3)
Brookfield Pl 250 Vesey St 15th Fl, New
York, NY 10281
Tel.: (212) 417-7000
Web Site:
https://www.brookfieldproperties.com
Real Estate Investment Trust
N.A.I.C.S.: 525990
Tyler Merritt (Dir-Leasing-Houston)

Subsidiary (Domestic):

1201 Louisiana Co. L.P. (4)
1201 Louisiana St Ste 304, Houston, TX
77002
Tel.: (416) 646-2473
Property Management Services
N.A.I.C.S.: 523940

1600 Smith Co. LLC (4)
1600 Smith St, Houston, TX 77002
Tel.: (713) 951-7400
Web Site:
http://www.brookfieldproperties.com
Emp.: 25
Property Management Services
N.A.I.C.S.: 523940

BOP 650 Mass LLC (4)
750 9th St NW, Washington, DC 20001-
4524
Tel.: (202) 467-7760
Real Estate Development Services
N.A.I.C.S.: 531390

EYP Realty, LLC (4)
725 S Figueroa St Ste 1850, Los Angeles,
CA 90017-5524
Tel.: (213) 955-7170
Sales Range: $50-74.9 Million
Emp.: 12
Real Estate Development Services
N.A.I.C.S.: 531390

One Allen Center Co. LLC (4)
500 Dallas St, Houston, TX 77002-4800
Tel.: (713) 651-1515
Real Estate Development Services
N.A.I.C.S.: 531390

Sunrise Tech Park Co. LLC (4)
750 9th St Nw 700, Washington, DC 20001-
4590
Tel.: (202) 467-7700
Real Estate Development Services
N.A.I.C.S.: 531390
Greg Myer (VP)

Two Ballston Plaza Co. LLC (4)
1110 N Glebe Rd, Arlington, VA 22201
Tel.: (703) 351-7900
Web Site:
http://www.brookfieldofficeproperties.com
Emp.: 3
Property Management Services
N.A.I.C.S.: 531311

Subsidiary (Domestic):

**Brookfield Residential Services
Ltd.** (3)
3190 Steeles Avenue East Suite 200,
Markham, L3R 1G9, ON, Canada
Tel.: (416) 510-8700
Web Site:
http://www.brookfieldresidential.com
Property Management Services
N.A.I.C.S.: 531311

**Royal LePage Real Estate Services
Ltd.** (3)
39 Wynford Dr, Toronto, M3C 3K5, ON,
Canada
Tel.: (416) 510-5800
Web Site: http://www.royallepage.ca
Real Estate Management Services
N.A.I.C.S.: 531210

Subsidiary (Non-US):

**Brookfield Properties Management
Corporation** (2)
Brookfield Place Suite 100 181 Bay Street,
Toronto, M5J 2T3, ON, Canada
Tel.: (416) 363-9491
Web Site:
http://www.brookfieldproperties.com
Real Estate Property Management Services
N.A.I.C.S.: 531312

Subsidiary (US):

Brookfield Property REIT Inc. (2)
250 Vesey St 15th Fl, New York, NY
10281-1023 (87%)
Tel.: (212) 417-7000
Web Site: http://bpy.brookfield.com
Rev.: $1,529,545,000
Assets: $21,879,964,000
Liabilities: $18,629,511,000
Net Worth: $3,250,453,000
Earnings: ($711,461,000)
Fiscal Year-end: 12/31/2020
Real Estate Investment Trust
N.A.I.C.S.: 525990
Brian W. Kingston (CEO)

Joint Venture (US):

Forever 21, Inc. (2)
2001 S Alameda St, Los Angeles, CA
90058 (25%)
Tel.: (213) 741-5100
Web Site: http://www.forever21.com
Sales Range: $1-4.9 Billion
Emp.: 6,000
Women's Apparel & Accessories
N.A.I.C.S.: 458110
Don W. Chang (Founder & Pres)

**Brookfield Renewable Partners
L.P.** (1)
73 Front Street 5th Floor, Hamilton, HM 12,
Bermuda (68%)
Tel.: (441) 2943304

Web Site: https://bep.brookfield.com
Rev.: $4,711,000,000
Assets: $64,111,000,000
Liabilities: $37,825,000,000
Net Worth: $26,286,000,000
Earnings: $138,000,000
Emp.: 3,400
Fiscal Year-end: 12/31/2022
Electric Power Generation & Distribution
N.A.I.C.S.: 221122
Bruce Flatt (CEO)

Subsidiary (Non-US):

**Brookfield Renewable Power Pre-
ferred Equity Inc.** (2)
Brookfield Place 181 Bay Street Suite 300,
PO Box 762, Toronto, M5J 2T3, ON,
Canada
Tel.: (416) 359-1955
Investment Management Service
N.A.I.C.S.: 523940
Richard J. Legault (Pres)

Holding (Non-US):

Isagen S.A. E.S.P. (2)
Carrera 30 10C - 280 Transversal Inferior,
El Poblado, Medellin, Colombia (99.73%)
Web Site: http://www.isagen.com.co
Sales Range: $800-899.9 Million
Emp.: 662
Hydroelectric & Geothermal Power Genera-
tion
N.A.I.C.S.: 221111
Camilo Marulanda Lopez (CEO)

Subsidiary (US):

Standard Solar, Inc. (2)
1355 Piccard Dr Ste 300, Rockville, MD
20850
Tel.: (301) 944-1200
Web Site: http://www.standardsolar.com
Develops & Integrates Solar Electricity Sys-
tems for Residential, Government & Com-
mercial Businesses
N.A.I.C.S.: 221118
Tony Clifford (Chief Dev Officer)

**Westinghouse Electric Company
LLC** (2)
1000 Westinghouse Dr, Cranberry, PA
16066 (51%)
Tel.: (412) 374-4111
Web Site:
http://www.westinghousenuclear.com
Nuclear Power Plant Construction, Mainte-
nance & Support Services; Nuclear Fuel
Supplier
N.A.I.C.S.: 237990
David A. Howell (Pres-Operating Plant
Svcs)

Affiliate (Non-US):

Mangiarotti S.p.A. (3)
(30%)
Web Site: http://www.mangiarotti.it
Pressure Equipment Design & Mfr
N.A.I.C.S.: 333248
Richard Gabbianelli (Chm)

Subsidiary (Domestic):

WEC Welding & Machining LLC (3)
1 Energy Dr, Lake Bluff, IL 60044 (100%)
Tel.: (847) 680-8100
Contracting Services for Maintenance of
Power Systems
N.A.I.C.S.: 238990

Subsidiary (Domestic):

WEC Carolina Energy Solutions (4)
244 East Mt Gallant Rd, Rock Hill, SC
29730 (100%)
Tel.: (803) 980-3060
Web Site:
http://www.carolinaenergysolutions.com
Welding & Machining Services
N.A.I.C.S.: 238990
Jason Beasley (Mgr-Product)

Subsidiary (Domestic):

WesDyne International, Inc. (3)
680 Waltz Mill Rd, Madison, PA
15663 (100%)
Tel.: (724) 722-5250
Web Site: http://www.wesdyne.com

Emp.: 80
Development & Application of Inspection Equipment & Services for Power Industry
N.A.I.C.S.: 541990
Greg Turley *(Pres)*

Subsidiary (Non-US):

Westinghouse Electric Germany GmbH (3)
Dudenstrasse 44, D 68167, Mannheim, Germany
Tel.: (49) 6213882007
Web Site:
http://www.westinghousenuclear.com
Sales Range: $100-124.9 Million
Emp.: 400
Nuclear Power Plant Construction, Maintenance & Support Services; Nuclear Fuel Supplier
N.A.I.C.S.: 237990

Westinghouse Energy Systems Europe S.A. (3)
Blue Tower Avenue Louise 326 18th floor, Box 60, 1050, Brussels, Belgium
Tel.: (32) 26457111
Nuclear Power Plant Construction, Maintenance & Support Services; Nuclear Fuel Supplier
N.A.I.C.S.: 237990
Anders Jackson *(Pres-European Reg)*

Brookfield Residential Properties Inc. (1)
4906 Richard Road SW, Calgary, T3E 6L1, AB, Canada
Tel.: (403) 231-8900
Web Site:
http://www.brookfieldresidential.com
Rev.: $1,938,358,000
Assets: $5,559,846,000
Liabilities: $2,514,600,000
Net Worth: $3,045,246,000
Earnings: $197,560,000
Emp.: 938
Fiscal Year-end: 12/31/2019
Real Estate Services
N.A.I.C.S.: 531390
Alan Norris *(Chm & CEO)*

Subsidiary (Domestic):

Brookfield Homes Ontario Ltd. (2)
7303 Warden Avenue Suite 100, Markham, L3R 5Y6, ON, Canada   **(100%)**
Tel.: (905) 477-5111
Web Site: http://www.brookfieldhomes.ca
Sales Range: $10-24.9 Million
Emp.: 50
Housing Developments
N.A.I.C.S.: 925110

Brookfield Residential (Alberta) LP (2)
200-10414 103 Ave, Edmonton, T5J 0J1, AB, Canada
Tel.: (780) 423-1910
Real Estate Development Services
N.A.I.C.S.: 531390

Canary Wharf Group PLC (1)
One Canada Square Canary Wharf, London, E14 5AB, United Kingdom
Tel.: (44) 2074182000
Web Site: https://group.canarywharf.com
Emp.: 1,000
Holding Company; Property Investors & Leasors
N.A.I.C.S.: 551112
George Iacobescu *(Chm)*

Center Parcs (Operating Company) Limited (1)
One Edison Rise New Ollerton, Newark, NG22 9DP, Notts, United Kingdom
Tel.: (44) 3448267723
Web Site: https://www.centerparcs.co.uk
Sales Range: $500-549.9 Million
Emp.: 30
Forest Resorts & Villages Operator
N.A.I.C.S.: 531311

Ember Resources Inc. (1)
Devon Tower 800 400 3rd Ave S W, Calgary, T2P 4H2, AB, Canada
Tel.: (403) 270-0803
Web Site: https://www.emberresources.com
Sales Range: $25-49.9 Million
Gas Production
N.A.I.C.S.: 221210

Fairfield Residential Company LLC (1)
5355 Mira Sorrento Pl Ste 100, San Diego, CA 92121
Tel.: (858) 457-2123
Web Site:
https://www.fairfieldresidential.com
Multifamily Real Estate Services
N.A.I.C.S.: 531390
Richard Boynton *(Sr VP-Acquisitions)*

Forest City Realty Trust, Inc. (1)
127 Public Sq Ste 3100, Cleveland, OH 44114
Tel.: (216) 621-6060
Web Site: http://www.forestcity.net
Rev.: $911,926,000
Assets: $8,063,287,000
Liabilities: $4,218,570,000
Net Worth: $3,844,717,000
Earnings: $206,030,000
Emp.: 1,473
Fiscal Year-end: 12/31/2017
Real Estate Investment Trust
N.A.I.C.S.: 525990
Deborah Ratner Salzberg *(Co-Founder, Pres-Washington & Exec VP)*

Subsidiary (Domestic):

Forest City Bayside Corporation (2)
50 Public Sq, Cleveland, OH 44113-2202   **(100%)**
Tel.: (216) 621-6060
Web Site: http://www.forestcity.net
Sales Range: $50-74.9 Million
Emp.: 100
Apartment Management
N.A.I.C.S.: 531210
James A. Ratner *(Exec VP)*

Subsidiary (Domestic):

Bayside Village Associates, L.P. (3)
3 Bayside Village Pl, San Francisco, CA 94107
Tel.: (415) 777-4850
Web Site: https://www.baysidevillage.com
Emp.: 45
Real Estate Development Services
N.A.I.C.S.: 531210

Subsidiary (Domestic):

Forest City Capital Corporation (2)
1170 Trml Twr 50 Pub Sq 1170 Terminal Tower, Cleveland, OH 44113   **(100%)**
Tel.: (216) 621-6060
Web Site: http://www.forestcity.net
Sales Range: $25-49.9 Million
Emp.: 6
Rental Property Financing Services
N.A.I.C.S.: 522292

Forest City Commercial Group (2)
50 Public Sq Ste 1100, Cleveland, OH 44113-2267   **(100%)**
Tel.: (216) 621-6060
Web Site: http://www.forestcity.net
Sales Range: $1-4.9 Billion
Emp.: 800
Commercial Buildings
N.A.I.C.S.: 531210
James A. Ratner *(Chm & CEO)*

Forest City Myrtle Associates, LLC (2)
1 Metrotech Ctr N 11, Brooklyn, NY 11201
Tel.: (718) 923-8400
Nonresidential Construction Services
N.A.I.C.S.: 531312

Forest City Ratner Companies, LLC (2)
1 MetroTech Ctr, Brooklyn, NY 11201   **(100%)**
Tel.: (718) 923-8400
Web Site: http://www.forestcity.net
Sales Range: $400-449.9 Million
Emp.: 300
Commercial Property Acquisition & Management Services
N.A.I.C.S.: 531312
Bruce C. Ratner *(Chm)*

Forest City Rental Properties Corporation (2)
50 Public Sq, Cleveland, OH 44113   **(100%)**
Tel.: (216) 621-6060

Web Site: http://www.forestcity.net
Sales Range: $300-349.9 Million
Emp.: 1,800
Real Estate Investment Services
N.A.I.C.S.: 531120

Subsidiary (Domestic):

Forest City Commercial Management, Inc. (3)
50 Public Sq Ste 1515, Cleveland, OH 44113
Tel.: (216) 416-3906
Real Estate Development Services
N.A.I.C.S.: 531210

Forest City Residential Group, Inc. (3)
50 Public Sq, Cleveland, OH 44113
Tel.: (216) 621-6060
Web Site: http://www.forestcity.net
Sales Range: $550-599.9 Million
Emp.: 1,500
Real Estate Manangement Services
N.A.I.C.S.: 531390

Subsidiary (Domestic):

Forest City Equity Services, Inc. (4)
50 Public Sq Ste 1170, Cleveland, OH 44113
Tel.: (216) 416-3500
Real Estate Development Services
N.A.I.C.S.: 531210

Forest City Residential Management, Inc. (4)
50 Public Sq Ste 1100, Cleveland, OH 44113
Tel.: (216) 621-6060
Real Estate Development Services
N.A.I.C.S.: 531210
George M. Cvijovic *(Co-Pres & COO)*

Forest City Stapleton Land, Inc. (4)
7351 E 29th Ave, Denver, CO 80238
Tel.: (303) 382-1800
Web Site: http://www.stapletondenver.com
Real Estate Development Services
N.A.I.C.S.: 531210

Subsidiary (Domestic):

Forest City Residential Group, LLC (3)
91 Sidney St, Cambridge, MA 02139
Tel.: (617) 679-9401
Real Estate Development Services
N.A.I.C.S.: 531210

Forest City Washington, Inc. (3)
301 Water St SE Ste 201, Washington, DC 20003
Tel.: (202) 496-6600
Web Site: http://www.fcwashington.com
Emp.: 3,000
Real Estate Development Services
N.A.I.C.S.: 531210

Subsidiary (Domestic):

Forest City Residential Development Inc. (2)
50 Public Sq, Cleveland, OH 44113   **(100%)**
Tel.: (216) 621-6060
Web Site: http://www.forestcity.net
Sales Range: $300-349.9 Million
Emp.: 489
Construction Contracting
N.A.I.C.S.: 236117

GrafTech International Ltd. (1)
982 Keynote Cir, Brooklyn Heights, OH 44131
Tel.: (216) 676-2000
Web Site: https://www.graftech.com
Rev.: $1,281,250,000
Assets: $1,604,178,000
Liabilities: $1,266,463,000
Net Worth: $337,715,000
Earnings: $382,962,000
Emp.: 1,347
Fiscal Year-end: 12/31/2022
Graphite & Carbon Products Mfr
N.A.I.C.S.: 335991
Timothy K. Flanagan *(Pres & CEO)*

Subsidiary (Non-US):

GrafTech Brasil Participacoes Ltda. (2)

Rodovia BA-522 / Km-7 Candeias, Bahia, Salvador, 43813-300, Brazil
Tel.: (55) 7121089462
Web Site: http://www.graftech.com
Carbon & Graphite Products Mfr
N.A.I.C.S.: 335991

GrafTech France S.N.C. (2)
Rue des Garennes, 62100, Calais, France
Tel.: (33) 321191420
Web Site: http://www.graftech.com
Carbon & Graphite Product Mfr
N.A.I.C.S.: 335991

GrafTech Germany GmbH (2)
Kaiserswerther Str 115, 40880, Ratingen, Germany
Tel.: (49) 15172447017
N.A.I.C.S.: 335210

GrafTech Hong Kong Limited (2)
13/F Gloucester Tower The Landmark 15 Queen s Road Central, Central, China (Hong Kong)
Tel.: (852) 27392820
N.A.I.C.S.: 811310

GrafTech RUS LLC (2)
35 Usacheva Str 7th Floor, 119048, Moscow, Russia
Tel.: (7) 4959379848
Web Site: http://www.graftech.com
Graphite & Carbon Electrode Distr
N.A.I.C.S.: 335991

GrafTech S.p.A. (2)
77 Via Monte Napoleone 8, 20121, Milan, MI, Italy
Tel.: (39) 041798380861
N.A.I.C.S.: 335210

GrafTech South Africa (Pty) Ltd. (2)
38 Rae Frankel Street Brackenhurst, Alberton, 1448, Gauteng, South Africa
Tel.: (27) 118674228
Web Site: http://www.graftech.com
Carbon & Graphite Electrode Distr
N.A.I.C.S.: 335991

GrafTech Switzerland S.A. (2)
Boulevard de l Arc-en-Ciel 36, 1030, Bussigny-pres-Lausanne, Switzerland
Tel.: (41) 218213111
N.A.I.C.S.: 335210

GrafTech UK Limited (2)
Hart Shaw Building Europa Link, Sheffield, S9 1XU, South Yorkshire, United Kingdom
Tel.: (44) 1142518850
N.A.I.C.S.: 335210

Subsidiary (Domestic):

GrafTech USA LLC (2)
800 Theresia St, Saint Marys, PA 15857-1831
Tel.: (814) 834-2801
Carbon & Graphite Product Mfr
N.A.I.C.S.: 335991

Subsidiary (Non-US):

Graftech Iberica S.L. (2)
Carretera de Astrain S/N Ororbia, 31171, Navarra, Spain
Tel.: (34) 948321200
N.A.I.C.S.: 335210

Subsidiary (Domestic):

Seadrift Coke L.P. (2)
8618 Hwy 185 N, Port Lavaca, TX 77979
Tel.: (361) 552-8887
Web Site: http://www.seadriftcoke.com
Petroleum-Based Needle Coke Mfr
N.A.I.C.S.: 324199

Subsidiary (Non-US):

Shanghai GrafTech Trading Co., Ltd. (2)
Unit 2104 of International Capital Plaza 1318 Sichuan Road North, Hongkou District, Shanghai, 200080, China
Tel.: (86) 2163258018
Web Site: http://www.graftech.com
Carbon & Graphite Electrode Distr
N.A.I.C.S.: 335991

Hammerstone Corporation (1)
2681 Hochwald Court SW, Calgary, T3E 7M3, AB, Canada

Brookfield Corporation—(Continued)

Tel.: (403) 297-1680
Web Site: http://www.hammerstonecorp.com
Sales Range: $50-74.9 Million
Emp.: 15
Limestone & Other Mineral Mining & Quarrying
N.A.I.C.S.: 212312

Hibernia REIT plc (1)
1WML Windmill Lane, Dublin, D02 F206, Ireland
Tel.: (353) 15369100
Web Site: http://www.hiberniareit.com
Rev.: $77,714,586
Assets: $1,582,953,722
Liabilities: $355,289,427
Net Worth: $1,227,664,294
Earnings: ($26,947,654)
Emp.: 35
Fiscal Year-end: 03/31/2021
Real Estate Investment Services
N.A.I.C.S.: 525990
Kevin Nowlan (CEO)

HomeServe plc (1)
Cable Drive, Walsall, WS2 7BN, United Kingdom
Tel.: (44) 1922426262
Web Site: http://www.homeserveplc.com
Rev.: $1,774,904,740
Assets: $2,439,640,280
Liabilities: $1,653,829,240
Net Worth: $785,811,040
Earnings: $165,656,120
Emp.: 8,634
Fiscal Year-end: 03/31/2022
Home Emergency & Repair Services
N.A.I.C.S.: 811490
Richard David Harpin (CEO-Grp, Founder & CEO-Grp)

Subsidiary (Non-US):

Aragonesa De Postventa S.L.U. (2)
Poligono Industrial Parque Tecnologico C/ Centro nave 40, Pinseque, 50298, Zaragoza, Spain
Tel.: (34) 976656788
Heating Air-conditioning Mfr & Distr
N.A.I.C.S.: 333415

Aujard SAS (2)
12 Av Du President Paul Seramy, 77870, Vulaines-sur-Seine, France
Tel.: (33) 164236793
Web Site: http://www.aujard.fr
Plumbing, Heating & Air-conditioning Services Provider
N.A.I.C.S.: 238220

Electro Gaz Service SA (2)
9 Rue Anna Marly, 69007, Lyon, France
Tel.: (33) 484313117
Web Site: https://www.electrogaz.fr
Plumbing, Heating & Air-conditioning Services Provider
N.A.I.C.S.: 238220

Subsidiary (US):

Environmental Systems Associates, Inc. (2)
9375 Gerwig Ln Ste J, Columbia, MD 21046
Tel.: (410) 381-7991
Web Site: http://esaheatac.com
Air Conditioner Installation Services
N.A.I.C.S.: 238220

Hays Cooling & Heating LLC (2)
24825 N 16th Ave Ste 115, Phoenix, AZ 85085
Air Conditioner Installation Services
N.A.I.C.S.: 238220

Subsidiary (Domestic):

Help-Link UK Ltd. (2)
1175 Century Way Thorpe Park, Leeds, LS15 8ZB, W Yorks, United Kingdom
Tel.: (44) 1134267683
Web Site: https://www.homeserve.com
Boiler & Central Heating Installation & Repair Services
N.A.I.C.S.: 238220
Andrew Reid (Mgr-Customer Svc)

Subsidiary (Domestic):

Miller Pattison Limited (3)

Unit 5 Park Square Thorncliffe Park, Chapeltown, Sheffield, S35 2PH, United Kingdom
Tel.: (44) 800564456
Web Site: http://www.millerpattison.co.uk
Construction Materials Whslr
N.A.I.C.S.: 423390
Steve Kane (Mgr-Bus Info Sys & Ops Support)

Subsidiary (Domestic):

HomeServe Assistance Limited (2)
Cable Drive, Walsall, United Kingdom (100%)
Tel.: (44) 8007830951
Web Site: http://www.homeserve.com
Sales Range: $100-124.9 Million
Home Furnishings Stores
N.A.I.C.S.: 449129

HomeServe Care Solutions Limited (2)
Cable Drive, Weston-Super-Mare, Walsall, WS2 7BN, United Kingdom (100%)
Tel.: (44) 1934423333
Web Site: http://www.homeserve.com
Insurance Related Activities
N.A.I.C.S.: 524298

HomeServe Claims Management (2)
Fulwood Park Caxton Road, Preston, PR2 9NZ, United Kingdom (100%)
Tel.: (44) 1772758758
Web Site: http://www.homeserve.com
Sales Range: $350-399.9 Million
Emp.: 750
Claims Adjusting
N.A.I.C.S.: 524291
Richard Harpin (Co-CEO)

HomeServe Enterprises Limited (2)
Cable Drive, Walsall, WS2 7BN, United Kingdom (100%)
Tel.: (44) 1922659800
Sales Range: $700-749.9 Million
Emp.: 1,000
Insurance Related Activities
N.A.I.C.S.: 524298

HomeServe GB Limited (2)
Cable Drive, Walsall, United Kingdom (100%)
Tel.: (44) 8007830951
Web Site: http://www.homeserve.com
Sales Range: $100-124.9 Million
Emp.: 500
Home Furnishings Stores
N.A.I.C.S.: 449129
Richard Harpin (CEO)

HomeServe Membership Limited (2)
Cable Drive, Walsall, WS2 7BN, United Kingdom
Tel.: (44) 8007830951
Home Emergency Services
N.A.I.C.S.: 624230
Martin John Bennett (CEO)

Subsidiary (Non-US):

HomeServe Servowarm Limited (2)
(100%)
Tel.: (44) 8456882266
Web Site: http://www.homeserve.com
Building Equipment & Machinery Installation Contractors
N.A.I.C.S.: 238220

HomeServe Spain SLU (2)
Parque Empresarial La Finca Paseo del Club Deportivo 1, Edificio 12, Pozuelo de Alarcon, 28223, Madrid, Spain
Tel.: (34) 912747201
Web Site: https://www.homeserve.es
N.A.I.C.S.: 811411
Fernando Prieto (CEO)

Subsidiary (US):

HomeServe USA Corp. (2)
601 Merritt 7 6th Fl, Norwalk, CT 06851
Web Site: https://www.homeserve.com
Home Emergency & Repair Dispatch Services
N.A.I.C.S.: 561990
Thomas Rusin (Chm)

Subsidiary (Domestic):

Canyon State Air Conditioning & Heating, Inc. (3)

13632 W Camino Del Sol, Sun City West, AZ 85375-4414
Tel.: (602) 755-6226
Web Site: http://canyonstateac.com
Rev.: $2,400,000
Emp.: 17
Plumbing, Heating & Air-Conditioning Contractors
N.A.I.C.S.: 238220
Christina Jaynes (VP)

Crawford Services, Inc. (3)
1405 Ave T, Grand Prairie, TX 75050
Tel.: (214) 271-8800
HVAC & Plumbing Services
N.A.I.C.S.: 238220
Tim Buford (Co-Founder, Pres & CEO)

Croppmetcalfe, Inc. (3)
8421 Hilltop Rd, Fairfax, VA 22031
Web Site: http://www.croppmetcalfe.com
Site Preparation Contractor
N.A.I.C.S.: 238910

Geisel Heating, Air Conditioning & Plumbing, Inc. (3)
633 Broad St, Elyria, OH 44035
Tel.: (909) 830-5650
Web Site: https://www.gogeisel.com
Plumbing, Heating & Air-Conditioning Contractors
N.A.I.C.S.: 238220

Gregg Mechanical Corp. (3)
4295 Arthur Kill Rd Ste 1A, Staten Island, NY 10309
Tel.: (800) 711-3479
Web Site: http://www.greggmechanical.com
Plumbing, Heating & Air-Conditioning Contractors
N.A.I.C.S.: 238220

HomeServe USA Energy Services (New England) LLC (3)
5 Constitution Way Ste B, Woburn, MA 01801
Tel.: (781) 359-2600
Heating, Cooling & Appliance Repair Services
N.A.I.C.S.: 238220

Sterling Air Services, LLC (3)
7256 S 89th Pl Ste 103, Mesa, AZ 85212
Tel.: (480) 885-0887
Web Site: https://www.sterlingair.us
Commercial Air, Rail & Water Transportation Equipment Rental & Leasing
N.A.I.C.S.: 532411

Taylor Heating, Inc. (3)
259 E Main St, Avon, NY 14414-4414
Tel.: (585) 226-2474
Web Site: http://www.taylorheating.com
Plumbing, Heating & Air-Conditioning Contractors
N.A.I.C.S.: 238220
Aurel Cournoyer (Mgr-Svcs)

Vincodo, LLC (3)
2300 E Lincoln Hwy Ste 317, Langhorne, PA 19047
Web Site: https://vincodo.com
Digital Marketing & Advertising Services
N.A.I.C.S.: 541613
Drew Brooke (VP-Mktg Svcs)

Worry Free Comfort Systems, Inc (3)
630 20th St N, Bessemer, AL 35020-4831
Tel.: (205) 544-4444
Web Site: http://www.freedomheating.com
Emp.: 50
Plumbing, Heating & Air-Conditioning Contractors
N.A.I.C.S.: 238220
Don Johnson (Owner)

Subsidiary (US):

HomeServe USA Energy Services LLC (2)
420 N 2nd Rd Unit 1, Hammonton, NJ 08037
Web Site: https://www.homeservesj.com
N.A.I.C.S.: 811411

HomeServe USA Repair Management Corp. (2)
7134 Lee Hwy, Chattanooga, TN 37421
N.A.I.C.S.: 811411

Subsidiary (Non-US):

ID Energies SAS (2)
Z A DArmanville Route De La Brique, 50700, Valognes, France
Tel.: (33) 233419501
Web Site: https://www.id-energies.com
N.A.I.C.S.: 811411

Lesage SAS (2)
Pa Du Landas - 16 Rue Gutenberg, 44160, Pontchateau, France
Tel.: (33) 240456650
Web Site: https://lesage-mecanique.fr
N.A.I.C.S.: 333613
Brivet Mecano Soudure (Dir)

Linacal S.L.U. (2)
Poligono Las Labrada Vial Estella D-1, Tudela, Navarra, Spain
Tel.: (34) 948411030
Web Site: http://linacal.com
Gas Boiler Services
N.A.I.C.S.: 238220

Mesos Gestion y Servicios S.L. (2)
Avenida de la Industria 18, 28823, Coslada, Madrid, Spain
Tel.: (34) 910010203
Web Site: http://mesos.in
Household Services
N.A.I.C.S.: 811490

Oscagas Hogar SLU (2)
Avda Pablo Ruiz Picasso 14, 50018, Zaragoza, Spain
Tel.: (34) 900816863
Web Site: https://www.oscagas.es
N.A.I.C.S.: 811411

Preventivi SRL (2)
Via Martiri di Bologna 13, 76123, Andria, BT, Italy
Tel.: (39) 0287196246
Web Site: https://pro.preventivi.it
Plumbing, Heating & Air-conditioning Services Provider
N.A.I.C.S.: 238220

Reparalia Direct SL (2)
Camino Cerro de los Gamos 1 Parque empresarial Edificio 5 y 6 planta 0, Pozuelo de Alarcon, 28224, Madrid, Spain
Tel.: (34) 912747201
Web Site: http://www.reparalia.com
Property Repair Services
N.A.I.C.S.: 624229

Reparalia S.A. (2)
Camino Cerro De Los Gamos Pq Empr Cerro De Los 1, Pozuelo De Alarcon, Madrid, 28224, Spain
Tel.: (34) 913729080
Property Repair Services
N.A.I.C.S.: 624229

Reseau Energies SAS (2)
Chemin des Carrieres, 14123, Fleury-sur-Orne, France
Tel.: (33) 231286390
Web Site: http://www.reseauenergies.fr
Wood Stove Mfr
N.A.I.C.S.: 333414

Roussin Energies SAS (2)
34 Allee des Balmes, 38600, Fontaine, France
Tel.: (33) 476260765
Web Site: https://www.roussin-energies.fr
N.A.I.C.S.: 811411

Subsidiary (US):

SJESP Plumbing Services LLC (2)
420 N 2nd Rd Unit 1, Hammonton, NJ 08037
Web Site: https://www.homeservesj.com
Plumbing, Heating & Air-conditioning Services Provider
N.A.I.C.S.: 238220

Service Line Warranties of America, Inc. (2)
4000 Town Center Blvd Ste 400, Canonsburg, PA 15317
Water Coverage Services
N.A.I.C.S.: 221310

Subsidiary (Non-US):

Service Line Warranties of Canada Inc. (2)

150 King Street Suite 200, Toronto, M5H
1J9, ON, Canada
Web Site: https://www.slwofc.ca
N.A.I.C.S.: 811411

Servicio Tecnico Uruena S.L.   **(2)**
Orixe - 54 / Taller Orixe - 56, 48015, Bilbao,
Bizkaia, Spain
Tel.: (34) 944758947
Web Site: http://serviciotecnicouruena.com
Plumbing, Heating & Air-conditioning Ser-
vices Provider
N.A.I.C.S.: 238220

Servicios Tecnicos Sate S.L.   **(2)**
Av de los Monegros 31, 22005, Huesca,
Spain
Tel.: (34) 974223937
Web Site: https://satehuesca.com
Gas Boiler Services
N.A.I.C.S.: 238220

**Societe Francaise de Garantie
S.A.**   **(2)**
Impasse Evariste Galois, 13016, Rousset,
Cedex, France
Tel.: (33) 488785900
Web Site: https://www.sfg.fr
Sales Range: $50-74.9 Million
Emp.: 150
Insurance Agencies & Brokerages
N.A.I.C.S.: 524210

Somgas Hogar S.L.   **(2)**
C/ Rocafort 22-2, 08205, Sabadell, Barce-
lona, Spain
Tel.: (34) 900816895
Web Site: https://somgas.com
Plumbing, Heating & Air-conditioning Ser-
vices Provider
N.A.I.C.S.: 238220

**Tecno Arasat Servicios de Manten-
imiento S.L.**   **(2)**
31 Baron de Eroles Street, 22400, Monzon,
Huesca, Spain
Tel.: (34) 974403107
Web Site: https://www.tecnoarasat.es
Gas Boiler Services
N.A.I.C.S.: 238220

Subsidiary (Domestic):

Vetted Limited   **(2)**
Building 2000 Lakeside North Harbour
Western Road, Portsmouth, PO6 3EN,
United Kingdom
Tel.: (44) 3300574446
Web Site: https://www.checkatrade.com
N.A.I.C.S.: 811411

Subsidiary (US):

eLocal USA LLC   **(2)**
PO Box 495, Dresher, PA 19025
Web Site: https://www.elocal.com
Advertising Services
N.A.I.C.S.: 541810

IPICO, Inc.   **(1)**
4480 Harvester Road, Burlington, L7L 4X2,
ON, Canada
Tel.: (905) 631-6310
Web Site: http://www.ipico.com
Sales Range: $1-9.9 Million
Emp.: 32
Radio-Frequency Identification Equipment
Designer & Mfr
N.A.I.C.S.: 334220

Subsidiary (Non-US):

IPICO South Africa (Pty) Ltd.   **(2)**
Scientia Techno Park Building C Unit 20,
Meiring Naude Street, Pretoria, 0020, South
Africa
Tel.: (27) 123497620
Emp.: 9
Sports Timing & Tracking System Services
N.A.I.C.S.: 334220
Marius Van Dyk *(Mgr)*

Insignia Energy Ltd.   **(1)**
2300 500 4th Ave SW, Calgary, T2P 2V6,
AB, Canada
Tel.: (403) 536-8132
Web Site: http://www.insigniaenergy.ca
Sales Range: $25-49.9 Million
Emp.: 15
Oil & Gas Exploration Services
N.A.I.C.S.: 211120

MediSolution Ltd.   **(1)**
13-217 avenue Leonidas, Rimouski, G5L
2T5, QC, Canada   **(60%)**
Tel.: (514) 850-5000
Web Site: https://www.medisolution.com
Sales Range: $25-49.9 Million
Emp.: 302
Healthcare & Service Industry Information
Technology Software & Services
N.A.I.C.S.: 513210

**Network International Holdings
PLC**   **(1)**
Network Building 1 Al Barsha 2 Level 1,
Dubai, United Arab Emirates
Tel.: (971) 2123362301
Web Site: https://www.network.ae
Rev.: $284,844,000
Assets: $1,248,729,000
Liabilities: $750,767,000
Net Worth: $497,962,000
Earnings: $5,598,000
Emp.: 1,309
Fiscal Year-end: 12/31/2020
Electronic Payment Services
N.A.I.C.S.: 522320

Subsidiary (Non-US):

Egyptian Smart Cards Company   **(2)**
B86- A7- Smart Village KM 28 Cairo Alex
Desert Road, Cairo, Egypt
Tel.: (20) 233455615
Web Site: http://www.egyptsmartcards.com
Online Payment Services
N.A.I.C.S.: 522320
Ahmed Radwan *(CFO)*

**Network International Payment Ser-
vices Proprietary Limited**   **(2)**
3rd Floor Letterstedt House Newlands on
Main Main Road, Claremont, Cape Town,
South Africa
Tel.: (27) 216812560
Online Payment Services
N.A.I.C.S.: 522320

**Network International Payments Ser-
vices Nigeria Limited**   **(2)**
Block B 4th Floor 3 Force Road Onikan,
Lagos, Nigeria
Tel.: (234) 19076001
Online Payment Services
N.A.I.C.S.: 522320

**Network International Services
Limited**   **(2)**
Abdul Raheem Al-Wakeed St Building No
43, Shmeisani, Amman, Jordan
Tel.: (962) 65606829
Online Payment Services
N.A.I.C.S.: 522320

OB Companies   **(1)**
7505 W Sand Lk Rd Ste 108, Orlando, FL
32819
Tel.: (407) 248-7878
Web Site: http://www.simplyss.com
Sales Range: $75-99.9 Million
Emp.: 50
Holding Company; Self Storage Facilities,
Commercial Real Estate, Retail & Office
Construction
N.A.I.C.S.: 551112
Jason Jacobson *(CFO)*

Royal Oak Ventures Inc.   **(1)**
Brookfield Place 181 Bay Street Suite 300,
PO Box 762, Toronto, M5J 2T3, ON,
Canada   **(100%)**
Tel.: (416) 359-8590
Sales Range: Less than $1 Million
Investment Holding Company
N.A.I.C.S.: 551112

TerraForm Global, Inc.   **(1)**
7550 Wisconsin Ave 9th Fl, Bethesda, MD
20814
Tel.: (240) 762-7700
Web Site: http://www.terraformglobal.com
Clean Power Generation
N.A.I.C.S.: 221118

TerraForm Power, Inc.   **(1)**
200 Liberty St 14th Fl, New York, NY
10281   **(100%)**
Tel.: (646) 992-2400
Web Site: https://www.terraformpower.com
Rev.: $941,240,000
Assets: $10,058,636,000

Liabilities: $7,450,728,000
Net Worth: $2,607,908,000
Earnings: ($148,684,000)
Emp.: 174
Fiscal Year-end: 12/31/2019
Holding Company; Renewable Power (Solar
& Wind Assets) Operator
N.A.I.C.S.: 551112

Vanti SA., ESP   **(1)**
Calle 71A No 5-38, Bogota,
Colombia   **(59.1%)**
Tel.: (57) 1 307 8121
Web Site: http://www.grupovanti.com
Natural Gas Distr
N.A.I.C.S.: 221210
Maria Eugenia Coronado Orjuela *(Pres)*

Vodafone New Zealand Ltd.   **(1)**
No 20 Via Back Harbour Ave, PO Box
92161, Auckland, 1142, New Zealand
Tel.: (64) 93552000
Web Site: http://www.vodafone.co.nz
Sales Range: $1-4.9 Billion
Emp.: 3,000
Cellular Communications Network Operator
N.A.I.C.S.: 517112
Tony Baird *(Dir-Wholesale & Infrastructure)*

**Wynyard Properties Holdings
Limited**   **(1)**
Level 12 301 Thakral House, George
Street, Sydney, 2000, NSW, Australia
Tel.: (61) 292728888
Holding Company; Real Estate Develope-
ment Services; Hotel Owner & Operator
N.A.I.C.S.: 551112

Subsidiary (Domestic):

Hilton on the Park Melbourne   **(2)**
192 Wellington Parade, Melbourne, 3002,
VIC, Australia
Tel.: (61) 394192000
Web Site:
   http://www.hiltonmelbourne.com.au
Hotel & Spa Services
N.A.I.C.S.: 721110

**Novotel Pacific Bay Coffs Harbour
Resort**   **(2)**
Pacific Highway, Coffs Harbour, 2450,
NSW, Australia
Tel.: (61) 266597000
Web Site:
   http://www.pacificbayresort.com.au
Sales Range: $25-49.9 Million
Emp.: 80
Hotels & Motels
N.A.I.C.S.: 721110

**Sovereign AOC Operations Pty
Limited**   **(2)**
L 12 301 George Street, Sydney, 2001,
NSW, Australia
Tel.: (61) 292728888
Property Development Services
N.A.I.C.S.: 531311

Sovereign Goldsea Pty Limited   **(2)**
Oasis Shopping Centre Victoria Ave, Broad-
beach, Gold Coast, 4218, QLD, Australia
Tel.: (61) 755923900
Emp.: 10
Property Development Services
N.A.I.C.S.: 531311
Michael Tree *(Mgr)*

**Sovereign Pacific Bay Property Man-
agement Pty Limited**   **(2)**
L 12 301 George Street, Sydney, 2000,
NSW, Australia
Tel.: (61) 2 9272 8888
Property Management Services
N.A.I.C.S.: 531311

**Sovereign Palm Cove Development
Nominees Pty Limited**   **(2)**
PO Box 53, Palm Cove, 4879, Australia
Tel.: (61) 740598400
Nominee Services
N.A.I.C.S.: 541199

**Sovereign Property Fund Pty
Limited**   **(2)**
Level 12 Wynyard House 301 George
Street, Sydney, 2000, NSW, Australia
Tel.: (61) 292728888
Real Estate Manangement Services
N.A.I.C.S.: 531390

**Sovereign Wynyard Finance Pty
Limited**   **(2)**
Level 12 Thakral House 301 George Street,
Sydney, 2000, NSW, Australia
Tel.: (61) 292728888
Property Management Services
N.A.I.C.S.: 531311

Wynyard Properties Pty Limited   **(2)**
14 Carrington St, Sydney, 2000, NSW, Aus-
tralia
Tel.: (61) 292991000
Emp.: 200
Hotel
N.A.I.C.S.: 721110
Michael Smith *(Mng Dir)*

**BROOKFIELD GLOBAL INFRA-
STRUCTURE SECURITIES IN-
COME FUND**
181 Bay Street Suite 300 Brookfield
Place, PO Box 762, Toronto, M5J
2T3, ON, Canada
Year Founded: 2013
BGI.UN—(TSX)
Rev.: $12,075,125
Assets: $81,234,088
Liabilities: $18,957,436
Net Worth: $62,276,652
Earnings: $10,471,331
Fiscal Year-end: 12/31/21
Investment Management Service
N.A.I.C.S.: 525990
Leonardo Anguiano *(Mng Dir & Port-
folio Mgr)*

**BROOKFIELD INFRASTRUC-
TURE PARTNERS L.P.**
73 Front Street, Hamilton, HM 12,
Bermuda
Tel.: (441) 2943309   **BM**
Web Site: https://bip.brookfield.com
BIP—(NYSE)
Rev.: $14,427,000,000
Assets: $72,969,000,000
Liabilities: $47,415,000,000
Net Worth: $25,554,000,000
Earnings: $1,375,000,000
Emp.: 52,000
Fiscal Year-end: 12/31/22
Holding Company; Infrastructure As-
sets Owner & Operator
N.A.I.C.S.: 551112
Mark Murski *(Mng Partner)*

Subsidiaries:

**Brookfield Infrastructure
Corporation**   **(1)**
Brookfield Place Suite 300 181 Bay Street,
Toronto, M5J 2T3, ON, Canada
Tel.: (416) 363-9491
Web Site: https://www.bip.brookfield.com
Rev.: $1,886,000,000
Assets: $10,178,000,000
Liabilities: $10,539,000,000
Net Worth: ($361,000,000)
Earnings: $1,619,000,000
Emp.: 2,300
Fiscal Year-end: 12/31/2022
Real Estate Asset Management Services
N.A.I.C.S.: 531390
Sam Pollock *(Mng Partner & CEO-
Infrastructure)*

Subsidiary (Non-US):

Triton International Limited   **(2)**
Victoria Pl 5th Fl 31 Victoria St, Hamilton,
HM 10, Bermuda
Tel.: (441) 2948033
Web Site: http://www.tritoninternational.com
Rev.: $1,679,686,000
Assets: $12,109,258,000
Liabilities: $8,904,895,000
Net Worth: $3,204,363,000
Earnings: $694,810,000
Emp.: 244
Fiscal Year-end: 12/31/2022
Cargo Container Leasing Services
N.A.I.C.S.: 532490
Michelle Gallagher *(VP & Controller)*

Brookfield Infrastructure Partners L.P.—(Continued)

Subsidiary (Domestic):

Triton Container International Limited   **(3)**
Canons Court 22 Victoria Street, Hamilton, HM 12, Bermuda
Tel.: (441) 295 2287
Container Mfr
N.A.I.C.S.: 332439
Roderick Romeo (Pres)

Subsidiary (US):

TAL International Group, Inc   **(4)**
100 Manhattanville Rd, Purchase, NY 10577-2135
Tel.: (914) 251-9000
Mfr of Intermodal Freight Containers & Distr of Used Shipping Containers
N.A.I.C.S.: 483111
John Burns (CFO & Sr VP)

Subsidiary (Non-US):

ICS Terminals (UK) Limited   **(5)**
271a CEME Marsh Way, Rainham, RM13 8EU, Essex, United Kingdom
Tel.: (44) 20 8596 5080
Web Site: http://www.spacewise.co.uk
Portable Offices & Containers Leasing Services
N.A.I.C.S.: 532490

Subsidiary (Non-US):

Triton Container (S) Pte Ltd   **(4)**
6 Temasek Boulevard 21-06 Suntec Tower 4, Singapore, 038986, Singapore
Tel.: (65) 6338 7227
Web Site: http://www.tritoncontainer.com
Emp.: 11
Cargo Container Leasing Services
N.A.I.C.S.: 532490
Jeanie Tan (VP)

Triton Container International B.V.   **(4)**
Veerhaven 4, 3016 CJ, Rotterdam, Netherlands
Tel.: (31) 104363400
Cargo Container Leasing Services
N.A.I.C.S.: 532490

Subsidiary (US):

Triton Container International Limited   **(4)**
55 Green St, San Francisco, CA 94111
Tel.: (206) 855-4181
Web Site: http://www.tritoncontainer.com
Cargo Container Leasing Services
N.A.I.C.S.: 532490

Subsidiary (Non-US):

Triton Container International, GmbH   **(4)**
Kleine Reichenstrasse 5, 20457, Hamburg, Germany
Tel.: (49) 4023893114
Web Site: http://www.tritoninternational.com
Cargo Container Leasing Services
N.A.I.C.S.: 532490

Triton Container South Africa (Pty) Ltd   **(4)**
212 2nd Floor The Cliffs Niagara Way Tyger Falls Bellville, Cape Town, 7530, South Africa
Tel.: (27) 21 914 2660
Cargo Container Leasing Services
N.A.I.C.S.: 532490
Gareth Weir (Gen Mgr)

Triton Container Sul Americana Transporte E Comercio Ltda.   **(4)**
Av Rio Branco 25-3 andar-Grupo A Centro, Rio de Janeiro, 20090-003, Brazil
Tel.: (55) 21 2518 1448
Web Site: http://www.trtn.com
Emp.: 4
Cargo Container Leasing Services
N.A.I.C.S.: 532490

Triton Container UK Limited   **(4)**
3rd Floor 40 New Bond Street, London, W1S 2RX, United Kingdom
Tel.: (44) 20 7493 2380

Web Site: http://www.tritoncontainer.com
Emp.: 10
Cargo Container Leasing Services
N.A.I.C.S.: 532490
Mark Bennett (Sr VP)

Triton International Australia Pty Ltd   **(4)**
Suite 410 Level 4 15 Lime Street, Sydney, 2000, NSW, Australia
Tel.: (61) 2 9299 9993
Web Site: http://www.trtn.com
Emp.: 5
Cargo Container Leasing Services
N.A.I.C.S.: 532490

Triton Italy s.r.l.   **(4)**
Largo San Giuseppe 3/15, 16121, Genoa, Italy
Tel.: (39) 010 576 971
Web Site: http://www.tritoncontainer.com
Emp.: 4
Cargo Container Leasing Services
N.A.I.C.S.: 532490
Renzo Fiumano (Dir-Mktg)

Triton Limited   **(4)**
33/F PCCW Tower Taikoo Place 979 King's Road, Quarry Bay, China (Hong Kong)
Tel.: (852) 2529 6118
Cargo Container Leasing Services
N.A.I.C.S.: 532490

Brookfield Infrastructure L.P.   **(1)**
73 Front St, Hamilton, HM 12, Bermuda
Tel.: (441) 2943309   **(70%)**
Infrastructure Asset Management Services
N.A.I.C.S.: 523940
Samuel Pollock (CEO & Mng Partner)

Holding (Non-US):

Brookfield Rail Pty. Ltd.   **(2)**
Tel.: (61) 892122800
Sales Range: $25-49.9 Million
Emp.: 100
Railroad Infrastructure Management Services
N.A.I.C.S.: 488210

Oy Rauma Stevedoring Ltd.   **(2)**
  (100%)
Tel.: (358) 283121
Sales Range: $100-124.9 Million
Emp.: 600
Port Operator & Marine Cargo Handling Services
N.A.I.C.S.: 488310

PD Ports Ltd.   **(2)**
17-27 Queen's Square, Middlesbrough, TS2 1AH, United Kingdom   **(100%)**
Tel.: (44) 1642877000
Web Site: https://www.pdports.co.uk
Sales Range: $250-299.9 Million
Emp.: 1,500
Holding Company; Port Operation & Logistic Services
N.A.I.C.S.: 551112
David Robinson (Chm)

Subsidiary (Domestic):

PD Ports Group Limited   **(3)**
17-27 Queens Square, Middlesbrough, TS2 1AH, United Kingdom   **(100%)**
Tel.: (44) 01642877000
Web Site: http://www.pdports.co.uk
Sales Range: $25-49.9 Million
Emp.: 30
Holding Company; Port Operation & Logistic Services
N.A.I.C.S.: 551112

Unit (Domestic):

PD Logistics   **(4)**
Crannaghmore Summerhill, Athlone, Felixstowe, N37 F6C1, Roscommon, United Kingdom
Tel.: (44) 906465720
Web Site: https://www.pdlogistics.ie
Sales Range: $10-24.9 Million
General Freight Warehousing & Distribution Services
N.A.I.C.S.: 493110

Subsidiary (Domestic):

PD Port Services Ltd.   **(4)**

Spurn House, Immingham, DN40 2NR, Lincs, United Kingdom   **(100%)**
Tel.: (44) 1469552700
Web Site: http://www.pdports.co.uk
Port Operation Services
N.A.I.C.S.: 488310

Holding (Non-US):

Rockpoint Gas Storage LP   **(2)**
400 - 607 8th Avenue SW, Calgary, T2P 0A7, AB, Canada
Tel.: (403) 513-8600
Web Site: http://www.rockpointgs.com
Holding Company; Natural Gas Storage Assets Investment & Management Services
N.A.I.C.S.: 551112
Kevin Donegan (VP-Fin)

Subsidiary (US):

Lodi Gas Storage, LLC   **(3)**
23265 N Rte 99 - PO Box 230, Acampo, CA 95220
Tel.: (209) 368-9277
Web Site: http://www.rockpointgs.com
Natural Gas Terminal & Pipeline Transportation Services
N.A.I.C.S.: 424710
Simon Dupere (Chm, Pres & CEO)

Wild Goose Storage, LLC   **(3)**
2780 W Liberty Rd, Gridley, CA 95948
Tel.: (530) 846-7351
Web Site: http://www.rockpointgs.com
Emp.: 100
Natural Gas Storage Services
N.A.I.C.S.: 424710

Joint Venture (Non-US):

TDF S.A.S.   **(2)**
Tel.: (33) 155951000
Web Site: http://www.tdf.fr
Television, Radio, Telecommunications & Satellite Communications Infrastructure Operator
N.A.I.C.S.: 517810
Olivier Huart (Chm & CEO)

EnerCare Inc.   **(1)**
7400 Birchmount Rd, Markham, L3R 5V4, ON, Canada
Tel.: (416) 649-1900
Web Site: http://corporate.enercare.ca
Rev.: $1,002,250,420
Assets: $1,597,655,243
Liabilities: $1,125,269,407
Net Worth: $472,385,836
Earnings: $44,221,897
Emp.: 4,259
Fiscal Year-end: 12/31/2017
Water Heater & Related Products Investment Services
N.A.I.C.S.: 523999
Geoff Lowe (CFO)

Subsidiary (US):

Service Experts LLC   **(2)**
1207 Avenue L, Plano, TX 75074
Tel.: (972) 424-4300
Web Site: http://www.serviceexperts.com
Sales Range: $1-9.9 Million
Emp.: 25
Refrigeration Repair Services
N.A.I.C.S.: 811412
Rob Comstock (Pres)

Subsidiary (Domestic):

Aramendia Plumbing, Heating & Air, Ltd.   **(3)**
17327 Green Mountain Rd, San Antonio, TX 78247
Tel.: (210) 654-1034
Web Site: https://www.aramendia.com
Sales Range: $1-9.9 Million
Emp.: 90
Plumbing, Heating & Air-Conditioning Contractors
N.A.I.C.S.: 238220
Joe Aramendia (Founder & Pres)

Genesee & Wyoming Inc.   **(1)**
20 West Ave, Darien, CT 06820
Tel.: (203) 202-8900
Web Site: http://www.gwrr.com
Rev.: $2,348,550,000
Assets: $7,868,461,000
Liabilities: $4,238,409,000

Net Worth: $3,630,052,000
Earnings: $244,418,000
Emp.: 8,000
Fiscal Year-end: 12/31/2018
Short Line & Regional Freight Railroad Services
N.A.I.C.S.: 482111
Jack Hellmann (CEO)

Subsidiary (Domestic):

Arizona & California Railroad Company   **(2)**
1301 S California Ave, Parker, AZ 85344
Tel.: (928) 669-6662
Sales Range: $10-24.9 Million
Emp.: 29
Short Line Railroad
N.A.I.C.S.: 482111

Arizona Eastern Railway Company   **(2)**
5903 S Calle de Loma, Claypool, AZ 85532
Tel.: (928) 473-2447
Rev.: $4,200,000
Emp.: 45
Railroad Services
N.A.I.C.S.: 482111

Arkansas Louisiana & Mississippi Railroad Co.   **(2)**
140 Plywood Mill Rd, Crossett, AR 71635
Tel.: (870) 364-9000
Sales Range: $1-9.9 Million
Emp.: 19
Short Line Railroads Services
N.A.I.C.S.: 482112

Arkansas Midland Railroad   **(2)**
314 Reynolds Rd Bldg 41, Malvern, AR 72104
Tel.: (501) 844-4444
Web Site: https://www.gwrr.com
Railroad Services
N.A.I.C.S.: 482111
Gene Cox (Gen Mgr)

Subsidiary (Non-US):

Atlantic and Western Railway LP   **(2)**
Tel.: (919) 776-7521
Web Site: http://www.gwrr.com
Sales Range: $1-9.9 Million
Emp.: 3
Railroad Line-Haul Services
N.A.I.C.S.: 488210

Subsidiary (Domestic):

Atlas Railroad Construction Co., Inc.   **(2)**
1370 Washington Pike Ste 202, Bridgeville, PA 15017
Tel.: (412) 677-2020
Web Site: http://gwrr.com
Emp.: 50
Short Line Railroads Services
N.A.I.C.S.: 482112

Bauxite & Northern Railway Company   **(2)**
6232 Cynamide Rd, Bauxite, AR 72011
Tel.: (501) 557-2600
Web Site: https://www.gwrr.com
Short Line Railroads Services
N.A.I.C.S.: 482112

Buffalo & Pittsburgh Railroad, Inc.   **(2)**
400 Meridian Center Ste 300, Rochester, NY 14618
Tel.: (585) 328-8601
Web Site: http://www.gwrr.com
Sales Range: $1-9.9 Million
Emp.: 100
Freight Transportation Arrangement
N.A.I.C.S.: 561110

Division (Domestic):

Allegheny & Eastern Railroad, LLC   **(3)**
1210 4th Ave, Warren, PA 16365
Tel.: (814) 726-3551
Short Line Railroads Services
N.A.I.C.S.: 482112

Branch (Domestic):

Buffalo & Pittsburgh Railroad, Inc.   **(3)**

201 N Penn St, Punxsutawney, PA 15765
Tel.: (814) 938-5500
Web Site: http://www.gwrr.com
Sales Range: $1-9.9 Million
Emp.: 10
Line-Haul Operating Railroads
N.A.I.C.S.: 482111

Joint Venture (Domestic):

CG Railway, LLC   **(2)**
601 Poydras St Ste 1625, New Orleans, LA
70130   **(40%)**
Tel.: (251) 266-5239
Web Site: http://www.cgrailway.com
Short Line Railroad
N.A.I.C.S.: 482112

Subsidiary (Domestic):

California Northern Railroad
Company   **(2)**
1801 Hanover Dr Ste D, Davis, CA 95616
Tel.: (530) 753-7826
Web Site: http://www.gwrr.com
Sales Range: $10-24.9 Million
Emp.: 40
Short Line Railroads Services
N.A.I.C.S.: 482112

Subsidiary (Non-US):

Cape Breton & Central Nova Scotia
Railway Limited   **(2)**
121 King Street, PO Box 2240, Stellarton,
B0K 1S0, NS, Canada
Web Site: http://www.gwrr.com
Sales Range: $25-49.9 Million
Emp.: 125
Short Line Railroad
N.A.I.C.S.: 482112

Subsidiary (Domestic):

Carolina Piedmont Railroad   **(2)**
268 E Main St, Laurens, SC 29360
Tel.: (864) 984-0040
Web Site: https://www.gwrr.com
Sales Range: $1-9.9 Million
Emp.: 9
Short Line Railroad
N.A.I.C.S.: 482111
Yurgen Harter *(Mgr-Ops)*

Cascade & Columbia River Railroad
Company   **(2)**
901 Omak Ave, Omak, WA 98841
Tel.: (509) 826-3752
Web Site: http://www.gwrr.com
Sales Range: $1-9.9 Million
Emp.: 8
Short Line Railroad
N.A.I.C.S.: 482111

Central Oregon & Pacific Railroad,
Inc.   **(2)**
333 SE Mosher, Roseburg, OR 97470
Tel.: (802) 527-3499
Sales Range: $25-49.9 Million
Emp.: 75
Short Line Railroads Services
N.A.I.C.S.: 482112

Central Railroad Company of
Indianapolis   **(2)**
1990 E Washington St, East Peoria, IL
61611
Tel.: (309) 698-2600
Web Site: http://www.gwrr.com
Short Line Railroads Services
N.A.I.C.S.: 482112

Chattahoochee Industrial
Railroad   **(2)**
160 CIRR Ln, Cedar Springs, GA 39832
Tel.: (229) 793-4546
Containerboard Mill Railroad Services
N.A.I.C.S.: 482111

Chattooga & Chickamauga Railway
Co.   **(2)**
413 W Villanow St, La Fayette, GA 30728
Tel.: (706) 638-9552
Web Site: https://www.gwrr.com
Freight Railroad Services
N.A.I.C.S.: 482111
Donnie Owens *(Mgr)*

Columbus & Chattahoochee Railroad,
Inc.   **(2)**

621 9th Ave, Columbus, GA 31901
Tel.: (229) 698-2000
Web Site: https://www.gwrr.com
Emp.: 21
Short Line Railroads Services
N.A.I.C.S.: 482112

Conecuh Valley Railway, L.L.C.   **(2)**
812 N Main St, Enterprise, AL 36330
Tel.: (904) 596-1086
Web Site: https://www.gwrr.com
Short Line Railroads Services
N.A.I.C.S.: 482112
Bill Jasper *(Pres)*

Connecticut Southern Railroad,
Inc.   **(2)**
440 Windsor St, Hartford, CT 06142
Web Site: https://www.gwrr.com
Sales Range: $1-9.9 Million
Emp.: 14
Short Line Railroads Services
N.A.I.C.S.: 482112

Dallas, Garland & Northeastern Rail-
road, Inc.   **(2)**
403 International Pkwy Ste 500, Richard-
son, TX 75081
Tel.: (972) 808-9800
Web Site: http://www.gwrr.com
Sales Range: $1-9.9 Million
Emp.: 95
Short Line Railroads Services
N.A.I.C.S.: 482112

Subsidiary (Domestic):

Texas Northeastern Railroad   **(3)**
403 International Pkwy Ste 500, Richard-
son, TX 75081-2899
Tel.: (972) 808-9800
Web Site: http://www.gwrr.com
Short Line Railroad
N.A.I.C.S.: 482112

Subsidiary (Domestic):

East Tennessee Railway, L.P.   **(2)**
132 Legion St, Johnson City, TN 37601
Tel.: (802) 527-3499
Web Site: https://www.gwrr.com
Sales Range: $1-9.9 Million
Emp.: 3
Short Line Railroads Services
N.A.I.C.S.: 482112

Eastern Alabama Railway, LLC   **(2)**
2413 Hill Rd, Sylacauga, AL 35151
Tel.: (251) 513-1100
Web Site: https://www.gwrr.com
Emp.: 10
Short Line Railroads Services
N.A.I.C.S.: 482112

Subsidiary (Non-US):

Ferrocarriles Chiapas-Mayab, S.A. de
C.V.   **(2)**
480 Colonial Centro Entre 44 Y 46, Merida,
CP 97000, Yucatain, Mexico
Tel.: (52) 9999302500
Web Site: http://www.rosasandxocolate.com
Sales Range: $100-124.9 Million
Emp.: 300
Freight Transportation Arrangement
N.A.I.C.S.: 488510

Subsidiary (Domestic):

First Coast Railroad Inc.   **(2)**
404 Gum St, Fernandina Beach, FL 32034
Tel.: (904) 261-0888
Web Site: https://www.gwrr.com
Short Line Railroads Services
N.A.I.C.S.: 482112

Fordyce and Princeton R.R. Co.   **(2)**
105 W 2nd Ave, Crossett, AR 71635-2803
Tel.: (870) 364-9000
Railroad Transportation Services
N.A.I.C.S.: 482111

Subsidiary (Non-US):

Freightliner Group Limited   **(2)**
6th Floor The Lewis Building 35 Bull Street,
Birmingham, B4 6EQ, United Kingdom
Tel.: (44) 2072003974
Web Site: http://www.freightliner.co.uk
Emp.: 80

Holding Company; Intermodal Rail Freight
Transportation Services
N.A.I.C.S.: 551112
Tim Shakerley *(Mng Dir-UK Rail)*

Subsidiary (Non-US):

ERS Railways B.V.   **(3)**
Albert Plesmanweg 61 B, 3088 GB, Rotter-
dam, Netherlands
Tel.: (31) 104285220
Web Site: http://www.ersrail.com
Line Haul Railroad Services
N.A.I.C.S.: 482111

Freightliner Australia Pty Ltd   **(3)**
Suite 1 Building 1 Pymble Corporate Centre
20 Bridge Street, Pymble, 2073, Australia
Tel.: (61) 294496222
Web Site:
     http://www.freightlineraustralia.com.au
Emp.: 8
Bulk Freight Rail Transportation Services
N.A.I.C.S.: 482112

Freightliner DE GmbH   **(3)**
Strasse am Flugplatz 6A, 12487, Berlin,
Germany
Tel.: (49) 30632234711
Web Site: https://de.freightliner.eu
Bulk Freight Rail Transportation
N.A.I.C.S.: 482112

Subsidiary (Domestic):

Freightliner Heavy Haul Limited   **(3)**
3rd Floor The Podium 1 Eversholt Street,
London, NW1 2FL, United Kingdom
Tel.: (44) 7739823448
Web Site: http://www.freightliner.co.uk
Short Line Railroads Services
N.A.I.C.S.: 482112

Freightliner Limited   **(3)**
Third Floor 90 Whitfield Street, Fitzrovia,
London, W1T 4EZ, United Kingdom
Tel.: (44) 3330168556
Web Site: http://www.freightliner.co.uk
Emp.: 70
Intermodal Rail Freight Transportation Ser-
vices
N.A.I.C.S.: 482111
Gary Long *(CEO)*

Subsidiary (Non-US):

Freightliner PL Sp. z o. o.   **(2)**
Ul Polna 11, 00-633, Warsaw, Poland
Tel.: (48) 226486655
Rail Freight Services
N.A.I.C.S.: 488210
Wojciech Jurkiewicz *(COO)*

Freightliner Scotland Ltd   **(2)**
100 Gartsherrie Road, Coatbridge, ML5
2DR, United Kingdom
Tel.: (44) 1236503700
Shunting Terminal Services
N.A.I.C.S.: 488210

GWI Acquisitions Pty Ltd   **(2)**
33 Richmond Road 5035, Adelaide, 5035,
SA, Australia
Tel.: (61) 883435455
Regional Rail Services
N.A.I.C.S.: 482111

GWI Holding BV   **(2)**
Industrial Road 17, 6662 NG, Elst, Nether-
lands
Tel.: (31) 481451034
Short Line Railroads Services
N.A.I.C.S.: 482112

Genesee & Wyoming Australia Pty
Ltd   **(2)**
Level 3 33 Richmond Road, Keswick, 5035,
SA, Australia
Tel.: (61) 883435455
Web Site: http://www.gwrr.com
Sales Range: $300-349.9 Million
Emp.: 484
Short Line Railroads Services
N.A.I.C.S.: 482112
Michael Morris *(CFO)*

Genesee & Wyoming Canada
Inc.   **(2)**
9001 boul de lAcadie Bureau 600, Mon-
treal, H4N 3H5, QC, Canada
Tel.: (514) 948-6999

Web Site: http://www.gwrr.com
Emp.: 40
Short Line Railroads Services
N.A.I.C.S.: 482112

Subsidiary (Domestic):

Huron Central Railway Inc.   **(3)**
30 Oakland Avenue, Sault Sainte Marie,
P6A 2T3, ON, Canada
Tel.: (705) 254-4511
Rail Freight Transportation Services
N.A.I.C.S.: 482111

Quebec Gatineau Railway   **(3)**
9001 Bureau 600, Montreal, H4N 3H5, QC,
Canada
Tel.: (514) 948-6999
Web Site: http://www.gwrr.com
Rail Transportation
N.A.I.C.S.: 482112

St. Lawrence & Atlantic Railroad
(Quebec) Inc.   **(3)**
9001 boul de l Acadie Bureau 600, Mon-
treal, H4N 3H5, QC, Canada
Tel.: (514) 948-6999
Web Site: http://www.gwrr.com
Short Line Railroad
N.A.I.C.S.: 482112

Western Labrador Rail Services
Inc,   **(3)**
Suite 210-1 210 Humber Avenue, Labrador
City, A2V 2W8, NL, Canada
Tel.: (709) 944-6564
Web Site: http://www.gwrr.com
Short Line Railroads Services
N.A.I.C.S.: 482112

Subsidiary (Domestic):

Genesee & Wyoming Railroad
Company   **(2)**
200 Meridian Ctr Ste 300, Rochester, NY
14618-3972
Tel.: (585) 328-8601
Sales Range: $200-249.9 Million
Emp.: 2,600
Line-Haul Operating Railroads
N.A.I.C.S.: 482111

Genesee & Wyoming Railroad Ser-
vices, Inc.   **(2)**
200 Meridian Ctr Blvd Ste 300, Rochester,
NY 14618
Tel.: (585) 328-8601
Emp.: 130
Short Line Railroads Services
N.A.I.C.S.: 482112

Georgia Central Railway, L.P.   **(2)**
186 Winge Rd, Lyons, GA 30436
Tel.: (912) 526-6165
Web Site: https://www.gwrr.com
Short Line Railroads Services
N.A.I.C.S.: 482112

Subsidiary (Non-US):

Goderich-Exeter Railway Company
Limited   **(2)**
101 Shakespeare Street Unit 2, Stratford,
N5A 3W5, ON, Canada
Tel.: (519) 271-4441
Web Site: http://www.gwrr.com
Short Line Railroads Services
N.A.I.C.S.: 482112

Subsidiary (Domestic):

Golden Isles Terminal Railroad,
Inc.   **(2)**
179 Penniman Cir, Brunswick, GA 31523
Tel.: (802) 527-3499
Web Site: https://www.gwrr.com
Short Line Railroads Services
N.A.I.C.S.: 482112

Heart of Georgia Railroad, Inc.   **(2)**
908 Elm Ave, Americus, GA 31709
Tel.: (229) 924-7662
Web Site: https://www.gwrr.com
Emp.: 11
Regional Rail Services
N.A.I.C.S.: 482111

Huron & Eastern Railway Company,
Inc.   **(2)**
101 Enterprise Dr, Vassar, MI 48768-9505

Brookfield Infrastructure Partners L.P.—(Continued)

Tel.: (989) 823-0090
Web Site: http://www.gwrr.com
Sales Range: $1-9.9 Million
Emp.: 20
Short Line Railroads Services
N.A.I.C.S.: 482112

Illinois & Midland Railroad, Inc. (2)
1500 N Grand Ave E, Springfield, IL 62702
Tel.: (217) 788-8601
Web Site: https://www.gwrr.com
Sales Range: $25-49.9 Million
Emp.: 80
Line-Haul Operating Railroads
N.A.I.C.S.: 482111

Indiana Southern Railroad, LLC (2)
202 W Illinois St, Petersburg, IN 47567
Tel.: (812) 354-8080
Sales Range: $10-24.9 Million
Emp.: 29
Short Line Railroads Services
N.A.I.C.S.: 482112

KWT Railway, Inc. (2)
908 Depot St, Paris, TN 38242
Web Site: http://www.gwrr.com
Rail Transportation Services
N.A.I.C.S.: 488210

Kiamichi Railroad Company L.L.C. (2)
800 Martin Luther King Blvd, Hugo, OK 74743
Tel.: (508) 916-7600
Emp.: 16
Short Line Railroads Services
N.A.I.C.S.: 482112

Kyle Railroad Company (2)
38 Railroad Ave, Phillipsburg, KS 67661
Tel.: (785) 628-7700
Sales Range: $25-49.9 Million
Emp.: 85
Short Line Railroads Services
N.A.I.C.S.: 482112

Louisiana & Delta Railroad, Inc. (2)
402 W Washington St, New Iberia, LA 70560
Tel.: (337) 364-9625
Sales Range: $10-24.9 Million
Emp.: 40
Short Line Railroads Services
N.A.I.C.S.: 482112

M & B Railroad L.L.C. (2)
119 22nd Ave, Meridian, MS 39301
Tel.: (601) 693-4351
Sales Range: $1-9.9 Million
Emp.: 10
Provider of Railroad Line-Haul Services
N.A.I.C.S.: 482111

Marquette Rail, LLC (2)
239 N Jebavy Dr, Ludington, MI 49431
Tel.: (231) 845-9000
Web Site: http://www.gwrr.com
Emp.: 30
Short Line Railroads Services
N.A.I.C.S.: 482112

Maryland Midland Railway, Inc. (2)
40 N Main St, Union Bridge, MD 21791
Tel.: (410) 775-7718
Short Line Railroads Services
N.A.I.C.S.: 482112

Michigan Shore Railroad (2)
101 Enterprise Dr, Vassar, MI 48768
Tel.: (989) 797-5100
Web Site: http://www.gwrr.com
Sales Range: $25-49.9 Million
Emp.: 70
Short Line Railroad
N.A.I.C.S.: 482112

Mid-Michigan Railroad, Inc. (2)
101 Enterprise Dr, Vassar, MI 48768-9505
Tel.: (989) 797-5124
Web Site: http://www.gwrr.com
Sales Range: $1-9.9 Million
Emp.: 18
Short Line Railroad
N.A.I.C.S.: 482111

Missouri & Northern Arkansas Railroad Company, Inc. (2)
514 N Orner, Carthage, MO 64836

Tel.: (417) 358-8800
Sales Range: $1-9.9 Million
Emp.: 130
Short Line Railroads Services
N.A.I.C.S.: 482112

New England Central Railroad, Inc. (2)
2 Federal St Ste 201, Saint Albans, VT 05478
Tel.: (802) 527-3411
Web Site: http://www.gwrr.com
Sales Range: $100-124.9 Million
Emp.: 250
Short Line Railroads Services
N.A.I.C.S.: 482112
Robert Richardson (Asst Gen Mgr)

North Carolina & Virginia Railroad Company, LLC (2)
214 Railroad St N, Ahoskie, NC 27910
Tel.: (904) 223-1110
Sales Range: $1-9.9 Million
Emp.: 8
Short Line Railroads Services
N.A.I.C.S.: 482112

Division (Domestic):

Chesapeake & Albemarle Railroad (3)
214 Railroad St N, Ahoskie, NC 27910
Tel.: (252) 332-2778
Sales Range: $1-9.9 Million
Emp.: 4
Short Line Railroad
N.A.I.C.S.: 482111

Virginia Southern Railroad (3)
Keysville Depot Railroad Ave PO Box 12, Keysville, VA 23947
Tel.: (919) 332-2778
Short Line Railroad
N.A.I.C.S.: 482112
Carl Hollowell (Gen Mgr)

Subsidiary (Domestic):

Ohio Central Railroad, Inc. (2)
47849 Papermill Rd, Coshocton, OH 43812
Tel.: (740) 622-8092
Web Site: https://www.gwrr.com
Short Line Railroad
N.A.I.C.S.: 482112

Ohio Southern Railroad, Inc. (2)
47849 Papermill Rd, Coshocton, OH 43812
Tel.: (740) 622-8092
Short Line Railroad
N.A.I.C.S.: 482112

Subsidiary (Non-US):

Ottawa Valley Railway (2)
445 Oak Street East, North Bay, P1B 1A3, ON, Canada
Tel.: (802) 527-3490
Web Site: https://www.gwrr.com
Emp.: 35
Short Line Railroad
N.A.I.C.S.: 482112

Subsidiary (Domestic):

Otter Tail Valley Railroad Company, Inc. (2)
200 N Mill St, Fergus Falls, MN 56537
Tel.: (218) 736-6073
Web Site: https://www.gwrr.com
Sales Range: $1-9.9 Million
Emp.: 8
Short Line Railroads Services
N.A.I.C.S.: 482112

Subsidiary (Non-US):

Pentalver Cannock Limited (2)
Pentalver Way, Cannock, WS11 8XY, United Kingdom
Tel.: (44) 3331508300
Container Operator
N.A.I.C.S.: 488490

Pentalver Transport Limited (2)
Western Docks Dock Gate 10, Southampton, SO15 1AW, United Kingdom
Tel.: (44) 3330168556
Web Site: https://www.pentalver.com
Emp.: 600
Freight Container Transport, Storage & Logistics Services

N.A.I.C.S.: 488320

Subsidiary (Domestic):

Portland & Western Railroad Inc (2)
1200 Howard Dr SE, Albany, OR 97321
Tel.: (802) 527-3499
Web Site: https://www.gwrr.com
Sales Range: $75-99.9 Million
Emp.: 200
Switching & Terminal Services
N.A.I.C.S.: 482111
Roberta Kane (VP-HR)

Providence & Worcester Railroad Company (2)
381 Southbridge St, Worcester, MA 01608
Tel.: (802) 527-3499
Web Site: https://www.gwrr.com
Short Line Railroads Services
N.A.I.C.S.: 482112
James Rivers (Asst Gen Mgr)

Puget Sound & Pacific Railroad (2)
501 N 2nd St, Elma, WA 98541
Tel.: (360) 807-4325
Web Site: http://www.gwrr.com
Sales Range: $10-24.9 Million
Emp.: 46
Short Line Railroads Services
N.A.I.C.S.: 482112

Rail Link, Inc. (2)
13901 Sutton Park Dr S Ste 125, Jacksonville, FL 32224
Tel.: (904) 223-1110
Web Site: http://www.gwrr.com
Sales Range: $1-9.9 Million
Emp.: 15
Short Line Railroads Services
N.A.I.C.S.: 482112

Subsidiary (Domestic):

The Bayline Railroad LLC (3)
2037 Industrial Dr, Panama City, FL 32045
Tel.: (850) 785-4609
Emp.: 35
Railroad Services
N.A.I.C.S.: 482111

Subsidiary (Domestic):

RailAmerica Transportation Corp. (2)
7411 Fullerton St Ste 300, Jacksonville, FL 32256
Tel.: (904) 538-6100
Short Line Railroads Services
N.A.I.C.S.: 482112

RailAmerica, Inc. (2)
13901 Sutton Park Dr S, Jacksonville, FL 32224
Tel.: (904) 538-6100
Sales Range: $800-899.9 Million
Emp.: 1,808
Short Line Railroads Services
N.A.I.C.S.: 482112
Christopher Liucci (Pres)

Subsidiary (Non-US):

Railcare Inc. (2)
500 Sherman Ave N Unit 80, Hamilton, L8L 8J6, ON, Canada
Tel.: (905) 527-8238
Short Line Railroads Services
N.A.I.C.S.: 482112

Subsidiary (Domestic):

Railroad Distribution Services, Inc. (2)
425 E Southlake Blvd, Southlake, TX 76092
Tel.: (501) 844-4484
Railroad Distribution Services
N.A.I.C.S.: 482111
Gene Cox (Gen Mgr)

Rapid City, Pierre & Eastern Railroad, Inc. (2)
246 Founders Park Dr Ste 202, Rapid City, SD 57701
Tel.: (605) 877-3699
Web Site: https://www.gwrr.com
Line-Haul Railroad Related Services
N.A.I.C.S.: 482111

Rockdale, Sandow & Southern Railroad Company (2)
PO Box 387, Rockdale, TX 76567

Tel.: (512) 446-3478
Short Line Railroads Services
N.A.I.C.S.: 482112

Salt Lake City Southern Railroad Company, Inc. (2)
4692 N 300 W, Provo, UT 84604
Tel.: (801) 221-7460
Short Line Railroads Services
N.A.I.C.S.: 482112

San Diego & Imperial Valley Railroad Company, Inc. (2)
1501 National Ave Ste 200, San Diego, CA 92113
Tel.: (928) 669-6662
Sales Range: $1-9.9 Million
Emp.: 15
Short Line Railroads Services
N.A.I.C.S.: 482112

San Joaquin Valley Railroad Co. (2)
221 N F St, Exeter, CA 93221
Tel.: (559) 592-1857
Sales Range: $25-49.9 Million
Emp.: 200
Short Line Railroads Services
N.A.I.C.S.: 482112
Dave Siegel (Dir-Sls & Mktg)

Savannah Port Terminal Railroad, Inc. (2)
2 Main St, Garden City, GA 31408
Tel.: (802) 527-3499
Web Site: https://www.gwrr.com
Short Line Railroads Services
N.A.I.C.S.: 482112

South Carolina Central Railroad Company, LLC (2)
621 Field Pond Rd, Darlington, SC 29540
Tel.: (843) 398-9850
Web Site: https://www.gwrr.com
Sales Range: $1-9.9 Million
Emp.: 28
Short Line Railroads Services
N.A.I.C.S.: 482112

Subsidiary (Non-US):

Southern Ontario Railway (2)
3258 Highway 6, PO Box 601, Jarvis, N0A 1J0, ON, Canada
Tel.: (905) 777-1234
Web Site: http://www.gwrr.com
Sales Range: $10-24.9 Million
Emp.: 35
Short Line Railroad
N.A.I.C.S.: 482112

Subsidiary (Domestic):

St. Lawrence & Atlantic Railroad Company (2)
225 First Flight Dr Ste 201, Auburn, ME 04210
Web Site: https://www.gwrr.com
Sales Range: $10-24.9 Million
Emp.: 75
Short Line Railroads Services
N.A.I.C.S.: 482112
Laurie Therrien (Mgr-Sls & Mktg)

Tazewell & Peoria Railroad, Inc. (2)
301 Wesley Rd, Creve Coeur, IL 61610
Tel.: (309) 694-8619
Web Site: https://www.gwrr.com
Short Line Railroads Services
N.A.I.C.S.: 482112

The Aliquippa & Ohio River Railroad Co. (2)
208 Islands Ave, McKees Rocks, PA 15136
Tel.: (740) 622-8092
Short Line Railroad
N.A.I.C.S.: 482112

The Central Railroad Company of Indiana (2)
2856 Cypress Way, Cincinnati, OH 45212
Tel.: (513) 860-1000
Web Site: https://www.gwrr.com
Short Line Railroad
N.A.I.C.S.: 482111

The Indiana & Ohio Railway Company (2)
2856 Cypress Way, Cincinnati, OH 45212
Tel.: (513) 860-1000

Sales Range: $10-24.9 Million
Emp.: 156
Line-Haul Operating Railroad
N.A.I.C.S.: 482111

The Pittsburgh & Ohio Central Railroad Company (2)
208 Islands Ave, McKees Rocks, PA 15136
Tel.: (412) 331-6200
Web Site: https://www.gwrr.com
Short Line Railroads Services
N.A.I.C.S.: 482112

The Prescott and Northwestern Railroad Company (2)
314 Reynolds Rd Bldg 41, Malvern, AR 72104
Web Site: https://www.gwrr.com
Rail Transportation Services
N.A.I.C.S.: 488210

Toledo, Peoria & Western Railway Corp. (2)
1990 E Washington St, East Peoria, IL 61611-2961
Tel.: (309) 698-2600
Web Site: https://www.gwrr.com
Sales Range: $10-24.9 Million
Emp.: 35
Short Line Railroad
N.A.I.C.S.: 482112

Tomahawk Railway Limited Partnership (2)
17 S Marinette St, Tomahawk, WI 54487
Tel.: (715) 453-2303
Sales Range: $1-9.9 Million
Emp.: 12
Provider of Railroad Line-Haul Services
N.A.I.C.S.: 482111
Katie Kaiser *(Mgr-Warehouse)*

Ventura County Railroad Company (2)
351 Warehouse Ave, Oxnard, CA 93030
Tel.: (559) 592-4247
Web Site: http://www.gwrr.com
Sales Range: $1-9.9 Million
Emp.: 25
Short Line Railroads Services
N.A.I.C.S.: 482112

Wellsboro & Corning Railroad, LLC (2)
900 Airport Rd Ste 6, West Chester, PA 19380
Tel.: (610) 458-0600
Web Site: http://www.gwrr.com
Short Line Railroads Services
N.A.I.C.S.: 482112

Wilmington Terminal Railroad, Limited Partnership (2)
2128 Burnett Blvd, Wilmington, NC 28401
Tel.: (910) 343-0461
Web Site: https://www.gwrr.com
Sales Range: $25-49.9 Million
Emp.: 6
Short Line Railroads Services
N.A.I.C.S.: 482112

Wiregrass Central Railway, L.L.C. (2)
812 N Main St, Enterprise, AL 36330
Tel.: (334) 347-6070
Web Site: https://www.gwrr.com
Line-Haul Railroad Related Services
N.A.I.C.S.: 482111

York Railway Company (2)
2790 W Market St, York, PA 17404
Tel.: (904) 710-0235
Web Site: https://www.gwrr.com
Sales Range: $1-9.9 Million
Emp.: 32
Rail Freight Transportation & Distribution Services
N.A.I.C.S.: 482111

Subsidiary (Non-US):

SLR Leasing Corp. (3)
605 Rue Principale Nord, PO Box 788, Richmond, J0B H20, BC, Canada
Tel.: (819) 826-1561
Web Site: http://www.gwrr.com
Rev.: $407,000
Emp.: 10
Locomotive Leasing Company
N.A.I.C.S.: 532411

St. Lawrence & Atlantic Railroad (Quebec) Inc. (3)
605 Rue Principale Nord C, Richmond, J0B 2H0, QC, Canada
Tel.: (819) 826-5460
Short Line Railroads Services
N.A.I.C.S.: 482112

Subsidiary (Domestic):

York Rail Logistics, Inc. (3)
2790 W Market St, York, PA 17404
Tel.: (717) 792-1425
Sales Range: $1-9.9 Million
Emp.: 4
Short Line Railroads Services
N.A.I.C.S.: 482112
Jarrod Hutcheson *(Gen Mgr)*

Subsidiary (Domestic):

Youngstown & Austintown Railroad, Inc. (2)
123 Division St Ext, Youngstown, OH 44510
Tel.: (740) 622-8092
Web Site: https://www.gwrr.com
Short Line Railroads Services
N.A.I.C.S.: 482112
Brian McClain *(Gen Mgr)*

Inter Pipeline Ltd. (1)
Suite 3200 215 2nd Street SW, Calgary, T2P 1M4, AB, Canada **(19.64%)**
Tel.: (403) 290-6000
Web Site: http://www.interpipeline.com
Petroleum Transporter
N.A.I.C.S.: 486990
Christian P. Bayle *(Pres & CEO)*

Subsidiary (Domestic):

Cold Lake Pipeline Limited Partnership (2)
2600 237 4th Ave SW, Calgary, T2P 4K3, AB, Canada
Tel.: (403) 290-6000
Sales Range: $50-74.9 Million
Emp.: 100
Crude Petroleum & Natural Gas Extraction
N.A.I.C.S.: 211120
Megan Joyce *(Mgr-HR)*

Plant (Domestic):

Inter Pipeline Ltd. - Cochrane Extraction Plant (2)
1/2 Mile S PM Rd, PO Box 219, Coleville, S0L 0K0, SK, Canada
Tel.: (403) 932-8555
Web Site: http://www.interpipeline.com
Emp.: 80
Pipeline Transportation Services
N.A.I.C.S.: 486910

Subsidiary (Non-US):

Inter Terminals Sweden AB (2)
Skarvikshamnen Smorjoljegatan 21, 418 34, Gothenburg, Vastergotland, Sweden
Tel.: (46) 31648300
Web Site: http://interterminals.com
Petroleum & Chemical Terminals Operation Services
N.A.I.C.S.: 424710
Cecilia Lonnroth *(Mgr-Comml)*

NuStar Eastham Limited (2)
Bankfields Drive, Wirral, CH62 0BA, United Kingdom
Tel.: (44) 1513271205
Warehousing & Storage Services
N.A.I.C.S.: 493190
Mark Burkey *(Gen Mgr)*

NuStar Grangemouth Limited (2)
The Docks, Grangemouth, FK3 8UD, United Kingdom
Tel.: (44) 1324486111
Warehousing & Storage Services
N.A.I.C.S.: 493190
Terry Keogh *(Gen Mgr)*

Simon Tanklager Gesellschaft mbH (2)
Essener Str 64, Mannheim, Germany
Tel.: (49) 6218998680
Web Site: http://www.simontanklager.com
General Warehousing & Storage
N.A.I.C.S.: 493110

Natural Gas Pipeline Company of America LLC (1)
1001 Louisiana St Ste 1000, Houston, TX 77002
Tel.: (713) 369-9000
Interstate Gas Transmission Services
N.A.I.C.S.: 486210

BROOKFIELD REINSURANCE LTD.

Ideation House 1st Floor 94 Pitts Bay Road, Pembroke, HM08, BM, Bermuda
Tel.: (441) 294-3316   BM
Web Site: https://bnre.brookfield.com
BNRE—(NYSE)
Rev.: $7,020,000,000
Assets: $61,643,000,000
Liabilities: $55,488,000,000
Net Worth: $6,155,000,000
Earnings: $797,000,000
Emp.: 4,000
Fiscal Year-end: 12/31/23
Reinsurance Products & Services
N.A.I.C.S.: 524130

Subsidiaries:

American Equity Investment Life Holding Company (1)
6000 Westown Pkwy, West Des Moines, IA 50266
Tel.: (515) 221-0002
Web Site: https://www.american-equity.com
Rev.: $2,835,970,000
Assets: $4,303,414,000
Liabilities: $1,280,154,000
Net Worth: $3,023,260,000
Earnings: $166,855,000
Emp.: 995
Fiscal Year-end: 12/31/2023
Holding Company
N.A.I.C.S.: 551112
Jeffrey D. Lorenzen *(Chief Risk Officer & Exec VP)*

Subsidiary (Domestic):

American Equity Investment Life Insurance Company (2)
6000 Westown Pkwy, West Des Moines, IA 50266-7711
Tel.: (515) 221-0002
Web Site: https://www.american-equity.com
Sales Range: $200-249.9 Million
Emp.: 500
Fire Insurance Services
N.A.I.C.S.: 524113
Ronald J. Grensteiner *(Pres)*

American Equity Investment Life Insurance Company of New York (2)
1979 Marcus Ave Ste 210, Lake Success, NY 11042
Web Site: https://www.eagle-lifeco.com
Fire Insurance Services
N.A.I.C.S.: 524113

Eagle Life Insurance Company (2)
6000 Westown Pkwy, West Des Moines, IA 50266
Tel.: (515) 221-0002
Web Site: https://www.eagle-lifeco.com
Sales Range: $25-49.9 Million
Emp.: 4
Investment Management Service
N.A.I.C.S.: 523940
John Michael Matovina *(CFO & Treas)*

Argo Group International Holdings, Ltd. (1)
90 Pitts Bay Road, Pembroke, HM 08, Bermuda
Tel.: (441) 2965858
Web Site: http://www.argolimited.com
Rev.: $1,754,900,000
Assets: $10,034,400,000
Liabilities: $8,801,500,000
Net Worth: $1,232,900,000
Earnings: ($185,700,000)
Emp.: 1,206
Fiscal Year-end: 12/31/2022
Holding Company; Insurance Services
N.A.I.C.S.: 551112
Marsh Duncan *(Pres-Excess & Surplus)*

Subsidiary (US):

AGI Properties Inc. (2)
175 E Houston St Ste 1300, San Antonio, TX 78205
Tel.: (210) 321-8400
Web Site: http://www.argogroupus.com
Rev.: $420,000
Emp.: 1,000
Real Estate Managers
N.A.I.C.S.: 531390

ARIS Title Insurance Corporation (2)
610 Broadway 4th Fl, New York, NY 10012
Tel.: (212) 563-3600
Web Site: http://www.aristitle.com
Insurance Brokerage Services
N.A.I.C.S.: 524210

Alteris Insurance Services, Inc. (2)
250 Summer St 3rd Fl, Boston, MA 02210
Tel.: (210) 342-8808
Insurance Providing Services
N.A.I.C.S.: 524298

Subsidiary (Non-US):

Argo Direct, Ltd. (2)
Exchequer Court 33 St Mary Axe, London, EC3A 8AA, United Kingdom
Tel.: (44) 2077127600
Sales Range: $100-124.9 Million
Emp.: 15
Insurance Policy Providing Services
N.A.I.C.S.: 524298

Division (US):

Argo Group International Holdings, Ltd. - Alteris Public Risk Solutions Division (2)
1901 W Kettleman Ln Ste 103, Lodi, CA 95242
Tel.: (949) 450-5000
General Insurance Services
N.A.I.C.S.: 524210

Subsidiary (US):

Argo Group US, Inc. (2)
379 Thornall St 2nd Fl St Fl Thornall, Edison, NJ 08837
Tel.: (732) 906-8100
Sales Range: $50-74.9 Million
Emp.: 50
Reinsurance Company
N.A.I.C.S.: 524130
Marsh Duncan *(Sr VP-Specialty Programs)*

Subsidiary (Non-US):

Argo Management Holdings, (2)
Exchequer Court 33 St Mary Axe, London, EC3A 8AA, United Kingdom
Tel.: (44) 20 7712 7600
Web Site: http://www.argolimited.com
Business Support Services
N.A.I.C.S.: 561499

Argo Managing Agency Limited (2)
1 Fen Court, London, EC3M 5BN, United Kingdom
Tel.: (44) 2077127600
Web Site: http://www.argolimited.com
General Insurance Services
N.A.I.C.S.: 524126
Dominic Kirby *(Mng Dir)*

Unit (US):

Argo Pro (2)
101 Hudson St 12th Fl, Jersey City, NJ 07302
Tel.: (732) 906-6718
General Insurance Services
N.A.I.C.S.: 524210
Craig Landi *(Pres)*

Subsidiary (Non-US):

Argo Re DIFC, Ltd. (2)
DIFC Presing Building 2 South Building 4th Fl, PO Box 482067, Dubai, 482067, United Arab Emirates
Tel.: (971) 4 389 4 000
Sales Range: $50-74.9 Million
Emp.: 6
General Insurance Services
N.A.I.C.S.: 524210

Brookfield Reinsurance Ltd.—(Continued)

Subsidiary (Domestic):

Argo Re, Ltd. (2)
29 Richmond Road, Pembroke, HM08, Bermuda
Tel.: (441) 2955485
Web Site: https://www.arielre.com
Sales Range: $50-74.9 Million
Emp.: 30
General Business Insurance Services
N.A.I.C.S.: 524126

Subsidiary (Non-US):

ArgoGlobal SE (3)
Strand Tower Floor 1 36 Strand, Sliema, SLM 1022, Malta
Tel.: (356) 234 23000
Web Site: http://www.argolimited.com
Insurance Underwriting Services
N.A.I.C.S.: 524127

Subsidiary (Non-US):

Argo Solutions, SA (2)
Avenue Marcel Thiry 79 BTE 3, 1200, Brussels, Belgium
Tel.: (32) 2 777 0909
Web Site: http://www.argolimited.com
Emp.: 3
Insurance & Reinsurance Service Providers
N.A.I.C.S.: 524298
Rudy Bogaerts (Mng Dir)

Argo Underwriting Agency, Ltd. (2)
Exchequer Court 33 Saint Mary Axe, London, EC3A 8AA, United Kingdom
Tel.: (44) 2077127600
Emp.: 150
Underwriting Agencies
N.A.I.C.S.: 523150

ArgoGlobal Assicurazioni S.p.A. (2)
Via Guido d'Arezzo 14, 00198, Rome, Italy
Tel.: (39) 0685379811
Property & General Liability Insurance Services
N.A.I.C.S.: 524126
David Mancazzo (CEO & Gen Mgr)

ArgoGlobal Underwriting (Dubai) Limited (2)
Unit 301 & 401 Level 3 Gate Precinct Building 2, PO Box 482067, Dubai International Financial Centre, Dubai, United Arab Emirates
Tel.: (971) 43894000
Insurance Agency & Brokerage Services
N.A.I.C.S.: 524210
Lina Hantas (Chief Underwriting Officer)

ArgoGlobal Underwriting Asia Pacific Pte Ltd. (2)
8 Marina View 14-01 & 15-01 Asia Square Tower 1, Singapore, 018960, Singapore
Tel.: (65) 64999330
Property & Casualty Insurance Provider
N.A.I.C.S.: 524130

Subsidiary (US):

Argonaut Claims Management, LLC (2)
175 E Houston, San Antonio, TX 78216-4156
Tel.: (210) 321-8400
Web Site: http://www.argogroup.com
Insurance Management Services
N.A.I.C.S.: 524298

Argonaut Claims Services, Ltd. (2)
5100 N O'Connor Blvd Ste 200, Irving, TX 75039
Tel.: (972) 506-2400
Web Site: http://www.argolimited.com
Sales Range: $25-49.9 Million
Emp.: 2
Online Advertisement Services
N.A.I.C.S.: 541810

Argonaut Insurance Company (2)
100 Marine Pkwy Ste 500, Redwood City, CA 94065 **(100%)**
Tel.: (650) 508-5400
Web Site: http://www.argolimited.com
Sales Range: $450-499.9 Million
Emp.: 29
Property & Casualty Insurance
N.A.I.C.S.: 524126

Argonaut Limited Risk Insurance Company (2)
711 Broadway St Ste 400, San Antonio, TX 78215-1816
Tel.: (210) 321-8400
Insurance Management Services
N.A.I.C.S.: 524298

Argonaut Management Services, Inc. (2)
711 Broadway St Ste 400, San Antonio, TX 78215-1816
Tel.: (210) 321-8400
Business Management Consulting Services
N.A.I.C.S.: 541611

Argonaut-Midwest Insurance Company (2)
PO Box 469012, San Antonio, TX 78246
Tel.: (210) 321-8400
Web Site:
   http://www.argonautautogroup.com
Insurance Management Services
N.A.I.C.S.: 524298

Argonaut-Southwest Insurance Company (2)
711 Broadway St Ste 400, San Antonio, TX 78215-1816
Tel.: (210) 321-8400
Sales Range: $200-249.9 Million
Emp.: 300
Insurance Management Services
N.A.I.C.S.: 524298

Subsidiary (Domestic):

Ariel Re BDA Limited (2)
29 Richmond Road, Hamilton, HM08, Bermuda
Tel.: (441) 2955485
Web Site: https://www.arielre.com
Property & Casualty Insurance Services
N.A.I.C.S.: 524126
Nancy McCombs (Asst VP)

Subsidiary (US):

Colony Agency Services, Inc. (2)
8720 Stony Point Pkwy Ste 400, Richmond, VA 23235
Tel.: (804) 560-2000
Web Site: http://www.argolimited.com
Insurance Brokerage Services
N.A.I.C.S.: 524210

Colony Insurance Group (2)
8720 Stony Pte Pkwy Ste 400, Richmond, VA 23235-6865
Tel.: (804) 327-1700
Web Site: http://www.colonyins.com
Sales Range: $100-124.9 Million
Emp.: 250
Environmental Insurance Management
N.A.I.C.S.: 524126

Colony Management Services (2)
8520 Stoney Pt Ste 300, Richmond, VA 23235 **(100%)**
Tel.: (804) 327-1700
Web Site: http://www.colonyspecility.com
Sales Range: $75-99.9 Million
Emp.: 300
Property & Casualty Underwriting
N.A.I.C.S.: 541611

Subsidiary (Domestic):

Colony Insurance Company (3)
8720 Stony Point Ste 300, Richmond, VA 23235
Tel.: (804) 327-1700
Web Site: http://www.argolimited.com
Sales Range: $75-99.9 Million
Emp.: 250
Property & Casualty Underwriting
N.A.I.C.S.: 524126

Subsidiary (US):

Colony Specialty (2)
8720 Stony Point Ste 400, Richmond, VA 23235
Tel.: (804) 560-2000
Web Site: http://www.argolimited.com
Sales Range: $100-124.9 Million
Emp.: 139
Property & Casualty Underwriting
N.A.I.C.S.: 524210

Colony Specialty Insurance Company (2)
PO Box 469012, San Antonio, TX 78246
Tel.: (804) 560-2000
Web Site: http://www.colonyspecialty.com
Property & Casualty Insurance Provider
N.A.I.C.S.: 524130

Grocers Insurance Agency, Inc. (2)
6400 So Lk Rd Ste 100, Portland, OR 97222-2189
Tel.: (503) 833-1600
Sales Range: $50-74.9 Million
Emp.: 100
General Insurance Services
N.A.I.C.S.: 524210
Eric Wilcoxen (Gen Mgr)

Insight Insurance Services, Inc. (2)
2000 S Batavia Ave Ste 300, Geneva, IL 60134
Tel.: (630) 208-1900
Web Site: http://www.insightinsurance.com
Insurance Services
N.A.I.C.S.: 524298

John Sutak Insurance Brokers, Inc. (2)
1 Embarcadero Ctr Suite 1040, San Francisco, CA 94111
Tel.: (415) 394-0700
Property & Casualty Insurance Provider
N.A.I.C.S.: 524130

Subsidiary (Domestic):

Peleus Reinsurance, Ltd. (2)
110 Pitts Bay Road, PO Box HM 1282 HM FX, Pembroke, HM08, Bermuda
Tel.: (441) 2965858
Commercial Property Reinsurance
N.A.I.C.S.: 524130

Subsidiary (US):

Rockwood Casualty Insurance Co. (2)
654 Main St, Rockwood, PA 15557
Tel.: (814) 926-4661
Web Site: http://www.argolimited.com
Sales Range: $125-149.9 Million
Emp.: 120
Property & Casualty Insurance Products & Services
N.A.I.C.S.: 524126

Somerset Casualty Insurance Company (2)
654 Main St, Rockwood, PA 15557
Tel.: (814) 926-4661
Web Site: http://www.rockwoodcasualty.com
Sales Range: $50-74.9 Million
Emp.: 100
Insurance Policy Services
N.A.I.C.S.: 524298

Sonoma Risk Management, LLC (2)
11150 W Olympic Blvd Ste 1140, Los Angeles, CA 90064
Tel.: (310) 954-1522
Property & Casualty Insurance Provider
N.A.I.C.S.: 524130

BROOKLINE PUBLIC RELATIONS INC.
Suite 202 239 10th Avenue SE, Calgary, T2G 0V9, AB, Canada
Tel.: (403) 538-5641
Web Site: http://www.brooklinepr.com
Sales Range: $1-9.9 Million
Emp.: 10
Public Relations
N.A.I.C.S.: 541820
Shauna MacDonald (Founder & Principal)

BROOKS FORGINGS LTD.
Doulton Road, Cradley Heath, Warley, B64 5QJ, West Midlands, United Kingdom
Tel.: (44) 1384563356
Web Site:
   http://www.brooksforgings.co.uk
Year Founded: 1960
Sales Range: $1-9.9 Million
Emp.: 60

Plumbing & Heating Equipment & Supplies (Hydronics) Merchant Wholesalers
N.A.I.C.S.: 423720
Steven Clive Brooks (Mng Dir)

BROOKS LABORATORIES LIMITED
201 The Summit Business Park Behind Guru Nanak Petrol Pump, Off Andheri Kurla Road Andheri East, Mumbai, 400093, India
Tel.: (91) 2269073100
Web Site: https://www.brookslabs.net
Year Founded: 2002
533543—(BOM)
Rev.: $12,556,130
Assets: $26,741,783
Liabilities: $8,407,158
Net Worth: $18,334,625
Earnings: ($2,636,170)
Emp.: 335
Fiscal Year-end: 03/31/22
Pharmaceuticals Mfr
N.A.I.C.S.: 325412
Atul Ranchal (Chm)

BROOKS MACDONALD GROUP PLC
21 Lombard Street, London, EC3V 9AH, United Kingdom
Tel.: (44) 2074996424
Web Site:
   https://www.brooksmacdonald.com
Year Founded: 2006
BRK—(AIM)
Rev.: $165,926,961
Assets: $256,808,665
Liabilities: $55,289,074
Net Worth: $201,519,591
Earnings: $31,785,583
Emp.: 449
Fiscal Year-end: 06/30/22
Financial Services
N.A.I.C.S.: 523940
Andrew Shepherd (Co-CEO-Intl & Deputy CEO-Grp)

Subsidiaries:

Braemar Group Limited (1)
Richmond House Heath Road, Hale, WA14 2XP, Cheshire, United Kingdom
Tel.: (44) 1619292300
Web Site: http://www.braemar-estates.com
Real Estate Investment & Property Management Services
N.A.I.C.S.: 531390
William Martin Robinson (Chm)

Subsidiary (Domestic):

Brooks Macdonald Funds Limited (2)
21 Lombard Street, London, EC3V 9AH, United Kingdom
Tel.: (44) 2074996424
Web Site: http://www.bm-funds.com
Investment Fund Management Services
N.A.I.C.S.: 523940

Brooks Macdonald Asset Management Limited (1)
21 Lombard Street, Mayfair, London, EC3V 9AH, United Kingdom
Tel.: (44) 2074996424
Web Site: http://www.bm-am.com
Sales Range: $100-124.9 Million
Emp.: 150
Investment Management Service
N.A.I.C.S.: 523999
Andrew Denham-Davis (Dir-Intermediary Sls)

Subsidiary (Domestic):

Brooks Macdonald Asset Management (Tunbridge Wells) Limited (2)
2 Mount Ephraim Road, Tunbridge Wells, TN1 1EE, Kent, United Kingdom
Tel.: (44) 1892554900
Web Site: http://www.bm-am.com

Sales Range: $50-74.9 Million
Emp.: 12
Asset & Pension Fund Management Services
N.A.I.C.S.: 523999

BROS EASTERN CO., LTD.
8F Ningbo Fortune Centre NO 188 Yongjiang Avenue, Yinzhou District, Ningbo, 315040, Zhejiang, China
Tel.: (86) 57487142999
Web Site: https://www.bros.com.cn
Year Founded: 2004
601339—(SHG)
Rev.: $981,264,614
Assets: $2,275,386,170
Liabilities: $863,900,898
Net Worth: $1,411,485,272
Earnings: $219,405,495
Fiscal Year-end: 12/31/22
Spinning Product Mfr
N.A.I.C.S.: 313110

Subsidiaries:

BROTEX (VIETNAM) CO., LTD (1)
Lot 34-6 Road D11 Phuoc Dong IP, Phuoc Dong Commune Go Dau District, Tay Ninh, Vietnam
Tel.: (84) 663530999
Yarn Distr
N.A.I.C.S.: 424990

Bros Holding Ltd. (1)
Flat J 6/F Leader Industrial Centre Phase Two 188-202 Texaco Road, Tsuen Wan, China (Hong Kong)
Tel.: (852) 2 615 3888
Web Site: http://www.bros.com.hk
Yarn Mfr & Distr
N.A.I.C.S.: 313110

Bros Spinning (Shenzhen) CO., Ltd. (1)
North of Huawang Road, Dalang Subdistrict Bao'an District, Shenzhen, China
Tel.: (86) 75528033999
Yarn Mfr & Distr
N.A.I.C.S.: 313110

Shenzhen Bros Eastern Textile Co., Ltd. (1)
24/F Golden Century No 6033 Shennan Boulevard, Shenzhen, China
Tel.: (86) 75528109999
Yarn Mfr & Distr
N.A.I.C.S.: 313110

BROSE FAHRZEUGTEILE GMBH & CO. KG
Ketschendorfer Strasse 38-50, D-96450, Coburg, Germany
Tel.: (49) 9561210
Web Site: http://www.brose.com
Year Founded: 1908
Sales Range: $1-4.9 Billion
Emp.: 8,790
Motor Vehicle Doors & Seats
N.A.I.C.S.: 336340
Kurt Sauernheimer *(Head-Door Sys Div)*

Subsidiaries:

Brose (Thailand) Co., Ltd. (1)
300/28 Moo 1, Eastern Seaboard Industrial Estate T Tasith A Pluakdaeng, 21140, Rayong, Thailand
Tel.: 33658633
Automobile Parts Distr
N.A.I.C.S.: 423120
Denis Reul *(Pres & Mng Dir)*

Brose AUNDE Fahrzeugistze GmbH (1)
Lochweg 15, 97318, Kitzingen, Germany
Tel.: (49) 93212643828
Web Site: http://www.brose-aunde.com
Automobile Parts Distr
N.A.I.C.S.: 423120
Markus Kussmaul *(Mng Dir)*

Brose Automotive La Suze S.A.S. (1)
Le Pre-Sec, 72210, La Suze-sur-Sarthe, France
Tel.: (33) 2 4377 6700
Automobile Parts Distr
N.A.I.C.S.: 423120

Brose Beijing Automotive Systems Co., Ltd. (1)
Building 1 & 2 No 23 Ding Ye Road Wulianhuan Industrial Development, Area Xihongmen Town Daxing, 100076, Beijing, China
Tel.: (86) 10 56590 888
Motor Vehicle Parts Mfr & Distr
N.A.I.C.S.: 336320

Brose Belvidere Inc. (1)
725 Logistics Dr, Belvidere, IL 61008
Tel.: (779) 552-7624
Automobile Parts Distr
N.A.I.C.S.: 423120
Piyush Kumar *(Production Mgr)*

Brose Bratislava, spol. s r.o. (1)
Priemyselny Park Lozorno 1006, 900 55, Lozorno, Slovakia
Tel.: (421) 260261100
Web Site: http://www.brose.com
Sales Range: $25-49.9 Million
Emp.: 30
Motor Vehicle Parts & Accessories Mfr
N.A.I.C.S.: 336390

Brose CZ spol. s r.o. (1)
Prumyslovy park 302, 74221, Koprivnice, Czech Republic
Tel.: (420) 556844118
Web Site: http://www.brose.com.de
Sales Range: $25-49.9 Million
Emp.: 50
Motor Vehicle Parts & Accessories Mfr
N.A.I.C.S.: 336390

Brose Canada Inc (1)
1500 Max Brose Drive, London, N6N 1P7, ON, Canada
Tel.: (519) 644-5200
Web Site: https://www.brose.com
Sales Range: $200-249.9 Million
Emp.: 600
Motor Vehicle Parts & Accessories Mfr
N.A.I.C.S.: 336390

Brose Changchun Automotive Systems Co., Ltd (1)
No 1177 Wen Zhou Street, Economical & Technological, Development Zone, 130033, Changchun, China
Tel.: (86) 43184991000
Web Site: http://www.brose.net
Motor Vehicle Design Services
N.A.I.C.S.: 336390

Brose China Co., Ltd. (1)
3/F No 557 Anchi Road, Anting, Shanghai, 201805, China
Tel.: (86) 21 3957 5555
Web Site: http://www.brose.com
Automotive Component Mfr & Distr
N.A.I.C.S.: 336320

Brose Chongqing Automotive Systems Co., Ltd. (1)
Zhenhua Road Taizi Information Industrial Park, Shapingba District, 401331, Chongqing, China
Tel.: (86) 23 6591 9111
Automotive Components Mfr
N.A.I.C.S.: 336320
Wolfgang Beuck *(Gen Mgr)*

Brose Delloyd Automotive Co., Ltd. (1)
300/28 Moo 1 Eastern Seaboard Industrial Estate Tasith, Pluakdaeng, Rayong, 21140, Thailand
Tel.: (66) 33 658 630
Automotive Component Mfr & Distr
N.A.I.C.S.: 336320

Brose Fahrzeugteile GmbH (1)
Gerhard-Stalling-Strasse 62, 26135, Oldenburg, Germany
Tel.: (49) 4412068610
Automobile Parts Distr
N.A.I.C.S.: 423120

Brose France S.A.S. (1)
Parc d'Activites Actipole, 134 Avenue Joseph Kessel, Voisins-le-Bretonneux, 78960, France

Tel.: (33) 130120980
Web Site: http://www.brose.net
Sales Range: $25-49.9 Million
Emp.: 25
Motor Vehicle Parts & Accessories Mfr
N.A.I.C.S.: 336390
Kurt Sauernheimer *(Pres)*

Brose Gent bvba (1)
Skaldenstraat 121, PO Box A2, 9042, Gent, Belgium
Tel.: (32) 92180888
Web Site: http://www.brose.com
Sales Range: $25-49.9 Million
Emp.: 120
Motor Vehicle Parts & Accessories Mfr
N.A.I.C.S.: 336390

Brose Guangzhou Automotive Systems Co., Ltd. (1)
1503 Kaichuang Avenue, Luogang District, Guangzhou, 510760, China
Tel.: (86) 2032307411
Automobile Parts Distr
N.A.I.C.S.: 423120

Brose Hungary Automotive Kft. (1)
Daimler ut 1, 6000, Kecskemet, Hungary
Tel.: (36) 76 58 1070
Automotive Component Mfr & Distr
N.A.I.C.S.: 336320
Agota Peto *(Mgr-Fin)*

Brose India Automotive Systems Pvt Ltd. (1)
Office no 202 2nd Floor Survey No-19/20 Panchshil Tech Park, Hinjewadi, Pune, 411 057, Maharashtra, India
Tel.: (91) 20 3043 7800
Web Site: http://www.brose.com
Emp.: 180
Automobile Component Distr
N.A.I.C.S.: 423120
Vasanth Kamath *(Gen Mgr)*

Brose Italia s.r.l. (1)
Corso Unione Sovietica 385, 10135, Turin, Italy
Tel.: (39) 011 02 63 500
Automobile Component Distr
N.A.I.C.S.: 423120

Brose Japan Ltd. (1)
KDX Nagoya Sakae Bldg 1 1F 4-5-3 Sakae, Naka-ku, Nagoya, 460-0008, Japan
Tel.: (81) 52 238 9300
Automobile Component Distr
N.A.I.C.S.: 423120

Brose Jefferson, Inc. (1)
25295 Guenther, Warren, MI 48091
Tel.: (586) 427-4601
Automotive Components Mfr
N.A.I.C.S.: 336320
Lisa Basila *(Mgr-HR)*

Brose Korea Ltd. (1)
12th Floor KANC 906-10 lui-dong, Yeongtong-gu Suwon-si, Ansan, 443-270, Gyeonggi-Do, Korea (South)
Tel.: (82) 315466160
Web Site: http://www.brose.net
Motor Vehicle Parts & Accessories Mfr
N.A.I.C.S.: 336390

Brose Limited (1)
Colliery Ln, Exhall, CV7 9NW, United Kingdom
Tel.: (44) 2476646410
Web Site: http://www.brose.com
Sales Range: $50-74.9 Million
Emp.: 270
Motor Vehicle Parts & Accessories Mfr
N.A.I.C.S.: 336390

Brose Melfi Automotive s.r.l. (1)
Zona Industriale San Nicola di Melfi Zona D1, 85025, Potenza, Italy
Tel.: (39) 0972 257 711
Automobile Component Distr.
N.A.I.C.S.: 423120

Brose Mexico, S.A. de C. V. (1)
Calle 2 No 7, Fracc Ind Benito Juarez, C P 76120, Queretaro, Mexico
Tel.: (52) 42118500
Web Site: http://www.brose.net
Motor Vehicle Parts & Accessories Mfr
N.A.I.C.S.: 336390

Brose New Boston, Inc. (1)

23400 Bell Rd, New Boston, MI 48164
Tel.: (734) 551-9497
Automobile Component Distr
N.A.I.C.S.: 423120
Luiz Cavacchinic Neto *(Engr-Quality)*

Brose North America, Inc. (1)
3933 Automation Ave, Auburn Hills, MI 48326
Tel.: (248) 339-4000
Web Site: http://www.brose.com
Sales Range: $100-124.9 Million
Emp.: 425
Motor Vehicle Parts & Accessories Mfr
N.A.I.C.S.: 336390
Michael Stoscheck *(Chm)*

Subsidiary (Domestic):

Brose Chicago, Inc. (2)
12543 S. Burley Ave, Chicago, IL 60633
Tel.: (773) 371-4750
Motor Vehicle Parts & Accessories Mfr
N.A.I.C.S.: 336390

Brose Tuscaloosa, Inc. (2)
10100 Brose Dr, Vance, AL 35490
Tel.: (205) 562-4800
Web Site: http://www.brose.com
Motor Vehicle Parts & Accessories Mfr
N.A.I.C.S.: 336390

Brose Prievidza spol. S.r.o. (1)
Max Brose 2909/20, 971 01, Prievidza, Slovakia
Tel.: (421) 463962000
Automobile Parts Distr
N.A.I.C.S.: 423120
Daniela Svetlakova *(Fin Mgr)*

Brose Puebla, S.A. de C.V. (1)
Camino San Lorenzo No 1214 Parque Industrial Empresarial, Cuautlancingo Sanctorum, 72730, Mexico, Puebla, Mexico
Tel.: (52) 222 229 1311
Automobile Component Distr
N.A.I.C.S.: 423120

Brose Queretaro S.A. de C.V. (1)
Max Brose No 1, Parque Industrial Aerotech, 76295, Colon, Mexico
Tel.: (52) 4424789664
Automobile Parts Distr
N.A.I.C.S.: 423120
Jesus Duran *(Mgr-Maintenance)*

Brose Russland LLC (1)
4th Lesnoy pereulok Bld 4 BC Capital Plaza, 125047, Moscow, Russia
Tel.: (7) 495 641 3749
Automobile Component Distr
N.A.I.C.S.: 423120
Igor Alexandrov *(Gen Dir)*

Brose S. A. (1)
C Illes Balears 2-6, 08730, Barcelona, Spain
Tel.: (34) 938917300
Web Site: http://www.brose.com
Sales Range: $100-124.9 Million
Emp.: 300
Motor Vehicle Parts & Accessories Mfr
N.A.I.C.S.: 336390

Brose Schliesssysteme GmbH & Co. KG (1)
Otto-Hahn-Strasse 34, Ronsdorf, 42369, Wuppertal, Germany
Tel.: (49) 20246670
Automobile Parts Distr
N.A.I.C.S.: 423120
Sebastian Knoche *(VP-Product Unit & Closure Sys)*

Brose Shanghai Automotive Systems Co., Ltd. (1)
No 585 Tashan Rd Anting Industrial Zone, Tashan Rd, Shanghai, China
Tel.: (86) 2139575555
Web Site: http://www.shbrose.com
Electrical Motor Vehicle Parts & Accessories Mfr
N.A.I.C.S.: 336390

Brose Shenyang Automotive Systems Co., Ltd. (1)
Shenyang Eu Economic Development Zone No 27-3 Puping Road, Shenyang, 110122, China
Tel.: (86) 2431141001
Automobile Parts Distr

Brose Fahrzeugteile GmbH & Co. KG—(Continued)
N.A.I.C.S.: 423120

Brose Sistemas de Fechaduras para Automoveis, Unipessoal Lda. (1)
Apartado 116, 3465168, Tondela, Portugal
Tel.: (351) 232811001
Sales Range: $25-49.9 Million
Emp.: 100
Motor Vehicle Parts & Accessories Mfr
N.A.I.C.S.: 336390

Brose Spartanburg, Inc. (1)
1171 Howell Rd Ste 300, Duncan, SC 29334
Tel.: (864) 485-2517
Automobile Parts Distr
N.A.I.C.S.: 423120
Jeremy Walsh (Mgr-Quality)

Brose Sweden AB (1)
Flygfaltsgatan 4, 423 37, Torslanda, Sweden
Tel.: (46) 317257000
Web Site: http://www.brose.net
Sales Range: $25-49.9 Million
Emp.: 70
Motor Vehicle Parts & Accessories Mfr
N.A.I.C.S.: 336390

Brose Taicang Automotive Systems Co., Ltd. (1)
No158 Dongting North Road New Zone of Taicang, Port Economic Technology Development Area, Taicang, 215400, China
Tel.: (86) 51253679210
Automobile Parts Distr
N.A.I.C.S.: 423120

Brose Togliatti Automotive LLC (1)
Severnaya Str 6a, 445141, Togliatti, Russia
Tel.: (7) 8482698628
Web Site: http://www.brose.com
Emp.: 80
Automobile Component Distr
N.A.I.C.S.: 423120
Maxim Gusev (Mng Dir)

Brose Wuhan Automotive Systems Co., Ltd. (1)
Building No 20 2nd Fengshu Road South Area Minying Technology Park, Hanyang District, 430056, Wuhan, China
Tel.: (86) 27 8421 5111
Automotive Component Mfr & Distr
N.A.I.C.S.: 336320
Ren Wei (Deputy Mgr-Logistics)

Brose do Brasil Ltda. (1)
Av Sul 151, Campo Largo da Roseira, CEP 83183-000, Curitiba, Brazil
Tel.: (55) 4133812000
Web Site: http://www.brose.net
Motor Vehicle Parts & Accessories Mfr
N.A.I.C.S.: 336390

Dongfeng Brose Automotive System Co., Ltd. (1)
No 67 Fengshu South Road, Economic Technological Development Zone, Wuhan, 430056, China
Tel.: (86) 2784215034
Automobile Parts Distr
N.A.I.C.S.: 423120
Du Juan (CFO)

Mando Brose Corporation (1)
75 Cheomdan-daero 60beon-gil, Yeonsu-gu, Incheon, 21990, Korea (South)
Tel.: (82) 322226114
Web Site: http://www.mandobrose.com
Automotive Part Mfr & Distr
N.A.I.C.S.: 336390
Jungsuk Lee (CEO)

Pressan Madeni Esya San. Ve Ticaret A.S. (1)
Hadimkoy Road No 16 Kirac-Esenyurt, Ataturk, 34522, Istanbul, Turkiye
Tel.: (90) 2128865557
Web Site: http://www.pressan.com
Automobile Parts Distr
N.A.I.C.S.: 423120
Ozan Paftali (Production Mgr)

RG Brose Automotive Components (Pty.) Ltd. (1)
6 Spruit Ave Industrial Sites, PO Box 899, Brits, 250, South Africa

Tel.: (27) 122502385
Web Site: http://www.rgbrose.co.za
Sales Range: $50-74.9 Million
Emp.: 120
Motor Vehicle Window Regulator & Door Module Mfr
N.A.I.C.S.: 336390
Michael Stoscheck (Chm)

Shanghai Brose Automotive Components Co., Ltd. (1)
No 299 Yuan Mao Road, Jading District, Shanghai, 201814, China
Tel.: (86) 21 69979 015
Automotive Component Mfr & Distr
N.A.I.C.S.: 336320
Zhang Rayman (Dir-Fin)

Shanghai Brose Electric Motors Co., Ltd. (1)
1126 Jiaxin Road, Shanghai, 201801, China
Tel.: (86) 21 6095 7888
Automotive Component Mfr & Distr
N.A.I.C.S.: 336320

BROTHER ENTERPRISES HOLDING CO., LTD.
No1 Xuelin Street, Haizhou Subdistrict, Haining, 314400, Zhejiang, China
Tel.: (86) 57380703928
Web Site: http://www.brother.com.cn
Year Founded: 1989
002562—(SSE)
Rev.: $478,954,944
Assets: $800,176,104
Liabilities: $326,584,440
Net Worth: $473,591,664
Earnings: $42,896,412
Emp.: 3,000
Fiscal Year-end: 12/31/22
Vitamin Products & Leather Chemicals Mfr
N.A.I.C.S.: 325998
Qian Zhida (Chm)

Subsidiaries:

Jiangsu Brother Vitamins Co., Ltd. (1)
South Area Marine Economic Comprehensive Development Zone, Dafeng District, Yancheng, Jiangsu, China
Tel.: (86) 51583551600
Pharmaceutical Ingredient Mfr
N.A.I.C.S.: 325412

Jiangxi Brother Pharmaceutical Co., Ltd. (1)
Jishan Industrial Park, Pengze County, Jiujiang, Jiangxi, China
Tel.: (86) 7925678111
Pharmaceutical Ingredient Mfr
N.A.I.C.S.: 325412

LANXESS CISA (Pty) Limited (1)
Karbochem Road, Private Bag X 6600, Newcastle, 2940, Kwazulu-Natal, South Africa
Tel.: (27) 343701118
Sales Range: $50-74.9 Million
Emp.: 220
Leather Tanning Chemicals Mfr
N.A.I.C.S.: 325998

BROTHER INDUSTRIES, LTD.
15-1 Naeshiro-cho, Mizuho-ku, Nagoya, 467-8561, Japan
Tel.: (81) 528242511   JP
Web Site: https://global.brother
Year Founded: 1908
BRTHF—(OTCIQ)
Rev.: $5,439,567,300
Assets: $5,923,280,490
Liabilities: $1,507,000,680
Net Worth: $4,416,279,810
Earnings: $209,173,450
Emp.: 40,538
Fiscal Year-end: 03/31/24
Home & Office Typewriters, Printers, Word Processors, Facsimile Machines, Sewing Machines & Other Various Electrical Appliances Mfr & Distr

N.A.I.C.S.: 333310
Toshikazu Koike (Chm)

Subsidiaries:

BETOP STAFF, LTD. (1)
18-1 Shioiri-cho T and I Showa Building 3rd floor, Mizuho-ku, Nagoya, 467-0851, Aichi, Japan
Tel.: (81) 52 824 3260
Web Site: https://www.betop.co.jp
Human Resource Consulting Services
N.A.I.C.S.: 541612

BMB (Shanghai) International Corp. (1)
Room 6F/6010 Yongxin Building 887 Huaihai Middle Road, Shanghai, 200020, China
Tel.: (86) 2164375401
Printing Equipment Mfr & Distr
N.A.I.C.S.: 333248

BMB International Corp. (1)
Shiba Park Bldg B-Kan 8th Floor 2-4-1 Shiba-Park, Minato-ku, Tokyo, 105-0011, Japan
Tel.: (81) 5058141068
Web Site: http://www.bmb.com
Peripheral Equipment Distr
N.A.I.C.S.: 423430

BROTHER CENTRAL AND EASTERN EUROPE GmbH (1)
Pfarrgasse 58, 1230, Vienna, Austria
Tel.: (43) 161007
Web Site: http://www.brother.com
Industrial Electronic Machinery Mfr
N.A.I.C.S.: 333248

BROTHER ENTERPRISE, LTD. (1)
26-1 Naeshiro-cho, Mizuho-ku, Nagoya, 467-0841, Aichi, Japan
Tel.: (81) 52 824 3239
Web Site: https://www.brother-enterprise.co.jp
Amusement Equipment Mfr
N.A.I.C.S.: 333310

BROTHER IBERIA, S.L.U. (1)
Calle Julian Camarillo 57, San Fdo de Henares, 28037, Madrid, Spain
Tel.: (34) 916557570
Web Site: http://www.brother.es
Sales Range: $25-49.9 Million
Emp.: 40
Industrial Machinery Mfr
N.A.I.C.S.: 333248

BROTHER INTERNATIONAL DEL PERU S.A.C. (1)
Tel.: (51) 16269200
Web Site: http://www.brother.com.pe
Emp.: 7
Industrial Machinery Mfr
N.A.I.C.S.: 333248

BROTHER INTERNATIONAL KOREA CO., LTD. (1)
7F 16 Teheran-ro 70-gil Daechi-dong Dongsan Building, Gangnam-gu, Seoul, Korea (South)
Industrial Electronic Machinery Mfr
N.A.I.C.S.: 333248

BROTHER LOGITEC LTD. (1)
1-4-20 Tobeshita, Minami-ku, Nagoya, 457-0842, Aichi, Japan
Tel.: (81) 52 824 2356
Web Site: https://www.brother-logitec.co.jp
Emp.: 203
Logistics Consulting Servies
N.A.I.C.S.: 541614

BROTHER POLSKA Sp. z o.o (1)
ul Garazowa 7, 02-651, Warsaw, Poland
Tel.: (48) 22 607 76 60
Web Site: http://www.brother.pl
Industrial Electronic Machinery Mfr
N.A.I.C.S.: 333248

BROTHER SEWING MACHINES EUROPE GmbH (1)
Konrad-Adenauer-Allee 1 - 11, 61118, Bad Vilbel, Germany
Tel.: (49) 610198140
Industrial Sewing Machine Distr
N.A.I.C.S.: 423830

BROTHER SOFTWARE DEVELOPMENT (HANGZHOU) LTD. (1)

25F Xiao Hong Building 1777 Bin Sheng Road, Bin Jiang District, Hangzhou, 310052, China
Tel.: (86) 571 8659 1639
Software Development Services
N.A.I.C.S.: 541511

Bellezza Club Japan Inc. (1)
15-1 Naeshirocho, Mizuho-ku, Nagoya, 467-0841, Aichi, Japan
Tel.: (81) 528243270
Electrical Equipment Distr
N.A.I.C.S.: 423610

Brother (China) Ltd. (1)
20F Building II Jin Hongqiao International Centre No 533, Loushanguan Road Changning, Shanghai, 200051, China (100%)
Tel.: (86) 213 133 2101
Web Site: http://www.brother-cn.net
Sales Range: $50-74.9 Million
Emp.: 100
Office Equipment & Sewing Machines Whslr
N.A.I.C.S.: 423420

Brother Commercial (Thailand) Ltd. (1)
21st Floor Rasa Building Rasa Tower 2 No 555 Phahonyothin Road, Chatuchak Subdistrict Chatuchak District, Bangkok, 10900, Thailand
Tel.: (66) 26657700
Web Site: https://www.brother.co.th
Printing Equipment Mfr & Distr
N.A.I.C.S.: 333248
Teerawut Suppapunpinyo (Mng Dir)

Brother Corporation (Asia) Ltd. (1)
Unit 606 6/F Exchange Tower 33 Wang Chiu Road, Kowloon Bay, Hong Kong, China (Hong Kong) (100%)
Tel.: (852) 27234198
Sales Range: $50-74.9 Million
Emp.: 20
Holding Company; Printers & Other Office Machinery Mfr
N.A.I.C.S.: 551112

Subsidiary (Non-US):

Brother Industries (Shenzhen) Ltd. (2)
G02414-1 Baochangli Bonded Transportation Industrial Park, Baolong Industrial Estate, Longgang District, Shenzhen, 518 116, China (100%)
Tel.: (86) 75584639697
Web Site: http://www.brother.com
Multi-Function Office Machinery Mfr
N.A.I.C.S.: 333310

Brother Technology (Shenzhen) Ltd. (2)
No 5 Jinlong 3rd Road Baolong Industrial Estate, Longgang District, Shenzhen, Guangdong, China (100%)
Tel.: (86) 75566844750
Printers, Facsimile Machines & Other Office Equipment Mfr
N.A.I.C.S.: 333248

Brother Finance (Japan), Ltd. (1)
15-1 Naeshiro-cho, Mizuho-ku, Nagoya, 467-8561, Japan (100%)
Tel.: (81) 52 824 2117
Web Site: http://www.brother.com
International Trade Financing Services
N.A.I.C.S.: 522299

Brother Finance (U.K.) plc (1)
Brother House 1 Tame Street, Audenshaw, Manchester, M34 5JE, United Kingdom (100%)
Tel.: (44) 161 931 2240
Web Site: http://www.brother.com
Sales Range: $50-74.9 Million
Emp.: 4
International Trade Financing Services
N.A.I.C.S.: 522299

Brother Holding (Europe) Ltd. (1)
Brother House 1 Tame Street, Audenshaw, M34 5JE, Manchester, United Kingdom
Tel.: (44) 161 330 6531
Web Site: http://www.brother.com
Sales Range: $50-74.9 Million
Emp.: 220
Computer Peripheral Equipment Mfr & Distr
N.A.I.C.S.: 334118

Brother Industrial Printing (Japan), Ltd. (1)
8-20-8 Nishikamata Azel Building No 3, Ota-ku, Tokyo, 144-0051, Japan
Tel.: (81) 337362733
Web Site: http://www.bipj.brother.co.jp
Printing Equipment Mfr & Distr
N.A.I.C.S.: 333248

Brother Industries (Philippines), Inc. (1)
Lot 1-B-2 Phase 1B Brgy Ulango, First Philippine Industrial Park, Tanauan, 4232, Batangas, Philippines
Tel.: (63) 434301030
Printing Equipment Mfr & Distr
N.A.I.C.S.: 333248

Brother Industries (U.K.) Ltd. (1)
Vauxhall Industrial Estate, Ruabon, Wrexham, LL14 6HA, United Kingdom (100%)
Tel.: (44) 197 881 3400
Web Site: https://www.biuk.co.uk
Sales Range: $50-74.9 Million
Emp.: 150
Office Machinery Mfr
N.A.I.C.S.: 333310

Subsidiary (Non-US):

Brother Industries (Slovakia) s.r.o. (2)
Osloboditelov 929/15, 963 01, Krupina, Slovakia (100%)
Tel.: (421) 455251400
Sales Range: $25-49.9 Million
Used Toner Cartridge Recycling Services
N.A.I.C.S.: 562920
Andy Dutton (Mgr)

Brother Industries (Vietnam) Ltd. (1)
5th Floor-Minh Long Building 17 Ms Huyen Thanh Quan, Ward 6 District 3, Ho Chi Minh City, Vietnam (100%)
Tel.: (84) 286 290 8787
Web Site: https://www.brother.com.vn
Sales Range: $125-149.9 Million
Emp.: 500
Printers, Facsimile Machines & Multi-Fucntion Office Machinery Mfr
N.A.I.C.S.: 333310

Brother Industries Technology (M) Sdn. Bhd. (1)
17 Jalan Firma 2 Kawasan Perindustrian Tebrau, 81100, Johor Bahru, Johor Darul Takzim, Malaysia
Tel.: (60) 73543888
Web Site: http://www.brother.com
Sales Range: $450-499.9 Million
Emp.: 2,500
Computer & Electronic Product Mfg
N.A.I.C.S.: 541512

Brother Industries Technology (Malaysia) Sdn. Bhd. (1)
17 Jalan Firma 2 Kawasan Perindustrian Tebrau, Johor Darul Takzim, 81100, Johor Bahru, Johor, Malaysia
Tel.: (60) 7 3543 888
Web Site: http://www.brother.com.my
Emp.: 1,800
Industrial Machinery Mfr
N.A.I.C.S.: 333248

Brother International Corporation - USA (1)
200 Crossing Blvd, Bridgewater, NJ 08807-0911 (100%)
Tel.: (908) 704-1700
Web Site: https://global.brother
Sales Range: $750-799.9 Million
Emp.: 1,100
Office Equipment & Sewing Machines Whslr
N.A.I.C.S.: 423420
Kazufumi Ikeda (Chm)

Subsidiary (Domestic):

BROTHER MOBILE SOLUTIONS, INC. (2)
11030 Cir Point Rd Ste 100, Westminster, CO 80020-2775
Tel.: (303) 460-1600
Web Site: http://www.brother-usa.com
Mobile Software Development Services
N.A.I.C.S.: 541511
Ravi Panjwani (Pres)

Brother Industries (U.S.A.), Inc. (2)
7819 N Brother Blvd, Bartlett, TN 38133 (100%)
Tel.: (901) 377-7777
Web Site: https://global.brother
Sales Range: $350-399.9 Million
Electronic Typewriters & Word Processors Mfr
N.A.I.C.S.: 333310

Subsidiary (Non-US):

Brother International Corporation (Canada) Ltd. (2)
1 Rue Hotel De Ville, Dollard-des-Ormeaux, Montreal, H9B 3H6, QC, Canada (100%)
Tel.: (514) 685-0600
Web Site: http://www.brother.ca
Sales Range: $75-99.9 Million
Emp.: 175
Office Equipment & Sewing Machines Whslr
N.A.I.C.S.: 423420
Martin Featherston (Pres)

Brother International Corporation de Argentina S.R.L. (2)
Av Santa Fe 2755 10 Piso Ciudad Autonoma de, C1425BGC, Buenos Aires, Argentina (100%)
Tel.: (54) 1148285400
Web Site: https://www.brother.com.ar
Office Equipment & Sewing Machines Whslr
N.A.I.C.S.: 423420

Brother International Corporation do Brazil, Ltda. (2)
Av Paulista 854 15th Floor, Edificio Top Center Bela Vista, Sao Paulo, 01310-913, Brazil (100%)
Tel.: (55) 1133713555
Web Site: https://www.brother.com.br
Sales Range: $25-49.9 Million
Emp.: 40
Office Equipment & Sewing Machines Whslr
N.A.I.C.S.: 423420

Brother International de Chile, Ltda. (2)
Edificio Matta Calle Rosario Norte 532 Oficina 901, Las Condes, Santiago, Chile (100%)
Tel.: (56) 24116500
Sales Range: $10-24.9 Million
Emp.: 16
Office Equipment & Sewing Machines Whslr
N.A.I.C.S.: 423420

Brother International de Mexico, S.A. de C.V. (2)
Av Santa Fe 428 Torre II Piso 2 Of 201 Col Santa Fe Cuajimalpa, Alcaldia Cuajimalpa de Morelos, CP 05348, Mexico, Mexico (100%)
Tel.: (52) 5585038700
Web Site: http://www.brother.com.mx
Sales Range: $50-74.9 Million
Emp.: 80
Office Equipment & Sewing Machines Whslr
N.A.I.C.S.: 423420

Brother International Taiwan Ltd. (1)
33F No 66 Sec 1 Zhongxiao W Rd, Zhongzheng Dist, Taipei, 10018, Taiwan
Tel.: (886) 223816188
Printing Equipment Mfr & Distr
N.A.I.C.S.: 333248

Brother Living Co., Ltd. (1)
1-1 Kawagishi-icchome, Mizuho-ku, Nagoya, 467-0845, Aichi, Japan
Tel.: (81) 52 824 2140
Web Site: http://www.brother.com
Building Maintenance & Security Services
N.A.I.C.S.: 561730

Brother Machinery (Asia) Ltd. (1)
Unit 1207-11 12/F 9 Wing Hong Street, Cheung Sha Wan, Kowloon, China (Hong Kong)
Tel.: (852) 27770010
Printing Equipment Mfr & Distr
N.A.I.C.S.: 333248

Brother Machinery Shanghai Ltd. (1)
Unit 01 5/F No 799 West Tianshan Rd, Changning District, Shanghai, 200335, China
Tel.: (86) 2122256666
Printing Equipment Mfr & Distr
N.A.I.C.S.: 333248

Brother Machinery Xian Co., Ltd. (1)
No 40 3rd Shang Lin Yuan Road Hi-Tech Industries Development Zone, Xi'an, 710119, Shaanxi, China (100%)
Tel.: (86) 29 8427 5569
Emp.: 1,000
High-End Industrial Sewing Machine Mfr
N.A.I.C.S.: 333248
Kozo Tamagawa (Mgr)

Brother Nordic A/S (1)
Baldershoj 22, 2635, Ishoj, Denmark
Tel.: (45) 43313131
Industrial Electronic Machinery Mfr
N.A.I.C.S.: 333248

Brother Real Estate, Ltd. (1)
15-1 Naeshiro-cho, Mizuho-ku, Nagoya, 467-0841, Aichi, Japan
Tel.: (81) 52 824 3431
Web Site: https://www.brother-bre.co.jp
Emp.: 78
Real Estate Manangement Services
N.A.I.C.S.: 531390

Brother Sales, Ltd. (1)
15-1 Naeshiro-cho, Mizuho-ku, Nagoya, 467-8577, Aichi Prefecture, Japan (100%)
Tel.: (81) 528243311
Web Site: https://www.brother.co.jp
Sales Range: $1-4.9 Billion
Emp.: 344
Printing Equipment Mfr
N.A.I.C.S.: 333248
Koichi Yasui (Pres)

Brother Sewing Machine (Shanghai) Co., Ltd. (1)
2201 Yongsheng Road, Jiading Industrial Zone, Shanghai, 201821, China (100%)
Tel.: (86) 21 6952 0891
Sewing machines Mfr
N.A.I.C.S.: 333248

Brother System Technology Development (Hangzhou) Ltd. (1)
2F 3F 4F 8 Building NO 88 Jiangling Road Xixing Street, Binjiang District, Hangzhou, 310051, Zhejiang, China
Tel.: (86) 57186591639
Printing Equipment Mfr & Distr
N.A.I.C.S.: 333248

Citronix Inc. (1)
2241 S Watson Rd Ste 111, Arlington, TX 76010
Tel.: (817) 633-3200
Web Site: http://www.citronix.com
Ink Jet Printer Mfr
N.A.I.C.S.: 325910

Domino Asia Pte. Ltd. (1)
33 Ubi Avenue 3 05-24 The Vertex Tower B, Singapore, Singapore
Tel.: (65) 66367636
Printing Equipment Mfr & Distr
N.A.I.C.S.: 333248

Domino Graph Tech AG (1)
Aeschwuhrstrasse 15, 4665, Oftringen, Switzerland
Tel.: (41) 627460650
Printing Equipment Mfr & Distr
N.A.I.C.S.: 333248

Domino Printing Sciences plc (1)
Trafalgar Way Bar Hill, Cambridge, CB23 8TU, United Kingdom
Tel.: (44) 195 478 2551
Web Site: https://www.domino-printing.com
Sales Range: $500-549.9 Million
Commercial Inkjet & Laser Printers Mfr & Distr
N.A.I.C.S.: 334118
Simon Howes (Product Mgr-Digital Colour Label Press)

Subsidiary (Non-US):

APS France S.a.r.l. (2)
La Pimpie-1 Rue Robert Schuman, 26120, Montelier, France
Tel.: (33) 475602155
Web Site: http://www.aps-direct.fr
Coding & Printing Machinery Distr
N.A.I.C.S.: 423440

Domino Amjet B.V. (2)
Hoofdveste 11a, 3992 DH, Houten, Netherlands
Tel.: (31) 306363333

Web Site: https://www.domino-printing.com
Coding & Printing Machinery Mfr & Distr
N.A.I.C.S.: 423430

Domino Amjet Iberica SAU (2)
Avenida Valdelaparra 4, Alcobendas, 28108, Madrid, Spain
Tel.: (34) 91 654 2141
Web Site: http://www.domino-spain.com
Coding & Printing Machinery Distr
N.A.I.C.S.: 423430

Domino China Limited (2)
No 1150 Yun Qiao Road, Jin Qiao Export Processing Zone Pudong New Area, Shanghai, 201206, China
Tel.: (86) 4008216818
Web Site: http://www.domino-printing.com
Industrial Coding & Printing Machinery Mfr & Distr
N.A.I.C.S.: 333248
Min Xiang (Mng Dir)

Domino Deutschland GmbH (2)
Lorenz-Schott-Strasse 3, 55252, Mainz-Kastel, Germany
Tel.: (49) 6134250405
Web Site: https://www.domino-printing.com
Investment Management Service
N.A.I.C.S.: 523150

Domino Korea Limited (2)
37 Sagimakgol-ro 62beon-gil Sangdaewon-dong Star Tower 2F, Jungwon-gu, Seongnam, Gyeonggi, Korea (South)
Tel.: (82) 2 797 1811
Web Site: https://www.domino-printing.com
Industrial Coding & Printing Machinery Distr
N.A.I.C.S.: 423830

Domino Laser GmbH (2)
Fangdieckstr 75a, 22547, Hamburg, Germany
Tel.: (49) 40888880
Web Site: http://www.dominolaser.com
Laser Marking Systems Mfr
N.A.I.C.S.: 333248
Frau Anja Wurow (Mgr-HR)

Subsidiary (US):

Domino North America (2)
1290 Lakeside Dr, Gurnee, IL 60031
Tel.: (847) 244-2501
Web Site: https://www.domino-printing.com
Industrial Coding & Printing Machinery Distr
N.A.I.C.S.: 423830
Frank Eickenberg (Pres)

Subsidiary (Non-US):

Domino Print and Apply AB (2)
Agnesfridsvagen 189, 213 75, Malmo, Scania, Sweden
Tel.: (46) 40 689 2500
Web Site: https://www.dominopa.com
Industrial Labelling Machinery Mfr
N.A.I.C.S.: 333993
Kent Anderson (Engr-Software)

Domino Printech India LLP (2)
Plot No 167 HSIIDC Udyog Vihar Phase 1, Gurgaon, 122016, Haryana, India
Tel.: (91) 1244886100
Web Site: https://www.domino-printing.com
Industrial Coding & Printing Machinery Distr
N.A.I.C.S.: 423830

Domino Printing Mexico SA de CV (2)
Calle 3 No 47 Int F-6, Ind Naucalpan Naucalpan de Juarez, 53370, Naucalpan, Edo de Mexico, Mexico
Tel.: (52) 5555767979
Web Site: https://www.domino-printing.com
Emp.: 2,800
Industrial Coding & Printing Machinery Distr
N.A.I.C.S.: 423830
Constantino de Llano (Mng Dir)

Domino Printing Solutions Inc. (2)
1-200 North Service Rd W Suite 317, Oakville, L6M 2Y1, ON, Canada
Web Site: https://www.domino-printing.com
Industrial Coding & Printing Machinery Distr
N.A.I.C.S.: 423830

Domino SAS (2)
Za Du Bel Air 2 Rue Hippolyte Mege Mouries, BP 31, 78120, Rambouillet, France
Tel.: (33) 130465678

BROTHER INDUSTRIES, LTD.

Brother Industries, Ltd.—(Continued)
Web Site: https://www.domino-printing.com
Coding & Printing Machinery Distr
N.A.I.C.S.: 423430

Subsidiary (Domestic):

Domino UK Ltd.   **(2)**
Trafalgar Way, Bar Hill, Cambridge, CB23
8TU, United Kingdom
Tel.: (44) 195 478 2551
Web Site: https://www.domino-printing.com
Ink Jet Printing Systems
N.A.I.C.S.: 334118

Subsidiary (Non-US):

Marque TDI - Technologias de Codifi-cacao S.A.   **(2)**
Sector X Soconorte Arm Business Complex
H L and M, Maia Industrial Zone, 4475-249,
Maia, Portugal
Tel.: (351) 22 986 6660
Web Site: https://www.marquetdi.pt
Coding & Printing Machinery Mfr
N.A.I.C.S.: 333310

Pri-Ma-Tech Verwaltungs GmbH **(2)**
Pastorstrasse 16, 56751, Polch, Rhineland-Palatinate, Germany
Tel.: (49) 265496440
Web Site: http://www.primatech.de
Coding & Printing Machinery Distr
N.A.I.C.S.: 423440
Josef Wetzl *(Mng Dir)*

Subsidiary (Domestic):

Purex International Limited   **(2)**
QWP House Island Drive Capitol Park
Thorne, Doncaster, DN8 5UE, South York-shire, United Kingdom
Tel.: (44) 140 574 6030
Web Site: https://www.purex.co.uk
Fume Extraction Equipment Mfr & Distr
N.A.I.C.S.: 333998
Trefor Jones *(Mng Dir)*

Subsidiary (Non-US):

Wiedenbach Apparatebau GmbH **(2)**
Industriepark 312, 78244, Gottmadingen,
Germany
Tel.: (49) 773 179 9110
Web Site: https://www.wiedenbach.com
Ink Jet Printers & Applications Solutions Mfr
N.A.I.C.S.: 334118
Michael Wohrmann *(Mng Dir)*

Subsidiary (Non-US):

Wiedenbach Apparatebau GmbH **(3)**
51-52 Victoria Rd, Old Town, Swindon, SN1
3AY, United Kingdom
Tel.: (44) 01793495015
Web Site: http://www.wiedenbach.com
Ink Jet Printers & Applications Solutions
N.A.I.C.S.: 423430

Domino Printing Technology Ltd. **(1)**
No 11 Dongzhou Road, Changshu Eco-nomic Development Zone, Jiangsu, 215513,
China
Tel.: (86) 51288801999
Printing Equipment Mfr & Distr
N.A.I.C.S.: 333248

Grandprix Leisure System Co., Ltd. **(1)**
Grand Prix Mikaho Building 3F Kita 23-jo
Higashi 7-5-1, Higashi-ku, Sapporo, 065-0023, Hokkaido, Japan
Tel.: (81) 117505000
Ink Jet Printer Mfr
N.A.I.C.S.: 325910

MIE BROTHER PRECISION INDUS-TRIES, LTD. **(1)**
1480 Higashino Saiku, Meiwa-cho Taki-gun,
Mie, 515-0321, Japan
Tel.: (81) 59 652 2811
Web Site: http://www.brother.com
Computer Peripheral Equipment Mfr
N.A.I.C.S.: 334118

**Nissei Gear Motor Mfg. (Changzhou)
Co., Ltd.** **(1)**
28 Fengqi Road, Wujin High-Tech Industry
Zone, Changzhou, Jiangsu, China
Tel.: (86) 51981663637

Printing Equipment Mfr & Distr
N.A.I.C.S.: 333248

Nissei Trading (Shanghai) Co., Ltd. **(1)**
Unit 2209 Jing An China Tower No 1701
West Beijing Road, Shanghai, 200040,
China
Tel.: (86) 2162884598
Printing Equipment Mfr & Distr
N.A.I.C.S.: 333248

**PT BROTHER INTERNATIONAL
SALES INDONESIA** **(1)**
Wisma 46 - Kota BNI 22nd Floor Suite 22
04-22 05, Jl Jend Sudirman Kav 1, Jakarta,
10220, Indonesia
Tel.: (62) 215744477
Industrial Electronic Machinery Distr
N.A.I.C.S.: 423830
Deny Santosa *(Gen Mgr-Sls & Mktg)*

Post Jet Systems Ltd. **(1)**
Unit 7 Beechwood Chineham Business
Park, Chineham, Basingstoke, RG24 8WA,
United Kingdom
Tel.: (44) 1256479585
Web Site: http://www.postjet.co.uk
Ink Jet Printer Mfr
N.A.I.C.S.: 325910
Jim Lambert *(Mng Dir)*

Standard Corp. **(1)**
Shinagawa NBS Building 7F 2-5-12 Konan,
Minato-ku, Tokyo, 108-0075, Japan
Tel.: (81) 368488181
Restaurant Operating Services
N.A.I.C.S.: 722511

Taiwan Brother Industries, Ltd. **(1)**
76 Kai Fa Rd, Kaohsiung, Taiwan **(100%)**
Tel.: (886) 73613111
Web Site: http://www.taiwanbrother.com
Sales Range: $125-149.9 Million
Emp.: 300
Household Appliances Mfr
N.A.I.C.S.: 449210

Teichiku Music, Inc. **(1)**
Shiba Park Building B Building 8F 2-4-1
Shiba Koen, Minato-ku, Tokyo, 105-0011,
Japan
Tel.: (81) 368602259
Web Site: https://www.teichiku.co.jp
Music Production Services
N.A.I.C.S.: 512250

Xian Brother Industries Co., Ltd. **(1)**
No 20 Gao Xin Road 3, Development Zone
of Hi-Tech Industries, Xi'an, Shaanxi,
China **(100%)**
Tel.: (86) 29 8831 5753
Web Site: http://www.brother.com
Sales Range: $100-124.9 Million
Emp.: 300
Industrial Sewing Machine Mfr
N.A.I.C.S.: 333248

Xing Inc. **(1)**
3-8 Momozono-cho, Mizuho-ku, Nagoya,
467-0855, Aichi, Japan **(99.97%)**
Tel.: (81) 52 825 1901
Web Site: https://www.xing.co.jp
Sales Range: $400-449.9 Million
Karaoke Network Content Data Services
N.A.I.C.S.: 518210
Yasushi Mizutani *(Pres)*

Subsidiary (Domestic):

Teichiku Entertainment, Inc. **(2)**
4-1 Shibakoen-nichome, Minato-ku, Tokyo,
105-8505, Japan **(100%)**
Tel.: (81) 36 860 2254
Web Site: https://www.teichiku.co.jp
Emp.: 120
Audio & Video Software Development Ser-vices
N.A.I.C.S.: 541511
Tsuyoshi Murakami *(Sr Mng Dir)*

Xing Music Entertainment, Inc. **(1)**
Shiba Park Bldg B 8Fl 2-4-1 Shibakoen,
Minato-ku, Tokyo, 105-0011, Japan
Tel.: (81) 354702725
Web Site: https://xme.co.jp
Music Publishers
N.A.I.C.S.: 512230

Yoshiteru Shimizu *(Auditor)*

Zhuhai Brother Industries Co., Ltd. **(1)**
254 Gangchang Road Gongbei, Zhuhai,
Guangdong, China **(100%)**
Tel.: (86) 756 861 0224
Web Site: http://www.brother.com.cn
Sales Range: $900-999.9 Million
Emp.: 3,000
Printing & Business Solutions Services
N.A.I.C.S.: 323120

BROTHERS TEXTILE MILLS LIMITED

135 Upper Mall, Lahore, Pakistan
Tel.: (92) 42 35757013
Web Site:
   http://www.brothersgrouppk.com
Sales Range: Less than $1 Million
Yarn Mfr
N.A.I.C.S.: 313110

BROTOMATIC S.L.

C San Miguel de Acha 2 - Pab 3,
01010, Vitoria, Alava, Spain
Tel.: (34) 945249411
Web Site: http://www.brotomatic.es
Industrial Equipment & Services
N.A.I.C.S.: 423830

BROWAVE CORPORATION

3F No30 Industry East Road, IX
Science-Based Industrial Park, Hsin-chu, 30075, Taiwan
Tel.: (886) 35630099
Web Site: https://www.browave.com
Year Founded: 1998
3163—(TPE)
Rev.: $90,881,255
Assets: $1,165,145,971
Liabilities: $1,079,535,065
Net Worth: $85,610,906
Earnings: $14,251,021
Fiscal Year-end: 12/31/23
Computer Component Mfr & Distr
N.A.I.C.S.: 334118
K. J. Wu *(Chm)*

BROWN & NEWIRTH LTD.

Elma House Beaconsfield Close, Hat-field, AL10 8YG, Hertfordshire, United
Kingdom
Tel.: (44) 1707255000   **UK**
Web Site:
   http://www.brownandnewirth.com
Year Founded: 1967
Sales Range: $10-24.9 Million
Emp.: 50
Jewelry Mfr & Whslr
N.A.I.C.S.: 339910
John Ball *(Dir)*

Subsidiaries:

Abbeycrest Thailand Ltd. **(1)**
12th Floor Bangkok Gem & Jewellery
Tower, 322/20-21 Surawong Road, 10500,
Bangkok, Thailand
Tel.: (66) 22 367 133
Web Site:
   http://www.abbeycrestinternational.com
Jewelry Mfr
N.A.I.C.S.: 339910

BROWN ADVISORY US SMALLER COMPANIES PLC

18 Hanover Square, London, W1S
1JY, United Kingdom
Tel.: (44) 2033018130
Web Site:
   https://www.brownadvisory.com
BASC—(LSE)
Assets: $195,193,516
Liabilities: $674,028
Net Worth: $194,519,488
Earnings: ($31,716,762)
Fiscal Year-end: 06/30/22

Portfolio Management & Investment
Advice
N.A.I.C.S.: 523940

BROWN BROS FORD LIN-COLN SALES & SERVICE

270 S E Marine Dr, Vancouver, V5X
2S6, BC, Canada
Tel.: (604) 321-5100
Web Site:
   http://www.brownbrosford.com
Rev.: $61,035,355
Emp.: 121
New & Used Car Dealers
N.A.I.C.S.: 441110
Pat Bultitude *(Mgr-Parts)*

BROWN COMMUNICATIONS GROUP

2275 Albert St, Regina, S4P 2V5, SK,
Canada
Tel.: (306) 352-6625   **SK**
Web Site: http://www.brown.ca
Year Founded: 1966
Rev.: $14,000,000
Emp.: 35
Communications, Full Service,
Internet/Web Design, Public Rela-tions, Strategic Planning
N.A.I.C.S.: 541810
Ken Christoffel *(Pres & CEO)*

Subsidiaries:

Brown Communications Group **(1)**
200-325 Manning Rd NE, Calgary, T2E
2P5, AB, Canada
Tel.: (403) 290-1285
Web Site: http://www.brown.ca
Emp.: 9
Communications, Full Service, Internet/Web
Design, Newspapers & Magazines, Public
Relations, Strategic Planning
N.A.I.C.S.: 541810
Linda Ducharme *(Gen Mgr)*

BROWN WINDOW CORPORA-TION

185 Snow Blvd, Concord, L4K 4N9,
ON, Canada
Tel.: (905) 738-6045
Web Site:
   http://www.brownwindow.com
Rev.: $10,417,645
Emp.: 70
Vinyl & Wooden Windows & Doors
Mfr
N.A.I.C.S.: 321911
Eros Gerardi *(Pres)*

BROWNE & CO.

100 Esna Park Drive, Markham, L3R
1E3, ON, Canada
Tel.: (905) 475-6104
Web Site: http://www.browneco.com
Sales Range: $250-299.9 Million
Emp.: 200
Import Kitchen & Tableware Mfr
N.A.I.C.S.: 332215
Michael Browne *(Pres)*

Subsidiaries:

Duncan Kitchen Grips Inc. **(1)**
100 Esna Park Dr, Markham, L3R-1E3, ON,
Canada
Tel.: (905) 752-3128
Web Site: http://www.kitchengrips.com
Mfr & Retailer of Kitchen Gloves, Pot Hold-ers, Oven Mitts & Barbecue Mitts
N.A.I.C.S.: 332215
Joanne Lockwood *(Mgr-Customer Svc-Intl)*

BROWNS BEACH HOTELS PLC

No 315 Vauxhall Street, 02, Colombo,
Sri Lanka
Tel.: (94) 112308308   **LK**
Year Founded: 1992

BBH—(COL)
Rev.: $2,225,092
Assets: $17,588,855
Liabilities: $18,216,987
Net Worth: ($628,132)
Earnings: ($3,385,387)
Emp.: 132
Fiscal Year-end: 03/31/23
Hotel & Restaurant Operator
N.A.I.C.S.: 721110
Deshamanya D. H. S. Jayawardena
(Chm)

BROWNS CAPITAL PLC
No 19 Dudley Senanayake Mawatha,
Colombo, 08, Sri Lanka
Tel.: (94) 0117474500   LK
Web Site:
  http://www.brownscapital.com
Year Founded: 2008
FLCH—(COL)
Sales Range: $1-9.9 Million
Investment Holding Company
N.A.I.C.S.: 551112
S. Kotakadeniya *(Mng Dir)*

BROWNS' CHEVROLET
12109 8th St, Dawson Creek, VIG
5A5, BC, Canada
Tel.: (250) 782-9155
Web Site:
  http://www.brownschev.com
Year Founded: 1982
Rev.: $13,602,054
Emp.: 45
New & Used Car Dealers
N.A.I.C.S.: 441110
Aaron Powell *(Gen Mgr)*

**BRQ SOLUCOES EM INFOR-
MATICA S.A.**
Av Copacabana 238 3 andar 18 do
Forte, 06465-903, Barueri, SP, Brazil
Tel.: (55) 1139270600
Web Site: http://www.brq.com
Year Founded: 1993
BRQB3—(BRAZ)
Rev.: $117,684,522
Assets: $68,153,946
Liabilities: $30,942,778
Net Worth: $37,211,168
Earnings: $12,462,594
Fiscal Year-end: 12/31/23
Software Publishing Services
N.A.I.C.S.: 513210
Benjamin Ribeiro Quadros *(Chm,
CEO & Dir-IR)*

BRS RESOURCES LTD.
Suite 404 999 Canada Place, Van-
couver, V6C 3E2, BC, Canada
Tel.: (604) 657-7004
Web Site:
  http://www.brsresources.com
Year Founded: 1967
BRS—(TSXV)
Assets: $209,261
Liabilities: $487,824
Net Worth: ($278,562)
Earnings: ($338,738)
Fiscal Year-end: 10/31/23
Oil & Gas Development Services
N.A.I.C.S.: 213112
Steven D. Moore *(CEO)*

**BRS VENTURES INVESTMENT
LTD**
Sky Tower Second Floor, Abu Dhabi,
United Arab Emirates
Tel.: (971) 26333413
Web Site:
  http://www.brsventures.com
Year Founded: 1975
Holding Company
N.A.I.C.S.: 551112
B.R. Shetty *(Founder & Chm)*

Subsidiaries:

Assam Company India Limited   **(1)**
Greenwood Tea Estate PO Dibrugarh, As-
sam, 786001, India
Tel.: (91) 33 2283 8306
Web Site: http://www.assamco.com
Rev.: $27,570,199
Assets: $169,736,399
Liabilities: $205,307,816
Net Worth: ($35,571,417)
Earnings: ($15,155,258)
Emp.: 16,958
Fiscal Year-end: 03/31/2019
Tea Producer; Oil & Gas Exploration Ser-
vices
N.A.I.C.S.: 311920
Sanjay Sharma *(CFO)*

BRUCE R SMITH LIMITED
Railroad 2, Simcoe, N3Y 4K1, ON,
Canada
Tel.: (519) 426-0904
Web Site: http://www.brsmith.com
Year Founded: 1947
Rev.: $49,477,473
Emp.: 500
Transportation Services
N.A.I.C.S.: 488999
Beth Knoll *(Chief Admin Officer)*

BRUCKNER GROUP GMBH
Konigsberger Str 5-7, 83313,
Siegsdorf, Germany
Tel.: (49) 8662 63 0
Web Site: http://www.brueckner.com
Holding Company
N.A.I.C.S.: 551112
Maximilian Schneider *(Mng Dir)*

Subsidiaries:

Brueckner Group USA, Inc.   **(1)**
200 Intl Dr Ste 105, Portsmouth, NH 03801
Tel.: (603) 929-3900
Web Site: http://www.brueckner-usa.com
Packaging Machinery & Equipment Mfr &
Distr
N.A.I.C.S.: 333993
Steven D. Hoenig *(Pres & CEO)*

Unit (Domestic):

Brueckner Group USA, Inc. -
Fraser   **(2)**
34203 James J Pompo Dr, Fraser, MI
48026
Tel.: (586) 294-7630
Web Site: http://www.brueckner-usa.com
Plastic Packaging Machinery & Equipment
Mfr & Distr
N.A.I.C.S.: 333310

BRUDER MANNESMANN AG
Lempstrasse 24, 42859, Remscheid,
Germany
Tel.: (49) 2191937070
Web Site: https://www.bmag-
  online.de
Year Founded: 1931
BMM—(MUN)
Rev.: $27,188,318
Assets: $42,112,640
Liabilities: $31,405,101
Net Worth: $10,707,539
Earnings: ($1,015,560)
Emp.: 59
Fiscal Year-end: 12/31/23
Steel Product Mfr & Distr
N.A.I.C.S.: 331210
Arthur Burgmans *(CEO)*

BRUNEL INTERNATIONAL N.V.
John M Keynesplein 33, 1066 EP,
Amsterdam, Netherlands
Tel.: (31) 203125000
Web Site:
  https://www.brunelinternational.net
Year Founded: 1975
BRNL—(EUR)
Rev.: $1,468,743,791
Assets: $674,780,881

Liabilities: $329,781,433
Net Worth: $344,999,448
Earnings: $35,499,503
Emp.: 12,539
Fiscal Year-end: 12/31/23
Business Consulting & Project Man-
agement Placement Services
N.A.I.C.S.: 561311
Aat Schouwenaar *(Chm-Supervisory
Bd)*

Subsidiaries:

Brunel Austria GmbH   **(1)**
Inssbrucker Bundesstrasse 126, 5020,
Salzburg, Austria
Tel.: (43) 66283000110
Web Site: https://www.brunel.net
Engineering Consulting Services
N.A.I.C.S.: 541330

Brunel Belgium N.V.   **(1)**
Stephenson Plaza Zone B Rood Blarenber-
glaan 3 A, 2800, Mechelen, Belgium
Tel.: (32) 15273333
Information Technology Services
N.A.I.C.S.: 541512

Brunel CZ S.R.O.   **(1)**
Probrezni 620/3, Karlin, 186 00, Prague,
Czech Republic
Tel.: (420) 226202446
Information Technology Services
N.A.I.C.S.: 541512

Brunel Canada Ltd   **(1)**
200 Ronson Drive Suite 320, Toronto, M9W
5Z9, ON, Canada   **(100%)**
Tel.: (416) 244-2402
Web Site: http://www.brunelcanada.ca
Sales Range: $10-24.9 Million
Emp.: 36
Employment Placement Agencies
N.A.I.C.S.: 561311
Jan Arie van Barneveld *(CEO)*

Brunel Car Synergies GmbH   **(1)**
Daimlerring 9, 31135, Hildesheim,
Germany   **(100%)**
Tel.: (49) 51211760
Web Site: http://www.brunel.de
Sales Range: $10-24.9 Million
Emp.: 35
Engineering & Financing Services
N.A.I.C.S.: 541330
Peter Bolz *(Gen Mgr)*

Brunel Energy Canada Inc   **(1)**
Ste 1810 Bow Valley Square 2 205 5th Av-
enue SW, Calgary, T2P 2V7, AB,
Canada   **(100%)**
Tel.: (403) 539-5009
Sales Range: $25-49.9 Million
Emp.: 10
Employment Placement Agencies
N.A.I.C.S.: 561311

Brunel Energy Europe BV   **(1)**
Molengraaffsingel 8, 2629, Delft,
Netherlands   **(100%)**
Tel.: (31) 203125000
Sales Range: $25-49.9 Million
Emp.: 200
Business Support Services
N.A.I.C.S.: 561499
Bracco Gartner *(Gen Mgr)*

Brunel Energy Holding BV   **(1)**
John M Keynesplein 33, 2909, Amsterdam,
Netherlands   **(100%)**
Tel.: (31) 102666400
Web Site: http://www.brunel.nl
Sales Range: $25-49.9 Million
Emp.: 300
Business Support Services
N.A.I.C.S.: 561499
Jan van Barneveld *(CEO)*

Brunel Energy Inc.   **(1)**
9811 Katy Fwy Ste 1000, Houston, TX
77024   **(100%)**
Tel.: (713) 333-1024
Web Site: http://www.brunelenergy.net
Sales Range: $25-49.9 Million
Emp.: 25
Employment Placement Agency
N.A.I.C.S.: 561311
Bracco Gartner *(Mng Dir)*

Brunel Energy Japan KK   **(1)**
Dogenzaka Square 6F 5-18, Maruyamacho
Shibuya-ku, Tokyo, 150-0044, Japan
Tel.: (81) 357843690
Information Technology Services
N.A.I.C.S.: 541512

Brunel Energy Korea Ltd.   **(1)**
802 190 Yeonhahaean ro, Yeoncho-myeon,
Geoje, 53208, Gyeongsangnam, Korea
(South)
Tel.: (82) 556878967
Construction Engineering Services
N.A.I.C.S.: 541330

Brunel Energy Kuwait W.L.L.   **(1)**
Office 22 & 23 Waha Mall, Dajeej Area, Al
Farwaniyah, 80000, Kuwait
Tel.: (965) 24337398
Information Technology Services
N.A.I.C.S.: 541512

Brunel Energy L.L.C.   **(1)**
Unit 2902 2903 2904 Swiss Tower, PO Box
5658, Cluster Y Jumeirah Lakes Tower,
Dubai, United Arab Emirates
Tel.: (971) 43153000
Sales Range: $350-399.9 Million
Emp.: 1,000
Oil & Gas Operations
N.A.I.C.S.: 213112

Brunel Energy Malaysia Sdn Bhd   **(1)**
25-2 Level 25 Menara AIA Sentral, 30 Jalan
Sultan Ismail, 50250, Kuala Lumpur, Malay-
sia
Tel.: (60) 321443451
Web Site: http://www.brunel.net
Sales Range: $25-49.9 Million
Emp.: 9
Engineeering Services
N.A.I.C.S.: 541330
Ganeashan Periasamy *(Gen Mgr)*

Brunel Energy Nigeria Ltd   **(1)**
Eshrow House No 7 Onikepoakande Street
Off Admiralty Way Road 12, Lekki Phase 1,
Victoria Island, Lagos, Nigeria
Tel.: (234) 1271 4023
Human Resource Consulting Services
N.A.I.C.S.: 541612
Mitch Sonariwo *(Country Mgr)*

Brunel Energy Pty Ltd   **(1)**
Level 2 101 St George's Terrace, Perth,
6000, WA, Australia
Tel.: (61) 893219600
Web Site: http://www.brunel.net
Sales Range: $50-74.9 Million
Emp.: 50
Drilling Oil & Gas Wells
N.A.I.C.S.: 213111
Paul Smith *(Dir)*

Brunel Energy Qatar W.L.L.   **(1)**
Office No 3108 F1 Bldg 3 Al Waab city
Comml District Salwa Rd, PO Box 24936,
Jaun St Al Saad, Doha, Qatar
Tel.: (974) 4320422
Web Site: http://www.brunel.net
Sales Range: $100-124.9 Million
Emp.: 200
Support Activities for Oil & Gas Operations
N.A.I.C.S.: 213112

Brunel Engineering Consultants
NV   **(1)**
Blareenbeerglaan 3 A, 2800, Mechelen,
Belgium
Tel.: (32) 15273333
Web Site: http://www.brunel.be
Sales Range: $50-74.9 Million
Emp.: 120
Engineeering Services
N.A.I.C.S.: 237310
Sandra Schuerewegen *(Dir-Brunel Engrg)*

Brunel GmbH   **(1)**
Langemarckstrasse 4, 16935, Bremen,
Germany   **(100%)**
Tel.: (49) 421169410
Web Site: http://www.brunel.de
Sales Range: $50-74.9 Million
Emp.: 60
Regulation Licensing & Inspection of Com-
mercial Sectors
N.A.I.C.S.: 926150
Banmivald Jen arei *(CEO)*

Brunel ICt NV   **(1)**

Brunel International N.V.—(Continued)

Blärenberglaan 3A, 2800, Mechelen, Belgium
Tel.: (32) 15273333
Web Site: http://www.brunel.be
Sales Range: $25-49.9 Million
Emp.: 120
Highway & Street Construction
N.A.I.C.S.: 541330
Sandra Schuerewegen (Mng Dir)

Brunel India Private Ltd. (1)
Unit No 04 and 05 Ground Floor C and B
Square Sangam Complex, C T S No 95 A
127 Andheri Kurla Road Village Chakala
Andheri East, Mumbai, 400059, India
Tel.: (91) 2267596759
Petrochemical Mfr
N.A.I.C.S.: 325110

Brunel International France Sarl (1)
8 rue Temara, 78100, Saint Germain-en-Laye, France
Tel.: (33) 139580097
Web Site: https://www.brunelenergy.net
Human Resource Consulting Services
N.A.I.C.S.: 541612

**Brunel International South East Asia
Pte Ltd** (1)
77 Robinson Rd 10-03, Singapore, 068896, Singapore
Tel.: (65) 65322480
Web Site: http://www.brunel.com.sg
Sales Range: $25-49.9 Million
Emp.: 70
Management Consulting Services
N.A.I.C.S.: 541618
Sil Hoeve (Gen Mgr)

Brunel International UK Ltd (1)
19 Spring Gardens, Cadogan Street, Manchester, M2 1FB, United Kingdom (100%)
Tel.: (44) 1618852130
Sales Range: $25-49.9 Million
Emp.: 20
Employment Placement Agencies
N.A.I.C.S.: 561311

Brunel Nederland BV (1)
Winthontlaan 6 J, 3526 KV, Utrecht, Netherlands (100%)
Tel.: (31) 203125000
Sales Range: $650-699.9 Million
Emp.: 2,550
Employment Placement Agencies
N.A.I.C.S.: 561311
Jan van Barneveld (CEO)

Brunel Oil & Gas Services WLL (1)
Building B1 Office No 104 Salwa Road, PO
Box 24936, Al Waab City Commercial District, Doha, Qatar
Tel.: (974) 40403434
Web Site: http://www.brunel.net
Emp.: 30
Oil & Gas Industry Recruitment Consulting
Services
N.A.I.C.S.: 541614
John Deneys (Reg Mgr)

**Brunel Recruitment Kazakhstan
LLP** (1)
12B Kurmangazy Str, 060011, Atyrau, Kazakhstan
Tel.: (7) 22307745
Engineering Consulting Services
N.A.I.C.S.: 541330

Brunel Suriname N.V. (1)
Grote Combeweg 37, Paramaribo, Suriname
Tel.: (597) 6202500
Information Technology Services
N.A.I.C.S.: 541512

Brunel Switzerland AG (1)
Leutschenbachstr 95, 8050, Zurich, Switzerland
Tel.: (41) 445423070
Web Site: https://www.brunel.net
Engineering Consulting Services
N.A.I.C.S.: 541330

**Brunel Technical Services (Thailand)
Limited** (1)
49/63 Moo 5 T Tungsukhla, Sriracha, Chon
Buri, 20230, Thailand (100%)
Tel.: (66) 384015913

Web Site: http://www.brunel.co.th
Sales Range: $75-99.9 Million
Emp.: 400
Professional Scientific & Technical Services
N.A.I.C.S.: 541990

**Brunel Technical Services Pte
Ltd** (1)
77 Robinson Rd 10-03, 068896, Singapore, Singapore (100%)
Tel.: (65) 65341352
Web Site: http://www.brunel.com.sg
Sales Range: $25-49.9 Million
Emp.: 100
Scientific & Technical Consulting Services
N.A.I.C.S.: 541690
William Anderson (Mng Dir)

**Brunel Technical Services Pty
Ltd** (1)
Level 8/40 The Esplanade, Perth, 6000, WA, Australia
Tel.: (61) 894295600
Sales Range: $25-49.9 Million
Emp.: 40
Technical Consulting Services
N.A.I.C.S.: 541690
Paul Smith (Mng Dir)

Brunel Vietnam Company Ltd. (1)
19/F Saigon Trade Centre 37 Ton Duc
Thang Street, District 1, Ho Chi Minh City, Vietnam
Tel.: (84) 822202344
Engineering Consulting Services
N.A.I.C.S.: 541330

Taylor Hopkinson Corporation (1)
1 Lincoln St 23rd Fl, Boston, MA 02111
Tel.: (617) 209-4781
Renewable Energy Distr
N.A.I.C.S.: 424490

Taylor Hopkinson Limited (1)
2nd Floor 58 Waterloo Street, Glasgow, G2
7DA, United Kingdom
Tel.: (44) 1414684900
Web Site: https://www.taylorhopkinson.com
Renewable Energy Distr
N.A.I.C.S.: 424490

Taylor Hopkinson Pte. Ltd. (1)
Level 24-01 CapitaGreen 138 Market
Street, Singapore, 048946, Singapore
Tel.: (65) 97247265
Recruitment Consulting Services
N.A.I.C.S.: 541612

BRUNELLO CUCINELLI S.P.A.
Viale Parco dell'Industria 5, 6073, Corciano, Perugia, Italy
Tel.: (39) 075697071
Web Site:
https://www.brunellocucinelli.com
0Q7S—(AIM)
Rev.: $996,865,380
Assets: $1,433,977,889
Liabilities: $1,008,033,817
Net Worth: $425,944,071
Earnings: $87,360,720
Emp.: 2,308
Fiscal Year-end: 12/31/22
Luxury Clothing & Accessories
N.A.I.C.S.: 315250

Subsidiaries:

Brunello Cucinelli (Sichuan) Fashion
Co., Ltd. (1)
25/F Chengdu IFS Tower 1 no 1 Hongxing
Road Section 3, Jinjiang District, Chengdu, 610014, China
Tel.: (86) 4006055085
Web Site: https://shop.brunellocucinelli.cn
Women Boutique Product Mfr
N.A.I.C.S.: 315250

Brunello Cucinelli Austria GmbH (1)
Bognergasse 4, AT 1010, Vienna, Austria
Tel.: (43) 15350225
Web Site: https://shop.brunellocucinelli.com
Women Boutique Product Mfr
N.A.I.C.S.: 315250

Brunello Cucinelli Brasil Ltda (1)
Av Magalhaes de Castro 12000 - Shopping
Cidade Jardim, Sao Paulo, 05502-001, Brazil

Tel.: (55) 1131989387
Women Boutique Product Mfr
N.A.I.C.S.: 315250

Brunello Cucinelli Denmark ApS (1)
Pilestraede 8B, 1112, Copenhagen, Denmark
Tel.: (45) 43326325
Web Site: https://shop.brunellocucinelli.com
Women Boutique Product Mfr
N.A.I.C.S.: 315250

Brunello Cucinelli Hellas SA (1)
Valaoritou 2, GR 106 71, Athens, Greece
Tel.: (30) 2107211303
Web Site: https://shop.brunellocucinelli.com
Women Boutique Product Mfr
N.A.I.C.S.: 315250

Brunello Cucinelli Kuwait for Ready-made & Novelty Clothes Retail
WLL (1)
Al Rai Sheikh Zayed Bin Sultan Al Nahyan
Road, Al Farwaniyah, 13052, Kuwait
Tel.: (965) 22200527
Clothing Accessory Distr
N.A.I.C.S.: 424350

Brunello Cucinelli Middle East
LLC (1)
The Dubai Mall Fashion Avenue Ground
Floor, Dubai, United Arab Emirates
Tel.: (971) 43941728
Clothing Accessory Distr
N.A.I.C.S.: 424350

Brunello Cucinelli Netherlands
B.V. (1)
PC Hooftstraat 99 III, 1071 BR, Amsterdam, Netherlands
Tel.: (31) 206860888
Women Boutique Product Mfr
N.A.I.C.S.: 315250

Brunello Cucinelli Retail Spain
SL (1)
Calle de Jose Ortega y Gasset 14, ES
28006, Madrid, Spain
Tel.: (34) 914313203
Web Site: https://shop.brunellocucinelli.com
Women Boutique Product Mfr
N.A.I.C.S.: 315250

Brunello Cucinelli Suisse SA (1)
Via Nassa 29, T 6900, Lugano, Switzerland
Tel.: (41) 919226784
Web Site: https://shop.brunellocucinelli.com
Women Boutique Product Mfr
N.A.I.C.S.: 315250

Sprl Brunello Cucinelli Belgium (1)
Boulevard de Waterloo 13, 1000, Brussels, Belgium
Tel.: (32) 25137802
Web Site: https://shop.brunellocucinelli.com
Women Boutique Product Mfr
N.A.I.C.S.: 315250

BRUNNER INVESTMENT
TRUST PLC
199 Bishopsgate, London, EC2M
3TY, United Kingdom
Tel.: (44) 2032467000   UK
Web Site: https://www.brunner.co.uk
Year Founded: 1927
BUT—(LSE)
Rev.: $28,317,133
Assets: $588,421,517
Liabilities: $44,376,827
Net Worth: $544,044,690
Earnings: $34,606,965
Fiscal Year-end: 11/30/20
Portfolio Management & Investment
Advice
N.A.I.C.S.: 523940
Carolan Dobson (Chm)

BRUNO SAINT HILAIRE SAS
20 Avenue du Prat Gimont, 31130, Balma, France
Tel.: (33) 5 6124 7880   FR
Web Site: http://www.bruno-saint-hilaire.com
Year Founded: 1973

Men & Women Clothing Designer Mfr
& Whslr
N.A.I.C.S.: 315990
Fabrice Dorr (Pres)

BRUNO'S CONTRACTING
(THUNDER BAY) LTD.
665 Hewitson St, Thunder Bay, P7B
5V5, ON, Canada
Tel.: (807) 623-1855   Ca
Web Site:
http://www.brunoscontracting.com
Year Founded: 1970
Building Contractors
N.A.I.C.S.: 236220

BRUNSWICK EXPLORATION
INC.
1100 Av des Canadiens-de-Montreal
Bureau 300, Montreal, H3B 2S2, QC, Canada
Tel.: (514) 861-4441   QC
Web Site: https://brwexplo.ca
Year Founded: 2007
BRW—(TSXV)
Rev.: $479,801
Assets: $17,886,146
Liabilities: $1,089,887
Net Worth: $16,796,258
Earnings: ($3,927,147)
Fiscal Year-end: 12/31/23
Metal Mining
N.A.I.C.S.: 212290
Robert P. Wares (Chm & Pres-Interim)

BRUNSWICK GROUP LIMITED
16 Lincoln's Inn Fields, London,
WC2A 3ED, United Kingdom
Tel.: (44) 2074045959   UK
Year Founded: 1987
Corporate Consulting Services
N.A.I.C.S.: 561499
Simon Sporborg (Mng Partner)

Subsidiaries:

Brunswick Group (Beijing) Co.,
Ltd. (1)
2605 Twin Towers (East) B12 Jianguomen-wai Avenue, Beijing, 100022, China
Tel.: (86) 1065662256
Web Site: https://www.brunswickgroup.com
Corporate Consulting Services
N.A.I.C.S.: 561499
Philip Lisio (Partner)

Brunswick Group (HK) Co., Ltd. (1)
22 Floor Onfem Tower, 29 Wyndham St
Central, Hong Kong, China (Hong Kong)
Tel.: (852) 35125000
Web Site: https://www.brunswickgroup.com
Corporate Consulting Services
N.A.I.C.S.: 561499
Tim Payne (Mng Partner)

Brunswick Group (Pty) Ltd. (1)
23 Fricker Rd, Illovo Boulevard, Illovo, Johannesburg, South Africa
Tel.: (27) 115027300
Web Site: https://www.brunswickgroup.com
Corporate Consulting Services
N.A.I.C.S.: 561499
Mark Carter (Mng Partner)

Brunswick Group GmbH (1)
WeiSSfrauenstraSSe 12-16, 60311, Frankfurt am Main, Germany
Tel.: (49) 6924005510
Web Site: https://www.brunswickgroup.com
Corporate Consulting Services
N.A.I.C.S.: 561499
Thomas Knipp (Sr Partner)

Branch (Domestic):

Brunswick Group (2)
TaubenstraSSe 20-22, 10117, Berlin, Germany
Tel.: (49) 30 2067 3360
Web Site: http://www.brunswickgroup.com
N.A.I.C.S.: 541810
Carl Count von Hohenthal (Partner)

Brunswick Group LLC (1)
1114 Ave of the Americas 24th Fl, New
York, NY 10036
Tel.: (212) 333-3810
Web Site: https://www.brunswickgroup.com
Corporate Consulting Services
N.A.I.C.S.: 561499
Steven Lipin (Partner)

Brunswick Group NV/SA (1)
Mezzanine Floor, 9-13 Rue Joseph II, 1000,
Brussels, Belgium
Tel.: (32) 22356511
Web Site: https://www.brunswickgroup.com
Corporate Consulting Services
N.A.I.C.S.: 561499
Philippe Blanchard (Partner)

Brunswick Gulf Ltd. (1)
PO Box 77800 Level 1 Blue Building two-
four54, Abu Dhabi, United Arab Emirates
Tel.: (971) 24012690
Web Site: https://www.brunswickgroup.com
Corporate Consulting Services
N.A.I.C.S.: 561499
Alex Blake Milton (Partner)

Branch (Domestic):

Brunswick Group (2)
Gate Village Building 1 PO Box 506691,
Dubai International, Finance Centre, Dubai,
United Arab Emirates
Tel.: (971) 4 365 8260
Web Site: http://www.brunswickgroup.com
N.A.I.C.S.: 541810
Rupert Young (Partner)

BRUNSWICK RESOURCES INC.
15 Gamble Street East Suite 204,
Rouyn-Noranda, J9X 3B6, QC,
Canada
Tel.: (819) 797-0596   AB
Web Site:
     http://www.brunswickresources.com
Year Founded: 2006
BRU—(TSXV)
Rev.: $1,429
Assets: $36,739
Liabilities: $247,604
Net Worth: ($210,865)
Earnings: ($55,725)
Fiscal Year-end: 12/31/19
Metal Mining Services
N.A.I.C.S.: 212290
Christian Dupont (Pres & CEO)

BRUUSH ORAL CARE, INC.
30 Wellington Street West 5th Floor,
Toronto, ON, Canada   BC
Web Site: https://www.bruush.com
Year Founded: 2017
BRSH—(NASDAQ)
Rev.: $2,632,000
Assets: $1,191,000
Liabilities: $2,593,000
Net Worth: ($1,402,000)
Earnings: ($8,765,000)
Emp.: 7
Fiscal Year-end: 10/31/22
Health Care Srvices
N.A.I.C.S.: 621610
Aneil Manhas (CEO, Founder & Chm)

BRVENIK A.D.
Zeleznicka 26, Raska, Serbia
Tel.: (381) 36 736 119
Year Founded: 2010
BRVN—(BEL)
Sales Range: Less than $1 Million
Emp.: 39
Construction Engineering Services
N.A.I.C.S.: 236116
Milivoje Miladinovic (Exec Dir)

BRYAH RESOURCES LIMITED
191B Carr Place, Leederville, 6007,
WA, Australia
Tel.: (61) 893210001   AU

Web Site: https://www.bryah.com.au
Year Founded: 2017
BYH—(ASX)
Rev.: $16,256
Assets: $8,296,669
Liabilities: $305,129
Net Worth: $7,991,540
Earnings: ($1,096,239)
Fiscal Year-end: 06/30/24
Mineral Exploration Services
N.A.I.C.S.: 213114
Neil Andrew Marston (Mng Dir & Sec)

BRYAST-D JSC
Pop Bogomil Str No 6, 9300, Dobrich,
9300, Bulgaria
Tel.: (359) 58601543
Web Site: https://www.bryast.com
Furniture Mfr
N.A.I.C.S.: 337214

BRYEN & LANGLEY LTD.
48 60 Footscray Rd, Eltham, London,
SE9 2SU, United Kingdom
Tel.: (44) 2088507775
Web Site: http://www.bryen-
langley.com
Year Founded: 1967
Sales Range: $50-74.9 Million
Emp.: 189
Construction & Maintainance Ser-
vices
N.A.I.C.S.: 237990
Paul McMahon (Dir-Contracts)

Subsidiaries:

Andara Tools and Plant Hire Ltd (1)
10 Orangery Lane, Eltham, London, SE9
1HN, United Kingdom
Tel.: (44) 20 8859 2804
Web Site: http://www.andaratools.com
Industrial Equipment Rental Services
N.A.I.C.S.: 532490

BRYMOR CONTRACTORS LTD.
Brymor House Parklands Business
Park Forest Rd, Denmead, Waterloo-
ville, PO7 6XP, Hampshire, United
Kingdom
Tel.: (44) 2392261515
Web Site: http://www.brymor.co.uk
Sales Range: $50-74.9 Million
Emp.: 150
Building Contractors
N.A.I.C.S.: 238190
Stephen J. Morton (Chm)

BRYTEX BUILDING SYSTEMS INC.
5610-97 Street, Edmonton, T6E 3J1,
AB, Canada
Tel.: (780) 437-7970
Web Site: https://www.brytex.com
Year Founded: 1987
Sales Range: $25-49.9 Million
Steel Building Mfr
N.A.I.C.S.: 332311
Al Stix (Pres)

BRYTON MARINE GROUP
8160 Highland Rd, Vernon, V1B
3W6, BC, Canada
Web Site: https://bryton.com
Holding Company
N.A.I.C.S.: 551112
Byron Bolton (CEO)

Subsidiaries:

All American Marine, Inc. (1)
200 Harris Ave, Bellingham, WA 98225
Tel.: (360) 647-7602
Web Site:
     http://www.allamericanmarine.com
Sales Range: $1-9.9 Million
Emp.: 35
Boatbuilding And Repairing, Nsk
N.A.I.C.S.: 336612

Matthew Mullett (Co-CEO)

BRZ INVESTIMENTOS S.A.
Rua Leopoldo Couto de Magalhaes
Jr 758, Cj 52 Itaim Bib, 4542000, Sao
Paulo, Brazil
Tel.: (55) 11353880080
Web Site:
     http://www.brzinvestimentos.com.br
Financial & Asset Management In-
vestment Services
N.A.I.C.S.: 523999
Nelson Rozental (Chm)

BS LIMITED
504 Trendset Towers Road no 2,
Banjara Hills, Hyderabad, 500034,
Andhra Pradesh, India
Tel.: (91) 40 4455 8888
Web Site: http://www.bslimited.in
Rev.: $72,342,425
Assets: $246,592,223
Liabilities: $331,003,510
Net Worth: ($84,411,287)
Earnings: ($127,596,640)
Emp.: 132
Fiscal Year-end: 03/31/18
Telecommunication & Power Struc-
tures Mfr
N.A.I.C.S.: 237130
Rajesh Agarwal (Chm & Mng Dir)

BSA LIMITED
Suite 1401 Level 14 Tower B The
Zenith 821 Pacific Highway, Chats-
wood, 2067, NSW, Australia
Tel.: (61) 297636200   AU
Web Site: https://www.bsa.com.au
BSA—(ASX)
Rev.: $357,320,368
Assets: $97,787,297
Liabilities: $103,221,117
Net Worth: ($5,433,819)
Earnings: ($32,365,398)
Emp.: 350
Fiscal Year-end: 06/30/22
Communications & Technical Service
Solutions; Satellite Installation Ser-
vices
N.A.I.C.S.: 517410
Michael Givoni (Chm)

Subsidiaries:

066 059 809 Pty Limited (1)
Unit 8 79-99 St Hilliers Rd, Auburn, 2144,
NSW, Australia
Tel.: (61) 287482400
Communication Network Installation Ser-
vices
N.A.I.C.S.: 238210

Allstaff Airconditioning (ACT) Pty
Limited (1)
Unit 4 65 Tennant Street, Fyshwick, 2609,
ACT, Australia
Tel.: (61) 262392828
Web Site: http://www.allstaff.com.au
Air Conditioning Equipment Installation Ser-
vices
N.A.I.C.S.: 238220

Allstaff Airconditioning (NSW) Pty
Limited (1)
Quad 2 Level 3 8 Parkview Drive Olympic
Park, Sydney, 2127, NSW, Australia
Tel.: (61) 298793377
Web Site: http://www.allstaffnsw.com.au
Air Conditioning Equipment Installation Ser-
vices
N.A.I.C.S.: 238220
Paul Carter (Mgr-Comml)

Allstaff Airconditioning (VIC) Pty
Limited (1)
379-383 Lower Dandenong Road, Dingley,
3172, VIC, Australia
Tel.: (61) 395513066
Web Site: http://www.allstaffvic.com.au
Air Conditioning Equipment Installation Ser-
vices
N.A.I.C.S.: 238220

Haydn Walsh (Gen Mgr)

BSA Advanced Property Solutions
(ACT) Pty Ltd (1)
6/55 Tennant Street, Fyshwick, 2609, ACT,
Australia
Tel.: (61) 26 239 1185
Property Management Services
N.A.I.C.S.: 531390

BSA Advanced Property Solutions
(NT) Pty Ltd (1)
Units 1 and 2 19 Mel Road, Berrimah,
0828, NT, Australia
Tel.: (61) 88 947 2595
Property Management Services
N.A.I.C.S.: 531390

BSA Advanced Property Solutions
(VIC) Pty Ltd (1)
34-40 Garden Blvd, Dingley Village, Mel-
bourne, 3172, VIC, Australia
Tel.: (61) 37 505 6600
Property Management Services
N.A.I.C.S.: 531390

BSA Communications & Utility Infra-
structure Pty Ltd (1)
Level 7 3 Thomas Holt Drive, Macquarie
Park, 2113, NSW, Australia
Tel.: (61) 28 748 2400
Property Management Services
N.A.I.C.S.: 531390

Burke Air Pty Limited (1)
U1 / 21 Frederick Street, Belmont, 6104,
WA, Australia
Tel.: (61) 8 6465 7300
Web Site: http://www.burkeair.com.au
Air Conditioning Equipment Installation Ser-
vices
N.A.I.C.S.: 238220
Ryan Hipps (Reg Gen Mgr)

Division (Domestic):

Burke Air Pty Limited - Kalgoorlie
Division (2)
U1 / 224 Boulder Rd, Kalgoorlie, 6430, WA,
Australia
Tel.: (61) 8 9022 3393
Web Site: http://www.burkeair.com.au
Emp.: 10
Air Conditioning Equipment Installation Ser-
vices
N.A.I.C.S.: 238220
Rod Thompson (Mgr)

Catalyst One Pty Ltd (1)
L7 3 Thomas Holt Drive, Macquarie Park,
Sydney, 2113, NSW, Australia
Tel.: (61) 29 763 6200
Web Site: https://catalystone.com.au
Property Management Services
N.A.I.C.S.: 531390

Complex Airconditioning Pty
Limited (1)
20 A Osburn St, Wodonga, 3690, VIC, Aus-
tralia
Tel.: (61) 260242055
Air Conditioning Equipment Installation Ser-
vices
N.A.I.C.S.: 238220

MEC Services Pty Limited (1)
Unit 1 19 Mel Road, Berrimah, 828, NT,
Australia
Tel.: (61) 8 8947 2595
Web Site: http://www.mecservices.net.au
Emp.: 30
Air Conditioning Equipment Installation Ser-
vices
N.A.I.C.S.: 238220
Damion Telford (Gen Mgr)

Triple 'M' Fire (1)
Quad 2 Level 3 68 Parkview Drive, Home-
bush Bay, 2127, NSW, Australia
Tel.: (61) 297636200
Web Site: http://www.triple-m.com.au
Emp.: 150
Fire Protection Solutions
N.A.I.C.S.: 922160
Rod Sekulich (Gen Mgr)

Triple M Mechanical Services Pty
Ltd (1)
Triple M Industrial Estate, Unit 5/47 Day

BSA Limited—(Continued)

Street North, Silverwater, 2128, NSW, Australia
Tel.: (61) 297378711
Web Site: http://www.triple-m.com.au
Mechanical Engineering Services
N.A.I.C.S.: 541330

Triple M Mechanical Services Pty Ltd **(1)**
56 Overlord Place, Acacia Ridge, 4110, QLD, Australia
Tel.: (61) 732721177
Web Site: http://www.triple-m.com.au
Sales Range: $25-49.9 Million
Emp.: 60
Mechanical Engineering Services
N.A.I.C.S.: 541330

BSB SA
Avenue Athena 2, B-1348, Louvain-la-Neuve, Belgium
Tel.: (32) 10483480
Year Founded: 1995
Sales Range: $25-49.9 Million
Emp.: 344
IT Consulting & Business Software Publisher
N.A.I.C.S.: 541611
Badreddine Ouali (Chm)

Subsidiaries:

Business Solutions Builders (Belgium) SA **(1)**
Boulevard du Regent 37-40, Brussels, 1000, Belgium
Tel.: (32) 10483480
Web Site: http://www.bsb.com
Sales Range: $25-49.9 Million
Emp.: 50
IT Services & Financial Software Publishers
N.A.I.C.S.: 513210
Marwan Hanifeh (CEO)

BSEL INFRASTRUCTURE REALTY LIMITED
737 7th Floor The Bombay Oilseeds and Oils Exchange Premises Co-op Sty, Plot No 2 3 and 4 The Commodity Exchange Sector-19 Vashi, Navi Mumbai, 400 705, Maharashtra, India
Tel.: (91) 2265123124
Web Site: https://www.bsel.com
532123—(BOM)
Rev.: $954,819
Assets: $110,033,175
Liabilities: $58,956,667
Net Worth: $51,076,508
Earnings: $663,101
Emp.: 3
Fiscal Year-end: 03/31/22
Real Estate Development Services
N.A.I.C.S.: 531390
Kirit Kanakiya (Chm & CEO)

Subsidiaries:

BSEL Infrastructure Realty FZE **(1)**
Saif Plus R-4-07/A Sharjah Airport International Free Zone, Sharjah, United Arab Emirates
Tel.: (971) 65575781
Real Estate Development Services
N.A.I.C.S.: 531210

BSF ENTERPRISE PLC
2 Portman Street, London, W1H 6DU, United Kingdom
Tel.: (44) 2032834590
Web Site: https://www.bsfenterprise.com
BSFA—(LSE)
Assets: $4,562,766
Liabilities: $509,490
Net Worth: $4,053,276
Earnings: ($1,052,946)
Fiscal Year-end: 09/30/22
Portfolio Management & Investment Advice
N.A.I.C.S.: 523940

Min Yang (Chm)

BSI STEEL LIMITED
46 Eden Park Drive Murrayfield Park Mkondeni, Kwazulu Natal, Pietermaritzburg, 3201, Gauteng, South Africa
Tel.: (27) 33 846 2222
Web Site: http://www.bsisteel.com
Year Founded: 1085
Rev.: $175,575,767
Assets: $110,320,561
Liabilities: $58,631,358
Net Worth: $51,689,203
Earnings: $4,152,380
Emp.: 440
Fiscal Year-end: 03/31/17
Steel Products Mfr & Distr
N.A.I.C.S.: 331210
Emmerentia Vermaak (Fin Dir)

BSL CORPORATION BERHAD
E-10-4 Megan Avenue 1 189 Jalan Tun Razak, 3 Bangsar South No 8 Jalan Kerinchi, 50400, Kuala Lumpur, Malaysia
Tel.: (60) 321810516   MY
Web Site: https://www.bslcorp.com.my
Year Founded: 1978
7221—(KLS)
Rev.: $45,461,717
Assets: $42,844,632
Liabilities: $13,766,087
Net Worth: $29,078,545
Earnings: ($2,175,462)
Fiscal Year-end: 12/31/22
Industrial Parts Mfr & Distr
N.A.I.C.S.: 333517
Tong Kwan Ngiam (Chm)

Subsidiaries:

BSL Eco Energy Sdn. Bhd. **(1)**
No 5-1 5-2 Jalan 3/1 Setia Eco Templer, 48000, Rawang, Selangor Darul Ehsan, Malaysia
Tel.: (60) 364204191
Web Site: https://bsleco.com
Solar Installation Services
N.A.I.C.S.: 221114

Ban Seng Lee Industries Sdn. Bhd. **(1)**
Lot 4220 Persimpangan Jalan Batu Arang Lebuhraya PLUS, 48000, Rawang, Selangor, Malaysia
Tel.: (60) 360919148
Metal Component Mfr
N.A.I.C.S.: 332999

Bsl Electronics & Technologies Sdn. Bhd. **(1)**
Lot 4212 Persimpangan Jalan Batu Arang Lebuhraya PLUS, 48000, Rawang, Selangor, Malaysia
Tel.: (60) 360919148
Electric Equipment Mfr
N.A.I.C.S.: 335999

Bsl Manufacturing Sdn. Bhd. **(1)**
Lot 4220 Persimpangan Jalan Batu Arang/Lebuhraya PLUS, 48000, Rawang, Selangor Darul Ehsan, Malaysia
Tel.: (60) 919148
Precision Metal Part Mfr
N.A.I.C.S.: 332721

Bsl Unify Pte. Ltd. **(1)**
60 Kaki Bukit Place 04-05 Eunos TechPark II, Singapore, 415979, Singapore
Tel.: (65) 705912
Web Site: https://www.bslunify.com
Semiconductor Equipment Mfr
N.A.I.C.S.: 333242

BSL LIMITED
26 Industrial Area Gandhi Nagar, Bhilwara, 311001, Rajasthan, India
Tel.: (91) 1482246801
Web Site: https://www.bslltd.com
BSL—(NSE)
Rev.: $44,047,049
Assets: $39,337,075

Liabilities: $28,652,073
Net Worth: $10,685,002
Earnings: $185,476
Emp.: 401
Fiscal Year-end: 03/31/21
Formal Suits Mfr
N.A.I.C.S.: 315250
Arun Churiwal (Chm & Mng Dir)

BSM CHEMICAL CO., LTD.
No 2 Noeleven Road Shangyu Industrial Park Hangzhou Bay, Shaoxing, 201900, Zhejiang, China
Tel.: (86) 57582738303
Web Site: https://en.bsmchem.com
Year Founded: 2003
300796—(SSE)
Rev.: $107,837,028
Assets: $294,943,896
Liabilities: $65,881,296
Net Worth: $229,062,600
Earnings: $21,464,352
Fiscal Year-end: 12/31/22
Chemical Product Mfr & Distr
N.A.I.C.S.: 325520
Feng Chen (Chm)

BSM GROUP LIMITED
BSM Center 119/122, Amin Market, Chittagong, Bangladesh
Tel.: (880) 31624372
Web Site: http://bsmgroupbd.com
Holding Company
N.A.I.C.S.: 551112
Abul Bashar Chowdhury (Chm)

Subsidiaries:

Modern Poly Industries Ltd. **(1)**
BSM Center 119/122 4th Floor, Amin Market, Chittagong, 4000, Bangladesh
Tel.: (880) 31624372
Web Site: http://modempolybd.com
Polyester Yarn
N.A.I.C.S.: 313110

BSN MEDIA HOLDINGS, INC.
3-18 Kawagishi-cho, Chuo-ku, Niigata, 951-8655, Japan
Tel.: (81) 252674111
Web Site: https://www.ohbsn.com
Year Founded: 1952
9408—(TKS)
Rev.: $152,301,010
Assets: $208,631,430
Liabilities: $48,193,510
Net Worth: $160,437,920
Earnings: $4,587,340
Fiscal Year-end: 03/31/24
Television Broadcasting Services
N.A.I.C.S.: 516120

BSP - BIOLOGICAL SIGNAL PROCESSING LTD.
30 HaBarzel Street, Tel Aviv, 6971918, Israel
Tel.: (972) 36474840
Web Site: http://www.bspmedical.com
Year Founded: 2000
BSP—(TAE)
Sales Range: Less than $1 Million
Medical Device Mfr & Distr
N.A.I.C.S.: 334510
Yair Granot (CTO)

BSP FINANCIAL GROUP LIMITED
Section 34 Allotment 6&7 Klinki Street Waigani Drive, PO Box 78, Port Moresby, Papua New Guinea
Tel.: (675) 3201212
Web Site: https://www.bsp.com.pg
Year Founded: 1974
BSP—(PNGX)
Rev.: $453,388,358
Assets: $7,012,548,307
Liabilities: $6,121,357,402

Net Worth: $891,190,905
Earnings: $254,563,685
Emp.: 4,000
Fiscal Year-end: 12/31/19
Banking Services
N.A.I.C.S.: 522110
Robin Fleming (CEO)

Subsidiaries:

BSP Capital Limited **(1)**
Ground Floor Ravalian Haus Waterfront, PO Box 2017, National Capital District, 121, Port Moresby, Papua New Guinea
Tel.: (675) 3214333
Web Site: https://www.bspcapital.com.pg
Financial Investment Services
N.A.I.C.S.: 523999

BSP Convertible Notes Limited **(1)**
Level 12 BSP Suva Central Building Cnr of Renwick Rd & Pratt Street, Suva, Fiji **(100%)**
Tel.: (679) 3214412
Financial Services
N.A.I.C.S.: 523999
Robin Gerard Fleming (Chm)

BSP Life (Fiji) Limited **(1)**
Level 7 BSP Life Centre Thomson Street, Suva, Fiji
Tel.: (679) 132700
Web Site: https://www.bsplife.com.fj
Financial Investment Services
N.A.I.C.S.: 523999
Munendra Naidu (CFO)

BSP Life (PNG) Limited **(1)**
Level 2 Waigani Banking Centre, PO Box 78, National Capital District, Port Moresby, Papua New Guinea
Tel.: (675) 3056214
Web Site: https://www.bsplife.com.pg
Financial Investment Services
N.A.I.C.S.: 523999
Nilson Singh (Country Mgr)

BSRM STEELS LIMITED
Ali Mansion 1207/1099 Sadarghat Road, Chittagong, Bangladesh
Tel.: (880) 2333354901
Web Site: https://www.bsrm.com
Year Founded: 1952
BSRMSTEEL—(CHT)
Rev.: $771,000,407
Assets: $701,442,342
Liabilities: $450,000,761
Net Worth: $251,432,581
Earnings: $27,176,866
Emp.: 1,557
Fiscal Year-end: 06/30/23
Steel Mfrs
N.A.I.C.S.: 331110
Alihussain Akberali (Chm)

BT GROUP PLC
1 Braham Street, London, E1 8EE, United Kingdom
Tel.: (44) 2073565000   UK
Web Site: https://www.bt.com
Year Founded: 1984
BT—(LSE)
Rev.: $26,252,209,078
Assets: $65,310,527,742
Liabilities: $49,508,962,458
Net Worth: $15,801,565,285
Earnings: $1,079,272,912
Emp.: 91,700
Fiscal Year-end: 03/31/24
Holding Company; Communications Products & Services
N.A.I.C.S.: 551112
Clive Selley (CEO-Openreach)

Subsidiaries:

BT Bilisim Hizmetleri Anonim Sirketi **(1)**
Cecen Sokak Akasya A Kule Kent Etabi Apt No 25 A / 28, Acibadem Mahallesi Merkez Uskudar, 34660, Istanbul, Turkiye
Tel.: (90) 2162506574
N.A.I.C.S.: 517810

BT Communications Ireland Limited (1)
2 Grand Canal Plaza Upper Grand Canal Street, Dublin, 4, Ireland
Tel.: (353) 14328846
Web Site: https://www.btireland.com
Internet Providing Services
N.A.I.C.S.: 517810
Shay Walsh (Mng Dir)

BT Telekom Hizmetleri Anonim Sirketi (1)
Cecen Sokak Akasya A Kule Kent Etabi Apt No 25 A / 28, Acibadem Mahallesi Merkez Uskudar, 34660, Istanbul, Turkiye
Tel.: (90) 2162506574
N.A.I.C.S.: 517810

British Telecommunications plc (1)
BT Centre 81 Newgate Street, London, EC1A 7AJ, United Kingdom (100%)
Tel.: (44) 2073565000
Web Site: http://www.btplc.com
Assets: $76,199,574,920
Liabilities: $48,550,167,160
Net Worth: $27,649,407,760
Earnings: $2,978,389,940
Fiscal Year-end: 03/31/2019
Communications Products & Services
N.A.I.C.S.: 517111
Simon Lowth (CFO)

Subsidiary (Non-US):

BT (Germany) GmbH & Co. OHG (2)
Barthstrasse 4, Munich, 80339, Germany
Tel.: (49) 8926000
Web Site: http://www.bt.com
Telecommunication Software Development Services
N.A.I.C.S.: 541511

BT Australasia Pty Limited (2)
Level 20 420 George Street, Sydney, 2000, NSW, Australia (100%)
Tel.: (61) 292691000
Sales Range: $50-74.9 Million
Emp.: 110
Telecommunication Services Provider
N.A.I.C.S.: 517111

Subsidiary (Domestic):

First State Computing Pty Ltd. (3)
Level 7, Underwood House 37-49 Pitt Street, Sydney, 2000, NSW, Australia
Computer Software Developer
N.A.I.C.S.: 334610

Subsidiary (Non-US):

BT Communications do Brasil Limitada (2)
Km 9 - Chacara Assay - Condominio Tech Town Unidade 27, Hortolandia, 13186 904, Sao Paulo, Brazil
Tel.: (55) 1930319600
Telecommunication Servicesb
N.A.I.C.S.: 517810

Subsidiary (Domestic):

BT Conferencing (2)
81 Newgate St, London, EC1A 7AJ, United Kingdom
Tel.: (44) 2073565000
Web Site: http://www.bt.com
Audio, Video & Web Collaboration Services
N.A.I.C.S.: 561499

Subsidiary (US):

BT Americas Inc. (3)
251 Little Falls Dr, Wilmington, DE 19808
Tel.: (703) 755-6733
Information Technology Services
N.A.I.C.S.: 518210

BT Conferencing, Inc. (3)
150 Newport Ave Ext Ste 400, North Quincy, MA 02171
Tel.: (781) 849-8136
Web Site: http://www.btconferencing.com
Sales Range: $150-199.9 Million
Emp.: 1,000
Audio, Video & Web Conferencing Services
N.A.I.C.S.: 561499

Subsidiary (Domestic):

BT Convergent Solutions Limited (2)
Cassini House Hanborough Business Park, Witney, OX29 8SD, Oxon, United Kingdom
Tel.: (44) 1993 885900
Sales Range: $100-124.9 Million
Emp.: 30
Telecommunication Servicesb
N.A.I.C.S.: 517810
Neil Pemberton (Gen Mgr)

Subsidiary (Non-US):

BT Espana S.A. (2)
Salvador De Madariaga 1 Planta 3, Madrid, 28027, Spain (100%)
Tel.: (34) 912708000
Web Site: http://www.bt.com
Sales Range: $150-199.9 Million
Emp.: 600
Telecommunication Services Provider
N.A.I.C.S.: 517111

BT Global Communications India Private Limited (2)
502 5th Floor Raheja Titanium II Off Western Express Highway, Jogeshwari E, Mumbai, 400 063, India
Tel.: (91) 2242430000
Telecommunication Servicesb
N.A.I.C.S.: 517810

Division (Domestic):

BT Global Services (2)
1 Braham Street, London, E1 8EE, United Kingdom (100%)
Tel.: (44) 2073565000
Web Site: http://wwwbtglobalservices.com
Sales Range: $15-24.9 Billion
Emp.: 37,000
Multi-Site Corporate Network Information Technology Services
N.A.I.C.S.: 517810
Bas Burger (CEO)

Subsidiary (Non-US):

BT Frontline Pte. Ltd. (3)
750 Chai Chee Road 02-01/02/03 The Oasis, Technopark at Chai Chee, 469000, Singapore, Singapore (100%)
Tel.: (65) 67737227
Web Site: http://www.frontline.com.sg
Sales Range: $800-899.9 Million
Emp.: 5,000
IT Consulting & Services
N.A.I.C.S.: 541690

Subsidiary (Non-US):

BT Hong Kong Limited (2)
38 F Porset House Taikoo Pl, 979 Kings Rd, Quarry Bay, China (Hong Kong) (100%)
Tel.: (852) 25323606
Web Site: http://www.bt.com
Sales Range: $25-49.9 Million
Emp.: 100
Telecommunication Servicesb
N.A.I.C.S.: 517111

Subsidiary (Domestic):

BT IT Services Limited (2)
3 Midland Way Barlborough Links, Barlborough, Chesterfield, S43 4XA, Derbyshire, United Kingdom
Tel.: (44) 1246574000
Web Site: http://www.btengageit.com
Sales Range: $75-99.9 Million
Emp.: 600
Information Technology Products, Consulting & Technology Services
N.A.I.C.S.: 541511

Subsidiary (US):

BT Ignite (2)
11440 Commerce Pk Dr, Reston, VA 20191
Tel.: (703) 755-6000
Sales Range: $75-99.9 Million
Emp.: 450
Global Telecommunications Supplier
N.A.I.C.S.: 541690

BT Infonet (2)
2160 E Grand Ave, El Segundo, CA 90245
Tel.: (310) 335-4700
Web Site: http://www.bt.com

Global Communications
N.A.I.C.S.: 517810

Subsidiary (Non-US):

BT Italia SpA (2)
Via Tucidide 14, Torre 7, 20134, Milan, Italy (100%)
Tel.: (39) 0283714000
Web Site: https://www.globalservices.bt.com
Sales Range: $800-899.9 Million
Emp.: 1,300
Communications Services & Solutions
N.A.I.C.S.: 517111

Subsidiary (Domestic):

BT Enia Telecomunicazioni S.P.A. (3)
Strada S Margherita 6/A, 43100, Parma, Italy
Tel.: (39) 0521496611
Web Site: http://www.btenia.it
Telecommunication Servicesb
N.A.I.C.S.: 517810

ERP Tech S.p.A. (3)
Via Darwin 85, 20019, Settimo Milanese, Italy (100%)
Tel.: (39) 02311828
Web Site: http://www.erptech.it
Sales Range: $10-24.9 Million
Emp.: 50
Management Consulting Services
N.A.I.C.S.: 541618

SPC Italia Srl (3)
Via Vittor Pisani 31, 20124, Milan, Italy (100%)
Tel.: (39) 02674971
Web Site: http://www.spcitalia.it
Data Processing Services
N.A.I.C.S.: 518210

Subsidiary (Non-US):

BT LatAm Brasil Ltda (2)
SP 101 - Campinas/Monte Mor Km 9 5 Cond Tech Town-Unid 27, Hortolandia, 13030-040, Sao Paulo, Brazil
Tel.: (55) 1930319600
Data Processing Services
N.A.I.C.S.: 518210
Javier Semerene (VP-Latin America)

Subsidiary (Domestic):

BT Property Ltd. (2)
BT Ctr 81 Newgate St, London, EC1A 7AJ, United Kingdom
Tel.: (44) 2073565000
Web Site: http://www.bt.com
Sales Range: $25-49.9 Million
Emp.: 20
Property Holding Company
N.A.I.C.S.: 531120

BT Redcare Group (2)
Monument 11-13 Great Tower St, London, EC3R 5AQ, United Kingdom
Tel.: (44) 800800828
Web Site: http://www.redcare.bt.com
Sales Range: $50-74.9 Million
Emp.: 150
Remote Monitoring & Tracking Systems Developer & Mfr
N.A.I.C.S.: 334511

Division (Domestic):

BT Redcare (3)
H1 Newgate Street BT Centre, London, EC1A 7AJ, United Kingdom
Tel.: (44) 8708506696
Web Site: http://www.redcare.bt.com
Sales Range: $25-49.9 Million
Emp.: 85
Wireless Data Communication Security Services
N.A.I.C.S.: 517112

Division (Domestic):

BT Retail (2)
BT Centre 81 Newgate St, London, EC1A 7AJ, United Kingdom
Tel.: (44) 2073565000
Web Site: http://www.bt.com
Sales Range: $15-24.9 Billion
Residential & Commercial Communications Products & Services

N.A.I.C.S.: 517111

Subsidiary (Non-US):

BT Singapore Pte Ltd (2)
Level 3 03-01/02 & 03-04 Block B Alexandra Technopark, 438B Alexandra Road, Singapore, 119968, Singapore
Tel.: (65) 62907100
Telecommunication Servicesb
N.A.I.C.S.: 517810

BT Switzerland AG (2)
Richtistrasse 5, 8304, Wallisellen, 8304, Zurich, Switzerland
Tel.: (41) 445432111
Telecommunication Servicesb
N.A.I.C.S.: 517810

Division (Domestic):

BT Wholesale (2)
BT Centre 81 Newgate Street, London, EC1A 7AJ, United Kingdom
Tel.: (44) 2073565000
Web Site: http://www.btwholesale.com
Sales Range: $5-14.9 Billion
Communications Network Voice & Internet Services
N.A.I.C.S.: 517111

Subsidiary (Domestic):

EE Limited (2)
1 Braham Street, London, E1 8EE, Herts, United Kingdom
Tel.: (44) 7953966150
Web Site: https://ee.co.uk
Emp.: 15,000
Wireless Telecommunication Services
N.A.I.C.S.: 517112
Stephen Harris (CFO)

ESPN Sports Media Limited (2)
3 Queen Caroline Street, Hammersmith, London, W6 9PE, United Kingdom
Tel.: (44) 20 7766 8473
Web Site: http://www.espn.co.uk
Sales Range: $75-99.9 Million
Sports Cable Channel
N.A.I.C.S.: 516210

Division (Domestic):

Openreach (2)
6 Gracechurch St, London, EC3V 0AT, United Kingdom
Tel.: (44) 2073565000
Web Site: https://www.openreach.com
Sales Range: $5-14.9 Billion
Communications Network Development, Maintenance & Support Services
N.A.I.C.S.: 811010
Nigel Cheek (Gen Counsel & Co-Sec)

Subsidiary (Non-US):

PlusNet Plc (2)
Endeavour Sheffield Digital Campus 1a Concourse Way, 2 Tenter Street, Sheffield, S1 2BJ, South Yorkshire, United Kingdom - England
Tel.: (44) 3301239123
Web Site: https://www.plus.net
Sales Range: $50-74.9 Million
Emp.: 200
Internet Services
N.A.I.C.S.: 517810

Subsidiary (Domestic):

Scoot (2)
Eaglescliffe Logistics Ctr, Durham Ln, Stockton-on-Tees, TS16 0RW, United Kingdom
Tel.: (44) 642881088
Web Site: http://www.scoot.co.uk
Consumer Information Services
N.A.I.C.S.: 541512
Edward Stevens (Founder & CEO)

Mainline Digital Communications Limited (1)
Suite 2 Willow House 328 Wetmore Road, Burton-on-Trent, DE14 1SP, Staffordshire, United Kingdom
Tel.: (44) 1283500100
Web Site: https://www.mainline.uk.com
Network Distribution Services
N.A.I.C.S.: 517810
Colin Buckley (Head-IT)

BT Group plc—(Continued)

BT HOLDING AG

Stadtturmstrasse 19, 5400, Baden,
Switzerland
Tel.: (41) 562005050　　**CH**
Investment Holding Company
N.A.I.C.S.: 551112
Peter Wanner *(Chm)*

Subsidiaries:

AZ Medien AG　　　　　　　　　　　**(1)**
Neumattstrasse 1, 5001, Aarau, Switzerland
Tel.: (41) 58 200 5858
Web Site: http://www.azmedien.ch
Sales Range: $400-449.9 Million
Emp.: 761
Multimedia Holding Company
N.A.I.C.S.: 551112
Dietrich Berg *(Mng Dir-Magazines & Books)*

Subsidiary (Domestic):

AZ Anzeiger AG　　　　　　　　　　**(2)**
Zuchwilerstrasse 21, CH-4501, Solothurn,
Switzerland　　　　　　　　　　**(100%)**
Tel.: (41) 326247511
Web Site: http://www.azeiger.ch
Newspaper Publishers
N.A.I.C.S.: 513110

AZ Fachverlage AG　　　　　　　　**(2)**
Neumattstrasse 1, CH-5001, Aarau,
Switzerland　　　　　　　　　　**(100%)**
Tel.: (41) 582005858
Web Site: http://www.azmedien.ch
Magazine Publisher
N.A.I.C.S.: 513120

Aargauer Zeitung AG　　　　　　　**(2)**
Neumattstrasse 1, 5001, Aarau,
Switzerland　　　　　　　　　　**(100%)**
Tel.: (41) 582005858
Web Site: http://www.aargauerzeitung.ch
Newspaper Publishers
N.A.I.C.S.: 513110

Radio 24 AG　　　　　　　　　　　**(2)**
Limmatstrasse 264, Zurich, 8005, Switzerland
Tel.: (41) 444482424
Web Site: http://www.radio24.ch
Sales Range: $25-49.9 Million
Emp.: 50
Radio Broadcasting Stations
N.A.I.C.S.: 516110
Florian Wanner *(Mng Dir)*

Radio 32 AG　　　　　　　　　　　**(2)**
Zuchwilerstrasse 21, CH-4501, Solothurn,
Switzerland　　　　　　　　　　**(61.3%)**
Tel.: (41) 582004232
Web Site: http://www.radio32.ch
Sales Range: $25-49.9 Million
Emp.: 32
Radio Broadcasting Stations
N.A.I.C.S.: 516110
Karin Fluckiger *(Editor-in-Chief)*

Solothurner Zeitung AG　　　　　　**(2)**
Zuchwilerstrasse 21, Solothurn, 4500,
Switzerland　　　　　　　　　　**(100%)**
Tel.: (41) 582004774
Web Site: http://www.solothurnerzeitung.ch
Emp.: 30
Newspaper Publishers
N.A.I.C.S.: 513110
Peter Wanner *(Publr)*

Tele M1 AG　　　　　　　　　　　**(2)**
Neumattstrasse 1, CH-5001, Aarau,
Switzerland　　　　　　　　　　**(100%)**
Tel.: (41) 582004600
Web Site: http://www.telem1.ch
Sales Range: $25-49.9 Million
Emp.: 50
Television Broadcasting Station
N.A.I.C.S.: 516120
Stephan Gassner *(Editor-in-Chief-News)*

TeleZuri AG　　　　　　　　　　　**(2)**
Heinrichstrasse 267, 8005, Zurich, Switzerland
Tel.: (41) 44 447 24 24
Web Site: http://www.telezueri.ch
Sales Range: $25-49.9 Million
Emp.: 60
Television Broadcasting
N.A.I.C.S.: 516120

Markus Gilli *(CEO)*

Weiss Medien AG　　　　　　　　　**(2)**
Obere Bahnhofstrasse 5, CH-8910, Affoltern
am Albis, Switzerland　　　　　　**(100%)**
Tel.: (41) 582005700
Web Site: http://www.affolteranzeiger.ch
Newspaper Publishers
N.A.I.C.S.: 513110

BT WEALTH INDUSTRIES PUBLIC COMPANY LTD.

593/3 Soi Ramkhamhaeng 39 Thep
Leela 1 Ramkhamhaeng Road, Wang
Thonglang, Bangkok, 10310, Thailand
Tel.: (66) 2314215052
Web Site:
　　https://www.btwealthindustries.com
Year Founded: 2012
BTW—(THA)
Rev.: $17,416,081
Assets: $22,582,073
Liabilities: $14,491,285
Net Worth: $8,090,788
Earnings: ($22,550,392)
Emp.: 372
Fiscal Year-end: 12/31/23
Steel Fabrication Product Mfr
N.A.I.C.S.: 332312
Sarawut Charuchinda *(Chm)*

Subsidiaries:

Best Tech & Engineering Limited　**(1)**
593/3 Soi Ramkhamhaeng 39 Thep Leela 1,
Ramkhamhaeng Road, Wangthonglang,
Bangkok, 10310, Thailand
Tel.: (66) 23142150
Web Site: https://www.bteng.com
Steel Products Mfr
N.A.I.C.S.: 332999

BTA BANK JSC

242 Nursultan Nazarbayev Ave, Samal 3 Micro District Medeu District,
050059, Almaty, Kazakhstan
Tel.: (7) 7272500111　　**KZ**
Web Site: http://www.bta.kz
Banking Services
N.A.I.C.S.: 522110
Rifat Anvarovich Samigullin *(Chm)*

BTB REAL ESTATE INVEST-MENT TRUST

1411 Crescent Street, Montreal, H3G
2B3, QC, Canada
Tel.: (514) 286-0188　　**QC**
Web Site: https://www.btbreit.com
Year Founded: 2006
BTBIF—(OTCIQ)
Rev.: $78,496,322
Assets: $883,898,954
Liabilities: $567,525,365
Net Worth: $316,373,589
Earnings: $32,517,815
Emp.: 52
Fiscal Year-end: 12/31/21
Real Estate Investment Services
N.A.I.C.S.: 525990
Michel Leonard *(Founder, Pres & CEO)*

Subsidiaries:

Complexe Lebourgneuf Phase II
Inc.　　　　　　　　　　　　　　**(1)**
815 Boulevard Lebourgneuf, Quebec, G2J
1C3, QC, Canada
Tel.: (418) 627-2566
Real Estate Development Services
N.A.I.C.S.: 531390

BTC DIGITAL LTD.

3rd Floor Tower A 2nd Shenyun West
Road, Tagen Knowledge & Innovation
Center Nanshan District, Shenzhen,
518000, Guangdong, China
Tel.: (86) 75582945250　　**Ky**

Web Site:
　　https://www.investor.metenedu-
　　edtechx.com
Year Founded: 2019
BTCT—(NASDAQ)
Rev.: $12,501,783
Assets: $32,063,789
Liabilities: $11,690,689
Net Worth: $20,373,100
Earnings: $8,122
Emp.: 16
Fiscal Year-end: 12/31/22
Holding Company
N.A.I.C.S.: 551112

BTC HEALTH LIMITED

Level 1 10 Oxley Road, Hawthorn,
3122, VIC, Australia
Tel.: (61) 800100282
Web Site:
　　https://www.btchealth.com.au
BTC—(ASX)
Rev.: $10,924
Assets: $3,438,039
Liabilities: $136,183
Net Worth: $3,301,856
Earnings: $704,652
Fiscal Year-end: 06/30/24
Investing Services
N.A.I.C.S.: 523999
Richard Spencer Treagus *(Chm)*

BTG HOTELS GROUP CO., LTD.

No 51 Fuxingmennei Avenue,
Xicheng District, Beijing, 100020,
China
Tel.: (86) 1066059316
Web Site: http://www.btghg.com
Year Founded: 1999
600258—(SHG)
Rev.: $714,548,587
Assets: $3,572,925,539
Liabilities: $2,083,270,588
Net Worth: $1,489,654,951
Earnings: ($81,736,654)
Fiscal Year-end: 12/31/22
Tour Operator
N.A.I.C.S.: 561520
Li Yun *(Chm)*

BTG PACTUAL

Av Brigadeiro Faria Lima 3477, Sao
Paulo, Brazil
Tel.: (55) 1133832000
Web Site: http://www.btgpactual.com
Year Founded: 1983
Asset Management Services
N.A.I.C.S.: 523940
Roberto Balls Sallouti *(CEO)*

BTG PACTUAL HOLDING S.A.

Avenida Brigadeiro Faria Lima 3 477
14th Floor, Sao Paulo, 04538-133,
SP, Brazil
Tel.: (55) 11 3383 2000　　**BR**
Web Site: http://www.btgpactual.com
Year Founded: 2008
Rev.: $4,309,598,714
Assets: $38,547,617,969
Liabilities: $31,965,611,113
Net Worth: $6,582,006,856
Earnings: $1,060,329,668
Emp.: 1,300
Fiscal Year-end: 12/31/16
Financial Holding Company
N.A.I.C.S.: 551111
Roberto Balls Sallouti *(CEO)*

Subsidiaries:

B&A Mineracao S.A.　　　　　　　**(1)**
Avenida do Contorno 5919 5 andar, Savassi, 30110-035, Belo Horizonte, Brazil
Tel.: (55) 31 2552 1588
Web Site: http://www.bamineracao.com
Holding Company; Fertilizer Minerals, Iron
Ore & Copper Mining

N.A.I.C.S.: 551112
Roger Agnelli *(Chm)*

Subsidiary (Domestic):

B&A Fertilizers Limited　　　　　　**(2)**
Avenida do Contorno 5919 5 andar, Savassi, 30110-035, Belo Horizonte, Brazil
Tel.: (55) 31 2552 1588
Fertilizer Mineral Mining
N.A.I.C.S.: 212390

Banco BTG Pactual S.A.　　　　　**(1)**
Praia de Botafogo 501 6th floor, Rio de Janeiro, 22250-040, RJ, Brazil　**(82.76%)**
Tel.: (55) 1133832000
Web Site: https://www.btgpactual.com
Rev.: $1,875,102,726
Assets: $102,033,139,348
Liabilities: $90,412,703,109
Net Worth: $11,620,436,239
Earnings: $2,113,294,173
Fiscal Year-end: 12/31/22
Investment Banking, Securities Brokerage &
Investment Advisory Services
N.A.I.C.S.: 523150
Marcelo Kalim *(CFO & Sr VP)*

Banco Pan S.A.　　　　　　　　　**(1)**
Av Paulista 1374 - 12 Floor, 01310-100,
Sao Paulo, SP, Brazil　　　　　**(50.6%)**
Tel.: (55) 1132645343
Web Site: http://www.bancopan.com.br
Rev.: $2,736,455,479
Assets: $10,237,832,623
Liabilities: $8,911,135,603
Net Worth: $1,326,697,021
Earnings: $105,767,860
Emp.: 8,107
Fiscal Year-end: 12/31/22
Commercial Banking Services
N.A.I.C.S.: 522110
Sergio Cutolo dos Santos *(Vice Chm)*

PPLA Participations Ltd　　　　　　**(1)**
Av Brigadeiro Faria Lima 3 477 14th andar,
Itaim Bibi, 04538-133, Sao Paulo, SP,
Brazil　　　　　　　　　　　　**(5.17%)**
Tel.: (55) 1133832000
Web Site: http://www.btgpactual.com
Sales Range: $200-249.9 Million
Holding Company; Open & Closed-End Investment Fund Management Services
N.A.I.C.S.: 551112
Marcelo Kalim *(CFO & Sr VP)*

Affiliate (Domestic):

Stigma Participacoes S.A.　　　　**(2)**
Av Brigadeiro Faria Lima 3477 1st Floor,
Sao Paulo, 04538-133, SP, Brazil
Tel.: (55) 11 3383 2000
Emp.: 500
Investment Banking Services
N.A.I.C.S.: 523150
Andre Santos Esteves *(CEO)*

BTHC X, INC.

1st Floor Chapel House 1-3 Chapel
Street, Guildford, GU1 3UH, Surrey,
United Kingdom
Tel.: (44) 1483443000　　**DE**
Year Founded: 2006
BTXI—(OTCBB)
Investment Services
N.A.I.C.S.: 523999
Michael E. Fasci *(CFO, Treas & Sec)*

BTM RESOURCES BERHAD

35-3 Jalan PJU 1/41 Dataran Prima,
Bangsar South City, 47301, Petaling
Jaya, Selangor, Malaysia
Tel.: (60) 378809523
Web Site:
　　https://www.btmresources.com.my
BTM—(KLS)
Rev.: $1,746,220
Assets: $9,633,986
Liabilities: $7,305,022
Net Worth: $2,328,964
Earnings: ($1,635,317)
Fiscal Year-end: 12/31/22
Timber Lamination Boards Mfr
N.A.I.C.S.: 321113
Tu Sang Yong *(Mng Dir)*

Subsidiaries:

BTM Marketing & Trading Sdn. Bhd. (1)
35-3 Jalan PJU 1/41 Dataran Prima, 47301, Petaling Jaya, Malaysia
Tel.: (60) 378809523
Timber & Lamination Board Mfr
N.A.I.C.S.: 321215

BTQ TECHNOLOGIES CORP
Suite 210 - 905 West Pender St, Vancouver, V6C 1L6, BC, Canada
Tel.: (778) 373-5499
Web Site:
http://www.sonoragoldcorp.com
Year Founded: 1998
BTQQF—(OTCQX)
Assets: $424,371
Liabilities: $10,979
Net Worth: $413,392
Earnings: ($105,446)
Fiscal Year-end: 01/31/20
Metal Exploration Services
N.A.I.C.S.: 213114
Robert G. Dinning *(CFO)*

BTS GROUP AB
Grevgatan 34, 114 53, Stockholm, Sweden
Tel.: (46) 858707000
Web Site: https://www.bts.com
Year Founded: 1985
BTS.B—(OTCIQ)
Rev.: $178,744,653
Assets: $239,287,787
Liabilities: $152,628,078
Net Worth: $86,659,709
Earnings: $4,300,878
Emp.: 1,025
Fiscal Year-end: 12/31/20
Business Acumen Education Simulations & Services
N.A.I.C.S.: 611430
Henrik Ekelund *(Founder, Pres & CEO)*

Subsidiaries:

BTS Asia Pacific Pte. Ltd. (1)
1 Finlayson Green Suite 16-01, Singapore, 049246, Singapore
Tel.: (65) 6 304 3032
Business Management Consulting Services
N.A.I.C.S.: 541611

BTS Australasia (1)
270 Bourbong Street, Bundaberg, 4670, QLD, Australia
Tel.: (61) 741542438
Web Site: http://www.bts.com.au
Business Management Solutions
N.A.I.C.S.: 541618

BTS BILBAO (1)
Simon Bolivar 27 10 dpt 19, Bilbao, 48010, Spain
Tel.: (34) 94 423 5594
Corporate Training & Development Solutions
N.A.I.C.S.: 611430

BTS Brussels NV (1)
Rue d'Arenberg 44, 1000, Brussels, Belgium
Tel.: (32) 2 27 415 10
Sales Range: $10-24.9 Million
Emp.: 4
Corporate Training & Development Services
N.A.I.C.S.: 611430
Gillian McCarron *(Gen Mgr)*

BTS Business Consulting (Thailand) Co.,Ltd. (1)
Thai CC Building Suite 181 18th Floor 889 South Sathorn Road, Yannawa Sathorn, Bangkok, 10120, Thailand
Tel.: (66) 2672 3780
Web Site: http://www.bts.com
Sales Range: $25-49.9 Million
Emp.: 3
Business Management Services
N.A.I.C.S.: 561499

BTS CHICAGO Limited (1)
33 N LaSalle St Ste 1210, Chicago, IL 60602
Tel.: (312) 263-6250
Web Site: http://www.bts.com
Sales Range: $10-24.9 Million
Emp.: 13
Corporate Training & Development Solutions
N.A.I.C.S.: 611430

BTS Consulting (Shanghai) Co., Ltd. (1)
Suite 506B 1376 Room 531 western manjing road, Shanghai Centre 1376 Nanjing Road West, Shanghai, 200040, China
Tel.: (86) 21 6289 8688
Emp.: 6
Corporate Training & Development Services
N.A.I.C.S.: 611430

BTS London (1)
37 Kensington High Street, London, W8 5ED, United Kingdom
Tel.: (44) 20 7368 4180
Web Site: http://www.bts.com
Business Management Solutions
N.A.I.C.S.: 541618

BTS MEXICO (1)
Moliere No 13 -P H, 11560, Mexico, Mexico
Tel.: (52) 55 5281 6972
Web Site: http://www.bts.com
Emp.: 13
Corporate Training & Development Services
N.A.I.C.S.: 611430

BTS Management SA (1)
C/o Lkm Associates sarl rue du Nant 8, 1207, Geneva, Switzerland
Tel.: (41) 22 807 24 00
Corporate Training & Development Services
N.A.I.C.S.: 611430

BTS SEOUL (1)
7th Floor Hanvit Building 107 Sajik-ro Jongo-Gu, Gangnam-gu, Seoul, 110-053, Korea (South)
Tel.: (82) 2 539 7676
Sales Range: $10-24.9 Million
Emp.: 3
Corporate Training & Development Services
N.A.I.C.S.: 611430
Yunho Chung *(Gen Mgr)*

BTS STAMFORD (1)
300 First Stamford Pl, Stamford, CT 06902
Tel.: (203) 316-2740
Web Site: http://www.bts.com
Corporate Training & Development Solutions
N.A.I.C.S.: 611430

BTS STOCKHOLM (1)
Grevgatan 34, 114 53, Stockholm, Sweden
Tel.: (46) 8 58 70 70 00
Sales Range: $10-24.9 Million
Emp.: 32
Corporate Training & Development Services
N.A.I.C.S.: 611430
Anna Sandperg *(Gen Mgr-Northern Europe)*

BTS South Africa (1)
267 West Avenue 1st janctuary, Lakefield Office Park, Centurion, 0046, Gauteng, South Africa
Tel.: (27) 12 663 6909
Sales Range: $25-49.9 Million
Emp.: 15
Business Management Solutions
N.A.I.C.S.: 541618
Deon Greyling *(Mng Dir)*

BTS Sverige AB (1)
Grevgatan 34, 114 53, Stockholm, Sweden
Tel.: (46) 858707000
Web Site: http://www.bts.com
Sales Range: $10-24.9 Million
Emp.: 35
Corporate Training & Development Solutions
N.A.I.C.S.: 611430

BTS TAIPEI (1)
12F Building A No 25 Ren Ai Road, Section 4, Taipei, Taiwan
Tel.: (886) 987 80 29 30
Business Consulting Services
N.A.I.C.S.: 561499

BTS TOKYO (1)
TS Kojimachi Bldg 3F 6-4-6 Kojimachi, Chiyoda-ku, Tokyo, 102-0083, Japan
Tel.: (81) 362729973
Web Site: http://www.bts.com
Corporate Training & Development Solutions
N.A.I.C.S.: 611430

BTS USA, Inc. (1)
222 Kearny St Ste 1000, San Francisco, CA 94108
Tel.: (415) 362-4200
Web Site: https://www.bts.com
Sales Range: $10-24.9 Million
Emp.: 40
Corporate Training & Development Services
N.A.I.C.S.: 611430

BTS United States (1)
300 First Stamford Pl, Stamford, CT 06902
Tel.: (203) 316-2740
Web Site: http://www.bts.com
Sales Range: $10-24.9 Million
Emp.: 25
Developer of Business Acumen Education Simulations & Services
N.A.I.C.S.: 611430

Subsidiary (Domestic):

Advantage Performance Group (2)
100 Smith Ranch Rd Ste 306, San Rafael, CA 94903
Tel.: (415) 925-6832
Web Site:
https://www.advantageperformance.com
Sales Range: $10-24.9 Million
Emp.: 7
Employee Performance Improvement Services
N.A.I.C.S.: 611430
Jonathan Hodge *(Pres & CEO)*

BTS Philadelphia (2)
6 Tower Bridge Ste 540 181 Washington St, Conshohocken, PA 19428
Tel.: (484) 391-2900
Web Site: http://www.smginc.com
Business Management Solutions
N.A.I.C.S.: 561499

BTS Scottsdale (2)
9455 E Ironwood Square Dr Ste 100, Scottsdale, AZ 85258
Tel.: (480) 948-2777
Web Site: http://www.bts.com
Sales Range: $10-24.9 Million
Employee Performance Improvement Services
N.A.I.C.S.: 611430

BTS in Amsterdam bv (1)
Barbara Strozzilaan 201, 1083 HN, Amsterdam, Netherlands
Tel.: (31) 20 615 15 14
Web Site: http://www.bts.com
Emp.: 3
Corporate Training & Development Services
N.A.I.C.S.: 611430

Business Training Solutions S.L. (1)
Calle Simon Bolivar 27-1 of 19, Bilbao, 48013, Spain
Tel.: (34) 944235594
Web Site: http://www.bts.com
Sales Range: $10-24.9 Million
Emp.: 13
Corporate Training & Development Solutions
N.A.I.C.S.: 611430
Philios Andreou *(Pres-Other Markets Unit)*

Catalysts for Profitability and Growth Ltd (1)
267 W Ave, Centurion, 46, South Africa
Tel.: (27) 126636909
Web Site: http://www.bts.com
Sales Range: $10-24.9 Million
Emp.: 14
Corporate Training & Development Services
N.A.I.C.S.: 611430

BTS GROUP HOLDINGS PUBLIC COMPANY LIMITED
15th floor TST Tower 21 Soi Choei Phuang Viphavadi-Rangsit Road, Chomphon Chatuchak, Bangkok, 10900, Thailand
Tel.: (66) 227386115   TH

Web Site: https://www.btsgroup.co.th
Year Founded: 1968
BTGRF—(OTCIQ)
Rev.: $670,656,668
Assets: $7,482,377,079
Liabilities: $5,656,551,646
Net Worth: $1,825,825,433
Earnings: ($198,916,317)
Emp.: 6,451
Fiscal Year-end: 03/31/24
Holding Company
N.A.I.C.S.: 551112
Keeree Kanjanapas *(Chm)*

Subsidiaries:

888 Media Co., Ltd. (1)
21 TST Tower 9th Floor Viphavadi-Rangsit Road Chomphon, Chatuchak, Bangkok, 10900, Thailand
Tel.: (66) 2273 8884
Advertising Management Services
N.A.I.C.S.: 541890

Bangkok Mass Transit System Public Company Limited (1)
BTS Building 1000 Phahonyothin Rd, Chomphon Chatuchak, Bangkok, 10900, Thailand
Tel.: (66) 26177300
Mass Transit Services
N.A.I.C.S.: 485113
Keeree Kanjanapas *(Chm)*

Subsidiary (Domestic):

Bangkok Smartcard System Co., Ltd. (2)
21 TST Tower 19th Floor Vibhavadi-Rangsit Road, Chomphon Chatuchak, Bangkok, 10900, Thailand
Tel.: (66) 2 617 8338
Web Site: https://rabbit.co.th
Financial Services
N.A.I.C.S.: 522320

VGI Public Company Limited (2)
21 TST Tower 9th Floor Viphavadi-Rangsit Road, Chomphon Chatuchak, Bangkok, 10900, Thailand (51%)
Tel.: (66) 22738884
Web Site: https://www.vgi.co.th
Rev.: $150,154,470
Assets: $781,053,684
Liabilities: $89,852,057
Net Worth: $691,201,627
Earnings: ($103,802,207)
Emp.: 1,705
Fiscal Year-end: 03/31/2024
Advertising Services
N.A.I.C.S.: 541890
Marut Arthakaivalvatee *(Vice Chm)*

Bangkok Payment Solutions Co., Ltd. (1)
123 Suntowers Building B 17th Floor Viphavadi-Rangsit Road, Chomphon Chatuchak, Bangkok, 10900, Thailand
Tel.: (66) 2 617 9880
Web Site: https://www.bkkps.co.th
Payment Solutions Services
N.A.I.C.S.: 522320

DNAL Co., Ltd. (1)
21 Soi Choei Phuang Viphavadi-Rangsit Road, Jompol Jatujak, Bangkok, 10900, Thailand
Tel.: (66) 2 273 8833
Office Building Rental Services
N.A.I.C.S.: 531120

HHT Construction Co., Ltd. (1)
11th Floor TST Tower 21 Soi Choei Phuang Viphavadi-Rangsit Road, Chomphon Chatujak, Bangkok, 10900, Thailand
Tel.: (66) 22738733
Construction Services
N.A.I.C.S.: 236220

Rabbit Internet Co., Ltd. (1)
1032/1-5 Krits Building 2nd Floor Rama 4 Rd, Thungmahamek Sathorn, Bangkok, 10120, Thailand
Tel.: (66) 20221222
Web Site: http://www.rabbitfinance.com
Financial Services
N.A.I.C.S.: 522320
Michael Steibl *(Mng Dir)*

BTS Group Holdings Public Company Limited—(Continued)

Rabbit Rewards Co., Ltd. (1)
21 TST Tower 19th Floor Viphavadi-Rangsit Road, Chomphon Chatuchak, Bangkok, 10900, Thailand
Tel.: (66) 26183777
Web Site: http://www.rewards.rabbit.co.th
Advertising Material Services
N.A.I.C.S.: 541870

Roctec Global Public Company Limited (1)
21 TST Building Floor 21 - 22 Vibhavadi Rangsit Rd, Chatuchak, Bangkok, 10900, Thailand (63.23%)
Tel.: (66) 29383388
Web Site: https://www.roctecglobal.co.th
Rev.: $72,186,942
Assets: $192,297,076
Liabilities: $67,281,888
Net Worth: $125,015,188
Earnings: $8,358,862
Emp.: 342
Fiscal Year-end: 03/31/2024
Advertising Services
N.A.I.C.S.: 541890
Chaiwat Atsawintarangkun (Chm)

Subsidiary (Non-US):

Trands Ad Vietnam Joint Stock Company (2)
35 Nguyen Hue, Ben Nghe Ward District 1, Ho Chi Minh City, Vietnam
Tel.: (84) 777009098
Web Site: https://transad.vn
Advertising Services
N.A.I.C.S.: 541850

Subsidiary (Domestic):

Trans.Ad Solutions Company Limited (2)
21 TST Tower 21/F Vibhavadi-Rangsit Road, Chomphon Chatuchak, Bangkok, 10900, Thailand
Tel.: (66) 200199002
Web Site: https://www.transad.co.th
Advertising Services
N.A.I.C.S.: 541810

Subsidiary (Non-US):

Roctec Technology Limited (3)
Room 1502-4 Kodak House II 321 Java Road, North Point, China (Hong Kong)
Tel.: (852) 28119898
Web Site: https://www.roctec.com.hk
Software Services
N.A.I.C.S.: 541519

Subsidiary (Non-US):

VGI Global Media (Malaysia) Sdn. Bhd. (2)
15th Floor Menara Manulife 6 Jalan Gelenggang, Bukit Damansara, 50490, Kuala Lumpur, Malaysia
Tel.: (60) 32 011 2338
Web Site: https://www.vgimalaysia.com
Transportation Services
N.A.I.C.S.: 485999

Sam Pao Petch Co., Ltd. (1)
100-100/1 Moo 4 Bangna-Trad Road Km 14, Bangchalong, Bang Phli, 10540, Samutprakarn, Thailand
Tel.: (66) 2336 1938 9
Real Estate Management Services
N.A.I.C.S.: 531390

Thana City Golf & Sports Club Co., Ltd. (1)
100/2 Moo 4 Bangna-Trad Highway Km 14, Banchalong, Bang Phli, 10540, Samut Prakarn, Thailand
Tel.: (66) 2336196872
Web Site: http://www.thanacitygolf.com
Golf Club Operator
N.A.I.C.S.: 713910

BTS SP. Z O.O.
ul Koksownicza 1, 42-523, Dabrowa Gornicza, Poland
Tel.: (48) 327575455
Web Site: http://www.btsdg.pl
Sales Range: $25-49.9 Million

Emp.: 75
Industrial Supply Distr
N.A.I.C.S.: 423840
Piotr Jaszczak (CEO)

BTSR INTERNATIONAL S.P.A.
Via S Rita, 21057, Olgiate Olona, Varese, Italy
Tel.: (39) 0331323202
Web Site: https://www.btsr.com
Electronic Products Mfr
N.A.I.C.S.: 334417

BTU METALS CORP.
1240-789 W Pender St, Vancouver, V6C 1H2, BC, Canada
Tel.: (604) 683-3995   BC
Web Site: https://www.btumetals.com
Year Founded: 2008
BTU.H—(OTCIQ)
Assets: $7,822,485
Liabilities: $341,785
Net Worth: $7,480,700
Earnings: ($1,189,642)
Fiscal Year-end: 04/30/21
Investment Services
N.A.I.C.S.: 523999
Mike England (Pres)

BUA CEMENT PLC
5th Floor BUA Towers PC 32 Churchgate Street, Victoria Island, Lagos, 23401, Nigeria
Tel.: (234) 14610671
Web Site: http://www.buacement.com
Year Founded: 2008
BUACEMEN—(NIGE)
Rev.: $520,479,667
Assets: $1,375,524,822
Liabilities: $939,651,401
Net Worth: $435,873,421
Earnings: $78,586,661
Emp.: 1,257
Fiscal Year-end: 12/31/23
Cement Mfr
N.A.I.C.S.: 327310
Yusuf Haliru Binji (CEO & Mng Dir)

BUALI INVESTMENT COMPANY
Ghaled Eslamboli Street Wezaraa Thirty-Seventh Ave Building 165, Tehran, Iran
Tel.: (98) 2188776064
Web Site: http://www.buali.com
Year Founded: 1984
BALI1—(THE)
Sales Range: Less than $1 Million
Investment Management Service
N.A.I.C.S.: 523999

BUALUANG OFFICE LEASEHOLD REIT
175 Sathorn City Tower Floors 7 21 and 26 Sathorn Tai Road, Thung Maha Mek Sathorn, Bangkok, 10120, Thailand
Tel.: (66) 26746488
Web Site: https://bworkreit.com
Year Founded: 2018
B-WORK—(THA)
Rev.: $18,040,229
Assets: $137,139,966
Liabilities: $30,145,663
Net Worth: $106,994,303
Earnings: $9,735,582
Fiscal Year-end: 12/31/23
Real Estate Development Services
N.A.I.C.S.: 531390
Voravan Tarapoom (Chm)

BUBALUS RESOURCES LIMITED
Level 2 22 Mount Street, Perth, 6000, WA, Australia
Tel.: (61) 61888181

Web Site: https://www.bubalusresources.com
Year Founded: 2021
BUS—(ASX)
Rev.: $76,637
Assets: $3,147,306
Liabilities: $57,604
Net Worth: $3,089,702
Earnings: ($261,643)
Fiscal Year-end: 06/30/24
Mineral Exploration Services
N.A.I.C.S.: 212390
Alec Pismiris (Chm)

BUBBLES INTERGROUP LTD
Floor 15 Menachem Begin Road 7, Ramat Gan, Tel Aviv, Israel
Tel.: (972) 0533310680
Year Founded: 2004
BBLS—(TAE)
Rev.: $37,883
Assets: $1,039,310
Liabilities: $1,701,029
Net Worth: ($661,718)
Earnings: ($374,798)
Fiscal Year-end: 12/31/20
Commerce & Services
N.A.I.C.S.: 513210
Gideon Amihood (Chm)

BUBBLR, INC.
2 Chapel Court, London, SE1 1HH, United Kingdom
Tel.: (44) 7494142733   WY
Web Site: http://www.bubblr.com
BBLR—(OTCQB)
Rev.: $142,212
Assets: $1,416,368
Liabilities: $1,330,091
Net Worth: $86,277
Earnings: ($4,390,880)
Emp.: 5
Fiscal Year-end: 12/31/22
Information Technology Services
N.A.I.C.S.: 541519
Steven S. Suanders (CEO)

BUBNY DEVELOPMENT S.R.O.
Na Porici 1047/26, 11000, Prague, Czech Republic
Tel.: (420) 221416311   CZ
Sales Range: $25-49.9 Million
Residential Property Development Services
N.A.I.C.S.: 236115
Ales Vobruba (Mng Dir)

BUBS AUSTRALIA LIMITED
Ground Floor 6 Tilley Lane, Sydney, 2086, NSW, Australia
Tel.: (61) 80028272878
Web Site: https://www.bubsaustralia.com
Year Founded: 1993
BUB—(ASX)
Rev.: $68,418,717
Assets: $96,494,727
Liabilities: $28,909,451
Net Worth: $67,585,276
Earnings: ($8,717,360)
Emp.: 65
Fiscal Year-end: 06/30/22
Litigation Funding Services
N.A.I.C.S.: 311514
Alan R. Van Noort (Chm)

BUCCANEER GOLD CORP.
82 Richmond Street East Suite 308, Toronto, M5C 1P1, ON, Canada
Tel.: (416) 848-7744   ON
Web Site: http://www.buccaneergold.com
Year Founded: 2004
BUCK—(TSXV)
Rev.: $2,842
Assets: $231,276
Liabilities: $37,324

Net Worth: $193,952
Earnings: ($82,116)
Fiscal Year-end: 09/30/20
Gold Mining
N.A.I.C.S.: 212220
James Longshore (CEO)

BUCHANAN FOREST PRODUCTS, LTD.
233 South Court Street, McIntyre Centre, Thunder Bay, P7B 2X9, ON, Canada
Tel.: (807) 345-0571
Lumber Mfr
N.A.I.C.S.: 321912
Bucky Henson (Pres)

BUCHANG PHARMACEUTICAL,INC
No 369 Zhonghua West Road, Heze, 274000, Shandong, China
Tel.: (86) 5305299167
Web Site: http://www.buchang.com
Year Founded: 2001
603858—(SHG)
Rev.: $2,099,155,879
Assets: $3,082,044,177
Liabilities: $1,358,626,932
Net Worth: $1,723,417,245
Earnings: ($214,776,086)
Fiscal Year-end: 12/31/22
Medicine Mfr & Distr
N.A.I.C.S.: 325412
Tao Zhao (Chm)

BUCHER INDUSTRIES AG
Murzlenstrasse 80, CH-8166, Niederweningen, Switzerland
Tel.: (41) 438158080
Web Site: https://www.bucherindustries.com
Year Founded: 1984
BUCN—(SWX)
Rev.: $3,597,177,708
Assets: $3,134,903,454
Liabilities: $1,399,279,932
Net Worth: $1,735,623,522
Earnings: $304,860,924
Emp.: 13,388
Fiscal Year-end: 12/31/21
Holding Company; Mechanical & Vehicle Mfr & Engineering
N.A.I.C.S.: 551112
Philip Mosimann (Chm)

Subsidiaries:

Artec Pulverisation SAS (1)
ZA de la Frise, Corpe, 85320, Lucon, France
Tel.: (33) 251284270
Web Site: https://www.artec-pulverisation.com
Farm Sprayer Mfr & Distr
N.A.I.C.S.: 333111

Arvel Industries Sarl (1)
ZA Perache, 63114, Coudes, France
Tel.: (33) 473969222
Web Site: http://www.arvel.fr
Industrial Cleaning Equipment Mfr & Distr
N.A.I.C.S.: 333310

Bucher Automation AG (1)
Thomas-Alva-Edison-Ring 10, 71672, Marbach am Neckar, Germany
Tel.: (49) 714125500
Automotive Parts Mfr & Distr
N.A.I.C.S.: 336390

Bucher Automation Hungary Kft. (1)
Ihasz utca 10, 1105, Budapest, Hungary
Tel.: (36) 14332523
Web Site: https://www.jetter.hu
Electric Appliances Mfr
N.A.I.C.S.: 334419

Bucher Automation Tettnang GmbH (1)
Tolnauer Strasse 3-4, 88069, Tettnang, Germany
Tel.: (49) 754253070

Automotive Parts Mfr & Distr
N.A.I.C.S.: 336390

Bucher Beteiligungen GmbH (1)
Industriestrasse 1, 79771, Klettgau, Germany
Tel.: (49) 77428520
Investment Management Service
N.A.I.C.S.: 523999

Subsidiary (Domestic):

Jetter AG (2)
Graeterstrasse 2, 71642, Ludwigsburg, Germany
Tel.: (49) 714125500
Web Site: https://www.jetter.de
Sales Range: $50-74.9 Million
Emp.: 249
Industrial Services
N.A.I.C.S.: 334512
Martin Jetter (Founder)

Subsidiary (Non-US):

Jetter Distribution Ltd. (3)
Kidderminster Rd, Alveley, Bridgnorth, WV15 6JF, Shropshire, United Kingdom
Tel.: (44) 1686640193
Sales Range: $25-49.9 Million
Emp.: 1
Electric Controllers Mfr
N.A.I.C.S.: 334513

Jetter Oy (3)
Laurinniityntie 6-8, 00440, Helsinki, Finland
Tel.: (358) 95657230
Web Site: https://www.jetter.fi
Sales Range: $25-49.9 Million
Emp.: 4
Automation Controls Mfr
N.A.I.C.S.: 334513
Harri Granholm (Mng Dir)

Jetter Technologies Pte Ltd. (3)
Blk 26 Kallang Place 03-15, 109674, Singapore, Singapore
Tel.: (65) 62787881
Web Site: http://www.jetter.com.sg
Sales Range: $50-74.9 Million
Emp.: 5
Automation Electric Controls Sales Distr
N.A.I.C.S.: 423610

Bucher Denwel, spol. s r.o. (1)
K Hajum 2, 155 00, Prague, Czech Republic
Tel.: (420) 270007400
Web Site: https://www.denwel.com
Pharmaceuticals Product Mfr
N.A.I.C.S.: 325412

Bucher Exzel, S.L. (1)
N7 C/Les Rotes 9, Industrial Polygon Elupuig, 46540, Valencia, Spain
Tel.: (34) 961445678
Web Site: https://www.bucherexzel.com
Juice Equipment Mfr & Distr
N.A.I.C.S.: 333241

Bucher Hidraulica Ltda. (1)
Rua Berto Cirio 1420, Canoas, Sao Luis, 92420-030, RS, Brazil
Tel.: (55) 5133613512
Construction Equipment & Industrial Hydraulic Mfr
N.A.I.C.S.: 333120

Bucher Hydraulics (Wuxi) Co., Ltd. (1)
No 225 Xitai Road, Meicun New District, Wuxi, 214112, Jiangsu, China
Tel.: (86) 51088551803
Web Site: https://www.bh-wx.cn
Construction Equipment & Industrial Hydraulic Mfr
N.A.I.C.S.: 333120

Bucher Hydraulics AG Frutigen (1)
Schwandistrasse 25, 3714, Frutigen, Switzerland
Tel.: (41) 336726111
Construction Equipment & Industrial Hydraulic Mfr
N.A.I.C.S.: 333120

Bucher Hydraulics Erding GmbH (1)
Albert-Einstein-Strasse 12, D-85435, Erding, Germany
Tel.: (49) 812297130

Construction Equipment & Industrial Hydraulic Mfr
N.A.I.C.S.: 333120

Bucher Hydraulics GmbH (1)
Industriestrasse 1, 79771, Klettgau, Germany (100%)
Tel.: (49) 77428520
Web Site: https://www.bucherhydraulics.com
Sales Range: $400-449.9 Million
Emp.: 500
Mobile & Industrial Hydraulics
N.A.I.C.S.: 333996

Subsidiary (Non-US):

Bucher Hidrolik Sistemleri Tic. Ltd. (2)
ISTOC33 Ada No 31-33, Mahmutbey, 34218, Istanbul, Turkiye
Tel.: (90) 2126590488
Hydraulic Equipment Distr
N.A.I.C.S.: 423830
Avni Bezmez (Gen Mgr)

Subsidiary (US):

Bucher Hydraulics (2)
1363 Michigan St NE, Grand Rapids, MI 49503-2003
Tel.: (616) 458-1306
Web Site: http://www.monarchhyd.com
Sales Range: $50-74.9 Million
Emp.: 250
Fluid Power Pumps & Motors
N.A.I.C.S.: 333996
Uwe Kronmuller (Mng Dir)

Subsidiary (Non-US):

Bucher Hydraulics (2)
Dawang Comprehensive Economic Development Zone, Zhaoqing, China
Tel.: (86) 7583642371
Hydraulics Mfr
N.A.I.C.S.: 333996

Bucher Hydraulics AG (2)
Industriestrasse 15, 6345, Neuheim, Switzerland (100%)
Tel.: (41) 417570333
Web Site: https://www.bucherhydraulics.com
Sales Range: $25-49.9 Million
Emp.: 190
N.A.I.C.S.: 333611

Subsidiary (Domestic):

Bucher Hydraulics Fruhgen AG (3)
Schwandistrasse 25, 3714, Frutigen, Switzerland (100%)
Tel.: (41) 336726111
Web Site: http://www.bucherhydraulics.com
Sales Range: $50-74.9 Million
Emp.: 300
N.A.I.C.S.: 333611
Aurelo Lemos (CEO)

Subsidiary (Non-US):

Bucher Hydraulics Co., Ltd (2)
No 22 Ding Hwu 5th Street, Kuasun Shiang, Taoyuan, Taiwan
Tel.: (886) 33 28 77 28
Web Site: http://www.bucherhydraulics.com
Hydraulic Cylinder Mfr
N.A.I.C.S.: 333995

Bucher Hydraulics Corp (2)
460 Newbold Street, London, N6E 1K3, ON, Canada
Tel.: (519) 686-5900
Web Site: https://www.fluidpack.com
Sales Range: $25-49.9 Million
Emp.: 25
Hydraulic Component Mfr & Distr
N.A.I.C.S.: 333995
Chris Countryman (Gen Mgr)

Bucher Hydraulics Corporation (2)
460 Newbold Street, London, N6E 1K3, ON, Canada
Tel.: (519) 686-5900
Web Site: http://www.fluidpack.com
Sales Range: $25-49.9 Million
Emp.: 12
Hydraulic Assemblies
N.A.I.C.S.: 811310
Chris Countryman (Gen Mgr)

Subsidiary (Domestic):

Bucher Hydraulics Dachau GmbH (2)
Ohmstr 8, 85221, Dachau, Germany
Tel.: (49) 813131170
Web Site: https://www.bucherhydraulics.com
Sales Range: $25-49.9 Million
Emp.: 20
Fluid Power Pump & Motor Mfr
N.A.I.C.S.: 333996
Heinz Klien (Gen Mgr)

Subsidiary (Non-US):

Bucher Hydraulics KK (2)
Sakae-Cho 723-1-102, Yoshikawa, 342-0050, Saitama-Ken, Japan
Tel.: (81) 489843713
Hydraulic Equipment Mfr
N.A.I.C.S.: 333995

Bucher Hydraulics Ltd (2)
Unit 9 Eastboro Fields, Hemdale, Nuneaton, CV11 6GL, Warwickshire, United Kingdom
Tel.: (44) 2476353568
Hydraulic Equipment Distr
N.A.I.C.S.: 423830

Bucher Hydraulics Pvt Ltd. (2)
Plot No-6 Sector 5 IMT Manesar, Gurgaon, 122050, Haryana, India
Tel.: (91) 1244700100
Web Site: https://www.bucherhydraulics.com
Emp.: 150
Hydraulic Equipment Distr
N.A.I.C.S.: 423830

Bucher Hydraulics S.p.A. (2)
Via P Colletta N 5, I 42100, Reggio nell'Emilia, Italy (100%)
Tel.: (39) 0522928411
Web Site: http://www.bucherhydraulics.it
Sales Range: $25-49.9 Million
Emp.: 200
N.A.I.C.S.: 333611

Bucher Hydraulics SAS (2)
50 Rue de l'Ile Napoleon, 68173, Rixheim, Cedex, France
Tel.: (33) 389642244
Hydraulic Component Distr
N.A.I.C.S.: 423830

Suzhou Bucher Hydraulics Co. Ltd (2)
No 168 Shexing Road Foho New Hi-tech industrial Development Zone, Wujiang, 215214, Jiangsu, China
Tel.: (86) 51263221299
Emp.: 100
Hydraulic Cylinder Mfr
N.A.I.C.S.: 333995

Bucher Hydraulics Remscheid GmbH (1)
Ringstrasse 65, 42897, Remscheid, Germany
Tel.: (49) 21914232510
Construction Equipment & Industrial Hydraulic Mfr
N.A.I.C.S.: 333120

Bucher Hydraulics Suzhou Co., Ltd. (1)
168 Shexing Road Foho New Hi-tech industrial Development Zone, Wujiang, 215214, Jiangsu, China
Tel.: (86) 51263221299
Construction Equipment & Industrial Hydraulic Mfr
N.A.I.C.S.: 333120

Bucher Iberica SL (1)
C/ Gavilan 15, 28946, Fuenlabrada, Spain
Tel.: (34) 916422850
Cleaning Equipment Mfr & Distr
N.A.I.C.S.: 333131

Bucher Management AG (1)
Flughafenstrasse 90, 8058, Zurich, Switzerland
Tel.: (41) 587501500
Sales Range: $25-49.9 Million
Emp.: 28
Business Management Consulting Services
N.A.I.C.S.: 541611
Philip Mosimann (CEO)

Bucher Merk Process GmbH (1)

Lippersmatt 2, 79725, Laufenburg, Germany
Tel.: (49) 776392720
Food Processing Equipment Mfr & Distr
N.A.I.C.S.: 333241

Bucher Municipal A/S (1)
Lillehojvej 15, 8600, Silkeborg, Denmark
Tel.: (45) 86821211
Cleaning Vehicle Services
N.A.I.C.S.: 561740

Bucher Municipal Coudes Sarl (1)
ZA Perache, 63114, Coudes, France
Tel.: (33) 473969222
Cleaning Equipment Mfr & Distr
N.A.I.C.S.: 333131

Bucher Municipal GmbH (1)
Schorlingstrasse 3, 30453, Hannover, Germany
Tel.: (49) 51121490
Web Site: https://www.buchermunicipal.com
Street Cleaning Snow Removal & Garbage Collection Services
N.A.I.C.S.: 488490

Bucher Municipal LLC (1)
Tulskaya 13B, 3248000, Kaluga, Russia
Tel.: (7) 4842926390
Street Cleaning Snow Removal & Garbage Collection Services
N.A.I.C.S.: 488490

Bucher Municipal Ltd. (1)
258 Seohaean-Ro, Siheung, 15086, Gyeonggi-Do, Korea (South)
Tel.: (82) 314988961
Sweepers Services
N.A.I.C.S.: 561790

Bucher Municipal North America (1)
105 Motorsports Rd, Mooresville, NC 28115
Tel.: (704) 658-1333
Web Site: https://www.buchermunicipal.com
Sweepers Services
N.A.I.C.S.: 561790

Bucher Municipal Pty Ltd (1)
65-73 Nantilla Road North, Clayton, AU-3179, VIC, Australia
Tel.: (61) 392716400
Web Site: https://www.buchermunicipal.com
Machinery & Vehicle Construction Mfr
N.A.I.C.S.: 333120

Bucher Municipal S.A.S. (1)
40 Avenue Eugene Gazeau, 60300, Senlis, France
Tel.: (33) 344533057
Automotive Parts Mfr & Distr
N.A.I.C.S.: 336390

Bucher Municipal SIA (1)
Ganibu iela 105, Ventspils, LV-3601, Latvia
Tel.: (371) 63661050
Web Site: https://www.buchermunicipal.com
Sweepers Services
N.A.I.C.S.: 561790

Bucher Municipal Wernberg GmbH (1)
Daimlerstrasse 18, 92533, Wernberg-Koblitz, Germany
Tel.: (49) 9604932670
Cleaning Equipment Mfr & Distr
N.A.I.C.S.: 333131

Bucher Schorling AG (1)
Murzlenstrasse 80, Niederweningen, 8166, Switzerland
Tel.: (41) 44 857 22 11
Web Site: http://www.bucherschoerling.com
Sales Range: $125-149.9 Million
Emp.: 450
Street Sweeping Truck Mfr & Distr
N.A.I.C.S.: 336120

Subsidiary (Non-US):

Beam A/S (2)
Salten Skovvej 4-6, 8653, Them, Denmark
Tel.: (45) 86 84 76 00
Web Site: http://www.beamsweepers.com
Sales Range: $25-49.9 Million
Emp.: 80
Street Sweeper Mfr
N.A.I.C.S.: 333998

Bucher Schorling Korea Ltd (2)
Sihwa Industrial Complex Chungwang-Dong

Bucher Industries AG—(Continued)

3Ma 819Ho, Siheung, 429-450, Kyunggi-do,
Korea (South)
Tel.: (82) 31 498 89 61 3
Sales Range: $25-49.9 Million
Emp.: 2
Trucks Mfr
N.A.I.C.S.: 336120
Jaewook Ha *(Gen Mgr)*

Bucher-Schoerling GmbH (2)
Schoerlingstrasse 3, 30453, Hannover,
Germany (100%)
Tel.: (49) 51121490
Web Site: http://www.bucherschoerling.de
Sales Range: $25-49.9 Million
Emp.: 25
N.A.I.C.S.: 336110

Giletta S.p.A. (2)
Via A De Gasperi 1, 12036, Revello, CN,
Italy (60%)
Tel.: (39) 0175258800
Web Site: https://www.buchermunicipal.com
Snow Removal Equipment Mfr
N.A.I.C.S.: 333998

Gmeiner GmbH (2)
Daimlerstrasse 18, 92533, Wernberg-
Koblitz, Germany
Tel.: (49) 9604 93267 0
Sales Range: $25-49.9 Million
Emp.: 4
Winter Maintenance Equipment Mfr & Distr
N.A.I.C.S.: 333310
Wilfried Muller *(Gen Mgr)*

Johnston Sweepers Ltd. (2)
Curtis Road, Dorking, RH4 1XF, Surrey,
United Kingdom
Tel.: (44) 1306 884722
Web Site: http://www.johnstonsweepers.com
Sales Range: $75-99.9 Million
Emp.: 45
Outdoor Surface Cleansing Equipment Mfr
N.A.I.C.S.: 333310
Chris Mitchell *(Mgr-Bus Support)*

Subsidiary (US):

Johnston North America Inc (3)
606 Performance Rd Ste A & B, Moores-
ville, NC 28115
Tel.: (704) 658-1333
Web Site:
  http://www.johnstonnorthamerica.com
Sales Range: $25-49.9 Million
Emp.: 13
Outdoor Surface Cleaning Equipment Distr
N.A.I.C.S.: 423850
Bob O'Hara *(Gen Mgr)*

Subsidiary (Non-US):

New Motion Limited (3)
Workshop 2 13/f Wah Lai Industrial Centre
No 10-14 Kwei Tei Street, Shatin, Fotan,
New Territories, China (Hong Kong)
Tel.: (852) 3102 7606
Web Site: http://www.newmotion.com.hk
Emp.: 15
Cleaning Machine & Equipment Distr
N.A.I.C.S.: 423850

P T Nasaral Kekal Medal (3)
Wisma Sawah Besar Mendawai I No 64-66,
Kebayoran Baro, 12130, Jakarta, Indonesia
Tel.: (62) 21723 1877
Sales Range: $50-74.9 Million
Emp.: 1
Cleaning Equipment Distr
N.A.I.C.S.: 423810
Alex Takarianto *(Gen Mgr)*

Subsidiary (Non-US):

MacDonald Johnston Ltd. (2)
65-73 Nantilla Road Clayton, Clayton North,
Melbourne, 3168, VIC, Australia
Tel.: (61) 3 9271 6400
Web Site: http://www.mje.com.au
Sales Range: $75-99.9 Million
Emp.: 260
Side Loader Bodies Mfr
N.A.I.C.S.: 336211

SIA Bucher Schoerling Baltic SA (2)
105 Ganibu Street, Ventspils, 3600, Latvia
Tel.: (371) 63661050

Sales Range: $25-49.9 Million
Emp.: 210
Transportation Equipment Mfr
N.A.I.C.S.: 336999
Christopher Wittwer *(Gen Mgr)*

Bucher Unipektin AG (1)
Murzlenstrasse 80, 8166, Niederweningen,
Switzerland
Tel.: (41) 448572300
Web Site: https://www.bucherunipektin.com
Construction Equipment & Industrial Hy-
draulic Mfr
N.A.I.C.S.: 333120

Bucher Unipektin Ltd (1)
Murzlenstrasse 80, 8166, Niederweningen,
Switzerland
Tel.: (41) 44 857 23 00
Web Site: http://www.bucherunipektin.com
Vacuum Evaporator Mfr & Installation Ser-
vices
N.A.I.C.S.: 332919

Subsidiary (Non-US):

Bucher Unipektin Co. Ltd. (2)
Asian Game Village Huiyuan Apartment
Room E1102 No 8 Beichendong Lu, Chao-
ang District, Beijing, 100101, China
Tel.: (86) 10 6499 13 88
Web Site: http://www.bucheralimentech.com
Sales Range: $25-49.9 Million
Emp.: 6
Soft Drinks Mfr
N.A.I.C.S.: 312111

Bucher Unipektin Sp. z o.o. (1)
Ul Lubomirskich 1e, 37-200, Przeworsk,
Poland
Tel.: (48) 166490139
Food Processing Equipment Mfr & Distr
N.A.I.C.S.: 333241

Bucher Vaslin S.r.l. (1)
L Duzzi Viale Trieste 56, Romans d Isonzo,
Giuliano di Roma, Italy
Tel.: (39) 0481908931
Grape Wine Distr
N.A.I.C.S.: 424820

Bucher Vaslin SA (1)
5 Rue Gaston Bernierq, BP 70028, 49290,
Chalonnes-sur-Loire, France (100%)
Tel.: (33) 241745050
Web Site: https://www.buchervaslin.com
Sales Range: $50-74.9 Million
Emp.: 200
Wine Production Equipment Mfr
N.A.I.C.S.: 333241

Subsidiary (Domestic):

Bucher Vaslin MS SA (2)
Rue Gaston Bernier, 70028, Rivesaltes,
France
Tel.: (33) 241745050
Web Site: http://www.buchervaslin.com
Sales Range: $25-49.9 Million
Emp.: 39
Grapes Reception Equipment Mfr
N.A.I.C.S.: 333241

Subsidiary (US):

Bucher Vaslin North America, Inc (2)
3100 Dutton Ave Ste 134D-132D, Santa
Rosa, CA 95407
Tel.: (707) 823-2883
Web Site: https://www.bvnorthamerica.com
Sales Range: $25-49.9 Million
Emp.: 12
Food Product Machinery Mfr
N.A.I.C.S.: 333241
Mea Leeman *(Dir-Sls & Mktg-Napa Valley)*

Subsidiary (Non-US):

Bucher Vaslin Sudamerica (2)
La Vara 02429, San Bernardo, Santiago,
Chile
Tel.: (56) 27733960
Sales Range: $25-49.9 Million
Emp.: 3
Wine Making Machinery Mfr
N.A.I.C.S.: 333248
Gallardo Osvaldo *(Gen Mgr)*

Bucher-Alimentech Ltd (2)
412c Lake Road, PO Box 14258, Takapuna,
Auckland, 0622, New Zealand

Tel.: (64) 95731333
Web Site: https://www.bucherunipektin.com
Emp.: 4
Food Processing Machinery Mfr
N.A.I.C.S.: 333241

Bucher-Guyer AG (1)
Murzlenstrasse 80, 8166, Niederweningen,
Switzerland (100%)
Tel.: (41) 587501500
Web Site: https://www.bucherindustries.com
Sales Range: $100-124.9 Million
Emp.: 500
Vehicles & Agricultural Vehicles Mfr
N.A.I.C.S.: 336110

Division (Domestic):

Bucher Landtechnik AG (2)
Murzlenstrasse 80, 8166, Niederweningen,
Switzerland (100%)
Tel.: (41) 448572600
Web Site: https://www.bucherlandtechnik.ch
Sales Range: $25-49.9 Million
Emp.: 450
Importer of Tractors
N.A.I.C.S.: 333924

Bucher Municipal AG (2)
Murzlenstrasse 80, 8166, Niederweningen,
Switzerland (100%)
Tel.: (41) 448572211
Web Site: https://www.buchermunicipal.com
Sales Range: $75-99.9 Million
Emp.: 450
Vehicles & Agricultural Vehicles Mfr
N.A.I.C.S.: 336110
Aurelio Lemos *(Pres)*

Bucher-Guyer AG Food Tech (2)
Niederweningen ZH, CH 8166, Nieder-
weningen, Switzerland (100%)
Tel.: (41) 448572211
Web Site: http://www.bucherguyer.ch
Sales Range: $25-49.9 Million
Emp.: 70
N.A.I.C.S.: 311423
Hartmut Haverland *(Mng Dir)*

**Bucher-Guyer AG Municipal
Vehicles** (2)
Murzlenstrasse 80, 8166, Niederweningen,
Switzerland (100%)
Tel.: (41) 438158080
Web Site: http://www.bucherguyer.ch
Mfr & Retailer of Municipal Vehicles
N.A.I.C.S.: 336110

Contifonte SA (1)
4 Impasse des Fabriques, BP 50060,
67706, Saverne, Cedex, France
Tel.: (33) 388018105
Web Site: https://www.contifonte.com
Rev.: $15,063,846
Emp.: 75
Agricultural Machinery Mfr
N.A.I.C.S.: 333111
Michel Siepert *(Gen Mgr)*

Emhart Glass S.A. (1)
Hinterbergstrasse 22, PO Box 2251, 6330,
Champagne, Switzerland (100%)
Tel.: (41) 417494200
Web Site: http://old.emhartglass.com
Sales Range: $50-74.9 Million
Emp.: 60
Industrial Equipment, Controls & Glass
Parts Supplier
N.A.I.C.S.: 423840

Subsidiary (Non-US):

Emhart Glass GmbH (2)
Hammfelddamm 4B, 41460, Neuss,
Germany (100%)
Tel.: (49) 213135950
Web Site: http://old.emhartglass.com
Sales Range: $25-49.9 Million
Emp.: 20
Marketing of Industrial Supplies
N.A.I.C.S.: 423840

Subsidiary (US):

Emhart Glass Inc (2)
123 Great Pond Dr, Windsor, CT 06095-
0220
Tel.: (860) 298-7340
Emp.: 50
Glass Container Parts Mfr & Distr
N.A.I.C.S.: 327215

Subsidiary (Domestic):

Emhart Glass International SA (2)
Hinterbergstrasse 22, 6312, Steinhausen,
Switzerland
Tel.: (41) 417494200
Sales Range: $25-49.9 Million
Emp.: 75
Glass Equipment Distr
N.A.I.O.O.: 424310
Edward Munz *(Gen Mgr)*

Subsidiary (Non-US):

Emhart Glass Japan Co Ltd. (2)
Parale Mitsui Bldg 15F 8 Higashida-cho,
Kawasaki-ku, Kawasaki, 210-0005, Japan
Tel.: (81) 442239613
Web Site: https://www.emhartglass.com
Sales Range: $25-49.9 Million
Emp.: 5
Glass Products Distr
N.A.I.C.S.: 424310
Yoshiya Shibagaki *(Pres)*

Emhart Glass Ltd. (2)
First Avenue The Village, Trafford Park,
Manchester, M17 1JZ, United
Kingdom (50%)
Tel.: (44) 1618761700
Web Site: http://www.gemhartglass.com
Sales Range: $25-49.9 Million
Emp.: 17
Industrial Equipment Supplier
N.A.I.C.S.: 423840
Mike Curry *(Mng Dir)*

Subsidiary (US):

Emhart Glass Manufacturing Inc. (2)
123 Great Pond Dr, Windsor, CT
06095 (100%)
Tel.: (860) 298-7340
Web Site: http://www.emhartglass.com
Sales Range: $25-49.9 Million
Emp.: 56
Container Glass Mfr
N.A.I.C.S.: 327213

Branch (Domestic):

Emhart Glass Manufacturing Inc. (3)
9875 18 St N, Saint Petersburg, FL
33716 (100%)
Tel.: (727) 471-1113
Web Site: http://emhartglass.com
Sales Range: $25-49.9 Million
Emp.: 25
Automated Inspection Equipment
N.A.I.C.S.: 333993

Subsidiary (Non-US):

Emhart Glass OOO (2)
Privolnaya Str 70, Moscow, 109431, Russia
Tel.: (7) 499 746 13 40
Web Site: http://www.emhartglass.com
Sales Range: $25-49.9 Million
Emp.: 6
Glass Processing Machinery Distr
N.A.I.C.S.: 423830

Emhart Glass Pte. Ltd. (2)
8 Jurong Town Hall Road 25-06 The JTC
Summit, Singapore, 609434,
Singapore (100%)
Tel.: (65) 67781466
Web Site: https://www.emhartglass.com
Sales Range: $25-49.9 Million
Emp.: 13
Marketing of Industrial Supplies
N.A.I.C.S.: 423840

Emhart Glass S.r.l. (2)
Edificio Filo d Acqua Torre Orsero Largo
delle Coffe 1/1, Casella Postale 35,
I-17100, Savona, Italy (100%)
Tel.: (39) 0195166200
Web Site:
  https://www.bucheremhartglass.com
Sales Range: $25-49.9 Million
Emp.: 30
Equipment, Controls & Parts Supplier to the
Glass Container Industry
N.A.I.C.S.: 423840
Peolo Revello *(Mng Dir)*

Emhart Glass Sdn Bhd (2)
No 20 Jalan Mahir 5 Taman Perindustrian
Cemerlang, 81800, Ulu Tiram, Johor, Ma-
laysia

Tel.: (60) 72720000
Web Site: https://www.emhartglass.com
Sales Range: $25-49.9 Million
Emp.: 120
Glass Container Mfr
N.A.I.C.S.: 327213

Emhart Glass Sweden AB   **(2)**
Universitetsallen 1, PO Box 710, SE-85121,
Sundsvall, Sweden   **(100%)**
Tel.: (46) 60199100
Web Site: https://old.emhartglass.com
Sales Range: $125-149.9 Million
Marketing of Industrial Supplies
N.A.I.C.S.: 423840
Bertil Bjugard *(Mng Dir)*

Emhart Glass Vision GmbH   **(1)**
Behringstr 6, 82152, Planegg, Germany
Tel.: (49) 8955279800
Glass Container Product Distr
N.A.I.C.S.: 423220

J. Hvidtved Larsen A/S   **(1)**
Lillehojvej 15, 8600, Silkeborg, Denmark
Tel.: (45) 86821211
Street Cleaning Snow Removal & Garbage
Collection Services
N.A.I.C.S.: 488490

J. Hvidtved Larsen Ireland Ltd.   **(1)**
Two Mile Borris, Thurles, Tipperary, Ireland
Tel.: (353) 862449395
Sewer Cleaning Unit Mfr
N.A.I.C.S.: 333310

J. Hvidtved Larsen UK Ltd.   **(1)**
Unit 1 Samson Road, Leicester, LE67 3FP,
Leicestershire, United Kingdom
Tel.: (44) 1530815687
Sewer Cleaning Unit Mfr
N.A.I.C.S.: 333310

Jetter Automation Hungary Kft.   **(1)**
Ihasz Utca 10, 1105, Budapest, Hungary
Tel.: (36) 14332523
Web Site: https://www.jetter.hu
Electronic Components Mfr
N.A.I.C.S.: 334419

**Jetter Automation Technology
(Shanghai) Co., Ltd.**   **(1)**
Room 105 Building 6 No 787 Kang Qiao
Road, Pudong New District, Shanghai,
201315, China
Tel.: (86) 2158691233
Automation Component Mfr
N.A.I.C.S.: 334419

KUHN S.A.   **(1)**
4 Impasse des Fabriques, BP 50060,
F-67706, Saverne, Cedex, France   **(99%)**
Tel.: (33) 388018100
Web Site: https://www.kuhn.fr
Sales Range: $800-899.9 Million
Emp.: 3,200
Agricultural Machinery Mfr
N.A.I.C.S.: 333111

Subsidiary (US):

KUHN North America, Inc.   **(2)**
1501 W 7th Ave, Brodhead, WI 53520
Tel.: (608) 897-2131
Web Site: https://www.kuhn-usa.com
Sales Range: $100-124.9 Million
Emp.: 300
Farm Machinery & Equipment
N.A.I.C.S.: 333111
Thierry Krier *(Pres & CEO)*

Subsidiary (Domestic):

Kuhn Krause, Inc.   **(3)**
305 S Monroe St, Hutchinson, KS 67504
Tel.: (620) 663-6161
Web Site: https://www.krauseco.com
Sales Range: $50-74.9 Million
Emp.: 230
Farm Equipment Mfr
N.A.I.C.S.: 333111
Jason Seeger *(Dir-Engrg)*

Subsidiary (Domestic):

KUHN-Huard S.A.   **(2)**
2 Rue du Quebec Zone HORIZON, F -
44110, Chateaubriant, CEDEX, France
Tel.: (33) 240557700
Web Site: https://www.kuhn.com

Sales Range: $50-74.9 Million
Emp.: 350
Agricultural Machinery Mfr
N.A.I.C.S.: 333111

Subsidiary (Non-US):

Kuhn Farm Machinery Ltd   **(2)**
Stafford Park 7, Telford, TF3 3BQ, Shrop-
shire, United Kingdom
Tel.: (44) 1952239300
Web Site: https://www.kuhn.co.uk
Emp.: 5,000
Agricultural Machinery Distr
N.A.I.C.S.: 423820
Sian Pritchard *(Mng Dir)*

Kuhn Farm Machinery Pty Ltd   **(2)**
313 - 325 Foleys Road, Deer Park, 3023,
VIC, Australia
Tel.: (61) 399821490
Web Site: https://www.kuhn.com.au
Agricultural Machinery Mfr
N.A.I.C.S.: 333111

Kuhn Farm Machinery Sarl   **(2)**
16 Mechnikova Str Office Ste 311-312,
Kiev, 1601, Ukraine
Tel.: (380) 44 2293875
Web Site: http://www.kuhn.com
Sales Range: $25-49.9 Million
Emp.: 1
Agricultural Machinery Mfr
N.A.I.C.S.: 333111

Subsidiary (Domestic):

Kuhn Group SAS   **(2)**
4 Impasse Des Fabriques, 67700, Saverne,
France
Tel.: (33) 388018100
Industrial Machinery Distr
N.A.I.C.S.: 423830

Subsidiary (Non-US):

Kuhn Iberica SA   **(2)**
Carretera A-131 Km 100, 22005, Huesca,
Spain
Tel.: (34) 974234440
Web Site: https://www.kuhn.es
Farm Machinery Distr
N.A.I.C.S.: 423820

Kuhn Italia Srl.   **(2)**
Via Cerca per Colturano 8, 20077, Meleg-
nano, MI, Italy
Tel.: (39) 02982161
Web Site: https://www.kuhn.it
Agricultural Machinery Distr
N.A.I.C.S.: 423820

Subsidiary (Domestic):

Kuhn MGM SAS   **(2)**
Parc De La Faisanderie, 67700, Monswiller,
France
Tel.: (33) 388018100
Agricultural Machinery & Equipment Mfr
N.A.I.C.S.: 333111

Subsidiary (Non-US):

Kuhn Maschinen-Vertrieb GmbH   **(2)**
Schopsdorfer industriestr 14, Genthin,
D-39291, Schopsdorf, Germany
Tel.: (49) 392259600
Web Site: https://www.kuhn.de
Agricultural Machinery Distr
N.A.I.C.S.: 423820

**Kuhn Maszyny Rolnicze Sp.
z.o.o**   **(2)**
Jelonek K/Poznania - Ul Orzechowa 1, 62-
002, Suchy Las, Poland
Tel.: (48) 618125235
Web Site: https://www.kuhn.com.pl
Sales Range: $25-49.9 Million
Emp.: 37
Farm Machinery & Equipment Distr
N.A.I.C.S.: 423820

Kuhn Vostok LLC   **(2)**
Aidarovskoye rural settlement industrial ter-
ritory, Ramonsky municipal district 3rd In-
dustrial zone street, Voronezh, 396002,
Russia
Tel.: (7) 4733746446
Web Site: https://www.kuhn.ru
Emp.: 25
Agricultural Machinery & Equipment Distr

N.A.I.C.S.: 423820

Kuhn do Brasil S/A   **(2)**
Rua Arno Pini 1380, Industrial District,
Passo Fundo, 99050-130, RS, Brazil
Tel.: (55) 5433166200
Web Site: https://www.kuhnbrasil.com.br
Sales Range: $75-99.9 Million
Emp.: 48
Agricultural Machinery Mfr
N.A.I.C.S.: 333111
Mario Wagner *(Gen Dir)*

Subsidiary (Domestic):

Kuhn-Audureau SA   **(2)**
Rue Quanquese, BP 19, F - 85260, La Co-
pechagniere, France
Tel.: (33) 251414700
Web Site: https://www.kuhn.com
Emp.: 20
Agricultural Machinery Mfr
N.A.I.C.S.: 333111

Kuhn-Blanchard SAS   **(2)**
24 rue de Nantes, Chaumes-en-Retz,
44680, Chemere, France
Tel.: (33) 240213024
Web Site: https://www.bucherind.com
Emp.: 200
Agricultural & Forestry Machinery Mfr
N.A.I.C.S.: 333111

Subsidiary (Non-US):

Kuhn-Geldrop B.V.   **(2)**
Nuenenseweg 165, PO Box 9, 5660 AA,
Geldrop, Netherlands
Tel.: (31) 402893300
Web Site: https://www.kuhn.nl
Sales Range: $75-99.9 Million
Emp.: 400
Farm Machinery & Equipment Mfr
N.A.I.C.S.: 333111

**Kuhn-Montana Industria de Maquinas
S/A**   **(1)**
Rua Francisco Dal Negro No 3400, Sao
Jose dos Pinhais, 83025-320, Brazil
Tel.: (55) 4121020200
Machinery & Vehicle Construction Mfr
N.A.I.C.S.: 333120

Maquiasfalt SL   **(1)**
Calle Gavilan 15, 28946, Fuenlabrada,
Spain
Tel.: (34) 916422850
Street Cleaning Snow Removal & Garbage
Collection Services
N.A.I.C.S.: 488490

SSV Environnement S.A.S.   **(1)**
5 Rue Robert Moinon, 95190, Goussain-
ville, France
Tel.: (33) 130111820
Web Site: https://www.ssvenvironnement.fr
Truck & Sweeper Rental Services
N.A.I.C.S.: 532120

**Shandong Sanjin Glass Machinery
Co., Ltd.**   **(1)**
577 Xinhuaroad, Zhoucun District, Zibo,
255300, Shandong, China
Tel.: (86) 5336181717
Web Site: https://www.sanjinglass.com
Emp.: 800
Machinery Gypsum Board Equipment &
Spare Parts Mfr
N.A.I.C.S.: 327420

futronic GmbH   **(1)**
Tolnauer Strasse 3-4, 88069, Tettnang, Ger-
many
Tel.: (49) 754253070
Web Site: https://www.futronic.de
Emp.: 90
Electric Equipment Mfr
N.A.I.C.S.: 335999
Michael Preuss *(Mng Dir)*

BUCHER LEICHTBAU AG
Industriestrasse 1a, 8117, Fallanden,
Switzerland
Tel.: (41) 44 806 24 24
Web Site: http://www.bucher-
group.com
Year Founded: 1953
Aircraft Equipment Mfr
N.A.I.C.S.: 336413

Beat Burlet *(CEO)*

Subsidiaries:

Bucher Aerospace Corp.   **(1)**
1310 Industry St Ste 100, Everett, WA
98203
Tel.: (425) 355-2202
Web Site: http://www.bucher-group.com
Sales Range: $25-49.9 Million
Emp.: 50
Aircraft Components Mfr
N.A.I.C.S.: 336413
Francisco Aguilera *(CEO)*

Bucher Interiors GmbH   **(1)**
Zur Dornheck 1517, Fleisbach, 36764,
Sinn, Germany
Tel.: (49) 277257696100
Aircraft Equipment Mfr
N.A.I.C.S.: 336413
Beat Burlet *(CEO)*

BUCHERER AG
Langensandstrasse 27, 6005, Lu-
cerne, Switzerland
Tel.: (41) 3697000
Web Site: http://www.bucherer.com
Year Founded: 1888
Watch & Jewelry Mfr & Retailer
N.A.I.C.S.: 423940
Jorg Baumann *(CMO)*

Subsidiaries:

SWISS LION AG   **(1)**
Lowenplatz 11, 6004, Lucerne, Switzerland
Tel.: (41) 41 410 61 81
Web Site: http://www.swisslion.ch
Watch Distr
N.A.I.C.S.: 423940
Ivo Carla *(Mng Dir)*

Tourneau, LLC   **(1)**
663 Fifth Ave, New York, NY 10022
Web Site: http://www.tourneau.com
Watches, Clocks & Jewelry Mfr & Retailer
N.A.I.C.S.: 458310
Richard Gellman *(VP-Adv & Mktg)*

BUCK-CHEMIE GMBH
Hertzstrasse 1, Herrenberg, 71083,
Germany
Tel.: (49) 703297690
Web Site: http://www.buck-chemie.de
Year Founded: 1966
Rev.: $18,374,869
Emp.: 50
Cleaning Consumer Goods Mfr
N.A.I.C.S.: 325180
Edgar Jaeschke *(Gen Mgr)*

BUCKET STUDIO CO., LTD.
21Eonju-ro 135gil, Gangnam-gu,
Seoul, 135925, Korea (South)
Tel.: (82) 234525079   **KR**
Web Site:
    http://www.candlemedia.co.kr
Year Founded: 1999
066410—(KRS)
Rev.: $34,245,198
Assets: $240,494,019
Liabilities: $141,358,591
Net Worth: $99,135,428
Earnings: ($150,029,843)
Emp.: 64
Fiscal Year-end: 12/31/22
Miscellaneous Goods Distr
N.A.I.C.S.: 512250
Keum Ki-Dong *(CFO)*

**BUCKING HORSE ENERGY
INC.**
Ste 900 609 West Hastings Street,
Vancouver, V6B 4W4, BC, Canada
Tel.: (604) 331-3398   **BC**
Web Site:
    http://www.buckinghorseenergy.com
Year Founded: 2006
Sales Range: $10-24.9 Million
Petroleum Exploration & Develop-
ment

Bucking Horse Energy Inc.—(Continued)

N.A.I.C.S.: 213112
Gordon Nielsen *(Chm, Pres, CEO, CFO, Treas & Sec)*

Subsidiaries:

Arrowhead Resources (U.S.A.)
Ltd. (1)
3964 Crystal Bridge Dr, Carbondale, CO
81623
Tel.: (970) 704-0471
Oil & Gas Field Exploration Services
N.A.I.C.S.: 213112

**BUCKINGHAMSHIRE BUILD-
ING SOCIETY**

High Street, Chalfont Saint Giles,
HP8 4QB, Buckinghamshire, United
Kingdom
Tel.: (44) 1494 879500
Web Site: http://www.bucksbs.co.uk
Year Founded: 1907
Rev.: $11,003,012
Assets: $365,651,783
Liabilities: $332,738,492
Net Worth: $32,913,290
Earnings: $1,680,160
Emp.: 44
Fiscal Year-end: 12/31/19
Mortgage Lender
N.A.I.C.S.: 522310
Tim Vigeon *(Head-Lending)*

**BUCKLAND CUSTOMS BRO-
KERS LTD.**

73 Gaylord Road, Saint Thomas,
N5P 3R9, ON, Canada
Tel.: (519) 631-4944
Web Site:
　　http://www.bucklandcustoms.com
Year Founded: 1945
Sales Range: $10-24.9 Million
Customs Brokerage & Logistics Ser-
vices
N.A.I.C.S.: 488510
Stephane Ethier *(COO)*

BUCKTHORN PARTNERS LLP

76 Brook Street, 55 Baker Street,
London, W1K 5EE, United Kingdom
Tel.: (44) 2039591070
Web Site:
　　http://www.buckthornpartners.com
Private Investment Firm
N.A.I.C.S.: 523999
Nicholas Gee *(Partner)*

Subsidiaries:

Acteon Group Ltd. (1)
Ferryside Ferry Rd, Norfolk, NR1 1SW,
United Kingdom
Tel.: (44) 1603227019
Web Site: https://www.acteon.com
Offshore Oil & Gas Engineering & Drilling
Services
N.A.I.C.S.: 213112
David Drysdale *(Exec VP-Infrastructure)*

Subsidiary (Domestic):

2H Offshore Engineering Ltd. (2)
Hollywood House Church St E, Woking,
GU21 6HJ, Surrey, United Kingdom
Tel.: (44) 1483774900
Web Site: https://www.2hoffshore.com
Sales Range: $25-49.9 Million
Marine Riser System Design, Construction
& Maintenance Services
N.A.I.C.S.: 237120
Yann Helle *(Mng Dir-London)*

Subsidiary (Non-US):

CAPE Group Pte. Ltd. (2)
10 Anson Road 12-14 International Plaza,
Singapore, 079903, Singapore
Tel.: (65) 62622282
Web Site: https://capegroupglobal.com

Sales Range: $25-49.9 Million
Emp.: 20
Holding Company
N.A.I.C.S.: 551112
Yogaprakash Mahalingam *(Gen Mgr)*

Subsidiary (Domestic):

Claxton Engineering Services
Ltd (2)
Bureside House North River Road Great
Yarmouth, Norfolk, NR30 1TE, United King-
dom
Web Site:
　　http://www.claxtonengineering.com
Sales Range: $75-99.9 Million
Emp.: 100
Oil & Natural Gas Well Engineering & Con-
sulting Services
N.A.I.C.S.: 213112
Laura Claxton *(COO)*

Subsidiary (Non-US):

Fluke Engenharia Ltda. (2)
Avenida Das Americas 3434 Bloco 2-Sala
201-Barra Da Tijuca, Rio de Janeiro,
22640-102, Brazil
Tel.: (55) 2134313899
Offshore Oil & Natural Gas Well Mooring
System Developer & Mfr
N.A.I.C.S.: 213112

Subsidiary (US):

InterAct PMTI, Inc. (2)
260 Maple Ct Ste 210, Ventura, CA 93003
Tel.: (805) 658-5600
Web Site: http://www.interactprojects.com
Oil & Gas Production Engineering, Project
Management & Consulting Services
N.A.I.C.S.: 213112

Subsidiary (Domestic):

InterMoor (2)
Tern Place House Tern Place Bridge of
Don, Aberdeen, AB23 8JX, United Kingdom
Tel.: (44) 1224701830
Web Site: https://acteon.com
Sales Range: $50-74.9 Million
Emp.: 20
Oil & Natural Gas Well Mooring & Anchor-
ing System Mfr
N.A.I.C.S.: 213112
Alan Duncan *(Mng Dir)*

Subsidiary (Non-US):

InterMoor Pte. Ltd. (3)
25 Loyang Crescent Block 103 06-02, Mail-
box No 5078, Tops Avenue 1, Singapore,
508988, Singapore
Tel.: (65) 65465928
Web Site: http://www.intermoor.com
Emp.: 22
Oil & Natural Gas Well Mooring & Anchor-
ing System Mfr
N.A.I.C.S.: 213112
Alan Duncan *(Mng Dir-UK)*

Subsidiary (Domestic):

Viking SeaTech Ltd. (3)
Peterseat Drive Peterseat Park, London,
AB12 3HT, Altens, United Kingdom
Tel.: (44) 1224516516
Web Site: http://www.vikingseatech.com
Marine Equipment Distr
N.A.I.C.S.: 423910

Subsidiary (US):

InterMoor Inc. (2)
101 Youngswood Rd, Morgan City, LA
70380
Tel.: (985) 385-3083
Web Site: http://www.intermoor.com
Sales Range: $50-74.9 Million
Integrated Mooring Systems Mfr for the Off-
shore Oil & Gas Industries
N.A.I.C.S.: 237120

Subsidiary (Non-US):

Menck GmbH (2)
Industrial Area Moorkarten, Am Springmoor
5A, Kaltenkirchen, 24568, Germany
Tel.: (49) 41919110

Web Site: http://www.menck.com
Sales Range: $50-74.9 Million
Oil & Gas Well Engineering, Construction &
Consulting Services
N.A.I.C.S.: 333132
Fabian Hippe *(Mng Dir)*

Subsidiary (Domestic):

Seatronics Ltd. (2)
Acteon House Peregrine Road, Aberdeen-
shire, Westhill, AB32 6JL, United Kingdom
Tel.: (44) 1224853100
Web Site: https://acteon.com
Sales Range: $25-49.9 Million
Emp.: 50
Subsea Electronic Equipment Supplier
N.A.I.C.S.: 423690
Derek Donaldson *(Mng Dir-Grp)*

Subsidiary (US):

Seatronics, Inc. (3)
1319 W Sam Houston Pkwy N Ste 150,
Houston, TX 77043
Tel.: (713) 464-3311
Web Site: http://www.seatronics-group.com
Sales Range: $25-49.9 Million
Emp.: 20
Subsea Electronic Equipment Supplier
N.A.I.C.S.: 423690
Jenell Pence *(Pres)*

Subsidiary (Domestic):

TEAM Energy Resources Ltd. (2)
Ferryside Ferry Road, Norwich, NR1 1SW,
United Kingdom
Tel.: (44) 1603767439
Web Site: https://www.team-energy.co.uk
Sales Range: $75-99.9 Million
Emp.: 25
Oil & Gas Well Engineering & Consulting
Services
N.A.I.C.S.: 213112

Coretrax Technology Limited (1)
Technology House Moss Road Gateway
Business Park, Aberdeen, AB12 3GQ,
United Kingdom
Tel.: (44) 1224 872020
Web Site: http://www.coretrax.com
Oilfield Equipment Supplier
N.A.I.C.S.: 423440
Kenny Murray *(Mng Dir)*

BUCKWOLD WESTERN LTD.

70-3239 Faithfull Ave, Saskatoon,
S7K 8H4, SK, Canada
Tel.: (306) 652-1660
Web Site: http://www.buckwold.com
Year Founded: 1925
Sales Range: $10-24.9 Million
Floor Covering Products Distr
N.A.I.C.S.: 444180
Bruce Buckwold *(Pres)*

Subsidiaries:

Wanke Cascade Distribution Ltd. (1)
6330 N Cutter Cir, Portland, OR 97217-
3997
Tel.: (503) 289-8609
Web Site: http://www.wanke.com
Sales Range: $25-49.9 Million
Emp.: 75
Floor Covering Distr
N.A.I.C.S.: 423220
Shawn Loomis *(Mgr-Sls-Resiential)*

BUCOVINA SA

Str Humorului Nr 62, Scheia, Su-
ceava, Romania
Tel.: (40) 230526271
Web Site: https://bucovina-sa.ro
Year Founded: 1991
BUCS—(BUC)
Rev.: $3,963,837
Assets: $2,116,870
Liabilities: $1,084,174
Net Worth: $1,032,696
Earnings: ($120,080)
Emp.: 63
Fiscal Year-end: 12/31/23
Cheese & Dairy Product Mfr
N.A.I.C.S.: 311513

Viorel Cibota *(Pres & Gen Mgr)*

BUDAMAR LOGISTICS AS

Horarska 12, 82109, Bratislava, Slo-
vakia
Tel.: (421) 421258312111
Web Site: http://www.budamar.sk
Year Founded: 2002
Logistic Services
N.A.I.C.S.: 488999
Peter Malec *(CEO)*

Subsidiaries:

ELH WBN Waggonbau Niesky
GmbH (1)
Am Waggonbau 11, 2906, Berlin, Germany
Tel.: (49) 3588240
Web Site: http://www.waggonbau-
niesky.com
Rail Vehicle Mfr
N.A.I.C.S.: 336510
Peter Schulze *(Head-HR & Procurist)*

**BUDAPEST PROPERTY UTILI-
ZATION AND DEVELOPMENT
PLC.**

Bajcsy Zsilinszky Ut 57, 1065, Buda-
pest, Hungary
Tel.: (36) 13322200
Web Site: http://www.bif.hu
Year Founded: 1994
Sales Range: $10-24.9 Million
Emp.: 44
Real Estate Manangement Services
N.A.I.C.S.: 531390
Gabor Angel *(CEO)*

BUDAPESTI INGATLAN NYRT

Polgar u 8-10, 1033, Budapest, 1033,
Hungary
Tel.: (36) 13322200
Web Site: https://www.bif.hu
BIF—(BUD)
Rev.: $28,206,390
Assets: $223,841,719
Liabilities: $71,711,411
Net Worth: $152,130,308
Earnings: $27,495,218
Emp.: 64
Fiscal Year-end: 12/31/22
Real Estate Development Services
N.A.I.C.S.: 531390
Anna Ungar *(Chm)*

BUDDHA AIR PVT. LTD.

Jawalakhel Lalitpur, PO Box 2167,
Kathmandu, Nepal
Tel.: (977) 015521015
Web Site: http://www.buddhaair.com
Sales Range: $150-199.9 Million
Emp.: 700
Oil Transportation Services
N.A.I.C.S.: 481111
Surendra B. Basnet *(Chm)*

BUDDS' BMW

2454 South Service Road West, Oak-
ville, L6L 5M9, ON, Canada
Tel.: (905) 827-6047
Web Site: http://www.buddsbmw.com
Year Founded: 1973
Rev.: $23,973,621
Emp.: 50
New & Used Car Dealers
N.A.I.C.S.: 441110
Rob Werstroh *(Gen Mgr)*

BUDDY PLATFORM LTD.

Level 2 333 King William Street, Ad-
elaide, 5000, SA, Australia
Tel.: (61) 8 6380 2555
Web Site: http://www.buddy.com
Rev.: $1,626,495
Assets: $20,252,249
Liabilities: $1,394,990
Net Worth: $18,857,259
Earnings: ($10,831,248)

Fiscal Year-end: 06/30/18
Business Computer Services
N.A.I.C.S.: 541519
David Peter McLauchlan *(Founder & CEO)*

Subsidiaries:

Buddy Platform, Inc. **(1)**
PO Box 2934, Kirkland, WA 98083-2934
Tel.: (252) 227-7014
Web Site: http://www.buddy.com
Software Publisher
N.A.I.C.S.: 513210

BUDGE BUDGE COMPANY LTD.
16A Brabourne Road 9th Floor, Kolkata, 700 001, West Bengal, India
Tel.: (91) 334 010 8000
Web Site: http://www.gayatrigroup.co
538789—(BOM)
Rev.: $28,605,022
Assets: $16,289,541
Liabilities: $14,210,660
Net Worth: $2,078,881
Earnings: ($2,185,611)
Emp.: 4,647
Fiscal Year-end: 03/31/21
Jute Mfr
N.A.I.C.S.: 313210
Ashok Kumar Poddar *(Chm)*

BUDGET RENT-A-CAR OF B.C. LTD
3691 No 3 Rd, Richmond, V6X 2B8, BC, Canada
Tel.: (604) 668-7100
Web Site: http://www.budgetbc.com
Year Founded: 1965
Rev.: $22,084,017
Emp.: 150
Automobile Renting & Leasing
N.A.I.C.S.: 532111
Sydney Belzberg *(Chm)*

BUDLEX SP ZOO
ul Kimczaka 1, Warsaw, Poland
Tel.: (48) 22 430 03 02
Web Site: http://www.budlex.pl
Year Founded: 1987
Construction & Engineering Services
N.A.I.C.S.: 236115
Malgorzata Mellem *(Vice Chm)*

BUDUCNOST A.D.
Second Railway Resort 11, Backa Palanka, Serbia
Tel.: (381) 21 6041 012
Year Founded: 1989
Sales Range: Less than $1 Million
Emp.: 71
Cereal Crop Farming Services
N.A.I.C.S.: 111998
Boris Strbac *(Gen Mgr)*

BUDUCNOST A.D.
Nikole Tesle 16, Conoplja, Serbia
Tel.: (381) 25 844 820
Year Founded: 1989
Sales Range: $1-9.9 Million
Emp.: 11
Cereal Crop Farming Services
N.A.I.C.S.: 111998
Rade Kosanovic *(Exec Dir)*

BUDUCNOST HLADENJE SLAP A.D.
Budvanska 2, Belgrade, Serbia
Tel.: (381) 112860131
Year Founded: 1989
BHSL—(BEL)
Sales Range: Less than $1 Million
Emp.: 10
Computer & Peripheral Equipment Maintenance Services
N.A.I.C.S.: 811210
Dordije Sabovic *(Exec Dir & Dir)*

BUDUCNOST JAGODINA A.D.
Kablovska bb, 35000, Jagodina, Serbia
Tel.: (381) 35 221 202
Web Site:
http://www.adbuducnost.com
Year Founded: 2000
Sales Range: Less than $1 Million
Packaging Services
N.A.I.C.S.: 561910

BUDUCNOST NOVI SAD A.D.
Privrednikova 8A, Novi Sad, Serbia
Tel.: (381) 21 48 99 721
Web Site: http://www.buducnostad.rs
Year Founded: 1957
Sales Range: Less than $1 Million
Emp.: 350
Building Construction Services
N.A.I.C.S.: 236115

BUDVAR CENTRUM SA
ul Przemyslowa 36, 98-220, Zdunska Wola, Poland
Tel.: (48) 438243132
Web Site: http://www.budvar.pl
Year Founded: 1997
Sales Range: $10-24.9 Million
Emp.: 300
PVC, Wooden & Aluminum Window & Door Mfr
N.A.I.C.S.: 332321
Marek Trzcinski *(Founder)*

BUDWEISER BREWING COMPANY APAC LIMITED
Suites 3012-16 Tower Two Times Square 1 Matheson Street, Causeway Bay, China (Hong Kong) Ky
Web Site:
https://www.budweiserapac.com
Year Founded: 2001
1876—(HKG)
Rev.: $6,478,000,000
Assets: $15,996,000,000
Liabilities: $5,163,000,000
Net Worth: $10,833,000,000
Earnings: $949,000,000
Emp.: 24,320
Fiscal Year-end: 12/31/22
Brewing Product Mfr
N.A.I.C.S.: 312120

BUDWORTH PROPERTIES LIMITED
1 Valley Rd, Birkenhead, CH41 7ED, United Kingdom
Tel.: (44) 151 6531700
Property Management Services
N.A.I.C.S.: 531311
Christopher Houghton *(Mng Dir)*

BUECHL HANDELS-UND BETEILIGUNGS-KG
Im Gewerbepark C 30, 93059, Regensburg, Germany
Tel.: (49) 9 41 46 46 40 De
Web Site: http://www.bueechl.de
Engineeering Services
N.A.I.C.S.: 541330

Subsidiaries:

Michael Glatt Maschinenbau GmbH **(1)**
Industriestrasse 2, 93326, Abensberg, Germany
Tel.: (49) 944391140
Web Site: http://www.glattistgutgmbh.de
Sales Range: $10-24.9 Million
Emp.: 80
Chemicals Pressure Container & Other Apparate Mfr
N.A.I.C.S.: 332999
Georg Hochreiter *(CEO & Mng Dir)*

BUETTNER S.A. INDUSTRIA E COMERCIO

R Edgar Von Buettner 941, 88355350, Brusque, SC, Brazil
Tel.: (55) 47 3211 4078
Web Site: http://www.buettner.com.br
Year Founded: 1898
Sales Range: $25-49.9 Million
Emp.: 743
Textile Product Mfr & Whslr
N.A.I.C.S.: 314120
Fabricio Pozzi Colzani *(Pres & CEO)*

BUFA GMBH & CO. KG
Stubbenweg 40, 26125, Oldenburg, Germany
Tel.: (49) 44193170 De
Web Site: http://www.buefa.de
Year Founded: 1883
Sales Range: $250-299.9 Million
Emp.: 500
Holding Company; Chemicals, Composite Materials & Cleaning Products Mfr
N.A.I.C.S.: 551112
Lothar Kempf *(Mng Dir-Segment Composites)*

Subsidiaries:

BUFA Composite Systems GmbH & Co. KG **(1)**
Hohe Looge 2-8, 26180, Rastede, Germany
Tel.: (49) 4402 975 0
Web Site:
http://www.buefacompositesystems.de
Composite Materials Mfr & Distr
N.A.I.C.S.: 325211
Lothar Kempf *(Mng Dir & Dir-Product Mgmt)*

Subsidiary (Non-US):

BUFA Composites Baltic OU **(2)**
Parnu mnt 130-3, 11317, Tallinn, Estonia
Tel.: (372) 5341 3545
Web Site:
http://www.buefacompositesystems.de
Composite Materials Distr
N.A.I.C.S.: 424690
Kait Vahter *(Gen Mgr)*

Subsidiary (Domestic):

BUFA Composites GmbH & Co. KG **(2)**
Stubbenweg 38, 26125, Oldenburg, Germany
Tel.: (49) 441 885 384 10
Web Site:
http://www.buefacompositesystems.de
Composite Materials Distr
N.A.I.C.S.: 424690
Felix Thalmann *(Mgr)*

BUFFALO CO., LTD.
9F Kawaguchi Center Building 1-8 Honmachi 4-chome, Kawaguchi, 332-0012, Saitama, Japan
Tel.: (81) 482278860
Web Site: https://buffalo.co.jp
Year Founded: 1983
3352—(TKS)
Rev.: $74,137,760
Assets: $56,138,730
Liabilities: $16,518,390
Net Worth: $39,620,340
Earnings: $753,540
Emp.: 261
Fiscal Year-end: 03/31/24
Retail Store Operator
N.A.I.C.S.: 459999
Yuji Sakamoto *(Pres & Exec Officer)*

BUFFALO COAL CORP.
16 Pieter Street 1st Floor Building 1 Manhattan Office Park, Centurion, Gauteng, South Africa
Tel.: (27) 11 656 3210 ON
Web Site:
http://www.buffalocoal.co.za
Year Founded: 2006
BUF—(TSXV)
Rev.: $25,515,289
Assets: $11,897,644

Liabilities: $40,076,972
Net Worth: ($28,179,329)
Earnings: ($3,182,971)
Emp.: 956
Fiscal Year-end: 12/31/21
Coal Mining Services
N.A.I.C.S.: 212114
Craig Wiggill *(Chm)*

Subsidiaries:

Forbes Coal (Pty) Ltd. **(1)**
Coalfields Commercial Rd R33, PO Box 684, Dundee, 3000, Kwazulu Natal, South Africa
Tel.: (27) 34 212 1455
Coal Mining Services
N.A.I.C.S.: 212115

BUFFALO DAVID BITTON
400 Sauve W, Montreal, H3L 1Z8, QC, Canada
Tel.: (514) 388-3551
Web Site:
http://www.buffalojeans.com
Year Founded: 1985
Sales Range: $100-124.9 Million
Emp.: 300
Denim Apparel Designer, Mfr & Retailer
N.A.I.C.S.: 458110
Gaby Bitton *(Pres)*

BUGOJNOPROMET D.D.
Dr Wagnera 11, 70230, Bugojno, Bosnia & Herzegovina
Tel.: (387) 30251453
BGPMRK3—(SARE)
Rev.: $59,108
Assets: $669,652
Liabilities: $21,435
Net Worth: $648,218
Earnings: ($97,185)
Emp.: 1
Fiscal Year-end: 12/31/20
Tobacco & Food Product Distr
N.A.I.C.S.: 445298

BUHLER AG
Gupfenstrasse 5, CH 9240, Uzwil, Switzerland
Tel.: (41) 719551111
Web Site:
http://www.buhlergroup.com
Year Founded: 1860
Rev.: $3,402,430,016
Assets: $4,152,095,296
Liabilities: $2,374,008,704
Net Worth: $1,778,086,592
Earnings: $207,599,616
Emp.: 12,767
Fiscal Year-end: 12/31/19
Food Processing Systems; Chemical Process Engineering; Die Casting; Mfr & Logistics
N.A.I.C.S.: 311999
Stefan Scheiber *(CEO)*

Subsidiaries:

Buhler (Canada) Inc. **(1)**
7270 Woodbine Av Suite 202, Markham, L3R 4B9, ON, Canada
Tel.: (905) 940-6910
Rice Distr
N.A.I.C.S.: 424490

Buhler Aeroglide **(1)**
100 Aeroglide Dr, Cary, NC 27511-6900
Tel.: (919) 851-2000
Web Site: http://www.aeroglide.com
Sales Range: $50-74.9 Million
Emp.: 220
Industrial Drying & Cooling Equipment Mfr
N.A.I.C.S.: 333241
Mark Paulson *(VP-Ops)*

Subsidiary (Non-US):

Buhler Aeroglide U.K. **(2)**
2 St Mary's Hill, Stamford, PE9 2DW, Lincs, United Kingdom

Buhler AG—(Continued)

Tel.: (44) 1780767007
Web Site: http://www.aeroglide.com
Sales Range: $25-49.9 Million
Emp.: 10
Thermal Processing Equipment Mfr
N.A.I.C.S.: 333248

Buhler Barth GmbH (1)
Daimlerstr 6, PO Box 12 45, 71688,
Freiberg am Neckar, Germany
Tel.: (49) 7141705201
Chocolate Mfr & Distr
N.A.I.C.S.: 311351
Joachim Essig (Head-Sls)

Buhler Farmila Vietnam Ltd. (1)
Lot 11 Street No 1 Tan Duc Industrial Park,
Duc Hoa, Long An, Vietnam
Tel.: (84) 723769045
Food Products Mfr
N.A.I.C.S.: 311919

Buhler GmbH (1)
Kolner Str 102-108, 51702, Bergneustadt,
Germany
Tel.: (49) 226140910
Chocolate Mfr & Distr
N.A.I.C.S.: 311351

Buhler Inc. (1)
13105 12th Ave N, Plymouth, MN 55441
Tel.: (763) 847-9900
Web Site: http://www.buhlerusa.com
Sales Range: $50-74.9 Million
Emp.: 170
Mfr & Wholesaler of Industrial Food Pro-
cessing Machinery & Equipment; Manufac-
turer of Bulk Conveying & Dust Control Sys-
tems & Machinery
N.A.I.C.S.: 333241
Jeff Lewin (Sr Mgr-Engrg)

Subsidiary (Domestic):

American Pellet Mill Services,
Inc. (2)
1001 Shaver St, Springdale, AR 72762
Tel.: (479) 751-2727
Rev.: $2,905,000
Emp.: 7
Pellet Mill Parts Mfr
N.A.I.C.S.: 333519
David Sparks (Pres)

Buhler Limited (1)
Unit 18E Isaac John Street Gra, Ikeja, La-
gos, Nigeria
Tel.: (234) 7053890504
Food Products Mfr
N.A.I.C.S.: 311919

Buhler Ltd (1)
Sukari Industrial Estate, PO Box 44553,
Ruiru, Nairobi, Kenya
Tel.: (254) 720180011
Food Products Mfr
N.A.I.C.S.: 424490

Buhler Ltd. (1)
No 1702 17th Floor 42 Tower 65 Soi
Sukhumvit 42 Sukhumvit Road, Phra Kha-
nong, Bangkok, 10110, Thailand
Tel.: (66) 27122570
Food Products Mfr
N.A.I.C.S.: 311919

Buhler P.J.S.C (1)
Buhler Building Farmanieh Lavasani Street
166, Tehran, 19377 43451, Iran
Tel.: (98) 2122691400
Emp.: 150
Food Products Mfr
N.A.I.C.S.: 424490

Buhler Pakistan (Pvt.) Ltd. (1)
Plot 499 Sundar Industrial Estate Raiwind
Road, Lahore, Pakistan
Tel.: (92) 4235298701
Emp.: 20
Food Products Mfr
N.A.I.C.S.: 311919
Andreas Aepli (Mgr-Country)

Buhler SA (1)
Villa Eplf n 110, Zeralda, Algiers, Algeria
Tel.: (213) 21321362
Food Products Mfr
N.A.I.C.S.: 424490

Buhler SORTEX Inc. (1)

2385 Arch-Airport Rd Ste 300, Stockton, CA
95206
Tel.: (209) 983-8400
Rice Distr
N.A.I.C.S.: 424490

Buhler Vietnam Company
Limited (1)
10th floor Mekong Tower Cong Hoa ward
13, Tan Binh, 235241, Ho Chi Minh City,
Vietnam
Tel.: (84) 838120740
Food Products Mfr
N.A.I.C.S.: 311919

Esau & Hueber GmbH. (1)
Kapellenweg 10, 86529, Schrobenhausen,
Germany
Tel.: (49) 825289850
Web Site: http://www.esau-hueber.de
Sales Range: $25-49.9 Million
Emp.: 55
Waste Treatment Services
N.A.I.C.S.: 237110

IdraPrince, Inc. (1)
670 Windcrest Dr, Holland, MI 49423
Tel.: (616) 394-8248
Web Site: http://www.prince-machine.com
Sales Range: $50-74.9 Million
Emp.: 230
Die Casting Machine Mfr
N.A.I.C.S.: 333517

Leybold Optics GmbH (1)
Siemensstrasse 88, 63755, Alzenau, Ger-
many
Tel.: (49) 6023 500 0
Optical Product Distr
N.A.I.C.S.: 423460
Antonio Requena (CEO & Mng Dir)

BUILD INVESTMENTS GROUP JSC
Bokehana 24, Nur-Sultan, 010000,
Kazakhstan
Tel.: (7) 7172360360
Web Site: http://www.bi-group.kz
Sales Range: $75-99.9 Million
Construction & Related Industries
Investment Services
N.A.I.C.S.: 523999
Askhat Omarov (Chm-Mgmt Bd)

Subsidiaries:

ABK-Concrete Plant LLP (1)
Building 6 Passage 60 Street, Nur-Sultan,
Kazakhstan
Tel.: (7) 87172532864
Construction Engineering Services
N.A.I.C.S.: 541330

BI-Cement LLP (1)
10/2 Syganak Street, Nur-Sultan, Kazakh-
stan
Tel.: (7) 87172661443
Construction Engineering Services
N.A.I.C.S.: 541330

Build Investments Group JSC -
Astana MDU Division (1)
Zhansugurov 14/3, Nur-Sultan, Kazakhstan
Tel.: (7) 7172 70 53 53
Construction Engineering Services
N.A.I.C.S.: 541330

Build Investments Group JSC - Con-
struction Materials Production
Division (1)
Building No 6/1 93 Street Industrial Area,
Nur-Sultan, Kazakhstan
Tel.: (7) 8 7172 53 30 00
Web Site: http://www.big-elit.kz
Construction Engineering Services
N.A.I.C.S.: 541330

BUILD KING HOLDINGS LIMITED
6/F Tower B Manulife Financial Cen-
tre 223 Wai Yip Street, Kwun Tong,
Kowloon, China (Hong Kong)
Tel.: (852) 22723680
Web Site: http://www.buildking.hk
0240—(HKG)
Rev.: $1,583,876,145

Assets: $933,367,958
Liabilities: $662,310,098
Net Worth: $271,057,860
Earnings: $54,718,665
Emp.: 3,390
Fiscal Year-end: 12/31/22
Construction Business
N.A.I.C.S.: 522292
Desmond Kam Chuen Chang (Exec
Dir)

Subsidiaries:

Leader Marine Cont. L.L.C. (1)
Office 503 Crystal Plaza Tower C King
Faisal Road, PO Box 39169, Sharjah,
United Arab Emirates
Tel.: (971) 65750083
Marine Construction Services
N.A.I.C.S.: 541330

Titan Foundation Limited (1)
6/F Tower B Manulife Financial Centre 223
Wai Yip Street, Kwun Tong, Kowloon, China
(Hong Kong)
Tel.: (852) 34603382
Civil Engineering Services
N.A.I.C.S.: 541330

Wuxi Qianhui Sewage Treatment Co.,
Ltd. (1)
Xiao Lu An Tou Xiao Xing Cun Qian Qiao
Zhen, Wuxi, 214151, China
Tel.: (86) 51083238119
Sewage Treatment Services
N.A.I.C.S.: 221320

BUILDERS CAPITAL MORTGAGE CORP.
260 1414 8th Street SW, Calgary,
T2R 1J6, AB, Canada
Tel.: (403) 685-9888
Web Site:
    https://www.builderscapital.ca
Year Founded: 2013
BCF—(TSXV)
Rev.: $3,530,274
Assets: $25,186,483
Liabilities: $3,003,768
Net Worth: $22,182,715
Earnings: $2,486,943
Fiscal Year-end: 12/31/23
Mortgage Investment Services
N.A.I.C.S.: 523999
Sandy L. Loutitt (Founder, Pres &
CEO)

BUILDERSMART PUBLIC COMPANY LIMITED
1055 Rama III Rd, Chong Nonsi Yan-
nawa, Bangkok, 10120, Thailand
Tel.: (66) 26834900
Web Site:
    https://www.buildersmart.com
Year Founded: 1999
BSM—(THA)
Rev.: $14,398,063
Assets: $36,341,375
Liabilities: $24,192,553
Net Worth: $12,148,822
Earnings: ($1,546,591)
Fiscal Year-end: 12/31/23
Construction Materials Distr
N.A.I.C.S.: 423390

Subsidiaries:

BuilderSmart (Vietnam) Limited (1)
90A/B 73 Ly Thuong Kiet, Ho Chi Minh City,
Vietnam
Tel.: (84) 8 3864 3525
Construction Materials Distr
N.A.I.C.S.: 423320

Builders Box (India) PVT. Ltd (1)
Unit G5-6 26 Race Course Road, Benga-
luru, 560 001, Karnataka, India
Tel.: (91) 80 412 26 332
Construction Materials Distr
N.A.I.C.S.: 423320

BUILDEX VENTURE CAPITAL

CORPORATION
3030 boul Le Carrefour, Bureau
1002, Laval, H7T 2P5, QC, Canada
Tel.: (450) 681-7744   Ca
Year Founded: 2010
Investment Services
N.A.I.C.S.: 523999
Pierre-Hubert Seguin (Sec)

BUILDING DREAMSTAR TECH-NOLOGY INC.
No 5002 Shennan East Road Suite
2016 King Building, Luohu District,
Shenzhen, 518001, Guangdong,
China
Tel.: (86) 85221274570   Ky
Year Founded: 2016
Emp.: 373
Holding Company
N.A.I.C.S.: 551112
Houde Li (Founder & Chm)

BUILDINGIQ, INC.
Suite 1102 46 Market Street, Sydney,
2000, NSW, Australia
Tel.: (61) 2 9360 0602
Web Site: http://www.buildingiq.com
Rev.: $5,480,519
Assets: $9,038,248
Liabilities: $5,088,510
Net Worth: $3,949,738
Earnings: ($8,050,990)
Fiscal Year-end: 12/31/19
Computer System Design Services
N.A.I.C.S.: 541512
Steve Nguyen (VP-Product & Mktg)

BUIMA GROUP, INC.
7F 2 No 283 Songjiang Rd, Zhong-
shan Dist, Taipei, 104, Taiwan
Tel.: (886) 225080656
Web Site: https://www.buima.com.tw
5543—(TPE)
Rev.: $111,204,233
Assets: $128,296,845
Liabilities: $86,303,818
Net Worth: $41,993,028
Earnings: $669,856
Fiscal Year-end: 12/31/22
Building Metal Product Mfr
N.A.I.C.S.: 332311
Li Wen-Hsuan (CFO)

Subsidiaries:

Buima Energy Inc. (1)
7F-2 No 283 Songjiang Rd, Zhongshan
Dist, Taipei, 10483, Taiwan
Tel.: (886) 225080656
Web Site: https://www.buimaenergy.com
Construction Material Services
N.A.I.C.S.: 811310

BUKA INVESTMENTS LIMITED
23 Saddle Drive Woodmead Office
Park, Woodmead, Sandton, 2191,
South Africa
Tel.: (27) 110869800   ZA
Web Site:
    https://www.imbaliebeauty.co.za
Year Founded: 2003
ILE—(JSE)
Rev.: $10,280
Assets: $185,944
Liabilities: $44,575
Net Worth: $141,369
Earnings: ($204,735)
Fiscal Year-end: 02/28/23
Skincare Product Whslr
N.A.I.C.S.: 424210
Paige Atkins (Sec)

BUKALAPAK.COM PT TBK
Metropolitan Tower Jl R A Kartini Kav
14 RT 10 RW 4 Cilandak Barat, Cilandak, South Jakarta, 12430, Indonesia
Tel.: (62) 2150982008

Web Site:
https://www.about.bukalapak.com
Year Founded: 2011
BUKA—(INDO)
Rev.: $288,221
Assets: $1,696,543
Liabilities: $51,434
Net Worth: $1,645,109
Earnings: ($89,458)
Emp.: 1,477
Fiscal Year-end: 12/31/23
Online Shopping Operator
N.A.I.C.S.: 423690
Rachmat Kaimuddin *(CEO)*

Subsidiaries:

PT Bina Unggul Kencana   (1)
GF 1 Blok C 30 No 7 Lindeteves Trade
Center LTC Jl Hayam Wuruk West, Jakarta,
Indonesia
Tel.: (62) 811 885 8392
Web Site: https://www.binaunggul.com
Hardware Product Retailer
N.A.I.C.S.: 444140

PT Buka Pengadaan Indonesia   (1)
Metropolitan Tower Jl RA Kartini Kav 14
West Cilandak, Jakarta, 12430, Indonesia
Tel.: (62) 2150982008
Web Site: https://www.bukalapak.com
Trading Services
N.A.I.C.S.: 425120

**BUKIT SEMBAWANG ESTATES
LTD**
2 Bukit Merah Central 13-01, Singa-
pore, 159835, Singapore
Tel.: (65) 68900333
Web Site:
https://www.bukitsembawang.sg
Year Founded: 1967
B61—(SES)
Rev.: $416,417,932
Assets: $1,184,618,005
Liabilities: $58,337,162
Net Worth: $1,126,280,844
Earnings: $52,498,703
Emp.: 31
Fiscal Year-end: 03/31/24
Holding Company
N.A.I.C.S.: 551112
Chee Seng Ng *(CEO)*

Subsidiaries:

Bukit Sembawang Rubber Company
Limited   (1)
250 Tanjong Pagar Rd Unit X09-01, St An-
drews Centre, Singapore, 88541, Singapore
Tel.: (65) 68900333
Web Site: http://www.bukitsembawang.sg
Sales Range: $50-74.9 Million
Emp.: 20
Financial & Investments Services
N.A.I.C.S.: 523999
Chee Seng Ng *(Gen Mgr)*

Subsidiary (Domestic):

Singapore United Estates (Private)
Limited   (2)
250 Tanjong Pagar Rd 09-01, St Andrew's
Ctr, Singapore, 088541, Singapore
Tel.: (65) 68900333
Sales Range: $25-49.9 Million
Emp.: 30
Property Development Services
N.A.I.C.S.: 531190

Singapore United Rubber Plantations
Limited   (2)
2 Bukit Merah Central 13-01, Singapore,
159835, Singapore
Tel.: (65) 68900333
Web Site: http://www.bukitsembawang.sg
Sales Range: $25-49.9 Million
Emp.: 32
Financial & Investments Services
N.A.I.C.S.: 523999
Ooi Chee Eng *(CEO)*

Bukit Sembawang View Pte Ltd   (1)
250 Cheng yung Paga Rd 6 09-01 Saint

Andrew Tower, Singapore, 88541, Singa-
pore
Tel.: (65) 68900333
Web Site: http://www.bukitsembawang.sg
Sales Range: $50-74.9 Million
Emp.: 25
Property Development Services
N.A.I.C.S.: 531190
Ng Chee *(Mng Dir)*

**BUKWANG PHARMACEUTI-
CAL CO., LTD.**
7 Sangdo-ro, Dongjak-gu, Seoul,
06955, Korea (South)
Tel.: (82) 28288114
Web Site: https://www.bukwang.co.kr
Year Founded: 1960
003000—(KRS)
Rev.: $146,427,483
Assets: $307,512,688
Liabilities: $99,005,689
Net Worth: $208,506,999
Earnings: ($1,898,213)
Emp.: 623
Fiscal Year-end: 12/31/22
Pharmaceutical Products Mfr & Sales
N.A.I.C.S.: 325412
Jae Young Lee *(CEO)*

Subsidiaries:

Anterogen Co., Ltd   (1)
345-30 Gasan-dong, Geumcheon-gu,
Seoul, 08589, Korea (South)
Tel.: (82) 221040391
Web Site: https://www.anterogen.com
Rev.: $5,055,305
Assets: $95,209,791
Liabilities: $13,300,799
Net Worth: $81,908,992
Earnings: ($5,244,054)
Emp.: 43
Fiscal Year-end: 12/31/2022
Drug Mfr & Distr
N.A.I.C.S.: 325411
Lee TaeHee *(Sr Mng Dir)*

Bukwang Medical Inc.   (1)
104 Bongam-ri, Eunhyeon-myeon, Yangju,
Gyeonggi, Korea (South)
Tel.: (82) 31 865 9334
Web Site: https://bkmedical.en.ec21.com
Medical Appliance Mfr
N.A.I.C.S.: 339112

**BULDAN TEKSTIL TIC. SAN.
LTD. STI.**
Yeni Yalova Yolu 12 km Alasar Mevkii
Ada Sok No 2, Bursa, Turkiye
Tel.: (90) 2242671018   TR
Real Estate Development Services
N.A.I.C.S.: 531390

**BULGAR CZECH INVEST
HOLDING AD**
Ul Belgrad 2 et 2, Plovdiv, 4000, Bul-
garia
Tel.: (359) 30162379
6B6—(BUL)
Sales Range: Less than $1 Million
Holding Company
N.A.I.C.S.: 551112

**BULGARIA HOLDING CO AD-
SOFIA**
25 Nezabravka Street, Sofia, 1113,
Bulgaria
Tel.: (359) 29712391
Holding Company
N.A.I.C.S.: 551112
Pirin Vasilev Atanassov *(Chm-Mgmt
Bd)*

**BULGARIAN AMERICAN
CREDIT BANK AD**
2 Slavyanska Str, Sofia, Bulgaria
Tel.: (359) 29658358
Web Site: https://www.bacb.bg
BACB—(BUL)
Rev.: $31,025,254
Assets: $1,466,276,711

Liabilities: $1,316,808,763
Net Worth: $149,467,947
Earnings: $23,255,990
Emp.: 357
Fiscal Year-end: 12/31/22
Financial & Insurance Services
N.A.I.C.S.: 522320
Vasil Stefanov Simov *(Chm-Mgmt Bd
& Exec Dir)*

**BULGARIAN INVESTMENT
GROUP REIT**
Tel.: (359) 8687196
Web Site: https://big-adsic.com
Year Founded: 2006
BGIG—(BUL)
Sales Range: Less than $1 Million
Real Estate Investment Services
N.A.I.C.S.: 531210

**BULGARIAN INVESTMENT
HOLDING**
4A Saborna Str fl 1 office 1, 1000,
Sofia, Bulgaria
Tel.: (359) 876874449   BG
Web Site: http://www.bulgartabac.bg
Year Founded: 1996
57B—(BUL)
Sales Range: $25-49.9 Million
Emp.: 2,109
Holding Company; Tobacco Products
Mfr & Retailer
N.A.I.C.S.: 551112
Ventzislav Zlatkov Cholakov *(Chm)*

Subsidiaries:

Blagoevgrad-BT AD   (1)
ul Pokrovnishko Shosse 1, 2700, Blago-
evgrad, Bulgaria
Tel.: (359) 73884826
Web Site: http://www.blagoevgrad-bt.com
Sales Range: $150-199.9 Million
Tobacco Product Mfr
N.A.I.C.S.: 312230

Bulgartabac-Trading AD   (1)
62 Graf Ignatiev St, 1000, Sofia, Bulgaria
Tel.: (359) 29306847
Tobacco Product Mfr
N.A.I.C.S.: 312230

Pleven-BT AD   (1)
Selo Yasen Plains vlg, Pleven, 5850, Bul-
garia
Tel.: (359) 64903258
Web Site: http://www.pleven-bt.com
Tobacco Processing Services
N.A.I.C.S.: 312230

Sofia-BT A.D.   (1)
Bul Tzar Boris III 134, Sofia, 1618, Bulgaria
Tel.: (359) 28189350
Web Site: http://www.bulgartabac.com
Emp.: 430
Cigarette Mfr
N.A.I.C.S.: 312230
Vladimir Gechev Zhekov *(Exec Dir)*

Yambol-Tabac A.D.   (1)
7 Yambolen St, 8600, Yambol, Yambol,
Bulgaria
Tel.: (359) 46 661782
Tobacco Product Mfr
N.A.I.C.S.: 312230

BULGARIAN NATIONAL BANK
1 Knyaz Alexander I Sq, 1000, Sofia,
Bulgaria
Tel.: (359) 291459
Web Site: http://www.bnb.bg
Year Founded: 1879
Sales Range: $350-399.9 Million
Emp.: 932
Banking Services
N.A.I.C.S.: 522110
Petko Krastev *(Sec)*

Subsidiaries:

Bulgarian Mint EAD   (1)
5006 Street, Gara Iskar, 1528, Sofia, Bulgaria

Tel.: (359) 2 8071867
Web Site: http://www.mint.bg
Coin, Medal, Badges & Insignia Mfr
N.A.I.C.S.: 339910

**BULGARIAN REAL ESTATE
FUND**
111 R Tsarigradsko shose Blvd floor
16, 1113, Sofia, Bulgaria
Tel.: (359) 29809309
Web Site: https://www.brefbg.com
BREF—(BUL)
Rev.: $12,751,959
Assets: $93,791,809
Liabilities: $18,872,944
Net Worth: $74,918,865
Earnings: $9,307,871
Emp.: 1
Fiscal Year-end: 12/31/23
Real Estate Investment Trust Ser-
vices
N.A.I.C.S.: 531190
Alexandar Georgiev *(Dir-IR)*

**BULGARIAN RIVER SHIPPING
J.S.CO.**
Otetz Paisii sq No 2, 7000, Ruse,
Bulgaria
Tel.: (359) 82833777
Web Site: https://www.brp.bg
BRP—(BUL)
Sales Range: Less than $1 Million
Transportation Services
N.A.I.C.S.: 488999

BULGARIAN ROSE PLC
Industrial zone 1, Karlovo, 4300, Plo-
vdiv, Bulgaria
Tel.: (359) 33593320
Web Site: https://bulgarianrose.bg
Year Founded: 1948
ROZA—(BUL)
Sales Range: Less than $1 Million
Essential Oil Mfr
N.A.I.C.S.: 325998

**BULGARIAN STOCK EX-
CHANGE - SOFIA AD**
6 Tri ushi St, 1000, Sofia, Bulgaria
Tel.: (359) 29370934
Web Site: https://www.bse-sofia.bg
Year Founded: 1997
BSE—(BUL)
Rev.: $9,701,468
Assets: $201,419,808
Liabilities: $183,670,575
Net Worth: $17,749,233
Earnings: $6,858,567
Emp.: 58
Fiscal Year-end: 12/31/23
Security Exchange
N.A.I.C.S.: 523210
Asen Yagodin *(Chm)*

Subsidiaries:

Balkan Services Ltd.   (1)
31 Ekzarh Yosif Str, 1000, Sofia, Bulgaria
Tel.: (359) 29809599
Web Site: http://www.balkanservices.com
Information Technology Consulting Services
N.A.I.C.S.: 541512
Slavi Slavov *(Partner & Head-NetSuite ERP
Dept)*

BULGARSKA ZAHAR AD
Ul Zavodska 1, Dolna Mitropolia,
5855, Pleven, Bulgaria
Tel.: (359) 64826125
BZAH—(BUL)
Sales Range: Less than $1 Million
Sugar Products Mfr
N.A.I.C.S.: 311314

**BULGARSKI TRANSPORTEN
HOLDING AD**
82 Hristo Botev Blvd, 4000, Plovdiv,
Bulgaria

Bulgarski Transporten Holding AD—(Continued)

Tel.: (359) 32626082
Web Site: https://www.bthold.com
Year Founded: 1996
BTRH—(BUL)
Sales Range: Less than $1 Million
Holding Company
N.A.I.C.S.: 551112
Svetla Koicheva Russeva (Chm-Mgmt Bd)

BULIGO CAPITAL ORD SHS
Moshe Aviv Tower 34th Floor 7 Jabotinsky Street, Ramat Gan, 5252269, Israel
Tel.: (972) 35755406
Web Site:
https://www.buligocapital.com
BLGO—(TAE)
Rev.: $20,952,000
Assets: $69,578,000
Liabilities: $3,603,000
Net Worth: $65,975,000
Earnings: $4,509,000
Fiscal Year-end: 06/30/23
Real Estate Services
N.A.I.C.S.: 531210
Itay Goren (Co-Founder & CEO)

BULL GROUP CO., LTD.
No 32 Sanhai Road, East District
Guanhaiwei Town Industrial Park, Cixi, Zhejiang, China
Tel.: (86) 4008832388
Web Site: https://www.gongniu.cn
Year Founded: 2008
603195—(SHG)
Rev.: $2,203,543,686
Assets: $2,774,613,680
Liabilities: $744,371,906
Net Worth: $2,030,241,775
Earnings: $543,367,010
Emp.: 1,000
Fiscal Year-end: 12/31/23
Electronic Product Mfr & Distr
N.A.I.C.S.: 334419
Liping Ruan (Chm & Gen Mgr)

BULL TRADING AND INVEST-MENTS LTD.
The 5th Hebrew Battalion, Sapir, Ashdod, 5252247, Israel
Tel.: (972) 35444566
Web Site: https://www.bull-trade.co.il
BULL—(TAE)
Rev.: $14,514,126
Assets: $106,707,066
Liabilities: $83,216,474
Net Worth: $23,490,592
Earnings: $4,610,108
Fiscal Year-end: 12/31/22
Investment Management Service
N.A.I.C.S.: 523999

BULL WILL CO., LTD.
3F No 199 Ruihu St, Neihu Dist, Taipei, 114, Taiwan
Tel.: (886) 287927788
Web Site: https://www.bullwill.com.tw
Year Founded: 1994
6259—(TPE)
Rev.: $18,901,510
Assets: $14,670,763
Liabilities: $4,587,312
Net Worth: $10,083,451
Earnings: $738,205
Emp.: 22
Fiscal Year-end: 12/31/22
Electronic Components Distr
N.A.I.C.S.: 423690
Jimmy Chang (Chm)

BULL-DOG SAUCE CO., LTD.
11-5 Kabuto-cho Nihombashi, Chuo-ku, Tokyo, 103-0026, Japan
Tel.: (81) 336686811

Web Site: http://www.bulldog.co.jp
Year Founded: 1926
2804—(TKS)
Rev.: $95,726,020
Assets: $223,067,670
Liabilities: $81,217,070
Net Worth: $141,850,600
Earnings: $958,450
Emp.: 211
Fiscal Year-end: 03/31/24
Sauce Products Mfr
N.A.I.C.S.: 311941
Yukitoshi Ishigaki (Pres & CEO)

BULLAND INVESTMENTS REIT
Christopher Columbus Blvd No 43, 1592, Sofia, Bulgaria
Tel.: (359) 29651444
Web Site: https://www.bulland.bg
Year Founded: 2005
LAND—(BUL)
Sales Range: Less than $1 Million
Real Estate Investment Services
N.A.I.C.S.: 531390
Danko Idakiev (CEO)

BULLER ELECTRICITY LTD.
24 Robertson Street, Westport, 7825, New Zealand
Tel.: (64) 3 788 8171   NZ
Web Site:
http://www.bullerelectricity.co.nz
Year Founded: 1993
Rev.: $7,804,248
Assets: $38,855,090
Liabilities: $7,729,213
Net Worth: $31,125,877
Earnings: $2,868,726
Emp.: 50
Fiscal Year-end: 03/31/19
Electricity Distribution Services
N.A.I.C.S.: 221122
Eamon J. Ginley (CEO)

Subsidiaries:

Pulse Energy Limited   (1)
Level 1 201 Hobson Street, Auckland, 1010, New Zealand   (56%)
Tel.: (64) 9 378 9981
Web Site: http://www.pulseenergy.co.nz
Sales Range: $50-74.9 Million
Electricity Retailer & Measuring Equipment Mfr
N.A.I.C.S.: 221122
Gary Holden (CEO)

BULLET EXPLORATION INC.
705 - 1030 West Georgia Street, PO Box 11110, STN Royal Center, Vancouver, V6E 2Y3, BC, Canada
Tel.: (778) 358-6172
Web Site:
https://bulletexploration.com
Year Founded: 2013
AMMO—(TSXV)
Rev.: $361
Assets: $990,538
Liabilities: $40,226
Net Worth: $950,313
Earnings: ($82,011)
Fiscal Year-end: 12/31/23
Real Estate Services
N.A.I.C.S.: 531311

BULLETIN RESOURCES LIM-ITED
Suite 11 139 Newcastle Street, Perth, 6000, WA, Australia
Tel.: (61) 892303585
Web Site:
https://www.bulletinresources.com
Year Founded: 2010
BNR—(ASX)
Rev.: $324,130
Assets: $8,336,099
Liabilities: $350,570

Net Worth: $7,985,529
Earnings: ($432,161)
Emp.: 2
Fiscal Year-end: 06/30/24
Gold Mining Services
N.A.I.C.S.: 212220
Paul Poli (Chm)

BULLION GOLD RESOURCES CORP.
410 rue Saint-Nicolas suite 236, Montreal, H2Y 2P5, QC, Canada
Tel.: (514) 317-7956
Web Site: https://www.bulliongold.ca
Year Founded: 2005
TTEXF—(OTCIQ)
Assets: $1,386,815
Liabilities: $39,183
Net Worth: $1,347,632
Earnings: ($139,714)
Fiscal Year-end: 12/31/23
Mineral Exploration Services
N.A.I.C.S.: 213114
Jonathan Hamel (Pres, CEO & Interim CFO)

BULLMAN MINERALS INC.
Suite 303 595 Howe Street, Vancouver, V6C 2T5, BC, Canada
Tel.: (604) 336-8618
Web Site:
http://www.bullmanminerals.com
Year Founded: 2010
Assets: $14,139,689
Liabilities: $3,260,793
Net Worth: $10,878,896
Earnings: ($837,400)
Fiscal Year-end: 11/30/17
Financial Management Services
N.A.I.C.S.: 523999
Andre C. Lambert (Mgr-Exploration)

BULPROS CONSULTING AD
Business Park Sofia Bldg 15 5th Floor, Sofia, 1766, Bulgaria
Tel.: (359) 2 489 5725   BG
Web Site: http://www.bulpros.com
Year Founded: 2010
Information Technology & Business Process Outsourcing Services
N.A.I.C.S.: 541690
Ivaylo Slavov (CEO)

Subsidiaries:

GBS Europa GmbH   (1)
An der RaumFabrik 33c, 76227, Karlsruhe, Germany
Tel.: (49) 721 4901 0
Web Site: http://www.gbs.com
Messaging Security & Workflow Management Solutions
N.A.I.C.S.: 541511
Ivaylo Slavov (Mng Dir)

Subsidiary (Non-US):

GBS Solutions NA LLC   (2)
4789 Yonge Street Suite 1116, Toronto, M2N 0G3, ON, Canada
Communication Service
N.A.I.C.S.: 517810
Philip Neelamegam (Country Mgr)

BULTEN AB
August Barks Gata 6A, Gothenburg, Sweden
Tel.: (46) 317345900
Web Site: http://www.bulten.com
BULTEN—(OMX)
Rev.: $390,045,600
Assets: $374,907,680
Liabilities: $191,421,440
Net Worth: $183,486,240
Earnings: $6,714,400
Emp.: 1,425
Fiscal Year-end: 12/31/20
Holding Company; Metal Fastener & Structure Mfr

N.A.I.C.S.: 551112
Kamilla Oresvard (Sr VP-Corp Comm)

Subsidiaries:

Bulten Fasteners (Tianjin) Co., Ltd.   (1)
Building P1 No 4 Shengda 2nd Branch Hoad, Xiqing Economic-Technological Development Zone, Tianjin, 300383, China
Tel.: (86) 2258105868
Fastener Equipment Mfr & Distr
N.A.I.C.S.: 332722
Edith Wang (Mng Dir)

Bulten Fasteners AB   (1)
August Barks gata 6A, PO Box 9148, 400 93, Gothenburg, Sweden
Tel.: (46) 317345900
Web Site: https://www.bulten.com
Metal Fastener Mfr
N.A.I.C.S.: 332722

Bulten GmbH   (1)
Industriestrasse 20, 59192, Bergkamen, Germany
Tel.: (49) 23899292000
Fastener Equipment Mfr & Distr
N.A.I.C.S.: 332722
Jurgen Niklas (Plant Mgr)

Bulten Hallstahammar AB   (1)
Industrigatan, 734 30, Hallstahammar, Sweden
Tel.: (46) 22021300
Fastener Equipment Mfr & Distr
N.A.I.C.S.: 332722
Juha Kauppinen (Plant Mgr)

Bulten Ltd.   (1)
Unit 25 Bloom Lane Normanby Enterprise Park, Scunthorpe, DN15 9AJ, United Kingdom
Tel.: (44) 1724852666
Fastener Equipment Mfr & Distr
N.A.I.C.S.: 332722
Lianne Brown (Sls Dir & Mng Dir)

Bulten North America LLC   (1)
10069 Wellman Rd, Streetsboro, OH 44241
Tel.: (234) 602-1258
Fastener Equipment Mfr & Distr
N.A.I.C.S.: 332722
Karen Hannum (Sls Dir & Mng Dir)

Bulten Polska S.A.   (1)
Bukietowa 60, 43-302, Bielsko-Biala, Poland
Tel.: (48) 334983600
Fastener Equipment Mfr & Distr
N.A.I.C.S.: 332722

Bulten Sweden AB   (1)
Terminalvagen 12 ARW, Box 8708, 402 75, Gothenburg, Sweden
Tel.: (46) 317644900
Fastener Equipment Mfr & Distr
N.A.I.C.S.: 332722

PSM Celada Fasteners S.R.L.   (1)
Via Porpora 24, 20131, Milan, Italy
Tel.: (39) 0229400630
Web Site: https://www.psmcelada.it
Fastener Distr
N.A.I.C.S.: 423710

PSM Fasteners (Hong Kong) Ltd.   (1)
Room 1601 16/F Chow Tai Fook Centre No 580 A-F Nathan Road, Mong Kok, Kowloon, China (Hong Kong)
Tel.: (852) 26525051
Automotive Parts Mfr & Distr
N.A.I.C.S.: 336390

PSM Fasteners AB   (1)
Datavagen 8A, 175 43, Jarfalla, Sweden
Tel.: (46) 8282815
Web Site: https://en.psmfasteners.se
Fastener Mfr
N.A.I.C.S.: 332722

PSM International Holdings Ltd.   (1)
Ferry Lane Pembroke Dock, Pembrokeshire, Pembroke, SA71 4RE, United Kingdom
Tel.: (44) 1646683501
Web Site: https://www.psminternational.com
Fastener Mfr & Distr
N.A.I.C.S.: 332722

PSM International Ltd. (1)
Ferry Lane, Pembroke Dock, Pembroke,
SA71 4RE, Pembrokeshire, United Kingdom
Tel.: (44) 164 668 3501
Web Site: https://www.psminternational.com
Industrial Fastener Systems, Spring Steel &
Plastic Fasteners, Wire Thread Inserts &
Automated Assembly Equipment
N.A.I.C.S.: 332722
Ian Atkinson (Mng Dir)

Subsidiary (Domestic):

**PSM International Fasteners
Limited** (2)
Ferry Lane, Pembroke, SA71 4RE, Pem-
brokeshire, United Kingdom
Tel.: (44) 1646683501
Web Site: https://www.psminternational.com
Aerospace & Commercial Fasteners &
Components
N.A.I.C.S.: 332999
Fernando Palmero (Mng Dir)

Subsidiary (US):

PSM Fastener Corporation (3)
10069 Wellman Rd, Streetsboro, OH 44241
Tel.: (234) 602-1258
Web Site: http://www.psminternational.com
Fasteners, Components & Fastening Sys-
tems Whslr
N.A.I.C.S.: 423510

Ram-Bul LLC (1)
5445 Hudson Industrial Pkwy, Hudson, OH
44236
Tel.: (330) 653-5135
Web Site: https://ram-bul.com
Emp.: 1,300
Automotive Parts Mfr & Distr
N.A.I.C.S.: 336390

BULVESTA HOLDING AD
Vitosha HPP Simeonovo 999, 1700,
Sofia, Bulgaria
Tel.: (359) 29628768
Web Site: http://www.bulvesta-
bg.com
BVH—(BUL)
Sales Range: Less than $1 Million
Investment Management Service
N.A.I.C.S.: 523940

**BUM BETON- UND MONIER-
BAU GMBH**
An der Vestischen 2, 45701, Herten,
Germany
Tel.: (49) 2366501990 De
Web Site: http://www.bumherne.de
Sales Range: $50-74.9 Million
Emp.: 100
Civil Engineering & Concrete Struc-
ture Repair Services
N.A.I.C.S.: 238110

BUMECH SA
ul Krakowska 191, 40-389, Katowice,
Poland
Tel.: (48) 327893850
Web Site: http://www.bumech.pl
BMC—(WAR)
Rev.: $169,576,219
Assets: $300,219,257
Liabilities: $113,221,544
Net Worth: $186,997,713
Earnings: ($6,576,219)
Fiscal Year-end: 12/31/23
Mining Machinery & Equipment Mfr
N.A.I.C.S.: 333131
Marcin Sutkowski (Chm)

**BUMHAN INDUSTRIES CO.,
LTD.**
62 Freetrade 4-gil, Masanhoewon-gu,
Changwon-si, Gyeongsangnam-do,
Korea (South)
Tel.: (82) 055 224 050
Web Site: https://bumhan.com
Emp.: 100
Air Compressor Mfr
N.A.I.C.S.: 333912

BUMI ARMADA BERHAD
Level 21 Menara Perak 24 Jalan
Perak, 50450, Kuala Lumpur, Malay-
sia
Tel.: (60) 323029000
Web Site:
https://www.bumiarmada.com
Year Founded: 1995
5210—(KLS)
Rev.: $464,320,639
Assets: $2,419,702,236
Liabilities: $1,205,156,952
Net Worth: $1,214,545,284
Earnings: $63,786,896
Emp.: 788
Fiscal Year-end: 12/31/23
Marine Transportation Services
N.A.I.C.S.: 483111
Tunku Ali Redhauddin Tuanku Muhriz
(Chm)

Subsidiaries:

Armada Marine Contractors Caspian
Pte. Ltd. (1)
Office 902 174 Hero of Turkmenistan Ata-
murad Niyazov street, Business Center of
Entrepreneur's Union, Ashgabat, 744013,
Turkmenistan
Tel.: (993) 12210172
Marine Transportation Services
N.A.I.C.S.: 488390

Bumi Armada (Singapore) Pte.
Ltd. (1)
1 Fusionopolis Walk 11-02 Solaris South
Tower, Singapore, 138628, Singapore
Tel.: (65) 66435060
Marine Transportation Services
N.A.I.C.S.: 488390

Bumi Armada Caspian LLC (1)
Kirova Street 1 3rd Floor, 414000, Astra-
khan, Russia
Tel.: (7) 8512292901
Marine Transportation Services
N.A.I.C.S.: 488390

Bumi Armada Engineering Sdn
Bhd (1)
Level 21 Menara Perak 24 Jalan Perak,
50450, Kuala Lumpur, Malaysia
Tel.: (60) 3 21715799
Web Site: http://www.bumiarmada.com
Offshore Engineering Services
N.A.I.C.S.: 541330

Bumi Armada Navigation Sdn.
Bhd. (1)
Lot 13840 Jalan Penghiburan Chukai,
24000, Kemaman, Terengganu, Malaysia
Tel.: (60) 98510100
Marine Transportation Services
N.A.I.C.S.: 488390

Subsidiary (Domestic):

Bumi Armada Navigation Labuan
Limited (2)
Block C No A11 Lot 1211 Manmohans
Warehouse Jalan Patau-Patau Wilayah, PO
Box 80226, Persekutuan, 87012, Labuan,
Malaysia
Tel.: (60) 87412327
Marine Transportation Services
N.A.I.C.S.: 488390

Bumi Armada UK Limited (1)
Level 4 Annan House 33-35 Palmerston
Road, Aberdeen, AB11 5QP, United King-
dom
Tel.: (44) 1224281600
Marine Transportation Services
N.A.I.C.S.: 488390

BUMITAMA AGRI LTD.
10 Anson Road 11-19 International
Plaza, Singapore, 079903, Singapore
Tel.: (65) 62221332
Web Site: https://www.bumitama-
agri.com
P8Z—(SES)
Rev.: $1,002,861,471
Assets: $1,248,974,980
Liabilities: $246,478,861

Net Worth: $1,002,496,119
Earnings: $190,350,050
Emp.: 32,831
Fiscal Year-end: 12/31/23
Crude Palm Oil & Palm Kernel Pro-
duction
N.A.I.C.S.: 111120
Gunawan Hariyanto Lim (Chm &
CEO)

**BUMRUNGRAD HOSPITAL
PUBLIC COMPANY LIMITED**
33 Sukhumvit Soi 3 Nana Nua
Sukhumvit Road, Khlong Toei Nua
Vadhana, Bangkok, 10110, Thailand
Tel.: (66) 20668888
Web Site:
https://www.bumrungrad.com
BH—(THA)
Rev.: $746,583,922
Assets: $852,758,900
Liabilities: $149,296,980
Net Worth: $703,461,920
Earnings: $205,953,192
Emp.: 4,194
Fiscal Year-end: 12/31/23
Hospital Services
N.A.I.C.S.: 622110
Chanvit Tanphiphat (Vice Chm)

Subsidiaries:

Asia Global Health Ltd. (1)
9th Floor Chinachem Hollywood Centre
1-13 Hollywood Road, Central, China (Hong
Kong)
Tel.: (852) 2526 0505
Web Site: http://www.globalhealthasia.com
Medical Insurance Services
N.A.I.C.S.: 524114

Asia Global Research Co., Ltd. (1)
5th floor Ploenchit Center 2 Sukhumvit Rd,
Klontoey, Bangkok, 10110, Thailand
Tel.: (66) 2667 1700
Web Site:
http://www.asiaglobalresearch.com
Clinical Research Services
N.A.I.C.S.: 541715
Jina Katchmart (Dir-Sls & Mktg)

Bumrungrad Health Network Co.,
Ltd. (1)
33 Sukhumvit Soi 3 Sukhumvit Road, Kh-
long Toei Nua Vadhana, Bangkok, 10110,
Thailand
Tel.: (66) 20668888
Holding Company
N.A.I.C.S.: 551112

Subsidiary (Non-US):

Bumrungrad Myanmar Co., Ltd. (2)
No 46/B GF-A Pantra Street, Dagon Town-
ship, Yangon, Myanmar
Tel.: (95) 9782302424
Medical Diagnostic Services
N.A.I.C.S.: 621512

Bumrungrad Medical Center Ltd.
(BMC) (1)
33 Sukhumvit 3 Soi Nana Nua, Klongtoey
Nua, Bangkok, 10110, Thailand (100%)
Tel.: (66) 26671000
Web Site: http://www.bumrungrad.com
Sales Range: $450-499.9 Million
Emp.: 4,000
Gen Medical & Surgical Hospitals
N.A.I.C.S.: 622110
Curtis Schroeder (CEO)

Health Horizons Enterprises Pte.
Ltd. (1)
8 Marina Boulevard 05-02 Marina Bay Fi-
nancial Centre, Singapore, 018981, Singa-
pore
Tel.: (65) 63381888
Holding Company
N.A.I.C.S.: 551112

Subsidiary (Non-US):

Bumrungrad Mongolia LLC (2)
Choidog-5 Peace Avenue 1st Khoroo,
Sukhbaatar District, Ulaanbaatar, Mongolia
Tel.: (976) 70129000

Financial Investment Services
N.A.I.C.S.: 523999

Life & Longevity Ltd. (1)
Room 337 3rd Fl South China C S Building
13-17 Wah Sing Street, Kwai Chung New
Territories, Tsuen Wan, China (Hong Kong)
Tel.: (852) 8818226
Financial Investment Services
N.A.I.C.S.: 523999

Ruenmongkol Co., Ltd. (1)
11/26 Sukhumvit Soi 1 Sukhumvit Road,
Khlong Toei Nua Vadhana, Bangkok, 10110,
Thailand
Tel.: (66) 20668888
Real Estate Services
N.A.I.C.S.: 531390

Vitallife Corporation Ltd. (1)
210 Sukhumvit Soi 1, Wattana, Bangkok,
Thailand
Tel.: (66) 2 6671270
Health Care Srvices
N.A.I.C.S.: 621999

**BUMYANG CONSTRUCTION
CO., LTD.**
114 Choryangjung-ro, Dong-gu, Bu-
san, Chungcheongnam-do, Korea
(South)
Tel.: (82) 415735631
Web Site: http://www.iby.co.kr
Year Founded: 1958
002410—(KRS)
Rev.: $91,848,878
Assets: $169,222,129
Liabilities: $110,472,822
Net Worth: $58,749,307
Earnings: ($7,334,627)
Emp.: 141
Fiscal Year-end: 12/31/22
Civil Construction Engineering Ser-
vices
N.A.I.C.S.: 541330
Hae-Ju Hwang (Dir)

**BUND CENTER INVESTMENT
LTD.**
Clarendon House 2 Church Street,
Hamilton, HM 11, Bermuda
Tel.: (441) 2955950 BM
Web Site:
https://www.bundcenter.com
Year Founded: 2009
BTE—(SES)
Rev.: $63,537,832
Assets: $310,177,232
Liabilities: $26,161,478
Net Worth: $284,015,754
Earnings: $8,707,112
Emp.: 454
Fiscal Year-end: 12/31/23
Investment Holding Company
N.A.I.C.S.: 551114
Frankle Widjaja (Chm & CEO)

BUNDESDRUCKEREI GMBH
Kommandantenstrasse 18, 10969,
Berlin, Germany
Tel.: (49) 3025980
Web Site:
http://www.bundesdruckerei.de
Year Founded: 1763
Secure Identification System Mfr
N.A.I.C.S.: 541512
Christian Helfrich (CFO)

Subsidiaries:

D-TRUST GmbH (1)
Kommandantenstrasse 15, 10969, Berlin,
Germany
Tel.: (49) 30 2593910
Electrical Equipment Distr
N.A.I.C.S.: 423610

Maurer Electronics GmbH (1)
Otto Maurer Dieterskircher Str 22, 88524,
Uttenweiler, Germany
Tel.: (49) 7374 92 180 0
Web Site: http://www.maurer-electronic.com

Bundesdruckerei GmbH—(Continued)

Electronic Components Mfr
N.A.I.C.S.: 334419
Otto Maurer (Mng Dir)

Veridos GmbH (1)
Oranienstrasse 91, 10969, Berlin,
Germany (40%)
Tel.: (49) 30 25899840
Web Site: http://www.veridos.com
Identity Products & Services
N.A.I.C.S.: 323111
Marc-Julian Siewert (CEO)

Subsidiary (US):

E-Seek, Inc. (2)
9471 Ridgehaven Ct Ste E, San Diego, CA
92123
Tel.: (858) 495-1900
Web Site: http://www.e-seek.com
Computer Peripheral Equipment Mfr
N.A.I.C.S.: 334118

iNCO Spolka z o.o. (1)
Wawrow 90, 66-403, Gorzow Wielkopolski,
Poland
Tel.: (48) 95 731 73 40
Web Site: http://www.incoscan.com
Electrical Equipment Distr
N.A.I.C.S.: 423610

BUNKA SHUTTER CO., LTD.
1-17-3 Nishikata, Bunkyo-ku, Tokyo,
113-8535, Japan
Tel.: (81) 358447111
Web Site: https://www.bunka-s.co.jp
Year Founded: 1955
5930—(TKS)
Rev.: $1,461,312,360
Assets: $1,367,470,190
Liabilities: $680,532,550
Net Worth: $686,937,640
Earnings: $69,947,020
Emp.: 5,290
Fiscal Year-end: 03/31/24
Shutters Mfr
N.A.I.C.S.: 332321
Toshihiko Shiozaki (Chm)

Subsidiaries:

Aiwa Insurance Service Co., Ltd. (1)
4-14-5 Nishisugamo, Toshima-ku, Tokyo,
170-0001, Japan
Tel.: (81) 368992031
Casualty Insurance Services
N.A.I.C.S.: 524126

Arco (Qld) Pty Ltd (1)
Building 9/84 Christensen Road South,
Stapylton, Southport, 4207, QLD, Australia
Tel.: (61) 738075364
Web Site: https://www.arcoqld.com.au
Construction Services
N.A.I.C.S.: 236220
Malou Luna (Officer-Procurement)

**BX Aiwa Insurance Service Co.,
Ltd.** (1)
4-14-5 Nishisugamo, Toshima-ku, Tokyo,
170-0001, Japan
Tel.: (81) 368992031
Construction Services
N.A.I.C.S.: 236220

BX Asahi Kenzai Co., Ltd. (1)
230-1 Enowaki Sadamithu Tsurugi-cho,
Mima-gun, Tokushima, 779-4103, Japan
Tel.: (81) 883551081
Construction Services
N.A.I.C.S.: 236220

BX BUNKA VIETNAM Co., Ltd. (1)
Lo C-9 KCN Thang Long II, Lieu Xa, Yen
My, Hung Yen, Vietnam
Tel.: (84) 2213974580
Web Site: https://www.bunka.vn
Emp.: 164
Doors Mfr & Whslr
N.A.I.C.S.: 332321

BX Bunka Australia Pty Ltd (1)
51 Perivale Street, Darra, 4076, QLD, Australia
Tel.: (61) 737176666
Construction Services

N.A.I.C.S.: 236220

BX Bunka Kougei Co., Ltd. (1)
753 Aza Nishihara Hiratsuka, Ageo, 362-0011, Saitama, Japan
Tel.: (81) 487794711
Construction Services
N.A.I.C.S.: 236220

BX Bunka Panel Co., Ltd. (1)
5-16-8 Minami, Suita, 564-0043, Osaka,
Japan
Tel.: (81) 663396115
Construction Services
N.A.I.C.S.: 236220

BX Kaneshin Co., Ltd. (1)
4-19-12 Okudo, Katsushika-ku, Tokyo, 124-0022, Japan
Tel.: (81) 336966781
Web Site: https://www.kaneshin.co.jp
Emp.: 115
Construction Services
N.A.I.C.S.: 236220

BX Kensei Co., Ltd. (1)
3726 Ooaza Noharu, Yamaga-machi, Kitsuki, 879-1307, Oita, Japan
Tel.: (81) 977750555
Construction Services
N.A.I.C.S.: 236220

BX Koun Co., Ltd. (1)
37-2 Shimobutai Aza, Inuyama, 484-0953,
Aichi, Japan
Tel.: (81) 568670661
Web Site: http://www.bunka-s.co.jp
Household Furniture Retailer
N.A.I.C.S.: 449110

**BX Nishiyama Tetsumou Co.,
Ltd.** (1)
4-57-21 Horikiri, Katsushika-ku, Tokyo, 124-0006, Japan
Tel.: (81) 336030111
Construction Services
N.A.I.C.S.: 236220

**BX Okinawa Bunka Shutter Co.,
Ltd.** (1)
667 Aza Nesabu, Tomigusuku, 901-0205,
Japan
Tel.: (81) 988506116
Building Material Mfr & Distr
N.A.I.C.S.: 327120

BX Rootes Co., Ltd. (1)
4-50-1 Minamishinmatsi, Matsubara, 580-0023, Osaka, Japan
Tel.: (81) 723328821
Construction Services
N.A.I.C.S.: 236220

BX Shinsei Seiki Co., Ltd. (1)
687 Kamodani-cho, Kasai, 675-2444, Japan
Tel.: (81) 790442671
Web Site: https://bxshinsei
Motor Parts Mfr & Distr
N.A.I.C.S.: 336320

BX TR Co., Ltd. (1)
753 Aza Nishihara Hiratsuka, Ageo, 362-0011, Saitama, Japan
Tel.: (81) 487713710
Construction Services
N.A.I.C.S.: 236220

BX Tetsuya Co., Ltd. (1)
380 Toyofuta, Kashiwa, 277-0872, Chiba,
Japan
Tel.: (81) 471339111
Construction Services
N.A.I.C.S.: 236220

BX Tohoku Tetsuya Co., Ltd. (1)
16 Hirose Tashiro, Tsuruoka, 997-0302,
Yamagata, Japan
Tel.: (81) 235574592
Construction Services
N.A.I.C.S.: 236220

BX Tosho Co., Ltd. (1)
30-20-8 Shinyokohama, Kouhoku-ku, Yokohama, 222-0033, Kanagawa, Japan
Tel.: (81) 455347500
Construction Services
N.A.I.C.S.: 236220

BX Yutori Form Co., Ltd. (1)
BX113 Building 4F 4-14-5 Nishisugamo,
Toshima-ku, Tokyo, 170-0001, Japan

Tel.: (81) 359077331
Web Site: https://www.yutoriform.co.jp
Renovation Design Services
N.A.I.C.S.: 236118

Bunka Kougei Co., Ltd. (1)
753 Aza Nishihara Hiratsuka, Ageo, 362-0011, Saitama, Japan
Tel.: (81) 487794711
Web Site: http://www.b-Kougei.com
Household Furniture Retailer
N.A.I.C.S.: 423210

Bunka Panel Kogyo Co., Ltd. (1)
5-16-8 Minami Suita, Suita, 564-0043,
Osaka, Japan
Tel.: (81) 663396115
Shutters Mfr
N.A.I.C.S.: 332321

Bunka Shutter Service Co., Ltd. (1)
4-14-5 Nishisugamo, Toshima-ku, Tokyo,
170-0001, Japan
Tel.: (81) 359803160
Construction Services
N.A.I.C.S.: 236220

Ecowood Co. Ltd. (1)
1-12-1 Hibikimatsi, Wakamatsu-ku, Kitakyushu, 808-0021, Fukuoka, Japan
Tel.: (81) 937512424
Construction Services
N.A.I.C.S.: 236220

Eurowindow., JSC (1)
Eurowindow Office Building No 02 Ton That
Tung, Dong Da, Hanoi, Vietnam
Tel.: (84) 2437474700
Web Site: https://www.eurowindow.biz
Construction Services
N.A.I.C.S.: 236220
Hannes Romauch (Gen Dir)

Okinawa Bunka Shutter Co., Ltd (1)
667 Aza Nesabu, Tomigusuku, Okinawa,
901-0205, Japan
Tel.: (81) 988506116
Web Site: http://www.bunka-s.co.jp
Fabricated Metal Mfr & Sales
N.A.I.C.S.: 332999
Hiroo Matsusaka (Pres)

Shinsei Seiki Co., Ltd (1)
687 Kamodani-cho, Kasai, Hyogo, 675-2444, Japan
Tel.: (81) 790441161
Web Site: http://www.shinseiseiki.co.jp
Sales Range: $50-74.9 Million
Emp.: 109
Metal Service Centers & Other Metal Merchant Whslr
N.A.I.C.S.: 423510
Kiyokazu Kokado (Pres)

TR Kenzai Co., Ltd. (1)
753 Aza Nishihara Hiratsuka, Ageo, 362-0011, Saitama, Japan
Tel.: (81) 48 771 3710
Web Site: http://www.bunka-s.co.jp
Home Remodeling Services
N.A.I.C.S.: 236118

Tenpal Co., Ltd. (1)
4-14-5 Nishisugamo, Toshima-ku, Tokyo,
170-0001, Japan
Web Site: http://www.tenpal.co.jp
Sales Range: $25-49.9 Million
Emp.: 100
Canvas & Related Product Mills
N.A.I.C.S.: 314910

Yutori Form Co., Ltd. (1)
4F BX113 Building 4-14-5 Nishisugamo,
Toshima-ku, Tokyo, 170-0001, Japan
Tel.: (81) 359077331
Web Site: https://www.yutoriform.co.jp
Sales Range: $100-124.9 Million
Emp.: 235
Remodeling & Renovation Services
N.A.I.C.S.: 236118

BUNKEIDO CO., LTD.
1-7-1 Enaka, Ekira-cho, Hashima,
501-6297, Gifu, Japan
Tel.: (81) 583981111
Web Site: https://www.bunkei.co.jp
Year Founded: 1900
9471—(NGO)
Rev.: $127,746,960

Assets: $186,765,920
Liabilities: $52,901,200
Net Worth: $133,864,720
Earnings: $7,492,320
Fiscal Year-end: 03/31/22
Educational Material Publishing Services
N.A.I.C.S.: 513130
Kuniteru Mizutani (Chm)

BUNKER HILL MINING CORP.
82 Richmond Street East, Toronto,
M5C 1P1, ON, Canada
Tel.: (416) 477-7771 NV
Web Site:
https://www.bunkerhillmining.com
Year Founded: 2007
BHLL—(OTCQB)
Rev.: $1,107,093
Assets: $61,989,678
Liabilities: $88,356,840
Net Worth: ($26,367,162)
Earnings: ($13,432,539)
Emp.: 20
Fiscal Year-end: 12/31/23
Mining Exploration Company
N.A.I.C.S.: 212220
Gerbrand Van Heerden (CFO)

BUNKYODO GROUP HOLDINGS CO., LTD.
Bunkyodo Mizonokuchi Main Store
5F 3-1-28 Hisamoto, Takatsu-ku, Kawasaki, 213-0011, Kanagawa, Japan
Tel.: (81) 448110118
Web Site:
https://www.bunkyodo.co.jp
Year Founded: 1949
9978—(TKS)
Rev.: $92,833,500
Assets: $62,504,780
Liabilities: $54,356,580
Net Worth: $8,148,200
Earnings: $261,240
Fiscal Year-end: 08/31/24
Holding Company
N.A.I.C.S.: 551111
Fujio Shimazaki (Pres)

BUNNY'S LIMITED
105 A Quaid-e-Azam Industrial Estate
Kot Lakhpat, Lahore, Pakistan
Tel.: (92) 042111442222
Web Site: https://bunnys.com
BNL—(PSX)
Rev.: $20,457,648
Assets: $14,608,152
Liabilities: $7,573,219
Net Worth: $7,034,933
Earnings: $473,087
Emp.: 758
Fiscal Year-end: 06/30/23
Yarn Mfr
N.A.I.C.S.: 313110

BUNZL PLC
York House 45 Seymour St, London,
W1H 7JT, United Kingdom
Tel.: (44) 2077255000 UK
Web Site: https://www.bunzl.com
Year Founded: 1940
BNZL—(LSE)
Rev.: $14,501,577,750
Assets: $10,439,160,600
Liabilities: $7,161,836,550
Net Worth: $3,277,324,050
Earnings: $571,414,800
Fiscal Year-end: 12/31/22
Holding Company; Outsourcing &
Distribution Services
N.A.I.C.S.: 551112
Andrew Mooney (Dir-Corp Dev)

Subsidiaries:

365 Healthcare Limited (1)
New Frontier House, Coalville, LE67 1PB,
Leicestershire, United Kingdom

Tel.: (44) 190 577 8365
Web Site: https://www.365healthcare.com
Medical Equipment Distr
N.A.I.C.S.: 423450

Abco Kovex (UK) Limited (1)
Unit 10, Peartree Industrial Estate Peartree
Lane, Dudley, DY2 0UW, West Midlands,
United Kingdom
Tel.: (44) 1384898931
Packing Material Mfr & Distr
N.A.I.C.S.: 326199

Abco Kovex Limited (1)
Swords Business Park, Swords, Dublin,
K67 C6A0, Ireland
Tel.: (353) 18077600
Web Site: https://abcokovex.com
Packing Material Mfr & Distr
N.A.I.C.S.: 326199

Aggora Limited (1)
Centech House Centech Park North Moons
Moat, Redditch, B98 9NR, Worcestershire,
United Kingdom
Tel.: (44) 845 117 7999
Web Site: https://aggora.co.uk
Catering Equipment Distr
N.A.I.C.S.: 423850

Allshoes Benelux B.V (1)
Barnsteenstraat 1a, 1812 SE, Alkmaar,
Netherlands
Tel.: (31) 725402716
Web Site: http://www.allshoes.nl
Shoe Distr
N.A.I.C.S.: 458210

Alpes Entretien Distribution SAS (1)
725 route des Vernes, 74370, Pringy,
France
Tel.: (33) 45 027 2007
Web Site: https://www.aednet.fr
Laundry Product Distr
N.A.I.C.S.: 423850

Arch Logistics, LLC (1)
1727 Bluff View Dr Unit Ste B, Dupo, IL
62239
Tel.: (314) 941-2139
Web Site: https://archlogisticsllc.com
N.A.I.C.S.: 541614

Banner Stakes LLC (1)
250 Melvin Henley Dr, Murray, KY 42071
Web Site: https://www.bannerstakes.com
Belt Barrier Mfr & Distr
N.A.I.C.S.: 326220

Baumer Betriebshygiene Vertriebsge-
sellschaft mbH (1)
Maysweg 11, 47918, Tonisvorst, Germany
Tel.: (49) 215 197 9800
Web Site: https://www.baeumer.info
Hygiene & Cleaning Product Distr
N.A.I.C.S.: 423990

Blanc SAS (1)
Zam du Bassin de Thau Rte de Sete, BP
99, Balaruc-Les-Bains, 34540, Montpellier,
France
Tel.: (33) 467516464
Web Site: https://sas-blanc.com
N.A.I.C.S.: 423850

Blyth s.r.o. (1)
Pratelstvi 1011/17, Uhrineves, 104 00,
Prague, Czech Republic
Tel.: (420) 27 209 9544
Web Site: https://www.blyth.cz
Emp.: 40
Sporting Goods Mfr
N.A.I.C.S.: 339920

Bodyguard Workwear Limited (1)
Adams Street, Birmingham, B7 4LS, West
Midlands, United Kingdom
Tel.: (44) 1213598880
Web Site:
https://www.bodyguardworkwear.co.uk
Safety Material Mfr & Distr
N.A.I.C.S.: 339113

Bourgogne Hygiene Entretien
SAS (1)
14 Rue Lavoisier, 21700, Nuits-St-Georges,
France
Tel.: (33) 380525142
Web Site: https://bhe-hedis.fr
N.A.I.C.S.: 423850

Bunzl Australasia Ltd (1)
Suite 8 9-11 Compark Circuit, PO Box 379,
Mulgrave, 3170, VIC, Australia
Tel.: (61) 395903000
Web Site: http://www.bunzl.com.au
Sales Range: $25-49.9 Million
Emp.: 36
Consumer Products Distr
N.A.I.C.S.: 423990

Bunzl CS s.r.o. (1)
Dolnokrcska 2029/54a, Krc, 140 00,
Prague, Czech Republic
Tel.: (420) 286000000
Web Site: http://www.bunzlcs.cz
Packaging Material Whslr
N.A.I.C.S.: 424130
Monika Urbanova *(Acct Mgr)*

Bunzl Canada, Inc. (1)
3150 Harvester Road Unit 100, Burlington,
L7N 3W8, ON, Canada
Tel.: (289) 266-1200
Web Site: https://bunzlcanada.ca
N.A.I.C.S.: 561910

Bunzl Catering Supplies Limited (1)
K60 Lister Road, Basingstoke, RG22 4AS,
Hampshire, United Kingdom
Tel.: (44) 1256383500
Web Site: https://www.bunzlcatering.co.uk
N.A.I.C.S.: 423850

Bunzl Distributie SRL (1)
Bucharest West Logistics Park Cladirea A2
unitatea C01 Str DE 287/1, Sat
Dragomiresti-Deal Comuna Dragomiresti-
Vale Judet Ilfov, Bucharest, 077096, Roma-
nia
Tel.: (40) 21 315 1081
Web Site: https://www.bunzlromania.ro
Personal Protection Goods Distr
N.A.I.C.S.: 423910

Bunzl Distribution Danmark A/S (1)
Greve Main 30, 2670, Greve, Denmark
Tel.: (45) 77403300
Web Site: http://www.bunzl.dk
Hygiene & Cleaning Product Distr
N.A.I.C.S.: 423990

Bunzl Distribution Oklahoma,
Inc. (1)
8000 Mid America Blvd, Oklahoma City, OK
73135
Tel.: (405) 324-9990
Packaging Material Distr
N.A.I.C.S.: 424130

Bunzl Distribution Spain, S.A.U. (1)
Filats 8 Pol In Prologis Park, Sant Boi Llo-
bregat, 08830, Barcelona, Spain
Tel.: (34) 902101353
Web Site: http://www.bunzlspain.com
Hygiene & Cleaning Product Distr
N.A.I.C.S.: 423990

Bunzl Grosshandel GmbH (1)
Elbestrasse 1-3, 45768, Marl, Germany
Tel.: (49) 236595385
Web Site: https://bunzl-grosshandel.de
Kitchen Equipment Distr
N.A.I.C.S.: 423440

Bunzl Healthcare GmbH (1)
Kitzingstr 15-19, 12277, Berlin, Germany
Tel.: (49) 30755110
Web Site: https://www.bunzl-healthcare.de
Hygiene Product Distr
N.A.I.C.S.: 424210

Bunzl Higiene E Limpeza Ltda. (1)
Avenida Alberto J Byington 1435 Santa Fe,
Osasco, 06273-050, Sao Paulo, Brazil
Tel.: (55) 113 646 2800
Web Site: https://www.bunzlhigiene.com.br
Cleaning Product Distr
N.A.I.C.S.: 423850

Bunzl Holding GmbH (1)
Buschgrundstr 23, 45894, Gelsenkirchen,
Nordrhein-Westfalen, Germany
Tel.: (49) 209 93030
Sales Range: $100-124.9 Million
Emp.: 150
Investment Management Service
N.A.I.C.S.: 523999
Hans-Georg Wieskus *(Mng Dir)*

Bunzl Ireland Limited (1)
Unit D9 Horizon Logistics Park, Harristown,

Dublin, K67 N4T2, Ireland
Tel.: (353) 18164800
Web Site: https://www.bunzlireland.ie
N.A.I.C.S.: 423850

Bunzl Magyarorszag Kft (1)
Vendel park Erdoalja u 3, 2051, Biatorbagy,
Hungary
Tel.: (36) 14645100
Web Site: https://www.bunzl.hu
Cleaning Product Whslr
N.A.I.C.S.: 423850
Simon Bernadett *(Mgr-Product)*

Bunzl Minneapolis, LLC (1)
10250 89th Ave N, Maple Grove, MN 55369
Tel.: (763) 571-1011
Packaging Material Distr
N.A.I.C.S.: 424130

Bunzl Outsourcing Services BV (1)
Rondebeltweg 82, Almere, 1329 BG, Neth-
erlands
Tel.: (31) 365478600
Web Site: http://www.bunzl.nl
Sales Range: $25-49.9 Million
Emp.: 100
Business Outsourcing Services
N.A.I.C.S.: 561439
Wilco Wieling *(Gen Mgr)*

Bunzl Retail, LLC (1)
Lamplight Way Agecroft Commerce Park,
Swinton, Manchester, M27 8UJ, United
Kingdom
Tel.: (44) 161 743 2222
Web Site: https://www.bunzlretail.com
Medical Equipment Retailer
N.A.I.C.S.: 423450
Helen Cockerham *(Mng Dir)*

Bunzl Romania SRL (1)
Building A2 Unit C01 Str DE 287/1
Dragomiresti-Deal, West Logistics Park
Dragomiresti-Vale Commune Ilfov County,
Bucharest, Romania
Tel.: (40) 213151081
Web Site: https://www.bunzlromania.ro
Packing Material Mfr & Distr
N.A.I.C.S.: 326199

Bunzl UK Ltd (1)
Ellerslie Square Industrial Estate Unit 9,
London, SW2 5DZ, United Kingdom
Tel.: (44) 2077339771
Janitorial Services
N.A.I.C.S.: 561720

Unit (Domestic):

Greenham (2)
Taylor Woolf House 671 London Road, Isle-
worth, TW7 4EX, Middlesex, United
Kingdom (100%)
Tel.: (44) 208 560 4422
Web Site: https://www.greenham.com
Sales Range: $250-299.9 Million
Emp.: 900
Personal Protection Equipment, Construc-
tion Tools, Cleaning & Hygiene & Mainte-
nance Products Supplier
N.A.I.C.S.: 425120

Protec Direct (2)
Unit 1 Brittania Park, Trident Drive,
Wednesbury, WS10 7XB, West Midlands,
United Kingdom
Tel.: (44) 333 003 5454
Web Site: https://www.protecdirect.co.uk
Sales Range: $50-74.9 Million
Emp.: 200
Safety Clothing Whslr
N.A.I.C.S.: 458110

Walsh - Blyth & Turton
Wholesale (2)
Chaddock Lane, Tyldesley Astley, Man-
chester, M29 7JT, United Kingdom
Tel.: (44) 333 999 2222
Web Site: https://www.wbtwholesale.co.uk
Personal Protection Equipment Whslr
N.A.I.C.S.: 423990

Bunzl USA Holdings LLC (1)
1 City Place Dr Ste 200, Saint Louis, MO
63141
Tel.: (314) 997-5959
Web Site: http://www.bunzldistribution.com
Sales Range: $75-99.9 Million
Emp.: 150
Packaging Material Distr

N.A.I.C.S.: 424130

Subsidiary (Domestic):

Bunzl USA, LLC (2)
One Cityplace Dr Ste 200, Saint Louis, MO
63141
Tel.: (314) 997-5959
Web Site: http://www.bunzldistribution.com
Sales Range: $50-74.9 Million
Emp.: 100
Fabricated Plastic Products Mfr; Outsourced
Service Provider
N.A.I.C.S.: 424130
Erica Glanz *(Sr Dir-Diversity & Inclusion-*
North America)

Subsidiary (Domestic):

Bunzl Distribution USA, LLC (3)
1 Cityplace Dr Ste 200, Saint Louis, MO
63141 (100%)
Tel.: (314) 997-5959
Web Site: https://bunzldistribution.com
Food Product Packaging Distr
N.A.I.C.S.: 424130
Jane Jennewein *(Sr VP-Fin)*

Earthwise Bag Company, Inc. (3)
2819 Burton Ave, Burbank, CA 91504-3224
Tel.: (818) 847-2174
Web Site: https://earthwisebags.com
Sales Range: $10-24.9 Million
Emp.: 16
Reusable Bags Mfr & Distr
N.A.I.C.S.: 424990
Stanley R. Joffe *(Co-Founder)*

International Sourcing Company
Inc. (3)
4025 Viscount Ave, Memphis, TN 38118
Tel.: (901) 458-5030
Web Site: http://www.cordovaisc.com
Importer & Distr of Safety Garments &
Products
N.A.I.C.S.: 315990
Printice Kincade *(Dir-IT)*

Packaging Film Sales, Inc. (3)
11620 E 51st Ave, Denver, CO 80239
Tel.: (303) 333-1320
Web Site: http://www.pfsdenver.com
Sales Range: $1-9.9 Million
Emp.: 4
Plastics Materials & Basic Forms & Shapes
Merchant Whslr
N.A.I.C.S.: 424610
Jeffrey May *(Pres)*

R3, LLC (3)
701 Emerson Rd, Saint Louis, MO 63141
Tel.: (314) 997-5959
Web Site: http://www.r3redistribution.com
Industrial, Food Service & Janitorial Sup-
plies Distr
N.A.I.C.S.: 423840
Patrick L. Larmon *(Pres & CEO)*

Subsidiary (Domestic):

R3 AWM (4)
2301 Lunt Ave, Elk Grove Village, IL 60007-
5625
Tel.: (847) 952-9000
Sales Range: $25-49.9 Million
Emp.: 80
Redistributor of Paper, Plastic Aluminum &
Allied Products
N.A.I.C.S.: 423840

R3 Metro South TEC (4)
1000 Amboy Ave, Perth Amboy, NJ 08861-
1916
Tel.: (732) 969-8700
Sales Range: $1-9.9 Million
Emp.: 35
Hardware & Paper Product Distr
N.A.I.C.S.: 423710
David Holtzman *(Pres)*

R3 Safety (4)
6021 Union Centre Blvd, Fairfield, OH
45014
Tel.: (513) 273-2800
Web Site: https://r3safety.net
Sales Range: $25-49.9 Million
Emp.: 60
Welding Machinery & Equipment Distr
N.A.I.C.S.: 423830

Bunzl plc—(Continued)

Subsidiary (Domestic):

SAS Safety Corp.   **(3)**
3031 Gardenia Ave, Long Beach, CA 90807
Tel.: (562) 427-2775
Web Site: http://www.sassafety.com
Sales Range: $25-49.9 Million
Emp.: 60
Industrial Safety Apparel & Accessories Mfr & Distr
N.A.I.C.S.: 315990

Steiner Industries, Inc.   **(3)**
5801 North Tripp Ave, Chicago, IL 60646
Tel.: (773) 588-3444
Web Site: https://www.steinerindustries.com
Sales Range: $10-24.9 Million
Emp.: 50
Ophthalmic Goods Mfr
N.A.I.C.S.: 339115
Robert Steiner (Owner)

Subsidiary (Domestic):

Western Safety Products, Inc.   **(2)**
505 South Lander St, Seattle, WA 98134-2024
Tel.: (206) 264-0808
Web Site: https://www.westernsafety.com
Durable Goods Merchant Whslr
N.A.I.C.S.: 423990

Bunzl Verpackungen GmbH   **(1)**
Elbestrasse 1-3, 45768, Marl, Germany
Tel.: (49) 236595385
Web Site: http://www.bunzl.de
Cleaning Product Distr
N.A.I.C.S.: 423850

Bunzl de Mexico S.A. de C.V.   **(1)**
Miguel Aleman Road Km 21 Col Prologis Park Apodaca Building 4-C, 66627, Apodaca, Nuevo Leon, Mexico
Tel.: (52) 8183139440
Web Site: http://www.bunzlmexico.com.mx
Hygiene & Cleaning Product Distr
N.A.I.C.S.: 423990

CM Supply ApS   **(1)**
Jydekrogen 7, 2625, Vallensbaek, Denmark
Tel.: (45) 70201610
Web Site: http://www.cmsupply.dk
Folding Paperboard Box Mfr
N.A.I.C.S.: 322212

Clean Care A/S   **(1)**
Indkildevej 2C, 9210, Aalborg, Denmark
Tel.: (45) 96341300
Web Site: http://www.cleancare.dk
Cleaning Product Distr
N.A.I.C.S.: 423850

Comptoir de Bretagne SAS   **(1)**
ZA La Teillais rue Jean-Marie David, BP 94102, 35741, Pace, Cedex, France
Tel.: (33) 299852100
Web Site: http://www.cdbpromo.com
Catering Equipment Distr
N.A.I.C.S.: 423850

Continental Chef Supplies Limited   **(1)**
2 Swan Road, South West Industrial Estate, Peterlee, SR8 2HS, County Durham, United Kingdom
Tel.: (44) 1915188080
Web Site: http://www.chefs.net
Catering Equipment Distr
N.A.I.C.S.: 423850

Cool-Pak, LLC   **(1)**
401 N Rice Ave, Oxnard, CA 93030
Tel.: (805) 981-2434
Web Site: https://cool-pak.com
Custom Print Packaging Mfr
N.A.I.C.S.: 326112
Paula Coffman (Dir-Supply Chain)

Corded Strap (NZ) Limited   **(1)**
10 Merton Place, Tahunanui, Nelson, New Zealand
Tel.: (64) 800 548 5459
Web Site: https://www.cordstrap.co.nz
Cargo Securing Accessory Mfr
N.A.I.C.S.: 333515

DPS Chile Comercial Limitada   **(1)**
Camino Coquimbo, 16000, Colina, Metropolitan, Chile

Tel.: (56) 225848900
Web Site: https://dpschile.cl
N.A.I.C.S.: 561910

DVS Equipamentos de Protecao Individual Ltda.   **(1)**
Rua Joseph Zarzour n 93 15 andar Jardim Guarulhos, Guarulhos, 07020-081, Sao Paulo, Brazil
Tel.: (55) 113 133 5766
Web Site: https://www.danny.com.br
Glove & Eyewear Mfr
N.A.I.C.S.: 339113

Daugeron & Fils SAS   **(1)**
12 Route de Montigny, La Genevraye, 77690, Montigny, France
Tel.: (33) 164453030
Web Site: http://www.daugeron.fr
Hygiene & Cleaning Product Distr
N.A.I.C.S.: 423990

De Ridder B.V   **(1)**
Industrieweg 11b, 1566 JN, Assendelft, Netherlands
Tel.: (31) 251315920
Web Site: http://www.deridderproducts.com
Grocery Product Services
N.A.I.C.S.: 445110

Deliver Net Limited   **(1)**
Healthcare House Snaygill Industrial Estate Keighley Road, Skipton, BD23 2QR, North Yorkshire, United Kingdom
Tel.: (44) 175 670 6050
Web Site: https://www.delivernet.co.uk
Sales Range: $25-49.9 Million
Emp.: 50
Healthcare Supplies Online
N.A.I.C.S.: 459999
Adele Farquharson (Mng Dir)

Dental Sorria Ltda.   **(1)**
Avenida Barao Homem de Melo 2212-Estoril, Belo Horizonte, 30494-080, Minas Gerais, Brazil
Tel.: (55) 3135248686
Web Site: http://www.dentalsorria.com.br
Surgical Appliance Distr
N.A.I.C.S.: 423450

Destiny Packaging, LLC   **(1)**
9621 Citation Ct Ste D, Monterey, CA 93940
Tel.: (831) 455-8000
Web Site: https://destinypackaging.com
Custom Print Packaging Mfr
N.A.I.C.S.: 326112
Radoslav Sertov (Gen Mgr)

Distrimondo AG   **(1)**
Oberebenestrasse 53, 5620, Bremgarten, Switzerland
Tel.: (41) 566482300
Web Site: http://www.distrimondo.ch
Cleaning Product Distr
N.A.I.C.S.: 423850
Dominik Arnold (Mgr-Bus Dev)

Diversified Distribution Systems, LLC   **(1)**
7351 Boone Ave N, Brooklyn Park, MN 55428
Tel.: (612) 813-5200
Web Site: http://www.ddsjit.com
Store Supplies Logistic Services
N.A.I.C.S.: 541614
Scott M. Kopas (VP-Global Logistics)

Espomega S. de R.L. de C.V   **(1)**
Avenida Pablo A Gonzalez Garza 820, 64030, Monterrey, Nuevo Leon, Mexico
Tel.: (52) 8180407070
Web Site: http://www.espomega.mx
Personal Protection Goods Distr
N.A.I.C.S.: 423910

Faru, S.L.U.   **(1)**
C/ Tarento nave 5, 50197, Zaragoza, Spain
Tel.: (34) 97 646 3737
Web Site: https://www.faru.es
Protection Equipment Mfr
N.A.I.C.S.: 339113

Fichot Hygiene SAS   **(1)**
Rue de Reaumur PA du Jardin, 28000, Chartres, France
Tel.: (33) 237841828
Web Site: https://fichot-hygiene.fr
N.A.I.C.S.: 423850
Adelina Chopard (Mgr)

Fire Rescue Safety Australia Pty Ltd.   **(1)**
17 Millrose Drive, Malaga, 6090, WA, Australia
Tel.: (61) 892706777
Web Site: https://www.frsa.com.au
Fire Rescue Services
N.A.I.C.S.: 922160

FoodHandler Inc.   **(1)**
2301 Lunt Ave, Elk Grove Village, IL 60007
Tel.: (847) 952-0884
Web Site: https://www.foodhandler.com
Food Safety Products Mfr
N.A.I.C.S.: 326199
John Mihelich (VP)

France Securite SAS   **(1)**
Rue Alain Colas, CS 61856, 29218, Brest, Cedex 1, France
Tel.: (33) 29 880 2535
Web Site: https://www.france-securite.fr
Health & Safety Product Distr
N.A.I.C.S.: 423850

GM Equipement S.A.S.   **(1)**
11 C rue des Aulnes, 69410, Champagne-au-Mont-d'Or, France
Tel.: (33) 297545380
Web Site: http://www.gm-equipement.com
Cleaning Product Distr
N.A.I.C.S.: 423850

Gama 29 SAS   **(1)**
530 rue Jacqueline Auriol ZA St Thudon CS60137, Guipavas, 29803, Brest, Cedex 9, France
Tel.: (33) 29 802 0109
Web Site: https://www.gama29.fr
Hygiene & Cleaning Product Distr
N.A.I.C.S.: 423990

Green Source, LLC   **(1)**
1262 S 650 W, Farmington, UT 84014
Tel.: (801) 540-5241
Web Site: http://www.greensourcellc.com
Lawn Product Distr
N.A.I.C.S.: 424910

Inkozell Zellstoff-Vertrieb GmbH   **(1)**
Malteserstrasse 139-143, 12277, Berlin, Germany
Tel.: (49) 8006647142
Web Site: http://www.inkozell.de
Medical Product Distr
N.A.I.C.S.: 423450

Interpath Services Pty. Ltd.   **(1)**
Unit 1/46 Sheehan Road, PO Box 340, Heidelberg, 3081, VIC, Australia
Tel.: (61) 394576277
Web Site: http://www.interpath.com.au
Science Consumable Distr
N.A.I.C.S.: 423490

Istanbul Ticaret Hirdavat Sanayi A.S.   **(1)**
Nato Yolu Caddesi Metanet Sokak No 2 Yukaridudullu, Umraniye, Istanbul, Turkiye
Tel.: (90) 2165277356
Web Site: http://www.isttic.com
Health & Safety Product Distr
N.A.I.C.S.: 423850

Istanbul Ticaret Is Guvenligi ve Endustriyel Sanayi Urunler A.S.   **(1)**
Camlica Mahallesi Anadolu Bulvari Timko Sokak O Blok No 5, Yenimahalle, Ankara, Turkiye
Tel.: (90) 3123547428
Web Site: http://www.istanbulticaret.com
Health & Safety Product Distr
N.A.I.C.S.: 423850

Jan-Mar Sales Limited   **(1)**
514 Kipling Avenue, Toronto, M8Z 5E3, ON, Canada
Tel.: (416) 255-8535
Web Site: http://www.jan-mar.com
Sales Range: $1-9.9 Million
Emp.: 28
Janitorial & Sanitation Products Supplier
N.A.I.C.S.: 423840
Pat Schaump (VP-Sls)

Joshen Paper & Packaging Co. Inc.   **(1)**
5800 Grant Ave, Cuyahoga Heights, OH 44105-5608
Tel.: (216) 441-5600

Web Site: https://www.joshen.com
Food Service Supplies & Containers
N.A.I.C.S.: 424130
Bob Reiner (Pres)

Subsidiary (Domestic):

A.D. Schinner Co.   **(2)**
8133 N Granville Woods Rd, Milwaukee, WI 53223
Tel.: (414) 434-0277
Packaging Services
N.A.I.C.S.: 561910

Division (Domestic):

Supply Pro Inc.   **(2)**
7075 Dort Hwy, Grand Blanc, MI 48439
Tel.: (810) 239-8658
Web Site: http://www.supplypro.net
Sales Range: $10-24.9 Million
Emp.: 100
Commercial & Industrial Sanitary Products Distr
N.A.I.C.S.: 423850

Juba Personal Protective Equipment, S.L.U.   **(1)**
Avenida Logrono 29-31, Santo Domingo de la Calzada, 26250, La Rioja, Spain
Tel.: (34) 941340885
Web Site: http://www.jubappe.es
Leather Band Mfr
N.A.I.C.S.: 316990
Rebeca Moneo (Mng Dir)

Keenpac (Switzerland) SA   **(1)**
Route des Jeunes 5D, Les Acacias, 1227, Les Geneveys-sur-Coffrane, Switzerland
Tel.: (41) 223621038
N.A.I.C.S.: 561910

Keenpac Italia S.r.l.   **(1)**
Corso Italia 6, 50123, Florence, Italy
Tel.: (39) 055282015
N.A.I.C.S.: 561910

King Belgium NV   **(1)**
Rue du Cerf 190/1, 1332, Genval, Belgium
Tel.: (32) 26550333
Web Site: https://www.kingbelgium.be
Medical Disposable Distr
N.A.I.C.S.: 423450

Kingsbury Packaging (Limavady) Ltd.   **(1)**
Aghanloo Rd, Aghanloo Industrial Estate, Londonderry, BT49 0HE, United Kingdom
Tel.: (44) 287 776 4926
Web Site: https://www.packagingni.com
Packaging Material Distr
N.A.I.C.S.: 424130

Kullanatmarket Elektronik Pazarlama Ticaret Anonim Sirketi   **(1)**
Akcaburgaz Mah 3137 Sok No 19 Kirac, Esenyurt, 34522, Istanbul, Turkiye
Tel.: (90) 2128866360
Web Site: https://www.kullanatmarket.com
N.A.I.C.S.: 423850

LSH Industrial Solutions Pte. Ltd.   **(1)**
1 Penjuru Close, Singapore, 608617, Singapore
Tel.: (65) 6 262 5252
Web Site: https://www.lsh.sg
Personal Protection Goods Distr
N.A.I.C.S.: 423910
Ching Chong Goh (Sr Mgr)

Lee Brothers Bilston Limited   **(1)**
Unit 1 Britannia Park Trident Drive, Wednesbury, WS10 7XB, West Midlands, United Kingdom
Tel.: (44) 1215674111
Web Site: https://www.leebrothers.co.uk
N.A.I.C.S.: 423810

Lightning Packaging Supplies Limited   **(1)**
Frobisher Way Hatfield Business Park, Hatfield, AL10 9TY, Hertfordshire, United Kingdom
Tel.: (44) 170 763 5343
Web Site:
   https://www.lightningpackaging.co.uk
Packaging Material Distr
N.A.I.C.S.: 424130

Ligne T SAS   **(1)**
50 avenue d'Allemagne - Za Albasud,

82000, Montauban, France
Tel.: (33) 56 366 7744
Web Site: https://www.ligne-t.com
Health & Safety Product Distr
N.A.I.C.S.: 423850

Lockhart Catering Equipment Limited (1)
Lockhart House Brunel Road, Theale, Reading, RG7 4XE, Berkshire, United Kingdom
Tel.: (44) 118 930 3900
Web Site: https://www.lockhart.co.uk
Catering Equipment Distr
N.A.I.C.S.: 423850

London Bio Packaging Limited (1)
York House 45 Seymour Street, London, W1H 7JT, United Kingdom
Tel.: (44) 207 471 3700
Web Site: https://www.londonbiopackaging.com
Packaging Material Distr
N.A.I.C.S.: 424130

M.L. Kishigo Manufacturing Company, LLC (1)
11250 Slater Ave, Fountain Valley, CA 92708
Tel.: (949) 852-1963
Web Site: https://www.kishigo.com
Industrial Safety Garments Designer & Mfr
N.A.I.C.S.: 315250
John Ambrosio *(VP-Enterprise Sls & Mktg)*

Majestic Products B.V. (1)
Jan Campertlaan 6, 3201 AX, Spijkenisse, Netherlands
Tel.: (31) 181475000
Web Site: http://www.majestic.nl
Personal Protection Goods Distr
N.A.I.C.S.: 423910

Marca Proteccion Laboral, S.L.U. (1)
Pol Ind Cabezo Beaza Avda Brusela R-100, 30353, Cartagena, Spain
Tel.: (34) 96 850 1132
Web Site: https://www.marcapl.com
Workwear Product Mfr
N.A.I.C.S.: 314999

Mat'hygiene SAS (1)
7 Route de Villiers, 77780, Bourron-Marlotte, France
Tel.: (33) 164456525
Web Site: http://www.mathygiene.fr
Electrical Equipment Distr
N.A.I.C.S.: 423610

Medshop Singapore Pte. Ltd. (1)
15 Greenwich Drive, Singapore, 534022, Singapore
Tel.: (65) 31634113
Web Site: https://www.medshop.com.sg
Pharmaceuticals Distr
N.A.I.C.S.: 424210

Meichaley Zahav Packages Ltd. (1)
PO 533, Modi'in-Maccabim-Re'ut, 7177904, Israel
Tel.: (972) 89125005
Web Site: https://www.mzahav.co.il
N.A.I.C.S.: 561910

Meier Verpackungen GmbH (1)
Diepoldsauer Strasse 37, 6845, Hohenems, Austria
Tel.: (43) 55 767 1770
Web Site: https://www.meierverpackungen.at
Packaging Services
N.A.I.C.S.: 561910

Mo Ha Ge Mommsen Handelsgesellschaft mbH (1)
Malteserstr 139, 12277, Berlin, Germany
Tel.: (49) 30755110
Web Site: http://www.mohage.de
Medical Product Distr
N.A.I.C.S.: 423450

MultiLine A/S (1)
Kirkebjergvej 17, 4180, Soro, Denmark
Tel.: (45) 70107700
Web Site: http://www.multiline.dk
Laundry Product Whslr
N.A.I.C.S.: 423850

Nelson Packaging Supplies Limited (1)

10 Merton Place, Tahunanui, Nelson, New Zealand
Tel.: (64) 3 548 5459
Web Site: https://www.nelpack.co.nz
Packaging & Labeling Services
N.A.I.C.S.: 561910

Neri S.p.A. (1)
Via 8 Marzo 6, 42025, Cavriago, RE, Italy
Tel.: (39) 0522948111
Web Site: http://www.nerispa.com
Footwear Mfr
N.A.I.C.S.: 316210

Nicolas Entretien SAS (1)
257 rue Pierre Pascal Fauvelle, BP 82073, 66011, Perpignan, Cedex, France
Tel.: (33) 46 868 3070
Web Site: https://www.nicolasentretien.fr
Hygiene & Cleaning Product Distr
N.A.I.C.S.: 423990

ORRU SAS (1)
267 Chemin des Plantades, 83130, La Garde, France
Tel.: (33) 49 414 7114
Web Site: https://www.orru-hedis.fr
Hygiene & Cleaning Product Distr
N.A.I.C.S.: 423990

PKA Klocker GmbH (1)
Friedrichstr 2, 40699, Erkrath, Germany
Tel.: (49) 2112 295 0560
Web Site: https://www.pka-kloecker.de
Work Wear Product Whslr
N.A.I.C.S.: 424350

Packaging 2 Buy Limited (1)
Frobisher Way Hatfield Business Park, Hatfield, AL10 9TY, Hertfordshire, United Kingdom
Tel.: (44) 170 763 5353
Web Site: https://www.packaging2buy.co.uk
Packaging Material Distr
N.A.I.C.S.: 424130
Caren Vint *(Mgr-Ops)*

Polaris Chemicals SPRL (1)
Avenue Sabin 23 Zoning Industriel Nord, 1300, Wavre, Belgium
Tel.: (32) 10231650
Web Site: http://www.polarischem.be
Hygiene & Cleaning Product Distr
N.A.I.C.S.: 423990

Portabrands Limited (1)
Unit 4 The Arena Mollison Avenue, Enfield, EN3 7NL, Middlesex, United Kingdom
Tel.: (44) 2084439109
Web Site: http://www.portabrands.com
Carrier Bag Retailer
N.A.I.C.S.: 424130

Prime Source, LLC (1)
10025 US Hwy 264 Alternate, Middlesex, NC 27557
Web Site: http://www.prime-sourcellc.com
Pesticide & Other Agricultural Chemical Mfr
N.A.I.C.S.: 325320

Proepta, S.A. DE C.V (1)
Galileo 11 Polanco Polanco IV Secc, 11550, Mexico, Mexico
Tel.: (52) 5541622222
Web Site: https://catalogo.proepta.mx
N.A.I.C.S.: 423830

Prorisk S.A.S. (1)
11C rue des Aulnes, 69410, Champagne-au-Mont-d'Or, France
Tel.: (33) 42 610 6595
Web Site: https://www.prorisk.fr
Medical Product Distr
N.A.I.C.S.: 423450

QS Nederland B.V. (1)
Bijsterhuizen 3005 C, 6604 LP, Wijchen, Netherlands
Tel.: (31) 243712710
Web Site: https://www.qualityservices.nl
N.A.I.C.S.: 322291

Quirumed, S.L.U. (1)
Carrer del Corretger 117 Parque Empresarial Tactica, 46980, Paterna, Valencia, Spain
Tel.: (34) 1224608942
Web Site: https://www.quirumed.com
N.A.I.C.S.: 423450

Revco Industries, Inc. (1)

10747 Norwalk Blvd, Santa Fe Springs, CA 90670
Tel.: (562) 777-1588
Web Site: https://www.blackstallion.com
Whol Work Clothing And Mfg Personal Safety Equip And Whol Industrial Pipe Fittings
N.A.I.C.S.: 423830
Steve Hwang *(Pres)*

Saebe Compagniet ApS (1)
Vesterlundvej 5-7, 2730, Herlev, Denmark
Tel.: (45) 70274545
Web Site: http://www.saebecompagniet.dk
Laundry Product Distr
N.A.I.C.S.: 423850

Secure Line S.r.l (1)
Via Marconi 35, 20089, Rozzano, MI, Italy
Tel.: (39) 0257512152
Web Site: http://www.secur-line.it
Personal Protection Goods Distr
N.A.I.C.S.: 423910

Secure Service S.r.l. (1)
Via AM Enriques Agnoletti 23, 42124, Reggio Emilia, RE, Italy
Tel.: (39) 052 230 7205
Web Site: https://www.secureservice.it
Personal Protection Goods Distr
N.A.I.C.S.: 423910

Shanghai Cosafety Technology Co., Ltd. (1)
Bldg 4 Lane 115 No 1276 Nanle Road, Songjiang, Shanghai, China
Tel.: (86) 2167755218
Web Site: http://www.cosafety.cn
Fire Fighting Safety Material Distr
N.A.I.C.S.: 423850

Shelby Group International, Inc. (1)
1255 Schilling Blvd W, Collierville, TN 38017-7190
Tel.: (901) 795-5810
Web Site: https://www.mcrsafety.com
Emp.: 300
Importer Work Glove & Rainwear Mfr
N.A.I.C.S.: 315990
Glen Herald *(COO)*

Subsidiary (Domestic):

Parmelee Industries, Inc. (2)
3119 B Terrace St, Kansas City, MO 64111
Tel.: (913) 599-5555
Web Site: http://www.ussafety.com
Sales Range: $10-24.9 Million
Emp.: 70
Industrial Personal Protective Equipment Including Safety Eyewear, Faceshields, Goggle Lenses, Welding Goggles, Helmets, Hearing Protectors & Respirators
N.A.I.C.S.: 339115
Terry Meyers *(Treas & VP)*

Subsidiary (Non-US):

Parmelee Limited (3)
Middlemore Lane West, Aldridge, Walsall, WS9 8BG, West Midlands, United Kingdom
Tel.: (44) 192 245 7421
Web Site: https://www.mcrsafetyeurope.com
Emp.: 20
Eyeglass Mfr & Distr
N.A.I.C.S.: 339115
Garry Dawson *(Mgr)*

Skien Storkjokken AS (1)
Bedriftsveien 24, 3735, Skien, Norway
Tel.: (47) 35521555
Catering Equipment Distr
N.A.I.C.S.: 423850

Sodiscol SAS (1)
RN 20 13 Rue des Battants, PO Box 50201, 31142, Saint-Alban-Leysse, France
Tel.: (33) 534272727
Web Site: http://www.sodiscol.fr
Hygiene & Cleaning Product Distr
N.A.I.C.S.: 423990

Sopecal Hygiene SAS (1)
Route de Samadet, BP 90045, 40500, Saint-Sever, France
Tel.: (33) 55 876 0484
Web Site: https://www.sopecal-hygiene.fr
Hygiene & Cleaning Product Distr
N.A.I.C.S.: 423990

TSN East, LLC (1)

1133 N W L St, Richmond, IN 47374
Tel.: (765) 962-1283
N.A.I.C.S.: 541614

TSN West, LLC (1)
PO Box 679, Frederick, CO 80530
Tel.: (303) 530-0600
N.A.I.C.S.: 512110

Talge Descartaveis do Brasil Ltda. (1)
Rua Fermino Vieira Cordeiro 380 Galpao 2 - Modulo B, Bairro Espinheiros, Itajai, 88317-200, SC, Brazil
Tel.: (55) 4732678600
Web Site: https://talge.com.br
N.A.I.C.S.: 424130

Tecno Boga Comercial Limitada (1)
Av Boulevard Norte Airport N 9649 ENEA, Pudahuel, Santiago, Chile
Tel.: (56) 223073286
Web Site: http://www.tecnoboga.cl
Footwear Mfr
N.A.I.C.S.: 316210

Tecnopacking, S.L.U. (1)
Pol Ind El Colomer Parcela 45 C/Castilla-Leon s/n Aptdo Correos 389, Onda, 12200, Castellon de la Plana, Spain
Tel.: (34) 964772236
Web Site: http://www.tecnopacking.com
Packaging Material Distr
N.A.I.C.S.: 424130

Tingley Rubber Corporation (1)
1551 S Washington Ave Ste 403, Piscataway, NJ 08854
Tel.: (908) 757-7474
Web Site: http://www.tingleyrubber.com
Molded Rubber Footwear, Protective Clothing, Over-the-Sock Protective Footwear Mfr
N.A.I.C.S.: 316210
Jim Towey *(VP-Mktg)*

Total Safety Supply Belgium BVBA (1)
Oudenaardsesteenweg 19, Gent, Belgium
Tel.: (32) 2429060
Web Site: http://www.totalsafetysupply.be
Personal Protection Goods Distr
N.A.I.C.S.: 423910

Tri-Star Packaging Supplies Limited (1)
Unit 4 The Arena Mollison Avenue, Enfield, EN3 7NL, Middlesex, United Kingdom
Tel.: (44) 208 443 9100
Web Site: https://tri-star.co.uk
Packaging Material Distr
N.A.I.C.S.: 424130

Varia-Pack NV (1)
Aarschotsesteenweg 114, Wilsele, 3012, Leuven, Belgium
Tel.: (32) 1 630 1301
Web Site: https://www.variapack.be
Packaging Material Whslr
N.A.I.C.S.: 424130

Vicsa Commerce & Trading (Shanghai) Co., Ltd. (1)
New Town Center 1101 N083 Lou Shan Guan Road, Shanghai, 200336, China
Tel.: (86) 2162368661
N.A.I.C.S.: 541614

Vicsa Safety Comercial Limitada (1)
Panamericana Norte 5151, Conchali, Santiago, Chile
Tel.: (56) 223073200
Web Site: http://www.vicsa.cl
Clothing Material Mfr
N.A.I.C.S.: 315250

Vicsa Safety Peru S.A.C. (1)
Av Santa Rosa 350 Ate, Lima, Peru
Tel.: (51) 17157200
Web Site: http://www.vicsasafety.com.pe
Personal Protection Goods Distr
N.A.I.C.S.: 423910

Vicsa Steelpro Colombia S.A.S (1)
Km 7 Via Medellin Celta Trade Park Lot 49 Bg 1 and 2, Funza, Cundinamarca, Colombia
Tel.: (57) 18234090
Web Site: http://www.steelprocolombia.com
Personal Protection Goods Distr
N.A.I.C.S.: 423910

Bunzl plc—(Continued)

Vicsa Steelpro S.A. (1)
Av Maipu 4180, 1636, Olivos, Buenos Aires, Argentina
Tel.: (54) 114 799 7903
Web Site: https://www.vicsa.com.ar
Hardware Products Distr
N.A.I.C.S.: 444140

Volk do Brasil Ltda (1)
Rua dos Eucaliptos 147-Capela Velha, Araucaria, 83705-320, Brazil
Tel.: (55) 41 2105 0055
Web Site: http://www.volkdobrasil.com.br
Industrial Machinery & Equipment Distr
N.A.I.C.S.: 423830

WGS AG (1)
Guterstrasse 4, 4313, Mohlin, Switzerland
Tel.: (41) 61 855 2020
Web Site: http://www.wgservices.ch
Cleaning Product Distr
N.A.I.C.S.: 423850

Weita AG (1)
Nordring 2, Basel-Landschaft, 4147, Aesch, Switzerland
Tel.: (41) 61 706 6600
Web Site: https://www.weita.ch
Cleaning Product Whslr
N.A.I.C.S.: 423850

Worldpack Trading B.V. (1)
Esp 125, 5633 AA, Eindhoven, Netherlands
Tel.: (31) 884942080
Web Site: http://www.worldpack.eu
Carrier Bag Retailer
N.A.I.C.S.: 424130
Jos Bergen *(Mng Dir)*

BUPA ARABIA FOR COOP-ERATIVE INSURANCE COM-PANY

Bupa Arabia Building Prince Saud Al Faisal Street, PO Box 23807, Al Khalidiyah District, Jeddah, 21436, Saudi Arabia
Tel.: (966) 920000456
Web Site: https://www.bupa.com.sa
Year Founded: 2008
8210—(SAU)
Rev.: $3,434,047,194
Assets: $3,815,609,119
Liabilities: $2,670,727,370
Net Worth: $1,144,881,749
Earnings: $229,987,735
Emp.: 2,200
Fiscal Year-end: 12/31/22
Insurance Agency Services
N.A.I.C.S.: 524210
Loay Hisham Nazer *(Chm)*

BURBANK AUSTRALIA PTY LTD

Burbank Business Pk Aberdeen Rd, Altona, 3018, VIC, Australia
Tel.: (61) 393280333
Web Site: http://www.burbank.com.au
Sales Range: $25-49.9 Million
Emp.: 267
Single Family Home Builder
N.A.I.C.S.: 236115
Anthony E. Sanfilippo *(CEO)*

BURBERRY GROUP PLC

Horseferry House Horseferry Road, London, SW1P 2AW, United Kingdom
Tel.: (44) 203 367 3000
Web Site: http://www.burberryplc.com
Year Founded: 1856
BRBY—(LSE)
Rev.: $3,836,916,720
Assets: $5,019,490,840
Liabilities: $2,824,057,600
Net Worth: $2,195,433,240
Earnings: $539,014,840
Emp.: 8,979
Fiscal Year-end: 04/02/22
Apparel Mfr & Retailer
N.A.I.C.S.: 458110
Gerry Murphy *(Chm)*

Subsidiaries:

Burberry (Austria) GmbH (1)
Kohlmarkt 2, 1010, Vienna, Wien, Austria
Tel.: (43) 15322820
Luxury Goods & Jewelry Retailer
N.A.I.C.S.: 458310

Burberry (Deutschland) GmbH (1)
Konigsallee 50, Nordrhein-Westfalen, 40212, Dusseldorf, Germany
Tel.: (49) 211320926
Luxury Goods & Jewelry Retailer
N.A.I.C.S.: 458310

Burberry (Shanghai) Trading Co., Ltd. (1)
60th Floor No 1717 Nanjing West Road, Jing'an District, Shanghai, China
Tel.: (86) 4001201154
Web Site: https://www.burberry.cn
Family Clothing & Accessories Retailer
N.A.I.C.S.: 458110

Burberry (Suisse) SA (1)
8 Rue Robert-Ceard, Geneva, Switzerland
Tel.: (41) 223113425
Luxury Goods & Jewelry Retailer
N.A.I.C.S.: 458310

Burberry Antwerp NV (1)
Boulevard de Waterloo 16, Brussels, Belgium
Tel.: (32) 25025878
Luxury Goods & Jewelry Retailer
N.A.I.C.S.: 458310

Burberry Czech Rep s.r.o. (1)
Parizska 11/67, 11000, Prague, Hlavni mesto Praha, Czech Republic
Tel.: (420) 222317445
Luxury Goods & Jewelry Retailer
N.A.I.C.S.: 458310

Burberry Limited (1)
444 Madison Ave, New York, NY 10022
Tel.: (212) 707-6500
Web Site: https://us.burberry.com
Sales Range: $50-74.9 Million
Emp.: 250
Apparel for Men & Women Mfr
N.A.I.C.S.: 458110
Virginie Costa *(CFO)*

BURCELIK BURSA CELIK DO-KUM SANAYI AS

OSB MAH MINARELICAVUS Yesil Cd NO 6, 16159, Bursa, Turkiye
Tel.: (90) 2242431107
Web Site: https://www.burcelik.com.tr
Year Founded: 1968
BURCE—(IST)
Rev.: $9,153,306
Assets: $17,410,841
Liabilities: $6,546,321
Net Worth: $10,864,519
Earnings: $915,647
Emp.: 198
Fiscal Year-end: 12/31/22
Industrial Machinery Mfr
N.A.I.C.S.: 333248
Safak Capar *(Gen Mgr)*

BURCELIK VANA SANAYI VE TICARET A.S.

Organized Industrial Zone Yellow Street No 15, Nilufer, 16140, Bursa, Turkiye
Tel.: (90) 2242431107
Web Site:
   https://www.burcelikvana.com
Year Founded: 1968
BURVA—(IST)
Emp.: 250
Industrial Machinery & Equipment Mfr & Whslr
N.A.I.C.S.: 333998
Renan Komurcuoglu *(CEO & Exec Dir)*

BURCKHARDT COMPRES-SION HOLDING AG

Franz-Burckhardt-Strasse 5, CH-

8404, Winterthur, Switzerland
Tel.: (41) 522625500
Web Site:
   https://www.burckhardt.com
Year Founded: 2002
BCHN—(SWX)
Rev.: $1,092,648,269
Assets: $1,185,739,400
Liabilities: $854,250,583
Net Worth: $331,488,817
Earnings: $100,241,460
Emp.: 3,104
Fiscal Year-end: 03/31/23
Reciprocating Compressor Mfr
N.A.I.C.S.: 333912
Marcel Pawlicek *(CEO)*

Subsidiaries:

Arkos Field Services, LP (1)
19750 FM 362 Ste 100, Waller, TX 77484
Tel.: (832) 783-5400
Web Site: http://www.arkos.com
Electronic Equipment Repair Services
N.A.I.C.S.: 811210
Bill Sayre *(Pres)*

Arkos Group LLC (1)
1303 Azle Hwy, Weatherford, TX 76085
Tel.: (817) 598-1600
Compressor Equipment Mfr
N.A.I.C.S.: 333912

Burckhardt Compression (Nether-lands) BV (1)
Nieuwe Waterwegstraat 7, 3115 HE, Schiedam, Netherlands
Tel.: (31) 104090599
Air & Gas Compressor Mfr & Distr
N.A.I.C.S.: 333912

Burckhardt Compression (Saudi Ara-bia) LLC (1)
1st Support Industrial Area - Road A120, Jubail, Saudi Arabia
Tel.: (966) 133400234
Compressor Equipment Mfr
N.A.I.C.S.: 333912

Burckhardt Compression AG (1)
Franz-Burckhardt-Strasse 5, PO Box 3352, 8404, Winterthur, Switzerland
Tel.: (41) 522615500
Reciprocating Compressor Mfr
N.A.I.C.S.: 333912

Subsidiary (Non-US):

Burckhardt Compression (Brasil) Ltda. (2)
Avenida Osvaldo Fregonezi 171 Conjunto 41 - Bairro Alves Dias, Sao Bernardo do Campo, Sao Paulo, 09851-015, Brasilien, Brazil (100%)
Tel.: (55) 1143442900
Sales Range: $25-49.9 Million
Emp.: 20
Air & Gas Compressor Mfr
N.A.I.C.S.: 333914

Burckhardt Compression (Canada) Inc. (2)
7956 Torbram Road Unit 9-C, Brampton, L6T 5A2, ON, Canada (100%)
Tel.: (905) 458-1623
Web Site:
   http://www.burckhardtcompression.ca
Sales Range: $25-49.9 Million
Emp.: 5
Appliance Repair & Maintenance
N.A.I.C.S.: 811412

Burckhardt Compression (Deutschland) GmbH (2)
Kruppstrasse 1c, 41469, Neuss, Germany (100%)
Tel.: (49) 213791700
Sales Range: $25-49.9 Million
Emp.: 50
Oil & Gas Field Machinery & Equipment Mfr
N.A.I.C.S.: 333132
Holger Korn *(Mng Dir)*

Burckhardt Compression (Espana) S.A. (2)
Avenida Camino de lo Cortao 37A, 28703, Madrid, Spain (100%)
Tel.: (34) 915675720

Sales Range: $25-49.9 Million
Emp.: 15
Oil & Gas Field Machinery & Equipment Mfr
N.A.I.C.S.: 333132
Javier Cuevas *(Mng Dir)*

Burckhardt Compression (France) S.A.S (2)
Romain Pazat ZA de l Horloge 17/21 Rue du Petit, Albi Le Cerianthe, 95800, Cergy, France (100%)
Tel.: (33) 175720350
Sales Range: $25-49.9 Million
Emp.: 11
Air & Gas Compressor Mfr
N.A.I.C.S.: 333914

Burckhardt Compression (India) Pvt. Ltd. (2)
Gate No 304 Village Kondhapuri Pune-Nagar Road, Tal Shirur Dist, Pune, 412 209, Maharashtra, India
Tel.: (91) 2067623829
Web Site: http://www.bc-india.com
Sales Range: $75-99.9 Million
Reciprocating Compressor Mfr
N.A.I.C.S.: 333248

Burckhardt Compression (Italia) S.r.l. (2)
Via delle Industrie 17/G, Milano, 20867, Caponago, MB, Italy (100%)
Tel.: (39) 0295548000
Web Site:
   https://www.burckhardtcompression.com
Sales Range: $25-49.9 Million
Emp.: 15
Ship Building & Repairing
N.A.I.C.S.: 336611

Burckhardt Compression (Japan) Ltd. (2)
Yokohama Blue Avenue 5F 4-4-2 Minatomirai, Nishi-ku, Yokohama, 220-0012, Kanagawa, Japan (100%)
Tel.: (81) 452646310
Sales Range: $25-49.9 Million
Emp.: 7
Air & Gas Compressor Mfr
N.A.I.C.S.: 333912

Burckhardt Compression (Middle East) FZE (2)
Roundabout 7 Jebel Ali Free Zone, PO Box 262944, Jebel Ali Free Zone, Dubai, United Arab Emirates
Tel.: (971) 48870042
Reciprocating Compressor Mfr
N.A.I.C.S.: 333912

Burckhardt Compression (Shanghai) Co. Ltd. (2)
Building 6 No 509 Renqing Road, Pudong District, Shanghai, 201201, China (100%)
Tel.: (86) 2150720880
Sales Range: $25-49.9 Million
Emp.: 30
Oil & Gas Field Machinery & Equipment Mfr
N.A.I.C.S.: 333132

Burckhardt Compression (UK) Ltd. (2)
Units 1 & 2 Arena 14 Bicester Park Charbridge Lane, Bicester, OX26 4SS, Oxfordshire, United Kingdom (100%)
Tel.: (44) 1869326800
Sales Range: $25-49.9 Million
Emp.: 25
Air & Gas Compressor Mfr
N.A.I.C.S.: 333912
Colin Webb *(Mng Dir)*

Subsidiary (US):

Burckhardt Compression (US) Inc. (2)
19750 FM 362 Rd, Waller, TX 77484
Tel.: (281) 582-1050
Sales Range: $1-9.9 Million
Reciprocating Compressor Sales & Servicing
N.A.I.C.S.: 423830

Burckhardt Compression Korea Busan Ltd. (1)
10 Mieumsandan 1ro 15beon-gil, Gangseo-gu, Busan, 46730, Korea (South)
Tel.: (82) 517111120
Compressor Equipment Mfr

N.A.I.C.S.: 333912

Burckhardt Compression Korea Ltd. (1)
105-dong 48 Yutongdanji 1-ro 58beon-gil, Gangseo-gu, Busan, 46721, Korea (South)
Tel.: (82) 518326030
Compressor Equipment Mfr
N.A.I.C.S.: 333912

Burckhardt Compression Singapore Pte Ltd. (1)
26 Soon Lee Road, Singapore, 628086, Singapore
Tel.: (65) 67958684
Compressor Equipment Mfr
N.A.I.C.S.: 333912

Burckhardt Compression South Africa (Pty) Ltd. (1)
5445 Proton Industrial Park 6 Proton Street, Chloorkop, Edenvale, 1619, South Africa
Tel.: (27) 105931915
Compressor Equipment Mfr
N.A.I.C.S.: 333912

Burckhardt Kompresor San. ve Tic. Ltd. (1)
Imes Industrial Site B Block Street 205 No 2, Umraniye, 34775, Istanbul, Turkiye
Tel.: (90) 2163138300
Compressor Equipment Mfr
N.A.I.C.S.: 333912

CSM Compressor Inc. (1)
9330-27 Ave, Edmonton, T6N 1B2, AB, Canada
Tel.: (780) 435-5722
Web Site: http://www.csm-compressor.com
Electronic Equipment Repair Services
N.A.I.C.S.: 811210
Tim Lillak (Gen Mgr)

MT Sealing Technology Inc (1)
Aspstrasse 8, 8472, Seuzach, Switzerland
Tel.: (41) 523205060
Web Site: http://www.mt-switzerland.ch
Sales Range: $25-49.9 Million
Emp.: 4
Sealing Components Mfr
N.A.I.C.S.: 339991
Rose Mary MacLeod (Gen Mgr)

PROGNOST Machinery Diagnostics Equipment & Services LLC (1)
PO Box 29861, Abu Dhabi, United Arab Emirates
Tel.: (971) 564998359
Compressor Equipment Mfr
N.A.I.C.S.: 333912

PROGNOST Systems GmbH (1)
Daimlerstr 10, PO Box 1905, 48432, Rheine, Germany
Tel.: (49) 5971808190
Web Site: https://prognost.info
Sales Range: $25-49.9 Million
Reciprocating Compressor Mfr
N.A.I.C.S.: 333415
Eike Drewes (Mng Dir)

Subsidiary (US):

PROGNOST Systems Inc. (2)
309 Ibis St Ste A, Webster, TX 77598
Tel.: (281) 480-9300
Monitoring Diagnostic System Mfr
N.A.I.C.S.: 325413

Shenyang Yuanda Compressor Co. Ltd. (1)
No 11 Zhongde Street, Economic and Technological Development Zone, Shenyang, Liaoning, China
Tel.: (86) 2425566050
Web Site: https://www.ydysj.com
Compressor Mfr
N.A.I.C.S.: 333912

BURCON NUTRASCIENCE CORPORATION
490-999 West Broadway, Vancouver, V5Z 1K5, BC, Canada
Tel.: (604) 733-0896   YT
Web Site: https://www.burcon.ca
Year Founded: 1998
BU—(NASDAQ)
Rev.: $134,138

Assets: $22,959,712
Liabilities: $862,461
Net Worth: $22,097,251
Earnings: ($8,024,947)
Emp.: 26
Fiscal Year-end: 03/31/22
Plant-Based Protein Products Researcher & Mfr
N.A.I.C.S.: 541715
Johann F. Tergesen (Founder, Pres & CEO)

Subsidiaries:

Burcon NutraScience (MB) Corp. (1)
1388 Waller Ave, Winnipeg, R3T 1P9, MB, Canada
Tel.: (204) 475-6207
Web Site: http://www.burcon.ca
Sales Range: $25-49.9 Million
Emp.: 15
Physical Research & Development Services
N.A.I.C.S.: 541715

BURE EQUITY AB
Nybrogatan 6, SE-114 34, Stockholm, Sweden
Tel.: (46) 86140020
Web Site: https://www.bure.se
Year Founded: 1992
BURE—(OMX)
Rev.: $785,828,960
Assets: $2,930,408,320
Liabilities: $5,859,840
Net Worth: $2,924,548,480
Earnings: $776,672,960
Emp.: 8
Fiscal Year-end: 12/31/21
Holding Company
N.A.I.C.S.: 551112
Patrik Tigerschiold (Chm)

Subsidiaries:

Allgon AB (1)
Kronborgsgrand 7, 164 46, Kista, Sweden   (98.66%)
Tel.: (46) 87929200
Web Site: http://www.allgon.se
Rev.: $61,532,727
Assets: $85,389,841
Liabilities: $49,198,532
Net Worth: $36,191,309
Earnings: $4,552,582
Emp.: 391
Fiscal Year-end: 12/31/2019
Wireless Equipment Product Mfr
N.A.I.C.S.: 334220
Johan Harden (CEO)

CR&T Ventures AB (1)
Goteborg, Gothenburg, Sweden   (100%)
Tel.: (46) 317086400
Securities & Commodity Exchanges
N.A.I.C.S.: 523210

Celemiab Group AB (1)
Nordenskioldsgatan 8, Malmo, 211 19, Sweden
Tel.: (46) 406602700
Sales Range: $25-49.9 Million
Emp.: 15
Marketing Consulting Services
N.A.I.C.S.: 541613
Kjell Lindqvist (Gen Mgr)

Citat AB (1)
PO Box 30159, 10425, Stockholm, Sweden   (100%)
Tel.: (46) 850661750
Web Site: http://www.citat.se
Sales Range: $50-74.9 Million
Emp.: 150
Plate Work Mfr
N.A.I.C.S.: 332313

IT Gymnasiet Sverige AB (1)
Origovagen 4, Gothenburg, Sweden   (100%)
Tel.: (46) 317341190
Sales Range: $10-24.9 Million
Emp.: 20
Colleges Universities & Professional Schools
N.A.I.C.S.: 611310

Mercuri International Group AB (1)
Gustav III s Boulevard 42, 169 03, Solna, Sweden   (100%)
Tel.: (46) 87052900
Web Site: https://mercuri.net
Sales Range: $25-49.9 Million
Emp.: 34
Holding Company
N.A.I.C.S.: 551112

Vittra AB (1)
Adolf Fredriks Kyrkogata 2, 111 37, Stockholm, Sweden   (100%)
Tel.: (46) 8 794 4200
Web Site: https://www.vittra.se
Emp.: 1,000
Elementary & Secondary Schools
N.A.I.C.S.: 611110
Anneli Wisen (Head-Ops)

BUREAU DE RECHERCHES GEOLOGIQUES ET MINIERE
3 Avenue Claude Guillemin, PO Box 36009, 45060, Orleans, Cedex, France
Tel.: (33) 238643434
Web Site: http://www.brgm.eu
Year Founded: 1959
Sales Range: $75-99.9 Million
Engineering & Environmental Services
N.A.I.C.S.: 541330
Pierre Toulhoat (Deputy CEO & Dir-Scientific)

Subsidiaries:

BRGM (1)
3 Ave Claude Guillemin, PO Box 6009, 45060, Orleans, France   (100%)
Tel.: (33) 238643439
Web Site: http://www.brgm.fr
Sales Range: $150-199.9 Million
Emp.: 850
Engineeering Services
N.A.I.C.S.: 541330

CFG Services SA (1)
3 Ave Claude Guillemin, Orleans, France   (100%)
Tel.: (33) 238643122
Web Site: http://www.cfgservices.fr
Sales Range: $25-49.9 Million
Emp.: 40
Engineeering Services
N.A.I.C.S.: 541330
Burno Lanouille (Pres)

IRIS Instruments SA (1)
1 Ave Buffon, PO Box 16007, Loiret, 45060, Orleans, Cedex 2, France   (51%)
Tel.: (33) 238638100
Web Site: http://www.iris-instruments.com
Sales Range: $25-49.9 Million
Emp.: 23
Instrument Mfr for Measuring & Testing Electricity & Electrical Signals
N.A.I.C.S.: 334515
Bernard Juano (Pres)

BUREAU VERITAS S.A.
Immeuble Newtime 40/52 Boulevard du Parc, 92200, Neuilly-sur-Seine, France
Tel.: (33) 155247000   FR
Web Site:
   https://group.bureauveritas.com
Year Founded: 1828
BVI—(EUR)
Rev.: $6,271,504,640
Assets: $7,101,534,720
Liabilities: $4,970,561,280
Net Worth: $2,130,973,440
Earnings: $551,393,920
Emp.: 62,031
Fiscal Year-end: 12/31/23
Holding Company; Product Testing & Certification, Conformity Assessment, Consulting & Training Services
N.A.I.C.S.: 551111
Matthieu de Tugny (Exec VP-Marine & Offshore Div)

Subsidiaries:

APP Corporation Pty Limited (1)
Level 7 116 Miller Street, Sydney, 2060, NSW, Australia
Tel.: (61) 299576211
Web Site: https://www.app.com.au
Real Estate Consulting Service
N.A.I.C.S.: 531390

Advanced Testing Laboratory, Inc. (1)
6954 Cornell Rd Ste 200, Cincinnati, OH 45242
Tel.: (513) 489-8447
Web Site: https://www.atlscience.com
Testing Laboratories
N.A.I.C.S.: 541380
Gregory A. Neal (CEO)

Bureau Veritas Australia Pty. Ltd. (1)
Level 11 500 Collins Street, Melbourne, 3000, VIC, Australia
Tel.: (61) 399220700
Web Site: https://www.bureauveritas.com.au
Emp.: 2,000
Scientific & Technical Support Services
N.A.I.C.S.: 561990

Subsidiary (Domestic):

Bureau Veritas Asset Integrity & Reliability Services Pty. Ltd. (2)
29 Rosegum Close, Warabrook, 2304, NSW, Australia
Tel.: (61) 249082500
Emp.: 30
Mining Services & Asset Management
N.A.I.C.S.: 213113
Ken Brown (Dir-Bus Dev & Special Projects)

Bureau Veritas International Trade Australia Pty. Ltd. (2)
29 Rosegum Close, Warabrook, 2304, NSW, Australia
Tel.: (61) 2 4908 2500
Coal Wholesale Trade Broker
N.A.I.C.S.: 425120

Bureau Veritas North America, Inc. (1)
100 SE 12th St, Fort Lauderdale, FL 33316
Tel.: (954) 236-8100
Web Site: https://www.bvna.com
Sales Range: $25-49.9 Million
Emp.: 70
Product Testing & Certification, Conformity Assessment, Consulting & Training Services
N.A.I.C.S.: 541380
Jorge Hercules (VP-Elevators & Certification Div)

Subsidiary (Domestic):

Bureau Veritas Consumer Products Services, Inc. (2)
100 Northpointe Pkwy, Buffalo, NY 14228
Tel.: (716) 505-3300
Web Site: http://www.us.bureauveritas.com
Product Testing & Certification Services
N.A.I.C.S.: 541380
Rick Rosati (VP-Governmental Affairs & Industry Standards)

Branch (Domestic):

Bureau Veritas North America, Inc. - Costa Mesa (2)
15 Musick Irvine, Costa Mesa, CA 92618
Tel.: (949) 716-6512
Web Site: http://www.us.bureauveritas.com
Sales Range: $1-9.9 Million
Emp.: 40
Scientific & Technical Consulting Services
N.A.I.C.S.: 541690

Subsidiary (Domestic):

DTI DiversiTech, Inc. (2)
16115 Cypress Rosehill Rd, Cypress, TX 77429
Tel.: (281) 304-1499
Web Site: http://www.dti-div.com
Sales Range: $10-24.9 Million
Emp.: 85
Oil & Gas Operations Support Activities
N.A.I.C.S.: 213112
Gerald L. Falls (Pres & CEO)

Bureau Veritas S.A.—(Continued)

Quiktrak Inc. (2)
8285 SW Nimbus Ave Ste 115/119, Beaverton, OR 97008-7172
Tel.: (503) 214-3000
Web Site: https://www.quiktrak.com
Sales Range: $10-24.9 Million
Emp.: 100
Industrial & Commercial Equipment Inspection Service
N.A.I.C.S.: 541990
Kim Plutte (COO & VP)

SIEMIC Inc. (2)
775 Montague Expy, Milpitas, CA 95035-6815
Tel.: (408) 526-1188
Web Site: http://www.siemic.com
Sales Range: $10-24.9 Million
Emp.: 100
Electric & Electronic Equipment Testing, Analysis & Certification Services
N.A.I.C.S.: 541380
Leslie Bai (Gen Mgr)

Bureau Veritas UK Limited (1)
Suite 206 Fort Dunlop, Fort Parkway, Birmingham, B24 9FD, United Kingdom
Tel.: (44) 1213772000
Web Site: http://www.bureauveritas.co.uk
Scientific & Technical Support Services
N.A.I.C.S.: 561990
Kyle Veitch (Dir-Technical, Quality & Risk)

Subsidiary (Domestic):

Inspectorate International Limited (2)
2 Perry Rd, Witham, CM8 3TU, Essex, United Kingdom
Tel.: (44) 1376536800
Web Site: http://www.inspectorate.com
Sales Range: $350-399.9 Million
Emp.: 7,000
Commodity Inspection & Testing Services
N.A.I.C.S.: 926150
David Lappage (Sec)

Subsidiary (US):

Inspectorate America Corporation (3)
12000 Aerospace Ave Ste 200, Houston, TX 77034
Tel.: (713) 944-2000
Web Site: http://www.inspectorate.com
Sales Range: $50-74.9 Million
Emp.: 100
Commodity Inspection & Testing Services
N.A.I.C.S.: 926140
Sergio Sanchez (VP-Food & Safety)

Subsidiary (Non-US):

Inspectorate Suisse S.A. (3)
Route de Cossonay 28b, PO Box 172, 1008, Prilly, Vaud, Switzerland
Tel.: (41) 216236230
Web Site: http://www.inspectorate.com
Sales Range: $25-49.9 Million
Emp.: 27
Commodity Inspection & Testing Services
N.A.I.C.S.: 926150
Kirill Doubrovine (Gen Mgr)

Subsidiary (Domestic):

MatthewsDaniel Limited (2)
No 10 Fenchurch Street, London, EC3M 3BE, United Kingdom
Tel.: (44) 2079291300
Emp.: 25
Holding Company; Loss Investigation & Risk Assessment Services
N.A.I.C.S.: 551112
Gary Mawditt (CEO)

Subsidiary (US):

Matthews-Daniel Company (3)
4544 Post Oak Place Dr Ste 160, Houston, TX 77027
Tel.: (713) 622-1633
Web Site: http://www.matdan.com
Sales Range: $10-24.9 Million
Loss Investigation & Risk Assessment Services
N.A.I.C.S.: 561611
James Vavasour (Pres & Dir-Marine)

Subsidiary (Domestic):

Matthews-Daniel International (London) Limited (3)
No 10 Fenchurch Street, London, EC3M 3BE, United Kingdom
Tel.: (44) 2079291300
Web Site: https://www.matdan.com
Loss Investigation & Risk Assessment Services
N.A.I.C.S.: 561611
Gary Mawditt (CEO)

California Code Check, Inc. (1)
250 N Westlake Blvd Ste 150, Westlake Village, CA 91362
Tel.: (805) 230-2888
Web Site:
   http://www.californiacodecheck.com
Engineering & Construction Consulting Services
N.A.I.C.S.: 541330
Bryan Spain (VP)

Galbraith Laboratories, Inc. (1)
2323 Sycamore Dr, Knoxville, TN 37921-1750
Tel.: (865) 546-1335
Web Site: http://www.galbraith.com
Emp.: 54
Chemical Testing Laboratory Services
N.A.I.C.S.: 541380
Jason Williams (Mgr-Bus Dev)

BURELLE S.A.
6 avenue de Provence, 75008, Paris, France
Tel.: (33) 140876500
Web Site: https://www.burelle.fr
BUR—(EUR)
Sales Range: $5-14.9 Billion
Emp.: 10,000
Holding Company
N.A.I.C.S.: 551112
Jean Burelle (Chm & CEO)

Subsidiaries:

Compagnie Plastic Omnium S.A. (1)
1 Allee Pierre Burelle, 92593, Levallois-Perret, Cedex, France (56.6%)
Tel.: (33) 140876400
Web Site: https://www.plasticomnium.com
Rev.: $7,877,260,286
Assets: $6,736,979,274
Liabilities: $4,972,548,291
Net Worth: $1,764,430,983
Earnings: $154,634,218
Emp.: 40,500
Fiscal Year-end: 12/31/2022
Plastic Components Mfr for Automotive, Medical, Pharmaceutical, Waste Management, Recreational Equipment & Recycling Industries
N.A.I.C.S.: 326199
Rodolphe Lapillonne (Chief Pur Performance Officer & Sr Exec VP)

Subsidiary (Non-US):

3P- Productos Plasticos Performantes SA (2)
Pista De Silla Km 6 700, PO Box 428, 46080, Valencia, Spain (100%)
Tel.: (34) 963896800
Web Site: http://www.plasticomnium.com
Sales Range: $50-74.9 Million
Emp.: 120
Plastics Products
N.A.I.C.S.: 326199

Subsidiary (Non-US):

3P GmbH (3)
Max Planck Str 27, Karben, 61184, Germany
Tel.: (49) 603948040
Web Site: http://www.3pcorporate.com
Sales Range: $25-49.9 Million
Emp.: 4
Plastics Products
N.A.I.C.S.: 326199

3P SpA (3)
Via Kennedy 38, Rodano Millepini, 20090, Milan, Italy (100%)
Tel.: (39) 0295328283
Web Site: http://www.3pcorporate.com

Sales Range: $25-49.9 Million
Emp.: 8
Plastics Products
N.A.I.C.S.: 326199

Subsidiary (US):

EPSCO International Inc. (2)
717 Georgia Ave, Deer Park, TX 77536-2513
Tel.: (281) 930-1340
Web Site: http://www.eadslink.com
Sales Range: $25-49.9 Million
Emp.: 50
Distr of Plastic Pipe
N.A.I.C.S.: 423720
Stuart Waldman (Controller)

Subsidiary (Non-US):

HBPO GmbH (2)
Rixbecker Strasse 75, 59552, Lippstadt, Germany (66.66%)
Tel.: (49) 2941 2838 0
Web Site: http://www.hbpogroup.com
Emp.: 760
Automobile Front-End Modules Mfr
N.A.I.C.S.: 336390
Martin Schuler (Pres & CEO)

Subsidiary (Domestic):

Inergy Automotive Systems S.A. (2)
18 Rue de Calais, 75009, Paris, France
Tel.: (33) 156022162
Web Site: http://www.inergyautomotive.com
Sales Range: $1-4.9 Billion
Emp.: 4,000
Automotive Fuel Systems Mfr
N.A.I.C.S.: 336310
Pierre Lecocq (CEO)

Subsidiary (Non-US):

Inergy Automotive Systems (Belgium) N.V. (3)
Grensstraat 12, 2200, Herentals, Belgium (100%)
Tel.: (32) 14849540
Web Site: http://www.inergyautomotive.com
Sales Range: $25-49.9 Million
Emp.: 80
Automotive Fuel Systems
N.A.I.C.S.: 336310
Peter Wijnants (Gen Mgr)

Inergy Automotive Systems Argentina S.A. (3)
Balcarce 1348, Florida, 1604, Buenos Aires, Argentina (50%)
Tel.: (54) 1147305700
Web Site: http://www.inergyautomotive.com
Sales Range: $1-9.9 Billion
Emp.: 250
Automobile Parts Mfr
N.A.I.C.S.: 336390
Leonard Baker (Plant Mgr)

Inergy Automotive Systems Belgium NV (3)
310 Rue De Ransbeek, Brussels, 1120, Belgium (50%)
Tel.: (32) 22642855
Web Site: http://www.inergyautomotive.com
Sales Range: $25-49.9 Million
Emp.: 90
Automotive Fuel Systems Mfr
N.A.I.C.S.: 336310
Wilfrid Schon (VP)

Subsidiary (Domestic):

Inergy Automotive Systems France (3)
92 rue du Marechal Leclerc, PO Box 80259, Venette, 60202, Compiegne, Cedex, France
Tel.: (33) 344903456
Web Site: http://www.inergyautomotive.com
Sales Range: $125-149.9 Million
Emp.: 500
Automotive Fuel Systems Mfr
N.A.I.C.S.: 326199

Subsidiary (Non-US):

Inergy Automotive Systems Germany GmbH (3)
Max Planck Strasse 27, D 61184, Karben, Germany (100%)
Tel.: (49) 603992900

Web Site: http://www.inergyautomotive.com
Sales Range: $50-74.9 Million
Emp.: 250
Automotive Fuel Systems Mfr
N.A.I.C.S.: 326199

Inergy Automotive Systems Germany GmbH (3)
Essener Strasse, 99819, Grossenlupnitz, Thuringen, Germany (100%)
Tel.: (49) 893692085192
Web Site: http://www.inergyautomotive.com
Sales Range: $25-49.9 Million
Emp.: 50
Automotive Fuel Systems Mfr
N.A.I.C.S.: 326199

Inergy Automotive Systems Germany GmbH (3)
Kesterbacher Str 23, 65479, Raunheim, Hessen, Germany (50%)
Tel.: (49) 614291340
Web Site: http://www.inergyautomotive.com
Sales Range: $25-49.9 Million
Emp.: 10
Automotive Fuel Systems Mfr
N.A.I.C.S.: 326199
Dieter Bruess (Gen Mgr)

Subsidiary (US):

Inergy Automotive Systems Inc. (3)
1549 W Beecher St, Adrian, MI 49221
Tel.: (517) 265-1100
Web Site: http://www.inergyautomotive.com
Rev.: $93,000,000
Emp.: 170
Plastic Automotive Parts
N.A.I.C.S.: 326199
John Dunn (Pres/CEO-Americas)

Subsidiary (Non-US):

Inergy Automotive Systems Mexico S.A. de C.V. (3)
Blvd Industria De La Transformacion 3150, Parque Industrial Saltillo, 25900, Ramos Arizpe, Coahuila, Mexico (100%)
Tel.: (52) 8444382200
Web Site: http://www.inergyautomotive.com
Emp.: 250
Automotive Fuel Systems Mfr
N.A.I.C.S.: 326199

Inergy Automotive Systems U.K. Ltd. (3)
Halesfield 6, Telford, TF7 4RQ, Stropshire, United Kingdom (100%)
Tel.: (44) 1952635588
Sales Range: $25-49.9 Million
Emp.: 50
Fuel Systems Mfr
N.A.I.C.S.: 336310

Subsidiary (Domestic):

Ludoparc S.A. (2)
131 151 Rue Du 1 Er Mai, 92000, Nanterre, France (100%)
Tel.: (33) 155669898
Web Site: http://www.plasticomnium.com
Sales Range: $25-49.9 Million
Emp.: 70
Playground Equipment Mfr
N.A.I.C.S.: 339920

Metroplast SA (2)
Rue Denis Papin, 71100, Chalon-sur-Saone, France (100%)
Tel.: (33) 385971200
Web Site: http://www.plasticomnium.com
Sales Range: $25-49.9 Million
Emp.: 50
Plastics Products
N.A.I.C.S.: 326199
Lesevere Oliser (Mgr)

Subsidiary (Non-US):

Plastic Omnium AB (2)
Vannhogsgatan 11, Vannhogsgatan 11, Trelleborg, 231 66, Sweden (100%)
Tel.: (46) 41012460
Web Site: http://www.plasticomnium.se
Sales Range: $25-49.9 Million
Emp.: 6
Plastics Products
N.A.I.C.S.: 326199
Christophe Gence (Gen Mgr)

Plastic Omnium AG (2)
Baselstrasse 61, 4124, Basel,
Switzerland (100%)
Tel.: (41) 615603634
Web Site: http://www.plasticomnium.com
Sales Range: $25-49.9 Million
Emp.: 40
Plastics Products
N.A.I.C.S.: 326199

Subsidiary (Domestic):

**Plastic Omnium Auto Exterieur
SA** (2)
1 rue du Parc, 92593, Levallois-Perret,
France (100%)
Tel.: (33) 140876400
Web Site: http://www.plasticomnium.com
Sales Range: $50-74.9 Million
Emp.: 200
Motor Vehicle Plastic Parts
N.A.I.C.S.: 326199
Andre Poirson (Mng Dir)

Subsidiary (Non-US):

Plastic Omnium Automotive Ltd (2)
Westminster Industrial Est Huntington Way,
Measham, Swadlincote, DE12 7DS,
Terbyshira, United Kingdom (100%)
Tel.: (44) 530273849
Web Site: http://www.plasticomnium.com
Sales Range: $50-74.9 Million
Emp.: 150
Automotive Plastic Products
N.A.I.C.S.: 326199

Plastic Omnium BV (2)
Nikkelstraat 31, 4823 DZ, Breda, Nether-
lands
Tel.: (31) 76 54 25 055
Web Site: http://www.plasticomnium.com
Plastics Product Mfr
N.A.I.C.S.: 326199

Plastic Omnium Do Brasil Ltda (2)
Avenida Hilario Jose Signorini 201 Distrito
Industrial Una II Bairro, Itaim, Taubate,
12085193, SP, Brazil
Tel.: (55) 12 2125 0900
Web Site: http://www.plasticomnium.com
Emp.: 400
Plastics Product Mfr
N.A.I.C.S.: 326199
Frederic Acha (Gen Mgr)

**Plastic Omnium Entsorgungstechnik
GmbH** (2)
Essener Strasse, 99819, Grossenlupnitz,
Germany (100%)
Tel.: (49) 369208510
Web Site: http://www.plasticomnium.com
Sales Range: $50-74.9 Million
Emp.: 200
Plastics Products
N.A.I.C.S.: 326199

**Plastic Omnium Equipamientos Exte-
riores SA** (2)
Calle Gobelas 47-49, La Florida, 28023,
Madrid, Spain (100%)
Tel.: (34) 917082970
Web Site: http://www.plasticomnium.com
Sales Range: $25-49.9 Million
Emp.: 20
Plastics Products
N.A.I.C.S.: 326199

Subsidiary (US):

Plastic Omnium Industries Inc. (2)
1050 Wilshire Dr, Troy, MI 48084
Tel.: (248) 458-0700
Plastics Product Mfr
N.A.I.C.S.: 423120

Subsidiary (Domestic):

Plastic Omnium Medical SA (2)
1 Rue du Parc, PO Box 7020, 92593, Per-
ret, France (100%)
Tel.: (33) 472767778
Web Site: http://www.plasticomnium.com.fr
Sales Range: $100-124.9 Million
Emp.: 300
Plastics Product Mfr
N.A.I.C.S.: 326199

Subsidiary (Non-US):

Plastic Omnium SA (2)

Calle Galvarino Gallardo 1754, Providencia,
Santiago, 6640677, Chile
Tel.: (56) 22360000
Web Site: http://www.plasticomnium.com
Sales Range: $25-49.9 Million
Emp.: 53
Plastics Products
N.A.I.C.S.: 326199

**Plastic Omnium Sistemas Urbanos
SA** (2)
Calle Gobelas 47-49, La Florida, 28023,
Madrid, Spain (100%)
Tel.: (34) 917082970
Web Site: http://www.plasticomnium.com
Sales Range: $25-49.9 Million
Emp.: 20
Plastics Products
N.A.I.C.S.: 326199

Subsidiary (Domestic):

**Plastic Omnium Systemes Urbains
SA** (2)
19 Ave Jules Carteret, PO Box 7020,
69342, Lyon, France (100%)
Tel.: (33) 472767778
Web Site: http://www.plasticomnium.com
Plastics Products
N.A.I.C.S.: 326199

Subsidiary (US):

Plastic Omnium, Inc (2)
5100 Old Pearman Dairy Rd, Anderson, SC
29625-1314
Tel.: (864) 260-0000
Web Site: http://www.plasticomnium.com
Sales Range: $150-199.9 Million
Emp.: 400
Automobile Bumpers Mfr
N.A.I.C.S.: 326199
Hugo Hernandez (Gen Mgr)

Subsidiary (Non-US):

Posedo Co., Ltd. (2)
140-2 Daejeon Ri Hapdeok-Eub Tangjin-
Goon, Seoul, Korea (South) (100%)
Tel.: (82) 41 362 2390
Web Site: http://www.posedo.co.kr
Sales Range: $25-49.9 Million
Emp.: 10
Plastics Product Mfr
N.A.I.C.S.: 326199

Subsidiary (Domestic):

**Produits Plastiques Performants -
3P** (2)
1 rue du Parc, 92593, Levallois-Perret,
France (100%)
Tel.: (33) 140876400
Web Site: http://www.plasticomnium.com
Sales Range: $200-249.9 Million
Emp.: 800
Plastics Products
N.A.I.C.S.: 326199

Transit SA (2)
19 Ave Jules Carteret, PO Box 7020,
69342, Lyon, France (100%)
Tel.: (33) 472767778
Web Site: http://www.plasticomnium.com
Wholesale of Plastic Products
N.A.I.C.S.: 424130

Signature S.A. (1)
63 Rue Edouard Colone, 92027, Nanterre,
Cedex, France (100%)
Tel.: (33) 140874300
Web Site: http://www.ciesignature.com
Sales Range: $150-199.9 Million
Emp.: 400
Signs, Safety Equipment & Road Marking
Mfr; Road Management Services
N.A.I.C.S.: 339950

Subsidiary (Non-US):

Berlack GmbH (2)
Kusterkamp 1, D-25355, Barmstedt, Ger-
many
Tel.: (49) 412392190
Web Site: http://www.berlack.de
Sales Range: $25-49.9 Million
Emp.: 16
Road Marking Products Mfr
N.A.I.C.S.: 339940

Subsidiary (Domestic):

Euroliners (2)
Zone Industrielle de Boulay 30 Rte du Gen-
eral de Rascas, 57220, Boulay,
France (100%)
Tel.: (33) 387794838
Web Site: http://www.euroliners.com
Sales Range: $25-49.9 Million
Emp.: 27
Road Marking Machines Mfr
N.A.I.C.S.: 333120

BURFORD CAPITAL LIMITED
Oak House Hirzel Street, Saint Peter
Port, GY1 2NP, Guernsey, United
Kingdom
Tel.: (44) 2035302000
Web Site:
https://www.burfordcapital.com
Year Founded: 2009
BUR—(NYSE)
Rev.: $152,158,000
Assets: $3,524,706,000
Liabilities: $1,584,016,000
Net Worth: $1,940,690,000
Earnings: ($72,066,000)
Emp.: 140
Fiscal Year-end: 12/31/21
Investment Management Service
N.A.I.C.S.: 523999

BURG-WACHTER KG
Altenhofer Weg 15, 58300, Wetter,
Germany
Tel.: (49) 2335965366 De
Web Site: http://www.burg-
waechter.de
Sales Range: $150-199.9 Million
Emp.: 700
Locks, Mailboxes & Safe Mfr & Distr
N.A.I.C.S.: 332510
Dietmar Luling (Mng Dir)

Subsidiaries:

BURG-WAECHTER S.A.R.L. (1)
2 Rue des Hetres, 67670, Paris, France
Tel.: (33) 388 591843
Hardware Products Distr
N.A.I.C.S.: 423710

Sanyo Video Vertrieb AG (1)
An der Strusbek 31, 22926, Ahrensburg,
Germany
Tel.: (49) 410247980
Web Site: http://www.santec-video.com
Rev.: $11,380,050
Emp.: 25
Security System Services
N.A.I.C.S.: 561621
Lars Christian Diestel (CEO)

**BURGAN COMPANY FOR
WELL DRILLING, TRADING &
MAINTENANCE KSCC**
West Industrial Shuaiba Block 3
Street 306, PO Box 47143, Fahaheel,
64022, Kuwait
Tel.: (965) 22263800
Web Site:
https://www.burgandrilling.com
Year Founded: 1970
ABAR—(KUW)
Rev.: $161,005,412
Assets: $647,756,932
Liabilities: $398,950,873
Net Worth: $248,806,058
Earnings: $10,199,158
Emp.: 3,015
Fiscal Year-end: 03/31/24
Oil Well Drilling & Maintenance Ser-
vices
N.A.I.C.S.: 213111
Ahmed Hamad Ahmed Al-Hamad
(Chm)

**BURGBAD AKTIENGESELL-
SCHAFT**

Bad Fredeburg Kirchplatz 10, 57392,
Schmallenberg, Germany
Tel.: (49) 297496170
Web Site: http://www.burgbad.com
Sales Range: $100-124.9 Million
Emp.: 628
Interior & Bathroom Furnishings Mfr
N.A.I.C.S.: 327110
Karl-Heinz Wennrich (Chm-Mgmt Bd)

**BURGESS ARCHITECTURAL
PRODUCTS LIMITED**
Brookfield Rd, Hinckley, LE10 2LL,
Leicestershire, United Kingdom
Tel.: (44) 1455618787
Web Site:
http://www.burgessceilings.co.uk
Sales Range: $25-49.9 Million
Emp.: 50
Metal Ceiling Tiles Mfr
N.A.I.C.S.: 332323
Joe Higgins (Dir-Sls)

BURGO GROUP S.P.A.
Via Piave 1, 36077, Altavilla Vicen-
tina, Italy
Tel.: (39) 0444396811
Web Site: http://www.burgo.com
Sales Range: $650-699.9 Million
Emp.: 4,983
Graphics Paper & Flexible Packaging
Papers Mfr
N.A.I.C.S.: 322120
Ignazio Capuano (CEO)

Subsidiaries:

Burgo Ardennes sa (1)
1 Rue de la Papeterie, 6760, Virton, Bel-
gium
Tel.: (32) 63 58 71 11
Coated Paper Mfr
N.A.I.C.S.: 322220

Burgo Benelux sa (1)
Romeinsesteenweg 468, 1853, Strombeek-
Bever, Belgium
Tel.: (32) 2333 3010
Emp.: 7
Paper Product Whslr
N.A.I.C.S.: 424110
Johan Blyaert (Mng Dir)

Burgo Central Europe GmbH (1)
Brahmsstr 32, 81677, Munich, Germany
Tel.: (49) 89 455 0350
Paper Products Mfr
N.A.I.C.S.: 322299

Burgo Deutschland Gmbh (1)
Brahmstrasse 32, 81677, Munich, Germany
Tel.: (49) 89 45 50 35 0
Coated Paper Mfr
N.A.I.C.S.: 322220
Guido Caccya (Gen Mgr)

Burgo Distribuzione Srl (1)
Via dei Missaglia 97-edificio B1, 20142, Mi-
lan, Italy
Tel.: (39) 02893941
Web Site:
http://www.burgodistribuzione.com
Paper Product Whslr
N.A.I.C.S.: 424110
Gianluigi Magarini (Dir-Comml)

Burgo Eastern Europe Sp. z o.o. (1)
Prosta 32, 00-838, Warsaw, Poland
Tel.: (48) 22 122 5206
Paper Products Mfr
N.A.I.C.S.: 322299

Burgo Energia Srl (1)
Corso Giulio Cesare 268 Edificio A, 10154,
Turin, Italy
Tel.: (39) 011 22 333 22
Web Site: http://www.burgoenergia.it
Eletric Power Generation Services
N.A.I.C.S.: 221111
Luigi Piombi (Mgr-Ops)

Burgo Factor Spa (1)
Via Cechov 50/2, 20152, Milan, Italy
Tel.: (39) 011 2233546
Web Site: http://www.burgofactor.it
Financial Factoring Services

Burgo Group S.p.A.—(Continued)
N.A.I.C.S.: 522299

Burgo France SARL (1)
6 rue Neuve Saint-Pierre, 75004, Paris, France
Tel.: (33) 15 578 2655
Paper Products Mfr
N.A.I.C.S.: 322299

Burgo Iberica Papel SA (1)
Via Augusta 9 Prai 1a, 08006, Barcelona, Spain
Tel.: (34) 93 487 5476
Paper Products Mfr
N.A.I.C.S.: 322299

Burgo North America Inc (1)
1 Landmark Sq, Stamford, CT 06901
Tel.: (203) 569-9000
Emp.: 10
Paper Product Whslr
N.A.I.C.S.: 424110
Giovanni Cattoni (Mng Dir)

Burgo Polaska Sp z o o (1)
ul Prosta 32, 00-838, Warsaw, Poland
Tel.: (48) 221225206
Web Site: http://www.burgogroup.com
Emp.: 4
Paper Product Whslr
N.A.I.C.S.: 424110
Katarzyna Borowska (Mng Dir)

Burgo UK ltd (1)
Office G Qld Stratford Business Park Falcon Drive, Old Stratford, Milton Keynes, MK19 6FG, United Kingdom
Tel.: (44) 1908 265800
Web Site: http://www.burgo.com
Emp.: 10
Paper Product Whslr
N.A.I.C.S.: 424110
Andrew Causer (Mng Dir)

Comecart S.p.A (1)
Via Piave 1, 12100, Cuneo, Italy
Tel.: (39) 0171 410410
Web Site: http://www.comecart.it
Paper Machinery Mfr
N.A.I.C.S.: 333243
Massimo Zambon (Mgr-Paper & Board)

BURGUNDY DIAMOND MINES LIMITED
Level 25 South 32 Tower 108 St Georges Terrace, Perth, 6000, WA, Australia
Tel.: (61) 63133945
Web Site: https://www.burgundy-diamonds.com
BDM—(ASX)
Rev.: $257,484,000
Assets: $666,985,000
Liabilities: $508,753,000
Net Worth: $158,232,000
Earnings: ($676,000)
Fiscal Year-end: 12/31/23
Oil & Gas Exploration
N.A.I.C.S.: 211120
Kim Truter (CEO)

Subsidiaries:

Arctic Canadian Diamond Company Ltd. (1)
900 - 606 4 Street SW, Calgary, T2P 1T1, AB, Canada
Tel.: (403) 910-1933
Web Site: http://www.ddmines.com
Diamond Exploration & Mining
N.A.I.C.S.: 212390

Subsidiary (Non-US):

Dominion Diamond (India) Private Limited (2)
9010 Bharat Diamond Bourse Bandra Kurla Complex, Bandra E, 400051, Mumbai, India
Tel.: (91) 2223699004
Web Site: http://www.harrywinston.co.in
Sales Range: $25-49.9 Million
Emp.: 15
Jewelry Watch Precious Stone & Precious Metal Whslr
N.A.I.C.S.: 423940

Holding (Domestic):

EKATI Diamond Mine (2)
#1102 4920 52nd Street, Yellowknife, X1A 3T1, NT, Canada
Tel.: (867) 669-6100
Diamond Mining
N.A.I.C.S.: 212390
Rob Cooper (Pres-Asset)

BURGUNDY TECHNOLOGY ACQUISITION CORPORATION
Boundary Hall Cricket Square, PO Box 1093, Georgetown, KY1-1102, Cayman Islands
Tel.: (345) 9457099   Ky
Year Founded: 2020
BTAQU—(NASDAQ)
Sales Range: Less than $1 Million
Investment Services
N.A.I.C.S.: 523999
Leo Apotheker (Chm & Co-CEO)

BURIRAM SUGAR PUBLIC COMPANY LIMITED
237 Moo 2 Baan Sao-Ae Hinlekfai, Kumueang, Buriram, 31190, Thailand
Tel.: (66) 44666592
Web Site:
   https://www.buriramsugar.com
BRR—(THA)
Rev.: $183,845,063
Assets: $259,765,851
Liabilities: $172,440,058
Net Worth: $87,325,793
Earnings: $15,757,371
Fiscal Year-end: 12/31/23
Sugar Mfr
N.A.I.C.S.: 311314
Sirichai Sombutsiri (Chm)

Subsidiaries:

Key Brand Fertilizer Company Limited (1)
237 Village No 2 Ban Sok Khu Road, Ban Karo Hin Lek Fai Subdistrict Khu Mueang District, Buriram, Thailand
Tel.: (66) 957492708
Web Site: http://www.thaikbf.com
Organic & Chemical Fertilizer Mfr
N.A.I.C.S.: 325311

Sugarcane Ecoware Co., Ltd. (1)
128/77 7th Fl Phayathai Plaza Phayathai Rd, Thug Phayathai Ratchathewi, Bangkok, Thailand
Tel.: (66) 815548320
Web Site: https://seweoware.com
Packaging Product Mfr & Distr
N.A.I.C.S.: 322220

BURKHALTER HOLDING AG
Flurstrasse 55, 8048, Zurich, Switzerland
Tel.: (41) 445376400
Web Site: https://www.burkhalter.ch
Year Founded: 1959
BRKN—(SWX)
Rev.: $1,378,451,396
Assets: $558,458,524
Liabilities: $408,680,772
Net Worth: $149,777,752
Earnings: $61,675,779
Emp.: 5,185
Fiscal Year-end: 12/31/23
Electrotechnical & Telecommunication Engineering Systems Distr & Installer
N.A.I.C.S.: 335999
Gaudenz F. Domenig (Chm)

Subsidiaries:

Alpha-Plan AG Rothrist (1)
Helblingstrasse 4, 4852, Rothrist, Aargau, Switzerland
Tel.: (41) 627851085
Web Site: http://www.alpha-plan.ch
Sales Range: $25-49.9 Million
Emp.: 16
Electrical Engineering Services
N.A.I.C.S.: 541330

As Stuber, Znl Der Sergio Lo Stanco Elektro AG (1)
Landshutstrasse 3, 3427, Utzenstorf, Switzerland
Tel.: (41) 326655060
Web Site: https://www.asstuber.ch
Emp.: 5
Electrical Engineering Services
N.A.I.C.S.: 541330

Bassi Elektro AG (1)
Poststrasse 43, 7050, Arosa, Graubunden, Switzerland
Tel.: (41) 813787878
Web Site: http://www.bassiarosa.ch
Sales Range: $25-49.9 Million
Emp.: 20
Electrical Engineering Services
N.A.I.C.S.: 541330
Karl Butzerin (Mng Dir)

Baumann Electro AG (1)
Breitfeldstrasse 10, 9015, Saint Gallen, Switzerland
Tel.: (41) 713118888
Web Site: http://www.baumann-electro.ch
Electrical Engineering Services
N.A.I.C.S.: 541330

Bieri Elektrotechnik AG (1)
Altelsweg 12, 3661, Uetendorf, Switzerland
Tel.: (41) 332220060
Web Site: http://www.bieri-elektrotechnik.ch
Emp.: 20
Electrical Engineering Services
N.A.I.C.S.: 541330

Burkhalter Automation AG (1)
Muttenzerstrasse 143, 4133, Pratteln, Basel, Switzerland
Tel.: (41) 616993939
Web Site: http://www.burkhalter-automation.ch
Sales Range: $25-49.9 Million
Emp.: 18
Industrial Automation Services
N.A.I.C.S.: 561990
Deborah Sig (Mng Dir)

Burkhalter Elektrotechnik AG (1)
Rheinweg 1a, 8200, Schaffhausen, Switzerland
Tel.: (41) 526200808
Web Site: http://www.bu-schaffhausen.ch
Emp.: 18
Electrical Engineering Services
N.A.I.C.S.: 541330

Burkhalter Services AG (1)
Vega-Strasse 3, Glattpark, 8152, Opfikon, Switzerland
Tel.: (41) 587339090
Electrical Engineering Services
N.A.I.C.S.: 541330

Burkhalter Technics AG (1)
Hohlstrasse 475, 8048, Zurich, Switzerland
Tel.: (41) 444321111
Web Site: http://www.burkhalter-technics.ch
Sales Range: $75-99.9 Million
Emp.: 500
Electrical Engineering Services
N.A.I.C.S.: 541330

Caviezel AG (1)
Bramabuelstrasse 4A Platz, Davos Platz, 7270, Davos, Graubunden, Switzerland
Tel.: (41) 81 410 00 00
Web Site: http://www.caviezel-ag.ch
Sales Range: $25-49.9 Million
Emp.: 45
Electrical Engineering Services
N.A.I.C.S.: 541330
Adis Crljenkovic (Mng Dir)

Derungs AG (1)
Via S Clau Sura 2, 7130, Ilanz, Switzerland
Tel.: (41) 819200000
Web Site: http://www.elektro-derungs.ch
Emp.: 16
Electrical Engineering Services
N.A.I.C.S.: 541330

Ebnother Elektro AG (1)
Kantonsstrasse 29, 8863, Buttikon, Switzerland
Tel.: (41) 554442901
Web Site: http://www.ebnoether-elektro.ch
Electrical Engineering Services
N.A.I.C.S.: 541330

Eigenmann AG (1)
Frauenfelderstrasse 13, 9542, Munchwilen, Aargau, Switzerland
Tel.: (41) 719600666
Web Site: http://www.eigenmann-elektro.ch
Electrical Engineering Services
N.A.I.C.S.: 541330

Electra Buin SA (1)
Via da Manarol 080, 7550, Scuol, Graubunden, Switzerland
Tel.: (41) 812586300
Web Site: http://www.buin.ch
Sales Range: $25-49.9 Million
Emp.: 25
Electrical Engineering Services
N.A.I.C.S.: 541330

Elektro Arber AG (1)
Romanshornerstrasse 2, 8280, Kreuzlingen, Thurgau, Switzerland
Tel.: (41) 716868050
Web Site: http://www.arber.ch
Sales Range: $25-49.9 Million
Emp.: 110
Electrical Engineering Services
N.A.I.C.S.: 541330
Andreas Haueter (Mng Dir)

Elektro Burkhalter AG (1)
Eymattstrasse 7, 3027, Bern, Switzerland
Tel.: (41) 319963333
Web Site: http://www.burkhalter-biel.ch
Emp.: 130
Electrical Engineering Services
N.A.I.C.S.: 541330

Elektro Christoffel, Znl Der Caviezel AG (1)
Obere Strasse 19, 7270, Davos, Switzerland
Tel.: (41) 814137455
Web Site: https://www.elektrochristoffel.ch
Emp.: 20
Electrical Engineering Services
N.A.I.C.S.: 541330

Elektro Gutzwiller AG (1)
Muhlemattstrasse 25, 4104, Oberwil, Basel, Switzerland
Tel.: (41) 614061010
Web Site: http://www.elektro-gutzwiller.ch
Sales Range: $25-49.9 Million
Emp.: 25
Electrical Engineering Services
N.A.I.C.S.: 541330
Marc Spuhler (Mng Dir)

Elektro Hunziker AG (1)
Moosweg 10, 3607, Thun, Switzerland
Tel.: (41) 332251010
Web Site: http://www.elektrohunziker.ch
Electrical Engineering Services
N.A.I.C.S.: 541330

Elektro Kalin AG (1)
Leutschenstrasse 19, 8807, Freienbach, Switzerland
Tel.: (41) 554223333
Web Site: https://www.elektro-kaelin.ch
Electrical Engineering Services
N.A.I.C.S.: 541330

Elektro Niklaus AG (1)
Grabenstrasse 12, 9220, Bischofszell, Switzerland
Tel.: (41) 714223737
Web Site: http://www.enb.ch
Emp.: 30
Electrical Engineering Services
N.A.I.C.S.: 541330

Elektro Pizol AG (1)
Malervastrasse 5, 7320, Sargans, Switzerland
Tel.: (41) 817236263
Web Site: http://www.elektro-pizol.ch
Sales Range: $25-49.9 Million
Emp.: 13
Electrical Engineering Services
N.A.I.C.S.: 541330
Armin Walser (Mng Dir)

Elektro Ruegg AG (1)
Voa Sporz 12, 7078, Lenzerheide, Graubunden, Switzerland
Tel.: (41) 813851717
Web Site: http://www.ruegg-elektro.ch
Emp.: 20
Electrical Engineering Services

N.A.I.C.S.: 541330
Andreas Handle *(Mng Dir)*

Elektro Schmidlin AG (1)
Prattelerstrasse 35, 4132, Muttenz, Switzerland
Tel.: (41) 614657878
Web Site: http://www.elektro-schmidlin.ch
Electrical Engineering Services
N.A.I.C.S.: 541330

Elektro Siegrist AG (1)
Dorfstrasse 2, 5082, Kaisten, Aargau, Switzerland
Tel.: (41) 628697070
Web Site: http://www.siegrist-elektro.ch
Sales Range: $25-49.9 Million
Emp.: 34
Electrical Engineering Services
N.A.I.C.S.: 541330

Elektro Stampfl AG (1)
Muhlenstrasse 24, 9000, Saint Gallen, Switzerland
Tel.: (41) 712227570
Web Site: https://www.elektro-stampfl.ch
Emp.: 20
Electrical Engineering Services
N.A.I.C.S.: 541330

Elektro Zurichsee AG (1)
Zugerstrasse 56, 8810, Horgen, Switzerland
Tel.: (41) 447255082
Web Site: http://www.elektro-zuerichsee.ch
Emp.: 25
Electrical Engineering Services
N.A.I.C.S.: 541330

Elektro-Bau AG Rothrist (1)
Helblingstrasse 4, 4852, Rothrist, Aargau, Switzerland
Tel.: (41) 627852424
Web Site: http://www.elektro-bau.ch
Electrical Engineering Services
N.A.I.C.S.: 541330

Elektrohuus von Allmen AG (1)
Gsteigstrasse 27, 3780, Gstaad, Switzerland
Tel.: (41) 337487748
Web Site: http://www.elektrohuus.ch
Sales Range: $25-49.9 Million
Emp.: 40
Electrical Engineering Services
N.A.I.C.S.: 541330
Bruno Zinger *(Mng Dir)*

Eletro Celio SA (1)
Via Industrie 23, 6512, Giubiasco, Ticino, Switzerland
Tel.: (41) 918573641
Web Site: http://www.celio.ch
Electrical Engineering Services
N.A.I.C.S.: 541330
Marco Celio *(Mng Dir)*

Eltel Sisa, Znl Der Elektrohuus Von Allmen AG (1)
Gewerbestrasse 1, 3770, Zweisimmen, Switzerland
Tel.: (41) 337298020
Web Site: https://www.eltel-sisa.ch
Emp.: 15
Electrical Engineering Services
N.A.I.C.S.: 541330

Fliri & Conrad Electro, Znl Der Electra Buin S.A. (1)
Via Val Mustair 156, 7536, Sta Maria, Switzerland
Tel.: (41) 818503939
Web Site: https://www.fliriconrad.ch
Emp.: 7
Electrical Engineering Services
N.A.I.C.S.: 541330

Fritz Wegmann Elektrische Anlagen AG (1)
Henauerstrasse 11, Niederuzwil, 9244, Uzwil, Switzerland
Tel.: (41) 719500529
Web Site: http://www.elektro-wegmann.ch
Electrical Engineering Services
N.A.I.C.S.: 541330

Gallati AG (1)
Grossmatte Ost 24 B, 6014, Lucerne, Switzerland
Tel.: (41) 2494070
Web Site: https://www.gallatiag.ch

Civil Engineering Services
N.A.I.C.S.: 541330

Grichting & Valterio Electro SA (1)
Route des Iles 38, 1950, Sion, Valais, Switzerland
Tel.: (41) 279481414
Web Site: http://www.grichting-valterio.ch
Sales Range: $25-49.9 Million
Emp.: 100
Electrical Engineering Services
N.A.I.C.S.: 541330

Guyer Warme Und Wasser AG (1)
Zurichbergstrasse 80, 8044, Zurich, Switzerland
Tel.: (41) 442684444
Web Site: https://www.guyer.ch
Plumbing Work Services
N.A.I.C.S.: 238220

Imwinkelried Luftung Und Klima AG (1)
Torweg 10, 3930, Visp, Switzerland
Tel.: (41) 279480720
Web Site: https://www.imwinkelried-group.ch
Ventilation & Air Conditioning Services
N.A.I.C.S.: 238220

K. Schweizer AG (1)
Hammerstrasse 121, 4005, Basel, Switzerland
Tel.: (41) 616993737
Web Site: http://www.ksag.ch
Electrical Engineering Services
N.A.I.C.S.: 541330

Kalte 3000 AG (1)
Luxwiesenstrasse 4, 7302, Landquart, Switzerland
Tel.: (41) 813000300
Web Site: https://www.kaelte3000.com
Cooling System Services
N.A.I.C.S.: 238220

Kolb Elektro AG (1)
Staatsstrasse 129, Oberriet, 9463, Saint Gallen, Switzerland
Tel.: (41) 717636060
Web Site: http://www.kolbelektro.ch
Electrical Installation Services
N.A.I.C.S.: 238210

Kreis Wasser AG (1)
Moosstrasse 52, 9014, Saint Gallen, Switzerland
Tel.: (41) 712742074
Web Site: https://www.kreiswasser.ch
Heating & Sanitary Services
N.A.I.C.S.: 541620

LKE Haustechnik AG (1)
Flurstrasse 4, CH- 7205, Zizers, Switzerland
Tel.: (41) 813226655
Web Site: https://www.lke-haustechnik.ch
Civil Engineering Services
N.A.I.C.S.: 541330

Langle & Staub Sanitarplanung GmbH (1)
Teufenerstrasse 25, 9001, Saint Gallen, Switzerland
Tel.: (41) 712222245
Web Site: https://www.slsanitaerplanung.ch
Building Technology Services
N.A.I.C.S.: 541350

M&H Elektro AG (1)
Alpenblickstrasse 26, Lachen, 8853, Schwyz, Switzerland
Tel.: (41) 554426644
Web Site: http://www.mhelektro.ch
Emp.: 30
Electrical Installation Services
N.A.I.C.S.: 238210

M. Kunz AG (1)
Landstrasse 44, 7252, Klosters, Switzerland
Tel.: (41) 814102200
Web Site: https://www.kunz.ch
Engineering Consulting Services
N.A.I.C.S.: 541330

Marcel Hufschmid AG (1)
Industriestrasse 55, PO Box 2259, 6302, Zug, Switzerland
Tel.: (41) 417696969
Web Site: http://www.hufschmid-elektro.ch
Sales Range: $25-49.9 Million
Emp.: 110
Electrical Engineering Services

N.A.I.C.S.: 541330
Stephen Ulrich *(CEO)*

Merinat S.A. (1)
Chaussee de la Guinguette 12, 1800, Vevey, Switzerland
Tel.: (41) 219258080
Web Site: https://www.merinat.ch
Emp.: 90
Electrical Engineering Services
N.A.I.C.S.: 541330

Oberholzer AG (1)
Pfaffikerstrasse 34, 8610, Uster, Zurich, Switzerland
Tel.: (41) 844667788
Web Site: http://www.oberholzer.ch
Sales Range: $25-49.9 Million
Emp.: 90
Electrical Engineering Services
N.A.I.C.S.: 541330

Pauli Elektro AG (1)
Einschlagweg 71, 3400, Burgdorf, Switzerland
Tel.: (41) 344207070
Web Site: https://www.paulielektro.ch
Emp.: 19
Electrical Engineering Services
N.A.I.C.S.: 541330

Perl-Pool AG (1)
Weinfelderstrasse 12, 8576, Mauren, Liechtenstein
Tel.: (423) 716362014
Civil Engineering Services
N.A.I.C.S.: 541330

Peter & Barbisch AG (1)
Malervastrasse 5, 7320, Sargans, Saint Gallen, Switzerland
Tel.: (41) 81 723 62 63
Web Site: http://www.peter-barbisch.ch
Sales Range: $25-49.9 Million
Emp.: 17
Electrical Engineering Services
N.A.I.C.S.: 541330

Rast Elektro AG (1)
Hauptstrass 15, Kublis, 7240, Davos, Switzerland
Tel.: (41) 813321127
Web Site: https://www.rastelektro.ch
Electrical Engineering Services
N.A.I.C.S.: 541330

Robert Widmer AG (1)
Reusseggstrasse 9, 6002, Lucerne, Switzerland
Tel.: (41) 414204833
Web Site: http://www.widmer-elektro.ch
Emp.: 50
Electrical Installation Services
N.A.I.C.S.: 238210

Russi Heizung-Sanitar AG (1)
Gemsstockstrasse 1, 6490, Andermatt, Switzerland
Tel.: (41) 8870387
Web Site: https://www.russiag.ch
Building Technology Services
N.A.I.C.S.: 541350

Schachenmann & Co. AG (1)
Hochbergerstrasse 60 B, 4057, Basel, Switzerland
Tel.: (41) 616992233
Web Site: http://www.schachenmann.ch
Providers of Electrical Services
N.A.I.C.S.: 238210

Schachenmann & Co. AG (1)
Hafenstrasse 92, 4127, Birsfelden, Switzerland
Tel.: (41) 613789800
Web Site: http://www.schachenmann.ch
Sales Range: $25-49.9 Million
Emp.: 100
Providers of Electrical Services
N.A.I.C.S.: 238210

Schild Elektro AG (1)
Sandweg 4, 3818, Grindelwald, Bern, Switzerland
Tel.: (41) 338531111
Web Site: http://www.schild-elektro.ch
Sales Range: $25-49.9 Million
Emp.: 20
Electrical Engineering Services
N.A.I.C.S.: 541330

Schmitter Elektro, Znl Der Elektro-Bau AG (1)
Bachweg 22, 4852, Rothrist, Switzerland
Tel.: (41) 627944444
Web Site: https://www.schmitter-elektro.ch
Electrical Engineering Services
N.A.I.C.S.: 541330

Schonholzer AG (1)
Kalchbuhlstrasse 18, 7000, Chur, Graubunden, Switzerland
Tel.: (41) 81 257 12 12
Web Site: http://www.schoenholzer-elektro.ch
Electrical Contracting Services
N.A.I.C.S.: 238210
Jan Hubert *(Mng Dir)*

Schultheis-Mockli AG (1)
Froschenweidstrasse 10, 8404, Winterthur, Switzerland
Tel.: (41) 522350101
Web Site: http://www.schultheismoeckli.ch
Electrical Engineering Services
N.A.I.C.S.: 541330

Sedelec Jura Bernois, Succursale De Sedelec S.A. (1)
Rue de la Combe-Aubert 22, Tramelan, 2720, Lausanne, Switzerland
Tel.: (41) 324874670
Electrical Engineering Services
N.A.I.C.S.: 541330

Sedelec La Vallee, Succursale De Sedelec S.A. (1)
Route Neuve 15, 1347, Le Sentier, Switzerland
Tel.: (41) 218459595
Electrical Engineering Services
N.A.I.C.S.: 541330

Sedelec SA (1)
Rue Blavignac 1, 1227, Carouge, Geneva, Switzerland
Tel.: (41) 228698000
Web Site: http://www.sedelec.ch
Emp.: 300
Electrical Engineering Services
N.A.I.C.S.: 541330
Schaller Eric *(Mng Dir)*

Sedelec SA Lausanne (1)
Av des Boveresses 48, 1010, Lausanne, Vaud, Switzerland
Tel.: (41) 216512000
Web Site: http://www.sedelec-lsne.ch
Electrical Engineering Services
N.A.I.C.S.: 541330

Sedelec Saignelegier, Succursale De Sedelec S.A. (1)
Chemin des Senailles 6, 2350, Saignelegier, Switzerland
Tel.: (41) 329513223
Electrical Engineering Services
N.A.I.C.S.: 541330

Sedelec Vevey, Succursale De Sedelec S.A. (1)
Av General-Guisan 31, 1800, Vevey, Switzerland
Tel.: (41) 219217888
Electrical Engineering Services
N.A.I.C.S.: 541330

Sedelec Yverdon, Succursale De Sedelec S.A. (1)
Rue de la Blancherie 2, 1400, Yverdon-les-Bains, Switzerland
Tel.: (41) 244252207
Electrical Engineering Services
N.A.I.C.S.: 541330

Sergio Lo Stanco Elektro AG (1)
Industriestrasse 8, 4562, Biberist, Switzerland
Tel.: (41) 326712020
Web Site: http://www.lostanco.ch
Electrical Installation Services
N.A.I.C.S.: 238210

Sprecher AG (1)
Landwasserstrasse 70, Davos, 7277, Glaris, Switzerland
Tel.: (41) 814132020
Web Site: https://www.sprecher-ag.ch
Engineering Consulting Services
N.A.I.C.S.: 541330

Burkhalter Holding AG—(Continued)

TZ Stromag (1)
Kantonsstrasse 132, 3902, Brig, Valais, Switzerland
Tel.: (41) 279222070
Web Site: http://www.stromag.ch
Electrical Engineering Services
N.A.I.C.S.: 541330

Tabelec Force El Commandes S.A. (1)
Chemin du Coteau 29 E, 1123, Aclens, Switzerland
Tel.: (41) 218026380
Web Site: https://www.tabelec.ch
Emp.: 25
Electrical Panel Mfr & Distr
N.A.I.C.S.: 335313

Triulzi AG (1)
Via Surpunt 62, 7500, Saint Moritz, Graubunden, Switzerland
Tel.: (41) 818373666
Web Site: http://www.triulzi.ch
Sales Range: $25-49.9 Million
Emp.: 45
Electrical Engineering Services
N.A.I.C.S.: 541330
Marco Triulzi (Mng Dir)

Ulrich Huber AG (1)
Neugutstrasse 4a, 7208, Malans, Switzerland
Tel.: (41) 813006090
Web Site: https://www.huber-malans.ch
Emp.: 27
Bathroom Remodelled & Maintenance Services
N.A.I.C.S.: 236118

Vuadens Controles SA (1)
Rue Oscar Bider 54, 1950, Sion, Valais, Switzerland
Tel.: (41) 273228480
Electrical Engineering Services
N.A.I.C.S.: 541330

Wisler Elektro AG (1)
Gewerbestrasse 6, 3532, Zaziwil, Switzerland
Tel.: (41) 317110080
Web Site: https://www.wislerelektro.ch
Emp.: 20
Electrical Engineering Services
N.A.I.C.S.: 541330

Wulser Lostorf AG (1)
Hauptstrasse 14, 4654, Lostorf, Switzerland
Tel.: (41) 627469292
Web Site: https://www.wuelser-haustechnik.ch
Building Technology Services
N.A.I.C.S.: 541350

Wulser Zofingen AG (1)
Muhlethalstrasse 67, 4800, Zofingen, Switzerland
Tel.: (41) 627469200
Web Site: https://www.wuelser-haustechnik.ch
Building Technology Services
N.A.I.C.S.: 541350

BURKI VERPACKUNGSTECH-NIK AG
Niedermattstrasse 14, Oberbipp, 4538, Bern, Switzerland
Tel.: (41) 326365353
Web Site: http://www.buerkiag.ch
Year Founded: 1863
Sales Range: $10-24.9 Million
Emp.: 10
Real Estate Agents & Brokers Offices
N.A.I.C.S.: 531210
Markus Frey (CEO)

BURLEY MINERALS LTD.
L3 30 Richardson Street, West Perth, 6005, WA, Australia
Tel.: (61) 893226283　　AU
Web Site:
　https://www.burleyminerals.com.au
Year Founded: 2020
BUR—(ASX)
Rev.: $17,552

Assets: $13,062,789
Liabilities: $176,102
Net Worth: $12,886,688
Earnings: ($864,301)
Fiscal Year-end: 06/30/23
Mineral Exploration Services
N.A.I.C.S.: 212390
Lisa Wynne (Sec)

BURN
Berkeley House 85 Sheen Rd, Richmond, TW9 1YJ, United Kingdom
Tel.: (44) 2083327204
Web Site:
　http://www.burnmarketing.com
Year Founded: 2005
Sales Range: $10-24.9 Million
Emp.: 14
N.A.I.C.S.: 541810
Guy McConnell (Mng Dir)

BURNAC CORPORATION
44 St Clair Avenue West, Toronto, M4V 3C9, ON, Canada
Tel.: (416) 964-3600
Web Site: http://www.burnac.com
Year Founded: 1964
Rev.: $19,127,889
Emp.: 60
Real Estate Services
N.A.I.C.S.: 531390
Joseph Burnett (Chm)

BURNCO ROCK PRODUCTS LTD
Main Floor 155 Glendeer Circle SE, PO Box 1480, Station T, Calgary, T2H 2P9, AB, Canada
Tel.: (403) 255-2600
Web Site: http://www.burnco.com
Year Founded: 1912
Sales Range: $75-99.9 Million
Emp.: 550
Readymix Concrete Mfr
N.A.I.C.S.: 327320
Tom Zais (CEO)

Subsidiaries:

BURNCO Colorado, LLC (1)
Centennial Dr, Milliken, CO 80543
Tel.: (970) 356-7523
Web Site: http://www.burnco-usa.com
Brick Stone & Related Material Provider
N.A.I.C.S.: 423320
Dana Rotkovich (Sls Mgr)

BURNING ROCK BIOTECH LIMITED
601 6/F Building 3 Standard Industrial Unit 2 No 7 Luoxuan 4th Road, International Biotech Island, Guangzhou, 510005, China
Tel.: (86) 2034037871　　Ky
Web Site: http://www.brbiotech.com
Year Founded: 2014
BNR—(NASDAQ)
Rev.: $86,293,694
Assets: $243,215,819
Liabilities: $65,746,394
Net Worth: $177,469,425
Earnings: ($148,802,608)
Emp.: 1,138
Fiscal Year-end: 12/31/22
Holding Company
N.A.I.C.S.: 551112
Yusheng Han (Founder, Chm & CEO)

BURNPUR CEMENT LIMITED
7/1 Anandilal Poddar Sarani Russel Street 5th Floor Flat, No 5B Kanchana Building, Kolkata, 700 001, India
Tel.: (91) 3322623167
Web Site:
　https://www.burnpurcement.com
Year Founded: 1980

BURNPUR—(NSE)
Rev.: $17,194,659
Assets: $39,017,638
Liabilities: $69,464,372
Net Worth: ($30,446,734)
Earnings: ($10,811,701)
Emp.: 105
Fiscal Year-end: 03/31/21
Cement Mfr & Distr
N.A.I.C.S.: 327310
Prem Prakash Sharma (Chm)

BURNSIDE WAR MEMORIAL HOSPITAL INC.
120 Kensington Rd, Toorak Gardens, 5065, SA, Australia
Tel.: (61) 0882027222
Web Site:
　https://www.burnsidehospital.asn.au
Health Care Srvices
N.A.I.C.S.: 621999
Alan Morrison (CEO)

Subsidiaries:

Sportsmed Sa Hospitals Pty Ltd (1)
32 Payneham Rd, 5069, Stepney, South, Australia
Tel.: (61) 61881301255
Web Site: http://www.sportsmed.com.au
Sales Range: $75-99.9 Million
Emp.: 150
Hospital Specialty, Except Psychiatric
N.A.I.C.S.: 621999

BURO HAPPOLD ENGINEERS LIMITED
Camden Mill 230 Lower Bristol Road, Bath, BA2 3DQ, United Kingdom
Tel.: (44) 1225320600　　UK
Web Site:
　http://www.burohappold.com
Year Founded: 1986
Sales Range: $200-249.9 Million
Emp.: 1,700
Engineeering Services
N.A.I.C.S.: 541330
James Bruce (CFO & COO)

Subsidiaries:

Buro Happold & Partner for Engineering Consultancy Co (1)
PO Box 34183, Riyadh, 11468, Saudi Arabia
Tel.: (966) 114191992
Engineeering Services
N.A.I.C.S.: 541330

Buro Happold ApS (1)
Lavendelstraede 17D 2, 1462, Copenhagen, Denmark
Tel.: (45) 33129800
Engineeering Services
N.A.I.C.S.: 541330
Rod Manson (Partner)

Buro Happold Consulting Engineers (Beijing) Limited (1)
Room 1609 Office Tower A Jianwai SOHO No 39 East 3rd Ring Road, Chaoyang District, Beijing, 100022, China
Tel.: (86) 1058697376
Engineeering Services
N.A.I.C.S.: 541330
Matthew Smith (Partner)

Buro Happold Consulting Engineers Limited (1)
7th Floor 702A Kamala Tower, PO Box 107455, Abu Dhabi, United Arab Emirates
Tel.: (971) 24967200
Engineeering Services
N.A.I.C.S.: 541330
Kevin Mitchell (Partner)

Buro Happold Consulting Engineers, Inc. (1)
800 Wilshire Blvd 16th Fl, Los Angeles, CA 90017
Tel.: (310) 945-4800
Engineeering Services
N.A.I.C.S.: 541330
David Herd (Mng Partner)

Buro Happold Engineers India Pvt. Ltd. (1)
Ackruti Corporate Park G1 LBS Marg Next to GE Gardens, Kanjur Marg, Mumbai, 400078, India
Tel.: (91) 2233414133
Engineeering Services
N.A.I.C.S.: 541330
Anil Hira (Partner)

Buro Happold International (Hong Kong) Limited (1)
5/F Tai Yau Building 181 Johnston Road, Wanchai, China (Hong Kong)
Tel.: (852) 36589608
Engineeering Services
N.A.I.C.S.: 541330
Steve Brown (Partner)

Buro Happold Limited (1)
Camden Mill 230 Lower Bristol Road, Bath, BA2 3DQ, United Kingdom
Tel.: (44) 1225320600
Web Site: https://www.burohappold.com
Engineering & Technical Consulting Services
N.A.I.C.S.: 541330
Claire Smith (Dir-Officer)

Buro Happold Polska Sp. z o.o. (1)
ul Sapiezynska 10a, 00-215, Warsaw, Poland
Tel.: (48) 225360300
Engineeering Services
N.A.I.C.S.: 541330
Ian Booth (Partner)

Happold Ingenieurburo GmbH (1)
Pfalzburger Strasse 43-44, 10717, Berlin, Germany
Tel.: (49) 308609060
Engineeering Services
N.A.I.C.S.: 541330
Paul Rogers (Partner)

BURSA CIMENTO FABRIKASI A.S.
Yeni Mahalle Uludag Caddesi No 170 Kestel, Bursa, Turkiye
Tel.: (90) 2243721560
Web Site:
　https://www.bursacement.com
Year Founded: 1966
BUCIM—(IST)
Rev.: $353,409,551
Assets: $407,063,330
Liabilities: $56,465,138
Net Worth: $350,598,191
Earnings: $63,295,000
Fiscal Year-end: 12/31/23
Cement Mfr
N.A.I.C.S.: 327310
Osman Nemli (Gen Mgr)

Subsidiaries:

Ares Cimento Insaat San. ve Tic. A.S. (1)
Haciilyas Mah Ulubatli Hasan Bulvari No 106, Bursa, Turkiye
Tel.: (90) 2243729667
Web Site: http://www.arescimento.com.tr
Cement Mfr
N.A.I.C.S.: 327310

Bursa Ares Cevre ve Enerji Teknolojileri Sanayi ve Ticaret A.S. (1)
Haciilyas Mahallesi Ulubatli Hasan Bulvari No 106, Bursa, Turkiye
Tel.: (90) 2243729667
Web Site: https://www.arescevre.com.tr
Construction Services
N.A.I.C.S.: 236115

Bursa Beton A.S. (1)
Haci Ilyas Mh Ulubatlihasan Blv No 106, Osmangazi, Bursa, Turkiye
Tel.: (90) 4441622
Web Site: http://www.bursabeton.com.tr
Readymix Concrete Mfr
N.A.I.C.S.: 327320

Bursa Beton Sanayi Ticaret A.S. (1)
Haci Ilyas Mh Ulubatlihasan Blv No 106, Osmangazi, 16220, Bursa, Turkiye
Tel.: (90) 4441622
Web Site: https://www.bursabeton.com.tr

Readymix Concrete Mfr
N.A.I.C.S.: 327320

CEMTAS Celik Makina Sanayi Ticaret A.S. (1)
Organize Sanayi Bolgesi AOS Bulvari No 3, 16140, Bursa, Turkiye
Tel.: (90) 2242431230
Web Site: https://www.cemtas.com.tr
Emp.: 400
Steel Products Mfr
N.A.I.C.S.: 331110

BURSA DE VALORI BUCUR-ESTI
34 - 36 Carol I Boulevard 020922 14th Floor, 20922, Bucharest, Romania
Tel.: (40) 213079500
Web Site: https://www.bvb.ro
Rev.: $9,308,669
Assets: $50,051,306
Liabilities: $21,902,820
Net Worth: $28,148,486
Earnings: $2,392,590
Emp.: 103
Fiscal Year-end: 12/31/18
Stock Exchange Services
N.A.I.C.S.: 523210
Marius-Alin Barbu *(Deputy Gen Mgr)*

BURSA MALAYSIA BERHAD
Exchange Square Bukit Kewangan, 50200, Kuala Lumpur, Malaysia
Tel.: (60) 320347000 MY
Web Site:
https://www.bursamalaysia.com
Year Founded: 1973
1818—(KLS)
Rev.: $127,670,899
Assets: $898,303,280
Liabilities: $731,793,862
Net Worth: $166,509,418
Earnings: $47,951,323
Emp.: 614
Fiscal Year-end: 12/31/22
Stock Exchange Services
N.A.I.C.S.: 523210
Rosidah Baharom *(CFO)*

Subsidiaries:

Bursa Malaysia Derivatives Berhad (1)
Exchange Square Bukit Kewangan, 50200, Kuala Lumpur, Malaysia
Tel.: (60) 320347000
Web Site: http://www.bursamalaysia.com
Securities Services
N.A.I.C.S.: 523999
Samuel Ho Hock Guan *(CEO & Dir-Derivatives Market)*

Bursa Malaysia IT Sdn Bhd (1)
4th Floor Exchange Square, Bukit Kewangan, 50200, Kuala Lumpur, Malaysia
Tel.: (60) 3 20267099
Web Site: http://www.klse.com
Securities Services
N.A.I.C.S.: 523999

Bursa Malaysia Information Sdn Bhd (1)
11th Floor Exchange Square, Bukit Kewangan, 50200, Kuala Lumpur, Malaysia
Tel.: (60) 320347084
Sales Range: $50-74.9 Million
Emp.: 5
Securities Services
N.A.I.C.S.: 523999

Bursa Malaysia Property Sdn Bhd (1)
Bukit Kewangan, 50200, Kuala Lumpur, Malaysia
Tel.: (60) 320347000
Web Site: http://www.bursamalaysia.com
Sales Range: $350-399.9 Million
Securities Services
N.A.I.C.S.: 523999

Labuan International Financial Exchange Inc. (1)
Unit B Level 7 Main Ofc Tower Financial

Park Complex, Jalan Merdeka, 87000, Labuan, Malaysia (100%)
Tel.: (60) 87451359
Web Site: http://www.lfx.com.my
Sales Range: $25-49.9 Million
Emp.: 6
Securities Services
N.A.I.C.S.: 523999

Malaysia Derivatives Exchange Berhad (1)
10th Floor Exchange Square, Bukit Kewangan, 50200, Kuala Lumpur, Malaysia
Tel.: (60) 320347000
Web Site: http://www.bursamalaysia.com.my
Securities Services
N.A.I.C.S.: 523999

Malaysian Central Depository Sdn Bhd (1)
6th Floor Exchange Square, Bukit Kewangan, 50200, Kuala Lumpur, Malaysia
Tel.: (60) 320262099
Securities Services
N.A.I.C.S.: 523999

Securities Clearing Automated Network Services Sdn Bhd (1)
6th Fl Exchange Square, Bukit Kewngan, 50200, Kuala Lumpur, Malaysia
Tel.: (60) 3 20268099
Securities Services
N.A.I.C.S.: 523999

Yayasan Bursa Malaysia (1)
15th Floor Exchange Square, Bukim Kewangan, Kuala Lumpur, 50200, Malaysia
Tel.: (60) 320347000
Securities Services
N.A.I.C.S.: 523999
Aidura Haron *(Head-Community Investment)*

BURSEI DE VALORI A MOLDOVEI
Stefan cel Mare Blvd 73 Room 352, MD2001, Chisinau, Moldova
Tel.: (373) 22277594
Web Site: http://www.moldse.md
Year Founded: 1994
Sales Range: $25-49.9 Million
Emp.: 20
Stock Exchange Services
N.A.I.C.S.: 523210
Corneliu Dodu *(Pres-Exchange)*

BURU ENERGY LIMITED
Level 2 16 Ord Street, West Perth, 6005, WA, Australia
Tel.: (61) 800337330
Web Site:
https://www.buruenergy.com
BRU—(OTCIQ)
Rev.: $9,058,486
Assets: $22,254,678
Liabilities: $9,373,411
Net Worth: $12,881,268
Earnings: ($21,371,194)
Emp.: 37
Fiscal Year-end: 12/31/22
Crude Petroleum Extraction Services
N.A.I.C.S.: 211120
Eric Charles Streitberg *(Chm)*

Subsidiaries:

2H Resources Pty Limited (1)
L2 16 Ord St, West Perth, 6005, WA, Australia
Tel.: (61) 892151800
Web Site: https://www.2hresources.com
Hydrogen Gas Exploration Services
N.A.I.C.S.: 221118

Buru Fitzroy Pty Limited (1)
Lot No 1 Princes Highway Cnr Bellambi Lane, Russell Vale, 2517, NSW, Australia
Tel.: (61) 242236800
Emp.: 16
Oil & Gas Exploration Services
N.A.I.C.S.: 213112

Geovault Pty Limited (1)
Level 2 16 Ord St, West Perth, 6005, WA, Australia

Tel.: (61) 92151800
Web Site: https://www.geovault.com.au
Oil & Gas Exploration Services
N.A.I.C.S.: 213112

BURUJ COOPERATIVE INSURANCE COMPANY
Tel.: (966) 112938383
Year Founded: 2009
8270—(SAU)
Rev.: $98,344,048
Assets: $211,655,656
Liabilities: $106,395,177
Net Worth: $105,260,478
Earnings: ($10,476,765)
Emp.: 205
Fiscal Year-end: 12/31/22
Insurance Agency Services
N.A.I.C.S.: 524210
Samer Kanj *(CEO)*

BURWILL HOLDINGS LIMITED
Unit 1402 14/F Office Tower Convention Plaza 1 Harbour Road, Wanchai, China (Hong Kong)
Tel.: (852) 2877 7368
Web Site: http://www.burwill.com
Rev.: $294,385,081
Assets: $232,220,609
Liabilities: $104,201,169
Net Worth: $128,019,440
Earnings: ($14,015,510)
Emp.: 259
Fiscal Year-end: 12/31/18
International Steel Trading
N.A.I.C.S.: 331512
Shing Chan *(Chm & Mng Dir)*

Subsidiaries:

Burwill Resources Limited (1)
Rm 1402 14 F Convention Plz Ofc Tower 1 Harbour RdWanchai, Wanchai, China (Hong Kong)
Tel.: (852) 28777368
Web Site: http://www.burwill.com
Sales Range: $75-99.9 Million
Emp.: 150
Steel Product Distr
N.A.I.C.S.: 423510
Sham Kai Man *(Mng Dir)*

Burwill Steel Pipes Limited (1)
Unit 1402 Ofc Tower Convention Plz 1 Harbour Rd, Wanchai, China (Hong Kong)
Tel.: (852) 26778839
Web Site: http://www.burwill-bsp.com
Sales Range: $25-49.9 Million
Emp.: 50
Steel Processing Services
N.A.I.C.S.: 331221
Mark Yin *(Pres)*

BURZA CENNYCH PAPIEROV V BRATISLAVE, A.S.
Vysoka 17, PO Box 151, 814 99, Bratislava, Slovakia
Tel.: (421) 249236111
Web Site: http://www.bsse.sk
Sales Range: $1-9.9 Million
Emp.: 30
Stock Exchange Services
N.A.I.C.S.: 523210

BUSAN INDUSTRIAL CO., LTD.
35 Jangin-ro, Sa Sang-Gu, Busan, Korea (South)
Tel.: (82) 513158338
Web Site: http://www.busanind.co.kr
Year Founded: 1976
011390—(KRS)
Rev.: $117,052,026
Assets: $103,298,736
Liabilities: $40,355,821
Net Worth: $62,942,916
Earnings: $3,481,241
Emp.: 37
Fiscal Year-end: 12/31/22
Readymix Concrete Mfr
N.A.I.C.S.: 327320

Chan-Jung Lee *(Dir-Accounting)*

BUSCANDO RESOURCES CORP.
520-999 West Hastings Street, Box 55, Vancouver, V6C 2W2, BC, Canada
Tel.: (604) 428-9480 BC
Web Site:
https://www.buscandoresources.com
Year Founded: 2017
BRCO—(CNSX)
Assets: $407,627
Liabilities: $19,748
Net Worth: $387,879
Earnings: ($84,979)
Fiscal Year-end: 12/31/21
Mineral Exploration Services
N.A.I.C.S.: 212220
Kyler Hardy *(CEO)*

BUSHIROAD, INC.
Sumitomo Nakanosakaue Building 1-38-1 Chuo, Nakano-Ku, Tokyo, 164-0001, Japan
Tel.: (81) 353480852
Web Site:
https://www.bushiroad.co.jp
Year Founded: 2007
7803—(TKS)
Rev.: $287,749,640
Assets: $314,763,100
Liabilities: $170,017,480
Net Worth: $144,745,620
Earnings: $5,000,880
Emp.: 853
Fiscal Year-end: 06/30/24
Application Development Services
N.A.I.C.S.: 541511
Yoshitaka Hashimoto *(Pres & COO)*

Subsidiaries:

Bushiroad Creative, Inc. (1)
Sumitomo Nakano Sakagami Building 1-38-1, Chuo Nakano-ku, Tokyo, Japan
Tel.: (81) 345004851
Web Site: https://bushiroad-creative.com
Merchandise Goods Mfr & Distr
N.A.I.C.S.: 339999

Bushiroad International Pte. Ltd. (1)
331 North Bridge Road 03-03 Odeon Towers, Singapore, 188720, Singapore
Tel.: (65) 63371153
Game Card Mfr
N.A.I.C.S.: 339930

Bushiroad Media, Inc. (1)
Sumitomo Nakano Sakagami Building 2nd Floor 1-38-1, Chuo Nakano-ku, Tokyo, 164-0011, Japan
Tel.: (81) 345004310
Web Site: http://bushiroad-media.com
Book Publishers
N.A.I.C.S.: 513130

Bushiroad Music, Inc. (1)
Sumitomo Nakano Sakagami Building 2nd Floor 1-38-1 Central, Nakano-ku, Tokyo, 164-0011, Japan
Tel.: (81) 345006633
Web Site: https://www.bushiroad-music.com
Emp.: 40
Music Content Production Services
N.A.I.C.S.: 512250

Bushiroad USA Inc. (1)
20690 Carrey Rd, Walnut, CA 91789
Tel.: (909) 869-9199
Game Card Mfr
N.A.I.C.S.: 339930

Sopratico Co., Ltd. (1)
4-17-3 Hanazono, Otaru, 047-0024, Hokkaido, Japan
Tel.: (81) 134240202
Web Site: https://www.sopratico.com
Fitness Club Services
N.A.I.C.S.: 713940

Theater Company Hikosen Inc. (1)
Sumitomo Nakano Sakagami Building 2nd Floor 1-38-1 Central, Nakano-ku, Tokyo,

Bushiroad, Inc.—(Continued)

164-0011, Japan
Tel.: (81) 345006810
Web Site: https://www.hikosen.co.jp
Musical Theater Services
N.A.I.C.S.: 711110

BUSHVELD MINERALS LIMITED

Illovo Edge Office Park 5 Harries Road 2nd Floor, Illovo, 2116, Johannesburg, South Africa
Tel.: (27) 112686555   **GY**
Web Site:
   http://www.bushveldminerals.com
BMN—(AIM)
Rev.: $148,450,000
Assets: $267,590,000
Liabilities: $266,780,000
Net Worth: $810,000
Earnings: ($30,330,000)
Fiscal Year-end: 12/31/22
Holding Company; Iron Ore Mining
N.A.I.C.S.: 551112
Fortune Mojapelo *(Founder & CEO)*

Subsidiaries:

Bushveld Energy Company (Pty) Limited   **(1)**
Corner of Fricker and Harries Roads Building 3 2nd Floor, Illovo Edge Office Block Illovo, Johannesburg, 2196, South Africa
Tel.: (27) 112686555
Web Site: https://www.bushveldenergy.com
Energy Development Services
N.A.I.C.S.: 221118
Mikhail Nikomarov *(Founder)*

BUSI GROUP S.R.L.

Via delle Brede 2, 25080, Paitone, Italy
Tel.: (39) 0306896956
Web Site: https://busigroup.eu
Year Founded: 1991
Industrial Control Product Mfr & Distr
N.A.I.C.S.: 335314

BUSINESS & INDUSTRIAL INSURANCE COMPANY LTD.

2nd Floor 72-West Benazir Plaza, Jinnah Avenue Blue Area, Islamabad, Pakistan
Tel.: (92) 51 2278957
Insurance Management Services
N.A.I.C.S.: 524298

BUSINESS ALIGNMENT PUBLIC COMPANY LIMITED

92/45 Sathorn Thani Building 2 16th Floor North Sathorn Rd, Bangrak, Bangkok, 10500, Thailand
Tel.: (66) 263668289   **TH**
Web Site:
   https://www.bizalignment.com
Year Founded: 2000
BIZ—(THA)
Rev.: $49,579,661
Assets: $43,132,360
Liabilities: $16,794,192
Net Worth: $26,338,168
Earnings: $5,882,961
Emp.: 25
Fiscal Year-end: 12/31/23
Medical Equipment Distr
N.A.I.C.S.: 423450
Sompong Chunekitiyanone *(CEO & COO)*

BUSINESS ALLIANCE JSC

Per Kapranova Building 3 P 2, Moscow, 123242, Russia
Tel.: (7) 4955891300
Web Site: http://www.leasing-ba.ru
Sales Range: Less than $1 Million
Automobile Leasing Services
N.A.I.C.S.: 532490

BUSINESS BRAIN SHOWA-OTA INC.

15F Hibiya Fort Tower 1-1-1 Nishi-Shinbashi, Minato-ku, Tokyo, 105-0003, Japan
Tel.: (81) 335071300
Web Site: https://www.bbs.co.jp
Year Founded: 1967
9650—(TKG)
Rev.: $226,180,980
Assets: $295,566,150
Liabilities: $101,212,320
Net Worth: $194,353,830
Earnings: $93,505,060
Emp.: 2,258
Fiscal Year-end: 03/31/24
Management Consulting Services
N.A.I.C.S.: 541618
Kazuhiro Komiya *(Pres & CEO)*

Subsidiaries:

BBS Outsourcing Kumamoto Inc. **(1)**
9F Fuji Suidocho Building 7-16 Suidocho, Chuo-ku, Kumamoto, 860-0844, Japan
Tel.: (81) 96 342 4742
Web Site: https://www.bos-k.co.jp
Emp.: 200
Outsourcing Business Services
N.A.I.C.S.: 561990

EP Consulting Services Corporation   **(1)**
Hibiya Fort Tower 16F 1-1-1 Nishi-Shinbashi, Minato-ku, Tokyo, 105-0003, Japan   **(100%)**
Tel.: (81) 5017434000
Sales Range: $25-49.9 Million
Emp.: 80
IT Staffing Services
N.A.I.C.S.: 541513

Financial Brain Systems Inc. **(1)**
1-1-1 Nishi-Shimbashi Hibiya Fort Tower 15th Floor, Minato-ku, Tokyo, 105-0003, Japan
Tel.: (81) 33 507 1320
Web Site: https://www.fbsc.co.jp
Emp.: 228
Investment Banking Services
N.A.I.C.S.: 523999

Global Security Experts Inc. **(1)**
Suzuebaydium 4th Floor 1-15-1 Kaigan, Minato-ku, Tokyo, 105-0022, Japan
Tel.: (81) 33 578 9001
Web Site: https://www.gsx.co.jp
Security Consulting Services
N.A.I.C.S.: 541690
Shiro Aoyagi *(Pres & CEO)*

ISS Inc.   **(1)**
5-15-1 Samourai, Nak-ku, Hamamatsu, 432-8021, Shizuoka, Japan
Tel.: (81) 53 456 1595
Web Site: http://www.iss-staffing.co.jp
Staff Recruitment Services
N.A.I.C.S.: 561311
Koichi Odawara *(Dir)*

Joyworks Inc.   **(1)**
1-18-3 Dogenzaka Premier Dogenzaka Building 2nd Floor, Shibuya-ku, Tokyo, 150-0043, Japan
Tel.: (81) 36 453 9472
Web Site: https://www.joyworks.jp
Application Development Services
N.A.I.C.S.: 541511

Medical & Welfare Information Center of Showa-ota Inc.   **(1)**
1-1-1 Nishi-Shimbashi Hibiya Fort Tower 15th Floor, Minato-ku, Tokyo, 105-0003, Japan
Tel.: (81) 33 507 1355
Web Site: https://www.mics-i.co.jp
Medical Devices
N.A.I.C.S.: 621111

PLM Japan Inc.   **(1)**
16th Floor Hibiya Fort Tower 1-1-1 Nishi-Shimbashi, Minato-ku, Tokyo, 105-0003, Japan
Tel.: (81) 335071340
Software Development Services
N.A.I.C.S.: 541511

BUSINESS BREAKTHROUGH, INC.

1-7 Rokubancho Chiyoda-ku, Tokyo, 102-0085, Japan
Tel.: (81) 358605530   **JP**
Year Founded: 1998
2464—(TKS)
Rev.: $49,403,140
Assets: $49,515,510
Liabilities: $17,959,370
Not Worth: $31,556,140
Earnings: $1,599,620
Fiscal Year-end: 03/31/24
Education Services
N.A.I.C.S.: 611710
Kenichi Ohmae *(Founder & Chm)*

BUSINESS CENTRIC SERVICES GROUP

130 Old Street, London, EC1V 9BD, United Kingdom
Tel.: (44) 845 880 8820
Web Site: http://www.bcsg.com
Year Founded: 2006
Sales Range: $10-24.9 Million
Emp.: 100
Information Technology Consultancy Services
N.A.I.C.S.: 541512
Phil Bircumshaw *(CTO)*

BUSINESS CONNEXION GROUP LIMITED

Business Connexion Park North 789 16th Road Randjespark, PO Box X48, Halfway House, Midrand, 1685, Gauteng, South Africa
Tel.: (27) 11 266 5111
Web Site: http://www.bcx.co.za
Year Founded: 1979
Holding Company; Information & Communication Technology Products & Services
N.A.I.C.S.: 551112
Lawrence Weitzman *(Mgr-Sls)*

Subsidiaries:

Accsys (Proprietary) Limited **(1)**
5 Grayston Office Park 128 Peter Road, Simba, Sandton, 2031, Gauteng, South Africa
Tel.: (27) 117198000
Web Site: http://www.accsys.co.za
Sales Range: $25-49.9 Million
Emp.: 75
Human Resource Software Development Services
N.A.I.C.S.: 541511
Teryl Schroenn *(CEO)*

Business Connexion (Pty) Limited   **(1)**
Business Connexion Park - South Block B, 789 16th Road Randjespark, Midrand, South Africa   **(100%)**
Tel.: (27) 112665111
Web Site: http://www.bcx.co.za
Sales Range: $700-749.9 Million
Emp.: 3,500
Custom Computer Programming Services
N.A.I.C.S.: 541511
Isaac Mophatlny *(CEO)*

Subsidiary (Domestic):

Business Connexion Communications (Pty) Limited   **(2)**
789 Business Connexion Park 16 Road Randjespark Halfway House, Midrand, 4685, Gauteng, South Africa
Tel.: (27) 112665111
Communication & Web Hosting Services
N.A.I.C.S.: 517810

Subsidiary (Non-US):

Business Connexion Limited **(2)**
Connexion House 4 Arlington Court Whittle Way Arlington Business Park, Stevenage, SG1 2FS, Hertfordshire, United Kingdom
Tel.: (44) 8456781122
Web Site: http://www.bcx.uk.com

Sales Range: $25-49.9 Million
Emp.: 25
Software Support Services
N.A.I.C.S.: 541511

Business Connexion Mozambique Limitada   **(2)**
Rua de Kassuende No 140, Bairro da Polana, Maputo, Mozambique
Tel.: (268) 21406530
Sales Range: $10-24.9 Million
Emp.: 50
Business Management Software Development Services
N.A.I.C.S.: 541511

Business Connexion Namibia (Pty) Limited   **(2)**
130 Jan Jonker Street, PO Box 6702, Windhoek, 9000, Namibia
Tel.: (264) 612040000
Web Site: http://www.bcx.co.za
Sales Range: $25-49.9 Million
Emp.: 113
Internet & Telecommunication Services
N.A.I.C.S.: 517111
Ferdi Graupe *(CEO)*

Business Connexion Networks (Nigeria) Limited   **(2)**
Adebola House 228A Awolowo Road, Lagos, Nigeria
Tel.: (234) 702 5337 980
Business Management Software Development Services
N.A.I.C.S.: 541511

Business Connexion Tanzania Limited   **(2)**
Mikocheni Area Plot No 6 Lucy Lameck Street, PO Box 76384, Kinondoni District, Dar es Salaam, 766384, Tanzania
Tel.: (255) 754310358
Web Site: http://www.bcx.co.za
Emp.: 30
Business Management Software Development Services
N.A.I.C.S.: 541511

Subsidiary (Domestic):

Business Connexion Technology Holdings (Pty) Limited   **(2)**
789 16th Road Randjespark, Midrand, 1685, South Africa
Tel.: (27) 112661000
Business Management Software Development Services
N.A.I.C.S.: 541511

CEB Maintenance Africa (Proprietary) Limited   **(1)**
5 Monza Rd, Westmead, Pinetown, 3610, KwaZulu-Natal, South Africa
Tel.: (27) 317003332
Web Site: http://www.ceb.co.za
Sales Range: $75-99.9 Million
Emp.: 400
Information Technology Support Services
N.A.I.C.S.: 541512

UCS Solutions (Proprietary) Limited   **(1)**
2nd Fl ABB Park The Crescent 3 Eglin Rd, Sunninghill, Johannesburg, 2157, Gauteng, South Africa
Tel.: (27) 115189000
Web Site: http://www.ucs-solutions.co.za
Sales Range: $75-99.9 Million
Emp.: 500
Business Management Solutions
N.A.I.C.S.: 561110
Jessica Knight *(CEO)*

Branch (Domestic):

UCS Solutions   **(2)**
7th Fl Newlands Terraces 8 Boundary Rd, PO Box 27, Rondebosch, Cape Town, 7701, South Africa   **(100%)**
Tel.: (27) 216804000
Web Site: http://www.ucs-solutions.co.za
Sales Range: $25-49.9 Million
Emp.: 100
Provider of Networking Services
N.A.I.C.S.: 541512

BUSINESS DEVELOPMENT BANK OF CANADA

5 Place Ville Marie Ground floor, Montreal, H3B 5E7, QC, Canada
Tel.: (514) 283-5904   Ca
Web Site: http://www.bdc.ca
Year Founded: 1944
Rev.: $1,177,786,771
Assets: $22,470,261,088
Liabilities: $16,785,521,681
Net Worth: $5,684,739,407
Earnings: $649,119,698
Emp.: 2,300
Fiscal Year-end: 03/31/19
Commericial Banking
N.A.I.C.S.: 522110
Jerome Nycz (Exec VP-Capital)

Subsidiaries:

Monarch Industries Limited   (1)
51 Burmac Rd, Winnipeg, R2J 4J3, MB, Canada
Tel.: (204) 786-7921
Web Site:
    http://www.monarchindustries.com
Hydraulic Cylinders & Metal Casting Mfr
N.A.I.C.S.: 333517
Roy Cook (Pres & CEO)

BUSINESS ONLINE PUBLIC COMPANY LIMITED

No 1023 MS Siam Tower 28 Floor Rama III Road Chong Nonsi, Yannawa, Bangkok, 10120, Thailand
Tel.: (66) 26573999
Web Site: https://www.bol.co.th
Year Founded: 1995
BOL—(THA)
Rev.: $22,865,301
Assets: $40,525,443
Liabilities: $10,474,531
Net Worth: $30,050,912
Earnings: $8,474,735
Emp.: 129
Fiscal Year-end: 12/31/23
Business Information Services
N.A.I.C.S.: 561499
Jack Min Intanate (Co-Chm)

Subsidiaries:

D&B (Thailand) Co., Ltd.   (1)
No 1023 MS Siam Tower 28th Floor Rama 3 Road, Chong Nonsi Sub-district Yannawa District, Bangkok, 10120, Thailand
Tel.: (66) 26573939
Credit Reporting Services
N.A.I.C.S.: 561450
Jack Min Intanate (Chm)

iBOL Co., Ltd.   (1)
900/21 25 Fl Rama III Rd Bangpongpang, Yannawa, Bangkok, 10120, Thailand
Tel.: (66) 2657 3988
Information Technology Consulting Services
N.A.I.C.S.: 541512

BUSINESSON COMMUNICATION CO., LTD.

230 Hakdong-ro Yubim Building 209-4 Nonhyeon-dong, Gangnam-Gu, Seoul, 06104, Korea (South)
Tel.: (82) 25590800
Web Site:
    https://www.businesson.co.kr
Year Founded: 2007
138580—(KRS)
Rev.: $30,844,548
Assets: $67,370,326
Liabilities: $8,680,852
Net Worth: $58,689,474
Earnings: $5,739,274
Emp.: 78
Fiscal Year-end: 12/31/21
Software Development Services
N.A.I.C.S.: 541511
Min-Chul Kang (CEO)

BUSS-SMS-CANZLER GMBH

Kaiserstrasse 13-15, Butzbach, 35510, Germany
Tel.: (49) 6033850

Web Site: http://www.sms-vt.com
Year Founded: 1919
Sales Range: $25-49.9 Million
Emp.: 218
Thermal Separation Components & Systems Mfr
N.A.I.C.S.: 333248
Harald Bechmann (Mng Dir)

BUSSEYS AND SABBERTON BROS. LTD.

95 Whiffler Road, Norwich, NR3 2EU, Norfolk, United Kingdom
Tel.: (44) 1603909986
Web Site: http://www.busseys.co.uk
Year Founded: 1911
Sales Range: $50-74.9 Million
Emp.: 210
New & Used Car Dealers
N.A.I.C.S.: 441110
Phil Collins (Dir-Ops)

BUSY BEE CLEANING SERVICES LTD.

Units 5 & 6 Kingsmill Park London Rd, Loudwater, High Wycombe, HP10 9UB, Bucks, United Kingdom
Tel.: (44) 1494530077
Web Site: http://www.bbcs.co.uk
Year Founded: 1983
Building & Industrial Cleaning Services
N.A.I.C.S.: 561710
Gary C. Stevens (Chm)

BUT'ONE INFORMATION CORPORATION

Block C 10th Floor Building 3 Huoju Road, Hi-Tech Development Zone, Xi'an, 710043, Shaanxi, China
Tel.: (86) 2982693206
Web Site: http://www.butone.com
Year Founded: 1994
600455—(SHG)
Rev.: $33,340,423
Assets: $130,727,465
Liabilities: $81,997,952
Net Worth: $48,729,513
Earnings: $3,769,178
Fiscal Year-end: 12/31/22
Software Development Services
N.A.I.C.S.: 541511
Ping Wang (Chm & Gen Mgr)

BUTANE INDUSTRIAL COMPANY

No 34 East Hoveize St North Sohrevardi St, 15599-43611, Tehran, Iran
Tel.: (98) 2183520000
Web Site:
    https://butaneindustrial.com
Year Founded: 1964
BOTA1—(THE)
Sales Range: Less than $1 Million
Household Appliances Mfr
N.A.I.C.S.: 335220

BUTCHER'S PET CARE LTD.

Baker Group House Dockham Way, Crick, NN6 7TZ, Northamptonshire, United Kingdom
Tel.: (44) 1788 825 872
Web Site:
    http://www.butchersdogfood.co.uk
Year Founded: 1987
Sales Range: $100-124.9 Million
Emp.: 259
Pet Food Mfr
N.A.I.C.S.: 311111
Francis Powell (Dir-Fin)

Subsidiaries:

Butcher's Pet Care Sp.z.o.o   (1)
ul kochowskiego 15, Warsaw, Poland
Tel.: (48) 223743033
Web Site: http://www.butcherspetcare.pl

Pet Care Services
N.A.I.C.S.: 812910

BUTLER CAPITAL PARTNERS SA

30 Cours Albert 1er, 75008, Paris, France
Tel.: (33) 1 45 61 55 80
Web Site:
    http://www.butlercapitalpartners.com
Year Founded: 1991
Emp.: 10
Privater Equity Firm
N.A.I.C.S.: 523999
Walter Butler (Founder & Mng Partner)

Subsidiaries:

Sernam S.A.   (1)
33 Ave Claude Gedussy, 92 110, Clichy, France
Tel.: (33) 146529000
Web Site: http://www.sernam.fr
Sales Range: $450-499.9 Million
Courier Service
N.A.I.C.S.: 492110

Subsidiary (Domestic):

Sernam Centre S.A.   (2)
5 Boulevard De Quebec, Orleans, France   (100%)
Tel.: (33) 238524545
Web Site: http://www.sernam.fr
Sales Range: $25-49.9 Million
Freight Transportation Arrangement
N.A.I.C.S.: 488510

Sernam Est S.A.   (2)
1 Chemin De La Rompure, Champigneulles, 54250, Nancy, France   (100%)
Tel.: (33) 383396565
Sales Range: $25-49.9 Million
Freight Transportation Arrangement
N.A.I.C.S.: 488510

Sernam IDF S.A.   (2)
142-176 Avenue de Stalingrad, 92700, Colombes, France   (100%)
Tel.: (33) 146529000
Freight Transportation Arrangement
N.A.I.C.S.: 488510

Sernam Nord S.A.   (2)
Tarcdunelanpoys Ruegessaules, 59811, Lesquin, France
Tel.: (33) 320494200
Sales Range: $25-49.9 Million
Freight Transportation Arrangement
N.A.I.C.S.: 488510
Ettyenne Georgge (Gen Mgr)

Sernam Ouest S.A.   (2)
ZA de la Hallerais, Vern-sur-Seiche, France   (100%)
Tel.: (33) 299327000
Web Site: http://www.sernam.fr
Freight Transportation Arrangement
N.A.I.C.S.: 488510

BUTN LIMITED

Suite 6 229 Balaclava Rd, Caulfield North, 3161, VIC, Australia
Tel.: (61) 1300992886   AU
Web Site: https://www.butn.co
Year Founded: 2015
BTN—(ASX)
Rev.: $7,729,312
Assets: $64,534,223
Liabilities: $54,338,247
Net Worth: $10,195,976
Earnings: ($4,258,580)
Fiscal Year-end: 06/30/23
Financial Investment Services
N.A.I.C.S.: 523999
Darryl Lasnitzki (CFO)

Subsidiaries:

Australian Factoring Company Pty. Ltd.   (1)
PO Box 2245, Caulfield East, 3161, VIC, Australia
Tel.: (61) 1300232669

Web Site:
    https://www.australianfactoring.com.au
Cash Financial Services
N.A.I.C.S.: 522320

Faultless Recovery Services Pty. Ltd.   (1)
PO Box 2018, Caulfield East, 3161, VIC, Australia
Tel.: (61) 448077216
Web Site: https://www.faultlessrs.com.au
Motor Vehicle Repair Services
N.A.I.C.S.: 811111

NZ Factoring Company Ltd.   (1)
Manners Street Post Shop Te Aro, PO Box 11058, Wellington, 6011, New Zealand
Tel.: (64) 220240159
Web Site:
    https://www.nzfactoringcompany.co.nz
Cash Financial Services
N.A.I.C.S.: 522320

BUTTE ENERGY INC.

Suite 1700 666 Burrard Street, Vancouver, V6C 2X8, BC, Canada
Tel.: (604) 318-0390
Web Site:
    http://www.butteenergy.com
Year Founded: 1992
BEN.H—(TSXV)
Rev.: $711
Assets: $273,117
Liabilities: $104,020
Net Worth: $169,098
Earnings: ($731,485)
Fiscal Year-end: 12/31/20
Petroleum & Gas Extraction Services
N.A.I.C.S.: 211120
JoAnne Odette (CFO)

BUTWAL POWER COMPANY LIMITED

Ganga Devi Marga-313 Buddha Nagar, PO Box 11728, Kathmandu, Nepal
Tel.: (977) 14784026   NP
Web Site: https://www.bpc.com.np
Year Founded: 1965
BPCL—(NEP)
Rev.: $17,839,892
Assets: $102,143,936
Liabilities: $49,006,509
Net Worth: $53,137,427
Earnings: ($307,376)
Emp.: 184
Fiscal Year-end: 07/16/23
Hydro Power Generation Services
N.A.I.C.S.: 221111
Padma Jyoti (Chm)

Subsidiaries:

Nepal Hydro & Electric Limited   (1)
Durbarmarg No 4, PO Box 1, Rupandehi District, Butwal, Nepal
Tel.: (977) 71530212
Web Site: https://nhe.com.np
Emp.: 250
Automotive Parts Mfr & Distr
N.A.I.C.S.: 336390

Nyadi Hydropower Limited   (1)
Ganga Devi Marg-313, PO Box 26305, Buddhanagar, Kathmandu, Nepal
Tel.: (977) 14791776
Web Site: https://nhl.com.np
Hydroelectric Power Generation Services
N.A.I.C.S.: 221111

BUUDAIN TSATSAL JOINT STOCK COMPANY

1st Bag Kherlen Soum, Kherlen, Ulaanbaatar, Khentii, Mongolia
Tel.: (976) 15 622 3055
Grain & Oilseed Farming Services
N.A.I.C.S.: 111191

BUXLY PAINTS LIMITED

X-3 Manghopir Road SITE, Karachi, Pakistan
Tel.: (92) 2138691571   PK

Buxly Paints Limited—(Continued)

Web Site: https://www.buxly.com
Year Founded: 1954
BUXL—(PSX)
Rev.: $2,076,033
Assets: $1,763,903
Liabilities: $1,114,978
Net Worth: $648,925
Earnings: $9,774
Emp.: 25
Fiscal Year-end: 06/30/23
Paints Mfr
N.A.I.C.S.: 325510
Shamshad Ali *(Chm)*

BUXTON RESOURCES LIMITED

Suite 1 First Floor 14 - 16 Rowland
Street, Subiaco, 6008, WA, Australia
Tel.: (61) 893806063
Web Site:
　http://www.buxtonresources.com.au
BUX—(ASX)
Rev.: $1,900,774
Assets: $2,987,337
Liabilities: $346,199
Net Worth: $2,641,138
Earnings: ($2,698,893)
Emp.: 8
Fiscal Year-end: 06/30/24
Mineral Mining Services
N.A.I.C.S.: 213115
Sam Wright *(Sec)*

BUYANG INTERNATIONAL HOLDING INC.

8 Buyang Road, Xicheng Jiedao,
Yongkang, Zhejiang, China
Tel.: (86) 57987270871
Year Founded: 2005
2457—(HKG)
Rev.: $67,462,806
Assets: $75,624,762
Liabilities: $19,325,603
Net Worth: $56,299,159
Earnings: $8,270,889
Emp.: 547
Fiscal Year-end: 12/31/22
Holding Company
N.A.I.C.S.: 551112
Jingjun Xu *(Deputy Chm)*

BUYSELL TECHNOLOGIES CO., LTD.

PALT Bldg 4-28-8 Yotsuya, Shinjuku-
Ku, Tokyo, 160-0004, Japan
Tel.: (81) 333590830
Web Site: https://www.buysell-
technologies.com
Year Founded: 2001
7685—(TKS)
Rev.: $301,849,660
Assets: $151,158,800
Liabilities: $90,113,900
Net Worth: $61,044,900
Earnings: $10,301,770
Emp.: 924
Fiscal Year-end: 12/31/23
Precious Metal Distr
N.A.I.C.S.: 423940
Hideki Yoshimura *(Chm)*

BUZBUZ CAPITAL CORP.

82 Richmond Street East, Toronto,
M5C 1P1, ON, Canada
Tel.: (647) 501-3290
Year Founded: 2018
BZBZ.P—(TSXV)
Assets: $344,062
Liabilities: $56,255
Net Worth: $287,807
Earnings: ($50,966)
Fiscal Year-end: 12/31/20
Business Consulting Services
N.A.I.C.S.: 522299
Richard Buzbuzian *(CEO)*

BUZZ CAPITAL 2, INC.

116 Albert St Suite 300, Ottawa, K1P
5G3, ON, Canada
Tel.: (613) 366-4242
Year Founded: 2018
BUZH.P—(TSXV)
Assets: $93,070
Liabilities: $11,654
Net Worth: $81,116
Earnings: ($59,359)
Fiscal Year-end: 12/31/23
Asset Management Services
N.A.I.C.S.: 523940
Patrick Lalonde *(CEO & CFO)*

BUZZ CAPITAL, INC.

950 Gladstone Ave 200, Ottawa, K1Y
3E6, ON, Canada
Tel.: (647) 559-2899
Web Site: https://buzzcapital.ca
BUZ.P—(TSXV)
Assets: $248,080
Liabilities: $12,069
Net Worth: $236,011
Earnings: ($87,731)
Fiscal Year-end: 12/31/23
Asset Management Services
N.A.I.C.S.: 523940

BUZZ TECHNOLOGIES, INC.

Level 3 163 10 Jalan Perak, Wilayah
Persekutuan, 50450, Kuala Lumpur,
Malaysia
Tel.: (60) 987 654 321 01
Web Site:
　http://www.buzzfintech.com
BZTG—(OTCIQ)
Sales Range: Less than $1 Million
Financial Investment Services
N.A.I.C.S.: 523999

BUZZI SPA

Via Luigi Buzzi 6, 15033, Casale
Monferrato, AL, Italy
Tel.: (39) 0142416111
Web Site: https://www.buzzi.com
Year Founded: 1872
BUZZI—(ITA)
Rev.: $4,614,532,243
Assets: $8,139,342,726
Liabilities: $2,119,831,200
Net Worth: $6,019,511,526
Earnings: $1,033,329,734
Emp.: 9,620
Fiscal Year-end: 12/31/23
Engineering & Construction Services
N.A.I.C.S.: 333120
Enrico Buzzi *(Chm)*

Subsidiaries:

Buzzi Unicem USA Inc.　　　　**(1)**
100 Brodhead Rd Ste 230, Bethlehem, PA
18017-8989
Tel.: (610) 882-5000
Web Site: https://www.buzziunicemusa.com
Sales Range: $75-99.9 Million
Emp.: 100
Portland Cement, Masonry Cement &
Ready-mixed Concrete
N.A.I.C.S.: 212312

Branch (Domestic):

Buzzi Unicem USA　　　　　　　**(2)**
10401 N Meridian St Ste 120, Indianapolis,
IN 46290
Tel.: (610) 882-5000
Web Site: http://www.buzziunicem.com
Sales Range: $25-49.9 Million
Emp.: 40
Mfr & Importer of Cement, Clinker & Ready
Mixed Concrete
N.A.I.C.S.: 327310

Cement Hranice a.s.　　　　　　**(1)**
Belotinska 288, 753 01, Hranice, Czech
Republic
Tel.: (420) 581829111
Web Site: https://www.cement.cz

Sales Range: $50-74.9 Million
Emp.: 200
Cement Mfr
N.A.I.C.S.: 327310

Cementos Hispania s.a.　　　　**(1)**
Avda de Felipe II 15, E-28009, Madrid,
Spain
Tel.: (34) 914314540
Web Site: http://www.dyckerhoff.com
Cement Mfr
N.A.I.C.S.: 327310

Ciments Luxembourgeois S.A.　**(1)**
50 S Rue Fandel Fomain, 4002, Esch-sur-
Alzette, Luxembourg　　　　　　**(100%)**
Tel.: (352) 5525251
Web Site: http://www.cimalux.lu
Sales Range: $10-24.9 Million
Emp.: 150
Mfr of Cement
N.A.I.C.S.: 327310

Deuna Zement GmbH　　　　　**(1)**
Industriestr 7, D 37355, Deuna, Germany
Tel.: (49) 3607680
Web Site: http://www.deuna-zement.com
Sales Range: $1-9.9 Million
Emp.: 146
Cement Mfr
N.A.I.C.S.: 327310

Dyckerhoff GmbH　　　　　　**(1)**
Biebricher Strasse 68, 65203, Wiesbaden,
Germany
Tel.: (49) 6116760
Web Site: https://www.dyckerhoff.com
Readymix Concrete Mfr
N.A.I.C.S.: 327320

Subsidiary (Non-US):

Cimalux S.A.　　　　　　　　　**(2)**
Tel.: (352) 5525251
Web Site: http://www.cimalux.lu
Readymix Concrete Mfr
N.A.I.C.S.: 327320

Subsidiary (Non-US):

Beton du Ried S.A.S.　　　　　**(3)**
Route de Hindisheim, BP 3, Krauterger-
sheim, Obernai, Cedex, France
Tel.: (33) 388481948
Web Site: https://www.betonduried.com
Readymix Concrete Mfr
N.A.I.C.S.: 327320

Subsidiary (Non-US):

Dyckerhoff Basal Nederland B.V. **(2)**
Kelvinbaan 44, 3439 MT, Nieuwegein,
Netherlands
Tel.: (31) 886078300
Web Site: https://www.dyckerhoff-basal.nl
Readymix Concrete Mfr
N.A.I.C.S.: 327320

Subsidiary (Domestic):

Dyckerhoff Basal Betonmörtel
B.V.　　　　　　　　　　　　　**(3)**
Hefbrugweg 101, 1332 AM, Almere, Nether-
lands
Tel.: (31) 886078400
Readymix Concrete Mfr
N.A.I.C.S.: 327320

Subsidiary (Domestic):

Betonmörtel Centrale Groningen
(B.C.G.) B.V.　　　　　　　　　**(4)**
Duinkerkenstraat 60, 9723 BT, Groningen,
Netherlands
Tel.: (31) 503138888
Web Site: https://www.bcgroningen.nl
Readymix Concrete Mfr
N.A.I.C.S.: 327320

Friesland Beton Heerenveen
B.V.　　　　　　　　　　　　　**(4)**
Wetterwille 27, 8447 GB, Heerenveen,
Netherlands
Tel.: (31) 513620550
Readymix Concrete Mfr
N.A.I.C.S.: 327320

Subsidiary (Non-US):

Dyckerhoff Polska Sp. z o.o.　　**(2)**
Zakladowa 3, 26-052, Nowiny, Poland

Tel.: (48) 413466000
Web Site: https://www.dyckerhoff.pl
Readymix Concrete Mfr
N.A.I.C.S.: 327320
Kieres Krzysztof *(Gen Dir)*

Subsidiary (Domestic):

GfBB pruftechnik GmbH & Co.
KG　　　　　　　　　　　　　　**(2)**
Liebigstrasse 16, 65439, Florsheim, Ger-
many
Tel.: (49) 2171342799
Web Site: https://www.betonpruefung.info
Construction Material Services
N.A.I.C.S.: 541380

Subsidiary (Non-US):

OOO Dyckerhoff Korkino
Cement　　　　　　　　　　　　**(2)**
Zavodskaya Street 1, Korkino, 456541,
Chelyabinsk, Russia
Tel.: (7) 3515233761
Readymix Concrete Mfr
N.A.I.C.S.: 327320

TOB Dyckerhoff Ukraina　　　　**(2)**
Pyrohivskyi shliakh Str bld 26, 03083, Kiev,
Ukraine
Tel.: (380) 445361953
Web Site: http://www.dyckerhoff.com.ua
Readymix Concrete Mfr
N.A.I.C.S.: 327320

Zapa Beton a.s.　　　　　　　　**(2)**
Michle c ev 417, 141 00, Prague, Czech
Republic
Tel.: (420) 226004444
Web Site: https://www.zapa.cz
Readymix Concrete Mfr
N.A.I.C.S.: 327320

Subsidiary (Non-US):

Zapa Beton SK s.r.o.　　　　　　**(3)**
Vajnorska 142, PO Box 99, 830 00, Brati-
slava, Slovakia
Tel.: (421) 249105411
Web Site: https://www.zapa.sk
Readymix Concrete Mfr
N.A.I.C.S.: 327320

Leschuplat GmbH　　　　　　　**(1)**
Linderhauser Str 135, D 42279, Wuppertal,
Germany
Tel.: (49) 202758860
Web Site: http://www.leschuplast.de
Sales Range: $25-49.9 Million
Emp.: 10
Cement Mfr
N.A.I.C.S.: 327310

Materiaux S.A.　　　　　　　　**(1)**
2A Rue Kalchesbreck, PO Box 2492, L
1852, Luxembourg, Luxembourg
Tel.: (352) 438811
Mfr of Cement
N.A.I.C.S.: 327310

Nordenhamer Transportbeton GmbH
& Co. KG　　　　　　　　　　　**(1)**
Weserstrasse 16, Elsfleth, 26931, Norden-
ham, Germany
Tel.: (49) 4404951111
Web Site: https://www.nordenhamer-tb.de
Readymix Concrete Mfr
N.A.I.C.S.: 327320

OAO Sucholoshskzement　　　　**(1)**
Ul Kunarskaja 20, Swerdlowsker Gebiet,
RUS 623520, Yekaterinburg, Suchoi Log,
Russia
Tel.: (7) 3437379038
Web Site: http://www.sl-cement.ru
Sales Range: $200-249.9 Million
Emp.: 1,000
Producer & Distr of Cement, Concrete &
Finishing Products
N.A.I.C.S.: 327310
Vladimir Aleksandrovich Klementyev *(Dir-
Mktg & Sls)*

RHEBAU Rheinische Beton- und
Bauindustrie GmbH & Co. KG　　**(1)**
Dusseldorfer Strasse 118, 41541, Dorma-
gen, Germany　　　　　　　　　**(100%)**
Tel.: (49) 213377030
Web Site: http://www.rhebau.de

Sales Range: $25-49.9 Million
Emp.: 100
Mfr of Cement
N.A.I.C.S.: 327310

Sibo-Gruppe GmbH & Co. KG (1)
Lienener Strasse 89, 49525, Lengerich,
Germany
Tel.: (49) 54196388501
Web Site: http://www.sibo.de
Readymix Concrete Mfr
N.A.I.C.S.: 327320

Sibobeton Ems GmbH & Co. KG (1)
Darmer Esch 81a, 49811, Lingen, Germany
Tel.: (49) 591912250
Readymix Concrete Mfr
N.A.I.C.S.: 327320

**Sibobeton Enger GmbH & Co.
KG** (1)
Vor der Nade 48, 32130, Enger, Germany
Tel.: (49) 5224974311
Readymix Concrete Mfr
N.A.I.C.S.: 327320

**Sibobeton Osnabruck GmbH & Co.
KG** (1)
Suberweg 62, 49090, Osnabruck, Germany
Tel.: (49) 54133579911
Readymix Concrete Mfr
N.A.I.C.S.: 327320

**Sibobeton Wilhelmshaven GmbH &
Co. KG** (1)
Hildesheimer Strasse 7, 26384, Wil-
helmshaven, Germany
Tel.: (49) 442193780
Readymix Concrete Mfr
N.A.I.C.S.: 327320

**Sudwest Lacke & Farben GmbH &
Co. KG** (1)
Iggelheimer Str 13, 67459, Boehl-Iggelheim,
Germany (100%)
Tel.: (49) 63247090
Web Site: https://www.suedwest.de
Sales Range: $10-24.9 Million
Emp.: 120
Paints, Stripper, Protective Coatings & Fin-
ishing Products
N.A.I.C.S.: 444180
Hans-Joerg von Rhade (Mng Dir)

**TUBAG Trass-Zement-Steinwerke
GmbH** (1)
Bundesstrasse, 56638, Kruft, Germany
Tel.: (49) 265281104
Web Site: http://www.quick-mik.de
Sales Range: $25-49.9 Million
Emp.: 15
Cement Mfr
N.A.I.C.S.: 327310
Carsten Peier (Gen Mgr)

BV HOLDING AG
Vordere Dorfgasse 12, 3073, Gumli-
gen, Switzerland
Tel.: (41) 31 380 18 50
Web Site: http://www.bvgroup.ch
Privater Equity Firm
N.A.I.C.S.: 523999
Patrick Schar (CEO)

BVE HOLDING SE
Am Wollelager 8, 27749, Delmen-
horst, Germany
Tel.: (49) 422115493011
Holding Company
N.A.I.C.S.: 551112
Sarah Stoppe-Ramadan (Vice Chm)

Subsidiaries:

Mesar Beratung (1)
Am Wollelager 8 Technologiezentrum,
27749, Delmenhorst, Germany
Tel.: (49) 42222093180
Web Site: http://www.mesar-beratung.com
Financial Advisory Services
N.A.I.C.S.: 523940

BVZ HOLDING AG
Rail Center Bahnhofplatz 7, CH-3900,
Brig, Switzerland
Tel.: (41) 848642442

Web Site: https://www.bvzholding.ch
BVZN—(SWX)
Sales Range: Less than $1 Million
Emp.: 655
Holding Company
N.A.I.C.S.: 551112
Alice Kalbermatter (Member-Mgmt Bd
& Head-Fin & Svcs)

BW ENERGY LIMITED
Washington Mall Phase 2 4th Floor
Suite 400 22 Church Street, Hamil-
ton, HM 1189, Bermuda
Tel.: (441) 2951422 BM
Web Site: https://www.bwenergy.no
Year Founded: 2016
BWE—(OSL)
Rev.: $507,300,000
Assets: $1,740,400,000
Liabilities: $1,042,800,000
Net Worth: $697,600,000
Earnings: $81,000,000
Emp.: 434
Fiscal Year-end: 12/31/23
Oil & Gas Distribution Services
N.A.I.C.S.: 237120
Carl K. Arnet (CEO)

BW EPIC KOSAN LTD.
8 Eu Tong Sen Street #22-89 The
Central, Singapore, 059818, Singa-
pore
Tel.: (65) 62307801
Web Site: http://www.bwek.com
BWEK—(OSL)
Rev.: $361,364,586
Assets: $987,307,980
Liabilities: $498,930,426
Net Worth: $488,377,554
Earnings: $21,367,655
Emp.: 2,034
Fiscal Year-end: 12/31/22
Pressurised Gas Carriers Owner &
Operator
N.A.I.C.S.: 213112
Charles Maltby (CEO)

Subsidiaries:

Lauritzen Kosan A/S (1)
15 Tuborg Havnevej, 2900, Hellerup, Den-
mark
Tel.: (45) 33968000
Web Site: http://www.j-l.com
Freight Transportation Services
N.A.I.C.S.: 488510
Mads Peter zacho (CEO)

BW GROUP LTD.
10 Pasir Panjang Road #17-02
Mapletree Business City, Singapore,
117438, Singapore
Tel.: (65) 6 705 5588 BM
Web Site: http://www.bwlpg.com
Year Founded: 1955
Rev.: $521,754,000
Assets: $2,259,944,000
Liabilities: $1,276,319,000
Net Worth: $983,625,000
Earnings: ($69,319,000)
Emp.: 1,798
Fiscal Year-end: 12/31/18
Holding Company
N.A.I.C.S.: 551112
Andreas Sohmen-Pao (Chm)

Subsidiaries:

BW Fleet Management Pte Ltd (1)
Mapletree Business City 18-01 10 Pasir
Panjang Road, Singapore, 117438, Singa-
pore
Tel.: (65) 6337 2133
Marine Transportation Services
N.A.I.C.S.: 483111
Surajit Chanda (Mgr-Fleet)

BW Maritime Pte Ltd. (1)
Mapletree Business City 18-01 10 Pasir
Panjang Road, Singapore, 117438, Singa-
pore

Tel.: (65) 63372133
Web Site: http://www.bwshipping.com
Holding Company; Marine Operations
N.A.I.C.S.: 551112

Subsidiary (Non-US):

BW Gas ASA (2)
Drammensveien 106, 0273, Oslo, Norway
Tel.: (47) 22120505
Web Site: http://www.bwgas.com
Sales Range: $550-599.9 Million
Emp.: 3,790
Gas & Marine Transportation Services
N.A.I.C.S.: 488330
Helmut Sohmen (Chm)

Subsidiary (Non-US):

Bergesen D.Y. Philippines, Inc. (3)
5th Fl Urban Bldg, 405 Sen Gil Puyat Ave,
Makati, 1209, Metro Manila,
Philippines (100%)
Tel.: (63) 28952469
Web Site: http://www.bergesen.no
Sales Range: $25-49.9 Million
Emp.: 40
Shipping Services
N.A.I.C.S.: 488330

Affiliate (Domestic):

BW LPG Limited (2)
10 Pasir Panjang Road 17-02 Mapletree
Business City, Singapore, 117438,
Singapore (45%)
Tel.: (65) 67055588
Web Site: http://www.bwlpg.com
Rev.: $699,028,000
Assets: $2,540,514,000
Liabilities: $981,392,000
Net Worth: $1,559,122,000
Earnings: $238,577,000
Emp.: 1,595
Fiscal Year-end: 12/31/2022
LPG Carrier
N.A.I.C.S.: 213112
Elaine Ong (CFO)

BW Shipping Philippines Inc. (1)
5/F Goodland Building 377 Senator Gil
Puyat Ave, Makati, 1200, Philippines
Tel.: (63) 2 895 2469
Web Site: http://www.bwphilippines.com
Marine Transportation Services
N.A.I.C.S.: 483111

BW Water Pte. Ltd. (1)
10 Pasir Panjang Road, Mapletree Busi-
ness City #17-02,, Singapore, 117438, Sin-
gapore
Tel.: (65) 64345832
Web Site: https://www.bw-water.com
Waste Water Solutions
N.A.I.C.S.: 221310
Matthew White (CEO)

Subsidiary (US):

SafBon Water Technology, Inc. (2)
9208 Palm River Rd Ste 302, Tampa, FL
33619
Tel.: (813) 549-0182
Web Site: https://www.safbonwater.com
Waste Water Treatment Services
N.A.I.C.S.: 221310

Hafnia Limited (1)
Mapletree Business City 18-01 10 Pasir
Panjang Road, Singapore, 117438, Singa-
pore
Tel.: (65) 64343770
Web Site: https://hafnia.com
Rev.: $1,832,544,000
Assets: $3,918,854,000
Liabilities: $1,909,850,000
Net Worth: $2,009,004,000
Earnings: $751,589,000
Emp.: 5,095
Fiscal Year-end: 12/31/2022
Freight Transportation Services
N.A.I.C.S.: 483111
Jens Christophersen (Exec VP-Comml)

BW IDEOL AS
PO Box 33, Skoyen, 0212, Oslo,
Norway NO
Web Site: https://www.bw-ideol.com
Year Founded: 2010

BWIDL—(EUR)
Rev.: $8,154,285
Assets: $155,166,016
Liabilities: $34,944,656
Net Worth: $120,221,359
Earnings: ($20,423,175)
Emp.: 74
Fiscal Year-end: 12/31/22
Engineeering Services
N.A.I.C.S.: 541330
Cynthia Moutier (Chief HR Officer)

BW OFFSHORE LIMITED
Karenslyst Alle 6, NO-0212, Oslo,
Norway
Tel.: (47) 23130000
Web Site:
https://www.bwoffshore.com
BWO—(OSL)
Rev.: $774,100,000
Assets: $3,498,600,000
Liabilities: $2,347,500,000
Net Worth: $1,151,100,000
Earnings: $129,500,000
Emp.: 1,733
Fiscal Year-end: 12/31/22
Floating Production Services for Oil &
Gas Industry
N.A.I.C.S.: 213112
Andreas Sohmen-Pao (Chm)

Subsidiaries:

BW Energy Gabon SA (1)
Boulevard du Bord de Mer Immeuble Bord
de Mer 3ieme Etage, BP 23771, Libreville,
Gabon
Tel.: (241) 1764849
Floating Production Services
N.A.I.C.S.: 213112

BW Offshore (UK) Limited (1)
First Floor Horizons House 81-83 Waterloo
Quay, Aberdeen, AB11 5DE, United King-
dom
Tel.: (44) 1224900260
Floating Production Services
N.A.I.C.S.: 213112
Colleen Gray (Sr Mgr-Human Capital-Ops)

BW Offshore China Ltd. (1)
Room 2301 No 18 Xin Jin Qiao Road, Pu-
dong, Shanghai, 201206, China
Tel.: (86) 2150302017
Floating Production Services
N.A.I.C.S.: 213112

BW Offshore Cyprus Ltd (1)
359 28th October Street WTC Cyprus Trust
Re Building 2ndFloor, CY-3107, Limassol,
Cyprus
Tel.: (357) 25814038
Floating Production Services for Oil & Gas
Industry
N.A.I.C.S.: 213112

BW Offshore Management B.V. (1)
Polarisavenue 17, 2132 JH, Hoofddorp,
Netherlands
Tel.: (31) 237271235
Floating Production Services
N.A.I.C.S.: 213112

BW Offshore Nigeria Ltd. (1)
South Atlantic Petroleum Towers 8th Floor
1, PO Box 50655, Adeola Odeku Street Vic-
toria Islands, Lagos, 234, Nigeria
Tel.: (234) 12705146
Floating Production Services for Oil & Gas
Industry
N.A.I.C.S.: 213112

BW Offshore Norway AS (1)
Karenslyst Alle 6, 0278, Oslo, Norway
Tel.: (47) 23130000
Floating Production Services
N.A.I.C.S.: 213112

**BW Offshore Shipholding Cyprus
Limited** (1)
359 28th October Street WTC Cyprus Trust
Re Building 2ndFloor, CY-3107, Limassol,
Cyprus
Tel.: (357) 25814038
Floating Production Services
N.A.I.C.S.: 213112

BW Offshore Limited—(Continued)

BW Offshore Singapore Pte. Ltd. (1)
30 Pasir Panjang Road 14-31/32, Mapletree Business City, Singapore, 117400, Singapore
Tel.: (65) 6 632 7888
Web Site: https://www.bwoffshore.com
Emp.: 250
Floating Production Services for Oil & Gas Industry
N.A.I.C.S.: 213112

BW Offshore USA Management, Inc. (1)
2925 Briar Park Ste 1295, Houston, TX 77042
Tel.: (713) 781-0670
Floating Production Services
N.A.I.C.S.: 213112

BW Offshore USA, LLC (1)
125 St James Dr W Ste 140, Saint Rose, LA 70087
Tel.: (504) 934-4950
Floating Production Services
N.A.I.C.S.: 213112

BW Offshore do Brasil Ltda (1)
Rua Lauro Muller 116 Sala 703, Torre do Rio Sul Botafogo, Rio de Janeiro, 22290-160, Brazil
Tel.: (55) 2122448350
Sales Range: $50-74.9 Million
Emp.: 50
Floating Production Services for Oil & Gas Industry
N.A.I.C.S.: 213112

Bergesen Worldwide Mexico, S.A, de CV (1)
Calle 68 Mz 8 Lote 16 Entre 35-A y 35-B, Col San Agustin del Palmar, 24110, Ciudad del Carmen, Campeche, Mexico
Tel.: (52) 9383842040
Floating Production Services
N.A.I.C.S.: 213112

Prosafe Production Nigeria Limited (1)
South Atlantic Petroleum Towers 8th Floor 1, Adeola Odeku Street Victoria Islands, Lagos, Nigeria
Tel.: (234) 12705146
Floating Production Services
N.A.I.C.S.: 213112

BWA GROUP PLC
One Bow Churchyard, Westminster, London, EC4A 9DQ, United Kingdom
Tel.: (44) 7836238172
Web Site:
    https://www.bwagroupplc.com
Rev.: $1,202
Assets: $1,142,829
Liabilities: $111,629
Net Worth: $1,031,200
Earnings: ($92,875)
Fiscal Year-end: 04/30/18
Investment Services
N.A.I.C.S.: 523999
James Montford Victor Butterfield (Sec)

BWB PARTNERS P/S
Avderodvej 27C, 3480, Kokkedal, Denmark
Tel.: (45) 48401200
Web Site: http://www.odinequity.dk
Year Founded: 2005
Sales Range: $25-49.9 Million
Emp.: 12
Privater Equity Firm
N.A.I.C.S.: 523999
Jacob Bergenholtz (Partner)

Subsidiaries:

DBB Jack-Up Services A/S (1)
Borneovej 28, 8000, Arhus, Denmark
Tel.: (45) 87 30 84 00
Web Site: http://www.dbbjackup.dk
Marine Vessel Operator
N.A.I.C.S.: 488330
Vagn Lehd Moller (Chm)

HYDRA Tech A/S (1)
Sigenvej 2, Vraa, 9760, Hjorring, Denmark
Tel.: (45) 98980200
Web Site: http://www.hydratech.dk
Sales Range: $50-74.9 Million
Emp.: 250
Hydraulic Cylinders Mfr & Distr
N.A.I.C.S.: 333248
Kim Weidemann (Pres & CEO)

Qubiqa Esbjerg A/S (1)
Morsogade 10, DK-6700, Esbjerg, Denmark
Tel.: (45) 75 12 01 99
Web Site: http://www.qubiqa.dk
Emp.: 200
Logistics Consulting Servies
N.A.I.C.S.: 541614
Carsten Sorensen (CEO)

SH Group A/S (1)
Kuopiovej 20, 5700, Svendborg, Denmark (100%)
Tel.: (45) 62 21 78 10
Web Site: http://www.shgroup.dk
Sales Range: $25-49.9 Million
Emp.: 250
Hydraulic & Mechanical Systems Design, Engineering & Pipe Work Services
N.A.I.C.S.: 541330
Morten Nielsen (CEO)

SSG A/S (1)
Knapholm 6, 2730, Herlev, Denmark
Tel.: (45) 70 15 38 00
Web Site: http://www.ssg.dk
Sales Range: $75-99.9 Million
Emp.: 304
Facility Services & Damage Control
N.A.I.C.S.: 561210
Michael Nielsen (CEO)

BWK GMBH UNTERNEHMENS BETEILIGUNGSGESELL-SCHAFT
Thouretstrasse 2, 70173, Stuttgart, Germany
Tel.: (49) 7112255760
Web Site: http://www.bwk.de
Sales Range: $25-49.9 Million
Emp.: 14
Investment Services
N.A.I.C.S.: 523999
Jochen Wolf (Exec Dir)

BWL LIMITED
Industrial Area, Bhilai, 490026, Chhattisgarh, India
Tel.: (91) 9830403897
Web Site: https://www.bhilaiwire.com
Year Founded: 1991
504643—(BOM)
Rev.: $14,466
Assets: $401,718
Liabilities: $1,405,369
Net Worth: ($1,003,651)
Earnings: ($108,587)
Emp.: 4
Fiscal Year-end: 03/31/21
Steel Products Mfr
N.A.I.C.S.: 331210
Sunil Khetawat (Chm, CEO & Mng Dir)

BWP TRUST
Level 14 Brookfield Place Tower 2, 123 St Georges Terrace, Perth, 6000, WA, Australia
Tel.: (61) 893274356　　　　AU
Web Site:
    https://www.bwptrust.com.au
Year Founded: 1998
BWP—(ASX)
Rev.: $116,493,055
Assets: $2,394,716,203
Liabilities: $586,790,195
Net Worth: $1,807,926,008
Earnings: $120,340,544
Fiscal Year-end: 06/30/24
Commercial Real Estate Management Services
N.A.I.C.S.: 531210

Michael J. Wedgwood (Mng Dir)

BWR EXPLORATION, INC.
82 Richmond Street East Suite 201, Toronto, M5C 1P1, ON, Canada
Tel.: (416) 203-8636　　　　Ca
Web Site: https://bwrexploration.com
Year Founded: 2011
BWR—(TSXV)
Assets: $64,349
Liabilities: $741,036
Net Worth: ($676,687)
Earnings: ($264,935)
Fiscal Year-end: 11/30/23
Metal Mining
N.A.I.C.S.: 212290
Neil D. Novak (Co-Founder, Pres & CEO)

BWT AKTIENGESELLSCHAFT
Walter Simmer Strasse 4, A-5310, Mondsee, Austria
Tel.: (43) 623250110　　　　AT
Web Site: http://www.bwt-group.com
Rev.: $652,923,619
Assets: $507,703,204
Liabilities: $299,745,427
Net Worth: $207,957,777
Earnings: $10,107,974
Emp.: 3,326
Fiscal Year-end: 12/31/16
Water Technology Services
N.A.I.C.S.: 488390
Andreas Weissenbacher (CEO)

Subsidiaries:

Anna International Limited (1)
Suite 2a Level 5, Plaza Commercial Centre, Sliema, Malta
Tel.: (356) 21335174
Other Miscellaneous Durable Goods Whslr
N.A.I.C.S.: 423990

BWT AQUA AG (1)
Hauptstrasse 192, CH-4147, Aesch, Switzerland
Tel.: (41) 617558899
Web Site: http://www.bwt-aqua.ch
Sales Range: $50-74.9 Million
Emp.: 180
General Purpose Machinery Mfr
N.A.I.C.S.: 333998
Thomas Muller (Mng Dir)

BWT Austria GmbH (1)
Walter-Simmer-Strasse 4, 5310, Mondsee, Austria
Tel.: (43) 623250110
Web Site: http://www.bwt.at
Emp.: 30
Waste Treatment Services
N.A.I.C.S.: 221310
Roland D'leteren (Gen Mgr)

BWT Belgium n.v. (1)
Leuvensesteenweg 633, 1930, Zaventem, Belgium
Tel.: (32) 27580310
Web Site: http://www.bwt.be
Sales Range: $25-49.9 Million
Emp.: 40
Other Support Activities for Water Transportation
N.A.I.C.S.: 488390

BWT Ceska Republika s.r.o. (1)
Lipova 196 - Cestlice, Prague, Czech Republic
Tel.: (420) 272680300
Sewage Treatment Facilities
N.A.I.C.S.: 221320

BWT France SAS (1)
103 rue Charles Michels, 93206, Saint Denis, France
Tel.: (33) 1 49 22 45 00
Waste Treatment Services
N.A.I.C.S.: 221310

BWT Hungaria Kft (1)
Keleti 7, Budaors, 2040, Hungary
Tel.: (36) 23415305
Web Site: http://www.bwt.hu

Sales Range: $25-49.9 Million
Emp.: 20
Other Commercial & Service Industry Machinery Mfr
N.A.I.C.S.: 333310
Gyula Patro (Mng Dir)

BWT International Trading Ltd (1)
Tower Gate Place Tal-Qroqq Street, Msida, MSD 1703, Malta
Tel.: (356) 2131 3060
Water Treatment & Distr
N.A.I.C.S.: 221310
John Tsaila (Gen Mgr)

BWT Malta Holdings Ltd. (1)
Tower Gate Pl Tal-Qroqq St, Msida, MSD 1703, Malta
Tel.: (356) 2131 3060
Investment Management Service
N.A.I.C.S.: 523999
John Psaila (Mng Partner)

BWT Nederland BV (1)
Energieweg 9, 2382 NA, Zoeterwoude, Netherlands
Tel.: (31) 88 750 90 00
Web Site: http://www.bwtnederland.nl
Sales Range: $50-74.9 Million
Emp.: 49
Waste Treatment Services
N.A.I.C.S.: 221310
Jan Aufenacker (Mng Dir)

BWT Pharma & Biotech Ltd. (1)
Unit 2A Ashbourne Business Park, Ashbourne, Meath, Ireland
Tel.: (353) 1 849 87 00
Web Site: http://www.bwt-group.com
Sales Range: $75-99.9 Million
Emp.: 20
Waste Treatment Services
N.A.I.C.S.: 221310
Patrick Archer (Gen Mgr)

BWT Polska Sp. z.o.o. (1)
Ul Polczynska 116, 01-304, Warsaw, Poland
Tel.: (48) 22 533 57 00
Waste Treatment Services
N.A.I.C.S.: 221310

Subsidiary (Non-US):

BWT Ukraine Ltd. (2)
Radyshcheva Lane 8 Kiev, 4073, Kiev, Ukraine
Tel.: (380) 44 390 76 18
Web Site: http://www.bwt.ua
Emp.: 11
Waste Treatment Services
N.A.I.C.S.: 221310
Evgeniy Doroshenko (Gen Mgr)

BWT Wassertechnik GmbH (1)
Industriestr 7, Schriesheim, 69198, Heidelberg, Germany
Tel.: (49) 6203730
Web Site: http://www.bwt.ge
Sales Range: $100-124.9 Million
Emp.: 300
Other Commercial & Service Industry Machinery Mfr
N.A.I.C.S.: 333310
lutz Huepner (Mng Dir)

Subsidiary (Domestic):

BWT water+more Deutschland GmbH (2)
Spiegelgasse 13, 65183, Wiesbaden, Germany
Tel.: (49) 611 58019 0
Web Site: http://www.water-and-more.com
Sales Range: $75-99.9 Million
Emp.: 1
Waste Treatment Services
N.A.I.C.S.: 221310
Frank Neuhausen (Gen Mgr)

Subsidiary (Non-US):

BWT water and more Iberica S.L. (3)
TCM 2 6 Pl Ofic 20 Avda Ernest Lluch 32, 8302, Mataro, Spain
Tel.: (34) 937023 204
Waste Treatment Services
N.A.I.C.S.: 221310

BWT water+more Italia srl (3)

Viale Giulio Cesare 20, 24124, Bergamo,
Italy
Tel.: (39) 035 210738
Waste Treatment Services
N.A.I.C.S.: 221310

Subsidiary (Domestic):

hobby-pool technologies GmbH   **(2)**
Rodgener Str 8-9, Ot Grosszoberitz, 06780,
Zorbig, Germany
Tel.: (49) 34956 3998 0
Swimming Pool Products Distr
N.A.I.C.S.: 423910

BWT Water Technology (Shanghai)
Co. Ltd.   **(1)**
248 Xintuan Rd 12 Workshop Qingpu Ind
Zone, 201707, Shanghai, China
Tel.: (86) 21 5986 7100
Sales Range: $50-74.9 Million
Emp.: 5
Waste Treatment Services
N.A.I.C.S.: 221310
Oliver Wake (Gen Mgr)

BWT water + more GmbH   **(1)**
Walter Simmer-Strasse 4, 5310, Mondsee,
Austria
Tel.: (43) 6232 5011 1164
Emp.: 45
Waste Treatment Services
N.A.I.C.S.: 221310
Andreas Weissenbacher (CEO)

Cilit SA   **(1)**
C/ Silici 71-73 Poligono Industrial del Este,
8940, Barcelona, Spain
Tel.: (34) 934740494
Waste Treatment Services
N.A.I.C.S.: 221310

Cillichemie Italiana Srl   **(1)**
Via Plinio 59, 20129, Milan, Italy
Tel.: (39) 02 2046343
Sales Range: $75-99.9 Million
Emp.: 100
Waste Treatment Services
N.A.I.C.S.: 221310
Lorenzo Tadini (Mng Dir)

Culligan (UK) Ltd.   **(1)**
Culligan House Unit 3 The Gateway Centre,
Coronation Rd, High Wycombe, HP12 3SU,
Buckinghamshire, United Kingdom **(100%)**
Tel.: (44) 1494 441286
Web Site: http://www.culligan.co.uk
Water Conditioning & Purification Equip-
ment & Related Products
N.A.I.C.S.: 333310

FuMA-Tech GmbH   **(1)**
Am Grubenstollen 11, 66386, Saint Ingbert,
Germany
Tel.: (49) 689492650
Web Site: http://www.fumatech.com
Sales Range: $25-49.9 Million
Emp.: 25
Support Activities for Water Transportation
N.A.I.C.S.: 488390
Bernd Bauer (Mng Dir)

HOH Birger Christensen AS   **(1)**
Roykenveien 142 A, PO Box 136, N-1371,
Asker, Norway
Tel.: (47) 67177000
Web Site: http://www.hoh.no
Sales Range: $50-74.9 Million
Emp.: 35
Water Supply & Irrigation Systems
N.A.I.C.S.: 221310

HOH Separtec OY   **(1)**
Varppeenkatu 28 19, 21201, Raisio, Finland
Tel.: (358) 24367300
Web Site: http://www.hoh.fi
Sales Range: $25-49.9 Million
Emp.: 14
Commercial & Service Industry Machinery
Mfr
N.A.I.C.S.: 333310

HOH Vattenteknik AB   **(1)**
Kantyxegatan 25, PO Box 9226, S-200 39,
Malmo, Sweden
Tel.: (46) 406914500
Web Site: http://www.vattenteknik.se
Sales Range: $25-49.9 Million
Emp.: 35
Commercial & Service Industry Machinery
Mfr

Paul Morin (Mng Dir)

HOH Water Technology A/S   **(1)**
Geminivej 24, 2670, Greve, Denmark
Tel.: (45) 43600500
Web Site: http://www.hoh.com
Sales Range: $25-49.9 Million
Emp.: 100
Consumer Electronics Repair & Mainte-
nance
N.A.I.C.S.: 811210
Henick Forslund (CEO)

OOO BWT   **(1)**
Ul Kasatkina 3a, 129301, Moscow, Russia
Tel.: (7) 4956828667
Web Site: http://www.bwt.ru
Sales Range: $75-99.9 Million
Emp.: 10
Waste Treatment Services
N.A.I.C.S.: 221310
Pavel Brunovsky (Gen Dir)

P & LS Beteiligungs GmbH   **(1)**
Walter-Simmer-Strasse 4, 5310, Mondsee,
Austria
Tel.: (43) 6232 5011 0
Waste Treatment Services
N.A.I.C.S.: 221310

P & LS Holding GmbH   **(1)**
Walter-Simmer-Str 4, 5310, Mondsee, Aus-
tria
Tel.: (43) 623250110
Web Site: http://www.bwt-group.com
Investment Management Service
N.A.I.C.S.: 523999
Andreas Weissenbacher (Member-Mgmt
Bd)

Subsidiary (Non-US):

BWT Pharma & Biotech AB   **(2)**
Kantyxegatan 25A, 21376, Malmo, Sweden
Tel.: (46) 40315440
Web Site: http://www.christ.se
Sales Range: $25-49.9 Million
Emp.: 20
Water Treatment & Management Engineer-
ing
N.A.I.C.S.: 541330

BWT Pharma & Biotech GmbH   **(2)**
Carl-Benz-Strasse 4, Bietigheim-Bissingen,
74321, Germany
Tel.: (49) 7142 3737 500
Web Site: http://www.bwt-pharma.com
Sales Range: $25-49.9 Million
Emp.: 60
Water Treatment & Management Engineer-
ing
N.A.I.C.S.: 541330
Stephan Stautmeaster (Mng Dir)

BWT UK Limited   **(2)**
BWT House The Gateway Centre Corona-
tion Road, High Wycombe, HP12 3SU,
Buckinghamshire, United Kingdom
Tel.: (44) 1494 838100
Web Site: http://www.bwt-uk.co.uk
Waste Treatment Services
N.A.I.C.S.: 221310

Best Water Technology (Ireland)
Ltd.   **(2)**
Unit 2A Ashbourne Business Park, Ash-
bourne, Ireland
Tel.: (353) 18498700
Sales Range: $50-74.9 Million
Emp.: 15
Water & Wastewater Sterilization Services
N.A.I.C.S.: 221310
Richard O'Neill (Mng Dir)

Christ Nishotech Water Systems Pte.
Ltd.   **(1)**
Plot No W159 MIDC Pawane, TTC Indus-
trial Area, Mumbai, 400 705, India   **(50%)**
Tel.: (91) 2227619274
Web Site: http://www.christ-nishotech.com
Water Treatment & Management Engineer-
ing
N.A.I.C.S.: 541330

Christ Pharma & Life Science Shang-
hai Ltd.   **(2)**
No 799 Yuyang Rd, Cangqiao Ind Zone,
201600, Shanghai, China
Tel.: (86) 21 59867200

Web Site: http://www.christ-austar.com
Sales Range: $25-49.9 Million
Emp.: 120
Service Industry Machinery Mfr
N.A.I.C.S.: 333310

WTA - Wassertechnischer Anlagen-
bau Plauen GmbH   **(1)**
Reissiger Gewerbering Eleven, 8525,
Plauen, Germany
Tel.: (49) 37 41 55 84 0
Waste Treatment Services
N.A.I.C.S.: 221310

arcana pool systems gmbh   **(1)**
Brunner Strasse 186, Gerasdorf Bei, 2201,
Vienna, Austria
Tel.: (43) 2246 28555
Web Site: http://www.mypool.at
Emp.: 15
Swimming Pool Equipments Distr
N.A.I.C.S.: 423910
Aralt Klanka (Gen Mgr)

BWX LIMITED

2 Darby Way, Dandenong South,
3175, VIC, Australia
Tel.: (61) 387856300
Web Site: http://www.bwxltd.com
BWX—(ASX)
Rev.: $151,956,930
Assets: $288,491,222
Liabilities: $213,003,885
Net Worth: $75,487,337
Earnings: ($257,126,468)
Emp.: 100
Fiscal Year-end: 06/30/22
Skin & Hair Care Products
N.A.I.C.S.: 456120
Ian Campbell (Chm)

Subsidiaries:

Mineral Fusion Natural Brands
LLC   **(1)**
1470 Cader Ln, Petaluma, CA 94954
Web Site: http://www.mineralfusion.com
Cosmetic Product Retailer
N.A.I.C.S.: 456120

The Good Collective Pty Ltd.   **(1)**
2 Darby Way, Dandenong South, 3175,
VIC, Australia
Tel.: (61) 387856300
Beauty Product Mfr & Distr
N.A.I.C.S.: 325620

Uspa Corporation Pty. Ltd.   **(1)**
2 Darby Way, Dandenong South, 3175,
VIC, Australia
Tel.: (61) 387856300
Web Site: http://www.uspa.com.au
Skin Care Product Retailer
N.A.I.C.S.: 456120

BXR GROUP B.V.

Jachthavenweg 109h, 1081 KM, Am-
sterdam, Netherlands
Tel.: (31) 20 504 6704
Web Site: http://www.bxrgroup.com
Investment Services
N.A.I.C.S.: 523999
Derk Stikker (CEO)

Subsidiaries:

BXR Partners Kft   **(1)**
Alkotas utca 53 MOM Park Centrum, 1123,
Budapest, Hungary
Tel.: (36) 14878000
Financial Advisory Services
N.A.I.C.S.: 523940

BXR Partners LLP   **(1)**
Marble Arch House 66 Seymour Street,
London, W1H 5BT, United Kingdom
Tel.: (44) 2072241900
Financial Advisory Services
N.A.I.C.S.: 523940

BXR Partners Pte. Ltd.   **(1)**
25 Duxton Hill 02-01, Singapore, 089608,
Singapore
Tel.: (65) 62293980
Financial Advisory Services
N.A.I.C.S.: 523940

Brazil Iowa Farms, LLC   **(1)**
207 Main St, Royal, IA 51357
Tel.: (712) 933-9400
Web Site: http://www.grupoiowa.org
Cultivation Services
N.A.I.C.S.: 115112
David Kruse (Pres)

BYBLOS BANK S.A.L.

Elias Sarkis Avenue, Ashrafieh, Bei-
rut, Lebanon
Tel.: (961) 1205050
Web Site:
http://www.byblosbank.com
Year Founded: 1950
BYB—(BEY)
Rev.: $13,985,722
Assets: $299,850,328
Liabilities: $247,799,960
Net Worth: $52,050,368
Earnings: ($17,218,052)
Fiscal Year-end: 12/31/22
Banking Services
N.A.I.C.S.: 522110
Semaan F. Bassil (Chm & Gen Mgr)

Subsidiaries:

Adonis Insurance & Reinsurance Co.
(ADIR) SAL   **(1)**
Dora highway Aya Commercial Center GF
1st Floor and 2nd Floor, Beirut, Lebanon
Tel.: (961) 1263263
Web Site: http://www.adirinsurance.com
Insurance Services
N.A.I.C.S.: 524210
Rene Klat (Chm)

Adonis Insurance & Reinsurance
Syria S.A.   **(1)**
Abu Rummaneh Al Mahdi Bin Baraka
Street-Building No 28, PO Box 33 509, Da-
mascus, Syria
Tel.: (963) 113344177
Web Site: http://www.adirinsurance-sy.com
Insurance Services
N.A.I.C.S.: 524210

Adonis Insurance Company Syria
S.A.   **(1)**
Abu Rummaneh Al Mahdi Bin Baraka Street
building No 28, PO Box 33 509, Damascus,
Syria
Tel.: (963) 113344177
Web Site: https://www.adirinsurance-sy.com
Individual & Business Insurance Services
N.A.I.C.S.: 524113

Byblos Bank Africa ltd.   **(1)**
Intersection of Mac Nimer and Baladiyya
Streets, PO Box 8121, Byblos Bank Africa
Tower, Khartoum, Sudan
Tel.: (249) 156552222
Web Site: http://www.byblosbankafrica.com
Sales Range: $50-74.9 Million
Emp.: 60
Commericial Banking
N.A.I.C.S.: 522110

Byblos Bank Armenia CJSC   **(1)**
Amiryan 18/3, Yerevan, 0002, Armenia
Tel.: (374) 60616100
Web Site:
https://www.byblosbankarmenia.am
Banking Services
N.A.I.C.S.: 522110
Hayk Stepanyan (CEO)

Byblos Bank Europe S.A.   **(1)**
Bld Bischoffsheim 1/8, PO Box 3 1 & 3 2,
1000, Brussels, Belgium
Tel.: (32) 25510020
Web Site: https://bbe.digital
Sales Range: $50-74.9 Million
Emp.: 55
Commericial Banking
N.A.I.C.S.: 522110

Byblos Bank Invest S.A.L   **(1)**
Byblos Tower Elias, Sarkis Avenue, Beirut,
Lebanon
Tel.: (961) 1335200
Web Site: http://www.byblosbank.com
Commericial Banking
N.A.I.C.S.: 522110

Byblos Bank Syria S.A.   **(1)**

Byblos Bank S.A.L.—(Continued)

Al Chaalan Amine Loutfi Hafez Street, PO
Box 5424, 5424, Damascus, Syria
Tel.: (963) 113348240
Web Site: http://www.byblosbank.com.lb
Sales Range: $100-124.9 Million
Emp.: 201
Commericial Banking
N.A.I.C.S.: 522110

BYBON GROUP COMPANY LIMITED

14th Floor Building 10 Futong East
Street, Chaoyang District, Beijing,
100102, China
Tel.: (86) 1064775967
Web Site: http://www.bybon.com
Year Founded: 2007
300736—(CHIN)
Rev.: $95,994,796
Assets: $22,785,276
Liabilities: $8,060,014
Net Worth: $14,725,262
Earnings: ($4,024,042)
Fiscal Year-end: 12/31/23
Electronic System Development Services
N.A.I.C.S.: 517112
Tiefeng Liu (Chm, Pres & Gen Mgr)

BYC CO., LTD.

984-74 Kongjwi Patjwi-ro Iseo-myeon,
Wanju-gun Yeongdeungpo-0547,
Seoul, Jeollabuk-do, Korea (South)
Tel.: (82) 7074308503
Web Site: https://www.byc.co.kr
Year Founded: 1946
001460—(KRS)
Rev.: $130,144,818
Assets: $513,024,844
Liabilities: $117,454,346
Net Worth: $395,570,499
Earnings: $27,064,747
Emp.: 570
Fiscal Year-end: 12/31/24
Apparel Product Mfr & Distr
N.A.I.C.S.: 315250
Dae-Hwan Kim (CEO)

BYCO PETROLEUM PAKISTAN LIMITED

9th-10th Floor The Harbour Front
Dolmen City, HC-3 Block-4 Marine
Drive Clifton, Karachi, 75600, Paki-
stan
Tel.: (92) 21111222081
Web Site: https://www.cnergyico.com
CNERGY—(PSX)
Rev.: $697,599,788
Assets: $1,313,968,698
Liabilities: $642,626,279
Net Worth: $671,342,419
Earnings: ($49,037,830)
Emp.: 1,300
Fiscal Year-end: 06/30/23
Crude Oil Refining & Marketing
N.A.I.C.S.: 324110
Amir Abbassciy (CEO)

Subsidiaries:

Byco Isomerisation Pakistan (Private)
Limited   (1)
Room No 406 407 4th Floor 55-B Islam-
abad Stock Exchange Towers, Jinnah Av-
enue Blue Area, Islamabad, Pakistan
Tel.: (92) 5128954712
Web Site: https://www.byco.com.pk
Petroleum Product Mfr
N.A.I.C.S.: 324199
Amir Abbassciy (CEO)

BYD COMPANY LIMITED

No 3009 BYD Road, Pingshan, Shen-
zhen, Guangdong, China
Tel.: (86) 75589888888
Web Site: https://www.byd.com
Year Founded: 1995

002594—(SSE)
Rev.: $33,115,175,572
Assets: $45,316,476,782
Liabilities: $29,345,221,367
Net Worth: $15,971,255,414
Earnings: $466,553,560
Emp.: 229,000
Fiscal Year-end: 12/31/21
Electric Equipment Mfr
N.A.I.C.S.: 335910
Wang Chuanfu (Founder & CEO)

Subsidiaries:

BYD (H.K.) Co., Limited   (1)
Unit 1712 17 F Tower 2 Grand Cent Plz No
138 Shatin Rural Comt Rd, Sha Tin, New
Territories, China (Hong Kong)
Tel.: (852) 23055128
Nickel & Lithium Batteries Sales
N.A.I.C.S.: 335910

BYD America Corporation   (1)
1500 W Shure Dr Ste 250, Arlington
Heights, IL 60004-1465
Tel.: (847) 690-9999
Storage Batteries Mfr & Sales
N.A.I.C.S.: 335910

BYD Australia Pty. Ltd.   (1)
Suite 401 Level 4 2-4 Lyonpark Road, Mac-
quarie Park, 2113, NSW, Australia
Tel.: (61) 1300293288
N.A.I.C.S.: 336320

BYD Chile S.p.A.   (1)
Room 701 Bucarest 150, 7510018, San-
tiago, Chile
Tel.: (56) 229023017
N.A.I.C.S.: 336320

BYD Company Limited - Huizhou
Plant 2   (1)
Xiangshui River Econ Develop Zone Daya
Bay, Huizhou, 516083, Guangdong, China
Tel.: (86) 7525118888
Ferrous Batteries Mfr
N.A.I.C.S.: 335910

BYD E-Motors Ecuador S.A   (1)
Av Rep Del Salvador y Naciones Unidas
ed, Mansion Blanca Torre Londres of 601,
Quito, Ecuador
Tel.: (593) 2260204
Automobile Parts Mfr
N.A.I.C.S.: 336390

BYD Electronic Hungary Kft   (1)
Ipari Park Puskas Tivadar Ut 8, Koppany-
monostor, 2903, Hungary
Tel.: (36) 34540840
Web Site: http://www.byd.com
Emp.: 2
Mobile Handset Components Mfr & Sales
N.A.I.C.S.: 334220
Wu Jinshen (Gen Mgr)

BYD Electronic International Co
Ltd   (1)
Part of Uint 1712 17th Floor Tower 2 Grand
Central Plaza, No 138 Shatin Rural Com-
mittee Road, Sha Tin, New Territories,
China (Hong Kong)
Tel.: (852) 21366185
Web Site: https://electronics.byd.com
Rev.: $14,840,813,026
Assets: $7,891,334,321
Liabilities: $4,341,950,598
Net Worth: $3,549,383,723
Earnings: $257,202,315
Emp.: 90,000
Fiscal Year-end: 12/31/2022
Telecommunication Servicesb
N.A.I.C.S.: 334210
Qian Li (Co-Sec)

BYD Europe B.V.   (1)
Gravelandseweg 256, 3125 BK, Schiedam,
Netherlands
Tel.: (31) 102070888
Web Site: http://www.byd.com
Sales Range: $25-49.9 Million
Emp.: 35
Nickel & Lithium Batteries Distr
N.A.I.C.S.: 423610
Isbrand Ho (Gen Mgr)

BYD European B.V.   (1)
S-Gravelandseweg 256, 3125 BK,

Schiedam, Netherlands
Tel.: (31) 102070888
Web Site: https://bydeurope.com
Electric Vehicle Mfr
N.A.I.C.S.: 336110

BYD Japan Co., Ltd.   (1)
Portside Dia-Bldg 5F 10-35 Sakae-cho,
Kanagawa-ku, Yokohama, 221-0052, Kana-
gawa, Japan
Tel.: (81) 456209788
Rechargeable Batteries Whslr
N.A.I.C.S.: 423610
Xuelang Liu (Pres)

BYD Korea Company Ltd.   (1)
58 Bukhang-Ro 177beon-Gil, Seo-gu, Incheon, 22856, Korea (South)
Tel.: (82) 325798818
N.A.I.C.S.: 336320

BYD Malaysia Sdn. Bhd.   (1)
Level 30 the Gardens North Tower Mid Val-
ley City Lingkaran Syed Putra, 59200,
Kuala Lumpur, Malaysia
Tel.: (60) 6564082135
N.A.I.C.S.: 336320

BYD Motor Colombia SAS   (1)
Tel.: (57) 16477928
Automobile Parts Mfr
N.A.I.C.S.: 336390

BYD Motors Inc.   (1)
888 E Walnut St Ste 200A, Pasadena, CA
91101
Tel.: (213) 748-3980
Web Site: https://en.byd.com
N.A.I.C.S.: 336320

BYD Motors Peru S.A.C.   (1)
Av Javier Prado Oeste 2501 Int 901,
Magdalena del Mar, Lima, Peru
Tel.: (51) 987857990
Automobile Mfr & Distr
N.A.I.C.S.: 336110

P.T. Byd Motor Indonesia   (1)
World Trade Centre WTC 5 Level 7 Jl Jen-
deral Sudirman No Kav 29-31, RT 8/RW 3
Kuningan Karet Kecamatan Setiabudi
Daerah Khusus Ibukota, South Jakarta,
12920, Indonesia
Tel.: (62) 2139738889
Automobile Mfr & Distr
N.A.I.C.S.: 336110

Shanghai BYD Company Limited   (1)
No 999 Xiangjing Rd, Songjiang Dist,
Shanghai, 201611, China
Tel.: (86) 21 57778888
Web Site: http://www.byd.com
Lithium Batteries Mfr & Sales
N.A.I.C.S.: 335910

BYGGFAKTA GROUP NORDIC HOLDCO AB

Lojtnantsgatan 9, 827 81, Ljusdal,
Sweden
Tel.: (46) 651552500
Web Site:
https://www.byggfaktagroup.com
Year Founded: 1936
BFG—(OMX)
Rev.: $203,199,300
Assets: $1,203,773,400
Liabilities: $444,054,960
Net Worth: $759,718,440
Earnings: $11,924,820
Emp.: 1,900
Fiscal Year-end: 12/31/22
Software Development Services
N.A.I.C.S.: 541511
Dario Aganovic (CEO)

Subsidiaries:

Armilar Business Services S.L.   (1)
Jose Abascal 44 - 1, 28003, Madrid, Spain
Tel.: (34) 900823900
Web Site: https://armilar.biz
Business Intelligence Services
N.A.I.C.S.: 561499

BCI Asia Vietnam Co. Ltd.   (1)
Viettel Tower Block A1 13th Floor 285 Cach
Mang Thang Tam Street, Ward 12 District
10, Ho Chi Minh City, Vietnam

Tel.: (84) 2862561010
Building Construction Services
N.A.I.C.S.: 541330

BCI Central Ltd.   (1)
Unit 2017 20/F The Metropolis Tower 10
Metropolis Drive, Hunghom, Kowloon,
China (Hong Kong)
Tel.: (852) 25380011
Building Construction Services
N.A.I.C.S.: 541330

BCI Central Sdn Bhd.   (1)
Unit 1106 Block B Phileo Damansara II
Jalan 16/11 Section 16, 46350, Petaling
Jaya, Selangor, Malaysia
Tel.: (60) 376611380
Building Construction Services
N.A.I.C.S.: 541330

BCI Central Singapore Pte. Ltd.   (1)
300 Beach Road 13-05, Singapore,
199555, Singapore
Tel.: (65) 65386836
Building Construction Services
N.A.I.C.S.: 541330

BCI New Zealand Pty. Ltd.   (1)
Ground Floor Building 5 660 Great South
Road Ellerslie, Auckland, 1051, New Zea-
land
Tel.: (64) 800942876
Building Construction Services
N.A.I.C.S.: 541330

BIM Shark Aps   (1)
Maribovej 3, 4000, Roskilde, Denmark
Tel.: (45) 33608888
Web Site: https://bimshark.com
Software Solutions Services
N.A.I.C.S.: 541511

Byggefakta A/S   (1)
Stationsparken 25 2nd Floor, 2600,
Glostrup, Denmark
Tel.: (45) 70253031
Web Site: https://www.byggefakta.dk
Building Construction Services
N.A.I.C.S.: 541330

Byggfakta Docu AS   (1)
Elisabeth Von Hubschs gate 6, 1534, Moss,
Norway
Tel.: (47) 69912400
Web Site: https://www.byggfakta.no
Emp.: 50
Construction Industry Project Distr
N.A.I.C.S.: 423320

CityMark Analys i Norden AB   (1)
Svardvagen 11, 182 33, Danderyd, Sweden
Tel.: (46) 812887887
Real Estate Development Services
N.A.I.C.S.: 531390

Construction Monitor LLC   (1)
2390 W UT 56 Bldg B Ste 4A, Cedar City,
UT 84721
Tel.: (805) 595-2450
Web Site:
http://www.constructionmonitor.com
Construction Market Research Services
N.A.I.C.S.: 541910

Familjehemsbanken AB   (1)
Tingsgatan 2A, 827 32, Ljusdal, Sweden
Tel.: (46) 58520057
Web Site:
https://www.familjehemsbanken.se
Contact Mediation Services
N.A.I.C.S.: 624190

Forecon Oy   (1)
Visiokatu 4, 33720, Tampere, Finland
Tel.: (358) 407041187
Web Site: https://www.forecon.fi
Building Construction Services
N.A.I.C.S.: 236220

Istav Media, s.r.o.   (1)
Nadrazni 762/32, Smichov, 150 00, Prague,
Czech Republic
Tel.: (420) 702111740
Web Site: https://www.istav.cz
Building Materials Mfr
N.A.I.C.S.: 327120

Magasinet Fastighetssverige AB   (1)
Tradgardsgatan 1, 411 08, Gothenburg,
Sweden
Tel.: (46) 31139116

Web Site: https://fastighetssverige.se
Real Estate Development Services
N.A.I.C.S.: 531390

**Newmarket Information (Publications)
Limited** (1)
Suite 8 The Mall Beacon Court, Sandyford,
Dublin, D18 C9H9, Ireland
Tel.: (353) 12999200
Web Site: https://www.cisireland.com
Construction Information Services
N.A.I.C.S.: 237130

**North America Procurement Council,
Inc.** (1)
320 W Ohio St Ste 300, Chicago, IL 60654
Tel.: (302) 450-1923
Web Site: https://www.napc.pro
Digital Procurement Services
N.A.I.C.S.: 541614

P.T. BCI Asia (1)
Menara Bidakara 2-18th Floor, Unit 1 Jl
Jenderal Gatot Subroto Kav 71-73, South
Jakarta, 12870, Indonesia
Tel.: (62) 2183708731
Building Construction Services
N.A.I.C.S.: 541330

ProdLib OY (1)
Otakaari 5, 02150, Espoo, Finland
Tel.: (358) 505914822
Web Site: https://www.prodlib.com
Software Design Services
N.A.I.C.S.: 541512

Prognoscentret AB (1)
Tulegatan 11, 113 53, Stockholm, Sweden
Tel.: (46) 84409360
Web Site: https://prognoscentret.se
Building Construction Services
N.A.I.C.S.: 236220

Prognosesenteret AS (1)
Karenslyst Alle 2, 0278, Oslo, Norway
Tel.: (47) 24115880
Web Site: https://prognosesenteret.com
Building Construction Services
N.A.I.C.S.: 236220

RPT Byggfakta OY (1)
Ruukinkuja 3, 02330, Espoo, Finland
Tel.: (358) 9809911
Web Site: https://www.rpt.fi
Real Estate & Construction Services
N.A.I.C.S.: 541330

Svenska Media i Ljusdal AB (1)
Tingsgatan 2A, 827 32, Ljusdal, Sweden
Tel.: (46) 65115050
Web Site: https://www.svenskamedia.se
Content Creation & Graphic Design Ser-
vices
N.A.I.C.S.: 541430

**Vortal Comercio Electronico, Consul-
tadoriae Multimedia, S.A.** (1)
Centro Comercial Brasilia - Praca Mouzinho
de Albuquerque no 113 5, 4100 359, Porto,
Portugal
Tel.: (351) 707202712
Information Technology Services
N.A.I.C.S.: 541519

BYGGMA ASA
Vennslaveien 233, PO Box 21,
4701, Vennesla, Norway
Tel.: (47) 38137100
Web Site: https://www.byggma.com
BMA—(OSL)
Rev.: $220,991,904
Assets: $318,563,865
Liabilities: $207,569,506
Net Worth: $110,994,359
Earnings: $5,996,422
Emp.: 675
Fiscal Year-end: 12/31/23
Building Materials Distr
N.A.I.C.S.: 444180
Geir Drangsland *(CEO)*

Subsidiaries:

AS Byggform (1)
Eternitveien 8, 3470, Slemmestad, Norway
Tel.: (47) 31289270
Web Site: http://www.byggform.no
Building Material Mfr & Distr

N.A.I.C.S.: 327120

Aneta Belysning AB (1)
Lagergatan 3, Box 3064, 350 33, Vaxjo,
Sweden
Tel.: (46) 470778400
Web Site: http://www.aneta.se
Textile Lamp Shade Mfr & Distr
N.A.I.C.S.: 335131

Aneta Lighting AS (1)
Bymoen 23, 4618, Kristiansand, Norway
Tel.: (47) 38137091
Web Site: https://anetalighting.com
Cable Distr
N.A.I.C.S.: 423610

Forestia AS (1)
Damvegen 31, 2435, Braskereidfoss, Nor-
way
Tel.: (47) 38137100
Web Site: https://www.forestia.com
Emp.: 200
Particle Board Mfr & Distr
N.A.I.C.S.: 321219
Halvor C. Olsen *(Mgr-Export)*

Huntonit AS (1)
Vennslavegen 233, 4700, Vennesla, Nor-
way
Tel.: (47) 38137100
Web Site: https://www.huntonit.com
Emp.: 190
Wall Panels Mfr
N.A.I.C.S.: 327390

Masonite Beams AB (1)
Strandvagen 36, 914 41, Rundvik, Sweden
Tel.: (46) 93039900
Web Site: https://www.masonite-beams.com
Building Material Mfr & Distr
N.A.I.C.S.: 327120

Scan Lamps AS (1)
Bymoen 23, 4618, Kristiansand, Norway
Tel.: (47) 38137100
Web Site: http://www.scan-lamps.no
Household Lighting Product Mfr & Whslr
N.A.I.C.S.: 335131

Smartpanel AS (1)
Habornveien 50, Gamle, 1630, Fredrikstad,
Norway
Tel.: (47) 69921920
Web Site: https://www.smartpanel.no
Emp.: 40
Wall Panel Mfr & Distr
N.A.I.C.S.: 327390

Uldal AS (1)
PO Box 98, 4795, Birkeland, Norway
Tel.: (47) 38137920
Web Site: https://www.uldal.no
Window & Door Mfr
N.A.I.C.S.: 321911

**BYGGMASTARE ANDERS J
AHLSTROM HOLDING AB**
Sturegatan 18, 114 36, Stockholm,
Sweden
Tel.: (46) 42210008
Web Site: https://byggmastaren.com
Year Founded: 1895
AJA.B—(OMX)
Rev.: $19,869,741
Assets: $156,755,603
Liabilities: $8,705,525
Net Worth: $148,050,078
Earnings: $12,416,757
Emp.: 377
Fiscal Year-end: 12/31/20
Property Management Services
N.A.I.C.S.: 531311

BYGGPARTNER GRUPPEN AB
Brunnsgatan 38, Box 848, 781 28,
Borlange, Sweden
Tel.: (46) 243559500
Web Site:
　https://byggpartnergruppen.se
Year Founded: 1992
BYGGP—(OMX)
Rev.: $370,638,868
Assets: $174,310,414
Liabilities: $144,229,959
Net Worth: $30,080,456

Earnings: ($8,746,148)
Emp.: 1,019
Fiscal Year-end: 12/31/22
Industrial Construction Services
N.A.I.C.S.: 236210
Sture Nilsson *(CEO)*

BYLOG GROUP CORP.
84/1 Bilang Hutan 402, Dalian,
116013, Liaoning, China
Tel.: (86) 85292895975　　　NV
Year Founded: 2015
BYLG—(OTCIQ)
Assets: $832
Liabilities: $259,113
Net Worth: ($258,281)
Earnings: ($81,193)
Fiscal Year-end: 03/31/21
Webpage Development Services
N.A.I.C.S.: 541511
Wah Leung *(Chm, Pres, CEO, CFO,
Treas & Sec)*

BYMAX CORP.
North District Sunshine Home Unit 2
Floor 6 Ste 201, Inner Mongolia,
Manzhouli, 021400, China
Tel.: (86) 6469707560　　　NV
Year Founded: 2019
Rev.: $10,800
Assets: $23,478
Liabilities: $11,700
Net Worth: $11,778
Earnings: $2,034
Fiscal Year-end: 04/30/21
Marketing Consulting Services
N.A.I.C.S.: 541613
Longjiang Li *(Pres, CEO & Treas)*

**BYNORDIC ACQUISITION
CORPORATION**
Tel.: (46) 707294100　　　DE
Web Site: https://bynordic.se
Year Founded: 2019
BYNO—(NASDAQ)
Assets: $179,842,619
Liabilities: $185,179,888
Net Worth: ($5,337,269)
Earnings: $1,160,817
Emp.: 5
Fiscal Year-end: 12/31/22
Investment Services
N.A.I.C.S.: 523999
Jonas Olsson *(Co-Founder & Chm)*

BYON CO., LTD.
8F kyobo building 13 Byeoryang-
sangga 1-ro, Cheongwon-gu, Gwa-
cheon, Gyeonggi, Korea (South)
Tel.: (82) 25160720
Web Site: https://www.by-on.co.kr
Year Founded: 1983
032980—(KRS)
Rev.: $10,366,490
Assets: $23,101,653
Liabilities: $4,850,368
Net Worth: $18,251,285
Earnings: ($7,613,340)
Emp.: 21
Fiscal Year-end: 12/31/22
Industrial Material Mfr
N.A.I.C.S.: 314910
Jinhyung Ryu *(CEO)*

Subsidiaries:

Miraecellbio Co., Ltd. (1)
502 1503 1509 15F 147 Seongsui-ro,
Seongdong-gu, Seoul, 04795, Korea
(South)
Tel.: (82) 245787589
Web Site: https://www.miraecellbio.com
Skin Care Products Distr
N.A.I.C.S.: 424210

BYOTROL LIMITED
Building 303 Ashton Thornton Sci-

ence Park Pool Lane Ince, Chester,
CH2 4NU, United Kingdom
Tel.: (44) 1925742000　　　UK
Web Site: https://byotrolplc.com
BYOT—(AIM)
Rev.: $5,702,346
Assets: $9,612,774
Liabilities: $2,652,485
Net Worth: $6,960,289
Earnings: ($2,101,126)
Emp.: 36
Fiscal Year-end: 03/31/23
Microbial Technology Products Mfr
N.A.I.C.S.: 339999
Denise Keenan *(Chief Comml Officer
& Sec)*

Subsidiaries:

**Byotrol Consumer Products
Limited** (1)
Building 303 Ashton Thornton Science Park
Pool Lane, Ince, Chester, CH2 4NU, United
Kingdom
Tel.: (44) 192 574 2000
Web Site: https://byotrolplc.com
Chemicals Mfr
N.A.I.C.S.: 325199
David Traynor *(CEO)*

Byotrol Inc. (1)
100 Corporate Dr Ste J, Spartanburg, SC
29303-5008
Tel.: (864) 278-8017
Web Site: http://www.byotrol.co.uk
Sales Range: $50-74.9 Million
Emp.: 7
Household Cleaning & Personal Care Prod-
ucts Distr
N.A.I.C.S.: 424690
Shea Phillips *(Gen Mgr)*

Byotrol Technology Limited (1)
Building 303 Thornton Scienane pool Lane
Ince, Chester, CH2 4NU, United Kingdom
Tel.: (44) 161 277 9518
Sales Range: $25-49.9 Million
Household Cleaning & Personal Care Prod-
ucts Distr
N.A.I.C.S.: 424690
David Traynor *(CEO)*

Medimark Scientific Limited (1)
East Point High Street, Seal, Sevenoaks,
TN15 0EG, Kent, United Kingdom
Tel.: (44) 173 276 3555
Web Site: https://medi-mark.co.uk
Pharmaceutical Products Distr
N.A.I.C.S.: 424210
Rick Hayman *(Mng Dir)*

BYRON ENERGY LIMITED
Level 4 480 Collins Street, Mel-
bourne, 3000, VIC, Australia
Tel.: (61) 386106583
Web Site:
　https://www.byronenergy.com.au
BYE—(ASX)
Rev.: $49,380,691
Assets: $168,543,619
Liabilities: $30,312,133
Net Worth: $138,231,486
Earnings: $10,073,729
Fiscal Year-end: 06/30/24
Oil & Gas Exploration Services
N.A.I.C.S.: 211120
Maynard Smith *(CEO)*

BYSTROBANK PJSC
268 Pushkinskaya Street, 426008,
Izhevsk, Russia
Tel.: (7) 8003332265
Web Site: http://www.bystrobank.ru
Year Founded: 1990
Sales Range: Less than $1 Million
Commercial Banking Services
N.A.I.C.S.: 522110
Vladislav Yurevich Kolpakov *(Chm-
Mgmt Bd & Pres)*

BYSTRONIC AG
Giesshuebelstrasse 45, CH-8045,
Zurich, Switzerland

Bystronic AG—(Continued)

Tel.: (41) 629563783
Web Site: https://www.bystronic.com
BYS—(SWX)
Rev.: $1,626,094,016
Assets: $1,303,676,160
Liabilities: $397,384,384
Net Worth: $906,291,776
Earnings: $140,871,108
Emp.: 4,717
Fiscal Year-end: 12/31/19
Holding Company; Sheet Metal Processing Systems, Glass Processing Systems, Automation Systems, Foam Materials, Sporting Goods, Graphic Coatings & Real Estate
N.A.I.C.S.: 551112
Kaspar W. Kelterborn *(CFO-Grp & Member-Exec Bd)*

Subsidiaries:

Ajungilak AS (1)
Professor Birkelandsvei 36, 1008, Oslo,
Norway (100%)
Tel.: (47) 23143700
Web Site: http://www.ajungilak.no
Sales Range: $50-74.9 Million
Emp.: 10
Toy & Hobby Goods & Supplies Whslr
N.A.I.C.S.: 423920

Beyeler Maschinenbau GmbH (1)
Muhlhauser Str 3, 99867, Gotha, Germany
Tel.: (49) 36213830
Web Site: http://www.bystronic.com
Sheet Metal Work Mfg
N.A.I.C.S.: 332322

Buttikofer AG (1)
Zetzwilerstrasse 763, Gontenschwil Aargau,
Aarau, 5728, Switzerland (100%)
Tel.: (41) 627670000
Web Site: http://www.foampartner.com
Sales Range: $25-49.9 Million
Emp.: 20
All Other Plastics Product Mfr
N.A.I.C.S.: 326199

Bystronic Laser AG (1)
Industriestr 21, Niederonz, 3362, Bern,
Switzerland (100%)
Tel.: (41) 629563333
Web Site: http://www.bystronic.com
Sales Range: $400-449.9 Million
Emp.: 600
Machine Tool (Metal Forming Types) Mfr
N.A.I.C.S.: 333517
Alex Waser *(CEO)*

Subsidiary (Non-US):

Bystronic (Tianjin) Machinery Co. Ltd. (2)
Economic Development Zone, Ninghe County, 301500, Tianjin, PRC,
China (100%)
Tel.: (86) 22 6958 9988
Web Site: http://www.bystronic.com
Sales Range: $25-49.9 Million
Emp.: 100
Research & Development & Pressbrakes Production
N.A.I.C.S.: 541715

Bystronic Asia Pte. Ltd. (2)
2 Leng Kee Road # 03-05, Thye Hong Centre, Singapore, 159086, Singapore (100%)
Tel.: (65) 64722478
Web Site: http://www.bystronic-glass.com
Sales Range: $25-49.9 Million
Emp.: 13
Industrial Machinery & Equipment Merchant Whslr
N.A.I.C.S.: 423830

Bystronic Austria GmbH (2)
Viennese Road 131, 4020, Linz,
Austria (100%)
Tel.: (43) 732341155
Web Site: http://www.bystronic.at
Machine Tool (Metal Forming Types) Mfr
N.A.I.C.S.: 333517

Bystronic Benelux B.V. (2)
Stek 8, Postbus 153, Hardinxveld-
Giessendam, 3371, Netherlands (100%)

Tel.: (31) 184611020
Web Site: http://www.bystronic.nl
Sales Range: $25-49.9 Million
Emp.: 24
Construction & Mining except Oil Well Machinery & Equipment Whslr
N.A.I.C.S.: 423810
Twes Wolters *(Office Mgr)*

Bystronic Deutschland GmbH (2)
Romerstrasse 14, Heimsheim, 71296,
Germany (100%)
Tel.: (49) 703346990
Web Site: http://www.bystronic.de
Emp.: 20
Industrial Machinery & Equipment Whslr
N.A.I.C.S.: 423830
Oliver Friz *(Gen Mgr)*

Bystronic France SAS (2)
Parc Technopolis 3rd Ave du Canada,
91940, Les Ulis, France (35%)
Tel.: (33) 169419984
Web Site: http://www.bystronic.com
Sales Range: $25-49.9 Million
Emp.: 45
Machine Tool (Metal Cutting Types) Mfr
N.A.I.C.S.: 423830

Bystronic Glass UK Ltd. (2)
Lodge Park, Hortonwood 30, Telford, TF3 4NA, Shropshire, United Kingdom (100%)
Tel.: (44) 1952677971
Web Site: http://www.bystronic-glass.com
Sales Range: $25-49.9 Million
Emp.: 18
Glass Product Mfr Made of Purchased Glass
N.A.I.C.S.: 327215

Bystronic Iberica S.A. (2)
Av Tenerife N 2 Edificio 1 3a Planta, Oficina D San Sebastian de los, 28700, Madrid,
Spain (100%)
Tel.: (34) 916544878
Web Site: http://www.bystronic.com
Farm & Garden Machinery & Equipment Whslr
N.A.I.C.S.: 423820

Subsidiary (US):

Bystronic Inc. (2)
200 Airport Rd, Elgin, IL 60123 (100%)
Tel.: (847) 214-0300
Web Site: http://www.bystronic.com
Flat Glass Mfr
N.A.I.C.S.: 327211
Gary Wisniewski *(Mgr-Sls Admin)*

Subsidiary (Non-US):

Bystronic Polska Sp. z o.o. (2)
Al Krakowska 81 Sekocin Nowy, 05090,
Raszyn, Poland (100%)
Tel.: (48) 223313770
Web Site: http://www.bystronic.pl
Sales Range: $25-49.9 Million
Emp.: 17
Engineeering Services
N.A.I.C.S.: 541330
Hugo Allemann *(Mng Dir)*

Subsidiary (Domestic):

Bystronic Sales AG (2)
Industriestrasse 21, Niederoenz, 3362, Niederlenz, Switzerland (100%)
Tel.: (41) 629563783
Web Site: http://www.bystronic.ch
Sales Range: $75-99.9 Million
Emp.: 500
Industrial Machinery & Equipment Whslr
N.A.I.C.S.: 423517
Philipp Burgener *(Exec Dir)*

Subsidiary (Non-US):

Bystronic Scandinavia AB (2)
Metallvagen 30A, 195 72, Rosersberg,
Sweden (100%)
Tel.: (46) 859441550
Web Site: http://www.bystronic.se
Emp.: 60
Industrial Machinery & Equipment Whslr
N.A.I.C.S.: 423830
Michael Kron *(Mng Dir)*

Bystronic UK Ltd. (2)
Maple Park Lowfields Avenue, LS126HH,

Leeds, West Yorkshire, United
Kingdom (100%)
Tel.: (44) 1132976666
Web Site: http://www.bystronic.com
Sales Range: $25-49.9 Million
Emp.: 80
Machine Tool (Metal Forming Types) Mfr
N.A.I.C.S.: 333517

Bystronic UK Ltd. (2)
6 Wayside Business Park Wilsons Lane, Coventry, CV6 6NY, Warwickshire, United
Kingdom (100%)
Tel.: (44) 844 848 5850
Web Site: http://www.bystronic.co.uk
Laser Cutting, Waterjet Cutting, Bending & Shearing Systems Mfr
N.A.I.C.S.: 333515

Bystronic do Brasil Ltda (2)
Rua Arapongas 285, 83040-200, Sao Jose dos Pinhais, Brazil (100%)
Tel.: (55) 4133982000
Web Site: http://www.bystronic.com
Sales Range: $25-49.9 Million
Emp.: 15
All Other Automotive Repair & Maintenance
N.A.I.C.S.: 811198

Colorsud SA (1)
Via Industria, 6814, Lamone, Switzerland
Tel.: (41) 919452461
Web Site: http://www.novacolor.it
Paint Varnish & Supplies Whslr
N.A.I.C.S.: 424950

Conzzeta Management AG (1)
Giesshubelstrasse 45, 8045, Zurich,
Switzerland (100%)
Tel.: (41) 444682466
Web Site: http://www.conzzeta-versicherungen.ch
Sales Range: $25-49.9 Million
Emp.: 2
All Other Business Support Services
N.A.I.C.S.: 561499
Rolf Meyer *(VP)*

Frina Mousse France S.a.r.l. (1)
BP 55, 1 Rue du Jasmin, 51381, Wittenheim, France (100%)
Tel.: (33) 389526652
Web Site: http://www.foampartner.com
Sales Range: $25-49.9 Million
Emp.: 23
Polystyrene Foam Product Manufacturing
N.A.I.C.S.: 326140
Patrick Stadelmann *(Mng Dir)*

Fritz Nauer AG (1)
Oberwolfhauserstrasse 9, Wolfhausen,
8633, Hinwil, Switzerland (100%)
Tel.: (41) 552536363
Web Site: http://www.foampartner.com
Sales Range: $50-74.9 Million
Emp.: 200
Polystyrene Foam Product Mfr
N.A.I.C.S.: 326140
Part Tenbrink *(Mng Dir)*

Mammut Sports Group AG (1)
Birren 5, 5703, Seon, Switzerland (100%)
Tel.: (41) 627698181
Web Site: http://www.mammut.ch
Sales Range: $50-74.9 Million
Emp.: 200
Sporting & Athletic Goods Manufacturing
N.A.I.C.S.: 339920
Oliver Pabst *(CEO)*

Mammut Sports Group GmbH (1)
Anschutzstr 5, 87700, Memmingen,
Germany (100%)
Tel.: (49) 833183920
Web Site: http://www.mammut.ch
Sales Range: $75-99.9 Million
Emp.: 150
Sporting & Recreational Goods & Supplies Whslr
N.A.I.C.S.: 423910

Mammut Sports Group Inc. (1)
458 Hurricane Ln Ste 111, Williston, VT 05495 (100%)
Tel.: (802) 985-5056
Web Site: http://www.mammut.ch
Sales Range: $25-49.9 Million
Emp.: 20
Sporting & Recreational Goods & Supplies Whslr

N.A.I.C.S.: 423910
William Supple *(CEO-North America)*

Neutex AG (1)
Oberwolfhauserstrasse 9, 8633, Zurich,
Wolfhausen, Switzerland (100%)
Tel.: (41) 552536363
Web Site: http://www.foampartner.com
Sales Range: $25-49.9 Million
Emp.: 33
All Other Miscellaneous Textile Product Mills
N.A.I.C.S.: 314999

Plazza AG (1)
Sieberstrasse 5, 8055, Zurich,
Switzerland (100%)
Tel.: (41) 444686070
Web Site: https://www.plazza.ch
Sales Range: Less than $1 Million
Real Estate Agents & Brokers Offices
N.A.I.C.S.: 531210
Ralph Siegle *(CEO & Member-Mgmt Bd)*

Reisgies Schaumstoff e GmbH (1)
Dieselstrasse 7, Leverkusen, 51381,
Germany (100%)
Tel.: (49) 21715080
Web Site: http://www.foampartner.com
Sales Range: $125-149.9 Million
Emp.: 150
All Other Rubber Product Mfr
N.A.I.C.S.: 326299

Swiss Lack Theler Perren AG (1)
Nellenstadel 3, Glis, Wallis, 3902, Switzerland
Tel.: (41) 279233939
Web Site: http://www.thelerperren.ch
Paint Varnish & Supplies Merchant Whslr
N.A.I.C.S.: 424950

Swisstex Inc. (1)
325 Bessie Rd, Piedmont, SC 29673 (100%)
Tel.: (864) 845-7541
Web Site: http://www.swisstex.com
Sales Range: $25-49.9 Million
Emp.: 15
Plastics Pipe & Pipe Fitting Mfr
N.A.I.C.S.: 326122
James Williams *(Mgr)*

Transall AG (1)
Giesshubelstrasse 45, Zurich,
Switzerland (100%)
Tel.: (41) 433994060
General Freight Trucking, Local
N.A.I.C.S.: 484110

BYT HOLDINGS LTD.
1000 - 595 Burrard Street, Vancouver, V7X 1S8, BC, Canada
Tel.: (416) 865-7878
BYT—(CNSX)
Rev.: $3,287,067
Assets: $5,398,167
Liabilities: $2,727,656
Net Worth: $2,670,511
Earnings: ($1,186,729)
Fiscal Year-end: 12/31/22
Engineeering Services
N.A.I.C.S.: 541330
Sunny Li *(Chm)*

BYTE POWER GROUP LIMITED
43 Nariel St, Newstead, 4006, QLD,
Australia
Tel.: (61) 736201688
Web Site:
http://www.bytepowergroup.com
Year Founded: 1988
BPG—(ASX)
Sales Range: $1-9.9 Million
Information Technology & Telecommunications Facilites, Products & Network Management Solutions
N.A.I.C.S.: 541990
Alvin Phua *(Chm, Mng Dir & CEO)*

Subsidiaries:

Byte Power (Hong Kong) Limited (1)
Room 2104 Island Palace Tower, 510 Kings

Road, North Point, China (Hong Kong) **(83.4%)**
Tel.: (852) 2907 9838
Software Development & Integration Services for the Telecommunications & Corporate Communications Markets
N.A.I.C.S.: 513210

Byte Power Pty Ltd **(1)**
Unit 13/76 Doggett street, Newstead, 4006, QLD, Australia **(100%)**
Tel.: (61) 736201688
Web Site: http://www.bytepower.com.au
Sales Range: $50-74.9 Million
Information Technology Products & Services
N.A.I.C.S.: 423430

Byte Power Technologies Pty Ltd **(1)**
Unit 1 75 Longland Street, Newstead, 4006, QLD, Australia **(100%)**
Tel.: (61) 736201688
Web Site: http://www.bytepower.com.au
Sales Range: $50-74.9 Million
Software Development & Integration Services for the Telecommunications & Corporate Communications Markets
N.A.I.C.S.: 513210

Power Tech Systems Pty Ltd **(1)**
Newstead, Brisbane, 4113, QLD, Australia **(100%)**
Tel.: (61) 397086866
Web Site: http://www.ptech.com.au
Power Supply Products Mfr & Distr
N.A.I.C.S.: 335311
Alvin Phua *(CEO)*

BYTE SOFTWARE HOUSE S.P.A.

Via Oropa 28, 10153, Turin, Italy
Tel.: (39) 0118185611   IT
Web Site: http://www.bytesh.com
Year Founded: 1974
Sales Range: $50-74.9 Million
Emp.: 500
Information Technology Services
N.A.I.C.S.: 541511
Robarto Gamarro *(Pres)*

BYTEK AUTOMOBILES INC.

1325 St Laurent Blvd, Ottawa, K1G 0Z7, ON, Canada
Tel.: (613) 745-6886
Web Site: http://www.bytekvw.ca
Year Founded: 1956
Sales Range: $10-24.9 Million
New & Used Car Dealers
N.A.I.C.S.: 441110
Andrew Crowe *(Gen Sls Mgr)*

BYUCKSAN CORPORATION

10F 14F Gwanghui Building Toegye-ro 307, Jung-gu, Seoul, Korea (South)
Tel.: (82) 222606114
Web Site: https://www.byucksan.com
Year Founded: 1958
007210—(KRS)
Rev.: $398,752,564
Assets: $461,595,966
Liabilities: $229,741,287
Net Worth: $231,854,679
Earnings: $8,973,125
Emp.: 399
Fiscal Year-end: 12/31/22
Construction Supply Mfr
N.A.I.C.S.: 327993
Sung-Shik Kim *(CEO)*

Subsidiaries:

Byucksan Paint & Coatings Co., Ltd. **(1)**
904 219 Gasandigital1-ro, Geumcheon-gu, Seoul, Korea (South)
Tel.: (82) 269583910
Web Site: https://www.byucksanpaint.co.kr
Emp.: 178
Chemical Product & Paint Mfr
N.A.I.C.S.: 325998
Sung Shik Kim *(Pres & CEO)*

Plant (Domestic):

Byucksan Corporation - Huna Plant 1 **(2)**
69 Nakdong-daero 970beon-gil, Sasang-gu, Busan, Korea (South)
Tel.: (82) 513105710
Chemical Product & Paint Mfr
N.A.I.C.S.: 325998

Byucksan Corporation - Huna Plant 2 **(2)**
39 Cheongma-ro 34beon-gi, Seo-gu, Incheon, Korea (South)
Tel.: (82) 325600780
Chemical Product & Paint Mfr
N.A.I.C.S.: 325998

BYUCKSAN ENGINEERING & CONSTRUCTION CO., LTD.

13 25 Yeouido Dong, Yeongdeungpo Gu, 150870, Seoul, Korea (South)
Tel.: (82) 27675114
Web Site: http://www.becco.co.kr
Year Founded: 1958
Sales Range: $1-4.9 Billion
Emp.: 580
Architectural & Civil Engineering Services
N.A.I.C.S.: 541310
Seong Gak Jang *(CEO)*

Subsidiaries:

Byucksan America Inc. **(1)**
4060 W Wash Blvd, Los Angeles, CA 90018
Tel.: (323) 735-3479
Civil Engineering Services
N.A.I.C.S.: 541330

BYWATERS LTD

Lea Riverside Twelvetrees Crescent Bow, London, E3 3JG, United Kingdom
Tel.: (44) 2070016000
Web Site: http://www.bywaters.co.uk
Year Founded: 1952
Rev.: $41,201,221
Emp.: 273
Recycling & Resource Management Services
N.A.I.C.S.: 562998
John S. Glover *(Mng Dir)*

BZ BANK AKTIENGESELL-SCHAFT

Egglirain 15, Wilen, 8832, Munchwilen, Switzerland
Tel.: (41) 447866111
Web Site: http://www.bzbank.ch
Year Founded: 1985
Sales Range: $1-9.9 Million
Emp.: 16
Private Bank
N.A.I.C.S.: 522110
Ralph Stadler *(Member-Mgmt Bd & Gen Counsel)*

Subsidiaries:

BZ Fund Management Aktiengesellschaft **(1)**
Egglirain 24, 8832, Munchwilen, Switzerland
Tel.: (41) 447866600
Web Site: http://www.bzfund.ch
Sales Range: $50-74.9 Million
Emp.: 4
Securities & Commodity Exchanges
N.A.I.C.S.: 523210

Intershop Holding AG **(1)**
Pulse 5 Giessereistrasse No 18, 8031, Zurich, Switzerland **(100%)**
Tel.: (41) 445441000
Web Site: http://www.intershop.ch
Sales Range: $50-74.9 Million
Emp.: 36
Real Estate Investment Company
N.A.I.C.S.: 525990
Cyrill M. Schneuwly *(CEO)*

BZAM LTD.

1570 - 200 Burrard Street, Vancouver, V6C 3L6, BC, Canada
Tel.: (905) 304-4201
Web Site: https://bzam.com
Year Founded: 2012
BZAMF—(OTCQX)
Rev.: $8,542,374
Assets: $261,850,588
Liabilities: $57,072,364
Net Worth: $204,778,224
Earnings: ($149,795,730)
Fiscal Year-end: 12/31/19
Organic Cannabis Services
N.A.I.C.S.: 111998
Bassam Alghanim *(Chm)*

C & C CONSTRUCTIONS LIMITED

Plot No 70 Sector 32, Gurgaon, 122001, Haryana, India
Tel.: (91) 1244536666
Web Site: https://www.candcinfrastructure.com
Year Founded: 1996
CANDC—(NSE)
Sales Range: $125-149.9 Million
Emp.: 1,179
Highways & Bridge Construction Services
N.A.I.C.S.: 237310
Gurjeet Singh Johar *(Chm)*

Subsidiaries:

C & C Towers Ltd **(1)**
Sector- 57 Mohali Phase- 6 ISBT Commercial Complex Gate No 5, Opposite Verka Milk Plant, Mohali, 140 501, Punjab, India
Tel.: (91) 172 4242300
Sales Range: $25-49.9 Million
Emp.: 18
Construction Engineering Services
N.A.I.C.S.: 541330
C. V. S. Sehgal *(Gen Mgr)*

C & I LEASING PLC.

2 C and I Leasing Drive Off Bisola Durosinmi Etti Drive, Off Admiralty Way Lekki Phase 1, Lagos, Nigeria
Tel.: (234) 9062979243
Web Site: https://www.c-ileasing.com
Year Founded: 1990
CILEASING—(NIGE)
Rev.: $37,550,587
Assets: $151,729,278
Liabilities: $115,548,007
Net Worth: $36,181,271
Earnings: $81,641
Emp.: 333
Fiscal Year-end: 12/31/21
Financial Lending Services
N.A.I.C.S.: 533110
Chukwuma Henry Okolo *(Chm)*

Subsidiaries:

Leasafric Ghana Limited **(1)**
No 5 East Legon Tetteh Quarshie Interchange Legon Road, PO Box CT2430, Accra, Ghana
Tel.: (233) 3027809013
Web Site: https://leasafric.com.gh
Car Rental Services
N.A.I.C.S.: 532111
Yusuff Olakunle Kareem *(Head-Fin & Acct)*

C & T REINFORCING STEEL CO (1987) LIMITED

93 Passmore Avenue, Scarborough, M1V 4S9, ON, Canada
Tel.: (416) 291-7349
Web Site: http://www.ctsteel.com
Rev.: $13,215,632
Emp.: 85
Reinforcing Steel Supplier
N.A.I.C.S.: 238120
Sam Costa *(Pres)*

C C P CONTACT PROBES CO., LTD.

5F No 8 Lane 24 Heping Road, Banchiao Dist, New Taipei City, 220, Taiwan
Tel.: (886) 229612525
Web Site: https://www.ccpcontactprobes.com
Year Founded: 1986
6217—(TPE)
Rev.: $87,848,716
Assets: $163,813,820
Liabilities: $72,894,794
Net Worth: $90,919,026
Earnings: ($221,165)
Emp.: 1,200
Fiscal Year-end: 12/31/23
Semiconductor Equipment Mfr
N.A.I.C.S.: 333242
Chih-Feng Chen *(Chm)*

Subsidiaries:

More Electronics ApS **(1)**
Lyngager 10 C, 2605, Broendby, Denmark
Tel.: (45) 43290600
Web Site: https://moreelectronics.dk
Electric Component Whslr
N.A.I.C.S.: 423690

NH Technology GmbH **(1)**
Giesserallee 21, 47877, Willich, Germany
Tel.: (49) 215481250
Web Site: https://www.nh-technology.de
Electrical Part Mfr
N.A.I.C.S.: 335210

C CHANNEL CORPORATION

Column Minamiaoyama 7F 7-1-5 Minamiaoyama, Minato-ku, Tokyo, 107-0062, Japan
Tel.: (81) 364536893
Web Site: https://corp.cchan.tv
Year Founded: 2015
7691—(TKS)
Rev.: $38,133,090
Assets: $14,178,450
Liabilities: $13,484,400
Net Worth: $694,050
Earnings: ($1,546,740)
Fiscal Year-end: 03/31/24
Media Advertising Services
N.A.I.C.S.: 541840
Akira Morikawa *(Pres & CEO)*

C CHENG HOLDINGS LIMITED

15th Floor North Tower World Finance Centre Harbour City, Tsim Sha Tsui, Kowloon, China (Hong Kong)
Tel.: (852) 25890000
Web Site: http://www.cchengholdings.com
1486—(HKG)
Rev.: $87,040,043
Assets: $106,360,883
Liabilities: $41,894,078
Net Worth: $64,466,805
Earnings: ($1,419,840)
Emp.: 1,130
Fiscal Year-end: 12/31/22
Architectural & Ladscaping Services
N.A.I.C.S.: 541310
Ronald Liang *(Co-Chm)*

Subsidiaries:

Cfu Come Limited **(1)**
Suite 1109-14 11/F Wharf T and T Centre Harbour City Tsim Sha Tsui, Kowloon, China (Hong Kong)
Tel.: (852) 81180002
Web Site: http://www.cfucome.com.hk
General Repair & Maintenance Services
N.A.I.C.S.: 811412

C DUGARD LTD

75 Old Shoreham Road, Hove, BN3 7BX, East Sussex, United Kingdom
Tel.: (44) 1273732286
Web Site: http://www.dugard.com
Year Founded: 1939
Rev.: $13,452,048
Emp.: 53

C Dugard Ltd—(Continued)

Machine Tools Mfr
N.A.I.C.S.: 333517
Sean Ford *(Mgr-Svc)*

Subsidiaries:

Dugard Middle East   (1)
403 4th Floor Liberty Building Al Mina
Road, Sharjah, United Arab Emirates
Tel.: (971) 502172071
Industrial Machine Tool Distr
N.A.I.C.S.: 333517

Dugard Rus LLC   (1)
Entuziastov highway property 1A room 87
office/floor 13/2, 143912, Moscow, Russia
Tel.: (7) 4959269060
Web Site: http://www.dugardrus.ru
Emp.: 8
Industrial Machine Tool Distr
N.A.I.C.S.: 333517

Machine Tools International Sp. z
o.o.   (1)
Ul M Buhla 61, 44-217, Rybnik, Poland
Tel.: (48) 324243219
Web Site: http://www.mti.pl
Industrial Machine Tool Distr
N.A.I.C.S.: 333517

C J O'SHEA GROUP LTD

Granard Business Centre Bunns
Lane Mill Hill, London, NW7 2DZ,
United Kingdom
Tel.: (44) 2089593600
Web Site: http://www.oshea.co.uk
Year Founded: 1966
Sales Range: $150-199.9 Million
Emp.: 175
Construction Services
N.A.I.C.S.: 236220
Crohan O'Shea *(Founder & Chm)*

Subsidiaries:

CJ O'Shea (Plant Hire) Ltd   (1)
Station Road, Smallford, Saint Albans, AL4
0HF, Herts, United Kingdom
Tel.: (44) 1727826748
Web Site: http://www.osheaplanthire.co.uk
Construction Engineering Services
N.A.I.C.S.: 541330

C MARKET A.D.

Jurija Gagarina 14, Belgrade, Serbia
Tel.: (381) 11 715 3557
Web Site: http://www.cmarket.rs
Year Founded: 1998
Sales Range: $250-299.9 Million
Grocery Store Operator
N.A.I.C.S.: 445110

C P S SHAPERS LIMITED

Plot No 31 New Mayur Vihar Near
Raj Vansh Vihar Garh Road, Meerut,
250002, India
Tel.: (91) 9084735560
Web Site:
   https://www.dermawear.co.in
Year Founded: 2012
CPS—(NSE)
Rev.: $4,494,534
Assets: $2,125,204
Liabilities: $1,912,253
Net Worth: $212,951
Earnings: $299,259
Emp.: 335
Fiscal Year-end: 03/31/23
Fitness Product Mfr
N.A.I.C.S.: 339920
Abhishek Kamal Kumar *(Chm)*

C&A MODAS S.A.

Alameda Araguaia 1 222/1 022, Ba-
rueri, 06455-000, SP, Brazil
Tel.: (55) 1121349530
Web Site: http://www.cea.com.br
Year Founded: 1841
Emp.: 100
Fashion Apparels Retailer

N.A.I.C.S.: 458110
Luiz Antonio De Moraes Carvalho
(Chm)

C&C GROUP PLC

Bulmers House Keeper Road, Crum-
lin, Dublin, D12 K702, Ireland
Tel.: (353) 15063900   IE
Web Site:
   https://www.candcgroupplc.com
Year Founded: 1935
CCR—(LSE)
Rev.: $2,223,936,974
Assets: $1,535,614,073
Liabilities: $737,858,839
Net Worth: $797,755,234
Earnings: $56,011,224
Emp.: 2,897
Fiscal Year-end: 02/28/23
Alcoholic & Non-Alcoholic Beverages
& Snacks Mfr
N.A.I.C.S.: 424820
Mark Chilton *(Gen Counsel & Sec)*

Subsidiaries:

Admiral Taverns Ltd.   (1)
4th Floor HQ Building 58 Nicholas Street,
Chester, CH1 2NP, United
Kingdom   **(46.65%)**
Tel.: (44) 1244321171
Web Site: https://www.admiraltaverns.co.uk
Pub Operator
N.A.I.C.S.: 722410
David Wigham *(Comml Dir)*

Bulmers Ltd   (1)
Annerville Clonmel, Tipperary, Ireland
Tel.: (353) 526172100
Web Site: https://bulmers.ie
Sales Range: $25-49.9 Million
Cider Mfr
N.A.I.C.S.: 312111

C & C International Ltd   (1)
3rd Fl Block 71 The Plaza, Parkwest Busi-
ness Park, Dublin, Ireland
Tel.: (353) 16161100
Web Site: http://www.bulmers.ie
Sales Range: $25-49.9 Million
Emp.: 40
Beverage Sales & Distr
N.A.I.C.S.: 424820

Instil Drinks Limited   (1)
109a Regents Park Road, London, NW1
8UR, United Kingdom
Tel.: (44) 2074491685
Web Site: http://www.instildrinks.co.uk
Wine Distr
N.A.I.C.S.: 424820
Mark Johnson *(Mng Dir)*

M. & J. Gleeson Investments
Ltd.   (1)
Bulmers House Keeper Road, Crumlin,
Dublin, 12, Ireland
Tel.: (353) 16269787
Web Site: http://www.gleesongroup.ie
Sales Range: $300-349.9 Million
Beverage Distr
N.A.I.C.S.: 424820
Stephen Meleady *(Gen Mgr)*

Subsidiary (Domestic):

Gilbey's of Ireland, Ltd.   (2)
Bulmer House, Keeper Road, Dublin, 12,
Ireland   **(100%)**
Tel.: (353) 7500660044
Rev.: $181,773,000
Emp.: 110
Wine Distr
N.A.I.C.S.: 424820
Matthew Clark Bibendum Limited   (1)
Whitchurch Lane, Bristol, BS14 0JZ, United
Kingdom
Tel.: (44) 3448223910
Web Site: https://www.matthewclark.co.uk
Alcoholic Beverage Distr
N.A.I.C.S.: 424820
Simon Jerrome *(Head-Wine Buying)*

C&C INTERNATIONAL CO.,
LTD.

39 Samseong 1-Ro 5-Gil, Hwaseong,
Gyeonggi-do, Korea (South)
Tel.: (82) 3180061600
Web Site:
   https://www.cnccosmetic.com
Year Founded: 1997
352480—(KRS)
Emp.: 356
Cosmetics Products Mfr
N.A.I.C.S.: 325620
Eun-Chul Bae *(CEO)*

C&D HOLSIN ENGINEERING
CONSULTING CO., LTD

11th Floor Building 4 Jinshan Fortune
Plaza 2368 Fangzhong Road, Huli
District, Xiamen, 361009, Fujian,
China
Tel.: (86) 5922932999
Web Site: https://www.holsin.cn
Year Founded: 1995
603909—(SHG)
Rev.: $177,047,110
Assets: $255,030,577
Liabilities: $108,135,266
Net Worth: $146,895,311
Earnings: $7,960,469
Fiscal Year-end: 12/31/22
Engineering Consulting Services
N.A.I.C.S.: 541330
Lin Weiguo *(Chm)*

C&D PROPERTY MANAGE-
MENT GROUP CO., LTD.

C&D International Building No 1699
Huandao East Road, Xiamen,
361008, China
Tel.: (86) 5922337924   VG
Web Site: http://www.cndservice.com
Year Founded: 2016
2156—(HKG)
Property Management Services
N.A.I.C.S.: 531311
Yuekai Zhuang *(Chm)*

C&G BEAULIEU GROUP INC.

368 Grand Boulevard Est, Saint-
Basile-Le-Grand, J3N 1M4, QC,
Canada
Tel.: (450) 653-9581
Web Site: http://www.cgbeaulieu.com
Year Founded: 1974
Sales Range: $10-24.9 Million
Emp.: 100
Construction Services
N.A.I.C.S.: 236220
Gaetan Beaulieu *(Pres)*

C&G ENVIRONMENTAL PRO-
TECTION HOLDINGS LIMITED

Office F 23/F MG Tower 133 Hoi Bun
Road, Kwun Tong, Kowloon, China
(Hong Kong)
Tel.: (852) 2219 8555
Web Site: http://www.cg-ep.com
Assets: $6,895
Liabilities: $245,803
Net Worth: ($238,908)
Earnings: ($272,874)
Fiscal Year-end: 12/31/18
Holding Company; Waste Incineration
Power Plants Construction & Opera-
tion
N.A.I.C.S.: 551112
Chik Tsan Lam *(Founder, Chm &
CEO)*

C&G HI TECH CO., LTD.

162 SeungryangGil, Wongok-Myeon,
Anseong, Gyeonggi-do, Korea
(South)
Tel.: (82) 316549222
Web Site: https://www.cnghitech.com
Year Founded: 2002
264660—(KRS)
Rev.: $147,862,797

Assets: $118,647,849
Liabilities: $47,040,366
Net Worth: $71,607,483
Earnings: $12,928,887
Emp.: 148
Fiscal Year-end: 12/31/22
Semiconductor Machinery Mfr
N.A.I.C.S.: 333242
Chang Ho Lee *(Mgr)*

C&G SYSTEMS INC.

Tennoz Central Tower 19th floor
2-2-24 Higashi-shinagawa,
Shinagawa-ku, Tokyo, 140-0002, Ja-
pan
Tel.: (81) 368640781
Web Site: https://www.cgsys.co.jp
Year Founded: 2007
6633—(TKS)
Rev.: $27,126,340
Assets: $39,590,560
Liabilities: $17,427,220
Net Worth: $22,163,340
Earnings: $482,120
Emp.: 241
Fiscal Year-end: 12/31/23
Software Development & Distr
N.A.I.C.S.: 541511
Shuji Yamaguchi *(Chm)*

Subsidiaries:

CGS Asia Co., Ltd.   (1)
Tel.: (66) 26619620
Web Site: https://www.smri.asia
Emp.: 26
Cad System Distr
N.A.I.C.S.: 423430

CGS NORTH AMERICA INC.   (1)
2160 Fasan Drive, Oldcastle, Windsor, N0R
1L0, ON, Canada
Tel.: (519) 737-6009
Web Site: https://www.camtool.com
Software Publishing Services
N.A.I.C.S.: 513210

PT. JWC Indonesia Energi   (1)
Centennial Tower Level 29 Unit D - F Jl
Jenderal Gatot Subroto, Karet Semanggi
Setiabudi, Jakarta, 12930, Indonesia
Tel.: (62) 212 960 1521
Web Site: https://www.jwcindonesia.com
Oil & Gas Distr
N.A.I.C.S.: 424720

Tritech International, LLC   (1)
1710 Todd Farm Dr, Elgin, IL 60123
Tel.: (847) 888-0333
Web Site: https://www.tritech-intl.com
Industrial Mold Mfr
N.A.I.C.S.: 333511

C&H COMMUNICATIONS

DTEC Dubai Silicon Oasis, Dubai,
United Arab Emirates
Tel.: (971) 44418580
Web Site:
   https://chcommunications.net
Year Founded: 2009
Event Management Services
N.A.I.C.S.: 541618

C&J CLARK LIMITED

40 High Street, PO Box 50, Street,
BA16 0EQ, Somerset, United King-
dom
Tel.: (44) 1458899901
Web Site: http://www.clarks.co.uk
Year Founded: 1825
Sales Range: $1-4.9 Billion
Emp.: 14,000
Men's, Women's & Children's Shoes
Mfr & Retailer
N.A.I.C.S.: 316210
Philip de Klerk *(CFO-Interim)*

Subsidiaries:

C&J Clark Canada, Ltd.   (1)
2881 Brighton Road, Oakville, L6H 6C9,
ON, Canada   **(100%)**
Tel.: (905) 829-1825

Web Site: http://www.clarkscanada.com
Sales Range: $25-49.9 Million
Emp.: 26
Shoe Distr
N.A.I.C.S.: 424340
George Molyneux *(Sr VP & Gen Mgr)*

Clarks Companies North America **(1)**
156 Oak St, Newton Upper Falls, MA 02464-1440
Tel.: (617) 964-1222
Web Site: http://www.clarksusa.com
Sales Range: $300-349.9 Million
Emp.: 1,000
Retailer of Shoes
N.A.I.C.S.: 424340
Robert Kiel *(Mgr-Sls)*

Division (Domestic):

Bostonian Wholesale Division **(2)**
156 Oak St, Newton Upper Falls, MA 02464
Tel.: (617) 964-1222
Web Site: http://www.bostonianshoe.com
Sales Range: $50-74.9 Million
Emp.: 300
Shoe Wholesaling
N.A.I.C.S.: 623110
Geralyn Breig *(Pres)*

Clarks Companies - IT Division **(2)**
620 S Union St, Kennett Square, PA 19348-3534 **(100%)**
Tel.: (610) 444-6550
Sales Range: $10-24.9 Million
Emp.: 40
Information Technology Services
N.A.I.C.S.: 541519
Jim Salzano *(Pres)*

C&L AEROSPACE PTY LTD.
5/37 Windorah St, Brisbane, 4053, QLD, Australia
Tel.: (61) 7 3354 8100 AU
Web Site: http://www.cla.aero
Year Founded: 1994
Aircraft Parts Distr & Maintenance Services
N.A.I.C.S.: 488190
Jameel Wazir *(Exec VP)*

Subsidiaries:

C&L Aviation Services **(1)**
40 Wyoming Ave, Bangor, ME 04401
Tel.: (207) 217-6050
Web Site: http://www.claerospace.com
Aircraft Engineering & Modification, Leasing & Parts Sales & Leasing
N.A.I.C.S.: 336411
Jack Kenney *(Mgr-Sls-Northern North America & Canada)*

C&N HOLDINGS LIMITED
3 Soon Lee Street 06-03 Pioneer Junction, Singapore, 627606, Singapore
Tel.: (65) 65600028 Ky
Web Site: https://www.irasia.com
Year Founded: 1992
8430—(HKG)
Rev.: $17,771,198
Assets: $13,320,991
Liabilities: $2,624,060
Net Worth: $10,696,931
Earnings: ($3,873,633)
Emp.: 130
Fiscal Year-end: 12/31/23
Logistics Management Services
N.A.I.C.S.: 541614
Lim Kang Chua *(Founder, Co-Chm & CEO)*

C&S ASSET MANAGEMENT CO., LTD.
907 Jeokseon Hyundai Building Jeokseon-dong, Jongno-gu, Seoul, 110-756, Korea (South)
Tel.: (82) 2 732 9676
Web Site: http://www.cnsamc.com
Year Founded: 1980
Rev.: $190,082,492

Assets: $208,800,443
Liabilities: $197,137,857
Net Worth: $11,662,586
Earnings: ($29,858,465)
Emp.: 5,362
Fiscal Year-end: 12/31/17
Asset & Facility Management Services
N.A.I.C.S.: 531390
Cho Seung-Yeon *(Mng Dir)*

C&S PAPER CO., LTD.
No 136 Caihong Ave, Western District, Zhongshan, Guangdong, China
Tel.: (86) 15625313492
Web Site:
https://www.zhongshungroup.com
002511—(SSE)
Rev.: $1,186,543,864
Assets: $1,154,063,428
Liabilities: $436,754,957
Net Worth: $717,308,471
Earnings: $48,456,344
Emp.: 4,500
Fiscal Year-end: 12/31/22
Household Paper Products Mfr
N.A.I.C.S.: 322291

Subsidiaries:

C&S Paper (Hubei) Co., Ltd. **(1)**
Eight-one Bridge of 107 National Rd, Xiaogan, Hubei, China
Tel.: (86) 7122515566
Paper Product Distr
N.A.I.C.S.: 424130

C&S Paper (Sichuan) Co., Ltd. **(1)**
No 80 Mudan Road, Pengzhou, Sichuan, China
Tel.: (86) 2883806688
Paper Product Distr
N.A.I.C.S.: 424130

C&S Paper Yunfu Co., Ltd. **(1)**
No168 Longbao Road Shuangdong Neighborhood Committees, Shuangdong Street, Luoding, Guangdong, China
Tel.: (86) 7663903888
Paper Product Distr
N.A.I.C.S.: 424130

Jiangmen Zhongshun Paper Industry Co., Ltd. **(1)**
The Energy Development Zone Yinzhouhu Paper Industry Base, Shuangshui Country Xinhui District, Jiangmen, Guangdong, China
Tel.: (86) 7506966816
Paper Product Distr
N.A.I.C.S.: 424130

Zhejiang Zhong Shun Paper Industry Co., Ltd. **(1)**
No 222 of Wei Third Road East Avenue, Zhapu Town, Jiaxing, Zhejiang, China
Tel.: (86) 57385581111
Paper Product Distr
N.A.I.C.S.: 424130

C&T DREAM CO., LTD.
60 Baekseokgongdan 7-Ro, Seobuk-gu, Cheonan, 31094, Chungcheongnam-do, Korea (South)
Tel.: (82) 264093978
Web Site: https://cntdream.com
Year Founded: 2009
286000—(KRS)
Emp.: 81
Cosmetics Products Mfr
N.A.I.C.S.: 325620
Taewoo Ahn *(CEO)*

C'BON COSMETICS CO., LTD.
7-18-12 Roppongi, Minato-ku, Tokyo, 106-8556, Japan
Tel.: (81) 449791234
Web Site: https://www.cbon.co.jp
Year Founded: 1966
4926—(TKS)
Rev.: $56,171,780
Assets: $58,220,880

Liabilities: $20,814,890
Net Worth: $37,405,990
Earnings: ($171,860)
Emp.: 694
Fiscal Year-end: 03/31/24
Cosmetics & Pharmaceutical Products Mfr & Sales
N.A.I.C.S.: 325620

Subsidiaries:

C'BON Cosmetics Co., Ltd. - Tochigi Factory **(1)**
2524 Takou Kamimikawa-machi, Kawachi, 329-0524, Tochigi, Japan
Tel.: (81) 285530485
Cosmetics Products Mfr
N.A.I.C.S.: 325620

C'S CREATE CO., LTD.
7F IVY East Building 11-11 Shibuya 3-Chome, Shibuya-Ku, Tokyo, 150-0002, Japan
Tel.: (81) 364185145
Web Site: https://www.cscreate.co.jp
Year Founded: 1999
8921—(TKS)
Real Estate Development Services
N.A.I.C.S.: 531311
Fujio Sato *(Pres)*

C'S MEN CO., LTD.
2F Nakasho Building 1-5-4 Nihonbashi Bakuro-cho, Chuo-ku, Tokyo, 103-0002, Japan
Tel.: (81) 356233781
Web Site: https://www.csmen.co.jp
Year Founded: 1989
3083—(TKS)
Rev.: $39,207,700
Assets: $13,463,910
Liabilities: $10,039,440
Net Worth: $3,424,470
Earnings: ($2,353,880)
Emp.: 119
Fiscal Year-end: 02/29/24
Men's Casual Clothing Retailer
N.A.I.C.S.: 458110
Shoji Kabashima *(Chm, Pres & CEO)*

C+G INFORMATIONSTECH-NOLOGIE GMBH
Seligenstadter Grund 7, 63150, Heusenstamm, Germany
Tel.: (49) 61049450
Web Site: http://www.cg-infogmbh.com
Year Founded: 1995
Sales Range: $10-24.9 Million
Computer Equipment Whslr
N.A.I.C.S.: 423430
Ortwin Hutter *(Founder & Mng Dir)*

C-COM SATELLITE SYSTEMS INC.
2574 Sheffield Road, Ottawa, K1B 3V7, ON, Canada
Tel.: (613) 745-4110
Web Site: https://www.c-comsat.com
Year Founded: 1997
CYSNF—(OTCQB)
Rev.: $6,263,688
Assets: $20,105,073
Liabilities: $823,507
Net Worth: $19,281,566
Earnings: $1,263,246
Emp.: 33
Fiscal Year-end: 11/30/23
Vehicle Mounted Antennas Mfr
N.A.I.C.S.: 339999
Leslie Klein *(Pres & CEO)*

C-LINK SQUARED LIMITED
No 1 Persiaran Sungai Buloh Taman Industri Sungai Buloh, Kota Damansara, 47810, Petaling Jaya, Selangor, Malaysia

Tel.: (60) 61573773 Ky
Web Site:
https://www.clinksquared.com
Year Founded: 2000
1463—(HKG)
Rev.: $26,155,800
Assets: $27,660,600
Liabilities: $5,915,498
Net Worth: $21,745,103
Earnings: $69,300
Emp.: 168
Fiscal Year-end: 12/31/22
Software Development Services
N.A.I.C.S.: 541511
Sheng Hwang Ling *(CEO)*

C-MER EYE CARE HOLDINGS LTD.
Suite 1535 Central Building 1-3 Pedder Street, Central, China (Hong Kong)
Tel.: (852) 39973266 Ky
Web Site:
https://www.cmermedical.com
Year Founded: 2012
3309—(HKG)
Rev.: $220,817,633
Assets: $369,965,093
Liabilities: $115,189,620
Net Worth: $254,775,473
Earnings: ($5,893,688)
Emp.: 2,115
Fiscal Year-end: 12/31/22
Surgical & Medical Product Distr
N.A.I.C.S.: 423450
Xiaoting Li *(Exec Dir)*

Subsidiaries:

Beijing C-MER Dennis Lam Eye Hospital Co., Ltd. **(1)**
1-3F Podium Floor Zitan Building No 27 Jianguo Road Gaobeidian, Chaoyang District, Beijing, China
Tel.: (86) 1053090996
Web Site: https://www.bjcmer.com
Eye Care Hospital Services
N.A.I.C.S.: 622310

C-QUADRAT INVESTMENT AG
Schottenfeldgasse 20, A-1070, Vienna, Austria
Tel.: (43) 1515660 AT
Web Site: https://www.c-quadrat.com
Year Founded: 1991
Sales Range: $75-99.9 Million
Investment Fund Services & Asset Management
N.A.I.C.S.: 525910
Cristobal Mendez de Vigo *(Grp Mng Dir & Mng Dir)*

C-RAD AB
Sjukhusvagen 12K, SE-753 09, Uppsala, Sweden
Tel.: (46) 184108288
Web Site: https://www.c-rad.se
CRAD.B—(OMX)
Rev.: $27,056,346
Assets: $33,025,448
Liabilities: $8,635,207
Net Worth: $24,390,241
Earnings: $1,753,679
Emp.: 59
Fiscal Year-end: 12/31/20
Radiation Therapy Equipment Mfr
N.A.I.C.S.: 334510
Lars Nyberg *(Chm)*

Subsidiaries:

C-RAD Australia & New Zealand Pty. Ltd. **(1)**
Level 22 44 Market Place, Sydney, 2000, NSW, Australia
Tel.: (61) 1300169776
Cancer Treatment Services
N.A.I.C.S.: 622310

C-RAD Incorporated **(1)**

C-RAD AB—(Continued)

70 SE 4th Ave, Delray Beach, FL 33483
Tel.: (561) 742-9260
Medical Equipment Mfr
N.A.I.C.S.: 339112

CYRPA International Sprl (1)
Rue de Stalle 140 3eme etage, Uccle,
1180, Brussels, Belgium
Tel.: (02) 03440504
Web Site: http://www.cyrpa.com
Laser Positioning Product Distr
N.A.I.C.S.: 423490

C. BROWN & SONS (STEEL) LTD

Cochrane House Pedmore Road,
Dudley, DY2 0RL, West Midlands,
United Kingdom
Tel.: (44) 1384 480048
Web Site:
http://www.cbrownsteels.co.uk
Year Founded: 1946
Sales Range: $75-99.9 Million
Emp.: 150
Steel Mfr & Distr
N.A.I.C.S.: 331513
Neville Brown (Mng Dir)

Subsidiaries:

C. Brown & Sons (Steel) Ltd (1)
Brenton Business Complex Bond Street,
Bury, BL9 7BE, Lancs, United Kingdom
Tel.: (44) 161 763 1454
Steel Mfrs
N.A.I.C.S.: 331513

C. C. MARINE DISTRIBUTORS INC.

460 Harry Walker Parkway South,
Newmarket, L3Y 8E3, ON, Canada
Tel.: (905) 830-0000
Web Site: http://www.ccmarine.ca
Sales Range: $10-24.9 Million
Marine Transportation Equipment &
Parts Distr
N.A.I.C.S.: 423860
Rick Chang (VP)

C. CARDASSILARIS & SONS - CARDICO S.A.

2nd Km Schimatari-oinoe Rd, 32009,
Oinofita, Greece
Tel.: (30) 22620 47700
Year Founded: 1980
Emp.: 110
Dried Fruit Mfr & Whslr
N.A.I.C.S.: 311423
Cardassilari Zoe (IR Officer)

C. CHRISTOPHEL MASCHI-NENHANDEL & VERMITTLUN-GEN GMBH

Taschenmacherstrasse 31-33, 23556,
Lubeck, Germany
Tel.: (49) 451899470
Web Site: http://www.christophel.com
Year Founded: 1984
Sales Range: $25-49.9 Million
Construction Machinery Distr
N.A.I.C.S.: 423810
Rudiger Christophel (Mng Dir)

C. HAFNER GMBH + CO. KG

Bleichstrasse 13-17, Pforzheim,
75173, Germany
Tel.: (49) 72319200
Web Site: http://www.c-hafner.de
Year Founded: 1850
Rev.: $57,934,800
Emp.: 181
Metals Recovery & Processing Ser-
vices
N.A.I.C.S.: 423940
Philipp Reisert (Mng Partner)

C. MAHENDRA EXPORTS LTD.

Tower C Office No CC - 6011 6th
Floor Bharat Diamond Bourse,
Bandra-Kurla Complex Bandra East,
Mumbai, 400 051, India
Tel.: (91) 22 26725555
Web Site: http://www.cmahendra.com
Year Founded: 1978
Sales Range: $100-124.9 Million
Emp.: 368
Diamond & Jewelry Distr & Exporter
N.A.I.C.S.: 423940
Mahendra Chandulal Shah (Chm &
Mng Dir)

Subsidiaries:

C. Mahendra Exports Ltd. - Diamond
Factory (1)
No 37 AK Road Opp to Umiya Temple,
395001, Surat, Gujarat, India
Tel.: (91) 26125464
Web Site: http://www.cmahendra.com
Sales Range: $400-449.9 Million
Diamond Mfr
N.A.I.C.S.: 339910

C.A. FABRICA NACIONAL DE CEMENTOS, S.A.C.A.

Av Principal De La Castellana Centro
Letonia Torre ING Bank piso 6, 1060,
Caracas, Venezuela
Tel.: (58) 2122763911
Web Site: http://www.fnc.com.ve
Year Founded: 1907
Emp.: 1,600
Cement Mfr
N.A.I.C.S.: 327310
Henri J. Sarcos G. (Dir Gen)

C.A. SPENCER INC.

2930 Dagenais Blvd West, Laval,
H7P 1T1, QC, Canada
Tel.: (450) 622-2420
Web Site: http://www.caspencer.ca
Year Founded: 1908
Rev.: $27,246,148
Emp.: 70
Hardwood Products Mfr
N.A.I.C.S.: 325194
Claude Cadrin (Pres)

C.BANNER INTERNATIONAL HOLDINGS LIMITED

Unit 2904 29th Floor Far East Fi-
nance Center 16 Harcourt Road,
Hong Kong, China (Hong Kong)
Tel.: (852) 2584791598
Web Site: http://www.cbanner.com.cn
1028—(HKG)
Rev.: $193,996,577
Assets: $241,292,142
Liabilities: $48,374,118
Net Worth: $192,918,024
Earnings: $2,073,146
Emp.: 4,363
Fiscal Year-end: 12/31/22
Women's Footwear Mfr & Retailer
N.A.I.C.S.: 316210
Yixi Chen (Chm)

C.E. INFO SYSTEMS LTD.

Plot No 237 First Second & Third
Floor, Okhla Industrial Estate Phase
3, New Delhi, 110020, India
Tel.: (91) 1146009900
Web Site: https://about.mappls.com
Year Founded: 1995
MAPMYINDIA—(NSE)
Rev.: $33,032,181
Assets: $70,510,413
Liabilities: $9,655,532
Net Worth: $60,854,880
Earnings: $11,884,646
Emp.: 510
Fiscal Year-end: 03/31/22
Software Development Services
N.A.I.C.S.: 541511

Rakesh Kumar Verma (Co-Founder,
Chm & Mng Dir)

C.E.MANAGEMENT INTE-GRATED LABORATORY CO.LTD

888-1 Shinonoi Ombegawa, Nagano,
388-8006, Japan
Tel.: (81) 262936688
Web Site: http://www.dksiken.co.jp
6171—(TKS)
Rev.: $51,941,340
Assets: $48,644,490
Liabilities: $15,810,700
Net Worth: $32,833,790
Earnings: $1,347,100
Emp.: 440
Fiscal Year-end: 12/31/23
Civil Engineering & Construction Re-
lated Services
N.A.I.C.S.: 238990
Yuji Shimodaira (Pres)

C.E.O GROUP JOINT STOCK COMPANY

Floor 5th CEO Tower Pham Hung
Road, Hanoi, Vietnam
Tel.: (84) 2437875136
Web Site:
https://www.ceogroup.com.vn
CEO—(HNX)
Rev.: $57,411,088
Assets: $388,303,738
Liabilities: $130,966,230
Net Worth: $257,337,507
Earnings: $4,993,358
Emp.: 1,270
Fiscal Year-end: 12/31/23
Architectural Services; Road Con-
struction
N.A.I.C.S.: 541310

Subsidiaries:

CEO Construction Joint Stock
Company (1)
12th Floor of CEO Tower Pham Hung, Me
Tri Ward Nam Tu Liem, Hanoi, Vietnam
Tel.: (84) 2437857440
Web Site: http://www.ceocons.com.vn
Emp.: 250
Building Construction Services
N.A.I.C.S.: 236220

CEO International Co., Ltd. (1)
5th Floor CEO Tower Pham Hung Road,
Hanoi, Vietnam
Tel.: (84) 2437875875
Real Estate Development Services
N.A.I.C.S.: 531390

CEO Service Development Joint
Stock Company (1)
Floor 4 & 12 CEO Tower HH2-1 Pham
Hung Street, Me Tri Ha New Urban Area
Me Tri Ward Nam Tu Liem District, Hanoi,
Vietnam
Tel.: (84) 2437856926
Web Site: http://www.ceos.com.vn
Human Resource Training Services
N.A.I.C.S.: 541612

CEO Tourism Joint Stock
Company (1)
Floor 2 CEO Tower Pham Hung Street, Me
Tri Ward Nam Tu Liem District, Hanoi, Viet-
nam
Tel.: (84) 2437535588
Web Site: http://www.ceotravel.com.vn
Travel Management Services
N.A.I.C.S.: 561599

Phu Quoc Housing & Urban Develop-
ment JSC (1)
Sonasea Villas and Resort Duong Bao,
Duong To Phu Quoc, Kien Giang, Vietnam
Tel.: (84) 2973980026
Real Estate Development Services
N.A.I.C.S.: 531390
Dao Ngoc (CEO)

Phu Quoc Investment & Development
JSC (1)

CEO Real Estate Transaction Floor 1st
Floor CEO Tower Pham Hung Street, Nam
Tu Liem District, Hanoi, Vietnam
Tel.: (84) 983060351
Web Site: http://www.sonasea.com.vn
Hotel Services
N.A.I.C.S.: 721110

South Can Tho Investment & Devel-
opment JSC (1)
No 88 Huynh Cuong Street, An Cu Ward
Ninh Kieu District, Can Tho, Vietnam
Tel.: (84) 904127761
Real Estate Development Services
N.A.I.C.S.: 531390

Van Don Tourism Development & Investment Joint Stock Company (1)
1st Floor - CEO Tower Pham Hung St, Hanoi, Vietnam
Tel.: (84) 348946868
Web Site:
http://www.sonaseavandonharborcity.vn
Hotel Services
N.A.I.C.S.: 721110

C.G. HACKING & SONS LIM-ITED

Calverts Buildings 50 Borough High
Street, London, SE1 1XW, United
Kingdom
Tel.: (44) 2074076451
Web Site: http://www.cghacking.com
Year Founded: 1972
Sales Range: $50-74.9 Million
Emp.: 10
Nuts Distr
N.A.I.C.S.: 111336
Christopher Hacking (Chm)

C.H. BAILEY PLC

Alexandra Dock, Newport, NP20 2NP,
South Wales, United Kingdom
Tel.: (44) 1633262961
Web Site:
http://www.chbaileyplc.co.uk
Rev.: $7,617,210
Assets: $29,706,489
Liabilities: $10,498,995
Net Worth: $19,207,494
Earnings: $2,538,276
Emp.: 129
Fiscal Year-end: 03/31/18
Engineering & Electrical Services
N.A.I.C.S.: 541330
Charles H. Bailey (CEO)

C.H. BOEHRINGER SOHN AG & CO. KG

Binger Strasse 173, 55216, Ingel-
heim, Germany
Tel.: (49) 6132770
Web Site: http://www.boehringer-
ingelheim.com
Year Founded: 1885
Rev.: $23,821,661,920
Assets: $37,492,912,800
Liabilities: $19,404,934,080
Net Worth: $18,087,978,720
Earnings: $3,047,139,060
Emp.: 51,015
Fiscal Year-end: 12/31/19
Holding Company; Pharmaceutical
Mfr & Whslr
N.A.I.C.S.: 551112
Hubertus von Baumbach (Chm-Mgmt
Bd)

Subsidiaries:

Boehringer Ingelheim (Canada)
Ltd. (1)
5180 South Service Road, Burlington, L7L
5H4, ON, Canada
Tel.: (905) 639-0333
Web Site: http://www.boehringer-
ingelheim.ca
Sales Range: $250-299.9 Million
Emp.: 700

Pharmaceuticals Research & Development;
Human Prescription Pharmaceuticals & Animal Health Products Sales & Marketing
N.A.I.C.S.: 424210

Boehringer Ingelheim (Hong Kong) Ltd. (1)
Suites 1504-7 Great Eagle Centre 23 Harbour Road, Wanchai, China (Hong Kong)
Tel.: (852) 25960033
Pharmaceuticals Product Mfr
N.A.I.C.S.: 325412
Zoe Leung *(Product Mgr-Respiratory)*

Boehringer Ingelheim (N.Z.) Limited (1)
42 Ormiston Rd East Tamaki, Manukau City, Auckland, New Zealand
Tel.: (64) 92748664
Sales Range: $25-49.9 Million
Emp.: 20
Pharmaceuticals Sales & Marketing
N.A.I.C.S.: 424210
Tony Davison *(Gen Mgr)*

Boehringer Ingelheim (Philippines) Inc. (1)
23rd Floor Citibank Tower 8741 Paseo de Roxas, Salcedo Village, Makati, 1227, Metro Menila, Philippines
Tel.: (63) 288670800
Web Site:
    http://www.boehringeringelheim.com
Sales Range: $25-49.9 Million
Provider of Pharmaceuticals & Animal Health Products
N.A.I.C.S.: 325412

Boehringer Ingelheim (Pty.) Ltd. (1)
404 Main Ave Ferndale, PO Box 3032, Johannesburg, Randburg, 2125, South Africa
Tel.: (27) 113482400
Web Site: http://www.boehringer-ingelheim.co.za
Sales Range: $75-99.9 Million
Emp.: 226
Holding Company; Pharmaceutical Products Mfr
N.A.I.C.S.: 551112

Subsidiary (Domestic):

Ingelheim Pharmaceuticals (Pty.) Ltd. (2)
404 Main Avenue, Private Bag X 3032, Randburg, 2125, South Africa
Tel.: (27) 113482400
Web Site:
    http://www.boehringeringelheim.com
Sales Range: $50-74.9 Million
Emp.: 200
Provider of Pharmaceuticals
N.A.I.C.S.: 325412

Boehringer Ingelheim (Schweiz) GmbH (1)
Hochbergerstrasse 60B, CH 4002, Basel, Switzerland
Tel.: (41) 612952525
Web Site: http://www.boehringer-ingelheim.ch
Sales Range: $50-74.9 Million
Provider of Pharmaceuticals, Animal Health Products & Nature-Based Consumer Health Care Products
N.A.I.C.S.: 325412

Subsidiary (Domestic):

Pharmaton S.A. (2)
Veaumureni, Bioggio, CH 6934, Switzerland
Tel.: (41) 916103111
Web Site: http://www.pharmaton.com
Sales Range: $50-74.9 Million
Emp.: 200
Developer of Pharmaceuticals
N.A.I.C.S.: 325412
Genovesi Michele *(Gen Mgr)*

Boehringer Ingelheim (Thai) Ltd. (1)
2922/207 - 208 Charn Issara Tower II 12 Floor New Petchburi Road, Bangkapi Huaykwang, Bangkok, 10320, Thailand
Tel.: (66) 23088500
Web Site: http://www.boehringer-ingelheim.com
Sales Range: $10-24.9 Million
Provider of Pharmaceutical Mfr
N.A.I.C.S.: 325412

Boehringer Ingelheim AB (1)
Hammarby Alle 29, 120 32, Stockholm, Sweden
Tel.: (46) 87212100
Web Site: http://www.boehringer-ingelheim.se
Sales Range: $25-49.9 Million
Provider of Pharmaceuticals
N.A.I.C.S.: 325412
Franz Zinsberger *(Mng Dir)*

Boehringer Ingelheim Animal Health Australia Pty. Ltd. (1)
Level 1 78 Waterloo Road, North Ryde, 2113, NSW, Australia
Tel.: (61) 288758800
Pharmaceuticals Product Mfr
N.A.I.C.S.: 325412

Boehringer Ingelheim Animal Health Belgium S.A. (1)
Vesalius Science Park Arianelaan 16, 1200, Brussels, Belgium
Tel.: (32) 27733456
Pharmaceuticals Product Mfr
N.A.I.C.S.: 325412
Fabien Danlois *(Product Mgr-Mktg)*

Boehringer Ingelheim Animal Health Japan Co., Ltd. (1)
ThinkPark Tower 2-1-1 Osaki, Shinagawa-ku, Tokyo, 141-6017, Japan
Tel.: (81) 364172800
Pharmaceuticals Product Mfr
N.A.I.C.S.: 325412

Boehringer Ingelheim Animal Health Netherlands B.V. (1)
Comeniusstraat 6, 1817 MS, Alkmaar, Netherlands
Tel.: (31) 725662411
Pharmaceuticals Product Mfr
N.A.I.C.S.: 325412

Boehringer Ingelheim Animal Health New Zealand Limited (1)
Level 3-2 Osterley Way, Manukau, 2104, New Zealand
Tel.: (64) 99801600
Pharmaceuticals Product Mfr
N.A.I.C.S.: 325412
Kim Ellett *(Head-Mktg)*

Boehringer Ingelheim Animal Health South Africa Pty. Ltd. (1)
404 Main Avenue, Ferndale Randburg, Johannesburg, 2194, South Africa
Tel.: (27) 113482400
Web Site: http://www.boehringer-ingelheim.co.za
Emp.: 120
Pharmaceuticals Product Mfr
N.A.I.C.S.: 325412
Muzi Nhlapo *(Mgr-Comml Quality)*

Boehringer Ingelheim Animal Health do Brasil Ltda. (1)
Fazenda Sao Francisco s/n, 13140-970, Paulinia, SP, Brazil
Tel.: (55) 1935785300
Pharmaceuticals Product Mfr
N.A.I.C.S.: 325412

Boehringer Ingelheim B.V. (1)
Comeniusstraat 6, 1817 MS, Alkmaar, Netherlands
Tel.: (31) 725662424
Web Site: http://www.boehringer-ingelheim.nl
Sales Range: $50-74.9 Million
Pharmaceuticals & Animal Health Products Mfr
N.A.I.C.S.: 325412

Boehringer Ingelheim BH d.o.o (1)
Grbavicka 4, Sarajevo-Novo, 71000, Sarajevo, Bosnia & Herzegovina
Tel.: (387) 5 1 2444600
Pharmaceutical Products Distr
N.A.I.C.S.: 424210

Boehringer Ingelheim C.A. (1)
Av La Estancia Torre A Piso 3 Oficina A32, Apartado Postal 1060, Centro Banaven Cubo Negro Chuao, Caracas, 64745, Venezuela
Tel.: (58) 2129597580
Web Site:
    http://www.sudamerica.boehringer-ingelheim.com

Sales Range: $50-74.9 Million
Pharmaceuticals Distr
N.A.I.C.S.: 424210

Boehringer Ingelheim Corp. (1)
900 Ridgebury Rd, Ridgefield, CT 06877-1058
Tel.: (203) 798-9988
Web Site:
    http://us.boehringer-ingelheim.com
Rev.: $3,167,427,500
Emp.: 6,493
Holding Company; Pharmaceutical Products & Chemical Drug Materials Developer & Mfr
N.A.I.C.S.: 551112
Wolfgang Baiker *(Pres & CEO)*

Subsidiary (Domestic):

Boehringer Ingelheim Chemicals, Inc. (2)
2820 N Normandy Dr, Petersburg, VA 23805-9372
Tel.: (804) 504-8600
Web Site:
    http://www.boehringeringelheim.com
Sales Range: $125-149.9 Million
Emp.: 375
Pharmaceutical Intermediates & Chemical Substances Mfr
N.A.I.C.S.: 325998
Ken Glaize *(Assoc Dir-Maintenance & Facilities Ops)*

Boehringer Ingelheim Fremont, Inc. (2)
6701 Kaiser Dr, Fremont, CA 94555-3616
Tel.: (510) 608-6500
Web Site: http://www.boehringer-ingelheim.us
Sales Range: $125-149.9 Million
Emp.: 300
Biopharmaceutical Mfr
N.A.I.C.S.: 325414
Jean-Michel Boers *(Pres, CEO & Mng Dir-US)*

Boehringer Ingelheim Pharmaceuticals, Inc. (2)
900 Ridgebury Rd, Ridgefield, CT 06877
Tel.: (203) 798-9988
Web Site: http://www.boehringer-ingelheim.us
Sales Range: $25-49.9 Million
Emp.: 100
Drugs Acting On The Cardiovascular System Except Diagnostic
N.A.I.C.S.: 325412
Jean-Michel Boers *(Pres, CEO & Mng Dir-US)*

Boehringer Ingelheim Vetmedica, Inc. (2)
3902 Gene Field Rd, Saint Joseph, MO 64506
Tel.: (816) 233-2571
Web Site: http://www.bi-vetmedica.com
Sales Range: $250-299.9 Million
Veterinary Serum Biologics Pharmaceuticals Insecticide & Efficiency Enhancer Mfr
N.A.I.C.S.: 325414

Boehringer Ingelheim Danmark A/S (1)
Strodamvej 52, 2100, Copenhagen, Denmark
Tel.: (45) 39158888
Web Site: http://www.boehringer-ingelheim.dk
Sales Range: $50-74.9 Million
Pharmaceuticals & Animal Health Products Mfr & Marketer
N.A.I.C.S.: 325412

Boehringer Ingelheim Ellas AE (1)
Ellinikou 2, Elliniko, 16777, Athens, Greece
Tel.: (30) 2108906300
Sales Range: $125-149.9 Million
Emp.: 299
Pharmaceuticals, Consumer Health Products & Animal Health Products Mfr & Distr
N.A.I.C.S.: 325412

Boehringer Ingelheim Espana, S.A. (1)
Prat de la Riba 50, San Cugat Del Valles, 08174, Barcelona, Spain
Tel.: (34) 934045100
Web Site: http://www.boehringer-ingelheim.es

Sales Range: $400-449.9 Million
Emp.: 1,515
Pharmaceuticals Mfr & Marketer
N.A.I.C.S.: 325412
Santiago Culi *(Mgr-Comm)*

Boehringer Ingelheim Europe GmbH (1)
Binger Strasse 150-175, 55216, Ingelheim, Germany
Tel.: (49) 6132 770
Holding Company; Regional Managing Office
N.A.I.C.S.: 551112

Subsidiary (Non-US):

Boehringer Ingelheim Austria GmbH (2)
Dr Boehringer Gasse 5-11, 1121, Vienna, Austria
Tel.: (43) 1801050
Web Site: http://www.boehringer-ingelheim.at
Researcher & Developer of Oncology Products & Manufacturer of Biopharmaceuticals
N.A.I.C.S.: 325412

Subsidiary (Domestic):

Boehringer Ingelheim Pharma Ges.m.b.H. (3)
Dr Boehringer Gasse 5-11, 1121, Vienna, Austria
Tel.: (43) 1801050
Web Site: http://www.boehringeringelheim.at
Sales Range: $450-499.9 Million
Pharmaceuticals Mfr & Marketer
N.A.I.C.S.: 325412

Unit (Domestic):

I.M.P. Research Institute of Molecular Pathology (3)
Campus-Vienna-Biocenter 1, 1030, Vienna, Austria
Tel.: (43) 179730
Web Site: http://www.imp.univie.ac.at
Sales Range: $25-49.9 Million
Research Services
N.A.I.C.S.: 541715

Subsidiary (Non-US):

Boehringer Ingelheim Finland Ky (2)
HTC Santa Maria 5 kerros Tammasaaren-katu 5, 00180, Helsinki, Finland
Tel.: (358) 103102800
Web Site: http://www.boehringer-ingelheim.fi
Sales Range: $50-74.9 Million
Emp.: 86
Pharmaceuticals Sales, Marketing & Clinical Trials
N.A.I.C.S.: 424210
Amos Gyllenbogel *(Mng Dir)*

Boehringer Ingelheim Norway KS (2)
Hagalokkveien 26, 1383, Asker, Norway
Tel.: (47) 66761300
Web Site: http://www.boehringer-ingelheim.no
Pharmaceuticals Sales & Marketing
N.A.I.C.S.: 424210

Boehringer Ingelheim Sp. z o.o. (2)
ul F Klimczaka 1, 02 797, Warsaw, Poland
Tel.: (48) 226990699
Web Site: http://www.boehringer-ingelheim.pl
Pharmaceutical Preparation Manufacturing
N.A.I.C.S.: 325412

Boehringer Ingelheim s.r.o. (2)
Na Porici 1079/3a, Nove Mesto, 110 00, Prague, Czech Republic
Tel.: (420) 234655111
Web Site: http://www.boehringer-ingelheim.cz
Sales Range: $10-24.9 Million
Provider of Pharmaceutical Mfr
N.A.I.C.S.: 325412

Boehringer Ingelheim France S.A.S. (1)
12 rue Andre Huet, 51721, Reims, Cedex, France
Tel.: (33) 326504533
Web Site: http://www.boehringer-ingelheim.fr

C.H. Boehringer Sohn AG & Co.
KG—(Continued)

Sales Range: $400-449.9 Million
Emp.: 1,282
Pharmaceutical Chemical & Animal Health
Product Mfr
N.A.I.C.S.: 325412

Subsidiary (Domestic):

LABSO Chimie Fine S.A.R.L. **(2)**
20 Rue Jean Duvert, 33290, Blanquefort,
France
Tel.: (33) 5 5635 5050
Sales Range: $1-9.9 Million
Emp.: 12
Mfr of Chemical Products
N.A.I.C.S.: 325998

Boehringer Ingelheim GmbH **(1)**
Binger Strasse 173, 55216, Ingelheim, Germany
Tel.: (49) 6132770
Web Site: http://www.boehringer-
ingelheim.com
Fiscal Year-end: 12/31/2019
Pharmaceutical Preparation Manufacturing
N.A.I.C.S.: 551112

Subsidiary (Domestic):

Boehringer Ingelheim Pharma GmbH
& Co. KG **(2)**
Binger Strasse 173, 55216, Ingelheim, Germany
Tel.: (49) 6132770
Web Site: http://www.boehringer-
ingelheim.de
Sales Range: $1-4.9 Billion
Pharmaceutical Products Developer & Mfr
N.A.I.C.S.: 325412

Boehringer Ingelheim Vetmedica
GmbH **(2)**
Binger Strasse 173, D 55216, Ingelheim,
Germany
Tel.: (49) 6132778219
Web Site:
http://www.boehringeringelheim.de
Sales Range: $50-74.9 Million
Emp.: 165
Animal Health Veterinary Pharmaceuticals
Mfr
N.A.I.C.S.: 325412

Boehringer Ingelheim microParts
GmbH **(2)**
Hauert 7, 44227, Dortmund, Germany
Tel.: (49) 23197990
Web Site: http://www.boehringer-
ingelheim.de
Pharmaceutical Preparation Mfr
N.A.I.C.S.: 325412

Boehringer Ingelheim Ilac Ticaret
A.S. **(1)**
Esentepe Mah Harman 1 Sok Nidakule Levent No 7-9 Kat 15, Sisli, 34394, Istanbul,
Turkiye
Tel.: (90) 2123291100
Web Site: http://www.boehringer-
ingelheim.com.tr
Sales Range: $100-124.9 Million
Emp.: 400
Pharmaceutical Preparation Mfr
N.A.I.C.S.: 325412
Evren Ozlu *(Chm & Gen Mgr)*

Boehringer Ingelheim India Private
Ltd. **(1)**
1102 Hallmark Business Plaza 11th Floor
Gurunanak Hospital Road, Near Gurunanak
Hospital Bandra East, Mumbai, 400051,
India
Tel.: (91) 2271456477
Pharmaceuticals Product Mfr
N.A.I.C.S.: 325412
Sharad Tyagi *(Mng Dir)*

Boehringer Ingelheim International
Trading (Shanghai) Co. Ltd. **(1)**
29/F Park Pl 1601 W Nanjing Rd, Jing An
Dist, Shanghai, 200040, China
Tel.: (86) 2158882200
Web Site: http://www.boehringer-
ingelheim.com.cn
Pharmaceuticals Sales & Marketing
N.A.I.C.S.: 424210

Boehringer Ingelheim Israel Ltd **(1)**
89 Medinat Ha-Yehudim Street, Herzliya
Pituach, Israel
Tel.: (972) 9 9730515
Pharmaceutical Products Distr
N.A.I.C.S.: 424210

Boehringer Ingelheim Italia
S.p.A. **(1)**
Via Lorenzini n 8, 20139, Milan, Italy
Tel.: (39) 0253551
Web Site: http://www.boehringer-ingelheim.it
Sales Range: $200-249.9 Million
Prescription & Over-the-Counter Pharmaceuticals Mfr
N.A.I.C.S.: 325412
Sergio Diniotti *(Mng Dir)*

Subsidiary (Domestic):

Bidachem S.p.A. **(2)**
Strada Statale 11 Padana Superiore n 8,
Fornovo San Giovanni, 24040, Bergamo,
Italy
Tel.: (39) 036335521
Web Site: http://www.boehringer-ingelheim.it
Sales Range: $50-74.9 Million
Provider of Chemical Products
N.A.I.C.S.: 325998

Boehringer Ingelheim Korea Ltd. **(1)**
16F Yonsei Foundation Severance Building
10 Tongil ro, Jung gu, Seoul, 04527, Korea
(South)
Tel.: (82) 27090112
Web Site: http://www.bikr.co.kr
Sales Range: $100-124.9 Million
Provider of Pharmaceuticals & Animal
Health Products
N.A.I.C.S.: 325412

Subsidiary (Domestic):

Boehringer Ingelheim Vetmedica Korea Ltd. **(2)**
Yonsei Severance Building 10 Tongil Ro,
Kolea, 100754, Seoul, Jung-Gu, Korea
(South)
Tel.: (82) 27090114
Web Site: http://www.bikr.co.kr
Sales Range: $10-24.9 Million
Emp.: 150
Provider of Animal Health Products
N.A.I.C.S.: 112990

Boehringer Ingelheim Ltd. **(1)**
Ellesfield Ave, Bracknell, RG12 8YS, Berkshire, United Kingdom
Tel.: (44) 1344424600
Web Site: http://www.boehringer-
ingelheim.com
Sales Range: $200-249.9 Million
Provider of Pharmaceuticals & Animal
Health Products
N.A.I.C.S.: 325412

Boehringer Ingelheim Ltda. **(1)**
Av de Padua No 11, Lisbon, 1800-294, Portugal
Tel.: (351) 213135300
Web Site:
http://www.boehringeringelheim.com
Sales Range: $25-49.9 Million
Pharmaceuticals Mfr
N.A.I.C.S.: 325412

Subsidiary (Domestic):

Unilfarma-Uniao Internacional de
Laboratorios Farmaceuticos,
Lda. **(2)**
Avenida Padua 11, 1800-294, Lisbon, Portugal
Tel.: (351) 213135300
Web Site: http://www.unilfarma.pai.pt
Sales Range: $25-49.9 Million
Pharmaceuticals Distr
N.A.I.C.S.: 424210

Boehringer Ingelheim Ltda. **(1)**
Isidora Goyenechea 3000 piso 18, Las
Condes, Santiago, Chile
Tel.: (56) 223275000
Web Site: http://www.boehringer-
ingelheim.com
Emp.: 80
Pharmaceuticals Distr
N.A.I.C.S.: 424210

Boehringer Ingelheim Peru
S.A.C. **(1)**

Canaval y Moreyra 480 Piso 20 Edificio
Chocavento, San Isidro, Lima, Peru
Tel.: (51) 14125000
Pharmaceuticals Product Mfr
N.A.I.C.S.: 325412
Patricia Corzo *(Sls Mgr)*

Boehringer Ingelheim Pharma Ges
mbH **(1)**
Innova Tower Office Building 7th floor 52
Abay avenue, 050008, Almaty, Kazakhstan
Tel.: (7) 727 250 00 73
Pharmaceutical Products Distr
N.A.I.C.S.: 424210

Boehringer Ingelheim Promeco, S.A.
de C.V. **(1)**
Maiz No 49, Xaltocan, 16090, Xochimilco,
Mexico
Tel.: (52) 5556298300
Web Site: http://www.boehringer-
ingelheim.com.mx
Sales Range: $200-249.9 Million
Mfr of Pharmaceuticals
N.A.I.C.S.: 325412

Boehringer Ingelheim Pty. Ltd. **(1)**
78 Waterloo Rd, North Ryde, 2113, NSW,
Australia
Tel.: (61) 288758800
Web Site:
http://www.boehringeringelheim.com
Sales Range: $100-124.9 Million
Mfr & Sales of Pharmaceuticals, Chemicals
& Animal Health Products
N.A.I.C.S.: 325412

Boehringer Ingelheim S.A. **(1)**
Complejo Empresarial Urbana Cazadores
de Coquimbo 2841 Piso 2, B1605AZE, Munro, Buenos Aires, Argentina
Tel.: (54) 11 47048600
Web Site:
http://www.sudamerica.boehringer-
ingelheim.com
Sales Range: $25-49.9 Million
Mfr & Distr of Prescription Medicines, Consumer Health Care Products & Animal
Health Products
N.A.I.C.S.: 325412

Boehringer Ingelheim S.A. **(1)**
Carrera 11 N 84A - 09 Piso 5 Torre Sur,
Bogota, DC, Colombia
Tel.: (57) 13199100
Web Site:
http://www.sudamerica.boehringer-
ingelheim.com
Pharmaceuticals & Animal Health Products
Mfr
N.A.I.C.S.: 325412

Boehringer Ingelheim Serbia
d.o.o. **(1)**
Sava Business Center Milentija Popovica
5a, 11070, Novi Beograd, Serbia
Tel.: (381) 11 3115960
Pharmaceutical Products Distr
N.A.I.C.S.: 424210

Boehringer Ingelheim Shanghai Pharmaceuticals Co., Ltd. **(1)**
22F No 138 Pudong Avenue, Shanghai,
200120, China
Tel.: (86) 2158882200
Web Site: http://www.boehringer-
ingelheim.com
Pharmaceuticals Mfr
N.A.I.C.S.: 325412

Boehringer Ingelheim Taiwan
Ltd. **(1)**
12th Floor No 2 Section 3 Minsheng East
Road, Zhongshan District, Taipei, 10478,
Taiwan
Tel.: (886) 225032636
Web Site: http://www.boehringer-
ingelheim.tw
Sales Range: $50-74.9 Million
Provider of Pharmaceuticals
N.A.I.C.S.: 325412

Boehringer Ingelheim Venture Fund
GmbH **(1)**
Binger Strasse 173, Ingelheim am Rhein,
55216, Ingelheim, Germany
Tel.: (49) 613277181170
Web Site: http://www.boehringer-ingelheim-
venture.com

Investment Fund Services
N.A.I.C.S.: 523940
Frank Kalkbrenner *(Head)*

Boehringer Ingelheim Veterinary Research Center GmbH & Co. KG **(1)**
Bemeroder Str 31, 30559, Hannover, Germany
Tel.: (49) 6132770
Pharmaceuticals Product Mfr
N.A.I.C.S.: 325412
Rocio Leon-Kempis *(Head-Bacteriology)*

Boehringer Ingelheim Vetmedica S.A.
de C.V. **(1)**
Calle 30 No 2614 Zona Industrial, Postal
1-2698, Apartado, 44940, Guadalajara,
Jalisco, Mexico
Tel.: (52) 3336688000
Web Site: http://www.boehringer-
ingelheim.mx
Sales Range: $25-49.9 Million
Human Pharmaceuticals & Animal Health
N.A.I.C.S.: 325412

Boehringer Ingelheim Zagreb
d.o.o. **(1)**
Radnicka 40-5, 10000, Zagreb, Croatia
Tel.: (385) 5 1 2444600
Pharmaceutical Products Distr
N.A.I.C.S.: 424210

Boehringer Ingelheim del Ecuador
Cia. Ltda. **(1)**
Av Los Shyris N 344 y Av Eloy Alfaro Edificio Parque Central Piso 15, Quito, Ecuador
Tel.: (593) 23979900
Web Site:
http://www.sudamerica.boehringer-
ingelheim.com
Sales Range: $1-9.9 Million
Pharmaceuticals Distr
N.A.I.C.S.: 424210

Boehringer Ingelheim do Brasil
Quimica e Farmaceutica Ltda. **(1)**
Rochavera Corporate Towers Av Nacoes
Unidas, 14 171 Marble Tower 18th floor,
Sao Paulo, 04794-000, Brazil
Tel.: (55) 11 4949 4700
Web Site: http://www.boehringer-
ingelheim.com.br
Sales Range: $125-149.9 Million
Pharmaceuticals & Animal Health Products
Mfr & Marketer
N.A.I.C.S.: 325412

Subsidiary (Domestic):

Solana Agro Pecuaria Ltda. **(2)**
Fazendo Nossa Senhora Iparecida, Zona
Rural, CEP 86700-970, Arapongas, Brazil
Medicinal Plants Production
N.A.I.C.S.: 325412

Boehringer Ingelheim s.a./n.v. **(1)**
Avenue Arnaud Fraiteur 15 23, 1050, Brussels, Belgium
Tel.: (32) 27733311
Web Site: http://www.boehringer-
ingelheim.be
Sales Range: $50-74.9 Million
Provider of Pharmaceuticals & Animal
Health Products
N.A.I.C.S.: 325412
Christian Wigsen *(Gen Mgr)*

Boehringer Ingelheim spol. s r.o. **(1)**
Na Porici 1079/3a, 110 00, Prague, Czech
Republic
Tel.: (420) 234 655 111
Web Site: http://www.boehringer-
ingelheim.cz
Emp.: 100
Pharmaceuticals Product Mfr
N.A.I.C.S.: 325412

Forschungsinstitut fur Molekulare Pathologie Gesellschaft mbH **(1)**
Campus-Vienna-Biocenter 1, 1030, Vienna,
Austria
Tel.: (43) 179730
Web Site: http://www.imp.ac.at
Emp.: 250
Biotechnology Research & Development
Services
N.A.I.C.S.: 541714
Harald Isemann *(Mng Dir-Fin & Admin)*

LLC Boehringer Ingelheim **(1)**

Leningradskoe highway 16A p 3, 125171, Moscow, Russia
Tel.: (7) 4955445044
Web Site: http://www.boehringer-ingelheim.ru
Pharmaceutical Products Distr
N.A.I.C.S.: 424210

Newport Laboratories, Inc. (1)
1520 Prairie Dr, Worthington, MN 56187
Web Site: http://www.newportlabs.com
Veterinary Laboratory Testing Services
N.A.I.C.S.: 541940

Nippon Boehringer Ingelheim Co. Ltd. (1)
ThinkPark Tower 2-1-1 Osaki, Shinagawa ku, Tokyo, 141-6017, Japan
Tel.: (81) 364172200
Web Site: http://www.boehringer-ingelheim.jp
Sales Range: $550-599.9 Million
Holding Company; Pharmaceutical Products Mfr
N.A.I.C.S.: 551112
Yoshiaki Aono (Pres)

Subsidiary (Domestic):

Boehringer Ingelheim Seiyaku Co., Ltd. (2)
5353 1 Higashine Kou, Higashine Shi, Yamagata, 999 3701, Japan
Tel.: (81) 237421193
Web Site: http://www.boehringeringelheim.co.jp
Sales Range: $25-49.9 Million
Emp.: 50
Pharmaceuticals Mfr & Distr
N.A.I.C.S.: 325412

Boehringer Ingelheim Vetmedica Japan (2)
2 8 8 Sarugaku Cho, Chiyoda-ku, Tokyo, 102-0073, Japan
Tel.: (81) 352807200
Web Site: http://www.boehringer-ingelheim.co.jp
Provider of Animal Health Products
N.A.I.C.S.: 325412

SSP Co. Ltd. (2)
2-12-4 Nihombashi-Hamacho, Chuo-ku, Tokyo, 103-8481, Japan
Tel.: (81) 3 3668 4511
Web Site: http://www.ssp.co.jp
Pharmaceutical Products Distr
N.A.I.C.S.: 424210

OOO Boehringer Ingelheim (1)
Leningradskoe shosse 16A p 3, 125171, Moscow, Russia
Tel.: (7) 4955445044
Web Site: http://www.boehringer-ingelheim.ru
Animal & People Health Services
N.A.I.C.S.: 923120
Oliver Koehncke (Head-Human Pharma & Gen Mgr)

PT Boehringer Ingelheim Indonesia (1)
Sampoerna Strategic Square North Tower Level 6, Jl Jendral Sudirman Kav 45-46, Jakarta, 12930, Indonesia
Tel.: (62) 215732375
Web Site: http://www.boehringer-ingelheim.com
Sales Range: $100-124.9 Million
Emp.: 390
Pharmaceutical Preparation Mfr & Marketer
N.A.I.C.S.: 325412

SCS Boehringer Ingelheim Comm. V. (1)
Avenue Arnaud Fraiteur 15-23, 1050, Brussels, Belgium
Tel.: (32) 2 773 33 11
Web Site: http://www.boehringer-ingelheim.be
Emp.: 150
Pharmaceutical Products Distr
N.A.I.C.S.: 424210

ViraTherapeutics GmbH (1)
Bundesstrasse 27, Rum, 6063, Innsbruck, Austria
Tel.: (43) 512272061
Web Site: http://www.viratherapeutics.com
Therapy Research & Development Services

N.A.I.C.S.: 541713
Knut Elbers (Co-CEO)

C.I. GROUP PUBLIC COMPANY LIMITED
1/1 Moo 7 Bangkoowad Road Bangkoowad, Amphoe Muang, Pathumthani, 12000, Thailand
Tel.: (66) 29765299
Web Site: https://www.cigpcl.com
Year Founded: 1983
CIG—(THA)
Rev.: $17,605,580
Assets: $37,157,700
Liabilities: $12,642,377
Net Worth: $24,515,323
Earnings: $241,110
Emp.: 136
Fiscal Year-end: 12/31/23
Air Conditioning Product Mfr & Distr
N.A.I.C.S.: 333415
Prung Boonpadung (Chm)

Subsidiaries:

C.I. Group Public Company Limited - Factory 2 (1)
789/75 Moo 1 Pinthong Industrial Park, Nongkham, Si Racha, 20230, Chonburi, Thailand
Tel.: (66) 38296920
Heat Exchanger Mfr
N.A.I.C.S.: 332410

C.I. Group Public Company Limited - Factory 3 (1)
526/1-3 Moo3 Teparak Road, Amphoe Muang, Samut Prakan, 10270, Thailand
Tel.: (66) 27583034
Heat Exchanger Mfr
N.A.I.C.S.: 332410

C.I. HOLDINGS BERHAD
Suite A-11-1 Level 11 Hampshire Office Place 157 Hampshire, No 1 Jalan Mayang Sari, 50450, Kuala Lumpur, Malaysia
Tel.: (60) 321827333
Web Site: https://www.cih.com.my
CIHLDG—(KLS)
Rev.: $1,131,675,132
Assets: $257,520,212
Liabilities: $147,471,323
Net Worth: $110,048,889
Earnings: $35,241,058
Fiscal Year-end: 06/30/23
Plumbing Products Mfr
N.A.I.C.S.: 332913
Pei Yee Chaw (Sr Mgr-Fin & Admin)

Subsidiaries:

Continental Resources Sdn. Bhd. (1)
Lot 2239 Jalan Rajawali Batu 9 Kampung Kebun Baru, Telok Panglima Garang, 42500, Kuala Langat, Selangor Darul Ehsan, Malaysia
Tel.: (60) 331220578
Web Site: https://www.crsb.com.my
Edible Oil Product Mfr
N.A.I.C.S.: 311225

Subsidiary (Domestic):

Palmtop Sdn Bhd (2)
PLO 470 Jalan Keluli 1, Kawasan Perindustrian Pasir Gudang, 81700, Pasir Gudang, Johor, Malaysia
Tel.: (60) 72526118
Web Site: https://www.palmtopvegeoil.com.my
Edible Oil Product Mfr
N.A.I.C.S.: 311225

Subsidiary (Non-US):

Continental Palms Pte. Ltd. (3)
114 Lavender Street CT Hub 2 12-84, Singapore, Singapore
Tel.: (65) 63845241
Edible Oil Product Mfr
N.A.I.C.S.: 311225

Doe Industries Sdn. Bhd. (1)

No 8 Jalan SS21/39, Damansara Utama, 47400, Petaling Jaya, Malaysia
Tel.: (60) 377278868
Web Site: https://www.doe.com.my
Emp.: 50
Tap Ware & Sanitary Fitting Product Mfr
N.A.I.C.S.: 332913
Robert Foo Loke Yean (CEO)

Subsidiary (Domestic):

Potex Industries Sdn. Bhd. (2)
No 8B Jalan SS21/39, Damansara Utama, 47400, Petaling Jaya, Selangor Darul Ehsan, Malaysia
Tel.: (60) 377251006
Web Site: https://www.potex.com.my
Bathroom Related Product Mfr & Distr
N.A.I.C.S.: 326199

C.J. COLEMAN & COMPANY LIMITED
Port Soken House 155 Minories, London, EC3 N1BT, United Kingdom
Tel.: (44) 2074882211 UK
Web Site: http://www.cjcoleman.com
Year Founded: 1973
Sales Range: $10-24.9 Million
Emp.: 25
Liability Insurance
N.A.I.C.S.: 524128
Jim Foster (Sec)

Subsidiaries:

Coleman & Large Ltd. (1)
4th Floor Europa House 49 Sandgate Road, Folkestone, CT20 1RQ, Kent, United Kingdom
Tel.: (44) 1303223883
Web Site: http://www.cjcoleman.com
Liability Insurance
N.A.I.C.S.: 524128

C.J.GELATINE PRODUCTS LIMITED
B-Shop-05 Ground Floor Plot-237 Azad Nagar Rahivasi Sangh, Acharya Donde Marg Sewree W, Mumbai, 400 015, Maharashtra, India
Tel.: (91) 7480423301 In
Web Site: https://www.cjgelatineproducts.com
Year Founded: 1980
507515—(BOM)
Rev.: $5,331,148
Assets: $4,443,392
Liabilities: $3,380,587
Net Worth: $1,062,806
Earnings: $47,294
Emp.: 102
Fiscal Year-end: 03/31/21
Gelatin Mfr
N.A.I.C.S.: 325998
Jaspal Singh (Chm & Mng Dir)

C.K. TANG LIMITED
5 Kadayanallur Street, Singapore, 69183, Singapore
Tel.: (65) 67375500
Web Site: http://www.tangs.com
Year Founded: 1932
Sales Range: $150-199.9 Million
Emp.: 686
Department Stores Owner & Operator
N.A.I.C.S.: 455110
Kevin M. Dyson (CEO)

C.O. CYPRUS OPPORTUNITY ENERGY PUBLIC LIMITED
13 Karaiskakis Str, Limassol, 3032, Cyprus
Tel.: (357) 25800000
GAS—(CYP)
Rev.: $51,025
Assets: $22,667
Liabilities: $189,786
Net Worth: ($167,119)
Earnings: ($468,207)
Fiscal Year-end: 12/31/19

Oil & Gas Exploration Services
N.A.I.C.S.: 213112
Rony Halman (Chm)

C.P. ALL PUBLIC COMPANY LIMITED
58/28 THE TARA Building Moo 2 Chaengwattana Rd, Bang Talad Pakkred, Nonthaburi, 11120, Thailand
Tel.: (66) 20719000
Web Site: https://www.cpall.co.th
Year Founded: 1988
CPALL—(OTCIQ)
Rev.: $25,333,088,562
Assets: $25,478,953,735
Liabilities: $17,184,942,998
Net Worth: $8,294,010,737
Earnings: $600,941,533
Emp.: 63,896
Fiscal Year-end: 12/31/23
Convenience Stores Services
N.A.I.C.S.: 455110
Korsak Chairasmisak (Vice Chm)

Subsidiaries:

24 Shopping Co., Ltd. (1)
119 Thara Sathorn Building Floor 9-10 Soi Sathorn 5 Sathon Tai Road, Bangkok, 10120, Thailand
Tel.: (66) 27807666
Web Site: http://www.24shopping.co.th
Electronic Shopping Services
N.A.I.C.S.: 423620

All Now Logistics Co., Ltd. (1)
127 Panjaphum Building 2 15th Floor South Sathorn Road, Thungmahamek Sathorn, Bangkok, 10120, Thailand
Tel.: (66) 20909100
Freight Forwarding & Transportation Services
N.A.I.C.S.: 532411

CP All Laos Company Limited (1)
No 239 Unit 16 Souphanouvong Road, Nongpanai Village Sikhottabong District, Vientiane, Laos
Tel.: (856) 2145350810
Web Site: https://cpalllaos.com
Convenience Retailer Services
N.A.I.C.S.: 445131

CP Axtra Public Company Limited (1)
1468 Phatthanakan Road Khwaeng, Phatthanakan Subdistrict Suan Luang District, Bangkok, 10250, Thailand
Tel.: (66) 20678999
Web Site: https://www.cpaxtra.com
Rev.: $7,289,089,481
Assets: $2,466,818,040
Liabilities: $1,710,103,570
Net Worth: $756,714,470
Earnings: $217,385,176
Emp.: 8,545
Fiscal Year-end: 12/31/2020
Discount Stores
N.A.I.C.S.: 424490
Prasert Jarupanich (Exec Dir)

CP Retailink Co., Ltd. (1)
159/30 Moo 3 Vibhavadi Rangsit Road Talad, Bangkhen Lake Si, Bangkok, 10210, Thailand
Tel.: (66) 279268009
Web Site: http://www.cpretailink.co.th
Retail Equipment Distr
N.A.I.C.S.: 423850

CP Wholesale India Private Limited (1)
7th & 8th Floor WeWork BlueOne Square 246 Phase IV, Udyog Vihar, Gurgaon, 122016, Haryana, India
Tel.: (91) 8601235687
Web Site: https://corporate.lotswholesale.com
N.A.I.C.S.: 424420

CPRAM Co., Ltd. (1)
177 Moo 4 Pathum Thanee-Lat Lum Kaeo Road, Rahaeng Lat Lum kaeo, Pathumthani, 12140, Thailand
Tel.: (66) 2 844 8100
Web Site: https://www.cpram.co.th
Food Products Mfr

C.P. All Public Company Limited—(Continued)

N.A.I.C.S.: 311813

Counter Service Co., Ltd. (1)
No 119 Thara Sathorn Building 4th-6th
Floor Sathorn Soi 5, South Sathorn Road
Thungmahamek Sathorn, Bangkok, 10120,
Thailand
Tel.: (66) 2 826 7788
Web Site: https://www.counterservice.co.th
Insurance Services
N.A.I.C.S.: 524210

**Gosoft (Thailand) Company
Limited** (1)
34 Flr 5 CP Tower 3 Phayathai Road,
Thung Phayathai Ratchathewi, Bangkok,
10400, Thailand
Tel.: (66) 2 071-1503
Web Site: https://www.gosoft.co.th
IT System Consulting Services
N.A.I.C.S.: 541690

**Indoguna (Cambodia) Company
Limited** (1)
Green Community Mall Building C Unit
A10-11 First Floor, Sangkat Khmuonh Khan
Sen Sok, Phnom Penh, Cambodia
Tel.: (855) 23901369
Web Site: https://www.indoguna-
cambodia.com
N.A.I.C.S.: 424470
Kham Phalleap (Mgr-Business Develop-
ment)

Indoguna (Singapore) Pte. Ltd. (1)
34/36/38 Senoko Drive, Singapore, 758221,
Singapore
Tel.: (65) 67550330
Web Site: http://www.indoguna.com
Catering Services
N.A.I.C.S.: 722310
Helene Raudaschl (Mng Dir)

Indoguna Dubai L.L.C. (1)
Building 24 Road 25 Al Quoz Industrial Area
4, PO Box 123125, Dubai, United Arab
Emirates
Tel.: (971) 43386304
Web Site: https://www.indogunadubai.com
N.A.I.C.S.: 424470
Karlo Pacheco (Mng Dir)

**Indoguna Lordly Company
Limited** (1)
Unit A 5/F & Unit B 7/F 29-37 Kwai Wing
Road, Sing Mei Industrial Building, Kwai
Chung, China (Hong Kong)
Tel.: (852) 27302025
Web Site: http://www.lordly.com.hk
Catering Services
N.A.I.C.S.: 722310
Kennis Cheung (Asst Gen Mgr)

**Indoguna Vina Food Service Com-
pany Limited** (1)
44B Phan Xich Long Str, Ward 3 Phu
Nhuan Dist, Ho Chi Minh City, Vietnam
Tel.: (84) 907091188
Web Site: http://www.indogunavina.com
Catering Services
N.A.I.C.S.: 722310

**Lotuss Stores (Malaysia) Sdn.
Bhd.** (1)
Level 3 No 3 Jalan 7A/62A, Bandar Men-
jalara, 52200, Kuala Lumpur, Malaysia
Tel.: (60) 1300131313
Web Site: https://corp.lotuss.com.my
Grocery Store Retailer
N.A.I.C.S.: 445110

**Makro (Cambodia) Company
Limited** (1)
No 5734 Street 1003, Bayab Village
Sangkat Phnom Penh Thmey Khan Sen
Sok, Phnom Penh, Cambodia
Tel.: (855) 23977355
Web Site: https://www.makrocambodia.com
N.A.I.C.S.: 424420

**Maxzi The Good Food Restaurant &
Cafe L.L.C.** (1)
Al Shafar Investment Building Al Quoz J,
PO Box 126113, Dubai, United Arab Emir-
ates
Tel.: (971) 43953988
Web Site: http://www.maxzi.ae
Catering Services

N.A.I.C.S.: 722310

Panyatara Co., Ltd. (1)
58/5 Moo 2 Chaeng Watthana Road, Bang
Talat Subdistrict Pak Kred District, Non-
thaburi, 11120, Thailand
Tel.: (66) 20716161
Web Site: http://www.panyatara.co.th
Training Services
N.A.I.C.S.: 611430

Siam Food Services Limited (1)
2439 Old Paknam Railway Road, Prakanong Klongtoey, Bangkok, 10110, Thailand
Tel.: (66) 27826000
Web Site:
https://www.siamfoodservices.com
N.A.I.C.S.: 424470
Preeyada Sripiboon (Mng Dir)

Thai Smart Card Co., Ltd. (1)
119 4th Floor Soi Sathorn 5 South Sathorn
Road Thungmahamek, Sathorn, Bangkok,
10120, Thailand
Tel.: (66) 20712260
Web Site: http://www.thaismartcard.co.th
Banking Services
N.A.I.C.S.: 522110

C.Q. PHARMACEUTICAL HOLDING CO., LTD.
No 303 Jinshi Avenue, Yubei District,
Chongqing, 401120, China
Tel.: (86) 2363910671
Web Site: http://www.cq-m.com.cn
Year Founded: 1999
000950—(SSE)
Rev.: $9,523,193,004
Assets: $8,984,416,428
Liabilities: $7,077,742,308
Net Worth: $1,906,674,120
Earnings: $133,700,112
Fiscal Year-end: 12/31/22
Agricultural Chemical Mfr
N.A.I.C.S.: 325320
Qiu Tian (Sec)

C.S. BACHLY BUILDERS LTD.
27 Nixon Road, Bolton, L7E 1J7, ON,
Canada
Tel.: (905) 951-3100
Web Site: http://www.bachly.com
Year Founded: 1962
Rev.: $14,767,900
Emp.: 47
Building Construction Services
N.A.I.C.S.: 236115
Scott Bachly (CEO)

C.S. LUMBER CO., INC.
1-16-3 Makuhari Hongo, Hanami-
gawa Ward, Chiba, 262-0033, Japan
Tel.: (81) 432138810
Web Site: https://www.c-s-
lumber.co.jp
7808—(TKS)
Rev.: $139,682,520
Assets: $155,546,520
Liabilities: $87,549,450
Net Worth: $67,997,070
Earnings: $9,485,350
Emp.: 321
Fiscal Year-end: 05/31/24
Timber Mfr & Distr
N.A.I.C.S.: 321215
Chiyosuke Nakai (Founder, Chm &
Pres)

C.S.A. CENTRO SERVIZI AU-TOCARRI S.R.L.
Via Emilia 43, Anzola dell'Emilia,
40011, Bologna, BO, Italy
Tel.: (39) 051 650 8611   IT
Web Site: http://www.csavic.it
New & Used Car Dealer
N.A.I.C.S.: 441110
Giovanni Terzitta (Dir Gen)

C.T.I. TRAFFIC INDUSTRIES CO., LTD.
16 Shih Chien Street, Kuan Tien,
Tainan City, Taiwan
Tel.: (886) 66991235
Web Site: https://www.ctico.com.tw
Year Founded: 1973
2230—(TPE)
Rev.: $15,770,150
Assets: $31,413,407
Liabilities: $12,930,901
Net Worth: $18,482,506
Earnings: $3,375,950
Fiscal Year-end: 12/31/22
Engine Parts Mfr
N.A.I.C.S.: 336310
Wan Chieh-Lu (Pres)

C.T.O. PUBLIC COMPANY LTD.
15 Ayion Omologiton Str, 1080, Nico-
sia, Cyprus
Tel.: (357) 24819200
Year Founded: 1976
CTO—(CYP)
Rev.: $1,089,595
Assets: $6,671,661
Liabilities: $2,096,244
Net Worth: $4,575,418
Earnings: ($1,356,243)
Emp.: 60
Fiscal Year-end: 12/31/19
Tobacco Product Mfr & Whslr
N.A.I.C.S.: 312230
Anastasios Elias Triandaphyllidis
(Chm)

C.UYEMURA & CO., LTD.
3-2-6 Dosho-machi, Chuo-ku, Osaka,
541-0045, Japan
Tel.: (81) 662028518
Web Site: https://www.uyemura.co.jp
Year Founded: 1848
4966—(TKS)
Rev.: $699,899,071
Assets: $979,511,088
Liabilities: $217,575,918
Net Worth: $761,935,170
Earnings: $93,717,830
Emp.: 1,547
Fiscal Year-end: 03/31/22
Chemical Product Mfr & Distr
N.A.I.C.S.: 325998
Hiroya Uyemura (Pres)

Subsidiaries:

**C.Uyemura & Co., Ltd. - Hirakata
Chemical Plant** (1)
5-1 Deguchi 1-chome, Hirakata, 573-0065,
Osaka, Japan
Tel.: (81) 728320161
Chemical Products Mfr
N.A.I.C.S.: 325199

PT. Uyemura Indonesia (1)
Suryacipta City of Industry JL Surya Lestari
Kav I-2F, Kutamekar Ciampel, Karawang,
41361, Jawa Barat, Indonesia
Tel.: (62) 2129614032
Web Site:
    http://www.indonesia.uyemura.co.jp
Plastic Plating Services
N.A.I.C.S.: 332813
Mitsuyasu Chikuma (Pres)

Sumix Corporation (1)
5-1 Deguchi 1-chome, Hirakata, 573-0065,
Osaka, Japan
Tel.: (81) 728320166
Web Site: http://www.sumix.co.jp
Plastic Plating Services
N.A.I.C.S.: 332813

Taiwan Uyemura Co., Ltd. (1)
No 7-1 Minzu St, Dayuan Dist, Taoyuan,
33759, Taiwan
Tel.: (886) 33866901
Web Site: http://www.uyemura.com.tw
Emp.: 293
Printed Circuit Board Mfr & Distr
N.A.I.C.S.: 334412

Uyemura (Malaysia) Sdn. Bhd. (1)
Plo 553 Jalan Keluli 8 Zone 12, Pasir Gu-
dang, 81700, Johor, Malaysia
Tel.: (60) 72511566
Web Site: https://www.uyemura.com.my
Emp.: 36
Electroplating Chemical Mfr
N.A.I.C.S.: 325992
Hiroya Uemura (Chm)

Uyemura (Shanghai) Co., Ltd. (1)
Room 1001-1003 10th Floor Shen Building
No 266 Hankou Road, Huangpu District,
Shanghai, 200001, China
Tel.: (86) 2163238833
Web Site: http://www.uyemura.com.cn
Emp.: 57
Surface Treatment Chemical Distr
N.A.I.C.S.: 424690
Shinji Miyazaki (Pres)

**Uyemura International (Hong Kong)
Co., Ltd.** (1)
Unit 12 39/F Cable TV Tower No 9 Hoi
Shing Road, Tsuen Wan, China (Hong
Kong)
Tel.: (852) 2414 4251
Web Site: https://www.uyemura.com.hk
Electroplating Equipment Mfr
N.A.I.C.S.: 333248

Subsidiary (Non-US):

Uyemura (Shenzhen) Co., Ltd. (2)
No 52 Qing Song Road Grand Industrial
Zone, Pingshan New District, Shenzhen,
518118, China
Tel.: (86) 75589929668
Web Site: https://www.uyemura.com
Electroplating Chemical Mfr
N.A.I.C.S.: 325992

**Uyemura International (Singapore)
Pte., Ltd.** (1)
2 Jurong East St 21 05-22/23 Imm Building,
Singapore, 609601, Singapore
Tel.: (65) 65631781
Web Site: http://www.uyemura.com.sg
Emp.: 16
Electroplating Chemical Distr
N.A.I.C.S.: 424690
Okuda Jiro (CEO)

**Uyemura International
Corporation** (1)
3990 Concours Ste 425, Ontario, CA 91764
Tel.: (909) 466-5635
Web Site: http://www.uyemura.com
Plating Chemical Distr
N.A.I.C.S.: 424690
Don Gudeczauskas (VP)

Uyemura Korea Co., Ltd. (1)
46 Jangangongdan 6-gil, Jangan-myeon,
Hwaseong, 18579, Gyeonggi-do, Korea
(South)
Tel.: (82) 3180474800
Web Site: https://www.uyemura.co.kr
Surface Treatment Chemical Distr
N.A.I.C.S.: 424690

C.W. MACKIE PLC
36 DR Wijewardena RD, 10, Co-
lombo, Sri Lanka
Tel.: (94) 115573573
Web Site: https://www.cwmackie.com
CWM—(COL)
Rev.: $63,938,444
Assets: $30,998,895
Liabilities: $17,188,339
Net Worth: $13,810,556
Earnings: $3,129,783
Emp.: 544
Fiscal Year-end: 03/31/23
Latex Crepe Rubber Mfr & Export
Services
N.A.I.C.S.: 325212
Camani Renuka Ranasinghe (Sec)

C21 INVESTMENTS INC.
170 - 601 West Cordova, Mailbox
107, Vancouver, V6B 1G1, BC,
Canada   BC
Web Site: https://www.cxxi.ca
Year Founded: 1987

CXXI—(CNSX)
Rev.: $28,285,200
Assets: $54,528,934
Liabilities: $23,481,926
Net Worth: $31,047,008
Earnings: ($3,305,285)
Emp.: 114
Fiscal Year-end: 01/31/24
Cannabis Brands & Products Mfr
N.A.I.C.S.: 111419
Michael Kidd *(CFO & Sec)*

Subsidiaries:

Silver State Relief LLC (1)
175 E Greg St, Sparks, NV 89431
Tel.: (775) 440-7777
Web Site: http://www.silverstaterelief.com
Cannabis Product Distr
N.A.I.C.S.: 459999

C29 METALS LIMITED
Suite 4 4 Douro Place, West Perth, 6005, WA, Australia
Tel.: (61) 861028072 AU
Web Site:
  https://www.c29metals.com.au
Year Founded: 2020
C29—(ASX)
Rev.: $20,144
Assets: $3,174,817
Liabilities: $263,748
Net Worth: $2,911,069
Earnings: ($1,722,654)
Fiscal Year-end: 06/30/23
Metal Exploration Services
N.A.I.C.S.: 213114

C2C METALS CORP.
1771 Robson Street - 1221, Vancouver, V6G 1C9, BC, Canada
Tel.: (604) 260-0289
Web Site: https://c2cmetals.com
CTOC—(CNSX)
Rev.: $15
Assets: $5,430,593
Liabilities: $167,687
Net Worth: $5,262,906
Earnings: ($173,128)
Fiscal Year-end: 12/31/20
Gold Exploration
N.A.I.C.S.: 212220
Lori Walton *(CEO)*

C3 METALS INC.
C3 Metals Inc 69 Yonge St, Toronto, M5J 2S1, ON, Canada
Tel.: (416) 572-2510 ON
Web Site: https://c3metals.com
Year Founded: 2010
CUC—(TSXV)
Rev.: $62,165
Assets: $41,281,366
Liabilities: $359,681
Net Worth: $40,921,685
Earnings: ($691,745)
Emp.: 3
Fiscal Year-end: 08/31/23
Metal Mining
N.A.I.C.S.: 212290

C4X DISCOVERY HOLDINGS PLC
Manchester One 53 Portland Street, Manchester, M1 3LD, United Kingdom
Tel.: (44) 161 235 5085
Web Site:
  http://www.c4xdiscovery.com
C4XD—(LSE)
Holding Company
N.A.I.C.S.: 551112
Clive Dix *(CEO)*

CA CULTURAL TECHNOLOGY GROUP LIMITED
Suites 2905 China Resources Build-

ing 26 Harbour Road, Hong Kong, China (Hong Kong)
Tel.: (852) 2 180 9699 Ky
Web Site:
  http://www.animatechina.com
1566—(HKG)
Rev.: $61,692,295
Assets: $284,910,371
Liabilities: $133,959,789
Net Worth: $150,950,582
Earnings: $9,155,258
Emp.: 284
Fiscal Year-end: 03/31/21
Holding Company; Toy Distr
N.A.I.C.S.: 551112
Jason Heung Chung Chong *(Exec Dir)*

CAA CLUB GROUP
60 Commerce Valley Drive East, Thornhill, L3T 7P9, ON, Canada
Tel.: (905) 771-3000
Web Site: http://www.caasco.com
Year Founded: 1903
Automobile Insurance Services
N.A.I.C.S.: 524210
Amy Bryson *(Chm)*

Subsidiaries:

Echelon General Insurance Company (1)
2680 Matheson Blvd E Ste 300, Mississauga, L4W 0A5, ON, Canada
Tel.: (905) 214-7880
Web Site: http://www.echelon-insurance.ca
Insurance Services
N.A.I.C.S.: 524113
Hemraj Singh *(CFO)*

Division (Domestic):

Echelon General Insurance Company Automobile Division (2)
2680 Matheson Blvd E Ste 300, Mississauga, L4W 0A5, ON, Canada
Tel.: (905) 214-7880
Web Site: http://www.echelon-insurance.ca
Sales Range: $75-99.9 Million
Insurance Services
N.A.I.C.S.: 524113

Echelon General Insurance Company Niche Products Division (2)
2680 Matheson Blvd, E Ste 300, Mississauga, L4W 0A5, ON, Canada
Tel.: (905) 214-7880
Insurance Services
N.A.I.C.S.: 524113

Manitoba Motor League (1)
870 Empress Street, Winnipeg, R3C 2Z3, MB, Canada
Tel.: (204) 262-6000
Web Site: http://www.caamanitoba.com
Automobile & Travel Services Club
N.A.I.C.S.: 561599

CAB CAKARAN CORPORATION BERHAD
Plot 21 Lorong Jelawat 4 Seberang Jaya Industrial Park, Seberang Jaya Perai, 13700, Penang, Malaysia
Tel.: (60) 43982233
Web Site: https://www.cab.com.my
CAB—(KLS)
Rev.: $475,342,952
Assets: $325,452,827
Liabilities: $161,071,895
Net Worth: $164,380,931
Earnings: $29,921,386
Emp.: 3,568
Fiscal Year-end: 09/30/23
Food Processing, Poultry Farming & Marine Products Mfr
N.A.I.C.S.: 333618
Hoon Phong Chuah *(Mng Dir)*

Subsidiaries:

CAB Marine Resources Sdn. Bhd. (1)
2235 Jalan Dato Kramat, Nibong Tebal,

14300, Malaysia
Tel.: (60) 45935868
Emp.: 10
Seafood Distr
N.A.I.C.S.: 424460

EC Grocer Pte. Ltd. (1)
22 Senoko South Road, Singapore, 758086, Singapore
Tel.: (65) 67542477
Web Site: http://www.ecgrocer.net
Food Products Distr
N.A.I.C.S.: 424420

Farm's Best Food Industries Sdn. Bhd. (1)
No 28 Jalan BJ6 Taman Perindustrian Belmas Johan, 48000, Rawang, Selangor Darul Ehsan, Malaysia
Tel.: (60) 360926077
Web Site: http://www.farmsbest.com.my
Poultry Product Mfr & Distr
N.A.I.C.S.: 311615

Kyros Kebab Sdn Bhd (1)
No 12 Jalan Segambut Lentang, 51200, Kuala Lumpur, Malaysia
Tel.: (60) 362592887
Web Site: https://www.kyroskebab.com.my
Restaurant Operators
N.A.I.C.S.: 722511

Pasaraya Jaya Gading Sdn. Bhd. (1)
A-257 Tingkat Satu Jalan Air Putih, Kuantan, 25300, Malaysia
Tel.: (60) 95602711
Supermarket Product Distr
N.A.I.C.S.: 445110

CABASSE GROUP
93 Place Pierre Duhem, 34000, Montpellier, France
Tel.: (33) 467471000 FR
Web Site: https://www.cabasse.com
Year Founded: 2003
ALCAB—(EUR)
Sales Range: $25-49.9 Million
Emp.: 30
Wireless Technology Products
N.A.I.C.S.: 334220
Alain Molinie *(Co-Founder, Chm & CEO)*

Subsidiaries:

Cabasse S.A. (1)
210 rue Rene Descartes, BP 10, 29280, Plouzane, France
Tel.: (33) 2 9805 8888
Web Site: http://www.cabasse.com
Sound Systems & Loudspeakers Designer, Mfr & Whslr
N.A.I.C.S.: 334310
Guy Bourreau *(Dir Gen)*

CABBEEN FASHION LIMITED
UnitA, 26/FBillion Plaza II 10 Cheung Yue Street, Cheung Sha Wan Kowloon, Hong Kong, China (Hong Kong)
Tel.: (852) 23195624
Web Site: http://www.cabbeen.com
2030—(HKG)
Rev.: $166,380,880
Assets: $308,600,604
Liabilities: $122,372,078
Net Worth: $186,228,526
Earnings: ($10,562,994)
Emp.: 333
Fiscal Year-end: 12/31/22
Casual Menswear Mfr & Sales
N.A.I.C.S.: 315250
Ziming Yang *(Chm & Co-CEO)*

Subsidiaries:

Guangzhou Cabbeen Clothing Co., Ltd. (1)
Cabbeen Apparel Building No 379 Sh, Guangzhou, 510507, China
Tel.: (86) 18620135025
Emp.: 400
Men Wear Distr
N.A.I.C.S.: 424350

CABINDA PARTICIPACOES S.A.
R Pamplona 818, 1405001, Sao Paulo, Brazil
Tel.: (55) 1135565555
CABI3B—(BRAZ)
Sales Range: Less than $1 Million
Financial Investment Services
N.A.I.C.S.: 523999
Danilo Gamboa *(Chm, CEO & Dir-IR)*

CABIO BIOTECH WUHAN CO., LTD.
No 999 Gaoxin Avenue East Lake High-tech Development Zone, Wuhan, 430073, Hubei, China
Tel.: (86) 2767845351
Web Site: https://www.cabio.com
Year Founded: 2004
688089—(SHG)
Rev.: $60,852,800
Assets: $226,160,307
Liabilities: $26,081,771
Net Worth: $200,078,536
Earnings: $9,037,955
Emp.: 406
Fiscal Year-end: 12/31/22
Food Products Mfr
N.A.I.C.S.: 311225
Dewei Yi *(Chm & Gen Mgr)*

CABKA GROUP GMBH
Christstrasse 30, 14059, Berlin, Germany
Tel.: (49) 30 473 9038 0 De
Web Site: http://www.cabka.com
Year Founded: 1993
Sales Range: $125-149.9 Million
Emp.: 400
Holding Company; Recycled Plastic Pallet & Material Handling Product Mfr & Distr
N.A.I.C.S.: 551112
Gat Ramon *(Chm-Mgmt Bd & CEO)*

Subsidiaries:

CABKA GmbH & Co. KG (1)
Anne-Frank-Strasse 1, 07806, Weira, Germany
Tel.: (49) 364846450
Recycled Plastic Pallet & Material Handling Products Mfr & Whslr
N.A.I.C.S.: 326199

CABKA North America, Inc. (1)
123 Byassee Dr, Saint Louis, MO 63042
Tel.: (314) 731-0302
Plastic Pallet Mfr
N.A.I.C.S.: 326199
Nathan Franck *(CEO)*

CABKA Spain S.L.U. (1)
Avenida Juan de la Cierva y Codorniu 8, Paterna, 46980, Valencia, Spain
Tel.: (34) 961102431
Plastic Pallet Mfr
N.A.I.C.S.: 326199

IPS - Innova Packaging Systems NV (1)
Rozendaalstraat 101, 8900, Ypres, Belgium
Tel.: (32) 57229110
Web Site: http://www.cabka-ips.com
Recycled Plastic Product Mfr
N.A.I.C.S.: 325991

CABKA N.V.
Johan Cruijff 65-71 Boulevard, 1101 DL, Amsterdam, Netherlands
Tel.: (31) 57229110 Nl
Web Site: https://www.cabka.com
Year Founded: 1994
CABKA—(EUR)
Rev.: $217,339,662
Assets: $200,227,398
Liabilities: $122,142,621
Net Worth: $78,084,778
Earnings: ($1,701,071)
Emp.: 603
Fiscal Year-end: 12/31/23

Cabka N.V.—(Continued)

Plastics Product Mfr
N.A.I.C.S.: 326199
Frank Roerink (CFO)

Subsidiaries:

System Technik GmbH (1)
Wielandstrasse 12, 99610, Sommerda, Germany
Tel.: (49) 363437020
Web Site: https://www.systemtechnik-online.de
Fare Management & Ticketing Services
N.A.I.C.S.: 561599

CABLE & WIRELESS (SEY-CHELLES) LTD.

Francis Rachel St, PO Box 4, Victoria, Mahe, Seychelles
Tel.: (248) 284004
Web Site:
http://www.cwseychelles.com
Telecommunication Servicesb
N.A.I.C.S.: 517810
Charles Hammond (CEO)

CABLE BAHAMAS LTD.

Marathon and Robinson Roads, PO Box CB 13050, Nassau, Bahamas
Tel.: (242) 6012200   BS
Web Site:
http://www.cablebahamas.com
Year Founded: 1994
CAB—(BISX)
Rev.: $231,090,604
Assets: $494,254,407
Liabilities: $469,315,810
Net Worth: $24,938,597
Earnings: ($7,042,235)
Emp.: 700
Fiscal Year-end: 06/30/23
Cable Television, Internet & Voice
Telecommunications Services
N.A.I.C.S.: 517111
John Gomez (COO)

Subsidiaries:

Summit Broadband Inc. (1)
4558 35th St Ste 100, Orlando, FL 32811
Tel.: (407) 996-8900
Web Site: http://www.summit-broadband.com
Telecommunications Resellers
N.A.I.C.S.: 517121
Patrick Antonio (Dir-Sls)

CABLE CORPORATION OF INDIA LTD.

Laxmi Building 4th Floor 6 Shoorji Vallabhdas Marg, Ballard Estate, Mumbai, 400001, India
Tel.: (91) 22 66144000
Web Site:
http://www.cablecorporation.com
Year Founded: 1957
Sales Range: $25-49.9 Million
Electronic Cable Mfr
N.A.I.C.S.: 334417
Maadhav M. Digraskar (CEO & Mng Dir)

Subsidiaries:

Cable Corporation of India Ltd. - Malegaon Plant (1)
Plot No F-3/1 MIDC Sinnar Industrial Area, Malegaon, Nashik, 422 103, India
Tel.: (91) 255130328
Power Cable Distr
N.A.I.C.S.: 423510

Cable Corporation of India Ltd. - Nashik Plant (1)
Plot No F-3/2 MIDC Sinnar Industrial Area, Malegaon, Nashik, 422 103, India
Tel.: (91) 2551230697
Power Cable Distr
N.A.I.C.S.: 423510

CABLEVISION HOLDING S.A.

Tacuari 1842 Piso 4, Buenos Aires, Argentina
Tel.: (54) 1143093417   Ar
Web Site:
https://www.cablevisionholding.com
Year Founded: 2016
CVH—(BUE)
Rev.: $850,187,385
Assets: $2,017,540,270
Liabilities: $1,068,583,203
Net Worth: $948,957,066
Earnings: ($196,761,676)
Fiscal Year-end: 12/31/22
Telecommunications Holding Company
N.A.I.C.S.: 551112
Sebastian Bardengo (Pres)

Subsidiaries:

Telecom Argentina S.A. (1)
Ensign Hipolito Bouchard 4191, Munro, C1107AAB, Buenos Aires,
Argentina (79.52%)
Tel.: (54) 1149684000
Web Site: https://hogares.telecom.com.ar
Assets: $8,941,922,060
Liabilities: $4,318,436,110
Net Worth: $4,623,485,950
Earnings: $60,686,560)
Emp.: 23,254
Fiscal Year-end: 12/31/2020
Telecommunications
N.A.I.C.S.: 517111
Mariano Marcelo Ibanez (Vice Chm)

Subsidiary (Domestic):

Cablevision S.A. (2)
Gral Hornos 690, Buenos Aires, 1272, Argentina
Tel.: (54) 11 5530 4589
Web Site:
http://www.cablevisionfibertel.com.ar
Cable Television Transmission & Distribution Services
N.A.I.C.S.: 517111

Subsidiary (Domestic):

Nextel Communications Argentina S.R.L. (3)
Olga Cossettini 363 Dique 4, C1107CCG, Buenos Aires, Argentina
Tel.: (54) 11 5359 0000
Web Site: http://www.nextel.com.ar
Digital Wireless Communication Services
N.A.I.C.S.: 517112

CABNET HOLDING BERHAD

No 18 PLO 184 Jalan Angkasa Mas 6 Kawasan Perindustrian Tebrau II, 81100, Johor Bahru, Johor, Malaysia
Tel.: (60) 73539008   MY
Web Site: https://www.cabnet.asia
Year Founded: 1995
CABNET—(KLS)
Rev.: $20,456,028
Assets: $20,939,193
Liabilities: $11,447,611
Net Worth: $9,491,582
Earnings: $38,088
Emp.: 152
Fiscal Year-end: 02/28/23
Holding Company
N.A.I.C.S.: 551112
Tay Hong Sing (CEO)

Subsidiaries:

AmpLogix Technology Sdn. Bhd. (1)
No 18 PLO 184 Jalan Angkasa Mas 6 Kawasan Perindustrian Tebrau II, 81100, Johor Bahru, Johor, Malaysia
Tel.: (60) 73539008
Web Site: https://www.amplogix.asia
Wireless Infrastructure Solution Services
N.A.I.C.S.: 517810

Cabnet M&E Sdn. Bhd. (1)
Setia Business Park 2 No 23 Jalan Perniagaan Setia 3, Taman Perniagaan Setia, 81100, Johor Bahru, Johor, Malaysia
Tel.: (60) 75628040

Web Site: https://www.ceemne.com.my
Electrical System Installation Services
N.A.I.C.S.: 811310

ITWin Technology Sdn. Bhd. (1)
No 18 PLO 184 Jalan Angkasa Mas 6 Kawasan Perindustrian Tebrau II, 81100, Johor Bahru, Johor, Malaysia
Tel.: (60) 73562969
Web Site: https://www.itwin.asia
Information Technology Solutions Services
N.A.I.C.S.: 541519

CABO DRILLING CORP.

120 Lonsdale Ave, North Vancouver, V7M 2E8, BC, Canada
Tel.: (604) 984-8894   YT
Web Site: https://www.cabo.ca
Year Founded: 1996
CBE—(TSXV)
Sales Range: $1-9.9 Million
Oil & Gas Drilling Services
N.A.I.C.S.: 213111
John A. Versfelt (Chm, Pres & CEO)

Subsidiaries:

Cabo Drilling (Atlantic) Corp (1)
171 Little Bay Rd, PO Box 488, Springdale, A0J 1T0, NL, Canada
Tel.: (709) 673-3801
Sales Range: $50-74.9 Million
Emp.: 50
Core Drilling Services
N.A.I.C.S.: 213111
John Versfelt (Gen Mgr)

Cabo Drilling (International) Inc. (1)
21 Goodfish Rd, Kirkland Lake, P2N 1H7, ON, Canada
Tel.: (705) 567-9311
Web Site: http://www.cabo.ca
Drilling Services
N.A.I.C.S.: 213114
Pierre Germain (Gen Mgr)

Cabo Drilling (Ontario) Corp. (1)
34 Duncan Avenue, PO Box 998, Kirkland Lake, P2N 3L3, ON, Canada
Tel.: (705) 567-9311
Sales Range: $100-124.9 Million
Emp.: 130
Oil Drilling Services
N.A.I.C.S.: 213111
Pierre Germain (Gen Mgr)

Cabo Drilling (Pacific) Corp. (1)
20 6th Street New West Minster, Surrey, V3L 2Y8, BC, Canada
Tel.: (604) 527-4201
Web Site: http://www.cabo.ca
Sales Range: $50-74.9 Million
Emp.: 7
Drilling Services
N.A.I.C.S.: 213111
John Versfelt (Chm, Pres & CEO)

Cabo Drilling (Panama) Corp., (1)
Aerea Especial Economica Panama Pacifico Andrews Boulevard, Edificio 466, Panama, Panama
Tel.: (507) 3162226
Web Site: http://www.cabo.ca
Sales Range: $50-74.9 Million
Emp.: 100
Drilling Services
N.A.I.C.S.: 213111
Herb Butler (Gen Mgr)

Forages Cabo Inc. (1)
3000 Boulevard Industriel, Chambly, J3L 4X3, QC, Canada
Tel.: (450) 572-1400
Sales Range: $25-49.9 Million
Emp.: 20
Geothermal Drilling Services
N.A.I.C.S.: 237110
Pierre Germain (Gen Mgr)

CABOT ENERGY PLC

93-95 Gloucester Place, London, W1U 6JQ, United Kingdom
Tel.: (44) 2074692900
Web Site: http://www.cabot-energy.com
Rev.: $12,204,000
Assets: $70,860,000

Liabilities: $18,921,000
Net Worth: $51,939,000
Earnings: ($6,106,000)
Emp.: 15
Fiscal Year-end: 12/31/18
Oil & Gas Exploration
N.A.I.C.S.: 211120
Scott Aitken (CEO)

Subsidiaries:

Northern Petroleum (GB) Limited (1)
Martin House 5 Martin Ln, London, EC4R 0DP, United Kingdom
Tel.: (44) 2074692900
Sales Range: $50-74.9 Million
Oil & Gas Exploration Services
N.A.I.C.S.: 213112

CABOT SQUARE CAPITAL LLP

One Connaught Place, London, W2 2ET, United Kingdom
Tel.: (44) 20 7579 9320   UK
Web Site:
http://www.cabotsquare.com
Year Founded: 1996
Privater Equity Firm
N.A.I.C.S.: 523999
James Clark (Founder & Partner)

Subsidiaries:

Premier Modular Limited (1)
Catfoss Lane, Brandesburton, YO25 8EJ, E Yorks, United Kingdom
Tel.: (44) 1964 545 000
Web Site: http://www.premiermodular.co.uk
Commercial & Institutional Modular Building Leasing Services
N.A.I.C.S.: 236220
Eugenio de Sa (Mng Dir)

CABRAL GOLD INC.

Suite 1500 - 409 Granville Street, Vancouver, V6C 1T2, BC, Canada
Tel.: (604) 676-5663
Web Site: https://cabralgold.com
CBR—(TSXV)
Rev.: $26,229
Assets: $6,535,550
Liabilities: $325,489
Net Worth: $6,210,062
Earnings: ($3,620,340)
Fiscal Year-end: 12/31/20
Oil & Gas Producing Services
N.A.I.C.S.: 211120
P. Mark Smith (Chm)

CABRINI HEALTH LIMITED

183 Wattletree Road, Malvern, 3144, VIC, Australia
Tel.: (61) 395081222   AU
Web Site: http://www.cabrini.com.au
Year Founded: 1948
Emp.: 4,170
Non-Profit Health Services Organization
N.A.I.C.S.: 813920
Michael Walsh (CEO)

Subsidiaries:

Cabrini Technology Services (1)
Unit 1 9-11 S Str, Rydalmere, 2140, NSW, Australia
Tel.: (61) 2 9764 7777
Web Site: http://www.awa.com.au
Sales Range: $25-49.9 Million
Emp.: 450
Information & Communications Technology Support Services
N.A.I.C.S.: 541990
Michael Schroeder (COO)

CAC CORPORATION

24-1 Hakozaki-cho Nihonbashi, Chuo-ku, Tokyo, 103-0015, Japan
Tel.: (81) 366678000
Web Site: http://www.cac.co.jp
Year Founded: 1966
Sales Range: $500-549.9 Million

Emp.: 1,305
Business Information & Computer Services
N.A.I.C.S.: 541519
Toshihiro Adachi *(Exec Officer)*

Subsidiaries:

CAC America Corporation **(1)**
457th Ave Ste 808, New York, NY 10123 **(100%)**
Tel.: (212) 482-8340
Web Site: http://www.cacamerica.com
Sales Range: $25-49.9 Million
Emp.: 50
Business Information & Computer Services
N.A.I.C.S.: 541519
Takayuki Havihara *(Pres)*

CAC EUROPE LIMITED **(1)**
60 Lombard Street, London, EC3V 9EA, United Kingdom
Tel.: (44) 2074648435
Web Site: http://www.caceurope.com
Computer Software Consulting Services
N.A.I.C.S.: 541512

CAC MARUHA NICHIRO SYSTEMS CORPORATION **(1)**
1-28-25 Shinkawa Tokyo Daiya Building 3gokan 6f, Chuo-ku, Tokyo, 104-0033, Japan
Tel.: (81) 335527432
Information Technology Consulting Services
N.A.I.C.S.: 541512

CAC Maruha Nichiro Systems Ltd. **(1)**
No 25-28 Tokyo Diamond Building 3 6 Fl Chuo-ku Shinkawa chome, Tokyo, 104-0033, Japan
Tel.: (81) 3 3552 7432
Web Site: http://www.cacmns.co.jp
Sales Range: $10-24.9 Million
Data Processing Hosting & Related Services
N.A.I.C.S.: 518210
Takashi Kano *(Pres & CEO)*

CAC Orbis Corporation **(1)**
Edobori Yatani Building 1-25-7 Edobori, Nishi-ku, Osaka, 550-0002, Japan
Tel.: (81) 664458888
Web Site: https://www.orbis-corp.jp
Sales Range: $25-49.9 Million
Emp.: 102
Custom Computer Programming Services
N.A.I.C.S.: 541511
Makoto Yamashita *(Pres)*

CAC Shanghai Corporation **(1)**
Unit 108 Area D2 Internet Treasure Land No 221 Huangxing Road, Yangpu District, Shanghai, 200090, Pudong, China
Tel.: (86) 2161940080
Web Site: https://www.cacshanghai.com
Emp.: 118
Business Information & Computer Services
N.A.I.C.S.: 541519

GoldenTech Computer Technology (Suzhou) Co.,Ltd. **(1)**
103 Sutong Rd Suzhou Industrial Park, 215021, Suzhou, China
Tel.: (86) 51267630301
Web Site: http://www.goldentech.com
Sales Range: $25-49.9 Million
Emp.: 100
Software & Systems Development
N.A.I.C.S.: 334610
Zhu Jian Ting *(Mgr)*

Inspirisys Solutions Limited **(1)**
First Floor, Dowlath Towers New Door Nos 57 59 61 & 63, Taylors Road Kilpauk, Chennai, 600010, Tamil Nadu, India
Tel.: (91) 4442252000
Web Site: www.inspirisys.com
Rev.: $47,362,770
Assets: $27,248,130
Liabilities: $27,140,295
Net Worth: $107,835
Earnings: ($1,820,910)
Emp.: 1,561
Fiscal Year-end: 03/31/2022
Integrated Information Technology Services
N.A.I.C.S.: 541513
Maqbool Hassan *(Pres-Enterprise Solutions & Svcs)*

CAC HOLDINGS CORPORATION
24-1 Nihonbashi-Hakozaki-cho, Chuo-Ku, Tokyo, 103-0015, Japan
Tel.: (81) 366678001
Web Site: https://www.cac-holdings.com
Year Founded: 1996
4725—(TKS)
Rev.: $358,321,510
Assets: $344,091,880
Liabilities: $114,758,740
Net Worth: $229,333,140
Earnings: $17,533,570
Emp.: 4,447
Fiscal Year-end: 12/31/23
Holding Company
N.A.I.C.S.: 551112
Akihiko Sako *(Chm)*

Subsidiaries:

ARK Systems Co., Ltd. **(1)**
11F Nihonbashi Hakozaki Building 24-1 Nihonbashi Hakozaki-cho, Chuo-ku, Tokyo, 103-0014, Japan
Tel.: (81) 336668140
Web Site: https://www.arksystems.co.jp
Emp.: 193
System Development & Integration Services
N.A.I.C.S.: 541512

CAC Croit Corporation **(1)**
Acropolis Tokyo 6-29 Shinogawamachi, Shinjuku-ku, Tokyo, 162-0814, Japan
Tel.: (81) 36 731 9550
Web Site: https://www.croit.com
Emp.: 581
Drug Development Support Services
N.A.I.C.S.: 541714
Akira Sasa *(Pres)*

CAC India Private Limited **(1)**
Indiana House A wing 6th Floor Makwana Road, Marol Naka Off Andheri Kurla Road Andheri - East, Mumbai, 400059, India
Tel.: (91) 222 920 5303
Web Site: https://cac-india.com
Healtcare Services
N.A.I.C.S.: 622110
Malcolm Mehta *(Pres)*

CEN Solutions Corp. **(1)**
NEC Annex 2F 2-31-25 Shiba, Minato-ku, Tokyo, 105-0014, Japan
Tel.: (81) 354399285
Web Site: https://www.censol.jp
Emp.: 35
System Development & Integration Services
N.A.I.C.S.: 541512

Hitec Systems Corporation **(1)**
1-17-21 Mukai-cho Hikojima, Shimonoseki, 750-0084, Yamaguchi, Japan
Tel.: (81) 832673128
Web Site: https://www.hitecsys.co.jp
Software Development Services
N.A.I.C.S.: 513210

Mitrais Pte. Ltd. **(1)**
10 Anson Road 03-05 International Plaza, Singapore, 079903, Singapore
Tel.: (65) 31581185
Software Services
N.A.I.C.S.: 541511
Wiwie Harris *(Pres)*

CACCO, INC.
1-5-31 Motoakasaka, Minato-Ku, Tokyo, 107-0051, Japan
Tel.: (81) 364474534
Web Site: https://www.cacco.co.jp
Year Founded: 2011
4166—(TKS)
Software Development Services
N.A.I.C.S.: 541511
Hiroyuki Iwai *(Founder, Chm, Pres & CEO)*

CACHET PHARMACEUTICAL CO., LTD.
Building 1 No 11 Kun Ming Hu South Road, Handian District, Beijing, 100195, China

Tel.: (86) 1088433464
Web Site: http://www.cachet.com.cn
Year Founded: 2003
002462—(SSE)
Rev.: $3,681,258,516
Assets: $2,324,548,044
Liabilities: $1,493,155,404
Net Worth: $831,392,640
Earnings: $41,690,376
Emp.: 1,200
Fiscal Year-end: 12/31/22
Pharmacy Owner & Operator
N.A.I.C.S.: 456110

CACONDE PARTICIPACOES S.A.
Rua Pamplona 818-Conjunto 92, 01405-001, Sao Paulo, Brazil
Tel.: (55) 1131315555
CACO3B—(BRAZ)
Sales Range: Less than $1 Million
Investment Management Service
N.A.I.C.S.: 523940
Danilo Gamboa *(Chm, CEO & Dir-IR)*

CAD IT S.P.A.
via Torricelli 44/a, 37136, Verona, Italy
Tel.: (39) 0458211111 IT
Web Site: http://www.caditgroup.com
Year Founded: 1977
Sales Range: $50-74.9 Million
Emp.: 624
Information Technology Services
N.A.I.C.S.: 541512
Paolo Dal Cortivo *(Mng Dir)*

Subsidiaries:

CAD S.r.l. **(1)**
Via Torricelli 44A, Verona, 37136, Italy
Tel.: (39) 0458211111
Sales Range: $200-249.9 Million
Emp.: 600
Information Technology Services
N.A.I.C.S.: 519290
Giuseppe Dal Cortivo *(Mng Dir)*

Cesbe S.r.l. **(1)**
Centro Studi Bancari Europei, Via Torricelli 44-A, Verona, 37126, Italy **(52%)**
Tel.: (39) 0458211111
Web Site: http://www.cesbe.it
Sales Range: $50-74.9 Million
Emp.: 600
Educational Support Services
N.A.I.C.S.: 611710

ELIData S.r.l. **(1)**
Via Sanadolo 19, Castiglione d Adda, Lodi, 26823, Italy **(51%)**
Tel.: (39) 0377901448
Web Site: http://www.elidata.it
Emp.: 18
Computer & Computer Peripheral Equipment & Software Merchant Whslr
N.A.I.C.S.: 423430
Marco Connizzoli *(Office Mgr)*

S.G.M. S.r.l. **(1)**
Via Torricelli 44/A, Verona, 37136, VR, Italy **(100%)**
Tel.: (39) 0458211111
Web Site: http://www.caditgroup.com
Testing Laboratories
N.A.I.C.S.: 541380

Smart Line S.r.l. **(1)**
Viale Montegrappa 306, Prato, 59100, Italy
Tel.: (39) 057 452011
Web Site: http://www.smart-line.it
Tax Collection Software Development Services
N.A.I.C.S.: 541511

Tecsit S.r.l. **(1)**
Via Silvio D amico 40, 00145, Rome, Italy **(70%)**
Tel.: (39) 0654225625
Web Site: http://www.tecsit.it
Switchgear & Switchboard Apparatus Mfr
N.A.I.C.S.: 335313

CADAC GROUP HOLDING B.V.

Nieuw Eyckholt 282, 6419 DJ, Heerlen, Netherlands
Tel.: (31) 889322322 Nl
Web Site: http://www.cadac.com
Sales Range: $150-199.9 Million
Emp.: 250
Holding Company; Digital Design Information Software Publisher, Whslr & Support Services
N.A.I.C.S.: 551112
Jan Baggen *(CEO)*

Subsidiaries:

Cadac Group B.V. **(1)**
Nieuw Eyckholt 282, 6419 DJ, Heerlen, Netherlands **(100%)**
Tel.: (31) 889322322
Web Site: http://www.cadac.com
Sales Range: $50-74.9 Million
Emp.: 175
Digital Design Information Software Publisher Services
N.A.I.C.S.: 513210
Jan Baggen *(CEO)*

NedGraphics B.V. **(1)**
Laanakkerweg 6, NL-4131 PN, Vianen, Netherlands **(60%)**
Tel.: (31) 347329600
Web Site: http://www.nedgraphics.nl
Sales Range: $25-49.9 Million
Emp.: 80
Design & Geographic Information Software Developer, Publisher & Distr
N.A.I.C.S.: 513210

CADELER A/S
Fairway House Arne Jacobsens Alle 7, DK-2300, Copenhagen, S, Denmark
Tel.: (45) 32463100
Web Site: https://www.cadeler.com
CADLR—(OSL)
Rev.: $117,226,419
Assets: $1,351,780,704
Liabilities: $316,769,912
Net Worth: $1,035,010,792
Earnings: $12,408,806
Emp.: 113
Fiscal Year-end: 12/31/23
Offshore Wind Farm Transportation & Installation Services
N.A.I.C.S.: 488390

Subsidiaries:

Eneti Inc. **(1)**
9 Boulevard Charles III, 98000, Monaco, Monaco
Tel.: (377) 97985715
Web Site: http://www.eneti-inc.com
Rev.: $199,326,000
Assets: $814,504,000
Liabilities: $99,190,000
Net Worth: $715,314,000
Earnings: $105,702,000
Emp.: 286
Fiscal Year-end: 12/31/2022
Deep Sea Transportation Services
N.A.I.C.S.: 483111
Cameron MacKey *(COO)*

CADENCE CAPITAL LIMITED
Level 6 131 Macquarie Street, Sydney, 2000, NSW, Australia
Tel.: (61) 282982450
Web Site: https://www.cadencecapital.com.au
CDM—(ASX)
Rev.: $24,469,151
Assets: $246,889,266
Liabilities: $43,807,847
Net Worth: $203,081,419
Earnings: $14,400,789
Fiscal Year-end: 06/30/24
Security Consulting Services
N.A.I.C.S.: 541690
Wayne Davies *(COO & Sec)*

CADENCE MINERALS PLC
c/o The Broadgate Tower 20 Prim-

Cadence Minerals plc—(Continued)
rose Street, London, EC2A 2EW,
United Kingdom
Tel.: (44) 2035826636　　　　**UK**
Web Site:
https://www.cadenceminerals.com
Year Founded: 2010
KDNC—(AIM)
Assets. $26,870,068
Liabilities: $393,651
Net Worth: $26,476,418
Earnings: ($6,826,175)
Emp.: 6
Fiscal Year-end: 12/31/22
Mineral Investment Services
N.A.I.C.S.: 523999
Donald Strang (Sec & Dir-Fin)

CADEX ELECTRONICS INC.
22000 Fraserwood Way, Richmond,
V6W 1J6, BC, Canada
Tel.: (604) 231-7777
Web Site: https://www.cadex.com
Year Founded: 1980
Rev.: $13,305,662
Emp.: 55
Battery Charging & Analyzing Equipment Mfr
N.A.I.C.S.: 334515
Isidor Buchmann (Founder & CEO)

Subsidiaries:

Cadex Electronics GmbH　　(1)
Farmstrasse 91-97, 64546, Moerfelden-
Walldorf, Germany
Tel.: (49) 6105975110
Electronic Components Distr
N.A.I.C.S.: 423690
Mario Ricker (Territory Mgr-Sls)

CADILLAC VENTURES INC.
269-1099 Kingston Road, Pickering,
L1V 1B5, ON, Canada
Tel.: (416) 970-3223　　　　**ON**
Web Site:
http://www.cadillacventures.com
Year Founded: 1995
CDC—(TSXV)
Assets: $3,558,503
Liabilities: $2,112,337
Net Worth: $1,446,166
Earnings: ($12,247,666)
Emp.: 2
Fiscal Year-end: 05/31/21
Gold Mining Services
N.A.I.C.S.: 212220
Norman E. Brewster (Pres & CEO)

Subsidiaries:

Cadillac Ventures Holdings Inc.　(1)
181 Bay St Ste 2840, Toronto, M5J 2T3,
ON, Canada
Tel.: (416) 203-7722
Investment Management Service
N.A.I.C.S.: 523999

CADOGAN ENERGY SOLUTIONS PLC
6th Floor 60 Gracechurch Street,
London, EC3V 0HR, United Kingdom
Tel.: (44) 2074878301
Web Site:
https://www.cadoganenergy.com
Year Founded: 2004
CAD—(LSE)
Rev.: $8,472,000
Assets: $37,432,000
Liabilities: $1,905,000
Net Worth: $35,527,000
Earnings: ($1,560,000)
Emp.: 75
Fiscal Year-end: 12/31/22
Oil & Gas Exploration Services
N.A.I.C.S.: 211120
Fady Khallouf (CEO)

Subsidiaries:

Cadogan Bitlyanske BV　　(1)
Tel.: (31) 205222555
Oil & Gas Exploration Services
N.A.I.C.S.: 213112

Cadogan Petroleum Holdings BV　(1)
Tel.: (31) 205222555
Oil & Gas Exploration Services
N.A.I.C.S.: 213112

Cadogan Petroleum Holdings Ltd　(1)
Tel.: (44) 2072450801
Oil & Gas Drilling Services
N.A.I.C.S.: 213111

LLC Astroinvest-Energy　　(1)
Tel.: (380) 532641880
Oil & Gas Exploration Services
N.A.I.C.S.: 213112

LLC Industrial Company
Gazvydobuvannya　　(1)
3 Myru Street, Poltava, 36022, Ukraine
Tel.: (380) 532503060
Oil & Gas Exploration Services
N.A.I.C.S.: 213112

CADRE AS
Rigetjonnveien 14, 4626, Kristiansand, Aust-Agder, Norway
Tel.: (47) 90048888　　　　**NO**
Web Site: https://www.cadre.no
Year Founded: 2023
Hydroelectric Power Generation Services
N.A.I.C.S.: 221111

CADSYS (INDIA) LTD.
803 8th Floor DSL ABACUS IT Park,
IDA Uppal, Himayat Nagar, Hyderabad, 500039, Telangana, India
Tel.: (91) 4045474843
Web Site:
https://www.cadsystech.com
Year Founded: 1989
CADSYS—(NSE)
Rev.: $4,343,933
Assets: $9,908,297
Liabilities: $2,948,706
Net Worth: $6,959,591
Earnings: ($732,583)
Emp.: 172
Fiscal Year-end: 03/31/21
Information Technology Services
N.A.I.C.S.: 541512
Ncv Harish Rangacharya (Mng Dir)

Subsidiaries:

Apex Advanced Technology LLC　(1)
205 Van Buren St Ste 120, Herndon, VA
20170
Tel.: (703) 709-3456
Engineeering Services
N.A.I.C.S.: 541330
Harish Rangacharya (CEO & Mng Dir)

Apex Engineers (India) Private
Limited　　(1)
Plot No 1716 G I D C Phase III, Vatva,
Ahmedabad, 382 445, Gujarat, India
Tel.: (91) 9601295126
Web Site: http://www.apexengineers.com
Wire Cable Coating Mfr
N.A.I.C.S.: 335929

Cadsys Technologies LLC　　(1)
8808 Colesville Rd, Silver Spring, MD
20910
Tel.: (703) 709-3480
Telecommunication Servicesb
N.A.I.C.S.: 517810

CADU INMOBILIARIA S.A DE C.V.
Av. Bonampak Smz 6, Mz 1 Lt 1 First
Floor, 77500, Cancun, Mexico
Tel.: (52) 9981931100
Web Site:
http://www.caduinmobiliaria.com
Year Founded: 2001

CADU—(MEX)
Rev.: $265,498,019
Assets: $665,512,606
Liabilities: $354,616,044
Net Worth: $310,896,562
Earnings: $17,766,853
Emp.: 2,592
Fiscal Year-end: 12/31/23
Real Estate Services
N.A.I.C.S.: 531210
Pedro Vaca Elguero (Chm)

CADUCEUS SOFTWARE SYSTEMS CORP.
42A High Street, Sutton Coldfield, W
Midlands, United Kingdom
Tel.: (44) 1216959585　　　　**NV**
Year Founded: 2006
CSOC—(OTCIQ)
Sales Range: Less than $1 Million
Emp.: 8
Software Services
N.A.I.C.S.: 513210
Derrick Gidden (Pres, CEO, CFO,
Treas & Sec)

CAE AUTOMOTIVE GMBH
Mercatorstr 15, 49080, Osnabruck,
Germany
Tel.: (49) 541 20071 0　　　　**De**
Web Site: http://www.cae-
automotive.de
Sales Range: $1-9.9 Million
Automotive Engineering Services
N.A.I.C.S.: 541330

CAE INC.
8585 Cote-de-Liesse, Saint Laurent,
H4T 1G6, QC, Canada
Tel.: (514) 341-6780　　　　**Ca**
Web Site: https://www.cae.com
Year Founded: 1947
CAE—(NYSE)
Rev.: $3,288,157,524
Assets: $8,164,265,220
Liabilities: $4,574,460,528
Net Worth: $3,589,804,692
Earnings: $181,410,732
Emp.: 13,000
Fiscal Year-end: 03/31/23
Simulation, Modelling & Training Solutions for Civil Aviation & Military
N.A.I.C.S.: 423610
Andrew Arnovitz (Sr VP-IR & Strategy)

Subsidiaries:

CAE Australia Pty Ltd.　　(1)
Building A 350 Parramatta Road, PO Box
6650, Campus Business Park, Homebush,
2140, NSW, Australia　　　(100%)
Tel.: (61) 297484844
Web Site: http://www.cae.com.au
Sales Range: $25-49.9 Million
Emp.: 100
Supplier of Integrated Sensor Stimulation
Products & Systems for Military Radar Testing; Commercial & Military Flight Simulators
& Control Systems
N.A.I.C.S.: 336419

CAE Aviation Training Peru S.A.　(1)
Av Elmer Faucett S/n Cdra 34 Urb Ind Bocanegra Callao, Lima, Peru
Tel.: (51) 13116060
Airline Pilot Training Services
N.A.I.C.S.: 611512

CAE Brunei Multi Purpose Training
Centre Sdn Bhd　　(1)
1 Digital Junction Jalan Paya Sailaila, Kg
Tungku Lebuh Raya Tungku Gadong A,
BE2119, Negara, Brunei Darussalam
Tel.: (673) 2459800
Airline Pilot Training Services
N.A.I.C.S.: 611512

CAE Center Brussels N.V.　　(1)
Airport Building 201, 1820, Steenokkerzeel,
Belgium
Tel.: (32) 27525711

Airline Pilot Training Services
N.A.I.C.S.: 611512

CAE Centre Copenhagen A/S　(1)
Kystvejen 40, 2770, Kastrup, Denmark
Tel.: (45) 72300700
Airline Pilot Training Services
N.A.I.C.S.: 611512

CAE Centre Hong Kong Limited　(1)
5/F South Wing HKA Training Academy
Tower, 28 Kwo Lo Wan Road Hong Kong
International Airport Lantau, Hong Kong,
China (Hong Kong)
Tel.: (852) 38917723
Airline Pilot Training Services
N.A.I.C.S.: 611512

CAE Centre Oslo AS　　(1)
Henrik Ibsens veg 12, 2060, Gardermoen,
Norway
Tel.: (47) 63946300
Airline Pilot Training Services
N.A.I.C.S.: 611512

CAE Centre Stockholm AB　　(1)
Kabinvagen 5, 19060, Stockholm, Sweden
Tel.: (46) 851839100
Web Site: https://www.cae.com
Airline Pilot Training Services
N.A.I.C.S.: 611512

CAE Colombia Flight Training
S.A.S.　　(1)
Diagonal 25G 95A - 85 3rd Floor, Avianca,
Bogota, Colombia
Tel.: (57) 16530010
Web Site: https://www.cae.com
Airline Pilot Training Services
N.A.I.C.S.: 611512

CAE Doss Aviation, Inc.　　(1)
2405 North Support Rd Bldg B DFW Airport, Dallas, TX 75261
Tel.: (972) 456-8080
Web Site: https://www.cae.com
Airline Training Services
N.A.I.C.S.: 611512

CAE Elektronik GmbH　　(1)
Steinfurt 11, 52222, Stolberg,
Germany　　　　　　　　(100%)
Tel.: (49) 24021060
Web Site: https://de.cae.com
Sales Range: $75-99.9 Million
Emp.: 500
Flight Simulation & Training Systems
N.A.I.C.S.: 611512

CAE Flight Training (India) Private
Limited　　(1)
Survey No 26 27 Anneshwara Panchayat,
Badaramanahalli Village Kasaba Hobli Devanahalli Taluk, Bengaluru, 562110, India
Tel.: (91) 8042854005
Airline Pilot Training Services
N.A.I.C.S.: 611512

CAE Flight Training Center Mexico,
S.A. de C.V.　　(1)
Ernesto Monroy Street 110, Parque Industrial Exportec II, 50200, Toluca, Mexico
Tel.: (52) 7222763400
Airline Pilot Training Services
N.A.I.C.S.: 611512

CAE Healthcare Inc.　　(1)
8585 Cote de Liesse, Saint Laurent, H4T
1G6, QC, Canada
Tel.: (514) 341-6780
Web Site: http://www.cae.com
Medical Training & Simulation Systems Developer
N.A.I.C.S.: 611699

Subsidiary (US):

Medical Education Technologies,
Inc.　　(2)
6300 Edgelake Dr, Sarasota, FL 34240
Tel.: (941) 377-5562
Web Site: http://www.meti.com
Sales Range: $50-74.9 Million
Emp.: 200
Medical Education & Simulation Technology
Solutions
N.A.I.C.S.: 611699

CAE India Private Limited　　(1)
Survey No 26 and 27 IVC Road Uganvadi
Post, Bandaramanahalli Village Devanahalli

Taluk, Bengaluru, 562110, India
Tel.: (91) 8026256000
Defense & Security Services
N.A.I.C.S.: 928110

CAE Kuala Lumpur Sdn Bhd (1)
Lot PT25B Jalan Klia S5 Klia, Southern
Support Zone, 64000, Sepang, Selangor
Darul Ehsan, Malaysia
Tel.: (60) 387778060
Web Site: https://www.cae.com
Airline Pilot Training Services
N.A.I.C.S.: 611512

CAE North East Training Inc. (1)
4 Apollo Dr, Whippany, NJ 07981
Tel.: (973) 581-7400
Airline Pilot Training Services
N.A.I.C.S.: 611512

**CAE Oxford Aviation Academy Phoe-
nix Inc.** (1)
5010 E Falcon Dr Ste 201, Mesa, AZ 85215
Tel.: (480) 948-4515
Airline Pilot Training Services
N.A.I.C.S.: 611512

CAE Singapore (S.E.A.) Pte Ltd. (1)
380 Jalan Besar 14-11/12 ARC 380, Singa-
pore, 209000, Singapore
Tel.: (65) 69046068
Airline Pilot Training Services
N.A.I.C.S.: 611512

**CAE Technology India Private
Limited** (1)
1st Floor Pine Valley Off Intermediate Ring
Road, Embassy Golf Links Business Park,
Bengaluru, 560071, India
Tel.: (91) 8041764639
Web Site: https://www.caetechnology.net
Engineering & IT Services
N.A.I.C.S.: 541519
Radhakrishnan Bageballi *(CTO)*

CAE UK plc (1)
Burgess Hill Innovation Drive York Road,
Burgess Hill, RH15 9TW, W Sussex, United
Kingdom (100%)
Tel.: (44) 1444247535
Web Site: https://www.cae.com
Sales Range: $75-99.9 Million
Emp.: 150
Military Simulation & Training
N.A.I.C.S.: 928110
Andrew Naismith *(Mng Dir)*

CAE USA, Inc. (1)
4908 Tampa W Blvd, Tampa, FL 33634
Tel.: (813) 885-7481
Web Site: https://www.cae.com
Simulated Flight Training & Services
N.A.I.C.S.: 611512

Flight Simulation Company B.V. (1)
Fokkerweg 300 1D, Oude Meer, 1438 AN,
Schiphol, Netherlands
Tel.: (31) 203043200
Web Site: http://www.fsctraining.com
Sales Range: $10-24.9 Million
Emp.: 40
Flight Training Services
N.A.I.C.S.: 611512

Oxford Aviation Academy Limited (1)
London Oxford Airport, Kidlington, Oxford,
OX5 1QX, United Kingdom
Tel.: (44) 1865841234
Sales Range: $50-74.9 Million
Emp.: 500
Flight Training
N.A.I.C.S.: 611512

Subsidiary (Domestic):

CAE Training & Services UK Ltd. (2)
Diamond Point Fleming Way, Crawley,
RH10 9DP, West Sussex, United Kingdom
Tel.: (44) 1293305901
Sales Range: $75-99.9 Million
Flight Training Systems
N.A.I.C.S.: 611512

Subsidiary (Non-US):

PARC Aviation, Ltd. (2)
Unit 21 Block 2 Woodford Business Park,
Santry, D17 E925, Dublin, 9, Ireland
Tel.: (353) 18161747
Sales Range: $10-24.9 Million
Emp.: 40

Aviation Specialist Personnel & Support
Solutions
N.A.I.C.S.: 561311
Sean Butler *(CEO)*

Pelesys Learning Systems Inc. (1)
125-13500 Maycrest Way, Richmond, V6V
2N8, BC, Canada
Tel.: (604) 233-6268
Web Site: http://pelesys.com
Training & Learning Management Services
N.A.I.C.S.: 513210

Presagis (1)
4700 de la Savane Suite 300, Montreal,
H4P 1T7, QC, Canada
Tel.: (514) 341-3874
Web Site: http://www.presagis.com
Sales Range: $10-24.9 Million
Emp.: 120
Simulation Software Development
N.A.I.C.S.: 513210
Jean-Michel Briere *(Pres)*

Presagis Europe (S.A.) (1)
2 Rue Jean Lantier, 75001, Paris, France
Tel.: (33) 130705000
Computer Software Development Services
N.A.I.C.S.: 541511

Presagis USA Inc. (1)
12424 Research Pkwy Ste 390, Orlando,
FL 32826
Tel.: (407) 380-7229
Computer Software Development Services
N.A.I.C.S.: 541511

Rotorsim S.r.l. (1)
2 Via Indipendenza, 21100, Sesto Calende,
Italy (50%)
Tel.: (39) 0331915573
Web Site: https://www.cae.com
Helicopter Flight Training Services
N.A.I.C.S.: 611512

Simcom, Inc. (1)
6989 Lee Vista Blvd, Orlando, FL
32822 (50%)
Tel.: (407) 275-1050
Web Site: https://www.simulator.com
Sales Range: $25-49.9 Million
Flight Training Services
N.A.I.C.S.: 611512
Eric Hinson *(CEO)*

Subsidiary (Domestic):

PrestoSIM, Inc. (2)
1000 Nolen Dr Ste 400, Grapevine, TX
76051-8622
Tel.: (817) 488-4870
Flight Training Services
N.A.I.C.S.: 611512

CAELUM CO., LTD.
6 Beombang 2-Ro, Gangseo-Gu, Bu-
san, 46727, Korea (South)
Tel.: (82) 519413511
Web Site: https://www.ewkinc.co.kr
Year Founded: 2009
258610—(KRS)
Rev.: $48,689,437
Assets: $86,832,315
Liabilities: $28,724,920
Net Worth: $58,107,395
Earnings: ($20,624,815)
Emp.: 47
Fiscal Year-end: 12/31/21
Geothermal Mfr
N.A.I.C.S.: 221116
Michael Yoonjune Kwon *(CEO)*

CAESARS GROUP
Mabanee 1 II Floor Block 1 Salhiya
Street, PO Box 5592, Kuwait, 13056,
Kuwait
Tel.: (965) 22450504
Web Site:
   http://www.caesarsgroup.net
Year Founded: 1973
Rev.: $15,000,000
Emp.: 2,500
N.A.I.C.S.: 551112
Ghazi Al Abdul Razzak *(Co-Owner)*

Subsidiaries:

Ajwan International Co. WLL (1)
Mabane Building No-1 2nd Floor Salhiya
Street, Kuwait, Kuwait
Tel.: (965) 22450504
Web Site: https://www.ajwancaesars.com
Information Technology Services
N.A.I.C.S.: 541511
S. K. Mishra *(CEO)*

**Al Afrah Al Sharqiya General Trading
and Contracting Company W.L.L.** (1)
PO Box 5592, Safat, Kuwait, Kuwait
Tel.: (965) 22450504
Web Site: http://www.caesarsgroup.net
Polyester Resins & Fiberglass Distr
N.A.I.C.S.: 423840

**Caesar Pac Carton & Paper Products
Co.** (1)
Free Trade Zone Phase1, PO Box 5592,
Safat, Kuwait, 13056, Kuwait
Tel.: (965) 4610077
Web Site: http://www.caesarpac.com
Emp.: 168
Folding Paperboard Box Mfr
N.A.I.C.S.: 322299

**Caesars General Trading and Con-
tracting Company W.L.L.** (1)
PO Box 5592, Safat, Kuwait, Kuwait
Tel.: (965) 2450504
Sales Range: $250-299.9 Million
Emp.: 550
Trading & Contracting Services
N.A.I.C.S.: 236220

Caesars Holidays (1)
PO Box 5592, Safat, 13056, Kuwait, Kuwait
Tel.: (965) 22450504
Web Site: http://www.caesarsgroup.net
Travel Services, Tour Packages & Hotel
Reservations
N.A.I.C.S.: 561599

**Caesars Int'l Shipping & Logistics Co.
W.L.L.** (1)
Al-Nafisi Tower M3 Abdullah Al- Mubarak
Street, Opposite Science Museum Mirqab,
Kuwait, Kuwait
Tel.: (965) 22467718
Web Site: https://caesarsshippingintl.com
Air Freight Services
N.A.I.C.S.: 481112

Caesars Travel Company (1)
PO Box 5592, Safat, Kuwait, Kuwait
Tel.: (965) 2450504
Travel Services
N.A.I.C.S.: 561599
P. N. J. Kumar *(Gen Mgr)*

Subsidiary (Domestic):

CAESARS CARGO CO. W.L.L. (2)
Dajeej Farwaniya Waha Mall Behind City
Center, Kuwait, Kuwait
Tel.: (965) 24344561
Web Site: http://www.caesarscargo.com
Emp.: 1,100
Warehousing & Storage Services
N.A.I.C.S.: 493190
P. N. J. Kumar *(CEO)*

Caesars Travel Group (1)
Al-Nafisi Tower Ground Floor Abdullah Al-
Mubarak Street, Opp Science Museum
Mirqab, Kuwait, Kuwait
Tel.: (965) 22423185
Web Site: https://www.caesarstravel.com
Corrugated Carton Mfr
N.A.I.C.S.: 322211
Ghazi Yousef Al Abdul Razzak *(Chm)*

Chattaya Ajwan Infotech Pvt. Ltd. (1)
A-601- 604 Behind Navrangpura Bus Stand
Opp Havmor Restaurant, Nirman Complex
Navrangpura, Ahmedabad, 380 009, Guja-
rat, India
Tel.: (91) 7926423468
Web Site: https://www.chattary.com
Web Based Software Services
N.A.I.C.S.: 541511
Manoj Jain *(CEO)*

CAESARSTONE LTD.
Kibbutz Sdot-Yam, MP Menashe,
Caesarea, 3780400, Israel

Tel.: (972) 46109368   II
Web Site:
   http://www.caesarstoneus.com
Year Founded: 1987
CSTE—(NASDAQ)
Rev.: $690,806,000
Assets: $752,981,000
Liabilities: $331,935,000
Net Worth: $421,046,000
Earnings: ($56,366,000)
Emp.: 2,111
Fiscal Year-end: 12/31/22
Quartz Countertops Mfr
N.A.I.C.S.: 327991
Ariel Halperin *(Chm)*

Subsidiaries:

Caesarstone Australia Pty Ltd (1)
Unit 3/1 Secombe Place, Moorebank, 2170,
NSW, Australia
Tel.: (61) 1300119119
Web Site: http://www.caesarstone.com.au
Sales Range: $50-74.9 Million
Emp.: 7
Quartz Countertop Mfr
N.A.I.C.S.: 327991

Caesarstone Canada Inc. (1)
8885 Jane Street, Concord, L4K 2M6, ON,
Canada
Tel.: (416) 479-8400
Web Site: http://www.caesarstone.ca
Quartz Countertop Mfr
N.A.I.C.S.: 327991

**Caesarstone South East Asia Pte
Ltd** (1)
3 Temasek Boulevard 03-357 Suntec City
Mall Tower 3, Singapore, 038983, Singa-
pore
Tel.: (65) 90113559
Web Site: https://www.caesarstone.sg
Emp.: 20
Quartz Countertop Mfr
N.A.I.C.S.: 327991

Caesarstone US (1)
6840 Hayvenhurst Ave Ste 100, Van Nuys,
CA 91406
Tel.: (818) 779-0099
Web Site: http://www.caesarstoneus.com
Quartz Countertop Mfr
N.A.I.C.S.: 327991

CAFCA LIMITED
54 Lytton Road, PO Box 1651, Ha-
rare, Zimbabwe
Tel.: (263) 242754075   ZW
Web Site: https://www.cafca.co.zw
Year Founded: 1947
CAC—(JSE)
Sales Range: $10-24.9 Million
Emp.: 154
Cable Mfr & Whslr
N.A.I.C.S.: 335929
H. Piniel Mkushi *(Chm)*

**CAFE DE CORAL HOLDINGS
LIMITED**
Cafe de Coral Centre 5 Wo Shui
Street Fo Tan, Sha Tin, New Territo-
ries, China (Hong Kong)
Tel.: (852) 26936218
Web Site:
   https://www.cafedecoral.com
Year Founded: 1986
0341—(HKG)
Rev.: $968,478,962
Assets: $886,330,697
Liabilities: $521,784,721
Net Worth: $364,545,976
Earnings: $2,947,193
Emp.: 17,954
Fiscal Year-end: 03/31/22
Holding Company; Restaurant Opera-
tor
N.A.I.C.S.: 551112
Mike Hung Chun Lim *(CFO)*

Subsidiaries:

Bloomcheer Limited (1)

Cafe de Coral Holdings Limited—(Continued)

Cafe De Coral Ctr, Sha Tin, China (Hong Kong) **(100%)**
Tel.: (852) 26936218
Web Site: http://www.cafetecoral.com
Full-Service Restaurants
N.A.I.C.S.: 722511

Cafe de Coral Fast Food Limited **(1)**
Cafe De Coral Contro No 5 -10 Wo Shui Street Fo Tan, New Territories, Sha Tin, China (Hong Kong) **(100%)**
Tel.: (852) 26936218
Web Site: http://www.cafedecoral.com
Sales Range: $10-24.9 Million
Emp.: 70
Full-Service Restaurants
N.A.I.C.S.: 722511

Cafe de Coral Group Limited **(1)**
10th Floor Cafe De Coral Center, Sha Tin, China (Hong Kong) **(100%)**
Tel.: (852) 26936218
Web Site: http://www.cafedecoral.com
Emp.: 2
Full-Service Restaurants
N.A.I.C.S.: 722511
Sunny Lo (Mng Dir)

China Inn Restaurants, Inc. **(1)**
285 Main St, Pawtucket, RI 02860-2907 **(100%)**
Tel.: (401) 723-3960
Full-Service Restaurants
N.A.I.C.S.: 722511

Dai Bai Dang Restaurants Inc **(1)**
165 E Paseo Del Centro, Fresno, CA 93720-4320
Tel.: (559) 448-8894
Web Site: http://www.daibaidang.com
Restaurant Operating Services
N.A.I.C.S.: 722511
Susan Sussan (Mgr)

Eldoon Limited **(1)**
10/f Cafe De Coral Center 5 Wo Shui St Fotan, Sha Tin, New Territories, China (Hong Kong)
Tel.: (852) 26936218
Catering Services
N.A.I.C.S.: 722320

Exo Enterprises Limited **(1)**
Cafe De Coral Ctr, Sha Tin, China (Hong Kong) **(100%)**
Tel.: (852) 26936218
Web Site: http://www.cafedecoral.com
Full-Service Restaurants
N.A.I.C.S.: 722511
Sunny Lo (CEO)

Kater International Limited **(1)**
Cafe de Coral Centre No 5-13 Wo Shui St Fo Tan, Sha Tin, China (Hong Kong)
Tel.: (852) 26936218
Full-Service Restaurants
N.A.I.C.S.: 722511

Scanfoods Limited **(1)**
9th Floor Cafe De Coral Centre, Sha Tin, China (Hong Kong) **(100%)**
Tel.: (852) 27302323
Web Site: http://www.scanfoods.com.hk
Meat & Meat Product Whslr
N.A.I.C.S.: 424470

Shenzhen Cafe de Coral Catering Company Limited **(1)**
G/F Dexing Building 1048 Jianshe Road, Shenzhen, 518001, China
Tel.: (86) 75582330173
Catering Services
N.A.I.C.S.: 722320

Yumi Yumi Caterers Limited **(1)**
10th Floor Cafe De Coral Ctr, Sha Tin, China (Hong Kong) **(100%)**
Tel.: (852) 26936218
Web Site: http://www.cafedecoral.com
Full-Service Restaurants
N.A.I.C.S.: 722511

CAFE SOLUVEL BRASILIA SA
R Sara 17, 20220070, Rio de Janeiro, Brazil
Tel.: (55) 35 2106 1900
Sales Range: $1-9.9 Million
Emp.: 205

Coffee Mfr & Whslr
N.A.I.C.S.: 311920
Ruy Barreto (Dir-IR)

CAFE24 CORP.
15 Boramae ro 5gil Sindaebang-dong Specialty Contractor Financial Bldg, Dongjak-gu, Seoul, 7071, Korea (South)
Tel.: (82) 232840300
Web Site:
https://www.cafe24corp.com
Year Founded: 2000
042000—(KRS)
Rev.: $214,239,035
Assets: $261,637,668
Liabilities: $131,715,786
Net Worth: $129,921,881
Earnings: ($38,245,657)
Emp.: 1,251
Fiscal Year-end: 12/31/22
Online Marketing Services
N.A.I.C.S.: 541511
Lee Jaesuk (CEO)

CAFFE NERO GROUP LTD.
3 Neal St, London, WC2H 9PU, United Kingdom
Tel.: (44) 2075205150
Web Site: http://www.caffenero.com
Sales Range: $150-199.9 Million
Emp.: 1,969
Coffee Retailer
N.A.I.C.S.: 311920
Michael Peegan (Dir-Intl Dev)

CAFFYNS PLC
4 Meads Road, Eastbourne, BN20 7DR, East Sussex, United Kingdom
Tel.: (44) 1323730201
Web Site:
https://www.caffynsplc.co.uk
CFYN—(LSE)
Rev.: $312,220,807
Assets: $124,223,463
Liabilities: $84,905,591
Net Worth: $39,317,872
Earnings: $3,134,303
Emp.: 402
Fiscal Year-end: 03/31/23
Automobile Dealership Operator
N.A.I.C.S.: 441110
Simon G. M. Caffyn (CEO)

CAFG AUSTRALEASE PTY. LTD.
781 Pacific Highway Suite 205 Level 2, Chatswood, 2067, NSW, Australia
Tel.: (61) 299571850
Web Site: http://www.cafga.com.au
Year Founded: 1977
Emp.: 35
Commercial & Personal Lending Services
N.A.I.C.S.: 522310
Teresa Koh (Acct Mgr)

CAFOM SA
3 avenue Hoche, 75008, Paris, France
Tel.: (33) 156603079   FR
Web Site: https://www.cafom.com
Year Founded: 1985
CAFO—(EUR)
Sales Range: $350-399.9 Million
Household Goods Retailer
N.A.I.C.S.: 455219
Herve Giaoui (Chm & CEO)

Subsidiaries:

Habitat International **(1)**
La Maison Blanche Rte De Quarante Sous, F 78630, Orgeval, France
Tel.: (33) 139224444
Web Site: http://www.habitat.net

Sales Range: $25-49.9 Million
Emp.: 80
Furniture Retailer
N.A.I.C.S.: 449110

Subsidiary (Domestic):

Habitat France SA **(2)**
35 avenue de Wagram, 75017, Paris, France **(100%)**
Tel.: (33) 170363285
Web Site: http://www.habitat.fr
Sales Range: $25-49.9 Million
Emp.: 15
Retail Furnishings & Fittings
N.A.I.C.S.: 449129

Vente-Unique.com SA **(1)**
9/11 Rue Jacquard, 93310, Le Pre-Saint-Gervais, France
Tel.: (33) 176496680
Web Site: https://www.vente-unique.com
Sales Range: $125-149.9 Million
Furniture Product Distr
N.A.I.C.S.: 423210
Sacha Vigna (CEO)

CAG HOLDING GMBH
Keisslergasse 26, Vienna, 0012, Austria
Tel.: (43) 1415650
Web Site: http://www.stoelzle.com
Sales Range: $100-124.9 Million
Emp.: 500
Investment Holding Company
N.A.I.C.S.: 551112
Johannes Scheck (CEO)

Subsidiaries:

Fried.v.Neuman GmbH **(1)**
Werkstrasse 1, 3182, Marktl, Austria
Tel.: (43) 2762 500 0
Web Site: http://www.neuman.at
Metal Products Mfr
N.A.I.C.S.: 332999

Subsidiary (Non-US):

Neuman (Xinhui) Alloy Material Co Ltd. **(2)**
No 46 Jinzhou Rd Xinhui, Economic Development Zone, Jiangmen, 529100, Guangdong, China
Tel.: (86) 750 636 2627
Aluminium Metal Product Mfr
N.A.I.C.S.: 332999

Neuman Aluminium Fliesspresswerk GmbH **(2)**
Wilhelm-Maybach-Str 15, 72108, Rottenburg am Neckar, Germany
Tel.: (49) 7472 15000
Glass Products Mfr
N.A.I.C.S.: 327215

Subsidiary (US):

Neuman Aluminium Impact Extrusion Inc. **(2)**
1418 Genicom Dr, Waynesboro, VA 22980
Tel.: (540) 213-8465
Aluminium Metal Product Mfr
N.A.I.C.S.: 332999
Pamela Meller (Controller)

Subsidiary (Non-US):

Neuman Aluminium Services s.r.o. **(2)**
Bystricka 1608, 96681, Zarnovica, Slovakia
Tel.: (421) 45 68137 42
Metal Products Mfr
N.A.I.C.S.: 332999

PWG Profilrollen-Werkzeugbau GmbH **(2)**
Industriestrasse 4, 96524, Neuhaus-Schierschnitz, Germany
Tel.: (49) 36764 8180
Web Site: http://www.pwgnet.de
Aluminium Metal Product Mfr
N.A.I.C.S.: 332999

PREFA Aluminiumprodukte s.r.o. **(1)**
K Zelenci 2883/14, Horni Pocernice, 193 00, Prague, Czech Republic
Tel.: (420) 234 496 501
Web Site: http://www.cz.prefa.com

Aluminium Metal Product Mfr
N.A.I.C.S.: 332999

PREFA France Sarl **(1)**
245 avenue des Massettes, 73 190, Challes-les-Eaux, France
Tel.: (33) 4 79 44 84 58
Web Site: http://www.prefa.fr
Aluminium Metal Product Mfr
N.A.I.C.S.: 332999

PREFA GmbH **(1)**
Aluminiumstr 2, 98634, Wasungen, Germany
Tel.: (49) 36941 785 39
Web Site: http://www.prefa-design.com
Aluminium Metal Parts Mfr
N.A.I.C.S.: 332999
Peter Asberg (Country Mgr)

PREFA Italia Srl **(1)**
Via Negrelli 23, 39100, Bolzano, Italy
Tel.: (39) 0471068680
Web Site: http://www.prefa.it
Aluminium Metal Product Mfr
N.A.I.C.S.: 332999

Prefa Hungaria Kft. **(1)**
Gyar u 2 Budaorsi Ipari Park, Pf 80, 2040, Budaors, Hungary
Tel.: (36) 23 511 670
Web Site: http://www.prefa.hu
Aluminium Metal Parts Mfr
N.A.I.C.S.: 332999

Prefa Schweiz AG **(1)**
Töggenburgerstr 28a, 9230, Flawil, Switzerland
Tel.: (41) 71 952 68 19
Web Site: http://www.prefa.ch
Aluminium Metal Product Mfr
N.A.I.C.S.: 332999

Sicrem S.p.A. **(1)**
Via GB Pirelli 56, 26026, Pizzighettone, Lombardy, Italy
Tel.: (39) 0372738011
Web Site: http://www.glanzstoff.com
Sales Range: $25-49.9 Million
Emp.: 270
Tire Reinforcement Fabrics Mfr
N.A.I.C.S.: 314994

Stolzle Lausitz GmbH **(1)**
Berliner Strasse 22-32, 02943, Weisswasser, Germany
Tel.: (49) 3576 268 0
Web Site: http://www.stoelzle-lausitz.com
Glass Products Mfr
N.A.I.C.S.: 327215
Johann Nagl (Mng Dir)

Stolzle-Oberglas GmbH **(1)**
Fabrikstrasse 11, 8580, Koflach, Austria
Tel.: (43) 3144 706
Web Site: http://www.stoelzle.com
Glass Products Mfr
N.A.I.C.S.: 327215

Subsidiary (Non-US):

Stoelzle Glass LLC **(2)**
Ul Dobrolyubova 3 b1 of 300, 127254, Moscow, Russia
Tel.: (7) 4956191325
Web Site: http://www.stoelzle.com
Emp.: 3
Glass Container Mfr
N.A.I.C.S.: 327213
Elena Golubchikova (Mng Dir)

Stoelzle Masnieres SAS **(2)**
Route Nationale, 59241, Masnieres, France
Tel.: (33) 3 27 72 27 00
Glass Container Mfr
N.A.I.C.S.: 327213

Stolzle Czestochowa Sp. z o.o. **(2)**
ul Warszawska 347, 42-209, Czestochowa, Poland
Tel.: (48) 343 604500
Glass Products Mfr
N.A.I.C.S.: 327215
Stanislaw Gorski (Plant Mgr)

Stolzle Flaconnage Ltd. **(2)**
Weeland Road, Knottingley, WF11 8AP, West Yorkshire, United Kingdom
Tel.: (44) 1977 607124
Web Site: http://www.stoelzle.com
Emp.: 300

Aluminium Metal Product Mfr
N.A.I.C.S.: 332999

Glass Products Mfr
N.A.I.C.S.: 327215
Thomas Riss *(CEO)*

Stolzle France SAS   (2)
Tour de l'Horloge 4 Place Louis Armand,
75603, Paris, Cedex, France
Tel.: (33) 173 020 360
Glass Products Mfr
N.A.I.C.S.: 327215
Franck Legrand *(Dir-Sls)*

Subsidiary (US):

Stolzle Glass USA, Inc.   (2)
494 8th Ave Ste 1400, New York, NY 10001
Tel.: (212) 590-2539
Web Site: http://www.stolzle-usa.com
Glass Products Mfr
N.A.I.C.S.: 327215
Neil Robson *(VP-Sls & Mktg-Prestige Spirits & Tableware)*

Subsidiary (Non-US):

Stolzle-Union s.r.o   (2)
U Sklarny 300, 330 24, Hermanova Hut,
Czech Republic
Tel.: (420) 377 882 511
Glass Products Mfr
N.A.I.C.S.: 327215
Libor Kraft *(Plant Mgr)*

TUBEX Holding GmbH   (1)
Fabrikstrasse 1, 72414, Rangendingen,
Germany
Tel.: (49) 7471 990 0
Web Site: http://www.tubex.de
Emp.: 300
Holding Company
N.A.I.C.S.: 551112
Leopold Werdich *(Mng Dir)*

Subsidiary (Non-US):

TUBEX Packaging Materials Co.
Ltd.   (2)
Xijia Industry Zone, Huicheng Town Xinhui
District, Jiangmen, 529100, Guangdong,
China
Tel.: (86) 750 6109993
Packaging Material Whslr
N.A.I.C.S.: 423840
Henry Liu *(Mng Dir)*

TUBEX Tubenfabrik Wolfsberg
GmbH   (2)
Am Industriepark 8, 9431, Saint Stefan,
Austria
Tel.: (43) 4352 37488 0
Metal Products Mfr
N.A.I.C.S.: 332999
Markus Leiss *(Acct Mgr)*

Subsidiary (Domestic):

TUBEX Wasungen GmbH   (2)
Aluminiumstrasse 1, 98634, Wasungen,
Germany
Tel.: (49) 36941 75 0
Plastics Product Mfr
N.A.I.C.S.: 326199

Subsidiary (Non-US):

TUBEX ZAO   (2)
Ul Kalinina 224a, Leningradskaya obl Tosno
region, 187010, Ulyanovsk, Russia
Tel.: (7) 8136193570
Glass Products Mfr
N.A.I.C.S.: 327215
Andrzej Zareba *(Exec Dir)*

Textilcord Steinfort S.A.   (1)
Rue Schwarzenhof, PO Box 11, 8401,
Steinfort, Luxembourg
Tel.: (352) 3998811
Web Site: http://www.glanzstoff.com
Sales Range: $125-149.9 Million
Emp.: 110
Tire Reinforcement Fabrics Mfr
N.A.I.C.S.: 314994

CAHYA MATA SARAWAK BER-HAD

Level 6 Wisma Mahmud Jalan Sungai Sarawak, 93100, Kuching, Sarawak, Malaysia
Tel.: (60) 82238888   MY

Web Site:
   https://www.cahyamata.com
Year Founded: 1974
2852—(KLS)
Rev.: $213,877,249
Assets: $1,027,683,598
Liabilities: $291,761,270
Net Worth: $735,922,328
Earnings: $61,360,000
Emp.: 2,000
Fiscal Year-end: 12/31/22
Investment Services
N.A.I.C.S.: 523999
Isaac Lugun *(Mng Dir)*

Subsidiaries:

CMS Cement Industries Sdn.
Bhd.   (1)
Lot 5895 Jalan Simen Raya Pending Indus-
trial Estate, 93450, Kuching, Malaysia
Tel.: (60) 82332111
Concrete Product Mfr & Retailer
N.A.I.C.S.: 327320

CMS Clinker Sdn. Bhd.   (1)
Lot 571 Jalan Mambong Off Jalan Puncak
Borneo, 93250, Kuching, Sarawak, Malay-
sia
Tel.: (60) 82610229
Web Site: http://www.cmsb.com.my
Sales Range: $50-74.9 Million
Emp.: 200
Clinker Mfr
N.A.I.C.S.: 327310

CMS Concrete Products Sdn.
Bhd.   (1)
Lot 212 Block 17 Kuching Central Land Dis-
trict Old Airport Road, 93250, Kuching,
Sarawak, Malaysia
Tel.: (60) 82618718
Web Site: http://www.cmsb.com.my
Sales Range: $25-49.9 Million
Emp.: 45
Readymix Concrete Mfr
N.A.I.C.S.: 327320

CMS Infra Trading Sdn. Bhd.   (1)
No 2128 Sublot 2 Jalan Utama Pending,
93450, Kuching, Sarawak, Malaysia
Tel.: (60) 82348950
Sales Range: $25-49.9 Million
Emp.: 16
Water Management Products Distr
N.A.I.C.S.: 423720
Julia Kelon *(Mgr-Fin & Admin)*

CMS Land Sdn. Bhd.   (1)
Level 5 Wisma Mahmud Jalan Sungai,
93100, Kuching, Sarawak, Malaysia
Tel.: (60) 82237777
Web Site: https://www.cmsproperty.com.my
Property Holding Development & Construc-
tion Services
N.A.I.C.S.: 531390

CMS Penkuari Sdn. Bhd.   (1)
9th Mile Kuching-Serian Road, Kuching,
93250, Sarawak, Malaysia
Tel.: (60) 82614913
Sales Range: $25-49.9 Million
Emp.: 28
Crushed Stone Aggregates Whslr
N.A.I.C.S.: 423320
Gohchii Bing *(Mng Dir)*

CMS Premix Sdn. Bhd.   (1)
Lot 353 Block 17 7th Mile Penrissen Road,
Kuching, 93818, Sarawak, Malaysia
Tel.: (60) 82614208
Web Site: http://www.cmsb.com.my
Sales Range: $25-49.9 Million
Emp.: 20
Premix Concrete Mfr & Distr
N.A.I.C.S.: 327320

CMS Property Development Sdn.
Bhd.   (1)
Level 5 Wisma Mahmud Jalan Sungai Sara-
wak, 93100, Kuching, Sarawak, Malaysia
Tel.: (60) 82237777
Web Site: http://www.cmsproperty.com.my
Sales Range: $25-49.9 Million
Emp.: 28
Commercial & Residential Property Devel-
opment Services
N.A.I.C.S.: 531210

CMS Quarries Sdn. Bhd.   (1)
7th Mile Kuching-Serian Rd, 93250, Kuch-
ing, Sarawak, Malaysia
Tel.: (60) 82615605
Web Site: http://www.cmsb.com.my
Sales Range: $50-74.9 Million
Emp.: 150
Crushed Stone Aggregates Mfr
N.A.I.C.S.: 333131
Haji Abdul Rahman *(Gen Mgr-Mktg)*

CMS Resources Sdn. Bhd.   (1)
7th Mile Old Airport Road, 93250, Kuching,
Malaysia
Tel.: (60) 82610226
Construction Material & Trading Services
N.A.I.C.S.: 423390

Subsidiary (Domestic):

Betong Premix Sdn. Bhd.   (2)
Lot 563 KM5 Jalan Betong, 95700, Betong,
Malaysia
Tel.: (60) 83472137
Construction Material & Trading Services
N.A.I.C.S.: 423390

Borneo Granite Sdn. Bhd.   (2)
Lot 71 Block 17, Kuching Central Land Dis-
trict 290 Pekan Batu 7 Kota Sentosa,
93250, Kuching, Malaysia
Tel.: (60) 82615605
Construction Material & Trading Services
N.A.I.C.S.: 423390

CMS Premix (Miri) Sdn. Bhd.   (2)
Mile 11 Miri-Bintulu Road, 98000, Miri, Ma-
laysia
Tel.: (60) 85491136
Construction Material & Trading Services
N.A.I.C.S.: 423390

PPES Concrete Product Sdn.
Bhd.   (2)
Lot 212 Block 17 Old Airport Road, Kuching
Central Land District, 93250, Kuching, Ma-
laysia
Tel.: (60) 82614436
Concrete Product Mfr & Retailer
N.A.I.C.S.: 327320

CMS Wires Sdn. Bhd.   (1)
Lot 87 Lorong Tenaga II Off Jalan Tenaga
Bintawa Industrial Estate, PO Box 3039,
93450, Kuching, Malaysia
Tel.: (60) 82334772
Construction Material & Trading Services
N.A.I.C.S.: 423390

CMS Works Sdn. Bhd.   (1)
Level 3-4 Lot 220-222 Section 63 KTLD
Lorong Ang Cheng Ho 9, Jalan Ang Cheng
Ho, 93100, Kuching, Malaysia
Tel.: (60) 82234823
Construction & Road Maintenance Services
N.A.I.C.S.: 237310

Subsidiary (Domestic):

CMS Pavement Tech Sdn. Bhd.   (2)
Level 4 Lot 220-222 Section 63 KTLD
Lorong Ang Cheng Ho 9, Jalan Ang Cheng
Ho, 93100, Kuching, Malaysia
Tel.: (60) 82240233
Construction & Road Maintenance Services
N.A.I.C.S.: 237310

CMS Roads Sdn. Bhd.   (1)
Lot 220-222 Section 63 KTLD Lorong Ang
Cheng Ho 9 Jalan Ang Cheng Ho, 93100,
Kuching, Malaysia
Tel.: (60) 82233311
Construction & Road Maintenance Services
N.A.I.C.S.: 237310

COPE Private Equity Sdn. Bhd.   (1)
Office Suite 1 Level 8 Ilham Tower No 8
Jalan Binjai, 50450, Kuala Lumpur, Malay-
sia
Tel.: (60) 323879008
Web Site: http://www.copepartners.com
Private Equity Investment Fund Services
N.A.I.C.S.: 523940
Azam Azman *(Mng Dir)*

Cahya Mata Alam Sdn. Bhd.   (1)
Sirim Berhad No 1 Persiaran Dato Menteri
Block 21 Section 2, 40700, Shah Alam, Se-
langor, Malaysia
Tel.: (60) 105295188

Web Site:
   https://www.thermasitemy.wixsite.com
Thermite Mfr
N.A.I.C.S.: 325991

Cahya Mata Cement Sdn. Bhd.   (1)
Lot 5895 Jalan Simen Raya Pending Indus-
trial Estate, PO Box 2000, 93740, Kuching,
Malaysia
Tel.: (60) 82332111
Web Site: https://cement.cahyamata.com
Cement Mfr
N.A.I.C.S.: 327310

Cahya Mata Development Sdn.
Bhd.   (1)
Level 5 Wisma Mahmud Jalan Sungai Sara-
wak, 93100, Kuching, Sarawak, Malaysia
Tel.: (60) 82237777
Web Site: https://www.cmsproperty.com.my
Property Development Services
N.A.I.C.S.: 531311

Cahya Mata Phosphate Industries
Sdn. Bhd.   (1)
No 482 S/Lot 4206 Parkcity Commerce
Square Phase 6, Jalan Tun Ahmad Zaidi,
97000, Bintulu, Malaysia
Tel.: (60) 82344575
Phosphate Mfr
N.A.I.C.S.: 325180

Cahya Mata Roads Sdn. Bhd.   (1)
Level 3-4 Lot 220 Section 63 KTLD Lorong
Ang Cheng Ho 9, Jalan Ang Cheng Ho,
93100, Kuching, Malaysia
Tel.: (60) 82256116
Road Maintenance Services
N.A.I.C.S.: 237310

PPES Works (Sarawak) Sdn.
Bhd.   (1)
Level 4 Wisma Mahmud Jalan Sungai,
Kuching, 93100, Sarawak, Malaysia
Tel.: (60) 82340588
Web Site: http://www.cmsb.com.my
Sales Range: $25-49.9 Million
Emp.: 100
Public Utility Construction & Engineering
Services
N.A.I.C.S.: 237990

PPESW BPSB JV Sdn. Bhd.   (1)
Level 2 Wisma Mahmud Jalan Sungai,
93100, Kuching, Sarawak, Malaysia
Tel.: (60) 8235299
Construction & Road Maintenance Services
N.A.I.C.S.: 237310

Projek Bandar Samariang Sdn.
Bhd.   (1)
No 5574 Jln Sultan Tengah Bandar Baru
Semariang, 93050, Kuching, Sarawak, Ma-
laysia
Tel.: (60) 82311887
Web Site: http://www.cmsproperty.com.my
Sales Range: $50-74.9 Million
Emp.: 24
Commercial Property Development Services
N.A.I.C.S.: 531210

Samalaju Industries Sdn. Bhd.   (1)
Level 6 Wisma Mahmud Jalan Sungai,
93100, Kuching, Sarawak, Malaysia
Tel.: (60) 82238888
Investment Holding Company Services
N.A.I.C.S.: 551112

Subsidiary (Domestic):

Malaysian Phosphate Additives
(Sarawak) Sdn. Bhd.   (2)
Level 5 Wisma Mahmud Jalan Sungai,
93100, Kuching, Sarawak, Malaysia
Tel.: (60) 82337995
Fertilizer Grade & Non-Phosphate Product
Mfr
N.A.I.C.S.: 325312

Samalaju Properties Sdn. Bhd.   (2)
Level 6 Wisma Mahmud Jalan Sungai Sara-
wak, 93100, Kuching, Sarawak, Malaysia
Tel.: (60) 82337995
Accommodation Services
N.A.I.C.S.: 721199

Subsidiary (Domestic):

Samalaju Hotel Management Sdn.
Bhd.   (3)

Cahya Mata Sarawak Berhad—(Continued)

Lot 1332 Block 1, Kemena Land District
Samalaju Industrial Park, 97000, Bintulu,
Sarawak, Malaysia
Tel.: (60) 86291999
Property Holding Development & Construction Services
N.A.I.C.S.: 531390

CAI LAY VETERINARY PHARMACEUTICAL JOINT STOCK COMPANY

Quarter 1 Ward 5, Cai Lay, Tien Giang, Vietnam
Tel.: (84) 2733826462
Web Site: https://mekovet.com.vn
Year Founded: 1990
MKV—(HNX)
Rev.: $11,963,400
Assets: $10,604,400
Liabilities: $3,242,400
Net Worth: $7,362,000
Earnings: $590,400
Fiscal Year-end: 12/31/22
Pharmaceuticals Product Mfr
N.A.I.C.S.: 325412

CAI PRIVATE EQUITY

Royal Bank Plaza South Tower, 200
Bay Street Suite 2320, Toronto, M5J
2J1, ON, Canada
Tel.: (416) 306-9810   Ca
Web Site: http://www.caifunds.com
Year Founded: 1989
Sales Range: $25-49.9 Million
Emp.: 20
Privater Equity Firm
N.A.I.C.S.: 523999
Mark Piotrowski (Mng Dir)

Subsidiaries:

CAI Capital Management Inc.   (1)
3429 Rue Drummond Ste 200, Montreal,
H3G 1X6, QC, Canada
Tel.: (514) 849-1642
Sales Range: $50-74.9 Million
Emp.: 12
Privater Equity Firm
N.A.I.C.S.: 523999

CAI Capital Management Inc.   (1)
Ste 2833 Bentall Three, 595 Burrard St,
Vancouver, V7X 1KB, BC, Canada
Tel.: (604) 637-3411
Sales Range: $50-74.9 Million
Emp.: 7
Privater Equity Firm
N.A.I.C.S.: 523999
Tracey L. McVicar (Mng Partner)

Corix Group
1188 West Georgia Street Suite 1160, Vancouver, V6E 4A2, BC, Canada
Tel.: (604) 697-6700
Web Site: http://www.corix.com
Sales Range: $400-449.9 Million
Utility Infrastructure System Design, Construction & Management Services; Owned
by CAI Capital Management Inc. & British
Columbia Investment Management Corporation
N.A.I.C.S.: 237110
Sue Paish (Chm)

Plastube Inc.   (1)
590 Simonds Street South, Granby, J2J
1E1, QC, Canada
Tel.: (450) 378-2633
Web Site: http://www.plastube.com
Sales Range: $50-74.9 Million
Mfr of Plastic Packaging Products
N.A.I.C.S.: 326199
Jose Mathieu (Pres & CEO)

CAIAC FUND MANAGEMENT AG

Haus Atzig Industriestrasse 2, PO
Box 27, Bendern, 9487, Gamprin,
Liechtenstein
Tel.: (423) 375 83 33
Web Site: http://www.caiac.li
Fund Management Services

N.A.I.C.S.: 523940
Thomas Jahn (CEO & Chm-Exec Bd)

CAIANO AS

Strandgata 92, 5528, Haugesund,
Norway
Tel.: (47) 52709070
Web Site: http://www.caiano.no
Sales Range: $25-49.9 Million
Emp.: 19
Investment Holding Company
N.A.I.C.S.: 551112
Kristian Eidesvik (Founder)

Subsidiaries:

Euro-Terminal AS   (1)
Skovveien 2A, PO Box 2613, Solli, Oslo,
0203, Norway
Tel.: (47) 2254 2690
Logistics Consulting Servies
N.A.I.C.S.: 541614

Subsidiary (Non-US):

Euro Terminal Sp z o o   (2)
Jana Soltana 1, Swinoujscie, 72-602, Poland
Tel.: (48) 91 321 65 11
Web Site: http://www.euro-terminal.com.pl
Emp.: 80
Logistics Consulting Servies
N.A.I.C.S.: 541614
Katarzyna Bulawa (Mng Dir)

Green Management Sp. z o.o.   (1)
Pulaskiego 6, 81-368, Gdynia, Poland
Tel.: (48) 58 770 1300
Web Site: http://www.greenmanagement.ro
Emp.: 15
Freight Forwarding Services
N.A.I.C.S.: 483211

Maloyterminalen AS   (1)
Gnr 106 Bnr 12, 6700, Maloy, Norway
Tel.: (47) 57 85 36 30
Logistics Consulting Servies
N.A.I.C.S.: 541614

Mosterfarm AS   (1)
Serklauwegen 91, 5440, Bomlo, Norway
Tel.: (47) 53422170
Web Site: http://www.mosterfarm.no
Steel Product Distr
N.A.I.C.S.: 423390

Reach Subsea ASA   (1)
Mollervegen 6, 5527, Haugesund,
Norway   (54.56%)
Tel.: (47) 40007710
Web Site: https://www.reachsubsea.no
Rev.: $107,291,059
Assets: $87,944,301
Liabilities: $34,421,116
Net Worth: $53,523,185
Earnings: $6,667,744
Emp.: 273
Fiscal Year-end: 12/31/2022
Logistics Management Services
N.A.I.C.S.: 541614
Kare Johannes Lie (Deputy Chm)

UAB Green Terminal   (1)
S Dariaus ir S Gireno 9 - 1, Klaipeda,
92223, Lithuania
Tel.: (370) 46 312683
Web Site: http://www.green.lt
Logistics Consulting Servies
N.A.I.C.S.: 541614

Wilson ASA   (1)
Damsgardsveien 135 Laksevag, 5160, Bergen, Norway   (90.1%)
Tel.: (47) 55308200
Web Site: https://www.wilsonship.no
Sales Range: $300-349.9 Million
Emp.: 1,650
Water Transportation Management Services
N.A.I.C.S.: 483211
Kristian Eidesvik (Chm)

Subsidiary (Non-US):

**NSA Schifffahrt und Transport
GmbH**   (2)
Alter Wall 55, 20457, Hamburg, Germany
Tel.: (49) 40370070
Web Site: http://www.nsa-hamburg.de
Emp.: 10

Marine Transportation Distr
N.A.I.C.S.: 488320
Peter Steinberg (Mgr-Port OPS)

Nesskip hf.   (2)
IS-170 Seltjarnarnes, Reykjavik, 170, Iceland
Tel.: (354) 563 9900
Web Site: http://www.nesskip.is
Emp.; 9
Marine Transportation Services
N.A.I.C.S.: 488320
Gardar Johanson (Gen Mgr)

Wilson Agency B.V.   (2)
Directiekade 15, 3089 JA, Rotterdam, Netherlands
Tel.: (31) 10 2952 888
Web Site: http://www.wilsonagency.nl
Marine Transportation Services
N.A.I.C.S.: 488320

Subsidiary (Domestic):

Wilson Agency Norge AS   (2)
Hammaren 23, 4056, Tananger, Norway
Tel.: (47) 9414 8560
Web Site: http://www.wilsonship.com
Emp.: 4
Marine Transportation Services
N.A.I.C.S.: 488320
Ton Trump (Mgr)

Subsidiary (Non-US):

Wilson Crewing Agency Ltd.   (2)
55/1 Vologodskaya St, 163001, Arkhangelsk, Russia
Tel.: (7) 8182650357
Web Site: http://www.wilson-crewing.com
Emp.: 1,200
Marine Transportation Services
N.A.I.C.S.: 488320

**Wilson Crewing Agency Odessa
Ltd.**   (2)
7 Mayakovskogo Lane, Odessa, 65000,
Ukraine
Tel.: (380) 48 723 4175
Web Site: http://www.wilson-crewing.com
Marine Transportation Services
N.A.I.C.S.: 488320

Subsidiary (Domestic):

Wilson EuroCarriers AS   (2)
Bradbenken 1, 5835, Bergen, Norway
Tel.: (47) 5530 8200
Marine Transportation Services
N.A.I.C.S.: 488320

Wilson Management AS   (2)
Bradbenken 1, 5835, Bergen, Norway
Tel.: (47) 5530 8200
Marine Transportation Services
N.A.I.C.S.: 488320

Subsidiary (Non-US):

Wilson Murmansk Ltd.   (2)
Lenina 102 Office 24, Murmansk, 183012,
Russia
Tel.: (7) 8152 458296
Marine Transportation Services
N.A.I.C.S.: 488320

Wilson NRL Transport GmbH   (2)
Dammstrasse 13, 47119, Duisburg, Germany
Tel.: (49) 203 809 570
Web Site: http://www.wilsonship.de
Marine Transportation Services
N.A.I.C.S.: 488320

Subsidiary (Domestic):

Wilson Ship Management AS   (2)
Bradbenken 1, 5835, Bergen, Norway
Tel.: (47) 5530 8200
Web Site: http://www.wilsonship.no
Marine Transportation Services
N.A.I.C.S.: 488320

ZAO Green Terminal   (1)
5-ya Prichalnaja str 1, 236035, Kaliningrad,
Russia
Tel.: (7) 4012 655882
Web Site: http://www.greenreefers.com
Emp.: 15
Logistics Consulting Servies
N.A.I.C.S.: 541614

Alexander Lobanov (Gen Mgr)

CAICA DIGITAL INC.

Lexington Aoyama 5-11-9 Minamiaoyama, Minato-Ku, Tokyo, 107-0062, Japan
Tel.: (81) 356573000
Web Site: https://www.caica.jp
Year Founded: 1989
2315—(TKS)
Rev.: $38,342,720
Assets: $21,064,390
Liabilities: $5,480,570
Net Worth: $15,583,820
Earnings: ($27,573,010)
Emp.: 398
Fiscal Year-end: 10/31/23
Information Services
N.A.I.C.S.: 519290
Nobu Suzuki (Pres & CEO)

CAIDA SECURITIES CO., LTD.

No 35 Ziqiang Road, Qiaoxi District,
Shijiazhuang, 050000, Hebei, China
Tel.: (86) 31166006224
Web Site: https://www.95363.com
Year Founded: 2002
600906—(SHG)
Rev.: $230,772,026
Assets: $6,155,624,241
Liabilities: $4,591,049,940
Net Worth: $1,564,574,301
Earnings: $42,467,588
Fiscal Year-end: 12/31/22
Securities Brokerage Services
N.A.I.C.S.: 523150
Zhang Ming (Chm & Gen Mgr)

CAIDAO CAPITAL LIMITED

5 F, Lee Kee Commercial Building
221 227 Queen's Road, Central,
China (Hong Kong)
Tel.: (852) 37933890
Web Site:
    http://www.caidaocapital.com
Year Founded: 2007
Asset Management & Investment
Banking Services
N.A.I.C.S.: 523150
Ming Lee (Founder & CEO)

CAIN INTERNATIONAL LIMITED

33 Davies Street, London, W1K 4LR,
United Kingdom
Tel.: (44) 2075699000
Web Site: http://www.cainint.com
Financial Services
N.A.I.C.S.: 523999
Jonathan Goldstein (Co-Founder &
CEO)

CAINA TECHNOLOGY CO., LTD.

No 23 Huanxi Road, Zhutang Town,
Jiangyin, 214421, Jiangsu, China
Tel.: (86) 51083166666
Web Site: https://www.caina.ltd
Year Founded: 2004
301122—(CHIN)
Rev.: $65,354,796
Assets: $258,810,552
Liabilities: $15,028,416
Net Worth: $243,782,136
Earnings: $22,726,548
Fiscal Year-end: 12/31/22
Medical Equipment Mfr & Distr
N.A.I.C.S.: 339112
Jun Lu (Chm)

CAIRN HOMES PLC

45 Mespil Road, Dublin, D02 KW81,
Ireland
Tel.: (353) 16964600
Web Site:
    https://www.cairnhomes.com

Year Founded: 2014
C5H—(ISE)
Rev.: $736,071,310
Assets: $1,147,919,197
Liabilities: $312,107,297
Net Worth: $835,811,900
Earnings: $94,306,215
Emp.: 350
Fiscal Year-end: 12/31/23
Residential Property Development Services
N.A.I.C.S.: 531311
Michael Stanley *(Co-Founder & CEO)*

CAIRO & ALEXANDRIA STOCK EXCHANGES

4A El Sherifien St, 11513, Cairo, Egypt
Tel.: (20) 223928698
Web Site: http://www.egyptse.com
Stock Exchange Services
N.A.I.C.S.: 523210
Mohamed Abdel Salam *(Chm)*

Subsidiaries:

Egypt for Information Dissemination   (1)
Block 72 off 90 Axis El Tagmoaa El Khames, New Cairo, Helwan, Egypt   **(100%)**
Tel.: (20) 226145000
Web Site: http://www.egidegypt.com
Sales Range: $75-99.9 Million
Stock Exchange Services
N.A.I.C.S.: 523999

Misr for Central Clearing, Depository & Registry SAE   (1)
70 El Gamhouria Street, Cairo, Egypt   **(35%)**
Tel.: (20) 25971581
Web Site: http://www.mcsd.com.eg
Stock Exchange Services
N.A.I.C.S.: 523999
Mohamed Soliman Abdel Salam *(Chm)*

CAIRO AMMAN BANK

Arar Street Wadi Saqra, PO Box 950661, Amman, 11195, Jordan
Tel.: (962) 6 500 7700
Web Site: http://www.cab.jo
Sales Range: $125-149.9 Million
Banking Services
N.A.I.C.S.: 522110
Yazid Adnan Al-Muftii *(Chm)*

CAIRO COMMUNICATION S.P.A.

Via Angelo Rizzoli 8, 20123, Milan, Italy
Tel.: (39) 02748131   IT
Web Site:
https://www.cairocommunication.it
CAI—(ITA)
Sales Range: $1-4.9 Billion
Book & Magazine Publisher; Internet Site Operator; Advertising Space & Time Sales
N.A.I.C.S.: 513130
Urbano Cairo *(Chm)*

Subsidiaries:

Cairo Editore S.p.A.   (1)
Corso Magenta 55, 20123, Milan, Italy   **(100%)**
Tel.: (39) 02460709
Web Site: http://www.cairoeditore.it
Sales Range: $25-49.9 Million
Emp.: 75
All Other Publishers
N.A.I.C.S.: 513199
Urbano Cairo *(Pres)*

Cairo Pubblicita S.p.A   (1)
Via Tucidide 56, Milan, Italy   **(100%)**
Tel.: (39) 027481111
Web Site: http://www.cairocommunication.it
Sales Range: $25-49.9 Million
Emp.: 50
Television Broadcasting

N.A.I.C.S.: 516120
Urbano Cairo *(Pres)*

Cairo Publishing Srl   (1)
Corso Magenta 55, 20123, Milan, Italy   **(100%)**
Tel.: (39) 02433131
Sales Range: $25-49.9 Million
Emp.: 100
All Other Publishers
N.A.I.C.S.: 513199
Urbano Cairo *(Pres)*

Cairo Sport Srl   (1)
Via Tucidide 56, Milan, Italy   **(100%)**
Tel.: (39) 027481111
Web Site: http://www.cairocommunication.it
Sales Range: $25-49.9 Million
Emp.: 25
Advertising Agencies
N.A.I.C.S.: 541810
Urbano Cairo *(Pres)*

Editoriale Giorgio Mondadori Spa   (1)
Corso Magenta 55, 20123, Milan, Italy   **(100%)**
Tel.: (39) 02460709
Web Site: http://www.cairoeditore.it
Sales Range: $25-49.9 Million
Emp.: 75
All Other Publishers
N.A.I.C.S.: 513199
Urbano Cairo *(Pres)*

IL Trovatore Srl   (1)
Via Tucidide 56, Milan, Italy   **(100%)**
Tel.: (39) 027481111
Sales Range: $25-49.9 Million
Emp.: 30
Software Publisher
N.A.I.C.S.: 513210
Urbano Cairo *(Pres)*

CAIRO DEVELOPMENT & INVESTMENT, (S.A.E.)

21 Misr Helwan El-Zeraea St Korniche El-Nile, Maadi, Egypt
Tel.: (20) 2 23807828
Web Site: http://www.cdicoeg.com
Year Founded: 1976
Real Estate Investment Services
N.A.I.C.S.: 523999
Hossam Mohamed Zaki Ibrahim *(Chm & Mng Dir)*

CAIRO INVESTMENT & REAL ESTATE DEVELOPMENT

36 Ahmed El-Sawy St, Nasr, Cairo, Egypt
Tel.: (20) 222747380
Web Site: https://cira.com.eg
Year Founded: 1992
CIRA.CA—(EGX)
Sales Range: Less than $1 Million
Education Management Services
N.A.I.C.S.: 611710
Hassan El Kalla *(Chm)*

CAIRO MEZZ PLC

33 Vasilissis Friderikis Palais D'Ivoire House 2nd floor, 1066, Nicosia, Cyprus
Tel.: (357) 22022738   CY
Web Site:
https://www.cairomezz.com.cy
Year Founded: 2020
CAIROMEZ—(ATH)
Rev.: $132,773,581
Assets: $193,696,809
Liabilities: $220,428
Net Worth: $193,476,380
Earnings: $132,460,621
Fiscal Year-end: 12/31/23
Holding Company
N.A.I.C.S.: 551112
Elena Papandreou *(CEO)*

CAIRO OIL & SOAP COMPANY

6 Falaky square, PO 1407, Cairo, Egypt
Tel.: (20) 27962508
Web Site: https://www.cairooil.com

Year Founded: 1963
COSG.CA—(EGX)
Sales Range: Less than $1 Million
Toilet Product Mfr
N.A.I.C.S.: 325611
Mohamed Ayman Korra *(Chm)*

CAIRO RESOURCES INC.

800 West Pender Street Suite 1430, Vancouver, V6C 2V6, BC, Canada
Tel.: (604) 638-8063   BC
Year Founded: 2010
QAI—(TSXV)
Assets: $15,697
Liabilities: $38,043
Net Worth: ($22,347)
Earnings: ($32,356)
Fiscal Year-end: 02/29/20
Investment Services
N.A.I.C.S.: 523999
Darryl Cardey *(CEO & CFO)*

CAIRO THREE A GROUP

62 Service Center El-Tagamoha, El Khames El-Katamia, Cairo, Egypt
Tel.: (20) 2 25657382
Web Site: http://www.cairothreea.com
Year Founded: 1981
Agricultural Commodities Supplier
N.A.I.C.S.: 112340
Ayman El Gamil *(Chm)*

Subsidiaries:

Egyptian Starch & Glucose Company   (1)
6 October Street 8 Mostorod, Cairo, Egypt
Tel.: (20) 2 48588701
Web Site: http://www.esgc.com.eg
Starch & Glucose Product Mfr
N.A.I.C.S.: 311221
Islam Gharieb *(Exec Mgr)*

CAISSA TOSUN DEVELOPMENT CO., LTD.

17F Tower B Lecheng Center No 24 Dongsanhuan Middle Road, Chaoyang District, Beijing, 570105, China
Tel.: (86) 18518400796
Web Site: http://www.hnacaissa.com
Year Founded: 1993
000796—(SSE)
Rev.: $44,881,668
Assets: $346,580,208
Liabilities: $438,988,680
Net Worth: ($92,408,472)
Earnings: ($143,434,044)
Fiscal Year-end: 12/31/22
Travel Services
N.A.I.C.S.: 722320
Chi Yongjie *(Chm)*

CAISSE DE DEPOT ET PLACEMENT DU QUEBEC

Price Building 65 rue Sainte-Anne 14th Floor, Quebec, G1R 3X5, QC, Canada
Tel.: (418) 684-2334   QC
Web Site: http://www.cdpq.com
Year Founded: 1965
Rev.: $9,615,785,760
Assets: $369,522,474,480
Liabilities: $41,123,677,320
Net Worth: $328,398,797,160
Earnings: $9,033
Emp.: 890
Fiscal Year-end: 12/31/21
Public Investment Portfolio Management
N.A.I.C.S.: 523940
Claude Bergeron *(Chief Risk Officer & Head-Depositor Rels)*

Subsidiaries:

AlixPartners, LLP   (1)
909 3rd Ave, New York, NY 10022
Tel.: (212) 490-2500
Web Site: http://www.alixpartners.com

Emp.: 2,000
Management Consulting Services
N.A.I.C.S.: 541618
Fred Crawford *(Mng Dir)*

Subsidiary (Non-US):

AlixPartners Argentina SRL   (2)
Avenida Corrientes 1750 Piso 12, C1042AAQ, Buenos Aires, Argentina
Tel.: (54) 11 5031 2900
Financial Advisory Services
N.A.I.C.S.: 523940

AlixPartners UK LLP   (2)
6 New Street Square, London, EC4A 3BF, United Kingdom
Tel.: (44) 20 7098 7400
Financial Advisory Services
N.A.I.C.S.: 523940
Nick Wood *(Mng Dir-Merger & Acq Services Practice-EMEA)*

CDP Capital Financing Inc.   (1)
1000 Place Jean Paul Riopelle, Montreal, H2Z 2B3, QC, Canada
Tel.: (514) 842-3261
Web Site: http://www.lacaisse.com
Sales Range: $250-299.9 Million
Emp.: 800
Holding Company
N.A.I.C.S.: 551112
Michael Sabia *(CEO)*

CDP Capital Real Estate Advisory   (1)
1000 Pl Jean Paul Riopelle Ste A 300, Montreal, H2Z 2B6, QC, Canada   **(100%)**
Tel.: (514) 875-3360
Web Site: http://www.cdpcapital.com
Sales Range: $300-349.9 Million
Emp.: 800
Management of a Portfolio Targeting Residential Properties & Non-Traditional Real Estate Investmentst
N.A.I.C.S.: 531210

CDP Capital Technologies   (1)
1000 Pl Jean Paul Riopelle, Montreal, H2Z 2B3, QC, Canada
Tel.: (514) 847-2000
Web Site: http://www.cdpcapital.com
Sales Range: $100-124.9 Million
Emp.: 800
Investor of Telecommunications, Media, Cultural Industries & Technologies
N.A.I.C.S.: 517111
Micheal Fabia *(Pres)*

CDP Capital US inc.   (1)
1211 6th Ave Ste 3001, New York, NY 10036
Tel.: (212) 596-6300
Web Site: http://www.nacaisse.com
Emp.: 20
Investment Management Service
N.A.I.C.S.: 523940
Peter Dannenbaum *(VP)*

CDP Financial, Inc.   (1)
1800 W Littleton Blvd, Littleton, CO 80120
Tel.: (303) 794-0706
Investment Management Service
N.A.I.C.S.: 523940

CDP Technologies   (1)
1000 Gean Paul Riopelle, Montreal, H2Z2B3, QC, Canada
Tel.: (514) 847-2613
Sales Range: $500-549.9 Million
Emp.: 800
N.A.I.C.S.: 524298

CDPQ China   (1)
Suite 903 Office Tower E1 Oriental Plaza No 1 Chang'an Ave East, Beijing, 100738, China
Tel.: (86) 10 6408 8718
Investment Management Service
N.A.I.C.S.: 523940

CDPQ Mortgage Corporation   (1)
65 Steamme St 13th Fl, Quebec, G1R 3X5, QC, Canada   **(100%)**
Tel.: (418) 656-6572
Web Site: http://www.mcap.com
Sales Range: $50-74.9 Million
Emp.: 2
Mortgage Loans & Securities
N.A.I.C.S.: 522310

Caisse de Depot et Placement du
Quebec—(Continued)

Capital CDPQ (1)
1000 Pl Jean Paul Riopelle, Montreal, H2Z
2B3, QC, Canada
Tel.: (514) 842-3261
Web Site: http://www.lacaisse.com
Sales Range: $500-549.9 Million
Emp.: 800
N.A.I.C.S.: 524298
Michael Sabia (Pres & CEO)

Capital International CDPQ (1)
1001 Sq Victoria, Montreal, H2Z 2A8, QC,
Canada (100%)
Tel.: (514) 842-3261
Web Site: http://www.lacaisse.com
Sales Range: $700-749.9 Million
Emp.: 1,500
Investments & International Networking
N.A.I.C.S.: 523150
Michael Sabia (Pres)

Centre CDP Capital (1)
1000 Pl Jean Paul Riopelle, Montreal, H2Z
2B3, QC, Canada
Tel.: (514) 842-3261
Web Site: http://www.lacaisse.com
Sales Range: $75-99.9 Million
Emp.: 750
Insurance Services
N.A.I.C.S.: 524298
Ginette Depelteau (Sr Principal & VP)

Clarios Global GP LLC (1)
Florist Twr 5757 N Green Bay Ave, Milwau-
kee, WI 53201
Tel.: (414) 524-1200
Web Site: http://www.clarios.com
Holding Company; Storage Battery Mfr &
Whslr
N.A.I.C.S.: 551112
Mark Wallace (CEO)

Subsidiary (Domestic):

**Johnson Controls Battery Group,
LLC** (2)
5757 N Green Bay Ave, Milwaukee, WI
53201
Tel.: (414) 524-1200
Web Site: http://www.johnsoncontrols.com
Sales Range: $1-4.9 Billion
Emp.: 2,000
Automotive Batteries Mfr & Whslr
N.A.I.C.S.: 335910

Subsidiary (Non-US):

Delkor Corp. Ltd. (3)
9th floor Korea Intellectual Property Center
Building 131 Teheran-ro, Gangnam-gu,
Seoul, 06133, Gyeongbuk, Korea (South)
Tel.: (82) 25298975
Web Site: https://www.delkor.com
Sales Range: $75-99.9 Million
Emp.: 400
Battery Mfr
N.A.I.C.S.: 335910

**Johnson Controls Autobatterie
GmbH** (3)
Tel.: (49) 51197502
Web Site: http://www.varta-automotive.com
Automotive Battery Mfr
N.A.I.C.S.: 335910

Subsidiary (Non-US):

Clarios VARTA Hannover GmbH (4)
Tel.: (49) 51179030
Web Site: http://www.varta-automotive.com
Automobile Batteries Mfr
N.A.I.C.S.: 335910

Johnson Controls Batterie AG (4)
Tel.: (41) 448708060
Web Site:
http://www.johnsoncontrolsbatterie.ch
Sales Range: $10-24.9 Million
Emp.: 15
Automotive Battery Mfr & Distr
N.A.I.C.S.: 335910

Johnson Controls Batteries Ltd. (4)
Tel.: (44) 1895838999
Sales Range: $10-24.9 Million
Emp.: 12
Automotive Battery Mfr
N.A.I.C.S.: 335910

Subsidiary (Domestic):

Optima Batteries, Inc. (3)
17500 E 22nd Ave, Aurora, CO 80011
Tel.: (888) 867-8462
Web Site: http://www.optimabatteries.com
Sales Range: $50-74.9 Million
Emp.: 190
Automotive Batteries
N.A.I.C.S.: 335910

Subsidiary (Non-US):

Optima Batteries AB (4)
Vendevagen 90, Danderyd, 182 32, Stock-
holm, Sweden
Tel.: (46) 858705304
Automotive Components
N.A.I.C.S.: 336390

**Constellation Insurance Holdings
Inc.** (1)
1211 Avenue of the Americas 30th floor,
New York, NY 10036
Web Site: https://www.constellationih.com
Emp.: 100
Holding Company
N.A.I.C.S.: 551111
Anurag Chandra (Founder & CEO)

Subsidiary (Domestic):

Ohio National Holdings, Inc. (2)
1 Financial Way, Cincinnati, OH 45242
Tel.: (513) 794-6100
Web Site: http://www.ohionational.com
Rev.: $2,388,716,000
Assets: $39,178,667,000
Liabilities: $36,713,380,000
Net Worth: $2,465,287,000
Earnings: $72,649,000
Fiscal Year-end: 12/31/2018
Mutual Insurance Holding Company; Insur-
ance & Financial Products & Services
N.A.I.C.S.: 551112

Subsidiary (Domestic):

Ohio National Equities, Inc. (3)
1 Financial Way Ste 100, Cincinnati, OH
45242
Tel.: (513) 794-6100
Web Site: http://www.ohionational.com
Sales Range: $50-74.9 Million
Emp.: 40
Wholesale Securities Brokerage & Dealing
Services
N.A.I.C.S.: 523150
Laurens N. Sullivan (VP-Institutional Sls)

**Ohio National Financial Services,
Inc.** (3)
One Financial Way, Cincinnati, OH
45242 (100%)
Tel.: (513) 794-6100
Web Site: http://www.ohionational.com
Sales Range: $75-99.9 Million
Emp.: 700
Holding Company
N.A.I.C.S.: 551112
Pamela A. Webb (Sr VP-HR & Corp Svcs)

Ohio National Investments, Inc. (3)
1 Financial Way, Montgomery, OH 45242
Tel.: (513) 794-6336
Emp.: 30
Investment Advisory Services
N.A.I.C.S.: 523940

**Ohio National Life Assurance
Corporation** (3)
1 Financial Way ste100, Cincinnati, OH
45242
Tel.: (513) 794-6100
Fire Insurance Services
N.A.I.C.S.: 524210

The O.N. Equity Sales Company (3)
1 Financial Way, Cincinnati, OH 45242
Tel.: (513) 794-6794
Web Site: http://www.joinonesco.com
Investment Management Service
N.A.I.C.S.: 523940
Patrick H. McEvoy (Pres)

**Demers, Manufacturier d'Ambulances
Inc.** (1)
28 Richelieu, Beloeil, J3G 4N5, QC,
Canada
Tel.: (450) 467-4683

Web Site: http://www.demers-
ambulances.com
Sales Range: $10-24.9 Million
Ambulances Designer & Mfr
N.A.I.C.S.: 336211
Benoit R. Lafortune (Exec VP)

Subsidiary (US):

Braun Industries, Inc. (2)
1170 Production Dr, Van Wert, OH 45891
Tel.: (419) 232-7020
Web Site: http://www.braunambulances.com
Customized Ambulance Mfr
N.A.I.C.S.: 336211
Kim Braun (Pres)

Subsidiary (Domestic):

Crestline Coach Ltd. (2)
126 Wheeler Street, Saskatoon, S7P 0A9,
SK, Canada
Tel.: (306) 934-8844
Web Site: http://www.crestlinecoach.com
Sales Range: $10-24.9 Million
Ambulance & Emergency Vehicle Mfr
N.A.I.C.S.: 336110
Steven Hoffrogge (Pres & CEO)

Subsidiary (US):

Medix Specialty Vehicles, Inc. (2)
3008 Mobile Dr, Elkhart, IN 46514-5524
Tel.: (574) 266-0911
Web Site: http://www.medixambulance.com
Rev.: $6,500,000
Emp.: 57
Light Truck & Utility Vehicle Mfr
N.A.I.C.S.: 336110
Art Brown (Mgr-Warranty & Svc-Electrical
Product Dev)

FNZ Holdings Ltd (1)
1 Tanfield, Edinburgh, EH3 5DA, United
Kingdom
Tel.: (44) 303 333 3330
Sales Range: $150-199.9 Million
Emp.: 220
Investment Management Service
N.A.I.C.S.: 523940

Subsidiary (Non-US):

Brand Addition GmbH (2)
Heydastrasse 13-15, 58093, Hagen, Ger-
many
Tel.: (49) 233195970
Web Site: http://www.brandaddition.de
Sales Range: $10-24.9 Million
Emp.: 50
Marketing of Promotional Goods
N.A.I.C.S.: 459110
Adelfo Marino (Mng Dir)

Subsidiary (Domestic):

FNZ (UK) Ltd (2)
Suite 1 3rd Floor 11-12 St James's Square,
London, SW1Y 4LB, United Kingdom
Tel.: (44) 131 473 1786
Web Site: http://www.fnz.com
Financial Related Software Services
N.A.I.C.S.: 541511
Adrian Durham (CEO)

Subsidiary (Non-US):

**European Bank for Financial Services
GmbH** (3)
Bahnhofstrasse 20, Aschheim, 80218, Ger-
many
Tel.: (49) 89 4 54 60890
Web Site: http://www.ebase.com
Financial Investment Services
N.A.I.C.S.: 523940
Rudolf Geyer (Mng Dir)

Fondsdepot Bank GmbH (3)
Windmuhlenweg 12, 95030, Hof, Germany
Tel.: (49) 928172580
Web Site: http://www.fondsdepotbank.de
Investment Account Administration Services
N.A.I.C.S.: 561499
Sabine Dittmann-Stenger (COO)

Ivanhoe Cambridge, Inc. (1)
1001 rue du Square-Victoria, Montreal, H2Z
2B5, QC, Canada
Tel.: (514) 841-7600
Web Site:
http://www.ivanhoecambridge.com

Sales Range: $150-199.9 Million
Emp.: 600
Operator & Manager of Shopping Centers
N.A.I.C.S.: 531120
Daniel Fournier (Chm & CEO)

Branch (Domestic):

Ivanhoe Cambridge (2)
95 Wellington Street West Suite 600, To-
ronto, M5J 2R2, ON, Canada (100%)
Tel.: (416) 369-1200
Web Site:
http://www.ivanhoecambridge.com
Sales Range: $75-99.9 Million
Emp.: 170
Shopping Center Space Leasing Services
N.A.I.C.S.: 581190
Daniel Fournier (Chm & CEO)

Unit (US):

**The Shops at Mary Brickell
Village** (2)
901 S Miami Ave Ste 206, Miami, FL 33130
Tel.: (305) 381-6130
Web Site:
http://www.marybrickellvillage.com
Shopping Center Property Manager
N.A.I.C.S.: 531312
Fernando Perez (Gen Mgr)

Madden Manufacturing Co., Inc. (1)
469 Dogwood Rd, Lake Ozark, MO 65049
Tel.: (573) 365-7040
Web Site: http://www.maddenmetals.com
Rev.: $1,240,000
Emp.: 10
Other Building Finishing Contractors
N.A.I.C.S.: 238390
Cory Hofeldt (VP-Ops)

New Look Vision Group, Inc. (1)
1 Place Ville Marie Suite 3670, Montreal,
H3B 3P2, QC, Canada
Tel.: (514) 877-4119
Web Site: http://www.newlookvision.ca
Rev.: $227,938,213
Assets: $295,615,273
Liabilities: $174,060,725
Net Worth: $121,554,548
Earnings: $14,844,126
Emp.: 2,599
Fiscal Year-end: 12/28/2019
Eye Wear Accessories Distr
N.A.I.C.S.: 423460
Antoine Amiel (Pres & CEO)

Subsidiary (Domestic):

IRIS The Visual Group Inc. (2)
3030 Boul Le Carrefour Suite 1200, Laval,
H7T 2P5, QC, Canada
Tel.: (450) 688-9060
Web Site: http://www.iris.ca
Eye Care Product Distr
N.A.I.C.S.: 423450

Otera Capital, Inc. (1)
World Trade Center 413 rue St-Jacques
Suite 700, Montreal, H2Y 1N9, QC, Canada
Tel.: (514) 847-5900
Web Site: http://www.oteracapital.com
Emp.: 70
Mortgage Lending Services
N.A.I.C.S.: 522292
Raymond McManus (Chm)

PetSmart, Inc. (1)
19601 N 27th Ave, Phoenix, AZ 85027
Tel.: (623) 587-2025
Web Site: https://www.petsmart.com
Sales Range: $5-14.9 Billion
Emp.: 50,000
Pet & Pet Supplies Retailers
N.A.I.C.S.: 459910
Raymond Svider (Chm)

Subsidiary (Domestic):

Chewy, Inc. (2)
7700 W Sunrise Blvd, Plantation, FL 33322
Tel.: (786) 320-7111
Web Site: https://www.chewy.com
Rev.: $11,147,720,000
Assets: $3,186,851,000
Liabilities: $2,676,607,000
Net Worth: $510,244,000
Earnings: $39,580,000
Emp.: 18,100
Fiscal Year-end: 01/28/2024

Animal Food Distr
N.A.I.C.S.: 459910
Raymond Svider *(Chm)*

SPIE Fleischhauer GmbH **(1)**
Oldenburger Allee 36, 30659, Hannover, Germany
Tel.: (49) 51190140
Web Site: http://www.spie-fleischhauer.com
Sales Range: $50-74.9 Million
Emp.: 407
Building Technology Services
N.A.I.C.S.: 926130
Michael Hartoung *(Mng Dir)*

Sebia SA **(1)**
Parc Technologique Leonard de Vinci, Lisses, 91008, France
Tel.: (33) 69 89 80 80
Web Site: http://www.sebia.com
Sales Range: $125-149.9 Million
Emp.: 400
Medical Diagnostic Equipment Mfr
N.A.I.C.S.: 339112
Benoit Adelus *(Chm & CEO)*

Subsidiary (Non-US):

ORGENTEC Diagnostika GmbH **(2)**
Carl-Zeiss-Strasse 49-51, 55129, Mainz, Germany
Tel.: (49) 6131 9258 0
Web Site: http://www.orgentec.com
Emp.: 120
Diagnostic Services
N.A.I.C.S.: 621511
Ralf Wehen *(Mng Dir)*

Subsidiary (US):

Corgenix Medical Corporation **(3)**
11575 Main St Ste 400, Broomfield, CO 80020
Tel.: (303) 457-4345
Web Site: http://www.corgenix.com
Sales Range: $10-24.9 Million
Specialized Diagnostic Test Kits Developer & Marketer for Vascular Diseases & Immunological Disorders
N.A.I.C.S.: 325413
James F. Widergren *(Pres)*

Subsidiary (US):

Sebia, Inc. **(2)**
1705 Corporate Dr, Norcross, GA 30093
Tel.: (770) 446-3707
Web Site: http://www.sebia-usa.com
Rev.: $3,300,000
Emp.: 22
Medical Diagnostic Equipment Mfr
N.A.I.C.S.: 339112
Theresa Heslin *(CEO)*

Zeus Scientific, Inc. **(2)**
199 & 200 Evans Way, 08876, Branchburg, NJ
Tel.: (908) 526-3744
Web Site: http://www.zeusscientific.com
Surgical & Medical Instrument Mfr
N.A.I.C.S.: 339112
Mark Kopnitsky *(VP-Science & Quality)*

Sodemex Developpement **(1)**
Edifice Price 65 rue Sainte-Anne 14e FL, Quebec, G1R 3X5, QC, Canada **(100%)**
Tel.: (418) 684-2334
Sales Range: $50-74.9 Million
Emp.: 2
Private Investments in Junior Exploration Companies
N.A.I.C.S.: 523999
Denis Landry *(Pres)*

Southern Star Central Corp. **(1)**
4700 Hwy 56, Owensboro, KY 42301
Tel.: (270) 852-5000
Web Site:
   http://www.southernstarcentralcorp.com
Natural Gas Transmission Services
N.A.I.C.S.: 486210
David L. Finley *(Chief Admin Officer)*

Sterling Infosystems, Inc. **(1)**
1 State St Plz 24th Fl, New York, NY 10004
Tel.: (212) 736-5100
Web Site: https://www.sterlingbackcheck.ca
Employment & Background Screening Services
N.A.I.C.S.: 561499
Lou Paglia *(Pres & COO)*

Subsidiary (Domestic):

EmployeeScreenIQ, Inc. **(2)**
PO Box 22627, Cleveland, OH 44122
Tel.: (216) 514-2800
Web Site: http://www.employeescreen.com
Background Screening Services
N.A.I.C.S.: 561499
Jason B. Morris *(Founder, Pres & COO)*

Transport Service Co. **(2)**
2001 Spring Rd Ste 400, Oak Brook, IL 60523
Tel.: (630) 472-5900
Web Site:
   http://www.transportserviceco.com
Sales Range: $125-149.9 Million
Emp.: 40
Contract Haulers
N.A.I.C.S.: 484121

Student Transportation Inc. **(1)**
3349 Highway 138 Building A, Ste C, Wall Township, NJ 07719
Tel.: (732) 280-4200
Web Site: https://ridesta.com
School & Charter Bus Transportation Services
N.A.I.C.S.: 485410
Patrick J. Walker *(CFO)*

Subsidiary (Domestic):

Student Transportation of America, Inc. **(2)**
3349 Hwy 138 Bldg B Ste D, Wall, NJ 07719-9671
Web Site: http://www.ridesta.com
School & Charter Bus Transportation Services
N.A.I.C.S.: 485410
Denis J. Gallagher *(VP-Ops)*

Subsidiary (Domestic):

Rick Bus Company, Inc. **(3)**
1399 Lower Ferry Rd, Ewing, NJ 08618
Tel.: (609) 392-7550
School Buses
N.A.I.C.S.: 485510

Subsidiary (Non-US):

Student Transportation of Canada, Inc. **(3)**
160 Saunders Road Unit 6, Barrie, L4N 9A4, ON, Canada
Tel.: (705) 721-2626
Web Site: http://www.ridestc.com
Student Transportation
N.A.I.C.S.: 485410

Subsidiary (Domestic):

Parkview Transit **(4)**
95 Forhan Ave, Newmarket, L3Y 8X6, ON, Canada
Tel.: (905) 775-5331
Web Site: http://www.parkviewtransit.ca
School Bus Transportation Services
N.A.I.C.S.: 485113

Techem GmbH **(1)**
Hauptstrasse 89, 65760, Eschborn, Germany
Tel.: (49) 61965220
Web Site: http://www.techem.de
Energy Billing & Energy Management Services
N.A.I.C.S.: 561499
Robert Woggon *(Head-Corp Comm)*

Subsidiary (Non-US):

Danuvius EOOD **(2)**
bul Ovtscha kupel 72 Et 2, 1618, Sofia, Bulgaria
Tel.: (359) 2 955 04 11
Energy & Water Metering Equipment Mfr
N.A.I.C.S.: 334515
Asya Angelova *(Country Mgr)*

Subsidiary (US):

Metron Sustainable Services Inc. **(2)**
5661 Airport Blvd, Boulder, CO 80301
Tel.: (303) 217-5990
Web Site:
   http://www.metronsubmetering.com
Energy Billing & Energy Management Services

N.A.I.C.S.: 561499
Rick Minogue *(Mng Dir)*

Subsidiary (Non-US):

Techem (Schweiz) AG **(2)**
Steinackerstrasse 55, 8902, Urdorf, Switzerland
Tel.: (41) 43 455 65 00
Web Site: http://www.techem.ch
Energy Billing & Energy Management Services
N.A.I.C.S.: 561499
Marcel Sporrer *(Mng Dir & Head-Fin)*

Techem Danmark A/S **(2)**
Trindsovej 7A-B, 8000, Arhus, Denmark
Tel.: (45) 87 44 77 00
Web Site: http://www.techem.dk
Energy Billing & Energy Management Services
N.A.I.C.S.: 561499
Carsten Hejgaard *(Mgr)*

Techem Energy Services B.V. **(2)**
Takkebijsters 17 A1, 4817 BL, Breda, Netherlands
Tel.: (31) 76 57 25 800
Web Site: http://www.techem.nl
Energy Billing & Energy Management Services
N.A.I.C.S.: 561499
Maikel van Loo *(Mng Dir)*

Techem Energy Services Middle East FZCO **(2)**
Dubai Silicon Oasis Headquaters Building, PO Box 341002, Office 603 D-Wing, Dubai, United Arab Emirates
Tel.: (971) 4 5015516
Web Site: http://www.techem.me
Energy Billing & Energy Management Services
N.A.I.C.S.: 561499

Techem Energy Services S.R.L. **(2)**
Strada Ronda nr 8 Sector 2, 024102, Bucharest, Romania
Tel.: (40) 21 323 21 21
Web Site: http://www.techem.ro
Energy Billing & Energy Management Services
N.A.I.C.S.: 561499

Techem Enerji Hizmetleri Sanayi ve Ticaret Limited Sirketi **(2)**
Gulbahar Mah Avni Dilligil Sok Celik Is Merkezi, No 11/A Daire 5 Sisli, 34394, Istanbul, Turkiye
Tel.: (90) 212 447 07 47
Web Site: http://www.techem.com.tr
Energy Billing & Energy Management Services
N.A.I.C.S.: 561499

Techem Norge A/S **(2)**
Dicks vei 10b, 1366, Lysaker, Norway
Tel.: (47) 22 02 14 59
Web Site: http://www.techem.no
Energy Billing & Energy Management Services
N.A.I.C.S.: 561499

Techem S.r.l. **(2)**
Via dei Buonvisi 61/D, 00148, Rome, Italy
Tel.: (39) 06 65191810
Web Site: http://www.techem.it
Energy Billing & Energy Management Services
N.A.I.C.S.: 561499
Octavio Manuel Prieto *(Mng Dir)*

Techem SAS **(2)**
Gay Lussac building 20 avenue Edouard Herriot, CS 9002, 92356, Le Plessis-Robinson, Cedex, France
Tel.: (33) 1 46 01 59 70
Web Site: http://www.techem.fr
Energy Billing & Energy Management Services
N.A.I.C.S.: 561499
Bruno Macre *(Dir)*

Techem Services e.o.o.d. **(2)**
jk Geo Milev Prof Georgi Pavlov No 3, 1111, Sofia, Bulgaria
Tel.: (359) 700 1 28 28
Web Site: http://www.techem.net
Energy Billing & Energy Management Services

N.A.I.C.S.: 561499

Techem Sverige AB **(2)**
Foretagsgatan 9, Box 5, 233 51, Svedala, Sweden
Tel.: (46) 102022800
Web Site: http://www.techem.se
Energy Billing & Energy Management Services
N.A.I.C.S.: 561499
Carsten Hejgaard *(CEO)*

Techem Techniki Pomiarowe Sp. z o.o. **(2)**
os Lecha 121, 61 298, Poznan, Poland
Tel.: (48) 61 623 35 00
Web Site: http://www.techem.pl
Energy Billing & Energy Management Services
N.A.I.C.S.: 561499
Wojciech Lubiniecki *(Chm-Mgmt Bd)*

Techem do Brasil Servicos de Medicao de Agua Ltda. **(2)**
Av Brig Luis Antonio 2 729, 13 andar Jardim Paulista, Sao Paulo, 01401 000, Brazil
Tel.: (55) 11 3059 3030
Web Site: http://www.techem.com.br
Energy Billing & Energy Management Services
N.A.I.C.S.: 561499
Eduardo Lacerda Soares *(Mng Dir)*

Techem spol. s r. o. **(2)**
Hattalova 12, 831 03, Bratislava, Slovakia
Tel.: (421) 2 49 10 64 11
Web Site: http://www.techem.sk
Energy Billing & Energy Management Services
N.A.I.C.S.: 561499
Eliana Kostolany *(Mng Dir)*

Techem spol. s r. o. **(2)**
Pocernicka 96, Malesice, 108 00, Prague, Czech Republic
Tel.: (420) 272 088 777
Web Site: http://www.techem.cz
Energy Billing & Energy Management Services
N.A.I.C.S.: 561499
Jiri Zerzan *(Mng Dir)*

Trencap L.P. **(1)**
1000 place Jean Paul Riopelle, Montreal, H2Z 2B3, QC, Canada **(64.74%)**
Tel.: (514) 847-2126
Holding Company
N.A.I.C.S.: 551112

Holding (Domestic):

Noverco Inc. **(2)**
1000 place Jean Paul Riopelle, Montreal, H2Z 2B3, QC, Canada **(61.1%)**
Tel.: (514) 847-2126
Holding Company; Gas Distribution
N.A.I.C.S.: 551112

Holding (Domestic):

Gaz Metro Inc. **(3)**
1717 Du Havre, Montreal, H2K 2X3, QC, Canada **(100%)**
Tel.: (514) 598-3444
Web Site: https://www.energir.com
Sales Range: $550-599.9 Million
Emp.: 1,500
Holding Company
N.A.I.C.S.: 551112

Subsidiary (Domestic):

Gaz Metro Limited Partnership **(4)**
1717 du Havre, Montreal, H2K 2X3, QC, Canada **(71%)**
Tel.: (514) 598-3444
Web Site: http://www.gazmetro.com
Natural Gas Distr
N.A.I.C.S.: 221210
Sophie Brochu *(Pres & CEO)*

Affiliate (Domestic):

Aqua-Rehab, Inc. **(5)**
2145 Rue Michelin, Laval, H7L 5B8, QC, Canada
Tel.: (450) 687-3472
Web Site: http://www.aquarehab.com
Sales Range: $1-9.9 Million
Emp.: 65

Caisse de Depot et Placement du
Quebec—(Continued)

Trenchless Rehabilitation of Underground
Infrastructures
N.A.I.C.S.: 611710

Subsidiary (Domestic):

Climatisation et Chauffage Urbains **(5)**
de Montreal (CCUM)
1350 Nobel, Boucherville, J4B 5H3, QC,
Canada
Tel.: (514) 398-9773
Web Site: http://www.ccum.com
Sales Range: $150-199.9 Million
Emp.: 20
Superheated Steam Distr
N.A.I.C.S.: 221330

Gaz Metro Plus Inc. **(5)**
1350 rue Nobel bureau 100, Boucherville,
J4B 5H3, QC, Canada
Tel.: (450) 641-6300
Web Site: http://www.gazmetroplus.com
Sales Range: $10-24.9 Million
Emp.: 200
Provider of Equipment Rental & Technical
Services
N.A.I.C.S.: 532412
Luc Genier (Pres)

Affiliate (Domestic):

Natural Gas Technology Centre **(5)**
1350 Nobel Bd Ste 150, Boucherville, J4B
5H3, QC, Canada
Tel.: (450) 449-4774
Web Site: http://www.ctgn.qc.ca
Sales Range: $1-9.9 Million
Emp.: 20
Research Center for Technological Develop-
ments for Natural Gas Applications
N.A.I.C.S.: 541715

Subsidiary (US):

Northern New England Energy
Corporation **(5)**
PO Box 467, Burlington, VT 05402-0700
Tel.: (802) 658-6555
Web Site: http://www.nneec.com
Natural Gas Distr
N.A.I.C.S.: 221210
Sophie Brochu (Pres & CEO)

Subsidiary (Domestic):

Green Mountain Power
Corporation **(6)**
163 Acorn Ln, Colchester, VT 05446-6612
Tel.: (802) 864-5731
Sales Range: $200-249.9 Million
Emp.: 192
Electricity Supplier
N.A.I.C.S.: 221122
Dawn D. Bugbee (CFO & VP)

Subsidiary (Domestic):

Vermont Electric Power Company,
Inc. **(7)**
366 Pinnacle Ridge Rd, Rutland, VT 05701
Tel.: (802) 773-9161
Web Site: http://www.velco.com
Sales Range: $25-49.9 Million
Emp.: 100
Electric Energy & Operator of Power Trans-
mission Infrastructure Distr
N.A.I.C.S.: 221121
Tom Dunn (Pres & CEO)

Vermont Yankee Nuclear Power
Corporation **(7)**
163 Acorn Ln, Colchester, VT 05446
Tel.: (802) 864-5731
Sales Range: $125-149.9 Million
Electric Power Distribution Services
N.A.I.C.S.: 221122
Dawn D. Bugbee (Pres)

Subsidiary (Domestic):

Vermont Gas Systems, Inc. **(6)**
85 Swift St, South Burlington, VT 05403-
7306
Tel.: (802) 863-4511
Web Site: http://www.vermontgas.com
Sales Range: $50-74.9 Million
Emp.: 130
Natural Gas Distr

N.A.I.C.S.: 221210
Don Rendall (Pres & CEO)

Subsidiary (Domestic):

TelDig Systems, Inc. **(5)**
575 Saint Joseph E, Quebec, G1K 3B7,
QC, Canada
Tel.: (418) 948-1314
Web Site: http://www.teldig.com
Sales Range: $150-199.9 Million
Emp.: 23
Damage Protection for Buried Infrastructure
Systems
N.A.I.C.S.: 221210

Joint Venture (Domestic):

Trans Quebec & Maritimes Pipeline
Inc. **(5)**
1 Place Ville-Marie 39th floor, Montreal,
H2B 4M7, QC, Canada
Tel.: (450) 462-5300
Web Site: http://www.gazoductqm.com
Sales Range: $75-99.9 Million
Emp.: 4
Natural Gas Distr
N.A.I.C.S.: 486210
David Marchand (CFO)

Holding (Domestic):

Valener Inc. **(3)**
1717 rue du Havre, Montreal, H2K 2X3,
QC, Canada
Tel.: (514) 598-6220
Web Site: http://www.valener.com
Rev.: $55,092,164
Assets: $739,225,961
Liabilities: $119,517,177
Net Worth: $619,708,784
Earnings: $40,669,902
Emp.: 2,150
Fiscal Year-end: 09/30/2018
Power Generation Services
N.A.I.C.S.: 221118
Martin Imbleau (Sr VP-Dev Communities)

USI Holdings Corporation **(1)**
100 Summit Lake Dr Ste 400, Valhalla, NY
10595
Tel.: (914) 749-8500
Web Site: http://www.usi.com
Holding Company; Insurance Agencies &
Services
N.A.I.C.S.: 551112
Edward J. Bowler (CFO & Sr VP-Corp Dev)

Subsidiary (Domestic):

USI Insurance Services LLC **(2)**
100 Summit Lk Dr Ste 400, Valhalla, NY
10595
Tel.: (866) 657-0861
Web Site: https://www.usi.com
Insurance Services
N.A.I.C.S.: 524101
Sanford Ware (VP)

Subsidiary (Domestic):

Accelerated Benefits **(3)**
5880 Venture Dr, Dublin, OH 43017
Tel.: (614) 791-1143
Web Site: http://www.accben.com
Insurance & Benefits Brokerage Firm
N.A.I.C.S.: 524210

Associated Financial Group, LLC **(3)**
12600 Whitewater Dr Ste 100, Minnetonka,
MN 55343-9437
Tel.: (952) 945-0200
Web Site: http://www.associatedbrc.com
Emp.: 400
Insurance Agency; Human Resource Con-
sulting, Risk & Employee Benefits Manage-
ment Services
N.A.I.C.S.: 524210
Mardi Burns (Sr VP)

Branch (Domestic):

Associated Financial Group, LLC -
Waukesha Office **(4)**
N16 W23250 Stone Rdg Dr Ste 5, Wauke-
sha, WI 53188
Tel.: (262) 542-8822
Web Site:
http://www.associatedfinancialgroup.com

Sales Range: $25-49.9 Million
Emp.: 30
Financial Services
N.A.I.C.S.: 523999

Subsidiary (Domestic):

Financial Resource Management
Group, Inc. **(4)**
6000 Clearwater Dr, Minnetonka, MN
55343-9437
Tel.: (952) 945-0200
Sales Range: $50-74.9 Million
Emp.: 1
Insurance & Pension Fund Management
Services
N.A.I.C.S.: 524292
Rick Thill (Gen Mgr)

Subsidiary (Domestic):

BOK Financial Insurance, Inc. **(3)**
821 17th St, Denver, CO 80202
Tel.: (303) 988-0446
Web Site: http://www.cobizins.com
Business Insurance & Employee Benefit
Consulting Services
N.A.I.C.S.: 525110

Beneficial Insurance Services,
LLC **(3)**
1818 Market St Ste 2100, Philadelphia, PA
19103
Tel.: (215) 925-7656
Sales Range: $1-9.9 Million
Emp.: 40
Insurance Services
N.A.I.C.S.: 524298
Joe Robinson (Pres)

Cavanah Associates, Inc. **(3)**
1100 Alakea St Ste 2600, Honolulu, HI
96813
Tel.: (808) 537-1970
Web Site: http://www.cavanah.com
Sales Range: $1-9.9 Million
Emp.: 19
Insurance Brokerage Services
N.A.I.C.S.: 524210

Chernoff Diamond & Co, LLC **(3)**
725 RXR Plaza E Tower, Uniondale, NY
11556
Tel.: (516) 683-6100
Human Resources & Executive Search
Consulting Services
N.A.I.C.S.: 541612
Frank J. Aiosa (Partner-Transaction Ser-
vices)

Cohen-Seltzer, Inc. **(3)**
520 W Pennsylvania Ave, Fort Washington,
PA 19034
Tel.: (215) 542-0600
Web Site: http://www.cosel.com
Insurance, Risk Management & Financial
Services
N.A.I.C.S.: 524210

Daul Insurance Agency, Inc. **(3)**
94 Westbank Expy Ste A, Gretna, LA 70054
Tel.: (504) 362-0667
Web Site: http://www.daulinsurance.com
Insurance Agencies & Brokerages
N.A.I.C.S.: 524210
Jerry Daul (Owner & Pres)

Full Service Insurance, Inc. **(3)**
903 Murfreesboro Rd, Franklin, TN 37064-
3002
Tel.: (615) 790-0990
Web Site: http://www.fullserviceins.com
Insurance Brokerage Services
N.A.I.C.S.: 524210
Eddie Fly (Mgr-Comml Lines Mktg)

Gaudreau Group Inc. **(3)**
2377 Boston Road, Wilbraham, MA 01095
Tel.: (413) 543-3534
Web Site: http://www.gaudreaugroup.com
Insurance Related Activities
N.A.I.C.S.: 524298
Jules O. Gaudreau (Pres)

Hildi Incorporated **(3)**
14852 Scenic Heights R Ste 205, Minne-
apolis, MN 55344
Tel.: (952) 934-5554
Web Site: http://www.hildiinc.com
Professional, Scientific & Technical Services
N.A.I.C.S.: 541990

Roxane Gilje (Office Mgr)

Marcotte Insurance Agency, Inc. **(3)**
9394 W Dodge Rd #250, Omaha, NE
68114
Tel.: (402) 398-9009
Insurance Agencies & Brokerages
N.A.I.C.S.: 524210
Amy Fredrickson (Acct Mgr)

Ritman & Associates, Inc. **(3)**
1154 Conner St, Noblesville, IN 46060-2808
Tel.: (317) 770-3000
Web Site: http://www.ritmanassoc.com
Insurance Agents
N.A.I.C.S.: 524210
Jennifer Ritman (Pres)

Scheetz & Hogan Insurance Agency,
Inc. **(3)**
1000 E North St, Greenville, SC 29601
Tel.: (864) 232-5162
Web Site: http://www.shfpins.com
Insurance Agencies & Brokerages
N.A.I.C.S.: 524210
Ronald D. Scheetz (Pres & CEO)

The Bert Company **(3)**
3645 W Lk Rd, Erie, PA 16505-3450
Tel.: (814) 838-0000
Insurance Brokerage & Consulting Services
N.A.I.C.S.: 524210

The Colburn Corp. **(3)**
3001 W Big Beaver Rd, Troy, MI 48084
Tel.: (248) 643-4800
Web Site: http://www.colburngroup.com
Sales Range: $1-9.9 Million
Emp.: 20
Insurance Agencies & Brokerages
N.A.I.C.S.: 524210
Harry S. Colburn (Principal)

U.S. Risk Insurance Group, Inc. **(3)**
8401 North Central Expy Ste 1000, Dallas,
TX 75225
Tel.: (214) 265-7090
Web Site: http://www.usrisk.com
Holding Company; Insurance Services
N.A.I.C.S.: 551112
Randall Goss (CEO)

Subsidiary (Domestic):

Continental Risk Insurance
Services **(4)**
330 S Fairmont Ave Ste 2, Lodi, CA 95240-
3843
Tel.: (209) 365-6130
Web Site:
https://www.continentalriskins.com
Emp.: 100
Insurance Agencies & Brokerages
N.A.I.C.S.: 524210
Jeana Ramos (VP)

Gumtree Wholesale Insurance Bro-
kers, Inc. **(4)**
2616 Lakeward Dr Ste 120, Jackson, MS
39216
Tel.: (601) 983-4005
Web Site: http://www.gumtree-ins.com
Insurance Brokerage Services
N.A.I.C.S.: 524210
Nick Myers (Dir-Mktg & Underwriting)

U.S. Risk, LLC **(4)**
8401 N Central Expy Ste 1000, Dallas, TX
75225
Tel.: (214) 265-7090
Web Site: http://www.usrisk.com
Sales Range: $100-124.9 Million
Emp.: 500
Provider of Insurance Services
N.A.I.C.S.: 524210
Randall G. Goss (CEO)

Subsidiary (Domestic):

KRB Management, Inc. **(5)**
365 Miron Dr Ste D, Southlake, TX 76092
Tel.: (817) 424-1996
Web Site: http://www.auminsur.com
Insurance Agent/Broker
N.A.I.C.S.: 524210
Kenneth Boyd (Chm, Pres & CEO)

U.S. Risk Brokers, Inc. **(5)**
201 Rue Iberville Ste 725, Lafayette, LA
70508-8521
Tel.: (337) 235-7745

Web Site: https://www.usrisk.com
Insurance Brokerage Services
N.A.I.C.S.: 524210

Subsidiary (Domestic):

Regency Insurance Brokerage Services, Inc. (6)
217 E Hallandale Bch Blvd, Hallandale, FL 33009
Tel.: (954) 458-6323
Insurance Agencies & Brokerages
N.A.I.C.S.: 524210
Paul A. Riemer *(CEO)*

Subsidiary (Domestic):

U.S. Risk Financial Services, Inc. (5)
2550 Meridian Ste 200, Franklin, TN 37067
Tel.: (214) 265-7090
Web Site: http://www.usrisk.com
Sales Range: $25-49.9 Million
Emp.: 7
Provider of Insurance Services
N.A.I.C.S.: 524210

U.S. Risk Management, Inc. (5)
10210 N Central Expy Ste 500, Dallas, TX 75231-3425
Tel.: (214) 696-4700
Web Site: http://www.usrisk.com
Sales Range: $50-74.9 Million
Emp.: 250
Insurance Services
N.A.I.C.S.: 524298
George Gorney *(CIO & Exec VP-Corp Shared Svcs)*

US E & O Brokers (5)
820 Gessner Ste 1680, Houston, TX 77024
Tel.: (713) 984-1370
Web Site: http://www.useo.com
Insurance Agencies & Brokerages
N.A.I.C.S.: 524210
Susan Kirby *(Branch Mgr)*

Subsidiary (Domestic):

U.S.I. Insurance Services of Massachusetts, Inc. (3)
12 Gill St Ste 5500, Woburn, MA 01801
Tel.: (781) 938-7500
Web Site: http://www.usi.com
Insurance Services
N.A.I.C.S.: 524210

Unit (Domestic):

USI Affinity (3)
3805 W Chester Pike Ste 200, Newtown Square, PA 19073
Tel.: (610) 833-1800
Web Site: http://www.usiaffinity.com
Insurance & Financial Risk Management Services
N.A.I.C.S.: 524298

Subsidiary (Domestic):

USI Colorado LLC (3)
6501 S Fiddlers Green Cir Ste 100, Greenwood Village, CO 80111
Tel.: (303) 837-8500
Web Site: http://www.usi.com
Insurance Brokers
N.A.I.C.S.: 524210

Unit (Domestic):

USI Consulting Group (3)
95 Glastonbury Blvd Ste 102, Glastonbury, CT 06033-6503
Tel.: (860) 633-5283
Web Site: https://www.usicg.com
Employee Benefit Consulting Services
N.A.I.C.S.: 541612
Christopher J. Martin *(Sr VP-Defined Contribution)*

Subsidiary (Domestic):

Hooker & Holcombe, Inc. (4)
65 Lasalle Road Ste 402, West Hartford, CT 06107
Tel.: (860) 521-8400
Web Site: http://www.hhconsultants.com
Rev.: $7,000,000
Emp.: 60
Employee Benefit Consulting Services
N.A.I.C.S.: 541611

Richard S. Sych *(Pres)*

Branch (Domestic):

USI Insurance Services LLC - Austin (3)
7600 C N Capital of Texas Hwy Ste 200, Austin, TX 78731-1184
Tel.: (512) 451-7555
Web Site: http://www.usi.com
Insurance Agent Broker & Service
N.A.I.C.S.: 524210

USI Insurance Services LLC - Dallas (3)
14241 Dallas Pkwy, Dallas, TX 75254
Tel.: (214) 443-3100
Web Site: http://www.usi.com
Insurance Agents, Brokers & Service
N.A.I.C.S.: 524210

USI Insurance Services LLC - Fort Lauderdale (3)
2400 E Commercial Blvd Ste 600, Fort Lauderdale, FL 33309-2185
Tel.: (954) 607-4000
Web Site: http://www.usi.com
Commercial Property & Casualty Insurance, Retirement Planning & Employee Benefit Services
N.A.I.C.S.: 524126

USI Insurance Services LLC - Houston (3)
9811 Katy Fwy Ste 500, Houston, TX 77024
Tel.: (713) 490-4600
Web Site: http://www.usi.com
Insurance Agents, Brokers & Service
N.A.I.C.S.: 524210

USI Insurance Services LLC - Phoenix (3)
2375 E Camelback Rd Ste 250, Phoenix, AZ 85016
Tel.: (602) 395-9111
Web Site: http://www.usi.com
Insurance Brokers
N.A.I.C.S.: 524210

USI Insurance Services LLC - San Angelo (3)
133 W Concho Ave Ste 109, San Angelo, TX 76903
Tel.: (325) 486-5143
Web Site: http://www.usi.com
Insurance Agents, Brokers & Service
N.A.I.C.S.: 524210

USI Insurance Services LLC - South Portland (3)
75 John Roberts Rd, South Portland, ME 04106
Tel.: (855) 874-0123
Web Site: http://www.usi.com
Personal Insurance Brokerage Services
N.A.I.C.S.: 524210

Subsidiary (Domestic):

USI Insurance Services of Connecticut, LLC (3)
530 Preston Ave, Meriden, CT 06450-1040
Tel.: (203) 634-5700
Web Site: http://www.usi.com
Insurance Services
N.A.I.C.S.: 524298

Venneberg Insurance, Inc. (3)
225 Harbor Dr, Sitka, AK 99835-0199
Tel.: (907) 747-8625
Web Site: http://www.vennberginsurance.com
Insurance Agencies & Brokerages
N.A.I.C.S.: 524210

Vista Insurance Partners of Illinois, Inc. (3)
6 W Hubbard St 4 Fl, Chicago, IL 60654
Tel.: (312) 755-0084
Web Site: http://www.ajrenner.com
Insurance Brokers
N.A.I.C.S.: 524210
Alison J. Renner *(CEO)*

CAISSE DES DEPOTS ET CONSIGNATIONS
56 rue de Lille, 75356, Paris, France
Tel.: (33) 158500000   FR

Web Site:
http://www.caissedesdepots.fr
Year Founded: 1816
Holding Company Financial Insurance Real Estate Service Industry & Private Equity Services
N.A.I.C.S.: 551112
Olivier Mareuse *(Dir-Asset Mgmt & Savings Funds)*

Subsidiaries:

Banque des Territoires (1)
56 rue de Lille, 75356, Paris, France
Tel.: (33) 01585000
Web Site:
https://www.banquedesterritoires.fr
Investment Banking & Securities Dealing
N.A.I.C.S.: 523150

Joint Venture (Domestic):

Compagnie Eiffage du Viaduc de Millau (2)
Peage de Saint Germain, BP 60457, 12104, Millau, France   **(49%)**
Tel.: (33) 565616161
Web Site: http://www.leviaducdemillau.com
Bridge Construction Services
N.A.I.C.S.: 237310
Immanuel Cachot *(Mng Dir)*

Caisse des Depots et Consignations - Banking Services (1)
56 Auedelille, Paris, 75356, SP, France   **(100%)**
Tel.: (33) 158500000
Web Site: http://www.caissedesdepots.fr
Sales Range: $1-4.9 Billion
Emp.: 9,500
Banking Services
N.A.I.C.S.: 521110
Pierre Ducret *(Mng Dir)*

Caisse des Depots et Consignations - Local & Regional Development (1)
72 avenue Pierre Mendes-France, F-75914, Paris, Cedex 13, France   **(100%)**
Tel.: (33) 158507661
Web Site: http://www.caissedesdepots.fr
Community & Public Works Development Services
N.A.I.C.S.: 925120

Subsidiary (Domestic):

Alteau S.A. (2)
43 Rue Boissiere, F-75116, Paris, France   **(51%)**
Tel.: (33) 153704540
Web Site: http://www.alteau.fr
Sales Range: $10-24.9 Million
Emp.: 150
Public & Commercial Water & Sanitation Systems Management
N.A.I.C.S.: 924110

Egis S.A. (1)
15 Avenue du Centre, 78286, Saint-Quentin-en-Yvelines, Cedex, France   **(75%)**
Tel.: (33) 1 3941 4000
Web Site: http://www.egis.fr
Infrastructure Engineering Services
N.A.I.C.S.: 541330
Nicolas Jachiet *(Pres & CEO)*

Subsidiary (Non-US):

Aeroservice Consultoria e Engenharia de Projeto Ltda (2)
Rua Dr Sodre 72, 04535-110, Sao Paulo, Brazil
Tel.: (55) 11 3047 8399
Bus Transportation Services
N.A.I.C.S.: 485210

Egis Algerie S.p.A. (2)
Cooperative des Jasmins - Lot n 2, Les Sources Bir Mourad Rais, Algiers, Algeria
Tel.: (213) 21 44 91 76
Bus Transportation Services
N.A.I.C.S.: 485210

Subsidiary (Domestic):

Egis Avia SA (2)
195 rue Jean-Jacques Rousseau, 92138, Issy-les-Moulineaux, France

Tel.: (33) 1 41 23 46 00
Bus Transportation Services
N.A.I.C.S.: 485210

Egis Bdpa SA (2)
15 avenue du centre CS 20538, Guyancourt, 78286, Saint-Quentin-en-Yvelines, France
Tel.: (33) 1 30 48 22 70
Bus Transportation Services
N.A.I.C.S.: 485210

Subsidiary (Non-US):

Egis Beijing Industrial Technical Co., LTD. (2)
16k Mansion Oriental Kenzo N 48, Dongzhimenwai Dajie, Beijing, China
Tel.: (86) 10 58 19 60 07
Bus Transportation Services
N.A.I.C.S.: 485210

Egis Cameroun (2)
Villa ex Serec, BP 911, Sic Hippodrome, Yaounde, Cameroon
Tel.: (237) 223 54 30
Bus Transportation Services
N.A.I.C.S.: 485210

Egis Easytrip Services SA (2)
EA House Damastown Ind Estate, Mulhuddart, Dublin, Ireland
Tel.: (353) 1 861 3203
Bus Transportation Services
N.A.I.C.S.: 485210

Subsidiary (Domestic):

Egis Eau SA (2)
ZAC de Pacheroux 6 avenue Jean-Jacques Rousseau, 63510, Aulnat, France
Tel.: (33) 4 73 60 35 14
Bus Transportation Services
N.A.I.C.S.: 485210

Subsidiary (Non-US):

Egis Eyser SA (2)
Arequipa 1 Bloque 3 2 planta, 28043, Madrid, Spain
Tel.: (34) 91 578 37 70
Web Site: http://www.egis-eyser.com
Bus Transportation Services
N.A.I.C.S.: 485210

Egis Geoplan Pvt. Ltd. (2)
3/1 Platform Road, Seshadripuram, Bengaluru, 560 020, Karnataka, India
Tel.: (91) 80 66997200
Web Site: http://www.egis-geoplan.com
Emp.: 150
Bus Transportation Services
N.A.I.C.S.: 485210

Egis India Consulting Engineers Private Limited (2)
13/6 SSR Corporate Park 8th Floor NH 2 Delhi Mathura Road Sector 27B, 121 003, Faridabad, Haryana, India
Tel.: (91) 129 4265100
Web Site: http://www.egis-india.com
Bus Transportation Services
N.A.I.C.S.: 485210

Egis International S.A. (2)
Astoria Building - Etaj 1 64 - 66 Dionisie Lupu Street Sector 1, Bucharest, 010468, Romania
Tel.: (40) 21 312 24 48
Bus Transportation Services
N.A.I.C.S.: 485210

Egis Kenya Limited (2)
Timau Plaza Argwings Kodek Road, PO Box 76672, Kilimani, 00508, Nairobi, Kenya
Tel.: (254) 72 22 36 298
Bus Transportation Services
N.A.I.C.S.: 485210

Egis Poland sp. z o.o. (2)
ul Domaniewska 39A, 02-672, Warsaw, Poland
Tel.: (48) 22 20 30 100
Web Site: http://www.egispoland.com
Emp.: 150
Bus Transportation Services
N.A.I.C.S.: 485210
Cezer Gsaganowski *(Mng Dir)*

Egis Projects Asia Pacific Pty Ltd (2)
Ste 701 Level 7 50 Clarence street, Syd-

Caisse des Depots et Consignations—(Continued)

ney, 2000, NSW, Australia
Tel.: (61) 2 9086 6488
Bus Transportation Services
N.A.I.C.S.: 485210

Egis Projects Canada Inc. (2)
12165 Harris Road Ste 101, Pitt Meadows,
V3Y2E9, BC, Canada
Tel.: (604) 460 5010
Bus Transportation Services
N.A.I.C.S.: 485210

Egis Projects Ireland Ltd (2)
Unit 24 Northwood House Northwood Business Park, Santry, Dublin, Ireland
Tel.: (353) 1 469 1200
Web Site: http://www.egis-projects.ie
Emp.: 20
Bus Transportation Services
N.A.I.C.S.: 485210
Steve Preece (Mng Dir)

Egis Projects Philippines, Inc. (2)
Unit 703 7F Citystate Centre 709 Shaw
Boulevard, Pasig, 1603, Philippines
Tel.: (63) 2635 34 40
Bus Transportation Services
N.A.I.C.S.: 485210

Egis Projects Polska Sp. z o.o. (2)
ul Emilii Plater 53, 00-113, Warsaw, Poland
Tel.: (48) 224 902 033
Web Site: http://www.egis-projects.com
Bus Transportation Services
N.A.I.C.S.: 485210

Subsidiary (Domestic):

Egis Rail S.A. (2)
168 170 Avenue Thiers, 69006, Lyon,
France
Tel.: (33) 4 37 72 40 50
Bus Transportation Services
N.A.I.C.S.: 485210

Subsidiary (Non-US):

**Egis Road Operation Croatia
D.o.o.** (2)
O&M Centre Velika Ves b, 49224, Lepajci,
Croatia
Tel.: (385) 49 382 830
Bus Transportation Services
N.A.I.C.S.: 485210

**Egis Road Operation India Private
Limited** (2)
T-305 3rd floor tirupati plaza Sector -XI
Pkt-4 Plot No 11, 110075, New Delhi, India
Tel.: (91) 124 478 7800
Bus Transportation Services
N.A.I.C.S.: 485210

Egis Ukraina LLC (2)
Flat 14 - 45/2 Pushkinska Street, 01004,
Kiev, Ukraine
Tel.: (380) 44 230 23 87
Web Site: http://www.egisukraina.com
Emp.: 50
Bus Transportation Services
N.A.I.C.S.: 485210
Arnaud Derugy (Office Mgr)

England TIR Group (2)
Pzale dell Autostrada 36, 47521, Cesena,
Italy
Tel.: (39) 0547639911
Bus Transportation Services
N.A.I.C.S.: 485210

PT Egis Indonesia (2)
Wisma PMI 4 Floor Jalan Wijaya I no 63,
Kebayoran Baru, 12160, Jakarta, Indonesia
Tel.: (62) 21 725 25 77
Web Site: http://www.egis-indonesia.co.id
Bus Transportation Services
N.A.I.C.S.: 485210

Transpass B.V. (2)
Jacobus Lipsweg 122, 3316 BP, Dordrecht,
Netherlands
Tel.: (31) 78 653 06 04
Web Site: http://www.transpass.eu
Emp.: 30
Bus Transportation Services
N.A.I.C.S.: 485210
Gerard Berg (Mng Dir)

Icade S.A. (1)

27 rue Camille Desmoulins, 92445, Paris,
Cedex, Issy-les-Moulineaux,
France (61.6%)
Tel.: (33) 141577000
Web Site: https://www.icade.fr
Rev.: $1,959,421,541
Assets: $19,661,342,543
Liabilities: $10,288,905,677
Net Worth: $9,372,436,866
Earnings: $58,385,495
Emp.: 1,243
Fiscal Year-end: 12/31/2022
Real Estate Investment Trust
N.A.I.C.S.: 525990
Marianne de Battisti (Head-Institutional Rels
& Comm)

Subsidiary (Domestic):

ANF Immobilier (2)
27 Rue Camille Desmoulins, Issy les Moulineaux, 92130, Paris, France
Tel.: (33) 14157 7000
Web Site: http://www.anf-immobilier.com
Real Estate Investment Services
N.A.I.C.S.: 525990

Capri Atlantique (2)
70 Cours De Verdun, 33000, Bordeaux,
France (100%)
Tel.: (33) 556000111
Web Site: http://www.capri-immo.fr
Property Development Company
N.A.I.C.S.: 236118

Capri Lyon Mediterranee (2)
103 Ave De Saxe, 69003, Lyon,
France (100%)
Tel.: (33) 472601080
Web Site: http://www.capri-immo.fr
Sales Range: $50-74.9 Million
Emp.: 150
Property Development Group
N.A.I.C.S.: 236118

Compagnie la Lucette S.A. (2)
7 rue Scribe, 75009, Paris, France (100%)
Tel.: (33) 1 42 25 86 86
Sales Range: $125-149.9 Million
Emp.: 40
Commercial, Office & Industrial Real Estate,
Developer & Manager
N.A.I.C.S.: 531190

EMGP (2)
50 Ave Du Pres Wilson, St Denis La Plaine,
93214, Paris, Cedex, France (100%)
Tel.: (33) 149464840
Property Leasing Services
N.A.I.C.S.: 531120

GFF (Ile de France) (2)
Tour Franklin La Defence 8, 92042, Paris,
Cedex, France (100%)
Tel.: (33) 44948686
Web Site: http://www.gff.fr
Property Management & Consultancy Services
N.A.I.C.S.: 921190

Icade Capri S.A. (2)
204 Ave De Colmar, 67100, Strasbourg,
France
Tel.: (33) 388237464
Web Site: http://www.capriimmo.fr
Sales Range: $25-49.9 Million
Emp.: 15
Property Development Company
N.A.I.C.S.: 236118

Promomidi (2)
13 Rue Paul Mesple, BP 1257, Toulouse,
31100, Cedex, France
Tel.: (33) 534613060
Web Site: http://www.capri-immo.fr
Property Development Group
N.A.I.C.S.: 236118

SCIC Habitat (2)
Latrium, 6 Pl Abel Gance, 92100,
Boulogne-Billancourt, France (100%)
Tel.: (33) 146944711
Web Site: http://www.scichabitat.fr
Constructor of Affordable Housing & Property Management Services
N.A.I.C.S.: 925110

**Services Conseil Expertise Territoire
S.A.** (2)
102 Ave du France, 75646, Paris, France
Tel.: (33) 155033000

Web Site: http://www.scet.fr
Sales Range: $125-149.9 Million
Emp.: 500
Property Consultancy Group
N.A.I.C.S.: 921190
Remi de Nijs (CEO)

Novethic (1)
56 rue de Lille, 75007, Paris, France
Tel.: (33) 158509814
Web Site: http://www.novethic.fr
Investment Consultants
N.A.I.C.S.: 523940
Anne Catherine Husson Traore (Dir Gen)

SA BPI-Groupe (1)
27-31 Avenue du General Leclerc, 94710,
Maisons-Alfort, Cedex, France (50%)
Tel.: (33) 1 4179 8000
Web Site: http://www.bpifrance.fr
Holding Company; Private Equity & Equity
Investment Services
N.A.I.C.S.: 551112
Arnaud Caudoux (Dir-Fin & Warranty Mgmt)

Subsidiary (Domestic):

Bpifrance Financement (2)
27-31 avenue du General Leclerc, 94710,
Maisons-Alfort, Cedex, France (89.7%)
Tel.: (33) 1 4179 8000
Web Site: http://www.bpifrance.fr
Investment Financing Services
N.A.I.C.S.: 522299
Nicolas Dufourcq (Chm & Dir Gen)

Bpifrance Participations (2)
27-31 avenue du General Leclerc, 94710,
Maisons-Alfort, Cedex, France
Tel.: (33) 1 4179 8000
Web Site: http://www.bpifrance.fr
Emp.: 2,000
Equity Investment Firm
N.A.I.C.S.: 523999
Nicolas Dufourcq (Chm & Dir Gen)

Subsidiary (Domestic):

Bpifrance Investissement SAS (3)
27-31 avenue du General Leclerc, 94710,
Maisons-Alfort, Cedex, France
Tel.: (33) 1 4179 8000
Web Site: http://www.bpifrance.fr
Emp.: 1,300
Investment Management Service
N.A.I.C.S.: 523940
Nicolas Dufourcq (Chm)

Subsidiary (Domestic):

BAOBAG SAS (4)
2-16 Boulevard de Vintimille, 13015, Marseilles, France
Tel.: (33) 491627719
Web Site: http://www.baobag.eu
Plastics Bag Mfr
N.A.I.C.S.: 326111
Alain Cavalier (Pres)

Saur SA (1)
1 Ave Eugene Freyssinet, 78064, Saint-
Quentin-en-Yvelines, France (47%)
Tel.: (33) 130602260
Web Site: http://www.saur.com
Sales Range: $1-4.9 Billion
Water Treatment & Sanitation Services
N.A.I.C.S.: 562219
Olivier Brousse (Mng Dir & Pres)

Subsidiary (Domestic):

Coved (2)
1 rue Antoine Lavoisier, 78064, Guyancourt,
France
Tel.: (33) 130602260
Sales Range: $550-599.9 Million
Sanitation Management Services
N.A.I.C.S.: 562998
Brousse Olivier (Mng Dir)

Stereau SAS (2)
1 rue Antoine Lavoisier, 78064, Saint-
Quentin-en-Yvelines, France
Tel.: (33) 130602260
Web Site: http://www.stereau.fr
Sales Range: $10-24.9 Million
Emp.: 50
Waste Treatment Services
N.A.I.C.S.: 562219
Caroline Catoire (CFO)

Societe Nationale Immobiliere (1)
125 Avenue de Lodeve, BP 6068, 34074,
Montpellier, Cedex, France (100%)
Tel.: (33) 467759640
Property Management Services
N.A.I.C.S.: 531110
Andre Yche (Chm-Mgmt Bd)

Transdev Group S.A. (1)
Immeuble Crystal 3 Allee de Grenelle,
92442, Issy-les-Moulineaux,
France (66%)
Tel.: (33) 174342000
Web Site: https://www.transdev.com
Sales Range: $5-14.9 Billion
Emp.: 37,000
Passenger Transportation Services
N.A.I.C.S.: 485999
Jean-Marc Janaillac (Chm & CEO)

Subsidiary (US):

SuperShuttle International, Inc. (2)
14500 N Northsight Blvd Ste 329, Scottsdale, AZ 85260
Tel.: (480) 609-3000
Web Site: http://www.supershuttle.com
Sales Range: $25-49.9 Million
Emp.: 1,000
Airport Transportation Services
N.A.I.C.S.: 485119
R. Brian Weir (Pres & CEO)

Subsidiary (Domestic):

**Golden Touch Transportation of New
York** (3)
45-02 Ditmars Blvd, Astoria, NY 11105
Tel.: (718) 886-5204
Web Site:
http://www.goldentouchtransportation.com
Sales Range: $25-49.9 Million
Emp.: 100
Scheduled Air Transportation
N.A.I.C.S.: 485999
Thomas Herrschaft (Pres)

Subsidiary (US):

Transdev North America, Inc. (2)
720 E Butterfield Ste 300, Lombard, IL
60148
Tel.: (630) 571-7070
Web Site: http://www.transdevna.com
Sales Range: $900-999.9 Million
Emp.: 90
Passenger & Freight Transportation Services
N.A.I.C.S.: 485113
Bill McCloud (Sr VP-Client Rels)

Subsidiary (Domestic):

Connex TCT LLC (3)
10511B Hardin Vly Rd, Knoxville, TN 37932
Tel.: (865) 693-9404
Passenger Transport Services Operator
N.A.I.C.S.: 485999

Branch (Domestic):

Veolia Transportation, Inc. (3)
2100 Huntingdon Ave, Baltimore, MD 21211
Tel.: (410) 727-7300
Web Site:
http://www.veoliatransportation.com
Sales Range: $125-149.9 Million
Passenger & Freight Transportation Services
N.A.I.C.S.: 485999
Michael J. Weidger (Gen Mgr-TheBus-Pub
Works & Transportation-Prince Georges
County)

Subsidiary (Domestic):

Transdev S.A. (2)
Latrium 6 Place Abel Gance, 92652,
Boulogne-Billancourt, France
Tel.: (33) 146944811
Web Site: http://www.transdev.fr
Sales Range: $1-4.9 Billion
Emp.: 21,600
Public Transportation Systems Operator
N.A.I.C.S.: 485999

Subsidiary (Non-US):

Transdev Sverige AB (2)
Fredsforsstigen 22-24, Box 14091, SE-167
14, Bromma, Sweden

Tel.: (46) 86295000
Web Site: http://www.transdev.se
Emp.: 3,500
Passenger Transport Services Operator
N.A.I.C.S.: 485999
Gunnar Schon *(CEO)*

Subsidiary (Non-US):

Boreal Norge AS **(3)**
Klubbgata 1, Stavanger, 4013, Norway
Tel.: (47) 91555888
Web Site: http://www.boreal.no
Passenger Transport Services Operator
N.A.I.C.S.: 485999

Veolia Transport Finland Oy **(3)**
Tuupakantie 7 A, 01740, Vantaa, Finland
Tel.: (358) 98789170
Web Site: http://www.veolia-transport.fi
Sales Range: $25-49.9 Million
Emp.: 10
Passenger Transport Services Operator
N.A.I.C.S.: 485999

Veolia Transport Polska Sp. z o.o.
ul. **(3)**
Ul Slominskiego15509, 00 195, Warsaw,
Poland
Tel.: (48) 226375170
Web Site: http://www.connex.se
Sales Range: $25-49.9 Million
Emp.: 12
Passenger Transport Services Operator
N.A.I.C.S.: 485999

Subsidiary (Non-US):

Transdev plc **(2)**
4th Floor Zone G7, Palestra, 197 Blackfairs
Road, London, SE 8NJ, United Kingdom
Tel.: (44) 8453007000
Web Site: http://www.transdevplc.co.uk
Sales Range: $250-299.9 Million
Emp.: 3,895
Public Transportation
N.A.I.C.S.: 485999

Subsidiary (Domestic):

London United Busways **(3)**
Busways House Wellington Road, Wellington Rd, Twickenham, TW2 5NX, Middlesex,
United Kingdom
Tel.: (44) 2084006665
Web Site: http://www.londonutd.co.uk
Sales Range: $400-449.9 Million
Emp.: 500
Bus Operating Company
N.A.I.C.S.: 485210
Richard Hall *(Mng Dir)*

Subsidiary (Non-US):

Veolia Transport Australasia **(2)**
Level 8 469 La Trobe Street, Melbourne,
3000, VIC, Australia
Tel.: (61) 386817500
Web Site: http://www.transdev.com.au
Sales Range: $400-449.9 Million
Emp.: 60
Passenger Transport Services Operator
N.A.I.C.S.: 485999
Peter Lodge *(Gen Mgr)*

Subsidiary (Domestic):

Transdev Sydney Pty Ltd **(3)**
190 Pyrmont Street, Pyrmont, 2009, Australia
Tel.: (61) 285845288
Web Site:
   http://www.transdevsydney.com.au
Emp.: 80
Passenger Transport Services Operator
N.A.I.C.S.: 485999
Tony Ralph *(Gen Mgr-Light Rail Implementation)*

Veolia Transport Australia Pty
Ltd **(3)**
Level 8 469 La Trobe Street, PO Box 5092,
Melbourne, 3000, VIC, Australia
Tel.: (61) 3 8681 7500
Web Site: http://www.veolia.com.au
Bus Transportation Services
N.A.I.C.S.: 485210

Subsidiary (Non-US):

Veolia Transport Ireland **(2)**

Luas Depot Red Cow Roundabout, Clondalkin, Dublin, 22, Ireland
Tel.: (353) 14614910
Web Site: http://www.veolia-transport.ie
Sales Range: $100-124.9 Million
Emp.: 350
Passenger Transport Services Operator
N.A.I.C.S.: 485999

Veolia Transport Nederland BV **(2)**
Mastbosstraat 12, PO Box 3306, 4800 DH,
Breda, Netherlands
Tel.: (31) 765281000
Web Site: http://www.connex.se
Passenger Transport Services Operator
N.A.I.C.S.: 485999

Veolia Transport RATP India Pvt.
Ltd. **(2)**
B1 Marble Arch 9 Prithviraj Road, 110011,
New Delhi, India
Tel.: (91) 11 2465 3457
Bus Transportation Services
N.A.I.C.S.: 485210
Apurba Dhar *(Dir-Bus Dev)*

Veolia Verkher GmbH **(2)**
Georgenstrasse 22, 10117, Berlin, Germany
Tel.: (49) 3020073343
Web Site: http://www.veolia-verkher.de
Passenger Transport Services Operator
N.A.I.C.S.: 485999

CAISSE FRANCAISE DE FINANCEMENT LOCAL
1-3 rue du Passeur de Boulogne,
92130, Issy-les-Moulineaux, France
Tel.: (33) 171289099   FR
Web Site:
   https://www.caissefrancaise.fr
Year Founded: 1998
DXAHB—(ASX)
Rev.: $3,021,683,127
Assets: $69,743,452,154
Liabilities: $68,151,567,224
Net Worth: $1,591,884,930
Earnings: $70,845,857
Fiscal Year-end: 12/31/23
Investment Management Service
N.A.I.C.S.: 523940
Philippe Mills *(Chm-Supervisory Bd)*

CAISSE REGIONALE DE CREDIT AGRICOLE MUTUEL ATLANTIQUE VENDEE SC
La Garde -134 route de Paris, 44300,
Nantes, Cedex, France
Tel.: (33) 251895115
Web Site: https://www.ca-atlantique-
   vendee.fr
CRAV—(EUR)
Commercial Banking Services
N.A.I.C.S.: 522110
Patrice Cheramy *(CEO)*

CAISSE REGIONALE DE CREDIT AGRICOLE MUTUEL BRIE PICARDIE SCA
500 rue Saint-Fuscien, FR-80095,
Amiens, Cedex, France
Tel.: (33) 322533333
Web Site: https://www.ca-
   briepicardie.fr
CRBP2—(EUR)
Sales Range: $650-699.9 Million
Commercial Banking Services
N.A.I.C.S.: 522110
Guillaume Rousseau *(CEO &
Member-Exec Bd)*

CAISSE REGIONALE DE CREDIT AGRICOLE MUTUEL D'ILLE-ET-VILAINE SC
4 rue Louis Braille, 35136, Saint-
Jacques-de-la-Lande, France
Tel.: (33) 299033535
Web Site: https://www.ca-
   illeetvilaine.fr
CIV—(EUR)
Sales Range: Less than $1 Million

Commercial Banking Services
N.A.I.C.S.: 522110
Guillaume Rousseau *(CEO)*

CAISSE REGIONALE DE CREDIT AGRICOLE MUTUEL DE LA TOURAINE ET DU POITOU SCACV
45 Boulevard Winston Churchill, BP
4114, 37041, Tours, Cedex, France
Tel.: (33) 247398100
Web Site: http://www.ca-
   tourainepoitou.fr
CRTO—(EUR)
Sales Range: $300-349.9 Million
Financial Investment Management
Services
N.A.I.C.S.: 523940
Philippe Chatain *(CEO)*

CAISSE REGIONALE DE CREDIT AGRICOLE MUTUEL DE NORD DE FRANCE SC
10 avenue Foch, BP 369, 59020,
Lille, Cedex, France
Tel.: (33) 320637000
Web Site: https://www.ca-
   norddefrance.fr
CNF—(EUR)
Commercial Banking Services
N.A.I.C.S.: 522110
Francois Mace *(CEO)*

CAISSE REGIONALE DE CREDIT AGRICOLE MUTUEL DE NORMANDIE SEINE SC
Cite de l Agriculture chemin de la
Breteque, BP 800, 76230, Bois-
Guillaume, France
Tel.: (33) 227766030
Web Site: http://www.ca-normandie-
   seine.fr
CCN—(EUR)
Sales Range: $350-399.9 Million
Financial Services
N.A.I.C.S.: 524126
Nicolas Denis *(CEO)*

CAISSE REGIONALE DE CREDIT AGRICOLE MUTUEL DE PARIS ET D'ILE DE FRANCE SC
26 quai de la Rapee, 75596, Paris,
France
Tel.: (33) 144732122
Web Site: https://www.ca-paris.fr
CAF—(EUR)
Sales Range: $1-4.9 Billion
Financial Investment Management
Services
N.A.I.C.S.: 523940
Olivier Gavalda *(CEO)*

CAISSE REGIONALE DE CREDIT AGRICOLE MUTUEL SUD RHONE ALPES
15-17 rue Paul Claudel, BP 67,
38100, Grenoble, France
Tel.: (33) 476867070
Web Site: https://www.ca-
   sudrhonealpes.fr
CRSU—(EUR)
Commercial Banking Services
N.A.I.C.S.: 522110
Christian Rouchon *(CEO)*

CAISSE REGIONALE DE CREDIT AGRICOLE TOULOUSE 31
6 place Jeanne d Arc, BP 40535,
31005, Toulouse, Cedex, France
Tel.: (33) 561269111
Web Site: http://www.ca-toulousain.fr
CAT31—(EUR)

Financial Support Services
N.A.I.C.S.: 523940
Nicolas Langevin *(CEO)*

CAITONG SECURITIES CO., LTD.
Caitong Shuangguan Building No 198
Tianmushan Road, Xihu District,
Hangzhou, 310007, Zhejiang, China
Tel.: (86) 57187821312
Web Site: https://www.ctsec.com
Year Founded: 1993
601108—(SHG)
Rev.: $677,675,644
Assets: $17,647,145,736
Liabilities: $13,017,519,394
Net Worth: $4,629,626,343
Earnings: $213,015,048
Fiscal Year-end: 12/31/22
Financial Banking Services
N.A.I.C.S.: 531390
Zhang Qicheng *(Chm)*

CAIXA ECONOMICA FEDERAL
Setor Bancario Sul Quadra 04 34
Bloco A, Brasilia, 70092-900, Brazil
Tel.: (55) 6135218600
Web Site: http://www.caixa.gov.br
Rev.: $28,207,506,392
Assets: $320,124,549,469
Liabilities: $300,156,291,816
Net Worth: $19,968,257,653
Earnings: $5,213,213,082
Fiscal Year-end: 12/31/19
Commercial Banking Services
N.A.I.C.S.: 522110
Pedro Duarte Guimaraes *(Chm)*

CAIXA ECONOMICA MONTEPIO GERAL
rua Aurea 219 a 241, PT-1100-062,
Lisbon, Portugal
Tel.: (351) 21 724 16
Web Site: http://www.montepio.pt
Sales Range: $900-999.9 Million
Emp.: 4,425
Banking Services
N.A.I.C.S.: 522110

Subsidiaries:

Banco Montepio Geral - Cabo Verde,
Sociedade Unipessoal, S.A. **(1)**
Rua da Comunicacao Social No 2 - 10 Esq
Apartado 261, Santiago Island, Praia, Cape
Verde
Tel.: (238) 2601630
Web Site: http://www.bmgcv.cv
Financial Services
N.A.I.C.S.: 541611

Montepio Valor - Sociedade Gestora
de Fundos de Investimento, S.A. **(1)**
Rua Soeiro Pereira Gomes Lote 1-7th Floor
C/D, Lisboa, 1600-198, Lisbon, Portugal
Tel.: (351) 210416003
Web Site: http://www.montepiovalor.pt
Real Estate Services
N.A.I.C.S.: 531210

CAIXA GERAL DE DEPOSITOS S.A.
Av Joao XXI 63, 1000-300, Lisbon,
Portugal
Tel.: (351) 217953000
Web Site: http://www.cgd.pt
Year Founded: 1876
Rev.: $2,109,866,405
Assets: $96,057,179,063
Liabilities: $86,464,450,240
Net Worth: $9,592,728,823
Earnings: $868,931,234
Emp.: 12,372
Fiscal Year-end: 12/31/19
Banking Services
N.A.I.C.S.: 523150
Maria Joao Borges Carioca Rodrigues *(Member-Exec Bd)*

Caixa Geral de Depositos S.A.—(Continued)

Subsidiaries:

A Promotora, Sociedade de Capital
de Risco, S.A.R.L.   **(1)**
Cha de Areia, Caixa Postal 735, Praia, 753,
Cape Verde
Tel.: (238) 2608472
Web Site: http://www.apromotora.cv
Commercial Banking Services
N.A.I.C.S.: 522110

Banco Caixa Geral, S.A.   **(1)**
Avda Madrid 83, 28902, Madrid,
Spain   **(100%)**
Tel.: (34) 91 682 5431
Web Site: http://www.bancocaixageral.es
Rev.: $56,587,000
Emp.: 250
International Banking
N.A.I.C.S.: 522299

Banco Comercial do Atlantico,
S.A.R.L.   **(1)**
Alexandre Albuquerque C P 474, Praia,
Cape Verde
Tel.: (238) 2604660
Web Site: http://www.bca.cv
Commercial Banking Services
N.A.I.C.S.: 522110

Banco Interatlantico, S.A.R.L.   **(1)**
Av Cidade de Lisboa, 131-A, Praia, San-
tiago, Cape Verde
Tel.: (238) 2603695
Web Site: http://www.bi.cv
Commercial Banking Services
N.A.I.C.S.: 522110

CGD Investimentos CVC   **(1)**
Av Pres Juscelino Kubitschek 1700 10 an-
dar, 04543-000, Sao Paulo, Brazil
Tel.: (55) 11 3074 8004
Web Site: http://www.cgdsecurities.com.br
Commercial Banking Services
N.A.I.C.S.: 522110

CGD North America Finance
LLC   **(1)**
733 3rd Ave 22nd Fl, New York, NY 10017
Tel.: (212) 557-0025
Commercial Banking Services
N.A.I.C.S.: 522110

Cabo Verde, S.A.R.L.   **(1)**
Chao de Areia, Caixa Postal 138, Praia,
138, Cape Verde
Tel.: (238) 260 86 00
Web Site: http://www.garantia.cv
Commercial Banking Services
N.A.I.C.S.: 522110

Caixa - Banco de Investimento,
S.A.   **(1)**
Av Joao XXI 63, 1000-300, Lisbon, Portugal
Tel.: (351) 21 313 73 00
Web Site: http://www.caixabi.pt
Commercial Banking Services
N.A.I.C.S.: 522110
Nuno Alexandre de Carvalho Martins (Vice
Chm)

Caixa Geral de Depositos
(France)   **(1)**
85 Ave Marceau, 75116, Paris,
France   **(100%)**
Tel.: (33) 00140695400
Web Site: http://www.cgd.fr
Sales Range: $450-499.9 Million
Emp.: 500
International Banking Services
N.A.I.C.S.: 522299

Caixa Gestao de Ativos, SGOIC,
SA   **(1)**
Ave Joao XXI 63 Floor 3, Allas, 1000-3000,
Lisbon, Portugal   **(88.3%)**
Tel.: (351) 217905457
Web Site: http://www.cgd.pt
Fund Management Company
N.A.I.C.S.: 523940

Caixa Leasing & Factoring, IFIC,
SA   **(1)**
Av 5 Outubro 175 12 andar, 1050 053, Lis-
bon, Portugal   **(100%)**
Tel.: (351) 217807940
Rev.: $75,000,000
Emp.: 200

Financial Leasing & Banking Services
N.A.I.C.S.: 522299

Caixa-Imobiliario-Sociedade de
Gestao e Investimento Imobiliario
S.A.   **(1)**
Ave Zuao 2163, Lisbon, 1000063,
Portugal   **(100%)**
Tel.: (351) 217953000
Sales Range: $150-199.9 Million
Emp.: 500
Real Estate Management
N.A.I.C.S.: 531210

Cares Multiassitance, S.A.   **(1)**
Rua de Ponta Delgada n 44 A e B, 1000-
243, Lisbon, Portugal
Tel.: (351) 210337200
Commercial Banking Services
N.A.I.C.S.: 522110

Cares RH - Companhia de Assisten-
cia e Representacao de Seguros,
S.A.   **(1)**
Avenida Jose Malhoa 13-7, 1070-157, Lis-
bon, Portugal
Tel.: (351) 214 414 441
Commercial Banking Services
N.A.I.C.S.: 522110

Cetra - Centro Tecnico de Reparacao
Automovel, S.A.   **(1)**
Rua Cidade de Bolama 1, Lisbon, Portugal
Tel.: (351) 21 854 0310
Commercial Banking Services
N.A.I.C.S.: 522110

Companhia Portuguesa de Resse-
guros, S.A.   **(1)**
Av Liberdade 227.4, 1250-142, Lisbon, Por-
tugal
Tel.: (351) 213530975
Commercial Banking Services
N.A.I.C.S.: 522110

E.A.P.S. - Empresa de Analise, Pre-
vencao e Seguranca, S.A.   **(1)**
Rua Nova da Trindade 3, 1200-301, Lisbon,
Portugal
Tel.: (351) 21 321 31 00
Web Site: http://www.safemode.pt
Emp.: 40
Commercial Banking Services
N.A.I.C.S.: 522110
Ramiro Martins (Gen Mgr)

Fundimo, S.A.   **(1)**
Av Joao XXI 63 2 Fl, 1000, Lisbon,
Portugal   **(100%)**
Tel.: (351) 217905450
Web Site: http://www.fundimo.pt
Rev.: $3,703,187
Emp.: 30
Real Estate Investment Fund
N.A.I.C.S.: 525990
George Madeira (Mng Dir)

GEP - Gestao de Peritagens Auto-
moveis, S.A.   **(1)**
Av 5 de Outubro 35 - 8, 1050-047, Lisbon,
Portugal
Tel.: (351) 91 955 92 00
Commercial Banking Services
N.A.I.C.S.: 522110

Imocaixa - Gestao Imobiliaria,
S.A.   **(1)**
Avenida 5 de Outubro 175 10, 1050-053,
Lisbon, Portugal
Tel.: (351) 217 905 455
Commercial Banking Services
N.A.I.C.S.: 522110

Imoleasing-Socciedade de Locacao
Financiera Imobiliaria SA   **(1)**
Av 5 de Outubro 175-12, 1050 053, Lisbon,
Portugal   **(68.4%)**
Tel.: (351) 217807940
Web Site: http://www.imoleasing.pt
Rev.: $73,041,176
Emp.: 39
Finance Leasing Services
N.A.I.C.S.: 522220

Locapor - Companhia Portuguesa
Locacao Financeria Mobiliaria,
S.A.   **(1)**
Ave 5 de Outubro 175 12, 1050053, Lisbon,
Portugal   **(62%)**

Tel.: (351) 217807940
Rev.: $208,541,825
Emp.: 100
Finance Leasing
N.A.I.C.S.: 522220
Paulo Pinheiro (Pres)

Orey Financial - Instituicao Financeira
de Credito, SA   **(1)**
Edificio Amoreiras Square R Carlos Alberto
da Mota Pinto n17 6, 1070-313, Lisbon,
Portugal
Tel.: (351) 213 407 000
Web Site: http://www.oreyfinancial.com
Financial Management Services
N.A.I.C.S.: 523999
Duarte Maia de Albuquerque dOrey (Chm)

CAJAVEC A.D.
Jovan Ducica 23A, 78000, Banja
Luka, Bosnia & Herzegovina
Tel.: (387) 51248352
CJVC—(BANJ)
Sales Range: $1-9.9 Million
Holding Company
N.A.I.C.S.: 551112

CAJAVEC SIP A.D.
Veselina Maslese 1/ix, 78000, Banja
Luka, Bosnia & Herzegovina
Tel.: (387) 51 211 624
Sales Range: Less than $1 Million
Emp.: 2
Real Estate Prorperty Leasing Ser-
vices
N.A.I.C.S.: 531190
Petko Zekanovic (Chm-Mgmt Bd)

Subsidiaries:

Cajavec usluzne djelatnosti a.d.   **(1)**
Jovana Ducica 23A, 78000, Banja Luka,
Bosnia & Herzegovina   **(66.35%)**
Tel.: (387) 51 214 929
Sales Range: Less than $1 Million
Accounting Services
N.A.I.C.S.: 541219

CAJAVEC-MEGA A.D.
Kralja Petra I Karadordevica 103,
78000, Banja Luka, Bosnia & Herze-
govina
Tel.: (387) 51921570
Web Site: http://www.cmega.ba
Year Founded: 1950
CMEG—(BANJ)
Sales Range: $1-9.9 Million
Emp.: 10
Real Estate Prorperty Leasing Ser-
vices
N.A.I.C.S.: 531190
Nace Brenk (Chm-Mgmt Bd)

CAKE BOX HOLDINGS PLC
22 Jute Lane, London, EN3 7PJ,
United Kingdom
Tel.: (44) 2080502026   UK
Web Site: https://www.cakebox.com
Year Founded: 2008
CBOX—(AIM)
Rev.: $29,748,816
Assets: $24,308,772
Liabilities: $9,181,541
Net Worth: $15,127,232
Earnings: $4,571,318
Emp.: 107
Fiscal Year-end: 03/31/21
Confectionery Product Retailer
N.A.I.C.S.: 445292
Pardip Dass (Co-Founder & CFO)

Subsidiaries:

Eggfree Cake Box Ltd.   **(1)**
201a Oxlow Lane, Dagenham, RM10 7YA,
United Kingdom
Tel.: (44) 2080501434
Celebration Cake Mfr
N.A.I.C.S.: 311811

CAKOVECKI MLINOVI D.D.

Mlinska Ulica 1, 40000, Cakovec,
Croatia
Tel.: (385) 40375555
Web Site: https://www.cak-mlinovi.hr
Year Founded: 1983
CKML—(ZAG)
Rev.: $220,353,240
Assets: $121,255,105
Liabilities: $31,098,355
Net Worth: $90,156,750
Earnings: $8,008,610
Emp.: 2,250
Fiscal Year-end: 12/31/23
Flour Milling Product Mfr
N.A.I.C.S.: 311211
Nino Varga (Chm-Mgmt Bd & Pres)

Subsidiaries:

METSS Ltd.   **(1)**
300 Westdale Ave, Westerville, OH 43082
Tel.: (614) 797-2200
Web Site: http://www.metss.com
Laboratory Testing Services
N.A.I.C.S.: 541380
Brian Collett (Mng Dir)

CAL-COMP ELECTRONICS
(THAILAND) PCL
191 54 191 57 18th Fl CTI Tower Ra-
chadapisek Road, Klongtoey, Bang-
kok, 10110, Thailand
Tel.: (66) 22615033   TH
Web Site: https://www.calcomp.co.th
Year Founded: 1989
CCET—(THA)
Rev.: $4,740,109,051
Assets: $2,654,984,644
Liabilities: $2,141,690,938
Net Worth: $513,293,706
Earnings: $21,600,376
Emp.: 43,583
Fiscal Year-end: 12/31/22
Electronic Products Mfr
N.A.I.C.S.: 334419
Sheng-Hsiung Hsu (Founder & Chm)

Subsidiaries:

Cal-Comp Automation and Industrial
4.0 Service (Thailand) Co., Ltd.   **(1)**
60 Moo 8 Sethakij Road Tambon Klong Maduea, Amphoe Krathum Baen, Samut Sakhon, 74110, Thailand
Tel.: (66) 34878165
Electronic Appliance Mfr & Distr
N.A.I.C.S.: 334413

Cal-Comp Electronics (Suzhou) Com-
pany Limited   **(1)**
No 2288 Jiangxing E Rd, Wujiang Eco-
nomic Development Z, Nanjing,
China   **(100%)**
Tel.: (86) 51263407000
Sales Range: $1-4.9 Billion
Emp.: 7,000
Electronic Components Mfr
N.A.I.C.S.: 334419

Cal-Comp Electronics (USA) Co.,
Ltd.   **(1)**
1940 Camino Vida Roble, Carlsbad, CA
92008
Tel.: (858) 587-6900
Printed Circuit Board Mfr
N.A.I.C.S.: 334418

Cal-Comp Electronics -
Mahachai   **(1)**
60 Moo 8 Sethakij Road Klon Maduea, Kra-
toom Bean, Samut Sakhon, 74110, Thai-
land
Tel.: (66) 34472000
Web Site: http://www.calcomp.co.th
Electronic Products Mfr
N.A.I.C.S.: 334419

Cal-Comp Electronics -
Petchaburi   **(1)**
138 Moo 4 Petchkasem Rd Tambon Sar-
pang, Khao Yoi District, Phetchaburi,
76140, Thailand
Tel.: (66) 324 477 6366
Web Site: http://www.calcomp.co.th

Electronic Products Mfr
N.A.I.C.S.: 334419

Cal-Comp Electronics and Communications Company Limited **(1)**
A Bldg No 147 Sec 3 Beishen Rd Wanshuen Tsuen, Shenkeng Shiang, Taipei, 222, Taiwan **(100%)**
Tel.: (886) 277058001
Web Site: http://www.calcomp.com.tw
Sales Range: $50-74.9 Million
Emp.: 100
Computer Peripheral Equipment & Software Whslr
N.A.I.C.S.: 423430

Cal-Comp Industria E Comercio De Eletronicos E Informatica Ltd. **(1)**
Av Torquato Tapajos 7503 Galpao 2 Modulos Contiguos 07 19 20 e 21, Taruma, Manaus, 69041-025, Brazil
Tel.: (55) 9221259906
Web Site: https://www.ccbr.com.br
Electronic Components Mfr & Distr
N.A.I.C.S.: 334416

Cal-Comp Optical Electronics (Suzhou) Company Limited **(1)**
No 2288 Jiangxing E Rd, Wujiang Economic Development Z, Nanjing, China **(100%)**
Tel.: (86) 51263407000
Sales Range: $1-4.9 Billion
Emp.: 7,000
Electronic Computer Mfr
N.A.I.C.S.: 334111

Cal-Comp Optical Electronics (Yueyang) Co., Ltd. **(1)**
No 8 Xinjinbao Road of Xianggugang East Road, Chenglingji Comprehensive Bonded Zone, Yueyang, China
Tel.: (86) 7303055888
Electronic Appliance Mfr & Distr
N.A.I.C.S.: 334413

Cal-Comp Precision (Thailand) Limited **(1)**
No 4 Moo 8 Sethakij Road, Tambol Klong Maduea Amphur Krathumbaen, Samut Sakhon, 74110, Thailand
Tel.: (66) 34849652
Precision Product Mfr & Distr
N.A.I.C.S.: 332721

Cal-Comp Precision (Yueyang) Co., Ltd. **(1)**
No 8 Xinjinbao Road of Xianggugang East Road, Chenglingji Comprehensive Bonded Zone, Yueyang, China
Tel.: (86) 7303050888
Electronic Appliance Mfr & Distr
N.A.I.C.S.: 334413

Cal-Comp Precision Holding Co., Ltd. **(1)**
The Grand Pavilion Commercial Centre Oleander Way 802 West Bay Road, PO Box 32052, Grand Cayman, KY1-1208, Cayman Islands
Tel.: (345) 226622660
Electronic Appliance Mfr & Distr
N.A.I.C.S.: 334413

Logistar International Holding Company Limited **(1)**
Palm Grove House, PO Box 438, Tortola, Virgin Islands (British) **(100%)**
Tel.: (284) 4942616
Holding Company
N.A.I.C.S.: 551112

Subsidiary (Domestic):

Wise Sigma International Holding Company Limited **(2)**
Beaufort House, PO Box 438, Tortola, Virgin Islands (British)
Tel.: (284) 4942616
Holding Company
N.A.I.C.S.: 551112

Power Digital Communication Co., Ltd. **(1)**
145 Sandan-ro 19 Beon-gil, Danwon-gu, Ansan, 15427, Gyeonggi-do, Korea (South)
Tel.: (82) 315990100
Web Site: http://www.dpc.co.kr
Electronic Components Mfr

N.A.I.C.S.: 334419

SMS Technologies, Inc. **(1)**
9877 Waples St, San Diego, CA 92121
Tel.: (858) 587-6900
Web Site: http://www.calcompusa.com
Sales Range: $50-74.9 Million
Emp.: 150
Electronic Components Mfr
N.A.I.C.S.: 334419

Total Electronics, LLC **(1)**
1 Technology Way, Logansport, IN 46947
Tel.: (574) 739-2929
Web Site: http://www.totalems.com
Electronic Components Mfr
N.A.I.C.S.: 334419

Zakang, Inc. **(1)**
C-402 Pundang Techno Park 151 Yatap-Dong, Pundang-Ku, Seongnam, Korea (South) **(100%)**
Tel.: (82) 317899013
Web Site: http://www.zakang.co.kr
Sales Range: $25-49.9 Million
Emp.: 40
Cellular & Wireless Telecommunications
N.A.I.C.S.: 517112

CALAC TRUCKING LTD.
202 Edson Street, Saskatoon, S7J 0P9, SK, Canada
Tel.: (306) 242-0155
Rev.: $40,636,138
Emp.: 320
Road Transportation & Trucking Services
N.A.I.C.S.: 484121
Timothy Mckechnie *(Pres & CEO)*

CALANCE CORPORATION
Suite No 201 Greenwood Plaza Greenwood City Sector 45, Gurgaon, 122002, India
Tel.: (91) 124 4047951 In
Web Site: http://www.calance.com
Sales Range: $10-24.9 Million
Emp.: 75
IT Services
N.A.I.C.S.: 541512
Sunil Chopra *(Co-Founder & COO)*

Subsidiaries:

Partners Consulting Services, Inc. **(1)**
7101 Village Dr, Buena Park, CA 90621
Tel.: (714) 573-7450
Web Site:
http://www.partnersconsulting.com
IT & Staffing Services
N.A.I.C.S.: 541512
Chad Decatur *(Sr Mgr-Sys Ops)*

CALASTONE LIMITED
Birchin Court 4th Floor 20 Birchin Lane, London, EC3V 9DU, United Kingdom
Tel.: (44) 2037004100
Web Site: https://www.calastone.com
Year Founded: 2007
Investment Management Service
N.A.I.C.S.: 523999

CALATA CORPORATION
Level 16 Tower 2 The Enterprise Center, Ayala Avenue Cor Paseo de Roxas, Makati, 1226, Philippines
Tel.: (63) 2 511 1701
Web Site: http://www.calatacorp.com
Year Founded: 1999
CAL—(PHI)
Sales Range: $25-49.9 Million
Agricultural Products Including Agrochemicals, Feeds, Fertilizers & Veterinary Medicines Distr
N.A.I.C.S.: 424910
Joseph Hernandez Calata *(Chm & Pres)*

Subsidiaries:

Agri Phil Corporation **(1)**

Level 16 Tower 2 The Enterprise Center Ayala Avenue corner, Paseo de Roxas, Makati, 1227, Philippines
Tel.: (63) 2 511 1701
Web Site: http://agri.com.ph
Agricultural Products Retailer & Distr
N.A.I.C.S.: 424690
Vanessa Gael Dalisay *(Gen Mgr)*

CALATRAVA CAPITAL S.A.
Lucka 2/4/6, 00-845, Warsaw, Poland
Tel.: (48) 22 398 96 71
Web Site:
http://www.calatravacapital.pl
Investment Management Service
N.A.I.C.S.: 523940
Jacek Dariusz Makowiecki *(Chm-Mgmt Bd)*

CALB GROUP CO., LTD.
No 1 Jiangdong Avenue, Jintan District, Changzhou, China
Tel.: (86) 5196890368 CN
Web Site: https://www.calb-tech.com
Year Founded: 2015
3931—(HKG)
Rev.: $3,739,184,343
Assets: $14,597,505,677
Liabilities: $8,175,015,923
Net Worth: $6,422,489,754
Earnings: $60,528,772
Emp.: 16,962
Fiscal Year-end: 12/31/23
Lithium Product Mfr
N.A.I.C.S.: 335910

CALBANK PLC
23 Independence Avenue, PO Box 14596, Accra, Ghana
Tel.: (233) 302680062
Web Site: https://www.calbank.net
Rev.: $159,247,224
Assets: $1,116,050,436
Liabilities: $955,531,533
Net Worth: $160,518,903
Earnings: $31,553,303
Emp.: 792
Fiscal Year-end: 12/31/18
Banking Services
N.A.I.C.S.: 522110
Samuel Kwame Boafo *(Head-People & Culture)*

Subsidiaries:

CAL Investments Limited **(1)**
4 Farm St Mayfair, London, W1J 5RD, United Kingdom
Tel.: (44) 2073993380
Web Site: http://www.calinvestments.com
Investment Management Service
N.A.I.C.S.: 541618
Martin H.J. Smetsers *(Mng Dir)*

CALBEE, INC.
Marunouchi Trust Tower Main 22nd Floor 1-8-3 Marunouchi, Chiyoda-ku, Tokyo, 100-0005, Japan
Tel.: (81) 352206222
Web Site: https://www.calbee.co.jp
Year Founded: 1949
2229—(TKS)
Rev.: $2,003,008,470
Assets: $1,931,164,380
Liabilities: $601,985,920
Net Worth: $1,329,178,460
Earnings: $131,446,460
Emp.: 4,939
Fiscal Year-end: 03/31/24
Snack Food Mfr
N.A.I.C.S.: 311919
Shuji Ito *(Pres & CEO)*

Subsidiaries:

Calbee (Hangzhou) Foods Co., Ltd. **(1)**
Room 3406-03 3406-04 3406-05 34th Floor Building 1, Gaode Land Center Jiangtan District, Hangzhou, Zhejiang, China

Tel.: (86) 57186893121
Web Site: http://www.calbee-hc.com
Snack Product Whslr
N.A.I.C.S.: 424450

Calbee America, Inc. **(1)**
2600 Maxwell Way, Fairfield, CA 94534 **(100%)**
Tel.: (707) 427-2500
Web Site: http://calbeena.com
Sales Range: $25-49.9 Million
Emp.: 60
Snack Food Mfr & Distr
N.A.I.C.S.: 311919
Gene Jensen *(Pres)*

Subsidiary (Domestic):

Warnock Food Products, Inc. **(2)**
20237 Masa St, Madera, CA 93638 **(80%)**
Tel.: (559) 661-4845
Web Site: http://www.warnockfoods.com
Snack Food Mfr
N.A.I.C.S.: 311919
Kraig Rawls *(CEO)*

Calbee Group (UK) Limited **(1)**
Seabrook House Duncombe Street, Bradford, BD8 9AJ, Yorkshire, United Kingdom
Tel.: (44) 3306600015
Web Site: https://www.calbee.co.uk
Snack Product Mfr & Whslr
N.A.I.C.S.: 311919

Calbee Logistics, Inc. **(1)**
43-167 Hiraide Industrial Park, Utsunomiya, 321-0905, Tochigi, Japan
Tel.: (81) 286623100
Web Site: http://www.callogi.co.jp
Confectionery Logistics Transportation Services
N.A.I.C.S.: 488510

Calbee Moh Seng Pte., Ltd. **(1)**
31 Jurong Port Road 06-06/07 Jurong Logistics Hub, Singapore, 619115, Singapore
Tel.: (65) 62921957
Web Site:
https://www.calbeemohseng.com.sg
Snack Product Mfr & Whslr
N.A.I.C.S.: 311919

Calbee North America, LLC **(1)**
2600 Maxwell Wy, Fairfield, CA 94534
Tel.: (707) 427-2500
Web Site: https://calbeeamerica.com
Snack Food Mfr
N.A.I.C.S.: 311919

Calbee Potato, Inc. **(1)**
31-4 Beppu-cho Zero, Obihiro, 089-1184, Hokkaido, Japan
Tel.: (81) 155534141
Web Site: https://www.calbee-potato.co.jp
Emp.: 253
Vegetable Whslr
N.A.I.C.S.: 424450

Calbee Tanawat Co., Ltd. **(1)**
3195/6 Wiboon Thani Building 1st Floor Rama 4 Road, Khlong Tan Subdistrict Khlong Toei District, Bangkok, 10110, Thailand
Tel.: (66) 26656220
Web Site: https://www.calbee.co.th
Snack Product Whslr
N.A.I.C.S.: 424450

Calnac Co., Ltd. **(1)**
Tokyo Prince 1-13-14 Asahi Seimei Prince Building, Kita-ku, Tokyo, 114-0002, Japan
Tel.: (81) 339147979
Web Site: http://www.calnac.co.jp
Food Packaging Product Whslr
N.A.I.C.S.: 424420

Japan Frito-Lay Ltd. **(1)**
Marunouchi Trust Tower Main Building 22F 1-8-3 Marunouchi, Chiyoda-ku, Tokyo, 100-0005, Japan
Tel.: (81) 120953306
Web Site: http://www.fritolay.co.jp
Snack Product Mfr & Whslr
N.A.I.C.S.: 311919

Potato Kaitsuka Co. Ltd. **(1)**
240-18 Ogami, Kasumigaura, 300-0132, Ibaraki, Japan
Tel.: (81) 298971815
Web Site: https://www.calbee-ksp.co.jp
Emp.: 361

Calbee, Inc.—(Continued)

Vegetable Whslr
N.A.I.C.S.: 424450

Studio Socio Inc. **(1)**
4th floor Suzuki Building 3-4-4 Uchikanda,
Chiyoda-ku, Tokyo, Japan
Tel.: (81) 352965702
Web Site: https://www.e-socio.co.jp
Snack Product Whslr
N.A.I.C.S.: 424450

CALCIALIMENT

ZI de la Gare, Pleudihen-sur-Rance,
22690, France
Tel.: (33) 296832142
Web Site:
http://www.calcialiment.com
Sales Range: $10-24.9 Million
Emp.: 100
Animal Feed Mfr
N.A.I.C.S.: 311119
Patrik Chwalowska (Mgr-Export)

CALCIMIN COMPANY

2nd No 13 8th St Ghaem magham
Farahani St, PO Box 1586868513,
Tehran, Iran
Tel.: (98) 21 88502317
Web Site: http://www.calcimin.com
Year Founded: 1964
KSIM—(THE)
Sales Range: Less than $1 Million
Zinc Ingot Mfr
N.A.I.C.S.: 331110

CALCITECH LTD.

10 route de l'aeroport, 1215, Geneva,
Switzerland
Tel.: (41) 227883092 **BM**
Web Site: http://www.calcitech.com
CLKTF—(OTCIQ)
Sales Range: Less than $1 Million
Emp.: 4
Chemicals Mfr
N.A.I.C.S.: 325998
Roger A. Leopard (Chm, Pres &
CEO)

CALCOM VISION LTD.

B-16 Site-C Surajpur Industrial Area,
Gautam Budh Nagar, Noida, 201306,
UP, India
Tel.: (91) 1202569761
Web Site:
https://www.calcomindia.com
517236—(BOM)
Rev.: $7,890,546
Assets: $10,547,778
Liabilities: $4,891,478
Net Worth: $5,656,301
Earnings: $103,522
Emp.: 150
Fiscal Year-end: 03/31/21
Television Mfr
N.A.I.C.S.: 334310
Sushil Kumar Malik (Chm & Mng Dir)

CALCORP LIMITED

D-131/A Block 4 Clifton, Karachi,
Pakistan
Tel.: (92) 21 38771130
Web Site: http://www.calcorp.com.pk
Year Founded: 1992
CPAL—(ISL)
Rev.: $261,938
Assets: $2,182,050
Liabilities: $1,635,431
Net Worth: $546,619
Earnings: $72,511
Emp.: 4
Fiscal Year-end: 06/30/21
Car Rental Business Services
N.A.I.C.S.: 532111
Shomaila Siddiqui (CFO & Sec)

CALCULUS VCT PLC

Calculus Capital 12 Conduit Street,
London, W1S 2XH, United Kingdom
Tel.: (44) 2074934940 **UK**
Web Site:
https://www.calculuscapital.com
Year Founded: 2010
CLC—(LSE)
Rev.: $361,154
Assets: $46,768,023
Liabilities: $171,073
Net Worth: $46,596,950
Earnings: $879,803
Fiscal Year-end: 02/28/23
Investment Management Service
N.A.I.C.S.: 523940
Jan Ward (Chm)

CALCUTTA STOCK EXCHANGE ASSOCIATION LTD.

7 Lyons Range, Kolkata, 700 001,
India
Tel.: (91) 3322104470
Web Site: http://www.cse-india.com
Sales Range: $50-74.9 Million
Emp.: 125
Stock Exchange Services
N.A.I.C.S.: 523210
Dhiraj Chakraborty (Deputy Gen Mgr-
Margin, HR & Bus Dev)

CALDAS GOLD CORP.

401 Bay Street Suite 2400, Toronto,
M5H 2Y4, ON, Canada
Tel.: (416) 360-4653
Web Site: http://www.caldasgold.ca
Mineral Mining Services
N.A.I.C.S.: 213114
Serafino Lacono (Chm & CEO)

CALDIC B.V.

Westerlaan 1, 3016 CK, Rotterdam,
Netherlands
Tel.: (31) 104136420 **NI**
Web Site: http://www.caldic.com
Global Full-Service Solution Provider
for Food, Pharma, Personal Care &
Industrial markets
N.A.I.C.S.: 311999
Olav van Caldenborgh (CEO)

Subsidiaries:

Caldic New Zealand Ltd. **(1)**
Level 3 Building 10 666 Great South Rd,
Ellerslie, Auckland, 1051, New Zealand
Tel.: (64) 99691605
Web Site: http://www.caldic.com
Food Ingredient Distr
N.A.I.C.S.: 424490
Steve Crockett (Mng Dir)

Caldic USA Inc. **(1)**
2425 Alft Ln, Elgin, IL 60124
Tel.: (847) 468-0001
Web Site: http://www.caldic.com
Global Full-Service Solution Provider for
Food, Pharma, Personal Care & Industrial
Markets
N.A.I.C.S.: 311999
Jill Wuthmann (Pres)

CALEDONIA (PRIVATE) INVESTMENTS PTY. LTD.

Level 7 Gold Fields House 1 Alfred
Street, Sydney, 2000, NSW, Australia
Tel.: (61) 2 9255 7600 **AU**
Web Site:
http://www.caledonia.com.au
Year Founded: 1992
Rev.: $2,546,495,000
Privater Equity Firm
N.A.I.C.S.: 523999
Mark Nelson (Chm)

CALEDONIA INVESTMENTS PLC

Cayzer House 30 Buckingham Gate,
London, SW1E 6NN, United Kingdom
Tel.: (44) 2078028080 **UK**

Web Site: https://www.caledonia.com
CLDN—(LSE)
Rev.: $851,426,212
Assets: $3,821,438,712
Liabilities: $43,311,268
Net Worth: $3,778,127,444
Earnings: $829,838,464
Emp.: 60
Fiscal Year ond: 03/31/22
Closed-End Investment Trust
N.A.I.C.S.: 525990
Jamie M. B. Cayzer-colvin (Head-
Funds)

Subsidiaries:

7IM Investment & Retirement Solu-
tions Ltd. **(1)**
55 Bishopsgate, London, EC2N 3AS,
United Kingdom
Tel.: (44) 207 760 8777
Web Site: https://www.7im.co.uk
Investment Management Service
N.A.I.C.S.: 541611
Dean Proctor (CEO)

Bloom Combustion (India) Private
Ltd. **(1)**
Block J-344 Near Quality Circle, MIDC-
Bhosari, Pune, 411026, India
Tel.: (91) 988 100 1342
Heating Equipment Mfr
N.A.I.C.S.: 333414

Bloom Engineering (Europa)
GmbH **(1)**
Buttgenbachstrasse 14, 40549, Dusseldorf,
Germany
Tel.: (49) 21 150 0910
Web Site: https://www.bloomeng.de
Burner Maintenance Services
N.A.I.C.S.: 238220

Bloom Engineering Co. Inc. **(1)**
5460 Horning Rd, Pittsburgh, PA 15236
Tel.: (412) 653-3500
Web Site: https://www.bloomeng.com
Heating Equipment Mfr
N.A.I.C.S.: 333414

Butcombe Brewery Ltd. **(1)**
Cox's Green, Wrington, Bristol, BS40 5PA,
United Kingdom
Tel.: (44) 193 486 3963
Web Site: https://butcombe.com
Beer Brewery Mfr
N.A.I.C.S.: 312120

Caledonia Group Services Ltd **(1)**
Cayzer House, London, SW1E 6NN, United
Kingdom **(100%)**
Tel.: (44) 2078028080
Web Site: http://www.caledonia.com
Sales Range: $50-74.9 Million
Miscellaneous Financial Investment Activi-
ties
N.A.I.C.S.: 523999
Will Wyatt (CEO)

Caledonia Treasury Ltd **(1)**
Cayzer House 30 Buckingham Gate, Lon-
don, SW1E 6NN, United Kingdom
Tel.: (44) 2078028080
Web Site: http://www.caledonia.com
Investment Management Service
N.A.I.C.S.: 523999
William White (Gen Mgr)

Cooke Optics Ltd. **(1)**
Cooke Close, Thurmaston, Leicester, LE4
8PT, United Kingdom
Tel.: (44) 116 264 0700
Web Site: https://cookeoptics.com
Sound Recording Studio Services
N.A.I.C.S.: 512240
Kees Van Oostrum (Chm)

DSE Development Ltd. **(1)**
Unit 9 Drakehouse Court Hamilton Road,
Sutton in Ashfield, NG17 5ES, Nottingham-
shire, United Kingdom
Tel.: (44) 172 389 3317
Web Site: https://www.dsedevelopment.com
Software Development Services
N.A.I.C.S.: 541511

Deep Sea Electronics India Pte.
Ltd. **(1)**
405 406 Pride Gateway, Baner, Pune,

411045, Maharashtra, India
Tel.: (91) 206 819 5900
Generator Control Module Mfr
N.A.I.C.S.: 335312

Partners Wealth Management
LLP **(1)**
20 St Andrew Street, London, EC4A 3AG,
United Kingdom
Tel.: (44) 207 444 4030
Web Site:
https://www.partnersmanagement.co.uk
Wealth Management Services
N.A.I.C.S.: 523999
James Roberts (Mng Partner)

Sterling Industries Ltd. **(1)**
South Buliding Brunel Road, Aylesbury,
HP19 8TD, Bucks, United
Kingdom **(100%)**
Tel.: (44) 1296 480 210
Web Site: http://www.sterling-industries.com
Sales Range: $50-74.9 Million
Emp.: 390
Holding Company; Heat Exchange & Com-
bustion Technologies Engineering Services
N.A.I.C.S.: 551112

Subsidiary (US):

Bloomfield Engineering Company
Inc. **(2)**
5460 Horning Rd, Pittsburgh, PA 15236
Tel.: (412) 653-3500
Web Site: http://www.bloomeng.com
Sales Range: $25-49.9 Million
Emp.: 174
Industrial Burners & Combustion Systems
Designer, Mfr & Maintenance Services
N.A.I.C.S.: 332410
Michael Binni (VP-Project Mgmt)

Subsidiary (Domestic):

Sterling Thermal Technology
Limited **(2)**
Brunel Road, Aylesbury, HP19 8TD, Buck-
inghamshire, United Kingdom
Tel.: (44) 1296487171
Web Site: http://www.sterlingtt.com
Sales Range: $10-24.9 Million
Emp.: 140
Heat Exchangers Designer & Mfr
N.A.I.C.S.: 332410

CALEDONIA MINING CORPORATION PLC

B006 Millais House Castle Quay,
Saint Helier, JE2 3EF, Channel Is-
lands, Jersey
Tel.: (44) 1534679800 **Ca**
Web Site:
https://www.caledoniamining.com
Year Founded: 1992
CMCL—(NYSEAMEX)
Rev.: $146,314,000
Assets: $328,303,000
Liabilities: $64,111,000
Net Worth: $264,192,000
Earnings: ($618,000)
Emp.: 2,332
Fiscal Year-end: 12/31/23
Gold Mining Services
N.A.I.C.S.: 212220
Steven Curtis (CEO)

Subsidiaries:

Caledonia Holdings Zimbabwe
(Limited) **(1)**
6th Floor Red Bridge East Gate Robert
Mugabe Road, PO Box CY1277, Cause-
way, Harare, Zimbabwe
Tel.: (263) 4701151
Web Site: http://www.caledoniamining.com
Emp.: 600
Mining Services
N.A.I.C.S.: 212290

Caledonia Holdings Zimbabwe (Pri-
vate) Limited **(1)**
Causeway, PO Box CY1277, Harare, Zim-
babwe
Tel.: (263) 4701151
Web Site: http://www.caledoniamining.com

Sales Range: $50-74.9 Million
Emp.: 3
Precious Metal Mining Services
N.A.I.C.S.: 212220

Greenstone Management Services
(Pty) Ltd.   (1)
4th Floor No 1 Quadrum Office Park,
Florida, 1709, South Africa
Tel.: (27) 114472499
Sales Range: $50-74.9 Million
Emp.: 10
Mining Services
N.A.I.C.S.: 212290
Stefan Hayden (CEO)

CALEDONIAN TRUST PLC

61a North Castle Street, Edinburgh,
EH2 3LJ, United Kingdom
Tel.: (44) 1312200416
Web Site:
https://www.caledoniantrust.com
CNN—(AIM)
Rev.: $415,462
Assets: $39,023,588
Liabilities: $7,452,525
Net Worth: $31,571,063
Earnings: ($1,767,751)
Emp.: 5
Fiscal Year-end: 06/30/22
Other Activities Related to Real Es-
tate
N.A.I.C.S.: 531390
Michael J. Baynham (Sec)

Subsidiaries:

Caledonian City Developments
Ltd.   (1)
61a N Castle St, Edinburgh, EH2 3LJ, Scot-
land, United Kingdom
Tel.: (44) 191 2221010
Sales Range: $50-74.9 Million
Emp.: 2
Property Development Services
N.A.I.C.S.: 531311

Caledonian Scottish Developments
Ltd.   (1)
61A N Castle Street, Edinburgh, EH2 3LJ,
United Kingdom
Tel.: (44) 1312200416
Property Development Services
N.A.I.C.S.: 531311
Michael J. Baynham (Sec)

South Castle Properties Ltd.   (1)
61a N Castle St, Edinburgh, EH2 3LJ, Scot-
land, United Kingdom
Tel.: (44) 1312200416
Web Site: http://www.caledoniantrust.com
Sales Range: $50-74.9 Million
Emp.: 2
Property Investment Services
N.A.I.C.S.: 531311
Michael J Baynham (Sec)

West Castle Properties Ltd.   (1)
61A N Castle St, Edinburgh, EH2 3LJ, Scot-
land, United Kingdom
Tel.: (44) 1312200416
Web Site: http://www.caledoniantrust.com
Property Investment Services
N.A.I.C.S.: 531311
Michael Baynham (Gen Mgr)

CALEFFI - S.P.A.

Via Belfiore 24, 46019, Viadana, Italy
Tel.: (39) 03757881   IT
Web Site: https://www.caleffionline.it
Year Founded: 1967
CLF—(ITA)
Sales Range: $50-74.9 Million
Home Furnishing Mfr & Retailer
N.A.I.C.S.: 314120
Giuliana Caleffi (Chm)

CALEFFI S.P.A.

SR 229 n 28010, Fontaneto
D'Agogna, Novara, Italy
Tel.: (39) 03228491
Web Site: http://www.caleffi.com
Year Founded: 1961
Sales Range: $350-399.9 Million

Emp.: 912
Hydronic System Mfr
N.A.I.C.S.: 423720
Marco Caleffi (Chm)

Subsidiaries:

Altecnic Ltd.   (1)
Mustang Drive, Stafford, ST16 1GW, United
Kingdom
Tel.: (44) 1785218200
Web Site: http://www.altecnic.co.uk
Sales Range: $25-49.9 Million
Emp.: 50
Hydronic Systems Distr
N.A.I.C.S.: 423720
Allan Sherwin (Mng Dir)

Caleffi Armaturen GmbH   (1)
Daimlerstrasse 3, Muhlheim am Main,
63165, Muhlheim, Germany
Tel.: (49) 610890910
Web Site: http://www.caleffi.com
Sales Range: $25-49.9 Million
Emp.: 30
Hydronic Systems Distr
N.A.I.C.S.: 423720
Thomas Brennecke (Mng Dir & Gen Mgr)

Caleffi France Consulting   (1)
45 Avenue Gambetta, Valence, 26000,
France
Tel.: (33) 475599586
Web Site: http://www.caleffi.fr
Sales Range: $50-74.9 Million
Emp.: 10
Hydronic Systems Distr
N.A.I.C.S.: 423720

Caleffi Internationa N.V.   (1)
Moesdijk 10-12, PO Box 10357, 6000 GJ,
Weert, Netherlands
Tel.: (31) 495547733
Web Site: http://www.caleffi.nl
Sales Range: $25-49.9 Million
Emp.: 20
Hydronic Systems Distr
N.A.I.C.S.: 423720
Walter Schincariol (Mgr)

Caleffi Lda.   (1)
Urbanizacao das Australias lote 17, Mil-
heiros Ap 1214, 4417-909, Maia, Codex,
Portugal
Tel.: (351) 229619410
Web Site: http://www.caleffi.pt
Sales Range: $50-74.9 Million
Emp.: 100
Hydronic Systems Distr
N.A.I.C.S.: 423720
Jorge Hamig Aires Pereira (Gen Mgr)

Caleffi North America, Inc.   (1)
3883 W Milwaukee Rd, Milwaukee, WI
53208
Tel.: (414) 421-1000
Web Site: http://www.caleffi.us
Sales Range: $25-49.9 Million
Emp.: 16
Hydronic Systems Distr
N.A.I.C.S.: 423720
Mark Olson (CEO)

CALEIDO GROUP S.P.A.

Via Gian Giacomo Mora 20, 20123,
Milan, Italy
Tel.: (39) 02 4507 0766
Web Site: http://www.caleido-
group.com
Tourism Services
N.A.I.C.S.: 713990
Vincenzo Saggiomo (CFO)

CALFRAC WELL SERVICES LTD.

Suite 500 407 - 8 Avenue SW, Cal-
gary, T2P 1E5, AB, Canada
Tel.: (403) 266-6000
Web Site: https://www.calfrac.com
CFW—(OTCIQ)
Rev.: $551,848,474
Assets: $713,801,556
Liabilities: $392,883,702
Net Worth: $320,917,854
Earnings: ($253,642,556)
Emp.: 2,350

Fiscal Year-end: 12/31/20
Oil & Gas Services
N.A.I.C.S.: 213112
Ronald P. Mathison (Chm)

Subsidiaries:

Calfrac Well Services (Argentina)
S.A.   (1)
Av del Libertador 1068 Piso 5 CABA, Bue-
nos Aires, Argentina
Tel.: (54) 1157767800
Oil & Natural Gar Mfr
N.A.I.C.S.: 333132

Calfrac Well Services Corp.   (1)
717-17 St Ste 1445, Denver, CO 80202
Tel.: (303) 293-2931
Oilfield Operation Services
N.A.I.C.S.: 213112
Fred L. Toney (Pres)

Calfrac Well Services Corp.   (1)
Suite 500 407 - 8 Avenue SW, Calgary,
T2P 1E5, AB, Canada
Tel.: (403) 266-6000
Web Site: http://www.calfrac.com
Sales Range: $100-124.9 Million
Oil & Gas Wells Drilling Services
N.A.I.C.S.: 213111

CALGARY CO-OPERATIVE AS-SOCIATION LIMITED

110 151-86 Ave SE, Calgary, T2H
3A5, AB, Canada
Tel.: (403) 219-6025   Ca
Web Site:
http://www.calgarycoop.com
Year Founded: 1956
Rev.: $961,965,805
Assets: $524,568,024
Liabilities: $140,624,217
Net Worth: $383,943,806
Earnings: $23,480,134
Emp.: 3,850
Fiscal Year-end: 10/30/21
Food, Drugs & Petroleum Retailer;
General Merchandise Stores
N.A.I.C.S.: 455219
Ken Keelor (CEO)

Subsidiaries:

Calgary Co-op Home Health Care
Limited   (1)
9309 MacLeod Trail SW, Calgary, T2J 0P6,
AB, Canada
Tel.: (403) 252-2266
Sales Range: $10-24.9 Million
Emp.: 60
Women Healthcare Services
N.A.I.C.S.: 621610
Linda Kealey (Gen Mgr)

CALGARY FLAMES LIMITED PARTNERSHIP

555 Saddledome Rise SE Station M,
PO Box 1540, Calgary, T2G 2W1,
AB, Canada
Tel.: (403) 777-2177   Ca
Web Site:
http://www.calgaryflames.com
Year Founded: 1980
Sales Range: $200-249.9 Million
Emp.: 950
Professional Hockey Team & Multi-
Purpose Entertainment Facility
N.A.I.C.S.: 711211
Brad Treliving (Gen Mgr)

CALGARY METAL RECYCLING INC.

3415 Ogden Road SE, Calgary, T2G
4N4, AB, Canada
Tel.: (403) 262-4542
Web Site:
https://www.calgarymetal.com
Year Founded: 1918
Rev.: $10,323,021
Emp.: 70
Metal Recycling Services
N.A.I.C.S.: 562920

Mark Clarke (CEO)

CALGARY TENT & AWNING LTD.

Bay 142 1220 28th Street NE, Cal-
gary, T2A 6A2, AB, Canada
Tel.: (403) 273-8368
Web Site:
https://www.calgarytent.com
Year Founded: 1928
Sales Range: $10-24.9 Million
Emp.: 10
Commercial & Residential Textile
Products Mfr
N.A.I.C.S.: 541490
Marty Way (Pres)

CALGRO M3 HOLDINGS LIM-ITED

Calgro M3 Building 33 Ballyclare
Drive Ballywoods Office Park, Bryan-
ston, Sandton, South Africa
Tel.: (27) 861225476   ZA
Web Site: http://www.calgrom3.com
Year Founded: 1995
CGR—(JSE)
Rev.: $80,551,999
Assets: $140,425,183
Liabilities: $79,480,407
Net Worth: $60,944,776
Earnings: $9,837,849
Emp.: 163
Fiscal Year-end: 02/28/23
Residential Building Development
Services
N.A.I.C.S.: 236115
Willem Jakobus Lategan (CEO)

CALIAN GROUP LTD.

770 Palladium Dr 4th Floor, Ottawa,
K2V 1C8, ON, Canada
Tel.: (613) 599-8600   Ca
Web Site: https://www.calian.com
Year Founded: 1982
74L—(DEU)
Rev.: $133,939,647
Assets: $523,379,414
Liabilities: $281,802,908
Net Worth: $241,576,507
Earnings: ($419,934)
Emp.: 4,500
Fiscal Year-end: 09/30/24
Management Consulting, Information
Technology, Systems Integration,
Outsourcing & Staffing Services
N.A.I.C.S.: 541690
Jacqueline Gauthier (Sr VP-
Corporate Development)

Subsidiaries:

Alio Health Services Inc.   (1)
770 Palladium Drive 4th Floor, Ottawa, K2V
1C8, ON, Canada
Tel.: (613) 287-2546
Web Site: https://www.aliohealth.com
Women Healthcare Services
N.A.I.C.S.: 621610

Allphase Clinical Research Services
Inc.   (1)
770 Palladium Drive 4th Floor, Ottawa, K2V
1C8, ON, Canada
Tel.: (613) 287-0366
Web Site: http://www.allphaseclinical.com
Clinical Development Services
N.A.I.C.S.: 541713

Calian Ltd.   (1)
770 Palladium Dr 4th floor, Ottawa,
K2V1C8, ON, Canada   (100%)
Tel.: (613) 599-8600
Web Site: https://www.calian.com
Sales Range: $25-49.9 Million
Emp.: 175
Provider of Technical & Professional Ser-
vices
N.A.I.C.S.: 541990
Desiree McCarthy (Gen Mgr)

Calian Group Ltd.—(Continued)

Division (Domestic):

Calian Ltd. - SED Systems Division (2)
18 Innovation Boulevard, PO Box 1464, Saskatoon, S7N 3R1, SK, Canada
Tel.: (306) 931-3425
Web Site: http://www.sedsystems.ca
Satellite Telemetry Operation Services
N.A.I.C.S.: 517810
Patrick Thera (Pres)

Branch (Domestic):

Calian Ltd. - Toronto (2)
2 Robert Speck Parkway Suite 620, Mississauga, L4Z 1H8, ON, Canada
Tel.: (905) 848-2818
Web Site: http://www.calian.com
Emp.: 7
Business Software Development Services
N.A.I.C.S.: 541511

Hawaii Pacific Teleport, LP (1)
91-340 Farrington Hwy, Kapolei, HI 96707
Tel.: (808) 216-2136
Sales Range: $1-9.9 Million
Emp.: 11
Information Services
N.A.I.C.S.: 519290
Christopher Guthrie (Principal)

InterTronic Solutions Inc. (1)
1701 Rue Chicoine Vaudreuil-Dorion, Quebec, J7V 8P2, QC, Canada
Tel.: (450) 424-5666
Web Site:
  https://www.intertronicsolutions.com
Television Antenna Mfr
N.A.I.C.S.: 334220

IntraGrain Technologies Inc. (1)
118 Husum Road RM of Sherwood, Regina, S4K 0A4, SK, Canada
Tel.: (306) 570-7979
Web Site: https://www.calianagriculture.com
Monitoring Cable Mfr
N.A.I.C.S.: 334519
Kyle Folk (Pres)

SatService Gesellschaft fur Kommunikationssysteme mbH (1)
Hardstrasse 9, Steisslingen, 78256, Konstanz, Germany
Tel.: (49) 77389979110
Web Site: https://satservicegmbh.de
Telecommunication Equipment Whslr
N.A.I.C.S.: 423690
Wilfried Megger (Mng Dir)

SimFront Simulation Systems Corporation (1)
329 March Road Suite 232, Ottawa, K2K 2E1, ON, Canada
Tel.: (613) 216-2300
Web Site: https://www.simfront.com
Space Aircraft Mfr
N.A.I.C.S.: 336411

Stratos Management Systems, Inc. (1)
840 W Sam Houston Pkwy N Ste 420, Houston, TX 77041
Tel.: (713) 780-7580
Web Site: http://www.computex.net
Information Technology Infrastructure & Hybrid Cloud Services
N.A.I.C.S.: 541512
Ken Brown (Co-Founder)

Tallysman Wireless Inc. (1)
36 Steacie Drive, Ottawa, K2K 2A9, ON, Canada
Tel.: (613) 591-3131
Web Site: https://www.tallysman.com
Telecommunications Equipment Mfr
N.A.I.C.S.: 334290
Gyles Panther (Pres & CTO)

CALIBRE GROUP LTD
Level 2 50 St Georges Terrace, Perth, 6000, WA, Australia
Tel.: (61) 8 9265 3000
Web Site:
  http://www.calibregroup.com
Year Founded: 2002
Sales Range: $300-349.9 Million

Engineeering Services
N.A.I.C.S.: 541330
Geoff Tomlinson (Chm)

CALIBRE MINING CORP.
Suite 1560 200 Burrard Street, PO Box 49167, Vancouver, V6C 3L6, BC, Canada
Tel.: (604) 681-9944
Web Site:
  https://www.calibremining.com
CXBMF—(OTCIQ)
Rev.: $242,748,000
Assets: $351,183,000
Liabilities: $121,035,000
Net Worth: $230,148,000
Earnings: $63,413,000
Emp.: 1,144
Fiscal Year-end: 12/31/20.
Gold, Silver & Copper Exploration Services
N.A.I.C.S.: 212220
Douglas B. Forster (Founder)

Subsidiaries:

Marathon Gold Corporation (1)
36 Lombard Street Suite 600, Toronto, M5C 2X3, ON, Canada
Tel.: (416) 861-0851
Web Site: https://www.marathon-gold.com
Rev.: $424,778
Assets: $124,068,043
Liabilities: $9,442,902
Net Worth: $114,625,142
Earnings: ($5,498,646)
Emp.: 14
Fiscal Year-end: 12/31/2020
Gold Mining Services
N.A.I.C.S.: 212220
Gil Lawson (COO)

CALIDA HOLDING AG
Bahnstrasse, Oberkirch, CH-6208, Sursee, Switzerland
Tel.: (41) 419254525
Web Site: https://www.calida-group.com
CALN—(SWX)
Rev.: $367,907,982
Assets: $370,362,528
Liabilities: $149,788,248
Net Worth: $220,574,279
Earnings: $41,042,129
Emp.: 2,500
Fiscal Year-end: 12/31/22
Holding Company; Men's & Women's Clothing Mfr
N.A.I.C.S.: 551112
Daniel Gemperle (COO)

Subsidiaries:

Aubade Handels GmbH (1)
Wallbrunnstrasse 2479539, Freiburg, Lorrach, Germany
Tel.: (49) 15166583749
Web Site:
  https://www.aubadehandelsgmbh.de
Refined Edible Oil Mfr
N.A.I.C.S.: 311225

Aubade Italia S.R.L. (1)
Via Magnaghi 2/8, 16129, Genoa, Italy (100%)
Tel.: (39) 059553669
Web Site: http://aubade.it
Womens & Girls Cut & Sew Lingerie Loungewear & Nightwear Mfr
N.A.I.C.S.: 315250

Aubade Paris (UK) Ltd. (1)
1 Pury Hill Cottage Alderton Road, Paulerspury North, Towcester, United Kingdom (100%)
Tel.: (44) 1327811289
Web Site: https://www.aubade.com
Emp.: 3
Womens & Girls Cut & Sew Lingerie Loungewear & Nightwear Mfr
N.A.I.C.S.: 315250

Aubade Paris SAS (1)

10 Rue du Colonel Driant, 75001, Paris, France (100%)
Tel.: (33) 170992000
Web Site: https://www.aubade.fr
Sales Range: $25-49.9 Million
Emp.: 130
Womens & Girls Cut & Sew Lingerie Loungewear & Nightwear Mfr
N.A.I.C.S.: 315250

Callda AG (1)
Industrie Munigen Sursee, 6210, Lucerne, Switzerland (100%)
Tel.: (41) 9254525
Sales Range: $100-124.9 Million
Emp.: 300
Womens & Girls Cut & Sew Lingerie Loungewear & Nightwear Mfr
N.A.I.C.S.: 315250

Calida Group Digital GmbH (1)
Gewerbepark BWB 2, 83052, Bruckmuhl, Germany
Tel.: (49) 80627213300
Web Site: https://calidagroup.digital
Underwear Mfr & Distr
N.A.I.C.S.: 315990

Lafuma Mobilier SAS (1)
6 Rue Victor Lafuma, 26140, Anneyron, France
Tel.: (33) 411923019
Web Site: https://www.lafuma-mobilier.fr
Outdoor Furniture Mfr
N.A.I.C.S.: 337122

Lafuma SA (1)
3 Impasse des Prairies, 74940, Annecy-le-Vieux, France (93.5%)
Tel.: (33) 475313131
Web Site: https://www.groupe-lafuma.com
Rev.: $194,265,869
Earnings: $6,849,015
Emp.: 1,559
Fiscal Year-end: 12/31/2018
Outdoor Garments, Backpacks, Tents, Sleeping Bags, Footwear & Camping Equipment Mfr
N.A.I.C.S.: 339920
Carine Rosiere (Sec)

Subsidiary (Domestic):

Eider S.A.S. (2)
21 rue du Pre Faucon PAE Les Glaisins, PO Box 60348 F, 74940, Annecy-le-Vieux, France
Tel.: (33) 450107250
Web Site: http://www.eider.com
Sales Range: $25-49.9 Million
Emp.: 50
Clothing & Footwear Mfr
N.A.I.C.S.: 315990

Subsidiary (US):

Lafuma America, Inc. (2)
140 Old Laramie Trl Ste 3, Lafayette, CO 80026
Tel.: (303) 527-1460
Web Site: https://www.lafuma.com
Sales Range: $25-49.9 Million
Emp.: 15
Outdoor Sporting Equipment & Apparel Mfr & Distr
N.A.I.C.S.: 423910
Guillaume Linossier (Gen Mgr)

Subsidiary (Non-US):

Lafuma BV (2)
Plesmanstraat 1, 3833 LA, Leusden, Netherlands
Tel.: (31) 334320499
Web Site: https://www.lafuma.com
Sales Range: $50-74.9 Million
Emp.: 5
Sporting Goods Whslr
N.A.I.C.S.: 423910

Lafuma Group GmbH (2)
Fabrikstr 35, 73266, Bietigheim-Bissingen, Germany
Tel.: (49) 702395110
Web Site: https://www.lafuma.com
Sales Range: $25-49.9 Million
Emp.: 15
Backpacks & Tents Mfr
N.A.I.C.S.: 314910

Lafuma HK Ltd. (2)

Room E 94 MG Tower Ste 133 Hoi Bun Road Kwun Tong, 1 13 Hollywood Rd, Kowloon, China (Hong Kong)
Tel.: (852) 25266632
Web Site: http://www.lafuma.com
Clothing Stores
N.A.I.C.S.: 458110

Lafuma Hungaria (2)
Kemeny Istvan utca 1, 9600, Sarvar, Hungary
Tel.: (36) 95320651
Sales Range: $75-99.9 Million
Emp.: 230
Sportswear Mfr
N.A.I.C.S.: 315250

Subsidiary (Domestic):

Millet (2)
21 rue du Pre Falcon PAE Les Glaisins, PO Box 60348 F, 74943, Annecy-le-Vieux, Cedex, France
Tel.: (33) 450695959
Web Site: http://www.millet.fr
Sales Range: $25-49.9 Million
Emp.: 70
Mountain Clothing & Backpacks Mfr
N.A.I.C.S.: 314910

Luemme, Inc. (1)
12186 SW 128th St, Miami, FL 33186
Tel.: (305) 253-9904
Web Site: http://www.cosabella.com
Rev.: $30,000,000
Emp.: 60
Lingerie, Swimwear & Apparel Retailer
N.A.I.C.S.: 458110
Valeria Campello (Pres)

Reich Online Services GmbH (1)
Hogeringer Strasse 27, 83071, Stephanskirchen, Germany
Tel.: (49) 8036943940
Web Site: http://www.reich-online.biz
Logistics & Consulting Services
N.A.I.C.S.: 541614
Theresia Steiner (Dir-HR)

CALIFORNIA SOFTWARE COMPANY LTD.
Workflo Greeta TowersIndustrial Estate OMR Phase 1, Perungudi, Chennai, 600096, India
Tel.: (91) 9444860882
Web Site: https://www.calsof.com
Year Founded: 1992
CALSOFT—(NSE)
Rev.: $198,608
Assets: $2,469,681
Liabilities: $1,114,987
Net Worth: $1,354,694
Earnings: $26,536
Emp.: 15
Fiscal Year-end: 03/31/21
Enterprise Software Products
N.A.I.C.S.: 541511
Vasudevan Mahalingam (CEO & Mng Dir)

CALIMA ENERGY LIMITED
4/246-250 Railway Parade, West Leederville, 6007, WA, Australia
Tel.: (61) 865003270 AU
Web Site: https://calimaenergy.com
Year Founded: 2001
CE1—(ASX)
Rev.: $751,311
Assets: $83,683,673
Liabilities: $26,872,148
Net Worth: $56,811,525
Earnings: ($1,886,111)
Fiscal Year-end: 12/31/23
Oil & Gas Exploration Services
N.A.I.C.S.: 211120
Jordan Kevol (CEO)

Subsidiaries:

Calima Energy Inc. (1)
2500 639 5 Avenue SW, Calgary, T2P 0M9, AB, Canada
Tel.: (403) 389-1226
Oil & Gas Exploration Services
N.A.I.C.S.: 213112

Micheal Dobovich *(Pres)*

CALIN TECHNOLOGY CO., LTD.
24 Chien Kuo Rd, Tan Tzu Dist, Taichung, 42760, Taiwan
Tel.: (886) 425353658
Web Site: https://www.calin.com.tw
Year Founded: 2002
4976—(TAI)
Rev.: $30,194,054
Assets: $101,989,597
Liabilities: $19,937,865
Net Worth: $82,051,732
Earnings: ($8,559,305)
Emp.: 423
Fiscal Year-end: 12/31/23
Optical Glass Lens Mfr
N.A.I.C.S.: 333310
Chia-Pin Liu *(Chm & Pres)*

CALIX LIMITED
Suite 301 Building 1 20 Bridge St, Pymble, 2073, NSW, Australia
Tel.: (61) 281997400   AU
Web Site: https://calix.global
Year Founded: 2005
CXL—(ASX)
Rev.: $16,152,511
Assets: $75,050,748
Liabilities: $18,958,333
Net Worth: $56,092,414
Earnings: ($17,501,335)
Emp.: 155
Fiscal Year-end: 06/30/24
Other Nonmetallic Mineral Mining & Quarrying
N.A.I.C.S.: 212390
Phil Hodgson *(CEO & Mng Dir)*

Subsidiaries:

Inland Environmental Resources, Inc.   (1)
1717 S Rustle St, Spokane, WA 99224
Web Site: https://ierwater.com
Wastewater Treatment Chemicals & Equipment Distr
N.A.I.C.S.: 562998
Doug Kelley *(Pres)*

CALLAGHAN INNOVATION RESEARCH LIMITED
69 Gracefield Road, PO Box 31310, Lower Hutt, 5040, New Zealand
Tel.: (64) 4 931 3000   NZ
Web Site:
    http://www.callaghan.govt.nz
Year Founded: 1992
Sales Range: $50-74.9 Million
Emp.: 500
Scientific Research & Development, Research Funding & Business Consulting Services
N.A.I.C.S.: 541715
Robin Hape *(Deputy Chm)*

CALLEJA S.A. DE C.V.
Prolongacion 59 Avenue South El Progreso Street Suite 2934, San Salvador, El Salvador
Tel.: (503) 22673600
Supermarkets, Groceries & Retail Stores
N.A.I.C.S.: 459999

Subsidiaries:

Almacenes Exito S.A.   (1)
Carrera 48 32B Sur 139, Medellin, Colombia
Tel.: (57) 43396565
Web Site: https://www.grupoexito.com.co
Retail Store Services
N.A.I.C.S.: 459999
Carlos Mario Giraldo Moreno *(Chm & CEO)*

CALLIDUS CAPITAL CORPORATION

4620 - 181 Bay Street Bay Wellington Tower Brokfield Place, PO Box 792, Toronto, M5J 2T3, ON, Canada
Tel.: (416) 945-3016   ON
Year Founded: 2003
Rev.: $273,944,606
Assets: $498,227,562
Liabilities: $502,220,049
Net Worth: ($3,992,488)
Earnings: ($134,567,428)
Emp.: 34
Fiscal Year-end: 12/31/18
Financial Lending Services
N.A.I.C.S.: 522310

Subsidiaries:

Altair Water & Drilling Services Inc.   (1)
38318 Rge Rd 281, Red Deer, T4E 1X8, AB, Canada
Tel.: (403) 348-0189
Web Site: http://www.altairwater.com
Water Well Drilling Services
N.A.I.C.S.: 213111

Bluberi Gaming Technologies Inc.   (1)
2120 Rue Letendre, Drummondville, J2C 7E9, QC, Canada
Tel.: (819) 475-5155
Web Site: http://www.bluberi.com
Digital Slot Gaming Services
N.A.I.C.S.: 713210

C & C Resources Inc.   (1)
1751 Quesnel-Hixon Rd, Quesnel, V2J 5Z5, BC, Canada
Tel.: (250) 992-7471
Web Site: http://www.ccresourcesinc.com
Emp.: 300
Wood Products Mfr
N.A.I.C.S.: 337111

Wabash Castings Inc.   (1)
3837 W Mill St, Wabash, IN 46992
Tel.: (270) 935-8084
Web Site: http://wabashcastings.com
Aluminum Casting Mfr & Distr
N.A.I.C.S.: 331524

CALLINEX MINES INC.
1100 1199 West Hastings Street, Vancouver, V6E 3T5, BC, Canada
Tel.: (604) 605-0885   BC
Web Site: https://www.callinex.ca
Year Founded: 2011
CNX—(OTCIQ)
Assets: $23,792,416
Liabilities: $1,546,228
Net Worth: $22,246,188
Earnings: ($901,250)
Fiscal Year-end: 09/30/21
Metal Mining Services
N.A.I.C.S.: 212290
Max Porterfield *(Pres & CEO)*

CALLISTA INDUSTRIES LTD.
Shop No 136-137/ 8 & 9 3rd Floor Empire Square Baben Ta-Bardoli, Surat, 394 602, Gujarat, India
Tel.: (91) 7977106490
Web Site:
    https://callistaindustries.com
Year Founded: 1989
Sales Range: Less than $1 Million
Textile Products Distr
N.A.I.C.S.: 424310
Rashmi Ravi Sharma *(Mng Dir)*

CALLISTA PRIVATE EQUITY GMBH & CO. KG
Konrad-Zuse-Platz 8, 81829, Munich, Germany
Tel.: (49) 89 207042430
Web Site: http://www.callista-pe.de
Privater Equity Firm
N.A.I.C.S.: 523999
Olaf Meier *(CEO)*

Subsidiaries:

MS Deutschland Beteiligungsgesellschaft mbH   (1)
Am Holm 25, Neustadt in Holstein, 23730, Germany
Tel.: (49) 45613960
Web Site: http://www.msdeutschland-gmbh.de
Cruise Ship Operator
N.A.I.C.S.: 483112
Frank Thuringer *(Mng Dir)*

MT Technologies GmbH   (1)
Hebbelstrasse 65, 85055, Ingolstadt, Germany
Tel.: (49) 84195300
Web Site: http://www.mt-technologies.com
Emp.: 300
Car Maintenance Services
N.A.I.C.S.: 811111

PCH Metals S.A.S.   (1)
13 Rue de lilet, Saint-Martin-sur-le-Pre, France
Tel.: (33) 326640357
Heating & Cooling System Mfr
N.A.I.C.S.: 333415

Reederei Peter Deilmann GmbH   (1)
Am Holm 25, 23730, Neustadt in Holstein, Germany
Tel.: (49) 4561 396 0
Web Site: http://www.deilmann-kreuzfahrten.de
Sales Range: $10-24.9 Million
Cruise Ship Operator
N.A.I.C.S.: 483112
Frank Thuringer *(Mng Dir)*

CALMARK SWEDEN AB
Greenhouse Labs Teknikringen 38A, 114 28, Stockholm, Sweden
Tel.: (46) 102040150
Web Site: https://en.calmark.se
Year Founded: 2007
9C7—(DEU)
Health Care Srvices
N.A.I.C.S.: 621610
Mathias Karlsson *(Founder)*

CALMENA ENERGY SERVICES INC.
1200 1122-4th Street SW, Calgary, T2R 1M1, AB, Canada
Tel.: (403) 225-3879   AB
Web Site: http://www.calmena.com
Year Founded: 2008
Sales Range: $75-99.9 Million
Emp.: 387
Oil & Gas Exploration Services
N.A.I.C.S.: 211120
John R. King *(Pres & CEO)*

CALMONT LEASING LTD
14610 Yellowhead Tr, Edmonton, T5L 3C5, AB, Canada
Tel.: (780) 454-0491
Web Site: http://www.calmontedm.ca
Year Founded: 1977
Rev.: $51,558,355
Emp.: 270
New & Used Truck Retailer
N.A.I.C.S.: 532120
Lawrence Pudlowski *(VP-Ops)*

Subsidiaries:

Calmont Truck Centre Ltd.   (1)
11403 174th St NW, Edmonton, T5S 2P4, AB, Canada
Tel.: (780) 451-2680
Web Site: https://www.volvotruckcentre.com
Truck Leasing Services
N.A.I.C.S.: 532120

CALNEX SOLUTIONS PLC
Calnex Solutions Oracle Campus, Linlithgow, EH49 7LR, United Kingdom
Tel.: (44) 1506671416   UK
Web Site: https://www.calnexsol.com
Year Founded: 2006

CLX—(AIM)
Rev.: $34,086,168
Assets: $48,119,750
Liabilities: $14,144,102
Net Worth: $33,975,648
Earnings: $7,340,280
Emp.: 116
Fiscal Year-end: 03/31/23
Telecommunication Servicesb
N.A.I.C.S.: 517410
Tommy Cook *(CEO)*

Subsidiaries:

Calnex Americas Corporation   (1)
2040 Martin Ave, Santa Clara, CA 95050
Tel.: (610) 739-6066
Network Services
N.A.I.C.S.: 516210

CALORIC ANLAGENBAU GMBH
Lohenstrasse 12, Grafelfing, 82166, Germany
Tel.: (49) 89898190
Web Site: http://www.caloric.de
Year Founded: 1965
Rev.: $25,067,147
Emp.: 50
Gas Generating Plant Mfr
N.A.I.C.S.: 333998
Florian von Linde *(Mng Dir)*

CALS REFINERIES LIMITED
Unit No 209 2nd Floor Suneja Tower-II, District Center Janakpuri, New Delhi, 110 058, India
Tel.: (91) 1145067736   In
Web Site: http://www.cals.in
Year Founded: 1984
Oil Refining Services
N.A.I.C.S.: 324110

CALTAGIRONE EDITORE S.P.A.
Via Barberini 28, 00187, Rome, Italy
Tel.: (39) 0645412200   IT
Web Site:
    https://www.caltagironeeditore.com
CED—(ITA)
Rev.: $147,261,063
Assets: $552,898,377
Liabilities: $136,194,621
Net Worth: $416,703,757
Earnings: ($54,382,782)
Emp.: 596
Fiscal Year-end: 12/31/20
Newspaper & Advertising Publishing Services
N.A.I.C.S.: 327420
Alessandro Caltagirone *(Vice Chm)*

Subsidiaries:

Ced Digital & Servizi Srl   (1)
Via del Tritone 152, 00187, Rome, Italy
Tel.: (39) 0645412200
Web Site: https://www.ceds.it
Telecommunication Servicesb
N.A.I.C.S.: 517810

Centro Stampa Veneto SpA   (1)
Via Torino 110, Venice, 30172, Italy   (99.91%)
Tel.: (39) 0416652111
Web Site: http://www.gazzettino.it
Sales Range: $50-74.9 Million
Emp.: 120
Periodical Publishers
N.A.I.C.S.: 513120
Roberto Papetti *(Mng Dir)*

Corriere Adriatico Srl   (1)
Via Barberini 28, 00187, Rome, Italy
Tel.: (39) 0714581
Web Site: https://www.corriereadriatico.it
Newspaper Publishers
N.A.I.C.S.: 513110

Il Gazzettino SpA   (1)
Via Torino 110, Mestre, 30172, Venice, Italy   (99.91%)
Tel.: (39) 041665111

Caltagirone Editore S.p.A.—(Continued)

Web Site: https://www.ilgazzettino.it
Newspaper Publishers
N.A.I.C.S.: 513110

Il Mattino SpA (1)
Centro Direzionale Torre Francesco - Isola
B5 33 piano, 80143, Naples, Italy (100%)
Tel.: (39) 0817947111
Web Site: httpoi://www.ilmattino.it
Emp.: 22
Newspaper Publishers
N.A.I.C.S.: 513110

Il Messaggero SpA (1)
Via Del Tritone 152, 00187, Rome,
Italy (100%)
Tel.: (39) 0647201
Web Site: https://www.ilmessaggero.it
Periodical Publishers
N.A.I.C.S.: 513120

**Imprese Tipografiche Venete
SpA** (1)
Via Torino 110, Venice, 110-30172,
Italy (100%)
Tel.: (39) 041665111
Newspaper Publishers
N.A.I.C.S.: 513110

Leggo Srl (1)
Via Barberini 28, 00187, Rome, Italy
Tel.: (39) 064620731
Web Site: https://www.leggo.it
Newspaper Publishers
N.A.I.C.S.: 513110

Piemme SpA (1)
Via Puccini 13, Campolongo Tapogliano,
33040, Udine, UD, Italy (100%)
Tel.: (39) 043199058
Web Site: https://piemme.com
Media Representatives
N.A.I.C.S.: 541840

Societa Editrice Padana SpA (1)
via Torino 110, Mestre, Italy (52%)
Tel.: (39) 0540 191 970
Publishing Services
N.A.I.C.S.: 513110

Stampa Napoli 2015 Srl (1)
Agglomerato Asi Pascarola, 80023, Cai-
vano, Italy
Tel.: (39) 0818360320.
Offset Printing Paper Mfr
N.A.I.C.S.: 323111

Vianini Lavori S.p.A. (1)
Via Barberini 68, 00187, Rome,
Italy (55%)
Tel.: (39) 06374921
Web Site: http://www.vianinigroup.it
Sales Range: $150-199.9 Million
Emp.: 41
Construction & Civil Engineering Services
N.A.I.C.S.: 541330
Mario Delfini (Chm)

CALTECH SURVEYS LTD.
300 1011 1st Street S W, Calgary,
T2R 1J2, AB, Canada
Tel.: (403) 263-8055
Web Site:
　http://www.caltechsurveys.com
Year Founded: 1990
Oil & Natural Gas Pipeline Surveys
N.A.I.C.S.: 541370
Jade McLeod (Pres)

CALTH INC.
321 54 Changeop-ro, Sujeong-gu,
Seongnam, Gyeonggi-do, Korea
(South)
Tel.: (82) 317540320
Web Site: https://www.thecalth.com
Year Founded: 2018
402420—(KRS)
Medical Device Mfr
N.A.I.C.S.: 339112

CALVALLEY ENERGY LTD.
PO Box 7090, Hadda Area, Sana'a,
Yemen
Tel.: (967) 1 41 5555

Web Site:
　http://www.calvalleypetroleum.com
Holding Company; Petroleum & Natural Gas Exploration & Extraction Services
N.A.I.C.S.: 551112
Les Kondratoff (Country Mgr-Yemen)

Subsidiaries:

Calvalley Petroleum (Cyprus)
Ltd. (1)
PO Box 7090, Hadda Area, Sana'a, Yemen
Tel.: (967) 1415555
Sales Range: $50-74.9 Million
Emp.: 50
Petroleum & Natural Gas Exploration & Ex-
traction Services
N.A.I.C.S.: 211120
Paul King (Gen Mgr)

CALVATIS GMBH
Dr Albert-Reimann-Strasse 16 A,
68526, Ladenburg, Germany
Tel.: (49) 62031050
Web Site: http://www.calvatis.com
Year Founded: 1929
Sales Range: $50-74.9 Million
Emp.: 400
Industrial Detergent & Disinfectant
Mfr
N.A.I.C.S.: 325611
Thomas Mohr (CEO)

Subsidiaries:

Calvatis Asia Pacific Co., Ltd (1)
406 Ratchadapisek Samsen nork, Huayk-
wang, Bangkok, 10310, Thailand
Tel.: (66) 22901213
Web Site: https://www.calvatisthai.com
Disinfectant & Cleaning Equipment Mfr
N.A.I.C.S.: 325612

Calvatis B.V. (1)
Cob Balkplein 1, Cothen, 3945 ER, Nether-
lands
Tel.: (31) 343 563959
Sales Range: $50-74.9 Million
Emp.: 5
Detergent & Disinfectant Distr
N.A.I.C.S.: 424690
Ton Buining (Office Mgr)

Calvatis GmbH (1)
Kaiser-Josef-Platz 41, Wels, 4600, Austria
Tel.: (43) 7242 42899 0
Web Site: http://www.calvatis.com
Year Founded:
Sales Range: $25-49.9 Million
Emp.: 12
Detergent & Disinfectant Distr
N.A.I.C.S.: 424690

Calvatis Hijyen San. ve Ds Tic. Ltd.
Sti. (1)
Sanayi Mah Isso San Sit R 2 Blok No 1-2,
34517, Esenyurt, Istanbul, Turkiye
Tel.: (90) 212 6231833
Detergent & Disinfectant Distr
N.A.I.C.S.: 424690

Calvatis OOO (1)
Leninskiy prospekt d 42 k1, 119119, Mos-
cow, Russia
Tel.: (7) 4959387136
Web Site: http://www.calvatis.ru
Detergent & Disinfectant Mfr & Distr
N.A.I.C.S.: 325611

Calvatis UAB (1)
B Sruogos Str 36, 10220, Vilnius, Lithuania
Tel.: (370) 52 340 336
Web Site: http://www.calvatis.com
Sales Range: $25-49.9 Million
Emp.: 15
Detergent & Disinfectant Distr
N.A.I.C.S.: 424690
Gedimaninas Gegucirs (Gen Mgr)

Calvatis srl (1)
Via-Carlo-Abarth 17, 39012, Merano, Italy
Tel.: (39) 0473 232016
Detergent & Disinfectant Mfr & Distr
N.A.I.C.S.: 325611

Calvatis srl (1)
str Fabricii nr 56, Cluj-Napoca, 400, Romania

Tel.: (40) 264415830
Sales Range: $50-74.9 Million
Emp.: 9
Detergent & Disinfectant Distr
N.A.I.C.S.: 424690

CALVETON UK LTD
4 Old Park Lane, London, W1K 1QW,
United Kingdom
Year Founded: 2017
Private Investment
N.A.I.C.S.: 523999
Sandeep Vyas (Founder)

CALVI HOLDING S.R.L.
Via 4 Novembre 2, 23807, Lecco,
Italy
Tel.: (39) 03999851
Web Site: http://www.calvi.it
Steel Profile Mfr
N.A.I.C.S.: 332322
Riccardo Chini (Chm & CEO)

Subsidiaries:

Falci S.r.l. (1)
Via Cuneo 3/5/7, Dronero, 12025, Cuneo,
Italy
Tel.: (39) 0171 5341
Web Site: http://www.falcisrl.com
Steel Products Mfr
N.A.I.C.S.: 331110

Fiav L. Mazzacchera S.p.A. (1)
Via Archimede 45, 20864, Agrate Brianza,
Italy
Tel.: (39) 039 3310 411
Web Site: http://www.fiav.it
Steel Products Mfr
N.A.I.C.S.: 331110

Hoesch Schwerter Profile GmbH (1)
Eisenindustriestrasse 1, 58239, Schwerte,
Germany
Tel.: (49) 2304 106 0
Web Site: http://www.hoesch-profile.com
Steel Products Mfr
N.A.I.C.S.: 331110
Dott Riccardo Chini (Mng Partner)

Rathbone Precision Metals, Inc. (1)
1241 Park St, Palmer, MA 01069-1606
Tel.: (413) 283-8961
Web Site: http://www.rathboneprofiles.com
Sales Range: $25-49.9 Million
Emp.: 50
Custom, Cold-Drawn Metal Shapes Mfr
N.A.I.C.S.: 331221
William Delaney (Controller)

Sipa S.p.A. (1)
Via G Galilei 32, 20866, Monza, Italy
Tel.: (39) 039 6076488
Web Site: http://www.sipaspa.com
Steel Products Mfr
N.A.I.C.S.: 331110
Alessandro Rizzetto (Area Mgr-Sls)

CALYSTENE
16 Rue Irene Joliot-Curie, 38320, Ey-
bens, France
Tel.: (33) 476412930
Web Site: http://www.calystene.com
Sales Range: $10-24.9 Million
Emp.: 35
Medical Software Systems Solutions
N.A.I.C.S.: 513210

CALYX VENTURES INC.
Suite 2200, HSBC Building 885 West
Georgia Street, Vancouver, V6C 3E8,
BC, Canada
Tel.: (604) 880-8822
Web Site: http://www.calyxbio.com
Year Founded: 2008
CYX—(TSXV)
Sales Range: Less than $1 Million
Holding Company; Biotechnology
Products Developer
N.A.I.C.S.: 551112
Roger Forde (Pres & CEO)

Subsidiaries:

Agrisoma Biosciences Inc. (1)
5929L Jeanne D'Arc Boulevard Suite 323,
Ottawa, K1C 7K2, ON, Canada (32%)
Tel.: (613) 323-3171
Web Site: http://www.agrisoma.com
Agricultural Biotechnology Products Devel-
oper & Mfr
N.A.I.C.S.: 325414

CAM ALTERNATIVES GMBH
Gereonshof 12, Cologne, 550670,
Germany
Tel.: (49) 221 937085 0
Web Site: http://www.cam-
　alternatives.com
Year Founded: 1998
Emp.: 70
Financial Investment Services
N.A.I.C.S.: 523999
Andreas Schmidt (Co-CEO & Part-
ner)

CAM CLARK FORD
417 Lantern Street, Red Deer, T4E
0A5, AB, Canada
Tel.: (403) 343-3673
Web Site:
　http://www.camclarkfordreddeer.com
Year Founded: 1983
Rev.: $50,051,310
Emp.: 55
New & Used Car Dealers
N.A.I.C.S.: 441110
Sean Bell (Gen Mgr)

CAM GROUP, INC.
Jixing Building 151 Shengli Avenue
North, Shijiazhuang, 050041, Hebei,
China
Tel.: (86) 31186964264
Year Founded: 1995
CAMG—(OTCIQ)
Sales Range: Less than $1 Million
Emp.: 14
Advertising Services
N.A.I.C.S.: 541890
Lijun Chen (Pres-China Agriculture
Media (Hebei) Co Ltd)

**CAM MEDIA CREATIVE
WORKS SP. Z O.O.**
ul Tamka 16 lok U4, 00-349, Warsaw,
Poland
Tel.: (48) 228280885
Web Site: http://www.cammedia.pl
Advertising Services
N.A.I.C.S.: 541810

**CAM RANH INTERNATIONAL
AIRPORT SERVICES JSC**
Cam Ranh International Airport, Cam
Nghia ward, Cam Ranh Bay, Khanh
Hoa, Vietnam
Tel.: (84) 2586265588
Web Site: https://cias.vn
Year Founded: 2009
CIA—(HNX)
Rev.: $10,614,800
Assets: $33,682,400
Liabilities: $1,326,000
Net Worth: $32,356,400
Earnings: $6,551,700
Fiscal Year-end: 12/31/22
Food Catering Services
N.A.I.C.S.: 722320

Subsidiaries:

Aviation Ground Service Company
Ltd. (1)
Cam Ranh International Airport, Cam Nghia
Ward, Cam Ranh Bay, Khanh Hoa, Vietnam
Tel.: (84) 2583971888
Web Site: https://www.ags.com.vn
Aircraft Maintenance Services
N.A.I.C.S.: 561720

CAM RESOURCES BERHAD

10th Floor Menara Hap Seng 1 and 3
Jalan P Ramlee, 50250, Kuala Lumpur, Malaysia
Tel.: (60) 323824288
Web Site:
https://www.camres.com.my
Year Founded: 2000
CAMRES—(KLS)
Rev.: $104,975,788
Assets: $41,454,729
Liabilities: $11,935,825
Net Worth: $29,518,904
Earnings: $3,435,070
Emp.: 409
Fiscal Year-end: 12/31/22
Aluminum & Stainless Steel Mfr
N.A.I.C.S.: 331513
Ming Toong Lim (Co-Sec)

Subsidiaries:

CAM Plastic Industry Sdn. Bhd. **(1)**
Lot 19971, Khathan Baru Industrial Estate
Kanthan Baru, 31200, Chemor, Perak, Malaysia
Tel.: (60) 52011088
Web Site: http://www.kiwiplastic.com.my
House Ware Plastic Product Mfr
N.A.I.C.S.: 326199

Central Aluminium Manufactory Sdn.
Bhd. **(1)**
Batu 12 Jalan Hutan Melintang, Hutan Melintang, 36400, Perak, Malaysia
Tel.: (60) 56411046
Web Site: https://www.camsink.com.my
Kitchen Sink Mfr
N.A.I.C.S.: 326191

Central Melamineware Sdn. Bhd. **(1)**
Railway Wharf Jalan Maharaja Lela, 36000,
Teluk Intan, Perak, Malaysia
Tel.: (60) 56223849
Tableware Product Mfr
N.A.I.C.S.: 332215

CAMANCHACA S.A.

Avenida El Golf No 99 Piso 10, Las
Condes, Santiago, Chile
Tel.: (56) 28732940   CL
Web Site: https://www.camanchaca.cl
Year Founded: 1965
CAMANCHACA—(SGO)
Rev.: $761,843,000
Assets: $888,920,000
Liabilities: $452,006,000
Net Worth: $436,914,000
Earnings: $5,397,000
Emp.: 4,100
Fiscal Year-end: 12/31/23
Aquaculture & Fishing Services
N.A.I.C.S.: 114111
Ricardo Garcia Holtz (CEO)

Subsidiaries:

Salmones Camanchaca S.A. **(1)**
Diego Portales 2000 piso 13, Puerto Montt,
Chile   **(70.29%)**
Tel.: (56) 652327200
Web Site:
https://www.salmonescamanchaca.cl
Rev.: $372,961,000
Assets: $422,576,000
Liabilities: $209,524,000
Net Worth: $213,052,000
Earnings: $44,704,000
Emp.: 1,770
Fiscal Year-end: 12/31/2022
Fishing Services
N.A.I.C.S.: 112511
Ricardo Garcia Holtz (CEO)

CAMARGO CORREA S.A.

Rua Funchal 160 Vila Olimpia,
04551-903, Sao Paulo, SP, Brazil
Tel.: (55) 1138415511   BR
Web Site:
http://www.camargocorrea.com.br
Year Founded: 1939
Sales Range: $5-14.9 Billion
Emp.: 49,186

Multi-Industry Holding Company
N.A.I.C.S.: 551112

Subsidiaries:

Cimpor - Cimentos de Portugal,
SGPS, S.A. **(1)**
Rua Alexandre Herculano 35, 1250-009,
Lisbon, Portugal   **(94.1%)**
Tel.: (351) 213118100
Web Site: http://www.cimpor.com
Rev.: $2,042,557,278
Assets: $5,324,005,053
Liabilities: $5,761,455,970
Net Worth: ($437,450,917)
Earnings: ($840,740,759)
Emp.: 7,747
Fiscal Year-end: 12/31/2016
Cement Mfr
N.A.I.C.S.: 327310
Paulo Sergio Oliveira Diniz (CFO)

Subsidiary (Domestic):

Agrepor Agregados - Extraccao De
Inertes S.A. **(2)**
Sangardao, Condeixa-A-Nova, 3151-999,
Coimbra, Portugal   **(100%)**
Tel.: (351) 239949620
Sales Range: $50-74.9 Million
Emp.: 20
Dimension Stone Mining & Quarrying
N.A.I.C.S.: 212311

Alempedras - Sociedade de Britas
Lda **(2)**
Casal Da Luz Bairro, Obidos, Lisbon,
Portugal   **(100%)**
Tel.: (351) 262959444
Nonmetallic Mineral Product Mfr
N.A.I.C.S.: 327999

Subsidiary (Non-US):

Amreyah Cement Compamy
S.A.E. **(2)**
El Gharbaneyat - Borg el Arab, Alexandria,
Egypt   **(96.39%)**
Tel.: (20) 34195600
Cement Mfr
N.A.I.C.S.: 327310
Luis Fernandes (Mng Dir)

Amreyah Cimpor Cement Company
S.A.E. **(2)**
El Gharbaneyat - Borg el Arab, Alexandria,
Egypt   **(97.29%)**
Tel.: (20) 3 41 95 600
Web Site: http://www.cimpor.pt
Concrete Block & Brick Mfr
N.A.I.C.S.: 327331

Asment de Temara S.A. **(2)**
Route Principale de Casablanca, Ain Attig
Temara, Rabat, Morocco   **(62.62%)**
Tel.: (212) 377476992
Web Site: http://www.asment.co.ma
Cement Mfr
N.A.I.C.S.: 327310

Subsidiary (Domestic):

Bepronor - Sociedade De Betao
Pronto Do Nordeste S.A. **(2)**
Rua Alexandre Herculano 35, 1250-009,
Lisbon, Portugal   **(100%)**
Tel.: (351) 278265347
Concrete Products Mfr
N.A.I.C.S.: 327390

Betabeiras - Betoes Da Beira
S.A. **(2)**
Rua De SAo Jose 149 2, Lisbon,
Portugal   **(88.95%)**
Tel.: (351) 213472038
Readymix Concrete Mfr
N.A.I.C.S.: 327320

Betao Liz S.A. **(2)**
R Qta Paizinho-Bloco 2 1-E, 2795-650, Carnaxide, Portugal   **(66.44%)**
Tel.: (351) 214247500
Web Site: http://www.bpcc.pt
Mixed Mode Transit Systems
N.A.I.C.S.: 485111

Subsidiary (Non-US):

Betocim SA **(2)**
QI lot Azzahra oulja, Sale, Rabat, Morocco

Tel.: (212) 3780 7826
Cement Product Mfr
N.A.I.C.S.: 327310

C.J.O.-Societe les Ciments De Jbel
Oust **(2)**
3 Rue de Touraine - Cite Jardins, Le Belvedere, 1002, Tunis, Tunisia   **(100%)**
Tel.: (216) 71780945
Web Site: http://www.cimpor.com
Cement Mfr
N.A.I.C.S.: 327310

CIMENTOS DE MOCAMBIQUE,
S.A. **(2)**
Estrada Velha 56, Matola, Mozambique
Tel.: (258) 21482507
Cement Mfr & Distr
N.A.I.C.S.: 423320

CIMPOR BETAO MOCAMBIQUE,
S.A. **(2)**
Av Angola-Maputo, Maputo, Mozambique
Tel.: (258) 2140 78 68
Cement Mfr
N.A.I.C.S.: 327310

CIMPOR HORMIGON ESPANA,
S.A. **(2)**
Avda Miguel de Fabra Parc 4 Pol Ind El
Nevero, Badajoz, 06006, Spain
Tel.: (34) 924 275 200
Readymix Concrete Mfr
N.A.I.C.S.: 327320

Subsidiary (Domestic):

CIMPOR TRADING, S.A. **(2)**
Rua Alexandre Herculano 35, Lisbon,
125009, Portugal
Tel.: (351) 21 311 81 00
Web Site: http://www.cimportrading.com
Construction Materials Whslr
N.A.I.C.S.: 423320

CIMPSHIP - TRANSPORTES MARITIMOS, S.A. **(2)**
Rua Ivens Edificio Dona Mecia Nr 3-B- 2-L,
Funchal, 9000-046, Portugal
Tel.: (351) 291200300
Marine Transportation Services
N.A.I.C.S.: 488390

Subsidiary (Non-US):

Canteras Prebetong S.L. **(2)**
Cl Brasil 56, 36204, Vigo, Spain **(98.41%)**
Tel.: (34) 986269000
Web Site: http://www.cimpor.es
Crushed & Broken Limestone Mining &
Quarrying
N.A.I.C.S.: 212312

Subsidiary (Domestic):

Cecisa - Comercio Internacional
S.A. **(2)**
Avenida Jose Malhoa n 22 - floors 6 to 11,
1099-020, Lisbon, Portugal
Tel.: (351) 213118100
Web Site: http://www.cimpor.com
Durable Goods Whslr
N.A.I.C.S.: 423990

Celfa - Socedade Industrial De Transformacao de Gessos S.A. **(2)**
Rua Alexandre Herculano 35, Lisbon,
Portugal   **(100%)**
Tel.: (351) 239501397
Gypsum Product Mfr
N.A.I.C.S.: 327420

Subsidiary (Non-US):

Cement Services Company
S.A.E. **(2)**
Km 55 Alexandria - Mattrouh Road Gharbanyat, Alexandria, Egypt **(98.38%)**
Tel.: (20) 2034195622
Management Consulting Services
N.A.I.C.S.: 541618

Subsidiary (Domestic):

Cement Trading Activities - Comercio
Internacional S.A. **(2)**
Rua Alexandre Herculano 35, Lisbon, 1250-009, Portugal   **(100%)**
Tel.: (351) 219408600
Web Site: http://www.cempro.com

Emp.: 250
Brick Stone & Related Construction Material
Merchant Whslr
N.A.I.C.S.: 423320

Subsidiary (Non-US):

Cementos Cosmos S.A. **(2)**
Brasil 56, Vigo, 36024, Spain   **(99.29%)**
Tel.: (34) 986269000
Web Site: http://www.cimpor.es
Emp.: 100
Cement Mfr
N.A.I.C.S.: 327310
Jorge Wagner (Gen Mgr)

Cementos de Andalucia S.L. **(2)**
Avda Agrupacion Cordoba 15, Cordoba,
Spain
Tel.: (34) 957013000
Sales Range: $25-49.9 Million
Emp.: 7
Construction Materials Whslr
N.A.I.C.S.: 423390
Evamuno De Morales (Asst Dir)

Subsidiary (Domestic):

Ciarga - Argamassas Secas S.A. **(2)**
Rua Alexandre Herculano 35, 1250-009,
Lisbon, Portugal   **(100%)**
Tel.: (351) 213118100
Web Site: http://www.cimpor.pt
Brick Stone & Related Construction Material
Whslr
N.A.I.C.S.: 423320

Cimadjuvantes - Comercializacao E
Producao De Adjuvantes Para Cimento Lda **(2)**
Edificio Cimpor, Pomar Velho, Faro,
1250009, Portugal   **(100%)**
Tel.: (351) 213118100
Chemical & Allied Products Whslr
N.A.I.C.S.: 424690
Ricardo Lima (CEO)

Cimentacor - Cimentos Dos Acores
Lda **(2)**
Rua Bento Dias Carreiro 6 Ribeira Grande,
Ribeira Grande, 9600-050, Sao Miguel,
Portugal   **(75%)**
Tel.: (351) 296201730
Cement Mfr
N.A.I.C.S.: 327310

Cimpor - Industria De Cimentos
S.A. **(2)**
Rua Alexandre Herculano 35, Lisbon, 1250-009, Portugal   **(100%)**
Tel.: (351) 213118100
Cement Mfr
N.A.I.C.S.: 327310

Cimpor - Servicos De Apoio A Gestao
De Empresas S.A. **(2)**
Rua Alexandre Herculano 35, 1250-009,
Lisbon, Portugal   **(100%)**
Tel.: (351) 213118100
Web Site: http://www.cimpor-portugal.pt
Business Support Services
N.A.I.C.S.: 561499

Cimpor Betao - Industria De Betao
Pronto S.A. **(2)**
Av Alm Gago Coutinho, Portela Sintra, Sintra, 2710-418, Portugal   **(100%)**
Tel.: (351) 219105540
Asphalt Paving Mixture & Block Mfr
N.A.I.C.S.: 324121

Cimpor Betao - Sociedade Gestora
De Participacoes Sociais S.A. **(2)**
Rua Alexandre Herculano 35, 1250-009,
Lisbon, Portugal   **(100%)**
Tel.: (351) 213118100
Web Site: http://www.cimpor.com
Holding Company
N.A.I.C.S.: 551112

Subsidiary (Non-US):

Cimpor Brasil Participacoes Ltda **(2)**
Av Maria Coelho Aguiar 215, Sao Paulo,
05805-000, Brazil   **(100%)**
Tel.: (351) 1137413000
Web Site: http://www.cimpor.com
Sales Range: $25-49.9 Million
Emp.: 100
Holding Company

Camargo Correa S.A.—(Continued)

N.A.I.C.S.: 551112

Subsidiary (Domestic):

Cimpor Internacional SGPS S.A. (2)
Rua Alexandre Herculano 35, Lisbon, 1250-009, Portugal (100%)
Tel.: (351) 213118100
Web Site: http://www.Cimpor.com
Emp.: 200
Holding Company
N.A.I.C.S.: 551112
Ricardo Manuel Simoes Bayao Horta (Chm)

Cimpor Investimentos SGPS S.A. (2)
Rua Alexandre Herculano 35, Lisbon, Portugal (100%)
Tel.: (351) 213118100
Holding Company
N.A.I.C.S.: 551112
Ricardo Manuel Simoes Bayao Horta (Chm)

Subsidiary (Non-US):

Companhia de Cimentos do Brasil Ltda (2)
Av Maria Coelho Aguiar 215 - Bloco E 8 Andar, Jardim Sao Luiz, 05805-000, Sao Paulo, Brazil (100%)
Tel.: (55) 1137413581
Web Site: http://www.cimpor.com.br
Sales Range: $50-74.9 Million
Emp.: 110
Cement Mfr
N.A.I.C.S.: 327310

Corporacion Noroeste S.A. (2)
Brasil asal 56, 36204, Vigo, Spain (99.54%)
Tel.: (34) 986269000
Web Site: http://www.pulmor.es
Sales Range: $10-24.9 Million
Emp.: 30
Management Consulting Services
N.A.I.C.S.: 541618
Ricardo Manuel Simoes Bayao Horta (Chm)

Subsidiary (Domestic):

Estabelecimentos Scial Do Norte S.A. (2)
Av Americo Duarte - SAo Pedro De Fins, 4425-504, Maia, Portugal (100%)
Tel.: (351) 219408732
Construction Materials Whslr
N.A.I.C.S.: 423390

Subsidiary (Non-US):

Firmes Y Hormigones Sani S.L. (2)
Carretera Nacional 630 Gijon - Sevilha Km 308, Almendralejo, 06200, Caceres, Spain (79.63%)
Tel.: (34) 924666113
Readymix Concrete Mfr
N.A.I.C.S.: 327320

Subsidiary (Domestic):

GEOFER - PRODUCAO E COMER-CIALIZACAO DE BENS E EQUIPA-MENTOS, S.A. (2)
Zona Industrial, Tramagal, 2206-906, Santarem, Portugal
Tel.: (351) 241899050
Sales Range: $25-49.9 Million
Emp.: 6
Cement Mfr & Distr
N.A.I.C.S.: 327310

Subsidiary (Non-US):

Hormigones Hercules S.L. (2)
Apartado 411, 21080, Huelva, Spain
Tel.: (34) 959282471
Readymix Concrete Mfr
N.A.I.C.S.: 327320

Subsidiary (Domestic):

Ibera - Industria De Betao S.A. (2)
Quinta da Madeira E N 114 KM 185, 7000-172, Evora, Portugal (66.44%)
Tel.: (351) 266758500
Web Site: http://ibera.pt
Sales Range: $25-49.9 Million
Emp.: 30
Readymix Concrete Mfr

N.A.I.C.S.: 327320
Vitor Basosa (Gen Mgr)

Jomatel - Empresa De Materiais de Construcao S.A. (2)
Estrada de Albarraque - Linho, Sintra, Portugal (90%)
Tel.: (351) 219239000
Mixed Mode Transit Systems
N.A.I.C.S.: 485111

Kandmad - Sociedade Gestora De Participacoes Sociais Lda (2)
Avenida Arriaga 77 1 Edificio Marina Forum Sala 103, Funchal, Portugal (99.93%)
Tel.: (351) 291206430
Holding Company
N.A.I.C.S.: 551112

Subsidiary (Non-US):

Morteros De Galicia S.L. (2)
Calle Brasil 56, 36204, Vigo, Spain (99.54%)
Tel.: (34) 986269000
Concrete Contractor
N.A.I.C.S.: 238110

NATAL PORTLAND CEMENT COM-PANY (PTY) LTD. (2)
199 Coedmore Road, Bellaire, Durban, 4006, South Africa
Tel.: (27) 31 450 4411
Web Site: http://www.npc.co.za
Sales Range: $125-149.9 Million
Emp.: 50
Cement Mfr & Distr
N.A.I.C.S.: 327310
Simon Jensen (Gen Mgr)

Occidental De Hormigones S.L. (2)
Poligono Ind El Nevero C/La Biela S/N, 6006, Badajoz, Spain (99.54%)
Tel.: (34) 924 27 0205
Web Site: http://www.cimpor.es
Readymix Concrete Mfr
N.A.I.C.S.: 327320

Prebetong Galicia S.A. (2)
C- Brasil 56, 36204, Vigo, Spain (98.41%)
Tel.: (34) 986269000
Web Site: http://www.vceaa.es
Emp.: 66
Readymix Concrete Mfr
N.A.I.C.S.: 327320
Pablo Punzom (Mng Dir)

Prebetong Lugo Hormigones S.A. (2)
Avenida Benigno Rivera Pg Industrial De Ceao S-N, 27003, Lugo, Spain (81.57%)
Tel.: (34) 982209121
Cement Mfr
N.A.I.C.S.: 327320

Prebetong Lugo S.A. (2)
Avenida Benigno Rivera S-N, 27003, Lugo, Spain (81.57%)
Tel.: (34) 982209121
Readymix Concrete Mfr
N.A.I.C.S.: 327320

Subsidiary (Domestic):

Prediana - Sociedade De Pre-Esforcados S.A. (2)
Rua Alexandre Herculano 35, 1250-009, Lisbon, Portugal (100%)
Tel.: (351) 266893908
Concrete Contractor
N.A.I.C.S.: 238110

SOGESSO - SOCIEDADE DE GES-SOS DE SOURE, S.A. (2)
Sao Jose Do Pinheiro, Soure, 3130-544, Portugal
Tel.: (351) 239506120
Construction Machinery Whslr
N.A.I.C.S.: 423830

Subsidiary (Non-US):

SOUTH COAST STONE CRUSHERS (PTY) LTD. (2)
Lot 2000 Quarry Rd Uvongo Port Shepstone, Margate, 4270, KwaZulu-Natal, South Africa
Tel.: (34) 314504411
Web Site: http://www.npc.co.za
Cement Mfr

N.A.I.C.S.: 327310
Dave Kendall (Gen Mgr-Sterkspruit Quarry)

Subsidiary (Domestic):

Sacopor - Sociedade De Embalagens E Sacos De Papel S.A. (2)
Quinta da Arrocazia Lote 1 - Santo Estevao, Alenquer, 2580-374, Lisbon, Portugal (100%)
Tel.: (351) 263730370
Sales Range: $25-49.9 Million
Emp.: 54
Nonfolding Sanitary Food Container Mfr
N.A.I.C.S.: 322219

Scoreco - Valorizacao De Residuos Lda (2)
Av Severian Falcao 8 - Edificio Cimpor, Prior Velho, 2685-378, Faro, Portugal
Tel.: (351) 219408743
Web Site: http://www.cimentos.com
Brick Stone & Related Construction Material Whslr
N.A.I.C.S.: 423320

Subsidiary (Non-US):

Servicios Y Materiales Para La Construccion S.A. (2)
Calle Brasil 56, 36204, Vigo, Spain (99.54%)
Tel.: (34) 986269000
Web Site: http://www.cimpor.es
Construction Materials Whslr
N.A.I.C.S.: 423390

Sociedad De Cementos Y Materiales De Construccion De Andalucia S.A. (2)
Avda de Agrapacion Cordoba 15, 14014, Cordoba, Spain
Tel.: (34) 957013000
Cement Mfr
N.A.I.C.S.: 327310
Joseph de la Vega (Plant Mgr)

Subsidiary (Domestic):

Transviaria - Gestao De Transportes S.A. (2)
Rua Alexandre Herculano 35, 1250-009, Lisbon, Portugal (100%)
Tel.: (351) 219408600
General Freight Trucking
N.A.I.C.S.: 484110

Construcoes e Comercio Camargo Correa SA (1)
Rua Funchal 160 Vila Olimpia, CEP 04551 903, Sao Paulo, Brazil
Tel.: (55) 1138415511
Engineering & Construction Services
N.A.I.C.S.: 237310

InterCement Brasil S.A. (1)
Rua Funchal 160 Vila Olimpia, 04551-903, Sao Paulo, SP, Brazil (99.89%)
Tel.: (55) 11 3848 7816
Web Site: http://www.intercement.com
Sales Range: $1-4.9 Billion
Emp.: 125
Cement & Concrete Mfr
N.A.I.C.S.: 327310
Paulo Nigro (CEO)

Subsidiary (Non-US):

Loma Negra Cia Industria Argentina SA (2)
Loma Negra Reconquista 1088 Piso 7, Buenos Aires, Argentina
Tel.: (54) 1143193000
Cement Product Mfr
N.A.I.C.S.: 327310

Santista Jeanswear S.A. (1)
Av Maria Coelho Aguiar 215 bloco A 2 andar, Jd Sao Luiz, Sao Paulo, SP 05804-900, Brazil
Tel.: (55) 112383 8800
Web Site: http://www.santistajeanswear.com.br
Denim & Cotton Fabric Mfr
N.A.I.C.S.: 313210

VBC Energia S.A. (1)
Av Eng Luis Carlos Berrini 1297, 13 andar Conjunto 132 Brooklin, Sao Paulo, Brazil
Tel.: (55) 1151027050

Electric Power Generation
N.A.I.C.S.: 221118

CAMARICO INVESTMENT GROUP LTD.
2416 - 19th Street, PO Box 1284, Nanton, Calgary, T0L 1R0, AB, Canada
Tel.: (403) 861-4779
Web Site: http://www.cerusenergy.com
Year Founded: 1996
Assets: $231,045
Liabilities: $1,500,390
Net Worth: ($1,269,344)
Earnings: ($14,571)
Fiscal Year-end: 12/31/18
Energy Investment Services
N.A.I.C.S.: 523999
R. Mackenzie Loree (CEO)

CAMAU TRADING JOINT STOCK COMPANY
70-72 De Tham Phuong 2, Ca Mau, Vietnam
Tel.: (84) 7803839220
Web Site: http://www.tncm.com.vn
CMV—(HOSE)
Rev.: $175,538,450
Assets: $21,873,904
Liabilities: $11,786,414
Net Worth: $10,087,490
Earnings: $609,801
Fiscal Year-end: 12/31/23
Trading Services
N.A.I.C.S.: 523160
Tuan Nguyen Quynh (Chm)

CAMBI ASA
Skysstasjon 11A, PO Box 78, 1371, Asker, Norway
Tel.: (47) 66779800
Web Site: https://www.cambi.no
Year Founded: 1996
CAMBI—(OSL)
Rev.: $90,208,757
Assets: $67,790,504
Liabilities: $36,504,711
Net Worth: $31,285,793
Earnings: $16,894,513
Emp.: 141
Fiscal Year-end: 12/31/23
Hazardous Waste Treatment Services
N.A.I.C.S.: 562211
Eirik Fadnes (CEO)

Subsidiaries:

Cambi Group AS (1)
Skysstasjon 11A, PO Box 78, 1371, Asker, Norway
Tel.: (47) 66779800
Thermal Hydrolysis Services
N.A.I.C.S.: 541380

Gronn Vekst AS (1)
Reddalsveien 211, N-4886, Grimstad, Norway
Tel.: (47) 91505673
Web Site: https://www.gronnvekst.no
Environment Renewable Services
N.A.I.C.S.: 541620

CAMBIE ROOFING & DRAIN-AGE CONTRACTORS LTD.
1367 East Kent Avenue N, Vancouver, V5X 4T6, BC, Canada
Tel.: (604) 261-1111
Web Site: https://www.cambieroofing.com
Year Founded: 1952
Rev.: $10,795,569
Emp.: 90
Roofing & Drainage Contract Services
N.A.I.C.S.: 238160
Knute Skujins (Pres)

CAMBIUM BIO LIMITED

16 Goodhope Street, Sydney, 2021, NSW, Australia
Tel.: (61) 1300995098
Web Site: https://www.cambium.bio
Year Founded: 2007
CMB—(ASX)
Rev.: $6,095,671
Assets: $6,520,540
Liabilities: $3,344,326
Net Worth: $3,176,214
Earnings: $2,113,965
Fiscal Year-end: 06/30/21
Regenerative Medicine Mfr
N.A.I.C.S.: 325412
Karolis Rosickas *(CEO)*

Subsidiaries:

Regeneus Animal Health Pty Ltd **(1)**
25 Bridge Street, Pymble, 2073, NSW, Australia
Tel.: (61) 294998010
Web Site: http://www.regeneus.com.au
Emp.: 25
Health Care Srvices
N.A.I.C.S.: 621999
John Martin *(CEO)*

CAMBIUM GLOBAL TIMBER-LAND LIMITED
Charter Place 23/27 Seaton Place, Saint Helier, JE1 1JY, Jersey
Tel.: (44) 148 173 7600
Web Site: http://www.cambium.je
TREE—(AIM)
Sales Range: $1-9.9 Million
Forestry Investment Services
N.A.I.C.S.: 523999
Robert James Rickman *(Mgr-Ops)*

CAMBRIA AFRICA PLC
Burleigh Manor, Douglas, IM1 5EP, Isle of Man
Tel.: (44) 2032878814   IM
Web Site:
  https://www.cambriaafrica.com
CMB—(AIM)
Rev.: $920,000
Assets: $6,847,000
Liabilities: $677,000
Net Worth: $6,170,000
Earnings: ($5,000)
Emp.: 9
Fiscal Year-end: 08/31/22
Investment Management Service
N.A.I.C.S.: 523940
Paul Turner *(Chm)*

Subsidiaries:

Gardoserv (Pvt) Limited **(1)**
No 27 Conald Road Graniteside, Harare, 00263, Zimbabwe
Tel.: (263) 4 756 532
Web Site: http://www.millchem.co.zw
Chemical Products Distr
N.A.I.C.S.: 424690

MSA Sourcing BV **(1)**
Binnenhof 45, 4871 BR, Etten-Leur, Netherlands
Tel.: (31) 76 5023098
Chemical Products Distr
N.A.I.C.S.: 424690

Millchem Zambia Limited **(1)**
Plot 7216 Kachidza Road, Lusaka, Zambia
Tel.: (260) 971 615 569
Web Site: http://www.millchemzambia.com
Chemical Products Distr
N.A.I.C.S.: 424690
Lionel Maiden *(Mng Dir)*

CAMBRIA AUTOMOBILES PLC
Dorcan Way, Swindon, SN3 3RA, United Kingdom
Tel.: (44) 1793 414200
Web Site:
  http://www.cambriaautomobiles.com
Year Founded: 2006
Rev.: $862,740,313
Assets: $339,529,957

Liabilities: $253,515,229
Net Worth: $86,014,728
Earnings: $13,054,355
Emp.: 1,076
Fiscal Year-end: 08/31/19
Car Dealership Owner & Operator
N.A.I.C.S.: 441110
Mark Lavery *(CEO)*

Subsidiaries:

Repair & Maintenance Plans
Limited **(1)**
21 Commerce Road Lynch Wood, Peterborough, PE2 6LR, United Kingdom
Tel.: (44) 3300947224
Web Site: http://www.ramplimited.co.uk
Automobile Parts Mfr
N.A.I.C.S.: 336390

CAMBRIAN FORD SALES INC
1615 Kingsway St, Sudbury, P3A 4S9, ON, Canada
Tel.: (705) 560-3673
Web Site:
  http://www.cambrianford.com
Rev.: $50,000,000
Emp.: 215
New & Used Car Dealers
N.A.I.C.S.: 441110
Teri Akkanen *(Controller)*

CAMBRICON TECHNOLOGIES CORPORATION LIMITED
Floors 11-14 16-17 Block D Zhizhen Building No 7 Zhichun Road, Haidian District, Beijing, 100191, China
Tel.: (86) 1083030796
Web Site: http://www.cambricon.com
Year Founded: 2016
688256—(SHG)
Rev.: $102,356,458
Assets: $810,166,912
Liabilities: $116,616,198
Net Worth: $693,550,714
Earnings: ($176,421,375)
Fiscal Year-end: 12/31/22
Software Development Services
N.A.I.C.S.: 541511
Tianshi Chen *(Chm & Gen Mgr)*

CAMBRIDGE BROADBAND NETWORKS LIMITED
Selwyn House Cambridge Business Park Cowley Road, Cambridge, CB4 0WZ, United Kingdom
Tel.: (44) 1223703000
Web Site: http://www.cbnl.com
Year Founded: 2000
Sales Range: $25-49.9 Million
Emp.: 100
Point-to-Multipoint Wireless Transmission Equipment Mfr
N.A.I.C.S.: 334220
William Ginn *(CFO)*

CAMBRIDGE BUILDING SOCIETY
51 Newmarket Road, PO Box 232, Cambridge, CB5 8FF, United Kingdom
Tel.: (44) 345 601 3344
Web Site:
  http://www.cambridgebs.co.uk
Year Founded: 1850
Rev.: $44,582,596
Assets: $2,080,130,708
Liabilities: $1,965,561,137
Net Worth: $114,569,572
Earnings: $3,731,502
Emp.: 138
Fiscal Year-end: 12/31/19
Mortgage Lending Services
N.A.I.C.S.: 522310
Victoria Stubbs *(Chief Risk Officer)*

CAMBRIDGE COGNITION

HOLDINGS PLC
Tunbridge Court, Bottisham, Cambridge, CB25 9TU, United Kingdom
Tel.: (44) 1223810700
Web Site:
  https://www.cambridgecognition.com
COG—(AIM)
Rev.: $15,921,484
Assets: $19,069,679
Liabilities: $18,949,760
Net Worth: $119,919
Earnings: ($516,284)
Emp.: 60
Fiscal Year-end: 12/31/22
Pharmaceuticals Mfr
N.A.I.C.S.: 325412
Steven Powell *(Chm)*

CAMBRIDGE LIFE SCIENCES LTD.
14 St Thomas Place Cambridgeshire Business Park, Cambridgeshire, Ely, CB7 4EX, Cambs, United Kingdom
Tel.: (44) 1353645200
Web Site:
  http://www.cambridgesciences.com
Year Founded: 1981
Sales Range: $10-24.9 Million
Emp.: 20
Pharmaceuticals Product Mfr
N.A.I.C.S.: 325412
Peter Blake *(CEO)*

CAMBRIDGE NUTRITIONAL SCIENCES PLC
9 Haymarket Square, Edinburgh, EH3 8FY, United Kingdom
Tel.: (44) 1259763030
Web Site:
  https://www.omegadiagnostics.com
ODX—(AIM)
Rev.: $11,859,498
Assets: $42,075,003
Liabilities: $9,931,947
Net Worth: $32,143,056
Earnings: ($2,857,064)
Emp.: 171
Fiscal Year-end: 03/31/21
Medical Diagnostic Equipment Mfr
N.A.I.C.S.: 334510
Kieron Harbinson *(Dir/Dir-Fin-Grp)*

Subsidiaries:

Cambridge Nutritional Sciences
Limited **(1)**
Eden Res Park Henry Crabb Rd, Littleport, CB6 1SE, Cambs, United Kingdom
Tel.: (44) 1353863279
Web Site: http://www.camnutri.com
Sales Range: $25-49.9 Million
Emp.: 70
Diagnostic Test Kits Distr
N.A.I.C.S.: 423450
Jamie Yexley *(Mgr-Site)*

Omega Diagnostics Limited **(1)**
Omega Diagnostics House, Hillfoots Business Village, Alva, FK12 5DQ, Scotland, United Kingdom
Tel.: (44) 1259763030
Web Site: http://www.omegadiagnostics.com
Sales Range: $25-49.9 Million
Immuno Diagnostic Test Kits Mfr
N.A.I.C.S.: 334510

CAMBRIDGE PLYMOUTH CHRYSLER LTD
289 Hespeler Rd, Cambridge, N1R 3H8, ON, Canada
Tel.: (519) 621-2830
Web Site: http://galtchrysler.ca
Year Founded: 1984
Rev.: $15,727,375
Emp.: 35
New Car Dealers
N.A.I.C.S.: 441110
Paul Beaudoin *(Pres)*

CAMBRIDGE PRO FAB INC.

84 Shaver Street, Brantford, N35 0H4, ON, Canada
Tel.: (519) 751-4351
Web Site:
  http://www.cambridgeprofab.com
Rev.: $10,172,559
Emp.: 80
Metal Fabrication & Other Industrial Equipment Mfr
N.A.I.C.S.: 332999

Subsidiaries:

Cambridge Pro Fab Inc. - Plant 2 **(1)**
84 Shaver Street, Brantford, N3T 5M1, ON, Canada
Tel.: (519) 751-4351
Industrial Equipment Mfr
N.A.I.C.S.: 332999

Cambridge Pro Fab Inc. - Plant 3 **(1)**
121 Avenue Road, Cambridge, N1R 1C2, ON, Canada
Tel.: (519) 620-0672
Industrial Equipment Mfr
N.A.I.C.S.: 332999

Cambridge Pro Fab Inc. - Plant 4 **(1)**
1362 Osprey Drive, Ancaster, L9G 4V5, ON, Canada
Tel.: (905) 648-2257
Industrial Equipment Mfr
N.A.I.C.S.: 332999

CAMBRIDGE TECHNOLOGY ENTERPRISES LTD.
Capital park 4th Floor Unit No 403B 404, Plot No 1 98 4 1 13 28 29 Survey No 72 Image Gardens Road Madhapur, Hyderabad, 500 081, Telangana, India
Tel.: (91) 4067234400
Web Site: https://www.ctepl.com
CTE—(NSE)
Rev.: $15,598,683
Assets: $18,342,485
Liabilities: $6,687,249
Net Worth: $11,655,236
Earnings: $1,337,102
Emp.: 258
Fiscal Year-end: 03/31/22
Technology Services & Outsourcing Company
N.A.I.C.S.: 541511
Dharani Raghurama Swaroop *(Exec Dir)*

Subsidiaries:

Cambridge Bizserve Inc. **(1)**
2nd Floor DCG Bldg, Crossing Bayabas Toril, Davao, 8025, Philippines
Tel.: (63) 9129338247
Software Development Services
N.A.I.C.S.: 541511

Cambridge Technology Inc. **(1)**
120 SE 6th St Ste 3-124, Topeka, KS 66603
Tel.: (785) 354-4300
Software Development Services
N.A.I.C.S.: 541511

Cambridge Technology Investments Pte. Ltd. **(1)**
51 Goldhill Plaza 07-10/11, Singapore, 308900, Singapore
Tel.: (65) 90228500
Software Development Services
N.A.I.C.S.: 541511

CAMBRIDGE UNIVERSITY PRESS
University Printing House Shaftesbury Road, Cambridge, CB2 8BS, United Kingdom
Tel.: (44) 1223358331
Web Site: http://www.cambridge.org
Sales Range: $200-249.9 Million
Emp.: 800

Cambridge University Press—(Continued)

Publishing Services
N.A.I.C.S.: 513130
Hanri Pieterse *(Mng Dir-Education)*

Subsidiaries:

Cambridge University Press India Private Limited **(1)**
Splendor Forum Plot no 3 3rd Floor, Jasola District Centre, New Delhi, 110 025, India
Tel.: (91) 1143543500
Web Site: http://www.cambridge.org
Book Publish Services
N.A.I.C.S.: 513130

Cambridge University Press Japan K.K. **(1)**
Sakura Building 1st Floor Nishiki-cho, 1-10-1 Kanda Chiyoda-ku, Tokyo, 101-0054, Japan
Tel.: (81) 332955875
Web Site: http://www.cambridge.org
Book Publishers
N.A.I.C.S.: 513130

Cambridge University Press, North America **(1)**
1 Liberty Plz, New York, NY 10006
Tel.: (212) 924-3900
Sales Range: $50-74.9 Million
Emp.: 150
Publisher of Books, Publications & Journals
N.A.I.C.S.: 513130

CAMBUCI S.A.
Avenida Getulio Vargas 930, Quince Saint Roch, Sao Roque, 18130-430, SP, Brazil
Tel.: (55) 47139500
Web Site: http://www.cambuci.com.br
Year Founded: 1945
CAMB3—(BRAZ)
Rev.: $94,623,596
Assets: $69,158,784
Liabilities: $21,176,919
Net Worth: $47,981,865
Earnings: $14,809,892
Emp.: 3,000
Fiscal Year-end: 12/31/23
Sporting Goods Mfr
N.A.I.C.S.: 339920
Roberto Estefan *(Dir-Investor Relations)*

CAMBUHY INVESTIMENTOS LTDA.
Rua Amauri 255 7 andar, 01448-000, Sao Paulo, Brazil
Tel.: (55) 11 3019 3400 **BR**
Web Site: http://www.cmby.com
Private Equity Firm Services
N.A.I.C.S.: 523999
Pedro Moreira Salles *(Co-Pres & Partner)*

Subsidiaries:

Alpargatas S.A. **(1)**
Av das Nacoes Unidas n 14261 Wing A 9th 10th and 11th floors, 04794-000, Sao Paulo, Brazil
Tel.: (55) 1145697322
Web Site: http://www.alpargatas.com.br
Rev.: $919,062,515
Assets: $1,119,566,663
Liabilities: $442,536,376
Net Worth: $677,030,287
Earnings: $64,206,159
Fiscal Year-end: 12/31/2019
Footwear, Sporting Goods & Textiles Mfr
N.A.I.C.S.: 316210
Adalberto Fernandes Granjo *(Chief Legal Affairs Officer)*

Subsidiary (Non-US):

Alpargatas France S.A.R.L. **(2)**
29 Blvrd, St Martin, 75003, Paris, France
Tel.: (33) 1 42 74 87 40
Web Site: http://www.alpargatas.com.br
Apparel Product Distr
N.A.I.C.S.: 424310

Alpargatas Italy S.R.L. **(2)**
Via Michelino 33, 40127, Bologna, Italy
Tel.: (39) 0510455127
Web Site:
Apparel Product Distr
N.A.I.C.S.: 424310

Alpargatas Portugal Limited **(2)**
Savd do Forte no 8 - Piso 2 - Fraccao Q1 Edificio Pujol, 2790-072, Lisbon, Portugal
Tel.: (351) 214 181 931
Web Site: http://www.alpargatas.com.br
Apparel Product Distr
N.A.I.C.S.: 424310

Plant (Domestic):

Alpargatas S.A. - Campina Grande Plant **(2)**
Av Assis de Chateaubriand 4324, Distrito Industrial, Campina Grande, 58105-421, Paraiba, Brazil
Tel.: (55) 83 3315 4000
Web Site: http://www.alpargatas.com.br
Footwear Product Mfr
N.A.I.C.S.: 316210

Alpargatas S.A. - Dupe Plant **(2)**
BR 408km 50 5, Carpina, 55819-320, Pernambuco, Brazil
Tel.: (55) 81 3622 8000
Web Site: http://www.alpargatas.com.br
Footwear Product Mfr
N.A.I.C.S.: 316210

Alpargatas S.A. - Joao Pessoa Plant **(2)**
Rua B1 - 1099 Av das Industrias, Distrito Industrial, Joao Pessoa, 58083-000, Paraiba, Brazil
Tel.: (55) 83 3229 3000
Web Site: http://www.alpargatas.com.br
Footwear Product Mfr
N.A.I.C.S.: 316210

Alpargatas S.A. - Mogi Mirim Plant **(2)**
Av Joao Pinto 100 Parque das Empresas, Mogi Mirim, Sao Paulo, 13803-360, Brazil
Tel.: (55) 19 3548 3000
Web Site: http://www.alpargatas.com.br
Footwear Product Mfr
N.A.I.C.S.: 316210

Alpargatas S.A. - Santa Rita Plant **(2)**
Rua/Av Contorno da BR 230 Km 41, s/n - Ligacao Santa Rita, Santa Rita do Sapucai, 58301-645, Paraiba, Brazil
Tel.: (55) 83 3044 8100
Web Site: http://www.alpargatas.com.br
Footwear Product Mfr
N.A.I.C.S.: 316210

Subsidiary (Non-US):

Alpargatas SAIC **(2)**
Oficina Central Azara 841, Buenos Aires, C1267ABQ, Argentina
Tel.: (54) 11 4124 2400
Web Site: http://www.alpargatas.com.ar
Apparel Product Mfr & Distr
N.A.I.C.S.: 315990
Diego Jose Mohadeb *(Mng Dir & VP)*

Alpargatas Spain S.L.U. **(2)**
Avenida Arroyo del Santo 4 Bis, 28037, Madrid, Spain
Tel.: (34) 914 009 288
Web Site: http://www.havaianas-store.com
Apparel Product Distr
N.A.I.C.S.: 424310

Alpargatas UK Ltd **(2)**
24 Bradmore Park Road, Hammersmith, London, W6 0DT, United Kingdom
Tel.: (44) 208 748 0333
Web Site: http://www.havaianas-store.com
Apparel Product Distr
N.A.I.C.S.: 424310

Subsidiary (US):

Alpargatas USA Inc. **(2)**
33 E 33rd St Ste 501, New York, NY 10016
Tel.: (646) 747-7171
Web Site: http://www.alpargatas.com.br
Apparel Product Distr
N.A.I.C.S.: 424310
Eno Polo *(Pres)*

CAMCO ACURA
1475 Carling Avenue, Ottawa, K1Z 7L9, ON, Canada
Tel.: (613) 728-8888
Web Site:
http://www.camcoacura.com
Rev.: $23,803,595
Emp.: 50
New & Used Car Dealers
N.A.I.C.S.: 441110

CAMDON CONSTRUCTION LTD
6780 76th Street, Red Deer, T4P 4G6, AB, Canada
Tel.: (403) 343-1233
Web Site: http://www.camdon.ca
Year Founded: 1984
Rev.: $17,002,568
Emp.: 60
Building Construction Services
N.A.I.C.S.: 236220
Troy Spelt *(Partner)*

CAMECO CORPORATION
2121 11th Street West, Saskatoon, S7M 1J3, SK, Canada
Tel.: (306) 956-6200 **Ca**
Web Site: https://www.cameco.com
Year Founded: 1988
CCJ—(NYSE)
Rev.: $1,911,618,527
Assets: $7,338,447,957
Liabilities: $2,836,483,711
Net Worth: $4,501,964,246
Earnings: $266,540,592
Emp.: 2,638
Fiscal Year-end: 12/31/23
Ownership & Operation of Uranium Mines
N.A.I.C.S.: 212290
Grant Isaac *(CFO & Sr VP)*

Subsidiaries:

Cameco Australia Pty. Ltd. **(1)**
Lvl 3 1060 Hay St, West Perth, 6005, WA, Australia
Tel.: (61) 894800675
Web Site: https://www.camecoaustralia.com
Uranium Mining Services
N.A.I.C.S.: 212290

Cameco Fuel Manufacturing Inc **(1)**
200 Dorset St E, Port Hope, L1A 3V4, ON, Canada
Tel.: (905) 885-4537
Web Site: http://www.cameco.com
Sales Range: $125-149.9 Million
Emp.: 300
Fuel Mfr
N.A.I.C.S.: 324110

NUKEM GmbH **(1)**
Industriestrasse 13, D 63755, Alzenau, Germany **(100%)**
Tel.: (49) 60239106
Web Site: http://www.nukem.de
Sales Range: $200-249.9 Million
Emp.: 50
Uranium Trading, Conversion & Enrichment Services
N.A.I.C.S.: 425120

Subsidiary (US):

NUKEM, Inc. **(2)**
285 Riverside Ave Ste 350, Westport, CT 06880 **(100%)**
Tel.: (203) 778-9420
Web Site: http://www.nukem.de
Sales Range: $50-74.9 Million
Emp.: 10
Uranium Trading, Conversion & Enrichment Services
N.A.I.C.S.: 425120

CAMEL GROUP CO., LTD.
No 125 Keji 2nd Rd East Lake High-Tech Development Zone, Wuhan, 430078, Hubei, China
Tel.: (86) 2752108948
Web Site: https://www.camelbatt.com

Year Founded: 1980
601311—(SHG)
Rev.: $1,884,920,670
Assets: $1,895,766,809
Liabilities: $614,821,021
Net Worth: $1,280,945,788
Earnings: $65,990,864
Emp.: 7,200
Fiscal Year-end: 12/31/22
Battery Mfr & Whslr
N.A.I.C.S.: 335910
Liu Changlai *(Chm)*

Subsidiaries:

Camel Power Trading Sdn. Bhd. **(1)**
No 23 Jalan Pemberita U1/49 Temasya Industrial Park, Glenmarie, 40150, Shah Alam, Selangor, Malaysia
Tel.: (60) 355699767
Web Site: https://www.camelpower.com.my
Automotive Battery Mfr & Distr
N.A.I.C.S.: 335910

Hubei Camel Special Power Supply Company **(1)**
Wuhan University Hi-tech Keyuan Road, Nanshan District, Shenzhen, Guangdong, China
Tel.: (86) 75586393232
Battery Mfr
N.A.I.C.S.: 335910

CAMELLIA PLC
Wrotham Place Bull Lane, Wrotham, TN15 7AE, Kent, United Kingdom
Tel.: (44) 1622746655 **UK**
Web Site: https://www.camellia.plc.uk
Year Founded: 1889
CAM—(AIM)
Rev.: $375,157,788
Assets: $721,787,427
Liabilities: $194,521,585
Net Worth: $527,265,842
Earnings: ($10,477,152)
Emp.: 106,760
Fiscal Year-end: 12/31/22
Holding Company
N.A.I.C.S.: 551112
Malcolm C. Perkins *(Chm)*

Subsidiaries:

AJT Engineering Limited **(1)**
Craigshaw Crescent West Tullos, Aberdeen, AB12 3TB, United Kingdom
Tel.: (44) 1224871791
Web Site: https://www.ajt-engineering.co.uk
Sales Range: $25-49.9 Million
Emp.: 75
Engineeering Services
N.A.I.C.S.: 541330

AKD Engineering Limited **(1)**
Horn Hill, Lowestoft, NR33 0PX, Suffolk, United Kingdom
Tel.: (44) 1502527800
Web Site: http://www.akd-engineering.co.uk
Sales Range: $25-49.9 Million
Emp.: 100
Fabricated Metal Products Mfr
N.A.I.C.S.: 332999
Andrew Quayle *(Mng Dir)*

Abbey Metal Finishing Company Limited **(1)**
Unit 2 Dodwells Bridge Industrial Estate Dodwells Road, Hinckley, LE10 3BZ, United Kingdom
Tel.: (44) 145 563 7284
Web Site: https://www.amfin.co.uk
Sales Range: $25-49.9 Million
Emp.: 70
Electroplating Plating Polishing Anodizing & Coloring
N.A.I.C.S.: 332813
Brendan Johnston *(Mng Dir)*

Affish B.V. **(1)**
Industrierondweg 24, Woudrichem, 8321 EC, Urk, Netherlands
Tel.: (31) 18 330 3484
Web Site: https://www.affish.nl
Sales Range: $50-74.9 Million
Emp.: 8
Fish & Seafood Whslr

N.A.I.C.S.: 424460

Atfin GmbH (1)
Robert-Drosten-Platz 1, 82380, Peissenberg, Germany
Tel.: (49) 8803491236
Web Site: http://www.aerotechfinishing.com
Etch Inspection Aerospace Services
N.A.I.C.S.: 488190

Bordure Limited (1)
Linton Park Linton, Maidstone, ME174AB, Kent, United Kingdom
Tel.: (44) 1622746655
Web Site: http://www.camellia.plc.uk
Sales Range: $25-49.9 Million
Emp.: 12
Holding Company
N.A.I.C.S.: 551112

British Metal Treatments Limited (1)
40 Battery Road, Great Yarmouth, NR30 3NN, Norfolk, United Kingdom
Tel.: (44) 149 384 4153
Web Site: https://www.bmtgalv.co.uk
Sales Range: $25-49.9 Million
Emp.: 25
Precision Turned Product Mfr
N.A.I.C.S.: 332721

Duncan Brothers Limited (1)
22 Kazi Nazrul Islam Avenue, Dhaka, 1000, Bangladesh
Tel.: (880) 258 611 7202
Web Site: https://www.duncanbd.com
Tea & Rubber Mfr
N.A.I.C.S.: 311920
Nazmul Hossain *(Asst Mgr)*

Duncan Lawrie Limited (1)
1 Hobart Place, London, SW1W 0HU, United Kingdom
Tel.: (44) 2072451234
Web Site: http://www.duncanlawrie.com
Sales Range: $50-74.9 Million
Emp.: 100
Financial Investment Services
N.A.I.C.S.: 523999

Subsidiary (Domestic):

Duncan Lawrie (2)
9 Queen Square, Bristol, BS1 4JE, United Kingdom
Tel.: (44) 1179271500
Web Site: http://www.duncanlawrie.com
Sales Range: $25-49.9 Million
Emp.: 8
Business Services
N.A.I.C.S.: 561499
Byron Coombs *(Mng Dir)*

Subsidiary (Non-US):

Duncan Lawrie (IOM) Limited (2)
14-15 Mount Havelock, Douglas, IM1 2QG, Isle of Man
Tel.: (44) 1624662200
Web Site: http://www.duncanlawrie.com
Sales Range: $25-49.9 Million
Emp.: 30
Financial Investment Services
N.A.I.C.S.: 523999
Nigel Gautrey *(Mng Dir)*

Duncan Lawrie Offshore Services Limited (2)
14-15 Mt Havelock, Douglas, IM1 2QG, Isle of Man
Tel.: (44) 1624662200
Web Site: http://www.duncanlawrie.com
Sales Range: $50-74.9 Million
Emp.: 100
Financial Investment Services
N.A.I.C.S.: 523999

Eastern Produce Cape (Pty) Limited (1)
Slangrivier Road Slangrivier Plaas, PO Box 1234, Wellington, Cape Town, 7655, South Africa
Tel.: (27) 218731625
Web Site: https://www.lintonparkwines.co.za
Sales Range: $10-24.9 Million
Emp.: 45
Grape Vineyards
N.A.I.C.S.: 111332

Eastern Produce Kenya Limited (1)
Tel.: (254) 722205342
Web Site: https://www.easternproduce.com

Sales Range: $25-49.9 Million
Emp.: 35
Coffee & Tea Mfr
N.A.I.C.S.: 311920
Ketan Shah *(Dir-Fin)*

Eastern Produce South Africa (Pty) Limited (1)
7 Windsor St, Tzaneen, 0850, Limpopo, South Africa
Tel.: (27) 153073120
Web Site: https://www.easternproduce.com
Sales Range: $25-49.9 Million
Emp.: 4
Roasted Nuts & Peanut Butter Mfr
N.A.I.C.S.: 311911

Goodricke Group Limited (1)
Camellia House 14 Gurusaday Road, Kolkata, 700 019, WB, India
Tel.: (91) 3322871816
Web Site: https://www.goodricke.com
Sales Range: $25-49.9 Million
Emp.: 100
Coffee & Tea Mfr
N.A.I.C.S.: 311920
Subrata Banerjee *(Sec & Sr Gen Mgr)*

Subsidiary (Domestic):

Amgoorie India Limited (2)
Camellia House 14 Gurusaday Road, 14 Gurusaday Road, Kolkata, 700019, WB, India
Tel.: (91) 3322873067
Web Site: http://www.goodricke.com
Sales Range: $25-49.9 Million
Emp.: 100
Coffee & Tea Mfr
N.A.I.C.S.: 311920

Koomber Tea Company Limited (2)
Camellia House, 14 Gurusaday Road, Kolkata, 700019, WB, India
Tel.: (91) 3322873067
Web Site: http://www.goodricke.com
Coffee & Tea Mfr
N.A.I.C.S.: 311920

Jing Tea Limited (1)
5 Hobart Place, Belgravia, London, SW1W 0HU, United Kingdom
Tel.: (44) 207 183 2113
Web Site: https://www.jingtea.com
Tea Mfr
N.A.I.C.S.: 311920

Kakuzi PLC (1)
Punda Milia Road Makuyu, PO Box 24, 1000, Thika, 01000, Kenya   **(50.7%)**
Tel.: (254) 602033012
Web Site: https://www.kakuzi.co.ke
Rev.: $32,841,363
Assets: $62,852,026
Liabilities: $12,197,340
Net Worth: $50,654,686
Earnings: $5,660,509
Emp.: 3,760
Fiscal Year-end: 12/31/2020
Tea Mfr
N.A.I.C.S.: 311920
Simon Odhiambo *(Head-Corp Affairs)*

Linton Park Plc (1)
Linton Park Linton, Maidstone, ME17 4AB, Kent, United Kingdom
Tel.: (44) 1622746655
Web Site: http://www.camellia.plc.uk
Sales Range: $25-49.9 Million
Emp.: 12
Holding Company
N.A.I.C.S.: 551112

Robertson Bois Dickson Anderson Limited (1)
Linton Park Linton, Maidstone, ME17 4AB, Kent, United Kingdom
Tel.: (44) 1622746655
Web Site: http://www.camellia.plc.uk
Sales Range: $25-49.9 Million
Emp.: 12
Holding Company
N.A.I.C.S.: 551112

Tiru Tea Company Limited (1)
Camellia House, 14 Gurusaday Rd, 700019, Kolkata, WB, India
Tel.: (91) 3322871816
Web Site: http://www.camellia.plc.uk
Coffee & Tea Mfr

N.A.I.C.S.: 311920

United Leasing Company Limited (1)
Camellia House 22 Kazi Nazrul, Islam Avenue, 1000, Dhaka, Bangladesh
Tel.: (880) 29669006
Web Site: http://www.ulc.com.bd
Sales Range: $350-399.9 Million
Emp.: 1,000
Insurance Services
N.A.I.C.S.: 524298

Unochrome Industries Limited (1)
Linton Park Linton, Maidstone, ME17 4AB, Kent, United Kingdom
Tel.: (44) 1622746655
Web Site: http://www.camellia.plc.uk
Sales Range: $25-49.9 Million
Emp.: 15
Holding Company
N.A.I.C.S.: 551112

Wylax International B.V. (1)
Burg Vd Lelystraat 2, Woudrichem, Utrecht, 4285, Netherlands
Tel.: (31) 183301333
Web Site: http://www.wylax.nl
Sales Range: $25-49.9 Million
Emp.: 50
Fish & Seafood Whslr
N.A.I.C.S.: 424460

CAMELOT ELECTRONIC TECHNOLOGY CO., LTD
No M1-0405A Yingfu Industrial Zone, Anfeng Industrial Park, High-tech Development Zone, Qingyuan, 511540, Guangdong, China
Tel.: (86) 7633983168
Web Site:
  https://www.camelotpcb.com
Year Founded: 2006
301282—(CHIN)
Rev.: $210,107,196
Assets: $343,457,712
Liabilities: $106,444,260
Net Worth: $237,013,452
Earnings: $19,792,188
Fiscal Year-end: 12/31/22
Electronic Component Mfr & Distr
N.A.I.C.S.: 334419
Jilin Li *(Chm & Gen Mgr)*

CAMELOT GHANA LIMITED
Osu La Road Behind 18th July Furniture Opposite Ghana Commercial Bank, Accra, Ghana
Tel.: (233) 21773120
Web Site:
  https://www.camelotprint.com
Year Founded: 1977
CMLT—(GHA)
Sales Range: $1-9.9 Million
Pre-Printed, Customized Forms & Security Printing
N.A.I.C.S.: 323111
Elisabeth Joyce Villars *(Founder & Chm)*

Subsidiaries:

Camelot Security Solutions Limited (1)
14th Floor New Africa House 31 Marina, Lagos, Nigeria
Tel.: (234) 8079215440
Security Printing Services
N.A.I.C.S.: 323111

CAMELOT INFORMATION SYSTEMS INC.
Beijing Publishing House A6 North Third Ring Road, Xicheng District, Beijing, 100120, China
Tel.: (86) 10 82019000   VG
Web Site:
  http://www.camelotchina.com
Year Founded: 1994
Sales Range: $200-249.9 Million
IT Services & Solutions
N.A.I.C.S.: 541519
Simon Yiming Ma *(CEO)*

CAMELOT MANAGEMENT CONSULTANTS AG
Theodor-Heuss-Anlage 12, 68165, Mannheim, Germany
Tel.: (49) 621 86298 0
Web Site: http://www.camelot-mc.com
Year Founded: 1996
Emp.: 200
Business Management Consulting Services
N.A.I.C.S.: 541611
Josef Packowski *(Founder & Mng Partner)*

Subsidiaries:

Camelot Management Consultants Inc. (1)
100 W Sixth St Ste 103, Media, PA 19063
Tel.: (610) 616-3868
Software Development Services
N.A.I.C.S.: 541511

Camelot Management Consultants Middle East DMCC (1)
Jumeirah Lakes Towers Cluster O Reef Tower First Level, PO Box 5003333, Dubai, United Arab Emirates
Tel.: (971) 43507441
Software Development Services
N.A.I.C.S.: 541511
Mark Barto *(Gen Mgr)*

CAMEO COMMUNICATION, INC.
5F No 158 Ruihu St, Neihu Dist, Taipei, 114, Taiwan
Tel.: (886) 277363000
Web Site: https://www.cameo.com.tw
Year Founded: 1991
6142—(TAI)
Rev.: $83,042,412
Assets: $139,282,378
Liabilities: $36,247,162
Net Worth: $103,035,216
Earnings: ($1,215,213)
Emp.: 195
Fiscal Year-end: 12/31/23
Wireless Adapters & Routers Mfr
N.A.I.C.S.: 334210
Wu Zongzhe *(Chm)*

CAMERIT AG
Wendenstrasse 1A, 20097, Hamburg, Germany
Tel.: (49) 40339620
Web Site: https://www.camerit.de
RTML—(DEU)
Rev.: $77,271
Assets: $7,627,742
Liabilities: $55,193
Net Worth: $7,572,548
Earnings: ($132,464)
Emp.: 1
Fiscal Year-end: 12/31/23
Financial Services
N.A.I.C.S.: 523999
Klaus Mutschler *(Deputy Chm-Supervisory Bd)*

CAMERON BALLOONS LTD.
Saint Johns St, Bedminster, Bristol, BS3 4NH, United Kingdom
Tel.: (44) 1179637216
Web Site:
  http://www.cameronballoons.co.uk
Year Founded: 1970
Sales Range: $10-24.9 Million
Emp.: 63
Hot-Air Balloon Mfr
N.A.I.C.S.: 336411
Nick Purvis *(Dir-Sls)*

Subsidiaries:

Cameron Balloons U.S. (1)
7399 Newman Blvd, Dexter, MI 48130   **(100%)**
Tel.: (734) 426-5525

Cameron Balloons Ltd.—(Continued)

Web Site: http://www.cameronballoons.com
Sales Range: $1-9.9 Million
Emp.: 15
Hot-Air Balloon Mfr.
N.A.I.C.S.: 336411
Dave Moody (Mgr-Engrg)

CAMERON THOMSON GROUP LTD.
390 Bay Street Suite 1706, Toronto, M5H 2Y2, ON, Canada
Tel.: (416) 350-5009   Ca
Web Site:
    http://www.cameronthomson.com
Holding Company; Media & Entertainment Outsourced Business Support Services
N.A.I.C.S.: 551112
Vania Giusto (Head-Admin)

Subsidiaries:

Cameron Thomson Entertainment Ltd.   (1)
390 Bay Street Suite 1706, Toronto, M5H 2Y2, ON, Canada
Tel.: (416) 350-5009
Web Site: http://www.cameronthomson.com
Motion Picture & Other Filmed Entertainment Production & Distribution Services
N.A.I.C.S.: 512110
David Plant (Pres)

WirelesStudios Inc.   (1)
390 Bay Street Suite 1706, Toronto, M5H 2Y2, ON, Canada
Tel.: (416) 350-5009
Web Site: http://www.wirelesstudios.com
Wireless Entertainment Media Distr
N.A.I.C.S.: 518210
Ronald W. Thomson (Founder, Pres & CEO)

CAMERONS BREWERY LTD.
Lion Brewery Waldon Street, Hartlepool, TS24 7QS, United Kingdom
Tel.: (44) 1429 852000
Web Site:
    http://www.cameronsbrewery.com
Sales Range: $50-74.9 Million
Emp.: 150
Beer Brewery
N.A.I.C.S.: 312120
Christopher David Soley (Gen Mgr)

CAMEROON AIRLINES SA
3 Avenue du General de Gaulle, BP 4092, Douala, Cameroon
Tel.: (237) 342 2525
Web Site: http://www.cameroon-airlines.com
Year Founded: 1961
Rev.: $70,180,000
Emp.: 1,400
Oil Transportation Services
N.A.I.C.S.: 481111

CAMEX LIMITED
Camex House Stadium - Commerce Road Navrangpura, Ahmedabad, 380 009, Gujarat, India
Tel.: (91) 7926462261
Web Site: https://www.camexltd.com
Year Founded: 1986
524440—(BOM)
Rev.: $24,544,980
Assets: $8,876,322
Liabilities: $3,449,109
Net Worth: $5,427,213
Earnings: $434,493
Emp.: 50
Fiscal Year-end: 03/31/22
Textile & Leather Product Mfr
N.A.I.C.S.: 314999
Chandraprakash Chopra (Chm & Mng Dir)

CAMEXIP S.A.

Strada Republicii Nr 9, 2064, Baicoi, Romania
Tel.: (40) 244 260 347
Web Site: http://www.camexipsa.ro
Rev.: $3,043,765
Assets: $950,411
Liabilities: $184,742
Net Worth: $765,669
Earnings: $1,295,333
Emp.: 60
Fiscal Year-end: 12/31/17
Industrial Equipment Mfr
N.A.I.C.S.: 811310

CAMFIL AB
Sveavagen 56 E, 111 34, Stockholm, Sweden
Tel.: (46) 854512500   SE
Web Site: http://www.camfil.se
Year Founded: 1963
Sales Range: $400-449.9 Million
Emp.: 103
Air Filters & Purification Equipment Mfr
N.A.I.C.S.: 333413
Johan Markman (Vice Chm)

Subsidiaries:

Camfil (Irl) Ltd   (1)
Clonshaugh Industrial Estate, Clonshaugh, Dublin, Ireland
Tel.: (353) 1848 49 77
Web Site: http://www.camfil.ie
Emp.: 45
Air Filter Mfr & Distr
N.A.I.C.S.: 333413

Camfil A/S   (1)
Literbuen 1-7, 2740, Skovlunde, Denmark
Tel.: (45) 4914 4433
Web Site: http://www.camfil.dk
Air Filter Mfr & Distr
N.A.I.C.S.: 333413
Else Marie Sorensen (Mng Dir)

Camfil AG   (1)
Zugerstrasse 88, 6314, Unterageri, Switzerland
Tel.: (41) 41 754 44 44
Web Site: http://www.camfil.ch
Air Filter Mfr & Distr
N.A.I.C.S.: 333413

Camfil Airfilter Sdn. Bhd.   (1)
Plot 9A Lorong Bemban 1 Bemban Industrial Estate, 31000, Batu Gajah, Malaysia
Tel.: (60) 53668888
Web Site: http://www.camfil.com.my
Emp.: 300
Air Filter Mfr & Distr
N.A.I.C.S.: 333413
Jorn Poulsen (Mng Dir)

Camfil Australia Pty Ltd   (1)
Lot 2 23-29 South Street, Rydalmere, 2116, NSW, Australia
Tel.: (61) 288325500
Web Site: https://www.camfil.com
Emp.: 21
Air Filter Mfr & Distr
N.A.I.C.S.: 333413
John Mahar (Gen Mgr)

Camfil Austria GmbH   (1)
Hermann-Mark-Gasse 7, 1100, Vienna, Austria
Tel.: (43) 1 713 37 83
Web Site: http://www.camfil.at
Air Filter Mfr & Distr
N.A.I.C.S.: 333413
Sascha Deifel (Mng Dir)

Camfil BV   (1)
Galvanistraat 50, 6716 AE, Ede, Netherlands
Tel.: (31) 318 63 33 46
Web Site: http://www.camfil.com
Air Filter Mfr & Distr
N.A.I.C.S.: 333413

Camfil Canada Inc.   (1)
2785 Francis Hughes Ave, Laval, H7L 3J6, QC, Canada
Tel.: (450) 629-3030
Web Site: https://www.camfil.com

Sales Range: $10-24.9 Million
Emp.: 200
Commercial & Industrial Air Filtration Equipment Mfr & Distr
N.A.I.C.S.: 333413
Dominique Mignacco (Pres)

Camfil Espana SA   (1)
C/Islo Alegranza Nave 13-14, San Sebastian de los Reyes, 28700, Madrid, Spain
Tel.: (34) 91 663 81 25
Web Site: http://www.camfil.es
Air Filter Mfr & Distr
N.A.I.C.S.: 333413
Carmelo De Las Heras (Controller-Fin)

Camfil India Pvt. Ltd.   (1)
Plot 32 Sector 3 IMT Manesar, Gurgaon, 122050, Haryana, India
Tel.: (91) 1244874100
Web Site: https://www.camfil.com
Air Filter Mfr
N.A.I.C.S.: 333413
P. K. S. V. Sagar (Mng Dir)

Camfil Ltd.   (1)
Knowsley Road, Haslingden, BB4 4EG, Lancashire, United Kingdom
Tel.: (44) 1706 23800
Web Site: http://www.camfilfarr.com
Rev.: $10,746,000
Emp.: 60
Commercial & Industrial Filters & Filtration Systems Mfr
N.A.I.C.S.: 333413

Camfil New Zealand Limited   (1)
Unit 30 930 Great South Road, PO Box 112097, Penrose, Auckland, 1642, New Zealand
Tel.: (64) 96360663
Web Site: https://www.camfil.com
Air Filter Mfr & Distr
N.A.I.C.S.: 333413
Terry Kelly (Gen Mgr)

Camfil Norge AS   (1)
Sven Oftedals vei 10, 0950, Oslo, Norway
Tel.: (47) 23 12 62 00
Web Site: http://www.camfil.no
Emp.: 30
Air Filter Mfr & Distr
N.A.I.C.S.: 333413
Ole Petter Kolby Hansen (Key Acct Mgr)

Camfil OY   (1)
Ruukinmestarintie 11, 02330, Espoo, Finland
Tel.: (358) 9 8190 380
Web Site: http://www.camfil.fi
Air Filter Mfr & Distr
N.A.I.C.S.: 333413
Marina Almark (Mgr-Customer Svc)

Camfil Polska Sp. z o.o.   (1)
ul Zbaszynska 4, 91-342, Lodz, Poland
Tel.: (48) 426559410
Web Site: http://www.camfil.pl
Air Filter Mfr & Distr
N.A.I.C.S.: 333413
Aleksander Bogusz (Mng Dir)

Camfil SA   (1)
Excelsiorlaan 67-69, 1930, Zaventem, Belgium
Tel.: (32) 2 705 80 70
Web Site: http://www.camfil.be
Emp.: 20
Air Filter Mfr & Distr
N.A.I.C.S.: 333413

Camfil SpA   (1)
Via Induno 2, 20092, Cinisello Balsamo, Milan, Italy
Tel.: (39) 0266048961
Web Site: http://www.camfil.it
Air Filter Mfr & Distr
N.A.I.C.S.: 333413
Marco Fiori (Mng Dir & Dir-Sls)

Camfil UAE   (1)
BA01-04 LIU10 JAFZA South V, Jebel Ali Free Zone, Dubai, United Arab Emirates
Tel.: (971) 48865882
Web Site: https://www.camfil.com
Air Filter Mfr & Distr
N.A.I.C.S.: 333413
Rahul Uppal (Area Mgr)

Camfil USA, Inc.   (1)
1 N Corporate Dr, Riverdale, NJ 07457

Tel.: (973) 616-7300
Web Site: https://www.camfil.com
Sales Range: $1-9.9 Million
Emp.: 20
Warm Air Heating & Air-Conditioning Equipment & Supplies Merchant Whslr
N.A.I.C.S.: 333413
Dominique Mignacco (Pres)

Camfil s.r.o.   (1)
Phemyselny Park Gena U E Sachsa 8, 934 01, Levice, Slovakia
Tel.: (421) 366357370
Web Site: https://www.camfil.com
Air Filter Mfr & Distr
N.A.I.C.S.: 333413
Frantisek Balint (Mgr-Sls)

CAMFIN S.P.A.
Piazza Borromeo 12, 20123, Milan, Italy
Tel.: (39) 0272583400   IT
Web Site: http://www.gruppocamfin.it
Year Founded: 1915
Emp.: 100
Investment Holding Company
N.A.I.C.S.: 551112
Luca Schinelli (Sec & Gen Mgr)

Subsidiaries:

Cam Immobiliare S.p.A.   (1)
Via Sempione 230, 20016, Pero, Italy   (100%)
Tel.: (39) 02353741
Activities Related to Real Estate
N.A.I.C.S.: 531390

Cam Partecipazioni S.p.A.   (1)
Viale Piero e Alberto Pirelli 25, 20126, Milan, MI, Italy   (100%)
Tel.: (39) 0272582400
Energy & Environmental Services
N.A.I.C.S.: 541620

Cam Petroli S.r.l.   (1)
Via Sempione 230, 20016, Pero, Italy   (50%)
Tel.: (39) 02353741
Web Site: http://www.gruppocamfin.it
Petroleum Bulk Stations & Terminals
N.A.I.C.S.: 424710

Perhopolis S.r.l.   (1)
Via Sempione 230, 20016, Pero, Italy   (100%)
Tel.: (39) 02353741
Activities Related to Real Estate
N.A.I.C.S.: 531390

CAMIL ALIMENTOS S.A.
Av. Doutora Ruth Cardoso 8501 12 Floor Pinheiros, Eldorado Business Tower, Sao Paulo, 05425-070, SP, Brazil
Tel.: (55) 1130399200
Web Site:
    https://www.camilalimentos.com.br
Year Founded: 1963
CAML3—(BRAZ)
Rev.: $2,318,319,829
Assets: $2,188,842,447
Liabilities: $1,552,604,221
Net Worth: $636,238,226
Earnings: $74,283,565
Emp.: 4,000
Fiscal Year-end: 02/28/24
Food Product Mfr & Distr
N.A.I.C.S.: 311423
Jacques Maggi Quarter (Chm)

CAMIMEX GROUP JOINT STOCK COMPANY
333 Cao Thang Str Ward 8, Ca Mau, Vietnam
Tel.: (84) 2903831608
Web Site:
    https://www.camimex.com.vn
CMX—(HOSE)
Rev.: $84,051,708
Assets: $141,141,394
Liabilities: $79,581,467
Net Worth: $61,559,928

Earnings: $2,758,422
Fiscal Year-end: 12/31/23
Seafood Export Services
N.A.I.C.S.: 311710

CAMINO MINERALS CORPO-RATION

Suite 1780 - 555 W Hastings Street, Vancouver, V6B 4N4, BC, Canada
Tel.: (604) 493-2058   BC
Web Site: https://caminocorp.com
Year Founded: 2009
COR—(TSXV)
Rev.: $32,305
Assets: $4,917,518
Liabilities: $1,467,539
Net Worth: $3,449,978
Earnings: ($2,320,526)
Fiscal Year-end: 07/31/23
Metal Mining Services
N.A.I.C.S.: 212290
Justin Bourassa *(CFO)*

CAMINOS DE LAS SIERRAS S.A.

Av Italia 700, 5101, Cordoba, Argentina
Tel.: (54) 351 498 2400   Ar
Web Site:
   http://www.camsierras.com.ar
Sales Range: $25-49.9 Million
Road & Bridge Construction Services
N.A.I.C.S.: 237310

CAMIRA FABRICS LTD.

The Watermill Wheatley Park, Mirfield, WF14 8HE, West Yorkshire, United Kingdom
Tel.: (44) 3330324568
Web Site:
   http://www.camirafabrics.com
Year Founded: 1974
Sales Range: $50-74.9 Million
Emp.: 250
Upholstery Fabric Mfr
N.A.I.C.S.: 313210

Subsidiaries:

Camira Fabrics GmbH   **(1)**
Hohenzollernstrasse 2, 71088, Holzgerlingen, Germany
Tel.: (49) 7031 608430
Web Site: http://www.camirafabrics.com
Emp.: 4
Fabric Distr
N.A.I.C.S.: 424310
Reiner Rupp *(Mgr)*

Camira Fabrics Ltd. - Lithuania Manufacturing Facility   **(1)**
Zemaiciu g 47, Ariogala, LT-60252, Raseiniai, Lithuania
Tel.: (370) 428 50155
Web Site: http://www.camirafabrics.com
Emp.: 215
Fabrics Mfr
N.A.I.C.S.: 313210
Marina Sargsian *(Dir-Admin & Fin)*

Camira Fabrics Ltd. - Meltham Manufacturing Facility   **(1)**
Meltham Mills Meltham Mills Road Meltham, Huddersfield, HD9 4AY, United Kingdom
Tel.: (44) 1924 490491
Fabric Product Mfr
N.A.I.C.S.: 313210

Camira Fabrics Shanghai Ltd   **(1)**
Room 2D01 Apollo Business Centre 1440 Yanan Road Middle, Shanghai, 20040, China
Tel.: (86) 21 61331812
Web Site: http://www.camirafabrics.com
Fabric Product Mfr
N.A.I.C.S.: 313210

Camira Group, Inc   **(1)**
2476 Waldorf Ct NW, Grand Rapids, MI 49544
Tel.: (616) 288-0655
Web Site: http://www.camirafabrics.com
Emp.: 7

Fabric Distr
N.A.I.C.S.: 424310
Rune Akselberg *(Pres)*

Luna Textiles   **(1)**
2415 3rd St Ste 280, San Francisco, CA 94107
Tel.: (415) 252-7125
Web Site: http://www.lunatextiles.com
Specialized Design Services
N.A.I.C.S.: 541490
Anna Hernandez *(Founder)*

CAMLIN FINE SCIENCES LTD.

2nd floor In G S Point CST Road kalina Santacruz East, Andheri E, Mumbai, 400098, India
Tel.: (91) 2267001000
Web Site: https://www.camlinfs.com
532834—(BOM)
Rev.: $197,259,330
Assets: $245,711,302
Liabilities: $141,281,554
Net Worth: $104,429,748
Earnings: $8,240,764
Emp.: 478
Fiscal Year-end: 03/31/22
Bulk Drugs, Fine Chemicals & Food Grade Products Mfr
N.A.I.C.S.: 325411
Ashish S. Dandekar *(Mng Dir)*

Subsidiaries:

Chemolutions Chemicals Ltd.   **(1)**
511 Highway Commercial Center Off I B Patel Road, Goregaon, Mumbai, 400063, Maharashtra, India
Tel.: (91) 2228479609
Sales Range: $25-49.9 Million
Emp.: 40
Food Grade Antioxidants Mfr
N.A.I.C.S.: 325998

Sangam Laboratories Ltd   **(1)**
ICC Chambers 3rd flr Saki Vihar Rd, Powai, Mumbai, 400 072, Maharashtra, India
Tel.: (91) 22 2847 9609
Sales Range: $25-49.9 Million
Emp.: 20
Bulk Drug Mfrs
N.A.I.C.S.: 424210

CAMMSYS CO., LTD

26 Venture-ro 100 beon-gil, Yeonsu-gu, 406 840, Incheon, 406 840, Korea (South)
Tel.: (82) 7046802500
Web Site: https://www.cammsys.net
Year Founded: 1993
050110—(KRS)
Rev.: $562,750,454
Assets: $269,396,739
Liabilities: $169,677,697
Net Worth: $99,719,042
Earnings: $4,824,992
Emp.: 144
Fiscal Year-end: 12/31/22
Semiconductor Fabrication Equipment Mfr & Sales
N.A.I.C.S.: 333242
Kwon Hyun-Jin *(CEO)*

Subsidiaries:

Cammsys Global Co., Ltd.   **(1)**
3rd Floor 26 Venture-ro 100beon-gil, Yeonsu-gu Songdo-dong, Incheon, Korea (South)   **(98%)**
Tel.: (82) 7046805797
Camera Module Mfr
N.A.I.C.S.: 333310

Cammsys VINA Co., Ltd.   **(1)**
KCN Ba Thien Xa Ba Hien, Binh Xuyen, Vinh Phuc, Vietnam
Tel.: (84) 978516668
Camera Module Mfr
N.A.I.C.S.: 333310
Nguyen Minh Nga *(Mgr-Logistics)*

Cevo Mobility Co., Ltd.   **(1)**
1F Orange County Bldg 993 Seongnam-daero, Joongwon-gu, Seongnam, Gyeonggi, Korea (South)

Tel.: (82) 15229282
Automotive Parts Mfr & Distr
N.A.I.C.S.: 336390

CAMOZZI GROUP

Via Eritrea 20-I, Brescia, 25126, Italy
Tel.: (39) 03037921
Web Site: http://www.camozzi.com
Year Founded: 1964
Sales Range: $100-124.9 Million
Emp.: 3,000
Machine Tools Mfr
N.A.I.C.S.: 333517
Ettore Camozzi *(CEO)*

Subsidiaries:

Camcasting srl   **(1)**
Via del Pavione 16/18, Paderno Franciacorta, Brescia, 25050, Italy
Tel.: (39) 030657181
Web Site: http://www.camcasting.it
Aluminium Products Mfr
N.A.I.C.S.: 331315

Camozzi Advanced Manufacturing S.p.A.   **(1)**
Via Rubattino 81, 20134, Milan, Italy
Tel.: (39) 022 171 1751
Metal Machinery Mfr
N.A.I.C.S.: 333519

Camozzi ApS   **(1)**
Metalvej 7F, 4000, Roskilde, Denmark
Tel.: (45) 46750202
Web Site: http://www.camozzi.dk
Automation Software Distr
N.A.I.C.S.: 423430

Camozzi Automation AB   **(1)**
Bronsyxegatan 7, 213 75, Malmo, Sweden
Tel.: (46) 40 600 5870
Web Site:
   https://se.automation.camozzi.com
Industrial Machine Tool Distr
N.A.I.C.S.: 423830

Camozzi Automation AS   **(1)**
Torgveien 10, 1400, Ski, Norway
Tel.: (47) 4 064 4920
Web Site:
   https://no.automation.camozzi.com
Industrial Machine Tool Distr
N.A.I.C.S.: 423830

Camozzi Automation ApS   **(1)**
Metalvej 7F, 4000, Roskilde, Denmark
Tel.: (45) 4 675 0202
Web Site:
   https://dk.automation.camozzi.com
Industrial Machine Tool Distr
N.A.I.C.S.: 423830

Camozzi Automation B.V.   **(1)**
De Vijf Boeken 1 A, 2911 BL, Nieuwerkerk, Netherlands
Tel.: (31) 18 031 6677
Web Site: https://nl.automation.camozzi.com
Industrial Machine Tool Distr
N.A.I.C.S.: 423830

Camozzi Automation GmbH   **(1)**
Lofflerweg 18, 6060, Hall in Tirol, Austria
Tel.: (43) 522 352 8880
Web Site:
   https://at.automation.camozzi.com
Industrial Machine Tool Distr
N.A.I.C.S.: 423830

Camozzi Automation GmbH   **(1)**
Porschestrasse 1, 73095, Albershausen, Germany
Tel.: (49) 716 191 0100
Web Site:
   https://de.automation.camozzi.com
Industrial Machine Tool Distr
N.A.I.C.S.: 423830

Camozzi Automation Ltd.   **(1)**
The Fluid Power Centre Watling Street, Nuneaton, CV11 6BQ, Warwickshire, United Kingdom
Tel.: (44) 247 637 4114
Web Site: https://store.camozzi.co.uk
Industrial Machine Tool Distr
N.A.I.C.S.: 423830
James Green *(Mgr)*

Camozzi Automation OU   **(1)**

Osmussaare 8, 13811, Tallinn, Estonia
Tel.: (372) 6119055
Web Site: http://www.camozzi.ee
Industrial Supplies Whslr
N.A.I.C.S.: 423840

Camozzi Automation S.p.A.   **(1)**
Via Eritrea 20/l, 25126, Brescia, Italy
Tel.: (39) 0303 7921
Web Site:
   https://en.automation.camozzi.com
Metal Machinery Mfr
N.A.I.C.S.: 333519

Camozzi Automation Sarl   **(1)**
5 Rue Louis Gattefosse-Parc de la Bandonniere, Saint-Priest, 69800, Lyon, France
Tel.: (33) 47 821 3408
Web Site: https://fr.automation.camozzi.com
Industrial Machine Tool Distr
N.A.I.C.S.: 423830

Camozzi Automation Sp. z o.o.   **(1)**
Ul Byczynska 44, Slaski, 46-310, Gorzow, Poland
Tel.: (48) 34 358 8305
Web Site: https://pl.automation.camozzi.com
Industrial Machine Tool Distr
N.A.I.C.S.: 423830

Camozzi Benelux B.V.   **(1)**
de Vijf Boeken 1A, 2911 BL, Nieuwerkerk, Netherlands
Tel.: (31) 180316677
Web Site: http://www.camozzi.nl
Industrial Supplies Whslr
N.A.I.C.S.: 423840
Edwin van den Haak *(Dir-Ops)*

Camozzi Digital S.r.l.   **(1)**
Via Cassala 48/50, 25126, Brescia, Italy
Tel.: (39) 0303 7921
Web Site: https://en.digital.camozzi.com
Industrial Automation Machinery Mfr
N.A.I.C.S.: 333248

Camozzi GmbH   **(1)**
Lofflerweg 18, 6060, Hall in Tirol, Austria
Tel.: (43) 5223528880
Web Site: http://www.camozzi.at
Industrial Supply Whslr
N.A.I.C.S.: 423840

Camozzi GmbH   **(1)**
Porschestrasse 1, 73095, Albershausen, Germany
Tel.: (49) 7161910100
Web Site: http://www.camozzi.de
Industrial Supplies Whslr
N.A.I.C.S.: 423840

Camozzi Group - Lumezzane Plant   **(1)**
Via Moretto 29, Lumezzane, Brescia, 25065, Italy
Tel.: (39) 0308920521
Machine Tools Mfr
N.A.I.C.S.: 333517

Camozzi Group - Polpenazze Plant   **(1)**
Via Borrine 23/25, Polpenazze, Brescia, 25080, Italy
Tel.: (39) 0365674046
Machine Tools Mfr
N.A.I.C.S.: 333517

Camozzi Iberica SL   **(1)**
Avda Altos Hornos de Vizcaya 33 C-1, 48901, Barakaldo, Vizcaya, Spain
Tel.: (34) 94 655 8958
Industrial Machine Tool Distr
N.A.I.C.S.: 423830

Camozzi India Private Limited   **(1)**
No D-44 Phase II Ext Hosiery complex, Noida, 201 305, Uttar Pradesh, India
Tel.: (91) 1204055252
Web Site: http://www.camozzi.in
Industrial Supply Whslr
N.A.I.C.S.: 423840

Camozzi Malaysia SDN. BHD.   **(1)**
30 & 32 Jalan Industri USJ 1/3 Taman Perindustrian USJ1, Subang Jaya, 47600, Selangor, Malaysia
Tel.: (60) 380238400
Web Site: http://www.camozzi.com.my
Emp.: 20
Industrial Supplies Whslr
N.A.I.C.S.: 423840

Camozzi Group—(Continued)

Camozzi Manufacturing srl (1)
Via Italia 73, Paitone, 25080, Italy
Tel.: (39) 0306901011
Web Site: http://www.camozzi-manufacturing.com
Machine Tools Mfr
N.A.I.C.S.: 333517

Camozzi Neumatica S.A. (1)
Prof Dr Pedro Chutro 3048, Buenos Aires, Argentina
Tel.: (54) 1149110816
Web Site: http://www.camozzi.com.ar
Industrial Supplies Whslr
N.A.I.C.S.: 423840

Camozzi Neumatica S.A. de C.V. (1)
Lago Tanganica 707 Col Ocho Cedros 2 seccion, Toluca, 50170, Mexico
Tel.: (52) 7222707880
Web Site: http://www.camozzi.com.mx
Industrial Supplies Whslr
N.A.I.C.S.: 423840

Camozzi Otomasyon A.S. (1)
Serifali Mahallesi Turgut Ozal Bulvari No 188, Dudullu Umraniye, 34755, Istanbul, Turkiye
Tel.: (90) 216 412 1111
Web Site: https://tr.automation.camozzi.com
Industrial Machine Tool Distr
N.A.I.C.S.: 423830

Camozzi Pneumatic Kazakhstan LLP (1)
Radostovets str 165b/72g off 615 Shevchenko, 050009, Almaty, Kazakhstan
Tel.: (7) 7273335334
Web Site: http://www.camozzi.kz
Industrial Supplies Whslr
N.A.I.C.S.: 423840

Camozzi Pneumatic LLC (1)
Floor 14 Leningradskaya Street 1A, Moscow, Russia
Tel.: (7) 4957354961
Web Site: http://www.camozzi.ru
Industrial Supplies Whslr
N.A.I.C.S.: 423840

Camozzi Pneumatics Inc (1)
2160 Redbud Blvd Ste 101, McKinney, TX 75069-8252
Tel.: (972) 548-8885
Web Site: http://www.camozzi-usa.com
Industrial Supplies Whslr
N.A.I.C.S.: 423840
Claudio Paris (Reg Mgr-Sls)

Camozzi Pneumatics Ltd. (1)
The Fluid Power Centre Watling St, Nuneaton, CV11 6BQ, Warwickshire, United Kingdom
Tel.: (44) 2476374114
Web Site: http://www.camozzi.co.uk
Industrial Supplies Whslr
N.A.I.C.S.: 423840
Shaun Gerber (Mgr-External Technical Sls)

Camozzi Pneumatik AB (1)
Bronsyxegatan 7, Box 9214, 20039, Malmo, Sweden
Tel.: (46) 406005800
Web Site: http://www.camozzi.se
Machine Tools Mfr
N.A.I.C.S.: 333517
Henrik Wahlstrom (Engr-Sls)

Camozzi Pneumatique Sarl (1)
5 Rue Louis Gattefosse - Parc de la Bandonniere, Saint-Priest-en-Jarez, 69800, France
Tel.: (33) 478213408
Web Site: http://www.camozzi.fr
Industrial Supplies Whslr
N.A.I.C.S.: 423840

Camozzi R.O. (1)
6th Floor Master Building 155 Hai Ba Trung St, Ward 6 District 3, Ho Chi Minh City, Vietnam
Tel.: (84) 854477588
Web Site: http://www.camozzi.com.vn
Emp.: 1,700
Industrial Supplies Whslr
N.A.I.C.S.: 423840

Camozzi S.r.o. (1)
V Chotejne 700/7, 102 00, Prague, Czech Republic
Tel.: (420) 27 269 0994
Web Site: https://cz.automation.camozzi.com
Industrial Machine Tool Distr
N.A.I.C.S.: 423830

Camozzi Technopolymers S.r.l. (1)
Via XXV Aprile 5, 25080, Brescia, Italy
Tel.: (39) 03 653 2128
Industrial Automation Machinery Mfr
N.A.I.C.S.: 333248

Camozzi Venezuela S.A. (1)
Calle 146 con Av 62, PO Box 529, Maracaibo, Venezuela
Tel.: (58) 2617360821
Web Site: http://www.camozzi.com.ve
Industrial Supplies Whslr
N.A.I.C.S.: 423840

Camozzi do Brasil Ltda. (1)
Rod Adauto Campo Dall Orto 2 200 Condo Techville - Shed 1, 13178-440, Sumare, Sao Paulo, Brazil
Tel.: (55) 1921374500
Web Site: http://www.camozzi.com.br
Industrial Supply Distr
N.A.I.C.S.: 423840

Campress Srl (1)
Via Cascina Croce 6/8, Paderno Franciacorta, Brescia, 25050, Italy
Tel.: (39) 0306857161
Web Site: http://www.campress.com
Metal Forging Services
N.A.I.C.S.: 332111

FE LLC Camozzi Automation (1)
Honabod FKY, Xonabod Zangiata District, Tashkent, Uzbekistan
Tel.: (998) 55 503 0115
Industrial Machine Tool Distr
N.A.I.C.S.: 423830

Fonderie Mora Gavardo Spa (1)
Via Giovanni Quarena 207, Gavardo, 25085, Brescia, Italy
Tel.: (39) 0365377711
Web Site: http://www.fonderiemoragavardo.it
Industrial Supplies Whslr
N.A.I.C.S.: 423840

Ingersoll Machines Tools, Inc. (IMTA) (1)
707 Fulton Ave, Rockford, IL 61103-4069
Tel.: (815) 987-6000
Web Site: http://www.ingersoll.com
Sales Range: $50-74.9 Million
Emp.: 200
Special Machine Tools Mfr
N.A.I.C.S.: 333517

Innse Milano Spa (1)
Via Raffaele Rubattino 81, Milan, Italy
Tel.: (39) 0221711751
Web Site: http://www.innsemilano.com
Industrial Machinery Mfr
N.A.I.C.S.: 333248

Innse-Berardi GmbH (1)
Porschestrasse 1, 73095, Albershausen, Germany
Tel.: (49) 7161 910 1080
Industrial Machine Tool Distr
N.A.I.C.S.: 423830

Innse-Berardi Inc. (1)
N59W14272 Bobolink Ave, Menomonee Falls, WI 53051
Tel.: (414) 379-4556
Industrial Machine Tool Distr
N.A.I.C.S.: 423830

Innse-Berardi spa (1)
via Attilio Franchi 20, Brescia, 25127, Italy
Tel.: (39) 030370611
Web Site: http://www.innse-berardi.com
Machine Tools Mfr
N.A.I.C.S.: 333517

LLC Camozzi (1)
Kirillovskaya Str 1-3 section D, Kiev, 04080, Ukraine
Tel.: (380) 445369520
Web Site: http://www.camozzi.ua
Machine Tools Mfr
N.A.I.C.S.: 333517

Marzoli Machines Textile srl (1)
Via San Alberto 10, Palazzolo, Brescia, Italy
Tel.: (39) 030 73091
Web Site: http://www.marzoli.it
Textile Machinery Mfr
N.A.I.C.S.: 333248
Marco Muratori (Mgr-Logistics)

Newton Officine Meccaniche Srl (1)
Via Gregorcic 32/34, Sant Andrea, Gorizia, 34170, Italy
Tel.: (39) 0481570511
Web Site: http://www.newton-srl.it
Industrial Machinery Mfr
N.A.I.C.S.: 333248

Subsidiary (US):

Marzoli International, Inc. (2)
100 Corporate Dr Corporate Ctr, Spartanburg, SC 29303
Tel.: (864) 599-7100
Web Site: http://www.marzoli.com
Textile Machinery Distr
N.A.I.C.S.: 423830

Subsidiary (Non-US):

Marzoli Textile Machinery Manufacturers Private Limited (2)
31 C Senapati Bapat Marg, Bengaluru, 560100, Karnataka, India
Tel.: (91) 9448022211
Textile Machinery Mfr
N.A.I.C.S.: 333248

Plastibenaco srl (1)
Via XXV Aprile 5, Castrezzone di Muscoline, Brescia, 25080, Italy
Tel.: (39) 036532128
Web Site: http://www.plastibenaco.com
Plastics Product Mfr
N.A.I.C.S.: 326199
Mauro Abate (Mgr-Production)

Shanghai Camozzi Automation Control Co., Ltd. (100%)
415 Ren De Road, Shanghai, 200434, China
Tel.: (86) 2159100999
Web Site: http://www.camozzi.com.cn
Machine Tools Mfr
N.A.I.C.S.: 333517
Luo Qian (Product Mgr)

CAMP WAHANOWIN
227 Eglinton Ave W, Toronto, M4R 1A9, ON, Canada
Tel.: (416) 482-2600
Web Site: http://www.wahanowin.com
Year Founded: 1955
Rev: $11,368,860
Emp.: 300
Camp & Vacation Services
N.A.I.C.S.: 721214
Harold Nashman (Founder)

CAMPAIGN MONITOR PTY LTD
201 Elizabeth St, Sydney, 2000, NSW, Australia
Tel.: (61) 2 9521 5312
Web Site: http://www.campaignmonitor.com
Year Founded: 2004
Email Campaign Software
N.A.I.C.S.: 513210
Wellford Dillard (CEO)

CAMPBELL FORD
1500 Carling Ave, Ottawa, K1Z 0A3, ON, Canada
Tel.: (613) 725-3611
Web Site: http://www.campbellford.com
Year Founded: 1920
Rev: $43,681,143
Emp.: 100
New & Used Car Dealers
N.A.I.C.S.: 441110
Don Hoddinott (Mgr-Campbell Leasing)

CAMPBELL POOLS INC.
4490 County Rd 17, Alfred, K0B 1A0, ON, Canada
Tel.: (613) 679-1213
Web Site: https://www.campbellpools.ca
Year Founded: 1989
Sales Range: $10-24.9 Million
Emp.: 35
Swimming Pool Accessories Distr
N.A.I.C.S.: 423990

CAMPBELLS/BEWLEY GROUP
Northern Cross Malahide Rd, Dublin, D17 K526, Ireland
Tel.: (353) 18160606
Web Site: http://www.bewleys.com
Year Founded: 1924
Sales Range: $125-149.9 Million
Emp.: 152
Confectionery Coffee & Tea Mfr
N.A.I.C.S.: 311352
John Cahill (CEO)

Subsidiaries:

Bewley's Ltd. (1)
Northern Cross Malahide Rd, Dublin, 17, Ireland (100%)
Tel.: (353) 18160606
Web Site: http://www.bewleys.com
Sales Range: $25-49.9 Million
Provider of Coffee, Tea & Bakery Products
N.A.I.C.S.: 311811
Jim Corbett (Mng Dir)

Bewley's Oriental Cafes Limited (1)
Northern Cross Malahide Rd, Dublin, 17, Ireland (100%)
Tel.: (353) 18160606
Web Site: http://www.bewleys.ie
Sales Range: $25-49.9 Million
Operator of Retail Cafe & Shop Units
N.A.I.C.S.: 812990

Campbell Catering Limited (1)
Newenham House Northern Cross Malahide Road, Dublin, D17 AY61, Ireland
Tel.: (353) 18160700
Contract & Commercial Catering Services
N.A.I.C.S.: 722320
Shane Flynn (Mng Dir-Food Svcs & Facilities Mgmt)

CAMPER & NICHOLSONS MARINA INVST. LTD.
Bordage House Le Bordage, Saint Peter Port, GY1 1BU, Guernsey
Tel.: (44) 20 3405 1782
Web Site: http://en.cnmarinas.com
Rev: $8,230,981
Assets: $67,681,303
Liabilities: $31,995,730
Net Worth: $35,685,573
Earnings: ($2,077,645)
Fiscal Year-end: 12/31/17
Investment Company
N.A.I.C.S.: 523940
Phil Ladmore (Dir-Comml & Legal)

Subsidiaries:

Camper & Nicholsons Marinas Ltd. (1)
5th Floor Cording House 34 St James's St, London, SW1A 1HD, United Kingdom
Tel.: (44) 20 34051782
Web Site: http://www.cnmarinas.com
Sales Range: $50-74.9 Million
Management & Consultancy Services
N.A.I.C.S.: 541618
David Mead (Dir-Fin-Ops)

Camper & Nicholsons USA, Inc. (1)
801 Seabreeze Blvd, Fort Lauderdale, FL 33316
Tel.: (954) 524-4250
Emp.: 12
Yacht Retailer
N.A.I.C.S.: 441222
Rusty Preston (Pres)

CAMPI SRL
Via Diamantina 15, 44122, Ferrara, Italy

Tel.: (39) 0532 770048
Web Site: http://www.campisrl.it
Industrial Machinery Mfr
N.A.I.C.S.: 333248

CAMPINE N.V.
Nijverheidsstraat 2, BE 2340, Beerse, Belgium
Tel.: (32) 14601511
Web Site: https://www.campine.com
Year Founded: 1912
CAMB—(EUR)
Rev.: $342,575,005
Assets: $137,700,194
Liabilities: $73,432,981
Net Worth: $64,267,213
Earnings: $17,056,983
Emp.: 228
Fiscal Year-end: 12/31/22
Chemical Products Mfr
N.A.I.C.S.: 325180
Patrick De Groote *(Chm)*

Subsidiaries:

Campine France S.A.S   (1)
679 Av de la Republique, 59800, Lille, France
Tel.: (33) 474023070
Battery Repair Services
N.A.I.C.S.: 811111

Campine recycled Polymers
S.A.S.   (1)
300 Avenue de l'epie, 69400, Arnas, France
Tel.: (33) 474023093
Recycled Polypropylene Compounds Mfr
N.A.I.C.S.: 325991

F.W. Hempel Metallurgical GmbH   (1)
Am Wehrhahn 50, 40211, Dusseldorf, Germany
Tel.: (49) 208620550
Web Site: https://www.metallurgical.de
Non-ferrous Metal Mfr & Distr
N.A.I.C.S.: 331492

CAMPION MARINE INC.
200 Campion Rd, Kelowna, V1X 7S8, BC, Canada
Tel.: (250) 765-7795
Web Site:
  http://www.campionboats.com
Year Founded: 1974
Rev.: $17,388,990
Emp.: 50
Boat Builders Repair & Maintenance
N.A.I.C.S.: 336612
Brock Elliott *(Gen Mgr)*

**CAMPLIFY HOLDINGS LIM-
ITED**
c/o Growthwise 59 Parry Street, Newcastle, 2300, NSW, Australia
Tel.: (61) 1300416133
Web Site:
  https://www.camplify.com.au
Year Founded: 2014
CHL—(ASX)
Rev.: $24,925,822
Assets: $73,720,834
Liabilities: $31,015,003
Net Worth: $42,705,831
Earnings: ($2,352,930)
Fiscal Year-end: 06/30/23
Holding Company
N.A.I.C.S.: 551112
Jonathan Milgate *(CTO)*

Subsidiaries:

PaulCamper GmbH   (1)
Landsberger Allee 117, D-10407, Berlin, Germany
Tel.: (49) 30609849722
Web Site: https://paulcamper.de
Recreational Vehicle Rental Agency Services
N.A.I.C.S.: 532120

CAMPOSOL HOLDING PLC
Ave El Derby 250 Santiago de Surco,

Urb El Derby de Monterrico, Lima, Peru
Tel.: (51) 16347100   CY
Web Site:
  http://www.camposol.com.pe
Year Founded: 2007
CMSL—(NYSE)
Rev.: $464,442,000
Assets: $1,127,865,000
Liabilities: $827,872,000
Net Worth: $299,993,000
Earnings: $20,088,000
Emp.: 19,000
Fiscal Year-end: 12/31/23
Holding Company
N.A.I.C.S.: 551112
Samuel Barnaby Dyer Coriat *(Chm)*

CAMPOSTANO GROUP S.P.A.
Via Paleocapa 6/3, Savona, 17100, Italy
Tel.: (39) 01984131
Web Site:
  http://www.campostano.com
Sales Range: $50-74.9 Million
Emp.: 180
Freight Forwarding, Shipping & Terminal Operation Services
N.A.I.C.S.: 488510

Subsidiaries:

Forest S.p.A.   (1)
Ponte Somalia Ponente, 16149, Genoa, Italy
Tel.: (39) 010415341
Web Site: http://www.campostano.com
Sales Range: $50-74.9 Million
Emp.: 11
Shipping Services
N.A.I.C.S.: 425120

**CAMPUS ACTIVEWEAR LIM-
ITED**
D1 Udyog Nagar Main Rohtak Road, New Delhi, 110041, India
Tel.: (91) 1143272500
Web Site:
  https://www.campusactivewear.com
Year Founded: 2005
543523—(BOM)
Rev.: $178,287,153
Assets: $140,988,550
Liabilities: $74,791,080
Net Worth: $66,197,470
Earnings: $14,042,084
Emp.: 839
Fiscal Year-end: 03/31/23
Footwear Mfr & Distr
N.A.I.C.S.: 316210

CAMROST-FELCORP INC.
95 St Clair Ave W Suite 1600, Toronto, M4V 1N6, ON, Canada
Tel.: (416) 486-1961
Web Site: http://www.camrost.com
Year Founded: 1976
Rev.: $12,780,908
Emp.: 40
Residential & Industrial Building Construction Services
N.A.I.C.S.: 236220
David Feldman *(Founder, Pres & CEO)*

Subsidiaries:

CamCorp Inc.   (1)
9732 Pflumm Rd, Lenexa, KS 66215
Tel.: (913) 831-0740
Web Site: http://www.camcorpinc.com
Design & Engineering Services
N.A.I.C.S.: 541330
Keith Horton *(Dir-Natl Sls)*

Subsidiary (Domestic):

CamCorp Manufacturing, Inc.   (2)
3 Coastal Dr, Willow Springs, MO 65793-3554
Tel.: (417) 469-4807

Emp.: 100
Construction Equipment Mfr
N.A.I.C.S.: 333991

CAMROVA RESOURCES INC.
55 York Street Suite 401, Toronto, M5J 1R7, ON, Canada
Tel.: (604) 685-2323   BC
Web Site:
  http://www.camrovaresources.com
Year Founded: 1985
CAV—(OTCIQ)
Assets: $1,529
Liabilities: $1,027,980
Net Worth: ($1,026,451)
Earnings: ($373,174)
Emp.: 3
Fiscal Year-end: 12/31/20
Copper, Zinc, Cobalt & Other Metal Mining & Processing Services
N.A.I.C.S.: 212230

Subsidiaries:

Baja International S.a r.l.   (1)
121 Avenue de la Faiencerie, 1511, Luxembourg, Luxembourg
Tel.: (352) 26 20 04 33
Mineral Exploration Services
N.A.I.C.S.: 213115

**CAMSING HEALTHCARE LIM-
ITED**
7500-E Beach Road 03-201 The Plaza, Singapore, 199595, Singapore
Tel.: (65) 62952027   SG
Year Founded: 1979
Sales Range: $10-24.9 Million
Emp.: 722
Investment Holding Company
N.A.I.C.S.: 551112
Ching Lo *(Chm)*

**CAMSING INTERNATIONAL
HOLDING LIMITED**
Suite 1602 Cheung Kong Center 2 Queen's Road Central, Central, China (Hong Kong)
Tel.: (852) 3158 8163
Web Site: http://www.camsingintl.com
Rev.: $373,669,658
Assets: $102,206,204
Liabilities: $39,956,994
Net Worth: $62,249,210
Earnings: $11,003,188
Emp.: 539
Fiscal Year-end: 06/30/18
Printed Circuit Board Mfr
N.A.I.C.S.: 334412
Hui Liu *(Exec Dir)*

Subsidiaries:

POW! Entertainment, Inc.   (1)
9440 Santa Monica Blvd Ste 620, Beverly Hills, CA 90210
Tel.: (310) 275-9933
Web Site: http://www.powentertainment.com
Multimedia Production & Entertainment Services
N.A.I.C.S.: 512110
Gill Champion *(Pres)*

CAMSON SEEDS LTD.
Corporate Block Golden Enclav C-7 7th Floor Old Airport Ro, Bengaluru, 560 017, India
Tel.: (91) 8040768900
Agriculture Product Mfr & Distr
N.A.I.C.S.: 311911
Dhirendra Kumar *(Chm & Mng Dir)*

**CAMST-COOPERATIVA AL-
BERGO MENSA SPETTACOLO
E TURISMO, SOC. COOP.
A.R.L.**
Via Tosarelli 318, 40055, Villanova di Castenaso, Bologna, Italy
Tel.: (39) 051 6017411   IT

Web Site: http://www.camst.it
Year Founded: 1945
Sales Range: $700-749.9 Million
Emp.: 14,000
Catering & Food Services Contractor
N.A.I.C.S.: 722320

Subsidiaries:

Ge.S.In. Gestione Servizi Integrati -
Societa Cooperativa   (1)
Via Colorno 63, 43122, Parma, Italy
Tel.: (39) 0521 600 111
Web Site: http://www.gesincoop.it
Sales Range: $50-74.9 Million
Emp.: 1,000
Construction & Facilities Management Services
N.A.I.C.S.: 561210
Antonio Costantino *(Dir Gen)*

CAMURUS AB
Ideon Science Park, SE-223 70, Lund, Sweden
Tel.: (46) 462865730
Web Site: https://www.camurus.com
Year Founded: 1991
CAMX—(OMX)
Rev.: $89,572,621
Assets: $122,274,486
Liabilities: $29,111,711
Net Worth: $93,162,775
Earnings: $5,203,199
Emp.: 176
Fiscal Year-end: 12/31/22
Pharmaceuticals Product Mfr
N.A.I.C.S.: 325412
Per-Olof Wallstrom *(Chm)*

Subsidiaries:

Camurus GmbH   (1)
Carl-Reuther-Str 1, 68305, Mannheim, Germany
Tel.: (49) 62185451096
Pharmaceuticals Mfr
N.A.I.C.S.: 325412

Camurus Ltd.   (1)
Royston Rd, Duxford, Cambridge, CB22 4QH, United Kingdom
Tel.: (44) 1223919700
Pharmaceuticals Mfr
N.A.I.C.S.: 325412

Camurus Pty. Ltd.   (1)
223 Liverpool Street, Darlinghurst, 2010, NSW, Australia
Tel.: (61) 1800142038
Web Site: https://buvidal.com.au
Medicinal Product Mfr & Distr
N.A.I.C.S.: 325411

**CAMUZZI GAS PAMPEANA
S.A.**
Av Alicia Moreau de Justo 240 Piso 3, C1107AAF, Buenos Aires, Argentina
Tel.: (54) 1157767000
Web Site:
  https://www.camuzzigas.com
Natural Gas Distribution Services
N.A.I.C.S.: 221210
Jaime Barba *(Chm)*

CAN (OFFSHORE) LTD
Hareness Road, Altens, Aberdeen, AB12 3LE, United Kingdom
Tel.: (44) 1224 870100
Web Site: http://www.cangroup.net
Year Founded: 1977
Sales Range: $100-124.9 Million
Emp.: 1,000
Engineering, Inspection & Maintenance Services
N.A.I.C.S.: 541330
Michael Freeman *(Mng Dir)*

Subsidiaries:

CAN AS   (1)
Slettestrandveien 4, 4032, Stavanger, Norway

CAN (Offshore) Ltd—(Continued)
Tel.: (47) 51 81 18 18
Web Site: http://www.can.no
Emp.: 80
Engineering Inspection & Maintenance Services
N.A.I.C.S.: 541330

CAN Geotechnical Ltd (1)
Smeckley Wood Close Chootorfield Trading Estate, Chesterfield, S41 9PZ, Derbyshire, United Kingdom
Tel.: (44) 1246 261111
Web Site: http://www.can.ltd.uk
Emp.: 3
Rock Faces, Soil Slopes & Retaining Walls Stabilization Services
N.A.I.C.S.: 541620
Gerald Borcherds (Mng Dir)

CAN Global Angola LDA (1)
Suite 15 Sonils Building Boavista Street, Luanda, Angola
Tel.: (244) 226 430 677
Engineering, Inspection & Maintenance Services
N.A.I.C.S.: 541330

CAN Middle East L.L.C. (1)
PO Box 52892, Abu Dhabi, United Arab Emirates
Tel.: (971) 2 644 1338
Engineering, Inspection & Maintenance Services
N.A.I.C.S.: 541330

CAN Structures Ltd (1)
Smeckley Wood Close Chesterfield Trading Estate, Chesterfield, S41 9PZ, Derbyshire, United Kingdom
Tel.: (44) 1246 261111
Web Site: http://www.can.ltd.uk
Environmental Construction & Maintenance Services
N.A.I.C.S.: 541330
James Wong (Dir-Ops)

CAN USA, Inc. (1)
1800 Jutland Dr, Harvey, LA 70058
Tel.: (504) 328-1567
Web Site: http://www.can-usa.net
Sales Range: $25-49.9 Million
Emp.: 100
Engineering, Inspection & Maintenance Services
N.A.I.C.S.: 541330
Clayton Hinyup (Pres)

CAN USA, Inc. (1)
171 Lodi St, Hackensack, NJ 07601
Tel.: (201) 996-9287
Sales Range: $25-49.9 Million
Emp.: 100
Engineering, Inspection & Maintenance Services
N.A.I.C.S.: 541330

CAN DON HYDRO POWER JOINT STOCK COMPANY
Thanh Binh Town, Bu Dop, Binh Phuoc, Vietnam
Tel.: (84) 2713563359
Web Site:
https://www.candon.com.vn
SJD—(HOSE)
Rev.: $17,749,372
Assets: $55,558,076
Liabilities: $13,676,917
Net Worth: $41,881,160
Earnings: $5,363,004
Emp.: 232
Fiscal Year-end: 12/31/23
Power Generation Services
N.A.I.C.S.: 221111
Mai Ngoc Hoan (Exec Dir)

CAN THO MINERAL & CEMENT JSC
Highway 80 Thoi Thuan Ward, Thot Not District Ho Chi Minh City, Can Tho, Vietnam
Tel.: (84) 2923859216
Web Site:
http://www.ximangcantho.vn

CCM—(HNX)
Rev.: $125,910,100
Assets: $73,238,500
Liabilities: $30,940,200
Net Worth: $42,298,300
Earnings: $5,301,100
Fiscal Year-end: 12/31/22
Cement Mfr & Whslr
N.A.I.C.S.: 327310

CAN THO PESTICIDES JOINT STOCK COMPANY
No 51 Truong Van Dien Street Phuoc Thoi Ward, O Mon District, Can Tho, Vietnam
Tel.: (84) 2923861770
Web Site:
https://www.tstcantho.com.vn
CPC—(HNX)
Rev.: $18,860,600
Assets: $12,375,100
Liabilities: $4,039,500
Net Worth: $8,335,600
Earnings: $956,000
Emp.: 190
Fiscal Year-end: 12/31/22
Pesticides & Agricultural Chemicals Mfr
N.A.I.C.S.: 325320

CAN-AMERI AGRI CO. INC.
Suite 700-595 Burrard St, Vancouver, V7X 1S8, BC, Canada
Tel.: (604) 245-5978   BC
Year Founded: 2014
Real Estate Services
N.A.I.C.S.: 531390

CAN-BOW MOTORS LTD.
707 Railway Avenue, Canmore, T1W 1P2, AB, Canada
Tel.: (403) 678-4222
Web Site: http://www.can-bow.com
Year Founded: 1977
New & Used Car Dealers
N.A.I.C.S.: 441110
Larry Algeo (Mgr-New Vehicle)

CAN-CAL RESOURCES LTD.
42 Springfield Avenue, Red Deer, T4N 0C7, AB, Canada
Tel.: (403) 342-6221   NV
Year Founded: 1995
Metal Mining Services
N.A.I.C.S.: 212290
Casey Douglass (Chm)

CAN-CELL INDUSTRIES INC.
14735-124 Avenue, Edmonton, T5L 3B2, AB, Canada
Tel.: (780) 447-1255
Web Site: https://www.can-cell.com
Year Founded: 1976
Rev.: $22,070,400
Emp.: 160
Building Hardware Products Mfr & Distr
N.A.I.C.S.: 325520
Harold Tiemstra (Pres)

CAN-DER CONSTRUCTION LTD
5410 97 St, Edmonton, T6E 5C1, AB, Canada
Tel.: (780) 436-2980
Web Site: http://www.cdlhomes.com
Year Founded: 1970
Rev.: $27,134,149
Emp.: 50
Building Construction Services
N.A.I.C.S.: 236220
Greg Christenson (Owner & Pres)

CAN-FITE BIOPHARMA LTD.
10 Bareket Street Kiryat Matalon, PO Box 7537, Petah Tiqwa, 49170, Israel

Tel.: (972) 39241114   II
Web Site: https://www.ir.canfite.com
Year Founded: 1994
CANF—(NYSEAMEX)
Rev.: $810,000
Assets: $9,283,000
Liabilities: $4,811,000
Net Worth: $4,472,000
Earnings: ($10,173,000)
Emp.: 8
Fiscal Year-end: 12/31/22
Biopharmaceutical Mfr
N.A.I.C.S.: 325412
Motti Farbstein (CFO & COO)

CAN-ONE BERHAD
2B-4 Level 4 Jalan SS 6/6 Kelana Jaya, 47301, Petaling Jaya, Selangor Darul Ehsan, Malaysia
Tel.: (60) 378048590
Web Site:
https://www.canone.com.my
CANONE—(KLS)
Rev.: $670,360,212
Assets: $902,343,492
Liabilities: $497,218,201
Net Worth: $405,125,291
Earnings: $18,600,635
Emp.: 5,782
Fiscal Year-end: 12/31/22
Tin Cans & Plastic Jerry Cans Mfr
N.A.I.C.S.: 332431
Khay Leong Chee (Exec Dir)

Subsidiaries:

BP MPak Sdn. Bhd. (1)
Plo 165 Jalan Cyber Utama Kawasan Perindustrian Senai 3, 81400, Senai, Johor, Malaysia
Tel.: (60) 75997797
Carton Box Mfr
N.A.I.C.S.: 322219

Box-Pak (Hanoi) Co., Ltd. (1)
No 12 Street 11 VSIP Bac Ninh, Phu Chan Commune Tu Son Town, Hanoi, Bac Ninh, Vietnam
Tel.: (84) 2413765966
Carton Box Mfr
N.A.I.C.S.: 322219

Can-One (USA), Inc. (1)
141 Burke St, Nashua, NH 03060
Tel.: (603) 704-9340
Web Site: https://can-one.com
Aluminium Beverage Can Mfr
N.A.I.C.S.: 332439

F & B Nutrition Sdn. Bhd. (1)
Lot 2234 Jalan Rajawali Batu 9 Kampung Kebun Baru, Telok Panglima Garang, 42500, Kuala Langat, Selangor, Malaysia
Tel.: (60) 37 622 2212
Web Site: https://fnbnutrition.com.my
Food Mfr
N.A.I.C.S.: 311999
Tan Beng Wah (Dir-Sls & Mktg)

KJO International Sdn. Bhd. (1)
No 106 Jalan Permata 1 Kawasan Industri Arab-Malaysian, 71800, Nilai, Malaysia
Tel.: (60) 67998899
Metal Tank Mfr
N.A.I.C.S.: 332431

Kian Joo Can (Vietnam) Co., Ltd. (1)
No 17 Dai Lo Doc Lap Vietnam Singapore Industrial Park, Thuan An District, Thuan An, Binh Duong, Vietnam
Tel.: (84) 6503782292
Metal Tank Mfr
N.A.I.C.S.: 332431

Kian Joo Can Factory Berhad (1)
Lot No 10 Jalan Perusahaan Satu, 68100, Batu Caves, Selangor Darul Ehsan, Malaysia   (97.48%)
Tel.: (60) 361896322
Web Site: http://www.kjcf.net
Rev.: $439,607,409
Assets: $658,086,390
Liabilities: $192,861,062
Net Worth: $465,235,328
Earnings: $4,153,206

Emp.: 3,193
Fiscal Year-end: 12/31/2018
Metal Tank Mfr
N.A.I.C.S.: 332431
Jin Hoe Yeoh (Grp Mng Dir)

Subsidiary (Domestic):

Bintang Seribu Sdn. Bhd. (2)
Lot 18 Jalan Pengapit 15-19, 40000, Shah Alam, Selangor, Malaysia   (100%)
Tel.: (60) 351912157
Corrugated & Solid Fiber Box Mfr
N.A.I.C.S.: 322211

Box-Pak (Malaysia) Berhad (2)
Lot 4 Jalan Perusahaan Dua, 68100, Batu Caves, Selangor, Malaysia   (54.83%)
Tel.: (60) 361896688
Web Site: https://www.boxpak.com.my
Sales Range: $50-74.9 Million
Emp.: 200
Corrugated & Solid Fiber Box Mfr
N.A.I.C.S.: 322211
Roslan A. Ghaffar (Chm)

Subsidiary (Non-US):

Box-Pak (Vietnam) Co., Ltd. (2)
No 22 Dai Lo Huu Nghi, Vietnam Singapore Industrial Park, Thuan An, Binh Duong, Vietnam   (54.83%)
Tel.: (84) 6503784490
Web Site: http://www.boxpak.com.my
Sales Range: $200-249.9 Million
Emp.: 750
Corrugated & Solid Fiber Box Mfr
N.A.I.C.S.: 322211

Subsidiary (Domestic):

Federal Metal Printing Factory Sdn. Bhd. (2)
Jalan Kawat 15/18, 40000, Shah Alam, Selangor, Malaysia   (100%)
Tel.: (60) 355192521
Emp.: 200
Corrugated & Solid Fiber Box Mfr
N.A.I.C.S.: 322211

Indastri Kian Joo Sdn. Bhd. (2)
Lot 10 Jalan Perusahaan Satu, Batu Caves, 68100, Selangor, Malaysia
Tel.: (60) 361896322
Tin Cans Mfr
N.A.I.C.S.: 332431
Ang Kok Kun (Gen Mgr)

KJ Can (Johore) Sdn. Bhd. (2)
6 Jalan Hasil 2 Kawasan Perindustrian, Jalan Hasil Tampoi, 81200, Johor Bahru, Johor Darul Takzim, Malaysia   (100%)
Tel.: (60) 72349958
Emp.: 150
Metal Tank Mfr
N.A.I.C.S.: 332431

KJ Can (Selangor) Sdn. Bhd. (2)
Lot 19 Jalan SU 4 Seksyen 22, 46300, Shah Alam, Selangor, Malaysia   (100%)
Tel.: (60) 351928660
Sales Range: $50-74.9 Million
Emp.: 106
Corrugated & Solid Fiber Box Mfr
N.A.I.C.S.: 322211

KJM Aluminium Can Sdn. Bhd. (2)
No 106 Jalan Permata 1, Kawasan Industri Arab-Malaysian, 71800, Nilai, Negeri, Malaysia   (100%)
Tel.: (60) 67998899
Sales Range: $50-74.9 Million
Emp.: 200
Corrugated & Solid Fiber Box Mfr
N.A.I.C.S.: 322211

KJO Systems Sdn. Bhd. (2)
No 106 Jalan Permata 1 Kawasan Industri Arab-Malaysian, Nilai, 71800, Malaysia
Tel.: (60) 6 799 8899
Web Site: http://www.kjcs.net
Sales Range: $50-74.9 Million
Emp.: 200
Packaging Machinery Mfr
N.A.I.C.S.: 333993

Kian Joo Canpack (Shah Alam) Sdn. Bhd. (2)
Lot 3 Jalan 15-18, 40000, Shah Alam, Selangor, Malaysia   (100%)
Tel.: (60) 355192521

Web Site: http://www.kjcf.net
Sales Range: $25-49.9 Million
Emp.: 100
Corrugated & Solid Fiber Box Mfr
N.A.I.C.S.: 322211

Kian Joo Canpack Sdn. Bhd. (2)
PT4974 Jalan Haruan 8, Taman Perindus-
trian Oakland, 70300, Seremban, Negeri,
Malaysia (100%)
Tel.: (60) 67677830
Sales Range: $50-74.9 Million
Emp.: 200
Corrugated & Solid Fiber Box Mfr
N.A.I.C.S.: 322211

Kian Joo Packaging Sdn Bhd (2)
Lot 6 Jalan Perusahaan 1, 68100, Batu
Caves, Selangor, Malaysia (100%)
Tel.: (60) 361896322
Web Site: http://www.kianjoocan.com.my
Sales Range: $50-74.9 Million
Emp.: 200
Metal Tank Mfr
N.A.I.C.S.: 332431

Kian Joo-Visypak Sdn.Bhd (2)
No 8 Jalan TP7 Taman Perindustrian UEP
Subang Jaya, 40400, Shah Alam,
Malaysia (100%)
Tel.: (60) 351923110
Web Site: http://www.kjvpet.com.my
Sales Range: $25-49.9 Million
Emp.: 80
Corrugated & Solid Fiber Box Mfr
N.A.I.C.S.: 322211
Anthony See (Mng Dir)

Metal-Pak (Malaysia) Sdn. Bhd. (2)
No 106 Jalan Permata 1, Kawasan Industri
Arab-Malaysian, 71800, Nilai, Negeri,
Malaysia (100%)
Tel.: (60) 67998899
Web Site: http://www.mtcma.com
Corrugated & Solid Fiber Box Mfr
N.A.I.C.S.: 322211

CAN2 TERMIK A.S.
Basak Cengiz Sokak Varyap Meridian
Sitesi No 1 1D/Villa 4, Barbaros Ma-
hallesi Bati Atasehir, 34746, Istanbul,
Turkiye
Tel.: (90) 2164741474
Web Site:
https://www.can2termik.com.tr
Year Founded: 2013
CANTE—(IST)
Rev.: $197,470,929
Assets: $601,574,360
Liabilities: $31,669,931
Net Worth: $569,904,429
Earnings: $15,130,078
Emp.: 794
Fiscal Year-end: 12/31/23
Information Technology Services
N.A.I.C.S.: 541512
Burak Altay (Chm)

CANA-DATUM MOULDS LTD.
55 Goldthorne Avenue, Toronto, M8Z
5S7, ON, Canada
Tel.: (416) 252-1212
Web Site: http://www.cana-
datum.com
Year Founded: 1986
Emp.: 105
Precision Tools & Dies Mfr
N.A.I.C.S.: 332721
Rodrigo Merino (Mgr-Mfg)

CANAAN INC.
28 Ayer Rajah Crescent 06-08, Soft-
ware Park No 8 Dongbeiwang West
Road Haidian District, Beijing,
139959, China
Tel.: (86) 1058741858   Ky
Web Site: https://www.canaan.io
Year Founded: 2013
CAN—(NASDAQ)
Rev.: $670,892,341
Assets: $731,430,362
Liabilities: $82,474,628
Net Worth: $648,955,734

Earnings: $74,514,756
Emp.: 541
Fiscal Year-end: 12/31/22
Computer Hardware Mfr
N.A.I.C.S.: 332510
Nangeng Zhang (Co-Chm & CEO)

CANACCORD GENUITY GROUP INC.
609 Granville Street Suite 2200, PO
Box 10337, Vancouver, V7Y 1H2,
BC, Canada
Tel.: (604) 643-7300
Web Site:
https://www.canaccordgenuity.com
Year Founded: 1950
CCORF—(OTCIQ)
Rev.: $1,126,756,162
Assets: $4,701,590,400
Liabilities: $3,658,207,198
Net Worth: $1,043,383,202
Earnings: ($40,837,532)
Emp.: 2,829
Fiscal Year-end: 03/31/23
Investment Services
N.A.I.C.S.: 523999
David J. Kassie (Chm)

Subsidiaries:

Canaccord Genuity (Australia)
Limited (1)
Financial Investment Services
N.A.I.C.S.: 523940

Canaccord Genuity (Dubai) Ltd. (1)
Gate Village Building 4 Suite 402 DIFC, PO
Box 507023, Dubai, United Arab Emirates
Tel.: (971) 44541215
Banking Services
N.A.I.C.S.: 523150

Canaccord Genuity (Hong Kong)
Limited (1)
Suite 1210 12/F ICBC Tower Three Garden
Road, Hong Kong, China (Hong Kong)
Tel.: (852) 39192500
Banking Services
N.A.I.C.S.: 523150

Canaccord Genuity Asia (Beijing)
Limited (1)
Unit 1421-1422 South Tower Beijing Kerry
Centre 1 Guanghua Road, Chaoyang Dis-
trict, Beijing, 100020, China
Tel.: (86) 1086229070
Banking Services
N.A.I.C.S.: 523150

Canaccord Genuity Corp. (1)
Pacific Centre Suite 2200 609 Granville
Street, PO Box 10337, Vancouver, V7Y
1H2, BC, Canada
Tel.: (604) 643-7300
Web Site: http://www.canaccordgenuity.com
Sales Range: $350-399.9 Million
Investment Banking Services
N.A.I.C.S.: 523150

Subsidiary (US):

Canaccord Genuity Inc. (2)
99 High St Ste 1200, Boston, MA 02110
Tel.: (617) 371-3900
Web Site: http://www.canaccordgenuity.com
Sales Range: $100-124.9 Million
Emp.: 225
Brokerage & Investment Financial Services
N.A.I.C.S.: 523150
Jeff Barlow (Pres)

Subsidiary (Domestic):

Canaccord Genuity Securities
LLC (3)
350 Madison Ave, New York, NY
10017 (100%)
Tel.: (212) 389-8000
Web Site: http://www.canaccordgenuity.com
Sales Range: $50-74.9 Million
Emp.: 50
Institutional & Private Client Stockbroking,
Market Making, Corporate Finance, Fund
Management & Financial Information Ser-
vices
N.A.I.C.S.: 525990

Gregory Miller (Mng Dir)

Subsidiary (Non-US):

Canaccord Genuity Limited (2)
41 Lothbury, London, EC2R 7AE, United
Kingdom
Tel.: (44) 2075234500
Web Site: http://www.canaccordgenuity.com
Institutional & Private Client Stockbroking,
Market Making, Corporate Finance, Fund
Management & Financial Information Ser-
vices
N.A.I.C.S.: 523150
David Esfandi (CEO-Wealth Mgmt-UK &
Europe)

Subsidiary (Domestic):

Canaccord Genuity Hawkpoint
Limited (3)
41 Lothbury, London, EC2R 7AE, United
Kingdom
Tel.: (44) 2076654500
Sales Range: $50-74.9 Million
Emp.: 125
Corporate Financial Advisory Services
N.A.I.C.S.: 523940

Canaccord Genuity Financial
Limited (1)
Level 23 Exchange Tower 2 The Espla-
nade, Perth, 6000, WA, Australia
Tel.: (61) 892631111
Financial Investment Services
N.A.I.C.S.: 523940

Canaccord Genuity Management
Company Limited (1)
38 Fitzwilliam Street Upper Grand Canal
Dock, Dublin, D02 KV05, Ireland
Tel.: (353) 16350210
Banking Services
N.A.I.C.S.: 523150

Canaccord Genuity SAS (1)
Washington Plaza 29 rue de Berri, 75008,
Paris, France
Tel.: (33) 156696666
Banking Services
N.A.I.C.S.: 523150

Canaccord Genuity SG Pte. Ltd. (1)
Six Battery Road Level 42, Singapore,
049909, Singapore
Tel.: (65) 62322187
Banking Services
N.A.I.C.S.: 523150

Canaccord Genuity Wealth (Interna-
tional) Limited (1)
Trafalgar Court Admiral Park, Saint Peter
Port, GY1 2JA, Guernsey
Tel.: (44) 1481733900
Banking Services
N.A.I.C.S.: 523150

Finlogik Inc. (1)
360 Saint-Jacques W Suite S-120, Mon-
treal, H2Y 1P5, QC, Canada
Tel.: (514) 938-8448
Web Site: http://www.finlogik.com
Software Services
N.A.I.C.S.: 541511

Jitneytrade Inc. (1)
360 Saint-Jacques St Suite G-102, Mon-
treal, H2Y 1P5, QC, Canada
Tel.: (416) 869-7368
Web Site: http://mybusinessmigration.com
Financial Services
N.A.I.C.S.: 523999

Petsky Prunier, LLC (1)
33 Whitehall St Fl 27, New York, NY 10004
Tel.: (212) 842-6020
Web Site: http://www.petskyprunier.com
Management Consulting Services
N.A.I.C.S.: 541611
Michael Petsky (Mng Dir)

CANACOL ENERGY LTD.
Suite 2000 215 9 Ave SW, Calgary,
T2P 1K3, AB, Canada
Tel.: (403) 561-1648   AB
Web Site:
https://www.canacolenergy.com
3B6—(DEU)
Rev.: $315,803,000

Assets: $1,233,428,000
Liabilities: $881,754,000
Net Worth: $351,674,000
Earnings: $86,237,000
Emp.: 396
Fiscal Year-end: 12/31/23
Oil & Gas Exploration Services
N.A.I.C.S.: 211120
Michael John Hibberd (Chm)

CANADA CARBON INC.
The Canadian Venture Building 82
Richmond Street East, Toronto, M5C
1P1, ON, Canada
Tel.: (905) 407-1212   Ca
Web Site:
https://www.canadacarbon.com
Year Founded: 1985
BRUZF—(OTCIQ)
Assets: $6,586,648
Liabilities: $957,552
Net Worth: $5,629,097
Earnings: $740,571
Fiscal Year-end: 12/31/22
Carbon Exploration Services
N.A.I.C.S.: 212290
R. Bruce Duncan (Chm)

CANADA CARTAGE CORPO-RATION.
1115 Cardiff Blvd, Mississauga, L5S
1L8, ON, Canada
Tel.: (800) 268-2228
Web Site:
https://www.canadacartage.com
Year Founded: 1914
GBUX—(OTC)
Emp.: 1,432
Truck Transportation
N.A.I.C.S.: 488999

CANADA COAL INC.
5213 Durie Rd, Mississauga, L5M
2C6, ON, Canada
Tel.: (604) 685-6375   ON
Web Site:
http://www.canadacoal.com
Year Founded: 2012
CCK—(TSXV)
Assets: $1,365,623
Liabilities: $18,683
Net Worth: $1,346,940
Earnings: ($222,817)
Fiscal Year-end: 09/30/19
Coal Exploration, Development &
Mining
N.A.I.C.S.: 213113
R. Bruce Duncan (Pres & CEO)

CANADA COMPUTATIONAL UNLIMITED CORP.
289 Dugas, Joliette, J6E 4H1, QC,
Canada
Tel.: (450) 756-3636   ON
Web Site: https://bysato.com
Year Founded: 2008
CCPUF—(OTCQB)
Rev.: $13,260,403
Assets: $16,373,839
Liabilities: $11,374,634
Net Worth: $4,999,205
Earnings: $586,348
Fiscal Year-end: 12/31/23
Investment Services
N.A.I.C.S.: 523999
Yvan Routhier (CEO)

CANADA CORDAGE, INC.
70 Dundas Street, Deseronto, K0K
1X0, ON, Canada
Tel.: (519) 745-7391   ON
Web Site:
http://www.canadacordage.com
Year Founded: 1978
Sales Range: $25-49.9 Million
Emp.: 100

Canada Cordage, Inc.—(Continued)

Rope Mfr & Distr
N.A.I.C.S.: 314994
Clement J. Girard *(VP-Sls)*

Subsidiaries:

Orion Ropeworks, Inc. **(1)**
953 Benton Ave, Winslow, ME 04901
Tel.: (000) 507-7073
Web Site: http://www.orionropeworks.com
Emp.: 60
Rope & Cordage Mfr
N.A.I.C.S.: 314994
Floyd Kierstead *(VP-Indus Products)*

CANADA DRUGS LTD.
24 Terracon Pl, Winnipeg, R2J 4G7,
MB, Canada
Tel.: (204) 654-5194
Web Site:
http://www.canadadrugs.com
Year Founded: 2001
Sales Range: $25-49.9 Million
Emp.: 250
Online & Mail Order Pharmacy
N.A.I.C.S.: 456110
Kris Thorkelson *(Founder & Pres)*

CANADA ENERGY PARTNERS INC.
650-669 Howe Street, Vancouver,
V6C 0B4, BC, Canada
Tel.: (520) 668-4101 **BC**
Year Founded: 2006
CE.H—(TSXV)
Assets: $143,328
Liabilities: $288,825
Net Worth: ($145,497)
Earnings: $143,015
Fiscal Year-end: 04/30/21
Natural Gas Exploration & Development Services
N.A.I.C.S.: 213112
Ricardo A. Chona *(Sr Engr)*

CANADA FORGINGS INC.
130 Hagar St, PO Box 308, Station
Main, Welland, L3B 5P8, ON,
Canada
Tel.: (905) 735-1220
Web Site: http://www.canforge.com
Year Founded: 1912
Sales Range: $10-24.9 Million
Emp.: 115
Open & Closed Die Forgings &
Seamless Rolled Rings Mfr
N.A.I.C.S.: 332111
G. Guilbeault *(Pres)*

CANADA GARDENWORKS LTD.
6250 Lougheed Hwy, Burnaby, V5B
2Z9, BC, Canada
Tel.: (604) 299-0621
Web Site:
https://www.gardenworks.ca
Year Founded: 1984
Rev.: $12,757,336
Emp.: 260
Garden & Floral Stores
N.A.I.C.S.: 444240
Michelle Martin *(CFO)*

CANADA GLOBAL (T.R) LTD
Moshe Aviv Tower 47th Floor 7 Jabotinsky Street, Ramat Gan, Israel
Tel.: (972) 37533214
Web Site: http://avivarlon.com
Year Founded: 2007
AVLN—(TAE)
Rev.: $2,169
Assets: $6,720,351
Liabilities: $110,352
Net Worth: $6,609,999
Earnings: ($8,924,136)
Fiscal Year-end: 12/31/22

Real Estate Manangement Services
N.A.I.C.S.: 531390
Eyal Lev-Ari *(Co-CEO)*

CANADA HOUSE WELLNESS GROUP INC.
1773 Bayly Street, Pickering, L1W
2Y7, ON, Canada **Ca**
Web Site: https://canadahouse.ca
CHV—(CNSX)
Rev.: $8,260,877
Assets: $28,938,102
Liabilities: $23,561,491
Net Worth: $5,376,610
Earnings: ($8,890,612)
Fiscal Year-end: 04/30/21
Holding Company; Medical Marijuana
Purveyor
N.A.I.C.S.: 551112
Paul Hart *(CFO)*

Subsidiaries:

Abba Medix Corp. **(1)**
1773 Bayly Street, Pickering, L1W 2Y7,
ON, Canada
Tel.: (416) 548-2420
Web Site: http://www.abbamedix.com
Sales Range: Less than $1 Million
Medical Marijuana Purveyor
N.A.I.C.S.: 111998

CANADA IRON INC.
170 University Ave Ste 900, Toronto,
M5H 3B3, ON, Canada
Tel.: (416) 346-1008 **ON**
Web Site:
http://www.canadaironinc.com
Mineral Resource Company Engaged
in the Acquisition, Exploration & Development of Quality Iron Ore
N.A.I.C.S.: 212210
Gary Handley *(Pres & CEO)*

CANADA LAND LIMITED
15/F Yat Chau Building 262 Des
Voeux Road, Central, China (Hong
Kong)
Tel.: (852) 28544333 **HK**
Web Site:
http://www.canadaland.com.hk
Year Founded: 1972
Sales Range: $1-9.9 Million
Emp.: 110
Real Estate Operations
N.A.I.C.S.: 531210
William Shue Lam Yip *(Chm)*

CANADA LANDS COMPANY LIMITED
1 University Ave Suite 1700, Toronto,
M5J 2P1, ON, Canada
Tel.: (416) 214-1250
Web Site: https://www.clc-sic.ca
Year Founded: 1956
Sales Range: $150-199.9 Million
Emp.: 100
Offices of Bank Holding Companies
N.A.I.C.S.: 551111
Robert A Howald *(Exec VP-Real Estate)*

CANADA MORTGAGE & HOUSING CORPORATION
700 Montreal Road, Ottawa, K1A
0P7, ON, Canada
Tel.: (613) 748-2000 **Ca**
Web Site: http://www.cmhc-schl.gc.ca
Year Founded: 1946
Rev.: $3,880,343,180
Assets: $193,413,191,720
Liabilities: $182,505,865,150
Net Worth: $10,907,326,570
Earnings: $1,038,618,490
Emp.: 1,900
Fiscal Year-end: 12/31/18
Mortgage Financing Services
N.A.I.C.S.: 522310

Evan W. Siddall *(Pres & CEO)*

CANADA NICKEL COMPANY, INC.
130 King Street West Suite 1900,
Toronto, M5X 1E3, ON, Canada
Tel.: (647) 256-1954
Web Site:
http://www.canadanickel.com
CNIKF—(OTCQX)
Assets: $112,894,672
Liabilities: $19,937,620
Net Worth: $92,957,052
Earnings: ($4,329,982)
Fiscal Year-end: 10/31/22
Metal Mining Services
N.A.I.C.S.: 212290
Mark Selby *(Chm & CEO)*

CANADA ONE MINING CORP.
Suite 250 - 750 West Pender Street,
Vancouver, V6C 2T7, BC, Canada
Tel.: (604) 313-4064 **BC**
Year Founded: 1979
CONE—(TSXV)
Assets: $213,959
Liabilities: $795,593
Net Worth: ($581,634)
Earnings: ($290,877)
Fiscal Year-end: 07/31/23
Gold & Uranium Exploration Services
N.A.I.C.S.: 212220
Michael Kinley *(CFO & Dir)*

CANADA PENSION PLAN INVESTMENT BOARD
One Queen Street East Suite 2500,
Toronto, M5C 2W5, ON, Canada
Tel.: (416) 868-4075 **Ca**
Web Site:
https://www.cppinvestments.com
Year Founded: 1997
Rev.: $25,856,249,720
Assets: $366,404,373,300
Liabilities: $79,094,792,700
Net Worth: $287,309,580,600
Earnings: $23,462,369,700
Emp.: 1,661
Fiscal Year-end: 03/31/19
Professional Investment Management
Services
N.A.I.C.S.: 524292
Edwin D. Cass *(Sr Mng Dir & Chief Investment Officer)*

Subsidiaries:

99 Cents Only Stores LLC **(1)**
4000 Union Pacific Ave, City of Commerce,
CA 90023
Tel.: (323) 980-8145
Web Site: https://www.99only.com
Sales Range: $1-4.9 Billion
Emp.: 17,000
All Other General Merchandise Retailers
N.A.I.C.S.: 455219

Air System Components, Inc. **(1)**
605 Shiloh Rd, Plano, TX 75074
Tel.: (972) 212-4888
Web Site: http://www.airsysco.com
Sales Range: $100-124.9 Million
Emp.: 300
Heating Air Conditioning & Ventilation System Component Mfr
N.A.I.C.S.: 333415

Unit (Domestic):

PennBarry **(2)**
605 Shiloh Rd, Plano, TX 75074
Tel.: (972) 212-4700
Web Site: http://www.pennbarry.com
Ventilators & Air-Moving Equipment Mfr
N.A.I.C.S.: 333415
Vince Snyder *(VP)*

Titus **(2)**
605 Shiloh Rd, Plano, TX 75074
Tel.: (972) 212-4800
Web Site: http://www.titus-hvac.com

Sales Range: $25-49.9 Million
Emp.: 60
Architectural & Ornamental Metal Work Mfr
N.A.I.C.S.: 493110
Keith Glasch *(VP-Sls & Mktg)*

Anglian Water Group Limited **(1)**
Lancaster House Lancaster Way Ermine
Business Park, Huntingdon, PE29 6XU,
Cambs, United Kingdom **(32.9%)**
Tel.: (44) 1480323000
Web Site: https://www.awg.com
Sales Range: $1-4.9 Billion
Emp.: 5,967
Holding Company; Water Supply, Sewerage
& Property Development Services
N.A.I.C.S.: 551112
Stephen Billingham *(Chm)*

Subsidiary (Domestic):

AWG Property Limited **(2)**
47 Melville Street, Edinburgh, EH4 7HL,
United Kingdom
Tel.: (44) 01313431000
Web Site: http://www.awgproperty.co.uk
Sales Range: $50-74.9 Million
Emp.: 30
Commercial & Residential Property Investment & Development
N.A.I.C.S.: 531390
Tony Donnelly *(Chm)*

Anglian Water Services Limited **(2)**
Lancaster House Lancaster Way Ermine
Business Park, Huntingdon, PE29 6XU,
Cambridgeshire, United Kingdom
Tel.: (44) 3457919155
Web Site: https://www.anglianwater.co.uk
Rev.: $1,719,141,394
Assets: $14,320,002,386
Liabilities: $12,272,438,616
Net Worth: $2,047,563,770
Earnings: ($41,623,856)
Emp.: 4,764
Fiscal Year-end: 03/31/2019
Water Supply Distribution & Sewerage Services
N.A.I.C.S.: 221310
Peter Simpson *(CEO & Member-Mgmt Bd)*

Antares Capital LP **(1)**
500 W Monroe St, Chicago, IL 60661
Tel.: (312) 638-4000
Web Site: http://www.antares.com
Specialty Corporate Financing Services
N.A.I.C.S.: 523999
Daniel L. Barry *(Sr Mng Dir)*

Arqiva Limited **(1)**
Crawley Ct, Winchester, SO21 2QA, United
Kingdom
Tel.: (44) 1962823434
Web Site: http://www.arqiva.com
Mobile Communication & Wireless Services
N.A.I.C.S.: 517112
Sean West *(CFO)*

Branch (Domestic):

Arqiva Limited **(2)**
Wireless House Warwick Technology Park,
Warwick, CV34 6DD, United Kingdom
Tel.: (44) 1926416000
Web Site: http://www.arqiva.com
Sales Range: $500-549.9 Million
Emp.: 250
Mobile Telecommunication Infrastructure
Services
N.A.I.C.S.: 517112

Affiliate (Domestic):

Digital One Ltd. **(2)**
30 Leicester Square, London, WC2H 7LA,
United Kingdom
Tel.: (44) 2072998670
Web Site: http://www.ukdigitalradio.com
Sales Range: $25-49.9 Million
Emp.: 6
Digital Radio Broadcasting
N.A.I.C.S.: 516210

Ascend Learning, LLC **(1)**
25 Mall Rd 6th Fl, Burlington, MA 01803
Tel.: (855) 856-7705
Web Site: https://www.ascendlearning.com
Holding Company; Education & Professional Assessment, Training & Certification
Products & Services
N.A.I.C.S.: 551112

Greg Sebasky *(CEO)*

Subsidiary (Domestic):

Assessment Technologies Institute, LLC   **(2)**
11161 Overbrook Rd, Leawood, KS 66211
Tel.: (913) 685-2740
Web Site: https://www.atitesting.com
Nursing Professional Testing Preparation &
Education Support Services
N.A.I.C.S.: 611430
Ada Woo *(VP)*

Subsidiary (Domestic):

MedHub, LLC   **(3)**
510 Marquette Ave S 3rd Fl, Minneapolis,
MN 55402
Tel.: (612) 253-0130
Web Site: https://www.medhub.com
Healthcare Education Program Management Software Publisher
N.A.I.C.S.: 513210

Subsidiary (Domestic):

ClickSafety.com, Inc.   **(2)**
25 Mall Rd, Burlington, MA 01803
Tel.: (800) 971-1080
Web Site: https://www.clicksafety.com
Online Compliance Course Interactive
Training Services
N.A.I.C.S.: 611430

Jones & Bartlett Learning, LLC   **(2)**
25 Mall Rd, Burlington, MA 01803
Tel.: (978) 443-5000
Web Site: https://www.jblearning.com
Instructional, Assessment & Educational
Books Publisher
N.A.I.C.S.: 513130

Asciano Limited   **(1)**
Level 4 476 St Kilda Road, Melbourne,
3004, VIC, Australia
Tel.: (61) 3 92487000
Web Site: http://www.asciano.com.au
Sales Range: $1-4.9 Billion
Ports & Rail Assets Management
N.A.I.C.S.: 485112
Roger Burrows *(CFO)*

Joint Venture (Non-US):

C3 Limited   **(2)**
58 Cross Road Sulphur Point, Tauranga,
3110, New Zealand
Tel.: (64) 75728972
Web Site: https://www.c3.co.nz
Emp.: 800
Marine Cargo Handling Services
N.A.I.C.S.: 488320
Chris Sutherland *(Gen Mgr-Logistics-New Zealand)*

Homeplus Co., Limited   **(1)**
398 Hwagokoro, Gangseo-gu, Seoul, 135-080, Korea (South)   **(21.5%)**
Tel.: (82) 234598000
Web Site: http://www.homeplus.co.kr
Hypermarkets, Supermarkets & Convenience Stores Operator & Franchisor
N.A.I.C.S.: 445110
Sang Hyun Kim *(CEO)*

Hotelbeds Group, S.L.U.   **(1)**
Camino de Son Fangos 100 Complejo Mirall Balear Tower A 5 andar 6A-7A, 07007,
Palma de Mallorca, Spain
Tel.: (34) 971 178 800
Web Site: http://group.hotelbeds.com
Holding Company; Online Wholesale & Retail Travel Agency
N.A.I.C.S.: 551112
Sam Turner *(Dir-Wholesale Sls & Sourcing)*

Subsidiary (Non-US):

HotelBeds Hong Kong Limited   **(2)**
Room 1029-1032 Star House 3 Salisbury
Road, Tsim Sha Tsui, Kowloon, China
(Hong Kong)
Tel.: (852) 21129998
Web Site: http://www.hotelbeds.com
Travel & Tour Accommodation Services
N.A.I.C.S.: 561520
Annie Cheung *(Mgr-Fin)*

Hotelbeds Pte. Ltd.   **(2)**
101 Thomson Road #16-01 United Square,
Singapore, 307591, Singapore
Tel.: (65) 63306666
Web Site: http://www.pacificworld.com
Travel & Tour Accommodation Services
N.A.I.C.S.: 561520

Subsidiary (Domestic):

Hotelbeds Spain, S.L.U.   **(2)**
Complejo Mirall Balear Cami de Son Fangos 100 Torre A 5 Planta, 07007, Palma de
Mallorca, Spain
Tel.: (34) 971 211601
Web Site: http://checkpickup.com
Travel & Tour Accommodation Services
N.A.I.C.S.: 561599

Hotelopia SL   **(2)**
Complex Mirall Balear Cami de Son Fangos
100 Torre A 5a Planta, CP 07007, Palma de
Mallorca, Spain
Tel.: (34) 902 430 419
Web Site: http://www.hotelopia.com
Hotel Operator
N.A.I.C.S.: 721110

Subsidiary (US):

Intercruises Shoreside & Port Services Inc.   **(2)**
711 12th Ave, New York, NY 10019
Tel.: (212) 459-9263
Web Site: http://www.intercruises.com
Ground Handling & Port Agency Services
N.A.I.C.S.: 488310
Simon O'Sullivan *(Pres-North America)*

Subsidiary (Non-US):

Intercruises Shoreside & Port Services Pty Ltd   **(2)**
Suite 101 Level 1 72 Pitt Street, Sydney,
2000, NSW, Australia
Tel.: (61) 295500047
Web Site: http://www.intercruises.com
Tour Operating Services
N.A.I.C.S.: 561520
Martin Bidgood *(Reg Dir)*

MicronNexus GmbH   **(2)**
Humboldthaus Am Sandtorkai 37, 20457,
Hamburg, Germany
Tel.: (49) 40 18 88 98 0
Web Site: http://www.carnect.com
Information Technology Consulting Services
N.A.I.C.S.: 541512
Christopher Paul Leonard *(Mng Dir)*

Subsidiary (US):

Tourico Holidays, Inc.   **(2)**
220 E Central Pkwy Ste 4000, Altamonte
Springs, FL 32701
Tel.: (407) 667-8700
Web Site: http://login.touricoholidays.com
Travel Tour Operator
N.A.I.C.S.: 561520
Uri Argov *(CEO)*

Informatica Corporation   **(1)**
2100 Seaport Blvd, Redwood City, CA
94063
Tel.: (650) 385-5000
Web Site: http://www.informatica.com
Sales Range: $1-4.9 Billion
Emp.: 3,664
Enterprise Data Integration Software & Services
N.A.I.C.S.: 513210
Charles Race *(Exec VP-Worldwide Field Ops)*

Subsidiary (Non-US):

AddressDoctor GmbH   **(2)**
Rontgenstr 9, 67133, Maxdorf, Germany
Tel.: (49) 623797740
Web Site: http://www.addressdoctor.com
Enterprise Data Integration Software Provider
N.A.I.C.S.: 541511
Earl E. Fry *(Mng Dir)*

Subsidiary (Domestic):

Compact Solutions LLC   **(2)**
1 Lincoln Ctr 18 W 140th W Butterfield Rdd
15th Fl, Oakbrook Terrace, IL 60181
Tel.: (708) 524-9500
Web Site: http://www.compactbi.com
Business Data Services

N.A.I.C.S.: 541512
Grzegorz Swietlik *(Dir-Polish Ops)*

Subsidiary (Non-US):

I.D.I. Informatica Data Integration Ltd.   **(2)**
Kiryat Atidim Bldg 8 29th Fl, Tel Aviv,
6158101, Israel
Tel.: (972) 35633600
Web Site: http://www.informatica.com
Sales Range: $25-49.9 Million
Emp.: 66
Data Integration Software Services
N.A.I.C.S.: 541511

IS Informatica Software Ltda.   **(2)**
Av Das Nacoes Unidas 12901-3 Andar,
Torre Norte Brooklin Novo, Sao Paulo,
04578-000, Brazil
Tel.: (55) 1130135446
Web Site: http://www.informatica.com
Sales Range: $25-49.9 Million
Data Integration Software Provider
N.A.I.C.S.: 541511

Group (Non-US):

Informatica Australia Pty. Ltd. - Asia/Pacific Headquarters   **(2)**
Level 5 255 George St, Sydney, 2000,
NSW, Australia
Tel.: (61) 289074400
Web Site: http://www.informatica.com
Sales Range: $75-99.9 Million
Emp.: 20
Enterprise Data Integration Software & Services
N.A.I.C.S.: 513210

Subsidiary (Non-US):

Informatica (Beijing) Information Technology Co., Ltd.   **(3)**
19F-06 E Tower Twin Towers B-12 Jian Guo
Men Wai Da Jie, Chao Yang District, Beijing, 100022, China
Tel.: (86) 1058793366
Web Site: http://www.informatica.com
Sales Range: $100-124.9 Million
Enterprise Data Integration Software & Services
N.A.I.C.S.: 513210
Wang Qun *(Pres-Greater China)*

Informatica Business Solutions Pvt. Ltd.   **(3)**
206 Navkar Chamber, MVRoad Marol Naka,
Andheri E, Mumbai, 59, India
Tel.: (91) 2240262643
Web Site: http://www.informatica.com
Sales Range: $100-124.9 Million
Enterprise Data Integration Software & Services
N.A.I.C.S.: 513210

Informatica Hong Kong   **(3)**
2/F Shui On Centre, 6-8 Harbour Road,
Wanchai, China (Hong Kong)
Tel.: (852) 28248860
Web Site: http://www.informatica.com
Sales Range: $100-124.9 Million
Enterprise Data Integration Software & Services
N.A.I.C.S.: 513210

Informatica Japan K.K   **(3)**
Sumitomo Ichigaya Bldg 1-1 Ichigaya-Honmuracho, Shinjuku-ku, Tokyo, 162-0845, Japan
Tel.: (81) 352297211
Web Site: http://www.informatica.com
Sales Range: $100-124.9 Million
Enterprise Data Integration Software & Services
N.A.I.C.S.: 513210

Informatica Korea Corporation   **(3)**
Samsung Life Insurance Yoido B/D 20F
Yoido-Dong, Youngdeungpo-Ku, Seoul, Korea (South)
Tel.: (82) 262935000
Web Site: http://www.informatica.com
Sales Range: $10-24.9 Million
Emp.: 15
Enterprise Data Integration Software & Services
N.A.I.C.S.: 513210
S. C. Choi *(Country Mgr)*

Informatica S.E.A. Pte., Ltd.   **(3)**
600 North Bridge Road, Parkview Square,
Singapore, 188778, Singapore
Tel.: (65) 63966679
Web Site: http://www.informatica.com
Sales Range: $25-49.9 Million
Emp.: 25
Enterprise Data Integration Software & Services
N.A.I.C.S.: 513210

Informatica Taiwan Co. Ltd.   **(3)**
Dunhua S Rd, Taipei, 105, Taiwan
Tel.: (886) 225770257
Web Site: http://www.informatica.com
Sales Range: $100-124.9 Million
Emp.: 25
Enterprise Data Integration Software & Services
N.A.I.C.S.: 513210

Subsidiary (Non-US):

Informatica International do Brazil Ltd. - Latin America Region Headquarters   **(2)**
Av Das Nacoes Unidas 12901 - 3 Andar
Torre Norte, Brooklin Novo, Sao Paulo,
04578-000, Brazil
Tel.: (55) 1130135446
Web Site: http://www.informatica.com
Sales Range: $100-124.9 Million
Emp.: 30
Enterprise Data Integration Software & Services
N.A.I.C.S.: 513210

Branch (Domestic):

Informatica - Rio de Janeiro   **(3)**
Praia de Botafogo 501 1 andar, Torre Pao
de Azucar, 22250-040, Rio de Janeiro, Brazil
Tel.: (55) 2125866091
Web Site: http://www.informatica.com
Sales Range: $100-124.9 Million
Emp.: 10
Enterprise Data Integration Software & Services
N.A.I.C.S.: 513210

Subsidiary (Non-US):

Informatica Software Services de Mexico S.A. de C.V.   **(3)**
Blvd Manuel Avila Camacho No 36, Piso 10
Lomas de Chapultepec, 11000, Mexico,
Mexico
Tel.: (52) 5591721463
Web Site: http://www.informatica.com
Sales Range: $25-49.9 Million
Emp.: 50
Enterprise Data Integration Software & Services
N.A.I.C.S.: 513210

Group (Non-US):

Informatica Nederland B.V. - EMEA Headquarters   **(2)**
Edisonbaan 14A, 3439 MN, Nieuwegein,
Netherlands
Tel.: (31) 306086700
Web Site: http://www.informatica.com
Sales Range: $100-124.9 Million
Emp.: 55
Enterprise Data Integration Software & Services
N.A.I.C.S.: 513210

Subsidiary (Non-US):

Informatica CZ, s.r.o.   **(3)**
Krehova 439/13, 162 00, Prague, 6, Czech
Republic
Tel.: (420) 235010244
Web Site: http://www.informatica.cz
Sales Range: $100-124.9 Million
Emp.: 10
Enterprise Data Integration Software & Services
N.A.I.C.S.: 513210
Radek Stastny *(Mng Dir)*

Informatica France S.A.S.   **(3)**
Tour CB 21 16 Place de l'Iris, rue Du General Leclerc, Paris, 92800, France
Tel.: (33) 141389200
Web Site: http://www.informatica.com
Rev.: $13,100,000

Canada Pension Plan Investment
Board—(Continued)

Emp.: 50
Enterprise Data Integration Software & Services
N.A.I.C.S.: 513210

Informatica GmbH　　(3)
Lyoner Strasse 15, 60528, Frankfurt, Germany
Tel.: (49) 699288090
Web Site: http://www.informatica.com
Sales Range: $100-124.9 Million
Enterprise Data Integration Software & Services
N.A.I.C.S.: 513210

Informatica Ireland Limited　　(3)
George's Quay House Townsend St, Dublin, 2, Ireland
Tel.: (353) 14004900
Web Site: http://www.informatica.com
Sales Range: $75-99.9 Million
Emp.: 50
Data Quality Software & Support Services
N.A.I.C.S.: 518210

Informatica Middle East FZ-LLC　　(3)
Al-Shatha Tower 2407, Dubai Internet City, Dubai, United Arab Emirates
Tel.: (971) 4 3642960
Web Site: http://www.informatica.com
Sales Range: $100-124.9 Million
Enterprise Data Integration Software & Services
N.A.I.C.S.: 513210

Informatica Software (Schweiz) AG　　(3)
Dreikonigstrasse 31A, 8002, Zurich, Switzerland
Tel.: (41) 432155600
Web Site: http://www.informatica.com
Sales Range: $100-124.9 Million
Enterprise Data Integration Software & Services
N.A.I.C.S.: 513210

Informatica Software Italia S.r.l.　　(3)
Via Conca del Naviglio 18, Milan, 20123, Italy
Tel.: (39) 0289827360
Web Site: http://www.informatica.com
Sales Range: $100-124.9 Million
Enterprise Data Integration Software & Services
N.A.I.C.S.: 513210

Informatica Software Ltd.　　(3)
6 Waltham Park Waltham Road, White Waltham, Maidenhead, SL6 3TN, Berkshire, United Kingdom
Tel.: (44) 1628511311
Web Site: http://www.informatica.com
Sales Range: $75-99.9 Million
Emp.: 130
Enterprise Data Integration Software & Services
N.A.I.C.S.: 513210

Informatica South Africa　　(3)
Kid House 812 Hammets Crossing 2 Selborne Rd Fourways, Maroelandal Fourways, Johannesburg, 2040, South Africa
Tel.: (27) 114629676
Web Site: http://www.informatica.co.za
Sales Range: $1-9.9 Million
Emp.: 5
Enterprise Data Integration Software & Services
N.A.I.C.S.: 513210

Informatica Turkey　　(3)
Idealtepe Mah Dik Sok No15/2, 34841 Kucukyali, Istanbul, Turkiye
Tel.: (90) 216 518 4447
Web Site: http://www.informatica.com.tr
Sales Range: $100-124.9 Million
Enterprise Data Integration Software & Services
N.A.I.C.S.: 513210

Itemfield Limited　　(3)
Street 8 Kiryat Atidim Building 29th Floor, Tel Aviv, 6158101, Israel
Tel.: (972) 35633600
Web Site: http://www.informatica.com
Sales Range: $10-24.9 Million
Emp.: 65

Enterprise Data Integration Software & Services
N.A.I.C.S.: 561210

Subsidiary (Non-US):

Informatica Research and Development Center LLC　　(2)
Office 702 Building 88A Sredniy Prospect VO, 199106, Saint Petersburg, Russia
Tel.: (7) 8123209143
Web Site: http://www.informatica.com
Sales Range: $25-49.9 Million
Emp.: 55
Data Integration Software Services
N.A.I.C.S.: 541511

Informatica Software Limited　　(2)
Unit36 Level23 One Island East 8 Westlands Road, Hong Kong, China (Hong Kong)
Tel.: (852) 37507620
Web Site: http://www.informatica.com
Emp.: 100
Enterprise Data Integration Software Provider
N.A.I.C.S.: 541511

Informatica Software Ltd.　　(2)
Bankers Hall West Tower 888-3rd Street SW 10th Floor, Calgary, T2P 5C5, AB, Canada
Tel.: (403) 668-6000
Web Site: http://www.informatica.com
Data Migration & Consolidation & Synchronization & Warehousing Service Provider
N.A.I.C.S.: 518210

Informatica Software de Mexico S. de R.L. de C.V.　　(2)
Blvd Del Centro No 26 Ofic 14, Naucalpan, 53140, Mexico, Mexico
Tel.: (52) 5591721434
Web Site: http://www.informatica.com
Enterprise Data Integration Software Services
N.A.I.C.S.: 541511

Subsidiary (Domestic):

StrikeIron, LLC　　(2)
15501 Weston Pkwy Ste 150, Cary, NC 27513
Tel.: (919) 467-4545
Web Site: http://www.strikeiron.com
Sales Range: $1-9.9 Million
Emp.: 25
Information Technology Services
N.A.I.C.S.: 541512

WisdomForce Technologies, Inc.　　(2)
8501 SE 76th Pl, Mercer Island, WA 98040
Tel.: (206) 407-9238
Web Site: http://www.wisdomforce.com
Software Publishing Services
N.A.I.C.S.: 513210
Sohaib Abbasi *(Chm, CEO & Pres)*

Keywords Studios Plc　　(1)
Whelan House South County Business Park, Dublin, 18, Ireland
Tel.: (353) 19022730
Web Site: https://www.keywordsstudios.com
Rev.: $745,432,765
Assets: $870,610,835
Liabilities: $269,390,244
Net Worth: $601,220,591
Earnings: $51,122,383
Emp.: 12,000
Fiscal Year-end: 12/31/2022
Video Game Technical Services
N.A.I.C.S.: 541990
Ross Graham *(Chm)*

Subsidiary (Non-US):

AMC RO Studios S.R.L.　　(2)
36 Stirbei Voda St 1st Floor DOMUS I Building, 1st District, 010113, Bucharest, Romania
Tel.: (40) 752219585
Web Site: https://amcstudio.ro
Digital Art Design Services
N.A.I.C.S.: 541430

Babel Media India Private Limited　　(2)
D-32 Infocity 2 Sector-33, Gurgaon, 122001, Haryana, India
Tel.: (91) 1244410482

Web Site: https://www.babelmedia.com
Outsourced Services
N.A.I.C.S.: 541214

Babel Media Limited　　(2)
4th Floor 110 High Holborn, London, WC1V 6JS, United Kingdom
Tel.: (44) 1273764100
Web Site: https://www.babelmedia.com
Video Game Technical Services
N.A.I.C.S.: 541990

Binari Sonori S.r.l.　　(2)
Viale Fulvio Testi 11, Cinisello Balsamo, 20092, Milan, Italy
Tel.: (39) 0261866310
Web Site: https://binarisonori.info
Audio Production Services
N.A.I.C.S.: 512240

Subsidiary (US):

Binari Sonori America Inc.　　(3)
350 N Glenoaks Blvd, Burbank, CA 91502
Tel.: (818) 729-8508
Video Game Technical Services
N.A.I.C.S.: 541990
Kirk Lambert *(Pres & Mgr-Ops)*

Subsidiary (US):

Blindlight LLC　　(2)
8335 Sunset Blvd, West Hollywood, CA 90069
Tel.: (323) 337-9090
Web Site: http://www.blindlight.com
Motion Picture Services
N.A.I.C.S.: 512110

Subsidiary (Non-US):

Cord Worldwide Ltd.　　(2)
4th Floor 110 High Holborn, London, WC1V 6JS, United Kingdom
Tel.: (44) 2035975350
Web Site: https://www.cordww.com
Musical Troop Services
N.A.I.C.S.: 711130

Descriptive Video Works Inc.　　(2)
147 W 3rd Avenue, Vancouver, V5Y 1E6, BC, Canada
Web Site: https://descriptivevideoworks.com
Entertainment & Studio Services
N.A.I.C.S.: 512110

Subsidiary (US):

GameSim, Inc.　　(2)
13501 Ingenuity Dr, Orlando, FL 32826
Tel.: (407) 688-0587
Web Site: http://www.gamesim.com
Game Development & Terrain Databases
N.A.I.C.S.: 513210
Derek Minton *(CTO)*

Heavy Iron Studios, Inc.　　(2)
1600 Rosecrans Ave Bldg 7 Ste 300, Manhattan Beach, CA 90266
Tel.: (310) 216-7703
Web Site: http://www.heavyiron.games
Motion Picture & Video Production
N.A.I.C.S.: 512110
Lyle Hall *(VP)*

High Voltage Software, Inc.　　(2)
2345 Pembroke Ave, Hoffman Estates, IL 60169
Tel.: (847) 490-9567
Web Site: https://www.high-voltage.com
Entertainment & Studio Services
N.A.I.C.S.: 512110

Subsidiary (Non-US):

Indigo Pearl Limited　　(2)
Indigo Pearl Keywords Studios 4th Floor 110 High Holborn, London, WC1V 6JS, United Kingdom
Tel.: (44) 2089644545
Web Site: https://www.indigopearl.com
Entertainment & Studio Services
N.A.I.C.S.: 512110

Jinglebell S.r.l.　　(2)
Via Marco d Oggiono 12, 20123, Milan, Italy
Tel.: (39) 028331141
Web Site: https://jinglebell.com
Entertainment & Studio Services
N.A.I.C.S.: 512110

Keywords International Co. Limited　　(2)
2F Toshin Building 4-33-10 Yoyogi, Shibuya-ku, Tokyo, 151-0053, Japan
Tel.: (81) 3 4588 6760
Video Game Technical Services
N.A.I.C.S.: 541990

Keywords International Corporation Inc.　　(2)
410 St-Nicolas Suite 600, Montreal, H2Y 2P5, QC, Canada
Tel.: (514) 789-0404
Video Game Technical Services
N.A.I.C.S.: 541990

Subsidiary (US):

Keywords International Inc.　　(2)
Plz Ctr 10900 NE 8th St Ste 1000 Bellevue, Seattle, WA 98004
Tel.: (425) 633-3226
Video Game Technical Services
N.A.I.C.S.: 541990

Subsidiary (Non-US):

Keywords International Pte. Limited　　(2)
20 Kallang Avenue 06-6A Lobby B Pico Creative Centre, Singapore, 339411, Singapore
Tel.: (65) 67098680
Emp.: 50
Video Game Technical Services
N.A.I.C.S.: 541990

Keywords Italia Srl　　(2)
Viale delle Province 2, 00162, Rome, Italy
Tel.: (39) 06 44 20 25 21
Web Site: http://www.keywordsintl.it
Video Game Technical Services
N.A.I.C.S.: 541990

Subsidiary (US):

Liquid Development LLC　　(2)
4200 Montrose Blvd 300, Houston, TX 77006
Tel.: (713) 521-9574
Web Site: http://www.liquiddev.com
Computer System Design Services
N.A.I.C.S.: 541512

Subsidiary (Non-US):

Liquid Violet Limited　　(2)
1st Floor 39 Earlham Street, London, WC2H 9LT, United Kingdom
Tel.: (44) 2039590770
Web Site: https://www.liquidviolet.co.uk
Audio Production Services
N.A.I.C.S.: 512240

Maverick Media Limited　　(2)
110 High Holborn, London, WC1V 6JS, United Kingdom
Tel.: (44) 2072913450
Web Site: https://maverickmedia.co.uk
Emp.: 12,000
Video Games Design & Development Services
N.A.I.C.S.: 512110

SPOV Ltd.　　(2)
4th Floor 110 High Holborn, London, WC1V 6JS, United Kingdom
Tel.: (44) 2077395862
Motion Picture Services
N.A.I.C.S.: 512110

Snowed In Studios, Inc.　　(2)
250 City Centre Ave, Ottawa, K1R 6K7, ON, Canada
Tel.: (613) 656-3372
Web Site: https://www.snowedin.ca
Video Game Design Services
N.A.I.C.S.: 532282

TV+SYNCHRON Berlin GmbH　　(2)
Moriz Seeler Str 5-7 Franz Ehrlich Haus, 12489, Berlin, Germany
Tel.: (49) 30677749415
Web Site: https://tv-synchron.de
Recording Studio Services
N.A.I.C.S.: 512240

Tantalus Media Pty. Limited　　(2)
12 Spring Street, Fitzroy, 3065, VIC, Australia
Tel.: (61) 396940900

Web Site: https://www.tantalus.com.au
Video Games Design & Development Services
N.A.I.C.S.: 512110

The TrailerFarm Limited **(2)**
Lees Housethird Floor West 22 - 33 Dyke Road, Brighton, BN1 3FE, United Kingdom
Tel.: (44) 1273329727
Web Site: https://thetrailerfarm.com
Video Game Design Services
N.A.I.C.S.: 532282

Subsidiary (US):

VMC Consulting Corporation **(2)**
11601 Willows Rd NE, Redmond, WA 98052 **(100%)**
Tel.: (425) 558-7700
Web Site: http://www.vmc.com
Quality Assurance, Localization & Support Services
N.A.I.C.S.: 541614

Subsidiary (Non-US):

Wizcorp Inc. **(2)**
Higashi-Nihonbashi 3-10-14 Sunrise Tachibana 6F, Chuo-ku, Tokyo, 103-0004, Japan
Tel.: (81) 34 550 1448
Web Site: https://www.wizcorp.jp
Sales Range: $1-9.9 Million
Emp.: 35
Mobile Application Development Services
N.A.I.C.S.: 541511
Guillaume Hansali (Founder & CEO)

d3t Ltd. **(2)**
Daresbury Point Greenwood Drive, Manor Park, Runcorn, WA7 1UG, Cheshire, United Kingdom
Tel.: (44) 1928575742
Web Site: https://www.d3tltd.com
Scientific & Technical Services
N.A.I.C.S.: 541990

Koch Filter Corporation **(1)**
625 W Hill St, Louisville, KY 40208
Tel.: (502) 634-4796
Web Site: http://www.kochfilter.com
Sales Range: $25-49.9 Million
Emp.: 250
Air Filter & Filtration Products Mfr
N.A.I.C.S.: 333413
Kim Trusty (Mgr-Customer Svc)

Neiman Marcus Group, Inc. **(1)**
1618 Main St, Dallas, TX 75201
Tel.: (214) 741-6911
Web Site: https://www.neimanmarcus.com
Sales Range: $1-4.9 Billion
Emp.: 10,000
Offices of Other Holding Companies
N.A.I.C.S.: 551112
T. Dale Stapleton (Chief Acctg Officer & Sr VP)

Subsidiary (Domestic):

Neiman Marcus Group LTD LLC **(2)**
1 Marcus Sq1618 Main St, Dallas, TX 75201
Tel.: (214) 743-7600
Web Site:
    http://www.neimanmarcusgroup.com
Rev.: $4,900,444,000
Assets: $7,545,903,000
Liabilities: $6,786,722,000
Net Worth: $759,181,000
Earnings: $251,131,000
Emp.: 13,500
Fiscal Year-end: 07/28/2018
Holding Company; Online & Specialty Store Fashion & Gift Retailer
N.A.I.C.S.: 551112
David B. Kaplan (Chm)

Subsidiary (Domestic):

Bergdorf Goodman, Inc. **(3)**
754 5th Ave, New York, NY 10019
Tel.: (212) 753-7300
Web Site:
    https://www.bergdorfgoodman.com
Sales Range: $150-199.9 Million
Men's & Women's Clothing Retailer
N.A.I.C.S.: 458110
Darcy Penick (Pres)

Unit (Domestic):

Neiman Marcus Stores **(3)**
1618 Main St, Dallas, TX 75201
Tel.: (214) 741-6911
Web Site: http://www.neimanmarcus.com
Sales Range: $1-4.9 Billion
Speciality Retailing Men's, Women's & Children's Clothing & Accessories
N.A.I.C.S.: 455110
Tim Adair (VP & Gen Mgr)

Nord Anglia Education, Inc. **(1)**
Level 12 St George's Building 2 Ice House Street, Central, China (Hong Kong)
Tel.: (852) 39511100
Web Site:
    http://www.nordangliaeducation.com
Holding Company; Private Elementary & Secondary Schools Operator
N.A.I.C.S.: 551112
Andrew Fitzmaurice (CEO)

Subsidiary (Non-US):

Nord Anglia Education Limited **(2)**
St Clements House 27-28 Lane, London, EC4N 7AE, United Kingdom
Tel.: (44) 2075319696
Web Site: http://www.nordanglia.com
Holding Company; Education Services
N.A.I.C.S.: 551112
Andrew Fitzmaurice (CEO)

Subsidiary (Non-US):

English International School Prague **(3)**
Brunelova 960/12, 14200, Prague, Czech Republic
Tel.: (420) 272181911
Web Site:
    http://www.nordangliaeducation.com
Colleges Universities & Professional Schools
N.A.I.C.S.: 611310
Mel Curtis (Principal)

Subsidiary (US):

IMG Academy, LLC **(3)**
5650 Bollettieri Blvd, Bradenton, FL 34210
Tel.: (941) 749-8660
Web Site: https://www.imgacademy.com
Boarding School Services
N.A.I.C.S.: 611110

Subsidiary (Non-US):

The British International School Bratislava **(3)**
J Valastana Dolinskeho 1, 84102, Bratislava, Slovakia
Tel.: (421) 269307081
Web Site:
    http://www.nordangliaeducation.com
Colleges Universities & Professional Schools
N.A.I.C.S.: 611310
Barbara Kanclerova (Bus Mgr)

The British International School Budapest **(3)**
Kiscelli Koz 17, Budapest, 1037, Hungary
Tel.: (36) 12009971
Web Site:
    http://www.nordangliaeducation.com
Colleges Universities & Professional Schools
N.A.I.C.S.: 611310
Eszter Valko (Bus Mgr)

The British International School Shanghai **(3)**
Puxi Campus No 111 Jinguang Road, Huacao Town Minhang, 201107, Shanghai, China
Tel.: (86) 2152263211
Web Site:
    http://www.nordangliaeducation.com
Colleges Universities & Professional Schools
N.A.I.C.S.: 611310
Neil Hopkin (Principal)

The British School Sp. z o.o. **(3)**
ul Limanowskiego 15, 02943, Warsaw, Poland
Tel.: (48) 228423281

Web Site:
    http://www.nordangliaeducation.com
Colleges Universities & Professional Schools
N.A.I.C.S.: 561499
Alun Yorath (Principal)

Pattern Energy Group LP **(1)**
1088 Sansome St, San Francisco, CA 94111
Tel.: (415) 283-4000
Web Site: http://www.patternenergy.com
Rev.: $541,000,000
Assets: $7,173,000,000
Liabilities: $4,589,000,000
Net Worth: $2,584,000,000
Earnings: ($31,000,000)
Emp.: 228
Fiscal Year-end: 12/31/2019
Wind Power
N.A.I.C.S.: 221115
Barry E. Davis (Chm)

Subsidiary (Domestic):

Hatchet Ridge Wind, LLC **(2)**
1 Pier Ste 3, San Francisco, CA 94111-2028
Tel.: (415) 283-4000
Wind Electric Power Generation Services
N.A.I.C.S.: 221115

Subsidiary (Non-US):

Mont Sainte-Marguerite Wind Farm L.P. **(2)**
226 Rue de l eglise St-Severin, Quebec, G0N 1V0, QC, Canada
Tel.: (418) 426-3838
Wind Electric Power Mfr
N.A.I.C.S.: 333611

Petco Holdings, Inc. **(1)**
10850 Via Frontera, San Diego, CA 92127
Tel.: (858) 453-7845
Web Site: http://www.petco.com
Sales Range: $1-4.9 Billion
Emp.: 17,000
Holding Company; Pet Food, Supplies & Services Retailer
N.A.I.C.S.: 551112
Justin Tichy (Chief Stores Officer)

Subsidiary (Domestic):

Petco Animal Supplies, Inc. **(2)**
10850 Via Frontera, San Diego, CA 92127
Tel.: (858) 453-7845
Web Site: http://www.petco.com
Sales Range: $1-4.9 Billion
Emp.: 9,900
Pet Food, Supplies & Services Retailer
N.A.I.C.S.: 459910
Justin Tichy (Chief Stores Officer)

Subsidiary (Domestic):

Petco Wellness, LLC **(3)**
2253 Air Park Rd, Rhinelander, WI 54501
Web Site: http://www.drsfostersmith.com
Emp.: 115
Pet Food, Supplies & Services Retailer
N.A.I.C.S.: 459910
Spencer Insolia (Pres)

Ports America, Inc. **(1)**
525 Washington Blvd Ste 1660, Jersey City, NJ 07310
Tel.: (732) 635-3899
Web Site: http://www.portsamerica.com
Sales Range: $1-4.9 Billion
Emp.: 10,000
Marine Port Operator
N.A.I.C.S.: 488310
Mark Montgomery (CEO)

Puget Energy, Inc. **(1)**
355 110th Ave NE, Bellevue, WA 98004
Tel.: (425) 454-6363
Web Site: https://www.pugetenergy.com
Rev.: $4,221,162,000
Assets: $17,187,514,000
Liabilities: $5,560,052,000
Net Worth: $11,627,462,000
Earnings: $414,345,000
Emp.: 3,250
Fiscal Year-end: 12/31/2022
Holding Company; Electric Power & Gas Distr
N.A.I.C.S.: 551112
Steven W. Hooper (Chm)

Subsidiary (Domestic):

Puget Sound Energy, Inc. **(2)**
355 110th Ave NE, Bellevue, WA 98004
Tel.: (425) 454-6363
Web Site: https://www.pse.com
Rev.: $4,216,173,000
Assets: $15,200,242,000
Liabilities: $5,542,394,000
Net Worth: $9,657,848,000
Earnings: $490,952,000
Emp.: 3,250
Fiscal Year-end: 12/31/2022
Electric Power & Natural Gas Distribution & Generation Services
N.A.I.C.S.: 221122
Steven W. Hooper (Chm)

Subsidiary (Domestic):

Puget Western, Inc. **(3)**
19515 North Creek Pkwy Ste 310, Bothell, WA 98011-8200
Tel.: (425) 487-6550
Web Site: http://www.pugetwestern.com
Sales Range: $25-49.9 Million
Emp.: 5
Real Estate Holding & Developing
N.A.I.C.S.: 237210
Joel Molander (Pres)

Qualtrics International Inc. **(1)**
333 W River Park Dr, Provo, UT 84604
Tel.: (385) 203-4999
Web Site: https://www.qualtrics.com
Rev.: $1,458,628,000
Assets: $3,395,851,000
Liabilities: $1,491,831,000
Net Worth: $1,904,020,000
Earnings: ($1,061,478,000)
Emp.: 5,600
Fiscal Year-end: 12/31/2022
Enterprise Data Collection & Analysis Solutions
N.A.I.C.S.: 513210
Brigid Archibald (Mng Dir-Asia Pacific & Japan)

Subsidiary (Domestic):

Clarabridge, Inc. **(2)**
11400 Commerce Park Dr Ste 500, Reston, VA 20191
Tel.: (571) 299-1800
Web Site: http://www.clarabridge.com
Test Analytics Software Developer
N.A.I.C.S.: 334610
Sid Banerjee (Founder, Vice Chm & Chief Strategy Officer)

Subsidiary (Domestic):

Market Metrix LLC **(3)**
125 E Sir Francis Drake Blvd Ste 300, Larkspur, CA 94939
Tel.: (415) 721-1300
Web Site: http://www.marketmetrix.com
Emp.: 35
Marketing Research & Public Opinion Polling
N.A.I.C.S.: 541910
Robert Honeycutt (CEO)

Ruskin Company **(1)**
3900 Doctor Greaves Rd, Grandview, MO 64030-1134
Tel.: (816) 761-7476
Web Site: http://www.ruskin.com
Sales Range: $200-249.9 Million
Emp.: 570
Air, Fire & Smoke Dampers, Louvres & Fibreglass Products Mfr
N.A.I.C.S.: 334512
Keith Glasch (Pres)

Division (Domestic):

Lau Industries **(2)**
4509 Springfield St, Dayton, OH 45431-0943
Tel.: (937) 253-2000
Web Site: http://www.lauparts.com
Sales Range: $25-49.9 Million
Emp.: 20
Fans & Blowers Mfr
N.A.I.C.S.: 333413
Anna Schlotterbeck (Mgr-Sls & Mktg)

Rooftop Systems Inc. **(2)**
1625 Diplomat Dr, Carrollton, TX 75006
Tel.: (972) 247-7447

Canada Pension Plan Investment Board—(Continued)

Web Site: http://www.rooftopsystems.com
Sales Range: $25-49.9 Million
Emp.: 350
Air Ducts & Sheet Metal Mfr
N.A.I.C.S.: 423390

Swartwout Division (2)
3900 Doctor Greaves Rd, Grandview, MO 64030-1134
Tel.: (816) 761-7476
Web Site: http://www.swartwout.com
Sales Range: $50-74.9 Million
Emp.: 115
Ventilators, Louvers, Heat & Smoke Units & Roof Curbs Mfr
N.A.I.C.S.: 238990

Selkirk Corporation (1)
1301 W President Bush Hwy Ste 330, Richardson, TX 75080
Tel.: (972) 943-6100
Web Site: http://www.selkirkinc.com
Sales Range: $550-599.9 Million
Chimneys & Venting Products Mfr
N.A.I.C.S.: 423720

Subsidiary (Non-US):

Selkirk Canada Corporation (2)
375 Green Rd, Stoney Creek, L8E 4A5, ON, Canada
Tel.: (905) 662-6600
Web Site: http://www.selkirkcorp.com
Sales Range: $25-49.9 Million
Emp.: 15
Chimney Pipes, Venting & Fireplace Mfr
N.A.I.C.S.: 327390
John Vukanovich (Pres-Mktg)

Waystar, Inc. (1)
888 W Market St Louisville, Louisville, KY 40202
Tel.: (844) 492-9782
Web Site: http://www.waystar.com
Computer Software (for Healthcare Services); Claims & Revenue Cycle Management & Healthcare Information
N.A.I.C.S.: 541511
Matthew Hawkins (CEO)

Subsidiary (Domestic):

Navicure, Inc. (2)
2055 Sugarloaf Cir Ste 600, Duluth, GA 30097
Tel.: (770) 342-0200
Web Site: http://www.navicure.com
Automated Web-Based Claims Management Solutions
N.A.I.C.S.: 513210

Recondo Technology, Inc. (2)
7900 E Union Ave 4th Fl, Denver, CO 80237
Tel.: (303) 974-2800
Web Site: http://www.recondotech.com
Software Solutions Provider
N.A.I.C.S.: 541511
Mike Mulcahy (VP-Payer Rels)

ZirMed, Inc. (2)
888 W Main St Ste 400, Louisville, KY 40202
Tel.: (844) 492-9782
Rev.: $2,665,973,183
Assets: $4,072,036,518
Liabilities: $2,724,669,054
Net Worth: $1,347,367,463
Earnings: $355,183,396
Emp.: 10,416
Fiscal Year-end: 12/31/2018
Healthcare Patient Billing Services
N.A.I.C.S.: 561499

eSolutions, Inc. (2)
8215 W 108th Ter, Olathe, KS 66210
Tel.: (866) 633-4726
Web Site: http://www.esolutionsinc.com
Healthcare Software Services
N.A.I.C.S.: 541511
Gerry McCarthy (CEO)

Subsidiary (Domestic):

Practice Insight, LLC (3)
1 Greenway Plz Ste 350, Houston, TX 77046
Tel.: (713) 333-6000

Web Site: http://www.practiceinsight.net
Health Care Software Systems
N.A.I.C.S.: 541511
J. Michael Reeves (Co-Founder & Chm)

CANADA POST CORPORATION
2701 Riverside Drive Suite N 1200, Ottawa, K1A 0B1, ON, Canada   Ca
Web Site: http://www.canadapost.ca
Year Founded: 1981
Rev.: $6,809,870,760
Assets: $8,055,681,480
Liabilities: $8,110,778,760
Net Worth: ($55,097,280)
Earnings: ($10,713,360)
Emp.: 68,000
Fiscal Year-end: 12/31/19
Postal Service
N.A.I.C.S.: 491110
Susan Margles (Chief People & Safety Officer)

Subsidiaries:

Canada Post International Ltd. (1)
2701 Riverside Dr Ste C0115, Ottawa, K1A 0B1, ON, Canada
Tel.: (613) 734-9800
Provider of Consulting Services, Postal Technology, Postal Transformation & e-Commerce Capabilities to the Global Postal Industry
N.A.I.C.S.: 541611

Innovapost, Inc. (1)
365 March Road, Ottawa, K2K 3N5, ON, Canada (51%)
Tel.: (613) 270-6262
Web Site: http://www.innovapost.com
Sales Range: $200-249.9 Million
Emp.: 700
Provider of IS/IT & eBusiness Solutions to the Global Postal Industry, Particularly to the Canada Post Group of Companies
N.A.I.C.S.: 561499

Intelcom Express Inc. (1)
1380 William Street Suite 200, Montreal, H3C 1R5, QC, Canada
Tel.: (514) 937-0430
Web Site: http://www.intelcomgroup.com
Emp.: 400
Provider of Delivery, Courier, Warehousing, Distribution & Logistics Management Services for Business
N.A.I.C.S.: 561499
Valerie Cloutier (Mgr-Customer Experience)

Progistix-Solutions Inc. (1)
Unit 300 Bldg 99 Signet Dr, North York, M9L 1T6, ON, Canada (100%)
Tel.: (416) 401-7000
Sales Range: $75-99.9 Million
Emp.: 300
Provider of Logistics Services to Businesses
N.A.I.C.S.: 561499
Jim Eckler (Pres & CEO)

epost (1)
393 University Ave 13th Fl, Toronto, M5G 2P7, ON, Canada (100%)
Tel.: (416) 313-4100
Provider of Online Mail Services
N.A.I.C.S.: 517121

CANADA POWER TECHNOLOGY LIMITED
161 Watline Avenue, Mississauga, L4Z 1P2, ON, Canada
Tel.: (905) 890-6900
Web Site: https://www.canadapowertech.com
Year Founded: 1987
Rev.: $10,817,105
Emp.: 35
Air-Cooled Engines Distr
N.A.I.C.S.: 811198
Tim Bequiri (Pres)

CANADA RARE EARTH CORP.
Suite 2110-650 West Georgia St, Vancouver, V6E 4N8, BC, Canada

Tel.: (604) 638-8886
Web Site:
  https://www.canadarareearth.com
RAREF—(OTCIQ)
Rev.: $4,010,133
Assets: $1,696,999
Liabilities: $1,692,426
Net Worth: $4,573
Earnings: $127,765
Fiscal Year-end: 03/31/23
Metal Mining Services
N.A.I.C.S.: 212290
Gordon J. Fretwell (Sec)

CANADA RENEWABLE BIOENERGY CORP.
Suite 2000 1066 West Hastings Street, Vancouver, V6E 3X2, BC, Canada
Tel.: (604) 285-6516   AB
Year Founded: 2007
Oil & Gas Exploration Services
N.A.I.C.S.: 211120

CANADA SILVER COBALT WORKS INC.
3028 Quadra Court, Coquitlam, V3B 5X6, BC, Canada
Tel.: (604) 828-1475   Ca
Web Site:
  http://www.canadacobaltworks.com
Year Founded: 2005
CCWOF—(OTCQB)
Assets: $1,972,476
Liabilities: $2,658,356
Net Worth: ($685,880)
Earnings: ($4,580,092)
Emp.: 2
Fiscal Year-end: 12/31/23
Silver Mining Services
N.A.I.C.S.: 212220
Frank J. Basa (CEO)

CANADABIS CAPITAL, INC.
255C Clearview Drive, Red Deer, T4E 3B6, AB, Canada
Web Site:
  https://www.canadabis.com
CANB—(TSXV)
Rev.: $5,371,373
Assets: $10,391,738
Liabilities: $8,967,009
Net Worth: $1,424,729
Earnings: ($2,097,222)
Fiscal Year-end: 07/31/21
Cannabis Product Distr
N.A.I.C.S.: 424210

CANADIAN ADVANCED TECHNOLOGY ALLIANCE
207 Bank St Suite 416, Ottawa, K2P 2N2, ON, Canada
Tel.: (613) 236-6550
Web Site: http://www.cata.ca
Sales Range: $25-49.9 Million
Emp.: 7
Technology Alliance
N.A.I.C.S.: 813910
John Reid (Pres & CEO)

Subsidiaries:

CATA Biometrics Group (1)
388 Albert St 2nd Fl, Ottawa, K1R 5B2, ON, Canada
Tel.: (613) 236-6550
Sales Range: $25-49.9 Million
Biometric Technology Alliance
N.A.I.C.S.: 813910

Canadian Association of Internet Providers (1)
388 Albert St 2nd Fl, Ottawa, K1R 5B2, ON, Canada
Tel.: (613) 232-2247
Web Site: http://www.caip.ca
Sales Range: $25-49.9 Million
Emp.: 6
Technology Trade Association

N.A.I.C.S.: 813910

CANADIAN APARTMENT PROPERTIES REAL ESTATE INVESTMENT TRUST
11 Church Street, Toronto, M5E 1W1, ON, Canada
Tel.: (416) 861-9404   Ca
Web Site: https://www.capreit.ca
Year Founded: 1997
CAR.UN—(OTCIQ)
Sales Range: $800-899.9 Million
Emp.: 897
Real Estate Investment Trust Services
N.A.I.C.S.: 525990
Jodi Lieberman (Chief HR Officer)

CANADIAN BACK INSTITUTE LIMITED PARTNERSHIP
Sun Life Financial Centre West Tower 3300 Bloor St W Ste 900, Toronto, M8X 2X2, ON, Canada
Tel.: (416) 231-0078
Web Site: http://www.cbi.ca
Emp.: 1,000
Health Care Management Services
N.A.I.C.S.: 621399
Dave Maxwell (COO-Rehabilitation Svcs)

Subsidiaries:

Care Point Medical Centres (1)
3993 Henning Dr, Suite 203, Burnaby, V5C 6N5, BC, Canada (100%)
Tel.: (604) 205-9466
Web Site: http://www.carepoint.ca
Sales Range: $1-9.9 Million
Emp.: 100
Healthcare Services
N.A.I.C.S.: 621111

CANADIAN BANK NOTE COMPANY LIMITED
145 Richmond Road, Ottawa, K1Z 1A1, ON, Canada
Tel.: (613) 722-3421   ON
Web Site: http://www.cbnco.com
Year Founded: 1910
Sales Range: $75-99.9 Million
Emp.: 750
High Security Printing Services
N.A.I.C.S.: 323120
Doug Arends (Chm)

Subsidiaries:

CBN Lottery Group (1)
18 Auriga Dr Ste 205, Ottawa, K2E 7T9, ON, Canada (100%)
Tel.: (613) 225-3018
Web Site: http://www.cbnco.com
Sales Range: $50-74.9 Million
Emp.: 214
Provider of High Security Printing Services
N.A.I.C.S.: 323120

Canadian Bank Note Design Inc. (1)
105 2507 12th St NE, Calgary, 22E-7F5, AB, Canada (100%)
Tel.: (403) 250-9510
Web Site: http://www.mcara.com
Sales Range: $25-49.9 Million
Emp.: 70
High Security Printing Services
N.A.I.C.S.: 323120
Rodger K. Grant (Gen Mgr)

Guyana Lottery Company Limited (1)
357 Lamaha Street North Cummingsburg, Georgetown, Guyana (100%)
Tel.: (592) 2260753
Web Site: http://www.guyana-lottery.com
Sales Range: $25-49.9 Million
Emp.: 40
Provider of Lottery Services
N.A.I.C.S.: 713290
Tracey Lewis (Gen Mgr)

McAra Printing (1)
105 2507 12th St NE, Calgary, T2E 7L5,

AB, Canada **(100%)**
Tel.: (403) 250-9510
Web Site: http://www.mcara.com
Sales Range: $25-49.9 Million
Emp.: 70
Printer of Government, Financial & Lottery Related Documents
N.A.I.C.S.: 323120
Rodger K. Grant (VP & Gen Mgr)

CANADIAN CANNABIS CORP.

100 Rutherford Road South, Brampton, L6W 2J2, ON, Canada
Tel.: (866) 790-3324   DE
Web Site:
   http://www.cdncannabis.com
Year Founded: 2011
Sales Range: Less than $1 Million
Medical Marijuana Mfr & Sales
N.A.I.C.S.: 325412

CANADIAN COMMERCIAL CORPORATION

350 Albert Street Suite 700, Ottawa, K1A 0S6, ON, Canada
Tel.: (613) 996-0034
Web Site: http://www.ccc.ca
Year Founded: 1946
Rev.: $11,357,923
Assets: $75,627,701
Liabilities: $56,014,377
Net Worth: $19,613,324
Earnings: $2,308,508
Emp.: 112
Fiscal Year-end: 03/31/22
Export Contracting Services
N.A.I.C.S.: 561499
Carl Marcotte (Pres & CEO)

CANADIAN FERRO REFRACTORIES

345 Arvin Ave, Stoney Creek, L8E 2M6, ON, Canada
Tel.: (905) 662-8381
Web Site: http://www.thermatex.ca
Sales Range: $25-49.9 Million
Emp.: 9
Mfr of Specialty Refractories for the Steel Industry
N.A.I.C.S.: 327120
John Flannigan (Pres)

CANADIAN GENERAL TOWER LIMITED

52 Middleton Street, PO Box 160, Cambridge, N1R 5T6, ON, Canada
Tel.: (519) 623-1630
Web Site: http://www.cgtower.com
Year Founded: 1946
Sales Range: $200-249.9 Million
Emp.: 1,100
Coated Fabrics & Plastic Film Mfr
N.A.I.C.S.: 322220
Craig Richardson (CEO)

Subsidiaries:

CGT SHANGHAI TRADING CO. LTD. **(1)**
2315-16 200 Middle Yincheng Road Bank of China Tower, Shanghai, 200120, China
Tel.: (86) 21 6888 1631
Coated Fabric Product Mfr
N.A.I.C.S.: 332999

CANADIAN GOLD SEAFOOD COMPANY

209 Aerotech Drive Unit 10B, Enfield, B2T 1K3, NS, Canada
Tel.: (902) 873-3766
Web Site:
   http://www.canadiangold.ns.ca
Year Founded: 1995
Rev.: $21,736,238
Emp.: 30
Seafood Processing Storage & Distr
N.A.I.C.S.: 311710
Doug McRae (Pres)

CANADIAN GOLDCAMPS CORP.

Suite 810-789 West Pender Street, Vancouver, V6C 1H2, BC, Canada
Tel.: (647) 640-2141
Web Site:
   https://goldcamps.s0.adnetcms.com
CAMP—(CNSX)
Rev.: $12,806
Assets: $34,004
Liabilities: $110,525
Net Worth: ($76,520)
Earnings: ($1,517,352)
Fiscal Year-end: 12/31/23
Metal Exploration Services
N.A.I.C.S.: 213115
Brendan Purdy (Pres & CEO)

CANADIAN HOSPITAL SPECIALTIES LIMITED

2060 Winston Park Dr Ste 400, Oakville, L6H 5R7, ON, Canada
Tel.: (905) 825-0628
Web Site: https://www.chsltd.com
Emp.: 100
Medical Device Mfr
N.A.I.C.S.: 339112
Mike Canzoneri (CEO)

Subsidiaries:

SandBox Medical LLC **(1)**
300 Oak St Ste 750, Pembroke, MA 02359-1959
Tel.: (781) 826-6905
Web Site: http://www.sandboxmedical.com
Rubber Products Mfr
N.A.I.C.S.: 326299
Eileen M. Gay (Mgr)

CANADIAN IMPERIAL BANK OF COMMERCE

81 Bay Street 12th Floor, Toronto, M5J 0E7, ON, Canada
Tel.: (416) 980-3096   Ca
Web Site: https://www.cibc.com
Year Founded: 1867
CM—(NYSE)
Rev.: $47,387,454,720
Assets: $412,752,005,520
Liabilities: $369,126,950,280
Net Worth: $43,625,055,240
Earnings: $5,289,095,280
Emp.: 48,074
Fiscal Year-end: 10/31/24
Banking Services
N.A.I.C.S.: 522110
Katharine Berghuis Stevenson (Chm)

Subsidiaries:

CIBC (U.K.) Holdings Limited **(1)**
150 Cheapside, London, EC2V 6ET, United Kingdom **(100%)**
Tel.: (44) 2072346000
Web Site: http://www.cibcwm.com
Sales Range: $150-199.9 Million
Emp.: 300
Holding Company
N.A.I.C.S.: 551112

CIBC Australia Ltd. **(1)**
Level 45 Gateway 1 Macquarie Place, Sydney, 2000, NSW, Australia
Tel.: (61) 292751300
Sales Range: $50-74.9 Million
Emp.: 13
Investment Management Service
N.A.I.C.S.: 523940

CIBC First Caribbean International Bank Limited **(1)**
The Michael Mansoor Building Warrens, PO Box 503, Warrens, Saint Michael, BB22026, Barbados
Tel.: (246) 3672300
Web Site: https://www.cibc.com
Rev.: $715,463,000
Assets: $12,521,108,000
Liabilities: $11,168,589,000
Net Worth: $1,352,519,000
Earnings: $260,761,000
Emp.: 2,598

Fiscal Year-end: 10/31/2023
Corporate & Retail Banking, Credit Card & Financial Management Services
N.A.I.C.S.: 523991
Patrick James McKenna (Chief Risk Officer)

CIBC Global Asset Management Inc. **(1)**
1000 De La Gauchetiere West Suite 3200, Montreal, H3B 4W5, QC, Canada
Tel.: (514) 875-7040
Web Site: http://www.cibc.com
Sales Range: $50-74.9 Million
Emp.: 90
Investment Management Service
N.A.I.C.S.: 523940
David Scandiffio (Pres & CEO)

CIBC Investor Services Inc. **(1)**
161 Bay Street 4th Floor, Toronto, M5J 2S8, ON, Canada
Tel.: (416) 980-3343
Web Site:
   http://www.investorsedge.cibc.com
Emp.: 200
Investment Management Service
N.A.I.C.S.: 523940

CIBC Mellon **(1)**
320 Bay Street, Toronto, M5H 4A6, ON, Canada **(50%)**
Tel.: (416) 643-5000
Web Site: http://www.cibcmellon.com
Emp.: 1,000
Investment Processing Services
N.A.I.C.S.: 523991
Kelly Hastings (Chief Risk Officer)

CIBC Private Wealth Group, LLC **(1)**
3290 Northside Pkwy NW 7th Fl, Atlanta, GA 30327
Tel.: (404) 881-3400
Web Site: https://private-wealth.us.cibc.com
N.A.I.C.S.: 525910
Beth McRae Mayfield (Mng Dir)

CIBC Reinsurance Company Limited **(1)**
FCIB Head Office 3rd Floor, Saint Michael, BB22026, Barbados
Tel.: (246) 367 2400
Web Site: http://www.cibc.com
Sales Range: $50-74.9 Million
Emp.: 9
Reinsurance Services
N.A.I.C.S.: 524130

CIBC Securities, Inc. **(1)**
161 Bay Street, Toronto, M5J 2S8, ON, Canada **(100%)**
Tel.: (416) 980-2211
Web Site: http://www.cibc.com
Sales Range: $200-249.9 Million
Emp.: 300
Security Brokers
N.A.I.C.S.: 523999

CIBC Trust Corporation **(1)**
55 Yonge St 10th Fl, Toronto, M5E 1J4, ON, Canada
Tel.: (416) 861-7000
Investment Management Service
N.A.I.C.S.: 523999

Canadian Imperial Holdings Inc. **(1)**
425 Lexington Ave, New York, NY 10017-3903 **(100%)**
Tel.: (212) 856-4000
Web Site: http://www.cibcwm.com
Sales Range: $150-199.9 Million
Emp.: 500
Bank Holding Company
N.A.I.C.S.: 551111

Subsidiary (Domestic):

Atlantic Trust Group, LLC **(2)**
1555 Peachtree St Ste 1100, Atlanta, GA 30309
Tel.: (404) 881-3400
Web Site: http://www.atlantictrust.com
Sales Range: $650-699.9 Million
Investment & Wealth Management Services
N.A.I.C.S.: 523940

Subsidiary (Domestic):

AT Investment Advisers, Inc. **(3)**
1 S Wacker Ste 3500, Chicago, IL 60606
Tel.: (312) 368-7700
Web Site: http://www.atlantictrust.com

Sales Range: $25-49.9 Million
Emp.: 50
Investment Advisory Services
N.A.I.C.S.: 523940

Branch (Domestic):

Atlantic Trust Group, LLC - Baltimore **(3)**
100 Internationall Dr 23rd Fl, Baltimore, MD 21202
Tel.: (410) 539-4660
Web Site: http://www.atlantictrust.com
Emp.: 5
Investment & Wealth Management Services
N.A.I.C.S.: 523940

Atlantic Trust Group, LLC - Boston **(3)**
100 Federal St, Boston, MA 02110
Tel.: (617) 357-9600
Web Site: http://www.atlantictrust.com
Sales Range: $50-74.9 Million
Emp.: 100
Investment & Wealth Management Services
N.A.I.C.S.: 523940

Subsidiary (Domestic):

CIBC Bank USA **(2)**
120 S LaSalle St, Chicago, IL 60603 **(100%)**
Tel.: (312) 564-2000
Web Site: http://us.cibc.com
Commericial Banking
N.A.I.C.S.: 522110
Larry D. Richman (Chm)

CIBC Inc. **(2)**
425 Lexington Ave, New York, NY 10017-3903 **(100%)**
Tel.: (212) 856-4000
Web Site: http://www.cibc.com
Sales Range: $50-74.9 Million
Emp.: 70
Corporate Banking & Financial Services
N.A.I.C.S.: 523150

Lodestar Investment Counsel, LLC **(2)**
150 S Wacker Dr Ste 3050, Chicago, IL 60606
Tel.: (312) 630-9666
Web Site: http://www.ldstr.com
Investment Advisory Services
N.A.I.C.S.: 523940

Cleary Gull Holdings Inc. **(1)**
411 E Wisconsin Ave Ste 1850, Milwaukee, WI 53202
Tel.: (414) 291-4550
Web Site: http://www.clearygull.com
Sales Range: $1-4.9 Billion
Emp.: 100
Holding Company; Investment Advisory, Wealth Management, Securities Brokerage & Dealing Services
N.A.I.C.S.: 551112
Gregory T. Gorlinski (Mng Dir)

Subsidiary (Domestic):

Cleary Gull Inc. **(2)**
411 E Wisconsin Ave Ste 1850, Milwaukee, WI 53202
Tel.: (414) 291-4550
Web Site: http://www.clearygull.com
Investment Advisory Wealth Management Security Brokerage & Dealing Services
N.A.I.C.S.: 523940
John R. Peterson (Mng Dir)

INTRIA Items Inc. **(1)**
155 Britannia Road East, Mississauga, L4Z 4B7, ON, Canada
Tel.: (905) 755-2400
Web Site: http://www.intriaitemsinc.com
Sales Range: $100-124.9 Million
Emp.: 150
Payment & Information Management Services
N.A.I.C.S.: 522320

Sentry Insurance Brokers Ltd. **(1)**
37 Pine Rd, Belleville, Saint Michael, BB11113, Barbados
Tel.: (246) 2280163
Web Site: https://sentrybrokers.com
N.A.I.C.S.: 524210
J. P. Stephen Ollivierre (Mng Dir)

Canadian Imperial Bank of Commerce—(Continued)

The CIBC Wood Gundy Corporation **(1)**
1621 Base Street, Toronto, M5J 2S8, ON, Canada **(100%)**
Tel.: (416) 980-2211
Web Site: http://www.woodgundy.com
Sales Range: $350-399.9 Million
Emp.: 1,000
Investment Securities Broker
N.A.I.C.S.: 523910

Subsidiary (Domestic):

CIBC Wood Gundy **(2)**
2200 255 Queens Avenue, London, N6A 5R8, ON, Canada
Tel.: (519) 663-5353
Web Site: http://www.cibcwoodgundy.com
Sales Range: $75-99.9 Million
Emp.: 120
Securities Brokerage Services
N.A.I.C.S.: 523150

CIBC Wood Gundy **(2)**
10180-101 Street Suite 1800, Edmonton, T5J 3S4, AB, Canada
Tel.: (780) 409-9904
Web Site: https://woodgundylocations.cibc.com
Sales Range: $75-99.9 Million
Emp.: 140
Securities Brokerage Services
N.A.I.C.S.: 523150

CIBC World Markets Inc. **(2)**
161 Bay St, Toronto, M5J 2S8, ON, Canada **(62.4%)**
Tel.: (416) 594-7000
Web Site: http://www.cibcwm.com
Sales Range: $600-649.9 Million
Emp.: 2,500
Investments & Financial Services
N.A.I.C.S.: 523150
Roman S. Dubczak *(Mng Dir & Head-Investment Banking-Global)*

Subsidiary (Domestic):

CIBC WM Real Estate Ltd. **(3)**
199 Bay Street 44th Floor Commerce Court, Toronto, M5L 1A2, ON, Canada
Tel.: (416) 594-7360
Web Site: http://www.cibc.com
Sales Range: $25-49.9 Million
Emp.: 5
Real Estate Brokerage Services
N.A.I.C.S.: 531210

CIBC Wood Gundy Financial Services Inc. **(3)**
200 King Street West Suite 700, Toronto, M5H 4A8, ON, Canada
Tel.: (800) 563-3193
Web Site: http://www.woodgundy.com
Sales Range: $1-4.9 Billion
Emp.: 300
Financial Management Services
N.A.I.C.S.: 523999

Subsidiary (Non-US):

CIBC World Markets (Japan) Inc. **(3)**
2-2-3 Uchisaiwaicho Hibiyakokusai Bldg 8f, Chiyoda-Ku, Tokyo, 100-0011, Japan
Tel.: (81) 355128866
Investment Management Service
N.A.I.C.S.: 523999

Subsidiary (US):

CIBC World Markets Corp. **(3)**
425 Lexington Ave, New York, NY 10017-6232
Tel.: (212) 667-7000
Securities Firm & Investment Banking
N.A.I.C.S.: 523120
Laurene Bielski Mahon *(Executives)*

Subsidiary (Non-US):

CIBC World Markets plc **(3)**
150 Cheapside, London, EC2V 6ET, United Kingdom **(100%)**
Tel.: (44) 20 7234 6000
Web Site: http://www.cibcwm.com
Sales Range: $150-199.9 Million
Emp.: 250
Investment Company
N.A.I.C.S.: 523910

CANADIAN LINEN & UNIFORM SERVICE CO.
75 Norfinch Dr, Toronto, M3N 1W8, ON, Canada
Tel.: (416) 849-5100
Web Site: http://www.canadianuniform.com
Year Founded: 1925
Sales Range: $125-149.9 Million
Emp.: 1,850
Linen Supply Services
N.A.I.C.S.: 812331
Bill Evans *(Pres & CEO)*

CANADIAN MANGANESE COMPANY INC.
55 University Avenue Suite 1805, Toronto, M5J 2H7, ON, Canada
Tel.: (647) 728-4106　　　　　Ca
Web Site: https://www.canadian.com
Year Founded: 2011
CDMNF—(OTCIQ)
Assets: $11,810,014
Liabilities: $667,986
Net Worth: $11,142,028
Earnings: ($1,373,308)
Emp.: 1
Fiscal Year-end: 12/31/22
Mineral Mining Services
N.A.I.C.S.: 213115
John F. Kearney *(Chm)*

CANADIAN METALS INC.
2700-1000 rue Sherbrooke Ouest, Montreal, H3A 3G4, QC, Canada
Tel.: (416) 303-6460
Web Site: https://canadian-metals.com
CME—(CNSX)
Assets: $10,002,552
Liabilities: $1,308,385
Net Worth: $8,694,167
Earnings: ($451,559)
Fiscal Year-end: 07/31/23
Gold Mining
N.A.I.C.S.: 212220
Arnab De *(CFO)*

CANADIAN NATIONAL RAILWAY COMPANY
935 de La Gauchetiere Street West, Montreal, H3B 2M9, QC, Canada
Tel.: (514) 399-7091　　　　　Ca
Web Site: https://www.cn.ca
Year Founded: 1919
CNI—(NYSE)
Rev.: $11,325,067,560
Assets: $37,970,306,640
Liabilities: $20,178,130,320
Net Worth: $17,792,176,320
Earnings: $3,826,913,760
Emp.: 22,604
Fiscal Year-end: 12/31/21
Freight & Railway Transportation Services
N.A.I.C.S.: 482111
Keith Reardon *(Sr VP-Consumer Product Supply Chain)*

Subsidiaries:

Autoport Limited **(1)**
1180 Main Road, Eastern Passage, B3G 1M4, NS, Canada
Tel.: (902) 465-6050
Transshipment & Vehicle Processing Services
N.A.I.C.S.: 493190
Emery Robidoux *(Gen Mgr)*

CN WorldWide North America **(1)**
16800 S Center St, Harvey, IL 60426 **(100%)**
Tel.: (708) 332-4532
Web Site: http://www.cnworldwide.com
Transportation Management, Warehousing & Distribution Services
N.A.I.C.S.: 488210

Canadian National Railway Company **(1)**
455 N Cityfront Plaza Dr, Chicago, IL 60611-5503
Tel.: (312) 755-7500
Web Site: http://www.cn.ca
Sales Range: $1-4.9 Billion
Emp.: 3,500
Rail Transportation Services
N.A.I.C.S.: 482111

Canadian National Railway Company **(1)**
17641 S Ashland Ave, Homewood, IL 60430
Tel.: (708) 332-4377
Web Site: http://www.cn.ca
Sales Range: $450-499.9 Million
Emp.: 2,000
Freight Railroad
N.A.I.C.S.: 482111

Lakeland & Waterways Railway **(1)**
Associative Ctr Ste 306, 13220 St Albert Trl, Edmonton, T5O 4W1, AB, Canada
Tel.: (780) 448-5855
Sales Range: $1-9.9 Million
Emp.: 24
Short Line Railroad
N.A.I.C.S.: 482112

Mackenzie Northern Railway **(1)**
Associative Ctr Ste 306, 13220 St Albert Trl, Edmonton, T5O 4W1, AB, Canada
Tel.: (780) 448-5855
Sales Range: $75-99.9 Million
Emp.: 200
Short Line Railroad
N.A.I.C.S.: 482112

CANADIAN NATURAL RESOURCES LTD.
2100 855-2nd Street SW, Calgary, T2P 4J8, AB, Canada
Tel.: (403) 517-7345
Web Site: https://www.cnrl.com
Year Founded: 1989
CNQ—(NYSE)
Rev.: $26,570,141,095
Assets: $56,109,182,241
Liabilities: $26,684,642,092
Net Worth: $29,424,540,149
Earnings: $6,081,849,745
Emp.: 10,272
Fiscal Year-end: 12/31/23
Petrochemicals Extraction Services
N.A.I.C.S.: 211120
N. Murray Edwards *(Chm)*

Subsidiaries:

CNR (ECHO) Resources Inc. **(1)**
855 2 St SW Suite 2500, Calgary, T2P 4J8, AB, Canada
Tel.: (403) 517-7000
Petroleum & Natural Gas Extraction Services
N.A.I.C.S.: 211120

CNR International **(1)**
SARL Immeuble Kharrat Angle Boul Botreau Roussel, PO Box 8707, Ave Nougoues O1, 1, Abidjan, Cote d'Ivoire **(100%)**
Tel.: http://www.cnrinternational.com
Sales Range: $50-74.9 Million
Emp.: 30
Oil/Gas Exploration & Production
N.A.I.C.S.: 211120

CNR International (Angola) Limited **(1)**
Rua Dos Enganos 1-1 Andar, 5876, Luanda, Angola
Tel.: (244) 2396145
Web Site: http://www.cnrinternational.com
Sales Range: $50-74.9 Million
Emp.: 17
N.A.I.C.S.: 211120

CNR International (Cote d'Ivoire) S A R L **(1)**
Immeuble Kharrat Angle Avenue Nougoues Boulevard Botreau Roussel, BP 8707, Le Plateau, Abidjan, Cote d'Ivoire
Tel.: (225) 20310015
N.A.I.C.S.: 213112

CNR International (Gabon) Limited **(1)**
Villa Pierre Marie Dong Quartier la Sabliere, BP 641, Libreville, Gabon
Tel.: (241) 241734646
Oil & Gas Exploration Services
N.A.I.C.S.: 213112

CNR International (South Africa) Limited **(1)**
Suite 1B Nautica The Waterclub Beach Road Granger Bay, Cape Town, 8005, South Africa
Tel.: (27) 214014140
Emp.: 1
Oil & Gas Exploration Services
N.A.I.C.S.: 213112
Gloria Hutchinson *(Gen Mgr)*

CNR International UK Limited **(1)**
(100%)
Oil/Gas Exploration & Production
N.A.I.C.S.: 211120
W. David R. Bell *(VP-Exploration)*

Devon Canada Corporation **(1)**
100 400-3rd Avenue SW, Calgary, T2P 4H2, AB, Canada **(100%)**
Tel.: (403) 232-7100
Web Site: http://www.dvn.com
Sales Range: $700-749.9 Million
Emp.: 1,100
Oil & Gas Exploration & Production
N.A.I.C.S.: 211120

Subsidiary (Domestic):

Devon ARL Corporation **(2)**
400 3rd Avenue Southwest Suite 100, Calgary, T2P 4H2, AB, Canada
Tel.: (403) 232-7100
Web Site: http://www.dvn.com
Oil & Gas Exploration
N.A.I.C.S.: 237120

Branch (Domestic):

Devon Canada **(2)**
5101 48th Ave, PO Box 277, Eaglesham, T0H 1H0, AB, Canada
Tel.: (780) 359-2650
Sales Range: $25-49.9 Million
Emp.: 25
Oil & Gas Exploration
N.A.I.C.S.: 211120

Subsidiary (Domestic):

Devon NEC Corporation **(2)**
400 3 Ave Sw Ste 2000, Calgary, T2P 4H2, AB, Canada
Tel.: (403) 232-7100
Web Site: http://www.dvn.com
Emp.: 15
Oil & Gas Exploration Services
N.A.I.C.S.: 213112

Horizon Construction Management Ltd. **(1)**
855 2 St SW Ste 2500, Calgary, T2P 4J8, AB, Canada
Tel.: (403) 517-6700
Web Site: http://www.cnrl.com
Oil & Gas Exploration Services
N.A.I.C.S.: 213112

Painted Pony Energy Ltd. **(1)**
1200 520 3 Avenue SW, Calgary, T2P 0R3, AB, Canada
Tel.: (403) 475-0440
Web Site: http://www.paintedpony.ca
Rev.: $228,121,870
Assets: $1,380,069,782
Liabilities: $721,332,825
Net Worth: $658,736,958
Earnings: ($178,192,256)
Emp.: 65
Fiscal Year-end: 12/31/2019
Petroleum & Natural Gas Exploration Services
N.A.I.C.S.: 213112
Patrick R. Ward *(Pres & CEO)*

CANADIAN NET REAL ESTATE INVESTMENT TRUST
106 Gun Avenue, Pointe-Claire, H9R 3X3, QC, Canada
Tel.: (450) 536-5328　　　　　QC
Web Site: https://www.cnetreit.com
Year Founded: 2006

CNNRF—(OTCIQ)
Rev.: $10,159,675
Assets: $164,048,809
Liabilities: $93,482,185
Net Worth: $70,566,624
Earnings: $7,526,454
Fiscal Year-end: 12/31/20
Real Estate Asset Management Services
N.A.I.C.S.: 531390
Jason Parravano (Pres & CEO)

CANADIAN NEXUS TEAM VENTURES CORP.

403 - 850 Harbourside Drive, Vancouver, V7P 0A3, BC, Canada
Tel.: (604) 960-1878   BC
Web Site: https://cnteamventures.ca
Year Founded: 1981
TEAM—(CNSX)
Rev.: $10,871
Assets: $1,066,610
Liabilities: $335,305
Net Worth: $731,305
Earnings: ($1,725,512)
Fiscal Year-end: 12/31/23
Mineral Exploration Services
N.A.I.C.S.: 213114

CANADIAN NORTH RE-SOURCES INC.

299 Courtneypark Drive East, Mississauga, L5T 2T6, ON, Canada
Tel.: (905) 696-8288   ON
Web Site:
  https://www.cnresources.com
Year Founded: 2013
CNRSF—(OTCQX)
Rev.: $68,847
Assets: $25,843,372
Liabilities: $2,618,255
Net Worth: $23,225,117
Earnings: $2,905,429
Fiscal Year-end: 12/31/22
Mineral Mining Services
N.A.I.C.S.: 213115
Carmelo Marrelli (CFO)

CANADIAN OIL RECOVERY & REMEDIATION ENTERPRISES LIMITED

141 Adelaide Street West Suite 110, Toronto, M5H 3L5, ON, Canada
Tel.: (416) 662-9455   Ca
Web Site: http://www.corre.com
Year Founded: 2007
CVR.H—(TSXV)
Rev.: $99,523
Assets: $51,394
Liabilities: $2,913,629
Net Worth: ($2,862,236)
Earnings: ($182,597)
Fiscal Year-end: 12/31/20
Oil & Gas Exploration Services
N.A.I.C.S.: 211120
John Lorenzo (CEO)

CANADIAN OVERSEAS PE-TROLEUM LIMITED

3200 715 - 5th Avenue SW, Calgary, T2P 2X6, AB, Canada
Tel.: (403) 262-5441
Web Site:
  https://www.canoverseas.com
Year Founded: 2004
XOP—(CNSX)
Rev.: $2,398,000
Assets: $98,778,000
Liabilities: $63,767,000
Net Worth: $35,011,000
Earnings: ($13,536,000)
Emp.: 23
Fiscal Year-end: 12/31/21
Oil & Gas Exploration & Development Services
N.A.I.C.S.: 213112

Harald Horst Ludwig (Chm)

CANADIAN PACIFIC KANSAS CITY LIMITED

7550 Ogden Dale Road S E, Calgary, T2C 4X9, AB, Canada
Tel.: (403) 319-7000   Ca
Web Site: https://www.cpkcr.com
Year Founded: 1881
CP—(NYSE)
Rev.: $9,366,030,000
Assets: $59,606,892,000
Liabilities: $27,968,286,000
Net Worth: $31,638,606,000
Earnings: $2,926,558,000
Emp.: 19,927
Fiscal Year-end: 12/31/23
Rail & Intermodal Freight Transportation Services
N.A.I.C.S.: 482111
Nadeem Velani (CFO & Exec VP)

Subsidiaries:

CP Finance Switzerland AG   (1)
Kreuzstrasse 100, 8645, Jona, Switzerland
Tel.: (41) 552112121
Rail Transport Services
N.A.I.C.S.: 488210

Cedar American Rail Holdings, Inc.   (1)
140 N Phillips Ave, Sioux Falls, SD 57104-6724
Tel.: (605) 782-1200
Holding Company
N.A.I.C.S.: 551112

Subsidiary (Domestic):

Dakota, Minnesota & Eastern Railroad Corporation   (2)
140 N Phillips Ave, Sioux Falls, SD 57104-2828
Tel.: (605) 782-1200
Sales Range: $250-299.9 Million
Emp.: 340
Railroads, Line-Haul Operating Services
N.A.I.C.S.: 482111

Delaware & Hudson Railway Company, Inc.   (1)
200 Clifton Corporate Pkwy, Clifton Park, NY 12065-3862
Tel.: (518) 383-7200
Web Site: http://www.cpr.ca
Emp.: 12
Railroad
N.A.I.C.S.: 482111

Kansas City Southern   (1)
427 West 12th St, Kansas City, MO 64105
Tel.: (816) 983-1303
Web Site: https://www.kcsouthern.com
Holding Company
N.A.I.C.S.: 551112
Patrick J. Ottensmeyer (Pres & CEO)

Subsidiary (Non-US):

Arrendadora KCSM, S. de R.L. de C.V.   (2)
Av Manuel L Barragan No 4850 Norte, Colonia Hidalgo, 64290, Monterrey, NL, Mexico
Tel.: (52) 11528283057911
N.A.I.C.S.: 541614

Kansas City Southern de Mexico S.A. de C.V.   (2)
Montes Urales No 625 Colonia Lomas de Chapultepec, Alcaldia Miguel Hidalgo, 11000, Mexico, DF, Mexico
Tel.: (52) 8183057911
Web Site: https://www.kcsouthern.com
Railroad Services
N.A.I.C.S.: 482112
Patrick J. Ottensmeyer (Pres)

Subsidiary (Domestic):

Meridian Speedway, LLC   (2)
4601 Hilry Huckaby Dr, Shreveport, LA 71107-5797
Tel.: (318) 676-6064

Sales Range: $50-74.9 Million
Emp.: 200
Freight Rail Transportation Services
N.A.I.C.S.: 482111

Pabtex, Inc.   (2)
209 Taft Ave, Port Arthur, TX 77642-0913
Tel.: (409) 962-8343
Freight Rail Transportation Services
N.A.I.C.S.: 482111

Subsidiary (Non-US):

Panama Canal Railway Company   (2)
Corozal One West Bldg T376, Panama, Panama
Tel.: (507) 3176070
Web Site: https://www.panarail.com
Sales Range: $400-449.9 Million
Emp.: 200
Railway Services
N.A.I.C.S.: 482112

Subsidiary (Domestic):

The Kansas City Southern Railway Company   (2)
427 W 12th St, Kansas City, MO 64105
Tel.: (816) 983-1303
Web Site: http://www.kcsouthern.com
Railroad
N.A.I.C.S.: 482111

The Texas Mexican Railway Company   (2)
1610 Woodstead Ct 470 Spring, The Woodlands, TX 77380
Tel.: (281) 465-7180
Railways Owners & Operators
N.A.I.C.S.: 482111

Mount Stephen Properties Inc.   (1)
7550 Ogden Dale Rd SE, Calgary, T2P 1K3, AB, Canada
Tel.: (403) 319-7000
Emp.: 5
Line Haul Railroad Operator
N.A.I.C.S.: 482111

Soo Line Corporation   (1)
14327 Huntington Ave, Savage, MN 55378-2678
Tel.: (952) 895-5277
Line Haul Railroad Operator
N.A.I.C.S.: 482111
Chris Goebel (Gen Mgr)

Soo Line Railroad Company   (1)
501 Marquette Ave, Minneapolis, MN 55402   (100%)
Tel.: (612) 904-5994
Railroad
N.A.I.C.S.: 522130

CANADIAN PALLADIUM RE-SOURCES, INC.

1558 West Hastings St, Vancouver, V6G 3J4, BC, Canada
Tel.: (604) 639-4452
DCNNF—(OTCIQ)
Rev.: $390,945
Assets: $3,283,362
Liabilities: $673,742
Net Worth: $2,609,620
Earnings: ($3,120,085)
Fiscal Year-end: 09/30/21
Mineral Exploration Services
N.A.I.C.S.: 213115
Wayne Tisdale (Pres & CEO)

CANADIAN PREFERRED SHARE TRUST

1501 McGill College Ave Suite 800, Montreal, H3A 3M8, QC, Canada
Investment Management Trust Services
N.A.I.C.S.: 523940
Jean-Guy Desjardins (Mgr-Fund)

CANADIAN PREMIUM SAND INC.

Suite 2000 715 5 Avenue SW, Calgary, T2P 2X6, AB, Canada
Tel.: (587) 355-3714   ON

Web Site: https://cpsglass.com
Year Founded: 2005
CPS—(TSXV)
Assets: $3,805,464
Liabilities: $3,096,794
Net Worth: $708,671
Earnings: ($1,955,529)
Fiscal Year-end: 09/30/21
Gold Mining Services
N.A.I.C.S.: 212220
Richard D. Williams (Founder & Sec)

CANADIAN PUREGAS EQUIP-MENT LIMITED

8410 Hwy 3, PO Box 280, Dunnville, N1A 2X5, ON, Canada
Tel.: (905) 774-8600   ON
Web Site:
  http://www.canadianpuregas.com
Year Founded: 1958
Sales Range: $1-9.9 Million
Emp.: 25
Dryers & Pressurization Systems Designer, Installer, Maintenance & Repair
N.A.I.C.S.: 333413
Ingolf Plath (Pres)

CANADIAN RESOURCES IN-COME TRUST

40 King Street West Scotia Plaza 26th Floor, PO Box 4085, Station A, Toronto, M5W 2X6, ON, Canada
Tel.: (416) 863-7144
Web Site:
  http://www.scotiamanaged.com
Year Founded: 1996
Assets: $8,673,931
Liabilities: $156,562
Net Worth: $8,517,370
Earnings: ($410,188)
Fiscal Year-end: 12/31/17
Financial Investment Services
N.A.I.C.S.: 523999
John B. Newman (Chm)

CANADIAN SILVER HUNTER INC.

65 Harbour Square suite 904, Toronto, M4J 2L4, ON, Canada
Tel.: (416) 707-4230   ON
Web Site:
  https://www.canadiansilverhunter.ca
Year Founded: 2006
AGH.H—(TSXV)
Assets: $354,582
Liabilities: $41,916
Net Worth: $312,666
Earnings: ($38,919)
Fiscal Year-end: 12/31/23
Silver Mining Services
N.A.I.C.S.: 212220
Jeffrey Hunter (Founder, Pres & CEO)

CANADIAN SOLAR INC.

545 Speedvale Avenue West, Guelph, N1K 1E6, ON, Canada
Tel.: (519) 837-1881   Ca
Web Site:
  https://www.canadiansolar.com
Year Founded: 2001
CSIQ—(NASDAQ)
Rev.: $7,468,610,000
Assets: $9,037,128,000
Liabilities: $6,730,434,000
Net Worth: $2,306,694,000
Earnings: $239,968,000
Emp.: 18,423
Fiscal Year-end: 12/31/22
Solar Power Device Mfr
N.A.I.C.S.: 334419
Shawn Qu (Founder, Chm, Pres & CEO)

Canadian Solar Inc.—(Continued)

Subsidiaries:

Astana Solar LLP   (1)
Turan Avenue, Nur-Sultan, 010000, Kazakhstan
Tel.: (7) 7172 551400
Web Site: http://astanasolar.kz
Solar Module Mfr
N.A.I.C.S.: 334413

CSI Solar Technologies Inc.   (1)
No 2 Changsheng Road Yangyuan Town, Changshu, 215562, China
Tel.: (86) 51252477677
Solar Module Mfr
N.A.I.C.S.: 334413

CSI Solartronics (Changshu) Co., Ltd.   (1)
Xinzhuang Industrial Park Yangyuan Town, Changshu, 215562, Jiangsu, China
Tel.: (86) 51252477677
Solar Wafer & Cells Mfr
N.A.I.C.S.: 334413

Canadian Solar (Australia) Pty., Ltd.   (1)
333 Drummond Street, Carlton, 3053, VIC, Australia
Tel.: (61) 386091844
Web Site: http://www.canadiansolar.com
Silicon Wafers Mfr
N.A.I.C.S.: 334413

Canadian Solar (USA) Inc.   (1)
1350 Treat Blvd Ste 500, Walnut Creek, CA 94597
Tel.: (925) 866-2700
Sales Range: $25-49.9 Million
Emp.: 65
Solar Cells Mfr & Distr
N.A.I.C.S.: 334413

Subsidiary (Domestic):

Recurrent Energy, LLC   (2)
300 California St 7th Fl, San Francisco, CA 94104
Tel.: (415) 675-1500
Web Site: http://www.recurrentenergy.com
Solar Electric Power Generation Services
N.A.I.C.S.: 221118
Donald P. Hutchison (Co-Founder)

Canadian Solar Construction S.R.L.   (1)
Via Mercato 3, 20121, Milan, Italy
Tel.: (39) 0239190730
Solar Electric Power Generation Services
N.A.I.C.S.: 221114

Canadian Solar EMEA GmbH   (1)
Radlkoferstrasse 2, 81373, Munich, Germany
Tel.: (49) 8951996890
Web Site: http://www.canadiansolar.com
Sales Range: $25-49.9 Million
Emp.: 50
Solar Cells & Module Mfr
N.A.I.C.S.: 334413

Canadian Solar Japan K.K.   (1)
Round-Cross Shinjuku 5-Chome 8F 5-17-5, Shinjuku-ku, Tokyo, 160-0022, Japan
Tel.: (81) 352918591
Web Site: http://www.canadiansolar.co.jp
Sales Range: $25-49.9 Million
Emp.: 100
Solar Cells & Module Mfr & Distr
N.A.I.C.S.: 334413
Yutaka Yamamoto (CEO)

Canadian Solar Manufacturing (Suzhou) Inc.   (1)
199 Lushan Road SND, Suzhou, 215129, Jiangsu, China
Tel.: (86) 51266908088
Web Site: http://www.canadiansolar.com
Emp.: 300
Wafer & Solar Cells Mfr
N.A.I.C.S.: 334413

Canadian Solar Projects K.K.   (1)
Shinjuku Mitsui Building 43F 2-1-1 Nishi-Shinjuku, Shinjuku-ku, Tokyo, 163-0443, Japan
Tel.: (81) 369112901
Web Site: https://canadiansolar-energy.co.jp

Solar Power Plant Distr
N.A.I.C.S.: 423690

Canadian Solar South Africa (Pty) Ltd.   (1)
4th Floor Suite F0405A Letterstedt, Newlands on Main Cnr Campground and Main Roads 7700, Cape Town, South Africa
Tel.: (27) 210014800
Web Site: https://www.canadiansolar.com
Solar Photovoltaic Product & Energy Solution Services
N.A.I.C.S.: 541690

Kazakhstan Solar Silicon LLP   (1)
st Sogrinskaya 223/6, Ust-Kamenogorsk, Oskemen, East Kazakhstan, Kazakhstan
Tel.: (7) 23 220 4150
Web Site: https://www.kazsolarsilicon.kz
Photovoltaic Silicon Cells Mfr
N.A.I.C.S.: 334413
Baizhumin Daniyar Anuarbekovich (Gen Dir)

MK KazSilicon LLP   (1)
Komarova St 1, Karatal District, Bastobe, 041011, Almaty Region, Kazakhstan
Tel.: (7) 283440373
Web Site: http://www.kazsilicon.kz
Metallurgical & Polycrystalline Silicon Mfr & Whslr
N.A.I.C.S.: 331110

CANADIAN SOLAR INFRA-STRUCTURE FUND, INC.
50th floor Mitsui Building 11 Nishi-iShinjuku 2chome, Shinjuku-ku, Tokyo, 160-0023, Japan
Tel.: (81) 362790311
Web Site:
  https://www.canadiansolarinfra.com
9284—(TKS)
Sales Range: Less than $1 Million
Investment Management Service
N.A.I.C.S.: 525990
Tetsuya Nakamura (Exec Dir)

CANADIAN SPIRIT RE-SOURCES INC.
900 140 4th Avenue SW, Calgary, T2P 3N3, AB, Canada
Tel.: (403) 294-5500   BC
Web Site: https://www.csri.ca
Year Founded: 1987
CSPUF—(OTCIQ)
Rev.: $18,186
Assets: $30,612,219
Liabilities: $2,412,993
Net Worth: $28,199,226
Earnings: ($1,547,445)
Fiscal Year-end: 12/31/20
Oil & Natural Gas Exploration Services
N.A.I.C.S.: 211120
Louisa DeCarlo (Chm, Pres & CEO)

CANADIAN TIRE CORPORA-TION LIMITED
2180 Yonge Street, PO Box 770, Station K, Toronto, M4P 2V8, ON, Canada
Tel.: (416) 480-3000   ON
Web Site:
  https://www.canadiantire.ca
Year Founded: 1927
CTC—(TSX)
Rev.: $12,304,424,910
Assets: $16,235,724,311
Liabilities: $11,474,846,716
Net Worth: $4,760,877,595
Earnings: $250,498,633
Emp.: 14,322
Fiscal Year-end: 12/31/23
Automobile Product Distr
N.A.I.C.S.: 441330
Mahes S. Wickramasinghe (Exec VP)

Subsidiaries:

Canadian Tire Bank   (1)
PO Box 3000, Welland, L3B 5S5, ON, Canada

Web Site: http://www.ctfs.com
Banking Services
N.A.I.C.S.: 522110

FGL Sports Ltd.   (1)
824 41st Ave NE, Calgary, T2E 3R3, AB, Canada
Tel.: (403) 717-1400
Web Site: http://www.forzanigroup.com
Sales Range: $1-4.9 Billion
Sporting Goods Retailer
N.A.I.C.S.: 459110

Helly Hansen Group AS   (1)
Munkedamsvelen 35 5th-7th Floor, 0250, Oslo, Norway
Tel.: (47) 2 105 0257
Web Site: https://www.hellyhansen.com
Holding Company; Rainwear & Other Outerwear Protective Garments Mfr & Distr
N.A.I.C.S.: 551112

Subsidiary (Domestic):

Helly Hansen AS   (2)
Munkedamsvelen 35 5th-7th Floor, N-0250, Oslo, Norway
Tel.: (47) 21 05 02 57
Web Site: http://www.hellyhansen.com
Rainwear & Other Outerwear Protective Garments Mfr & Distr
N.A.I.C.S.: 315250

Subsidiary (Non-US):

Helly Hansen Benelux B.V.   (2)
Holtum Noordweg 77, Born, 6121 RE, Netherlands
Tel.: (31) 467 440 214
Web Site: http://www.hellyhansen.com
Apparel Distr
N.A.I.C.S.: 424350

Helly Hansen Schweiz AG   (2)
Thurgauerstrasse 117, CH 8052, Zurich, Switzerland
Tel.: (41) 435 020133
Web Site: http://www.hellyhansen.com
Apparel Mfr & Distr
N.A.I.C.S.: 424350

Helly-Hansen (UK) Ltd.   (2)
Unit G3A Birkbeck House Colliers Way Phoenix Park, Nottingham, NG8 6AT, United Kingdom
Tel.: (44) 115 896 2388
Web Site: http://www.hellyhansen.com
Apparel Distr
N.A.I.C.S.: 424310

Subsidiary (US):

Helly-Hansen (US), Inc.   (2)
14218 8th St E Ste 100A, Sumner, WA 98390
Web Site: http://www.hellyhansen.com
Rainwear, Polypropylene Underwear, Outerwear, Skiwear & Sailing Gear Mfr & Distr
N.A.I.C.S.: 315250
Scott Sutherland (Dir-Fin)

Subsidiary (Non-US):

Helly-Hansen Deutschland Gmbh   (2)
Balanstrasse 73/Haus 10, D 81541, Munich, Germany
Tel.: (49) 8990420110
Web Site: http://www.hellyhansen.com
Apparel Distr
N.A.I.C.S.: 424350

MUSTO Limited   (2)
Birkbeck House Colliers Way, Nottingham, NG8 6AT, United Kingdom
Tel.: (44) 115 896 2387
Web Site: https://www.musto.com
Apparel Distr
N.A.I.C.S.: 424310

Marks Work Wearhouse Ltd.   (1)
30 1035 64th Ave SE Ste 30, Calgary, T2H 2J7, AB, Canada   (100%)
Tel.: (403) 255-9220
Web Site: http://www.marks.com
Sales Range: $250-299.9 Million
Emp.: 2,863
Retailer of Women's & Men's Workwear, Casual Wear, Custom Uniforms & Related Apparel
N.A.I.C.S.: 458110

Division (Domestic):

Marks Work Wearhouse   (2)
33 Heritage Meadows Way SE Unit 1120, Heritage Meadows Plaza, Calgary, T2H 3B8, AB, Canada   (100%)
Tel.: (403) 278-4885
Web Site: http://www.marks.com
Sales Range: $75-99.9 Million
Emp.: 300
Operator of Retail Clothing Stores
N.A.I.C.S.: 458110

CANADIAN UNIVERSITIES TRAVEL SERVICE LIMITED
45 Charles St E Ste 100, Toronto, M4Y 1S2, ON, Canada
Tel.: (416) 966-2887
Web Site: http://www.travelcuts.com
Sales Range: $150-199.9 Million
Emp.: 380
Travel Agency
N.A.I.C.S.: 561510
Rodney Hurd (Pres)

CANADIAN UTILITIES & TELE-COM INCOME FUND
121 King Street West Suite 2600, PO Box 113, Toronto, M5H 3T9, ON, Canada
Tel.: (416) 681-3966   ON
Year Founded: 2010
UTE.UN—(TSX)
Rev.: $2,948,919
Assets: $11,934,561
Liabilities: $687,668
Net Worth: $11,246,894
Earnings: $2,522,846
Fiscal Year-end: 12/31/19
Closed-End Investment Fund
N.A.I.C.S.: 525990
John P. Mulvihill (Chm, Pres, CEO & Sec)

CANADIAN WESTERN BANK
Suite 3000 10303 Jasper Avenue, Edmonton, T5J 3X6, AB, Canada
Tel.: (780) 423-8888
Web Site: https://www.cwb.com
Year Founded: 1984
CBWBF—(OTCIQ)
Rev.: $1,221,847,043
Assets: $32,417,795,066
Liabilities: $29,497,562,601
Net Worth: $2,920,232,465
Earnings: $263,547,003
Emp.: 2,712
Fiscal Year-end: 10/31/22
Commercial Banking Services
N.A.I.C.S.: 522110
Robert Lawrence Phillips (Chm)

Subsidiaries:

CWB McLean & Partners Wealth Management Ltd.   (1)
801 - 10th Avenue SW, Calgary, T2R 0B4, AB, Canada
Tel.: (403) 234-0005
Web Site:
  http://www.cwbmcleanpartners.com
Financial Services
N.A.I.C.S.: 523999
Kevin Dehod (Pres & CEO)

Canadian Direct Financial   (1)
Suite 3000 10303 Jasper Avenue NW, Edmonton, T5J 3X6, AB, Canada
Tel.: (780) 441-2249
Web Site: https://www.motivefinancial.com
Loan Services
N.A.I.C.S.: 522291

Canadian Western Trust   (1)
Suite 300 - 750 Cambie Street, Vancouver, V6B 0A2, BC, Canada   (100%)
Tel.: (604) 685-2081
Web Site: https://www.cwt.ca
Sales Range: $50-74.9 Million
Emp.: 75
Trust, Deposits & Lending
N.A.I.C.S.: 522210

Division (Domestic):

Optimum Mortgage (2)
1010 10303 Jasper Ave, Edmonton, T5J
3X6, AB, Canada
Web Site: http://www.optimummortgage.ca
Mortgage Lending Services
N.A.I.C.S.: 522310

McLean & Partners Wealth Manage-
ment Ltd. (1)
801 10th Avenue SW, Calgary, T2R 0B4,
AB, Canada
Tel.: (403) 234-0005
Web Site: https://www.cwbwealth.com
Wealth Management Services
N.A.I.C.S.: 523940

National Leasing Group Inc. (1)
1525 Buffalo Place, Winnipeg, R3T 1L9,
MB, Canada
Web Site:
   http://www.cwbnationalleasing.com
Equipment Leasing Services
N.A.I.C.S.: 532490

CANAF INVESTMENTS INC.
1100-1111 Melville Street, Vancouver,
V6E 3V6, BC, Canada
Tel.: (604) 283-6110
Web Site:
   https://www.canafinvestments.com
Year Founded: 1996
CAFZF—(OTCIQ)
Rev.: $24,410,033
Assets: $10,283,550
Liabilities: $2,661,198
Net Worth: $7,622,352
Earnings: $2,217,535
Fiscal Year-end: 10/31/23
Mineral Exploration Services
N.A.I.C.S.: 213114
Christopher Way (Pres & CEO)

Subsidiaries:

Quantum Screening and Crushing
(Proprietary) Limited (1)
78 Sutherland Street, Newcastle, 765,
Kwazulu-Natal, South Africa
Tel.: (27) 343127750
Web Site: http://www.southern-col.co.za
Sales Range: $25-49.9 Million
Emp.: 30
Coal Prodcuts Mfr
N.A.I.C.S.: 324199
Peter Cronje (Mgr)

Subsidiary (Domestic):

Southern Coal (Proprietary)
Limited (2)
45 Harding Street, Newcastle, 2940,
Kwazulu-Natal, South Africa
Tel.: (27) 343127750
Web Site: http://www.southern-coal.co.za
Emp.: 3
Anthracite Mining Services
N.A.I.C.S.: 212115

CANAFARMA HEMP PROD-
UCTS CORP.
2080-777 Hornby Street, Vancouver,
V6Z 1S4, BC, Canada
Tel.: (214) 704-7942
Web Site:
   http://www.canafarmacorp.com
CNFA—(CNSX)
Rev.: $1,804,188
Assets: $6,761,461
Liabilities: $6,860,469
Net Worth: ($99,008)
Earnings: ($17,801,347)
Fiscal Year-end: 06/30/20
Pharmaceuticals Product Mfr
N.A.I.C.S.: 325412
Vitaly Fargesen (Sr VP-Strategic
Plng)

CANAGOLD RESOURCES
LTD.
Suite 1250625 Howe Street, Vancou-
ver, V6C 2T6, BC, Canada

Tel.: (604) 685-9700   BC
Web Site:
   https://www.canagoldresources.com
CANA—(DEU)
Rev.: $1,000
Assets: $32,628,000
Liabilities: $3,115,000
Net Worth: $29,513,000
Earnings: ($2,705,000)
Emp.: 3
Fiscal Year-end: 12/31/22
Gold Mining
N.A.I.C.S.: 212220
Chris Pharness (Sr VP-Sustainability
& Permitting)

CANAL BANK, S.A.
Ave Costa Del Sol, Panama, Panama
Tel.: (507) 8005625
Web Site: http://www.canalbank.com
Rev.: $24,381,559
Assets: $532,359,690
Liabilities: $485,950,627
Net Worth: $46,409,063
Earnings: $807,315
Fiscal Year-end: 12/31/21
Commercial Banking Services
N.A.I.C.S.: 522110
Raul Quevedo (Exec VP & Gen Mgr)

CANALASKA URANIUM LTD.
Suite 580 625 Howe Street, Vancou-
ver, V6C 2T6, BC, Canada
Tel.: (604) 688-3211   BC
Web Site: https://www.canalaska.com
CVV—(OTCIQ)
Rev.: $28,944
Assets: $12,665,113
Liabilities: $1,649,046
Net Worth: $11,016,067
Earnings: ($4,837,620)
Emp.: 1
Fiscal Year-end: 04/30/22
Uranium Mining Services
N.A.I.C.S.: 212290
Thomas Graham Jr. (Chm)

CANALI S.P.A.
Via Lombardia 17/19 Sovico, 20845,
Milan, Monza and Brianza, Italy
Tel.: (39) 0223345876   IT
Web Site: http://www.canali.com
Year Founded: 1934
Sales Range: $200-249.9 Million
Emp.: 1,600
Men Apparel Mfr & Distr
N.A.I.C.S.: 315210
Elisabetta Canali (Dir-Grp Comm)

Subsidiaries:

Canali USA Inc. (1)
415 W 13th St 2nd Fl, New York, NY 10014
Tel.: (212) 767-0205
Sales Range: $25-49.9 Million
Emp.: 25
Men's Apparel
N.A.I.C.S.: 315210
Lisa Ranieri-Emanuel (Mgr-PR)

CANAM COAL CORP.
202 1201-5th Street SW, Calgary,
T2R 0Y6, AB, Canada
Tel.: (403) 262-3797   AB
Web Site: http://www.canamcoal.com
Year Founded: 1994
Sales Range: $50-74.9 Million
Coal Mining & Production Services
N.A.I.C.S.: 212115
Eric Hallmark (CFO)

CANAMERA ENERGY METALS
CORP.
Suite 710 1030 West Georgia Street,
Vancouver, V6E 2Y3, BC, Canada
Tel.: (604) 910-1804   BC
Year Founded: 2018
EMET—(CNSX)

Assets: $226,673
Liabilities: $44,426
Net Worth: $182,248
Earnings: ($53,584)
Fiscal Year-end: 04/30/21
Mineral Exploration Services
N.A.I.C.S.: 213115
Daryn Gordon (CFO)

CANAMEX GOLD CORP.
Suite 804-750 West Pender Street,
Vancouver, V6C 3T7, BC, Canada
Tel.: (604) 833-4278   BC
Web Site:
   http://www.canamexgold.com
Year Founded: 2009
CSQ—(CNSX)
Sales Range: Less than $1 Million
Gold Exploration Services
N.A.I.C.S.: 212220
Mike Stark (Chm)

CANAQUEST MEDICAL CORP
37-4120 Ridgeway Drive, Missis-
sauga, L5L 5S9, ON, Canada
Tel.: (416) 704-3040   Ca
Web Site: https://ir.canaquest.com
Year Founded: 2008
CANQF—(OTCIQ)
Assets: $104,000
Liabilities: $848,000
Net Worth: ($744,000)
Earnings: ($615,000)
Emp.: 4
Fiscal Year-end: 03/31/23
Medical & Botanical Mfr
N.A.I.C.S.: 325411
Paul Ramsay (Co-Founder, Chm &
Pres)

CANARA BANK
No 112 JC Road, Bengaluru, 560002,
Karnataka, India
Tel.: (91) 8022115526   In
Web Site:
   https://www.canarabank.com
Year Founded: 1906
532483—(BOM)
Rev.: $127,845,559
Assets: $1,610,071,554
Liabilities: $1,524,882,464
Net Worth: $85,189,090
Earnings: $3,945,669
Emp.: 88,213
Fiscal Year-end: 03/31/21
Commercial Banking Services
N.A.I.C.S.: 522110
Debashish Mukherjee (Exec Dir)

Subsidiaries:

CAN FIN HOMES LIMITED (1)
No 29/1 Sir M N Krishna Rao Road Lalbagh
West, Basavanagudi, Bengaluru, 560 004,
India
Tel.: (91) 8026567655
Web Site: https://www.canfinhomes.com
Rev.: $275,515,859
Assets: $3,013,066,152
Liabilities: $2,656,827,401
Net Worth: $356,238,751
Earnings: $62,252,231
Emp.: 756
Fiscal Year-end: 03/31/2021
Housing Loan Financial Services
N.A.I.C.S.: 522299
Shamila M. (Gen Mgr)

Canara Bank (Tanzania) Ltd. (1)
Plot No 16/1 Elia Complex Zanaki - Bibi Titi
Street, P B No 491, Dar es Salaam, Tanza-
nia
Tel.: (255) 222112530
Web Site: https://www.canarabank.co.tz
Emp.: 25
Banking Services
N.A.I.C.S.: 522110

Canara Bank Securities Ltd. (1)
VII Floor Maker Chambers III, Nariman
Point, Mumbai, 400 021, India

Tel.: (91) 2222802400
Web Site: https://www.canmoney.in
Banking Services
N.A.I.C.S.: 522110
Debashish Mukherjee (Chm)

Canara Robecco Asset Management
Company Ltd. (1)
4th Floor Construction House 5 Walchand
Hirachand Marg, Ballard Estate Fort, Mum-
bai, 400001, Maharashtra, India
Tel.: (91) 8002092726
Web Site: https://www.canararobeco.com
N.A.I.C.S.: 523940

Canbank Computer Services
Limited (1)
218 I Floor JP Royale Sampige Road Near
14th Cross, Malleswaram, Bengaluru, 560
003, India (100%)
Tel.: (91) 8023469661
Web Site: https://www.ccsl.co.in
Sales Range: $25-49.9 Million
Emp.: 90
Custom Computer Programming Services
N.A.I.C.S.: 541511

Canbank Factors Limited (1)
No 67/1 Kanakapura Main Road Near Lal-
bagh West Gate, Basavanagudi, Bengaluru,
560 004, India (80%)
Tel.: (91) 8022420245
Web Site: https://www.canbankfactors.com
Sales Range: $50-74.9 Million
Emp.: 25
Activities Related to Credit Intermediation
N.A.I.C.S.: 522390
P. V. Bharathi (Vice Chm)

Canbank Financial Services
Limited (1)
Naveen Complex 6th Floor M G Road, 14
M G Road, 560001, Bengaluru,
India (100%)
Tel.: (91) 8025583844
Sales Range: $50-74.9 Million
Emp.: 2
Activities Related to Credit Intermediation
N.A.I.C.S.: 522390

Canbank Venture Capital Fund
Limited (1)
No 29 2nd floor DwarakanathBhavan K R
Road, Bengaluru, 560 004, India
Tel.: (91) 8041518461
Web Site: https://canbank.vc
Sales Range: $50-74.9 Million
Emp.: 11
Open-End Investment Funds
N.A.I.C.S.: 525910
K. Baskaran (Mng Dir)

Syndicate Bank Ltd. (1)
Door No 16/355 16/365 A, Udupi District,
Manipal, 576 104, Karnataka, India
Tel.: (91) 8202571181
Web Site: http://www.syndicatebank.in
Rev.: $3,434,319,410
Assets: $44,880,021,969
Liabilities: $42,187,566,757
Net Worth: $2,692,455,212
Earnings: ($371,080,009)
Emp.: 31,521
Fiscal Year-end: 03/31/2019
Banking Services
N.A.I.C.S.: 522110
Uday Sankar Majumder (CFO & Gen Mgr)

Subsidiary (Domestic):

Syndbank Services Limited (2)
10/1 1st Floor Rajdhoot Complex Mysore
Bank Circle Avenue Road, Bengaluru, 560
002, Karnataka, India
Tel.: (91) 80 41486575
Web Site: http://www.syndbankservices.in
Sales Range: $50-74.9 Million
Emp.: 5
Commercial Banking Services
N.A.I.C.S.: 522110
D. K. Kundu (Mng Dir)

CANARC RESOURCES CORP.
Suite 810-625 Howe Street, Vancou-
ver, V6C 2T6, BC, Canada
Tel.: (604) 685-9700
Web Site: http://www.canarc.net
Gold Ore Mining Services

Canarc Resources Corp.—(Continued)
N.A.I.C.S.: 212220
Garry Biles *(Pres & COO)*

CANARE ELECTRIC CO., LTD.
5F LIVMO Rising Bldg 3-19-1 Shin-yokohama, Kohoku-ku, Yokohama, 222-0033, Japan
Tel.: (81) 456207332
Web Site: https://www.canare.co.jp
Year Founded: 1970
5819—(TKS)
Rev.: $91,262,480
Assets: $134,057,720
Liabilities: $13,378,830
Net Worth: $120,678,890
Earnings: $8,422,920
Emp.: 125
Fiscal Year-end: 12/31/23
Cable Products Mfr
N.A.I.C.S.: 335929
Masahiro Nakajima *(Pres)*

Subsidiaries:

Canare Corporation **(1)**
45 Commerce Wy Unit C, Totowa, NJ 07512
Tel.: (973) 837-0070
Web Site: https://www.canare.com
Cable & Connector Mfr & Distr
N.A.I.C.S.: 334417

Canare Corporation of America **(1)**
45 Commerce Way Unit C, Totowa, NJ 07512
Tel.: (973) 837-0070
Web Site: https://www.canare.com
Communication Equipment Mfr
N.A.I.C.S.: 335929

Canare Corporation of Korea **(1)**
Korea Canary Building 1488-10 Gaeyang 3-Dong, Gangseo-gu, Seoul, Korea (South)
Tel.: (82) 226682560
Web Site: http://www.canare.co.kr
Video Cable Connector Mfr & Distr
N.A.I.C.S.: 334417

Canare Corporation of Taiwan **(1)**
4F No 512-6 Yuan-San Road, Chung-Ho City, Taipei, 235, Taiwan
Tel.: (886) 2 2222 1010
Web Site: http://www.canare.com.tw
Communication Equipment Distr
N.A.I.C.S.: 423610

Canare Electric (Shanghai) Co., Ltd. **(1)**
999 Ning Qiao Road, Jinjiao Export Processing Zone, Shanghai, China
Tel.: (86) 2150326650
Web Site: https://www.canare.com
Cable & Connector Mfr & Distr
N.A.I.C.S.: 334417

Canare Electric Corporation of Tianjin Co., Ltd. **(1)**
Room 1806 Full Tower 9 Dongsanhuan Middle Road, Chaoyang District, Beijing, 100020, China
Tel.: (86) 1085911490
Video Cable Connector Mfr & Distr
N.A.I.C.S.: 334417

Canare Electric India Private Limited **(1)**
Suite 104 L Block Market CSC Sarita Vihar, Delhi, 110076, India
Tel.: (91) 1141052365
Web Site: http://www.canare.in
Video Cable Connector Mfr & Distr
N.A.I.C.S.: 334417

Canare Europe GmbH **(1)**
Hoffeldstr 104 Hof 4Hoffeldstr 104 Hof 4, 40235, Dusseldorf, Germany
Tel.: (49) 21191734503
Web Site: http://www.canare.eu
Video Cable Connector Mfr & Distr
N.A.I.C.S.: 334417

Canare France SAS **(1)**
14-30 rue de Mantes, 92700, Colombes, France
Tel.: (33) 1 42 42 16 23
Web Site: http://www.canare.fr
Communication Equipment Mfr

N.A.I.C.S.: 335929
Jean Lepicard *(Mgr)*

Canare Middle East FZCO **(1)**
Dubai Airport Free Zone DAFZA Industrial Park Beirut St, PO Box 20218, W/H no 27 QD-06 Opposite to FEWA Commercial Bank of Dubai Al Qusais, Dubai, United Arab Emirates
Tel.: (971) 4 323 3450
Web Site: https://www.canare-me.com
Video Cable Connector Mfr & Distr
N.A.I.C.S.: 334417
Momen Nabil *(Gen Mgr)*

Canare Singapore Private Limited **(1)**
4012 Ang Mo Kio Ave 10 02-08/09 Techplace I, Singapore, 569628, Singapore
Tel.: (65) 6 293 5692
Web Site: https://www.canare.com.sg
Video Cable Connector Mfr & Distr
N.A.I.C.S.: 334417

CANARGO ENERGY CORPORATION
70 Kostava Street, Tbilisi, 0171, Georgia
Tel.: (995) 233 25 27   DE
Sales Range: $1-9.9 Million
Emp.: 150
Holding Company; Oil & Gas Exploration Services
N.A.I.C.S.: 551112
Vincent McDonnell *(Chm, Pres, CEO, COO & Chief Comml Officer)*

Subsidiaries:

CanArgo Limited **(1)**
PO Box 291, Saint Peter Port, GY1 3RR, Guernsey
Tel.: (44) 1481729980
Oil & Gas Exploration Services
N.A.I.C.S.: 211120

Subsidiary (Non-US):

CanArgo Georgia Ltd **(2)**
70 Kostava Street, Tbilisi, 0171, Georgia
Tel.: (995) 599 56 23 65
Emp.: 200
Oil & Gas Exploration Services
N.A.I.C.S.: 211120
David Ramsay *(Dir Gen, COO & Country Mgr)*

CANARIABIO INC.
23 Yongsugol-gil, Dongnam-gu, Cheonan, 31202, Korea (South)
Tel.: (82) 415638200
Web Site: http://www.hdfeed.co.kr
016790—(KRS)
Rev.: $121,259,343
Assets: $208,065,508
Liabilities: $175,566,600
Net Worth: $32,498,908
Earnings: ($216,870,114)
Emp.: 96
Fiscal Year-end: 12/31/22
Animal Feed Mfr
N.A.I.C.S.: 311119

CANARYS AUTOMATIONS LIMITED
566 & 567 30th Main Attimabbe Road Banagirinagara, Banashankari 3rd Stage, Bengaluru, Karnataka, India, 560085
Tel.: (91) 8026799915
Web Site: https://ecanarys.com
Year Founded: 1988
CANARYS—(NSE)
Rev.: $1,728,812
Assets: $3,631,487
Liabilities: $3,535,082
Net Worth: $96,404
Earnings: ($165,315)
Emp.: 326
Fiscal Year-end: 03/31/23
Software Development Services
N.A.I.C.S.: 541511

Raghu Chandrashekhariah *(CFO)*

CANASIL RESOURCES INC.
1760-750 West Pender Street, Vancouver, V6C 2T8, BC, Canada
Tel.: (604) 708-3788
Web Site: https://www.canasil.com
CNSUF—(OTCIQ)
пov.: $1,000
Assets: $472,636
Liabilities: $71,766
Net Worth: $400,871
Earnings: ($1,742,865)
Fiscal Year-end: 12/31/21
Mineral Properties Acquisition & Development; Gold, Silver, Copper & Zinc Mining
N.A.I.C.S.: 212220
Graham H. Scott *(Sec)*

Subsidiaries:

Minera Canasil, S.A. de C.V. **(1)**
Tel.: (52) 6181296082
Mineral Exploration Services
N.A.I.C.S.: 213115

CANATURE HEALTH TECHNOLOGY GROUP CO., LTD.
No 518 & 508 Chuan Da Road, Pudong, Shanghai, 201299, China
Tel.: (86) 2158599999
Web Site: https://www.canature-global.com
Year Founded: 2001
300272—(CHIN)
Rev.: $180,959,395
Assets: $278,598,596
Liabilities: $92,217,099
Net Worth: $186,381,497
Earnings: $4,047,808
Emp.: 600
Fiscal Year-end: 12/31/20
Water Purification Products Mfr
N.A.I.C.S.: 221310
Lijun Zhao *(Chm)*

CANBAS CO., LTD.
2-2-1 Otemachi, Numazu, 410-0801, Japan
Tel.: (81) 559543666
Web Site: https://www.canbas.co.jp
Year Founded: 2000
4575—(TKS)
Sales Range: $1-9.9 Million
Emp.: 20
Cancer Pharmaceutical Researcher, Developer & Mfr
N.A.I.C.S.: 325412
Takumi Kawabe *(Pres & CEO)*

CANBRIDGE PHARMACEUTICALS INC.
Suite 301 3F Timeloit No 17 RongChuang Road, Chaoyang, Beijing, China
Tel.: (86) 1084148018   Ky
Web Site: https://www.canbridgepharma.com
Year Founded: 2012
1228—(HKG)
Rev.: $14,243,326
Assets: $54,741,083
Liabilities: $60,250,055
Net Worth: ($5,508,972)
Earnings: ($52,453,063)
Emp.: 100
Fiscal Year-end: 12/31/23
Pharmaceutical Product Mfr & Distr
N.A.I.C.S.: 325412
Chris Chen *(VP)*

CANBURG LIMITED
Hopton Industrial Works, London Road, Devizes, SN10 2EU, Wilts, United Kingdom
Tel.: (44) 1380729090   UK
Web Site: http://www.canburg.com

Year Founded: 2009
Sales Range: $50-74.9 Million
Emp.: 400
Holding Company; Wood Household Furniture & Kitchen Cabinetry Designer, Mfr & Distr
N.A.I.C.S.: 551112
Leo Caplan *(Owner, Chm & CEO)*

Subsidiaries:

Mark Wilkinson Furniture Limited **(1)**
The Hopton Works Hopton Industrial Works, London Rd, Devizes, SN10 2EU, Wilts, United Kingdom
Tel.: (44) 1380850007
Web Site: http://www.mwf.com
Sales Range: $25-49.9 Million
Emp.: 300
Wood Household Furniture & Kitchen Cabinetry Designer Mfr
N.A.I.C.S.: 337122
Mark Wilkinson *(Founder)*

Smallbone & Co (Devizes) Limited **(1)**
The Hopton Works Hopton Industrial Works, London Rd, Devizes, SN10 2EU, Wilts, United Kingdom
Tel.: (44) 1380729090
Web Site: http://www.smallbone.co.uk
Sales Range: $25-49.9 Million
Emp.: 180
Wood Household Furniture & Kitchen Cabinetry Designer, Mfr & Distr; Ceramic & Stone Wall & Floor Tile Mfr & Distr
N.A.I.C.S.: 337122
Cameron Patfield *(Gen Mgr)*

CANCOM SE
Erika-Mann-Strasse 69, 80636, Munich, Germany
Tel.: (49) 89540540   De
Web Site: https://www.cancom.de
Year Founded: 1992
COK—(MUN)
Rev.: $1,680,895,965
Assets: $1,709,320,618
Liabilities: $910,030,428
Net Worth: $799,290,190
Earnings: $40,655,532
Emp.: 5,225
Fiscal Year-end: 12/31/23
Holding Company; IT Infrastructure & Professional Services
N.A.I.C.S.: 551112

Subsidiaries:

CANCOM Financial Services GmbH **(1)**
Messerschmittstrasse 20 Scheppach, 89343, Jettingen, Germany
Tel.: (49) 82259960
Information Technology Services
N.A.I.C.S.: 513210

CANCOM ICT Service GmbH **(1)**
Erika-Mann-Strasse 69, 80636, Munich, Germany
Tel.: (49) 893681680
Information Technology Services
N.A.I.C.S.: 513210

CANCOM IT Solutions GmbH **(1)**
Industriestrasse 3, 70565, Stuttgart, Germany
Tel.: (49) 711735820
Sales Range: $25-49.9 Million
Emp.: 10
Information Technology Solutions
N.A.I.C.S.: 541512

Subsidiary (Domestic):

acentrix GmbH **(2)**
Erika-Mann-Strasse 69, 80339, Munich, Germany
Tel.: (49) 8954054520
Web Site: http://www.acentrix.de
Sales Range: $10-24.9 Million
Information Technology Solutions
N.A.I.C.S.: 541512
Thomas Heinz *(Mng Dir)*

CANCOM NSG GIS GmbH **(1)**
Messerschmittstr 20, D-89343, Jettingen,

Bavaria, Germany
Tel.: (49) 8225 996 1381
Web Site: http://www.cancom.de
Recruitment Services
N.A.I.C.S.: 561311

CANCOM NSG GmbH (1)
Ridlerstrasse 37, 80339, Munich, Bavaria,
Germany
Tel.: (49) 893681680
Web Site: http://www.cancom.de
Sales Range: $25-49.9 Million
Emp.: 80
Information Technology Solutions
N.A.I.C.S.: 541512

CANCOM Physical Infrastructure GmbH (1)
Wettmannsberger Weg 30 Allgau, 87437,
Kempten, Germany
Tel.: (49) 831521910
Information Technology Services
N.A.I.C.S.: 513210
Christian Steininger (Mng Dir)

CANCOM Public BV (1)
Rue Montoyer 25, 1000, Brussels, Belgium
Tel.: (32) 25373504
Information Technology Services
N.A.I.C.S.: 513210
Nancy Anthoons (Ops Mgr)

CANCOM Public GmbH (1)
Granatenstrasse 19-20, 13409, Berlin, Germany
Tel.: (49) 304976918300
Information Technology Services
N.A.I.C.S.: 541511

CANCOM SYSDAT GmbH (1)
Kirchweg 2, Cologne, 50858, Germany
Tel.: (49) 2219488101
Web Site: http://www.cancom.de
Sales Range: $25-49.9 Million
Emp.: 150
Information Technology Solutions
N.A.I.C.S.: 541511
Manfred Hoevel (VP)

CANCOM VVM GmbH (1)
Am Kabellager 5, 51063, Cologne, Germany
Tel.: (49) 221948810
Web Site: http://www.cancom-pironet.de
Information Technology Services
N.A.I.C.S.: 513210
Matthias Renneberg (Head-Network Infrastructure Svc)

CANCOM a+d IT Solutions GmbH (1)
Heinrich-Bablik-Strasse 17, 2345, Brunn am
Gebirge, Austria
Tel.: (43) 506050
Web Site: http://www.cancom.at
Information Technology Solutions
N.A.I.C.S.: 541512

CANCOM on line GmbH (1)
Granatenstrasse 19-20, 13409, Berlin, Germany
Tel.: (49) 30396038620
Web Site: http://www.onlinedaten-gmbh.cancom.de
Information Technology Services
N.A.I.C.S.: 513210
Tatjana Limberg (Sls Mgr)

CANCOM, Inc. (1)
6700 Koll Center Pkwy Ste 250, Pleasanton, CA 94566
Tel.: (925) 965-0700
Information Technology Services
N.A.I.C.S.: 513210
Scott Spencer (Acct Mgr-Enterprise)

NWC Services GmbH (1)
Karlsruher Strasse 34, 75179, Pforzheim,
Germany
Tel.: (49) 72311270
Web Site: https://www.nwc-services.de
Information Technology Services
N.A.I.C.S.: 541511

CANDAX ENERGY INC.
36 Toronto Street Suite 1000, Toronto, M5C 2C5, ON, Canada
Tel.: (447) 983-7438   BC
Year Founded: 2004

CAX—(TSX)
Energy Production & Development
Services
N.A.I.C.S.: 221112

Subsidiaries:

Candax Madagascar Ltd. (1)
Immeuble SANTA Lot 3E Etage, Antananarivo, 101, Madagascar
Tel.: (261) 20 22 265 58
Web Site: http://www.candax.com
Energy Production & Development Services
N.A.I.C.S.: 221112

Falcan Chaal Petroleum, Ltd (1)
Rue Du Lac Windermere Les Berges Du
Lac, Tunis, 1053, Tunisia
Tel.: (216) 71962611
Sales Range: $50-74.9 Million
Emp.: 15
Natural Gas Exploration Service
N.A.I.C.S.: 213112

CANDEAL CO., LTD.
111 Kitayamabushicho, Shinjuku-ku,
Tokyo, 162-0853, Japan
Tel.: (81) 368621701
Web Site: https://www.candeal.co.jp
Year Founded: 2014
1446—(TKS)
Rev.: $87,270,810
Assets: $44,135,250
Liabilities: $24,949,710
Net Worth: $19,185,540
Earnings: $1,588,160
Fiscal Year-end: 09/30/23
Building Repair & Inspection Services
N.A.I.C.S.: 541350

CANDELARIA MINING CORP.
Suite 1201, 1166 Alberni Street, Vancouver, V6E 3Z3, BC, Canada
Tel.: (604) 349-5992   BC
Web Site:
   https://www.candelariamining.com
Year Founded: 2012
CAND—(OTCIQ)
Assets: $14,301,643
Liabilities: $3,211,259
Net Worth: $11,090,384
Earnings: ($4,067,074)
Fiscal Year-end: 04/30/21
Investment Services
N.A.I.C.S.: 523999
Manuel Gomez (Chm)

CANDENTE COPPER CORP.
Suite 801 - 1112 West Pender Street,
Vancouver, V6E 2S1, BC, Canada
Tel.: (604) 689-1957   Ca
Web Site:
   http://www.candentecopper.com
Year Founded: 1997
DNT—(LIM)
Assets: $65,996,849
Liabilities: $580,200
Net Worth: $65,416,649
Earnings: $1,175,913
Emp.: 14
Fiscal Year-end: 12/31/21
Copper Ore Exploration & Mining Development Services
N.A.I.C.S.: 213114
Joanne C. Freeze (Founder, Pres & CEO)

Subsidiaries:

Canariaco Copper Peru S.A. (1)
Calle Antequera 777 -Oficina 1101, San
Isidro, Lima, Peru
Tel.: (51) 5117152001
Copper Exploration Services
N.A.I.C.S.: 212230

CANDEREL MANAGEMENT INC.
900-2000 Peel Street, Montreal, H3A
2W5, QC, Canada

Tel.: (514) 842-8636
Web Site: http://www.canderel.com
Year Founded: 1975
Sales Range: $25-49.9 Million
Real Estate Development Services
N.A.I.C.S.: 531190
Douglas Pascal (Vice Chm)

Subsidiaries:

Canderel Commercial Services Inc. (1)
1750 - 360 Albert Street, Ottawa, K1R 7X7,
ON, Canada
Tel.: (613) 688-3558
Real Estate Development Services
N.A.I.C.S.: 531390
Daniel D. Peritz (Sr VP)

Canderel Pacific Inc. (1)
1590-505 Burrard Street Box 96, Vancouver, V7X 1M5, BC, Canada
Tel.: (604) 639-5987
Web Site: https://www.canderel.com
Real Estate Development Services
N.A.I.C.S.: 531390
Bryce Margetts (VP)

Canderel Residential Inc. (1)
1075 Bay Street Suite 400, Toronto, M5S
2B1, ON, Canada
Tel.: (416) 593-6366
Web Site:
   http://www.canderelresidential.com
Residential Property Management Services
N.A.I.C.S.: 531311
Brett Miller (CEO)

Cominar Real Estate Investment Trust (1)
2820 Laurier Blvd Suite 850, Quebec, G1V
0C1, QC, Canada
Tel.: (514) 213-0295
Web Site: http://www.cominar.com
Rev.: $517,337,410
Assets: $5,002,116,576
Liabilities: $2,870,809,579
Net Worth: $2,131,306,997
Earnings: ($257,586,812)
Emp.: 535
Fiscal Year-end: 12/31/2020
Real Estate Investment Trust
N.A.I.C.S.: 525990
Wally Commisso (Exec VP-Ops & Property Mgmt)

CANDOUR TECHTEX LTD.
110 TV Industrial Estate 52 SK Ahire
Marg Worli, Mumbai, 400 030, India
Tel.: (91) 9820150865
Web Site: https://www.cteil.com
522292—(BOM)
Rev.: $9,663,595
Assets: $8,047,496
Liabilities: $5,231,383
Net Worth: $2,816,114
Earnings: $150,628
Emp.: 7
Fiscal Year-end: 03/31/21
Yarn Mfr
N.A.I.C.S.: 313110
Jayesh Ramniklal Mehta (Founder & Mng Dir)

Subsidiaries:

Chandni Machines Limited (1)
110 52 TV Industrial Estate S K Ahire Marg
Worli, Mumbai, 400030, Maharashtra, India
Tel.: (91) 919820150865
Web Site: https://www.cml.net.in
Rev.: $5,927,570
Assets: $5,854,997
Liabilities: $5,151,952
Net Worth: $703,044
Earnings: $4,682
Emp.: 7
Fiscal Year-end: 03/31/2021
Industrial Machinery Mfr
N.A.I.C.S.: 333248
Bharat Keshavlal Shah (Exec Dir)

CANDOVER INVESTMENTS PLC

34 Lime Street, London, EC3M 7AT,
United Kingdom
Tel.: (44) 2074899848   UK
Web Site:
   http://www.candoverinvestments.com
Year Founded: 1980
Private Equity Investment Trust
N.A.I.C.S.: 525920
Malcolm Fallen (CEO)

Subsidiaries:

Candover Services Limited (1)
20 Old Bailey, London, EC4M 7LN, United
Kingdom
Tel.: (44) 2074899848
Investment Management Service
N.A.I.C.S.: 523999

CANDRAFT DETAILING, INC.
889 Carnarvon St, New Westminster,
V3M 1G2, BC, Canada
Tel.: (604) 525-0055
Web Site: http://www.candraft.com
Year Founded: 1979
Sales Range: $10-24.9 Million
Emp.: 50
Bridge Drafting & Detailing Services
N.A.I.C.S.: 541340
John Cooper (Founder & Pres)

CANDY TOY - INDUSTRIA E COMERCIO DE ALIMENTOS E PLASTICOS LTDA
Rua Dona Rima Simao, Duartina,
Sao Paulo, 17470-009, Brazil
Tel.: (55) 1432821059
Web Site:
   https://www.candytoy.com.br
Year Founded: 2011
Food Product Mfr & Distr
N.A.I.C.S.: 333241

CANDYM ENTERPRISES LTD.
95 Clegg Rd, Markham, L6G 1B9,
ON, Canada
Tel.: (905) 474-1555
Web Site: http://www.candym.com
Rev.: $17,248,140
Emp.: 48
Gift Wares Mfr & Distr
N.A.I.C.S.: 424990
Bruce Brown (Gen Mgr-Sls)

CANEFCO LIMITED
10 Milner Business Ct Ste 301, Scarborough, M1B 3C6, ON, Canada
Tel.: (416) 335-6556
Web Site: http://www.canefco.com
Sales Range: $10-24.9 Million
Emp.: 15
Custom Mfr, Designer & Installer of
Industrial Heat Processing Equipment, Specializing in the Aluminum
Industry
N.A.I.C.S.: 333414

CANEO SA
14 Faubourg des Ancetres, BP
40269, 90000, Belfort, France
Tel.: (33) 384267542
Web Site: http://www.caneo.eu
Soft Drink & Juice Mfr & Sales
N.A.I.C.S.: 312111
Renaud Meger-Tissiere (Co-Chm)

CANERECTOR INC.
1 Sparks Avenue, North York, M2H
2W1, ON, Canada
Tel.: (416) 225-6240
Web Site:
   https://www.canerector.com
Year Founded: 1947
Sales Range: $500-549.9 Million
Emp.: 2,000
Steel Work & Blast Furnace Mfr
N.A.I.C.S.: 333994
William Nickel (Pres)

Canerector Inc.—(Continued)

Subsidiaries:

Associated Valve (1)
703 19th Ave, Nisku, T9E 7V9, AB, Canada (100%)
Tel.: (780) 979-0505
Web Site: http://www.associatedvalve.com
Sales Range: $50-74.9 Million
Emp.: 5
Valve Mfr
N.A.I.C.S.: 332919

C.E. MacPherson Division of Conrex Steel Ltd. (1)
468 Rideau St, Kingston, K7K 3B1, ON, Canada (100%)
Tel.: (613) 549-2001
Web Site: http://www.conrex.kingston.net
Sales Range: $1-9.9 Million
Emp.: 16
Pipe & Steel Fittings Mfr
N.A.I.C.S.: 332919

Capitol Equipment (1)
85 Talbot Street East, PO Box 606, Jarvis, N0A 1J0, ON, Canada (100%)
Tel.: (519) 587-4571
Web Site:
http://www.capitolequipmentrentals.com
Sales Range: $50-74.9 Million
Emp.: 30
Agriculture Equipment Rentals
N.A.I.C.S.: 333111
Terry Furler (Gen Mgr)

Capitol Pipe & Steel (1)
101 261200 Wagonville Way, Rocky View, Calgary, T4A 0E3, AB, Canada (100%)
Tel.: (403) 279-2428
Web Site: http://www.capitolpipe.ca
Sales Range: $50-74.9 Million
Emp.: 7
Pipe & Steel Products Mfr & Distr
N.A.I.C.S.: 326122
Elsi Bayer (Office Mgr)

Capitol Pipe Supports (1)
85 Talbot St E, PO Box 606, Jarvis, N0A 1J0, ON, Canada (100%)
Tel.: (519) 587-2264
Sales Range: $50-74.9 Million
Emp.: 20
N.A.I.C.S.: 425120

Douglas Barwick (1)
599 Cure Boivin, Boisbriand, J7G 2A8, QC, Canada (100%)
Tel.: (450) 435-3648
Web Site: http://www.douglasbarwick.com
Sales Range: $50-74.9 Million
Emp.: 40
Stainless Steel Pipes & Fittings Mfr
N.A.I.C.S.: 331210

Douglas Barwick Inc. (1)
150 California Ave, PO Box 756, Brockville, K6V 5W1, ON, Canada (100%)
Tel.: (613) 342-8471
Web Site: http://www.douglasbarwick.com
Sales Range: $25-49.9 Million
Emp.: 65
Stainless Steel Pipe & Pipe Fittings Mfr
N.A.I.C.S.: 331210
Pierre Desormeaux (Gen Mgr)

Formweld Fittings (1)
8118 Progress Dr, Milton, FL 32583-8725
Tel.: (850) 626-4888
Web Site: http://www.formweldfitting.com
Sales Range: $1-9.9 Million
Emp.: 20
Mfr of Buttweld Fittings
N.A.I.C.S.: 332313
Kapen Winwit (Pres)

Niagara Structural Steel (1)
23 Smith St, PO Box 730, Saint Catharines, L2R6Y6, ON, Canada (100%)
Tel.: (905) 684-2022
Web Site:
http://www.niagarastructuralsteel.com
Sales Range: $50-74.9 Million
Emp.: 30
Steel Mfrs
N.A.I.C.S.: 238120
Iain Fox (Gen Mgr)

Niagarasteel (1)

23 Smith St, PO Box 730, Saint Catharines, L2R 6Y6, ON, Canada (100%)
Tel.: (905) 688-1943
Web Site: http://www.niagarasteel.com
Sales Range: $1-9.9 Million
Emp.: 8
Steel Plate Rolling & Fabrication
N.A.I.C.S.: 425120

Norsteel Limited (1)
234 Des Plonniers, Sept-Iles, G4R 4K2, QC, Canada (100%)
Tel.: (418) 962-7744
Sales Range: $50-74.9 Million
Emp.: 4
Steel Mfrs
N.A.I.C.S.: 238120

Quality Fabrication, Inc. (1)
9631 Irondale Ave, Chatsworth, CA 91311
Tel.: (818) 709-8505
Web Site: http://www.quality-fab.com
Sheet Metalwork, Nsk
N.A.I.C.S.: 332322

TIW Steel Platework Inc. (1)
23 Smith Street, PO Box 730, Saint Catharines, L2R 6Y6, ON, Canada
Tel.: (905) 684-9421
Web Site: http://www.tiwsteelplatework.ca
Sales Range: $75-99.9 Million
Emp.: 120
Design, Manufacture & Construction of Field Erected Steel Platework Structures
N.A.I.C.S.: 238120
John Raposo (Mgr-Gen Sls)

TIW Western, Inc. (1)
7770 44th St SE, Calgary, T2C 2L5, AB, Canada (100%)
Tel.: (403) 279-8310
Web Site: http://www.tiwwestern.com
Sales Range: $50-74.9 Million
Emp.: 80
Structural Steel Services
N.A.I.C.S.: 238120

CANEX METALS INC.
Suite 1620 7347th Avenue SW, Calgary, T2P 3E8, AB, Canada
Tel.: (403) 233-2636 **AB**
Web Site:
https://www.canexmetals.ca
Year Founded: 1971
NOMNF—(OTCIQ)
Rev.: $18,340
Assets: $4,473,791
Liabilities: $74,189
Net Worth: $4,399,602
Earnings: ($404,293)
Fiscal Year-end: 09/30/23
Mineral Exploration Services
N.A.I.C.S.: 213114
Shane W. Ebert (Pres & CEO)

CANFOR CORPORATION
100-1700 West 75th Avenue, Vancouver, V6P 6G2, BC, Canada
Tel.: (604) 661-5241 **BC**
Web Site: https://www.canfor.com
Year Founded: 1966
CFP—(TSX)
Rev.: $6,011,743,572
Assets: $4,829,718,492
Liabilities: $1,693,479,744
Net Worth: $3,136,238,748
Earnings: $1,141,190,064
Emp.: 7,391
Fiscal Year-end: 12/31/21
Holding Company; Forest Products; Pulp, Paper, Lumber & Hardboard
N.A.I.C.S.: 551112
Donald Kayne (Pres & CEO)

Subsidiaries:

Anthony Forest Products Company, LLC (1)
295 Cooper Dr, El Dorado, AR 71730-5614
Tel.: (870) 862-3414
Web Site: http://www.anthonyforest.com
Lumber & Engineered Wood Products Mfr
N.A.I.C.S.: 321113
Chris Webb (Natl Sls Mgr)

Plant (Domestic):

Anthony Forest Products Co., Inc. - Arkansas Laminating Plant (2)
295 Cooper Dr, El Dorado, AR 71730
Tel.: (870) 862-2995
Web Site: http://www.anthonyforest.com
Laminated Wood Product Mfr
N.A.I.C.S.: 321114

Anthony Forest Products Co., Inc. - Arkansas Sawmill (2)
1236 Urbana Rd, El Dorado, AR 71730
Tel.: (870) 962-3206
Web Site: http://www.anthonyforest.com
Sawmills
N.A.I.C.S.: 321113

Anthony Forest Products Co., Inc. - Georgia Laminating Plant (2)
256 Edison Rd, Washington, GA 30673
Tel.: (706) 678-7405
Web Site: http://www.anthonyforest.com
Laminated Wood Product Mfr
N.A.I.C.S.: 321114

Anthony Forest Products Co., Inc. - Texas Chip Mill (2)
18410 Country Rd 2153, Troup, TX 75789
Tel.: (903) 842-3714
Web Site: http://www.anthonyforest.com
Chip Mill
N.A.I.C.S.: 321113

Balfour Lumber Company, Inc. (1)
800 W Clay St, Thomasville, GA 31792
Tel.: (229) 226-0611
Web Site: http://www.balfourlumber.com
Sawmills & Lumber Yard
N.A.I.C.S.: 321113
Jim Conner (Mgr-HR)

Beadles Lumber Company, Inc. (1)
900 6th St NE, Moultrie, GA 31768 (55%)
Tel.: (229) 985-6996
Web Site: http://www.beadleslumber.com
General Sawmills & Planing Mills; Pulpwood
N.A.I.C.S.: 321113

Canadian Forest Products Ltd. (1)
100 1700 W 75th Ave, Vancouver, V6P 6G2, BC, Canada (100%)
Tel.: (604) 661-5241
Web Site: http://www.canfor.com
Sales Range: $25-49.9 Million
Emp.: 200
Integrated Forest Products Company
N.A.I.C.S.: 113210

Unit (Domestic):

Canadian Forest Products - Chetwynd (2)
4700 50th St, PO Box 180, Chetwynd, V0C 1J0, BC, Canada (100%)
Tel.: (250) 788-2231
Web Site: http://www.canfor.com
Sales Range: $25-49.9 Million
Emp.: 150
Timber Tracts & Sawmilling
N.A.I.C.S.: 113110
Travis Peterson (Gen Mgr)

Canadian Forest Products - Clear Lake (2)
Sta A, PO Box 9000, V2L 4W2, Prince George, BC, Canada (100%)
Tel.: (250) 964-5000
Sales Range: $25-49.9 Million
Emp.: 200
Timber Tracts & Sawmilling Services
N.A.I.C.S.: 113110
Mark Todd (Mgr-HR)

Canadian Forest Products - Englewood Logging (2)
5000 Railway Ave, Woss, V0N 3P0, BC, Canada (100%)
Tel.: (250) 281-2300
Sales Range: $75-99.9 Million
Logging Operations
N.A.I.C.S.: 113310

Canadian Forest Products - Grande Prairie (2)
9401 101st St, PO Box 100, Grande Prairie, T8V 3A3, AB, Canada (100%)
Tel.: (780) 538-7749
Sales Range: $25-49.9 Million
Emp.: 200
Timber Tracts & Sawmilling

N.A.I.C.S.: 113110

Canadian Forest Products - Isle Pierre (2)
Bag Service 5410 Isle Pierre Rd, PO Box 6000, Prince George, V2N 2K3, BC, Canada (100%)
Tel.: (250) 441-5900
Sales Range: $25-49.9 Million
Emp.: 100
Timber Tracts & Sawmilling
N.A.I.C.S.: 113110
Al Stearns (Mgr-Pharma)

Canadian Forest Products - Prince George Pulp & Paper Mills (2)
Prince George 7689, PO Box 6000, Prince George, V2N 2K3, BC, Canada (100%)
Tel.: (250) 563-0161
Web Site: http://www.canfor.com
Emp.: 300
Paper Mfr
N.A.I.C.S.: 322120
Peter Lovell (Gen Mgr)

Canfor Panel & Fibre (2)
430 Canfor Ave, New Westminster, V3L 5G2, BC, Canada (100%)
Tel.: (604) 529-6300
Web Site: http://www.canforpfd.com
Sales Range: $25-49.9 Million
Emp.: 144
Panel & Fiber Mat
N.A.I.C.S.: 444110

Canfor Corporation - Camden Plant (1)
1281 Sanders Creek Rd, Camden, SC 29020-1026
Tel.: (803) 425-1810
Web Site: http://www.canfor.com
Timber Product Mfr
N.A.I.C.S.: 321999

Canfor Corporation - Canal Flats Sawmill Facility (1)
9006 Grainger Rd, Canal Flats, V0B 1B0, BC, Canada
Tel.: (250) 349-5294
Sales Range: $50-74.9 Million
Emp.: 18
Timber Product Mfr
N.A.I.C.S.: 321999
Pascal Buzon (Mng Dir)

Canfor Corporation - Chetwynd Sawmill Facility (1)
4700 50th Street, PO Box 180, Chetwynd, V0C 1J0, BC, Canada
Tel.: (250) 788-2231
Web Site: http://www.canfor.com
Sales Range: $50-74.9 Million
Emp.: 20
Timber Product Mfr
N.A.I.C.S.: 321999

Canfor Corporation - Fort St John Sawmill Facility (1)
9312 259 Road RR 1 Site 13 Compartment 2, Fort Saint John, V1J 4M6, BC, Canada
Tel.: (250) 787-3600
Web Site: http://www.canfor.com
Timber Product Mfr
N.A.I.C.S.: 327910

Canfor Corporation - Graham Plant (1)
4408 Mt Herman-Rock Creek Rd, Graham, NC 27253
Tel.: (336) 376-3130
Web Site: http://www.canfor.com
Timber Product Mfr
N.A.I.C.S.: 321999

Canfor Corporation - Intercontinental Pulp (CPLP) Facility (1)
2533 Prince George Pulp Mill Road, PO Box 6000, Prince George, V2N 2K3, BC, Canada
Tel.: (250) 563-0161
Sales Range: $125-149.9 Million
Emp.: 50
Paper Products Mfr
N.A.I.C.S.: 322299

Canfor Corporation - Isle Pierre Sawmill Facility (1)
5410 Isle Pierre Road Bag Service, PO Box 6000, Prince George, V2N 2K3, BC, Canada

Tel.: (250) 441-5900
Web Site: http://www.canfor.com
Sales Range: $50-74.9 Million
Emp.: 13
Timber Product Mfr
N.A.I.C.S.: 321999

Canfor Corporation - Marion
Plant **(1)**
402 Highway 576 Bypass, Marion, SC
29571-1519
Tel.: (843) 423-1385
Web Site: http://www.canfor.com
Timber Product Mfr
N.A.I.C.S.: 321999

Canfor Corporation - Polar Sawmill
Facility **(1)**
36654 Hart Highway General Delivery, Bear
Lake, V0J 3G0, BC, Canada
Tel.: (250) 972-4700
Web Site: http://www.canfor.com
Sales Range: $50-74.9 Million
Emp.: 22
Timber Product Mfr
N.A.I.C.S.: 321999

Canfor Corporation - Prince George
Pulp & Paper (CPLP) Facility **(1)**
2789 Prince George Pulp Mill Road, PO
Box 6000, Prince George, V2N 2K3, BC,
Canada
Tel.: (250) 563-0161
Paper Products Mfr
N.A.I.C.S.: 322299

Canfor Corporation - Quesnel Saw-
mill Facility **(1)**
1920 Brownmiller Road, Quesnel, V2J 6S1,
BC, Canada
Tel.: (250) 992-5581
Timber Product Mfr
N.A.I.C.S.: 321999

Canfor Corporation-Polar
Division **(1)**
General Delivery 366 54 Hart Highway,
Bear Lake, V0J 3G0, BC, Canada **(100%)**
Tel.: (250) 972-4700
Web Site: http://www.canfor.com
Sales Range: $50-74.9 Million
Emp.: 200
Sawmill & Planing Mill
N.A.I.C.S.: 321113

Canfor Europe **(1)**
2 Ave De La Foresterie, 1170, Brussels,
Belgium **(100%)**
Tel.: (32) 26725561
Sales Range: $25-49.9 Million
Emp.: 7
Sales Office for Pulp & Paper
N.A.I.C.S.: 322120

Canfor Japan Corporation **(1)**
1-1-3 Toranomon Tokyo Toranomon Toho
Building 4F, Minato-ku, Tokyo, 105-0001,
Japan
Tel.: (81) 335931205
Web Site: http://www.canfor.com.jp
Sales Range: $50-74.9 Million
Emp.: 5
Lumber & Plywood Products Marketer &
Whslr
N.A.I.C.S.: 423310
Jason Nomura *(Pres)*

Joint Venture (Domestic):

Canfor Georgia-Pacific Japan
Corporation **(2)**
Arco Tower 16F 1-8-1 Shimo-Meguro,
Meguro-ku, Tokyo, 153-0064,
Japan **(50%)**
Tel.: (81) 354345778
Web Site: http://www.canforpulp.com
Sales Range: $50-74.9 Million
Marketing Consulting Services
N.A.I.C.S.: 541613

Chemtrade Pulp Chemicals
Limited **(1)**
2711 Pulp Mill Rd, PO Box 2390, Prince
George, V2N 2S6, BC, Canada **(100%)**
Tel.: (250) 565-8700
Sales Range: $25-49.9 Million
Emp.: 40
Produces Sodium Chlorate Used in the
Pulp Mill Bleaching Process

N.A.I.C.S.: 325998

Daaquam Lumber Inc. **(1)**
2590 Boul Laurier Suite 740, Quebec, G1V
4M6, QC, Canada
Tel.: (418) 659-2422
Web Site: http://www.daaquam.com
Sales Range: $50-74.9 Million
Emp.: 20
Lumber & Stud Mfr
N.A.I.C.S.: 321999

Elliott Sawmilling Company, Inc. **(1)**
4426 Steep Bottom Rd, Estill, SC 29918-
4745
Tel.: (803) 625-3331
Web Site: http://www.elliottsawmilling.com
Sawmills
N.A.I.C.S.: 321113
Richard H. Elliott *(Pres)*

Wynndel Box and Lumber Co.
Ltd. **(1)**
1140 Winlaw Road, Wynndel, V0B 2N1,
BC, Canada
Tel.: (250) 866-5231
Web Site: http://www.wynnwood.ca
Emp.: 100
Wood Products Mfr
N.A.I.C.S.: 337211
Michael Combs *(CEO)*

CANFOR PULP PRODUCTS INC.

101-161 East 4th Avenue, Vancouver,
V5T 1G4, BC, Canada
Tel.: (604) 661-5241
Web Site: https://www.canfor.com
8CP—(DEU)
Rev.: $661,107,560
Assets: $510,310,096
Liabilities: $255,759,144
Net Worth: $254,550,952
Earnings: ($72,567,032)
Emp.: 7,580
Fiscal Year-end: 12/31/23
Pulp & Paper Products Supplier
N.A.I.C.S.: 322299
David M. Calabrigo *(Sec & Sr VP-
Corp Dev & Legal Affairs)*

CANG BAO TIAN XIA INTER-NATIONAL ART TRADE CEN-TER, INC.

Unit 609 Shengda Plaza No 61
Guoxing Ave, Meilan District, Haikou,
570203, Hainan, China
Tel.: (86) 89866186181 NV
Web Site: http://www.txcb.com
TXCB—(OTCEM)
Rev.: $1,303,486
Assets: $20,442,325
Liabilities: $33,898,796
Net Worth: ($13,456,471)
Earnings: ($8,445,157)
Emp.: 33
Fiscal Year-end: 06/30/21
Powertrain Product Mfr & Distr
N.A.I.C.S.: 336330
Xingtao Zhou *(Founder, Chm, Pres,
CEO & CFO)*

CANGGANG RAILWAY LIM-ITED

Yangzhuang Station Yangerzhuang
Town, Huanghua, Cangzhou, Hebei,
China
Tel.: (86) 3177610979 Ky
Web Site: http://www.czcgtl.com
Year Founded: 2009
2169—(HKG)
Railway Freight Transportation Ser-
vices
N.A.I.C.S.: 487110
Yongliang Liu *(Founder)*

CANGO INC.

6-8/F New Bund Oriental Plaza II 556
West Haiyang Road, Pudong New
Area, Shanghai, 200127, China

Tel.: (86) 2131830016 Ky
Web Site:
https://www.cangoonline.com
Year Founded: 2010
CANG—(NYSE)
Rev.: $303,425,275
Assets: $1,074,960,020
Liabilities: $412,800,341
Net Worth: $662,159,679
Earnings: ($170,248,160)
Emp.: 827
Fiscal Year-end: 12/31/22
Automotive Transaction Services
N.A.I.C.S.: 441227
Xiaojun Zhang *(Co-Founder & Chm)*

CANICA AS

Slemdalsveien 70, 0370, Oslo, Nor-
way
Tel.: (47) 2413 3000 NO
Web Site: http://wwww.canica.no
Year Founded: 1985
Investment Holding Company
N.A.I.C.S.: 551112
Stein Erik Hagen *(Founder)*

CANICKEL MINING LIMITED

1655-999 West Hastings Street, PO
Box 35, Vancouver, V6C 2W2, BC,
Canada
Tel.: (778) 372-1806 ON
Web Site: http://www.canickel.com
Year Founded: 1937
CMLGF—(OTCIQ)
Assets: $5,974,363
Liabilities: $78,559,963
Net Worth: ($72,585,600)
Earnings: ($6,974,308)
Emp.: 2
Fiscal Year-end: 12/31/22
Nickel Mining & Exploration Services
N.A.I.C.S.: 212230
Kevin Zhu *(CEO)*

CANLAN ICE SPORTS COR-PORATION

6501 Sprott Street, Burnaby, V5B
3B8, BC, Canada
Tel.: (604) 291-0626 Ca
Web Site:
https://www.canlansports.com
Year Founded: 1956
QV5—(DEU)
Rev.: $65,054,343
Assets: $92,123,885
Liabilities: $58,403,246
Net Worth: $33,720,639
Earnings: $328,477
Emp.: 1,000
Fiscal Year-end: 12/31/23
Ice Rinks Development Services
N.A.I.C.S.: 713940
Michael F. Gellard *(Exec VP)*

Subsidiaries:

Les Quatre Glaces (1994) Inc **(1)**
5880 Boul Taschereau Blvd, Brossard, J4W
1M6, QC, Canada
Tel.: (450) 462-2113
Web Site: http://www.Canlanicesports.com
Emp.: 50
Ice Sports Facility Operation Services
N.A.I.C.S.: 711310

CANMAX TECHNOLOGIES CO., LTD.

99 Shuangma Street Suzhou Indus-
trial Park, Suzhou, 215121, China
Tel.: (86) 51262852266
Web Site:
https://www.canmax.com.cn
300390—(CHIN)
Rev.: $2,391,075,180
Assets: $2,845,547,172
Liabilities: $869,770,980
Net Worth: $1,975,776,192
Earnings: $924,644,916

Fiscal Year-end: 12/31/22
Antistatic Clean Technology Mfr
N.A.I.C.S.: 333248

Subsidiaries:

Wuxi Yushou Medical Appliances Co,
Ltd. **(1)**
No 215 Xigang Road, Dongbeitang Town
Xishan District, Wuxi, 214191, Jiangsu,
China
Tel.: (86) 5108 377 7555
Web Site: https://www.chinasyringe.com
Pharmaceutical & Medicine Mfr
N.A.I.C.S.: 325412

CANN GLOBAL LIMITED

Level 21 133 Castlereagh Street,
Sydney, 2000, NSW, Australia
Tel.: (61) 83791832
Web Site:
http://www.canngloballimited.com
Year Founded: 2007
CGB—(ASX)
Rev.: $430,858
Assets: $10,077,817
Liabilities: $2,804,831
Net Worth: $7,272,987
Earnings: ($6,956,500)
Fiscal Year-end: 06/30/22
Bauxite Mining Services
N.A.I.C.S.: 212390
Pnina Feldman *(Chm)*

CANN GROUP LIMITED

Ground Floor 262-276 Lorimer Street,
Bundoora, Port Melbourne, 3207,
VIC, Australia
Tel.: (61) 390957088 AU
Web Site:
https://www.canngrouplimited.com
Year Founded: 2014
CAN—(ASX)
Rev.: $12,736,378
Assets: $61,946,447
Liabilities: $52,650,908
Net Worth: $9,295,539
Earnings: ($34,216,079)
Fiscal Year-end: 06/30/24
Medicinal Product Mfr & Distr
N.A.I.C.S.: 325411
Philip Robert Nicholas Jacobsen
(Deputy Chm)

CANN-IS CAPITAL CORP.

100 King Street West Suite 1600 1
First Canadian Place, Toronto, M5X
1G5, ON, Canada
Tel.: (416) 862-4479 ON
Year Founded: 2017
NIS.P—(TSXV)
Assets: $114,338
Liabilities: $18,612
Net Worth: $95,726
Earnings: ($73,972)
Fiscal Year-end: 12/31/20
Business Consulting Services
N.A.I.C.S.: 522299
Jonathan Graff *(CEO)*

CANNA 8 INVESTMENT TRUST

199 Bay Street Suite 4000, Toronto,
M5L 1A9, ON, Canada
Tel.: (647) 218-3849 ON
Year Founded: 2018
RCR.P—(TSXV)
Assets: $159,526
Liabilities: $9,386
Net Worth: $150,140
Earnings: ($103,936)
Fiscal Year-end: 12/31/21
Business Consulting Services
N.A.I.C.S.: 522299

CANNABIS POLAND S.A.

Ul Jana Styki 23, 03-928, Warsaw,
Poland

Cannabis Poland S.A.—(Continued)

Tel.: (48) 789560105
Web Site: https://www.cp-sa.pl
Year Founded: 2012
CBD—(WAR)
Pharmaceutical Product Mfr & Distr
N.A.I.C.S.: 325412

CANNABIS SUISSE CORP

Lerzenstrasse 12, 8953, Dietikon, Switzerland
Tel.: (41) 15022082098   NV
Web Site:
   http://www.cannabissuisse.com
Year Founded: 2016
CSUI—(OTCIQ)
Rev.: $11,086
Assets: $383,592
Liabilities: $748,337
Net Worth: ($364,745)
Earnings: ($389,135)
Emp.: 1
Fiscal Year-end: 05/31/23
Cannabis Cigarettes & Health Supplements Mfr
N.A.I.C.S.: 325412
Suneetha Nandana Silva Sudusinghe *(Pres, CEO, CFO & Treas)*

CANNABIX TECHNOLOGIES INC.

501-3292 Production Way, Burnaby, V5A 4R4, BC, Canada
Tel.: (604) 551-7831   BC
Web Site:
   https://www.cannabixtech.com
Year Founded: 2011
BLO—(CNSX)
Assets: $8,121,180
Liabilities: $63,189
Net Worth: $8,057,992
Earnings: ($7,230,964)
Fiscal Year-end: 04/30/21
Marijuana Breathalyzer Device Mfr
N.A.I.C.S.: 339112
Ravinder S. Mlait *(CEO)*

CANNAMERICA BRANDS CORP.

10th Floor 595 Howe Street, Vancouver, V6C 2T5, BC, Canada
Web Site:
   http://www.cannamericabrands.com
CANA—(OTCIQ)
Rev.: $302,347
Assets: $238,937
Liabilities: $3,969,884
Net Worth: ($3,730,947)
Earnings: ($2,777,847)
Fiscal Year-end: 03/31/21
Cannabis Product Mfr
N.A.I.C.S.: 325412
Dan Anglin *(Pres & CEO)*

CANNAPHARMARX, INC.

Suite 3600 888 3rd Street SW, Calgary, T2P 5C5, AB, Canada
Tel.: (949) 652-6838   DE
Web Site:
   https://www.cannapharmarx.com
Year Founded: 1998
CPMD—(OTCIQ)
Rev.: $5,269,560
Assets: $11,745,650
Liabilities: $23,898,863
Net Worth: ($12,153,213)
Earnings: $3,688,456
Emp.: 21
Fiscal Year-end: 12/31/23
Pharmaceuticals Product Mfr
N.A.I.C.S.: 325412
Oliver Foeste *(CFO)*

CANNARA BIOTECH, INC.

333 Decarie Blvd Suite 200, Saint Laurent, H4N 3M9, QC, Canada

Tel.: (514) 543-4200
Web Site: https://www.cannara.ca
8CB0—(DEU)
Rev.: $53,270,082
Assets: $105,575,601
Liabilities: $46,086,545
Net Worth: $59,489,057
Earnings: $5,181,282
Emp.: 461
Fiscal Year-end: 08/31/23
Pharmaceuticals Product Mfr
N.A.I.C.S.: 325412
Nicholas Sosiak *(CFO)*

Subsidiaries:

ShopCBD.com Inc.   **(1)**
113 N San Vicente Blvd 2nd Fl, Beverly Hills, CA 90211
Web Site: http://www.shopcbd.com
Health & Wellness Product Retailer
N.A.I.C.S.: 456199

CANNAWORLD VENTURES INC.

308-9080 University Crescent, Burnaby, V5A 0B7, BC, Canada
Tel.: (604) 868-2540
Web Site:
   https://www.cannaworldventure.com
Year Founded: 2015
Venture Capital & Private Equity Principals
N.A.I.C.S.: 523999

CANNIBBLE FOODTECH LTD.

PO Box 4250, Rosh Ha'Ayin, 4856602, Israel
Tel.: (972) 7863226055   II
Web Site:
   https://www.cannibble.world
Year Founded: 2018
PLCN—(CNSX)
Rev.: $221,000
Assets: $981,000
Liabilities: $1,138,000
Net Worth: ($157,000)
Earnings: ($2,161,000)
Fiscal Year-end: 12/31/21
Food Products Distr
N.A.I.C.S.: 424490
Yoav Bar Joseph *(CEO & Co-Founder)*

CANNINDAH RESOURCES LIMITED

Tel.: (61) 755578791
Web Site:
   https://www.cannindah.com.au
CAE—(ASX)
Rev.: $7,415
Assets: $10,972,687
Liabilities: $1,793,991
Net Worth: $9,178,696
Earnings: ($1,240,772)
Fiscal Year-end: 06/30/23
Metal Mining
N.A.I.C.S.: 212290
Thomas Pickett *(Chm)*

CANNOVUM CANNABIS AG

Stresemannstrasse 23, 10963, Berlin, Germany
Tel.: (49) 1785811701
Web Site: https://en.cannovum.de
Year Founded: 2018
27N0—(DEU)
Assets: $452,589
Liabilities: $298,046
Net Worth: $154,542
Earnings: ($3,499,282)
Fiscal Year-end: 12/31/23
Pharmaceutical Product Mfr & Distr
N.A.I.C.S.: 325412

CANNTAB THERAPEUTICS LIMITED

223 Riviera Drive, Markham, 1A2 B3C, ON, Canada
Tel.: (416) 875-3609   Ca
Web Site: https://canntab.ca
Year Founded: 2010
PILL—(CNSX)
Assets: $4,975,961
Liabilities: $3,201,157
Net Worth: $1,774,804
Earnings: ($3,457,507)
Fiscal Year-end: 05/31/21
Cannabis Resin Extended Release Capsules & Tablets Mfr & Seller
N.A.I.C.S.: 325412
Robert Lefler *(Dir-Operations)*

CANNY ELEVATOR CO., LTD.

No 888 Kangli Road FOHO New and Hi-Tech Development Zone, Suzhou, 215213, Jiangsu, China
Tel.: (86) 51263297851
Web Site: https://www.canny-elevator.com
Year Founded: 1997
002367—(SSE)
Rev.: $718,087,032
Assets: $946,422,360
Liabilities: $492,881,220
Net Worth: $453,541,140
Earnings: $38,510,316
Emp.: 5,000
Fiscal Year-end: 12/31/22
Elevator Mfr
N.A.I.C.S.: 333921
Christopher Wiltshire *(Chief Bus Officer)*

CANOE FINANCIAL LP

Suite 3900 350 7th Avenue SW, Calgary, T2P 3N9, AB, Canada
Tel.: (403) 571-5550   AB
Web Site:
   http://www.canoefinancial.com
Year Founded: 2008
Rev.: $2,428,245,000
Emp.: 45
Open & Closed-End Investment Fund Management Services
N.A.I.C.S.: 523940
Rafi G. Tahmazian *(Head-Energy Sector)*

Subsidiaries:

Canoe EIT Income Fund   **(1)**
421-7th Ave SW Suite 2750, Calgary, T2P 4K9, AB, Canada
Web Site: http://www.canoefinancial.com
Rev.: $133,330,028
Assets: $2,007,482,744
Liabilities: $255,458,606
Net Worth: $1,752,024,138
Earnings: $94,183,852
Emp.: 93
Fiscal Year-end: 12/31/2023
Closed-End Investment Fund
N.A.I.C.S.: 525990
Rafi G. Tahmazian *(Sr Portfolio Mgr)*

CANON INC.

30-2 Shimomaruko 3-chome, Ohta-ku, Tokyo, 146-8501, Japan
Tel.: (81) 337582111   JP
Web Site: https://global.canon
Year Founded: 1937
77510—(TKS)
Rev.: $34,009,295,760
Assets: $45,988,595,840
Liabilities: $15,995,803,120
Net Worth: $29,992,792,720
Earnings: $2,078,470,240
Emp.: 184,034
Fiscal Year-end: 12/31/21
Photograph Equipment Mfr
N.A.I.C.S.: 325412
Toshizo Tanaka *(CFO & Exec VP)*

Subsidiaries:

ASPAC Inc.   **(1)**

3-17-7 Shibaura Ryoshintaji Bldg, Minato-Ku, Tokyo, 108-0023, Japan
Tel.: (81) 3 6435 4890
Web Site: http://www.canon.com
Sales Range: $150-199.9 Million
Emp.: 641
Computer Software Development Services
N.A.I.C.S.: 541511

Canon (China) Co., Ltd.   **(1)**
Floor 33 China Life Financial Center Building 23 Zhenzhi Road, Chaoyang District, Beijing, 100005, China   **(100%)**
Tel.: (86) 1085139999
Web Site: https://www.canon.com.cn
Sales Range: $75-99.9 Million
Emp.: 1,220
Office Machines, Cameras & Computer Peripherals Sales
N.A.I.C.S.: 423420

Subsidiary (Domestic):

Canon Dalian Business Machines, Inc.   **(2)**
Economic and Technical Development Zone, No 23 Huai He West Road, Dalian, 116600, China   **(50%)**
Tel.: (86) 41187613333
Web Site: http://www.canon.com
Sales Range: $50-74.9 Million
Emp.: 1,271
Mfr & Recycler of Toner Cartridges
N.A.I.C.S.: 325992

Canon Optical Industrial Equipment (Shanghai) Inc.   **(2)**
3F-4F South Wing Building 5 Innovation Galaxy No 210 Wenshui Rd, Jing'an District, Shanghai, 200001, China
Tel.: (86) 2123163200
Web Site: http://www.canon.com
Sales Range: $25-49.9 Million
Emp.: 663
Semiconductor Equipment Mfr
N.A.I.C.S.: 334413

Canon Optical Industrial Equipment Service (Shanghai) Inc.   **(2)**
3-4F South Wing Building 5 Innovation Galaxy No 210 Wenshui Rd, Jing'an District, Shanghai, 200072, China
Tel.: (86) 2123163200
Sales Range: $25-49.9 Million
Emp.: 94
Electronic Components Mfr
N.A.I.C.S.: 334419

Canon Zhongshan Business Machines Co., Ltd.   **(2)**
No 2 Huan Mao 3 Road Zhongshan Torch Hi-Tech, Industrial Development Zone, Zhongshan, Guangdong, China
Tel.: (86) 760 89957888
Web Site: http://www.canon.com
Photocopying Machinery Mfr
N.A.I.C.S.: 333310

Canon Zhuhai, Inc.   **(2)**
No 2323 Middle of Jiuzhou Road, Zhuhai, 519020, Guangdong, China
Tel.: (86) 756 8888101
Web Site: http://www.canon.com
Digital Camera & Printer Mfr
N.A.I.C.S.: 333310

Tianjin Canon Co., Ltd.   **(2)**
1 Xijiang Street Jiefangnan Road, Hexi District, Tianjin, 300221, China
Tel.: (86) 22 8824 2111
Digital Camera & Printer Mfr
N.A.I.C.S.: 333310

Canon (Suzhou) Inc.   **(1)**
No 266 Mayun Road, High-tech Zone, Suzhou, 215129, China
Tel.: (86) 51266612111
Web Site: http://www.canon-suzhou.com.cn
Color Digital Copier Mfr & Distr
N.A.I.C.S.: 333248

Canon ANELVA Corporation   **(1)**
5-1 Kurigi 2-chome, Asao-ku, Kawasaki, 215-8550, Kanagawa, Japan
Tel.: (81) 449805111
Web Site: https://anelva.canon
Sales Range: $550-599.9 Million
Emp.: 1,061
Mfr of Vacuum Thin-Film Deposition & Processing Equipment

N.A.I.C.S.: 334413
Junro Sakai *(Pres)*

Canon Australia Pty. Ltd. **(1)**
(100%)
Tel.: (61) 298052000
Web Site: http://www.canon.com.au
Sales Range: $200-249.9 Million
Emp.: 600
Sales of Office Machines, Photographic
Equipment & Computer Peripherals
N.A.I.C.S.: 459410
Jason McLean *(Dir-Consumer Imaging & Svcs)*

Subsidiary (Domestic):

Canon Finance Australia Pty. Ltd. **(2)**
Building A The Park Estate 5 Talavera
Road, Macquarie Park, 2113, NSW,
Australia **(100%)**
Tel.: (61) 298052000
Web Site: http://www.canon.com.au
Sales Range: $550-599.9 Million
Emp.: 12
Provider of Leasing & Rental Services
N.A.I.C.S.: 531120

Subsidiary (Non-US):

Canon Finance New Zealand Ltd. **(3)**
Akoringi Bus Pk 28 The Warehouse Way,
PO Box 33336, Northcourt Takapuna, Auck-
land, 0740, New Zealand **(100%)**
Tel.: (64) 94890300
Web Site: http://www.cfnz.co.nz
Sales Range: $50-74.9 Million
Emp.: 7
Provider of Leasing & Rental Services
N.A.I.C.S.: 531120

Subsidiary (Non-US):

Canon New Zealand Ltd. **(2)**
28 The Warehouse Way, Akoranga Busi-
ness Park, Auckland, 0627, New
Zealand **(100%)**
Tel.: (64) 800222666
Web Site: http://www.canon.co.nz
Sales Range: $25-49.9 Million
Emp.: 374
Sales of all Canon Products
N.A.I.C.S.: 449210
Brad Gibbons *(Gen Mgr-Consumer Imaging & Svcs)*

Division (Domestic):

Canon Professional Printing **(2)**
Level 3 Building 1 195 Wellington Road,
Clayton, 3168, VIC, Australia **(100%)**
Tel.: (61) 397303333
Web Site: http://www.oce.com
Sales Range: $25-49.9 Million
Emp.: 100
Printing Equipment Distr
N.A.I.C.S.: 423420

Subsidiary (Domestic):

Converga Pty Limited **(2)**
Unit 16 39 Herbert Street, Saint Leonards,
2065, NSW, Australia
Tel.: (61) 294337000
Web Site: http://www.converga.com.au
Business Process Outsourcing Services
N.A.I.C.S.: 541511
Brian Parkes *(Gen Mgr-Ops)*

Inland Technology **(2)**
Unit 6 13-19 Ringers Road, PO Box 1720,
Tamworth, 2340, NSW, Australia **(100%)**
Tel.: (61) 267556600
Web Site:
https://www.inlandtechnology.com.au
Sales Range: $25-49.9 Million
Emp.: 9
Sales of Business Machines
N.A.I.C.S.: 423420
Peter Ryan *(Owner)*

**Canon Business Machines (Philip-
pines), Inc.** **(1)**
Lot 4 Phase 1B, First Philippine Industrial
Park, Tanauan, 4232, Batangas, Philippines
Tel.: (63) 437405111
Web Site: https://bmp.canon
Laser Printer Mfr

N.A.I.C.S.: 333248

Canon Chemicals, Inc. **(1)**
(100%)
Tel.: (81) 298762111
Web Site: http://www.canon-kasei.co.jp
Sales Range: $450-499.9 Million
Emp.: 1,344
Mfr of Toner Cartridges, Chemical Products
& Plastic Precision-Molded Parts
N.A.I.C.S.: 325998

Canon Components, Inc. **(1)**
3461-1 Oaza-Shichihongi Kamisato-machi,
Kodama-gun, Saitama, 369-0393,
Japan **(100%)**
Tel.: (81) 495333111
Web Site: https://compo.canon
Sales Range: $200-249.9 Million
Emp.: 1,020
Mfr & Sales of Contact Image Sensors,
Printer Cartridges & Printed Circuits
N.A.I.C.S.: 334118
Tomoaki Matsumoto *(Pres & CEO)*

Canon Ecology Industry Inc. **(1)**
1234 Matate, Bando, 306-0605, Ibaraki,
Japan
Tel.: (81) 297 36 3101
Web Site: http://www.canon-ecology.co.jp
Sales Range: $150-199.9 Million
Emp.: 700
Toner Cartridge Repair & Maintenance Ser-
vices
N.A.I.C.S.: 811210

**Canon Electron Tubes & Devices
Co., Ltd.** **(1)**
1385 Shimoishigami, Otawara, 324-8550,
Tochigi, Japan
Tel.: (81) 287266531
Web Site: https://etd.canon
Emp.: 415
Electron Tube Mfr & Distr
N.A.I.C.S.: 334419
Hironori Nakamuta *(Pres)*

**Canon Electronics Business Systems
Inc.** **(1)**
1248 Shimokagemori, Chichibu, 369-1892,
Saitama, Japan
Tel.: (81) 494211621
Sales Range: $25-49.9 Million
Emp.: 28
Laser Printer Distr
N.A.I.C.S.: 424120

Canon Electronics, Inc. **(1)**
1248 Shimokagemori Chichibu-shi, Sai-
tama, 3691892, Japan **(100%)**
Tel.: (81) 494233111
Web Site: https://www.canon-elec.co.jp
Rev.: $682,915,890
Assets: $929,818,050
Liabilities: $122,657,000
Net Worth: $807,161,050
Earnings: $46,552,940
Emp.: 5,527
Fiscal Year-end: 12/31/2023
Electronic Component Sales; Magnetic
Components, Document Scanners, Micro-
graphics & Handheld Information Terminals
N.A.I.C.S.: 334118
Hisashi Sakamaki *(Pres & CEO)*

Subsidiary (Non-US):

e-System Corporation **(2)**
Web Site: http://www.e-system.co.jp
Sales Range: $50-74.9 Million
Emp.: 400
CRM Consulting, Integration, Technical
Support & Application Support Services
N.A.I.C.S.: 541512

Subsidiary (Domestic):

EC Concierge Corporation **(3)**
6th Floor Asano Bldg 1-3-11 Nihonbashi
Chuou-ku, 103-0027, Tokyo,
Japan **(100%)**
Tel.: (81) 335169320
Computer Facilities Management Services
N.A.I.C.S.: 541513

Canon Emirates LLC **(1)**
Web Site: http://www.canon-emirates.ae
Sales Range: $25-49.9 Million
Emp.: 89
Photocopying Machinery Mfr

N.A.I.C.S.: 333310

Canon Eurasia A.S. **(1)**
Degirmen Sokak Nida Kule Is Merkezi No
18/10 K 1 Kozyatagi, Kadikoy, 34742, Istan-
bul, Turkiye
Tel.: (90) 2165716800
Web Site: http://www.canon.com.tr
Sales Range: $50-74.9 Million
Emp.: 12
Digital Camera & Printer Mfr
N.A.I.C.S.: 333310
Roman Troedthandl *(Mng Dir)*

Canon Europa N.V. **(1)**
Bovenkerkerweg 59, 1185 XB, Amstelveen,
Netherlands **(100%)**
Tel.: (31) 205458545
Web Site: http://www.canon-europe.com
Sales Range: $25-49.9 Million
Emp.: 543
Office & Photographic Equipment Distr
N.A.I.C.S.: 423410

Subsidiary (Non-US):

Axis AB **(2)**
Emdalavaegen 14, SE-228 69, Lund, Swe-
den
Tel.: (46) 462721800
Web Site: http://www.axis.com
Rev.: $1,046,764,368
Assets: $609,860,160
Liabilities: $235,633,320
Net Worth: $374,226,840
Earnings: $89,532,144
Emp.: 3,087
Fiscal Year-end: 12/31/2017
Holding Company; Security Network Sys-
tems Products & Services
N.A.I.C.S.: 551112
Ray Mauritsson *(Pres & CEO)*

Subsidiary (Domestic):

Axis Communications AB **(3)**
Granden 1, 223 69, Lund, Sweden
Tel.: (46) 462721800
Web Site: https://www.axis.com
Commercial Security Systems Sales & Ser-
vices
N.A.I.C.S.: 561621
Ray Mauritsson *(Pres & CEO)*

Subsidiary (Non-US):

Axis Communications **(4)**
Via de los Poblados 3 Edif 6 - Pl 1, Tres
Cantos, 28033, Madrid, Spain
Tel.: (34) 918034643
Network Video Solutions Mfr
N.A.I.C.S.: 334310

Axis Communications (S) Pte Ltd **(4)**
7 Temasek Boulevard 41-01/02/03 Suntec
Tower 1, Singapore, 038987, Singapore
Tel.: (65) 68362777
Network Video Solutions Mfr
N.A.I.C.S.: 334310

**Axis Communications (SA) (Pty)
Ltd** **(4)**
The Crossing 372 Main Road, 3012 William
Nicol Drive, Bryanston, 2021, Johannes-
burg, South Africa
Tel.: (27) 115486780
Emp.: 19
Network Video Cameras & Print Servers
Mfr
N.A.I.C.S.: 334310
Sasha Bonheim *(Mgr-PR Mktg)*

Axis Communications (UK) Ltd **(4)**
1 Capability Green, Luton, LU1 3LU, Bed-
fordshire, United Kingdom
Tel.: (44) 1582283760
Emp.: 37
Network Video Cameras & Print Servers
Mfr
N.A.I.C.S.: 334310
Katherine Bramwell *(Acct Mgr-Distr-
Watford)*

Axis Communications BV **(4)**
Riviumboulevard 301 gebouw oost 3de
verdieping, 2909 LK, Capelle aan den IJs-
sel, Netherlands
Tel.: (31) 107504600
Network Video Solutions Mfr
N.A.I.C.S.: 334310

Axis Communications GmbH **(4)**
Adalperostrasse 86, 85737, Ismaning, Ger-
many
Tel.: (49) 893588170
Network Video Solutions Mfr
N.A.I.C.S.: 334310

Axis Communications KK **(4)**
Shinjuku Front Tower 19F 2-21-1 Kita-
Shinjuku, Shinjuku-ku, Tokyo, 169-0074,
Japan
Tel.: (81) 359372929
Network Video Solutions Mfr
N.A.I.C.S.: 334310

**Axis Communications Korea Co.
Ltd.** **(4)**
Rm 1406 Zei Platz 186 Gasan digital 1-ro,
Geumcheon-gu, Seoul, Korea (South)
Tel.: (82) 27809636
Web Site: http://www.axis.co.kr
Network Video Solutions Mfr
N.A.I.C.S.: 334310

Axis Communications OOO **(4)**
Leningradsky prospekt 31 A Building 1
etazh 16, 125284, Moscow, Russia
Tel.: (7) 495 940 6682
Emp.: 26
Network Video Solutions Mfr
N.A.I.C.S.: 334310

Axis Communications Pty Ltd **(4)**
Level 4 South Tower 80 Collins Street, Mel-
bourne, 3000, VIC, Australia
Tel.: (61) 399821111
Network Video Solutions Mfr
N.A.I.C.S.: 334310

**Axis Communications Taiwan Co.,
Ltd.** **(4)**
6F No 39 Ln 258 Ruiguang Road, Neihu
Dist, Taipei, 114, Taiwan
Tel.: (886) 226573858
Web Site: http://tw.axis.com
Network Video Solutions Mfr
N.A.I.C.S.: 334310

**Shanghai Axis Communication Equip-
ment Trading Co. Ltd** **(4)**
Rm 2606 26/F Yueda889 Center 1111
Changshou Road, Shanghai, 200042,
China
Tel.: (86) 2164311690
Network Video Solutions Mfr
N.A.I.C.S.: 334310

Subsidiary (Non-US):

Canon (Schweiz) AG **(2)**
(90%)
Sales of all Canon Products
N.A.I.C.S.: 449210

Subsidiary (Domestic):

**Canon (Schweiz) AG -
Glattbrugg** **(3)**
Sagereistrasse 10, Glattbrugg, 8152, Switz-
erland
Tel.: (41) 448291111
Sales Range: $50-74.9 Million
Emp.: 250
Marketing & Sales of Office Equipment &
Graphics Plotters
N.A.I.C.S.: 423420

Subsidiary (Non-US):

Canon (U.K.) Ltd. **(2)**
(100%)
Web Site: http://www.canon.co.uk
Digital Imaging Technology
N.A.I.C.S.: 333310

Subsidiary (Non-US):

**Canon Ireland Business Equipment
Ltd.** **(3)**
3006 Lake Drive Citywest Business Cam-
pus, Dublin, 24, Ireland **(100%)**
Tel.: (353) 12052400
Web Site: http://www.canon.ie
Sales Range: $25-49.9 Million
Emp.: 64
Photocopiers, Plotters & Printers
N.A.I.C.S.: 424120

Canon UK **(3)**
(100%)

Canon Inc.—(Continued)

Sales Range: $50-74.9 Million
Emp.: 250
Mfr, Sales & Marketing of Copiers, Printers, Plotters & Supplies
N.A.I.C.S.: 333310

Subsidiary (Non-US):

Canon Austria GmbH **(2)**
(100%)
Tel.: (43) 1680880
Web Site: http://www.canon.at
Emp.: 300
Sales of all Canon Products
N.A.I.C.S.: 449210

Subsidiary (Domestic):

Canon East Europe Vertriebsgesell-schaft mbH **(3)**
Oberlaaer Strasse 233, 1100, Vienna, Austria **(100%)**
Tel.: (43) 1680880
Web Site: http://www.canon-europe.com
Sales Range: $150-199.9 Million
Emp.: 300
Copier & Fax Machine Sales
N.A.I.C.S.: 423420

Subsidiary (Non-US):

Canon Hungaria Kft. **(3)**
Graphisoft Park 1 Hx building utca 7, 1031, Budapest, Hungary **(100%)**
Tel.: (36) 12375900
Web Site: http://www.canon.hu
Sales Range: $25-49.9 Million
Emp.: 80
Sales of Copy & Fax Machines
N.A.I.C.S.: 423420

Subsidiary (Non-US):

Oce-Hungaria Kft. **(4)**
Web Site: http://www.oce.hu
Sales Range: $25-49.9 Million
Emp.: 100
Printing & Office Solutions & Business Services
N.A.I.C.S.: 323120

Subsidiary (Non-US):

Canon Polska Sp. z o.o. **(3)**
ul Gottlieba Daimlera 2, 02-460, Warsaw, Poland **(100%)**
Tel.: (48) 224306000
Web Site: https://www.canon.pl
Sales Range: $25-49.9 Million
Emp.: 60
Sales of Copy & Fax Machines
N.A.I.C.S.: 423420

Subsidiary (Domestic):

OPTOPOL Technology S.A. **(4)**
ul Zabia 42, 42-400, Zawiercie, Poland
Tel.: (48) 326709173
Web Site: https://www.optopol.com
Sales Range: $50-74.9 Million
Emp.: 20
Diagnostic Equipment Mfr & Distr
N.A.I.C.S.: 334510

Subsidiary (Non-US):

Canon Slovakia s.r.o. **(3)**
Karadzicova 8 building CBC I, 821 08, Bratislava, Slovakia
Tel.: (421) 257104011
Web Site: https://www.canon.sk
Sales Range: $50-74.9 Million
Emp.: 10
Sales of Photographic Equipment
N.A.I.C.S.: 423410

Subsidiary (Non-US):

Canon Belgium N.V./S.A. **(2)**
Berkenlaan 3, Machelen, 1831, Diegem, Belgium **(100%)**
Tel.: (32) 27220411
Web Site: https://www.canon.be
Emp.: 460
Sales of Business Machines
N.A.I.C.S.: 423420

Canon Bulgaria EOOD **(2)**
251 Ring Road Business Centre Delta 2nd

---

floor office 201 Mladost 4, 1715, Sofia, Bulgaria
Tel.: (359) 29751630
Sales Range: $25-49.9 Million
Emp.: 11
Digital Camera & Printer Mfr
N.A.I.C.S.: 333310
Secareanu Petronius *(Mng Dir)*

Canon CEE GmbH **(2)**
Oberlaaer Strasse 233, 1100, Vienna, Austria
Tel.: (43) 1680890
Web Site: https://www.canon-cee.com
Sales Range: $25-49.9 Million
Emp.: 101
Digital Camera & Printer Scanner Distr
N.A.I.C.S.: 423410

Canon CZ spol s.r.o. **(2)**
Prague Marina Office Center Jankovcova 1595/14a - entrance A, Holesovice, 170 00, Prague, 7, Czech Republic
Tel.: (420) 225280111
Web Site: https://www.canon.cz
Sales Range: $25-49.9 Million
Emp.: 220
Sales of Copy & Fax Machines
N.A.I.C.S.: 423420

Canon Danmark A/S **(2)**
Tel.: (45) 70155005
Web Site: http://www.canon.dk
Sales Range: $50-74.9 Million
Digital Camera & Printer Mfr
N.A.I.C.S.: 333310

Canon Deutschland GmbH **(2)**
Europark Fichtenhain A10, 47807, Krefeld, Germany **(100%)**
Tel.: (49) 21513450
Web Site: http://www.canon.de
Sales of Office Products, Computer Peripherals & Photographic Equipment
N.A.I.C.S.: 459410

Subsidiary (Domestic):

Canon Giessen GmbH **(3)**
Canonstrasse 1, 35394, Giessen, Germany
Tel.: (49) 6414060
Web Site: https://www.canon-giessen.de
Sales Range: $50-74.9 Million
Emp.: 315
Mfr & Remanufacturer of Copy Machines
N.A.I.C.S.: 423420

Oce-Deutschland GmbH **(3)**
Solingerstr 5 7, D 45481, Mullheim, Germany **(100%)**
Tel.: (49) 20848450
Web Site: http://www.oce.com
Sales Range: $200-249.9 Million
Service & Sales of Printing Equipment
N.A.I.C.S.: 423830

Subsidiary (Domestic):

Oce Printing Systems GmbH **(4)**
Siemens Allee 2, PO Box 1260, 85586, Poing, Germany **(100%)**
Tel.: (49) 8121720
Web Site: http://www.oce.com
Emp.: 1,000
Provider of Solutions for Printing Systems
N.A.I.C.S.: 323111

Oce-Deutschland Leasing GmbH **(4)**
Solinger Str 5-7, 45481, Mullheim, Germany
Tel.: (49) 20848450
Web Site: http://www.oce.de
Sales Range: $150-199.9 Million
Emp.: 300
Leasing of Printing Equipment
N.A.I.C.S.: 532420

Subsidiary (Non-US):

Canon Espana, S.A. **(2)**
Parque Empresarial La Moraleja Av de Europa 6, Alcobendas, 28108, Madrid, Spain
Tel.: (34) 915384500
Web Site: https://www.canon.es
Sales Range: $50-74.9 Million
Emp.: 865
Cameras & Photographic Supplies Sales
N.A.I.C.S.: 449210

Subsidiary (Domestic):

Oce-Espana S.A. **(3)**

Mas Blau Osona 2, El Prat De Llobregat, E 08820, Barcelona, Spain **(100%)**
Tel.: (34) 934844848
Web Site: http://www.oce.es
Sales Range: $50-74.9 Million
Emp.: 225
Marketing & Sales of Office Equipment
N.A.I.C.S.: 423420

Subsidiary (Domestic):

Oce-Renting S.A. **(4)**
Businnes Park Mas Blau Osona 2, Barcelona, 08820, Spain **(100%)**
Tel.: (34) 934844800
Web Site: http://www.oce.es
Sales Range: $50-74.9 Million
Emp.: 200
N.A.I.C.S.: 459410

Subsidiary (Non-US):

Canon Europe Ltd. **(2)**
6 Roundwood Ave, Uxbridge, UB11 1JA, Middlesex, United Kingdom **(100%)**
Tel.: (44) 2085888000
Web Site: http://www.canon-europe.com
Sales Range: $75-99.9 Million
Sales of all Canon Products
N.A.I.C.S.: 449210
Hiroyuki Imamura *(Exec VP-Digital Printing & Solutions)*

Subsidiary (Non-US):

Canon (Irl) Business Equipment Ltd. **(3)**
3006 Lake Drive Citywest, Saggart, Dublin, 24, Ireland **(100%)**
Tel.: (353) 12052415
Web Site: http://www.canon.ie
Sales Range: $75-99.9 Million
Emp.: 120
Sales of Business Machines, IT Support & Consulting
N.A.I.C.S.: 423420

Subsidiary (Domestic):

Canon Technology Europe Ltd **(3)**
The Braccans London Road, Bracknell, RG12 2XH, Berks, United Kingdom **(100%)**
Tel.: (44) 344354700
Web Site: http://www.cre.canon.co.uk
Sales Range: $25-49.9 Million
Emp.: 100
Provider of Computer Research Services
N.A.I.C.S.: 541715

Subsidiary (Non-US):

Canon France S.A. **(2)**
17 Quai du President Paul Doumer, 92414, Courbevoie, France **(100%)**
Tel.: (33) 1 41 997777
Web Site: http://www.canon.fr
Sales of Business Machines
N.A.I.C.S.: 459410

Subsidiary (Domestic):

Canon Bretagne S.A. **(3)**
Les Landes de Beauge, 35341, Liffre, Cedex, France **(100%)**
Tel.: (33) 299235111
Web Site: https://www.canon-bretagne.fr
Sales Range: $250-299.9 Million
Emp.: 600
Mfr of Low-Speed Copy Machines & Toner Cartridges; Recycler of Toner Cartridges
N.A.I.C.S.: 423420

Canon Research Centre France S.A.S. **(3)**
Rue De La Touche Lambert Rennes, 35517, Cesson Sevigne, Atalante, France **(100%)**
Tel.: (33) 299876800
Sales Range: $25-49.9 Million
Emp.: 70
Developer of Image Processing Technology, Wireless Communications & Multimedia Network Infrastructures
N.A.I.C.S.: 541512

Oce-France S.A. **(3)**
12 Avenue de l'Europe, 77144, Montevrain, France **(100%)**
Tel.: (33) 820 12 04 10
Web Site: http://www.oce.fr

Sales Range: $200-249.9 Million
Emp.: 600
Mfr & Sales of Copier Products
N.A.I.C.S.: 424120

Subsidiary (Domestic):

Oce-France Financement S.A. **(4)**
32 Pacenneus NeaJran, 93883, Neuilly-sur-Seine, France
Tel.: (33) 145925055
Web Site: http://www.oce.fr
Sales Range: $350-399.9 Million
Provider of Financial Services for Oce France
N.A.I.C.S.: 523999

Subsidiary (Non-US):

Canon Italia S.p.A. **(2)**
(100%)
Tel.: (39) 0282481
Web Site: http://www.canon.it
Sales Range: $75-99.9 Million
Sales of all Canon Products
N.A.I.C.S.: 449210

Canon Luxembourg S.A. **(2)**
West Side Village Complex Building E Rue Pafebruch 89E, 8308, Capellen, Luxembourg
Tel.: (352) 4847961
Web Site: https://www.canon.lu
Sales Range: $25-49.9 Million
Digital Camera & Printer Mfr
N.A.I.C.S.: 333310

Canon Middle East, FZ-LLC **(2)**
Dubai Internet City Canon Building, PO Box 500 007, Dubai, United Arab Emirates
Tel.: (971) 43915050
Web Site: https://en.canon-me.com
Sales Range: $25-49.9 Million
Sales of Business Machines
N.A.I.C.S.: 423420

Subsidiary (Domestic):

Canon Nederland N.V. **(2)**
Bovenkerkerweg 59, 1185 XB, Amstelveen, Netherlands **(100%)**
Tel.: (31) 736815815
Web Site: http://www.canon.nl
Sales Range: $125-149.9 Million
Emp.: 876
Sales of Business Machines
N.A.I.C.S.: 423420

Subsidiary (Domestic):

Canon Nederland N.V. - 's-Hertogenbosch **(3)**
Brabantlaan 2, PO Box 800, 5216 TV, 's-Hertogenbosch, Netherlands **(100%)**
Tel.: (31) 736815815
Web Site: http://www.oce.nl
Emp.: 876
Office Equipment Distr
N.A.I.C.S.: 423420

Subsidiary (Non-US):

Canon Norge A.S. **(2)**
Hallagerbakken 110, PO Box 33, 1201, Oslo, Norway **(100%)**
Tel.: (47) 2262 9200
Web Site: http://www.canon.no
Sales Range: $100-124.9 Million
Sales of all Canon Products
N.A.I.C.S.: 449210

Canon Oy **(2)**
Huopalahdentie 24, PL 1, 00350, Helsinki, Finland **(100%)**
Tel.: (358) 1054420
Web Site: http://www.canon.fi
Sales Range: $75-99.9 Million
Sales of all Canon Products
N.A.I.C.S.: 449210

Subsidiary (Domestic):

Canon North-East Oy **(3)**
Huopalahdentie 24, PL1, 00351, Helsinki, Finland **(100%)**
Tel.: (358) 01054400
Web Site: http://www.canon.fi
Sales of all Canon Products
N.A.I.C.S.: 423420

Oce-Finland Oy **(3)**

Huopalahdentie 24, 2150, Helsinki, Finland
Tel.: (358) 207438710
Web Site: http://www.oce.com
Sales Range: $25-49.9 Million
Emp.: 15
Printing Software Development Services
N.A.I.C.S.: 541511
Jari-Pekka Koskenmies *(Mng Dir)*

Subsidiary (Non-US):

Canon Portugal S.A.   **(2)**
Lagoas Park Edificio 15 Piso O e 1, 2740-262, Porto Salvo, Portugal
Tel.: (351) 214 704 000
Web Site: http://www.canon.pt
Sales Range: $50-74.9 Million
Digital Camera & Printer Mfr
N.A.I.C.S.: 333310

Subsidiary (Domestic):

Oce Portugal Equipamentos Graficos S.A.   **(3)**
Edificio Canon Rua Alfredo da Silva 14, Miraflores, Amadora, 2610-016, Alfragide, Portugal   **(100%)**
Tel.: (351) 214125700
Web Site: http://www.oce.pt
Sales Range: $25-49.9 Million
Emp.: 56
N.A.I.C.S.: 459410

Subsidiary (Non-US):

Canon South Africa Pty. Ltd.   **(2)**
Ground Floor Block C Southdowns Office Park, PO Box 68497, Corner of Karee John Vorster Drive Southdowns, Centurion, 0062, South Africa   **(100%)**
Tel.: (27) 126754900
Web Site: https://www.canon.co.za
Emp.: 143
Sales of Consumer Products
N.A.I.C.S.: 532289

Canon Svenska AB   **(2)**
Bjornstigen 85, 170 73, Solna, Sweden   **(100%)**
Tel.: (46) 87448500
Web Site: http://www.canon.se
Sales Range: $25-49.9 Million
Emp.: 200
Sales of all Canon Products
N.A.I.C.S.: 449210

I.R.I.S. Group S.A.   **(2)**
Rue du Bosquet 10, 1348, Louvain-la-Neuve, Belgium
Tel.: (32) 10451364
Web Site: http://www.iriscorporate.com
Emp.: 161
Software & Technology Services
N.A.I.C.S.: 541512
Olivier Colin *(CFO)*

Subsidiary (Non-US):

I.R.I.S. France s.a.   **(3)**
Tel.: (33) 156707070
Web Site: http://www.iriscorporate.com
Sales Range: $25-49.9 Million
Emp.: 15
Developer & Marketer of Computer Software; Information Technology Services
N.A.I.C.S.: 541512

Subsidiary (US):

I.R.I.S. Inc.   **(3)**
955 NW 17th Ave Unit D, Delray Beach, FL 33445
Tel.: (561) 921-0854
Sales Range: $25-49.9 Million
Emp.: 8
Computer Software Design & Consulting Services
N.A.I.C.S.: 541519

Subsidiary (Non-US):

I.R.I.S. Luxembourg s.a.   **(3)**
Ecoparc - SolarWind Rue de l'Industrie 13, L 8399, Windhof, Luxembourg   **(100%)**
Tel.: (352) 3903261
Web Site: http://www.irislink.com
Sales Range: $10-24.9 Million
Emp.: 40
Developer & Marketer of Computer Software; Information Technology Services
N.A.I.C.S.: 541512

Subsidiary (Domestic):

I.R.I.S. eCommunication   **(3)**
10 rue du Bosquet, 1348, Louvain-la-Neuve, Belgium
Tel.: (32) 10832450
Web Site: http://www.irisecom.com
Sales Range: $25-49.9 Million
Emp.: 20
Developer & Marketer of Advanced Web Content Management Solutions for Professional Associations, Companies & Industries
N.A.I.C.S.: 541519

Canon Finetech Inc.   **(1)**
5540-11 Sakatemachi, Joso-shi, Ibaraki, 303 8503, Japan   **(100%)**
Tel.: (81) 297270111
Web Site: http://www.canon-finetech.co.jp
Rev.: $1,741,315,257
Emp.: 1,600
Business Machines & Peripherals Mfr
N.A.I.C.S.: 334118

Plant (Domestic):

Canon Finetech Inc. - Fukui Plant   **(2)**
29-73-3 Ishibashi-cho, Fukui, 910-3138, Fukui, Japan
Tel.: (81) 776 85 1300
Web Site: http://www.canon-finetech.co.jp
Photocopying Machinery Mfr
N.A.I.C.S.: 333310

Canon Finetech Inc. - Ibaraki Plant   **(2)**
5540-11 Sakatemachi, Joso, 303-8503, Ibaraki, Japan
Tel.: (81) 297 27 0111
Web Site: http://www.canon-finetech.co.jp
Photographic Machinery Mfr
N.A.I.C.S.: 333310

Subsidiary (Non-US):

Canon Finetech Nisca (Shenzhen) Inc.   **(2)**
No 3 Chuanxin Industrial Park Jingtian Road Xintian Community, Guanhu Street Longhua District, Shenzhen, 518110, Guangdong, China
Tel.: (86) 75583596300
Web Site: http://www.canon-fn.com.cn
Emp.: 1,744
Photocopying Machinery Mfr
N.A.I.C.S.: 333310

Subsidiary (Domestic):

Nisca Corporation   **(2)**
430-1 Kobayashi Minamikoma-gun, Fujikawa-cho, Yamanashi, 400-0593, Japan
Tel.: (81) 556 22 3929
Web Site: http://www.nisca.co.jp
Rev.: $267,688,320
Emp.: 827
Photocopying Machinery & Printer Mfr
N.A.I.C.S.: 333310
Noriyoshi Ueda *(Pres)*

Canon Finetech Nisca Inc.   **(1)**
14-1 Chuo 1-chome, Misato, 341-8527, Saitama, Japan
Tel.: (81) 489492111
Web Site: https://ftn.canon
Emp.: 1,478
Printer Mfr & Distr
N.A.I.C.S.: 333248
Junichi Yoshitake *(Pres)*

Canon Hi-Tech (Thailand) Ltd.   **(1)**
Hi-Tech Industrial Estate 89 Moo 1 Bhan Lain, Bang Pa-in, Phra Nakhon Si Ayutthaya, 13160, Thailand   **(100%)**
Tel.: (66) 35350080
Web Site: http://www.canon.co.th
Sales Range: $1-4.9 Billion
Emp.: 9,036
Software Publisher
N.A.I.C.S.: 513210

Canon HongKong Co., Ltd.   **(1)**
Tel.: (852) 21702828
Sales Range: $200-249.9 Million
Emp.: 700
Marketer of All Canon Products
N.A.I.C.S.: 449210

Subsidiary (Domestic):

Canon Electronic Business Machines (H.K.) Co., Ltd.   **(2)**

17th Fl Tower 1 Ever Gain Plz 88 Container Port Road, Kwai Chung, NT, China (Hong Kong)
Tel.: (852) 23058400
Sales Range: $25-49.9 Million
Emp.: 50
Mfr & Marketing of Personal Information Products
N.A.I.C.S.: 541512
Yuji Suzuki *(Pres)*

Canon Engineering Hong Kong Co., Ltd.   **(2)**
5/F Manhattan Centre No 8 Kwai Cheong Road, Kwai Chung, NT, China (Hong Kong)
Tel.: (852) 27592662
Sales Range: $50-74.9 Million
Emp.: 86
Electronic Components Mfr
N.A.I.C.S.: 334419
Osamu Izawa *(Mng Dir)*

Canon Imaging Systems Inc.   **(1)**
Plaka 2 1-2 Sasakuchi, Chuo-ku, Niigata, 950-0911, Japan
Tel.: (81) 252446335
Web Site: https://imgsys.canon
Sales Range: $75-99.9 Million
Emp.: 514
Photocopying Software Development Services
N.A.I.C.S.: 541511

Canon Inc., Taiwan   **(1)**
Tel.: (886) 425322123
Sales Range: $400-449.9 Million
Emp.: 1,600
Mfr of Compact Cameras, EF Lenses & Lens Units for Image Scanners & Multimedia Projectors
N.A.I.C.S.: 333310

Canon India Pvt. Ltd.   **(1)**
7th Floor Tower B Building 5 DLP Epitome, DLF Phase III, Gurgaon, 122002, Haryana, India   **(100%)**
Tel.: (91) 1147192613
Web Site: https://in.canon
Sales Range: $75-99.9 Million
Emp.: 940
Sales of Copy Machines & Software
N.A.I.C.S.: 423420
Gary Lee *(CFO & VP)*

Canon Information Technologies Philippines, Inc.   **(1)**
Techno Plaza One 18 Orchard Road, Eastwood, Quezon City, 1110, Philippines
Tel.: (63) 2 421 1000
Sales Range: $75-99.9 Million
Emp.: 40
Application Software Development Services
N.A.I.C.S.: 541511
Lu Xueli *(Pres)*

Canon Korea Consumer Imaging Inc.   **(1)**
Canon Bldg 5F 168-12 Samseong-dong, Gangnam-gu, Seoul, 135-090, Korea (South)
Tel.: (82) 2 2191 8500
Web Site: http://www.canon-ci.co.kr
Sales Range: $25-49.9 Million
Emp.: 90
Digital Camera Mfr
N.A.I.C.S.: 333310

Canon Machinery Inc.   **(1)**
85 Minami Yamada-cho, Kusatsu, 525-8511, Shiga, Japan
Tel.: (81) 77 563 8511
Web Site: http://www.canon-machinery.co.jp
Rev.: $376,606,090
Emp.: 1,061
Electronic Components Mfr
N.A.I.C.S.: 334419
Masahiro Okabe *(Mng Dir)*

Subsidiary (Non-US):

Canon Machinery (Dalian) Co., Ltd.   **(2)**
No 23-3 Huai He West Road Dalian Economic Technical Development Zone, Dalian, 116600, Liaoning, China
Tel.: (86) 41187531126
Sales Range: $25-49.9 Million
Emp.: 62
Photographic Machinery Mfr
N.A.I.C.S.: 333310

Takahiro Tsubota *(Mng Dir)*

Canon Machinery (Malaysia) Sdn Bhd.   **(2)**
Lot 47 Persiaran Subang Hi-Tech, Subang Hi-Tech, 47500, Shah Alam, Selangor Darul Ehsan, Malaysia
Tel.: (60) 356332127
Web Site: http://www.canon.com.my
Sales Range: $25-49.9 Million
Emp.: 186
Semiconductor Equipment Mfr
N.A.I.C.S.: 334413

Canon Marketing (Malaysia) Sdn. Bhd.   **(1)**
No 6-2-01 Canon Tower Jalan Pengaturcara U1/51A, UOA Business Park Tower 6 Seksyen U1, 40150, Shah Alam, Selangor, Malaysia   **(100%)**
Tel.: (60) 355682333
Web Site: https://my.canon
Sales Range: $100-124.9 Million
Emp.: 504
Sales of all Canon Products
N.A.I.C.S.: 449210

Canon Marketing (Philippines), Inc.   **(1)**
7th Floor Ground Floor Commerce and Industry Plaza, Campus Avenue corner Park Avenue McKinley Hill Brgy Pinagsama, Taguig, 1634, Philippines   **(100%)**
Tel.: (63) 288849090
Web Site: https://ph.canon
Sales Range: $10-24.9 Million
Emp.: 262
Sales of Business Machines
N.A.I.C.S.: 423420

Canon Marketing (Taiwan) Co., Ltd.   **(1)**
19th Floor No 100 Section 2 Roosevelt Road, Zhongzheng District, Taipei, 10084, Taiwan   **(100%)**
Tel.: (886) 266328888
Web Site: https://tw.canon
Sales Range: $50-74.9 Million
Emp.: 152
Sales of Business Machines
N.A.I.C.S.: 423420

Canon Marketing (Thailand) Co., Ltd.   **(1)**
No 98 Sathorn Square Office Tower Building Floor 22-24, North Sathorn Road Silom Subdistrict Bang Rak District, Bangkok, 10500, Thailand   **(55%)**
Tel.: (66) 23449999
Web Site: https://th.canon
Sales Range: $200-249.9 Million
Emp.: 600
Sales of all Canon Products
N.A.I.C.S.: 449210

Canon Marketing Japan Inc.   **(1)**
Canon S Tower 16-6 Konan 2-chome, Minato-ku, Tokyo, 108-8011, Japan
Tel.: (81) 367199111
Web Site: https://cweb.canon.jp
Rev.: $4,321,163,570
Assets: $3,951,724,940
Liabilities: $863,966,130
Net Worth: $3,087,758,810
Earnings: $258,735,370
Emp.: 16,089
Fiscal Year-end: 12/31/2023
Office Equipment Marketer; IT Consulting Services
N.A.I.C.S.: 423420
Masahiro Sakata *(Pres)*

Subsidiary (Non-US):

Canon Advanced Technologies Taiwan, Inc.   **(2)**
9F-1 No 25 Puding Road, Hsin-chu, Taiwan
Tel.: (886) 3 5797 500
Web Site: http://www.canon-at.com.tw
Semiconductor Testing Equipment Mfr
N.A.I.C.S.: 334515
Yasuhisa Oba *(Chm)*

Subsidiary (Domestic):

Canon Business Support Inc.   **(2)**
CANON Konan Building 13-29 Konan 2-chome, Minato-ku, Tokyo, 108-0075, Japan   **(100%)**
Tel.: (81) 367199369

Canon Inc.—(Continued)

Web Site: http://www.canon-bs.co.jp
Emp.: 612
Real Estate & Assets Management Services
N.A.I.C.S.: 561499
Yoshitaka Kinari (Pres & CEO)

Subsidiary (Domestic):

OAI, Inc. (3)
2-13-29 Konan, Minato-Ku, Tokyo, 108-0075, Japan
Tel.: (81) 367199383
Business Process Outsourcing Services
N.A.I.C.S.: 561499

Subsidiary (Domestic):

Canon Customer Support Inc. (2)
Canon MJ Makuhari Office 16F 7-2 Nakase 1-chome, Mihama-ku, Chiba, 261-0023, Japan
Tel.: (81) 432119312
Emp.: 804
Business Process Outsourcing Services
N.A.I.C.S.: 561499
Jill Nakamura (Gen Mgr)

Canon MJ IT Group Holdings Inc. (2)
Nomura Fudosan Tennozu Building 4-12 Higashishinagawa 2-chome, Shinagawa-ku, Tokyo, 140-8526, Japan
Tel.: (81) 3 6701 3600
Web Site: http://www.canon-mj.co.jp
Sales Range: $25-49.9 Million
Emp.: 5
Investment Management Service
N.A.I.C.S.: 523940

Subsidiary (Domestic):

Canon IT Solutions Inc. (3)
Canon S Tower 2-16-6 Konan, Minato-ku, Tokyo, 108-0075, Japan
Tel.: (81) 367013300
Web Site: https://www.canon-its.co.jp
Emp.: 3,778
Software Consulting Services
N.A.I.C.S.: 541512

Subsidiary (Domestic):

Canon ITS Medical Inc. (4)
Nomura Fudosan Tennozu Building 4-11 Higashishinagawa 2-chome, Shinagawa-ku, Tokyo, 140-8526, Japan
Tel.: (81) 367013610
Emp.: 191
Medical Equipment Mfr
N.A.I.C.S.: 339112

Subsidiary (US):

Canon Software America, Inc. (4)
1 Canon Plz, Lake Success, NY 11042-1198
Tel.: (516) 327-2270
Software Development Services
N.A.I.C.S.: 541511

Subsidiary (Domestic):

Qualysite technologies Inc. (4)
195-3 Toyohara Mirai Building 2, Nago, 905-2172, Okinawa, Japan
Tel.: (81) 980500600
Web Site: https://www.qualysite.co.jp
Emp.: 220
Software Development Services
N.A.I.C.S.: 541511

SuperStream Inc. (4)
Nomura Fudosan Tennozu Bldg 2-4-11 Higashi-shinagawa, Shinagawa-ku, Tokyo, 140-8526, Japan
Tel.: (81) 367013647
Web Site: https://www.superstream.canon-its.co.jp
Sales Range: $25-49.9 Million
Emp.: 13
Software Development Services
N.A.I.C.S.: 541511
Satoshi Tsunoda (Pres & CEO)

Subsidiary (Domestic):

Edifist Learning Inc. (3)
4F Yomiuri Yaesu Building 2-8-7 Kyobashi, Chuo-ku, Tokyo, 104-0031, Japan

Tel.: (81) 332821311
Web Site: https://www.edifist.co.jp
Sales Range: $10-24.9 Million
Information Technology Training Services
N.A.I.C.S.: 611430
Toshiro Kamei (Pres)

Subsidiary (Domestic):

Canon Print square Inc. (2)
Canon Konan Building 13-29 Konan 2-chome, Minato-ku, Tokyo, 108-8011, Japan
Tel.: (81) 3 6719 9594
Web Site: http://www.canon.com
Photocopying Machinery Leasing Services
N.A.I.C.S.: 532420

Canon Software, Inc. (2)
3-9-7 Mita, Minato Ku, 108-8317, Tokyo, Japan **(100%)**
Tel.: (81) 334559911
Web Site: http://www.canon-soft.co.jp
Rev.: $144,691,200
Emp.: 861
Software Publisher
N.A.I.C.S.: 513210

Subsidiary (Domestic):

Canon Software Information Systems Inc. (3)
Osaka Sakaisuji Bldg 2-2-13 Bakuromachi, Chuo-ku, Osaka, 541-0059, Japan
Tel.: (81) 6 6125 4828
Web Site: http://www.canon-js.co.jp
Rev.: $37,513,370
Emp.: 267
Networking Software Development Services
N.A.I.C.S.: 541511

Subsidiary (Domestic):

ELK Corporation (2)
1-31-1-402 Kaidori, Tama-shi, Tokyo, 206-0012, Japan
Tel.: (81) 5037000179
Emp.: 337
Medical Device Mfr
N.A.I.C.S.: 339112
Koji Ishwata (Pres)

Showa Information Systems Co., Ltd. (2)
No 45 Kowa Bldg 1-15-9 Minami Aoyama, Minato-Ku, Tokyo, 107-0062, Japan
Tel.: (81) 3 3403 7101
Web Site: http://www.sis.co.jp
Rev.: $135,876,840
Emp.: 380
Precision Printing System Mfr
N.A.I.C.S.: 333248

TOKYO NISSAN COMPUTER SYSTEM CO., LTD. (2)
3F Tokyu Fudosan Ebisu Bldg 1-18-18 Ebisu, Shibuya-Ku, Tokyo, 150-0013, Japan
Tel.: (81) 332802711
Web Site: http://www.tcs-net.co.jp
Sales Range: Less than $1 Million
Emp.: 151
Computer Hardware & Software Whslr
N.A.I.C.S.: 449210
Kojiro Yoshimaru (Pres)

withPhoto Inc. (2)
2-2-43 Higashi-Shinagawa, Shinagawa-ku, Tokyo, Japan
Tel.: (81) 3 3740 0531
Web Site: http://www.canon.com
Photographic Mail Ordering Services
N.A.I.C.S.: 541511

Canon Medical Finance Co., Ltd. (1)
Ningyocho 2-14-10 Urbannet Nihonbashi Building 5F, Nihonbashi Chuo-ku, Tokyo, 103-0013, Japan
Tel.: (81) 363714591
Web Site: https://finance.medical.canon
N.A.I.C.S.: 523150
Jun Tanaka (Dir-Rep)

Canon Medical Systems Corporation (1)
1385 Shimoishigami, Otawara, 324-8550, Tochigi, Japan
Tel.: (81) 287266200
Web Site: https://global.medical.canon
Medical Equipment Mfr
N.A.I.C.S.: 339112

Canon Medical Systems Europe B.V. (1)
Bovenkerkerweg 59, 1185 XB, Amstelveen, Netherlands
Tel.: (31) 882285000
Web Site: https://eu.medical.canon
Medical Equipment Mfr
N.A.I.C.S.: 339112

Canon Medical Systems USA, Inc. (1)
2441 Michelle Dr, Tustin, CA 92780
Web Site: https://us.medical.canon
Medical Equipment Mfr
N.A.I.C.S.: 339112
Yuji Hamada (Pres & CEO)

Canon Mold Co., Ltd. (1)
812-2 Kashiwai, Kasama, 309-1713, Ibaraki, Japan
Tel.: (81) 296778171
Web Site: https://mold.canon
Sales Range: $125-149.9 Million
Emp.: 517
Precise Plastic Molding Mfr
N.A.I.C.S.: 326199

Canon Opto (Malaysia) Sdn. Bhd. (1)
Jalan Selisik Seksyen 26, Prai, 40400, Shah Alam, Selangor Darul Ehsan, Malaysia **(50%)**
Tel.: (60) 351912100
Sales Range: $800-899.9 Million
Emp.: 2,700
Optical Lenses, Video Camcorder Lenses & Compact Cameras Mfr
N.A.I.C.S.: 333310

Canon Optron, Inc. (1)
(100%)
Tel.: (81) 296213700
Sales Range: $25-49.9 Million
Emp.: 200
Polisher of Optical Crystals for Steppers, Cameras & Telescopes & Manufacturer of Vapor Deposition Materials
N.A.I.C.S.: 333310
Hiroshi Oku (Pres)

Canon Precision Inc. (1)
4-1 Seinobukuro 5-chome, Hirosaki, 036-8072, Aomori, Japan **(100%)**
Tel.: (81) 172322911
Emp.: 2,400
DC Micromotors & Ultrasonic Motor-Related Units Mfr & Distr
N.A.I.C.S.: 335312
Takeji Yabu (Pres)

Canon Production Printing Germany GmbH & Co.KG (1)
PO Box 1260, 85581, Poing, Germany
Tel.: (49) 8121720
Printing Equipment Whslr
N.A.I.C.S.: 423830

Canon Production Printing Netherlands B.V. (1)
Van der Grintenstraat 10, 5914 HH, Venlo, Netherlands
Tel.: (31) 773592222
Web Site: http://cpp.canon
Emp.: 1,900
Printer Mfr & Distr
N.A.I.C.S.: 333248

Canon Ru LLC (1)
Serebryanicheskaya Naberezhnaya 29 8th Floor, Business Center Silver City, 109028, Moscow, Russia
Tel.: (7) 4952585600
Web Site: http://www.canon.ru
Sales Range: $50-74.9 Million
Emp.: 200
Digital Camera & Printer Mfr
N.A.I.C.S.: 333310

Canon Sales Co., Inc. (1)
(100%)
Sales Range: $1-4.9 Billion
Emp.: 15,813
R&D & Corporate Administration
N.A.I.C.S.: 541715

Canon Semiconductor Engineering Korea Inc. (1)
5th-6th floor 607 Teheran-ro, Gangnam-gu, Seoul, 135-090, Korea (South)
Tel.: (82) 264450013

Web Site: https://sekr.canon
Sales Range: $75-99.9 Million
Emp.: 523
Sales of Semiconductor Equipment
N.A.I.C.S.: 423690

Canon Semiconductor Equipment Inc. (1)
Tel.: (81) 297352531
Sales Range: $450-499.9 Million
Emp.: 1,345
Sales of Business Machines
N.A.I.C.S.: 459410

Canon Semiconductor Equipment Taiwan, Inc. (1)
9F-1 No 25 Puding Road, East District, Hsinchu, 300, Taiwan **(100%)**
Tel.: (886) 36686600
Web Site: https://setw.canon
Sales Range: $75-99.9 Million
Emp.: 150
Sales of Semiconductor Equipment
N.A.I.C.S.: 423690

Canon Singapore Pte. Ltd. (1)
1 Fusionopolis Place 14-10 Galaxis, Singapore, 138522, Singapore
Tel.: (65) 67998888
Web Site: https://sg.canon
Sales Range: $250-299.9 Million
Emp.: 1,000
Sales of Business Machines
N.A.I.C.S.: 423420

Subsidiary (Non-US):

Canon MailCom Malaysia Sdn. Bhd. (2)
No 3 Jalan Astaka U8/82 Taman Perindustrian Bukit Jelutong Seksyen U8, Bukit Jelutong, 40150, Shah Alam, Selangor Darul Ehsan, Malaysia **(100%)**
Tel.: (60) 378452555
Web Site: https://www.canon-mc.com.my
Business Process Outsourcing Services
N.A.I.C.S.: 561499
Kensaku Konishi (Chm & CEO)

Subsidiary (Domestic):

TECH Semiconductor Singapore Pte. Ltd. (2)
No 1 Woodlands Industrial Park D Street 1, Singapore, 738799, Singapore
Tel.: (65) 6365 1998
Web Site: http://www.techsemiconductor.com.sg
Sales Range: $350-399.9 Million
Mfr of Semiconductors
N.A.I.C.S.: 334413

Canon System & Support (1)
Canon S Tower 16-6 Konan 2-chome, Minato-ku, Tokyo, 108-8225, Japan **(100%)**
Tel.: (81) 367197111
Web Site: http://www.canon-sas.co.jp
Sales Range: $150-199.9 Million
Emp.: 4,632
Sales & Servicer of Business Machines
N.A.I.C.S.: 423420

Canon Technical Information Services Inc. (1)
30-2 Shimomaruko 3-chome, Ohta-ku, Tokyo, 146-8501, Japan
Tel.: (81) 337576241
Sales Range: $25-49.9 Million
Emp.: 82
Translation Services
N.A.I.C.S.: 541930

Canon Tokki Corporation (1)
10-1 Shinko-cho, Mitsuke-shi, Niigata, 954-0076, Japan
Tel.: (81) 258615050
Web Site: https://tokki.canon
Sales Range: $100-124.9 Million
Emp.: 647
Vacuum Product Mfr
N.A.I.C.S.: 334419
Teruhisa Tsugami (Chm & CEO)

Canon U.S.A., Inc. (1)
1 Canon Plz, Lake Success, NY 11042 **(100%)**
Tel.: (516) 328-5000
Web Site: http://www.usa.canon.com
Rev.: $9,722,099,712

Emp.: 900
Photographic & Office Products Importer, Marketer & Distr
N.A.I.C.S.: 423420
Seymour Liebman *(Chief Admin Officer & Gen Counsel)*

Subsidiary (Domestic):

Canon Business Process Services, Inc. **(2)**
261 Madison Ave, New York, NY 10016 **(100%)**
Tel.: (212) 502-2100
Web Site: https://www.cbps.canon.com
Sales Range: $550-599.9 Million
Emp.: 65
Business Process Outsourcing Services
N.A.I.C.S.: 561499
Joseph R. Marciano *(Pres & CEO)*

Subsidiary (Non-US):

Canon Canada, Inc. **(2)**
6390 Dixie Rd, Mississauga, L5T 1P7, ON, Canada **(100%)**
Tel.: (905) 795-1111
Web Site: http://www.canon.ca
Sales Range: $125-149.9 Million
Emp.: 500
Marketing of Canon Products
N.A.I.C.S.: 423410

Subsidiary (Domestic):

Oce-Canada, Inc. **(3)**
4711 Young St Ste 1100, Toronto, M2N 6K8, ON, Canada **(100%)**
Tel.: (416) 224-5600
Web Site: http://www.oce.ca
Sales Range: $25-49.9 Million
Emp.: 80
Document Management & Printing Equipment Distr
N.A.I.C.S.: 423420

Subsidiary (Domestic):

Canon Development Americas, Inc. **(2)**
15975 Alton Pkwy, Irvine, CA 92618
Tel.: (949) 932-3100
Sales Range: $25-49.9 Million
Emp.: 100
Digital Software Developer
N.A.I.C.S.: 423430

Canon Financial Services, Inc. **(2)**
158 Gaither Dr Ste 200, Mount Laurel, NJ 08054
Tel.: (856) 813-1000
Web Site: http://www.cfs.canon.com
Leasing of Cannon Products
N.A.I.C.S.: 532490

Canon Information Technology Services Inc. **(2)**
850 Greenbrier Cir Ste K, Chesapeake, VA 23320-2644
Tel.: (757) 579-7100
Web Site: https://www.cits.canon.com
Rev.: $14,100,000
Emp.: 500
Technical Support Center for Canon Printers & Products
N.A.I.C.S.: 811210
Doris Higginbotham *(Pres)*

Canon Information and Imaging Solutions, Inc. **(2)**
1 Canon Plz, Lake Success, NY 11042
Tel.: (516) 328-5000
Web Site: http://www.ciis.canon.com
Software Consulting Services
N.A.I.C.S.: 541512

Division (Domestic):

Canon Latin America, Inc. **(2)**
703 Waterford Way Ste 400, Miami, FL 33126-4675 **(100%)**
Tel.: (305) 260-7400
Web Site: http://www.canonlatinamerica.com
Sales Range: $25-49.9 Million
Emp.: 80
Canon Sales & Marketing for Latin America
N.A.I.C.S.: 333310

Subsidiary (Non-US):

Canon Argentina S.A. **(3)**

San Martin 344 Piso 19, Buenos Aires, C1004AAH, Argentina **(100%)**
Tel.: (54) 11 5554 9800
Web Site: http://www.canonarg.com.ar
Sales Range: $10-24.9 Million
Sales of Business Machines
N.A.I.C.S.: 423420

Canon Chile S.A. **(3)**
9th Floor Torre Centenario Building, Miraflores, Santiago, Chile **(100%)**
Tel.: (56) 224622157
Web Site: http://www.canon.cl
Sales Range: $50-74.9 Million
Emp.: 130
Sales of Business Machines
N.A.I.C.S.: 423420

Canon Mexicana, S. de R.L. de C.V. **(3)**
(100%)
Web Site: http://www.canon.com.mx
Sales Range: $50-74.9 Million
Sales of all Canon Products
N.A.I.C.S.: 449210
Yasuhiro Suzuki *(Sr VP & Gen Mgr)*

Canon Panama, S.A. **(3)**
Tel.: (507) 2798900
Emp.: 200
Sales of all Canon Products
N.A.I.C.S.: 449210

Canon do Brasil Industrial e Comercio Limitada **(3)**
Av do Cafe 277, Torre B-6 andar-Vila Guarani, Sao Paulo, 04311-000, S P, Brazil **(100%)**
Tel.: (55) 1149505312
Web Site: https://www.canon.com.br
Sales Range: $25-49.9 Million
Sales of Copy & Fax Machines
N.A.I.C.S.: 423420

Subsidiary (Domestic):

Canon Solutions America, Inc. **(2)**
1 Canon Park, Melville, NY 11747
Tel.: (631) 330-5000
Web Site: https://www.csa.canon.com
Sales Range: $1-4.9 Billion
Emp.: 7,000
Office Machinery Distribution & Support Services
N.A.I.C.S.: 423420
Seymour Liebman *(Vice Chm)*

Unit (Domestic):

Canon Solutions America, Inc. - Burlington **(3)**
300 Commerce Sq Blvd, Burlington, NJ 08016 **(100%)**
Tel.: (609) 387-8700
Sales Range: $50-74.9 Million
Emp.: 200
Office Products Distr
N.A.I.C.S.: 423420

Canon Solutions America, Inc. - Chicago **(3)**
225 W Washington Ste 600, Chicago, IL 60606 **(100%)**
Tel.: (312) 986-0100
Holding Company
N.A.I.C.S.: 325992

Canon Solutions America, Inc. - Gardena **(3)**
110 W Walnut St, Gardena, CA 90248-3100
Tel.: (310) 217-3000
Web Site: http://www.solutions.canon.com
Sales Range: $75-99.9 Million
Emp.: 250
Office Products Distr
N.A.I.C.S.: 423420

Canon Solutions America, Inc. - Salt Lake City **(3)**
345 W Bearcat Dr Ste B, Salt Lake City, UT 84115
Tel.: (801) 461-7600
Web Site: http://www.canonbusinesssolutions.com
Sales Range: $50-74.9 Million
Emp.: 85
Office Equipment Distr
N.A.I.C.S.: 423420

Canon Solutions America, Inc. - Schaumburg **(3)**

425 N Martingale Rd Ste 100, Schaumburg, IL 60173-2212 **(100%)**
Tel.: (847) 706-3400
Web Site: https://l.csa.canon.com
Sales Range: $250-299.9 Million
Emp.: 605
Office Products Distr
N.A.I.C.S.: 423420

Canon Solutions America, Inc. - Trumbull **(3)**
100 Oakview Dr, Trumbull, CT 06611-4724
Tel.: (203) 365-7000
Office Equipment Distr
N.A.I.C.S.: 423420
John C. Chillock *(VP-Customer Svc Ops)*

Subsidiary (Domestic):

Canon U.S. Life Sciences, Inc. **(2)**
9800 Medical Ctr Dr, Rockville, MD 20850
Tel.: (301) 762-7070
Web Site: http://www.culs.canon.com
Sales Range: $10-24.9 Million
Emp.: 37
Clinical Diagnostic Research & Development Services
N.A.I.C.S.: 541715

Canon USA, Inc. **(2)**
15955 and 15975 Alton Pkwy, Irvine, CA 92618 **(100%)**
Tel.: (949) 753-4000
Sales Range: $75-99.9 Million
Emp.: 200
Mfr of Image Finding Systems, Cameras, Lenses & Printers
N.A.I.C.S.: 423410
Yoshinori Shimono *(CFO, Treas, Sr VP & Gen Mgr-Fin & Acctg)*

Canon USA, Inc. **(2)**
3300 N 1st St, San Jose, CA 95134-1900 **(100%)**
Web Site: http://www.usa.canon.com
Rev.: $1,700,000
Emp.: 10
Computer Peripherals & Software
N.A.I.C.S.: 449210

Canon Virginia, Inc. **(2)**
12000 Canon Blvd, Newport News, VA 23606-4201 **(100%)**
Sales Range: $400-449.9 Million
Copying Machines Mfr
N.A.I.C.S.: 333310
Toru Nishizawa *(Pres & CEO)*

Subsidiary (Domestic):

Custom Integrated Technology Inc. **(3)**
120 Enterprise Dr, Newport News, VA 23603-1368
Tel.: (757) 887-0211
Web Site: http://www.usa.canon.com
Rev.: $10,100,000
Emp.: 90
Computer Printers & Copiers Mfr
N.A.I.C.S.: 334118

Subsidiary (Domestic):

Molecular Imprints, Inc. **(2)**
1807 W Braker Ln Bldg C-300, Austin, TX 78758-3605
Tel.: (512) 339-7760
Web Site: https://cnt.canon.com
Sales Range: $1-9.9 Million
Emp.: 75
Nanopatterning Systems & Solutions for Hard Disk Drive & Semiconductor Industries
N.A.I.C.S.: 333242

Canon Vietnam Co., Ltd. **(1)**
Lot A1 Thang Long Industrial Park, Kim Chung commune Dong Anh District, Hanoi, Vietnam
Tel.: (84) 2438812111
Web Site: https://cvn.canon
Sales Range: $1-4.9 Billion
Emp.: 22,747
Printer & Toner Cartridge Mfr
N.A.I.C.S.: 334118
Niimura Minoru *(Gen Dir)*

Subsidiary (Domestic):

Canon Electronics Vietnam Co., Ltd. **(2)**
Road 206 Section B Pho Noi A Industrial

Park, Van Lam District, Yen My, Hung Yen, Vietnam
Tel.: (84) 2213587311
Sales Range: $400-449.9 Million
Emp.: 3,476
Electronic Components Mfr
N.A.I.C.S.: 334419
Wayne Hartley *(Gen Dir)*

Canon Marketing Vietnam Company Limited **(2)**
7th Floor Friendship Tower 31 Le Duan, Ben Nghe Ward District 1, Ho Chi Minh City, Vietnam
Tel.: (84) 2838200466
Web Site: http://www.canon.com.vn
Sales Range: $25-49.9 Million
Emp.: 2
Photographic Equipment Distr
N.A.I.C.S.: 423410

Canon Wind Inc. **(1)**
564-1 Sako, Oita, 870-0292, Japan
Tel.: (81) 975241122
Sales Range: $25-49.9 Million
Emp.: 32
Digital Camera Parts Mfr
N.A.I.C.S.: 333310

Fukushima Canon Inc. **(1)**
2 Nihon Enoki Sakurashita, Fukushima, 960-2193, Japan
Tel.: (81) 245932111
Web Site: https://fukushima.canon
Emp.: 1,590
Commercial Photo Printer Mfr
N.A.I.C.S.: 325910

Milestone Systems A/S **(1)**
Banemarksvej 50 C, 2605, Brondby, Denmark
Tel.: (45) 88300300
Web Site: https://www.milestonesys.com
Emp.: 589
IP Video Management Software
N.A.I.C.S.: 513210
Kenneth Hune Petersen *(CMO & Chief Sls Officer)*

Subsidiary (Non-US):

Milestone Sistemas do Brasil **(2)**
Rua Joaquim Floriano 466 cj 1908 sala 1, Ed Office BR Itaim Bibi, Sao Paulo, 04534-002, SP, Brazil
Tel.: (55) 11 21374421
IP Video Management Software
N.A.I.C.S.: 513210

Milestone Systems (Australia) Pty Limited **(2)**
A5/8 Rogers St, Bundoora, Port Melbourne, 3207, VIC, Australia
Tel.: (61) 385184790
IP Video Management Software
N.A.I.C.S.: 513210

Milestone Systems Bulgaria **(2)**
2 Donka Ushlinova str Garitage Park Building 1 Floor 2, 1766, Sofia, Bulgaria
Tel.: (359) 24426172
IP Video Management Software
N.A.I.C.S.: 513210

Milestone Systems France SARL **(2)**
9 Avenue Edouard Belin, 92500, Rueil-Malmaison, France
Tel.: (33) 184021080
IP Video Management Software
N.A.I.C.S.: 513210

Milestone Systems Germany GmbH **(2)**
Maximilianstrasse 54, 80538, Munich, Germany
Tel.: (49) 8920000757
IP Video Management Software
N.A.I.C.S.: 513210

Subsidiary (US):

Milestone Systems Inc. **(2)**
8905 SW Nimbus Ave Ste 400, Beaverton, OR 97008
Tel.: (503) 350-1100
Web Site: https://www.milestonesys.com
Emp.: 120
IP Video Management Software
N.A.I.C.S.: 513210

CANON INC.

Canon Inc.—(Continued)

Subsidiary (Non-US):

Milestone Systems Italia S.r.l. (2)
Via Arnesano 2, 20092, Cinisello Balsamo, MI, Italy
Tel.: (39) 0294751082
IP Video Management Software
N.A.I.C.S.: 513210

Milestone Systems K.K. (2)
Canon Konan Building 2-13-29 Konan, Minato-ku, Tokyo, 108-0075, Japan
Tel.: (81) 345795657
IP Video Management Software
N.A.I.C.S.: 513210

Milestone Systems Pte. Ltd. (2)
10 Eunos Road 8 12-03 North Lobby, Singapore Post Centre, Singapore, 408600, Singapore
Tel.: (65) 31589911
IP Video Management Software
N.A.I.C.S.: 513210

Milestone Systems Spain S.L. (2)
Calle Pallars 99 3rd floor office 34, 08018, Barcelona, Spain
Tel.: (34) 933937064
IP Video Management Software
N.A.I.C.S.: 513210

Milestone Systems UAE (2)
Al Falak Street Aurora Tower Office 1806 18th floor, Dubai Media City, Dubai, United Arab Emirates
Tel.: (971) 145592710
Emp.: 11
IP Video Management Software
N.A.I.C.S.: 513210
Peter Biltsted (Dir-Sls-Middle East & Africa)

Milestone Systems UK Ltd. (2)
Landmark Building 450 Brook Drive, Green Park, Reading, RG2 6UU, United Kingdom
Tel.: (44) 1184024726
IP Video Management Software
N.A.I.C.S.: 513210

Miyazaki Canon Inc. (1)
11700-1 Minami Takanabe, Takanabe Town Koyu District, Miyazaki, 884-8611, Japan
Tel.: (81) 983222111
Web Site: https://miyazaki.canon
Emp.: 963
Camera Mfr
N.A.I.C.S.: 333310

Miyazaki Daishin Canon Co., Ltd. (1)
(50%)
Web Site: http://www.daishin-canon.co.jp
Digital Camera Mfr
N.A.I.C.S.: 333310

Nagahama Canon Inc. (1)
1280 Kunitomomachi, Nagahama-Shi, Shiga, 526-0001, Japan
(100%)
Tel.: (81) 749642111
Sales Range: $200-249.9 Million
Emp.: 1,000
Mfr of Chemical Products, Solar Cells & Printer Cartridges
N.A.I.C.S.: 325998

Nagasaki Canon Inc. (1)
925-1 Orishikisego Hasami-cho, Higashisonogi-gun, Nagasaki, 859-3793, Japan
Tel.: (81) 956851111
Sales Range: $400-449.9 Million
Emp.: 1,125
Digital Camera Mfr
N.A.I.C.S.: 333310

Oita Canon Inc. (1)
710 Shimohara Aki-cho, Akimachi Higashi-kunisaki Gun, Kunisaki, 873-0292, Oita, Japan
Tel.: (81) 978672111
Camera Mfr
N.A.I.C.S.: 333310

Oita Canon Materials Inc. (1)
1-111 Kumano, Kitsuki, 873-8501, Oita, Japan
Tel.: (81) 978642111
Web Site: https://mtrl.canon
Sales Range: $450-499.9 Million
Emp.: 1,550
Specialty Chemicals Mfr

N.A.I.C.S.: 325998

Quality ElectroDynamics LLC (1)
700 Beeta Dr Ste 100, Mayfield Village, OH 44143 **(70%)**
Tel.: (440) 638-5106
Web Site: http://www.qualedyn.com
Sales Range: $10-24.9 Million
Emp.: 130
Designs & Manufactures MRI Radio Frequency Coil Technology for Human Body Imaging
N.A.I.C.S.: 621512
Hiroyuki Fujita (Founder & CEO)

Toshiba Medical Systems Corporation (1)
1385 Shimoishigami, Otawara-shi, Tochigi, 324-8550, Japan **(100%)**
Medical Diagnostic Imaging Systems & Products Developer, Mfr & Distr
N.A.I.C.S.: 811210
Toshio Takiguchi (Pres & CEO)

Subsidiary (US):

Vital Images, Inc. (2)
5850 Opus Pkwy Ste 300, Minnetonka, MN 55343-4411
Tel.: (952) 487-9500
Web Site: http://www.vitalimages.com
Emp.: 238
Medical Equipment Distr; Health Imaging Informatics Solutions
N.A.I.C.S.: 423450
Stephen S. Andersen (Exec VP-Intl & Gen Mgr-HII)

Subsidiary (Non-US):

Vital Images China (3)
L24 Tower 3 China Cental Place 77 Jianguo Road, Chaoyang District, Beijing, 10025, China
Tel.: (86) 40000 84825
Web Site: http://www.vitalimages.com
Medical Equipment Distr
N.A.I.C.S.: 423450

Vital Images Europe B.V. (3)
Zilverstraat 1, 2718 RP, Zoetermeer, Netherlands
Tel.: (31) 792065800
Web Site: http://www.vitalimages.com
Medical Equipment Distr; Health Imaging Informatics Solutions
N.A.I.C.S.: 423450
Marc Lamont (Mng Dir-EMEA)

Ueno Canon Materials Inc. (1)
410-7 Todaimachi Mita, Iga-Shi, Iga, 518-0022, Mie, Japan
Tel.: (81) 595243111
Web Site: https://ueno.canon
Sales Range: $50-74.9 Million
Emp.: 250
Mfr of Chemical Products for Copying Machines & Printers
N.A.I.C.S.: 325998

CANONICAL GROUP LIMITED

5th Floor Blue Fin Building 110 Southwark Street, London, SE1 0SU, United Kingdom
Tel.: (44) 20 7630 2401
Web Site: http://www.canonical.com
Year Founded: 2004
Sales Range: $75-99.9 Million
Emp.: 400
Software Development & Support Services
N.A.I.C.S.: 513210

Subsidiaries:

Canonical USA Inc. (1)
Ste 212 Lexington Corporate Ctr 10 Maguire Rd, Lexington, MA 02421
Tel.: (781) 761-9080
Application Software Development Services
N.A.I.C.S.: 541511

CANOPY FINANCE LIMITED

301 Corporate Arena Off Aarey Piramal X Road 3rd Floor, Behind Mahindra Gardens Goregaon West, Mumbai, 400062, India

Tel.: (91) 9892108869
Web Site: http://www.canopyfinance.org
Year Founded: 1981
539304—(BOM)
Rev.: $673,864
Assets: $981,775
Liabilities: $52,530
Net Worth: $929,245
Earnings: $113,411
Fiscal Year-end: 03/31/21
Financial Support Services
N.A.I.C.S.: 523999
Lalit Kumar Tapadia (Mng Dir & Compliance Officer)

CANOPY GROWTH CORPORATION

1 Hershey Drive, Smiths Falls, K7A 0A8, ON, Canada
Web Site: https://www.canopygrowth.com
Year Founded: 2009
CGC—(NASDAQ)
Rev.: $352,730,834
Assets: $1,908,057,583
Liabilities: $1,313,507,573
Net Worth: $594,550,010
Earnings: ($2,564,437,440)
Emp.: 1,572
Fiscal Year-end: 03/31/23
Medical Marijuana Mfr & Supplier
N.A.I.C.S.: 325411
Christelle Gedeon (Chief Legal Officer)

Subsidiaries:

Hiku Brands Company Ltd. (1)
6 2322 Dominion Road, West Kelowna, Vancouver, V1Z 2W8, BC, Canada
Tel.: (416) 899-9422
Web Site: http://www.hiku.com
Assets: $18,237,188
Liabilities: $10,223,287
Net Worth: $8,013,901
Earnings: ($4,970,869)
Fiscal Year-end: 12/31/2017
Pharmaceutical Products
N.A.I.C.S.: 325412

Mettrum Health Corp. (1)
314 Bennett Road, Bowmanville, L1C 3K5, ON, Canada
Tel.: (844) 638-8786
Investment Services
N.A.I.C.S.: 523999

The Supreme Cannabis Company, Inc. (1)
178R Ossington Avenue, Toronto, M6J 2Z7, ON, Canada
Tel.: (416) 630-7272
Web Site: http://www.supreme.ca
Pharmaceuticals Mfr
N.A.I.C.S.: 325412
John Alexander Fowler (Founder, Chief Advocacy Officer & Mng Dir-Flower & Concentrates)

Subsidiary (Domestic):

BlissCo Cannabis Corp. (2)
#2 - 20133 102nd Ave, Vancouver, V6L 1R3, BC, Canada
Tel.: (604) 484-9119
Web Site: http://www.blissco.com
Sales Range: Less than $1 Million
Cannabis Research & Cultivation
N.A.I.C.S.: 111419

CANOX CORPORATION

1-1-12 Nagono, Nishi-ku, Nagoya, 451-8570, Aichi, Japan
Tel.: (81) 52 564 3511
Web Site: http://www.canox.co.jp
Year Founded: 1897
Sales Range: $25-49.9 Million
Emp.: 190
Steel Product Distr
N.A.I.C.S.: 423510
Mikio Kinoshita (Pres)

CANPRO CONSTRUCTION LTD.

555 Dupplin Rd, Victoria, V8Z 1C2, BC, Canada
Tel.: (250) 475-0975
Web Site: http://www.canpro-ltd.com
Year Founded: 1984
Building Construction Services
N.A.I.C.S.: 236220
Don Wagner (Owner)

CANSEL SURVEY EQUIPMENT, LTD.

3900 North Fraser Way, Burnaby, V5J 5H6, BC, Canada
Tel.: (888) 222-6735
Web Site: http://www.cansel.ca
Year Founded: 1966
Civil Engineering Services
N.A.I.C.S.: 541330
Martin Trudelle (Pres)

Subsidiaries:

California Surveying & Drafting Supply, Inc. (1)
4733 Auburn Blvd, Sacramento, CA 95841
Tel.: (916) 344-0232
Web Site: http://www.csdsinc.com
Surveying, Drafting & Engineering Supplies & Services
N.A.I.C.S.: 541360
Dan Soldavini (Mgr-Sls-Media & Drafting Equipment)

CANSINO BIOLOGICS, INC.

No 185 South Street Economic and Technological Development Zone, West District Biomedicine Park, Tianjin, 300457, China
Tel.: (86) 2258213766
Web Site: http://www.cansinotech.com
Year Founded: 2009
688185—(SHG)
Rev.: $658,757,343
Assets: $1,819,244,190
Liabilities: $509,622,883
Net Worth: $1,309,621,308
Earnings: $292,184,646
Emp.: 1,946
Fiscal Year-end: 12/31/21
Vaccine Product Mfr
N.A.I.C.S.: 325414
Xuefeng Yu (Founder, Chm, CEO & Gen Mgr)

CANSO CREDIT INCOME FUND

3080 Yonge Street Suite 3037, Toronto, M4N 3N1, ON, Canada
Tel.: (416) 640-4275
Web Site: http://lysanderfunds.com
PBY.UN—(TSX)
Rev.: $26,928,569
Assets: $170,032,092
Liabilities: $44,432,785
Net Worth: $125,599,306
Earnings: $17,382,470
Fiscal Year-end: 12/31/21
Closed-End Investment Fund
N.A.I.C.S.: 525990
Richard Usher-Jones (Pres)

CANSO ENTERPRISES LTD.

Avenue Javier Rojo Gomez 630, Leyes de Reforma Istapalapa, Mexico, 09310, Mexico
Tel.: (52) 55 10843026
Year Founded: 2013
Metal Mining
N.A.I.C.S.: 212290
Jim Burns (Pres, CEO, CFO, Principal Acctg Officer, Treas & Sec)

CANSO FORD SALES

9 MacIntosh Ave, Port Hawkesbury, B9A 3K4, NS, Canada

Tel.: (902) 625-1338
Web Site:
    http://cansoford.connection.com
Year Founded: 1979
Rev.: $11,561,746
Emp.: 26
Used & New Car Dealers
N.A.I.C.S.: 441110
Chris Kennedy *(Mgr-Collision Center)*

CANSO SELECT OPPORTUNITIES CORP.
100 York BoulevardSuite 550, Richmond Hill, L4B1J8, ON, Canada
Tel.: (647) 956-6264
Web Site:
    https://www.selectopportunities.com
Year Founded: 2018
CSOC.A—(TSXV)
Rev.: $22,575
Assets: $9,441,100
Liabilities: $27,474
Net Worth: $9,413,626
Earnings: ($845,924)
Fiscal Year-end: 12/31/20
Investment Management Service
N.A.I.C.S.: 525990
Brian Carney *(Pres & CEO)*

CANSTAR RESOURCES INC.
550-220 Bay Street, Toronto, M5J 2W4, ON, Canada
Tel.: (647) 557-3442
Web Site:
    https://www.canstarresources.com
Year Founded: 1997
CSRNF—(OTCIQ)
Assets: $10,363,035
Liabilities: $160,392
Net Worth: $10,202,643
Earnings: ($6,927,138)
Fiscal Year-end: 06/30/22
Mineral Exploration Services
N.A.I.C.S.: 213114
John E. Hurley *(CFO)*

CANTABIL RETAIL INDIA LIMITED
B-16 Lawrence Road Industrial Area, New Delhi, 110035, India
Tel.: (91) 41414188
Web Site:
    https://www.cantabilnational.com
533267—(BOM)
Rev.: $12,964,456
Assets: $58,503,600
Liabilities: $41,571,553
Net Worth: $16,932,047
Earnings: $175,075
Emp.: 2,178
Fiscal Year-end: 03/31/21
Clothing Mfr & Retailer
N.A.I.C.S.: 458110
Vijay Bansal *(Chm & Mng Dir)*

CANTARGIA AB
Scheelevagen 27, SE 223 63, Lund, Sweden
Tel.: (46) 462756260   SE
Web Site: https://www.cantargia.com
Year Founded: 2010
CANTA—(OMX)
Rev.: $912,267
Assets: $44,470,482
Liabilities: $7,971,939
Net Worth: $36,498,544
Earnings: ($34,824,805)
Emp.: 26
Fiscal Year-end: 12/31/22
Pharmaceuticals Mfr
N.A.I.C.S.: 325412
Thoas Fioretos *(Co-Founder)*

CANTERBURY RESOURCES LTD.
Suite 301 55 Miller Street, Pyrmont, 2009, NSW, Australia
Tel.: (61) 293928020
Web Site:
    https://www.canterburysources.com
Year Founded: 2011
CBY—(ASX)
Rev.: $363,506
Assets: $8,340,648
Liabilities: $832,508
Net Worth: $7,508,140
Earnings: ($470,871)
Fiscal Year-end: 06/30/24
Gold Ore & Silver Ore Mining
N.A.I.C.S.: 212220
John Anderson *(Chm)*

CANTERRA MINERALS CORPORATION
580 625 Howe Street, Vancouver, V6C 2T6, BC, Canada
Tel.: (604) 687-6644   BC
Web Site:
    https://www.canterraminerals.com
CTMCF—(OTCQB)
Assets: $5,983,702
Liabilities: $300,113
Net Worth: $5,683,589
Earnings: ($3,753,929)
Emp.: 5
Fiscal Year-end: 12/31/21
Minerals Exploration & Mining
N.A.I.C.S.: 212390
Randy C. Turner *(Chm)*

CANTEX MINE DEVELOPMENT CORP.
203 - 1634 Harvey Ave, Kelowna, V1Y 6G2, BC, Canada
Tel.: (250) 860-8582
Web Site: https://www.cantex.ca
CD—(TSXV)
Rev.: $69,403
Assets: $10,112,038
Liabilities: $5,243,340
Net Worth: $4,868,699
Earnings: ($7,264,184)
Fiscal Year-end: 07/31/19
Mineral Exploration Services
N.A.I.C.S.: 213114
Chad Ulansky *(Pres & CEO)*

CANTILLANA SA/NV
Pontstraat 84, Deurle, Sint-Martens-Latem, 9831, Belgium
Tel.: (32) 9280 7780   BE
Web Site: http://www.cantillana.com
Year Founded: 1875
Sales Range: $25-49.9 Million
Emp.: 250
Plaster & Mortar Mfr
N.A.I.C.S.: 327120
Piet Bogaert *(Dir-Sls)*

Subsidiaries:

Cantillana B.V.   (1)
Munnikenlandse Maaskade 2a, Poederoijen, Zaltbommel, 5307TE, Netherlands
Tel.: (31) 183 44 7800
Web Site: http://www.cantillana.com
Plaster & Mortar Mfr
N.A.I.C.S.: 327120
Fredrick Sdades *(Gen Mgr)*

Cantillana GmbH   (1)
Deilbachtal 63, 45257, Essen, Germany
Tel.: (49) 201 43 62 83 00
Emp.: 8
Building Materials Distr
N.A.I.C.S.: 423320

Cantillana SAS   (1)
Zl des Iscles 785 Avenue de la Durance, F-13160, Chateaurenard, France
Tel.: (33) 4 9094 2060
Web Site: http://www.cantillana.com
Plaster & Mortar Mfr
N.A.I.C.S.: 327120

CANTINE RIUNITE & CIV S.C.AGR.
Via Giacomo Brodolini 24, 42040, Campegine, Italy
Tel.: (39) 0522905711   IT
Web Site: http://www.riunite.it
Year Founded: 1950
Sales Range: $600-649.9 Million
Emp.: 1,500
Holding Company; Wineries & Wine Whslr
N.A.I.C.S.: 551112
Benini Flancesca *(Dir-Comml)*

Subsidiaries:

Gruppo Italiano Vini S.p.A.   (1)
Villa Belvedere, Frazione Di Bardolino, Calmasino, 37010, Veneto, Italy
Tel.: (39) 0456269600
Web Site: http://www.gruppoitalianovini.com
Sales Range: $200-249.9 Million
Emp.: 330
Holding Company; Wineries & Wine Whslr
N.A.I.C.S.: 551112
Rolando Chiossi *(Vice Chm & Head-Fin Ops)*

Subsidiary (Domestic):

Bigi S.p.A.   (2)
Localita Ponte Giulio no 3, IT-05018, Orvieto, Terni, Italy
Tel.: (39) 0763315888
Web Site: http://www.cantinebigi.it
Sales Range: $25-49.9 Million
Emp.: 20
Winery & Wine Whslr
N.A.I.C.S.: 312130
Massimo Panattoni *(Mgr)*

Holding (US):

Frederick Wildman & Sons Ltd.   (2)
307 E 53rd St, New York, NY 10022-4985   (75%)
Tel.: (212) 355-0700
Web Site: http://www.frederickwildman.com
Sales Range: $25-49.9 Million
Emp.: 75
French & Italian Wines Importer
N.A.I.C.S.: 424820
Tim Master *(Dir-Specialty Spirits & Trade Education)*

CANTONI MOTOR S.A.
Grazynskiego 22, 43-300, Bielsko-Biala, Poland
Tel.: (48) 334994805
Web Site:
    http://www.cantonigroup.com
Sales Range: $10-24.9 Million
Emp.: 20
Electric Motor Mfr
N.A.I.C.S.: 335312
Luca Cantoni *(Chm)*

Subsidiaries:

Besel S.A.   (1)
Ul Elektryczna 8, 49-300, Brzeg, Poland
Tel.: (48) 774162861
Web Site: http://www.besel.pl
Electric Motor Mfr
N.A.I.C.S.: 335312

CELMA INDUKTA SA   (1)
ul 3 Maja 19, 43-400, Cieszyn, Poland
Tel.: (48) 334701700
Industrial Machinery Mfr
N.A.I.C.S.: 332510

Celma S.A.   (1)
Ul 3 Maja 19, 43 400, Cieszyn, Poland
Tel.: (48) 338519100
Web Site: http://www.motors.celma.pl
Electric Motor Mfr
N.A.I.C.S.: 335312

Emit S.A.   (1)
Narutowicza 72, Zychlin, 99 320, Poland
Tel.: (48) 242851014
Web Site: http://www.emit-motor.com.pl
Low & High Voltage Induction Motors Mfr
N.A.I.C.S.: 335312
Barbara Studzinska *(Dir-Comml)*

FANA Narzedzia Sp.z.o.o.   (1)
ul Grazynskiego 22, 43-300, Bielsko-Biala, Poland
Tel.: (48) 334994805
Industrial Machinery Mfr
N.A.I.C.S.: 332510

Fenes S.A.   (1)
gen Franciszka Kleeberga 2, 08 110, Siedlce, Poland
Tel.: (48) 256325251
Web Site: http://www.fenes.com.pl
Cutting Tools for Metalworking & Woodworking Mfr
N.A.I.C.S.: 333519

Narmod Sp. z o.o.   (1)
Ul Narutowicza 72, 99-320, Zychlin, Poland
Tel.: (48) 242854789
Industrial Machinery Mfr
N.A.I.C.S.: 332510

ZPN BESEL-FORMIT ltd.   (1)
ul Elektryczna 8; 49-300, Brzeg, Poland
Tel.: (48) 774162861
Industrial Machinery Mfr
N.A.I.C.S.: 332510

CANTOURAGE GROUP SE
Feurigstrasse 54, 10827, Berlin, Germany
Tel.: (49) 30470135050   De
Web Site:
    https://www.cantourage.com
Year Founded: 2019
HIGH—(DEU)
Rev.: $1,832,432
Assets: $49,773,706
Liabilities: $916,216
Net Worth: $48,857,490
Earnings: $44,155
Fiscal Year-end: 12/31/23
Pharmaceutical Products Distr
N.A.I.C.S.: 424210
Bernd Fischer *(CFO)*

CANTRONIC SYSTEMS INC.
8-62 Fawcett Rd, Coquitlam, V3K 6V5, BC, Canada
Tel.: (604) 516-6667   BC
Web Site:
    https://www.cantronics.com
Year Founded: 2005
Sales Range: $10-24.9 Million
Emp.: 300
Infrared Imaging Camera & Night Vision Surveillance Systems Mfr & Distr
N.A.I.C.S.: 561621
Kevin Tao Su *(CFO)*

Subsidiaries:

AIRT Academy of Infrared Training Inc.   (1)
67A Clipper St, Coquitlam, V3K 6X2, BC, Canada
Tel.: (360) 676-1915
Web Site: http://www.infraredtraining.net
Emp.: 15
Training Services
N.A.I.C.S.: 611430

Actiontop Electronics (Shenzhen) Co. Ltd   (1)
13F Block B1 Nanshan Zhiyuan No 1001 Xueyuan Road Nanshan Distric, Longgang District, Shenzhen, 518129, Guangdong, China
Tel.: (86) 75589390905
Web Site: http://www.actiontop.com
Emp.: 150
Surveillance Equipment Mfr
N.A.I.C.S.: 334511
Alec Weingart *(CEO & Pres)*

Beijing Advanced VideoInfo Technology Co., Ltd   (1)
Jiahuiyua Huaao International Building B Area 10th Floor, Beijing, 100097, China
Tel.: (86) 10 58930606
Web Site: http://www.avinfo.cn
Surveillance Equipments Mfr & Distr
N.A.I.C.S.: 334511

Cantronic Systems Inc.—(Continued)

Subsidiary (Domestic):

Liaoning Daoheng Technology Co.,
Ltd　　　　　　　　　　　　(2)
No 9 d1 1F Baike Mansion Kehuan Road,
Shenyang, 110000, Liaoning, China
Tel.: (86) 2483601302
Surveillance Equipment Mfr
N.A.I.C.S.: 334511

Cantronic Security Systems (China)
Co., Ltd　　　　　　　　　(1)
F 17 Multimedia Plaza No 757 Guangzhong
West Road, Shanghai, 200072, China
Tel.: (86) 21 6630 6600
Web Site: http://www.cantronics.com.cn
Surveillance Equipment Mfr
N.A.I.C.S.: 334290
James Zahn (CEO)

Cantronic Systems Inc.　　　(1)
F.17 Multimedia Plaza No. 757
Guangzhong W. Road, Pudong District,
Shanghai, 200122, China
Tel.: (86) 2166306600
Web Site: http://www.cantronics.com
Infrared Imaging Camera & Night Vision
Surveillance Systems Mfr & Distr
N.A.I.C.S.: 423410

QWIP Technologies, Inc.　　(1)
499 Nibus St Ste D, Brea, CA 92821
Tel.: (866) 391-6970
Web Site: http://www.cantronics.com
Surveillance Equipments Mfr & Sales
N.A.I.C.S.: 334511
Alex Hong (Dir-Engrg & Bus Dev)

Shenzhen Huanghe Digital Technol-
ogy Co. Ltd　　　　　　　(1)
6th Floor 1st Building Yuehai Industrial Park
Yuehai Road, Nanshan, Shenzhen, 518054,
Guangdong, China
Tel.: (86) 75533631190
Web Site: http://www.histream.cn
Surveillance Equipment Mfr
N.A.I.C.S.: 334511

**CANUC RESOURCES CORPO-
RATION**
130 Queens Quay E Suite 607, To-
ronto, M5A 3Y5, ON, Canada
Tel.: (416) 548-9748　　　　ON
Web Site:
　　https://www.canucresources.ca
Year Founded: 1997
CNUCF—(OTCQB)
Rev.: $221,372
Assets: $107,211
Liabilities: $493,074
Net Worth: ($385,863)
Earnings: $1,285,491
Fiscal Year-end: 12/31/22
Gold Mining Services
N.A.I.C.S.: 212220
Christopher J. Berlet (Pres & CEO)

CANUELAS MILL S.A.C.I.F.I.A
John F Kennedy 160, Buenos Aires,
B1814BKD, Argentina
Tel.: (54) 22 2643 2885　　　Ar
Web Site:
　　http://www.molinocanuelas.com.ar
Year Founded: 1977
Sales Range: $1-4.9 Billion
Food Product Mfr & Distr
N.A.I.C.S.: 311821
Aldo Adriano Navilli (Pres & CEO)

**CANUSA AUTOMOTIVE WARE-
HOUSING INC.**
257 Hamilton Crescent, Dorchester,
N0L 1G4, ON, Canada
Tel.: (519) 268-7070
Web Site: http://www.canusa.on.ca
Year Founded: 1981
Rev.: $21,384,980
Emp.: 140
Automobile Parts Mfr & Distr
N.A.I.C.S.: 456130
Ivor Jones (Pres)

**CANUSA WOOD PRODUCTS
LIMITED**
1281 W Georgia St Ste 203, Vancou-
ver, V6E 3J7, BC, Canada
Tel.: (604) 687-2254　　　　Ca
Web Site:
　　http://www.canusawood.com
Year Founded: 1975
Sales Range: $10-24.9 Million
Emp.: 15
Timber & Panel Products Importer
N.A.I.C.S.: 423310

**CANVEST ENVIRONMENTAL
PROTECTION GROUP COM-
PANY LIMITED**
Unit 6803B Level 68 International
Commerce Centre 1 Austin Road
West, Kowloon, China (Hong Kong)
Tel.: (852) 26686596
Web Site:
　　http://www.canvestenvironment.com
1381—(HKG)
Rev.: $1,051,447,238
Assets: $3,292,073,078
Liabilities: $2,144,075,063
Net Worth: $1,147,998,015
Earnings: $173,331,533
Emp.: 4,762
Fiscal Year-end: 12/31/22
Waste-To-Energy Conversion Ser-
vices
N.A.I.C.S.: 562998
Loretta Wing Yee Lee (Chm)

CANXGOLD MINING CORP.
888 Dunsmuir Street, Suite 888, Van-
couver, V6C 3K4, BC, Canada
Tel.: (604) 221-8936　　　　BC
Web Site:
　　http://www.goldendawnmineral.com
L93—(DEU)
Assets: $3,321,741
Liabilities: $12,617,589
Net Worth: ($9,295,848)
Earnings: ($3,310,180)
Fiscal Year-end: 11/30/22
Mineral Mining & Exploration Ser-
vices
N.A.I.C.S.: 212390
Christopher R. Anderson (CEO)

**CANYON BRIDGE CAPITAL
PARTNERS, INC.**
45/F China World Tower A No 1 Jian-
guomenwai Avenue, Beijing, 100004,
China
Tel.: (86) 10 5781 0600
Web Site:
　　http://www.canyonbridge.com
Privater Equity Firm
N.A.I.C.S.: 523999
Ray Bingham (Co-Founder & Partner)

Subsidiaries:

Imagination Technologies Group
Limited　　　　　　　　　(1)
Home Park Estate, Kings Langley, WD4
8LZ, Hertfordshire, United Kingdom
Tel.: (44) 1923260511
Web Site: http://www.imgtec.com
Develops & Licenses Silicon & Software
Intellectual Property for System-On-Chip
Devices Targeting Multimedia & Communi-
cation Applications
N.A.I.C.S.: 334413
David Harold (CMO)

Subsidiary (Non-US):

Imagination Technologies India Pvt.
Ltd.　　　　　　　　　　(2)
2nd Floor Bajaj IT Tower Building Bajaj
Brandview, Survey no 25 A/1 Plot No 38
Wakdewadi Shivajinagar, Pune, 411005,
Maharashtra, India
Tel.: (91) 206626 8100
Web Site: http://www.imgtec.com

Audio & Video Systems Design Services
N.A.I.C.S.: 334413

Imagination Technologies KK　(2)
1-7-11 Higashi Gotanda AIOS Gotanda
Building 3 Floor, Shinagawa, Tokyo, 141
0022, Japan
Tel.: (81) 357954648
Web Site: http://www.imgtec.com
Multimedia & Communications Semiconduc-
tors Sales
N.A.I.C.S.: 423690

Subsidiary (Domestic):

Imagination Technologies Ltd.　(2)
Imagination House, Home Park Estate,
Kings Langley, WD4 8LZ, Hertfordshire,
United Kingdom
Tel.: (44) 1923260511
Web Site: http://www.imgtec.com
Develops & Licenses Silicon & Software
Intellectual Property for System-On-Chip
Devices Targeting Multimedia & Communi-
cation Applications
N.A.I.C.S.: 334413

**CANYON CREEK FOOD COM-
PANY LTD.**
8704 53Ave, Edmonton, T5E 5G2,
AB, Canada
Tel.: (780) 463-2991
Web Site:
　　https://www.canyoncreekfood.com
CYF—(TSXV)
Rev.: $5,613,017
Assets: $4,326,499
Liabilities: $26,848,417
Net Worth: ($22,521,918)
Earnings: ($1,318,976)
Fiscal Year-end: 05/31/21
Food Products Mfr
N.A.I.C.S.: 311999
Belva Rode (CFO)

CANYON CREEK TOYOTA INC.
370 Canyon Meadows Drive SE, Cal-
gary, T2J 7C6, AB, Canada
Tel.: (403) 278-6066
Web Site:
　　https://www.canyoncreektoyota.com
Year Founded: 2018
Rev.: $30,865,457
Emp.: 62
New & Used Car Dealers
N.A.I.C.S.: 441110

CANYON RESOURCES LTD
945 Wellington Street, Perth, 6005,
WA, Australia
Tel.: (61) 863852263　　　　AU
Web Site:
　　https://www.canyonresources.com
CAY—(ASX)
Rev.: $408,544
Assets: $29,738,610
Liabilities: $445,739
Net Worth: $29,292,871
Earnings: ($6,369,303)
Emp.: 11
Fiscal Year-end: 06/30/24
Gold Mining Services
N.A.I.C.S.: 212220
Phillip Gallagher (Mng Dir)

Subsidiaries:

Camalco SA　　　　　　　(1)
Y Building Nouvelle Route De Bastos, PO
Box 35616, Yaounde, Cameroon
Tel.: (237) 22 221 7091
Web Site: https://www.camalco.net
Mining Services
N.A.I.C.S.: 213113

CAP ENERGY PLC
2nd Floor 20 Berkeley Square, London, W1J 6EQ, United Kingdom
Tel.: (44) 207 491 9196
Web Site:
　　http://www.capenergy.co.uk

Sales Range: Less than $1 Million
Emp.: 3
Oil & Gas Exploration
N.A.I.C.S.: 211120
Lina Haidar (CEO)

CAP PARTS AG
Elterleiner Strasse 15, 09481, Sche-
ibonborg, Gormany
Tel.: (49) 373496980
Web Site: http://www.capparts.de
Year Founded: 1933
Sales Range: $10-24.9 Million
Emp.: 110
Electronic Device Packaging Prod-
ucts Mfr
N.A.I.C.S.: 327110
Hans-Gerd Meixner (CEO)

CAP S.A.
Gertrudis Echenique 220 Las Con-
des, Santiago, Chile
Tel.: (56) 28186000
Web Site: https://www.cap.cl
CAP—(SGO)
Rev.: $2,964,899,000
Assets: $7,006,540,000
Liabilities: $3,345,428,000
Net Worth: $3,661,112,000
Earnings: $87,971,000
Emp.: 5,870
Fiscal Year-end: 12/31/23
Iron Ore & Steel Mfr
N.A.I.C.S.: 331110
Rodolfo Krause (Chm)

Subsidiaries:

Armacero Industrial y Comercial
Ltda　　　　　　　　　　(1)
Calle Interior N 700 Panamericana Norte
Km 17 1 2, Lampa, Santiago, Chile
Tel.: (56) 2 544 99 01
Web Site: http://www.armacero.cl
Sales Range: $50-74.9 Million
Emp.: 140
Steel Bar Mfr
N.A.I.C.S.: 331110

Compania Minera del Pacifico
S.A　　　　　　　　　　(1)
P Pablo Munoz 675, IV Region Coquimbo,
La Serena, Elqui, Chile
Tel.: (56) 51208000
Web Site: http://www.cmp.cl
Iron Mine Deposits Onwership & Operation
Services
N.A.I.C.S.: 212210
Erick Weber (Pres)

Subsidiary (Domestic):

Imopac Ltda.　　　　　　(2)
Calle Brasil 1050, Vallenar, Chile
Tel.: (56) 51208609
Iron Ore Mining Services
N.A.I.C.S.: 212210

Manganesos Atacama S.A.　(2)
Vulcano N 75, IV Region, Coquimbo, Elqui,
Chile
Tel.: (56) 51322299
Web Site: http://www.manganeso.cl
Manganese Ferroalloys Mfr
N.A.I.C.S.: 331110

Minera Hierro Atacama S.A.　(2)
Brasil N 1050, III Region, Vallenar, Huasco,
Chile
Tel.: (56) 51 208 400
Iron Ore Mining Services
N.A.I.C.S.: 212210

Grupo Cintac S.A.　　　　(1)
Camino Lonquen 11011, Maipu, Chile
Tel.: (56) 224849200
Web Site: https://www.grupocintac.com
Iron Mfr & Distr
N.A.I.C.S.: 331210

INTASA S.A.　　　　　　(1)
Gertrudis Echedique 220, Las Condes,
Santiago, Chile
Tel.: (56) 5202903
Web Site: http://www.intasa.cl

Sales Range: Less than $1 Million
Metal Products Mfr
N.A.I.C.S.: 332111
Roberto De Andraca Barbas *(Chm)*

Novacero S.A. **(1)**
Calle J y Calle Tercera Quitumbe Turubamba, Y Rio Coca Planta Baja, Quito, Pichincha, Ecuador **(100%)**
Tel.: (593) 23891900
Web Site: http://www.novacero.com
Structured Iron & Steel Products Mfr
N.A.I.C.S.: 331110
Ramiro Garzon *(Pres)*

Subsidiary (Non-US):

Cintac S.A. **(2)**
Camino A Melipilla 8920, PO Box 14294 C 21, Maipu, Chile **(50.93%)**
Tel.: (56) 224849200
Web Site: https://www.cintac.cl
Sales Range: $250-299.9 Million
Emp.: 632
Construction Services
N.A.I.C.S.: 532412
Roberto de Andraca Barbas *(Chm & Pres)*

Petropac Ltda **(1)**
Pedro Pablo Munoz N 675, Region IV Coquimbo, La Serena, Elqui, Chile
Tel.: (56) 51 208153
Web Site: http://www.petropac.cl
Sales Range: $50-74.9 Million
Emp.: 10
Fuel Oil Terminals Operation Services
N.A.I.C.S.: 424710

Puerto Las Losas S.A. **(1)**
Av Gertrudis Echenique 220 6th Floor, Las Condes, Santiago, Chile
Tel.: (56) 228186103
Web Site: http://www.puertolaslosas.cl
Mining & Metal Services
N.A.I.C.S.: 213114

Tubos Argentinos S.A. **(1)**
Marcos Sastre 698, El Talar, B1618EXN, Buenos Aires, Argentina
Tel.: (54) 91137815988
Web Site: http://www.tubosarg.com.ar
Steel Pole Mfr
N.A.I.C.S.: 331210

CAP-XX LTD.
Unit 1 13A Stanton Road, Seven Hills, 2147, NSW, Australia
Tel.: (61) 294200690 AU
Web Site: https://www.cap-xx.com
Year Founded: 1997
CPX—(AIM)
Rev.: $4,257,917
Assets: $9,317,621
Liabilities: $4,074,622
Net Worth: $5,242,998
Earnings: ($3,784,105)
Fiscal Year-end: 06/30/22
Electronic Components Mfr
N.A.I.C.S.: 334416
Anthony Kongats *(Founder)*

CAP10 PARTNERS LLP
3rd Floor 12 Charles II Street, St James' Park, London, SW1Y 4QU, United Kingdom
Web Site:
https://www.cap10partners.com
Year Founded: 2021
Private Equity
N.A.I.C.S.: 523999
Fabrice Nottin *(Partner)*

Subsidiaries:

Sureserve Group plc **(1)**
Unit 1 Yardley Business Park Luckyn Lane, Basildon, SS14 3GL, Essex, United Kingdom
Tel.: (44) 2039615210
Web Site: http://www.sureservegroup.co.uk
Rev.: $331,302,688
Assets: $166,684,569
Liabilities: $84,778,752
Net Worth: $81,905,817
Earnings: $15,412,837
Emp.: 2,381

Fiscal Year-end: 09/30/2021
Energy Support Services
N.A.I.C.S.: 541690
Bob Holt *(Chm)*

Subsidiary (Domestic):

Everwarm Limited **(2)**
3 Inchcorse Place, Whitehill Industrial Estate, Bathgate, EH48 2EE, United Kingdom
Tel.: (44) 8001977755
Web Site: http://www.everwarmgroup.com
Emp.: 350
Electronic Services
N.A.I.C.S.: 238210

H20 Nationwide Limited **(2)**
Repton Court Enterprise Park Repton Close, Basildon, SS13 1LN, United Kingdom
Tel.: (44) 1268282700
Water Treatment & Distribution Services
N.A.I.C.S.: 221310

H2O Nationwide Limited **(2)**
Repton Court Enterprise Park Repton Close, Basildon, SS13 1LN, United Kingdom
Tel.: (44) 1268282700
Duct & Water Tank Cleaning Services
N.A.I.C.S.: 562998

K & T Heating Services Limited **(2)**
Crossways Point 15 Victory Way, Crossways Business Park, Dartford, DA2 6DT, Kent, United Kingdom
Tel.: (44) 2082694500
Gas Compliance Services
N.A.I.C.S.: 541990
Jim Day *(Founder)*

Providor Limited **(2)**
Unit 2 Craven Court Willie Snaith Road, Newmarket, CB8 7FA, Suffolk, United Kingdom
Tel.: (44) 1223652410
Gas Compliance Services
N.A.I.C.S.: 541990
Colin Laidlaw *(Mng Dir)*

Sure Maintenance Limited **(2)**
Unit 16 The Matchworks Speke Road, Liverpool, L19 2RF, United Kingdom
Tel.: (44) 8459569700
Gas Compliance Services
N.A.I.C.S.: 541990
Pat Coleman *(Mng Dir)*

Sureserve Fire & Electrical Limited **(2)**
Unit 2 Regents Business Park 6 Jubilee Road, Burgess Hill, RH15 9TL, West Sussex, United Kingdom
Tel.: (44) 8452262223
Electronic Services
N.A.I.C.S.: 238210

CAPACIT'E INFRAPROJECTS LIMITED
6th floor 605-607 A Wing Shrikant Chambers, Next to R K Studios Sion Trombay Road Chembur, Mumbai, 400 071, Maharashtra, India
Tel.: (91) 2271733717 In
Web Site: https://www.capacite.in
Year Founded: 2012
540710—(BOM)
Rev.: $246,806,414
Assets: $358,149,751
Liabilities: $211,623,539
Net Worth: $146,526,212
Earnings: $13,008,013
Emp.: 1,433
Fiscal Year-end: 03/31/23
Construction Engineering Services
N.A.I.C.S.: 541330
Rahul R. Katyal *(Mng Dir)*

CAPALLIANZ HOLDINGS LIMITED
8 Wilkie Road 03-01 Wilkie Edge, Singapore, 228095, Singapore
Tel.: (65) 68262549 SG
Web Site: https://www.cwxglobal.com

594—(CAT)
Rev.: $3,315,000
Assets: $75,901,000
Liabilities: $40,472,000
Net Worth: $35,429,000
Earnings: ($1,649,000)
Emp.: 63
Fiscal Year-end: 06/30/23
Holding Company; Petroleum & Natural Gas Exploration, Development & Extraction
N.A.I.C.S.: 551112
Jeffrey Pang Kee Chai *(CEO)*

CAPARO GROUP LTD.
103 Baker St, London, W1U 6LN, United Kingdom
Tel.: (44) 2074861417 UK
Web Site: http://www.caparo.com
Year Founded: 1968
Sales Range: $150-199.9 Million
Emp.: 7,000
Holding Company; Engineered Steel Products Mfr & Whslr
N.A.I.C.S.: 551112
Swraj Paul *(Founder & Chm)*

Subsidiaries:

Caparo Engineering India Ltd. **(1)**
3C/3 Ecotech-II Udyog Vihar, Noida, 201306, Uttar Pradesh, India
Tel.: (91) 1206642500
Steel Product Mfr & Distr
N.A.I.C.S.: 332312

Caparo Middle East FZ **(1)**
Warehouse 23 Street S300 Jebel Ali Free Zone South, PO Box 17241, Dubai, United Arab Emirates
Tel.: (971) 48015300
Web Site: http://caparomiddleeast.com
Electrical Products Distr
N.A.I.C.S.: 423610

Caparo plc **(1)**
103 Baker St, London, W1U 6LN, United Kingdom
Tel.: (44) 2074861417
Web Site: http://www.caparo.com
Emp.: 10
Holding Company
N.A.I.C.S.: 551112

Subsidiary (US):

Bull Moose Tube Company **(2)**
1819 Clarkson Rd Ste 100, Chesterfield, MO 63017-5071 **(100%)**
Tel.: (636) 537-2600
Web Site: http://www.bullmoosetube.com
Sales Range: $75-99.9 Million
Steel Pole Mfr
N.A.I.C.S.: 331210

Plant (Domestic):

Bull Moose Tube Company - Casa Grande Plant **(3)**
1001 N Jefferson Ave, Casa Grande, AZ 85122
Tel.: (520) 836-3455
Mechanical Steel Tube & Pipe Mfr
N.A.I.C.S.: 331210

Bull Moose Tube Company - Chicago Heights Plant **(3)**
555 E 16th St, Chicago Heights, IL 60411
Tel.: (708) 750-7700
Mechanical Steel Tube & Pipe Mfr
N.A.I.C.S.: 331210

Bull Moose Tube Company - Gerald Plant **(3)**
406 E Industrial Dr/Hwy 50, Gerald, MO 63037
Tel.: (573) 764-3315
Web Site: http://www.bullmoosetube.com
Mechanical Steel Tube & Pipe Mfr
N.A.I.C.S.: 331210

Bull Moose Tube Company - Masury Plant **(3)**
1433 Standard Ave SE, Masury, OH 44438
Tel.: (330) 448-4878
Mechanical Steel Tube & Pipe Mfr
N.A.I.C.S.: 331210

Bull Moose Tube Company - Trenton Plant **(3)**
195 N Industrial Dr, Trenton, GA 30752
Tel.: (706) 657-3900
Mechanical Steel Tube & Pipe Mfr
N.A.I.C.S.: 331210

Subsidiary (Domestic):

Bull Moose Tubes **(3)**
29851 County Rd 20 W, Elkhart, IN 46515 **(100%)**
Tel.: (574) 295-8070
Web Site: http://www.bullmoosetube.com
Sales Range: $25-49.9 Million
Emp.: 100
Steel Pole Mfr
N.A.I.C.S.: 331210

Subsidiary (Non-US):

Bull Moose Tubes Ltd. **(3)**
2170 Queensway Dr, Burlington, L7R 3T1, ON, Canada **(100%)**
Tel.: (905) 637-8261
Web Site: http://www.bullmoosetube.com
Sales Range: $25-49.9 Million
Emp.: 48
Steel Pole Mfr
N.A.I.C.S.: 331210

Subsidiary (Non-US):

Caparo India Pvt. Ltd. **(2)**
7 Maruti Joint Venture Complex Delhi-Gurgaon Road, Gurgaon, 122015, Haryana, India
Tel.: (91) 124-431 8000
Web Site: http://www.caparo.com
Metal Stamping Mfr
N.A.I.C.S.: 332119
Rajesh Soni *(COO)*

Subsidiary (Domestic):

Caparo Fasteners Limited **(3)**
Plot No A-7 RIICO, Chopanki, Bhiwadi, Rajasthan, India
Tel.: (91) 9772209803
Web Site: http://www.caparo.co.in
Fastner & Bolt Mfr
N.A.I.C.S.: 332722

Caparo Tubes Limited **(3)**
Steel Tube Road, Dewas, 455 001, Madhya Pradesh, India
Tel.: (91) 9711030940
Web Site: http://www.caparo.co.in
Welded Precision Tube Mfr
N.A.I.C.S.: 331210

Subsidiary (Domestic):

Caparo Industries plc **(2)**
103 Baker Street, London, W1U 6LN, West Midlands, United Kingdom
Tel.: (44) 2074861417
Web Site: http://www.caparo.com
Holding Company; Steel Products Mfr
N.A.I.C.S.: 551112

Subsidiary (Domestic):

Bridge Aluminium Limited **(3)**
365 Fosse Way, Syston, LE7 1NL, Leics, United Kingdom
Tel.: (44) 121 556 0995
Aluminum Cast Mfr
N.A.I.C.S.: 331524

Caparo Atlas Fastenings Limited **(3)**
Heath Rd, PO Box 6, Darlaston, WS10 8UL, W Midlands, United Kingdom
Tel.: (44) 1212242000
Web Site:
http://www.caparoatlasfastenings.com
Bolt & Fasteners Mfr
N.A.I.C.S.: 332722

Caparo Engineering Ltd. **(3)**
Caparo House Popes' Lane, Oldbury, B69 4PJ, West Midlands, United Kingdom **(100%)**
Tel.: (44) 1212024400
Web Site: http://www.caparo.com
Sales Range: $25-49.9 Million
Emp.: 25
Metal Products Mfr
N.A.I.C.S.: 332999

Caparo Group Ltd.—(Continued)

Division (Domestic):

CMT Engineering   **(4)**
Congreaves Road, PO Box 36, Cradley
Heath, B64 7DQ, W Midlands, United
Kingdom   **(100%)**
Tel.: (44) 1384 563 200
Web Site: http://www.cmt-engineering.co.uk
Sales Range: 325-49.9 Million
Emp.: 138
Pipe Fitting & Insulation Component Mfr
N.A.I.C.S.: 332919

**Caparo Engineering Ltd. - Clydesdale
Jones Division**   **(4)**
Neachells Lane, Willenhall, WV13 3SN,
West Midlands, United Kingdom
Tel.: (44) 1902 308000
Web Site: http://www.clydesdale-jones.com
Mechanical Steel Tube & Pipe Mfr
N.A.I.C.S.: 331210
Angad Paul (CEO)

Clydesdale Forge   **(4)**
Brenda Road, Hartlepool, TS25 2BP, United
Kingdom
Tel.: (44) 1429268101
Web Site: http://www.clydesdale-forge.co.uk
Sales Range: $25-49.9 Million
Metal Products Mfr
N.A.I.C.S.: 332999
Mike Wilson (Mgr-Mktg)

Subsidiary (Domestic):

Caparo Merchant Bar plc   **(3)**
Caparo House, PO Box 15, Scunthorpe,
DN16 1XL, United Kingdom
Tel.: (44) 1724853333
Web Site: http://www.cmbplc.co.uk
Sales Range: $50-74.9 Million
Emp.: 140
Merchant Bar Rolling Mill
N.A.I.C.S.: 331221
Steven Unwin (Mng Dir)

Caparo Modular Systems Ltd.   **(3)**
Neachells Lane, Willenhall, WV13 3SN,
United Kingdom   **(100%)**
Tel.: (44) 1902305221
Web Site: http://www.willenhall-
manufacturing.co.uk
Automobile Body Panels, Truck & Tractor
Cabs
N.A.I.C.S.: 336120
Yen Whila (Mng Dir)

Caparo Precision Strip Limited   **(3)**
Tident Steel Works Albion Road, West Bro-
mwich, B70 8BH, W Midlands, United King-
dom
Tel.: (44) 121 553 3031
Web Site: http://www.jbslees.co.uk
Emp.: 250
Rolled Steel Strip Mfr
N.A.I.C.S.: 331221

Division (Domestic):

**Caparo Precision Strip Ltd. - Ductile
Stourbridge Cold Mills Division**   **(4)**
Charles Street, West Midlands, Willenhall,
WV13 1HQ, United Kingdom
Tel.: (44) 1902 365 400
Web Site: http://www.dscm.co.uk
Steel Strips Mfr
N.A.I.C.S.: 331221

Subsidiary (Domestic):

Caparo Precision Tubes Ltd.   **(3)**
Popes Ln, Oldbury, B69 4PF, W Midlands,
United Kingdom
Tel.: (44) 1215435700
Web Site:
http://www.caparoprecisiontubes.co.uk
Sales Range: $25-49.9 Million
Iron and Steel Mfr
N.A.I.C.S.: 331210
Rob Sweetnam (Mng Dir)

Division (Domestic):

**Caparo Precision Tubes Ltd. - Cap-
aro Drawn Products Division**   **(4)**
Phoenix Street, West Bromwich, B70 0AS,
W Midlands, United Kingdom
Tel.: (44) 121 543 5700

Mechanical Steel Tube & Pipe Mfr
N.A.I.C.S.: 331210

Division (Domestic):

**Caparo Steel Products Ltd. - Hub Le
Bas Division**   **(3)**
Rose Street Bradley, Bilston, WV14 8TS, W
Midlands, United Kingdom
Tel.: (44) 1902 493 506
Web Site: http://www.nublebas.co.uk
Emp.: 35
Aluminium Products Mfr
N.A.I.C.S.: 331210
Andy Guy (Mng Dir)

Subsidiary (Domestic):

Caparo Tube Components Ltd.   **(3)**
Tafarnaubach Industrial Estate, Tredegar,
Gwent, NP22 3AA, United Kingdom
Tel.: (44) 1495 724333
Web Site: http://www.caparo-tubes.co.uk
Emp.: 25
Welded Steel Tube Mfr
N.A.I.C.S.: 331210

Subsidiary (Domestic):

Caparo Testing Technologies Ltd   **(2)**
Popes Lane, Oldbury, B69 4PF, W Mid-
lands, United Kingdom
Tel.: (44) 800 121 4602
Web Site: http://www.caparotesting.com
Corrosion Testing Services
N.A.I.C.S.: 541380
Andrea Owen (Mgr-Bus Dev)

Plant (Non-US):

**Caparo Testing Technologies Ltd -
Middle East Facility**   **(3)**
Office 2B 235 East Wing 4B, PO Box
17241, Dubai Airport Free Zone, Dubai,
United Arab Emirates
Tel.: (971) 4 8831808
Corrosion Testing Services
N.A.I.C.S.: 541380

Subsidiary (Domestic):

Caparo Wire Limited   **(2)**
Ash Road, Wrexham Industrial Estate, Wr-
exham, LL13 9JT, United Kingdom
Tel.: (44) 1978 666 800
Web Site: http://www.caparo-wire.co.uk
Sales Range: $25-49.9 Million
Emp.: 70
Mfr of Specialized Wire for Fasteners,
Ropes, Chains, Bedding & Seating
N.A.I.C.S.: 332618
Bernard Darlington (Mng Dir)

Subsidiary (US):

XL Specialized Trailers, Inc.   **(2)**
1086 S 3rd St PO Box 400, Manchester, IA
52057
Tel.: (563) 927-4900
Web Site:
    http://www.xlspecializedtrailer.com
Emp.: 150
Mfr of Customized Heavy-Haul Truck Trail-
ers
N.A.I.C.S.: 336212
Steve Fairbanks (Pres & CEO)

CAPCARGO AG
Ifangstrasse 12, 8302, Kloten, Swit-
zerland
Tel.: (41) 44 578 04 00   **CH**
Web Site: http://www.capcargo.com
Year Founded: 2011
Logistic Software Development Ser-
vices
N.A.I.C.S.: 541511
Oliver Franz (Chm & CFO)

**CAPCELLENCE MITTEL-
STANDSPARTNER GMBH**
Gasstrabe 4, 22761, Hamburg, Ger-
many
Tel.: (49) 40 307 007 00   **De**
Web Site:
    http://www.capcellence.com
Sales Range: $25-49.9 Million
Emp.: 15

Privater Equity Firm
N.A.I.C.S.: 523999
Spyros Chaveles (Mng Partner)

Subsidiaries:

**4WHEELS Service + Logistik
GmbH**   **(1)**
Worringer Str 57, 40211, Dusseldorf, Ger-
many
Tel.: (49) 2 11 90 60 90
Web Site: http://www.4wheels.de
Sales Range: $25-49.9 Million
Emp.: 330
Tire Warehousing Services
N.A.I.C.S.: 493110
Christoph Gerigk (CEO)

THE Machines Yvonand SA   **(1)**
Rue de l industrie 5, 1462, Yvonand, Vaud,
Switzerland
Tel.: (41) 244235050
Web Site: http://www.the-machines.ch
Sales Range: $25-49.9 Million
Emp.: 55
Irrigation Pipe Systems Mfr
N.A.I.C.S.: 327332
Wolfgang Reith (CEO)

CAPCOM CO., LTD.
3-1-3 Uchihirano-machi, Chuo-ku,
Osaka, 540-0037, Japan
Tel.: (81) 669203600   **JP**
Web Site: https://www.capcom.co.jp
Year Founded: 1979
CCOEF—(OTCIQ)
Rev.: $1,007,430,100
Assets: $1,609,376,360
Liabilities: $319,890,950
Net Worth: $1,289,485,410
Earnings: $286,702,140
Emp.: 3,531
Fiscal Year-end: 03/31/24
Video Game Software & Hardware
Developer
N.A.I.C.S.: 334610
Kenzo Tsujimoto (Chm & CEO)

Subsidiaries:

**CAPCOM ENTERTAINMENT KOREA
CO., LTD.**   **(1)**
13 floor Yeon-bong Building 416 Teheran
Road Gangmam-gu, Seocho-gu, Seoul, Ko-
rea (South)
Tel.: (82) 25252160
Web Site: http://www.capcomkorea.com
Sales Range: $25-49.9 Million
Emp.: 10
Electronic Game Machines Mfr & Sales
N.A.I.C.S.: 339930
Igo Shunzo (Mgr)

**CAPCOM INTERACTIVE CANADA,
INC**   **(1)**
405 The West Mall, Toronto, M9C 5J1, ON,
Canada
Tel.: (647) 788-1600
Sales Range: $25-49.9 Million
Emp.: 40
Video Games Development & Publishing
Services
N.A.I.C.S.: 513210
Vera Dobric (Mgr-Office)

CE Europe Ltd.   **(1)**
The Metro Building 2nd Floor 1 Butterwick,
Hammersmith, London, W6 8DL, United
Kingdom   **(100%)**
Tel.: (44) 800 587 6638
Web Site: https://www.capcom-europe.com
Sales Range: $25-49.9 Million
Emp.: 35
Developer of Video Game Software & Hard-
ware
N.A.I.C.S.: 339930

**CEG INTERACTIVE ENTERTAIN-
MENT GmbH**   **(1)**
Borselstrabe 20, Hamburg, 22765, Ger-
many
Tel.: (49) 406965620
Sales Range: $25-49.9 Million
Emp.: 15
Video Games Distr
N.A.I.C.S.: 423990

Capcom Asia Co., Ltd.   **(1)**
Unit 504-505 5/F New East Ocean Centre 9
Science Museum Road, Tsim Tsa Tsui,
China (Hong Kong)   **(100%)**
Tel.: (852) 2 366 1001
Web Site: http://www.capcomasia.com.hk
Sales Range: $25-49.9 Million
Emp.: 7
Developer of Video Game Software & Hard-
ware
N.A.I.C.S.: 339930

Capcom Co., Ltd. - Ueno Facility   **(1)**
3902 Hatta, Iga, 518-1155, Mie, Japan
Tel.: (81) 59 520 2030
Web Site: https://www.capcom.co.jp
Video Games Distr
N.A.I.C.S.: 423990

**Capcom Entertainment France,
SAS**   **(1)**
32 Rue du Vieil Abreuvoir, 78100, Saint-
Germain, France
Tel.: (33) 130618660
Web Site: https://www.capcomfrance.fr
Software Development Services
N.A.I.C.S.: 541511

**Capcom Entertainment Germany
GmbH**   **(1)**
Borselstrasse 20, 22765, Hamburg, Ger-
many
Tel.: (49) 8001801976
Web Site: https://capcom-germany.de
Software Development Services
N.A.I.C.S.: 541511

Capcom Entertainment, Inc.   **(1)**
800 Concar Dr Ste 300, San Mateo, CA
94402-2649
Tel.: (650) 350-6500
Web Site: http://www.capcom.com
Sales Range: $100-124.9 Million
Emp.: 100
Developer of Video Game Software & Hard-
ware
N.A.I.C.S.: 423920
Darin Johnston (Mgr-E-Commerce & Event
Sls)

Capcom Inc   **(1)**
800 Concar Dr Ste 300, San Mateo, CA
94402-2649
Tel.: (650) 350-6500
Web Site: http://www.capcom.com
Mfr of Video Games
N.A.I.C.S.: 513210

Capcom USA, Inc.   **(1)**
185 Berry St Ste 1200, San Francisco, CA
94107   **(100%)**
Tel.: (650) 350-6500
Web Site: https://www.capcom.com
Sales Range: $100-124.9 Million
Emp.: 120
Mfr of Pinball Machines, Video Games; Op-
erator of Arcades; Consumer Video Games
Whslr
N.A.I.C.S.: 713120
Kiichiro Urata (CEO)

Captron Co., Ltd.   **(1)**
3-1-3 Uchihirano-machi, Chuo-ku, Osaka,
540-0037, Japan   **(100%)**
Tel.: (81) 6 6920 3626
Web Site: http://www.capcom.co.jp
Sales Range: $400-449.9 Million
Emp.: 1,200
Developer of Video Game Software & Hard-
ware
N.A.I.C.S.: 339930

Enterrise Co. Ltd.   **(1)**
2-13-8 Higashi Ueno Arcadia Ueno Building
3F, Taito-ku, Tokyo, 110-0015, Japan
Tel.: (81) 59 520 9720
Web Site: https://www.enterrise.co.jp
Amusement Equipment Mfr & Sales
N.A.I.C.S.: 339999

Flagship Co., Ltd.   **(1)**
6th Fl Nakano F Bldg 4 44 18 Honmachi,
Nakano Ku, Tokyo, 164 0012, Japan
Tel.: (81) 353288071
N.A.I.C.S.: 336991

K2 CO., LTD   **(1)**
2-2-14 Awajicho DAIWA Kitahama Building
6F, Chuo-ku, Osaka, 541-0047, Japan
Tel.: (81) 66 920 7680

Web Site: https://www.k2-games.com
Emp.: 70
Home Video Game Development Services
N.A.I.C.S.: 541511

CAPCON LIMITED

Kings House Business Centre Station Road, Kings Langley, WD4 8LZ, United Kingdom
Tel.: (44) 1923 242202   UK
Web Site: http://www.capcon.co.uk
Year Founded: 1983
Emp.: 60
Investigation Services
N.A.I.C.S.: 561611
Marcus Jones (Mng Dir)

Subsidiaries:

Capcon Argen Limited   (1)
Carlton House 19 West St, Epsom, KT18 7RL, Surrey, United Kingdom
Tel.: (44) 8700675070
Sales Range: $25-49.9 Million
Emp.: 10
Investigations & Risk Management Services
N.A.I.C.S.: 561611
Lesley Shark (Gen Mgr)

CAPE EMPOWERMENT TRUST LIMITED

2nd Fl Sunclare Bldg, 21 Dreyer St, 7700, Claremont, South Africa
Tel.: (27) 216839050
Web Site: http://www.capemp.co.za
Sales Range: $10-24.9 Million
Emp.: 10
Security & Services
N.A.I.C.S.: 541690
Jeremy de Villiers (Mng Dir)

CAPE INDUSTRIES LTD.

1303 Yangsan-daero Sangbuk-myeon, Soto-ri, Yangsan, Gyeong-sangnam, Korea (South)
Tel.: (82) 553701234
Web Site: https://www.cape.co.kr
Year Founded: 1983
064820—(KRS)
Rev.: $467,640,178
Assets: $1,786,225,335
Liabilities: $1,604,798,164
Net Worth: $181,427,171
Earnings: ($413,311)
Emp.: 218
Fiscal Year-end: 12/31/22
Cylinder Liner Mfr
N.A.I.C.S.: 333618
Hyoung Suk Jung (Pres & CEO)

CAPE POINT HOLDINGS, INC.

Campos Eliseos 400 601B Colonia Polanco Reforma, Delegacion Miguel Hidalgo, Mexico, CP 11560, Mexico
Tel.: (52) 55 70980527   FL
Web Site:
   http://www.capepointholdings.com
Year Founded: 2016
Emp.: 2
Broadband Service Provider
N.A.I.C.S.: 517111
Porfirio Sanchez-Talavera (Chm & CEO)

CAPELLA MINERALS LIMITED

8681 Clay St, Mission, V4S 1E7, BC, Canada
Tel.: (604) 314-2662
Web Site:
   https://capellaminerals.com
Year Founded: 2005
CMIL—(TSXV)
Rev.: $8,214
Assets: $4,181,312
Liabilities: $1,738,831
Net Worth: $2,442,482
Earnings: ($1,806,497)
Fiscal Year-end: 05/31/19

Mineral Exploration Services
N.A.I.C.S.: 213114
Robert Cameron McLean (VP-Exploration)

Subsidiaries:

Minera Mariana Argentina S.A.   (1)
Espana 776 -Tercer piso Dto 1, Mendoza, M5500DXU, Argentina
Tel.: (54) 2614293982
Web Site: http://www.mineramariana.com.ar
Mineral Mining Services
N.A.I.C.S.: 213114

CAPELLA TELECOMMUNICA-TIONS INC.

747 Monaghan Road, Peterborough, K9J 5K2, ON, Canada
Tel.: (705) 748-3255
Web Site: http://www.capella.ca
Year Founded: 1993
Telecommunication Services Provider
N.A.I.C.S.: 517810
Vincent Garneau (Reg Mgr)

CAPELLI SA

58 avenue du Marechal Foch
CS30354, 69006, Lyon, France
Tel.: (33) 478474929
Web Site: https://capelli-immobilier.fr
CAPLI—(EUR)
Sales Range: $200-249.9 Million
Home Construction Services
N.A.I.C.S.: 236116
Christopher Capelli (Chm & CEO)

CAPEVIN HOLDINGS LIMITED

Millennia Park 16 Stellentia Avenue, Stellenbosch, 7600, South Africa
Tel.: (27) 21 888 3311   ZA
Web Site: http://www.capevin.com
CVH—(JSE)
Sales Range: Less than $1 Million
Investment Management Service
N.A.I.C.S.: 523940
C. A. Otto (Chm)

CAPEVIN INVESTMENTS LIM-ITED

57 Main St, 7646, Paarl, South Africa
Tel.: (27) 218073911
Web Site: http://www.kwv.co.za
Sales Range: $75-99.9 Million
Emp.: 360
Fund Investment
N.A.I.C.S.: 523910
Albert W. Eksteen (Sec)

CAPFIN INDIA LIMITED

C-12 Raj Nagar C H B Society Pitam Pura, Delhi, 110 034, India
Tel.: (91) 9811225111   In
Web Site: http://www.capfinindia.com
Year Founded: 1995
539198—(BOM)
Rev.: $20,479
Assets: $413,778
Liabilities: $3,092
Net Worth: $410,686
Earnings: $5,289
Fiscal Year-end: 03/31/21
Investment Management Service
N.A.I.C.S.: 523150
Rachita Mantry (CFO)

CAPGEMINI SE

Place de l' Etoile 11 Rue de Tilsitt, 75017, Paris, France
Tel.: (33) 147545000   FR
Web Site:
   https://www.capgemini.com
Year Founded: 1967
CAP—(EUR)
Rev.: $19,465,147,520
Assets: $26,964,780,960
Liabilities: $19,454,093,360
Net Worth: $7,510,687,600

Earnings: $1,172,969,200
Emp.: 324,684
Fiscal Year-end: 12/31/21
Holding Company; Consulting, Information Technology & Outsourcing Services
N.A.I.C.S.: 551112
Daniel Bernard (Vice Chm)

Subsidiaries:

23red Limited   (1)
20 North Down St, London, N19DG, United Kingdom
Tel.: (44) 2073230313
Web Site: http://www.23red.com
Sales Range: $10-24.9 Million
Emp.: 60
N.A.I.C.S.: 541810
Tristan Cavanagh (Art Dir)

AIVE BST SPA   (1)
Centro Direzionale Valecenter Via E Mattei 1/C, 30020, Marcon, Venice, Italy
Tel.: (39) 041 5957511
Web Site: http://www.aivebst.it
Financial Management Services
N.A.I.C.S.: 523999
Andrea Falleni (Mng Dir)

AIVE SPA   (1)
Centro Direzionale Valecenter Via E Mattei 1/c, Marcon, 30020, Venice, Italy
Tel.: (39) 0415 95 75 11
Web Site: http://www.aive.com
Information Technology Consulting Services
N.A.I.C.S.: 541512

AIVEBS SPA   (1)
Centro Direzionale Valecenter Via E Mattei 1/c, 30020, Marcon, Venice, Italy
Tel.: (39) 041 5957511
Web Site: http://www.aivebs.it
Information Technology Consulting Services
N.A.I.C.S.: 541512

Artesys SA   (1)
23 Rue du Renard, 75004, Paris, France
Tel.: (33) 1 44 61 11 00
Web Site: http://www.artesys.eu
Sales Range: $25-49.9 Million
Emp.: 100
Information Technology Consulting Services
N.A.I.C.S.: 541512
Eric Chenneveau (CEO)

CHCS Services Inc.   (1)
411 N Baylen St, Pensacola, FL 32501
Tel.: (850) 432-1700
Web Site: http://www.chcsservices.com
Insurance Services
N.A.I.C.S.: 524113
Partha Deka (VP & Head-TPA)

CPM Braxis ERP Tecnologia da Informacao Ltda.   (1)
Alameda araguaia 2096, Alphaville, Barueri, 06455-000, Brazil
Tel.: (55) 1137089100
Information Technology Consulting Services
N.A.I.C.S.: 541512

CPM Braxis Outsourcing S.A.   (1)
Sede Alameda Araguaia N 2 096, Alphaville Baruari, Sao Paulo, 06455-000, Brazil
Tel.: (55) 11 3708 9100
Business Process Outsourcing Services
N.A.I.C.S.: 561499

CPM Braxis USA Corp.   (1)
19495 Biscayne Blvd 708 Ste 400, Miami, FL 33180-2318
Tel.: (305) 932-6010
Information Technology Consulting Services
N.A.I.C.S.: 541512

CS Consulting GmbH   (1)
Robert-Koch-Str 45, 50931, Cologne, Germany
Tel.: (49) 2215080770
Web Site: http://www.csconsulting-gmbh.com
Banking Information Technology Consulting Services
N.A.I.C.S.: 541512

Cap Sogeti 2005 S.A.S.   (1)
11 Rue de Tilsitt, 75017, Paris, France
Tel.: (33) 1 47 54 50 00
Web Site: http://www.capgemini.com

Sales Range: $25-49.9 Million
Emp.: 40
Management Consulting Services
N.A.I.C.S.: 541618

Capgemini Argentina S.A.   (1)
Edificio Republica 8th floor Tucuman 1, C1048, Buenos Aires, Argentina
Tel.: (54) 1152979200
Web Site: https://www.capgemini.com
Management Consulting Services
N.A.I.C.S.: 541618

Capgemini Asia Pacific   (1)
Level 7 77 King Street, PO Box 4287, Sydney, 2000, NSW, Australia   (100%)
Tel.: (61) 292934000
Web Site: http://www.capgemini.com
Sales Range: $50-74.9 Million
Emp.: 100
Holding Company
N.A.I.C.S.: 551112
Luc-Francois Salvador (Chm-Asia Pacific & Middle East)

Subsidiary (Non-US):

Capgemini (Shanghai)   (2)
28F SML Center No 610 Xujiahui Road, Zhangjiang High-Tech Park, Shanghai, 200025, China   (100%)
Tel.: (86) 2161822688
Web Site: https://www.capgemini.com
Sales Range: $25-49.9 Million
Emp.: 200
Consultancy & IT Services
N.A.I.C.S.: 541618

Subsidiary (Domestic):

Capgemini Australia Pty Ltd   (2)
Level 7 77 King Street, Sydney, 2000, NSW, Australia
Tel.: (61) 292934000
Web Site: http://www.capgemini.com
IT Services & Business Consultancy
N.A.I.C.S.: 541611
Olaf Pietschner (Mng Dir-Australia & New Zealand)

Subsidiary (Domestic):

RXP Services Ltd.   (3)
Level 15 31 Queen Street, Melbourne, 3000, VIC, Australia
Tel.: (61) 386305800
Web Site: http://www.rxpservices.com.au
Rev.: $98,714,702
Assets: $116,068,666
Liabilities: $37,337,635
Net Worth: $78,731,032
Earnings: ($946,275)
Emp.: 469
Fiscal Year-end: 06/30/2019
IT & Communication Consulting Services
N.A.I.C.S.: 541690
Ross Fielding (CEO)

Subsidiary (Domestic):

RXP Services Limited   (4)
Level 15 31 Queen St, Melbourne, 3000, VIC, Australia
Tel.: (61) 386305800
Web Site: http://rxpservices.com
Information Technology Consulting Services
N.A.I.C.S.: 541512

Vanguard Integration International Pty Ltd   (4)
SE 11 01 343 Little Collins St, Melbourne, VIC, Australia
Tel.: (61) 3 82562083
Information Technology Consulting Services
N.A.I.C.S.: 541512

Subsidiary (Non-US):

Capgemini Business Services Asia Ltd.   (2)
501A 9 Queen Rd Central, Quarry Bay, China (Hong Kong)   (100%)
Tel.: (852) 22991548
Sales Range: $10-24.9 Million
Emp.: 50
IT Services & Business Consultancy
N.A.I.C.S.: 541611

Capgemini China   (2)
WeWork 3/F Wonderful World Commercial Plaza, 38 East 3rd Ring North Road Cha-

Capgemini SE—(Continued)

oYang District, Beijing, 100026, China
Tel.: (86) 1065637388
Web Site: https://www.capgemini.com
Sales Range: $25-49.9 Million
Emp.: 100
IT Services & Business Consulting Services
N.A.I.C.S.: 541611

Capgemini Consulting India Pvt. Ltd. (2)
SEP SEP2 B 3 Godrej Industries, Complex Eastern Express Hwy, Vikhroli, Mumbai, 400 079, India (100%)
Tel.: (91) 2267557000
IT Services & Business Consultancy
N.A.I.C.S.: 541611

Subsidiary (Domestic):

Capgemini Financial Services Australia Pty Ltd. (2)
Level 16 595 Collins Street, Melbourne, 3000, VIC, Australia
Tel.: (61) 3 9613 3000
Web Site: http://www.capgemini.com
Financial Investment Services
N.A.I.C.S.: 523999

Capgemini Asia Pacific Pte. Ltd. (1)
6 Battery Road 16-07/08, Singapore, 049909, Singapore
Tel.: (65) 62246620
Information Technology Consulting Services
N.A.I.C.S.: 541512

Subsidiary (Non-US):

Praxis Technology Co. Ltd. (2)
Room 1506 No 800 Dongfang Road, Pudong New District, Shanghai, 200122, China
Tel.: (86) 2158205592
Information Technology Consulting Services
N.A.I.C.S.: 541512

Capgemini Business Services (India) Ltd. (1)
4th Floor Btp Block B, Agrahara Village, Bengaluru, 560100, Karnataka, India
Tel.: (91) 22 67557000
Sales Range: $650-699.9 Million
Emp.: 5,000
Business Process Outsourcing Services
N.A.I.C.S.: 561499

Capgemini Business Services Australia Pty Ltd. (1)
Level 8 68 Grenfell Street, Adelaide, 5000, SA, Australia
Tel.: (61) 8 8113 8000
Web Site: http://www.capgemini.com
Emp.: 90
Information Technology Consulting Services
N.A.I.C.S.: 541512

Capgemini Business Services Chile Ltda. (1)
Americo Vespucio 1737 Piso 6, Huechuraba, Santiago, Chile
Tel.: (56) 2 8975700
Financial Management Services
N.A.I.C.S.: 523999

Capgemini Business Services Guatemala S.A. (1)
15 Avenida 5-00, Guatemala, Guatemala
Tel.: (502) 22230010
Web Site: https://www.capgemini.com
Business Process Outsourcing Services
N.A.I.C.S.: 561499
Christian Chilliwack (Gen Mgr)

Capgemini Business Services USA LLC (1)
2099 S State College Blvd 600, Anaheim, CA 92806-6137
Tel.: (714) 787-1550
Sales Range: $10-24.9 Million
Emp.: 50
Business Process Outsourcing Services
N.A.I.C.S.: 561499

Capgemini Canada Inc. (1)
685 Centre Street SW Suite 1150, Calgary, T2R 0C5, AB, Canada
Tel.: (403) 716-3636
Web Site: https://www.capgemini.com
Information Technology Consulting Services

N.A.I.C.S.: 541512

Capgemini Consulting Osterreich AG (1)
Millenium Tower 22nd floor Handelskai 94-96, A-1200, Vienna, Austria (100%)
Tel.: (43) 1211630
Web Site: https://www.capgemini.com
Sales Range: $75-99.9 Million
Emp.: 260
Management Consulting, Information Technology & Outsourcing Services
N.A.I.C.S.: 541611

Capgemini Consulting S.A.S. (1)
Tour Europlaza - 20 Avenue Andre Prothin, 92927, Paris, France
Tel.: (33) 149673000
Web Site: http://www.capgemini-consulting.fr
Emp.: 1,000
Information Technology Consulting Services
N.A.I.C.S.: 541512
Pierre-Yves Cros (CEO)

Capgemini Consulting Slovakia d.o.o (1)
Zelezniciarska 13, 81104, Bratislava, Slovakia
Tel.: (421) 44455678
Management Consulting, Information Technology & Outsourcing Services
N.A.I.C.S.: 541611

Capgemini Czech Republic s.r.o (1)
Hadovka Office Park Evropska 2588 33a, 160 00, Prague, Czech Republic
Tel.: (420) 22 280 3678
Web Site: http://www.capgemini.com
Management Consulting, Information Technology & Outsourcing Services
N.A.I.C.S.: 541611

Capgemini Danmark A/S (1)
Delta Park 40, 2665, Vallensbaek, Denmark
Tel.: (45) 35154100
Web Site: https://www.capgemini.com
Emp.: 100
Information Technology Consulting Services
N.A.I.C.S.: 541512

Capgemini Deutschland Holding GmbH (1)
Potsdamer Platz 5, 10785, Berlin, Germany
Tel.: (49) 30887030
Web Site: https://www.capgemini.com
Holding Company; Investment Management Services
N.A.I.C.S.: 551112
Hans-Peter Berger (Gen Counsel)

Subsidiary (Domestic):

Cap Gemini Telecom Media & Networks Deutschland GmbH (2)
Berliner Str 76, 63065, Offenbach, Hessen, Germany
Tel.: (49) 21156611000
Data Processing Services
N.A.I.C.S.: 518210

Capgemini Deutschland GmbH (2)
Alt-Moabit 98, 10559, Berlin, Germany (100%)
Tel.: (49) 30887030
Web Site: https://www.capgemini.com
Sales Range: $550-599.9 Million
Emp.: 300
Consultancy & IT Services
N.A.I.C.S.: 541611

Branch (Domestic):

Capgemini Deutschland GmbH - Cologne (3)
Gustav-Heinemann-Ufer 72a, 50968, Cologne, Germany
Tel.: (49) 221379920
Web Site: http://www.capgemini.com
Consultancy & IT Services
N.A.I.C.S.: 541611

Capgemini Deutschland GmbH - Hamburg (3)
Lubecker Strasse 128, 22087, Hamburg, Germany
Tel.: (49) 402544910
Web Site: http://www.capgemini.com
Consultancy & IT Services
N.A.I.C.S.: 541611

Capgemini Deutschland GmbH - Munich (3)
Olof-Palme-Strasse 14, 81829, Munich, Germany
Tel.: (49) 89383380
Web Site: http://www.capgemini.com
Sales Range: $25-49.9 Million
Emp.: 100
Consultancy & IT Services
N.A.I.C.S.: 541611

Capgemini Deutschland GmbH - Offenbach (3)
Berliner Strasse 76, 63065, Offenbach, Germany
Tel.; (49) 6995150
Web Site: http://www.de.capgemini.com
Sales Range: $50-74.9 Million
Emp.: 200
IT Consulting Services
N.A.I.C.S.: 541611
Peter Lempp (Office Mgr)

Capgemini Deutschland GmbH - Stuttgart (3)
Loffelstrasse 46, 70597, Stuttgart, Germany
Tel.: (49) 711505050
Web Site: http://www.capgemini.com
Sales Range: $25-49.9 Million
Emp.: 250
Consultancy & IT Services
N.A.I.C.S.: 541611

Subsidiary (Domestic):

Capgemini Outsourcing Services GmbH (2)
Klaus-Bungert-Str 3, 40882, Dusseldorf, Germany
Tel.: (49) 21021011000
Web Site: https://www.capgemini.com
Emp.: 40
Business Process Outsourcing Services
N.A.I.C.S.: 561499

Capgemini Engineering (1)
96 Avenue Charles de Gaulle, 92200, Neuilly-sur-Seine, France
Tel.: (33) 146417000
Web Site: http://www.altran.com
Rev.: $3,449,129,627
Assets: $5,332,183,130
Liabilities: $3,396,367,738
Net Worth: $1,935,815,392
Earnings: $92,600,095
Emp.: 46,693
Fiscal Year-end: 12/31/2018
Engineering & Technology Consulting & Related Services
N.A.I.C.S.: 541330
Pascal Brier (Exec VP-Strategy, Tech & Innovation)

Subsidiary (Non-US):

Altran (Switzerland) S.A. (2)
Avenue De Savoie 10, 1003, Lausanne, Switzerland
Tel.: (41) 21 331 15 30
Web Site: http://www.altran.ch
Sales Range: $25-49.9 Million
Emp.: 200
Information Technology Consulting Services
N.A.I.C.S.: 541512
Nicolas Mayer (CEO & Member-Exec Bd)

Altran AG (2)
Avenue De Savoie 10, 1003, Lausanne, Switzerland
Tel.: (41) 21 331 15 30
Information Technology Consulting Services
N.A.I.C.S.: 541511

Altran B.V. (2)
Herculesplein 24, 3584 AA, Utrecht, Netherlands
Tel.: (31) 888275000
Web Site: http://www.altran.nl
Sales Range: $25-49.9 Million
Emp.: 125
Business Management Consulting Services
N.A.I.C.S.: 541611

Altran Belgium SA (2)
Orion Business Park Chaussee de Liege 624 Building A Jambes, Namur, 5100, Belgium
Tel.: (32) 81354370
Engineeering Services
N.A.I.C.S.: 541330

Subsidiary (Domestic):

Altran CIS France (2)
14 Bis Terrasse Bellini, Puteaux, 92800, France
Tel.: (33) 1 48 88 70 00
Web Site: http://www.altran.com
Information Technology Consulting Services
N.A.I.C.S.: 541512

Subsidiary (Non-US):

Altran Canada Inc (2)
7575 Rte Transcanadienne Bureau 500, Montreal, H4T 1V6, QC, Canada
Tel.: (514) 331-0155
Engineering Consulting Services
N.A.I.C.S.: 541330

Altran Deutschland Holding GmbH (2)
Schillerstr 20, Frankfurt am Main, 60313, Germany
Tel.: (49) 696605530
Investment Management Service
N.A.I.C.S.: 523999

Subsidiary (Domestic):

Altran Xype Deutschland GmbH (3)
Karnapp 25, 21079, Hamburg, Germany
Tel.: (49) 407971560
Web Site: http://www.altran.com
Sales Range: $25-49.9 Million
Emp.: 9
Engineering Consulting Services
N.A.I.C.S.: 541690

Subsidiary (Non-US):

Altran Innovacion S.L.U. (2)
Parque Empresarial Las Mercedes C/Campezo 1 Edificio 1, 28022, Madrid, Spain
Tel.: (34) 91 550 41 00
Sales Range: $350-399.9 Million
Emp.: 216
Information Technology Consulting Services
N.A.I.C.S.: 541512

Altran International B.V. (2)
Walaardt Sacrestraat 405, Schiphol, 1117 BM, Netherlands
Tel.: (31) 20 4498390
Web Site: http://www.altran.nl
Sales Range: $25-49.9 Million
Emp.: 150
Information Technology Consulting Services
N.A.I.C.S.: 541512
Lars Seegers (CEO)

Altran Italia S.p.A. (2)
Via Goito 52, 185, Rome, Italy
Tel.: (39) 06 91659500
Web Site: http://www.altran.it
Sales Range: $350-399.9 Million
Emp.: 200
Management Consulting Services
N.A.I.C.S.: 541611
Marcel Alain Patrignani (CEO)

Altran Luxembourg S.A.N.V. (2)
26-28 Rue Edward Steichen, 2540, Luxembourg, Luxembourg
Tel.: (352) 26 30 85 1
Web Site: http://www.altran.be
Sales Range: $50-74.9 Million
Emp.: 60
Financial Management Services
N.A.I.C.S.: 523999
Pascal Laffineur (CEO)

Altran Norway AS (2)
Inkognitogata 35, Oslo, 256, Norway
Tel.: (47) 22 20 71 30
Web Site: http://www.altran.se
Sales Range: $25-49.9 Million
Emp.: 20
Enterprise Content Management Consulting Services
N.A.I.C.S.: 541618
Fredrik Nyberg (CEO-Scandinavia & Member-Exec Bd)

Altran Osterreich GmbH (2)
Gumpendorferstrasse 21, 1060, Vienna, Austria
Tel.: (43) 31242030
Web Site: http://www.altran.at

Sales Range: $25-49.9 Million
Emp.: 4
Information Technology Consulting Services
N.A.I.C.S.: 541512

Altran Portugal S.A. (2)
Edificio Expo 98 Av D Joao II - Lote 1 07 2
1 Piso 2, 1990-096, Lisbon, Portugal
Tel.: (351) 210 331 600
Web Site: http://www.altran.pt
Sales Range: $75-99.9 Million
Emp.: 400
Information Technology Consulting Services
N.A.I.C.S.: 541512
Celia Reis (CEO)

Altran Praxis Limited (2)
22 St Lawwrence Street South Gate, Bath,
BA1 1AN, United Kingdom
Tel.: (44) 1225 466991
Web Site: http://www.altran.com
Emp.: 15
Software Development Services
N.A.I.C.S.: 541511

Subsidiary (Domestic):

Altran Praxis SAS (2)
950 Avenue De Roumanille Batiment Teck,
BP 305, 6906, Sophia-Antipolis, France
Tel.: (33) 4 92 38 11 11
Sales Range: $25-49.9 Million
Emp.: 80
Security Software Development Services
N.A.I.C.S.: 541511
Karim Alami (Mgr)

Subsidiary (Non-US):

Altran S.A.N.V. (2)
Avenue De Tervuren 142-144 Tervurenlaan
142-144, Tervurenlaan 142-144, 1150, Brussels, Belgium
Tel.: (32) 27376811
Web Site: http://www.altran.be
Emp.: 15
Engineering Consulting Services
N.A.I.C.S.: 541690
Christelle Roux (Acct Mgr-Global)

Altran Shangai Ltd. (2)
Unit 1801 Silver Tower 85 Taoyuan Road,
Shanghai, 200021, China
Tel.: (86) 21 6407 9499
Web Site: http://www.altran.com
Business Management Consulting Services
N.A.I.C.S.: 541618
Fabrice Boyer (CEO)

Subsidiary (US):

Altran Solutions Corp. (2)
10 North Ave, Burlington, MA 01803
Tel.: (781) 993-5500
Web Site: http://www.altransolutions.com
Emp.: 150
Engineeering Services
N.A.I.C.S.: 541330
Gene Porzio (Dir-Transmission & Distr)

Subsidiary (Non-US):

Altran Sverige AB (2)
Sodra Hamngatan 37-41, 411 06, Gothenburg, Sweden
Tel.: (46) 317465550
Web Site: http://www.altran.se
Sales Range: $75-99.9 Million
Emp.: 400
Information Technology Consulting Services
N.A.I.C.S.: 541512

Altran Technologies India Ltd. (2)
Office No- 554 Regus-Green Boulevard
Level 5 Tower-c Green Boulevard, Block B
Noida Sector-62, Noida, 201 201, Uttar
Pradesh, India
Tel.: (91) 1206608051
Web Site: http://www.altran.co.in
Information Technology Consulting Services
N.A.I.C.S.: 541690

Altran Technologies Sweden AB (2)
Lofstroms Alle 5, 172 66, Sundbyberg,
Sweden
Tel.: (46) 8 705 86 40
Web Site: http://www.altran.se
Sales Range: $25-49.9 Million
Emp.: 15
Information Technology Consulting Services
N.A.I.C.S.: 541512

Altran Technologies UK Ltd. (2)
2nd Floor Shackleton House 4 Battlebridge
Lane, London, SE1 2HP, United Kingdom
Tel.: (44) 203 117 0700
Web Site: http://www.altran-tech.co.uk
Automotive Information Technology Consulting Services
N.A.I.C.S.: 541512
Fabrice Boyer (Mng Dir & Dir-Acting ASDR
Div)

Altran UK Limited (2)
2nd Floor Shackleton House 4 Battlebridge
Lane, London, SE1 2HP, United Kingdom
Tel.: (44) 203 117 0700
Web Site: http://www.altran.co.uk
Sales Range: $75-99.9 Million
Emp.: 500
Information Technology Consulting Services
N.A.I.C.S.: 541512
Mike Simms (CEO)

Subsidiary (US):

Altran USA Holdings Inc. (2)
451 D St Ste 110, Boston, MA 02210-1988
Tel.: (617) 204-1000
Investment Management Service
N.A.I.C.S.: 523999
Robert Alder (VP-Power Engrg & Design-
North America)

Subsidiary (Non-US):

**CHS Data Systems Gesellschaft fur
Systementwicklung und Beratung
GmbH** (2)
Bahnhofplatz 18-20, 56068, Koblenz, Germany
Tel.: (49) 261 915990
Information Technology Consulting Services
N.A.I.C.S.: 541512

Cambridge Consultants Ltd (2)
29 Cambridge Science Park Milton Rd, Milton, Cambridge, CB4 0DW, United Kingdom
Tel.: (44) 1223420024
Web Site:
https://www.cambridgeconsultants.com
Sales Range: $25-49.9 Million
Emp.: 380
Technology Consulting Services
N.A.I.C.S.: 541690
Richard Traherne (Chief Comml Officer)

Subsidiary (US):

Cambridge Consultants, Inc. (3)
745 Atlantic Ave Ste 600, Boston, MA 02111
Tel.: (617) 532-4700
Web Site:
http://www.cambridgeconsultants.com
Business Management Consulting Services
N.A.I.C.S.: 541611

**Synapse Product Development,
Inc.** (3)
1511 6th Ave Ste 400, Seattle, WA 98101
Tel.: (206) 381-0898
Web Site: http://www.synapse.com
Engineeering Services
N.A.I.C.S.: 541330
Jeff Hebert (Pres)

Subsidiary (Domestic):

DATACEP SA (2)
Immeuble Le Libertis 2 Rue Paul Vaillant
Couturier, 92300, Levallois-Perret, France
Tel.: (33) 1 46 17 51 00
Web Site: http://www.datacep.fr
Information Technology Consulting Services
N.A.I.C.S.: 541512

DIOREM (2)
2 Rue Paul Vaillant Couturier, 92300,
Levallois-Perret, France
Tel.: (33) 1 48 88 74 60
Web Site: http://www.diorem.fr
Sales Range: $10-24.9 Million
Emp.: 12
Professional Training Services
N.A.I.C.S.: 611430
Bruno Koenig (Gen Mgr)

Subsidiary (US):

Frog Design, Inc. (2)
1130 Howard St, San Francisco, CA 94103
Tel.: (415) 442-4804

Web Site: http://www.frogdesign.com
Business Innovation & Marketing Services
N.A.I.C.S.: 561499

Subsidiary (Domestic):

NSI S.A. (2)
6 Avenue Du Pre De Challes, 74 943,
Annecy-le-Vieux, France
Tel.: (33) 450 094 630
Web Site: http://www.nsi.fr
Sales Range: $10-24.9 Million
Electronic Software Development Services
N.A.I.C.S.: 541511
Yvan Chabanne (Mng Dir)

Subsidiary (Non-US):

**SUTHERLAND CONSULTING
LIMITED** (2)
Hidden Orchard, Benniworth, Market Rasen, LN8 6JH, Lincolnshire, United Kingdom
Tel.: (44) 150 731 3400
Web Site:
https://www.sutherlandconsulting.co.uk
Emp.: 2
Information Technology Consulting Services
N.A.I.C.S.: 541512
Chris Burford-Bradshaw (Founder)

Capgemini Espana S.L. (1)
C/ Hornos Altos S/N Ed INCUVATIC 2, La
Felguera, 33930, Asturias, Spain (100%)
Tel.: (34) 985675767
Web Site: https://www.capgemini.com
Sales Range: $350-399.9 Million
Emp.: 2,000
Management Consulting, Information Technology & Outsourcing Services
N.A.I.C.S.: 541611

Branch (Domestic):

**Capgemini Espana S.L. -
Barcelona** (2)
Avda Diagonal 199, 08018, Barcelona,
Spain
Tel.: (34) 93 495 8600
Web Site: https://www.capgemini.com
Emp.: 400
Management Consulting, Information Technology & Outsourcing Services
N.A.I.C.S.: 541611

Capgemini Financial Services International Inc. (1)
6400 Shafer Ct, Rosemont, IL 60018
Tel.: (847) 384-6100
Information Technology Consulting Services
N.A.I.C.S.: 541512

**Capgemini Financial Services USA
Inc.** (1)
6400 Shafer Ct Ste 100, Rosemont, IL
60018-4944
Tel.: (847) 384-6100
Financial Management Services
N.A.I.C.S.: 523999

Capgemini Finland Oy (1)
Keilaranta 10 E, 02150, Espoo, Finland
Tel.: (358) 945 2651
Web Site: http://www.capgemini.com
Emp.: 600
Information Technology Consulting Services
N.A.I.C.S.: 541512
Mikko Valorinta (Sr VP-Application Svcs &
Country Mgr)

Capgemini France S.A.S. (1)
Place de l Etoile - 11 rue de Tilsitt, 75017,
Paris, Cedex 16, France (100%)
Tel.: (33) 147545000
Web Site: https://www.capgemini.com
Sales Range: $25-49.9 Million
Emp.: 50
Holding Company
N.A.I.C.S.: 551112

Branch (Domestic):

Capgemini France - Grenoble (2)
95 chemin de l Etoile, 38330, Montbonnot-
Saint-Martin, France
Tel.: (33) 47 639 9400
Web Site: https://www.capgemini.com
Sales Range: $75-99.9 Million
Emp.: 500
Information Technology Consulting Services

N.A.I.C.S.: 541690

Capgemini France - Rennes (2)
7 Rue Claude Chappe Cesson Sévigne,
35577, Rennes, Cedex, France
Tel.: (33) 29 927 4545
Web Site: https://www.capgemini.com
Sales Range: $100-124.9 Million
Emp.: 300
Provider of Information Technology Consulting Services
N.A.I.C.S.: 518210

Capgemini Gouvieux S.A.S. (1)
67 rue de Chantilly, Les Fontaines
Capgemini Campus, 60270, Gouvieux,
France
Tel.: (33) 344629100
Management Consulting Services
N.A.I.C.S.: 541611

**Capgemini Government Solutions
LLC** (1)
1765 Greensboro Station Pl Ste 300,
McLean, VA 22102
Tel.: (571) 336-1600
Management Consulting Services
N.A.I.C.S.: 541618
Doug Lane (Pres & CEO)

Capgemini India Private Ltd. (1)
Plant-2 A Wing Godrej IT Park Godrej &
Boyce Compound LBS, Marg Vikhroi West,
Mumbai, 400079, India
Tel.: (91) 22 67557000
Emp.: 370
Information Technology Consulting Services
N.A.I.C.S.: 541512
Ananth Chandramouli (Head-Local Bus
Svcs-India & Middle East)

Capgemini Italia SpA (1)
Via Di Torre Spaccata 140, 00173, Rome,
Italy
Tel.: (39) 0699740000
Web Site: https://www.capgemini.com
Management Consulting, Information Technology & Outsourcing Services
N.A.I.C.S.: 541611

Branch (Domestic):

Capgemini Italia (2)
Via Marcello Nizzoli 6, 20147, Milan,
Italy (100%)
Tel.: (39) 02414931
Web Site: http://www.capgemini.com
Management Consulting, Information Technology & Outsourcing Services
N.A.I.C.S.: 541611

Capgemini Italia (2)
Corso Novara 10, 80143, Naples, Italy
Tel.: (39) 06231901
Web Site: http://www.capgemini.com
Management Consulting, Information Technology & Outsourcing Services
N.A.I.C.S.: 541611

Capgemini Italia (2)
Lungo Dora Colletta 75, 10153, Turin, Italy
Tel.: (39) 01106581
Web Site: http://www.capgemini.com
Management Consulting, Information Technology & Outsourcing Services
N.A.I.C.S.: 541611

Capgemini Italia SpA (2)
Via Paolo Emilio Taviani snc, 19125, La
Spezia, Italy
Tel.: (39) 018728381
Web Site: http://www.capgemini.com
Management Consulting, Information Technology & Outsourcing Services
N.A.I.C.S.: 541611

Capgemini Ltd (1)
1 Avenue Road, Aston, Birmingham, B6
4DU, West Midlands, United Kingdom
Tel.: (44) 330 588 8000
Software Development Services
N.A.I.C.S.: 541511

Capgemini Magyarorszag Kft (1)
Retkoz Utca 5, 1118, Budapest, Hungary
Tel.: (36) 17011432
Web Site: http://www.capgemini.com
Sales Range: $25-49.9 Million
Emp.: 6
Information Technology Consulting Services
N.A.I.C.S.: 541512

Capgemini SE—(Continued)

Capgemini Middle East FZ LLC (1)
Al Shatha Tower Office No F27-14, PO Box
502420, Dubai, United Arab Emirates
Tel.: (971) 4 4335690
Information Technology Consulting Services
N.A.I.C.S.: 541512

Capgemini Nederland B.V. (1)
Reykjavikplein 1, 0543 KA, Utrecht,
Netherlands (100%)
Tel.: (31) 302030500
Web Site: https://www.capgemini.com
Sales Range: $1-4.9 Billion
Emp.: 5,000
Holding Company
N.A.I.C.S.: 551112
Jeroen Groenevelt (Mng Dir)

Subsidiary (Non-US):

Capgemini Belgium N.V/S.A (2)
Hermeslaan 9, Machelen, 1831, Diegem,
Brussels, Belgium (100%)
Tel.: (32) 27081111
Web Site: https://www.capgemini.com
Sales Range: $150-199.9 Million
Emp.: 800
Professional Techical Services; Manage-
ment Consultancy
N.A.I.C.S.: 541611

Subsidiary (Domestic):

**Capgemini Business Services
BV** (2)
Reykjavikplein 1, 3524 KA, Utrecht, Nether-
lands
Tel.: (31) 306898989
Web Site: http://www.capgemini.com
Emp.: 5,000
Business Process Outsourcing Services
N.A.I.C.S.: 561499

**Capgemini Educational Services
B.V.** (2)
Reykjavikplein 1, 3543 KA, Utrecht, Nether-
lands
Tel.: (31) 306896600
Web Site: http://www.academy.capgemini.nl
Sales Range: $10-24.9 Million
Emp.: 50
Educational Support Services
N.A.I.C.S.: 611710

Capgemini Outsourcing B.V (2)
Reykjavic Plein 1, 3528 BJ, Utrecht,
Netherlands (100%)
Tel.: (31) 306894422
Web Site: http://www.capgemini.nl.co
Sales Range: $600-649.9 Million
Emp.: 5,000
Outsourcing Consultancy Services
N.A.I.C.S.: 541611
Peter Barbier (Mng Dir)

Capgemini Shared Services BV (2)
Reykjavikplein 1, Utrecht, 3524 KA, Nether-
lands
Tel.: (31) 306898989
Web Site: http://www.nl.capgemini.com
Business Process Outsourcing Services
N.A.I.C.S.: 561499
Jeroen Versteeg (Gen Mgr)

Capgemini Norge AS (1)
Karenslyst Alle 20, 0278, Oslo, Norway
Tel.: (47) 23508100
Web Site: https://www.capgemini.com
Emp.: 700
Information Technology Consulting Services
N.A.I.C.S.: 541512

Capgemini North America Inc. (1)
623 5th Ave 33rd Fl, New York, NY 10022
Tel.: (917) 934-8000
Web Site: http://www.us.capgemini.com
Information Technology Consulting Services
N.A.I.C.S.: 541512
Tim Bridges (Head-Application Svcs)

**Capgemini Outsourcing Services
S.A.S.** (1)
55 Quai Marcel-Dassault Cedex, Saint-
Cloud, 92212, France
Tel.: (33) 157585100
Business Process Outsourcing Services
N.A.I.C.S.: 561499

Capgemini Philippines SBOS (1)

3rd Floor One World Square McKinley Hill,
Fort Bonifacio, Taguig, 1634, Philippines
Tel.: (63) 2 667 6000
Sales Range: $25-49.9 Million
Emp.: 200
Information Technology Consulting Services
N.A.I.C.S.: 541512

Capgemini Polska Sp. Z o. o (1)
Ul Zwirki i Wigury 16a, 02-092, Warsaw,
Poland
Tel.: (48) 224647000
Web Site: https://www.capgemini.com
Emp.: 80
Information Technology Consulting Services
N.A.I.C.S.: 541512

**Capgemini Portugal, Servicos de
Consultoria e Informatica, SA** (1)
Avenida do Colegio Militar 37-F, Torre Co-
lombo Oreante Piso 10, 1500-180, Lisbon,
Portugal (100%)
Tel.: (351) 214122200
Web Site: http://www.pt.capgemini.com
Sales Range: $25-49.9 Million
Emp.: 100
Consultancy & IT Services
N.A.I.C.S.: 541611

Capgemini Retail Solutions B.V. (1)
Hoogoorddreef 15 Atlas Arena, Amsterdam
Zuidoost, Amsterdam, 1101 BA, Noord-
Holland, Netherlands
Tel.: (31) 203129966
Information Technology Consulting Services
N.A.I.C.S.: 541512

Capgemini Schweiz AG (1)
World Trade Center Leutschenbachstrasse
95, 8050, Zurich, Switzerland (100%)
Tel.: (41) 445602400
Web Site: http://www.capgemini.com
Sales Range: $10-24.9 Million
Emp.: 170
Management & Information Technology
Consulting Services, Systems Integration &
Technology Development, Design & Out-
sourcing Capabilities
N.A.I.C.S.: 541611

Branch (Domestic):

Capgemini Schweiz AG (2)
Amsler Laffon Str 9, CH 8201, Schaff-
hausen, Switzerland (100%)
Tel.: (41) 445602600
Sales Range: $10-24.9 Million
Emp.: 80
Data Processing Software Development &
Related Services
N.A.I.C.S.: 518210

Capgemini Schweiz AG (Basel) (2)
Leutschenbachstrasse 95, Zurich, 8050,
Switzerland (100%)
Tel.: (41) 445602400
Web Site: http://www.capgemini.com
Sales Range: $10-24.9 Million
Emp.: 40
Management Consulting, Information Tech-
nology & Outsourcing Services
N.A.I.C.S.: 541611

Capgemini Schweiz AG (Genf) (2)
Avenue Louis Casai 18, 1209, Geneva, Pe-
tit Lancy, Switzerland
Tel.: (41) 445602400
Web Site: http://www.capgemini.com
Management Consulting, Information Tech-
nology & Outsourcing Services
N.A.I.C.S.: 541611

Capgemini Service S.A.S (1)
Place de l'Etoile 11 rue de Tilsitt, 75017,
Paris, France
Tel.: (33) 147545000
Web Site: https://www.capgemini.com
Emp.: 40
Information Technology Consulting Services
N.A.I.C.S.: 541512
M. Paul Hermelin (CEO)

**Capgemini Services Malaysia Sdn
Bhd** (1)
Suite 15-01 GTower 199 Jalan Tun Razak,
50400, Kuala Lumpur, Malaysia
Tel.: (60) 321681954
Web Site: https://www.capgemini.com
Information Technology Consulting Services
N.A.I.C.S.: 541512

**Capgemini Services Romania
s.r.l.** (1)
Green Court 4 Gara Herastrau street build-
ing C 4th floor, District 2, 020334, Bucha-
rest, Romania
Tel.: (40) 212098010
Web Site: http://www.capgemini.com
Emp.: 300
Information Technology Consulting Services
N.A.I.C.S.: 541512

Capgemini Singapore Pte. Ltd. (1)
12 Marina Boulevard 30-01, Marina Bay
Financial Centre Tower 3, Singapore,
018982, Singapore
Tel.: (65) 64701700
Web Site: https://www.capgemini.com
Management Consulting Services
N.A.I.C.S.: 541611

Capgemini Slovensko, S.r.o. (1)
Prievozska 2b, Bratislava, 821 08, Slovakia
Tel.: (421) 2 444 556 78
Web Site: http://www.sk.capgemini.com
Emp.: 50
Information Technology Consulting Services
N.A.I.C.S.: 541512
Ivo Petrencik (Mng Dir)

**Capgemini Solutions Private
Limited** (1)
Akruti Softech Park 4th Floor MIDC Cross
Road No 21, MIDC Andheri East, Mumbai,
400093, Maharashtra, India
Tel.: (91) 22 6693 0500
Web Site: http://www.capgemini.com
Information Technology Consulting Services
N.A.I.C.S.: 541512

Capgemini Suisse SA (1)
Avenue de Rumine 13, 1005, Lausanne,
Switzerland
Tel.: (41) 213175011
Web Site: https://www.capgemini.com
Sales Range: $10-24.9 Million
Emp.: 50
Management Consulting, Information Tech-
nology & Outsourcing Services
N.A.I.C.S.: 541611

Capgemini Sverige AB (1)
Fleminggatan 18, PO Box 825, Bromma,
112 26, Stockholm, Sweden (100%)
Tel.: (46) 853685000
Web Site: https://www.capgemini.com
Rev.: $7,391,668,065
Emp.: 1,350
Management Consulting, Information Tech-
nology & Outsourcing Services
N.A.I.C.S.: 541611

Capgemini Technologies LLC (1)
2250 Corporate Park Dr 406, Herndon, VA
20171-2898
Tel.: (703) 673-9100
Information Technology Consulting Services
N.A.I.C.S.: 541512

**Capgemini Technology Services India
Limited** (1)
Rajiv Gandhi Infotech Park Plot No 14
Phase III MIDC SEZ, Village Man Taluka
Mulshi Haveli Hinjewadi, Pune, 411 057,
Maharashtra, India
Tel.: (91) 2066991000
Web Site: https://www.capgemini.com
Computer System Design Services
N.A.I.C.S.: 541512

**Capgemini Technology Services Ma-
roc S.A.** (1)
Park CasaNearShore Shore 8A 8 B and
Shore 16 - 1100 Boulevard, Al Qods Sidi
Maarouf, 20270, Casablanca, Morocco
Tel.: (212) 522461800
Web Site: https://www.capgemini.com
Information Technology Consulting Services
N.A.I.C.S.: 541512

**Capgemini Technology Services
S.A.S.** (1)
Tour Europlaza 20 Avenue Andre Prothin,
92400, Courbevoie, Hauts De Seine,
France
Tel.: (33) 149673000
Information Technology Consulting Services
N.A.I.C.S.: 541512

Capgemini U.S. (1)

623 5th Ave 33rd Fl, New York, NY
10022 (100%)
Tel.: (212) 314-8000
Web Site: http://www.us.capgemini.com
Sales Range: $700-749.9 Million
Emp.: 3,000
Information Technology Consulting Services
N.A.I.C.S.: 541618

Capgemini UK (1)
No 1 Forge End, Woking, GU21 6DB, Sur-
rey, United Kingdom (100%)
Tel.: (44) 3305888000
Sales Range: $1-4.9 Billion
Emp.: 8,000
Management Consulting, Information Tech-
nology & Outsourcing Services
N.A.I.C.S.: 541611
Christine Hodgson (Chm)

Capgemini Universite (1)
67 Rue de Chantilly, Route de chacilly,
60270, Gouvieux, France (100%)
Tel.: (33) 344629100
Web Site: http://www.les-fontaines.com
Sales Range: $25-49.9 Million
Emp.: 30
Information Technology Consulting Services
N.A.I.C.S.: 518210

**Capgemini do Brasil, Servicos de
Consultoria e Informatica Ltda.** (1)
Rua Samuel Morse 120 Conjunto 71 - 7
Andar, Sao Paulo, 04576-060, Brazil
Tel.: (55) 1155026802
Information Technology Consulting Services
N.A.I.C.S.: 541512

ENTERPRIME FINANCE SRL (1)
Centro Direzionale Valecenter Via E Mattei
1/C, 30020, Marcon, Venice, Italy
Tel.: (39) 041 5957511
Financial Software Development Services
N.A.I.C.S.: 541511

Fahrenheit 212 (1)
665 Broadway Ste 402, New York, NY
10012
Tel.: (646) 654-1212
Sales Range: $10-24.9 Million
Emp.: 25
Advetising Agency
N.A.I.C.S.: 541810
Mark Payne (Founder, Pres & Partner)

**I&S IT-Beratung & Service
GmbH** (1)
Martin-Schmeisser-Weg 10, 44227, Dort-
mund, Germany
Tel.: (49) 231 975186 0
Web Site: http://www.is-do.de
Emp.: 2
Information Technology Consulting Services
N.A.I.C.S.: 541512

**IGATE Computer Systems (Suzhou)
Co., Ltd.** (1)
Building No 3 Suzhou Software & Technol-
ogy Park No 2 Keling Road, Suzhou New
District, Suzhou, 215163, China
Tel.: (86) 51266616666
Web Site: http://www.capgemini.com
Information Technology Services
N.A.I.C.S.: 541511

IGATE Singapore Pte Ltd. (1)
6 Battery Road #14-05/06, Singapore,
049909, Singapore
Tel.: (65) 62246620
Web Site: http://www.sg.capgemini.com
Information Technology Services
N.A.I.C.S.: 541511

**Immobiliere Les Fontaines
S.A.R.L.** (1)
67 Route de Chantilly, 60270, Gouvieux,
France
Tel.: (33) 344629393
Web Site: https://www.les-fontaines.com
Sales Range: $50-74.9 Million
Emp.: 50
Event Management Services
N.A.I.C.S.: 711310
Lydia Petitcolin (Mgr-Comm)

Inergi LP (1)
20 Dundas Street West Suite 831, Toronto,
M5G 2C2, ON, Canada
Tel.: (416) 345-5705
Management Consulting Services

N.A.I.C.S.: 541618
Brad Sandbrook *(Sr Project Mgr)*

Itelios S.A.S.   **(1)**
19 Rue de Provence, 75009, Paris, France
Tel.: (33) 140980200
Web Site: http://www.en.itelios.com
Emp.: 180
Ecommerce Services
N.A.I.C.S.: 519290

**KONEXUS Consulting Group
GmbH**   **(1)**
Osterbekstrasse 90c, 22083, Hamburg,
Germany
Tel.: (49) 4069658510
Web Site: http://www.konexus-
   consulting.com
Management Consulting Services
N.A.I.C.S.: 541618

Leidos Cyber, Inc.   **(1)**
225 Foxborough Blvd, Foxboro, MA 02035
Tel.: (508) 718-6700
Cyber Security Solution Services
N.A.I.C.S.: 541511

Lyons Consulting Group Inc.   **(1)**
20 N Wacker Ste 1750, Chicago, IL 60606
Tel.: (312) 506-2020
Web Site: http://www.lyonscg.com
Business Consulting & IT Services
N.A.I.C.S.: 541618
Dave Barr *(Exec VP)*

Prosodie France S.A.   **(1)**
150 Rue Gallieni, 92100, Boulogne-
Billancourt, France
Tel.: (33) 1 46 84 11 11
Web Site: http://www.prosodie.com
Sales Range: $150-199.9 Million
Emp.: 65
Information Technology Consulting Services
N.A.I.C.S.: 541512

Prosodie Iberica S.L.U.   **(1)**
Calle Puerto de Somport 9 Edificio Oxxeo,
28050, Madrid, Spain
Tel.: (34) 902636333
Web Site: http://www.prosodie.es
Software Development Services
N.A.I.C.S.: 541512

REALTA' INFORMATCA SRL   **(1)**
Via Assarotti 9, 10122, Turin, Italy
Tel.: (39) 011 5619585
Web Site: http://www.realtainformatica.it
Information Technology Consulting Services
N.A.I.C.S.: 541512

Sogeti   **(1)**
145-151 Quai du President Roosevelt, Issy-
les-Moulineaux, 92130, Paris,
France   **(100%)**
Tel.: (33) 158445566
Web Site: http://www.sogeti-transiciel.com
Emp.: 100
IT & Other Professional Technical Services
N.A.I.C.S.: 541512
Michiel Boreel *(CTO)*

Subsidiary (Non-US):

SOGETI N.V./S.A.   **(2)**
Av Jules Bordet 160, Evere, 1140, Belgium
Tel.: (32) 2 538 92 92
Information Technology Consulting Services
N.A.I.C.S.: 541512

Sogeti Belgium   **(2)**
Jules Bordetlaan 160, 1140, Brussels, Bel-
gium
Tel.: (32) 25389292
Web Site: http://www.sogeti.be
Sales Range: $75-99.9 Million
Emp.: 500
IT Consulting Services
N.A.I.C.S.: 541512
Eric De Saqui De Sannes *(CEO)*

Subsidiary (Domestic):

Sogeti Corporate Services SAS   **(2)**
22-24 Rue Street Gouverneur General Eb-
oue, 75016, Issy-les-Moulineaux, France
Tel.: (33) 15500120
Emp.: 40
Information Technology Consulting Services
N.A.I.C.S.: 541512

Subsidiary (Non-US):

Sogeti Deutschland GmbH   **(2)**

Balcke-Durr-Allee 7, 40882, Ratingen,
Germany   **(100%)**
Tel.: (49) 21021014000
Web Site: https://www.sogeti.de
Sales Range: $25-49.9 Million
IT & Other Professional Technical Services
N.A.I.C.S.: 541512

Sogeti Espana SL   **(2)**
Avda Diagonal 199 - 5 Planta, 08018, Bar-
celona, Spain   **(100%)**
Tel.: (34) 932530188
Web Site: http://www.sogeti.es
Emp.: 200
IT & Other Professional Technical Services
N.A.I.C.S.: 541512
Sergio Zernis *(Mng Dir)*

Sogeti Finland Oy   **(2)**
Keilaranta 10, 02150, Espoo, Finland
Tel.: (358) 207 463 880
Web Site: http://www.sogeti.fi
Sales Range: $25-49.9 Million
Emp.: 93
Information Technology Consulting Services
N.A.I.C.S.: 541512
Juha Vaitilo *(Chief Sls Officer & Dir-Sls)*

Subsidiary (Domestic):

Sogeti France S.A.S.   **(2)**
145-151 Quai du President Roosevelt,
92130, Issy-les-Moulineaux, France
Tel.: (33) 158445566
Web Site: http://www.fr.sogeti.com
Emp.: 65
Information Technology Consulting Services
N.A.I.C.S.: 541512

Subsidiary (Non-US):

Sogeti High Tech GmbH   **(2)**
Hein-Sass-Weg 38, 21129, Hamburg, Ger-
many
Tel.: (49) 40 743 781 94
Web Site: http://www.sogeti-hightech.de
Sales Range: $75-99.9 Million
Emp.: 28
Aerospace Engineering & Consulting Ser-
vices
N.A.I.C.S.: 541330
Arne Vieth *(Mng Dir)*

Subsidiary (Domestic):

Sogeti High Tech S.A.S.   **(2)**
24 Rue du Gouverneur Eboue, Issy-les-
Moulineaux, 92130, France
Tel.: (33) 1 40 93 73 00
Web Site: http://www.sogeti-hightech.fr
Sales Range: $75-99.9 Million
Information Technology Consulting Services
N.A.I.C.S.: 541512
Dominique Lafond *(CEO)*

Subsidiary (Non-US):

Sogeti Ireland Ltd.   **(2)**
Plaza 256 Blanchardstown Corporate Busi-
ness Park 2, Ballycoolin, Dublin, Ireland
Tel.: (353) 1 639 0100
Web Site: http://www.ie.sogeti.com
Sales Range: $25-49.9 Million
Emp.: 90
Software Development Services
N.A.I.C.S.: 541511
Jeff Schmalbach *(CEO)*

Sogeti Luxembourg S.A.   **(2)**
Route de Longwy 36, L-8080, Bertrange,
Luxembourg
Tel.: (352) 314401
Web Site: https://www.sogeti.lu
Rev.: $52,855,600
Emp.: 50
Information Technology Consulting Services
N.A.I.C.S.: 541512

Sogeti Nederland B.V.   **(2)**
Lange Dreef 17, 4131 NJ, Vianen, Nether-
lands
Tel.: (31) 886606600
Web Site: https://www.sogeti.nl
Sales Range: $700-749.9 Million
IT & Other Professional Technical Services
N.A.I.C.S.: 541512

Sogeti Norge AS   **(2)**
Karenslyst Alle 20, 0278, Oslo, Norway
Tel.: (47) 4 000 5089
Web Site: https://www.sogeti.no

Information Technology Consulting Services
N.A.I.C.S.: 541512
Morten Lovstad *(CEO)*

Sogeti PSF S.A.   **(2)**
Route de Longwy 36, 8080, Bertrange, Lux-
embourg
Tel.: (352) 31 44 01
Web Site: http://www.sogeti.com
Sales Range: $600-649.9 Million
Emp.: 500
Information Technology Consulting Services
N.A.I.C.S.: 541512
Philippe Margraff *(Gen Mgr)*

Sogeti Sverige AB   **(2)**
Svetsarvagen 4, 171 41, Solna,
Sweden   **(100%)**
Tel.: (46) 853682000
Web Site: https://www.sogeti.se
Sales Range: $25-49.9 Million
IT & Other Professional Technical Services
N.A.I.C.S.: 541512
Stefen Ek *(Mng Dir)*

Sogeti UK Ltd.   **(2)**
85 London Wall, London, EC2M 7AD,
United Kingdom
Tel.: (44) 3305888200
Web Site: http://www.uk.sogeti.com
Sales Range: $10-24.9 Million
Emp.: 40
Information Technology Consulting Services
N.A.I.C.S.: 541512
Paul Atwal *(CFO)*

Subsidiary (US):

Sogeti USA LLC   **(2)**
7735 Paragon Rd Ste A, Dayton, OH 45459
Tel.: (937) 433-3334
Web Site: http://www.us.sogeti.com
Sales Range: $400-449.9 Million
IT & Other Professional Technical Services
N.A.I.C.S.: 541512
Rajnish Nath *(CEO)*

Branch (Domestic):

Sogeti USA LLC   **(3)**
Owings Mills Corp Campus 10055 Red Run
Blvd Ste 100, Owings Mills, MD 21117-4860
Tel.: (410) 581-5022
Web Site: http://www.sogeti.com
Sales Range: $50-74.9 Million
Emp.: 150
Contract Computer Programming
N.A.I.C.S.: 518210
John Rogan *(Exec VP-Sls & Mktg)*

Sogeti USA LLC   **(3)**
4 Westbrook Corporate Ctr Ste 800,
Westchester, IL 60154-5755
Tel.: (708) 531-0011
Web Site: http://www.us.sogeti.com
Sales Range: $25-49.9 Million
Emp.: 30
Contract Computer Programming Services
N.A.I.C.S.: 518210

Sogeti USA LLC   **(3)**
222 W Las Colinas Blvd Ste 960, Irving, TX
75039
Tel.: (972) 892-3407
Sales Range: $25-49.9 Million
Emp.: 140
Contract Computer Programming Services
N.A.I.C.S.: 541618
Fraser Ashworth *(Branch Mgr)*

Sogeti USA LLC   **(3)**
10100 Innovation Dr Ste 200, Dayton, OH
45342   **(100%)**
Tel.: (937) 291-8100
Web Site: http://www.us.sogeti.com
Sales Range: $25-49.9 Million
Emp.: 100
Contract Computer Programming Services
N.A.I.C.S.: 541618

Sogeti USA LLC   **(3)**
8201 Greensboro Dr Ste 1002, McLean, VA
22102-3840
Tel.: (703) 734-1511
Web Site: http://www.us.sogeti.com
Sales Range: $25-49.9 Million
Emp.: 12
Contract Computer Programming Services
N.A.I.C.S.: 541519

Sogeti USA LLC   **(3)**

4445 Lake Forest Dr Ste 550, Cincinnati,
OH 45242
Tel.: (513) 563-6622
Web Site: http://www.us.sogeti.com
Sales Range: $50-74.9 Million
Emp.: 250
IT & Other Professional Technical Services
N.A.I.C.S.: 541512

Sogeti USA LLC   **(3)**
Beacon Pl 6055 Rockside Woods Blvd Ste
170, Independence, OH 44131
Tel.: (216) 654-2230
Web Site: http://www.us.sogeti.com
IT & Other Professional Technical Services
N.A.I.C.S.: 541512

Sogeti USA LLC   **(3)**
8395 Keystone Crossing Ste 200, India-
napolis, IN 46240
Tel.: (317) 810-4400
Web Site: http://www.us.sogeti.com
Sales Range: $25-49.9 Million
Emp.: 100
IT & Other Professional Technical Services
N.A.I.C.S.: 541519

Sogeti USA LLC   **(3)**
7101 College Blvd Ste 1150, Overland
Park, KS 66210
Tel.: (913) 451-9600
Web Site: http://www.us.sogeti.com
IT & Other Professional Technical Services
N.A.I.C.S.: 541512

Sogeti USA LLC   **(3)**
31555 W 14 Mile Rd Ste 301, Farmington
Hills, MI 48334
Tel.: (248) 702-1900
Web Site: http://www.us.sogeti.com
Sales Range: $1-9.9 Million
Emp.: 125
IT Services
N.A.I.C.S.: 541512

Sogeti USA LLC   **(3)**
1820 NW 118th St, Des Moines, IA 50325
Tel.: (515) 282-4802
Web Site: http://www.sogeti.com
Sales Range: $25-49.9 Million
Emp.: 78
Provider of IT Services
N.A.I.C.S.: 541511

Sogeti USA LLC   **(3)**
8425 Pulsar Pl Ste 300, Columbus, OH
43240
Tel.: (614) 847-4477
Web Site: http://www.us.sogeti.com
Sales Range: $50-74.9 Million
Emp.: 150
IT Services
N.A.I.C.S.: 541511

Sogeti USA LLC   **(3)**
14301 FNB Pkwy Ste 206, Omaha, NE
68154
Tel.: (402) 492-8877
Web Site: http://www.us.sogeti.com
Sales Range: $10-24.9 Million
Emp.: 50
IT Services
N.A.I.C.S.: 541512

CAPILLARY TECHNOLOGIES
INTERNATIONAL PTE LTD.
50 Raffles Place 19-00 Singapore
Land Tower, Singapore, 048623, Sin-
gapore
Tel.: (65) 83337488
Web Site:
   https://www.capillarytech.com
Year Founded: 2012
Information Technology Services
N.A.I.C.S.: 518210
Sameer Garde *(CEO)*

Subsidiaries:

Brierley & Partners, Inc.   **(1)**
5465 Legacy Dr Ste 300, Plano, TX 75024-
3821
Tel.: (214) 760-8700
Web Site: http://www.brierley.com
Sales Range: $200-249.9 Million
Emp.: 150
Customer Loyalty Programs Services
N.A.I.C.S.: 541810

Capillary Technologies International Pte Ltd.—(Continued)

Jim Huppenthal *(Sr VP-Creative Svcs)*

Branch (Domestic):

Brierley & Partners - Los Angeles (2)
5700 Wilshire Blvd Ste 650, Los Angeles, CA 90036-3654
Tel.: (323) 932-7272
Web Site: http://www.brierley.com
Emp.: 40
Advertising Agencies
N.A.I.C.S.: 541810
Jim Huppenthal *(Sr VP-Creative Svcs)*

Subsidiary (Non-US):

Brierley Europe Limited (2)
The Johnson Bldg 77 Hatton Garden, London, EC1N 0JS, United Kingdom
Tel.: (44) 207 153 0550
Web Site: http://www.brierley.com
Emp.: 12
Advertising Agencies
N.A.I.C.S.: 541810

Brierley+Partners Japan, Inc. (2)
6-4-6 TS Kojimachi BLDG 5F, Kojimachi Chiyoda-ku, Tokyo, 102-0083, Japan
Tel.: (81) 352157770
Web Site: https://brierley.jp
Consulting Design Services
N.A.I.C.S.: 541490
Yuki Kudo *(Pres)*

CAPILLION INTERNATIONAL PTE. LTD.
6 Temasek Boulevard, #21-01 Suntec Tower 4, Singapore, 038986, Singapore
Tel.: (65) 6225 5650   **SG**
Web Site: http://www.capillion.com
Sales Range: $50-74.9 Million
Content Management System, Customer Relationship Management & Internet Marketing Services
N.A.I.C.S.: 561499
Jack Lan *(Chm)*

CAPINFO COMPANY LIMITED
F5 Longfu Building 95 Longfusi Street, Dongcheng, Beijing, 100010, China
Tel.: (86) 1088511155   **CN**
Web Site: http://www.capinfo.com.cn
Year Founded: 1998
1075—(HKG)
Rev.: $199,782,706
Assets: $356,706,331
Liabilities: $171,207,212
Net Worth: $185,499,119
Earnings: $19,741,620
Emp.: 1,816
Fiscal Year-end: 12/31/22
IT Services & Software
N.A.I.C.S.: 541512
Donghui Yu *(Pres)*

CAPITA PLC
65 Gresham Street, London, EC2V 7NQ, United Kingdom
Tel.: (44) 2078085200   **UK**
Web Site: https://www.capita.com
Year Founded: 1984
CPI—(OTCIQ)
Rev.: $4,320,943,900
Assets: $4,266,499,328
Liabilities: $3,863,935,348
Net Worth: $402,563,980
Earnings: $308,473,984
Emp.: 53,330
Fiscal Year-end: 12/31/21
Business Process Outsourcing Services
N.A.I.C.S.: 541611
Ian Powell *(Chm)*

Subsidiaries:

ACC Loan Management DAC (1)

76 Sir John Rogerson's Quay Floors 6 7 and 8, International Financial Services Centre, Dublin, D01 H2T6, Ireland
Tel.: (353) 1 607 6268
Web Site: https://www.accloanmanagement.ie
Loan Management Services
N.A.I.C.S.: 522390

AMT-SYBEX Ltd. (1)
The Spirella Building, Bridge Road, Letchworth, SG6 4ET, Hertfordshire, United Kingdom
Tel.: (44) 1462476400
Web Site: http://www.amt-sybex.com
Sales Range: $50-74.9 Million
Emp.: 250
Systems Technology Consulting Services
N.A.I.C.S.: 541690
Leonard Hayes *(Dir-Technical)*

Agiito Limited (1)
Pentagon House Sir Frank Whittle Road, Derby, DE21 4XA, United Kingdom
Tel.: (44) 3303900000
Web Site: https://www.agiito.com
Travel & Event Management Services
N.A.I.C.S.: 561510

Applied Language Solutions (1)
Riverside Court Huddersfield Road, Huddersfiled Rd Delph, Oldham, OL3 5FZ, Greater Manchester, United Kingdom (100%)
Tel.: (44) 845 367 7000
Web Site: https://www.capitatranslation.com
Sales Range: $10-24.9 Million
Emp.: 150
Language Translation Services
N.A.I.C.S.: 541930

Artificial Labs Ltd. (1)
10 Bow Lane, London, EC4M 9AL, United Kingdom
Tel.: (44) 2038808461
Web Site: https://artificial.io
Information Technology Services
N.A.I.C.S.: 541519

BDML Connect Limited (1)
The Connect Ctr Kingston Crescent, North End, Portsmouth, PO2 8QL, United Kingdom
Tel.: (44) 8706061389
Sales Range: $200-249.9 Million
Emp.: 450
Automobile Insurance Services
N.A.I.C.S.: 524126

BSI Group Limited (1)
389 Chiswick High Road, London, W4 4AL, United Kingdom
Tel.: (44) 3450869001
Finance Investment Services
N.A.I.C.S.: 523999

Call Centre Technology Limited (1)
Oxleigh House 540 Bristol Business Park, Coldharbour Lane, Bristol, BS16 1EJ, United Kingdom
Tel.: (44) 844 2252057
Web Site: http://www.cctonline.co.uk
Sales Range: $25-49.9 Million
Emp.: 60
Business Process Outsourcing Services
N.A.I.C.S.: 561499
Martin Deaker *(Dir-Svcs)*

Capita Business Services Limited (1)
17-19 Rochester Row, London, SW1P 1LA, United Kingdom
Tel.: (44) 8000223414
Web Site: https://www.capita-ld.co.uk
Training & Consultancy Services
N.A.I.C.S.: 611710

Capita Commercial Services Limited (1)
71 Victoria St, Westminster, London, SW1H 0XA, United Kingdom
Tel.: (44) 20 7799 1525
Web Site: http://www.capitainsuranceservices.co.uk
Business Support Services
N.A.I.C.S.: 561499

Capita Customer Services (Germany) GmbH (1)
Rudower Chaussee 4, 12489, Berlin, Germany

Tel.: (49) 30809690
Web Site: https://capita-europe.com
Emp.: 5,500
Information Technology Services
N.A.I.C.S.: 541519

Capita Customer Services AG (1)
Muhlentalstrasse 2, 8200, Schaffhausen, Switzerland
Tel.: (41) 716669700
Information Technology Services
N.A.I.C.S.: 541519

Capita Insurance Services Limited (1)
65 Gresham Street, London, EC2V 7NQ, United Kingdom
Tel.: (44) 2077094500
Web Site: https://www.capitainsuranceservices.co.uk
Sales Range: $200-249.9 Million
Emp.: 300
Commercial Insurance Management Services
N.A.I.C.S.: 524298
Sue Perry *(Mgr-MGA Investments)*

Capita International Development (1)
Beacon House 27 Clarendon Road 88 Main Street, Belfast, BT1 3PR, Northern Ireland, United Kingdom
Tel.: (44) 28 9261 0930
Sales Range: $50-74.9 Million
Emp.: 30
Financial Consulting Services
N.A.I.C.S.: 523999

Capita International Financial Services Ltd. (1)
2 Grand Canal Square, Grand Canal Harbour, Dublin, 2, Ireland (100%)
Tel.: (353) 1 224 0300
Web Site: http://www.capitaifs.com
Sales Range: $100-124.9 Million
Emp.: 200
International Financial Services
N.A.I.C.S.: 522320

Capita Life & Pensions Limited (1)
141 Castle St, Salisbury, SP1 3TB, Wiltshire, United Kingdom
Tel.: (44) 1722414888
Sales Range: $200-249.9 Million
Emp.: 300
Pension Administration Services
N.A.I.C.S.: 524292

Subsidiary (Domestic):

Capita Life & Pensions Regulated Services Limited (2)
141 Castle St, Salisbury, SP1 3TB, Wiltshire, United Kingdom
Tel.: (44) 1722414888
Web Site: https://www.capitaipservices.co.uk
Sales Range: $200-249.9 Million
Emp.: 300
Pension Administration Services
N.A.I.C.S.: 524292

Subsidiary (Domestic):

Western Mortgage Services Limited (3)
65 Gresham Street, London, EC2V 7NQ, United Kingdom
Tel.: (44) 2077991525
Mortgage & Nonmortgage Loan Brokers
N.A.I.C.S.: 522310

Capita Life & Pensions Services Limited (1)
65 Gresham Street, London, EC2V 7NQ, United Kingdom
Tel.: (44) 2077094500
Web Site: https://www.capitalifeandpensions.co.uk
Emp.: 12,000
Investment Banking Services
N.A.I.C.S.: 523150
Tony Brown *(Mng Dir-Portfolio)*

Capita Mortgage Software Solutions Ltd. (1)
Jessop House Jessop Avenue, Cheltenham, GL50 3SH, Glos, United Kingdom
Tel.: (44) 1242214000
Web Site: https://www.capita-software.co.uk

Mortgage Origination & Servicing Software & Services
N.A.I.C.S.: 541511
Steven Barker *(Fin Dir)*

Capita Resourcing Limited (1)
Kings Chase, 107 King St, Maidenhead, SL6 1DP, Berkshire, United Kingdom
Tel.: (44) 1628408100
Web Site: https://www.capitaresourcing.co.uk
Sales Range: $25-49.9 Million
Emp.: 100
Business Process Outsourcing Services
N.A.I.C.S.: 541611

Division (Domestic):

ThirtyThree (2)
The Observatory 40 Clerkenwell Close, London, EC1R 0AW, United Kingdom
Tel.: (44) 20 7336 4533
Web Site: http://www.thirtythree.co.uk
Employer Branding, Research, Employee Engagement & Digital Media Services
N.A.I.C.S.: 541613
Andy Bamford *(CEO)*

Subsidiary (Non-US):

ThirtyThree APAC Limited (3)
11F 151 Hollywood Road, Central, China (Hong Kong)
Tel.: (852) 3711 3088
Web Site: http://www.thirtythreeapac.com
Employer Branding, Research, Employee Engagement & Digital Media Services
N.A.I.C.S.: 541613

Subsidiary (US):

ThirtyThree USA Inc. (3)
36 Cooper Sq 4th Fl, New York, NY 10003
Tel.: (646) 395-5200
Web Site: https://www.thirtythreeus.com
Emp.: 15
Employer Branding, Research, Employee Engagement & Digital Media Services
N.A.I.C.S.: 541613

Capita Secure Information Systems Limited (1)
Methuen Park Bath Road, Chippenham, SN14 0TW, United Kingdom
Tel.: (44) 8456041999
Web Site: http://www.capitasecuresystems.co.uk
Sales Range: $150-199.9 Million
Emp.: 900
Security Software Development Services
N.A.I.C.S.: 541511

Capita Symonds Limited (1)
Business Ctr CastleWay House, 17 Preston New Rd, Blackburn, BB2 1AU, United Kingdom
Tel.: (44) 1254273000
Web Site: http://www.capitasymonds.co.uk
Sales Range: $150-199.9 Million
Emp.: 550
Infrastructure Consulting Services
N.A.I.C.S.: 541310
Ian Buckley *(Exec Dir-Infrastructure & Regions)*

Capita Trust Company Limited (1)
7th Floor Phoenix House 18 King William Street, London, EC4N 7HE, United Kingdom
Tel.: (44) 20 7800 4100
Web Site: http://www.capitafiduciary.com
Financial Management Services
N.A.I.C.S.: 523999
Chris Searson *(CEO)*

Capita West GmbH (1)
Nassauerring 39-41, 47803, Krefeld, Germany
Tel.: (49) 21513691000
Telecommunication Services
N.A.I.C.S.: 517810

Club 24 Limited (1)
Hepworth House, Leeds, LS2 8AE, United Kingdom
Tel.: (44) 8453309030
Sales Range: $200-249.9 Million
Emp.: 8,000
Customer Management Outsourcing Services
N.A.I.C.S.: 541611

ComputerLand UK Ltd. (1)
Discovery House Mere Way, Ruddington Fields, Ruddington, NG11 6JW, Nottinghamshire, United Kingdom
Tel.: (44) 1159318000
Web Site: http://www.computerland.co.uk
Sales Range: $125-149.9 Million
Emp.: 500
Systems Integration & Technical Support Services
N.A.I.C.S.: 541512

Contact Associates Limited (1)
Suite D5B First Floor Victoria House Victoria Street, Taunton, TA1 3FA, Somerset, United Kingdom
Tel.: (44) 1823273060
Web Site: https://www.contact-associates.co.uk
Educational Institution Services
N.A.I.C.S.: 611710

Equita Limited (1)
42-44 Henry Street, Northampton, NN1 4BZ, United Kingdom
Tel.: (44) 1604628360
Web Site: https://equita.co.uk
Tax Preparation Services
N.A.I.C.S.: 541213

Evolvi Rail Systems Limited (1)
Templegate House, 115-123 High St, Orpington, Kent, United Kingdom
Tel.: (44) 871 521 9871
Web Site: http://www.evolvi.co.uk
Online Rail Travelling Solution Provider
N.A.I.C.S.: 513199
Ken Cameron *(Mng Dir)*

Fire Service College Limited (1)
London Road, Moreton-in-Marsh, GL56 0RH, Gloucestershire, United Kingdom
Tel.: (44) 1608650831
Web Site: https://www.fireservicecollege.ac.uk
Fire Prevention & Protection Services
N.A.I.C.S.: 922160

IBS OPENSystems (UK) Limited (1)
Newhouse Overbridge Square Cambridge Lane, Newbury, RG14 5UX, United Kingdom
Tel.: (44) 1635550088
Web Site: http://www.ibsopensystems.com
Sales Range: $25-49.9 Million
Emp.: 40
Software Solutions Provider
N.A.I.C.S.: 513210

Market Mortgage Limited (1)
612 Wimborne Road, Bournemouth, BH9 2EN, United Kingdom
Tel.: (44) 1202850390
Web Site: https://themortgagemarket.info
Financial Institution Services
N.A.I.C.S.: 523999

Premier Medical Group Limited (1)
Premier House, Eco Business Park, Ludlow, SY8 1ES, United Kingdom
Tel.: (44) 345 600 6738
Web Site: https://www.premiermedical.co.uk
Emp.: 230
Medical Reporting & Screening Services
N.A.I.C.S.: 621999
Harry Bruenjes *(Founder)*

Ross & Roberts Limited (1)
42-44 Henry Street, Northampton, NN1 4BZ, United Kingdom
Tel.: (44) 1458550480
Web Site: https://www.rossandroberts.com
Tax Preparation Services
N.A.I.C.S.: 541213

Service Birmingham Limited (1)
Birmingham City Council Council House, Victoria Sq, Birmingham, B1 1BB, United Kingdom
Tel.: (44) 1213031111
Web Site: http://www.birmingham.gov.uk
Sales Range: $25-49.9 Million
Emp.: 55
Professional & Management Services
N.A.I.C.S.: 561110

Sigma Seven Limited (1)
Gordon Lamb House 3 Jackson's Entry, Edinburgh, EH8 8PJ, United Kingdom
Tel.: (44) 131 557 1803

Web Site: http://www.sigmaseven.co.uk
Emp.: 30
Mobile Software Development Services
N.A.I.C.S.: 541511

Smart DCC Limited (1)
2nd Floor Ibex House 42-47 Minories, London, EC3N 1DY, United Kingdom
Tel.: (44) 2037258656
Web Site: https://www.smartdcc.co.uk
Information Technology Services
N.A.I.C.S.: 541519

Smiths Consulting Ltd. (1)
New Broad Street House, 35 New Broad Street, London, EC2M 1NH, United Kingdom
Tel.: (44) 8454581607
Web Site: http://www.smithsconsulting.co.uk
Sales Range: $10-24.9 Million
Emp.: 52
Management Consulting Services
N.A.I.C.S.: 541611

Stirling Park LLP (1)
24 Blythswood Square, Glasgow, G2 4BG, United Kingdom   **(100%)**
Tel.: (44) 1415655767
Web Site: https://www.stirlingpark.co.uk
Sales Range: $25-49.9 Million
Emp.: 150
Debt Collection Services
N.A.I.C.S.: 561440

Synetrix Limited (1)
Innovation Centre Keele Science Park, Keele, ST5 5NB, Staffordshire, United Kingdom
Tel.: (44) 1782 338 200
Web Site: http://www.synetrix.co.uk
Software Consultancy Services
N.A.I.C.S.: 541511

TELAG AG (1)
Hardturmstrasse 101, 8005, Zurich, Switzerland
Tel.: (41) 442764444
Web Site: https://www.telag.ch
Emp.: 200
Telecommunication Servicesb
N.A.I.C.S.: 532490

Tascor Services Limited (1)
Surety House 18 Concorde Road, Patchway, Bristol, BS34 5TB, United Kingdom
Tel.: (44) 1179 336 600
Web Site: http://www.tascor.co.uk
Sales Range: $300-349.9 Million
Emp.: 2,000
Forensic Medical Services, Custody & Secure Transport Services
N.A.I.C.S.: 561621

Team24 Limited (1)
33 Soho Square, London, W1D 3QU, Surrey, United Kingdom
Tel.: (44) 330 024 1111
Web Site: https://www.team24.co.uk
Health Care Recruitment Services
N.A.I.C.S.: 541612

The G2G3 Group Ltd. (1)
145 Morrison Street, Edinburgh, EH3 8FJ, United Kingdom
Tel.: (44) 1314613333
Web Site: http://www.g2g3.com
Digital Transformation Training Services
N.A.I.C.S.: 611430

Trustmarque Solutions Limited (1)
York Biotech Campus, Sand Hutton, York, YO41 1LZ, United Kingdom
Tel.: (44) 845 210 1500
Web Site: https://www.trustmarque.com
Emp.: 1,000
Software & Software Licensing Distr
N.A.I.C.S.: 423430
Angelo Di Ventura *(Dir-Sls & Mktg)*

Updata Infrastructure UK Ltd. (1)
The Omnibus Building Lesbourne Road, Reigate, RH2 7LD, Surrey, United Kingdom
Tel.: (44) 8545650555
Web Site: https://www.updata.net
Sales Range: $25-49.9 Million
Emp.: 150
Internet Service Provider
N.A.I.C.S.: 517810
Andrew Bullock *(Mng Dir-Networking Connectivity)*

CAPITAL & REGIONAL PLC
Strand Bridge House 138-142 Strand, London, WC2R 1HH, United Kingdom
Tel.: (44) 2079328000   UK
Web Site: https://www.capreg.com
Year Founded: 2006
CAL—(LSE)
Rev.: $98,706,244
Assets: $911,437,436
Liabilities: $683,612,020
Net Worth: $227,825,416
Earnings: ($276,160,248)
Emp.: 295
Fiscal Year-end: 12/31/20
Real Estate Investing Management Services
N.A.I.C.S.: 523999
Liz Hardy *(Gen Mgr-The Mall Walthamstow)*

Subsidiaries:

Capital & Regional Property Management Limited   (1)
52 Grosvenor Gardens, London, SW1W 0AU, United Kingdom   **(100%)**
Tel.: (44) 2079328000
Web Site: http://www.capreg.com
Sales Range: $25-49.9 Million
Emp.: 60
Land Subdivision
N.A.I.C.S.: 237210
Hugh Scott-Barrett *(CEO)*

CAPITAL A BHD
RedQ Jalan Pekeliling 5 Lapangan Terbang Antarabangsa, 64000, Kuala Lumpur, Selangor Darul Ehsan, Malaysia
Tel.: (60) 386604333   MY
Web Site: https://www.capitala.com
Year Founded: 2017
5099—(KLS)
Rev.: $3,198,201,153
Assets: $6,193,981,539
Liabilities: $8,506,723,609
Net Worth: ($2,312,742,070)
Earnings: ($20,965,172)
Emp.: 17,428
Fiscal Year-end: 12/31/23
Holding Company; Airline Owner & Operator
N.A.I.C.S.: 551112
Riad Asmat *(CEO-Malaysia)*

Subsidiaries:

AirAsia Berhad (1)
RedQ Jalan Pekeliling 5 Lapangan Terbang Antarabangsa, Kuala Lumpur, 64000, Selangor Darul Ehsan, Malaysia
Tel.: (60) 386604333
Web Site: http://www.airasia.com
Oil Transportation Services
N.A.I.C.S.: 481111
Riad Asmat *(CEO)*

Asia Digital Engineering Sdn. Bhd. (1)
Redq Jalan Pekeliling 5 Kuala Lumpur International Airport 2, 64000, Sepang, Selangor, Malaysia
Tel.: (60) 386604333
Web Site: http://www.ade.aero
Aircraft Maintenance Services
N.A.I.C.S.: 488190

PT Teleportasi Bisnis Indonesia (1)
Jalan Anggrek Neli Murni Blok A no 97 slipi kemanggisan, Jakarta Barat, 11480, Indonesia
Tel.: (62) 2122123106
Web Site: http://www.teleport.asia
Logistic Services
N.A.I.C.S.: 488510

RedBeat Academy Sdn. Bhd. (1)
East Wing Level 4 Stesen Sentral, 50470, Kuala Lumpur, Malaysia
Tel.: (60) 105001122
Web Site: http://www.redbeatacademy.com
Education Training Services
N.A.I.C.S.: 611710

CAPITAL AIRPORTS HOLDING COMPANY (CAH)
28 Bldg Tianzhu Rd A Block, Tianzhu Port Industry Zone, Shunyi District, Beijing, 100621, China
Tel.: (86) 10 64563947
Web Site: http://www.cah.com.cn
Year Founded: 2002
Sales Range: $5-14.9 Billion
Emp.: 50,000
Holding Company: Air Transportation Services
N.A.I.C.S.: 551112
Li Peiying *(Pres)*

Subsidiaries:

Beijing Airport Foods Service Co., Ltd.   (1)
28 Building Tianzhu Road A Blcok, Tianzhu Port Industry Zone, Shunyi District, Beijing, 100621, China
Tel.: (86) 64563947
Airport Restaurant Services
N.A.I.C.S.: 488119

CAPITAL APPRECIATION LTD.
Unit 2 44 Saturn Crescent Linbro Business Park, Sandton, 2196, South Africa
Tel.: (27) 100251000
Web Site: https://www.capitalappreciation.co.za
Year Founded: 2015
CTA—(JSE)
Rev.: $52,551,939
Assets: $87,843,767
Liabilities: $8,875,516
Net Worth: $78,968,251
Earnings: $4,853,822
Emp.: 524
Fiscal Year-end: 03/31/23
Commercial Banking Services
N.A.I.C.S.: 522110
Michael Motty Sacks *(Chm)*

Subsidiaries:

African Resonance Business Solutions Proprietary Limited   (1)
54 Melville Road, Illovo, Johannesburg, 2196, South Africa
Tel.: (27) 117501600
Web Site: http://www.africanresonance.com
Payment Device Mfr & Distr
N.A.I.C.S.: 334513

Dashpay Proprietary Limited   (1)
54 Melville Road, Illovo, Johannesburg, South Africa
Tel.: (27) 860012729
Web Site: http://www.dashpay.co.za
Financial Management Services
N.A.I.C.S.: 541611

Synthesis Software Technologies Proprietary Limited   (1)
Unit 59a 4th Floor 3 Melrose Boulevard, Melrose Arch, Johannesburg, South Africa
Tel.: (27) 876543300
Web Site: https://www.synthesis.co.za
Computer Software Development Services
N.A.I.C.S.: 541511
Jake Shepherd *(Founder & Dir-Technical)*

CAPITAL ASSET PLANNING, INC.
6F JRE Dojima Tower 2-4-27 Dojima, Kita-ku, Osaka, 530-0003, Japan
Tel.: (81) 647965666
Web Site: https://www.cap-net.co.jp
3965—(TKS)
Rev.: $57,046,140
Assets: $39,314,050
Liabilities: $16,987,640
Net Worth: $22,326,410
Earnings: $1,566,890
Emp.: 344
Fiscal Year-end: 09/30/23
Information Technology Services
N.A.I.C.S.: 541512
Masakazu Kitayama *(Pres)*

Capital Bank—(Continued)

CAPITAL BANK
54 Issam Ajlouni St Shmeisani, PO
Box 941283, Amman, 11194, Jordan
Tel.: (962) 65100220
Web Site: http://www.capitalbank.jo
Year Founded: 1995
EXFB—(AMM)
Rev.: $183,760,639
Assets: $3,877,024,971
Liabilities: $3,375,349,362
Net Worth: $501,675,610
Earnings: $42,739,263
Emp.: 888
Fiscal Year-end: 12/31/20
Commercial & Investment Banking
Services
N.A.I.C.S.: 522110
Saher Abdul-Hadi Daoud (Head-
Compliance)

Subsidiaries:

Capital Investment & Brokerage
Company Limited   **(1)**
PO Box 940982, Amman, 11194, Jordan
Tel.: (962) 65200330
Investment Brokerage Services
N.A.I.C.S.: 523999

Capital Investment Company   **(1)**
Shmesani Issam Ajluni St 45, PO Box
940982, Amman, 11194, Jordan
Tel.: (962) 6 520 0330
Web Site: http://www.capitalinv.jo
Sales Range: $50-74.9 Million
Emp.: 40
Financial Management Services
N.A.I.C.S.: 523999

CAPITAL BANK - GRAWE GRUPPE AG
Burgring 16, 8010, Graz, Austria
Tel.: (43) 31680720
Web Site: http://www.capitalbank.at
Rev.: $82,335,426
Assets: $1,167,150,382
Liabilities: $440,498,238
Net Worth: $726,652,144
Earnings: $57,772,259
Emp.: 172
Fiscal Year-end: 12/31/19
Banking Services
N.A.I.C.S.: 522110
Christian Jauk (Member-Exec Bd)

Subsidiaries:

BK Immo Vorsorge GmbH   **(1)**
Burgring 16, 8010, Graz, Austria
Tel.: (43) 3169071990
Web Site: http://www.bkimmo.at
Real Estate Management Services
N.A.I.C.S.: 531390

Capital Bank   **(1)**
Wallnerstrasse 4/1, 1010, Vienna, Austria
Tel.: (43) 131614
Sales Range: $100-124.9 Million
Emp.: 200
Banking Services
N.A.I.C.S.: 522110
Christian Jauk (Mng Dir)

CAPITAL BANK KAZAKHSTAN JSC
103 Nazarbayev Avenue, Almaty,
050000, Kazakhstan
Tel.: (7) 273316677
Web Site: http://www.capitalbank.kz
Year Founded: 1992
Sales Range: $25-49.9 Million
Emp.: 40
Commercial Banking Services
N.A.I.C.S.: 522110
Orifdzhan Shadiev (Chm)

CAPITAL CLEAN ENERGY CARRIERS CORP.
3 Iassonos Street, 18537, Piraeus,
18537, Greece

Tel.: (30) 2104584950   **MH**
Web Site:
  https://www.capitalcleanenergy.com
CPLP—(NASDAQ)
Rev.: $299,071,000
Assets: $1,996,764,000
Liabilities: $1,358,338,000
Net Worth: $638,426,000
Earnings: $125,421,000
Fiscal Year-end: 12/31/22
Holding Company; Deep-Sea Freight
Transportation Services
N.A.I.C.S.: 551112
Keith B. Forman (Chm)

CAPITAL CONCEPT LIMITED AD
Tzarigradsko shose Blvd 115G,
Megapark Business Building Floor 5
Office B, 1784, Sofia, Bulgaria
Tel.: (359) 2 405 3500
Web Site: http://www.ccl.bg.com
Year Founded: 2008
CCL—(BUL)
Sales Range: Less than $1 Million
Information Services
N.A.I.C.S.: 519290

CAPITAL DGMC INC.
1155 boulevard Rene-Levesque West
Bureau 2660, Montreal, H3B 4S5,
QC, Canada
Tel.: (514) 238-5091   **QC**
Sales Range: $1-9.9 Million
Investment Services
N.A.I.C.S.: 523999
Daniel Dumont (Pres & CEO)

CAPITAL DYNAMICS LTD.
30-32 Whitfield Street Whitfield Court
2nd Floor, London, W1T 2RQ, United
Kingdom
Tel.: (44) 20 7297 0200   **UK**
Web Site: http://www.capdyn.com
Year Founded: 1988
Emp.: 160
Asset Manager & Private Equity Firm
N.A.I.C.S.: 523940
Dario Bertagna (VP)

Subsidiaries:

Capital Dynamics AG   **(1)**
Bahnhofstrasse 22, 6301, Zug, Switzerland
Tel.: (41) 748 8444
Web Site: http://www.capdyn.com
Emp.: 150
Equity Investment & Portfolio Management
Services
N.A.I.C.S.: 523999
Thomas Kubr (Chm)

Capital Dynamics, Inc.   **(1)**
10 E 53rd St 17th Fl, New York, NY 10022
Tel.: (212) 798-3400
Web Site: http://www.capdyn.com
Investment Advice
N.A.I.C.S.: 523940
Hina Ahmad (COO)

CAPITAL ENGINEERING NETWORK PUBLIC COMPANY LIMITED
1011 Supalai Grand Tower 17th Floor
Rama 3 Road Chongnonsi, Yannawa,
Bangkok, 10120, Thailand
Web Site: http://www.cenplc.com
CEN—(THA)
Rev.: $34,223,397
Assets: $93,396,324
Liabilities: $17,409,203
Net Worth: $75,987,121
Earnings: ($11,312,805)
Emp.: 277
Fiscal Year-end: 12/31/23
Industrial Steel, Aluminium & Related
Wire Ropes Mfr
N.A.I.C.S.: 331222

Wutichai Leenabanchong (Chm, Chm
& CEO)

Subsidiaries:

Sky Tower Public Company
Limited   **(1)**
1011 Supalai Grand Tower 17th Floor Rama
3 Road, Chongnonsi Yannawa, Bangkok,
10120, Thailand
Tel.: (66) 20491041
Web Site: https://skytower.co.th
Rev.: $5,467,456
Assets: $33,415,246
Liabilities: $7,594,657
Net Worth: $25,820,589
Earnings: ($6,311,450)
Emp.: 155
Fiscal Year-end: 12/31/2023
Transmission Line Towers Mfr
N.A.I.C.S.: 237130
Chokchai Niamratana (Deputy Mng Dir-
Corp Svcs)

CAPITAL ENVIRONMENT HOLDINGS LIMITED
Unit 1613-1618 16/F Bank of America
Tower 12 Harcourt Road, Central,
China (Hong Kong)
Tel.: (852) 25263438   **Ky**
Web Site: http://www.cehl.com.hk
3989—(HKG)
Rev.: $644,289,282
Assets: $2,827,374,638
Liabilities: $1,888,929,245
Net Worth: $938,445,394
Earnings: $428,689,357
Emp.: 3,674
Fiscal Year-end: 12/31/22
Investment Holding Company
N.A.I.C.S.: 551112
Guoxian Cao (Chm)

Subsidiaries:

Biomax Environmental Technology
(Beijing) Limited   **(1)**
Floor 14 Sanyuan Building No 18 Xibahe
Dongli Chaoyang District, Beijing, 100028,
China
Tel.: (86) 1084603818
Waste Recycling Services
N.A.I.C.S.: 562920

Biomax Environmental Technology
(Shanghai) Company Limited   **(1)**
7/F No 270 Wusong Road Yaojiang Interna-
tional Plaza Hongkou District, Shanghai,
200080, China
Tel.: (86) 2131358886
General Consulting Services
N.A.I.C.S.: 541618

Waste Management NZ Limited   **(1)**
318 East Tamaki Road, Private Bag 14 919,
East Tamaki, Auckland, 2013, New Zealand
Tel.: (64) 80 010 1010
Web Site:
  https://www.wastemanagement.co.nz
Waste & Environmental Services
N.A.I.C.S.: 562112
Craig Wilson (Gen Mgr-Sls)

Subsidiary (Domestic):

Budget Bins Limited   **(2)**
86 Lunn Ave Mount Wellington, Private Bag
14919, Panmure, 1741, Auckland, New
Zealand
Tel.: (64) 800244224
Web Site: https://www.budgetbins.co.nz
Waste Management Services
N.A.I.C.S.: 562111
Tom Nickels (Mng Dir)

ERS New Zealand Ltd   **(2)**
4 Caerphilly Place, Hillsborough,
Christchurch, New Zealand
Tel.: (64) 3 376 6256
Web Site: http://www.ersnz.co.nz
Sales Range: $25-49.9 Million
Emp.: 7
Waste Management Services
N.A.I.C.S.: 562998

Living Earth Limited   **(2)**
30 Neales Road East Tamaki, PO Box

204253, Highbrook, Penrose, 2161, New
Zealand
Tel.: (64) 95251003
Web Site: http://www.livingearth.co.nz
Organic Composting Services
N.A.I.C.S.: 562219

Affiliate (Domestic):

Midwest Disposals Ltd.   **(2)**
49-53 Malden St, Palmerston North, New
Zealand
Tel.: (64) 63578378
Solid Waste Collection
N.A.I.C.S.: 562111

Subsidiary (Domestic):

Waste Management Technical Services (NZ) Ltd.   **(2)**
16-30 Neales Road East Tamaki, Auckland,
2013, New Zealand
Tel.: (64) 92747963
Waste Management Services
N.A.I.C.S.: 562998

CAPITAL ESTATE LIMITED
Unit 1701 17/F YF Life Tower 33
Lockhart Road, Wanchai, China
(Hong Kong)
Tel.: (852) 25292678
Web Site:
  http://www.capitalestate.com.hk
0193—(HKG)
Rev.: $14,980,640
Assets: $145,423,918
Liabilities: $25,001,999
Net Worth: $120,421,919
Earnings: ($3,798,977)
Emp.: 80
Fiscal Year-end: 07/31/21
Property & Investment Holding
N.A.I.C.S.: 523940
Yat Ming Hung (Sec)

Subsidiaries:

Foshan Fortuna Hotel Company
Limited   **(1)**
B 82 Lecong Dadao Lecong Town, Shunde
Dist, Foshan, 528315, Guangdong, China
Tel.: (86) 2033363233
Home Management Services
N.A.I.C.S.: 721110

CAPITAL EYE INVESTMENTS LIMITED
4th Floor The Mall Offices 11 Cra-
dock Avenue Rosebank, Melrose
North, Johannesburg, 2017, South
Africa
Tel.: (27) 117121300
Web Site: http://www.capitaleye.co.za
Year Founded: 2011
Sales Range: $150-199.9 Million
Emp.: 2,315
Holding Company
N.A.I.C.S.: 551112
Lindsey Ord (COO)

Subsidiaries:

Fernridge Consulting (Proprietary)
Limited   **(1)**
26th Fl UCS Bldg 209 Smit St Corner Harri-
son St, PO Box 31266, Braamfontein, Jo-
hannesburg, 2001, Gauteng, South Africa
Tel.: (27) 117121715
Web Site: http://www.fernridge.co.za
Sales Range: $25-49.9 Million
Emp.: 12
Business Consulting Services
N.A.I.C.S.: 541611
Stephen Walters (Mng Dir)

GAAP Point-of-Sale (Proprietary)
Limited   **(1)**
Building 4 Constantia Park 546 16th Road,
Midrand, 1685, Gauteng, South Africa
Tel.: (27) 110874200
Web Site: http://www.gaap.co.za
Sales Range: $25-49.9 Million
Emp.: 51
Restaurant Software Development Services
N.A.I.C.S.: 541511

J. P. d'Abbadie *(Mng Dir)*

**Just Dynamics Software Solutions
(Pty) Ltd** (1)
15E Riley Road Riley Road Office Park CIB
Building 1, Bedfordview, Johannesburg,
2008, South Africa
Tel.: (27) 114214800
Web Site: http://www.just-dynamics.co.za
Sales Range: $25-49.9 Million
Emp.: 35
Software Support Services
N.A.I.C.S.: 541512

**UCS Software Manufacturing (Propri-
etary) Limited** (1)
267 West Avenue, Centurion, 0157, Gau-
teng, South Africa
Tel.: (27) 126438300
Web Site: http://www.ucssm.com
Sales Range: $25-49.9 Million
Emp.: 52
Retail Management Software Development
Services
N.A.I.C.S.: 541511
Grant Wellbeloved *(CEO)*

**Ultisales Retail Software (Proprietary)
Limited** (1)
Meerlus Bldg 263 W Ave, Centurion, Gau-
teng, South Africa
Tel.: (27) 126821300
Web Site: http://www.ultisales.com
Sales Range: $25-49.9 Million
Emp.: 11
Retail Management Software Development
Services
N.A.I.C.S.: 541511

**Universal Knowledge Software (Pro-
prietary) Limited** (1)
UCS House 21st Fl 209 Smit St, Braamfon-
tein, Johannesburg, 2001, Gauteng, South
Africa
Tel.: (27) 117121750
Web Site: http://www.uks.co.za
Sales Range: $25-49.9 Million
Emp.: 18
Library Management Software Development
Services
N.A.I.C.S.: 541511
Neesha Ramsumar *(Mng Dir)*

CAPITAL FINANCE HOLDINGS LIMITED
Unit 2613A 26/F Mira Place Tower A
132 Nathan Road Tsimshatsui, Kow-
loon, China (Hong Kong)
Tel.: (852) 37521000   Ky
Web Site:
  http://www.capitalfinance.hk
8239—(HKG)
Rev.: $5,926,583
Assets: $37,594,650
Liabilities: $24,676,988
Net Worth: $12,917,663
Earnings: ($545,828)
Emp.: 45
Fiscal Year-end: 12/31/22
Holding Company
N.A.I.C.S.: 551112
Wei Zhang *(Chm & CEO)*

CAPITAL FINANCIAL PRESS LIMITED
Suite 2418 Jardine House 1 Con-
naught Place, Hong Kong, China
(Hong Kong)
Tel.: (852) 28507799
Web Site: http://www.capitalfp.com
Financial Services
N.A.I.C.S.: 523940
Kennis Wong *(Acct Dir)*

CAPITAL FOR COLLEAGUES PLC
1 Portland Street, Manchester, M1
3BE, United Kingdom
Tel.: (44) 161 233 4891
Web Site:
  http://www.capitalforcolleagues.com
Investment Services

N.A.I.C.S.: 523999
John Eckersley *(CEO)*

CAPITAL FORD LINCOLN WIN-NIPEG
555 Empress Street, Winnipeg, R3G
3H1, MB, Canada
Tel.: (204) 772-2411
Web Site:
  http://www.capitalfordwinnipeg.ca
New & Used Car Dealers
N.A.I.C.S.: 441110
Ron Gagnon *(Mgr-Parts)*

CAPITAL GRAND EST SAS
550 boulevard Gonthier d'Andernach,
67400, Illkirch-Graffenstaden, France
Tel.: (33) 367106102
Web Site:
  http://www.capitalgrandest.eu
Holding Company
N.A.I.C.S.: 551112

Subsidiaries:

**Stevenin Nollevaux Forges Et
Estampage** (1)
Rue De La Semoy, 08800, Les Hautes-
Rivieres, Ardennes, France
Tel.: (33) 324534045
Web Site: http://www.stevenin-
  nollevaux.com
Sheet Metalwork Products Mfr
N.A.I.C.S.: 332119

CAPITAL HOLDING GROUP REIT
49 Hristo Botev blvd Capital City
Center fl 2 office CCC, 4000, Plovdiv,
4000, Bulgaria
Tel.: (359) 887404060
Web Site:
  https://www.capitalholdinggroup.bg
CHG—(BUL)
Sales Range: Less than $1 Million
Emp.: 250
Real Estate Investment Services
N.A.I.C.S.: 531210
Veselin Stoychev Chipev *(Chm)*

CAPITAL HOTELS PLC.
1 Ladi Kwali Street Wuse Zone 4,
Abuja, Nigeria
Tel.: (234) 94612000   NG
Web Site:
  http://www.capitalhotelsng.org
Year Founded: 1981
CAPHOTEL—(NIGE)
Rev.: $5,083,192
Assets: $47,260,327
Liabilities: $9,197,149
Net Worth: $38,063,178
Earnings: ($631,242)
Emp.: 567
Fiscal Year-end: 12/31/20
Restaurant Operators
N.A.I.C.S.: 722511
Robert Itawa *(Exec Dir)*

CAPITAL INDIA FINANCE LIM-ITED
Level - 20 Birla Aurora, Dr Annie Be-
sant Road, Mumbai, 400030, India
Tel.: (91) 2245036000
Web Site: https://capitalindia.com
Year Founded: 1994
530879—(BOM)
Rev.: $72,630,135
Assets: $221,991,151
Liabilities: $127,267,768
Net Worth: $94,723,383
Earnings: ($2,824,540)
Emp.: 278
Fiscal Year-end: 03/31/22
Textile Product Mfr & Investment
Management Services
N.A.I.C.S.: 314999

Rachit Malhotra *(Compliance Officer
& Sec)*

CAPITAL INDUSTRIAL FINAN-CIAL SERVICES GROUP LIM-ITED
5/F Bank of East Asia Harbour View
Centre 56 Gloucester Road, Wan-
chai, China (Hong Kong)
Tel.: (852) 28774500   HK
Web Site: http://www.shougang-
  grand.com.hk
0730—(HKG)
Rev.: $47,256,345
Assets: $255,794,453
Liabilities: $31,984,013
Net Worth: $223,810,440
Earnings: $4,110,218
Emp.: 50
Fiscal Year-end: 12/31/22
Holding Company; Computer-
Generated Video Content Production
& Distr, Property Investment & Man-
agement & Financial Investment Ser-
vices
N.A.I.C.S.: 551112
Liang Xu *(Chm)*

Subsidiaries:

**SCG Finance Corporation
Limited** (1)
Room 1-4 11 F Harcourt House 39 Glouc-
ester Road, Wanchai, Hong Kong, China
(Hong Kong)
Tel.: (852) 28774500
Web Site: http://www.shougang-
  grand.com.hk
Real Estate Investment Services
N.A.I.C.S.: 531390

**South China International Leasing
Company Limited** (1)
23rd Floor Times Financial Center 4001
Shennan Avenue, Futian District, Shenzhen,
China
Tel.: (86) 75533336988
Web Site: http://www.nf-leasing.com
Investment Services
N.A.I.C.S.: 523999

CAPITAL INTERNATIONAL GROUP LIMITED
Capital House Circular Road, Doug-
las, IM1 1AG, Isle of Man
Tel.: (44) 1624 654 200   IM
Web Site: http://www.capital-iom.com
Year Founded: 1996
Holding Company; Securities Broker-
age & Dealing, Custody, Investment
Management & Other Financial Ser-
vices
N.A.I.C.S.: 551112
Peter Long *(Founder)*

Subsidiaries:

CILSA Investments (Pty) Ltd. (1)
Office NG101A Great Westerford 240 Main
Road, Rondebosch, 7700, South Africa
Tel.: (27) 212011070
Web Site: http://www.capital-sa.com
Emp.: 10
Investment Management Service
N.A.I.C.S.: 523940
Mark Wilkinson *(Mng Dir)*

Capital Financial Markets Limited (1)
20 Bunhill Row, London, EC1Y 8UE, United
Kingdom
Tel.: (44) 2036970560
Web Site:
  http://www.capitalfinancialmarkets.co.uk
Financial Investment Management Services
N.A.I.C.S.: 523940

Capital International Limited (1)
Capital House Circular Road, Douglas, IM1
1AG, Isle of Man
Tel.: (44) 1624 654 200
Web Site: http://www.capital-island.com
Emp.: 70

Securities Brokerage & Dealing, Custody,
Investment Management & Other Financial
Services
N.A.I.C.S.: 523150
Peter Long *(Chm)*

**Capital Treasury Services
Limited** (1)
Finch Hill House Bucks Road, PO Box 58,
Douglas, IM99 1DT, Isle of Man
Tel.: (44) 1624689300
Financial Investment Management Services
N.A.I.C.S.: 523940
R. C. Floate *(Sec)*

CAPITAL LIMITED
9th Floor The CORE Building, Ebene,
Mauritius
Tel.: (230) 4643250   BM
Web Site: https://www.capdrill.com
Year Founded: 2004
CAPD—(LSE)
Rev.: $318,424,000
Assets: $467,748,000
Liabilities: $194,601,000
Net Worth: $273,147,000
Earnings: $38,530,000
Emp.: 2,739
Fiscal Year-end: 12/31/23
Mineral Exploration & Mining Ser-
vices
N.A.I.C.S.: 213115
Jamie Phillip Boyton *(Chm)*

Subsidiaries:

**Capital Drilling (Singapore) Pte.
Ltd.** (1)
23 Amoy St, Singapore, 69858, Singapore
Tel.: (65) 62279050
Web Site: http://www.capdrill.com
Emp.: 15
Mineral Drilling Services
N.A.I.C.S.: 213115

Capital Drilling Chile S.A. (1)
El Juncal 111 2 Piso Parque Industrial Port-
ezuelo, Quilicura, Santiago, Chile
Tel.: (56) 2 2738 6640
Web Site: http://www.capdrill.com
Mineral Drilling Services
N.A.I.C.S.: 213115
Andrew Triggs *(Gen Mgr)*

**Capital Drilling Egypt (Limited Liability
Company)** (1)
52 Ahmed Fakhry, Cairo, Nasr, Egypt
Tel.: (20) 222700699
Mineral Drilling Services
N.A.I.C.S.: 213115
Brian Rudd *(CEO)*

**Capital Drilling Mozambique
Limitada** (1)
Rua 3 De Fevereiro No 108, Tete, Mozam-
bique
Tel.: (258) 25 222 174
Web Site: http://www.capdrill.com
Mineral Drilling Services
N.A.I.C.S.: 213115

Capital Drilling Zambia Limited (1)
Plot 609T Zambezi Rd, Roma, Lusaka,
Zambia
Tel.: (260) 211292337
Mineral Drilling Services
N.A.I.C.S.: 213115
Bert Gerritsen *(Gen Mgr)*

**Supply Force International Pte
Ltd** (1)
23 Amoy St, Singapore, 69858, Singapore
Tel.: (65) 62279050
Web Site: http://www.captdrill.com
Logistics Consulting Servies
N.A.I.C.S.: 541614

CAPITAL MERCHANT BANK-ING AND FINANCE LIMITED
Battisputali, Kathmandu, Nepal
Tel.: (977) 1 447 1458
Web Site: http://www.cmbfl.com.np
Year Founded: 2002
CMB—(NEP)
Sales Range: Less than $1 Million

Capital Merchant Banking and Finance Limited—(Continued)

Financial & Banking Services
N.A.I.C.S.: 522110

CAPITAL METALS PLC
47 Charles Street, London, W1J 5EL, United Kingdom
Tel.: (44) 2077667555
Web Site: http://www.epoil.co.uk
PAL—(AIM)
Rev.: $111,000
Assets: $8,138,000
Liabilities: $1,307,000
Net Worth: $6,831,000
Earnings: ($7,886,000)
Emp.: 13
Fiscal Year-end: 03/31/21
Crude Palm Oil Producer
N.A.I.C.S.: 111120
Geoffrey Brown (Exec Dir)

CAPITAL MINING LIMITED
Level 11 216 St Georges Terrace, Perth, 6000, WA, Australia
Tel.: (61) 86 245 3534
Web Site:
http://www.capitalmining.com.au
CMY—(ASX)
Sales Range: Less than $1 Million
Mineral Exploration & Evaluation
N.A.I.C.S.: 213115
Robert Crossman (Chm)

CAPITAL PARTNERS S.A.
ul Marszalkowska 126/134, 00-008, Warsaw, Poland
Tel.: (48) 222759990
Web Site: https://c-p.pl
Year Founded: 2002
CPA—(WAR)
Rev.: $101,626
Assets: $417,754
Liabilities: $26,049
Net Worth: $391,705
Earnings: ($390,701)
Fiscal Year-end: 12/31/23
Investment Management Service
N.A.I.C.S.: 523940
Konrad Korobowicz (Vice Chm-Mgmt Bd)

Subsidiaries:

Towarzystwo Funduszy Inwestycyjnych Capital Partners SA **(1)**
Ul Krolewska 16, 00-103, Warsaw, Poland
Tel.: (48) 223306900
Web Site: http://www.tficp.pl
Bond Investment Services
N.A.I.C.S.: 523940
Joanna Kwiatkowska (VP)

CAPITAL PEOPLE S.A.
451 B19 Route de Lennik, 1070, Brussels, Belgium
Tel.: (32) 4 349 55 55
Web Site:
http://www.capitalpeople.eu
Privater Equity Firm
N.A.I.C.S.: 523999
Jean-Paul Rosette (CEO)

Subsidiaries:

Carat Duchatelet S.A. **(1)**
Rue Winston Churchill 413, Liege, 4020, Belgium
Tel.: (32) 43495555
Web Site: http://www.caratbyduchatelet.com
Rev.: $17,447,220
Emp.: 50
Mobile Security Company
N.A.I.C.S.: 561621
Jean-Paul Rosette (CEO)

Division (Domestic):

Centigon **(2)**

Rue Winston Churchill 413, 4020, Liege, Belgium
Tel.: (32) 43495555
Web Site: http://www.caratsecurity.com
Sales Range: $50-74.9 Million
Emp.: 110
Armored Vehicle Mfr
N.A.I.C.S.: 336211

Plant (Non-US):

Centigon Brazil **(3)**
Alameda Jurua 762 Alphaville, Sao Paulo, 06455-010, Brazil
Tel.: (55) 1146894200
Web Site: http://www.centigon.com
Sales Range: $25-49.9 Million
Emp.: 80
Armored Vehicle Mfr
N.A.I.C.S.: 336211
Marcus Leloann (Gen Mgr)

Centigon Colombia **(3)**
Calle 21 No 69B-05, 95118, Bogota, Colombia
Tel.: (57) 14051414
Web Site: http://www.centigon.com
Sales Range: $50-74.9 Million
Armored Vehicle Mfr
N.A.I.C.S.: 336211

Centigon France **(3)**
42 rue d Armor Maroue, BP 90447, 22400, Lamballe, France
Tel.: (33) 296501280
Web Site: http://www.centigon.com
Emp.: 170
Mobile Security Service
N.A.I.C.S.: 561621

Subsidiary (Non-US):

Centigon Mexico **(2)**
Blvd Adolfo Lopez Mateos No 1491 Col Afonso XIII, Mexico, 01460, Mexico
Tel.: (52) 55 917 10 200
Armored Vehicle Distr
N.A.I.C.S.: 423110

Centigon Venezuela **(2)**
Avenida Principal de Boleita Norte Galpon, No 5 Antiguo Diaro de Caracas, Caracas, Venezuela
Tel.: (58) 2 12 239 94 65
Armored Vehicle Distr
N.A.I.C.S.: 423110

CAPITAL POINT LTD.
Azrieli Center Round Tower 22nd floor, Tel Aviv, 67021, Israel
Tel.: (972) 36070320
Web Site: http://www.capitalpoint.co.il
Year Founded: 2000
CPTP—(TAE)
Rev.: $8,567,205
Assets: $45,963,530
Liabilities: $7,151,264
Net Worth: $38,812,266
Earnings: $472,717
Fiscal Year-end: 12/31/23
Miscellaneous Financial Investment Activities
N.A.I.C.S.: 523999

CAPITAL POWER CORPORATION
1200 - 10423 101 St NW, Edmonton, T5H 0E9, AB, Canada
Tel.: (780) 392-5100
Web Site:
https://www.capitalpower.com
Year Founded: 2009
CPX—(TSX)
Rev.: $1,401,063,480
Assets: $6,970,897,080
Liabilities: $4,679,598,960
Net Worth: $2,291,298,120
Earnings: $101,696,400
Emp.: 825
Fiscal Year-end: 12/31/20
Gas & Electric Power Distribution & Generation Services
N.A.I.C.S.: 221118
Brian Vaasjo (Pres & CEO)

Subsidiaries:

Frederickson Power, LP **(1)**
18610 50th Ave E, Tacoma, WA 98446 **(50.15%)**
Sales Range: $1-9.9 Million
Emp.: 16
Fiscal Year-end: 10/15/2012
Electric Power Generation
N.A.I.C.S.: 221118
Epcor Utilities (Principal)

CAPITAL PROFESSIONAL LIMITED
6th floor Reading Bridge George Street, Reading, RG1 8LS, United Kingdom
Tel.: (44) 845 475 7500
Web Site: http://www.ascotlloyd.co.uk
Year Founded: 2011
Financial Planning Services
N.A.I.C.S.: 523940

CAPITAL REALM FINANCIAL HOLDINGS GROUP LIMITED
Room 3702 37/F 118 Connaught Road West, Sheung Wan, Hong Kong, China (Hong Kong)
Tel.: (852) 31021690
Web Site:
http://www.chinainvestment.com.hk
Year Founded: 1998
0204—(HKG)
Rev.: $1,302,698
Assets: $30,395,685
Liabilities: $1,502,101
Net Worth: $28,893,584
Earnings: ($2,580,890)
Emp.: 10
Fiscal Year-end: 03/31/22
Investment Management Service
N.A.I.C.S.: 523940
Chan Kwan Pak (Sec)

CAPITAL SECURITIES CORPORATION
11F No 156 Sec 3 Minsheng E Rd, Songshan Dist, Taipei, 105, Taiwan
Tel.: (886) 24128878
Web Site: https://www.capital.com.tw
6005—(TAI)
Rev.: $416,829,312
Assets: $8,074,519,202
Liabilities: $6,656,404,732
Net Worth: $1,418,114,469
Earnings: $149,481,436
Emp.: 1,842
Fiscal Year-end: 12/31/23
Corporate Banking Services
N.A.I.C.S.: 523150
Alex Jiunn-Chih Wang (Chm)

Subsidiaries:

CSC Financial Services Limited **(1)**
Unit 3204-07 32/F Cosco Tower 183 Queen Road, Central, China (Hong Kong)
Tel.: (852) 25309966
Financial Management Services
N.A.I.C.S.: 523999

CSC Futures (HK) Ltd. **(1)**
3/F FWD Financial Centre 308 Des Voeux Road, Central, China (Hong Kong)
Tel.: (852) 25309966
Emp.: 28
Financial Investment Management Services
N.A.I.C.S.: 523999
Sam Kao (Mng Dir)

CSC International Holdings Ltd. **(1)**
18F New Shanghai International Tower No 360 Pudong Road S, Shanghai, 200120, China
Tel.: (86) 215 888 7188
Web Site: http://www.capital.com.tw
Investment Management Service
N.A.I.C.S.: 523999

Subsidiary (Non-US):

CSC Finance Ltd. **(2)**
Unit 3204-07 32/F Cosco Tower 183 Queen Road, Central, Hong Kong, China (Hong Kong)
Tel.: (852) 25309966
Financial Management Services
N.A.I.C.S.: 523999

CSC Securities (HK) Ltd. **(2)**
Tel.: (852) 25309966
Financial Investment Management Services
N.A.I.C.S.: 523999

Capital Securities (Hong Kong) Ltd. **(2)**
Unit 3204-07 32/F Cosco Tower 183 Queen Road, Central, China (Hong Kong)
Tel.: (852) 25309966
Securities Brokerage Services
N.A.I.C.S.: 523150

Capital Insurance Advisory Corp. **(1)**
14F No 156 Sec 3 Minsheng E Rd, Songshan Dist, Taipei, 10596, Taiwan
Tel.: (886) 287896777
General Insurance Services
N.A.I.C.S.: 524210

Capital Insurance Agency Corp. **(1)**
14F No 156 Sec 3 Minsheng E Rd, Songshan Dist, Taipei, 10596, Taiwan
Tel.: (886) 287896777
General Insurance Services
N.A.I.C.S.: 524210

Capital Investment Management Corp. **(1)**
Tel.: (886) 287806789
Investment Management Service
N.A.I.C.S.: 523999

CAPITAL SPORTS GROUP OF COMPANIES
1000 Palladium Drive, Kanata, K2V 1A5, ON, Canada
Tel.: (613) 599-0250
Web Site:
http://www.ottawasenators.com
Sales Range: $50-74.9 Million
Emp.: 200
Holding Company
N.A.I.C.S.: 551112

Subsidiaries:

Canadian Tire Centre **(1)**
1000 Palladium Drive, Ottawa, K2V 1A5, ON, Canada
Tel.: (613) 599-0100
Web Site:
http://www.canadiantirecentre.com
Sports & Entertainment Complex
N.A.I.C.S.: 711310

Ottawa Senators Hockey Club **(1)**
Scociabank Pl Ctr 1000 Palladium Dr, Kanata, K2V 1A5, ON, Canada
Tel.: (613) 599-0250
Web Site: http://www.ottawasenators.com
Emp.: 800
Professional Hockey Franchise
N.A.I.C.S.: 711211
Mark Bonneau (Chief Revenue Officer)

CAPITAL SQUARE PARTNERS PTE LTD.
160 Robinson Road Ste #10-01 SBF Center, Singapore, 068914, Singapore
Tel.: (65) 6202 4732
Web Site:
http://www.capitalsquarepartners.com
Privater Equity Firm
N.A.I.C.S.: 523999
Sudip Banerjee (Operating Partner)

CAPITAL TRADE LINKS LIMITED
Office No 102103 1st Floor Surya Kiran Building 19 K G Marg C P, C-2 Sector-4 Vaishali, Ghaziabad, 201010, Uttar Pradesh, India
Tel.: (91) 7042353322

Web Site: https://www.capitaltrade.in
Year Founded: 1984
538476—(BOM)
Rev.: $1,331,530
Assets: $6,643,687
Liabilities: $2,330,710
Net Worth: $4,312,977
Earnings: $337,237
Emp.: 16
Fiscal Year-end: 03/31/22
Financial Services
N.A.I.C.S.: 523999
Santosh Gupta *(CFO)*

CAPITAL TRUST LIMITED
205 Centrum Mall Sultanpur MG
Road, New Delhi, 110030, India
Tel.: (91) 9999074312
Web Site: https://www.capitaltrust.in
Year Founded: 1985
511505—(BOM)
Rev.: $15,641,289
Assets: $55,570,720
Liabilities: $37,729,201
Net Worth: $17,841,519
Earnings: ($3,224,744)
Emp.: 2,301
Fiscal Year-end: 03/31/21
Financial Support Services
N.A.I.C.S.: 523999
Yogen Khosla *(Mng Dir)*

CAPITAL VC LIMITED
Room 2302 23rd Floor New World
Tower 1, 18 Queens Road, Central,
China (Hong Kong)
Tel.: (852) 37560081 Ky
Web Site: http://www.capital-vc.com
2324—(HKG)
Assets: $48,419,788
Liabilities: $7,512,915
Net Worth: $40,906,874
Earnings: ($19,063,772)
Emp.: 20
Fiscal Year-end: 09/30/23
Investment Services
N.A.I.C.S.: 523940
Yuet Ching Chan *(Sec)*

CAPITAL WORLD LIMITED
01-02-01 and 02 Pangsapuri Jentayu
Jalan Tampoi, Kawasan Perindustrian
Tampoi Johor Bahru, 81200, Johor,
Malaysia
Tel.: (60) 72386622 Ky
Web Site:
 http://www.capitalworld.com.sg
Year Founded: 2013
1D5—(CAT)
Rev.: $1,722,328
Assets: $89,025,608
Liabilities: $41,067,725
Net Worth: $47,957,884
Earnings: $9,725,079
Emp.: 19
Fiscal Year-end: 06/30/23
Investment Holding Company; Real
Estate Development Services
N.A.I.C.S.: 551112
Siow Chien Fu *(CEO & Exec Dir)*

Subsidiaries:

Capital City Property Sdn Bhd **(1)**
1132 Jalan Tampoi, Kawasan Perindustrian
Tampoi, 81200, Johor Bahru, Johor, Malaysia
Tel.: (60) 72386622
Web Site: https://capitalcity.com.my
Property Development Services
N.A.I.C.S.: 531311

CAPITALAND ASCOTT TRUST MANAGEMENT LIMITED
No 30-01 Capital Tower 168 Robinson Road, Singapore, 068912, Singapore
Tel.: (65) 67132888 SG

Web Site:
 https://investor.ascottreit.com
Year Founded: 2006
HMN—(SES)
Rev.: $227,980,556
Assets: $5,096,095,063
Liabilities: $2,214,703,740
Net Worth: $2,881,391,323
Earnings: $57,704,622
Emp.: 1,400
Fiscal Year-end: 12/31/21
Real Estate Investment Trust Services
N.A.I.C.S.: 531120

CAPITALAND CHINA TRUST
168 Robinson Road 30-01 Capital
Tower, Singapore, 068912, Singapore
Tel.: (65) 67132888 SG
Web Site: https://www.clct.com.sg
Year Founded: 2006
AU8U—(SES)
Rev.: $276,259,941
Assets: $3,783,805,951
Liabilities: $1,953,338,634
Net Worth: $1,830,467,317
Earnings: $124,501,250
Emp.: 482
Fiscal Year-end: 12/31/23
Real Estate Investment Management
Services
N.A.I.C.S.: 531120
Tze Wooi Tan *(CEO)*

CAPITALAND INDIA TRUST
168 Robinson Road, 30-01 Capital
Tower, Singapore, 068912, Singapore
Tel.: (65) 67132888 SG
Web Site: https://www.clint.com.sg
Year Founded: 2007
CY6U—(SES)
Rev.: $177,272,589
Assets: $2,825,270,770
Liabilities: $1,583,770,354
Net Worth: $1,241,500,416
Earnings: $119,300,916
Emp.: 20
Fiscal Year-end: 12/31/23
Real Estate Investment Services
N.A.I.C.S.: 523999
Mary Judith De Souza *(Co-Sec)*

CAPITALAND INVESTMENT LIMITED
168 Robinson Road 30-01 Capital
Tower, Singapore, 068912, Singapore
Tel.: (65) 67132888 SG
Web Site:
 https://www.capitaland.com
Year Founded: 1985
9CI—(SES)
Rev.: $2,062,986,291
Assets: $25,293,071,508
Liabilities: $11,779,177,473
Net Worth: $13,513,894,035
Earnings: $246,758,059
Emp.: 9,900
Fiscal Year-end: 12/31/23
Asset Management Services
N.A.I.C.S.: 525990
Michelle Chai Ping Koh *(Sec)*

Subsidiaries:

CLI Singapore Pte. Ltd. **(1)**
168 Robinson Road 30-01 Capital Tower,
Singapore, 068912, Singapore
Tel.: (65) 67132888
N.A.I.C.S.: 531390

CapitaLand (Japan) Kabushiki
Kaisha **(1)**
Mita Kokusai Building 16F 1-4-28 Mita,
Minato-ku, Tokyo, 108-0073, Japan
Tel.: (81) 364539730
Web Site: http://www.capitaland.co.jp
Real Estate Management Services
N.A.I.C.S.: 531390

CapitaLand (Vietnam) Holdings Pte
Ltd **(1)**
8th Floor Vista Tower 628C Hanoi Highway,
An Phu Ward District 2, Ho Chi Minh City,
Vietnam
Tel.: (84) 2835191067
Web Site: http://www.capitaland.com.vn
Sales Range: $50-74.9 Million
Emp.: 80
Holding Company
N.A.I.C.S.: 551112

Subsidiary (Domestic):

CapitaLand-Vista Joint Venture Co.,
Ltd. **(2)**
30th Floor Saigon Trade Center 37 Ton Duc
Thang Street, District 1, Ho Chi Minh City,
Vietnam **(90%)**
Tel.: (84) 8 3910 6688
Web Site: http://www.thevista.com.vn
Real Estate Management Services
N.A.I.C.S.: 531390

CapitaLand China Holdings Pte
Ltd **(1)**
268 Xizang Road Middle, 19-01 Raffles City
Shanghai, 200001, Shanghai,
China **(100%)**
Tel.: (86) 21 3311 4633
Holding Company; Real Estate Development
N.A.I.C.S.: 551112
Jen Yuh Loh *(CEO)*

Subsidiary (Domestic):

CapitaLand (China) Investment Co.,
Ltd **(2)**
12/f Raffles Center No 1 Dongzhimens Avenue, Dongcheng Dis, Beijing, 100007,
China
Tel.: (86) 1065630828
Real Estate Management Services
N.A.I.C.S.: 531390

CapitaLand Commercial Limited **(1)**
39 Robinson Rd 18-01 Robinson Point, Singapore, 068911, Singapore **(100%)**
Tel.: (65) 65361188
Web Site:
 http://www.capitalandcommercial.com
Sales Range: $150-199.9 Million
Emp.: 400
Commercial Properties Management Services
N.A.I.C.S.: 531312
Khai Meng Wen *(Deputy Chm)*

CapitaLand Commercial Trust Management Limited **(1)**
168 Robinson Road No 30-01 Capital
Tower, Singapore, 068912, Singapore
Tel.: (65) 67132888
Rev.: $305,607,597
Assets: $7,552,773,196
Liabilities: $2,205,889,074
Net Worth: $5,346,884,122
Earnings: $259,081,792
Emp.: 124
Fiscal Year-end: 12/31/2019
Holding Company
N.A.I.C.S.: 551112

Subsidiary (Domestic):

CapitaLand Commercial Trust **(2)**
168 Robinson Road No 30-01 Capital
Tower, Singapore, 068912, Singapore
Tel.: (65) 6713 2888
Web Site: http://www.cct.com.sg
Sales Range: $350-399.9 Million
Real Estate Investment Trust
N.A.I.C.S.: 525990
Ming Yan Lim *(Deputy Chm)*

CapitaLand Fund Management
Limited **(1)**
39 Robinson Road 18-01 Robinson Point,
Singapore, 068911, Singapore **(100%)**
Tel.: (65) 5361188
Web Site:
 http://www.capitalandcommercial.com
Sales Range: $200-249.9 Million
Emp.: 400
Provider of Property Fund Management
N.A.I.C.S.: 523940

CapitaLand GCC Holdings Pte
Ltd **(1)**

39 Robinson Road 16-01 Robinson Point,
Singapore, 068911, Singapore
Tel.: (65) 6622 6000
Sales Range: $50-74.9 Million
Emp.: 17
Real Estate Management Services
N.A.I.C.S.: 531390
Wei Siong Ku *(VP)*

CapitaLand Integrated Commercial
Trust **(1)**
168 Robinson Road 30-01 Capital Tower,
Singapore, 068912, Singapore
Tel.: (65) 67132888
Web Site: http://www.cmt.com.sg
Rev.: $1,155,934,791
Assets: $18,332,068,173
Liabilities: $7,660,174,880
Net Worth: $10,671,893,294
Earnings: $644,103,742
Emp.: 486
Fiscal Year-end: 12/31/2023
Real Estate Investment Management Services
N.A.I.C.S.: 525990
Tony Tee Hieong Tan *(CEO)*

CapitaLand International Pte.
Ltd. **(1)**
168 Robinson Road 30-01 Capital Tower,
Singapore, 068912, Singapore
Tel.: (65) 67132888
Real Estate Management Services
N.A.I.C.S.: 531390

CapitaLand Mall Asia Limited **(1)**
168 Robinson Road 30-01 Capital Tower,
Singapore, 068912, Singapore
Tel.: (65) 67132888
Web Site:
 http://www.capitalandmallasia.com
Sales Range: $250-299.9 Million
Shopping Mall Developer
N.A.I.C.S.: 237210

CapitaLand Residential Limited **(1)**
8 Shenton Way Unit 21-01, Singapore,
68811, Singapore **(100%)**
Tel.: (65) 68202188
Web Site:
 http://www.capitalandresidential.com
Sales Range: $75-99.9 Million
Emp.: 150
Developer of Condominiums
N.A.I.C.S.: 531311

Subsidiary (Domestic):

CapitaLand Residential Singapore
Pte Ltd **(2)**
8 Shenton Way 21-01, Singapore, 068811,
Singapore
Tel.: (65) 68202188
Web Site:
 http://www.capitalandresidential.com
Sales Range: $50-74.9 Million
Emp.: 100
Real Estate Management Services
N.A.I.C.S.: 531390

CapitaLand Singapore Limited **(1)**
168 Robinson Road 30-01 Capital Tower,
Singapore, 068912, Singapore
Tel.: (65) 67132888
Real Estate Management Services
N.A.I.C.S.: 531390
David Leong *(VP)*

CapitaLand Treasury Limited **(1)**
168 Robinson Road 30-01, Singapore,
068912, Singapore
Tel.: (65) 68233200
Real Estate Development Services
N.A.I.C.S.: 531390

CapitaLand UK Management Ltd **(1)**
Citadines London Barbican 7-21 Goswell
Road, London, EC1M 7AH, United Kingdom
Tel.: (44) 20 3119 3430
Real Estate Management Services
N.A.I.C.S.: 531390

CapitalValue Homes Limited **(1)**
8 Shenton Way 29-03, Singapore, 068811,
Singapore
Tel.: (65) 68265312
Web Site: http://www.capitavaluehomes.com
Real Estate Management Services
N.A.I.C.S.: 531390

CapitaLand Investment Limited—(Continued)

Raffles Holdings Limited (1)
250 North Bridge Road, 15-03/04 Raffles
City Tower, Singapore, 179101,
Singapore (100%)
Tel.: (65) 63985777
Real Estate Investment & Management
Services
N.A.I.C.S.: 525990

The Ascott Limited (1)
168 Robinson Road #30-01 Capital Tower,
Singapore, 068912, Singapore (100%)
Tel.: (65) 6713 2888
Web Site: http://www.theascottlimited.com
Sales Range: $100-124.9 Million
Emp.: 3,200
Serviced Residence Units Owner & Man-
ager
N.A.I.C.S.: 531110
Meenu Singh (Dir-Sls-Somerset Panorama
Muscat-Oman)

Subsidiary (Domestic):

**Ascott International Management
(2001) Pte Ltd** (2)
8 Shenton Way 13-01, Singapore, 068811,
Singapore
Tel.: (65) 62208222
Web Site: http://www.the-ascott.com
Sales Range: $50-74.9 Million
Emp.: 100
Property Management Services
N.A.I.C.S.: 531311

Subsidiary (Non-US):

**Ascott Property Management (Bei-
jing) Co., Ltd** (2)
No 108 B Jianguo Rd, Chaoyang District,
Beijing, 100022, China
Tel.: (86) 1065678100
Property Management Services
N.A.I.C.S.: 531311

Subsidiary (Domestic):

**Ascott Residence Trust Management
Limited** (2)
168 Robinson Road 30-01 Capital Tower,
Singapore, 068912, Singapore
Tel.: (65) 67132888
Web Site: http://www.ascottreit.com
Residential Property Management Services
N.A.I.C.S.: 531311
Beh Siew Kim (CEO)

Subsidiary (Non-US):

**Citadines Melbourne on Bourke Pty
Ltd** (2)
131-135 Bourke Street, Melbourne, 3000,
VIC, Australia
Tel.: (61) 390398888
Web Site: http://www.citadines.com.au
Residential Property Management Services
N.A.I.C.S.: 531311

Subsidiary (Domestic):

The Ascott (Europe) Pte Ltd (2)
8 Shenton Way 13-01 Temasek Tower, Sin-
gapore, 068811, Singapore
Tel.: (65) 62208222
Web Site: http://www.the-acott.com
Sales Range: $75-99.9 Million
Emp.: 110
Real Estate Management Services
N.A.I.C.S.: 531390

The Ascott Capital Pte Ltd (2)
8 Shenton Way 13-01 8 Shenton Way, Sin-
gapore, 068811, Singapore
Tel.: (65) 62208222
Web Site: http://www.the-ascott.com
Emp.: 100
Real Estate Management Services
N.A.I.C.S.: 531390

CAPITALGROUP LIMITED
Ground Floor 5 Eglon Street, Parnell,
Auckland, 1052, New Zealand
Tel.: (64) 93090506 NZ
Web Site:
　　http://www.capitalgroup.co.nz
Year Founded: 1996
Sales Range: $25-49.9 Million

Emp.: 5
Privater Equity Firm
N.A.I.C.S.: 523999
Greig Allison (Co-Founder)

Subsidiaries:

BBQ Factory Pty. Ltd. (1)
91 Darley Street, Mona Vale, 2103, NSW,
Australia
Tel.: (61) 299991891
Web Site: http://www.bbqfactory.co.nz
Sales Range: $25-49.9 Million
Emp.: 100
Barbeque & Spa Pool Retailer
N.A.I.C.S.: 459999
Russell Whittaker (Owner)

**CAPITALONLINE DATA SER-
VICE CO., LTD.**
Building 9 Yard No 18 Ziyue Road,
Chaoyang, Beijing, 100012, China
Tel.: (86) 4008105300
Web Site:
　　https://www.capitalonline.net
Year Founded: 2005
300846—(SSE)
Rev.: $171,695,160
Assets: $304,697,484
Liabilities: $132,784,704
Net Worth: $171,912,780
Earnings: ($26,541,216)
Fiscal Year-end: 12/31/22
Software Development Services
N.A.I.C.S.: 541511
Ning Qu (Chm & Gen Mgr)

**CAPITALPART PARTICIPA-
COES S.A.**
R Iguatemi 354 - Cj 301, 1451010,
Sao Paulo, Brazil
Tel.: (55) 21 3231 8200
Year Founded: 1998
Assets: $12,285
Liabilities: $34,832
Net Worth: ($22,548)
Fiscal Year-end: 12/31/15
Financial Investment Services
N.A.I.C.S.: 523999
Marcos Navajas (CFO & COO)

**CAPITALWORKS INVESTMENT
PARTNERS (PTY) LTD**
6 Benmore Road, Johannesburg,
2010, South Africa
Tel.: (27) 113013000
Web Site:
　　http://www.capitalworksip.com
Year Founded: 2006
Equity Investment Firm
N.A.I.C.S.: 523999
Darshan Daya (Partner)

Subsidiaries:

Sovereign Food Investments Ltd. (1)
9 Kruis River Road, Uitenhage, 6229, South
Africa
Tel.: (27) 419951700
Web Site: http://www.sovereignfoods.co.za
Poultry Producers
N.A.I.C.S.: 311119
Chris Coombes (CEO)

**The Building Company Proprietary
Limited** (1)
1st Floor Execujet Building Tower Road
Cape Town, PO Box 155, International Air-
port Co-ordinates S 33 58 17 267 & E 18
36 7 506, Cape Town, 7525, South Africa
Tel.: (27) 21 927 5000
Web Site: https://thebuildingco.co
Building Materials Distr
N.A.I.C.S.: 423390
Steve du Toit (CEO)

CAPITAN SILVER CORP.
550-800 West Pender Street, Vancouver, V6C 2V6, BC, Canada
Tel.: (778) 327-6671
Web Site: https://capitansilver.com

CAPT—(TSXV)
Assets: $6,874,611
Liabilities: $156,552
Net Worth: $6,718,059
Earnings: ($718,726)
Fiscal Year-end: 09/30/21
Mining & Exploration Services
N.A.I.C.S.: 213114
Alberto Orozco (CEO)

**CAPITANIA SECURITIES II FII
FUND**
Rua Tavares Cabral 102-82, 05423-
030, Sao Paulo, SP, Brazil
Tel.: (55) 1168538800
Financial Advisory Services
N.A.I.C.S.: 523940

**CAPITEC BANK HOLDINGS
LIMITED**
5 Neutron Road, Techno Park, Stel-
lenbosch, 7600, South Africa
Tel.: (27) 218095900 ZA
Web Site:
　　https://www.capitecbank.co.za
Year Founded: 2001
CPI—(JSE)
Rev.: $1,362,804,846
Assets: $10,962,231,646
Liabilities: $8,663,380,105
Net Worth: $2,298,851,540
Earnings: $558,040,167
Emp.: 15,746
Fiscal Year-end: 02/29/24
Bank Holding Company
N.A.I.C.S.: 551111
Andre Pierre du Plessis (CFO)

Subsidiaries:

Capitec Bank Limited (1)
1 Quantum Street, Techno Park, Stellenbo-
sch, 7600, South Africa
Tel.: (27) 218095900
Web Site: http://www.capitecbank.co.za
Commericial Banking
N.A.I.C.S.: 522110

Subsidiary (Domestic):

**Mercantile Bank Holdings
Limited** (2)
142 West Street, Sandown, Johannesburg,
2196, South Africa
Tel.: (27) 113020300
Web Site: http://www.mercantile.co.za
International Banking & Financial Services
N.A.I.C.S.: 522299
Teixeira Mei (CFO)

CAPITOL HEALTH LIMITED
Level 2 288 Victoria Parade, Mel-
bourne, 3002, VIC, Australia
Tel.: (61) 393483333
Web Site:
　　https://www.capitolhealth.com.au
Year Founded: 2005
CAJ—(ASX)
Rev.: $156,794,871
Assets: $213,330,662
Liabilities: $139,437,099
Net Worth: $73,893,563
Earnings: ($9,856,437)
Emp.: 1,000
Fiscal Year-end: 06/30/24
Diagnostic Imaging Product Mfr
N.A.I.C.S.: 621512
Andrew Demetriou (Chm)

Subsidiaries:

Capital Radiology Pty Ltd (1)
54 - 56 Princes Highway, Dandenong,
3175, VIC, Australia
Tel.: (61) 87889888
Web Site:
　　https://www.capitalradiology.com.au
Health Care Srvices
N.A.I.C.S.: 621999

Capital Radiology WA Pty Ltd (1)

PO Box 551, Melbourne, 8002, VIC, Austra-
lia
Tel.: (61) 39 348 3333
Web Site:
　　https://www.capitalradiology.com.au
Medical Diagnostic Imaging Services
N.A.I.C.S.: 621512

Lime Avenue Radiology Pty Ltd (1)
287 Oxley Ave, PO Box 498, Margate,
4019, QLD, Australia
Tel.: (61) 73 283 9200
Web Site: https://limeradiology.com.au
Medical Diagnostic Imaging Services
N.A.I.C.S.: 621512

CAPITOL W.B.C. PLC
1st Floor Office Cr Whateley's Drive,
Kenilworth, CV8 2GY, United King-
dom
Tel.: (44) 2071933550 UK
Web Site: http://www.wbc-
　　capitol.co.uk
Year Founded: 1995
Fire Prevention Products Mfr
N.A.I.C.S.: 325998
Radomir Krkic (Dir-Intl Dev)

Subsidiaries:

Capitol W.B.C. d.o.o. (1)
Tresnjinog Cveta 11, 11000, Belgrade, Ser-
bia
Tel.: (381) 116302451
Sales Range: $50-74.9 Million
Emp.: 5
Fertilizer Mining Services
N.A.I.C.S.: 212390
Nedeljko Dzudzelija (Gen Mgr)

CAPITON AG
Bleibtreustrasse 33, 10707, Berlin,
Germany
Tel.: (49) 303159450 De
Web Site: http://www.capiton.de
Year Founded: 1999
Rev.: $636,608,832
Emp.: 20
Equity Investment Firm
N.A.I.C.S.: 523999
Stefan Theis (Chm-Supervisory Bd &
Sr Partner)

Subsidiaries:

AEMtec GmbH (1)
Carl-Scheele-Strasse 16, 12489, Berlin,
Germany
Tel.: (49) 30 6392 7300
Web Site: http://www.aemtec.com
Sales Range: $50-74.9 Million
Emp.: 140
Chip Card Mfr
N.A.I.C.S.: 334419

GPE-Plast Engineering GmbH (1)
Oderstrasse 68, 24539, Neumunster, Ger-
many
Tel.: (49) 432181122
Web Site: http://www.gpe-group.de
Engineering Solutions
N.A.I.C.S.: 541330
Burkhard Kroger (Mng Dlr)

CAPLAND ASCENDAS REIT
168 Robinson Road 30-01 Capital
Tower, Singapore, 068912, Singapore
Tel.: (65) 67132888
Web Site: https://www.capitaland-
　　ascendasreit.com
Year Founded: 2001
A17U—(SES)
Rev.: $1,120,789,214
Assets: $13,840,538,507
Liabilities: $6,107,396,801
Net Worth: $7,733,141,706
Earnings: $127,451,337
Emp.: 50
Fiscal Year-end: 12/31/23
Real Estate Investment Management
Services
N.A.I.C.S.: 531120

Lawden Tan *(Head-Investment & Bus Dev Strategy)*

CAPLIN POINT LABORATORIES LIMITED

Ashvich Tower No 3 Developed Plots Industrial Estate, Perungudi, Chennai, 600 096, Tamil Nadu, India
Tel.: (91) 4424968000
Web Site: https://www.caplinpoint.net
Year Founded: 1990
524742—(BOM)
Rev.: $178,563,840
Assets: $237,007,680
Liabilities: $30,909,060
Net Worth: $206,098,620
Earnings: $42,103,425
Emp.: 743
Fiscal Year-end: 03/31/22
Pharmaceutical Product Mfr & Distr
N.A.I.C.S.: 325412
Vinod Kumar Srinivasan *(Compliance Officer & Sec)*

Subsidiaries:

Caplin Point Laboratories Limited - CP-I Factory **(1)**
R S No 85/3, Suthukeny Village, Pondicherry, 605 502, India
Tel.: (91) 413 267 4402
Pharmaceuticals Product Mfr
N.A.I.C.S.: 325412

Caplin Point Laboratories Limited - CP-II Factory **(1)**
19 Chinnapuliyur Village, Thiruvallur District, Gummidipoondi, India
Tel.: (91) 44 2794 0274
Pharmaceutics Product Mfr
N.A.I.C.S.: 325412

Caplin Steriles Limited **(1)**
1st Floor Ashvich Towers, No 3 Developed Plots Industrial Estate Perungudi, Chennai, 600096, Tamil Nadu, India
Tel.: (91) 4424968000
Web Site: https://www.caplinsteriles.net
Ophthalmic Product Mfr
N.A.I.C.S.: 339115
Sathya Narayanan M. *(CFO)*

CAPMAN FINANCIALS LIMITED

Office No 19 1st Floor Goyal Shopping Arcade S V Road, Borivali West, Mumbai, 400 092, India
Tel.: (91) 22 28940941
Rev.: $144,687
Assets: $1,139,978
Liabilities: $143,520
Net Worth: $996,458
Earnings: $69,552
Fiscal Year-end: 03/31/16
Financial Services
N.A.I.C.S.: 523999
Jagdishbhai K. Bodra *(Compliance Officer)*

CAPMAN PLC

Ludviginkatu 6 4 fl, 00130, Helsinki, Finland
Tel.: (358) 207207500   **FI**
Web Site: https://www.capman.com
Year Founded: 1989
CAPMAN—(HEL)
Rev.: $72,881,502
Assets: $291,940,427
Liabilities: $138,536,585
Net Worth: $153,403,842
Earnings: $44,300,669
Emp.: 186
Fiscal Year-end: 12/31/22
Holding Company; Private Equity & Real Estate Investment Services
N.A.I.C.S.: 551112
Andreas Tallberg *(Chm)*

Subsidiaries:

CapMan (Guernsey) Ltd. **(1)**

Hambro House St Julian's Ave, PO Box 86, Saint Peter Port, GY1 3AE, Guernsey
Tel.: (44) 481726521
Web Site: http://www.capman.com
Investment Company
N.A.I.C.S.: 525910

CapMan AB **(1)**
Stureplan 13 3rd fl, PO Box 5745, 111 45, Stockholm, Sweden
Tel.: (46) 841073130
Sales Range: $50-74.9 Million
Emp.: 20
Investment Company
N.A.I.C.S.: 525910

CapMan Capital Management Oy **(1)**
Ludviginkatu 6, 130, Helsinki, Finland **(100%)**
Tel.: (358) 504062254
Privater Equity Firm
N.A.I.C.S.: 523999

Holding (Domestic):

Fortaco Group Oy **(2)**
Plaza Business Park Ayritie 24, 01510, Vantaa, Finland
Tel.: (358) 10 757 6000
Web Site: https://www.fortacogroup.com
Sales Range: $400-449.9 Million
Emp.: 2,600
Material Handling Equipment Mfr
N.A.I.C.S.: 333248
Lars Hellberg *(Pres & CEO)*

Joint Venture (Domestic):

Innofactor Plc **(2)**
Keilaranta 9, FI-02150, Espoo, Finland
Tel.: (358) 102729000
Web Site: https://www.innofactor.com
Rev.: $76,764,515
Assets: $60,236,348
Liabilities: $33,472,912
Net Worth: $26,763,436
Earnings: $3,582,992
Emp.: 564
Fiscal Year-end: 12/31/2022
Software, Digital Document, Business Process Management, Customer-Specific Integration & CRM Solutions
N.A.I.C.S.: 513210
Sami Ensio *(Pres, CEO & Mgr-Finland)*

Affiliate (Non-US):

GAP AG **(3)**
Hospitalstrasse 6, D-99817, Eisenach, Germany **(23%)**
Tel.: (49) 3691886923
Web Site: http://www.gapag.de
Application Software Solutions
N.A.I.C.S.: 423430

Subsidiary (Domestic):

PlanMill Ltd. **(3)**
Hameentie 19, 00500, Helsinki, Finland
Tel.: (358) 10 322 9110
Web Site: https://www.planmill.com
Business Management Services
N.A.I.C.S.: 513210
Thomas Hood *(CEO & Partner)*

Holding (US):

Nansen Inc. **(2)**
150 N Michigan Ave Ste 1950, Chicago, IL 60601-7550
Tel.: (203) 519-2370
Web Site: http://www.nansen.com
Computer Related Services
N.A.I.C.S.: 541519

CapMan Fund Investment SICAV-SIF **(1)**
7A Rue Robert Stumper, 2557, Luxembourg, Luxembourg
Tel.: (352) 26 49 58 42 05
Investment Management Service
N.A.I.C.S.: 523999

CapMan Growth Equity Oy **(1)**
Ludviginkatu 6, 00100, Helsinki, Finland
Tel.: (358) 207207500
Web Site: http://www.capman.com
Investment Services
N.A.I.C.S.: 523999

CapMan Norway AS **(1)**
Dronning Mauds Gt 3, PO Box 1235, 0250, Oslo, Norway **(100%)**
Tel.: (47) 23237575
Web Site: http://www.capman.com
Sales Range: $50-74.9 Million
Emp.: 5
Investment Company
N.A.I.C.S.: 525910

CapMan Private Equity Advisors Limited **(1)**
10 Arbat Str, 119002, Moscow, Russia
Tel.: (7) 4956204885
Web Site: http://www.capman.com
Emp.: 10
Privater Equity Firm
N.A.I.C.S.: 523999
Hans Christian Dall Nygard *(CEO & Sr Partner)*

CapMan Procurement Services (CaPS) Oy **(1)**
Ludviginkatu 6 4 fl, 00130, Helsinki, Finland
Tel.: (358) 400435476
Web Site: https://caps.fi
Internal Procurement Services
N.A.I.C.S.: 541990
Maximilian Marschan *(Founder & Mng Partner)*

CapMan Public Market Manager S.A. **(1)**
7A Rue Robert Stumper, 2557, Luxembourg, Luxembourg
Tel.: (352) 26 49 58 42 05
Sales Range: $50-74.9 Million
Emp.: 1
Venture Capital Services
N.A.I.C.S.: 523910
Sella Komulaimen *(Gen Mgr)*

CapMan Real Estate Denmark, filial av CapMan AB **(1)**
Regnbuepladsen 7 3rd fl, 1551, Copenhagen, Denmark
Tel.: (45) 20435563
Real Estate Development Services
N.A.I.C.S.: 531390

CapMan Real Estate Oy **(1)**
Korkeavuorenkatu 32, 130, Helsinki, Finland
Tel.: (358) 207207500
Real Estate Development Services
N.A.I.C.S.: 531390
Mika Matikainen *(Sr Partner)*

Subsidiary (Domestic):

Dividum Oy **(2)**
Korkeavuorenkatu 32, 00100, Helsinki, Finland
Tel.: (358) 207207500
Sales Range: $50-74.9 Million
Emp.: 100
Real Estate Development Services
N.A.I.C.S.: 531390
Lennart Simonsen *(CEO)*

CapMan Sweden AB **(1)**
Box 5745, 114 87, Stockholm, Sweden
Tel.: (46) 854585470
Equity Fund Management Services
N.A.I.C.S.: 523940

JAY Solutions Oy **(1)**
Urho Kekkosen katu 2c, 00100, Helsinki, Finland
Tel.: (358) 504062254
Web Site: https://jaysolutions.com
Financial Services
N.A.I.C.S.: 523999
Jaakko Leikko *(CTO)*

CAPMONT GMBH

Prinzregentenstrasse 56, 80538, Munich, Germany
Tel.: (49) 89954296150
Web Site: https://www.cmont.com
Privater Equity Firm
N.A.I.C.S.: 523940

CAPPELLE PIGNENES N.V.

Kortrijkstraat 153, Menen, 8930, Belgium
Tel.: (32) 56521200   **BE**
Web Site: http://www.cappelle.be

Year Founded: 1890
Sales Range: $10-24.9 Million
Emp.: 250
Pigment Sales
N.A.I.C.S.: 424950
Philippe Verhelle *(Dir-Translation Svcs)*

Subsidiaries:

Cappelle Freres (UK) Ltd. **(1)**
PO Box 2, 77A London Rd., Grays, RM17 5YY, Essex, United Kingdom
Tel.: (44) 1375384084
Mfr of Pigments for Paint, Printing Ink & Plastics Industries
N.A.I.C.S.: 325180

Cappelle Inc. **(1)**
PO Box 169, Alpharetta, GA 30009
Tel.: (770) 663-8226
Web Site: http://www.Cappelle.de
Mfr of Pigments for Paint, Printing Ink & Plastics Industries
N.A.I.C.S.: 325180
John Heiskell *(Office Mgr)*

Gebroeders Cappelle Freres S.A.R.L. **(1)**
Kortrijkstraat 115, 8930, Menen, Belgium
Tel.: (32) 56511801
Web Site: http://www.cappelle.be
Mfr of Pigments for Paint, Printing Ink & Plastics Industries
N.A.I.C.S.: 325180

CAPRAL LIMITED

71 Ashburn Road, Bundamba, 4304, QLD, Australia
Tel.: (61) 738167000   **AU**
Web Site: https://www.capral.com.au
Year Founded: 1938
CAA—(ASX)
Rev.: $447,421,157
Assets: $289,626,047
Liabilities: $150,172,332
Net Worth: $139,453,716
Earnings: $21,687,215
Emp.: 1,100
Fiscal Year-end: 12/31/23
Rolling Mill, Extrusion, Aluminum Plant & Smelter
N.A.I.C.S.: 331318
Tertius Campbell *(CFO)*

Subsidiaries:

Austex Dies Pty Limited **(1)**
13 Montore Road, Minto, 2560, NSW, Australia
Tel.: (61) 29 820 0300
Web Site: https://www.austexdies.com
Aluminum Extruded Product Mfr
N.A.I.C.S.: 331313
Alessandro Ferrari *(Mng Dir)*

Capral Aluminium-Sheets **(1)**
71 Ashburn Road, PO Box 12, Bundamba, 4304, QLD, Australia **(100%)**
Tel.: (61) 73 816 7000
Web Site: https://www.capral.com.au
Sales Range: $25-49.9 Million
Emp.: 50
N.A.I.C.S.: 331318

National Aluminium Limited **(1)**
49 Business Parade North, East Tamaki, Auckland, 2013, New Zealand
Tel.: (64) 92721700
Web Site: https://altus.co.nz
Sales Range: $100-124.9 Million
Emp.: 80
N.A.I.C.S.: 331318

CAPRI GLOBAL CAPITAL LIMITED

502 Tower A Peninsula Business Park Senapati Bapat Marg, Lower Parel, Mumbai, 400013, India
Tel.: (91) 2240888100
Web Site: https://www.capriloans.in
Year Founded: 1997
531595—(BOM)
Rev.: $199,972,091
Assets: $1,609,964,948

Capri Global Capital Limited—(Continued)

Liabilities: $1,123,278,839
Net Worth: $486,686,109
Earnings: $27,935,271
Emp.: 7,900
Fiscal Year-end: 03/31/23
Investment Banking Services
N.A.I.C.S.: 523150
Rajesh Sharma *(Mng Dir)*

CAPRI HOLDINGS LIMITED

33 Kingsway, London, WC2B 6UF,
United Kingdom
Tel.: (44) 2076328600   VG
Web Site:
    http://www.capriholdings.com
CPRI—(NYSE)
Rev.: $5,170,000,000
Assets: $6,689,000,000
Liabilities: $5,089,000,000
Net Worth: $1,600,000,000
Earnings: ($229,000,000)
Emp.: 10,200
Fiscal Year-end: 03/30/24
Holding Company; Women's & Men's
Fashion Apparel & Accessories De-
signer & Retailer
N.A.I.C.S.: 551112
John D. Idol *(Chm & CEO)*

Subsidiaries:

Gianni Versace S.p.A   **(1)**
Via Montenapoleone11, 20121, Milan, MI,
Italy   **(100%)**
Tel.: (39) 0276008528
Web Site: https://www.versace.com
Apparel & Accessories Mfr
N.A.I.C.S.: 315990
Jonathan Akeroyd *(CEO)*

Jimmy Choo PLC   **(1)**
10 Howick Place, London, SW1P 1GW,
United Kingdom
Tel.: (44) 2073685000
Web Site: http://www.us.jimmychoo.com
Designer Shoes & Handbags Mfr
N.A.I.C.S.: 316210
Hannah Colman *(CEO)*

MK Holetown (Barbados) Inc.   **(1)**
Limegrove Lifestyle Centre Holetown St
James, Holetown, BB24016, Barbados
Tel.: (246) 2466210470
Clothes & Accessories Retailer
N.A.I.C.S.: 458110

Michael Kors (Austria) GmbH   **(1)**
Tel.: (43) 216622271
Emp.: 2
Women's & Men's Fashion Apparel & Ac-
cessories Retailer
N.A.I.C.S.: 458110

Michael Kors (Bucharest Store)
S.R.L.   **(1)**
Baneasa Shopping City Soseaua Bucuresti-
Ploiesti 42d Unit 20, 13696, Bucharest,
013696, Romania
Tel.: (40) 314361163
Web Site: https://www.michaelkors.eu
Fragrance Product Mfr
N.A.I.C.S.: 316210

Michael Kors (Canada) Co.   **(1)**
9600 Rue Meilleur, Montreal, H2N 2E3, QC,
Canada
Tel.: (514) 383-4141
Web Site: http://www.michael-
korscanada.com
Women's & Men's Fashion Apparel & Ac-
cessories Retailer
N.A.I.C.S.: 458110

Michael Kors (Czech Republic)
s.r.o.   **(1)**
Centrum Chodov - Roztylsk 2321/19, 148
00, Prague, 11, Czech Republic
Tel.: (420) 226203261
Web Site: https://www.michaelkors.eu
Clothing Apparel Distr
N.A.I.C.S.: 458110
Dianoa Vanzarova *(Gen Mgr)*

Michael Kors (Germany) GmbH   **(1)**

Theatiner Strasse 36, 80333, Munich, Ger-
many
Tel.: (49) 8945205100
Sales Range: $25-49.9 Million
Emp.: 5
Women's & Men's Fashion Apparel & Ac-
cessories Retailer
N.A.I.C.S.: 458110

Michael Kors (Netherlands) B.V.   **(1)**
Herikerbergweg 238-Luna Arena, 1101 CM,
Amsterdam, Netherlands
Tel.: (31) 205755600
Women's & Men's Fashion Apparel & Ac-
cessories Retailer
N.A.I.C.S.: 458110

Michael Kors (Switzerland)
GmbH   **(1)**
Strada Regina 42, 6934, Bioggio, Switzer-
land
Tel.: (41) 91 910 11 11
Women's & Men's Fashion Apparel & Ac-
cessories Retailer
N.A.I.C.S.: 458110

Michael Kors (UK) Limited   **(1)**
90 Whitfield Street, London, W1T 4EZ,
United Kingdom
Tel.: (44) 8003580598
Web Site: https://www.michaelkors.co.uk
Emp.: 3
Women's & Men's Fashion Apparel & Ac-
cessories Retailer
N.A.I.C.S.: 458110

Michael Kors (USA), Inc.   **(1)**
11 W 42nd St, New York, NY 10036
Tel.: (212) 201-8100
Holding Company; Regional Managing Of-
fice; Women's & Men's Fashion Apparel &
Accessories Designer & Retailer
N.A.I.C.S.: 551112
Joshua Schulman *(CEO)*

Subsidiary (Domestic):

Michael Kors, LLC   **(2)**
11 W 42nd St, New York, NY 10036
Tel.: (212) 201-8100
Web Site: http://www.michaelkors.com
Rev.: $30,600,000
Emp.: 160
Women's & Men's Clothing & Accessories
Designer & Retailer
N.A.I.C.S.: 541400
Michael Kors *(Chief Creative Officer)*

Subsidiary (Domestic):

Michael Kors Retail, Inc.   **(3)**
11 W 42nd St, New York, NY 10036
Tel.: (212) 201-8100
Holding Company; Women's & Men's Fash-
ion Apparel & Accessories Retailer
N.A.I.C.S.: 551112

Subsidiary (Domestic):

Michael Kors Stores (California),
Inc.   **(4)**
1 Meadowlands Plz 12th Fl, East Ruther-
ford, NJ 07073
Tel.: (201) 453-5069
Women's & Men's Fashion Apparel & Ac-
cessories Retailer
N.A.I.C.S.: 458110

Michael Kors Stores, LLC   **(4)**
11 W 42nd St, New York, NY 10036
Tel.: (212) 201-8100
Web Site: http://www.michaelkors.com
Women's & Men's Fashion Apparel & Ac-
cessories Retailer
N.A.I.C.S.: 458110

Michael Kors Belgium BVBA   **(1)**
Zetellaan 137, 3630, Maasmechelen, Bel-
gium
Tel.: (32) 89723588
Women's & Men's Fashion Apparel & Ac-
cessories Retailer
N.A.I.C.S.: 458110

Michael Kors Italy S.R.L.   **(1)**
Emp.: 24
Women's & Men's Fashion Apparel & Ac-
cessories Retailer
N.A.I.C.S.: 458110

Michael Kors Japan K.K.   **(1)**

4-11-6 Jingumae, Tokyo, Japan
Tel.: (81) 357725325
Women's & Men's Fashion Apparel & Ac-
cessories Retailer
N.A.I.C.S.: 458110
Daisuke Yamazaki *(Pres)*

Michael Kors Limited   **(1)**
Rm 1001 10/F Miramar Twr 132 Nathan Rd,
Tsim Tsa Tsui, China (Hong Kong)
Tel.: (852) 39285559
Women's & Men's Fashion Apparel & Ac-
cessories Retailer
N.A.I.C.S.: 458110

Michael Kors Spain, S.L.   **(1)**
Calle Serrano 32, 28001, Madrid, Spain
Tel.: (34) 917813157
Jean Apparel Mfr
N.A.I.C.S.: 315250

Versace Australia Pty Limited   **(1)**
Shop 2 161 Collins Street, Melbourne,
3000, VIC, Australia
Tel.: (61) 383064628
Clothes & Accessories Retailer
N.A.I.C.S.: 458110

Versace Austria GmbH   **(1)**
Trattnerhof 1, 1010, Vienna, Austria
Tel.: (43) 15332531
Clothes & Accessories Retailer
N.A.I.C.S.: 458110

Versace Belgique SA   **(1)**
Boulevard De Waterloo 7, 1000, Brussels,
Belgium
Tel.: (32) 25118559
Clothes & Accessories Retailer
N.A.I.C.S.: 458110

Versace Canada, Inc.   **(1)**
106 Yorkville Avenue, Toronto, M5R 1B9,
ON, Canada
Tel.: (647) 954-1800
Clothes & Accessories Retailer
N.A.I.C.S.: 458110

Versace Deutschland GmbH   **(1)**
Goethestrasse 22, 60313, Frankfurt, Ger-
many
Tel.: (49) 6921657997
Clothes & Accessories Retailer
N.A.I.C.S.: 458110

Versace France S.A.   **(1)**
45 Avenue Montaigne, 75008, Paris, France
Tel.: (33) 147428802
Clothes & Accessories Retailer
N.A.I.C.S.: 458110

Versace Monte-Carlo S.A.M.   **(1)**
Allee Francois Blanc Casino De Montecarlo,
98000, Monte Carlo, Monaco
Tel.: (377) 97987155
Clothes & Accessories Retailer
N.A.I.C.S.: 458110

CAPRICE RESOURCES LIM-ITED

Level 2 7 Havelock Street, West
Perth, 6005, WA, Australia
Tel.: (61) 861413136   AU
Web Site:
    https://www.capriceresources.com
Year Founded: 2018
CRS—(ASX)
Rev.: $8,826
Assets: $11,885,440
Liabilities: $958,830
Net Worth: $10,926,610
Earnings: ($1,035,196)
Fiscal Year-end: 06/30/24
Support Activities for Metal Mining
N.A.I.C.S.: 213114
Oonagh Malone *(Sec)*

CAPRICORN ENERGY PLC

50 Lothian Road, Edinburgh, EH3
9BY, United Kingdom
Tel.: (44) 1314753000   UK
Web Site:
    https://www.capricornenergy.com
CRNCY—(OTCIQ)
Rev.: $394,700,000
Assets: $1,635,300,000

Liabilities: $509,700,000
Net Worth: $1,125,600,000
Earnings: ($393,800,000)
Emp.: 204
Fiscal Year-end: 12/31/20
Explorer & Producer of Oil & Gas
N.A.I.C.S.: 211120
Nicoletta Giadrossi *(Chm)*

Subsidiaries:

Cairn Energy Hydrocarbons
Limited   **(1)**
50 Lothian Rd, Edinburgh, EH3 9BY, Scot-
land, United Kingdom
Tel.: (44) 1314753000
Web Site: http://www.carinenergy.com
Oil & Gas Exploration Services
N.A.I.C.S.: 211120

Cairn Energy Lumbini Limited   **(1)**
50 Lothian Road, Edinburgh, EH3 9BY,
United Kingdom
Tel.: (44) 1314753030
Sales Range: $100-124.9 Million
Oil & Gas Exploration Services
N.A.I.C.S.: 213112

Cairn UK Holdings Limited   **(1)**
50 Lothian Road, Edinburgh, EH3 9BY,
United Kingdom   **(100%)**
Tel.: (44) 131 475 3000
Web Site: http://www.cairnenergy.com
Holding Company
N.A.I.C.S.: 551112

Capricorn Americas Mexico S. de
R.L. de C.V.   **(1)**
Torre Mayor Avenida de la Reforma 505
Piso 36, Colonia, 06500, Cuauhtemoc,
Mexico
Tel.: (52) 551 328 7900
Oil & Gas Exploration Services
N.A.I.C.S.: 213112

Capricorn Energy Limited   **(1)**
50 Lothian Road, Edinburgh, EH3 9BY,
United Kingdom
Tel.: (44) 1314753000
Holding Company; Oil & Gas Exploration
Services
N.A.I.C.S.: 551112

UAH Limited   **(1)**
4th Floor Wellington House 125 Strand,
London, WC2R 0AP, United Kingdom
Tel.: (44) 208 049 7620
Oil & Gas Exploration Services
N.A.I.C.S.: 213111

CAPRICORN INVESTMENT PARTNERS LIMITED

Suncorp House Suite 1B 103 Bols-
over Street, PO Box 564, Rockhamp-
ton, 4700, QLD, Australia
Tel.: (61) 7 4920 4600
Web Site:
    http://www.capinvest.com.au
Investment Advisory Services
N.A.I.C.S.: 523940
David French *(Chm)*

Subsidiaries:

The Pentad Group Pty. Ltd.   **(1)**
4 Prospect Hill Road, Camberwell, 3124,
VIC, Australia
Tel.: (61) 3 9813 0133
Web Site: http://www.pentad.com.au
Emp.: 30
Financial Planning Services
N.A.I.C.S.: 523940
Christopher Heyworth *(Principal)*

CAPRICORN METALS LTD.

Level 3 40 Kings Park Road, West
Perth, 6005, WA, Australia
Tel.: (61) 892124600   AU
Web Site:
    https://www.capmetals.com.au
CMM—(ASX)
Rev.: $240,273,770
Assets: $416,372,194
Liabilities: $209,865,117
Net Worth: $206,507,077

Earnings: $58,185,096
Emp.: 134
Fiscal Year-end: 06/30/24
Gold Exploration Services
N.A.I.C.S.: 212220
Stephen Evans (Gen Mgr-Operations)

CAPRICORN SOCIETY LIMITED
28 Troode Street, West Perth, 6005, WA, Australia
Tel.: (61) 8 6250 9500
Web Site: http://www.capricorn.coop
Rev.: $72,572,903
Assets: $290,055,917
Liabilities: $141,740,476
Net Worth: $148,315,441
Earnings: $14,275,249
Emp.: 200
Fiscal Year-end: 06/30/19
Automobile Service Stations
N.A.I.C.S.: 811111
Bradley Gannon (CEO-Automotive)

CAPRICORN SYSTEMS GLOBAL SOLUTIONS LIMITED
8-2-686/B/6/401 4th Floor 12th Square Building Road Number 12, Banjara Hills, Hyderabad, 500034, India
Tel.: (91) 4023399499   In
Web Site: https://www.capricornsys-global.com
Year Founded: 1985
512169—(BOM)
Rev.: $180,259
Assets: $518,600
Liabilities: $41,964
Net Worth: $476,636
Earnings: ($59,642)
Emp.: 6
Fiscal Year-end: 03/31/21
Software Development Services
N.A.I.C.S.: 541511
Madhav Rao Dundigalla (CFO & Compliance Officer)

CAPRO CORP.
12 F Baeksang Building 12 insadong 7 gil, Jangno-gu, Seoul, 110-300, Korea (South)
Tel.: (82) 23991200
Web Site: https://www.hcccapro.co.kr
Year Founded: 1969
006380—(KRS)
Rev.: $327,652,676
Assets: $231,791,689
Liabilities: $211,387,388
Net Worth: $20,404,300
Earnings: ($142,820,509)
Emp.: 204
Fiscal Year-end: 12/31/22
Caprolactam, Ammonium Sulfate & Inorganic Fertilizers Producer
N.A.I.C.S.: 325314
Yoo Ik-Sang (Pres & CEO)

CAPROCK MINING CORP.
77 King Street West Suite 2905, Toronto, M5K 1H1, ON, Canada
Tel.: (647) 466-0506   ON
Web Site: https://www.caprockmining.com
Year Founded: 2020
CAPR—(CNSX)
Mining Services
N.A.I.C.S.: 212210
Vishal Gupta (Pres & CEO)

CAPROLACTAM CHEMICALS LIMITED
B-31 Mahad Industrial Area MIDC, Raigad, Mahad, 402302, Maharashtra, India
Tel.: (91) 2145233427
Web Site: https://www.caprolactam.in

Year Founded: 1992
507486—(BOM)
Rev.: $873,904
Assets: $954,588
Liabilities: $397,649
Net Worth: $556,939
Earnings: $88,802
Fiscal Year-end: 03/31/21
Specialty Chemicals Mfr
N.A.I.C.S.: 325998
Zaver S. Bhanushali (Chm & Mng Dir)

CAPSENSIXX AG
Bettinastrasse 57-59, 60325, Frankfurt am Main, 60325, Germany
Tel.: (49) 6924747990
Web Site: https://www.capsensixx.de
Year Founded: 2001
CPX—(MUN)
Assets: $53,051,992
Liabilities: $34,981,640
Net Worth: $18,070,352
Earnings: $3,256,416
Emp.: 118
Fiscal Year-end: 12/31/23
Investment Management Service
N.A.I.C.S.: 523940

CAPSTONE COPPER CORP.
510 West Georgia Street Suite 2100, Vancouver, V6B 0M3, BC, Canada
Tel.: (604) 684-8894
Web Site: https://capstonecopper.com
CS—(TSX)
Copper Mining Services
N.A.I.C.S.: 212230

CAPSTONE SYSTEMS, INC.
42nd FL Hanzhong Str 1 Qinhuai District, International Financial Center, Nanjing, 210005, Jiangsu, China
Tel.: (86) 25 57625881   NV
Year Founded: 2015
CPSN—(OTCIQ)
Sales Range: Less than $1 Million
Kitchen Sinks & Cabinets Distr
N.A.I.C.S.: 423210
Xiuping Fang (Chm, Pres, CEO, CFO, Chief Acctg Officer, Treas & Sec)

CAPSTONE TECHNOLOGIES GROUP INC.
No 2 Longbao Street Xiaodian zone, Taiyuan, 030031, Shanxi, China
Tel.: (86) 3517963988   NV
Web Site: http://www.chinabilingualedu.com
Year Founded: 2009
CATG—(OTCIQ)
Assets: $156,674
Liabilities: $277,907
Net Worth: ($121,233)
Earnings: ($122,956)
Emp.: 2
Fiscal Year-end: 08/31/21
Education Services
N.A.I.C.S.: 611710

CAPTAIN PIPES LTD.
Survey No 257 Plot No 23 to 28 NH27 Captain Gate, Shapar Veraval, Rajkot, 360024, Gujarat, India
Tel.: (91) 9909029066
Web Site: https://www.captainpipes.com
Year Founded: 2010
538817—(BOM)
Rev.: $11,326,552
Assets: $4,771,535
Liabilities: $2,601,349
Net Worth: $2,170,186
Earnings: $700,463
Emp.: 41

Fiscal Year-end: 03/31/22
Pipes & Piping Products Mfr
N.A.I.C.S.: 326122
Gopal D. Khichadia (Mng Dir)

CAPTAIN POLYPLAST LTD.
Survey No 267 Plot No 10A and 11 NH 27 Captain Gate, Shapar Veraval, Rajkot, 360024, Gujarat, India
Tel.: (91) 2827253006
Web Site: https://www.captainpolyplast.com
536974—(BOM)
Rev.: $25,547,026
Assets: $28,854,530
Liabilities: $19,814,982
Net Worth: $9,039,549
Earnings: $376,180
Emp.: 308
Fiscal Year-end: 03/31/22
HDPE Pipes & Irrigation Equipment Mfr & Distr
N.A.I.C.S.: 326122
Ramesh D. Khichadia (Chm & Mng Dir)

CAPTAIN TECHNOCAST LIMITED
Survey No 257 Plot No 4 6/9 National Highway-27 At-Shapar, Veraval Dist, Rajkot, 360 024, Gujarat, India
Tel.: (91) 2827252411   In
Web Site: https://www.captaintechnocast.com
Year Founded: 2010
540652—(BOM)
Rev.: $6,967,315
Assets: $5,565,105
Liabilities: $3,152,317
Net Worth: $2,412,788
Earnings: $374,829
Emp.: 122
Fiscal Year-end: 03/31/22
Industrial Metal Parts Mfr & Distr
N.A.I.C.S.: 331512
Ramesh D. Khichadia (Chm)

CAPTII LIMITED
140 Paya Lebar Road No 10-14 AZ Paya Lebar, Singapore, 409015, Singapore
Tel.: (65) 62977100
Web Site: https://www.captii.com
Year Founded: 1998
AWV—(SES)
Rev.: $13,846,096
Assets: $36,412,179
Liabilities: $4,095,281
Net Worth: $32,316,898
Earnings: ($8,874,498)
Emp.: 190
Fiscal Year-end: 12/31/23
Holding Company
N.A.I.C.S.: 551112
Tze Leng Wong (Chm)

Subsidiaries:

GlobeOSS (Brunei) Sdn. Bhd.   (1)
8th Floor PGGMB Building Jalan Kianggeh, BS8111, Bandar Seri Begawan, Brunei Darussalam
Tel.: (673) 2367033
Software Development Services
N.A.I.C.S.: 541511

GlobeOSS Pte Ltd   (1)
140 Payar Lebar Road 10-14 AZ Payar Lebar, Payar Lebar, Singapore, 409015, Singapore
Tel.: (65) 6 297 7100
Web Site: http://www.unifiedcomms.com
Business Management Services
N.A.I.C.S.: 561110

GlobeOSS Sdn Bhd   (1)
Unit No 3B-08-01 Level 8 Tower 3B UOA Business Park Shah Alam, No 1 Jalan Pengaturcara U1/51A Seksyen U1, 40150, Shah Alam, Selangor, Malaysia

Tel.: (60) 35 569 8856
Web Site: https://www.globeoss.com
Sales Range: $10-24.9 Million
Emp.: 40
Business Management Services
N.A.I.C.S.: 561110
Wan Kuan Ann (CEO)

Unified Communications Pte Ltd   (1)
140 Paya Lebar Rd Unit 10-14 Az paya Lebar, Singapore, 409015, Singapore
Tel.: (65) 62977100
Sales Range: $25-49.9 Million
Emp.: 9
Telecommunication Servicesb
N.A.I.C.S.: 517111
Ting Fei Ho (Grp Head-Bus Dev)

CAPTIVA VERDE WELLNESS CORP.
632 Foster Avenue, Coquitlam, V3J 2L7, BC, Canada
Tel.: (949) 903-5906   BC
Year Founded: 2015
CPIVF—(OTCIQ)
Assets: $7,632,537
Liabilities: $1,430,402
Net Worth: $6,202,135
Earnings: ($2,835,947)
Fiscal Year-end: 10/31/22
Real Estate Investment Services
N.A.I.C.S.: 531210

CAPTIVISION INC.
Unit 18B Nailsworth Mills Estate Avening Road, Nailsworth, GL6 0BS, United Kingdom
Tel.: (44) 1865688221   Ky
Year Founded: 2023
CAPT—(NASDAQ)
Emp.: 98
Glass Products Mfr
N.A.I.C.S.: 327215

CAPTOR CAPITAL CORP.
4 King Street West Suite 401, Toronto, M5H 1B6, ON, Canada
Tel.: (416) 504-3978   ON
Web Site: https://www.captorcapital.com
Year Founded: 2003
NMV—(DEU)
Rev.: $27,159,632
Assets: $25,008,847
Liabilities: $21,248,831
Net Worth: $3,760,016
Earnings: ($11,919,367)
Fiscal Year-end: 03/31/24
Investment & Merchant Banking Services
N.A.I.C.S.: 523999
John Zorbas (Pres)

Subsidiaries:

Chai Cannabis Co. Inc.   (1)
10665 Merritt St, Castroville, CA 95012
Tel.: (831) 453-7180
Web Site: http://www.chaicannabis.com
Cannabis Product Retailer
N.A.I.C.S.: 459999

CAPTOR THERAPEUTICS S.A.
Dunska 11, 54 427, Wroclaw, Poland
Tel.: (48) 537869089   PL
Web Site: https://www.captortherapeutics.com
Year Founded: 2015
CTX—(WAR)
Rev.: $3,316,334
Assets: $24,442,044
Liabilities: $7,052,706
Net Worth: $17,389,338
Earnings: ($17,732,000)
Emp.: 104
Fiscal Year-end: 12/31/23
Biotechnology Research & Development Services
N.A.I.C.S.: 541714

Captor Therapeutics S.A.—(Continued)

Michal Walczak *(Chief Scientific Officer)*

CAPTURE
22a Leathermarket Street, London, FE1 3HP, United Kingdom
Tel.: (44) 20 3553 5555
Web Site:
    http://www.capturemarketing.co.uk
Year Founded: 2008
Sales Range: $10-24.9 Million
Emp.: 42
Digital Marketing Services
N.A.I.C.S.: 541613
Matt Lee *(Co-Founder)*

CAPULA LIMITED
Orion House, Stone Business Park, Stone, ST15 0LT, Staffordshire, United Kingdom
Tel.: (44) 1785827000   UK
Web Site: http://www.capula.co.uk
Year Founded: 1969
Information Technology Systems for Nuclear, Power Generation & Utilities Markets
N.A.I.C.S.: 541512
Mark Hardy *(Mng Dir)*

Subsidiaries:

Capula Nuclear   (1)
1414 Charlton Court Gloucester Business Park, Gloucester, GL3 4AE, United Kingdom
Tel.: (44) 1452650000
Web Site: http://www.capulanuclear.co.uk
Information Technology Consulting Services
N.A.I.C.S.: 541512
Natalie Smalley *(Head-Bus Sector)*

CAPVEST LIMITED
100 Pall Mall, London, SW1Y 5NQ, United Kingdom
Tel.: (44) 2073897900   UK
Web Site: http://www.capvest.com
Year Founded: 1999
Privater Equity Firm
N.A.I.C.S.: 523999
Seamus Philip FitzPatrick *(Mng Partner)*

Subsidiaries:

Brownie Brittle, LLC   (1)
2253 Vista Pkwy #8, West Palm Beach, FL 33411
Web Site: http://www.browniebrittle.com
Sales Range: $10-24.9 Million
Cookie Mfr
N.A.I.C.S.: 311821
Jan Grywczynski *(CEO)*

CapVest Partners LLP   (1)
100 Pall Mall St. James's, London, SW1Y 5NQ, United Kingdom
Tel.: (44) 2073897900
Web Site: https://www.capvest.com
Investment Services
N.A.I.C.S.: 523999

Holding (US):

Datasite LLC   (2)
Baker Ctr 733 S Marquette Ave Ste 600, Minneapolis, MN 55402
Tel.: (888) 311-4100
Web Site: https://www.datasite.com
Software Development Services
N.A.I.C.S.: 513210

Cardinal Foods AS   (1)
Brynsveien 5, 0667, Oslo, Norway   (52%)
Tel.: (47) 22 72 88 60
Web Site: http://www.cardinalfoods.no
Sales Range: $200-249.9 Million
Emp.: 300
Poultry Products & Eggs Producer & Distr
N.A.I.C.S.: 112390
Torfinn Prytz Higdem *(CEO)*

Karro Food Group Limited   (1)
Hugden Way, Malton, YO17 9HG, N York-

shire, United Kingdom
Tel.: (44) 1653693031
Web Site: http://www.karro.co.uk
Pork Food Products
N.A.I.C.S.: 112210
Mike Roberts *(Dir-Technical)*

Subsidiary (Domestic):

Young's Seafood Limited   (2)
Hoss House Wickham Road, Grimsby, DN31 3SW, United Kingdom
Tel.: (44) 1472 585858
Web Site: http://www.youngsseafood.co.uk
Fresh, Frozen, Own-label & Branded Fish Products & Frozen Seafood Distr
N.A.I.C.S.: 424460
Marina Richardson *(Controller-Mktg)*

Recochem Group, Inc.   (1)
8725 Holgate Crescent, Milton, L9T 5G7, ON, Canada
Tel.: (905) 878-5544
Web Site: http://www.recochem.com
Chemical Products Mfr
N.A.I.C.S.: 325998
Fred Moudy *(Gen Mgr-Ops)*

Subsidiary (US):

Paint Over Rust Products, Inc.   (2)
64 S Jefferson Rd, Whippany, NJ 07981
Tel.: (973) 887-1999
Web Site: http://www.por15.com
Sales Range: $1-9.9 Million
Emp.: 25
Miscellaneous Chemical Product & Preparation Mfr
N.A.I.C.S.: 325998
Tom Slutsker *(Pres & CEO)*

Second Nature Brands, Inc.   (1)
1200 E 14 Mile Rd, Madison Heights, MI 48071
Tel.: (800) 527-6887
Web Site:
    https://secondnaturebrandsus.com
Snack & Treats Products Mfr
N.A.I.C.S.: 311919
Victor Mehren *(CEO)*

Valeo Foods Ltd.   (1)
Merrywell Industrial Estate, Ballymount, Dublin, 12, Ireland
Tel.: (353) 14051500
Web Site: https://valeofoods.ie
Grocery Product Mfr & Whslr
N.A.I.C.S.: 311421
Ian Ainsworth *(Mng Dir-UK)*

Subsidiary (Non-US):

Bakery Foods Limited   (2)
Heanor Gate Road, Heanor, DE75 7RJ, Derbs, United Kingdom
Tel.: (44) 1773760121
Web Site:
    http://www.matthewwalkerpuddings.co.uk
Sales Range: $25-49.9 Million
Emp.: 200
Christmas Puddings Mfr
N.A.I.C.S.: 311999

Subsidiary (Domestic):

Batchelors Ltd.   (2)
72 74 Bannow Rd Cabra W, PO Box 88, Dublin, 7, Ireland
Tel.: (353) 18380133
Web Site: http://www.batchelors.ie
Sales Range: $25-49.9 Million
Canned Vegetables & Fruit Juice & Distr
N.A.I.C.S.: 311422
Seamus Kearney *(Mng Dir)*

Subsidiary (Non-US):

Fox's Confectionery Limited   (2)
Sunningdale Road, Braunstone, Leicester, LE3 1UE, United Kingdom
Tel.: (44) 116 287 3561
Web Site: http://www.bigbearuk.com
Confectionery Mfr
N.A.I.C.S.: 311340

Irish Biscuits (N.I.) Limited   (2)
PO Box 3, Hillsborough, Co Down, United Kingdom
Tel.: (44) 2892682644
Biscuits, Food & Drinks Products Distr

N.A.I.C.S.: 445298

Tangerine Confectionery Ltd.   (2)
Quality House, Vicarage Lane, Blackpool, FY4 4NQ, United Kingdom
Tel.: (44) 1253761201
Web Site: http://www.tangerineuk.net
Sales Range: $250-299.9 Million
Emp.: 150
Confectionery Mfr
N.A.I.C.S.: 311340
Steven Joseph *(Chm)*

Division (Domestic):

Tangerine Confectionery Ltd. - Lion Confectionery Division   (3)
Westgate, Cleckheaton, BD19 5EB, W Yorkshire, United Kingdom
Tel.: (44) 274872537
Web Site: http://www.tangerineuk.net
Sales Range: $25-49.9 Million
Emp.: 70
Confectionery Mfr
N.A.I.C.S.: 311352

CAPVIS AG
Grabenstrasse 17, 6340, Baar, Switzerland
Tel.: (41) 433005858   CH
Web Site: http://www.capvis.com
Investment Management Service
N.A.I.C.S.: 523940
Marc Battenfeld *(Partner & Head-Risk Mgmt)*

Subsidiaries:

Amann Girrbach AG   (1)
Herrschaftswiesen 1, 6842, Koblach, Austria
Tel.: (43) 5523 62333 200
Web Site: http://www.amanngirrbach.com
Dental Equipment & Supplies Mfr
N.A.I.C.S.: 339114

Subsidiary (US):

Amann Girrbach America Inc.   (2)
5265 Pkwy Plz Blvd, Charlotte, NC 28217-1967
Tel.: (210) 262-7306
Web Site: http://www.amanngirrbach.com
Dental Equipment & Supplies Mfr
N.A.I.C.S.: 339114
Robert Maietta *(Treas)*

Subsidiary (Non-US):

Amann Girrbach Asia Pte. Ltd.   (2)
80 Anson Road 25-06 Fuji Xerox Towers, Singapore, 079907, Singapore
Tel.: (65) 6592 5190
Dental Equipment & Supplies Mfr
N.A.I.C.S.: 339114

Amann Girrbach Brasil Ltda.   (2)
Av Marechal Floriano Peixoto, 2590, Reboucas, Brazil
Tel.: (55) 41 3287 0897
Dental Equipment & Supplies Mfr
N.A.I.C.S.: 339114

Amann Girrbach China Co., Ltd.   (2)
3A Building B Golden Resources Business Center, No 2 Lan Dian Chang East Road Haidian District, 100097, Beijing, China
Tel.: (86) 10 8886 6064 800
Web Site: http://www.amammgirrbach.com
Dental Equipment & Supplies Mfr
N.A.I.C.S.: 339114

Amann Girrbach GmbH   (2)
Durrenweg 40, 75177, Pforzheim, Germany
Tel.: (49) 7231 957 100
Dental Equipment & Supplies Mfr
N.A.I.C.S.: 339114

Hennecke GmbH   (1)
Birlinghovener Strasse 30, Saint Augustin, 53757, Germany   (100%)
Tel.: (49) 22413390
Web Site: http://www.hennecke.com
Emp.: 500
Polyurethane Materials & Products Mfr
N.A.I.C.S.: 326150

Subsidiary (US):

Hennecke Inc. Polyurethane Technology   (2)

1000 Energy Dr, Bridgeville, PA 15017
Tel.: (724) 271-3686
Web Site: http://www.hennecke.com
Polyurethane Products Mfr
N.A.I.C.S.: 326150

ProXES GmbH   (1)
Stephanplatz 2, 31789, Hameln, Germany
Tel.: (49) 5151 583 0
Web Site: http://www.proxes-group.com
Holding Company; Processing Technologies Designer, Mfr & Whslr
N.A.I.C.S.: 551112
Bernd F. Kessler *(Chm)*

Subsidiary (Non-US):

FrymaKoruma AG   (2)
Theodorshofweg 6, 4310, Rheinfelden, Switzerland
Tel.: (41) 61 836 4141
Web Site: http://www.frymakoruma.com
Processing & Packaging Machinery Mfr & Whslr
N.A.I.C.S.: 333998
Markus Schroder *(CEO)*

Subsidiary (Domestic):

ProXES Technology GmbH   (2)
Fischerstrasse 10, 79395, Neuenburg, Germany
Tel.: (49) 763170670
Web Site: http://www.frymakoruma.com
Processing & Packaging Machinery Whslr
N.A.I.C.S.: 423830

Stephan Machinery GmbH   (2)
Stephanplatz 2, 31789, Hameln, Germany
Tel.: (49) 5151 583 0
Web Site: http://www.stephan-machinery.com
Food Processing Machinery Designer, Mfr & Whslr
N.A.I.C.S.: 333241
Olaf Pehmoller *(Chm-Mgmt Bd & CEO)*

Wer liefert was GmbH   (1)
ABC Strasse 21, 20354, Hamburg, Germany
Tel.: (49) 40 254 40 0
Web Site: http://www.wlw.de
Business Information Services
N.A.I.C.S.: 519290
Peter F Schmid *(Mng Dir)*

CAPXON INTERNATIONAL ELECTRONIC CO LTD
Room 1303 13th Floor OfficePlus Wan Chai No 303 Hennessy Road, Wanchai, China (Hong Kong)
Tel.: (852) 25981308
Web Site:
    http://www.capxongroup.com
Rev.: $195,740,909
Assets: $232,735,407
Liabilities: $128,218,888
Net Worth: $104,516,519
Earnings: $13,243,476
Emp.: 2,348
Fiscal Year-end: 12/31/19
Capacitor Mfr
N.A.I.C.S.: 335999
Yin Fung Chan *(Sec & Controller-Fin)*

Subsidiaries:

Capxon Electronic (Shenzhen) Co. Ltd.   (1)
Tang Wei Indus Section Tang Wei Vlg Gong Ming, New Guangming Dist, Shenzhen, 518106, Guangdong, China
Tel.: (86) 755 27177888
Sales Range: $900-999.9 Million
Capacitors Mfr & Sales
N.A.I.C.S.: 334416

Capxon Electronic Industrial Company Limited   (1)
5F 165 Datong Rd Sec 2, Taipei, Taiwan
Tel.: (886) 286926611
Web Site: http://www.Capxon.com.tw
Sales Range: $25-49.9 Million
Emp.: 44
Aluminum Electrolytic Capacitors Mfr
N.A.I.C.S.: 334416

Capxon Europe GmbH   (1)

Sandwiesenstrasse 15, 72793, Pfullingen, Baden-Wurttemberg, Germany
Tel.: (49) 7121701777
Web Site: http://www.capxon-europe.com
Sales Range: $50-74.9 Million
Emp.: 3
Electronic Components Distr
N.A.I.C.S.: 423690

CAQ HOLDINGS LIMITED
Suite 91 262 Lord Street, West Perth, 6000, WA, Australia
Tel.: (61) 892288860   AU
Web Site:
   https://www.caqholdings.com
CAQ—(ASX)
Rev.: $2,431,185
Assets: $46,328,709
Liabilities: $5,542,366
Net Worth: $40,786,343
Earnings: ($347,387)
Fiscal Year-end: 12/31/22
Property Development Services
N.A.I.C.S.: 531311
Ivan Cheng (CFO)

Subsidiaries:

Haikou Peace Base Industry Development Co. Ltd.   (1)
Plot 003 Haikou Integrated Free Trade Zone No 69 South First Ring, Laocheng Economic Development Zone Chengmai County, Haikou, 571924, Hainan, China
Tel.: (86) 89867201261
Web Site: https://www.hpbhk.com
Jewelry Retailer
N.A.I.C.S.: 458310

CAR & GENERAL (KENYA) LIMITED
New Cargen House Lusaka Road Industrial Area, PO Box 20001, 200, Nairobi, Kenya
Tel.: (254) 206943000   KE
Web Site: https://www.cargen.com
CGEN—(NAI)
Rev.: $207,027,428
Assets: $161,410,594
Liabilities: $117,851,072
Net Worth: $43,559,523
Earnings: ($2,080,050)
Emp.: 3,743
Fiscal Year-end: 12/31/23
Power Generator Whslr
N.A.I.C.S.: 423610
Nicholas Ng'ang'a (Chm)

Subsidiaries:

Car & General (Tanzania) Limited   (1)
Azikiwe street Next to New Post office, PO Box 1552, Dar es Salaam, Tanzania
Tel.: (255) 222113016
Automobile Parts Distr
N.A.I.C.S.: 423120

Car & General (Uganda) Limited   (1)
Plot 81 Jinja Road, PO Box 207, Kampala, Uganda
Tel.: (256) 144234560
Automobile Parts Distr
N.A.I.C.S.: 423120

Cummins C&G Limited   (1)
New Cargen House Lusaka Road, PO Box 20001, Industrial Area, 00200, Nairobi, Kenya
Tel.: (254) 206943000
Automobile Parts Distr
N.A.I.C.S.: 423120

NIIT C&G Limited   (1)
Barclays Plaza Loita Street, PO Box 20001, 00200, Nairobi, Kenya
Tel.: (254) 742376314
Automobile Parts Distr
N.A.I.C.S.: 423120

NIIT Learning Limited   (1)
1st Floor Barclays Plaza Loita St, Nairobi, Kenya
Tel.: (254) 742376314
Education Management Services

N.A.I.C.S.: 611430

Watu Credit Limited   (1)
PO Box 10556, Nyali, 80101, Mombasa, Kenya
Tel.: (254) 742376314
Automobile Parts Distr
N.A.I.C.S.: 423120

CAR AUCTION CO., LTD.
Prince Hyoryeong Building 502 4 Hyoryeong-ro 34-gil, Seocho-gu, Seoul, Korea (South)
Tel.: (82) 16615777   KR
Web Site: http://www.car-auction.co.kr
Used Car Distr
N.A.I.C.S.: 441120

CAR HOUSE HOLDING CO., LTD.
Building 3 No 16 Science and Technology 4th Road Songshan Lake, High-Tech Industrial Development Zone, Dongguan, 523808, Guangdong, China
Tel.: (86) 76938897488   VG
Year Founded: 2018
Rev.: $30,930,083
Assets: $35,733,262
Liabilities: $19,787,993
Net Worth: $15,945,269
Earnings: $4,415,215
Emp.: 534
Fiscal Year-end: 06/30/19
Holding Company
N.A.I.C.S.: 523999
Haitao Jiang (Chm & CEO)

CAR KLEEN NEW ZEALAND LTD.
Unit E 1066 Great South Road, Mount Wellington, Auckland, 1060, New Zealand
Tel.: (64) 92761060
Web Site: http://www.carkleen.co.nz
Sales Range: $25-49.9 Million
Emp.: 13
Car Wash Equipment Whslr
N.A.I.C.S.: 423850
Steve Jans (Mng Dir)

CAR MATE MFG. CO., LTD.
5-33-11 Nagasaki, Toshima-ku, Tokyo, 1710051, Japan
Tel.: (81) 359261226
Web Site: https://www.carmate.co.jp
7297—(TKS)
Rev.: $105,462,550
Assets: $136,708,020
Liabilities: $39,554,240
Net Worth: $97,153,780
Earnings: $1,401,320
Emp.: 365
Fiscal Year-end: 03/31/24
Automotive Accessories Mfr & Sales
N.A.I.C.S.: 336390
Takaaki Murata (Chm)

Subsidiaries:

Car Mate USA, Inc.   (1)
383 Van Ness Ave Ste 1603, Torrance, CA 90501
Tel.: (310) 533-1647
Web Site: https://www.carmate-home.com
Automobile Parts Mfr
N.A.I.C.S.: 336390

CAR TELEMATICS SA
31 avenue du General Leclerc, 92100, Boulogne-Billancourt, France
Tel.: (33) 8 25162016
Web Site: http://www.cartelematics.fr
Sales Range: $1-9.9 Million
Emp.: 11
Geolocation Services
N.A.I.C.S.: 517112
Eric Felix (Chm & CEO)

CARABAO GROUP PUBLIC COMPANY LIMITED
393 Silom Building 393 7th-10th Floor Silom Road, Bangrak, Bangkok, 10500, Thailand
Tel.: (66) 26366111
Web Site:
   https://www.carabaogroup.com
Year Founded: 2001
CBG—(THA)
Rev.: $555,841,519
Assets: $570,513,315
Liabilities: $240,279,441
Net Worth: $330,233,874
Earnings: $55,473,782
Emp.: 2,750
Fiscal Year-end: 12/31/23
Energy Drink Mfr
N.A.I.C.S.: 311999
Sathien Setthasit (Chm & CEO)

Subsidiaries:

Asia Can Manufacturing Co., Ltd.   (1)
88/4 Moo 2 Phimphawat-Saenphudat Rd Tambon Phimph Amphoe, Bangprakong, Bangkok, 24130, Chachoengsao, Thailand
Tel.: (66) 38088461
Energy Drink Mfr & Distr
N.A.I.C.S.: 312111

Asia Pacific Glass Co., Ltd.   (1)
88 88/1 Moo 2 Phimphawat-Saenphudat Rd Tambon Phimph Amphoe, Bangprakong, Bangkok, 24130, Chachoengsao, Thailand
Tel.: (66) 38989499
Energy Drink Mfr & Distr
N.A.I.C.S.: 312111

Asia Packaging Manufacturing Co., Ltd.   (1)
88/5 Moo 2 Phimphawat-Saenphudat Rd, Tambon Phimpha Amphoe, Bang Pakong, 24130, Thailand
Tel.: (66) 33050726
Beverage Mfr & Distr
N.A.I.C.S.: 312111

Carabao Tawandang Co., Ltd.   (1)
88/2 88/3 Moo 2 Phimphawat-Saenphudat Rd Tambon Phimph Amphoe, Bangprakong, Bangkok, 24130, Chachoengsao, Thailand
Tel.: (66) 38989488
Energy Drink Mfr & Distr
N.A.I.C.S.: 312111

Intercarabao Limited   (1)
1420 Arlington Business Park, Theale, Reading, RG7 4SA, Berkshire, United Kingdom
Tel.: (44) 1189073052
Web Site: https://www.carabaoenergy.co.uk
Energy Drink Mfr & Distr
N.A.I.C.S.: 312111

CARACAL GOLD PLC
27-28 Eastcastle Street, London, W1W 8DH, United Kingdom   UK
Web Site:
   https://www.caracalgold.com
Year Founded: 2015
GCAT—(LSE)
Rev.: $5,256,539
Assets: $11,381,097
Liabilities: $20,386,631
Net Worth: ($9,005,534)
Earnings: ($6,480,954)
Emp.: 499
Fiscal Year-end: 06/30/23
Gold Ore & Silver Ore Mining
N.A.I.C.S.: 212220
Riaan Lombard (COO)

CARACAS PAPER COMPANY, S.A.
Avenida Aragua, Maracay, 2103, Carabobo, Venezuela
Tel.: (58) 2432311711
Web Site: http://www.capaco.com
Year Founded: 1953
Emp.: 350

Paper Products Mfr
N.A.I.C.S.: 322211
Gonzalo Penagos (Gen Mgr)

CARAD SA
5 Falirou, Piraeus, 185 43, Greece
Tel.: (30) 2104203625
Web Site: http://www.carad.gr
Household Appliance Distr
N.A.I.C.S.: 423620

CARASENT ASA
Radhusgata 30 B, 151, Oslo, Norway
Tel.: (47) 97969493   NO
Web Site: https://carasent.com
Year Founded: 1997
CARA—(OSL)
Rev.: $23,984,901
Assets: $107,510,717
Liabilities: $13,589,320
Net Worth: $93,921,397
Earnings: ($4,565,786)
Emp.: 165
Fiscal Year-end: 12/31/23
Investment Holding Company; Cloud Data Solutions
N.A.I.C.S.: 551112
Johan Lindqvist (Chm)

Subsidiaries:

Carasent Norge AS   (1)
Radhusgata 30B, 0151, Oslo, Norway
Tel.: (47) 677900
Web Site: https://carasent.no
Emp.: 170
Cloud Based Medical Record Services
N.A.I.C.S.: 518210

Evimeria EMR AB   (1)
Nellickevagen 20, 412 63, Gothenburg, Sweden
Tel.: (46) 317181400
Web Site: http://www.evimeria.se
Program Development Services
N.A.I.C.S.: 541511

Medrave Software AB   (1)
Kungsgatan 84, 112 27, Stockholm, Sweden
Tel.: (46) 84497257
Web Site: https://www.medrave.com
Healthcare Management Consulting Services
N.A.I.C.S.: 621610

Medrave Software AS   (1)
Radhusgata 30B, 0151, Oslo, Norway
Tel.: (47) 33311878
Web Site: https://www.medrave.com
Healthcare Management Consulting Services
N.A.I.C.S.: 621610

Metodika AB   (1)
Vikdalsgrand 10A, Nacka Strand, 131 52, Stockholm, Sweden
Tel.: (46) 857842800
Web Site: https://www.metodika.com
Healthcare Management Consulting Services
N.A.I.C.S.: 621610

CARASSO MOTORS LTD.
Merkaz Logisti Ta Do'ar 90 P'ark Ra'am, Bneyi Ayish, 6086000, Israel
Tel.: (972) 88631111
Web Site:
   http://www.carassotradein.co.il
Year Founded: 2007
CRSM—(TAE)
Rev.: $1,297,062,281
Assets: $1,961,988,642
Liabilities: $1,442,429,042
Net Worth: $519,559,600
Earnings: $55,308,191
Emp.: 317
Fiscal Year-end: 12/31/23
New Car Dealers
N.A.I.C.S.: 441110

CARASSO REAL ESTATE LTD.

CARASSO REAL ESTATE LTD.

Carasso Real Estate Ltd.—(Continued)

24th Rival St 2nd Floor, Tel Aviv,
6777861, Israel
Tel.: (972) 36381102   II
Web Site: https://en.carasso-
nadlan.co.il
Year Founded: 1933
CRSR—(TAE)
Rov.: $122,622,736
Assets: $1,036,950,391
Liabilities: $681,537,218
Net Worth: $355,413,173
Earnings: $4,740,157
Fiscal Year-end: 12/31/23
Lessors of Other Real Estate Property
N.A.I.C.S.: 531190

CARAVAN EAST FABRICS LIMITED

Suit No 215 2nd Floor Kawish Crown
Shahrah-e-Faisal, Karachi, Pakistan
Tel.: (92) 21 4321753
Textile Products Mfr
N.A.I.C.S.: 313210

CARAVAN ENERGY CORPORATION

220 333 Termnal Avenue, Vancouver,
V6A 4C1, BC, Canada
Tel.: (604) 681-1194   BC
Web Site:
https://www.caravanenergy.com
Year Founded: 2020
CNRG—(CNSX)
Mineral Exploration Services
N.A.I.C.S.: 213115

CARAVANE 185 INC

86 Principale, Saint-Antonin, G0L
2J0, QC, Canada
Tel.: (418) 867-2111
Web Site:
http://www.caravane185.com
Year Founded: 1992
Sales Range: $10-24.9 Million
Recreational Vehicle Dealers
N.A.I.C.S.: 441210
Gilles D'Amours (Pres)

CARAVEL MINERALS LIMITED

Suite 1 245 Churchill Ave, Subiaco,
6008, WA, Australia
Tel.: (61) 894266400
Web Site:
https://www.caravelminerals.com.au
CVV—(ASX)
Rev.: $856,631
Assets: $8,638,586
Liabilities: $729,175
Net Worth: $7,909,412
Earnings: ($4,277,097)
Fiscal Year-end: 06/30/24
Gold & Base Metals Exploration
N.A.I.C.S.: 212220
Daniel Davis (CFO & Sec)

CARAVELLE INTERNATIONAL GROUP

60 Paya Lebar Road #05-47 Paya
Lebar Square, Singapore, 409051,
Singapore
Tel.: (65) 83048372
Web Site:
http://www.caravelleglobal.com
Year Founded: 2022
HTCO—(NASDAQ)
Transportation Services
N.A.I.C.S.: 483111

Subsidiaries:

Pacifico Acquisition Corp.   (1)
521 Fifth Ave 17th Fl, New York, NY 10175
Tel.: (646) 886-8892
Investment Services
N.A.I.C.S.: 523999

Subsidiary (Non-US):

Topsheen Shipping Singapore Pte.
Ltd.   (2)
60 Paya Lebar Road 06-17 Paya Lebar
Square, Singapore, 409051, Singapore
Tel.: (65) 62241088
Web Site: https://www.topsheen.com.sg
Transportation Services
N.A.I.C.S.: 532411

CARAVELLE SA

6 Place des Etats-Unis, 75116, Paris,
France
Tel.: (33) 1 5365 6700   FR
Web Site: http://www.caravelle.fr
Year Founded: 1995
Investment Holding Company
N.A.I.C.S.: 551112
Marc-Olivier Laurent (VP)

Subsidiaries:

Belambra VVF SNC   (1)
28 rue d'Arcueil, F-94253, Gentilly, Cedex,
France   (61%)
Tel.: (33) 155013000
Web Site: http://www.belambra-vvf.fr
Sales Range: $200-249.9 Million
Emp.: 2,500
Vacation Resort & Tour Operator
N.A.I.C.S.: 721214
Olivier Colcombet (Chm-Mgmt Bd & CEO)

CARBACID INVESTMENTS PLC

ALN House Eldama Ravine Close
OffEldama Ravine Road Westlands,
PO Box 764, Sarit Centre, 00606,
Nairobi, Kenya
Tel.: (254) 704852487   KE
Web Site: https://www.carbacid.com
Year Founded: 1970
CARB—(NAI)
Rev.: $13,079,062
Assets: $38,859,432
Liabilities: $7,229,229
Net Worth: $31,630,202
Earnings: $6,201,649
Emp.: 76
Fiscal Year-end: 07/31/23
Chemical Products Mfr
N.A.I.C.S.: 325199
Dennis N. O. Awori (Chm)

CARBERY GROUP

Carbery Ballineen, Cork, Ireland
Tel.: (353) 23 8822200   IE
Web Site: http://www.carbery.com
Year Founded: 1965
Sales Range: $300-349.9 Million
Emp.: 200
Food Ingredients, Flavors & Cheese
Mfr
N.A.I.C.S.: 311513
T. J. Sullivan (Chm)

Subsidiaries:

Synergy Flavors, Inc.   (1)
1230 Karl Ct, Wauconda, IL 60084
Tel.: (847) 487-1022
Web Site: http://www.synergytaste.com
Flavoring Mfr
N.A.I.C.S.: 311930

Subsidiary (Domestic):

Sethness-Greenleaf, Inc.   (2)
1826 N Lorel Ave, Chicago, IL 60639
Tel.: (773) 889-1400
Web Site: http://www.synergytaste.com
Flavoring Mfr
N.A.I.C.S.: 311930

Subsidiary (Non-US):

Synergy (Corby) Ltd   (2)
5 Sallow Road Weldon Industrial Estate,
Corby, NN17 5JX, Northants, United Kingdom
Tel.: (44) 1536 262003
Flavour & Essence Distr
N.A.I.C.S.: 424490

Mark Embery (Mgr-Sls-Savoury-Europe)

Synergy (High Wycombe) Ltd   (2)
Hillbottom Road Sands Industrial Estate,
High Wycombe, HP12 4HJ, Bucks, United
Kingdom
Tel.: (44) 1494 492222
Flavour & Essence Distr
N.A.I.C.S.: 424490
Hugh Evans (Mgr-Mktg-Europe & Asia)

Synergy Aromas Ltda   (2)
Rua Jose de Rezende de Meirelles 3845,
Vinhedo, Sao Paulo, 13280-000, Brazil
Tel.: (55) 19 3826 7222
Flavour & Essence Distr
N.A.I.C.S.: 424490
Phillip Ross (Dir-Technical)

Subsidiary (Domestic):

Synergy Flavors (NY) Company,
LLC   (2)
86 White St, Rochester, NY 14608
Tel.: (585) 232-6647
Flavour & Essence Distr
N.A.I.C.S.: 424490

Synergy Flavors (OH), LLC   (2)
2991 Hamilton-Mason Rd, Hamilton, OH
45011
Tel.: (513) 892-7100
Flavour & Essence Distr
N.A.I.C.S.: 424490

Synergy Flavors (OH). LLC   (2)
2991 Hamilton-Mason Rd, Hamilton, OH
45011
Tel.: (513) 892-7100
Web Site: http://www.synergytaste.com
Flavor Extracts Mfr
N.A.I.C.S.: 311999

Subsidiary (Non-US):

Synergy Flavours (Thailand) Ltd   (2)
888/22 Moo 9 Soi Roongcharoen Lieb
Klong Suvarnabhumi Road, Bang Pla, Bang
Phli, Samutprakarn, Thailand
Tel.: (66) 2 181 6710
Web Site: http://www.synergytaste.com
Emp.: 27
Flavour & Essence Distr
N.A.I.C.S.: 424490
Siraschayar Natrthong (Mgr-Technical)

Synergy Ireland   (2)
Ballineen, Cork, Ireland
Tel.: (353) 23 88 22000
Flavour & Essence Distr
N.A.I.C.S.: 424490

CARBINE RESOURCES LIMITED

Suite 23 513 Hay Street, Subiaco,
6008, WA, Australia
Tel.: (61) 861420986   AU
Web Site:
http://www.carbineresources.com.au
Year Founded: 2006
Rev.: $86,296
Assets: $3,348,727
Liabilities: $211,379
Net Worth: $3,137,347
Earnings: ($1,956,298)
Fiscal Year-end: 12/31/17
Gold Exploration Services
N.A.I.C.S.: 212220
Evan Cranston (Chm)

CARBIOS SACA

Biopole Clermont-Limagne 3 rue
Emile Duclaux, 63360, Saint-
Beauzire, France
Tel.: (33) 33473865176
Web Site: https://www.carbios.com
ALCRB—(EUR)
Rev.: $2,017,998
Assets: $71,517,959
Liabilities: $10,957,129
Net Worth: $60,560,830
Earnings: ($7,548,763)
Emp.: 31
Fiscal Year-end: 12/31/20
Chemical Recycling Services

N.A.I.C.S.: 562998
Martin Stephan (Deputy CEO)

Subsidiaries:

SAS Carbiolice   (1)
4 Rue Andre Messager, 63200, Riom,
France
Tel.: (33) 473330300
Web Site: http://www.carbiolice.com
Emp.: 25
Plastic Recycling Services
N.A.I.C.S.: 562920
Nadia Auclair (Pres)

CARBON GREEN INC.

Vysoka 26, 81106, Bratislava, Slovakia
Tel.: (421) 2 52926300   NV
Sales Range: Less than $1 Million
Tire Recycling Services
N.A.I.C.S.: 423130
David W. Thursfield (COO)

Subsidiaries:

True Health Studio, Inc.   (1)
2688 Arbutus Street, Vancouver, V6J 2C7,
BC, Canada
Tel.: (604) 221-8783
Web Site: http://www.truehealthstudio.com
Chiropractic & Massaging Services
N.A.I.C.S.: 621310
Marcus Wong (Owner)

CARBON MINERALS LIMITED

Suite 3 Level 2 66 Clarence Street,
Sydney, 2000, NSW, Australia
Tel.: (61) 292993655   AU
Web Site:
http://www.carbonminerals.com.au
CRM—(ASX)
Rev.: $43,502
Assets: $3,100,981
Liabilities: $560,926
Net Worth: $2,540,055
Earnings: ($171,037)
Fiscal Year-end: 12/31/22
Natural Gas Exploration Service
N.A.I.C.S.: 211130
Marcus Paul Lincoln Smith (Chm &
CEO)

CARBON REVOLUTION LIMITED

Building NR Geelong Technology
Precinct 75 Pigdons Road, Waurn
Ponds, Geelong, 3216, VIC, Australia
Tel.: (61) 352713500   AU
Web Site: https://www.carbonrev.com
Year Founded: 2007
CBR—(ASX)
Rev.: $30,905,040
Assets: $126,326,342
Liabilities: $40,190,496
Net Worth: $86,135,846
Earnings: ($32,881,044)
Emp.: 400
Fiscal Year-end: 06/30/22
Software Development Services
N.A.I.C.S.: 541511
Ashley Denmead (CTO)

CARBONXT GROUP LIMITED

Level 8 210 George Street, Sydney,
2000, NSW, Australia
Tel.: (61) 292909600   AU
Web Site: http://www.carbonxt.com
Year Founded: 2006
CG1—(ASX)
Rev.: $10,099,237
Assets: $21,935,900
Liabilities: $14,767,824
Net Worth: $7,168,076
Earnings: ($5,421,006)
Fiscal Year-end: 06/30/24
Carbon Product Mfr & Distr
N.A.I.C.S.: 325180
Warren Murphy (Mng Dir)

CARBOPRESS S.P.A.
Via delle Suore 319, 41122, Modena, Italy
Tel.: (39) 059 735 35 20
Web Site: http://www.carbopress.com
Composite Parts Mfr & Automotive & Motor Sport Applications
N.A.I.C.S.: 332710

Subsidiaries:

Gurit (Hungary) Kft. (1)
Kukorica Street HRSZ 8133/21, 8000, Szekesfehervar, Hungary
Tel.: (36) 22502170
Wind Energy Equipment Mfr
N.A.I.C.S.: 333611
Katalin Kellner (Mgr-HR)

CARCETTI CAPITAL CORP.
3300 205 5th Avenue SW, Calgary, T2P 2V7, AB, Canada
Tel.: (713) 677-0439
Web Site: https://carcetti.com
KUB—(TSXV)
Rev.: $623,000
Assets: $7,194,000
Liabilities: $6,992,000
Net Worth: $202,000
Earnings: ($42,287,000)
Emp.: 3
Fiscal Year-end: 12/31/22
Oil & Gas Exploration Services
N.A.I.C.S.: 211120
Patrick McGrath (CEO & Interim & CFO)

CARCLO PLC
47 Wates Way, PO Box 88, Mitcham, CR4 4HR, Surrey, United Kingdom
Tel.: (44) 13918975785   UK
Web Site: https://www.carclo-plc.com
Year Founded: 1924
CAR—(LSE)
Rev.: $178,130,001
Assets: $152,334,090
Liabilities: $137,921,759
Net Worth: $14,412,331
Earnings: ($4,913,803)
Emp.: 1,116
Fiscal Year-end: 03/31/23
Specialty Wire, Cable & Technical Plastic Product Mfr
N.A.I.C.S.: 326199
Nick Sanders (Chm)

Subsidiaries:

Birkett Cutmaster Limited (1)
Middleton Business Park Cartwright Street, PO Box 30, Cleckheaton, BD19 5LY, Yorkshire, United Kingdom (100%)
Tel.: (44) 1274870311
Web Site: http://www.birkett-cutmaster.co.uk
Sales Range: $50-74.9 Million
Emp.: 9
Industrial Equipment Wholesale
N.A.I.C.S.: 423830
Bryn Pritchaid (Mng Dir)

Bruntons Aero Products Limited (1)
Units 1-3 Block 1 Inveresk Industrial Estate, Musselburgh, EH21 7PA, East Lothian, United Kingdom
Tel.: (44) 131 665 3888
Web Site: https://www.bruntons.co.uk
Sales Range: $25-49.9 Million
Emp.: 54
Aerospace Products Mfr
N.A.I.C.S.: 336413
Alan Hook (Mng Dir)

Carclo Diagnostic Solutions Ltd (1)
Springstone House 27 Dewsbury Road, PO Box 88, Ossett, WF5 9WS, West Yorkshire, United Kingdom
Tel.: (44) 208 685 0500
Web Site:
http://www.carclodiagnosticsolutions.com
Electromedical Apparatus Mfr
N.A.I.C.S.: 334510
Martin Day (Mgr-Mktg)

Carclo Precision Optics (1)

Units 6-7 Faraday Rd Rabans Lane Industrial Area, Aylesbury, HP19 8RY, United Kingdom (100%)
Tel.: (44) 1753 575011
Web Site: http://www.carclo-optics.com
Sales Range: $25-49.9 Million
Emp.: 17
Plastic Optical Component & Moulding Mfr
N.A.I.C.S.: 333310
Neil Collis (Gen Mgr)

Carclo Technical Plastics (1)
Mossburn Ave, Harthill, ML7 5NP, Lanerkshire, United Kingdom (100%)
Tel.: (44) 501751447
Web Site: http://www.carclo.com
Sales Range: $50-74.9 Million
Emp.: 200
Technical Plastics Mfr
N.A.I.C.S.: 326199

Carclo Technical Plastics (Brno) (1)
s.r.o
Turanka 98/1277, Brno, 627 00, Czech Republic
Tel.: (420) 532 190 711
Plastics Product Mfr
N.A.I.C.S.: 326199

Carclo Technical Plastics Ltd (1)
600 Depot St, Latrobe, PA 15650-1617
Tel.: (724) 539-1833
Sales Range: $25-49.9 Million
Emp.: 60
Technical Plastics Mfr
N.A.I.C.S.: 326199

Carclo Technical Plastics Ltd. (1)
111 Buckingham Ave, Slough, SL1 4PF, Berks, United Kingdom (100%)
Tel.: (44) 01753575011
Web Site: http://www.carclo-optics.com
Sales Range: $25-49.9 Million
Emp.: 15
Technical Plastics Mfr
N.A.I.C.S.: 326199

Carclo Technical Plastics Ltd. (1)
Ploughland House, PO Box 14, 62 George St, Wakefield, WF11ZF, United Kingdom (100%)
Tel.: (44) 1554749000
Sales Range: $25-49.9 Million
Emp.: 60
Technical Plastics Mfr
N.A.I.C.S.: 326199

Subsidiary (Non-US):

Carclo Technical Plastics Shanghai (2)
Co. Limited
No 21 Lianxi Road Lianxi Village Huangdu Town, Jiading District, Shanghai, 201804, China
Tel.: (86) 2169595189
Plastics Product Mfr
N.A.I.C.S.: 424610
Geoffrey Tregoning (Gen Mgr)

Carclo Technical Plastics Mitcham (1)
Ltd.
47 Wates Way, Mitcham, CR4 4HR, Surrey, United Kingdom (100%)
Tel.: (44) 2086850500
Web Site: http://www.carclo-ctp.co.uk
Sales Range: $50-74.9 Million
Emp.: 150
Technical Plastics Mfr
N.A.I.C.S.: 326199
Patrick Ward (Mng Dir)

Conductive Inkjet Technology (1)
Limited
Brookmount Ct Kirkwood Rd, Cambridge, CB4 2QH, United Kingdom
Tel.: (44) 1223424323
Web Site: http://www.conductiveinkjet.com
Sales Range: $25-49.9 Million
Emp.: 20
Electronic Products Mfr
N.A.I.C.S.: 334419

Estab Platt Freres S.A. (1)
108 122 Blvd De Lyon, PO Box 165, 59053, Roubaix, France (100%)
Tel.: (33) 320893700
Web Site: http://www.eccplatt.fr
Sales Range: $25-49.9 Million
Emp.: 40
Mfr of Flexible Card Clothing

N.A.I.C.S.: 332999

Jacottet Industrie SAS (1)
40 bis avenue d'Orleans, CS 70 304, 28008, Chartres, Cedex, France
Tel.: (33) 23 728 6128
Web Site: https://www.jacottet-industrie.com
Aerospace Cables Mfr
N.A.I.C.S.: 334511
Alan Hook (Mng Dir)

Wipac Limited (1)
London Rd, Buckingham, MK18 1BH, United Kingdom
Tel.: (44) 1280 822800
Web Site: http://www.wipac.com
Sales Range: $50-74.9 Million
Emp.: 150
Lighting Product Mfr
N.A.I.C.S.: 335132
Neil Sibley (Mng Dir)

CARDIEX LIMITED
Suite 301 55 Lime St, Barangaroo, 2000, NSW, Australia
Tel.: (61) 298748761
Web Site:
https://www.atcormedical.com
Year Founded: 2005
CDX—(ASX)
Rev.: $3,961,670
Assets: $9,483,796
Liabilities: $4,418,274
Net Worth: $5,065,522
Earnings: ($9,048,423)
Fiscal Year-end: 06/30/22
Medical Device Mfr
N.A.I.C.S.: 334510
Craig Cooper (CEO)

Subsidiaries:

AtCor Medical Inc. (1)
1 Pierce Pl Ste 225w, Itasca, IL 60143-2613
Tel.: (630) 228-8871
Web Site: http://www.atcormedical.com
Sales Range: $25-49.9 Million
Emp.: 15
Biomedical Diagnostic Equipment Suppliers
N.A.I.C.S.: 423450
Dean Winter (VP)

AtCor Medical Pty Limited (1)
Unit 11 West Ryde Corporate Centre 1059-1063 Victoria Road, Ryde, 2114, NSW, Australia
Tel.: (61) 298748761
Web Site: http://www.atcormedical.com
Sales Range: $25-49.9 Million
Emp.: 15
Medical Equipment Mfr
N.A.I.C.S.: 334510
Mark Harding (Dir-Sls)

CARDIFF CAR CITY PTY LIMITED
54 Macquarie Road, Cardiff, 2285, NSW, Australia
Tel.: (61) 249046777
Web Site:
http://www.cardiffcarcity.com.au
Sales Range: $25-49.9 Million
Emp.: 90
Car Dealership Owner & Operator
N.A.I.C.S.: 441110
Clayton Smart (CEO)

CARDIFF INTERNATIONAL AIRPORT LTD.
Cardiff Airport, Vale of Glamorgan, Cardiff, CF62 3BD, United Kingdom
Tel.: (44) 1446711111   UK
Web Site: http://www.cardiff-airport.com
Sales Range: $50-74.9 Million
Emp.: 150
Airport Operator
N.A.I.C.S.: 488119
Debra Barber (CEO)

CARDINAL CO., LTD.

2-6-14 Shigita, Joto-ku, Osaka, 536-0015, Japan
Tel.: (81) 6 6934 4141
Year Founded: 1967
7855—(JAS)
Sales Range: Less than $1 Million
Cards Mfr
N.A.I.C.S.: 323111
Hironao Yamada (Pres)

CARDINAL ENERGY LTD.
600 400 - 3rd Avenue SW, Calgary, T2P 4H2, AB, Canada
Tel.: (403) 234-8681   AB
Web Site:
https://www.cardinalenergy.ca
Year Founded: 2010
CJ—(TSX)
Rev.: $297,656,168
Assets: $879,893,613
Liabilities: $315,221,487
Net Worth: $564,672,126
Earnings: ($26,278,342)
Emp.: 177
Fiscal Year-end: 12/31/19
Oil & Gas Exploration
N.A.I.C.S.: 211120
Laurence Broos (VP-Fin)

CARDIOCOMM SOLUTIONS, INC.
18 Wynford Drive Suite 305, North York, M2J 0B5, ON, Canada
Tel.: (416) 977-9425   BC
Web Site:
https://www.cardiocommsolution.com
Year Founded: 1989
EKG—(TSXV)
Rev.: $653,036
Assets: $282,103
Liabilities: $806,480
Net Worth: ($524,376)
Earnings: ($49,758)
Emp.: 30
Fiscal Year-end: 12/31/20
Cardiac Management & Diagnostic Tools Software Solutions
N.A.I.C.S.: 513210
Robert E. Caines (Chm)

Subsidiaries:

CardioView Inc. (1)
4286 Morgan Cres, West Vancouver, V7V 2N9, BC, Canada
Web Site: http://www.cardioview.com
Software Development Services
N.A.I.C.S.: 513210

CARDIOL THERAPEUTICS, INC.
2265 Upper Middle Road East Suite 602, Oakville, L6H 0G5, ON, Canada
Tel.: (289) 910-0850
Web Site: https://www.cardiolrx.com
CRDL—(NASDAQ)
Assets: $27,111,257
Liabilities: $6,245,107
Net Worth: $20,866,150
Earnings: ($20,778,822)
Emp.: 17
Fiscal Year-end: 12/31/23
Pharmaceuticals Product Mfr
N.A.I.C.S.: 325412
Andrew Hamer (Chief Medical Officer)

CARDNO LIMITED
Level 11 North Tower Green Square 515 St Paul's Terrace, Locked Bag 4006, Fortitude Valley, 4006, QLD, Australia
Tel.: (61) 733699822   AU
Web Site: http://www.cardno.com
Year Founded: 1945
COLDF—(OTCIQ)
Rev.: $8,146,132
Assets: $75,235,261

Cardno Limited—(Continued)

Liabilities: $7,069,635
Net Worth: $68,165,626
Earnings: $390,261,941
Emp.: 4,000
Fiscal Year-end: 06/30/22
Holding Company; Infrastructure Engineering, Project Management & Environmental Consulting Services
N.A.I.C.S.: 551112
Jackie McPhee *(Mgr-Corporate Marketing)*

Subsidiaries:

Cardno (NSW/ACT) Pty. Ltd. (1)
Tel.: (61) 29 496 7700
Web Site: http://www.cardno.com.au
Sales Range: $25-49.9 Million
Emp.: 170
Engineering Consulting Services
N.A.I.C.S.: 541330

Cardno (NZ) Limited (1)
Level 4 272 Parnell Road, Parnell, Auckland, 1052, New Zealand
Tel.: (64) 99762111
Engineeering Services
N.A.I.C.S.: 541330

Cardno (PNG) Ltd. (1)
Level 2 CHM Corporate Park Corner of Kawai, Drive and Waigani Industrial Estate Drive Gordons NCD, Port Moresby, 1826, Papua New Guinea
Tel.: (675) 3254606
Web Site: http://www.cardnoem.com
Sales Range: $25-49.9 Million
Emp.: 42
Engineering Consulting Services
N.A.I.C.S.: 541330

Cardno (Qld) Pty. Ltd. (1)
Level 11 North Tower, PO Box 359, Hervey Bay, 4211, QLD, Australia
Tel.: (61) 741245455
Engineering Consulting Services
N.A.I.C.S.: 541330

Cardno (WA) Pty. Ltd. (1)
11 Harvest Ter, West Perth, 6005, WA, Australia
Tel.: (61) 892733888
Sales Range: $25-49.9 Million
Emp.: 100
Engineering Consulting Services
N.A.I.C.S.: 541330
David James *(Gen Mgr)*

Cardno Alexander Browne Pty. Ltd. (1)
Locked Bag 4006, Fortitude Valley, 4006, QLD, Australia
Tel.: (61) 733699822
Engineering Consulting Services
N.A.I.C.S.: 541330

Cardno Bowler (1)
73 Delta Street, Geebung, Brisbane, 4034, QLD, Australia
Tel.: (61) 738653212
Web Site: http://www.cardno.com
Engineering Consulting Services
N.A.I.C.S.: 541330

Cardno Bowler Pty. Ltd. (1)
1 Fox Road, Acacia Ridge, 4110, QLD, Australia
Tel.: (61) 72 800 6500
Web Site: https://constructionsciences.net
Sales Range: $25-49.9 Million
Emp.: 45
Geotechnical Engineering & Consulting Services
N.A.I.C.S.: 541330

Cardno ChemRisk, LLC (1)
235 Pine St 23rd Fl, San Francisco, CA 94104
Tel.: (415) 896-2400
Web Site: https://www.cardnochemrisk.com
Scientific Consulting Services
N.A.I.C.S.: 541690

Cardno Chemrisk - San Francisco (1)
235 Pine St 23rd Fl, San Francisco, CA 94104

Tel.: (415) 896-2400
Web Site: http://www.cardnochemrisk.com
Business Consulting Services
N.A.I.C.S.: 541690
Dennis J. Paustenbach *(Pres & Sr Principal)*

Cardno Christchurch (1)
Unit 1C 155 Blenheim Road, Riccarton, Christchurch, 8042, New Zealand
Tel.: (64) 33665428
Web Site: http://www.cardno.com
Sales Range: $25-49.9 Million
Emp.: 15
Surveying & Land Development Consulting Services
N.A.I.C.S.: 541320
Darcy Brittliff *(Mgr-Engrg)*

Cardno Ecology Lab Pty. Ltd. (1)
Level 9 The Forum 203 Pacific Highway St Leonards, Brookvale, 2065, NSW, Australia
Tel.: (61) 299074440
Web Site: http://www.cardno.com.au
Sales Range: $25-49.9 Million
Emp.: 15
Environmental Engineering Services
N.A.I.C.S.: 541330
Peggy O'Donneoo *(Mgr)*

Cardno Emerging Markets (Australia) Pty. Ltd. (1)
Level 4 501 Swanston Street, Hawthorn, 3000, VIC, Australia
Tel.: (61) 398192877
Web Site: http://www.cardno.com
Sales Range: $25-49.9 Million
Emp.: 40
Construction Engineering Services
N.A.I.C.S.: 541330
Martin Mason *(Mgr-IT)*

Cardno Emerging Markets (East Africa) Limited (1)
87 Rhapta Road Lantana Place, PO Box 39636, Westlands, 00623, Nairobi, Kenya
Tel.: (254) 20 444 5630
Web Site: http://cardnoem.agrisystems.co.uk
Sales Range: $25-49.9 Million
Emp.: 10
Agricultural Consulting Services
N.A.I.C.S.: 541690

Cardno Emerging Markets Belgium s.a, (1)
Avenue Louise 479, Box 53, 1050, Brussels, Belgium
Tel.: (32) 22820333
Engineeering Services
N.A.I.C.S.: 541330

Cardno Entrix (Colombia) S.A.S. (1)
Cra 7B Bis No 126-36 Barrio Santa Barbara, Bogota Distrito, Bogota, 07603, Colombia
Tel.: (57) 17953853
Engineeering Services
N.A.I.C.S.: 541330

Cardno Eppell Olsen Pty. Ltd. (1)
ILevel 11 Green Square - North Tower 515 St Paul's Terrace, Fortitude Valley, 4006, QLD, Australia
Tel.: (61) 733102401
Traffic Management Services
N.A.I.C.S.: 488111

Cardno Holdings Pty. Ltd. (1)
Level 11 515 St Paul's Terrace, Locked Bag 4006, Fortitude Valley, 4006, QLD, Australia
Tel.: (61) 73 369 9822
Web Site: http://www.Cardno.com.au
Emp.: 400
Investment Management Service
N.A.I.C.S.: 523940

Cardno ITC Pty. Ltd. (1)
Tel.: (61) 294958100
Web Site: http://www.itcgroup.net.au
Sales Range: $25-49.9 Million
Emp.: 50
Construction Engineering Services
N.A.I.C.S.: 541330

Subsidiary (Non-US):

Cardno ITC (QLD) Pty. Ltd. (2)
Tel.: (61) 294958100
Web Site: http://www.cardnoitc.com.au

Sales Range: $25-49.9 Million
Construction Engineering Services
N.A.I.C.S.: 541330

Cardno ITC (VIC) Pty. Ltd. (2)
Tel.: (61) 386108000
Web Site: http://www.cardnoitc.com.au
Sales Range: $25-49.9 Million
Emp.: 22
Engineering Consulting Services
N.A.I.C.S.: 541330

Cardno ITC (WA) Pty. Ltd. (2)
Tel.: (61) 894869924
Web Site: http://www.cardno.com
Sales Range: $25-49.9 Million
Emp.: 12
Construction Engineering Services
N.A.I.C.S.: 541330

Cardno Low & Hooke Pty. Ltd. (1)
Level 1 910 Pacific Highway, Gordon, 2072, NSW, Australia
Tel.: (61) 294967700
Sales Range: $25-49.9 Million
Emp.: 180
Engineering Consulting Services
N.A.I.C.S.: 541330

Cardno Pty. Ltd. (1)
16 Burelli Street Level 1 Ground Fl, Wollongong, 2500, NSW, Australia
Tel.: (61) 2 4228 4133
Web Site: http://www.cardno.com
Sales Range: $25-49.9 Million
Emp.: 100
Civil Engineering Services
N.A.I.C.S.: 541330
Andrew David Buckley *(Mng Dir)*

Cardno Spectrum Survey Pty. Ltd. (1)
61 Eagan Street, Kalgoorlie, 6430, WA, Australia
Tel.: (61) 8 9021 8343
Web Site: http://www.cardno.com
Surveying & Mapping Services
N.A.I.C.S.: 541370
Kylie Sprott *(Gen Mgr-Global Bus Srvcs)*

Cardno UK Limited (1)
Oxford House Oxford Road, Thame, OX9 2AH, Oxfordshire, United Kingdom
Tel.: (44) 1844216500
Web Site: http://www.cardno.uk.com
Sales Range: $25-49.9 Million
Emp.: 20
Engineering Consulting Services
N.A.I.C.S.: 541330

Subsidiary (Domestic):

Cardno Emerging Markets (UK) Limited (2)
Suite 3 Oxford House Oxford Road, Thame, OX9 2AH, Oxfordshire, United Kingdom
Tel.: (44) 1844216500
Sales Range: $25-49.9 Million
Agricultural Consulting Services
N.A.I.C.S.: 541690
Gerome Rich *(Mng Dir)*

Micro Drainage Limited (2)
Jacobs Well West Street, Newbury, RG14 1BD, Berkshire, United Kingdom
Tel.: (44) 1635582555
Web Site: http://www.microdrainage.co.uk
Sales Range: $25-49.9 Million
Emp.: 20
Drainage Management Software Development Services
N.A.I.C.S.: 541511
Paul Ramhaw *(Mng Dir)*

Cardno Ullman & Nolan Pty. Ltd. (1)
L 11 515 St Pauls Tce, Fortitude Valley, 4006, QLD, Australia
Tel.: (61) 731002199
Web Site: http://www.cardno.com.au
Emp.: 400
Engineering Consulting Services
N.A.I.C.S.: 541330
Geoff Hadwen *(Mgr-Div)*

Cardno United States of America (1)
5415 SW Westgate Dr Ste 100, Portland, OR 97221
Tel.: (503) 734-1800
Web Site: http://www.cardno.com
Engineering Consulting

N.A.I.C.S.: 541330

Subsidiary (Domestic):

Cardno ENTRIX, Inc. (2)
5252 Westchester St, Houston, TX 77005-4141
Tel.: (713) 666-6223
Web Site: http://www.entrix.com
Sales Range: $25-49.9 Million
Emp.: 250
Environmental Consulting & Natural Resource Management Services
N.A.I.C.S.: 541620

Cardno ERI, Inc. (2)
20372 N Sea Cir, Lake Forest, CA 92630
Tel.: (949) 340-1020
Web Site: http://www.cardnoeri.com
Sales Range: $1-9.9 Million
Emp.: 50
Environmental Consulting Services
N.A.I.C.S.: 541620

Cardno Emerging Markets (USA), Ltd. (2)
Colonial Pl 3rd Ste 800 2107 Wilson Blvd, Arlington, VA 22201-3096
Tel.: (703) 373-7600
Sales Range: $25-49.9 Million
Emp.: 80
Engineering Consulting Services
N.A.I.C.S.: 541330
Patti Espey *(CFO)*

Cardno Haynes Whaley, Inc. (2)
3700 W Sam Houston Pkwy S Ste 100, Houston, TX 77042
Tel.: (713) 868-1591
Web Site: http://www.cardno.com
Sales Range: $1-9.9 Million
Emp.: 83
Structural Engineering Services
N.A.I.C.S.: 541330
John D. Rohrer *(Exec VP)*

Cardno TBE (2)
380 Park Pl Blvd Ste 300, Clearwater, FL 33759
Tel.: (727) 531-3505
Web Site: http://www.cardno.com
Sales Range: $50-74.9 Million
Emp.: 70
Engineeering Services
N.A.I.C.S.: 541330
Craig Snyder *(COO)*

Subsidiary (Domestic):

Cardno TBE (Michigan), Inc. (3)
4500 Empire Way Ste 4, Lansing, MI 48917
Tel.: (517) 322-0822
Web Site: http://www.tbegroup.com
Construction Engineering Services
N.A.I.C.S.: 541330

Subsidiary (Domestic):

Cardno WRG, Inc. (2)
6720 SW Macadam Ave Ste 200, Portland, OR 97219
Tel.: (503) 419-2500
Web Site: http://www.cardno.com
Sales Range: $25-49.9 Million
Emp.: 45
Environmental Engineering Services
N.A.I.C.S.: 541330
Matt Lewis *(Branch Mgr)*

EM-Assist, Inc. (2)
90 Blue Ravine Rd Ste 180, Folsom, CA 95630
Tel.: (916) 355-8444
Web Site: https://www.em-assist.com
Sales Range: $10-24.9 Million
Emp.: 10
Environmental Program Management & Training Solutions
N.A.I.C.S.: 541620
Gregg Alex *(Exec VP)*

Cardno Victoria Pty. Ltd. (1)
Level 4 501 Swanston Street, Melbourne, 3000, VIC, Australia
Tel.: (61) 384157777
Web Site: http://www.cardno.com.au
Sales Range: $50-74.9 Million
Emp.: 270
Commercial Construction Services
N.A.I.C.S.: 237990

Entrix Americas, SA (1)
Calle Miguel Angel E6-111 y Alberti Urbanizacion la Primavera I, Cumbaya, 170157, Quito, Pichincha, Ecuador
Tel.: (593) 23550110
Engineering Services
N.A.I.C.S.: 541330

TGM Group Pty Ltd (1)
Level 1 27-31 Myers St, PO Box 1137, Geelong, 3220, VIC, Australia
Tel.: (61) 352024600
Web Site: http://www.tgmgroup.com
Emp.: 130
Engineering Services
N.A.I.C.S.: 541330
Leigh Prossor (Mgr-Engrg)

XP Software Pty. Ltd. (1)
4006 Fortitude Valley, Belconnen, Queensland, 4006, ACT, Australia
Tel.: (61) 262531844
Web Site: http://www.xpsolutions.com
Sales Range: $25-49.9 Million
Emp.: 10
Water Resource Software Development Services
N.A.I.C.S.: 541511

CARDON GROUP INC.
5774 - 10 St NE, Calgary, T2E 8W7, AB, Canada
Tel.: (587) 393-5185
Web Site:
https://www.cardongroup.ca
Year Founded: 2017
Private Equity
N.A.I.C.S.: 523940

Subsidiaries:

Teldon Media Group, Inc (1)
100-12751 Vulcan Way, Richmond, V6V 3C8, BC, Canada
Tel.: (888) 983-5366
Web Site: http://www.teldon.com
Publishing, Digital Printing & Marketing Services
N.A.I.C.S.: 323111
Monika Vent (Mgr-Creative Svcs)

Subsidiary (US):

By Design Publishing (2)
11626 North Tracey Road, Hayden, ID 83835
Tel.: (877) 423-4567
Web Site:
http://www.bydesignpublishing.com
Periodical Publishers
N.A.I.C.S.: 513120

CARDS OFF SA
79/81 rue du faubourg Poissonniere, 75009, Paris, France
Tel.: (33) 144701621
Web Site: http://www.cardsoff.com
Sales Range: Less than $1 Million
Emp.: 13
Financial Transaction Software & Systems
N.A.I.C.S.: 522320
Philippe Mendil Mendil (Chm & Mng Dir)

CARE CANADA
Suite 100 9 Gurdwara Road, Ottawa, K2E 7X6, ON, Canada
Tel.: (613) 228-5600
Web Site: http://www.care.ca
Sales Range: $100-124.9 Million
Emp.: 56
Aid & Development Organization
N.A.I.C.S.: 624230
Barbara Grantham (Pres)

CARE PROPERTY INVEST NV
Horstebaan 3, 2900, Schoten, Belgium
Tel.: (32) 32229494
Web Site:
https://carepropertyinvest.be

CPINV—(EUR)
Rev.: $44,466,091
Assets: $920,218,234
Liabilities: $466,040,284
Net Worth: $454,177,950
Earnings: $24,398,880
Emp.: 15
Fiscal Year-end: 12/31/20
Real Estate Support Services
N.A.I.C.S.: 531390
Mark Suykens (Chm)

CARE RATINGS LIMITED
4th Floor Godrej Coliseum Somaiya Hospital Road, Off Eastern Express Highway Sion East, Mumbai, 400022, India
Tel.: (91) 2267543404
Web Site:
https://www.careratings.com
Year Founded: 1993
534804—(BOM)
Rev.: $37,999,847
Assets: $92,446,665
Liabilities: $11,029,625
Net Worth: $81,417,040
Earnings: $10,246,414
Emp.: 517
Fiscal Year-end: 03/31/24
Credit Analysis & Research Services
N.A.I.C.S.: 561499
Umesh Ikhe (CTO)

Subsidiaries:

Care Kalypto Risk Technologies and Advisory Services Pvt. Ltd. (1)
2nd floor Apeejay Commercial Complex Sector 17, Vashi, Mumbai, 400 703, India
Tel.: (91) 22 3918 0406
Web Site: http://www.kalyptorisk.com
Credit Risk Management Services
N.A.I.C.S.: 561499
Abhisheik Vishwakarma (Pres)

Care Ratings (Africa) Private Limited (1)
5th Floor MTML Square 63 Cyber City, Ebene, Mauritius
Tel.: (230) 59553060
Financial Services
N.A.I.C.S.: 523999
Saurav Chatterjee (CEO)

Care Ratings Nepal Ltd. (1)
Star Mall 5th Floor Putalisadak, Kathmandu, Nepal
Tel.: (977) 14012628
Credit Rating Services
N.A.I.C.S.: 561450
Achin Nirwani (CEO)

Care Risk Solutions Private Limited (1)
Office No 602 6th Floor Rustomjee Aspiree Off Eastern Express Highway, Sion East, Mumbai, 400 022, India
Tel.: (91) 2261748900
Web Site: https://carerisksolutions.com
Financial Services
N.A.I.C.S.: 523999

CARE SERVICE CO., LTD.
5F Omori Miyuki Building 23 Omorikita 1chome, Ota-Ku, Tokyo, 143-0016, Japan
Tel.: (81) 357531170
Web Site: https://www.care.co.jp
Year Founded: 1991
2425—(TKS)
Rev.: $63,700,570
Assets: $25,494,770
Liabilities: $8,031,150
Net Worth: $17,463,620
Earnings: $2,491,970
Emp.: 1,491
Fiscal Year-end: 03/31/24
Nursing Care Services
N.A.I.C.S.: 623110
Toshio Fukuhara (Chm & Co-CEO)

CARE TWENTYONE CORPORATION
2-2-2 Dojima, Kita-ku, Osaka, 530-0003, Japan
Tel.: (81) 664565633
Web Site: https://www.tanoshii-ie.jp
Year Founded: 1993
2373—(TKS)
Rev.: $291,384,820
Assets: $225,596,710
Liabilities: $186,474,090
Net Worth: $39,122,620
Earnings: $42,540
Emp.: 5,906
Fiscal Year-end: 10/31/23
Nursing Care Services
N.A.I.C.S.: 623110
Taira Yoda (Chm & Pres)

CAREBOOK TECHNOLOGIES INC.
1400-2045 Stanley Street, Montreal, H3A 2V4, QC, Canada
Tel.: (514) 499-2848 　　BC
Web Site: https://www.carebook.com
Year Founded: 2018
CRBKF—(OTCIQ)
Rev.: $6,903,484
Assets: $6,904,976
Liabilities: $11,648,790
Net Worth: ($4,743,814)
Earnings: ($13,292,228)
Fiscal Year-end: 12/31/22
Software Development Services
N.A.I.C.S.: 541511
Charles Martin (CTO)

CAREER CO., LTD.
14th floor Carrot Tower 4-1-1 Taishido, Setagaya-ku, Tokyo, 154-0004, Japan
Tel.: (81) 368639450
Web Site: https://www.careergift.co.jp
6198—(TKS)
Rev.: $126,145,280
Assets: $36,201,540
Liabilities: $21,780,480
Net Worth: $14,421,060
Earnings: $2,680,020
Fiscal Year-end: 09/30/23
Human Resource Management Services
N.A.I.C.S.: 541612
Ichiro Kawashima (Founder, Chm & Pres)

CAREER DESIGN CENTER CO., LTD.
Akasaka Long Beach Bldg 3-21-20 Akasaka, Minato-ku, Tokyo, 107-0052, Japan
Tel.: (81) 335601622
Web Site: https://cdc.type.jp
Year Founded: 1993
2410—(TKS)
Rev.: $106,683,280
Assets: $54,614,560
Liabilities: $17,433,680
Net Worth: $37,180,880
Earnings: ($1,635,920)
Fiscal Year-end: 09/30/20
Employment Consulting Services
N.A.I.C.S.: 611710
Hiromi Tada (Chm, Pres, CEO & Dir-Rep)

CAREER POINT LTD.
CP Tower Road No 1 IPIA, Kota, 324 005, Rajasthan, India
Tel.: (91) 7446630500
Web Site: https://www.cpil.in
533260—(BOM)
Rev.: $8,096,375
Assets: $70,864,999
Liabilities: $6,591,039
Net Worth: $64,273,960

Earnings: $3,129,699
Emp.: 206
Fiscal Year-end: 03/31/22
Educational Support Services
N.A.I.C.S.: 611710
Pramod Maheshwari (Chm, CEO & Mng Dir)

CAREER TECHNOLOGY (MFG.) CO., LTD.
No 248 Bo-ai St, Shulin District, Taipei, Taiwan
Tel.: (886) 286868868
Web Site:
https://www.careergroups.com
Year Founded: 1992
6153—(TAI)
Rev.: $321,612,205
Assets: $684,510,488
Liabilities: $284,723,231
Net Worth: $399,787,257
Earnings: ($109,479,737)
Emp.: 4,595
Fiscal Year-end: 12/31/23
Flexible Printed Circuit Mfr
N.A.I.C.S.: 326112
Hsien-Chi Fu (CFO)

Subsidiaries:

Career Electronic (Kunshan) Co., Ltd. (1)
18 Chin-Sha-Chiang South Road Kunshan Development Zone, Kunshan, Jiangshu, China
Tel.: (86) 512 5771 8998
Flexible Printed Circuit Board Mfr
N.A.I.C.S.: 334412

Career Technology (H.K.) Ltd. (1)
Rm 8 13F Laurels Industrial Centre 32 Tai Yau St, San Po Kong, Kowloon, China (Hong Kong)
Tel.: (852) 2 320 1185
Web Site: http://www.careergroups.com
Emp.: 5
Printed Circuits Distr
N.A.I.C.S.: 423690

Career Technology (S) Pte. Ltd. (1)
47 Kallang Pudding Road 11-12, Singapore, 349318, Singapore
Tel.: (65) 6 745 8891
Web Site: http://www.careergroups.com
Sales Range: $50-74.9 Million
Emp.: 3
Printed Circuits Distr
N.A.I.C.S.: 423690
Cecilia Chia (Mgr)

Career Technology (Suzhou) Co., Ltd. (1)
28 Chungqui Road Panyang Industrial Park, Huangdai Town, Suzhou, 215143, Jiangsu, China
Tel.: (86) 51265716688
Web Site: http://www.careergroups.com
Flexible Printed Circuit Mfr
N.A.I.C.S.: 334413
Eric Hsiao (Sr Mgr-Admin Department)

Elcoflex (Suzhou) Co., Ltd. (1)
Suhong Industrial Square Block A2 No 81 Suhong West Street, Suzhou, 215021, Jiangsu, China
Tel.: (86) 5126 767 1225
Web Site: http://www.elcoflex.com
Flexible Printed Circuits Distr
N.A.I.C.S.: 423690

KJC Corporation (1)
44-15 Choong-Moo Building 702-708 Yeouido-dong, Youngdeungpo-gu, Seoul, 702-708, Korea (South)
Tel.: (82) 53633966
Web Site: http://www.kjcor.co.kr
Display Accessories Distr
N.A.I.C.S.: 423610

CAREERINDEX, INC.
1-8-1 Shimomeguro Meguro-Ku, Tokyo, 153-0064, Japan
Tel.: (81) 354347730
Web Site:
http://www.careerindex.co.jp

CareerIndex, Inc.—(Continued)

Year Founded: 2005
6538—(TKS)
Rev.: $24,899,870
Assets: $26,592,030
Liabilities: $12,790,350
Net Worth: $13,801,680
Earnings: ($10,582,610)
Emp.: 37
Fiscal Year-end: 03/31/24
Employment Placement Services
N.A.I.C.S.: 561311
Hirotaka Itakura *(Founder, Chm, Pres & CEO)*

CAREERLINK CO., LTD.
2-1-1 Nishi-Shinjuku Shinjuku-ku, Tokyo Shinjuku Mitsui Building 33rd floor, Tokyo, 163-0433, Japan
Tel.: (81) 363117321
Web Site:
https://www.careerlink.co.jp
6070—(TKS)
Rev.: $289,458,510
Assets: $140,191,490
Liabilities: $44,511,740
Net Worth: $95,679,750
Earnings: $14,548,610
Emp.: 909
Fiscal Year-end: 03/31/24
Employment Placement Services
N.A.I.C.S.: 561311
Motoaki Narisawa *(Pres)*

CAREGEN CO.,LTD.
Caregen Building 46-38 LS-ro 91beon-gil, Dongan-gu, Anyang, 14119, Gyeonggi-do, Korea (South)
Tel.: (82) 314209200
Web Site: https://www.caregen.co.kr
Year Founded: 2001
214370—(KRS)
Rev.: $52,997,917
Assets: $179,531,715
Liabilities: $13,876,591
Net Worth: $165,655,125
Earnings: $20,913,734
Emp.: 179
Fiscal Year-end: 12/31/22
Cosmetics Products Mfr
N.A.I.C.S.: 456120
Yongji Chung *(CEO)*

CAREL INDUSTRIES S.P.A.
Via dell'Industria 11, Brugine, 35020, Padua, Italy
Tel.: (39) 0499716611   IT
Web Site: https://www.careluk.com
Year Founded: 1973
CRL—(ITA)
Rev.: $588,012,087
Assets: $691,197,928
Liabilities: $452,424,995
Net Worth: $238,772,933
Earnings: $67,045,111
Emp.: 2,299
Fiscal Year-end: 12/31/22
Control Systems Developer, Mfr & Dstr
N.A.I.C.S.: 334519
Luigi Rossi Luciani *(Chm)*

Subsidiaries:

Alfaco Polska Sp.z.o.o.   (1)
ul Krakowska 141-155, 50-428, Wroclaw, Poland
Tel.: (48) 713400575
Web Site: https://alfaco.pl
Air Conditioning Systems Whslr
N.A.I.C.S.: 423740

C.R.C. S.r.l.   (1)
Via dell'Industria 11, Brugine, 35020, Padua, Italy
Tel.: (39) 0499731800
Refrigeration Control System Mfr
N.A.I.C.S.: 334512

CFM Sogutma Ve Otomasyon A.S.   (1)
AOSB 10044 St No 9, 35620, Cigli, Izmir, Turkiye
Tel.: (90) 2324590888
Web Site: https://www.cfm.com.tr
Air Conditioning Systems Whslr
N.A.I.C.S.: 423740

Carel (Thailand) Co. Ltd.   (1)
34 Thiam Ruammitr Rd, Huaykwang, Bangkok, 10310, Thailand
Tel.: (66) 2 126 6211
Refrigeration Control System Mfr
N.A.I.C.S.: 334512

Carel ACR Systems India Pvt. Ltd.   (1)
402 403 Vikas Commercial Next to Tridev Apartments Bhakti Marg, Mulund West, Mumbai, 400 080, India
Tel.: (91) 2241192929
Refrigeration Control System Mfr
N.A.I.C.S.: 334512

Carel Asia Ltd.   (1)
Rm 11 8/F Shatin Galleria 18 Shan Mei St Fotan, Shatin, Hong Kong, China (Hong Kong)
Tel.: (852) 26936223
Refrigeration Control System Mfr
N.A.I.C.S.: 334512

Carel Australia Pty Ltd   (1)
Unit 37 11-21 Underwood Rd, Homebush, 2140, NSW, Australia
Tel.: (61) 287629200
Refrigeration Control System Mfr
N.A.I.C.S.: 334512

Carel Controls Iberica SL   (1)
C/ Laurea Miro 401 Nau 10, Sant Feliu de Llobregat, 08980, Barcelona, Spain
Tel.: (34) 933298700
Refrigeration Control System Mfr
N.A.I.C.S.: 334512

Carel Controls South Africa Pty Ltd   (1)
Unit 5 Capital Hill Industrial Park Morkels Close off le Roux Ave, Midrand, Johannesburg, South Africa
Tel.: (27) 118051558
Refrigeration Control System Mfr
N.A.I.C.S.: 334512

Carel Deutschland GmbH   (1)
Am Spielacker 34, 63571, Gelnhausen, Germany
Tel.: (49) 605196290
Refrigeration Control System Mfr
N.A.I.C.S.: 334512

Carel Electronic Suzhou Ltd.   (1)
No 56 Shilin Road, Suzhou, 215151, Jiangsu, China
Tel.: (86) 51289173288
Refrigerator Equipment Mfr
N.A.I.C.S.: 333415

Carel France SAS   (1)
1 Rue Paul, Rieupeyroux, 69800, Saint Priest, France
Tel.: (33) 472478888
Refrigeration Control System Mfr
N.A.I.C.S.: 334512

Carel Japan Co., Ltd.   (1)
Tel.: (81) 364320170
Web Site: https://www.carel-japan.com
Emp.: 1
Refrigeration Control System Mfr
N.A.I.C.S.: 334512

Carel Mexicana S. de RL. de CV.   (1)
Ignacio Sepulveda S/N int 120 Col La Encarnacion, Apodaca, CP 66633, Mexico, NL, Mexico
Tel.: (52) 8110861587
Refrigeration Control System Mfr
N.A.I.C.S.: 334512

Carel Middle East DWC-CLC   (1)
Business Park Oce No A5-1-0106 Dubai Aviation City-Logistics City, PO Box 644328, Dubai, United Arab Emirates
Tel.: (971) 48879359
Refrigeration Control System Mfr
N.A.I.C.S.: 334512

Carel Nordic AB   (1)
Florettgatan 12, 254 67, Helsingborg, Sweden
Tel.: (46) 424506690
Refrigeration Control System Mfr
N.A.I.C.S.: 334512

Carel Russia LLC   (1)
Tel.: (7) 8123229353
Air Conditioning Equipment Mfr & Dstr
N.A.I.C.S.: 333415

Carel Sud America Instrumentacao Eletronica Ltda   (1)
Rodovia Visconde de Porto Seguro 2660-Galpao I Vila Pagano, Valinhos, 13278-327, Brazil
Tel.: (55) 1938266799
Refrigeration Control System Mfr
N.A.I.C.S.: 334512

Carel UK Ltd.   (1)
Unit 2 Roebuck Place 110 Roebuck Road, Chessington, KT9 1EU, United Kingdom
Tel.: (44) 2083913540
Refrigeration Control System Mfr
N.A.I.C.S.: 334512

Carel Ukraine LLC   (1)
Vidradnyi Ave 95 1K, 03061, Kiev, Ukraine
Tel.: (380) 444656612
Refrigeration Control System Mfr
N.A.I.C.S.: 334512

Enginia S.r.l.   (1)
Viale Lombardia 78, 20056, Trezzo-sull Adda, MI, Italy
Tel.: (39) 0295749357
Web Site: https://www.enginiasrl.com
Refrigerator Equipment Mfr
N.A.I.C.S.: 333415

Eurotec Ltd.   (1)
Unit C 750 Great South Road, Penrose, Auckland, 1061, New Zealand
Tel.: (64) 95791990
Web Site: https://eurotec.co.nz
Electronic Equipment Whslr
N.A.I.C.S.: 423690

HygroMatik GmbH   (1)
Lise-Meitner-Str 3, 24558, Henstedt-Ulzburg, 24558, Germany
Tel.: (49) 41938950
Web Site: http://www.hygromatik.de
Sales Range: $25-49.9 Million
Emp.: 50
Industrial & Commercial Fan & Blower Mfr
N.A.I.C.S.: 333413
Maike Nielsen *(Reg Mgr)*

Kiona Sp. Z o.o.   (1)
Street Trzy Lipy 3, 80172, Gdansk, Poland
Tel.: (48) 221046000
Software Services
N.A.I.C.S.: 541511

Klingenburg GmbH   (1)
Brusseler Str 77, 45968, Gladbeck, Germany
Tel.: (49) 204396360
Web Site: https://www.klingenburg.de
Heat Exchanger Mfr
N.A.I.C.S.: 332410

Klingenburg International Sp. z o.o.   (1)
Ul Metalowcow 5, 58100, Swidnica, Poland
Tel.: (48) 748515400
Web Site: https://www.klingenburg.pl
Heat Exchanger Mfr
N.A.I.C.S.: 332410

Klingenburg UK Ltd.   (1)
Unit 8 The Glenmore Centre Shearway Business Park Pent Road, Folkestone, CT19 4RJ, Kent, United Kingdom
Tel.: (44) 1303275598
Web Site: https://www.klingenburg.uk
Electric Equipment Mfr
N.A.I.C.S.: 334419

Klingenburg USA, LLC   (1)
2626 Glenwood Ave Ste 550, Raleigh, NC 27608
Tel.: (336) 884-5050
Heat Exchanger Mfr
N.A.I.C.S.: 332410

Recuperator S.p.A.   (1)

Via Valfurva 13, 20027, Rescaldina, MI, Italy
Tel.: (39) 033118531
Web Site: https://www.recuperator.eu
Solar Energy Equipment Distr
N.A.I.C.S.: 423690

Senva Inc.   (1)
1825 NW 167th Pl, Beaverton, OR 97006
Tel.: (503) 336-1273
Web Site: https://senvainc.com
Sensor Mfr
N.A.I.C.S.: 334419

CARELABS CO., LTD.
11th floor Estawor 16 Yeoksam-ro 2-gil, Gangnam-gu, Seoul, Korea (South)
Tel.: (82) 269292340
Web Site: https://www.carelabs.co.kr
Year Founded: 2012
263700—(KRS)
Rev.: $67,194,714
Assets: $138,565,571
Liabilities: $68,326,001
Net Worth: $70,239,570
Earnings: ($20,037,023)
Emp.: 73
Fiscal Year-end: 12/31/22
Software Development Services
N.A.I.C.S.: 541511

CAREMILE CO., LTD.
14th Floor Seshin Building 541 Dosan-daero, Gangnam-gu, Seoul, 06136, Korea (South)
Tel.: (82) 1644 8567   KR
Web Site: https://www.caremile.co.kr
Year Founded: 2017
Emp.: 100
Medical Instrument Mfr & Distr
N.A.I.C.S.: 339112

CAREMOLI SPA
via Ettore Majorana 10, Nova Milanese, 20834, Monza e Brianza, Italy
Tel.: (39) 0362364567
Web Site:
http://www.caremoligroup.com
Year Founded: 1998
Sales Range: $10-24.9 Million
Food Product Manufacturing
N.A.I.C.S.: 311999
Andrea Caremoli *(Pres & CEO)*

Subsidiaries:

Caremoli Deutschland GmbH   (1)
Am Wallgraben 99, Stuttgart, 70565, Germany
Tel.: (49) 7117072000
Grain Product Distr
N.A.I.C.S.: 424590

Caremoli India, Pvt. Ltd.   (1)
E 261-262 RIICO Agrofood Park Boranada, Jodhpur, 342003, Rajasthan, India
Tel.: (91) 9414102900
Grain Product Distr
N.A.I.C.S.: 424590
Vinay dhir *(Mgr-Export Documentation)*

Caremoli USA, Inc.   (1)
1110 Brickell Ave Ste 407, Miami, FL 33131
Tel.: (305) 579-4290
Web Site: http://www.caremoligroup.com
Sales Range: $1-9.9 Million
Emp.: 50
Food Product Manufacturing
N.A.I.C.S.: 311999
Daryna Piddubna *(Mgr-Acctg)*

CARENET INC.
Sumitomo Fudosan Chiyoda Fujimi Bldg 1- 8-19, Chiyoda-ku, Tokyo, 1020071, Japan
Tel.: (81) 352145800
Web Site: https://www.carenet.co.jp
Year Founded: 1996
2150—(TKS)
Rev.: $72,566,150
Assets: $100,451,120

Liabilities: $18,909,030
Net Worth: $81,542,090
Earnings: $10,705,900
Emp.: 100
Fiscal Year-end: 12/31/23
Medical Support Services
N.A.I.C.S.: 541690
Motoyasu Ono *(Chm & CEO)*

CAREPLUS GROUP BERHAD

Lot 120 and 121 Jalan Senawang 3
Senawang Industrial Estate, 70450,
Seremban, Negeri Sembilan, Malaysia
Tel.: (60) 66772781
Web Site: https://www.careplus.com
CAREPLS—(KLS)
Rev.: $65,057,832
Assets: $76,319,824
Liabilities: $19,482,632
Net Worth: $56,837,193
Earnings: ($46,707,894)
Emp.: 730
Fiscal Year-end: 06/30/23
Glove Mfr
N.A.I.C.S.: 315990
Sor Hua Tea *(Sec)*

Subsidiaries:

Careglove Global Sdn. Bhd.   **(1)**
Lot 17479 Lorong Senawang 3/2 Off Jalan
Senawang 3, Senawang Industrial Estate,
70450, Seremban, Negeri Sembilan, Malaysia
Tel.: (60) 67292133
Hand Glove Mfr & Distr
N.A.I.C.S.: 315990

MASTERCLEAN TECHNOLOGIES
(M) SDN BHD   **(1)**
Lot 110 Lorong Senawang 4/3 Off Jalan
Senawang Empat, Senawang Industrial Estate, 70450, Seremban, Negeri Sembilan,
Malaysia
Tel.: (60) 66772781
Web Site: http://www.careplus.com
Gloves Mfr & Whslr
N.A.I.C.S.: 339113

NEXV Synergy Sdn. Bhd.   **(1)**
Lot PT 3962 & 3963 Jalan Haruan 2 Pusat
Komersial Oakland, 70300, Seremban,
Negeri Sembilan, Malaysia   **(100%)**
Tel.: (60) 67292180
Web Site: https://www.evdrive.com.my
Electric Vehicle Distr
N.A.I.C.S.: 423110

Rubbercare Protection Products Sdn
Bhd   **(1)**
Lot 120 121 Jalan Senawang 3 Senawang
Industrial Estate, Senawang Industrial Estate, 70450, Seremban, Negeri Sembilan,
Malaysia
Tel.: (60) 66772781
Web Site:
   https://www.rubbercare.careplus.com
Sales Range: $50-74.9 Million
Emp.: 96
Rubber Gloves Mfr & Distr
N.A.I.C.S.: 339113

CARERAY DIGITAL MEDICAL TECHNOLOGY CO., LTD.

5th Floor Building B3 BIOBAY No
218 Xinghu Street, Suzhou, 215123,
Jiangsu, China
Tel.: (86) 51286860288
Web Site: https://www.careray.com
Year Founded: 2007
688607—(SHG)
Rev.: $28,721,796
Assets: $126,736,735
Liabilities: $8,217,121
Net Worth: $118,519,615
Earnings: ($789,596)
Fiscal Year-end: 12/31/22
Medical Product Mfr & Distr
N.A.I.C.S.: 339112
Liu Jianqiang *(Chm & Gen Mgr)*

CARERX CORPORATION

320 Bay St Suite 1200, Toronto, M5H
4A6, ON, Canada
Tel.: (647) 361-4499   Ca
Web Site: https://www.carerx.ca
Year Founded: 2001
CRRX—(TSX)
Rev.: $205,450,196
Assets: $221,241,300
Liabilities: $156,869,826
Net Worth: $64,371,474
Earnings: $17,781,224
Emp.: 555
Fiscal Year-end: 12/31/21
Healthcare Services Including Surgical Procedures, Disability Management, Third-Party Medical Assessments & Drug Trial Administration
Support
N.A.I.C.S.: 622110
Kevin Dalton *(Chm)*

Subsidiaries:

Don Mills Surgical Unit Ltd.   **(1)**
20 Wynford Dr Ste 103, Don Mills, Toronto,
M3C 1J4, ON, Canada
Tel.: (416) 441-2111
Web Site:
   http://www.centrichealthsurgical.com
Sales Range: $10-24.9 Million
Emp.: 10
Rehabilitation Services
N.A.I.C.S.: 624310
Sara Mooney *(Gen Mgr)*

Work Able Centres Inc.   **(1)**
65 Cedar Pointe Drive Unit 8088, Barrie,
L4N 5R7, ON, Canada
Tel.: (705) 727-1688
Web Site: http://www.workable.ca
Sales Range: $10-24.9 Million
Emp.: 4
Rehabilitation Services
N.A.I.C.S.: 624310
Shawn Ratcliffe *(Gen Mgr)*

Subsidiary (Domestic):

Work Able Centres North York
Inc.   **(2)**
4 Lansing Sq, North York, M2J 5A2, ON,
Canada
Tel.: (416) 490-8484
Web Site: http://www.workable.ca
Sales Range: $10-24.9 Million
Emp.: 100
Rehabilitation Services
N.A.I.C.S.: 624310
Mike Weller *(Gen Mgr)*

CARESPAN HEALTH, INC.

Royal Centre 1055 West Georgia St
Suite 1500, Vancouver, V6E 4N7,
BC, Canada
Tel.: (604) 602-0001   BC
Year Founded: 2018
CSPN—(TSXV)
Rev.: $5,756,681
Assets: $2,697,445
Liabilities: $3,396,970
Net Worth: ($699,525)
Earnings: ($6,860,852)
Fiscal Year-end: 12/31/21
Asset Management Services
N.A.I.C.S.: 523940
Rembert de Villa *(CEO)*

CARESTREAM MEDICAL LTD.

Unit 103-19099 25 Avenue, Surrey,
BC, Canada
Tel.: (888) 310-2186
Web Site:
   http://www.carestreammedical.com
Medical Products Mfr & Distr
N.A.I.C.S.: 339112
Sarj Dhesi *(Pres)*

Subsidiaries:

Christie Medical Holdings, Inc.   **(1)**
1256 Union Ave 3rd Floor, Memphis, TN
38104

Tel.: (901) 721-0330
Web Site: http://www.christiemed.com
Medical Laboratory Operating Services
N.A.I.C.S.: 621511

CARETEQ LIMITED

Level 10 99 Queen St, Melbourne,
3000, VIC, Australia
Tel.: (61) 395634212   AU
Web Site:
   https://www.careteq.com.au
Year Founded: 2016
CTQ—(ASX)
Rev.: $4,141,559
Assets: $4,935,747
Liabilities: $2,618,631
Net Worth: $2,317,115
Earnings: ($2,687,375)
Fiscal Year-end: 06/30/23
Information Technology Services
N.A.I.C.S.: 541512
Alex Boyd *(COO)*

Subsidiaries:

Embedded Health Solutions Pty.
Ltd.   **(1)**
1 01 3 Joseph Avenue, Mentone, 3194,
VIC, Australia   **(100%)**
Tel.: (61) 395634212
Web Site: https://embeddedhealth.com.au
Ward Medication Management Services
N.A.I.C.S.: 621999

CAREY GROUP PLC

Carey House Great Central Way,
Wembley, HA9 0HR, Middlesex,
United Kingdom
Tel.: (44) 2089000221
Web Site: http://www.carey-plc.co.uk
Rev.: $247,070,828
Emp.: 70
Construction Services
N.A.I.C.S.: 236220
John Carey *(Chm)*

Subsidiaries:

Carey Group PLC   **(1)**
Carey House Dardistown Cloughran, Dublin, Ireland
Tel.: (353) 18427300
Building Construction Services
N.A.I.C.S.: 236220
Joseph O'Hagan *(Dir-Ops)*

CARGIANT LTD.

44-45 Hythe Road, London, NW10
6RS, White City, United Kingdom
Tel.: (44) 20 8969 5511
Web Site: http://www.cargiant.co.uk
Year Founded: 1977
Sales Range: $500-549.9 Million
Emp.: 560
New & Used Car Dealer
N.A.I.C.S.: 441110
Geoffrey Warren *(Chm)*

CARGILLS (CEYLON) PLC

Tel.: (94) 112427777
Web Site:
   https://www.cargillsceylon.com
CARG—(COL)
Rev.: $727,201,403
Assets: $523,720,888
Liabilities: $368,794,429
Net Worth: $154,926,460
Earnings: $24,145,990
Emp.: 9,485
Fiscal Year-end: 03/31/22
Ice Cream & Dairy Products Mfr
N.A.I.C.S.: 311514
Louis R. Page *(Chm)*

CARGILLS BANK LIMITED

No 696 Galle Road, Colombo, 03, Sri
Lanka
Tel.: (94) 11 764 06 40

Web Site:
   http://www.cargillsbank.com
Rev.: $23,479,327
Assets: $184,565,035
Liabilities: $124,374,203
Net Worth: $60,190,833
Earnings: $670,515
Emp.: 586
Fiscal Year-end: 12/31/18
Banking Services
N.A.I.C.S.: 522110
Sajeewanie Solangaarachchi *(Asst
Gen Mgr-Legal)*

CARGO BOAT DEVELOPMENT CO. PLC

328 Galle Road, 3, Colombo, 3, Sri
Lanka
Tel.: (94) 1124489689
Year Founded: 1980
CABO—(COL)
Rev.: $344,193
Assets: $7,611,122
Liabilities: $483,499
Net Worth: $7,127,623
Earnings: $474,030
Fiscal Year-end: 03/31/23
Real Estate Services
N.A.I.C.S.: 531390

CARGO CARRIERS LTD.

11a Grace Road Mountainview Observatory, Johannesburg, 2198,
South Africa
Tel.: (27) 114858700
Web Site:
   http://www.cargocarriers.co.za
Rev.: $52,138,494
Assets: $61,624,806
Liabilities: $21,451,633
Net Worth: $40,173,174
Earnings: $1,947,043
Emp.: 538
Fiscal Year-end: 02/28/18
Logistics, Transport & Information
Technology Solutions
N.A.I.C.S.: 484110
Garth D. Bolton *(Exec Dir)*

CARGOJET INC.

2281 North Sheridan Way, Mississauga, L5K 2S3, ON, Canada
Tel.: (905) 501-7373
Web Site: https://www.cargojet.com
Year Founded: 2005
CJT—(TSX)
Rev.: $592,811,784
Assets: $1,165,440,744
Liabilities: $636,306,552
Net Worth: $529,134,192
Earnings: $130,953,672
Emp.: 1,126
Fiscal Year-end: 12/31/21
Air Cargo Services
N.A.I.C.S.: 488190
Ajay K. Virmani *(Pres & CEO)*

Subsidiaries:

Cargojet Holdings Ltd.   **(1)**
3486 21 Street East Edmonton International
Airport, Edmonton, T5J 2T2, AB, Canada
Tel.: (780) 890-8606
Emp.: 12
Investment Management Service
N.A.I.C.S.: 523940
Sean Walsh *(Gen Mgr)*

Cargojet Partnership Ltd   **(1)**
Unit 170-4840 Miller Road, Richmond,
V7d1k7, BC, Canada
Tel.: (604) 244-8868
Emp.: 50
Scheduled Freight Air Transportation Services
N.A.I.C.S.: 481112
Lyle Gibson *(Gen Mgr)*

CARGOLUX AIRLINES INTERNATIONAL S.A.

Cargolux Airlines International S.A.—(Continued)

Luxembourg Airport, L-2990, Luxem-
bourg, Luxembourg
Tel.: (352) 4211 3925
Web Site: http://www.cargolux.com
Year Founded: 1970
Sales Range: $5-14.9 Billion
Emp.: 1,710
Cargo Airlines
N.A.I.C.S.: 481112
Richard Forson (CEO)

CARGOPORT LOGISTICS, C.A.
Calle Guasipati Edificio Piarde Edif
Tv Guayana Ofic 2-E Piso 2, Puerto
Ordaz, Bolivar, Venezuela
Tel.: (58) 2869235515
Web Site: http://www.cargoport.com
Logistic Services
N.A.I.C.S.: 488510

**CARGOSOL LOGISTICS LIM-
ITED**
319320 Lodha Supremus Mahakali
Caves Road Near Hotel Bindras,
Andheri East, Mumbai, 400099, India
Tel.: (91) 2266126000
Web Site: https://www.cargosol.com
Year Founded: 2004
543621—(BOM)
Rev.: $20,422,385
Assets: $7,742,869
Liabilities: $4,530,819
Net Worth: $3,212,050
Earnings: $504,286
Emp.: 75
Fiscal Year-end: 03/31/23
Logistics Consulting Servies
N.A.I.C.S.: 541614

CARGOTEC CORPORATION
Porkkalankatu 5, 00180, Helsinki,
Finland
Tel.: (358) 207774000   FI
Web Site: https://www.cargotec.com
CGCBV—(HEL)
Rev.: $4,071,615,600
Assets: $4,946,490,952
Liabilities: $3,046,403,672
Net Worth: $1,900,087,280
Earnings: $303,006,808
Emp.: 11,174
Fiscal Year-end: 12/31/21
Cargo-Handling Solutions for Ships,
Ports, Terminals & Defense Custom-
ers
N.A.I.C.S.: 488320
Ilkka Herlin (Chm)

Subsidiaries:

All Set Marine Lashing AB   (1)
Gustavslundsv Gen 151A, Box 14112, 167
14, Bromma, Sweden
Tel.: (46) 8 807570
Web Site: http://www.allset.se
Cargo Handling Services
N.A.I.C.S.: 488320

Bromma (Malaysia) Sdn. Bhd.   (1)
Lot 19 Jalan Kelebang 1/6 Zon Perindus-
trian Bebas Kinta, 31200, Chemor, Perak,
Malaysia
Tel.: (60) 5 290 9200
Web Site: http://www.bromma.com
Sales Range: $100-124.9 Million
Emp.: 450
Crane Spreader & Rotator Mfr
N.A.I.C.S.: 333924

Cargotec (ARE) GULF WLL   (1)
Plot No 50 Shop Nos 12 & 13 M-9 Mussa-
fah Industrial Area n a, Abu Dhabi, United
Arab Emirates
Tel.: (971) 25541690
Crane & Hydraulic Equipment Distr
N.A.I.C.S.: 423830

Cargotec (Shanghai) Trading Company Limited   (1)
No 191 Hua Shen Rd Wai Gao Qiao Free

Trade Zone, Shanghai, 200131, China
Tel.: (86) 2158666658
Cargo Handling Services
N.A.I.C.S.: 488320

Cargotec ACT B.V.   (1)
Proostwetering 26, Utrecht, 3543 AE, Neth-
erlands
Tel.: (31) 302415422
Sales Range: $25-49.9 Million
Emp.: 15
Industrial Control Equipment Mfr
N.A.I.C.S.: 335314
Rudi De Vos Burchart (Acct Mgr)

Cargotec Argentina S.R.L.   (1)
Goncalves Dias 466, Barracas, 1274, Bue-
nos Aires, Argentina
Tel.: (54) 115263307
Web Site: http://www.cargotecargentina.com
Cargo Handling Services
N.A.I.C.S.: 488320

Cargotec Australia Pty. Ltd.   (1)
Ste 2 Level 2 768 Lorimer St, Melbourne,
3207, VIC, Australia
Tel.: (61) 392347000
Web Site: http://www.cargotec.com
Sales Range: $25-49.9 Million
Emp.: 24
Cargo Handling Services
N.A.I.C.S.: 488320

Cargotec Belgium NV   (1)
Heizegemweg 7, 2030, Antwerp, Belgium
Tel.: (32) 3 541 77 22
Web Site: http://www.kalmarbelgium.be
Cargo Handling Equipment Distr
N.A.I.C.S.: 423830
Pol Lenaerts (Mgr-Sls)

Cargotec Brazil Industria e Comercio
de Equipamentos para Movimentacao
de Cargas Ltda   (1)
Av Santos Dummont 3365 Vicente de Car-
valho Guaruja, Sao Paulo, 11460-006, Bra-
zil
Tel.: (55) 13 3308 2222
Web Site: http://www.cargotec.com
Emp.: 50
Marine Cargo Handling Services
N.A.I.C.S.: 488320

Cargotec Brazil Ltda   (1)
Rua Alexandre Herculano 197, Santos,
11050-031, Sao Paulo, Brazil
Tel.: (55) 1333082222
Web Site: http://www.kalmarglobal.com.br
Cargo Handling Services
N.A.I.C.S.: 488320

Cargotec CHS Asia Pacific Pte
Ltd.   (1)
15 Tukang Innovation Drive, Singapore,
618299, Singapore
Tel.: (65) 65973888
Web Site: http://www.kalmarglobal.com
Cargo Handling Services
N.A.I.C.S.: 488320

Cargotec Chile - S.A.   (1)
El Juncal 071-B Portezuelo, Quilicura, San-
tiago, Chile
Tel.: (56) 27386993
Web Site: http://www.cargotec.com
Sales Range: $25-49.9 Million
Emp.: 40
Marine Cargo Handling Services
N.A.I.C.S.: 488320

Cargotec Crane & Electrical Services
Inc.   (1)
1180 McLester St Ste 2, Elizabeth, NJ
07201
Tel.: (908) 351-0285
Web Site: http://www.kalmarusa.com
Cargo Handling Services
N.A.I.C.S.: 488320

Cargotec Cyprus Ltd.   (1)
Titos Building Office 201 58 Gladstone
Street, Limassol, 3041, Cyprus
Tel.: (357) 25763670
Web Site: http://www.cargotec.com
Emp.: 2
Marine Cargo Handling Services
N.A.I.C.S.: 488320

Cargotec Czech Republic s.r.o   (1)
Podebradska 57 Prague 9, Prague, 19800,
Czech Republic

Tel.: (420) 226 238 600
Web Site: http://www.cargotec.com
Sales Range: $25-49.9 Million
Emp.: 2
Cargo Handling Services
N.A.I.C.S.: 488320

Cargotec Engineering Italy S.r.l. (1)
Via Massa Avenza 2, Massa, 54100, Italy
Tel.: (39) 0585256015
Sales Range: $25-49.9 Million
Emp.: 8
Marine Cargo Handling Services
N.A.I.C.S.: 488320
Claudia Fontanini (Gen Mgr)

Cargotec Finland Oy   (1)
Porkkalankatu 5, 00180, Helsinki, Finland
Tel.: (358) 207774000
Web Site: https://www.cargotec.com
Emp.: 10,000
Load Handling Equipment & Logistics Ser-
vices
N.A.I.C.S.: 488320

Subsidiary (Non-US):

Cargotec Austria GmbH   (2)
Portendorf 8, Klagenfurt, 9020, Austria
Tel.: (43) 463 717 88
Web Site: http://www.kalmarind.at
Sales Range: $25-49.9 Million
Emp.: 45
Cargo Handling Equipment Distr
N.A.I.C.S.: 423830

Cargotec France S.A.S.   (2)
38-40 Ave Roger Hennequin, PO Box 34, F
78192, Trappes, Cedex, France
Tel.: (33) 130511836
Web Site: http://www.hiab.fr
Sales Range: $50-74.9 Million
Net Worth: $725,468
Emp.: 65
Mfr Cranes & Loaders & Industrial Equip-
ment & Machinery
N.A.I.C.S.: 333923

Cargotec Italia S.r.l.   (2)
Via Al Molo Giano, I-16128, Genoa, Italy
Tel.: (39) 03351394779
Web Site: http://www.cargotec.com
Sales Range: $1-9.9 Million
Emp.: 14
Cargo Access Equipment & Engineering &
Service Solutions for the Maritime Transpor-
tation Industry
N.A.I.C.S.: 488320

Cargotec Netherlands B.V.   (2)
Hesselingen 42, PO Box 1086, 7944 HR,
Meppel, Netherlands
Tel.: (31) 522253831
Web Site: http://www.hiab.nl
Sales Range: $25-49.9 Million
Emp.: 100
Mfr of Cranes, Loaders & Industrial Machin-
ery
N.A.I.C.S.: 333924

Cargotec Netherlands b.v.   (2)
Waalhaven OZ 123 22, 3081 AD, Rotter-
dam, Netherlands
Tel.: (31) 102832121
Web Site: http://www.macgregor-group.com
Sales Range: $1-9.9 Million
Emp.: 22
Cargo Access Equipment & Engineering &
Service Solutions for the Maritime Transpor-
tation Industry
N.A.I.C.S.: 488320

Cargotec Poland Sp. Z O.O.   (2)
Poznanska 94 Jawczyce, 05-850, Ozarow
Mazowiecki, Poland
Tel.: (48) 22 721 0270
Web Site: https://www.hiab.com
Sales Range: $25-49.9 Million
Emp.: 11
Engineeering Services
N.A.I.C.S.: 541330

Cargotec Rus LLC   (2)
Naberezhnaya Obvodnogo Kanala 118A,
Liter ZH Office 503, Saint Petersburg,
190005, Russia
Tel.: (7) 8123375450
Web Site: http://www.cargotec.com
Sales Range: $50-74.9 Million
Emp.: 22

Bulk Handling Equipment, Hatch Covers,
Cargo Cranes, Lashing Bridges, Lashing
Equipment, Offshore Loading Solutions &
RoRo Equipment
N.A.I.C.S.: 333120

Subsidiary (US):

Cargotec USA Inc.   (2)
12233 Williams Rd, Perrysburg, OH 43551
Tel.: (419) 402-0000
Web Site: http://www.hiab.com
Sales Range: $50-74.9 Million
Emp.: 148
Mfr of Fork Lifts & Cranes
N.A.I.C.S.: 423830
Roland Sunden (Pres)

Subsidiary (Non-US):

Hiab AB   (2)
Kopmanbergsvagen 5, 824 83, Hudiksvall,
Sweden
Tel.: (46) 65091442
Web Site: http://www.hiab.com
Sales Range: $100-124.9 Million
Emp.: 30
Loader Cranes Manufacturing & Marketing
N.A.I.C.S.: 333924
Scott Hall (Sr VP-Sls & Svcs)

Subsidiary (US):

Galfab, Inc.   (3)
612 West 11th St, Winamac, IN 46996-1211
Tel.: (574) 946-7767
Web Site: https://www.galfab.com
Waste Handling Equipment Mfr
N.A.I.C.S.: 333248
Don Galbreath (Founder)

Subsidiary (Non-US):

Hiab Chile S.A.   (2)
El Juncal 071 B, Portezuelo, Santiago, Qui-
licura, Chile
Tel.: (56) 27386993
Web Site: http://www.hiab.cl
Sales Range: $25-49.9 Million
Emp.: 45
Mfr Loader Cranes
N.A.I.C.S.: 423830

Hiab Cranes, S.L.   (2)
Poligono Industrial de Malpica Calle E 86,
Zaragoza, 50016, Spain
Tel.: (34) 976579800
Web Site: http://www.hiab.com
Sales Range: $50-74.9 Million
Net Worth: $379,407
Emp.: 200
Mfr Loader Cranes
N.A.I.C.S.: 333923

Hiab Denmark A/S   (2)
Industrikrogen 14, 2635, Ishoj, Denmark
Tel.: (45) 49192424
Web Site: http://www.zepro.dk
Sales Range: Less than $1 Million
Net Worth: $1,005,100
Loader Cranes Manufacturing, Sales & Mar-
keting
N.A.I.C.S.: 333924

Hiab GmbH   (2)
Emil Berliner Strasse 29, PO Box 101446,
Langenhagen, 30835, Germany
Tel.: (49) 51177050
Web Site: http://www.hiab.com
Rev.: $445,615,904
Emp.: 80
Cargo-Handling Solutions
N.A.I.C.S.: 488320

Hiab Hana Co. Ltd.   (2)
356 Taesung-Ri Gangnae-Myon,
Chongwon-gun, Chongju, 363-893, Chun-
gbuk, Korea (South)
Tel.: (82) 43 231 6300
Web Site: http://www.hiabhana.com
Sales Range: $10-24.9 Million
Net Worth: $796,500
Emp.: 74
Loader Cranes Mfr & Sales
N.A.I.C.S.: 333924

Hiab KK   (2)
3831 1 Ikonobe Cho, Tsuzuki Ku, Yokohama, 224 0053, Kanagawa, Japan
Tel.: (81) 459348291
Web Site: http://www.hiab.jp

Sales Range: $25-49.9 Million
Emp.: 44
Crane Equipment Mfg & Sales
N.A.I.C.S.: 423830
Fhinichi Tomioka *(Pres)*

Hiab Ltd.   **(2)**
Cargotec Industrial Pk, Ellesmere, SY12
9JW, United Kingdom
Tel.: (44) 1691623100
Web Site: http://www.hiab.com
Sales Range: $25-49.9 Million
Emp.: 55
Mfr Loader Cranes & Ground Level De-
mountables
N.A.I.C.S.: 333923

Hiab S.A.   **(2)**
Poligono Las Fronteras, 28850, Torrejon de
Ardoz, Madrid, Spain
Tel.: (34) 916270100
Web Site: http://www.hiab.com
Sales Range: $50-74.9 Million
Net Worth: $12,455,786
Emp.: 44
Loader Cranes Mfr, Sales, Marketing & Ser-
vice
N.A.I.C.S.: 333924

Hiab S.A. de C.V.   **(2)**
San Andres Atoto 16 A Col San Esteban,
53550, Naucalpan, Edo De Mexico, Mexico
Tel.: (52) 5553587411
Web Site: http://www.hiab.com.mx
Sales Range: $1-9.9 Million
Emp.: 70
Mfr Crane & Loaders
N.A.I.C.S.: 333923

Hiab S.A./N.V.   **(2)**
Parc Industriel 8, BE 1440, Wauthier Brain,
Belgium
Tel.: (32) 23662036
Web Site: http://www.hiab.be
Sales Range: $10-24.9 Million
Net Worth: $354,600
Emp.: 15
Mfr Cranes & Loaders
N.A.I.C.S.: 333923

Kalmar B.V.   **(2)**
Wilhelminakade 901, 3072 AP, Rotterdam,
Netherlands
Tel.: (31) 10 294 6666
Web Site: https://www.kalmar.nl
Mfr of Cranes, Loaders, Tractors, De-
mountables & Other Industrial Machinery
N.A.I.C.S.: 333923

Kalmar Belgium nv/sa   **(2)**
Heizegemweg 7, 2030, Antwerp, Belgium
Tel.: (32) 35410966
Mfr of Cranes, Tractors, Forklifts & Other
Industrial Machinery
N.A.I.C.S.: 811310

Kalmar Danmark A/S   **(2)**
Industrivej 3, 3550, Slangerup, Denmark
Tel.: (45) 70220260
Web Site: http://www.kalmarind.com
General Industrial Machine Mfr
N.A.I.C.S.: 333995

Kalmar Industries AB   **(2)**
Torggatan 3, 169908, Lidhult, Sweden
Tel.: (46) 37226010
Web Site: http://www.kalmarind.com
Emp.: 835
Mfr of Cranes, Tractors, Forklifts & Other
Industrial Machinery
N.A.I.C.S.: 333923

Subsidiary (Non-US):

Cargotec Asia Limited   **(3)**
2nd Fl Yoo Hoo Tower 38-42 Kwai Fung
Crescent, Kwai Chung, NT, China (Hong
Kong)
Tel.: (852) 29448383
Web Site: http://www.kalmarglobal.com
Sales Range: $50-74.9 Million
Emp.: 90
Develop, Mfr & Sell Material Handling
Equipment
N.A.I.C.S.: 423390

Subsidiary (Domestic):

Cargotec Sweden AB   **(3)**
Kronborgsgrand 23, 164 46, Kista, Sweden
Tel.: (46) 84453800

Web Site: https://www.kalmarglobal.se
Sales Range: $25-49.9 Million
Net Worth: $2,760,600
Emp.: 120
Mfr of Cranes, Forklifts, Demountables &
Other Industrial Machinery
N.A.I.C.S.: 333923

Subsidiary (Non-US):

**Kalmar Equipment (Australia) Pty.
Ltd.**   **(3)**
Ste 2 Level 2 768 Lorimer St, Melbourne,
3207, VIC, Australia
Tel.: (61) 397010311
Web Site: http://www.kalmar.com
Emp.: 50
Heavy Equipment Repair Services
N.A.I.C.S.: 811310

Kalmar France S.A.   **(3)**
265 Boulevard Jules Durand, 76085, Le
Havre, France
Tel.: (33) 235248300
Web Site: http://www.kalmar.fr
Sales Range: $10-24.9 Million
Emp.: 35
Mfr Industrial Machinery & Equipment
N.A.I.C.S.: 333248

**Kalmar HebeFahrzeuge
HandelsgesmbH**   **(3)**
Porpendors 8, 9020, Klagenfurt, Austria
Tel.: (43) 463717880
Web Site: http://www.kalmarind.com
Sales Range: $25-49.9 Million
Emp.: 50
Mfr Industrial Heavy Equipment
N.A.I.C.S.: 336999

Subsidiary (US):

Kalmar Industries Corporation   **(3)**
21 Englehard Dr, Monroe, NJ 08831-3722
Tel.: (609) 860-0150
Web Site: http://www.kalmarind.com
Sales Range: $25-49.9 Million
Emp.: 50
Inland Material Handling Equipment Service
& Sales
N.A.I.C.S.: 339999
Andy DePalma *(Mgr-Customer Support)*

**Kalmar Industries Magnum
Division**   **(3)**
1301 Cherokee Trace, White Oak, TX
75693-3530
Tel.: (903) 759-5490
Sales Range: $1-9.9 Million
Emp.: 44
Mfr Industrial Trucks & Tractors
N.A.I.C.S.: 333924

Subsidiary (Non-US):

Kalmar Ltd.   **(3)**
Cargotec Industrial Park, Ellesmere, SY12
9JW, United Kingdom
Tel.: (44) 1691 623100
Web Site: http://www.kalmarind.co.uk
Sales Range: $100-124.9 Million
Emp.: 60
Cargo Handling Solutions
N.A.I.C.S.: 488320
Antti Kaunonen *(Pres)*

Kalmar Norway AS   **(3)**
Carl Bergersens vei 5, 1481, Hagan, Nor-
way
Tel.: (47) 67062020
Web Site: https://www.kalmar.no
Cargo Handling Services
N.A.I.C.S.: 488320
Maija Eklof *(VP-Mktg & Comm)*

Kalmar South East Asia Pte. Ltd.   **(3)**
No 2 Gul St 4, Jurong, 629234, Singapore
Tel.: (65) 68653880
Sales Range: $1-9.9 Million
Net Worth: $302,827
Emp.: 50
Heavy Industrial Equipment
N.A.I.C.S.: 333248
Edward Soon Jan Houng *(Mng Dir)*

Division (US):

Kalmar USA Inc.   **(3)**
415 E Dundee St, Ottawa, KS 66067-1543

Tel.: (785) 242-2200
Web Site: https://www.kalmarusa.com
Sales Range: $100-124.9 Million
Emp.: 305
Industrial Truck Mfr
N.A.I.C.S.: 333924

Subsidiary (Domestic):

Kalmar Industries Oy AB   **(2)**
Vainetin Kapu 5, PO Box 387, Nuolialantic
62, 33101, Tampere, Finland
Tel.: (358) 32658111
Web Site: http://www.kalmarind.com
Mfr of Tractors, Forklifts, Loaders, Cranes &
Other Industrial Machinery
N.A.I.C.S.: 333923

Subsidiary (Non-US):

**Kalmar Industries South Africa (Pty)
Ltd**   **(2)**
Off 1100 11th Flr Mansion Hse 12 Joe
Slovo St, Durban, 4001, Kwazulu-Natal,
South Africa
Tel.: (27) 31 327 1808
Web Site: http://www.cargotec.com
Emp.: 42
Business Management Consulting Services
N.A.I.C.S.: 541611

**Kalmar Port Machinery (Shenzhen)
Co., Ltd**   **(2)**
No 191 Hua Shen Road Wai Gao Qiao
Free Trade Zone, Shanghai, 200131, China
Tel.: (86) 755 2685 6700
Web Site: http://www.kalmarasia.com
Cargo Handling Equipment Distr
N.A.I.C.S.: 423830

Subsidiary (Domestic):

Loglift Jonsered AB   **(2)**
Nesteentie 36, FI 21200, Raisio, Finland
Tel.: (358) 204552599
Web Site: http://www.cargotech.com
Sales Range: $10-24.9 Million
Emp.: 200
Mfr Timber Cranes & Production Loaders
N.A.I.C.S.: 333923

Cargotec Germany Gmbh   **(1)**
Emil-Berliner-Strasse 29, Langenhagen,
30851, Germany
Tel.: (49) 511 77050
Marine Cargo Handling Services
N.A.I.C.S.: 488320

**Cargotec Holding Netherlands
B.V.**   **(1)**
Steenwijkerstraatweg 78 7942, 7942 HR,
Meppel, Netherlands
Tel.: (31) 522253831
Investment Management Service
N.A.I.C.S.: 523999

Cargotec Holding Sweden AB   **(1)**
70 Kungsgatan, Stockholm, 111 22, Swe-
den
Tel.: (46) 86775300
Investment Management Service
N.A.I.C.S.: 523999

Cargotec Iberia SA   **(1)**
C/Limite s/n Poligono Las Fronteras, Torre-
jon de Ardoz, 28850, Madrid, Spain
Tel.: (34) 916 270 100
Sales Range: $25-49.9 Million
Emp.: 20
Industrial Machinery Whslr
N.A.I.C.S.: 423830
Eduardo Prat *(Gen Mgr)*

Cargotec India Private Limited   **(1)**
WeWork 10A-117 126 10th Floor Tower-1
Seawoods Grand Central, Sector 40 Sea-
woods, Navi Mumbai, 400706, Maharashtra,
India
Tel.: (91) 2267736666
Web Site: http://www.indital.in
Emp.: 50
Marine Cargo Handling Services
N.A.I.C.S.: 488320

**Cargotec Industries (China) Co.,
Ltd**   **(1)**
No 550 South Xin Yuan Road, Pudong,
Shanghai, 201306, China
Tel.: (86) 21 6118 4800
Web Site: http://www.cargotec.com

Emp.: 50
Marine Cargo Handling Services
N.A.I.C.S.: 488320

Cargotec Korea Limited   **(1)**
173-5 Songjeong-dong, Haeundae-gu, Bu-
san, 612-050, Gwangyeoksi, Korea (South)
Tel.: (82) 517048150
Web Site: http://www.macgregor.com
Marine Cargo Handling Services
N.A.I.C.S.: 488320

Cargotec Solutions LLC   **(1)**
415 E Dundee St, Ottawa, KS 66067
Tel.: (785) 242-2200
Heavy Duty Material Handling Equipment
Mfr & Distr
N.A.I.C.S.: 333310

Cargotec Solutions Oy   **(1)**
Satamakaari 35, 00980, Helsinki, Finland
Tel.: (358) 32658111
Cargo Handling Services
N.A.I.C.S.: 488320

**Cargotec Terminal Solutions (Malay-
sia) Sdn Bhd**   **(1)**
No 8 Lorong Sultan Hishamuddin 1 Selat
Klang Utara, Kelang, 42000, Selangor, Ma-
laysia
Tel.: (60) 3 31762998
Emp.: 65
Cargo Handling Services
N.A.I.C.S.: 488320
Dinesh Nair *(Gen Mgr)*

Cargotec UK Ltd.   **(1)**
Cargotec Industrial Park, Ellesmere, SY12
9JW, United Kingdom
Tel.: (44) 1691 623100
Web Site: http://www.cargotec.com
Emp.: 100
Cargo Handling Services
N.A.I.C.S.: 488320

Cargotec Ukraine, LLC   **(1)**
54-A Petropavlivska Street, 04086, Kiev,
Ukraine
Tel.: (380) 444682019
Web Site: http://www.cargotec.com
Cargo Handling Services
N.A.I.C.S.: 488320

**Cargotec de Mexico, S.A. de
C.V.**   **(1)**
San Andres Atoto 16A Col San Esteban,
Naucalpan, 53550, Mexico
Tel.: (52) 55 53587411
Web Site: http://www.kalmarind-
latinamerica.com
Marine Cargo Handling Services
N.A.I.C.S.: 488320

Del Equipment (UK) Ltd.   **(1)**
Building 1 Windrush Park Road Windrush
Industrial Park, Witney, OX29 7HA, Oxford-
shire, United Kingdom
Tel.: (44) 1993 708811
Web Site: http://www.del-tailifts.co.uk
Sales Range: $25-49.9 Million
Emp.: 100
Tail Lift Mfr
N.A.I.C.S.: 333924

Effer S.p.A.   **(1)**
Via IV Novembre 12, 40061, Minerbio, BO,
Italy
Tel.: (39) 051 418 1211
Web Site: https://www.effer.com
Industrial Machinery Equipment Distr
N.A.I.C.S.: 423830

Hiab (Pty) Ltd   **(1)**
Corner Fordicks & Aberdein Road Rood-
ekop, Germiston, 1422, Gauteng, South
Africa
Tel.: (27) 118651425
Web Site: http://www.hiab.com
Sales Range: $25-49.9 Million
Emp.: 74
Load Handling Machinery Mfr
N.A.I.C.S.: 333248

Hiab Austria GmbH   **(1)**
Waldschulgasse 3, 2700, Wiener Neustadt,
Austria
Tel.: (43) 262222300
Cargo Handling Services
N.A.I.C.S.: 488320

Hiab Benelux B.V.   **(1)**

Cargotec Corporation—(Continued)

Hesselingen 42, 7922 HR, Meppel, Netherlands
Tel.: (31) 522253831
Food Transportation Services
N.A.I.C.S.: 488490

Hiab Germany GmbH (1)
Osterbrooksweg 42, D-22869, Schenefeld, Germany
Tel.: (49) 8009886031
Transport Equipment Mfr & Distr
N.A.I.C.S.: 336999

Hiab Iberia, S.L. (1)
C/Limite s/n Poligono Industrial Las Fronteras, Torrejon de Ardoz, 28850, Madrid, Spain
Tel.: (34) 916270100
Industrial Machinery Equipment Distr
N.A.I.C.S.: 423830

Hiab Italia S.r.l. (1)
Viale Certosa 138, 20156, Milan, Italy
Tel.: (39) 023 910 0848
Web Site: https://www.hiab.com
Industrial Machinery Equipment Distr
N.A.I.C.S.: 423830

Hiab Load Handling Equipment
(Shanghai) Co., Ltd (1)
International Capital Plaza 12F 1318 Sichuan Road N, Shanghai, 200080, China
Tel.: (86) 21 2606 3000
Web Site: http://www.hiab.com
Emp.: 40
Load Handling Machinery Distr
N.A.I.C.S.: 333248

Hiab Norway AS (1)
Carl Bergersens Vei 5, 1481, Hagan, Norway
Tel.: (47) 67067500
Machinery Equipment Whslr
N.A.I.C.S.: 423830

Hiab Sdn Bhd (1)
27-1 Jalan Bandar 14 Pusat Bandar, Puchong, 47100, Selangor, Malaysia
Tel.: (60) 3 5882 2903
Web Site: http://www.hiab.com
Sales Range: $25-49.9 Million
Emp.: 12
Truck Mounted Crane & Hooklift Distr
N.A.I.C.S.: 423830

Interhydraulik Zepro GmbH (1)
Waldschulgasse 3, 2700, Wiener Neustadt, Austria
Tel.: (43) 262222300
Web Site: http://www.interhydraulik.at
Sales Range: $25-49.9 Million
Emp.: 10
Industrial Machinery Mfr & Distr
N.A.I.C.S.: 333248

International MacGREGOR-Navire
Holding BV (1)
Albert Plesmanweg 95 -97, 3088 GC, Rotterdam, Netherlands
Tel.: (31) 10 2832121
Sales Range: $200-249.9 Million
Emp.: 300
Investment Management Service
N.A.I.C.S.: 523999

Inver Port Services Pty. Ltd. (1)
Web Site:
     http://www.inverportservices.com.au
Port & Harbor Operation Services
N.A.I.C.S.: 488310
Robert Cebulski (Gen Mgr)

Kalmar Austria GmbH (1)
Portendorf 8, 9020, Klagenfurt, Austria
Tel.: (43) 463717880
Web Site: https://www.kalmar.at
Cargo Handling Services
N.A.I.C.S.: 488320

Kalmar Germany GmbH (1)
Max-Born-Strasse 2, 22761, Hamburg, Germany
Tel.: (49) 40 547 3050
Web Site: https://www.kalmar.de
Forklift Services
N.A.I.C.S.: 811310

Kalmar Italia S.r.l. (1)
Via Tagliolini 108, 16152, Genoa, Italy

Tel.: (39) 0106018926
Web Site: https://www.kalmarglobal.it
Cargo Handling Equipment Services
N.A.I.C.S.: 488320

Kalmar Middle East DMCC (1)
JBC 5 Unit 3501 Cluster W Jumeirah Lake Towers, PO Box 282574, Dubai, United Arab Emirates
Tel.: (971) 44286644
Cargo Handling Equipment Services
N.A.I.C.S.: 488320

Kalmar Netherlands B.V. (1)
Wilhelminakade 901, 3072, Rotterdam, Netherlands
Tel.: (31) 102946666
Web Site: https://www.kalmar.nl
Cargo Handling Equipment Services
N.A.I.C.S.: 811490

Kalmar Portugal, S.A. (1)
Rua Nossa Sra da Conceicao 3 M, Carnaxide, 2790-111, Lisbon, Portugal
Tel.: (351) 214164600
Cargo Handling Equipment Services
N.A.I.C.S.: 811490

Kalmar Spain Cargo Handling Solu-
tions S.A. (1)
Avda Virgen del Carmen 15, 11201, Algeciras, Spain
Tel.: (34) 956667564
Cargo Handling Equipment Services
N.A.I.C.S.: 488320

Kalmar Turkey Yuk Tasima Sistemleri
Anonim Sirketi (1)
Ramazanoglu Mah Kaynarca Cad No 26 Kurtkoy, Pendik, 34912, Istanbul, Turkiye
Tel.: (90) 2164594394
Web Site: http://www.kalmar.com.tr
Motor Vehicle Maintenance & Repair Services
N.A.I.C.S.: 811198

MacGREGOR (UKR) A.O. (1)
Bolshaya Arnautskaya St House 15 Room 78, Odessa, 65012, Ukraine
Tel.: (380) 48 221 0142
Marine Cargo Handling Services
N.A.I.C.S.: 488320

MacGREGOR Hydramarine AS (1)
Andoyfaret 15, Kristiansand, 4623, Norway
Tel.: (47) 91 68 60 00
Web Site: http://www.cargotec.com
Emp.: 400
Load Handling Equipment Mfr
N.A.I.C.S.: 333248

MacGREGOR Plimsoll Pte Ltd (1)
48 Tuas Road, Singapore, 638500, Singapore
Tel.: (65) 68613922
Web Site: http://www.plimsollcorp.com
Cargo Handling Equipment Mfr
N.A.I.C.S.: 333310

MacGREGOR Shanghai Trading Co.,
Ltd. (1)
12F International Capital Plaza 1318 North Sichuan Road, 200080, Shanghai, China
Tel.: (86) 2126063000
Cargo Handling Equipment Mfr
N.A.I.C.S.: 333310
Charley Xiao (Mgr-Svc)

MacGregor Belgium N.V. (1)
Heizegemweg 7, 2030, Antwerp, Belgium
Tel.: (32) 4025444444
Cargo Handling Equipment Services
N.A.I.C.S.: 811490

MacGregor Croatia d.o.o. (1)
Vrh Martinscice 93B, 51221, Rijeka, Kostrena, Croatia
Tel.: (385) 51289717
Web Site: http://www.cargotec.com
Sales Range: $25-49.9 Million
Emp.: 8
Cargo Handling Services
N.A.I.C.S.: 488320

MacGregor Germany GmbH (1)
Reichsbahnstrasse 72, Hamburg, DE-22525, Germany
Tel.: (49) 40254440
Web Site: http://www.macgregor.com
Marine Cargo Handling Services
N.A.I.C.S.: 488320

MacGregor Greece Ltd (1)
Aktimiouli 47-49, Piraeus, 18536, Greece
Tel.: (30) 2104283838
Web Site: http://www.macgregor.com
Emp.: 10
Cargo Handling Services
N.A.I.C.S.: 488320

MacGregor Group AB (1)
Fiskhamnsgatan 2, PO Box 4113, 400 40, Gothenburg, Sweden
Tel.: (46) 31850700
Web Site: http://www.macgregor-group.com
Sales Range: $450-499.9 Million
Emp.: 130
Mfr of Marine Cargo Handling & Stowage Systems
N.A.I.C.S.: 488390
John Carnall (Sr VP-Lifecycle Support Div-Global)

Subsidiary (Non-US):

Cargotec Denmark A/S (2)
Smedeholm 11, DK 2730, Herlev, Denmark
Tel.: (45) 44538484
Web Site: http://www.macgregor.com
Sales Range: $50-74.9 Million
Emp.: 15
Cargo Access Equipment for Ships & Engineering & Service Solutions for Maritime Transportation Industry
N.A.I.C.S.: 488320

MacGregor (ARE) LLC (2)
Al Quoz Industrial Area 4 Street 14B, Dubai, United Arab Emirates
Tel.: (971) 43413933
Web Site: http://www.macgregor-group.com
Sales Range: $25-49.9 Million
Emp.: 67
Marine Cargo Handling Services
N.A.I.C.S.: 488320

MacGregor (AUS) Pty. Ltd. (2)
2 Gordon Place, PO Box 662, Balmain, 2567, NSW, Australia
Tel.: (61) 246474149
Web Site: http://www.macgregor.com
Sales Range: $50-74.9 Million
Emp.: 2
Cargo Access Equipment for Ship Repair & Maintenance Services & Engineering & Service Solutions for the Maritime Transportation Industry
N.A.I.C.S.: 488320

MacGregor (CHN) Ltd. (2)
Room 1001-1005 10th Floor Surbana International Building, No 1318 North Sichuan Road Hongkou District, Shanghai, 200080, China
Tel.: (86) 2163912798
Web Site: https://www.macgregor.cn
Sales Range: $75-99.9 Million
Emp.: 160
Engineering & Service Solutions for the Maritime Industry
N.A.I.C.S.: 333120

MacGregor (CYPRUS) Ltd. (2)
Titos Bldg Office 201 58 Gladstone St, Limassol, 3041, Cyprus
Tel.: (357) 25 76 36 70
Web Site: http://www.macgregor.com
Emp.: 2
Cargo Handling Equipment Mfr
N.A.I.C.S.: 333923

MacGregor (ESP) S.A. (2)
Edificio Tmb 2 Fl Dock A 2 Port Of Bilbao, ES 48980, Santurce, Vizcaya, Spain
Tel.: (34) 944807339
Web Site: http://www.macgregor-group.com
Sales Range: $1-9.9 Million
Emp.: 10
Cargo Access Equipment for Ships & Engineering & Service Solutions for the Maritime Transportation Industry
N.A.I.C.S.: 333120

MacGregor (GBR) Ltd. (2)
83 Somerset Rd, Wirral, CH61 8SS, Pensby, United Kingdom
Tel.: (44) 7768334412
Web Site: http://www.macgregor-group.com
Sales Range: $50-74.9 Million
Emp.: 10
Cargo Access Equipment & Engineering & Service Solutions for the Maritime Transportation Industry

MacGregor (GRC) E.P.E. (2)
47-49 Akti Miaouli, 18576, Piraeus, Greece
Tel.: (30) 2104283838
Web Site: http://www.macgregor.com
Sales Range: $50-74.9 Million
Emp.: 10
Cargo Access Equipment for Ships & Engineering & Service Solutions for the Maritime Transportation Industry
N.A.I.C.S.: 333120

MacGregor (HRV) d.o.o. (2)
Vrh Martinscice 93B, Kostrena, Rijeka, 51221, Croatia
Tel.: (385) 51289718
Web Site: http://www.macgregor-group.com
Sales Range: $50-74.9 Million
Emp.: 10
Cargo Access Equipment for Ships & Engineering & Service Solutions for the Maritime Transportation Industry
N.A.I.C.S.: 333120

MacGregor (Hong Kong) Ltd. (2)
Unit 3551 12 35th Fl Tower 1 Millenium City 1, 388 Kwun Tong Rd, Kowloon, China (Hong Kong)
Tel.: (852) 23941008
Web Site: http://www.macgregor-group.com
Sales Range: $50-74.9 Million
Emp.: 67
Cargo Access Equipment, Repair & Maintenance Services & Engineering & Service Solutions for the Maritime Transportation Industry
N.A.I.C.S.: 488320

MacGregor (KOR) Ltd. (2)
173 5 Song Jeong Dong Haeungae Gu, Busan, 612 040, Korea (South)
Tel.: (82) 1062250121
Web Site: http://www.macgregor.com
Sales Range: $1-9.9 Million
Emp.: 28
Engineering & Service Solutions for the Maritime Transportation Industry
N.A.I.C.S.: 333120

MacGregor (NOR) A/S (2)
Skur 39, PO Box 337, 0050, Oslo, Vippetangen, Norway
Tel.: (47) 23103400
Web Site: http://www.macgregor-group.com
Sales Range: $50-74.9 Million
Emp.: 6
Cargo Access Equipment for Ships & Engineering & Service Solutions for the Maritime Transportation Industry
N.A.I.C.S.: 488320

MacGregor (POL) Sp. z o.o. (2)
Czechoslowacka 3, 81336, Gdynia, Poland
Tel.: (48) 587855110
Web Site: http://www.macgregor.com
Sales Range: $1-9.9 Million
Emp.: 74
Cargo Access Equipment for Ships & Engineering & Service Solutions for the Maritime Transportation Industry
N.A.I.C.S.: 333120

MacGregor (PRT) Lda. (2)
Av Alianca Povo MFA, Cova da Piedade, 2800, Almada, Portugal
Tel.: (351) 12744359
Web Site: http://www.macgregor-group.com
Sales Range: $25-49.9 Million
Emp.: 46
Cargo Access Equipment & Engineering & Service Solutions for the Maritime Transportation Industry
N.A.I.C.S.: 333922

MacGregor (SGP) Pte. Ltd. (2)
12 Benoi Crescent, Singapore, 629975, Singapore
Tel.: (65) 62652322
Web Site: http://www.macgregor-group.com
Sales Range: $50-74.9 Million
Emp.: 25
Cargo Access Equipment for Ship Repair & Maintenance Services & Engineering & Service Solutions for the Maritime Transportation Industry
N.A.I.C.S.: 488320

Joint Venture (Non-US):

MacGregor BLRT Baltic OU (2)

103 Kopli Str, 11712, Tallinn, Estonia
Tel.: (372) 6102200
Cargo Handling Services
N.A.I.C.S.: 488320

Subsidiary (Non-US):

MacGregor Conver GmbH **(2)**
Zum Panrepel 41, 28307, Bremen, Germany
Tel.: (49) 421839183
Web Site: http://www.macgregor-group.com
Sales Range: $25-49.9 Million
Emp.: 24
Engineering & Service Solutions for the Maritime Transportation Industry
N.A.I.C.S.: 488320

MacGregor France S.A.S **(2)**
5 Bis Rue De Bel Air, PO Box 437, 44474, Carquefou, Cedex, France
Tel.: (33) 240305000
Sales Range: $25-49.9 Million
Emp.: 40
Cargo Access Equipment for Ships & Engineering & Service Solutions for the Maritime Transportation Industry
N.A.I.C.S.: 488320
Vilhelm Roberts *(Mng Dir)*

MacGregor Kayaba Ltd. **(2)**
9 F Suzue Baydium Bldg 1-15-1 Kaigan, Tokyo, 105 0022, Minato-Ku, Japan
Tel.: (81) 354031966
Web Site: http://www.macgregor-group.com
Sales Range: $75-99.9 Million
Emp.: 100
Engineering & Service Solutions for the Maritime Transportation Industry
N.A.I.C.S.: 333120

MacGregor Oy **(2)**
Hallimestarinkatu 6, PO Box 116, 20780, Kaarina, Finland
Tel.: (358) 241211
Web Site: http://www.macgregor-group.com
Sales Range: $10-24.9 Million
Designs Shipboard Cargo Handling Equipment & Engineering & Service Solutions for the Maritime Transportation Industry
N.A.I.C.S.: 488320

MacGregor Plimsoll (Tianjin) Co., Ltd **(2)**
No.8 XinYe Street One West TEDA, Tianjin, 300462, China
Tel.: (86) 2259829200
Load Handling Equipment Mfr
N.A.I.C.S.: 333248

MacGregor Plimsoll Offshore Services Pte Ltd **(2)**
15 Tukang Innovation Drive, Singapore, 618299, Singapore
Tel.: (65) 68613922
Cargo Handling Services
N.A.I.C.S.: 488320

MacGregor Plimsoll Sdn Bhd **(2)**
Lot 14695 Kg Jaya Batu 2 Jalan Air Putih, Kemaman, Terengganu, 24000, Malaysia
Tel.: (60) 98592129
Web Site: http://www.cargotec.com
Sales Range: $25-49.9 Million
Emp.: 3
Cargo Handling Services
N.A.I.C.S.: 488320

PT MacGregor Plimsoll Indonesia **(2)**
Puri Industrial ParkBlok D No 2 Batam Centre, Batam, Indonesia
Tel.: (62) 7787482171
Marine Cargo Handling Services
N.A.I.C.S.: 488320

Subsidiary (Domestic):

TTS Marine AB **(2)**
Kampegatan 3, S-41104, Gothenburg, Sweden
Tel.: (46) 317257900
Web Site: http://www.ttsgroup.com
Sales Range: $250-299.9 Million
Emp.: 100
RoRo Vessel Ramps, Doors & Lifts Designer & Mfr
N.A.I.C.S.: 336999

Subsidiary (Non-US):

TTS Bohai Machinery Co., Ltd. **(3)**

Beihai Industry Park Sujia Dalian Wan Street, Dalian, 116013, China
Tel.: (86) 4118 711 2670
Web Site: http://www.tts-marine.com
Sales Range: $25-49.9 Million
Emp.: 3
Marine Cargo Handling Cranes Mfr
N.A.I.C.S.: 333923

TTS Greece Ltd. **(3)**
Akti Miaouli 81 Stoa Loumou, 18538, Piraeus, Greece
Tel.: (30) 2104294480
Emp.: 10
Industrial Equipment Distr
N.A.I.C.S.: 423830
Dimithri Manolias *(Gen Mgr)*

Subsidiary (Domestic):

TTS Hua Hai AB **(3)**
Kampegatan 3, Gothenburg, 411 04, Sweden
Tel.: (46) 317257900
Marine Equipment Mfr
N.A.I.C.S.: 336999

Subsidiary (Non-US):

TTS Hua Hai Ships Equipment Co., Ltd. **(3)**
18th Floor 3255 Zhoujiazui Road, 200093, Shanghai, China
Tel.: (86) 216 539 8257
Web Site: https://tts-huahai.com
Sales Range: $25-49.9 Million
Emp.: 80
Marine Cargo Vessel Equipment Mfr
N.A.I.C.S.: 336999

TTS Korea Inc **(3)**
Rm 625 Ocean Tower 760-3 Woo 1-dong, Haeundae-gu, 612-726, Busan, Korea (South)
Tel.: (82) 51 740 6081
Oil & Gas Industry Machinery Distr
N.A.I.C.S.: 423830

TTS Marine AS **(3)**
Barstolveien 26, 4606, Kristiansand, Norway **(100%)**
Tel.: (47) 38049500
Web Site: http://www.tts-marine.com
Sales Range: $50-74.9 Million
Emp.: 150
Marine Cargo Crane After Sales Services
N.A.I.C.S.: 488320

TTS Marine GmbH **(3)**
An der Reeperbahn 6, 28217, Bremen, Germany **(100%)**
Tel.: (49) 421 520 08 0
Web Site: http://www.ttsgroup.com
Marine Cargo Handling Vessel Equipment Mfr
N.A.I.C.S.: 336999

Subsidiary (Non-US):

TTS Marine Equipment (Dalian) Co., Ltd. **(4)**
Tuchengzi Cun Dalianwan Street, Ganjingzi District, Dalian, China
Tel.: (86) 411 8711 9663
Marine Equipment Installation Services
N.A.I.C.S.: 238990

TTS Marine Korea Co., Ltd. **(4)**
1664-10 Songjeong-Dong, Gangseo-Gu, Busan, 648-270, Korea (South) **(100%)**
Tel.: (82) 518318401
Web Site: http://www.ttsgroup.com
Sales Range: $25-49.9 Million
Emp.: 70
Industrial Machinery Mfr
N.A.I.C.S.: 333248

TTS Marine Ostrava S.r.o **(4)**
ul Reky 808, 72000, Ostrava, Hrabova, Czech Republic **(100%)**
Tel.: (420) 596782708
Industrial Machinery Mfr
N.A.I.C.S.: 333248

Subsidiary (US):

TTS Marine Inc. **(3)**
14730 Vickery Dr, Houston, TX 77032
Tel.: (954) 493-6405
Web Site: http://www.tts-marine.no

Sales Range: $25-49.9 Million
Emp.: 14
Cargo Vessel Systems & Equipment Services
N.A.I.C.S.: 561990

Subsidiary (Non-US):

TTS Marine S.r.l **(3)**
Ponte Colombo, Genoa, 16126, Italy **(100%)**
Tel.: (39) 0102481205
Web Site: http://www.tts-marine.com
Sales Range: $25-49.9 Million
Emp.: 2
Transportation Equipment Mfr
N.A.I.C.S.: 336999

TTS Marine Shanghai Co., Ltd. **(3)**
No 389 Er Rd GaoDong Industrial Park, PuDong, Shanghai, 200137, China **(100%)**
Tel.: (86) 2158485300
Web Site: http://www.tts-marine.com
Sales Range: $50-74.9 Million
Marine Cargo Handling Cranes Mfr
N.A.I.C.S.: 333923

TTS Offshore Handling Equipment AS
Folke Bernadottesvei 38, PO Box 3566, 5845, Bergen, Norway **(100%)**
Tel.: (47) 55348400
Web Site: http://www.ttsgroup.com
Emp.: 50
Marine Cargo Handling Cranes Mfr
N.A.I.C.S.: 333923

TTS Singapore Pte. Ltd. **(3)**
16 Enterprise Road Enterprise 10, Singapore, 627699, Singapore
Tel.: (65) 6867 9070
Web Site: http://www.tts-singapore.com
Sales Range: $25-49.9 Million
Emp.: 12
Cargo Handling Equipment Distr
N.A.I.C.S.: 423860
Maurice Tan *(Gen Mgr)*

TTS Vietnam **(3)**
6th Floor Harbour View Building No 12 Tran Phu Str, 3500, Haiphong, Vietnam
Tel.: (84) 31 3 686 518
Sales Range: $25-49.9 Million
Emp.: 29
Marine Cargo Handling Services
N.A.I.C.S.: 488320
Dan Magnusson *(Gen Mgr)*

MacGregor Japan Ltd. **(1)**
9/F Suzue Baydium Building 1-15-1 Kaigan, Minato-Ku, 105-0022, Tokyo, Japan
Tel.: (81) 354031966
Web Site: http://www.macgregor.com
Marine Cargo Handling Services
N.A.I.C.S.: 488320

MacGregor Poland Sp. z o.o. **(1)**
ul Czechoslowacka 3, 81-336, Gdynia, Poland
Tel.: (48) 4025444444
Cargo Handling Equipment Services
N.A.I.C.S.: 811490

Moffett Engineering Ltd **(1)**
Ardee Road, Dundalk, Ireland
Tel.: (353) 429359500
Sales Range: $50-74.9 Million
Emp.: 170
Hydraulic System Mfr
N.A.I.C.S.: 333923

Navis Holding LLC **(1)**
55 Harrison St Ste 600, Oakland, CA 94607
Tel.: (510) 267-5000
Web Site: http://www.navis.com
Sales Range: $100-124.9 Million
Emp.: 150
Investment Management Service
N.A.I.C.S.: 523999
Chuck Schneider *(Chief Customer Officer & Interim Gen Mgr-Americas)*

Navis India Technologies Private Limited **(1)**
Phase III Unit No 4 9th floor CSIR Road, Chennai, 600 113, India
Tel.: (91) 444 590 3000
Web Site: https://www.navis.com
Logistics Consulting Servies
N.A.I.C.S.: 541614

O'Leary's Material Handling Services Pty Ltd **(1)**
6 Montgomery Way, Malaga, Perth, 6090, WA, Australia
Tel.: (61) 8 9248 6674
Web Site: http://www.olearys.com.au
Sales Range: $25-49.9 Million
Emp.: 15
Tail Lift Mfr & Whslr
N.A.I.C.S.: 333921
Shing Wing *(Owner)*

Platform Crane Services Mexico S. de. R.L. **(1)**
Calle 61 No 1A Col Revolution Cd del Carmen, 24120, Campeche, Mexico
Tel.: (52) 938 286 1528
Oil & Gas Exploration Services
N.A.I.C.S.: 213112

Siwertell AB **(1)**
Angsvagen 5, Gunnarstorp, 267 90, Bjuv, Sweden
Tel.: (46) 42 85800
Web Site: http://www.siwertell.com
Emp.: 120
Cargo Handling Services
N.A.I.C.S.: 488320

Tagros d.o.o. **(1)**
Vojkovo nabrezje 38, Capodistria, 6000, Koper, Slovenia
Tel.: (386) 5 923 5515
Web Site: https://www.tagros.si
Emp.: 49
Motor Vehicle Maintenance & Repair Services
N.A.I.C.S.: 811198

Triplex Chile Ltda. **(1)**
Av Americo Vespucio 464, Parque industrial Las Arucas Ciudad De, Talcahuano, Chile
Tel.: (56) 412186620
Web Site: http://www.triplexchile.cl
Industrial Equipment Distr
N.A.I.C.S.: 423830

Waltco Lift Corp. **(1)**
285 Northeast Ave, Tallmadge, OH 44278-1428
Tel.: (330) 633-9191
Web Site: http://www.waltcoliftgates.com
Sales Range: $25-49.9 Million
Emp.: 100
Hydraulic Liftgate Mfr & Distr
N.A.I.C.S.: 333923
Steve Miller *(Pres)*

Z-Lyften Produktion AB **(1)**
Mossvagen 8, 641 49, Katrineholm, Sweden
Tel.: (46) 150489550
Web Site: http://www.z-lyften.se
Tail Lift Mfr
N.A.I.C.S.: 333998

Zepro Danmark A/S **(1)**
Industrikrogen 14, 2635, Ishoj, Denmark
Tel.: (45) 4 399 3300
Web Site: https://www.hiab.com
Cargo Handling Equipment Distr
N.A.I.C.S.: 423830

CARGOTRANS MARITIME LIMITED

Shyam Paragon 1st Floor DBZ-S/61 A, Opp Main Office of Gandhidham Muncipality Near Rotary Bhavan, Kutch, 370201, Gujarat, India
Tel.: (91) 2836236582
Web Site: https://www.cargotrans.in
Year Founded: 2012
543618—(BOM)
Rev.: $1,447,112
Assets: $1,447,112
Liabilities: $731,600
Net Worth: $715,513
Earnings: $288,986
Emp.: 75
Fiscal Year-end: 03/31/21
Freight Forwarding Services
N.A.I.C.S.: 488510

CARIBBEAN AIRLINES LIMITED

Caribbean Airlines Limited—(Continued)

Iere House Golden Grove Road,
Piarco, West Indies, Trinidad & To-
bago
Tel.: (868) 6257200
Web Site: http://www.caribbean-
airlines.com
Year Founded: 1940
Sales Range: $650-699.9 Million
Emp.: 1,984
Air Carrier
N.A.I.C.S.: 481111
Colville Carrington *(VP-Maintenance
& Engrg)*

CARIBBEAN CREAM LTD.
Kencot 3 South Road, Kingston, 10,
Jamaica
Tel.: (876) 9061127
Web Site:
https://www.caribcream.com
Year Founded: 2006
KREMI—(JAM)
Rev.: $12,979,105
Assets: $9,658,247
Liabilities: $3,870,755
Net Worth: $5,787,492
Earnings: $698,723
Fiscal Year-end: 02/28/21
Ice Cream Product Mfr & Distr
N.A.I.C.S.: 311520
Christopher Clarke *(CEO & Mng Dir)*

CARIBBEAN DEVELOPMENT BANK
Wildey, PO Box 408, Saint Michael,
Barbados
Tel.: (246) 4311600
Web Site: http://www.caribank.org
Sales Range: $10-24.9 Million
Emp.: 200
Banking Services
N.A.I.C.S.: 522110
William Warren Smith *(Pres)*

CARIBBEAN DISCOVERY, S.A. DE C.V.
Puerto Aventuras, Quintana Roo Isla
Mujeres, Cancun, Mexico
Tel.: (52) 998 849 4757   MX
Web Site:
http://www.caribbeantravel.com
Year Founded: 1990
Marine Mammal & Animal Park Op-
erator
N.A.I.C.S.: 712190
Eduardo Albor *(Pres & CEO)*

CARIBBEAN DIVERSIFIED INVESTMENTS INC.
175 Commerce Valley Drive West
Suite 310, Markham, L3T 7P6, ON,
Canada
Tel.: (905) 763-3001   BC
Web Site:
http://www.caribbeaninvestments.ca
Year Founded: 2011
Investment Services
N.A.I.C.S.: 523999
Christopher Malone *(Pres & CEO)*

CARIBBEAN INVESTMENT HOLDINGS LIMITED
Craigmuir Chambers, Road Town,
Tortola, Virgin Islands (British)
Tel.: (284) 2277132   BZ
Web Site: http://www.cihltd.co
CIHL—(BERM)
Rev.: $51,400,000
Assets: $1,010,200,000
Liabilities: $874,300,000
Net Worth: $135,900,000
Earnings: $12,600,000
Fiscal Year-end: 03/31/22
Bank Holding Company

N.A.I.C.S.: 551111
Michael Coye *(CFO)*

Subsidiaries:

The Belize Bank Limited   **(1)**
60 Market Square, Belize, Belize
Tel.: (501) 2277132
Web Site: http://www.belizebank.com
Commericial Banking
N.A.I.C.S.: 522110
Philip C. Johnson *(Pres)*

CARIBBEAN PRODUCERS JAMAICA LTD.
1 Guinep Way Montego Freeport
Saint James, Montego Bay, Jamaica
Tel.: (876) 2896282
Web Site: https://www.cpj.com
Year Founded: 1994
CPJ—(JAM)
Rev.: $142,581,482
Assets: $90,113,477
Liabilities: $57,826,021
Net Worth: $32,287,456
Earnings: $6,247,527
Emp.: 392
Fiscal Year-end: 06/30/23
Food Product Mfr & Distr
N.A.I.C.S.: 311999
David Lowe *(CEO)*

CARIBBEAN RESOURCES CORPORATION
333 Bay Street Suite 1100, Toronto,
M5H 2R2, ON, Canada
Tel.: (416) 360-8725
Web Site:
http://www.caribbeanresources.ca
Year Founded: 1990
Sales Range: $100-124.9 Million
Mineral Exploration Services
N.A.I.C.S.: 213114
Peter Volk *(Gen Counsel)*

CARIBOO CHEVROLET BUICK GMC
370 Mackenzie Avenue South, Wil-
liams Lake, V2G 1C7, BC, Canada
Tel.: (250) 392-7185
Web Site: http://www.cariboogm.ca
New & Used Car Dealers
N.A.I.C.S.: 441110

CARIBOO ROSE RESOURCES LTD.
Suite 110 - 325 Howe Street, Van-
couver, V6C 1Z7, BC, Canada
Tel.: (604) 681-7913   Ca
Web Site:
https://www.cariboorose.com
Year Founded: 2006
CRB—(TSXV)
Rev.: $63
Assets: $1,980,513
Liabilities: $163,105
Net Worth: $1,817,409
Earnings: ($117,352)
Fiscal Year-end: 02/28/21
Metal Exploration Services
N.A.I.C.S.: 213114
J. William Morton *(Pres & CEO)*

CARILLION PLC
Carillion House 84 Salop Street,
Wolverhampton, WV3 0SR, West
Midlands, United Kingdom
Tel.: (44) 1902422431   UK
Web Site: http://www.carillionplc.com
CLLN—(LSE)
Emp.: 31,628
Civil Engineering, Facilities Manage-
ment & Infrastructure Services
N.A.I.C.S.: 561210
John Denning *(Dir-Corp Affairs)*

Subsidiaries:

1st Insulation Partners Limited   **(1)**
Unit G02 Magna 34 Temple Close, Rother-
ham, S60 1FH, South Yorkshire, United
Kingdom
Tel.: (44) 1709389300
Web Site: http://www.firstinsulation.co.uk
Sales Range: $25-49.9 Million
Emp.: 25
Insulation Installation Services
N.A.I.C.S.: 238290

AFR Limited   **(1)**
Avoncraft House, 20 Burrowfield, Welwyn
Garden City, AL7 4SR, United Kingdom
Tel.: (44) 1707320207
Central Heating & Maintenance Services
N.A.I.C.S.: 238220

Al Futtaim Carillion   **(1)**
Near Dubai Municipality Used Car Show-
room Complex Aweer, Dubai, 1811, United
Arab Emirates   **(50%)**
Tel.: (971) 43331200
Web Site: http://www.afcarillion.ae
Sales Range: $1-4.9 Billion
Emp.: 24,000
Civil Engineering Contractors
N.A.I.C.S.: 237990
Richard Howson *(CEO)*

Carillion (AMBS) Ltd   **(1)**
84 Salop St, Wolverhampton, WV3 0SR,
West Midlands, United Kingdom
Tel.: (44) 1902 422431
Web Site: http://www.carillionplc.com
Facilities Management Services
N.A.I.C.S.: 561210

Carillion (Aspire Construction) Hold-
ings No 2 Ltd   **(1)**
Construction House 24 Birch Street,
Wolverhampton, WV1 4HY, West Midlands,
United Kingdom
Tel.: (44) 1902 422431
Investment Management Service
N.A.I.C.S.: 523999

Carillion Alawi LLC   **(1)**
Ruwi, PO Box 1436, Ruwi, PC 112,
Oman   **(100%)**
Tel.: (968) 24590347
Web Site: http://www.carillionplc.com
Civil Engineering Contractors
N.A.I.C.S.: 237110

Carillion Construction (Caribbean)
Ltd.   **(1)**
Southern Main Road, Couva, Trinidad &
Tobago   **(100%)**
Civil Engineering Contractors
N.A.I.C.S.: 237110

Carillion Construction Canada   **(1)**
7077 Kelle St, Concord, L4K 0B6, ON,
Canada   **(100%)**
Tel.: (416) 233-5811
Sales Range: $25-49.9 Million
Emp.: 80
Civil Engineering Contractors
N.A.I.C.S.: 237110

Carillion Construction Ltd   **(1)**
Radius Court, Bracknell, RG12 2UP, Berk-
shire, United Kingdom
Tel.: (44) 1344 828500
Sales Range: $25-49.9 Million
Emp.: 80
Construction Engineering Services
N.A.I.C.S.: 541330

Carillion Defence   **(1)**
24 Birch St, Wolverhampton, WV1 4HY,
United Kingdom
Tel.: (44) 1902316696
Web Site: http://www.carillionplc.com
Construction & Facilities Management Ser-
vices for the Defense Industry
N.A.I.C.S.: 236220

Carillion Energy Services Limited   **(1)**
Partnership House City W Business Park,
Tyne And Wear, Newcastle upon Tyne, NE3
3AF, United Kingdom
Tel.: (44) 1912473800
Web Site:
http://www.renewables.carillionenergy.com
Sales Range: $25-49.9 Million
Emp.: 150
Architectural & Engineering Activities

N.A.I.C.S.: 541320
Derek Holes *(Mgr-Bus)*

Carillion Facilities Management   **(1)**
Hetton Court The Oval, Hunslet, Leeds,
LS10 2AU, United Kingdom   **(100%)**
Tel.: (44) 1132705533
Property Asset Management & Facilities
Support Services
N.A.I.C.S.: 561210

Carillion Fleet Management Ltd   **(1)**
Construction House 24 Birch Street,
Wolverhampton, WV3 0SR, West Midlands,
United Kingdom
Tel.: (44) 8451282999
Web Site: http://www.carillionplc.com
Fleet Management Services
N.A.I.C.S.: 532112

Carillion Piling   **(1)**
1st Fl Radius Ct Eastern Rd, RG12 2UP,
Bracknell, Berks, United Kingdom - England
Tel.: (44) 1344828500
Sales Range: $25-49.9 Million
Emp.: 70
Specialty Engineering & Construction Ser-
vices
N.A.I.C.S.: 541330

Carillion Planned Maintenance   **(1)**
12 14 Lombard Road, London, SW11 3AY,
United Kingdom
Tel.: (44) 2072286400
Sales Range: $25-49.9 Million
Emp.: 60
Technical & Building Maintenance Services
N.A.I.C.S.: 561210

Carillion Private Finance Ltd   **(1)**
24 Birch Street, Wolverhampton, WV1 4HY,
United Kingdom
Tel.: (44) 1902 316 733
Emp.: 1
Financial Management Services
N.A.I.C.S.: 523999
Kai Becker *(Mng Dir)*

Carillion Services Ltd   **(1)**
24 Birch St, Wolverhampton, WV1 4HY,
West Midlands, United Kingdom
Tel.: (44) 1902 422431
Web Site: http://www.carillionplc.com
Emp.: 100
Construction Engineering Services
N.A.I.C.S.: 541330

Mico Services Limited   **(1)**
Unit 14 Seaway Dr Seaway Pde Industrial
Estate, Port Talbot, SA12 7BR, W Glamor-
gan, United Kingdom
Tel.: (44) 1639825770
Sales Range: $75-99.9 Million
Emp.: 124
Energy Efficiency Service Provider
N.A.I.C.S.: 926130

Permarock Products Limited   **(1)**
Jubilee Dr Loughborough, Leicester, LE11
5TW, United Kingdom
Tel.: (44) 1509262924
Web Site: http://www.permarock.com
Sales Range: $25-49.9 Million
Emp.: 38
External Wall Insulation Service Provider
N.A.I.C.S.: 238310

Postworth Ltd   **(1)**
Courtyard Woodlands, Bristol, BS32 4NH,
Avon, United Kingdom
Tel.: (44) 870 128 5160
Construction Engineering Services
N.A.I.C.S.: 541330

TPS Consult Limited   **(1)**
Centre Tower Whitgift Centre, Croydon,
CR9 0AU, United Kingdom
Tel.: (44) 2082564000
Web Site: http://www.tpsconsult.co.uk
Sales Range: $50-74.9 Million
Emp.: 240
Architectural & Engineering Consulting Ser-
vices
N.A.I.C.S.: 541310
Frank Huidobro *(Mng Dir)*

Division (Domestic):

Carillion Specialist Services   **(2)**
Centre Tower Whitgift Centre, Croydon,
CR9 0AU, United Kingdom

Tel.: (44) 20 8265 4000
Building Inspection Services
N.A.I.C.S.: 541350

eaga Insurance Services Limited (1)
Lawrence House Harborough Road, Market Harborough Bowden Business Vlg, Leicester, LE16 7SA, United Kingdom
Tel.: (44) 1858545000
Sales Range: $50-74.9 Million
Emp.: 19
Insurance Services
N.A.I.C.S.: 524210

CARIMALO
La Loge Rue Jean Jaures, BP417, 22600, Saint-Barnabe, Cedex, Cotes d'Amor, France
Tel.: (33) 296267461
Web Site: http://www.carimalo.fr
Construction Services
N.A.I.C.S.: 236210
Yann Carimalo (Dir)

CARIMIN PETROLEUM BER-HAD
B-1-6 Megan Avenue 1 189 Jalan Tun Razak, 50400, Kuala Lumpur, Malaysia
Tel.: (60) 321687000
Web Site: https://www.carimin.com
Year Founded: 1989
CARIMIN—(KLS)
Rev.: $56,367,878
Assets: $70,778,070
Liabilities: $28,663,223
Net Worth: $42,114,848
Earnings: $1,699,583
Emp.: 43
Fiscal Year-end: 06/30/22
Oil & Gas Engineering & Technical Operations
N.A.I.C.S.: 213112
Mokhtar Hashim (Mng Dir)

CARINDALE PROPERTY TRUST
Level 30 85 Castlereagh Street, Sydney, 2000, NSW, Australia
Tel.: (61) 293587877   AU
Web Site:
    https://www.carindaleproperty.com
CDP—(ASX)
Rev.: $38,641,159
Assets: $517,379,806
Liabilities: $163,693,910
Net Worth: $353,685,896
Earnings: $5,090,812
Fiscal Year-end: 06/30/24
Commercial Shopping Centers Real Estate Investment Trust
N.A.I.C.S.: 525990
Peter Kenneth Allen (CEO)

CARISBROOKE SHIPPING LIMITED
38 Medina Road, Cowes, PO31 7DA, Isle of Wight, United Kingdom
Tel.: (44) 1983 284100
Web Site: http://www.carisbrooke.co
Sales Range: $100-124.9 Million
Emp.: 90
Manage Fleet Dry Cargo & Multi-Purpose Vessel Operates
N.A.I.C.S.: 488320
Robert Webster (CEO & COO)

Subsidiaries:

Carisbrooke Shipping (Germany) GmbH (1)
Flughafenallee 26, D-28199, Bremen, Germany
Tel.: (49) 421 597 65 491
Freight Transportation
N.A.I.C.S.: 488510

Carisbrooke Shipping BV (1)
Scheepmakerij 230, 3331 MB, Zwijndrecht, Netherlands

Tel.: (31) 78 625 1973
Freight Transportation
N.A.I.C.S.: 488510

Carisbrooke Shipping GmbH (1)
Ledastrasse 24, 26789, Leer, Germany
Tel.: (49) 4919994341
Freight Transportation
N.A.I.C.S.: 488510

Soetermeer Fekkes - Zwijndrecht (1)
Scheepmakerij 230, 3331 MB, Zwijndrecht, Netherlands
Tel.: (31) 786251900
Web Site: http://www.sfck.nl
Freight Transportation
N.A.I.C.S.: 488510

CARISTRAP INTERNATIONAL INC.
1760 Fortin Boulevard, Laval, H7S 1NH, QC, Canada
Tel.: (450) 667-4700
Web Site: http://www.caristrap.com
Year Founded: 1954
Sales Range: $1-9.9 Million
Emp.: 250
Polyester Cord Strapping Systems Mfr
N.A.I.C.S.: 314994
Audrey Karass (Pres)

Subsidiaries:

CARISTRAP EUROPE d.o.o. (1)
Mihovljan bb, 49252, Mihovljan, Croatia
Tel.: (385) 49 354 287
Web Site: http://www.caristrap.com
Emp.: 37
Industrial Strapping Mfr
N.A.I.C.S.: 332999
Audrey Karras (Gen Mgr)

CARL BENNET AB
Arvid Wallgrens Backe 20, Gothenburg, 41346, Sweden
Tel.: (46) 317416400   SE
Web Site: http://www.carlbennetab.se
Year Founded: 1989
Investment Holding Company
N.A.I.C.S.: 551112
Carl Bennet (Owner, Chm & CEO)

Subsidiaries:

Dragesholm AB (1)
Dragesholm 2663, 268 76, Kagerod, Sweden
Tel.: (46) 70 622 11 44
Crop Farming Services
N.A.I.C.S.: 111998

Elanders AB (1)
Flojelbergsgatan 1 C, 431 35, Molndal, Sweden (73.4%)
Tel.: (46) 317500000
Web Site: https://www.elanders.com
Rev.: $1,348,996,208
Assets: $1,054,661,328
Liabilities: $699,677,104
Net Worth: $354,984,224
Earnings: $35,635,152
Emp.: 6,058
Fiscal Year-end: 12/31/2020
Graphics Services for Commercial Printing, Packaging & E-Commerce
N.A.I.C.S.: 323111
Carl Bennet (Chm)

Subsidiary (Domestic):

AB Repronik (2)
Box 13033, 40151, Gothenburg, Sweden (100%)
Tel.: (46) 317072970
Sales Range: $10-24.9 Million
Emp.: 45
Provider of Graphical Production Servcies
N.A.I.C.S.: 541430

Subsidiary (US):

Bergen Shippers Corp. (2)
5903 Westside Ave, North Bergen, NJ 07047 (80%)
Tel.: (201) 854-1512
Web Site: http://www.bergenlogistics.com

General Warehousing & Storage
N.A.I.C.S.: 493110
Anil Shetty (CFO)

Subsidiary (Domestic):

Elanders (2)
Design Veg 2, PO Box 137, 43533, Molnlycke, Sweden
Tel.: (46) 317500000
Web Site: http://www.elanders.com
Sales Range: $300-349.9 Million
Emp.: 180
Provider of Graphical Development Services
N.A.I.C.S.: 541430
Magnus Nilsson (Pres)

Subsidiary (Non-US):

Elanders (Beijing) Printing Company Ltd (2)
No 30 YuHua Road Beijing TianZhu Airport Industrial Zone, ShunYi District, Beijing, China
Tel.: (86) 10 80 48 33 00
Printing Services
N.A.I.C.S.: 323111

Subsidiary (Domestic):

Elanders Digitaltryck AB (2)
Designvagan 2, PO Box 137, Molnlycke, 43523, Sweden (100%)
Tel.: (46) 317500000
Web Site: http://www.elanders.se
Sales Range: $25-49.9 Million
Emp.: 200
Provider of Graphical Media Services
N.A.I.C.S.: 541430

Elanders Gummessons AB (2)
Designvagen 2 Molnlycke, PO Box 807, Gothenburg, 43523, Sweden (100%)
Tel.: (46) 515723200
Web Site: http://www.elanders.com
Sales Range: $10-24.9 Million
Emp.: 200
Provider of Graphical Media Services
N.A.I.C.S.: 541430
Jonas Brannerud (CEO & Mng Dir)

Subsidiary (Non-US):

Elanders Hindson Ltd. (2)
Merlin Way New York Bus Pk, North Tyneside, Newcastle, NE27 0QG, United Kingdom (100%)
Tel.: (44) 1912800400
Web Site: http://www.elanders.com
Sales Range: $25-49.9 Million
Emp.: 150
Provider of Graphical Design Services
N.A.I.C.S.: 541430
Paul Jacques (Dir-Fin)

Elanders Hungary Kft (2)
Ujmajor u 2, 8999, Budapest, Hungary
Tel.: (36) 92 57 25 00
Web Site: http://www.elanders-hungary.com
Emp.: 200
Printing Services
N.A.I.C.S.: 323111
Ova Tadlar (Gen Mgr)

Elanders Italy S.r.l. (2)
Via Delle Industrie 8, 31050, Ponzano Veneto, Italy
Tel.: (39) 0422 44 22 53
Printing Equipment Distr
N.A.I.C.S.: 423410

Elanders Ltd (2)
Merlin Way New York Business Park, North Tyneside, NE27 0QG, United Kingdom
Tel.: (44) 191 280 0400
Web Site: http://www.elanders.com
Packing & Crating Services
N.A.I.C.S.: 488991

Subsidiary (Domestic):

Elanders Novum AB, Stockholm (2)
Marieholmsgatan 10, 415 02, Gothenburg, Sweden
Tel.: (46) 31840155
Web Site: http://www.elanders.se
Graphic Services
N.A.I.C.S.: 541430

Subsidiary (Non-US):

Elanders Polska Sp. z.o.o. (2)
Ul Mazowiecka 2, Plonsk, Warsaw, 9100, Tonsk, Poland (100%)
Tel.: (48) 236622316
Web Site: http://www.elanders.com
Sales Range: $25-49.9 Million
Emp.: 60
Provider of Graphical Servcies
N.A.I.C.S.: 541430
Magnus Nilsson (Mng Dir)

Elanders Reproducao de Imagens Ltda (2)
Avenida Ferraz Alvim 832-Serraria, 09980-025, Diadema, Brazil
Tel.: (55) 11 3195 3400
Printing Services
N.A.I.C.S.: 323111

Subsidiary (Domestic):

Elanders Stockholm (2)
Bux 518, 1615, Vallingby, Sweden
Tel.: (46) 86346000
Web Site: http://www.elanders.com
Provider of Graphical Media Services
N.A.I.C.S.: 541430

Elanders Svenskt Tryck AB (2)
Bruksvagen, Box 2052, Surte, 44502, Gothenburg, Sweden (100%)
Tel.: (46) 31979800
Sales Range: $10-24.9 Million
Emp.: 45
Provider of Graphical Media Services
N.A.I.C.S.: 541430

Elanders Sverige AB (2)
Designvagen 2, 435 33, Molnlycke, Sweden (100%)
Tel.: (46) 31 750 0000
Web Site: http://www.elanders.com
Sales Range: $10-24.9 Million
Emp.: 50
Graphic Media Services
N.A.I.C.S.: 541430
Magnus Sahlen (Mgr-IT)

Subsidiary (Non-US):

Elanders UK Ltd. (2)
32 Kings Rd, Harrogate, HG15JW, N Yorkshire, United Kingdom (100%)
Tel.: (44) 1423530362
Web Site: http://www.elanders.co.uk
Sales Range: $25-49.9 Million
Emp.: 15
Provider of Graphical Design Services
N.A.I.C.S.: 541430
Kevin Rogers (Mng Dir)

Subsidiary (US):

ElandersUSA, LLC (2)
4525 Acworth Industrial Dr, Acworth, GA 30101
Tel.: (770) 917-7000
Web Site: http://www.elandersamericas.com
Emp.: 50
Offset Printing Services
N.A.I.C.S.: 323111
Tom Sheehan (Pres)

Subsidiary (Non-US):

LGI Logistics Group International GmbH (2)
Hewlett-Packard-Strasse 1/1, 71083, Herrenberg, Germany
Tel.: (49) 7032 2291 0
Web Site: http://www.lgi.de
Sales Range: $450-499.9 Million
Emp.: 4,000
Third-Party Logistics Services
N.A.I.C.S.: 488510
Andreas Bunz (CEO & Member-Mgmt Bd)

Holding (Domestic):

ITG GmbH Internationale Spedition und Logistik (3)
Eichenstrasse 2, Oberding, 85445, Schwaig, Germany
Tel.: (49) 8122 567 0
Web Site: http://www.itg.de
Sales Range: $150-199.9 Million
Emp.: 1,000
Logistics & Freight Forwarding Services

Carl Bennet AB—(Continued)

N.A.I.C.S.: 488510
Thomas Bogner (Head-Corp Comm & Mktg)

Subsidiary (US):

Midland Information Resources
Inc. **(2)**
5440 Corporate Pk Dr, Davenport, IA 52807
Tel.: (563) 359-3696
Web Site: http://www.midlandcorp.com
Sales Range: $25-49.9 Million
Emp.: 192
Information Management & Digital Printing
Solutions
N.A.I.C.S.: 323111
Thomas Sheehan (Pres & CEO)

Subsidiary (Non-US):

dom Deutsche Online Medien
GmbH **(2)**
Anton Schmidt Str 5 15, 71332, Waiblingen,
Germany
Tel.: (49) 71 51 165 17 0
Photographic Services
N.A.I.C.S.: 541921

Subsidiary (Domestic):

myphotobook GmbH **(3)**
Oranienstr 183, 10999, Berlin, Germany
Tel.: (49) 1805 846 846
Web Site: http://www.myphotobook.de
Software Development Services
N.A.I.C.S.: 541511

Lifco AB **(1)**
Verkmastaregatan 1, 745 85, Enkoping,
Sweden
Tel.: (46) 727175933
Web Site: https://lifco.se
Rev.: $2,133,958,400
Assets: $3,036,862,080
Liabilities: $1,723,769,600
Net Worth: $1,313,092,480
Earnings: $296,532,320
Emp.: 6,265
Fiscal Year-end: 12/31/2021
Mail Order for Dental Supplies & Consum-
ables
N.A.I.C.S.: 444180
Per Waldemarson (Pres & CEO)

Subsidiary (Domestic):

Brokk AB **(2)**
Risbergsgatan 67, Skelleftea, 93127, Swe-
den
Tel.: (46) 910711800
Web Site: http://www.brokk.com
Emp.: 80
Remote Controlled Demolition Machinery
Mfr
N.A.I.C.S.: 333120
Martin Krupicka (Mng Dir)

Subsidiary (US):

Brokk, Inc. **(3)**
1144 Village Way, Monroe, WA 98272
Tel.: (360) 794-1277
Web Site: http://www.brokkinc.com
Sales Range: $25-49.9 Million
Emp.: 15
Remote Controlled Demolition Machinery
Mfr
N.A.I.C.S.: 333120
Lars Lindgren (Pres)

Subsidiary (Non-US):

KINSHOFER GmbH **(2)**
Hauptstrasse 76, 83666, Waakirchen, Ger-
many
Tel.: (49) 802188990
Web Site: http://www.kinshofer.com
Sales Range: $25-49.9 Million
Emp.: 200
Construction Machinery Mfr
N.A.I.C.S.: 333120
Thomas Friedrich (Mng Dir)

Subsidiary (Non-US):

KINSHOFER Aponox Oy **(3)**
Terminaalitie 10, FI 13430, Hameenlinna,
Finland
Tel.: (358) 757540200

Sales Range: $25-49.9 Million
Emp.: 6
Construction Machinery Mfr
N.A.I.C.S.: 333120

KINSHOFER CZ s.r.o. **(3)**
Cs Legii 568, 37810, Ceske Velenice,
Czech Republic
Tel.: (420) 384795110
Web Site: http://www.kinshofer.com
Construction Machinery Mfr
N.A.I.C.S.: 333120

KINSHOFER France S.A.R.L. **(3)**
BP 20100, 67213, Obernai, France
Tel.: (33) 388 3955 00
Web Site: http://www.kinshofer.com
Sales Range: $25-49.9 Million
Emp.: 2
Construction Machinery Mfr
N.A.I.C.S.: 333120
Friedrich Thomas (Gen Mgr)

KINSHOFER UK Ltd. **(3)**
4 Milton Industrial Court Horsfield Way,
Bredbury, Stockport, SK6 2TA, Cheshire,
United Kingdom
Tel.: (44) 1614067046
Sales Range: $25-49.9 Million
Emp.: 7
Construction Machinery Mfr
N.A.I.C.S.: 333120

Prolec Ltd. **(3)**
25 Benson Rd, Nuffield Industrial Estate,
Poole, BH17 0GB, Dorset, United Kingdom
Tel.: (44) 1202681190
Web Site: http://www.prolec.co.uk
Sales Range: $25-49.9 Million
Emp.: 30
Sensor Mfr
N.A.I.C.S.: 334511

Subsidiary (Non-US):

M+W Dental GmbH **(2)**
Reichardsweide 40, 63654, Budingen, Ger-
many
Tel.: (49) 6042880088
Web Site: http://www.mwdental.de
Sales Range: $50-74.9 Million
Emp.: 200
Dental Consumables & Small Appliances
Mfr
N.A.I.C.S.: 423450
Reinhold Kuhn (Mng Dir)

Subsidiary (US):

Parkell Inc. **(2)**
300 Executive Dr, Edgewood, NY 11717
Tel.: (631) 249-1134
Web Site: http://www.parkell.com
Surgical & Medical Instrument Mfr
N.A.I.C.S.: 339112
Karen Mitchell (CEO)

Subsidiary (Domestic):

Proline Group AB **(2)**
Djupdalsvagen 3, Box 114, 191 22, Sollen-
tuna, Sweden
Tel.: (46) 8594 774 50
Web Site: http://www.proline-group.com
Pipeline Renovation Services
N.A.I.C.S.: 541990

Sorb Industri AB **(2)**
Risbergsgatan 67, 931 36, Skelleftea, Swe-
den
Tel.: (46) 91017400
Sawmill Equipment, Demolition, Contract
Manufacturing & Business Development
Services
N.A.I.C.S.: 333243

Subsidiary (Domestic):

Renholmen AB **(3)**
PO Box 10, Byske, 934 24, Sweden
Tel.: (46) 91240800
Web Site: http://www.renholmen.se
Sales Range: $1-9.9 Million
Emp.: 30
Sawmill Equipment
N.A.I.C.S.: 333243
Per Jonsson (CEO)

Subsidiary (Domestic):

Renholmen AB **(4)**

Strandvagen 64, PO Box 33, S 870 52,
Nyland, Sweden **(100%)**
Tel.: (46) 612771730
Web Site: http://www.renholmen.se
Sales Range: $25-49.9 Million
Emp.: 1
Sawmill Equipment Mfr
N.A.I.C.S.: 333243

Mentor Media Ltd **(1)**
No 1 Bukit Batok Street 22 07-01, Singa-
pore, 659592, Singapore
Tel.: (65) 6631 3333
Web Site: http://www.mentormedia.com
Logistics Consulting Services
N.A.I.C.S.: 541614

Subsidiary (Non-US):

Mentor Media (Chongqing) Co.,
Ltd **(2)**
No 22 Xi Yuan Yi Lu Shapingba District HP
PC Factory, Level 3 nit 4 5 6, Chongqing,
401332, China
Tel.: (86) 23 8652 9808
Logistics Consulting Services
N.A.I.C.S.: 541614

Mentor Media (Kunshan) Co.,
Ltd **(2)**
No 48 Factory Building Central Avenue
Kunshan Export Processing Zone, Kun-
shan, China, Jiangsu, China
Tel.: (86) 512 5772 0005
Logistics Consulting Services
N.A.I.C.S.: 541614

Mentor Media (Shenzhen) Co.,
Ltd **(2)**
Unit 302-304 No 6 Hongmian Dao Futian
Free Trade Zone, Shenzhen, 518038,
Guangdong, China
Tel.: (86) 755 8248 0428
Logistics Consulting Services
N.A.I.C.S.: 541614

Mentor Media (Songjiang) Co.,
Ltd **(2)**
10th Building in Phase IV of Royal Industry
Park, No 175 Ximaojing Road, Shanghai,
201613, China
Tel.: (86) 21 5774 9930
Logistics Consulting Services
N.A.I.C.S.: 541614

Mentor Media (Suzhou) Co., Ltd **(2)**
No 85 Zi Jin Road, Suzhou New HiTech
Industrial Park, Suzhou, 215011, Jiangsu,
China
Tel.: (86) 512 6878 5998
Logistics Consulting Services
N.A.I.C.S.: 541614

Subsidiary (US):

Mentor Media (USA) Supply Chain
Management Inc **(2)**
1770 S Vineyard Ave, Ontario, CA 91761
Tel.: (909) 930-0800
Logistics Consulting Services
N.A.I.C.S.: 541614

Subsidiary (Non-US):

Mentor Media (Xiamen) Co., Ltd **(2)**
8F East Side of 37 Building No 52, HuLi
Dadao HuLi District, Xiamen, 361006, Fu-
jian, China
Tel.: (86) 592 570 3399
Logistics Consulting Services
N.A.I.C.S.: 541614

Mentor Media CBZ (Chongqing) Co.,
Ltd **(2)**
2-2 Workshop Zone B Xi Yong CBZ No 60
Xi Qu Er Lu, Shapingba District, Chongqing,
401331, China
Tel.: (86) 23 6562 0388
Logistics Consulting Services
N.A.I.C.S.: 541614

Mentor Media Czech s.r.o **(2)**
Skrobarenska 6, 617 00, Brno, Czech Re-
public
Tel.: (420) 515 577 401
Logistics Consulting Services
N.A.I.C.S.: 541614

Mentor Media Japan
Godogaisha **(2)**

6F Toyo Building 1-2-10 Nihonbashi, Chuo-
ku, Tokyo, 103-0027, Japan
Tel.: (81) 3 4577 9658
Web Site: http://www.mentormedia.com
Emp.: 2
Logistics Consulting Services
N.A.I.C.S.: 541614
Nozomu Hayatsu (Gen Mgr)

Mentor Media Juarez S.A. de
C.V **(2)**
Avenida Libre Comercio No 2164 Parque
Industrial las Americas, Ciudad Juarez,
32596, Chihuahua, Mexico
Tel.: (52) 656 257 1600
Logistics Consulting Services
N.A.I.C.S.: 541614

Shanghai Mentor Media Co., Ltd **(2)**
Floor 2 Building C No 2727 Jinke Road
Zhangjiang High-Tech Park, Pudong,
Shanghai, 201203, China
Tel.: (86) 21 5834 1893
Emp.: 100
Software Development Services
N.A.I.C.S.: 513210
Khoo Lou Jing (Mgr)

Shanghai Mentor Media Printing Co.,
Ltd **(2)**
25 Yun Qiao Road T22/32 Jinqiao Export
Processing Zone, Pudong, Shanghai,
201206, China
Tel.: (86) 21 5031 3116
Web Site:
Software Development Services
N.A.I.C.S.: 513210

Symbrio AB **(2)**
Ostgotagatan 12, Stockholm, 11625, Swe-
den
Tel.: (46) 8204950
Web Site: http://www.symbrio.com
Emp.: 45
Purchasing & Invoicing Software Developer
N.A.I.C.S.: 513210
Johan Ouchterlony (CEO)

Subsidiary (Non-US):

Symbrio AS **(2)**
Grenseveien 97A, Oslo, Norway
Tel.: (47) 90080730
Purchasing & Invoicing Software Developer
N.A.I.C.S.: 513210

CARL DATA SOLUTIONS, INC.
Suite 1500 409 Granville Street, Van-
couver, V6C 1T2, BC, Canada
Tel.: (778) 379-0275 **BC**
Web Site: https://www.infinitii.ai
Year Founded: 2014
Y31—(DEU)
Rev.: $1,759,224
Assets: $696,441
Liabilities: $1,629,019
Net Worth: ($932,578)
Earnings: ($740,950)
Emp.: 20
Fiscal Year-end: 06/30/24
Software Publishing Services
N.A.I.C.S.: 513210
Greg Johnston (Pres & CEO)

Subsidiaries:

infinitii ai **(1)**
Ste B 9036 35th Ave SW, Seattle, WA
98126
Tel.: (778) 379-0275
Web Site: https://www.infinitii.ai
Data Processing Services
N.A.I.C.S.: 518210

CARL FROH GMBH
Hachener Str 157, 59846, Sundern,
Germany
Tel.: (49) 2935810
Web Site: http://www.carl-froh.de
Sales Range: $75-99.9 Million
Emp.: 180
Steel Tube & Component Mfr
N.A.I.C.S.: 331210
Andreas Jekat (Co-Mng Dir)

CARL MAHR HOLDING GMBH

Brauweg 38, D 37073, Gottingen, Germany
Tel.: (49) 55170730
Web Site: http://www.mahr.de
Year Founded: 1861
Sales Range: $150-199.9 Million
Emp.: 1,500
Measuring Instruments Mfr
N.A.I.C.S.: 334513
Stephan Gais *(Chm & Mng Partner)*

Subsidiaries:

Mahr AG   **(1)**
Zurcherstrasse 68, 8800, Thalwil, Switzerland
Tel.: (41) 44 723 39 99
Measuring & Controlling Device Mfr
N.A.I.C.S.: 334519

Mahr Austria GmbH   **(1)**
Hirschstettner Strasse 19-21, 1220, Vienna, Austria
Tel.: (43) 120436730
Web Site: http://www.mahr.de
Sales Range: $25-49.9 Million
Emp.: 9
Measuring & Controlling Device Mfr
N.A.I.C.S.: 334519
Martin Schober *(Mng Dir)*

Mahr China Ltd.   **(1)**
Unit G 14th-Floor CDW Building, 388 Castle Peak Road, Tsuen Wan, China (Hong Kong)
Tel.: (852) 23579683
Web Site: http://www.mahr.de
Sales Range: $50-74.9 Million
Emp.: 10
Industrial Machinery & Equipment Whslr
N.A.I.C.S.: 423830
Lych Wong *(Mng Dir)*

Mahr Corporation de Mexico S.A. de C.V.   **(1)**
Francisco G Sada 690 Col Chepevera, Monterrey, 64030, Nuevo Leon, Mexico
Tel.: (52) 8183332010
Web Site: http://www.mahr.com
Sales Range: $25-49.9 Million
Emp.: 18
Industrial Machinery Mfr
N.A.I.C.S.: 333248
Geogre Escarcega *(Gen Mgr)*

Mahr Federal, Inc.   **(1)**
1144 Eddy St, Providence, RI
02905-4511   **(100%)**
Tel.: (401) 784-3100
Web Site: http://www.mahr.com
Sales Range: $100-124.9 Million
Emp.: 300
Dimensional Measuring Instruments Mfr
N.A.I.C.S.: 334513
Tony Picone *(Pres)*

Mahr GmbH   **(1)**
Carl-Zeiss-Promenade 10, 07745, Jena, Germany
Tel.: (49) 3641642696
Web Site: http://www.mahr.com
Sales Range: $25-49.9 Million
Emp.: 30
Electrical Equipment & Component Mfr
N.A.I.C.S.: 335999
Holger Hage *(Mng Dir)*

Mahr Japan Co., Ltd.   **(1)**
712-4-1 Soyado-cho, Kohoku-ku, Yokohama, 222-0032, Japan
Tel.: (81) 455403591
Web Site: http://www.mahr.de
Emp.: 10
Industrial Machinery & Equipment Merchant Whslr
N.A.I.C.S.: 423830
Shoei Katano *(Mng Dir)*

Mahr Korea Ltd.   **(1)**
Hyein B/D 2F 200 Jangchungdan-ro, Jung-Gu, Seoul, 100-391, Korea (South)
Tel.: (82) 25794981
Web Site: http://www.mahr.co.kr
Sales Range: $50-74.9 Million
Emp.: 13
Industrial Machinery & Equipment Merchant Whslr
N.A.I.C.S.: 423830
Jung Cho *(Gen Mgr)*

Mahr Malaysia Sdn. Bhd.   **(1)**
No 130 Block B 1, Leisure Commerce Sq No 9 Jalan, Petaling Jaya, 47150, Selangor, Malaysia
Tel.: (60) 378772060
Web Site: http://www.mahr.com
Sales Range: $25-49.9 Million
Emp.: 5
Power-Driven Handtool Mfr
N.A.I.C.S.: 333991

Mahr Metering Systems Corporation   **(1)**
1415 A Cross Beam Dr, Charlotte, NC 28217
Tel.: (704) 525-7128
Web Site: http://www.mmscusa.com
Sales Range: $25-49.9 Million
Emp.: 20
Industrial Machinery & Equipment Whslr
N.A.I.C.S.: 423830
Carl Mahr *(Mng Dir)*

Mahr Metering Systems GmbH   **(1)**
Carl -Mahr Str 1, PO Box 1853, 37073, Gottingen, 37073, Germany
Tel.: (49) 5517073100
Web Site: http://www.mahr.de
Relay & Industrial Control Mfr
N.A.I.C.S.: 335314

Mahr Metrology India Private Ltd.   **(1)**
Mahr Metrology India Private Ltd, Anna Nagar East, 600102, Chennai, India
Tel.: (91) 4442170531
Web Site: http://www.mahr.in
Sales Range: $25-49.9 Million
Emp.: 12
Electromedical & Electrotherapeutic Apparatus Mfr
N.A.I.C.S.: 334510
R. Ganesan *(Mng Dir)*

Mahr Polska s.p.o.o.   **(1)**
Ul Pulawska 5/4, 02515, Warsaw, Poland
Tel.: (48) 607 665446
Measuring & Controlling Device Distr
N.A.I.C.S.: 423830

Mahr Precision Metrology Suzhou Ltd.   **(1)**
399 Su Hong Road Suzhou Industrial Park, Suzhou, 215122, China
Tel.: (86) 512 62585862
Measuring & Controlling Device Distr
N.A.I.C.S.: 423830
Wolf Gang *(Gen Mgr)*

Mahr S.E.A. Co. Ltd.   **(1)**
c/o Mahr China Ltd Room 103A G/F Riley House, 88 Lei Muk Road, Kwai Chung, China (Hong Kong)
Tel.: (852) 23579683
Web Site: http://www.mahr.de
Emp.: 12
Industrial Machinery Mfr
N.A.I.C.S.: 333248

Mahr Trading Co., Ltd.   **(1)**
Room 1706A Gui Du Tower No 27 Nan Bin He Road, Xuanwu District, Beijing, 100055, China
Tel.: (86) 10 6332448 1
Web Site: http://www.mahr.com.hk
Measuring & Controlling Device Distr
N.A.I.C.S.: 423830

Mahr U.K. plc.   **(1)**
19 Drakes Mews, Crownhill, Milton Keynes, MK8 0ER, Buckinghamshire, United Kingdom   **(100%)**
Tel.: (44) 908563700
Web Site: http://www.mahr.com
Sales Range: $25-49.9 Million
Emp.: 14
Dial Indicators & Precision Instruments
N.A.I.C.S.: 811210

Mahr do Brasil Ltda.   **(1)**
Av Washington Luis 703, 04662-001, Sao Paulo, Brazil
Tel.: (55) 11 28775566
Measuring & Controlling Device Distr
N.A.I.C.S.: 423830

Mahr, spol s.r.o.   **(1)**
Ulice Kpt Jarose 552, Probostov, 41712, Prague, Czech Republic

Tel.: (420) 417816711
Web Site: http://www.mahr.de
Sales Range: $50-74.9 Million
Emp.: 150
Cutting Tool & Machine Tool Accessory Mfr
N.A.I.C.S.: 333515

CARL SCHAEFER GMBH & CO. KG
Altstadter Kirchenweg 23, 75175, Pforzheim, Germany
Tel.: (49) 723115760
Web Site: http://www.carl-schaefer.com
Year Founded: 1861
Rev.: $19,311,600
Emp.: 33
Metal Recovery Services
N.A.I.C.S.: 423510
Timo Richardon *(Head-Sls)*

Subsidiaries:

Carl Schaefer (Austria) GmbH   **(1)**
Gewerbestrasse 30, 2422, Parndorf, Burgenland, Austria
Tel.: (43) 21425215213
Metal Product Distr
N.A.I.C.S.: 423510
Schnelle Daniel *(Mng Dir)*

Carl Schaefer (Casting) GmbH & Co. KG   **(1)**
Maystrasse 6, 75172, Pforzheim, Germany
Tel.: (49) 72314194720
Web Site: http://www.cs-casting.de
Metal Products Mfr
N.A.I.C.S.: 331513
Regina Rudorfer *(Mng Dir)*

Carl Schaefer Hungary Kft.   **(1)**
PO Box 545, 1397, Budapest, Hungary
Tel.: (36) 13242480
Metal Product Distr
N.A.I.C.S.: 423510
Zuzana Papucsekova *(Head-Sls & Mktg)*

Domus Aurea GmbH   **(1)**
Heustr 1, 70174, Stuttgart, Germany
Tel.: (49) 7118703800
Web Site: http://www.domus-aurea.de
Metal Product Distr
N.A.I.C.S.: 423510

CARL-ZEISS-STIFTUNG
Carl Zeiss Strasse 22, 73447, Oberkochen, Germany
Tel.: (49) 7364200
Web Site: http://www.zeiss.de
Year Founded: 1846
Emp.: 31,000
Optical Instruments, Lenses & Eyecare Products Mfr
N.A.I.C.S.: 333310
Karl Lamprecht *(Pres & CEO)*

Subsidiaries:

Carl Zeiss (N.Z.) Ltd.   **(1)**
15B Paramount Drive, Henderson, 0610, Auckland, New Zealand
Tel.: (64) 9 838 5626
Web Site: http://www.zeiss.co.nz
Emp.: 7
Optical Instrument Distr
N.A.I.C.S.: 423450

Carl Zeiss 3D Automation Gmbh   **(1)**
Carl Zeiss Strasse 32, Aalen, 73431, Germany
Tel.: (49) 7361 6336 0
Web Site: http://www.taster.zeiss.de
Industrial Machinery Mfr
N.A.I.C.S.: 333310

Carl Zeiss 3D Metrology Services Gmbh   **(1)**
Felix-Wankel-Strasse 6, Ostfildern, 73760, Germany
Tel.: (49) 711 341678 10
Industrial Machinery Mfr
N.A.I.C.S.: 333310

Carl Zeiss 3D Metrology Services Gmbh Koln   **(1)**
Ruth-Hallensleben-Strasse 6, Cologne,

50739, Germany
Tel.: (49) 221 8286 400
Industrial Equipment Mfr
N.A.I.C.S.: 334513

Carl Zeiss 3D Metrology Services Gmbh Munchen   **(1)**
Carl-Zeiss-Strasse 8a, Garching, 85748, Germany
Tel.: (49) 89 3 74 99 44 0
Web Site: http://www.zeiss.com
Emp.: 20
Industrial Machinery Mfr
N.A.I.C.S.: 333310
Matthias Schneider *(Mng Dir)*

Carl Zeiss 3D Metrology Services Gmbh Peine   **(1)**
Woltorfer Strasse 77 D, Peine, 31224, Germany
Tel.: (49) 5171 79091 0
Industrial Machinery Mfr
N.A.I.C.S.: 333310

Carl Zeiss A/S   **(1)**
Blokken 76, Birkerod, 3460, Denmark
Tel.: (45) 70 15 70 15
Web Site: http://www.zeiss.dk
Emp.: 40
Optical Instruments, Surgical Microscopes & Lenses Mfr
N.A.I.C.S.: 333310

Carl Zeiss AB   **(1)**
Tegeluddsvagen 76, Stockholm, 11528, Sweden   **(100%)**
Tel.: (46) 84592500
Web Site: http://www.zeiss.se
Sales Range: $25-49.9 Million
Emp.: 50
Mfr of Optical Instruments & Lenses
N.A.I.C.S.: 333310
Walter Heger *(Mng Dir)*

Carl Zeiss AG   **(1)**
Carl Zeiss Strasse 22, 73447, Oberkochen, Germany   **(100%)**
Tel.: (49) 7364200
Web Site: http://www.zeiss.de
Sales Range: $800-899.9 Million
Emp.: 4,000
Lens Mfr
N.A.I.C.S.: 333310
Michael F. Kaschke *(Pres & CEO-Mgmt Bd)*

Subsidiary (Non-US):

Carl Zeiss Canada Ltd.   **(2)**
45 Valleybrook D, Toronto, M3B 2S6, ON, Canada   **(60%)**
Tel.: (416) 449-4660
Web Site: http://www.zeiss.ca
Sales Range: $25-49.9 Million
Emp.: 150
Production of Scientific, Medical & Optical Instruments
N.A.I.C.S.: 339112

Subsidiary (Domestic):

Carl Zeiss Meditec AG   **(2)**
Carl Zeiss Promenade 10, 7745, Jena, Germany   **(100%)**
Tel.: (49) 3641640
Sales Range: $75-99.9 Million
Emp.: 400
Medical Supply Mfr
N.A.I.C.S.: 334510
James V. Mazzo *(Pres-Ophthalmic Devices-Global)*

Subsidiary (Non-US):

D.O.R.C. Dutch Ophthalmic Research Center (International) B.V.   **(3)**
Kerkweg 47e, 3214 VC, Zuidland, Netherlands
Tel.: (31) 181458080
Web Site: http://dorcglobal.com
Sales Range: $100-124.9 Million
Emp.: 300
Surgical Instrument Mfr
N.A.I.C.S.: 339112
Ger Vijfvinkel *(Pres)*

Subsidiary (US):

Dutch Ophthalmic USA, Inc.   **(4)**
10 Continental Dr Bldg 1, Exeter, NH 03833
Tel.: (603) 778-6929

Carl-Zeiss-Stiftung—(Continued)

Web Site:
http://www.dutchophthalmicusa.com
Sales Range: $25-49.9 Million
Emp.: 10
Surgical Instrument Mfr
N.A.I.C.S.: 339112
Ger Vijfvinkel (Pres)

Subsidiary (US):

Katalyst Surgical, LLC (3)
754 Goddard Ave, Chesterfield, MO 63005-1100
Web Site: http://www.katalystsurgical.com
Surgical & Medical Instrument Mfr
N.A.I.C.S.: 339112
Gregg Scheller (CEO)

Subsidiary (US):

Carl Zeiss Meditec, Inc. (2)
5300 Central Pkwy, Dublin, CA 94568
Tel.: (925) 557-4100
Web Site: http://www.meditec.zeiss.com
Sales Range: $75-99.9 Million
Emp.: 500
Medical Optics Mfr
N.A.I.C.S.: 333310

Subsidiary (Domestic):

Aaren Scientific Inc. (3)
1040 S Vintage Ave Bldg A, Ontario, CA 91761-1569
Tel.: (909) 937-1033
Web Site: http://www.aareninc.com
Sales Range: $10-24.9 Million
Emp.: 130
Optical Instruments & Intraocular Lenses Mfr
N.A.I.C.S.: 333310
Kim Dyer (Mgr-Mktg)

Laser Diagnostic Technologies (3)
Ste 210 10805 Rancho Bernardo Rd, San Diego, CA 92127-5703
Tel.: (858) 673-7900
Rev.: $16,000,000
Emp.: 120
Surgical & Medical Instruments
N.A.I.C.S.: 339112

Subsidiary (Domestic):

Carl Zeiss Microscopy GmbH (2)
Carl Zeiss Promenade 10, Jena, 37085, Germany
Tel.: (49) 551 50600
Optical Instruments, Lenses & Eyecare Products Mfr
N.A.I.C.S.: 333310

Subsidiary (Non-US):

Carl Zeiss Pty Ltd (2)
Tenancy Office 4 Level 1 40 52 Talavera Road, PO Box 501, North Ryde, 2113, NSW, Australia (100%)
Tel.: (61) 1300367244
Web Site: http://www.zeiss.com.au
Sales Range: $25-49.9 Million
Emp.: 40
Surgical Instruments & Instruments for Ophthalmology
N.A.I.C.S.: 339112
Hilke Fitzsimons (Gen Mgr)

Subsidiary (Domestic):

Carl Zeiss Sports Optics GmbH (2)
Gloelstr 3-5, 35576, Wetzlar, Germany (100%)
Tel.: (49) 8009347733
Web Site: http://www.zeiss.de
Sales Range: $150-199.9 Million
Emp.: 800
Mfr of Optical Instruments
N.A.I.C.S.: 333310

Subsidiary (US):

Carl Zeiss Sports Optics, LLC (2)
13017 N Kingston Ave, Chester, VA 23836-8333
Tel.: (804) 530-8300
Sales Range: $25-49.9 Million
Emp.: 96
Binoculars, Riflescopes, Ophthalmic Lenses & Coatings Mfr

N.A.I.C.S.: 339115
Michael A. Jensen (Pres)

Carl Zeiss, Inc. (2)
1 Zeiss Dr, Thornwood, NY 10594-1939
Tel.: (914) 747-1800
Web Site: http://www.zeiss.com
Sales Range: $300-349.9 Million
Emp.: 700
Distr of Scientific Instruments: Laboratory Microscopes, Surgical Microscopes & Ophthalmic Diagnostic Equipment
N.A.I.C.S.: 423450
Jim Sharp (Pres)

Carl Zeiss AG (1)
Feldbachstrasse 81, 8714, Feldbach, Switzerland
Tel.: (41) 552547333
Web Site: https://www.zeiss.ch
Mfr of Optical Instruments & Lenses
N.A.I.C.S.: 333310

Subsidiary (US):

Capture 3d, Inc. (2)
3207 S Shannon St, Santa Ana, CA 92704
Tel.: (714) 546-7278
Web Site: http://www.capture3d.com
Sales Range: $1-9.9 Million
Emp.: 16
Computer & Software Stores
N.A.I.C.S.: 449210
Richard P. White (Pres)

Carl Zeiss AS (1)
Kabelgaten 8, N0580, Oslo, Norway (100%)
Tel.: (47) 23172393
Web Site: http://www.zeiss.no
Emp.: 20
Eyeglass Lenses & Visual Devices
N.A.I.C.S.: 339115

Carl Zeiss Argentina S.A. (1)
Calle Nahuel Huapi 4015/25, 1430 BCO, Buenos Aires, Argentina (100%)
Tel.: (54) 11 4545 6661
Web Site: http://www.zeiss.com
Mfr of Optical Instruments & Lenses
N.A.I.C.S.: 333310

Carl Zeiss Automated Inspection GmbH & Co. KG (1)
An der Lehmgrube 9, Ohringen, 74613, Germany
Tel.: (49) 79419100 0
Web Site: http://www.zeiss.com
Emp.: 50
Industrial Equipment Mfr
N.A.I.C.S.: 334513
Kaiudo Modrech (Gen Mgr)

Carl Zeiss B.V. (1)
Graaf Engelbertlaan 75, PO Box 310, 4837 DS, Breda, Netherlands (100%)
Tel.: (31) 763035430
Web Site: http://www.micro-shop.zeiss.com
Sales Range: $25-49.9 Million
Emp.: 100
Optical Instrument & Lense Mfr
N.A.I.C.S.: 333310

Carl Zeiss CMP GmbH (1)
Koenigsallee 9-21, Gottingen, Germany
Tel.: (49) 5515060636
Semiconductor Components Mfr
N.A.I.C.S.: 334413
Michael Eikenbusch (Mgr-Production Objectives)

Carl Zeiss Co. Ltd. (1)
2F BR Elitel Bldg 141-1 Sangsu-dong, Mapo-gu, Seoul, 121 828, Korea (South) (100%)
Tel.: (82) 231402600
Web Site: http://www.zeiss.co.kr
Sales Range: $25-49.9 Million
Emp.: 50
Mfr of Optical Instruments & Lenses
N.A.I.C.S.: 333310

Carl Zeiss Co. Ltd. (1)
Fl 8 Thosapol Land Bldg 230, Rajchadapisek Rd Huaykwang, Bangkok, 10310, Thailand (49%)
Tel.: (66) 227406435
Web Site: http://www.zeiss.com.sg
Sales Range: $25-49.9 Million
Emp.: 15
Mfr of Optical Instruments & Lenses

N.A.I.C.S.: 333310

Carl Zeiss Co., Ltd. (1)
22 Honshio-cho, Shinjuku-ku, Tokyo, 160-0003, Japan
Tel.: (81) 3 3355 0341
Medical Equipment Mfr
N.A.I.C.S.: 334510

Carl Zeiss Co., Ltd. (1)
5F 1 No 150 Section 2 Gongdao 5th Road, Hsinchu, Taiwan
Tel.: (886) 35753747
Medical Device Mfr
N.A.I.C.S.: 339112

Carl Zeiss Far East Company Limited (1)
Tower 1 13th Floor 5-7 Ever Gain Plz No 88 Container Port Rd, Kwaichung, Kwai Chung, New Territories, China (Hong Kong) (100%)
Tel.: (852) 23320402
Web Site: http://www.carlzeiss.com
Sales Range: $25-49.9 Million
Emp.: 40
Mfr of Optical Instruments & Lenses
N.A.I.C.S.: 333310
Bjorn Franken (Dir-Sls & Mktg)

Carl Zeiss Fixture Systems GmbH (1)
Auf Rodert 5 - 7, Tholey, 66636, Germany
Tel.: (49) 15114225370
Industrial Equipment Mfr
N.A.I.C.S.: 334513

Carl Zeiss GmbH (1)
LaxenburgerStrasse 2, Vienna, 1030, Austria (100%)
Tel.: (43) 1795180
Web Site: http://www.zeiss.at
Sales Range: $25-49.9 Million
Emp.: 80
Mfr of Optical Instruments & Lenses
N.A.I.C.S.: 333310
Peter Amend (Gen Mgr)

Carl Zeiss IMT Co., Ltd. (1)
3-35-22 Tarumi-cho, Suita-shi, Osaka, 564-0062, Japan
Tel.: (81) 6 63378031
Web Site: http://www.zeiss.co.jp
Industrial Equipment Mfr
N.A.I.C.S.: 334513
Keiji Ueda (Pres)

Carl Zeiss IMT Iberia S.L.U. (1)
Ronda de Poniente 5, Tres Cantos, 28760, Spain
Tel.: (34) 91203 3700
Web Site: http://www.zeiss.es
Emp.: 100
Measuring & Controlling Device Mfr
N.A.I.C.S.: 334513
Ramon Larino (Mgr-Svcs)

Carl Zeiss Iberia, S.L. (1)
Frederic Mompou 3, Piso 6 B, Sant Just Desvern, 08960, Spain
Tel.: (34) 93 480 29 52
Emp.: 40
Optical Instrument & Lens Mfr
N.A.I.C.S.: 333310
Irene Guirado Reverte (Acct Mgr)

Carl Zeiss India Pte. Ltd. (1)
Plot No 03 Jigani Link Road Bommasandra Industrial Area, Bengaluru, 560 099, Karnataka, India
Tel.: (91) 80 4343 8000
Web Site: http://www.zeiss.co.in
Optical Instrument Mfr
N.A.I.C.S.: 333310
Aslam Sher Khan (Mgr-Natl Sls)

Carl Zeiss Industrial Metrology, LLC (1)
6250 Sycamore Ln N, Maple Grove, MN 55369
Tel.: (763) 744-2400
Web Site: http://www.zeiss.com
Emp.: 250
Measuring & Controlling Device Mfr
N.A.I.C.S.: 334513
Israel Gonzalez (VP-Svc)

Carl Zeiss Industrielle Messtechnik Austria Gmbh (1)
Puntigamer Strasse 127, Graz, 8055, Austria

Tel.: (43) 5 93477
Web Site: http://www.zeiss.at
Measuring & Controlling Device Mfr
N.A.I.C.S.: 334513

Carl Zeiss Innovationszentrum fur Messtechnik Gmbh (1)
Bertolt-Brecht-Allee 24, Dresden, 01309, Germany
Tel.: (49) 351 213911 0
Automobile Parts Mfr
N.A.I.C.S.: 336390

Carl Zeiss Instruments s.r.l. (1)
Str Fluierului 21B, 021423, Bucharest, Romania (100%)
Tel.: (40) 4253000
Web Site: http://www.zeiss.com
Sales Range: $25-49.9 Million
Emp.: 4
Mfr of Optical Instruments & Lenses
N.A.I.C.S.: 333310

Carl Zeiss Japan Group (1)
22 Honshio-cho, Shinjuku-ku, Tokyo, 160-0003, Japan
Tel.: (81) 333550341
Web Site: http://www.zeiss.co.jp
Scientific Instruments Laboratory Microscopes, Surgical Microscopes & Ophthalmic Equipment & Ophthalmic Diagnostic Equipment Distr
N.A.I.C.S.: 423490

Carl Zeiss Jena GmbH (1)
Carl-Zeiss-Promenade 10, Jena, Germany
Tel.: (49) 3641640
Semiconductor Components Mfr
N.A.I.C.S.: 334413
Gerhard Kolb (Acct Mgr)

Carl Zeiss Ltd. (1)
15-20 Woodfield Road, Welwyn Garden City, AL7 1LU, Herts, United Kingdom (100%)
Tel.: (44) 1707871200
Web Site: http://www.zeiss.co.uk
Sales Range: $50-74.9 Million
Emp.: 150
Mfr of Optical Instruments & Lenses
N.A.I.C.S.: 333310

Carl Zeiss MENA FZE (1)
Jebel Ali, Dubai, 262212, United Arab Emirates
Tel.: (971) 4 8807781
Optical Instrument Mfr & Distr
N.A.I.C.S.: 333310
Salil Kumar (Mgr-Ops)

Carl Zeiss MES Solutions GmbH (1)
Postgasse 1, Ulm, Germany
Tel.: (49) 7318801770
Web Site: http://www.guardus-mes.de
Software Services
N.A.I.C.S.: 541511
Simone Cronjager (Mng Dir-Sls)

Carl Zeiss Meditec Co., Ltd. (1)
2-10-9 Kojimachi, Chiyoda-ku, Tokyo, Japan
Tel.: (81) 570021311
Web Site: http://www.zeiss.co.jp
Health Care Srvices
N.A.I.C.S.: 621999

Carl Zeiss Meditec France S.A.S. (1)
100 Route de Versailles, Marly-le-Roi, France
Tel.: (33) 134802100
Medical Device Mfr
N.A.I.C.S.: 339112

Carl Zeiss Meditec Production, LLC (1)
1040 S Vintage Ave Bldg A, Ontario, CA 91761
Tel.: (909) 937-1033
Medical Device Mfr
N.A.I.C.S.: 339112

Carl Zeiss Meditec SAS (1)
Avenue Paul Langevin, La Rochelle, France
Tel.: (33) 546448550
Medical Device Mfr
N.A.I.C.S.: 339112

Carl Zeiss Meditec Vertriebsgesellschaft mbH (1)
Rudolf-Eber-Strasse 11, Oberkochen, Germany

Tel.: (49) 7364206000
Semiconductor Components Mfr
N.A.I.C.S.: 334413

Carl Zeiss Microscopy Co., Ltd. **(1)**
7 Honshio-cho, Shinjuku-Ku, Tokyo, 160-
0003, Japan
Tel.: (81) 3 3355 0332
Optical Instrument & Lens Mfr
N.A.I.C.S.: 333310

Carl Zeiss Microscopy Limited **(1)**
509 Coldhams Lane, Cambridge, CB1 3JS,
United Kingdom
Tel.: (44) 1223 401 500
Web Site: http://www.zeiss.co.uk
Optical Instrument Mfr
N.A.I.C.S.: 333310
Paul Adely *(Branch Mgr)*

Carl Zeiss Microscopy, LLC **(1)**
1 N Broadway, White Plains, NY 10601
Medical Device Mfr
N.A.I.C.S.: 339112

Carl Zeiss N.V-S.A. **(1)**
Ikaroslaan 49, 1930, Zaventem, Belgium
Tel.: (32) 27193911
Web Site: http://www.zeiss.be
Sales Range: $25-49.9 Million
Emp.: 40
Mfr of Optical Instruments & Lenses
N.A.I.C.S.: 333310
Stefan Claes *(Chm-Mgmt Bd)*

Carl Zeiss OIM Gmbh **(1)**
Daimlerstrasse 19, Wangen, 73117, Ger-
many
Tel.: (49) 7161 1 56 53 00
Measuring & Controlling Device Mfr
N.A.I.C.S.: 334513

Carl Zeiss Opton Kft. **(1)**
Bocskai ut 134-146, 1113, Budapest, Hun-
gary
Tel.: (36) 6 1 309 7930
Web Site: http://www.zeiss.hu
Optical Instruments & Lenses Mfr
N.A.I.C.S.: 333310

Carl Zeiss Oy **(1)**
Niittyvillankuja 4B, Vantaa, 01510, Finland
Tel.: (358) 207 940890
Web Site: http://www.zeiss.fi
Optical Instrument & Lens Mfr & Distr
N.A.I.C.S.: 333310
Petteri Valtonen *(Area Mgr-Sls)*

Carl Zeiss Pte. Ltd. **(1)**
50 Kaki Bukit Place 0501, 415926, Singa-
pore, Singapore **(100%)**
Tel.: (65) 67419600
Web Site: http://www.zeiss.com.sg
Sales Range: $25-49.9 Million
Emp.: 50
Mfr of Optical Instruments & Lenses
N.A.I.C.S.: 333310

Carl Zeiss Pty. Ltd. **(1)**
363 Oak Avenue Randburg, PO Box 3003,
Ferndale, 2194, South Africa
Tel.: (27) 118869510
Web Site: http://www.zeiss.co.za
Emp.: 68
Microscopes, Binoculars, Optical Lens,
Ophthalmic Products & Laboratory Products
Mfr & Distr
N.A.I.C.S.: 334516
Gail Giordani *(Mng Dir)*

Carl Zeiss QEC GmbH **(1)**
Ruth-Hallensleben-Strasse 6, Cologne, Ger-
many
Tel.: (49) 2218286400
Industrial Machinery Mfr
N.A.I.C.S.: 333248

Carl Zeiss S.A.S **(1)**
60 Rte De Sartrouville, BP No 66, 78230,
Le Pecq, France **(100%)**
Tel.: (33) 33134802000
Web Site: http://www.zeiss.fr
Mfr of Optical Instruments
N.A.I.C.S.: 333310

Carl Zeiss S.p.A. **(1)**
Viale Delle Industrie 1820, 20020, Arese,
Italy **(100%)**
Tel.: (39) 02937731
Web Site: http://www.zeiss.it
Provider of Optical Products

N.A.I.C.S.: 327215

Carl Zeiss SBE, LLC **(1)**
1 N Broadway, White Plains, NY 10601
Optical Device Mfr
N.A.I.C.S.: 333310

Carl Zeiss SMT GmbH **(1)**
Rudolf-Eber-Str 2, Oberkochen, Germany
Tel.: (49) 7364200
Semiconductor Components Mfr
N.A.I.C.S.: 334413
Ulrich Hahn *(Sls Mgr)*

Carl Zeiss Sdn. Bhd. **(1)**
Suites P5 16 & P5 17 Building Information
Centre, Lot 2 Jalan 243/51A, Petaling Jaya,
46100, Selangor, Malaysia
Tel.: (60) 3 7877 5058
Web Site: http://www.zeiss.com
Optical Instrument Distr
N.A.I.C.S.: 423450
Km Yee *(Mgr-Sls)*

Carl Zeiss Services S.a.r.l. **(1)**
25 rue Saint Blaise, Sable-sur-Sarthe,
France
Tel.: (33) 243551887
Web Site: http://www.zeiss-services.com
Measuring Instrument Distr
N.A.I.C.S.: 423830

Carl Zeiss Shanghai Co., Ltd. **(1)**
1/F Ke Yuan Building 11 Ri Nan Road
Waigaoqiao Free Trade Zone, Shanghai,
200131, China
Tel.: (86) 400 690 0401
Web Site: http://www.zeiss.com.cn
Optical Instrument Mfr
N.A.I.C.S.: 333310

Carl Zeiss Slovakia, s.r.o. **(1)**
Racianska 12481/77/A, Bratislava, 831 02,
Slovakia
Tel.: (421) 2 5564 6791
Web Site: http://www.zeiss.sk
Measuring & Controlling Device Mfr
N.A.I.C.S.: 334513

Carl Zeiss Sp. z o. o. **(1)**
Ul Mangalia 4, 02 758, Warsaw,
Poland **(100%)**
Tel.: (48) 228587819
Web Site: http://www.zeiss.pl
Sales Range: $25-49.9 Million
Emp.: 15
Mfr of Optical Instruments & Lenses
N.A.I.C.S.: 333310

Carl Zeiss Spectroscopy GmbH **(1)**
Carl-Zeiss-Promenade 10, Jena, Germany
Tel.: (49) 3641642838
Semiconductor Components Mfr
N.A.I.C.S.: 334413
Christian Korth *(Mng Dir)*

**Carl Zeiss Sport Optikai Hungaria
Kft.** **(1)**
Ernst Abbe utza 1-2, 4700, Mateszalka,
Hungary
Tel.: (36) 44 501194
Web Site: http://www.zeiss.hu
Optical Instrument Mfr
N.A.I.C.S.: 333310

Carl Zeiss Suzhou Co., Ltd. **(1)**
Modern Industrial Square 3-B-2 333 Xingpu
Rd Suzhou Industrial Park, Suzhou, Ji-
angsu, China
Tel.: (86) 512 6287 1388
Optical Instrument Mfr
N.A.I.C.S.: 333310

Carl Zeiss Technika Kft. **(1)**
Neumann Janos utca 3, 2040, Budaors,
Hungary
Tel.: (36) 23 802 800
Emp.: 7
Optical Instrument & Lens Mfr
N.A.I.C.S.: 333310
Antal Igaz *(Dir-Sls)*

**Carl Zeiss Teknoloji Cozumleri Ticaret
Limited Sirketi** **(1)**
Nidakule Atasehir Kuzey Barbaros Mah Be-
gonya Sok No 3 Kat 8, Atasehir, Istanbul,
Turkiye
Tel.: (90) 2164256475
Web Site: http://www.zeiss.com.tr
Medical Device Mfr
N.A.I.C.S.: 339112

**Carl Zeiss Vietnam Company
Limited** **(1)**
58 Nguyen Dinh Chieu Street, Da Kao
Ward District 1, Ho Chi Minh City, Vietnam
Tel.: (84) 2839118670
Medical Device Mfr
N.A.I.C.S.: 339112

**Carl Zeiss Vision (Malaysia) Sdn.
Bhd.** **(1)**
A-5-8 Kuchai Exchange No 43 Jalan Kuchai
Maju 13, 58200, Kuala Lumpur, Malaysia
Tel.: (60) 379899700
Web Site: http://www.zeiss.com.my
Optical Instrument & Lens Mfr
N.A.I.C.S.: 333310

Carl Zeiss Vision AB **(1)**
Boplatsgatan 6, Po Box 15035, 213 76,
Malmo, Sweden
Tel.: (46) 40 685 6000
Web Site: http://www.zeiss.se
Emp.: 35
Optical Instrument & Len Mfr
N.A.I.C.S.: 333310

Carl Zeiss Vision Argentina S.A **(1)**
1558 Capital Federal, C1037ACD, Buenos
Aires, Argentina
Tel.: (54) 11 43722452
Optical Instrument & Lens Mfr
N.A.I.C.S.: 333310

**Carl Zeiss Vision Australia Group Pty.
Ltd.** **(1)**
6 Sherriffs Rd, Lonsdale, 5160, SA, Austra-
lia
Tel.: (61) 883928114
Optical Instrument & Lens Mfr
N.A.I.C.S.: 333310

Carl Zeiss Vision Belgium NV **(1)**
Ikaroslaan 49, Zaventem, Belgium
Tel.: (32) 27193911
Eyeglass Device Mfr
N.A.I.C.S.: 333310

Carl Zeiss Vision Columbia Ltda. **(1)**
Av Centenario 108 A-85, Bogota, Colombia
Tel.: (57) 4046860
Optical Instrument Mfr
N.A.I.C.S.: 333310

Carl Zeiss Vision Danmark A/S **(1)**
Boplatsgatan 6, PO Box 128, Copenhagen,
20031, Denmark
Tel.: (45) 70 25 70 00
Web Site: http://www.zeiss.dk
Emp.: 45
Optical Instrument Mfr
N.A.I.C.S.: 333310

Carl Zeiss Vision Espana **(1)**
c/Tomas Lopez 3 4, 28009, Madrid,
Spain **(100%)**
Tel.: (34) 91 3096200
Web Site: http://www.zeiss.es
Sales Range: $25-49.9 Million
Emp.: 60
Optical Instruments & Lenses Mfr
N.A.I.C.S.: 333310

**Carl Zeiss Vision France Holding
S.A.S.** **(1)**
7 rue Augustin Fresnel, 35306, Fougeres,
France
Tel.: (33) 820 013535
Web Site: http://www.zeiss.fr
Optical Instrument Mfr
N.A.I.C.S.: 333310

**Carl Zeiss Vision Hungary Optikai
Kft.** **(1)**
Ernst Abbe utca 1-2, Mateszalka, Hungary
Tel.: (36) 44501202
Eyeglass Device Mfr
N.A.I.C.S.: 333310

**Carl Zeiss Vision International
GmbH** **(1)**
Gartenstrasse 97, 73430, Aalen, Germany
Web Site: http://www.vision.zeiss.com
Sales Range: $1-4.9 Billion
Emp.: 10,000
Mfr of Eyeglasses & Lenses
N.A.I.C.S.: 333310
Michael Hoffmann *(CEO)*

Subsidiary (Non-US):

Alpha Lens Company Ltd. **(2)**

76-77 Capitol Industrial Park Capitol Way,
London, NX9 0EW, United Kingdom
Tel.: (44) 2089491901
Sales Range: $25-49.9 Million
Emp.: 50
Ophthalmic Products Mfr & Supply
N.A.I.C.S.: 333310

Carl Zeiss Vision **(2)**
5th Fl Nissei Fushimi Machi Building, 4 4 1
Fushimi Machi Chuo Ku, Osaka, 541 0044,
Japan
Tel.: (81) 662022672
Sales Range: $25-49.9 Million
Emp.: 100
Eyeglass Lenses Mfr
N.A.I.C.S.: 333310

Carl Zeiss Vision **(2)**
Calle 7 Sur No 1111, Tijuana, 22500,
Mexico
Tel.: (52) 6646233734
Optical Lense Services
N.A.I.C.S.: 456130

Carl Zeiss Vision **(2)**
Avenida San Andres Atoto 165-B, Naucal-
pan de Juarez, Mexico, 53550, Mexico
Tel.: (52) 5555767033
Web Site: http://www.aolens.com
Sales Range: $25-49.9 Million
Emp.: 100
Optical Lense Services
N.A.I.C.S.: 333310

**Carl Zeiss Vision (Guangzhou)
Ltd.** **(2)**
No 1389 Jui Fo West Road, Baiyun District,
Guangzhou, 510555, China
Tel.: (86) 2087490088
Web Site: http://www.joffray.com
Eyeglass Lenses Mfr
N.A.I.C.S.: 333310

Carl Zeiss Vision Australia Ltd. **(2)**
24 Heath St, Lonsdale, 5160, SA, Australia
Tel.: (61) 883928899
Sales Range: $150-199.9 Million
Eyeglass Lenses Mfr
N.A.I.C.S.: 333310

**Carl Zeiss Vision Brasil Industria Op-
tica Ltda.** **(2)**
Rua Luiz Winter 222 Duarte da Silveira,
25665-431, Petropolis, RJ, Brazil
Tel.: (55) 24 2233 7012
Eyeglass Lenses Mfr
N.A.I.C.S.: 333310

Subsidiary (Domestic):

Carl Zeiss Vision GmbH **(2)**
Turnstrasse 27, 73430, Aalen, Germany
Tel.: (49) 7361 598 5000
Web Site: http://www.vision.zeiss.com
Sales Range: $25-49.9 Million
Emp.: 8
Eyeglass Lenses Mfr
N.A.I.C.S.: 333310
Spiller Rudols *(Gen Mgr)*

Subsidiary (US):

Carl Zeiss Vision Inc. **(2)**
12121 Scripps Summit Dr, San Diego, CA
92130-4682
Tel.: (858) 790-7700
Web Site: http://www.vision.zeiss.com
Sales Range: $650-699.9 Million
Plastic & Glass Eyeglass Lenses Mfr &
Sales
N.A.I.C.S.: 339115
Cindy Brown *(Mgr-Trade Show & Events)*

Subsidiary (Domestic):

Great Lakes Coating Laboratory **(3)**
1784 Larchwood Dr, Troy, MI 48083-2223
Tel.: (248) 524-0550
Web Site: http://www.carl-zeiss.com
Sales Range: $50-74.9 Million
Emp.: 120
Optical Goods Mfr & Sales
N.A.I.C.S.: 333310

Kansas City Opthalmics LLC **(3)**
13731 E 42nd Ter, Independence, MO
64055
Tel.: (816) 478-4901

Sales Range: $25-49.9 Million
Emp.: 6
Optical Services
N.A.I.C.S.: 456130

Subsidiary (Non-US):

Carl Zeiss Vision Ireland Ltd. (2)
Whitemill Industrial Estate, Wexford, Ireland
Tel.: (353) 5363700
Sales Range: $75-99.9 Million
Optical Lense Services
N.A.I.C.S.: 456130

Carl Zeiss Vision Italia SPA (2)
Via SEP Mazzucchelli No 17, Castiglione
Olona, 21043, Varese, Lombardia, Italy
Tel.: (39) 0331851111
Web Site: http://www.zeiss.it
Sales Range: $75-99.9 Million
Emp.: 400
Eyeglass Lenses & Magnifying Vision Mfr
N.A.I.C.S.: 333310
Michele D'adamo (Gen Mgr)

Carl Zeiss Vision Swiss AG (2)
Helsinkistrasse 9, Basel, 4142, Switzerland
Tel.: (41) 613388100
Sales Range: $25-49.9 Million
Emp.: 15
Optical Products Mfr & Sales
N.A.I.C.S.: 333310

Carl Zeiss Vision UK Ltd. (2)
Unit 9 Holford Way, Holford, Birmingham,
B6 7AX, United Kingdom
Tel.: (44) 1213324404
Web Site: http://www.vision.zeiss.co.uk
Sales Range: $75-99.9 Million
Eyeglass Lenses Mfr
N.A.I.C.S.: 333310

Carl Zeiss Vision Venezuela Industria Optica C.A. (2)
Av Francisco de Miranda, Centro Profe-
sional Miranda, piso 2 ofc 2C, Caracas,
1060, Venezuela
Tel.: (58) 212 264 6231
Web Site: http://www.solaven.com
Sales Range: $25-49.9 Million
Emp.: 5
Eyeglass Lenses Mfr
N.A.I.C.S.: 333310

Carl Zeiss Vision Manufactura de Mexico S. de R.L. de C.V. (1)
Blvd Insurgentes No 18600, Tijuana, 22580,
Mexico
Tel.: (52) 664 134 0800
Optical Instrument & Lens Mfr
N.A.I.C.S.: 333310

Carl Zeiss Vision Mexico S. de R.L. de C.V. (1)
Proton No 12 Parque Industrial, 53489,
Naucalpan, Mexico
Tel.: (52) 55 3000 3100
Optical Instrument Mfr
N.A.I.C.S.: 333310

Carl Zeiss Vision Portugal S.A. (1)
Av D Joao II Lote 1 12 02 Parque das Na-
coes, Edificio Adamastor Torre B Piso 3,
1990-077, Lisbon, Portugal
Tel.: (351) 218 981 150
Web Site: http://www.zeiss.pt
Emp.: 130
Optical Instrument Mfr
N.A.I.C.S.: 333310

Carl Zeiss Vision Singapore Pte. Ltd. (1)
Blk 1200 Depot Road, Singapore, 109675,
Singapore
Tel.: (65) 6275 3383
Optical Instrument Mfr
N.A.I.C.S.: 333310

Carl Zeiss Vision South Africa Ltd. (1)
363 Oak Avenue Ferndale, Randburg,
2094, South Africa
Tel.: (27) 11 538 4200
Optical Instrument Mfr
N.A.I.C.S.: 333310

Carl Zeiss X-ray Microscopy, Inc. (1)
4385 Hopyard Rd Ste 100, Pleasanton, CA
94588

Tel.: (925) 701-3600
Optical Instrument Mfr
N.A.I.C.S.: 333310

Carl Zeiss d.o.o. (1)
Leskoskova cesta 6, Ljubljana, 1000, Slove-
nia
Tel.: (386) 1 5138240
Emp.: 11
Optical Instrument & Lens Mfr
N.A.I.C.S.: 333310
Joze Moljk (Reg Mgr-Sls)

Carl Zeiss d.o.o. (1)
A Heinza 3, Zagreb, 10000, Croatia
Tel.: (385) 1 4633438
Web Site: http://www.micro-shop.zeiss.com
Emp.: 5
Optical Instrument & Lens Mfr
N.A.I.C.S.: 333310
Petar Cvjeticanin (Area Mgr-Sls)

Carl Zeiss de Mexico, S.A. de C.V. (1)
Av Miguel A De Quevedo 496, Coyoacan,
4010, Catarina, Mexico (100%)
Tel.: (52) 5559990200
Web Site: http://www.zeiss.com.mx
Sales Range: $25-49.9 Million
Emp.: 50
Mfr of Optical Instruments & Lenses
N.A.I.C.S.: 333310

Carl Zeiss do Brasil Ltda. (1)
Av das Nacoes Unidas, Sao Paulo, 04795-
100, Brazil
Tel.: (55) 11 5693 5500
Web Site: http://www.zeiss.com.br
Optical Instrument & Lens Mfr
N.A.I.C.S.: 334513
Rodrigo Guarana Santos (Dir-Medical Div)

Carl Zeiss spol. s.r.o. (1)
Radlecka 14 3201, Prague, 15000, Czech
Republic (50%)
Tel.: (420) 233101221
Web Site: http://www.zeiss.cz
Sales Range: $25-49.9 Million
Emp.: 80
Mfr of Optical Products
N.A.I.C.S.: 327215
Andreas Mohr (Mng Dir)

Carl Zeiss spol. s.r.o. (1)
Racianska 12481/77/A, 831 02, Bratislava,
Slovakia (100%)
Tel.: (421) 255646791
Web Site: http://www.zeiss.sk
Sales Range: $25-49.9 Million
Emp.: 11
Mfr of Optical Instruments & Lenses
N.A.I.C.S.: 333310

FCI Ophthalmics Inc. (1)
30 Corporate Park Dr Ste 310/320, Pem-
broke, MA 02359
Web Site: http://www.fci-ophthalmics.com
Medical Device Mfr
N.A.I.C.S.: 339112
Jan Willem DeCler (Treas)

France Chirurgie Instrumentation (F.C.I.) SAS (1)
20-22 rue Louis Armand, 75015, Paris,
France
Tel.: (33) 1 53 98 98 98
Web Site: http://www.fci.fr
Ophthalmic Goods Mfr
N.A.I.C.S.: 339115

GOM Americas Inc. (1)
Portal Ste 442 9319 Robert D Snyder Rd,
Charlotte, NC 28223
Tel.: (704) 912-1600
Industrial Machinery Mfr
N.A.I.C.S.: 333248
David Linford (VP & Gen Mgr)

GOM France SAS (1)
9 rue Leonard de Vinci ZA de la Mare du
Milieu, Guibeville, Dammarie-les-Lys,
France
Tel.: (33) 164592240
Industrial Machinery Mfr
N.A.I.C.S.: 333248

GOM GmbH (1)
Schmitzstrasse 2, Braunschweig, Germany
Tel.: (49) 531390290
Web Site: http://www.gom.com

Emp.: 500
Industrial Machinery Mfr
N.A.I.C.S.: 333248

GOM Italia S.R.L. (1)
Via della Resistenza 121/A, Buccinasco, MI,
Italy
Tel.: (39) 0245701564
Industrial Machinery Mfr
N.A.I.C.S.: 333248

GOM UK Limited (1)
14 The Cobalt Centre Siskin Parkway East,
Coventry, CV3 4PE, United Kingdom
Tel.: (44) 2476639920
Industrial Machinery Mfr
N.A.I.C.S.: 333248
Kevin Hawley (Sls Mgr)

**Holometric Technologies Forschungs-
und Entwicklungs-Gmbh** (1)
Willy-Messerschmitt-Str 1, 73457, Essingen,
Germany
Tel.: (49) 736596450
Web Site: http://www.holometric.de
Measuring & Controlling Device Mfr
N.A.I.C.S.: 334513

Hyaltech Ltd. (1)
Starlaw Business Park, Livingston, EH54
8TE, United Kingdom
Tel.: (44) 1506401000
Medical Device Mfr
N.A.I.C.S.: 339112

ICC Ukraine Ltd. (1)
10 Dovzhenko St Apt 13, 3057, Kiev,
Ukraine
Tel.: (380) 444555128
Web Site: http://www.zeiss.com
Provider of Optical Products
N.A.I.C.S.: 327215

JV ZEISS-BelOMO OOO (1)
Ul Makajonok 23, Minsk, Belarus
Tel.: (375) 172118001
Medical Device Mfr
N.A.I.C.S.: 339112

KLEO Halbleitertechnik Gmbh (1)
Karlsdorfer Strasse 50, 88069, Tettnang,
Germany
Tel.: (49) 7542 5391 30
Web Site: http://www.kleotech.de
Emp.: 20
Electronic Equipment Distr
N.A.I.C.S.: 423690
Andreas Knipp (Mng Dir)

Meisterhaus Laboratorio Optico Ltda. (1)
33 Gen Argolo R Sao Cristovao, 29021-
390, Rio de Janeiro, Brazil
Tel.: (55) 21 3578 4400
Optical Instrument & Lens Mfr
N.A.I.C.S.: 333310

OOO Optec (1)
Kutuzovsky Projezd 16, 123995, Moscow,
Russia
Tel.: (7) 4956600125
Medical Device Mfr
N.A.I.C.S.: 339112

Ooo Carl Zeiss (1)
Serebryanicheskaya Embankment 29,
109028, Moscow, Russia (100%)
Tel.: (7) 8002000567
Web Site: http://www.zeiss.ru
Sales Range: $25-49.9 Million
Emp.: 80
Provider of Optical Products
N.A.I.C.S.: 327215

OptiMedi Sp. z o.o. (1)
Ul Grunwaldzka 10, Slupsk, Poland
Tel.: (48) 593070670
Web Site: http://www.optimedi.pl
Medical Device Mfr
N.A.I.C.S.: 339112

Optiswiss AG (1)
Lyon-Strasse 26, 4053, Basel, Switzerland
Tel.: (41) 61 337 15 15
Web Site: http://www.optiswiss.com
Optical Instrument & Lens Mfr
N.A.I.C.S.: 333310
Denis-Andre Zaugg (Chm & CEO)

Optiswiss France SARL (1)

15 rue de Huningue, 68300, Saint Louis,
France
Tel.: (33) 3 89 89 42 00
Optical Instrument & Lens Mfr
N.A.I.C.S.: 333310

Schott AG (1)
(100%)
Tel.: (49) 6131660
Web Site: http://www.cohott.com
Sales Range: $1-4.9 Billion
Glass Mfr
N.A.I.C.S.: 327212
Frank Heinricht (Chm-Mgmt Bd)

Subsidiary (Non-US):

Gemtron de Mexico S.A. de C.V. (2)
AV C F E No 645 Manzana 5 Zona Indus-
trial del Potosi 2a Seccion, 78090, San Luis
Potosi, Mexico
Tel.: (52) 444 824 0100
Optical Instrument & Lens Mfr
N.A.I.C.S.: 333310
Manuel Tafoya (Fin Mgr)

Subsidiary (Domestic):

Jenaer Glaswerk GmbH (2)
Otto Schott Strasse 13, 7745, Jena,
Germany (100%)
Tel.: (49) 36416810
Web Site: http://www.schott.com
Sales Range: $100-124.9 Million
Emp.: 500
Mfr of Glass Products
N.A.I.C.S.: 327215

Subsidiary (Non-US):

NEC SCHOTT Components Corporation (2)
3-1 Nichiden Minakuchi-cho, Koka, 528-
0034, Shiga, Japan (100%)
Tel.: (81) 748 63 6610
Web Site: http://www.nec-schott.co.jp
Sales Range: $75-99.9 Million
Emp.: 190
Automotive Parts Mfr & Distr
N.A.I.C.S.: 336390

PT. SCHOTT Igar Glass (2)
Jl Meranti 3 Blok L8-06B Delta Silicon Ind
Park Lippo Cikarang, 17550, Bekasi, Indo-
nesia
Tel.: (62) 21 2864 0088
Optical Instrument Mfr & Distr
N.A.I.C.S.: 333310

**SCHOTT (Shanghai) Precision Mate-
rials & Equipment International Trad-
ing Co., Ltd.** (2)
Unit 301 Innov Tower 1801 Hong Mei Road,
200233, Shanghai, China
Tel.: (86) 21 33678000
Glass Product Distr
N.A.I.C.S.: 423460

SCHOTT Benelux B.V. (2)
Randweg 3A, 4104 AC, Culemborg, Nether-
lands
Tel.: (31) 345 470640
Web Site: http://www.schott.com
Emp.: 10
Building Materials Distr
N.A.I.C.S.: 423390
Antoon Wesselink (Gen Mgr)

SCHOTT Brasil Ltda. (2)
Av Francisco Nakasato 1801, Itupeva,
13295-000, Sao Paulo, Brazil
Tel.: (55) 11 4591 0288
Glass Products Mfr
N.A.I.C.S.: 327215
Valdemar Junque Jr. (Mgr-IT)

SCHOTT Brasil Ltda. Divisao Vitrofarma (2)
Av Francisco Nakasato 1801, Itupeva,
13295-000, Sao Paulo, Brazil (100%)
Tel.: (55) 1145910288
Web Site: http://www.schott.com
Sales Range: $25-49.9 Million
Emp.: 50
Tubing Mfr
N.A.I.C.S.: 331210

SCHOTT Brazil (2)
Rua Ivan De Oliveira Lima 155, CEP 20760
600, Rio de Janeiro, Brazil (100%)

Tel.: (55) 2125993100
Web Site: http://www.schott.com
Sales Range: $50-74.9 Million
Emp.: 200
Laboratory Glass Mfr
N.A.I.C.S.: 327215

Subsidiary (US):

SCHOTT DiamondView Armor Products, LLC (2)
1515 Garnet Mine Rd, Boothwyn, PA 19061
Tel.: (610) 558-4084
Glass Products Mfr
N.A.I.C.S.: 327215

Subsidiary (Non-US):

SCHOTT Envases Argentina S.A. (2)
Primera Junta 3181, Munro, Buenos Aires, 1605, Argentina
Tel.: (54) 11 4756 2800
Web Site: http://www.schott.com
Emp.: 200
Glass Products Mfr
N.A.I.C.S.: 327215
Christian Schmidt (Gen Mgr)

SCHOTT Envases Farmaceuticos S.A. (2)
Autopista Medellin 500 mts via Cota, Cundinamarca, Colombia
Tel.: (57) 1335 3600
Glass Products Mfr
N.A.I.C.S.: 327215

SCHOTT Flat Glass do Brasil Ltda. (2)
Rua Turmalina 543, Indaiatuba, 13347-040, Sao Paulo, Brazil
Tel.: (55) 19 3936 8997
Glass Products Mfr
N.A.I.C.S.: 327215

SCHOTT France Pharma Systems SAS (2)
Route de Paris, BP 18, 89140, Pont-sur-Yonne, France
Tel.: (33) 3 86 67 28 82
Web Site: http://www.schott.com
Emp.: 150
Pharmaceuticals Product Mfr
N.A.I.C.S.: 325412
Laurent Lamy (Gen Mgr)

SCHOTT Gemtron Canada Corporation (2)
125 Albert Street, PO Box 460, Midland, L4R 4L3, ON, Canada
Tel.: (705) 526-3771
Glass Products Mfr
N.A.I.C.S.: 327215

Joint Venture (US):

SCHOTT Gemtron Corporation (2)
615 Hwy 68, Sweetwater, TN 37874-1911
Tel.: (423) 337-3522
Web Site: http://www.gemtron.net
Sales Range: $50-74.9 Million
Emp.: 250
Mfr of Tempered & Decorative Glass For Uses Including Shower Doors, Ovens & Shelving; Joint Venture of Schott Glaswerke & AFG Industries, Inc.
N.A.I.C.S.: 327211
Christian Mias (COO)

Branch (Domestic):

SCHOTT Gemtron Corporation (3)
2000 Chestnut St, Vincennes, IN 47591-1760
Tel.: (812) 882-2680
Web Site: http://www.gemtron.com
Sales Range: $75-99.9 Million
Glass Tempering & Tempered Glass; Ceramics
N.A.I.C.S.: 327215

Subsidiary (Domestic):

SCHOTT Glas Export GmbH (2)
Rheinallee 145, 55120, Mainz, Germany (100%)
Tel.: (49) 613132100
Web Site: http://www.schott.com

Sales Range: $50-74.9 Million
Emp.: 200
Exporter of Laboratory Glass Products
N.A.I.C.S.: 327215
Bernard Langner (Mng Dir)

Subsidiary (Non-US):

SCHOTT Glass (Malaysia) Sdn. Bhd. (2)
2024 Tingkat Perusahaan 6 Zon Perindustrian Bebas Dua, 13600, Perai, Penang, Malaysia
Tel.: (60) 4 3898100
Glass Products Mfr
N.A.I.C.S.: 327215

SCHOTT Glass India Pvt. Ltd. (2)
Dynasty A Wing 303/304 3rd Floor Andheri Kurla Road, Andheri, 400 059, Mumbai, India
Tel.: (91) 2644 220216
Glass Products Mfr
N.A.I.C.S.: 327215
Akash Chaurasia (Asst Gen Mgr-Fin & Acct)

SCHOTT Glass Technologies (Suzhou) Co., Ltd. (2)
79 Huoju Road Science &Technology Industrial Park, Suzhou New District, 215009, Suzhou, China
Tel.: (86) 512 68095989
Glass Products Mfr
N.A.I.C.S.: 327215

Subsidiary (US):

SCHOTT Government Services, LLC (2)
2451 Crystal Dr Ste 450, Arlington, VA 22202
Tel.: (703) 418-1409
Web Site: http://www.us.schott.com
Emp.: 6
Glass Products Mfr
N.A.I.C.S.: 327215
Scott Custer (Pres)

Subsidiary (Non-US):

SCHOTT Iberica, S.A. (2)
Pi i Gibert 1 25, PO Box 2, Sant Adria de Besos, 08950, Barcelona, Spain (100%)
Tel.: (34) 934626900
Web Site: http://www.schott.es
Sales Range: $25-49.9 Million
Emp.: 150
Provider of Aluminum Products
N.A.I.C.S.: 331524

SCHOTT Iberica, S.A. Commercial Division (2)
Pi I Gibert 1-25, Apartado de Correos No. 2, 08930, Barcelona, Spain (100%)
Tel.: (34) 932283200
Web Site: http://www.schott.es
Sales Range: $25-49.9 Million
Emp.: 85
Producer of Ophthalmic Glass; Processor of Flat Glass; Manufacturer of Protective Glass for Industrial Applications
N.A.I.C.S.: 327211
Manuel Gutierrez (Gen Mgr)

SCHOTT Italvetro S.p.A. (2)
Via del Brennero, 55023, Lucca, Borgo a Mozzano, Italy
Tel.: (39) 0583 80721
Glass Products Mfr
N.A.I.C.S.: 327215

SCHOTT MiniFAB Pty Ltd (2)
1 Dalmore Drive Scoresby, Melbourne, 3179, VIC, Australia (100%)
Tel.: (61) 3 9039 2550
Web Site: http://www.schott-minifab.com
Bio Technology Services
N.A.I.C.S.: 541714
Greg Wolters (Head)

SCHOTT Nippon K.K. (2)
6F 3-13-45 Senzui, Asaka, 351-0024, Saitama, Japan
Tel.: (81) 48 460 3056
Glass Products Mfr
N.A.I.C.S.: 327215
Akihito Konuma (Asst Mgr)

SCHOTT Orim Cam Sanayi ve Ticaret A.S. (2)

Organize Sanayi Bolgesi G O Pasa Mah 25 Sok No 5, 59500, Tekirdag, Cerkezkoy, Turkiye
Tel.: (90) 282 725 18 60
Glass Products Mfr
N.A.I.C.S.: 327215
Adem Yuksel (Mgr-Logistics & Plng)

SCHOTT Schweiz AG (2)
St Josefenstrasse 20, 9001, Saint Gallen, Switzerland
Tel.: (41) 71 274 16 00
Web Site: http://www.schott.com
Glass Products Mfr
N.A.I.C.S.: 327215
Frank Bellemann (Gen Mgr)

SCHOTT Singapore Pte. Ltd. (2)
8 Admiralty Street 05-01 Admirax, 757438, Singapore, Singapore
Tel.: (65) 6488 2366
Optical Instrument & Glass Product Distr
N.A.I.C.S.: 423460

SCHOTT Solar S.L. (2)
Apartado de Correos 32, 41870, Aznalcollar, Sevilla, Spain
Tel.: (34) 955 73 31 00
Solar Power Generation Services
N.A.I.C.S.: 221114
Luis Alberto Sola Panos (Mng Dir)

Subsidiary (Domestic):

SCHOTT Spezialglas AG (2)
Hattenderg Strasse 10, 55122, Mainz, Germany (83.9%)
Tel.: (49) 61316601288
Web Site: http://www.schott.com
Sales Range: $700-749.9 Million
Emp.: 4,000
Producer of Ophthalmic Glass; Processor of Flat Glass; Manufacturer of Protective Glass for Industrial Applications
N.A.I.C.S.: 333310
Klaus Hofmann (Dir-Corp PR)

Subsidiary (US):

SCHOTT North America Inc (3)
400 York Ave, Duryea, PA 18642-2026 (100%)
Tel.: (570) 457-7485
Web Site: http://www.us.schott.com
Sales Range: $125-149.9 Million
Emp.: 300
Production of Special Glasses
N.A.I.C.S.: 327211

Division (Domestic):

SCHOTT North America, Inc. - Architecture Division (4)
555 Taxter Rd, Elmsford, NY 10523
Tel.: (914) 831-2200
Building Architectural Design Services
N.A.I.C.S.: 541310

SCHOTT North America, Inc. - Baron Systems & Solutions Division (4)
5530 Shepherdsville Rd, Louisville, KY 40228
Tel.: (502) 657-4437
Printed Circuit Board Mfr
N.A.I.C.S.: 334412

SCHOTT North America, Inc. - Flat Glass Division (4)
2000 Chestnut St, Vincennes, IN 47591
Tel.: (812) 882-2680
Glass Products Mfr
N.A.I.C.S.: 327215

SCHOTT North America, Inc. - Pharmaceutical Packaging Division (4)
30 Lebanon Valley Pkwy, Lebanon, PA 17042
Tel.: (717) 228-4200
Pharmaceutical Packaging Services
N.A.I.C.S.: 561910
Christopher Cassidy (VP-Sls & Mktg)

SCHOTT North America, Inc. - Electronic Packaging Division (4)
15 Wells St, Southbridge, MA 01550
Tel.: (508) 765-7400
Web Site: http://www.schott.com
Emp.: 75
Electrical Component Mfr
N.A.I.C.S.: 334413

Andreas Becker (Gen Mgr)

SCHOTT North America., Inc. - Lighting & Imaging Division (4)
122 Charlton St, Southbridge, MA 01550
Tel.: (508) 765-9744
Light Emitting Diode Mfr
N.A.I.C.S.: 334419

Subsidiary (Non-US):

SCHOTT Taiwan Ltd. (2)
8F-3 No 126 Sec 4 Nanking E Road 105, Taipei, Taiwan
Tel.: (886) 2 2570 9626
Optical Instrument & Lens Mfr
N.A.I.C.S.: 333310
Wayne Kao (Deputy Gen Mgr)

Subsidiary (Domestic):

SCHOTT Technical Glass Solutions Gmbh (2)
Otto Schott Strasse 13, 07745, Jena, Germany
Tel.: (49) 3641 681 4600
Glass Products Mfr
N.A.I.C.S.: 327215

Subsidiary (Non-US):

SCHOTT Termofrost AB (2)
Korpralsvagen, PO Box 991, 67129, Arvika, Sweden
Tel.: (46) 570 472 00
Glass Products Mfr
N.A.I.C.S.: 327215
Krister Borg (Mgr-Fin)

SCHOTT Termofrost AS (2)
Sandaasveien 45 B, 0956, Oslo, Norway
Tel.: (47) 6698 3660
Glass Products Mfr
N.A.I.C.S.: 327215
Linda Hemmingsen (Mng Dir)

SCHOTT UK Ltd. (2)
Drummond Road ST16 3EL, Stafford, United Kingdom
Tel.: (44) 1785 223166
Glass Products Mfr
N.A.I.C.S.: 327215
Andrew Dayer (Mgr-Sls & Mktg)

SCHOTT VTF SAS (2)
43 rue de la Liberation, 57870, Troisfontaines, France
Tel.: (33) 3 8723 1011
Web Site: http://www.schott.com
Emp.: 350
Cabinet Door & Panel Mfr
N.A.I.C.S.: 337110
Michael Kettler (Gen Mgr)

SCHOTT Xinkang Pharmaceutical Packaging Co., Ltd. (2)
No 8 Zuoku Industrial Zone, Hu Zhen, 321404, Zhejiang, China
Tel.: (86) 578 3551678
Pharmaceutical Packaging Services
N.A.I.C.S.: 561910

SCHOTT de Mexico, S.A. de C.V. (2)
Col Los Reyes Zona Industrial Calle Amistad No 9, 54073, Tlalnepantla, Mexico
Tel.: (52) 55 8851 7743
Glass Products Mfr
N.A.I.C.S.: 327215

SFAM Societe Francaise d'Ampoules Mecaniques SARL (2)
Rte De Bordeaux, 47700, Casteljaloux, France (100%)
Tel.: (33) 553930240
Web Site: http://www.schott.com
Sales Range: $25-49.9 Million
Emp.: 70
Mfr of Optical Instruments
N.A.I.C.S.: 333310

Zeiss-BelOMO OOO (1)
23 Makayonok St, 220114, Minsk, Belarus
Tel.: (375) 17 267 11 90
Web Site: http://www.belomo.by
Optical Instrument & Lens Mfr
N.A.I.C.S.: 333310

CARLIER PLASTIQUES

Carlier Plastiques—(Continued)

15 Chaussee Brunehaut, 62470,
Calonne-Ricouart, Pas De Calais,
France
Tel.: (33) 321655454
Web Site: http://www.carlier-
plastiques.com
Year Founded: 1957
Sales Range: $25-49.9 Million
Emp.: 103
Plastics Product Mfr
N.A.I.C.S.: 326199
Jean-Brice Guerin *(Chm)*

Subsidiaries:

citp SAS   (1)
21 avenue Georges Washington, BP 654,
62412, Bethune, Cedex, France
Tel.: (33) 3 21 68 69 00
Web Site: http://www.boilermaking-citp.com
Emp.: 51
Plastics Product Mfr
N.A.I.C.S.: 326199
Jean Claude Rousseau *(CEO)*

Plant (Domestic):

citp SAS - Lyon Plant   (2)
P A de la vallee de l'Ozon, Chaponnay,
69970, Lyon, France
Tel.: (33) 4 78 96 07 74
Plastics Product Mfr
N.A.I.C.S.: 326199
Abdel Bessas *(Coord-Safety & Environ-
ment)*

CARLIN GOLD CORPORATION

405-375 Water Street, Vancouver,
V6B 5C6, BC, Canada
Tel.: (604) 638-1402
Web Site: https://www.carlingold.com
CGD—(TSXV)
Assets: $1,890,933
Liabilities: $557,214
Net Worth: $1,333,719
Earnings: $60,846
Fiscal Year-end: 12/31/21
Gold Exploration Services
N.A.I.C.S.: 212220
K. Wayne Livingstone *(Pres & CEO)*

CARLING CAPITAL PART-NERS PTY LTD.

3 Spring Street, Sydney, 2000, NSW,
Australia
Tel.: (61) 2 9247 7744
Web Site:
  http://www.carlingcapital.com
Privater Equity Firm
N.A.I.C.S.: 523999
Maxim Carling *(Mng Partner)*

Subsidiaries:

Paterson Resources Limited   (1)
Level 2 23 Railway Road, Subiaco, 6008,
WA, Australia
Tel.: (61) 865591792
Web Site:
  https://www.patersonresources.com.au
Rev.: $1,360
Assets: $5,156,882
Liabilities: $458,773
Net Worth: $4,698,110
Earnings: $(1,118,302)
Emp.: 1
Fiscal Year-end: 06/30/2024
Mineral Exploration Services
N.A.I.C.S.: 213115
Sarah Smith *(CFO & Sec)*

CARLING MOTORS CO. LIMITED

1638 Carling Ave, Ottawa, K2A 1C5,
ON, Canada
Tel.: (613) 694-2817
Web Site:
  http://www.carlingmotors.ca
Year Founded: 1956
New & Used Car Dealers
N.A.I.C.S.: 441110

Sean Brennan *(Dir-Fixed Ops)*

CARLIT CO., LTD.

1-17-10 Kyobashi, Chuo-ku, Tokyo,
104-0031, Japan
Tel.: (81) 368937070
Web Site: https://www.carlithd.co.jp
Year Founded: 2013
4275—(TKS)
Rev.: $241,773,970
Assets: $364,515,060
Liabilities: $121,432,310
Net Worth: $243,082,750
Earnings: $17,172,780
Emp.: 1,081
Fiscal Year-end: 03/31/24
Holding Company
N.A.I.C.S.: 551112
Hideo Okamoto *(Exec Officer & Dir)*

Subsidiaries:

Asia Giken Co., Ltd.   (1)
72-39 Nishiminatomachi, Kokurakita-ku, Ki-
takyushu, 803-0801, Fukuoka, Japan
Tel.: (81) 93 562 0170
Web Site: https://www.asiagiken.co.jp
Welding Machine Mfr & Distr
N.A.I.C.S.: 333992

Carlit Sangyo Co., Ltd.   (1)
2470 Handa, Shibukawa, 377-0004,
Gunma, Japan
Tel.: (81) 279 23 8818
Web Site: http://www.carlitsangyou.co.jp
Emp.: 40
Engineering, Construction & Termite Control
Services
N.A.I.C.S.: 541330

Carlit Singapore Pte., Ltd.   (1)
1 Paya Lebar Link 04-01 Quarter 1, Paya
Lebar, 408533, Singapore
Tel.: (65) 69558475
Web Site: http://www.csg.com.sg
Emp.: 3
Chemical & Electronic Material Distr
N.A.I.C.S.: 423690

Daiichi Yakuhin Kogyo Co., Ltd.   (1)
1-17-10 Kyobashi, Chuo-ku, Tokyo, 104-
0031, Japan
Tel.: (81) 3 3564 5651
Web Site: http://www.carlithd.co.jp
Emp.: 7
Industrial Chemicals & Explosives Raw Ma-
terials Whslr
N.A.I.C.S.: 424690
Satoshi Sakano *(Pres)*

Fuji Shoji Co., Ltd.   (1)
6-8-24 Nakatsu, Kita-ku, Osaka, 531-0071,
Japan
Tel.: (81) 664582521
Web Site: https://www.fuji-syoji.jp
Emp.: 64
Paint Whslr & Industrial Painting Services
N.A.I.C.S.: 238320
Osamu Sawamura *(Pres)*

JC Bottling Co., Ltd.   (1)
1-17-10 Kyobashi, Chuo-ku, Tokyo, 104-
0031, Japan
Tel.: (81) 362287735
Web Site: https://www.jcbottling.co.jp
Soft Drink Bottler
N.A.I.C.S.: 312111
Takeshi Kimura *(Pres)*

Japan Abrasive Grain, Ltd.   (1)
1-17-10 Kyobashi, Chuo-ku, Tokyo, 104-
0031, Japan
Tel.: (81) 3 6685 2100
Web Site: http://www.jag.co.net
Emp.: 4
Abrasives & Fire-Resistant Materials Mfr &
Whslr
N.A.I.C.S.: 327910
Akihide Kamiya *(Pres)*

Japan Carlit (Shanghai) Co., Ltd.   (1)
Room 1710 Shanghai Mart No 2299 Yanan
Road West, Changning District, Shanghai,
China
Tel.: (86) 216 235 0896
Electronic Material Distr
N.A.I.C.S.: 423690

Japan Carlit Co., Ltd.   (1)
1-17-10 Kyobashi, Chuo-ku, Tokyo, 104-
0031, Japan
Tel.: (81) 366852020
Web Site: https://www.carlit.co.jp
Emp.: 363
Chemical & Electronic Materials Mfr & Distr
N.A.I.C.S.: 325998

Japex.Co., Ltd.   (1)
SAPIA Tower 1-7-12 Marunouchi, Chiyoda-
ku, Tokyo, 100-0005, Japan
Tel.: (81) 36 268 7000
Emp.: 1,780
Industrial Explosive Product Distr
N.A.I.C.S.: 424690

Namitakiko Co., Ltd.   (1)
1-13-13 Kobayashi-nishi, Taisho-ku, Osaka,
551-0013, Japan
Tel.: (81) 6 6553 0155
Web Site: http://www.namitakiko.co.jp
Emp.: 90
Fire-Resistant & Heat-Resistant Metal Mate-
rials Mfr & Whslr
N.A.I.C.S.: 332999
Eizi Kokubu *(Exec Officer)*

SD Network Co., Ltd.   (1)
1-3-26 Otacho, Suma-ku, Kobe, Japan
Tel.: (81) 78 733 6542
Web Site: https://sdnetwork.co.jp
Emp.: 22
Building Construction Services
N.A.I.C.S.: 236220

Silicon Technology Corporation   (1)
1-17-10 Kyobashi, Chuo-ku, Tokyo, 104-
0031, Japan
Tel.: (81) 3 5159 3301
Web Site: http://www.s-tc.co.jp
Emp.: 111
Semiconductor Silicon Wafer Mfr & Whslr
N.A.I.C.S.: 334413
Masayasu Konishi *(Pres)*

Toyo Spring Industrial Co., Ltd.   (1)
Matsudo Daiichi Seimei Building 2nd Floor
14-2 Honcho, Matsudo, 271-0091, Chiba,
Japan
Tel.: (81) 47 313 9030
Web Site: https://www.tohatsu-i.co.jp
Emp.: 150
Automobile Parts Mfr & Distr
N.A.I.C.S.: 336390

CARLO GAVAZZI HOLDING AG

Sumpfstrasse 3, PO Box 152, CH-
6312, Steinhausen, Switzerland
Tel.: (41) 417474525
Web Site:
  https://www.carlogavazzi.com
GAV—(SWX)
Rev.: $232,373,614
Assets: $205,484,479
Liabilities: $59,271,619
Net Worth: $146,212,860
Earnings: $31,296,009
Emp.: 1,103
Fiscal Year-end: 03/31/23
Holding Company
N.A.I.C.S.: 551112
Vittorio Rossi *(CEO-Automation Com-
ponents)*

Subsidiaries:

CARLO GAVAZZI GmbH   (1)
Pfnorstrasse 10 - 14, 64293, Darmstadt,
Germany
Tel.: (49) 61 518 1000
Web Site: https://www.gavazzi.de
Electronic Component Mfr & Distr
N.A.I.C.S.: 334419

Carlo Gavazzi (Canada) Inc.   (1)
2660 Meadowvale Boulevard, Mississauga,
L5N 6M6, ON, Canada
Tel.: (905) 542-0979
Web Site: http://www.carlogavazzionline.com
Sales Range: $25-49.9 Million
Emp.: 15
Instrument Mfr for Measuring & Testing
Electricity & Electrical Signals
N.A.I.C.S.: 334515

Carlo Gavazzi AB   (1)

Vastra Kyrkogatan 1, 652 24, Karlstad,
Sweden   **(100%)**
Tel.: (46) 5 485 1125
Web Site: https://gavazzi.se
Sales Range: $25-49.9 Million
Emp.: 20
Electrical & Electronic Appliance Television
& Radio Set Merchant Whslr
N.A.I.C.S.: 423620

Carlo Gavazzi AG   (1)
Sumpfstrasse 3, SuisseSumpfstrasse 32,
6312, Steinhausen, Switzerland   **(100%)**
Tel.: (41) 41 747 4535
Web Site: https://gavazziautomation.com
Other Management Consulting Services
N.A.I.C.S.: 541618

Carlo Gavazzi AS   (1)
Melkeveien 13, 3919, Porsgrunn,
Norway   **(100%)**
Tel.: (47) 3 593 0800
Web Site: https://gavazzi.no
Sales Range: $25-49.9 Million
Emp.: 14
Other Electronic Parts & Equipment Whslr
N.A.I.C.S.: 423690

Carlo Gavazzi Automacao Ltda   (1)
Av Francisco Matarazzo 1752 Conj 2108,
Barra Funda, Sao Paulo, 05001-200, Brazil
Tel.: (55) 113 052 0832
Web Site: https://gavazziautomation.com
Electric Equipment Mfr
N.A.I.C.S.: 334419

Carlo Gavazzi Automation (China) Co
Ltd   (1)
Unit 2308 23/F News Building Block 1 1002
Middle Shennan Zhong Road, Zhong Road
Futian District, Shenzhen, 518027,
China   **(100%)**
Tel.: (86) 7558 369 9500
Web Site: https://gavazziautomation.com
Sales Range: $25-49.9 Million
Emp.: 70
Commercial Industrial & Institutional Electric
Lighting Fixture Mfr
N.A.I.C.S.: 335132
Jackie Fu *(Mng Dir)*

Carlo Gavazzi Automation (M) Sdn
Bhd   (1)
D12-06-G Block D12 Pusat Perdagangan
Dana 1 Jalan PJU 1A/46, 47301, Petaling
Jaya, Selangor, Malaysia   **(100%)**
Tel.: (60) 37 842 7299
Web Site: https://gavazziautomation.com
Sales Range: $25-49.9 Million
Emp.: 7
All Other Industrial Machinery Mfr
N.A.I.C.S.: 333248

Carlo Gavazzi Automation Hong
Kong Ltd   (1)
Unit No 16 on 25th Floor One Midtown No
11 Hoi Shing Road, Tsuen Wan, New Terri-
tories, China (Hong Kong)   **(100%)**
Tel.: (852) 2 626 1316
Web Site: https://www.carlogavazzi.com
Sales Range: $25-49.9 Million
Emp.: 25
Other Electronic Component Mfr
N.A.I.C.S.: 334419

Carlo Gavazzi Automation Singapore
Pte Ltd   (1)
61 Tai Seng Avenue 05-06 Print Media Hub
Paya Lebar iPark, Singapore, 534167,
Singapore   **(100%)**
Tel.: (65) 6 746 6990
Web Site: http://www.gavazzi-
automation.com.sg
Sales Range: $25-49.9 Million
Emp.: 19
Electrical & Electronic Appliance Television
& Radio Set Merchant Whslr
N.A.I.C.S.: 423620
Songyang-Lee *(Mng Dir)*

Carlo Gavazzi Automation Spa   (1)
Via Milano 13, 20045, Lainate, MI,
Italy   **(100%)**
Tel.: (39) 0293 1761
Web Site: https://gavazziautomation.com
Electrical Apparatus & Equipment Wiring
Supplies & Related Equipment Merchant
Whslr
N.A.I.C.S.: 423610

Carlo Gavazzi BV (1)
Wijkermeerweg 23, 1948 NT, Beverwijk,
Netherlands (100%)
Tel.: (31) 25 122 9345
Web Site: https://gavazziautomation.com
Sales Range: $50-74.9 Million
Emp.: 7
Other Electronic Parts & Equipment Whslr
N.A.I.C.S.: 423690

Carlo Gavazzi Gmbh (1)
Ketzergasse 374, 1230, Vienna,
Austria (100%)
Tel.: (43) 1 888 4112
Web Site: https://gavazziautomation.com
Sales Range: $25-49.9 Million
Emp.: 4
Other Electronic Component Mfr
N.A.I.C.S.: 334419

Carlo Gavazzi Handel A/S (1)
Over Hadstenvej 40, 8370, Hadsten,
Denmark (100%)
Tel.: (45) 8 960 6100
Web Site: https://gavazziautomation.com
Sales Range: $25-49.9 Million
Emp.: 20
Other Electronic Parts & Equipment Whslr
N.A.I.C.S.: 423690
Michael Rasmussen *(Mng Dir)*

Carlo Gavazzi Inc. (1)
750 Hastings Ln, Buffalo Grove, IL
60089-6904 (100%)
Tel.: (847) 465-6100
Web Site: https://www.gavazzionline.com
Sales Range: $25-49.9 Million
Emp.: 25
Engineeering Services
N.A.I.C.S.: 541330
Fred Shirzadi *(Pres & CEO)*

Carlo Gavazzi Industri A/S (1)
Over Hadstenvej 40, 8370, Hadsten,
Denmark (100%)
Tel.: (45) 89606100
Web Site: http://www.gavazzi.dk
Sales Range: $25-49.9 Million
Emp.: 20
Semiconductor & Related Device Mfr
N.A.I.C.S.: 334413
Savio Fion *(Mng Dir)*

Subsidiary (Non-US);

**CARLO GAVAZZI INDUSTRI
KAUNAS UAB** (2)
Raudondvario Pl 101, 47184, Kaunas,
Lithuania
Tel.: (370) 37328227
Web Site: http://www.gavazzi-
automation.com
Sales Range: $50-74.9 Million
Industrial Automation Component Distr
N.A.I.C.S.: 423690
Ernestas Greicius *(Mgr-Ops)*

Carlo Gavazzi LDA (1)
Rua dos Jeronimos 38-B, 1400-212, Lis-
bon, Portugal (100%)
Tel.: (351) 21 361 7060
Web Site: https://gavazziautomation.com
Sales Range: $50-74.9 Million
Emp.: 4
Other Electronic Parts & Equipment Whslr
N.A.I.C.S.: 423690

Carlo Gavazzi Logistics Spa (1)
Via Milano 13, 20020, Lainate,
Italy (100%)
Tel.: (39) 0293176431
Web Site: http://www.carlogavazzi.com
Sales Range: $25-49.9 Million
Emp.: 40
Electrical Apparatus & Equipment Wiring
Supplies & Related Equipment Merchant
Whslr
N.A.I.C.S.: 423610

Carlo Gavazzi Marketing Ag (1)
Sumpfstrasse 32, 6312, Steinhausen,
Switzerland (100%)
Tel.: (41) 417474535
Web Site: http://www.carlogavazzi.com
Other Management Consulting Services
N.A.I.C.S.: 541618

**Carlo Gavazzi Mexico S.A. de
C.V.** (1)
Circuito Puericultores 22 Ciudad Satelite,

EDOMEX Naucalpan de Juarez, 53100,
Mexico, Mexico
Electric Equipment Mfr
N.A.I.C.S.: 334419

Carlo Gavazzi Oy AB (1)
Petaksentie 2-4, Helsinki, 630,
Finland (100%)
Tel.: (358) 97562000
Sales Range: $25-49.9 Million
Emp.: 6
Other Electronic Component Mfr
N.A.I.C.S.: 334419

**Carlo Gavazzi Participation Danmark
A/S** (1)
Over Hadstenvej 40, Hadsten, 8370,
Denmark (100%)
Tel.: (45) 89606100
Web Site: http://www.carlogavazzi.com
Sales Range: $25-49.9 Million
Emp.: 25
Switchgear & Switchboard Apparatus Mfr
N.A.I.C.S.: 335313
Savio Fion *(Mng Dir)*

Subsidiary (Non-US):

**CARLO GAVAZZI AUTOMATION
(KUNSHAN) Co Ltd** (2)
Kunjia Road 347 Kunshan Development
Zone, Kunshan, 215334, Jiangsu, China
Tel.: (86) 512 57639310
Web Site: http://www.gavazzi-
automation.com
Electronic Automation Component Mfr
N.A.I.C.S.: 334419

**CARLO GAVAZZI CONTROLS
SpA** (2)
Via Safforze 8, 32100, Belluno, Italy
Tel.: (39) 0437355811
Web Site: http://www.gavazzi-
automation.com
Electronic Component Mfr & Distr
N.A.I.C.S.: 334419

CARLO GAVAZZI Ltd (2)
B42 Bulebel Industrial Estate, Zejtun, ZTN
3000, Malta
Tel.: (356) 23601100
Web Site: http://www.carlogavazzi.com.mt
Electronic Automation Component Mfr &
Distr
N.A.I.C.S.: 334419
Stefan Farrugia *(Mgr-Logistics & IT)*

CARLO GAVAZZI SA (2)
Avda Iparraguirre 80-82, 48940, Leioa, Bi-
zkaia, Spain
Tel.: (34) 94 480 4037
Web Site: http://www.carlogavazzi.es
Sales Range: $25-49.9 Million
Automation Component Mfr & Distr
N.A.I.C.S.: 333248

Carlo Gavazzi Sa (1)
Mechelsesteenweg 311, 1800, Vilvoorde,
Belgium (100%)
Tel.: (32) 2 257 4120
Web Site: https://gavazziautomation.com
Sales Range: $25-49.9 Million
Emp.: 25
Other Electronic Component Mfr
N.A.I.C.S.: 334419
Peter Martins *(Mng Dir)*

Carlo Gavazzi Sarl (1)
Zac de Paris Nord II 69 rue de la Belle
Etoile, 95956, Roissy-en-France, Cedex,
France (100%)
Tel.: (33) 14 938 9860
Web Site: https://gavazziautomation.com
Sales Range: $25-49.9 Million
Emp.: 15
Other Electronic Parts & Equipment Whslr
N.A.I.C.S.: 423690

Carlo Gavazzi Services Ag (1)
Sumpfstrasse 3, 6312, Steinhausen,
Switzerland (100%)
Tel.: (41) 7474525
Web Site: http://www.carlogavazzi.com
Emp.: 9
Other Management Consulting Services
N.A.I.C.S.: 541618

Carlo Gavazzi Spa (1)
Via Milano 13, 20045, Lainate, MI,
Italy (100%)

Tel.: (39) 0293 1761
Web Site: https://gavazziautomation.com
Other Electronic Parts & Equipment Whslr
N.A.I.C.S.: 423690

Carlo Gavazzi UK Ltd (1)
4 4 Frimley Business Park, Frimley, Cam-
berley, GU16 7SG, Surrey, United
Kingdom (100%)
Tel.: (44) 127 685 4110
Web Site: http://www.carlogavazzi.co.uk
Sales Range: $25-49.9 Million
Emp.: 14
Other Electronic Parts & Equipment Whslr
N.A.I.C.S.: 423690

Carlo Gavazzi Unipessoal Lda (1)
Rua Jeronimos 38-B, 1400-212, Lisbon,
Portugal
Tel.: (351) 213617060
Electrical Equipment Distr
N.A.I.C.S.: 423610

CARLOS CASADO SA
Edificio Torre Alem Plaza Avda Lean-
dro N Alem 855 piso 15, 1001, Bue-
nos Aires, Argentina
Tel.: (54) 1143110170
Web Site:
https://www.carloscasadosa.com
Year Founded: 1883
Farming Services
N.A.I.C.S.: 115116
Pedro Aller *(Gen Mgr)*

CARLSBERG A/S
J C Jacobsens Gade 1, 1799, Co-
penhagen, Denmark
Tel.: (45) 33273300   DK
Web Site:
https://www.carlsberggroup.com
Year Founded: 1847
CARLA—(CSE)
Rev.: $10,999,274,380
Assets: $20,862,041,810
Liabilities: $12,813,888,890
Net Worth: $8,048,152,920
Earnings: $1,322,045,630
Emp.: 40,000
Fiscal Year-end: 12/31/21
Brewery Operator
N.A.I.C.S.: 312120
Flemming Besenbacher *(Chm-
Supervisory Bd)*

Subsidiaries:

A/S Aldaris (1)
Tvaika Iela 44, Riga, 1005, Latvia
Tel.: (371) 6 702 3200
Web Site: https://www.aldaris.lv
Sales Range: $100-124.9 Million
Emp.: 40
Beverage Products Mfr & Distr
N.A.I.C.S.: 312120

AB Svyturys (1)
Kuliu Vartu g 7, 92276, Klaipeda,
Lithuania (57%)
Tel.: (370) 8 46 484000
Web Site: http://www.svyturys.lt
Mfr of Beer
N.A.I.C.S.: 312120

Aldaris JSC (1)
Tvaika Iela 44, Riga, 1005, Latvia
Tel.: (371) 80009001
Web Site: https://www.aldaris.lv
Beverage Mfr & Distr
N.A.I.C.S.: 311999

Brasseries Kronenbourg (1)
Boulevard De L'europe 67212, PO Box 13,
67037, Obernai, Cedex, France
Tel.: (33) 388274488
Web Site: http://wwwbrasseries-
kronenbourg.com
Sales Range: $350-399.9 Million
Emp.: 2,000
Brewery
N.A.I.C.S.: 312120

CTDD Beer Imports Ltd. (1)
5565 Av Christophe-Colomb, Montreal, H2J
3H3, QC, Canada
Tel.: (514) 938-3883

Sales Range: $50-74.9 Million
Emp.: 3
Alcoholic Beverage Distr
N.A.I.C.S.: 424820

**Carlsberg Accounting Service Centre
Sp. z.o.o.** (1)
Male Garbary 9, Poznan, 61756, Poland
Tel.: (48) 61 844 11 00
Web Site: http://www.carlsberggroup.com
Sales Range: $75-99.9 Million
Emp.: 300
Accounting Services
N.A.I.C.S.: 541219

Carlsberg Breweries A/S (1)
1 J C Jacobsens Gade, 1799, Copenhagen,
Denmark
Tel.: (45) 33273300
Emp.: 2,000
Beer Mfr
N.A.I.C.S.: 312120
Ceest Hart *(CEO)*

**Carlsberg Brewery Hong Kong
Limited** (1)
18/F One Harbourfront 18 Tak Fung Street,
Hung Hom, Kowloon, China (Hong
Kong) (51%)
Tel.: (852) 3 189 8282
Web Site:
https://www.carlsberghongkong.com.hk
Sales Range: $25-49.9 Million
Emp.: 200
N.A.I.C.S.: 312120

Subsidiary (Non-US):

Carlsberg (Singapore) Pte. Ltd. (2)
18 Ah Hood Road 07-51 Hiap Hoe Building
At Zhongshan Park, Singapore, 329983,
Singapore (100%)
Tel.: (65) 62953395
Web Site:
https://www.carlsbergsingapore.com.sg
Sales Range: $25-49.9 Million
Emp.: 68
N.A.I.C.S.: 312120

**Carlsberg Brewery Malaysia
Berhad** (1)
No 55 Persiaran Selangor Section 15,
40200, Shah Alam, Selangor,
Malaysia (50%)
Tel.: (60) 355226688
Web Site:
https://www.carlsbergmalaysia.com.my
Sales Range: $150-199.9 Million
Emp.: 700
Brewer of Beers & Ales
N.A.I.C.S.: 312120
Pearl Ming Choo Lai *(Dir-CSR & Corp
Comm)*

Subsidiary (Domestic):

Carlsberg Marketing Sdn BHD (2)
No 55 Persiaran Selangor Section 15, Shah
Alam, 40200, Selangor, Malaysia
Tel.: (60) 355226688
Web Site:
https://www.carlsbergmalaysia.com.my
Sales Range: $125-149.9 Million
Emp.: 30
Alcoholic Beverage Distr
N.A.I.C.S.: 424820

Carlsberg Brewing Limited (1)
140 Bridge St, Northampton, NN1 1PZ,
United Kingdom (100%)
Tel.: (44) 604668866
Web Site: http://www.carlsberg.co.uk
Rev.: $1,500,000
Emp.: 2,867
Brewers of Beer
N.A.I.C.S.: 445320

Carlsberg Canada Inc. (1)
1425 North Service Rd E, Oakville, L6H
1A7, ON, Canada
Tel.: (905) 829-0299
Web Site: https://www.carlsberg.com
Beverage Product Distr
N.A.I.C.S.: 424820

**Carlsberg Chongqing Breweries
Company Limited** (1)
No 9 Hengshan East Road, Liangjiang New
District, Chongqing, China
Tel.: (86) 4001600132

Carlsberg A/S—(Continued)

Web Site:
https://www.carlsbergchina.com.cn
Beer Beverage Mfr
N.A.I.C.S.: 312120

Carlsberg Croatia (1)
Ulica Danica 3, 48000, Koprivnica,
Croatia (40%)
Tel.: (385) 4 865 7011
Web Site: https://www.carlsbergcroatia.hr
Emp.: 300
Provider of Beverage Services
N.A.I.C.S.: 312120

Carlsberg Danmark A/S (1)
JC Jacobsens Gade 1, 1799, Copenhagen,
Denmark
Tel.: (45) 3 327 3327
Web Site:
https://compliance.carlsberggroup.com
Beer Mfr
N.A.I.C.S.: 312120
Soren Brinck (Mng Dir)

**Carlsberg Denmark A/S
Fredericia** (1)
Vester Ringvej 111, 7000, Fredericia,
Denmark (100%)
Tel.: (45) 22126129
Web Site: http://www.carlsbergdanmark.dk
Sales Range: $100-124.9 Million
Emp.: 332
Beer Distiller
N.A.I.C.S.: 312120

Carlsberg Deutschland GmbH (1)
Jurgen-Topfer-Strasse 50 house 18, 22763,
Hamburg, Germany
Tel.: (49) 4 038 1010
Web Site:
https://www.carlsbergdeutschland.de
Beer Mfr
N.A.I.C.S.: 312120

**Carlsberg Ejendomme Holding
A/S** (1)
Bag Elefanterne Ny Carlsberg Vej 140,
1760, Copenhagen, Denmark
Tel.: (45) 33273300
Web Site: https://www.carlsberggroup.com
Real Estate Development Services
N.A.I.C.S.: 531390
Jakob Stilov (Dir-Real Estate)

Carlsberg Finans A/S (1)
Ny Carlsberg Vej 100, 1799, Copenhagen,
Denmark (100%)
Tel.: (45) 33273300
Web Site: https://www.carlsberg.com
Sales Range: $750-799.9 Million
Emp.: 100
Financial Services
N.A.I.C.S.: 561499
Jorgen Buhl Rasmussen (CEO)

Carlsberg GB Limited (1)
Carlsberg Brewery 140 Bridge Street,
Northampton, NN1 1PZ, United Kingdom
Tel.: (44) 1604668866
Web Site: http://www.carlsberg.co.uk
Beverages Mfr
N.A.I.C.S.: 312120

**Carlsberg Hungary Sales Limited Li-
ability Company** (1)
Neumann Janos Utca 3, 2040, Budaors,
Hungary
Tel.: (36) 23 88 85 55
Web Site: http://www.carlsberggroup.com
Sales Range: $25-49.9 Million
Emp.: 30
Alcoholic Beverage Distr
N.A.I.C.S.: 424820

Carlsberg Importers SA (1)
Industrielaan 16-20, Ternat, 1740,
Belgium (100%)
Tel.: (32) 25835000
Web Site: http://www.carlsberg.be
Sales Range: $25-49.9 Million
Emp.: 48
Provider of Brewing Services
N.A.I.C.S.: 312120
Paul Haelterman (Gen Mgr)

Carlsberg India Pvt Ltd (1)
IREO Grand View Tower 3rd Floor Golf
Course Extension Road Sector-58, Gur-

gaon, 122101, Haryana, India
Tel.: (91) 1244554444
Web Site: https://www.carlsbergindia.com
Sales Range: $250-299.9 Million
Emp.: 537
Alcoholic Beverage Distr
N.A.I.C.S.: 312120
Nilesh Patel (Mng Dir & VP)

Subsidiary (Domestic):

Parag Breweries Ltd (2)
2 J L Nehru Road, Kolkata, 700 013, West
Bengal, India
Tel.: (91) 3213 251443
Alcoholic Beverage Mfr & Distr
N.A.I.C.S.: 312120

Carlsberg Insurance A/S (1)
Ny Carlsberg Vej 100, 1799, Copenhagen,
Denmark
Tel.: (45) 33273300
Emp.: 200
General Insurance Services
N.A.I.C.S.: 524298
Yutaka Usuda (CEO)

Carlsberg International A/S (1)
Ny Carlsberg Vej 100, 1799, Copenhagen,
Denmark
Tel.: (45) 33273300
Web Site: https://www.carlsbergbyen.dk
Emp.: 180
Beer Mfr
N.A.I.C.S.: 312120
Carsten Hanel (CIO)

Carlsberg Invest A/S (1)
Ny Carlsberg Vej 100, 1799, Copenhagen,
Denmark
Tel.: (45) 33273300
Web Site: https://www.carlsberg.com
Investment Management Service
N.A.I.C.S.: 523999

Carlsberg Italia S.p.A. (1)
Via Ramazzotti 12, 20045, Lainate, MI,
Italy (100%)
Tel.: (39) 029 353 6911
Web Site: https://www.carlsbergitalia.it
Emp.: 259
Beer Mfr
N.A.I.C.S.: 312120

Carlsberg Kazakhstan Ltd. (1)
270 V Kazybayev str, 050014, Almaty, Ka-
zakhstan
Tel.: (7) 7273210100
Web Site: https://carlsbergkazakhstan.kz
Alcoholic Beverage Distr
N.A.I.C.S.: 424820

**Carlsberg Marston's Brewing Com-
pany Ltd.** (1)
Marston s House Brewery Road, Wolver-
hampton, WV1 4JT, United
Kingdom (60%)
Tel.: (44) 3457585685
Web Site:
https://www.carlsbergmarstons.co.uk
Beverage Mfr & Distr
N.A.I.C.S.: 311999

Carlsberg Okocim SA. (1)
Ul Bokserska 66, 02 690, Warsaw,
Poland (45%)
Tel.: (48) 225431440
Web Site: http://www.carlsberg.pl
Sales Range: $25-49.9 Million
Emp.: 150
Mfr of Beer
N.A.I.C.S.: 312120

Carlsberg Polska S. A. (1)
Ul Krakowiakow 34, 02-255, Warsaw, Po-
land
Tel.: (48) 225431400
Web Site: https://www.carlsbergpolska.pl
Emp.: 150
Alcoholic Beverages Mfr
N.A.I.C.S.: 312120
Paul Davies (CEO)

Carlsberg Sverige AB (1)
Evenemangsgatan 31, 169 79, Solna, Swe-
den
Tel.: (46) 87577000
Web Site: https://www.carlsbergsverige.se
Sales Range: $400-449.9 Million
Emp.: 950
Beverage Products Mfr & Distr

Carlsberg UK Ltd (1)
140 Bridge Street, Northampton, NN1 1PZ,
United Kingdom
Tel.: (44) 1600000000
Web Site: http://www.carlsberguk.co.uk
Emp.: 42,000
Beer Mfr
N.A.I.C.S.: 424810
Tomasz Blawat (CEO)

Ceylon Brewery Ltd. (1)
83 George Road de Silva Mawatha, 13,
Colombo, Sri Lanka (8%)
Tel.: (94) 33153542
Sales Range: $50-74.9 Million
Emp.: 165
Beverages
N.A.I.C.S.: 312120

**Dali Beer (Group) Limited
Company** (1)
13D No 308 Binjiang Road Central,
Guangzhou, China
Tel.: (86) 20 34691778
Alcoholic Beverage Distr
N.A.I.C.S.: 424820

**Danish Malting Group Polska Sp.
z.o.o.** (1)
ul Swietokrzyska 27, 09-200, Sierpc, Poland
Tel.: (48) 242758400
Web Site: http://www.dmgp.pl
Sales Range: $25-49.9 Million
Emp.: 30
Malt Mfr
N.A.I.C.S.: 311213

Dyland BV (1)
Gooiberg 26, Bussum, 1406 SP, Nether-
lands
Tel.: (31) 356919285
Beverage Products Mfr & Distr
N.A.I.C.S.: 312120

**Ejendomsaktieselskabet af 4. marts
1982** (1)
Ny Carlsberg Vej 100, 1799, Copenhagen,
Denmark
Tel.: (45) 33223929
Property Management Services
N.A.I.C.S.: 531312

Emeraude S.A.S. (1)
8 rue Henri Farman, 93290, Tremblay,
France
Tel.: (33) 148688230
Web Site: https://www.emeraudesas.com
Painting & Wall Covering Services
N.A.I.C.S.: 238920

Euro Distributors Sdn BHD (1)
No 55 Psn Selangor Seksyen 15, 40200,
Shah Alam, Selangor, Malaysia
Tel.: (60) 355191621
Sales Range: $150-199.9 Million
Emp.: 40
Beverage Product Distr
N.A.I.C.S.: 424820

**Feldschlosschen Beverages Holding
Ltd.** (1)
Theophil Roniger Strasse, 4310, Rhein-
felden, Switzerland (100%)
Tel.: (41) 848125000
Web Site:
https://www.feldschloesschen.swiss
Sales Range: $350-399.9 Million
Emp.: 600
Producer, Buyer & Distributer of Beer,
Sweet Drinks, Mineral Water
N.A.I.C.S.: 312130
Gerard Schaller (Dir-Sls)

Subsidiary (Domestic):

Feldschlosschen Beverages Ltd. (2)
Theophil Roniger Strasse, 4310, Rhein-
felden, Switzerland (100%)
Tel.: (41) 848125000
Web Site:
https://www.feldschloesschen.swiss
Sales Range: $150-199.9 Million
Emp.: 700
Brewers of Beer
N.A.I.C.S.: 312120

**Feldschlosschen Getranke Holding
AG** (1)

Theophil Roniger-Strasse, CH-4310, Rhein-
felden, Switzerland
Tel.: (41) 848125000
Web Site:
https://www.feldschloesschen.swiss
Emp.: 1,700
Investment Management Service
N.A.I.C.S.: 523999
Thomas Amstutz (CEO)

Gorkha Brewery Limited (1)
Hattisar, PO Box 4140, Kathmandu, Nepal
Tel.: (977) 14444445
Web Site: https://www.gorkhabrewery.com
Sales Range: $50-74.9 Million
Emp.: 225
Brewery Mfr
N.A.I.C.S.: 312120
Surendra Silwal (Deputy Mng Dir)

Holsten-Brauerei AG (1)
Jurgen-Topfer-Strasse 50, 22763, Hamburg,
Germany (98%)
Tel.: (49) 4042236951
Web Site: https://www.holsten-pilsener.de
Sales Range: $800-899.9 Million
Emp.: 2,840
Mfr of Beer & Non-Alcoholic Beverages
N.A.I.C.S.: 312120

Hue Brewery Ltd. (1)
Thuan An St, Hue, Vietnam (50%)
Tel.: (84) 54850166
Web Site: http://www.huda.com.vn
Sales Range: $1-9.9 Million
Emp.: 297
N.A.I.C.S.: 312120

Mythos Brewery S.A. (1)
Industrial Zone, 570 22, Thessaloniki,
Greece
Tel.: (30) 2310568400
Web Site: http://www.mythosbrewery.gr
Brewery
N.A.I.C.S.: 312120

Nuuk Imeq A/S (1)
Qeqertanut 1, Box 1075, 3900, Nuuk,
Greenland
Tel.: (299) 329588
Web Site: https://www.nuukimeq.dk
Brewers of Beer
N.A.I.C.S.: 312120

OAO Baltika Breweries (1)
6 Verkhny per d 3, 194292, Saint Peters-
burg, Russia (100%)
Tel.: (7) 8003333303
Web Site: https://eng.baltika.ru
Sales Range: $1-4.9 Billion
Emp.: 12,000
Beer Producer
N.A.I.C.S.: 312120
Herman Epstein (VP-IT)

Oy Sinebrychoff AB (1)
Sinebrychoffinaukio 1, 04250, Kerava,
Finland (100%)
Tel.: (358) 9294991
Web Site: https://www.sinebrychoff.fi
Emp.: 700
Mfr of Beer
N.A.I.C.S.: 312120

Subsidiary (Non-US):

Carlsberg Sweden AB (2)
Evenemangsgatan 31, PO Box 164, 169
79, Solna, Sweden (100%)
Tel.: (46) 8 757 7000
Web Site: https://www.carlsbergsverige.se
Sales Range: $75-99.9 Million
Emp.: 500
Brewer, Bottler & Distributor of Malt Bever-
ages
N.A.I.C.S.: 312120
Peter Hammarstedt (Mng Dir)

OAO Vena (2)
1 Farforovskata Str, 192171, Saint Peters-
burg, Russia (66%)
Tel.: (7) 8123262100
Web Site: http://www.vv.daltika.ru
Mfr of Beer
N.A.I.C.S.: 312120

Pripps Ringnes AB (1)
Bryggerivagen 10, Bromma, 168 67, Swe-
den
Tel.: (46) 87577000
Beverage Product Distr

N.A.I.C.S.: 424820
Mark Jensen *(Mng Dir)*

Ringnes A/S **(1)**
Thorvald Meyersgate 2A, 0307, Oslo, Norway
Tel.: (47) 2 206 9500
Web Site: https://www.ringnes.no
Rev.: $439,410
Emp.: 1,500
Producers of Carbonated Soft Drinks & Beer
N.A.I.C.S.: 312111
Anders Roed *(CEO & Mng Dir)*

Saku Olletehase AS **(1)**
Tel.: (372) 6508400
Web Site: https://www.saku.ee
Sales Range: $50-74.9 Million
Emp.: 150
Beverage Products Mfr & Distr
N.A.I.C.S.: 312120
Jaan Harms *(Dir-Sls)*

South-East Asia Brewery Ltd. **(1)**
167 Minh Khai, Minh Khai ward Hai Ba Trung District, Hanoi, Vietnam **(35%)**
Tel.: (84) 243 863 1871
Web Site: http://www.halida.com.vn
Sales Range: $100-124.9 Million
Emp.: 327
N.A.I.C.S.: 312120

T&C Italia S.R.L. **(1)**
Via S Giorgio 34/D, 61049, Urbania, PU, Italy
Tel.: (39) 0721799065
Web Site: https://www.tectartufi.it
Food Product Mfr & Distr
N.A.I.C.S.: 333241

Traitomic A/S **(1)**
Gamle Carlsberg Vej 10, DK-1799, Copenhagen, Denmark
Tel.: (45) 22515262
Web Site: https://www.traitomic.com
Foodstuff Mfr & Distr
N.A.I.C.S.: 333241

United Romanian Breweries Bereprod SRL **(1)**
B-dul Birunitei 89, Pantelimon Ilfov, Bucharest, Romania
Tel.: (40) 212055012
Web Site: http://www.tuborg.ro
Sales Range: $150-199.9 Million
Emp.: 750
Mfr of Beer
N.A.I.C.S.: 312120

Waterloo Brewing Ltd. **(1)**
400 Bingemans Centre Drive, Kitchener, N2B 3X9, ON, Canada
Tel.: (519) 742-2732
Web Site: http://waterloobrewing.com
Rev.: $87,431,875
Assets: $102,818,074
Liabilities: $74,089,516
Net Worth: $28,728,558
Earnings: $4,539,212
Emp.: 250
Fiscal Year-end: 01/31/2022
Beer Mfr
N.A.I.C.S.: 312120
George H. Croft *(Pres & CEO)*

CARLTON INVESTMENTS LIMITED
Level 15 478 George Street, Sydney, 2000, NSW, Australia
Tel.: (61) 293736732 AU
Web Site:
https://www.carltoninvestments.com
Year Founded: 1938
CIN—(ASX)
Rev.: $27,763,087
Assets: $702,546,071
Liabilities: $115,120,192
Net Worth: $587,425,879
Earnings: $25,888,755
Emp.: 2
Fiscal Year-end: 06/30/24
Investment Management Service
N.A.I.C.S.: 523940
Alan G. Rydge *(Chm)*

CARLTON RESOURCES PLC

Suite 5 Sicilian House, Sicilian Avenue, London, WC1A 2QH, United Kingdom
Tel.: (44) 2074005740
Web Site:
http://www.carltonresourcesplc.com
Sales Range: $25-49.9 Million
Emp.: 4
Investment Services
N.A.I.C.S.: 523999

CARLUCCIO'S LTD.
35 Rose Street, Covent Garden, London, WC2E 9EB, United Kingdom
Tel.: (44) 2075803050 UK
Web Site: http://www.carluccios.com
Year Founded: 1991
Sales Range: $75-99.9 Million
Emp.: 1,566
Holding Company; Italian Restaurant Operator
N.A.I.C.S.: 551112
Simon Kossoff *(Founder)*

CARLY HOLDINGS LIMITED
Tel.: (61) 290001215 AU
Web Site: https://investors.carly.co
CL8—(ASX)
Rev.: $2,403,956
Assets: $6,331,648
Liabilities: $8,557,495
Net Worth: ($2,225,847)
Earnings: ($2,789,370)
Fiscal Year-end: 06/30/24
Software Developer
N.A.I.C.S.: 513210
Chris Noone *(CEO)*

CARLYLE COMMODITIES CORP.
1500-409 Granville St, Vancouver, V6C 1T2, BC, Canada
Tel.: (604) 715-4751
Web Site:
https://www.carlylecommodities.com
CCCFF—(OTCQB)
Assets: $4,953,236
Liabilities: $479,136
Net Worth: $4,474,100
Earnings: ($1,763,422)
Fiscal Year-end: 02/28/23
Mineral Exploration Services
N.A.I.C.S.: 212390
Morgan Good *(Founder & CEO)*

CARLYLE MOTOR PRODUCTS LTD
Junction 9 13, Carlyle, S0C 0R0, SK, Canada
Tel.: (306) 453-6741
Web Site:
http://www.carlylemotorproduct.com
Year Founded: 1986
Sales Range: $10-24.9 Million
Emp.: 32
New & Used Car Dealers
N.A.I.C.S.: 441110
Bill Wyatt *(Controller)*

CARMANAH TECHNOLOGIES CORPORATION
250 Bay Street, Victoria, V9A 3K5, BC, Canada
Tel.: (250) 380-0052 AB
Web Site: https://www.carmanah.com
Year Founded: 1996
Rev.: $30,719,000
Assets: $70,837,000
Liabilities: $10,878,000
Net Worth: $59,959,000
Earnings: $943,000
Emp.: 82
Fiscal Year-end: 12/31/18
Renewable & Energy-Efficient Technology Solutions Integrator Focusing

on Solar-Powered LED Lighting, Solar Power Systems (Off Grid & Grid Tie) & LED Illuminated Signage
N.A.I.C.S.: 334413

Subsidiaries:

Information Display Company **(1)**
10950 SW 5th St Ste 330, Beaverton, OR 97005
Tel.: (800) 421-8325
Web Site: http://www.informationdisplay.com
Radar Speed Display Signs Mfr
N.A.I.C.S.: 334290
Gary Odell *(Pres)*

Sol, Inc. **(1)**
3210 SW 42nd Ave, Palm City, FL 34990
Tel.: (772) 286-9461
Web Site: http://www.solarlighting.com
Sales Range: $1-9.9 Million
Emp.: 10
Solar Powered Lighting Equipment Mfr
N.A.I.C.S.: 335139
Mimi Drabit *(Mgr-Sls)*

CARMAT SAS
36 avenue de l'Europe Immeuble l'Etendard, 78140, Velizy-Villacoublay, Cedex, France
Tel.: (33) 139456450
Web Site: https://www.carmatsa.com
Year Founded: 2008
ALCAR—(EUR)
Rev.: $20,527,652
Assets: $58,581,521
Liabilities: $86,225,853
Net Worth: ($27,644,332)
Earnings: $59,464,621
Emp.: 182
Fiscal Year-end: 12/31/23
Implantable Artificial Heart Mfr
N.A.I.C.S.: 339112
Philippe Pouletty *(Founder)*

CARMECO SA
Sos Mangaliei Nr 74, Constanta, Romania
Tel.: (40) 341803100
CRMC—(BUC)
Rev.: $180,064
Assets: $2,761,109
Liabilities: $146,684
Net Worth: $2,614,426
Earnings: $3,510
Emp.: 4
Fiscal Year-end: 12/31/23
Meat Processing Services
N.A.I.C.S.: 311612

CARMESIN SA
1 Pantelimon Road Sector 2, PB 39-F5, 73381, Bucharest, Romania
Tel.: (40) 21 2520355
Web Site: http://www.carmesin.ro
Emp.: 35
Metal Forging, Stamping, Extruding, Drawing, Rolling & Powder Metallurgy
N.A.I.C.S.: 332111
Ion Popovici *(Gen Mgr)*

CARMEUSE HOLDING SA
Boulevard de Lauzelle 65, 1348, Louvain-la-Neuve, Belgium
Tel.: (32) 010481600
Web Site: http://www.carmeuse.be
Year Founded: 1860
Crushed & Broken Limestone
N.A.I.C.S.: 327410
Yves Willems *(Pres & CEO-Americas)*

Subsidiaries:

Carmeuse North America **(1)**
11 Stanwix St 21th Fl, Pittsburgh, PA 15222-1312
Tel.: (412) 995-5500
Web Site: http://www.carmeusena.com
Sales Range: $50-74.9 Million
Emp.: 100

Lime & Lime Related Environmental Technologies Mfr
N.A.I.C.S.: 327410
Bruce Routhieaux *(VP-Sls)*

Subsidiary (Domestic):

Carmeuse Lime & Stone **(2)**
103 Holly St, Chatsworth, GA 30705
Tel.: (706) 695-1562
Web Site: http://www.carmeuse.com
Sales Range: $50-74.9 Million
Emp.: 70
Industrial Filler Products Operations
N.A.I.C.S.: 212390
Mark Davis *(Area Mgr-Ops)*

Carmeuse Lime & Stone **(2)**
1696 Oranda Rd, Strasburg, VA 22657-3731
Tel.: (540) 465-5161
Web Site: http://www.carmeusena.com
Industrial Minerals
N.A.I.C.S.: 212312
Jim Bottom *(Plant Mgr)*

Carmeuse Lime & Stone **(2)**
684 Pkwy Dr, Buchanan, VA 24066
Tel.: (540) 254-1241
Web Site: http://www.carmeusena.com
Sales Range: $50-74.9 Million
Emp.: 75
Industrial Minerals
N.A.I.C.S.: 212312

Carmeuse Lime & Stone **(2)**
11 Stanwix St Ste 21, Pittsburgh, PA 15222
Tel.: (412) 995-5500
Web Site: http://www.carmeusena.com
Sales Range: $50-74.9 Million
Emp.: 100
Industrial Minerals
N.A.I.C.S.: 212312
Joe Bourdage *(Dir-H&S)*

Carmeuse Lime & Stone **(2)**
165 Steel Dr, Portage, IN 46368
Tel.: (219) 787-9190
Web Site: http://www.carmeusena.com
Sales Range: $50-74.9 Million
Emp.: 15
Industrial Minerals
N.A.I.C.S.: 212312
Ron Vessel *(Plant Mgr)*

Carmeuse Lime & Stone **(2)**
486 Clinch Vly Rd, Luttrell, TN 37779-9414
Tel.: (865) 992-3841
Web Site: http://www.carmeusena.com
Sales Range: $25-49.9 Million
Emp.: 100
Industrial Mineral Mfr
N.A.I.C.S.: 327992
Jack Fahler *(COO)*

Carmeuse Lime & Stone, Inc. **(2)**
11 Stanwix St, Pittsburgh, PA 15222
Tel.: (814) 453-6721
Web Site: http://www.carmeusena.com
Sales Range: $50-74.9 Million
Emp.: 25
Sand Crushed Limestone
N.A.I.C.S.: 212312
Roger Davis *(Mgr-Sls)*

Subsidiary (Domestic):

Yager Materials LLC **(3)**
5001 E HWY 60, Owensboro, KY 42303
Tel.: (270) 926-3611
Web Site: http://www.yagermaterials.com
Sales Range: $50-74.9 Million
Emp.: 50
Common Sand Mining
N.A.I.C.S.: 212321
James B. Yager *(Sec)*

Subsidiary (Domestic):

Carmeuse Lime Inc. **(2)**
3245 E 103rd St, Chicago, IL 60617 **(100%)**
Tel.: (773) 221-9400
Sales Range: $50-74.9 Million
Emp.: 85
Lime Processing
N.A.I.C.S.: 212312

Carmeuse N.A. **(2)**
11 Stanwix St 21th Fl, Pittsburgh, PA 15222-1312 **(100%)**

Carmeuse Holding SA—(Continued)

Tel.: (412) 995-5500
Web Site: http://www.carmeusena.com
Sales Range: $25-49.9 Million
Emp.: 100
Mfr of Chemical & Metallurgical Lime &
Lime-Related Environmental Technologies
N.A.I.C.S.: 327410
Kevin Whyte *(Gen Counsel & VP)*

Superior Minerals Company (2)
4843 W 124th St, Savage, MN 55378
Tel.: (952) 894-0323
Mineral Processor & Distr
N.A.I.C.S.: 327992
Jonathan Wilmshurst *(Pres)*

STT Enviro Corp. (1)
8485 Parkhill Drive, Milton, L9T 5E9, ON,
Canada
Tel.: (905) 875-5587
Web Site: http://www.sttsystems.com
Dry & Liquid Materials Storage, Handling &
Conveying Systems
N.A.I.C.S.: 333248

CARMILA SA

58 Avenue Emile Zola TSA 48002,
92100, Boulogne-Billancourt, Cedex,
France
Tel.: (33) 158336300
Web Site: https://www.carmila.com
CARM—(EUR)
Rev.: $481,074,897
Assets: $7,029,273,689
Liabilities: $3,243,980,142
Net Worth: $3,785,293,546
Earnings: $236,703,000
Emp.: 273
Fiscal Year-end: 12/31/22
Portfolio Management Services
N.A.I.C.S.: 523940
Alexandre De Palmas *(CEO)*

Subsidiaries:

Galimmo SA (1)
37 Rue de la Victoire, 75009, Paris,
France **(93%)**
Tel.: (33) 153205861
Web Site: https://www.galimmo.com
Real Estate Investment Services
N.A.I.C.S.: 531190
Eric Ravoire *(CEO)*

Next Tower S.A.S. (1)
2 Rue Kellermann, 59100, Roubaix, France
Tel.: (33) 972101007
Web Site: https://www.next-tower.fr
Digital Technology Services
N.A.I.C.S.: 541490

CARMIT CANDY INDUSTRIES LTD.

4 Hayated st Industrial area Tziporit,
Nof HaGalil, Israel
Tel.: (972) 39637000
Web Site:
https://www.carmitcandy.com
Year Founded: 1973
CRMT—(TAE)
Rev.: $64,894,598
Assets: $68,137,587
Liabilities: $47,993,368
Net Worth: $20,144,218
Earnings: $143,943
Emp.: 70
Fiscal Year-end: 12/31/23
Chocolate & Confectionery Manufac-
turing from Cacao Beans
N.A.I.C.S.: 311351
Steve Grun *(CEO)*

CARNA BIOSCIENCES INC.

BMA 3F 1-5-5 Minatojima-
Minamimachi, Chuo-ku, Kobe, 650-
0047, Japan
Tel.: (81) 783027039
Web Site: https://www.carnabio.com
Year Founded: 2003
4572—(TKS)
Rev.: $11,521,250

Assets: $30,834,410
Liabilities: $3,346,480
Net Worth: $27,487,930
Earnings: ($8,167,680)
Emp.: 65
Fiscal Year-end: 12/31/23
Pharmaceuticals Mfr
N.A.I.C.S.: 325412
Kohichiro Yoshino *(Pres & CEO)*

Subsidiaries:

CarnaBio USA Inc. (1)
209 W Central St Ste 307, Natick, MA
01760
Tel.: (508) 650-1244
Web Site: https://shop.carnabio.com
Sales Range: $25-49.9 Million
Emp.: 6
Biological Products Distr
N.A.I.C.S.: 325414

CARNABY RESOURCES LIMITED

78 Churchill Avenue, Subiaco, 6008,
WA, Australia
Tel.: (61) 65003236
Web Site:
https://www.carnabyresources.com
CNB—(ASX)
Rev.: $555,733
Assets: $19,932,494
Liabilities: $2,052,869
Net Worth: $17,879,625
Earnings: ($8,070,475)
Fiscal Year-end: 06/30/24
Mineral Exploration Services
N.A.I.C.S.: 213115
Greg Barrett *(Sec)*

CARNARVON ENERGY LIMITED

Level 2 76 Kings Park Road, West
Perth, 6005, WA, Australia
Tel.: (61) 893212665
Web Site: http://carnarvon.com.au
CVN—(ASX)
Rev.: $5,838,675
Assets: $178,679,887
Liabilities: $839,343
Net Worth: $177,840,544
Earnings: ($438,034)
Fiscal Year-end: 06/30/24
Oil & Gas Exploration & Production
Services
N.A.I.C.S.: 211120
Adrian C. Cook *(CEO & Mng Dir)*

CARNATION INDUSTRIES LTD.

222 A J C Bose Road, Kolkata,
700017, West Bengal, India
Tel.: (91) 3322878229
Web Site:
http://www.carnationindustries.com
530609—(BOM)
Rev.: $12,053
Assets: $1,946,954
Liabilities: $2,008,871
Net Worth: ($61,916)
Earnings: ($1,058,803)
Emp.: 16
Fiscal Year-end: 03/31/21
Grey Iron, Iron Castings, Manhole
Covers & Frames Mfr
N.A.I.C.S.: 331511
Ravindra Prakash Sehgal *(Co-Mng Dir)*

CARNAVALE RESOURCES LIMITED

Level 2 Suite 9 389 Oxford Street,
Hawthorn, 6016, WA, Australia
Tel.: (61) 893809098
Web Site:
https://www.carnavaleresources.com
CAV—(ASX)
Rev.: $2,565
Assets: $7,272,772

Liabilities: $403,799
Net Worth: $6,868,973
Earnings: ($1,082,334)
Emp.: 3
Fiscal Year-end: 06/30/22
Gold & Copper Assets Developer
N.A.I.C.S.: 212230
Ron Gajewski *(Chm)*

CARNEGIE CLEAN ENERGY LIMITED

21 North Mole Drive, PO Box 39,
North Fremantle, 6159, WA, Australia
Tel.: (61) 861688400
Web Site:
https://www.carnegiece.com
CCE—(ASX)
Rev.: $298,719
Assets: $14,955,650
Liabilities: $867,620
Net Worth: $14,088,030
Earnings: ($1,549,296)
Emp.: 25
Fiscal Year-end: 06/30/24
Miscellaneous Financial Investment
Activities
N.A.I.C.S.: 523999
Grant Jonathan Mooney *(Sec)*

CARNIVAL GROUP INTERNATIONAL HOLDINGS LIMITED

18/F Everbright Centre 108 Glouces-
ter Road, Wanchai, China (Hong
Kong)
Tel.: (852) 29076111
Web Site: http://www.0996.com.hk
0996—(HKG)
Rev.: $13,440,232
Assets: $2,266,218,713
Liabilities: $2,133,143,211
Net Worth: $133,075,502
Earnings: ($499,693,284)
Emp.: 182
Fiscal Year-end: 12/31/20
Investment Services
N.A.I.C.S.: 523999
Stella Yuen Ying Chan *(Sec)*

Subsidiaries:

Po Sun Piece Goods Company
Limited (1)
9 Queens Rd, Central, China (Hong Kong)
Tel.: (852) 23983878
Textile & Fabrics Whslr
N.A.I.C.S.: 424310

CARNIVAL INDUSTRIAL CORPORATION

6F No 25 Sec 4 Renai Rd, Daan
Dist, Taipei, 106, Taiwan
Tel.: (886) 27113171
Web Site:
https://www.carnival.com.tw
Year Founded: 1969
1417—(TAI)
Rev.: $48,950,422
Assets: $117,146,665
Liabilities: $32,481,473
Net Worth: $84,665,192
Earnings: ($2,164,786)
Fiscal Year-end: 12/31/23
Apparel Product Mfr
N.A.I.C.S.: 315990
Li-Lien Yen Chen *(Chm)*

CARO HOLDINGS, INC.

28th Floor Cityland Pasong Tamo
Tower U2807 2210 Chino Roces Av-
enue, Makati, 1230, Philippines
Tel.: (63) 28938909 NV
Web Site:
http://www.caroholdings.com
Year Founded: 2016
Rev.: $13
Assets: $266,292
Liabilities: $391,054

Net Worth: ($124,762)
Earnings: ($356,479)
Fiscal Year-end: 03/31/23
Investment Services
N.A.I.C.S.: 523999
Christopher McEachnie *(CEO, Treas
& Sec)*

CAROL INFO SERVICES LTD.

Wockhardt Towers Bandra-Kurla
Comples, Bandra East, Mumbai,
400051, India
Tel.: (91) 22 2653 4444
Web Site:
http://www.carolinfoservices.com
Sales Range: Less than $1 Million
Emp.: 100
Pharmaceuticals Product Mfr
N.A.I.C.S.: 325412
G. B. Parulkar *(Chm & Mng Dir)*

CAROLYN RIVER PROJECTS LTD.

2640 Tempe Knoll Drive, North Van-
couver, V6C 1V5, BC, Canada
Tel.: (604) 908-0233 NV
Year Founded: 2004
Sales Range: Less than $1 Million
Mineral Mining & Exploration Ser-
vices
N.A.I.C.S.: 212290
Steve Bolton *(Pres, CEO, CFO,
Treas & Sec)*

CARON TRANSPORTATION SYSTEMS PARTNERSHIP

301 Streambank Avenue, Sherwood
Park, T8H 1N1, AB, Canada
Tel.: (780) 449-6688
Web Site:
https://www.carontransport.ca
Year Founded: 1990
Rev.: $38,085,752
Emp.: 400
Transportation Services
N.A.I.C.S.: 486990

Subsidiaries:

Interload Services Ltd. (1)
13310 156 St NW, Edmonton, T5V 1L3, AB,
Canada
Tel.: (780) 451-7900
Freight Forwarding Services
N.A.I.C.S.: 484121

CAROS CO., LTD.

122 Naecheon-gil Naecheon-ri
Seotan-myeon, Pyeongtaek,
Gyeonggi-do, Korea (South)
Tel.: (82) 316123000 KR
Web Site: http://www.caros.co.kr
Year Founded: 2009
Household Appliance Mfr & Distr
N.A.I.C.S.: 335210
Yoo Young-Min *(CEO)*

CARPATAIR SA

Str Ion Ionescu de la Brad nr 15,
300246, Timisoara, Romania
Tel.: (40) 256 300 900
Web Site: http://www.carpatair.com
Year Founded: 1999
Airline Services
N.A.I.C.S.: 481211

Subsidiaries:

Moldavian Airlines (1)
Chisinau Airport Hotel 80/3, MD-2026, Chi-
sinau, Moldova
Tel.: (373) 22529356
Sales Range: $25-49.9 Million
Emp.: 200
Oil Transportation Services
N.A.I.C.S.: 481111
Nicolae Petrov *(Pres & CEO)*

CARPATERRA CAPITAL PARTNERS SRO

Rytirska 13, 110 00, Prague, 1, Czech Republic
Tel.: (420) 226 205 060
Web Site: http://www.carpaterra.com
Privater Equity Firm
N.A.I.C.S.: 523999

Subsidiaries:

C-Energy Bohemia Sro **(1)**
Prumyslova 748, Plana nad Luznici, 391 02, South Bohemia, Czech Republic
Tel.: (420) 380071800
Web Site: http://www.c-energy.cz
Electrical Energy Distr
N.A.I.C.S.: 335999
Ivo Nejdl (CEO)

Subsidiary (Domestic):

Teplarna Tabor, a.s. **(2)**
U Cihelny 2128, Tabor, 39049, Czech Republic **(51.95%)**
Tel.: (420) 381417235
Electric Power Generation & Distribution Services
N.A.I.C.S.: 221118

CARPATHIA CAPITAL SA

ul Archbishop A Baraniaka 6, 61-131, Poznan, Poland
Tel.: (48) 797289406
Web Site:
https://www.carpathiacapital.eu
CRPC—(BUC)
Rev.: $745,136
Assets: $14,023,947
Liabilities: $23,787,963
Net Worth: ($9,764,017)
Earnings: ($2,967,188)
Emp.: 19
Fiscal Year-end: 12/31/19
Financial Advisory Services
N.A.I.C.S.: 523940
Sebastian Huczek (VP)

CARPENE MALVOLTI S.P.A.

Via A Carpene 1, 31015, Conegliano, Italy
Tel.: (39) 0438364611
Web Site: http://www.carpene-malvolti.com
Year Founded: 1868
Sales Range: $10-24.9 Million
Emp.: 39
Wine, Brandy & Grappa Producer
N.A.I.C.S.: 312130
Etile Carpene (Owner & Pres)

CARPENTER TAN HOLDINGS LIMITED

Room 708 7th Floor Witty Commercial Building 1A-1L Tung Choi Street, Mong Kok, Kowloon, China (Hong Kong)
Tel.: (852) 51187186978
Web Site: http://www.ctans.com
0837—(HKG)
Rev.: $50,698,721
Assets: $120,163,522
Liabilities: $17,137,917
Net Worth: $103,025,605
Earnings: $16,599,997
Emp.: 720
Fiscal Year-end: 12/31/21
Wooden Handcrafts Including Combs, Furniture & Accessories Mfr
N.A.I.C.S.: 321999
Chuan Tan (Co-Founder & Chm)

Subsidiaries:

Carpenter Tan Development Company Limited **(1)**
1009 10/F Nan Fung Commercial Centre 19 Lam Lok Street Kowloon Bay, Kowloon, China (Hong Kong)
Tel.: (852) 25122333
Wooden Furniture Mfr
N.A.I.C.S.: 337122

CARPETRIGHT PLC

Purfleet Bypass, Purfleet, RM19 1TT, Essex, United Kingdom
Tel.: (44) 1708802000 UK
Web Site:
http://www.carpetright.plc.uk
Year Founded: 1988
CPR—(LSE)
Rev.: $490,349,328
Assets: $256,595,844
Liabilities: $193,525,550
Net Worth: $63,070,294
Earnings: $27,918,440
Emp.: 3,181
Fiscal Year-end: 04/27/19
Retail Floor Coverings & Carpet Services
N.A.I.C.S.: 449121
Wilf Walsh (CEO)

Subsidiaries:

Carpetland BV **(1)**
Franciscusdreef 60, 3565 AC, Utrecht, Netherlands **(100%)**
Tel.: (31) 302631263
Web Site: http://www.carpetright.nl
Sales Range: $125-149.9 Million
Emp.: 500
Miscellaneous Retail Stores
N.A.I.C.S.: 459999

Carpetland NV **(1)**
Rue du Stalle 215, 1620, Drogenbos, Belgium **(100%)**
Tel.: (32) 23712411
Sales Range: $25-49.9 Million
Emp.: 20
Floor Covering Stores
N.A.I.C.S.: 449121

Carpetright of London Limited **(1)**
Amberley House New Road, Rainham, RA13 8QN, United Kingdom **(100%)**
Tel.: (44) 1708525522
Miscellaneous Retail Stores
N.A.I.C.S.: 459999

Fontainebleau Vastgoed BV **(1)**
Franciscusdreef 60, 3565 AC, Utrecht, Netherlands **(100%)**
Tel.: (31) 302631261
Web Site: http://www.carpetright.nl
Sales Range: $50-74.9 Million
Emp.: 25
Real Estate Property Lessors
N.A.I.C.S.: 531190

CARPEVIGO HOLDING AG

Marktplatz 20, 83607, Holzkirchen, Germany
Tel.: (49) 80246083830
Web Site: https://www.carpevigo.de
Year Founded: 2006
A1MBGZ—(MUN)
Sales Range: Less than $1 Million
Electric Equipment Mfr
N.A.I.C.S.: 335999
Jens F. Neureuther (CEO)

CARR'S FLOUR MILLS LTD.

Hutchisons Mill East Bridge, Kirkcaldy, KY1 2SR, United Kingdom
Tel.: (44) 1592 267191 UK
Web Site: http://www.carrs-flourmills.co.uk
Flour Milling
N.A.I.C.S.: 311211

CARR'S GROUP PLC

Warwick Mill Business Centre, Warwick Bridge, Carlisle, CA4 8RR, Cumbria, United Kingdom
Tel.: (44) 1228554600
Web Site:
https://www.carrsgroup.com
Year Founded: 1831
CARR—(LSE)
Rev.: $566,514,101
Assets: $356,406,931
Liabilities: $172,797,024
Net Worth: $183,609,906
Earnings: $13,104,713
Emp.: 1,153
Fiscal Year-end: 08/28/21
Holding Company; Agriculture & Engineering Services
N.A.I.C.S.: 551112
Neil Austin (Dir-Fin)

Subsidiaries:

Afgritech Limited **(1)**
Old Croft, Carlisle, CA3 9BA, United Kingdom
Tel.: (44) 1228554600
Web Site: http://www.carrsgroup.com
Other Animal Food Mfr
N.A.I.C.S.: 311119
Tim David (CEO)

Animal Feed Supplement Inc. **(1)**
11094 Business 212, Belle Fourche, SD 57717 **(100%)**
Tel.: (605) 892-3421
Web Site: https://newgensupplements.com
Sales Range: $25-49.9 Million
Emp.: 50
Other Animal Food Mfr
N.A.I.C.S.: 311119
Dick Wark (Pres & CEO)

Animax Ltd. **(1)**
Shepherds Grove Industrial Estate West, Stanton, Bury Saint Edmunds, IP31 2AR, Suffolk, United Kingdom
Tel.: (44) 135 925 2181
Web Site: https://animax-vet.com
Animal Health Products Mfr
N.A.I.C.S.: 311119

Bendalls Engineering **(1)**
46 Brunthill Road, Carlisle, CA3 0EH, United Kingdom **(100%)**
Tel.: (44) 1228815350
Web Site: https://www.bendalls.co.uk
Sales Range: $25-49.9 Million
Emp.: 80
Engineeering Services
N.A.I.C.S.: 541330

Bibby Agriculture Limited **(1)**
Network House, Oxon Business Park, Shrewsbury, SY3 5AB, United Kingdom
Tel.: (44) 1743237890
Web Site: https://bibbyagri.com
Sales Range: $25-49.9 Million
Emp.: 70
Other Animal Food Mfr
N.A.I.C.S.: 311119

Carrs Billington Agriculture (Sales) Ltd. **(1)**
Montgomery Way Rosehill Industrial Estate, Carlisle, CA1 2UY, Cumbria, United Kingdom **(51%)**
Tel.: (44) 1228210275
Web Site: https://www.carrs-billington.com
Sales Range: $25-49.9 Million
Emp.: 45
Farm & Garden Machinery & Equipment Whslr
N.A.I.C.S.: 423820
Tim Davies (Chm)

Carrs Billington Agriculture (Sales), Annan **(1)**
Annan Business Park, Annan, DG12 6TZ, Dumfriesshire, United Kingdom **(100%)**
Tel.: (44) 1461202772
Web Site: http://www.carrs-milling.com
Hog & Pig Farming & Sales
N.A.I.C.S.: 112210

Carrs Engineering Limited **(1)**
Brunthill Road Kingstown Industrial Estate, Carlisle, CA3 0EH, Cumbria, United Kingdom
Tel.: (44) 1228815350
Sales Range: $25-49.9 Million
Emp.: 80
Fabricated Metal Products Mfr
N.A.I.C.S.: 332999
Chrise Woodhead (Gen Mgr)

Carrs Properties Limited **(1)**
Oldcroft Stanwix, Carlisle, CA3 9BA, Cumbria, United Kingdom
Tel.: (44) 1228554600

Emp.: 25
Farm Supplies Merchant Whslr
N.A.I.C.S.: 424910
Tamothy Davies (CEO)

NW Total Engineered Solutions Ltd. **(1)**
Andrews Way, Barrow-in-Furness, LA14 2UE, Cumbria, United Kingdom
Tel.: (44) 122 981 1000
Web Site: https://www.nwtotal.co.uk
Carbon Steel Pipe Equipment Mfr
N.A.I.C.S.: 331210

NuVision Engineering, Inc. **(1)**
2403 Sidney St Ste 700, Pittsburgh, PA 15203-2181
Tel.: (412) 586-1810
Engineering Software & Consulting Services
N.A.I.C.S.: 541330
Robert Mullens (VP-Safety, QA, Decon & Field Ops)

Scotmin Nutrition Limited **(1)**
13 Whitfield Drive Heathfield Industrial Estate, Ayr, KA8 9RX, United Kingdom
Tel.: (44) 1292280909
Web Site: https://www.scotmin.com
Sales Range: $25-49.9 Million
Emp.: 30
Animal Supplements Distr
N.A.I.C.S.: 424590
Neil Dale (Mgr-Bus Dev)

Walischmiller Engineering GmbH **(1)**
Schiessstattweg 16, 88677, Markdorf, Germany
Tel.: (49) 75 449 5140
Web Site: https://www.hwm.com
Sales Range: $25-49.9 Million
Emp.: 125
Robot Grip Tongs Mfr
N.A.I.C.S.: 333248

CARREFOUR SA

93 Avenue de Paris, 91300, Massy, France
Tel.: (33) 164505000 FR
Web Site: https://www.carrefour.com
Year Founded: 1959
CRERF—(OTCIQ)
Rev.: $93,727,784,537
Assets: $62,005,740,157
Liabilities: $47,228,170,886
Net Worth: $14,777,569,270
Earnings: $993,487,140
Emp.: 305,333
Fiscal Year-end: 12/31/23
Holding Company; Supermarkets, Hypermarkets & Convenience Stores Owner & Operator
N.A.I.C.S.: 551112
Noel Prioux (Exec Dir-Latin America)

Subsidiaries:

Atacadao S.A. **(1)**
Avenida Morvan Dias de Figueiredo 6169 Vila Maria Baixa, Sao Paulo, 02170-901, Brazil
Tel.: (55) 1129678261
Web Site: http://www.atacadao.com.br
Rev.: $19,638,368,474
Assets: $16,582,827,896
Liabilities: $12,859,798,375
Net Worth: $3,723,029,522
Earnings: ($114,227,487)
Fiscal Year-end: 12/31/2023
Consumer Goods Distr
N.A.I.C.S.: 445110
Jose Roberto Meister Mussnich (CEO)

BLO DISTRIBUTION **(1)**
Route de Paris Zi, Mondeville, 14120, France
Tel.: (33) 231702000
Super Market Stores Operating Services
N.A.I.C.S.: 445110

Bellevue Distribution SA **(1)**
Rue De La Poste, 36000, Chateauroux, France **(100%)**
Tel.: (33) 254085240
Grocery Distr
N.A.I.C.S.: 424490

CHALLENGER SARL **(1)**
35 Cours Napoleon, 20000, Ajaccio, France

Carrefour SA—(Continued)

Tel.: (33) 495210855
Super Market Stores Operating Services
N.A.I.C.S.: 445110

CLAIREFONTAINE SA   **(1)**
27 route de la Loire, 44450, La Chapelle-
Basse-Mer, France
Tel.: (33) 2 40333260
Sales Range: $25-49.9 Million
Emp.: 10
Paper Products & Stationery Material Mfr
N.A.I.C.S.: 322230

CLV DISTRIBUTION   **(1)**
3 rue Georges Clemenceau, 69470, Cours-
la-Ville, France
Tel.: (33) 4 74 89 72 96
Supermarket Operating Services
N.A.I.C.S.: 445110

COLIBRI   **(1)**
8 Place de la Madeleine, Paris, France
Tel.: (33) 1 42 60 59 22
Web Site: http://www.colibri.com
General Retail Store Operating Services
N.A.I.C.S.: 455219

CONTINENT 2001   **(1)**
13 Quai De Marne, Epernay, 51200, France
Tel.: (33) 326532979
Super Market Stores Operating Services
N.A.I.C.S.: 445110

COSG   **(1)**
33 Avenue Emile Zola, 92100, Boulogne-
Billancourt, France
Tel.: (33) 141042600
Sales Range: $700-749.9 Million
Emp.: 400
Business Management Services
N.A.I.C.S.: 541618

Cardadel SA   **(1)**
58 Avenue Du Marechal Leclerc, Cosne-
Cours-sur-Loire, 58200, France   **(100%)**
Tel.: (33) 386266549
Sales Range: $25-49.9 Million
Emp.: 25
Super Market Stores Operating Services
N.A.I.C.S.: 445110

Carrefour Asia Limited   **(1)**
14th Floor Tower 1 Admiralty, Hong Kong,
China (Hong Kong)   **(100%)**
Tel.: (852) 22834000
Sales Range: $25-49.9 Million
Emp.: 100
Owner & Operator of Hypermarkets, Super-
markets, Grocery & Convenience Stores
N.A.I.C.S.: 445110

Subsidiary (Non-US):

**CHENGDU YUSHENG INDUSTRIAL
DEVELOPMENT CO LTD**   **(2)**
Rm 2401 Minshan Restaurant, Jinjiang,
Chengdu, 610021, China
Tel.: (86) 2885583333
Super Market Stores Operating Services
N.A.I.C.S.: 445110

Subsidiary (Domestic):

**Carrefour Global Sourcing Asia
Limited**   **(2)**
18/F One Kowloon 1 Wang Yuen St, Kow-
loon, China (Hong Kong)
Tel.: (852) 25866400
Sales Range: $50-74.9 Million
Emp.: 11
Vegetables & Canned Fruits Distr
N.A.I.C.S.: 424480

Subsidiary (Non-US):

Carrefour Singapore Pte Ltd   **(2)**
8 Temasek Blvd 04-01/2/3, Suntec Twr
Three, 38988, Singapore,
Singapore   **(100%)**
Tel.: (65) 63336868
Web Site: http://www.carrefour.com.sg
Sales Range: $25-49.9 Million
Owner & Operator of Supermarkets, Hyper-
markets, Grocery & Convenience Stores
N.A.I.C.S.: 445110

**Carrefour South East Asia Pte.
Ltd.**   **(2)**
8 Temasek Boulevard 04-01/02/03 Suntec

Tower 3, Singapore, 039192, Singapore
Tel.: (65) 62113102
Super Market Stores Operating Services
N.A.I.C.S.: 445110

Carrefour Taiwan   **(2)**
Presicarre Corporation, 6F-1,137 Nan King
East Road, Section 2, 104, Taipei, Taiwan
Tel.: (886) 225063400
Web Site: http://www.carrefour.com.tw
Hypermarkets, Supermarkets, Grocery &
Convenience Stores
N.A.I.C.S.: 457110
Chun-chao Wang (CEO)

**Cencar Limited (Carrefour
Thailand)**   **(2)**
15th Floor Q House Building, 11 South
Sethorn Road, Tungmahamek Sathorn,
10120, Bangkok, Thailand
Tel.: (66) 26773399
Owner & Operator of Hypermarkets, Super-
markets, Grocery & Convenience Stores
N.A.I.C.S.: 445110

**DIA TIANTIAN (SHANGHAI) MAN-
AGEMENT CONSULTING SERVICE
CO. LTD**   **(2)**
A G 7/F International Ship Finance Mansion
No 720 Pudong Ave, Shanghai, 200120,
China
Tel.: (86) 2150368282
Web Site: http://www.diatiantian.com
Management Consulting Services
N.A.I.C.S.: 541611

**WUHAN HANFU SUPERMARKET
CO. LTD**   **(2)**
No 687 Hanyang Road, Wuhan, 430051,
China
Tel.: (86) 27 84882020
Super Market Stores Operating Services
N.A.I.C.S.: 445110

**Xuzhou Yuejia Commercial Co.,
Ltd.**   **(2)**
No 6 Zhongshan North Road, Gulou, Xu-
zhou, 221005, China
Tel.: (86) 51687880001
Super Market Stores Operating Services
N.A.I.C.S.: 445110
Lee Hill (Gen Mgr)

Carrefour Belgium SA   **(1)**
Ave Des Olympiades 20, PO Box 1140,
Evere, Brussels, 1140, Belgium   **(100%)**
Tel.: (32) 27292111
Web Site: http://www.carrefour.eu
Sales Range: $200-249.9 Million
Emp.: 1,000
Operator of Supermarkets, Hypermarkets,
Convenience Stores & Grocery Stores
N.A.I.C.S.: 445110

Subsidiary (Domestic):

Carrefour Finance SA   **(2)**
Avenue Louise 240, Brussels, 1050, Bel-
gium
Tel.: (32) 26261960
Sales Range: $50-74.9 Million
Emp.: 15
Financial Management Services
N.A.I.C.S.: 523999

FOURCAR BELGIUM SA   **(2)**
240 Avenue Louise, Brussels, 1052, Bel-
gium
Tel.: (32) 26261960
Trade Shows Organisation Services
N.A.I.C.S.: 561920

**QUIEVRAIN RETAIL ASSOCIATE
NV**   **(2)**
Avenue Docteur Schweitzer 30, 7340,
Wasmes, Belgium
Tel.: (32) 65 80 32 92
Sales Range: $25-49.9 Million
Emp.: 8
Food Store Operating Services
N.A.I.C.S.: 445298

ROTHIDI SA   **(2)**
Rue De La Bruyere 215, Rixensart, 1332,
Walloon Brabant, Belgium
Tel.: (32) 26 53 63 68
Super Market Stores Operating Services
N.A.I.C.S.: 445110

Unit (Domestic):

**Supertransport - Traffic Center
Kontich**   **(2)**

Neerveld 1, 2550, Kontich,
Belgium   **(100%)**
Tel.: (32) 34514681
Web Site: http://www.supertransport.be
Sales Range: $10-24.9 Million
Emp.: 50
Distribution Services
N.A.I.C.S.: 541614

**Supertransport - Traffic Center Nord
(KDC)**   **(2)**
Drevendaal 3, St Katelijne Waver, 2860,
Mechelen, Belgium   **(100%)**
Tel.: (32) 5306580
Web Site: http://www.supertransport.be
Distribution Services
N.A.I.C.S.: 541614

**Supertransport - Traffic Center
Sud**   **(2)**
Rue De lindustrie 21, 1400, Nivelles,
Belgium   **(100%)**
Tel.: (32) 67634814
Web Site: http://www.supertransport.be
Distribution Services
N.A.I.C.S.: 541614

**Supertransport - Traffic Center
Vilvoorde**   **(2)**
Drevendaal 3 St Katelinje Waver, Waver,
2860, Vilvoorde, Belgium   **(100%)**
Tel.: (32) 22572630
Distribution Services
N.A.I.C.S.: 541614

Carrefour Ceska Republika   **(1)**
Podbabska 17, Dejvice, 160 00, Prague,
Czech Republic   **(100%)**
Tel.: (420) 233013300
Web Site:
    http://www.carrefour.czechtrade.us
Sales Range: $100-124.9 Million
Emp.: 300
Owner & Operator of Hypermarkets, Super-
markets, Grocery & Convenience Stores
N.A.I.C.S.: 445110

Carrefour China Holdings BV   **(1)**
Overschiestraat 186 D, Amsterdam, 1062
XK, Netherlands
Tel.: (31) 20 669 5858
Sales Range: $50-74.9 Million
Emp.: 4
Holding Company
N.A.I.C.S.: 551112

Carrefour France   **(1)**
ZI Route de Paris, BP 83, 14120, Mondev-
ille, France
Tel.: (33) 231706088
Web Site: http://www.carrefour.fr
Super Market Stores Operating Services
N.A.I.C.S.: 445110

Subsidiary (Domestic):

Carrefour Administratif France   **(2)**
66 Avenue Charles de Gaulle, 92200,
Neuilly-sur-Seine, France   **(100%)**
Tel.: (33) 1 4641 5800
Super Market Stores Operating Services
N.A.I.C.S.: 445110

Carrefour Drive   **(2)**
102 rue de Paris, 91300, Massy,
France   **(100%)**
Tel.: (33) 169193000
Web Site: http://www.carrefour.fr
Sales Range: $25-49.9 Million
Emp.: 10
Grocery Pick-up Services
N.A.I.C.S.: 812990

Carrefour Hypermarches   **(2)**
1 Rue Jean Mermoz, BP75, 91002,
Courcouronnes, France   **(100%)**
Tel.: (33) 160913737
Web Site: http://www.carrefour.fr
Owner & Operator of Hypermarkets
N.A.I.C.S.: 445110
George Plassa (Gen Mgr)

Carrefour Import SAS   **(2)**
102 rue de Paris, 91300, Massy,
France   **(100%)**
Tel.: (33) 164869000
Product Import Services
N.A.I.C.S.: 425120

Carrefour Property Gestion   **(2)**
66/70 Avenue Charles de Gaulle, 92200,

Neuilly-sur-Seine, France   **(100%)**
Tel.: (33) 1 4641 5800
Real Estate Acquisition & Store Develop-
ment
N.A.I.C.S.: 531390

Carrefour Station Service   **(2)**
Quartier Les Salles Route Nationale 7,
83480, Puget-sur-Argens, France   **(100%)**
Tel.: (33) 494176560
Super Market Stores Operating Services
N.A.I.C.S.: 445110

**Carrefour Systemes d'Informations
France**   **(2)**
Route De Paris Zi, 14120, Mondeville,
France   **(100%)**
Tel.: (33) 2 31 70 60 00
Information Technology Support Services
N.A.I.C.S.: 541513

Carrefour Italia SpA   **(1)**
Via Caldera 21, 20153, Milan, Italy **(100%)**
Tel.: (39) 0248251
Web Site: http://www.carrefouritalia.it
N.A.I.C.S.: 444140

Carrefour Latin America   **(1)**
Cuyo 3323/3337, Martinez, 1640, Buenos
Aires, Argentina
Tel.: (54) 1140037000
Web Site: http://www.carrefour.com.ar
Holding Company
N.A.I.C.S.: 551112

Subsidiary (Domestic):

Carrefour Argentina S.A.   **(2)**
Cuyo 3323/3337, Martinez, 1640, Buenos
Aires, Argentina
Tel.: (54) 1140037000
Web Site: http://www.carrefour.com.ar
Owner & Operator of Supermarkets, Hyper-
markets, Grocery & Convenience Stores
N.A.I.C.S.: 445110
Daniel Fernandez (Exec Dir)

Subsidiary (Non-US):

Carrefour Brasil   **(2)**
213 Rua George Eastman, CEP 04719,
Sao Paulo, Brazil   **(80%)**
Tel.: (55) 11 37796000
Web Site: http://www.grupocarrefour.com.br
Sales Range: $25-49.9 Million
Emp.: 170
Owner & Operator of Hypermarkets, Super-
markets, Grocery & Convenience Stores
N.A.I.C.S.: 445110

Carrefour Monaco   **(1)**
Avenue Albert 2BP 233, Monaco, 98004,
Monaco
Tel.: (377) 92055700
Supermarket Operating Services
N.A.I.C.S.: 445110

Carrefour Nederland B.V.   **(1)**
186 D Gebouw Spring Overschiestraat,
1062 XK, Amsterdam, Netherlands **(100%)**
Tel.: (31) 206695858
Sales Range: $25-49.9 Million
Emp.: 4
Owner & Operator of Hypermarkets, Super-
markets, Grocery & Convenience Stores
N.A.I.C.S.: 445110
F. Tassan (Gen Mgr)

Subsidiary (Domestic):

ALCYON BV   **(2)**
Overschiestraat 186d Geb Spring, Amster-
dam, 1062 XK, Netherlands
Tel.: (31) 206695858
Sales Range: $25-49.9 Million
Emp.: 4
Super Market Stores Operating Services
N.A.I.C.S.: 445110

CADAM BV   **(2)**
Overschiestraat 186d, Amsterdam, 1062
XK, Netherlands
Tel.: (31) 206695858
Super Market Stores Operating Services
N.A.I.C.S.: 445110

Carrefour Property B.V.   **(2)**
Overschiestraat 186d, Amsterdam, 1062
XK, Netherlands
Tel.: (31) 206695858
Property Management Services

N.A.I.C.S.: 531311

FOURCAR BV (2)
Overschiestraat 186d, Amsterdam, 1062
XK, Netherlands
Tel.: (31) 206695858
Super Market Stores Operating Services
N.A.I.C.S.: 445110

FRANCOFIN BV (2)
Overschiestraat 186d, Amsterdam, 1062
XK, Netherlands
Tel.: (31) 206695858
Emp.: 4
Super Market Stores Operating Services
N.A.I.C.S.: 445110

MILDEW BV (2)
Overschiestraat 186 d, Amsterdam, 1062
XK, Netherlands
Tel.: (31) 900 9888
Super Market Stores Operating Services
N.A.I.C.S.: 445110

SOCA BV (2)
Overschiestraat 186D, Amsterdam, 1062
XK, Netherlands
Tel.: (31) 206695858
Super Market Stores Operating Services
N.A.I.C.S.: 445110

Carrefour Polska Sp. z o.o. (1)
Al Jerozolimskie 148, 02326, Warsaw, Po-
land
Tel.: (48) 225724700
Sales Range: $1-4.9 Billion
Emp.: 15,397
Owner & Operator of Hypermarkets, Super-
markets, Grocery & Convenience Stores
N.A.I.C.S.: 445110

Subsidiary (Domestic):

**Carrefour Polska Proper Sp. z
o.o.** (2)
ul Targowa 72, Warsaw, 03-734, Poland
Tel.: (48) 22 517 2110
Super Market Stores Operating Services
N.A.I.C.S.: 445110

**Carrefour Procurement International
AG & Co. KG** (1)
Schliengener Strasse 25, 79379, Mullheim,
Germany
Tel.: (49) 763170040
Super Market Stores Operating Services
N.A.I.C.S.: 445110

**Carrefour Property Development
SA** (1)
58 avenue Emile Zola, 92100, Boulogne-
Billancourt, France
Tel.: (33) 146415800
Web Site: http://www.cardety.com
Sales Range: Less than $1 Million
Real Estate Support Services
N.A.I.C.S.: 531390
Francis Mauger (Chm & CEO)

Carrefour Property Espana, SLU (1)
Avda Matapinonera s/n Edificio Abside 5
Planta, 28703, San Sebastian de los
Reyes, Madrid, Spain
Tel.: (34) 916634419
Web Site: http://www.carrefourproperty.es
Construction Services
N.A.I.C.S.: 236220

Carrefour Property France SAS (1)
93 Avenue de Paris, 91342, Massy, Cedex,
France
Tel.: (33) 158336100
Web Site: http://www.carrefourproperty.fr
Construction Services
N.A.I.C.S.: 236220

Carrefour Property Italia SRL (1)
Via Caldera 21, 20153, Milan, Italy
Tel.: (39) 02482525
Web Site: http://www.carrefourproperty.it
Construction Services
N.A.I.C.S.: 236220

Carrefour Romania S.A. (1)
Str Gara Herastrau nr 4C Green Court Cla-
direa B etaj 7 Sector 2, 4th Floor For The
Procurement Department Sector 2, Bucha-
rest, Romania
Tel.: (40) 212067400
Web Site: http://www.carrefour.ro
Food Products Distr

N.A.I.C.S.: 445110
Gabriela Stanica (Chief Info, Data Officer &
Dir-E-commerce)

**Carrefour Sabanci Ticaret Merkezi AS
CarrefourSA** (1)
CarrefourSA Plaza Cevizli Mahallesi Tugay
Yolu Caddesi No 67 A Blok B, Maltepe, Is-
tanbul, Turkiye **(58.2%)**
Tel.: (90) 2166 55 0000
Web Site: http://www.carrefoursa.com
Sales Range: $125-149.9 Million
Emp.: 500
Supermarkets & Other Stores Operator
N.A.I.C.S.: 445110

Carrefour Slovensko s.r.o. (1)
Panonska Cesta 16a, Bratislava, 851 04,
Slovakia
Tel.: (421) 268 292 111
Super Market Stores Operating Services
N.A.I.C.S.: 445110
Stephane Sellier (Gen Mgr)

Carrefour Voyages SAS (1)
1 Rue Jean Mermoz-ZAE St Guenault,
91002, Evry, Cedex, France
Tel.: (33) 164991818
Web Site: http://www.voyages.carrefour.fr
Travel Services
N.A.I.C.S.: 561599

Carrefour World Trade SA (1)
Route de l'Aeroport 10, Geneva, 1215,
Switzerland
Tel.: (41) 227107311
Web Site: http://www.carrefour.com
Sales Range: $25-49.9 Million
Emp.: 18
Super Market Stores Operating Services
N.A.I.C.S.: 445110
Jean Pierre Noeel (Mng Dir)

**Carrefoursa Turkiye Genel
Mudurluk** (1)
CarrefourSA Plaza Cevizli Mahallesi Tugay
Yolu Caddesi No 67 A, Blok B Maltepe,
34750, Istanbul, Turkiye
Tel.: (90) 2166550000
Web Site: http://www.carrefour.com.tr
Hypermarkets, Supermarkets, Grocery &
Convenience Stores Operator
N.A.I.C.S.: 445110

**Centros Comerciales Carrefour,
S.A.** (1)
Ctra de Burgos Km 14500, 28108, Alcoben-
das, Madrid, Spain **(77%)**
Tel.: (34) 914908900
Web Site: http://www.carrefour.es
Owner & Operator of Hypermarkets, Super-
markets, Grocery & Convenience Stores
N.A.I.C.S.: 445110

Subsidiary (Domestic):

Carrefour Canarias, S.A. (2)
Avenida Manuel Hermoso Rojas 16, 38003,
Santa Cruz de Tenerife, Spain
Tel.: (34) 922236000
Super Market Stores Operating Services
N.A.I.C.S.: 445110

**Carrefour Espana Properties,
S.L.** (2)
Avenida Matapinonera S/N-Ed Abside
Planta 5, Madrid, Spain
Tel.: (34) 916634335
Property Management Services
N.A.I.C.S.: 531311

Carrefour Navarra, S.L. (2)
Avenida Baranain S/N, 31008, Pamplona,
Spain
Tel.: (34) 948194100
Web Site: http://www.carrefour.com
Super Market Stores Operating Services
N.A.I.C.S.: 445110

Carrefour Norte, S.L. (2)
Carretera Trapaga A Barakaldo S/N, Ses-
tao, 48910, Spain
Tel.: (34) 944729100
Super Market Stores Operating Services
N.A.I.C.S.: 445110

Subsidiary (Non-US):

**DIA PORTUGAL SUPERMERCADOS
SA** (2)

R Carlos Mardel 49 1, Lisbon, 1900-117,
Portugal
Tel.: (351) 218452240
Supermarket Operating Services
N.A.I.C.S.: 445110

Subsidiary (Domestic):

GROUP SUPECO MAXOR SL (2)
Av Angel Sallent S/N, Terrassa, 8224, Spain
Tel.: (34) 937333006
Sales Range: $25-49.9 Million
Emp.: 54
Super Market Stores Operating Services
N.A.I.C.S.: 445110
Fidel Murillo (Gen Mgr)

INVERSIONES PRYCA, S.A. (2)
Calle Campezo 16, Madrid, 28022, Spain
Tel.: (34) 913018900
Super Market Stores Operating Services
N.A.I.C.S.: 445110

VIAJES CARREFOUR, S.L.U. (2)
Burgos Km 14500, 28108, Alcobendas,
Spain **(100%)**
Tel.: (34) 916630900
Web Site: http://www.viajes.carrefour.es
Travel Agency
N.A.I.C.S.: 561510

**Champion Supermarches France
SAS** (1)
4 Rue Brest, 35000, Rennes, France
Tel.: (33) 299592893
Sales Range: $25-49.9 Million
Emp.: 5
Super Market Stores Operating Services
N.A.I.C.S.: 445110

DISTRIVAL SA (1)
9 Rue Louis Pasteur, 26000, Valence,
France
Tel.: (33) 475800881
Soft Drink Distr
N.A.I.C.S.: 424490

ED SAS (1)
120 rue du General Malleret Joinville, Vitry-
sur-Seine, 94405, France
Tel.: (33) 1 47 18 17 17
Super Market Stores Operating Services
N.A.I.C.S.: 445110

FALDIS SA (1)
167 Rue Neuve Grange, 88000, Epinal,
France
Tel.: (33) 329641313
Super Market Stores Operating Services
N.A.I.C.S.: 445110

Flortine (1)
Avenue Des Peupliers, 27400, Louviers,
France **(100%)**
Tel.: (33) 2 32 25 93 03
Supermarket Operating Services
N.A.I.C.S.: 445110

GEDEL SARL (1)
Avenue De Madrazes, 24200, Sarlat-la-
Caneda, France
Tel.: (33) 553592453
Super Market Stores Operating Services
N.A.I.C.S.: 445110

GENEDIS SAS (1)
Zone Industrielle Route de Paris, 14120,
Mondeville, France
Tel.: (33) 2 31 70 60 00
Hypermarket & Supermarket Stores Operat-
ing Services
N.A.I.C.S.: 445110

GUILVIDIS (1)
Zone Industrielle Route De Paris, 14120,
Mondeville, France
Tel.: (33) 298581884
Super Market Stores Operating Services
N.A.I.C.S.: 445110

Greenweez SAS (1)
301 rue des Marais, Saint-Jorioz, 74410,
Annecy, France
Tel.: (33) 486139110
Web Site: http://www.greenweez.com
Electronic Shopping Services
N.A.I.C.S.: 445110

Guyenne et Gascogne SA (1)
60 avenue du Capitaine Resplandy, 64 101,
Bayonne, Cedex, France

Tel.: (33) 559445500
Web Site:
  http://www.guyenneetgascogne.com
Sales Range: $500-549.9 Million
Emp.: 2,047
Food-Based Retail Group Operating Hyper-
markets & Supermarkets
N.A.I.C.S.: 445110
Marc Leguillette (Sec)

HYPERDEMA SA (1)
C/O Daniel Schneuwly Avocat Rue De
Romont 35, Fribourg, 1700, Switzerland
Tel.: (41) 263472222
Super Market Stores Operating Services
N.A.I.C.S.: 445110

Hyparlo S.A. (1)
100 route de Paris, BP 51, 69751, Char-
bonnieres, Cedex, France
Tel.: (33) 4 7259 2097
Web Site: http://www.hyparlo.fr
Emp.: 4,792
Supermarket Operator
N.A.I.C.S.: 445110
Jean-Michel Arlaud (Vice Chm & Mng Dir)

IMMODIS (1)
180 rue Garibaldi, 76300, Sotteville-les-
Rouen, France
Tel.: (33) 2 32 18 22 88
Super Market Stores Operating Services
N.A.I.C.S.: 445110

IMOREAL (1)
90 rue Sierck, 57480, Rettel, France
Tel.: (33) 3 82 83 70 67
Supermarket Store Operator
N.A.I.C.S.: 445110

Immobiliere Carrefour S.A.S. (1)
Route De Paris, BP 186, 14120, Mondev-
ille, Calvados, France
Tel.: (33) 231706000
Real Estate Acquisition & Development
Services
N.A.I.C.S.: 531390

Interdis SNC (1)
Zone Industrielle Route De Paris, 14120,
Mondeville, France **(100%)**
Tel.: (33) 169193000
Super Market Stores Operating Services
N.A.I.C.S.: 445110

LODIAF S.A. (1)
Avenue des Peupliers, 27400, Louviers,
France
Tel.: (33) 232259303
Supermarket Operating Services
N.A.I.C.S.: 445110

La Chartreuse (1)
Rue Saint Georges, Cahors,
France **(100%)**
Tel.: (33) 565351737
Home Management Services
N.A.I.C.S.: 721110

Lefaubas (1)
Zone Industrielle Route De Paris, 14120,
Mondeville, France **(100%)**
Tel.: (33) 545781933
Supermarket Operating Services
N.A.I.C.S.: 445110

Logdis SAS (1)
Avenue Gabriel Voisin, 13300, Salon-de-
Provence, France **(100%)**
Tel.: (33) 4 90 17 20 00
Super Market Stores Operating Services
N.A.I.C.S.: 445110

MAICHE DISTRIBUTION SA (1)
Place Du Champ De Foire, 25120, Maiche,
Doubs, France
Tel.: (33) 381643060
Super Market Stores Operating Services
N.A.I.C.S.: 445110

Maison Johanes Boubee SAS (1)
1 Rue De Grassi, 33006, Bordeaux, France
Tel.: (33) 556488787
Wine Distr
N.A.I.C.S.: 424820

Montel Distribution SA (1)
Quartier Saint Christophe, 04000, Digne-
les-Bains, France
Tel.: (33) 4 92 36 63 36
Web Site: http://www.montel-distribution.fr

Carrefour SA—(Continued)

Food Whslr & Distr
N.A.I.C.S.: 445298

OOSHOP (1)
Zone Industrielle Route De Paris, 14120, Mondeville, France
Tel.: (33) 146852031
Super Market Stores Operating Services
N.A.I.C.S.: 445110

PHILIBERT SARL (1)
12 Rue De La Grange, 67000, Strasbourg, France
Tel.: (33) 388326535
Toy Stores Operating Services
N.A.I.C.S.: 459120

PHIVETOL SA (1)
Zone Industrielle Route De Paris, Mondeville, 14120, France
Tel.: (33) 233321813
Supermarket Operating Services
N.A.I.C.S.: 445110

POULAIN DISTRIBUTION (1)
Zone Industrielle Rue De La Belle Jardiniere, Equeurdreville-Hainneville, 50120, France
Tel.: (33) 233034874
Industrial Equipment Whsr
N.A.I.C.S.: 423830
Pauline Jacques (Gen Mgr)

PRODIM SAS (1)
Zone Industrielle Les Estroublans 29 Boulevard De L Europe, BP 30216, 13746, Vitrolles, France
Tel.: (33) 4 42 10 88 00
Cleaning Equipment Distr
N.A.I.C.S.: 423850

PROFIDIS (1)
Route De Paris, Mondeville, 14120, France
Tel.: (33) 2 31 70 60 00
Financial Services
N.A.I.C.S.: 523999

PROMOHYPERMARKT AG (1)
C/O Daniel Schneuwly Rue De Romont 35, Fribourg, 1700, Switzerland
Tel.: (41) 263471630
Hypermarket & Supermarket Stores Operating Services
N.A.I.C.S.: 445110

PT Alfa Retailindo Tbk (1)
Jl Lodan Street No 80-81 Cikokol, Jakarta, 14430, Indonesia
Tel.: (62) 21 690 9080
Grocery Whslr
N.A.I.C.S.: 445110

QUERCY (1)
Zac Des Grands Camps, 46090, Mercues, France
Tel.: (33) 565303905
Supermarket Operating Services
N.A.I.C.S.: 445110

ROTONDE (1)
105 Boulevard du Montparnasse, 75006, Paris, Ile-de-France, France
Tel.: (33) 143266884
Super Market Stores Operating Services
N.A.I.C.S.: 445110

Rue du Commerce SAS (1)
44/50 Avenue du Capitaine Glarner, 93400, Saint-Ouen, France (100%)
Tel.: (33) 892465666
Web Site: http://www.rueducommerce.fr
Ecommerce Services
N.A.I.C.S.: 425120

S.D.O (1)
13 Allee Du Clos Des Charmes, Collegien, 77090, France
Tel.: (33) 160060045
Super Market Stores Operating Services
N.A.I.C.S.: 445110

S.L.M. DISTRIBUTION (1)
Rte de Paris, 14120, Mondeville, France
Tel.: (33) 2 31 84 44 37
Plumbing & Heating Equipment Distr
N.A.I.C.S.: 423720

SOBRECO (1)
25 Avenue Florissant, 74100, Annemasse, France

Tel.: (33) 450950874
Super Market Stores Operating Services
N.A.I.C.S.: 445110

SODITA (1)
1 Chemin De Geles, 33320, Le Taillan-Medoc, France
Tel.: (33) 556576363
Supermarket Operating Services
N.A.I.C.S.: 445110

SOREDIS SA (1)
Rue De Sierck, 57480, Rettel, France
Tel.: (33) 3 82 83 70 67
Web Site: http://www.soredis.com
Super Market Stores Operating Services
N.A.I.C.S.: 445110

STEMA SNC (1)
15 Cours Gambetta, Montpellier, 34000, France
Tel.: (33) 467926010
Super Market Stores Operating Services
N.A.I.C.S.: 445110

STROFI SA (1)
Zone Industrielle Route De Paris, Mondeville, 14120, France
Tel.: (33) 235200764
Super Market Stores Operating Services
N.A.I.C.S.: 445110

SUPERDIS SA (1)
Zone Industrielle Le Vaillant Lot N 13 2 Rue Jean Moulin, Le Bourget, 93350, France
Tel.: (33) 148364544
Real Estate Manangement Services
N.A.I.C.S.: 531390

Shanghai Global Sourcing Consulting Co., Ltd. (1)
10E Huamin Empire Plaza 726 Yan An West Road, Shanghai, 200050, China
Tel.: (86) 2162121515
Web Site: http://www.gsc-china.com
Electronic Machinery Equipment Mfr
N.A.I.C.S.: 334111

So.bio SAS (1)
Batiment I Parc Espace France 4 voie romaine, 33610, Canejan, France
Tel.: (33) 557103040
Web Site: http://www.sobio.fr
Food Products Distr
N.A.I.C.S.: 445110

Soessardis Sarl (1)
Rue Rouen, 95420, Magny-en-Vexin, France
Tel.: (33) 1 34 67 36 30
Super Market Stores Operating Services
N.A.I.C.S.: 445110

Soval SA (1)
78 Rue Gabriel Peri, Dombasle-sur-Meurthe, 54110, France (100%)
Tel.: (33) 383482320
Super Market Stores Operating Services
N.A.I.C.S.: 445110

Supeco Investment SRL (1)
Strada Barbu Vacarescu nr 154 - 158 magazin Carrefour Market Barbu, Vacarescu etaj 2 Sector 2, Bucharest, 020284, Romania
Tel.: (40) 212023883
Web Site: http://www.supeco.ro
Food Products Distr
N.A.I.C.S.: 445110

VIADIX SAS (1)
Zone Industrielle Route De Paris, Mondeville, 14120, France
Tel.: (33) 490257681
Super Market Stores Operating Services
N.A.I.C.S.: 445110

CARREFOURSA CARREFOUR SABANCI TICARET MERKEZI A.S.
CarrefourSA Plaza Cevizli Mahallesi Tugay Yolu Caddesi No 67 A Blok B, Maltepe, Istanbul, Turkiye
Tel.: (90) 2166550000　　TR
Web Site:
　https://www.carrefoursa.com
Year Founded: 1963
CRFSA—(IST)
Sales Range: $900-999.9 Million

Supermarket Operator
N.A.I.C.S.: 445110
Laurent Charles Rene Vallee (Deputy Chm)

CARRIANNA GROUP HOLDINGS COMPANY LIMITED
26/F Wyler Centre Phase II, 200 Tai Lin Pai Road, Kwai Chung, New Territories, China (Hong Kong)
Tel.: (852) 2 426 1021
Web Site: http://www.carrianna.com
0126—(HKG)
Rev.: $100,755,307
Assets: $913,387,348
Liabilities: $387,354,671
Net Worth: $526,032,677
Earnings: $3,238,817
Emp.: 1,400
Fiscal Year-end: 03/31/22
Property Investment & Development Services
N.A.I.C.S.: 531312
John Hung Ming Ma (Vice Chm)

Subsidiaries:

Carrianna (Chiu Chow) Restaurant Limited (1)
1/F 151 Gloucester Road, Wanchai, China (Hong Kong)
Tel.: (852) 25111282
Restaurant Management Services
N.A.I.C.S.: 722511

CARRIE ARRAN RESOURCES INC.
141 Adelaide Street West Suite 301, Toronto, M5H 3L5, ON, Canada
Tel.: (416) 628-5940　　Ca
Metal Mining Services
N.A.I.C.S.: 212290

CARRIESOFT CO., LTD.
1101 20 Digitalro 31-gil, Guro-Gu, Seoul, Korea (South)
Tel.: (82) 222891452
Web Site: https://www.carriesoft.com
Year Founded: 2014
317530—(KRS)
Rev.: $7,737,521
Assets: $11,464,353
Liabilities: $2,945,089
Net Worth: $8,519,264
Earnings: ($1,077,197)
Emp.: 51
Fiscal Year-end: 12/31/22
Animated Cartoon Production Services
N.A.I.C.S.: 512110
Johnson Zhao (Sls Mgr)

CARROLL SOUTH SHORE MOTORS INC.
15133 Hebbville Highway, PO Box 306, Bridgewater, B4V 2W9, NS, Canada
Tel.: (902) 543-2493
Web Site:
　http://www.carrollsouthshore.ns.ca
Year Founded: 1926
Rev.: $19,896,146
Emp.: 41
New & Used Car Dealers
N.A.I.C.S.: 441110
Adam Gladwin (Gen Mgr)

CARRY WEALTH HOLDINGS LIMITED
2001 20th Floor Shui On Centre 6-8 Harbour Road, Wanchai, China (Hong Kong)
Tel.: (852) 23108180
Web Site:
　http://www.carrywealth.com
0643—(HKG)
Rev.: $63,625,560

Assets: $32,477,565
Liabilities: $17,393,678
Net Worth: $15,083,888
Earnings: ($972,188)
Emp.: 488
Fiscal Year-end: 12/31/22
Apparel Product Mfr
N.A.I.C.S.: 315900
Haifeng Li (Chm & CEO)

Subsidiaries:

Carry Wealth Limited (1)
Room 2701 27F One Kowloon 1 Wang Yuen Street, Kowloon Bay, Kowloon, China (Hong Kong)
Tel.: (852) 23108180
Sales Range: $25-49.9 Million
Emp.: 100
Apparel Product Mfr
N.A.I.C.S.: 315120

PT Aneka Garmentama Indah (1)
Jl Raya Cakung Cilincing Blok F 3-4, 10310, Jakarta, Indonesia (95%)
Tel.: (62) 214404224
Broadwoven Fabric Mills
N.A.I.C.S.: 313210

PT Caterindo Garment Industri (1)
Jl Nusantara II Blok E 2-3, Tanjung Priuk, 14310, Jakarta, Indonesia (95%)
Tel.: (62) 214356070
Men's & Boys' Clothing Mfr
N.A.I.C.S.: 315250

Topwell Group Development Ltd (1)
Room 2701 27F One Kowloon 1 Wang Yuen Street, Kowloon Bay, Kowloon, China (Hong Kong)
Tel.: (852) 23108180
Sales Range: $25-49.9 Million
Emp.: 100
Apparel Product Mfr
N.A.I.C.S.: 315120
James Le (Mgr)

CARS GALORE LTD.
Melton Court Gibson Lane, Melton, HU14 3HH, East Yorkshire, United Kingdom
Tel.: (44) 1482638499
Web Site:
　http://www.carsgaloreonline.co.uk
Year Founded: 2005
Sales Range: $25-49.9 Million
Emp.: 6
Used Automobile Purchasing & Retailing Services
N.A.I.C.S.: 423110
Noel Parkinson (Founder & Mng Dir)

CARSALES.COM LIMITED
449 Punt Road, Locked Bag 9001, Richmond, 3121, VIC, Australia
Tel.: (61) 390938600
Web Site:
　https://www.carsales.com.au
Year Founded: 1997
CAR—(OTCIQ)
Rev.: $327,288,785
Assets: $891,531,788
Liabilities: $170,929,327
Net Worth: $720,602,461
Earnings: $100,533,322
Emp.: 1,200
Fiscal Year-end: 06/30/21
Online Motor Vehicle Advertising Services
N.A.I.C.S.: 541890
Cameron McIntyre (CEO)

Subsidiaries:

Automotive Data Services Pty. Ltd. (1)
449 Punt Road, Locked Bag 9001, Richmond, 3121, VIC, Australia
Tel.: (61) 1300671378
Web Site: https://www.redbook.com.au
Sales Range: $25-49.9 Million
Emp.: 20
Data Processing Services
N.A.I.C.S.: 518210

Russ Booth (Gen Mgr)

Discount Vehicles Australia Pty Ltd (1)
Level 4 449 Punt Road, Locked Bag 9001, Richmond, 3121, VIC, Australia
Tel.: (61) 39 093 8791
Web Site:
https://www.discountnewcars.au
Car Dealing Services
N.A.I.C.S.: 441110

Equipment Research Group Pty. Ltd. (1)
Level 4 449 Punt Road, Richmond, 3122, VIC, Australia
Tel.: (61) 390938600
Web Site:
http://www.erginternational.com.au
Sales Range: $25-49.9 Million
Emp.: 200
Business Management Services
N.A.I.C.S.: 541611

Red Book Automotive Data Services (Beijing) Limited (1)
6F Suite 602-1 602-2 Fairmont Tower Building 1, No 33 Guangshun North Avenue Chaoyang District, Beijing, 100037, China
Tel.: (86) 1085235568
Sales Range: $25-49.9 Million
Emp.: 7
Data Processing Services
N.A.I.C.S.: 518210

Red Book Automotive Services (M) Sdn. Bhd. (1)
A 10 5 Northpoint Offices Mid Vly City No 1 Medan Syed Putra Utara, Kuala Lumpur, 59200, Malaysia
Tel.: (60) 322824599
Web Site:
http://www.redbookasiapacific.com
Sales Range: $25-49.9 Million
Emp.: 5
Data Processing Services
N.A.I.C.S.: 518210
Oani Nazlan (Mgr-Sls)

CARSGEN THERAPEUTICS HOLDINGS LIMITED
CMC Preparation Center Building 12 No 388 Yindu Road, Xuhui District, Shanghai, China   Ky
Web Site: https://www.carsgen.com
Year Founded: 2014
2171—(HKG)
Rev.: $7,827,869
Assets: $312,529,630
Liabilities: $63,069,617
Net Worth: $249,460,013
Earnings: ($103,538,159)
Emp.: 516
Fiscal Year-end: 12/31/23
Holding Company
N.A.I.C.S.: 551112
Huamao Wang (COO)

CARSOME SDN. BHD.
Level 9 KYM Tower No 8 Jalan PJU 7/6, Mutiara Damansara, Petaling Jaya, 47800, Malaysia
Tel.: (60) 323301515
Web Site: http://www.carsome.my
Year Founded: 2015
Car Dealers & E-commerce Platform
N.A.I.C.S.: 441110
Melanie Mei (Head-Mktg)

Subsidiaries:

iCar Asia Limited (1)
Suite 18 01 Level 18 Centerpoint North Tower, Mid Valley City Lingkaran Syed Putra, 59200, Kuala Lumpur, Malaysia (100%)
Tel.: (60) 3 2776 6000
Web Site: http://www.icarasia.com
Rev.: $10,769,373
Assets: $29,867,060
Liabilities: $9,472,951
Net Worth: $20,394,109
Earnings: ($8,174,112)
Emp.: 394
Fiscal Year-end: 12/31/2020

Online Motor Vehicle Classified Advertising & Websites
N.A.I.C.S.: 541890
Hamish Stone (CEO)

CARSON CUMBERBATCH PLC
Tel.: (94) 112039200
Web Site:
https://www.cumberbatch.com
CARS—(COL)
Rev.: $908,095,405
Assets: $1,495,906,360
Liabilities: $878,450,987
Net Worth: $617,455,373
Earnings: $79,445,230
Emp.: 13,407
Fiscal Year-end: 03/31/22
Investment Holding Company
N.A.I.C.S.: 551112
Hariharan Selvanathan (Deputy Chm & CEO-Grp-Plantations, Oils & Fats)

Subsidiaries:

Agro Harapan Lestar (Private) Limited (1)
Level 20 East Tower World Trade Centre Echelon Square, Colombo, Sri Lanka
Tel.: (94) 114357777
Management Services
N.A.I.C.S.: 561110

Carsons Management Services (Private) Limited (1)
Investment Management Service
N.A.I.C.S.: 523999

Ceylon Guardian Investment Trust PLC (1)
No 61 Janadhipathi Mawatha, 1, Colombo, 1, Sri Lanka
Tel.: (94) 112039200
Rev.: $2,829,820
Assets: $87,684,799
Liabilities: $1,867,768
Net Worth: $85,817,031
Earnings: ($12,796,433)
Emp.: 20
Fiscal Year-end: 03/31/2019
Investment Management Service
N.A.I.C.S.: 523940

Ceylon Investment PLC (1)
No 61 Janadhipathi Mawatha, 1, Colombo, 1, Sri Lanka
Tel.: (94) 114739200
Rev.: $1,241,806
Assets: $36,943,305
Liabilities: $2,023,121
Net Worth: $34,920,183
Earnings: ($3,523,584)
Fiscal Year-end: 03/31/2020
Investment Management Service
N.A.I.C.S.: 523940

Equity One PLC (1)
No 61 Janadhipathi Mawatha, 01, Colombo, Sri Lanka
Tel.: (94) 112039200
Sales Range: Less than $1 Million
Emp.: 15
Property Development & Management Services
N.A.I.C.S.: 531312

Equity Two PLC (1)
61 Janadhipathi Mawatha, 1, Colombo, 01, Sri Lanka
Tel.: (94) 112039200
Rev.: $486,389
Assets: $6,665,983
Liabilities: $1,634,799
Net Worth: $5,031,184
Earnings: $337,818
Emp.: 6
Fiscal Year-end: 03/31/2023
Real Estate Services
N.A.I.C.S.: 531390
Ajith Prashantha Weeratunge (Exec Dir)

Galle Face Capital Partners PLC (1)
No 61 Janadhipathi Mawatha, Colombo, 01, Sri Lanka
Tel.: (94) 112039200
Web Site:
http://www.carsoncumberbatch.com
Rev.: $106,625
Assets: $4,339,943

Liabilities: $94,802
Net Worth: $4,245,141
Earnings: $1,433,724
Fiscal Year-end: 03/31/2024
Investment Management Service
N.A.I.C.S.: 523940

Good Hope PLC (1)
61 Janadhipathi Mawatha, 1, Colombo, 1, Sri Lanka
Tel.: (94) 112039200
Rev.: $24,157
Assets: $42,584,501
Liabilities: $107,057
Net Worth: $42,477,444
Earnings: $12,623
Fiscal Year-end: 03/31/2023
Crude Palm Oil Mfr
N.A.I.C.S.: 311225

Goodhope Asia Holdings Ltd (1)
No 1 Kim Seng Promenade 15-04 Great World City East Tower, Singapore, 237994, Singapore
Tel.: (65) 66900120
Palm Oil Processing Services
N.A.I.C.S.: 311225
Sanjaya Upasena (COO-Oil Palm Plantations Segment & Dir)

Subsidiary (Non-US):

Agro Harapan Lestari Sdn. Bhd. (2)
Suite 3 02 3rd Floor Wisma E and C 2 Lorong Dungun Kiri, Damansara Heights, Kuala Lumpur, 50490, Malaysia
Tel.: (60) 320934660
Web Site: http://www.goodhopeasia.com
Emp.: 50
Palm Oil Plantation Services
N.A.I.C.S.: 311224

PT Agro Harapan Lestari (2)
Menara Global Building 5th Floor Jl Jend Gatot Subroto Kav 27, Jakarta, 12950, Indonesia
Tel.: (62) 21 52892260
Web Site: http://www.goodhopeasia.com
Palm Oil Plantation Services
N.A.I.C.S.: 311224

Subsidiary (Domestic):

PT Agro Indomas (3)
Jalan P Antasari II No 26, PO Box 233, Sampit, Central Kalimantan, Indonesia
Tel.: (62) 542593560
Palm Oil Plantation Services
N.A.I.C.S.: 115112

Indo-Malay PLC (1)
61 Janadhipathi Mawatha, 1, Colombo, 1, Sri Lanka
Tel.: (94) 112039200
Rev.: $129,734
Assets: $56,747,530
Liabilities: $308,730
Net Worth: $56,438,800
Earnings: $118,918
Fiscal Year-end: 03/31/2022
Crude Palm Oil Mfr
N.A.I.C.S.: 311225

Luxury Brands (Private) Limited (1)
No 254 Colombo Road, 11650, Biyagama, Sri Lanka
Tel.: (94) 778065814
Web Site: https://www.luxurybrands.lk
Beer, Wine & Spirit Distr
N.A.I.C.S.: 424810

Pegasus Hotels of Ceylon PLC (1)
No 61 Janadhipathi Mawatha, 1, Colombo, 01, Sri Lanka
Tel.: (94) 112039200
Rev.: $2,395,946
Assets: $9,394,504
Liabilities: $3,243,211
Net Worth: $6,151,293
Earnings: ($303,425)
Emp.: 241
Fiscal Year-end: 03/31/2023
Hotel Services
N.A.I.C.S.: 721110
D. Chandima Rajakaruna Gunawardena (Chm)

Premium Oils & Fats Sdn. Bhd. (1)
Suite 6 03 Level 6 Wisma UOA Damansara II 6 Changkat Semantan, Damansara Heights, 50490, Kuala Lumpur, Malaysia

Tel.: (60) 320826200
Edible Oil & Fat Refining Services
N.A.I.C.S.: 311225

Premium Vegitable Oils Sdn. Bhd. (1)
PLO 66 Jalan Timah Dua Pasir Gudang Industrial Estate, PO Box 39, 81707, Pasir Gudang, Johor, Malaysia
Tel.: (60) 72596699
Web Site: http://www.premiumveg.com
Edible Oil & Fat Refining Services
N.A.I.C.S.: 311225

Selinsing PLC (1)
61 Janadhipathi Mawatha, 1, Colombo, 1, Sri Lanka
Tel.: (94) 112039200
Rev.: $165,170
Assets: $60,114,159
Liabilities: $202,953
Net Worth: $59,911,207
Earnings: $149,582
Fiscal Year-end: 03/31/2022
Crude Palm Oil Producer
N.A.I.C.S.: 311225
Hariharan Selvanathan (Deputy Chm)

Shalimar (Malay) PLC (1)
61 Janadhipathi Mawatha, 1, Colombo, 1, Sri Lanka
Tel.: (94) 112039200
Rev.: $5,212
Assets: $43,021,875
Liabilities: $1,187
Net Worth: $43,020,688
Earnings: ($1,348)
Fiscal Year-end: 03/31/2023
Crude Palm Oil Producer
N.A.I.C.S.: 311225

CARSON RIVER VENTURES CORP.
Suite 820 -1130 West Pender Street, Vancouver, V6E 4A4, BC, Canada
Tel.: (778) 839-2909   BC
Year Founded: 2021
CRIV—(CNSX)
Assets: $758,040
Liabilities: $69,240
Net Worth: $688,800
Earnings: ($315,296)
Fiscal Year-end: 09/30/23
Mineral Exploration Services
N.A.I.C.S.: 212220
Jeff Cocks (Pres & CEO)

CARTAMUNDI N.V.
Visbeekstraat 22, 2300, Turnhout, Belgium
Tel.: (32) 14 42 0201
Web Site: http://www.cartamundi.com
Year Founded: 1970
Sales Range: $100-124.9 Million
Emp.: 2,200
Playing Card & Board Game Mfr & Distr
N.A.I.C.S.: 339930
Chris Van Doorslaer (CEO)

Subsidiaries:

ASS/ Spielkartenfabrik Altenburg GmbH (1)
Leipziger Strasse 7, 04600, Altenburg, Germany
Tel.: (49) 34475820
Web Site: https://www.spielkarten.com
Game Product Retailer
N.A.I.C.S.: 339930

Carta Mundi Asia Pacific Pte. Ltd. (1)
114 Lavender Street CT Hub 2, 238729, Singapore, Singapore (100%)
Tel.: (65) 62273292
Sales Range: $25-49.9 Million
Emp.: 10
Game Toy & Childrens Vehicle Mfr
N.A.I.C.S.: 339930
Stefan Magnus (Mng Dir)

Carta Mundi Hungary Kft. (1)
Maros street 12, 1122, Budapest, Hungary (100%)

Cartamundi N.V.—(Continued)
Tel.: (36) 13189430
Sales Range: $50-74.9 Million
Emp.: 3
Durable Goods Whslr
N.A.I.C.S.: 423990

Carta Mundi UK Ltd. (1)
Units 8-17 Sandhurst Kings Rd, Charfleets
Industrial Est, Oanvey, 338OQY, Essex,
United Kingdom (100%)
Tel.: (44) 1268511522
Web Site: http://www.cartamundi.co.uk
Sales Range: $25-49.9 Million
Emp.: 30
Retailers Stores
N.A.I.C.S.: 459999
Paul Roberts *(Mng Dir)*

Carta Mundi, Inc. (1)
4809 S Westmoreland Rd, Dallas, TX
75237-1619
Tel.: (423) 279-9200
Web Site: http://www.cartamundiusa.com
Sales Range: $50-74.9 Million
Emp.: 100
Playing Card Mfr
N.A.I.C.S.: 423920
Michael Szul *(VP)*

Cartamundi - Digital NV (1)
Deinsesteenweg 108b, 9031, Drongen,
Belgium
Tel.: (32) 92260907
Web Site: https://cartamundi-digital.com
Gambling Services
N.A.I.C.S.: 713290

Cartamundi Espana, S.L. (1)
Calle Salvador Pau 32-bajo, 46021, Valen-
cia, Spain
Tel.: (34) 963696601
Web Site: https://cartamundi.es
Playing Card Mfr
N.A.I.C.S.: 323111

Cartamundi Italy SA (1)
Viale Garibaldi 46/B, Mestre, 30173, Ven-
ice, Italy
Tel.: (39) 0418501274
Web Site: https://cartamundi.it
Playing Card Mfr
N.A.I.C.S.: 323111

Cartamundi Nordic AB (1)
Torshamnsgatan 35, 164 40, Kista, Sweden
Tel.: (46) 851443640
Web Site: https://cartamundi.se
Playing Card Mfr
N.A.I.C.S.: 323111

Cartamundi North America East
Longmeadow LLC (1)
443 Shaker Rd, East Longmeadow, MA
01028
Tel.: (413) 526-2000
Playing Card Mfr
N.A.I.C.S.: 323111

Cartamundi Polska Sp. z o.o. (1)
Pollanki 18, 30-740, Krakow, Poland
Tel.: (48) 122962170
Web Site: https://cartamundi.pl
Playing Card Mfr
N.A.I.C.S.: 323111
Robert Gasiorek *(Acct Mgr)*

Copag da Amazonia S.A. (1)
Av Eng Luis Carlos Berrini 1645-3rd floor,
Sao Paulo, 04571-011, Brazil
Tel.: (55) 1121643650
Playing Card Mfr
N.A.I.C.S.: 323111

Japan Card Products Co., Ltd. (1)
1-11-1 Inari, Soka, Saitama, Japan
Tel.: (81) 489312421
Web Site: https://www.cardproducts.com
Paper Toy Mfr
N.A.I.C.S.: 339930

Konigsfurt Urania Verlag GmbH (1)
Ringstrasse 32, 24103, Kiel, Germany
Tel.: (49) 4315470940
Web Site: https://www.koenigsfurt-
urania.com
Card Deck & Set Mfr
N.A.I.C.S.: 322230

Parksons Cartamundi Pvt. Ltd. (1)

Unit No 701/A 7th Floor Indiabulls Finance
Centre - Tower 1, Senapati Bapat Marg El-
phinstone Road, Mumbai, 400 013, India
Tel.: (91) 2266245221
Web Site:
    https://www.parksonscartamundi.com
Playing Card Mfr & Distr
N.A.I.C.S.: 323111

Spielkartenfabrik Altenburg
GmbH (1)
Leipziger Strasse 7, Altenburg, 04600,
Leipzig, Germany
Tel.: (49) 34475820
Web Site: http://www.spielkarten.com
Sales Range: $50-74.9 Million
Emp.: 125
Game Toy & Childrens Vehicle Mfr
N.A.I.C.S.: 339930

The United States Playing Card
Company (1)
300 Gap Way, Erlanger, KY 41018
Tel.: (800) 543-2273
Web Site: http://www.usplayingcard.com
Playing Cards, Games & Playing Cards Ac-
cessories Mfr
N.A.I.C.S.: 339930
Michael Slaughter *(Pres)*

CARTE INTERNATIONAL INC.
1995 Logan Avenue, Winnipeg, R2R
0H8, MB, Canada
Tel.: (204) 633-7220
Web Site: https://carte.ca
Year Founded: 1973
Rev.: $36,516,879
Emp.: 200
Electrical Utilities Mfr & Distr
N.A.I.C.S.: 334416
Brian Klaponski *(Pres & CEO)*

CARTER DODGE CHRYSLER
LTD
4650 Lougheed Highway, Burnaby,
V5C 4A6, BC, Canada
Tel.: (604) 299-9181
Web Site:
    http://www.carterdodgechrysler.com
New & Used Car Dealer
N.A.I.C.S.: 441110
Sadhu Thiara *(Gen Mgr)*

CARTER MOTOR CARS LTD
2390 Burrard Street, Vancouver, V6J
3J1, BC, Canada
Tel.: (604) 736-2821
Web Site:
    https://www.carterhonda.com
Year Founded: 1984
Rev.: $59,731,181
Emp.: 115
New & Used Car Dealers
N.A.I.C.S.: 441110
Geoff Jessup *(Gen Mgr)*

CARTIER RESOURCES INC.
1740 Chemin Sullivan bureau 1000,
Val d'Or, J9P 7H1, QC, Canada
Tel.: (819) 874-1331
Web Site:
    https://www.ressourcescartier.com
Year Founded: 2006
6CA—(DEU)
Rev.: $106,157
Assets: $35,689,456
Liabilities: $3,885,006
Net Worth: $31,804,450
Earnings: ($1,048,039)
Fiscal Year-end: 12/31/23
Mineral Exploration Services
N.A.I.C.S.: 213114
Philippe Cloutier *(Pres & CEO)*

CARTIER SAADA
285-291 Industrial Zone Sidi Ghanem, 40110, Marrakech, Morocco
Tel.: (212) 524336868
Web Site:
    https://www.cartiersaada.com

Year Founded: 1947
CRS—(CAS)
Sales Range: $10-24.9 Million
Food Preservation Services
N.A.I.C.S.: 424480
Hassan Debbarh *(Gen Mgr)*

CARTIER SILVER CORPORA-
TION
20 Adelaide Street East Suite 200,
Toronto, M5C 2T6, ON, Canada
Tel.: (416) 360-8006
Web Site:
    https://cartiersilvercorp.com
CRTIF—(OTCIQ)
Assets: $9,026,348
Liabilities: $1,115,223
Net Worth: $7,911,124
Earnings: ($3,464,522)
Fiscal Year-end: 12/31/22
Iron Ore Mining
N.A.I.C.S.: 212210
Miles Nagamatsu *(CFO)*

CARTIERA LUCCHESE S.P.A.
Via Ciarpi 77, Lu, 55016, Porcari,
Italy   IT
Tel.: (39) 0583 2140
Web Site: http://www.lucartgroup.com
Year Founded: 1953
Sales Range: $550-599.9 Million
Emp.: 1,400
Machine-Glazed Packaging Paper,
Tissue Paper & Converted Paper
Products Mfr & Distr
N.A.I.C.S.: 322120
Massimo Pasquini *(CEO)*

Subsidiaries:

Airtissue S.r.l. (1)
Via Boccardo 1, IT-16121, Genoa,
Italy (100%)
Tel.: (39) 010 55411
Web Site: http://www.tenderly.it
Sales Range: $125-149.9 Million
Emp.: 300
Tissue Paper Products Mfr
N.A.I.C.S.: 322291

Fato Professional S.p.A. (1)
Via Galileo Galilei 4, Torre di Mosto, IT-
30020, Santo Stino di Livenza, VE,
Italy (100%)
Tel.: (39) 0390421 312 811
Web Site: http://www.fato.com
Converted Machine-Glazed Packaging &
Tissue Paper Products Mfr
N.A.I.C.S.: 322299

Lucart Iberica S.L.U. (1)
Calle Trafalgar 4 10th andar, Barcelona,
8010, Spain (100%)
Tel.: (34) 93 268 0440
Paper Product Whslr
N.A.I.C.S.: 424130

Lucart SAS (1)
10 Rue Maurice Mougeot, BP 35, F-88600,
Laval, France (100%)
Tel.: (33) 3 2955 7878
Web Site: http://www.novatissue.com
Sales Range: $75-99.9 Million
Emp.: 230
Tissue Paper & Converted Tissue Paper
Products Mfr
N.A.I.C.S.: 322120

CARTRADE TECH LTD.
12th Floor Vishwaroop It Park S Pra-
navanandji Marg Sector 30A, Vashi,
Navi Mumbai, 400705, Maharashtra,
India
Tel.: (91) 2267398888
Web Site:
    https://www.cartradetech.com
Year Founded: 2000
CARTRADE—(NSE)
Rev.: $48,996,702
Assets: $311,324,095
Liabilities: $28,174,938
Net Worth: $283,149,157

Earnings: ($16,564,548)
Emp.: 542
Fiscal Year-end: 03/31/22
Car Dealer
N.A.I.C.S.: 441110
Vinay Sanghi *(Chm, CEO & Mng Dir)*

Subsidiaries:

Adroit Inspection Services Private
Limited (1)
H-182 1st Floor Sector 63, Noida, 201301,
Uttar Pradesh, India
Tel.: (91) 1204369000
Web Site: https://www.adroitauto.in
Emp.: 1,200
Automotive Inspection Services
N.A.I.C.S.: 811198
Jyoti Jain *(CEO)*

Shiram Automall India Limited (1)
7th Floor Best Business Park Netaji Sub-
hash Place, Pitampura, Delhi, 110034, India
Tel.: (91) 1141414444
Emp.: 1,400
Motor Vehicles Mfr
N.A.I.C.S.: 336110
Lakshmi Narayanan Subramanian *(Chm)*

CARTRIDGE SAVE LIMITED
5-6 Gregson Road, Stockport, SK5
7SS, United Kingdom
Tel.: (44) 161 968 5994
Web Site:
    http://www.cartridgesave.co.uk
Year Founded: 2003
Sales Range: $10-24.9 Million
Emp.: 33
Printer Cartridge Whslr
N.A.I.C.S.: 424120
Ian Cowley *(Mng Dir)*

CARTU GROUP JSC
39a Chavchavadze Avenue, Tbilisi,
0162, Georgia
Tel.: (995) 32 292 5592   GE
Sales Range: $100-124.9 Million
Emp.: 295
Bank Holding Company
N.A.I.C.S.: 551111
Nato Khaindrava *(Mgr-Fin)*

Subsidiaries:

Cartu Bank JSC (1)
39a I Chavchavadze Avenue, Tbilisi, 0162,
Georgia (100%)
Tel.: (995) 322008080
Web Site: http://www.cartubank.ge
Rev.: $32,834,338
Assets: $463,926,527
Liabilities: $351,689,501
Net Worth: $112,237,026
Earnings: $7,743,404
Emp.: 301
Fiscal Year-end: 12/31/2019
Retail & Commercial Banking
N.A.I.C.S.: 522110
Nato Khaindrava *(CEO)*

CARVAJAL EMPAQUES SA
Calle 29 Norte 6A-40, Cali, Colombia
Tel.: (57) 26612161
Web Site:
    http://www.carvajalempaques.com
PFCARPAK—(COLO)
Sales Range: Less than $1 Million
Packaging Services
N.A.I.C.S.: 561910
Pedro Felipe Carvajal Cabal *(CEO)*

CARVAJAL S.A.
Calle 29 Norte No 6A-40, Cali, Co-
lombia
Tel.: (57) 2 667 5011   Co
Web Site: http://www.carvajal.com
Investment Holding Company
N.A.I.C.S.: 551112
Ricardo Obregon Trujillo *(Chm &
Pres)*

Subsidiaries:

Carvajal Pulpa y Papel S.A.   (1)
Carretera Antigua A Yumbo Km 12, Apartado Aereo 4412, Yumbo Valle, Cali, Colombia   (83.78%)
Tel.: (57) 26698859
Web Site:
    http://www.carvajalpulpaypapel.com
Emp.: 950
Pulp & Paper Mill Operator
N.A.I.C.S.: 322120
Eugenio Castro Carvajal *(Pres)*

CARWOOD MOTOR UNITS LTD

Herald Way, Binley, Coventry, CV3 2RQ, United Kingdom
Tel.: (44) 2476449533
Web Site: http://www.carwood.co.uk
Year Founded: 1966
Rev.: $26,892,591
Emp.: 110
Vehicle Parts Mfr
N.A.I.C.S.: 336390
Gary Carter *(Founder & Chm)*

Subsidiaries:

Carwood (BDS) Motor Unit Ltd   (1)
5 Pexton Road, Kellythorpre Industrial Estate, Driffield, YO25 9DJ, United Kingdom
Tel.: (44) 1482212400
Automobile Parts Mfr
N.A.I.C.S.: 336390

Carwood (HK) Limited   (1)
Unit 10B 23rd Floor Cable TV Tower 9 Hoi Shing Road, Tsuen Wan, China (Hong Kong)
Tel.: (852) 24986427
Web Site: http://www.carwood.com.hk
Automobile Parts Distr
N.A.I.C.S.: 423120

Carwood (Rewind) Yeovil ltd   (1)
12 Buckland Rd, Pen Mill Trading Estate, Yeovil, BA21 5EA, Somerset, United Kingdom
Tel.: (44) 1935476255
Electrical Equipment Repair Services
N.A.I.C.S.: 811210

Carwood Motor Units Ltd - Ollerton Factory   (1)
Unit 1 & 2 Whitewater Place Maun Way, Boughton Industrial Estate South Newark-on-Trent, Ollerton, NG22 9ZD, Nottinghamshire, United Kingdom
Tel.: (44) 1623863600
Automotive Components Mfr
N.A.I.C.S.: 336390

CARYSIL LIMITED

A-702 7th floor Kanakia Wall Street Chakala Andheri Kurla Road, Andheri East, Mumbai, 400059, India
Tel.: (91) 9967073658
Web Site: https://www.carysil.com
524091—(BOM)
Rev.: $67,426,673
Assets: $75,529,845
Liabilities: $40,457,918
Net Worth: $35,071,928
Earnings: $8,907,512
Emp.: 539
Fiscal Year-end: 03/31/22
Kitchen Accessories Mfr & Distr
N.A.I.C.S.: 332215
Chirag A. Parekh *(Chm & Mng Dir)*

Subsidiaries:

United Granite LLC   (1)
15 Sage Ln, Fredericksburg, VA 22405-4525
Tel.: (540) 720-6600
Web Site:
    https://www.landmarksurfaces.com
Brick, Stone & Related Construction Material Merchant Whslr
N.A.I.C.S.: 423320

CAS CORPORATION

262 Geurugogaero Gwangjeokmy-eon, Yangju-si, Yangju, Gyeonggi-do, Korea (South)
Tel.: (82) 215775578
Web Site: https://www.globalcas.com
Year Founded: 1983
016920—(KRS)
Rev.: $129,134,266
Assets: $134,078,620
Liabilities: $86,922,296
Net Worth: $47,156,324
Earnings: $2,100,602
Emp.: 326
Fiscal Year-end: 12/31/22
Electronic Scale Mfr & Distr
N.A.I.C.S.: 333998

Subsidiaries:

CAS (Zhejiang) Electronics Co., Ltd.   (1)
No 99 Changjiang Road Hui Streets With Loose Hair House Community, Jiashan, Zhejiang, China
Tel.: (86) 57384599000
Electronic Scale Mfr
N.A.I.C.S.: 333998

CAS Corporation - CAS Chemical Factory   (1)
69 Chungjusandan 5-ro, Chungju, Chungcheongbuk-do, Korea (South)
Tel.: (82) 438417888
Electronic Scale Mfr
N.A.I.C.S.: 333998

CAS Corporation - Rutherford Branch   (1)
99 Murry Hill Pkwy, East Rutherford, NJ 07073
Tel.: (201) 933-9002
Electronic Scale Mfr
N.A.I.C.S.: 333998

CAS Polska Sp. z o.o.   (1)
Ul Pola Karolinskie 4, 02-401, Warsaw, Poland
Tel.: (48) 222559000
Web Site: https://wagicas.pl
Electronic Scale Mfr
N.A.I.C.S.: 333998

CAS Weighing India Pvt. Ltd.   (1)
788 Udyog Vihar Phase -V, Gurgaon, 122 016, Haryana, India
Tel.: (91) 1242342621
Electronic Scale Mfr
N.A.I.C.S.: 333998
Anil Kumar Kavtiyal *(Mgr-Production)*

CASA ALBA - INDEPENDENTA SA

Str Ocnei Nr 33, Sibiu, Romania
Tel.: (40) 269 505000
Sales Range: Less than $1 Million
Emp.: 1
Real Estate Prorperty Leasing Services
N.A.I.C.S.: 531190
Szitas Stefan *(Pres)*

CASA DE BOLSA FINAMEX, S.A.B. DE C.V.

Av Americas No 1545 Pisos 18 Y 19, Providencia 5Ta Seccion, 27-28 Col Juarez Del, 44638, Guadalajara, Mexico
Tel.: (52) 3338184400
Web Site:
    http://www.finamex.com.mx
Year Founded: 1974
FINAMEX—(MEX)
Rev.: $59,038,421
Assets: $5,743,872,741
Liabilities: $5,633,691,257
Net Worth: $110,181,485
Earnings: $11,901,957
Emp.: 257
Fiscal Year-end: 12/31/23
Investment Management Service
N.A.I.C.S.: 523940
Eduardo Arturo Carrillo Madero *(Chm & CEO)*

CASA DEL MAR BEACH RESORT N.V.

LG Smith Boulevard 51-53, Oranjestad, Aruba
Tel.: (297) 5827000
Web Site: http://www.casadelmar-aruba.com
Sales Range: $25-49.9 Million
Emp.: 220
Resort & Hotel
N.A.I.C.S.: 721110
Bob Curtis *(Gen Mgr)*

CASA HOLDINGS LTD.

15 Kian Teck Crescent, Singapore, 628884, Singapore
Tel.: (65) 62680066
Web Site: https://casa.sg
Year Founded: 1976
C04—(SES)
Rev.: $17,383,475
Assets: $70,277,881
Liabilities: $27,431,641
Net Worth: $42,846,239
Earnings: $1,273,805
Emp.: 100
Fiscal Year-end: 09/30/23
Holding Company; Household Appliances, Electronic Goods & Building Materials Distr
N.A.I.C.S.: 551112
Soo Kong Lim *(Founder & CEO)*

Subsidiaries:

Unicasa Pty Ltd   (1)
81 Milperra Road, Revesby, 2212, NSW, Australia
Tel.: (61) 297720388
Bathroom Product Mfr
N.A.I.C.S.: 326199

CASA MINERALS INC.

470 Granville St Suite 822, Vancouver, V6C 1V5, BC, Canada
Tel.: (604) 678-9587   BC
Web Site:
    https://www.casaminerals.com
Year Founded: 2010
0CM—(DEU)
Assets: $2,787,260
Liabilities: $298,389
Net Worth: $2,488,871
Earnings: ($210,260)
Fiscal Year-end: 12/31/23
Investment Services
N.A.I.C.S.: 523999
Farshad Shirvani *(Founder, Founder, Pres, Pres & CEO)*

CASA, INC.

Shinjuku Sumitomo Building 2-6-1 Nishi-Shinjuku, Shinjuku-ku, Tokyo, 163-0230, Japan
Tel.: (81) 353391143
Web Site: https://www.casa-inc.co.jp
Year Founded: 2008
7196—(TKS)
Rev.: $79,578,160
Assets: $104,761,840
Liabilities: $53,465,690
Net Worth: $51,296,150
Earnings: $4,289,450
Fiscal Year-end: 01/31/24
Real Estate Rental Services
N.A.I.C.S.: 531210
Masatake Miyachi *(Pres & CEO)*

CASABLANCA GROUP LIMITED

5th Floor Yan Hing Centre 9-13 Wong Chuk Yeung Street, Fo Tan, Sha Tin, NT, China (Hong Kong)
Tel.: (852) 23061699
Web Site:
    https://www.casablanca.com.hk
Year Founded: 1993

2223—(HKG)
Rev.: $38,270,783
Assets: $61,816,590
Liabilities: $11,356,935
Net Worth: $50,459,655
Earnings: $588,668
Emp.: 519
Fiscal Year-end: 12/31/22
Bedding Products Mfr & Distr
N.A.I.C.S.: 314999
Sze Kin Cheng *(Co-Founder & Chm)*

Subsidiaries:

Casablanca Home (Shenzhen) Limited   (1)
Shop No 139-11 Bianfang Branch Residential Area Meilin Road, Futian District, Shenzhen, Guangdong, China
Tel.: (86) 75523991199
Home Textile Product Distr
N.A.I.C.S.: 423220
Yi Kai Lin *(Deputy Gen Mgr)*

CASCADE BREWERY COMPANY

131 Cascade Road, Hobart, 7004, TAS, Australia
Tel.: (61) 362218300
Web Site:
    http://www.cascadebreweryco.com
Sales Range: $25-49.9 Million
Emp.: 130
Brewery
N.A.I.C.S.: 312120
Mike Unsworth *(Gen Mgr)*

CASCADERO COPPER CORPORATION

395 901 West Third Street, North Vancouver, V7P 3P9, BC, Canada
Tel.: (604) 985-3327
Web Site:
    https://www.cascadero.com
Year Founded: 2003
C5C—(DEU)
Assets: $563,966
Liabilities: $191,140
Net Worth: $372,826
Earnings: ($219,293)
Fiscal Year-end: 11/30/22
Mineral Properties Exploration Services
N.A.I.C.S.: 213114
Natasha Tsai *(CFO)*

Subsidiaries:

Cascadero Minerals S.A.   (1)
Rivadavia 378, A4400BTH, Salta, Argentina
Tel.: (54) 3874228252
Metal Mining Services
N.A.I.C.S.: 213114

Salta Exploraciones S.A.   (1)
Pasaje Franco Sosa 490, 4400, Salta, Argentina
Tel.: (54) 387 4950717
Sales Range: $50-74.9 Million
Emp.: 9
Gold Mining Services
N.A.I.C.S.: 212220

CASCADES INC.

404 Marie-Victorin Blvd, Kingsey Falls, J0A 1B0, QC, Canada
Tel.: (819) 363-5100   QC
Web Site: https://www.cascades.com
Year Founded: 1964
CADNF—(OTCIQ)
Rev.: $3,277,150,800
Assets: $3,707,891,400
Liabilities: $2,293,125,000
Net Worth: $1,414,766,400
Earnings: ($24,949,200)
Emp.: 10,000
Fiscal Year-end: 12/31/22
Boxboard, Fine Papers, Tissue Papers, Containerboard & Specialty Products Mfr

Cascades Inc.—(Continued)

N.A.I.C.S.: 322211
Alain Lemaire *(Co-Founder & Chm)*

Subsidiaries:

Cascades Boxboard Group Inc.　**(1)**
1061 Parent St, Saint-Bruno, J3V 6R7, QC,
Canada　　　　　　　　　　　**(100%)**
Tel.: (450) 461-8000
Web Site: http://www.cascades.com
Sales Range: $50-74.9 Million
Emp.: 150
Boxboard Mfr
N.A.I.C.S.: 322130

Plant (Domestic):

Cascades Boxboard Group Inc. -
Cobourg　　　　　　　　　　　**(2)**
Building 1E Northon Industrial Park, Co-
bourg, K9A 4L1, ON, Canada
Tel.: (905) 372-5199
Web Site: http://www.cascades.com
Sales Range: $25-49.9 Million
Emp.: 85
Boxboard Container Mfr
N.A.I.C.S.: 322212
Alain Levac *(Gen Mgr)*

Cascades Boxboard Group Inc. -
East Angus　　　　　　　　　　**(2)**
2 Rue Angus Nord, CP 2001, East Angus,
J0B 1R0, QC, Canada
Tel.: (819) 832-5300
Web Site: http://www.cascade.com
Sales Range: $25-49.9 Million
Emp.: 80
Coated Boxboard Mfr
N.A.I.C.S.: 322130

Cascades Boxboard Group Inc. -
Lachute　　　　　　　　　　　**(2)**
695 Cristini Blvd, Lachute, J8H 4N6, QC,
Canada
Tel.: (450) 566-3200
Sales Range: $50-74.9 Million
Emp.: 150
Paperboard & Box Mfr
N.A.I.C.S.: 322130

Cascades Boxboard Group Inc. -
Winnipeg　　　　　　　　　　　**(2)**
531 Golspie, Winnipeg, R2K 2T9, MB,
Canada
Tel.: (204) 667-6600
Web Site: http://www.cascades.com
Sales Range: $50-74.9 Million
Emp.: 191
Folding Cartons Mfr
N.A.I.C.S.: 322212
Herb Vielhaber *(Gen Mgr)*

Cascades Groupe Carton Plat
Jonquiere　　　　　　　　　　　**(2)**
4010 Chemim St Andre, Jonquiere, G7S
5K5, QC, Canada　　　　　　**(100%)**
Tel.: (418) 542-9544
Sales Range: $50-74.9 Million
Emp.: 130
N.A.I.C.S.: 322130

Subsidiary (Non-US):

Cascades S.A.S.　　　　　　　　**(2)**
Avenue Maurice Franck, F-73110, Paris,
France　　　　　　　　　　　**(100%)**
Tel.: (33) 479653232
Sales Range: $25-49.9 Million
Emp.: 331
Cartons & Packaging Materials Mfr
N.A.I.C.S.: 322130
Stephane Thiollier *(Pres/CEO-Careo)*

Subsidiary (Non-US):

Cascades Djupafors A.B.　　　　**(3)**
Haggatorpsvagen 45, PO Box 501, 37225,
Ronneby, Sweden
Tel.: (46) 457461700
Web Site: http://www.cascades.com
Sales Range: $50-74.9 Million
Emp.: 150
Mfr of Cartons & Packaging Materials
N.A.I.C.S.: 322212

Subsidiary (Domestic):

Norampac Inc.　　　　　　　　　**(2)**

1061 rue Parent, Saint-Bruno, J3V 6R7,
QC, Canada
Tel.: (450) 461-8600
Web Site: http://www.cascades.com
Packaging Materials Mfr
N.A.I.C.S.: 322212

Plant (Domestic):

Norampac Inc. - Drummondville　**(3)**
600 Rue Janelle St, Drummondville, J2C
5Z3, QC, Canada
Tel.: (819) 475-4567
Web Site: http://www.norampac.com
Sales Range: $25-49.9 Million
Emp.: 180
Carton Box Mfr
N.A.I.C.S.: 322130

Norampac Inc. - Newfoundland　**(3)**
110 Clyde Ave Donovans Industrial Park,
CP 8875, Saint John's, A1B 3T2, NL,
Canada
Tel.: (709) 747-1200
Sales Range: $25-49.9 Million
Emp.: 65
Corrugated Packaging Container Mfr
N.A.I.C.S.: 322211

Norampac Inc. - Vaudreuil　　　**(3)**
400 Forbes St, Vaudreuil-Dorion, J7V 6N8,
QC, Canada
Tel.: (450) 455-5731
Web Site: http://www.norampac.com
Sales Range: $150-199.9 Million
Emp.: 170
N.A.I.C.S.: 322130

Subsidiary (US):

Norampac Industries Inc.　　　　**(3)**
4001 Packard Rd, Niagara Falls, NY 14303
Tel.: (716) 285-3681
Web Site: http://www.norampac.com
Sales Range: $50-74.9 Million
Emp.: 200
Corrugated Medium Paper Mfr
N.A.I.C.S.: 322130

Plant (Domestic):

Norampac Industries Inc. -
Lancaster　　　　　　　　　　　**(4)**
4444 Walden Ave, Lancaster, NY 14086
Tel.: (716) 651-2000
Web Site: http://www.cascades.com
Sales Range: $25-49.9 Million
Emp.: 125
Corrugated Packaging Container Mfr
N.A.I.C.S.: 322211

Subsidiary (US):

Norampac New England Inc.　　**(3)**
720 Thompson Rd CP 246, Thompson, CT
06277
Tel.: (860) 923-9563
Web Site: http://www.cascades.com
Sales Range: $25-49.9 Million
Emp.: 75
Corrugated Packaging Container Mfr
N.A.I.C.S.: 322211

Norampac New York City Inc.　　**(3)**
55-15 Grand Ave, Maspeth, NY 11378
Tel.: (718) 386-3200
Web Site: http://www.cascades.com
Sales Range: $50-74.9 Million
Emp.: 148
Corrugated Product Mfr
N.A.I.C.S.: 322211

Norampac Schenectady Inc.　　**(3)**
Bldg 801 Corporation Park, Schenectady,
NY 12302
Tel.: (518) 346-6151
Sales Range: $50-74.9 Million
Emp.: 150
Corrugated Packaging Box Mfr
N.A.I.C.S.: 322211
Craig Griffith *(Gen Mgr)*

Cascades Canada ULC　　　　　**(1)**
2755 rue Viau, Montreal, H1V 3J4, QC,
Canada
Tel.: (514) 251-3800
Emp.: 53
Packaging Materials Mfr
N.A.I.C.S.: 322219

Cascades Specialty Products
Group　　　　　　　　　　　　**(1)**
404 Marie-Victorin Boulevard, PO Box 30,
Kingsey Falls, J0A 1B0, QC, Canada
Tel.: (819) 363-5100
Sales Range: $25-49.9 Million
Emp.: 2,000
Industrial Packaging, Consumer Product
Packaging, Specialty Papers & Recycled
Paper & Plastic Products
N.A.I.C.S.: 322212
Luc Langevin *(Pres & COO)*

Subsidiary (Domestic):

Cascades Conversion, Inc.　　　**(2)**
457 Marie Victorin St, Kingsey Falls, J0A
1B0, QC, Canada　　　　　　**(100%)**
Tel.: (819) 363-5400
Emp.: 85
Headers & Cardboard Mfr
N.A.I.C.S.: 322130

Cascades East Angus, Inc.　　　**(2)**
248 Rue Wagner, East Angus, J0B 1R0,
QC, Canada　　　　　　　　　**(100%)**
Tel.: (819) 832-2451
Web Site: http://www.cascade.com
Sales Range: $50-74.9 Million
Emp.: 300
Paperboard Mills
N.A.I.C.S.: 322130

Subsidiary (US):

Cascades Enviropac HPM LLC　**(2)**
236 Stevens St Sw, Grand Rapids, MI
49507-1528
Tel.: (616) 243-4870
Packaging Products Mfr
N.A.I.C.S.: 322220

Subsidiary (Domestic):

Cascades Enviropac Inc　　　　**(2)**
541 Melchers Street, Berthierville, J0K 1A0,
QC, Canada
Tel.: (450) 836-1799
Sales Range: $25-49.9 Million
Emp.: 46
Honeycomb Packaging Products Mfr
N.A.I.C.S.: 322220

Plant (Domestic):

Cascades Enviropac St-Cesaire　**(3)**
1850 avenue de l'Union, Saint Cesaire, J0L
1T0, QC, Canada
Tel.: (450) 469-3389
Web Site: http://www.cascades.com
Sales Range: $25-49.9 Million
Emp.: 31
Paper & Pulp Mfr
N.A.I.C.S.: 322120

Subsidiary (Domestic):

Cascades Forma-Pak, Inc.　　　**(2)**
406 Marie-Victorin CP 129, Kingsey
Falls, J0A 1B0, QC, Canada　**(100%)**
Tel.: (819) 363-5060
Web Site: http://www.cascades.com
Sales Range: $10-24.9 Million
Emp.: 57
N.A.I.C.S.: 322130

Cascades Inopak　　　　　　　**(2)**
500 rue Lauzon, Drummondville, J2B 2Z3,
QC, Canada　　　　　　　　　**(100%)**
Tel.: (819) 472-5757
Web Site: http://www.cascades.com
Sales Range: $1-9.9 Million
Emp.: 84
Plastic Containers & Coin Wrappers Mfr
N.A.I.C.S.: 322130

Subsidiary (Non-US):

Cascades La Rochette　　　　　**(2)**
23 Avenue Maurice Franck, 73110, Seine-
et-Marne, La Rochette, France
Tel.: (33) 4 79 65 32 32
Web Site: http://borntobeconverted.com
Emp.: 335
Mfr & Distr of Rochblanc, Rochcoat,
Rochperle Premium Paper Products
N.A.I.C.S.: 322120

Subsidiary (Domestic):

Cascades Lupel, Inc.　　　　　　**(2)**

700 Notre Dame E St, PO Box 23, Trois
Rivieres, G9A 5E3, QC, Canada　**(100%)**
Tel.: (819) 373-4307
Web Site: http://www.cascades.com
Sales Range: $25-49.9 Million
Emp.: 55
N.A.I.C.S.: 322130
Julie Lafontaine *(Mgr)*

Subsidiary (US):

Cascades Moulded Pulp, Inc.　　**(2)**
112 Cascades Way, Rockingham, NC
28380
Tel.: (910) 997-2775
Web Site: http://www.cascades.com
Sales Range: $25-49.9 Million
Emp.: 27
Beverage Tray Mfr
N.A.I.C.S.: 322212

Subsidiary (Domestic):

Cascades Multi-Pro, Inc.　　　　**(2)**
495 rue Haggerty, Drummondville, J2C
3G5, QC, Canada　　　　　　**(100%)**
Tel.: (819) 478-5983
Web Site: http://www.cascades.com
Sales Range: $25-49.9 Million
Emp.: 55
Carton Mfr
N.A.I.C.S.: 322130

Cascades Papier Kingsey Falls　**(2)**
408 Marie-Victorin, CP 150, Kingsey
Falls, J0A 1B0, QC, Canada
Tel.: (819) 363-5200
Sales Range: $25-49.9 Million
Emp.: 68
Uncoated Paperboard Mfr
N.A.I.C.S.: 322130

Subsidiary (US):

Cascades Plastics Inc.　　　　　**(2)**
7501 S Spoede Ln, Warrenton, MO 63383
Tel.: (636) 456-9576
Sales Range: $25-49.9 Million
Emp.: 70
Mfr of Polystyrene Foam Containers for
Packaging & Food Presentation
N.A.I.C.S.: 326140
Peirre Renaud *(Gen Mgr)*

Subsidiary (Domestic):

Cascades Recovery Inc.　　　　**(2)**
66 Shorncliffe Road, Toronto, M8Z 5K1,
ON, Canada
Tel.: (416) 231-2525
Web Site: http://www.recoverycascades.com
Sales Range: $10-24.9 Million
Discarded Paper & Cardboard Collection &
Transportation Services
N.A.I.C.S.: 562119
Albino Metauro *(Co-Founder)*

Subsidiary (US):

Cascades Recovery U.S., Inc.　　**(2)**
1845 Emerson St, Rochester, NY 14606
Tel.: (585) 527-8110
Web Site: http://www.cascades.com
Emp.: 81
Discarded Paper & Cardboards Collection &
Transportation Services
N.A.I.C.S.: 562119

Plant (US):

Cascades Sonoco, Inc. -
Birmingham　　　　　　　　　　**(2)**
170 Cleage Dr, Birmingham, AL 35217
Tel.: (205) 854-8574
Web Site: http://www.cascades.com
Sales Range: $25-49.9 Million
Emp.: 73
Paper Idustry Machinery Mfr
N.A.I.C.S.: 333243

Subsidiary (Domestic):

Plastiques Cascades, Inc.　　　**(2)**
455 boul Marie-Victorin, Kingsey Falls, J0A
1B0, QC, Canada　　　　　　**(100%)**
Tel.: (819) 363-5300
Web Site: http://www.cascades.com
Sales Range: $50-74.9 Million
Emp.: 170
N.A.I.C.S.: 322130

Cascades Tenderco Inc.   **(1)**
404 Marie Victorin Blvd, Kingsey Falls, J0A
1B0, QC, Canada
Tel.: (819) 363-5100
Web Site: http://www.cascades.com
Paper & Pulp Mfr
N.A.I.C.S.: 322120

Cascades Tissue Group   **(1)**
77 Marie-Victorin Blvd, Candiac, J5R 1C2,
QC, Canada
Web Site: http://www.pro.cascades.com
Sales Range: $50-74.9 Million
N.A.I.C.S.: 322130

Plant (Domestic):

Cascades Groupe Tissu - Agincourt &
Scarborough   **(2)**
45 Milliken Blvd, Toronto, M1V 1V3, ON,
Canada
Tel.: (416) 329-5200
Web Site: http://www.cascades.com
Sales Range: $50-74.9 Million
Tissue Paper Mfr
N.A.I.C.S.: 322120

Cascades Tissue Group - Kingsey
Falls   **(2)**
467 boul Marie-Victorin CP 210, Kingsey
Falls, J0A 1B0, QC, Canada
Tel.: (819) 363-5600
Web Site: http://www.cascade.com
Sales Range: $50-74.9 Million
Emp.: 185
Specialty Tissue Paper Mfr
N.A.I.C.S.: 322130

Cascades Tissue Group -
Lachute   **(2)**
115 Rue Princesse, Lachute, J8H 4M3, QC,
Canada
Tel.: (450) 562-8585
Web Site: http://www.cascades.com
Sales Range: $50-74.9 Million
Emp.: 146
Paper Hand Towel & Tissue Paper Mfr
N.A.I.C.S.: 322120

Cascades Tissue Group - Laval   **(2)**
2345 autoroute des Laurentides, Laval,
H7S 1Z7, QC, Canada
Tel.: (450) 688-1152
Web Site: http://www.cascades.com
Sales Range: $25-49.9 Million
Emp.: 54
Napkin Mfr
N.A.I.C.S.: 322291

Subsidiary (US):

Cascades Tissue Group - New York
Inc.   **(2)**
510 S Main St, Mechanicville, NY 12118
Tel.: (518) 664-8400
Web Site: http://www.cascades.com
Emp.: 42
Tissue Paper Mfr
N.A.I.C.S.: 322120

Cascades Tissue Group - Oregon
Inc.   **(2)**
1300 Kaster Rd, Saint Helens, OR 97051
Tel.: (503) 397-2900
Web Site: http://www.cascades.com
Sales Range: $25-49.9 Million
Emp.: 94
Tissue Paper Mfr
N.A.I.C.S.: 322120

Cascades Tissue Group - Pennsylva-
nia Inc. (Pittston)   **(2)**
901 Sathers Dr CP 6000, Pittston, PA
18640
Tel.: (570) 388-6161
Web Site: http://www.cascades.com
Sales Range: $50-74.9 Million
Tissue Paper Mfr
N.A.I.C.S.: 322120
William Roepke *(Branch Mgr)*

Cascades Tissue Group - Pennsylva-
nia Inc. (Ransom)   **(2)**
1 Main St, Ransom, PA 18653
Tel.: (570) 388-6161
Sales Range: $25-49.9 Million
Emp.: 75
Tissue Paper Mfr
N.A.I.C.S.: 322291

Plant (US):

Cascades Tissue Group -
Rockingham   **(2)**
805 Midway Rd, Rockingham, NC 28379
Tel.: (910) 895-4033
Web Site: http://www.cascades.com
Sales Range: $50-74.9 Million
Emp.: 62
Mfr of Jumbo Rolls of Tissue Paper, Con-
verted Tissue & Paper Towels
N.A.I.C.S.: 322291

Subsidiary (US):

Cascades Tissue Group - Tennessee
Inc.   **(2)**
1535 Thomas St, Memphis, TN 38107-1002
Tel.: (901) 523-9118
Web Site: http://www.cascades.com
Sales Range: $25-49.9 Million
Emp.: 49
Tissue Paper Mfr
N.A.I.C.S.: 322120

IFC Disposables Inc.   **(2)**
250 Kleer Vu Dr, Brownsville, TN 38012
Tel.: (731) 779-0959
Web Site: http://www.cascades.com
Sales Range: $25-49.9 Million
Emp.: 56
Disposable Wiping Cloth Products Mfr
N.A.I.C.S.: 325612

Cascades Transport Inc.   **(1)**
2 Parenteau Street, PO Box 300, Kingsey
Falls, J0A 1B0, QC, Canada
Tel.: (819) 363-5800
Sales Range: $50-74.9 Million
Emp.: 205
General Freight Trucking Services
N.A.I.C.S.: 484121
Yan Lambert *(Gen Mgr)*

Cascades USA Inc.   **(1)**
148 Hudson River Rd, Waterford, NY 12188
Tel.: (518) 880-3632
Web Site: http://www.cascades.com
Packaging Product & Tissue Paper Mfr
N.A.I.C.S.: 322220

Unit (Domestic):

Cascades IFC   **(2)**
250 Kleer Vu, Brownsville, TN 38012-0469
Tel.: (731) 779-0959
Web Site: http://www.cascades.com
Sales Range: $10-24.9 Million
Emp.: 50
Supplier of Disposable Industrial & Food
Service Fabrics & Wiping Products
N.A.I.C.S.: 313230

Orchids Paper Products
Company   **(1)**
4826 Hunt St, Pryor, OK 74361
Tel.: (918) 825-0616
Web Site: http://www.orchidspaper.com
Paper Products Mfr
N.A.I.C.S.: 322120
Pierre Lebeau *(Mgr-Prod)*

R.D.M Arnsberg GmbH   **(1)**
Hellefelder Strasse 51, 59821, Arnsberg,
Germany
Tel.: (49) 2931851
Coated Recycled Carton Board Mfr
N.A.I.C.S.: 322130

R.D.M Barcelona Cartonboard
S.A.   **(1)**
Carrer Potassi 7, Castellbisbal, 08755, Bar-
celona, Spain
Tel.: (34) 936311000
Coated Recycled Carton Board Mfr
N.A.I.C.S.: 322130

R.D.M La Rochette S.A.S.   **(1)**
23 Avenue Maurice Franck, Valgelon-La
Rochette, 73110, Seine-et-Marne, France
Tel.: (33) 479653232
Packaging Materials Mfr
N.A.I.C.S.: 322219

CASCADIA BLOCKCHAIN
GROUP CORP.
Richmond Centre 6060, PO Box
43166, Richmond, V6Y 3Y3, BC,
Canada

Tel.: (604) 773-5180   BC
Web Site:
   https://www.cascadiacorp.com
Year Founded: 2011
CK—(CNSX)
Rev.: $2
Assets: $28,415
Liabilities: $798,902
Net Worth: ($770,487)
Earnings: ($288,849)
Fiscal Year-end: 01/31/24
Electronic Hardware & Software
N.A.I.C.S.: 334419
Danny Deng *(Pres & CEO)*

CASCADIA MOTIVATION INC
14-4646 Riverside Drive, Red Deer,
T4N 6Y5, AB, Canada
Tel.: (403) 340-8687
Web Site:
   http://www.cascadiamotivation.com
Year Founded: 1984
Sales Range: $10-24.9 Million
Performance Improvement Services
N.A.I.C.S.: 561499
Keri Lefaivre *(Dir-Travel Ops)*

CASCO LTD.
Aviation Centre Star Industrial Estate
Partridge Green, Horsham, RH13
8RA, West Sussex, United Kingdom
Tel.: (44) 1403711444
Web Site: http://www.casco.co.uk
Year Founded: 1982
Sales Range: $25-49.9 Million
Emp.: 27
Aircraft Parts Distr
N.A.I.C.S.: 423860
David Elwick *(Mng Dir)*

Subsidiaries:

CASCO Russia   **(1)**
Nagatinskaya naberezhnaya 16 - 348, Mos-
cow, 115533, Russia
Tel.: (7) 9032367460
Aircraft Parts Distr
N.A.I.C.S.: 423860

CASCO Singapore   **(1)**
Suite Draycott Suntec Tower 2 9 Temasek
Boulevard, Singapore, 38989, Singapore
Tel.: (65) 94488732
Aircraft Parts Distr
N.A.I.C.S.: 423860

CASDON LIMITED
Cornford Road, Blackpool, FY4 4QW,
Lancashire, United Kingdom
Tel.: (44) 1253766411   UK
Web Site: http://www.casdon.co.uk
Year Founded: 1946
Sales Range: $10-24.9 Million
Toy Mfr & Whslr
N.A.I.C.S.: 339930
Paul M. Cassidy *(Chm)*

Subsidiaries:

Casdon Toys Ltd.   **(1)**
Cornford Road, Blackpool, FY4 4QW,
Lancs, United Kingdom
Tel.: (44) 1253 766 411
Web Site: http://www.casdon.com
Toy Mfr & Whslr
N.A.I.C.S.: 339930
Paul M. Cassidy *(Chm)*

CASE 'N DRUM OIL LP
3462 White Oak Road, London, N6E
2Z9, ON, Canada
Tel.: (519) 681-3772
Web Site: http://www.cndoil.ca
Year Founded: 1977
Rev.: $15,215,366
Emp.: 35
Lubricant Supplier
N.A.I.C.S.: 424720
Gord Poole *(Gen Mgr)*

CASE GROUP AB

Tel.: (46) 86620690
Web Site: https://www.casefonder.se
Year Founded: 2004
CASE—(OMX)
Rev.: $12,802,895
Assets: $33,044,454
Liabilities: $6,061,509
Net Worth: $26,982,946
Earnings: $43,679
Emp.: 17
Fiscal Year-end: 12/31/23
Asset Management Services
N.A.I.C.S.: 523999
Oscar Andrassy *(CFO)*

CASELLA WINES PTY. LTD.
Walkley Rd, PO Box 281, Yenda,
2681, NSW, Australia
Tel.: (61) 269613000
Web Site:
   http://www.casellawines.com
Year Founded: 1965
Sales Range: $300-349.9 Million
Emp.: 450
Wine Mfr
N.A.I.C.S.: 312130
Bob Powell *(Mgr-Sls-Australia)*

Subsidiaries:

Peter Lehmann Wines Limited   **(1)**
Para Road, Tanunda, 5352, SA,
Australia   **(99.1%)**
Tel.: (61) 885659555
Web Site:
   http://www.peterlehmannwines.com
Wine Mfr
N.A.I.C.S.: 312130
Paul Turale *(Dir-Intl Sls & Mktg)*

CASETEK HOLDINGS LIMITED
2F No 96 Ligong St, Beitou District,
Taipei, 112, Taiwan
Tel.: (886) 255630588   Ky
Web Site:
   http://www.casetekholdings.com
5264—(TAI)
Rev.: $336,381,044
Assets: $518,314,480
Liabilities: $176,073,599
Net Worth: $342,240,881
Earnings: ($3,253,623)
Emp.: 1,118
Fiscal Year-end: 12/31/20
Dies, Molds & Electronic Products
Mfr
N.A.I.C.S.: 333511
Gary Chuang *(CEO)*

Subsidiaries:

Kai Jia Computer Accessory Co.,
Ltd.   **(1)**
No 95 Changjiang Road Jiashan Economic
Development Zone, Jiaxing, Zhejiang,
China
Tel.: (86) 57384607777
Electronic Component Mfr & Whslr
N.A.I.C.S.: 334419

Ri Ming (Shanghai) Co., Ltd.   **(1)**
No 88 Tinghua Road Tinglin Town Jinshan
District, Shanghai, China
Tel.: (86) 2131219800
Electronic Component Mfr & Whslr
N.A.I.C.S.: 334419

Ri-Kuan Metal Corporation   **(1)**
96 Ligong Street 112 Beitou District, Taipei,
Taiwan
Tel.: (886) 255630588
Iron & Aluminum Whslr
N.A.I.C.S.: 423510

Ri-Teng Computer Accessory (Shang-
hai) Co., Ltd.   **(1)**
1168 Ronghua Road Songjiang District,
Shanghai, China
Tel.: (86) 2161951868
Electronic Component Mfr & Whslr
N.A.I.C.S.: 334419

Sheng Rui Electronic Technology
(Shanghai) Co., Ltd.   **(1)**

Casetek Holdings Limited—(Continued)

No 113 Lane 171 Linsheng Road Tinglin
Town Jinshan District, Shanghai, China
Tel.: (86) 2131219800
Electronic Component Mfr & Whslr
N.A.I.C.S.: 334419

CASEWARE INTERNATIONAL, INC.
469 King St W 2nd Floor, Toronto,
M5V 1K4, ON, Canada
Tel.: (416) 867-9504
Web Site: http://www.caseware.com
Year Founded: 1988
Sales Range: $1-9.9 Million
Emp.: 30
Software Solutions to Accountants &
Auditors
N.A.I.C.S.: 513210
Dwight W. Wainman (Founder)

Subsidiaries:

Audimation Services, Inc.   (1)
1250 Wood Branch Park Dr, Houston, TX
77079
Tel.: (281) 749-0200
Web Site: http://www.audimation.com
Sales Range: $1-9.9 Million
Emp.: 24
Computer And Software Stores, Nsk
N.A.I.C.S.: 449210
Carolyn Newman (Pres)

CASH CANADA GROUP LTD.
17316 107 Ave, Edmonton, T5S 1E9,
AB, Canada
Tel.: (780) 424-1080   AB
Web Site:
http://www.cashcanada.com
Year Founded: 1988
Sales Range: $10-24.9 Million
Emp.: 100
Pawn Shop Owner & Operator; Loan
Services
N.A.I.C.S.: 455219
Tim Latimer (CEO)

CASH CONVERTERS INTERNATIONAL LIMITED
Level 11 141 St Georges Terrace,
Perth, 6000, WA, Australia
Tel.: (61) 892219111
Web Site:
https://www.cashconverters.com
CCV—(ASX)
Rev.: $255,450,720
Assets: $319,202,723
Liabilities: $178,066,239
Net Worth: $141,136,484
Earnings: $11,616,586
Emp.: 783
Fiscal Year-end: 06/30/24
Second Hand Goods Purchasing &
Reselling Services
N.A.I.C.S.: 459510
Peter Cumins (Deputy Chm)

Subsidiaries:

Cash Converters (Stores) Pty
Ltd   (1)
260 Smith Street, Collingwood, 3066, VIC,
Australia
Tel.: (61) 392307302
Web Site:
http://www.cashconverters.com.au
Financial & Secondary Marketing Services
N.A.I.C.S.: 522299

Cash Converters Pty Ltd   (1)
Level 11 141 St Georges Terrace, Perth,
6000, WA, Australia
Tel.: (61) 892219111
Web Site: https://www.cashconverters.com
Financial & Broking Services
N.A.I.C.S.: 522299

Cash Converters UK Holdings
PLC   (1)
15-17 Gentlemens Field Westmill Rd, Ware,
SG12 0EF, Hertfordshire, United Kingdom

Tel.: (44) 1920485696
Web Site: http://www.cashconverters.co.uk
Sales Range: $50-74.9 Million
Emp.: 15
Financial & Broking Services
N.A.I.C.S.: 522299
David Patrick (CEO)

Safrock Finance Corporation (QLD)
Pty Ltd   (1)
Level 2 9 Mcinroy St, Taringa, Brisbane,
QLD 4068, Queensland, Australia
Tel.: (61) 738769411
Web Site: http://www.safrock.net
Sales Range: $50-74.9 Million
Emp.: 50
Personal Loan Services
N.A.I.C.S.: 522291

CASH FINANCIAL SERVICES GROUP LIMITED
22/F Manhattan Place 23 Wang Tai
Road, Kowloon Bay, Hong Kong,
China (Hong Kong)
Tel.: (852) 22878788
Web Site: http://www.cfsg.com.hk
0510—(HKG)
Rev.: $8,770,980
Assets: $134,274,458
Liabilities: $91,070,063
Net Worth: $43,204,395
Earnings: ($8,899,245)
Emp.: 78
Fiscal Year-end: 12/31/22
Investment Banking & Securities
Dealing Services
N.A.I.C.S.: 523150
Bankee Pak Hoo Kwan (Chm &
CEO)

Subsidiaries:

CASH Asset Management
Limited   (1)
21/F Low Block Grand Millennium Plaza
181 Queens Road, Central, China (Hong
Kong)
Tel.: (852) 22878848
Web Site: http://www.cash.com.hk
Asset Management Services
N.A.I.C.S.: 523940

CASH E-Trade Limited   (1)
21 F Low Block Grand Millennium Plz, 181
Queens Rd, Central, China (Hong Kong)
Tel.: (852) 22878888
Web Site: http://www.cash.com.hk
Administrative Management Services
N.A.I.C.S.: 561110

CASH Frederick Taylor Limited   (1)
21 F Low Block Grand Millennium Plz, 181
Queen St, Central, China (Hong Kong)
Tel.: (852) 21392323
Web Site: http://www.cash.com.hk
Financial Advisory Consultancy
N.A.I.C.S.: 541611

CASH Wealth Management
Limited   (1)
9/F Low Block Grand Millennium Plaza 181
Queens Road Central, Hong Kong, China
(Hong Kong)
Tel.: (852) 21392323
Financial Services
N.A.I.C.S.: 523150

Celestial Commodities Limited   (1)
21 F Low Block Grand Millennium Plz, 181
Queens Rd, Central, China (Hong Kong)
Tel.: (852) 22878888
Web Site: http://www.cashon-line.com.hk
Electronic Trading Services
N.A.I.C.S.: 425120
Carrie Law (Mgr-HR)

Celestial Securities Limited   (1)
21 F Low Block Grand Millennium Plz, 181
Queens Rd, Central, China (Hong Kong)
Tel.: (852) 22878788
Web Site: http://www.cash.com.hk
Sales Range: $200-249.9 Million
Securities & Foreign Exchange Trading
Services
N.A.I.C.S.: 523210

CASH FLOW SPOLKA AKCYJNA
Ul Perla 14, 41-300, Dabrowa Gornicza, Poland
Tel.: (48) 32 763 20 00
Financial Services
N.A.I.C.S.: 523999

CASH.LIFE AG
Dr-Gustav-Adolph-Str 2, 82049, Pullach, Germany
Tel.: (49) 1802000393   De
Web Site: http://www.cashlife.de
Year Founded: 1999
Sales Range: $200-249.9 Million
Fire Insurance Services
N.A.I.C.S.: 524210
Andreas Benninger (Chm-Supervisory
Bd)

CASHBUILD LIMITED
Tel.: (27) 112481500
Web Site:
https://www.cashbuild.co.za
CSB—(JSE)
Rev.: $562,595,348
Assets: $331,274,253
Liabilities: $228,002,461
Net Worth: $103,271,792
Earnings: $6,067,977
Emp.: 6,046
Fiscal Year-end: 06/25/23
Building Material Retailer
N.A.I.C.S.: 444140
Shane A. Thoresson (Dir-Ops)

CASHDASH UK LTD.
North West House 119 Marylebone
Road, London, NW1 5PU, United
Kingdom
Web Site: http://www.rapyd.net
Year Founded: 2016
Fintech-as-a-Service Platform
N.A.I.C.S.: 518210
Arik Shtilman (Co-Founder & CEO)

CASHWAY FINTECH CO., LTD.
No 30 West 8 Avenue Pilot Free
Trade Zone, Tianjin, 300308, China
Tel.: (86) 2224828888
Web Site:
https://en.cashwaytech.com
Year Founded: 2004
603106—(SHG)
Rev.: $82,149,500
Assets: $311,222,995
Liabilities: $104,324,824
Net Worth: $206,898,171
Earnings: $21,348,073)
Emp.: 500
Fiscal Year-end: 12/31/22
Banking Equipment Mfr & Distr
N.A.I.C.S.: 334118
Jiang Haoran (Chm & Pres)

CASI PHARMACEUTICALS, INC.
1701-1703 China Central Office
Tower 1 No 81 Jianguo Road, Chaoyang District, Beijing, 100025, China
Tel.: (86) 1065618789   Ky
Web Site:
https://www.casipharmaceutical.com
Year Founded: 2022
CASI—(NASDAQ)
Holding Company; Pharmaceutical
Developer & Mfr
N.A.I.C.S.: 551112
Alexander A. Zukiwski (Chief Medical
Officer & Exec VP)

Subsidiaries:

CASI Pharmaceuticals (China) Co.,
Ltd.   (1)
1701-1702 China Central Office Tower 1 No
81 Jianguo Road, Chaoyang District, Bei-

jing, 100025, China
Tel.: (86) 1065086067
Pharmaceutical Product Developer, Mfr &
Distr
N.A.I.C.S.: 325412

CASIL TELECOMMUNICATIONS HOLDINGS LIMITED
Ste 1701 17th Fl Central Plz, Wanchai, China (Hong Kong)
Tel.: (852) 25861185   Ky
Web Site:
http://www.castelecom.com
Sales Range: $10-24.9 Million
Emp.: 300
Holding Company; Electronic & Telecommunication Products Designer,
Developer, Mfr, Marketer, System Integration & Professional System Services
N.A.I.C.S.: 551112
Wang Xiaodong (CEO)

CASIN REAL ESTATE DEVELOPMENT GROUP CO., LTD.
25th Floor Building 1 No 1 Honghuang Road, Jiangbei District,
Chongqing, 400020, Guangdong,
China
Tel.: (86) 1059282532
Web Site: http://www.casindev.com
Year Founded: 1989
000838—(SSE)
Rev.: $589,069,260
Assets: $1,501,586,424
Liabilities: $1,303,442,712
Net Worth: $198,143,712
Earnings: ($32,235,840)
Fiscal Year-end: 12/31/22
Real Estate Development Services
N.A.I.C.S.: 531311
Xiannian Xian (Chm, Pres & Chm-
Supervisory Bd)

CASING MACRON TECHNOLOGY CO., LTD.
11F No 98 Shing De Rd, San Chung,
New Taipei City, Taiwan
Tel.: (886) 229998658
Web Site: https://www.casing.com.tw
Year Founded: 1994
3325—(TPE)
Rev.: $33,330,050
Assets: $55,957,634
Liabilities: $26,104,712
Net Worth: $29,852,922
Earnings: ($2,870,119)
Fiscal Year-end: 12/31/22
Computer Peripheral Equipment Mfr
N.A.I.C.S.: 334118
Yi Chang Hsiao (Chm)

CASINOS AUSTRIA AG
Renn Weg 44, 1038, Vienna, Austria
Tel.: (43) 5077750
Web Site: http://www.casinos.at
Sales Range: $1-4.9 Billion
Emp.: 9,642
Casino Management & Development
Services
N.A.I.C.S.: 713210
Martin Skopek (Member-Mgmt Bd)

Subsidiaries:

Casinos Austria International
GmbH   (1)
Rennwet 44, Vienna, 1038, Austria
Tel.: (43) 1534400
Web Site: http://www.casinos.at
Sales Range: $150-199.9 Million
Emp.: 3,000
Casino Management & Development Services
N.A.I.C.S.: 713210
Reinhard Bernkop-Schnurch (Head-New
Bus & Strategy)

Casinos Austria International Holdings GmbH **(1)**
Rennweg 44, Vienna, 1038, Austria
Tel.: (43) 5077750
Web Site: http://www.casinos.com
Sales Range: $25-49.9 Million
Emp.: 45
Holding Company
N.A.I.C.S.: 551112
Karl Stoss *(Mng Dir)*

Congress Casino Baden GmbH **(1)**
Kaiser-Franz-Ring 1, 2500, Baden, Austria
Tel.: (43) 2252 444 96
Casino Operator
N.A.I.C.S.: 713210

CASIO COMPUTER CO., LTD.

6-2 Hon-machi 1-chome, Shibuya-ku, Tokyo, 151-8543, Japan
Tel.: (81) 353344111   **JP**
Web Site: https://world.casio.com
Year Founded: 1957
CAC1—(DEU)
Rev.: $1,776,953,080
Assets: $2,312,805,950
Liabilities: $784,884,620
Net Worth: $1,527,921,330
Earnings: $78,718,490
Emp.: 9,594
Fiscal Year-end: 03/31/24
Mfr of Digital Watches & Calculators, Musical Instruments, Personal Computers, T.V.'s
N.A.I.C.S.: 334111
Yuichi Masuda *(Sr Exec Mng Officer & Sr Gen Mgr-Product Dev & Timepiece Bus Unit)*

Subsidiaries:

CXD NEXT Co., Ltd. **(1)**
Shimomoto Building 10F 1-46-3 Hatsudai, Shibuya-Ku, Tokyo, 151-0061, Japan
Tel.: (81) 35 302 3760
Web Site: https://www.cxdnext.co.jp
Electronic Payment Services
N.A.I.C.S.: 541512

Casio (China) Co., Ltd. **(1)**
11/F Global Harbor Tower B 1188 North KaiXuan Road, PuTuo District, Shanghai, 200062, Changning, China
Tel.: (86) 216 197 4898
Web Site: http://world.casio.com
Emp.: 420
Sales & Marketing of Casio Products in China
N.A.I.C.S.: 334111

Casio (Guangzhou) Co., Ltd. **(1)**
2F/3F No 1505 Kaichuang Avenue, Huangpu District, Guangzhou, 510760, Guangdong, China
Tel.: (86) 208 222 0488
Web Site: http://world.casio.com
Logistics Management Services
N.A.I.C.S.: 541614

Casio (Thailand) Co., Ltd. **(1)**
60/70 Moo 19, Nava Nakorn Industrial Estate, 12120, Pathumthani, Thailand
Tel.: (66) 252906114
Sales Range: $200-249.9 Million
Emp.: 880
Calculators, Musical Instruments & Watches Mfr
N.A.I.C.S.: 459140

Casio America, Inc. **(1)**
570 Mount Pleasant Ave, Dover, NJ 07801-1631
Tel.: (973) 361-5400
Web Site: https://www.casio.com
Sales Range: $75-99.9 Million
Emp.: 200
Electronic Musical Instruments Mfr
N.A.I.C.S.: 423420
Shigenori Itoh *(Chm & CEO)*

Casio Benelux B.V. **(1)**
Prof W H Keesomlaan 6E, 1183 DJ, Amstelveen, Netherlands
Tel.: (31) 205451070
Web Site: https://www.casio-europe.com
Sales Range: $25-49.9 Million
Emp.: 13

Calculators, Musical Instruments & Watches Mfr
N.A.I.C.S.: 459140
M. Asada *(Mng Dir)*

Casio Brasil Comercio De Produtos Eletronicos Ltda. **(1)**
Rua Loefgreen 1057 Conj 401/404 Vila Clementino, Sao Paulo, 04040-030, Brazil
Tel.: (55) 1150858090
Web Site: http://world.casio.com
Calculators & Watches Mfr
N.A.I.C.S.: 423940

Casio Canada, Ltd. **(1)**
141 McPherson Street, Markham, L3R 3L3, ON, Canada **(100%)**
Tel.: (905) 248-4400
Web Site: http://www.casioca.com
Sales Range: $25-49.9 Million
Emp.: 23
Markets & Sales of Calculators, Musical Instruments & Watches
N.A.I.C.S.: 459140

Casio Computer (Hong Kong) Ltd. **(1)**
Units 4102-4111 Level 41 Metroplaza Tower 1 No 223 Hing Fong Rd, 22 TakFung St Hunghon, Kwai Fong, New Territories, China (Hong Kong) **(100%)**
Tel.: (852) 2 377 2288
Web Site: http://www.casio.com
Sales Range: $50-74.9 Million
Emp.: 100
Mfr of Electronic Calculators & Timepieces
N.A.I.C.S.: 423690
Katsuyoshi Hosokawa *(Mng Dir)*

Casio Electronic Manufacturing Co., Ltd. **(1)**
4084 Miyadera, Iruma, 358-0014, Saitama, Japan
Tel.: (81) 429348900
Electronic Components Mfr
N.A.I.C.S.: 334419

Casio Electronic Technology (Zhongshan) Co., Ltd. **(1)**
Avenue West 46, Torch Hi-Tech Industrial Development Zone, Zhongshan, 528437, Guangdong, China
Tel.: (86) 7608 858 0668
Web Site: https://www.casio.co.jp
Calculators, Musical Instruments & Watches Mfr
N.A.I.C.S.: 459140

Casio Electronics (Shaoguan) Co., Ltd. **(1)**
257 Huarong Dadao South Guanguang Industrial Park, Guandu Town Wengyuan County, Shaoguan, 512625, China
Tel.: (86) 7512888088
Electronic Product Mfr & Distr
N.A.I.C.S.: 334419

Casio Electronics (Shenzhen) Co., Ltd. **(1)**
3/F 5/F and Room 902A Philips Research and Development Building, No 12 Shihua Road Futian Free Trade Zone Futian District, Shenzhen, 518038, Guangdong, China
Tel.: (86) 7558 359 0620
Web Site: http://world.casio.com
Mfr of Electronics
N.A.I.C.S.: 334419

Casio Electronics Co., Ltd. **(1)**
Harp View 12 Priestley Way, London, NW2 7JD, United Kingdom **(100%)**
Tel.: (44) 208 450 9131
Web Site: https://www.casio.co.uk
Sales Range: $50-74.9 Million
Emp.: 150
Marketing of Computers
N.A.I.C.S.: 449210

Casio Espana, S.L. **(1)**
Torre Diagonal Litoral Josep Pla No 2, Edificio B2 Planta 12, 08019, Barcelona, Spain
Web Site:
  http://www.escuelaslibresdemercurio.com
Emp.: 40
Calculators, Musical Instruments & Watches Mfr
N.A.I.C.S.: 459140

Casio Europe GmbH **(1)**

Casio-Platz 1, 22848, Norderstedt, Germany **(60%)**
Tel.: (49) 4 052 8650
Web Site: https://www.casio-europe.com
Sales Range: $150-199.9 Million
Emp.: 378
Sales of Computers
N.A.I.C.S.: 423430
Kazuyuki Yamashita *(Mng Dir)*

Casio France S.A. **(1)**
23 Avenue Carnot Immeuble ILIADE - Batiment A, 91300, Massy, France
Tel.: (33) 16 919 2060
Web Site: https://www.casio-europe.com
Emp.: 70
Calculators, Musical Instruments & Watches Mfr
N.A.I.C.S.: 459140

Casio India Company Private Ltd **(1)**
A-41 First Floor Mathura Road, Mohan Cooperative Industrial Estate, New Delhi, 110044, India **(100%)**
Tel.: (91) 116 699 9200
Web Site: https://www.casio-intl.com
Sales Range: $25-49.9 Million
Emp.: 60
Mfr of Communications Equipment
N.A.I.C.S.: 334220
Kulbhushan Seth *(VP)*

Casio Information Systems Co., Ltd. **(1)**
3-3-5 Nihombashihongokucho Nihombashitoku Bldg, Chuo-Ku, Tokyo, 103-0021, Japan
Tel.: (81) 352004730
Web Site: http://w3.cjnet.co.jp
Computer Peripheral Equipment Distr
N.A.I.C.S.: 423430
Haruo Ohsawa *(Gen Mgr)*

Casio Italia S.r.l. **(1)**
Via Ludovico di Breme No.9, 20156, Milan, Italy
Tel.: (39) 02 40708611
Calculators, Musical Instruments & Watches Mfr
N.A.I.C.S.: 459140

Casio Korea Co., Ltd. **(1)**
654-4 Bongam-Dong, Masan, Kyung Sang Namdo, Korea (South) **(100%)**
Tel.: (82) 552967111
Mfr of Electronic Timepieces
N.A.I.C.S.: 334519

Casio Latin America S.A. **(1)**
Ruta 8 km 17 500 Edificio Biotec Office 103, Zonamerica, 91600, Montevideo, Uruguay
Tel.: (598) 25185319
Electronic Product Mfr & Distr
N.A.I.C.S.: 334419

Casio Malaysia, Sdn. Bhd. **(1)**
Unit 20-06 Level 20 Q Sentral 2A Jalan Stesen Sentral 2, Kuala Lumpur Sentral, 50470, Kuala Lumpur, Malaysia
Tel.: (60) 327421253
Web Site: https://www.casio.com
Electronic Product Distr
N.A.I.C.S.: 423690

Casio Marketing (Thailand) Co., Ltd. **(1)**
208 Wireless Road Building 6th Floor Unit 601 Wireless Road, Lumpini Pathumwan, Bangkok, 10330, Thailand
Tel.: (66) 26514588
Electronic Product Mfr & Distr
N.A.I.C.S.: 334419

Casio Mexico Marketing, S. de R. L. de C.V. **(1)**
Av Insurgentes Sur No 1457 Piso 21 Oficina 01, Col Insurgentes Mixcoac, 03920, Mexico, Mexico
Tel.: (52) 5590002071
Web Site: https://www.casiomx.com
Sales Range: $25-49.9 Million
Emp.: 20
Calculators, Musical Instruments & Watches Mfr
N.A.I.C.S.: 459140

Casio Micronics Co., Ltd. **(1)**
10-6 Imai 3-chome Ome City, Tokyo, 198-8555, Japan **(75%)**

Tel.: (81) 428321551
Web Site: http://www.casio-micronics.co.jp
Sales Range: $75-99.9 Million
Emp.: 345
Electronic Parts Developer, Mfr & Sales
N.A.I.C.S.: 334419

Casio Middle East & Africa FZE **(1)**
Jafza View 19 - Downtown, PO Box 18607, Jebel Ali, Dubai, United Arab Emirates
Tel.: (971) 48850688
Electronic Product Mfr & Distr
N.A.I.C.S.: 334419

Casio Philippines Corporation **(1)**
First Cavite Industrial Estate Brgy, Langkaan, Dasmarinas, Cavite, Philippines
Tel.: (63) 402 0788
Mfr of Pagers
N.A.I.C.S.: 334220

Casio Scandinavia AS **(1)**
Hillerenveien 82, Mathopen, 5174, Bergen, Norway
Tel.: (47) 55197990
Web Site: http://www.casio.no
Calculators, Musical Instruments & Watches Mfr
N.A.I.C.S.: 459140

Casio Singapore Pte., Ltd. **(1)**
238B Thomson Road 18-01/08 Novena Square Tower B, 10-02 TripleOne Somerset, Singapore, 307685, Singapore
Tel.: (65) 6 480 7118
Web Site: https://www.casio-intl.com
Emp.: 100
Calculators, Musical Instruments & Watches Mfr
N.A.I.C.S.: 459140
Shigeru Watanabe *(Mng Dir)*

Casio Taiwan Co., Ltd. **(1)**
Chung Hsiao East Road sixth 21 Hao 7, Nangang, 11575, Taipei, Taiwan **(100%)**
Tel.: (886) 2 2653 2588
Web Site: http://www.casio.com.tw
Sales Range: $25-49.9 Million
Emp.: 40
Mfr of Timepiece Cases & Electronic Calculators
N.A.I.C.S.: 334519

Casio Techno Co., Ltd. **(1)**
2-23 Kanda Sakumacho Casio Akihabara Building, Chiyoda-ku, Tokyo, 101-0025, Japan
Tel.: (81) 35 821 7611
Web Site: https://www.casiotechno.co.jp
Emp.: 245
Electronic Device Distr
N.A.I.C.S.: 423690

Casio Timepiece (Dongguan) Co., Ltd. **(1)**
No 222 Bubugao Road, Wusha District Changan Town, Dongguan, China
Tel.: (86) 76983589732
Electronic Product Mfr & Distr
N.A.I.C.S.: 334419

Casio, Inc. **(1)**
570 Mount Pleasant Ave, Dover, NJ 07801-1620
Tel.: (973) 361-5400
Web Site: http://www.casio.com
Sales Range: $450-499.9 Million
Emp.: 300
Consumer Electronics Mfr
N.A.I.C.S.: 423420
Larry Sampey *(Gen Mgr)*

Kofu Casio Co., Ltd. **(1)**
217 Ichouhata, Tokyo, 409-3896, Yamanashi, Japan
Tel.: (81) 55 273 3111
Web Site: http://www.kofu-casio.co.jp
Electric Device Mfr
N.A.I.C.S.: 334419

Limited Liability Company Casio **(1)**
77 Butyrskaya Street, 127015, Moscow, Russia
Tel.: (7) 4957256466
Web Site: http://www.casio.ru
Sales Range: $25-49.9 Million
Emp.: 36
Electronic Components Mfr
N.A.I.C.S.: 334419

Yamagata Casio Co., Ltd. **(1)**

Casio Computer Co., Ltd.—(Continued)

5400-1 Oaza Higashine ko, Higashine, 999-3701, Yamagata, Japan
Tel.: (81) 23 743 5111
Web Site: https://www.yamagata-casio.co.jp
Electronic Devices Mfr & Distr
N.A.I.C.S.: 334419
Yutaka Shinoda *(Auditor)*

CASPAR ASSET MANAGEMENT SA

Ul Polwiejska 32, 61-888, Poznan, Poland
Tel.: (48) 618551614
Web Site: https://www.caspar.com.pl
Year Founded: 2010
CSR—(WAR)
Asset Management Services
N.A.I.C.S.: 523940
Lukasz Zymiera *(Mgr-Portfolio)*

CASPIAN BEVERAGE HOLD-ING JSC

211 Gogol Street, 050026, Almaty, Kazakhstan
Tel.: (7) 727 2421806
Web Site: http://www.zhigulevskoe.kz
Sales Range: $10-24.9 Million
Beer Producer & Sales
N.A.I.C.S.: 312120

CASPIAN CORPORATE SER-VICES LIMITED

105 Surya Towers 1st Floor F Block SP Road, Secunderabad, 500 003, India
Tel.: (91) 4023410031
Web Site:
https://www.caspianservices.in
Year Founded: 2011
534732—(BOM)
Rev.: $54,049
Assets: $574,281
Liabilities: $9,383
Net Worth: $564,898
Earnings: $20,726
Emp.: 2
Fiscal Year-end: 03/31/21
Financial Management Services
N.A.I.C.S.: 523940
Leena Modi *(Mng Dir)*

CASPIAN ENERGY INC.

885 West Georgia Street, 2200 HSBC Building, Vancouver, V6C 3E8, BC, Canada
Tel.: (403) 252-2462   BC
Web Site:
http://www.caspianenergyinc.com
Year Founded: 1982
CKZ.H—(TSXV)
Sales Range: $1-9.9 Million
Emp.: 2
Oil & Gas Explorer
N.A.I.C.S.: 213112
Wei Zhao *(CEO)*

CASPIAN SERVICES INC.

2nd floor 134 Azerbayeva str, Almaty, 050010, Kazakhstan
Tel.: (7) 727 321 80 90
Web Site:
http://www.caspianservicesinc.com
Year Founded: 1999
Marine Cargo Handling Services
N.A.I.C.S.: 488320
Alexey Kotov *(Pres & CEO)*

CASPIAN SUNRISE PLC

5 New Street Square, London, EC4A 3TW, United Kingdom
Tel.: (44) 8456525236
Web Site:
https://www.caspiansunrise.com
Year Founded: 2006

CASP—(AIM)
Rev.: $36,650,000
Assets: $134,920,000
Liabilities: $63,460,000
Net Worth: $71,460,000
Earnings: $11,110,000
Fiscal Year-end: 12/31/23
Crude Petroleum Extraction Services
N.A.I.C.S.: 211120
Kuat Rafikuly Oraziman *(CEO)*

Subsidiaries:

Roxi Petroleum Kazakhstan LLP   **(1)**
Oil & Gas Exploration Services
N.A.I.C.S.: 211120

CASPIN RESOURCES LIMITED

Principal Place of Business Ground Floor 675 Murray Street, West Perth, 6005, WA, Australia
Tel.: (61) 863732000   AU
Web Site: https://www.caspin.com.au
Year Founded: 2020
CPN—(ASX)
Rev.: $230,686
Assets: $3,013,530
Liabilities: $821,600
Net Worth: $2,191,930
Earnings: ($7,298,216)
Fiscal Year-end: 06/30/23
Exploration & Mining Services
N.A.I.C.S.: 213115
Steven Wood *(CFO)*

CASPIY COMMODITY EX-CHANGE JSC

st Syganak building No 47 block A 14th floor, Yesil district, Z05K7B3, Nur-Sultan, Kazakhstan
Tel.: (7) 172644009
Web Site: https://ccx.kz
Year Founded: 2011
EXCS—(KAZ)
Rev.: $754,354
Assets: $4,666,148
Liabilities: $1,864,778
Net Worth: $2,801,371
Earnings: ($320,834)
Fiscal Year-end: 12/31/20
Commodity Trading Services
N.A.I.C.S.: 523160
Tanayev Erik Maratovich *(Pres)*

CASS PAK INDUSTRIES LIM-ITED

4th Floor Sheikh Sultan Trust Bldg No 2 26-Civil Lines 10, Beaumont Road, Karachi, Pakistan
Tel.: (92) 21 5688541
Electrical Cables Mfr
N.A.I.C.S.: 335999

CASSA CENTRALE BANCA-CREDITO COOPERATIVO DEL NORD EST SPA

Via G Segantini 5, 38122, Trento, Italy
Tel.: (39) 0461313111   IT
Web Site: http://www.cassacentrale.it
Year Founded: 1974
Holding Company
N.A.I.C.S.: 551111
Sartori Mario *(Gen Mgr)*

Subsidiaries:

Claris Leasing SpA   **(1)**
Pizza Rinaldi 8, 31100, Treviso, Italy
Tel.: (39) 0422 427411
Web Site: http://www.clarisleasing.it
Sales Range: $1-9.9 Million
Emp.: 26
Commercial Banking Services
N.A.I.C.S.: 522110

CASSA DEPOSITI E PRESTITI S.P.A.

Via Goito 4, 00185, Rome, Italy

Tel.: (39) 0642211   IT
Web Site: http://www.cdp.it
Year Founded: 1850
Rev.: $23,948,355,041
Assets: $502,508,415,875
Liabilities: $458,617,516,684
Net Worth: $43,890,899,192
Earnings: $1,998,055,332
Emp.: 33,571
Fiscal Year-end: 12/31/19
Public Finance & Investment Services
N.A.I.C.S.: 921130
Fabrizio Palermo *(CEO & Gen Mgr)*

Subsidiaries:

Ansaldo Energia Switzerland AG   **(1)**
Haselstrasse 18, 5401, Baden, Switzerland
Tel.: (41) 56 525 1900
Eletric Power Generation Services
N.A.I.C.S.: 221118

Ansaldo Russia LLC   **(1)**
Sadovnicheskaya Street 14 Bld 2 Str, 115035, Moscow, Russia
Tel.: (7) 495 225 8647
Eletric Power Generation Services
N.A.I.C.S.: 221118

Ansaldo Thomassen Gulf LLC   **(1)**
Gas Turbine Industrial Workshop-ICA D III, Abu Dhabi, United Arab Emirates
Tel.: (971) 2 611 9500
Mechanical Engineering Services
N.A.I.C.S.: 541330

CDP Equity SpA   **(1)**
San Marco Street 21 A, 20121, Milan, Italy   **(100%)**
Tel.: (39) 0246744333
Web Site: http://www.cdpequity.it
Equity Investment Holding Company
N.A.I.C.S.: 551112
Giovanni Gorno Tempini *(Chm)*

Holding (Domestic):

Ansaldo Energia S.p.A.   **(2)**
Via Nicola Lorenzi 8, 16152, Genoa, GE, Italy   **(87.6%)**
Tel.: (39) 0106551
Web Site: http://www.ansaldoenergia.it
Rev.: $1,337,693,379
Assets: $4,201,320,200
Liabilities: $3,604,445,918
Net Worth: $596,874,282
Earnings: ($126,248,333)
Emp.: 3,308
Fiscal Year-end: 12/31/2020
Power Generation & Plant Engineering Services
N.A.I.C.S.: 221122
Giuseppe Zampini *(Chm)*

Subsidiary (Domestic):

Ansaldo Nucleare SpA   **(3)**
Via Nicola Lorenzi 8, 16152, Genoa, Italy
Tel.: (39) 0106551
Web Site: http://www.ansaldonucleare.it
Nuclear Power Plant Engineering Services
N.A.I.C.S.: 541330

Subsidiary (Non-US):

Asia Power Projects Private Ltd.   **(3)**
8th Floor Prince Towers 25 & 26 College Road, Chennai, 600006, Tamil Nadu, India
Tel.: (91) 4428230712
Web Site: http://www.ansaldoenergia.co.in
Sales Range: $25-49.9 Million
Emp.: 10
Power Plant Construction Services
N.A.I.C.S.: 237990
R. S. Raghavan *(Mng Dir)*

Thomassen Energy B.V.   **(3)**
Havelandseweg 8d, 6991 GS, Rheden, Netherlands
Tel.: (31) 264975800
Web Site: http://thomassen.energy
Support Services for Industrial Gas Turbine Systems
N.A.I.C.S.: 333611
Mark Kooister *(Comml Dir)*

Holding (Domestic):

Societa Interbancaria per l'Automazione-Cedborsa S.p.A.   **(2)**

Via Gonin 36, Milan, 20147, Italy   **(25.7%)**
Tel.: (39) 02 6084 1
Web Site: http://www.sia.eu
Sales Range: $450-499.9 Million
Emp.: 1,494
Financial Transaction Processing & Technology Infrastructure Management Services
N.A.I.C.S.: 522320
Giuliano Asperti *(Chm)*

Subsidiary (Domestic):

Emmecom s.r.l.   **(3)**
Corso Casale 20, 10131, Turin, Italy
Tel.: (39) 0848 782 444
Web Site: http://www.sia.eu
Telecommunication Servicesb
N.A.I.C.S.: 517112

Kedrios S.p.A.   **(3)**
Via Roncaglia 8, 20146, Milan, Italy   **(81%)**
Tel.: (39) 0248501
Web Site: http://www.kedrios.it
Sales Range: $25-49.9 Million
Emp.: 290
Computer Systems Design & Consulting Services
N.A.I.C.S.: 541512

Subsidiary (Non-US):

Perago Financial Systems Enablers (Pty) Ltd   **(3)**
Glenfield Office Park Block C Oberon Avenue, Faerie Glen, Pretoria, 0043, South Africa   **(75%)**
Tel.: (27) 124704800
Web Site: http://www.perago.com
Sales Range: $100-124.9 Million
Emp.: 300
Payment System Infrastructure Design Services
N.A.I.C.S.: 541512
Philip Tromp *(CEO)*

Subsidiary (Domestic):

RA Computer S.p.A.   **(3)**
10/A Via Padre Reginaldo Giuliani, 20125, Milan, Italy
Tel.: (39) 02 661551
Web Site: http://www.racomputer.it
Software Development Services
N.A.I.C.S.: 541511
Angelo Cislaghi *(Dir-Bus-Payment Sys & Trade Fin)*

Subsidiary (Non-US):

SIA Central Europe Zrt.   **(3)**
Aliz utca 4 7th floor Office Garden III, 1117, Budapest, Hungary
Tel.: (36) 1 4212 200
Web Site: http://www.sia.eu
Emp.: 50
Information Technology Consulting Services
N.A.I.C.S.: 541512

Subsidiary (Domestic):

Thesia S.p.A.   **(3)**
Via T Taramelli 26, 20124, Milan, Italy   **(55%)**
Tel.: (39) 02 6946 1
Web Site: http://www.thesia.it
Computer Systems Design & Consulting Services
N.A.I.C.S.: 541512

CDP Immobiliare S.r.l.   **(1)**
Via Alessandria 220, 00198, Rome, Italy
Tel.: (39) 06 4211 61
Web Site: http://www.cdpimmobiliare.it
Real Estate Development Services
N.A.I.C.S.: 531210
Giorgio Righetti *(Chm)*

CDP Immobiliare SGR S.p.A.   **(1)**
Via Alessandria 220, 00198, Rome, Italy
Tel.: (39) 064 204 5499
Web Site: https://www.cdpisgr.it
Asset Management Services
N.A.I.C.S.: 523940

CDP Technologies AS   **(1)**
Hundsvaergata 8, PO Box 144, 6001, Alesund, Norway
Tel.: (47) 99080900
Web Site: https://cdpstudio.com
Software Solutions Services

N.A.I.C.S.: 541511
Oyvind Stevenson (Mng Dir)

Castor Drilling Solution AS (1)
Skibasen 39, 4636, Kristiansand, Norway
Tel.: (47) 95803611
Web Site: https://www.cds.as
Drilling Solution Services
N.A.I.C.S.: 213111
Oyvind V. Reiten (CEO)

Fincantieri Infrastructure Opere Maritime S.p.A. (1)
Tel.: (39) 0454648511
Maritime Design & Construction Services
N.A.I.C.S.: 236116

Fintecna S.p.A. (1)
Via Benedetto Croce 32, 00142, Rome, Italy
Tel.: (39) 0677610001
Web Site: http://www.fintecna.it
Equity Investment Firm
N.A.I.C.S.: 523999

Fondo Italiano di Investimento SGR S.p.A. (1)
Via San Marco 21A, 20121, Milan, Italy
Tel.: (39) 0263 5321
Web Site: https://www.fondoitaliano.it
Industrial Investment Services
N.A.I.C.S.: 523999
Antonio Pace (CEO & Gen Mgr)

HMS IT S.p.A. (1)
Via Salvatore Quasimodo 136, 00144, Rome, Italy
Tel.: (39) 0672577100
Web Site: https://www.hmsit.it
System Integration Services
N.A.I.C.S.: 541512

Marine Interiors Cabins S.p.A. (1)
Via Redipuglia 163, 34077, Ronchi dei Legionari, Gorizia, Italy
Tel.: (39) 0668635777
Emp.: 370
Marine Interior Design & Construction Services
N.A.I.C.S.: 541410

New SIA Greece S.A. (1)
23 the Km National Road, Lamia, Athens, Greece
Tel.: (30) 210 624 4000
Web Site: https://www.newsiagreece.eu
Information & Communication Technology Services
N.A.I.C.S.: 519290

Quadrante S.p.A (1)
25 Lungo Lago Buozzi, Omegna, 28887, Verbano-Cusio-Ossola, Italy
Tel.: (39) 0323 66 01 11
Real Estate Development Services
N.A.I.C.S.: 531210

SACE S.p.A. (1)
Piazza Poli 37/42, 00187, Rome, Italy (100%)
Tel.: (39) 066736000
Web Site: http://www.sace.it
Export Credit, Credit Assurance, Investment Protection, Factoring & Other Credit Intermediation Services
N.A.I.C.S.: 522299
Giovanni Castellaneta (Chm)

Subsidiary (Domestic):

SACE Fct S.p.A. (2)
Via A De Togni 2, 20123, Milan, Italy
Tel.: (39) 02 4344991
Financial Services
N.A.I.C.S.: 523999
Franco Pagliardi (Gen Mgr)

SIA Central Europe. A.S. (1)
Rontgenova 1, PO Box 79, 851 01, Bratislava, Slovakia
Tel.: (421) 26 828 5111
Management Services
N.A.I.C.S.: 541611

SIA Croatia d.o.o. (1)
Varsavska 1, 10000, Zagreb, Croatia
Tel.: (385) 1 639 2902
Management Services
N.A.I.C.S.: 541611

SIA Czech Republic. S.r.o. (1)

V Celnici 1031/4, 110 00, Prague, Czech Republic
Tel.: (420) 22 223 2980
Management Services
N.A.I.C.S.: 541611

SIA RS d.o.o. (1)
Bulevar Zorana Djindica 144v, 11070, Belgrade, Serbia
Tel.: (381) 11 207 1106
Management Services
N.A.I.C.S.: 541611

SIA Romania Payment Technologies S.r.l. (1)
Street Ing G Constantinescu No 4B Floor 6 Building B and Street G, Constantinescu no 2-4 LOT 2 2nd District, 020339, Bucharest, Romania
Tel.: (40) 73 294 0905
Management Services
N.A.I.C.S.: 541611

Simest S.p.A. (1)
Corso Vittorio Emanuele II 323, 00186, Rome, Italy (76%)
Tel.: (39) 0800020030
Web Site: https://www.simest.it
Investment, Advisory & Corporate Financing Services
N.A.I.C.S.: 523999

Support Logistic Services S.r.l. (1)
Via Montenero 67, Guidonia Montecelio, 00012, Rome, Italy
Tel.: (39) 0774572835
Web Site: https://www.slsitalia.it
Intercommunication Services
N.A.I.C.S.: 517810

Vard Accommodation Tulcea S.r.l. (1)
22 Ing Dumitru Ivanov Street, 820242, Tulcea, Romania
Tel.: (40) 240534542
Marine Interior Design & Construction Services
N.A.I.C.S.: 541410

Vard Electro US Inc. (1)
15995 N Bakers Landing Ste 125, Houston, TX 77079
Tel.: (713) 595-7900
Web Site: https://vardelectrous.com
Electrical Engineering Design Services
N.A.I.C.S.: 541330
Pierre Poulain (Pres)

CASSA DI RISPARMIO DI ASTI S.P.A.
Piazza Liberta 23, 14100, Asti, AT, Italy
Tel.: (39) 02 4540 3768 IT
Web Site: http://www.bancacrasti.it
Year Founded: 1842
Retail & Commercial Banking
N.A.I.C.S.: 522110
Aldo Pia (Chm)

Subsidiaries:

Cassa di Risparmio di Biella e Vercelli S.p.A. (1)
Via Carso 15, 13900, Biella, BI, Italy (60.42%)
Tel.: (39) 01535081
Web Site: http://www.biverbanca.it
Sales Range: $200-249.9 Million
Emp.: 747
Retail & Commercial Banking Services
N.A.I.C.S.: 522110
Roberto De Battistini (Deputy Chm)

CASSA RURALE ED ARTIGIANA DI BINASCO CREDITO COOPERATIVO
via Filippo Turati 2, 20082, Binasco, Italy
Tel.: (39) 0290024
Year Founded: 1920
Commercial Banking Services
N.A.I.C.S.: 522110

CASSIAR GOLD CORP.
Suite 450 - 800 West Pender Street, Vancouver, V6C 2V6, BC, Canada

Tel.: (236) 878-6160 AB
Web Site: https://cassiargold.com
Year Founded: 2009
756—(DEU)
Assets: $34,962,087
Liabilities: $4,030,868
Net Worth: $30,931,219
Earnings: ($1,313,894)
Emp.: 7
Fiscal Year-end: 09/30/23
Tungsten & Zinc Mining
N.A.I.C.S.: 212230
Tyler Rice (Pres)

CASSIDY GOLD CORP.
432 Royal Avenue, Kamloops, V2B 3P7, BC, Canada
Tel.: (250) 574-5011
Web Site:
http://www.cassidygold.com
Year Founded: 1984
Mineral Exploration Services
N.A.I.C.S.: 213114
James T. Gillis (Pres)

CASSIUS MINING LIMITED
Suite 18 Level 4 3 spring street, Sydney, 2000, NSW, Australia
Tel.: (61) 407233153
Web Site:
https://www.cassiusmining.com
Year Founded: 2014
CMD—(ASX)
Rev.: $8
Assets: $1,167,733
Liabilities: $457,124
Net Worth: $710,609
Earnings: ($277,272)
Fiscal Year-end: 06/30/22
Mineral Exploration Services
N.A.I.C.S.: 213115
Wayne John Kernaghan (Sec)

CASSIUS VENTURES LTD.
3083 Three Bentall Centre 595 Burrard Street, Vancouver, V7X 1L3, BC, Canada
Tel.: (604) 558-1107 BC
Web Site:
https://www.cassiusventures.com
Year Founded: 2007
CZ.H—(TSXV)
Assets: $1,290
Liabilities: $298,608
Net Worth: ($297,318)
Earnings: ($33,428)
Fiscal Year-end: 10/31/22
Investment Services
N.A.I.C.S.: 523999
John Alan Thomas (Chm, Pres & CEO)

CAST S.A.
3 rue Marcel Allegot, 92190, Meudon, France
Tel.: (33) 146902100
Web Site:
http://www.castsoftware.com
Year Founded: 1990
CAS—(EUR)
Sales Range: $25-49.9 Million
Emp.: 365
Software Development Services
N.A.I.C.S.: 541511
Vincent Delaroche (Founder, Chm & CEO)

Subsidiaries:

Cast Benelux SA (1)
Avenue de Messidorlaan, 1180, Brussels, Belgium
Tel.: (32) 26466511
Information Technology Services
N.A.I.C.S.: 541519

Cast Italia S.R.L. (1)
Via San Vittore 49, 20123, Milan, Italy
Tel.: (39) 0287286150

Information Technology Services
N.A.I.C.S.: 541519

Cast Software Espana SL (1)
Gustavo Fernandez Balbuena 11 Loft 2B, 28002, Madrid, Spain
Tel.: (34) 915155672
Information Technology Services
N.A.I.C.S.: 541519

Cast Software Inc. (1)
321 W 44th St Ste 501, New York, NY 10036
Tel.: (212) 871-8330
Software Development Services
N.A.I.C.S.: 541511
Vincent Delaroche (Chm & CEO)

Cast Software India Private Limited (1)
4th Floor J P & Devi Jambukeshwar Arcade 69 Millers Road, Bengaluru, 560052, India
Tel.: (91) 8049132525
Information Technology Services
N.A.I.C.S.: 541519

Cast Software Ltd. (1)
Third Floor 87 Worship Street, London, EC2A 2BE, United Kingdom
Tel.: (44) 2073970550
Information Technology Services
N.A.I.C.S.: 541519
Aditya Singh (Mktg Mgr)

CASTA DIVA GROUP
Via Lomazzo 34a, 20154, Milan, Italy
Tel.: (39) 023450817
Web Site:
https://www.castadivagroup.com
CDG—(ITA)
Communication Company
N.A.I.C.S.: 541890
Andrea De Micheli (Chm)

Subsidiaries:

Blue Note SpA (1)
Via Pietro Borsieri 37, Milan, Italy
Tel.: (39) 02 69016888
Web Site: http://www.bluenotemilano.com
Musical Entertainment, Exhibitions & Other Cultural & Artistic Events
N.A.I.C.S.: 711310

CASTEC KOREA CO., LTD.
55 Mieumsandan 4-ro, Gangseo-gu, Busan, Korea (South)
Tel.: (82) 519744282
Web Site: https://www.castec.co.kr
Year Founded: 1958
071850—(KRS)
Rev.: $139,608,634
Assets: $197,792,728
Liabilities: $128,505,671
Net Worth: $69,287,057
Earnings: ($4,740,283)
Emp.: 279
Fiscal Year-end: 12/31/22
Automotive Parts, Compressors & Turbine Mfr
N.A.I.C.S.: 336310
Sang-Won Yoon (Pres)

CASTECH INC.
Building No 9 Zone F 89 Ruanjian Avenue, Fuzhou, 350003, Fujian, China
Tel.: (86) 59183771604
Web Site: https://www.castech.com
Year Founded: 1988
002222—(SSE)
Rev.: $107,880,552
Assets: $222,483,456
Liabilities: $22,121,424
Net Worth: $200,362,032
Earnings: $31,785,156
Emp.: 1,000
Fiscal Year-end: 12/31/22
Photoelectronic Material Mfr
N.A.I.C.S.: 334419

CASTEL FRERES SA

Castel Freres SA—(Continued)

21 24 Rue Georges Guynemer, Blanquefort, 3290, France
Tel.: (33) 556955400
Web Site: http://www.groupe-castel.com
Year Founded: 1949
Sales Range: $1-4.9 Billion
Emp.: 500
Beverages Mfr
N.A.I.C.S.: 312130
Pierre Castel (Pres)

Subsidiaries:

Castel Malawi Limited   (1)
Malimidwe Road Makata Indusrial Area,
Blantyre, 1050, Malawi   **(59.48%)**
Tel.: (265) 1872999
Web Site: http://www.carlsberg.mw
Brewery
N.A.I.C.S.: 312120
Alfred Msowoya (Mgr-Warehouse)

CASTELAN LTD.
Alpha House, Sunnyside Road North,
Weston-super-Mare, BS23 3QY,
Somerset, United Kingdom
Tel.: (44) 870 320 3333
Web Site:
   http://www.castelangroup.com
Retail Warranty Services
N.A.I.C.S.: 524298
Martin John Napper (CEO)

CASTELBAJAC CO., LTD.
49 Harmony-ro 177beon-gil, Yeonsu-gu, Incheon, 06228, Korea (South)
Tel.: (82) 234980330
Web Site: https://www.hyungji.com
Year Founded: 2016
308100—(KRS)
Rev.: $47,370,420
Assets: $91,178,652
Liabilities: $44,467,023
Net Worth: $46,711,628
Earnings: ($7,105,713)
Emp.: 78
Fiscal Year-end: 12/31/22
Apparel Product Mfr
N.A.I.C.S.: 315120
Jun Ho Choi (CEO)

CASTELL HOWELL FOODS LTD.
Cross Hands Food Park, Carmarthen,
SA14 6SX, Dyfed, United Kingdom
Tel.: (44) 1269846060
Web Site:
   http://www.castellhowellfoods.co.uk
Sales Range: $100-124.9 Million
Emp.: 280
General Grocery Whslr
N.A.I.C.S.: 424410
David B Jones (Mng Dir)

CASTELLUM AB
Ostra Hamngatan 16, PO Box 2269,
403 14, Gothenburg, Sweden
Tel.: (46) 31607400
Web Site: https://www.castellum.se
CAST—(OMX)
Rev.: $973,454,858
Assets: $15,817,499,824
Liabilities: $8,156,034,845
Net Worth: $7,661,464,979
Earnings: ($1,150,753,489)
Emp.: 535
Fiscal Year-end: 12/31/23
Real Estate Services
N.A.I.C.S.: 531390
Per Berggren (Chm)

Subsidiaries:

Aspholmen Fastigheter AB   (1)
Tradgardsgatan 14, Box 1824, 701 18, Ore-
bro, Sweden   **(100%)**
Tel.: (46) 1 927 6500

Web Site:
   http://www.aspholmenfastigheter.se
Sales Range: $25-49.9 Million
Emp.: 33
Lessors of Other Real Estate Property
N.A.I.C.S.: 531190

Eklandia Fastighets AB   (1)
Lilla Bommen 6, Box 8725, 402 75, Goth-
enburg, Sweden
Tel.: (46) 31 744 0900
Web Site: http://www.eklandia.se
Sales Range: $25-49.9 Million
Emp.: 35
Other Real Estate Property Lessors
N.A.I.C.S.: 531190

Fastighets AB Briggen   (1)
Lilla Nygatan 7, Box 3158, 200 22, Malmo,
Sweden   **(100%)**
Tel.: (46) 40383720
Web Site: http://www.briggen.se
Sales Range: $25-49.9 Million
Emp.: 37
Other Holding Companies Offices
N.A.I.C.S.: 551112
Gunnar Ostenson (Mng Dir)

Fastighets AB Brostaden   (1)
Torsgatan 11, Johanneshov, 111 23, Stock-
holm, Sweden   **(100%)**
Tel.: (46) 86023300
Web Site: http://www.brostaden.se
Sales Range: $25-49.9 Million
Emp.: 40
Other Real Estate Property Lessors
N.A.I.C.S.: 531190
Anders Nilsson (Mng Dir)

Fastighets AB Corallen   (1)
Jonkopingsvagen 41, 33121, Varnamo,
Sweden
Tel.: (46) 370694900
Web Site: http://www.corallen.se
Emp.: 35
Other Holding Companies Offices
N.A.I.C.S.: 551112

Harry Sjogren AB   (1)
Kraketorpsgatan 20, Molndal, 43153,
Sweden   **(100%)**
Tel.: (46) 317066500
Web Site: http://www.harrysjogren.se
Sales Range: $25-49.9 Million
Emp.: 27
Other Real Estate Property Lessors
N.A.I.C.S.: 531190

CASTELNAU GROUP LIMITED
Les Banques Trafalgar Court, PO
Box 255, Saint Peter Port, GY1 3QL,
Guernsey
Tel.: (44) 2086000100   **GY**
Web Site:
   https://www.castelnaugroup.com
Year Founded: 2021
CGL—(LSE)
Rev.: $692,713
Assets: $177,550,120
Liabilities: $3,310,408
Net Worth: $174,239,712
Earnings: ($43,037,219)
Fiscal Year-end: 12/31/22
Investment Management Service
N.A.I.C.S.: 523999
Graham Elliott Shircore (CEO)

Subsidiaries:

Rawnet Limited   (1)
39 - 51 High St, Ascot, SL5 7HY, Berkshire,
United Kingdom
Tel.: (44) 1344266233
Web Site: https://www.rawnet.com
Digital Strategy & Design Services
N.A.I.C.S.: 541613

CASTIK CAPITAL S.A.R.L.
1 Boulevard de la Foire, 1528, Lux-
embourg, Luxembourg
Tel.: (352) 28669097   **LU**
Web Site: http://www.castik.lu
Year Founded: 2014
Privater Equity Firm
N.A.I.C.S.: 523999
Michael Phillips (Partner)

Subsidiaries:

Castik Capital Partners GmbH   (1)
Mohlstrasse 28, 81675, Munich, Germany
Tel.: (49) 899446640
Financial Investment Management Services
N.A.I.C.S.: 523940

Waterlogic Plc   (1)
Suite 4 2nd Floor The Avenue Sandyford,
Dublin, Ireland
Tel.: (353) 12931960
Web Site: http://www.waterlogic.com
Emp.: 10
Holding Company; Water Filtration & Dis-
pensing Equipment Mfr & Distr
N.A.I.C.S.: 551112
Jeremy Ben-David (Founder & CEO)

Subsidiary (Non-US):

Aqua Cure (Scotland) Limited   (2)
Lawgrove Place Inveralmond Industrial Es-
tate, Perth, PH1 3XQ, Perthshire, United
Kingdom
Tel.: (44) 1738 626 648
Web Site:
   http://www.aquacurescotland.co.uk
Water Filtration & Dispensing Equipment
Distr
N.A.I.C.S.: 423440

Aqua Cure Limited (UK)   (2)
Aqua Cure House Hall Street, Southport,
PR9 0SE, United Kingdom
Tel.: (44) 1704 516916
Web Site: http://www.aquacure.co.uk
Water Filtration & Dispensing Equipment
Distr
N.A.I.C.S.: 423440

Escowa AB   (2)
Bergkallavagen 30, 192 79, Sollentuna,
Sweden
Tel.: (46) 8 557 731 00
Web Site: http://www.escowa.se
Water Filtration & Dispensing Equipment
Distr
N.A.I.C.S.: 423440
Mattias Kallemyr (Mng Dir)

WLI (UK) Limited   (2)
Belvedere Basing View, Basingstoke, RG21
4HG, United Kingdom
Tel.: (44) 1256 400 110
Web Site: http://www.waterlogic.com
Water Purification Equipment Technical
Support Services
N.A.I.C.S.: 541990

Subsidiary (Domestic):

WLI Trading Ltd.   (2)
Suite 4 2nd Floor The Avenue, Sandyford,
Dublin, Ireland
Tel.: (353) 1 293 1960
Web Site: http://www.waterlogic.com
Water Filtration & Dispensing Equipment
Distr
N.A.I.C.S.: 423440

Subsidiary (US):

Waterlogic Americas LLC   (2)
77 McCullough Dr Ste 9, New Castle, DE
19720
Tel.: (888) 826-6537
Web Site: http://www.waterlogicusa.com
Water Filtration & Dispensing Equipment
Distr
N.A.I.C.S.: 423440
Sergio Leynarie (Pres)

Subsidiary (Domestic):

Merus Refreshment Services
Inc.   (3)
115 Queen Pkwy Ste A, West Columbia,
SC 29169-4679
Tel.: (803) 739-9779
Web Site: http://www.merusinc.com
Direct Selling Establishments
N.A.I.C.S.: 561910
Patty Davis (Mgr)

Subsidiary (Non-US):

Waterlogic Australia Pty   (2)
1 Farr Street, PO Box 57, Marrickville,
2204, NSW, Australia
Tel.: (61) 2 9335 2800

Web Site:
   http://www.waterlogicaustralia.com.au
Water Filtration Equipment Distr & Services
N.A.I.C.S.: 423440
David Wicks (CEO)

Subsidiary (US):

Waterlogic Commercial Products,
LLC   (2)
11710 Stonegate Circle, Omaha, NE 68164
Tel.: (402) 905-2001
Web Site: http://www.waterlogic.us
Water Filtration & Dispensing Equipment
Distr
N.A.I.C.S.: 423440
Bob Junk (Pres)

Subsidiary (Non-US):

Waterlogic Danmark AS   (2)
Ihouse Lene Haus Vej 15, 7430, Ikast, Den-
mark
Tel.: (45) 70238055
Web Site: http://www.waterlogic.dk
Water Filtration & Dispensing Equipment
Distr
N.A.I.C.S.: 423440

Waterlogic France SA   (2)
8 Rue Du Commandant d Estienne d
Orves, Boulevard Gallieni, Villeneuve-la-
Garenne, 92390, France
Tel.: (33) 140807751
Web Site: http://www.waterlogic.fr
Water Filtration & Dispensing Equipment
Distr
N.A.I.C.S.: 423440
Philippe Barnetche (Mng Dir)

Waterlogic GmbH   (2)
Kleinsachsenheimerstrasse 26-1, 74321,
Bietigheim-Bissingen, Germany
Tel.: (49) 7142 92903 0
Web Site: http://www.waterlogic.de
Water Filtration & Dispensing Equipment
Distr
N.A.I.C.S.: 423440
Olaf Wilhelm (Mng Dir)

Waterlogic Norge AS   (2)
Trollasveien 34-36, Trollasen, 1414, Oslo,
Norway
Tel.: (47) 815 51 960
Web Site: http://www.waterlogic.no
Water Filtration & Dispensing Equipment
Distr
N.A.I.C.S.: 423440
Erik Gulbrandsen (Mng Dir)

Subsidiary (US):

Waterlogic USA (WEST)   (2)
185 Mason Cir Ste B, Concord, CA 94520
Tel.: (925) 521-9100
Web Site: http://www.waterlogicusa.com
Water Dispensers & Coffee Machine Distri-
bution & Support Services
N.A.I.C.S.: 561499
Barry Taylor (Pres)

Xexec Limited   (1)
Mountcliff House 154 Brent Street, London,
NW4 2DR, United Kingdom
Tel.: (44) 2082016483
Web Site: http://www.xexec.com
Sales Range: $25-49.9 Million
Emp.: 45
Platform & Interface Development Services
N.A.I.C.S.: 541511
Dipika Parmar (Coord-Accts)

Subsidiary (US):

Xexec Inc.   (2)
195 Plymouth St 3rd Fl, Brooklyn, NY
11201
Tel.: (844) 576-2457
Software Development Services
N.A.I.C.S.: 541511

CASTILLIAN METAIS LTDA.
Av Afonso Pena 2770 Sala 200, Belo
Horizonte, 30130-007, Brazil
Tel.: (55) 31 3505 5200
Sales Range: $50-74.9 Million
Emp.: 100
Gold Mining Services
N.A.I.C.S.: 212220

Helio Diniz *(Mgr-South America)*

CASTILLO COPPER LIMITED
45 Ventnor Avenue, West Perth, 6005, WA, Australia
Tel.: (61) 893894407   AU
Web Site:
https://www.castillocopper.com
CCZ—(ASX)
Rev.: $301,538
Assets: $7,159,933
Liabilities: $74,881
Net Worth: $7,085,052
Earnings: ($976,128)
Fiscal Year-end: 06/30/24
Copper Mining Services
N.A.I.C.S.: 212230
Robert N. Scott *(Chm)*

CASTINGS PLC
Lichfield Road, Brownhills, WS8 6JZ, West Midlands, United Kingdom
Tel.: (44) 1543374341
Web Site: https://www.castings.plc.uk
CGS—(LSE)
Rev.: $201,734,111
Assets: $224,287,198
Liabilities: $45,749,733
Net Worth: $178,537,465
Earnings: $11,611,221
Emp.: 1,167
Fiscal Year-end: 03/31/22
Iron Supplies
N.A.I.C.S.: 212210
Steve J. Mant *(Sec & Dir-Fin)*

Subsidiaries:

CNC Speedwell Limited   (1)
Lichfield Road, Brownhills, WS8 6LH, West Midlands, United Kingdom
Tel.: (44) 1543363880
Web Site: http://www.cncspeedwell.co.uk
Sales Range: $50-74.9 Million
Emp.: 365
Ductile Iron Castings Mfr
N.A.I.C.S.: 331511

William Lee Limited   (1)
Callywhite Lane, Dronfield, S18 2XU, Derbyshire, United Kingdom
Tel.: (44) 1246416155
Web Site: http://www.wmlee.co.uk
Sales Range: $100-124.9 Million
Emp.: 400
Iron Casting Mfr
N.A.I.C.S.: 331511
Chris Hodson *(Dir-Sls)*

CASTLE BRIDGE IMPACT MEDIA INC.
3 Banyatelep Visegrad, Budapest, 2025, Hungary
Tel.: (36) 702 472 9058   NV
Year Founded: 2017
Vacuum Cleaner Distr
N.A.I.C.S.: 423620
Mester Frigyes *(Pres, Treas & Sec)*

CASTLE FUELS INC.
1639 E Trans Canada Hwy, Kamloops, V2C 3Z5, BC, Canada
Tel.: (250) 372-5035
Web Site: https://www.castlefuels.ca
Rev.: $21,375,238
Emp.: 25
Petroleum Product Whslr
N.A.I.C.S.: 324110
Robert R. Vandriel *(Owner & Pres)*

CASTLE HILL RSL CLUB LTD.
77 Castle St, Castle Hill, 2154, NSW, Australia
Tel.: (61) 288584800   UK
Web Site:
http://www.castlehillrsl.com.au
Sales Range: $125-149.9 Million
Emp.: 208
Recreational Services
N.A.I.C.S.: 721214

Warren E. Glenny *(Pres)*

CASTLE MINERALS LIMITED
Suite 9 11 Ventnor Ave, West Perth, 6005, WA, Australia
Tel.: (61) 893227018
Web Site:
https://www.castleminerals.com
CDT—(ASX)
Rev.: $58,824
Assets: $738,745
Liabilities: $397,716
Net Worth: $341,028
Earnings: ($1,923,994)
Emp.: 4
Fiscal Year-end: 06/30/24
Gold Exploration & Mining Services
N.A.I.C.S.: 212220
Michael Atkins *(Chm)*

Subsidiaries:

Carlie Mining Ltd.   (1)
13 Shippi Link, PO Box CT9, East Cantonments Cantonments Post Office, Accra, Ghana
Tel.: (233) 208118388
Gold Exploration Services
N.A.I.C.S.: 212220

CASTLE PEAK HOLDINGS PUBLIC COMPANY LIMITED
9-14th Floor CPH Tower 899 Petchkasem Road Bangkae Subdistrict, Khet Bangkae, Bangkok, 10160, Thailand
Tel.: (66) 4550300
Web Site:
https://www.castlepeak.co.th
Year Founded: 1976
CPH—(THA)
Rev.: $36,814,581
Assets: $47,384,608
Liabilities: $15,488,370
Net Worth: $31,896,238
Earnings: $2,286,652
Emp.: 1,833
Fiscal Year-end: 12/31/23
Jacket & Apparel Mfr
N.A.I.C.S.: 315990
Boonchoo Pongchaloem *(Chm & Pres)*

Subsidiaries:

C.P.G. Garment Co., Ltd.   (1)
2 Soi Petchakasem 50/2 Petchkasem Road Bangwah, Khet Pasricharoen, Bangkok, 10160, Thailand
Tel.: (66) 2 457 4142
Garments Mfr
N.A.I.C.S.: 315120

Castle Peak Real Estate Co., Ltd.   (1)
393 Moo 4 th Floor CPS Tower Petkasem Road, Bangkhae, Bangkok, 10160, Thailand
Tel.: (66) 2 8011802
Real Estate Development Services
N.A.I.C.S.: 531390

CASTLE PEAK MINING LTD.
2411 Bennie Place, Port Coquitlam, V3B 7M6, BC, Canada
Tel.: (604) 362-7685
Web Site:
https://www.castlepeakmining.com
CAP—(TSXV)
Assets: $2,610,867
Liabilities: $12,541
Net Worth: $2,598,327
Earnings: ($147,105)
Fiscal Year-end: 12/31/20
Gold Exploration Services
N.A.I.C.S.: 212220
Brian Lock *(Chm & CEO-Interim)*

CASTLE PRIVATE EQUITY AG
Schutzenstrasse 6, CH-8808, Pfaffikon, Switzerland

Tel.: (41) 554159494   CH
Web Site: https://www.castlepe.com
Year Founded: 1997
CPEN—(SWX)
Rev.: $94,000
Assets: $106,465,000
Liabilities: $372,000
Net Worth: $106,093,000
Earnings: ($17,375,000)
Emp.: 700
Fiscal Year-end: 12/31/22
Investment Management Service
N.A.I.C.S.: 523999
Benedikt Meyer *(Gen Mgr)*

Subsidiaries:

LGT Fund Managers (Ireland) Ltd.   (1)
Third Floor 30 Herbert Street, Dublin, D02 W332, Ireland
Tel.: (353) 12648600
Investment Management Service
N.A.I.C.S.: 523940

CASTLEBAR CAPITAL CORP.
600 1090 West Georgia St, Vancouver, V6E 3V7, BC, Canada
Tel.: (778) 549-6714   BC
Year Founded: 2018
CBAR.P—(TSXV)
Assets: $133,184
Liabilities: $10,770
Net Worth: $122,414
Earnings: ($39,586)
Fiscal Year-end: 12/31/20
Business Consulting Services
N.A.I.C.S.: 522299
Gary Economo *(CEO)*

CASTLECAP CAPITAL, INC.
2032 45 Av SW, Calgary, T2T 2P5, AB, Canada
Tel.: (403) 680-8511   AB
Year Founded: 2018
CSTL.P—(TSXV)
Rev.: $319
Assets: $118,630
Liabilities: $3,598
Net Worth: $115,031
Earnings: ($20,654)
Fiscal Year-end: 12/31/20
Business Consulting Services
N.A.I.C.S.: 522299

CASTLENET TECHNOLOGY, INC.
No 14 Ln 141 Sec 3 Beishen Rd, Shenkeng Dist, New Taipei City, 222004, Taiwan
Tel.: (886) 222673858
Web Site:
https://www.castlenet.com.tw
Year Founded: 1998
8059—(TPE)
Rev.: $35,820,936
Assets: $86,120,314
Liabilities: $27,709,596
Net Worth: $58,410,718
Earnings: $509,833
Fiscal Year-end: 12/31/22
Network Communication Equipment Mfr
N.A.I.C.S.: 334210

CASTLES TECHNOLOGY CO., LTD
6F No 2075 Sec 3 Beixin Rd, Xindian District, New Taipei City, 231, Taiwan
Tel.: (886) 289131771   TW
Web Site:
https://www.castlestech.com
Year Founded: 1993
5258—(TAI)
Rev.: $263,090,281
Assets: $228,575,582
Liabilities: $103,470,417
Net Worth: $125,105,165

Earnings: $30,461,884
Emp.: 1,000
Fiscal Year-end: 12/31/23
Electronic Product Mfr & Distr
N.A.I.C.S.: 335999
Winston Fong *(CEO)*

Subsidiaries:

Castles Technology Europe S.r.l.   (1)
Via Achille Papa 30, 20149, Milan, Italy
Tel.: (39) 02 36768 760
Electronic Payment Device Mfr
N.A.I.C.S.: 334511

Castles Technology International Corp.   (1)
53 Perimeter Ctr E Ste 275, Atlanta, GA 30346
Tel.: (470) 273-6350
Electronic Payment Device Mfr
N.A.I.C.S.: 334511

Castles Technology Singapore Pte. Ltd.   (1)
1557 Keppel Road Blk C 03-33, Singapore, 89066, Singapore
Tel.: (65) 81268469
Electronic Payment Device Mfr
N.A.I.C.S.: 334511

Castles Technology Spain SL   (1)
Calle Retama N 7 Planta 12, 28045, Madrid, Spain
Tel.: (34) 910884332
Electronic Payment Device Mfr
N.A.I.C.S.: 334511

Castles Technology UK & Ireland Ltd.   (1)
Unit 6 Milford Trading Estate Blakey Road, Salisbury, SP1 2UD, Wiltshire, United Kingdom
Tel.: (44) 87 130 2021
Financial Services
N.A.I.C.S.: 522320

CASTLEVIEW PROPERTY FUND LTD.
13 Hudson Street De Waterkant, Cape Town, 7925, South Africa
Tel.: (27) 212762040
Web Site:
https://www.castleview.co.za
CVW—(JSE)
Rev.: $110,134,188
Assets: $1,151,534,316
Liabilities: $600,567,377
Net Worth: $550,966,939
Earnings: $16,080,545
Fiscal Year-end: 03/31/24
Investment Management Service
N.A.I.C.S.: 525990
James Templeton *(CEO)*

CASTOR MARITIME INC.
223 Christodoulou Chatzipavlou Street, Hawaii Royal Gardens, 3036, Limassol, Cyprus
Tel.: (357) 25357767   MH
Web Site:
https://www.castormaritime.com
Year Founded: 2017
CTRM—(NASDAQ)
Rev.: $97,515,511
Assets: $605,041,979
Liabilities: $143,861,727
Net Worth: $461,180,252
Earnings: $36,980,474
Emp.: 1
Fiscal Year-end: 12/31/23
Marine Shipping Services
N.A.I.C.S.: 488510
Petros Panagiotidis *(Founder, Chm, Pres, CEO, CFO & Treas)*

CASTORAMA RUS LLC
Derbenevskaya Naberezhnaya Building 7 Building 8 3rd Floor, 115114, Moscow, Russia
Tel.: (7) 4952802555
Web Site: http://www.castorama.ru

Castorama RUS LLC—(Continued)

Year Founded: 2004
Supermarket Operating Services
N.A.I.C.S.: 445110

CASTRICO CO., LTD.

3F Shinmei Nihonbashi Bldg 16-15
Nihonbashi Koami-cho Chuo-ku, To-
kyo, 103-0016, Japan
Tel.: (81) 356148181
Web Site: http://www.tripleone.net
Year Founded: 1995
6695—(TKS)
Rev.: $20,540,800
Assets: $7,143,430
Liabilities: $4,264,050
Net Worth: $2,879,380
Earnings: $926,170
Emp.: 55
Fiscal Year-end: 10/31/19
Electronic Equipment Mfr & Distr
N.A.I.C.S.: 334413
Hideaki Shioda (CEO)

CASTRO MODEL LTD.

31 Ort Israel Street, Bat Yam, 59590,
Israel
Tel.: (972) 523327090
Web Site: https://www.castro.com
Year Founded: 1950
CAST—(TAE)
Rev.: $487,506,278
Assets: $594,668,591
Liabilities: $429,678,402
Net Worth: $164,990,189
Earnings: $11,736,151
Emp.: 1,890
Fiscal Year-end: 12/31/23
Other Miscellaneous Nondurable
Goods Merchant Wholesalers
N.A.I.C.S.: 424990
Esther Rotter (CEO)

CAT RESOURCE & ASSET HOLDINGS, INC.

Jose Cojuangco Sons Bldg 119 de la
Rosa Street, Legaspi Village, Makati,
Philippines
Tel.: (63) 2 818 3911
Year Founded: 2014
Holding Company
N.A.I.C.S.: 551112

Subsidiaries:

Central Azucarera de Tarlac, Inc. (1)
119 Dela Rosa St, Legaspi Village, Makati,
1200, Philippines
Tel.: (63) 28183911
Web Site: http://www.luisitasugar.com
Sales Range: $10-24.9 Million
Cane Sugar Mfr
N.A.I.C.S.: 311314
Martin Ignacio P. Lorenzo (Chm)

CAT STRATEGIC METALS CORPORATION

1010 789 W Pender St, Vancouver,
V6C 1H2, BC, Canada
Tel.: (604) 674-3145   BC
Web Site: https://catstrategic.com
Year Founded: 2010
CATTF—(OTCIQ)
Assets: $401,509
Liabilities: $661,365
Net Worth: ($259,856)
Earnings: ($1,570,066)
Fiscal Year-end: 12/31/22
Gold Mining Services
N.A.I.C.S.: 212220
Robert Rosner (Chm, Pres & CEO)

CAT TECHNOLOGIES LIMITED

5-4-736 Nampally Stn Road, Hyderabad, 500 001, India
Tel.: (91) 4023202769

Web Site:
https://www.cattechnologies.com
531682—(BOM)
Assets: $1,127,074
Liabilities: $660,519
Net Worth: $466,555
Earnings: ($603,780)
Fiscal Year-end: 03/31/23
Software Development Services
N.A.I.C.S.: 541511
Dhiraj Kumar Jaiswal (Founder &
Mng Dir)

Subsidiaries:

CATT Ltd.   (1)
Bluecross Digital 275 Hagley Road,
Edgbaston, Birmingham, B16 9NB, United
Kingdom
Tel.: (44) 1214544242
Software Development Services
N.A.I.C.S.: 541511

CAT9 GROUP INC.

Room 2001 Dading Century Square
No 387 Tianren Road, Wuhou Dis-
trict, Chengdu, 610000, Sichuan,
China
Tel.: (86) 28 85594777   DE
Year Founded: 2015
CATN—(OTCIQ)
Rev.: $1,572,261
Assets: $517,821
Liabilities: $1,237,584
Net Worth: ($719,763)
Earnings: ($372,978)
Emp.: 16
Fiscal Year-end: 12/31/20
Investment Services
N.A.I.C.S.: 523999
Wenfa Sun (Chm, Pres & CEO)

CATACAP MANAGEMENT AS

Oster Alle 42 7, DK-2100, Copenha-
gen, O, Denmark
Tel.: (45) 71 99 19 00
Web Site: http://catacap.dk
Privater Equity Firm
N.A.I.C.S.: 523999
Vilhelm Hahn-Petersen (Partner)

Subsidiaries:

GSV Materieludlejning AS   (1)
Baldersbuen 5, 2640, Hedehusene, Den-
mark
Tel.: (45) 70 12 13 15
Web Site: http://www.gsv.dk
Machinery & Equipment Rental Services
N.A.I.C.S.: 532412

Subsidiary (Domestic):

Ramirent A/S   (2)
Hundigevej 85, Greve, 2670, Denmark
Tel.: (45) 43958888
Web Site: http://www.ramirent.dk
Machinery & Equipment Rental Services
N.A.I.C.S.: 532412
Carsten Boris (Mgr-Sourcing)

CATALANO SEAFOOD LIMITED

301 Collier Road, Bassendean, 6054,
WA, Australia
Tel.: (61) 893780900   AU
Web Site: https://catalanos.net.au
Year Founded: 1969
CSF—(ASX)
Rev.: $11,034,376
Assets: $5,558,374
Liabilities: $2,358,953
Net Worth: $3,199,422
Earnings: ($3,984,743)
Emp.: 80
Fiscal Year-end: 06/30/22
Fish & Seafood Merchant Wholesal-
ers
N.A.I.C.S.: 424460
Nick Catalano (CEO)

CATALINA RESOURCES LTD

Unit 38 18 Stirling Hwy, Nedlands,
6009, WA, Australia
Tel.: (61) 861181672
Web Site:
https://catalinaresources.com.au
CTN—(ASX)
Rev.: $194,707
Assets: $4,005,465
Liabilities: $630,019
Net Worth: $3,375,446
Earnings: ($554,647)
Fiscal Year-end: 06/30/24
Other Metal Ore Mining
N.A.I.C.S.: 212290
Sanjay Kumar Loyalka (Founder &
Sec)

CATALYST INVESTMENT MANAGERS PTY. LIMITED

Level 9 151 153 Macquarie St, Syd-
ney, 2000, NSW, Australia
Tel.: (61) 0292701200   AU
Web Site:
http://www.catalystinvest.com.au
Sales Range: $25-49.9 Million
Emp.: 10
Privater Equity Firm
N.A.I.C.S.: 523999
Brian Gatfield (Chm)

Subsidiaries:

Cirrus Media Pty. Limited   (1)
Level 2 26-32 Pyrmont Bridge Road,
Locked Bag 2999, Pyrmont, 2009, NSW,
Australia
Tel.: (61) 284840888
Web Site: http://www.cirrusmedia.com.au
Sales Range: $150-199.9 Million
Emp.: 300
Trade Journals Publisher & Information
Services
N.A.I.C.S.: 513120
Gloria Madden (Dir-HR)

Unit (Domestic):

Catch   (2)
Tower 1 L13 495 Victoria Ave, Locked Bag
2999, Chatswood, 2067, NSW, Australia
Tel.: (61) 294222999
Web Site: http://www.catch.com.au
Sales Range: $50-74.9 Million
Emp.: 150
Online Business Directory Publisher
N.A.I.C.S.: 513140
Cherie Nelson (Mgr-Sls & Mktg)

CATALYST MEDIA GROUP PLC

City Registrars Quadrant House Floor
6 4 Thomas More Square, London,
E1W 1YW, United Kingdom
Tel.: (44) 2077348111
Web Site: https://www.cmg-plc.com
CMX—(AIM)
Rev.: $33,943
Assets: $48,307,629
Liabilities: $71,765
Net Worth: $48,235,864
Earnings: $33,205,448
Fiscal Year-end: 06/30/22
Digital Multi-Media Content Distr
N.A.I.C.S.: 541519

CATALYST METALS LIMITED

Level 1 30 Richardson Street, West
Perth, 6005, WA, Australia
Tel.: (61) 863240090
Web Site:
https://www.catalystmetals.com.au
CYL—(ASX)
Rev.: $211,681,356
Assets: $227,351,094
Liabilities: $92,481,971
Net Worth: $134,869,123
Earnings: $15,730,502
Emp.: 500
Fiscal Year-end: 06/30/24

Mineral Explorer
N.A.I.C.S.: 213115
Stephen Boston (Chm)

Subsidiaries:

Superior Gold, Inc.   (1)
70 University Ave Suite 1410, Toronto, M5J
2M4, ON, Canada
Tel.: (647) 925-1293
Web Site: http://www.superior-gold.com
Rev.: $106,147,000
Assets: $109,166,000
Liabilities: $72,034,000
Net Worth: $37,132,000
Earnings: ($4,773,000)
Fiscal Year-end: 12/31/2020
Metal Exploration Services
N.A.I.C.S.: 213114

Vango Mining Limited   (1)
Aurora Place Building 1 Level 29 88 Phillip
Street, Sydney, 2000, NSW,
Australia   (100%)
Tel.: (61) 272089611
Web Site: http://www.vangomining.com
Rev.: $327,706
Assets: $43,647,274
Liabilities: $10,255,129
Net Worth: $33,392,145
Earnings: ($3,688,468)
Fiscal Year-end: 06/30/2021
Gold & Base Metals Mining
N.A.I.C.S.: 212220
Bruce McInnes (Chm)

CATANA GROUP SA

Zone Technique du Port, 66140,
Canet-en-Rousillon, France
Tel.: (33) 468801313
Web Site:
https://www.catanagroup.com
CATG—(EUR)
Sales Range: $100-124.9 Million
Emp.: 250
Sail Construction & Distribution Ser-
vices
N.A.I.C.S.: 336612
Olivier Poncin (Founder)

CATAPULT GROUP INTERNATIONAL LTD.

The Clocktower, 1 Aurora Lane, Vic-
toria, 3008, Australia
Tel.: (61) 3 9095 8401
Web Site:
http://www.catapultsports.com
Year Founded: 2006
Athlete Tracking Equipment Mfr
N.A.I.C.S.: 334519
Adir Shiffman (Chm)

Subsidiaries:

XOS Digital Inc.   (1)
181 Ballardvale Street, Wilmington, MA
01887   (100%)
Tel.: (407) 447-5220
Web Site: http://www.xosdigital.com
Audio-Visual Equipment & Technology for
Sports Teams & Arenas
N.A.I.C.S.: 334310
Matt Bairos (CEO)

CATARC AUTOMOTIVE PROVING GROUND CO., LTD.

Dafeng Port Economic Zone, Dafeng
District, Yancheng, 224100, Jiangsu,
China
Tel.: (86) 51569860935
Web Site: https://www.capg.com.cn
Year Founded: 2011
301215—(SSE)
Rev.: $45,590,688
Assets: $438,265,620
Liabilities: $55,462,212
Net Worth: $382,803,408
Earnings: $19,973,304
Fiscal Year-end: 12/31/22
Automotive Services
N.A.I.C.S.: 541420
Zhang Jiahe (Chm)

CATCHA DIGITAL BERHAD
Co-labs Coworking The Starling Plus
7 Jalan SS 21/39, Damansara
Utama, 47400, Petaling Jaya, Malaysia
Tel.: (60) 376604908
Web Site:
    https://www.catchadigital.com
CATCHA—(KLS)
Rev.: $5,131,483
Assets: $10,983,198
Liabilities: $201,035
Net Worth: $10,782,164
Earnings: $448,503
Fiscal Year-end: 12/31/23
Online Media & Magazine Publishing
N.A.I.C.S.: 513120
Yit Chan Tai (Co-Sec)

CATCHA INVESTMENT CORP.
45-7 the Boulevard, Mid Valley City,
592005, Kuala Lumpur, Malaysia
Tel.: (60) 322970999   Ky
Year Founded: 2020
CHAA—(NYSEAMEX)
Rev.: $2,774,613
Assets: $28,262,634
Liabilities: $38,230,237
Net Worth: ($9,967,603)
Earnings: ($6,189,645)
Emp.: 4
Fiscal Year-end: 12/31/23
Investment Services
N.A.I.C.S.: 523999
Patrick Grove (Chm & CEO)

CATCHER TECHNOLOGY CO., LTD.
No 398 Ren Ai Street, YungKang
Dist, T'ainan, 710, Taiwan
Tel.: (886) 62539000
Web Site: https://www.catcher-
    group.com
Year Founded: 1988
2474—(TAI)
Rev.: $591,055,408
Assets: $8,384,177,747
Liabilities: $3,218,572,330
Net Worth: $5,165,605,417
Earnings: $299,275,472
Emp.: 1,624
Fiscal Year-end: 12/31/23
Electronic Products Mfr
N.A.I.C.S.: 335999

Subsidiaries:

Catcher Technology (Suqian) Co.,
Ltd.   (1)
NO 21 Gu Cheng Road, SuSu Industrial
Park, Suqian, Jiangsu, China
Tel.: (86) 52784675858
Magnesium Alloy Die Casting Mfr
N.A.I.C.S.: 331529

Cepheus International Co., Ltd.   (1)
No 70-2 Chung Ho Villa Shuei Shaing
Hsiang, Chiayi, Taiwan
Tel.: (886) 52894822
Investment Management Service
N.A.I.C.S.: 523940

Cygnus International Co., Ltd.   (1)
66/4-6 Moo 4 Suksawad Road Bangperng,
Prapradaeng District, Samut Prakan,
10230, Thailand
Tel.: (66) 24626316
Web Site: https://www.cygnusintl.com
Waste Water Treatment Services
N.A.I.C.S.: 221320

Envio Technology (Suqian) Co.,
Ltd.   (1)
NO 21 Gu Cheng Road, SuSu Industrial
Park, Suqian, Jiangsu, China
Tel.: (86) 52780975858
Magnesium Alloy Die Casting Mfr
N.A.I.C.S.: 331529

Meeca Technology (Suzhou Industrial
Park) Co., Ltd.   (1)
No 107 Chang Yang Street, Industrial Park,

Suzhou, China
Tel.: (86) 51262955858
Magnesium Alloy Die Casting Mfr
N.A.I.C.S.: 331529

Meeca Technology (Taizhou) Co.,
Ltd.   (1)
No 227 XiangTai Road, Taizhou, China
Tel.: (86) 52386695959
Magnesium Alloy Die Casting Mfr
N.A.I.C.S.: 331529

Topo Technology (Suzhou) Co.,
Ltd.   (1)
No 111 Chang Yang Street, Industrial Park,
Suzhou, China
Tel.: (86) 51262655858
Magnesium Alloy Die Casting Mfr
N.A.I.C.S.: 331529

Topo Technology (Taizhou) Co.,
Ltd.   (1)
No 227 XiangTai Road, Taizhou, China
Tel.: (86) 52386695858
Magnesium Alloy Die Casting Mfr
N.A.I.C.S.: 331529

Uranus International Co., Ltd.   (1)
4F No 12 Lane 538 Zhongzheng Rd, Taipei,
Taiwan
Tel.: (886) 286673636
Web Site: http://www.uranus.tw
Emp.: 30
Clothing Store Operator
N.A.I.C.S.: 458110
Bac Wang (Gen Mgr)

Vito Technology (Suqian) Co.,
Ltd.   (1)
No 21 Gu Cheng Road, SuSu Industrial
Park, Suqian, Jiangsu, China
Tel.: (86) 52780985858
Magnesium Alloy Die Casting Mfr
N.A.I.C.S.: 331529

CATEKS D.D.
Zrinsko-Frankopanska 25, 40000,
Cakovec, Hrvatska, Croatia
Tel.: (385) 40379444
Web Site: https://www.cateks.hr
Year Founded: 1874
CTKS—(ZAG)
Sales Range: Less than $1 Million
Textile Products Mfr
N.A.I.C.S.: 313310
Davor Sabolic (CEO)

CATELLA AB
Birger Jarlsgatan 6, PO Box 5894,
102 40, Stockholm, Sweden
Tel.: (46) 84633310   SE
Web Site: http://www.catella.com
Asset Management & Financial Advisory Services
N.A.I.C.S.: 523940
Johan Claesson (Chm)

Subsidiaries:

Amplion Asset Management Oy   (1)
Aleksanterinkatu 15 B, 100, Helsinki, Finland
Tel.: (358) 10 5220 100
Web Site: http://www.amplion.fi
Asset Management Services
N.A.I.C.S.: 531390
Timo Nurminen (CEO)

Catella Bank SA   (1)
Parc d'Activites 38 r Pafebruch, 8308,
Capellen, Luxembourg
Tel.: (352) 27 751 101
Web Site: http://www.catella.com
Emp.: 150
Real Estate Development Services
N.A.I.C.S.: 531210
Stefan Carlsson (Chm)

Catella Corporate Finance Goteborg
HB   (1)
Ostra Hamngatan 19, 411 10, Gothenburg,
Sweden
Tel.: (46) 31 60 01 70
Web Site: http://www.catella.se
Real Estate Development Services
N.A.I.C.S.: 531210
Anne Almlund Rosengren (Mng Dir)

Catella Corporate Finance Malmo
AB   (1)
Norra Vallgatan 60, 211 22, Malmo, Sweden
Tel.: (46) 40 622 12 00
Real Estate Development Services
N.A.I.C.S.: 531210
Jarl Olsson (Head-Property Advisory)

Catella Corporate Finance SIA   (1)
Duntes 6, 1013, Riga, Latvia
Tel.: (371) 6 7847 382
Real Estate Development Services
N.A.I.C.S.: 531210

Catella Corporate Finance Vilnius
UAB   (1)
Vilniaus g 10, 01116, Vilnius, Lithuania
Tel.: (370) 524 211 01
Real Estate Development Services
N.A.I.C.S.: 531210

Catella France SARL   (1)
4 rue de Lasteyrie, 75116, Paris, France
Tel.: (33) 56 79 79 79
Real Estate Development Services
N.A.I.C.S.: 531210

Catella Investment Management
A/S   (1)
Kongens Nytorv 26 1, 1050, Copenhagen,
Denmark
Tel.: (45) 33 93 75 93
Real Estate Development Services
N.A.I.C.S.: 531210
Peter Gronholt-Pedersen (Mgr-Asset)

Catella Property Benelux SA   (1)
Avenue Louise 326 Tour Bleue, 1050, Brussels, Belgium
Tel.: (32) 2 230 70 00
Real Estate Development Services
N.A.I.C.S.: 531210

Catella Property GmbH   (1)
Bleichstrasse 8-10, 40211, Dusseldorf, Germany
Tel.: (49) 211 527 00 0
Web Site: http://www.catella.de
Real Estate Development Services
N.A.I.C.S.: 531210

Catella Property Spain S.A.   (1)
Fortuny 45 Bajo Dcha, 28010, Madrid,
Spain
Tel.: (34) 91 411 74 96
Real Estate Development Services
N.A.I.C.S.: 531210
Borja Marquez de Amilibia (Mng Dir & Partner)

Catella Real Estate AG   (1)
Alter Hof 5, 80331, Munich, Germany
Tel.: (49) 89 189 16 65 0
Web Site: http://www.catella-realestate.de
Emp.: 30
Real Estate Investment Services
N.A.I.C.S.: 531210
Bernhard Fachtner (Member-Mgmt Bd)

IPM Informed Portfolio Management
AB   (1)
Master Samuelsgatan 6, 11144, Stockholm,
Sweden
Tel.: (46) 8 20 19 29
Web Site: http://www.ipm.se
Emp.: 48
Investment Management Service
N.A.I.C.S.: 523940
Anders Lindell (Chm & Partner)

OU Catella Corporate Finance
Tallin   (1)
Vana-Viru 13/Aia 4-17, 10111, Tallinn, Estonia
Tel.: (372) 5680 4410
Real Estate Development Services
N.A.I.C.S.: 531210

CATENA AB
Landskronavagen 23, SE- 252 32,
Helsingborg, Sweden
Tel.: (46) 424492200   SE
Web Site:
    https://www.catenafastigheter.se
Year Founded: 1967
CATE—(OMX)
Rev.: $179,482,601

Assets: $3,325,490,954
Liabilities: $1,599,062,906
Net Worth: $1,726,428,048
Earnings: $97,881,551
Emp.: 65
Fiscal Year-end: 12/31/23
Logistics Consulting Servies
N.A.I.C.S.: 541614
Sofie Bennsten (Deputy CEO& CFO)

CATENA MEDIA PLC
Quantum Place Triq Ix Xatt, Ta Xbiex,
Gzira, GZR 1052, Malta
Tel.: (356) 2131032   Mt
Web Site:
    https://www.catenamedia.com
Year Founded: 2012
CTM—(OMX)
Rev.: $84,720,168
Assets: $267,166,354
Liabilities: $73,787,394
Net Worth: $193,378,960
Earnings: ($31,109,394)
Emp.: 231
Fiscal Year-end: 12/31/23
Media Advertising Services
N.A.I.C.S.: 541840
Fiona Ewins-Brown (Chief HR Officer)

CATENAE INNOVATION PLC
26 Lansdowne Terrace, Newcastle
upon Tyne, NE3 1HP, United Kingdom
Tel.: (44) 1915808545   UK
Web Site:
    http://www.catenaeinnovation.com
Year Founded: 2003
CTEA—(LSE)
Rev.: $20,295
Assets: $997,446
Liabilities: $315,291
Net Worth: $682,155
Earnings: ($1,044,339)
Emp.: 4
Fiscal Year-end: 09/30/20
Software Development Services
N.A.I.C.S.: 541511
Edward Guy Meyer (CEO)

CATENON S.A.
Paseo De La Castellana 259C 20th
Floor South Office, 28046, Madrid,
Spain
Tel.: (34) 913096980
Web Site: https://www.catenon.com
COM—(MAD)
Sales Range: Less than $1 Million
Emp.: 90
Executive Search Service
N.A.I.C.S.: 561312

CATERING INTERNATIONAL & SERVICES S.A.
40 C Avenue de Hambourg, 13008,
Marseille, France
Tel.: (33) 491165300
Web Site: https://www.cis-
    integratedservices.com
Year Founded: 1992
ALCIS—(EUR)
Rev.: $360,054,090
Assets: $229,242,742
Liabilities: $157,553,814
Net Worth: $71,688,928
Earnings: $3,723,369
Emp.: 14,000
Fiscal Year-end: 12/31/23
Catering Services
N.A.I.C.S.: 722320
Regis Arnoux (Founder, Chm, CEO &
Mgr-Publication)

Subsidiaries:

Cis Brazil Ltda   (1)
R Fiscal Juca 950, Macae, 27930-480, Rio

Catering International & Services S.A.—(Continued)

de Janeiro, Brazil
Tel.: (55) 2227919150
Web Site: http://cisbrasil.com.br
Catering Services
N.A.I.C.S.: 722320

Cis Commodity Inspection Services B.V. (1)
Spoorhaven 8, 2651 AV, Berkel en Roden-rijs, Netherlands
Tel.: (31) 102140589
Web Site: https://www.cis-inspections.com
Commodity Inspection Services
N.A.I.C.S.: 541380

Cis Tchad S.A.R.L. (1)
Avenue Tombalbaye, PO Box 6081, N'djamena, Chad
Tel.: (235) 22516344
Web Site: https://www.cis-chad.com
Emp.: 250
Business Support Services
N.A.I.C.S.: 541611

SARL CIEPTAL (1)
Zone Industrielle de Hassi Messaoud, PO Box 128, Ouargla, Algeria
Tel.: (213) 29 79 74 40
Web Site: http://www.cieptal.com
Catering Management Services
N.A.I.C.S.: 722320

CATHAY CHEMICAL WORKS, INC.
12th Fl No 320 Chung Hsiao E Rd Sec 4, Taipei, 10694, Taiwan
Tel.: (886) 2278111619
Web Site: https://www.ccwi.com.tw
Year Founded: 1962
1713—(TAI)
Rev.: $15,579,024
Assets: $98,620,357
Liabilities: $5,504,366
Net Worth: $93,115,991
Earnings: $11,457,699
Fiscal Year-end: 12/31/23
Chemical Product Mfr & Distr
N.A.I.C.S.: 325180
Jou-Er Ing (Chm)

CATHAY INDUSTRIAL BIO-TECH LTD.
3F Building 5 1690 Cailun Road, Zhangjiang High-tech Park, Shang-hai, 201203, China
Tel.: (86) 2150801916   Ky
Web Site:
http://www.cathaybiotech.com
Sales Range: $100-124.9 Million
Emp.: 1,204
Chemical Intermediates Mfr
N.A.I.C.S.: 325998
Xiucai Liu (Founder, Chm & CEO)

CATHAY INDUSTRIES EU-ROPE N.V.
Industriepark II Pamelstraat-Oost 442, B-9400, Ninove, Belgium
Tel.: (32) 54 311410
Web Site:
http://www.cathayindustries.eu
Synthetic Iron Oxide Pigments Mfr
N.A.I.C.S.: 325180
Roger Currie (CFO)

Subsidiaries:

Hoover Color Corporation (1)
PO Box 218, Hiwassee, VA 24347-0218
Tel.: (540) 980-7233
Web Site: http://www.hoovercolor.com
Iron Oxide Pigments Mfr
N.A.I.C.S.: 325130
Charles Hoover (Pres & CEO)

CATHAY INTERNATIONAL HOLDINGS LIMITED
Suites 1203-4 12/F Li Po Chun Champers 189 Des Voeux Road, Central, China (Hong Kong)

Tel.: (852) 28289289   BM
Web Site: http://www.cathay-intl.com.hk
Year Founded: 2001
CTI—(LSE)
Rev.: $79,761,000
Assets: $355,623,000
Liabilities: $263,577,000
Net Worth: $92,046,000
Earnings: ($11,264,000)
Emp.: 1,461
Fiscal Year-end: 12/31/19
Pharmaceutical Products Mfr & Distr
N.A.I.C.S.: 325412
Zhen Tao Wu (Founder)

Subsidiaries:

Xi'an Haotian Bio-Engineering Tech-nology Co. Limited (1)
Huahai 21 Tuanjienan Road Xi'an Hi-tech Industries Development Zone, Xi'an, 710075, Shaanxi, China
Tel.: (86) 29 88324612
Web Site: http://www.htinc.cn
Emp.: 300
Plant Extract & Chemical Intermediate Mfr
N.A.I.C.S.: 325998

Yangling Dailyhealth Bio-Engineering Technology Co. Limited (1)
5 Xinqiao South Road Yangling Demonstra-tion Zone, Xi'an, 712100, Shaanxi, China
Tel.: (86) 2987071799
Web Site: http://www.htinc.cn
Pharmaceuticals Mfr
N.A.I.C.S.: 325412

CATHAY INVESTMENTS LIM-ITED
Office 37 Airport House Purley Way, Croydon, CR0 0XZ, Surrey, United Kingdom
Tel.: (44) 208 722 5951
Web Site: http://www.cathay-investments.com
Year Founded: 2003
Investment Services
N.A.I.C.S.: 523999
Benjamin Ka Ping Chaing (Mng Dir)

Subsidiaries:

Amethyst Group Limited (1)
Lodge Road, Staplehurst, TN12 0QW, Kent, United Kingdom
Tel.: (44) 1789470880
Web Site: http://www.amethystgroup.co.uk
Portfolio Management Services
N.A.I.C.S.: 523940
Nick John (Mgr-Distr Centre)

Cathay Composites Ltd (1)
Alchorne Place Portsmouth, Portsmouth, PO3 5QU, Hampshire, United Kingdom
Tel.: (44) 8456503663
Fiberglass Distr
N.A.I.C.S.: 424310
Annukka Villanen (Mgr-Sls)

Euroresins International GmbH (1)
Zeiloch 20, 76646, Bruchsal, Germany
Tel.: (49) 7251 302 79 13
Resin Product Distr
N.A.I.C.S.: 424690

Subsidiary (Non-US):

Euroresins Scandinavia Oy (2)
Vasarakuja 1, 67100, Kokkola, Finland
Tel.: (358) 68245800
Resin Product Distr
N.A.I.C.S.: 424690
Joni Saarinen (Mgr-Sls)

Euroresins UK Ltd. (1)
Cloister Way Bridges Road, Ellesmere Port, CH65 4EL, Cheshire, United Kingdom
Tel.: (44) 1513488800
Web Site: http://www.euroresins.com
Premium Composite Products Distr
N.A.I.C.S.: 424690
Edie Putwain (Mng Dir)

Marpex Chemicals Ltd. (1)
Office 37 Airport House Purley Way, Croy-don, CR0 0XZ, United Kingdom

Tel.: (44) 2087225900
Web Site: http://www.marpex.com
Paint Distr
N.A.I.C.S.: 424950
Martyn Gough (Mng Dir)

Perkins Group Services (1)
45 Cobham Road, Ferndown, Dorset, BH21 7QZ, United Kingdom
Tel.: (44) 1202891890
Web Site: http://www.perkinsgroup.co.uk
Toy Distr
N.A.I.C.S.: 423920
Terry Pugh (Dir-Comml & Trading)

Williams of Swansea Limited (1)
Prydwen Road Swansea West Industrial Park, Fforestfach, Swansea, SA5 4HW, United Kingdom
Tel.: (44) 8456448388
Web Site: http://www.williamsdirect.co.uk
Stationery Product Distr
N.A.I.C.S.: 424120

CATHAY MEDIA & EDUCATION GROUP, INC.
22F Block 12 Wanda Plaza No 93 Jianguo Road, Chaoyang, Beijing, 100022, China
Tel.: (86) 1058205558   Ky
Web Site:
http://www.cathaymedia.com
Year Founded: 2017
1981—(HKG)
Educational Support Services
N.A.I.C.S.: 611710
Shulin Pu (Founder, Chm & CEO)

CATHAY ORGANISATION HOLDINGS LTD
22 Martin Road 03-01, Singapore, 239058, Singapore
Tel.: (65) 63378181
Web Site: http://www.cathay.com.sg
Year Founded: 1935
Sales Range: $25-49.9 Million
Emp.: 200
Entertainment, Leisure, Lifestyle & Property Management Services
N.A.I.C.S.: 512199
Suhaimi Rafdi (CEO)

Subsidiaries:

Cathay Cineplexes Sdn Bhd (1)
Level 2 No 2A Jalan PJU 7/3 eCurve, 47800, Petaling Jaya, Malaysia
Tel.: (60) 377270724
Web Site:
http://www.cathayholdings.com.my
Cinema Operator
N.A.I.C.S.: 512131

Cathay-Keris Films Pte Ltd (1)
11 Unity St 02-01 Robertson Walk, Singa-pore, 237995, Singapore
Tel.: (65) 63378181
Cinema Operator
N.A.I.C.S.: 512131

E2Max Centre Pte Ltd (1)
8 Grange Road Cathay Cine Orchid Level 9, Singapore, 239695, Singapore
Tel.: (65) 62359249
Web Site: http://www.e2max.com.sg
Online Game Development Services
N.A.I.C.S.: 541511

Hangout Hotels International Pte Ltd (1)
10A Upper Wilkie Road, Singapore, 228119, Singapore
Tel.: (65) 64385588
Web Site: http://www.hangouthotels.com
Home Management Services
N.A.I.C.S.: 561110

CATHAY PACIFIC AIRWAYS LIMITED
Cathay Pacific City 8 Scenic Road Hong Kong International Airport, Lan-tau, Hong Kong, China (Hong Kong)
Tel.: (852) 27473333   HK

Web Site:
https://www.cathaypacific.com
Year Founded: 1946
CPCAY—(OTCIQ)
Rev.: $5,879,811,260
Assets: $25,360,950,460
Liabilities: $16,042,274,440
Net Worth: $9,318,676,020
Earnings: ($712,743,480)
Emp.: 16,700
Fiscal Year-end: 12/31/21
Passenger & All-Freight Transporta-tion Airline Services
N.A.I.C.S.: 561599
Ronald Lam (CEO)

Subsidiaries:

Asia Miles Limited (1)
PO Box 1024, Tsuen Wan, China (Hong Kong)
Tel.: (852) 27473838
Web Site: https://www.asiamiles.com
Travel Arrangement Services
N.A.I.C.S.: 561510
Paul Smitton (CEO)

Cathay Pacific Catering Services (H.K.) Ltd. (1)
11 Catering Road East Hong Kong Interna-tional Airport, Lan Tau Island, China (Hong Kong)
Tel.: (852) 21162288
Web Site: https://www.cathaydining.com
Sales Range: $250-299.9 Million
Emp.: 1,644
Airline Catering Services
N.A.I.C.S.: 722320

Cathay Pacific Services Limited (1)
3 Chun Wan Road Hong Kong International Airport Lantau, Hong Kong, China (Hong Kong)
Tel.: (852) 27679888
Web Site:
https://www.cathaycargoterminal.com
Air Cargo Services
N.A.I.C.S.: 488119
Aldous Chung (Head-Quality)

Global Logistics System (HK) Com-pany Limited (1)
2/F South Tower Cathay Pacific City 8 Sce-nic Road, Hong Kong International Airport Lantau, Hong Kong, China (Hong Kong)
Tel.: (852) 28331880
Web Site: http://www.glshk.com
Air Cargo Services
N.A.I.C.S.: 488119
Simon Ng (CEO)

Hong Kong Airport Services Ltd. (1)
4/F Cathay Dragon House 11 Tung Fai Road, Hong Kong International Airport, Lan Tau Island, China (Hong Kong)
Tel.: (852) 29280770
Web Site: https://www.has.com.hk
Air Terminal Ramp Handling Services
N.A.I.C.S.: 561499
Agatha Lee (CEO)

Hong Kong Dragon Airlines Limited (1)
Level 5 Dragonair House No 11 Tung Fai Rd Hong Kong Intl Airport, Lan Tau Island, China (Hong Kong)
Tel.: (852) 31933193
Web Site: http://www.dragonair.com
Sales Range: $600-649.9 Million
Emp.: 1,500
Passenger & All-Freight Transportation Air-line Services
N.A.I.C.S.: 481111
Algernon Yau (CEO)

Vogue Laundry Services Limited (1)
95-99 Fuk Hi Street, Yuen Long Industrial Estate, Yuen Long, New Territories, China (Hong Kong)
Tel.: (852) 24603506
Web Site: https://www.voguelaundry.com
Commercial Laundry Services
N.A.I.C.S.: 812332

CATHEDRA BITCOIN INC.
320 638 Broughton Street, Vancou-ver, V6G 3K3, BC, Canada

Tel.: (604) 477-9997 BC
Web Site: https://cathedra.com
Year Founded: 2011
FORT—(TSXV)
Rev.: $1,288,040
Assets: $8,593,775
Liabilities: $154,679
Net Worth: $8,439,097
Earnings: ($812,024)
Fiscal Year-end: 06/30/19
Investment Services
N.A.I.C.S.: 523999
Aydin Kilic *(Founder)*

CATHEDRAL ENERGY SERVICES LTD.
6030 - 3rd Street SE, Calgary, T2H
1K2, AB, Canada
Tel.: (403) 265-2560
Web Site: https://actenergy.com
Year Founded: 2009
CET—(TSX)
Rev.: $31,740,229
Assets: $50,284,958
Liabilities: $19,014,098
Net Worth: $31,270,861
Earnings: ($21,693,407)
Emp.: 118
Fiscal Year-end: 12/31/20
Oil & Natural Gas Extraction Services
N.A.I.C.S.: 213111
Rod Maxwell *(Chm)*

Subsidiaries:

Cathedral Energy Services Inc. (1)
6622 Willowbrook Park Dr, Houston, TX
77066
Tel.: (281) 440-1010
Web Site:
https://www.cathedralenergyservices.com
Oil & Natural Gas Extraction Services
N.A.I.C.S.: 213111

Compass Directional Services
Ltd (1)
400 525 11th Ave SW200, Calgary, T2R
0C9, AB, Canada
Tel.: (403) 237-8799
Web Site:
http://www.compassdirectional.com
Rev.: $22,271,797
Emp.: 35
Drilling Contractor
N.A.I.C.S.: 213111
Rob Savoy *(Pres)*

CATHERWOOD TOWING LTD.
32885 Mission Way, Mission, V2V
6E4, BC, Canada
Tel.: (604) 826-9221
Web Site:
https://www.catherwoodtowing.com
Year Founded: 1971
Emp.: 75
Tug Boat Towing Operations
N.A.I.C.S.: 336612
Trevor Sexton *(CEO)*

CATHOLIC CHURCH INSURANCE LIMITED
485 La Trobe Street, Melbourne,
3000, VIC, Australia
Tel.: (61) 399343000
Web Site:
http://www.ccinsurance.org.au
Rev.: $170,323,400
Assets: $1,033,124,411
Liabilities: $641,469,549
Net Worth: $391,654,863
Earnings: ($11,089,779)
Emp.: 221
Fiscal Year-end: 06/30/19
Insurance Services
N.A.I.C.S.: 524126
Paul A. Gallagher *(Chm)*

CATHRX LTD
5 Parkview Drive, Sydney Olympic
Park, Sydney, 2127, NSW, Australia

Tel.: (61) 293975700 AU
Web Site:
http://www.khelixmedical.com
Sales Range: Less than $1 Million
Emp.: 25
Cardiac Catheter Device Mfr
N.A.I.C.S.: 334510
Roman Greifeneder *(COO)*

CATO SMS
Stationsplein Noord-Ooost 438, 1117
CL, Schiphol, Netherlands
Tel.: (31) 204350580
Web Site: http://www.cato-sms.com
Year Founded: 2019
Regulatory & Clinical Research Services
N.A.I.C.S.: 325412
Mark A. Goldberg *(Exec Chm)*

Subsidiaries:

Cato Research, Ltd. (1)
4364 S Alston Ave Ste 100, Durham, NC
27713
Tel.: (919) 361-2286
Web Site: http://www.cato.com
Rev.: $19,655,000
Emp.: 300
Contract Research Organization
N.A.I.C.S.: 541715
Allen Cato *(Co-Founder & CEO)*

Nuventra, Inc. (1)
2525 Meridian Pkwy Ste 280, Durham, NC
27713-5244
Web Site: http://www.nuventra.com
Scientific & Technical Consulting Services
N.A.I.C.S.: 541690
David Y. Mitchell *(Chief Scientific Officer)*

CATTLELAND FEEDYARDS LTD.
PO Box 2265, Strathmore, T1P 1K2,
AB, Canada
Tel.: (403) 934-4030
Web Site:
https://www.cattlelandfeedyard.com
Year Founded: 1976
Sales Range: $10-24.9 Million
Beef Cattle Feedlots
N.A.I.C.S.: 112112
Keith Gregory *(Gen Mgr)*

CATTLES LIMITED
The Zenith Building 26 Spring Gardens, Manchester, M2 1AB, United
Kingdom
Tel.: (44) 1618384513 UK
Web Site: http://www.cattles.co.uk
Year Founded: 1927
Sales Range: $750-799.9 Million
Emp.: 4,082
Financial Service for the Consumer
Credit Market Services
N.A.I.C.S.: 522320
Margaret Young *(Chm)*

Subsidiaries:

C L Finance Limited (1)
Lawrence House, Riverside Drive, Cleckheaton, BD19 4DH, United
Kingdom (100%)
Tel.: (44) 1924444466
Sales Range: $25-49.9 Million
Emp.: 200
Financial Investment Activities
N.A.I.C.S.: 561440

Cattles Invoice Finance (Oxford)
Limited (1)
Park House The Quadrant, Abingdon Science Park, Abingdon, OX143YS, Oxford,
United Kingdom (100%)
Tel.: (44) 1235849999
Sales Range: $50-74.9 Million
Emp.: 25
Financial Investment Activities
N.A.I.C.S.: 523999

Welcome Financial Services
Limited (1)

Mere Way Ruddington Fields Business
Park, Nottingham, NG11 6NZ, United Kingdom
Tel.: (44) 1159849200
Web Site: http://www.wfs.co.uk
Sales Range: $200-249.9 Million
Emp.: 400
Financial Investment Activities
N.A.I.C.S.: 523999
Robert D. East *(Mng Dir)*

CATTORINI HNOS. S.A.
Crisologo Larralde 1461, B1869AAQ,
Buenos Aires, Argentina
Tel.: (54) 1142042020
Year Founded: 1952
Glass Containers
N.A.I.C.S.: 327213

CATVISION LIMITED
E-14 &15 Sector-8, Noida, 201301,
UP, India
Tel.: (91) 7669300112
Web Site:
https://www.catvisionindia.com
Year Founded: 1985
531158—(BOM)
Rev.: $3,060,775
Assets: $3,996,567
Liabilities: $1,505,262
Net Worth: $2,491,305
Earnings: $17,770
Emp.: 61
Fiscal Year-end: 03/31/22
Cable TV Products Mfr
N.A.I.C.S.: 423690
Syed Athar Abbas *(Mng Dir)*

CAULDRON ENERGY LIMITED
Ground Floor 20 Kings Park Road,
West Perth, 6005, WA, Australia
Tel.: (61) 407981867
Web Site:
https://www.cauldronenergy.com.au
CAULF—(OTCIQ)
Rev.: $650
Assets: $3,290,942
Liabilities: $850,113
Net Worth: $2,440,829
Earnings: ($1,421,243)
Fiscal Year-end: 06/30/22
Uranium Mining & Exploration Services
N.A.I.C.S.: 212290
Simon Youds *(Chm)*

CAUSEWAY AERO GROUP LTD.
Unit 2 Ballinderry Business Par, 58
Ballinderry Road, Lisburn, BT28 2SA,
Northern Ireland, United Kingdom
Tel.: (44) 2896208050
Web Site: http://www.causeway.aero
Year Founded: 2000
Turnkey Single-Source Solutions Provider
N.A.I.C.S.: 334511
Pete Hinds *(VP-Enrng & Bus Dev)*

Subsidiaries:

Race Completions Ltd (1)
Units 7 & 8 Simmonds Buildings Bristol
Road, Hambrook, Bristol, BS16 1RY, United
Kingdom
Tel.: (44) 117 964 9083
Web Site: http://www.racecomp.co.uk
Aircraft Interior Services
N.A.I.C.S.: 336360
Rick Crosby *(Mng Dir)*

CAUSEWAY TECHNOLOGIES LIMITED
Sterling House 20 Station Road, Gerrards Cross, SL9 8EL, Bucks, United
Kingdom
Tel.: (44) 1628 552000 UK
Web Site: https://www.causeway.com
Year Founded: 1999

Emp.: 100
Cloud Software Solutions Services
N.A.I.C.S.: 513210
Phil Brown *(CEO)*

Subsidiaries:

Yotta Limited (1)
Yotta House 8 Hamilton Ter, Leamington
Spa, CV32 4LY, Warks, United Kingdom
Tel.: (44) 8454596882
Web Site: http://www.yottadcl.com
Sales Range: $25-49.9 Million
Emp.: 35
Highway Surveying Services
N.A.I.C.S.: 541370
Nick Smee *(Mng Dir)*

CAVALCADE FORD LINCOLN SALES
420 Ecclestone Dr, Bracebridge, P1L
1V9, ON, Canada
Tel.: (705) 645-8731
Web Site: http://cavalcadeford.com
Rev.: $17,635,033
Emp.: 40
New & Used Car Dealers
N.A.I.C.S.: 441110
Chris Tonge *(Mgr-Fixed Ops)*

CAVALIER RESOURCES LIMITED
Level 2 22 Mount Street, Perth, 6000,
WA, Australia
Tel.: (61) 861888181 AU
Web Site:
https://www.cavalierresources.com
Year Founded: 2019
CVR—(ASX)
Rev.: $742
Assets: $4,289,701
Liabilities: $282,720
Net Worth: $4,006,981
Earnings: ($225,363)
Fiscal Year-end: 06/30/22
Exploration & Mining Services
N.A.I.C.S.: 213115
Damon Cox *(Sec)*

CAVATINA HOLDING SA
Ul Wielicka 28 B, 30-552, Krakow,
Poland
Tel.: (48) 536288119
Web Site: https://www.cavatina.pl
Year Founded: 2007
CAV—(WAR)
Rev.: $23,962,652
Assets: $796,221,289
Liabilities: $498,560,212
Net Worth: $297,661,076
Earnings: $22,993,140
Fiscal Year-end: 12/31/23
Holding Company
N.A.I.C.S.: 551112
Daniel Draga *(VP)*

CAVE INTERACTIVE CO., LTD.
Nakameguro GT Tower 2-1-1 Kameguro, Meguro-ku, Tokyo, 153-0051,
Japan
Tel.: (81) 353663310
Web Site: https://www.cave.co.jp
Year Founded: 1994
3760—(TKS)
Rev.: $81,131,140
Assets: $94,899,770
Liabilities: $50,044,310
Net Worth: $44,855,460
Earnings: $9,749,750
Emp.: 97
Fiscal Year-end: 05/31/24
Mobile Entertainment Services
N.A.I.C.S.: 711410
Hirofumi Ando *(COO)*

CAVE SHEPHERD & CO., LTD.
24 Broad St, Bridgetown, BB11000,
Barbados

Cave Shepherd & Co., Ltd.—(Continued)

Tel.: (246) 6294268
Web Site:
http://www.caveshepherd.com
Year Founded: 1906
CSP—(BARB)
Rev.: $15,535,500
Assets: $48,606,000
Liabilities: $17,516,000
Net Worth: $31,090,000
Earnings: $6,770,500
Fiscal Year-end: 12/31/22
Retail Tourism & Financial Services
N.A.I.C.S.: 459999
Ian P. Gibson (CFO)

Subsidiaries:

Cave Shepherd Card (Barbados)
Inc. (1)
One Haggatt Hall, Saint Michael, BB11059,
Barbados
Tel.: (246) 5394444
Web Site: https://paycedigital.com
Financial Services
N.A.I.C.S.: 523999
Alison Browne-Ellis (CEO)

Duty Free Caribbean Holdings
Ltd. (1)
24 Broad St, Bridgetown,
Barbados (40%)
Tel.: (246) 227 1325
Web Site: http://www.dutyfreecaribbean.com
Emp.: 300
Holding Company; Duty Free Retail Stores
Owner & Operator
N.A.I.C.S.: 551112
Peter Allan (CEO)

CAVENDISH FINANCIAL PLC
One Bartholomew Close, London,
EC1A 7BL, United Kingdom
Tel.: (44) 2072200500 UK
Web Site: https://www.finncap.com
Year Founded: 2007
CAV—(AIM)
Rev.: $71,359,048
Assets: $90,448,591
Liabilities: $45,558,295
Net Worth: $44,890,296
Earnings: $8,840,115
Emp.: 155
Fiscal Year-end: 03/31/22
Investment Banking Services
N.A.I.C.S.: 523150
Richard Snow (Co-CFO)

Subsidiaries:

Cavendish Corporate Finance
LLP (1)
1 Bartholomew Close, London, EC1A 7BL,
United Kingdom
Tel.: (44) 2079080000
Financial Advisory Services
N.A.I.C.S.: 523940
John Farrugia (Mng Partner & Head-Tech)

Cavendish Securities plc (1)
6 7 8 Tokenhouse Yard, London, EC2R
7AS, United Kingdom
Tel.: (44) 2073978900
Web Site: http://www.cenkos.com
Rev.: $43,328,918
Assets: $76,360,888
Liabilities: $41,569,313
Net Worth: $34,791,575
Earnings: $2,449,327
Emp.: 91
Fiscal Year-end: 12/31/2020
Securities Dealing & Investment Banking
N.A.I.C.S.: 523150
Joe Nally (Head-Natural Resources)

**CAVERTON OFFSHORE SUP-
PORT GROUP PLC**
1 Prince Kayode Akingbade Close
Victoria Island, Lagos, Nigeria
Tel.: (234) 12275656
Web Site: https://www.caverton-
offshore.com
Year Founded: 2008

CAVERTON—(NIGE)
Rev.: $21,634,638
Assets: $55,112,455
Liabilities: $46,122,599
Net Worth: $8,989,856
Earnings: $3,823,184
Emp.: 293
Fiscal Year-end: 12/31/22
Oil & Gas Distribution Services
N.A.I.C.S.: 213112
Chesa Okoroafor (CFO)

Subsidiaries:

Caverton Helicopters Limited (1)
Shell Warri Operations Ogunu, Warri, Delta,
Nigeria
Tel.: (234) 8057500999
Oil & Gas Services
N.A.I.C.S.: 213112

CAVINKARE PVT. LTD.
Cavin Villa No 12, Cenotaph Road,
Chennai, 600 018, India
Tel.: (91) 44 66317560 In
Web Site: http://www.cavinkare.com
Year Founded: 1983
Sales Range: $125-149.9 Million
Emp.: 1,000
Consumer Products Mfr
N.A.I.C.S.: 325611
C. K. Ranganathan (Founder, Chm &
Mng Dir)

**CAVMONT CAPITAL HOLD-
INGS ZAMBIA PLC.**
Anglo American Building 1st Floor 74
Independence Avenue, PO Box
38474, Lusaka, Zambia
Tel.: (260) 7160 1 224280
Holding Company
N.A.I.C.S.: 551112
Charles Henry de Beauvoir Carey
(CEO & Mng Dir)

CAVOTEC SA
Corso Elvezia 16, CH-6900, Lugano,
Switzerland
Tel.: (41) 919114010 CH
Web Site: https://www.cavotec.com
CCC—(OMX)
Rev.: $159,560,760
Assets: $180,968,055
Liabilities: $133,644,507
Net Worth: $47,323,548
Earnings: ($15,855,817)
Emp.: 627
Fiscal Year-end: 12/31/22
Power Supply Equipment Design &
Manufacturing Services
N.A.I.C.S.: 333613
Patrik Tigerschiold (Chm)

Subsidiaries:

Cavotec (Swiss) S.A. (1)
Via S Balestra 27, CH 6900, Lugano, Swit-
zerland
Tel.: (41) 919114010
Web Site: http://www.cavotec.com
Sales Range: $25-49.9 Million
Emp.: 20
Power Supply Equipment Design & Manu-
facturing Services
N.A.I.C.S.: 333613

Subsidiary (Non-US):

Cavotec Alfo GmbH (2)
Am Aggerberg 5, 51491, Overath, Germany
Tel.: (49) 220660950
Web Site: http://www.cavotecalfo.com
Power Supply Equipment Design & Manu-
facturing Services
N.A.I.C.S.: 333613

Cavotec Australia (2)
24 Garnet Way, Maddington, Perth, 6109,
NSW, Australia
Tel.: (61) 249565788
Web Site: http://www.cavotec.com.au
Emp.: 40

Power Supply Equipment Design & Manufacturing Services
N.A.I.C.S.: 333613

Cavotec Canada Inc. (2)
860 Denison St 6, Markham, L3R 4H1, ON,
Canada
Tel.: (905) 415-2233
Web Site: http://www.cavotec.com
Sales Range: $25-49.9 Million
Emp.: 6
Power Supply Equipment Design & Manu-
facturing Services
N.A.I.C.S.: 333613

Cavotec Connectors AB (2)
Blockvagen 12, 247 56, Lund, Sweden
Tel.: (46) 46202112
Web Site:
http://www.cavotecconnectors.com
Power Supply Equipment Design & Manu-
facturing Services
N.A.I.C.S.: 333613

Subsidiary (US):

Cavotec Dabico US Inc. (2)
5665 Corporate Ave, Cypress, CA 90630
Tel.: (714) 545-7900
Sales Range: $10-24.9 Million
Aircraft Ground Support Equipment
N.A.I.C.S.: 336413

Subsidiary (Non-US):

Cavotec Dabico UK Ltd. (3)
32 Jay Avenue Teesside Industrial Estate,
Thornaby, Stockton-on-Tees, TS17 9LZ,
United Kingdom
Tel.: (44) 1642608245
Web Site: http://www.cavotec.com
Aircraft Ground Support Equipment
N.A.I.C.S.: 336413

Subsidiary (Non-US):

Cavotec Danmark AS (2)
Rolundvej 19, 5260, Odense, Denmark
Tel.: (45) 63131300
Sales Range: $25-49.9 Million
Emp.: 6
Power Supply Equipment Design & Manu-
facturing Services
N.A.I.C.S.: 333613

Cavotec Deutschland GmbH (2)
Ludwig Erhard Str 1a, 65760, Eschborn,
Germany
Tel.: (49) 6196509500
Web Site: http://www.cavotec.com
Emp.: 20
Power Supply Equipment Design & Manu-
facturing Services
N.A.I.C.S.: 333613

Cavotec Deutschland Holdings
GmbH (2)
Ludwig-Erhard-StraSSe 1a, 65760, Es-
chborn, Germany
Tel.: (49) 6196509500
Web Site: http://www.cavotec.com
Power Supply Equipment Design & Manu-
facturing Services
N.A.I.C.S.: 333613

Cavotec Finland Oy (2)
Olarinluoma 14 B, 02200, Espoo, 02200,
Finland
Tel.: (358) 98870200
Web Site: http://www.cavotec.com
Sales Range: $25-49.9 Million
Emp.: 8
Power Supply Equipment Design & Manu-
facturing Services
N.A.I.C.S.: 333613

Cavotec Fladung GmbH (2)
Heimbach 26, 63776, Mombris, Germany
Tel.: (49) 602997100
Web Site: http://www.fladung.com
Sales Range: $25-49.9 Million
Power Supply Equipment Design & Manu-
facturing Services
N.A.I.C.S.: 333613

Cavotec Hong Kong Ltd. (2)
Room 09 23rd floor Kimberland Center No
55 Wing Hong street, Lai Chi Kok, Kow-
loon, China (Hong Kong)
Tel.: (852) 27916161
Web Site: http://www.cavotec.com

Sales Range: $25-49.9 Million
Emp.: 5
Power Supply Equipment Design & Manu-
facturing Services
N.A.I.C.S.: 333613

Cavotec Iberica S.L. (2)
Muelle Poniente sn Business World, 03001,
Alicante, Spain
Tel.: (34) 066084054
Sales Range: $25-49.9 Million
Emp.: 3
Marine Engineering Services
N.A.I.C.S.: 541330
Jason Smith Hurtado (Reg Mgr-Sls)

Cavotec India Ltd. (2)
901 902 903-9th Floor Lunkad Sky Vista-
New Airport Road, Viman Nagar, Pune,
411057, Maharashtra, India
Tel.: (91) 2040224440
Sales Range: $25-49.9 Million
Emp.: 12
Power Supply Equipment Design & Manu-
facturing Services
N.A.I.C.S.: 333613

Cavotec Latin America S.A. (2)
Bogota 1362, B1640DDL, Buenos Aires,
Argentina
Tel.: (54) 1148362726
Web Site: http://www.cavotec.com
Sales Range: $25-49.9 Million
Emp.: 5
Power Supply Equipment Design & Manu-
facturing Services
N.A.I.C.S.: 333613

Cavotec Micro-control GmbH (2)
Hoerlbacher Strasse 20, 93326, Kelheim,
Germany
Tel.: (49) 9443 92860 0
Power Supply Equipment Design & Manu-
facturing Services
N.A.I.C.S.: 333613

Cavotec Micro-control as (2)
Blockvagen 12, Box 284, Hell, 7517,
Stjordal, Norway
Tel.: (47) 74839860
Sales Range: $25-49.9 Million
Power Supply Equipment Design & Manu-
facturing Services
N.A.I.C.S.: 333613

Cavotec Middle East FZE (2)
Jafza One Tower Office-AB1409, PO Box
261211, Jebel Ali Free Zone, Dubai, 61124,
United Arab Emirates
Tel.: (971) 48838350
Sales Range: $25-49.9 Million
Power Supply Equipment Design & Manu-
facturing Services
N.A.I.C.S.: 333613
Juergen Strommer (Mng Dir)

Cavotec MoorMaster Ltd (2)
Level 1, Unit 9, Amuri Park, 404 Barbadoes
St, Christchurch, 8141, New Zealand
Tel.: (64) 33771226
Power Supply Equipment Design & Manu-
facturing Services
N.A.I.C.S.: 333613

Subsidiary (Non-US):

Cavotec Group Holdings NV (3)
Ohmweg 19, Alblasserdam, 2952 BD, Neth-
erlands
Tel.: (31) 78 693 12 00
Crane & Gantries Machinery Mfr
N.A.I.C.S.: 333923

Subsidiary (Non-US):

Cavotec International Ltd (4)
Unit 5 Saint Annes Industrial Estate, Lim-
eoak Way, Stockton-on-Tees, TS18 2LS,
United Kingdom
Tel.: (44) 1642 608245
Web Site: http://www.cavotec.com
Sales Range: $25-49.9 Million
Emp.: 25
Lift Handling Equipment Mfr
N.A.I.C.S.: 333924

Subsidiary (Domestic):

Cavotec Nederland B.V. (4)
Pompmolenlaan 13C, 3447 GK, Woerden,
Netherlands (100%)

Tel.: (31) 348433032
Web Site: http://www.cavotec.com
Power Supply Equipment Distr
N.A.I.C.S.: 333613
Sietse Nap *(Mng Dir)*

Subsidiary (Non-US):

Cavotec Realty Italia Srl **(4)**
Via Luigi Galvani 1, Nova Milanese, 20054,
Milan, Italy
Tel.: (39) 0362367606
Emp.: 100
Aircraft Equipment Mfr
N.A.I.C.S.: 336413

Cavotec Realty Norway AS **(4)**
Gevinglia 112, Hell, Stjordal, Nord-
Trondelag, Norway
Tel.: (47) 74839860
Power Transmission Equipment Distr
N.A.I.C.S.: 423830

Subsidiary (Non-US):

Cavotec Norge AS **(2)**
Strandveien 6, Mjondalen, 3050, Norway
Tel.: (47) 32274300
Web Site: http://www.cavotec.com
Sales Range: $25-49.9 Million
Emp.: 25
Power Supply Equipment Design & Manu-
facturing Services
N.A.I.C.S.: 333613

Cavotec RMS SA **(2)**
ZI les Bethunes 16 Avenue du Fief, Saint-
Ouen-l'Aumone, 95077, France
Tel.: (33) 130379900
Web Site: http://www.cavotec.com
Sales Range: $25-49.9 Million
Emp.: 10
Power Supply Equipment Design & Manu-
facturing Services
N.A.I.C.S.: 333613

Cavotec Shanghai Ltd. **(2)**
Unit 11 No 1951 Duhui Rd, Xinzhuang In-
dustrial Zone, Shanghai, 200008, Minhang
District, China
Tel.: (86) 2154429778
Web Site: http://www.cavotec.com
Sales Range: $25-49.9 Million
Emp.: 90
Power Supply Equipment Design & Manu-
facturing Services
N.A.I.C.S.: 333613

Cavotec Singapore PTE Ltd. **(2)**
21 Toh Guan Road East 01-10, Toh Guan
Centre, Singapore, 608609, Singapore
Tel.: (65) 68622545
Web Site: http://www.cavotec.com
Emp.: 4
Power Supply Equipment Design & Manu-
facturing Services
N.A.I.C.S.: 333613

Cavotec South Africa (Pty.) Ltd. **(2)**
PO Box 16897, Atlasville, Johannesburg,
1465, Gauteng, South Africa
Tel.: (27) 119630015
Sales Range: $25-49.9 Million
Emp.: 5
Power Supply Equipment Design & Manu-
facturing Services
N.A.I.C.S.: 333613

Cavotec Specimas S.p.A. **(2)**
Via Galvani 1, 20054, Nova Milanese, Italy
Tel.: (39) 0362455101
Web Site: http://www.specimas.it
Sales Range: $25-49.9 Million
Power Supply Equipment Design & Manu-
facturing Services
N.A.I.C.S.: 333613
Patrick Rosenwald *(Mng Dir)*

Cavotec Sverige AB **(2)**
Fagerstagatan 5, 163 53, Spanga, Sweden
Tel.: (46) 855652200
Sales Range: $25-49.9 Million
Emp.: 16
Power Supply Equipment Design & Manu-
facturing Services
N.A.I.C.S.: 333613
Erik Chilo *(Mng Dir)*

Subsidiary (US):

Cavotec US Holdings Inc **(2)**

2711 Cranlyn Rd, Shaker Heights, OH
44122
Tel.: (216) 464-5461
Investment Management Service
N.A.I.C.S.: 523999

Cavotec USA Inc. **(2)**
500 S Main St Bldg Ste 1 Ste 109, Moores-
ville, NC 28115
Tel.: (704) 873-3009
Web Site: http://www.cavotec.com
Sales Range: $25-49.9 Million
Power Supply Equipment Design & Manu-
facturing Services
N.A.I.C.S.: 333613

INET Airport Systems, Inc. **(2)**
4111 N Palm St, Fullerton, CA 92835
Tel.: (714) 888-2700
Web Site: http://www.inetas.com
Sales Range: $10-24.9 Million
Wholesale Aircraft Parts & Equipment Mfr &
Sales
N.A.I.C.S.: 336413

Cavotec CIS Ltd. **(1)**
Of 206 84a Shkolnaya Str, Vidnoe, Mos-
cow, 142703, Russia
Tel.: (7) 495 663 91 97
Sales Range: $25-49.9 Million
Emp.: 6
Engineeering Services
N.A.I.C.S.: 541330
Andrei Bondar *(Deputy Mng Dir)*

Cavotec Engineering Services India
Pvt. Ltd. **(1)**
901 902 903 9th Floor Lunkad Sky Vista,
Koregoan Park, Pune, 411014, Maharash-
tra, India
Tel.: (91) 20 6725 5000
Web Site: http://www.cavotec.com
Sales Range: $25-49.9 Million
Emp.: 30
Engineeering Services
N.A.I.C.S.: 541330

Cavotec Korea Ltd **(1)**
5th Floor Gookto Building 160-7 Garak-
dong, Song pa-gu, Seoul, Korea (South)
Tel.: (82) 5 663 91 97
Automated Crane System Mfr
N.A.I.C.S.: 333923

Cavotec MSL Holdings Limited - Ca-
votec Italia Division **(1)**
Via Galvani 1, 20834, Nova Milanese,
Monza and Brianza, Italy
Tel.: (39) 0362 36 76 06
Sales Range: $25-49.9 Million
Emp.: 5
Marine Engineering Services
N.A.I.C.S.: 541330
Elio Crovetto *(Gen Mgr)*

CAWACHI LIMITED
1293 Soshima, Tokyo, 323-0061,
Tochigi, Japan
Tel.: (81) 285371111
Web Site: http://www.cawachi.co.jp
Year Founded: 1980
2664—(TKS)
Rev.: $1,890,195,600
Assets: $1,296,346,590
Liabilities: $560,686,640
Net Worth: $735,659,950
Earnings: $31,152,930
Emp.: 2,722
Fiscal Year-end: 03/31/24
Pharmaceutical Products Distr
N.A.I.C.S.: 424210

**CAXTON AND CTP PUBLISH-
ERS AND PRINTERS LTD.**
368 Jan Smuts Avenue, Craighall,
Johannesburg, 2196, South Africa
Tel.: (27) 118890600
Web Site: https://www.caxton.co.za
CAT—(JSE)
Rev.: $368,326,556
Assets: $484,585,547
Liabilities: $99,233,093
Net Worth: $385,352,454
Earnings: $39,706,588
Emp.: 4,275

Fiscal Year-end: 06/30/23
Printing, Publishing & Distribution
N.A.I.C.S.: 323111
P. M. Jenkins *(Chm)*

Subsidiaries:

CTP Digital Services Pty Ltd. **(1)**
456 Granite Drive Kya Sands Business
Park, Kya Sands, Johannesburg, 2163,
South Africa
Tel.: (27) 117083570
DVD & CD Mfr
N.A.I.C.S.: 334610

Cognition Holdings Limited **(1)**
Cognition House Cnr Bram Fischer Drive &
Will Scarlet Road, Randburg, 2194, South
Africa **(75.52%)**
Tel.: (27) 112930000
Web Site:
https://www.cognitionholdings.co.za
Rev.: $4,182,805
Assets: $14,061,976
Liabilities: $1,465,480
Net Worth: $12,596,496
Earnings: $510,364
Emp.: 85
Fiscal Year-end: 06/30/2023
Investment Management Services; Tele-
communications
N.A.I.C.S.: 523940
Mark Allan Smith *(CEO)*

Subsidiary (Domestic):

Adcheck Proprietary Limited **(2)**
Cognition House Cnr Bram Fischer Dr and
Will Scarlet Rd, Blairgowrie Randburg, Jo-
hannesburg, 2194, South Africa
Tel.: (27) 11 615 7007
Web Site: https://www.adcheck.co.za
Advertising Services
N.A.I.C.S.: 541890
Angela Adamson *(Mng Dir)*

BMI Sports Info Proprietary
Limited **(2)**
Cnr Bram Fischer & Will Scarlet Drive,
Ferndale, Randburg, 2194, South Africa
Tel.: (27) 11 293 0000
Web Site: https://www.bmisportinfo.co.za
Sports Track Services
N.A.I.C.S.: 611620

Flip File (Pty) Ltd. **(1)**
14 Purdey Road, Sheffield Business Park
Philippi, Cape Town, South Africa
Tel.: (27) 21 691 0477
Web Site: https://www.flipfile.co.za
Stationery Product Mfr
N.A.I.C.S.: 322230

Health Spas Guide (Pty) Ltd. **(1)**
58 Nelson Road, Berea, Durban, 4001,
South Africa
Tel.: (27) 861771772
Web Site: http://www.healthspas.co.za
Spa Services
N.A.I.C.S.: 812199

Highway Mail (Pty) Ltd. **(1)**
115 Escom Road, New Germany, Pinetown,
South Africa
Tel.: (27) 317164444
Web Site: https://www.highwaymail.co.za
Newspaper Publishers
N.A.I.C.S.: 513110

Shumani Mills Communications (Pty)
Ltd. **(1)**
2 Koets Street Tygerberg Business Park,
Cape Town, 7500, South Africa
Tel.: (27) 219516391
Web Site: https://www.shumanimills.co.za
Printing Services
N.A.I.C.S.: 323113

Zululand Observer (Pty) Ltd. **(1)**
105A Bullion Boulevard, Richards Bay,
South Africa
Tel.: (27) 357990500
Web Site: http://www.zululandobserver.co.za
Newspaper Publishers
N.A.I.C.S.: 513110
Gavin Anthony *(Mng Dir)*

Zululand Observer (Pty) Ltd. **(1)**
105A Bullion Boulevard, Richards Bay,
South Africa

Tel.: (27) 357990500
Web Site: http://www.zululandobserver.co.za
Newspaper Publishers
N.A.I.C.S.: 513110
Gavin Anthony *(Mng Dir)*

Zululand Observer (Pty) Ltd. **(1)**
105A Bullion Boulevard, Richards Bay,
South Africa
Tel.: (27) 357990500
Web Site: http://www.zululandobserver.co.za
Newspaper Publishers
N.A.I.C.S.: 513110
Gavin Anthony *(Mng Dir)*

Zululand Observer (Pty) Ltd. **(1)**
105A Bullion Boulevard, Richards Bay,
South Africa
Tel.: (27) 357990500
Web Site: http://www.zululandobserver.co.za
Newspaper Publishers
N.A.I.C.S.: 513110
Gavin Anthony *(Mng Dir)*

**CAYENNE ENTERTAINMENT
TECHNOLOGY CO., LTD.**
3F No 31 Lane 583 Ruiguang Road,
Neihu District, Taipei, 11492, Taiwan
Tel.: (886) 287512168
Web Site:
https://www.cayennetech.com.tw
Year Founded: 2006
4946—(TPE)
Rev.: $3,567,020
Assets: $5,359,285
Liabilities: $3,895,007
Net Worth: $1,464,278
Earnings: ($3,667,761)
Fiscal Year-end: 12/31/22
Online Game Development Services
N.A.I.C.S.: 541511
Teng Jun-Tse *(Chm)*

CAYENNE GOLD MINES LTD.
470 Granville St Ste 422, Vancouver,
V6C 1V5, BC, Canada
Tel.: (604) 687-8623   BC
Year Founded: 2001
Emp.: 10
Gold Mining & Exploration Services
N.A.I.C.S.: 212220
H. Alexander Briden *(Pres & CEO)*

CAYMAN AIRWAYS LTD.
181 Owen Roberts Dr, PO Box
10092, Georgetown, KY1-1001,
Grand Cayman, Cayman Islands
Tel.: (345) 9498200   Ky
Web Site:
http://www.caymanairways.com
Year Founded: 1968
Sales Range: $75-99.9 Million
Emp.: 333
Airline
N.A.I.C.S.: 481111
Fabian Whorms *(Pres & CEO)*

**CAYMAN ENGLEY INDUS-
TRIAL CO., LTD.**
No 2379 Zhuoyue Str High-Tech De-
velopment Zone, Changchun, Jilin,
China
Tel.: (86) 4318 502 2771   Ky
Web Site: http://www.engley.com
Year Founded: 2015
2239—(TAI)
Rev.: $3,316,100,528
Assets: $4,958,476,490
Liabilities: $2,898,486,532
Net Worth: $2,059,989,958
Earnings: $126,469,646
Fiscal Year-end: 12/31/20
Automobile Body Part Mfr & Distr
N.A.I.C.S.: 336310
Chi-Pin Lin *(Chm & Gen Mgr)*

Subsidiaries:

Changchun Engley Automobile Industry Co., Ltd. **(1)**

Cayman Engley Industrial Co., Ltd.—(Continued)

888 Shunda Rd High-tech Zone, Changchun, Jilin, China
Tel.: (86) 431870308016
Automobile Parts Mfr & Distr
N.A.I.C.S.: 336370

CAYMAN GOLDEN CENTURY WHEEL GROUP LIMITED
Fl 4 Willow House Cricket Sq, PO Box 2084, Georgetown, KY1-1112, Cayman Islands
Tel.: (345) 27808863
900280—(KRS)
Rev.: $271,274,510
Assets: $1,093,479,089
Liabilities: $191,732,540
Net Worth: $901,746,549
Earnings: ($1,099,592,236)
Emp.: 397
Fiscal Year-end: 12/31/23
Tire Mfr & Distr
N.A.I.C.S.: 326211

CAYMAN ISLANDS MONETARY AUTHORITY
80 Shedden Road Elizabethan Square, PO Box 10052, Georgetown, KY1 - 1001, Grand Cayman, Cayman Islands
Tel.: (345) 9497089
Web Site: http://www.cimoney.com.ky
Year Founded: 1997
Sales Range: $10-24.9 Million
Banking Services
N.A.I.C.S.: 521110
Cindy Scotland (Mng Dir)

CAYMAN ISLANDS STOCK EXCHANGE LIMITED
4th Floor Elizabethan Square, PO Box 2408, KY1-1105, Georgetown, Cayman Islands
Tel.: (345) 9456060
Web Site: http://www.csx.ky
Sales Range: $25-49.9 Million
Emp.: 8
Stock Exchange Services
N.A.I.C.S.: 523210
Eva Holt (Deputy Head-Listings & Compliance)

CAZ (THAILAND) PUBLIC COMPANY LIMITED
239 Huaypong-Nongbon Rd T Huaypong, A Muangrayong, Rayong, 21150, Thailand
Tel.: (66) 38606242
Web Site: https://www.caz.co.th
Year Founded: 2014
CAZ—(THA)
Rev.: $92,341,213
Assets: $67,335,449
Liabilities: $38,685,385
Net Worth: $28,650,104
Earnings: $6,390,674
Emp.: 3,726
Fiscal Year-end: 12/31/23
Building Construction Services
N.A.I.C.S.: 236210
C. S. Hong (CEO)

CAZALY RESOURCES LIMITED
Level 2 38 Richardson Street, West Perth, 6005, WA, Australia
Tel.: (61) 893226283
Web Site:
    http://www.cazalyresources.com.au
CAZ—(ASX)
Rev.: $198,628
Assets: $10,773,161
Liabilities: $261,428
Net Worth: $10,511,733
Earnings: ($595,789)
Fiscal Year-end: 06/30/24

Minerals Exploration
N.A.I.C.S.: 213115
Clive Bruce Jones (Co-Mng Dir)

CAZOO GROUP LTD.
27 Old Gloucester Street, London, WC1N 3AX, United Kingdom
Tel.: (44) 2039013488   Ky
Web Site: https://www.cazoo.co.uk
Year Founded: 2018
CZOO—(NYSE)
Rev.: $1,695,236,973
Assets: $1,174,297,459
Liabilities: $1,075,728,345
Net Worth: $98,569,114
Earnings: ($955,677,384)
Emp.: 3,226
Fiscal Year-end: 12/31/22
Used Car Dealers
N.A.I.C.S.: 441120
Paul Woolf (CFO)

CB AUSTRALIA LIMITED
Level 8 3 Spring Street, Sydney, 2000, NSW, Australia
Tel.: (61) 292239223
Web Site: http://www.cbal.com.au
Sales Range: $1-9.9 Million
Emp.: 168
Real Estate Services
N.A.I.C.S.: 531390
John Bell (COO & Sec)

Subsidiaries:

Admerex (Singapore) Pte Limited   (1)
51 Goldhill Plz No 22-01, Goldhill Plz, Singapore, 308900, Singapore
Tel.: (65) 62582318
Software Development Services
N.A.I.C.S.: 513210

CB ENERGOTRANSBANK JSC
Ul Clinical D 83-A, 236016, Kaliningrad, Russia
Tel.: (7) 4012590099
Web Site:
    http://www.energotransbank.com
Sales Range: Less than $1 Million
Commercial Banking Services
N.A.I.C.S.: 522110

CB ENGINEERING LTD
5040 - 12A Street SE, Calgary, T2G 5K9, AB, Canada
Tel.: (403) 259-6220
Web Site: http://www.cbeng.com
Year Founded: 1974
Rev.: $12,520,073
Emp.: 45
Industrial Equipment Distr
N.A.I.C.S.: 423830
Craig Bowyer (Founder)

CB GROUP MANAGEMENT CO., LTD.
223 Minamiaoyama, Minato-Ku, Tokyo, 107-0062, Japan
Tel.: (81) 337965075   JP
Web Site: https://www.cbgm.co.jp
Year Founded: 1920
9852—(TKS)
Rev.: $973,547,240
Assets: $351,658,610
Liabilities: $188,477,540
Net Worth: $163,181,070
Earnings: $13,596,770
Emp.: 35
Fiscal Year-end: 03/31/24
Holding Company
N.A.I.C.S.: 551112
Seiichiro Kojima (Pres)

CB INDUSTRIAL PRODUCT HOLDING BERHAD
Lot 4 Jalan Waja 15 Kawasan Perusahaan Telok Panglima Garang,

42500, Shah Alam, Selangor, Malaysia
Tel.: (60) 331227117   MY
Web Site: https://www.cbip.com.my
Year Founded: 1980
CBIP—(KLS)
Rev.: $183,073,575
Assets: $269,918,591
Liabilitio: $82,318,805
Net Worth: $187,599,696
Earnings: $16,379,190
Fiscal Year-end: 12/31/23
Palm Oil Mill Processing Equipment Trading Services
N.A.I.C.S.: 333241
Chee Meng Mak (Exec Dir)

Subsidiaries:

AVP Engineering (M) Sdn. Bhd.   (1)
Lot 4 Jalan Waja 16 Kawasan Perusahaan Telok Panglima Garang, 42500, Telok Panglima Garang, Selangor Darul Ehsan, Malaysia
Tel.: (60) 331228262
Web Site: https://www.avp.com.my
Ambulances & Fire Fighting Vehicle Mfr
N.A.I.C.S.: 336211

Advance Boilers Sdn. Bhd.   (1)
Lot 6074 Jalan Haji Abdul Manan, Meru, 42200, Kapar, Selangor, Malaysia
Tel.: (60) 333928091
Web Site:
    http://www.advanceboilers.com.my
Boiler Mfr
N.A.I.C.S.: 332410

Avecpalm Marketing Resources Sdn. Bhd.   (1)
No 1 Jalan Astaka U8 / 83 Seksyen 8, Bukit Jelutong, 40150, Shah Alam, Selangor, Malaysia
Tel.: (60) 378454115
Web Site: http://www.avecpalm.com
Oil Mill Equipment Mfr
N.A.I.C.S.: 333132

PT Berkala Maju Bersama   (1)
JlNila Putih No 08 Kelurahan Bukit Tunggal, Kecamatan Jekan Raya, Kalimantan, Indonesia
Tel.: (62) 5363233427
Web Site: http://www.pt-bmb.com
Palm Oil Plant Production Services
N.A.I.C.S.: 115112

PalmitEco Engineering Sdn. Bhd.   (1)
Lot 4 Jalan Waja 15 Kawasan Perusahaan, 42500, Teluk Panglima Garang, Selangor, Malaysia
Tel.: (60) 33 122 7117
Web Site: https://www.palmiteco.com.my
Oil Mill Equipment Mfr
N.A.I.C.S.: 333132
Lim Chai Beng (Mng Dir)

TPG Aeronautik Sdn. Bhd.   (1)
Lot 4 Jalan Waja 16 Kawasan Perusahaan, 42500, Teluk Panglima Garang, Selangor, Malaysia
Tel.: (60) 331228262
Web Site: http://www.tpgaeronautik.com
Aeronautic Product Distr
N.A.I.C.S.: 423860

TPG Oil & Gas Sdn. Bhd.   (1)
Lot 2859 PLO71 Jalan Nibong 5 Kawasan Perindustrian, Tanjung Langsat Pasir Gudang, 81700, Johor Bahru, Malaysia
Tel.: (60) 7 255 5678
Web Site: https://www.tpgog.com.my
Oil & Gas Operation Services
N.A.I.C.S.: 213112
Lim Chai Beng (Chm)

CB KHLYNOV JSC
Ul Uritskogo 40, Kirov, 610002, Russia
Tel.: (7) 8332252777
Web Site: http://www.bank-hlynov.ru
Sales Range: Less than $1 Million
Mortgage Banking Services
N.A.I.C.S.: 522292

CB KUBAN CREDIT LIMITED LIABILITY COMPANY
House Number 32 Krasnoarmeyskaya Street, 350000, Krasnodar, Russia
Tel.: (7) 8612748889
Web Site: http://www.kubankredit.ru
Year Founded: 1993
Sales Range: Less than $1 Million
Commercial Banking Services
N.A.I.C.S.: 522110

CB LOCKO-BANK JSC
39/80 Leningradsky av, 125167, Moscow, Russia
Tel.: (7) 8002505050
Web Site: http://www.lockobank.ru
Year Founded: 1994
Rev.: $129,837,330
Assets: $2,134,213,740
Liabilities: $1,846,157,790
Net Worth: $288,055,950
Earnings: $33,472,950
Emp.: 1,628
Fiscal Year-end: 12/31/20
Commercial Banking Services
N.A.I.C.S.: 522110

CB RENAISSANCE CREDIT LLC
Ul Kozhevnicheskaya 14, Moscow, 115114, Russia
Tel.: (7) 4957834600
Web Site: http://www.rencredit.ru
Sales Range: Less than $1 Million
Financial Support Services
N.A.I.C.S.: 541611
Alexey Valeryevich Levchenko (Chm-Mgmt Bd)

CB SOLIDARNOST JSC
90 Kuibyshev Street, 443099, Samara, Russia
Tel.: (7) 8007009220
Web Site: http://www.solid.ru
Sales Range: Less than $1 Million
Mortgage Banking Services
N.A.I.C.S.: 522292
Vyacheslav Petrovich Arbuzov (Chm-Mgmt Bd-Acting)

CBA ASSET MG OR
8 rue Bovy-Lysberg, 1204, Geneva, Switzerland
Tel.: (41) 228071474
Year Founded: 1994
CBAM—(BUL)
Sales Range: Less than $1 Million
Asset Management Services
N.A.I.C.S.: 523940

CBAK ENERGY TECHNOLOGY, INC.
CBAK Industrial Park Meigui Street, Huayuankou Economic Zone, Dalian, 116450, Liaoning, China
Tel.: (86) 41139185985   NV
Web Site: https://www.cbak.com.cn
CBAT—(NASDAQ)
Rev.: $248,725,485
Assets: $244,032,734
Liabilities: $119,654,237
Net Worth: $124,378,497
Earnings: ($9,448,446)
Emp.: 1,063
Fiscal Year-end: 12/31/22
Rechargeable Batteries Mfr
N.A.I.C.S.: 335910
Yunfei Li (Chm, Pres & CEO)

Subsidiaries:

Nanjing Cbak New Energy Technology Co., Ltd.   (1)
Cangxi Rd 5, Gaochun Economic Development Zone, Nanjing, China
Tel.: (86) 2557878089

Web Site: https://en.cbak.com.cn
Lithium Battery Mfr & Distr
N.A.I.C.S.: 335311

CBC CO., LTD.
2 15 13 Tsukishima, Chuo-ku, Tokyo,
104-0052, Japan
Tel.: (81) 335364500   JP
Web Site: http://www.cbc.co.jp
Year Founded: 1925
Sales Range: $10-24.9 Million
Emp.: 432
Electronic Components & Plastics Mfr
N.A.I.C.S.: 325211
Masataro Doi (COO & VP)

Subsidiaries:

CBC (Beijing) Trading Co., Ltd.   (1)
Room B905-A Tian Yuan Gang Center No
C2 Dong San Huan Bei-Lu, Chao Yang Dis-
trict, Beijing, 100027, China
Tel.: (86) 10 6410 8081
Emp.: 20
Resin Product Mfr
N.A.I.C.S.: 325211
Takeshi Ikeno (Gen Mgr)

CBC (Deutschland) GmbH   (1)
Hansaallee 191, Dusseldorf, 40549,
Germany   (100%)
Tel.: (49) 211530670
Web Site: http://www.cbc-de.com
Sales Range: $25-49.9 Million
Emp.: 40
Mfr & Supplier of CCTV Equipment & Opti-
cal Lenses
N.A.I.C.S.: 333310
Fumiya Sagawa (Mng Dir)

CBC (Europe) Ltd.   (1)
7-8 Garrick Industrial Ctr Irving Way, Lon-
don, NW9 6AQ, United Kingdom   (100%)
Tel.: (44) 2087323333
Web Site: http://www.cbceurope.com
Mfr & Supplier of CCTV Equipment & Opti-
cal Lenses
N.A.I.C.S.: 333310

CBC (Guangzhou) Trading Co.,
Ltd   (1)
Room 1207 CITIC Plaza No 233 Tian He
North Road, Guangzhou, China
Tel.: (86) 20 8752 0039
Resin Product Mfr
N.A.I.C.S.: 325211
Shusaku Kawai (Gen Mgr)

CBC (H.K.) Co., Ltd.   (1)
Tower 5 8901 sem, Unit 901 9/F Tower 5
China Hon, Kowloon, China (Hong
Kong)   (100%)
Tel.: (852) 28871326
Web Site: http://www.cbc.co.hk
Emp.: 14
N.A.I.C.S.: 325211
Kawai Shusaku (Gen Mgr)

CBC (H.K.) Co., Ltd. - Kwun Tong
Branch   (1)
423 China Hong Kong City, 53 Canton Rd,
Kowloon, China (Hong Kong)   (100%)
Tel.: (852) 23458686
Web Site: http://www.cbc.co.hk
N.A.I.C.S.: 325211

CBC (Poland) Sp.zo.o.   (1)
UL G Morcinka 5 Paw 6, 1496, Warsaw,
Poland   (100%)
Tel.: (48) 226384440
Web Site: http://www.cbcpoland.pl
Mfr & Supplier of CCTV Equipment & Opti-
cal Lenses
N.A.I.C.S.: 333310

CBC (Shanghai) Trading Co.,
Ltd.   (1)
Room B-2703 Dawning Centre No 500
HongBaoShi Road, Changning District,
Shanghai, China
Tel.: (86) 21 32092626
Web Site: http://www.cbc-china.cn
Emp.: 55
Plastics Mfr & Distr
N.A.I.C.S.: 325211

CBC (Thailand) Co., Ltd.   (1)
21st Fl ITF Tower 140/48 Silom Rd, Bang-

kok, 10500, Thailand   (100%)
Tel.: (66) 22316181
Web Site: http://www.cbcthailand.com
Emp.: 20
N.A.I.C.S.: 325211
Utaro Doi (Pres)

CBC America Co., Ltd.   (1)
20521 Earl St, Torrance, CA 90503-3006
Tel.: (310) 793-1500
Web Site: http://www.cbcamerica.com
Distr of Security Camera Lenses, Tubes &
Products
N.A.I.C.S.: 334220
Jim Holihan (VP)

CBC America Co., Ltd.   (1)
55 Mall Dr, Commack, NY
11725-5703   (100%)
Tel.: (631) 864-9700
Web Site: http://www.cbcamerica.com
Distr of Optical Lenses & Security Cameras
N.A.I.C.S.: 423410

Subsidiary (Domestic):

Broadsight Systems Inc.   (2)
1124 Louise Rd, Winston Salem, NC 27107
Tel.: (336) 837-1272
Web Site:
    http://www.broadsightsystems.com
Emp.: 25
Video Equipment Mfr
N.A.I.C.S.: 334310
Joseph Fleming (Plant Mgr)

Division (Domestic):

CBC AMERICA Corp. - LOS ANGE-
LES Division   (2)
21241 S Western Ave Ste 160, Torrance,
CA 90501
Tel.: (310) 222-8600
Web Site: http://www.canganzsecurity.com
Resin Product Mfr
N.A.I.C.S.: 325211

CBC CORPORATION (INDIA) Pvt.
Ltd.   (1)
2nd Floor B Wing Marwah Centre Krishanlal
Marwah Marg, Andheri East, Mumbai, 400
072, India
Tel.: (91) 22 2857 9798
Web Site: http://www.global-cbc.com
Emp.: 10
Resin Product Mfr
N.A.I.C.S.: 325211
Durgesh Sharma (Mng Dir)

CBC Co (Milan) Ltd   (1)
Via E Majorana 2, Nova, 20054, Milan,
Italy   (100%)
Tel.: (39) 0362365079
Web Site: http://www.cbc.it
Mfr & Supplier of CCTV Equipment & Opti-
cal Lenses
N.A.I.C.S.: 333310

CBC Co. (Paris) Ltd.   (1)
1 Ave Des Marguerites Zone D Activites
Des Petits Carreaux, 94389, Bonneuil,
France   (100%)
Tel.: (33) 143990424
Web Site: http://www.cbcfrance.com
Mfr & Supplier of CCTV Equipment & Opti-
cal Lenses
N.A.I.C.S.: 333310

CBC Co., Ltd. - Mishima Factory (1)
100 Hirata, Mishima, 411-0821, Shizuoka,
Japan
Tel.: (81) 55 991 7300
Web Site: http://www.cbc.co.jp
Resin Product Mfr
N.A.I.C.S.: 325211

CBC EUROPE S.r.l.   (1)
Via E Majorana 2, 20834, Nova Milanese,
Monza and Brianza, Italy
Tel.: (39) 0362 365079
Web Site: http://www.cbceurope.it
Resin Product Mfr
N.A.I.C.S.: 325211

CBC FORMA Co., Ltd.   (1)
700/869 Moo 5 Amata Nakorn Industrial
Estate, Nongkhaka, 20160, Chonburi, Thai-
land
Tel.: (66) 38 185 462
Resin Product Mfr
N.A.I.C.S.: 325211

CBC IBERIA S.A.   (1)
Av Digonal 605 8-3, 08028, Barcelona,
Spain
Tel.: (34) 93 444 7597
Web Site: http://www.cbciberia.es
Resin Product Mfr
N.A.I.C.S.: 325211

CBC INGS (CHANGSHU) Co.,
Ltd.   (1)
No 32 Xietang Road Fangbang Industrial
Park Yushan, New High-Tech Industrial
Park, Changshu, 215523, Jiangsu, China
Tel.: (86) 512 5233 2211
Resin Product Mfr
N.A.I.C.S.: 325211

CBC INGS (DONG GUAN) Co.,
Ltd.   (1)
Zhen An West Road No 303 Shang Jiao
Industrial Changan-Zhen, Dongguan,
523878, Guang Dong, China
Tel.: (86) 769 8238 9200
Web Site: http://www.dgcbc.cn
Plastic Molding Mfr
N.A.I.C.S.: 325211

CBC INGS AMERICA Inc.   (1)
3137 E 6th St, Muscle Shoals, AL 35660
Tel.: (256) 383-7600
Web Site: http://www.cbcings.com
Automobile Parts Mfr
N.A.I.C.S.: 336390
Kevin Hayashi (CEO)

CBC OPTICAL INDUSTRIES BD Co.,
Ltd.   (1)
Sector-3 Plot No 16-17 K E P Z North Pat-
enga, Chittagong, Bangladesh
Tel.: (880) 3 1250 1783
Optical Instrument Mfr
N.A.I.C.S.: 333310

CBC OPTRONICS (BD) Co.,
Ltd.   (1)
Sector-6 Plot No 16-19 C E P Z South, Hal-
ishahar, Chittagong, Bangladesh
Tel.: (880) 31 74 0181
Resin Product Mfr
N.A.I.C.S.: 325211
Yasumi Matsuo (Mng Dir)

CBC OPTRONICS (BEIJING) Co.,
Ltd.   (1)
No 1 Fushun St Jingwei Industry Area Bei-
fang Town, Huairou District, Beijing,
101400, China
Tel.: (86) 10 6168 1338
Optical Instrument Mfr
N.A.I.C.S.: 333310
Kimura Tetsuro (Mgr)

CBC.S PTE LTD - Trade Division (1)
15 Jalankilong Barat No 04 03, San Ctr,
Singapore, 159357, Singapore
Tel.: (65) 62751221
Web Site: http://www.cbc.co.jp
Emp.: 20
Mfr & Marketer of Plastics, Electronic Com-
ponents, Clothing, Metals, Food & Other
Products
N.A.I.C.S.: 333310
N Ohta (Mng Dir)

CBC.S PTE Ltd. - Distribution
Division   (1)
15 Jalan Kilang Barat, #04-03 Front Tech
Ctr, Singapore, 159357, Singapore (100%)
Tel.: (65) 62751221
Web Site: http://www.cbcsingapore.com
Emp.: 10
N.A.I.C.S.: 325211
Yuki Tsubota (Gen Mgr)

PT. CBC PRIMA   (1)
MidPlaza IIBuilding 12th Floor Jl Jend
Sudirman Kav 10-11, Jakarta, 10220, Indo-
nesia
Tel.: (62) 21 570 7590
Resin Product Mfr
N.A.I.C.S.: 325211

Procos S.p.A.   (1)
Via G Matteotti 249, Novara, 28062, Cam-
eri, Italy
Tel.: (39) 0321 64 22 11
Web Site: http://www.procos.it
Pharmaceutical Product Whslr
N.A.I.C.S.: 424210

T-CBC (Taiwan) Co., Ltd.   (1)
Rm 1401 Chia Hsing Bldg 96 Chung Shan
N Rd Sec 2, Taipei, 104, Taiwan (100%)
Tel.: (886) 225223901
Web Site: http://www.cbc.co.jp
N.A.I.C.S.: 325211

TERRA FRUCTI S.A.S.   (1)
2250 Route de Nohic, Fronton, 31620,
France
Tel.: (33) 5 61 82 40 88
Resin Product Mfr
N.A.I.C.S.: 325211

**CBH COMPAGNIE BANCAIRE
HELVETIQUE SA**
Boulevard Emile-Jaques-Dalcroze 7,
PO Box 3754, 1211, Geneva, Swit-
zerland
Tel.: (41) 22 839 01 00   CH
Web Site: http://www.cbhbank.com
Year Founded: 1975
Private Banking Services
N.A.I.C.S.: 523150
Philippe Cordonier (CEO)

CBK HOLDINGS LIMITED
Room 1501 Vanta Industrial Centre,
21-33 Tai Lin Pai Road, Kwai Chung,
New Territories, China (Hong Kong)
Tel.: (852) 2 604 9660   Ky
Web Site: http://www.cbk.com.hk
Year Founded: 2004
8428—(HKG)
Rev.: $3,521,412
Assets: $4,737,822
Liabilities: $2,199,367
Net Worth: $2,538,455
Earnings: ($8,837,065)
Emp.: 136
Fiscal Year-end: 03/31/22
Restaurant Operators
N.A.I.C.S.: 722511
Lap Ping Chan (Exec Dir)

CBL INTERNATIONAL LIMITED
Level 23-2 Menara Permata Sapura
Kuala Lumpur City Centre, 50088,
Kuala Lumpur, Malaysia
Tel.: (60) 327068280   Ky
Web Site: https://www.banle-intl.com
Year Founded: 2022
BANL—(NASDAQ)
Rev.: $435,897,718
Assets: $53,461,908
Liabilities: $28,162,233
Net Worth: $25,299,675
Earnings: $1,132,650
Emp.: 35
Fiscal Year-end: 12/31/23
Marine Fuel Logistic Services
N.A.I.C.S.: 488320
Sing Chung Raymond Chiu (Pres,
CEO, CFO & Sr VP)

Subsidiaries:

Banle Energy International
Limited   (1)
Suite 3602 - 3A Skyline Tower 39 Wang
Kwong Road, Kowloon Bay, China (Hong
Kong)
Tel.: (852) 28821228
Marine Fuel Distr
N.A.I.C.S.: 457210

Banle International (Malaysia) Sdn.
Bhd.   (1)
Suite 19-9-6 Level 9 UOA Centre No 19
Jalan Pinang, 50450, Kuala Lumpur, Malay-
sia
Tel.: (60) 327032966
Marine Fuel Distr
N.A.I.C.S.: 457210

Banle International Marketing
Limited   (1)
No 1 - 23A First Floor Paragon Jalan Mus-
tapha, 87000, Labuan, Malaysia
Tel.: (60) 87599260
Marine Fuel Distr
N.A.I.C.S.: 457210

CBL International Limited—(Continued)

Majestic Energy (Singapore) Pte. Ltd. (1)
Level 17 Frasers Tower 182 Cecil St, Singapore, 069547, Singapore
Tel.: (65) 69569204
Marine Fuel Distr
N.A.I.C.S.: 457210

CBLT INC.
855 Brant Street, Burlington, L7R 2J6, ON, Canada
Tel.: (416) 890-1232
Web Site: http://www.cbltinc.com
Year Founded: 2008
CBLT—(TSXV)
Rev.: $607,706
Assets: $580,137
Liabilities: $439,503
Net Worth: $140,634
Earnings: $336,118
Fiscal Year-end: 05/31/21
Mineral Exploration Services
N.A.I.C.S.: 212290
Peter M. Clausi (Pres & CEO)

CBO TERRITORIA
Cours de l Usine La Mare, CS 91005, 97833, Sainte-Marie-la-Blanche, Cedex, France
Tel.: (33) 262203204
Web Site:
https://www.cboterritoria.com
Year Founded: 2004
CBOT—(EUR)
Sales Range: $125-149.9 Million
Emp.: 70
Real Estate Development & Management Services
N.A.I.C.S.: 237210

CBPE CAPITAL LLP
2 George Yard, London, EC3V 9DH, United Kingdom
Tel.: (44) 2070651100   UK
Web Site:
http://www.cbpecapital.com
Year Founded: 1984
Privater Equity Firm
N.A.I.C.S.: 523999
Sean Dinnen (Mng Partner)

CBR MANAGEMENT GMBH
Theatinerstrasse 7, 80333, Munich, Germany
Tel.: (49) 892113777
Web Site: http://www.equivest.de
Sales Range: $25-49.9 Million
Emp.: 7
Privater Equity Firm
N.A.I.C.S.: 523999
Wolfgang Behrens-Ramberg (Co-Founder)

Subsidiaries:

EquiVest GmbH & Co (1)
Theatinerstrasse 7, 80333, Munich, Germany
Tel.: (49) 89 2113777
Web Site: http://www.equivest.de
Investment Management Service
N.A.I.C.S.: 523999

SELLNER Holding GmbH (1)
Windsbacher Str 40, 91564, Neuendettelsau, Germany
Tel.: (49) 98745050
Web Site: http://www.sellner.de
Sales Range: $350-399.9 Million
Motor Vehicle Interior Surface Mfr
N.A.I.C.S.: 336360

CBRAIN A/S
Dampfaergevej 30, 2100, Copenhagen, Denmark
Tel.: (45) 72161811
Web Site: https://www.cbrain.com

CBRAIN—(CSE)
Rev.: $27,191,041
Assets: $46,691,554
Liabilities: $22,165,791
Net Worth: $24,525,763
Earnings: $5,553,385
Emp.: 164
Fiscal Year-end: 12/31/22
Software Development Services
N.A.I.C.S.: 541511
Per Tejs Knudsen (Founder & CEO)

CBRE LIMITED
Saint Martins Court 10 Paternoster Row, London, EC4M 7HP, United Kingdom
Tel.: (44) 2071822000   UK
Web Site: http://www.cbre.com
Emp.: 1,500
Commercial Real Estate Brokerage Services; Regional Managing Office
N.A.I.C.S.: 531210
Jonathan Priestley (Sr Dir-Industrial & Logistics Team)

CBS CONSTRUCTION LTD.
150 MacKay Crescent, Fort McMurray, T9H 4W8, AB, Canada
Tel.: (780) 743-1810
Web Site:
https://www.cbsconstruction.ca
Year Founded: 1978
Rev.: $61,480,757
Emp.: 380
Construction Services
N.A.I.C.S.: 236220
Garry Fizzell (Owner)

CBZ HOLDINGS LIMITED
5 Campbell Road Pomona Borrowdale, PO Box 3313, Harare, Zimbabwe
Tel.: (263) 242748050
Web Site: https://www.cbz.co.zw
CBZ—(ZIM)
Sales Range: Less than $1 Million
Investment & Financial Management Services
N.A.I.C.S.: 523940
Rumbidzay Angeline Jakanani (Sec)

Subsidiaries:

CBZ Asset Management Company (Private) Limited (1)
1st Floor Cecil House 2 Central Avenue, Harare, Zimbabwe
Tel.: (263) 4702809
Sales Range: $50-74.9 Million
Emp.: 40
Financial Marketing Services
N.A.I.C.S.: 523999

CBZ Bank Limited (1)
60 Kwame Nkrumah Avenue, PO Box 3313, Harare, Zimbabwe
Tel.: (263) 4749714
Web Site: http://www.cbz.co.zw
Sales Range: $350-399.9 Million
Emp.: 900
Full Banking Services
N.A.I.C.S.: 522110

CBZ Insurance (Private) Limited (1)
Beverley Court 5th Floor South Wing 100 Nelson Mandela Avenue, Harare, Zimbabwe
Tel.: (263) 242 799 2349
Financial Services
N.A.I.C.S.: 523999

CBZ Properties (Pvt) Limited (1)
8th Floor Sapphire House Corner, PO Box 3313, Speke Avenue Angwa Street, Harare, Zimbabwe
Tel.: (263) 4759110
Property Management Services
N.A.I.C.S.: 531312
Chris Nazare (Mgr)

CC JAPAN INCOME & GROWTH TRUST PLC

29 Wellington Street Central Square, Leeds, LS1 4DL, United Kingdom
Tel.: (44) 8716640300
Web Site:
https://www.ccjapanincome.com
CCJI—(LSE)
Rev.: $11,612,579
Assets: $257,349,037
Liabilities: $7,039,778
Net Worth: $250,309,259
Earnings: ($32,182,037)
Fiscal Year-end: 10/31/20
Investment Management Service
N.A.I.C.S.: 525990
Richard Aston (Mgr-Portfolio)

CC LAND HOLDINGS LIMITED
25/F China Resources Building 26 Harbour Road, Wanchai, China (Hong Kong)
Tel.: (852) 28207000   BM
Web Site: http://www.ccland.com.hk
1224—(HKG)
Rev.: $63,541,920
Assets: $3,340,121,198
Liabilities: $1,441,451,888
Net Worth: $1,898,669,310
Earnings: ($247,393,478)
Emp.: 75
Fiscal Year-end: 12/31/22
Investment Services; Land, Property & Manufacturing
N.A.I.C.S.: 523999
Wai Fai Leung (Exec Dir)

Subsidiaries:

Touyun Biotech Group Ltd (1)
12/F Kwan Chart Tower 6 Tonnochy Road, Hong Kong, China (Hong Kong)
Tel.: (852) 22707200
Web Site: http://www.hinatouyun.com.hk
Rev.: $41,225,085
Assets: $113,181,368
Liabilities: $77,033,970
Net Worth: $36,147,398
Earnings: ($25,838,640)
Emp.: 570
Fiscal Year-end: 12/31/2022
Investment Holding Company
N.A.I.C.S.: 551112
Liang Wang (Chm)

CC NAPRED JSC
115 Mihajla Pupina Street, 11070, Belgrade, Serbia
Tel.: (381) 11 7113740
Web Site: http://www.napred.net
Emp.: 130
Civil Engineering Services
N.A.I.C.S.: 237990
Dobroslav Bojovic (CEO)

CCC S.A.
Ul Strefowa 6, 59-101, Polkowice, Poland
Tel.: (48) 768458400
Web Site: http://firma.ccc.eu
CCC—(WAR)
Rev.: $2,371,577,149
Assets: $1,845,450,435
Liabilities: $1,605,913,681
Net Worth: $239,536,753
Earnings: ($31,326,936)
Fiscal Year-end: 01/31/24
Footwear Distr
N.A.I.C.S.: 424340
Dariusz Milek (Chm-Supervisory Bd)

Subsidiaries:

CCC Shoes & Bags Sp. z o.o. (1)
Ul Strefowa 6, 59-101, Polkowice, Poland
Tel.: (48) 768458400
Footwear Distr
N.A.I.C.S.: 424340

CCC Shoes & Bags d.o.o. (1)
Vladimira Popovica 6, Novi Beograd, 11000, Belgrade, Serbia
Tel.: (381) 114082052
Shoe Distr

N.A.I.C.S.: 458210

CCC Shoes Bulgaria EOOD (1)
Serdika Offices Fl 10 Office 1001 Sitnyakovo Blvd 48, Sofia, 1505, Bulgaria
Tel.: (359) 24398083
Shoe Distr
N.A.I.C.S.: 458210

Gino Rossi S.A. (1)
ul Owocowa 24, 76-200, Slupsk, Poland   (90.02%)
Tel.: (48) 598422608
Web Site: https://www.gino-rossi.com
Shoes & Apparel Product Mfr
N.A.I.C.S.: 316990
Tomasz Malicki (Chm-Mgmt Bd)

Karl Voegele AG (1)
Burgerfeldstrasse 15, 8730, Uznach, Switzerland
Tel.: (41) 84 883 0838
Web Site: https://voegele-shoes.com
Footwear Distr
N.A.I.C.S.: 424340

CCCG REAL ESTATE CORPORATION LIMITED
9th Floor Building B Fortune Building No 9 Honghu East Road, Yubei District, Chongqing, 401120, China
Tel.: (86) 2367530016
Web Site:
https://www.cccgrealestate.com
Year Founded: 1993
000736—(SSE)
Rev.: $5,400,773,820
Assets: $19,277,932,284
Liabilities: $16,604,540,784
Net Worth: $2,673,391,500
Earnings: $4,765,176
Fiscal Year-end: 12/31/22
Real Estate Development Services
N.A.I.C.S.: 531312
Li Yongqian (Chm)

CCI EUROPE A/S
Axel Kiers Vej 11, Hoejbjerg, 8270, Arhus, Denmark
Tel.: (45) 8733 5588
Web Site: http://www.ccieurope.com
Year Founded: 1979
Editorial & Advertising Services
N.A.I.C.S.: 541810
Dan Korsgaard (CEO)

Subsidiaries:

Escenic AS (1)
Grev Wedels plass 7, 0151, Oslo, Norway   (100%)
Tel.: (47) 95073440
Web Site: http://www.escenic.com
Web Publisher & Content Management Services
N.A.I.C.S.: 518210
Mark Van Den Kamp (Mgr)

CCIAM FUTURE ENERGY LIMITED
Rooms 1801-4 Harcourt House 39 Gloucester Road, Wanchai, China (Hong Kong)
Tel.: (852) 21140682   HK
0145—(HKG)
Rev.: $2,971,515
Assets: $7,671,803
Liabilities: $5,192,565
Net Worth: $2,479,238
Earnings: ($6,626,430)
Emp.: 14
Fiscal Year-end: 12/31/22
Investment Management Service
N.A.I.C.S.: 523940

CCID CONSULTING COMPANY LIMITED
Room 311 No 2 Building No 28 Zhen Xing Road, Chang Ping District, Beijing, 100048, China

Tel.: (86) 1088558866   CN
Web Site:
   http://www.ccidconsulting.com
Rev.: $34,461,199
Assets: $48,246,737
Liabilities: $14,628,827
Net Worth: $33,617,911
Earnings: $9,240,539
Emp.: 321
Fiscal Year-end: 12/31/19
Management & Strategy Consultancy
Services
N.A.I.C.S.: 541611
Huifeng Sun *(Gen Mgr)*

CCK CONSOLIDATED HOLDINGS BERHAD

Lot 999 Section 66 Jalan Keluli Bintawa Industrial Estate, 93450, Kuching, Sarawak, Malaysia
Tel.: (60) 82336520
Web Site: https://www.cck.com.my
Year Founded: 1970
CCK—(KLS)
Rev.: $187,459,314
Assets: $106,951,085
Liabilities: $30,284,265
Net Worth: $76,666,820
Earnings: $13,359,856
Emp.: 2,800
Fiscal Year-end: 12/31/22
Poultry Services
N.A.I.C.S.: 112340
Jan Moi Voon *(Co-Sec)*

Subsidiaries:

P.T. Bonanza Pratama Abadi   **(1)**
Jl Aji Iskandar RT 16 Juata Laut, Tarakan, Kalimantan Utara, Indonesia
Tel.: (62) 8115921280
Web Site: https://bonanzapratamaabadi.com
Shrimp Processing Services
N.A.I.C.S.: 114112

CCK FINANCIAL SOLUTIONS PTY LIMITED

Level 1 133 St Georges Terrace, Perth, 6000, WA, Australia
Tel.: (61) 892237600   AU
Web Site: http://www.cck.com.au
Year Founded: 1981
Computer Software Developer
N.A.I.C.S.: 513210
Helen Glastras *(COO)*

Subsidiaries:

CCK Financial Solutions (Consulting)
Pty. Ltd.   **(1)**
L 3 12 St Georges Ter, Perth, 6000, WA, Australia
Tel.: (61) 892237600
Web Site: http://www.cck.com.au
Emp.: 21
Financial Software Consulting Services
N.A.I.C.S.: 541511
Joseph Wong *(Mng Dir)*

CCK Financial Solutions (Malaysia)
Sdn. Bhd.   **(1)**
Ste 13 08 13th Fl Wisma UOA II, 21 Jalan Pinang, Kuala Lumpur, 50450, Malaysia
Tel.: (60) 321633529
Web Site: http://www.cck.com.au
Treasury Management Services
N.A.I.C.S.: 541618
Yin Shuey Tian *(Country Mgr)*

CCL INDUSTRIES INC.

111 Gordon Baker Road Suite 801, Toronto, M2H 3R1, ON, Canada
Tel.: (416) 756-8500   ON
Web Site: https://www.cclind.com
Year Founded: 1951
1C9—(DEU)
Rev.: $5,021,245,952
Assets: $6,738,841,904
Liabilities: $3,247,771,120
Net Worth: $3,491,070,784
Earnings: $400,364,624

Emp.: 25,700
Fiscal Year-end: 12/31/23
Labels, Aluminum Cans & Packaging
& Plastic Tubes Mfr
N.A.I.C.S.: 561910
Donald G. Lang *(Chm)*

Subsidiaries:

CCL Container   **(1)**
105 Gordon Baker Rd, Willowdale, M2H
3P8, ON, Canada   **(100%)**
Tel.: (416) 756-8500
Web Site: http://www.cclcontainer.com
Sales Range: $25-49.9 Million
Emp.: 10
Recyclable Aluminum Aerosol Cans, Aluminum Bottles, Barrier Systems & Other Specialty Aluminum Packaging Mfr
N.A.I.C.S.: 331315

Subsidiary (US):

CCL Container (Hermitage), Inc.   **(2)**
1 Llodio Dr, Hermitage, PA
16148-9015   **(100%)**
Tel.: (724) 981-4420
Web Site: http://www.cclcontainer.com
Sales Range: $75-99.9 Million
Emp.: 400
Aluminum Cans & Packaging Mfr
N.A.I.C.S.: 332431
Eric Frantz *(VP & Gen Mgr)*

CCL Container Mexico   **(1)**
Av De la Luz 85 Frac Industrial La Luz, Cuautitlan, 54730, Izcalli, Mexico
Tel.: (52) 5558726322
Web Site: http://www.cclind.com
Specialty Packaging Products
N.A.I.C.S.: 327213

CCL Design GmbH   **(1)**
Lindgesfeld 26, 42653, Solingen, Germany
Tel.: (49) 212 3827 0
Web Site: http://www.ccl-design.de
Films & Aluminium Product Mfr
N.A.I.C.S.: 322220

CCL Industries Corp.   **(1)**
161 Worcester Rd Ste 603, Framingham, MA 01701
Tel.: (508) 872-4511
Web Site: https://www.cclind.com
Specialty Packaging Mfr
N.A.I.C.S.: 561910

Subsidiary (Domestic):

Avery Products Corporation   **(2)**
50 Pointe Dr, Brea, CA 92821
Tel.: (714) 674-8500
Web Site: http://www.avery.com
Sales Range: $750-799.9 Million
Emp.: 450
Self-Adhesive Labels, Binders & Sheet Protectors Mfr
N.A.I.C.S.: 322299

Subsidiary (Domestic):

AVERY OFFICE PRODUCTS
PUERTO RICO L.L.C.   **(3)**
Citibank Tower 250 Ponce de Leon Ave Ste 1002, San Juan, PR 00918
Tel.: (787) 753-3135
Information Services
N.A.I.C.S.: 327910

Subsidiary (Non-US):

Avery Office Products Pty. Ltd.   **(3)**
11 Carrington Road, Castle Hill, 2154, NSW, Australia
Tel.: (61) 2 9843 0777
Web Site: http://www.averyproducts.com.au
Emp.: 60
Flexible Packaging Products Mfr
N.A.I.C.S.: 322220

Avery TICO S.r.l.
Via Honduras 15, 00040, Pomezia, RM, Italy
Tel.: (39) 06910461
Web Site: http://www.avery.it
Labels & Office Products Whslr
N.A.I.C.S.: 424120

Subsidiary (Domestic):

Lodging Access Systems, LLC   **(3)**

55 Skyline Dr, Lake Mary, FL 32746
Web Site: https://www.rfidhotel.com
Sales Range: $10-24.9 Million
Emp.: 19
Key Card Mfr
N.A.I.C.S.: 339999
Stephen Brooks *(Chm)*

pc/nametag, Inc.   **(3)**
124 Horizon Dr, Verona, WI 53593
Tel.: (608) 845-1850
Web Site: https://www.pcnametag.com
Sales Range: $10-24.9 Million
Emp.: 60
Name Tag & Other Meeting & Identification
Supplies Mfr & Whslr
N.A.I.C.S.: 423490
Darryl Anunson *(Mgr-IT)*

Subsidiary (Domestic):

CCL Label TubeDec   **(2)**
92 Ark Rd, Lumberton, NJ 08048
Tel.: (856) 273-0700
Sales Range: $75-99.9 Million
Emp.: 300
Label Mfr
N.A.I.C.S.: 561910
Matthew Rybacki *(Acct Mgr)*

CCL Label, Inc.   **(2)**
161 Worcester Rd Ste 603, Framingham,
MA 01701   **(100%)**
Tel.: (508) 872-4511
Web Site: http://www.ccllabel.com
Sales Range: $25-49.9 Million
Emp.: 6
Business Services
N.A.I.C.S.: 322299
Geoffrey Martin *(CEO)*

Subsidiary (Domestic):

CCL Insertco, LLC   **(3)**
1831 D Portal St, Baltimore, MD 21224
Tel.: (410) 633-6525
Web Site: http://www.ccl-label.com
Emp.: 100
Healthcare Products Packaging Services
N.A.I.C.S.: 561910
Dave Joesten *(Gen Mgr)*

Branch (Domestic):

CCL Label   **(3)**
15 Controls Dr, Shelton, CT
06484-0511   **(100%)**
Tel.: (203) 926-1253
Web Site: http://www.cclind.com
Sales Range: $25-49.9 Million
Emp.: 80
Mfr of Pressure Sensitive Labels
N.A.I.C.S.: 561910
Jake Martin *(Gen Mgr)*

CCL Label   **(3)**
1209 W Bailey, Sioux Falls, SD 57104
Tel.: (605) 336-7940
Web Site: http://www.ccllabel.com
Emp.: 500
Mfr of Pressure Sensitive Labels
N.A.I.C.S.: 323111

CCL Label   **(3)**
576 College Commerce Way, Upland, CA
91786
Tel.: (909) 608-2260
Web Site: http://www.ccllabel.com
Sales Range: $25-49.9 Million
Mfr of Pressure Sensitive Labels
N.A.I.C.S.: 322220

CCL Label   **(3)**
1862 Suncast Ln, Batavia, IL 60510
Tel.: (630) 406-9147
Web Site: http://www.ccllabel.com
Sales Range: $10-24.9 Million
Label Printing Services
N.A.I.C.S.: 323111

CCL Label   **(3)**
Urb Industrial El Retiro Highway 102 Km 33
2, San German, PR 00683
Tel.: (787) 892-1268
Web Site: http://www.ccllabel.com
Healthcare Products Packaging Services
N.A.I.C.S.: 561910

Subsidiary (Domestic):

CCL Label Portland, Inc   **(3)**

2511 Nw 30th Ave, Portland, OR 97210-2015
Tel.: (503) 274-9782
Emp.: 13
Beverage Products Packaging Services
N.A.I.C.S.: 561910
Jon Cates *(Gen Mgr)*

CCL Label Sioux Falls, Inc   **(3)**
1209 W Bailey St, Sioux Falls, SD 57104-1313
Tel.: (605) 336-7940
Web Site: http://www.ccl-label.com
Sales Range: $75-99.9 Million
Food Products Packaging Services
N.A.I.C.S.: 561910

Branch (Domestic):

CCL Label/Auto-Sleeve   **(3)**
2003 Case Pkwy S Unit 3, Twinsburg, OH
44240-2310
Tel.: (330) 487-2200
Web Site: http://www.ccl-autosleeve.com
Sales Range: $1-9.9 Million
Emp.: 2
Stretch-Sleeve Labels Mfr
N.A.I.C.S.: 561910

Subsidiary (Domestic):

CCL Tube (Wilkes-Barre), Inc   **(2)**
1 Lasley Ave, Wilkes Barre, PA 18706
Tel.: (570) 824-8485
Web Site: http://www.ccltube.com
Health Care Products Labeling Services
N.A.I.C.S.: 561910

CCL Tube, Inc.   **(2)**
2250 E 220th St, Los Angeles, CA 90810
Tel.: (310) 635-4444
Web Site: http://www.ccltube.com
Sales Range: $50-74.9 Million
Emp.: 200
Plastic Tube Packaging Mfr
N.A.I.C.S.: 326199
Andy Iseli *(VP & Gen Mgr)*

Checkpoint Systems, Inc.   **(2)**
101 Wolf Dr, Thorofare, NJ 08086
Tel.: (856) 848-1800
Web Site:
   http://www.checkpointsystems.com
Sales Range: $5-14.9 Billion
Integrated Electronic Security Systems Mfr
N.A.I.C.S.: 334290
Carol P. Roy *(Sr VP-Global HR)*

Division (Domestic):

Alpha Security Products   **(3)**
1510 4th St SE, Canton, OH 44707
Tel.: (800) 633-2155
Web Site: http://www.alphaworld.com
Tracking, Security & Merchandising Solutions Mfr & Marketer
N.A.I.C.S.: 561621

Subsidiary (Non-US):

CKP (CZ) s.r.o.   **(3)**
Golcova 1/2, 148 00, Prague, 4, Czech
Republic
Tel.: (420) 244910194
Web Site: http://www.ckp-cz.cz
Integrated Electronic Security Systems Distr
N.A.I.C.S.: 561621

Checkpoint Portugal LDA   **(3)**
Rua Nova dos Mercadores, 20D Parque
das Nacoes Sul, 1900-180, Lisbon, Portugal
Tel.: (351) 219897200
Web Site:
   http://www.checkpointsystems.com
Integrated Electronic Security Systems Provider
N.A.I.C.S.: 561621

Checkpoint Solutions GmbH   **(3)**
Ersheimer Str 69, 69434, Hirschhorn, Germany
Tel.: (49) 62729280
Integrated Electronic Security Systems Distr
N.A.I.C.S.: 561621

Checkpoint Systems (Aust/NZ) Pty
Ltd.   **(3)**
80 Lewis Road, Wantirna, 3152, VIC, Australia
Tel.: (61) 1300 369 338

CCL Industries Inc.—(Continued)

Web Site:
http://www.checkpointsystems.com
Integrated Electronic Security Systems Provider
N.A.I.C.S.: 561621

Checkpoint Systems (M) Sdn. Bhd. (3)
8 Jalan Udang Harimau 1 Segambut Bahagia, 52100, Kuala Lumpur, Malaysia
Tel.: (60) 3.6179 2662
Integrated Electronic Security Systems Mfr
N.A.I.C.S.: 561621

Checkpoint Systems (UK) Ltd. (3)
7 Fulmar House VOTEC Center, Hambridge Lane, Newbury, RG14 5TN, Berks, United Kingdom
Tel.: (44) 1635567070
Web Site:
http://www.checkpointsystems.com
Integrated Electronic Security Systems Distr
N.A.I.C.S.: 561621

Checkpoint Systems Benelux B.V. (3)
Akkermansbeekweg 12, 7061 ZA, Terborg, Netherlands
Tel.: (31) 88 008 2555
Web Site:
http://www.checkpointsystems.com
Integrated Electronic Security Systems Distr
N.A.I.C.S.: 561621

Checkpoint Systems CEE Sp. z.o.o. (3)
Kiekrz ul Kierska 78, 62-090, Rokietnica, Poland
Tel.: (48) 61 271 7010
Web Site:
http://www.checkpointsystems.com
Integrated Electronic Security Systems Provider
N.A.I.C.S.: 561621

Checkpoint Systems Danmark A/S (3)
Brydehusvej 30, 2750, Ballerup, Denmark
Tel.: (45) 44841444
Communication Equipment Mfr
N.A.I.C.S.: 334290

Checkpoint Systems Espana S.L.U. (3)
Avenida de Burgos 12 Planta 16 Derecha, Madrid, 28036, Spain
Tel.: (34) 914322500
Web Site:
http://www.checkpointsystems.com
Integrated Electronic Security Systems & Software Solutions
N.A.I.C.S.: 561621

Checkpoint Systems France SASU (3)
6 Rue Jean Pierre Timbaud, CS 50501, Quentin en Yvelines, 78180, Montigny-le-Bretonneux, Cedex, France
Tel.: (33) 130473047
Web Site:
http://www.checkpointsystems.com
Integrated Electronic Security Systems & Software Solutions
N.A.I.C.S.: 561621

Checkpoint Systems GmbH (3)
Ersheimer Str 69, Neckar, D-69434, Hirschhorn, Germany
Tel.: (49) 6272 9280
Web Site:
http://www.checkpointsystems.com
Integrated Electronic Security Systems Services
N.A.I.C.S.: 561621

Checkpoint Systems Hong Kong Limited (3)
Room A 4/F Sha Tin Industrial Centre, 5-7 Yuen Siu Wai Tin New Territories, Hong Kong, China (Hong Kong)
Tel.: (852) 25272327
Labelling & Marking Solutions
N.A.I.C.S.: 424120

Checkpoint Systems India Private Limited (3)
Plot-438 Udyog Vihar Phase, 122016, Gurgaon, Haryana, India

Tel.: (91) 124 4399758
Web Site: http://www.checknet.checkpt.com
Communication Equipment Mfr
N.A.I.C.S.: 334290

Checkpoint Systems Italia S.p.A. (3)
via Leonardo da Vinci 14, Cusago, Milan, 20090, Italy
Tel.: (39) 02 903551
Web Site:
http://www.checkpointsystems.com
Security Systems Provider
N.A.I.C.S.: 561621

Checkpoint Systems Japan Co. Ltd. (3)
2-4-7 Shibadaimon Hamamatsucho West Place, Minato-ku, Tokyo, 1005-002, Japan
Tel.: (81) 35425 8040
Web Site:
http://www.checkpointsystems.com
Communication Equipment Mfr
N.A.I.C.S.: 334290

Subsidiary (Domestic):

Checkpoint Manufacturing Japan Co., Ltd. (4)
2-4-7 Shiba-daimon Hamamatsu-cho West Place, Minato-ku, Tokyo, 105-0012, Japan
Tel.: (81) 467872551
Web Site:
http://www.checkpointsystems.com
Integrated Electronic Security Systems Mfr
N.A.I.C.S.: 334419

Subsidiary (Non-US):

Checkpoint Systems Mexico (3)
Parque Industrial FINSA Av Michoacan No 20, Modulo 21 Col Renovacion, CP 09209, Mexico, Mexico
Tel.: (52) 55 51485800
Web Site: http://www.checkpointsystem.com
Integrated Electronic Security Systems Distr
N.A.I.C.S.: 561621

Checkpoint Systems S.A. (3)
Costa Rica 5379 Area de Promocion El Triangulo, Buenos Aires, Argentina
Tel.: (54) 1156509888
Web Site: http://checkpt.com.ar
Integrated Electronic Security Systems Distr
N.A.I.C.S.: 561621

Checkpoint Systems Sverige AB (3)
Skeppet Arans Vag 17, 42671, Vastra Frolunda, Sweden
Tel.: (46) 31 769 1170
Web Site: http://www.checkpointsystems.com
Integrated Electronic Security Systems Distr
N.A.I.C.S.: 561621

Checkpoint do Brasil Ltda. (3)
Rodovia Engenheiro Miguel Melhado Campos Km 79, Santa Candida Vinhedo, SP 13280-000, Sao Paulo, Brazil
Tel.: (55) 19 3876 9300
Web Site: http://www.checkpt.com.br
Integrated Electronic Security Systems Provider
N.A.I.C.S.: 561621

Ennte AS (3)
Slynga 10, 2005, Raelingen, Norway
Tel.: (47) 22903300
Web Site: http://www.ennte.no
Integrated Electronic Security Systems Distr
N.A.I.C.S.: 561621

METO FENIX Handels GmbH (3)
Jochen Rindt Strasse 13, 1230, Vienna, Austria
Tel.: (43) 1 616 24 11
Web Site: http://www.fenix.at
Integrated Electronic Security Systems Distr
N.A.I.C.S.: 561621

METO International GmbH (3)
Ersheimer Strasse 69, 69434, Hirschhorn, Germany
Tel.: (49) 62729280
Web Site: https://www.meto.com
Labelling & Marking Solutions
N.A.I.C.S.: 424120
Peter Sperl (Mng Dir)

Nordic Retail A/S (3)
Brydehusvej 30, Ballerup, 2750, Denmark
Tel.: (45) 44841444
Web Site: http://www.nordic-retail.com
Integrated Electronic Security Systems Distr

N.A.I.C.S.: 561621
Bo Bennetsen (Dir)

Subsidiary (Domestic):

PrettyWork Creative LLC (2)
PO Box 2663, Cypress, TX 77410
Tel.: (281) 826-4572
Web Site:
http://www.prettyworkcreative.com
Media Representatives
N.A.I.C.S.: 541840

CCL Label (1)
35 Mclachlan Dr, Etobicoke, M9W 1E4, ON, Canada (100%)
Tel.: (416) 675-3161
Sales Range: $75-99.9 Million
Emp.: 200
Basic & Unique Labeling Solutions
N.A.I.C.S.: 561910
Guenther Birkner (Pres-Healthcare & Specialty Bus)

Subsidiary (Domestic):

CCL Label (2)
80 Paramount Rd, Winnipeg, R2X 2W3, MB, Canada (100%)
Tel.: (416) 756-8500
Web Site: http://www.cclind.com
Sales Range: $25-49.9 Million
Emp.: 50
Basic & Unique Labeling Solutions
N.A.I.C.S.: 561910

Subsidiary (Non-US):

CCL Label Ireland (2)
70 74 Broomhill Rd, Tallaght Indus Est, Dublin, Ireland
Tel.: (353) 14513555
Web Site: http://ccllabel.com
Adhesive Labels & Heat Seal Lidding Mfr
N.A.I.C.S.: 322220
Gerard Molloy (Sls Dir)

CCL Label de Mexico S.A. de C.V. (2)
Michoacan 20 Mod 21, Col Renovacion, 09209, Mexico, Mexico (100%)
Tel.: (52) 5551485800
Web Site: http://www.ccllabel.com
Toiletries Mfr
N.A.I.C.S.: 325620
Ben Lilienthal (Mng Dir/VP)

Etiquetas CCL S.A. de C.V. (2)
Michoacan 20 Mod 21 Col Renovacion, 9209, Mexico, Mexico
Tel.: (52) 55 5148 5800
Web Site: http://www.ccllabel.com
Emp.: 20
Personal Care Products Labeling Services
N.A.I.C.S.: 561910

CCL Label (Ashford) Limited (1)
Foster Road Ashford Business Park, Sevington, Ashford, TN24 0SH, Kent, United Kingdom
Tel.: (44) 1233 503 333
Adhesive Label Mfr
N.A.I.C.S.: 322220

CCL Label (Guangzhou) Co., Ltd. (1)
No 8 Yongfeng Road Yonghe Zone, 511356, Guangzhou, China
Tel.: (86) 20 8298 6800
Personal Care Products Labeling Services
N.A.I.C.S.: 561910

CCL Label (Hefei) Co., Ltd (1)
Gengyun Road No 100 Hefei Economic & Technological Development Zone, 230601, Hefei, Anhui, China
Tel.: (86) 551 385 1680
Web Site: http://ccl-label.com
Beverage Product Labeling Services
N.A.I.C.S.: 561910

CCL Label (Thai) Ltd. (1)
Wellgrow Industrial Estate KM 36 Bangna-Trad Highway 69 Moo5, Bangsamark Bangpakong, Chachoengsao, 24180, Thailand
Tel.: (66) 38 571 381
Web Site: http://www.ccl-label.com
Digital Printing & Labeling Services
N.A.I.C.S.: 561910
Kittipong Kulratanasinsuk (Mng Dir)

CCL Label (Vic) Pty. Ltd. (1)
120 Merrindale Drive, Croydon South, Melbourne, VIC, VIC, Australia
Tel.: (61) 3 9751 7107
Label Printing Services
N.A.I.C.S.: 323111

CCL Label A/S (1)
Nyager 11-13, Brondby, 2605, Copenhagen, Denmark
Tel.: (45) 43 45 68 00
Web Site: http://www.ccllabel.dk
Sales Range: $75-99.9 Million
Emp.: 200
Label Distr
N.A.I.C.S.: 424310

CCL Label GmbH (1)
Industriestrasse 2, 83607, Holzkirchen, Germany
Tel.: (49) 80 24 3 08 0
Beverage Product Labeling Services
N.A.I.C.S.: 561910
Wolfgang Zollner (Gen Mgr)

CCL Label Limited (1)
Pioneer Way, Castleford, WF10 5QU, Wakefield, United Kingdom
Tel.: (44) 1977 711 111
Web Site: http://www.ccllabel.co.uk
Sales Range: $25-49.9 Million
Emp.: 2
Adhesive Label Mfr
N.A.I.C.S.: 322220

CCL Label Meerane GmbH (1)
Bruckenweg 5, Meerane, 08393, Germany
Tel.: (49) 3764 5020
Web Site: http://www.ccl-label.com
Emp.: 160
Food Products Labeling Services
N.A.I.C.S.: 561910

CCL Label S.A.S (1)
5 rue Rene Descartes, 41350, Vineuil, France
Tel.: (33) 2 1854 8041
Web Site: http://www.ccllabel.com
Personal Care Products Packaging Services
N.A.I.C.S.: 561910

CCL Label S.r.l. (1)
Via Commercio 2, 20049, Concorezzo, Milan, Italy
Tel.: (39) 039 6043565
Web Site: http://www.ccl-label.com
Label Distr
N.A.I.C.S.: 424310

CCL Label Sp z o.o (1)
ul Kierska 78 Kiekrz, 62-090, Rokietnica, Poland
Tel.: (48) 618960500
Web Site: http://www.ccl-label.com
Sales Range: $25-49.9 Million
Emp.: 150
Personal Care Products Packaging Services
N.A.I.C.S.: 561910

CCL Label Vietnam Company Limited (1)
No 8 VSIP 2 Street No 6 Vietnam Hoa Phu Ward, Thu Dau Mot, Binh Duong, Vietnam
Tel.: (84) 650 3628130
Personal Care Products Labeling Services
N.A.I.C.S.: 561910

CCL Label do Brasil S/A (1)
Miguel Melhados Campos S N Km 79, Vinhedo, 13280 000, Sao Paulo, Brazil
Tel.: (55) 1938769300
Web Site: http://www.ccllabel.com.br
Emp.: 200
Food Products Labeling Services
N.A.I.C.S.: 561910

CCL Package Label S.N.C (1)
20 Rue Arago, 91385, Chilly-Mazarin, France
Tel.: (33) 1 6454 4141
Web Site: http://www.ccl-label.com
Healthcare Products Packaging Services
N.A.I.C.S.: 561910

CCL Secure Pty Ltd (1)
PO Box 223, Craigieburn, 3064, VIC, Australia
Tel.: (61) 393030700
Web Site: http://www.cclsecure.com

Currency Printing Services
N.A.I.C.S.: 323111

Clinical Systems, Inc. (1)
377 Oak St, Garden City, NY 11530
Tel.: (516) 745-6200
Web Site: http://www.clinsys.net
Sales Range: $1-9.9 Million
Emp.: 34
Clinical Packaging & Labeling Services
N.A.I.C.S.: 561910
Roger Halvorsen (Pres)

Data Management, Incorporated (1)
537 New Britain Ave, Unionville, CT 06085
Tel.: (860) 677-8586
Web Site: http://www.datamanage.com
Rev.: $6,578,000
Emp.: 60
Business Support Services
N.A.I.C.S.: 561499
Bryan Gallagher (Pres & COO)

Faubel & Co. Nachfolger GmbH (1)
Schwarzenberger Weg 45, Melsungen, 34212, Germany
Tel.: (49) 566173090
Web Site: http://www.faubel.de
Sales Range: $25-49.9 Million
Emp.: 160
Packaging Plastic Label Mfr
N.A.I.C.S.: 322220
Martin Kuge (Mng Dir)

Subsidiary (US):

Faubel Pharma Services Corp. (2)
3 3rd St Ste 103, Bordentown, NJ 08505
Tel.: (908) 730-7563
Commercial Printing Services
N.A.I.C.S.: 323111

Innovia Films America, Inc. (1)
6001 Gun Club Rd, Winston Salem, NC 27103
Tel.: (336) 766-9448
Web Site: https://www.innoviafilms.com
Polypropylene Film Mfr
N.A.I.C.S.: 326113
Renee Bumgarner (Mgr-HR & Acctg)

CCL INTERNATIONAL LIMITED
M-4 B 1/1 Gupta Tower Commercial Complex, Azadpur, New Delhi, 110033, India
Tel.: (91) 1204214258
Web Site: https://www.cclil.com
Year Founded: 1991
531900—(BOM)
Rev.: $4,154,702
Assets: $8,402,565
Liabilities: $2,136,796
Net Worth: $6,265,768
Earnings: $65,163
Emp.: 32
Fiscal Year-end: 03/31/21
Infrastructure Development Services
N.A.I.C.S.: 237310
Rama Gupta (Chm & Mng Dir)

CCL PRODUCTS (INDIA) LIMITED
7-1-24/2/D Greendale, Ameerpet, Hyderabad, 500 016, Telangana, India
Tel.: (91) 4023732455
Web Site:
    https://www.cclproducts.com
Year Founded: 1994
CCL—(NSE)
Rev.: $283,165,401
Assets: $354,481,355
Liabilities: $152,159,826
Net Worth: $202,321,529
Earnings: $36,701,888
Emp.: 613
Fiscal Year-end: 03/30/23
Coffee Mfr
N.A.I.C.S.: 311920
Sridevi Dasari (Compliance Officer & Sec)

CCOOP GROUP CO., LTD.

No 103 Jiefang Road, Xincheng District, Xi'an, 710005, Shaanxi, China
Tel.: (86) 2987481871
Web Site:
    http://www.cnminsheng.com
Year Founded: 1992
000564—(SSE)
Rev.: $197,318,160
Assets: $3,907,444,320
Liabilities: $2,248,629,552
Net Worth: $1,658,814,768
Earnings: ($130,567,788)
Fiscal Year-end: 12/31/22
Departmental Store Operator
N.A.I.C.S.: 455110
Zhu Yandong (Chm)

Subsidiaries:

China Shun Ke Long Holdings Ltd. (1)
Floor 3 Huale Building No 60 Hebin North Road, Foshan, 528315, China
Tel.: (86) 75728854768
Web Site: http://www.skl.com.cn
Rev.: $89,682,044
Assets: $54,730,588
Liabilities: $29,913,484
Net Worth: $24,817,104
Earnings: ($3,381,955)
Emp.: 1,079
Fiscal Year-end: 12/31/2022
Holding Company
N.A.I.C.S.: 551112

CCR S.A.
Av chedid jafet 222 Block B 5th Floor Vila Olimpia, 04551065, Sao Paulo, 04551065, SP, Brazil
Tel.: (55) 1130485900   BR
Web Site:
    https://www.grupoccr.com.br
Year Founded: 1998
CCRO3—(BRAZ)
Rev.: $3,384,409,377
Assets: $9,767,993,162
Liabilities: $7,430,310,844
Net Worth: $2,337,682,318
Earnings: $331,510,154
Emp.: 17,000
Fiscal Year-end: 12/31/23
Infrastructure Investment & Service Solutions
N.A.I.C.S.: 237310
Renato Alves Vale (CEO)

Subsidiaries:

CCR Espana - Concesiones y Participaciones S.L. (1)
Portuetxe Kalea 0, Donostia, 20001, San Sebastian, Gipuzkoa, Spain
Tel.: (34) 943 22 66 81
Traffic Support Services
N.A.I.C.S.: 516210

Companhia da Metro da Bahia SA (1)
Rua Afeganistao s/n, Calabetao, Salvador, 41227-002, Bahia, Brazil
Tel.: (55) 7132051100
Web Site: http://www.ccrmetrobahia.com.br
Highway Renovation Services
N.A.I.C.S.: 237310

Concessionaria da Rodovia Presidente Dutra SA (1)
Rod Presidente Dutra BR 116 - SP/RJ s/n KM 184 3, PO Box 183, Santa Isabel, 07500-000, Sao Paulo, Brazil
Tel.: (55) 1127952400
Web Site: http://www.novadutra.com.br
Highway Renovation Services
N.A.I.C.S.: 237310

Concessionaria da Rodovia dos Lagos SA (1)
Rodovia RJ-124 km 21 5 Latino Melo, Rio Bonito, Rio de Janeiro, 28800-000, Brazil
Tel.: (55) 2136349800
Web Site:
    http://www.rodoviadoslagos.com.br
Highway Renovation Services
N.A.I.C.S.: 237310

Concessionaria de Rodovias Integradas do Oeste S/A (1)
Rod Presidente Castello Branco km 24 lado par Conjunto Norte, 06463-400, Barueri, Brazil
Tel.: (55) 1126646060
Web Site: http://www.viaoeste.com.br
Highway Renovation Services
N.A.I.C.S.: 237310

Concessionaria do Rodoanel Oeste S.A. (1)
Rod Presidente Castello Branco km 24 lado par Conjunto Norte, 06463-400, Barueri, Sao Paulo, Brazil
Tel.: (55) 1126646097
Web Site: http://www.rodoaneloeste.com.br
Highway Renovation Services
N.A.I.C.S.: 237310

Green Airports Inc. (1)
2000 Post Rd, Warwick, RI 02886
Tel.: (401) 737-8222
Traffic Support Services
N.A.I.C.S.: 516210

Sociedade de Activities em Multimidia Ltda. (1)
Av Chedid Jafet 222-Bloco C-Cj 51C-5 Andar, Vila OlimpiaÂ , 04551-065, Sao Paulo, Brazil
Tel.: (55) 1131949400
Web Site: http://www.sammnet.com.br
Multimedia Communication Services
N.A.I.C.S.: 517810

CCR TECHNOLOGIES LIMITED
255 17 Avenue SW Suite 205, Calgary, T2S 2T8, AB, Canada
Tel.: (403) 543-6699
Web Site: http://www.reclaim.com
Sales Range: $1-9.9 Million
Emp.: 16
Chemical Purification Technology Mfr
N.A.I.C.S.: 325998
Terry Trofimuk (VP-Engrg & Tech)

Subsidiaries:

CCR Technologies Ltd. (1)
1500 City West Blvd 550, Houston, TX 77042-2346
Tel.: (281) 988-5800
Web Site: http://www.reclaim.com
Provider of Chemical Purification Technology
N.A.I.C.S.: 562211

CCS INFOTECH LIMITED
CCS Towers 14 Periyar Road T Nagar, Chennai, 600 017, Tamil Nadu, India
Tel.: (91) 44 2834 1121
Web Site: http://www.ccsinfotech.com
Sales Range: $10-24.9 Million
Laptop Computers Export & Mfr
N.A.I.C.S.: 334111
Ratna Kumar (Co-Founder)

Subsidiaries:

CCS INFOTECH SINGAPORE PTE LTE (1)
11 - 06 Sim Lim Tower 10 Jalan Besar, Singapore, 208787, Singapore
Tel.: (65) 9069 2150
Sales Range: $25-49.9 Million
Emp.: 25
Computer Peripheral Equipment Mfr
N.A.I.C.S.: 334111
Ramesh Balaraman (Head-Bus Ops)

CCS SUPPLY CHAIN MANAGEMENT CO., LTD.
11th Floor South Wing of Central Office Building Zhuangsheng Square, No 10 Xuanwumen Street Xicheng District, Beijing, 100052, Henan, China
Tel.: (86) 1056735789
Web Site: https://www.intlccs.com
Year Founded: 2000
600180—(SHG)
Rev.: $7,844,741,274

Assets: $4,281,306,298
Liabilities: $3,224,053,189
Net Worth: $1,057,253,109
Earnings: $64,556,299
Emp.: 500
Fiscal Year-end: 12/31/22
Coal Whslr
N.A.I.C.S.: 423520
Li Qunli (Chm & Proo)

CCSL LIMITED
Suite 710 Level 7 530 Little Collins Street, Melbourne, 3000, VIC, Australia
Tel.: (61) 396 168600
Web Site: http://www.ccsl.com.au
Investment Management Service
N.A.I.C.S.: 523940
Mark Cerche (Chm)

CCT FORTIS HOLDINGS LIMITED
26A Fortis Tower 7779 Gloucester Road, New Territories, Hong Kong, China (Hong Kong)
Tel.: (852) 21028138   VG
Web Site: https://www.cct-fortis.com
Year Founded: 1980
0138—(HKG)
Rev.: $103,530,000
Assets: $425,722,500
Liabilities: $276,165,000
Net Worth: $149,557,500
Earnings: ($59,542,500)
Emp.: 325
Fiscal Year-end: 12/31/22
Holding Company; Cordless Telecommunication, Multimedia & Electronics Products
N.A.I.C.S.: 551112
Clement Shiu Tong Mak (Chm & CEO)

Subsidiaries:

AHM Engineering Company Limited (1)
Unit 1217 12/F KITEC 1 Trademart Drive, Kowloon Bay, China (Hong Kong)
Tel.: (852) 2 323 2688
Web Site: https://www.ahmhk.com
Electronic Equipment Distr
N.A.I.C.S.: 423690
Mazon Chan Muk Hing (Mng Dir)

Blackbird Heritage Motorworks Limited (1)
Unit 11 G/F 18 Ka Yip Street, Chai Wan, China (Hong Kong)
Tel.: (852) 2 881 8805
Web Site: https://www.blackbird-heritagemotorworks.com
Automotive Repair Services
N.A.I.C.S.: 811111

CCT Marketing Limited (1)
18F Cct Telecom Bldg 11 Wo Shing St Fotan, Sha Tin, New Territories, China (Hong Kong)
Tel.: (852) 26958333
Sales Range: $25-49.9 Million
Emp.: 100
Telecommunications Equipment Mfr
N.A.I.C.S.: 335999

CCT Tech (HK) Limited (1)
18/f CCT Telecom Bldg 11 Wo Shing St, Sha Tin, New Territories, China (Hong Kong)
Tel.: (852) 26958333
Electronic Products Mfr
N.A.I.C.S.: 334419

CCT Tech International Limited (1)
2208 22nd Floor St Georges Building, 2 Ice House Street, Central, China (Hong Kong)
Tel.: (852) 21028138
Web Site: http://www.cct-tech.com.hk
Sales Range: $25-49.9 Million
Emp.: 20
Electronic Parts & Equipment Whslr
N.A.I.C.S.: 423690
Clement Shiu Tong Mak (Chm & CEO)

CCT Fortis Holdings Limited—(Continued)

CCT Telecom (HK) Limited (1)
18th Fl CCT Telecom Bldg, Fotan, China
(Hong Kong)
Tel.: (852) 26958333
Electronic Parts & Equipment Whslr
N.A.I.C.S.: 423690
Flora Cheng (Mng Dir)

CCT Telecom Securities Limited (1)
Rm 2208 22/f St Georges Bldg 2 Ice House
St, Central District, Hong Kong, China
(Hong Kong)
Tel.: (852) 21028138
Securities Brokerage Services
N.A.I.C.S.: 523150

**Huiyang CCT Plastic Products
Co.,Ltd** (1)
CC Telecom Tech Park Sanhe Economic
Development Zone Huiyang, Huizhou,
516213, Guangdong, China
Tel.: (86) 7523500138
Plastics Product Mfr
N.A.I.C.S.: 326199

**Huiyang CCT Telecommunications
Products Co., Ltd** (1)
Inside Zhongjian Technology Park Sanhe
Economic Development Zone, Huizhou,
516213, Guangdong, China
Tel.: (86) 7523500138
Telecommunication Products Mfr
N.A.I.C.S.: 334419

Neptune Holding Limited (1)
18th Floor no 11 Wo Shing Street Cct Tele-
com Building, Fotan, China (Hong
Kong) (100%)
Tel.: (852) 28873031
Web Site: http://www.cct.com.hk
Sales Range: $50-74.9 Million
Emp.: 100
Plastics Materials & Basic Forms & Shapes
Whslr
N.A.I.C.S.: 424610

**Rich Full International Industries
Limited** (1)
Rm 121 1/f Southorn Ctr 130 135 Hennessy
Rd, Wan Chai, Hong Kong, China (Hong
Kong)
Tel.: (852) 28922698
Electronic Components Mfr
N.A.I.C.S.: 334419

Tradeeasy Holdings Limited (1)
20/F Pan Asia Centre 137 Wai Yip Street,
Kwun Tong, Kowloon, China (Hong Kong)
Tel.: (852) 21620888
Web Site: https://www.tradeeasy.com
Emp.: 500
On-Line & Off-Line Marketing Solutions to
Sellers
N.A.I.C.S.: 541613
Danny Kwok Cheung Yip (Mng Dir)

Wiltec Industries Limited (1)
9th Floor Power Industrial Bldg, 9-15 Wo
Heung St, Fotan, China (Hong Kong)
Tel.: (852) 23754388
Web Site: http://www.wiltechk.com
Sales Range: $25-49.9 Million
Emp.: 40
Plastics Product Mfr
N.A.I.C.S.: 326199

CCV RISK SOLUTIONS LIMITED
Towergate House Eclipse Park Sit-
tingbourne Road, Maidstone, ME14
3EN, Kent, United Kingdom
Tel.: (44) 1732 466402
Web Site:
http://www.ccventures.co.uk
Year Founded: 2006
Sales Range: $200-249.9 Million
Emp.: 650
Insurance Intermediary
N.A.I.C.S.: 524298
Peter Cullum (Chm)

Subsidiaries:

Protectagroup Acquisitions Ltd. (1)
Motaquote House, Dinas Isaf Industrial Es-

tate, Williamstown, CF40 1NY, Wales,
United Kingdom
Tel.: (44) 1443420700
Web Site: http://www.protectagroup.co.uk
Sales Range: $50-74.9 Million
Emp.: 80
Acquisition Vehicle
N.A.I.C.S.: 523999

Subsidiary (Domestic):

Culver Insurance Brokers Ltd. (2)
Llanmaes Michaelston Road, Saint Fagans,
Cardiff, CF5 6DU, United Kingdom
Tel.: (44) 2920670067
Web Site: http://ch.sitedesignlondon.co.uk
Insurance Services
N.A.I.C.S.: 524126

CD CAPITAL ASSET MANAGE-MENT LTD
105 Piccadilly, London, W1J 7NJ,
United Kingdom
Tel.: (44) 2073891450
Web Site: http://www.cd-capital.com
Investment Services
N.A.I.C.S.: 523999

Subsidiaries:

Verdant Minerals Ltd. (1)
Unit 20 90 Frances Bay Drive Stuart Park,
Darwin, 0820, NT, Australia (67%)
Tel.: (61) 889420385
Web Site:
http://www.verdantminerals.com.au
Rev.: $64,546
Assets: $39,364,050
Liabilities: $355,274
Net Worth: $39,008,775
Earnings: ($2,118,413)
Fiscal Year-end: 06/30/2018
Potash, Uranium, Base Metals & Gold Ex-
ploration Services
N.A.I.C.S.: 212290
Nigel Doyle (Mgr-Exploration)

CD DEUTSCHE EIGENHEIM AG
Plauener Strabe 163-165 House G,
13053, Berlin, Germany
Tel.: (49) 30263911500
Web Site: https://investor.deutsche-
eigenheim.ag
Building Construction Services
N.A.I.C.S.: 236210
Michael Stueber (Member-Mgmt Bd)

CD PROJEKT S.A.
ul Jagiellonska 74, Building E, 03-
301, Warsaw, Poland
Tel.: (48) 225196900
Web Site: https://www.cdprojekt.com
Year Founded: 1994
CDR—(WAR)
Rev.: $137,026,771
Assets: $369,097,870
Liabilities: $78,455,392
Net Worth: $290,642,478
Earnings: $46,085,054
Emp.: 185
Fiscal Year-end: 12/31/19
Game Video Production Services
N.A.I.C.S.: 512199
Adam Michal Kicinski (Pres & Co-
CEO)

CDC GROUP PLC
123 Victoria St, London, SW1E6DA,
United Kingdom
Tel.: (44) 2079634700
Web Site: http://www.cdcgroup.com
Year Founded: 1948
Sales Range: $700-749.9 Million
Emp.: 50
Emerging Markets-Focused Invest-
ment Services
N.A.I.C.S.: 523999
Miriam de Lacy (Dir-Corp Comm)

Subsidiaries:

Plateno Group Co. Ltd. (1)
Plateno Group Plaza No 300 Xin Jiao Xi
Road, Haizhu District, Guangzhou, Guang-
dong, China
Tel.: (86) 20 8911 5109
Web Site: http://www.plateno-group.com
Hotel Owner & Operator
N.A.I.C.S.: 721110
Lynn Meng (Pres & CEO-Plateno Internet
Company)

CDF INTERNATIONAL COOP-ERATIEF U.A.
Zwarteweg 149, 1431 VL, Aalsmeer,
Netherlands
Tel.: (31) 297345991
Web Site: http://www.cdfintl.com
Year Founded: 2007
Sales Range: $350-399.9 Million
Holding Company; Tobacco Whslr
N.A.I.C.S.: 551112
Tariq Rafique (Chm)

Subsidiaries:

CdF Colombia S.A. (1)
Carrera 3ra 6A-100 Edificio Torre Empre-
sarial Oficina 903, Cartagena, Bolivar, Co-
lombia
Tel.: (57) 56656260
Tobacco Distr
N.A.I.C.S.: 424940
Raymundo Delgado Gonzalez (Controller-
Fin)

CdF Domitab SA (1)
Carretera de las Cienagas - Jacagua, San-
tiago, Dominican Republic
Tel.: (809) 8095759366
Tobacco Distr
N.A.I.C.S.: 424940

CDG CO., LTD.
HERBIS Osaka 7F 2-5-25 Umeda,
Kita-ku, Osaka, 530-0001, Japan
Tel.: (81) 661335200
Web Site: https://www.cdg.co.jp
Year Founded: 1974
2487—(TKS)
Rev.: $74,740,667
Assets: $52,771,721
Liabilities: $12,124,215
Net Worth: $40,647,506
Earnings: $2,497,522
Fiscal Year-end: 12/31/23
Marketing & Promotion Consulting
Services
N.A.I.C.S.: 541613
Noriaki Sogabe (Auditor)

CDG PACKAGING HOLDING AG
Promenadeplatz 12, 80333, Munich,
Germany
Tel.: (49) 89244118332
Eco-Friendly Paper Packaging Prod-
ucts
N.A.I.C.S.: 322220
Zizu Wu (Chm-Supervisory Bd)

CDG PETCHEM LIMITED
Shyam-Arihant 1-8-304 to 307/10 &
11 Patigadda Road, Secunderabad,
500 003, Telangana, India
Tel.: (91) 4066494900
Web Site: http://www.urbaknitt.com
Year Founded: 2011
534796—(BOM)
Rev.: $5,598,263
Assets: $3,914,804
Liabilities: $3,323,098
Net Worth: $591,705
Earnings: ($20,713)
Emp.: 3
Fiscal Year-end: 03/31/21
Polypropylene Sheet Mfr
N.A.I.C.S.: 326113

Manoj Kumar Dugar (Chm & Mng
Dir)

CDH CHINA MANAGEMENT COMPANY LIMITED
25th Floor Fortune Financial Center 5
Dong San Huan Central Road, Cha-
oyang District, Beijing, 100020, China
Tel.: (86) 10 8507 6998
Web Site: http://www.cdhfund.com
Year Founded: 2002
Private Equity & Investment Services
N.A.I.C.S.: 523940
Li Guo (CFO)

Subsidiaries:

CDH Investments Management
(Hong Kong) Limited (1)
1503 International Commerce Center 1 Aus-
tin Road West, Kowloon, China (Hong
Kong)
Tel.: (852) 3518 8000
Web Site: http://www.cdhfund.com
Privater Equity Firm
N.A.I.C.S.: 523999
Dan Li (Mng Dir)

Fujian Nanping Nanfu Battery Co.,
Ltd. (1)
109 Industry Road, Nanping, 353000, Fu-
jian, China (79%)
Tel.: (86) 5998733999
Web Site: http://www.nanfu.com
Storage Battery Mfr & Distr
N.A.I.C.S.: 335910

Sinomem Technology Limited (1)
10 Ang Mo Kio St 65 06-10 Techpoint, Sin-
gapore, 569059, Singapore
Tel.: (65) 64816966
Web Site: http://www.suntar.com
Holding Company; Water Purification Solu-
tions
N.A.I.C.S.: 551112
Xinguang Lan (Mng Dir)

Subsidiary (Non-US):

Microdyn-Nadir (Xiamen) Co.,
Ltd. (2)
No 66 Jinting North Road, Xinglin, Xiamen,
361022, Fujian, China
Tel.: (86) 5926775500
Web Site: http://www.microdyn-nadir.com
Sales Range: $25-49.9 Million
Membrane Materials Mfr
N.A.I.C.S.: 326299
Hans Jorg Heckmann (Mng Dir-Asia)

SCT Suntar Ceramic Technology
(Xiamen) Co., Ltd. (2)
Suntar Technological Park Zhongya Industry
City, Xinglin, Xiamen, Fujian, China
Tel.: (86) 5926778100
Web Site: http://www.suntar.com
Sales Range: $50-74.9 Million
Poly Membrane Products Mfr
N.A.I.C.S.: 326299

Subsidiary (Domestic):

Suntar Membrane Technology (Singa-
pore) Pte Ltd (2)
10 Ang Mo Kio Street 65 06-10, Singapore,
569059, Singapore
Tel.: (65) 64816966
Web Site: http://www.sinomem.com
Sales Range: $25-49.9 Million
Emp.: 5
Polymer Membranes Mfr
N.A.I.C.S.: 326299

Subsidiary (Non-US):

Suntar Membrane Technology (Xia-
men) Co., Ltd. (2)
Sanda Technology Park Zhongya Industrial
City, Xinglin, Xiamen, 361022, Fujian, China
Tel.: (86) 5926778100
Web Site: http://www.suntar.com
Sales Range: $50-74.9 Million
Polymer Membranes Mfr
N.A.I.C.S.: 326299

Sirtex Medical Limited (1)
Level 33 101 Miller Street, North Sydney,
2060, NSW, Australia

Tel.: (61) 2 9964 8400
Web Site: http://www.sirtex.com
Sales Range: $150-199.9 Million
Liver Cancer Treatment & Medical Services
N.A.I.C.S.: 923120
Darren Smith *(CFO & Sec)*

Subsidiary (Domestic):

Sirtex Global Pty. Ltd. **(2)**
Level 33 101 Miller Street, PO Box 6244,
Sydney, 2059, Australia
Tel.: (61) 299648400
Web Site: http://www.sirtex.com
Sales Range: $10-24.9 Million
Emp.: 60
Liver Cancer Treatment Services
N.A.I.C.S.: 622310
David Cade *(Mgr)*

Subsidiary (Non-US):

Sirtex Medical Europe GmbH **(2)**
Walter-Flex Str 2, 53113, Bonn, Nordrhein-
Westfalen, Germany
Tel.: (49) 2281840730
Web Site: http://www.sirtex.com
Sales Range: $10-24.9 Million
Emp.: 30
Liver Cancer Treatment Services
N.A.I.C.S.: 622310
Nigel Lange *(CEO)*

Subsidiary (Domestic):

Sirtex Medical Products Pty. Ltd. **(2)**
Level 33 101 Miller Street, North Ryde,
2060, NSW, Australia
Tel.: (61) 299648400
Web Site: http://www.sirtex.com
Emp.: 55
Liver Cancer Treatment Services
N.A.I.C.S.: 622310
Darren Smith *(CFO)*

Sirtex SIR-Spheres Pty. Ltd. **(2)**
Level 33 101 Miller Street, North Sydney,
2060, NSW, Australia
Tel.: (61) 299648400
Web Site: http://www.sirtex.com
Sales Range: $25-49.9 Million
Emp.: 50
Microcapsules Mfr
N.A.I.C.S.: 325412
Kevin R. M. Smith *(Chief Compliance Officer & Gen Counsel)*

Sirtex Technology Pty. Ltd. **(2)**
PO Box 760, North Ryde, 1670, NSW, Australia
Tel.: (61) 299361426
Web Site: http://www.sirtex.com
Sales Range: $10-24.9 Million
Emp.: 70
Liver Cancer Treatment Services
N.A.I.C.S.: 622310
Michael Tapner *(Project Mgr-R&D)*

Subsidiary (US):

Sirtex Wilmington LLC **(2)**
Unit 2 416 Upton Dr, Wilmington, MA 01887
Tel.: (888) 474-7839
Web Site: http://www.sirtex.com
Emp.: 30
Cancer Treatment Services
N.A.I.C.S.: 622310
Michael Mangano *(Pres)*

CDI INTERNATIONAL LIMITED
SCO 856 Chandigarh Kalka Rd, NAC
Manimajra, Chandigarh, 160101, India
Tel.: (91) 1722734331
Produce, Distribute & Finance Films
& Television Serials Including Animation
N.A.I.C.S.: 512191
Suresh Kumar *(Chm & Mng Dir)*

Subsidiaries:

Laser Infomedia Ltd. **(1)**
SCO 856 NAC Manimajra Chandigarh - Kalka Rd, Chandigarh, 160101, India
Tel.: (91) 1722734331
Multimedia Production Services
N.A.I.C.S.: 512110

CDL HOSPITALITY TRUSTS
390 Havelock Road 02-06 Kings
Centre, Singapore, 169662, Singapore
Tel.: (65) 66648888 **SG**
Web Site: https://www.cdlht.com
Year Founded: 2006
J85—(SES)
Rev.: $195,073,847
Assets: $2,501,426,947
Liabilities: $1,072,765,280
Net Worth: $1,428,661,667
Earnings: $93,891,540
Emp.: 2,204
Fiscal Year-end: 12/31/23
Trust Management Services
N.A.I.C.S.: 523940
Annie Gan *(CFO)*

CDL INVESTMENTS NEW ZEALAND LIMITED
Level 13 280 Queen Street, PO Box
3248, Shortland Street, Auckland,
1140, New Zealand
Tel.: (64) 93535077
Web Site:
https://www.cdlinvestments.co.nz
CDI—(NZX)
Rev.: $63,727,127
Assets: $190,538,595
Liabilities: $5,661,406
Net Worth: $184,877,189
Earnings: $21,641,181
Fiscal Year-end: 12/31/20
Property Investment, Development &
Management Services
N.A.I.C.S.: 523940
Colin Sim *(Chm)*

Subsidiaries:

CDL Land New Zealand Limited **(1)**
Level 2 159 Hurstmere Road, Takapuna,
New Zealand
Tel.: (64) 93535077
Web Site: https://cdlinvestments.co.nz
Property Investment Services
N.A.I.C.S.: 531190

CDMV INC.
2999 Choquette Blvd, PO Box 608,
Saint-Hyacinthe, J2S 7C2, QC,
Canada
Tel.: (450) 771-2368
Web Site: http://www.cdmv.com
Year Founded: 1972
Rev.: $117,491,000
Emp.: 200
Pets Accessories Distr
N.A.I.C.S.: 423450
Denis Huard *(Gen Mgr)*

CDN MAVERICK CAPITAL CORP.
Suite 2150-555 West Hastings Street,
Vancouver, V6B 4N6, BC, Canada
Tel.: (604) 662-7902 **BC**
Web Site:
https://www.cdnmaverick.com
Year Founded: 1969
338B—(DEU)
Rev.: $135,595
Assets: $5,013,105
Liabilities: $499,580
Net Worth: $4,513,525
Earnings: $549,305
Fiscal Year-end: 12/31/23
Mineral Exploration Services
N.A.I.C.S.: 213114
Sandy MacDougall *(Chm, Pres & CEO)*

Subsidiaries:

Green Energy Inc. **(1)**
2305 W Huntington Dr, Tempe, AZ 85282
Tel.: (602) 454-7000
Metal Mining Services
N.A.I.C.S.: 213114

CDN MSOLAR CORP.
5300 Lancing Road, Richmond, V7C
3A1, BC, Canada
Tel.: (604) 999-8253 **BC**
Web Site: http://www.cdn-msolar.com
Year Founded: 2013
Assets: $6,206
Liabilities: $257,061
Net Worth: ($250,855)
Fiscal Year-end: 03/31/17
Energy-Savings Building Technology
Systems
N.A.I.C.S.: 238290

CDP HOLDINGS, LTD.
Building D106 1733 Lianhua Road,
Shanghai, 201103, China
Tel.: (86) 2133295800 **Ky**
Year Founded: 2006
Rev.: $108,282,546
Assets: $66,132,532
Liabilities: $130,132,919
Net Worth: ($64,000,387)
Earnings: ($4,535,296)
Emp.: 756
Fiscal Year-end: 12/31/18
Holding Company
N.A.I.C.S.: 551112

CDP-TRAVISSULLY LTD.
9 Lower John St, London, W1F 9DZ,
United Kingdom
Tel.: (44) 207 437 4224 **UK**
Year Founded: 1960
Sales Range: $10-24.9 Million
Emp.: 25
Advetising Agency
N.A.I.C.S.: 541810
Simon North *(CEO)*

CDR ADVANCE CAPITAL S.P.A.
Via Aldo Moro 3/A, 13900, Biella,
Italy
Tel.: (39) 015 405679
Web Site:
http://www.compagniadella.com
Business Consulting Services
N.A.I.C.S.: 541618
Mauro Girardi *(Chm & CEO)*

CDRL S.A.
Pianowo Ul Kwiatowa 2, 64-000, Koscian, Poland
Tel.: (48) 655118700
Web Site: https://www.cdrl.pl
Year Founded: 2003
CDL—(WAR)
Rev.: $69,908,790
Assets: $53,981,707
Liabilities: $32,873,476
Net Worth: $21,108,232
Earnings: $1,039,634
Emp.: 1,400
Fiscal Year-end: 12/31/23
Apparel Mfr & Distr
N.A.I.C.S.: 315990
Marek Dworczak *(Chm-Mgmt Bd & Pres)*

CDS CO., LTD.
Meieki Dia Meitetsu Bldg 1-1-17
Meieki, Nishi-ku, Nagoya, 451-0045,
Aichi, Japan
Tel.: (81) 525875410
Web Site: https://www.cds-japan.jp
Year Founded: 1980
2169—(NGO)
Rev.: $64,235,216
Assets: $71,139,742
Liabilities: $16,359,432
Net Worth: $54,780,311
Earnings: $6,593,987
Emp.: 560
Fiscal Year-end: 12/31/23

3D CAD Designer & Support Services
N.A.I.C.S.: 541519
Akinori Shibazaki *(Pres)*

Subsidiaries:

BYNAS Co., Ltd **(1)**
917-2 Hishiike Shimomiyake Heiwa-cho,
Inazawa, 490-1312, Aichi, Japan
Tel.: (81) 56 769 6981
Web Site: https://www.bynas.com
Robot Systems Mfr
N.A.I.C.S.: 333248

MCOR Co., Ltd. **(1)**
124-1 Aza Nibanwake Kitano-cho, Okazaki,
444-0951, Aichi, Japan
Tel.: (81) 564325480
Web Site: http://www.mcor.co.jp
Rev.: $33,415,200
Emp.: 277
Computer Aided Design Consultancy Services
N.A.I.C.S.: 541512

Metaform Langues SARL **(1)**
Les espaces de La Pardieu 2 Avenue Michel Ange, PO Box 12, 63000, Clermont-Ferrand, Cedex 1, France
Tel.: (33) 47 328 0072
Web Site: https://metaform-langues.fr
Translation & Interpretation Services
N.A.I.C.S.: 541930

PMC Co., Ltd. **(1)**
31F World Trade Center Bldg 2-4-1
Hamamatsu-cho, Minato-ku, Tokyo, 105-6131, Japan
Tel.: (81) 334333220
Web Site: http://www.pmcnet.co.jp
Emp.: 60
Document Preparation Services
N.A.I.C.S.: 561410
Akinori Shibazaki *(Chm)*

SAS SB Traduction **(1)**
7 Place de Jaude, 63000, Clermont-Ferrand, France
Tel.: (33) 473 289 965
Web Site: http://www.sbtrad.com
Emp.: 8
Translation & Interpretation Services
N.A.I.C.S.: 541930

SB Traduction Sarl **(1)**
7 place de Jaude, 63000, Clermont-Ferrand, France
Tel.: (33) 473289965
Web Site: https://www.sbtrad.com
Language Translation Services
N.A.I.C.S.: 541930

Torindo Co., Ltd **(1)**
6F PMO Tamachi 5-31-17 Shiba, Minato-ku,
Tokyo, 108-0014, Japan
Tel.: (81) 36 809 5813
Web Site: https://www.torindo.ne.jp
Translation & Localization Services
N.A.I.C.S.: 541930
Akinori Shibazaki *(Chm)*

CDT ENVIRONMENTAL TECHNOLOGY INVESTMENT HOLDINGS LIMITED
C1 4th Floor Building 1 Financial
Base No 8 Kefa Road, Nanshan District, Shenzhen, 518057, China
Tel.: (86) 75586667996 **Ky**
Web Site: https://www.cdthb.cn
Year Founded: 2016
CDTG—(NASDAQ)
Rev.: $34,209,919
Assets: $72,891,561
Liabilities: $40,805,318
Net Worth: $32,086,243
Earnings: $7,024,054
Emp.: 107
Fiscal Year-end: 12/31/23
Holding Company
N.A.I.C.S.: 551112
Yunwu Li *(Chm & CEO)*

CDU PLC
Gordon Mill, Barngate Street, Leek,
ST13 8AP, Staffs, United Kingdom

CDU plc—(Continued)

Tel.: (44) 1538 399141   UK
Web Site: http://www.cduplc.com
Sales Range: $10-24.9 Million
Emp.: 90
Mfr, Marketer & Whslr of Ladieswear
N.A.I.C.S.: 315120
Stephen James Thwaite (CEO)

CDW HOLDING LTD.

Rm 6-10 11/F CCT Telecom Building
No 11 Wo Shing Street, Fotan, Sha-
tin, China (Hong Kong)
Tel.: (852) 26341511
Web Site: https://www.cdw-
holding.com.hk
Year Founded: 2004
CDWHF—(OTCIQ)
Rev.: $147,992,000
Assets: $117,538,000
Liabilities: $58,936,000
Net Worth: $58,602,000
Earnings: $14,241,000
Emp.: 499
Fiscal Year-end: 12/31/22
Holding Company
N.A.I.C.S.: 551112
Philip Hua Cheung Dymo (CFO)

Subsidiaries:

Tomoike Industrial (H.K.) Limited   (1)
Room 1-10 11F CCT Telecom bldg 11 Wo
Shing St, Fo Tan, Sha Tin, China (Hong
Kong)
Tel.: (852) 2 688 5223
Web Site: https://tomoike.com.hk
Other Electronic Parts & Equipment Whslr
N.A.I.C.S.: 423690

Subsidiary (Non-US):

Tomoike Industrial Co., Ltd.   (2)
12/F Kintetsu Shin-Namba Bldg 1-4-38
Minato-machi, Naniwa-ku, Osaka, 556-
0017, Japan
Tel.: (81) 676687666
Web Site: http://www.tomoike.net
Emp.: 55
Precision Products Mfr & Distr
N.A.I.C.S.: 332216

Tomoike Precision Machinery (Shang-
hai) Co., Limited   (2)
Chenbao Road 58 Malu Ind City, Jiading
District, Shanghai, 201801, China
Tel.: (86) 2169154464
Emp.: 430
Office Automation Machinery Parts Mfr &
Distr
N.A.I.C.S.: 333248

CE BRANDS, INC.

1400 350-7th Avenue SW, Calgary,
T2P 3N9, AB, Canada
Tel.: (403) 536-0025   Ca
Web Site: https://www.cebrands.ca
Year Founded: 2018
CEBI—(TSXV)
Rev.: $1,427,511
Assets: $1,017,157
Liabilities: $8,407,753
Net Worth: ($7,390,596)
Earnings: $3,081,853
Emp.: 21
Fiscal Year-end: 03/31/24
Business Consulting Services
N.A.I.C.S.: 522299
Craig Smith (Chm & CEO)

CE CAPITAL PARTNER GMBH

Cremon 11, 20457, Hamburg, Ger-
many
Tel.: (49) 40 38 61 88 07
Web Site: http://www.cec-partners.de
Investment Company
N.A.I.C.S.: 523999
Nicolas Neumann (Mng Partner)

Subsidiaries:

Walter Hundhausen GmbH   (1)

Ostendamm 23, PO Box 1329, 58239,
Schwerte, Germany
Tel.: (49) 23041050
Web Site: http://www.walter-hundhausen.de
Iron & Steel Automotive Castings
N.A.I.C.S.: 332111
Andreas Beck (Mng Dir)

CE HOLDINGS CO., LTD.

15-chome Kita-1-21 Heiwa-dori,
Shiroishi-ku, Sapporo, 003-0029,
Hokkaido, Japan
Tel.: (81) 118611600
Web Site: https://www.ce-hd.co.jp
Year Founded: 1996
4320—(TKS)
Rev.: $96,650,880
Assets: $79,719,960
Liabilities: $33,046,490
Net Worth: $46,673,470
Earnings: $4,870,830
Emp.: 608
Fiscal Year-end: 09/30/23
Holding Company
N.A.I.C.S.: 551112
Yasuaki Sugimoto (Chm, Pres & CIO)

CEAT LTD.

463 Dr Annie Besant Road Worli,
Mumbai, 400 030, India
Tel.: (91) 2224930621
Web Site: https://ceat.com
500878—(BOM)
Rev.: $1,546,793,430
Assets: $1,314,198,795
Liabilities: $842,314,200
Net Worth: $471,884,595
Earnings: $24,896,235
Emp.: 8,207
Fiscal Year-end: 03/31/23
Tiles Mfr
N.A.I.C.S.: 339999
Anant Vardhan Goenka (Mng Dir)

CEBU LANDMASTERS, INC.

10th Floor Park Centrale Tower J M
del Mar St Cebu I T Park, Cebu, Phil-
ippines
Tel.: (63) 322314870   PH
Web Site:
https://www.cebulandmasters.com
Year Founded: 2003
CLI—(PHI)
Rev.: $232,173,150
Assets: $1,386,363,793
Liabilities: $1,013,374,417
Net Worth: $372,989,376
Earnings: $55,554,130-
Emp.: 691
Fiscal Year-end: 12/31/21
Real Estate Development Services
N.A.I.C.S.: 531312
Rosario B. Soberano (Treas & Exec
VP)

CEC ENVIRONMENTAL PRO-
TECTION CO., LTD.

No 1800 Cheng xin Street, Jiangning
District, Nanjing, 211102, Jiangsu,
China
Tel.: (86) 2586529992
Web Site: https://www.ce-ep.com
Year Founded: 2001
300172—(CHIN)
Rev.: $141,693,311
Assets: $407,341,594
Liabilities: $142,922,242
Net Worth: $264,419,353
Earnings: $12,087,141
Emp.: 200
Fiscal Year-end: 12/31/23
Water Processing Equipment System
Integration Mfr
N.A.I.C.S.: 221310
Wang Zhengfu (Chm)

CEC INTERNATIONAL HOLD-
INGS LIMITED

2/F Hing Win Factory Building 110
How Ming Street, Kwun Tong, Hong
Kong, China (Hong Kong)
Tel.: (852) 23415539   BM
Web Site: https://www.ceccoils.com
Year Founded: 1979
0759—(I IKQ)
Rev.: $215,781,383
Assets: $116,929,103
Liabilities: $48,902,370
Net Worth: $68,026,733
Earnings: $6,319,538
Emp.: 1,400
Fiscal Year-end: 04/30/23
Holding Company; Coils, Ferrite Ma-
terials, Inductors, Transformers, Line
Filters & Capacitors Designer & Mfr
N.A.I.C.S.: 551112
Kazuaki Fukuoka (Mgr-Bus Dev-Pur-
Retail Bus)

Subsidiaries:

CEC-Coils Singapore Pte Ltd.   (1)
69 Ubi Crescent 04-07 CES Building, Sin-
gapore, 408561, Singapore   (100%)
Tel.: (65) 62223321
Web Site: http://www.ceccoils.com
Sales Range: $50-74.9 Million
Emp.: 6
Coils & Other Electronic Components Mfr &
Sales
N.A.I.C.S.: 334416

Chongqing CEC-Technology
Limited   (1)
Rooms 2103 and 04 International Trade
Center No 38 Qing Nian Road, Yu Zhong
District, Chongqing, 400010, China
Tel.: (86) 236 372 0759
Electronic Component Mfr & Distr
N.A.I.C.S.: 334419

Coils Electronic (Zhongshan) Co.,
Ltd.   (1)
No 71 Li Xin Jie Yong An Lu, Dong Feng
Zhen, Zhongshan, 528425, Guangdong,
China   (100%)
Tel.: (86) 7602 260 1608
Web Site: https://www.ceccoils.com
Coils, Ferrite Materials, Inductors, Trans-
formers, Line Filters & Capacitors Designer
& Mfr
N.A.I.C.S.: 334416

Coils Electronic Co., Limited   (1)
2/F Hing Win Factory Building 110 How
Ming Street, Kwun Tong, Hong Kong, China
(Hong Kong)   (100%)
Tel.: (852) 23415539
Web Site: http://www.ceccoils.com
Sales Range: $50-74.9 Million
Emp.: 150
Coils, Ferrite Materials, Inductors, Trans-
formers, Line Filters & Capacitors Designer
& Mfr
N.A.I.C.S.: 334416

Coils Property Management
Limited   (1)
2/F Hing Win Factory Building 110 How
Ming Street, Kwun Tong, China (Hong
Kong)
Tel.: (852) 2 341 5539
Web Site: http://www.ceccoils.com
Property Investment Services
N.A.I.C.S.: 531390

Dongguan Coils Electronic Co.
Ltd.   (1)
Bei An Guan Li Au, Huang Jiang Zhen,
Dongguan, 523759, Guangdong,
China   (100%)
Tel.: (86) 769 362 2565
Coils & Other Electronic Components Mfr &
Sales
N.A.I.C.S.: 334416

Gaozhou Coils Electronic Co,
Ltd.   (1)
Zone 6 Jin Shan Kai Fa Qu Daidao,
Gaozhou, 525200, Guangdong, China
Tel.: (86) 668 613 6100
Coil Mfr & Distr
N.A.I.C.S.: 334416

Nanjing Guo Zhong Magnetic Mate-
rial Co., Ltd.   (1)
357 Yao Xin Road, Nanjing Economic and
Technical Development Zone, Nanjing,
210038, China   (100%)
Tel.: (86) 258 580 4419
Web Site: https://www.ceccoils.com
Ferrite Powder Mfr & Sales
N.A.I.C.S.: 325998

Tonichi Ferrite Co., Ltd.   (1)
Lin Jin Xie 71 Yong An Lu, Dong Feng
Zhen, Zhongshan, 528425, Guangdong,
China   (100%)
Tel.: (86) 76022601608
Web Site: http://www.ceccoils.com
Sales Range: $900-999.9 Million
Coils & Other Electronic Components Mfr &
Sales
N.A.I.C.S.: 334416

Zhongshan Coils Metalwork Co.,
Ltd.   (1)
No 4 Zhan Xing Lu Da Huan Gong Ye Qu
Zhang Jia Bian, Zhongshan, 528437,
Guangdong, China
Tel.: (86) 7608 531 6691
Coil Mfr
N.A.I.C.S.: 334416

CECCON FRERES SA

Ave Des Iles Prolongee, 74000,
Annecy, Haute Savoie, France
Tel.: (33) 450571156
Web Site: http://www.ceccon-freres.fr
Sales Range: $25-49.9 Million
Emp.: 226
Constructopn Services
N.A.I.C.S.: 236210
Christophe Ceccon (Mgr-DP)

CECEP COSTIN NEW MATERI-
ALS GROUP LIMITED

Unit 2703-04 27/F Tower 6 The Gate-
way, 9 Canton Road Tsimshatsui,
Kowloon, China (Hong Kong)
Tel.: (852) 35280390   Ky
Web Site:
http://www.costingroup.com
Year Founded: 1999
Sales Range: $150-199.9 Million
Emp.: 765
Holding Company; Nonwoven Fabrics
Mfr & Whslr
N.A.I.C.S.: 551112
Jackson Wai Shing Chim (CEO &
Dir-Strategic Plng)

CECEP ENVIRONMENTAL
PROTECTION CO., LTD.

Fengcheng 12th Road Economic De-
velopment Zone, Xi'an, 710018,
Shaanxi, China
Tel.: (86) 2986531336
Year Founded: 1993
300140—(CHIN)
Rev.: $865,484,615
Assets: $4,836,100,215
Liabilities: $2,929,197,561
Net Worth: $1,906,902,655
Earnings: $99,729,335
Fiscal Year-end: 12/31/23
Transformer Equipment Mfr
N.A.I.C.S.: 335311

Subsidiaries:

MP Biomedicals, LLC.   (1)
6 Thomas, Irvine, CA 92618
Tel.: (949) 833-2500
Surgical & Medical Instrument Mfr
N.A.I.C.S.: 339112

CECEP GUOZHEN ENVIRON-
MENTAL PROTECTION TECH-
NOLOGY CO., LTD.

14-16th Floor Zhongxin Network Security Building, No 2688 Innovation
Avenue High-tech Zone, Hefei,
230088, Anhui, China

Tel.: (86) 55165324976
Web Site: https://www.gzep.com.cn
Year Founded: 1997
300388—(CHIN)
Rev.: $575,499,600
Assets: $2,106,836,784
Liabilities: $1,516,599,396
Net Worth: $590,237,388
Earnings: $56,853,576
Fiscal Year-end: 12/31/22
Sewage Treatment Services
N.A.I.C.S.: 221320
Wang Di (Co-Chm)

CECEP SOLAR ENERGY CO., LTD.

7F CECEP Building No 42 Xizhimen
North Avenue, Haidian District, Bei-
jing, 100082, China
Tel.: (86) 1083052461
Web Site: http://www.tynen.cecep.cn
Year Founded: 1993
000591—(SSE)
Rev.: $1,296,787,752
Assets: $6,528,585,960
Liabilities: $3,462,532,164
Net Worth: $3,066,053,796
Earnings: $194,670,216
Fiscal Year-end: 12/31/22
Pharmaceutical Product Mfr & Distr
N.A.I.C.S.: 325412
Zhang Huixue (Chm & Gen Mgr)

CECEP TECHAND ECOLOGY & ENVIRONMENT CO., LTD.

7th Floor Agricultural Science Busi-
ness Office Building, No 8133 Hongli
West Road Futian District, Shenzhen,
518040, Guangdong, China
Tel.: (86) 75582927368
Web Site:
  https://www.sztechand.com
Year Founded: 2001
300197—(CHIN)
Rev.: $199,704,891
Assets: $4,279,439,099
Liabilities: $3,457,211,069
Net Worth: $822,228,030
Earnings: ($208,860,789)
Emp.: 4,000
Fiscal Year-end: 12/31/23
Ecological Environment Engineering
Services
N.A.I.C.S.: 541330
He Liang (Chm)

CECEP WIND-POWER CORPO-RATION CO., LTD.

Floor 11 & 12 Block A Energy Saving
Building, No 42 Xizhimen North
Street Haidian District, Beijing,
100082, China
Tel.: (86) 1083052221
Web Site: http://www.fd-en.cecep.cn
Year Founded: 2006
601016—(SHG)
Rev.: $735,723,083
Assets: $6,145,372,752
Liabilities: $3,817,221,764
Net Worth: $2,328,150,989
Earnings: $228,883,843
Fiscal Year-end: 12/31/22
Wind Electric Power Generation Ser-
vices
N.A.I.C.S.: 221115
Rui Jia (Deputy Gen Mgr)

CECONOMY AG

Kaistr 3, 40221, Dusseldorf, Germany
Tel.: (49) 21154087000   De
Web Site: https://www.ceconomy.de
Year Founded: 1996
CEC—(DEU)
Rev.: $26,236,434,640
Assets: $13,101,636,080
Liabilities: $12,225,900,960

Net Worth: $875,735,120
Earnings: $284,951,680
Emp.: 52,000
Fiscal Year-end: 09/30/21
Consumer Electronic Products Distr
N.A.I.C.S.: 423620
Stephanie Ritschel (VP-IR)

Subsidiaries:

24-7 ENTERTAINMENT ApS   (1)
Gothersgade 12 3-4 Floor, 1123, Copenha-
gen, Denmark
Tel.: (45) 36958959
Web Site: http://www.247entertainment.com
Sales Range: $25-49.9 Million
Emp.: 50
Music & Ringtones Distr
N.A.I.C.S.: 512250

Accelerate Commerce GmbH   (1)
Balanstrasse 73 Haus 19, 81541, Munich,
Germany
Tel.: (49) 8416340
Web Site: http://www.startupcreasphere.com
Accelerator Services
N.A.I.C.S.: 561499

DTB Deutsche Technikberatung
GmbH   (1)
Kalscheurener Str 2-2a, 50354, Hurth, Ger-
many
Tel.: (49) 22116531677
Web Site: https://www.deutsche-
  technikberatung.de
Computer Support & Services
N.A.I.C.S.: 541519
Till Steinmaier (Founder & CEO)

Imtron GmbH   (1)
Web Site: http://www.imtron.eu
Household Appliances Mfr
N.A.I.C.S.: 335220

MEDIA MARKT - BUDAORS Video
TV Hifi Elektro Foto Computer
Kereskedelmi Kft.   (1)
Petofi Sandor U 64, 2040, Budaors, Hun-
gary
Tel.: (36) 13586600
Consumer Electronics Retail Store Operat-
ing Services
N.A.I.C.S.: 449210

MEDIA MARKT ALACANT VIDEO-
TV-HIFI-ELEKTRO-COMPUTER-
FOTO, S.A.   (1)
Avenida Antonio Ramos Carratala S/N, Ali-
cante, 3015, Spain
Tel.: (34) 966020200
Web Site: http://www.mediamarkt.es
Emp.: 100
Consumer Electronics Retailer
N.A.I.C.S.: 449210
Eua Iuorra (Mng Dir)

MEDIA MARKT ALCALA DE GUA-
DAIRA VIDEO-TV-HIFI-ELEKTRO-
COMPUTER-FOTO S.A.   (1)
MediaMarkt - Ctra Sevilla-Malaga km 7,
41500, Alcala de Henares, Spain
Tel.: (34) 955657700
Web Site: https://www.mediamarkt.es
Consumer Electronics Retailer
N.A.I.C.S.: 449210

MEDIA MARKT ALCALA DE
HENARES VIDEO-TV-HIFI-
ELEKTRO-COMPUTER-FOTO,
S.A.   (1)
MediaMarkt - P C La Dehesa - C/ Humanes
11, 28805, Alcala de Henares, Spain
Tel.: (34) 918783500
Web Site: https://www.mediamarkt.es
Consumer Electronics Retailer
N.A.I.C.S.: 449210

MEDIA MARKT ALCORCON VIDEO-
TV-HIFI-ELEKTRO-COMPUTER-
FOTO, S.A.   (1)
MediaMarkt - C/ Estambul S/N Ed L5,
28922, Alcorcon, Spain
Tel.: (34) 912111300
Web Site: https://www.mediamarkt.es
Consumer Electronics Retailer
N.A.I.C.S.: 449210

MEDIA MARKT ALFAFAR VIDEO-TV-
HIFI-ELEKTRO-COMPUTER-FOTO,

S.A.   (1)
MediaMarkt - CC IKEA Alfafar - C/Alcalde
Jose Puertes S/N, 46910, Alfafar, Spain
Tel.: (34) 963425600
Web Site: https://www.mediamarkt.es
Consumer Electronics Retailer
N.A.I.C.S.: 449210

MEDIA MARKT ALFRAGIDE -
PRODUTOS INFORMATICOS E
ELECTRONICOS, LDA   (1)
Rua Casal do Canas 5, Zona Comercial de
Alfragide, 2790-204, Carnaxide, Portugal
Tel.: (351) 211127100
Consumer Electronics Retail Store Operat-
ing Services
N.A.I.C.S.: 449210

MEDIA MARKT Basilix NV   (1)
Avenue Charles-Quint 420, 1082, Sint-
Agatha-Berchem, Belgium
Tel.: (32) 24813600
Web Site: https://www.mediamarkt.be
Electronic Appliance Retailer
N.A.I.C.S.: 449210
Ioannis Tsouvala (Mgr-Store)

MEDIA MARKT Braine-l'Alleud
SA   (1)
Chaussee de Charleroi 18, 1420, Braine-
l'Alleud, Belgium
Tel.: (32) 23893230
Web Site: https://www.mediamarkt.be
Electronic Appliance Retailer
N.A.I.C.S.: 449210
Magali Gaspard (Sls Mgr)

MEDIA MARKT Bruxelles Rue Neuve
- MEDIA MARKT Brussel Nieuwstraat
SA   (1)
Rue Neuve 111-123, 1000, Brussels, Bel-
gium
Tel.: (32) 22271570
Electronic Appliance Retailer
N.A.I.C.S.: 449210
Magali Gaspard (Sls Mgr)

MEDIA MARKT CARTAGENA
VIDEO-TV-ELEKTRO-COMPUTER-
FOTO, S.A.   (1)
Plaza Mediterraneo 10-12, 30353, Carta-
gena, Spain
Tel.: (34) 968323900
Consumer Electronics Retail Store Operat-
ing Services
N.A.I.C.S.: 449210

MEDIA MARKT CASTELLO DE LA
Plana VIDEO-TV-HIFI-ELEKTRO-
COMPUTER-FOTO, S.A.   (1)
Calle De Grecia N 4, Castellon de la Plana,
12006, Spain
Tel.: (34) 964739600
Web Site: http://www.mediamarkt.es
Consumer Electronics Retail Store Operat-
ing Services
N.A.I.C.S.: 449210

MEDIA MARKT CENTURY CENTER
NV   (1)
De Keyserlei 7, 2018, Antwerp, Belgium
Tel.: (32) 32241040
Super Market Stores Operating Services
N.A.I.C.S.: 445110

MEDIA MARKT CORDOBA VIDEO-
TV-ELEKTRO-COMPUTER-FOTO,
S.A.   (1)
CC Los Patios de Azahara Ctra Palma del
Rio Km 4 5 s/n, 14013, Cordoba, Spain
Tel.: (34) 957229800
Super Market Stores Operating Services
N.A.I.C.S.: 445110

MEDIA MARKT DONOSTI VIDEO-
TV-HIFI-ELEKTRO-COMPUTER-
FOTO, S.A.   (1)
Travesia Garbera C Com Garbera 1, San
Sebastian, 20017, Spain
Tel.: (34) 943447700
Consumer Electronics Retail Store Operat-
ing Services
N.A.I.C.S.: 449210

MEDIA MARKT Debrecen Video-TV-
Hifi-Elektro-Photo-Computer-
Kereskedelmi Kft.   (1)
Csapo U 30, 4024, Debrecen, Hungary

Tel.: (36) 13586600
Consumer Electronics Retail Store Operat-
ing Services
N.A.I.C.S.: 449210

MEDIA MARKT GAVA VIDEO-TV-
HIFI-ELEKTRO-COMPUTER-FOTO
S.A.   (1)
Calle Progres C Com Barnasud 69, Barce-
lona, 8012, Spain
Tel.: (34) 936735400
Super Market Stores Operating Services
N.A.I.C.S.: 445110

MEDIA MARKT GIRONA VIDEO-TV-
HIFI-ELEKTRO-COMPUTER-FOTO,
S.A.   (1)
C/ Vitoria-Gazteiz 8, 17003, Gerona, Spain
Tel.: (34) 972010702
Web Site: https://www.mediamarkt.es
Consumer Electronics Retail Store Operat-
ing Services
N.A.I.C.S.: 449210

MEDIA MARKT Gosselies/Charleroi
N.V.   (1)
Rue de Namur 140, Gosselies, 6041, Charl-
eroi, Belgium
Tel.: (32) 71259440
Super Market Stores Operating Services
N.A.I.C.S.: 445110

MEDIA MARKT L HOSPITALET
VIDEO-TV-HIFI-ELEKTRO-
COMPUTER-FOTO S.A.   (1)
Avenida Mare De Deu De Bellvitge 3,
L'Hospitalet de Llobregat, 8907, Spain
Tel.: (34) 934128900
Consumer Electronics Retailer
N.A.I.C.S.: 449210

MEDIA MARKT LAS PALMAS DE
GRAN CANARIA VIDEO-TV-HIFI-
ELEKTRO-COMPUTER-FOTO,
S.A.   (1)
Plaza Felo Monzon C C Y De Ocio 7 Pal-
mas 7, Las Palmas, 35002, Spain
Tel.: (34) 928423409
Consumer Electronics Retailer
N.A.I.C.S.: 449210

MEDIA MARKT LEGANES VIDEO-
TV- HIFI-ELEKTRO-COMPUTER-
FOTO, S.A.   (1)
C C Parquesur-Avda Gran Bretana s/n,
28916, Leganes, Spain
Tel.: (34) 914951100
Web Site: https://www.mediamarkt.es
Consumer Electronics Retailer
N.A.I.C.S.: 449210

MEDIA MARKT LEON VIDEO-TV-
HIFI-ELEKTRO-COMPUTER-FOTO,
S.A.   (1)
C C Espacio Leon - Avda del Pais Leones
12 Lc 1 22, 24010, Leon, Spain
Tel.: (34) 987277300
Web Site: https://www.mediamarkt.es
Consumer Electronics Retailer
N.A.I.C.S.: 449210

MEDIA MARKT LOGRONO VIDEO-
TV-HIFI-ELEKTRO-COMPUTER-
FOTO, S.A.U.   (1)
Calle Lerida C Com Berceo 4, Logrono,
26006, Spain
Tel.: (34) 941279300
Consumer Electronics Retailer
N.A.I.C.S.: 449210

MEDIA MARKT MALAGA-CENTRO
VIDEO-TV-HIFI-ELEKTRO-
COMPUTER-FOTO, S.A.   (1)
Calle Explanada De La Estacion F1-21 F2-
21, Malaga, Spain
Tel.: (34) 951940200
Consumer Electronics Retailer
N.A.I.C.S.: 449210

MEDIA MARKT MATARO VIDEO-TV-
HIFI-ELEKTRO-COMPUTER-FOTO,
S.A.   (1)
CC Mataro Parc - C/ Strasburg 5, 08304,
Mataro, Spain
Tel.: (34) 937413700
Web Site: https://www.mediamarkt.es
Super Market Stores Operating Services
N.A.I.C.S.: 445110

Ceconomy AG—(Continued)

MEDIA MARKT MOLLET VIDEO-TV-HIFI-ELEKTRO-COMPUTER-FOTO, S.A.U. (1)
CC SPLAU - Plana del Galet 1 Local 47-48-49, 08820, El Prat de Llobregat, Spain
Tel.: (34) 934753000
Web Site: https://www.mediamarkt.es
Consumer Electronics Retail Store Operating Services
N.A.I.C.S.: 449210

MEDIA MARKT Megapark Video TV Hifi Elektro Photo Computer Kereskedelmi Kft. (1)
Martirok Utja 292, Budapest, 1201, Hungary
Tel.: (36) 14219900
Consumer Electronics Retail Store Operating Services
N.A.I.C.S.: 449210
Norbert Rakhel (Gen Mgr)

MEDIA MARKT Miskolc Video TV Hifi Elektro Photo Computer Kereskedelmit Kft (1)
Kiraly Ut 1/A, 3533, Miskolc, Hungary
Tel.: (36) 46524900
Web Site: https://www.mediamarkt.hu
Consumer Electronics Retail Store Operating Services
N.A.I.C.S.: 449210

MEDIA MARKT Polus Center Video TV Hifi Photo Computer Kereskedelmi Kft (1)
Szentmihalyi Ut 131, Budapest, 1152, Hungary
Tel.: (36) 14155000
Super Market Stores Operational Services
N.A.I.C.S.: 445110

MEDIA MARKT SALAMANCA VIDEO-TV-HIFI-ELEKTRO-COMPUTER-FOTO, S.A. (1)
CC Los Capuchinos-Crta Salamanca-Sta Marta Km 6 s/n, Santa Marta de Tormes, 37900, Salamanca, Spain
Tel.: (34) 923284300
Web Site: https://www.mediamarkt.es
Consumer Electronics Retailer
N.A.I.C.S.: 449210

MEDIA MARKT SAN SEBASTIAN DE LOS REYES VIDEO-TV-HIFI-ELEKTRO-COMPUTER-FOTO, S.A. (1)
C C Megapark Ctra Nacional A-1 Salida 19, 28700, San Sebastian, Spain
Tel.: (34) 912030500
Consumer Electronics Retailer
N.A.I.C.S.: 449210

MEDIA MARKT SANT CUGAT DEL VALLES VIDEO-TV-HIFI-ELEKTRO-COMPUTER-FOTO, S.A. (1)
Avda Via Augusta 2-14, 8174, Sant Cugat del Valles, Barcelona, Spain
Tel.: (34) 935835200
Web Site: http://www.mediamarkt.es
Emp.: 100
Consumer Electronics Retailer
N.A.I.C.S.: 449210

MEDIA MARKT SATURN ADMINISTRACION ESPANA, S.A.U. (1)
Barbara Martinez Guitart Parque de Negocios Mas Blau C/ Garrotxa, N 2-4 Edificio Oceano II, 8820, El Prat de Llobregat, Spain
Tel.: (34) 934756433
Business Management Consulting Services
N.A.I.C.S.: 541611

MEDIA MARKT SATURN, S.A. (1)
Calle La Garrotxa Parq Empre Mas Blau - Ed Oceano Ii 2, El Prat de Llobregat, 8820, Spain
Tel.: (34) 934753000
Super Market Stores Operating Services
N.A.I.C.S.: 445110

MEDIA MARKT SEVILLA-SANTA JUSTA VIDEO-TV-HIFIi-ELEKTRO-COMPUTER-FOTO, S.A. (1)
El mirador de Santa Justa - Avda Kansas City s/n, 41007, Seville, Spain
Tel.: (34) 954589800

MEDIA MARKT SIERO VIDEO-TV-HIFI-ELEKTRO-COMPUTER-FOTO, S.A. (1)
C C Parque Principado - C/ Paredes s/n, 33429, Lugones, Asturias, Spain
Tel.: (34) 985031000
Web Site: https://www.mediamarkt.es
Consumer Electronics Retailer
N.A.I.C.S.: 449210

MEDIA MARKT SINTRA - PRODUTOS INFORMATICOS E ELECTRONICOS, LDA (1)
Sintra Retail Park Loja 4 Alto do Forte, Alto do Forte, 2635-047, Rio de Mouro, Portugal
Tel.: (351) 210098100
Web Site: http://www.mediamarkt.com
Consumer Electronics Retail Store Operating Services
N.A.I.C.S.: 449210
Francisco Ribeiro (Gen Mgr)

MEDIA MARKT Sint-Pieters-Leeuw N.V. (1)
Bergensesteenweg 65, 1600, Woluwe-Saint-Lambert, Belgium
Tel.: (32) 23712370
Web Site: https://www.mediamarkt.be
Super Market Stores Operating Services
N.A.I.C.S.: 445110

MEDIA MARKT Stop Shop Video TV Hifi Elektro Photo Computer Kereskedelmi Kft. (1)
Becsi Ut 136, 1037, Budapest, Hungary
Tel.: (36) 14393950
Consumer Electronics Online Retail Services
N.A.I.C.S.: 449210

MEDIA MARKT Szeged Video-TV-Hifi-Elektro-Photo-Computer-Kereskedelmi Kft. (1)
Londoni Krt 3, 6724, Szeged, Hungary
Tel.: (36) 62624900
Web Site: https://www.mediamarkt.hu
Consumer Electronics Retail Store Operating Services
N.A.I.C.S.: 449210

MEDIA MARKT Szekesfeharvar Video TV Hifi Elektro Photo Computer Kereskedelmi Kft. (1)
Palotai Ut 6, 8000, Szekesfehervar, Hungary
Tel.: (36) 13586600
Web Site: https://www.mediamarkt.hu
Consumer Electronics Retail Store Operating Services
N.A.I.C.S.: 449210

MEDIA MARKT TARRAGONA VIDEO-TV-HIFI-ELEKTRO-COMPUTER-FOTO S.A. (1)
Josep Maria Folch I Torres 10 - Poligono Les Gavarres, 43006, Tarragona, Spain
Tel.: (34) 977258300
Web Site: https://www.mediamarkt.es
Super Market Stores Operating Services
N.A.I.C.S.: 445110

MEDIA MARKT TV-HiFi-Elektro GmbH Bad Kreuznach (1)
Wollsteiner Str 10, 55543, Bad Kreuznach, Germany
Tel.: (49) 22122243333
Consumer Electronics Retail Store Operating Services
N.A.I.C.S.: 449210

MEDIA MARKT TV-HiFi-Elektro GmbH Berlin-Hohenschonhausen (1)
Prerower Platz 1, Hohenschonhausen, 13051, Berlin, Germany
Tel.: (49) 22122243333
Consumer Electronics Retail Store Operating Services
N.A.I.C.S.: 449210

MEDIA MARKT TV-HiFi-Elektro GmbH Berlin-Spandau (1)
An den Freiheitswiesen 5, Spandau, 13597, Berlin, Germany
Tel.: (49) 22122243333

MEDIA MARKT TV-HiFi-Elektro GmbH Berlin-Wedding (1)
Pankstr 32-39, Wedding, 13357, Berlin, Germany
Tel.: (49) 22122243333
Consumer Electronics Retail Store Operating Services
N.A.I.C.S.: 449210

MEDIA MARKT TV-HiFi-Elektro GmbH Castrop-Rauxel (1)
Siemensstr 16, 44579, Castrop-Rauxel, Germany
Tel.: (49) 22122243333
Consumer Electronics Retailer
N.A.I.C.S.: 449210

MEDIA MARKT TV-HiFi-Elektro GmbH Dietzenbach (1)
Offenbacher Str 9, 63128, Dietzenbach, Germany
Tel.: (49) 22122243333
Sales Range: $25-49.9 Million
Emp.: 32
Consumer Electronics Retail Store Operating Services
N.A.I.C.S.: 449210
Stephan Held (Gen Mgr)

MEDIA MARKT TV-HiFi-Elektro GmbH Dresden-Mickten (1)
Peschelstr 39 Im Elbe Park, Mickten, 1139, Dresden, Germany
Tel.: (49) 35185110
Web Site: http://www.mediamarkt.de
Consumer Electronics Retailer
N.A.I.C.S.: 449210
Schieder Dietmar (Gen Mgr)

MEDIA MARKT TV-HiFi-Elektro GmbH Frankfurt Borsigallee (1)
Borsigallee 39, 60388, Frankfurt, Germany
Tel.: (49) 22122243333
Web Site: http://www.mediamarkt.de
Emp.: 7
Consumer Electronics Online Retail Services
N.A.I.C.S.: 449210

MEDIA MARKT TV-HiFi-Elektro GmbH Friedrichshafen (1)
Meistershofener Str 14 Im Bodensee-Center, 88045, Friedrichshafen, Germany
Web Site: http://www.mediamarkt.de
Emp.: 6
Consumer Electronics Retailer
N.A.I.C.S.: 449210

MEDIA MARKT TV-HiFi-Elektro GmbH Gutersloh (1)
Vennstr 40, 33330, Gutersloh, Germany
Tel.: (49) 22122243333
Consumer Electronics Retailer
N.A.I.C.S.: 449210

MEDIA MARKT TV-HiFi-Elektro GmbH Hannover-Wulfel (1)
Hildesheimer Str 410, 30519, Hannover, Germany
Tel.: (49) 22122243333
Sales Range: $25-49.9 Million
Emp.: 7
Consumer Electronics Retail Store Operating Services
N.A.I.C.S.: 449210
Horst Tiede (Gen Mgr)

MEDIA MARKT TV-HiFi-Elektro GmbH Limburg (1)
Hohenstr 10, 65549, Limburg, Germany
Tel.: (49) 64312160
Web Site: http://www.mediamarktlimburg.de
Emp.: 4
Consumer Electronics Retail Store Operating Services
N.A.I.C.S.: 449210
Soo-Cheol Shin (Gen Mgr)

MEDIA MARKT TV-HiFi-Elektro GmbH Magdeburg (1)
Am Pfahlberg 7, 39128, Magdeburg, Germany
Tel.: (49) 22122243333
Emp.: 12
Consumer Electronics Retail Store Operating Services

N.A.I.C.S.: 449210
Harald Christel (Mgr)

MEDIA MARKT TV-HiFi-Elektro GmbH Marburg (1)
Erlenring 19, 35037, Marburg, Germany
Tel.: (49) 22122243333
Consumer Electronics Retail Store Operating Services
N.A.I.C.S.: 449210

MEDIA MARKT TV-HiFi-Elektro GmbH Nienburg (1)
Schlossplatz 5, 31582, Nienburg, Germany
Tel.: (49) 22122243333
Emp.: 150
Consumer Electronics Retail Store Operating Services
N.A.I.C.S.: 449210
Seek Peace (Gen Mgr)

MEDIA MARKT TV-HiFi-Elektro GmbH Nurnberg-Langwasser (1)
Oppelner Str 213, 90473, Nuremberg, Germany
Tel.: (49) 22122243333
Consumer Electronics Retail Store Operating Services
N.A.I.C.S.: 449210

MEDIA MARKT TV-HiFi-Elektro GmbH Rheine (1)
Emsstrasse 36, 48431, Rheine, Germany
Tel.: (49) 22122243333
Consumer Electronics Retail Store Operating Services
N.A.I.C.S.: 449210

MEDIA MARKT TV-HiFi-Elektro GmbH Rodental (1)
Nikolaus-August-Otto-Str 17, Rodental, 96472, Germany
Tel.: (49) 956330860
Web Site: http://www.mediamarkt.de
Emp.: 35
Consumer Electronics Retail Store Operating Services
N.A.I.C.S.: 449210
Robert Lang (Gen Mgr)

MEDIA MARKT TV-HiFi-Elektro GmbH Rosenheim (1)
Georg-Aicher-Str 6-10, 83026, Rosenheim, Germany
Tel.: (49) 22122243333
Consumer Electronics Retail Store Operating Services
N.A.I.C.S.: 449210

MEDIA MARKT TV-HiFi-Elektro GmbH Saarbrucken (1)
Breslauer Str 1a, 66121, Saarbrucken, Germany
Tel.: (49) 22122243333
Consumer Electronics Retail Store Operating Services
N.A.I.C.S.: 449210

MEDIA MARKT TV-HiFi-Elektro GmbH Singen (1)
Unter den Tannen 3, 78224, Singen, Germany
Tel.: (49) 77317930
Web Site: http://www.mediamarkt.de
Sales Range: $25-49.9 Million
Emp.: 6
Consumer Electronics Retail Store Operating Services
N.A.I.C.S.: 449210
Michael Scholz (Gen Mgr)

MEDIA MARKT TV-HiFi-Elektro GmbH Stuhr (1)
3-K-Weg 25a, 28816, Stuhr, Germany
Tel.: (49) 22243333
Web Site: https://www.mediamarkt.de
Consumer Electronics Retailer
N.A.I.C.S.: 449210

MEDIA MARKT TV-HiFi-Elektro GmbH Trier (1)
Ostallee 3-5 Alleencenter Direkt am Hbf, 54290, Trier, Germany
Tel.: (49) 22243333
Web Site: https://www.mediamarkt.de
Consumer Electronics Retail Store Operating Services
N.A.I.C.S.: 449210

MEDIA MARKT TV-HiFi-Elektro GmbH Ulm (1)

Blaubeurer Str 24, 89077, Ulm, Germany
Tel.: (49) 22243333
Web Site: https://www.mediamarkt.de
Consumer Electronics Retailer
N.A.I.C.S.: 449210

MEDIA MARKT TV-HiFi-Elektro
GmbH Zella-Mehlis (1)
Industriestr 4, 98544, Zella-Mehlis, Germany
Tel.: (49) 22243333
Web Site: https://www.mediamarkt.de
Consumer Electronics Online Retail Services
N.A.I.C.S.: 449210
Udo Amarell (Gen Mgr)

MEDIA MARKT TV-Hifi-Elektro
GmbH (1)
Maria-Probst-Str 6, 80939, Munich, Germany
Tel.: (49) 22122243333
Consumer Electronics Online Retail Services
N.A.I.C.S.: 449210

MEDIA MARKT TV-Hifi-Elektro Wien
XI Gesellschaft m.b.H. (1)
Landwehrstrasse 6, 1110, Vienna, Austria
Tel.: (43) 176716200
Web Site: http://www.mediamarkt.at
Consumer Electronics Retailer
N.A.I.C.S.: 449210

MEDIA MARKT TV-Hifi-Elektro Wien
XIII GmbH (1)
Mantlergasse 34-36, Vienna, 1130, Austria
Tel.: (43) 187744110
Web Site: http://www.mediamark.at
Consumer Electronics Retailer
N.A.I.C.S.: 449210

MEDIA MARKT TWEE TORENS
HASSELT NV (1)
Biezenstraat 51, 3500, Hasselt, Belgium
Tel.: (32) 11294900
Web Site: https://www.mediamarkt.be
Super Market Stores Operating Services
N.A.I.C.S.: 445110

MEDIA MARKT VITORIA-GASTEIZ
VIDEO-TV-HIFI-ELEKTRO-
COMPUTER-FOTO, S.A. (1)
CC Boulevard - C/Zaramaga 1, 01013,
Vitoria-Gasteiz, Spain
Tel.: (34) 945129600
Web Site: https://www.mediamarkt.es
Super Market Stores Operating Services
N.A.I.C.S.: 445110

MEDIA MARKT Worgl TV-Hifi-Elektro
GmbH (1)
Innsbrucker Strasse 95, 6300, Worgl, Austria
Tel.: (43) 7009999
Web Site: https://www.mediamarkt.at
Super Market Stores Operating Services
N.A.I.C.S.: 445110

MEDIA MARKT ZARAGOZA
PUERTO VENECIA VIDEO-TV-HIFI-
ELEKTRO-COMPUTER-FOTO,
S.A. (1)
CC Puerto Venecia - C Teatro Malibran 18-
20, 50007, Zaragoza, Spain
Tel.: (34) 976720400
Web Site: https://www.mediamarkt.es
Sales Range: $25-49.9 Million
Emp.: 19
Consumer Electronics Retail Store Operating Services
N.A.I.C.S.: 449210

MEDIA MARKT- West End Video TV
Hifi Elektro Photo Computer Kereskedelmi Kft. (1)
Vaci ut 1-3, 1062, Budapest, Hungary
Tel.: (36) 12386900
Web Site: https://www.mediamarkt.hu
Consumer Electronics Online Retail Services
N.A.I.C.S.: 449210

MEDIA MARKT-SATURN BELGIUM
N.V (1)
Brusselsesteenweg 496 Bus 2, Zellik, 1731,
Asse, Belgium
Tel.: (32) 24643555
Web Site: http://www.media-saturn.com

Sales Range: $25-49.9 Million
Emp.: 100
Super Market Stores Operating Services
N.A.I.C.S.: 445110

MEDIA Markt TV-HiFi-Elektro GmbH
Aschaffenburg (1)
Mainaschaffer Str 115, 63741, Aschaffenburg, Germany
Tel.: (49) 22122243333
Consumer Electronics Retail Store Operating Services
N.A.I.C.S.: 449210

MEDIA Markt TV-HiFi-Elektro GmbH
Bayreuth (1)
Spinnereistr 4, 95445, Bayreuth, Germany
Tel.: (49) 22122243333
Consumer Electronics Retail Store Operating Services
N.A.I.C.S.: 449210

MEDIA Markt TV-HiFi-Elektro GmbH
Berlin-Biesdorf (1)
Wankelstrasse 5, 85046, Ingolstadt, Germany
Tel.: (49) 841 634 4545
Web Site: http://www.mediamarkt.com
Consumer Electronics Retailer
N.A.I.C.S.: 449210
Helga Kellerhals (Co-Founder)

MEDIA Markt TV-HiFi-Elektro GmbH
Berlin-Gropiusstadt (1)
Johannisthaler Chaussee 309, Gropiusstadt, 12351, Berlin, Germany
Tel.: (49) 22122243333
Consumer Electronics Retail Store Operating Services
N.A.I.C.S.: 449210

MEDIA Markt TV-HiFi-Elektro GmbH
Berlin-Neukolln (1)
Karl-Marx-Str 66, Neukolln, 12043, Berlin, Germany
Tel.: (49) 22122243333
Consumer Electronics Retail Store Operating Services
N.A.I.C.S.: 449210

MEDIA Markt TV-HiFi-Elektro GmbH
Heidelberg (1)
Hebelstr 22, 69115, Heidelberg, Germany
Tel.: (49) 22122243333
Consumer Electronics Retail Store Operating Services
N.A.I.C.S.: 449210

MEDIA Markt TV-HiFi-Elektro GmbH
Nurnberg-Kleinreuth (1)
Web Site: http://www.mediamarkt.de
Consumer Electronics Retail Store Operating Services
N.A.I.C.S.: 449210

MEDIA Markt TV-HiFi-Elektro Licht
GmbH Ingolstadt (1)
Eriagstr 28, 85053, Ingolstadt, Germany
Tel.: (49) 22243333
Web Site: https://www.mediamarkt.de
Electronic Retail Stores Operating Services
N.A.I.C.S.: 449210

MEDIA-Markt TV-HiFi-Elektro GmbH
Aachen (1)
Franzstr 6, 52064, Aachen, Germany
Web Site: http://www.mediamarkt.de
Consumer Electronics Retail Store Operating Services
N.A.I.C.S.: 449210

MEDIA-SATURN (PORTUGAL),
SGPS, UNIPESSOAL LDA (1)
Rua Casal Do Canas 5, Carnaxide, 2790-
204, Portugal
Tel.: (351) 210042000
Emp.: 1
Consumer Electronics Retail Store Operating Services
N.A.I.C.S.: 449210
Lee Reborse (Reg Mgr)

Media - Saturn Beteiligungsges
.m.b.H. (1)
Scs-Burocenter/B 2, Voesendorf, 2334,
Austria
Tel.: (43) 1699070
Consumer Electronics Retail Store Operating Services

N.A.I.C.S.: 449210

Media Markt 14 - Produtos Electronicos Lda (1)
Rua Casal do Canas n 5 Zona Comercial
de, Alfragide, 2790-204, Carnaxide, Portugal
Tel.: (351) 211127100
Electronic Appliance Retailer
N.A.I.C.S.: 449210

Media Markt 3 De Mayo Santa Cruz
De Tenerife S.A. (1)
Nivaria Center Calle Nivaria Tejera 2,
38003, Santa Cruz de Tenerife, Spain
Tel.: (34) 922849300
Web Site: https://www.mediamarkt.es
Electronic Appliance Retailer
N.A.I.C.S.: 449210
Sonia Rivero Perez (Mgr-In Store Fulfillment)

Media Markt Aigle SA (1)
Chemin Sous-le-Grand-Pre 4, 1860, Aigle,
Switzerland
Tel.: (41) 244682525
Web Site: https://www.mediamarkt.ch
Electronic Appliance Retailer
N.A.I.C.S.: 449210

Media Markt Alexandrium B.V. (1)
Watermanweg 325, 3067 GA, Rotterdam,
3067 GA, Netherlands
Tel.: (31) 102863888
Web Site: https://www.mediamarkt.nl
Electronic Retail Stores Operating Services
N.A.I.C.S.: 449210

Media Markt Alkmaar B.V. (1)
Noorderkade 172, 1823 CJ, Alkmaar, Netherlands
Tel.: (31) 725180400
Web Site: https://www.mediamarkt.nl
Electronic Retail Stores Operating Services
N.A.I.C.S.: 449210

Media Markt Almere B.V. (1)
Brouwerstraat 3, 1315 BL, Almere, 1315
BL, Netherlands
Tel.: (31) 365307500
Web Site: https://www.mediamarkt.nl
Electronic Retail Stores Operating Services
N.A.I.C.S.: 449210

Media Markt Alphen aan den Rijn
B.V. (1)
Sint Jorisstraat 15, 2405 DB, Alphen aan
den Rijn, Netherlands
Tel.: (31) 172428300
Web Site: https://www.mediamarkt.nl
Electronic Retail Stores Operating Services
N.A.I.C.S.: 449210

Media Markt Amersfoort B.V. (1)
Eemplein 3, 3812 EA, Amersfoort, Netherlands
Tel.: (31) 334452500
Web Site: https://www.mediamarkt.nl
Electronic Appliance Retailer
N.A.I.C.S.: 449210
Maurits Meijers (Chief Customer Officer)

Media Markt Amsterdam Centrum
B.V. (1)
Oosterdokskade 67, 1011 DL, Amsterdam,
Netherlands
Tel.: (31) 205213600
Web Site: https://www.mediamarkt.nl
Electronic Appliance Retailer
N.A.I.C.S.: 449210
Ricardo van Dijk (Mng Dir)

Media Markt Amsterdam Noord
B.V. (1)
Buikslotermeerplein 226, 1025, Amsterdam,
Netherlands
Tel.: (31) 206345300
Web Site: https://www.mediamarkt.nl
Electronic Retail Stores Operating Services
N.A.I.C.S.: 449210

Media Markt Amsterdam West
B.V. (1)
Zuidermolenweg 20, 1069 CG, Amsterdam,
Netherlands
Tel.: (31) 206675700
Web Site: https://www.mediamarkt.nl
Electronic Appliance Retailer
N.A.I.C.S.: 449210

Media Markt Amstetten TV-Hifi-
Elektro GmbH (1)
Waidhofnerstrasse 1, Amstetten, 3300, Austria
Tel.: (43) 7472620000
Web Site: http://www.mediamarkt.at
Consumer Electronics Retail Stores
N.A.I.C.S.: 449210
Markus Janku (Mgr)

Media Markt Apeldoorn B.V. (1)
De Voorwaarts 13, 7321 MA, Apeldoorn,
Netherlands
Tel.: (31) 553681700
Web Site: https://www.mediamarkt.nl
Electronic Appliance Retailer
N.A.I.C.S.: 449210
Sjon Bomhof (Bus Mgr-Unit)

Media Markt Arena B.V. (1)
Johan Cruijff Boulevard 123, 1101 DM, Amsterdam, Netherlands
Tel.: (31) 205641616
Web Site: https://www.mediamarkt.nl
Consumer Electronics Online Retail Services
N.A.I.C.S.: 449210

Media Markt Arnhem B.V. (1)
Velperplein 13, 6811 AG, Arnhem, 6811 AG,
Netherlands
Tel.: (31) 263520800
Web Site: https://www.mediamarkt.nl
Electronic Retail Stores Operating Services
N.A.I.C.S.: 449210

Media Markt Assen B.V. (1)
Crown work 21, 9401 BA, Assen, Netherlands
Tel.: (31) 592332600
Web Site: https://www.mediamarkt.nl
Electronic Appliance Retailer
N.A.I.C.S.: 449210
Randy Bommer (Chief Customer Officer)

Media Markt
Augsburg-Oberhausen (1)
Schonbachstr 192, 86154, Augsburg, Germany
Web Site: http://www.mediamarkt.de
Consumer Electronics Retail Store Operator
N.A.I.C.S.: 449210

Media Markt Aveiro - Produtos Informaticos E Electronicos, Lda (1)
Aveiro Shopping Center-Quinta do Simao,
3800-042, Aveiro, Portugal
Tel.: (351) 234001100
Electronic Appliance Retailer
N.A.I.C.S.: 449210
Francisco Macambira (Mng Dir-Store)

Media Markt Badajoz S.A. (1)
Avda de Elvas S/N Esquina C/Santiago
Soutullo S/N, 06006, Badajoz, Spain
Tel.: (34) 924209000
Web Site: https://www.mediamarkt.es
Electronic Appliance Retailer
N.A.I.C.S.: 449210
Antonio Vadillo (Mgr-Customer Experience)

Media Markt Baden-Baden (1)
Im Gewerbepark Cite 7, 76532, Baden-
Baden, Germany
Web Site: http://www.mediamarkt.de
Consumer Electronics Retail Store Operating Services
N.A.I.C.S.: 449210

Media Markt Basel AG (1)
Guterstrasse 115, 4053, Basel, Switzerland
Tel.: (41) 613651515
Web Site: https://www.mediamarkt.ch
Electronic Appliance Retailer
N.A.I.C.S.: 449210
Theodore Fischer (Sls Mgr)

Media Markt Bekescsaba Video TV
Hifi Elektro Photo Computer Kereskedelmi Kft. (1)
Andrassy ut 37-43, 5600, Bekescsaba,
Hungary
Tel.: (36) 13586600
Web Site: https://www.mediamarkt.hu
Electronic Appliance Retailer
N.A.I.C.S.: 449210
Attila Gyokos (Dir-Store)

Media Markt Benfica - Produtos Informaticos E Electronicos, Lda (1)

Ceconomy AG—(Continued)

Av Eusebio da Silva Ferreira Estadio SLB,
1500-313, Lisbon, Portugal
Tel.: (351) 210078115
Electronic Appliance Retailer
N.A.I.C.S.: 449210
Nuno Baltazar *(Mgr-Store)*

**Media Markt Bergen op Zoom
D.V.** **(1)**
Burgemeester van de Laarstraat 17, 4615
PB, Bergen-op-Zoom, Netherlands
Tel.: (31) 164218600
Web Site: https://www.mediamarkt.nl
Super Market Stores Operating Services
N.A.I.C.S.: 445110

Media Markt Biel-Brugg AG **(1)**
Erlenstrasse 40, 2555, Brugg, Switzerland
Tel.: (41) 323747878
Web Site: https://www.mediamarkt.ch
Electronic Appliance Retailer
N.A.I.C.S.: 449210
Steyaert Rob *(Mgr-Store)*

**Media Markt Bilbao - Zubiarte,
S.A.** **(1)**
Leizaola Lehendakariaren Kalea 2, 48011,
Bilbao, Spain
Tel.: (34) 944287000
Web Site: https://www.mediamarkt.es
Electronic Appliance Retailer
N.A.I.C.S.: 449210
Urko Cantalapiedra *(Mng Dir-Store)*

**Media Markt Boras TV-Hifi-Elektro
AB** **(1)**
Knalleland Algardsvagen 11, 506 30, Boras,
Sweden
Tel.: (46) 770778787
Web Site: https://www.mediamarkt.se
Consumer Electronics Retail Store Operating
Services
N.A.I.C.S.: 449210

**Media Markt Braga - Produtos Infor-
maticos E Electronicos, Lda** **(1)**
Lugar da Senra de Baixo Lamacaes, 4715-
276, Braga, Portugal
Tel.: (351) 253003100
Electronic Appliance Retailer
N.A.I.C.S.: 449210
Antunes Jorge *(Mng Dir-Store)*

Media Markt Breda B.V. **(1)**
Kruisvoort 14, 4814 RZ, Breda, 4814 RZ,
Netherlands
Tel.: (31) 765258100
Web Site: https://www.mediamarkt.nl
Electronic Retail Stores Operating Services
N.A.I.C.S.: 449210

Media Markt Brugge NV **(1)**
Maalse Steenweg 338, Sint Kruis, 8310,
Bruges, Belgium
Tel.: (32) 50729940
Web Site: https://www.mediamarkt.be
Electronic Appliance Retailer
N.A.I.C.S.: 449210
Steyaert Rob *(Mgr-Store)*

Media Markt Brussel Docks NV **(1)**
Avenue Lambermont 1, 1000, Brussels,
Belgium
Tel.: (32) 24232245
Web Site: https://www.mediamarkt.be
Electronic Appliance Retailer
N.A.I.C.S.: 449210
Abdellatif Boulif *(Mgr-Floor)*

**Media Markt Burs TV-Hifi-Elektro
GmbH** **(1)**
Zimbapark Almteilweg 1, Burs, 4024,
Bludenz, Austria
Tel.: (43) 57009999
Electronic Appliance Retailer
N.A.I.C.S.: 449210

**Media Markt CXXIX TV-HiFi-Elektro
GmbH Ingolstadt** **(1)**
Wankelstr 5, Ingolstadt, 85053, Germany
Tel.: (49) 8416340
Web Site: http://www.media-saturn.com
Emp.: 300
Super Market Stores Operating Services
N.A.I.C.S.: 445110

Media Markt Chur AG
Rascharenstrasse 65, 7000, Chur, Switzerland

Tel.: (41) 812864949
Electronic Appliance Retailer
N.A.I.C.S.: 449210

**Media Markt Collado Villalba,
S.A,** **(1)**
C C Planet Ocio Av Juan Carlos I 46 Cra,
Collado Villalba, 28400, A Coruna, Spain
Tel.: (34) 918561500
Electronic Appliance Retailer
N.A.I.C.S.: 449210
Juan Carlos Montalvo *(Bus Mgr-B2B)*

Media Markt Conthey SA **(1)**
Route Cantonale 11, Conthey, 1964, Walli-
sellen, Switzerland
Tel.: (41) 273454444
Electronic Appliance Retailer
N.A.I.C.S.: 449210

Media Markt Crissier SA **(1)**
Rue de Morges 13, 1023, Crissier, Switzer-
land
Tel.: (41) 217036060
Electronic Appliance Retailer
N.A.I.C.S.: 449210
Yannick Amstutz *(Deputy Mng Dir & Mgr-
Admin)*

Media Markt Cruquius B.V. **(1)**
Cruquiusplein 10, 2142 EV, Cruquius, 2142
EV, Netherlands
Tel.: (31) 235438800
Electronic Store Operating Services
N.A.I.C.S.: 449210

Media Markt Den Bosch B.V. **(1)**
Tinnegieterstraat 26, 5232 BM, Den Bosch,
Netherlands
Tel.: (31) 736402000
Electronic Appliance Retailer
N.A.I.C.S.: 449210
Joep van Gulik *(Sls Mgr)*

Media Markt Den Haag B.V. **(1)**
Grote Marktstraat 48A, 2511 BJ, Hague,
Netherlands
Tel.: (31) 703306400
Electronic Retail Stores Operating Services
N.A.I.C.S.: 449210

Media Markt Deurne NV **(1)**
Krijgsbaan 1a, 2100, Deurne, Belgium
Tel.: (32) 34512700
Electronic Appliance Retailer
N.A.I.C.S.: 449210
Lambot Koen *(Mgr-Store)*

Media Markt Deventer B.V. **(1)**
Boreelplein 38, Deventer, 7411 EH, Nether-
lands
Tel.: (31) 570685700
Super Market Stores Operating Services
N.A.I.C.S.: 445110

**Media Markt Diagonal Mar-Barcelona
Video-TV-Hifi-Elektro-Computer-Foto
S.A.** **(1)**
C C Diagonal Mar Av Diagonal 3 Pl B Lc
14000, 08019, Barcelona, Spain
Tel.: (34) 934857200
Electronic Appliance Retailer
N.A.I.C.S.: 449210

Media Markt Doetinchem B.V. **(1)**
Burg van Nispenstraat 16, 7001 BS, Doet-
inchem, Netherlands
Tel.: (31) 314320700
Electronic Appliance Retailer
N.A.I.C.S.: 449210
Viola Schoots *(Mgr-Customer Solution)*

Media Markt Dordrecht B.V. **(1)**
Johan de Wittstraat 15, 3311 KG, Dor-
drecht, Netherlands
Tel.: (31) 786115000
Electronic Appliance Retailer
N.A.I.C.S.: 449210
Marcella de Ronde *(Mgr-Customer Experi-
ence)*

Media Markt Drachten B.V. **(1)**
Raadhuisplein 37, 9203 CZ, Drachten,
Netherlands
Tel.: (31) 512570800
Electronic Appliance Retailer
N.A.I.C.S.: 449210
Age van Dijk *(Chief Customer Officer)*

Media Markt Duiven B.V. **(1)**
Cartograaf 3, 6921 EZ, Duiven, Netherlands

Tel.: (31) 263170100
Electronic Appliance Retailer
N.A.I.C.S.: 449210
Jordy Kreuzen *(Mgr-Customer Solution)*

Media Markt E-Commerce AG **(1)**
Allmendstrasse 23, 8953, Dietikon, Switzer-
land
Tel.: (41) 447493636
Electronic Appliance Retailer
N.A.I.C.S.: 449210
Marcel Bachmann *(Mgr-Online Content)*

Media Markt Ede B.V. **(1)**
Brouwerstraat 21b, 6711 AS, Ede, 6711 AS,
Netherlands
Tel.: (31) 318477400
Electronic Retail Stores Operating Services
N.A.I.C.S.: 449210

Media Markt Eindhoven B.V. **(1)**
Boschdijktunnel 1, 5611 AG, Eindhoven,
Netherlands
Tel.: (31) 402358800
Sales Range: $50-74.9 Million
Emp.: 16
Consumer Electronics Retailer
N.A.I.C.S.: 449210
Hans Duineveld *(Mng Dir)*

**Media Markt Eindhoven Ekkersrijt
B.V.** **(1)**
Ekkersrijt 4086, 5692 DA, Son en Breugel,
Netherlands
Tel.: (31) 499462600
Electronic Appliance Retailer
N.A.I.C.S.: 449210
Timo Fijneman *(Mgr-Customer Solution)*

Media Markt Emmen B.V. **(1)**
Noorderplein 90, 7811 MG, Emmen, Neth-
erlands
Tel.: (31) 591637200
Electronic Appliance Retailer
N.A.I.C.S.: 449210
Erik Wemmenhove *(Mgr-Customer Solution)*

Media Markt Enschede B.V. **(1)**
Klanderij 63, 7511 HS, Enschede, 7511 HS,
Netherlands
Tel.: (31) 534814000
Super Market Stores Operating Services
N.A.I.C.S.: 445110

**Media Markt Eskilstuna TV-Hifi-
Elektro AB** **(1)**
Albertina Nystroms vag 2, 632 22, Eskil-
stuna, Sweden
Tel.: (46) 770778787
Electronic Appliance Retailer
N.A.I.C.S.: 449210
Johan Holm *(Mng Dir)*

Media Markt Esplugues, S.A. **(1)**
C/Laurea Miro 4, 08950, Esplugues de Llo-
bregat, Barcelona, Spain
Tel.: (34) 933746400
Electronic Part & Component Whslr
N.A.I.C.S.: 449210

**Media Markt Feldkirch TV-Hifi-Elektro
GmbH** **(1)**
Konigshofstrasse 79, Altenstadt, 6804,
Feldkirch, Austria
Tel.: (43) 57009999
Electronic Part & Component Whslr
N.A.I.C.S.: 449210

Media Markt Ferrol, SA **(1)**
Parque Ferrol Avenida Buque Escola
Galatea S/N, 15405, El Ferrol, Spain
Tel.: (34) 981338300
Electronic Part & Component Whslr
N.A.I.C.S.: 449210

Media Markt Finestrat S.A.U. **(1)**
Av Pais Valencia 14, Finestrat, 03509, Ali-
cante, Spain
Tel.: (34) 966815600
Electronic Part & Component Whslr
N.A.I.C.S.: 449210

**Media Markt Gaia - Produtos Infor-
maticos E Electronicos, Lda** **(1)**
Rua D Henrique de Cernache, Santa
Marinha, 4400-625, Vila Nova de Gaia,
Portugal
Tel.: (351) 220034500
Electronic Part & Component Whslr
N.A.I.C.S.: 449210

Media Markt Gandia S.A. **(1)**
CC Pz Mayor Gandia Av Blasco Ibanez
S/N, 46701, Gandia, Spain
Tel.: (34) 962826900
Electronic Part & Component Whslr
N.A.I.C.S.: 449210

**Media Markt Gavle TV-Hifi-Elektro
AB** **(1)**
Valbo Kopctad Valbovagon 331, 818 32,
Valbo, Sweden
Tel.: (46) 770778787
Electronic Part & Component Whslr
N.A.I.C.S.: 449210

**Media Markt Goteborg-Backebol TV-
Hifi-Elektro AB** **(1)**
Backebol Homecenter Transportgatan, His-
ingsbacka, 422 46, Gothenburg, Sweden
Tel.: (46) 770778787
Electronic Part & Component Whslr
N.A.I.C.S.: 449210

**Media Markt Goteborg-Hogsbo TV-
HiFi-Elektro AB** **(1)**
Lona Knapes gata 1, 421 32, Vastra Frol-
unda, Sweden
Tel.: (46) 770778787
Electronic Part & Component Whslr
N.A.I.C.S.: 449210

**Media Markt Goteborg-Torpavallen
TV-Hifi-Elektro AB** **(1)**
Torpavallsgatan 4D, 416 73, Gothenburg,
Sweden
Tel.: (46) 770778787
Electronic Part & Component Whslr
N.A.I.C.S.: 449210

**Media Markt Granada - Nevada,
S.A.** **(1)**
Parque Comercial Nevada Shopping Calle
Hipocrates S/N, Armilla, 18100, Granada,
Spain
Tel.: (34) 958145800
Electronic Part & Component Whslr
N.A.I.C.S.: 449210

Media Markt Grancia SA **(1)**
Centro Lugano Sud, 6916, Grancia, Swit-
zerland
Tel.: (41) 919853232
Electronic Part & Component Whslr
N.A.I.C.S.: 449210

Media Markt Granges-Paccot AG **(1)**
Route de Morat 1, 1763, Granges-Paccot,
Switzerland
Tel.: (41) 264606060
Electronic Part & Component Whslr
N.A.I.C.S.: 449210
Antonio Guarino *(Mgr-Store)*

Media Markt Groningen B.V. **(1)**
Westerhaven 48-50, 9718 AC, Groningen,
9718 AC, Netherlands
Tel.: (31) 503172800
Super Market Stores Operating Services
N.A.I.C.S.: 445110

**Media Markt Groningen Sontplein
B.V.** **(1)**
Sontplein 3C, 9723 BZ, Groningen, Nether-
lands
Tel.: (31) 503173000
Electronic Part & Component Whslr
N.A.I.C.S.: 449210
Mark Kremer *(Mgr-Customer Solution)*

**Media Markt Gyor Video TV Hifi,
Elektro Photo Computer Kereske-
delmi Kft.** **(1)**
Budai ut 1, 9027, Gyor, Hungary
Tel.: (36) 13586600
Electronic Part & Component Whslr
N.A.I.C.S.: 449210

Media Markt Heerlen B.V. **(1)**
Corio Center 9, 6411 LX, Heerlen, 6411 LX,
Netherlands
Tel.: (31) 455763700
Super Market Stores Operating Services
N.A.I.C.S.: 445110

**Media Markt Helsingborg TV-Hifi-
Elektro AB** **(1)**
Marknadsvagen 5, Odakra, 254 69, Hels-
ingborg, Sweden
Tel.: (46) 770778787
Electronic Part & Component Whslr

N.A.I.C.S.: 449210
Imad Alaouie *(Mgr-Svc)*

Media Markt Hengelo B.V. (1)
The Square 130, 7559 SR, Hengelo, Netherlands
Tel.: (31) 742657500
Web Site: https://www.mediamarkt.nl
Super Market Stores Operating Services
N.A.I.C.S.: 445110

Media Markt Herstal SA (1)
Rue des Naiveux 2, 4040, Herstal, Belgium
Tel.: (32) 42407040
Web Site: https://www.mediamarkt.be
Electronic Part & Component Whslr
N.A.I.C.S.: 449210

Media Markt Hoofddorp B.V. (1)
Burgemeester van Stamplein 282, 2132 BH, Hoofddorp, Netherlands
Tel.: (31) 235563000
Web Site: https://www.mediamarkt.nl
Electronic Part & Component Whslr
N.A.I.C.S.: 449210
R, Soederhuijzen *(Chief Customer Officer)*

Media Markt Hoorn B.V. (1)
CJK van Aalstweg 15, 1625 NV, Hoorn, Netherlands
Tel.: (31) 229206100
Web Site: https://www.mediamarkt.nl
Electronic Part & Component Whslr
N.A.I.C.S.: 449210
E. Wielinga *(Chief Customer Officer)*

Media Markt Imst TV-Hifi-Elektro GmbH (1)
Industriezone 30a, Imst, 6460, Austria
Tel.: (43) 541261001
Sales Range: $25-49.9 Million
Emp.: 3
Consumer Electronics Retailer
N.A.I.C.S.: 449210
Herrn Jelen Zoran *(Gen Mgr)*

Media Markt Jemappes/Mons SA (1)
Avenue Wilson 510, Jemappes, 7012, Mons, Belgium
Tel.: (32) 65395940
Web Site: https://www.mediamarkt.be
Electronic Part & Component Whslr
N.A.I.C.S.: 449210
Nicolas Smet *(Sls Mgr)*

Media Markt Jonkoping TV-Hifi-Elektro AB (1)
Solasvagen 4A, 553 03, Jonkoping, Sweden
Tel.: (46) 770778787
Web Site: https://www.mediamarkt.se
Consumer Electronics Retail Store Operating Services
N.A.I.C.S.: 449210

Media Markt Kalmar TV-Hifi-Elektro AB (1)
Olandsleden 3, 393 56, Kalmar, Sweden
Tel.: (46) 770778787
Web Site: https://www.mediamarkt.se
Consumer Electronics Retail Store Operating Services
N.A.I.C.S.: 449210

Media Markt Kecskemet Video TV Hifi Elektro Photo Computer Kereskedelmi Kft. (1)
Dunafoldvarl ut 2, 6000, Kecskemet, Hungary
Tel.: (36) 76512900
Electronic Part & Component Whslr
N.A.I.C.S.: 449210

Media Markt Kispest Video TV HiFi Elektro Photo Computer Kereskedelmi Kft. (1)
Ulloi ut 201 231, 1191, Budapest, Hungary
Tel.: (36) 12781900
Electronic Part & Component Whslr
N.A.I.C.S.: 449210

Media Markt Kortrijk NV (1)
Steenpoort 2 W305, 8500, Kortrijk, Belgium
Tel.: (32) 56265670
Electronic Part & Component Whslr
N.A.I.C.S.: 449210

Media Markt Kristianstad TV-Hifi-Elektro AB (1)

Harakarvagen 4, 291 61, Kristianstad, Sweden
Tel.: (46) 770778787
Web Site: https://www.mediamarkt.se
Electronic Part & Component Whslr
N.A.I.C.S.: 449210

Media Markt Las Arenas S.A. (1)
CC Las Arenas -Carretera El Rincon S/N, de Gran Canaria, 35010, Las Palmas, Spain
Tel.: (34) 928495400
Web Site: https://www.mediamarkt.es
Electronic Part & Component Whslr
N.A.I.C.S.: 449210
Nazira Zerene *(Head-Svc)*

Media Markt Leeuwarden B.V. (1)
Plein de Centrale 12, 8924 CZ, Leeuwarden, 8924 CZ, Netherlands
Tel.: (31) 582344900
Web Site: https://www.mediamarkt.nl
Super Market Stores Operating Services
N.A.I.C.S.: 445110

Media Markt Leidschendam B.V. (1)
Liguster 102, 2262 AC, Leidschendam, Netherlands
Tel.: (31) 703306500
Web Site: https://www.mediamarkt.nl
Electronic Part & Component Whslr
N.A.I.C.S.: 449210
Jolanda Bras *(Mgr-Customer Experience)*

Media Markt Leiria - Produtos Informaticos E Electronicos, Lda (1)
Quinta do Pisao Parceiros, 2400-504, Leiria, Portugal
Tel.: (351) 244003700
Electronic Part & Component Whslr
N.A.I.C.S.: 449210

Media Markt Leoben TV-Hifi-Elektro GmbH (1)
Hauptplatz 19, Leoben, 8700, Austria
Tel.: (43) 384243700
Consumer Electronics Retail Store Operating Services
N.A.I.C.S.: 449210

Media Markt Liege Mediacite SA (1)
Shopping Mediacite Boulevard Poincare 7-225, 4020, Liege, Belgium
Tel.: (32) 43493200
Web Site: https://www.mediamarkt.be
Electronic Part & Component Whslr
N.A.I.C.S.: 449210

Media Markt Liege Place Saint-Lambert SA (1)
Galeries Saint Lambert 27, 4000, Liege, Belgium
Tel.: (32) 42509710
Web Site: https://www.mediamarkt.be
Electronic Part & Component Whslr
N.A.I.C.S.: 449210
Jonathan Vicovan *(Mgr-Floor)*

Media Markt Liezen TV-Hifi-Elektro GmbH (1)
Salzburger Strasse 1, 8940, Liezen, Austria
Tel.: (43) 154699
Electronic Part & Component Whslr
N.A.I.C.S.: 449210

Media Markt Linz TV-Hifi-Elektro GmbH (1)
Industriezeile 76, 4020, Linz, Austria
Tel.: (43) 154699
Electronic Part & Component Whslr
N.A.I.C.S.: 449210

Media Markt Lleida, SA (1)
Avda President Josep Irla 1 Esquina C/Marie Curie, 25001, Lleida, Spain
Tel.: (34) 973188600
Web Site: https://www.mediamarkt.es
Electronic Part & Component Whslr
N.A.I.C.S.: 449210

Media Markt Lorca S.A. (1)
CC Almenara - Camino de enmedio S/N Dptc Campillo, 30813, Lorca, Spain
Tel.: (34) 968498300
Web Site: https://www.mediamarkt.es
Electronic Part & Component Whslr
N.A.I.C.S.: 449210

Media Markt Lund TV-Hifi-Elektro AB (1)

Avtalsvagen 4, Lund, 227 61, Sweden
Tel.: (46) 46190100
Consumer Electronics Retail Store Operating Services
N.A.I.C.S.: 449210

Media Markt Maastricht B.V. (1)
Franciscus Romanusweg 2, 6221 AE, Maastricht, 6221 AE, Netherlands
Tel.: (31) 433501100
Web Site: https://www.mediamarkt.nl
Electronic Retail Stores Operating Services
N.A.I.C.S.: 449210

Media Markt Machelen NV (1)
Woluwelaan 11, 1830, Machelen, Belgium
Tel.: (32) 22392210
Electronic Part & Component Whslr
N.A.I.C.S.: 449210

Media Markt Madrid - Plaza Del Carmen S.A.U. (1)
Plaza del Carmen 2, 28013, Madrid, Spain
Tel.: (34) 915951100
Web Site: https://www.mediamarkt.es
Electronic Part & Component Whslr
N.A.I.C.S.: 449210

Media Markt Madrid - Vallecas S.A. (1)
Avenida de la Albufera Centro Comercial Albufera Plaza 153, Albufera Plaza 153, 28038, Madrid, Spain
Tel.: (34) 916858000
Web Site: https://www.mediamarkt.es
Electronic Part & Component Whslr
N.A.I.C.S.: 449210
Marcos Lopez Garcia *(Mgr-Customer Experience)*

Media Markt Madrid Benlliure SA (1)
C/ Alcala 106, 28009, Madrid, Spain
Tel.: (34) 915297100
Web Site: https://www.mediamarkt.es
Electronic Part & Component Whslr
N.A.I.C.S.: 449210

Media Markt Madrid Castellana SA (1)
Paseo de la Castellana 200, 28046, Madrid, Spain
Tel.: (34) 913537200
Web Site: https://www.mediamarkt.es
Electronic Part & Component Whslr
N.A.I.C.S.: 449210

Media Markt Madrid Plenilunio Video-TV-Hifi-Elektro-Computer-Foto S.A. (1)
Poligono de las Mercedes-Centro Comercial Plenilunio-C/Arrastaria 20, 28022, Madrid, Spain
Tel.: (34) 913019900
Web Site: https://www.mediamarkt.es
Electronic Part & Component Whslr
N.A.I.C.S.: 449210

Media Markt Malaga - Plaza Mayor S.A. (1)
Plaza Mayor P de Ocio Alfonso Ponce de Leon 3 L-A04, 29004, Malaga, Spain
Tel.: (34) 951299800
Web Site: https://www.mediamarkt.es
Electronic Part & Component Whslr
N.A.I.C.S.: 449210

Media Markt Malaga-Centro Vfdeo-TV-Hifi-Elektro-Computer-Foto, SA (1)
C/ Station Esplanade s/n, 29002, Malaga, Spain
Tel.: (34) 951940200
Web Site: https://www.mediamarkt.es
Electronic Part & Component Whslr
N.A.I.C.S.: 449210

Media Markt Malmo-Svagertorp TV-Hifi-Elektro AB (1)
Langhusgatan 3-5, 215 86, Malmo, Sweden
Tel.: (46) 770778787
Web Site: https://www.mediamarkt.se
Electronic Part & Component Whslr
N.A.I.C.S.: 449210

Media Markt Massalfassar S.A. (1)
Parque Comercial El Manar S/N, 46560, Valencia, Spain
Tel.: (34) 961369400
Web Site: https://www.mediamarkt.es
Electronic Part & Component Whslr

N.A.I.C.S.: 449210

Media Markt Meyrin SA (1)
Ch de Riantbosson 15-21, 1217, Meyrin, Switzerland
Tel.: (41) 227198080
Web Site: https://www.mediamarkt.ch
Electronic Part & Component Whslr
N.A.I.C.S.: 449210

Media Markt Middelburg B.V. (1)
Mortiereboulevard 4, 4336 RA, Middelburg, 4336 RA, Netherlands
Tel.: (31) 118607000
Web Site: https://www.mediamarkt.nl
Consumer Electronics Online Retail Services
N.A.I.C.S.: 449210

Media Markt Murcia Nueva Condomina Video-TV-Hifi-Elektro-Computer-Foto S.A. (1)
CC Nueva Condomina-Autovia A7 Km 760 s/n, Churra, 30110, Murcia, Spain
Tel.: (34) 968374400
Web Site: https://www.mediamarkt.es
Electronic Part & Component Whslr
N.A.I.C.S.: 449210

Media Markt Nieuwegein B.V. (1)
Raadstede 41, 3431 HA, Nieuwegein, Netherlands
Tel.: (31) 306004500
Web Site: https://www.mediamarkt.nl
Electronic Part & Component Whslr
N.A.I.C.S.: 449210
E. Yildiz *(Chief Customer Officer)*

Media Markt Norrkoping TV-Hifi-Elektro AB (1)
PO Box 57, StockSund, 18207, Stockholm, Sweden
Tel.: (46) 11321100
Consumer Electronics Retail Store Operating Services
N.A.I.C.S.: 449210

Media Markt Nyiregyhaza Video TV Hifi Elektro Photo Computer Kereskedelmi Kft (1)
Laszlo u 12, 4400, Nyiregyhaza, Hungary
Tel.: (36) 13586600
Web Site: https://www.mediamarkt.hu
Consumer Electronics Retail Store Operating Services
N.A.I.C.S.: 449210

Media Markt Oberwart TV-Hifi-Elektro GmbH (1)
Europastrasse 1, 7400, Oberwart, Austria
Tel.: (43) 57009999
Web Site: https://www.mediamarkt.at
Electronic Part & Component Whslr
N.A.I.C.S.: 449210

Media Markt Oftringen AG (1)
Spitalweidstrasse 1, 4665, Oftringen, Switzerland
Tel.: (41) 627891111
Web Site: https://www.mediamarkt.ch
Electronic Part & Component Whslr
N.A.I.C.S.: 449210

Media Markt Oostakker NV (1)
Sint Jozefsstraat 10 1 1, 3500, Hasselt, Belgium
Tel.: (32) 11 29 49 00
Web Site: http://www.mediamarkt.be
Sales Range: $25-49.9 Million
Emp.: 7
Super Market Stores Operating Services
N.A.I.C.S.: 445110
Bart Somers *(Gen Mgr)*

Media Markt Oostende NV (1)
Torhoutsesteenweg 639, 8400, Oostende, Belgium
Tel.: (32) 59295960
Web Site: https://www.mediamarkt.be
Electronic Part & Component Whslr
N.A.I.C.S.: 449210

Media Markt Orebro TV-Hifi-Elektro AB (1)
Marieberg Saljarevagen 10C, 70236, Orebro, Sweden
Tel.: (46) 770778787
Web Site: https://www.mediamarkt.se
Consumer Electronics Retail Store Operating Services

Ceconomy AG—(Continued)

N.A.I.C.S.: 449210

Media Markt Orihuela SA (1)
CC Zenia Boulevard-C/Jade 2 Lc MS-01, Orihuela, 03189, Alicante, Spain
Tel.: (34) 965359900
Web Site: https://www.mediamarkt.es
Electronic Part & Component Whslr
N.A.I.C.S.: 449210
David Rodriguez Pedraza *(Mgr-Customer Experience)*

Media Markt Palma De Mallorca Fan SAU (1)
Avda Cardenal Rossell S/N, Illes Balears, 07007, Palma de Mallorca, Spain
Tel.: (34) 871203800
Web Site: https://www.mediamarkt.es
Electronic Part & Component Whslr
N.A.I.C.S.: 449210

Media Markt Palma De Mallorca S.A. (1)
Center D Oci Ocimax C/Bisbe Pere Puigdorfila 1, Baleares, 07010, Palma de Mallorca, Spain
Tel.: (34) 871203200
Web Site: https://www.mediamarkt.es
Electronic Part & Component Whslr
N.A.I.C.S.: 449210

Media Markt Pecs Video TV Hifi Elektro Photo Computer Kereskedelmit Kft. (1)
Bajcsy-Zsilinszky u 11, 7622, Pecs, Hungary
Tel.: (36) 13586600
Web Site: https://www.mediamarkt.hu
Electronic Part & Component Whslr
N.A.I.C.S.: 449210

Media Markt Placa De Catalunya, S.A.U. (1)
C Fontanella 6 8, 08010, Barcelona, Spain
Tel.: (34) 932666500
Electronic Part & Component Whslr
N.A.I.C.S.: 449210

Media Markt Polska Bis Spofka z ograniczona odpowiedzialnoscia Bydgoszcz II spofka komandytowa (1)
ul Jagiellonska 94 B, 85-027, Bydgoszcz, 85-027, Poland
Tel.: (48) 799353535
Web Site: https://mediamarkt.pl
Electronic Part & Component Whslr
N.A.I.C.S.: 449210

Media Markt Polska Bis Spofka z ograniczona odpowiedzialnoscia Gdansk IV Spofka Komandytowa (1)
al Grunwaldzka 141, 80-264, Gdansk, 80-264, Poland
Tel.: (48) 799353535
Web Site: https://mediamarkt.pl
Electronic Part & Component Whslr
N.A.I.C.S.: 449210

Media Markt Polska Bis Spofka z ograniczona odpowiedzialnoscia Katowice III Spofka Komandytowa (1)
ul Alpejska 6, 40-506, Katowice, Poland
Tel.: (48) 799353535
Web Site: https://mediamarkt.pl
Electronic Part & Component Whslr
N.A.I.C.S.: 449210

Media Markt Polska Bis Spofka z ograniczona odpowiedzialnoscia Poznan IV Spofka Komandytowa (1)
ul Stanislawa Matyi 2, 61-586, Poznan, Poland
Tel.: (48) 799353535
Web Site: https://mediamarkt.pl
Electronic Part & Component Whslr
N.A.I.C.S.: 449210

Media Markt Polska Bis Spofka z ograniczona odpowiedzialnoscia Szczecin III Spofka Komandytowa (1)
ul Struga 31A, 70-784, Szczecin, Poland
Tel.: (48) 799353535
Web Site: https://mediamarkt.pl
Electronic Part & Component Whslr
N.A.I.C.S.: 449210

Media Markt Polska Bis Spofka z ograniczona odpowiedzialnoscia Ty
chy Spofka Komandytowa (1)
ul Towarowa 2A, 43-100, Tychy, Poland
Tel.: (48) 799353535
Web Site: https://mediamarkt.pl
Electronic Part & Component Whslr
N.A.I.C.S.: 449210

Media Markt Polska Bis sp. z o.o. Wroclaw V spofka komandytowa (1)
ul Legnicka 58, 54-204, Wroclaw, Poland
Tel.: (48) 799353535
Web Site: https://mediamarkt.pl
Electronic Part & Component Whslr
N.A.I.C.S.: 449210

Media Markt Polska Bis spofka z ograniczona odpowiedzialnoscia Lubin Spofka Komandytowa (1)
ul Gen Wl Sikorskiego 20, 59-300, Lubin, Poland
Tel.: (48) 799353535
Web Site: https://mediamarkt.pl
Electronic Part & Component Whslr
N.A.I.C.S.: 449210

Media Markt Polska Bis spofka z ograniczona odpowiedzialnoscia Poznan III spofka komandytowa (1)
Al Solidarnosci 47, 61-696, Poznan, Poland
Tel.: (48) 799353535
Web Site: https://mediamarkt.pl
Electronic Part & Component Whslr
N.A.I.C.S.: 449210

Media Markt Polska Sp. z o.o. (1)
Al Jerozolimskie 179, 02-222, Warsaw, Poland
Tel.: (48) 799353535
Web Site: https://mediamarkt.pl
Consumer Electronics Retail Store Operating Services
N.A.I.C.S.: 449210

Media Markt Polska Sp. z o.o. Biafystok Spofka Komandytowa (1)
ul Czeslawa Milosza 2, 15-265, Bialystok, 15-265, Poland
Tel.: (48) 799353535
Web Site: https://mediamarkt.pl
Electronic Appliance Retailer
N.A.I.C.S.: 449210

Media Markt Polska Sp. z o.o. Chorzow Spofka Komandytowa (1)
ul Katowicka 160, Chorzow, 41-500, Poland
Tel.: (48) 799353535
Web Site: https://mediamarkt.pl
Electronic Appliance Retailer
N.A.I.C.S.: 449210

Media Markt Polska Sp. z o.o. Chorzow Spolka Komandytowa (1)
ul Katowicka 160, 41-500, Chorzow, Poland
Tel.: (48) 799353535
Web Site: https://mediamarkt.pl
Consumer Electronics Retail Store Operating Services
N.A.I.C.S.: 449210

Media Markt Polska Sp. z o.o. Elblag Spolka Komandytowa (1)
ul plk Stanislawa Dabka 152, 82-300, Elblag, Poland
Tel.: (48) 799353535
Web Site: https://mediamarkt.pl
Electronic Appliance Retailer
N.A.I.C.S.: 449210
Sylwester Grynhagel *(Mgr-Small Store)*

Media Markt Polska Sp. z o.o. Gdansk II Spolka Komandytowa (1)
ul Zlota Karczma 26, 80-298, Gdansk, 80-298, Poland
Tel.: (48) 799353535
Web Site: https://mediamarkt.pl
Electronic Appliance Retailer
N.A.I.C.S.: 449210

Media Markt Polska Sp. z o.o. Gdynia I Spofka Komandytowa (1)
ul Kcynska 27C, 81-005, Gdynia, 81-005, Poland
Tel.: (48) 799353535
Web Site: https://mediamarkt.pl
Electronic Appliance Retailer
N.A.I.C.S.: 449210

Media Markt Polska Sp. z o.o. Gfogow Spofka Komandytowa (1)
ul Poniatowskiego 12, Glogow, Warsaw,
67-200, Poland
Tel.: (48) 799353535
Electronic Appliance Retailer
N.A.I.C.S.: 449210

Media Markt Polska Sp. z o.o. Gliwice Spofka Komandytowa (1)
ul Pszczynska 315, Gliwice, 44-100, Poland
Tel.: (48) 799353535
Electronic Appliance Retailer
N.A.I.C.S.: 449210

Media Markt Polska Sp. z o.o. Gorzow Wielkopolski Spofka Komandytowa (1)
ul Mysliborska 48A, 66-400, Gorzow Wielkopolski, 66-400, Poland
Tel.: (48) 799353535
Web Site: https://mediamarkt.pl
Electronic Appliance Retailer
N.A.I.C.S.: 449210

Media Markt Polska Sp. z o.o. Kalisz Spofka Komandytowa (1)
ul Poznanska 121-131, 62-800, Kalisz, 62-800, Poland
Web Site: https://mediamarkt.pl
Electronic Appliance Retailer
N.A.I.C.S.: 449210

Media Markt Polska Sp. z o.o. Konin Spofka Komandytowa (1)
ul Ogrodowa 31 D, Konin, Stare Miasto, 62-571, Poland
Tel.: (48) 799353535
Electronic Appliance Retailer
N.A.I.C.S.: 449210

Media Markt Polska Sp. z o.o. Konin Spolka Komandytowa (1)
Ogrodowa 31D, Stare Miasto, 62-571, Warsaw, Konin, Poland
Tel.: (48) 799353535
Web Site: https://mediamarkt.pl
Super Market Stores Operating Services
N.A.I.C.S.: 445110

Media Markt Polska Sp. z o.o. Koszalin Spofka Komandytowa (1)
I Paderewskiego 1, 75-736, Koszalin, 75-736, Poland
Tel.: (48) 799353535
Web Site: https://mediamarkt.pl
Electronic Appliance Retailer
N.A.I.C.S.: 449210

Media Markt Polska Sp. z o.o. Krakow II Spofka Komandytowa (1)
ul Zakopianska 105, Krakow, 30-418, Poland
Tel.: (48) 799353535
Electronic Appliance Retailer
N.A.I.C.S.: 449210

Media Markt Polska Sp. z o.o. Krakow II Spolka Komandytowa (1)
ul Zakopianska 105, 30-418, Krakow, Poland
Tel.: (48) 799353535
Web Site: https://mediamarkt.pl
Consumer Electronics Retail Store Operating Services
N.A.I.C.S.: 449210

Media Markt Polska Sp. z o.o. Legnica Spofka Komandytowa (1)
ul Schumana 17, 59-220, Legnica, 59-220, Poland
Tel.: (48) 799353535
Web Site: https://mediamarkt.pl
Electronic Appliance Retailer
N.A.I.C.S.: 449210

Media Markt Polska Sp. z o.o. Nowy Sacz Spofka Komandytowa (1)
ul Tarnowska 33, Nowy Sacz, 33-300, Poland
Tel.: (48) 799353535
Electronic Appliance Retailer
N.A.I.C.S.: 449210
Marcin Mirek *(Mgr-Bus Dev)*

Media Markt Polska Sp. z o.o. Nowy Sacz Spolka Komandytowa (1)
ul Tarnowska 33, 33-300, Nowy Sacz, Poland
Tel.: (48) 799353535
Web Site: https://mediamarkt.pl

Consumer Electronics Retail Store Operating Services
N.A.I.C.S.: 449210

Media Markt Polska Sp. z o.o. Pfock Spofka Komandytowa (1)
ul Wyszogrodzka 127, 09-410, Plock, 09-410, Poland
Tel.: (48) 799353535
Web Site: https://mediamarkt.pl
Electronic Appliance Retailer
N.A.I.C.S.: 449210

Media Markt Polska Sp. z o.o. Piotrkow Trybunalski Spolka Komandytowa (1)
Ul J Slowackiego 123, 97-300, Piotrkow Trybunalski, Poland
Tel.: (48) 799353535
Web Site: https://mediamarkt.pl
Consumer Electronics Retail Store Operating Services
N.A.I.C.S.: 449210

Media Markt Polska Sp. z o.o. Poznan II Spofka Komandytowa (1)
ul Bukowska 156, 60-197, Poznan, 60-197, Poland
Tel.: (48) 799353535
Web Site: https://mediamarkt.pl
Electronic Appliance Retailer
N.A.I.C.S.: 449210

Media Markt Polska Sp. z o.o. Radom Spofka Komandytowa (1)
Al Grzecznarowskiego 28, 26-604, Radom, 26-604, Poland
Tel.: (48) 799353535
Web Site: https://mediamarkt.pl
Electronic Appliance Retailer
N.A.I.C.S.: 449210

Media Markt Polska Sp. z o.o. Rybnik Spofka Komandytowa (1)
ul Zorska 2, 44-203, Rybnik, 44-203, Poland
Tel.: (48) 799353535
Web Site: https://mediamarkt.pl
Electronic Appliance Retailer
N.A.I.C.S.: 449210

Media Markt Polska Sp. z o.o. Sfupsk Spofka Komandytowa (1)
ul Szczecinska 58, 76-200, Slupsk, 76-200, Poland
Tel.: (48) 799353535
Web Site: https://mediamarkt.pl
Electronic Appliance Retailer
N.A.I.C.S.: 449210

Media Markt Polska Sp. z o.o. Tarnow Spofka Komandytowa (1)
ul Nowodabrowska 127, 33-100, Tarnow, 33-100, Poland
Tel.: (48) 799353535
Web Site: https://mediamarkt.pl
Electronic Appliance Retailer
N.A.I.C.S.: 449210

Media Markt Polska Sp. z o.o. Torun Spofka Komandytowa (1)
ul Zolkiewskiego 15, 87-100, Torun, 87-100, Poland
Tel.: (48) 799353535
Web Site: https://mediamarkt.pl
Electronic Appliance Retailer
N.A.I.C.S.: 449210

Media Markt Polska Sp. z o.o. Wafbrzych Spofka Komandytowa (1)
ul 1 Maja 64, 58-300, Walbrzych, 58-300, Poland
Tel.: (48) 799353535
Web Site: https://mediamarkt.pl
Electronic Appliance Retailer
N.A.I.C.S.: 449210

Media Markt Polska Sp. z o.o. Zamosc Spofka Komandytowa (1)
ul Przemyslowa 10, 22-400, Zamosc, 22-400, Poland
Tel.: (48) 799353535
Web Site: https://mediamarkt.pl
Electronic Appliance Retailer
N.A.I.C.S.: 449210

Media Markt Polska Sp. z o.o. Bielsko-Biafa Spolka Komandytowa (1)

ul Sarni Stok 2, Bielsko-Biala, 43-300, Poland
Tel.: (48) 799353535
Electronic Appliance Retailer
N.A.I.C.S.: 449210

**Media Markt Polska Sp. z.o.o.
Bielsko-Biala Spolka
Komandytowa** (1)
Jerozolimskie 179, Warsaw, 02-222, Poland
Tel.: (48) 338284100
Super Market Stores Operating Services
N.A.I.C.S.: 445110

**Media Markt Polska Sp. z.o.o.
Czeladz Spofka Komandytowa** (1)
ul Bedzinska 80, 41-250, Czeladz, 41-250, Poland
Tel.: (48) 799353535
Web Site: https://mediamarkt.pl
Electronic Appliance Retailer
N.A.I.C.S.: 449210

**Media Markt Polska Sp. z.o.o. Cze-
stochowa Spofka Komandytowa** (1)
ul Kisielewski 8/16, 42-200, Czestochowa, 42-200, Poland
Tel.: (48) 799353535
Web Site: https://mediamarkt.pl
Electronic Appliance Retailer
N.A.I.C.S.: 449210

**Media Markt Polska Sp. z.o.o.
Gdansk I Spofka Komandytowa** (1)
Al Grunwaldzka 309, 80-309, Gdansk, 80-309, Poland
Tel.: (48) 799353535
Web Site: https://mediamarkt.pl
Electronic Appliance Retailer
N.A.I.C.S.: 449210

**Media Markt Polska Sp. z.o.o.
Gdansk I Spolka Komandytowa** (1)
Al Jerozolimskie 179, 02-222, Warsaw, Mazowieckie, Poland
Tel.: (48) 799353535
Web Site: https://mediamarkt.pl
Consumer Electronics Retail Store Operating Services
N.A.I.C.S.: 449210

**Media Markt Polska Sp. z.o.o. Kato-
wice I Spofka Komandytowa** (1)
Kosciuszki 229, 40-600, Katowice, 40-600, Poland
Tel.: (48) 799353535
Web Site: https://mediamarkt.pl
Electronic Appliance Retailer
N.A.I.C.S.: 449210

**Media Markt Polska Sp. z.o.o. Kato-
wice I Spolka Komandytowa** (1)
ul Alpejska 6, 40-506, Katowice, Poland
Tel.: (48) 799353535
Web Site: https://mediamarkt.pl
Consumer Electronics Retail Store Operating Services
N.A.I.C.S.: 449210

**Media Markt Polska Sp. z.o.o. Kielce
Spofka Komandytowa** (1)
ul Radomska 8, 25-451, Kielce, 25-451, Poland
Tel.: (48) 799353535
Web Site: https://mediamarkt.pl
Electronic Appliance Retailer
N.A.I.C.S.: 449210
Jacek Smigaj (Mgr)

**Media Markt Polska Sp. z.o.o. Kra-
kow I Spolka Komandytowa** (1)
Al Pokoju 67, 31-580, Krakow, 31-580, Poland
Tel.: (48) 799353535
Web Site: https://mediamarkt.pl
Electronic Appliance Retailer
N.A.I.C.S.: 449210

**Media Markt Polska Sp. z.o.o. Lublin
Spofka Komandytowa** (1)
ul Tomasza Zana 31, 20-601, Lublin, 20-601, Poland
Tel.: (48) 799353535
Web Site: https://mediamarkt.pl
Electronic Appliance Retailer
N.A.I.C.S.: 449210
Piotr Persona (Mgr-Market)

**Media Markt Polska Sp. z.o.o. Ol-
sztyn Spofka Komandytowa** (1)

al Gen Sikorskiego 2B, 10-088, Olsztyn, 10-088, Poland
Tel.: (48) 799353535
Web Site: https://mediamarkt.pl
Electronic Appliance Retailer
N.A.I.C.S.: 449210

**Media Markt Polska Sp. z.o.o. Opole
Spofka Komandytowa** (1)
ul Sosnowskiego 16a, 45-273, Opole, Poland
Tel.: (48) 799353535
Web Site: https://mediamarkt.pl
Electronic Appliance Retailer
N.A.I.C.S.: 449210

**Media Markt Polska Sp. z.o.o. Rz-
eszow Spofka Komandytowa** (1)
ul Rejtana 36, 35-959, Rzeszow, 35-959, Poland
Tel.: (48) 799353535
Web Site: https://mediamarkt.pl
Electronic Appliance Retailer
N.A.I.C.S.: 449210

**Media Markt Polska Sp. z.o.o. War-
schau II Spofka Komandytowa** (1)
ul Ostrobramska 79, 04-175, Warsaw, 04-175, Poland
Tel.: (48) 799353535
Web Site: https://mediamarkt.pl
Electronic Appliance Retailer
N.A.I.C.S.: 449210

**Media Markt Polska Sp. z.o.o. War-
schau III Spofka Komandytowa** (1)
Al Krakowska 61, 02-183, Warsaw, Poland
Tel.: (48) 799353535
Web Site: https://mediamarkt.pl
Electronic Appliance Retailer
N.A.I.C.S.: 449210

**Media Markt Polska Sp. z.o.o. War-
schau IV Spofka Komandytowa** (1)
ul Gorczewska 212/226, 01-460, Warsaw, 01-460, Poland
Tel.: (48) 799353535
Web Site: https://mediamarkt.pl
Electronic Appliance Retailer
N.A.I.C.S.: 449210

**Media Markt Polska Sp. z.o.o. Wro-
claw I Spolka Komandytowa** (1)
Pl Dominikanski 3, 50-159, Wroclaw, 50-159, Poland
Tel.: (48) 799353535
Web Site: https://mediamarkt.pl
Electronic Appliance Retailer
N.A.I.C.S.: 449210

**Media Markt Polska Sp. z.o.o. Wro-
claw II Spolka Komandytowa** (1)
Al Karkonoska 85, 53-015, Wroclaw, Poland
Tel.: (48) 799353535
Web Site: https://mediamarkt.pl
Super Market Stores Operating Services
N.A.I.C.S.: 445110

**Media Markt Polska Sp. z.o.o. Zabrze
Spolka Komandytowa** (1)
ul Szkubacza 1, 41-800, Zabrze, 41-800, Poland
Tel.: (48) 799353535
Web Site: https://mediamarkt.pl
Electronic Appliance Retailer
N.A.I.C.S.: 449210

**Media Markt Polska Sp. z.o.o. todz I
Spolka Komandytowa** (1)
ul Brzezinska 27/29, 92-103, Lodz, 92-103, Poland
Tel.: (48) 799353535
Web Site: https://mediamarkt.pl
Electronic Appliance Retailer
N.A.I.C.S.: 449210
Pawel Glogowski (Project Mgr)

**Media Markt Polska Sp. z.o.o. todz II
Spolka Komandytowa** (1)
Al Pilsudskiego 15, 90-307, Lodz, 90-307, Poland
Tel.: (48) 799353535
Web Site: https://mediamarkt.pl
Electronic Appliance Retailer
N.A.I.C.S.: 449210

**Media Markt Puerto Real Video-TV-
Hifi-Electro-Computer-Foto, S.A.** (1)
P I Tres Caminos C/ Calamar S/N, 11100,

Puerto Real, Spain
Tel.: (34) 956598600
Electronic Appliance Retailer
N.A.I.C.S.: 449210

**Media Markt Quart De Poblet,
S.A.** (1)
C/ De la Saleta s/n A3 Madrid Exit 345, Quart de Poblet, 46930, Valencia, Spain
Tel.: (34) 963860700
Web Site: https://www.mediamarkt.es
Electronic Appliance Retailer
N.A.I.C.S.: 449210

Media Markt Region Bern AG (1)
Feldstrasse 30, 3073, Muri, Switzerland
Tel.: (41) 319505656
Web Site: https://www.mediamarkt.ch
Electronic Appliance Retailer
N.A.I.C.S.: 449210
Dominik Schupbach (Mgr-Store)

**Media Markt Ried TV-Hifi-Elektro
GmbH** (1)
Weberzeile 1, 4910, Ried im Innkreis, Austria
Tel.: (43) 57009999
Web Site: https://www.mediamarkt.at
Electronic Appliance Retailer
N.A.I.C.S.: 449210

Media Markt Rijswijk B.V. (1)
Pr W Alexander Promenade 69-83, 2284 DJ, Rijswijk, 2284 DJ, Netherlands
Tel.: (31) 703728200
Web Site: https://www.mediamarkt.nl
Super Market Stores Operational Services
N.A.I.C.S.: 445110

**Media Markt Rivas-Vaciamadrid
Video-TV-Hifi-Electro-Computer-Foto
S.A.** (1)
CC Rivas Futura - C/Isaac Peral 2 Ed A Lc A1b, 28529, Rivas-Vaciamadrid, Spain
Tel.: (34) 917794900
Web Site: https://www.mediamarkt.es
Electronic Appliance Retailer
N.A.I.C.S.: 449210

Media Markt Roermond B.V (1)
Schaarbroekerweg 32-34, 6042 EJ, Roermond, Netherlands
Tel.: (31) 475371500
Web Site: https://www.mediamarkt.nl
Sales Range: $25-49.9 Million
Emp.: 10
Super Market Stores Operational Services
N.A.I.C.S.: 445110

Media Markt Roeselare NV (1)
Brugsesteenweg 435-439, 8800, Roeselare, Belgium
Tel.: (32) 51259110
Electronic Store Operating Services
N.A.I.C.S.: 449210

**Media Markt Rotterdam Beijerlandse-
laan B.V.** (1)
Beijerlandselaan 2, 3074 EJ, Rotterdam, Netherlands
Tel.: (31) 104925900
Consumer Electronics Retailer
N.A.I.C.S.: 449210

**Media Markt San Juan De Aznal-
farache Video-TV-Hifi-Electro-
Computer-Foto, S.A.** (1)
Ctra Sevilla to Mairena del Aljarafe - PC Cavaleri s/n, San Juan de Aznalfarache, 41920, Seville, Spain
Tel.: (34) 954479000
Electronic Appliance Retailer
N.A.I.C.S.: 449210
Jorge Rodriguez Garcia (Mgr-Store)

**Media Markt Santander Video-TV-
Hifi-Electro-Computer-Foto, SA** (1)
CC Nuevo Alisal - c/ Joaquin Rodrigo 10, 39011, Santander, Spain
Tel.: (34) 942247300
Web Site: https://www.mediamarkt.es
Electronic Appliance Retailer
N.A.I.C.S.: 449210

**Media Markt Santiago De Compos-
tela S.A.** (1)
Rua de Malta Costa Vella Industrial Estate 2, 15704, Santiago de Compostela, Spain
Tel.: (34) 981550200
Web Site: https://www.mediamarkt.es

Electronic Appliance Retailer
N.A.I.C.S.: 449210

**Media Markt Saturn Holding Mag-
yarorszag Kft.** (1)
Europa utca 9-11 BILK J1 building, Budapest, 1239, Hungary
Tel.: (36) 13586600
Electronic Appliance Retailer
N.A.I.C.S.: 449210
Judit Felfalusi (Product Mgr-Accessories)

**Media Markt Saturn Holding Neder-
land B.V.** (1)
Ruth Leijting Prins Alexanderplein 32-36, 3067 GC, Rotterdam, Netherlands
Tel.: (31) 102076500
Emp.: 350
Super Market Stores Operating Services
N.A.I.C.S.: 445110
Gordon Scholz (CEO)

Media Markt Schoten NV (1)
Bredabaan 1305, 2900, Schoten, Belgium
Tel.: (32) 36802740
Electronic Appliance Retailer
N.A.I.C.S.: 449210

**Media Markt Setubal - Produtos Infor-
maticos e Electronicos, LDA.** (1)
Retail Park - loja 1 EN n 10 Alto da Cascalheira, 2910-297, Setubal, Portugal
Tel.: (351) 265004100
Electronic Appliance Retailer
N.A.I.C.S.: 449210
Pedro Perico (Bus Mgr-Enterprises)

Media Markt Singen GmbH (1)
Unter den Tannen 3, 78224, Singen, Germany
Tel.: (49) 77317930
Web Site: http://www.mediamarkt.com
Sales Range: $1-4.9 Billion
Emp.: 5
Electronics Retailer
N.A.I.C.S.: 449210
Michael Scholz (Mng Dir)

**Media Markt Skovde TV-Hifi-Elektro
AB** (1)
Norra Metallvagen 8, 541 39, Skovde, Sweden
Tel.: (46) 500773100
Consumer Electronics Retail Store Operating Services
N.A.I.C.S.: 449210

**Media Markt Soroksar Video TV Hifi
Elektro Photo Computer Kereske-
delmi Kft.** (1)
Bevasarlo utca 4, 1239, Budapest, Hungary
Tel.: (36) 12318900
Web Site: https://www.mediamarkt.hu
Electronic Appliance Retailer
N.A.I.C.S.: 449210

**Media Markt Spittal TV-Hifi-Elektro
GmbH** (1)
Villacher Strasse 79-83, 9800, Spittal an der Drau, Austria
Tel.: (43) 57009999
Web Site: https://www.mediamarkt.at
Super Market Stores Operating Services
N.A.I.C.S.: 445110

Media Markt St. Gallen AG (1)
Herisauerstrasse 5, 9015, Saint Gallen, Switzerland
Tel.: (41) 713130404
Web Site: https://www.mediamarkt.ch
Electronic Appliance Retailer
N.A.I.C.S.: 449210

**Media Markt St. Lorenzen TV-Hifi-
Elektro GmbH** (1)
Dr Reinhard Machold-Strasse 7, 8642, Sankt Lorenzen im Murztal, Austria
Tel.: (43) 57009999
Web Site: https://www.mediamarkt.at
Super Market Stores Operating Services
N.A.I.C.S.: 445110

**Media Markt Steyr TV-Hifi-Elektro
GmbH** (1)
Ennser Strasse 23, 4400, Steyr, Austria
Web Site: http://www.mediamarkt.at
Emp.: 3
Electronic Goods Store Operating Services
N.A.I.C.S.: 449210

Ceconomy AG—(Continued)

Media Markt Stockholm-Barkarby TV-Hifi-Elektro AB (1)
Enkopingsvagen 27, 177 38, Jarfalla, Sweden
Tel.: (46) 855588100
Consumer Electronics Retail Store Operating Services
N.A.I.C.S.: 449210

Media Markt Stockholm-Gallerian TV-Hifi-Elektro AB (1)
Hamngatan 37, 111 53, Stockholm, Sweden
Tel.: (46) 770778787
Electronic Appliance Retailer
N.A.I.C.S.: 449210
Kim Andersson (Dir-Store)

Media Markt Stockholm-Heron City TV-HiFi-Elektro AB (1)
Dialoggatan 2, 141 75, Kungens Kurva, Sweden
Tel.: (46) 770778787
Web Site: https://www.mediamarkt.se
Consumer Electronics Retail Store Operating Services
N.A.I.C.S.: 449210

Media Markt Stockholm-Lanna TV-Hifi-Elektro AB (1)
Truckvagen 2, 142 53, Skogas, Sweden
Tel.: (46) 770778787
Web Site: https://www.mediamarkt.se
Electronic Appliance Retailer
N.A.I.C.S.: 449210

Media Markt Stockholm-Nacka TV-Hifi-Elektro AB (1)
Forumvagen 12, 131 53, Nacka, Sweden
Tel.: (46) 770778787
Web Site: https://www.mediamarkt.se
Consumer Electronics Retail Store Operating Services
N.A.I.C.S.: 449210

Media Markt Stockholm-Taby TV-Hifi-Elektro AB (1)
Attundafaltet 2, 183 34, Taby, Sweden
Tel.: (46) 770778787
Web Site: https://www.mediamarkt.se
Electronic Appliance Retailer
N.A.I.C.S.: 449210

Media Markt Sundsvall TV-Hifi-Elektro AB (1)
Gesallvagen 11, 863 41, Sundsvall, Sweden
Tel.: (46) 770778787
Web Site: https://www.mediamarkt.se
Consumer Electronics Retail Store Operating Services
N.A.I.C.S.: 449210

Media Markt Szolnok Video Tv Hifi Elektro Photo Computer Kereskedelmi Kft. (1)
Felso Szandai ret 1, 5000, Szolnok, Hungary
Tel.: (36) 13586600
Web Site: https://www.mediamarkt.hu
Electronic Appliance Retailer
N.A.I.C.S.: 449210

Media Markt Szombathely Video-TV-Hifi-Elektro-Photo-Computer-Kereskedelmi Kft. (1)
Varasd u 1, 9700, Szombathely, Hungary
Tel.: (36) 94520900
Web Site: https://www.mediamarkt.hu
Electronic Appliance Retailer
N.A.I.C.S.: 449210

Media Markt TV-HiFi-Elektro GmbH Dusseldorf Bilk (1)
Friedrichstr 129-133, 40217, Dusseldorf, Germany
Tel.: (49) 22122243333
Consumer Electronics Online Retail Services
N.A.I.C.S.: 449210

Media Markt TV-HiFi-Elektro Athens I Commercial Anonymi Eteria (1)
Leontos 4 Elestherias, 16452, Athens, Greece
Tel.: (30) 2112117800
Consumer Electronics Retailer
N.A.I.C.S.: 449210

Media Markt TV-HiFi-Elektro Athens II Commercial Anonymi Eteria (1)
49 Kifissias Ave, 15123, Maroussi, Greece
Tel.: (30) 2111809800
Electronic Appliance Retailer
N.A.I.C.S.: 449210

Media Markt TV-HiFi-Elektro GmbH & Co. KG Bruchsal (1)
Im Wondolrot 5, 76616, Bruchsal, Germany
Tel.: (49) 22122243333
Consumer Electronics Retail Store Operating Services
N.A.I.C.S.: 449210

Media Markt TV-HiFi-Elektro GmbH Aalen (1)
Carl-Zeiss-Str 96, 73431, Aalen, Germany
Tel.: (49) 22122243333
Electronic Appliance Retailer
N.A.I.C.S.: 449210

Media Markt TV-HiFi-Elektro GmbH Albstadt (1)
Sonnenstr 30, 72458, Albstadt, Germany
Tel.: (49) 22122243333
Electronic Appliance Retailer
N.A.I.C.S.: 449210

Media Markt TV-HiFi-Elektro GmbH Alzey (1)
Karl-Heinz-Kipp-Str 23, 55232, Alzey, Germany
Tel.: (49) 22122243333
Consumer Electronics Retail Store Operating Services
N.A.I.C.S.: 449210

Media Markt TV-HiFi-Elektro GmbH Amberg (1)
Am Bergsteig 1, 92224, Amberg, Germany
Tel.: (49) 22122243333
Electronic Appliance Retailer
N.A.I.C.S.: 449210

Media Markt TV-HiFi-Elektro GmbH Ansbach (1)
Rothenburger Str 15, 91522, Ansbach, Germany
Tel.: (49) 22122243333
Electronic Appliance Retailer
N.A.I.C.S.: 449210

Media Markt TV-HiFi-Elektro GmbH Augsburg-Goggingen (1)
Eichleitnerstr 34, 86159, Augsburg, Germany
Tel.: (49) 22122243333
Consumer Electronics Retail Store Operating Services
N.A.I.C.S.: 449210

Media Markt TV-HiFi-Elektro GmbH Berlin-Charlottenburg (1)
Krumme Str 48, Charlottenburg, 10627, Berlin, Germany
Tel.: (49) 22122243333
Sales Range: $25-49.9 Million
Emp.: 10
Consumer Electronics Retail Store Operating Services
N.A.I.C.S.: 449210
Marco Wegener (Gen Mgr)

Media Markt TV-HiFi-Elektro GmbH Berlin-Mitte (1)
Grunerstr 20, 10179, Berlin, Germany
Tel.: (49) 22122243333
Electronic Appliance Retailer
N.A.I.C.S.: 449210

Media Markt TV-HiFi-Elektro GmbH Berlin-Prenzlauer Berg (1)
Greifswalder Str 140, 10409, Berlin, Germany
Tel.: (49) 22122243333
Consumer Electronics Retail Store Operating Services
N.A.I.C.S.: 449210

Media Markt TV-HiFi-Elektro GmbH Berlin-Schoneweide (1)
Schnellerstr 21, 12439, Berlin, Germany
Tel.: (49) 22122243333
Consumer Electronics Retail Store Operating Services
N.A.I.C.S.: 449210

Media Markt TV-HiFi-Elektro GmbH Berlin-Steglitz (1)

Web Site: http://www.mediamarkt.de
Consumer Electronics Retail Store Operating Services
N.A.I.C.S.: 449210

Media Markt TV-HiFi-Elektro GmbH Berlin-Tegel (1)
Am Borsigturm 2, 13507, Berlin, Germany
Tel.: (49) 22122243333
Electronic Appliance Retailer
N.A.I.C.S.: 449210

Media Markt TV-HiFi-Elektro GmbH Berlin-Tempelhof (1)
Tempelhofer Damm 227, 12099, Berlin, Germany
Tel.: (49) 22122243333
Consumer Electronics Retail Store Operating Services
N.A.I.C.S.: 449210

Media Markt TV-HiFi-Elektro GmbH Bielefeld (1)
Engersche Str 96, 33611, Bielefeld, Germany
Tel.: (49) 22122243333
Consumer Electronics Retail Store Operating Services
N.A.I.C.S.: 449210

Media Markt TV-HiFi-Elektro GmbH Bischofsheim (1)
Neben Dem Muhlweg 4b, 65474, Bischofsheim, Germany
Tel.: (49) 61449630
Web Site: http://www.mediamarkt.de
Consumer Electronics Retailer
N.A.I.C.S.: 449210
Oliver Wolf (Gen Mgr)

Media Markt TV-HiFi-Elektro GmbH Bochum (1)
Web Site: http://www.mediamarkt.de
Consumer Electronics Retailer
N.A.I.C.S.: 449210

Media Markt TV-HiFi-Elektro GmbH Bochum-Ruhrpark (1)
Am Einkaufszentrum 10, 44791, Bochum, Germany
Tel.: (49) 22122243333
Consumer Electronics Retailer
N.A.I.C.S.: 449210

Media Markt TV-HiFi-Elektro GmbH Bonn (1)
Friedensplatz 1, 53111, Bonn, Germany
Tel.: (49) 22122243333
Electronic Appliance Retailer
N.A.I.C.S.: 449210

Media Markt TV-HiFi-Elektro GmbH Brandenburg an der Havel (1)
Sankt-Annen-Str 23, Brandenburg an der Havel, 14776, Brandenburg, Germany
Tel.: (49) 22122243333
Consumer Electronics Retail Store Operating Services
N.A.I.C.S.: 449210

Media Markt TV-HiFi-Elektro GmbH Braunschweig (1)
Hintern Brudern 27-30, 38100, Braunschweig, Germany
Tel.: (49) 22122243333
Web Site: http://www.mediamarkt.de
Consumer Electronics Retail Store Operating Services
N.A.I.C.S.: 449210

Media Markt TV-HiFi-Elektro GmbH Bremen (1)
Hans-Bredow-Str 19, 28307, Bremen, Germany
Tel.: (49) 22122243333
Electronic Appliance Retailer
N.A.I.C.S.: 449210

Media Markt TV-HiFi-Elektro GmbH Bremen-Waterfront (1)
AG-Weser-Str 3, 28237, Bremen, Germany
Tel.: (49) 22122243333
Electronic Appliance Retailer
N.A.I.C.S.: 449210

Media Markt TV-HiFi-Elektro GmbH Buchholz in der Nordheide (1)
Nordring 2, 21244, Buchholz, Germany
Tel.: (49) 22243333
Web Site: https://www.mediamarkt.de
Consumer Electronics Retailer

N.A.I.C.S.: 449210

Media Markt TV-HiFi-Elektro GmbH Buxtehude (1)
Luneburger Schanze 17, 21614, Buxtehude, Germany
Tel.: (49) 22243333
Electronic Appliance Retailer
N.A.I.C.S.: 449210

Media Markt TV-HiFi-Elektro GmbH Chemnitz (1)
Thomas-Mann-Platz 1, 09130, Chemnitz, Germany
Tel.: (49) 22122243333
Sales Range: $25-49.9 Million
Emp.: 6
Consumer Electronics Retailer
N.A.I.C.S.: 449210
Tobias Boettner (Gen Mgr)

Media Markt TV-HiFi-Elektro GmbH Chemnitz-Rohrsdorf (1)
Ringstr 29, 09247, Chemnitz, Germany
Tel.: (49) 22122243333
Consumer Electronics Retailer
N.A.I.C.S.: 449210

Media Markt TV-HiFi-Elektro GmbH Coburg (1)
Niorter Str 20, 96450, Coburg, Germany
Tel.: (49) 22122243333
Electronic Appliance Retailer
N.A.I.C.S.: 449210

Media Markt TV-HiFi-Elektro GmbH Cottbus/Grob Gaglow (1)
Am Seegraben 20c, 03051, Cottbus, Germany
Tel.: (49) 22122243333
Consumer Electronics Retailer
N.A.I.C.S.: 449210

Media Markt TV-HiFi-Elektro GmbH Deggendorf (1)
Hans-Kramer-Strasse 31, 94469, Deggendorf, Germany
Tel.: (49) 22122243333
Sales Range: $25-49.9 Million
Emp.: 3
Consumer Electronics Retailer
N.A.I.C.S.: 449210
Anton Strasser (Gen Mgr)

Media Markt TV-HiFi-Elektro GmbH Dessau (1)
Am Eichengarten 2, 06842, Dessau, Germany
Tel.: (49) 22122243333
Consumer Electronics Retailer
N.A.I.C.S.: 449210

Media Markt TV-HiFi-Elektro GmbH Donauworth (1)
Artur-Proeller-Str 11, 86609, Donauworth, Germany
Tel.: (49) 22122243333
Electronic Appliance Retailer
N.A.I.C.S.: 449210

Media Markt TV-HiFi-Elektro GmbH Dorsten (1)
Europaplatz 10, 46282, Dorsten, Germany
Tel.: (49) 22122243333
Electronic Appliance Retailer
N.A.I.C.S.: 449210

Media Markt TV-HiFi-Elektro GmbH Dortmund-Horde (1)
Seekante 1, 44263, Dortmund, Germany
Tel.: (49) 22122243333
Electronic Appliance Retailer
N.A.I.C.S.: 449210

Media Markt TV-HiFi-Elektro GmbH Dortmund-Oespel (1)
Wulfshofstr 6-8, 44149, Dortmund, Germany
Tel.: (49) 22122243333
Electronic Appliance Retailer
N.A.I.C.S.: 449210

Media Markt TV-HiFi-Elektro GmbH Dresden Centrum (1)
Prager Str 15, 01069, Dresden, Germany
Tel.: (49) 22122243333
Consumer Electronics Retail Store Operating Services
N.A.I.C.S.: 449210

Media Markt TV-HiFi-Elektro GmbH
Duisburg (1)
August-Bebel-Platz 20, 47169, Duisburg,
Germany
Tel.: (49) 20399420
Web Site: http://www.mediamarkt.de
Consumer Electronics Retail Store Operat-
ing Services
N.A.I.C.S.: 449210
Uwe Goettert *(Gen Mgr)*

Media Markt TV-HiFi-Elektro GmbH
Duisburg-Grobenbaum (1)
Kenlastr 37, 47269, Duisburg, Germany
Tel.: (49) 22122243333
Sales Range: $25-49.9 Million
Emp.: 15
Consumer Electronics Online Retail Ser-
vices
N.A.I.C.S.: 449210
Dirk Heiss *(Gen Mgr)*

Media Markt TV-HiFi-Elektro GmbH
Dusseldorf (1)
Metrostr 16, 40235, Dusseldorf, Germany
Tel.: (49) 22122243333
Consumer Electronics Online Retail Ser-
vices
N.A.I.C.S.: 449210

Media Markt TV-HiFi-Elektro GmbH
Egelsbach (1)
Kurt-Schumacher-Ring 3, 63329, Egels-
bach, Germany
Tel.: (49) 61039430
Web Site: http://www.mediamarkt.de
Emp.: 45
Consumer Electronics Online Retail Ser-
vices
N.A.I.C.S.: 449210
Darren Fitzpatrick *(Mng Dir)*

Media Markt TV-HiFi-Elektro GmbH
Eiche (1)
Web Site: http://www.mediamarkt.de
Consumer Electronics Retail Store Operat-
ing Services
N.A.I.C.S.: 449210

Media Markt TV-HiFi-Elektro GmbH
Eisenach (1)
Am Stadtweg 4, 99817, Eisenach, Germany
Tel.: (49) 22122243333
Web Site: https://www.mediamarkt.de
Electronic Appliance Retailer
N.A.I.C.S.: 449210

Media Markt TV-HiFi-Elektro GmbH
Eislingen (1)
Steinbeisstr 2, 73054, Eislingen, Germany
Tel.: (49) 22122243333
Electronic Appliance Retailer
N.A.I.C.S.: 449210

Media Markt TV-HiFi-Elektro GmbH
Elmshorn (1)
Ramskamp 98, 25337, Elmshorn, Germany
Tel.: (49) 22122243333
Electronic Appliance Retailer
N.A.I.C.S.: 449210

Media Markt TV-HiFi-Elektro GmbH
Emden (1)
Fritz-Reuter-Str 11, 26721, Emden, Ger-
many
Tel.: (49) 22122243333
Consumer Electronics Retail Store Operat-
ing Services
N.A.I.C.S.: 449210

Media Markt TV-HiFi-Elektro GmbH
Erding (1)
im West Erding Park Johann-Auer-Str 2,
85435, Erding, Germany
Tel.: (49) 22122243333
Web Site: http://www.mediamarkt.de
Consumer Electronics Online Retail Ser-
vices
N.A.I.C.S.: 449210

Media Markt TV-HiFi-Elektro GmbH
Erfurt Thuringen-Park (1)
Nordhauser Str 73t, 99091, Erfurt, Germany
Tel.: (49) 36178380
Web Site: http://www.mediamarkt.de
Consumer Electronics Online Retail Ser-
vices
N.A.I.C.S.: 449210
Martin Sonntag *(Gen Mgr)*

Media Markt TV-HiFi-Elektro GmbH
Erfurt-Daberstedt (1)
Hermsdorfer Str 4, 99099, Erfurt, Germany
Tel.: (49) 22122243333
Consumer Electronics Online Retail Ser-
vices
N.A.I.C.S.: 449210

Media Markt TV-HiFi-Elektro GmbH
Erlangen (1)
Frauenauracher Str 108, 91056, Erlangen,
Germany
Tel.: (49) 22122243333
Sales Range: $25-49.9 Million
Emp.: 6
Consumer Electronics Retail Store Operat-
ing Services
N.A.I.C.S.: 449210
Wolfgang Kohl *(Gen Mgr)*

Media Markt TV-HiFi-Elektro GmbH
Eschweiler (1)
Auerbachstr 30, 52249, Eschweiler, Ger-
many
Tel.: (49) 22122243333
Electronic Appliance Retailer
N.A.I.C.S.: 449210

Media Markt TV-HiFi-Elektro GmbH
Essen (1)
Gladbecker Str 413, 45326, Essen, Ger-
many
Tel.: (49) 22122243333
Web Site: http://www.mediamarkt.de
Emp.: 12
Consumer Electronics Online Retail Ser-
vices
N.A.I.C.S.: 449210

Media Markt TV-HiFi-Elektro GmbH
Esslingen (1)
Weilstr 227, 73733, Esslingen, Germany
Tel.: (49) 22122243333
Consumer Electronics Online Retail Ser-
vices
N.A.I.C.S.: 449210

Media Markt TV-HiFi-Elektro GmbH
Fellbach (1)
Buhlstrasse 140, 70736, Fellbach, Germany
Tel.: (49) 22122243333
Electronic Appliance Retailer
N.A.I.C.S.: 449210

Media Markt TV-HiFi-Elektro GmbH
Flensburg (1)
Langberger Weg 4, 24941, Flensburg, Ger-
many
Tel.: (49) 22122243333
Web Site: http://www.mediamarkt.de
Consumer Electronics Retail Store Operat-
ing Services
N.A.I.C.S.: 449210

Media Markt TV-HiFi-Elektro GmbH
Frankfurt (1)
Tituscorso 6, 60439, Frankfurt am Main,
Germany
Tel.: (49) 699580180
Web Site: http://www.mediamarkt.de
Consumer Electronics Distr
N.A.I.C.S.: 423620
Mariano Garcia Barroso *(Mng Dir)*

Media Markt TV-HiFi-Elektro GmbH
Freiburg (1)
Bettackerstr 1-3, 79115, Freiburg, Germany
Tel.: (49) 22122243333
N.A.I.C.S.: 423610
Mario Medewaldt *(Mng Dir)*

Media Markt TV-HiFi-Elektro GmbH
Fulda (1)
Petersberger Strasse 36, 36037, Fulda,
Germany
Tel.: (49) 22122243333
Consumer Electronics Retailer
N.A.I.C.S.: 449210

Media Markt TV-HiFi-Elektro GmbH
Gifhorn (1)
Braunschweiger Strasse 34, 38518, Gif-
horn, Germany
Tel.: (49) 22122243333
Electronic Appliance Retailer
N.A.I.C.S.: 449210

Media Markt TV-HiFi-Elektro GmbH
Gottingen (1)
Hannoversche Str 53c, 37075, Gottingen,
Germany
Tel.: (49) 22122243333
Consumer Electronics Retail Store Operat-
ing Services
N.A.I.C.S.: 449210

Media Markt TV-HiFi-Elektro GmbH
Greifswald (1)
Anklamer Landstr 1, 17491, Greifswald,
Germany
Tel.: (49) 22122243333
Consumer Electronics Online Retail Ser-
vices
N.A.I.C.S.: 449210

Media Markt TV-HiFi-Elektro GmbH
Grundau-Lieblos (1)
Rudolf-Walther-Str 6, Lieblos, 63584, Grun-
dau, Germany
Tel.: (49) 22122243333
Sales Range: $25-49.9 Million
Emp.: 100
Consumer Electronics Retail Store Operat-
ing Services
N.A.I.C.S.: 449210
Pier Meier *(Gen Mgr)*

Media Markt TV-HiFi-Elektro GmbH
Gunthersdorf (1)
Einkaufszentrum Nova Eventis,
Gunthersdorf, 6237, Leuna, Gunthersdorf,
Germany
Web Site: http://www.mediamarkt.de
Emp.: 7
Consumer Electronics Retailer
N.A.I.C.S.: 449210

Media Markt TV-HiFi-Elektro GmbH
Halberstadt (1)
Quedlinburger Landstr 12, 38820, Halber-
stadt, Germany
Web Site: http://www.mediamarkt.de
Consumer Electronics Retailer
N.A.I.C.S.: 449210

Media Markt TV-HiFi-Elektro GmbH
Halstenbek (1)
Gartnerstr 169, 25469, Halstenbek, Ger-
many
Tel.: (49) 22122243333
Consumer Electronics Retailer
N.A.I.C.S.: 449210

Media Markt TV-HiFi-Elektro GmbH
Hamburg- Wandsbek (1)
Friedrich-Ebert-Damm 110, 22047, Ham-
burg, Germany
Tel.: (49) 22122243333
Consumer Electronics Retailer
N.A.I.C.S.: 449210

Media Markt TV-HiFi-Elektro GmbH
Hamburg-Altona (1)
Paul-Nevermann-Platz 15, 22765, Ham-
burg, Germany
Tel.: (49) 22122243333
Consumer Electronics Retail Store Operat-
ing Services
N.A.I.C.S.: 449210

Media Markt TV-HiFi-Elektro GmbH
Hamburg-Billstedt (1)
Billstedter Platz 37j, Billstedt, 22111, Ham-
burg, Germany
Tel.: (49) 22122243333
Consumer Electronics Retail Store Operat-
ing Services
N.A.I.C.S.: 449210

Media Markt TV-HiFi-Elektro GmbH
Hamburg-Harburg (1)
Hannoversche Str 86, 21079, Hamburg,
Germany
Tel.: (49) 22122243333
Electronic Appliance Retailer
N.A.I.C.S.: 449210

Media Markt TV-HiFi-Elektro GmbH
Hamburg-Hummelsbuttel (1)
Poppenbutteler Weg 31, 22339, Hamburg,
Germany
Tel.: (49) 22122243333
Consumer Electronics Retail Store Operat-
ing Services
N.A.I.C.S.: 449210

Media Markt TV-HiFi-Elektro GmbH
Hamburg-Nedderfeld (1)
Nedderfeld 70, 22529, Hamburg, Germany
Tel.: (49) 22122243333
Consumer Electronics Retail Store Operat-
ing Services
N.A.I.C.S.: 449210

Media Markt TV-HiFi-Elektro GmbH
Hameln (1)
Bocklerstr 5, 31789, Hameln, Germany
Tel.: (49) 51519950
Web Site: http://www.mediamarkt.de
Consumer Electronics Retail Store Operat-
ing Services
N.A.I.C.S.: 449210

Media Markt TV-HiFi-Elektro GmbH
Hannover-Vahrenheide (1)
Vahrenwalder Str 211, 30165, Hannover,
Germany
Tel.: (49) 22122243333
Consumer Electronics Retail Store Operat-
ing Services
N.A.I.C.S.: 449210

Media Markt TV-HiFi-Elektro GmbH
Heide (1)
Schanzenstr 11 Im Gewerbegebiet Ost,
Heide, Germany
Web Site: http://www.mediamarkt.de
Consumer Electronics Retail Store Operat-
ing Services
N.A.I.C.S.: 449210

Media Markt TV-HiFi-Elektro GmbH
Heidelberg-Rohrbach (1)
Hertzstr 1, 69126, Heidelberg, Germany
Tel.: (49) 22122243333
Electronic Appliance Retailer
N.A.I.C.S.: 449210

Media Markt TV-HiFi-Elektro GmbH
Heilbronn (1)
Edisonstr 5, 74076, Heilbronn, Germany
Tel.: (49) 22122243333
Electronic Appliance Retailer
N.A.I.C.S.: 449210

Media Markt TV-HiFi-Elektro GmbH
Henstedt-Ulzburg (1)
Kirchweg 88, 24558, Henstedt-Ulzburg,
Germany
Tel.: (49) 419375190
Web Site: http://www.mediamark.de
Consumer Electronics Retail Store Operat-
ing Services
N.A.I.C.S.: 449210
Jurgen Koch *(Mgr)*

Media Markt TV-HiFi-Elektro GmbH
Heppenheim (1)
Tiergartenstr 7, 64646, Heppenheim, Ger-
many
Tel.: (49) 22122243333
Consumer Electronics Retail Store Operat-
ing Services
N.A.I.C.S.: 449210

Media Markt TV-HiFi-Elektro GmbH
Hildesheim (1)
Bavenstedter Str 65, 31135, Hildesheim,
Germany
Tel.: (49) 22122243333
Web Site: http://www.mediamarkt.de
Consumer Electronics Retail Store Operat-
ing Services
N.A.I.C.S.: 449210

Media Markt TV-HiFi-Elektro GmbH
Hof (1)
An der Michaelisbrucke 2, 95028, Hof, Ger-
many
Tel.: (49) 22122243333
Electronic Appliance Retailer
N.A.I.C.S.: 449210

Media Markt TV-HiFi-Elektro GmbH
Holzminden (1)
Humboldtstr 4, 37603, Holzminden, Ger-
many
Tel.: (49) 22122243333
Web Site: http://www.mediamarkt.de
Consumer Electronics Retail Store Operat-
ing Services
N.A.I.C.S.: 449210

Media Markt TV-HiFi-Elektro GmbH
Homburg/Saar (1)
Talstr 38d, 66424, Homburg, Germany
Tel.: (49) 22122243333

Ceconomy AG—(Continued)

Consumer Electronics Retail Store Operating Services
N.A.I.C.S.: 449210

Media Markt TV-HiFi-Elektro GmbH Huckelhoven (1)
Am Landabsatz 5, 41836, Huckelhoven, Germany
Tel.: (49) 22122243333
Consumer Electronics Retail Store Operating Services
N.A.I.C.S.: 449210

Media Markt TV-HiFi-Elektro GmbH Idar-Oberstein (1)
John-F Kennedy Str 1, 55743, Idar-Oberstein, Germany
Tel.: (49) 22122243333
Consumer Electronics Retail Store Operating Services
N.A.I.C.S.: 449210
Michael Kusch (Mng Dir)

Media Markt TV-HiFi-Elektro GmbH Itzehoe (1)
Otto-F -Alsen-Str 2, 25524, Itzehoe, Germany
Tel.: (49) 22122243333
Consumer Electronics Retail Store Operating Services
N.A.I.C.S.: 449210

Media Markt TV-HiFi-Elektro GmbH Jena (1)
Stadtrodaer Str 105, 07747, Jena, Germany
Tel.: (49) 22122243333
Electronic Appliance Retailer
N.A.I.C.S.: 449210

Media Markt TV-HiFi-Elektro GmbH Kaiserslautern (1)
Hohenecker Str 26, 67663, Kaiserslautern, Germany
Tel.: (49) 63131720
Web Site: http://www.mediamarkt.de
Sales Range: $25-49.9 Million
Emp.: 45
Consumer Electronics Retail Store Operating Services
N.A.I.C.S.: 449210
Patrick Janiesch (Gen Mgr)

Media Markt TV-HiFi-Elektro GmbH Karlsfeld (1)
Munchner Str 173, 85757, Karlsfeld, Germany
Tel.: (49) 22122243333
Electronic Appliance Retailer
N.A.I.C.S.: 449210

Media Markt TV-HiFi-Elektro GmbH Karlsruhe (1)
Unterweingartenfeld 4, 76135, Karlsruhe, Germany
Tel.: (49) 22122243333
Electronic Appliance Retailer
N.A.I.C.S.: 449210

Media Markt TV-HiFi-Elektro GmbH Karlsruhe-Ettlinger Tor (1)
Ettlinger Tor Platz 1, 76133, Karlsruhe, Germany
Tel.: (49) 22122243333
Electronic Appliance Retailer
N.A.I.C.S.: 449210

Media Markt TV-HiFi-Elektro GmbH Kassel (1)
Knorrstrasse 28, 34134, Kassel, Germany
Tel.: (49) 22122243333
Consumer Electronics Retail Store Operating Services
N.A.I.C.S.: 449210

Media Markt TV-HiFi-Elektro GmbH Kempten (1)
August-Fischer-Platz 1, Allgau, 87435, Kempten, Germany
Tel.: (49) 22122243333
Sales Range: $25-49.9 Million
Emp.: 60
Consumer Electronics Retail Store Operating Services
N.A.I.C.S.: 449210

Media Markt TV-HiFi-Elektro GmbH Kiel (1)
Muhlendamm 5, 24113, Kiel, Germany

Tel.: (49) 22122243333
Consumer Electronics Retail Store Operating Services
N.A.I.C.S.: 449210

Media Markt TV-HiFi-Elektro GmbH Kirchheim (1)
Stuttgarter Str 1, 73230, Kirchheim, Germany
Tel.: (49) 22122243333
Electronic Appliance Retailer
N.A.I.C.S.: 449210

Media Markt TV-HiFi-Elektro GmbH Koblenz (1)
Carl-Zeiss-Str 8, 56070, Koblenz, Germany
Tel.: (49) 22122243333
Consumer Electronics Retail Store Operating Services
N.A.I.C.S.: 449210

Media Markt TV-HiFi-Elektro GmbH Koln Hohe Strasse (1)
Hohe Str 121, 50667, Cologne, Germany
Web Site: http://www.mediamarkt.de
Consumer Electronics Retail Store Operating Services
N.A.I.C.S.: 449210

Media Markt TV-HiFi-Elektro GmbH Koln-Chorweiler (1)
Florenzer Str 24-28, Chorweiler, 50765, Cologne, Germany
Tel.: (49) 221500630
Electronic Appliance Retailer
N.A.I.C.S.: 449210

Media Markt TV-HiFi-Elektro GmbH Koln-Kalk (1)
Vietorstr 7 In Den Koln-Arcaden, 51103, Cologne, Germany
Tel.: (49) 221899920
Web Site: http://www.mediamarkt.de
Consumer Electronics Retail Store Operating Services
N.A.I.C.S.: 449210
Daniel Kobernick (Gen Mgr)

Media Markt TV-HiFi-Elektro GmbH Koln-Marsdorf (1)
Max-Planck-Str 24, Koln-Marsdorf, 50858, Cologne, Germany
Tel.: (49) 22122243333
Consumer Electronics Retail Store Operating Services
N.A.I.C.S.: 449210

Media Markt TV-HiFi-Elektro GmbH Konstanz (1)
Schneckenburgstr 2, 78467, Konstanz, Germany
Tel.: (49) 22122243333
Consumer Electronics Online Retail Services
N.A.I.C.S.: 449210

Media Markt TV-HiFi-Elektro GmbH Krefeld (1)
Blumentalstr 151-155, 47803, Krefeld, Germany
Tel.: (49) 22122243333
Consumer Electronics Retailer
N.A.I.C.S.: 449210

Media Markt TV-HiFi-Elektro GmbH Kulmbach (1)
Kronacher Str 27, 95326, Kulmbach, Germany
Tel.: (49) 22122243333
Electronic Appliance Retailer
N.A.I.C.S.: 449210

Media Markt TV-HiFi-Elektro GmbH Lahr (1)
Im Gotzmann 8, 77933, Lahr, Germany
Tel.: (49) 22122243333
Electronic Appliance Retailer
N.A.I.C.S.: 449210

Media Markt TV-HiFi-Elektro GmbH Landau/Pfalz (1)
Klaus-von-Klitzing-Str 5, 76829, Landau, Germany
Tel.: (49) 22122243333
Consumer Electronics Retailer
N.A.I.C.S.: 449210

Media Markt TV-HiFi-Elektro GmbH Landsberg/Lech (1)

Am Penzinger Feld 21, 86899, Landsberg am Lech, Germany
Tel.: (49) 22122243333
Sales Range: $25-49.9 Million
Emp.: 5
Consumer Electronics Retailer
N.A.I.C.S.: 449210
Thorsten Matthies (Gen Mgr)

Media Markt TV-HiFi-Elektro GmbH Landshut (1)
Gaussstr 1, 84030, Landshut, Germany
Tel.: (49) 22122243333
Electronic Appliance Retailer
N.A.I.C.S.: 449210
Nils Amarell (Mgr-Store)

Media Markt TV-HiFi-Elektro GmbH Leipzig Hofe am Bruhl (1)
Bruhl 1, 04109, Leipzig, Germany
Tel.: (49) 22122243333
Electronic Appliance Retailer
N.A.I.C.S.: 449210

Media Markt TV-HiFi-Elektro GmbH Leipzig Paunsdorf (1)
Paunsdorfer Allee 1, 04329, Leipzig, Germany
Tel.: (49) 22122243333
Consumer Electronics Online Retail Services
N.A.I.C.S.: 449210

Media Markt TV-HiFi-Elektro GmbH Lingen (1)
Lookenstr 22-24, 49808, Lingen, Germany
Tel.: (49) 22122243333
Consumer Electronics Retailer
N.A.I.C.S.: 449210

Media Markt TV-HiFi-Elektro GmbH Lubeck (1)
Herrenholz 14, 23556, Lubeck, Germany
Web Site: http://www.mediamarkt.de
Sales Range: $25-49.9 Million
Emp.: 75
Consumer Electronics Retailer
N.A.I.C.S.: 449210

Media Markt TV-HiFi-Elektro GmbH Ludwigsburg (1)
Heinkelstr 1-11, 71634, Ludwigsburg, Germany
Tel.: (49) 22122243333
Consumer Electronics Retailer
N.A.I.C.S.: 449210
Boris Hartmann (Gen Mgr)

Media Markt TV-HiFi-Elektro GmbH Ludwigshafen (1)
Hedwig-Laudien-Ring 2, Oggersheim, 67071, Ludwigshafen, Germany
Tel.: (49) 22122243333
Web Site: http://www.mediamarkt.de
Consumer Electronics Retail Store Operating Services
N.A.I.C.S.: 449210

Media Markt TV-HiFi-Elektro GmbH Magdeburg-Bordepark (1)
Salbker Chaussee 67, 39118, Magdeburg, Germany
Tel.: (49) 22122243333
Electronic Appliance Retailer
N.A.I.C.S.: 449210

Media Markt TV-HiFi-Elektro GmbH Main-Taunus-Zentrum (1)
Main Taunus Zentrum, 65843, Sulzbach, Germany
Tel.: (49) 22122243333
Consumer Electronics Retail Store Operating Services
N.A.I.C.S.: 449210

Media Markt TV-HiFi-Elektro GmbH Mainz (1)
Haifa Allee 1, 55128, Mainz, Germany
Tel.: (49) 22122243333
Emp.: 120
Consumer Electronics Retail Store Operating Services
N.A.I.C.S.: 449210

Media Markt TV-HiFi-Elektro GmbH Mannheim (1)
Flossworthstr 65, 68199, Mannheim, Germany
Tel.: (49) 22122243333

Consumer Electronics Retail Store Operating Services
N.A.I.C.S.: 449210

Media Markt TV-HiFi-Elektro GmbH Mannheim-Sandhofen (1)
Frankenthalerstr 129, Sandhofen, 68307, Mannheim, Germany
Tel.: (49) 22122243333
Electronic Appliance Retailer
N.A.I.C.S.: 449210

Media Markt TV-HiFi-Elektro GmbH Marktredwitz (1)
Waldershofer Str 10, 95615, Marktredwitz, Germany
Tel.: (49) 22122243333
Electronic Appliance Retailer
N.A.I.C.S.: 449210

Media Markt TV-HiFi-Elektro GmbH Meerane (1)
Guteborner Allee 1, 08393, Meerane, Germany
Tel.: (49) 22122243333
Consumer Electronics Retail Store Operating Services
N.A.I.C.S.: 449210

Media Markt TV-HiFi-Elektro GmbH Memmingen (1)
Fraunhoferstr 9, 87700, Memmingen, Germany
Tel.: (49) 22122243333
Consumer Electronics Retail Store Operating Services
N.A.I.C.S.: 449210

Media Markt TV-HiFi-Elektro GmbH Monchengladbach (1)
Breitenbachstr 50, 41065, Monchengladbach, Germany
Tel.: (49) 22122243333
Consumer Electronics Retail Store Operating Services
N.A.I.C.S.: 449210

Media Markt TV-HiFi-Elektro GmbH Muhldorf/Inn (1)
Siemensstr 4, 84453, Muhldorf, Germany
Tel.: (49) 86319850
Web Site: http://www.mediamarket.de
Consumer Electronics Retail Store Operating Services
N.A.I.C.S.: 449210
Joerg Meier (Gen Mgr)

Media Markt TV-HiFi-Elektro GmbH Mulheim (1)
Mannesmannallee 31, Dumpten, 45475, Mulheim an der Ruhr, Germany
Tel.: (49) 22122243333
Consumer Electronics Retail Store Operating Services
N.A.I.C.S.: 449210

Media Markt TV-HiFi-Elektro GmbH Munchen-Haidhausen (1)
Einsteinstr 130, 81675, Munich, Germany
Tel.: (49) 22122243333
Sales Range: $50-74.9 Million
Emp.: 150
Consumer Electronics Retail Store Operating Services
N.A.I.C.S.: 449210
Edel Schlecht (Gen Mgr)

Media Markt TV-HiFi-Elektro GmbH Munchen-Pasing (1)
Pasinger Banhofsplatz 5, 81241, Munich, Germany
Tel.: (49) 89820830
Web Site: http://www.mediamarkt.de
Consumer Electronics Retail Store Operating Services
N.A.I.C.S.: 449210
Bernhard Reimers (Mng Dir)

Media Markt TV-HiFi-Elektro GmbH Munchen-Solln (1)
Drygalski-Allee 31, 81477, Munich, Germany
Tel.: (49) 22122243333
Consumer Electronics Retail Store Operating Services
N.A.I.C.S.: 449210

Media Markt TV-HiFi-Elektro GmbH Munster (1)

Robert-Bosch-Str 2, 48153, Munster, Germany
Tel.: (49) 22122243333
Consumer Electronics Retail Store Operating Services
N.A.I.C.S.: 449210

Media Markt TV-HiFi-Elektro GmbH Neu-Ulm (1)
Bahnhofstrase 1, 89231, Neu-Ulm, Germany
Web Site: http://www.mediamarkt.de
Consumer Electronics Retail Store Operating Services
N.A.I.C.S.: 449210

Media Markt TV-HiFi-Elektro GmbH Neubrandenburg (1)
Web Site: http://www.mediamarkt.de
Consumer Electronics Retail Store Operating Services
N.A.I.C.S.: 449210

Media Markt TV-HiFi-Elektro GmbH Neuburg an der Donau (1)
Am Sudpark 7, 86633, Neuburg an der Donau, Germany
Tel.: (49) 22122243333
Electronic Appliance Retailer
N.A.I.C.S.: 449210

Media Markt TV-HiFi-Elektro GmbH Neumunster (1)
Gansemarkt 1, Neumunster, 24534, Germany
Tel.: (49) 43219150
Web Site: http://www.mediamarkt.de
Emp.: 50
Consumer Electronics Retail Store Operating Services
N.A.I.C.S.: 449210
Peter Schneider *(Gen Mgr)*

Media Markt TV-HiFi-Elektro GmbH Neunkirchen (1)
Kirkeler Str 50, 66538, Neunkirchen, Germany
Web Site: http://www.mediamarkt.de
Emp.: 4
Consumer Electronics Retail Store Operating Services
N.A.I.C.S.: 449210

Media Markt TV-HiFi-Elektro GmbH Neuss (1)
Konrad-Adenauer-Ring 95, 41464, Neuss, Germany
Tel.: (49) 22122243333
Consumer Electronics Retail Store Operating Services
N.A.I.C.S.: 449210

Media Markt TV-HiFi-Elektro GmbH Neustadt an der Weinstrasse (1)
Chemnitzer Str 33, Neustadt an der Weinstrasse, 67433, Neustadt, Germany
Tel.: (49) 632139780
Web Site: http://www.mediamarkt.de
Super Market Stores Operating Services
N.A.I.C.S.: 445110
Michael Wageck *(Area Mgr-Brown Goods)*

Media Markt TV-HiFi-Elektro GmbH Neuwied (1)
Langendorfer Str 84-86, 56564, Neuwied, Germany
Tel.: (49) 22122243333
Electronic Appliance Retailer
N.A.I.C.S.: 449210

Media Markt TV-HiFi-Elektro GmbH Nordhausen (1)
Pferdemarkt 1, 99734, Nordhausen, Germany
Tel.: (49) 22122243333
Electronic Appliance Retailer
N.A.I.C.S.: 449210

Media Markt TV-HiFi-Elektro GmbH Nordhorn (1)
Denekamper Str 185, 48529, Nordhorn, Germany
Tel.: (49) 22122243333
Consumer Electronics Retail Store Operating Services
N.A.I.C.S.: 449210

Media Markt TV-HiFi-Elektro GmbH Offenburg (1)

Heinrich-Hertz Str 6, 77656, Offenburg, Germany
Tel.: (49) 22122243333
Consumer Electronics Retail Store Operating Services
N.A.I.C.S.: 449210

Media Markt TV-HiFi-Elektro GmbH Oldenburg (1)
Posthalterweg 15, 26129, Oldenburg, Germany
Tel.: (49) 22122243333
Consumer Electronics Retail Store Operating Services
N.A.I.C.S.: 449210

Media Markt TV-HiFi-Elektro GmbH Oststeinbek (1)
Willinghusener Weg 1, 22113, Oststeinbek, Germany
Tel.: (49) 22122243333
Electronic Appliance Retailer
N.A.I.C.S.: 449210

Media Markt TV-HiFi-Elektro GmbH Paderborn (1)
Pohlweg 110, 33100, Paderborn, Germany
Tel.: (49) 22122243333
Consumer Electronics Retail Store Operating Services
N.A.I.C.S.: 449210

Media Markt TV-HiFi-Elektro GmbH Papenburg (1)
An der Alten Werft 13, 26871, Papenburg, Germany
Tel.: (49) 22122243333
Electronic Appliance Retailer
N.A.I.C.S.: 449210

Media Markt TV-HiFi-Elektro GmbH Passau (1)
Regensburger Str 37, 94036, Passau, Germany
Tel.: (49) 22122243333
Electronic Appliance Retailer
N.A.I.C.S.: 449210

Media Markt TV-HiFi-Elektro GmbH Peine (1)
Hesebergweg 45, 31228, Peine, Germany
Tel.: (49) 22122243333
Consumer Electronics Retail Store Operating Services
N.A.I.C.S.: 449210

Media Markt TV-HiFi-Elektro GmbH Pforzheim (1)
Wilhelm-Becker-Str 15, 75179, Pforzheim, Germany
Tel.: (49) 22122243333
Consumer Electronics Retail Store Operating Services
N.A.I.C.S.: 449210

Media Markt TV-HiFi-Elektro GmbH Pirmasens (1)
Zweibrucker Str 232, 66954, Pirmasens, Germany
Tel.: (49) 22122243333
Consumer Electronics Retail Store Operating Services
N.A.I.C.S.: 449210

Media Markt TV-HiFi-Elektro GmbH Plauen (1)
Durerstr 28, 8527, Plauen, Germany
Web Site: http://www.mediamarkt.de
Consumer Electronics Retail Store Operating Services
N.A.I.C.S.: 449210

Media Markt TV-HiFi-Elektro GmbH Potsdam (1)
Sterncenter 4, 14480, Potsdam, Germany
Tel.: (49) 22122243333
Sales Range: $50-74.9 Million
Emp.: 120
Super Market Stores Operating Services
N.A.I.C.S.: 445110

Media Markt TV-HiFi-Elektro GmbH Ravensburg (1)
Gansbuhl 2, 88212, Ravensburg, Germany
Tel.: (49) 75136390
Web Site: http://www.mediamarkt.de
Emp.: 30
Super Market Stores Operating Services
N.A.I.C.S.: 445110

Tobias Bechter *(Gen Mgr)*

Media Markt TV-HiFi-Elektro GmbH Recklinghausen (1)
Web Site: http://www.mediamarkt.de
Consumer Electronics Retail Store Operating Services
N.A.I.C.S.: 449210

Media Markt TV-HiFi-Elektro GmbH Regensburg (1)
Bajuwarenstr 29, 93053, Regensburg, Germany
Tel.: (49) 22122243333
Sales Range: $25-49.9 Million
Emp.: 7
Consumer Electronics Retail Store Operating Services
N.A.I.C.S.: 449210
Thomas Schuster *(Gen Mgr)*

Media Markt TV-HiFi-Elektro GmbH Rendsburg (1)
Friedrichstadter Strasse 54-56, 24768, Rendsburg, Germany
Tel.: (49) 22122243333
Electronic Appliance Retailer
N.A.I.C.S.: 449210

Media Markt TV-HiFi-Elektro GmbH Reutlingen (1)
Unter den Linden 8, 72762, Reutlingen, Germany
Tel.: (49) 712134540
Web Site: http://www.mediamarkt.de
Consumer Electronics Retail Store Operating Services
N.A.I.C.S.: 449210
Peter Haas *(Gen Mgr)*

Media Markt TV-HiFi-Elektro GmbH Rostock (1)
Ostseeparkstr 3, Lambrechtshagen, 18069, Rostock, Germany
Tel.: (49) 22122243333
Consumer Electronics Retail Store Operating Services
N.A.I.C.S.: 449210

Media Markt TV-HiFi-Elektro GmbH Rostock-Brinckmansdorf (1)
Timmermannsstrat 11a, 18055, Rostock, Germany
Tel.: (49) 22122243333
Consumer Electronics Retail Store Operating Services
N.A.I.C.S.: 449210

Media Markt TV-HiFi-Elektro GmbH Saarbrucken-Saarterrassen (1)
Dr-Tietz-Str 13, 66115, Saarbrucken, Germany
Tel.: (49) 22122243333
Consumer Electronics Retail Store Operating Services
N.A.I.C.S.: 449210

Media Markt TV-HiFi-Elektro GmbH Saarlouis (1)
Dieselstrasse, 66740, Saarlouis, Germany
Tel.: (49) 22122243333
Consumer Electronics Retail Store Operating Services
N.A.I.C.S.: 449210

Media Markt TV-HiFi-Elektro GmbH Schiffdorf-Spaden (1)
Neufelder Weg 3, Schiffdorf-Spaden, 27619, Cuxhaven, Germany
Tel.: (49) 22122243333
Electronic Appliance Retailer
N.A.I.C.S.: 449210

Media Markt TV-HiFi-Elektro GmbH Schwabach (1)
Am Falbenholzweg 15, 91126, Schwabach, Germany
Tel.: (49) 22122243333
Electronic Appliance Retailer
N.A.I.C.S.: 449210

Media Markt TV-HiFi-Elektro GmbH Schwedt (1)
Landgrabenpark 1, 16303, Schwedt an der Oder, Germany
Tel.: (49) 22122243333
Consumer Electronics Retail Store Operating Services
N.A.I.C.S.: 449210

Media Markt TV-HiFi-Elektro GmbH Schweinfurt (1)
Friedrich-Ratzer-Str 3, 97424, Schweinfurt, Germany
Tel.: (49) 972165000
Web Site: http://www.mediamarkt.de
Consumer Electronics Retail Store Operating Services
N.A.I.C.S.: 449210
Rainer Haffke *(Gen Mgr)*

Media Markt TV-HiFi-Elektro GmbH Schwerin (1)
Marienplatz 5-7, 19053, Schwerin, Germany
Tel.: (49) 22122243333
Consumer Electronics Retail Store Operating Services
N.A.I.C.S.: 449210

Media Markt TV-HiFi-Elektro GmbH Siegen (1)
Hauptplatz 1, 57076, Siegen, Germany
Tel.: (49) 22122243333
Consumer Electronics Retail Store Operating Services
N.A.I.C.S.: 449210

Media Markt TV-HiFi-Elektro GmbH Sindelfingen (1)
Tilsiter Str 15, 71065, Sindelfingen, Germany
Tel.: (49) 22122243333
Consumer Electronics Retail Store Operating Services
N.A.I.C.S.: 449210

Media Markt TV-HiFi-Elektro GmbH Sinsheim (1)
Neulandstr 2, 74889, Sinsheim, Germany
Tel.: (49) 22122243333
Electronic Appliance Retailer
N.A.I.C.S.: 449210

Media Markt TV-HiFi-Elektro GmbH Speyer (1)
Wormser Landstr 94, 67346, Speyer, Germany
Tel.: (49) 22122243333
Electronic Appliance Retailer
N.A.I.C.S.: 449210

Media Markt TV-HiFi-Elektro GmbH Stade (1)
Haddorfer Grenzweg 2a, 21682, Stade, Germany
Tel.: (49) 414140750
Consumer Electronics Retail Store Operating Services
N.A.I.C.S.: 449210

Media Markt TV-HiFi-Elektro GmbH Stralsund (1)
Grunhufer Bogen 13-17 Im Strelapark EKZ, 18437, Stralsund, Germany
Tel.: (49) 22243333
Web Site: https://www.mediamarkt.de
Consumer Electronics Retailer
N.A.I.C.S.: 449210

Media Markt TV-HiFi-Elektro GmbH Straubing (1)
Aiterhofener Str 222, 94315, Straubing, Germany
Tel.: (49) 22243333
Web Site: https://www.mediamarkt.de
Sales Range: $25-49.9 Million
Emp.: 5
Consumer Electronics Retailer
N.A.I.C.S.: 449210
Reinhard Weigl *(Gen Mgr)*

Media Markt TV-HiFi-Elektro GmbH Stuttgart-Feuerbach (1)
Heilbronner Str 393-397, Stuttgart-Feuerbach, 70469, Stuttgart, Germany
Tel.: (49) 22243333
Web Site: https://www.mediamarkt.de
Sales Range: $25-49.9 Million
Emp.: 10
Consumer Electronics Retailer
N.A.I.C.S.: 449210
Henning Hommel *(Gen Mgr)*

Media Markt TV-HiFi-Elektro GmbH Stuttgart-Vaihingen (1)
Schwabenplatz 1 in der Schwabengalerie, Stuttgart-Vaihingen, 70563, Stuttgart, Germany
Tel.: (49) 711782400

Ceconomy AG—(Continued)

Web Site: http://www.mediamarkt.de
Emp.: 120
Consumer Electronics Retailer
N.A.I.C.S.: 449210
Christoph Breier (Gen Mgr)

Media Markt TV-HiFi-Elektro GmbH Traunreut (1)
Wagner Street 4, 83301, Traunreut, Germany
Tel.: (49) 22243333
Web Site: https://www.mediamarkt.de
Super Market Stores Operating Services
N.A.I.C.S.: 445110

Media Markt TV-HiFi-Elektro GmbH Traunstein (1)
Web Site: http://www.mediamarkt.de
Consumer Electronics Retail Store Operating Services
N.A.I.C.S.: 449210

Media Markt TV-HiFi-Elektro GmbH Velbert (1)
Friedrichstr 303, 42551, Velbert, Germany
Tel.: (49) 22243333
Web Site: https://www.mediamarkt.de
Electronic Appliance Retailer
N.A.I.C.S.: 449210

Media Markt TV-HiFi-Elektro GmbH Viernheim (1)
Burgermeister-Neff-Str 17, 68519, Viernheim, Germany
Tel.: (49) 22243333
Web Site: https://www.mediamarkt.de
Sales Range: $25-49.9 Million
Emp.: 80
Consumer Electronics Retailer
N.A.I.C.S.: 449210
Stefan Gross (Gen Mgr)

Media Markt TV-HiFi-Elektro GmbH Waltersdorf bei Berlin (1)
Am Rondell 3, 12529, Schonefeld, Germany
Tel.: (49) 22243333
Web Site: https://www.mediamarkt.de
Electronic Appliance Retailer
N.A.I.C.S.: 449210

Media Markt TV-HiFi-Elektro GmbH Weiden (1)
Regensburger Str 61, 92637, Weiden, Germany
Tel.: (49) 96138810
Web Site: http://www.mediamarkt.de
Emp.: 4
Consumer Electronics Retail Store Operating Services
N.A.I.C.S.: 449210
Cheryl Powell (Gen Mgr)

Media Markt TV-HiFi-Elektro GmbH Weilheim (1)
Munchener Str 75, 82362, Weilheim, Germany
Tel.: (49) 22243333
Web Site: https://www.mediamarkt.de
Consumer Electronics Retailer
N.A.I.C.S.: 449210

Media Markt TV-HiFi-Elektro GmbH Weiterstadt (1)
Robert-Koch-Str 18, 64331, Weiterstadt, Germany
Tel.: (49) 22243333
Web Site: https://www.mediamarkt.de
Consumer Electronics Retailer
N.A.I.C.S.: 449210

Media Markt TV-HiFi-Elektro GmbH Wetzlar (1)
Am Forum 1, 35576, Wetzlar, Germany
Tel.: (49) 22243333
Web Site: https://www.mediamarkt.de
Consumer Electronics Retail Store Operating Services
N.A.I.C.S.: 449210

Media Markt TV-HiFi-Elektro GmbH Wiesbaden (1)
Hasengartenstr 25, 65189, Wiesbaden, Germany
Tel.: (49) 22243333
Web Site: https://www.mediamarkt.de
Consumer Electronics Retailer

N.A.I.C.S.: 449210

Media Markt TV-HiFi-Elektro GmbH Wiesbaden-Appelallee (1)
Appelallee 69, 65203, Wiesbaden, Germany
Tel.: (49) 22243333
Web Site: https://www.mediamarkt.de
Consumer Electronics Retailer
N.A.I.C.S.: 449210
Thomas Stark (Gen Mgr)

Media Markt TV-HiFi-Elektro GmbH Wolfsburg (1)
Brandgehaege 3, 38444, Wolfsburg, Germany
Tel.: (49) 22243333
Web Site: https://www.mediamarkt.de
Consumer Electronics Retailer
N.A.I.C.S.: 449210

Media Markt TV-HiFi-Elektro GmbH Worms (1)
Schonauer Str 14 Im WEP, 67547, Worms, Germany
Tel.: (49) 22243333
Web Site: https://www.mediamarkt.de
Consumer Electronics Retailer
N.A.I.C.S.: 449210

Media Markt TV-HiFi-Elektro GmbH Wuppertal (1)
Friedrich-Engels-Allee 34, 42103, Wuppertal, Germany
Tel.: (49) 20226540
Consumer Electronics Retail Store Operating Services
N.A.I.C.S.: 449210
Pierre Schuermann (Mgr)

Media Markt TV-HiFi-Elektro GmbH Wurzburg (1)
Am Handelshof 2, 97076, Wurzburg, Germany
Tel.: (49) 22243333
Web Site: https://www.mediamarkt.de
Consumer Electronics Online Retail Services
N.A.I.C.S.: 449210

Media Markt TV-HiFi-Elektro GmbH Wurzburg - Alfred-Nobel-Strasse (1)
Alfred-Nobel-Str 3, 97080, Wurzburg, Germany
Tel.: (49) 931465860
Web Site: http://www.mediamarkt.de
Emp.: 50
Consumer Electronics Online Retail Services
N.A.I.C.S.: 449210
Christoph Tuleja (Pres)

Media Markt TV-HiFi-Elektro GmbH Zwickau (1)
Franz-Mehring-Str 169, 08058, Zwickau, Germany
Tel.: (49) 22243333
Web Site: https://www.mediamarkt.de
Electronic Appliance Retailer
N.A.I.C.S.: 449210

Media Markt TV-Hifi-Elektro GmbH Goslar (1)
Im Schleeke 6-8, 38640, Goslar, Germany
Tel.: (49) 53213970
Web Site: http://www.mediamarkt.de
Consumer Electronics Retailer
N.A.I.C.S.: 449210

Media Markt TV-Hifi-Elektro GmbH Nagold (1)
Haiterbacher Str 66, 72202, Nagold, Germany
Tel.: (49) 22122243333
Electronic Appliance Retailer
N.A.I.C.S.: 449210

Media Markt TV-Hifi-Elektro GmbH Nurnberg-Schoppershof (1)
Aussere Bayreuther Str 80, 90491, Nuremberg, Germany
Tel.: (49) 22122243333
Consumer Electronics Retail Store Operating Services
N.A.I.C.S.: 449210

Media Markt TV-Hifi-Elektro Wien XXI Gesellschaft m.b.H. (1)
Brunner Strasse 72a, 1210, Vienna, Austria

Tel.: (43) 154699
Electronic Appliance Retailer
N.A.I.C.S.: 449210

Media Markt Tatabanya Video TV Hifi Elektro Photo Computer Kereskedelmi Kft. (1)
Blathy Otto u 1, 2800, Tatabanya, Hungary
Tel.: (36) 13586600
Web Site: https://www.mediamarkt.hu
Consumer Electronics Retail Store Operating Services
N.A.I.C.S.: 449210

Media Markt Telde Vfdeo-TV-Hifi-Elektro- Computer- Foto, SA (1)
C C Las Terrazas - Autovia G C 1 Km 5 5 Salida Cortijo Jinamar, 35220, Telde, Spain
Tel.: (34) 928578000
Web Site: https://www.mediamarkt.es
Electronic Appliance Retailer
N.A.I.C.S.: 449210

Media Markt Tenerife Video-TV-Hifi-Elektro-Computer-Foto, SA (1)
CC Continental - C/Bentagay 1-3, 38111, Santa Cruz de Tenerife, Spain
Tel.: (34) 922472200
Web Site: https://www.mediamarkt.es
Electronic Appliance Retailer
N.A.I.C.S.: 449210

Media Markt Terrassa SA (1)
Parc Valles Shopping and Leisure Center Avda Textil 47, 08223, Terrassa, Spain
Tel.: (34) 937356600
Web Site: https://www.mediamarkt.es
Electronic Appliance Retailer
N.A.I.C.S.: 449210
Jaime Borraz (Mgr-Store)

Media Markt The Corner B.V. (1)
Binnenwegplein 50-52, 3012 KA, Rotterdam, 3012 KA, Netherlands
Tel.: (31) 104335000
Web Site: https://www.mediamarkt.nl
Sales Range: $50-74.9 Million
Emp.: 200
Consumer Electronics Retailer
N.A.I.C.S.: 449210

Media Markt Toledo S.A. (1)
CC La Abadia - Ctra From Toledo to Bargas, 45003, Toledo, Spain
Tel.: (34) 925389900
Web Site: https://www.mediamarkt.es
Electronic Appliance Retailer
N.A.I.C.S.: 449210

Media Markt Turnhout NV (1)
Parklaan 4, 2300, Turnhout, Belgium
Tel.: (32) 14558870
Web Site: https://www.mediamarkt.be
Electronic Appliance Retailer
N.A.I.C.S.: 449210
Nathalie Vos (Mng Dir-Store)

Media Markt Umea TV-Hifi-Elektro AB (1)
Klockarbacken Lagervagen 3, 901 37, Umea, Sweden
Tel.: (46) 770778787
Web Site: https://www.mediamarkt.se
Supermarket Operating Services
N.A.I.C.S.: 445110

Media Markt Uppsala TV-Hifi-Elektro AB (1)
Bolandsgatan 16G, 753 23, Uppsala, Sweden
Tel.: (46) 770778787
Web Site: https://www.mediamarkt.se
Consumer Electronics Retail Store Operating Services
N.A.I.C.S.: 449210

Media Markt Utrecht B.V. (1)
Gildenkwartier 181, 3511 DG, Utrecht, Netherlands
Tel.: (31) 302337100
Consumer Electronics Online Retail Services
N.A.I.C.S.: 449210

Media Markt Utrecht The Wall B.V. (1)
Hertogswetering 187, 3543 AS, Utrecht, Netherlands
Tel.: (31) 302425400
Web Site: https://www.mediamarkt.nl

Electronic Appliance Retailer
N.A.I.C.S.: 449210
R. Bommer (Chief Customer Officer)

Media Markt Valencia Colon SA (1)
MediaMarkt - C/ Colon 6, 46004, Valencia, Spain
Tel.: (34) 961258000
Web Site: https://www.mediamarkt.es
Electronic Appliance Retailer
N.A.I.C.S.: 449210

Media Markt Valladolid Vfdeo-TV-Hifi-Elektro-Computer-Foto, SA (1)
C/ Me falta un Tornillo 3, Arroyo de la Encomienda, 47195, Valladolid, Spain
Tel.: (34) 983365900
Web Site: https://www.mediamarkt.es
Electronic Appliance Retailer
N.A.I.C.S.: 449210

Media Markt Vasteras TV-Hifi-Elektro AB (1)
Hallsta Gardsgata 17, 721 38, Vasteras, Sweden
Tel.: (46) 770778787
Web Site: https://www.mediamarkt.se
Consumer Electronics Retail Store Operating Services
N.A.I.C.S.: 449210

Media Markt Venlo B.V. (1)
Maasstraat 12, 5911 DP, Venlo, Netherlands
Tel.: (31) 773551501
Web Site: https://www.mediamarkt.nl
Electronic Appliance Retailer
N.A.I.C.S.: 449210
Jos Prevos (Chief Customer Officer)

Media Markt Video-TV-Hifi-Elektro-Computer-Foto Grancia AG (1)
Tel.: (41) 919853232
Web Site: https://www.mediamarkt.ch
Consumer Electronics Retail Store Operating Services
N.A.I.C.S.: 449210

Media Markt Vigo Video-TV-Hifi-Elektro-Computer-Foto S.A. (1)
CC A Laxe - C/Canovas del Castillo 1 Pl Bj Lc 8, 36202, Vigo, Spain
Tel.: (34) 986819000
Web Site: https://www.mediamarkt.es
Electronic Appliance Retailer
N.A.I.C.S.: 449210

Media Markt Vocklabruck TV-Hifi-Elektro GmbH (1)
Linzer Strasse 50, 4840, Vocklabruck, Austria
Tel.: (43) 7009999
Web Site: https://www.mediamarkt.at
Consumer Electronics Retailer
N.A.I.C.S.: 449210

Media Markt Wels TV-Hifi-Elektro GmbH (1)
Gunskirchenerstrasse 7, 4600, Wels, Austria
Tel.: (43) 7009999
Web Site: https://www.mediamarkt.at
Consumer Electronics Retailer
N.A.I.C.S.: 449210

Media Markt Wien III TV-Hifi-Elektro GmbH (1)
Landstrasser Hauptstrasse 1b/Top 201, 1030, Vienna, Austria
Tel.: (43) 7009999
Web Site: https://www.mediamarkt.at
Electronic Appliance Retailer
N.A.I.C.S.: 449210

Media Markt Wien XV TV-Hifi-Elektro GmbH (1)
Gablenzgasse 5-13, 1150, Vienna, Austria
Tel.: (43) 7009999
Web Site: https://www.mediamarkt.at
Electronic Appliance Retailer
N.A.I.C.S.: 449210

Media Markt Wien XXII TV-Hifi-Elektro GmbH (1)
Zwerchackerweg 2, Vienna, 1220, Austria
Tel.: (43) 1732440
Web Site: http://www.mediamarkt.at
Sales Range: $50-74.9 Million
Emp.: 121
Super Market Stores Operating Services

N.A.I.C.S.: 445110
Thomas Maszat *(Gen Mgr)*

Media Markt Zaandam B.V. (1)
Hermitage 14-17, 1506 TX, Zaandam, Netherlands
Tel.: (31) 756510500
Web Site: http://www.mediamarkt.nl
Electronic Retail Stores Operating Services
N.A.I.C.S.: 449210
F. van der Werff *(Dir)*

Media Markt Zell am See TV-Hifi-Elektro GmbH (1)
Kitzsteinhornstrasse 40, 5700, Zell am See, Austria
Tel.: (43) 7009999
Web Site: https://www.mediamarkt.at
Consumer Electronics Retailer
N.A.I.C.S.: 449210

Media Markt Zoetermeer B.V. (1)
Burgemeester van Leeuwenpassage 30, 2711 JV, Zoetermeer, Netherlands
Tel.: (31) 793294100
Web Site: https://www.mediamarkt.nl
Sales Range: $25-49.9 Million
Emp.: 10
Electronic Retail Stores Operating Services
N.A.I.C.S.: 449210
Hans Hogenhuis *(Gen Mgr)*

Media Markt Zurich AG (1)
Kalanderplatz 1, 8045, Zurich, Switzerland
Tel.: (41) 442069696
Web Site: https://www.mediamarkt.ch
Electronic Appliance Retailer
N.A.I.C.S.: 449210

Media Markt Zwijnaarde NV (1)
Oudenaardsesteenweg 76-86, 9000, Zwijnaarde, Belgium
Tel.: (32) 93829550
Web Site: https://www.mediamarkt.be
Electronic Appliance Retailer
N.A.I.C.S.: 449210

Media Markt Zwolle B.V. (1)
Maagjesbolwerk 44, 8011 LL, Zwolle, Netherlands
Tel.: (31) 384263000
Web Site: https://www.mediamarkt.nl
Electronic Appliance Retailer
N.A.I.C.S.: 449210

Media Markt zwei TV-HiFi-Elektro GmbH Dresden-Prohlis (1)
Dohnaer Str 246 Im Kaufpark, 01239, Dresden, Germany
Tel.: (49) 22243333
Web Site: https://www.mediamarkt.de
Consumer Electronics Retail Store Operating Services
N.A.I.C.S.: 449210

Media Marktparets Del Valles SA (1)
Carrer Comte Montemolin 16, 08150, Parets del Valles, Spain
Tel.: (34) 935918800
Web Site: https://www.mediamarkt.es
Electronic Appliance Retailer
N.A.I.C.S.: 449210
Cristina Pla *(Mgr-HR)*

Media Saturn - Servicos de Apoio Adminstrativo, Lda. (1)
R Casal do Canas N 5 Zona Comercial de Alfragide, 2790-204, Carnaxide, Portugal
Tel.: (351) 210042100
Super Market Stores Operating Services
N.A.I.C.S.: 445110

Media Saturn Hellas Company Administration Anonymi Eteria (1)
4 Leontos Str & Eleutherias, Argyroupolis, 16452, Athens, Greece
Tel.: (30) 2109978501
Web Site: http://www.mediamarkt.com
Emp.: 95
Business Management Consulting Services
N.A.I.C.S.: 541611
Dimitris Katravas *(CEO & VP)*

Media Saturn Holding Polska Sp. z. o. o. (1)
Al Jerozolimskie 179, 02-222, Warsaw, Poland
Tel.: (48) 799353535
Investment Management Service
N.A.I.C.S.: 523999

Media Saturn Multichannel SAU Madrid-Islazul (1)
Centro Comercial IslaAzul - C/ Calderilla 1, 28054, Madrid, Spain
Tel.: (34) 914521500
Web Site: http://www.mediamarkt.es
Electronic Equipment Store
N.A.I.C.S.: 449210
Angel Sanchez *(Mgr)*

Media-Saturn Holding Sweden AB (1)
Iverness Vaagen 2, 18766, Taby, Sweden
Tel.: (46) 87323100
Web Site: http://www.media-saturn.com
Sales Range: $50-74.9 Million
Emp.: 150
Consumer Electronics Retail Store Operating Services
N.A.I.C.S.: 449210
Ter Kaufmann *(Gen Mgr)*

Media-Saturn-Holding GmbH (1)
Media-Saturn-Strasse 1, 85053, Ingolstadt, Germany   **(78.38%)**
Tel.: (49) 22243333
Web Site:
  https://www.mediamarktsaturn.com
Consumer Electronics Retailer
N.A.I.C.S.: 449210
Karsten Wildberger *(Member-Mgmt Bd)*

Subsidiary (Domestic):

Media-Saturn Deutschland GmbH (2)
Wankelstr 5, 85046, Ingolstadt, Germany
Tel.: (49) 8416340
Web Site:
  https://www.mediamarktsaturn.com
Super Market Stores Operating Services
N.A.I.C.S.: 445110

Media-Saturn Verwaltung Deutschland GmbH (2)
Wankelstrasse 5, 85053, Ingolstadt, Germany
Tel.: (49) 8416340
Super Market Stores Operating Services
N.A.I.C.S.: 445110

media-saturn-e-business GmbH (2)
Wankelstr 5, 85053, Ingolstadt, Germany
Tel.: (49) 8416340
Web Site: http://www.mediasaturn.com
Consumer Electronics Online Retail Store Operating Services
N.A.I.C.S.: 425120

MediaMarkt Central Warehouse N.V. (1)
Biezenstraat 51, 3500, Hasselt, Belgium
Tel.: (32) 11294900
Electronic Appliance Retailer
N.A.I.C.S.: 449210

Mediamarket S. p. A. (1)
Via Enrico Fermi 4, Curno, 24035, Bergamo, Italy
Tel.: (39) 0352021111
Electronic Products Retail Store Operating Services
N.A.I.C.S.: 449210

Mediamarket S.p.A.con Socio Unico (1)
Via A Furlanelli 69, Verano Brianza, 20843, Giussano, MB, Italy
Tel.: (39) 0800882288
Web Site: https://www.mediaworld.it
N.A.I.C.S.: 423610

Power Service GmbH (1)
Bergweg 50a, 63322, Rodermark, Germany
Tel.: (49) 6074629747
Web Site: https://www.power-service-gmbh.com
Consumer Electronic & Household Appliance Services
N.A.I.C.S.: 811210

SATURN BUDA Video TV Hifi Elektro Photo Computer Kereskedelmi Kft. (1)
Lovohaz Utca 2-4, Budapest, 1024, Hungary
Tel.: (36) 13363200
Super Market Stores Operating Services
N.A.I.C.S.: 445110

SATURN Brugge NV (1)
Frank van Ackerpromenade 2 Roltrap Stationsplein, 8000, Brugge, Belgium
Tel.: (32) 50729940
Electronic Products Store Operating Services
N.A.I.C.S.: 449210

SATURN Liege Mediacite N.V. (1)
Shopping Mediacite Boulevard Poincare 7/225, 4020, Liege, Belgium
Tel.: (32) 43493200
Super Market Stores Operating Services
N.A.I.C.S.: 445110

SATURN MADRID-PLENILUNIO ELEKTRO, S.A. (1)
Centro Comercial Plenilunio - C/ Aracne s/n, 28022, Madrid, Spain
Tel.: (34) 913939900
Consumer Electronics Retailer
N.A.I.C.S.: 449210

SATURN MEIR ANTWERPEN (1)
Stadsfeestzaal Meir 78, 2000, Antwerp, Belgium
Tel.: (32) 32028660
Super Market Stores Operating Services
N.A.I.C.S.: 445110

SATURN PEST Video TV HiFi Elektro Photo Computer Kereskedelmi Kft. (1)
Ulloi Ut 201-231, Budapest, 1191, Hungary
Tel.: (36) 13484000
Ceramic Furniture Distr
N.A.I.C.S.: 423210

SATURN PLANET Sp. z o.o. (1)
Jerozolimskie 179, Warsaw, 02-222, Poland
Tel.: (48) 225171100
Super Market Stores Operating Services
N.A.I.C.S.: 445110

SATURN TENERIFE 3 DE MAYO ELECTRO, S.A. (1)
C C Tres de Mayo C/ Nivaria Tejera 2, 38003, Santa Cruz de Tenerife, Spain
Tel.: (34) 922849300
Super Market Stores Operating Services
N.A.I.C.S.: 445110

SATURN Volketswil AG (1)
Industriestrasse 15, 8604, Volketswil, Switzerland
Tel.: (41) 442078888
Super Market Stores Operating Services
N.A.I.C.S.: 445110

SATURN Wilrijk NV (1)
Kernenergiestraat 56, 2610, Wilrijk, Belgium
Tel.: (32) 37407460
Super Market Stores Operating Services
N.A.I.C.S.: 445110

Saturn Duna Video Tv Hifi Elektro Photo Computer Kereskedelmi Kft. (1)
Vaci Ut 178, 1138, Budapest, Hungary
Tel.: (36) 14653900
Consumer Electronics Retail Store Operating Services
N.A.I.C.S.: 449210

Saturn Electro Handelsgesellschaft mbH Bremen (1)
Papenstrasse 5, 28195, Bremen, Germany
Tel.: (49) 22243333
Web Site: https://www.saturn.de
Consumer Electronics Retail Store Operating Services
N.A.I.C.S.: 449210

Saturn Electro-Handelsgesellschaft mbH Augsburg (1)
Willy-Brandt-Platz 1, 86153, Augsburg, Germany
Tel.: (49) 22243333
Web Site: https://www.saturn.de
Electronic Appliance Retailer
N.A.I.C.S.: 449210

Saturn Electro-Handelsgesellschaft mbH Bad Homburg (1)
Louisenstrasse 90, 61348, Bad Homburg, Germany
Tel.: (49) 22243333
Web Site: https://www.saturn.de
Electronic Appliance Retailer
N.A.I.C.S.: 449210

Saturn Electro-Handelsgesellschaft mbH Baunatal (1)
Fuldastrasse 1-5, 34225, Baunatal, Germany
Tel.: (49) 22243333
Web Site: https://www.saturn.de
Electronic Appliance Retailer
N.A.I.C.S.: 449210

Saturn Electro-Handelsgesellschaft mbH Berlin-Kopenick (1)
Elcknerplatz 8, 12555, Berlin, Germany
Tel.: (49) 22243123
Web Site: https://www.saturn.de
Electronic Appliance Retailer
N.A.I.C.S.: 449210

Saturn Electro-Handelsgesellschaft mbH Berlin-Leipziger Platz (1)
Vossstrasse 24, 10117, Berlin, Germany
Tel.: (49) 22243123
Web Site: https://www.saturn.de
Electronic Appliance Retailer
N.A.I.C.S.: 449210

Saturn Electro-Handelsgesellschaft mbH Berlin-Markische Zeile (1)
Kurt-Schumacher-Damm 1-15, 13405, Berlin, Germany
Tel.: (49) 22243333
Web Site: https://www.saturn.de
Electronic Appliance Retailer
N.A.I.C.S.: 449210

Saturn Electro-Handelsgesellschaft mbH Berlin-Marzahn (1)
Marzahner Promenade 1a, 12679, Berlin, Germany
Tel.: (49) 22243333
Web Site: https://www.saturn.de
Electronic Appliance Retailer
N.A.I.C.S.: 449210

Saturn Electro-Handelsgesellschaft mbH Berlin-Schlo15stra15e (1)
Treitschkestr 7, 12163, Berlin, Germany
Tel.: (49) 22243333
Web Site: https://www.saturn.de
Electronic Appliance Retailer
N.A.I.C.S.: 449210

Saturn Electro-Handelsgesellschaft mbH Berlin-Treptow (1)
Elsenstrasse 111-114, 12435, Berlin, Germany
Tel.: (49) 30536340
Electronic Appliance Retailer
N.A.I.C.S.: 449210

Saturn Electro-Handelsgesellschaft mbH Bocholt (1)
Berliner Platz 2, 46395, Bocholt, Germany
Tel.: (49) 22122243333
Web Site: http://www.saturn.de
Consumer Electronics Online Retail Services
N.A.I.C.S.: 449210

Saturn Electro-Handelsgesellschaft mbH Bochum (1)
Kortumstrasse 72 - 74, 44787, Bochum, Germany
Tel.: (49) 22243333
Web Site: https://www.saturn.de
Electronic Appliance Retailer
N.A.I.C.S.: 449210

Saturn Electro-Handelsgesellschaft mbH Braunschweig (1)
Platz am Ritterbrunnen 1, 38100, Braunschweig, Germany
Tel.: (49) 22243333
Web Site: https://www.saturn.de
Electronic Appliance Retailer
N.A.I.C.S.: 449210

Saturn Electro-Handelsgesellschaft mbH Bremen-Habenhausen (1)
Steinsetzerstrasse 13, Habenhausen, 28279, Bremen, Germany
Tel.: (49) 22243333
Web Site: https://www.saturn.de
Electronic Retail Stores Operating Services
N.A.I.C.S.: 449210

Saturn Electro-Handelsgesellschaft mbH Celle (1)
Nordwall 27, 29221, Celle, Germany
Tel.: (49) 22243333

Ceconomy AG—(Continued)

Web Site: https://www.saturn.de
Electronic Appliance Retailer
N.A.I.C.S.: 449210

Saturn Electro-Handelsgesellschaft mbH Chemnitz (1)
Ringstrasse 3, 09247, Chemnitz, Germany
Tel.: (49) 22243333
Web Site: http://www.saturn.de
Electronic Appliance Retailer
N.A.I.C.S.: 449210

Saturn Electro-Handelsgesellschaft mbH Chemnitz-Zentrum (1)
Neumarkt 2, 09111, Chemnitz, Germany
Tel.: (49) 22243333
Web Site: https://www.saturn.de
Consumer Electronics Online Retail Services
N.A.I.C.S.: 449210
Ingo Eizhhof *(Mgr)*

Saturn Electro-Handelsgesellschaft mbH Darmstadt (1)
Ludwigsplatz 6, 64283, Darmstadt, Germany
Tel.: (49) 22243333
Web Site: https://www.saturn.de
Super Market Stores Operating Services
N.A.I.C.S.: 445110

Saturn Electro-Handelsgesellschaft mbH Delmenhorst (1)
Seestrasse 7, 27755, Delmenhorst, Germany
Tel.: (49) 422198310
Super Market Stores Operating Services
N.A.I.C.S.: 445110

Saturn Electro-Handelsgesellschaft mbH Dortmund (1)
Westenhellweg 70-84, 44137, Dortmund, Germany
Tel.: (49) 22243333
Web Site: https://www.saturn.de
Consumer Electronics Online Retail Services
N.A.I.C.S.: 449210
Rudolf Nies *(Gen Mgr)*

Saturn Electro-Handelsgesellschaft mbH Dortmund-Eving (1)
Evinger Strasse 170, Eving, 44339, Dortmund, 44339, Germany
Tel.: (49) 231941880
Web Site: https://www.saturn.de
Consumer Electronics Retail Store Operating Services
N.A.I.C.S.: 449210

Saturn Electro-Handelsgesellschaft mbH Dresden (1)
Webergasse 1, 01067, Dresden, Germany
Tel.: (49) 22243333
Web Site: https://www.saturn.de
Electronic Appliance Retailer
N.A.I.C.S.: 449210

Saturn Electro-Handelsgesellschaft mbH Duisburg (1)
Konigstrasse 48, 47051, Duisburg, Germany
Tel.: (49) 22243333
Web Site: https://www.saturn.de
Consumer Electronics Retail Store Operating Services
N.A.I.C.S.: 449210
Georg Lenke *(Gen Mgr)*

Saturn Electro-Handelsgesellschaft mbH Erfurt (1)
Anger 1-3, 99084, Erfurt, Germany
Web Site: http://www.saturn.de
Consumer Electronics Retail Store Operating Services
N.A.I.C.S.: 449210

Saturn Electro-Handelsgesellschaft mbH Erlangen (1)
Nurnberger Strasse 7, 91052, Erlangen, Germany
Tel.: (49) 22243333
Web Site: https://www.saturn.de
Consumer Electronics Retail Store Operating Services
N.A.I.C.S.: 449210

Saturn Electro-Handelsgesellschaft mbH Essen (1)

Limbecker Platz 1a, 45127, Essen, Germany
Tel.: (49) 22122243333
Web Site: https://www.saturn.de
Electronic Appliance Retailer
N.A.I.C.S.: 449210

Saturn Electro-Handelsgesellschaft mbH Esslingen (1)
Berliner Strasse 2, 73728, Esslingen, 73728, Germany
Tel.: (49) 711345500
Web Site: https://www.saturn.de
Consumer Electronics Retail Store Operating Services
N.A.I.C.S.: 449210
Martin Puritscher *(Gen Mgr)*

Saturn Electro-Handelsgesellschaft mbH Euskirchen (1)
Veybachstrasse 3, 53879, Euskirchen, many
Tel.: (49) 22122243333
Web Site: https://www.saturn.de
Electronic Appliance Retailer
N.A.I.C.S.: 449210

Saturn Electro-Handelsgesellschaft mbH Flensburg (1)
Holm 57-61, 24937, Flensburg, Germany
Tel.: (49) 461500950
Web Site: https://www.saturn.de
Electronic Appliance Retailer
N.A.I.C.S.: 449210

Saturn Electro-Handelsgesellschaft mbH Frankfurt/Main (1)
Zeil 106- 110, 60313, Frankfurt am Main, Germany
Tel.: (49) 69219310
Web Site: https://www.saturn.de
Electronic Appliance Retailer
N.A.I.C.S.: 449210

Saturn Electro-Handelsgesellschaft mbH Freiburg (1)
Schiffstrasse 5 - 9, 79098, Freiburg, Germany
Tel.: (49) 76138380
Web Site: https://www.saturn.de
Consumer Electronics Retail Store Operating Services
N.A.I.C.S.: 449210

Saturn Electro-Handelsgesellschaft mbH Freising (1)
Isarstrasse 1, 85356, Freising, Germany
Tel.: (49) 81615490
Web Site: https://www.saturn.de
Consumer Electronics Retail Store Operating Services
N.A.I.C.S.: 449210

Saturn Electro-Handelsgesellschaft mbH Furth (1)
Wurzburgerstrasse 6, 90762, Furth, many
Tel.: (49) 911975950
Electronic Appliance Retailer
N.A.I.C.S.: 449210

Saturn Electro-Handelsgesellschaft mbH Gottingen (1)
Weender Strasse 75, 37073, Gottingen, Germany
Tel.: (49) 55149950
Consumer Electronics Retail Store Operating Services
N.A.I.C.S.: 449210

Saturn Electro-Handelsgesellschaft mbH Gummersbach (1)
Web Site: http://www.saturn.de
Consumer Electronics Retail Store Operating Services
N.A.I.C.S.: 449210

Saturn Electro-Handelsgesellschaft mbH Hagen (1)
Mittelstrasse 20, 58095, Hagen, Germany
Tel.: (49) 233190780
Web Site: https://www.saturn.de
Electronic Appliance Retailer
N.A.I.C.S.: 449210

Saturn Electro-Handelsgesellschaft mbH Hamburg-Altstadt (1)
Monckebergstrasse 1, 20095, Hamburg, Germany

Tel.: (49) 40309580
Web Site: https://www.saturn.de
Consumer Electronics Retail Store Operating Services
N.A.I.C.S.: 449210

Saturn Electro-Handelsgesellschaft mbH Hamm (1)
Richard-Matthaei-Platz 1, 59065, Hamm, Germany
Tel.: (49) 238191900
Web Site: https://www.saturn.de
Electronic Appliance Retailer
N.A.I.C.S.: 449210

Saturn Electro-Handelsgesellschaft mbH Hanau (1)
Web Site: http://www.saturn.de
Consumer Electronics Retail Store Operating Services
N.A.I.C.S.: 449210

Saturn Electro-Handelsgesellschaft mbH Hannover (1)
Ernst-August-Platz 3, 30159, Hamburg, Germany
Tel.: (49) 51145020
Web Site: https://www.saturn.de
Electronic Appliance Retailer
N.A.I.C.S.: 449210

Saturn Electro-Handelsgesellschaft mbH Hattingen (1)
Reschop Carre Platz 1, 45525, Hattingen, Germany
Tel.: (49) 232468640
Web Site: https://www.saturn.de
Consumer Electronics Retail Store Operating Services
N.A.I.C.S.: 449210

Saturn Electro-Handelsgesellschaft mbH Hilden (1)
Warringtonplatz 10, 40721, Hilden, Germany
Tel.: (49) 210333170
Web Site: https://www.saturn.de
Electronic Appliance Retailer
N.A.I.C.S.: 449210

Saturn Electro-Handelsgesellschaft mbH Ingolstadt (1)
Am Westpark 7, 85057, Ingolstadt, Germany
Tel.: (49) 84149150
Web Site: https://www.saturn.de
Super Market Stores Operating Services
N.A.I.C.S.: 445110

Saturn Electro-Handelsgesellschaft mbH Isernhagen (1)
Opelstrasse 3-5, 30916, Isernhagen, Germany
Tel.: (49) 511646430
Web Site: https://www.saturn.de
Super Market Stores Operating Services
N.A.I.C.S.: 445110

Saturn Electro-Handelsgesellschaft mbH Jena (1)
Goethestrasse 3, 07743, Jena, Germany
Tel.: (49) 364122080
Web Site: https://www.saturn.de
Electronic Appliance Retailer
N.A.I.C.S.: 449210

Saturn Electro-Handelsgesellschaft mbH Kaiserslautern (1)
Merkurstrasse 62-64, 67663, Kaiserslautern, Germany
Tel.: (49) 63141420
Web Site: https://www.saturn.de
Super Market Stores Operating Services
N.A.I.C.S.: 445110

Saturn Electro-Handelsgesellschaft mbH Karlsruhe-Durlach (1)
Durlacher Allee 111, Durlach, 76137, Karlsruhe, Germany
Tel.: (49) 721893310
Web Site: https://www.saturn.de
Super Market Stores Operating Services
N.A.I.C.S.: 445110

Saturn Electro-Handelsgesellschaft mbH Kassel (1)
Konigsplatz 61, 34117, Kassel, Germany
Tel.: (49) 56170140
Web Site: https://www.saturn.de

Super Market Stores Operating Services
N.A.I.C.S.: 445110

Saturn Electro-Handelsgesellschaft mbH Kempten (1)
Ursulasrieder Strasse 1, 87437, Kempten, Germany
Tel.: (49) 83154080
Web Site: https://www.saturn.de
Super Market Stores Operating Services
N.A.I.C.S.: 445110

Saturn Electro-Handelsgesellschaft mbH Kerpen (1)
Sindorfer Strasse 32, 50171, Kerpen, Germany
Tel.: (49) 223576170
Web Site: https://www.saturn.de
Electronic Appliance Retailer
N.A.I.C.S.: 449210

Saturn Electro-Handelsgesellschaft mbH Kiel (1)
Holstenstrasse 1, 24103, Kiel, Germany
Tel.: (49) 431557000
Web Site: https://www.saturn.de
Electronic Appliance Retailer
N.A.I.C.S.: 449210
Konrad Warthun *(Mgr-B2B)*

Saturn Electro-Handelsgesellschaft mbH Kleve (1)
Stechbahn 19-23, 47533, Kleve, Germany
Tel.: (49) 282171960
Web Site: https://www.saturn.de
Electronic Appliance Retailer
N.A.I.C.S.: 449210

Saturn Electro-Handelsgesellschaft mbH Koblenz (1)
Carl-Zeiss-Str 8, 56070, Koblenz, Germany
Tel.: (49) 22122243333
Web Site: https://www.mediamarkt.de
Super Market Stores Operating Services
N.A.I.C.S.: 445110

Saturn Electro-Handelsgesellschaft mbH Krefeld (1)
Neusser Strasse 35, 47798, Krefeld, Germany
Tel.: (49) 215193110
Web Site: https://www.saturn.de
Super Market Stores Operating Services
N.A.I.C.S.: 445110

Saturn Electro-Handelsgesellschaft mbH Landshut (1)
Ludwig-Erhard-Strasse 9, 84034, Landshut, Germany
Tel.: (49) 871975140
Web Site: https://www.saturn.de
Super Market Stores Operating Services
N.A.I.C.S.: 445110

Saturn Electro-Handelsgesellschaft mbH Leipzig (1)
Willy-Brandt-Platz 5, 04109, Leipzig, Germany
Tel.: (49) 22122243333
Web Site: http://www.saturn.de
Super Market Stores Operating Services
N.A.I.C.S.: 445110

Saturn Electro-Handelsgesellschaft mbH Leipzig-Hauptbahnhof (1)
Willy-Brandt-Platz 5, 04109, Leipzig, Germany
Tel.: (49) 341140530
Web Site: https://www.saturn.de
Super Market Stores Operating Services
N.A.I.C.S.: 445110

Saturn Electro-Handelsgesellschaft mbH Leonberg (1)
Leonbergerstrasse 98-108, 71229, Leonberg, Germany
Tel.: (49) 7152979610
Web Site: https://www.saturn.de
Electronic Appliance Retailer
N.A.I.C.S.: 449210

Saturn Electro-Handelsgesellschaft mbH Lubeck (1)
Danischburger Landstrasse 81, 23569, Lubeck, Germany
Tel.: (49) 45181030
Web Site: https://www.saturn.de
Super Market Stores Operating Services
N.A.I.C.S.: 445110

Saturn Electro-Handelsgesellschaft mbH Ludenscheid **(1)**
Thunenstrasse 2-8, 58511, Ludenscheid, Germany
Tel.: (49) 22122243333
Web Site: http://www.saturn.de
Super Market Stores Operating Services
N.A.I.C.S.: 445110

Saturn Electro-Handelsgesellschaft mbH Ludwigsburg **(1)**
stable 1, 71634, Ludwigsburg, Germany
Tel.: (49) 22122243333
Web Site: http://www.saturn.de
Super Market Stores Operating Services
N.A.I.C.S.: 445110

Saturn Electro-Handelsgesellschaft mbH Ludwigshafen **(1)**
Rathausplatz 20, 67059, Ludwigshafen, Germany
Tel.: (49) 621586600
Web Site: http://www.saturn.de
Super Market Stores Operating Services
N.A.I.C.S.: 445110
Hartmut Kunkies *(Mng Dir)*

Saturn Electro-Handelsgesellschaft mbH Lunen **(1)**
Willy-Brandt-Platz 6, 44532, Lunen, Germany
Tel.: (49) 230691020
Web Site: https://www.saturn.de
Sales Range: $25-49.9 Million
Emp.: 43
Super Market Stores Operating Services
N.A.I.C.S.: 445110
Horst Lewald *(Mng Dir)*

Saturn Electro-Handelsgesellschaft mbH Magdeburg **(1)**
Ernst-Reuter-Allee 11, 39104, Magdeburg, Germany
Tel.: (49) 39153530
Web Site: http://www.saturn.de
Super Market Stores Operating Services
N.A.I.C.S.: 445110

Saturn Electro-Handelsgesellschaft mbH Mainz **(1)**
Am Brand 41, 55116, Mainz, 55116, Germany
Tel.: (49) 61311460
Web Site: https://www.saturn.de
Sales Range: $25-49.9 Million
Emp.: 40
Super Market Stores Operating Services
N.A.I.C.S.: 445110

Saturn Electro-Handelsgesellschaft mbH Mannheim **(1)**
City Center N7 5-6, 68161, Mannheim, Germany
Tel.: (49) 22122243333
Electronic Appliance Retailer
N.A.I.C.S.: 449210

Saturn Electro-Handelsgesellschaft mbH Marl **(1)**
Bergstrasse 218 - 222, 45768, Marl, Germany
Tel.: (49) 236569800
Web Site: https://www.saturn.de
Super Market Stores Operating Services
N.A.I.C.S.: 445110

Saturn Electro-Handelsgesellschaft mbH Moers **(1)**
Hombergerstrasse 20-22, 47441, Moers, Germany
Tel.: (49) 22122243333
Web Site: http://www.saturn.de
Emp.: 53
Super Market Stores Operating Services
N.A.I.C.S.: 445110

Saturn Electro-Handelsgesellschaft mbH Mulheim **(1)**
Humboldtring 13, 45472, Mulheim an der Ruhr, Germany
Tel.: (49) 20878290
Web Site: https://www.saturn.de
Sales Range: $25-49.9 Million
Emp.: 20
Super Market Stores Operating Services
N.A.I.C.S.: 445110

Saturn Electro-Handelsgesellschaft mbH Munchen **(1)**

Neuhauser Strasse 39, 80331, Munich, Germany
Tel.: (49) 89510850
Web Site: https://www.saturn.de
Consumer Electronics Online Retail Store Operating Services
N.A.I.C.S.: 449210

Saturn Electro-Handelsgesellschaft mbH Munster **(1)**
Ludgeristrasse 100, 48143, Munster, Germany
Tel.: (49) 251414410
Web Site: https://www.saturn.de
Electronic Appliance Retailer
N.A.I.C.S.: 449210

Saturn Electro-Handelsgesellschaft mbH Neckarsulm **(1)**
Rotelstrasse 33, 74172, Neckarsulm, 74172, Germany
Tel.: (49) 713215670
Web Site: https://www.saturn.de
Super Market Stores Operating Services
N.A.I.C.S.: 445110

Saturn Electro-Handelsgesellschaft mbH Neu-Isenburg **(1)**
Hermesstrasse 4, 63263, Neu-Isenburg, Germany
Tel.: (49) 22122243333
Web Site: http://www.saturn.de
Super Market Stores Operating Services
N.A.I.C.S.: 445110

Saturn Electro-Handelsgesellschaft mbH Norderstedt **(1)**
De-Gasperi-Passage 8, 22850, Norderstedt, Germany
Tel.: (49) 402419260
Web Site: https://www.saturn.de
Electronic Appliance Retailer
N.A.I.C.S.: 449210

Saturn Electro-Handelsgesellschaft mbH Nurnberg **(1)**
Vordere Ledergasse 30, 90403, Nuremberg, Germany
Tel.: (49) 91124950
Web Site: https://www.saturn.de
Electronic Appliance Retailer
N.A.I.C.S.: 449210

Saturn Electro-Handelsgesellschaft mbH Oberhausen **(1)**
Centroallee 4, 46047, Oberhausen, Germany
Tel.: (49) 22122243333
Web Site: http://www.saturn.de
Emp.: 7
Super Market Stores Operating Services
N.A.I.C.S.: 445110

Saturn Electro-Handelsgesellschaft mbH Oldenburg **(1)**
Schlossplatz 3, 26122, Oldenburg, Germany
Tel.: (49) 44120540
Web Site: https://www.saturn.de
Consumer Electronics Online Retail Store Operating Services
N.A.I.C.S.: 449210

Saturn Electro-Handelsgesellschaft mbH Paderborn **(1)**
Kamp 30-32, 33098, Paderborn, Germany
Tel.: (49) 525187180
Web Site: https://www.saturn.de
Electronic Appliance Retailer
N.A.I.C.S.: 449210

Saturn Electro-Handelsgesellschaft mbH Passau **(1)**
Grunaustrasse 2, 94032, Passau, Germany
Tel.: (49) 851966290
Web Site: https://www.saturn.de
Electronic Appliance Retailer
N.A.I.C.S.: 449210
Zuhal Korotczuk *(Mgr-Customer Experience)*

Saturn Electro-Handelsgesellschaft mbH Pforzheim **(1)**
Karlsruher Strasse 51 - 57, 75179, Pforzheim, Germany
Tel.: (49) 723113570
Web Site: https://www.saturn.de
Super Market Stores Operating Services
N.A.I.C.S.: 445110

Saturn Electro-Handelsgesellschaft mbH Potsdam **(1)**
Babelsberger Strasse 4/6, 14473, Potsdam, Germany
Tel.: (49) 222243123
Web Site: https://www.saturn.de
Electronic Appliance Retailer
N.A.I.C.S.: 449210

Saturn Electro-Handelsgesellschaft mbH Regensburg **(1)**
Weichser Weg 5, 93059, Regensburg, Germany
Tel.: (49) 222243123
Web Site: https://www.saturn.de
Electronic Appliance Retailer
N.A.I.C.S.: 449210

Saturn Electro-Handelsgesellschaft mbH Remscheid **(1)**
Alleestrasse 74, 42853, Remscheid, Germany
Tel.: (49) 222243123
Web Site: https://www.saturn.de
Super Market Stores Operating Services
N.A.I.C.S.: 445110

Saturn Electro-Handelsgesellschaft mbH Reutlingen **(1)**
Ferdinand-Lassalle-Strasse 7, 72770, Reutlingen, Germany
Tel.: (49) 22122243333
Web Site: http://www.saturn.de
Super Market Stores Operating Services
N.A.I.C.S.: 445110

Saturn Electro-Handelsgesellschaft mbH Rostock **(1)**
Kropeliner Strasse 54, 18055, Rostock, Germany
Tel.: (49) 222243123
Web Site: https://www.saturn.de
Super Market Stores Operating Services
N.A.I.C.S.: 445110

Saturn Electro-Handelsgesellschaft mbH Saarbrucken **(1)**
Triererstrasse 1, 66111, Saarbrucken, Germany
Tel.: (49) 222243123
Web Site: https://www.saturn.de
Super Market Stores Operating Services
N.A.I.C.S.: 445110

Saturn Electro-Handelsgesellschaft mbH Schweinfurt **(1)**
Giegler-Pascha-Strasse Stadtgalerie 2, 97421, Schweinfurt, Germany
Tel.: (49) 972147400
Super Market Stores Operating Services
N.A.I.C.S.: 445110

Saturn Electro-Handelsgesellschaft mbH Senden **(1)**
Berliner Strasse 13, 89250, Senden, Germany
Tel.: (49) 22122243333
Web Site: http://www.saturn.de
Electronic Gadgets Store
N.A.I.C.S.: 449210

Saturn Electro-Handelsgesellschaft mbH Stuttgart-City **(1)**
Konigstrasse 26, 70173, Stuttgart, Germany
Tel.: (49) 222243123
Web Site: https://www.saturn.de
Electronic Appliance Retailer
N.A.I.C.S.: 449210

Saturn Electro-Handelsgesellschaft mbH Troisdorf **(1)**
Wilhelm-Hamacher-Platz 22, 53840, Troisdorf, Germany
Tel.: (49) 222243123
Web Site: https://www.saturn.de
Electronic Appliance Retailer
N.A.I.C.S.: 449210

Saturn Gerasdorf Electro-Handelsges.m.b.H. **(1)**
G3 Platz Top A-001, Gerasdorf, 2201, Vienna, Austria
Tel.: (43) 154633
Electronic Appliance Retailer
N.A.I.C.S.: 449210

Saturn Graz V VertriebsgmbH **(1)**
Lazarettgurtel 55, 8020, Graz, Austria
Tel.: (43) 31670970

Super Market Stores Operating Services
N.A.I.C.S.: 445110

Saturn Groningen B.V. **(1)**
Sontplein 3C, 9723 BZ, Groningen, Netherlands
Tel.: (31) 503173000
Electronic Retail Stores Operating Services
N.A.I.C.S.: 449210

Saturn Haid Electro-Handelsges .m.b.H **(1)**
Ikeaplatz 8, 4053, Haid, Austria
Tel.: (43) 7229791700
Supermarket Operating Services
N.A.I.C.S.: 445110

Saturn Heerhugowaard B.V. **(1)**
Th van Doesburgweg 1, 1703 DL, Heerhugowaard, Netherlands
Tel.: (31) 725757000
Electronic Retail Stores Operating Services
N.A.I.C.S.: 449210

Saturn Hoofddorp B.V. **(1)**
Burgemeester van Stamplein 282, 2132 BH, Hoofddorp, Netherlands
Tel.: (31) 235563000
Electronic Retail Stores Operating Services
N.A.I.C.S.: 449210

Saturn Innsbruck Electro-Handelsges .m.b.H. **(1)**
Maria-Theresien-Strasse 31, 6020, Innsbruck, Austria
Tel.: (43) 01 54 633
Web Site: http://www.saturn.at
Consumer Electronics Retail Store Operating Services
N.A.I.C.S.: 449210

Saturn Klagenfurt Electro-Handelsges .m.b.H. **(1)**
St Veiter Ring 20/Shop 118, 9020, Klagenfurt, Austria
Tel.: (43) 4635150000
Super Market Stores Operating Services
N.A.I.C.S.: 445110

Saturn Kortrijk N.V. **(1)**
Shopping K-in-Kortrijk Steenpoort 2 W305, 8500, Kortrijk, Belgium
Tel.: (32) 56265670
Super Market Stores Operating Services
N.A.I.C.S.: 445110

Saturn Luxembourg S.A. **(1)**
45-47 Avenue de la Gare, 1610, Luxembourg, Luxembourg
Tel.: (352) 266464666
Web Site: http://www.saturn.lu
Electronic Appliance Retailer
N.A.I.C.S.: 449210
Erwann Savary *(Office Mgr)*

Saturn Mega Markt GmbH Wuppertal **(1)**
Neumarkt 1, 42103, Wuppertal, Germany
Tel.: (49) 222243123
Web Site: https://www.saturn.de
Electronic Appliance Retailer
N.A.I.C.S.: 449210

Saturn Mons N.V. **(1)**
Rue De La Chaussee 68, Mons, 7000, Belgium
Tel.: (32) 65404970
Supermarkets Operation Services
N.A.I.C.S.: 445110

Saturn Planet Sp. z o.o. Krakow I Spolka Komandytowa **(1)**
Pawia 5, 31-154, Krakow, Poland
Tel.: (48) 126193100
Web Site: http://www.saturn.com
Consumer Electronics Retail Store Operating Services
N.A.I.C.S.: 449210

Saturn Planet Sp. z o.o. Tychy Spolka Komandytowa **(1)**
Towarowa 2A, 43-100, Tychy, Poland
Tel.: (48) 323236100
Sales Range: $25-49.9 Million
Emp.: 60
Consumer Electronics Retail Store Operating Services
N.A.I.C.S.: 449210

Saturn Planet Sp. z o.o. Warszawa III Spolka Komandytowa **(1)**

Ceconomy AG—(Continued)

Glebocka 13, 03-287, Warsaw, Poland
Tel.: (48) 225093100
Consumer Electronics Retail Store Operating Services
N.A.I.C.S.: 449210

Saturn Planet Sp. z o.o. Wroclaw II Spolka Komandytowa (1)
Plac Grunwaldzki 22, 50-370, Wroclaw, Poland
Tel.: (48) 713358100
Sales Range: $25-49.9 Million
Emp.: 6
Super Market Stores Operating Services
N.A.I.C.S.: 445110

Saturn Rotterdam Zuidplein B.V. (1)
Cartograaf 3, 6921 EZ, Duiven, Netherlands
Tel.: (31) 263170100
Electronic Store Operating Services
N.A.I.C.S.: 449210

Saturn Techno-Electro-Handelsgesellschaft mbH (1)
Maybachstrasse 115, 50670, Cologne, Germany
Tel.: (49) 222243123
Web Site: https://www.saturn.de
Electronic Appliance Retailer
N.A.I.C.S.: 449210

Saturn Techno-Markt Electro GmbH & Co. oHG (1)
Konigsallee 56, 40212, Dusseldorf, Germany
Tel.: (49) 211520230
Web Site: http://www.saturn.de
Consumer Electronics Retail Store Operating Services
N.A.I.C.S.: 449210

Saturn Techno-Markt Electro-Handelsgesellschaft mbH (1)
Hurth-Park L056, 50354, Hurth, Germany
Tel.: (49) 122243333
Web Site: https://www.saturn.de
Consumer Electronics Retailer
N.A.I.C.S.: 449210

Saturn Techno-Markt Electro-Handelsgesellschaft mbH Dusseldorf - Flingern (1)
Werdenerstrasse 87, 40233, Dusseldorf, Germany
Tel.: (49) 211164840
Electronic Appliance Retailer
N.A.I.C.S.: 449210

Saturn Tilburg B.V. (1)
Pieter Vreedeplein 152, 5038 BW, Tilburg, Netherlands
Tel.: (31) 135328800
Electronic Retail Stores Operating Services
N.A.I.C.S.: 449210

Saturn Wien X VertriebsgmbH (1)
Columbusplatz 7-8 Untere Favoritenstrasse, Vienna, 1100, Austria
Tel.: (43) 160550
Web Site: http://www.saturn.at
Emp.: 70
Super Market Stores Operating Services
N.A.I.C.S.: 445110
Mathaias Thupenschek (Gen Mgr)

Saturn Wien XIV Electro-Handelsges.m.b.H. (1)
Albert Schweitzer Gasse 6, 1140, Vienna, Austria
Tel.: (43) 154633
Electronic Appliance Retailer
N.A.I.C.S.: 449210

Saturn Wien XX VertriebsgmbH (1)
Handelskai 94-96, 1200, Vienna, Austria
Tel.: (43) 124090900
Web Site: http://www.saturn.com
Emp.: 88
Super Market Stores Operating Services
N.A.I.C.S.: 445110

Saturn Wien XXII Electro-Handelsges .m.b.H. (1)
SCS Burocenter B2, Vosendorf, 2334, Austria
Tel.: (43) 1201210
Web Site: http://www.saturn.at
Super Market Stores Operating Services

N.A.I.C.S.: 445110

Saturn Wien XXIII Electro-Handelsges .m.b.H. (1)
Breitenfurter Str 372/Top 101, 1230, Vienna, Austria
Tel.: (43) 1863210
Web Site: http://www.saturn.at
Super Market Stores Operating Services
N.A.I.C.S.: 445110

Saturn-Mega Markt GmbH Halle (1)
Leipziger Strasse 94, 6018, Halle, Germany
Tel.: (49) 122243333
Web Site: https://www.saturn.de
Consumer Electronics Retail Store Operating Services
N.A.I.C.S.: 449210

Saturn-Mega Markt GmbH Trier (1)
Simeonstrasse 53, 54290, Trier, Germany
Tel.: (49) 122243123
Web Site: https://www.saturn.de
Electronic Appliance Retailer
N.A.I.C.S.: 449210
Thomas Ernst (Mgr-B2B)

redcoon Logistics GmbH (1)
Web Site: http://www.mediamarktsaturn.com
Logistic Services
N.A.I.C.S.: 488510

xplace GmbH (1)
Tuchmacherweg 12, 37079, Gottingen, Germany
Tel.: (49) 5514887980
Web Site: https://www.xplace-group.com
Electronic Parts Whslr
N.A.I.C.S.: 423690

CEDAR CAPITAL PARTNERS LIMITED
45 Albemarle Street, London, W1S 4JL, United Kingdom
Tel.: (44) 20 7484 3560
Web Site: http://www.cedarcp.com
Year Founded: 2004
Hotel Asset Management
N.A.I.C.S.: 721110
Ramsey Mankarious (Founder)

Subsidiaries:

Shelborne South Beach Hotel (1)
1801 Collins Ave, Miami Beach, FL 33139
Tel.: (305) 531-1271
Web Site: http://www.shelborne.com
Hotel
N.A.I.C.S.: 721110

CEDAR CO., LTD.
2-1-1 Adachi, Kokurakita Ward, Kitakyushu, 802-0042, Fukuoka, Japan
Tel.: (81) 939327005
Web Site: https://www.cedar-web.com
Year Founded: 1981
2435—(TKS)
Rev.: $114,379,440
Assets: $134,381,300
Liabilities: $127,149,960
Net Worth: $7,231,340
Earnings: $1,341,830
Emp.: 2,029
Fiscal Year-end: 03/31/24
Nursing Care Services
N.A.I.C.S.: 623110
Yoshitada Yamasaki (Chm)

CEDAR DEVELOPMENT CO., LTD.
Cedar Center No 2511 Kaichuang Avenue, Huangpu District, Guangzhou, 510700, Guangdong, China
Tel.: (86) 2085518189
Web Site: http://www.sinoer.com
Year Founded: 2003
002485—(SSE)
Rev.: $239,634,720
Assets: $385,635,276
Liabilities: $189,521,748
Net Worth: $196,113,528

Earnings: ($48,984,156)
Emp.: 6,000
Fiscal Year-end: 12/31/22
Men's Clothing Mfr & Distr
N.A.I.C.S.: 315250
Su Qi (Chm & Gen Mgr)

CEDAR HOLDINGS GROUP CO., LTD.
62F Intel Finance Center 5 Zhujiang West Road Tianhe, Guangzhou, 510623, China
Tel.: (86) 20 3891 1638
Web Site: http://www.cedarhd.com
Sales Range: Less than $1 Million
Emp.: 31,065
Investment Management Service
N.A.I.C.S.: 523940
Jing Zhang (CEO)

CEDAR SHAKE & SHINGLE BUREAU
No 2 7101 Horne St, Mission, V2V 7A2, BC, Canada
Tel.: (604) 820-7700
Web Site:
http://www.cedarbureau.org
Year Founded: 1915
Sales Range: $10-24.9 Million
Emp.: 5
Certi-Label Cedar Roofing & Sidewall Products
N.A.I.C.S.: 321999
Lynne Christensen (Dir-Ops)

CEDAR WOODS PROPERTIES LIMITED
Ground Floor 50 Colin Street, West Perth, 6005, WA, Australia
Tel.: (61) 894801500
Web Site:
https://www.cedarwoods.com.au
CWP—(ASX)
Rev.: $257,978,097
Assets: $496,522,434
Liabilities: $188,836,137
Net Worth: $307,686,297
Earnings: $27,039,263
Emp.: 99
Fiscal Year-end: 06/30/24
Residential, commercial & Industries Construction
N.A.I.C.S.: 236117
Paul S. Freedman (Sec)

Subsidiaries:

Lonnegal Property Pty. Ltd. (1)
50 Colin Street, West Perth, 6005, WA, Australia
Tel.: (61) 894801500
Web Site:
http://www.cedarwoodsproperty.com.au
Sales Range: $50-74.9 Million
Emp.: 30
Real Estate Agency
N.A.I.C.S.: 531210
Paul Sadleir (Mng Dir)

CEDARBRAE VOLKSWAGEN LTD
666 Markham Rd, Scarborough, M1H 2A7, ON, Canada
Tel.: (416) 438-1900
Rev.: $21,168,197
Emp.: 46
New & Used Car Dealers
N.A.I.C.S.: 441110

CEDARLAKE ACQUISITION CORP.
Suite 2306 23/F Tower 1 The Gateway 25 Canton Road, Tsim Sha Tsui, Kowloon, China (Hong Kong)
Tel.: (852) 3841 1011
Year Founded: 2021
CEDAU—(NYSE)
Emp.: 3

Investment Services
N.A.I.C.S.: 523999
Yi Bao (Chm & CEO)

CEDAROME CANADA INC.
21 rue Paul Gauguin, Candiac, J5R 3X8, QC, Canada
Tel.: (450) 659-8000
Web Site: http://www.cedarome.com
Year Founded: 1984
Chemical Product Mfr & Distr
N.A.I.C.S.: 325620

CEDIMA GMBH
Larchenweg 3, Celle, 29227, Germany
Tel.: (49) 514188540
Web Site: http://www.cedima.com
Year Founded: 1984
Sales Range: $25-49.9 Million
Emp.: 100
Diamond Tools & Construction Industry Machinery Development & Sales
N.A.I.C.S.: 333515

CEE PROPERTIES REIT
Ul Apostol Karamitev 16 vh A et 9 ap 9-1, 1172, Sofia, 1172, Bulgaria
Tel.: (359) 28655226
5CG—(BUL)
Sales Range: Less than $1 Million
Financial Investment Services
N.A.I.C.S.: 523999

CEEJAY FINANCE LIMITED
C J House Mota Pore, Nadiad, 387 001, Gujarat, India
Tel.: (91) 2682562633
Web Site:
https://www.ceejayfinance.com
Year Founded: 1993
530789—(BOM)
Rev.: $2,451,199
Assets: $11,323,671
Liabilities: $3,571,523
Net Worth: $7,752,149
Earnings: $678,746
Emp.: 63
Fiscal Year-end: 03/31/22
Financial Services
N.A.I.C.S.: 523999
Deepak Patel (Mng Dir)

CEENIK EXPORTS (INDIA) LIMITED
D-396 / 2 TTC Industrial Area Turbhe MIDC, Juhi Nagar, Mumbai, 400705, India
Tel.: (91) 2246187866
Web Site:
https://www.ceenikexports.in
531119—(BOM)
Rev.: $267,088
Assets: $3,948,708
Liabilities: $2,508,030
Net Worth: $1,440,677
Earnings: ($84,123)
Emp.: 8
Fiscal Year-end: 03/31/21
Garment Product Mfr & Whslr
N.A.I.C.S.: 315250
Narain N. Hingorani (Chm & Mng Dir)

CEEPOWER CO., LTD.
No 20 North Jinzhou Road Jinshan Industrial Zone, Cangshan District, Fuzhou, 350002, Fujian, China
Tel.: (86) 59186550308
Web Site: https://www.ceepower.com
Year Founded: 1999
300062—(CHIN)
Rev.: $233,741,279
Assets: $427,903,821
Liabilities: $240,504,403
Net Worth: $187,399,418
Earnings: $7,352,891

Emp.: 1,000
Fiscal Year-end: 12/31/23
Electrical & Electronic Manufacturing Company; Electric Power Supply Systems
N.A.I.C.S.: 335311

CEEREF S.A.
42 rue de la Vallee, L-2661, Luxembourg, Luxembourg
Tel.: (352) 262 626 67
Web Site: http://www.ceeref.com
Year Founded: 2006
Rev.: $6,686,906
Assets: $53,026,224
Liabilities: $5,248,644
Net Worth: $47,777,579
Earnings: $921,737
Fiscal Year-end: 12/31/15
Real Estate Investment & Development
N.A.I.C.S.: 523999
Igor Lah *(Member-Mgmt Bd)*

CEESEG AG
Wallnerstrasse 8, PO Box 73, 1010, Vienna, Austria
Tel.: (43) 1531650
Web Site: http://www.ceeseg.com
Year Founded: 2009
Sales Range: $50-74.9 Million
Emp.: 80
Stock Exchange Operator
N.A.I.C.S.: 523210
Heimo Scheuch *(Chm-Supervisory Bd)*

Subsidiaries:

Burza cennych papiru Praha, a.s. **(1)**
Rybna 14, Prague, 1, Czech
Republic **(92.74%)**
Tel.: (420) 221831111
Web Site: http://www.pse.cz
Sales Range: $1-9.9 Million
Emp.: 50
Stock Exchange Services
N.A.I.C.S.: 523210

Wiener Boerse AG **(1)**
Wallnerstrasse 8, PO Box 73, 1010, Vienna, Austria **(100%)**
Tel.: (43) 1531650
Web Site: http://www.wienerborse.at
Stock Exchange Services
N.A.I.C.S.: 523210
Bernhard Stamm *(Head-Fin, HR & Facility Mgmt)*

Joint Venture (Domestic):

CCP Austria Abwicklungsstelle fur Borsengeschafte GmbH **(2)**
Strauchgasse 1-3, A-1010, Vienna, Austria **(50%)**
Tel.: (43) 5332244
Web Site: http://www.ccpa.at
Banking Services
N.A.I.C.S.: 522110
Wolfgang Aubrunner *(Mng Dir)*

CEETA INDUSTRIES LIMITED
Plot No 34-38 KIADB industrial Area
Sathyamangalam, Tumkur, 572104, Karnataka, India
Tel.: (91) 8162970239
Web Site: https://www.ceeta.com
514171—(BOM)
Rev.: $493,523
Assets: $3,664,786
Liabilities: $163,554
Net Worth: $3,501,232
Earnings: $63,791
Emp.: 18
Fiscal Year-end: 03/31/21
Granite Slab Mfr
N.A.I.C.S.: 327991
Krishna Murari Poddar *(Mng Dir)*

CEF (SOC) LIMITED

CEF House Block C Upper Grayston Office Park 152 Ann Crescent, Strathavon, Sandton, 2031, South Africa
Tel.: (27) 10 201 4700 **ZA**
Web Site: http://www.cefgroup.co.za
Sales Range: $1-4.9 Billion
Emp.: 2,100
Energy Holding Company
N.A.I.C.S.: 551112
A. Haffejee *(Sec)*

Subsidiaries:

African Exploration Mining and Finance Corporation **(1)**
150 Linden Street Block E Upper Grayston Office Park, Strathavon Sandton, Johannesburg, 2196, South Africa
Tel.: (27) 10 201 8107
Coal Mining & Distr
N.A.I.C.S.: 213113
Sizwe Madondo *(CEO)*

Petroleum Agency SA **(1)**
Tygerpoort Building 7 Mispel Street, Bellville, 7530, Cape Town, South Africa
Tel.: (27) 21 938 3500
Web Site:
http://www.petroleumagencysa.com
Oil & Gas Exploration Services
N.A.I.C.S.: 211120
P. Fusi *(Chm)*

The Petroleum Oil & Gas Corporation of South Africa (SOC) Limited **(1)**
151 Frans Conradie Driver, Parow, 7500, South Africa
Tel.: (27) 21 929 3000
Web Site: http://www.petrosa.co.za
Rev.: $840,379,716
Assets: $1,281,550,937
Liabilities: $1,247,056,813
Net Worth: $34,494,124
Earnings: ($144,166,352)
Emp.: 1,248
Fiscal Year-end: 03/31/2019
Oil & Natural Gas Exploration & Production Services
N.A.I.C.S.: 211120
Nhlanhla Gumede *(Chm-Interim)*

Subsidiary (Non-US):

PetroSA Europe BV **(2)**
Willemswerf Boompjes 40, 3000AP, Rotterdam, Netherlands
Tel.: (31) 10 400 7353
Web Site: http://www.petrosa.co.za
Oil & Gas Exploration Services
N.A.I.C.S.: 211120
Motsehoa Brenda Madumise *(Chm)*

CEFC ANHUI INTERNATIONAL HOLDING CO., LTD.
Wujiang Town, Hexian County, Ma'anshan, 238251, Anhui, China
Tel.: (86) 551 65848120
Web Site:
http://www.huaxingchem.com
Rev.: $143,354,540
Assets: $107,588,600
Liabilities: $247,744,560
Net Worth: ($140,155,960)
Earnings: ($169,670,130)
Fiscal Year-end: 12/31/18
Holding Company
N.A.I.C.S.: 551112
Yong Li *(Chm)*

CEFC CHINA ENERGY COMPANY LIMITED
111 Xingguo Road, Xuhui District, Shanghai, 200031, China
Tel.: (86) 2123576747
Web Site: http://en.cefc.co
Sales Range: $25-49.9 Billion
Holding Company; Energy & Financial Services
N.A.I.C.S.: 551112
Jianming Ye *(Chm)*

Subsidiaries:

ZDAS, a.s. **(1)**

Strojirenska 675/6 Zdar nad Sazavou 1, 591 01, Zdar nad Sazavou, Czech
Republic **(63%)**
Tel.: (420) 566641111
Web Site: http://www.zdas.cz
Metallurgical Products & Forging Machines Mfr
N.A.I.C.S.: 333517
Miroslav Sabart *(CEO)*

CEFC GLOBAL STRATEGIC HOLDINGS, INC.
111 Xing Guo Road D8, Xuhui District, Shanghai, 200030, China
Tel.: (86) 21 5856 5351 **NV**
Year Founded: 2010
Assets: $116,227
Liabilities: $374,425
Net Worth: ($258,198)
Earnings: ($49,127)
Emp.: 4
Fiscal Year-end: 02/28/17
Investment Services
N.A.I.C.S.: 523999
Chau To Chan *(Chm & Pres)*

CEFLA S.C.
Via Bicocca 14/c, Imola, 40026, Italy
Tel.: (39) 0542 653441
Web Site: http://www.cefla.com
Year Founded: 1932
Sales Range: $450-499.9 Million
Emp.: 1,700
Holding Company
N.A.I.C.S.: 551112
Andrea Formica *(CEO)*

Subsidiaries:

CEFLA Asia Pte Ltd **(1)**
BLK 2 Bukit Batok St 24 Unit 06-04, Singapore, 659480, Singapore
Tel.: (65) 65665255
Digital Printing Services
N.A.I.C.S.: 323111

Cefla Arredamenti Group **(1)**
Via Selice Provinciale 23/A, Imola, 40026, Italy
Tel.: (39) 0542 653111
Shelving, Rack & Point-of-Purchase Display Mfr
N.A.I.C.S.: 337215
Eleonora Zanotti *(Mktg Mgr)*

Cefla Dental Group **(1)**
Via Bicocca 14, 40026, Imola, Italy
Tel.: (39) 0542 653111
Dental Equipment & Supplies Mfr
N.A.I.C.S.: 339114
Claudia Poli *(Mgr-Ops)*

Cefla Deutschland GmbH **(1)**
Eisbachstrasse 2, Meckenheim, 53343, Germany
Tel.: (49) 22259090474
Dental Equipment Distr
N.A.I.C.S.: 423450

Cefla Finishing Europe **(1)**
1 rue de Marienthal, Bischwiller, 67240, France
Tel.: (33) 388537300
Digital Printing Services
N.A.I.C.S.: 323111

Cefla Finishing Europe Deutschland **(1)**
Giso-Ring 44, Marktoberdorf, 87616, Germany
Tel.: (49) 83421260
Digital Printing Services
N.A.I.C.S.: 323111

Cefla Finishing Group **(1)**
Via Bicocca 14/C, 40026, Imola, Italy
Tel.: (39) 0542 653441
Finishing Equipment Mfr
N.A.I.C.S.: 333248
Riccardo Quattrini *(Mng Dir)*

Subsidiary (US):

Cefla North America Inc. **(2)**
6125 Harris Technology Blvd, Charlotte, NC 28269

Tel.: (704) 598-0020
Web Site: http://www.cefla.com
Emp.: 50
Finishing Equipment Mfr
N.A.I.C.S.: 333248
Massimo Di Russo *(VP)*

Subsidiary (Domestic):

Delle Vedove USA, Inc. **(3)**
6125 Harris Technology Blvd, Charlotte, NC 28269
Tel.: (704) 598-0020
Sales Range: $25-49.9 Million
Emp.: 20
Sawmill & Woodworking Machinery Mfr
N.A.I.C.S.: 333243
Marco Belluz *(Program Dir)*

Cefla Finishing India Pvt. Ltd. **(1)**
8/13 2nd Floor Lakshmikanth Complex Nandhini Layout, Bengaluru, 560 096, India
Tel.: (91) 9902098256
Digital Printing Services
N.A.I.C.S.: 323111

Cefla Finishing Russia **(1)**
Proletarskiy Prospekt 10 Office 706, Shelkovo, 141100, Moscow, Russia
Tel.: (7) 4959811128
Digital Printing Services
N.A.I.C.S.: 323111

Cefla Impianti Group **(1)**
Via Selice Provinciale 23/A, Imola, 40026, Italy
Tel.: (39) 0542 653111
Civil & Industrial Engineering Services
N.A.I.C.S.: 237990

Cefla Ladenbau **(1)**
Leinenweber Strasse 11, Bad Hersfeld, 36251, Germany
Tel.: (49) 66218012270
Industrial Machinery & Equipment Distr
N.A.I.C.S.: 423830

Cefla Middle East FZE **(1)**
Warehouse No FZS2AB02 Jebel Ali Free Zone, PO Box 261 633, Dubai, United Arab Emirates
Tel.: (971) 148862722
Digital Printing Services
N.A.I.C.S.: 323111
Fabio Vito Grazioso *(Mng Dir)*

Cefla Polska Sp. z.o.o. **(1)**
ul Utrata 4 p 38, 03-877, Warsaw, Poland
Tel.: (48) 226796492
Web Site: http://www.cefla-serwis.pl
Digital Printing Services
N.A.I.C.S.: 323111

Cefla S.C. - Duspohl Plant **(1)**
An der Heller 7-13, Schloss Holte-Stukenbrock, Germany
Tel.: (49) 520792910
Digital Printing Services
N.A.I.C.S.: 323111

Cefla S.C. - Falcioni Plant **(1)**
Via della Meccanica 3, 61122, Pesaro, Italy
Tel.: (39) 072148551
Digital Printing Services
N.A.I.C.S.: 323111

Cefla S.C. - Madrid Plant **(1)**
c/ Joaquin Turina 2 oficina 7B, Pozuelo de Alarcon, 28224, Madrid, Spain
Tel.: (34) 916439506
Shelve Mfr
N.A.I.C.S.: 337122

Cefla S.C. - Paris Plant **(1)**
15-17 Avenue de la Liberation, Melun, France
Tel.: (33) 1641914
Shelve Mfr
N.A.I.C.S.: 337122

Cefla Soc. Coop. A.R.L. **(1)**
Via Gargano 23, 20139, Milan, Italy
Tel.: (39) 0256804615
Shelve Mfr
N.A.I.C.S.: 337122

DV-System **(1)**
6125 Harris Technology Blvd, Charlotte, NC 28269
Tel.: (704) 598-0020
Digital Printing Services
N.A.I.C.S.: 323111

Cefla S.C.—(Continued)

Delle Vedove S.p.A. (1)
Via delle Industrie 9, Valvasone, 33098,
Pordenone, Italy
Tel.: (39) 0542653441
Digital Printing Services
N.A.I.C.S.: 323111

Elca Technologies s.r.l. (1)
Via Gambellara 40/O, Imola, Bologna, Italy
Tel.: (39) 0542653751
Web Site: http://www.elca-technologies.com
Application Software Development Services
N.A.I.C.S.: 541511
Erika Franceschelli (Mgr-Procurement)

Filomarket s.r.l. (1)
Via UE Terracini 13, 40026, Imola, Bologna,
Italy
Tel.: (39) 0542634611
Web Site: http://www.filomarket.com
Shelve Mfr
N.A.I.C.S.: 337122

Mocom S.r.l. (1)
Via Saliceto 22, Castelmaggiore, 40013,
Bologna, Italy
Tel.: (39) 051703168
Web Site: http://www.mocom.it
Dental Equipment Mfr
N.A.I.C.S.: 334510

QR s.r.l. (1)
Via Silvestrini 20, 37135, Verona, Italy
Tel.: (39) 0458202727
Web Site: http://www.newtom.it
Dental Equipment Mfr
N.A.I.C.S.: 339114

**Suzhou Victor Medical Equipment
Co., Ltd.** (1)
No 85 Suli road, Suzhou, Jiangsu, China
Tel.: (86) 51265657989
Web Site:
   http://www.victordentalequipment.cn
Dental Equipment Distr
N.A.I.C.S.: 423450

Zenith R.S. (1)
Gorodok -17 street r p Bolshie Vyazemi,
Odinzovo District, Moscow, Russia
Tel.: (7) 4955982660
Metal Shelve Mfr & Distr
N.A.I.C.S.: 332322

CEGEDIM S.A.

137 rue d Aguesseau, 92100,
Boulogne-Billancourt, France
Tel.: (33) 149092200 FR
Web Site: https://www.cegedim.com
Year Founded: 1969
CGM—(EUR)
Rev.: $591,963,836
Assets: $948,827,373
Liabilities: $624,558,636
Net Worth: $324,268,737
Earnings: $12,878,630
Emp.: 5,691
Fiscal Year-end: 12/31/22
Market Research & Technology Services for the Healthcare & Pharmaceutical Industry
N.A.I.C.S.: 541611
Jean-Claude Labrune (Chm & CEO)

Subsidiaries:

3S/Tracere (1)
137 rue d'Aguesseau, Boulogne-Billancourt,
92100, France
Tel.: (33) 1 49 09 22 00
Web Site: http://www.cegedim.com
Sample Management Systems
N.A.I.C.S.: 541611

BSV SARL (1)
137 rue d'Aguesseau, 92100, Boulogne-
Billancourt, France
Tel.: (33) 147569966
Web Site: https://www.bsv.fr
Computer Software Development Services
N.A.I.C.S.: 541511

Cegedim Activ SASU (1)
114-116 rue d Aguesseau, 92100,
Boulogne-Billancourt, France
Tel.: (33) 562241717

Web Site: http://www.cegedim-
insurance.com
Insurance Services
N.A.I.C.S.: 524210
M. Philippe Simon (Pres & Dir-Publ)

Cegedim Cloud SASU (1)
137 rue d Aguesseau, 92100, Boulogne-
Billancourt, Cedex, France
Tel.: (33) 149092222
Web Site: http://www.cegedim.cloud
Emp.: 120
Computer Software Development Services
N.A.I.C.S.: 541511
Jerome Dury (CTO)

**Cegedim Customer Information
SRL** (1)
Str Modrogan nr 20 Sector 1, 011826, Bucharest, Romania
Tel.: (40) 372139500
Professional Services
N.A.I.C.S.: 541990
Silviu Moise (Mgr-IT Svcs)

**Cegedim Logiciels Medicaux
SAS** (1)
121 rue d Aguesseau, 92100, Boulogne-
Billancourt, France
Tel.: (33) 141863600
Web Site: http://www.cegedim-logiciels.com
Software Publisher
N.A.I.C.S.: 513210
Emmanuel Bertrand (Dir-Sls & Mktg)

Cegedim Maroc SARL (1)
Arribat Center-Immeuble D et E-2eme
Etage Avenue Omar Ibn Khattad, Adgal,
10090, Rabat, Morocco
Tel.: (212) 538045800
Professional Services
N.A.I.C.S.: 541990
Naoual Kalda (Mgr-Bus Unit)

Cegedim Media SARL (1)
137 rue d'Aguesseau, 92100, Boulogne-
Billancourt, France
Tel.: (33) 149097800
Web Site: https://www.cegedim-media.fr
Media Services
N.A.I.C.S.: 541840
Pascal Charon (Mgr-IT)

Cegedim Outsourcing SAS (1)
15 rue Paul Dautier, 78140, Velizy-
Villacoublay, France
Tel.: (33) 134583500
Web Site: https://www.cegedim-
outsourcing.fr
Emp.: 400
Information Technology Services
N.A.I.C.S.: 541519
Sonia Goumain (Mktg Mgr)

Cegedim RX Limited (1)
Suite B Part 2nd Floor Building 2 Station
Approach, Buckshaw Village, Chorley, PR7
7NR, Lancashire, United Kingdom
Tel.: (44) 3303033342
Web Site: http://www.cegedimrx.co.uk
Innovative Engineering Services
N.A.I.C.S.: 541330
Adam Dennett (Comml Dir)

Cegedim RX SRL (1)
Str Modrogan nr 20 - Sector 1, 011826, Bucharest, Romania
Tel.: (40) 372139500
Web Site: http://www.pharmec.ro
Healtcare Services
N.A.I.C.S.: 621999
Catalin Burghelea (Dir-Natl Support)

Cegedim SRH Ltd. (1)
Cegedim House Pound Road, Chertsey,
KT16 8EH, Surrey, United Kingdom
Tel.: (44) 8708881034
Professional Services
N.A.I.C.S.: 541990
Amel Kemmoun (Mgr-Comml Acct)

Cegedim SRH SA (1)
Boulevard de la Cluse 35, 1205, Geneva,
Switzerland
Tel.: (41) 228791500
Professional Services
N.A.I.C.S.: 541990
Isabelle Rey (Ops Mgr)

Cegedim Sante SASU (1)
137, rue d'Aguesseau Boulogne-Billancourt,

92100, Ile-de-France, France
Tel.: (33) 49092200
Web Site: https://www.cegedim-sante.com
Software Devolpement
N.A.I.C.S.: 513210

Subsidiary (Domestic):

Visiodent S.A. (2)
30bis rue du Bailly, 93210, La Plaine Saint-
Denis, France
Tel.: (33) 149465800
Web Site: http://www.visiodent.com
Sales Range: $1-9.9 Million
Software Development Services
N.A.I.C.S.: 541511

Cosytec SA (1)
Parc Club Orsay University 4 Rue Jean Rostand, 91893, Orsay, Cedex, France
Tel.: (33) 160193738
Web Site: http://www.cosytec.fr
Software Publisher
N.A.I.C.S.: 513210

Docavenue SASU (1)
137 rue d Aguesseau, 92100, Boulogne-
Billancourt, France
Tel.: (33) 149093499
Web Site: http://www.docavenue.com
Healtcare Services
N.A.I.C.S.: 621999
Laurent Labrune (Pres)

**Health Data Management Partners
SA** (1)
Route de Lennik 451, 1070, Anderlecht,
Belgium
Tel.: (32) 27264200
Web Site: http://www.hdmp.com
Health Care Consulting Services
N.A.I.C.S.: 541611
Philippe Quertemont (Dir-Dev)

In Practice Systems Ltd. (1)
Studio F5 Battersea Studios 1 82 Silver-
thorne Road, London, SW8 3HE, United
Kingdom
Tel.: (44) 3303033335
Web Site: http://www.visionhealth.co.uk
Innovative Engineering Services
N.A.I.C.S.: 541330
Andrew Neill (Reg Mgr)

MedExact SAS (1)
127 rue d'Aguesseau, 92100, Boulogne-
Billancourt, France
Tel.: (33) 685237227
Web Site: https://www.medexact.com
Digital Marketing Services
N.A.I.C.S.: 541613
Jean-Louis Lompre (Pres)

NetEDI Ltd. (1)
Unit 9 Kings Court King Street, Leyland,
Preston, PR25 2LE, United Kingdom
Tel.: (44) 1772977781
Web Site: http://www.netedi.co.uk
Information Technology Services
N.A.I.C.S.: 541511
Steve Martin (CEO)

Pharmastock (1)
137 rue d'Aguesseau, Amilly, Boulogne-
Billancourt, 45200, France
Tel.: (33) 238876081
Sales Range: $25-49.9 Million
Emp.: 20
Sample Management Systems
N.A.I.C.S.: 541611

RESIP (1)
17 rue de l'Ancienne Mairie, Boulogne-
Billancourt, 62200, France
Tel.: (33) 321103400
Web Site: http://www.resip.fr
Scientific Database Management Services
N.A.I.C.S.: 541611

RM Ingenierie SAS (1)
Avenue de la Gineste BP 3351, 12033, Rodez, Cedex, France
Tel.: (33) 565760333
Web Site: http://www.rmingenierie.net
Software Publisher
N.A.I.C.S.: 513210

Rue de la Paye SAS (1)
137 rue d'Aguesseau, 92100, Boulogne-
Billancourt, France
Tel.: (33) 144060797

Web Site: http://www.ruedelapaye.com
Payroll Services
N.A.I.C.S.: 541214

Smart RX SAS (1)
137 rue d Aguesseau, 92100, Boulogne-
Billancourt, France
Tel.: (33) 825556001
Web Site: http://www.smart-rx.com
Computer Programming Services
N.A.I.C.S.: 541511
Thomas Heufke (Reg Dir-Sls)

**Stacks Consulting e Ingeniera en
Software SL** (1)
Carrer d'Arago 182 Entresuelo, 08021, Barcelona, Spain
Tel.: (34) 900525858
Professional Services
N.A.I.C.S.: 541990
Laura Benitez Garcia (Mgr-IS Area & Software Architecture Area)

**Stacks Servicios Technologicos SL
Chile Ltda** (1)
Luis Thayer Ojeda 0130 of 1201 and 1202,
Providencia, Santiago, Chile
Tel.: (56) 23334669
Technical Consulting Services
N.A.I.C.S.: 541690

XimantiX Software GMBH (1)
Landsberger Str 478, 81241, Munich, Germany
Tel.: (49) 8945230830
Web Site: http://www.ximantix.de
Invoice Receipt & Dispatch Services
N.A.I.C.S.: 541219
Reinhard Wild (Mng Dir)

CEGEKA GROEP NV

Universiteitslaan 9, 3500, Hasselt,
Belgium
Tel.: (32) 11240234 BE
Web Site: http://www.cegeka.com
Sales Range: $300-349.9 Million
Emp.: 4,200
Holding Company; Information Technology Support & Outsourcing Services
N.A.I.C.S.: 551112
Stephan Daems (CFO)

Subsidiaries:

Cegeka Health Care NV (1)
Universiteitslaan 9, 3500, Hasselt, Belgium
Tel.: (32) 1124 0234
Web Site: http://www.cegeka.com
Emp.: 3,500
Health Care Industry Management Software
& Data Services
N.A.I.C.S.: 518210
Christoph Neut (Gen Mgr)

Cegeka NV (1)
Universiteitslaan 9, 3500, Hasselt, Belgium
Tel.: (32) 1124 0234
Web Site: http://www.cegeka.com
Information Technology Support & Outsourcing Services
N.A.I.C.S.: 541519
Andre Knaepen (Founder & Chm)

Subsidiary (Non-US):

Brain Force S.p.A. (2)
Via Alessandro Volta 16, 20093, Cologno
Monzese, MI, Italy
Tel.: (39) 02 254 4271
Web Site: http://www.brainforce.it
Sales Range: $25-49.9 Million
Emp.: 250
Software Publisher
N.A.I.C.S.: 513210
Stefania Donnabella (CEO)

CEGEKA Deutschland GmbH (2)
Wilhelm-Wagenfeld-Str 30, 80807, Munich,
Germany
Tel.: (49) 89748330
Web Site: http://www.brainforce.com
Software Publisher
N.A.I.C.S.: 513210
Martin Friedrich (Mng Dir)

Subsidiary (Non-US):

Brain Force B.V. (3)

Gildetrom 27-33, 3905 TB, Veenendaal, Netherlands
Tel.: (31) 318 410 000
Web Site: http://www.brainforce.nl
Emp.: 350
Computer Programming Services
N.A.I.C.S.: 541519
Zander Colaers (COO)

Brain Force GmbH (3)
Wiener Str 51, 3040, Neulengbach, Austria
Tel.: (43) 2772 55464 40
Web Site: http://www.brainforce.at
Software Publisher
N.A.I.C.S.: 513210
Markus Zulechner (Co-CEO)

Brain Force Software s.r.o. (3)
Mala Stepanska 1929/9, 120 00, Prague, 2, Czech Republic
Tel.: (420) 296 331 111
Web Site: http://www.brainforce.com
Software Publisher
N.A.I.C.S.: 513210
Brahomir Hruby (Mng Dir)

Cegeka Nederland Holding B.V. (1)
Bastion 4, 3905 NJ, Veenendaal, Netherlands
Tel.: (31) 318 41 0000
Web Site: http://www.cegeka.com
Holding Company; Regional Managing Office; Information Technology Support & Outsourcing Services
N.A.I.C.S.: 551112
Jan Willem van den Bos (Comml Dir-Outsourcing)

Computer Task Group, Inc. (1)
300 Corporate Pkwy Ste 214N, Amherst, NY 14226
Tel.: (716) 882-8000
Web Site: https://www.ctg.com
Rev.: $325,080,000
Assets: $181,619,000
Liabilities: $75,640,000
Net Worth: $105,979,000
Earnings: $6,609,000
Emp.: 3,200
Fiscal Year-end: 12/31/2022
IT Application Management, Consulting, Software Development & Integration & Staffing Solutions
N.A.I.C.S.: 541511
Stephan Daems (Treas & Sec)

Subsidiary (Non-US):

Computer Task Group (Holdings) Ltd. (2)
11 Beacontree Plaza, Gillette Way, Reading, RG2 0BS, Berkshire, United Kingdom
Tel.: (44) 1189750877
Web Site: http://www.ctg.com
Sales Range: $25-49.9 Million
Emp.: 25
Holding Company
N.A.I.C.S.: 551112

Computer Task Group Belgium N.V. (2)
Culliganlaan 1D, 1831, Diegem, Belgium
Tel.: (32) 27205170
Web Site: http://be.ctg.com
Emp.: 350
Software Development Services
N.A.I.C.S.: 541511
Filip J. L. Gyde (Gen Mgr)

Subsidiary (Domestic):

e-trinity N.V. (3)
Eigenlostraat 27 B, Saint-Niklaas, 9100, Belgium
Tel.: (32) 37600490
Web Site: http://www.etrinity.eu
Emp.: 20
Information Technology Services
N.A.I.C.S.: 541512
Bart Briers (CEO & Mng Dir)

Subsidiary (Non-US):

Computer Task Group of Canada, Inc.
1 Yonge St Suite 1801, Toronto, M5E 1W7, ON, Canada (100%)
Tel.: (416) 868-1212
Web Site: http://www.ctt.com

Sales Range: $1-9.9 Million
Emp.: 3
Computer Programming, Software Services, Consulting
N.A.I.C.S.: 541511

Subsidiary (Domestic):

Computer Task Group of Delaware, Inc. (2)
300 Corporate Pkwy Ste 214N, Amherst, NY 14226
Tel.: (716) 882-8000
Web Site: http://www.ctg.com
Software Development Services
N.A.I.C.S.: 541511

Subsidiary (Non-US):

Computer Task Group of Luxembourg PSF (2)
10A rue des Merovingiens, 8070, Bertrange, Luxembourg
Tel.: (352) 2987271
Web Site: http://lux.ctg.com
Sales Range: $350-399.9 Million
Emp.: 200
Software Development Services
N.A.I.C.S.: 541511
Caroline Simon (Mng Dir)

Nouvelles Solutions Informatiques-N.S.I. (1)
Chaussee de Bruxelles 174 A, 4340, Awans, Belgium
Tel.: (32) 42399150
Web Site: http://www.nsi-sa.be
Software Development Services
N.A.I.C.S.: 541511

CEIBA INVESTMENTS LIMITED
Les Echelons Court Les Echelons, Saint Peter Port, GY1 1AR, Guernsey
Tel.: (44) 1481743030 GY
Web Site: https://ceibainvest.com
Year Founded: 1995
CBA—(LSE)
Rev.: $19,095,234
Assets: $220,151,102
Liabilities: $38,630,626
Net Worth: $181,520,476
Earnings: ($11,284,821)
Fiscal Year-end: 12/31/22
Investment Management Service
N.A.I.C.S.: 523999
John Herring (Chm)

CELADON PHARMACEUTICALS PLC
32-33 Cowcross Street, London, EC1M 6DF, United Kingdom
Tel.: (44) 2031500252 UK
Web Site: https://celadonpharma.com
Year Founded: 2018
Rev.: $19,100
Assets: $7,428,256
Liabilities: $43,205
Net Worth: $7,385,050
Earnings: ($250,935)
Emp.: 4
Fiscal Year-end: 08/31/19
Investment Management Service
N.A.I.C.S.: 523940
Alexander Anton (Chm)

CELADOR PRODUCTIONS LTD.
38 Long Acre, London, WC2E 9JT, United Kingdom
Tel.: (44) 2072408101
Web Site:
http://www.cplproductions.co.uk
Year Founded: 1983
Sales Range: $25-49.9 Million
Emp.: 100
Television Production Company
N.A.I.C.S.: 516120
Danielle S. Lux (Mng Dir)

CELARTEM TECHNOLOGY INC.

5th Floor Sumitomo Higashi-Shimbashi Bldg 5, 2-11-7 Higashi-Shimbashi, Minato-ku, Tokyo, 105-0021, Japan
Tel.: (81) 355747231 JP
Web Site: http://www.celartem.com
Year Founded: 1996
Sales Range: $25-49.9 Million
Emp.: 103
Digital Contents Supply Chain Software & Technology Applications
N.A.I.C.S.: 541512
Syuichi Fujimoto (Pres)

Subsidiaries:

Beijing CEE Technology Co., Ltd. (1)
Yaojiayuan Road 105 Lake International a 9-storey, Chaoyang, Beijing, 100025, China
Tel.: (86) 10 56505280
Web Site: http://www.c-ee.cn
Software Application Services
N.A.I.C.S.: 513210

Lizardtech (1)
1008 Western Ave Ste 200, Seattle, WA 98104
Tel.: (206) 652-5211
Web Site: http://www.lizardtech.com
Sales Range: $50-74.9 Million
Software Publishing & Application Services
N.A.I.C.S.: 513210
Nahhe Nomie (CFO)

CELCOMDIGI BERHAD
D House Lot 10 Jalan Delima 1/1 Subang Hi-Tech Industrial Park, 40000, Subang Jaya, Selangor, Malaysia
Tel.: (60) 357211800
Web Site:
https://corporate.celcomdigi.com
CDB—(KLS)
Rev.: $1,433,504,974
Assets: $7,944,812,063
Liabilities: $4,492,021,164
Net Worth: $3,452,790,899
Earnings: $161,623,069
Emp.: 3,818
Fiscal Year-end: 12/31/22
Wireless Telecommunication Services
N.A.I.C.S.: 517112
Albern Murty (CEO)

Subsidiaries:

Celcom Axiata Berhad (1)
No 6 Persiaran Barat Seksyen 52, 46200, Petaling Jaya, Selangor, Malaysia
Tel.: (60) 372002222
Web Site: https://www.celcom.com.my
Telecommunication Servicesb
N.A.I.C.S.: 517810
Mohamad Idham Nawawi (CEO)

Subsidiary (Domestic):

Celcom Transmission (M) Sdn Bhd (2)
Level 10 Block F 3 Two Square No 2 Jalan 19/1, Petaling Jaya, 46300, Malaysia
Tel.: (60) 372602122
Web Site: http://www.celcom.com.my
Sales Range: $100-124.9 Million
Emp.: 40
Telecommunication Servicesb
N.A.I.C.S.: 517810

Digi Telecommunications Sdn Bhd (1)
Lot36 Jln Kilang Kolombong, Sedco Light Industrial Estate, 88450, Kota Kinabalu, Malaysia
Tel.: (60) 88438800
Internet Providing Services
N.A.I.C.S.: 517810

CELEBI HAVA SERVISI AS
Nuri Demirag Street No 39, Tayakadin District Arnavutkoy, 34149, Istanbul, Turkiye
Tel.: (90) 2129529200

CLEBI—(IST)
Rev.: $187,549,491
Assets: $248,662,940
Liabilities: $148,219,508
Net Worth: $100,443,432
Earnings: $33,357,132
Emp.: 13,475
Fiscal Year-end: 12/31/22
Air Freight Transportation Services
N.A.I.C.S.: 481212
Can Celebioglu (Chm)

Subsidiaries:

Celebi Nas Airport Services India Pvt. Ltd. (1)
E8 - 3016 Level 3 New T2 Chhatrapati Shivaji International Airport, Andheri East, Mumbai, 400 099, India
Tel.: (91) 2266859377
Web Site: https://www.celebinas.in
Emp.: 3,000
Ground Handling Services
N.A.I.C.S.: 713990

CELEBI HOLDING A.S.
Anel Is Merkezi Saray Mah Site Yolu Sok No 5 Kat 7-10, Umraniye, 34768, Istanbul, Turkiye
Tel.: (90) 2166666600
Web Site: http://www.celebi.com
Sales Range: $350-399.9 Million
Emp.: 1,000
Holding Services
N.A.I.C.S.: 551112
A. Cemil Erman (Dir Gen)

Subsidiaries:

CELEBI Ground Handling Hungary Kft. (1)
Liszt Ferenc International Airport, 1185, Budapest, Hungary
Tel.: (36) 70 296 0000
Web Site: http://www.celebihandling.hu
Airport Ground Handling Services
N.A.I.C.S.: 488119
Pal Schneider (Mgr-QSAR)

Ce-Tur Celebi Tourism Trade Inc. (1)
Ebulula Mardin Cad Maya Meridyen Is Merkezi Kat 4, Akatlar Besiktas, 34335, Istanbul, Turkiye
Tel.: (90) 212 352 04 14
Web Site: http://www.cetur.com.tr
Car Rental Services
N.A.I.C.S.: 532111

Celebi Bandirma Uluslararasi Limani Isletmeciligi A.S. (1)
Mehmet Akif Ersoy Caddesi Bandirma Limani, Bandirma, 10200, Balikesir, Turkiye
Tel.: (90) 266 714 04 04
Web Site: http://www.portofbandirma.com.tr
Bulk Cargo Transportation Distr
N.A.I.C.S.: 488320

Celebi Cargo GmbH (1)
Web Site: http://www.celebicargo.de
Freight Transportation Services
N.A.I.C.S.: 488510
M. Sanli Sekercioglu (CEO)

Celebi Delhi Cargo Terminal Management India Pvt. Ltd. (1)
Airport Cargo Handling Services
N.A.I.C.S.: 488119

Celebi Ground Handling Inc. (1)
Anel Is Merkezi Saray Mah Site Yolu Sok No 5 Kat 7-10, Umraniye, 34768, Istanbul, Turkiye
Tel.: (90) 216 666 67 67
Web Site: http://www.celebihandling.com.tr
Airport Ground Handling Services
N.A.I.C.S.: 488119

Celebi Ground Services Austria GmbH (1)
Vienna International Airport Versorgungsstrasse Objekt 951, 1300, Vienna, Austria
Tel.: (43) 1 9977007
Web Site: http://www.celebihandling.at
Airport Ground Handling Services
N.A.I.C.S.: 488119
Ozgun Ozbek (Mgr-Fin & Project Mgr)

Celebi Iplik Tic. ve San. A.S.—(Continued)

CELEBI IPLIK TIC. VE SAN. A.S.
Bagdat Cad Beach Yolu Sok Yasarbey Apt K 4 D 7 Caddebostan, Kadikoy, 34728, Istanbul, Turkiye
Tel.: (90) 2163550382   TR
Real Estate Development Services
N.A.I.C.S.: 531390

CELEBRITY FASHIONS LIMITED
SDF-IV C2 3rd Main Road MEPZ SEZ, Tambaram, Chennai, 600 045, Tamil Nadu, India
Tel.: (91) 4443432000
Web Site:
https://www.celebritygroup.com
Year Founded: 1998
532695—(BOM)
Rev.: $43,683,232
Assets: $21,683,352
Liabilities: $18,482,105
Net Worth: $3,201,247
Earnings: $737,366
Emp.: 3,993
Fiscal Year-end: 03/31/23
Garments Mfr & Distr
N.A.I.C.S.: 315250
Vidyuth Rajagopal (Mng Dir)

CELEBRITY NATIONAL FINANCIAL SERVICE SAOG
2nd Fl Off No 26 Fortune Bldg Al Qurum Al Harthy Complex, PO Box 300, 118, Muscat, Oman
Tel.: (968) 24559700
Web Site: http://www.nscoman.com
Year Founded: 1997
Sales Range: Less than $1 Million
Investment Advisory Services
N.A.I.C.S.: 523940

CELEKULA A.D.
Dusana Popovica 22, Nis, Serbia
Tel.: (381) 18 4536 947
Web Site: http://www.celekula.com
Year Founded: 1948
CKLAN—(BEL)
Sales Range: Less than $1 Million
Construction Product Mfr
N.A.I.C.S.: 327331
Dusan Ignjatovic (CEO)

CELEMICS, INC.
19F 20F Bldg A Byc Highcity 131 Gasandigital 1-Ro, Geumcheon-Gu, Seoul, 08506, Korea (South)
Tel.: (82) 267468067
Web Site: https://www.celemics.com
Year Founded: 2010
331920—(KRS)
Rev.: $6,695,097
Assets: $17,036,166
Liabilities: $2,778,222
Net Worth: $14,257,944
Earnings: ($3,679,247)
Emp.: 79
Fiscal Year-end: 12/31/22
Chemicals Mfr
N.A.I.C.S.: 325998
Sangseok Lee (CFO)

CELEST PAPER KLIPPAN AB
Fabriksvagen 2, 264 39, Klippan, Sweden
Tel.: (46) 43514040
Web Site: http://www.celestpaper.se
Sales Range: $10-24.9 Million
Emp.: 30
Paper Mills
N.A.I.C.S.: 322120
Ronny Andersson (Owner)

Subsidiaries:

Klippan AB   (1)
Kvarnbygatan 8, PO Box 213, 431 23, Molndal, Sweden   (100%)
Tel.: (46) 31675000
Web Site: http://www.klippan.com
Newsprint Mill
N.A.I.C.S.: 322120

CELESTIAL ASIA SECURITIES HOLDINGS LIMITED
28/F Manhattan Place 23 Wang Tai Road, Kowloon, China (Hong Kong)
Tel.: (852) 22878888
Web Site: http://www.cash.com.hk
1049—(HKG)
Rev.: $154,388,093
Assets: $227,784,105
Liabilities: $190,646,670
Net Worth: $37,137,435
Earnings: ($4,494,248)
Emp.: 536
Fiscal Year-end: 12/31/22
Investment Services
N.A.I.C.S.: 523999
Suzanne Wing Sheung Luke (Sec)

Subsidiaries:

CASH Quant-Finance Lab Limited   (1)
Unit 518 5/F No 12 Science Park West Avenue Hong Kong Science Park, Hong Kong, China (Hong Kong)
Tel.: (852) 22878031
Web Site: http://www.qflab.cashalgo.com
Financial Services
N.A.I.C.S.: 541611

Moli Group Limited   (1)
6F The Point-Jing An No 555 Anyuan Rd, Shanghai, 200040, China
Tel.: (86) 2132279848
Web Site: http://ir.moliyo.com
Sales Range: $100-124.9 Million
Emp.: 300
Online Game Development Services
N.A.I.C.S.: 541511

CELESTIAL BIOLABS LIMITED
Plot No 59 Road No 12 TSIIC Tech Park, IDA Nacharam, Hyderabad, 500076, Telangana, India
Tel.: (91) 4029888003
Web Site:
http://wwwcelestialbiolabs.com
Rev.: $6,662,014
Assets: $17,731,320
Liabilities: $1,813,285
Net Worth: $15,918,036
Earnings: $537,800
Emp.: 101
Fiscal Year-end: 03/31/18
Research & Development, Commercial Production & Marketing of Chemical Enzymes
N.A.I.C.S.: 325411
Aditya Narayan Singh (Chm & Mng Dir)

CELESTIAL GREEN VENTURES PLC
Merchant's Hall 25/26 Merchant's Quay, Dublin, 8, Ireland
Tel.: (353) 1 444 3662
Web Site:
http://www.celestialventures.com
Carbon Mfr
N.A.I.C.S.: 335991
Ciaran Kelly (CEO)

CELHART DONARIS SA
Sos Vizirului Km 10, Braila, Romania
Tel.: (40) 239 675110
Sales Range: Less than $1 Million
Emp.: 4
Paper & Paperboard Mfr
N.A.I.C.S.: 322120

CELIK D.O.O
Novosadska b.b., 21234, Backi Jarak, Serbia
Tel.: (381) 21 847 606
Web Site: http://www.celikdoo.rs
Year Founded: 1971
Sheet Metal Mfr
N.A.I.C.S.: 332322

CELL BIOTECH CO., LTD.
50 Aegibong-ro 409beon-gil Gaegok-ri Wolgot-myeon, Gimpo, 415-872, Gyeonggi-do, Korea (South)
Tel.: (82) 319876205
Web Site: https://www.cellbiotech.in
Year Founded: 1995
049960—(KRS)
Rev.: $38,753,249
Assets: $88,848,237
Liabilities: $5,941,712
Net Worth: $82,906,526
Earnings: $6,351,259
Emp.: 140
Fiscal Year-end: 12/31/22
Biological Product Mfr
N.A.I.C.S.: 325414

Subsidiaries:

Cell Biotech International Co., Ltd.   (1)
4F 3000TOWER 274 Seocho-daero, Seocho-gu, Seoul, Korea (South)
Tel.: (82) 226686077
Biology Product Mfr
N.A.I.C.S.: 325414

CELLA SPACE LTD.
Sree Kailas 57/2993-94 Paliam Rd, Ernakulam, Kochi, 682016, Kerala, India
Tel.: (91) 4842373230
Web Site: https://www.sreekailas.com
Year Founded: 1991
532701—(BOM)
Rev.: $756,278
Assets: $6,044,630
Liabilities: $9,208,863
Net Worth: ($3,164,234)
Earnings: $140,677
Emp.: 2
Fiscal Year-end: 03/31/22
Paper Mills
N.A.I.C.S.: 322120
Subramoniam Sivathanu Pillai (Founder)

CELLARMASTER WINES PTY LIMITED
Level 2 26 Waterloo St cnr of Waterloo & Cooper Streets, Surry Hills, 2010, NSW, Australia
Tel.: (61) 293338008
Web Site:
http://www.cellarmasters.com.au
Sales Range: $1-4.9 Billion
Emp.: 900
Wine Retailer
N.A.I.C.S.: 312130
Stuart Robinson (Dir-Cellar & Brand Mgr-Portfolio)

CELLAVISION AB
Mobilvagen 12, 223 62, Lund, Sweden
Tel.: (46) 464601600
Web Site:
https://www.cellavision.com
Year Founded: 1994
CEVI—(OMX)
Rev.: $69,042,588
Assets: $100,741,881
Liabilities: $34,418,259
Net Worth: $66,323,622
Earnings: $15,301,385
Emp.: 200
Fiscal Year-end: 12/31/21

Digital Image Analysis, Artificial Intelligence & Automated Microscopy Products Mfr
N.A.I.C.S.: 339112
Adam Morell (VP-Engrg)

Subsidiaries:

CellaVision Canada Inc.   (1)
2 Bloor St West Suite 2120, Toronto, M4W 3E2, ON, Canada
Tel.: (561) 741-3003
Web Site: https://www.cellavision.com
Electronic Diagnostic Instruments Distr
N.A.I.C.S.: 423450

CellaVision Inc.   (1)
4107 Burns Rd, Palm Beach Gardens, FL 33410
Tel.: (561) 741-3003
Web Site: http://www.cellavision.com
Electronic Diagnostic Instruments Distr
N.A.I.C.S.: 423450

CellaVision Japan K.K.   (1)
9th Floor Sotestu KS Building 1-1-5 Kitasaiwai, Nishi-ku, Yokohama, 220-0004, Kanagawa, Japan
Tel.: (81) 452870638
Emp.: 3
Electronic Diagnostic Instruments Distr
N.A.I.C.S.: 423450

RAL Diagnostics SAS   (1)
Technopole Montesquieu, 33650, Martillac, France
Tel.: (33) 557960404
Web Site: https://www.ral-diagnostics.fr
Medical Equipment Mfr
N.A.I.C.S.: 339112

CELLCUBE ENERGY STORAGE SYSTEMS INC.
393 University Avenue Suite 1810, Toronto, M5G 1E6, ON, Canada
Web Site:
http://www.cellcubeenergy.com
Year Founded: 1986
CUBE—(CSE)
Mineral Exploration Services
N.A.I.C.S.: 213114
Stefan Schauss (CEO)

CELLECOR GADGETS LIMITED
Crown Height 703 7th Floor Sector 10 Rohini, New Delhi, 110085, India
Tel.: (91) 8527578792
Web Site: https://www.cellcor.com
Year Founded: 2020
CELLECOR—(NSE)
Rev.: $32,146,857
Assets: $8,515,064
Liabilities: $6,835,452
Net Worth: $1,679,612
Earnings: $981,519
Emp.: 211
Fiscal Year-end: 03/31/23
Electronic Product Distr
N.A.I.C.S.: 423620
Varsha Bansal (Sec)

CELLECT BIOTECHNOLOGY LTD.
23 Hata as Street, Kfar Saba, 44425, Israel
Tel.: (972) 9 9741444   II
Web Site: http://www.cellect.co
Year Founded: 2011
APOP—(NASDAQ)
Assets: $6,079,671
Liabilities: $1,428,081
Net Worth: $4,651,590
Earnings: ($5,613,270)
Emp.: 12
Fiscal Year-end: 12/31/20
Biological Product Mfr
N.A.I.C.S.: 325414
Shai Yarkoni (Founder & CEO)

CELLECTIS S.A.

8 rue de la Croix Jarry, 75013, Paris, France
Tel.: (33) 181691600   FR
Web Site: https://www.cellectis.com
Year Founded: 1999
CLLS—(NASDAQ)
Rev.: $59,564,000
Assets: $261,216,000
Liabilities: $135,275,000
Net Worth: $125,941,000
Earnings: ($81,074,000)
Emp.: 236
Fiscal Year-end: 12/31/22
Genome Research & Development Services
N.A.I.C.S.: 541715
Stephan Reynier *(Chief Regulatory & Pharmaceutical Compliance Officer)*

Subsidiaries:

Cellectis therapeutics   (1)
102 Avenue Gaston Roussel, 93230, Romainville, France
Tel.: (33) 141839900
Health Care Srvices
N.A.I.C.S.: 621999

Ectycell SASU   (1)
4 Rue Pierre Fontaine, 91058, Evry, France
Tel.: (33) 141839900
Pluripotent Stem Cells Mfr
N.A.I.C.S.: 325412

CELLFIE GLOBAL CO.,LTD.
17 Hosandong-Ro 7-gil, Dalseo-Gu, Daegu, 42715, Korea (South)
Tel.: (82) 535923433
Web Site: https://www.cardnsoft.com
Year Founded: 1998
068940—(KRS)
Rev.: $29,058,258
Assets: $33,412,299
Liabilities: $13,732,419
Net Worth: $19,679,880
Earnings: $7,639,857
Emp.: 91
Fiscal Year-end: 12/31/22
Smart, Combi, 3D Lenticular & Specialty Cards Mfr
N.A.I.C.S.: 334118
Yoo Ki-Jong *(CEO)*

CELLGENTEK CO., LTD.
579-4 Yuseong-daero Yuseong-gu, Daejeon, 34196, Korea (South)
Tel.: (82) 15442340
Web Site: http://www.pcpia21.co.kr
Year Founded: 2001
Healthcare Software Development Services
N.A.I.C.S.: 541511
Hoe-Ryul Kim *(CEO)*

CELLHIRE PLC
Park House, Clifton Park, York, YO30 5PB, United Kingdom
Tel.: (44) 1904610610
Web Site: http://www.cellhire.co.uk
Year Founded: 1987
Telecommunication Servicesb
N.A.I.C.S.: 517112
Tim Williams *(Chm & CEO)*

Subsidiaries:

Cellhire (Germany) GmbH   (1)
Pfalzer-Wald-Strasse 70, 81539, Munich, Germany
Tel.: (49) 8966011790
Web Site: http://www.cellhire.de
Wireless Telecommunication Services
N.A.I.C.S.: 517112

Cellhire France SA   (1)
53 Rue du Capitaine Guynemer, 92418, Courbevoie, Cedex, France
Tel.: (33) 141437940
Web Site: http://www.cellhire.fr
Wireless Telecommunication Services
N.A.I.C.S.: 517112

Cellhire USA LLC   (1)
3520 W Miller Rd Ste 100, Garland, TX 75041
Tel.: (877) 244-7242
Web Site: http://www.cellhire.com
Wireless Telecommunication Services
N.A.I.C.S.: 517112
Kristi Overbeck *(Mgr-Fin & HR)*

CELLID CO., LTD.
142 dong 5F Gwanak-ro 1, Gwanak-gu, Seoul, 8826, Korea (South)
Tel.: (82) 232857860
Web Site: https://www.cellid.co.kr
Year Founded: 2006
299660—(KRS)
Rev.: $368,160
Assets: $35,172,619
Liabilities: $17,961,991
Net Worth: $17,210,628
Earnings: ($17,537,129)
Emp.: 69
Fiscal Year-end: 12/31/22
Pharmaceutical Product Mfr & Distr
N.A.I.C.S.: 325412
Chang Yuil Kang *(CEO)*

CELLIVERY THERAPEUTICS INC.
K Biz Dmc Tower 121-904 F9 189 Sungam Ro, Mapogu, Seoul, 03929, Korea (South)
Tel.: (82) 231518900
Web Site: https://www.cellivery.com
Year Founded: 2014
268600—(KRS)
Pharmaceutical Preparation Mfr
N.A.I.C.S.: 325412
Daewoong Jo *(Founder, CEO & Dir-Res)*

CELLMARK AB
Lilla Bommen 3C 4th Floor, 411 04, Gothenburg, Sweden
Tel.: (46) 31100300
Web Site: http://www.cellmark.com
Year Founded: 1984
Sales Range: $1-4.9 Billion
Emp.: 750
Pulp, Paper, Chemicals & Metals Supply Chain Services
N.A.I.C.S.: 541614
Hans Kling *(Pres, CEO & Sr VP-Metals Div)*

Subsidiaries:

CellMark Asia Pte Ltd   (1)
271 Bukit Timah Road 03-13 Balmoral Plaza, Singapore, 259708, Singapore
Tel.: (65) 6603 1288
Chemical Products Distr
N.A.I.C.S.: 424690
Kelly Ng *(Dir-Fin)*

CellMark Belgium NV   (1)
Verlorenbroodstraat 63b, 9820, Merelbeke, Belgium
Tel.: (32) 9 218 7180
Sales Range: $75-99.9 Million
Emp.: 10
Chemical, Mineral, Raw Material & Industrial Product Wholesale Trade Agency
N.A.I.C.S.: 425120
Luc Vereecken *(Mng Dir)*

CellMark Chemicals Ltd.   (1)
Regal Ct 42-44 High St, Slough, SL1 1EL, Berks, United Kingdom
Tel.: (44) 1753 245 530
Sales Range: $50-74.9 Million
Emp.: 75
Chemical, Mineral, Raw Material & Industrial Product Wholesale Trade Agency
N.A.I.C.S.: 425120

CellMark Chemicals Singapore Pte Ltd.   (1)
271 Bukit Timah Road Unit 03-13 Balmoral Plaza, Singapore, 259708, Singapore
Tel.: (65) 6603 1288
Sales Range: $50-74.9 Million
Emp.: 4

Chemical, Mineral, Raw Material & Industrial Product Wholesale Trade Agency
N.A.I.C.S.: 425120
Jason Yu *(Gen Mgr)*

CellMark China Ltd   (1)
Room 2101 Windsor House Tower 311 Gloucester Road, Causeway Bay, China (Hong Kong)
Tel.: (852) 2882 1208
Metal Product Distr
N.A.I.C.S.: 423510

CellMark Deutschland GmbH   (1)
Hamborner Str 53, 40472, Dusseldorf, Germany
Tel.: (49) 211 52380
Metal Product Distr
N.A.I.C.S.: 423510

CellMark Espana SA   (1)
C/Pere i Pons n 9-11 floor 12 P 3, Barcelona, 08035, Spain
Tel.: (34) 93 494 9900
Sales Range: $50-74.9 Million
Emp.: 20
Chemical, Mineral, Raw Material & Industrial Product Wholesale Trade Agency
N.A.I.C.S.: 425120

CellMark Hellas SA   (1)
26 Mylopotamou Str & 4 Tsokatou Str, 115 26, Athens, Greece
Tel.: (30) 210 6982 560
Web Site: http://www.cellmark.com
Emp.: 8
Chemical Products Distr
N.A.I.C.S.: 424690
Philon Panagopoulos *(Mng Dir)*

CellMark Iberica SL   (1)
Gran via Carles III 124, 8034, Barcelona, Spain
Tel.: (34) 93 414 5887
Chemical Products Distr
N.A.I.C.S.: 424690

CellMark India Private Limited   (1)
105 Town Centre II 1st Floor Andheri Kurla Road Saki Naka, Andheri East, Mumbai, 400059, India
Tel.: (91) 22 28528226
Web Site: http://www.cellmark.com
Emp.: 5
Chemical Products Distr
N.A.I.C.S.: 424690

CellMark Italy S.r.l   (1)
Viale Francesco Restelli 5, 20124, Milan, Italy
Tel.: (39) 02 668 931
Chemical Products Distr
N.A.I.C.S.: 424690

CellMark Japan   (1)
7F Shinjuku i-Land Tower 6-5-1 Nishi-Shinjuku, Shinjuku-ku, Shinjuku, 163-1307, Japan   (100%)
Tel.: (81) 333496600
Sales Range: $50-74.9 Million
Emp.: 20
Chemical, Mineral, Raw Material & Industrial Product Wholesale Trade Agency
N.A.I.C.S.: 425120
Masaru Sakamoto *(Pres)*

CellMark Kimya Tic AS   (1)
Fenerbahce mah Cengiz Topel sok Humbaraci apt D5 Kalamis, Kadikoy, 34726, Istanbul, Turkiye
Tel.: (90) 216 337 1060
Chemical Products Distr
N.A.I.C.S.: 424690
Emel Benzer *(Product Mgr)*

CellMark Ltd   (1)
Room 1105 Doosan We ve Pavilion 81 Sambong-Ro, Jongno-Gu, Seoul, 110-858, Korea (South)
Tel.: (82) 2 7568721
Chemical Products Distr
N.A.I.C.S.: 424690

CellMark M.E. LLC   (1)
201 Al Reem Tower Al Maktoum Street, PO Box 32436, Dubai, United Arab Emirates
Tel.: (971) 42271716
Web Site: http://www.cellmark.com
Emp.: 2
Pulp & Paper Product Distr
N.A.I.C.S.: 424110

A. K. Menon *(Gen Mgr)*

CellMark Paper Canada Inc   (1)
28-1817 Wellington Avenue, Winnipeg, R3H 0T8, MB, Canada
Tel.: (204) 784-5242
Pulp & Paper Product Distr
N.A.I.C.S.: 424110

CellMark Paper SA de CV   (1)
Insurgentes Sur 1898 Piso 15 Colonia Florida Delegacion Alvaro, Obregon, 01030, Mexico, Mexico
Tel.: (52) 55 53229240
Pulp & Paper Product Distr
N.A.I.C.S.: 424110

CellMark Papier SAS   (1)
1 Avenue Sonia Delaunay, 94506, Champigny-sur-Marne, France
Tel.: (33) 148810058
Sales Range: $25-49.9 Million
Emp.: 15
Paper Product Whslr
N.A.I.C.S.: 424110

CellMark Peru S.A.C.   (1)
Calle Mariano de los Santos 135, San Isidro, Lima, Peru
Tel.: (51) 1 4214299
Recyclable Material Distr
N.A.I.C.S.: 423930

CellMark Pulp and Paper Inc   (1)
1 Biscayne Tower 2 S Biscayne Blvd Ste 2500, Miami, FL 33131
Tel.: (305) 459-4100
Web Site: http://www.cellmark.com
Emp.: 30
Pulp & Paper Product Distr
N.A.I.C.S.: 424110

CellMark Recycling Benelux BV   (1)
Heuvel 7, 5664 HK, Geldrop, Netherlands
Tel.: (31) 40 2924040
Recyclable Material Distr
N.A.I.C.S.: 423930
Ron van den Akker *(Mng Dir)*

CellMark SA   (1)
1 Rue Pedro Meylan, 1208, Geneva, Switzerland
Tel.: (41) 22 7074102
Web Site: http://www.cellmark.com
Emp.: 6
Pulp & Paper Product Distr
N.A.I.C.S.: 424110
Anderson Frederik *(Gen Mgr)*

CellMark Shanghai Co Ltd   (1)
Units 803-806 Ocean Towers 550 Yan an Road (E), Huang Pu District, Shanghai, 200001, China
Tel.: (86) 21 6473 0266
Chemical Products Distr
N.A.I.C.S.: 424690

CellMark Taiwan Co Ltd   (1)
11th Floor - 7 No 58 Min Chuan East Road Sec 3, PO Box 101-351, Taipei, Taiwan
Tel.: (886) 2 25031773
Chemical Products Distr
N.A.I.C.S.: 424690
Shyu Joseph *(Vice Gen Mgr)*

CellMark Thailand Co Ltd   (1)
2024/139-140 Rimtangrodfai Road Phrakanong, Klong Toey, Bangkok, 10260, Thailand
Tel.: (66) 2 3331300
Web Site: http://www.cellmark.com
Emp.: 10
Recyclable Material Distr
N.A.I.C.S.: 423930
Kamol Vichakchon *(Mng Dir)*

CellMark UK Ltd   (1)
Fairburn House Park Lane, Allerton, WF10 2AT, Bywater, United Kingdom
Tel.: (44) 7889 190048
Web Site: http://www.cellmark.com
Chemical Products Distr
N.A.I.C.S.: 424690

CellMark USA, LLC   (1)
333 Ludlow St 8th Fl, Stamford, CT 06902
Tel.: (203) 541-9000
Sales Range: $50-74.9 Million
Emp.: 40
Chemical, Mineral, Raw Material & Industrial Product Wholesale Trade Agency

CellMark AB—(Continued)

N.A.I.C.S.: 425120
Tom Sliker *(Exec VP)*

Cellmark AB (Shanghai) (1)
Room 2007 Rui Jin Building, 205 South
Mao Ming Road, Shanghai, 200020, China
Tel.: (86) 2164730266
Web Site: http://www.cellmark.com
Sales Range: $25-49.9 Million
Emp.: 14
Books, Periodicals & Newspapers
N.A.I.C.S.: 424920
Henry Peng *(Mgr-Pulp)*

Cellmark Inc. (1)
22 Pelican Way, San Rafael, CA 94901
Tel.: (415) 927-1700
Web Site: http://www.cellmark.com
Sales Range: $50-74.9 Million
Emp.: 60
Paper & Wood Pulp Whslr
N.A.I.C.S.: 424110
Victor E. Rice *(Sr VP)*

PT CellMark Interindo Trade (1)
Jl Raya Jatiwaringin No 54 Pondok Gebe,
PO Box 8538, 17411, Jakarta, Indonesia
Tel.: (62) 21 8480130
Pulp & Paper Product Distr
N.A.I.C.S.: 424110

Singapore Pulp (Pte) Ltd. (1)
271 Bukit timach Rd 03/13 Balmoral Plz,
259008, Singapore, Singapore
Tel.: (65) 67378830
Sales Range: $125-149.9 Million
Emp.: 20
Acacia Pulp Marketer
N.A.I.C.S.: 322110

CELLNEX TELECOM, S.A.

Paseo Zona Franca 105, 8038, Barcelona, Spain
Tel.: (34) 935678910   ES
Web Site: https://www.cellnex.com
Year Founded: 2008
CLNX—(BIL)
Rev.: $4,369,979,495
Assets: $47,879,607,166
Liabilities: $31,532,971,077
Net Worth: $16,346,636,089
Earnings: ($320,764,084)
Emp.: 3,018
Fiscal Year-end: 12/31/23
Telecommunication Servicesb
N.A.I.C.S.: 551112
Jose Manuel Aisa Mancho *(Dir-Corp Fin & M&A)*

Subsidiaries:

Adesal Telecom S.L. (1)
Av Ausias March 20 Bjos, 46006, Valencia,
Spain   **(60.08%)**
Tel.: (34) 96 302 9327
Web Site: https://www.adesaltelecom.com
Telecommunication Software Development
Services
N.A.I.C.S.: 541511
Javier Marti de Veses Estades *(Pres)*

Breedlink BV (1)
Papendorpseweg 75-79, 3528 BJ, Utrecht,
Netherlands
Tel.: (31) 88 205 4400
Web Site: https://www.breedlink.nl
Broadband Connection Services
N.A.I.C.S.: 517111

Cellnex Austria Gmbh (1)
Schubertring 6, 1010, Vienna, Austria
Tel.: (43) 13950678200
Web Site: https://www.cellnex.com
N.A.I.C.S.: 517111

**Cellnex Connectivity Solutions
Limited** (1)
Level 4 R 2 Blagrave Street, Reading, RG1
1AZ, United Kingdom
Tel.: (44) 2045268553
Web Site: https://www.cellnex.com
N.A.I.C.S.: 517111

Cellnex Denmark ApS (1)
Orestads Boulevard 114 4th Floor, 2300,
Copenhagen, Denmark

Tel.: (45) 31116100
Web Site: https://www.cellnex.com
N.A.I.C.S.: 517111

Cellnex Ireland Limited (1)
Suite 311 Q House 76 Furze Rd Sandyford
Business Park, Sandyford, Dublin, D18
YV50, Ireland
Tel.: (353) 14825890
Emp.: 50
Wireless Telecoms Infrastructure Operator
N.A.I.C.S.: 561520

Cellnex Italia, S.r.L. (1)
Via Cesare Giulio Viola 43, 00148, Rome,
Italy
Tel.: (39) 0686950882
Web Site: https://www.cellnex.com
N.A.I.C.S.: 517111

Cellnex Poland Sp Z.o.o. (1)
Ul Marcina Kasprzaka 4, 01-211, Warsaw,
Poland
Tel.: (48) 226675678
Web Site: https://www.cellnex.com
N.A.I.C.S.: 517111

Cellnex Sweden AB (1)
Solna Strandvag 84, 17154, Stockholm,
Sweden
Tel.: (46) 302770077
Web Site: https://www.cellnex.com
Wireless Telecommunication Services
N.A.I.C.S.: 517410

Cellnex UK Limited (1)
4th Floor 2 Blagrave Street, Reading, RG1
1AZ, Berkshire, United Kingdom
Tel.: (44) 2045268553
Emp.: 350
Wireless Telecoms Infrastructure Operator
N.A.I.C.S.: 561520

Commscon Italia, S.r.L. (1)
Via Cufra 23, 20159, Milan, Italy
Tel.: (39) 0269010026
Web Site: https://www.commscon.it
N.A.I.C.S.: 517111

**OMTEL Estructuras de Comunica-
coes S.A.** (1)
Av Fontes Pereira de Melo No 6 70 direito,
Lisbon, Portugal
Tel.: (351) 210529700
Emp.: 3,000
Wireless Telecoms Infrastructure Operator
N.A.I.C.S.: 561520

Shere Group Limited (1)
2 River Court Albert Dr Woking, London,
GU21 5RP, United Kingdom   **(100%)**
Tel.: (44) 1483 732100
Web Site: http://www.cellnextelecom.com
Railway Transportation Services
N.A.I.C.S.: 482112

Shere Masten B.V. (1)
Papendorpseweg 75-79, 3528 BJ, Utrecht,
Netherlands
Tel.: (31) 882054400
N.A.I.C.S.: 517111

Sintel S.r.L (1)
Via San Pietro 134/B, 21042, Caronno Per-
tusella, VA, Italy
Tel.: (39) 029 645 0068
Web Site: https://www.sintel-srl.it
Home & Building Automation Services
N.A.I.C.S.: 238210

Zenon Digital Radio, S.L. (1)
Lincoln 11 1-3, 08006, Barcelona, Spain
Tel.: (34) 93 193 5746
Web Site: https://www.zenonradio.com
Wireless Radio Product Distr
N.A.I.C.S.: 423690
Ramon Sanchez *(Mgr-Sls)*

CELLNOVO GROUP SA

13 rue de Londres, 75009, Paris,
France
Tel.: (33) 155319170
Web Site: http://www.cellnovo.com
CLNV—(EUR)
Mobile Application Software Publisher
N.A.I.C.S.: 513210
John Brooks *(Chm)*

CELLO ELECTRONICS (UK) LTD.

Tumbledown, Wensley, Leyburn, DL8
4HL, North Yorkshire, United King-
dom
Tel.: (44) 7931263565
Web Site:
    http://www.celloelectronics.com
Year Founded: 1996
Sales Range: $50-74.9 Million
Television Mfr
N.A.I.C.S.: 334220
Brian Palmer *(CEO)*

CELLO PRODUCTS INC.

210 Avenue Road, Cambridge, N1R
8H5, ON, Canada
Tel.: (519) 621-9150
Web Site: http://www.cello.on.ca
Year Founded: 1946
Rev.: $19,775,000
Emp.: 70
Copper Solder & Cast Brass Fittings
Mfr
N.A.I.C.S.: 332913
Harry Lee *(Founder)*

CELLO WORLD LIMITED

Cello House Corporate Avenue
Sonawala Road Sonawala Industry
Estate, Goregaon E, Mumbai,
400063, India
Tel.: (91) 7400001965
Web Site: https://www.celloworld.com
Year Founded: 1958
CELLO—(NSE)
Rev.: $110,267,554
Assets: $105,908,317
Liabilities: $85,330,545
Net Worth: $20,577,772
Earnings: $1,659,555
Emp.: 5,502
Fiscal Year-end: 03/31/23
Household Product Distr
N.A.I.C.S.: 423620

CELLSCREEN DIRECT LIM-
ITED

Suite 39-40 112 McEvoy Street, Alex-
andria, 2015, NSW, Australia
Tel.: (61) 2 9009 6606
Web Site:
    http://www.cellscreendirect.com
Sales Range: Less than $1 Million
Molecular Diagnostic Testing &
Sample Processing Services
N.A.I.C.S.: 325413
Alison Coutts *(Chm)*

CELLSEED INC.

15 F East Wing Telecom Center
Building 2-5-10 Aomi, Koto-Ku, To-
kyo, 135-0064, Japan
Tel.: (81) 352866231
Web Site: https://www.cellseed.com
Year Founded: 2001
7776—(TKS)
Rev.: $1,558,480
Assets: $13,474,560
Liabilities: $3,533,200
Net Worth: $9,941,360
Earnings: ($8,847,520)
Emp.: 50
Fiscal Year-end: 12/31/21
Novel Surface & Cell Culture Prod-
ucts Researcher, Developer & Mfr
N.A.I.C.S.: 325413
Setsuko Hashimoto *(Pres & CEO)*

CELLSOURCE CO., LTD.

Shibuya Cast 11F 12321 Shibuya,
Shibuya-Ku, Tokyo, 150-0002, Japan
Tel.: (81) 364555308
Web Site:
    https://www.cellsource.co.jp
Year Founded: 2015
4880—(TKS)
Medicinal Product Mfr
N.A.I.C.S.: 339112

Takeshi Amemiya *(CFO)*

CELLSTAR (ASIA) CORPORA-
TION LIMITED

509 510 5 Fl Block B Sing Tao Bldg,
1 Wang Kwong Rd, Kowloon, China
(Hong Kong)
Tel.: (852) 27570998   HK
Wireless Communications Products &
Solutions
N.A.I.C.S.: 334220

CELLSTAR CHILE, S.A.

Adva Pdte. Eduardo Frie, Montalva
4251, Communa de Conchali, San-
tiago, Chile
Tel.: (56) 2 550 1700   CL
Web Site: http://cl.cellstar.com
Sales Range: $1-9.9 Million
Emp.: 147
Wireless Communications Products &
Solutions
N.A.I.C.S.: 334220

CELLSTOP SYSTEMS, INC.

1166 Alberni Street Suite 1405,
Burnaby, V6E 3Z3, BC, Canada
Tel.: (604) 633-2442
Electronic Products Mfr
N.A.I.C.S.: 334419
T. M. Williams *(CEO)*

CELLTRION PHARM. INC.

82 2sandan-ro Ochang-eup,
Cheogwon-gu, Cheongju,
Chungchengbuk-do, Korea (South)
Tel.: (82) 437177000
Web Site:
    https://www.celltrionph.com
Year Founded: 1976
068760—(KRS)
Rev.: $296,092,383
Assets: $459,988,729
Liabilities: $186,333,448
Net Worth: $273,655,282
Earnings: $19,911,280
Emp.: 874
Fiscal Year-end: 12/31/22
Pharmaceutical Preparation Mfr
N.A.I.C.S.: 325412
Jung Jin Seo *(Chm)*

Subsidiaries:

Celltrion Healthcare Co., Ltd. (1)
19 Academy-ro 51beon-gil, Yeonsu-gu, In-
cheon, 406-840, Korea (South)
Tel.: (82) 32 850 6400
Web Site:
    https://www.celltrionhealthcare.com
Pharmaceuticals Product Mfr
N.A.I.C.S.: 325412
Man Hoon Kim *(Co-CEO)*

**Celltrion Pharm. Inc. - Jincheon
Factory** (1)
47-17 Banji-gil Iwol-myeon, Jincheon, 365-
823, Chungcheongbuk-do, Korea (South)
Tel.: (82) 435331611
Web Site:
Pharmaceuticals Product Mfr
N.A.I.C.S.: 325412

CELLTRION, INC.

23 Academy-ro, Yeonsu-gu, Incheon,
Korea (South)
Tel.: (82) 328505000
Web Site:
    https://www.celltrion.com-us
Year Founded: 2002
068270—(KRS)
Rev.: $1,615,450,270
Assets: $14,783,734,615
Liabilities: $2,072,161,268
Net Worth: $12,711,573,347
Earnings: $397,583,216
Emp.: 2,529
Fiscal Year-end: 12/31/23
Pharmaceutical Product Mfr & Distr
N.A.I.C.S.: 325412

Jungjin Seo *(Chm)*

Subsidiaries:

Celltrion USA, Inc. **(1)**
1 Evertrust Plz Ste 1207, Jersey City, NJ
07302
Web Site: https://www.celltrionusa.com
N.A.I.C.S.: 325412

CELLULAC LIMITED
Second Floor Unit 14 Galway Technology Park, Parkmore, Galway, Ireland
Tel.: (353) 91 766 582   IE
Web Site: http://www.cellulac.co.uk
Year Founded: 2009
Industrial Biochemical Equipment Designer & Mfr
N.A.I.C.S.: 333248
Gerard Brandon *(CEO)*

Subsidiaries:

Pursuit Marine Drive Limited **(1)**
Shackleton House Kingfisher Way, Hinchingbrooke Business Park, Huntingdon,
PE29 6HB, Cambs, United Kingdom
Tel.: (44) 1480 422 050
Web Site: http://www.pdx.biz
Industrial Biochemical Machinery Designer,
Mfr & Distr
N.A.I.C.S.: 333248

CELLULAR GMBH
Grosse Elbstrasse 39, 22767, Hamburg, Germany
Tel.: (49) 40 5071 990   De
Web Site: http://www.cellular.de
Emp.: 130
Advetising Agency
N.A.I.C.S.: 541810
Roman Kocholl *(Co-CEO)*

CELLULAR GOODS PLC
9th Floor 16 Great Queen Street,
London, WC2B 5DG,
United Kingdom   UK
Web Site: https://cellular-goods.com
Year Founded: 2018
CBX—(LSE)
Rev.: $39,244
Assets: $6,966,957
Liabilities: $378,984
Net Worth: $6,587,972
Earnings: ($8,132,684)
Emp.: 5
Fiscal Year-end: 08/31/22
Biotechnology Research & Development Services
N.A.I.C.S.: 541714
Bruna Nikolla *(CFO)*

CELLULARLINE SPA
Via Lambrakis 1/A, 42122, Reggio
Emilia, Italy
Tel.: (39) 0522334002
Web Site:
    https://www.cellularlinegroup.com
Year Founded: 1990
CELL—(ITA)
Rev.: $135,812,638
Assets: $345,368,806
Liabilities: $93,138,667
Net Worth: $252,230,138
Earnings: ($4,723,811)
Emp.: 254
Fiscal Year-end: 12/31/21
Connectivity Device Mfr & Distr
N.A.I.C.S.: 334417
Antonio Luigi Tazartes *(Chm)*

Subsidiaries:

Pegaso s.r.l. **(1)**
Via del Lavoro 14/16 ZA Est, San Bonifacio,
37047, Verona, Italy
Tel.: (39) 0457665570
Web Site: http://www.pegaso-nardi.com
Industrial Machinery Mfr
N.A.I.C.S.: 333248

Systema s.r.l. **(1)**
Viale Como 40, 20833, Giussano, MB, Italy
Tel.: (39) 036231391
Web Site: http://www.systemasrl.it
Software Development Services
N.A.I.C.S.: 541511

CELLUMED CO., LTD
Rm 402 130 Digital-ro, Geumcheon-gu, Seoul, Korea (South)
Tel.: (82) 221040475
Web Site: https://www.cellumed.co.kr
Year Founded: 1997
049180—(KRS)
Rev.: $93,639,397
Assets: $71,527,300
Liabilities: $29,243,085
Net Worth: $42,284,215
Earnings: ($4,272,902)
Emp.: 73
Fiscal Year-end: 12/31/22
Human Tissue Bank
N.A.I.C.S.: 621991
Yoo In-soo *(CEO)*

Subsidiaries:

Endotec, Inc. **(1)**
20 Vly St Ste 210, South Orange, NJ 07079
Tel.: (973) 762-6100
Web Site: http://www.endotec.com
Medical Equipment Mfr & Distr
N.A.I.C.S.: 423450
Michael J. Pappas *(Co-Founder)*

CELON PHARMA SA
Ogrodowa 2A, Kielpin, 05-092, Lomianki, Poland
Tel.: (48) 227515933
Web Site:
    https://www.celonpharma.com
Year Founded: 2002
CLN—(WAR)
Rev.: $53,681,777
Assets: $190,651,476
Liabilities: $41,286,997
Net Worth: $149,364,479
Earnings: ($3,129,363)
Emp.: 488
Fiscal Year-end: 12/31/21
Pharmaceuticals Product Mfr
N.A.I.C.S.: 325412
Jacek Glinka *(Vice Chm)*

CELOXICA HOLDINGS PLC
20 Craven Terrace, London, W2
3QH, oxon, United Kingdom
Tel.: (44) 2072622008
Web Site: http://www.celoxica.com
Year Founded: 1996
Sales Range: $10-24.9 Million
Emp.: 37
Accelerated Computing & Electronic
System-Level (ESL) Designer & Services
N.A.I.C.S.: 541512
Jean-Marc Bouhelier *(Chm & CEO)*

Subsidiaries:

Celoxica Inc. **(1)**
Ste 185 Lakeview Plaza 4516 Seton Ctr
Pkwy, Austin, TX 78759   **(100%)**
Tel.: (512) 795-8170
Electronic System Level Design Technology
N.A.I.C.S.: 513210

Celoxica Ltd **(1)**
34 Porchester Road, London, W2 6ES,
United Kingdom   **(100%)**
Tel.: (44) 2073133180
Web Site: http://www.celoxica.com
Electronic System Level Design Technology
N.A.I.C.S.: 513210

CELSA GROUP
Pol Industrial del Llobregat C/Coure
11, 08755, Castellbisbal, Barcelona,
Spain
Tel.: (34) 937730400
Web Site: http://www.celsagroup.com

Year Founded: 1967
Sales Range: $5-14.9 Billion
Emp.: 9,657
Steel Production
N.A.I.C.S.: 331110
Joan Puiggali *(Mgr)*

Subsidiaries:

Barna Steel SA
Carrer de la Ferralla 12 pol Ind San Vicente, 8755, Castellbisbal, Barcelona, Spain
Tel.: (34) 937 730 400
Steel Products Mfr
N.A.I.C.S.: 331110

CELSA Huta Ostrowiec Sp. z **(1)**
o.o.
Ul Samsonowicza 2, 27-400, Ostroweic
Swietokrzyski, Polaska, Poland
Tel.: (48) 41 249 30 00
Web Site: http://www.celsaho.com
Steel Products Mfr
N.A.I.C.S.: 331110

Celsa Armeringsstal AS **(1)**
Mo Industripark, 8626, Mo i Rana, Norway
Tel.: (47) 47703333
Web Site:
    www.celsaarmeringsstaal.com
Steel Products Mfr
N.A.I.C.S.: 331110
Hatling Frank *(Mgr-IT)*

Celsa Atlantic S.A. **(1)**
Calle Lugar de Lendos s/n, Laracha, 15145,
A Coruna, Spain
Tel.: (34) 937 730 500
Web Site: http://www.celsaatlantic.com
Steel Products Mfr
N.A.I.C.S.: 331110
Josep Cortina *(Dir-Comml)*

Celsa France S.A.S. **(1)**
Rond Point Claudius Magnin, 64340, Boucau, France
Tel.: (33) 5 59 64 41 00
Web Site: http://www.celsafrance.com
Steel Products Mfr
N.A.I.C.S.: 331110

Celsa Germany **(1)**
Barthelsmuhlring 16, 76870, Kandel, Germany
Tel.: (49) 7275 98830
Steel Products Mfr
N.A.I.C.S.: 331110

Celsa Steel (UK) Ltd. **(1)**
Building 58 Castle Works East Moors Road,
Cardiff, CF24 5NN, United Kingdom
Tel.: (44) 2920351800
Web Site: http://www.celsauk.com
Sales Range: $25-49.9 Million
Emp.: 500
Steel Mfrs
N.A.I.C.S.: 331110
Luis Sanz *(Mng Dir)*

Subsidiary (Domestic):

Express Reinforcements Ltd. **(2)**
Eaglesbush Works, Milland Road, Neath,
SA11 1NJ, United Kingdom
Tel.: (44) 1639645555
Web Site:
    http://www.expressreinforcements.co.uk
Sales Range: $25-49.9 Million
Emp.: 80
Steel Reinforcing Product Mfr
N.A.I.C.S.: 331110
Andrew Lodge *(Mng Dir)*

ROM Group Limited **(2)**
Eastern Avenue Trent Valley, Lichfield,
WS13 6RN, United Kingdom
Tel.: (44) 1543 414 111
Web Site: http://www.rom.co.uk
Sales Range: $50-74.9 Million
Reinforcements, Wire & Fencing Mfr
N.A.I.C.S.: 332618

Subsidiary (Domestic):

RFA-Tech Ltd. **(3)**
South Yorkshire Industrial Estate Whaley
Road, Barugh, Barnsley, S75 1HT, United
Kingdom
Tel.: (44) 870 011 2881
Web Site: http://www.rfa-tech.co.uk

Construction Product Mfr
N.A.I.C.S.: 332618
Kathy Wallis *(Mgr-Comml)*

Celsa Steel Service A/S **(1)**
Frodebjergvej 6, 3650, Olstykke, Denmark
Tel.: (45) 47 16 00 30
Web Site: http://www.celsa-steelservice.dk
Steel Production
N.A.I.C.S.: 331110

Celsa Steel Service AB **(1)**
Stationsgatan 55, PO Box 119, 301 04, Halmstad, Sweden
Tel.: (46) 35 154 000
Web Site: http://www.celsa-steelservice.se
Steel Products Mfr
N.A.I.C.S.: 331110
Thomas Eriksson *(Mgr-Technical Dev)*

Celsa Steel Service AS **(1)**
Vitaminveien 5b, PO Box 59, Nydalen,
0409, Oslo, Norway
Tel.: (47) 23 39 38 00
Web Site: http://www.celsa-steelservice.no
Steel Products Mfr
N.A.I.C.S.: 331110
Gunvor Holmer *(Controller)*

Celsa Steel Service Oy **(1)**
Jokitie 35, 10410, Aminnefors, Finland
Tel.: (358) 19 22131
Web Site: http://www.celsa-steelservice.fi
Steel Products Mfr
N.A.I.C.S.: 331110
Pasi Hassinen *(Production Mgr)*

Global Steel Wire, S.A. **(1)**
Poligono Industrial Nuvea Montana S/N,
39011, Santander, Cantabria, Spain
Tel.: (34) 942 200 200
Web Site: http://www.globalsteelwire.com
Steel Products Mfr
N.A.I.C.S.: 331110
Tania Malo *(Mgr-Export)*

Moreda Riviere Trefilerias, SA **(1)**
Montclar 61 Poligono Polizur, 8290, Cerdanyola del Valles, Barcelona, Spain
Tel.: (34) 935 944 400
Web Site: http://www.moreda.com
Steel Products Mfr
N.A.I.C.S.: 331110
Marc Font Zapater *(Dir-Comml)*

Nervacero, S.A. **(1)**
Barrio Ballonti S/N, Valle de Trapaga,
48510, Vizcaya, Spain
Tel.: (34) 944 939 000
Web Site: http://www.nervacero.com
Steel Products Mfr
N.A.I.C.S.: 331110

Trefilerias Quijano, S.A. **(1)**
Avd de Jose Maria Quijano s/n, 39400, Los
Corrales de Buelna, Cantabria, Spain
Tel.: (34) 942 830 000
Web Site: http://www.tquijano.com
Steel Products Mfr
N.A.I.C.S.: 331110

CELSIUS RESOURCES LIMITED
Level 5 191 St Georges Terrace,
Perth, 6000, WA, Australia
Tel.: (61) 893244516
Web Site:
    https://celsiusresources.com
CLA—(ASX)
Rev.: $432
Assets: $19,690,986
Liabilities: $712,734
Net Worth: $18,978,252
Earnings: ($1,559,426)
Fiscal Year-end: 06/30/24
Thermal Coal Mining Services
N.A.I.C.S.: 212114
William Oliver *(Chm)*

Subsidiaries:

Makilala Mining Company, Inc. **(1)**
Unit 1901 Boni Prime Building McKinley
Business Park 20th Drive, Bonifacio Global
City, Taguig, Philippines
Tel.: (63) 253104061
Web Site: https://www.makilalamining.com

Celsius Resources Limited—(Continued)

Mineral Resources Exploration & Development Services
N.A.I.C.S.: 523910

CELSYS, INC.
Pacific Marks Shinjuku 4-15-7 Nishi-Shinjuku, Shinjuku-ku, Tokyo, 160-0023, Japan
Tel.: (81) 333723156   JP
Web Site: https://www.celsys.com
Year Founded: 2012
3663—(TKS)
Rev.: $57,365,190
Assets: $60,626,590
Liabilities: $13,407,190
Net Worth: $47,219,400
Earnings: $4,438,340
Emp.: 284
Fiscal Year-end: 12/31/23
Holding Company
N.A.I.C.S.: 551112
Kei Narushima *(Vice Chm & Pres)*

Subsidiaries:

CELSYS, Inc.   **(1)**
Pacific Marks Shinjuku 4-15-7 Nishi-Shinjuku, Shinjuku-ku, Tokyo, 160-0023, Japan
Tel.: (81) 3 3372 3156
Web Site: http://www.celsys.co.jp
Sales Range: $25-49.9 Million
Emp.: 138
Software Development Services
N.A.I.C.S.: 541511
Kei Narushima *(Pres)*

Candera GmbH   **(1)**
Semmelweisstrasse 34, 4020, Linz, Austria
Tel.: (43) 73 290 3050
Web Site: https://cgistudio.at
Software Services
N.A.I.C.S.: 541511
Sandor Peterbencze *(Mgr-Quality)*

CELTIC MINERALS LTD.
172 St Germain Av, Toronto, M5M 1W1, ON, Canada
Tel.: (416) 561-1007   AB
Year Founded: 1994
Gold & Base Metal Mining Services
N.A.I.C.S.: 212220

CELTIC PHARMA LIMITED
Cumberland House, 1 Victoria Street 4th Floor, Hamilton, HM 11, Bermuda
Tel.: (441) 299 7440
Web Site:
http://www.celticpharma.com
Pharmaceutical Development Services
N.A.I.C.S.: 325412
Stephen Evans-Freke *(Mng Gen Partner)*

CELTIC PLC
Celtic Park, Glasgow, G40 3RE, Scotland, United Kingdom
Tel.: (44) 8712261888   UK
Web Site: https://www.celticfc.com
Year Founded: 1887
CCP—(LSE)
Rev.: $157,457,027
Assets: $275,644,590
Liabilities: $121,902,174
Net Worth: $153,742,416
Earnings: $16,916,077
Emp.: 1,050
Fiscal Year-end: 06/30/24
Football & Soccer Team Operator
N.A.I.C.S.: 711211
Brendan Rodgers *(Mgr-Leicester City)*

Subsidiaries:

Celtic F.C.   **(1)**
Celtic Park, Glasgow, G40 3RE, United Kingdom
Tel.: (44) 871 226 1888

Web Site: https://www.celticfc.com
Sales Range: $50-74.9 Million
Emp.: 100
Football Club & Support Services
N.A.I.C.S.: 711211

CELULOSA ARGENTINA S.A.
Av Santa Fe 1821 piso 7, C1123AAA, Buenos Aires, Argentina
Tel.: (54) 1148918500
Web Site:
https://www.celulosaargentina.com
Year Founded: 1929
Paper & Forest Product Mfr
N.A.I.C.S.: 322299
Douglas Albrecht *(Chm)*

CELYAD ONCOLOGY SA
Rue Andre Dumont 9, 1435, Mont-Saint-Guibert, Belgium
Tel.: (32) 10394100
Web Site: https://www.celyad.com
Year Founded: 2007
CLYYF—(OTCEM)
Rev.: $112,595
Assets: $17,973,211
Liabilities: $11,014,415
Net Worth: $6,958,796
Earnings: ($9,325,494)
Emp.: 12
Fiscal Year-end: 12/31/23
Stem Cell-Based Pharmaceuticals for Cardiovascular Disease
N.A.I.C.S.: 325412
Michel E. Lussier *(Founder)*

CEM INTERNATIONAL LTD.
Westmead House Westmead, Farnborough, GU14 7LP, Hampshire, United Kingdom
Tel.: (44) 1252449407   UK
Web Site: http://www.cem-international.co.uk
Business Support Services
N.A.I.C.S.: 561499

CEMACON S.A.
Calea Turzii No 178 K Floor 1, Municipiul, Cluj-Napoca, Romania
Tel.: (40) 374998848
Web Site: https://www.cemacon.ro
Year Founded: 1969
CEON—(BUC)
Rev.: $54,858,534
Assets: $149,351,554
Liabilities: $68,120,418
Net Worth: $81,231,136
Earnings: $15,607,423
Emp.: 286
Fiscal Year-end: 12/31/22
Ceramic Block Mfr
N.A.I.C.S.: 327110
Liviu Ionel Stoleru *(Chm & CEO)*

CEMAT A/S
c/o DLA Piper Denmark Law Firm P/S, Oslo Plads 2, DK-2100, Copenhagen, Denmark
Tel.: (45) 33340058
Web Site: https://www.en.cemat.dk
CEMAT—(OMX)
Rev.: $4,975,198
Assets: $38,708,966
Liabilities: $12,834,974
Net Worth: $25,873,991
Earnings: $1,678,389
Emp.: 20
Fiscal Year-end: 12/31/23
Holding Company
N.A.I.C.S.: 551112
Jaroslaw Lipinski *(CEO & Member-Mgmt Bd)*

Subsidiaries:

CeMat Real Estate S.A.   **(1)**
ul Wolczyriska 133, 01-919, Warsaw, woj mazowieckie, Poland

Tel.: (48) 225698702
Web Site: https://cematrealestate.com
Real Estate Services
N.A.I.C.S.: 531390

CEMATRIX CORPORATION
9727-40 Street SE, Calgary, T2C 2P4, AB, Canada
Tel.: (403) 219-0484   Ca
Web Site: https://www.cematrix.com
Year Founded: 1999
CVX—(TSXV)
Rev.: $17,680,310
Assets: $34,724,627
Liabilities: $10,019,442
Net Worth: $24,705,185
Earnings: ($1,517,623)
Fiscal Year-end: 12/31/21
Concrete Product Mfr & Distr
N.A.I.C.S.: 327390
Randy Boomhour *(COO)*

Subsidiaries:

CEMATRIX (Canada) Inc.   **(1)**
5440-53 Street SE, Calgary, T2C 4B6, AB, Canada
Tel.: (403) 219-0484
Emp.: 20
Concrete Products Mfr & Distr
N.A.I.C.S.: 327390
Steve Bent *(VP)*

Subsidiary (Domestic):

CEMATRIX (Calgary) Ltd.   **(2)**
5440 53 St SE, Calgary, T2C 4B6, AB, Canada
Tel.: (403) 219-0484
Web Site: http://www.cematrix.com
Emp.: 28
Construction Materials Distr
N.A.I.C.S.: 423390

Subsidiary (US):

CEMATRIX (USA) Inc.   **(2)**
28 Larkspur Ln, Bristol, IL 60512
Tel.: (630) 917-2376
Sales Range: $25-49.9 Million
Emp.: 1
Concrete Products Mfr
N.A.I.C.S.: 327390
Steve La Vallee *(Project Mgr)*

MixOnSite USA, Inc.
1501 Abbott Ct, Buffalo Grove, IL 60089
Tel.: (847) 415-9603
Web Site: https://www.mixonsite.com
Concrete Contractor Services
N.A.I.C.S.: 238110

Pacific International Grout Company   **(1)**
3850 Mustang Way, Bellingham, WA 98226
Tel.: (360) 733-5270
Web Site: https://pigcoinc.com
Concrete Construction Services
N.A.I.C.S.: 237990
Patrick Stephens *(Pres)*

CEMBRA MONEY BANK AG
Bandliweg 20, 8048, Zurich, Switzerland
Tel.: (41) 444398572   CH
Web Site: https://www.cembra.ch
Year Founded: 2009
CMBN—(SWX)
Rev.: $564,145,233
Assets: $8,484,800,443
Liabilities: $7,071,939,024
Net Worth: $1,412,861,419
Earnings: $187,694,013
Emp.: 929
Fiscal Year-end: 12/31/22
Banking, Sales Financing, Consumer Lending, Credit Card Issuing & Insurance Brokerage Services
N.A.I.C.S.: 522110
Felix A. Weber *(Chm)*

Subsidiaries:

Swissbilling AG   **(1)**

Rue du Caudray 4, 1020, Renens, Switzerland
Tel.: (41) 582261050
Web Site: https://www.swissbilling.ch
Financial Transaction Services
N.A.I.C.S.: 522320

cashgate AG   **(1)**
Bionstrasse 4, CH 9001, Saint Gallen, Switzerland
Tel.: (41) 800554433
Web Site: http://www.cashgate.ch
Credit & Leasing Services
N.A.I.C.S.: 525990

CEMBRE S.P.A.
via Serenissima 9, 25135, Brescia, Italy
Tel.: (39) 03036921   IT
Web Site: https://www.cembre.com
Year Founded: 1969
CMB—(ITA)
Rev.: $241,555,148
Assets: $268,943,449
Liabilities: $46,928,556
Net Worth: $222,014,893
Earnings: $44,062,163
Emp.: 863
Fiscal Year-end: 12/31/23
Electrical Connectors & Tools Mfr
N.A.I.C.S.: 335931
Anna Maria Onofri *(Vice Chm)*

Subsidiaries:

CEMBRE AS   **(1)**
Fossnes Senter, Stokke, 3160, Norway   **(100%)**
Tel.: (47) 33361765
Web Site: http://www.cembre.com
Sales Range: $25-49.9 Million
Emp.: 2
Electrical Connectors & Tools
N.A.I.C.S.: 335931

CEMBRE Espana SL   **(1)**
Calle Verano 6 & 8, 28850, Torrejon de Ardoz, Madrid, Spain   **(100%)**
Tel.: (34) 914852580
Sales Range: $25-49.9 Million
Emp.: 50
Electrical Connectors & Tools
N.A.I.C.S.: 335931

CEMBRE GmbH   **(1)**
Heidemannstrasse 166, 80939, Munich, Germany   **(100%)**
Tel.: (49) 893580676
Web Site: http://www.cembre.de
Sales Range: $25-49.9 Million
Emp.: 12
Electrical Connectors & Tools
N.A.I.C.S.: 335931

CEMBRE Inc.   **(1)**
                                      (100%)
Tel.: (732) 225-7415
Sales Range: $25-49.9 Million
Emp.: 30
Electrical Connectors & Tools
N.A.I.C.S.: 335931

CEMBRE Ltd.   **(1)**
Dunton Park Kingsbury Road, Curdworth, Sutton Coldfield, B76 9EB, West Midlands, United Kingdom   **(100%)**
Tel.: (44) 1675470440
Web Site: http://www.cembre.co.uk
Sales Range: $25-49.9 Million
Emp.: 100
Electrical Connectors & Tools Mfr
N.A.I.C.S.: 335931

CEMBRE Sarl   **(1)**
                                      (100%)
Tel.: (33) 160491190
Web Site: http://www.cembre.com
Sales Range: $25-49.9 Million
Emp.: 25
Electrical Connectors & Tools Mfr
N.A.I.C.S.: 335931

General Marketing srl   **(1)**
Via Gallarate 112, 20151, Milan, Italy   **(100%)**
Tel.: (39) 0233402817
Web Site: http://www.generalmarketing.it

Sales Range: $75-99.9 Million
Emp.: 350
Electrical Connectors & Tools
N.A.I.C.S.: 561499

CEMENTIR HOLDING N.V.

200 Corso Di Francia, 00191, Rome,
Italy
Tel.: (39) 06324931   **IT**
Web Site:
  https://www.cementirholding.com
Year Founded: 1947
CEM—(ITA)
Rev.: $1,875,185,625
Assets: $2,721,987,913
Liabilities: $940,385,280
Net Worth: $1,781,602,633
Earnings: $217,314,915
Emp.: 3,045
Fiscal Year-end: 12/31/22
Holding Company; Cement & Cement
Products Mfr
N.A.I.C.S.: 551112
Marco Maria Bianconi *(Chief M&A,
Integration, Corp Dev & IR Officer)*

Subsidiaries:

Aalborg Portland A/S   **(1)**
Rordalsvej 44, 9220, Aalborg,
Denmark   **(100%)**
Tel.: (45) 98167777
Web Site: https://www.aalborgportland.dk
Sales Range: $250-299.9 Million
Grey & White Cement Mfr
N.A.I.C.S.: 327120

Subsidiary (Non-US):

Aalborg White Italia Srl   **(2)**
Via del Bragozzo 11, 48100, Ravenna, Italy
Tel.: (39) 0544430319
Concrete Contractor
N.A.I.C.S.: 238110

Aalborg Portland Belgium SA   **(1)**
Noorderlaan 147 B 9, B-2030, Antwerp,
Belgium
Tel.: (32) 472864729
Web Site: https://www.aalborgportland.be
Cement Product Mfr
N.A.I.C.S.: 325520

Aalborg Portland France SAS   **(1)**
Avenue Bachelar, BP 10255, 17305,
Rochefort, Cedex, France
Tel.: (33) 671388249
Web Site: https://www.aalborgportland.fr
Cement Product Distr
N.A.I.C.S.: 423320

Aalborg Portland Holding A/S   **(1)**
Rordalsvej 44, Aalborg Ost, 9220, Aalborg,
Denmark
Tel.: (45) 98167777
Web Site:
  https://www.aalborgportlandholding.com
Cement Mfr
N.A.I.C.S.: 327310
Francesco Caltagirone Jr. *(CEO)*

Subsidiary (Non-US):

Aalborg Portland (Anqing) Co.,
Ltd.   **(2)**
Guanbing Yangqiao Town of Anqing,
Anqing, 246007, Anhui, China
Tel.: (86) 5565367733
Web Site:
  https://www.aalborgportland.com.cn
White Cement Product Mfr & Distr
N.A.I.C.S.: 325520

Aalborg Portland Malaysia Sdn
Bhd   **(2)**
Lot 75244 Pinji Estate, PO Box 428, 30750,
Ipoh, Perak, Malaysia
Tel.: (60) 387033000
Web Site:
  https://www.aalborgportland.com.my
White Cement Mfr & Distr
N.A.I.C.S.: 325520

Compagnie des Ciments Belges
SA   **(2)**
Grand'Route 260, Gaurain-Ramecroix,
7530, Tournai, Belgium

Tel.: (32) 69252511
Web Site: http://www.ccb.be
Emp.: 400
Cement Product Distr
N.A.I.C.S.: 423320
Eddy Fostier *(Gen Mgr)*

Sinai White Portland Cement Co.
SAE   **(2)**
604 A El Safa Street, New Maadi, Cairo,
Egypt
Tel.: (20) 227542760
Web Site:
  https://www.sinaiwhitecement.com
Cement Product Mfr & Distr
N.A.I.C.S.: 325520

Aalborg Portland Islandi EHF   **(1)**
Baejarlind 4, 201, Kopavogur, Iceland
Tel.: (354) 5454800
Web Site: https://www.aalborgportland.is
Cement Product Distr
N.A.I.C.S.: 423320
Magnus Eyjolfsson *(Mng Dir)*

Aalborg Portland OOO   **(1)**
Street Vorovskogo House 18A Premise 317,
Kingisepp District, Kingisepp, 188480, Len-
ingrad, Russia
Tel.: (7) 8123467414
Web Site: https://www.aalborgportland.ru
Cement Product Distr
N.A.I.C.S.: 423320

Aalborg Portland Polska Sp.z.o.o   **(1)**
Ul Targowa 24, 03-733, Warsaw, Poland
Tel.: (48) 224608870
Web Site: https://www.aalborgportland.pl
White Cement Product Distr
N.A.I.C.S.: 423320

Aalborg Portland US Inc.   **(1)**
PO Box 492, Whitehouse, NJ 08888
Tel.: (908) 534-4021
Cement Product Distr
N.A.I.C.S.: 423320
Michael Grapsy *(CEO)*

Subsidiary (Domestic):

Aalborg Cement Company Inc.   **(2)**
PO Box 678, Somerville, NJ 08876
Tel.: (908) 534-4021
Cement Product Distr
N.A.I.C.S.: 423320
Alex Narcise *(Mng Dir)*

Vianini Pipe Inc.   **(2)**
81 County Line Rd, Branchburg, NJ 08876
Tel.: (908) 534-4021
Web Site: https://www.vianinipipe.com
Concrete Pipe Mfr & Distr
N.A.I.C.S.: 327332
Michael Grapsy *(CEO)*

Cementir Delta S.p.A.   **(1)**
Corso Di Francia 200, Rome, Italy
Tel.: (39) 0636308082
Web Site: http://www.cementirholding.it
New Single-Family Housing Construction
N.A.I.C.S.: 236115

Cimbeton Hazirbeton ve Prefabrik
Yapi Elemanlari Sanayi ve Ticaret
A.S.   **(1)**
Egemenlik Mah Isik Cad No 5 Isikkent Bor-
nova, Izmir, Turkiye
Tel.: (90) 2324720172
Web Site: https://www.cimbeton.com
Rev.: $37,297,599
Assets: $17,086,231
Liabilities: $14,994,996
Net Worth: $2,091,235
Earnings: $1,074,545
Fiscal Year-end: 12/31/2022
Concrete Products Mfr
N.A.I.C.S.: 327390
Walter Montevecchi *(Chm)*

Kars Cimento AS   **(1)**
Merkez Bozkale Koyu Mevkii, 36210, Kars,
Turkiye
Tel.: (90) 4742426230
Cement Product Mfr & Distr
N.A.I.C.S.: 325520

Kudsk & Dahl A/S   **(1)**
Vojensvej 7, 6500, Vojens, Denmark
Tel.: (45) 70707292
Web Site: https://www.kudsk-dahl.dk
Sand & Gravel Production Services

N.A.I.C.S.: 212321

Lehigh White Cement Company   **(1)**
7660 Imperial Way, Allentown, PA
18195   **(63.25%)**
Tel.: (610) 366-4600
Web Site:
  http://www.lehighwhitecement.com
Cement Mfr & Distr
N.A.I.C.S.: 327310
Larry Rowland *(Mgr-Mktg & Technical Svcs)*

Plant (Domestic):

Lehigh White Cement Company -
Waco Plant   **(2)**
100 S Wickson Rd, Waco, TX 76702-2576
Tel.: (254) 772-9350
Web Site:
  http://www.lehighwhitecement.com
White Cement Mfr
N.A.I.C.S.: 327310
Tom Del Vecchio *(Plant Mgr)*

Neales Waste Management Ltd.   **(1)**
501 Green Place Walton Summit Centre,
Bamber Bridge, Preston, PR5 8AY, United
Kingdom
Tel.: (44) 1254506302
Web Site: http://www.neales-waste.co.uk
Hazardous Waste Services
N.A.I.C.S.: 562211

Skane Grus AB   **(1)**
Norra Rorum Bergtakt, 243 92, Hoor, Swe-
den
Tel.: (46) 205709
Web Site: https://www.skanegrus.se
Quarry Services
N.A.I.C.S.: 212321

Unicon A/S   **(1)**
Tel.: (45) 70100590
Web Site: https://www.unicon.dk
Sales Range: $100-124.9 Million
Produces & Markets Ready-Mix Concrete,
Precast Concrete Products & Related Ser-
vices in Denmark, Sweden, USA, Spain &
Portugal
N.A.I.C.S.: 327332

CEMENTO POLPAICO S.A.

Av El Bosque Norte 0177 Casilla 223
Correo 35, Las Condes, Santiago,
Chile
Tel.: (56) 2600 6206200
Web Site: http://www.polpaico.cl
Year Founded: 1948
Cement & Construction Products &
Services
N.A.I.C.S.: 327332

Subsidiaries:

Cemento Polpaico S.A. - Mejillones
Grinding Plant   **(1)**
Av Longitudinal 2500, Mejillones, Chile
Tel.: (56) 55622420
Web Site: http://www.polpaico.cl
Construction Materials Whslr
N.A.I.C.S.: 423320

Compania Minera Polpaico Ltd.   **(1)**
Av El Bosque Norte 177, Piso 5 Las Con-
des, Santiago, Chile
Tel.: (56) 23376300
Web Site: http://www.polpaico.cl
Construction Materials Whslr
N.A.I.C.S.: 423320

CEMENTOS BIO-BIO S.A.

Avenida Gran Bretana 1725, PO Box
93-C, Santiago, Chile
Tel.: (56) 412546000   **CL**
Web Site: http://www.cementos.cl
CEMENTOS—(SGO)
Sales Range: Less than $1 Million
Cement Mfr
N.A.I.C.S.: 327310
Juan Hernan Briones Goich *(Chm &
Pres)*

CEMENTOS MOLINS S.A.

CN-340 no 2 al 38 Km 1242 3 Sant
Vicenc dels Horts, 8620, Barcelona,
Spain

Tel.: (34) 936806000
Web Site: https://www.cemolins.es
Year Founded: 1928
CMO—(BAR)
Rev.: $1,048,303,994
Assets: $2,074,924,861
Liabilities: $777,050,236
Net Worth: $1,297,874,625
Earnings: $162,516,101
Emp.: 6,266
Fiscal Year-end: 12/31/23
Cement Supplier & Mfr
N.A.I.C.S.: 327310
Juan Molins Amat *(Pres)*

Subsidiaries:

CEMENTOS ARTIGAS S.A   **(1)**
Maria Orticochea 4707, PO Box 112,
12900, Montevideo, Uruguay
Tel.: (598) 23092810
Web Site: http://www.cemartigas.com.uy
Cement Mfr & Distr
N.A.I.C.S.: 327310

Cementos Avellaneda S.A.   **(1)**
Defensa 113 6 piso 6, Buenos Aires,
C1065AAA, Argentina
Tel.: (54) 11 4331 7081
Cement & Concrete Mfr
N.A.I.C.S.: 327310

Cementos Molins Industrial, S.A.   **(1)**
Ctra N-340 Km 1 242 300, PO Box 40,
Sant Vicenc dels Horts, 08620, Barcelona,
Spain
Tel.: (34) 936806030
Web Site: http://www.cmi.cemolins.es
Cement Mfr & Distr
N.A.I.C.S.: 327310

Itacamba Cemento S.A.   **(1)**
Calle Bernardo Cadario 3060 Sobode Build-
ing second floor, Santa Cruz, Bolivia
Tel.: (591) 33481007
Web Site: http://www.itacamba.com
Cement Mfr
N.A.I.C.S.: 327310

Portcemen S.A.   **(1)**
Lugar Moll Contradic 1 Nave, Barcelona,
08039, Spain
Tel.: (34) 934430514
Building Materials Whslr
N.A.I.C.S.: 423320

Prefabricaciones y Contratas,
S.A.U.   **(1)**
Espronceda 38 Local 3, 28003, Madrid,
Spain
Tel.: (34) 913430348
Web Site: http://www.preconsa.es
Concrete Mfr
N.A.I.C.S.: 327390

Promotora Mediterranea-2, S.A.   **(1)**
CN- 340 n 2 al 38 Km 1242 3, Sant Vicenc
dels Horts, 08620, Barcelona, Spain
Tel.: (34) 936806000
Web Site: http://www.promsa.com
Emp.: 200
Concrete Mfr
N.A.I.C.S.: 327390

Promsa   **(1)**
CN- 340 n 2 al 38 Km 1242 3, Santo Vin-
cenco dels Horts, 08620, Barcelona, Spain
Tel.: (34) 936806000
Web Site: http://www.promsa.com
Sales Range: $450-499.9 Million
Emp.: 2,000
Concrete Distributor & Mfr
N.A.I.C.S.: 327310

Propamsa, S.A.U.   **(1)**
C/ Ciments Molins s/n Pol Ind Les Fallulles,
Santo Vincenco dels Horts, 08620, Barce-
lona, Spain
Tel.: (34) 936806040
Web Site: http://www.propamsa.es
Glue Mfr
N.A.I.C.S.: 325520

Societe Tuniso-Andalouse de Ciment
Blanc   **(1)**
Immeuble Alyssa Rue Du Lac Tanganica,
Les Berges du Lac, 1053, Tunis, Tunisia
Tel.: (216) 70020880
Web Site: http://www.sotacib.com

Cementos Molins S.A.—(Continued)

Cement Mfr
N.A.I.C.S.: 327310

Surma Holdings B.V. **(1)**
Strawinskylaan 3127 8e verdiepin, 1077ZX,
Amsterdam, Netherlands **(50%)**
Tel.: (31) 88 560 9950
Holding Company
N.A.I.C.S.: 551112

Holding (Non-US):

**LafargeHolcim Bangladesh
Limited** **(2)**
NinaKabbo Level 7 227/A Bir Uttam Mir
Shawkat Sarak, Tejgaon, Dhaka, 1208,
Bangladesh
Tel.: (880) 222281002
Web Site: https://www.lafargeholcim.com.bd
Rev.: $238,199,527
Assets: $343,615,954
Liabilities: $114,007,572
Net Worth: $229,608,382
Earnings: $45,029,379
Emp.: 70,000
Fiscal Year-end: 12/31/2021
Holding Company; Cement Mfr
N.A.I.C.S.: 551112
Narayan Prasad Sharma *(Dir-Ops-LUMPL)*

CEMENTOS PACASMAYO S.A.A.

Calle La Colonia 150 Urbanizacion El
Vivero Surco, Lima, Peru
Tel.: (51) 13176000 **Pe**
Web Site:
  https://www.cementos.com.pe
CPAC—(NYSE)
Rev.: $2,115,746,000
Assets: $3,314,161,000
Liabilities: $2,119,026,000
Net Worth: $1,195,135,000
Earnings: $176,828,000
Emp.: 1,713
Fiscal Year-end: 12/31/22
Cement, Lime & Concrete Mfr & Distr
N.A.I.C.S.: 327310
Eduardo Hochschild Beeck *(Chm)*

Subsidiaries:

Suzorite Mica Products, Inc. **(1)**
1475 Graham Bell St, Boucherville, J4B
6A1, QC, Canada **(100%)**
Tel.: (450) 655-2450
Sales Range: $1-9.9 Million
Emp.: 29
Supplier of Phlogopite Mica
N.A.I.C.S.: 212390

CEMEPE INVESTIMENTOS S.A.

Praca Tiradentes 10 Sala 304 Parte
Centro, Rio de Janeiro, 20060-070,
Brazil
Tel.: (55) 2132066000 **BR**
Web Site:
  https://www.cemepe.com.br
Year Founded: 1991
MAPT3—(BRAZ)
Sales Range: Less than $1 Million
Financial Services
N.A.I.C.S.: 541611
Flavio Jardim Vargas *(Dir-Investor
Relations)*

CEMEX, S.A.B. DE C.V.

Av Ricardo Margain Zozaya 32, San
Pedro, 66265, Garza Garcia, Nuevo
Leon, Mexico
Tel.: (52) 88884327 **MX**
Web Site: https://www.cemex.com
Year Founded: 1906
CX—(NYSE)
Rev.: $17,388,000,000
Assets: $28,433,000,000
Liabilities: $16,317,000,000
Net Worth: $12,116,000,000
Earnings: $182,000,000
Emp.: 46,000

Fiscal Year-end: 12/31/23
Cement Mfr
N.A.I.C.S.: 551112
Fernando Angel Gonzalez Olivieri
(CEO)

Subsidiaries:

APO Cement Corporation **(1)**
Barangay Tina an, City of Naga, Cebu,
3242, Philippines
Tel.: (63) 24893300
Cement Mfr
N.A.I.C.S.: 327310

CEMEX AB **(1)**
Jorgen Kocksgatan 4, 211 20, Malmo, Swe-
den
Tel.: (46) 40317550
Web Site: http://www.cemex.se
Concrete Distr
N.A.I.C.S.: 423320

CEMEX AS **(1)**
Meierisvingen 2 C, 1383, Asker, Norway
Tel.: (47) 22 92 43 70
Web Site: http://www.cemex.no
Cement Mfr & Distr
N.A.I.C.S.: 327310

CEMEX Asia Holdings Ltd. **(1)**
Tel.: (65) 63338010
Web Site: http://www.cemex.com
Sales Range: $50-74.9 Million
Emp.: 20
Holding Company
N.A.I.C.S.: 551112

Subsidiary (Non-US):

Solid Cement Corp. **(2)**
Tel.: (63) 28493585
Cement Mfr
N.A.I.C.S.: 327310

**CEMEX Asian Southeast
Corporation** **(1)**
34th Floor Petron Mega Plaza Building, 358
Sen Gil J Puyat Avenue, Makati City, Philip-
pines
Tel.: (63) 288493600
Investment Services
N.A.I.C.S.: 523999

Subsidiary (Domestic):

Cemex Holdings Philippines, Inc. **(2)**
8th Floor Petron Mega Plaza 358 Senator
Gil J Puyat Avenue, Makati, 1200, Metro
Manila, Philippines **(89.86%)**
Tel.: (63) 288493600
Web Site:
  https://www.cemexholdingphilippines.com
Rev.: $310,826,993
Assets: $1,208,853,897
Liabilities: $455,038,765
Net Worth: $753,815,132
Earnings: ($36,347,476)
Fiscal Year-end: 12/31/2022
Cement Product Mfr & Distr
N.A.I.C.S.: 327310
Ignacio Alejandro Mijares Elizondo *(Pres &
CEO)*

CEMEX Brazil **(1)**
Rua Desembargador Cesar Do Rego No 2
Colonia Antonio Aleixo, Manaus, Brazil
Tel.: (55) 9221255150
Cement Mfr
N.A.I.C.S.: 327310

Subsidiary (Domestic):

**Cimentos Vencemos do Amazonas,
Ltda.** **(2)**
Rua des Cezar do Rego 2, Manaus, 69083-
200, Brazil
Tel.: (55) 9221255150
Cement Mfr
N.A.I.C.S.: 327310

CEMEX Colombia, S.A. **(1)**
calle 99 No 9A-54 piso 8, Bogota,
Colombia **(98%)**
Tel.: (57) 16039000
Web Site: https://www.cemexcolombia.com
Sales Range: $200-249.9 Million
Emp.: 950
Cement Mfr
N.A.I.C.S.: 327310

CEMEX Costa Rica S.A. **(1)**
 (98%)
Tel.: (506) 22012000
Web Site: http://www.cemexcostarica.com
Sales Range: $50-74.9 Million
Emp.: 220
Cement Mfr
N.A.I.C.S.: 327310

Subsidiary (Non-US):

CEMEX Nicaragua, S.A. **(2)**
Tel.: (505) 22558918
Web Site: https://www.cemexnicaragua.com
Building Materials Mfr
N.A.I.C.S.: 327120

CEMEX Czech Republic k.s. **(1)**
Laurinova 2800/4, 155 00, Prague, 5, Stod-
ulky, Czech Republic
Tel.: (420) 800111212
Web Site: https://www.cemex.cz
Emp.: 1,000
Readymix Concrete Mfr
N.A.I.C.S.: 327320

CEMEX Deutschland AG **(1)**
Theodorstrasse 178, 40472, Dusseldorf,
Germany
Tel.: (49) 21144700
Web Site: http://www.cemex.de
Holding Company, Building Materials
N.A.I.C.S.: 551112

CEMEX Dominicana, S.A. **(1)**
Av Winston Churchill 67 Torre Acropolis
Piso 20, Ensanche Piantini, Santo Do-
mingo, Dominican Republic
Tel.: (809) 6834901
Web Site:
  https://www.cemexdominicana.com
Sales Range: $125-149.9 Million
Emp.: 457
Cement Mfr
N.A.I.C.S.: 327310

CEMEX Egypt **(1)**
3 Abbas El Akkad Street Nasr City, Cairo,
Egypt
Tel.: (20) 22407 8600
Web Site: http://www.cemex.com.eg
Cement & Concrete Mfr
N.A.I.C.S.: 327310

Subsidiary (Domestic):

Assiut Cement Company **(2)**
334 South 90th Stree, Assiut, Cairo,
Egypt **(96%)**
Tel.: (20) 224078600
Cement Mfr
N.A.I.C.S.: 327310

CEMEX Espana S.A. **(1)**
Hernandez de Tejada 1, 28027, Madrid,
Spain **(99.88%)**
Tel.: (34) 913779200
Web Site: https://www.cemex.es
Sales Range: $1-4.9 Billion
Emp.: 200
Cement Mfr
N.A.I.C.S.: 327310

Subsidiary (Non-US):

CEMEX Jamaica Limited **(2)**
Sir Florizel Glasspole Hwy, PO Box 448,
Rockfort, Kingston, West Indies, Jamaica
Tel.: (876) 8769286231
Industrial Product Distr
N.A.I.C.S.: 423840

Plant (Domestic):

**Cemex Espana S.A. - Gador
Plant** **(2)**
Paraje Venta de Araoz s/n, Gador, Almeria,
04560, Spain
Tel.: (34) 950 31 00 11
Web Site: http://www.cemex.es
Cement Mfr
N.A.I.C.S.: 327310

Subsidiary (Non-US):

Cemex Haiti S.A. **(2)**
Delmas 48, 6110, Port-au-Prince, HT-6110,
Haiti
Tel.: (509) 29409930
Industrial Product Distr
N.A.I.C.S.: 423840

Cemex Latam Holdings SA **(2)**
Calle 99 No 9A-54 Piso 8, Bogota,
Colombia **(73.17%)**
Tel.: (57) 16039051
Web Site: http://www.cemexlatam.com
Rev.: $4,486,800
Assets: $7,336,851
Liabilities: $4,210,439
Net Worth: $3,126,413
Earnings: $51,350
Fiscal Year-end: 12/31/2023
Building Materials Distr
N.A.I.C.S.: 444180
Jesus Gonzalez *(CEO)*

Subsidiary (Non-US):

Cemento Bayano, S.A. **(3)**
Plaza Credicorp Bank Panama Floor 28
Calle 50 between c/59 and 60, N/A 7262
Bella Vista, Panama, Panama
Tel.: (507) 2788700
Building Materials Mfr
N.A.I.C.S.: 327120
Holding Company

CEMEX France S.A. **(1)**
7 rue des Solets Parc Icade, Silic 423,
94150, Rungis, Cedex, France
Tel.: (33) 1497944
Web Site: https://www.cemex.fr
Sales Range: $450-499.9 Million
Emp.: 2,100
Production, Distribution, Marketing & Sale
of Cement, Ready-Mix Concrete, Aggre-
gates & Clinker
N.A.I.C.S.: 327310

Subsidiary (Domestic):

CEMEX France Gestion (S.A.S.) **(2)**
2 Rue du Verseau SILIC 423, Rungis,
94583, Ile-de-France, France
Tel.: (33) 149794444
Web Site: http://www.cemex.fr
Concrete Product Mfr & Distr
N.A.I.C.S.: 327390

CEMEX Guatemala **(1)**
12 Calle 2-25 Zone 10 AVIA Building Level
16 Office 1601 Zone 10, Guatemala, Guatemala
Tel.: (502) 22045600
Web Site:
  https://www.cemexguatemala.com
Cement Mfr
N.A.I.C.S.: 327310

CEMEX Holdings (Israel) Limited **(1)**
155 Bialik, Ramat Gan, 52523, Israel
Tel.: (972) 3 7519464
Investment Management Service
N.A.I.C.S.: 523940

Subsidiary (Domestic):

**Readymix Industries (Israel)
Limited** **(2)**
155 Bialik Street, Ramat Gan, 5252346,
Israel
Tel.: (972) 37519464
Sales Range: $50-74.9 Million
Emp.: 110
Readymix Concrete Mfr
N.A.I.C.S.: 327320
Gil Lidge *(CEO-Concrete Div)*

Division (Domestic):

Concrete Industry Div **(3)**
155 Bialik St, Ramat Gan, 5252346, Israel
Tel.: (972) 37519464
Readymix Concrete Mfr
N.A.I.C.S.: 327320

Subsidiary (Domestic):

Lime & Stone Production Co Ltd **(3)**
155 Bialik Street, Ramat Gan, Israel
Tel.: (972) 37554777
Web Site: http://www.readymix.co.il
Concrete Block Mfr
N.A.I.C.S.: 327331

**Readymix Concrete Products (Israel)
Ltd** **(3)**
Ad Halom Industrial Zone, Ashdod, Israel
Tel.: (972) 88548888
Web Site: http://www.readymix.co.il
Concrete Pipe Mfr
N.A.I.C.S.: 327332
Erez Avieli *(CEO)*

CEMEX Hrvatska d.d. **(1)**
Cesta dr Franje Tudmana 45, 21212, Kastel
Sucurac, Croatia
Tel.: (385) 21201111
Web Site: https://www.cemex.hr
Concrete Products Mfr
N.A.I.C.S.: 327390

CEMEX Innovation Holding Ltd. **(1)**
Romerstrasse 13, Brugg, 2555, Bern, Swit-
zerland
Tel.: (41) 323667800
Industry Product Distr
N.A.I.C.S.: 423830

CEMEX Mexico, S.A. de C.V. **(1)**
Av Ricardo Margain Zozaya 325, Garza
Garcia, 66225, Nuevo Leon, Mexico
Tel.: (52) 81 8888 8888
Web Site: http://www.cemex.com
Cement & Ready Mix Concrete Mfr
N.A.I.C.S.: 327310

CEMEX Netherlands B.V. **(1)**
Tel.: (31) 206424288
Cement & Ready Mix Concrete Mfr
N.A.I.C.S.: 327310

Subsidiary (Non-US):

New Sunward Holding B.V. **(2)**
Tel.: (31) 206422048
Investment Management Service
N.A.I.C.S.: 523940

**New Sunward Holding Financial Ven-
tures B.V.** **(2)**
Tel.: (31) 206422048
Investment Management Service
N.A.I.C.S.: 523940

CEMEX Oy **(1)**
Fiskarsinkatu 7 A 2 Kerros, 20750, Turku,
Finland
Tel.: (358) 207121434
Web Site: http://www.cemexfinland.fi
Cement Distr
N.A.I.C.S.: 423320

CEMEX Polska Sp.z.o.o. **(1)**
ul Krakowiakow 46, 02-255, Warsaw, Ma-
zovia, Poland
Tel.: (48) 225714100
Web Site: https://www.cemex.pl
Sales Range: $75-99.9 Million
Emp.: 130
Cement Mfr
N.A.I.C.S.: 327310

CEMEX SIA **(1)**
Lielirbes liela 17a - 28, Riga, 1046, Latvia
Tel.: (371) 67033400
Web Site: http://www.cemex.lv
Emp.: 300
Cement & Concrete Product Mfr
N.A.I.C.S.: 327310

CEMEX UK **(1)**
CEMEX House Coldharbour Lane, Egham,
TW20 8TD, Surrey, United Kingdom
Tel.: (44) 1932568833
Web Site: http://www.cemex.co.uk
Rev.: $7,293,579,776
Emp.: 350
Materials & Services to the Construction
Industry & Maintenance of the Environment;
Cement Mfr
N.A.I.C.S.: 327310

Subsidiary (Domestic):

**CEMEX Paving Solutions
Limited** **(2)**
Cemex House Savile Street, Sheffield, S4
7UL, United Kingdom
Web Site: http://www.cemex.co.uk
Sales Range: $50-74.9 Million
Emp.: 240
Cement Mfr & Road Surfacing Services
N.A.I.C.S.: 488490

CEMEX Specialist Products **(2)**
Waldorf Way Denby Dale Rd, Wakefield,
WF2 8DH, W Yorkshire, United Kingdom
Tel.: (44) 924362081
Web Site: http://www.thermabate.co.uk
Sales Range: $25-49.9 Million
Emp.: 20
Foam Products Mfr
N.A.I.C.S.: 326140

CEMEX UK Marine Ltd. **(2)**
Baltic Wharf Elm St Marine Parade, South-
ampton, SO14 5JF, Hamps, United King-
dom
Tel.: (44) 2380720200
Web Site: http://www.cemex.co.uk
Sales Range: $25-49.9 Million
Emp.: 25
Freight Transportation Services
N.A.I.C.S.: 483113

CEMEX UK Materials Limited **(2)**
CEMEX House Binley Business Park Harry
Weston Road, Coventry, CV3 2TY, Warcs,
United Kingdom
Tel.: (44) 1788542111
Sales Range: $125-149.9 Million
Emp.: 260
Holding Company
N.A.I.C.S.: 551112

Subsidiary (Domestic):

**CEMEX Ready Mixed Concrete (East
Midlands) Ltd.** **(3)**
RMC House Long Ln, Attenborough, Not-
tingham, NG9 6BL, Notts, United Kingdom
Tel.: (44) 59220660
Sales Range: $25-49.9 Million
Emp.: 50
Readymix Concrete Mfr
N.A.I.C.S.: 327320

Subsidiary (Domestic):

Chesterfield Macadam **(2)**
49 Birmington Rd N, Chesterfield, S41 9BE,
Derbys, United Kingdom
Tel.: (44) 246261400
Sales Range: $25-49.9 Million
Emp.: 4
Supplier of Coated Stone
N.A.I.C.S.: 327991

Subsidiary (Non-US):

Island Aggregates Limited **(2)**
Island House Isle of Man Business Park,
Douglas, IM2 2QZ, Isle of Man
Tel.: (44) 1624651965
Web Site:
https://www.islandaggregates.com
Sales Range: $50-74.9 Million
Emp.: 60
Sand, Gravel & Ready-Mixed Concrete
N.A.I.C.S.: 212321
Mike Shaw *(Mng Dir)*

Subsidiary (Domestic):

Nottingham Coated Stone **(2)**
Private Rd 4 Colwick Industrial Estate,
Netherfield, NG4 2JT, Nottinghamshire,
United Kingdom
Tel.: (44) 1159400171
Web Site: http://www.cemex.com
Sales Range: $50-74.9 Million
Emp.: 4
Suppliers of Coated Stone
N.A.I.C.S.: 212319

Sheffield Coated Stone **(2)**
Woodside Depot Rutland Street, Attercliffe,
Sheffield, S3 9PA, S Yorkshire, United King-
dom
Tel.: (44) 1143273393
Web Site:
https://www.sheffieldcoatedstone.co.uk
Sales Range: $50-74.9 Million
Emp.: 6
Suppliers of Coated Stone
N.A.I.C.S.: 212319

CEMEX de Puerto Rico Inc. **(1)**
12 Amelia St, Guaynabo, PR
00968 **(100%)**
Tel.: (787) 783-3000
Web Site: https://www.cemexpuertorico.com
Cement, Concrete & Other Construction
Materials Mfr
N.A.I.C.S.: 327310

Division (Domestic):

**CEMEX de Puerto Rico Inc. - Lime
Division** **(2)**
State Rd 123 Km 8, Ponce, PR 00731
Tel.: (787) 842-3000
Web Site: http://www.cemexpuertorico.com

Sales Range: $1-9.9 Million
Emp.: 37
Hydrated Lime Mfr
N.A.I.C.S.: 327410

Subsidiary (Domestic):

**Desarrollos Multiples Insulares,
Inc.** **(2)**
PO Box 364487, San Juan, PR
00936 **(100%)**
Tel.: (787) 783-3000
Web Site: http://www.prcements.com
Rev.: $119,634
Emp.: 2
Real Estate Sales
N.A.I.C.S.: 531210

Ready Mix Concrete, Inc. **(2)**
PO Box 364487, San Juan, PR
00936-4487 **(100%)**
Tel.: (787) 783-3000
Web Site: http://www.cemexpuertorico.com
Pre-Mixed Concrete Production
N.A.I.C.S.: 327320

CEMEX el Salvador S.A. de C.V. **(1)**
Avenida Albert Einstein Edificio Constru-
mark 3 nivel No 4 Antiguo, Cuscatlan, San
Salvador, El Salvador
Tel.: (503) 25298300
Cement Mfr
N.A.I.C.S.: 327310

CEMEX, Inc. **(1)**
10100 Katy Fwy Ste 300, Houston, TX
77043
Tel.: (713) 650-6200
Sales Range: $1-4.9 Billion
Emp.: 4,100
Cement, Concrete Products, Construction
Aggregates & Specialty Minerals Mfr
N.A.I.C.S.: 327320
Francisco Aguilera Mendoza *(VP-Trading-
Americas)*

Subsidiary (Domestic):

American Transit Mix Cemex **(2)**
2638 Nathan Ave, Modesto, CA 95354-4025
Tel.: (209) 529-4115
Rev.: $140,000,000
Emp.: 330
Readymix Concrete Mfr
N.A.I.C.S.: 327320

Unit (Domestic):

CEMEX Canada **(2)**
3990 E Concourse St Ste 200, Ontario, CA
91764-5456
Tel.: (909) 974-5500
Web Site: http://www.cemexusa.com
Rev.: $90,000,000
Emp.: 500
Mfr of Ready-Mixed Concrete
N.A.I.C.S.: 327332

CEMEX Concrete Products **(2)**
929 Gessner Rd Ste 2100, Houston, TX
77024
Tel.: (713) 650-6200
Web Site: http://www.cemexusa.com
Sales Range: $25-49.9 Million
Emp.: 100
Concrete Products
N.A.I.C.S.: 327331

Subsidiary (Domestic):

**CEMEX Construction Materials
Florida, LLC** **(2)**
1501 Belvedere Rd, West Palm Beach, FL
33406-1501
Tel.: (561) 833-5555
Web Site: http://www.cemexusa.com
Sales Range: $1-4.9 Billion
Concrete Block, Pipe, Aggregate, Ready
Mixed Concrete & Cement Mfr
N.A.I.C.S.: 327331

Subsidiary (Domestic):

Steel Construction Systems **(3)**
11250 Astronaut Blvd, Orlando, FL
32837-9204 **(55%)**
Tel.: (407) 438-1664
Web Site: https://www.steelconsystems.com
Sales Range: $10-24.9 Million
Emp.: 40
Metal Building Components Mfr

N.A.I.C.S.: 332311

Subsidiary (Domestic):

CEMEX Corp. **(2)**
10100 Katy Fwy Ste 300, Houston, TX
77043
Tel.: (713) 650-6200
Web Site: http://www.cemexusa.com
Emp.: 150
Cement Mfr & Distr
N.A.I.C.S.: 327310

CEMEX Materials LLC **(2)**
1501 Belvedere Rd, West Palm Beach, FL
33406-1501
Tel.: (561) 833-5555
Web Site: http://www.cemex.com
Emp.: 200
Concrete Products Mfr
N.A.I.C.S.: 327331

Unit (Domestic):

CEMEX, Inc. - Lakeland **(2)**
PO Box 3858, Lakeland, FL 33802
Tel.: (863) 688-5787
Sales Range: $200-249.9 Million
Emp.: 700
Readymix Concrete Mfr
N.A.I.C.S.: 327320

**CEMEX, Inc. - McKellington
Canyon** **(2)**
1 McKelligon Canyon Rd, El Paso, TX
79930
Tel.: (915) 565-4681
Web Site: http://www.cemexusa.com
Sales Range: $125-149.9 Million
Emp.: 500
Readymix Concrete Mfr
N.A.I.C.S.: 327320

CEMEX, Inc. - Mesa **(2)**
4646 E Van Buren Ste 250, Mesa, AZ
85008
Tel.: (602) 416-2600
Sales Range: $25-49.9 Million
Emp.: 90
Readymix Concrete Mfr
N.A.I.C.S.: 327320

CEMEX, Inc. - Naples **(2)**
1425 E Wiggins Pass Rd, Naples, FL 34110
Tel.: (239) 597-3162
Web Site: http://www.cemex.com
Sales Range: $25-49.9 Million
Emp.: 60
Readymix Concrete Mfr
N.A.I.C.S.: 327320

**Ready Mix USA - East
Tennessee** **(2)**
2209 W Blount Ave, Knoxville, TN 37920-
1956
Tel.: (865) 573-4501
Concrete & Limestone Mfr
N.A.I.C.S.: 212312

**Rinker Materials-Concrete Pipe &
Stormwater Treatment** **(2)**
800 Industrial Dr, Middletown, DE 19709
Tel.: (302) 378-8920
Web Site: https://www.rinkerpipe.com
Sales Range: $25-49.9 Million
Emp.: 50
Concrete Block & Brick Mfr
N.A.I.C.S.: 327332

**Rinker Materials-Environmental
Services** **(2)**
1200 NW 137th Ave, Miami, FL 33182-1803
Tel.: (305) 790-6648
Web Site: http://www.cemexusa.com
Sales Range: $25-49.9 Million
Emp.: 100
Non-Clay Refractories & Hydraulic Cement
Mfr
N.A.I.C.S.: 327331

Rinker Materials-Harrisburg **(2)**
5601 Pharr Mill Rd, Harrisburg, NC 28075-
7597
Tel.: (704) 455-1100
Web Site: http://www.rinkerpipe.com
Sales Range: $25-49.9 Million
Emp.: 30
Concrete Products Mfr
N.A.I.C.S.: 327332

Rinker Materials-Twin Mountain **(2)**

CEMEX, S.A.B. de C.V.—(Continued)

3700 Hwy 528, Bernalillo, NM 87004-6600
Tel.: (505) 867-2394
Web Site: http://www.rinkerpipe.com
Sales Range: $50-74.9 Million
Emp.: 30
Crushed & Broken Granite Mfr
N.A.I.C.S.: 212313

Cemex Falcon LLC   (1)
Jebel Ali Industrial Area, PO Box 66429,
Dubai, United Arab Emirates
Tel.: (971) 48801212
Cement Mfr & Distr
N.A.I.C.S.: 327310

Cemex Supermix LLC   (1)
New Mussafah, Abu Dhabi, United Arab
Emirates
Tel.: (971) 25515501
Ready Mix Mfr & Distr
N.A.I.C.S.: 327310

Cemex Topmix LLC   (1)
Al Quoz Industrial Area 3, Dubai, United
Arab Emirates
Tel.: (971) 43470427
Ready Mix Mfr & Distr
N.A.I.C.S.: 327310

Neoris N.V.   (1)
Strawinskylaan 1637 Tower B Lev, 1077,
Amsterdam, Netherlands
Tel.: (31) 205022812
N.A.I.C.S.: 327120

Readymix Limited   (61.2%)
Killeen Road, Dublin, 12, Ireland
Tel.: (353) 18658700
Sales Range: $75-99.9 Million
Emp.: 355
Readymix Concrete Mfr
N.A.I.C.S.: 327320
Adrian Auer (Chm)

Unit (Domestic):

Readymix   (2)
Maudlins, Naas, Kildare, Ireland
Tel.: (353) 145879355
Emp.: 60
Concrete Pipe Mfr
N.A.I.C.S.: 327332

Readymix (ROI) Ltd   (2)
Arden, Tullamore, Offaly, Ireland
Tel.: (353) 50621485
Web Site: http://www.readymix.ie
Sales Range: $25-49.9 Million
Emp.: 50
Readymix Concrete Mfr
N.A.I.C.S.: 327320

Trinidad Cement Limited   (1)
Southern Main Road, Claxton Bay, Trinidad
& Tobago   (63.83%)
Tel.: (868) 2258254
Web Site: https://www.tclgroup.com
Rev.: $329,564,406
Assets: $358,403,335
Liabilities: $210,213,597
Net Worth: $148,189,738
Earnings: $25,156,757
Emp.: 651
Fiscal Year-end: 12/31/2023
Oilwell Cement Mfr
N.A.I.C.S.: 327310
Francisco Aguilera Mendoza (Deputy Chm
& CEO)

Subsidiary (Non-US):

Arawak Cement Company
Limited   (2)
Checker Hall, Saint Lucy, BB27178, Barba-
dos
Tel.: (246) 4399880
Web Site:
   https://www.arawakcement.com.bb
Sales Range: $50-74.9 Million
Emp.: 248
Cement Mfr
N.A.I.C.S.: 327310
Sheryllyn Welch-Payne (Mgr-Procurement)

Caribbean Cement Co., Ltd.   (2)
Rockfort, PO Box 448, Kingston,
Jamaica   (74.08%)
Tel.: (876) 92862315

Web Site: https://www.caribcement.com
Rev.: $179,835,257
Assets: $214,821,452
Liabilities: $58,774,121
Net Worth: $156,047,332
Earnings: $36,177,536
Emp.: 600
Fiscal Year-end: 12/31/2023
Cement Mfr
N.A.I.C.S.: 327310
Parris A. Lyew-Ayee (Chm)

Subsidiary (Domestic):

Jamaica Gypsum & Quarries
Limited   (3)
PO Box 11, Rockfort, Kingston, Jamaica
Tel.: (876) 928 6102
Sales Range: $50-74.9 Million
Emp.: 5
Gypsum, Anhydrite, Fines & Shale Produc-
tion
N.A.I.C.S.: 212319
Marchel Burrell (Mgr-Health & Safety)

Rockfort Mineral Bath Complex
Limited   (3)
Caribbean Cement Company Limited, PO
Box 448, Kingston, Jamaica
Tel.: (876) 9386551
Sales Range: $50-74.9 Million
Emp.: 10
Mineral Mining Services
N.A.I.C.S.: 212390

Subsidiary (Non-US):

Premix & Precast Concrete
Incorporated   (2)
Black Bess, Saint Peter, Barbados
Tel.: (246) 422 0762
Concrete Products Mfr
N.A.I.C.S.: 327390

Subsidiary (Domestic):

Readymix (West Indies) Limited   (2)
Tumpuna Road, Guanapo, Arima, Trinidad
& Tobago
Tel.: (868) 643 2429
Web Site: http://www.rml.co.tt
Sales Range: $50-74.9 Million
Emp.: 125
Premixed Concrete Mfr & Marketer
N.A.I.C.S.: 327320
Michael Glenn Hamel-Smith (Chm)

TCL Ponsa Manufacturing Limited
(TPM)   (2)
Pacific Avenue Point Lisas Industrial Estate,
Point Lisas, WI, Trinidad & Tobago
Tel.: (868) 6794120
Web Site: https://www.tclgroup.com
Sales Range: $50-74.9 Million
Emp.: 55
Mfr & Sales of Single Use Polypropylene
Slings & Jumbo Bags
N.A.I.C.S.: 424130

Subsidiary (Non-US):

TCL Trading Limited   (2)
Fair Play Complex, Box 885, The Valley,
Anguilla
Tel.: (264) 497 3593
Cement Products Whslr
N.A.I.C.S.: 423320
Jaris Liburd (Gen Mgr)

CEMMAC AS
Cementarska 14, Horne Srnie, 91
442, Dubnica nad Vahom, Slovakia
Tel.: (421) 326576211
Web Site: http://www.cemmac.sk
Year Founded: 1883
1CEM01AE—(BRA)
Sales Range: Less than $1 Million
Cement Mfr
N.A.I.C.S.: 327310
Martin Kebisek (Chm-Mgmt Bd &
CEO)

CEMOI CHOCOLATIER SAS
2980 ave, Perpignan, France
Tel.: (33) 468563535
Web Site: http://group.cemoi.com
Year Founded: 1962

Chocolate Mfr
N.A.I.C.S.: 311999
Joaquin Munoz (Head-Sustainability)

Subsidiaries:

Chris Candies, Inc.   (1)
1557 Spring Garden Ave, Pittsburgh, PA
15212
Tel.: (412) 322-9400
Chocolate & Confectionery Mfr
N.A.I.C.S.: 311351
Mark E. McDonel (VP)

CEMTAS CELIK MAKINA
SANAYI VE TICARET A.S.
Organize Sanayi Bolgesi Ali Osman
Sonmez, Bulvari No 3, 16140, Bursa,
Turkiye
Tel.: (90) 2242431230
Web Site: https://www.cemtas.com.tr
Year Founded: 1970
CEMTS—(IST)
Rev.: $11,741,648
Assets: $486,883,104
Liabilities: $7,506,487
Net Worth: $479,376,617
Earnings: $79,400,144
Emp.: 289
Fiscal Year-end: 12/31/22
Steel & Steel Products Mfr & Mar-
keter
N.A.I.C.S.: 331513
M. Cuneyt Pekman (Member-Mgmt
Bd)

CENCOSUD S.A.
Av Kennedy 9001 Piso 4, Las Con-
des, Santiago, Chile
Tel.: (56) 229590000   CL
Web Site: https://www.cencosud.com
CENCOSUD—(SGO)
Rev.: $16,152,774,302
Assets: $15,406,444,189
Liabilities: $10,551,037,245
Net Worth: $4,855,406,944
Earnings: $331,681,743
Emp.: 121,657
Fiscal Year-end: 12/31/23
Supermarkets, Homecenters & Malls
Owner & Operator
N.A.I.C.S.: 445110
Horst Paulmann Kemna (Chm)

Subsidiaries:

Banco Paris S.A.   (1)
Morande 115 Piso 4, Santiago, Chile
Tel.: (56) 2 410 11 00
Web Site: http://www.bancoparis.cl
Financial Management Services
N.A.I.C.S.: 523999

Subsidiary (Domestic):

Administradora de Servicios Paris
Ltda.   (2)
Piso 7 9001 Av Kennedy, Santiago, Chile
Tel.: (56) 2 959 0700
Supermarket Operator
N.A.I.C.S.: 445110

Viajes Paris S.A.   (2)
Coyancura 2270, Santiago, Chile
Tel.: (56) 23367015
Web Site: http://www.viajesparis.cl
Travel Agency Services
N.A.I.C.S.: 561510

Cencosud de Puerto Rico Inc
S.A.   (1)
Agustinas 785 2 Piso, Santiago,
Chile   (49%)
Tel.: (56) 600 450 5000
Web Site: http://www.tarjetacencosud.cl
Retail Credit Card Administration & Sales
Financing Services
N.A.I.C.S.: 522210

Cencosud Peru S.A.   (1)
Calle Augusto Angulo Nro 130, Miraflores,
Lima, 18, Peru
Tel.: (51) 1 626 0000
Supermarket Operator

N.A.I.C.S.: 445110

Subsidiary (Domestic):

E.Wong S.A.   (2)
Calle Augusto Angulo Suite 130, Miraflores,
Lima, 18, Peru
Tel.: (51) 1 626 0000
Web Site: http://www.ewong.com
Supermarket Operator
N.A.I.C.S.: 445110

Cencosud Retail S.A.   (1)
Av Kennedy 9001 Piso 7, Las Condes,
Santiago, Chile
Tel.: (56) 2 959 0700 959
Supermarket Operator
N.A.I.C.S.: 445110
Javiera Espina Ross (Product Mgr)

Cencosud S.A.   (1)
Parana 3617, Martinez, 1640, Buenos Ai-
res, Argentina
Tel.: (54) 1147331400
Web Site: http://www.easy.com.ar
Sales Range: $1-4.9 Billion
Emp.: 640
Supermarket Operator
N.A.I.C.S.: 445110
Horst Paulmann (Pres)

Subsidiary (Domestic):

Blaisten SA   (2)
Avenida Juan Bautista Alberdi 3922/2, Bue-
nos Aires, C1407GZS, Argentina
Tel.: (54) 1146362000
Web Site: http://www.blaisten.com.ar
Construction Materials Retailer
N.A.I.C.S.: 423320

Cencosud Viajes Argentina S.A.   (2)
Parana 3617, Martinez, 1640, Buenos Ai-
res, Argentina
Tel.: (54) 1147331000
Retail Store Operator
N.A.I.C.S.: 459999

Disco S.A.   (2)
Larrea 833, Buenos Aires, Argentina
Tel.: (54) 49 611952
Web Site: http://www.disco.com.ar
Sales Range: $500-549.9 Million
Supermarket Operations
N.A.I.C.S.: 445110

Jumbo Retail Argentina S.A.   (2)
1111 Suipacha Street 18th Floor, Buenos
Aires, 1640, Argentina
Tel.: (54) 810 999 58626
Web Site: http://www.jumbo.com.ar
Sales Range: $1-4.9 Billion
Supermarket Operator
N.A.I.C.S.: 445110

Unicenter S.A.   (2)
Parana 3745, Martinez, B1640FRE, Buenos
Aires, Argentina
Tel.: (54) 11 4733 1111
Web Site: http://www.unicenter.com.ar
Shopping Mall Operator
N.A.I.C.S.: 445110

Cencosud Shopping Center S.A.   (1)
Avenida Presidente Kennedy 9001 Piso
4-5, Las Condes, Santiago, Chile
Tel.: (56) 2 9590000
Web Site: http://www.cencosudshopping.cl
Shopping Mall Operator
N.A.I.C.S.: 531120

EUROFASHION Ltda   (1)
San Ignacio 700, Quilicura, Santiago, Chile
Tel.: (56) 2 677 9010
Web Site: http://www.eurofashion.cl
Supermarket Operator
N.A.I.C.S.: 445110

East Colombia S.A.   (1)
Nit 900 155 107 1 Calle 175 No 22 13, Me-
zanine, Bogota, Colombia
Tel.: (57) 1 742 9800
Web Site: http://www.easy.com.co
Home Improvement Store Operator
N.A.I.C.S.: 444110

Johnsons Mega San Bernardo
S.A.   (1)
Nuble 1034, Santiago, Chile
Tel.: (56) 2 3872100
Supermarket Operator

N.A.I.C.S.: 445110

Mega Johnsons Vina del Mar S.A. (1)
Avenida Benidorm 961 Loc 253, Vina del Mar, Chile
Tel.: (56) 32 2384700
Departmental Store Operator
N.A.I.C.S.: 445110

Perini Comercial de Alimentos Ltda. (1)
Av Vasco da Gama 3051, Salvador, 40230-731, Brazil
Tel.: (55) 71 3203 0062
Web Site: http://www.perini.com.br
Sales Range: $300-349.9 Million
Emp.: 750
Food Products Mfr & Distr
N.A.I.C.S.: 424420

RETAIL S.A. (1)
Nueva Lyon 72 Piso 6, Santiago, Chile
Tel.: (56) 2 898 3002
Supermarket Operator
N.A.I.C.S.: 445110

Santa Isabel S.A. (1)
Avenida Kennedy 9001 4th Floor, Las Condes, Santiago, Chile
Tel.: (56) 29590000
Web Site: http://www.santaisabel.cl
Sales Range: $800-899.9 Million
Emp.: 5,000
Supermarket Operator
N.A.I.C.S.: 445110

CENERGY HOLDINGS SA
Avenue Marnix 30, 1000, Brussels, Belgium
Tel.: (32) 22240960
Web Site:
    https://www.cenergyholdings.com
Year Founded: 2016
CENER—(EUR)
Rev.: $1,538,968,271
Assets: $1,833,309,950
Liabilities: $1,464,616,879
Net Worth: $368,693,071
Earnings: $65,206,130
Emp.: 2,691
Fiscal Year-end: 12/31/22
Power Transmission Services
N.A.I.C.S.: 221121
Alexios Alexiou *(CEO)*

Subsidiaries:

Fulgor S.A. (1)
33 Amaroussiou Halandriou Str, Amaroussion, 151 25, Greece
Tel.: (30) 2106787416
Fiber Optic Cable Mfr & Distr
N.A.I.C.S.: 335921

CENGILD G.I. MEDICAL CENTRE
Unit 2-3 & 2-4 Nexus Bangsar South No 7, Jalan Kerinchi, 59200, Kuala Lumpur, Malaysia
Tel.: (60) 32 242 7000
Web Site: https://www.cengild.com
Year Founded: 2017
CENGILD—(KLS)
Health Care Srvices
N.A.I.C.S.: 621610
Huck Joo Tan *(Chm)*

CENIT AG
Industriestrasse 52-54, D-70565, Stuttgart, Germany
Tel.: (49) 711782530
Web Site: https://www.cenit.com
CSH—(MUN)
Rev.: $180,846,058
Assets: $102,556,812
Liabilities: $50,082,714
Net Worth: $52,474,098
Earnings: $2,847,060
Emp.: 711
Fiscal Year-end: 12/31/20
Software & Consulting Services
N.A.I.C.S.: 541512

Oliver Riedel *(Chm-Supervisory Bd)*

Subsidiaries:

CENIT France SARL (1)
Campus Millennials Batiment Alve 2 - 2eme etage, Impasse Pueyo Blagnac, 31700, Toulouse, France
Tel.: (33) 582083310
Web Site: http://www.cenit.fr
Information Technology Consulting Services
N.A.I.C.S.: 541512

CENIT Japan K. K. (1)
Teiken Tokyo BLDG 8F 2-17-13 Takanawa, Minato-ku, Tokyo, 108-0074, Japan
Tel.: (81) 3 5422 6691
Web Site: http://www.cenit.jp
Emp.: 5
Information Technology Consulting Services
N.A.I.C.S.: 541512

CENIT North America Inc. (1)
691 N Squirrel Rd Ste 275, Auburn Hills, MI 48326
Tel.: (248) 309-3240
Web Site: http://www.cenit.us
Information Technology Consulting Services
N.A.I.C.S.: 541512

CENIT S.R.L. (1)
Tel.: (40) 332430574
Web Site: http://www.cenit.ro
Information Technology Consulting Services
N.A.I.C.S.: 541512

CENIT Schweiz AG (1)
Im Langhag 7b, 8307, Effretikon, Switzerland
Tel.: (41) 523541010
Web Site: http://www.cenit-ag.ch
Information Technology Consulting Services
N.A.I.C.S.: 541512
Alfonso Panichella *(Mng Dir)*

Coristo GmbH (1)
Steubenstrasse 46, 68163, Mannheim, Germany
Tel.: (49) 62158679390
Information Technology Services
N.A.I.C.S.: 541519

ISR Information Products AG (1)
Hintern Brudern 23, 38100, Braunschweig, Germany
Tel.: (49) 53112080
Web Site: https://isr.de
Emp.: 250
Information Technology Services
N.A.I.C.S.: 541511

KEONYS SAS (1)
24 Quai Gallieni Batiment A, 92158, Suresnes, France
Tel.: (33) 181938193
Information Technology Services
N.A.I.C.S.: 541519

Subsidiary (Non-US):

KEONYS Belgique SPRL (2)
Dreve Richelle 161, 1410, Waterloo, Belgium
Tel.: (32) 23575360
Information Technology Services
N.A.I.C.S.: 541519

KEONYS NL BV (2)
Duwboot 15, 3991 CD, Houten, Netherlands
Tel.: (31) 307920271
Information Technology Services
N.A.I.C.S.: 541519

CENIT CO., LTD.
7F 218 Dogok-ro, Gangnam-gu, Seoul, Korea (South)
Tel.: (82) 25981250
Web Site: https://www.cenit.kr
Year Founded: 1995
037760—(KRS)
Rev.: $122,794,712
Assets: $151,572,986
Liabilities: $75,423,094
Net Worth: $76,149,892
Earnings: $7,277,002
Emp.: 263
Fiscal Year-end: 12/31/22
Stainless Steel Coil Mfr
N.A.I.C.S.: 331110

Choi Chang Woo *(Sr VP)*

CENLUB INDUSTRIES LTD.
Plot No 233-234 Sector-58
Ballabgarh, Faridabad, 121004, Haryana, India
Tel.: (91) 8826794470
Web Site: https://www.cenlub.in
522251—(BOM)
Rev.: $5,778,059
Assets: $7,632,903
Liabilities: $3,053,205
Net Worth: $4,579,698
Earnings: $547,734
Emp.: 225
Fiscal Year-end: 03/31/21
Lubrication Systems Mfr
N.A.I.C.S.: 811191
Madhu Mittal *(Chm & Mng Dir)*

Subsidiaries:

Cenlub Industries Ltd. - Faridabad Plant - I (1)
35 DLF Industrial Estate-I, Faridabad, 121 003, Haryana, India
Tel.: (91) 129 2275483
Lubrication System Mfr
N.A.I.C.S.: 333914

CENNTRO ELECTRIC GROUP LIMITED
Unit 7 35-39 William Street, Double Bay, 2028, NSW, Australia
Tel.: (61) 92750000   AU
Web Site:
    http://www.nakedbrands.com
Year Founded: 1947
CENN—(NASDAQ)
Rev.: $57,548,041
Assets: $114,955,158
Liabilities: $50,826,829
Net Worth: $64,128,329
Earnings: ($49,140,774)
Emp.: 506
Fiscal Year-end: 01/31/21
Holding Company
N.A.I.C.S.: 551112
Justin Davis-Rice *(Chm & CEO)*

Subsidiaries:

Naked Brand Group Inc. (1)
180 Madison Ave Ste 505, New York, NY 10016
Tel.: (646) 653-7710
Web Site: http://www.nakedbrands.com
Undergarment Mfr & Whslr
N.A.I.C.S.: 315250
Justin Davis-Rice *(Chm & CEO)*

CENOMI RETAIL
UWalk A3 Building 1st Floor University Walk Beside Muvi Cinema, PO Box 359, Prince Turki Ibn Abdulaziz Al Awwal Road, Riyadh, 11411, Saudi Arabia
Tel.: (966) 114350000
Web Site:
    https://www.cenomiretail.com
Year Founded: 1990
4240—(SAU)
Rev.: $1,577,148,362
Assets: $2,197,362,162
Liabilities: $2,158,605,154
Net Worth: $38,757,007
Earnings: $10,139,969
Emp.: 9,903
Fiscal Year-end: 03/31/22
Clothing Whslr
N.A.I.C.S.: 458110
Fawaz A. Alhokair *(Co-Founder)*

CENOTEC CO., LTD.
1256-4 Hammadae-ro Gaya-eup, Haman, Gyeongsangnam, Korea (South)
Tel.: (82) 555849181
Web Site: https://cenotec.com

Year Founded: 2015
222420—(KRS)
Rev.: $26,638,994
Assets: $73,886,283
Liabilities: $44,834,550
Net Worth: $29,051,733
Earnings: ($55,449)
Emp.: 114
Fiscal Year-end: 12/31/22
Investment Holding Company
N.A.I.C.S.: 551112

CENOVUS ENERGY INC.
225 6 Ave SW, Calgary, T2P 1N2, AB, Canada
Tel.: (403) 766-2000   Ca
Web Site: https://www.cenovus.com
Year Founded: 2009
CVE—(NYSE)
Rev.: $74,468,297,600
Assets: $72,375,496,000
Liabilities: $33,832,507,200
Net Worth: $38,542,988,800
Earnings: $5,515,921,600
Emp.: 6,925
Fiscal Year-end: 12/31/23
Oil & Gas Exploration & Production Services
N.A.I.C.S.: 211120
Kam S. Sandhar *(Exec VP-Strategy & Corp Dev)*

Subsidiaries:

BP Husky Refinery (1)
4001 Cedar Point Rd, Oregon, OH 43616-1310
Tel.: (419) 698-6200
Sales Range: $125-149.9 Million
Petroleum Refining Services; Owned by BP plc & Husky Energy, Inc.
N.A.I.C.S.: 324110

CENSOF HOLDINGS BERHAD
Unit B 10 06 6th Floor Dataran 3 Two Jalan 19/1, 46300, Petaling Jaya, Selangor, Malaysia
Tel.: (60) 379627888   MY
Web Site: https://www.censof.com
CENSOF—(KLS)
Rev.: $21,430,899
Assets: $28,083,809
Liabilities: $6,205,503
Net Worth: $21,878,307
Earnings: $1,082,116
Emp.: 372
Fiscal Year-end: 03/31/24
Financial Management Software
N.A.I.C.S.: 513210
Mohammad Ibrahim Mohammad Zain *(Chm)*

Subsidiaries:

Beyond4 Sdn. Bhd. (1)
Menara HLX Level 6 No 3 Jalan Kia Peng, Kuala Lumpur, Malaysia
Tel.: (60) 37 960 1922
Web Site: https://www.beyond4.tech
Information Technology Services
N.A.I.C.S.: 541511

Cendee Sdn. Bhd. (1)
Unit B-10-06 6th Floor Dataran 3 Two Jalan 19/1, 46300, Petaling Jaya, Selangor, Malaysia
Tel.: (60) 379627888
Software Services
N.A.I.C.S.: 541511

Cognitive Consulting Sdn. Bhd. (1)
25-2 Level 25 Oval Damansara 685 Jalan Damansara, Taman Tun Dr Ismail, 60000, Kuala Lumpur, Wilayah Persekutuan, Malaysia
Tel.: (60) 377312981
Web Site: https://www.cognitive.com.my
Information Technology Consulting Services
N.A.I.C.S.: 518210

Knowledgecom Corporation Sdn. Bhd. (1)
Unit C 15-03 Block C Dataran 3 Dua 3 Two

Censof Holdings Berhad—(Continued)

Square No 2 Jalan 19/1, 46300, Petaling Jaya, Selangor, Malaysia
Tel.: (60) 37 960 1922
Web Site: www.knowledgecom.my
Education & Software Services
N.A.I.C.S.: 611710

Netsense Busines Solutions Pte. Ltd. (1)
33 Ubi Avenue 3 08-67 Vertex Tower A, Singapore, 408868, Singapore
Tel.: (65) 6 681 6504
Web Site: https://netsensebs.com
Business Solution Services
N.A.I.C.S.: 541511
Abdul Rehman (Dir-Bus Dev)

PT Praisindo Teknologi (1)
Jl Empu Sendok No 53 Senopati Kebayoran baru, Jakarta, 12110, Indonesia
Tel.: (62) 2152 654 2324
Web Site: https://www.praisindo.com
Information Technology Services
N.A.I.C.S.: 541511
Muhammad Suryadi (Chm)

T-Melmax Sdn. Bhd. (1)
A-3 Block A Level 3 Sunway PJ 51A Jalan SS9A/19, Seri Setia, 47300, Petaling Jaya, Selangor, Malaysia
Tel.: (60) 37 877 9500
Web Site: https://www.cpay.com.my
Electronic Banking Services
N.A.I.C.S.: 522110

CENTAMIN PLC
2 Mulcaster Street, Saint Helier, JE2 3NJ, Jersey
Tel.: (44) 1534828700   JE
Web Site: https://www.centamin.com
CEE—(TSX)
Rev.: $891,262,000
Assets: $1,523,243,000
Liabilities: $144,637,000
Net Worth: $1,378,606,000
Earnings: $194,885,000
Emp.: 4,477
Fiscal Year-end: 12/31/23
Holding Company; Gold Exploration & Mining
N.A.I.C.S.: 551112
Darren Le Masurier (Sec)

Subsidiaries:

Centamin Egypt Limited (1)
Suite 8 7 The Esplanade, Mount Pleasant, 6153, WA, Australia
Tel.: (61) 893162640
Web Site: https://www.centamin.com
Emp.: 1
Holding Company
N.A.I.C.S.: 551112

Subsidiary (Domestic):

Pharaoh Gold Mines NL (2)
Suite 8 7 The Esplanade, Mount Pleasant, 6153, WA, Australia
Tel.: (61) 893162640
Emp.: 1
Holding Company; Gold Ore Mining
N.A.I.C.S.: 551112

Affiliate (Non-US):

Sukari Gold Mines (3)
361 El-Horreya Road, Sedi gaber, Alexandria, Egypt (50%)
Tel.: (20) 3 541 1259
Gold Ore Mining
N.A.I.C.S.: 212220
Youssef El-Raghy (Gen Mgr)

Centamin Group Services UK Limited (1)
9-10 Savile Row, London, W1S 3PF, United Kingdom
Tel.: (44) 2081766261
Mining Exploration Services
N.A.I.C.S.: 213114

CENTAR ZA PUTEVE VOJVODINE A.D.

Jovana Dordevica 2, Novi Sad, Serbia
Tel.: (381) 21 557 698
Year Founded: 2001
Sales Range: $1-9.9 Million
Engineering Consulting Services
N.A.I.C.S.: 541330

CENTARA EHF
Borgartun 26, 105, Reykjavik, Iceland
Tel.: (354) 5918700
Web Site: http://www.centara.com
Software Devolopment
N.A.I.C.S.: 513210
Stefan Stefansson (Partner)

Subsidiaries:

Wise Iausnir ehf (1)
Borgartun 26 4th Floor, 105, Reykjavik, Iceland
Tel.: (354) 545 3200
Web Site: http://www.wise.is
Business Management Software Development Services
N.A.I.C.S.: 541511
Hrannar Erlingsson (Mng Dir)

CENTAUR IMPORT MOTORS (1977) LTD.
3819 MacLeod Trail SW, Calgary, T2G 2R3, AB, Canada
Tel.: (403) 287-2544
Web Site: http://www.centaursubaru.ca
Year Founded: 1977
Rev.: $10,286,554
Emp.: 32
New & Used Car Dealers
N.A.I.C.S.: 441110
Peter Busse (Mgr-Sls)

CENTAUR MEDIA PLC
10 York Road, London, SE1 7ND, United Kingdom
Tel.: (44) 2079704000   UK
Web Site: https://www.centaurmedia.com
Year Founded: 1982
CAU—(LSE)
Rev.: $43,990,128
Assets: $90,424,152
Liabilities: $26,339,768
Net Worth: $64,084,384
Earnings: ($19,551,168)
Emp.: 416
Fiscal Year-end: 12/31/20
Holding Company; Business Publishing, Information & Exhibition Services
N.A.I.C.S.: 551112
Swagatam Mukerji (CEO)

Subsidiaries:

E-consultancy.com Limited (1)
Floor M 10 York Road, London, SE1 7ND, United Kingdom
Tel.: (44) 207 970 4322
Web Site: https://econsultancy.com
Digital Marketing Services
N.A.I.C.S.: 541613

Market Makers Incorporated Limited (1)
Antenna House St Marys Gate, Sheffield, S2 4QA, United Kingdom
Tel.: (44) 845 468 0880
Web Site: https://www.marketmakers.co.uk
Advertising Services
N.A.I.C.S.: 541810

Taxbriefs Limited (1)
Street Giles House 50 Poland Street, London, W1F 7AX, United Kingdom
Tel.: (44) 2072500967
Web Site: http://www.taxbriefs.co.uk
Sales Range: $25-49.9 Million
Emp.: 15
Financial Books Publishing Services
N.A.I.C.S.: 513130

The Profile Group (UK) Limited (1)

79 Wells Street, London, W1T 3QN, United Kingdom
Tel.: (44) 20 7970 4299
Web Site: http://www.profilegroup.co.uk
Sales Range: $1-9.9 Million
Emp.: 50
Forward Planning & Industry Contact Information Services
N.A.I.C.S.: 519290

CENTAURUS ENERGY INC.
1250 639 - 5th Avenue SW, Calgary, T2P 0M9, AB, Canada
Tel.: (403) 264-1915   AB
Web Site: https://www.ctaurus.com
CTA—(OTCIQ)
Rev.: $22,971,000
Assets: $39,241,000
Liabilities: $64,542,000
Net Worth: ($25,301,000)
Earnings: ($38,020,000)
Emp.: 72
Fiscal Year-end: 12/31/20
Oil & Gas Exploration & Development
N.A.I.C.S.: 213112
David D. Tawil (CEO)

Subsidiaries:

Madalena Energy S.A. (1)
Lola Mora 421 13th Floor, Buenos Aires, C1011ABE, Argentina
Tel.: (54) 11 4363 9600
Emp.: 40
Oil & Gas Exploration Services
N.A.I.C.S.: 211120
Ruy Riavitz (Gen Mgr)

CENTAURUS METALS LIMITED
Tel.: (61) 864258420
Web Site: https://www.centaurus.com.au
CTTZF—(OTCQX)
Rev.: $409,835
Assets: $43,975,231
Liabilities: $6,180,075
Net Worth: $37,795,156
Earnings: ($32,660,806)
Fiscal Year-end: 12/31/22
Exploration For Base Metals, Gold & Other Mineral Resources
N.A.I.C.S.: 213114
Darren P. Gordon (CEO & Mng Dir)

CENTENARI E ZINELLI SPA
Corso Italia 62, 20025, Legnano, MI, Italy
Tel.: (39) 0331453968   IT
Web Site: http://www.zinelli.it
Year Founded: 1872
Sales Range: $50-74.9 Million
Emp.: 404
Yarns & Textiles
N.A.I.C.S.: 313110

CENTENARY INTERNATIONAL CORP.
Reconquista 656 Third Floor Suite B, Buenos Aires, 1003, Argentina
Tel.: (54) 1143127075
Freight Forwarding Services
N.A.I.C.S.: 488510
Carlos Fabian De Sousa (Pres, CEO & Sec)

CENTENARY UNITED HOLDINGS LIMITED
40 Rainbow Road Western, Zhongshan, 528400, China
Tel.: (86) 76088160318   Ky
Web Site: http://www.car2000.com.cn
Year Founded: 1999
1959—(HKG)
Rev.: $280,618,463
Assets: $125,898,926
Liabilities: $91,932,656
Net Worth: $33,966,270
Earnings: ($3,345,030)

Emp.: 846
Fiscal Year-end: 12/31/22
Holding Company
N.A.I.C.S.: 551112
Hau Kit Law (Founder, Chm & CEO)

CENTENIAL SURGICAL SUTURE LTD.
F-29 MIDC Murbad, Thane, 421 401, India
Tel.: (91) 2524222905
Web Site: https://www.centenialindia.com
Year Founded: 1995
531380—(BOM)
Rev.: $5,053,994
Assets: $9,561,143
Liabilities: $5,524,687
Net Worth: $4,036,455
Earnings: $131,286
Emp.: 258
Fiscal Year-end: 03/31/21
Suture Mfr
N.A.I.C.S.: 339113
Mahima Bathwal (Compliance Officer & Sec)

CENTENNIAL MINING LIMITED
1/10 Mary Street, Como, 6152, WA, Australia
Tel.: (61) 8 9367 4504
Web Site: http://www.centennialmining.com
Year Founded: 2011
Sales Range: $200-249.9 Million
Gold Mining
N.A.I.C.S.: 212220
Dale Rogers (Chm)

CENTENNIAL OPTICAL LTD.
158 Norfinch Drive, Toronto, M3N 1X6, ON, Canada
Tel.: (416) 739-8539
Web Site: http://www.centennialoptical.com
Year Founded: 1967
Sales Range: $25-49.9 Million
Emp.: 125
Eyeglass Lense Distr
N.A.I.C.S.: 333310
Allen Nightingale (Pres)

CENTENNIAL WINDOWS & DOORS
687 Sovereign Road, London, N5V 4K8, ON, Canada
Tel.: (519) 451-0508
Web Site: http://www.centennialwindows.com
Year Founded: 1981
Sales Range: $10-24.9 Million
Windows & Doors Mfr
N.A.I.C.S.: 332321

CENTER INTERNATIONAL GROUP CO LTD
No 10 Yongchang East 4th Road, Beijing Economic and Technological Development Zone, Beijing, 100176, China
Tel.: (86) 1067856668
Web Site: https://www.centerint.com
Year Founded: 2001
603098—(SHG)
Rev.: $594,399,532
Assets: $1,038,815,037
Liabilities: $659,855,444
Net Worth: $378,959,593
Earnings: $7,513,871
Emp.: 1,800
Fiscal Year-end: 12/31/22
Metal Building Cladding System Mfr & Distr
N.A.I.C.S.: 339910
Aisen Liu (Chm)

Subsidiaries:

Lanzhou CENTER Steel Structure Co., Ltd (1)
Tower A No 13 Building Zhongguang Complex No 87 Zhangye Road, Chengguan District, Lanzhou, 730030, China
Tel.: (86) 9318488709
Metal Building Cladding System Distr
N.A.I.C.S.: 423330

CENTER-INVEST BANK PJSC
62 Sokolova Avenue, 344000, Rostov-na-Donu, Russia
Tel.: (7) 8632000000
Web Site: http://centrinvest.com
Year Founded: 1992
Sales Range: Less than $1 Million
Emp.: 1,572
Commercial Banking Services
N.A.I.C.S.: 522110
Sergey Smirnov (CFO & Member-Exec Bd)

CENTERAC TECHNOLOGIES LTD.
307 Regent Chambers, Nariman Point, Mumbai, 400021, Maharashtra, India
Tel.: (91) 2261100102
Web Site: https://www.centerac.in
531621—(BOM)
Rev.: $86,352
Assets: $85,800
Liabilities: $83,031
Net Worth: $2,770
Earnings: $20,515
Emp.: 2
Fiscal Year-end: 03/31/24
Information Technology Consulting Services
N.A.I.C.S.: 519290

CENTERPULSE AUSTRALIA PTY LTD
Level 5, 384 Eastern Valley Way, Chatswood, Sydney, 2067, Australia
Tel.: (61) 2 94177922
Sales Range: $25-49.9 Million
Emp.: 40
Medical & Hospital Equipment Mfr
N.A.I.C.S.: 423450

CENTERRA GOLD INC.
1 University Avenue Suite 1500, Toronto, M5J 2P1, ON, Canada
Tel.: (416) 204-1953   Ca
Web Site:
    https://www.centerragold.com
Year Founded: 2002
CGAU—(NYSE)
Rev.: $850,194,000
Assets: $2,335,909,000
Liabilities: $525,618,000
Net Worth: $1,810,291,000
Earnings: ($77,209,000)
Emp.: 1,150
Fiscal Year-end: 12/31/22
Gold Mining Services
N.A.I.C.S.: 212220
Dennis C. Kwong (VP-Bus Dev & Exploration)

Subsidiaries:

Kumtor Gold Company (1)
24 Ibraimov Street, 720031, Bishkek, Kyrgyzstan
Tel.: (996) 312900707
Web Site: https://www.kumtor.kg
Emp.: 4,706
Gold Ore Mining Services
N.A.I.C.S.: 212220
Deon Badenhorst (Pres)

Oksut Madencilik A.S. (1)
Gaziosmanpasa Mahallesi Turan Emeksiz Caddesi No 1 ic Kapi 3, Cankaya, Ankara, Turkiye
Tel.: (90) 3124088700

Web Site:
    https://www.oksutmadencilik.com.tr
Gold Ore Mining Services
N.A.I.C.S.: 212220
Daniel Richard Desjardins (Chm)

Thompson Creek Metals Company Inc. (1)
26 W Dry Creek Cir, Littleton, CO 80120
Tel.: (303) 761-8801
Molybdenum Mining Services
N.A.I.C.S.: 212290

Subsidiary (Domestic):

Cyprus Thompson Creek Mining Company (2)
26 W Dry Creek Cir Ste 225, Littleton, CO 80120
Tel.: (208) 838-2200
Emp.: 55
Molybdenum Mining Services
N.A.I.C.S.: 212290
Jim Kopp (Gen Mgr)

Thompson Creek Metals Company USA (2)
26 W Dry Creek Cir Ste 225, Littleton, CO 80120
Tel.: (303) 761-8801
Metal Mining Services
N.A.I.C.S.: 212290

Thompson Creek Mining Co. (2)
PO Box 600, Challis, ID 83226
Tel.: (208) 838-2200
Web Site: http://www.tcreek.com
Molybdenum Ores Mining
N.A.I.C.S.: 212230
Bert Doughty (Mgr-Environmental/Safety)

CENTESSA PHARMACEUTICALS PLC
3rd Floor 1 Ashley Road, Babraham, Altrincham, WA14 2DT, Cheshire, United Kingdom
Tel.: (44) 7391789784   UK
Web Site: https://centessa.com
Year Founded: 2020
CNTA—(NASDAQ)
Rev.: $2,342,000
Assets: $444,307,000
Liabilities: $108,138,000
Net Worth: $336,169,000
Earnings: ($216,207,000)
Emp.: 83
Fiscal Year-end: 12/31/22
Holding Company
N.A.I.C.S.: 551112
Saurabh Saha (CEO)

CENTOGENE N.V.
Am Strande 7, 18055, Rostock, Germany
Tel.: (49) 38180113500   NL
Web Site:
    https://www.centogene.com
Year Founded: 2018
CNTG—(NASDAQ)
Rev.: $52,380,747
Assets: $83,266,782
Liabilities: $110,551,479
Net Worth: ($27,284,697)
Earnings: ($38,346,644)
Emp.: 493
Fiscal Year-end: 12/31/23
Holding Company
N.A.I.C.S.: 551112
Arndt Rolfs (Co-Founder)

CENTR BRANDS CORP.
100-2318 Oak Street, Vancouver, V6H 4J1, BC, Canada
Tel.: (604) 733-1514   BC
Web Site:
    http://www.findyourcentr.com
Year Founded: 2010
CNTR—(CNSX)
Rev.: $762,547
Assets: $2,379,278
Liabilities: $6,007,916
Net Worth: ($3,628,638)

Earnings: ($14,257,039)
Emp.: 27
Fiscal Year-end: 05/31/21
Metal Mining
N.A.I.C.S.: 212290
Joseph E. Meehan (Pres & CEO)

CENTRAIS ELETRICAS BRASILEIRAS S.A.
Rua da Quitanda 196, Centro, Rio de Janeiro, CEP 20091-005, Brazil
Tel.: (55) 2125144526   BR
Web Site: https://www.eletrobras.com
Year Founded: 1962
EBR—(NYSE)
Rev.: $7,410,291,754
Assets: $53,257,085,253
Liabilities: $30,829,197,328
Net Worth: $22,427,887,925
Earnings: $942,641,340
Emp.: 8,328
Fiscal Year-end: 12/31/23
Holding Company; Electric Power Distr
N.A.I.C.S.: 551112
Luiz Henrique Hamann (Chief Distr Officer)

Subsidiaries:

Centrais Eletricas do Norte do Brasil SA (1)
SCN-Qd 06-Conj A Bloco B 413, Brasilia, 70 716-901, Brazil
Tel.: (55) 6134295151
Web Site: http://www.eletronorte.gov.br
Sales Range: $1-4.9 Billion
Emp.: 2,213
Energy Generation & Transmission Services
N.A.I.C.S.: 221111

Subsidiary (Domestic):

Manaus Energia S/A (2)
Av 7 de Setembro 2414, Cachoeirinha, Manaus, Brazil
Tel.: (55) 8007013001
Web Site: http://www.manausenergia.com.br
Power Generation & Transmission Services
N.A.I.C.S.: 221122

Centro de Pesquisas de Energia Eletrica (1)
Tel.: (55) 2125986000
Web Site: http://www.cepel.br
Research Center
N.A.I.C.S.: 541715

Companhia Energetica de Roraima (1)
Av Presidente Castelo Branco 1163 Calunga, Boa Vista, 69303035, Roraima, Brazil
Tel.: (55) 9540091500
Electric Power Generation & Distribution Services
N.A.I.C.S.: 221118

Companhia Hidreletrica do Sao Francisco (1)
Rua Delmiro Gouveia 333, San Martin, Recife, 50761-901, Pernambuco, Brazil
Web Site: http://www.chesf.gov.br
Electric Power Generation & Distribution Services
N.A.I.C.S.: 221118

Companhia Hidro Eletrica do Sao Francisco SA (1)
Rua Delmiro Gouveia 333 - Bongi, Recife, 50761-901, Pernambuco, Brazil
Tel.: (55) 8132292000
Web Site: http://www.chesf.gov.br
Sales Range: $1-4.9 Billion
Emp.: 5,625
Energy Generation & Transmission Services
N.A.I.C.S.: 221122

Companhia de Geracao Termica de Energia Eletrica (1)
Rua Sete de Setembro 539, Porto Alegre, 90010-190, Brazil
Tel.: (55) 5132871500
Web Site: http://www.cgtee.gov.br

Sales Range: $250-299.9 Million
Emp.: 500
Energy Generation Services
N.A.I.C.S.: 221118

Eletrobras Eletronorte (1)
Tel.: (55) 6134295151
Electric Power Generation & Distribution Services
N.A.I.C.S.: 221118

Eletrobras Termonuclear SA (1)
Rua da Candelaria 65 Centro, Rio de Janeiro, 20091-020, Brazil
Tel.: (55) 2125887000
Web Site: http://www.eletronuclear.gov.br
Sales Range: $1-4.9 Billion
Emp.: 2,000
Nuclear Power Generation
N.A.I.C.S.: 221113

Eletrosul Centrais Eletricas S.A. (1)
Deputado Antonio Edu Vieira 999, CP 5091, Pantanal, Florianopolis, 88040901, Santa Catarina, Brazil
Tel.: (55) 4832317000
Web Site: http://www.eletrosul.gov.br
Emp.: 2,000
Electric Power Transmission Services
N.A.I.C.S.: 221121

Subsidiary (Domestic):

Porto Velho Transmissora de Energia S.A. (2)
Rua Deputado Antonio Edu Vieira 999 Salao Terreo - Pantanal, Florianopolis, 88040-901, Santa Catarina, Brazil
Tel.: (55) 48 3231 7277
Sales Range: $400-449.9 Million
Emp.: 1,000
Electric Power Transmission Services
N.A.I.C.S.: 221121

Furnas Centrais Eletricas S.A. (1)
Tel.: (55) 2125283112
Web Site: http://www.furnas.com.br
Sales Range: $1-4.9 Billion
Emp.: 5,545
Energy Production Services
N.A.I.C.S.: 221111

Subsidiary (Domestic):

Retiro Baixo Energetica S.A. (2)
Rod BR 040 Sentido Brasilia Km 377, Pompeu, MG, Brazil
Tel.: (55) 3837291300
Web Site: https://www.rbe.com.br
Hydroelectric Power Generation Services
N.A.I.C.S.: 221111

CENTRAIS ELETRICAS DE SANTA CATARINA S.A. - CELESC
Avenida Itamarati 160, Itacorubi, 88034-900, Florianopolis, 88034-900, SC, Brazil
Tel.: (55) 32315000   BR
Web Site: http://www.celesc.com.br
Year Founded: 1955
CLSC4—(BRAZ)
Rev.: $2,143,762,591
Assets: $2,535,241,827
Liabilities: $1,930,900,356
Net Worth: $604,341,472
Earnings: $114,793,199
Fiscal Year-end: 12/31/23
Holding Company
N.A.I.C.S.: 551112
Julius Caesar Pungan (Dir-Investor Relations)

CENTRAL A.D.
Marsala Tita 92, 21460, Vrbas, Serbia
Tel.: (381) 21 707 376
Web Site: http://www.hotelbacka.rs
Year Founded: 1955
Sales Range: Less than $1 Million
Emp.: 33
Home Management Services
N.A.I.C.S.: 721110

Central a.d.—(Continued)

CENTRAL ALBERTA CO-OP LTD.

6201-46 Avenue, Red Deer, T4N
6Z1, AB, Canada
Tel.: (403) 343-2667   Ca
Web Site: http://www.centralab.coop
Year Founded: 2008
Emp.: 750
Food Stores & Pharmacies; Gas
Bars, Home & Agro Centre Operator
N.A.I.C.S.: 455219
Richard Lemke (Second VP)

CENTRAL AREA ELECTRICAL MECHANICAL JOINT STOCK COMPANY

Hoa Cam Industrial Zone Hoa Tho
Tay Ward, Cam Le District, Da Nang,
Vietnam
Tel.: (84) 2362218455
Web Site: https://www.cemc.com.vn
CJC—(HNX)
Rev.: $3,836,845
Assets: $5,097,383
Liabilities: $3,480,428
Net Worth: $1,616,955
Earnings: ($98,669)
Emp.: 340
Fiscal Year-end: 12/31/21
Mechanical & Electrical Equipment
Mfr
N.A.I.C.S.: 333613

CENTRAL ASIA DEVELOPMENT GROUP, INC.

350 Orchard Road #16-09/10, Singapore, 238868, Singapore
Tel.: (65) 68872234   MD
Web Site: http://www.cadg.com
Sales Range: $25-49.9 Million
Emp.: 100
Engineering, Logistics, Aid Management & Development Services
N.A.I.C.S.: 561990
Raju K. Shaulis (Pres)

CENTRAL ASIA METALS PLC

36 Carnaby Street, London, W1F
7DR, United Kingdom
Tel.: (44) 2078989001
Web Site:
https://www.centralasiametals.com
CAML—(AIM)
Rev.: $220,855,000
Assets: $443,045,000
Liabilities: $74,925,000
Net Worth: $368,120,000
Earnings: $33,805,000
Emp.: 1,072
Fiscal Year-end: 12/31/22
Copper, Gold & Molybdenum Mining
& Exploration Services
N.A.I.C.S.: 212230
Howard Nicholson (Dir-Technical)

Subsidiaries:

Kounrad Copper Company LLP   (1)
Zhunis Abugaliev St 4 Business Center No
2, Balkhash, Karaganda, Kazakhstan
Tel.: (7) 7103646465
Web Site: https://www.kounrad.kz
Metals Mfr
N.A.I.C.S.: 332313

Sary Kazna LLP   (1)
Junisa Abugaliyeva St 4 BC No 2,
Balkhash, Karaganda, Kazakhstan
Tel.: (7) 7103645065
Metals Mfr
N.A.I.C.S.: 332313

CENTRAL ASIAN MINERALS & RESOURCES PLC

34 North Quay, Douglas, IM1 4LB,
Isle of Man
Tel.: (44) 1624 679 000   IM

Web Site: http://www.camarplc.com
Investment Services
N.A.I.C.S.: 523999
Oliver John Vaughan (Chm)

CENTRAL AUTOMOTIVE PRODUCTS LTD.

4-2-30 Nakanoshima, Kita-ku, Osaka,
530-0005, Japan
Tel.: (81) 664435182   JP
Web Site: https://www.central-auto.co.jp
Year Founded: 1943
8117—(TKS)
Rev.: $259,977,910
Assets: $379,328,070
Liabilities: $49,376,700
Net Worth: $329,951,370
Earnings: $52,377,640
Emp.: 260
Fiscal Year-end: 03/31/24
Automotive Parts & Accessories & Air
Conditioner Parts Development, Mfr
& Sales; New & Used Car Sales
N.A.I.C.S.: 336390
Shinichiro Sakata (Pres & CEO)

Subsidiaries:

CAPCO Private Ltd.   (1)
2 Kallang Avenue 09-11 CT Hub, Singapore, 339407, Singapore
Tel.: (65) 62941915
Sales Range: $25-49.9 Million
Emp.: 10
Business Support Services
N.A.I.C.S.: 561499

CAPCO U.S.A., Inc.   (1)
               (100%)
Sales Range: $25-49.9 Million
Emp.: 1
Distribution of Automotive Products
N.A.I.C.S.: 488510

Capco (Malaysia) Sdn. Bhd.   (1)
Suite 10 Etiqa Twins Level 25 Tower2 11
Jalan Pinang, 50450, Kuala Lumpur, Malaysia
Tel.: (60) 32 726 9906
Automobile Parts Distr
N.A.I.C.S.: 423120

Capco Guangzhou, Ltd.   (1)
3806-B Room 38/F Office Tower CITIC
Plaza 233 Tianhe North Road, Guangzhou,
510613, China
Tel.: (86) 203 888 2954
Automobile Parts Distr
N.A.I.C.S.: 423120

Capco Middle East Fzco   (1)
6WA310 Dubai Airport Free Zone, PO Box
54852, Dubai, United Arab Emirates
Tel.: (971) 4 214 6362
Automobile Parts Distr
N.A.I.C.S.: 423120

CENTRAL BANK & FINANCIAL SERVICES AUTHORITY OF IRELAND

Dame Street, PO Box 559, Dublin, 2,
Ireland
Tel.: (353) 14344000
Web Site: http://www.centralbank.ie
Sales Range: $800-899.9 Million
Emp.: 963
Central Bank
N.A.I.C.S.: 521110
John Hurley (Governor)

CENTRAL BANK OF ARMENIA

Vazgen Sargsyan Str 6, 375010, Yerevan, Benin
Tel.: (229) 10583841
Web Site: http://www.cba.am
Sales Range: $100-124.9 Million
Emp.: 531
Central Bank
N.A.I.C.S.: 522110
Arthur Javadyan (Governor)

Subsidiaries:

Armenian Card CJSC   (1)
32/1 Garegin Nzhdehi St, Yerevan, 0026,
Armenia
Tel.: (374) 10 440380
Web Site: http://www.arca.am
Financial Transaction Processing Services
N.A.I.C.S.: 522320
Ishkhan Mkhitaryan (CEO)

Panarmenian Bank OJSC   (1)
9 Grigor Lusavorich str 1st floor, Yerevan,
0015, Armenia
Tel.: (374) 10 56 8000
Web Site: http://www.panarmenianbank.am
Commercial Banking Services
N.A.I.C.S.: 522110
Vahram Nercissiantz (Chm & CEO)

CENTRAL BANK OF BAHRAIN

PO Box 27, Manama, Bahrain
Tel.: (973) 17547777
Web Site: http://www.cbb.gov.bh
Sales Range: $125-149.9 Million
Emp.: 303
Central Bank
N.A.I.C.S.: 521110
Khalid Hamad Abdul-Rahman Hamad
(Exec Dir-Banking Supervision)

CENTRAL BANK OF BARBADOS

Tom Adams Financial Centre, Spry
Street, Bridgetown, Barbados
Tel.: (246) 2464366870
Web Site:
http://www.centralbank.org.bb
Sales Range: $125-149.9 Million
Emp.: 300
Central Bank
N.A.I.C.S.: 521110
Michael D. Carrington (Controller-Fin)

CENTRAL BANK OF BELIZE

Gabourel Ln, PO Box 852, Belize,
Belize
Tel.: (501) 2236194
Web Site:
http://www.centralbank.org.bz
Sales Range: $50-74.9 Million
Emp.: 109
Central Bank
N.A.I.C.S.: 521110

CENTRAL BANK OF EGYPT

54 Elgomhoreya Street, 11511, Cairo,
Egypt
Tel.: (20) 27702770
Web Site: http://www.cbe.org.eg
Year Founded: 1961
Central Bank
N.A.I.C.S.: 521110
Tarek Hassan Aly Amer (Governor)

CENTRAL BANK OF INDIA LIMITED

Chander Mukhi Nariman Point, Mumbai, 400 021, India
Tel.: (91) 2266387777
Web Site:
https://www.centralbankofindia.co.in
Year Founded: 1911
532885—(BOM)
Rev.: $16,896,973
Assets: $5,677,957
Liabilities: $1,421,102
Net Worth: $4,256,855
Earnings: $3,208,513
Emp.: 30,770
Fiscal Year-end: 03/31/23
Central Bank
N.A.I.C.S.: 521110
Anand Kumar Das (Officer-
Compliance, Sec & Asst Gen Mgr-
MBD)

Subsidiaries:

Cent Bank Home Finance
Limited   (1)
6th Floor Central Bank of India Mumbai
Main Office Building MG Road, Fort Flora
Fountain Hutatma Chowk, Mumbai, 400023,
India
Tel.: (91) 8008896606
Web Site: https://www.cbhfl.com
N.A.I.C.S.: 522292
Malladi Venkat Murali Krishna (Chm)

Centbank Financial Services
Limited   (1)
55 MG Road Fort, Mumbai, 400001, India
Tel.: (91) 2222616217
Investment Banking Services
N.A.I.C.S.: 523150

Indo Zambia Bank Ltd.   (1)
Plot No 6907 Cairo Road, PO Box 35411,
Lusaka, Zambia   (20%)
Tel.: (260) 211225080
Web Site: http://www.izb.co.zm
Banking Services
N.A.I.C.S.: 522110
Michael Gondwe (Chm)

CENTRAL BANK OF IRAQ

Al-Rasheed Street, Baghdad, Iraq
Tel.: (964) 1 8165170
Web Site: http://www.cbiraq.org
Central Bank
N.A.I.C.S.: 521110

CENTRAL BANK OF JORDAN

Po-Box-37, PO Box 37, Amman,
11118, Jordan
Tel.: (962) 64630301
Web Site: http://www.cbj.gov.jo
Sales Range: $200-249.9 Million
Emp.: 578
Banking Services
N.A.I.C.S.: 522110
Umayya Salah Toukan (Chm)

CENTRAL BANK OF KENYA

Haile Salassie Avenue, PO Box
60000, 200, Nairobi, Kenya
Tel.: (254) 202860000
Web Site:
http://www.centralbank.go.ke
Sales Range: $1-9.9 Million
Central Bank
N.A.I.C.S.: 521110
Aggrey Jonathan K. Bett (Dir-Deposit
Protection Fund Board)

CENTRAL BANK OF KUWAIT

Arabian Gulf Road Sharq, PO Box
526, Safat, Kuwait, 13006, Kuwait
Tel.: (965) 1814444   KW
Web Site: http://www.cbk.gov.kw
Year Founded: 1969
Central Bank
N.A.I.C.S.: 521110
Salem Abdulaziz Al-Sabah (Chm &
Governor)

CENTRAL BANK OF LESOTHO

Corner Airport and Moshoeshoe
Roads, PO Box 1184, Maseru, 100,
Lesotho
Tel.: (266) 22314281
Web Site:
http://www.centralbank.org.ls
Year Founded: 1978
Sales Range: $25-49.9 Million
Emp.: 200
Central Bank
N.A.I.C.S.: 521110
M. P. Makhetha (Deputy Chm)

CENTRAL BANK OF LIBYA

PO Box 1103, Tripoli, Libya
Tel.: (218) 213333591
Web Site: http://www.cbl.gov.ly
Central Bank
N.A.I.C.S.: 521110

CENTRAL BANK OF NIGERIA
33 Abubakar Tafawa Balewa Way
Central Business Dist, PMB 0187,
Cadastral Zone, Abuja, Nigeria
Tel.: (234) 946236011
Web Site: http://www.cenbank.org
Sales Range: $550-599.9 Million
Emp.: 4,862
Central Bank
N.A.I.C.S.: 521110
Chukwuma C. Soludo *(Chm & Governor)*

CENTRAL BANK OF OMAN
PO BOX 1161, PO Box 1161, Ruwi,
112, Oman
Tel.: (968) 24777777
Web Site: http://www.cbo-oman.org
Sales Range: $125-149.9 Million
Emp.: 600
Central Bank
N.A.I.C.S.: 521110
Tahir Bin Salim Abdullah Al Amri
(Pres)

CENTRAL BANK OF SAMOA
PO Box Private Bag, Apia, Samoa
(Western)
Tel.: (685) 34100
Web Site: http://www.cbs.gov.ws
Sales Range: $25-49.9 Million
Emp.: 100
Central Bank
N.A.I.C.S.: 521110
Gilbert Wongsin *(Mgr-Fin Institutions)*

CENTRAL BANK OF SEY-CHELLES
Independence Avenue, PO Box 701,
Victoria, Mahe, 701, Seychelles
Tel.: (248) 4282000
Web Site: http://www.cbs.sc
Sales Range: $50-74.9 Million
Emp.: 135
Central Bank
N.A.I.C.S.: 521110
Caroline Abel *(Chm)*

CENTRAL BANK OF SOLO-MON ISLANDS
PO Box 634, Honiara, Solomon Islands
Tel.: (677) 21791
Web Site: http://www.cbsi.com.sb
Year Founded: 1983
Sales Range: $1-9.9 Million
Emp.: 73
Central Bank
N.A.I.C.S.: 521110
Denton H. Rarawa *(Chm & Governor)*

CENTRAL BANK OF SRI LANKA
30 Janadhipathi Mawatha, PO Box
590, Colombo, 01, Sri Lanka
Tel.: (94) 112477000   LK
Web Site: http://www.cbsl.gov.lk
Year Founded: 1950
Rev.: $833,006,314
Assets: $10,469,224,207
Liabilities: $9,165,548,749
Net Worth: $1,303,675,459
Earnings: $753,085,340
Emp.: 1,421
Fiscal Year-end: 12/31/18
Central Bank
N.A.I.C.S.: 521110
S. J. A. Handagama *(Asst Governor)*

CENTRAL BANK OF SWAZI-LAND
Umntsholi Building Warner Street, PO
Box 546, H100, Mbabane, Eswatini
Tel.: (268) 4082000
Web Site:
http://www.centralbank.org.sz

Year Founded: 1974
Sales Range: $125-149.9 Million
Emp.: 300
Central Bank
N.A.I.C.S.: 521110
Refiloe Mamogobo *(Sec)*

CENTRAL BANK OF THE RUS-SIAN FEDERATION
12 Neglinnaya Street, 107016, Moscow, Russia
Tel.: (7) 4993003000
Web Site: http://www.cbr.ru
Sales Range: $1-4.9 Billion
Emp.: 4,417
Central Bank
N.A.I.C.S.: 521110
Georgy I. Luntovskiy *(Deputy Chm)*

Subsidiaries:

Asian - Pacific Bank PJSC   **(1)**
Voznesensky Per 11/1, 125009, Moscow,
Russia
Tel.: (7) 4959883061
Web Site: http://www.atb.su
Mortgage Banking Services
N.A.I.C.S.: 522292
Sergey Avramov *(Chm-Exec Bd)*

Moscow Industrial Bank PC
JSCB   **(1)**
M-35 Ul Balchug 2, Moscow, 115035, Russia
Tel.: (7) 4959502190
Web Site: http://www.minbank.ru
Sales Range: Less than $1 Million
Commercial Banking Services
N.A.I.C.S.: 522110

Otkritie Holding JSC   **(1)**
2/4 Letnikovskaya St, 115114, Moscow,
Russia   **(99.9%)**
Tel.: (7) 4952320300
Web Site: http://www.openholding.ru
Bank Holding Company
N.A.I.C.S.: 551111
Ruben Aganbegyan *(Chm & CEO)*

Subsidiary (Domestic):

AGD DIAMONDS JSC   **(2)**
Troitskiy prospect house 168, 163001,
Arkhangelsk, Russia
Tel.: (7) 8182464046
Web Site: http://www.agddiamond.ru
Mining & Exploration Services
N.A.I.C.S.: 212290
Sergei Sergeevich Neruchev *(Gen Dir)*

Public Joint-Stock Company Bank
Otkritie Financial Corporation   **(2)**
Letnikovskaya str building 2 block 4, Moscow, 115114, Russia
Tel.: (7) 495 232 2514
Web Site: http://www.open.ru
Sales Range: $1-4.9 Billion
Corporate Banking Services
N.A.I.C.S.: 522110
Kseniya Yudaeva *(Chm-Supervisory Bd)*

Subsidiary (Domestic):

Baltic Leasing LLC   **(3)**
10-Th Krasnoarmeyskaya Street 22 Lit,
190103, Saint Petersburg, Russia
Tel.: (7) 8126709080
Web Site: http://www.baltlease.ru
Emp.: 950
Financial Lending Services
N.A.I.C.S.: 522222
Dmitry V. Korchagov *(Gen Dir)*

OJSC Rosgosstrakh Bank   **(3)**
43 Bld 2 Myasnitskaya Street, 107078,
Moscow, Russia   **(99.99%)**
Tel.: (7) 495 925 80 80
Web Site: http://www.rgsbank.ru
Banking Services
N.A.I.C.S.: 522110
Danil Khachaturov *(CEO)*

CENTRAL BANK OF THE UNITED ARAB EMIRATES
PO Box 854, Abu Dhabi, United Arab
Emirates

Tel.: (971) 26652220
Web Site: http://www.centralbank.ae
Sales Range: $400-449.9 Million
Central Bank
N.A.I.C.S.: 521110
Sultan Bin Nasser Al Suwaidi *(Governor)*

CENTRAL BANK OF THE UNITED REPUBLIC OF TANZA-NIA
Mirambo Street No 10, PO Box 2939,
Dar es Salaam, Tanzania
Tel.: (255) 22 2233000
Web Site: http://www.bot-tz.org
Sales Range: $75-99.9 Million
Emp.: 100
Central Bank
N.A.I.C.S.: 521110
Benno Ndulu *(Governor & Chm)*

CENTRAL BANK OF TRINIDAD & TOBAGO
Eric Williams Plaza Independence
Square, PO Box 1250, Port of Spain,
Trinidad & Tobago
Tel.: (868) 6254835
Web Site: http://www.central-bank.org.tt
Year Founded: 1964
Central Bank
N.A.I.C.S.: 521110
Alister Noel *(Sr Mgr-Ops)*

CENTRAL CHINA LAND ME-DIA CO., LTD.
Block A China Henan Publishing Industrial Park No 39 Jinshui East
Road, Zhengzhou, 450016, Henan,
China
Tel.: (86) 37187528527
Web Site: http://www.zyddcm.com
Year Founded: 1989
000719—(SSE)
Rev.: $1,351,890,540
Assets: $2,218,488,480
Liabilities: $830,218,896
Net Worth: $1,388,269,584
Earnings: $144,918,072
Fiscal Year-end: 12/31/22
Books Publishing Services
N.A.I.C.S.: 513130
Jiangyan Lin *(Pres)*

CENTRAL CHINA MANAGE-MENT COMPANY LIMITED
Room 212 313 Block C Jianye Office
Building Nongye East Road,
Zhengzhou, Henan, China   Ky
Web Site:
https://www.centralchinamgt.com
Year Founded: 2020
9982—(HKG)
Rev.: $92,796,080
Assets: $412,661,330
Liabilities: $78,979,908
Net Worth: $333,681,421
Earnings: $46,495,711
Emp.: 912
Fiscal Year-end: 12/31/22
Property Management Services
N.A.I.C.S.: 531311
Jun Wang *(CEO)*

CENTRAL CHINA NEW LIFE LIMITED
Unit 1905 PICC Plaza No 24
Shangwu Waihuan Road, Zhengdong
New, Zhengzhou, Henan, China
Tel.: (86) 4009617777   Ky
Web Site:
http://www.ccnewlife.com.cn
Year Founded: 1994
9983—(HKG)
Property Management Services
N.A.I.C.S.: 531311

Jun Wang *(Chm & CEO)*

CENTRAL CHINA REAL ES-TATE LIMITED
Block E Jianye Office Building, Nongye East Road, Zhengzhou, Henan,
China
Tel.: (86) 37166516000   Ky
Web Site: https://www.jianye.com.cn
Year Founded: 1992
0832—(HKG)
Rev.: $2,712,829,851
Assets: $16,519,220,232
Liabilities: $16,613,963,330
Net Worth: ($94,743,098)
Earnings: ($437,016,337)
Emp.: 2,690
Fiscal Year-end: 12/31/23
Real Estate Development Services
N.A.I.C.S.: 531390
Xujun Yuan *(CEO)*

CENTRAL CHINA SECURITIES CO., LTD.
19th Floor Building Zhongyuan-guangfa, 10 Shangwuwaihuan Road,
Zhengzhou, 450018, Henan, China
Tel.: (86) 95377   CN
Web Site: http://www.ccnew.com
Year Founded: 2002
601375—(SSE)
Rev.: $264,099,420
Assets: $7,045,642,656
Liabilities: $5,050,927,908
Net Worth: $1,994,714,748
Earnings: $14,963,832
Fiscal Year-end: 12/31/22
Investment Management & Securities
Brokerage Services
N.A.I.C.S.: 523150
Mingjun Jian *(Bd of Dirs & Chm)*

Subsidiaries:

Central China Equity Exchange Co.,
Ltd.   **(1)**
No 23 Business Outer Ring Road, Zhengdong New District, Zhengzhou, China
Tel.: (86) 37161775086
Financial Brokerage Services
N.A.I.C.S.: 523150

CENTRAL COAST LEAGUES CLUB LIMITED
Dane Drive, Gosford, 2250, NSW,
Australia
Tel.: (61) 243259888
Web Site: http://www.cclc.com.au
Year Founded: 1954
Rev.: $21,693,669
Assets: $28,819,939
Liabilities: $7,486,586
Net Worth: $21,333,353
Earnings: $265,201
Fiscal Year-end: 06/30/19
Entertainment Services
N.A.I.C.S.: 713910
Edward Johnson *(Deputy Chm)*

CENTRAL DEVELOPMENT HOLDINGS LTD.
Room 2202 22/F Chinachem Century
Tower 178 Gloucester Road, Wanchai, China (Hong Kong)
Tel.: (852) 3 695 0000   Ky
Web Site: http://www.475hk.com
0475—(HKG)
Rev.: $7,251,256
Assets: $30,325,778
Liabilities: $23,448,822
Net Worth: $6,876,956
Earnings: ($3,501,936)
Emp.: 39
Fiscal Year-end: 03/31/21
Holding Company; Fine Jewelry Designer, Mfr & Distr
N.A.I.C.S.: 551112

Central Development Holdings
Ltd.—(Continued)

Yangjun Hu *(Exec Dir)*

Subsidiaries:

Guangzhou Noble Jewelry
Limited　　　　　　　　　　　　　**(1)**
(100%)
Jewelry Processing Services
N.A.I.C.S.: 339910

Guangzhou Sinoble Jewelry
Limited　　　　　　　　　　　　　**(1)**
No 4 Three St Xiangping Rd Xiaoping In-
dust Park, Sha Tou Panyu Dist,
Guangzhou, China　　　　　　　**(100%)**
Tel.: (86) 2034811766
Jewelry Mfr & Distr
N.A.I.C.S.: 339910

NEF Power (Taizhou) Co., Ltd.　**(1)**
Building A4 No 1 Yaojia Road, Hailing Dis-
trict, Taizhou, Jiangsu, China
Tel.: (86) 52386260739
Web Site: https://www.nefpower.com
Solar Energy Product Mfr
N.A.I.C.S.: 335999

Shanghai Noble Concepts Jewelry
Limited　　　　　　　　　　　　　**(1)**
Shanghai City Temple First Shopping Ctr
Co Ltd Hall 3-1, No 88 Lishui Rd, Shanghai,
China
Tel.: (86) 2163553156
Web Site: http://www.nobleconcepts.com.cn
Emp.: 30
Jewelry Mfr
N.A.I.C.S.: 339910

CENTRAL EQUITY LIMITED
Level 4 32 Power St, Southbank,
3006, VIC, Australia
Tel.: (61) 396001111
Web Site:
　http://www.centralequity.com.au
Sales Range: $150-199.9 Million
Emp.: 200
Property Development & Manage-
ment Services
N.A.I.C.S.: 531311
Dennis Wilson *(Mng Dir)*

CENTRAL FINANCE COM-
PANY PLC
84 Raja Veediya, Kandy, Sri Lanka
Tel.: (94) 812227000　　　　　**LK**
Web Site: https://www.cf.lk
Year Founded: 1957
CFIN—(COL)
Rev.: $206,414,064
Assets: $615,023,649
Liabilities: $309,282,435
Net Worth: $305,741,214
Earnings: $38,709,059
Emp.: 2,304
Fiscal Year-end: 03/31/22
Financial Services Holding Company
N.A.I.C.S.: 551111
Eranjith Harendra Wijenaike *(CEO,
Mng Dir & Mng Dir)*

Subsidiaries:

Central Finance Company PLC - City
Office　　　　　　　　　　　　　　**(1)**
No 270 Vauxhall Street, Colombo, 02, Sri
Lanka
Tel.: (94) 11 230 0555
Web Site: https://www.cf.lk
Corporate Office
N.A.I.C.S.: 551114

Holding (Domestic):

Central Industries PLC　　　　　**(2)**
No 312 Nawala Road, Rajagirya, Sri
Lanka　　　　　　　　　　　　**(49.98%)**
Tel.: (94) 117421421
Web Site: http://www.nationalpvc.com
Rev.: $14,426,943
Assets: $13,518,365
Liabilities: $2,738,571
Net Worth: $10,779,794

Earnings: $2,141,037
Emp.: 343
Fiscal Year-end: 03/31/2023
Water Supply Pipes & Pipe Fittings Mfr
N.A.I.C.S.: 326122
G. Shamil N. Peiris *(Chm)*

Kandy Private Hospitals Ltd　　　**(1)**
No 254 Katugastota Road, Kandy, Central
Province, Sri Lanka
Tel.: (94) 812234309
Sales Range: $25-49.9 Million
Emp.: 105
General Medical Services
N.A.I.C.S.: 622110

CENTRAL FINANCE LIMITED
Kupondole Road, PO Box 7062, Lal-
itpur, Kathmandu, Nepal
Tel.: (977) 15970005
Web Site:
　https://www.centralfinance.com.np
Year Founded: 1996
CFCL—(NEP)
Rev.: $6,959,765
Assets: $61,836,410
Liabilities: $52,835,796
Net Worth: $9,000,614
Earnings: $308,614
Fiscal Year-end: 07/16/23
Financial Services
N.A.I.C.S.: 523999
Sanjoj Man Shrestha *(Chm)*

CENTRAL GENERAL DEVEL-
OPMENT CO., LTD.
3-3-7 Iidabashi, Chiyoda-ku, Tokyo,
102-8125, Japan
Tel.: (81) 332393611
Web Site: https://www.central-
gd.co.jp
Year Founded: 1959
3238—(TKS)
Rev.: $211,024,250
Assets: $241,859,900
Liabilities: $176,136,670
Net Worth: $65,723,230
Earnings: $5,975,440
Emp.: 89
Fiscal Year-end: 03/31/24
Real Estate Services
N.A.I.C.S.: 531210

CENTRAL GLASS CO., LTD.
Kowa-Hitotsubashi Building 7-1
Kanda-Nishikicho 3-chome, Chiyoda-
ku, Tokyo, 101-0054, Japan
Tel.: (81) 332597111　　　　　　**JP**
Web Site: https://www.cgc-jp.com
Year Founded: 1936
4044—(TKS)
Rev.: $1,059,840,790
Assets: $1,417,210,440
Liabilities: $623,679,940
Net Worth: $793,530,500
Earnings: $82,479,580
Emp.: 3,314
Fiscal Year-end: 03/31/24
Glass & Chemicals Mfr & Sales
N.A.I.C.S.: 327211
Nobuyuki Tokunaga *(Exec Officer)*

Subsidiaries:

Apollo Scientific Limited　　　　**(1)**
Whitefield Rd, Bredbury, Stockport, SK6
2QR, Cheshire, United Kingdom
Tel.: (44) 1614060505
Web Site: http://www.apolloscientific.co.uk
Sales Range: $25-49.9 Million
Emp.: 70
Fluorine Chemicals Mfr & Sales
N.A.I.C.S.: 325180

Carlex Glass America, LLC　　　**(1)**
7200 Centennial Blvd, Nashville, TN 37209
Tel.: (615) 350-7500
Web Site: https://www.carlex.com
Holding Company; Automotive & Float
Glass Mfr
N.A.I.C.S.: 551112

David Kaufman *(Sr VP-Ops)*
Subsidiary (Domestic):

Carlex Glass Company, LLC　　**(2)**
77 Excellence Way, Vonore, TN 37885
Tel.: (423) 884-1105
Web Site: http://www.carlex.com
Emp.: 300
Automotive Glass Mfr
N.A.I.C.S.: 327215
Jim Shepherd *(Pres)*

Plant (Domestic):

Carlex Glass Company, LLC -
Ligonier　　　　　　　　　　　　**(3)**
860 W US 6, Ligonier, IN 46767-0260
Tel.: (260) 894-7750
Mfr of Windshields
N.A.I.C.S.: 327211

Subsidiary (Non-US):

Carlex Glass Luxembourg, S.A.　**(3)**
Zone Industrielle Potaschberg, 6776,
Grevenmacher, Luxembourg
Tel.: (352) 7194941
Web Site: http://www.carlex.com
Emp.: 250
Automotive Glass Mfr & Distr
N.A.I.C.S.: 327215
David Kaufman *(Mng Dir & Sr VP-Ops)*

Central Chemical Co., Ltd.　　　**(1)**
Kowa-Hitotsubashi Building 7-1 Kanda-
Nishikicho 3 chome, Chiyoda-ku, Tokyo,
101-0054, Japan
Tel.: (81) 332592400
Web Site: https://www.cgc-jp.com
Sales Range: $125-149.9 Million
Emp.: 300
Fertilizers Mfr & Whslr
N.A.I.C.S.: 325314

Central Engineering Co., Ltd.　　**(1)**
5272-4 Okiube, Ube, 755-0001, Yamaguchi,
Japan
Tel.: (81) 836331301
Emp.: 120
General Plant Engineering Services
N.A.I.C.S.: 541330

Central Glass Chemspec Company
Ltd.　　　　　　　　　　　　　　**(1)**
20 Chuncheng Road, High and New Tech-
nology Zone, Quzhou, 324004, Zhejiang,
China
Tel.: (86) 5703888333
Electrolyte Mfr & Whslr
N.A.I.C.S.: 325412

Central Glass Chubu Co., Ltd.　　**(1)**
3773 Dotsubo Sennonji Tomida-cho,
Nakagawa-ku, Nagoya, 454-0971, Aichi,
Japan
Tel.: (81) 524317532
Architectural Glass Mfr & Whslr
N.A.I.C.S.: 327211
Kobayashi Syuichi *(Pres)*

Central Glass Czech S.R.O.　　　**(1)**
Evropska 859/115a, 160 00, Praha 6, Czech
Republic
Tel.: (420) 246097230
Electrolyte Mfr & Whslr
N.A.I.C.S.: 325412

Central Glass Engineering Co.,
Ltd.　　　　　　　　　　　　　　**(1)**
7-21 Izumi 2-chome, Suginami-ku, Tokyo,
168-0063, Japan
Tel.: (81) 353013210
Web Site: http://www.cgc-jp.com
Architectural Glass Mfr
N.A.I.C.S.: 238150

Central Glass Europe Limited　　**(1)**
60 Moorgate, Bredbury, London, EC2R
6EJ, Cheshire, United Kingdom
Tel.: (44) 2045161260
Sales Range: $25-49.9 Million
Emp.: 2
Investigation & Information Services
N.A.I.C.S.: 561611

Central Glass Fiber Co., Ltd.　　**(1)**
926-1 Okuchi-cho, Matsusaka, 515-0001,
Mie, Japan
Tel.: (81) 598511611
Web Site: https://www.cgc-jp.com

Emp.: 250
Glass Fibers Mfr
N.A.I.C.S.: 327212

Central Glass Germany GmbH　**(1)**
Kantstrasse 2, Westfalen, 33790, Halle,
Germany
Tel.: (49) 520166130
Web Site: http://www.cg-germany.com
Sales Range: $25-49.9 Million
Emp.: 60
Glass Mfr & Suppliers
N.A.I.C.S.: 327211

Central Glass Hokkaido Co., Ltd.　**(1)**
Izumi Central Building 2-7-21, Izumi
Suginami-ku, Tokyo, 168-0063, Hokkaido,
Japan
Tel.: (81) 353005280
Web Site: http://www.cgco.co.jp
Architectural Glass Mfr & Supplier
N.A.I.C.S.: 327211

Central Glass International, Inc.　**(1)**
2033 Gateway Pl 5th Fl Ste 520, San Jose,
CA 95110-3712
Tel.: (408) 573-6909
Sales Range: $25-49.9 Million
Emp.: 2
Glass Whslr
N.A.I.C.S.: 423390
Yokusu Kuriyama *(Mgr)*

Central Glass Korea Co., Ltd.　　**(1)**
Teheran ro 116 Dong Kyung Bldg 8th Fl,
Gangnam-gu, Seoul, Korea (South)
Tel.: (82) 25553992
Glass Products Whslr
N.A.I.C.S.: 423390

Central Glass Kyushu Co., Ltd.　**(1)**
127-4 Ishibashi Yusu Kasuyamachi,
Kasuya-gun, Fukuoka, 811-2305, Japan
Tel.: (81) 92 624 2810
Web Site: http://www.cgc-jp.com
Architectural Glass Mfr & Whslr
N.A.I.C.S.: 327211
Shuichi Sarasawa *(Pres)*

Central Glass Module Co., Ltd.　**(1)**
2333 Suozuka Shimokoyama, Shimotsuke,
329-0502, Tochigi, Japan
Tel.: (81) 285534251
Web Site: http://www.cgco.co.jp
Sales Range: $25-49.9 Million
Emp.: 50
Automotive Parts Mfr & Sales
N.A.I.C.S.: 441330

Central Glass Plant Services Co.,
Ltd.　　　　　　　　　　　　　　**(1)**
1624-3 Azashinchi Okuchi-cho, Matsusaka,
515-0001, Mie, Japan
Web Site: http://www.cgc-jp.com
Crates & Pallets Mfr
N.A.I.C.S.: 321920

Central Glass Sales Co., Ltd.　　**(1)**
Izumi Central Building 2-7-21 Izumi,
Suginami-ku, Tokyo, 168-0063, Japan
Tel.: (81) 353005280
Architectural Glass Mfr & Whslr
N.A.I.C.S.: 327212

Central Glass Tohoku Co., Ltd.　**(1)**
Izumi Central Building 2-7-21, Izumi
Suginami-ku, Tokyo, 168-0063, Miyagi, Ja-
pan
Tel.: (81) 353005280
Architectural Glass Mfr & Suppliers
N.A.I.C.S.: 327211

Central Glass Tokyo Co., Ltd.　　**(1)**
14-5 Yagumo-Dai 2-chome, Chofu-Shi, To-
kyo, 182-0015, Japan
Tel.: (81) 424857662
Web Site: http://www.cgtokyo.co.jp
Sales Range: $75-99.9 Million
Emp.: 220
Glass Mfr & Whslr
N.A.I.C.S.: 327211

Central Glass Trading (Shanghai)
Co., Ltd.　　　　　　　　　　　　**(1)**
Room 612 Shanghai Intl Trade Center 2201
Yan An Road West, Shanghai, 200336,
China
Tel.: (86) 216 219 9791
Web Site: http://www.cgco.com.cn
Trading Services
N.A.I.C.S.: 425120

Central Glass Wool Co., Ltd. **(1)**
4387-1 Aza Komeno, Takakicho, Kasugai,
486-0804, Aichi, Japan
Tel.: (81) 568811361
Sales Range: $25-49.9 Million
Emp.: 70
Glass Door Mfr
N.A.I.C.S.: 327215

Central Insulation Co., Ltd. **(1)**
4387-1 Aza Komeno Takakicho, Kasugai,
486-0804, Aichi, Japan
Tel.: (81) 568877716
Web Site: http://www.cgc-jp.com
Glass Wool Mfr & Processor
N.A.I.C.S.: 327215

Central Kasei Chemical Co., Ltd. **(1)**
5254-7 Okiube, Ube, 755-0001, Yamaguchi,
Japan
Tel.: (81) 836345848
Compound Fertilizer Mfr
N.A.I.C.S.: 325314

Central Saint-Gobain Co., Ltd. **(1)**
Kowa Hitotsubashi Building 2F 3-7-1,
Kanda Nishiki-cho Chiyoda-ku, Tokyo, 101-
0054, Japan **(65%)**
Tel.: (81) 332597694
Sales Range: $25-49.9 Million
Emp.: 40
Automotive Glass Sales
N.A.I.C.S.: 811122
Koshinori Nakayama *(Pres)*

Giga Gas & Electronic Materials
Company **(1)**
12th Floor No 170 Dunhua North Road,
Songshan District, Taipei, 10045, Taiwan
Tel.: (886) 223116602
Web Site: https://www.giga-gas.com.tw
Emp.: 26
Special Glass Whslr
N.A.I.C.S.: 423390

JCEL Co., Ltd. **(1)**
742 Chung Hunng Donhng Yeosusandan
ro, Yeosu, Jeollanam-do, Korea (South)
Tel.: (82) 616919506
Electrolyte Mfr & Whslr
N.A.I.C.S.: 325412

Japan Tempered & Laminated Glass
Co., Ltd. **(1)**
401 Hataosa, Hirata-cho, Kaizu, 503-0304,
Gifu, Japan
Tel.: (81) 584673888
Web Site: http://www.cgco.co.jp
Automotive & Architecture Glass Mfr
N.A.I.C.S.: 327211

Jiangxi Tinci Central Advanced Mate-
rials Co., Ltd. **(1)**
South Jinsha road 88, High Tech Industrial
Park, Jiujiang, Hukou county Jiangxi, China
Tel.: (86) 7927181000
Electrolyte Mfr & Whslr
N.A.I.C.S.: 325412

Matsusaka Plant Sakai
Manufacturing **(1)**
6 Chikko-Minamimachi, Sakai-ku, Sakai,
590-0987, Osaka, Japan
Tel.: (81) 722213541
Web Site: http://www.cgc-jp.com
Flat Glass Mfr
N.A.I.C.S.: 327211

Mie Glass Industry Co., Ltd. **(1)**
1565-1 Shinchi Oguchi-cho, Matsusaka,
515-0001, Mie, Japan
Tel.: (81) 598533400
Web Site: https://www.mie-glass.co.jp
Glass Mfr
N.A.I.C.S.: 327212

Niigata Yoshino Gypsum Co.,
Ltd. **(1)**
901-1 Tarodai, Kita-ku, Niigata, 950-3101,
Japan
Tel.: (81) 252552521
Web Site: http://www.cgco.co.jp
Gypsum Plasters Mfr
N.A.I.C.S.: 327420

Saint-Gobain Central Sekurit
(Qingdao) Co., Ltd. **(1)**
201 Liaohe Road, Qingdao Economic Development Zone, Shangdong, China
Tel.: (86) 53258718326

Automotive Glass Mfr & Whslr
N.A.I.C.S.: 327212
Qunyi Bi *(Project Mgr)*

SynQuest Laboratories, Inc. **(1)**
13201 Rachael Blvd Rt 2054, Alachua, FL
32615
Tel.: (386) 462-0788
Sales Range: $25-49.9 Million
Emp.: 40
Fluorine Chemicals Mfr & Sales
N.A.I.C.S.: 325180
Frank Waters *(CEO)*

Taiwan Central Glass Co., Ltd. **(1)**
40-21 Po-Kung Keng Hsi-Hu Tsun Sanyi
Hsiang, Miao-li, 36705, Taiwan
Tel.: (886) 37876586
Emp.: 100
Glass Mfr & Suppliers
N.A.I.C.S.: 327212

Tosho Central Co., Ltd. **(1)**
2nd floor Kowa Hitotsubashi Building Annex
3-5-1, Kanda Nishikicho Chiyoda-ku, Tokyo,
101-0054, Japan
Tel.: (81) 332597447
Web Site: https://toshocentral.co.jp
Glass Mfr & Whslr
N.A.I.C.S.: 327212

Ube Yoshino Gypsum Co., Ltd. **(1)**
5254-11 Okiube, Ube, 755-0001, Yamagu-
chi, Japan
Tel.: (81) 836216158
Gypsum Plasters Mfr
N.A.I.C.S.: 327420

Yue Sheng Industrial Co., Ltd. **(1)**
No 40-5 Bogongkeng, Xihu Village Sanyi
Township, Hsinchu, Taiwan
Tel.: (886) 37871811
Web Site: https://www.twys.com.tw
Emp.: 129
Glass Mfr
N.A.I.C.S.: 327212

CENTRAL GLOBAL BERHAD
Lot 77 and 78 Persiaran 11 Kawasan
Perusahaan Bakar Arang, 08000,
Sungai Petani, Kedah Darul Aman,
Malaysia
Tel.: (60) 44227888 **MY**
Web Site:
https://www.cgbgroup.com.my
Year Founded: 1972
Rev.: $20,072,736
Assets: $19,821,503
Liabilities: $7,279,088
Net Worth: $12,542,414
Earnings: ($915,777)
Emp.: 1,500
Fiscal Year-end: 12/31/18
Adhesive Product Mfr
N.A.I.C.S.: 325520
Yuk Thin Wong *(Mng Dir)*

Subsidiaries:

CIC Marketing Sdn. Bhd. **(1)**
A5-06 Blok A Plaza Dwi Tasik Jalan 5/106,
56000, Kuala Lumpur, Malaysia
Tel.: (60) 391718966
Masking Tape Automotive Mfr
N.A.I.C.S.: 322220
Chew Eh Peng *(Mgr-Domestic Sls Div)*

CICS Distributors Pte. Ltd. **(1)**
No 11 Yishun Industrial Street 1 North
Spring Bizhub 01-116, Singapore, 768089,
Singapore
Tel.: (65) 64547787
Tape Distr
N.A.I.C.S.: 424130

Proventus Bina Sdn. Bhd. **(1)**
B2-50-2 Dataran Niaga Sungai Besi Mid-
fields Square East Jalan 11/108C, Leb-
uhraya Sungai Besi, 57100, Kuala Lumpur,
Malaysia **(51%)**
Tel.: (60) 390440190
Web Site: http://www.proventusbina.com.my
Adhesive Tape & Label Mfr
N.A.I.C.S.: 322220

CENTRAL GLOBAL CARGO GMBH
Langer Kornweg 34 D, 65451, Kel-
sterbach, Germany
Tel.: (49) 610790480
Web Site: http://www.central-
global.de
Year Founded: 1993
Rev.: $10,014,846
Emp.: 33
Logistic Services
N.A.I.C.S.: 488390
Werner Eyhorn *(Founder & Mng Dir)*

CENTRAL GROUP
4 Floor Montevideo street 9, 1037,
Budapest, Hungary
Tel.: (36) 13223636
Web Site: https://www.central-
invest.com
Emp.: 100
Investment Services
N.A.I.C.S.: 523999

Subsidiaries:

CENTRAL-FUND Kockazati
Tokealap-kezelo Zrt **(1)**
4 Floor Montevideo Street 9, 1037, Buda-
pest, Hungary
Tel.: (36) 13223636
Web Site: https://www.central-invest.com
Investment Services
N.A.I.C.S.: 523999

Subsidiary (Non-US):

Wydawnictwa Szkolne i Pedagog-
iczne SA **(2)**
Al Jerusalem 96, 00-807, Warsaw, Poland
Tel.: (48) 22 576 25 00
Web Site: http://www.wsip.pl
Educational Book Publisher
N.A.I.C.S.: 513130

CENTRAL GROUP COMPANY LIMITED
22 Soi Somkid Ploenchit Lumpini Pa-
thumwan, Bangkok, 10330, Thailand
Tel.: (66) 2 101 8000 **TH**
Web Site:
http://www.centralgroup.com
Year Founded: 1947
Holding Company
N.A.I.C.S.: 551112
Tos Chirathivat *(Exec Chm & CEO)*

Subsidiaries:

Central Food Retail Company
Limited **(1)**
1697 Phaholyothin Rd Kwang Chatuchak
Khet, Chatuchak, Bangkok, 10900, Thailand
Tel.: (66) 2937171622
Web Site: http://www.tops.co.th
Sales Range: $400-449.9 Million
Emp.: 5,500
Grocery Retailer
N.A.I.C.S.: 445110
Chiranun Poopat *(Sr VP-Buying, Mdsg &
Mktg)*

Subsidiary (Domestic):

Central Retail Corporation (CRC) CO.
Limited **(2)**
Central World Bldg 8th Floor, 999/9 Rama1
Rd Pathumwan, 10330, Bangkok, Thailand
Tel.: (66) 2309507175
Web Site: http://www.central.co.th
Grocery Product Whslr
N.A.I.C.S.: 424490

Subsidiary (Domestic):

Robinson Department Store PCL **(3)**
9/9 14th-17th Floor Rama 9 Road Huai
Khwang, Bangkok, 10310, Thailand
Tel.: (66) 2 169 2500
Web Site: http://www.robinson.co.th
Rev.: $966,382,975
Assets: $868,317,101
Liabilities: $292,545,007
Net Worth: $575,772,094
Earnings: $94,713,010
Emp.: 5,953
Fiscal Year-end: 12/31/2018

Departmental Store Operator
N.A.I.C.S.: 455110

Subsidiary (Domestic):

CR Chiang Mai (Thailand) Co.,
Ltd. **(4)**
2 Maheedon Road Haiya, Amphur Muang,
Chiang Mai, 50100, Thailand
Tel.: (66) 53 203 640
Departmental Store Operator
N.A.I.C.S.: 455110

CR Had Yai (Thailand) Co., Ltd. **(4)**
9 Thammanoonvithi Road, Hadyai,
Songkhla, 90110, Thailand
Tel.: (66) 74 220 150
Departmental Store Operator
N.A.I.C.S.: 455110

CR Nakorn Sri Thammarat (Thailand)
Co., Ltd. **(4)**
89/201 Pattanakarn Kukwang Road, Klung
Sub District Mueng Nakorn Sri Thammarat
District, Nakhon Si Thammarat, 80000,
Thailand
Tel.: (66) 7531801220
Departmental Store Services
N.A.I.C.S.: 455110

CR Phuket (Thailand) Co., Ltd. **(4)**
36 Tilok Utis Road, Talard Yai Sub District
Muang Phuket District, Phuket, 83000,
Thailand
Tel.: (66) 7625650012
Departmental Store Services
N.A.I.C.S.: 455110

CR Ratchaburi (Thailand) Co.,
Ltd. **(4)**
265 Sri Suriyawongse Road, Na Mueng
Sub District Mueng Ratchaburi District,
Ratchaburi, 70000, Thailand
Tel.: (66) 3233451023
Departmental Store Services
N.A.I.C.S.: 455110

CR Ubon Ratchathani (Thailand) Co.,
Ltd. **(4)**
221 Chayangkook Road Naimuang, Amphur
Muang, Ubon Ratchathani, 34000, Thailand
Tel.: (66) 45 241 887
Departmental Store Operator
N.A.I.C.S.: 455110

Had Yai (Thailand) Co., Ltd. **(4)**
9 Thammanoon Vithi Road, Had Yai Sub
District Had Yai District, Songkhla, 90110,
Thailand
Tel.: (66) 743545039
Departmental Store Services
N.A.I.C.S.: 455110

Selfridges & Co. **(1)**
400 Oxford Street, London, W1A 1AB,
United Kingdom **(50%)**
Tel.: (44) 1133698040
Web Site: http://www.selfridges.com
Departmental Store Operator
N.A.I.C.S.: 455110
Paul Kelly *(CEO)*

CENTRAL HOLDING GROUP CO., LTD.
Office 5509 55th Floor The Center,
99 Queen's Road Central, Central,
China (Hong Kong)
Tel.: (852) 25206188 **Ky**
Web Site:
http://www.wangyang.com.hk
Year Founded: 1996
1735—(HKG)
Sales Range: Less than $1 Million
Emp.: 382
Construction Engineering Services
N.A.I.C.S.: 541330
Zhuyun Yu *(Chm & CEO)*

CENTRAL HYDROPOWER JOINT STOCK COMPANY
Da Nang Industrial Park An Hai Bac
Ward, Son Tra District, Da Nang,
Vietnam
Tel.: (84) 236 3959110 **VN**
Web Site: http://www.chp.vn

Central Hydropower Joint Stock Company—(Continued)

Year Founded: 2004
Rev.: $34,421,358
Assets: $124,221,244
Liabilities: $49,065,352
Net Worth: $75,155,892
Earnings: $16,413,363
Fiscal Year-end: 12/31/17
Hydroelectric Power Generation
N.A.I.C.S.: 221111

CENTRAL INSTITUTE FOR EX-PERIMENTAL ANIMALS

3-25-12 Tonomachi, Kawasaki-ku, Kawasaki, 210-0821, Japan
Tel.: (81) 44 201 8510 **JP**
Web Site: http://www.ciea.or.jp
Year Founded: 1952
Emp.: 120
Research Center for Experimental Animals
N.A.I.C.S.: 541715
Ryuta Nomura (Chm & CEO)

Subsidiaries:

CLEA Japan, Inc. (1)
1-2-7 Higashiyama, Meguro-ku, 153-8533, Tokyo, Japan
Tel.: (81) 35704 7272
Web Site: http://www.clea-japan.com
Emp.: 318
Lab Animal Production & Sales; Research Animal Feed & Breeding Mfr
N.A.I.C.S.: 541715
Shigenobu Kimoto (Dir)

Subsidiary (Domestic):

Kyudo Co., Ltd. (2)
883-1 Tateishi-cho, Saga, 841-0075, Tosu, Japan
Tel.: (81) 942 82 6519
Web Site: http://www.kyudo.co.jp
Life Science Research Including Pharmaceuticals, Agricultural Chemicals, Food Additives & Cosmetics
N.A.I.C.S.: 541715
Mitsutoshi Tsuruta (Dir)

CENTRAL INSURANCE COMPANY LIMITED

7-8 Central Insurance Bhaban Motijheel C/A 3rd & 4th floor, Dhaka, 1000, Bangladesh
Tel.: (880) 9560251
Web Site: https://www.cicl-bd.com
Year Founded: 1987
CENTRALINS—(CHT)
Rev.: $1,694,942
Assets: $34,645,493
Liabilities: $10,372,198
Net Worth: $24,273,294
Earnings: $961,303
Emp.: 451
Fiscal Year-end: 12/31/23
General Insurance Services
N.A.I.C.S.: 524210
Mohammed Musa (Chm)

CENTRAL IRON ORE LIMITED

Level 2 49-51 York Street, Sydney, 2000, NSW, Australia
Tel.: (61) 293977521 **AU**
Web Site:
https://www.centralironoreltd.com
CIO—(TSXV)
Rev.: $102,096
Assets: $1,845,149
Liabilities: $432,911
Net Worth: $1,412,238
Earnings: ($217,370)
Fiscal Year-end: 06/30/21
Iron Mining Services
N.A.I.C.S.: 212210
David Deitz (CFO)

CENTRAL JAPAN RAILWAY COMPANY

JR Central Towers 1-1-4 Meieki, Nakamura-ku, Nagoya, 450-6101, Aichi, Japan
Tel.: (81) 525642413 **JP**
Web Site: https://global.jr-central.co.jp
Year Founded: 1987
9022—(NGO)
Rev.: $9,251,965,643
Assets: $62,863,620,747
Liabilities: $37,709,276,511
Net Worth: $25,154,344,235
Earnings: $1,449,732,408
Emp.: 18,727
Fiscal Year-end: 03/31/23
Railways Transport Services
N.A.I.C.S.: 482111
Koei Tsuge (Chm)

Subsidiaries:

Chuoh Linen Supply Co., Ltd. (1)
3-1-17 Nihonbashi 6F Nihonbashi Hirose Building, Chuo-ku, Tokyo, 103-0027, Japan
Tel.: (81) 332716191
Web Site: https://www.chuolinen.co.jp
N.A.I.C.S.: 336360
Yasuyuki Hamasaki (Pres)

Hamamatsu Terminal Development Co., Ltd. (1)
6-1 Sunayama-cho, Naka-Ku, Hamamatsu, 430-0926, Shizuoka, Japan
Tel.: (81) 534574000
Web Site: https://www.may-one.co.jp
Real Estate Lending Services
N.A.I.C.S.: 531190

JR Central Building Co., Ltd. (1)
1-1-3 Meieki JR Gate Tower the 27th floor JR Central Building, Nakamura ku, Nagoya, 450-6627, Aichi, Japan (100%)
Tel.: (81) 525868760
Web Site: http://www.towers.co.jp
Emp.: 70
Real Estate Lending Services
N.A.I.C.S.: 531390

JR Central Consultants Company (1)
Aqua Town Nayabashi 5-33-10 Meieki, Nakamura-ku, Nagoya, 450-0002, Aichi, Japan
Tel.: (81) 527467100
Web Site: https://www.jrcc.co.jp
N.A.I.C.S.: 541310
Makoto Iwata (Pres)

JR Central Passengers Co., Ltd. (1)
8F Nihombashi hirose bldg, Tokyo, 1030027, Tokyo, Japan (100%)
Tel.: (81) 332732941
Web Site: http://www.jr-cp.com
Sales Range: $800-899.9 Million
Emp.: 3,024
Food & Beverage Stores
N.A.I.C.S.: 445298
Watanabe Kazutoshi (Pres)

JR Development and Management Corporation of Shizuoka (1)
29 Asa Shizuoka Building 5th Floor, Niello Aoi Ward, Shizuoka, 420-0851, Japan (100%)
Tel.: (81) 542825896
Web Site: http://www.asty-shizuoka.co.jp
Real Estate Lending Services
N.A.I.C.S.: 531390
Hajimie Kobayashi (Pres & CEO)

JR Tokai Agency Co., Ltd. (1)
2-1-95 Konan Jrtokaishinagawa Bldg Bto7f, Minato-Ku, Tokyo, 108-0075, Japan (90%)
Tel.: (81) 366884288
Web Site: http://www.jrta.co.jp
Emp.: 211
Advertising Agency Services
N.A.I.C.S.: 541810
Mitsushi Akutsu (Pres & CEO)

JR Tokai Bus Company (1)
3-103 Omoto, Nakagawa-Ku, Nagoya, 454-0828, Aichi, Japan
Web Site: http://www.jrtbinm.co.jp
Passenger Bus Transportation Services
N.A.I.C.S.: 485999

JR Tokai Construction Co., Ltd. (1)
15-12 Takebashi-cho, Nakamura-ku, Nagoya, 453-0016, Aichi, Japan
Tel.: (81) 524532525
Web Site: https://www.jken.co.jp
Sales Range: $100-124.9 Million
Emp.: 415
Civil Engineering & Construction Services
N.A.I.C.S.: 237990

JR Tokai Corporation (1)
1-4-1 Meieki JR Central Towers 32F, Nakamura ku, Nagoya, 450-6032, Aichi, Japan (70%)
Tel.: (81) 528568053
Web Site: http://www.jrtc.co.jp
Building Materials & Office Supplies & Furnitures Distr
N.A.I.C.S.: 423390
Hiroyoshi Okamoto (Exec Dir)

JR Tokai Food Service Co., Ltd. (1)
1-18-15 Minamieki Neo Sasashima Building 6F, Nakamura-ku, Nagoya, 450-0003, Aichi, Japan
Tel.: (81) 525871752
Web Site: https://www.jrt-food-service.co.jp
Emp.: 184
Food & Beverage Sales
N.A.I.C.S.: 445298
Masaya Sakata (Pres)

JR Tokai Hotels Co., Ltd. (1)
Meieki chome No 1 No 4, Nakamura-ku, Nagoya, 450-6002, Aichi, Japan (100%)
Tel.: (81) 525841215
Web Site: http://www.associa.com
Sales Range: $100-124.9 Million
Emp.: 1,000
Home Management Services
N.A.I.C.S.: 721110

JR Tokai Information Systems Company (1)
46-30 Higashi Ozone Cho, Higashi-ku, Nagoya, 461 0022, Japan (100%)
Tel.: (81) 529303301
Web Site: http://www.jtis.co.jp
Sales Range: $200-249.9 Million
Emp.: 461
System Development & Maintenance Services
N.A.I.C.S.: 541519
Takashitoshi Yoshida (CEO & Pres)

JR Tokai Logistics Co., Ltd. (1)
Nagoya Ksul 11th floor No 18 Taihe Sanchome, Nakamura ku, Nagoya, 453-0801, Aichi, Japan (90%)
Tel.: (81) 52 856 6811
Web Site: http://www.jrtl.co.jp
Automobile Cargo Transportation & Freight Logistics
N.A.I.C.S.: 541614

JR Tokai Real Estate Co., Ltd. (1)
Nisshin Building 11F 1-8-27 Konan, Minato-ku, Tokyo, 108-0075, Japan (100%)
Tel.: (81) 343462451
Web Site: https://www.jr-estate.com
Emp.: 295
Real Estate Lending Services
N.A.I.C.S.: 531390
Junichi Hirasawa (Pres & CEO)

JR Tokai Takashimaya Co., Ltd. (1)
1-1-4 Meieki, Nakamura-Ku, Nagoya, 450-6001, Aichi, Japan (59.2%)
Tel.: (81) 525661101
Web Site: https://www.jr-takashimaya.co.jp
Emp.: 1,029
Department Store Operations
N.A.I.C.S.: 455110

JR Tokai Tours, Inc. (1)
Sanei Bldg 2nd-5th Floors 1-5-8 Kyobashi, Chuo-ku, Tokyo, 104 0031, Japan (70%)
Tel.: (81) 332749774
Web Site: http://www.jrtours.co.jp
Sales Range: $800-899.9 Million.
Emp.: 35
Travel Agency Services
N.A.I.C.S.: 561510
Osamu Yoshida (Pres)

Nagoya Station Area Development Corporation (1)
Nagoya Station Taiko-Dori Exit Building 15-27 Tsubaki-Cho, Nakamura-ku, Nagoya, 453-0015, Japan

Tel.: (81) 525592159
Web Site: https://www.nsk-eki.com
N.A.I.C.S.: 541330
Shunsuke Kono (Pres)

Shin-Yokohama Station Development Co., Ltd. (1)
5-4-1 Nippon Life Shin-Yokohama Building 2-4-1 Shin-Yokohama, Kohoku-ku, Yokohama, 222 0033, Kanagawa, Japan
Tel.: (81) 454739427
Web Site: http://www.cubicplaza.com
Sales Range: $50-74.9 Million
Emp.: 55
Real Estate Lending Services
N.A.I.C.S.: 531390

Shizuoka Terminal Development Company Limited (1)
49 Kurogane-Cho, Aoi-ku, Shizuoka, 420-0851, Japan
Tel.: (81) 542551081
Web Site: https://www.parche.co.jp
N.A.I.C.S.: 531190
Seigo Hata (Pres)

Tokai Kiosk Company (1)
3-22-8 Meieki, Nakamura-Ku, Nagoya, 450-0002, Aichi, Japan (100%)
Tel.: (81) 525626011
Web Site: http://www.kiosk.co.jp
Emp.: 2,650
Grocery Wholesale & Retail Sales
N.A.I.C.S.: 445110

Tokai Rolling Stock & Machinery Co., Ltd. (1)
Shin-Sasajima Building 23-23-27 Minamieki, Nakamura-ku, Nagoya, 450-0003, Aichi, Japan (60.5%)
Tel.: (81) 525662081
Web Site: http://www.t-ckk.co.jp
Emp.: 80
Rolling Stock & Machinery Maintenance
N.A.I.C.S.: 488210

Tokai Transport Service Company (1)
8-1 Yasuji-cho, Nishi-ku, Nagoya, 452-0815, Aichi, Japan (100%)
Tel.: (81) 525043051
Web Site: http://www.tkj-i.co.jp
Rail Travel Services
N.A.I.C.S.: 488210

Tokyo Station Development Co., Ltd. (1)
11th Floor Marunouchi Central Building 1-9-1 Marunouchi, Chiyoda-ku, Tokyo, 100-0005, Japan (100%)
Tel.: (81) 332100071
Web Site: http://www.tokyoeki-1bangai.co.jp
Real Estate Lending Services
N.A.I.C.S.: 531390

Toyohashi Station Building Co., Ltd. (1)
No 0532-55-2711 Nishijyuku Hanada-cho, Toyohashi, 440-0075, Aichi, Japan
Tel.: (81) 532552711
Web Site: https://www.toyohashi-kalmia.jp
Real Estate Leasing & Tenant Management Services
N.A.I.C.S.: 531390

CENTRAL MACHINE & MARINE INC.

649 McGregor Rd, Sarnia, N7T 7H5, ON, Canada
Tel.: (519) 337-3722
Web Site: http://www.centralmm.ca
Year Founded: 1973
Emp.: 125
Industrial Machinery Mfr
N.A.I.C.S.: 333248
Iain Pennington (VP-Fin & Admin)

CENTRAL MOTEK CO., LTD.

115 Modular Industry Road, Buk-Gu, Ulsan, Korea (South)
Tel.: (82) 522901300
Web Site:
https://www.centralmotek.co.kr
Year Founded: 1994
308170—(KRS)
Rev.: $324,515,059

Assets: $228,080,633
Liabilities: $148,429,006
Net Worth: $79,651,627
Earnings: $865,724
Emp.: 145
Fiscal Year-end: 12/31/22
Motor Vehicle Parts Mfr
N.A.I.C.S.: 336390
Seonggyun Park *(Mng Dir)*

CENTRAL MOUNTAIN AIR LTD.

6431 Airport Road, Box 998, Smithers, V0J 2N0, BC, Canada
Tel.: (250) 877-5000
Web Site: https://www.flycma.com
Year Founded: 1987
Sales Range: $75-99.9 Million
Emp.: 300
Oil Transportation Services
N.A.I.C.S.: 481111
Doug McCrea *(Pres)*

CENTRAL PATTANA PUBLIC COMPANY LIMITED

31st Floor The Offices at Centralworld 999/9 Rama 1 Road, Patumwan, Bangkok, 10330, Thailand
Tel.: (66) 20219999   TH
Web Site:
https://www.centralpattana.co.th
Year Founded: 1980
CPN—(THA)
Rev.: $1,411,047,684
Assets: $8,170,036,164
Liabilities: $5,233,857,120
Net Worth: $2,936,179,043
Earnings: $444,668,751
Emp.: 5,736
Fiscal Year-end: 12/31/23
Construction Services
N.A.I.C.S.: 236210
Narttaya Chirathivat *(Exec VP)*

Subsidiaries:

CPN Pattaya Co., Ltd.   (1)
999/9 Rama I Rd, Patumwan, Bangkok, BKK 10330, Thailand
Tel.: (66) 26675555
Web Site: http://www.cpn.co.th
Retail Developer
N.A.I.C.S.: 459999

Subsidiary (Domestic):

Grand Canal Land Public Company Limited   (2)
161 Rama 9 Road Huay Khwang, Huay Kwang District, Bangkok, 10310, Thailand   (50.43%)
Tel.: (66) 22462323
Web Site: http://www.grandcanalland.com
Rev.: $48,555,117
Assets: $879,706,782
Liabilities: $391,108,931
Net Worth: $488,597,851
Earnings: $12,688,805
Emp.: 172
Fiscal Year-end: 12/31/2023
Real Estate Development Services
N.A.I.C.S.: 531390
Prapanpong Vejjajiva *(Vice Chm)*

Rama 9 Square Co., Ltd.   (1)
33/4 Rama IX Rd, Huai Khwang, Bangkok, 10310, Thailand
Tel.: (66) 22462323
Shopping Complex Services
N.A.I.C.S.: 531120

Siam Future Development PCL   (1)
5th-6th floor Esplanade Ratchadapisek 99 Ratchadapisek Road, Din Daeng, Bangkok, 10400, Thailand   (96.89%)
Tel.: (66) 26609000
Web Site: http://www.siamfuture.com
Sales Range: $10-24.9 Million
Real Estate Developers
N.A.I.C.S.: 531390
Pongkit Suttapong *(Vice Chm)*

CENTRAL PETROLEUM LIMITED

Level 7 369 Ann Street, Brisbane, 4000, QLD, Australia
Tel.: (61) 731813800   AU
Web Site:
https://www.centralpetroleum.com
CTP—(ASX)
Rev.: $24,809,212
Assets: $69,203,906
Liabilities: $47,465,630
Net Worth: $21,738,276
Earnings: $8,294,666
Emp.: 81
Fiscal Year-end: 06/30/24
Crude Petroleum Extraction Services
N.A.I.C.S.: 211120
Daniel C. M. White *(Gen Counsel-Grp & Co-Sec)*

CENTRAL PETROVIETNAM FERTILIZER & CHEMICALS JOINT STOCK COMPANY

Lot A2 Nhon Binh Industrial Park, Nhon Binh ward, Quy Nhon, Binh Dinh, Vietnam
Tel.: (84) 563848488
Web Site: https://pce.vn
Year Founded: 2005
PCE—(HNX)
Rev.: $130,768,306
Assets: $9,397,473
Liabilities: $1,706,339
Net Worth: $7,691,134
Earnings: $862,687
Emp.: 52
Fiscal Year-end: 12/31/23
Fertilizer & Other Chemical Product Mfr
N.A.I.C.S.: 325998
Hai Thanh Mai *(Chm & Member-Mgmt Bd)*

CENTRAL PHARMACEUTICALS LIMITED

2-A/1 South-West Darus Salam Road 2nd Floor Mirpur-1, Dhaka, 1216, Bangladesh
Tel.: (880) 29038733   BD
Web Site: https://www.centralphl.com
Year Founded: 1980
CENTRALPHL—(CHT)
Rev.: $267,529
Assets: $11,564,638
Liabilities: $5,454,298
Net Worth: $6,110,340
Earnings: ($400,961)
Emp.: 575
Fiscal Year-end: 06/30/23
Pharmaceutical Preparation Mfr
N.A.I.C.S.: 325412
Morsheda Ahmed *(Chm)*

CENTRAL PLAINS ENVIRONMENT PROTECTION CO., LTD.

Floor 10 Building A Oriental Dingsheng Center No 6 Caigao Street, Zhengzhou, 450018, Henan, China
Tel.: (86) 37155326788
Web Site: http://www.cpepgc.com
Year Founded: 1996
000544—(SSE)
Rev.: $872,833,104
Assets: $3,740,400,612
Liabilities: $2,679,821,820
Net Worth: $1,060,578,792
Earnings: $60,175,440
Fiscal Year-end: 12/31/22
Sewage Treatment Services
N.A.I.C.S.: 221320
Liang Weigang *(Chm)*

CENTRAL PLAZA HOTEL PUBLIC COMPANY LIMITED

1695 Phaholyothin Road, Chatuchak, Bangkok, 10900, Thailand
Tel.: (66) 27691234
Web Site:
http://www.centralhotelsresorts.com
Year Founded: 1980
CENTEL—(THA)
Rev.: $649,853,241
Assets: $1,582,310,231
Liabilities: $997,945,874
Net Worth: $584,364,356
Earnings: $36,671,344
Emp.: 4,023
Fiscal Year-end: 12/31/23
Holding Company; Hotel & Resort Owner & Operator; Fast Food Franchises Owner & Operator
N.A.I.C.S.: 551112
Supatra Chirathivat *(Sr VP-Corp Affairs & Social Responsibilities)*

Subsidiaries:

Centara Villas Phuket   (1)
701 Patak Road Karon Beach, Muang, Phuket, 83100, Thailand
Tel.: (66) 7 637 2299
Web Site:
https://www.centarahotelsresorts.com
Sales Range: $10-24.9 Million
Emp.: 100
Home Management Services
N.A.I.C.S.: 721110

Central Krabi Bay Resort   (1)
396-396/1 Moo 2 Ao Nang, Amphur Muang, Krabi, 81180, Thailand
Tel.: (66) 75637789
Hotel & Resort
N.A.I.C.S.: 721110

Central Mae Sot Hill Hotel Co Ltd   (1)
Tel.: (66) 555326018
Web Site:
http://www.centralhotelsresorts.com
Hotels & Motels
N.A.I.C.S.: 721110

Central Restaurants Group Co., Ltd   (1)
5th 6th 7th 8th Floor Central Silom Tower 306 Soi Silom 30 Silom Road, Suriyawongse Bangrak, Bangkok, 10500, Thailand
Tel.: (66) 263579309
Web Site: https://www.crg.co.th
Home Management Services
N.A.I.C.S.: 721110
Nathaporn Montolsopon *(VP-Bus Dev)*

Central Samui Beach Resort Co., Ltd.   (1)
38/2 Moo 3 Borpud Chaweng Beach Koh Samui, Surat Thani, 84320, Thailand
Tel.: (66) 77230500
Sales Range: $50-74.9 Million
Emp.: 335
Home Management Services
N.A.I.C.S.: 721110
Martin Heiniter *(Gen Mgr)*

Central Samui Village Co., Ltd.   (1)
111 Moo 2 Maret Natien Beach, Ko Samui, 84310, Surat Thani, Thailand
Tel.: (66) 77424020
Web Site:
http://www.centralhotelresorts.com
Emp.: 90
Home Management Services
N.A.I.C.S.: 721110
Paul Maneerat *(Gen Mgr)*

Central World Hotel Co., Ltd.   (1)
999/99 Rama 1 Road Pathumwan, Bangkok, 10330, Thailand
Tel.: (66) 21001234
Sales Range: $100-124.9 Million
Emp.: 870
Home Management Services
N.A.I.C.S.: 721110

Karon Phuket Hotel Co., Ltd.   (1)
16 Patak Road Soi 24 Karon Beach, Phuket, Thailand
Tel.: (66) 76398350
Web Site: https://www.karon-phuket-hotels.com
Hotel & Motel Services
N.A.I.C.S.: 721110

Eric A. Conger *(CEO & Mng Dir)*

Sofitel Central Hua Hin Resort   (1)
1 Damnernkasem Road, Hua Hin, Prachuab-Khirikhan, 77110, Thailand
Tel.: (66) 32512021
Web Site: http://www.accorhotels-asia.com
Hotel Services
N.A.I.C.S.: 721110
Peter Nilsson *(Gen Mgr)*

CENTRAL PUERTO S.A.

Avenida Thomas Edison 2701, C1104BAB, Buenos Aires, Argentina
Tel.: (54) 1143175900   Ar
Web Site:
https://www.centralpuerto.com
Year Founded: 1989
CEPU—(NYSE)
Rev.: $1,205,559,274
Assets: $4,541,307,739
Liabilities: $1,433,791,950
Net Worth: $3,107,515,789
Earnings: $226,837,123
Emp.: 865
Fiscal Year-end: 12/31/22
Power Generation Services
N.A.I.C.S.: 221111
Justo Pedro Saenz *(Mgr-Admin)*

CENTRAL REFRIGERATION AND AIR CONDITIONING LTD.

28 Chicago Street Central Otago, Alexandra, 9320, New Zealand
Tel.: (64) 34487600
Web Site:
http://www.heatpumpcentral.co.nz
Emp.: 10
Heating & Air-Conditioning Contractor
N.A.I.C.S.: 238220
Ken Rogers *(Mgr-Appliance Svc)*

CENTRAL REINSURANCE CORPORATION

12F No 53 Sec 2 Nanjing E Rd, Zhongshan Dist, Taipei, 104, Taiwan
Tel.: (886) 225115211
Web Site: https://www.centralre.com
Year Founded: 1968
2851—(TAI)
Rev.: $722,022,112
Assets: $1,762,572,941
Liabilities: $1,139,455,498
Net Worth: $623,117,443
Earnings: $68,345,725
Emp.: 178
Fiscal Year-end: 12/31/23
Reinsurance Services
N.A.I.C.S.: 524130
Kuo-Cheng Chang *(Vice Chm)*

CENTRAL SECURITY PATROLS CO., LTD.

Shinjuku NS Bldg 2-4-1 Nishishinjuku, Shinjuku-ku, Tokyo, 163-0831, Japan
Tel.: (81) 120810602
Web Site: https://www.we-are-csp.co.jp
Year Founded: 1972
9740—(TKS)
Rev.: $482,190,900
Assets: $456,900,870
Liabilities: $174,910,300
Net Worth: $281,990,570
Earnings: $38,151,290
Emp.: 3,628
Fiscal Year-end: 02/29/24
Computer Security Surveillance Services
N.A.I.C.S.: 561612
Takashi Sawamoto *(Pres)*

Subsidiaries:

CSP Building & Service Inc.   (1)
6th floor Sumitomo Suidobashi Building

Central Security Patrols Co., Ltd.—(Continued)

2-7-8, Kanda Sarugakucho Chiyoda - ku, Tokyo, 101-0064, Japan
Tel.: (81) 355777360
Web Site: https://www.csp-bs.co.jp
Emp.: 60
Construction Services
N.A.I.C.S.: 236220

C&P Creative Service Co., Ltd   **(1)**
Nishi-Shinjuku Matsuya Building 3F 4-31-6 Yoyogi, Shibuya-ku, Tokyo, 151-0053, Japan
Tel.: (81) 353331706
Web Site: https://www.cspcs.co.jp
Emp.: 112
Call Center Services
N.A.I.C.S.: 561422

CTD Networks Co., Ltd.   **(1)**
15-10 Kobunacho Nihonbashi, Chuo-ku, Tokyo, 103-0024, Japan
Tel.: (81) 356440911
Web Site: https://www.ctd.co.jp
Construction Services
N.A.I.C.S.: 236220

Grasphere Japan Co., Ltd.   **(1)**
NNT Building 3-1-11 Nihonbashi Ningyocho, Chuo-ku, Tokyo, 103-0013, Japan
Tel.: (81) 366617151
Web Site: https://www.grasphere.com
Electric Equipment Mfr
N.A.I.C.S.: 334419

Kansai CSP K.K.   **(1)**
1-11-16 Nishinakajima Shin-Osaka CSP Building, Yodogawa-ku, Osaka, 532-0011, Japan
Tel.: (81) 663091111
Web Site: https://www.kncsp.co.jp
Security Alarm Services
N.A.I.C.S.: 561612

Leon Co.   **(1)**
1425-1 Takenohana Mikage Nitta, Komoro, 384-0808, Nagano, Japan
Tel.: (81) 267232551
Web Site: https://www.leon-c.jp
Hotel & Restaurant Management Services
N.A.I.C.S.: 721110

Naganoken Patrol Co.   **(1)**
1425-1 Mikage Shinden, Komoro, 384-0808, Nagano, Japan
Tel.: (81) 267255363
Web Site: https://www.np-c.co.jp
Emp.: 270
Security Services
N.A.I.C.S.: 561612

CENTRAL SPORTS CO., LTD.
Kayabacho Tower 1-21-2 Shinkawa, Chuo-ku, Tokyo, 104-0033, Japan
Tel.: (81) 355431800   JP
Web Site:
   https://company.central.co.jp
Year Founded: 1970
4801—(TKS)
Rev.: $299,955,190
Assets: $275,161,080
Liabilities: $111,081,050
Net Worth: $164,080,030
Earnings: $7,667,600
Emp.: 1,176
Fiscal Year-end: 03/31/24
Fitness Clubs Owner & Operator
N.A.I.C.S.: 713940
Tadaharu Goto *(Chm)*

Subsidiaries:

Meiji Sports Plaza Co., Ltd.   **(1)**
580 Horikawacho, Saiwai-Ku, Kawasaki, 212-0013, Kanagawa, Japan   **(100%)**
Tel.: (81) 335231205
Web Site: http://www.meijisp.jp
Sales Range: $25-49.9 Million
Emp.: 1,018
Fitness Center Operator
N.A.I.C.S.: 713940
Seiji Goto *(Pres)*

CENTRAL TANSHI CO., LTD.
3-chome-3-14 Nihonbashihongoku-cho, Tokyo, 103-0021, Japan

Tel.: (81) 332426611
Web Site: http://www.central-tanshi.com
Loan, Security & Financial Brokerage Services
N.A.I.C.S.: 523150
Onishi Yoshihisa *(Chm)*

Subsidiaries:

Central Tanshi FX Co., Ltd.   **(1)**
3-5-27 Mita Mita Twin Bldg Nishikan 14F, Tokyo, 108-0073, Japan
Tel.: (81) 3 5419 3300
Investment Banking & Financial Services
N.A.I.C.S.: 523150

Nittan Capital Group Co., Ltd.   **(1)**
3 3 14 Nihonbashi Hongokucho, Chuo, Tokyo, 103-0021, Japan
Tel.: (81) 3 3271 8450
Web Site: http://www.nittan-capital.com
Foreign Currency Exchange Services
N.A.I.C.S.: 523160
Mikihisa Fujiki *(Pres)*

CENTRAL VIETNAM METAL CORPORATION
69 Quang Trung Hai Chau 1 Ward, Hai Chau District, Da Nang, Vietnam
Tel.: (84) 236829628
Web Site:
   http://www.cevimetal.com.vn
KMT—(HNX)
Rev.: $393,081,600
Assets: $80,116,900
Liabilities: $66,648,200
Net Worth: $13,468,700
Earnings: $886,900
Fiscal Year-end: 12/31/23
Steel Products Distr & Mfr
N.A.I.C.S.: 423510
Anh Hoang Nguyen *(Gen Dir & Member-Mgmt Bd)*

CENTRAL WEALTH GROUP HOLDINGS LIMITED
Unit 6706B-08A Level 67 International Commerce Centre, 1 Austin Road West, Kowloon, China (Hong Kong)
Tel.: (852) 25112338
Web Site: http://www.cwghl.com
0139—(HKG)
Rev.: $35,424,600
Assets: $261,872,250
Liabilities: $120,890,400
Net Worth: $140,981,850
Earnings: ($13,437,225)
Emp.: 130
Fiscal Year-end: 12/31/22
Investment Holding Company
N.A.I.C.S.: 551112
Patrick Pui Tong Szeto *(Sec & Controller-Fin)*

Subsidiaries:

139 Enterprises Limited   **(1)**
Rm 1603 16th Floor Harcourt House 39 Gloucester Road, Wanchai, China (Hong Kong)   **(100%)**
Tel.: (852) 25112338
Web Site: http://www.icubetech.com.hk
Administrative Support Services
N.A.I.C.S.: 561110

Central Wealth Securities Investment Limited   **(1)**
Unit 6708A level 67 International Commerce Centre 1 Austin Road West, Kowloon, China (Hong Kong)
Tel.: (852) 3 958 4600
Web Site: https://www.cwsi.com.hk
Financial Investment Services
N.A.I.C.S.: 523999

Chongqing Electronics Limited   **(1)**
Room 1603-5 Harcourt House 39 Gloucester Rd, Wanchai, China (Hong Kong)   **(100%)**
Tel.: (852) 28022433
Web Site: http://www.chongqing.com.hk

Sales Range: $100-124.9 Million
Consumer Electronics Mfr
N.A.I.C.S.: 334310

Sino Electronics Limited   **(1)**
Rm 427 18 F Kodak House II 321 Java Rd, North Point, China (Hong Kong)   **(100%)**
Tel.: (852) 28118727
Consumer Electronics Whslr
N.A.I.C.S.: 423620

CENTRAL WIRE INDUSTRIES LTD
1 North Street, Perth, K7H 2S2, ON, Canada
Tel.: (613) 267-3752
Web Site: http://www.centralwire.com
Year Founded: 1955
Stainless Steel & High Nickel Alloy Wire Mfr
N.A.I.C.S.: 332618

Subsidiaries:

Sanlo, Inc.   **(1)**
400 State Hwy 212, Michigan City, IN 46360
Tel.: (219) 879-0241
Web Site: http://www.sanlo.com
Wire Rope & Mechanical Cable Assemblies Mfr
N.A.I.C.S.: 332618
Paul Freel *(Production Mgr)*

CENTRAL-ASIAN POWER ENERGY COMPANY JSC
Karasai batyr Str 89, 050012, Almaty, Kazakhstan
Tel.: (7) 7272584941
Web Site: http://www.capec.kz
Rev.: $385,423,175
Assets: $971,141,027
Liabilities: $543,782,935
Net Worth: $427,358,091
Earnings: $23,289,928
Emp.: 8,970
Fiscal Year-end: 12/31/16
Electricity Generation Services
N.A.I.C.S.: 237130
Alexander Yakovlevich Klebanov *(Chm)*

Subsidiaries:

Astana Investment house JSC   **(1)**
Al-Farabi Ave 5 BC Nurly Tau block 1 A office 206, Almaty, A15E2Y1, Kazakhstan
Tel.: (7) 273307094
Web Site: https://investdom.kz
Security Brokerage Services
N.A.I.C.S.: 523150

Caustic JSC   **(1)**
building 28/1, Northern Industrial Zone, Pavlodar, 140000, Kazakhstan
Tel.: (7) 182731220
Web Site: https://www.caustic.kz
Chemicals Mfr
N.A.I.C.S.: 325998

Central Asian Electric Power Corporation JSC   **(1)**
Business Center SAAD 12 Floor 2 Dostyk St, Nur-Sultan, 010000, Kazakhstan
Tel.: (7) 717 264 5777
Web Site: http://www.caepco.kz
Rev.: $353,482,497
Assets: $888,774,418
Liabilities: $595,996,248
Net Worth: $292,778,170
Earnings: ($12,968,946)
Emp.: 10,441
Fiscal Year-end: 12/31/2020
Eletric Power Generation Services
N.A.I.C.S.: 221111
Alexander Klebanov *(Chm)*

North-Kazakhstan regional Electric Distribution Company JSC   **(1)**
A Shazhimbayev St 144, North Kazakhstan region, Petropavl, Kazakhstan
Tel.: (7) 152411451
Electric Power Distribution Services
N.A.I.C.S.: 221122

Pavlodar heating networks LLP   **(1)**

Kamzin street 149, Pavlodar, 140000, Kazakhstan
Tel.: (7) 182571058
Electric Power Distribution Services
N.A.I.C.S.: 221122

CENTRALAND LIMITED
21st Fl No 12 CBD ShangWu Wai Huan Rd, Zhengdongxin District, 450016, Zhengzhou, Henan, China
Tel.: (86) 63890406
NAKD—(TSX)
Sales Range: $25-49.9 Million
Property Development Services
N.A.I.C.S.: 531312
Tao Yan *(CEO)*

CENTRALE BANK VAN ARUBA
JE Irausquin Blvd 8, PO Box 18, Oranjestad, Aruba
Tel.: (297) 2975252100
Web Site: http://www.cbaruba.org
Sales Range: $50-74.9 Million
Emp.: 90
Central Bank
N.A.I.C.S.: 521110
J. R. Semeleer *(Pres)*

CENTRALE BANK VAN SURI-NAME
Waterkant 16-20, Paramaribo, Suriname
Tel.: (597) 473741
Web Site: http://www.cbvs.sr
Year Founded: 1957
Sales Range: $125-149.9 Million
Emp.: 330
Central Bank
N.A.I.C.S.: 521110
Gilmorel Hoefdroed *(Pres)*

CENTRALE DEL LATTE DI TO-RINO & C. S.P.A.
Via Filadelfia 220, 10137, Turin, Italy
Tel.: (39) 0113240200
Web Site:
   http://www.centralelatte.torino.it
Year Founded: 1950
Milk & Dairy Products Producer & Marketer
N.A.I.C.S.: 311514
Riccardo Pozzoli *(CEO)*

Subsidiaries:

Centrale Latte Rapallo S.p.A.   **(1)**
Via Santa Maria del Campo 175, 16035, Rapallo, Italy
Tel.: (39) 0185260101
Web Site: http://www.lattetigullio.it
Fluid Milk Producer
N.A.I.C.S.: 311511

Centrale del Latte di Vicenza S.p.A.   **(1)**
Via Faedo 60, 36100, Vicenza, Italy
Tel.: (39) 0444 239811
Web Site: http://centralelattevicenza.com
Creamery Butter Producer
N.A.I.C.S.: 311512

Frascheri S.p.A.   **(1)**
Centrale del Latte, Via Cesare Battisti 29 Bardine, 17057, Savona, Italy
Tel.: (39) 0197908005
Web Site: http://www.frascheri.it
Dry Condensed & Evaporated Dairy Product Mfr
N.A.I.C.S.: 311514

CENTRALE KREDIETVERLEN-ING NV
Mannebeekstraat 33, 8790, Waregem, Belgium
Tel.: (32) 56629281
Web Site: http://www.ckv.be
Real Estate Management Services
N.A.I.C.S.: 531210
Hans Schrauwen *(Chief Risk Officer)*

CENTRALE TECHNIQUE D'APPROVISIONNEMENT IN-DUSTRIEL

11 Rue Louis Armand, 92600, Asnieres, France
Tel.: (33) 141115500
Web Site: http://www.cta-france.com
Rev.: $21,700,000
Emp.: 18
Motor Vehicle Supplies & New Parts
N.A.I.C.S.: 423120
Christian Legall *(Dir)*

CENTRAS SECURITIES JSC

Manasa St 32A second floor office 201, Bostandyk district, 050008, Al-maty, Kazakhstan
Tel.: (7) 272598877
Web Site: https://www.cesec.kz
Year Founded: 2004
CSEC—(KAZ)
Assets: $12,028,693
Liabilities: $271,032
Net Worth: $11,757,662
Earnings: $1,509,316
Fiscal Year-end: 12/31/23
Investment Services
N.A.I.C.S.: 523999
Kamarov Talgat *(Chm & CEO)*

CENTRE BRETAGNE MO-TOCULTURE

21 Boulevard Nominoe, 35740, Pace, Ille Et Vilaine, France
Tel.: (33) 299606192
Web Site: http://www.cbm-jd.com
Rev.: $30,300,000
Emp.: 50
Garden Machinery Mfr
N.A.I.C.S.: 423820
Lo C. Lemoine *(Mgr-Fin)*

CENTRE TESTING INTERNA-TIONAL CORPORATION

CTI Building Xing Dong Community, Xin an Sub-district Bao an District, Shenzhen, 518101, Guangdong, China
Tel.: (86) 75533683666
Web Site: https://www.cti-cert.com
Year Founded: 2003
300012—(CHIN)
Rev.: $663,259,879
Assets: $992,212,474
Liabilities: $293,942,578
Net Worth: $698,269,896
Earnings: $114,323,770
Emp.: 11,091
Fiscal Year-end: 12/31/21
Product Testing & Consulting Ser-vices
N.A.I.C.S.: 541380
Richard Shentu *(Pres)*

Subsidiaries:

CTI U.S. Inc.   **(1)**
44191 Airport Rd Ste D, California, MD 20619
Tel.: (301) 862-2726
Web Site: https://www.ctic.us
Software & System Development Services
N.A.I.C.S.: 541511

Centre Testing International (Beijing) Co., Ltd.   **(1)**
Buildings 20 21 and 22 No 99 Kechuang 14th Street, Beijing Economic and Techno-logical Development Zone, Beijing, China
Tel.: (86) 1056930400
Technical Testing Services
N.A.I.C.S.: 541380

Centre Testing International (Hong Kong) Co., Ltd.   **(1)**
Room 1511 Chun Moon House, Ko Chun Court Yau Tong, Kowloon, China (Hong Kong)
Tel.: (852) 90125518
Technical Testing Services

N.A.I.C.S.: 541380

Centre Testing International Group (Shandong) Co., Ltd.   **(1)**
No 39 Fengmao Road, High-Tech Industrial Development Zone, Qingdao, China
Tel.: (86) 53258820500
Technical Testing Services
N.A.I.C.S.: 541380

Hangzhou Huaan Testing Technology Co., Ltd.   **(1)**
Room 105 280 Building 1 No 600 21 Street, Overseas Students Pioneer Park Qiantang District, Hangzhou, China
Tel.: (86) 57128026668
Technical Testing Services
N.A.I.C.S.: 541380

Imat (Shenyang) Automotive Technol-ogy Co., Ltd.   **(1)**
68-G6/G7 Guizhuxiang Street, Sujiatun, Shenyang, 110100, China
Tel.: (86) 2431578083
Engineeering Services
N.A.I.C.S.: 541330

Imat Automotive Technology Services Mexico S. de R.L. de C.V.   **(1)**
Carretera Estatal 200 16 270 Parque Indus-trial Global Park-Bodega 44, El Marques, Queretaro, Mexico
Tel.: (52) 4426283864
Engineeering Services
N.A.I.C.S.: 541330

Imat automotive technology services inc.   **(1)**
2152 NW Pkwy SE Ste G, Marietta, GA 30067
Tel.: (678) 402-0975
Engineering Consulting Services
N.A.I.C.S.: 541330

Imat-uve automotive testing center (Pty.) ltd.   **(1)**
Tortelduif Street 7, Upington, 8800, South Africa
Tel.: (27) 661373006
Engineeering Services
N.A.I.C.S.: 541330

Poly Ndt Pte. Ltd.   **(1)**
60 Pandan Loop, Pandan Industrial Estate, Singapore, 128275, Singapore
Tel.: (65) 67754011
Web Site: https://www.polyndt.com.sg
Technical Testing Services
N.A.I.C.S.: 541380

Shanghai Imat Automotive Technol-ogy Service Co., Ltd.   **(1)**
2nd Floor Building 2 No 777 Xin Jun Huan Road, Minhang, Shanghai, 201114, China
Tel.: (86) 2131073712
Engineeering Services
N.A.I.C.S.: 541330

Suzhou CTI Testing Technology Co., Ltd.   **(1)**
No 3286 Chengyang Road, Xiangcheng District, Suzhou, China
Tel.: (86) 51267591186
Technical Testing Services
N.A.I.C.S.: 541380

CENTRE VEHICULES INDUS-TRIELS

33 Avenue Du Grand Sud, 37170, Chambray les Tours, Indre-et-Loire, France
Tel.: (33) 247807510
Rev.: $24,200,000
Emp.: 48
New & Used Car Dealers
N.A.I.C.S.: 441110
Mohamed Boudali *(Pres)*

CENTRELEC

2 Avenue du Canal de Berry, BP 2230, 03101, Montlucon, Cedex, France
Tel.: (33) 4 70022136
Year Founded: 1995
Rev.: $11,000,000
Emp.: 77

Electrical Contracting Services
N.A.I.C.S.: 238210
Jean-Yves Martin *(Mng Dir)*

CENTREMANOR LTD.

Freshwater House,158-162 Shaftes-bury Avenue, WC2H8HR, London, United Kingdom
Tel.: (44) 2078361555
Web Site:
     http://www.centremanor.co.uk
Emp.: 3
Investment Holding Company
N.A.I.C.S.:
Benzion S. Freshwater *(Chm & Mng Dir)*

Subsidiaries:

Daejan Holdings PLC   **(1)**
Freshwater House 158-162 Shaftesbury Avenue, London, WC2H 8HR, United Kingdom   **(100%)**
Tel.: (44) 2078361555
Web Site: https://www.daejanholdings.com
Sales Range: $150-199.9 Million
Emp.: 206
Holding Company; Property Investment & Trading
N.A.I.C.S.: 551112
B. S. E. Freshwater *(Chm & Mng Dir)*

Subsidiary (Domestic):

Bampton (Redbridge) Limited   **(2)**
158-162 Shattsburry Ave, London, WC2 H8HR, United Kingdom
Tel.: (44) 2078361555
Web Site: http://www.hithdorn.co.uk
Emp.: 130
Property Development Services
N.A.I.C.S.: 236220
Benzion Freshwater *(Chm)*

Brickfield Properties Limited   **(2)**
High Holborn House, London, WC1V 6RL, United Kingdom
Tel.: (44) 2078361555
Real Estate Investment Services
N.A.I.C.S.: 523999
Benzion S.E. Freshwater *(CEO)*

City and Country Properties (Birming-ham) Limited   **(2)**
Freshwater House 158-162 Shaftesbury Ave, London, WC2H 8HR, United Kingdom
Tel.: (44) 2078361555
Sales Range: $75-99.9 Million
Emp.: 130
Property Management Services
N.A.I.C.S.: 531312
Benzion Freshwater *(Chm & Mng Dir)*

City and Country Properties (Camber-ley) Limited   **(2)**
Freshwater House 158-162 Shaftesbury Avenue, London, WC2H 8HR, United King-dom
Tel.: (44) 2078361555
Web Site: http://www.hightorn.co.uk
Property Management Services
N.A.I.C.S.: 531312

City and Country Properties (Mid-lands) Limited   **(2)**
Freshwater House 158-162 Shaftesbury Avenue, London, WC2H 8HR, United King-dom
Tel.: (44) 2078361555
Web Site: http://www.daejanholdings.com
Property Management Services
N.A.I.C.S.: 531312
B. Freshwater *(Mng Dir & CEO)*

Daejan (Brighton) Limited   **(2)**
Freshwater House 158-162 Shaftesbury Avenue, London, WC2H 8HR, United King-dom
Tel.: (44) 2078361555
Property Management Services
N.A.I.C.S.: 531312

Daejan (Cambridge) Limited   **(2)**
Freshwater House 158-162 Shaftesbury Avenue, London, WC2H 8HR, United King-dom
Tel.: (44) 2078361555
Investment Management Service

N.A.I.C.S.: 523999

Daejan (Cardiff) Limited   **(2)**
Freshwater House 158-162 Shaftesbury Avenue, London, WC2H 8HR, United King-dom
Tel.: (44) 2078361555
Residential Real Estate Management Ser-vices
N.A.I.C.S.: 531311

Daejan (Dartford) Limited   **(2)**
Freshwater House 158-162 Shaftesbury Avenue, London, WC2H 8HR, United King-dom
Tel.: (44) 2078361555
Emp.: 100
Property Management Services
N.A.I.C.S.: 531312
David Green *(Mgr-Sls)*

Daejan (Kingston) Limited   **(2)**
Freshwater House 158-162 Shaftesbury Avenue, London, WC2H 8HR, United King-dom
Tel.: (44) 2078361555
Investment Management Service
N.A.I.C.S.: 523999

Daejan (Lauderdale) Limited   **(2)**
Freshwater House 158-162 Shaftesbury Avenue, London, WC2H 8HR, United King-dom
Tel.: (44) 2078361555
Emp.: 200
Investment Management Service
N.A.I.C.S.: 523999
Andrew Colao *(Gen Mgr)*

Daejan (Reading) Limited   **(2)**
Freshwater House 158-162 Shaftesbury Avenue, London, WC2H 8HR, United King-dom
Tel.: (44) 2078361555
Investment Management Service
N.A.I.C.S.: 523999

Daejan (Taunton) Limited   **(2)**
Freshwater House 158-162 Shaftesbury Avenue, London, WC2H 8HR, United King-dom
Tel.: (44) 2078361555
Investment Management Service
N.A.I.C.S.: 523999

Daejan (Traders) Limited   **(2)**
158-162 Shaftesbury Avenue, London, WC2H 8HR, United Kingdom
Tel.: (44) 2078361555
Investment Management Service
N.A.I.C.S.: 523999

Daejan (UK) Limited   **(2)**
Freshwater House 158 162 Shaftesbury Avenue, London, WC2H 8HR, United King-dom
Tel.: (44) 2078361555
Investment Management Service
N.A.I.C.S.: 523999

Daejan (US) Limited   **(2)**
Freshwater House 158-162 Shaftesbury Avenue, London, WC2H 8HR, United King-dom
Tel.: (44) 2078361555
Property Management Services
N.A.I.C.S.: 531312

Daejan (Warwick) Limited   **(2)**
Freshwater House 158-162 Shaftesbury Avenue, London, WC2H 8HR, United King-dom
Tel.: (44) 2078361555
Web Site: http://www.highdorn.co.uk
Emp.: 110
Investment Management Service
N.A.I.C.S.: 523999
Benzion Freshwater *(Chm & Mng Dir)*

Daejan Commercial Properties Limited   **(2)**
158/162 Shaftesbury Avenue, London, WC2H 8HR, United Kingdom
Tel.: (44) 2078361555
Commercial Property Management Services
N.A.I.C.S.: 531312

Daejan Developments Limited   **(2)**
Freshwater House 158-162 Shaftesbury Ave, Kingsway, London, WC2H 8HR, United Kingdom

Centremanor Ltd.—(Continued)

Tel.: (44) 2078361555
Web Site: http://www.highdorn.co.uk
Emp.: 100
Real Estate Investment
N.A.I.C.S.: 531390

Daejan Enterprises Limited (2)
Freshwater House 158-162 Shaftesbury Avenue, London, WO2II I0III1, United Kingdom
Tel.: (44) 2078361555
Emp.: 200
Investment Management Service
N.A.I.C.S.: 523999
Benny Fashoulta (Gen Mgr)

Daejan Estates Limited (2)
High Holborn House, London, WC1V 6RL, United Kingdom
Tel.: (44) 2078361555
Web Site: http://www.daejanholdings.com
Sales Range: $50-74.9 Million
Emp.: 25
Real Estate Property Lessors
N.A.I.C.S.: 531190
Benzion S.E. Freshwater (CEO)

Daejan Investments (Grove Hall) Limited (2)
Freshwater House 158/162 Shaftesbury Avenue, London, WC2H 8HR, United Kingdom
Tel.: (44) 2078361555
Emp.: 200
Investment Management Service
N.A.I.C.S.: 523999
S. Reshwater (Mng Dir)

Daejan Investments (Harrow) Limited (2)
162 Shaftesbury Avenue, London, WC2H 8HR, United Kingdom
Tel.: (44) 2078361555
Investment Management Service
N.A.I.C.S.: 523999

Daejan Investments Limited (2)
Freshwater House 158-162 Shaftesbury Avenue, London, WC2H 8HR, United Kingdom
Tel.: (44) 2078361555
Emp.: 100
Investment Management Service
N.A.I.C.S.: 523999
James Southgate (CFO)

Daejan Properties Limited (2)
Freshwater House 158-162 Shaftesbury Avenue, London, WC2H 8HR, United Kingdom
Tel.: (44) 2078361555
Web Site: http://www.daejanholdings.com
Sales Range: $50-74.9 Million
Emp.: 100
Investment Management Service
N.A.I.C.S.: 523999

Daejan Retail Properties Limited (2)
158/162 Shaftesbury Avenue, London, WC2H 8HR, United Kingdom
Tel.: (44) 2078361555
Property Management Services
N.A.I.C.S.: 531312

Pegasus Investment Company Limited (2)
13-17 Burlington Place, London, SW6 4NL, United Kingdom
Tel.: (44) 2078361555
Investment Management Service
N.A.I.C.S.: 523999

The Halliard Property Co. Limited (2)
Freshwater House 158-162 Shaftesbury Avenue, London, WC2H 8HR, United Kingdom
Tel.: (44) 2078361555
Investment Management Service
N.A.I.C.S.: 523999

CENTREPOINT ALLIANCE LIMITED
Level 8 309-315 George Street, Sydney, 2000, NSW, Australia
Tel.: (61) 289873000   **NI**

Web Site:
https://www.centrepointalliance.com
CAF—(ASX)
Rev.: $191,933,182
Assets: $39,404,005
Liabilities: $17,144,224
Net Worth: $22,259,781
Earnings: $5,186,337
Emp.: 187
Fiscal Year-end: 06/30/24
Insurance Company
N.A.I.C.S.: 524126
Debra K. Anderson (Co-Sec)

Subsidiaries:

Enzumo Corporation Pty Ltd (1)
Level 5 127 Creek Street, Brisbane, 4000, QLD, Australia
Tel.: (61) 1300720276
Web Site: https://www.enzumo.com
Financial Advisory Services
N.A.I.C.S.: 523940

xseedwealth Pty Ltd (1)
Level 8 309 George Street, Sydney, 2000, NSW, Australia
Tel.: (61) 1800882473
Web Site: https://www.xseedwealth.com.au
Investment Planning Services
N.A.I.C.S.: 523940
Toni Zafirovski (Specialist-Risk)

CENTREX LIMITED
Level 10 44 Waymouth Street, Adelaide, 5000, SA, Australia
Tel.: (61) 882133100   **AU**
Web Site:
https://www.centrexlimited.com.au
CXM—(ASX)
Rev.: $20,466,899
Assets: $36,645,571
Liabilities: $22,763,924
Net Worth: $13,881,647
Earnings: ($12,902,740)
Emp.: 25
Fiscal Year-end: 06/30/24
Iron Ore Exploration
N.A.I.C.S.: 212210
Alastair Watts (Gen Mgr-Exploration)

CENTRIA INC.
3131 St-martin W 500, Laval, H7T 2Z5, QC, Canada
Tel.: (514) 849-8000
Web Site: http://www.centria.ca
Sales Range: $25-49.9 Million
Emp.: 6
Investment
N.A.I.C.S.: 525910
Jean-Guy Desjardins (Chm & CEO)

Subsidiaries:

Centria Capital (1)
1501 McGill College Avenue Office 800, Montreal, H3A 3M8, QC, Canada
Tel.: (514) 849-8000
Web Site: http://www.centria.com
Sales Range: $100-124.9 Million
Financial Investment Services
N.A.I.C.S.: 525910

Centria Commerce (1)
3131 St-Martin Blvd West Ste 500, Laval, H7T 2Z5, QC, Canada
Tel.: (514) 874-0122
Web Site: http://www.centriacommerce.ca
Sales Range: $50-74.9 Million
Emp.: 50
Electronic Commerce Specializing in Integrated Management Solutions for Construction Projects
N.A.I.C.S.: 525990
Gilbert Doyon (VP-Fin & Admin)

CENTRIC HOLDING B.V.
Antwerpseweg 8, 2800 PB, Gouda, Netherlands
Tel.: (31) 182 64 80 00   **NI**
Web Site: http://www.centric.eu
Year Founded: 1992
Sales Range: $500-549.9 Million

Emp.: 4,501
Holding Company IT & Software Solutions
N.A.I.C.S.: 551112
Guust Sturm (COO)

Subsidiaries:

Centric Belgium NV (1)
Siomonolaan 12, 0020, Oostkamp, Belgium
Tel.: (32) 50 833 333
Information Technology Consulting Services
N.A.I.C.S.: 541511
Pieter Taghon (Mgr-Unit)

Centric Financial Professionals B.V. (1)
Einsteinweg 12, 3404 LL, IJsselstein, Netherlands   (100%)
Tel.: (31) 306088000
Web Site: http://www.centric.eu
Business Process Outsourcing & Staffing Services
N.A.I.C.S.: 541611

Centric Germany GmbH (1)
Kreuzerkamp 9, 40878, Ratingen, Germany
Tel.: (49) 2102 20700
Information Technology Consulting Services
N.A.I.C.S.: 541511

Centric IT Solutions Romania (1)
Str Palat Nr 3C Cladirea E3 United Business Center 4 Etaj 4, 700032, Iasi, Romania
Tel.: (40) 332 710 760
Information Technology Consulting Services
N.A.I.C.S.: 541511
Gabriel Csergo (Mgr-Competence)

Centric IT Solutions Switzerland AG (1)
Rumlangerstrasse 9, 8105, Zurich, Switzerland
Tel.: (41) 44 508 28 28
Information Technology Consulting Services
N.A.I.C.S.: 541511

Centric Netherlands Holding B.V. (1)
Antwerpseweg 8, 2803 PB, Gouda, Netherlands
Tel.: (31) 182 64 80 00
Web Site: http://www.centric.eu
Emp.: 1,000
Holding Company
N.A.I.C.S.: 551112
Karim Henkensen (Gen Mgr)

Centric Norway (1)
Kongens gate 6 5 etg, 0153, Oslo, Norway
Tel.: (47) 2 360
Information Technology Consulting Services
N.A.I.C.S.: 541511
Pal Andre Loberg (Bus Mgr)

Centric Sweden AB (1)
Hamngatan 33, Sundbyberg, 172 66, Stockholm, Sweden
Tel.: (46) 8 618 65 00
Information Technology Consulting Services
N.A.I.C.S.: 541511
Klas Bonde (CEO)

Oranjewoud N.V. (1)
Monitorweg 29, 1322 BK, Almere, Netherlands   (95.7%)
Tel.: (31) 365308191
Web Site: http://www.oranjewoud.nl
Sales Range: $1-4.9 Billion
Emp.: 10,187
Engineering Consulting Services
N.A.I.C.S.: 541330
Gerard P. Sanderink (CEO)

Subsidiary (Non-US):

Antea Belgium N.V. (2)
Roderveldlaan 1, 2600, Antwerp, Belgium
Tel.: (32) 3 221 55 00
Web Site: http://www.anteagroup.be
Emp.: 23
Engineering & Environmental Consulting Services
N.A.I.C.S.: 541620
Kris Van Malderen (CEO)

Antea S.A.S. (2)
ZAC du Moulin - 803 boulevard, PO Box 30602, Duhamel du Monceau, 45166, Olivet, Cedex, France

Tel.: (33) 238282300
Web Site: http://www.anteagroup.com
Engineering & Environmental Consulting Services
N.A.I.C.S.: 541620

Subsidiary (US):

Antea USA, Inc. (2)
5910 Rice Creek Pkwy Ste 100, Saint Paul, MN 55126-5023
Tel.: (651) 639-9449
Web Site: http://www.anteagroup.com
Sales Range: $50-74.9 Million
Emp.: 600
Engineering & Environmental Consulting Services
N.A.I.C.S.: 541620
Bob Karls (Dir-Environ)

Subsidiary (Non-US):

GeoIngenierla S.A. (2)
Calle 35 No 7 25 Piso 12, Bogota, Colombia
Tel.: (57) 1 327 63 00
Web Site: http://www.geoingenieria.com
Sales Range: $75-99.9 Million
Emp.: 400
Engineering & Environmental Consulting Services
N.A.I.C.S.: 541620

Subsidiary (Domestic):

Strukton Groep N.V. (2)
Westkanaaldijk 2, 3542 DA, Utrecht, Netherlands
Tel.: (31) 302486911
Web Site: http://www.strukton.com
Emp.: 4,300
Rail Systems, Buildings & Civil Infrastructure Maintenance & Construction Services
N.A.I.C.S.: 236210
Gerard P. Sanderink (Chm-Mgmt Bd)

Subsidiary (Domestic):

Strukton Bouw B.V. (3)
Westkanaaldijk 2, 3542 DA, Utrecht, Netherlands
Tel.: (31) 30 248 69 11
Web Site: http://www.strukton.com
Sales Range: $250-299.9 Million
Emp.: 40
Property Development Services
N.A.I.C.S.: 236220
Gert Jan Vos (Chm-Mgmt Bd)

Strukton Civiel B.V. (3)
Westkanaaldijk 2, 3542 DA, Utrecht, Netherlands
Tel.: (31) 30 248 69 11
Web Site: http://www.strukton.com
Sales Range: $500-549,9 Million
Emp.: 100
Civil Engineering Services
N.A.I.C.S.: 237990
Jos J. Hegeman (Chm-Mgmt Bd)

Strukton Integrale Projecten B.V. (3)
Westkanaaldijk 2, Utrecht, 3542, Netherlands
Tel.: (31) 30 248 69 11
Web Site: http://www.struktonpps.com
Engineeering Services
N.A.I.C.S.: 541330
Erik A. Hermsen (CEO)

Strukton Railinfra N.V. (3)
Westkanaaldijk 2, 3542 DA, Utrecht, Netherlands
Tel.: (31) 302407200
Web Site: http://www.struktonrail.com
Sales Range: $800-899.9 Million
Emp.: 3,200
Rail Infrastructure & Information Systems
N.A.I.C.S.: 485112
Aike Schoots (Chm-Mgmt Bd & CEO)

Subsidiary (Domestic):

Strukton Rail Short Line bv (4)
Veemarktweg 2A, 5223 AA, Den Bosch, Netherlands   (100%)
Tel.: (31) 736901600
Web Site: http://www.struktonrail.com
Passenger Railway Operator
N.A.I.C.S.: 488210
Jacob Zeeman (Mng Dir)

Subsidiary (Domestic):

Strukton Systems B.V. **(3)**
Welbergweg 60, 7556 PE, Hengelo, Netherlands
Tel.: (31) 742558800
Web Site: http://strukton.com
Sales Range: $25-49.9 Million
Emp.: 80
Electrical Engineering Services
N.A.I.C.S.: 541330
Lex Sezenter *(Gen Dir)*

Strukton Worksphere B.V. **(3)**
Westkanaaldijk 2, 3542 DA, Utrecht, Netherlands
Tel.: (31) 346588888
Web Site: http://www.worksphere.nl
Sales Range: $300-349.9 Million
Emp.: 1,500
Engieeering Services
N.A.I.C.S.: 541330

CENTRIC HOLDINGS S.A.
20 Makrigianni, 18344, Moschato, Greece
Tel.: (30) 2109480000
Web Site: https://www.centric.gr
CENTR—(ATH)
Sales Range: $1-9.9 Million
Emp.: 53
Electronic Games & Computer Peripheral Products Whslr
N.A.I.C.S.: 423920
Maria Arvaniti *(CFO)*

CENTRICA PLC
Millstream Maidenhead Road, Windsor, SL4 5GD, Berkshire, United Kingdom
Tel.: (44) 1753494000   UK
Web Site: https://www.centrica.com
Year Founded: 1997
CNA—(OTCIQ)
Rev.: $18,717,404,400
Assets: $22,893,559,200
Liabilities: $21,884,407,200
Net Worth: $1,009,152,000
Earnings: ($501,422,400)
Emp.: 19,743
Fiscal Year-end: 12/31/22
Holding Company; Gas Distr; Electricity Supplier; Security Services; Financial Services
N.A.I.C.S.: 551112
Michael Young *(CIO-Grp)*

Subsidiaries:

Accord Energy Ltd. **(1)**
Charter Court, 50 Windsor Road, Slough, SL1 2HA, Berkshire, United Kingdom   **(100%)**
Tel.: (44) 1753758058
Sales Range: $50-74.9 Million
Emp.: 50
Natural Gas Distr to Worldwide Market
N.A.I.C.S.: 211130

Bord Gais Energy Limited **(1)**
1 Warrington Place, PO Box 10943, Dublin, 2, Ireland
Tel.: (353) 16110151
Web Site: https://www.bordgaisenergy.ie
Energy Power Generation & Distribution Services
N.A.I.C.S.: 221118

British Gas Services Limited **(1)**
Lakeside House 30 The Causeway, Staines-upon-Thames, TW18 3BY, United Kingdom   **(100%)**
Tel.: (44) 1784874000
Web Site: http://www.britishgas.co.uk
Sales Range: $1-4.9 Billion
Emp.: 1,100
Gas Energy & Services for Homes & Businesses
N.A.I.C.S.: 221210

Subsidiary (Domestic):

Centrica Connected Home Limited **(2)**
Millstream Maidenhead Road, Windsor, SL4 5GD, Berkshire, United Kingdom
Tel.: (44) 8009808614
Web Site: http://www.hivehome.com
Internet Application Development Services
N.A.I.C.S.: 518210
Kass Hussain *(Dir-Product & Technology)*

Caythorpe Gas Storage Limited **(1)**
119-123 Marfleet Lane, Hull, HU9 5RN, East Yorkshire, United Kingdom
Tel.: (44) 7881 816369
Web Site:
http://www.caythorpegasstorage.com
Gas Storage Facilities Management Services
N.A.I.C.S.: 493190

Centrica Brigg Limited **(1)**
Scawby Brook, Brigg, DN20 9LT, North Lincolnshire, United Kingdom
Tel.: (44) 1652650011
Web Site: http://www.centrica.com
Sales Range: $50-74.9 Million
Emp.: 35
Eletric Power Generation Services
N.A.I.C.S.: 221118

Centrica Business Solutions BV **(1)**
Wiegerbruinlaan 2A, 1422 CB, Uithoorn, Netherlands
Tel.: (31) 297293200
Web Site:
https://www.centricabusinesssolutions.nl
Solar Energy Equipment Distr
N.A.I.C.S.: 221114

Centrica Business Solutions Italia S.r.l. **(1)**
Via Emilio Cornalia 26, 20124, Milan, MI, Italy
Tel.: (39) 0266703639
Web Site:
https://www.centricabusinesssolutions.it
Solar Energy Equipment Distr
N.A.I.C.S.: 221114

Centrica Energy Limited **(1)**
Sully Moors Road Penarth South Glamorgan, Slough, CF64 5YU, Berkshire, United Kingdom
Tel.: (44) 1446720220
Sales Range: $50-74.9 Million
Emp.: 35
Eletric Power Generation Services
N.A.I.C.S.: 221118

Centrica Energy Trading A/S **(1)**
Skelagervej 1, 9000, Aalborg, Denmark
Tel.: (45) 99395500
Renewable Energy Services
N.A.I.C.S.: 237130

Centrica Hive Canada Inc. **(1)**
Suite 1850 10303 Jasper Avenue, Edmonton, T5J 3N6, AB, Canada
Web Site: https://www.hivehome.com
Electronic Components Mfr
N.A.I.C.S.: 334419

Centrica Hive Limited **(1)**
Millstream Maidenhead Road, Windsor, SL4 5GD, Berkshire, United Kingdom
Tel.: (44) 3332029614
Web Site: https://hivehome.com
Electronic Components Mfr
N.A.I.C.S.: 334419

Centrica Hive US Inc. **(1)**
12 Greenway Plz Ste 250, Houston, TX 77046
Electronic Components Mfr
N.A.I.C.S.: 334419

Centrica RPS Limited **(1)**
Roosecote Power Station Roose, Barrow-in-Furness, LA13 0PQ, Cumbria, United Kingdom
Tel.: (44) 1229845630
Sales Range: $50-74.9 Million
Emp.: 32
Electric Power Distr
N.A.I.C.S.: 221122

Centrica SHB Limited **(1)**
South Marsh Rd Stallingborough South Humber Bank Powerstation, Stallingborough, DN41 8BZ, South Humberside, United Kingdom
Tel.: (44) 1469577236
Sales Range: $75-99.9 Million
Emp.: 60
Electric Power Transmission Services

N.A.I.C.S.: 221121

Centrica Storage Limited **(1)**
1st Floor 20 Kingston Road, Staines-upon-Thames, TW18 4LG, United Kingdom
Tel.: (44) 1784415300
Web Site: http://www.centrica-sl.co.uk
Sales Range: $50-74.9 Million
Emp.: 70
Oil & Gas Field Services
N.A.I.C.S.: 213112
Greg McKenna *(Mng Dir)*

Centrica Telecommunications Ltd. **(1)**
Onetel Chiswick Park Bldg 1 3rd Fl, 566 Chiswick High Rd, London, W4 5BY, United Kingdom   **(100%)**
Tel.: (44) 8458188000
Web Site: http://www.onetel.co.uk
Sales Range: $75-99.9 Million
Emp.: 150
Telephone & Internet Service Provider
N.A.I.C.S.: 517111

SmartWatt Energy, Inc. **(1)**
3 Rosell Dr, Ballston Lake, NY 12019
Tel.: (518) 406-5079
Web Site: http://www.smartwattenergy.net
Sales Range: $25-49.9 Million
Emp.: 130
Energy Consulting Services
N.A.I.C.S.: 541690
Chris Covell *(Pres)*

Spirit Energy Danmark ApS **(1)**
Radhuspladsen 16, 1550, Copenhagen, Denmark
Tel.: (45) 22529900
Oil & Energy Services
N.A.I.C.S.: 213112

Spirit Energy Limited **(1)**
1st Floor 20 Kingston Road, Staines-upon-Thames, London, TW18 4LG, United Kingdom   **(69%)**
Tel.: (44) 224411800
Oil & Gas Exploration & Production Companies.
N.A.I.C.S.: 213112

Subsidiary (Non-US):

Spirit Energy Norge AS **(2)**
Veritasveien 29, PO Box 520, 4003, Stavanger, Norway
Tel.: (47) 5 131 0000
Web Site: https://www.spirit-energy.com
Natural Gas Purchasing & Distribution Services
N.A.I.C.S.: 221210

Spirit Energy Nederland BV **(1)**
Polarisavenue 39, 2132 JH, Hoofddorp, Netherlands
Tel.: (31) 235569200
Oil & Energy Services
N.A.I.C.S.: 213112

The Centrica Gas Production LP **(1)**
Millstream Maidenhead Road, Windsor, SL4 5GD, United Kingdom
Tel.: (44) 1753494000
Natural Gas Extraction Services
N.A.I.C.S.: 211130

Venture North Sea Gas Limited **(1)**
Kings Close 62 Huntly Street, Aberdeen, AB10 1RS, Aberdeenshire, United Kingdom
Tel.: (44) 1224 619000
Oil & Natural Gas Extraction Services
N.A.I.C.S.: 213112

CENTRICUS PARTNERS LP
2nd Floor 7 Library Place, Saint Helier, JE2 3NL, Jersey
Tel.: (44) 1534 884 500   JE
Web Site: http://www.centricus.com
Year Founded: 2016
Investment Holding Company
N.A.I.C.S.: 551112
Dalinc Ariburnu *(Co-Founder)*

Subsidiaries:

CIFC LLC **(1)**
250 Park Ave 4th Fl, New York, NY 10177
Tel.: (212) 624-1200
Web Site: http://www.cifc.com

Emp.: 75
Holding Company; Investment Advisory & Management Services
N.A.I.C.S.: 551112
Rahul Agarwal *(CFO-Fin, Tech & Ops)*

Subsidiary (Domestic):

CIFC Corp. **(2)**
250 Park Ave 4th Fl, New York, NY 10177
Tel.: (212) 624-1200
Web Site: http://www.cifc.com
Holding Company; Investment Advisory & Asset Management Services
N.A.I.C.S.: 551112
Claudette Kraus *(Mng Dir & Head-Originations)*

Subsidiary (Domestic):

CIFC Asset Management LLC **(3)**
250 Park Ave 4th Fl, New York, NY 10177
Tel.: (212) 624-1200
Web Site: http://www.cifc.com
Investment Management Service
N.A.I.C.S.: 523940
Conor Daly *(Mng Dir, Head-European Credit & Sr Portfolio Mgr)*

CENTRLNYI TELEGRAF
Tel.: (7) 4955044444   RU
CNTL—(MOEX)
Sales Range: Less than $1 Million
Telecommunication Related Services
N.A.I.C.S.: 517810

CENTRO CARDIOLOGICO MONZINO S.P.A.
Via Carlo Parea 4, 20138, Milan, Italy
Tel.: (39) 02580021
Web Site:
https://www.cardiologicomonzino.it
Year Founded: 1981
Educational Support Services
N.A.I.C.S.: 611710

CENTRO DE IMAGEM DIAGNOSTICOS S.A.
Rua Marselhesa 500 7 andar, Sao Paulo, 04020-060, Brazil
Tel.: (55) 1143691387
Web Site: http://www.alliar.com
Year Founded: 1992
AALR3—(BRAZ)
Rev.: $210,862,153
Assets: $477,254,774
Liabilities: $308,506,990
Net Worth: $168,747,783
Earnings: ($39,069,554)
Emp.: 5,000
Fiscal Year-end: 12/31/23
Health Care Diagnostic Services
N.A.I.C.S.: 621512

Subsidiaries:

Clinica Sabedotti Ltda. **(1)**
R Cel Dulcidio 1425 Centro, Ponta Grossa, 84010-280, Brazil
Tel.: (55) 4232194602
Web Site: http://www.clinicasabedotti.com.br
Diagnostic Services
N.A.I.C.S.: 622110

Laboratorio de Analises Clinicas Sao Lucas Ltda. **(1)**
Av Dois 529 Centro, Rio Claro, 13500-410, Brazil
Tel.: (55) 1935311380
Diagnostic Services
N.A.I.C.S.: 622110

Plani Jacarei Diagnosticos Medicos Ltda. **(1)**
Avenida Major Acacio Ferreira 500 Centro, Jacarei, 12327-530, Brazil
Tel.: (55) 1237975411
Diagnostic Services
N.A.I.C.S.: 622110

Pro Imagem Ltda. **(1)**
Rua Itacolomi 456 Alto da Boa Vista, 14025-250, Ribeirao Preto, Brazil
Tel.: (55) 1634563456
Web Site: http://www.proimagemrp.com.br

Centro de Imagem Diagnosticos
S.A.—(Continued)

Diagnostic Services
N.A.I.C.S.: 622110

Sonimed Diagnosticos Ltda. **(1)**
Amadeu Amaral Square 27 Paraiso, Sao
Paulo, 01327-010, Brazil
Tel.: (55) 30593044
Web Site: http://www.sonimed.com.br
Diagnostic Services
N.A.I.C.S.: 622110

CENTRO ESCOLAR UNIVERSITY

9 Mendiola Street, San Miguel, Manila, 1005, Philippines
Tel.: (63) 7356861
Web Site: https://www.ceu.edu.ph
CEU—(PHI)
Rev.: $33,507,269
Assets: $128,055,134
Liabilities: $33,008,645
Net Worth: $95,046,489
Earnings: $7,057,068
Emp.: 976
Fiscal Year-end: 03/31/23
Education Services
N.A.I.C.S.: 611310
Maria Clara Perlita Erna V. Yabut
(VP-Res & Evaluation)

CENTROCREDIT BANK

Build 1 31/2 Pyatnitskaya St, 119017,
Moscow, Russia
Tel.: (7) 4959568626
Web Site: http://www.cbr.ru
Year Founded: 1989
Rev.: $75,979,485
Assets: $1,115,930,864
Liabilities: $656,173,202
Net Worth: $459,757,662
Earnings: ($80,130,520)
Emp.: 493
Fiscal Year-end: 12/31/16
Banking Services
N.A.I.C.S.: 522110
Andrey Tarasov *(Chm)*

CENTROISTOK A.D.

Zeleni bulevar 23, 19210, Bor, Serbia
Tel.: (381) 30434200
Web Site: https://centroistokbor.co.rs
Year Founded: 1954
CRIS—(BEL)
Sales Range: Less than $1 Million
Emp.: 17
Grocery Store Operator
N.A.I.C.S.: 445110

CENTRON TELECOM INTERNATIONAL HOLDING LTD

Room 1606 16th Floor Tai Tung
Building 8 Fleming Road, Wanchai,
China (Hong Kong)
Tel.: (852) 2648 2811
Web Site: http://www.centron.com.hk
Rev.: $230,601,527
Assets: $418,690,039
Liabilities: $168,147,749
Net Worth: $250,542,289
Earnings: $16,987,597
Emp.: 1,300
Fiscal Year-end: 12/31/16
Wireless Telecommunication Equipment Mfr & Sales
N.A.I.C.S.: 532490
Guoyu Dai *(Exec Dir)*

Subsidiaries:

Centron Communication System (xiamen) Co., LTD **(1)**
207 No 26 Guan Ri Rd Software Park II,
Xiamen, Fujian, China
Tel.: (86) 592 5630388
Web Site: http://www.centroncom.cn
Television Broadcasting Equipment Mfr
N.A.I.C.S.: 334220

CENTROPROJEKT-ARCHITECTURE, ENGINEERING & STRUCTURAL SYSTEMS LTD.

Zahumska 26, 11000, Belgrade, Serbia
Tel.: (381) 11 2423 636
Web Site: http://www.centroprojekt-aik.rs
Year Founded: 1950
Sales Range: $1-9.9 Million
Emp.: 34
Architectural & Landscape Designing
Services
N.A.I.C.S.: 541320

CENTROPROM A.D.

Nusiceva 15, Belgrade, Serbia
Tel.: (381) 113336362
Web Site: https://www.centroprom.rs
Year Founded: 1930
CNPR—(BEL)
Rev.: $2,946,721
Assets: $6,163,046
Liabilities: $34,259
Net Worth: $6,128,787
Earnings: $2,903,868
Emp.: 9
Fiscal Year-end: 12/31/22
Food Product Whslr
N.A.I.C.S.: 424420
Snezana Milovic *(Exec Dir)*

CENTROSLAVIJA A.D.

Branka Bajica 9, Novi Sad, Serbia
Tel.: (381) 21 547 903
Year Founded: 2004
CSNS—(BEL)
Sales Range: $1-9.9 Million
Emp.: 1
Construction Engineering Services
N.A.I.C.S.: 541330
Nenad Bobar *(Dir)*

CENTROTEC SE

Am Patbergschen Dorn 9, D-59929,
Brilon, Germany
Tel.: (49) 2961966310
Web Site: https://www.centrotec.de
Rev.: $729,005,343
Assets: $658,556,070
Liabilities: $400,820,291
Net Worth: $257,735,779
Earnings: $26,241,679
Emp.: 3,222
Fiscal Year-end: 12/31/19
Energy Savings Systems & Engineering Plastics
N.A.I.C.S.: 541715
Guido A. Krass *(Chm-Supervisory Bd)*

Subsidiaries:

Air Instal B.V. **(1)**
Elbingstraat 8, 7418 EP, Deventer, Netherlands
Tel.: (31) 570625959
Web Site: http://www.airinstall.nl
Ventilation System Mfr
N.A.I.C.S.: 333415

Bricon AG **(1)**
Silbernstrasse 10, 8953, Dietikon, Zurich,
Switzerland
Tel.: (41) 43 455 48 50
Web Site: http://www.bricon.ch
Spine Implants Mfr
N.A.I.C.S.: 339113

Brink Climate Systems B.V. **(1)**
Wethouder Wassebaliestraat 8, 7951 SN,
Staphorst, Netherlands
Tel.: (31) 522469944
Web Site: http://www.brinkclimatesystems.nl
Sales Range: $50-74.9 Million
Emp.: 150
Air Conditioning & Heating Units Mfr
N.A.I.C.S.: 333415

Brink Climate Systems Deutschland GmbH **(1)**
Ridderstrasse 20-22, 48683, Ahaus, Germany
Tel.: (49) 256198450
Web Site:
http://www.brinkclimatesystems.de
Ventilation System Mfr & Whslr
N.A.I.C.S.: 333415

Brink Climate Systems France S.A.S. **(1)**
11 Bd Ampere Batiment B, 44470, Carquefou, Cedex, France
Tel.: (33) 228248829
Web Site: http://www.brinkclimatesystems.fr
Research & Development Services
N.A.I.C.S.: 541715

Brink-Innosource GmbH **(1)**
Vidda Strassa 22, Ahaus, 48683, Nordrhein-Westfalen, Germany
Tel.: (49) 2734435506
Web Site:
http://www.brinkclimatesystems.de
Sales Range: $25-49.9 Million
Emp.: 8
Ventilation Equipment Distr
N.A.I.C.S.: 423730
Martin Klein-Reesink *(Mng Dir)*

CENTROTEC Composites GmbH **(1)**
Am Patbergschen Dorn 9, D-59929, Brilon,
Nordrhein-Westfalen, Germany
Tel.: (49) 2961 96 631 0
Web Site: http://www.centrotec-composites.de
Sales Range: $50-74.9 Million
Emp.: 5
Roofing Materials & Photovoltaic System
Mfr
N.A.I.C.S.: 238160

CENTROTEC J I Asia Pte. Ltd. **(1)**
18 Kaki Bukit Road 3 03-16 Entrepreneur
Business Centre, Singapore, 415978, Singapore
Tel.: (65) 67442242
Web Site: http://www.centrotec.com.sg
Sales Range: $50-74.9 Million
Emp.: 2
Roofing Materials Mfr & Distr
N.A.I.C.S.: 321215

CENTROTHERM Systemtechnik GmbH **(1)**
Am Patbergschen Dorn 9, 59929, Brilon,
Nordrhein-Westfalen, Germany
Tel.: (49) 2961 96 700
Web Site: http://www.centrotherm.com
Sales Range: $125-149.9 Million
Emp.: 300
Plastic Gas Flue Systems Mfr
N.A.I.C.S.: 326199

Subsidiary (US):

CENTROTHERM Eco Systems, LLC **(2)**
400 S Pearl St, Albany, NY 12202
Tel.: (518) 434-3400
Web Site: http://www.centrotherm.us.com
Sales Range: $25-49.9 Million
Emp.: 20
Polypropylene Flue Gas Systems Mfr &
Distr
N.A.I.C.S.: 326121
Joel Dzekciorius *(VP-Ops)*

Centrotec Building Technology (Jiaxing) Co. Ltd. **(1)**
Room 1101-3 Building 1 No 1539 Chengnan Road, Jiaxing, 314001, Zhejiang, China
Tel.: (86) 57382810099
Research & Development Services
N.A.I.C.S.: 541715

Comfort Expert B.V. **(1)**
Elbingstraat 8, PO Box 2110, 7418 EP, Deventer, Netherlands
Tel.: (31) 881700900
Web Site: http://www.comfortexpert.nl
Ventilation System Mfr
N.A.I.C.S.: 333415

Deveko Klimaatbeheersing B.V. **(1)**
Elbingstraat 8, Postbus 579, 7400 AN, Deventer, Overijssel, Netherlands
Tel.: (31) 570625959
Web Site: http://www.deveko.nl
Sales Range: $25-49.9 Million
Emp.: 25
Plumbing & Electrical Engineering Services
N.A.I.C.S.: 238220
Tom Geluk *(Gen Mgr)*

EnEV-Air GmbH **(1)**
Ridderstrasse 22, 48683, Ahaus, Nordrhein-Westfalen, Germany
Tel.: (49) 256198450
Web Site: http://www.enev-air.de
Ventilation Equipments Mfr & Distr
N.A.I.C.S.: 335210

Golu Klimaatbeheersing B.V. **(1)**
Nieuwegracht 25, 3763 LP, Soest, Utrecht,
Netherlands
Tel.: (31) 35 60 21 084
Web Site: http://www.golu.nl
Sales Range: $25-49.9 Million
Emp.: 15
Plumbing & Electrical Engineering Services
N.A.I.C.S.: 238220
Peter Vries *(Mgr)*

Holmak HeatX B.V. **(1)**
Wethouder Wassebaliestraat 8, 7951 SN,
Staphorst, Netherlands
Tel.: (31) 522469900
Web Site: http://www.holmak.eu
Electronic Computer Mfr
N.A.I.C.S.: 334111
Mark Lammers *(CEO)*

Kempair Klimaatbeheersing B.V. **(1)**
Hastelweg 274, 5652 CN, Eindhoven,
Noord-Brabant, Netherlands
Tel.: (31) 402511431
Web Site: http://www.kempair.nl
Emp.: 19
Plumbing & Electrical Engineering Services
N.A.I.C.S.: 238220
Peter Vennix *(Mgr)*

Kuntschar u. Schluter GmbH **(1)**
Unterm Dorfe 8, Ippingh, 34466, Wolfhagen, Hesse, Germany
Tel.: (49) 569298800
Emp.: 65
Plumbing & Electrical Engineering Services
N.A.I.C.S.: 238220

Moller Medical GmbH **(1)**
Wasserkuppenstrasse 29-31, Hessen,
36043, Fulda, Germany
Tel.: (49) 661941950
Web Site: http://www.moeller-medical.com
Sales Range: $50-74.9 Million
Emp.: 190
Medical Device Mfr
N.A.I.C.S.: 339112
Peter Schrempp *(Mng Dir)*

Ned Air B.V. **(1)**
Constructieweg 49, 8263 BC, Kampen,
Netherlands
Tel.: (31) 383370833
Web Site: http://www.ned-air.nl
Sales Range: $25-49.9 Million
Emp.: 80
Air Conditioning & Heating Units Mfr
N.A.I.C.S.: 333415
Klaas Roos *(Officer-Mktg & Comm)*

PRO-Klima D.o.o. **(1)**
Gradna 78E, 10430, Samobor, Croatia
Tel.: (385) 16546343
Web Site: http://www.proklima.hr
Ventilation System Mfr
N.A.I.C.S.: 333415

Rolf Schmidt Industri Plast A/S **(1)**
Jernet 4H, 6000, Kolding, Denmark
Tel.: (45) 75534166
Web Site: http://www.rsip.com
Sales Range: $25-49.9 Million
Emp.: 50
Extruded Plastic Products Mfr & Conveyor
Belts Distr
N.A.I.C.S.: 325211
Flemming Andreassen *(Dir-Fin)*

Ubbink B.V. **(1)**
Verhuellweg 9, 6984 AA, Doesburg, Netherlands
Tel.: (31) 313480200
Web Site: http://www.ubbink.nl
Sales Range: $50-74.9 Million
Emp.: 250
Environmental Engineering Services

N.A.I.C.S.: 237130

Subsidiary (Non-US):

Ubbink (UK) Ltd. **(2)**
Unit 2 Redbourne Park Liliput Road, Brackmills Industrial Estate, Northampton, NN4 7DT, United Kingdom
Tel.: (44) 1604000000
Web Site: http://www.ubbink.co.uk
Sales Range: $25-49.9 Million
Emp.: 30
Environmental Engineering Services
N.A.I.C.S.: 237130

Ubbink France S.A.S. **(1)**
13 Rue De Bretagne Za Malabry, PO Box 4301, 44 243, La Chapelle-sur-Erdre, France
Tel.: (33) 251134646
Web Site: http://www.ubbink.fr
Sales Range: $25-49.9 Million
Emp.: 70
Environmental Engineering Services
N.A.I.C.S.: 237130

Ubbink NV **(1)**
Jan Samijnstraat 9, 9050, Gentbrugge, Belgium
Tel.: (32) 92371100
Web Site: http://www.ubbink.be
Sales Range: $25-49.9 Million
Emp.: 25
Environmental Engineering Services
N.A.I.C.S.: 237130

Wolf Energiesparsysteme OOO **(1)**
Dmitrovskoe shosse buil 71B 5th floor room 18, 127238, Moscow, Russia
Tel.: (7) 4952874940
Ventilation System Whslr
N.A.I.C.S.: 423730

Wolf Energiesystemen B.V. **(1)**
Blauwe Engel 1, 8265 NL, Kampen, Netherlands
Tel.: (31) 383335086
Web Site: http://www.nl.wolf.eu
Ventilation System Whslr
N.A.I.C.S.: 423730

Wolf France S.A.S. **(1)**
Parc Galvani 4 rue Galvani, 91349, Massy, Cedex, France
Tel.: (33) 160136470
Web Site: http://france.wolf.eu
Sales Range: $25-49.9 Million
Emp.: 20
Heating & Ventilation Equipments Distr
N.A.I.C.S.: 423730

Wolf GmbH **(1)**
Industriestrasse 1, 84048, Mainburg, Germany
Tel.: (49) 8751740
Web Site: http://www.wolf-heiztechnik.de
Emp.: 1,230
Heating Boilers & Air-Conditioning Units Mfr
N.A.I.C.S.: 333414
Bernhard Steppe *(Member-Mgmt Bd-Sls)*

Wolf HVAC Systems Co., Ltd. **(1)**
Unit 203 Building B No 388 North Fuquan Road, Shanghai, 200335, China
Tel.: (86) 2161256246
Ventilation System Whslr
N.A.I.C.S.: 423730

Wolf Italia S.R.L. **(1)**
Via XXV Aprile 17, 20097, San Donato Milanese, Italy
Tel.: (39) 025161641
Ventilation System Whslr
N.A.I.C.S.: 423730

Wolf Power Systems GmbH **(1)**
Unterm Dorfe 8, 34466, Wolfhagen, Germany
Tel.: (49) 569298800
Web Site: http://www.wolf-ps.de
Ventilation System Mfr
N.A.I.C.S.: 333415

medimondi AG **(1)**
Wasserkuppenstrasse 29-31, 36043, Fulda, Germany
Tel.: (49) 661941950
Web Site: http://www.medimondi.com
Sales Range: $50-74.9 Million
Emp.: 190
Medicinal Product Mfr

N.A.I.C.S.: 326121

Subsidiary (Domestic):

CENTROPLAST Engineering Plastics GmbH **(2)**
Unterm Ohmberg 1, 34431, Marsberg, Germany
Tel.: (49) 299297040
Web Site: http://www.centroplast.de
Sales Range: $25-49.9 Million
Emp.: 80
Extruded Plastic Products Mfr
N.A.I.C.S.: 325211
Matthias Schlesies *(Mng Dir)*

CENTROTEXTIL A.D.
Knez Mihailova 1-3, 11000, Belgrade, Serbia
Tel.: (381) 11 218 36 41
Web Site:
http://www.centrotextil.co.rs
Year Founded: 1946
Textile Import & Export Services
N.A.I.C.S.: 314999
Mirko Rasic *(Gen Dir)*

CENTROTHERM PHOTOVOLTAICS AG
Johannes Schmid Strasse, 89143, Blaubeuren, Germany
Tel.: (49) 7344 9180   De
Web Site: http://www.centrotherm-pv.de
Sales Range: $800-899.9 Million
Emp.: 1,928
Solar Cell & Silicon Production Equipment Mfr
N.A.I.C.S.: 333248
Robert M. Hartung *(Chm)*

Subsidiaries:

Centrotherm Photovoltaics Italia S.R.L. **(1)**
Via Giorgione 46, 31100, Treviso, Italy
Tel.: (39) 0422590451
Web Site: http://www.centrotherm.de
Sales Range: $50-74.9 Million
Emp.: 3
Solar Cells Whslr
N.A.I.C.S.: 423690

Centrotherm Photovoltaics Technology GmbH **(1)**
Johannes Schmid Strasse 8, 89143, Blaubeuren, Germany
Tel.: (49) 734491880
Web Site: http://www.centrotherm.de
Sales Range: $200-249.9 Million
Emp.: 900
Photovoltaic Systems Mfr
N.A.I.C.S.: 334413

Centrotherm Photovoltaics Technology Shanghai Co. Ltd. **(1)**
1st Fl Bldg 13 27 Xin Jin Qiao Rd, Pudong, 201206, Shanghai, China
Tel.: (86) 2150301089
Web Site: http://www.centrotherm-pv.com
Sales Range: $25-49.9 Million
Emp.: 20
Solar Cell Mfr
N.A.I.C.S.: 334413
Renjun Wan *(Gen Mgr)*

Centrotherm Photovoltaics USA Inc. **(1)**
100 Cummings Ctr Ste 325k, Beverly, MA 01915-6119
Tel.: (978) 922-1997
Sales Range: $50-74.9 Million
Emp.: 5
Solar Cells Whslr
N.A.I.C.S.: 423690

Centrotherm SiTec GmbH **(1)**
Johannes Schmid Strasse 8, 89143, Blaubeuren, Germany
Tel.: (49) 73449187849
Web Site: http://www.sitec.centrotherm.de
Sales Range: $400-449.9 Million
Emp.: 1,400
Semiconductor Machinery Mfr
N.A.I.C.S.: 333242
Dirk Stenkamp *(CEO)*

Centrotherm Sud Europe SAS **(1)**
1Ter Bd Aristide Briand, 31600, Muret, France
Tel.: (33) 561439005
Web Site: http://www.centrotherm-ts.com
Sales Range: $25-49.9 Million
Emp.: 6
Furnace Mfr
N.A.I.C.S.: 333994

FHR Anlagenbau GmbH **(1)**
Am Hugel 2, Ottendorf-Okrilla, 01458, Bautzen, Germany
Tel.: (49) 352055200
Web Site: http://www.fhr.biz
Thin Film Equipment Mfr
N.A.I.C.S.: 334413

GP Solar GmbH **(1)**
Turmstrasse 22, 78467, Konstanz, Germany
Tel.: (49) 753128248400
Sales Range: $50-74.9 Million
Emp.: 120
Solar Cell Mfr
N.A.I.C.S.: 334413
Eric Ruland *(Mng Dir)*

Subsidiary (Domestic):

GP Inspect GmbH **(2)**
Fraunhoferstrasse 15, 82152, Martinsried, Germany
Tel.: (49) 8918904680
Sales Range: $10-24.9 Million
Emp.: 30
Research & Develpoment Services
N.A.I.C.S.: 541715

CENTROTRANS A.D.
Stefana Nemanje br 13, Istocno Sarajevo, Bosnia & Herzegovina
Tel.: (387) 57340771
Web Site: http://www.centrotrans-ad.com
Year Founded: 1993
Logistic Services
N.A.I.C.S.: 541614

CENTROTRANS TRANSPORT ROBE D.D. SARAJEVO
Kurta Schorka 18, 71000, Sarajevo, Bosnia & Herzegovina
Tel.: (387) 3 345 4214
Web Site: http://www.centrotrans-ctr.com
CTRBR—(SARE)
Rev.: $97,673
Assets: $4,611,702
Liabilities: $1,964,011
Net Worth: $2,647,691
Earnings: $3,759
Emp.: 7
Fiscal Year-end: 12/31/20
Transportation Services
N.A.I.C.S.: 488490

CENTROTRANS-EUROLINES D.D.
Kurta Schorka 14, Sarajevo, 71000, Bosnia & Herzegovina
Tel.: (387) 3 377 0800
Web Site: http://www.centrotrans.com
Year Founded: 1963
CTBURK4—(SARE)
Rev.: $14,077,401
Assets: $28,415,931
Liabilities: $13,363,661
Net Worth: $15,052,270
Earnings: ($795,559)
Emp.: 493
Fiscal Year-end: 12/31/20
Passenger Transportation Services
N.A.I.C.S.: 488490

CENTROTRANS-TRANZIT D.D.
ul Kurta Schorka br 8, 71000, Sarajevo, Bosnia & Herzegovina
Tel.: (387) 3 354 4138
Web Site:
http://www.centrotranstranzit.com

CTRTR—(SARE)
Rev.: $341,336
Assets: $5,291,208
Liabilities: $793,725
Net Worth: $4,497,482
Earnings: ($526,025)
Emp.: 16
Fiscal Year-end: 12/31/20
Food Transportation Services
N.A.I.C.S.: 484110

CENTRUM CAPITAL LTD.
Centrum House CST Road Vidya Nagari Marg Kalina, Santa Cruz East, Mumbai, 400 098, India
Tel.: (91) 2242159000
Web Site: https://www.centrum.co.in
Year Founded: 1977
CENTRUM—(NSE)
Rev.: $70,044,333
Assets: $431,338,731
Liabilities: $325,380,920
Net Worth: $105,957,811
Earnings: ($5,706,888)
Emp.: 39
Fiscal Year-end: 03/31/21
Investment Banking Services
N.A.I.C.S.: 523150
Alpesh Shah *(Compliance Officer & Sec)*

Subsidiaries:

Centrum Financial Services Limited **(1)**
Centrum House C S T Road Vidyanagari Marg Kalina Santacruz East, Mumbai, 40009, India
Tel.: (91) 224 215 9000
Investment Banking Services
N.A.I.C.S.: 523999

Centrum Microcredit Limited **(1)**
402 Level 4 Kirol Road, Neelkanth Corporate Park Vidyavihar West, Mumbai, 400 086, India
Tel.: (91) 226 275 6212
Web Site:
https://www.centrummicrocredit.com
Financial Services
N.A.I.C.S.: 523999
Prashant Thakker *(Exec Dir & CEO)*

Centrum Wealth Limited **(1)**
Centrum House CST Road Vidyanagari Marg, Kalina Santacruz East, Mumbai, 400098, India
Tel.: (91) 224 215 9000
Web Site: https://www.centrumwealth.co.in
Wealth Management Services
N.A.I.C.S.: 523940
S. Ganashyam *(Mng Dir)*

Club 7 Holidays Limited **(1)**
203 2nd FloorFortune 2000 B-Wing Bandra Kurla Complex, Bandra E, Mumbai, 700 026, India
Tel.: (91) 2266467400
Web Site: http://www.club7holidays.co.in
Sales Range: $25-49.9 Million
Emp.: 100
Travel & Tour Operator
N.A.I.C.S.: 561520
Barun Bhattacharya *(Asst Mgr-Product Dev)*

Pyxis Finvest Limited **(1)**
208 P J Towers Dalal Street Fort, Kalina Santacruz East, Mumbai, 400 001, India
Tel.: (91) 2242159000
Web Site: https://www.pyxisfinvest.com
Rev.: $238,023
Assets: $4,008,989
Liabilities: $1,944,968
Net Worth: $2,064,021
Earnings: ($1,885,845)
Emp.: 3
Fiscal Year-end: 03/31/2021
Financial Services
N.A.I.C.S.: 525990
Shailendrate Apte *(CFO)*

CENTRUM MEDYCZNE ENEL-MED S.A.
ul Slominskiego 19 lok 524, 00-195, Warsaw, Poland

Centrum Medyczne ENEL-MED S.A.—(Continued)

Tel.: (48) 224317701
Web Site: https://www.enel.pl
Year Founded: 1993
ENE—(WAR)
Rev.: $157,150,914
Assets: $120,939,532
Liabilities: $80,203,760
Net Worth: $40,735,772
Earnings: $2,090,701
Emp.: 2,000
Fiscal Year-end: 12/31/23
Hospital Management & Other Medical Related Services
N.A.I.C.S.: 622110
Anna Rozwadowska *(Member-Mgmt Bd)*

CENTRUM NOWOCZESNYCH TECHNOLOGII S.A.
ul Partyzantow 11, Sosnowiec, Poland
Tel.: (48) 32 294 40 11
Web Site: http://www.cntsa.pl
Year Founded: 1968
CNT—(WAR)
Sales Range: Less than $1 Million
Construction Engineering Services
N.A.I.C.S.: 237990
Jacek Tazbirek *(Chm-Mgmt Bd & Gen Mgr)*

CENTUM ELECTRONICS LTD.
44 KHB Industrial Area Yelahanka Newtown, Bengaluru, 560 106, India
Tel.: (91) 8041436000 In
Web Site:
https://www.centumelectronics.com
CENTUM—(NSE)
Rev.: $107,557,086
Assets: $125,984,177
Liabilities: $98,886,197
Net Worth: $27,097,980
Earnings: ($7,297,973)
Emp.: 1,172
Fiscal Year-end: 03/31/22
Electronic Components Mfr
N.A.I.C.S.: 334413
Apparao V. Mallavarapu *(Chm & Mng Dir)*

Subsidiaries:

Centum Adetel Transportation System SAS **(1)**
4 Chemin du Ruisseau, 69134, Ecully, France
Tel.: (33) 472180840
Web Site: http://www.adetelsolution.com
Rail Transportation Services
N.A.I.C.S.: 488210

CENTUM INVESTMENT COMPANY LIMITED
9th Floor or 8th Floor South Tower Two Rivers, PO Box 10518, 00100, Nairobi, Kenya
Tel.: (254) 202230518 KE
Web Site: https://www.centum.co.ke
Year Founded: 1967
CTUM—(NAI)
Rev.: $70,501,094
Assets: $578,901,573
Liabilities: $276,694,648
Net Worth: $302,206,925
Earnings: $19,788,268
Emp.: 1,088
Fiscal Year-end: 03/31/24
Investment Management Service
N.A.I.C.S.: 523999
James M. Mworia *(CEO-Grp & Mng Dir)*

Subsidiaries:

Athena Properties Limited **(1)**
The Gate House Two Rivers Development Off Northern Bypass Entrance, PO Box 10518-00100, Nairobi, Kenya

Tel.: (254) 20 228 6000
Web Site: https://www.athena-properties.com
Real Estate Development Services
N.A.I.C.S.: 531390
Samuel Kariuki *(Mng Dir)*

Jafari Credit Limited **(1)**
2nd floor Caxton House Kenyatta Avenue, Nairobi, Kenya
Tel.: (254) 708509573
Web Site: https://www.jafaricredit.co.ke
Credit Institution Operator
N.A.I.C.S.: 522390

Nabo Capital Limited **(1)**
5th Floor International House, PO Box 10518-00100, Nairobi, Kenya
Tel.: (254) 709902700
Web Site: http://www.nabocapital.com
Investment Management Service
N.A.I.C.S.: 523940
Robert Bunyi *(Chm)*

Pearl Marina Estates Limited **(1)**
Acacia Mall Level 4 Office Number 327, PO Box 10946, Kampala, Uganda
Tel.: (256) 704271855
Web Site: http://www.pearlmarina.co.ug
Real Estate Development Services
N.A.I.C.S.: 531390
James Mugerwa *(Mng Dir)*

Two Rivers Development Limited **(1)**
Limuru Road, Nairobi, Kenya
Tel.: (254) 70 919 0508
Web Site: https://www.tworivers-development.com
Construction Development Services
N.A.I.C.S.: 236220
Christopher J. Kirubi *(Chm)*

Vipingo Development Limited **(1)**
PO Box 117 - 80119, Vipingo, Mombasa, Kenya
Tel.: (254) 74 040 0215
Web Site:
https://www.vipingodevelopment.com
Construction Development Services
N.A.I.C.S.: 236220
Raphael Nyamai *(Asst Gen Mgr)*

Zohari Credit Limited **(1)**
Applewood Park 1st Floor Suite 205 Wood Street Off Wood Avenue, PO Box 10518-00100, Kilimani, Nairobi, Kenya
Tel.: (254) 709902000
Web Site: https://www.zoharileasing.com
Credit Institution Operator
N.A.I.C.S.: 522390

Zohari Leasing Limited **(1)**
Applewood Park 1st Floor Suite 205 Wood Street Off Wood Avenue, PO Box 10518-00100, Kilimani, Nairobi, Kenya
Tel.: (254) 70 990 2000
Web Site: https://www.zoharileasing.com
Industrial Machinery Leasing Services
N.A.I.C.S.: 532490

CENTURIA CAPITAL LIMITED
Tel.: (61) 289238923 AU
Web Site:
https://www.centuria.com.au
Year Founded: 1991
CNI—(ASX)
Rev.: $241,321,640
Assets: $1,519,111,951
Liabilities: $594,688,009
Net Worth: $924,423,942
Earnings: $69,069,570
Emp.: 400
Fiscal Year-end: 06/30/23
Investment Management Service
N.A.I.C.S.: 523999
Jason C. Huljich *(Co-CEO)*

Subsidiaries:

360 Capital Group Limited **(1)**
Suite 3701 Level 37 1 Macquarie Place, Sydney, 2000, NSW, Australia
Tel.: (61) 284058860
Web Site: https://www.360capital.com.au
Rev.: $14,680,932
Assets: $219,486,806
Liabilities: $56,142,911
Net Worth: $163,343,894

Earnings: ($9,873,204)
Emp.: 18
Fiscal Year-end: 06/30/2024
Holding Company; Real Estate Investment & Fund Management Services
N.A.I.C.S.: 551112
Tony Robert Pitt *(Founder, Exec Chm & Mng Dir)*

Subsidiary (Domestic):

360 Capital Investment Management Limited **(2)**
Level 8 56 Pitt Street, Sydney, 2000, NSW, Australia
Tel.: (61) 2 8405 8860
Web Site: http://www.360capital.com.au
Real Estate Trust & Investment Fund Management Services
N.A.I.C.S.: 523940
Tony Robert Pitt *(Mng Dir)*

Affiliate (Domestic):

360 Capital REIT **(3)**
Level 8 56 Pitt Street, Sydney, 2000, NSW, Australia
Tel.: (61) 284058860
Web Site: http://www.360capital.com.au
Rev.: $40,362,889
Assets: $154,591,858
Liabilities: $12,760,894
Net Worth: $141,830,963
Earnings: $25,839,758
Fiscal Year-end: 06/30/2022
Real Estate Investment Trust
N.A.I.C.S.: 525990
Tony Robert Pitt *(Mng Dir/Mng Dir-Grp)*

Subsidiary (Domestic):

URB Investments Limited **(4)**
Level 2 160 Pitt Street Mall, Sydney, 2000, NSW, Australia
Tel.: (61) 292107000
Sales Range: $1-9.9 Million
Portfolio Management Services
N.A.I.C.S.: 523940

Subsidiary (Domestic):

Trafalgar Corporate Pty. Limited **(2)**
Level 4 111 Harrington Street, Grosvenor Place, Sydney, 2000, NSW, Australia **(100%)**
Tel.: (61) 2 9252 4211
Sales Range: $50-74.9 Million
Real Estate Investment & Fund Management Services
N.A.I.C.S.: 531390

Subsidiary (Domestic):

Trafalgar Managed Investments Limited **(3)**
Level 4 111 Harrington Street, Grosvenor Place, Sydney, 2000, NSW, Australia **(100%)**
Tel.: (61) 2 9252 4211
Property Investment Management Services
N.A.I.C.S.: 523940

Centuria Capital NZ No.1 Ltd. **(1)**
Level 2 Bayleys House 30 Gaunt Street, Wynyard Quarter, Auckland, 1010, New Zealand **(90.8%)**
Tel.: (64) 93006161
Web Site: http://www.centuria.co.nz
Commercial & Industrial Property Management Services
N.A.I.C.S.: 531390
Mark E. Francis *(CEO)*

Centuria Industrial REIT **(1)**
Suite 39 01 Level 39 100 Miller Street, Sydney, 2060, NSW, Australia
Tel.: (61) 89238923
Web Site: http://www.centuria.com.au
Rev.: $152,197,978
Assets: $2,593,114,203
Liabilities: $952,002,928
Net Worth: $1,641,111,275
Earnings: $32,151,013
Fiscal Year-end: 06/30/2024
Real Estate Investment Trust
N.A.I.C.S.: 525990
Peter Done *(Chm)*

Centuria Office REIT **(1)**
Level 41 Chifley Tower 2 Chifley Square, North Sydney, 2000, NSW, Australia

Tel.: (61) 289238923
Web Site: http://www.centuria.com.au
Rev.: $107,893,429
Assets: $1,320,686,888
Liabilities: $602,252,735
Net Worth: $718,434,153
Earnings: ($112,677,786)
Emp.: 85
Fiscal Year-end: 06/30/2024
Real Estate Investment Trust
N.A.I.C.S.: 525990

Centuria Property Funds Limited **(1)**
Level 41 Chifley Tower 2 Chifley Square, Sydney, 2000, NSW, Australia
Tel.: (61) 289238923
Sales Range: $50-74.9 Million
Emp.: 5
Property Fund Management Services
N.A.I.C.S.: 525910

Centuria Property Funds No. 2 Limited **(1)**
Level 23 111 Pacific Highway, North Sydney, Sydney, 2060, NSW, Australia **(100%)**
Tel.: (61) 289238923
Property Fund Management Services
N.A.I.C.S.: 525910

Over Fifty Funds Management Pty Ltd **(1)**
Level 32 120 Collins Street, Melbourne, 3000, VIC, Australia
Tel.: (61) 396166500
Web Site: http://www.centuria.com.au
Sales Range: $50-74.9 Million
Emp.: 20
Financial Management Services
N.A.I.C.S.: 523999

Over Fifty Seniors Equity Release Pty Ltd **(1)**
GPO Box 695, Melbourne, 3001, VIC, Australia
Tel.: (61) 396166523
Web Site: https://www.overfifty.com.au
Portfolio Management Services
N.A.I.C.S.: 523940

Primewest (Northlands) Pty Ltd **(1)**
Wanneroo Rd and Amelia St, Balcatta, 6021, WA, Australia
Tel.: (61) 89 261 6666
Web Site:
https://www.primewestnorthlands.com.au
Shopping Mall Center Services
N.A.I.C.S.: 531120
Casey Parker *(Mgr)*

CENTURION CORPORATION LIMITED
45 Ubi Road 1 05-01, Singapore, 408696, Singapore
Tel.: (65) 67453288
Web Site:
https://www.centurioncorp.com.sg
OU8—(SES)
Rev.: $156,968,113
Assets: $1,306,590,926
Liabilities: $646,412,936
Net Worth: $660,177,990
Earnings: $133,237,143
Emp.: 486
Fiscal Year-end: 12/31/23
Holding Company; Dormitory Management Services; Optical Storage Media Mfr
N.A.I.C.S.: 551112
Chee Min Kong *(CEO)*

Subsidiaries:

CSL Student Living (Selegie) Pte. Ltd. **(1)**
1A Short Street, Singapore, 188210, Singapore
Tel.: (65) 62386339
Web Site: http://www.dwellstudent.com.sg
Accommodation Services
N.A.I.C.S.: 721110
Adeline Loh *(Ops Mgr)*

CSL Student Living Benikea KP Ltd. **(1)**
188-5 Hoegi-ro, Dongdaemun-gu, Seoul,

02446, Korea (South)
Tel.: (82) 29570700
Web Site: https://www.dwellstudent.co.kr
Accommodation Services
N.A.I.C.S.: 721110
Kong Chee Min *(CEO)*

Centurion - Lian Beng (Papan) Pte. Ltd. (1)
5C Jalan Papan 02-29, Singapore, 619420, Singapore
Tel.: (65) 62551028
Real Estate Services
N.A.I.C.S.: 531390

Centurion Dormitories Pte Ltd. (1)
45 Ubi Road 1 05-01, Singapore, 408696, Singapore
Tel.: (65) 67453288
Web Site: http://www.centurioncorp.com.se
Emp.: 100
Dormitory Building & Management Services
N.A.I.C.S.: 531311

Subsidiary (Non-US):

Centurion Dormitories Sdn Bhd (2)
No 17 Jalan Ekoperniagaan 1/23 Taman Ekoperniagaan, Tebrau IV, 81100, Johor Bahru, Johor, Malaysia
Tel.: (60) 75559366
Dormitory Management Services
N.A.I.C.S.: 531311

Centurion Dormitory (Westlite) Pte Ltd. (1)
28 Toh Guan Road East 02-01, Westlite Dormitory, Singapore, 608596, Singapore
Tel.: (65) 63163018
Web Site: http://www.centurioncorp.com.sg
Emp.: 12
Dormitory Building & Management Services
N.A.I.C.S.: 531311
Majid Deen *(Mgr-Grp Dormitory)*

Centurion Student Services (UK) Ltd. (1)
Lower Chatham Street, Manchester, M1 5SX, United Kingdom
Tel.: (44) 1612005540
Accommodation Services
N.A.I.C.S.: 721110
Lauren Newton *(Mgr-Accommodation)*

Centurion Student Services Pty. Ltd. (1)
5-17 Flemington Road, North Melbourne, 3051, VIC, Australia
Tel.: (61) 383302000
Accommodation Services
N.A.I.C.S.: 721110

Dwell Adelaide Student Living Pty. Ltd. (1)
12-18 Synagogue Place, Adelaide, 5000, SA, Australia
Tel.: (61) 884709291
Accommodation Services
N.A.I.C.S.: 721110

Dwell US Student Living LLC (1)
200 College St, New Haven, CT 06510
Tel.: (203) 428-4758
Web Site: https://www.dwellstudent.us
Hospitality Services
N.A.I.C.S.: 722513
Mirjana Hernandez *(Reg Dir-Ops)*

SM Summit Holdings Pte Ltd. (1)
45 Ubi Road 1 04-02, Singapore, 408696, Singapore
Tel.: (65) 67453288
Holding Company
N.A.I.C.S.: 551112

Subsidiary (Domestic):

Summit CD Manufacture Pte Ltd (2)
45 Ubi Road 1 04-02, Singapore, 408696, Singapore
Tel.: (65) 67453288
Web Site: https://www.smsummit.com.sg
Sales Range: $25-49.9 Million
Emp.: 100
Compact Disc Mfr
N.A.I.C.S.: 334610

SM Summit Investment Pte. Ltd. (1)
45 Ubi Road 1 04-02, Singapore, 408696, Singapore

Tel.: (65) 67453288
Web Site: http://www.centurioncorp.com
Emp.: 100
Investment Management Service
N.A.I.C.S.: 523999
Kong Cadmine *(CEO)*

Summit Creations Pte. Ltd. (1)
45 Ubi Road 1 04-02, Singapore, 408696, Singapore
Tel.: (65) 67453288
Web Site: https://www.smsummit.com.sg
Compact Disc Mfr
N.A.I.C.S.: 334610

Summit Hi-Tech Pte Ltd (1)
45 Ubi Road 1 Summit Building, Singapore, 408696, Singapore
Tel.: (65) 67453288
Web Site: http://www.smsummit.com.sg
Compact Disc Mfr
N.A.I.C.S.: 334610

Summit Technology Australia Pty Ltd (1)
Tel.: (61) 2 8756 4488
Web Site: http://www.summittechnology.com.au
Compact & Digital Versatile Discs Mfr
N.A.I.C.S.: 334610

Subsidiary (Non-US):

Summit Printing (Australia) Pty Limited (2)
Tel.: (61) 2 8756 4488
Web Site: http://www.summitprinting.com.au
Optical Discs Processing & Printing Serivces
N.A.I.C.S.: 323111

WOW Vision Pte Ltd (1)
62 Ubi Road 1 Oxley Bizhub 2 10-14, Singapore, 408734, Singapore
Tel.: (65) 67457798
Web Site: https://www.wowvision.com
Sales Range: $50-74.9 Million
Emp.: 5
Audio Visual Equipments Distr
N.A.I.C.S.: 423430
Dinesh Tripathi *(CEO)*

Westlite Dormitory (Bukit Minyak) Sdn. Bhd. (1)
No 38 Jalan Perniagaan Seri Tambun, Taman Westlite Dormitory Bukit Tambun, 14100, Simpang Empat, Penang, Malaysia
Tel.: (60) 45059900
Accommodation Services
N.A.I.C.S.: 721110
Tony Teh *(Bus Mgr)*

Westlite Dormitory (JB Techpark) Sdn. Bhd. (1)
Lot 46 Jalan Teknologi Johor Taman Teknologi, 81400, Senai, Johor, Malaysia
Tel.: (60) 75559366
Accommodation Services
N.A.I.C.S.: 721110

Westlite Dormitory (Pasir Gudang) Sdn. Bhd. (1)
lock 74 Jalan Tembusu Perjiranan 9 Taman Air Biru, 81700, Pasir Gudang, Johor, Malaysia
Tel.: (60) 75559366
Accommodation Services
N.A.I.C.S.: 721110

Westlite Dormitory (SN II) Sdn. Bhd. (1)
Lot 6214 Mukim, 81400, Senai, Johor, Malaysia
Tel.: (60) 75559366
Accommodation Services
N.A.I.C.S.: 721110

Westlite Dormitory (Senai) Sdn. Bhd. (1)
Lot 6212 Mukim, 81400, Senai, Johor, Malaysia
Tel.: (60) 75559366
Accommodation Services
N.A.I.C.S.: 721110

Westlite Dormitory (Tampoi) Sdn. Bhd. (1)
Lot 2051 Jalan Bayu Kempas Baru, 81200, Johor Bahru, Johor, Malaysia
Tel.: (60) 75559366

Accommodation Services
N.A.I.C.S.: 721110

Westlite Dormitory (Tebrau) Sdn. Bhd. (1)
PLO 250 Jalan Firma 2 Kawasan Perindustrian Tebrau IV, 81100, Johor Bahru, Johor, Malaysia
Tel.: (60) 75559366
Accommodation Services
N.A.I.C.S.: 721110

Westlite Dormitory (Toh Guan) Pte. Ltd. (1)
28 Toh Guan Road East, Singapore, 608596, Singapore
Tel.: (65) 63163018
Real Estate Services
N.A.I.C.S.: 531390

Westlite Dormitory (Woodlands) Pte. Ltd. (1)
2 Woodlands Sector 2 01-01, Singapore, 737723, Singapore
Tel.: (65) 62506616
Real Estate Services
N.A.I.C.S.: 531390

Westlite Dormitory Management Pte. Ltd. (1)
45 Ubi Road 1 05-01, Singapore, 408696, Singapore
Tel.: (65) 67453288
Real Estate Services
N.A.I.C.S.: 531390

Westlite Dormitory Management Sdn. Bhd. (1)
No 17 Jalan Ekoperniagaan 1/23 Taman Ekoperniagaan Taman Ekoperniagaan, 81100, Johor Bahru, Johor, Malaysia
Tel.: (60) 75559366
Real Estate Services
N.A.I.C.S.: 531390

Westlite Juniper (Mandai) Pte. Ltd. (1)
23 Mandai Estate, Singapore, 729937, Singapore
Tel.: (65) 63681709
Real Estate Services
N.A.I.C.S.: 531390

CENTURION FINANCE SA

ul Aleksandra Zajac 22, 40-749, Katowice, Poland
Tel.: (48) 735100333
Web Site: https://www.centurionsa.pl
Year Founded: 2011
6F4—(DEU)
Investment Management Service
N.A.I.C.S.: 523999
Bartosz Boszko *(Pres)*

CENTURION GROUP LTD

Unit 6 Kirkhill Commercial Park, Dyce Avenue, Dyce, AB21 0LQ, Aberdeen, United Kingdom
Tel.: (44) 1224 215400
Web Site: http://www.centuriongroup.co.uk
Energy Support Services
N.A.I.C.S.: 335929
Fernando Assing *(Pres & CEO)*

Subsidiaries:

ATR Holdings Ltd (1)
16 Denmore Road, Aberdeen, AB23 8JW, Scotland, United Kingdom
Tel.: (44) 1224 222777
Energy Equipment Retals
N.A.I.C.S.: 335929
Keith Moorhouse *(CEO)*

Subsidiary (Domestic):

Antler Ltd (2)
Northown House, 11-21 Northdown Street, London, N1 9BN, United Kingdom
Tel.: (44) 330961000
Web Site: http://www.antler.co.uk
Luggage & Travelware Mfr
N.A.I.C.S.: 316990

CENTURION MINERALS LTD.

Suite 520 470 Granville St, Vancouver, V6C 1V5, BC, Canada
Tel.: (604) 484-2161　　Ca
Web Site: https://www.centurionminerals.com
Year Founded: 2005
CTN—(TSXV)
Rev.: $74,878
Assets: $152,229
Liabilities: $1,341,275
Net Worth: ($1,189,047)
Earnings: ($326,290)
Fiscal Year-end: 07/31/21
Mineral Properties Exploration Services
N.A.I.C.S.: 213114
David G. Tafel *(Pres & CEO)*

CENTURION SAFETY PRODUCTS LIMITED

Howlett Way, Thetford, IP24 1HZ, Thetford, United Kingdom
Tel.: (44) 1842754266
Web Site: http://www.centurionsafety.co.uk
Year Founded: 1879
Sales Range: $10-24.9 Million
Emp.: 119
Safety Products Distr
N.A.I.C.S.: 423840
Del Parkinson *(Dir-Comml)*

CENTURY CITY INTERNATIONAL HOLDINGS LTD

11th Floor 68 Yee Wo Street, Causeway Bay, China (Hong Kong)
Tel.: (852) 28947888
Web Site: https://www.centurycity.com.hk
0355—(HKG)
Rev.: $510,663,000
Assets: $5,367,074,250
Liabilities: $2,985,170,250
Net Worth: $2,381,904,000
Earnings: ($50,936,250)
Emp.: 1,720
Fiscal Year-end: 12/31/22
Building Construction
N.A.I.C.S.: 236220
Donald Tung Fan *(Exec Dir)*

Subsidiaries:

Metropolitan Metro Asia (Ma On Shan) Limited (1)
G07 We Go Mall 16 Po Tai Street, Ma On Shan, Hong Kong, New Territories, China (Hong Kong)
Tel.: (852) 24887038
Web Site: https://asia.metropolitanfnb.com
Restaurant Services
N.A.I.C.S.: 722511

Paliburg Holdings Limited (1)
11th Floor 68 Yee Wo Street, Causeway Bay, China (Hong Kong) **(62.3%)**
Tel.: (852) 28947888
Web Site: https://www.paliburg.com.hk
Rev.: $510,471,750
Assets: $5,327,868,000
Liabilities: $2,982,416,250
Net Worth: $2,345,451,750
Earnings: ($47,991,000)
Emp.: 1,620
Fiscal Year-end: 12/31/2022
Property Development & Investment Construction Services
N.A.I.C.S.: 236220
Po Man Lo *(Exec Dir)*

Subsidiary (Domestic):

Bauhinia Hotels Limited (2)
119 - 121 Connaught Road, Central, China (Hong Kong)
Tel.: (852) 3 426 3333
Web Site: https://www.thebauhinia.com.hk
Hotel Operator
N.A.I.C.S.: 721110

Cosmopolitan International Holdings Limited (2)

Century City International Holdings Ltd—(Continued)

11 F 68 Yee Wo Street, Causeway Bay,
China (Hong Kong)
Tel.: (852) 28947888
Web Site: https://www.cosmoholdings.com
Rev.: $8,977,008
Assets: $744,085,620
Liabilities: $551,350,806
Net Worth: $192,734,814
Earnings: ($15,929,030)
Emp.: 100
Fiscal Year-end: 12/31/2020
Holding Company
N.A.I.C.S.: 551112
Yuk Sui Lo (Chm & CEO)

Regal Hotels International Holdings
Limited (2)
11th Floor 68 Yee Wo Street, Causeway
Bay, China (Hong Kong) (68.4%)
Tel.: (852) 28947888
Web Site: https://www.regal.com.hk
Rev.: $233,465,250
Assets: $3,856,594,500
Liabilities: $2,149,191,000
Net Worth: $1,707,403,500
Earnings: ($52,440,750)
Emp.: 1,430
Fiscal Year-end: 12/31/2022
Home Management Services
N.A.I.C.S.: 721110
Eliza Sau Fun Lam (Sec)

Subsidiary (Domestic):

Metropolitan Central Kitchen
Limited (3)
Workshop A12-14 3/F Block A, Yau Tong
Industrial City 17 Ko Fai Road Yau Tong,
Kowloon, China (Hong Kong)
Tel.: (852) 2 659 8678
Web Site: https://www.metropolitanfnb.com
Catering Services
N.A.I.C.S.: 722320

Regal Estate Management
Limited (3)
11 F 68 Yee Wo St, Causeway Bay, China
(Hong Kong)
Tel.: (852) 28947888
Web Site: https://www.regalhotel.com
Sales Range: $75-99.9 Million
Emp.: 200
Real Estate Property Management Services
N.A.I.C.S.: 531311

Subsidiary (Non-US):

Regal Hotels Investment & Manage-
ment (Shanghai) Ltd (3)
807 Charity Building 88 Cao Xi Road N,
Xujiahui, Shanghai, 200030, China
Tel.: (86) 2154258080
Web Site: http://www.regalhotelchina.com
Sales Range: $25-49.9 Million
Emp.: 10
Home Management Services
N.A.I.C.S.: 561110
Pen Poon (Gen Mgr)

Subsidiary (Domestic):

Regal Riverside Hotel Limited (2)
34-36 Tai Chung Kiu Road, Sha Tin, China
(Hong Kong)
Tel.: (852) 2 649 7878
Web Site: https://www.regalhotel.com
Hotel Operator
N.A.I.C.S.: 721110

CENTURY ENERGY INTERNA-
TIONAL HOLDINGS LIMITED
Flat O 10/F Yue Cheung Centre 1-3
Wong Chuk Yeung Street, Fo Tan
New Territories, Hong Kong, China
(Hong Kong)
Tel.: (852) 25901288 Ky
Web Site:
 http://www.chinaoilgangrans.com
8132—(HKG)
Rev.: $14,274,346
Assets: $16,147,909
Liabilities: $32,226,427
Net Worth: ($16,078,518)
Earnings: ($4,296,195)
Emp.: 115

Fiscal Year-end: 03/31/21
Investment Holding Company
N.A.I.C.S.: 551112
Changjun Rong (Vice Chm)

Subsidiaries:

Sun Fair Electric Wire & Cable (HK)
Company Limited (1)
Room Q 10th Floor Yue Choong Contro 1 3
Wong Chuk Yeung Street, Fotan, Sha Tin,
New Territories, China (Hong Kong)
Tel.: (852) 26063380
Web Site: https://www.sunfairw.com.hk
Electrical Equipment Mfr & Distr
N.A.I.C.S.: 335999

CENTURY ENTERTAINMENT
INTERNATIONAL HOLDINGS
LIMITED
G02 Shun Tak Centre 168-200 Con-
naught Road, Sheung Wan, Central,
China (Hong Kong)
Tel.: (852) 2 559 5925
Web Site: http://www.ceihldg.com
0959—(HKG)
Rev.: $25,796
Assets: $17,225,924
Liabilities: $20,665,821
Net Worth: ($3,439,897)
Earnings: ($474,002)
Emp.: 10
Fiscal Year-end: 03/31/22
Gaming & Entertainment Services
N.A.I.C.S.: 713290
Man Sun Ng (CEO & Chm)

CENTURY EXTRUSIONS LIM-
ITED
113 Park Street N Block 2nd Floor,
Kolkata, 700 016, India
Tel.: (91) 3322291012
Web Site:
 https://www.centuryextrusions.com
Year Founded: 1988
CENTEXT—(NSE)
Rev.: $44,644,805
Assets: $15,934,297
Liabilities: $8,123,014
Net Worth: $7,811,282
Earnings: $715,784
Emp.: 399
Fiscal Year-end: 03/31/23
Aluminum Extruded Product Mfr
N.A.I.C.S.: 331318
J. K. Malpani (Pres)

CENTURY GINWA RETAIL
HOLDINGS LIMITED
Unit 301 3/F OfficePlus Wan Chai
303 Hennessy Road, Wanchai, China
(Hong Kong)
Tel.: (852) 2 865 3039 BM
Web Site: http://www.cgrh.com.hk
Year Founded: 2000
0162—(HKG)
Rev.: $77,317,580
Assets: $1,104,559,068
Liabilities: $827,515,554
Net Worth: $277,043,515
Earnings: ($58,440,882)
Emp.: 1,050
Fiscal Year-end: 12/31/21
Holding Company
N.A.I.C.S.: 551112
Qin Chuan (CEO)

CENTURY GLOBAL COM-
MODITIES CORPORATION
200 University Avenue Suite 1401,
Toronto, M5H 3C6, ON, Canada
Tel.: (416) 977-3188
Web Site:
 https://www.centuryglobal.ca
CNT—(TSX)
Rev.: $6,820,252
Assets: $19,026,948
Liabilities: $2,071,456

Net Worth: $16,955,492
Earnings: ($2,167,882)
Emp.: 29
Fiscal Year-end: 03/31/22
Investment Services
N.A.I.C.S.: 523999
Sandy C. K. Chim (Founder, Chm,
Pres & CEO)

Subsidiaries:

Century Food Company Limited (1)
Room 905-906 9/F Houston Centre 63
Mody Road, Tsim Sha Tsui, Kowloon, China
(Hong Kong)
Tel.: (852) 39518700
Web Site: http://www.centuryfood.com
Food Products Distr
N.A.I.C.S.: 424490

CENTURY GROUP INTERNA-
TIONAL HOLDINGS LIMITED
Office D 16/F Kings Wing Plaza 1 No
3 On Kwan Street Shek Mun, Sha
Tin, New Territories, China (Hong
Kong)
Tel.: (852) 2 635 4488 Ky
Web Site:
 http://www.cherishholdings.com
2113—(HKG)
Rev.: $31,926,419
Assets: $14,351,734
Liabilities: $8,448,706
Net Worth: $5,903,028
Earnings: ($4,109,561)
Emp.: 207
Fiscal Year-end: 03/31/21
Site Formation Services
N.A.I.C.S.: 238910

CENTURY INVESTMENT
GROUP P.L.C.
Arramtha-Alhassan Industrial City, PO
Box 39, Ar Ramtha, Irbid, 21467,
Jordan
Tel.: (962) 7395900
Web Site:
 https://www.centurygroup.jo
Year Founded: 1995
CEIG—(AMM)
Rev.: $922,573
Assets: $16,653,797
Liabilities: $7,499,103
Net Worth: $9,154,694
Earnings: ($1,386,163)
Emp.: 8
Fiscal Year-end: 12/31/23
Financial Investment Services
N.A.I.C.S.: 523999
Riad Al-Khashman (Chm)

CENTURY IRON & STEEL IN-
DUSTRIAL CO., LTD.
No 1119 Sec 1 Zhongshan Rd,
Guanyin Dist, Taoyuan, 328, Taiwan
Tel.: (886) 34730201
Web Site: https://www.century.com.tw
9958—(TAI)
Rev.: $474,691,699
Assets: $1,160,898,776
Liabilities: $713,617,913
Net Worth: $447,280,862
Earnings: $43,802,673
Emp.: 325
Fiscal Year-end: 12/31/23
Structural Steel Mfr
N.A.I.C.S.: 238120
Wen-Hsiang Lai (Chm)

Subsidiaries:

Century Iron & Steel Industrial Co.,
Ltd. - Taoyuan Plant (1)
No 119 Sec 1 Zhongshan Rd Guanyin Dist,
Taoyuan, Taiwan
Tel.: (886) 34730201
Steel Products Mfr
N.A.I.C.S.: 332312

Century Wind Power Co., Ltd. (1)

No 1119 Sec 1 Zhongshan Rd Guanyin
Dist, Taoyuan, Taiwan
Tel.: (886) 34730201
Steel Product Mfr & Distr
N.A.I.C.S.: 332312

Myanmar Century Steel Sturcture
Limited (1)
Lot No A-2 Zone A, Thilawa Special Eco-
nomic Zone, Yangon, Myanmar
Tel.: (95) 9976360668
Steel Products Mfr
N.A.I.C.S.: 331110

CENTURY LEGEND HOLD-
INGS LTD
Unit 906 9th Floor Capital Centre 151
Gloucester Road, Wanchai, China
(Hong Kong)
Tel.: (852) 28489300
Web Site: http://www.clh.com.hk
0079—(HKG)
Rev.: $4,638,578
Assets: $67,667,438
Liabilities: $31,849,118
Net Worth: $35,818,320
Earnings: ($3,484,958)
Emp.: 45
Fiscal Year-end: 12/31/22
Travel & Gaming Business
N.A.I.C.S.: 311615
Evans Tania Ming Tak Chu (Exec Dir)

Subsidiaries:

Century Legend Finance Limited (1)
Rm 3403-4 34 F W Tower Shun Tak Ctr
168-200 Connaught Rd, Central, China
(Hong Kong)
Tel.: (852) 25252669
Sales Range: $50-74.9 Million
Emp.: 25
Commercial & Personal Loan Lending Ser-
vices
N.A.I.C.S.: 522310

Century Legend Management
Limited (1)
Rm 03-04 34 F Shun Tak Ctr W Tower 168-
200 Connaught Rd, Central, China (Hong
Kong)
Tel.: (852) 25252669
Property Management Services
N.A.I.C.S.: 531311

Headquarters Limited (1)
Retail 4 2/F LHT Tower 31 Queen's Road,
Central, China (Hong Kong)
Tel.: (852) 2 868 9092
Web Site: https://www.hq-headquarters.com
Hair Salon Operation Services
N.A.I.C.S.: 812112

CENTURY PACIFIC FOOD, INC.
7F 8F 19F Centerpoint Building Julia
Vargas corner Garnet Street, Ortigas
Business Center, Pasig, 1605, Metro
Manilla, Philippines
Tel.: (63) 286338555
Web Site:
 https://www.centurypacific.com.ph
Year Founded: 1978
CNPF—(PHI)
Rev.: $291,361,091
Assets: $930,614,676
Liabilities: $337,484,242
Net Worth: $593,130,433
Earnings: $100,734,125
Fiscal Year-end: 12/31/23
Food Mfr
N.A.I.C.S.: 311999
Christopher T. Po (Chm)

Subsidiaries:

Century Pacific Food, Inc. - Canned
Meat Plant (1)
Lot 7 Blk 7 LIIP Avenue Laguna Interna-
tional Industrial Park Mamplasan, Laguna,
Binan, 4024, Philippines
Tel.: (63) 22367550
Canned Meat Distr
N.A.I.C.S.: 424470

Century Pacific Food, Inc. - Coconut
Products Plant **(1)**
Purok Lansong Makar-Siguel Rd, General
Santos, 9500, South Cotabato, Philippines
Tel.: (63) 835521831
Coconut Product Distr
N.A.I.C.S.: 424490

Century Pacific Food, Inc. - Dairy &
Mixes Plant **(1)**
No 32 Arturo Drive Bagumbayan, Taguig,
1607, Philippines
Tel.: (63) 27763331
Grocery Product Distr
N.A.I.C.S.: 424490

Century Pacific Food, Inc. - General
Santos City Plant **(1)**
National Highway Brgy Tambler, General
Santos, 9500, South Cotabato, Philippines
Tel.: (63) 833807461
Canned & Processed Fish Distr
N.A.I.C.S.: 424460

Century Pacific Food, Inc. - Zam-
boanga Plant **(1)**
Purok 1 Dumagsa Talisayan, Zamboanga,
7000, Zamboanga del Norte, Philippines
Tel.: (63) 629918177
Canned & Processed Fish Distr
N.A.I.C.S.: 424460

CENTURY PAPER & BOARD
MILLS LIMITED

Lakson Square Building No 2 Sarwar
Shaheed Road, Karachi, 74200, Paki-
stan
Tel.: (92) 2135698000
Web Site:
https://www.centurypaper.com.pk
Year Founded: 1984
CEPB—(KAR)
Rev.: $177,978,010
Assets: $132,940,917
Liabilities: $68,841,824
Net Worth: $64,099,092
Earnings: $18,379,495
Emp.: 1,646
Fiscal Year-end: 06/30/21
Paper Mfr
N.A.I.C.S.: 322120
Aftab Ahmad *(CEO)*

CENTURY PEAK HOLDINGS
CORP.

14th Floor BDO Equitable Tower,
Paseo De Roxas Salcedo Village,
Makati, Philippines
Tel.: (63) 288560999   PH
Web Site:
https://www.centurypeakmetals.com
Year Founded: 2003
CPM—(PHI)
Rev.: $45,709,964
Assets: $197,559,282
Liabilities: $154,613,907
Net Worth: $42,945,375
Earnings: ($1,173,465)
Emp.: 150
Fiscal Year-end: 12/31/23
Metal Mining Services
N.A.I.C.S.: 212290
Wilfredo D. Keng *(Chm, Chm, Pres,
Pres & CEO)*

CENTURY PLYBOARDS (I)
LTD.

CENTURY HOUSE P15/1 Taratala
Road, Kolkata, 700088, India
Tel.: 3339403950
Web Site: https://www.centuryply.com
CENTURYPLY—(NSE)
Rev.: $293,158,770
Assets: $247,274,801
Liabilities: $74,438,705
Net Worth: $172,836,095
Earnings: $26,101,312
Emp.: 6,365
Fiscal Year-end: 03/31/21
Plywood Mfr

N.A.I.C.S.: 321211
Hari Prasad Agarwal *(Vice Chm)*

Subsidiaries:

Aegis Business Ltd. **(1)**
36-A Shakespeare Sarani, Kolkata, 700
017, West Bengal, India
Tel.: (91) 98300 45600
Web Site: http://www.aegisbusiness.net
Welding & Refractory Product Mfr
N.A.I.C.S.: 333992

Auro Sundram Ply & Door Pvt.
Ltd. **(1)**
Plot No 356 Raipur Ind Area Gagalheri
Road, Bhagwanpur Haridwar, Roorkee,
247661, Uttarakhand, India
Tel.: (91) 9528024275
Web Site: http://www.lomexply.com
Emp.: 1,000
Plywood Mfr
N.A.I.C.S.: 321211

Cement Manufacturing Co. Ltd **(1)**
Satyam Towers 3 Alipore Road 1st Floor
Unit No 9B, Kolkata, 700 027, India
Tel.: (91) 33 24484169
Web Site: http://www.cmcl.co.in
Sales Range: $25-49.9 Million
Emp.: 100
Cement Mfr
N.A.I.C.S.: 327310
Sajjan Bhajanka *(Chm)*

CENTURY PROPERTIES
GROUP, INC.

35F Century Diamond Tower, Century
City Kalayaan Avenue, Makati, 1210,
Philippines
Tel.: (63) 277935500
Web Site: https://www.century-
properties.com
CPG—(PHI)
Rev.: $199,723,368
Assets: $968,063,245
Liabilities: $582,412,521
Net Worth: $385,650,724
Earnings: $25,215,442
Emp.: 1,025
Fiscal Year-end: 12/31/22
Real Estate Development Services
N.A.I.C.S.: 531390
Jose E. B. Antonio *(Founder & Chm)*

CENTURY SAGE SCIENTIFIC
HOLDINGS LIMITED

Building H8 Privy Council No 10 Jia-
chuang Road, Opto-Mechatronics
Industrial Park Tongzhou District, Bei-
jing, 101111, China
Tel.: (86) 1059671700
Web Site: http://www.css-group.net
1450—(HKG)
Rev.: $59,755,082
Assets: $62,745,602
Liabilities: $48,286,789
Net Worth: $14,458,813
Earnings: ($2,301,296)
Emp.: 685
Fiscal Year-end: 12/31/22
Computer Hardware & Software Pro-
ducer
N.A.I.C.S.: 334118
Chi Sum Lo *(Chm & CEO)*

Subsidiaries:

Century Sage Scientific (Taiwan)
Limited **(1)**
281 2 Tiding Blvd, Neihu Dist, Taipei, 114,
Taiwan
Tel.: (886) 287511276
Television Broadcasting Services
N.A.I.C.S.: 516120

Cogent (Beijing) Technology Com-
pany Limited **(1)**
Block A Bldg H6-Privy Council No 10 Jiach-
uang Rd, Tongzhou District, Beijing, 101111,
China
Tel.: (86) 1080821774

Web Site: https://www.cogent-
technologies.net
Software Development Services
N.A.I.C.S.: 541511

CENTURY SUNSHINE GROUP
HOLDINGS LIMITED

Suite 1104 11th Floor Tower 6 The
Gateway 9 Canton Road, Tsim Sha
Tsui, Kowloon, China (Hong Kong)
Tel.: (852) 28022165
Web Site:
http://www.centurysunshine.com.hk
0509—(HKG)
Rev.: $67,779,638
Assets: $556,030,178
Liabilities: $405,221,520
Net Worth: $150,808,658
Earnings: ($134,559,293)
Emp.: 674
Fiscal Year-end: 12/31/22
Holding Company; Agricultural Prod-
ucts
N.A.I.C.S.: 325314
Wen Fu Chi *(Chm)*

Subsidiaries:

Rare Earth Magnesium Technology
Group Holdings Limited **(1)**
Suite 1105 11th Floor Tower 6 The Gateway
9 Canton Road, Tsim Sha Tsui, Kowloon,
China (Hong Kong) **(72.31%)**
Tel.: (852) 28022165
Web Site: http://www.remt.com.hk
Rev.: $48,947,123
Assets: $238,829,685
Liabilities: $99,095,805
Net Worth: $139,733,880
Earnings: $179,010
Emp.: 377
Fiscal Year-end: 12/31/2022
Electronic Hand Held Products Design Mfr
& Sales
N.A.I.C.S.: 334111
Samson Wai Ho Tam *(Co-Founder & Chm)*

Subsidiary (Domestic):

Group Sense Limited **(2)**
Room 13-24 2/F Sino Industrial Plaza 9 Kai
Cheung Road, Kowloon Bay, Kowloon,
China (Hong Kong)
Tel.: (852) 2 832 8228
Web Site: https://www.gsl.com.hk
Electronic Products Sales
N.A.I.C.S.: 423690

Group Sense Mobile-Tech
Limited **(2)**
Unit 13-24 2/F Sino Industrial Plaza 9 Kai
Cheung Road, Kowloon Bay, Kowloon, NT,
China (Hong Kong)
Tel.: (852) 2 832 8228
Web Site: https://www.gsml.com.hk
Communication Equipment Mfr
N.A.I.C.S.: 334210

Shandong Hongri Chemical Joint
Stock Company Limited **(1)**
East Section of Hubei Road, Luozhuang
District, Linyi, 276021, Shandong, China
Tel.: (86) 5398280028
Web Site: http://www.hongrihuagong.com
Chemical Products Mfr
N.A.I.C.S.: 325998

CENTURY TEXTILES AND IN-
DUSTRIES LIMITED

Century Bhavan Dr Annie Besant
Road Worli, Mumbai, 400030, Maha-
rashtra, India
Tel.: (91) 2224957000
Web Site:
https://www.centurytextind.com
Year Founded: 1897
CENTURYTEX—(NSE)
Rev.: $365,572,935
Assets: $913,658,655
Liabilities: $415,789,920
Net Worth: $497,868,735
Earnings: $4,587,765)
Emp.: 4,268

Fiscal Year-end: 03/31/21
Textile, Pulp Paper Products & Ce-
ment Mfr
N.A.I.C.S.: 314999
Kumar Mangalam Birla *(Vice Chm)*

Subsidiaries:

Birla Century Exports Private
Limited **(1)**
Century Bhavan Dr Annie Besant Road,
Worli, Mumbai, 400030, India
Tel.: (91) 2224957000
Web Site: http://www.birlacentury.com
Textile & Fabric Mfr
N.A.I.C.S.: 313310
R. K. Dalmia *(Pres)*

Birla Estates Private Limited **(1)**
Birla Aurora Level 8 Dr Annie Besant Rd,
Worli, Mumbai, 400 030, India
Tel.: (91) 2262874100
Web Site: http://www.birlaestates.com
Residential & Commercial Building Con-
struction Services
N.A.I.C.S.: 236220
K. T. Jithendran *(CEO)*

Century Textiles and Industries Lim-
ited - Birla Century Division **(1)**
Century Bhavan Dr Annie Besant Road,
Worli, Mumbai, 400 030, India
Tel.: (91) 222 495 7000
Web Site: https://www.birlacentury.com
Emp.: 100
Textile Products Mfr
N.A.I.C.S.: 314999

Century Textiles and Industries Lim-
ited - Century Denim Division **(1)**
Century Bhavan Dr Annie Besant Road,
Worli, Mumbai, 400030, India
Tel.: (91) 22 2495 7000
Web Site: http://www.centurytextind.com
Emp.: 75
Denim Fabric Mfr
N.A.I.C.S.: 313210
Vinoth Gupta *(Mgr-Sls)*

Plant (Domestic):

Century Textiles and Industries Lim-
ited - Century Denim Works **(2)**
Village & Post Satrati Tehsil - Kasrawad,
Tehsil - Kasrawad, Khargone, 451 660,
Madhya Pradesh, India
Tel.: (91) 7285 255277
Web Site: http://www.centurydenim.com
Denim Fabric Mfr
N.A.I.C.S.: 313210

Century Textiles and Industries Lim-
ited - Century Pulp and Paper
Division **(1)**
611 DLF Tower-B, Jasola District Center,
New Delhi, 110025, Uttranchal, India
Tel.: (91) 114 882 2222
Web Site:
https://www.centurypaperindia.com
Pulp & Paper Mfr
N.A.I.C.S.: 322110
J.P. Narain *(CEO)*

Century Textiles and Industries Lim-
ited - Century Rayon Division **(1)**
Industry House 159 Churchgate Reclamma-
tion, Mumbai, 400 020, Maharashtra, India
Tel.: (91) 222 202 7570
Web Site: https://www.centuryrayon.co.in
Sales Range: $25-49.9 Million
Emp.: 70
Rayon Yarn Mfr
N.A.I.C.S.: 313110
O. R. Chitlange *(Head-Bus)*

Plant (Domestic):

Century Textiles and Industries Lim-
ited - Century Rayon Plant **(2)**
Murbad Road, PO Box No 22, Shahad,
Thane, 421103, Maharashtra, India
Tel.: (91) 2512733670
Rayon Yarn Mfr
N.A.I.C.S.: 313110

Century Textiles and Industries Lim-
ited - Century Yarn Division **(1)**
Century Bhavan Dr Annie Besant Road,
Worli, Mumbai, 400 030, India

Century Textiles and Industries Limited—(Continued)

Tel.: (91) 22 2495 7000
Web Site: http://www.centuryyarn.com
Emp.: 50
Cotton Yarn Mfr
N.A.I.C.S.: 313110
Vinodh Gupta (Gen Mgr)

Plant (Domestic):

Century Textiles and Industries Limited - Century Yarn Works   (2)
Village and Post Satrati, Tehsil - Kasrawad, Khargone, 451 660, Madhya Pradesh, India
Tel.: (91) 7285 255277
Web Site: http://www.centuryyarn.com
Emp.: 70
Cotton Yarn Mfr
N.A.I.C.S.: 313110
Vinod Gupta (Gen Mgr-Mktg)

Century Textiles and Industries Limited - Cottons by Century Division   (1)
Centuary Bhavan Dr Annie Besant Road, Worli, Mumbai, 400 030, India
Tel.: (91) 22 2495 7000
Web Site: http://www.centurytextind.com
Emp.: 250
Textile Products Mfr
N.A.I.C.S.: 314999

CENTURY21 REAL ESTATE OF JAPAN LTD.

7F Kita-Aoyama YOSHIKAWA Building 2-12-16 Kita-Aoyama, Minato-ku, Tokyo, 107-0061, Japan
Tel.: (81) 334970956
Web Site:
    https://www.century21japan.co.jp
Year Founded: 1971
8898—(TKS)
Sales Range: $25-49.9 Million
Real Estate Sales & Services
N.A.I.C.S.: 531210
Kunihiro Osada (Pres & CEO)

CENTURYTOUCH LTD, INC.

Stanton House 31 Westgate, Grantham, NG31 6LX, United Kingdom
Tel.: (44) 1476 591111   DE
Web Site:
    http://www.centurytouch.com
Year Founded: 2010
Property Development & Hotel Management Services
N.A.I.C.S.: 237210
Eric Yew Kee Wong (Chm & Mng Dir)

CEO EVENT MEDYA AS

Balmumcu Mh Morbasan Sk Koza Is Merkezi B-Blok 12/17, Besiktas, 34347, Istanbul, Turkiye
Tel.: (90) 2122216501
Web Site:
    https://www.ceoevent.com.tr
Year Founded: 2006
CEOEM—(IST)
Rev.: $6,851,833
Assets: $4,715,541
Liabilities: $1,340,226
Net Worth: $3,375,315
Earnings: $860,878
Fiscal Year-end: 12/31/22
Event Management Services
N.A.I.C.S.: 711310
Bulent Uygun (CEO)

CEOTRONICS AG

Adam-Opel-Str 6, 63322, Rodermark, Germany
Tel.: (49) 607487510
Web Site:
    https://www.ceotronics.com
CEK—(MUN)
Rev.: $31,976,992
Assets: $47,290,982
Liabilities: $25,814,703
Net Worth: $21,476,279

Earnings: $1,349,012
Emp.: 135
Fiscal Year-end: 05/31/24
Data Communications Equipment Mfr
N.A.I.C.S.: 334290
Thomas H. Gunther (CEO & Member-Exec Bd)

Subsidiaries:

CT-Video GmbH   (1)
Gewerbegebiet Rothenschirmbach 9, 06295, Eisleben, Germany
Tel.: (49) 3477661490
Web Site: http://www.ct-video.com
Sales Range: $25-49.9 Million
Emp.: 40
Surveillance Equipment Mfr
N.A.I.C.S.: 334511

CeoTronics (Schweiz) AG   (1)
Grundstr 16, 6343, Rotkreuz, Switzerland
Tel.: (41) 417905838
Web Site: http://www.ceotronics.ch
Sales Range: $25-49.9 Million
Emp.: 2
Radio Communication Devices Mfr
N.A.I.C.S.: 334220

CeoTronics S.L.   (1)
C/Ciudad de Frias 7 y 9 Nave 19, E-28021, Madrid, Spain
Tel.: (34) 91460825051
Communication Equipment Mfr,
N.A.I.C.S.: 334290
Roberto Gil Gonzalez (Mng Dir)

CeoTronics S.a.r.l.   (1)
Bat Delta T ZA du Tuboeuf Allee des Pleus, 77170, Brie-Comte-Robert, France
Tel.: (33) 160183300
Web Site: http://www.ceotronics.fr
Sales Range: $50-74.9 Million
Emp.: 2
Communication Equipment Distr
N.A.I.C.S.: 423690

CeoTronics, Inc.   (1)
2133 Upton Dr Ste 126 PMB 513, Virginia Beach, VA 23452-6664
Tel.: (757) 549-6220
Web Site: https://www.ceotronicsusa.com
Sales Range: $25-49.9 Million
Emp.: 25
Communication Equipment Mfr
N.A.I.C.S.: 334220
Thomas H. Gunther (CEO)

CEPATWAWASAN GROUP BERHAD

Lot 70 Block 6 Prima Square Mile 4 North Road, 90000, Sandakan, Sabah, Malaysia
Tel.: (60) 89272773
Web Site:
    https://www.cepatgroup.com
CEPAT—(KLS)
Rev.: $75,574,180
Assets: $105,383,069
Liabilities: $19,902,857
Net Worth: $85,480,212
Earnings: $7,033,862
Fiscal Year-end: 12/31/22
Oil Palm Cultivation Services
N.A.I.C.S.: 311225
Fei San Seow (Co-Sec)

CEPD N.V.

Strawinskylaan 709 Tower A Floor 7, Strawinskylaan 709, 1077 XX, Amsterdam, Netherlands
Tel.: (31) 20 670 1316
Web Site: http://www.cepd.nl
Pharmaceutical Products Distr
N.A.I.C.S.: 456110
Jacek Szwajcowski (Vice Chm)

Subsidiaries:

Business Support Solution S.A.   (1)
Ul Pojezierska 90 A, 93 341, Lodz, Poland
Tel.: (48) 42 200 7000
Web Site: http://www.bssce.com
Pharmaceutical Support Services
N.A.I.C.S.: 325412

CEPD Management Sp. z o.o.   (1)
Ul 17 Stycznia 45B, 02-146, Warsaw, Poland
Tel.: (48) 22 329 6400
Web Site: http://www.cepd.nl
Emp.: 1
Pharmacy Management Services
N.A.I.C.S.: 456110
Andrew Benson (Gen Mgr)

DOZ S.A.   (1)
Aleje Jerozolimskie 134, 02-305, Warsaw, Poland
Tel.: (48) 22 329 6500
Web Site: http://www.dozsa.pl
Online Medical Information
N.A.I.C.S.: 513199

Eubioco S.A.   (1)
Ul Pojezierska 90-A, 91-341, Lodz, Poland
Tel.: (48) 42 200 7930
Web Site: http://www.eubioco.eu
Emp.: 4
Pharmaceutical Services
N.A.I.C.S.: 325412
Oliver Brown (Gen Mgr)

Farm-Serwis Sp. z o.o.   (1)
Ul Zbaszynska 3, 91 342, Lodz, Poland
Tel.: (48) 42 200 7176
Pharmaceutical Support Services
N.A.I.C.S.: 325412

Pharmalink Sp. z o.o.   (1)
Ul Zbaszynska 3, 91 342, Lodz, Poland
Tel.: (48) 42 200 7555
Web Site: http://www.pharmalink.pl
Pharmaceutical Support Services
N.A.I.C.S.: 325412

Pharmena S.A.   (1)
Ul Wolczanska 178, 90-530, Lodz, Poland
Tel.: (48) 42 291 3370
Web Site: http://www.pharmena.pl
Emp.: 15
Pharmaceutical Services
N.A.I.C.S.: 325412
Konrad Palka (Gen Mgr)

ePRUF S.A.   (1)
Ul Zbaszynska 3, 91 342, Lodz, Poland
Tel.: (48) 42 200 7568
Web Site: http://www.epruf.pl
Pharmaceutical Services
N.A.I.C.S.: 325412

CEPOVETT

150 Ancienne Route De Beaujeu
Villefranche-sur-Saone, PO Box 90421, Gleize, 69653, Gleize, Cedex, France
Tel.: (33) 474624700
Web Site: http://www.cepovett.com
Year Founded: 1948
Rev.: $22,500,000
Emp.: 200
Mens & Boys Work Clothing
N.A.I.C.S.: 315250
Nicolas Sandjian (CEO)

CEPROCIM S.A.

6 Preciziei Blvd Sector 6, 62203, Bucharest, Romania
Tel.: (40) 213188884
Web Site: https://www.ceprocim.ro
Year Founded: 1949
CEPO—(BUC)
Rev.: $1,189,542
Assets: $2,275,206
Liabilities: $95,016
Net Worth: $2,180,190
Earnings: $14,352
Emp.: 51
Fiscal Year-end: 12/31/22
Natural Sciences & Engineering Research Development
N.A.I.C.S.: 541715
Constantin Ignat (Deputy Gen Dir-Economic)

CEPS PLC

11 Laura Place, Bath, BA2 4BL, United Kingdom
Tel.: (44) 1225483030

Web Site: https://www.cepsplc.com
CEPS—(AIM)
Rev.: $37,784,718
Assets: $28,962,342
Liabilities: $21,845,881
Net Worth: $7,116,461
Earnings: $1,553,145
Fiscal Year-end: 12/31/23
Investment Holding Company
N.A.I.C.S.: 551112
David A. Horner (Chm)

Subsidiaries:

Aford Awards Limited   (1)
Grange House Bearsted Green Business Centre, Bearsted, Maidstone, ME14 4DZ, Kent, United Kingdom
Tel.: (44) 1622738711
Web Site: https://www.afordawards.co.uk
Trophies & Award Distr
N.A.I.C.S.: 459999

BRCS (Building Control) Limited   (1)
Amber Court 51 Church Street, Elsecar, Barnsley, S74 8HT, United Kingdom
Tel.: (44) 122 674 3959
Web Site: https://brcs.co.uk
Building Control Services
N.A.I.C.S.: 541350
Andrew Pearson (Project Mgr)

Friedman's Ltd.   (1)
Unit E 3 Tudor Road, Altrincham Business Park, Altrincham, WA14 5RZ, Cheshire, United Kingdom
Tel.: (44) 1619759002
Web Site: https://www.friedmans.co.uk
Sales Range: $25-49.9 Million
Emp.: 7
Fabrics Mfr
N.A.I.C.S.: 313240
David Kaitiff (Gen Mgr)

Sunline Direct Mail Ltd.   (1)
Cotton Way Weldon Rd Indus Est, Loughborough, LE11 5FJ, Leicestershire, United Kingdom
Tel.: (44) 1509263434
Web Site: http://www.sunline.co.uk
Sales Range: $50-74.9 Million
Emp.: 150
Polywrapping & Mailing Services
N.A.I.C.S.: 561431

CEPS, A.S.

Elektrárenská 774/2, 101 52, Prague, Czech Republic
Tel.: (420) 800199100
Web Site: https://www.ceps.cz
Year Founded: 1998
Emp.: 330
Electronic Services
N.A.I.C.S.: 926130

CEQUENCE ENERGY LTD.

Suite 1400 215 - 9th Avenue SW, Calgary, T2P 1K3, AB, Canada
Tel.: (403) 229-3050   AB
Web Site: http://www.cequence-energy.com
Year Founded: 2006
Rev.: $45,782,772
Assets: $207,899,611
Liabilities: $96,260,217
Net Worth: $111,639,394
Earnings: $(7,109,076)
Emp.: 14
Fiscal Year-end: 12/31/18
Oil & Gas Exploration Services
N.A.I.C.S.: 211120
Todd J. Brown (CEO)

CER A.D.

Dr Dragisa Misovica 169, Cacak, Serbia
Tel.: (381) 32372651
Web Site: http://cer.co.rs
Year Founded: 1953
CERC—(BEL)
Sales Range: $1-9.9 Million
Emp.: 62
Ventilation Equipment Mfr

N.A.I.C.S.: 335210
Ljubinko Mirkovic *(Exec Dir)*

CERA SANITARYWARE LTD.
9 GIDC Industrial Estate, Mehsana
Dist, Kadi, 382715, Gujarat, India
Tel.: (91) 2764242329
Web Site: https://www.cera-india.com
CERA—(NSE)
Rev.: $170,555,208
Assets: $188,049,730
Liabilities: $67,457,891
Net Worth: $120,591,840
Earnings: $13,643,762
Emp.: 2,473
Fiscal Year-end: 03/31/21
Sanitary Ware Mfr & Distr
N.A.I.C.S.: 332999
Atul Sanghvi *(CEO)*

CERA SCRL
Philipssite 5 Boite 10, Leuven, Bel-
gium
Tel.: (32) 70695242
Web Site: http://www.cera.be
Sales Range: $25-49.9 Million
Emp.: 43
Holding Company
N.A.I.C.S.: 551112
Franky Depickere *(Mng Dir)*

Subsidiaries:

KBC Ancora SCA   (1)
Muntstraat 1, 3000, Leuven, Belgium
Tel.: (32) 16279672
Web Site: https://www.kbcancora.be
Rev.: $335,562,794
Assets: $3,943,540,476
Liabilities: $187,573,702
Net Worth: $3,755,966,774
Earnings: $322,544,014
Fiscal Year-end: 06/30/2023
Investment Management Services; Owned
63% by Cera SCRL
N.A.I.C.S.: 523999
Franky Depickere *(Mng Dir)*

CERAGON NETWORKS LTD.
24 Raoul Wallenberg Street, Tel Aviv,
6971920, Israel
Tel.: (972) 35431000   II
Web Site: http://www.ceragon.com
Year Founded: 1996
CRNT—(NASDAQ)
Rev.: $295,173,000
Assets: $289,318,000
Liabilities: $169,535,000
Net Worth: $119,783,000
Earnings: ($19,689,000)
Emp.: 988
Fiscal Year-end: 12/31/22
Point-to-Point Wireless Backhaul
Telecommunications Products & Ser-
vices Designer, Developer, Mfr &
Whslr
N.A.I.C.S.: 334220
Ira Palti *(Pres & CEO)*

Subsidiaries:

Ceragon Italy   (1)
Centro Direzionale Colombirolo Edificio A
Via Roma 74, 20051, Cassina de' Pecchi,
Italy
Tel.: (39) 0233293334
Emp.: 4
Telecommunication Servicesb
N.A.I.C.S.: 334220

Ceragon Moscow   (1)
11 Marshal Katukov Street Building 2 office
23, Moscow, Russia
Tel.: (7) 4957500176
Web Site: http://www.ceragon.com
Telecommunication Servicesb
N.A.I.C.S.: 334220

Ceragon Networks (HK) Ltd.   (1)
Rm 308B Tower B Grand Pacific Bldg 8A
Guanghua Rd, Chaoyang District, Beijing,
100026, China
Tel.: (86) 1065815798

Ceragon Networks (India) Private
Limited   (1)
The Genesis A-32 Mohan Cooperative In-
dustrial Estate, Mathura Road, New Delhi,
110044, India
Tel.: (91) 1166244700
Sales Range: $25-49.9 Million
Emp.: 50
Telecommunication Servicesb
N.A.I.C.S.: 334220
Ram Prakash Tripathi *(Pres & Mng Dir)*

Ceragon Networks (Nigeria)
Limited
Web Site: http://www.ceragon.com
Point-to-Point Wireless Backhaul Telecom-
munications Products & Services Whslr
N.A.I.C.S.: 517810

Ceragon Networks (UK) Limited   (1)
4 Oak Tree Park Burnt Meadow Road,
North Moons Moat, Redditch, B98 9NW,
Worcestershire, United Kingdom
Tel.: (44) 1527591900
Web Site: http://www.ceragon.com
Sales Range: $25-49.9 Million
Emp.: 6
Telecommunication Servicesb
N.A.I.C.S.: 334220

Ceragon Networks APAC (S) Pte
Ltd   (1)
Web Site: http://www.ceragon.com
Point-to-Point Wireless Backhaul Telecom-
munications Products & Services Whslr
N.A.I.C.S.: 517810

Ceragon Networks AS   (1)
Kokstadveien 23, 5257, Kokstad, Norway
Tel.: (47) 55225100
Web Site: http://www.ceragon.com
Sales Range: $350-399.9 Million
Emp.: 200
Telecommunication Servicesb
N.A.I.C.S.: 517112

Ceragon Networks Australia Pty
Ltd   (1)
Suite 106 1 Cassins Avenue, North Sydney,
2060, NSW, Australia
Tel.: (61) 289074000
Point-to-Point Wireless Backhaul Telecom-
munications Products & Services Whslr
N.A.I.C.S.: 517810

Ceragon Networks Hellas S.A.   (1)
13A Anapafseos Str, Attica, 15125, Vrilissia,
Greece
Tel.: (30) 2106108998
Point-to-Point Wireless Backhaul Telecom-
munications Products & Services Whslr
N.A.I.C.S.: 517810

Ceragon Networks Philippines,
Inc.   (1)
Unit 2A Country Space 1 Bldg No 133 Sen
Gil Puyat Ave, Salcedo Village, Makati,
1500, Philippines
Web Site: http://www.ceragon.com
Point-to-Point Wireless Backhaul Telecom-
munications Products & Services Designer,
Developer, Mfr & Whslr
N.A.I.C.S.: 334210

Ceragon Networks S.A. de C.V.   (1)
Av Chapultepec 480 Floor 3 4, Col Roma
Norte Del Cuauhtemoc, 06700, Mexico, DF,
Mexico
Tel.: (52) 5591718560
Sales Range: $25-49.9 Million
Emp.: 25
Telecommunication Servicesb
N.A.I.C.S.: 334220
Billy Cain *(Pres)*

Ceragon Networks SARL   (1)
6 Place du Village, ZAC Barbanniers,
92230, Gennevilliers, France
Tel.: (33) 140867002
Web Site: http://www.ceragon.com
Emp.: 8
Point-to-Point Wireless Backhaul Telecom-
munications Products & Services Whslr
N.A.I.C.S.: 517810

Ceragon Networks do Brasil Ltda (1)

Tel.: (55) 1146894800
Web Site: http://www.ceragon.com
Sales Range: $1-9.9 Million
Emp.: 40
Telecommunication Servicesb
N.A.I.C.S.: 517810

Branch (Non-US):

Ceragon Colombia   (2)
Carrera 47 No 91-67, Bogota, DC, Colom-
bia
Tel.: (57) 1 257 1999
Web Site: http://www.ceragon.com
Telecommunication Servicesb
N.A.I.C.S.: 517810

Ceragon Networks, Inc.   (1)
10 Forest Ave Ste 120, Paramus, NJ 07652
Tel.: (201) 845-6955
Web Site: http://www.ceragon.com
Point-to-Point Wireless Backhaul Telecom-
munications Products & Services Designer,
Developer, Mfr & Whslr
N.A.I.C.S.: 334220

Ceragon Poland   (1)
Ul Smolenskiego 4/6, 01 698, Warsaw, Po-
land
Tel.: (48) 226393505
Web Site: http://www.ceragon.com
Sales Range: $25-49.9 Million
Emp.: 10
Telecommunication Servicesb
N.A.I.C.S.: 517810

Ceragon Thailand   (1)
Level 32 Interchange 21 No 399 Sukhumvit
Road North, Klongtoey Wattana, Bangkok,
10110, Thailand
Tel.: (66) 6565724170
Point-to-Point Wireless Backhaul Telecom-
munications Products & Services Whslr
N.A.I.C.S.: 517810

Ceragon USA   (1)
Web Site: http://www.ceragon.com
Sales Range: $25-49.9 Million
Emp.: 40
Telecommunication Equipment Sales
N.A.I.C.S.: 517810

CERAMAX INC.
8200 Decarie Blvd Ste 155, Montreal,
H4P 2P5, QC, Canada
Tel.: (514) 336-8155
Sales Range: $25-49.9 Million
Emp.: 20
Ceramic Wall & Floor Tile Mfr
N.A.I.C.S.: 327120
Maxime Giordanengo *(Pres)*

CERAMIC INDUSTRIES LIM-
ITED
Farm 2 Old Potchefstroom Road,
1939, Vereeniging, South Africa
Tel.: (27) 169303600
Web Site: http://www.ceramic.co.za
Year Founded: 1976
Sales Range: $150-199.9 Million
Emp.: 452
Tiles, Sanitary Ware & Bathroom
Ware Mfr
N.A.I.C.S.: 327110
David R. Alston *(CFO)*

Subsidiaries:

National Ceramic Industries Pty
Ltd   (1)
175 Racecourse Road, Rutherford, Mait-
land, 2320, NSW, Australia
Tel.: (61) 249318400
Web Site:
    https://www.nationalceramicindustry.com
Emp.: 60
Tiles & Bathroom Ware Mfr
N.A.I.C.S.: 327110

CERAMICA CARABOBO SACA
Avenida Lisandro Alvarado fund Gua-
camaya Cl de Servicio Sec, Valencia,
2001, Venezuela
Tel.: (58) 2418134276

Ceramic Wall & Floor Tile Mfr & Retailer
N.A.I.C.S.: 327120

CERAMICA CHIARELLI S.A.
R Domingos Brunelli 180, 13840020,
Mogi-Guacu, SP, Brazil
Tel.: (55) 19 3861 0642
Year Founded: 1936
Ceramic Tile Mfr & Whslr
N.A.I.C.S.: 327120
Luis Roberto Chiarelli *(Chm)*

CERAMICA LIMA S.A.
Av Alfredo Mendiola 1465, Lima,
Peru
Tel.: (51) 16140300
Web Site: http://www.celima-
trebol.com
Sales Range: $10-24.9 Million
Emp.: 1,000
Mfr of Plumbing Fixtures
N.A.I.C.S.: 327110

Subsidiaries:

Briggs Industries, Inc.   (1)
300 Eagle Rd, Goose Creek, SC 29445-
6024
Tel.: (843) 569-7887
Web Site: http://www.briggsplumbing.com
Distr of Porcelain-on-Steel & Vitreous China
Plumbing Fixtures & Brassware
N.A.I.C.S.: 327110

CERAMIKA NOWA GALA S.A.
ul Ceramiczna 1, 26-200, Konskie,
Poland
Tel.: (48) 41 390 1100
Web Site: http://www.nowa-
gala.com.pl
Year Founded: 1995
Rev.: $39,915,001
Assets: $56,916,090
Liabilities: $17,393,012
Net Worth: $39,523,078
Earnings: ($5,614,897)
Fiscal Year-end: 12/31/18
Ceramic Products Mfr
N.A.I.C.S.: 212323
Zbigniew Polakowski *(Chm-Mgmt Bd)*

Subsidiaries:

Ceramika Gres SA   (1)
ul Ceramic 1, Kopaniny, 26-200, Konskie,
Poland
Tel.: (48) 413759311
Web Site: http://www.ceramikagres.pl
Ceramic Tile Mfr
N.A.I.C.S.: 327120

CERCLE ENTREPRISE
Parc d'activites des charmes, BP
12033, 71601, Paray-le-Monial, Ce-
dex, France
Tel.: (33) 385816008
Web Site: http://www.cercle-
entreprise.fr
Sales Range: $10-24.9 Million
Emp.: 30
Engineeering Services
N.A.I.C.S.: 541300
Jean-Louis Labaune *(Mgr-DP)*

CEREAL PLANET PLC
Tel.: (380) 573417671
Web Site: https://www.cereal.com.ua
Year Founded: 2012
Groat Producing Services
N.A.I.C.S.: 111199
Anatoly Vlasenko *(Owner & CEO)*

CEREALCOM SA
Sos Tr Magurele Nr 1, Teleorman,
Alexandria, Romania
Tel.: (40) 247313440
Web Site:
    https://www.cerealcomteleorman.ro

CEREALCOM SA

Cerealcom SA—(Continued)
CCOM—(BUC)
Rev.: $2,095,958
Assets: $20,666,323
Liabilities: $3,162,959
Net Worth: $17,503,364
Earnings: $70,297
Emp.: 24
Fiscal Year-end: 12/31/23
Grain Product Whslr
N.A.I.C.S.: 424510

CEREBRA INTEGRATED TECHNOLOGIES LTD.

S-5 Off 3rd Cross St Netaji Nagar, Peenya 1st Stage, Bengaluru, 560 058, India
Tel.: (91) 80042546969
Web Site:
　https://www.cerebracomputers.com
CEREBRAINT—(NSE)
Rev.: $9,566,316
Assets: $52,403,497
Liabilities: $11,670,518
Net Worth: $40,732,979
Earnings: $168,291
Emp.: 169
Fiscal Year-end: 03/31/21
Information Technology Services
N.A.I.C.S.: 519290
V. Ranganathan (Mng Dir)

Subsidiaries:

Cerebra LPO India Limited.　　(1)
S-5/1 Off 3rd Cross Peenya Industrial Area Peenya 1st Stage, Rajajinagar, Bengaluru, 560 058, India
Tel.: (91) 8022046969
Web Site: https://cerebracomputers.com
Legal Process Outsourcing Services
N.A.I.C.S.: 541199
Shobha Srinivas (CEO)

Cerebra Middle East FZCO　　　(1)
A4-109 Dubai Digital Park, Dubai Silicon Oasis, Dubai, United Arab Emirates
Tel.: (971) 4 333 8410
Web Site: https://www.cerebra-me.com
Security System Services
N.A.I.C.S.: 561621
V. Ranganathan (Mng Dir)

Geeta Monitors Private Limited.　(1)
381/1 N S Iyengar street, Seshadripuram, Bengaluru, 560 020, India
Tel.: (91) 80 23466365
Web Site: http://www.geetaelectronics.in
Computer Hardware & Software Distr
N.A.I.C.S.: 423430
Vijaya Mohan (Gen Mgr)

CERERIA SGARBI S.P.A.

Strada Quaglia 26, Santena, Turin, 10026, Italy
Tel.: (39) 035996711　　　　IT
Web Site: http://www.sgarbi.it
Sales Range: $10-24.9 Million
Emp.: 100
Candle Mfr
N.A.I.C.S.: 339999

Subsidiaries:

Price's Patent Candle Ltd.　　　(1)
16 Hudson Road, Bedford, MK41 0LZ, United Kingdom
Tel.: (44) 1234264500
Web Site: http://www.prices-candles.co.uk
Candle Mfr
N.A.I.C.S.: 339999
Piergiorgio Ambroggio (Dir)

CERES INC.

3-6-6 Kita-aoyama Minato-ku, Tokyo, 107-0061, Japan
Tel.: (81) 354143229
Web Site: http://www.ceres-inc.jp
Year Founded: 2005
3696—(TKS)
Rev.: $170,656,300
Assets: $183,737,350

Liabilities: $112,518,300
Net Worth: $71,219,050
Earnings: $3,197,590
Emp.: 220
Fiscal Year-end: 12/31/23
Internet Marketing Services
N.A.I.C.S.: 541613
Satoshi Miyagi (Pres & CEO)

CERES POWER HOLDINGS PLC

Viking House Foundry Lane, Horsham, RH13 5PX, W Sussex, United Kingdom
Tel.: (44) 1403273463　　　　UK
Web Site: https://www.ceres.tech
CWR—(OTCIQ)
Rev.: $43,015,285
Assets: $200,279,993
Liabilities: $35,303,435
Net Worth: $164,976,557
Earnings: ($20,115,980)
Emp.: 325
Fiscal Year-end: 12/31/20
Development & Commercial Exploitation Of Microgeneration Products
N.A.I.C.S.: 311119
Richard Preston (CFO)

Subsidiaries:

Ceres Power Limited　　　　　(1)
Viking House Foundry Lane, Horsham, RH13 5PX, West Sussex, United Kingdom
Tel.: (44) 1293400404
Sales Range: $25-49.9 Million
Emp.: 40
Fuel Cell Mfr
N.A.I.C.S.: 335999

CERESCO

164 chemin de la Grande Ligne, Saint-Urbain-Premier, J0S 1Y0, QC, Canada
Tel.: (450) 427-3831
Web Site: http://www.sgceresco.com
Year Founded: 1987
Rev.: $40,386,207
Emp.: 90
Agricultural Services
N.A.I.C.S.: 926140

Subsidiaries:

Ceresco Marketing inc.　　　　(1)
Yokohama Just 1 Bldg 12-6 2 Chome, Takashima Nishi-Ku, Yokohama, 220-0011, Kanagawa, Japan
Tel.: (81) 454536561
Soybean Distr
N.A.I.C.S.: 424510

CERESPO CO., LTD.

1-21-5 Kita-Otsuka, Toshima-Ku, Tokyo, 170-0004, Japan
Tel.: (81) 359741111
Web Site: https://www.cerespo.co.jp
Year Founded: 1977
9625—(TKS)
Sales Range: $25-49.9 Million
Event Management Services
N.A.I.C.S.: 711310
Toshihiko Inaba (Pres)

CERIC TECHNOLOGIES

42 rue de Paradis, F-75010, Paris, France
Tel.: (33) 153055500　　　　FR
Web Site: http://www.ceric.fr
Year Founded: 1960
Sales Range: $25-49.9 Million
Emp.: 85
Building Material Industrial Plant & Manufacturing Equipment Design, Construction & Installation Services
N.A.I.C.S.: 236210
Patrick Hebrard (CEO)

CERILLION PLC

---

25 Bedford Street, London, WC2E 9ES, United Kingdom
Tel.: (44) 2079276000　　　　UK
Web Site: https://www.cerillion.com
Year Founded: 1999
CER—(AIM)
Rev.: $49,866,152
Assets: $67,205,365
Liabilities: $20,241,813
Net Worth: $46,963,552
Earnings: $16,460,795
Fiscal Year-end: 09/30/23
Telecommunication Management Services
N.A.I.C.S.: 517810
Louis Tancred Hall (CEO)

Subsidiaries:

Cerillion Inc.　　　　　　　　(1)
625 Liberty Ave, Pittsburgh, PA 15222-3152
Telecommunication Equipment Mfr & Distr
N.A.I.C.S.: 334290

Cerillion Technologies India Private Limited　　　　　　　　　　(1)
Cyber City Tower V Level - 2 Wing - B, Magarpatta City Hadapsar, Pune, 411 013, India
Tel.: (91) 2067488000
Telecommunication Equipment Mfr & Distr
N.A.I.C.S.: 334290

Cerillion Technologies Limited　(1)
25 Bedford Street, London, WC2E 9ES, United Kingdom
Tel.: (44) 2079276000
Telecommunication Equipment Mfr & Distr
N.A.I.C.S.: 334290

CERINNOV GROUP SA

2 Rue Columbia Parc d Ester, 87068, Limoges, France
Tel.: (33) 555042454
Web Site: https://www.cerinnov.com
ALPCV—(EUR)
Sales Range: $10-24.9 Million
Decorating Machine Mfr & Distr
N.A.I.C.S.: 333517
Arnaud Hory (CEO)

Subsidiaries:

Cerinnov Inc.　　　　　　　　(1)
720 Corporate Cir Ste N-O, Golden, CO 80401
Tel.: (720) 370-5600
Industrial Machinery Mfr & Distr
N.A.I.C.S.: 333310
Vincent Stempfer (Sls Mgr)

Cerinnov Limited　　　　　　　(1)
Unit 2 Dewsbury Road, Stoke-on-Trent, ST4 2TE, United Kingdom
Tel.: (44) 1782280055
Industrial Machinery Distr
N.A.I.C.S.: 423830

Cerinnov SAS　　　　　　　　(1)
2 rue Columbia Parc d'Ester, 87068, Limoges, Cedex, France
Tel.: (33) 555042454
Innovative Machinery Equipment Mfr & Distr
N.A.I.C.S.: 333248

Cerinnov, Unipessoal Lda.　　　(1)
Rua Paulo VI 2490, Vale Sepal, 2415-614, Leiria, Portugal
Tel.: (351) 244817800
Innovative Machinery Equipment Mfr & Distr
N.A.I.C.S.: 333248

Sas Cristallerie de Saint Paul　(1)
Emaux Soyer Pont de Saint-Paul de Ribes, Condat, 87920, Vienne, France
Tel.: (33) 555390117
Innovative Machinery Equipment Mfr & Distr
N.A.I.C.S.: 333248

Wistra Cerinnov Gmbh　　　　(1)
Wilhelm-Mauser-Strasse 41-43, D-50827, Cologne, Germany
Tel.: (49) 2212820890
Industrial Machinery Distr
N.A.I.C.S.: 423830
Bernd Rapprich (Sls Mgr)

CERMAK A HRACHOVEC A.S.

Smichovska 31, Praha 5, Prague, 155000, Czech Republic
Tel.: (420) 251091311
Web Site: http://www.cerhra.cz
Year Founded: 1993
Sewerage Pipe Construction
N.A.I.C.S.: 237120
Miroslav Vull (Dir)

CEROS HOLDING AG

Pilatusstrasse 38, 6002, Lucerne, Switzerland
Tel.: (41) 4104470　　　　CH
Web Site: http://www.ceros.de
Holding Company; Private Equity Firm
N.A.I.C.S.: 551112
Bruno Hofstetter (Pres)

Subsidiaries:

CEROS Financial Services, Inc.　(1)
1445 Research Blvd Ste 530, Rockville, MD 20850
Tel.: (866) 842-3356
Web Site: http://www.cerosfs.com
Emp.: 12
Investment Management Brokering Services
N.A.I.C.S.: 523999
Catherine Ayers - Rigsby (Pres)

CEROS Vermogensverwaltung AG　　　　　　　　　　　　(1)
Bockenheimer Landstrasse 101, 60325, Frankfurt, Germany
Tel.: (49) 699757070
Web Site: http://www.ceros.de
Emp.: 6
Asset Management
N.A.I.C.S.: 523999
Mark Ross (Member-Exec Bd)

CERRADO GOLD INC.

200 Bay St Suite 3205, Toronto, M5J 2T6, ON, Canada
Tel.: (416) 342-1091　　　　ON
Web Site:
　https://www.cerradogold.com
Year Founded: 2018
CERT—(TSXV)
Rev.: $32,194,000
Assets: $67,610,000
Liabilities: $63,449,000
Net Worth: $4,161,000
Earnings: ($12,569,000)
Fiscal Year-end: 12/31/20
Business Consulting Services
N.A.I.C.S.: 522299
Cliff Hale-Sanders (Pres)

Subsidiaries:

Voyager Metals Inc.　　　　　(1)
501-110 Yonge Street, Toronto, M5C 1T4, ON, Canada
Tel.: (647) 932-1604
Web Site: http://www.vanadiumone.com
Assets: $8,202,450
Liabilities: $3,895,217
Net Worth: $4,307,233
Earnings: ($1,861,600)
Fiscal Year-end: 02/28/2022
Mineral Exploration Services
N.A.I.C.S.: 212290
Pierre-Jean Lafleur (VP-Exploration)

CERRO DE PASCO RESOURCES INC.

205 68 de la Gare Av SaintSauveur, Trois Rivieres, J0R 1R0, QC, Canada
Tel.: (576) 476-7000　　　　Ca
Web Site:
　https://www.pascoresources.com
Year Founded: 2003
N8HP—(DEU)
Rev.: $40,591,297
Assets: $35,877,778
Liabilities: $51,671,785
Net Worth: ($15,794,007)
Earnings: ($18,609,343)

Fiscal Year-end: 12/31/22
Metal Mining
N.A.I.C.S.: 212290
Guy Goulet *(CEO)*

CERRO GRANDE MINING CORPORATION

Avenida Santa Maria 2224, Providencia, 7520426, Santiago, Chile
Tel.: (56) 225696224   Ca
Web Site:
https://www.cegmining.com
Year Founded: 2007
CEGMF—(OTCIQ)
Assets: $1,168,000
Liabilities: $6,783,000
Net Worth: ($5,615,000)
Earnings: ($387,000)
Fiscal Year-end: 09/30/23
Mineral Properties Exploration & Development
N.A.I.C.S.: 213115
Mario A. Hernandez *(Exec VP & Dir-Claims & Land Mgmt)*

Subsidiaries:

Cerro Grande Mining
Corporation   (1)
Avenida Santa Maria 2224, Providencia, 7520426, Santiago, Chile   **(100%)**
Tel.: (56) 998374476
Web Site: https://www.cegmining.com
Explorer & Developer of Mining Properties
N.A.I.C.S.: 213115

CERRO MINING CORP.

200 Granville Street Suite 2820, Vancouver, V6C 1S4, BC, Canada
Tel.: (778) 987-3203
Year Founded: 1987
CRX—(TSXV)
Rev.: $18,049
Assets: $6,943
Liabilities: $248,347
Net Worth: ($241,404)
Earnings: ($107,383)
Fiscal Year-end: 01/31/20
Mineral Properties Exploration Services
N.A.I.C.S.: 213114
Andrew Bowering *(CEO)*

CERSANIT ROMANIA SA

Str Aleea Plopilor 10, Neamt, Roman, Romania
Tel.: (40) 233 740416
Web Site: http://www.cersanit.ro
Sales Range: $10-24.9 Million
Emp.: 555
Bathroom Equipment Whslr
N.A.I.C.S.: 423220

CERSANIT S.A.

Al Solidarnosci 36, 25-323, Kielce, Poland
Tel.: (48) 413158004
Web Site: http://www.rovese.com
Sales Range: $400-449.9 Million
Bathroom Furnishings Mfr
N.A.I.C.S.: 327110
Ireneusz Kazimierski *(Chm-Mgmt Bd)*

CERTECH SPA

Via Don Pasquino Borghi 8/10 S Antonio, 42013, Casalgrande, Italy
Tel.: (39) 0536 824294
Web Site: http://www.certech.it
Year Founded: 1977
Ceramic Components Mfr
N.A.I.C.S.: 327110

Subsidiaries:

Eurorubber S.p.A.   (1)
Via Tarona 8, 43010, Pontetaro, PR, Italy
Tel.: (39) 0521679911
Web Site: http://www.eurorubber.it

Sales Range: $25-49.9 Million
Emp.: 60
Mfr & Distribution of Tires & Retreaded Tires
N.A.I.C.S.: 441340

CERTINA HOLDING AG

23 Tumblinger St, 80337, Munich, Germany
Tel.: (49) 892108960
Web Site: http://www.certina.de
Sales Range: $150-199.9 Million
Emp.: 1,300
Holding Company Services
N.A.I.C.S.: 551112
Andras v. Kontz *(Dir-Corp Dev)*

Subsidiaries:

AFT Automation Limited   (1)
Regus Building Central Boulevard Blythe Valley Business Park, Solihull, B90 8AG, United Kingdom
Tel.: (44) 1564 711017
Industrial Machinery & Equipment Distr
N.A.I.C.S.: 423830

AFT Automation and Conveying Systems (Shanghai) Co. Ltd.   (1)
No 1 Building No 5825 Hu Yi Road Waigang Town, Jia Ding District, Shanghai, 201821, China
Tel.: (86) 21 3950 7200
Industrial Machinery & Equipment Distr
N.A.I.C.S.: 423830

AFT Automatisierungs- und Fordertechnik GmbH & Co. KG   (1)
An der Wiese 14, 79650, Schopfheim, Germany
Tel.: (49) 7622 3998 0
Industrial Machinery & Equipment Distr
N.A.I.C.S.: 423830

AFT Korea Co. Ltd.   (1)
404 3 Da Shiwha Ind Complex, 429-450, Siheung, Kyeonggi-do, Korea (South)
Tel.: (82) 31 499 0445
Web Site: http://www.skaft.co.kr
Industrial Machinery & Equipment Distr
N.A.I.C.S.: 423830
Chaiwoo Shim *(Pres & CEO)*

AFT-Forderanlagen Bautzen GmbH & Co. KG   (1)
Edisonstrasse 1, 02625, Bautzen, Germany
Tel.: (49) 3591 3788 0
Industrial Machinery & Equipment Distr
N.A.I.C.S.: 423830

C.M.V. s.r.l.   (1)
Via A Costa 1-3 Cadriano di Granarolo Emilia, 40057, Bologna, Italy
Tel.: (39) 051 766324
Web Site: http://www.cmvsaune.com
Construction Engineering Services
N.A.I.C.S.: 541330
Grizzo Giuseppe *(Gen Mgr)*

CAM Systems GmbH   (1)
Westendstr 193, 80686, Munich, Germany
Tel.: (49) 89 189 080 0
Web Site: http://www.cam-systems.de
Software Development Services
N.A.I.C.S.: 541511
Uwe Brauer *(Mng Dir)*

COI GmbH   (1)
Am Weichselgarten 23, 91058, Erlangen, Germany
Tel.: (49) 9131 93 99 0
Web Site: http://www.coi.de
Emp.: 45
Website & Content Development Services
N.A.I.C.S.: 541513
Giovanni Santamaria *(CEO)*

Certina Construction AG   (1)
Via Valcellina A/2, 33097, Spilimbergo, Pordenone, Italy
Tel.: (39) 0427 594111
Bathroom Fixture Mfr
N.A.I.C.S.: 327110

Eiffel Deutschland Stahltechnologie
GmbH   (1)
Hackethalstrasse 4, 30179, Hannover, Germany
Tel.: (49) 51167990

Web Site: http://www.eiffel.de
Sales Range: $25-49.9 Million
Emp.: 180
Steel Mfrs
N.A.I.C.S.: 331513

Subsidiary (Domestic):

Eiffel Deutschland Stahltechnologie GmbH - Duisburg   (2)
Friedrich Ebert Strasse 134, 47229, Duisburg, Germany
Tel.: (49) 2065823010
Web Site: http://www.eiffel.de
Steel Mfrs
N.A.I.C.S.: 331513

Feintool Technology AG   (1)
Industriering 3, Lyss, 3250, Terne, Switzerland   **(85%)**
Tel.: (41) 323875111
Web Site: http://www.feintool.com
Sales Range: $100-124.9 Million
Emp.: 300
Fineblanking Technology of Automotive Gearboxes
N.A.I.C.S.: 333612
Heinz Loosli *(Head-Sys Parts)*

HORN Glass Industries AG   (1)
Bergstrasse 2, 95703, Plossberg, Germany
Tel.: (49) 9636 9204 0
Web Site: http://www.hornglass.com
Heating Equipment Mfr
N.A.I.C.S.: 333414
Maximilian Sollfrank *(CEO & Mng Dir)*

Subsidiary (Non-US):

HORN Glass Asia Pacific SDN.
BHD.   (2)
62C Jalan SS 21/62 Damansara Utama, 47400, Petaling Jaya, Selangor, Malaysia
Tel.: (60) 3 7729 1207
Web Site: http://www.hornglass.asia
Heating Equipment Distr
N.A.I.C.S.: 423720

HORN Glass Technology (Beijing) Co., Ltd   (2)
Room 718 Golden Land Building 32 Liang-MaQiao Road, ChaoYang, Beijing, 100125, China
Tel.: (86) 1064637797
Web Site: http://www.hornglass.com.cn
Heating Equipment Distr
N.A.I.C.S.: 423720

Pibiviesse S.r.l.   (1)
Via Bergamina 24, Nerviano, 20014, MI, Italy
Tel.: (39) 0331408711
Web Site: http://www.pibiviesse.it
Oil & Gas Mfr; Large Size Valves
N.A.I.C.S.: 332919

Pruss Armaturen AG   (1)
Schulenburger Landstr 261, 30419, Hannover, Germany
Tel.: (49) 511 27986 0
Web Site: http://www.pruss.de
Industrial Valve Mfr
N.A.I.C.S.: 332911
Ralf Nosko *(Mng Dir)*

Rebhan FPS Kunststoff-Verpackungen GmbH   (1)
Kronacher Strasse 19, 96342, Stockheim, Germany
Tel.: (49) 9265 75 0
Web Site: http://www.rebhan-group.com
Plastic Packaging Container Mfr
N.A.I.C.S.: 326199
Anika Sovuksu *(Key Acct Mgr)*

SCAM SPA   (1)
Via Campagna 80, 21056, Induno Olona, Varese, Italy
Tel.: (39) 0332 202861
Web Site: http://www.scamtrucks.it
Light Tactical Vehicle Mfr
N.A.I.C.S.: 336110
Andrea Aviano *(Mgr-ICT & Logistic)*

Vitaviva Italia Srl   (1)
Loc Lanciano 9, 62022, Castelraimondo, Macerata, Italy
Tel.: (39) 0737 6451
Web Site: http://www.vitaviva.it
Bathroom Fixture Mfr

N.A.I.C.S.: 327110

CERVANTES CORPORATION LIMITED

Shop 11 South Shore Piazza 85 The Esplanade, South Perth, 6151, WA, Australia
Tel.: (61) 8 6436 2300   AU
Web Site:
http://www.cervantescorp.com.au
Rev.: $59,908
Assets: $1,535,091
Liabilities: $1,204,597
Net Worth: $330,494
Earnings: ($248,213)
Emp.: 1
Fiscal Year-end: 06/30/18
Seafood Mfr & Whslr
N.A.I.C.S.: 311710
Patrick J. O'Neill *(Sec)*

CES ENERGY SOLUTIONS CORP.

Suite 1400 332 6th Avenue SW, Calgary, T2P 0B2, AB, Canada
Tel.: (403) 269-2800
Web Site:
https://www.cesenergysolutions.com
CEU—(OTCIQ)
Rev.: $935,935,438
Assets: $850,806,163
Liabilities: $470,090,044
Net Worth: $380,716,119
Earnings: $39,023,256
Emp.: 1,812
Fiscal Year-end: 12/31/21
Drilling Fluid Systems Designer
N.A.I.C.S.: 213112
Kyle D. Kitagawa *(Chm)*

Subsidiaries:

AES Drilling Fluids, LLC   (1)
1625 Broadway Ste 1480, Denver, CO 80202
Tel.: (303) 820-2800
Web Site: https://www.aesfluids.com
Sales Range: $50-74.9 Million
Oil & Gas Drilling Services
N.A.I.C.S.: 213111

Catalyst Oilfield Services   (1)
11999 E US Hwy, Gardendale, TX 79758
Tel.: (432) 563-0727
Web Site: http://www.jacamcatalyst.com
Site Preparation Contractor
N.A.I.C.S.: 238910
Trey Womack *(Founder & Pres)*

Clear Environmental Solutions
Inc.   (1)
720 - 736 8th Avenue Southwest, Calgary, T2P 1H4, AB, Canada
Tel.: (403) 263-5953
Web Site: http://clearenv.com
Sales Range: $25-49.9 Million
Environmental Engineering Services
N.A.I.C.S.: 541330

CES LIMITED

7th Floor Tower A Ramky Selenium Nanakramguda Gachibowli, Hyderabad, 500 032, India
Tel.: (91) 4042421122   In
Web Site: https://www.cesltd.com
512341—(BOM)
Rev.: $56,611,337
Assets: $41,025,991
Liabilities: $18,354,028
Net Worth: $22,671,963
Earnings: $3,175,084
Emp.: 839
Fiscal Year-end: 03/31/24
Business Management Services
N.A.I.C.S.: 518210
Murali Krishna Tummala *(Chm)*

Subsidiaries:

CES Technology Services Private
Limited   (1)

CES Limited—(Continued)

7th Floor Tower-A Ramky Selenium Building, Financial District, Hyderabad, 500 032, India
Tel.: (91) 4042421111
Web Site: http://www.cestechservices.com
IT Services
N.A.I.C.S.: 541511

CESAR SA
ZI Clos Bonnet 154 Blvd Jean Moulin, 49400, Saumur, France
Tel.: (33) 2 41 50 26 54
Web Site: http://www.cesar-group.fr
ALCES—(EUR)
Sales Range: $1-9.9 Million
Party Items Mfr
N.A.I.C.S.: 339930
Daniel Velasco *(Chm)*

CESARE PACIOTTI S.P.A.
Via Sant Andrea 8, Milan, 20121, Italy
Tel.: (39) 0276013887
Web Site: http://www.cesare-paciotti.com
Year Founded: 1948
Sales Range: $1-9.9 Million
Emp.: 200
Footwear Designer & Mfr
N.A.I.C.S.: 316210
Maximiliano Bennettin *(Mng Dir)*

CESC LIMITED
CESC House Chowringhee Square, Kolkata, 700 001, India
Tel.: (91) 22256040
Web Site: https://www.cesc.co.in
Year Founded: 1897
CESC—(NSE)
Rev.: $1,749,871,305
Assets: $5,117,858,655
Liabilities: $3,639,483,120
Net Worth: $1,478,375,535
Earnings: $191,656,920
Emp.: 6,920
Fiscal Year-end: 03/31/22
Electric Utility Services
N.A.I.C.S.: 221122
Sanjiv Goenka *(Chm)*

Subsidiaries:

CESC Properties Limited (1)
CESC House Chowringhee Sq, Kolkata, 700 001, India
Tel.: (91) 3322256040
Property Development Services
N.A.I.C.S.: 531311

ISGN Solutions, Inc. (1)
600-A N John Rodes Blvd, Melbourne, FL 32934
Web Site: http://www.isgn.com
Mortgage Technology, Software & Services
N.A.I.C.S.: 513210

Subsidiary (Domestic):

ISGN Fulfillment Services, Inc. (2)
707 Grant St Ste 300, Pittsburgh, PA 15219
Tel.: (412) 261-4791
Mortgage Loan Fulfillment Services
N.A.I.C.S.: 541191

Kota Electricity Distribution Limited (1)
Jai Height Kotri Gumanpura Road, Kota, 324007, India
Tel.: (91) 1413532000
Electricity Distribution Services
N.A.I.C.S.: 221122
Ravishankar P. Shukla *(Head-Comml)*

Music World Retail Limited (1)
2 St George Gate Road 7th Floor Hastings, Kolkata, 700022, West Bengal, India
Tel.: (91) 33 222 36 337
Web Site: http://www.musicworld.in
Music Publishing Services
N.A.I.C.S.: 512230

Nalanda Power Company Limited (1)
Regd Clfice 6 Church Lane 1st Floor, Kolkata, 700 001, India
Tel.: (91) 3322109358
Electric Power Generation
N.A.I.C.S.: 221118

Spencer's Retail Limited (1)
Mani Square EM Bypass 164/1 Maniktala Main Road Near Apollo Hospital, Kolkata, 700 054, West Bengal, India
Tel.: (91) 3340313712
Web Site: http://www.spencersretail.com
Supermarket & Grocery Stores
N.A.I.C.S.: 445110

Subsidiary (Domestic):

Natures Basket Ltd. (2)
Godrej One 3rd Floor, Pirojshanagar Eastern Express Highway, Mumbai, 400079, Vikhroli, India
Tel.: (91) 08880077745
Fruit Retail Store
N.A.I.C.S.: 445230
Avani Davda *(Mng Dir)*

CESI S.P.A.
Via Rubattino 54, 1-20134, Milan, Italy
Tel.: (39) 02 21251
Web Site: http://www.cesi.it
Year Founded: 1956
Sales Range: $125-149.9 Million
Management & Technical Consulting Servcies
N.A.I.C.S.: 541690
Giacomo Marini *(Dir-Consulting, Solutions, and Svcs Div)*

Subsidiaries:

EnerNex LLC (1)
620 Mabry Hood Rd Ste 300, Knoxville, TN 37932
Tel.: (865) 218-4600
Web Site: http://www.enernex.com
Electric Power Research, Engineering & Consulting Services
N.A.I.C.S.: 541620
Jeff Lamoree *(Pres & CEO)*

CESP - COMPANHIA ENERGETICA DE SAO PAULO
Av Nossa Senhora do Sabara 5312, Pedreira, 04447-011, Sao Paulo, Brazil
Tel.: (55) 1156132100
Web Site: http://www.cesp.com.br
CESP—(BRAZ)
Rev.: $286,402,678
Assets: $2,796,121,785
Liabilities: $1,155,485,829
Net Worth: $1,640,635,956
Earnings: ($92,605,873)
Emp.: 568
Fiscal Year-end: 12/31/23
Electric Power Generation & Distribution
N.A.I.C.S.: 221118
Mituo Hirota *(Member-Exec Bd & Dir-Generation)*

CESSATECH A/S
Kanonbadsvej 2, 1437, Copenhagen, Denmark
Tel.: (45) 93872309
Web Site: https://www.cessatech.com
Year Founded: 2020
8GN—(DEU)
Assets: $1,230,484
Liabilities: $1,508,154
Net Worth: ($277,669)
Earnings: ($3,838,318)
Emp.: 4
Fiscal Year-end: 12/31/23
Pharmaceutical Product Mfr & Distr
N.A.I.C.S.: 325412

CESSOT DECORATION SARL

14 rue Croix la Comtesse, Nogent le Rotrou, 28400, Le Mans, France
Tel.: (33) 237534200
Web Site: http://www.cessot-decoration.fr
Rev.: $21,800,000
Emp.: 105
Hardware
N.A.I.C.S.: 332510
Claude Tournier *(Mng Partner)*

CESTNE SATVBY AS
Majerska cesta 69, 974 01, Banska Bystrica, Slovakia
Tel.: (421) 484141251
Web Site: https://www.cestnestavbybb.sk
Year Founded: 1992
1CSB01AE—(BRA)
Sales Range: Less than $1 Million
Road Construction Services
N.A.I.C.S.: 237310
Milan Franik *(Chm, Chm-Mgmt Bd & Gen Dir)*

CESTNE STAVBY AS
Majerska route 69, Banska Bystrica, 974 01, Slovakia
Tel.: (421) 484141251
Web Site: http://www.cestnestavbybb.sk
Civil Engineering & Construction Services
N.A.I.C.S.: 541330
Milan Franik *(Chm-Mgmt Bd)*

CETC ACOUSTIC-OPTIC-ELECTRONIC TECHNOLOGY INC.
No 111 Yongjia Avenue, Bishan District, Chongqing, 402760, China
Tel.: (86) 2361954095
Web Site: http://www.jialingmotor.com
Year Founded: 1875
600877—(SHG)
Rev.: $219,739,661
Assets: $398,843,925
Liabilities: $95,588,111
Net Worth: $303,255,815
Earnings: $31,328,688
Fiscal Year-end: 12/31/22
Motorcycle & Related Parts Mfr & Distr
N.A.I.C.S.: 336991

Subsidiaries:

Shenzhen Ruijing Industrial Co. Ltd. (1)
No 168 Xiakeng 1 Road Building C1, Hengli Industrial Park Longgang District, Shenzhen, China
Tel.: (86) 75584829563
Web Site: http://www.rjsz.net
Electronic Supply Mfr
N.A.I.C.S.: 334419
Abbott Hou *(Sls Dir)*

CETC CYBERSPACE SECURITY TECHNOLOGY CO., LTD.
333 Yunhua Road, Chengdu, 610095, Sichuan, China
Tel.: (86) 2862386000
Web Site: https://en.cetccst.com.cn
Year Founded: 1998
002268—(SSE)
Rev.: $482,699,412
Assets: $1,062,371,700
Liabilities: $325,433,160
Net Worth: $736,938,540
Earnings: $43,052,256
Fiscal Year-end: 12/31/22
Security Product Mfr
N.A.I.C.S.: 561621
Chen Xin *(Chm)*

CETC DIGITAL TECHNOLOGY CO., LTD
19th Floor CETC Information Technology Building No 127 Bailianjing Road, Pudong New Area, Shanghai, 200126, China
Tel.: (86) 2133390000
Web Site: https://www.shecc.com
Year Founded: 1993
600850—(SHG)
Rev.: $1,385,961,787
Assets: $1,561,456,691
Liabilities: $954,010,629
Net Worth: $607,446,062
Earnings: $73,008,070
Emp.: 3,000
Fiscal Year-end: 12/31/22
Software Development Services
N.A.I.C.S.: 541512
Jiang Bo *(Chm)*

CETIS, D.D.
Copova ulica 24, 3000, Celje, Slovenia
Tel.: (386) 34278500
Web Site: https://www.cetis.si
CETG—(LJU)
Rev.: $75,312,948
Assets: $111,236,340
Liabilities: $30,404,018
Net Worth: $80,832,321
Earnings: $17,982,117
Emp.: 283
Fiscal Year-end: 12/31/23
Documents, Cards, Forms, Labels & Flexible Packaging
N.A.I.C.S.: 323111
Srecko Gorenjak *(Member-Mgmt Bd)*

Subsidiaries:

Amba Co., proizvodnja in trgovina d.o.o., Ljubljana (1)
Leskoskova 11, Ljubljana, 1000, Slovenia
Tel.: (386) 15874300
Web Site: http://www.amba-tc.si
Sales Range: $25-49.9 Million
Emp.: 36
Flexo Printing Technology Services
N.A.I.C.S.: 323111
Bostjan Jambrovic *(Chm)*

Cetis-ZG d.o.o. (1)
Industrijska 11, 10431, Sveta Nedelja, Croatia
Tel.: (385) 13335000
Web Site: https://www.cetis.hr
Sales Range: $25-49.9 Million
Emp.: 20
Security Printing Services
N.A.I.C.S.: 323111
Luana Vozila *(Gen Mgr)*

CETTIRE LIMITED
Level 40 140 William Street, Melbourne, 3000, VIC, Australia
Tel.: (61) 383913081
Web Site: https://www.cettire.com
Year Founded: 2017
CTT—(ASX)
Rev.: $271,387,508
Assets: $65,704,526
Liabilities: $44,188,291
Net Worth: $21,516,235
Earnings: $10,409,816
Fiscal Year-end: 06/30/23
Clothing Accessory Distr
N.A.I.C.S.: 458110
Fiona Van Wyk *(Sec)*

CETUS CAPITAL ACQUISITION CORP.
Floor 3 No 6 Lane 99 Zhengda Second Street, Wenshan District, Taipei, 11602, Taiwan
Tel.: (886) 920518827
Year Founded: 2022
CETU—(NASDAQ)
Rev.: $1,394,622

Assets: $60,494,983
Liabilities: $62,996,129
Net Worth: ($2,501,146)
Earnings: $52,056
Fiscal Year-end: 12/31/23
Investment Management Service
N.A.I.C.S.: 523999

CEVA SANTE ANIMALE SA
10 Avenue de la Ballastiere, 33500, Libourne, France
Tel.: (33) 557554040
Web Site: http://www.ceva.com
Pharmaceutical Products & Animal Vaccine Research & Development Services
N.A.I.C.S.: 541714
Mark Heffernan *(Sr VP-Biotherapeutics)*

Subsidiaries:

Scout Bio, Inc. **(1)**
100 N 18th St Ste 300, Philadelphia, PA 19103
Tel.: (650) 325-5153
Web Site: http://www.scoutbio.co
Biotechnology Research & Development Services
N.A.I.C.S.: 541714
Damian Lismore *(CFO)*

Thundershirt, LLC **(1)**
112A Broadwat St, Durham, NC 27701
Web Site: http://www.thundershirt.com
Chemicals Mfr
N.A.I.C.S.: 325998
Phil Blizzard *(Founder)*

CEVITAL S.P.A.
Ilot D No 6 ZHUN Garidi II, Kouba, 16005, Algiers, Algeria
Tel.: (213) 2356 3802   DG
Web Site: http://www.cevital.com
Year Founded: 2007
Sales Range: $1-4.9 Billion
Emp.: 13,000
Investment Holding Company
N.A.I.C.S.: 311999
Issad Rebrab *(Founder & Chm)*

Subsidiaries:

BATICOMPOS spa **(1)**
Beni Mancour Boudjellil Daira de tazmalt wilaya de, BP 75, Bejaia, 06026, Algeria
Tel.: (213) 34 34 01 69
Web Site: http://www.baticompos.com.dz
Sheet Metal Mfr
N.A.I.C.S.: 332322

CEVITAL Minerals, Spa **(1)**
30 Rue Djenane El Malik, Hydra, 16035, Algiers, Algeria
Tel.: (213) 21 608 491
Web Site: http://www.cevital-minerals.com
Mineral Exploration Services
N.A.I.C.S.: 213114

Ceviagro SpA **(1)**
Domaine Chaib Mohamed Eac N 29 El Hamiz Dar El Beida, Algiers, Algeria
Tel.: (213) 770 25 01 48
Potato Farming Services
N.A.I.C.S.: 111211

Cevital Food Processing Industry **(1)**
Nouveau Quai Port de, Bejaia, Algeria
Tel.: (213) 34202000
Web Site: http://www.cevital.com
Food Processing Services
N.A.I.C.S.: 311423

Cevital-MTP spa **(1)**
165 Lotissement Saidoune Mohamed Kouba, Algiers, Algeria
Tel.: (213) 21286424
Web Site: http://www.cevicar.com
Car Rental Services
N.A.I.C.S.: 532111

MFG Spa **(1)**
29 Route de meftah - I Arbaa, 9300, Blida, Algeria
Tel.: (213) 21 448 644
Web Site: http://www.mfg-dg.com

Flat Glass Mfr & Distr
N.A.I.C.S.: 327211

Subsidiary (Non-US):

M.F.G. EUROPE S.r.l. **(2)**
Via della Magliana 1, 12049, Cuneo, Trinita, Italy
Tel.: (39) 0172 484001
Web Site: http://www.mfg-eu.com
Flat Glass Mfr & Distr
N.A.I.C.S.: 327211
Fodil Laoudi *(CEO)*

MFG Tunisia **(2)**
Residence Riadh El Bouhaira n 29, Berges du Lac, 1053, Tunis, Tunisia
Tel.: (216) 67 19 63 020
Flat Glass Mfr & Distr
N.A.I.C.S.: 327211

Nolis-SPA **(1)**
138 Lotissement Mohamed Saidoun Kouba, Algiers, Algeria
Tel.: (213) 21 290 230
Web Site: http://www.nolis-spa.com
Sea Transportation Services
N.A.I.C.S.: 483111

Oxxo SA **(1)**
3 Route de Jalogny, PO Box 23, 71250, Cluny, France
Tel.: (33) 385595566
Web Site: http://www.oxxobatiment.fr
Sales Range: $125-149.9 Million
Emp.: 288
PVC Window Frame Mfr
N.A.I.C.S.: 326199

SAMHA Home Appliance SPA **(1)**
Samha Home Appliance Zone Industrielle Route de Batna, BP 78, Setif, 19000, Algeria
Tel.: (213) 36 62 51 41
Emp.: 1,800
Household Products Mfr
N.A.I.C.S.: 335220

Sodi Automotive Spa **(1)**
216 rue Hassiba Ben Bouali, Algiers, Algeria
Tel.: (213) 21 675 721
Web Site: http://www.sodiautomotive.com
Automobile Parts Distr
N.A.I.C.S.: 423110

CEVOTEC GMBH
Biberger Str 93, 82008, Unterhaching, Germany
Tel.: (49) 8923141650
Web Site: https://www.cevotec.com
Year Founded: 2015
Composite Material Mfr
N.A.I.C.S.: 321918

CEWE STIFTUNG & CO. KGAA
Meerweg 30-32, 26133, Oldenburg, Germany
Tel.: (49) 4414040
Web Site: https://www.cewe.de
CWC—(STU)
Rev.: $861,239,374
Assets: $735,133,265
Liabilities: $305,462,906
Net Worth: $429,670,359
Earnings: $63,262,790
Emp.: 3,731
Fiscal Year-end: 12/31/23
Photofinishing Services
N.A.I.C.S.: 812921
Frank Zweigle *(Member-Mgmt Bd)*

Subsidiaries:

CEWE Magyarorszag Kft **(1)**
Peace Road 21-29, 1135, Budapest, Hungary
Tel.: (36) 14511088
Web Site: http://www.cewe.hu
Online Printing Services
N.A.I.C.S.: 323111

CEWE Sp. z o. o. **(1)**
Ul Strzelecka 11, 47-230, Kedzierzyn-Kozle, Poland
Tel.: (48) 774063180
Web Site: http://www.cewe.pl

Online Printing Services
N.A.I.C.S.: 323111

Cewe Color AG & Co. OHG **(1)**
Meerweg 30 32, D 26133, Oldenburg, Germany
Tel.: (49) 4414040
Web Site: http://www.cewe.de
Photofinishing Services
N.A.I.C.S.: 812921

Subsidiary (Non-US):

CEWE COLOR Belgium S.A. **(2)**
Blauwesteenstraat 87, 2550, Kontich, Belgium
Tel.: (32) 3 4 51 92 00
Photofinishing Services
N.A.I.C.S.: 812921

CEWE COLOR Danmark A.S. **(2)**
Segaltvej 16, 8541, Skodstrup, Denmark
Tel.: (45) 86991422
Photofinishing Services
N.A.I.C.S.: 812921

CEWE COLOR Limited **(2)**
Unit 4 Spartan Close Titan Bus Ctr Tachbrook Park, Warwick, CV34 6RR, Warwickshire, United Kingdom
Tel.: (44) 1926463107
Web Site: http://www.cewe-photoworld.co.uk
Sales Range: $25-49.9 Million
Emp.: 80
Photofinishing Services
N.A.I.C.S.: 812921

CEWE COLOR Magyarorszag Kft **(2)**
Beke ut 21-29, 1135, Budapest, Hungary
Tel.: (36) 14511088
Web Site: http://www.cewe-fotokonyv.hu
Sales Range: $25-49.9 Million
Emp.: 60
Photofinishing Services
N.A.I.C.S.: 812921

CEWE COLOR Nederland B.V. **(2)**
Industrieweg 73, 8071 CS, Nunspeet, Netherlands
Tel.: (31) 341255355
Photofinishing Services
N.A.I.C.S.: 812921

CEWE COLOR S.A.S **(2)**
189 rue d Aubervilliers, 75886, Paris, Cedex 18, France
Tel.: (33) 153266666
Photofinishing Services
N.A.I.C.S.: 812921

CEWE COLOR Sp. z o. o **(2)**
Ul Strzelecka 11, 47230, Kedzierzyn-Kozle, Opole, Poland
Tel.: (48) 774063000
Web Site: http://www.cewecolor.pl
Sales Range: $25-49.9 Million
Emp.: 60
Photofinishing Services
N.A.I.C.S.: 812921

CeWe Color, a.s. **(2)**
Kloknerova 2278/24, 148 00, Prague, Czech Republic
Tel.: (420) 272071400
Web Site: http://www.cewe.cz
Sales Range: $25-49.9 Million
Emp.: 80
Photofinishing Services
N.A.I.C.S.: 812921

Subsidiary (Domestic):

Diginet Gmbh & Co. KG **(2)**
161 Industriestrasse, D 50999, Cologne, Nordhein-Westfalen, Germany
Tel.: (49) 221 2236 886 0
Web Site: http://www.pixum.de
Photofinishing Services
N.A.I.C.S.: 812921
Daniel Attallah *(Founder, CEO & Mng Dir)*

Fotocolor GmbH **(2)**
Freiburger Str 20, 79427, Eschbach, Germany
Tel.: (49) 76345050
Web Site: http://www.cewe.de
Photofinishing Services
N.A.I.C.S.: 812921

Subsidiary (Non-US):

Fotojoker Sp. z o. o. **(2)**

Ul Armii Krajowej 38, 47-220, Kedzierzyn-Kozle, Opole, Poland
Tel.: (48) 728464402
Web Site: http://www.fotojoker.pl
Sales Range: $25-49.9 Million
Emp.: 50
Camera & Photofinishing Equipment Sales
N.A.I.C.S.: 423410

Japan Photo Holding Norge AS **(2)**
Laguneveien 1 Radal, 5239, Bergen, Norway
Tel.: (47) 66822660
Web Site: http://www.support.japanphoto.no
Sales Range: $75-99.9 Million
Emp.: 300
Photofinishing Services
N.A.I.C.S.: 812921

Subsidiary (Domestic):

diron Wirtschaftsinformatik GmbH & Co. KG **(2)**
Otto-Hahn-Str 21, 48161, Munster, Nordrhein-Westfalen, Germany
Tel.: (49) 251979200
Web Site: http://www.diron.de
Sales Range: $10-24.9 Million
Emp.: 40
Photofinishing Services
N.A.I.C.S.: 812921

DeinDesign GmbH **(1)**
Otto-Meffert-Strasse 3, 55543, Bad Kreuznach, Germany
Tel.: (49) 6719708070
Web Site: https://www.deindesign.de
Mobile Accessory Part Retailer
N.A.I.C.S.: 441330
Gerd Dussler *(Mng Dir)*

Futalis GmbH **(1)**
Angerstr 40-42, 04177, Leipzig, Germany
Tel.: (49) 34139298790
Web Site: https://www.futalis.de
Pet Product Retailer
N.A.I.C.S.: 459910

Hertz Systemtechnik GmbH **(1)**
Reinersweg 68, 27751, Delmenhorst, Germany
Tel.: (49) 4221972300
Web Site: https://www.hertz.st
Emp.: 45
Software Development Services
N.A.I.C.S.: 541511

Saxoprint GmbH **(1)**
Enderstrasse 92c, 01277, Dresden, Germany
Tel.: (49) 3512044444
Web Site: https://www.saxoprint.de
Online Printing Services
N.A.I.C.S.: 323111

Subsidiary (Domestic):

Laserline GmbH **(2)**
Fraunhofer Strasse, 56218, Mulheim-Karlich, Germany
Tel.: (49) 26309644000
Industrial Laser Equipment Mfr
N.A.I.C.S.: 333992

Subsidiary (Non-US):

Saxoprint AG **(2)**
Tel.: (41) 435880088
Online Printing Services
N.A.I.C.S.: 323111

Saxoprint EURL **(2)**
Equinox Tower 21 Alleyways of Europe, 92110, Clichy, France
Tel.: (33) 974487000
Web Site: http://www.saxoprint.fr
Online Printing Services
N.A.I.C.S.: 323111

Saxoprint Ltd. **(2)**
GW2 Great West House Great West Road, London, TW8 9HU, United Kingdom
Tel.: (44) 2036080777
Web Site: http://www.saxoprint.co.uk
Online Printing Services
N.A.I.C.S.: 323111

Viaprinto GmbH & Co. KG **(1)**
Martin-Luther-King-Weg 30a, 48155, Munster, Germany
Tel.: (49) 25197920200

CEWE Stiftung & Co. KGaA—(Continued)

Web Site: https://www.viaprinto.de
Photo Printing Services
N.A.I.C.S.: 519290

CEYLON GRAIN ELEVATORS PLC
Tel.: (94) 112522556
Web Site: https://www.prima.com.lk
Year Founded: 1982
GRAN.N0000—(COL)
Rev.: $60,526,677
Assets: $58,405,045
Liabilities: $13,573,779
Net Worth: $44,831,266
Earnings: $12,503,472
Emp.: 745
Fiscal Year-end: 12/31/23
Veterinary Food Mfr
N.A.I.C.S.: 311111
Subsidiaries:

Three Acre Farms PLC   **(1)**
15 Rock House Lane, 15, Colombo, Sri Lanka
Tel.: (94) 2522556
Rev.: $27,685,513
Assets: $23,278,350
Liabilities: $3,940,668
Net Worth: $19,337,682
Earnings: $2,193,825
Emp.: 238
Fiscal Year-end: 12/31/2022
Poultry Farming Services
N.A.I.C.S.: 112390
C. C. K. Primus (CEO)

CEYLON GRAPHITE CORP.
1100 1111 Melville St, Vancouver, V6E 4A6, BC, Canada
Tel.: (604) 765-8657
Web Site:
https://www.ceylongraphite.com
Year Founded: 2017
CYLYF—(OTCQB)
Assets: $3,560,519
Liabilities: $3,170,246
Net Worth: $390,274
Earnings: ($2,554,607)
Fiscal Year-end: 03/31/21
Graphite Exploration Services
N.A.I.C.S.: 212390
Sasha Jacob (Founder & CEO)

CEYLON HOTELS CORPORATION PLC
327 Union Place, 2, Colombo, 2, Sri Lanka
Tel.: (94) 117765555
Web Site: https://www.chcplc.com
Year Founded: 1966
CHOT.N0000—(COL)
Rev.: $2,253,404
Assets: $64,862,157
Liabilities: $16,133,293
Net Worth: $48,728,864
Earnings: ($2,049,402)
Emp.: 240
Fiscal Year-end: 03/31/21
Hotel & Restaurant Operator
N.A.I.C.S.: 721110

CEYLON LAND & EQUITY PLC
Tel.: (94) 1123147505
Year Founded: 1958
KZOO.N0000—(COL)
Rev.: $105,801
Assets: $9,944,232
Liabilities: $2,267,336
Net Worth: $7,676,896
Earnings: $929,673
Fiscal Year-end: 03/31/23
Stationary Equipment Distr
N.A.I.C.S.: 423420
Rajiyah S. V. (Chm)

CEYLON TEA BROKERS PLC

Level 7 Millennium House 4658 Nawam Mawatha, 2, Colombo, 2, Sri Lanka
Tel.: (94) 114607777
Web Site:
https://www.ceylonteabrokers.com
CTBL.N0000—(COL)
Rev.: $4,614,125
Assets: $15,475,112
Liabilities: $12,760,047
Net Worth: $2,715,065
Earnings: $101,591
Emp.: 114
Fiscal Year-end: 03/31/22
Tea Mfr
N.A.I.C.S.: 311920
Chrisantha Perera (Chm)

CEYLON TOBACCO COMPANY LTD.
178 Srimath Ramanathan Mawatha, 1500, Colombo, Sri Lanka
Tel.: (94) 112496200
Web Site:
https://www.ceylontobacco.com
Year Founded: 1906
Cigarette Mfr
N.A.I.C.S.: 312230
William Pegel (Chm)

CEYONIQ TECHNOLOGY GMBH
Boulevard 9, 33613, Bielefeld, Germany
Tel.: (49) 52193181000
Web Site: http://www.ceyoniq.com
Sales Range: $10-24.9 Million
Software Development Services
N.A.I.C.S.: 541511
Oliver Kreth (CEO)

CEZ, A.S.
Duhova 2/1444, 140 53, Prague, 4, Czech Republic
Tel.: (420) 211041111   CZ
Web Site: https://www.cez.cz
Year Founded: 1992
CEZ—(MUN)
Rev.: $15,043,092,480
Assets: $36,928,210,800
Liabilities: $26,014,205,360
Net Worth: $10,914,005,440
Earnings: $1,320,313,280
Emp.: 29,563
Fiscal Year-end: 12/31/23
Electricity Distribution Services
N.A.I.C.S.: 221122
Tomas Pleskac (Chief Renewable Energy & Distr Officer)
Subsidiaries:

AZ KLIMA a.s.   **(1)**
Tilhonova 115a, CZ 627 00, Brno, Czech Republic   **(100%)**
Tel.: (420) 544 500 8111
Web Site: http://www.azklima.com
Ventilation & Cooling Technologies, Production of Ducts & Air-Handling Units Mfr
N.A.I.C.S.: 333415

AZ Klima SK, s.r.o.   **(1)**
Nova Roznavska 134/A, 831 04, Bratislava, Slovakia
Tel.: (421) 244880574
Electrical & Plumbing Services
N.A.I.C.S.: 238220

AirPlus, spol. s r.o.   **(1)**
Modlany 22, Modlany, 417 13, Teplice, Czech Republic
Tel.: (420) 417851360
Web Site: http://www.air-plus.cz
Ventilation & Air Conditioning Installation Services
N.A.I.C.S.: 238220

Astellas Pharma d.o.o.   **(1)**
Rezidenca 3rd Floor Smartinska Cesta 53, 1000, Ljubljana, Slovenia
Tel.: (386) 1 401 1400

Pharmaceutical Product Whslr
N.A.I.C.S.: 424210
Adam Pearson (Gen Mgr)

Baltic Green Construction sp. z o.o.   **(1)**
Marynarska 11, 02-674, Warsaw, Poland
Tel.: (48) 224440881
Electric Power Generation Services
N.A.I.C.S.: 221118

CEZ Bohunice a.s.   **(1)**
Duhova 2/1444, Prague, 140 53, Czech Republic
Tel.: (420) 211 041 111
Electric Power Generation Services
N.A.I.C.S.: 221118
Daniel Benes (CEO)

CEZ Bulgaria EAD   **(1)**
140 G S Rakovski Str, Sofia, 1000, Bulgaria
Tel.: (359) 700 10 010
Web Site: http://www.cez.bg
Electric Power Generation Services
N.A.I.C.S.: 221118

CEZ Chorzow B.V.   **(1)**
Hogehilweg 5d, Amsterdam, 1101 CA, Netherlands
Tel.: (31) 207586694
Emp.: 2
Electric Power Distribution Services
N.A.I.C.S.: 221122
Derk Berend Blik (Mng Dir)

Subsidiary (Non-US):

Elektrocieplownia Chorzow ELCHO sp. z.o.o.   **(2)**
M Sklodowskiej-Curie 30, 41-503, Chorzow, Poland
Tel.: (48) 327714001
Sales Range: $50-74.9 Million
Emp.: 100
Power Plant Construction Services
N.A.I.C.S.: 237130

CEZ Deutschland GmbH   **(1)**
Am Sandtorkai 74, 20457, Hamburg, Germany
Tel.: (49) 4099999530
Web Site: http://www.cezdeutschland.de
Electric Power Generation Services
N.A.I.C.S.: 221118

CEZ Distribuce, a. s.   **(1)**
Teplicka 874/8, 405 02, Decin, Czech Republic
Tel.: (420) 840 840 840
Web Site: http://www.cezdistribuce.cz
Electric Power Distribution Services
N.A.I.C.S.: 221122

CEZ Distribucne sustavy a.s.   **(1)**
Frantiskanska 4, 917 01, Trnava, Slovakia
Tel.: (421) 911100459
Web Site: http://www.escods.sk
Electric Power Distribution Services
N.A.I.C.S.: 221122

CEZ Elektro Bulgaria AD   **(1)**
140 G S Rakovski Str, Sofia, 1000, Bulgaria
Tel.: (359) 700 10 010
Web Site: http://www.cez.bg
Electric Power Distribution Services
N.A.I.C.S.: 221122
Kremena Stoyanova (Co-Chm-Supervisory Bd)

CEZ Energeticke produkty, s.r.o.   **(1)**
Komenskeho 534, Hostivice, 253 01, Czech Republic
Tel.: (420) 211 046 504
Web Site: http://www.cezep.cz
Sales Range: $75-99.9 Million
Emp.: 32
Electric Power Generation & Distribution Services
N.A.I.C.S.: 221118
Paul Sleska (Dir-Administration-Finance)

Subsidiary (Domestic):

In Projekt Louny Engineering S.r.o.   **(2)**
Na Valich 899, 440 01, Louny, Czech Republic
Tel.: (420) 415627900
Web Site: http://www.inprojekt.cz
Emp.: 17
Engineeering Services

N.A.I.C.S.: 541330
Pavel Mrzena (Mng Dir)

CEZ Energeticke sluzby, s.r.o.   **(1)**
Vystavni 1144/103, 703 00, Ostrava, Czech Republic
Tel.: (420) 596903401
Eletric Power Generation Services
N.A.I.C.S.: 221118

CEZ Energo, s.r.o.   **(1)**
Duhova 1531/3, Michle, 140 00, Prague, 4, Czech Republic
Tel.: (420) 771281073
Web Site: https://www.cezenergo.cz
N.A.I.C.S.: 335312
Martin Vaclavek (CEO)

CEZ Energoservis Spol, s.r.o.   **(1)**
Brafova 16, 674 01, Trebic, Czech Republic   **(100%)**
Tel.: (420) 568815013
Web Site: http://www.cezenergoservis.cz
Sales Range: $75-99.9 Million
Emp.: 270
Machine Maintenance Services
N.A.I.C.S.: 811310

CEZ Esco Bulgaria EOOD   **(1)**
159 Tsarigradsko Shose Blvd Benchmark Business Center, 17844, Sofia, Bulgaria
Tel.: (359) 897470146
Web Site: http://www.cez-esco.bg
Ventilation & Air Conditioning Installation Services
N.A.I.C.S.: 238220
Dusan Riban (Exec Dir)

CEZ Esco Polska sp. z o.o.   **(1)**
Al Jerozolimskie 61, 00-697, Warsaw, Poland
Tel.: (48) 222180141
Eletric Power Generation Services
N.A.I.C.S.: 221118

CEZ Esco, a.s.   **(1)**
Duhova 1444/2, Michle, 140 00, Prague, Czech Republic
Tel.: (420) 371101101
Web Site: http://www.cezesco.cz
Eletric Power Generation Services
N.A.I.C.S.: 221118
Kamil Cermak (CEO)

CEZ Finance B.V.   **(1)**
Hogehilweg 5d, Amsterdam, 1101 CA, Netherlands
Tel.: (31) 207586694
Financial Management Services
N.A.I.C.S.: 523999
Jiri Postolka (Mng Dir)

CEZ Hungary Ltd.   **(1)**
Retkoz Utca 5, 1118, Budapest, Hungary
Tel.: (36) 12669324
Web Site: http://www.cez.hu
Electric Power Distribution Services
N.A.I.C.S.: 221122

CEZ ICT Services, a. s.   **(1)**
Duhova 3/1531, 140 53, Prague, Czech Republic
Tel.: (420) 841842843
Natural Gas Distribution Services
N.A.I.C.S.: 221210

CEZ Logistika, s.r.o.   **(1)**
28 Rijna 568 147, 709 02, Prague, Ostrava, Czech Republic   **(100%)**
Tel.: (420) 591 113 839
Sales Range: $75-99.9 Million
Emp.: 160
Electrical Fitting Whslr
N.A.I.C.S.: 423610

CEZ MH B.V.   **(1)**
Hogehilweg 5d, Amsterdam, 1101 CA, Netherlands
Tel.: (31) 207586694
Electric Power Generation & Distribution Services
N.A.I.C.S.: 221122
Jiri Postolka (Mng Dir)

CEZ Obnovitelne zdroje, s.r.o.   **(1)**
Krizikova 788, 500 03, Hradec Kralove, Czech Republic
Tel.: (420) 492112821
Natural Gas Distribution Services
N.A.I.C.S.: 221210

CEZ Poland Distribution B.V. (1)
Hogehilweg 5d, Amsterdam, 1101 CA,
Netherlands
Tel.: (31) 207586694
Electric Power Distribution Services
N.A.I.C.S.: 221122

Subsidiary (Non-US):

Eco-Wind Construction S.A. (2)
Ul Marynarska 11, Warsaw, 2672, Poland
Tel.: (48) 22 444 08 81
Web Site: http://www.ecowind.pl
Sales Range: $25-49.9 Million
Emp.: 15
Wind Farm Development Services
N.A.I.C.S.: 237130
Jaromir Pecenka (Pres)

Elektrownia Skawina S.A. (2)
Pilsudskiego 10, 32-050, Skawina, Poland
Tel.: (48) 12 276 20 00
Web Site: http://www.cezpolska.pl
Sales Range: $250-299.9 Million
Emp.: 421
Electric Power Generation & Distribution
Services
N.A.I.C.S.: 221118

CEZ Polska sp. z o.o. (1)
Rondo ONZ 1, 00-124, Warsaw, Poland
Tel.: (48) 22 544 94 80
Web Site: http://www.cezpolska.pl
Sales Range: $100-124.9 Million
Emp.: 10
Electric Power Generation & Distribution
Services
N.A.I.C.S.: 221122

Subsidiary (Domestic):

CEZ Chorzow S.A. (2)
ul M Sklodowskiej - Curie 30, 41-503, Chor-
zow, Poland
Tel.: (48) 327714001
Eletric Power Generation Services
N.A.I.C.S.: 221118

CEZ Produkty Energetyczne Polska
sp. z o.o. (1)
Ul M Sklodowskiej - Curie 30, 41-503,
Chorzow, Poland
Tel.: (48) 32 770 42 51
Web Site: http://www.cezpolska.pl
Eletric Power Generation Services
N.A.I.C.S.: 221118

CEZ Shperndarje Sh.A. (1)
Egt Tower 12 1 Abdyl Frasheri, Tirana,
1000, Albania
Tel.: (355) 42421480
Web Site: http://www.cez.al
Electric Power Distribution Services
N.A.I.C.S.: 221122

CEZ Sprava majetku, s.r.o. (1)
Teplicka 874/8, Decin, 405 49, Czech Re-
public
Tel.: (420) 840 840 840
Property Management Services
N.A.I.C.S.: 531312

CEZ Srbija d.o.o. (1)
6 Bulevar Mihajla Pupina, Novi Beograd,
Belgrade, 11070, Serbia
Tel.: (381) 112200701
Sales Range: $75-99.9 Million
Emp.: 2
Electric Power Distr
N.A.I.C.S.: 221122

CEZ Trade Albania Sh.P.K. (1)
EGT Tower 12/1 2nd Floor Rr Abdyl Frash-
eri, Tirana, Albania
Tel.: (355) 4 242 1480
Web Site: http://www.cez.al
Electric Power Generation & Distribution
Services
N.A.I.C.S.: 221118

CEZ Trade Bulgaria EAD (1)
Pozitano 2 Square Floor 7, Sofia, 1000,
Bulgaria
Tel.: (359) 28959123
Web Site: http://www.cez-trade.bg
Natural Gas Distribution Services
N.A.I.C.S.: 221210
Vladimir Dichev (CEO)

CEZ Trade Polska sp. z o.o. (1)
Rondo ONZ 1, 00-124, Warsaw, Poland

Tel.: (48) 22 544 94 60
Web Site: http://www.cezpolska.pl
Sales Range: $75-99.9 Million
Emp.: 10
Eletric Power Generation Services
N.A.I.C.S.: 221118

CEZ Vanzare S.A. (1)
Depozitelor Street No 2, Gorj County, Targu
Jiu, 210238, Romania
Tel.: (40) 251929
Natural Gas Distribution Services
N.A.I.C.S.: 221210
Cornelia Szabo (Pres & Exec Dir)

CEZ, a.s. - Dukovany Nuclear Power
Station (1)
Jaderna Elektrarna Dukovany, 675 50, Du-
kovany, Czech Republic
Tel.: (420) 561 101 111
Electric Power Generation & Distribution
Services
N.A.I.C.S.: 221118

CEZ, a.s. - Hodonin Power Plant (1)
Elektrarna Hodonin U Elektrarny 1, 695 23,
Hodonin, Czech Republic
Tel.: (420) 511 100 111
Web Site: http://www.cez.cz
Eletric Power Generation Services
N.A.I.C.S.: 221118

CEZ, a.s. - Hydro Power
Stations (1)
Vodni Elektrarny, 252 07, Stechovice,
Czech Republic
Tel.: (420) 211 026 111
Web Site: http://www.cez.cz
Eletric Power Generation Services
N.A.I.C.S.: 221118

CEZ, a.s. - Ledvice Power
Station (1)
Elektrarna Ledvice, 418 48, Bilina, Czech
Republic
Tel.: (420) 411 101 111
Electric Power Generation & Distribution
Services
N.A.I.C.S.: 221118

CEZ, a.s. - Melnik Power Station (1)
Elektrarna Melnik, 277 03, Horni Pocaply,
Czech Republic
Tel.: (420) 311 101 111
Emp.: 50
Eletric Power Generation Services
N.A.I.C.S.: 221118
Andreas Geyr (Gen Mgr)

CEZ, a.s. - Porici Power Stations (1)
Elektrarny Porici, 541 37, Trutnov, Czech
Republic
Tel.: (420) 492 102 111
Eletric Power Generation Services
N.A.I.C.S.: 221118

CEZ, a.s. - Prunerov Power
Stations (1)
Elektrarny Prunerov, 432 01, Kadan, Czech
Republic
Tel.: (420) 471 101 111
Web Site: http://www.cez.cz
Electric Power Generation & Distribution
Services
N.A.I.C.S.: 221118

CEZ, a.s. - Temelin Nuclear Power
Station (1)
Jaderna Elektrarna Temelin, 373 05, Teme-
lin, Czech Republic
Tel.: (420) 381101111
Sales Range: $1-4.9 Billion
Emp.: 146
Electric Power Generation & Distribution
Services
N.A.I.C.S.: 221118
Milos Stepanovsky (Gen Mgr)

CEZ, a.s. - Tisova Power Plant (1)
Elektrarna Tisova Postovni Prihradka 98,
356 69, Sokolov, Czech Republic
Tel.: (420) 351 101 111
Eletric Power Generation Services
N.A.I.C.S.: 221118

CEZ, a.s.- Tusimice Power
Stations (1)
Elektrarny Tusimice, 432 01, Kadan, Czech
Republic
Tel.: (420) 471111111

Emp.: 2,000
Eletric Power Generation Services
N.A.I.C.S.: 221118

CEZData, s.r.o. (1)
Guldenerova 2577 19, 303 28, Plzen,
Czech Republic (100%)
Tel.: (420) 37 800 2931
Web Site: http://www.cezdata.cz
Sales Range: $25-49.9 Million
Emp.: 70
Information Systems & Technology Services
N.A.I.C.S.: 541519

CEZTel, a.s. (1)
Fugnerovo Nam 1866 5, Prague, 2, Czech
Republic (100%)
Tel.: (420) 224086301
Web Site: http://www.cez.cz
Sales Range: $25-49.9 Million
Emp.: 80
Telecommunication Servicesb
N.A.I.C.S.: 517810

CEZnet, a.s. (1)
Fugnerovo Nam 1866 5, 12000, Prague,
Czech Republic (100%)
Tel.: (420) 0211046312
Web Site: http://www.ceznet.cz
Sales Range: $125-149.9 Million
Emp.: 256
Telecommunication & Data Services
N.A.I.C.S.: 517810

D-I-E Elektro AG (1)
Goschwitzer Strasse 56, 07745, Jena, Ger-
many
Tel.: (49) 364129340
Web Site: http://www.die-eag.com
Electrical Engineering Services
N.A.I.C.S.: 541330

Distributie Energie Oltenia S.A. (1)
Str Calea Severinului No 97 Ground Floor 2
3 4, Dolj County, Craiova, 200769, Roma-
nia
Tel.: (40) 251408008
Web Site: http://www.distributieoltenia.ro
Eletric Power Generation Services
N.A.I.C.S.: 221118

Domat Control System s.r.o. (1)
Udernicka 11, 85101, Bratislava, Slovakia
Tel.: (421) 911165038
Electronic Monitoring Equipment Mfr
N.A.I.C.S.: 334515

Domat Control System s.r.o. (1)
U Panasonicu 376, Stare Civice, 530 06,
Pardubice, Czech Republic
Tel.: (420) 461100823
Web Site: http://www.domat-int.com
Electronic Monitoring Equipment Mfr
N.A.I.C.S.: 334515

EAB Elektroanlagenbau GmbH
Rhein/Main (1)
Dieselstrasse 8, 63128, Dietzenbach, Ger-
many
Tel.: (49) 607423890
Web Site: http://www.eab-rhein-main.de
Electrical Maintenance Services
N.A.I.C.S.: 238210

ENESA a.s. (1)
U Voborniku 852/10, Vysocany, 190 00,
Prague, Czech Republic
Tel.: (420) 466053511
Web Site: http://www.enesa.cz
Oil & Energy Services
N.A.I.C.S.: 213112

ETS Efficient Technical Solutions
GmbH (1)
Am Scherhubel 14, Schnaittenbach, 92253,
Amberg, Germany
Tel.: (49) 96227197600
Web Site: http://www.ets-tec.de
Engineering Consultancy Services
N.A.I.C.S.: 541330
Yvonne Lache (Mgr-Location)

Elektrarna Pocerady, a.s. (1)
Vaclava Rezace 315, 434 01, Most, Czech
Republic
Tel.: (420) 411112221
Electric Power Generation Services
N.A.I.C.S.: 221118

Elektro-Decker GmbH (1)
Holzstrasse 7-11a, 45141, Essen, Germany

Tel.: (49) 201831220
Web Site: http://www.elektro-decker.eu
Electrical Maintenance Services
N.A.I.C.S.: 238210

Elektro-Technik-Pfisterer-GmbH (1)
Dorfstrasse 58, Pankofen, 94447, Plattling,
Germany
Tel.: (49) 9931891272
Web Site: http://www.elektro-technik-
pfisterer.de
Software Development Services
N.A.I.C.S.: 541511

Elektrownie Wiatrowe Lubiechovo sp.
z.o.o. (1)
Chobolanska 29, Szczecin, 71-023, Poland
Tel.: (48) 914315485
Web Site: http://www.amerbil.pl
Electric Power Generation & Distribution
Services
N.A.I.C.S.: 221118
Ryszard Bilski (CEO)

Elevion GmbH (1)
Goschwitzer Strasse 56, 07745, Jena, Ger-
many
Tel.: (49) 36412934100
Web Site: http://www.elevion.de
Engineering Consultancy Services
N.A.I.C.S.: 541330

Elevion Group B.V. (1)
Herikerberweg 157, 1101CN, Amsterdam,
Netherlands
Tel.: (31) 07586692
Web Site: https://www.eleviongroup.com
Decarbonization & Energy Efficiency Solu-
tions
N.A.I.C.S.: 541690
Jaroslav Macek (CEO)

Subsidiary (Non-US):

Sercoo Group GmbH (2)
Friedrich-Ebert-Strasse 125, 49811, Lingen,
Germany
Tel.: (49) 59171050
Web Site: http://www.sercoo-group.de
Investment Services
N.A.I.C.S.: 523999
John Thalmann (Head-Controlling)

En.plus GmbH (1)
Joseph-von-Fraunhofer-Str 2, 39106,
Magdeburg, Germany
Tel.: (49) 3915045270
Web Site: http://www.en-plus.eu
Ventilation & Air Conditioning Installation
Services
N.A.I.C.S.: 238220

Energeticke Opravny, a.s. (1)
Prunerov C 375, 432 01, Kadan, Czech
Republic (100%)
Tel.: (420) 471 105 067
Web Site: http://www.eopru.cz
Sales Range: $75-99.9 Million
Emp.: 415
Power Equipment Repair Services
N.A.I.C.S.: 811210

Energeticke centrum s.r.o. (1)
Otin 3, 377 01, Jindrichuv Hradec, Czech
Republic
Tel.: (420) 384 322 701
Web Site: http://www.ecjh.cz
Sales Range: $75-99.9 Million
Emp.: 47
Electric Power Generation & Distribution
Services
N.A.I.C.S.: 221118
Radek Kozak (Mng Dir)

Energotrans, a.s. (1)
Duhova 1444/2, Michle, 140 00, Prague,
Czech Republic
Tel.: (420) 311102991
Natural Gas Distribution Services
N.A.I.C.S.: 221210

Euroklimat sp. z o.o. (1)
ul Obornicka 68, 62-002, Suchy Las, Po-
land
Tel.: (48) 616460025
Web Site: http://www.euroklimat.pl
Electrical Contracting Services
N.A.I.C.S.: 238210

FDLnet.CZ, s.r.o. (1)

CEZ, a.s.—(Continued)

Brezova 1306, Frydlant, 464 01, Liberec,
Czech Republic
Tel.: (420) 483101111
Web Site: http://www.fdlnet.cz
Internet Services
N.A.I.C.S.: 517112

GWE Warme- und Energietechnik
GmbH & Co. KG   **(1)**
Am Anger 35, 33332, Gutersloh, Germany
Tel.: (49) 552290350
Web Site: http://www.gwe-energie.de
Engineering Consultancy Services
N.A.I.C.S.: 541330

HA.EM Ostrava s.r.o.   **(1)**
At the Riding Hall 2767, 702 00, Ostrava,
Czech Republic
Tel.: (420) 596611198
Web Site: http://www.haem.cz
Heating Equipment Installation Services
N.A.I.C.S.: 238220
Josef Stacha (Chm)

Hermos AG   **(1)**
Gartenstrasse 19, 95490, Mistelgau, Germany
Tel.: (49) 92799910
Web Site: http://www.hermos.com
Software Development Services
N.A.I.C.S.: 541511

Hermos Gesellschaft fur Steuer-,
Mess- und Regeltechnik mbH   **(1)**
Pfutschbergstrasse 14, 98257, Suhl, Germany
Tel.: (49) 3681807950
Web Site: http://www.hermos-arn.com
Control & Measurement Device Retailer
N.A.I.C.S.: 423610

Hermos Systems GmbH   **(1)**
Hamburger Strasse 65, 01157, Dresden,
Germany
Tel.: (49) 351811540
Web Site: http://www.hermos-systems.de
Information Technology Services
N.A.I.C.S.: 541511

Hermos sp. z o.o.   **(1)**
ul Powstancow Slaskich 1, Lesnica, 47-150,
Strzelce Opolskie, Poland
Tel.: (48) 774615246
Software Development Services
N.A.I.C.S.: 541511

High-Tech Clima S.A.   **(1)**
Sos Berceni Nr 11 Vis-a-vis de IMGB
Doosan, Jud Ilfov, 077160, Popesti-
Leordeni, Romania
Tel.: (40) 212550320
Web Site: http://www.climat.ro
Electrical Contracting Services
N.A.I.C.S.: 238210

Hormen CE a.s.   **(1)**
Na dolinach 168/6, Podoli, 147 00, Prague,
Czech Republic
Tel.: (420) 244470408
Web Site: http://www.hormen.cz
Lamp Mfr
N.A.I.C.S.: 335139

ISP West s.r.o.   **(1)**
Vilemovska 1602, 347 01, Tachov, Czech
Republic
Tel.: (420) 725729462
Web Site: http://www.ispwest.cz
Information Technology Services
N.A.I.C.S.: 541519

Inewa Srl   **(1)**
via A Volta 13/A at NOI Techpark, 39100,
Bolzano, Italy
Tel.: (39) 04711631950
Web Site: http://www.inewa.it
Technical & Administrative Consultancy
Services
N.A.I.C.S.: 541611

Jager & Co. Gesellschaft mit be-
schrankter Haftung   **(1)**
Grimmestrasse 85, 59821, Arnsberg, Germany
Tel.: (49) 293110568
Web Site: http://www.jaeger-co-heizung.de
Drain Cleaning Services
N.A.I.C.S.: 561790

KART, spol. s r.o.   **(1)**
Duhova 1444/2, Michle, 140 00, Prague,
Czech Republic
Tel.: (420) 601388461
Web Site: http://www.kart.cz
Comprehensive Support Services
N.A.I.C.S.: 561990

Kotouc Stramberk Spol, s.r.o.
Stramberk 500, 742 67, Zenklava, Czech
Republic   **(64.87%)**
Tel.: (420) 556813174
Web Site: http://www.kotouc.cz
Sales Range: $200-249.9 Million
Emp.: 430
Limestone Miner
N.A.I.C.S.: 212312

Lomy Morina Spol, s.r.o.   **(1)**
Morina, 267 17, Beroun, Czech
Republic   **(52.46%)**
Tel.: (420) 311702111
Web Site: http://www.lomy-morina.cz
Sales Range: $100-124.9 Million
Emp.: 170
Limestone Miner
N.A.I.C.S.: 212312

MARTIA a.s.   **(1)**
Mezni 2854/4, 400 11, Usti nad Labem,
Czech Republic
Tel.: (420) 475 650 111
Technical Consulting Services
N.A.I.C.S.: 541690

Metrolog sp. z o.o.   **(1)**
ul Kosciuszki 97, Czarnkow, 64-700, Trz-
cianka, Poland
Tel.: (48) 672553439
Web Site: http://www.metrolog.com.pl
Comprehensive Investment Services
N.A.I.C.S.: 523999

Moser & Partner Ingenieurburo
GmbH   **(1)**
Salzbergstrasse 13, Absam, 6067,
Innsbruck, Austria
Tel.: (43) 522322112
Web Site: http://www.moser-partner.at
Engineeering Services
N.A.I.C.S.: 541330

OEM Energy sp. z o.o.   **(1)**
Ul Skladowa 17, 41-500, Chorzow, Poland
Tel.: (48) 501510511
Web Site: http://www.oemenergy.pl
Architecture & Planning Services
N.A.I.C.S.: 541310

OSC, a.s.   **(1)**
Stankova 18A, 612 00, Brno, Czech
Republic   **(66.67%)**
Tel.: (420) 541643111
Web Site: http://www.osc.cz
Sales Range: $25-49.9 Million
Emp.: 70
Electrical Machinery & Instruments Mfr; En-
gineering Services
N.A.I.C.S.: 335999

Rudolf Fritz GmbH   **(1)**
Hans-Sachs-Strasse 19, 65428, Rus-
selsheim, Germany
Tel.: (49) 61426980
Web Site: http://www.rudolf-fritz.de
Electrical Dealing Services
N.A.I.C.S.: 238210

SD - KOMES, a.s.   **(1)**
Moskevska 14/1, 434 01, Most, Czech Re-
public
Tel.: (420) 476 146 000
Rubber Belt & Petroleum Products Whslr
N.A.I.C.S.: 423840

SD - Rekultivace, a.s.   **(1)**
Tusimice 7, Kadan, 432 01, Czech Republic
Tel.: (420) 474 60 4001
Sales Range: $25-49.9 Million
Emp.: 60
Agricultural Reclamation Services
N.A.I.C.S.: 562910

SKODA PRAHA Invest s.r.o.   **(1)**
Duhova 2/1444, Prague, 140 74, Czech
Republic
Tel.: (420) 211 045 300
Web Site: http://www.spinvest.cz
Power Plant Construction Services
N.A.I.C.S.: 237130
Milos Mostecky (Dir-Comml)

Severoceske doly a.s.   **(1)**
Bozeny Nemcove 5359, CZ-430 01, Cho-
mutov, Czech Republic   **(100%)**
Tel.: (420) 474 602 111
Web Site: http://www.sdas.cz
Sales Range: $600-649.9 Million
Coal Mining
N.A.I.C.S.: 212114

Subsidiary (Domestic):

GEOMET s.r.o.   **(2)**
Ruska 287, 417 01, Dubi, Czech Republic
Tel.: (420) 417536139
Web Site: http://www.geomet-cz.com
Lithium Mining Services
N.A.I.C.S.: 212390

Joint Venture (Non-US):

Mitteldeutsche Braunkohlengesell-
schaft mbH   **(2)**
Gluck-Auf-Strasse 1, 06711, Zeitz,
Germany   **(50%)**
Tel.: (49) 34416840
Web Site: https://www.mibrag.de
Coal Mining
N.A.I.C.S.: 212114
Armin Eichholz (Chm-Mgmt Bd)

Subsidiary (Domestic):

Prodeco, a.s.   **(2)**
Dulni 437, Mostecke Predmesti, 41801,
Bilina, Czech Republic
Tel.: (420) 417804911
Web Site: http://www.prodeco.cz
Emp.: 700
Winding Machinery Distr
N.A.I.C.S.: 423810
Lubos Straka (Chm & Gen Dir)

Revitrans, a.s.   **(2)**
Dulni No 429, 418 01, Bilina, Czech Repub-
lic
Tel.: (420) 417805820
Web Site: http://www.revitrans.cz
Construction Machinery & Equipment
Rental Services
N.A.I.C.S.: 532412

SD - Kolejova doprava, a.s.   **(2)**
Tusimice 7, 432 01, Kadan, Czech Republic
Tel.: (420) 474602161
Web Site: http://www.sd-kd.cz
Logistic Services
N.A.I.C.S.: 488510

Severomoravska Energetika, a.s. **(1)**
28 Rijna 3123 152, 709 02, Ostrava, Morav-
ska, Czech Republic   **(99.13%)**
Tel.: (420) 840840840
Web Site: http://www.cez.cz
Sales Range: $600-649.9 Million
Emp.: 1,555
Electricity Distr & Supplier
N.A.I.C.S.: 221122

Subsidiary (Domestic):

Energetika Vitkovice, a.s.   **(2)**
Vystavni 1144 103, 706 02, Ostrava, Vitkov-
ice, Czech Republic   **(100%)**
Tel.: (420) 597015300
Sales Range: $400-449.9 Million
Emp.: 560
Electricity Distr
N.A.I.C.S.: 221122

Sinit, a.s.   **(2)**
Emila Filly 296 13, 709 00, Ostrava, Mari-
anske Hory, Czech Republic   **(100%)**
Tel.: (420) 596 673 110
Web Site: http://www.sinit.cz
Sales Range: $25-49.9 Million
Emp.: 30
Electrical Equipment & Wiring Whslr
N.A.I.C.S.: 423610

Stmem, a.s.   **(2)**
Trzni 8, 750 02, Prerov, Czech
Republic   **(100%)**
Tel.: (420) 581281111
Web Site: http://www.sme.cz
Sales Range: $25-49.9 Million
Emp.: 60
Electrical Machinery & Instruments Mfr &
Repair Services
N.A.I.C.S.: 335999

ePRIM, a.s.   **(2)**

28 Rijna 568 147, 709 02, Ostrava, Morav-
ska, Czech Republic   **(100%)**
Tel.: (420) 596673839
Sales Range: $25-49.9 Million
Emp.: 50
Wiring Materials Whslr
N.A.I.C.S.: 423610

Sigma Energo, s.r.o.   **(1)**
Na Nivkach 299, Trebic, 674 01, Czech
Republic   **(51%)**
Tel.: (420) 568822160
Web Site: http://www.sigma-energo.cz
Sales Range: $25-49.9 Million
Emp.: 90
Pumps & Compressors Maintenance & Re-
furbishment Services
N.A.I.C.S.: 811210

Skoda Praha, a.s.   **(1)**
Duhova 2/1444, 160 41, Prague, 6, Czech
Republic   **(100%)**
Tel.: (420) 224396444
Web Site: http://www.skodapraha.cz
Sales Range: $75-99.9 Million
Emp.: 340
Energy Designer & Engineering Services
N.A.I.C.S.: 541330

Spravbytkomfort, a.s.   **(1)**
Volgogradska 88, 080 01, Presov, Slovakia
Tel.: (421) 517567701
Web Site: http://www.spravbytkomfort.sk
Housing Management Services
N.A.I.C.S.: 531311
Natalia Banduricova (Chm)

Stredoceska Energeticka, a.s.   **(1)**
Vinohradska 325 8, 120 21, Prague, Czech
Republic   **(97.72%)**
Tel.: (420) 222 031 111
Web Site: http://www.cez.cz
Sales Range: $1-4.9 Billion
Emp.: 1,548
Electricity Distr
N.A.I.C.S.: 221122

Subsidiary (Domestic):

Eltraf, a.s.   **(2)**
Kralice 49, 285 04, Uhlirske Janovica,
Czech Republic   **(51%)**
Tel.: (420) 327543617
Web Site: http://www.eltraf.cz
Sales Range: $25-49.9 Million
Emp.: 30
Electric Equipment Mfr
N.A.I.C.S.: 335999

STE Obchodni Sluzby Spol, s
r.o.   **(2)**
Vinohradska 8, Prague, 2, Czech
Republic   **(74.42%)**
Tel.: (420) 222032518
Web Site: http://www.cez.cz
Sales Range: $25-49.9 Million
Emp.: 65
Material & Technical Supplies Whslr
N.A.I.C.S.: 423610

Syneco tec GmbH   **(1)**
Salzbergstrasse 13a, Absam, 6067,
Innsbruck, Austria
Tel.: (43) 522354393
Web Site: http://www.synecotec.com
Engineering Consultancy Services
N.A.I.C.S.: 541330

Telco Pro Services, a. s.   **(1)**
Duhova 1531/3, Michle, Prague, Czech
Republic
Tel.: (420) 910707070
Web Site: http://www.telcoproservices.cz
Telecommunication Servicesb
N.A.I.C.S.: 517810
Michal Drapala (Chm & Gen Mgr)

Tepelne hospodarstvi mesta Usti nad
Labem s.r.o.   **(1)**
Malatova 2437/11, 400 11, Usti nad Labem,
Czech Republic
Tel.: (420) 472774777
Web Site: http://www.thmu.cz
Home Appliance Product Distr
N.A.I.C.S.: 423620

Teplarna Trmice, a.s.   **(1)**
Edisonova 453, Trmice, 400 04, Czech Re-
public
Tel.: (420) 475 256 111

Sales Range: $300-349.9 Million
Emp.: 345
Electric Power Generation & Distribution
Services
N.A.I.C.S.: 221118
Petr Kreissl *(Chm)*

Subsidiary (Domestic):

ULITEP, spol. s r.o. **(2)**
Spitalske Nam 11, 400 01, Usti nad Labem,
Czech Republic
Tel.: (420) 475 214 481
Monitoring & Testing Equipment Mfr
N.A.I.C.S.: 334511

Teplo Klasterec s.r.o. **(1)**
Jana Amos Komenskeho 450 Miretice u
Klasterce nad Ohri, 431 51, Klasterec nad
Ohri, Czech Republic
Tel.: (420) 774560074
Web Site: http://www.teploklasterec.cz
Home Appliance Product Distr
N.A.I.C.S.: 423620

Trafo CZ, a.s. **(1)**
Koutnikova 208/12, 503 01, Hradec Kral-
ove, Czech Republic **(100%)**
Tel.: (420) 492112164
Web Site: https://www.trafocz.cz
Transformers Mfr & Repair Services
N.A.I.C.S.: 334416
Ales Radnik *(Mng Dir)*

UJV Rez, a. s. **(1)**
Hlavni 130, Husinec, 250 68, Rez, Czech
Republic
Tel.: (420) 266172000
Web Site: http://www.ujv.cz
Engineeering Services
N.A.I.C.S.: 541330
Daniel Jiricka *(Chm & CEO)*

Ustav Jaderneho Vyzkumu Rez,
a.s. **(1)**
Husinec Rez 130, 250 68, Rez, Czech
Republic **(52.46%)**
Tel.: (420) 266172000
Web Site: http://www.nri.cz
Sales Range: $25-49.9 Million
Emp.: 858
Nuclear Technology Research & Develop-
ment Services
N.A.I.C.S.: 221113

Subsidiary (Domestic):

Centrum vyzkumu Rez s.r.o. **(2)**
Husinec-Rez Cp 130, Rez, 25068, Czech
Republic
Tel.: (420) 266 173 181
Web Site: http://www.cvrez.cz
Sales Range: $25-49.9 Million
Emp.: 300
Nuclear Power Research & Development
Services
N.A.I.C.S.: 541715
Jaroslav Klimesova *(Gen Mgr)*

EGP INVEST, spol. s r.o. **(2)**
Antonina Dvoraka 1707, 688 01, Uhersky
Brod, Czech Republic
Tel.: (420) 572 610 311
Web Site: http://www.egpi.cz
Sales Range: $25-49.9 Million
Emp.: 11
Nuclear Energy Consulting Services
N.A.I.C.S.: 541690

LACOMED, spol. s r.o. **(2)**
Husinec - Rez No 130, 250 68, Rez, Czech
Republic
Tel.: (420) 220941165
Web Site: http://www.lacomed.cz
Medical Product Distr
N.A.I.C.S.: 424210
Michael Bauer *(CEO)*

Ustav aplikovane mechaniky Brno,
s.r.o. **(2)**
Resslova 972, 611 00, Brno, Czech Repub-
lic
Tel.: (420) 541 321 291
Web Site: http://www.uam.cz
Sales Range: $10-24.9 Million
Emp.: 30
Technical Consulting Services
N.A.I.C.S.: 541690
Lubomir Junek *(Mng Dir)*

Vychodoceska Energetika, a.s. **(1)**

Sladkovskeho 215, 501 03, Hradec Kralove,
Czech Republic **(98.83%)**
Tel.: (420) 495841111
Web Site: http://www.cez.cz
Sales Range: $1-4.9 Billion
Emp.: 1,600
Electrical Energy Distr
N.A.I.C.S.: 221122

Subsidiary (Domestic):

VCE Elektrarny, s.r.o. **(2)**
Krizikova 788, 500 03, Hradec Kralove,
Czech Republic **(98.83%)**
Tel.: (420) 495842218
Web Site: http://www.vceelektrarny.cz
Sales Range: $200-249.9 Million
Emp.: 485
Hydraulic Power Plant Operator
N.A.I.C.S.: 221118

VCE Montaze, a.s. **(2)**
Arnosta Z Pardubic 2082, 531 17, Pardu-
bice, Czech Republic **(98.83%)**
Tel.: (420) 466871111
Electrical Equipment Repair & Maintenance
Services
N.A.I.C.S.: 811114

Vyzkumny a zkusebni ustav Plzen
s.r.o. **(1)**
Tylova 1581/46, 301 00, Plzen, Czech Re-
public
Tel.: (420) 371430700
Design & Engineering Services
N.A.I.C.S.: 541330

Zapadoceska Energetika, a.s. **(1)**
Guldenerova 19, 303 28, Plzen, Czech
Republic **(99.13%)**
Tel.: (420) 37 800 1111
Web Site: http://www.cez.cz
Sales Range: $300-349.9 Million
Emp.: 1,330
Electrical Devices Designer, Mfr & Repair
Services
N.A.I.C.S.: 811114

Subsidiary (Domestic):

Lidrone Spol, s.r.o. **(2)**
Zeleznicni 34, 326 00, Plzen, Czech
Republic **(100%)**
Tel.: (420) 378003832
Waste Processing Services
N.A.I.C.S.: 562998

e-Dome a. s. **(1)**
Plynarenska 7/C, 821 09, Bratislava, Slova-
kia
Tel.: (421) 911020333
Web Site: http://www.e-dome.sk
Electric Energy Services
N.A.I.C.S.: 221118

CF COMUNICACION, S.L.
Calle Albarracin 56, 28037, Madrid,
Spain
Tel.: (34) 91 375 0581 ES
Web Site:
http://www.cfcomunicacion.com
Year Founded: 1994
Document Storage, Translation &
Printing Services
N.A.I.C.S.: 561410
Carlos Pellicer *(Partner & Dir)*

CF ENERGY CORP.
Suite 308 3100 Steeles Avenue East,
Markham, L3R 8T3, ON, Canada
Tel.: (647) 313-0066 Ca
Web Site: https://www.cfenergy.com
Year Founded: 2006
CFY—(TSXV)
Rev.: $61,125,352
Assets: $183,552,112
Liabilities: $127,302,394
Net Worth: $56,249,718
Earnings: $420,704
Fiscal Year-end: 12/31/23
Oil & Gas Exploration Services
N.A.I.C.S.: 211120
Ann Siyin Y. Lin *(Chm & CEO)*

CF ITALIA SRL

Corso Columbo 46, 21013, Gallarate,
Italy
Tel.: (39) 033175071
Web Site: http://www.cfitalia.it
Industrial Sewing Machine Producer
N.A.I.C.S.: 321999

Subsidiaries:

Euromac Sistemas de Confeccion,
S.A. **(1)**
c/Felix Campllonch 4-6, 08301, Barcelona,
Mataro, Spain
Tel.: (34) 93 775 7969
Web Site: http://www.euromac.es
Marketing of Industrial Sewing Machines
N.A.I.C.S.: 423830

Necchi S.p.A. **(1)**
Via Primo Levi 6 - Zone Industriale, 27049,
Pavia, Stradella, Italy
Tel.: (39) 03825141
Web Site: http://www.necchi.it
Sales Range: $50-74.9 Million
Emp.: 424
Mfr of Industrial Sewing Machines
N.A.I.C.S.: 333310

Rimoldi da Amazonia Ind. e Com.
Ltda. **(1)**
Maestro Gabriel Migliori 237, Baillo do Li-
mao, CEP 02712, Sao Paulo, SP, Brazil
Tel.: (55) 8577433
Mfr of Industrial Sewing Machines
N.A.I.C.S.: 333310

Rimoldi of America Inc. **(1)**
2315 NW 107th Ave Ste M 43 Box 85, Mi-
ami, FL 33172-2116
Tel.: (305) 477-9943
Web Site: http://www.cfrimoldi.com
Sales Range: $50-74.9 Million
Emp.: 7
Mfr of Industrial Sewing Machines
N.A.I.C.S.: 423830

CFC GROUP PTY. LTD.
Unit A2 118 Railway Street, Hazel-
mere, West Perth, 6005, WA, Austra-
lia
Tel.: (61) 8 9270 5150 AU
Web Site: http://www.cfc.com.au
Year Founded: 1971
Sales Range: $500-549.9 Million
Emp.: 1,100
Holding Company; Agricultural &
Construction Equipment Distr
N.A.I.C.S.: 551112
Philip Cardaci *(Chm)*

Subsidiaries:

Cape Crushing & Earthmoving Con-
tractors Pty. Ltd. **(1)**
16 Kalamunda Road, South Guilford, Perth,
6055, WA, Australia
Tel.: (61) 8 9379 6800
Web Site: http://www.capecrushing.com.au
Sales Range: $150-199.9 Million
Emp.: 275
Crushing & Earthmoving Contractors; Min-
ing Services
N.A.I.C.S.: 238910
Mike Heddon *(Co-Founder)*

Centurion Transport Co. Pty Ltd **(1)**
13 Yagine Close Airport, Hazelmere, Perth,
6105, WA, Australia
Tel.: (61) 8 9278 3000
Web Site: http://www.centurion.net.au
Logistics Services to the Resources, Energy
& Retail Sectors
N.A.I.C.S.: 541614
Andrew Ford *(Exec Gen Mgr-Major Ac-
counts)*

JCB Construction Equipment
Australia **(1)**
434-442 South Gippsland Hwy, Dandenong,
3175, VIC, Australia
Tel.: (61) 3 9797 3444
Web Site: http://www.cea.net.au
Emp.: 30
Construction & Agricultural Equipment Distr
N.A.I.C.S.: 423810
Anthony Whelan *(Exec Gen Mgr)*

Underground Services Australia Pty
Ltd **(1)**
1 Eyre Street, Rivervale, Perth, 6103, WA,
Australia
Tel.: (61) 8 9272 0100
Web Site:
http://www.undergroundservices.com.au
Sales Range: $75-99.9 Million
Emp.: 200
Utility Infrastructure Installation & Mainte-
nance Services
N.A.I.C.S.: 237130
Tim Abrahams *(Exec Gen Mgr)*

CFC UNDERWRITING LIMITED
85 Gracechurch Street, London,
EC3V 0AA, United Kingdom
Tel.: (44) 207 220 8500 UK
Web Site:
http://www.cfcunderwriting.com
Year Founded: 1999
Cyber Insurance Services
N.A.I.C.S.: 524298
David Walsh *(Founder & CEO)*

CFF FLUID CONTROL LIMITED
503 A wing Delphi Orchard Avenue
Hiranandani Gardens Powai, Mum-
bai, 400076, India
Tel.: (91) 912246086806
Web Site:
https://www.cffdefensys.com
Year Founded: 2012
543920—(BOM)
Rev.: $8,617,247
Assets: $10,748,017
Liabilities: $7,719,318
Net Worth: $3,028,699
Earnings: $1,228,482
Fiscal Year-end: 03/31/23
Shipboard Product Mfr
N.A.I.C.S.: 336611

CFF GMBH & CO. KG
Arnstaedter Strasse 2, Gehren,
98694, Ilmenau, Germany
Tel.: (49) 36783 882 0 De
Web Site: http://www.cff.de
Cellulose Fibre Products Mfr
N.A.I.C.S.: 325220
Markus Zott *(Mng Dir)*

Subsidiaries:

CFF Belgium N.V. **(1)**
Eurolaan 5 Industriezone TTS Zone B,
9140, Temse, Belgium
Tel.: (32) 37111636
Web Site: http://www.cff.de
Dietary Fiber Sales
N.A.I.C.S.: 325220

CFI HOLDING S.A.
Ul Teatralna 10-12, 50-055, Wroclaw,
Poland
Tel.: (48) 713488010
Web Site: http://cfiholding.pl
CFI—(WAR)
Rev.: $59,779,725
Assets: $417,384,653
Liabilities: $165,256,351
Net Worth: $252,128,302
Earnings: $18,136,433
Fiscal Year-end: 12/31/23
Holding Company
N.A.I.C.S.: 551112
Joanna Feder-Kawczynska *(Supervi-
sory Board of Directors & Chm-Mgmt
Bd)*

CFI HOLDINGS LIMITED
1 Wynne St, PO Box 510, Harare,
Zimbabwe
Tel.: (263) 4791260 ZW
Year Founded: 1908
CFI—(ZIM)
Rev.: $558,139,438
Assets: $404,891,814
Liabilities: $639,515,652

CFI Holdings Limited—(Continued)

Net Worth: ($234,623,838)
Earnings: ($256,226,686)
Emp.: 1,774
Fiscal Year-end: 09/30/23
Holding Company; Property Development
N.A.I.C.S.: 551112

CFI-COMPAGNIE FONCIERE INTERNATIONALE
72 rue du Faubourg Saint-Honore, 75008, Paris, France
Tel.: (33) 140078103
Web Site: https://www.cfi-france.com
CFI—(EUR)
Sales Range: $50-74.9 Million
Emp.: 1
Real Estate Investment Services
N.A.I.C.S.: 531390
Alain Benon (CEO)

CFM HOLDINGS LIMITED
3 Ang Mo Kio Street 62 05 16 LINK AMK, Singapore, 569139, Singapore
Tel.: (65) 64812888
Web Site:
    https://www.cfmholdings.com
Year Founded: 1979
5EB—(CAT)
Rev.: $22,029,641
Assets: $22,575,769
Liabilities: $6,288,996
Net Worth: $16,286,773
Earnings: $7,816,228
Emp.: 541
Fiscal Year-end: 06/30/23
Die Design Services
N.A.I.C.S.: 238390
Janet Fong Li Lim (Co-Founder & CEO)

Subsidiaries:

CFM Infratrade Pte. Ltd.   (1)
3 Ang Mo Kio Street 62 05-16, Singapore, 569139, Singapore
Tel.: (65) 64831522
Medical & ESD Product Distr
N.A.I.C.S.: 423450

CFM Slovakia s.r.o.   (1)
Radlinskeho 17, 052 01, Spisska Nova Ves, Kosice, Slovakia
Tel.: (421) 534188888
Web Site: https://www.cfmsk.sk
Sales Range: $50-74.9 Million
Emp.: 180
Metal Stamping Mfr
N.A.I.C.S.: 332119
Maros Stanko (Head-Sls)

CHINA Dalian CFM Precision Tooling Co., Ltd.   (1)
Room 1-1A No 99 Huai He Zhong Road Dalian Economic Development Zone, Dalian, 116600, China
Tel.: (86) 41187407678
Emp.: 60
Automobile Parts Mfr
N.A.I.C.S.: 336390

Cheong Fatt Holdings Pte. Ltd.   (1)
3 Ang Mo Kio Street 62 LINK AMK 05-16, Singapore, 569139, Singapore
Tel.: (65) 64812888
Warehousing & Logistics Services
N.A.I.C.S.: 541614

Cheong Fatt Metal Factory Pte Ltd   (1)
3 Ang Mo Kio Street 62, Singapore, 569139, Singapore
Tel.: (65) 64812888
Web Site: http://www.cfmholdings.com
Sales Range: $25-49.9 Million
Emp.: 15
Metal Stamping Mfr
N.A.I.C.S.: 332119

Han Tong Metal Component Sdn Bhd   (1)
No 4 Jalan Haji Saat Sungai Tiram, Ulu Ti-

ram, 81800, Johor, Malaysia   **(100%)**
Tel.: (60) 78616666
Web Site: http://www.cfmholdings.com
Sales Range: $50-74.9 Million
Emp.: 150
Metal Stamping Mfr
N.A.I.C.S.: 332119

Hantong Metal Component (KL) Sdn Bhd   (1)
Lot 1911-A Kawasan Perindustrian Kampung Baru Balakong, Kampung Baru Balakong, 43300, Seri Kembangan, Selangor, Malaysia
Tel.: (60) 389618882
Web Site: http://www.cfmholdings.com
Sales Range: $25-49.9 Million
Emp.: 57
Metal Stamping Mfr
N.A.I.C.S.: 332119

Hantong Metal Component Sdn Bhd   (1)
No 4 Jalan Haji Saat Sungai Tiram, 81800, Ulu Tiram, Johor, Malaysia
Tel.: (60) 78616666
Emp.: 101
Metal Stamping Mfr
N.A.I.C.S.: 332119

PT Hantong Precision Manufacturing Batam   (1)
Komplek Citra Buana Centre Park 2 Kelurahan Kampung Seraya, Kecamatan Batu Ampar, Batam, 29432, Riau Islands, Indonesia
Tel.: (62) 778428222
Emp.: 115
Metal Stamping Mfr
N.A.I.C.S.: 332119
Soh Thomas (Gen Mgr)

CFM INDOSUEZ WEALTH SA
11 Boulevard Albert 1er, BP 499, 98000, Monaco, Monaco
Tel.: (377) 93102050
Year Founded: 1922
MLCFM—(EUR)
Sales Range: $125-149.9 Million
Wealth Management Services
N.A.I.C.S.: 522180
Mathieu Ferragut (CEO)

CFN PRECISION LTD.
1000 Creditstone Road, Vaughan, L4K 4P8, ON, Canada
Tel.: (905) 669-8191
Web Site: http://cfnprecision.com
Year Founded: 1981
Rev.: $10,302,885
Emp.: 95
Aircraft Parts & Auxiliary Equipment Mfr
N.A.I.C.S.: 336413
Craig Jerry (Mgr-Sls)

CFOAM LIMITED
Level 1 33 Ord Street, West Perth, 6005, WA, Australia
Tel.: (61) 892261524   AU
Web Site: https://cfoam.com.au
Year Founded: 2016
CFO—(ASX)
Rev.: $49
Assets: $7,786,484
Liabilities: $4,568,554
Net Worth: $3,217,930
Earnings: ($4,599,797)
Fiscal Year-end: 06/30/22
Foam Product Mfr & Distr
N.A.I.C.S.: 326150
Gary Steinepreis (Sec)

Subsidiaries:

CFOAM LLC   (1)
The Millennium Ctr 1142 Middle Creek Rd, Triadelphia, WV 26059-1138
Tel.: (304) 907-2220
Graphite Carbon Foam Product Mfr & Distr
N.A.I.C.S.: 335991
Alain Bouruet-Aubertot (Pres & CEO)

CFS GROUP, INC.
550 Marshall Avenue, Dorval, H9P 1C9, QC, Canada
Tel.: (416) 237-1234
Web Site: http://www.ifscos.com
Year Founded: 1892
Sales Range: $75-99.9 Million
Emp.: 255
Producer of Industrial Products, Coatings, Chemicals & Fertilizers
N.A.I.C.S.: 212390
Domenic Scozzafava (CFO & Sec)

Subsidiaries:

Castec, Inc. & Ona Corporation   (1)
400 Orrton Ave, Reading, PA 19611
Tel.: (610) 378-1381
Sales Range: $25-49.9 Million
Emp.: 50
Producer of Industrial Products, Chemicals & Fertilizers
N.A.I.C.S.: 327120

IFS Coatings, Inc.   (1)
3601 N Interstate 35, Gainesville, TX 76240
Tel.: (940) 668-1062
Web Site: http://www.ifscoatings.com
Sales Range: $25-49.9 Million
Emp.: 30
Powdered Coatings Mfr
N.A.I.C.S.: 325510
Glen Nathan (Pres)

IFS Industries, Inc.   (1)
400 Orrton Ave, Reading, PA 19603   **(100%)**
Tel.: (610) 378-1381
Web Site: http://www.ifscos.com
Sales Range: $50-74.9 Million
Emp.: 98
Adhesives, Coatings & Polymers Mfr
N.A.I.C.S.: 325520
Patrick Donahue (Pres & Mng Dir)

Subsidiary (Domestic):

Ona Polymers LLC   (2)
2326 Lonnecker Dr, Garland, TX 75041
Tel.: (972) 840-0364
Web Site: http://www.onapolymers.com
Paints Mfr
N.A.I.C.S.: 325510
Omer Javed (VP)

IFS Industries, Inc.   (1)
2222 Lonnecker Dr, Garland, TX 75041
Tel.: (972) 864-2202
Web Site: http://www.ifscos.com
Sales Range: $25-49.9 Million
Emp.: 15
Producer of Industrial Products, Chemicals & Fertilizers
N.A.I.C.S.: 327120
Eric Delong (VP-Sls)

Multibond, Inc.   (1)
550 Marshall Ave, Dorval, H9P 1C9, QC, Canada   **(100%)**
Tel.: (514) 937-3965
Web Site: http://www.ifscos.com
Sales Range: $50-74.9 Million
Emp.: 40
Producer of Industrial Products, Chemicals & Fertilizers
N.A.I.C.S.: 212390

Multibond, Inc.   (1)
103 The East Mall, Etobicoke, M8Z 5X9, ON, Canada   **(100%)**
Tel.: (416) 237-1234
Sales Range: $50-74.9 Million
Emp.: 12
Producer of Industrial Products, Chemicals & Fertilizers
N.A.I.C.S.: 212390

R.C. Multibond Dural S.R.L.   (1)
Str Abatorulvi NR3, Craiova, COD 1156, Jud Dolj, Romania
Tel.: (40) 51 264 448
N.A.I.C.S.: 325110

Refractory Sales & Service Co., Incorporated   (1)
1750 Hwy 150, Bessemer, AL 35022-4044   **(100%)**
Tel.: (205) 424-3980
Web Site: http://www.rssdixie.com

Producer of Industrial Products, Chemicals & Fertilizers
N.A.I.C.S.: 327120

CFS INVESTMENT AND IMPORT EXPORT TRADING JSC
2nd Floor FLC Landmark Tower Building Le Duc Tho Street, My Dinh 2 Nam Tu Liem District, Hanoi, Vietnam
Tel.: (84) 437956869
Web Site: https://www.cfscorp.vn
Year Founded: 2009
KLF—(HNX)
Rev.: $142,671,300
Assets: $238,391,700
Liabilities: $64,752,000
Net Worth: $173,639,700
Earnings: $668,000
Fiscal Year-end: 12/31/21
Travel Services
N.A.I.C.S.: 721199
Duc Cong Nguyen (Gen Mgr & Deputy Gen Mgr)

CFT GMBH
Beisenstrasse 39-41, 45964, Gladbeck, Germany
Tel.: (49) 204348110
Web Site: http://www.cft-gmbh.com
Year Founded: 1999
Sales Range: $25-49.9 Million
Dedusting Systems Mfr
N.A.I.C.S.: 333998
Reinhold Both (Mng Dir)

CG-VAK SOFTWARE & EXPORTS LTD.
171 Mettupalayam Road, Coimbatore, 641 043, India
Tel.: (91) 4222434491
Web Site:
    https://www.cgvakindia.com
Year Founded: 1995
531489—(BOM)
Rev.: $6,129,937
Assets: $5,167,944
Liabilities: $848,741
Net Worth: $4,319,203
Earnings: $950,265
Emp.: 240
Fiscal Year-end: 03/31/21
Computer Software Development Services
N.A.I.C.S.: 541511
Antonio G. Stevens (Deputy Gen Mgr-Bus Dev)

Subsidiaries:

CG-VAK Software USA Inc.   (1)
1661 Tice Valley Blvd Ste 101, Walnut Creek, CA 94595
Tel.: (925) 262-8211
Web Site: http://www.cgvakusa.com
Software Development Services
N.A.I.C.S.: 541511

CGE CONTINENTAL GLASS ENGINEERING GMBH
Kattrepel 2 Montanhof, 20095, Hamburg, Germany
Tel.: (49) 405701020
Web Site: http://www.continental-glass.com
Year Founded: 1960
Rev.: $19,035,720
Emp.: 10
Glass Manufacturing Equipment Supply Services
N.A.I.C.S.: 423830
Ulrich Steffes (Mng Dir)

CGE GAS NATURAL SA
Avenida Presidente Riesco 5561 Piso 17, Santiago, 7561127, Chile
Tel.: (56) 226807000

Web Site:
http://www.gasnaturalchile.cl
CGEGAS—(SGO)
Sales Range: Less than $1 Million
Natural Gas Distribution Services
N.A.I.C.S.: 221210
Pablo Sobarzo Mierzo (CEO)

CGE MINAS INDUSTRIA E CO-MERCIO DE ARTEFATOS PLASTICOS LTDA.
Rod MG 050 S N Km 29, Mateus
Leme, 35670 000, MG, Brazil
Tel.: (55) 3135351833   BR
Web Site: http://www.tgemg.com.br
Sales Range: $125-149.9 Million
Emp.: 1,000
Mfr of Motor Vehicle Plastic Parts &
Accessories
N.A.I.C.S.: 336340

Subsidiaries:

CGE Sociedade Fabricadora de Pe-
cas Plasticas Ltda.   (1)
Rua Gen Castilho De Lima 150, 09371 340,
Maua, SP, Brazil   (100%)
Tel.: (55) 45126600
Web Site: http://www.cge.ind.br
Sales Range: $10-24.9 Million
Emp.: 300
Mfr of Motor Vehicle Plastic Parts & Acces-
sories
N.A.I.C.S.: 336340

CGG
27 Avenue Carnot, 91300, Massy,
France
Tel.: (33) 164474500   FR
Web Site: https://www.cgg.com
Year Founded: 1931
CGG—(EUR)
Rev.: $927,400,000
Assets: $2,889,400,000
Liabilities: $1,830,600,000
Net Worth: $1,058,800,000
Earnings: $43,300,000
Emp.: 3,416
Fiscal Year-end: 12/31/22
Holding Company; Oil & Gas Field
Geophysical Surveying Services &
Geophysical Equipment Mfr
N.A.I.C.S.: 551112
Yuri Baidoukov (CFO-Grp)

Subsidiaries:

Ardiseis FZCO   (1)
Jebel Ali Free Zone, PO Box 261159,
Dubai, United Arab Emirates
Tel.: (971) 4 883 9464
Sales Range: $50-74.9 Million
Emp.: 10
Oil & Gas Exploration Equipment Distr
N.A.I.C.S.: 423830

CGG Airborne Surveys (Pty) Ltd. (1)
Hangar 109 B C & D Lanseria Airport, Jo-
hannesburg, 1500, Gauteng, South Africa
Tel.: (27) 11 659 1119
Sales Range: $25-49.9 Million
Emp.: 7
Airborne Geophysical Surveying & Mapping
Services
N.A.I.C.S.: 541360
Teo Hage (Mng Dir)

CGG Americas Inc.   (1)
10300 Town Park Dr, Houston, TX 77072
Tel.: (832) 351-8300
Web Site: http://www.cgg.com
Sales Range: $150-199.9 Million
Holding Company; Regional Managing Of-
fice; Oil & Gas Geophysical Products &
Services
N.A.I.C.S.: 551112

Representative Office (Non-US):

CGG - Argentina   (2)
Maipu 757 2nd Fl, Buenos Aires,
C1006ACI, Argentina
Tel.: (54) 1143259653
Web Site: http://www.cgg.com

Sales Range: $25-49.9 Million
Emp.: 24
Geophysical Services
N.A.I.C.S.: 541360

CGG - Peru   (2)
Avenue 858, 193, San Isidro, Lima, Peru
Tel.: (51) 12224585
Web Site: http://www.cgg.com
Sales Range: $25-49.9 Million
Emp.: 5
Seismic & Geological Services
N.A.I.C.S.: 541360

Group (Non-US):

CGG Canada   (2)
1410 401 9th Ave S W, Calgary, T2P 3C5,
AB, Canada
Tel.: (403) 205-6000
Web Site: http://www.cgg.com
Sales Range: $1-9.9 Million
Data Services
N.A.I.C.S.: 518210

Subsidiary (Domestic):

CGG Geophysical (Canada)
Corporation   (3)
715 5 Ave SW Ste 2200, Calgary, T2P 5A2,
AB, Canada
Tel.: (403) 205-6000
Web Site: http://www.cgg.com
Geophysical Exploration Services
N.A.I.C.S.: 541360

Hampson Russel Limited
Partnership   (3)
715 5 Ave SW Ste 510, Calgary, T2P 2X6,
AB, Canada
Tel.: (403) 266-3225
Web Site: http://www.cgg.com
Software Development Services
N.A.I.C.S.: 541511

Subsidiary (Domestic):

Hampson-Russell Software Services
LP   (4)
715 5th Ave SW Ste 510, Calgary, T2P
2X6, AB, Canada
Tel.: (403) 266-3225
Sales Range: $25-49.9 Million
Emp.: 49
Geophysical Software & Services
N.A.I.C.S.: 541511

Subsidiary (Non-US):

CGG Geophysical (Chile) SA   (2)
Avda Nueva Tajamar 481 Torre Norte Piso
21, Las Condes, Santiago, Chile
Tel.: (56) 23471000
Web Site: http://www.cgg.com
Geophysical Surveying Services
N.A.I.C.S.: 541360

Subsidiary (Domestic):

CGG Holding (U.S.) Inc.   (2)
10300 Town Park Dr, Houston, TX 77072
Tel.: (832) 351-8300
Investment Management Service
N.A.I.C.S.: 523999

Unit (Domestic):

CGG Marine USA   (3)
6100 Hillcroft, Houston, TX 77081
Tel.: (713) 369-5600
Marine Broadband & Seismic Surveying
Services
N.A.I.C.S.: 213112

Subsidiary (Non-US):

CGG do Brasil Ltda.   (2)
Av Presidente Wilson 231 Saloes 1501
1502 1503 1504, Rio de Janeiro, 20030-
021, Brazil
Tel.: (55) 2121267450
Web Site: http://www.cgg.com
Sales Range: $25-49.9 Million
Emp.: 40
Geophysical Software & Services
N.A.I.C.S.: 541360

CGG Aviation (Australia) Pty Ltd. (1)
Main Country Office 1 Ord Street, West
Perth, 6005, WA, Australia
Tel.: (61) 892146200

Web Site: http://www.cgg.com
Sales Range: $25-49.9 Million
Airborne Geophysical Surveying & Mapping
Services
N.A.I.C.S.: 541360

CGG Data Services AG   (1)
Bahnhofstrasse 29, 6300, Zug, Switzerland
Tel.: (41) 417280808
Holding Company; Geophysical Software &
Services
N.A.I.C.S.: 551112

Subsidiary (Non-US):

CGG Jason (Australia) Pty. Ltd. (2)
69 Outram St, West Perth, Perth, 6005,
WA, Australia
Tel.: (61) 8 9420 6057
Web Site: http://jason.cgg.com
Seismic Inversion & Reservoir Characteriza-
tion Software & Services
N.A.I.C.S.: 423430

Subsidiary (US):

CGG Jason (U.S.) Inc.   (2)
10300 Town Park Dr, Houston, TX 77072
Tel.: (832) 351-8300
Web Site: http://jason.cgg.com
Seismic Inversion & Reservoir Characteriza-
tion Software & Services
N.A.I.C.S.: 513210
Howard Titchmarsh (Bus Mgr)

CGG Jakarta   (1)
Graha Paramita 6th Floor Jalan Denpasar
Blok D-2, Kuningan, Jakarta, 129440, Indo-
nesia
Tel.: (62) 212522240
Web Site: http://www.cgg.com
Sales Range: $25-49.9 Million
Emp.: 100
Computer Related Services
N.A.I.C.S.: 518210

CGG Marine (Australia) Pty. Ltd. (1)
69 Outram Street, West Perth, Perth, 6005,
WA, Australia
Tel.: (61) 8 9481 2043
Sales Range: $50-74.9 Million
Emp.: 23
Marine Broadband & Seismic Surveying
Services
N.A.I.C.S.: 213112

CGG Marine (Norway) AS   (1)
Hoffsveien 1c, Oslo, 275, Norway
Tel.: (47) 22134600
Web Site: http://www.fugro.geoteam.no
Marine Broadband & Seismic Surveying
Services
N.A.I.C.S.: 213112

CGG Marine Resources Norge
AS   (1)
O H Bangs Vei 70, 1322, Hovik,
Norway   (100%)
Tel.: (47) 6711 6500
Emp.: 4
Marine Engineering Services
N.A.I.C.S.: 541330

CGG Seismic Imaging (Australia) Pty.
Ltd.   (1)
38 Ord Steet, West Perth, 6005, WA, Aus-
tralia
Tel.: (61) 8 9322 2490
Subsurface Seismic Geophysical Data Ac-
quisition, Processing & Analysis Services
N.A.I.C.S.: 518210
Tony Weatherall (Country Mgr)

CGG Seismic Imaging (Norway)
AS   (1)
Hoffsveien 1C, 0213, Oslo, Norway
Tel.: (47) 2213 4600
Subsurface Seismic Geophysical Data Ac-
quisition, Processing & Analysis Services
N.A.I.C.S.: 518210

CGG Seismic Imaging (UK)
Limited   (1)
Horizon House Azalea Drive, Swanley, BR8
8JR, Kent, United Kingdom   (100%)
Tel.: (44) 13 2266 8011
Sales Range: $25-49.9 Million
Emp.: 70
Subsurface Seismic Geophysical Data Ac-
quisition, Processing & Analysis Services

N.A.I.C.S.: 518210

CGG Services S.A.   (1)
27 Avenue Carnot, 91341, Massy, Cedex,
France
Tel.: (33) 164473000
Sales Range: $25-49.9 Million
Oil & Gas Field Geophysical Surveying Ser-
vices
N.A.I.C.S.: 213112

Subsidiary (Domestic):

CGG Explo SARL   (2)
27 Avenue Carnot, 91341, Massy, Cedex,
France   (100%)
Tel.: (33) 164473000
Web Site: http://www.cggveritas.com
Sales Range: $75-99.9 Million
Emp.: 300
Engineering, Marine & Geological Services
N.A.I.C.S.: 541330

CGG I SA   (2)
1 Rue Leon Migaux, 91341, Massy,
France   (100%)
Tel.: (33) 164473000
Sales Range: $25-49.9 Million
Emp.: 200
Engineering Services
N.A.I.C.S.: 541330

Subsidiary (Non-US):

CGG Services (Australia) Pty.
Ltd.   (2)
1 Ord Street, West Perth, 6005, WA, Aus-
tralia
Tel.: (61) 892146200
Sales Range: $25-49.9 Million
Emp.: 80
Geophysical Surveying Services
N.A.I.C.S.: 541360
Sadia Imran (Mgr-HR)

CGG Services (Canada) Inc.   (2)
715-5th Avenue S W Suite 2200, Calgary,
T2P 5A2, AB, Canada
Tel.: (403) 205-6000
Sales Range: $25-49.9 Million
Emp.: 20
Oil & Gas Field Geophysical Information
Services
N.A.I.C.S.: 541360

CGG Services (Norway) AS   (2)
Carlkonowsgt 34, 5162, Laksevag,
Norway   (100%)
Tel.: (47) 56113100
Sales Range: $25-49.9 Million
Marine Seismic Services
N.A.I.C.S.: 541360

Subsidiary (Domestic):

Exploration Investment Resources II
AS   (3)
Carl Konows Gate 34, 5162, Laksevag,
Norway   (100%)
Tel.: (47) 56113100
Web Site: http://www.cgg.com
Sales Range: $25-49.9 Million
Emp.: 90
Architectural Services
N.A.I.C.S.: 541310

Exploration Vessel Resources
AS   (3)
Carl Konows gate 34, 5162, Laksevag,
Norway   (100%)
Tel.: (47) 56113100
Web Site: http://www.cgg.com
Sales Range: $25-49.9 Million
Emp.: 100
Water Transportation Services
N.A.I.C.S.: 488390

Multiwave Geophysical Company
AS   (3)
Carl Konows Gate 34, Laksevag, 5162,
Norway   (100%)
Tel.: (47) 56113100
Web Site: http://www.cgg.com
Sales Range: $25-49.9 Million
Emp.: 100
Architectural Services
N.A.I.C.S.: 541310

Subsidiary (Non-US):

CGG Services (Singapore) Pte.
Ltd.   (2)

CGG—(Continued)

9 Serangoon North Ave 5, Singapore, 554531, Singapore
Tel.: (65) 67235500
Oil & Gas Exploration Services
N.A.I.C.S.: 213112

Subsidiary (US):

CGG Services (U.S.) Inc. (2)
17200 Park Row, Houston, TX 77084-5935
Tel.: (281) 492-6688
Oil & Gas Geophysical Services
N.A.I.C.S.: 213112

Subsidiary (Non-US):

CGG Services (UK) Ltd. (2)
Crompton Way Manor Royal Estate, Crawley, RH10 9QN, United Kingdom
Tel.: (44) 1293683000
Oil & Gas Exploration Equipment Mfr
N.A.I.C.S.: 333132

Subsidiary (Domestic):

CGG NPA Satellite Mapping Ltd. (3)
Crockham Park, Edenbridge, TN8 6SR, Kent, United Kingdom
Tel.: (44) 17 3286 5023
Sales Range: $25-49.9 Million
Emp.: 35
Geophysical Mapping Services
N.A.I.C.S.: 541360
Michael King (Mgr-Offshore Svcs)

Subsidiary (Non-US):

CGG Services Holding (Latin America) B.V. (2)
Schiphol Boulevard 299, Luchthaven Schiphol, Amsterdam, 1118 BH, Netherlands
Tel.: (31) 202065970
Holding Company
N.A.I.C.S.: 551112

CGG Services Holding B.V. (2)
Schiphol Boulevard 299, Luchthaven Schiphol, Amsterdam, 1118 BH, Netherlands
Tel.: (31) 202065970
Web Site: http://www.cgg.com
Sales Range: $50-74.9 Million
Emp.: 11
Holding Company
N.A.I.C.S.: 551112

CGG Services India Private Ltd. (2)
AWFIS 12B Empire Tower Reliable Tech Park B Wing Thane - Belapur Rd, Gavate Wadi MIDC Airoli, Mumbai, 400 708, India
Tel.: (91) 9769977490
Sales Range: $25-49.9 Million
Emp.: 35
Geographical Software Development Services
N.A.I.C.S.: 541511
Lam Pham (Mng Dir)

CGG Services de Mexico SA de CV (2)
Lago Victoria No 74 Piso 11 Granada, Miguel Hidalgo, Mexico, 11520, Mexico
Tel.: (52) 5591527400
Web Site: http://www.cgg.com
Sales Range: $25-49.9 Million
Emp.: 18
Geophysical Surveying Services
N.A.I.C.S.: 541360

CGG Technology Services (Beijing) Co. Ltd. (2)
Room O-403 Lido Hotel No 6 JiangTai Road, Beijing, 100004, China
Tel.: (86) 1064371837
Technical Software Training Services
N.A.I.C.S.: 611430

De Regt Germany GmbH (1)
Frankischer Friedhof 1, 44319, Dortmund, Germany
Tel.: (49) 23165556411
Environmental Management Services
N.A.I.C.S.: 541620

De Regt Marine Cables Bv (1)
Zaag 2-4, 2931 LD, Krimpen aan de Lek, Netherlands
Tel.: (31) 180668800
Web Site: http://www.deregtcables.com
Cable Mfr

N.A.I.C.S.: 335929

Exgeo CA (1)
Av Fco De Miranda Edificio Parque Cristal Urbanizacion, Los Palos Grandes, Caracas, Venezuela
Tel.: (58) 212 2855334
Web Site: http://www.exgeo.com
Sales Range: $50-74.9 Million
Emp.: 25
Oil & Gas Exploration Services
N.A.I.C.S.: 213112
Marco Antonio Suarez (Gen Mgr)

Geoscience (Beijing) Ltd. (1)
A 1206-1209 Ocean International Center No 56 East 4th Ring Road, Chaoyang District, Beijing, 100025, China
Tel.: (86) 10 5908 1801
Geophysical Software Products & Services
N.A.I.C.S.: 423430

Lasa Prospeccoes Sa (1)
Salao 1502 Parte Centro, Rio de Janeiro, 20030-021, Brazil
Tel.: (55) 2121267450
Environmental Management Services
N.A.I.C.S.: 541620

Multifield Geophysics AS (1)
Carl Konows Gate 34, Laksevag, 5162, Norway
Tel.: (47) 56114800
Web Site: http://www.multifield-geophysics.com
Sales Range: $25-49.9 Million
Emp.: 120
Geophysical Surveying Services
N.A.I.C.S.: 541360

Pt Cgg Services Indonesia (1)
Graha Paramita Building 6th Floor Jalan Denpasar Raya Blok D2, Setiabudi, Kuningan, 129440, Jakarta, Indonesia
Tel.: (62) 212522240
Environmental Management Services
N.A.I.C.S.: 541620
Tenny Yoan (Mgr-Fin & Acctg)

Robertson (UK) Limited (1)
Tyn-y-Coed Pentywyn Road, Llandudno, LL30 1SA, United Kingdom
Tel.: (44) 1492 581 811
Web Site: http://www.robertson-cgg.com
Sales Range: $25-49.9 Million
Emp.: 250
Geophysical & Geological Software & Services
N.A.I.C.S.: 513210
Paul Watson (Mng Dir)

Subsidiary (US):

Robertson (USA) Inc. (2)
6100 Hillcroft 5th Fl, Houston, TX 77081
Tel.: (713) 369-6100
Web Site: http://www.robertson-cgg.com
Sales Range: $25-49.9 Million
Emp.: 100
Geophysical & Geological Software & Services
N.A.I.C.S.: 423430
Guy M. Oliver (Pres)

Seismic Support Services (1)
Bldg 1 4 Tessinsky Lane, 109028, Moscow, Russia
Tel.: (7) 495 644 08 05
Oil & Gas Exploration Services
N.A.I.C.S.: 213112

Sercel Holding SA (1)
16 Rue de Bel Air, BP 30439, 44474, Carquefou, Cedex, France
Tel.: (33) 240301181
Emp.: 600
Holding Company
N.A.I.C.S.: 551112

Subsidiary (Non-US):

Hebei Sercel-JunFeng Geophysical Prospecting Equipment Co., Ltd. (2)
PO Box 121-7, Xushui, 072550, Hebei, China (51%)
Tel.: (86) 312 864 8351
Navigational Services to Shipping
N.A.I.C.S.: 483111
Thierry Le Roux (Chm)

Sercel Beijing Technological Services Co Ltd. (2)

6 Jiang Tai Lu, Beijing, 100016, Chaoyang, China
Tel.: (86) 1064376710
Information Technology Consulting Services
N.A.I.C.S.: 541512

Sercel Canada Ltd (2)
1108-55th Ave NE, Calgary, T2EY4, AB, Canada (100%)
Tel.: (403) 275 3511
Web Site: http://www.sercel.com
Sales Range: $25-49.9 Million
Emp.: 7
Measuring & Controlling Device Mfr
N.A.I.C.S.: 334519

Sercel England Ltd (2)
Birchwood Way Cotes Park Industrial Estate, Alfreton, DE554QQ, United Kingdom
Tel.: (44) 1773605078
Web Site: http://www.sercel.com
Sales Range: $25-49.9 Million
Emp.: 63
Measuring & Controlling Device Mfr
N.A.I.C.S.: 334519

Subsidiary (Domestic):

Sercel S.A (2)
16 rue de Bel Air, BP 30439, 44474, Carquefou, Cedex, France
Tel.: (33) 240301181
Web Site: https://www.sercel.com
High Tech Integrated Equipment Mfr
N.A.I.C.S.: 333248

Branch (Domestic):

Sercel - Les Ulis (3)
Mini Parc du Verger Batiment E Zone de Cortaboeuf, 1 Rue de Terre Neuve, 91940, Les Ulis, France
Tel.: (33) 0169938360
Web Site: http://www.sercel.com
Sales Range: $25-49.9 Million
Emp.: 30
Geophysical Services & Manufacturer of Geophysical Equipment
N.A.I.C.S.: 541360

Subsidiary (Non-US):

Sercel Singapore Pte Ltd (2)
68 Loyang Way, Singapore, 508758, Singapore (100%)
Tel.: (65) 65450411
Sales Range: $25-49.9 Million
Emp.: 45
Motor Vehicle Electrical & Electronic Equipment Mfr
N.A.I.C.S.: 336320

Subsidiary (US):

Sercel, Inc. (2)
17200 Park Row, Houston, TX 77084-5935
Tel.: (281) 492-6688
Web Site: http://www.sercel.com
Measuring & Controlling Device Mfr
N.A.I.C.S.: 334519

Sercel-GRC (1)
13914 E Admiral Pl ste B, Tulsa, OK 74116-2107
Tel.: (918) 834-9600
Web Site: http://www.sercel-grc.com
Sales Range: $10-24.9 Million
Emp.: 45
Downhole Sensors & Temperature Gauges for Oil & Gas Industry
N.A.I.C.S.: 334513

Veritas DGC (Malaysia) Sdn. Bhd. (1)
Level 56 Tower 2 Petronas Twin Towers, Kuala Lumpur, 50888, Malaysia
Tel.: (60) 323821100
Sales Range: $25-49.9 Million
Emp.: 23
Processing Seismic Data
N.A.I.C.S.: 518210

CGI INC.
1350 Rene-Levesque Blvd West 15th floor, Montreal, H3G 1T4, QC, Canada
Tel.: (514) 841-3200
Web Site: http://www.cgi.com
Year Founded: 1976

GIB—(NYSE)
Rev.: $9,486,547,628
Assets: $11,750,644,308
Liabilities: $6,285,454,739
Net Worth: $5,465,189,569
Earnings: $1,070,997,644
Emp.: 80,000
Fiscal Year-end: 09/30/21
Information Technology & Business Process Services; Consulting Services
N.A.I.C.S.: 541690
Serge Godin (Co-Founder & Co-Chm)

Subsidiaries:

Annams Systems, Corp. (1)
2420 Camino Ramon Ste 130, San Ramon, CA 94583
Tel.: (925) 355-0700
Web Site: http://www.annams.com
Sales Range: $1-9.9 Million
Emp.: 50
Computer Integrated Systems Design
N.A.I.C.S.: 541512

Subsidiary (Domestic):

Sunflower Systems (2)
2420 Camino Ramon Ste 130, San Ramon, CA 94583
Tel.: (925) 355-0700
Web Site: http://www.sunflowersystems.com
Asset Management Solutions & Software Services
N.A.I.C.S.: 513210

Sunflower Systems (2)
2001 Jefferson Davis Hwy Ste 1211, Arlington, VA 22202 (100%)
Tel.: (703) 835-9388
Web Site: http://www.sunflowersystems.com
Asset Management Solutions & Software Services
N.A.I.C.S.: 513210

CGI Federal, Inc. (1)
12601 Fair Lakes Cir, Fairfax, VA 22030
Tel.: (703) 227-6000
Web Site: http://www.cgifederal.com
Sales Range: $200-249.9 Million
Emp.: 1,000
Information Technology Services for US Government
N.A.I.C.S.: 541690
Edward J. Jopeck (Dir-Bus Consulting)

CGI IT UK Limited (1)
Spaces 100 Avebury Boulevard, Milton Keynes, MK9 1FH, United Kingdom
Tel.: (44) 2076379111
N.A.I.C.S.: 541611

CGI Information Systems & Management Consultants Australia Pty Ltd (1)
Suite 2 Level 20 1 Market Street, Sydney, 2000, NSW, Australia (100%)
Tel.: (61) 292341300
Web Site: http://www.cgi.com
Sales Range: $25-49.9 Million
Emp.: 100
Systems Integration & Consulting Services
N.A.I.C.S.: 541512

CGI Information Systems & Management Consultants Deutschland GmbH (1)
Heerdter Lohweg 35, 40549, Dusseldorf, NRW, Germany (100%)
Tel.: (49) 21153550
Web Site: http://www.cgi.com
Sales Range: $100-124.9 Million
Emp.: 287
Systems Integration & Consulting Services
N.A.I.C.S.: 541512

CGI Information Systems & Management Consultants Espana S.A. (1)
Avenida Manoteras 32 Parque Empresarial La Moraleja, Alcobendas, 28108, Madrid, Spain (100%)
Tel.: (34) 916578100
Web Site: http://www.cgi.com
Sales Range: $50-74.9 Million
Emp.: 200
Systems Integration & Consulting Services

N.A.I.C.S.: 541512

CGI Information Systems & Management Consultants Inc. (1)
1130 Sherbrooke St West 7th Fl, Montreal,
H3A 2M8, QC, Canada (100%)
Tel.: (514) 841-3200
Web Site: http://www.cgi.ca
Sales Range: $550-599.9 Million
Emp.: 2,000
Computer Consulting & Systems Integration
Services
N.A.I.C.S.: 541512

Branch (Domestic):

CGI (2)
1350 Rene-Levesque Blvd West 15th Floor,
Montreal, H3G 1T4, QC, Canada (100%)
Tel.: (514) 841-3200
Web Site: http://www.cgi.ca
Sales Range: $150-199.9 Million
Emp.: 1,000
Research & Development in Technology
Solutions & Performance Platforms
N.A.I.C.S.: 541511
Guy Vigeant (Pres-Ops)

CGI Inc. (2)
930 Jacques Cartier East 3rd Fl, Chicoutimi, G7H 7K9, QC, Canada (100%)
Tel.: (418) 696-6789
Web Site: http://www.cgi.com
Sales Range: $75-99.9 Million
Emp.: 430
Information Technology Consulting Services
N.A.I.C.S.: 541611

CGI Information Systems (2)
275 Slater St 14th Fl, Ottawa, K1P 5H9,
ON, Canada
Tel.: (613) 234-2155
Web Site: http://www.cgi.ca
Sales Range: $200-249.9 Million
Emp.: 700
Systems Integration & Consulting Services
N.A.I.C.S.: 541512

CGI Information Systems (2)
800 5th Ave SW Ste 900, Calgary, T2P
3T6, AB, Canada (100%)
Tel.: (403) 218-8300
Web Site: http://www.cgi.com
Sales Range: $25-49.9 Million
Emp.: 150
Remote Database Administration
N.A.I.C.S.: 541512
Shawn Derby (Sr VP-Western Canada Ops)

Joint Venture (Domestic):

Innovapost, Inc. (2)
365 March Road, Ottawa, K2K 3N5, ON,
Canada (49%)
Tel.: (613) 270-6262
Web Site: http://www.innovapost.com
Sales Range: $200-249.9 Million
Emp.: 700
Provider of IS/IT & eBusiness Solutions to
the Global Postal Industry, Particularly to
the Canada Post Group of Companies
N.A.I.C.S.: 561499

**CGI Information Systems & Management Consultants Netherlands
B.V.** (1)
Prinses Beatrixlaan 614, 2595 BM, Hague,
Netherlands (100%)
Tel.: (31) 703787000
Web Site: http://www.cgi.com
Sales Range: $25-49.9 Million
Emp.: 30
Systems Integration & Consulting Services
N.A.I.C.S.: 541512

CGI Information Systems & Management Consultants Polska (1)
ul Krolewska 16 Saski Crescent 5th Floor,
00-103, Warsaw, Poland
Tel.: (48) 225265700
Web Site: http://www.cgi.com
Sales Range: $50-74.9 Million
Emp.: 100
Systems Integration & Consulting Services
N.A.I.C.S.: 541511

CGI Information Systems & Management Consultants Portugal (1)
Rua Tomas da Fonseca, Torresde Lisboa

Torre G12 Fl D, 1600-209, Lisbon,
Portugal (100%)
Tel.: (351) 217219000
Web Site: http://www.cgi.com
Sales Range: $25-49.9 Million
Emp.: 50
Systems Integration & Consulting Services
N.A.I.C.S.: 541512

CGI Information Systems & Management Consultants SA/NV (1)
Avenue du Boulevard/Bolwerklaan 21 b26,
1210, Brussels, Belgium (100%)
Tel.: (32) 22089111
Web Site: http://www.cgi.com
Sales Range: $25-49.9 Million
Emp.: 20
Systems Integration & Consulting Services
N.A.I.C.S.: 541512

**CGI Information Systems & Management Consultants Switzerland
SA** (1)
Weltpoststrasse 20, Postflach 263, CH
3000, Bern, Switzerland (100%)
Tel.: (41) 313564444
Web Site: http://www.cgi.com
Sales Range: $25-49.9 Million
Emp.: 30
Systems Integration & Consulting Services
N.A.I.C.S.: 541512

CGI Information Systems & Management Consultants UK Ltd. (1)
Broadlands House, Primett Road, Stevenage, SG1 3EE, Hertsfordshire, United
Kingdom
Tel.: (44) 1438317966
Web Site: http://www.cgi.com
Sales Range: $125-149.9 Million
Emp.: 360
Systems Integration & Consulting Services
N.A.I.C.S.: 541512

CGI Information Systems & Management Consultants, Inc. (1)
12 Corporate Woods Blvd, Albany, NY
12211
Tel.: (518) 436-0772
Web Site: http://www.cgi.com
Sales Range: $1-9.9 Million
Emp.: 60
Computer Integrated Systems Design Services
N.A.I.C.S.: 541512

CGI Limited (1)
250 Brook Drive, Green Park, Reading,
RG2 6UA, United Kingdom
Tel.: (44) 8450707765
Sales Range: $5-14.9 Billion
Emp.: 40,000
Holding Company; Computer Consultancy,
Systems Integration, Project Management,
Products & Outsourcing Services
N.A.I.C.S.: 551112
Michael Read (Project Mgr)

Subsidiary (Non-US):

Affecto Plc (2)
Keilaranta 17 C, FI-02150, Espoo, Finland
Tel.: (358) 20577711
Web Site: http://www.affecto.com
Sales Range: $100-124.9 Million
Business Intelligence; Document & Knowledge Management; Digital Location-Based
Information Systems; Payroll & Material
Management Solutions; Cartographic Services
N.A.I.C.S.: 541519

Subsidiary (Non-US):

Affecto Denmark A/S (3)
Lyngbyvej 28, DK-2100, Copenhagen, Denmark
Tel.: (45) 39 25 00 00
Web Site: http://www.affecto.com
Information Technology Consulting Services
N.A.I.C.S.: 519290

Affecto Norway AS (3)
Kongens gate, PO Box 324, Sentrum,
0103, Oslo, Norway (100%)
Tel.: (47) 22 40 20 00
Web Site: http://www.affecto.no
Business Management Software Development Services
N.A.I.C.S.: 541511

Affecto Poland Sp.z. o.o. (3)
Metropolitan Pitsudskiego 2, 00-078, Warsaw, Poland (100%)
Tel.: (48) 224651440
Web Site: http://www.affecto.pl
Business Management Consulting Services
N.A.I.C.S.: 541611

Affecto Sweden AB (3)
Jakobsbergsgatan 31, 111 44, Stockholm,
Sweden (100%)
Tel.: (46) 8 444 98 00
Web Site: http://www.affecto.com
Business Administration Software Development Services
N.A.I.C.S.: 541511

UAB CGI Lithuania (3)
Perkunkiemio g 4A, LT-12128, Vilnius,
Lithuania (100%)
Tel.: (370) 52123712
Web Site: http://www.affecto.com
IT Services
N.A.I.C.S.: 541519
Giedre Uzubale (Partner-Bus & HR)

Subsidiary (Non-US):

CGI AB (2)
Torshamnsgatan 24, Kista, 164 98, Stockholm, Sweden
Tel.: (46) 86702000
Sales Range: $1-4.9 Billion
Emp.: 9,000
IT Consulting Services
N.A.I.C.S.: 541690
Asa Thoft (Mgr-PR)

CGI Belgium NV/SA (2)
Leonardo Da Vincilaan 19, B 1831, Brussels, Diegem, Belgium (100%)
Tel.: (32) 27086100
Web Site: http://www.cgi.com
Sales Range: $75-99.9 Million
Emp.: 400
IT Consulting Services
N.A.I.C.S.: 541690

**CGI Business Process Outsourcing
BV** (2)
Siriusdreef 30, Hoofddorp, 2132 WT, Noord-Holland, Netherlands
Tel.: (31) 885640000
Web Site: http://www.cgi.com
Business Process Outsourcing Services
N.A.I.C.S.: 561499

CGI Czech Republic Sro (2)
Na Okraji 335 42, Prague, 16200, Czech
Republic
Tel.: (420) 284020111
Sales Range: $75-99.9 Million
Emp.: 600
IT Consulting Services
N.A.I.C.S.: 541690
Stefan Szabo (Mng Dir)

CGI Danmark AS (2)
Lautrupvang 10, Ballerup, 2750, Denmark
Tel.: (45) 44 78 40 00
Web Site: http://www.cgi.dk
IT Consulting Services
N.A.I.C.S.: 541690

**CGI Deutschland GmbH & Co.
KG** (2)
Leinfelder Strasse 60, Leinfelden-Echterdingen, 70771, Germany
Tel.: (49) 711728460
Web Site: http://www.de.cgi.com
Sales Range: $25-49.9 Million
Emp.: 250
Management Consulting Services
N.A.I.C.S.: 541611
Torsten Strass (Mng Dir)

CGI France S.A.S. (2)
17 Place des Reflets CB16, 17 place des
Reflets, 92097, Courbevoie, Cedex,
France (100%)
Tel.: (33) 157874000
Web Site: http://www.cgi.fr
Sales Range: $25-49.9 Million
Emp.: 15
Computer Consulting Services
N.A.I.C.S.: 541511
Jean-Marc Lazzari (Pres)

Branch (Domestic):

**CGI France S.A.S. -
Aix-en-Provence** (2)

1330 rue Guillibert de la Lauziere, Europarc
de Pichaury - Bat B1, 13856, Aix-en-Provence, Cedex 3, France
Tel.: (33) 442972220
Web Site: http://www.cgi.com
Computer Consulting Services
N.A.I.C.S.: 541511

CGI France S.A.S. - Bordeaux (3)
Parc d Activites Kennedy 3, 1 Avenue Neil
Armstrong, 33700, Merignac, Bordeaux,
France
Tel.: (33) 557929500
Computer Consulting Services
N.A.I.C.S.: 541511
Andy Green (Pres)

CGI France S.A.S. - Brest (3)
Immeuble Grand Large, Quai de la Douane,
29200, Brest, France
Tel.: (33) 2 98 80 98 80
Sales Range: $10-24.9 Million
Emp.: 30
Computer Consulting Services
N.A.I.C.S.: 541511

CGI France S.A.S. - Lille (3)
8 rue Anatole France, 59043, Lille, France
Tel.: (33) 320438840
Sales Range: $75-99.9 Million
Emp.: 400
Computer Consulting Services
N.A.I.C.S.: 541511

CGI France S.A.S. - Lyon (3)
Bat Docksite 47-49 rue des Docks, CS 20
218, 69336, Lyon, Cedex, France
Tel.: (33) 469646000
Sales Range: $25-49.9 Million
Emp.: 100
Computer Consulting Services
N.A.I.C.S.: 541511
Debu Sabien (Gen Mgr)

CGI France S.A.S. - Montpellier (3)
Parc Euromedecine, 61/67 rue Guillaume
Dupuytren, 34196, Montpellier, Cedex,
France
Tel.: (33) 467637110
Sales Range: $25-49.9 Million
Emp.: 20
Computer Consulting Services
N.A.I.C.S.: 541511

CGI France S.A.S. - Nantes (3)
9 Boulevard Ampere, BP 10727, 44481,
Carquefou, Cedex, France
Tel.: (33) 228015470
Web Site: http://www.cgi.com
Sales Range: $25-49.9 Million
Emp.: 500
Computer Consulting Services
N.A.I.C.S.: 541511

CGI France S.A.S. - Niort (3)
141 avenue Salvador Allende, 79000, Niort,
France
Tel.: (33) 549260707
Sales Range: $25-49.9 Million
Computer Consulting Services
N.A.I.C.S.: 541511

CGI France S.A.S. - Pau (3)
37 Rte de Tarbes, Idron, 64320, Pau,
France
Tel.: (33) 559806170
Sales Range: $25-49.9 Million
Computer Consulting Services
N.A.I.C.S.: 541511
Annie Falanchere (Project Mgr)

CGI France S.A.S. - Rennes (3)
Espace Sivigni, ZA La Rigourdihre, 35510,
Cesson Sevigne, France
Tel.: (33) 299837388
Sales Range: $25-49.9 Million
Emp.: 75
Computer Consulting Services
N.A.I.C.S.: 541511

CGI France S.A.S. - Strasbourg (3)
9 B Rue Du Parc, Valparc Oberhausbergen,
67088, Strasbourg, Cedex, France
Tel.: (33) 388568787
Sales Range: $10-24.9 Million
Computer Consulting Services
N.A.I.C.S.: 541511

CGI France S.A.S. - Toulouse (3)
15 avenue du Docteur Maurice Grynfogel,
31000, Toulouse, France

CGI Inc.—(Continued)

Tel.: (33) 567692222
Sales Range: $10-24.9 Million
Computer Consulting Services
N.A.I.C.S.: 541511
Sylvain Laduree *(Dir-Agency)*

Subsidiary (Domestic):

Umanis S.A. (3)
7-9 rue Paul Vaillant-Couturier, 92300,
Levallois-Perret, France **(70.6%)**
Tel.: (33) 140896800
Web Site: http://www.groupeumanis.com
Sales Range: $150-199.9 Million
Computer Consulting & Applications Engi-
neering Services
N.A.I.C.S.: 541519
Laurent Piepszownik *(Pres & CEO)*

Subsidiary (Non-US):

**CGI Information Systems and Man-
agement Consultants (Australia) Pty
Ltd** (2)
13th Floor 100 Pacific Highway, North Syd-
ney, 2060, NSW, Australia **(100%)**
Tel.: (61) 2 8062 3000
Web Site: http://www.cgi.com.au
Sales Range: $25-49.9 Million
Emp.: 150
IT Consulting Services
N.A.I.C.S.: 541690

Branch (Domestic):

CGI Australia Pty Ltd. (3)
Ground Fl 436 Elgar Rd, Box Hill, 3128,
VIC, Australia **(100%)**
Tel.: (61) 398430600
Sales Range: $25-49.9 Million
Emp.: 100
IT Consulting Services
N.A.I.C.S.: 541690
Colin Holgate *(Pres-APAC)*

Subsidiary (Non-US):

CGI Luxembourg S.A. (2)
7 Zone d'activites Bourmicht, L 8070, Ber-
trange, Luxembourg **(100%)**
Tel.: (352) 4852220
Sales Range: $25-49.9 Million
Emp.: 150
IT Consulting Services
N.A.I.C.S.: 541690

CGI Malaysia Sdn. Bhd. (2)
Avenue 7 Bangsar South City No 8 Jalan
Kerinchi, Level 5 Menara PNS Tower 7,
59200, Kuala Lumpur, Selangor Darul Eh-
san, Malaysia **(100%)**
Tel.: (60) 32386 8600
Sales Range: $25-49.9 Million
Emp.: 100
IT Consulting Services
N.A.I.C.S.: 541690

CGI Nederland B.V. (2)
Siriusdreef 30, Hoofddorp, 2132 WT,
Netherlands **(100%)**
Tel.: (31) 88 564 0000
Web Site: http://www.cginederland.nl
Sales Range: $75-99.9 Million
Emp.: 400
Prepackaged Software Services
N.A.I.C.S.: 334610

Branch (Domestic):

CGI Nederland B.V. - Arnhem (3)
Meander 901, 6825 MH, Arnhem, Nether-
lands
Tel.: (31) 88 564 0000
Web Site: http://www.cginederland.nl
Sales Range: $100-124.9 Million
Emp.: 300
Prepackaged Software Services
N.A.I.C.S.: 334610

CGI Nederland B.V. - Groningen (3)
Eemsgolaan 1, 9727 DW, Groningen, Neth-
erlands
Tel.: (31) 88 564 0000
Sales Range: $75-99.9 Million
Emp.: 350
Prepackaged Software Services
N.A.I.C.S.: 541511

Subsidiary (Non-US):

CGI Norge AS (2)
Grenseveien 86, 0605, Oslo, Norway
Tel.: (47) 22577000
Web Site: http://www.cginorge.no
IT Consulting Services
N.A.I.C.S.: 541690

CGI South America (2)
Brooklin Novo AvDdas Nacoes Unidas 12
495 5th & 6th Floors, Brooklin Novo, 04578
000, Sao Paulo, SP, Brazil **(100%)**
Tel.: (55) 1121653000
Sales Range: $25-49.9 Million
Emp.: 75
IT Consulting Services
N.A.I.C.S.: 541690
Edson F. Leite *(VP)*

CGI Suomi Oy (2)
Karvaamokuja 2 PL 38, Helsinki, 00381,
Finland
Tel.: (358) 10 302 010
Web Site: http://www.cgi.fi
IT Consulting Services
N.A.I.C.S.: 541690

CGI Sverige AB (2)
Torshamnsgatan 24, Kista, Stockholm, 164
40, Sweden
Tel.: (46) 8 6702000
Web Site: http://www.cgi.se
Information Technology Consulting Services
N.A.I.C.S.: 541512

Subsidiary (Domestic):

CGI UK Ltd. (2)
250 Brook Drive, Green Park, Reading,
RG2 6UA, United Kingdom **(100%)**
Tel.: (44) 845 070 7765
Web Site: http://www.cgi-group.co.uk
Sales Range: $25-49.9 Million
Emp.: 100
Computer Consulting Services
N.A.I.C.S.: 541512

Branch (Domestic):

CGI UK Ltd. - Aberdeen (3)
Seafield House Floor 3C Hill of Rubislaw,
Aberdeen, AB15 6BL, United Kingdom
Tel.: (44) 1224 388988
Sales Range: $25-49.9 Million
Emp.: 100
Computer Consulting Services
N.A.I.C.S.: 541512

CGI UK Ltd. - Bridgend (3)
Technology Dr Science Pk, Bridgend, CF31
3NA, Midgomargan, United Kingdom
Tel.: (44) 656765000
Sales Range: $25-49.9 Million
Emp.: 100
Computer Consulting Services
N.A.I.C.S.: 541512

CGI UK Ltd. - Bristol (3)
400 Park Ave Aztec W, Almondsbury, Bris-
tol, BS32 4TR, United Kingdom
Tel.: (44) 454614455
Sales Range: $25-49.9 Million
Emp.: 200
Computer Consulting Services
N.A.I.C.S.: 541512

CGI UK Ltd. - Cardiff (3)
Newport Road Saint Mellons, Cardiff, CF3
5WW, United Kingdom
Tel.: (44) 2920721111
Computer Consulting Services
N.A.I.C.S.: 541512

CGI UK Ltd. - Edinburgh (3)
81 George St, EH129Dj, Edinburgh, Scot-
land, United Kingdom
Tel.: (44) 315278500
Computer Consulting Services
N.A.I.C.S.: 541512

CGI UK Ltd. - Leatherhead (3)
Chaucer House & Keats House The Office
Park, Springfield Dr, Leatherhead, KT22
7LP, Surrey, United Kingdom
Tel.: (44) 1372369576
Sales Range: $75-99.9 Million
Computer Consulting Services
N.A.I.C.S.: 541512
Tim Gregory *(Pres)*

CGI UK Ltd. - Manchester (3)
Kingston House Towers Business Pk,
Wilmslow Rd, Manchester, M20 2LX, Dids-
bury, United Kingdom
Tel.: (44) 1614388000
Sales Range: $25-49.9 Million
Computer Consulting Services
N.A.I.C.S.: 541512

Unit (Non-US):

CGI-Dubai (2)
Dubai Internet City Bldg 4 301 Fl, PO Box
26379, Dubai, 26379, United Arab Emirates
Tel.: (971) 43916200
Sales Range: $25-49.9 Million
Emp.: 80
IT Consulting Services
N.A.I.C.S.: 541690
Raymond McMann *(CEO)*

Subsidiary (Non-US):

CGITI Portugal SA (2)
Av Jose Malhoa 16A, 1079 159, Lisbon,
Portugal
Tel.: (351) 210 018 000
Web Site: http://www.cgi.com.pt
IT Consulting Services
N.A.I.C.S.: 541690

**CGI Technologies & Solutions
Inc.** (1)
1130 Random Hills, Fairfax, VA
22033 **(100%)**
Tel.: (703) 267-8679
Web Site: http://www.cgi.com
Sales Range: $900-999.9 Million
Emp.: 6,500
Systems Integration & Consulting Services
N.A.I.C.S.: 541512

**Computer Technology Solutions,
Inc.** (1)
300 Riverchase Pkwy E, Birmingham, AL
35244-1813
Tel.: (205) 259-2300
Web Site: http://www.askcts.com
Custom Computer Programming Services
N.A.I.C.S.: 541511
Brendan Thompson *(Pres)*

**Conseillers en gestion et informatique
CGI Inc.** (1)
1130 Sherbrooke St W 7 Fl, Montreal, H3A
2M8, QC, Canada
Tel.: (514) 841-3200
Information Technology Consulting Services
N.A.I.C.S.: 541511

**Momentum Consulting
Corporation** (1)
14750 NW 77th Ct Ste 313, Miami Lakes,
FL 33016
Tel.: (305) 817-2622
Web Site: http://www.momentumcc.com
Sales Range: $1-9.9 Million
Emp.: 135
IT Consulting Services
N.A.I.C.S.: 541690
Mayte Fernandez *(Co-CEO & Mng Partner)*

**Paragon Computer Professionals
Inc.** (1)
25 Commerce Dr, Cranford, NJ 07016-0248
Tel.: (908) 709-6767
Web Site: http://www.cgi.com
Provider of Computer Related Services
N.A.I.C.S.: 541512
Daniel J. O'Connor *(CEO)*

Subsidiary (Non-US):

**Consult Paragon Computer Profes-
sionals LTD.** (2)
1st Flr 6 BTM Layout 1st Stage 1st Phase,
100 Feet Ring Road, Bengaluru, 560068,
India
Tel.: (91) 8041187900
Sales Range: $10-24.9 Million
Emp.: 40
Computer Management & Consulting Ser-
vices
N.A.I.C.S.: 541690
Muralidharan Jayaraman *(Dir-Ops)*

SCISYS Group plc (1)
Methuen Park, Chippenham, SN14 0GB,
Wilts, United Kingdom
Tel.: (44) 1249 466 466

Web Site: http://www.scisys.com
Rev.: $74,117,113
Assets: $75,924,198
Liabilities: $42,252,021
Net Worth: $33,672,177
Earnings: $1,822,313
Emp.: 648
Fiscal Year-end: 12/31/2018
Information & Communication Technology
Software & Services
N.A.I.C.S.: 513210
Klaus Heidrich *(CEO)*

Subsidiary (Domestic):

SCISYS UK Holding Limited (2)
Methuen Park, Chippenham, SN14 0GB,
United Kingdom
Tel.: (44) 1249466466
Web Site: http://www.scisys.co.uk
Sales Range: $50-74.9 Million
Information & Communication Technology
Software & Services
N.A.I.C.S.: 513210

Subsidiary (Non-US):

SCISYS Deutschland GmbH (3)
Borgmannstrasse 2, 44894, Bochum,
Nordrhein-Westfalen, Germany
Tel.: (49) 234 92580
Web Site: http://www.scisys.co.uk
Sales Range: $50-74.9 Million
Emp.: 120
Media Broadcasting Technology Solutions
N.A.I.C.S.: 541519

Branch (Domestic):

SCISYS Deutschland GmbH (4)
Europaplatz 4, Darmstadt, 64293, Germany
Tel.: (49) 6151 428530
Web Site: http://www.scisys.co.uk
Emp.: 25
Information & Communication Technology
Services
N.A.I.C.S.: 541512

Division (Domestic):

SciSys UK Ltd. (3)
Methuen Park, Chippenham, SN14 0GB,
Wilts, United Kingdom
Tel.: (44) 1249466466
Web Site: http://www.scisys.co.uk
Sales Range: $50-74.9 Million
Emp.: 150
Satellite & Space Systems Software
N.A.I.C.S.: 513210

Subsidiary (Non-US):

**Science Systems (Space)
Limited** (3)
Science Systems Clothier Rd, BS4 5SS,
Bristol, United Kingdom - England
Tel.: (44) 1179717251
Web Site: http://www.scisys.co.uk
Sales Range: $50-74.9 Million
Emp.: 150
Software Reproducing
N.A.I.C.S.: 334610

CGIFT AG
Schoppenstehl 22, 20095, Hamburg,
Germany
Tel.: (49) 4085416868
Web Site:
 https://deutschewasserkraft.com
Year Founded: 1998
Gift & Gift Card Retailer
N.A.I.C.S.: 459420
Delf Ness *(Chm)*

CGN MINING CO. LTD.
Room 1903 19/F China Resources
Building No 26 Harbour Road, Wan-
chai, China (Hong Kong)
Tel.: (852) 34238700 Ky
Web Site: http://www.cgnmc.com
Year Founded: 1994
1164—(HKG)
Rev.: $465,206,700
Assets: $875,377,643
Liabilities: $448,489,920
Net Worth: $426,887,723
Earnings: $65,651,663

Emp.: 22
Fiscal Year-end: 12/31/22
Holding Company
N.A.I.C.S.: 551112
Junjing An *(CEO)*

CGN NEW ENERGY HOLD-INGS CO., LTD.
15/F Harbour Centre 25 Harbour Road, Wanchai, China (Hong Kong)
Tel.: (852) 25933222
Web Site: http://www.cgnne.com
1811—(HKG)
Rev.: $2,430,056,000
Assets: $8,343,933,000
Liabilities: $6,844,074,000
Net Worth: $1,499,859,000
Earnings: $214,421,000
Emp.: 1,936
Fiscal Year-end: 12/31/22
Power Generation Services
N.A.I.C.S.: 221118

CGN NUCLEAR TECHNOLOGY DEVELOPMENT CO., LTD.
19th Floor North Building CGN Building 2002 Shennan Road, Futian District, Shenzhen, 518000, China
Tel.: (86) 75588619331
Web Site: https://www.cgnnt.com.cn
Year Founded: 2011
000881—(SSE)
Rev.: $975,065,364
Assets: $1,680,927,768
Liabilities: $734,390,280
Net Worth: $946,537,488
Earnings: $27,904,500
Fiscal Year-end: 12/31/22
Investment Services
N.A.I.C.S.: 523999
Yi Weijing *(Sec)*

CGN POWER CO., LTD.
18/F CGN Tower South Building No 2002, Shennan Boulevard, Shenzhen, 518035, China
Tel.: (86) 75584430888
Web Site:
https://www.en.cgnp.com.cn
Year Founded: 2014
1816—(HKG)
Rev.: $11,429,530,786
Assets: $57,494,787,990
Liabilities: $34,607,112,583
Net Worth: $22,887,675,407
Earnings: $2,360,125,670
Emp.: 19,038
Fiscal Year-end: 12/31/23
Electronic Services
N.A.I.C.S.: 238210

Subsidiaries:

China Nuclear Power Engineering Co., Ltd. **(1)**
Daya Bay Nuclear Power Base, Dapeng New District, Shenzhen, 518124, China
Tel.: (86) 75584472966
Web Site: http://www.en.cnpec.com.cn
Nuclear Power & Thermal Power Services
N.A.I.C.S.: 221118
Chen Ying Jian *(Gen Mgr)*

Daya Bay Nuclear Power Operations and Management Co., Ltd. **(1)**
01st Floor Daya Bay Nuclear Power Base, Shenzhen, 518124, Guangdong, China
Tel.: (86) 75584477888
Web Site: https://en.dnmc.com.cn
Nuclear Power Generation Services
N.A.I.C.S.: 221113

Nanjing Xinsu Thermoelectricity Co., Ltd. **(1)**
No 10 Shuanglong Road Zhonghuamenwai, Jiangning District, Nanjing, China
Tel.: (86) 2552104842
Nuclear Power Generation Services
N.A.I.C.S.: 221113

CGS INTERNATIONAL, INC.
3E Amery St N N Fairview Subdivision, Quezon City, 1121, Philippines
Tel.: (63) 284412083 NV
Year Founded: 2012
CGSI—(OTCIQ)
Assets: $91,680
Liabilities: $450,233
Net Worth: ($358,553)
Earnings: ($112,953,812)
Fiscal Year-end: 04/30/22
Media Related Advertising Services
N.A.I.C.S.: 541890
Ramon Mabanta *(CEO & Officer)*

CGS MANAGEMENT AG
Huobstrasse 14, Po Box 355, Pfaffikon, 8808, Switzerland
Tel.: (41) 554161640 CH
Web Site: http://www.cgs-management.com
Year Founded: 1995
Sales Range: $25-49.9 Million
Emp.: 12
Privater Equity Firm
N.A.I.C.S.: 523999
Rolf Lanz *(Mng Partner)*

Subsidiaries:

Masa GmbH **(1)**
Masa-Strasse 2, 56626, Andernach, Germany
Tel.: (49) 263292920
Web Site: http://www.masa-group.com
Building Material Production Equipment Mfr
N.A.I.C.S.: 333248
Hyun-Dee Ro *(Mgr-Mktg)*

Subsidiary (Non-US):

Masa Concrete Plants India Pvt. Ltd. **(2)**
5B KIADB Bommasandra Ind Area Attibele Hobli, Anekal Taluk, Bengaluru, 560 099, India
Tel.: (91) 8026283888
Construction Machinery & Equipment Distr
N.A.I.C.S.: 423810
Frank Reschke *(Member-Mgmt Bd)*

Masa Middle East FZCO **(2)**
PO Box 16867, Jebel Ali Free Zone, Dubai, United Arab Emirates
Tel.: (971) 48833476
Construction Machinery & Equipment Distr
N.A.I.C.S.: 423810
Cristian Brugioli *(Member-Mgmt Bd)*

Masa Tianjin Building Material Machinery Co., Ltd.
No 28 Xinghua Branch Road 3 Xiqing Economic Development Area, Tianjin, 300385, China
Tel.: (86) 2283983788
Web Site: http://www.masa-group.com.cn
Construction Machinery & Equipment Distr
N.A.I.C.S.: 423810
Jason Ji *(Member-Mgmt Bd)*

Subsidiary (US):

Masa-USA, LLC **(2)**
2231 Holmgren Way, Green Bay, WI 54304
Tel.: (920) 497-0390
Web Site: http://www.masa-usa.com
Construction Machinery & Equipment Distr
N.A.I.C.S.: 423810
Jose Diaz *(Member-Mgmt Bd)*

CGX ENERGY INC.
333 Bay Street Suite 2400, Toronto, M5H 2T6, ON, Canada
Tel.: (416) 364-5569 ON
Web Site:
https://www.cgxenergy.com
CGXEF—(OTCIQ)
Rev.: $2,333,280
Assets: $84,881,480
Liabilities: $21,453,756
Net Worth: $63,427,724
Earnings: ($3,193,577)
Fiscal Year-end: 12/31/23

Oil & Gas Exploration & Production Services
N.A.I.C.S.: 211120
Suresh Narine *(Chm)*

Subsidiaries:

CGX Resources Inc. **(1)**
120 Adelaide Street West Suite 512, Toronto, M5H 1T1, ON, Canada **(100%)**
Tel.: (416) 364-6653
Natural Gas Exploration Service
N.A.I.C.S.: 211130

ON Energy Inc. **(1)**
130 Adelaide St W Ste 2700, Toronto, M5H 1T5, ON, Canada **(85.5%)**
Tel.: (416) 364-5569
Energy Exploration Services
N.A.I.C.S.: 541360

CH BIOTECH R&D CO., LTD.
No 89 Wenxian Rd, Nantou County, Nantou, 540001, Taiwan
Tel.: (886) 497009198
Web Site: https://www.chbio.com.tw
Year Founded: 2013
6534—(TAI)
Emp.: 187
Crop Farming Services
N.A.I.C.S.: 111998
Chenpang Wu *(Chm)*

CH MEDIA HOLDING AG
Neumattstrasse 1, Aargau, Aarau, 5000, Switzerland
Tel.: (41) 58 200 54 21
Web Site: http://chmedia.ch
Year Founded: 2018
Holding Company; Media Production
N.A.I.C.S.: 551112
Michael Wanner *(CEO)*

CH. CHARILAOU GROUP PLC
Agia Varvara Industrial Area Warehouse E Agia Varvara, 2560, Nicosia, Cyprus
Tel.: (357) 22526640
Web Site:
http://www.charilaougroup.com
Year Founded: 1993
CHCH—(CYP)
Rev.: $1,942,592
Assets: $2,266,882
Liabilities: $254,776
Net Worth: $2,012,106
Earnings: $145,991
Fiscal Year-end: 12/31/19
Tourism Management Services
N.A.I.C.S.: 561520

CH. KARNCHANG PUBLIC COMPANY LIMITED
587 Viriyathavorn Building Sutthisarnvinijchai Rd, Dindaeng Subdistrict Dindaeng District, Bangkok, 10400, Thailand
Tel.: (66) 22770460
Web Site: https://www.ch-karnchang.co.th
Year Founded: 1972
CK—(THA)
Rev.: $1,108,005,305
Assets: $2,824,189,514
Liabilities: $2,064,950,291
Net Worth: $759,239,223
Earnings: $46,545,708
Emp.: 1,434
Fiscal Year-end: 12/31/23
General Contractors
N.A.I.C.S.: 236220
Plew Trivisvavet *(Bd of Dirs & Chm-Exec Bd)*

Subsidiaries:

Bangkok Expressway and Metro Public Company Limited **(1)**
587 Sutthisanvinitchai Rd Ratchadaphisek, Din Daeng, Bangkok, 10400, Thailand

Tel.: (66) 26414611
Web Site: http://www.becl.co.th
Sales Range: $350-399.9 Million
Emp.: 660
Highway, Street & Bridge Construction Services
N.A.I.C.S.: 237310

Bangkok Metro Public Company Limited **(1)**
189 Rama LX Road, Huai Khwang District, Bangkok, Thailand
Tel.: (66) 23542000
Web Site: http://www.bangkokmetro.co.th
Commercial & Institutional Building Construction
N.A.I.C.S.: 236220

Bangpa-in Cogeneration Limited **(1)**
No 587 Sutthisarnvinijchai Road, Dindaeng District, Bangkok, 10400, Thailand **(35%)**
Tel.: (66) 22750026
Electric Power & Steam Generation & Distribution Services
N.A.I.C.S.: 221118
Woravuth Anuruxwonpsri *(Mng Dir)*

CH. Karnchang (Lao) Co., Ltd **(1)**
10 Thadeua Road Thaphalansay, Vientiane, Lao People's Democratic Republic
Tel.: (856) 21353390
Construction Materials Distr
N.A.I.C.S.: 423320

CH. Karnchang - Tokyu Construction Co Ltd **(1)**
587 Viriyathavorn Building 7-8th Floor Sutthisarn Road Ratchadaphisek, Dindaeng, Bangkok, 10400, Thailand **(55%)**
Tel.: (66) 22775004
Web Site: https://chtokyu.co.th
Emp.: 200
Specialty Trade Contractors
N.A.I.C.S.: 238990

CH. Karnchang Real Estate Co., Ltd. **(1)**
587 Sutthisarn Road, Dindaeng District, Bangkok, Thailand **(99%)**
Tel.: (66) 22750026
Web Site: http://www.ch-karnchang.co.th
Residential Property Managers
N.A.I.C.S.: 531311

Construction Material Supply Co., Ltd. **(1)**
587 Sutthisarn Road 17th Floor Viriyathavorn Building, Dindaeng District, Bangkok, 10400, Thailand **(99.99%)**
Tel.: (66) 22749801
Construction Materials Whslr
N.A.I.C.S.: 423390

SouthEast Asia Energy Limited **(1)**
587 Viriyathavorn Bldg 20th Fl, Suthisarn Rd Dindaeng, Bangkok, 10400, Thailand **(28.5%)**
Tel.: (66) 22754873
Web Site: http://www.sean.co.th
Hydroelectric Power Operations
N.A.I.C.S.: 221111

CHA BIOTECH CO., LTD.
CHA Complex 335 Pangyoro Bundagu, Seongnam, Gyeonggido, Korea (South)
Tel.: (82) 318817400
Web Site: http://www.chabio.com
Year Founded: 2000
085660—(KRS)
Rev.: $647,795,059
Assets: $1,232,575,335
Liabilities: $732,540,172
Net Worth: $500,035,163
Earnings: ($53,428,509)
Emp.: 229
Fiscal Year-end: 12/31/22
Pharmaceuticals Product Mfr
N.A.I.C.S.: 325412
Sang Hoon Ho *(CEO)*

Subsidiaries:

ONDA Entertainment Co., Ltd. **(1)**
113-12 Dangha-ro Namsa-myeon, Cheoin-gu, Yongin, Gyeonggi-do, Korea (South)
Tel.: (82) 317056234

CHA Biotech Co., Ltd.—(Continued)

Web Site: http://www.diostech.co.kr
Rev.: $302,730,336
Assets: $142,954,883
Liabilities: $78,695,402
Net Worth: $64,259,480
Earnings: ($4,035,008)
Emp.: 135
Fiscal Year-end: 12/31/2022
Camera Lenses Mfr
N.A.I.C.S.: 333310
Hyo Sung Yoo (CEO)

SEOUL CRO Inc. (1)
4-6FL 10 Bongeunsa-ro 6-gil, Gangnam-gu,
Seoul, '06123, Korea (South)
Tel.: (82) 234470181
Web Site: https://en.seoulcro.com
Clinical Testing Services
N.A.I.C.S.: 541380

CHA VACCINE INSTITUTE
560 Dunchon-Daero, Jungwon-Gu,
Seongnam, 13230, Gyeonggi-do, Korea (South)
Tel.: (82) 317378208
Web Site:
https://www.chavaccine.com
Year Founded: 2000
261780—(KRS)
Vaccine Product Mfr
N.A.I.C.S.: 325414
Hong Mo Moon (Founder & Co-CEO)

**CHAARAT GOLD HOLDINGS
LIMITED**
Palm Grove House, PO Box 438,
Road Town, Tortola, VG1110, Virgin
Islands (British)
Tel.: (284) 2074992612   VG
Web Site: https://www.chaarat.com
CGH—(LSE)
Rev.: $92,434,000
Assets: $171,558,000
Liabilities: $94,682,000
Net Worth: $76,876,000
Earnings: ($3,588,000)
Emp.: 1,169
Fiscal Year-end: 12/31/21
Gold Exploration & Mining Services
N.A.I.C.S.: 212220
Martin Andersson (Chm)

Subsidiaries:

Chaarat Operating Company
GmbH   (1)
19 Razzakov Street Business Centre
Rossiya 15th Floor, 720040, Bishkek, Kyrgyzstan
Tel.: (996) 312 398 039
Gold Ore Mining Services
N.A.I.C.S.: 212220

Chaarat Zaav CJSC   (1)
Ibraimov koch 103, Bishkek, Kyrgyzstan
Tel.: (996) 31 297 6100
Web Site: https://chaarat.kg
Gold Ore Mining Services
N.A.I.C.S.: 212220

CHABIOTECH CO., LTD.
CHA Complex 335 Pangyoro, Bundanggu, Seongnam, Gyeonggido,
Korea (South)
Tel.: (82) 318817400
Web Site: https://en.chabio.com
Year Founded: 2002
085660—(KRS)
Rev.: $626,889,292
Assets: $1,192,797,425
Liabilities: $708,899,494
Net Worth: $483,897,932
Earnings: ($51,704,253)
Emp.: 229
Fiscal Year-end: 12/31/22
Health Care Srvices
N.A.I.C.S.: 621610
Sang-Hoon Oh (CEO)

Subsidiaries:

CHA Hollywood Medical Center,
L.P.   (1)
1300 N Vermont Ave, Los Angeles, CA
90027
Tel.: (213) 413-3000
Web Site:
https://www.hollywoodpresbyterian.com
Healthcare Services
N.A.I.C.S.: 621999

Matica Biotechnology, Inc.   (1)
150 Venture Dr Ste 101, College Station,
TX 77845
Tel.: (979) 321-7500
Web Site: https://www.maticabio.com
Biotechnology Research & Development
Services
N.A.I.C.S.: 541714

CHADHA PAPERS LTD.
C/o Wave One Project Office Plot No
L-2A 2nd Floor Sector 18, Noida,
201301, Uttar Pradesh, India
Tel.: (91) 1204120849
Web Site:
https://www.chadhapapers.com
Year Founded: 1990
531946—(BOM)
Rev.: $48,639,291
Assets: $29,524,090
Liabilities: $34,551,003
Net Worth: ($5,026,913)
Earnings: ($1,227,981)
Emp.: 510
Fiscal Year-end: 03/31/21
Paper Products Mfr
N.A.I.C.S.: 322299
Sanmeet Singh (Exec Dir)

**CHADORMALU MINING & IN-
DUSTRIAL COMPANY**
No 56 Esfandyar Blvd Vali-e Asr,
19686 53647, Tehran, Iran
Tel.: (98) 2188882858
Web Site:
https://www.chadormalu.com
Year Founded: 1992
CHML—(THE)
Sales Range: Less than $1 Million
Iron Ore Mining Services
N.A.I.C.S.: 212210

CHAGALA GROUP LIMITED
23 Baisheshek str, Almaty, 050040,
Kazakhstan
Tel.: (7) 7273550484   KZ
Web Site:
https://www.chagalagroup.com
Year Founded: 1994
Rev.: $19,107,000
Assets: $87,701,000
Liabilities: $21,596,000
Net Worth: $66,105,000
Earnings: $885,000
Fiscal Year-end: 12/31/17
Commercial Properties Development
Services
N.A.I.C.S.: 531390
Elmira Abdrakhmanova (Head-Legal
Dept)

Subsidiaries:

Caspi Limited LLP   (1)
1 Ismagulov str, Shagala hotel, 060002,
Atyrau, Kazakhstan
Tel.: (7) 7122996096
Real Estate Development Services
N.A.I.C.S.: 531390

Chagala Cooperatief U.A.   (1)
Johannes Vermeerplein 11, 1071 DV, Amsterdam, Netherlands
Tel.: (31) 20 6717452
Oil & Gas Exploration Services
N.A.I.C.S.: 213112

Chagala International Holding
B.V.   (1)
Johannes Vermeerplein 11, 1071 DV, Am-

sterdam, Netherlands
Tel.: (31) 206717452
Investment Management Service
N.A.I.C.S.: 523999

Chagala Management LLP   (1)
23 Baisheshek Str, Almaty, 050040, Kazakhstan
Tel.: (7) 7272980131
Web Site: http://www.chagalagroup.com
Emp.: 65
Shopping Mall Management Services
N.A.I.C.S.: 531120

**CHAHUA MODERN HOUSE-
WARES CO.LTD**
168 Jiaokeng Road Gushan, Jin an
District, Fuzhou, 350014, Fujian,
China
Tel.: (86) 59183620836
Web Site:
https://www.chahuahouseware.com
Year Founded: 1997
603615—(SHG)
Rev.: $94,898,382
Assets: $192,419,323
Liabilities: $23,167,207
Net Worth: $169,252,116
Earnings: ($2,636,895)
Fiscal Year-end: 12/31/22
Houseware Product Mfr & Distr
N.A.I.C.S.: 321999
Chen Kuisheng (Chm)

CHAI CHA NA MINING INC.
3045 Southcreek Road Unit 11, Mississauga, L4X 2E9, ON, Canada
Tel.: (905) 624-2266   Ca
Year Founded: 2007
Sales Range: Less than $1 Million
Gold Mining Services
N.A.I.C.S.: 212220
Frederick Fisher (Pres & CEO)

**CHAI WATANA TANNERY
GROUP PUBLIC COMPANY
LIMITED**
No 176/1 1480 Moo 1 Sukhumvit
Road Km 30 Taiban, Mueang, Samut
Prakan, 10280, Thailand
Tel.: (66) 23892510
Web Site: https://www.cwt.co.th
Year Founded: 1972
CWT—(THA)
Rev.: $52,147,542
Assets: $105,655,468
Liabilities: $55,789,404
Net Worth: $49,866,064
Earnings: ($9,658,179)
Fiscal Year-end: 12/31/23
Leather Mfr
N.A.I.C.S.: 316990

**CHAILEASE HOLDING COM-
PANY LIMITED**
No 362 Ruiguang Road, Neihu District, Taipei, 11492, Taiwan
Tel.: (886) 287526388   Ky
Web Site:
https://www.chaileaseholding.com
Year Founded: 1977
CHLRA—(LUX)
Rev.: $3,049,292,124
Assets: $29,495,196,511
Liabilities: $24,388,239,752
Net Worth: $5,106,956,758
Earnings: $814,329,613
Emp.: 7,787
Fiscal Year-end: 12/31/23
Financial Services
N.A.I.C.S.: 551112
Fong-Long Chen (Chm)

Subsidiaries:

Chailease Berjaya Credit Sdn.
Bhd.   (1)
A-05-01 Level 5 Block A PJ8 No 23 Jalan
Barat Seksyen 8, 46050, Petaling Jaya, Se-

langor, Malaysia
Tel.: (60) 376660888
Web Site: https://www.chailease.com.my
Financial Management Services
N.A.I.C.S.: 541611
Jenny Loh (Mgr-HR)

Chailease Berjaya Finance
Corporation   (1)
5F 45 San Miguel Building San Miguel Ave
Ortigas Center, Pasig, Metro Manila, Philippines
Tel.: (63) 27236388
Financial Management Services
N.A.I.C.S.: 541611

Chailease Consumer Finance Co.,
Ltd.   (1)
392 Sec 1 Neihu Rd, Neihu Dist, New Taipei City, 114006, Taiwan
Tel.: (886) 227986488
N.A.I.C.S.: 523999
Chen Fenglong (Chm)

Chailease Energy Integration Co.,
Ltd.   (1)
6F No 362 Ruiguang Rd, Neihu Dist, New
Taipei City, 114, Taiwan
Tel.: (886) 287526388
N.A.I.C.S.: 221114

Chailease Finance Co., Ltd.   (1)
1-12F No 362 Rueiguang Rd, Neihu District, Taipei, 11492, Taiwan
Tel.: (886) 287526388
Web Site: https://www.chailease.com.tw
Sales Range: $350-399.9 Million
Emp.: 600
Financial Support Services
N.A.I.C.S.: 522299
Albert F. L. Chen (Chm)

Subsidiary (Domestic):

Apex Credit Solutions Inc.   (2)
6F No 420 Fuxing N Rd, Zhongshan Dist,
Taipei, 104, Taiwan
Tel.: (886) 225122866
Financial Management Services
N.A.I.C.S.: 541611

Chailease Auto Rental Co., Ltd.   (2)
5F No 362 Ruiguang Rd, Neihu Dist, Taipei,
114, Taiwan
Tel.: (886) 287526388
Financial Management Services
N.A.I.C.S.: 541611

Chailease Insurance Brokers Co.,
Ltd.   (2)
1-12F No 362 Rueiguang Rd, Neihu District, Taipei, 11492, Taiwan
Tel.: (886) 287526388
Web Site:
https://chainsurance.chailease.com.tw
Financial Management Services
N.A.I.C.S.: 541611

Subsidiary (Non-US):

Chailease International Leasing Com-
pany Limited   (2)
28 Fl Saigon Trade Centre 37 Ton Duc
Thang St, Dist 1, Ho Chi Minh City, Vietnam
Tel.: (84) 287 301 6010
Web Site: https://www.chailease.com.vn
Finance & Leasing Services
N.A.I.C.S.: 532490
Quoc Vuong Tran (Officer-Mktg)

Chailease International Trading Com-
pany Limited   (2)
26-27-28 Fl Saigon Trade Centre 37 Ton
Duc Thang St, Dist 1, Ho Chi Minh City,
Vietnam
Tel.: (84) 2899996011
Web Site:
https://www.chaileasetrade.com.vn
Finance & Leasing Services
N.A.I.C.S.: 532490
Nguyen Thi Cam Nhung (Deputy Mgr)

Chailease Finance International
Corp.   (1)
4th Floor Building 13 West Zone Airport
Business Park, No 76 Huan He North Road
Airport Economic Zone, Tianjin, China
Tel.: (86) 2284861168
Financial Lending Services

N.A.I.C.S.: 533110

Chailease International Finance Corporation (1)
Building 1 Lane 631 Jinzhong Road, Changning District, Shanghai, 200336, China
Tel.: (86) 215 208 0101
Web Site: https://www.chailease.com.cn
Equipment Leasing Services
N.A.I.C.S.: 522220

Subsidiary (Domestic):

Jirong Real Estate Co., Ltd. (2)
Building 1 Lane 631 Jinzhong Rd, Changning District, Shanghai, China
Tel.: (86) 2152080101
Financial Management Services
N.A.I.C.S.: 541611

Chailease International Financial Leasing Corp. (1)
Building 1 Lane 631 Jinzhong Road, Changning District, Shanghai, China
Tel.: (86) 2152080101
Web Site: https://www.chailease.com.cn
Construction Industry Equipment Leasing Services
N.A.I.C.S.: 532412

Chailease Royal Finance Plc (1)
12F No 146 Key Stone Building Preah Norodom Blvd 41, Khan Chamkar Mon, Phnom Penh, Cambodia
Tel.: (855) 23973328
Financial Management Services
N.A.I.C.S.: 541611

Chailease Royal Leasing Plc (1)
No 146 11th Floor Street Norodom Blvd, Sangkat Tonle Bassak Khan Chamkar Mon, Phnom Penh, Cambodia
Tel.: (855) 11888408
Financial Management Services
N.A.I.C.S.: 541611
Younay Lim *(Officer-HR)*

Chung Ming Co., Ltd. (1)
No 28 Silin Ln, Situn Dist, Taichung, 40762, Taiwan
Tel.: (886) 427061109
Web Site: https://chungming-parts.com
Die-casting Product Mfr & Distr
N.A.I.C.S.: 331523

Fina Finance & Trading Co., Ltd. (1)
5F No 362 Ruiguang Road, Neihu District, Taipei, Taiwan
Tel.: (886) 287976168
Web Site: http://www.finatrade.com.tw
Sales Range: $50-74.9 Million
Emp.: 100
Equipment & Machinery Leasing Services
N.A.I.C.S.: 532420
Albert F. L. Chen *(Chm)*

Grand Pacific Financial Corp. (1)
901 Corporate Center Dr Ste 300, Monterey Park, CA 91754
Tel.: (323) 780-8881
Web Site: https://www.gpusa.com
Investment Banking Services
N.A.I.C.S.: 523150

Grand Pacific Financing Corp. (1)
901 Corporate Center Dr Ste 300, Monterey Park, CA 91754
Tel.: (323) 780-8881
Web Site: https://www.gpusa.com
Real Estate Services
N.A.I.C.S.: 531390
Tony Chen *(VP)*

PT Chailease Indonesia Finance (1)
Wisma 46 28th Floor Jl Jenderal Sudirman Kav 1 Kel, Karet Tengsin Kec Tanah Abang, Jakarta Pusat, Indonesia
Tel.: (62) 2125096888
Web Site: https://www.chailease.co.id
Vehicle Financing Services
N.A.I.C.S.: 522220

Tung Feng Inc. (1)
5F No 79-1 Zhouzi St, Neihu District, Taipei, 114, Taiwan
Tel.: (886) 227972077
Web Site: https://www.tungfeng.com
Construction Engineering Services
N.A.I.C.S.: 541330

CHAIN CHON INDUSTRIAL CO., LTD.
No 178 Ta Guan Rd, Hsien, Taoyuan, Taiwan
Tel.: (886) 33841688
Web Site:
https://www.chainchon.com
Year Founded: 1980
5014—(TPE)
Rev.: $596,207,235
Assets: $273,524,998
Liabilities: $173,124,660
Net Worth: $100,400,338
Earnings: $12,113,592
Emp.: 75
Fiscal Year-end: 12/31/22
Stainless Steel Mfr
N.A.I.C.S.: 331513
Li-Ching Po *(Chm & Pres)*

Subsidiaries:

Chain Chon Stainless Steel Sdn. Bhd. (1)
Lot 2 Jalan Perusahaan 2 Kawasan Perusahaan Beranang, 43700, Beranang, Selangor, Malaysia
Tel.: (60) 387232448
Web Site: https://chainchon.my
Stainless Steel Distr
N.A.I.C.S.: 423510

Ningbo Chain Chon Metal Technology Co., Ltd. (1)
No 9 Tonghe East Road Camel Street, Zhenhai District, Ningbo, Zhejiang, China
Tel.: (86) 57488232345
Stainless Steel Material Distr
N.A.I.C.S.: 423390

Tianjin Chain Chon Stainless Steel Co., Ltd. (1)
Chaonan Industrial Park, Ma Jia Dian Township Bao Di District, Tianjin, China
Tel.: (86) 2229648000
Stainless Steel Material Distr
N.A.I.C.S.: 423390

CHAINQUI CONSTRUCTION DEVELOPMENT CO., LTD.
6F No 329 Xinhu 2nd Rd, Neihu Chiu, Taipei, 114, Taiwan
Tel.: (886) 287918888
Web Site: https://www.gtg.com.tw
2509—(TAI)
Rev.: $7,307,956
Assets: $315,511,450
Liabilities: $172,246,601
Net Worth: $143,264,850
Earnings: ($7,829,818)
Fiscal Year-end: 12/31/23
Construction Engineering Services
N.A.I.C.S.: 541330
Yung-I Li *(Chm)*

CHAINTECH TECHNOLOGY CORP.
3F No 48-3 Mincyuan Rd, Xindian Dist, New Taipei City, 231, Taiwan
Tel.: (886) 229138833
Web Site:
http://www.chaintech.com.tw
Year Founded: 1986
2425—(TAI)
Rev.: $223,140,022
Assets: $119,726,965
Liabilities: $37,290,754
Net Worth: $82,436,211
Earnings: $7,626,312
Fiscal Year-end: 12/31/23
Memory Cards Mfr
N.A.I.C.S.: 323111
Kao Shu Jung *(Chm, Pres & Gen Mgr)*

Subsidiaries:

Fortech Electronics Co., Ltd. (1)
No 218 Bu Bu Gao Road Jiang Bei Wu Sha Zone Chang An, Dongguan, Guangdong, China

Tel.: (86) 76985546130
Solar Equipment Mfr
N.A.I.C.S.: 332510

CHAIRMAN'S BRANDS CORPORATION
77 Progress Avenue, Toronto, M1P 2Y7, ON, Canada
Tel.: (416) 288-8515
Web Site:
http://www.chairmansbrands.com
Year Founded: 1982
Sales Range: $10-24.9 Million
Emp.: 75
Fastfood Restaurant Services
N.A.I.C.S.: 722513

Subsidiaries:

241 Pizza (2006) Ltd. (1)
77 Progress Avenue, Toronto, M1P 2Y7, ON, Canada
Tel.: (416) 646-0987
Web Site: http://www.241pizza.com
Sales Range: $10-24.9 Million
Emp.: 50
Fastfood Restaurant Services
N.A.I.C.S.: 722513

Coffee Time Donuts Incorporated (1)
77 Progress Avenue, Toronto, M1P 2Y7, ON, Canada
Tel.: (416) 288-8515
Web Site: http://www.coffeetime.ca
Sales Range: $10-24.9 Million
Emp.: 40
Fastfood Restaurant Services
N.A.I.C.S.: 722513
Dan Lepidas *(Exec VP)*

Eggsmart Corporation (1)
6124 Tecumseh Rd E, Windsor, N8T 1E6, ON, Canada
Tel.: (519) 945-5092
Web Site: http://www.eggsmart.ca
Emp.: 7
Restaurant Operators
N.A.I.C.S.: 722511
Thair Binham *(Mgr)*

New Orleans Pizza Canada Inc (1)
77 Progress Avenue, Toronto, M1P 2Y7, ON, Canada
Tel.: (416) 646-0987
Web Site: http://www.neworleanspizza.ca
Food Products Distr
N.A.I.C.S.: 424490

Robins Donuts (1)
77 Progress Avenue, Toronto, M1P 2Y7, ON, Canada
Tel.: (416) 646-0987
Web Site: http://www.robinsdonuts.com
Emp.: 50
Fastfood Restaurant Services
N.A.I.C.S.: 722513
Dan Lepidas *(Exec VP)*

CHAKANA COPPER CORP.
Suite 1012 - 1030 West Georgia Street, Vancouver, V6E 2Y3, BC, Canada
Tel.: (604) 638-8063   BC
Web Site:
https://www.chakanacopper.com
Year Founded: 2011
CHKKF—(OTCQB)
Assets: $8,122,352
Liabilities: $639,689
Net Worth: $7,482,663
Earnings: ($5,733,861)
Fiscal Year-end: 03/31/22
Mineral Mining
N.A.I.C.S.: 212290
David Kelly *(Pres & CEO)*

CHAKRATEC ORD SHS
Hamelacha 4B, Lod, 7152008, Israel
Tel.: (972) 544232082
Web Site: http://www.chakratec.com
Year Founded: 2013
CKRT—(TAE)
Assets: $10,460,177
Liabilities: $1,171,281

Net Worth: $9,288,895
Earnings: ($4,514,650)
Real Estate Services
N.A.I.C.S.: 531210
Avi Cohen *(Chm)*

CHAKWAL SPINNING MILLS LTD.
7/1-E-3 Main Boulevard Gulberg III, Lahore, Pakistan
Tel.: (92) 4235717510
Web Site:
https://www.chakwalspinningmill.com
Year Founded: 1988
Rev.: $6,907,310
Assets: $6,408,385
Liabilities: $6,100,684
Net Worth: $307,701
Earnings: ($344,738)
Fiscal Year-end: 06/30/19
Yarn & Thread Mfr
N.A.I.C.S.: 313110
Khawaja Mohammad Jawed *(Chm)*

CHALET HOTELS LTD.
Raheja Tower 4th Floor Block G Plot No C-30 Bandra Kurla Complex, Bandra E, Mumbai, 400 051, India
Tel.: (91) 2226564000
Web Site:
https://www.chalethotels.com
Year Founded: 1986
542399—(BOM)
Rev.: $72,309,374
Assets: $606,428,823
Liabilities: $423,383,415
Net Worth: $183,045,408
Earnings: ($11,120,519)
Emp.: 1,853
Fiscal Year-end: 03/31/22
Hotel & Resort Operator
N.A.I.C.S.: 721110
Hetal Gandhi *(Chm)*

Subsidiaries:

Seapearl Hotels Private Limited (1)
4th Floor Raheja Tower Plot No C-30 Block G Bandra Kurla Complex, Bandra East, Mumbai, 400051, India
Tel.: (91) 2226564000
Hotel Operator
N.A.I.C.S.: 721110

CHALICE MINING LIMITED
Level 3 46 Colin Street, West Perth, 6005, WA, Australia
Tel.: (61) 893223960   AU
Web Site: https://chalicemining.com
CHLWF—(OTCIQ)
Rev.: $3,363,406
Assets: $113,961,183
Liabilities: $5,259,120
Net Worth: $108,702,062
Earnings: ($26,374,395)
Emp.: 66
Fiscal Year-end: 06/30/24
Support Activities for Nonmetallic Minerals (except Fuels) Mining
N.A.I.C.S.: 213115
Timothy Rupert Barr Goyder *(Chm)*

Subsidiaries:

Cgm (West Yilgarn) Pty. Ltd. (1)
Level 1 2A 300 Fitzgerald Street, North Perth, 6006, WA, Australia
Tel.: (61) 861669107
Web Site: https://www.westernyilgarn.com.au
Nickel Mining Services
N.A.I.C.S.: 212230

CHALKIS HEALTH INDUSTRY CO., LTD.
No 8 Qingnian Road Sunshine Plaza, Urumqi, 830000, Xinjiang, China
Tel.: (86) 9918852972
Web Site:
https://www.chalkistomato.com

Chalkis Health Industry Co., Ltd.—(Continued)

Year Founded: 1994
000972—(SSE)
Rev.: $82,736,316
Assets: $115,880,544
Liabilities: $101,781,576
Net Worth: $14,098,968
Earnings: $3,663,036
Emp.: 1,320
Fiscal Year-end: 12/31/22
Tomato Product Mfr
N.A.I.C.S.: 111219
Liu Hong (Chm & Sec-Party)

Subsidiaries:

Tianjin Chalton Tomato Product Co.,
Ltd.　　　　　　　　　　　　　　(1)
No 98 Free Trade Rd, Airport Industrial
Park Free Trade Zone, Tianjin, 300308,
China
Tel.: (86) 2258992345
Web Site: http://www.chalkistomato.com
Canned Tomato Paste Mfr
N.A.I.C.S.: 311421

CHALLAND PIPELINE LTD
Highway 11 South, PO Box 1807,
Rocky Mountain House, T4T 1B4,
AB, Canada
Tel.: (403) 845-2469
Web Site: https://www.challand.ca
Year Founded: 1974
Rev.: $39,610,513
Emp.: 250
Pipeline Construction
N.A.I.C.S.: 237120

CHALLANI CAPITAL LIMITED
No 15 New Giri Road Opp Hotel Ac-
cord Off G N Chetty Road, T Nagar,
Chennai, 600017, India
Tel.: (91) 4428342111
Web Site:
　　https://www.indoasiafinance.com
Year Founded: 1990
530747—(BOM)
Rev.: $4,192
Assets: $1,898,402
Liabilities: $830,389
Net Worth: $1,068,013
Earnings: ($124,769)
Emp.: 4
Fiscal Year-end: 03/31/20
Financial Management Services
N.A.I.C.S.: 523999
Padam J. Challani (Mng Dir)

CHALLENGER ACQUISITIONS LIMITED
55 Mount Row, Saint Peter Port, GY1
1NU, Guernsey
Tel.: (44) 1481740820　　　　　　GY
Web Site: http://www.challenger.com
Year Founded: 2014
Assets: $351,519
Liabilities: $4,407,306
Net Worth: ($4,055,788)
Earnings: ($2,548,192)
Investment Management Service
N.A.I.C.S.: 523940
Mark Gustafson (Co-CEO)

CHALLENGER ENERGY GROUP PLC
The Engine House Alexandra Road,
Castletown, IM9 1TG, Isle of Man
Tel.: (44) 1624647883　　　　　　IM
Web Site: https://cegplc.com
Year Founded: 2005
CEG—(AIM)
Rev.: $3,590,000
Assets: $117,010,000
Liabilities: $18,560,000
Net Worth: $98,450,000
Earnings: ($19,560,000)
Emp.: 75

Fiscal Year-end: 12/31/23
Oil & Gas Exploration Services
N.A.I.C.S.: 213112
Simon Craig Potter (CEO)

Subsidiaries:

Columbus Energy Resources
PLC　　　　　　　　　　　　　　(1)
Suite 114 90 Long Acre, London, WO2E
9RA, United Kingdom
Tel.: (44) 20 7203 2039
Web Site: http://www.columbus-erp.com
Sales Range: $10-24.9 Million
Oil & Gas Exploration & Production Ser-
vices
N.A.I.C.S.: 211120
Stewart Ahmed (CTO)

Subsidiary (Non-US):

West Indian Energy Group Ltd.　(2)
43 Carlos Street, Woodbrook, Chaguanas,
Trinidad & Tobago
Tel.: (868) 8686281128
Web Site: http://www.westindianenergy.com
Oil & Gas Services
N.A.I.C.S.: 213112
Stacey Bowman-Lamsee (Mgr-Corp Svcs)

CHALLENGER GEOMATICS LTD.
9945 50th Street Suite 200, Edmon-
ton, T6A 0L4, AB, Canada
Tel.: (780) 424-5511
Web Site:
　　http://www.challengergeomatics.com
Year Founded: 1984
Sales Range: $10-24.9 Million
Geomatics Services
N.A.I.C.S.: 541370
Peter Heil (Mgr-Bus Dev)

CHALLENGER GOLD LIMITED
Level 1 100 Havelock Street, West
Perth, 6005, WA, Australia
Tel.: (61) 863852743　　　　　　AU
Web Site: https://challengergold.com
CEL—(ASX)
Rev.: $14,548,548
Assets: $117,786,931
Liabilities: $9,157,704
Net Worth: $108,629,227
Earnings: $19,756,949
Emp.: 1
Fiscal Year-end: 06/30/22
Oil & Gas Exploration Services
N.A.I.C.S.: 211120
Robert Anthony Willes (Mng Dir)

CHALLENGER LIMITED
Level 2 5 Martin Place, Sydney,
2000, NSW, Australia
Tel.: (61) 299947000　　　　　　AU
Web Site:
　　https://www.challenger.com.au
CGF—(ASX)
Rev.: $424,549,092
Assets: $22,307,123,406
Liabilities: $19,712,819,958
Net Worth: $2,594,303,448
Earnings: $86,605,878
Emp.: 676
Fiscal Year-end: 06/30/24
Financial & Insurance Services
N.A.I.C.S.: 525990
Peter L. Polson (Chm)

Subsidiaries:

Challenger Diversified Property
Group　　　　　　　　　　　　　(1)
Level 2 5 Martin Place, Sydney, 2000,
NSW, Australia　　　　　　　(100%)
Tel.: (61) 299947000
Web Site: http://www.challenger.com.au
Sales Range: $50-74.9 Million
Retail & Industrial Real Estate Investment
Trust
N.A.I.C.S.: 525990

Challenger Group Holdings
Limited　　　　　　　　　　　　(1)
Level 2 5 Martin Place, Sydney, 2000,
NSW, Australia　　　　　　　(100%)
Tel.: (61) 299947000
Web Site: http://www.challengergroup.com
Sales Range: $200-249.9 Million
Emp.: 500
Miscellaneous Financial Investment Activi-
ties
N.A.I.C.S.: 523999

Challenger Group Services Pty
Ltd　　　　　　　　　　　　　　(1)
Level 2 5 Martin Place, Sydney, 2000,
NSW, Australia　　　　　　　(100%)
Tel.: (61) 299947000
Web Site: http://www.challengergroup.com
Sales Range: $75-99.9 Million
Emp.: 450
Other Management Consulting Services
N.A.I.C.S.: 541618

Challenger International Nominees
Ltd　　　　　　　　　　　　　　(1)
Level 2 5 Martin Place, Sydney, 2000,
NSW, Australia　　　　　　　(100%)
Tel.: (61) 299947000
Web Site: http://www.challengergroup.au
Sales Range: $75-99.9 Million
Emp.: 475
Other Management Consulting Services
N.A.I.C.S.: 541618

Challenger Life Holdings Pty
Limited　　　　　　　　　　　　(1)
Level 2 5 Martin Place, Sydney, 2000,
NSW, Australia　　　　　　　(100%)
Tel.: (61) 299947000
Web Site: http://www.challenger.com.au
Sales Range: $150-199.9 Million
Emp.: 600
Other Holding Companies Offices
N.A.I.C.S.: 551112

Challenger Limited　　　　　　(1)
3rd Floor 181 Queen Victoria Street, Lon-
don, EC4V 4EG, United Kingdom　(100%)
Tel.: (44) 2078320900
Web Site: http://www.challenger.com.au
Sales Range: $25-49.9 Million
Emp.: 15
Business Services
N.A.I.C.S.: 561499

Challenger Managed Investments
Ltd　　　　　　　　　　　　　　(1)
Level 2 5 Martin Place, Sydney, 2000,
NSW, Australia　　　　　　　(100%)
Tel.: (61) 299947000
Web Site: http://www.challenger.com.au
Sales Range: $50-74.9 Million
Emp.: 35
Miscellaneous Financial Investment Activi-
ties
N.A.I.C.S.: 523999

Challenger Portfolio Management
Limited　　　　　　　　　　　　(1)
Level 2 5 Martin Place, Sydney, 2000,
NSW, Australia　　　　　　　(100%)
Tel.: (61) 299947000
Web Site: http://www.challenger.com.au
Sales Range: $75-99.9 Million
Emp.: 500
Other Management Consulting Services
N.A.I.C.S.: 541618

Challenger Property Asset Manage-
ment Pty Limited　　　　　　　(1)
Level 2 5 Martin Place, Sydney, 2000,
NSW, Australia　　　　　　　(100%)
Tel.: (61) 299947000
Web Site: http://www.challengergroup.com
Sales Range: $25-49.9 Million
Emp.: 700
Management Services
N.A.I.C.S.: 562998

Fidante Partners Europe Limited　(1)
Bridge House L3 181 Queen Victoria Street,
London, EC4V 4EG, United Kingdom
Tel.: (44) 2078320900
Web Site: http://www.fidante.com
Emp.: 216
Investment Services
N.A.I.C.S.: 523999
John O'Keeffe (Head-Strategy & Dev)

CHALLENGER MOTOR FREIGHT INC.

300 Maple Grove Rd, Cambridge,
N3E 1B7, ON, Canada
Tel.: (519) 653-6226
Web Site: http://www.challenger.com
Year Founded: 1975
Sales Range: $150-199.9 Million
Emp.: 1,300
Trucking Operator
N.A.I.C.S.: 484110
Daniel Einwechter (Founder, Chm,
Pres & CEO)

CHALLENGER TECHNOLO-GIES LTD.
1 Ubi Link Challenger TecHub, Singa-
pore, 408553, Singapore
Tel.: (65) 63189800
Web Site:
　　http://www.challengerasia.com
Year Founded: 1984
573—(SES)
Rev.: $213,778,060
Assets: $165,084,760
Liabilities: $42,549,354
Net Worth: $122,535,406
Earnings: $13,435,446
Emp.: 271
Fiscal Year-end: 12/31/21
IT Products Retailer
N.A.I.C.S.: 449210
Leong Thye Loo (CEO)

Subsidiaries:

CBD eVision Pte Ltd　　　　　　(1)
1 Ubi Link, Singapore, 408553, Singapore
Tel.: (65) 6 288 8233
Web Site: https://www.cbd-evision.com
Sales Range: $25-49.9 Million
Emp.: 6
LED Technology Mfr
N.A.I.C.S.: 334413

Challenger Technologies (M) Sdn
Bhd　　　　　　　　　　　　　　(1)
L4 16 4th Fl Mines Shopping Fair Jalan Du-
lang Mines Resort City, Mines Resort City,
Seri Kembangan, 43300, Malaysia
Tel.: (60) 389469000
Web Site: http://www.challenger.my
Sales Range: $25-49.9 Million
Emp.: 50
Software Services
N.A.I.C.S.: 513210

Incall Systems Pte. Ltd.　　　　(1)
89C Science Park Drive 01-09 The Ruther-
ford, Singapore, 118261, Singapore
Tel.: (65) 6 893 3303
Web Site: https://www.incallsystems.com
Customer Interaction Centre Services
N.A.I.C.S.: 561422
Fiona Yeo (Dir-Sls & Mktg)

Valore (Shenzhen) Private
Limited　　　　　　　　　　　　(1)
Room 4302 Century Plaza No 3018 Shen-
nan Middle Road, FuTian District, Shen-
zhen, Guangdong, China
Tel.: (86) 75583835270
Web Site: http://www.valore.en.china.cn
Emp.: 100
Electronic Accessory Product Mfr
N.A.I.C.S.: 334419

CHALMERS GROUP OF COM-PANIES
6400 Northam Drive, Mississauga,
L4V1J1, ON, Canada
Tel.: (905) 362-6400
Web Site:
　　http://www.chalmersgroup.com
Holding Company
N.A.I.C.S.: 551112
H. S. Takhar (Chm & CEO)

Subsidiaries:

Lynx Product Group, LLC.　　　(1)
650 Lake St, Wilson, NY 14172
Tel.: (716) 751-3100
Sales Range: $1-9.9 Million
Emp.: 38
Commercial & Pressing Machine Mfr

N.A.I.C.S.: 333310
Donald Basil *(Pres)*

Primus Sterilizer Company, LLC **(1)**
8719 S 135th St Ste 300, Omaha, NE
68138
Tel.: (402) 344-4200
Web Site: http://www.primus-sterilizer.com
Dental Equipment & Supplies Mfr
N.A.I.C.S.: 339114
Dave Schall *(Dir-Sls)*

CHAM BANK
Al-Najmeh Square, PO Box 33979,
Damascus, Syria
Tel.: (963) 11 33919
Web Site: http://www.chambank.sy
Year Founded: 2006
Commercial Banking Services
N.A.I.C.S.: 522110
Ali Yousef ALawadi *(Chm)*

CHAM FOODS (ISRAEL) LTD.
1 Ha-Barzel st, Tel Aviv, 69710, Israel
Tel.: (972) 4 911 4436
Web Site: http://www.cham.co.il
Year Founded: 1971
CHAM—(TAE)
Rev.: $7,432,917
Assets: $9,858,389
Liabilities: $4,539,492
Net Worth: $5,318,897
Earnings: $234,132
Emp.: 700
Fiscal Year-end: 12/31/20
Food Ingredient Mfr
N.A.I.C.S.: 311999

CHAM GROUP AG
Fabrikstrasse 5, CH-6330, Cham,
Switzerland
Tel.: (41) 41 5080820   CH
Web Site: http://chamgroup.ch
Rev.: $3,749,608
Assets: $399,128,859
Liabilities: $76,454,182
Net Worth: $322,674,677
Earnings: $45,611,362
Emp.: 13
Fiscal Year-end: 12/31/20
Holding Company; Specialty Coated
Papers Developer, Mfr & Distr
N.A.I.C.S.: 551112
Philipp Buhofer *(Chm)*

Subsidiaries:

Cham Immobilien AG   **(1)**
Fabrikstrasse, 6330, Cham,
Switzerland   **(100%)**
Tel.: (41) 415080820
Web Site: http://chamgroup.ch
Industrial Real Estate Investment & Development
N.A.I.C.S.: 531390
Lukas Fehr *(Head-Dev)*

Cham Paper Group Schweiz AG   **(1)**
Fabrikstrasse, Cham, 6330,
Switzerland   **(100%)**
Tel.: (41) 41 785 3333
Web Site: http://www.champaper.ch
Sales Range: $150-199.9 Million
Emp.: 40
Coated Specialty Papers Mfr & Distr
N.A.I.C.S.: 322120
Susanne Oste *(Mng Dir)*

Industrieverwaltungsgesellschaft
Cham AG   **(1)**
Fabrikstrasse, Cham, 6330, ZG, Switzerland
Tel.: (41) 417 853333
Sales Range: $150-199.9 Million
Emp.: 35
Intellectual Property Administrative Services
N.A.I.C.S.: 533110

CHAMAK HOLDINGS LTD.
55-B Rama Road Industrial Area,
New Delhi, 110 015, India
Tel.: (91) 1145691047

Web Site:
http://www.chamakholdings.com
Year Founded: 1984
539600—(BOM)
Rev.: $10,730,740
Assets: $3,189,963
Liabilities: $2,871,381
Net Worth: $318,582
Earnings: $176,066
Emp.: 7
Fiscal Year-end: 03/31/21
Holding Company
N.A.I.C.S.: 551112
Anubhav Kathuria *(Mng Dir)*

CHAMAN LAL SETIA EXPORT LTD.
530307—(BOM)
Rev.: $127,813,222
Assets: $84,764,425
Liabilities: $28,860,550
Net Worth: $55,903,875
Earnings: $8,869,483
Emp.: 196
Fiscal Year-end: 03/31/22
Basmati Rice Mfr & Distr
N.A.I.C.S.: 311212
Vijay Kumar Setia *(Chm & Co-Mng Dir)*

CHAMBAL BREWERIES & DISTILLERIES LIMITED
House No 30 2nd Floor DAV School
Kei Pass, Talwandi, Kota, 324005,
Rajasthan, India
Tel.: (91) 7443500607
Web Site:
https://www.chambalkota.in
Year Founded: 1985
512301—(BOM)
Rev.: $14,617
Assets: $502,821
Liabilities: $1,733
Net Worth: $501,088
Earnings: ($50,970)
Emp.: 3
Fiscal Year-end: 03/31/23
Beer & Liquor Whslr
N.A.I.C.S.: 424810
Vinod Jhamnani *(CFO)*

CHAMBERLIN PLC
Chuckery Road, Walsall, WS1 2DU,
West Midlands, United Kingdom
Tel.: (44) 1922707100   UK
Web Site:
http://www.chamberlin.co.uk
Year Founded: 1890
CMH—(LSE)
Rev.: $20,906,945
Assets: $15,811,839
Liabilities: $15,305,185
Net Worth: $506,654
Earnings: $89,410
Emp.: 185
Fiscal Year-end: 03/31/22
Holding Company; Metal Castings &
Engineered Products Mfr
N.A.I.C.S.: 551112
Neil Davies *(Sec & Dir-Fin)*

Subsidiaries:

Chamberlin & Hill Castings
Limited   **(1)**
Chuckery Road, Walsall, WS1 2DU, W Midlands, United Kingdom
Tel.: (44) 1922 721 411
Web Site: http://www.chcastings.co.uk
Non-Ferrous Die Castings Foundry
N.A.I.C.S.: 331523

Petrel Limited   **(1)**
22 Fortnum Close Mackadown Lane Kitts
Green, Birmingham, B33 0LB, West Midlands, United Kingdom   **(100%)**
Tel.: (44) 121 783 7161
Web Site: http://www.petrel-ex.co.uk
Emp.: 50

Hazardous Area Lighting & Control Equipment Mfr & Distr
N.A.I.C.S.: 335132
Tony Glasscoe *(Mng Dir)*

Russell Ductile Castings Limited   **(1)**
Dawes Lane, Scunthorpe, DN15 6UW,
United Kingdom   **(100%)**
Tel.: (44) 1724862152
Web Site: http://www.russellductile.co.uk
Sales Range: $25-49.9 Million
Emp.: 100
Ductile & Gray Iron Castings Foundry
N.A.I.C.S.: 331511

CHAMBERS & COOK FREIGHT LTD.
European House Perrywell Road,
Witton, Birmingham, B6 7AT, United
Kingdom
Tel.: (44) 1213561441   UK
Web Site: http://www.ccfreight.com
Year Founded: 1925
Sales Range: $10-24.9 Million
Emp.: 89
Freight Transportation & Logistics
Services
N.A.I.C.S.: 484110
Chris Blackburn *(Dir-Ops)*

CHAMP PRIVATE EQUITY PTY. LTD.
Level 23 Aurora Place 88 Phillip
Street, Sydney, 2000, NSW, Australia
Tel.: (61) 282488888   AU
Web Site:
http://www.champequity.com.au
Year Founded: 2000
Privater Equity Firm
N.A.I.C.S.: 523999
Cameron Buchanan *(Mng Dir-Investment)*

Subsidiaries:

ATF Services Pty. Ltd.   **(1)**
9 Harbord St, Clyde, Granville, 2142, NSW,
Australia
Tel.: (61) 2 8860 8100
Web Site: http://www.atfservices.com.au
Fencing Services
N.A.I.C.S.: 238990

Alleasing Pty Ltd   **(1)**
Level 5 88 Phillip Street, Sydney, 2000,
NSW, Australia
Tel.: (61) 2 9850 5100
Web Site: http://www.alleasing.com.au
Asset Management & Financial leasing Services
N.A.I.C.S.: 541618
Peter Grover *(Head-Northern Reg)*

Blue Star Print Group Limited   **(1)**
30 Constellation Drive Mairangi Bay, Auckland, New Zealand   **(84%)**
Tel.: (64) 94770400
Web Site: http://www.bluestargroup.com.au
Sales Range: $400-449.9 Million
Emp.: 12
Printing Services
N.A.I.C.S.: 323111
Greg Howell *(CEO)*

CHAMP Private Equity Pte. Ltd.   **(1)**
50 Raffles Place Suite 32-01 Singapore
Land Tower, Singapore, 48623, Singapore
Tel.: (65) 6576 9179
Financial Management Services
N.A.I.C.S.: 523999
Maureen Lim *(Sr Accountant)*

Centric Wealth Group   **(1)**
10 O'Connell Street, Sydney, 2000, NSW,
Australia
Tel.: (61) 2 9250 6500
Web Site: http://www.centricwealth.com.au
Investment Advisory Services
N.A.I.C.S.: 523940
Terry Paule *(Chm)*

Jaybro Group Pty. Ltd.   **(1)**
29 Penelope Crescent, Arndell Park, 2148,
NSW, Australia
Tel.: (61) 300 885 364
Web Site: http://www.jaybro.com.au

Construction Supplies Distr
N.A.I.C.S.: 423490
Jeremy Joyce *(CEO & Mng Dir)*

Miclyn Express Offshore Limited   **(1)**
10 Hoe Chiang Road 09-01 Keppel Towers,
Singapore, 089315, Singapore   **(50%)**
Tel.: (65) 65456211
Web Site: http://www.meogroup.com
Rev.: $161,050,000
Assets: $830,831,000
Liabilities: $544,029,000
Net Worth: $286,802,000
Earnings: ($96,143,000)
Emp.: 1,500
Fiscal Year-end: 06/30/2017
Offshore Support Vessels
N.A.I.C.S.: 488390
Diederik de Boer *(Exec Dir)*

Pepperstone Group Limited   **(1)**
Level 5 530 Collins Street, Melbourne,
3000, VIC, Australia
Tel.: (61) 3 9020 0155
Web Site: http://www.pepperstone.com
Foreign Exchange & Contract For Difference Brokerage Services
N.A.I.C.S.: 523160
Tamas Szabo *(CEO)*

CHAMPADOR
Avenue Jean Ducourtieux, 24530,
Champagnac-de-Belair, Dordogne,
France
Tel.: (33) 553026363
Web Site:
http://champador.pagesperso-orange.fr
Rev.: $21,800,000
Emp.: 220
Cookies & Crackers
N.A.I.C.S.: 311821
Alain Teot *(Pres)*

CHAMPAGNE ALAIN THIENOT S.A.S.
14 Rue Des Moissons, Reims, 51100,
France
Tel.: (33) 326775010
Web Site: http://www.thienot.com
Sales Range: $100-124.9 Million
Winery Services
N.A.I.C.S.: 312130

Subsidiaries:

Champagne Canard-Duchene
S.A.   **(1)**
1 Rue Edmond Canard, 51500, Ludes,
France   **(100%)**
Tel.: (33) 326610998
Web Site: http://www.canard-duchene.fr
Sales Range: $25-49.9 Million
Emp.: 15
Champagne Mfr
N.A.I.C.S.: 312130
Alexis Petit Gats *(Mgr)*

CHAMPAGNE HENRIOT
81 Rue Coquebert, 51100, Reims,
Marne, France
Tel.: (33) 326895300
Web Site: http://www.champagne-henriot.com
Rev.: $20,700,000
Emp.: 27
Wines, Brandy & Brandy Spirits
N.A.I.C.S.: 312130
Catherine Guerlet *(Mgr-Fin)*

CHAMPAGNE LAURENT-PERRIER
Domaine Laurent Perrier, 51150,
Tours-sur-Marne, France
Tel.: (33) 326589122
Web Site: http://www.laurent-perrier.com
Year Founded: 1812
Sales Range: $250-299.9 Million
Emp.: 200
Champagne Producer
N.A.I.C.S.: 312130

Champagne Laurent-Perrier—(Continued)

Stephane Dalyac *(Chm-Mgmt Bd)*

Subsidiaries:

Laurent-Perrier UK Ltd. **(1)**
66-68 Chapel Street, Marlow, SL7 1DE,
Bucks, United Kingdom **(100%)**
Tel.: (44) 1628475404
Web Site: http://www.laurent-perrier.co.uk
Sales Range: $25-49.9 Million
Emp.: 20
Importer & Exporter of Champagne
N.A.I.C.S.: 424820
David Hesketh *(Mng Dir)*

CHAMPAGNE POL ROGER

1 Rue Henri Winston Churchill, BP
199, 51206, Epernay, France
Tel.: (33) 326595800
Web Site: http://www.polroger.com
Rev.: $28,100,000
Emp.: 52
Wines, Brandy & Brandy Spirits
N.A.I.C.S.: 312130
Patrice Noyelle *(Pres & CEO)*

CHAMPION BEAR RE-SOURCES LTD.

2005 - 9th Street SW, Calgary, T2T
3C4, AB, Canada
Tel.: (403) 229-9522
Web Site:
  https://www.championbear.com
Year Founded: 1987
CBA—(TSXV)
Rev.: $56,634
Assets: $3,796,045
Liabilities: $2,497,051
Net Worth: $1,298,994
Earnings: ($235,870)
Fiscal Year-end: 12/31/23
Mineral Exploration Services
N.A.I.C.S.: 213114
Richard D. Kantor *(Pres)*

CHAMPION BUILDING MATE-RIALS CO., LTD.

No 2007 Linzhupengcuo No 13 Da-puli, Miaoli, Zhunan, Taiwan
Tel.: (886) 37583775
Web Site:
  https://www.champion.com.tw
1806—(TAI)
Rev.: $102,608,224
Assets: $263,047,997
Liabilities: $84,908,496
Net Worth: $178,139,501
Earnings: $13,375
Emp.: 1,753
Fiscal Year-end: 12/31/23
Construction Material & Tile Mfr
N.A.I.C.S.: 327120
Jung Te Lin *(CEO)*

CHAMPION ELECTRIC MET-ALS INC.

401 Bay St Suite 2704, Toronto, M5H
2Y4, ON, Canada
Tel.: (416) 567-9087   Ca
Web Site: https://www.champem.com
Year Founded: 1978
CHELF—(OTCQB)
Assets: $936,546
Liabilities: $311,076
Net Worth: $625,470
Earnings: ($1,976,653)
Emp.: 1
Fiscal Year-end: 12/31/22
Gold Exploration Services
N.A.I.C.S.: 213114
Bruce Reid *(Chm)*

CHAMPION IRON LIMITED

91 Evans Street, Rozelle, 2039,
NSW, Australia
Tel.: (61) 298107816   AU

Web Site:
  https://www.championiron.com
Year Founded: 2006
CIAFF—(OTCQX)
Rev.: $1,040,735,648
Assets: $1,727,190,674
Liabilities: $785,213,490
Net Worth: $941,977,184
Earnings: $149,727,422
Emp.: 1,014
Fiscal Year-end: 03/31/23
Iron Ore Exploration & Mining Development
N.A.I.C.S.: 213114
Jorge Estepa *(Co-Sec)*

Subsidiaries:

Champion Iron Limited - Toronto
Head Office **(1)**
20 Adelaide St E Ste 200, Toronto, M5C
2T6, ON, Canada
Tel.: (416) 866-2200
Web Site:
  http://www.championironmines.com
Sales Range: $25-49.9 Million
Corporate Office; Iron Ore Exploration &
Mining Development Services
N.A.I.C.S.: 551114
Alexandre Belleau *(COO)*

CHAMPION MICROELEC-TRONIC CORP.

5F No 11 Yuanqu 2nd Rd East Dist,
East District, Hsin-chu, 300, Taiwan
Tel.: (886) 35679979
Web Site:
  https://www.championmicro.com.tw
Year Founded: 1999
3257—(TAI)
Rev.: $35,118,544
Assets: $61,281,302
Liabilities: $7,086,268
Net Worth: $54,195,034
Earnings: $8,156,251
Emp.: 73
Fiscal Year-end: 12/31/23
Semiconductor Devices Mfr
N.A.I.C.S.: 334413

Subsidiaries:

Champion Microelectronic **(1)**
960 Saratoga Ave Ste 125, San Jose, CA
95129
Tel.: (408) 985-1898
Web Site: https://www.champion-micro.com
Semiconductor & Related Device Mfr
N.A.I.C.S.: 334413

CHAMPION REAL ESTATE IN-VESTMENT TRUST

Suite 3008 30th Floor Great Eagle
Centre 23 Harbour Road, Wanchai,
China (Hong Kong)
Tel.: (852) 28791288   HK
Web Site:
  https://www.championreit.com
CMPNF—(OTCIQ)
Rev.: $335,515,866
Assets: $8,336,278,579
Liabilities: $2,300,549,797
Net Worth: $6,035,728,782
Earnings: ($245,091,569)
Emp.: 18
Fiscal Year-end: 12/31/22
Real Estate Investment Trust
N.A.I.C.S.: 525990
Ka Shui Lo *(Chm)*

CHAMPION TECHNOLOGY HOLDINGS LTD

Units 4214-15 42nd Floor 188 Con-naught Road West, Shek Tong Tsui,
Hong Kong, China (Hong Kong)
Tel.: (852) 29096288
Web Site: http://www.tricor.com.hk
CPIHF—(OTCIQ)
Rev.: $7,863,782
Assets: $23,093,224

Liabilities: $3,795,365
Net Worth: $19,297,859
Earnings: ($6,469,637)
Emp.: 28
Fiscal Year-end: 06/30/22
Software Devolement
N.A.I.C.S.: 513210
Lim Ka Liu *(Exec Dir)*

Subsidiaries:

Hong Kong IT Alliance Limited **(1)**
Unit 701 7/F No 1 Ning Foo Street, Chai
Wan, China (Hong Kong)
Tel.: (852) 28968838
Web Site: http://www.hkitalliance.com
Information Technology Development Services
N.A.I.C.S.: 541512
Paul Kan Man-Lok *(Chm)*

Kannet Limited **(1)**
3 F Kantone Ctr 1 Ning Foo St, Chai Wan,
China (Hong Kong)
Tel.: (852) 28971111
Web Site: http://www.kannethk.com
News & Entertainment Website Portals
N.A.I.C.S.: 516210
Walter Wellington *(Pres)*

Kantone Holdings Ltd **(1)**
Unit 4213 42nd Floor Hong Kong Plaza 188
Connaught Road West, No 168-200 Con-naught Road Central, Hong Kong, China
(Hong Kong) **(59.04%)**
Tel.: (852) 28971111
Web Site: http://www.tricor.com.hk
Rev.: $16,477,840
Assets: $20,507,433
Liabilities: $3,317,108
Net Worth: $17,190,325
Earnings: $587,891
Emp.: 167
Fiscal Year-end: 06/30/2022
Network Equipment
N.A.I.C.S.: 517112
Stephen Alan Gentry *(CEO-Multitone)*

Subsidiary (Domestic):

Kantone Paging Company
Limited **(2)**
3 F Kantone Ctr No 1 Ning Foo St, Chai
Wan, China (Hong Kong)
Tel.: (852) 28969399
Emp.: 100
Pagers Sales & Paging Services
N.A.I.C.S.: 449210

Subsidiary (Non-US):

Multiton Elektronik GmbH **(2)**
Rossstr 11, 40476, Dusseldorf,
Germany **(100%)**
Tel.: (49) 21 146 9020
Web Site: https://www.multitone.de
Sales Range: $25-49.9 Million
Emp.: 50
Electrical Equipment & Component Mfr
N.A.I.C.S.: 335999
Stephen Gentry *(Mng Dir)*

Multiton Electronics Plc **(2)**
Multitone House Shortwood Copse Lane,
Shortwood Copse Lane Hampshire, Basing-stoke, RG23 7NL, United Kingdom
Tel.: (44) 125 632 0292
Web Site: https://www.multitone.com
Emp.: 180
Radio & Television Broadcasting & Wireless
Communications Equipment Mfr
N.A.I.C.S.: 334220
Stephen Gentry *(CEO)*

Y28.COM Limited **(1)**
3 F Kantone Ctr 1 Ning Foo St, Chai Wan,
China (Hong Kong)
Tel.: (852) 28986668
Web Site: http://www.y28.com
News & Entertainment Website Portals
N.A.I.C.S.: 516210

CHAMPIONS (UK) PLC.

Barrington House Leake Road
Costock, Loughborough, LE12 6XA,
Leicestershire, United Kingdom
Tel.: (44) 1509 85 29 27

Web Site:
  http://www.championsukplc.com
Year Founded: 2003
Sales Range: $10-24.9 Million
Emp.: 60
Brand Management Agency Services
N.A.I.C.S.: 926150
Matthew Hayes *(Mng Dir)*

CHAMPLAIN FINANCIAL COR-PORATION

1000 Rue Sherbrooke Ouest Bureau
1700, Montreal, H3A 3G4, QC,
Canada
Tel.: (514) 282-3585
Web Site:
  http://www.champlaincanada.com
Year Founded: 2004
Privater Equity Firm
N.A.I.C.S.: 523999
Pierre Simard *(Pres)*

Subsidiaries:

Naya Waters Inc. **(1)**
214 4 - 2030 boulevard Pie IX, Montreal,
H1V 2C8, QC, Canada
Tel.: (450) 562-7911
Web Site: http://www.naya.com
Sales Range: $25-49.9 Million
Retail of Natural Spring Water
N.A.I.C.S.: 312112

CHAMPLAIN MOTORS LTD.

1810 Main St W, Moncton, E1E 4S7,
NB, Canada
Tel.: (506) 857-1800
Web Site:
  http://www.champlain.nissan.ca
Year Founded: 1971
Rev.: $12,346,183
Emp.: 30
New & Used Car Dealers
N.A.I.C.S.: 441110
Terry Gibson *(Gen Mgr)*

CHAMS HOLDING COMPANY

8 Louis Solomon Street Victoria Is-land, Lagos, Nigeria
Tel.: (234) 9053936425
Web Site: https://www.chamsplc.com
Year Founded: 1985
CHAMS—(NIGE)
Rev.: $10,914,219
Assets: $21,497,549
Liabilities: $10,559,137
Net Worth: $10,938,412
Earnings: $22,879
Emp.: 19
Fiscal Year-end: 12/31/31
Computer System Design Services
N.A.I.C.S.: 541512
Mayowa Olaniyan *(Exec Dir)*

Subsidiaries:

Card Center Ltd. **(1)**
8 Louis Solomon Close Victoria Island, La-gos, Nigeria
Tel.: (234) 8080345389
Web Site: https://cardcentre.com.ng
Computer Storage Device Mfr & Distr
N.A.I.C.S.: 334112

Card Centre Nigeria Limited **(1)**
8 Louis Solomon Close Victoria Island, La-gos, Nigeria
Tel.: (234) 8080345389
Smart Card Distribution Services
N.A.I.C.S.: 561990

Chams Access Limited **(1)**
8 Louis Solomon Close Victoria Island, La-gos, Nigeria
Tel.: (234) 12914988
Web Site: https://chamsaccess.com
Information Technology Services
N.A.I.C.S.: 541511

Chams Switch Limited **(1)**
8 Louis Solomon Close Victoria Island,
106104, Lagos, Nigeria
Tel.: (234) 8033944566

Information Technology Services
N.A.I.C.S.: 541511
Emmanuel Ojo *(Mng Dir)*

CHANDIS
Centre Du Grand Pin, 72560,
Change, Sarthe, France
Tel.: (33) 243783010
Rev.: $20,900,000
Emp.: 66
Grocery Stores
N.A.I.C.S.: 445110
Samuel Chevallier *(Pres)*

CHANDLER CORPORATION
Level 46 UOB Plaza 1 80 Raffles
Place, Singapore, 048624, Singapore
Tel.: (65) 6210 5555
Web Site:
http://www.chandlergroup.com
Year Founded: 1986
Investment Holding Company
N.A.I.C.S.: 551112
Richard F. Chandler *(Founder &
Chm)*

**CHANDRA BHAGAT PHARMA
LTD.**
323-F Bhagat Bhuvan Dr Ambedkar
Rd, Matunga East, Mumbai, 400019,
Maharashtra, India
Tel.: (91) 2224146154
Web Site:
https://www.cbcpharma.com
Year Founded: 1944
542934—(BOM)
Pharmaceuticals Product Mfr
N.A.I.C.S.: 325412
Prachi Pranav Bhagat *(CFO)*

**CHANDRA PRABHU INTERNA-
TIONAL LTD.**
14 Rani Jhansi Road, New Delhi,
110055, India
Tel.: (91) 1123516567
Web Site: https://www.cpil.com
530309—(BOM)
Rev.: $30,852,455
Assets: $4,964,687
Liabilities: $2,339,585
Net Worth: $2,625,101
Earnings: $779,435
Emp.: 16
Fiscal Year-end: 03/31/21
Petrochemical Products Mfr
N.A.I.C.S.: 325110
Amar Singh *(CFO)*

**CHANDRIMA MERCANTILES
LIMITED**
B-712 Seven Floor Tiitanium City
Center Near Sachin Tower, 100 Feet
Anandnagar Road, Ahmedabad,
380015, Gujarat, India
Tel.: (91) 9157877415
Web Site:
https://chandrimamercantiles.co.in
540829—(BOM)
Rev.: $2,706,264
Assets: $2,249,988
Liabilities: $2,261,051
Net Worth: ($11,063)
Earnings: $2,052
Fiscal Year-end: 03/31/22
Investment Management Service
N.A.I.C.S.: 523940
Pranav Trivedi *(Mng Dir & CFO)*

CHANEL S.A.
135 Ave Charles De Gaulle, 92521,
Neuilly-sur-Seine, Cedex, France
Tel.: (33) 146434000
Web Site: http://www.chanel.com
Sales Range: $5-14.9 Billion
Emp.: 2,000

Cosmetics, Fragrances & Clothing
Mfr
N.A.I.C.S.: 315210
Gerard Wertheimer *(Co-Owner)*
Subsidiaries:

Barrie Knitwear Ltd.   **(1)**
Burnfoot Indust Est, Hawick, TD9 8RJ,
Scotland, United Kingdom   **(100%)**
Tel.: (44) 1450365500
Web Site: http://www.barrie.co.uk
Sales Range: $50-74.9 Million
Emp.: 200
Cashmere Knitwear & Apparel Designer,
Mfr & Distr
N.A.I.C.S.: 315990
Clive Brown *(Dir-Sls)*

Chanel, Inc.   **(1)**
9 W 57th St Fl 44, New York, NY 10019-
2701
Tel.: (212) 688-5055
Web Site: http://www.chanel.com
Sales Range: $200-249.9 Million
Emp.: 300
Fragrances, Cosmetics & Mens & Womens
Accessories Mfr
N.A.I.C.S.: 325620
Cathy Yang *(Dir-Bus Intelligence Sys)*

Subsidiary (Domestic):

Fragrances Exclusive Inc.   **(2)**
600 Madison Ave, New York, NY
10022-1615   **(100%)**
Tel.: (212) 891-5100
Sales Range: $25-49.9 Million
Emp.: 12
Distr of Fragrances
N.A.I.C.S.: 424210

St. Supery, Inc.   **(2)**
8440 St Helena Hwy, Rutherford, CA 94573
Tel.: (707) 963-4507
Web Site: http://www.stsupery.com
Sales Range: $1-9.9 Million
Emp.: 60
Vineyard & Winery
N.A.I.C.S.: 312130
Emma J. Swain *(CEO)*

**CHANG CHUN EURASIA
GROUP CO., LTD.**
No 1128 Gongnong Road, Changc-
hun, 130012, Jilin, China
Tel.: (86) 43187666905
Web Site:
https://www.eurasiagroup.com.cn
Year Founded: 1992
600697—(SHG)
Rev.: $971,619,906
Assets: $2,988,275,411
Liabilities: $2,377,430,013
Net Worth: $610,845,398
Earnings: ($22,379,816)
Fiscal Year-end: 12/31/22
Departmental Store Operator
N.A.I.C.S.: 455110
Heping Cao *(Chm)*

**CHANG HWA COMMERCIAL
BANK LTD.**
No 57 Sec 2 Zhongshan N Rd,
Zhongshan Dist, Taipei, 10412, Tai-
wan
Tel.: (886) 25362951
Web Site: https://www.bankchb.com
2801—(TAI)
Rev.: $2,027,422,662
Assets: $90,700,501,485
Liabilities: $84,822,439,515
Net Worth: $5,878,061,970
Earnings: $405,907,576
Emp.: 6,734
Fiscal Year-end: 12/31/23
Commercial Banking Services
N.A.I.C.S.: 522110
Cheng-Ching Wu *(Mng Dir)*
Subsidiaries:

CHB Insurance Brokerage Company,
Ltd.   **(1)**

6th Floor 57 Sec 2 Chung Shan N Road,
Taipei, 104, Taiwan
Tel.: (886) 225362951
Sales Range: $1-4.9 Billion
Emp.: 6,000
Insurance Agencies & Brokerages
N.A.I.C.S.: 524210
Frank Chen *(Pres)*

CHB Life Insurance Agency Com-
pany, Ltd.   **(1)**
6th Floor 57 Sec 2, Chung Shan N Road,
Taipei, Taiwan
Tel.: (886) 225362951
Web Site: http://www.chb.com.tw
Sales Range: $10-24.9 Million
Insurance Agencies & Brokerages
N.A.I.C.S.: 524210

Chang Hwa Bank (Taichung)   **(1)**
2 Tsu Yu Rd, Taichung, 40045, Taiwan
Tel.: (886) 422230001
Commercial Banking Services
N.A.I.C.S.: 522110

Chang Hwa Bank (Taipei)   **(1)**
No 57 Sec 2 Zhongshan N Rd, Zhongshan
Dist, Taipei, 10412, Taiwan
Tel.: (886) 22 536 2951
Web Site: http://www.chb.com.tw
Sales Range: $350-399.9 Million
Emp.: 800
Commercial Banking Services
N.A.I.C.S.: 522110

Chang Hwa Commercial Bank - New
York Branch   **(1)**
685 3rd Ave 29th Fl, New York, NY 10017
Tel.: (212) 651-9769
Rev.: $6,923,000
Emp.: 25
Commericial Banking
N.A.I.C.S.: 522110
James Chen *(Mgr)*

Chang Hwa International
Banking   **(1)**
7th Fl No 57 Sec 2 Chung Shan N Road, Tai-
pei, 10412, Taiwan
Tel.: (886) 225621919
Commericial Banking
N.A.I.C.S.: 522110

**CHANG JIA M&E ENGINEER-
ING CORP.**
8F No 1 Ln 10 Jihu Rd, Neihu Dist,
Taipei, Taiwan
Tel.: (886) 266066789
Year Founded: 1993
4550—(TPE)
Rev.: $42,377,263
Assets: $54,271,394
Liabilities: $26,588,938
Net Worth: $27,682,456
Earnings: $3,346,590
Fiscal Year-end: 12/31/22
Mechanical & Electrical Engineering
Services
N.A.I.C.S.: 541330
Alvin Wang *(Chm)*

**CHANG TYPE INDUSTRIAL
CO., LTD.**
No 41 Nan-tsuen Road, Houli Dist,
Taichung, Taiwan
Tel.: (886) 425580669
Web Site: https://www.toty.com.tw
Year Founded: 1989
1541—(TAI)
Rev.: $110,468,945
Assets: $130,097,677
Liabilities: $67,597,859
Net Worth: $62,499,818
Earnings: $3,766,964
Emp.: 278
Fiscal Year-end: 12/31/23
Machine Tools Mfr
N.A.I.C.S.: 333517

**CHANG WAH ELECTRONMA-
TERIALS, INC.**
6F No 16 East 7th St, Nanzih Dist,
Kaohsiung, 811, Taiwan

Tel.: (886) 73622663
Web Site: https://www.cwei.com.tw
Year Founded: 1989
8070—(TAI)
Emp.: 78
Electronic Products Mfr
N.A.I.C.S.: 334419
Canon Huang *(Pres & Gen Mgr)*

**CHANG WAH TECHNOLOGY
CO., LTD.**
811 No 24 Kaifa Rd, Nanzi Dist, Ka-
ohsiung, 811, Taiwan
Tel.: (886) 79628202
Web Site:
https://www.cwtcglobal.com
Year Founded: 2009
6548—(TPE)
Rev.: $451,217,334
Assets: $588,708,126
Liabilities: $270,619,986
Net Worth: $318,088,141
Earnings: $88,952,537
Emp.: 2,139
Fiscal Year-end: 12/31/22
Electronic Components Mfr
N.A.I.C.S.: 334419
Chia-Neng Huang *(CEO)*
Subsidiaries:

Malaysian SH Electronics Sdn.
Bhd.   **(1)**
Lot 5 7 & 9 Jalan Ragum 15/17, 40200,
Shah Alam, Selangor, Malaysia
Tel.: (60) 355198140
Semiconductor Materials Mfr & Distr
N.A.I.C.S.: 334413

SH Asia Pacific Pte. Ltd.   **(1)**
10 Eunos Road 8 05-04/05 Singapore Post
Centre, Singapore, 408600, Singapore
Tel.: (65) 69147908
Semiconductor Equipment Mfr & Distr
N.A.I.C.S.: 333242

SH Electronics Chengdu Co.,
Ltd.   **(1)**
No7 Xin Yuan Nan Er Lu, Singapore Indus-
trial Park Chengdu Hi-Tech Development
Zone, Sichuan, 610041, China
Tel.: (86) 2885155577
Semiconductor Equipment Mfr & Distr
N.A.I.C.S.: 333242

SH Electronics Suzhou Co., Ltd.   **(1)**
No 123 Longtan Rd, 3rd District Suzhou
Industrial Park, Suzhou, 215126, China
Tel.: (86) 51262836501
Semiconductor Equipment Mfr & Distr
N.A.I.C.S.: 333242

SH Precision Chengdu Co., Ltd.   **(1)**
No 6 Workshop 8 Kexin Road, Chengdu
Hi-Tech Zone West Park, Sichuan, 611731,
China
Tel.: (86) 2887958880
Semiconductor Equipment Mfr & Distr
N.A.I.C.S.: 333242

Shanghai Chang Wah Electromateri-
als Inc.   **(1)**
21F-1 Zhao Feng Plaza 1027 Changning
Road, Shanghai, 2000050, China
Tel.: (86) 2152419000
Semiconductor Equipment Mfr & Distr
N.A.I.C.S.: 333242

**CHANG YIH CERAMIC JOINT
STOCK COMPANY**
Ton Duc Thang Street Nhon Trach 1
Industrial Park, Nhon Trach, Dong
Nai, Vietnam
Tel.: (84) 2513560770
Web Site: http://www.changyih-
ceramic.com
Year Founded: 2000
Sales Range: $10-24.9 Million
Ceramic Products Mfr
N.A.I.C.S.: 327120
Chen Hui Zun *(Chm)*

**CHANG-HO FIBRE CORPORA-
TION**

Chang-Ho Fibre Corporation—(Continued)

9F No 270 Chung Hsiao E Rd Sec 4,
Taipei, Taiwan
Tel.: (886) 227419299
Web Site: https://www.chang-
ho.com.tw
Year Founded: 1982
1468—(TAI)
Rev.: $34,431,896
Assets: $90,717,973
Liabilities: $49,469,536
Net Worth: $41,248,437
Earnings: $1,830,766
Emp.: 228
Fiscal Year-end: 12/31/23
Fabric Product Mfr
N.A.I.C.S.: 313320

Subsidiaries:

Chang-Ho Fibre Corporation - Nan-
kan Factory　　　　　　　　(1)
No 277 Sec 1 Nankan Rd, Luzhu Township,
Taoyuan, 338, Taiwan
Tel.: (886) 33222248
Textile Mfr
N.A.I.C.S.: 313210

CHANGAN MINSHENG APLL LOGISTICS CO., LTD.
No 1881 Jinkai Road, Yubei District,
Chongqing, 401122, China
Tel.: (86) 2389182222
Web Site: http://www.camsl.com
Year Founded: 2001
1292—(HKG)
Rev.: $1,080,707,940
Assets: $690,242,764
Liabilities: $386,715,654
Net Worth: $303,527,110
Earnings: $6,530,846
Emp.: 4,397
Fiscal Year-end: 12/31/22
Motor Vehicle Parts Distr
N.A.I.C.S.: 423120
Shikang Xie (Chm)

CHANGBAI MOUNTAIN TOUR-ISM CO., LTD.
Changbai Mountain Protection and
Development Zone, Chibei District,
Yanji, 133613, Jilin, China
Tel.: (86) 4335310666
Web Site: https://www.cbmt.com.cn
603099—(SHG)
Rev.: $27,329,506
Assets: $150,268,955
Liabilities: $23,037,969
Net Worth: $127,230,985
Earnings: ($8,056,938)
Emp.: 1,000
Fiscal Year-end: 12/31/22
Tourism Services
N.A.I.C.S.: 561510
Kun Wang (Chm, Pres & Sec-Interim)

CHANGCHAI CO., LTD.
No 123 Huaide Middle Road,
Changzhou, 213002, Jiangsu, China
Tel.: (86) 51986600341
Web Site:
　https://www.changchai.com.cn
Year Founded: 1913
000570—(SSE)
Rev.: $306,358,416
Assets: $732,798,144
Liabilities: $261,451,476
Net Worth: $471,346,668
Earnings: $10,765,872
Emp.: 500
Fiscal Year-end: 12/31/22
Diesel Engine Mfr
N.A.I.C.S.: 333618
He Jianjiang (Sec)

CHANGCHUN GAS CO., LTD.
No 421 Yan an Avenue, Chaoyang

District, Changchun, 130021, Jilin,
China
Tel.: (86) 43185954615
Web Site: http://www.ccrq.com.cn
Year Founded: 1993
600333—(SHG)
Rev.: $266,210,994
Assets: $850,957,829
Liabilities: $561,776,834
Net Worth: $289,180,995
Earnings: ($13,839,172)
Fiscal Year-end: 12/31/22
Coal Product Mfr & Distr
N.A.I.C.S.: 324199
Dong Zhiyu (Sec)

CHANGCHUN GROUP
7th Floor No 301 Songjiang Rd,
Zhongshan District, 10483, Taipei,
Taiwan
Tel.: (886) 225038131
Web Site: http://www.ccp.com.tw
Year Founded: 1949
Sales Range: $350-399.9 Million
Emp.: 1,200
Holding Company
N.A.I.C.S.: 551112
L. S. Liao (Chm)

Subsidiaries:

Chang Chiang Chemical (Shanghai)
Co., Ltd.
Room 708 Lotus Square 1st Building No
7866 HuMin Road, MinHang District,
Shanghai, China
Tel.: (86) 21 6428 4415
Chemical Products Mfr
N.A.I.C.S.: 325199

Chang Chiang Chemical Co.,
Ltd.　　　　　　　　　　　(1)
No 237 16th Fl Songkiang Rd, Taipei, 104,
Taiwan
Tel.: (886) 225097431
Sales Range: $25-49.9 Million
Emp.: 10
Antioxidants & PVC Products
N.A.I.C.S.: 325211

Chang Chun Chemical (JiangSu) Co.,
Ltd.　　　　　　　　　　　(1)
ChangChun road Riverside Industrial Park,
ChangShu Economy Development Zone,
Changshu, China
Tel.: (86) 512 5264 8000
Chemical Products Mfr
N.A.I.C.S.: 325199

Chang Chun Chemical (ZhangZhou)
Co., Ltd.　　　　　　　　　(1)
Baosheng Rd LongChi Development Area,
Zhangzhou, 363107, Fujian, China
Tel.: (86) 596 626 9085
Chemical Products Mfr
N.A.I.C.S.: 325199

Chang Chun Japan Co., Ltd.　(1)
2-8-6 Hon-Cho Nihonbashi, Chuo-Ku, To-
kyo, 103-0023, Japan
Tel.: (81) 3 5847 4521
Chemical Products Distr
N.A.I.C.S.: 424690
Ricky Chan (Gen Mgr)

Chang Chun PetroChemical Co.,
LTD.　　　　　　　　　　　(1)
7th Floor No 301 Songjiang Rd, Zhongshan
District, Taipei, 104070, Taiwan
Tel.: (886) 225001800
Web Site: https://www.ccp.com.tw
Emp.: 200
Chemical Products Mfr
N.A.I.C.S.: 325998

Chang Chun Plastics Co., LTD.　(1)
301 Songkiang Rd 7th Fl, Taipei, 104, Tai-
wan
Tel.: (886) 225038131
Web Site: http://www.ccp.com
Sales Range: $50-74.9 Million
Emp.: 400
Plastics Products
N.A.I.C.S.: 326199

Chang Long Chemical (ShenZhen)
Co., Ltd.　　　　　　　　　(1)
4th Floor No 21 ShiHua Road FuLin Logis-
tics Building, Futian Free Trade Zone,
Shenzhen, 518038, Guangdong, China
Tel.: (86) 755 8359 5716
Chemical Products Mfr
N.A.I.C.S.: 325199

ChangChun PetroChemical Co.,
Ltd.　　　　　　　　　　　(1)
301 Songkiang Rd 7th Fl, Taipei, 104, Tai-
wan
Tel.: (886) 225038131
Web Site: http://www.ccp.com.tw
Sales Range: $125-149.9 Million
Emp.: 800
Chemicals Mfr
N.A.I.C.S.: 325180

Dairen Chemical Corporation　(1)
9th Fl 301 Song Kiang Rd, Taipei, 104,
Taiwan　　　　　　　　　　(60%)
Tel.: (886) 225020238
Web Site: http://www.dcc.com.tw
Sales Range: $25-49.9 Million
Emp.: 90
Chemical Products
N.A.I.C.S.: 325998
Suhon Lin (Chm)

Subsidiary (Non-US):

Dairen Chemical (Jiangsu) Co.
Ltd.　　　　　　　　　　　(2)
1 Dalian Rd, Chemical Industry Park,
Yangzhou, 211900, Jiangsu, China (100%)
Tel.: (86) 51483268888
Web Site: http://www.dcc.com.tw
Sales Range: $50-74.9 Million
Chemicals Mfr
N.A.I.C.S.: 325998

Dairen Chemical (M) Sdn. Bhd.　(2)
Plo 18 Tanjung Langsat Industrial Est, Mu-
kim Sungai Tiram Pasir Gudan, Johor,
81700, Malaysia　　　　　　(100%)
Tel.: (60) 72565800
Web Site: http://www.dcc.com.tw
Sales Range: $25-49.9 Million
Emp.: 70
Chemicals Mfr
N.A.I.C.S.: 325998
Jong Yuh Lih (Mng Dir)

PT. Chang Chun DPN Chemical
Industry　　　　　　　　　(1)
Cikarang Industrial Estate Jl Jababeka XI
Blok G18-G23, Cikarang Bekasi, Jakarta,
17530, Indonesia
Tel.: (62) 218934205
Sales Range: $50-74.9 Million
Emp.: 200
Resins
N.A.I.C.S.: 325211
Chen Leeng Ye (Gen Mgr)

RCCT Technology Co., Ltd.　(1)
301 SongJiang Road 7th Floor, Taipei, 104,
Taiwan　　　　　　　　　　(100%)
Tel.: (886) 225187919
Web Site: http://www.rcct.com.tw
Flexible Copper Clad Laminate; Joint Ven-
ture of Chang Chun Corporation & Rogers
Corporation
N.A.I.C.S.: 326130

Sumitomo Bakelite (Taiwan) Corpora-
tion Limited　　　　　　　　(1)
No 1 Hwa Syi Road, Ta Fa Industries Dis-
trict Ta Liao, Kaohsiung, Taiwan
Tel.: (886) 77871285
Web Site: http://www.sumibe.co.jp
Epoxy Moulding Compound Mfr
N.A.I.C.S.: 325211

TOK Taiwan Co., Ltd.　　　(1)
4F No 95 Beida Rd, Hsin-chu, 30044, Tai-
wan
Tel.: (886) 35345953
Web Site: https://toktaiwan.com
Sales Range: $25-49.9 Million
Emp.: 40
Photolithography Materials Mfr & Supplier;
Owned by ChangChung Group & Tokyo
Ohka Kogyo Co., Ltd.
N.A.I.C.S.: 425120

Tai Hong Circuit Ind. Co., LTD.　(1)
No 81 Guangfu Road, Hsinchu Expanded

Industrial Zone, Hukou, 303, Hsinchu, Tai-
wan
Tel.: (886) 35985111
Web Site: https://www.tci.com.tw
Sales Range: $100-124.9 Million
Emp.: 1,100
Circuit Printing Board; Owned by ChangC-
hun Group, Mitsubishi Gas Chemical Com-
pany, Inc & Japan Printed Circuit Ind Co
N.A.I.C.S.: 334112

Tsu-Kong Co., LTD.　　　　(1)
301 Songkiang Rd 8th Fl, Taipei, 104, Tai-
wan
Tel.: (886) 225020221
Web Site: http://www.ccp.com.tw
Epoxy Moulding Compounds for Semicon-
ductor Encapsulation Mold Cleaner
N.A.I.C.S.: 333511

CHANGCHUN HIGH & NEW TECHNOLOGY INDUSTRY (GROUP) INC.
27F Hairong Plaza, Goxin District,
Changchun, 130021, Jilin, China
Tel.: (86) 80557027
Web Site: https://www.cchn.com.cn
000661—(SSE)
Rev.: $2,016,786,608
Assets: $4,256,708,421
Liabilities: $790,788,810
Net Worth: $3,465,919,611
Earnings: $627,559,191
Fiscal Year-end: 12/31/23
Pharmaceuticals Product Mfr
N.A.I.C.S.: 325412
Ma Ji (Chm)

Subsidiaries:

GeneScience Pharmaceuticals Co.,
Ltd.　　　　　　　　　　　(1)
72 Tianhe Street, Changchun High-tech
Dev Zone, Changchun, 130012, Jilin, China
Tel.: (86) 43185195060
Web Site: http://www.en.gensci-china.com
Pharmaceuticals Product Mfr
N.A.I.C.S.: 325412

CHANGCHUN JILIN UNIVER-SITY ZHENGYUAN INFORMA-TION TECHNOLOGIES CO., LTD.
4 / F AVIC technology building 56
Zhichun Road, Haidian District, Bei-
jing, 100086, China
Tel.: (86) 1062618866
Web Site: https://en.jit.com.cn
Year Founded: 1999
003029—(SSE)
Rev.: $68,961,672
Assets: $257,240,880
Liabilities: $61,625,772
Net Worth: $195,615,108
Earnings: ($4,724,460)
Fiscal Year-end: 12/31/22
Information Technology Services
N.A.I.C.S.: 541512
Fengliang Yu (Chm & Gen Mgr)

CHANGCHUN UP OPTOTECH CO., LTD.
No 588 Yingkou Road, Economic and
Technological Development Zone,
Changchun, 130033, Jilin, China
Tel.: (86) 43186176633
Web Site: https://www.up-china.com
Year Founded: 2001
002338—(SSE)
Rev.: $88,039,224
Assets: $271,119,420
Liabilities: $82,173,312
Net Worth: $188,946,108
Earnings: $11,483,316
Emp.: 700
Fiscal Year-end: 12/31/22
Photoelectric Measurement & Control
Equipment Mfr
N.A.I.C.S.: 333310
Jinsong Gao (Pres)

CHANGCHUN YIDONG CLUTCH CO., LTD.

No 2555 Chaoran Street Hitech Industrial Development Zone, Changchun, 130103, Jilin, China
Tel.: (86) 43185158520
Web Site: http://www.ccyd.com.cn
Year Founded: 1992
600148—(SHG)
Rev.: $77,308,550
Assets: $149,052,487
Liabilities: $62,435,712
Net Worth: $86,616,775
Earnings: ($1,151,617)
Emp.: 1,217
Fiscal Year-end: 12/31/22
Automobile Clutch Mfr
N.A.I.C.S.: 336350
Meng Qinghong *(Chm & Gen Mgr)*

CHANGCHUN ZHIYUAN NEW ENERGY EQUIPMENT CO., LTD.

No 888 Yumin Road Chaoyang Economic Development Zone, Changchun, 130000, Jilin, China
Tel.: (86) 43185011202
Web Site:
https://en.zynewenergy.com
Year Founded: 2014
300985—(SSE)
Rev.: $23,283,936
Assets: $226,331,820
Liabilities: $60,279,336
Net Worth: $166,052,484
Earnings: ($7,239,024)
Fiscal Year-end: 12/31/22
Energy Distribution Services
N.A.I.C.S.: 221122
Yuan Zhang *(Chm)*

CHANGDA INTERNATIONAL HOLDINGS, INC.

10th Floor Chenhong Bldg No 301East Dong Feng St, Weifang, China
Tel.: (86) 536 8513228   NV
Sales Range: $75-99.9 Million
Emp.: 190
Holding Company; Chemical & Microbial Organic-Inorganic Compound Fertilizers Mfr
N.A.I.C.S.: 551112
Leodegario Quinto Camacho *(CFO)*

CHANGE CAPITAL PARTNERS LLP

Thomas House 84 Eccleston Square, London, SW1V 1PX, United Kingdom
Tel.: (44) 2078089110
Web Site:
http://www.changecapital.com
Year Founded: 2003
Sales Range: $25-49.9 Million
Emp.: 15
Privater Equity Firm
N.A.I.C.S.: 523999
Roger Holmes *(Partner)*

CHANGE FINANCIAL LIMITED

Suite 3E Level 3 340 Adelaide St, Brisbane, 4000, QLD, Australia
Tel.: (61) 396618200   AU
Web Site:
https://www.changefinancial.com
Year Founded: 2011
CCA—(ASX)
Rev.: $10,638,843
Assets: $12,944,240
Liabilities: $7,066,092
Net Worth: $5,878,148
Earnings: ($2,569,771)
Fiscal Year-end: 06/30/24
Banking Services
N.A.I.C.S.: 522110
Ian Leijer *(CFO)*

CHANGE, INC.

19F Shiroyama Trust Tower 4-3-1 Toranomon, Minato - ku, Tokyo, 105-0001, Japan
Tel.: (81) 364357348
Web Site: https://www.change-jp.com
Year Founded: 2022
3962—(TKS)
Rev.: $244,669,150
Assets: $590,438,250
Liabilities: $275,392,430
Net Worth: $315,045,820
Earnings: $28,588,250
Fiscal Year-end: 03/31/24
Information Technology Consulting Services
N.A.I.C.S.: 541512
Takehiko Kubo *(Auditor)*

CHANGFENG (GROUP) CO., LTD.

19/F Hualing Mansion No 111 Er Road Furong Middle Road, Changsha, 410011, Hunan, China
Tel.: (86) 7462881664
Year Founded: 1950
Sales Range: $900-999.9 Million
Emp.: 3,600
Holding Company; Automobile Mfr
N.A.I.C.S.: 551112
Jianxin Li *(Chm)*

Subsidiaries:

Anhui Changfeng Yangzi Automobile
Manufacturing Co., Ltd,   (1)
Yangzi Industrial Zone, Chuzhou, Anhui, China
Tel.: (86) 550 3160498
Web Site: http://www.cfyzmotor.com
Sales Range: $200-249.9 Million
Emp.: 900
Automobile Mfr
N.A.I.C.S.: 336110

CHANGGAO ELECTRIC GROUP CO., LTD.

NO 393 Jinxingbei Road, Wangcheng District, Changsha, 410219, Hunan, China
Tel.: (86) 73188585095
Web Site:
https://www.changgaogroup.com
Year Founded: 1998
002452—(SSE)
Rev.: $171,695,160
Assets: $456,999,192
Liabilities: $161,672,004
Net Worth: $295,327,188
Earnings: $8,150,220
Fiscal Year-end: 12/31/22
Electric Equipment Mfr
N.A.I.C.S.: 335999
Ma Xiaowu *(Chm)*

CHANGHAE ETHANOL CO., LTD.

15 Wonmanseong-ro, Deokjin-gu, Jeonju, 54854, Jeollabuk-do, Korea (South)
Tel.: (82) 632147800
Web Site: https://www.chethanol.com
Year Founded: 1966
004650—(KRS)
Rev.: $83,932,577
Assets: $149,630,179
Liabilities: $45,872,244
Net Worth: $103,757,935
Earnings: $59,492
Emp.: 62
Fiscal Year-end: 12/31/22
Ethyl Alcohol Mfr
N.A.I.C.S.: 325193
Sung-woo Lim *(Chm)*

CHANGHONG HUAYI COMPRESSOR CO., LTD.

No 1 Changhong Avenue High-tech Development Zone, Jingdezhen, 333000, Jiangxi, China
Tel.: (86) 7988470206
Web Site: https://www.hua-yi.cn
Year Founded: 1994
000404—(SSE)
Rev.: $1,838,605,392
Assets: $1,765,305,360
Liabilities: $1,079,445,744
Net Worth: $685,859,616
Earnings: $36,890,100
Fiscal Year-end: 12/31/22
Compressor Mfr
N.A.I.C.S.: 333912
Xiubiao Yang *(Chm)*

Subsidiaries:

Huayi Compressor Barcelona, S.L.   (1)
Antoni Forrellad 2, Sant Quirze del Valles, 08192, Barcelona, Spain
Tel.: (34) 937106008
Web Site: https://www.huayicompressor.es
Emp.: 400
Air & Gas Compressor Mfr
N.A.I.C.S.: 333912

Jiaxipera Compressor Limited
Company   (1)
No 588 Yazhong Road, Nanhu District, Jiaxing, 314006, Zhejiang, China
Tel.: (86) 57382586166
Web Site: https://www.jiaxipera.com
Emp.: 4,000
Air & Gas Compressor Mfr
N.A.I.C.S.: 333912

CHANGHONG MEILING CO.,LTD.

No 2163 Lianhua Road Economic and Technological Development Zone, Hefei, 230601, Anhui, China
Tel.: (86) 55162219021
Web Site: http://www.meiling.com
Year Founded: 1992
000521—(SSE)
Rev.: $2,838,216,888
Assets: $2,274,530,544
Liabilities: $1,496,849,328
Net Worth: $777,681,216
Earnings: $34,333,416
Fiscal Year-end: 12/31/22
Household Electrical Appliance Mfr
N.A.I.C.S.: 335220
Wu Dinggang *(Chm)*

CHANGHUAT CORPORATION BERHAD

Ste 3 6 Level 3 Menara Pelangi No 2 Jalan Kuning, Taman Pelangi, 80400, Johor Bahru, Malaysia
Tel.: (60) 73341750
Sales Range: $10-24.9 Million
Plastic Injection Components Mfr
N.A.I.C.S.: 621111

CHANGJIANG PUBLISHING & MEDIA CO., LTD.

Block B No 268 Xiongchu Street, Wuchang, Wuhan, 430070, China
Tel.: (86) 2787673688
600757—(SHG)
Rev.: $883,823,504
Assets: $1,751,045,129
Liabilities: $560,192,588
Net Worth: $1,190,852,540
Earnings: $102,398,508
Fiscal Year-end: 12/31/22
Book Publishers
N.A.I.C.S.: 513130

CHANGJIANG RUNFA MEDICINE CO., LTD.

Gold town Shandong Road Town, Zhangjiagang, 215633, Jiangsu, China
Tel.: (86) 51256926615

Web Site: http://www.runfa-machinery.cn
Sales Range: $150-199.9 Million
Elevator Mfr
N.A.I.C.S.: 333921
Qiqin Qiu *(Vice Chm & Gen Mgr)*

CHANGJIANG SECURITIES COMPANY LIMITED

No 88 Huaihai Road, Jianghan District, Wuhan, 430023, Hubei, China
Tel.: (86) 2765799886
Web Site: http://www.cjsc.com
Year Founded: 1997
000783—(SSE)
Rev.: $894,569,832
Assets: $22,321,545,948
Liabilities: $17,988,719,112
Net Worth: $4,332,826,836
Earnings: $212,033,484
Fiscal Year-end: 12/31/22
Securities Brokerage Services
N.A.I.C.S.: 523150
Jin Caijiu *(Chm)*

Subsidiaries:

China Mobile Games & Entertainment
Group Limited   (1)
Block A 15/F Huajian Building 233 Tianfu Road, Tianhe District, Guangzhou, China
Tel.: (86) 20 85613455
Web Site: http://www.cmge.com
Holding Company; Mobile Game Developer
N.A.I.C.S.: 551112
Han Di Sin *(Vice Chm)*

CHANGLAN TECHNOLOGY GROUP CO., LTD

No 223 Tongzipo West Road Lugu Industrial Park, Hi-tech Development Zone, Changsha, 410205, Hunan, China
Tel.: (86) 73185541801
Web Site:
https://www.changlangroup.com
Year Founded: 1958
002879—(SSE)
Rev.: $138,842,964
Assets: $311,654,304
Liabilities: $75,008,700
Net Worth: $236,645,604
Earnings: $4,176,900
Emp.: 500
Fiscal Year-end: 12/31/22
Electrical Device Mfr & Distr
N.A.I.C.S.: 335931
Yu Tao *(Chm)*

CHANGLIN COMPANY LIMITED

No 898 West Huang He Road, Changzhou, 213136, Jiangsu, China
Tel.: (86) 519 86781288
Web Site:
http://www.changlin.com.cn
Year Founded: 1961
Sales Range: $125-149.9 Million
Construction Machinery Mfr & Whslr
N.A.I.C.S.: 333120
Wei Yan Wang *(Pres)*

CHANGMAO BIOCHEMICAL ENGINEERING COMPANY LIMITED

No 1228 Chang jiang Bei Road New North Zone, Xinbei District, Changzhou, 213034, Jiangsu, China
Tel.: (86) 51985776812
Web Site:
https://changmaobio.todayir.com
Year Founded: 1992
0954—(HKG)
Rev.: $102,496,774
Assets: $169,428,402
Liabilities: $60,071,825
Net Worth: $109,356,577
Earnings: $11,422,663

Changmao Biochemical Engineering Company Limited—(Continued)

Emp.: 497
Fiscal Year-end: 12/31/22
Organic Acids Mfr
N.A.I.C.S.: 325998
Xin Sheng Rui *(Founder, Chm, Compliance Officer-Compliance, Gen Mgr & Exec Dir)*

CHANGMING INDUSTRIAL MANAGEMENT GROUP HOLDING

Room 113 Level 11 Building D No 1 Ji, Yanta, Xi'an, 7100000, China
Tel.: (86) 2988810915
Year Founded: 2005
Mineral Exploration Services
N.A.I.C.S.: 212290
Zhoubin Ren *(Pres)*

CHANGS ASCENDING ENTERPRISE CO., LTD.

9 Keya East Road, Xitun District, Taichung, 407, Taiwan
Tel.: (886) 425658768
Web Site: https://www.caec.com.tw
Year Founded: 1997
8038—(TPE)
Rev.: $6,484,445
Assets: $33,660,851
Liabilities: $19,531,376
Net Worth: $14,129,475
Earnings: ($887,440)
Fiscal Year-end: 12/31/22
Battery Mfr
N.A.I.C.S.: 335910
James Chang *(CFO)*

CHANGSHA BROAD HOMES INDUSTRIAL GROUP CO., LTD.

No 248 Yinshuang Road, Yuelu, Changsha, Hunan, China
Tel.: (86) 73188911568   CN
Web Site: https://www.bhome.com.cn
Year Founded: 1988
2163—(HKG)
Rev.: $313,412,814
Assets: $1,323,046,202
Liabilities: $849,856,223
Net Worth: $473,189,980
Earnings: ($113,593,568)
Emp.: 2,866
Fiscal Year-end: 12/31/22
Prefabricated Building Product Mfr
N.A.I.C.S.: 332311
Jian Zhang *(Founder & Chm)*

CHANGSHA DIALINE NEW MATERIAL SCIENCE & TECHNOLOGY CO., LTD.

No 108 Huanlian Road Changsha High-tech Development Zone, Changsha, 410205, Hunan, China
Tel.: (86) 73189862939
Web Site: https://www.diamsaw.com
Year Founded: 2009
300700—(CHIN)
Rev.: $119,454,547
Assets: $304,341,004
Liabilities: $121,783,403
Net Worth: $182,557,601
Earnings: $15,839,625
Fiscal Year-end: 12/31/23
Cutting Tool Mfr & Distr
N.A.I.C.S.: 333515

CHANGSHA JINGJIA MICRO-ELECTRONICS CO., LTD.

No 1 Meixihu Road, Yuelu District, Changsha, 410221, Hunan, China
Tel.: (86) 73182737008
Web Site: http://www.jingjiamicro.com
Year Founded: 2006

300474—(CHIN)
Rev.: $162,011,772
Assets: $554,389,056
Liabilities: $91,865,124
Net Worth: $462,523,932
Earnings: $40,569,984
Fiscal Year-end: 12/31/22
Electronic Products Mfr
N.A.I.C.S.: 334419
Wanhui Zeng *(Chm, Pres & Gen Mgr)*

CHANGSHA TONGCHENG HOLDINGS CO., LTD.

No 589 Laodong West Road, Yuhua District, Changsha, 410007, Hunan, China
Tel.: (86) 73185534994
000419—(SSE)
Rev.: $299,123,604
Assets: $734,498,388
Liabilities: $264,064,320
Net Worth: $470,434,068
Earnings: $20,463,300
Fiscal Year-end: 12/31/22
Holding Company
N.A.I.C.S.: 551112

CHANGSHENG CHINA PROPERTY COMPANY LIMITED

Unit D 10th Floor China Overseas Building 139 Hennessy Road, 1 Harbour Road, Wanchai, China (Hong Kong)
Tel.: (852) 28322910
Web Site: http://www.cschina.com.hk
Sales Range: $25-49.9 Million
Emp.: 170
Real Estate Developers
N.A.I.C.S.: 236220
Shek Cheong Chau *(Chm)*

CHANGSHU FENGFAN POWER EQUIPMENT CO., LTD.

No 8 Renmin South Road, West District Shanghu Town Industrial Concentration Zone, Changshu, 215551, Jiangsu, China
Tel.: (86) 51251885888
Web Site: https://www.cstower.cn
Year Founded: 1993
601700—(SHG)
Rev.: $384,554,084
Assets: $672,040,802
Liabilities: $302,410,733
Net Worth: $369,630,069
Earnings: $4,527,619
Emp.: 2,000
Fiscal Year-end: 12/31/22
Steel Tower Mfr
N.A.I.C.S.: 331110
Wang Jianxiang *(Chm)*

CHANGSHU GUORUI TECHNOLOGY CO., LTD.

2 Qingdao Road Yushan High-tech Industrial Development Zone, Changshu, 215500, Jiangsu, China
Tel.: (86) 4001015915
Web Site: https://www.cs-grkj.com
Year Founded: 1993
300600—(CHIN)
Rev.: $27,629,840
Assets: $163,286,771
Liabilities: $30,381,739
Net Worth: $132,905,032
Earnings: ($3,258,522)
Fiscal Year-end: 12/31/23
Electric Equipment Mfr
N.A.I.C.S.: 335931
Ge Ying *(Chm)*

CHANGSHU TIANYIN ELEC-TROMECHANICAL CO., LTD.

No 8 Yingbin Road Bixi New District,

Changshu, Suzhou, 215513, Jiangsu, China
Tel.: (86) 51252691551
Web Site: https://www.tyjd.cc
300342—(CHIN)
Rev.: $117,830,700
Assets: $303,362,280
Liabilities: $92,638,728
Net Worth: $210,723,552
Earnings: $1,097,928
Emp.: 360
Fiscal Year-end: 12/31/22
Refrigerator Compressor Parts & Components Mfr
N.A.I.C.S.: 333415

CHANGTIAN PLASTIC & CHEMICAL LIMITED

18 Xinsheng Road Xinyang Industrial Zone, Haicang District, Xiamen, 361026, Fujian, China
Tel.: (86) 5926517000
Web Site:
http://www.changtian.com.sg
Adhesive Tape Mfr
N.A.I.C.S.: 325520
Junqing Yang *(Exec Dir)*

Subsidiaries:

Xiamen Changtian Enterprise Co., Ltd.   **(1)**
No 18 Xinsheng Road Xinyang Industrial Zone, Haicang District, Xiamen, 361026, Fujian, China
Tel.: (86) 5926807002
Web Site: http://www.chang-tian.com.cn
Chemical Products Mfr & Sales
N.A.I.C.S.: 326199

CHANGYOU ALLIANCE GROUP LIMITED

Room 501A Tower 1 Poly International Plaza Zone 7 Wangjing East Park, Chaoyang District, Beijing, 100102, China
Tel.: (86) 1084463988   Ky
Web Site:
http://www.fortunetecomm.com
Year Founded: 2001
1039—(HKG)
Rev.: $30,191,335
Assets: $21,678,602
Liabilities: $37,937,484
Net Worth: ($16,258,882)
Earnings: ($6,843,377)
Emp.: 48
Fiscal Year-end: 12/31/22
E-Commerce Platform Developer
N.A.I.C.S.: 561499
Jerome Cheng *(Chm)*

CHANGYUAN GROUP LTD.

5th Floor Building 6 New Material Port Changyuan 1st High-tech Zone, Nanshan District, Shenzhen, 518057, Guangdong, China
Tel.: (86) 75526718868   CN
Web Site: https://www.cyg.com
Year Founded: 1986
600525—(SHG)
Rev.: $1,068,879,324
Assets: $1,933,991,720
Liabilities: $1,154,150,211
Net Worth: $779,841,509
Earnings: $94,583,422
Emp.: 7,400
Fiscal Year-end: 12/31/22
Electronic Components Mfr & Distr
N.A.I.C.S.: 334419
Wu Qiquan *(Chm & Pres)*

Subsidiaries:

CYG Consulting and Engineering Co., Ltd.   **(1)**
No 1 1st Floor Building 13 No 87 Moxiang Road, Jinjiang District, Chengdu, Sichuan, China

Tel.: (86) 2867672902
Electro Mobile Related Materials Mfr & Distr
N.A.I.C.S.: 335999

CYG Contron Co., Ltd.   **(1)**
No 11 of the 6th Tecnology Road, National high-tech Industries Development Zone, Zhuhai, 519085, Guangdong, China
Tel.: (86) 7563838888
Web Site: https://www.contron.com.cn
Electro Mobile Related Materials Mfr & Distr
N.A.I.C.S.: 335999

CYG ET Co., Ltd.   **(1)**
4/F B2 Building 4 No 5 Keji Eighth Road, Tangjiawan Town New & High Technology Industrial Development Zone, Zhuhai, China
Tel.: (86) 13584049339
Web Site: https://www.cyg-et.com
Emp.: 400
Automation Equipment Mfr & Distr
N.A.I.C.S.: 334413

CYG Electric Co., Ltd.   **(1)**
No 89 Jinfeng North Road, Phase II Science & Technology Innovation Coast High-tech Zone, Zhuhai, China
Tel.: (86) 7563630222
Electro Mobile Related Materials Mfr & Distr
N.A.I.C.S.: 335999

CYG Flywheel Co., Ltd.   **(1)**
Room 310 Building1 Aili Center Cangqian Street, Yuhang District, Hangzhou, Zhejiang, China
Tel.: (86) 57188779861
Electro Mobile Related Materials Mfr & Distr
N.A.I.C.S.: 335999

CYG Insulator Co., Ltd.   **(1)**
Jinghui Road No 2, Niushan Foreign Trade Economy Industrial Park Dongcheng District, Dongguan, China
Tel.: (86) 76922291876
Web Site: https://www.cyginsulator.com
Railway Insulator Equipment Mfr & Distr
N.A.I.C.S.: 333248

CYG Meditech Technology Co., Ltd.   **(1)**
Building 5 Huigu Valley, Liaobu Town, Dongguan, Guangdong, China
Tel.: (86) 1866629289
Web Site: https://www.cygmd.com
Emp.: 230
Medical Equipment Mfr & Distr
N.A.I.C.S.: 339112

CYG Sunri Co., Ltd.   **(1)**
No 13 Keji North 1st Road, North Area of Hi-Tech Industrial Park Nanshan District, Shenzhen, 518057, China
Tel.: (86) 75533018888
Web Site: https://global.sznari.com
Emp.: 1,700
Energy Storage System Mfr & Distr
N.A.I.C.S.: 335910

CYG Tiangong Co., Ltd.   **(1)**
New Industrial Park, Economic Development Zone Hong'an County, Huanggang, Hubei, China
Tel.: (86) 7135319280
Electric Equipment Mfr
N.A.I.C.S.: 334419

CYGIA Co., Ltd.   **(1)**
3rd Road Xinqing Science & Technology Industrial Park, Doumen District, Zhuhai, China
Tel.: (86) 7566318588
Web Site: https://www.cygia.com
Electric Equipment Mfr
N.A.I.C.S.: 334419

Changyuan Electronics (Shenzhen) Co., Ltd.   **(1)**
A/ F6 Changyuan New Material Port Keyuan Road, Shenzhen, China
Tel.: (86) 755 26549490
Web Site: http://www.heat-shrink-manufacturer.com
Heat Shrink Tube Mfr
N.A.I.C.S.: 322219

Dongguan Salipt Co., Ltd.   **(1)**
Sanlian Technological Park Jingxiang Village Liaobu Town, Dongguan, Guangdong, China
Tel.: (86) 769 81120150
Web Site: http://www.salipt.com

Sales Range: $50-74.9 Million
Emp.: 20
Polyolefin Fiber Mfr
N.A.I.C.S.: 325220

OptoFidelity Ltd. (1)
No 9 Jinding Science & Technology Eighth Road, High-tech Zone, Zhuhai, China
Tel.: (86) 7566990032
Electro Mobile Related Materials Mfr & Distr
N.A.I.C.S.: 335999

CHANGZHENG ENGINEERING CO., LTD.
No 141 Jinghai 4th Road, Beijing Economic & Technological Development Zone, Beijing, 101111, China
Tel.: (86) 1056325888
Web Site: http://www.china-ceco.com
Year Founded: 2007
603698—(SHG)
Rev.: $351,878,932
Assets: $680,621,152
Liabilities: $240,156,222
Net Worth: $440,464,930
Earnings: $23,461,135
Fiscal Year-end: 12/31/22
Chemical Engineering Services
N.A.I.C.S.: 541330
Jiang Congbin (Chm)

CHANGZHOU ALMADEN STOCK CO., LTD.
No 639 Qinglong East Road, Changzhou, 213021, Jiangsu, China
Tel.: (86) 51988880015
Web Site: https://www.czamd.com
Year Founded: 2006
002623—(SSE)
Rev.: $1,589,577,314
Assets: $3,827,578,698
Liabilities: $1,252,445,926
Net Worth: $2,575,132,772
Earnings: $42,243,120
Emp.: 1,500
Fiscal Year-end: 12/31/21
Glass Coating Mfr
N.A.I.C.S.: 327211
Lin Jinxi (Chm)

Subsidiaries:

Jiangsu Almaden Power Investment Co., Ltd. (1)
No 616 Qinglong East Road, Changzhou, Jiangsu, China
Tel.: (86) 51988880016
Engineeering Services
N.A.I.C.S.: 541330

CHANGZHOU AOHONG ELECTRONICS CO., LTD.
No 15 Xinke Road, Xinbei District, Changzhou, 213000, Jiangsu, China
Tel.: (86) 51969887878
Web Site: https://www.czaohong.com
Year Founded: 2005
605058—(SHG)
Rev.: $158,112,204
Assets: $339,998,031
Liabilities: $125,545,582
Net Worth: $214,452,450
Earnings: $18,683,772
Fiscal Year-end: 12/31/22
Electronic Product Mfr & Distr
N.A.I.C.S.: 334419
Dinghong Chen (Chm & Gen Mgr)

Subsidiaries:

Changzhou Haihong Electronics Co., Ltd. (1)
16 Xingtang Rd, Binjiang Economic Development Zone, Changzhou, 213000, China
Tel.: (86) 51969887878
Electric Equipment Mfr
N.A.I.C.S.: 334419

CHANGZHOU ARCHITECTURAL RESEARCH INSTITUTE

GROUP CO., LTD.
No 10 Mushu Road, Changzhou, 213015, Jiangsu, China
Tel.: (86) 51986980929
Web Site: https://www.czjky.com
Year Founded: 2003
301115—(CHIN)
Rev.: $191,454,830
Assets: $549,709,294
Liabilities: $157,862,816
Net Worth: $391,846,478
Earnings: $14,167,352
Fiscal Year-end: 12/31/23
Architectural Services
N.A.I.C.S.: 541310
Jiangjin Yang (Chm)

CHANGZHOU KAIDI ELECTRICAL, INC.
No 2 Hengcui Road, Henglin Town, Changzhou, 213000, Jiangsu, China
Tel.: (86) 51967898510
Web Site: https://www.czkaidi.cn
Year Founded: 1992
605288—(SHG)
Rev.: $164,541,289
Assets: $350,712,082
Liabilities: $58,476,881
Net Worth: $292,235,201
Earnings: $6,820,520
Emp.: 3,000
Fiscal Year-end: 12/31/22
Electrical Equipment Mfr & Distr
N.A.I.C.S.: 335999
Rongqing Zhou (Chm)

Subsidiaries:

Jiangyin Kaiyan Metal Manufacturing Co., Ltd. (1)
66 Guibin Road Ligang Street, Jiangyin, Jiangsu, China
Tel.: (86) 51086632187
Linear Actuator & Other Electrical Product Mfr
N.A.I.C.S.: 333995

Kaidi Electrical Europe GmbH (1)
Leopoldstrasse 244, 80807, Munich, Germany
Tel.: (49) 89208039206
Web Site: https://kaidi.eu
Linear Actuator & Other Electrical Product Mfr
N.A.I.C.S.: 333995

Kaidi LLC (1)
342 E 40th St, Holland, MI 49423
Tel.: (616) 546-1950
Web Site: http://www.kaidiofficeusa.com
Emp.: 2,500
Linear Actuator & Other Electrical Product Mfr
N.A.I.C.S.: 333995
Sean McCarthy (Dir-Ops-North America)

CHANGZHOU LANGBO SEALING TECHNOLOGY CO., LTD.
No 1 Jinbo Road, Yaotan Subdistrict Jintan District, Changzhou, 213200, Jiangsu, China
Tel.: (86) 51982300228
Web Site: http://www.jmp-seal.com
Year Founded: 1985
603655—(SHG)
Rev.: $24,720,818
Assets: $79,230,037
Liabilities: $5,229,900
Net Worth: $74,000,137
Earnings: $2,146,014
Fiscal Year-end: 12/31/22
Rubber Product Mfr & Distr
N.A.I.C.S.: 326199
Wang Shuguang (Chm)

CHANGZHOU NRB CORPORATION
52 Hanjiang Road, New Hi-Tech District, Changzhou, 213022, Jiangsu, China

Tel.: (86) 51985158888
Web Site: https://www.nrb.com.cn
Year Founded: 1994
002708—(SSE)
Rev.: $208,894,140
Assets: $380,898,180
Liabilities: $206,212,500
Net Worth: $174,685,680
Earnings: ($32,883,084)
Emp.: 1,700
Fiscal Year-end: 12/31/22
Automotive Precision Bearings Mfr
N.A.I.C.S.: 332991
Li Shuhua (Chm)

CHANGZHOU QIANHONG BIOPHARMA CO., LTD.
No 518 Yunhe Road Life and Health Industrial Park, Xinbei District, Changzhou, 213125, Jiangsu, China
Tel.: (86) 51985156026
Web Site: https://en.qhsh.com.cn
Year Founded: 1971
002550—(SSE)
Rev.: $323,418,420
Assets: $393,953,976
Liabilities: $52,303,212
Net Worth: $341,650,764
Earnings: $45,406,764
Emp.: 1,300
Fiscal Year-end: 12/31/22
Biopharmaceutical Products Mfr, Distr, Importer & Exporter
N.A.I.C.S.: 325412
Yaofang Wang (Chm)

CHANGZHOU RANTO METALWORK CO., LTD.
Ma'an Luoyang, Changzhou, 213101, Jiangsu, China
Tel.: (86) 519 8878 1504   CN
Web Site: http://www.ranto.cn
Year Founded: 1993
Automotive & Industrial Metal Components Mfr
N.A.I.C.S.: 332119
Victor Wang (Supvr-Engrg Dept)

CHANGZHOU SHENLI ELECTRICAL MACHINE INC
No 289 Xingdong Road Economic Development Zone, Changzhou, 213013, China
Tel.: (86) 51988408518
Web Site: https://www.czshenli.com
Year Founded: 1991
603819—(SHG)
Rev.: $206,357,856
Assets: $213,258,558
Liabilities: $105,707,708
Net Worth: $107,550,851
Earnings: ($11,312,000)
Emp.: 700
Fiscal Year-end: 12/31/22
Motor Accessory Mfr & Distr
N.A.I.C.S.: 335314
Chen Meng (Chm)

CHANGZHOU TENGLONG AUTO PARTS CO., LTD.
No 15 Tenglong Road Economic Development Zone, Wujin District, Changzhou, 213149, Jiangsu, China
Tel.: (86) 51969692888
Web Site: https://www.cztl.com
Year Founded: 1997
603158—(SHG)
Rev.: $374,828,281
Assets: $573,871,999
Liabilities: $271,818,135
Net Worth: $302,053,864
Earnings: $17,329,600
Fiscal Year-end: 12/31/22
Automobile Parts Mfr
N.A.I.C.S.: 336110
Jiang Xuezhen (Chm)

Subsidiaries:

Changzhou Tengxing Auto Accessories Manufacturing Co., Ltd. (1)
No 58 Dongfeng Road, Yuli Town Wujin District, Changzhou, China
Tel.: (86) 51983738851
Motor Vehicle Parts Mfr
N.A.I.C.S.: 336390

Chongqing Changteng Auto Parts Manufacturing Co., Ltd. (1)
No 15 Park Avenue, Luohuang Industrial Park Area B Jianjin District, Chongqing, China
Tel.: (86) 2347630259
Motor Vehicle Parts Mfr
N.A.I.C.S.: 336390

Jiangsu Flexible Auto Parts Co., Ltd. (1)
No 1 Tenglong Road Wujin Economic Development Zone, Changzhou, China
Tel.: (86) 51968852668
Motor Vehicle Parts Mfr
N.A.I.C.S.: 336390

Liuzhou Longrun Auto Parts Manufacturing Co., Ltd. (1)
No 4 Standard Factory in the East Second Floor, Building No 1 Guantang Pioneer Park Area B Liudong New District, Nanning, Guangxi, China
Tel.: (86) 7726668681
Auto Parts Mfr & Retailer
N.A.I.C.S.: 336390

Tianjin Tenglong United Auto Parts Co., Ltd. (1)
No 2 Secondary Branch Kaituo Road Taida Microelectronics Mndustry, Baitai Town Jingnan District, Tianjin, China
Tel.: (86) 2258052518
Motor Vehicle Parts Mfr
N.A.I.C.S.: 336390

Wuhan Tenglong United Auto Accessories Manufacturing Co., Ltd. (1)
Floor 1-2 Building No 11 Wuhan Huading Packaging & Printing, Industrial Park Area A Road No 4 Economic Development Zone Hannan Dist, Wuhan, China
Tel.: (86) 2784736880
Motor Vehicle Parts Mfr
N.A.I.C.S.: 336390

Wuhu Tenglong Auto Parts Co., Ltd. (1)
No 2-8 Fengminghu South Road, Economic And Technological Development Zone, Wuhu, China
Tel.: (86) 5535998077
Motor Vehicle Parts Mfr
N.A.I.C.S.: 336390

Xiamen Da Jun Accurate Industrial Co., Ltd. (1)
Xia Mei Xiang Ping St, West Hong Tang Village Tong An District, Xiamen, China
Tel.: (86) 5927899156
Motor Vehicle Parts Mfr
N.A.I.C.S.: 336390

Zhejiang Richleo Environmettal Technology Co., Ltd. (1)
West Street Kowloon Avenue Road on the 2nd, Wenling, Zhejiang, China
Tel.: (86) 57681697988
Motor Vehicle Parts Mfr
N.A.I.C.S.: 336390

CHANGZHOU TIANSHENG NEW MATERIALS CO., LTD.
No 508 Longjin Road, Tianning Economic Development Zone, Changzhou, 213018, China
Tel.: (86) 51986929011
Web Site: https://www.tschina.com
Year Founded: 1998
300169—(CHIN)
Rev.: $82,080,264
Assets: $191,521,044
Liabilities: $153,686,052
Net Worth: $37,834,992
Earnings: ($26,355,888)
Emp.: 661

Changzhou Tiansheng New Materials Co.,
Ltd.—(Continued)

Fiscal Year-end: 12/31/22
Macromolecule Foam Materials Mfr &
Distr
N.A.I.C.S.: 337910

CHANGZHOU TRONLY NEW ELECTRONIC MATERIALS CO., LTD.

Qianjia Industrial Park, Changzhou,
Jiangsu, China
Tel.: (86) 51988380708
Web Site: https://www.tronly.com
300429—(CHIN)
Rev.: $125,103,420
Assets: $522,497,196
Liabilities: $250,354,260
Net Worth: $272,142,936
Earnings: ($13,009,464)
Emp.: 1,000
Fiscal Year-end: 12/31/22
Photoresist Chemical Materials Mfr
N.A.I.C.S.: 325998

Subsidiaries:

Chunmo International Co., Ltd. (1)
No 38 East Guanhe Road, Changzhou,
213101, Jiangsu, China
Tel.: (86) 51985226278
Chemical Products Distr
N.A.I.C.S.: 424690

CHANGZHOU XIANGMING INTELLIGENT DRIVE SYSTEM CORPORATION

No 518 Zhongwu Avenue,
Changzhou, 213011, Jiangsu, China
Tel.: (86) 51988389998
Web Site:
   https://www.xiangming.com
Year Founded: 1995
301226—(SSE)
Rev.: $90,232,272
Assets: $150,543,900
Liabilities: $23,653,188
Net Worth: $126,890,712
Earnings: $9,089,496
Fiscal Year-end: 12/31/22
Motor Product Mfr
N.A.I.C.S.: 335312
Min Zhang (Chm)

CHANGZHOU XINGYU AUTOMOTIVE LIGHTING SYSTEM CO., LTD.

No 182 Qinling Road, Xinbei District,
Changzhou, 213022, Jiangsu, China
Tel.: (86) 51985156063
Web Site: http://www.xyl.cn
Year Founded: 2000
601799—(SHG)
Rev.: $1,158,018,442
Assets: $1,858,428,693
Liabilities: $661,979,008
Net Worth: $1,196,449,685
Earnings: $132,175,972
Fiscal Year-end: 12/31/22
Automobile Light Lamp Mfr & Distr
N.A.I.C.S.: 335139
Shujun Li (Sec, VP, Controller &
Deputy Gen Mgr)

CHANGZHOU ZHONGYING SCIENCE & TECHNOLOGY CO., LTD.

No 28 Zhengqiang Road, Zhonglou
District, Changzhou, 213012, Jiangsu, China
Tel.: (86) 51983253357
Web Site: https://en.czzyst.cn
Year Founded: 2006
300936—(SSE)
Rev.: $34,812,180
Assets: $142,681,500
Liabilities: $17,801,316

Net Worth: $124,880,184
Earnings: $4,835,376
Fiscal Year-end: 12/31/22
Electronic Product Mfr & Distr
N.A.I.C.S.: 334419
Weizhong Yu (Chm & Gen Mgr)

CHANHIGH HOLDINGS LIMITED

17th and 18th Floors Cang Hai Industry Building No 3388 Cang Hai Road,
Yinzhou District, Ningbo, Zhejiang,
China
Tel.: (86) 23319999   Ky
Web Site:
   http://www.chanhigh.com.hk
Year Founded: 2001
2017—(HKG)
Rev.: $283,376,059
Assets: $321,318,317
Liabilities: $188,377,207
Net Worth: $132,941,110
Earnings: $4,647,100
Emp.: 533
Fiscal Year-end: 12/31/22
Landscape Architectural Services
N.A.I.C.S.: 541320
Tianbin Peng (Chm)

CHANJET INFORMATION TECHNOLOGY COMPANY LIMITED

Floor 3 Building 3 Yard 9 Yongfeng
Road, Haidian District, Beijing, China
Tel.: (86) 1062434214   CN
Web Site: https://www.chanjet.com
Year Founded: 2010
1588—(HKG)
Rev.: $95,492,920
Assets: $213,236,291
Liabilities: $113,227,546
Net Worth: $100,008,745
Earnings: ($29,778,138)
Emp.: 1,207
Fiscal Year-end: 12/31/22
Enterprise Software
N.A.I.C.S.: 513210
Yuchun Yang (Pres & Exec Dir)

CHANNEL FOUR TELEVISION CORPORATION

124 Horseferry Road, London, SW1P
2TX, United Kingdom
Tel.: (44) 2073964444
Web Site: http://www.channel4.com
Rev.: $1,291,926,000
Assets: $1,055,838,000
Liabilities: $550,872,000
Net Worth: $504,966,000
Earnings: ($32,790,000)
Emp.: 903
Fiscal Year-end: 12/31/19
Public Television Broadcasting Network
N.A.I.C.S.: 516120
Jonathan Allan (COO)

Subsidiaries:

Box Television Ltd. (1)
Mappin House 4, Winsley Street, London,
W1W 8HF, United Kingdom (50%)
Tel.: (44) 2071828000
Web Site: http://www.boxtv.co.uk
Sales Range: $25-49.9 Million
Emp.: 60
Cable Television Broadcasting
N.A.I.C.S.: 516210
Matt Rennie (Mng Dir)

CHANNEL HOLDINGS INC.

18 Pall Mall 2nd Floor, London,
SW1Y 5LU, United Kingdom
Tel.: (44) 207 389 5016   NV
Web Site:
   http://www.universalgoldmining.net
Year Founded: 2006
REHB—(OTCIQ)

Gold Mining Services
N.A.I.C.S.: 212220
Craig Lees Baxter Niven (Interim
CEO, Interim CFO & Asst Sec)

CHANNEL INFRASTRUCTURE NZ LIMITED

Port Marsden Highway, Ruakaka,
0171, New Zealand
Tel.: (64) 94328311   NZ
Web Site: https://channelnz.com
CHI—(NZX)
Rev.: $52,773,325
Assets: $566,344,498
Liabilities: $256,241,627
Net Worth: $310,102,871
Earnings: $7,153,110
Emp.: 135
Fiscal Year-end: 12/31/22
Petroleum Refiner
N.A.I.C.S.: 324110
Denise Jensen (CFO & Sec)

Subsidiaries:

Independent Petroleum Laboratory
Limited (1)
12 Ralph Trimmer Drive, Ruakaka, 0171,
Northland, New Zealand
Tel.: (64) 94328567
Web Site: https://www.ipl.co.nz
Sales Range: $25-49.9 Million
Emp.: 45
Laboratory Testing Services
N.A.I.C.S.: 541380
Russell Baddeley (CEO)

CHANNEL ISLANDS STOCK EXCHANGE

One Lefebvre Street, PO Box 623,
Saint Peter Port, GY1 4PJ, Guernsey
Tel.: (44) 481713831
Web Site: http://www.cisx.com
Stock Exchange Services
N.A.I.C.S.: 523210
Jon Moulton (Chm)

CHANNEL MICRON HOLDINGS COMPANY LIMITED

Building 24 Chuansha International
Precision Park No 6999, Chuansha
Road Pudong New Area, Shanghai,
China
Tel.: (86) 2158599778   Ky
Web Site: http://www.micron.com.my
Year Founded: 1989
2115—(HKG)
Holding Company
N.A.I.C.S.: 551112
Yew Sum Ng (Chm)

Subsidiaries:

Micron (M) Sdn. Bhd. (1)
Lot PT 14274 Jalan SU 8 Persiaran Tengku
Ampuan, 40400, Shah Alam, Selangor,
Malaysia
Tel.: (60) 351923333
Fan Filter Mfr
N.A.I.C.S.: 333413

Micron Cleanroom (Philippines)
Inc. (1)
Units 906 and 910 Page I Building 1215
Acacia Ave, Madrigal Business Park Ayala
Alabang, Muntinlupa, Philippines
Tel.: (63) 288503019
Cleanroom Design Services
N.A.I.C.S.: 541410

CHANNEL NINE ENTERTAINMENT LTD

Asaf Ali Road 3/12 Ground Floor,
New Delhi, 110002, India
Tel.: (91) 11 32315575
Web Site:
   http://www.channelnine.com
Year Founded: 2002
Television, Films & Video Game Production & Distribution
N.A.I.C.S.: 512110

Hitesh Khandelwal (Sec)

CHANSON INTERNATIONAL HOLDING

No 26 Culture Road, Tianshan District, Urumqi, 830000, Xinjiang, China
Tel.: (86) 9912302709   Ky
Year Founded: 2019
CHSN—(NASDAQ)
Rev.: $13,272,075
Assets: $27,329,186
Liabilities: $26,152,137
Net Worth: $1,177,049
Earnings: ($1,288,205)
Emp.: 354
Fiscal Year-end: 12/31/22
Holding Company
N.A.I.C.S.: 551112
Gang Li (Chm & CEO)

CHANT SINCERE CO., LTD.

7F 2 No 188 Sec 3 Datong Rd, Xizhi
Dist, New Taipei City, 221, Taiwan
Tel.: (886) 286471251
Web Site: https://www.coxoc.com.tw
6205—(TAI)
Rev.: $44,976,714
Assets: $120,181,231
Liabilities: $37,858,431
Net Worth: $82,322,800
Earnings: $5,540,273
Emp.: 44
Fiscal Year-end: 12/31/23
Electronic Components Mfr
N.A.I.C.S.: 334416

Subsidiaries:

David Electronics Co., Ltd. (1)
9F-2 No 188 Sec 3 Ta-Tung Road, Xizhi
Dist, New Taipei City, Taiwan
Tel.: (886) 286471376
Web Site: https://www.daec.com.tw
Connectivity Cables Mfr
N.A.I.C.S.: 335921

Zhuhai David Electronics Co.,
Ltd. (1)
9F-2 No 188 Sec 3 Ta-Tung Road, Xizhi
Dist, New Taipei City, Taiwan
Tel.: (886) 286471376
Web Site: https://www.daec.com.tw
Electronic Components Mfr & Distr
N.A.I.C.S.: 334419

CHANT WEST HOLDINGS LIMITED

Suite 1003 Level 10 45 Clarence
Street, Sydney, 2000, NSW, Australia
Tel.: (61) 29 361 1400
Web Site:
   http://www.chantwestholdings.com
CWL—(ASX)
Sales Range: $1-9.9 Million
Investment Services
N.A.I.C.S.: 523999
Brendan Burwood (CEO)

CHANTIER CATANA

Zone Technique du Port, Canet,
66140, France
Tel.: (33) 468801313
Rev.: $24,200,000
Emp.: 130
Boatbuilding & Repairing
N.A.I.C.S.: 336612
Olivier Poncin (Pres)

CHANTIERS AMEL S.A.

8 rue Joseph Cugnot, 17183, Perigny, Charente Maritime, France
Tel.: (33) 546551731
Web Site: http://www.amel.fr
Year Founded: 1968
Sales Range: $25-49.9 Million
Boatbuilding & Repairing Services
N.A.I.C.S.: 336612
Emmanuel Poujeade (Fin Dir)

CHANTIERS DE L'ATLANTIQUE SA
Avenue Antoine Bourdelle, BP 90180, 44613, Saint-Nazaire, Cedex, France
Tel.: (33) 251109100   FR
Web Site: http://www.chantiers-atlantique.com
Ship Building & Repair Services
N.A.I.C.S.: 336611
Laurent Castaing *(Pres)*

Subsidiaries:

Chantiers de l'Atlantique
Services   (1)
Avenue Chatonay, BP 30156, 44613, Saint-Nazaire, France
Tel.: (33) 2 51 10 91 00
Web Site: http://www.chantiers-atlantique.com
Ship Building Services
N.A.I.C.S.: 336611

CHANTLER TRANSPORT
3235 Clifford Court, Innisfil, L9S 3V8, ON, Canada
Tel.: (705) 431-4022
Web Site:
    http://www.chantlertransport.com
Year Founded: 1999
Rev.: $24,429,600
Emp.: 107
Transportation & Delivery Freight Services
N.A.I.C.S.: 488999
Steve Chantler *(Pres)*

CHAODA MODERN AGRICULTURE HOLDINGS LIMITED
No 29 Tongpan Road, Fuzhou, 350003, Fujian, China
Tel.: (86) 591 2837 8888
Web Site: http://www.chaoda.com.hk
Sales Range: $1-4.9 Billion
Emp.: 23,236
Agricultural Products Producer
N.A.I.C.S.: 111998
Andy Chi Po Chan *(CFO)*

Subsidiaries:

Chaoda Vegetable & Fruits
Limited   (1)
Rm 2705 27 F China Resources Bldg 26 Harbour Rd, Wanchai, China (Hong Kong)
Tel.: (852) 28450168
Web Site: http://www.chaodo.com.hk
Sales Range: $25-49.9 Million
Emp.: 20
Fruit & Vegetable Farming Services
N.A.I.C.S.: 111419

CHAOJU EYE CARE HOLDINGS LIMITED
24/F East Zone Block A Shouke Buiding No 14, Yard West 3rd Ring South Road Fengtai District, Beijing, China   Ky
Web Site:
    https://www.chaojueye.com
Year Founded: 1988
2219—(HKG)
Rev.: $151,684,641
Assets: $417,213,812
Liabilities: $65,064,763
Net Worth: $352,149,048
Earnings: $28,067,459
Emp.: 2,162
Fiscal Year-end: 12/31/22
Holding Company
N.A.I.C.S.: 551112
Bozhou Zhang *(CEO)*

CHAOPRAYA MAHANAKORN PCL
909/1 CMC Tower 6th Floor Unit 601 602 Somdejprachataksin Road, Dao Khanong Khet Thon Buri, Bangkok, 10600, Thailand

Tel.: (66) 24689000   TH
Web Site: https://www.cmc.co.th
Year Founded: 1994
CMC—(THA)
Rev.: $38,684,031
Assets: $221,598,288
Liabilities: $152,508,485
Net Worth: $69,089,803
Earnings: ($5,614,492)
Emp.: 1,454
Fiscal Year-end: 12/31/23
Real Estate Development Services
N.A.I.C.S.: 531390
Wichian Padhayanun *(Chm, CEO & Chief Project Officer)*

CHAOWEI POWER HOLDINGS LIMITED
No 18 Chengnan Road Huaxi Industrial Function Area, Changxing, 313100, Zhejiang, China
Tel.: (86) 5726562868   Ky
Web Site: http://www.chaowei.com.hk
Year Founded: 1998
0951—(HKG)
Rev.: $4,483,049,360
Assets: $2,804,958,234
Liabilities: $1,848,791,272
Net Worth: $956,166,962
Earnings: $82,534,000
Emp.: 16,977
Fiscal Year-end: 12/31/22
Motive Battery Mfr
N.A.I.C.S.: 335910
Mingming Zhou *(Founder, Chm & CEO)*

Subsidiaries:

Chaowei Power (Hong Kong)
Limited   (1)
Unit 1308A 13/F Lippo Sun Plaza 28 Canton Road, Tsim Sha Tsui, Kowloon, China (Hong Kong)
Tel.: (852) 31041602
Web Site: https://www.chaowei.com.hk
Electric Battery Mfr & Whslr
N.A.I.C.S.: 335910

Zhejiang Chaowei Chuangyuan Industrial Co., Ltd.   (1)
No 18 South Road, Changxin County, Hangzhou, Zhejiang, China
Tel.: (86) 5726203313
Web Site: https://www.chaowei-lib.com
Emp.: 1,000
Electric Battery Mfr & Whslr
N.A.I.C.S.: 335910

CHAOZHOU THREE-CIRCLE GROUP CO., LTD.
Sanhuan Industrial District, Fengtang, Chaozhou, 515646, Guangdong, China
Tel.: (86) 7682360888
Web Site: https://www.cctc.cc
Year Founded: 1970
300408—(SSE)
Rev.: $722,974,356
Assets: $2,750,910,552
Liabilities: $349,591,788
Net Worth: $2,401,318,764
Earnings: $211,261,284
Emp.: 500
Fiscal Year-end: 12/31/22
Ceramic Electronic Component Mfr
N.A.I.C.S.: 334419
Li Gang *(Chm)*

Subsidiaries:

HONG KONG THREE-CIRCLE
ELECTRONIC CO., LTD.   (1)
Flat D 5/F Houston Ind Bldg 32-40 Wang Lung St, Tsuen Wan, New Territories, China (Hong Kong)
Tel.: (852) 24073751
Electronic Product Distr
N.A.I.C.S.: 423690

Nanchong Three Circle Electronic Co.
Ltd.   (1)
Xing'an Road, Gaoping District, Nanchong, 637000, Sichuan, China
Ceramic Products Mfr
N.A.I.C.S.: 327110

Nanchong Three-Circle Electronics
Co., Ltd.   (1)
Xing'an Road, Gaoping District, Nanchong, Sichuan, China
Tel.: (86) 817 355 3279
Micro Dispensing System Mfr
N.A.I.C.S.: 333914

SHENZHEN THREE-CIRCLE ELECTRONIC CO., LTD.   (1)
Project Department China West Sanhuan Technology Building, 1161 Guangqiao Road Guangming District, Shenzhen, 518040, Guangdong, China
Tel.: (86) 75583400756
Ceramic Products Mfr
N.A.I.C.S.: 327110

Vermes Microdispensing GmbH   (1)
Rudolf-Diesel-Ring 2, 83607, Holzkirchen, Germany
Tel.: (49) 8 024 6440
Web Site: https://www.vermes.com
Micro Dispensing System Mfr
N.A.I.C.S.: 333914
Jurgen Stadtler *(CEO & Mng Dir)*

CHAPEL DOWN GROUP PLC
Chapel Down Winery Small Hythe Road, Tenterden, TN30 7NG, Kent, United Kingdom
Tel.: (44) 1580763033   UK
Web Site:
    https://www.chapeldown.com
Year Founded: 2002
CDGP—(LSE)
Rev.: $25,417,135
Assets: $64,527,995
Liabilities: $21,198,108
Net Worth: $43,329,888
Earnings: $1,927,985
Emp.: 86
Fiscal Year-end: 12/31/23
Beverage Product Mfr
N.A.I.C.S.: 312112
Andrew Carter *(CEO)*

CHAPMAN FREEBORN AIRCHARTERING LTD.
3 City Place Beehive Ring Road Gatwick, London, RH6 0PA, West Sussex, United Kingdom
Tel.: (44) 1293832796
Web Site: http://www.chapman-freeborn.com
Year Founded: 1973
Sales Range: $700-749.9 Million
Emp.: 250
Aircraft Charter Services
N.A.I.C.S.: 481219
Darren Banham *(Pres-Bus-US)*

Subsidiaries:

Chapman Freeborn Airchartering
(China) Ltd.   (1)
Suite 9D CITIC Building, 19 Jianguomenwai St, Beijing, 100004, China
Tel.: (86) 10 8526 1728
Aircraft Charter Services
N.A.I.C.S.: 481219

Chapman Freeborn Airchartering (Italia) SRL   (1)
Lungo Dora Colletta 67, 10153, Turin, Italy
Tel.: (39) 011 450 0858
Aircraft Charter Services
N.A.I.C.S.: 481219

Chapman Freeborn Airchartering
(Shanghai) Co Ltd.   (1)
8F Taiping Finance Tower, 488 Yin Cheng Zhong Road Lujiazui, Pudong, Shanghai, 200120, China
Tel.: (86) 10 8526 1728
Aircraft Charter Services

N.A.I.C.S.: 481219

Chapman Freeborn Airchartering
(South Africa) PTY LTD   (1)
Suite 201Colltin Place, C37 Lakefield Avenue, Benoni, South Africa
Tel.: (27) 87 150 3626
Aircraft Charter Services
N.A.I.C.S.: 481219

Chapman Freeborn Airchartering
BV   (1)
Boeingavenue 201-219, 1119 PD, Schiphol-Rijk, Netherlands
Tel.: (31) 206538888
Aircraft Charter Services
N.A.I.C.S.: 532411

Chapman Freeborn Airchartering
BVBA   (1)
Nieuwpoortsesteenweg 887, Office 54-55-56-57, Oostende, 8400, Belgium
Tel.: (32) 59 56 31 31
Aircraft Charter Services
N.A.I.C.S.: 481219

Chapman Freeborn Airchartering
Consulting (Shanghai) Co., Ltd.   (1)
Suite 2201 22/F Sino Life Tower 707 Zhangyang Road, Pudong, Shanghai, China
Tel.: (86) 1085261728
Aircraft Charter Services
N.A.I.C.S.: 532411

Chapman Freeborn Airchartering Fretamento e Logistica do Brasil
Ltda.   (1)
Alameda Vicente Pinzon, 144 CJ 111 Vila Olimpia, Sao Paulo, 04547-130, Brazil
Tel.: (55) 11 3047 1100
Emp.: 7
Aircraft Charter Services
N.A.I.C.S.: 481219
Maria Terasa Faria *(Country Mgr)*

Chapman Freeborn Airchartering
Limited   (1)
Suite 9D CITIC Building 19 Jianguomenwai St, Beijing, 100004, China
Tel.: (86) 1085261728
Aircraft Charter Services
N.A.I.C.S.: 532411

Chapman Freeborn Airchartering
Ltd.   (1)
3601 Highway 7 Suite 400, Markham, L3R 0M3, ON, Canada
Tel.: (905) 943-4964
Web Site: http://www.chapman-freeborn.com
Aircraft Charter Distr
N.A.I.C.S.: 481219

Chapman Freeborn Airchartering Pte
Ltd.   (1)
300 Tampines Avenue 5 #09-02, NTUC Income Tampines Junction, Singapore, 529653, Singapore
Tel.: (65) 6542 1316
Aircraft Charter Services
N.A.I.C.S.: 481219

Chapman Freeborn Airchartering Pvt.
Ltd.   (1)
Suite #302 G5 Building, Terminal 1D IG Airport, New Delhi, 110037, India
Tel.: (91) 11 42371016
Aircraft Charter Services
N.A.I.C.S.: 481219

Chapman Freeborn Airchartering
S.L   (1)
Calle de las Eras 5 1, 28411, Madrid, Spain
Tel.: (34) 918427768
Aircraft Chertering Services
N.A.I.C.S.: 532411

Chapman Freeborn Airchartering Sp
z.o.o   (1)
ul Bokserska 66, 02 690, Warsaw, Poland
Tel.: (48) 2244 501 50
Web Site: http://www.chapman-freeborn.com
Emp.: 10
Aircraft Charter Services
N.A.I.C.S.: 481219

Chapman Freeborn Airchartering,
Inc.   (1)

Chapman Freeborn Airchartering Ltd.—(Continued)

12121 Wickchester Ln Ste 520, Houston, TX 77079
Tel.: (281) 447-5667
Aircraft Charter Services
N.A.I.C.S.: 481219

Chapman Freeborn Airchartering, Inc.   (1)
550 W Cypress Creek Rd Ste 410, Fort Lauderdale, FL 33309
Tel.: (954) 202-0750
Aircraft Charter Services
N.A.I.C.S.: 481219

Chapman Freeborn Airmarketing GmbH   (1)
Albin Kobis Strasse 6, 51147, Cologne, Germany
Tel.: (49) 2203 95576 0
Aircraft Charter Services
N.A.I.C.S.: 481219

Chapman Freeborn Airmarketing GmbH   (1)
Main Airport Center, Unterschweinstiege 2 - 14 9th Floor, 60549, Frankfurt, Germany
Tel.: (49) 69 698039 10
Aircraft Charter Services
N.A.I.C.S.: 481219

Chapman Freeborn Airmarketing GmbH   (1)
Frachtzentrum Modul B Raum 329 3rd Floor, Munich, D-85356, Germany
Tel.: (49) 89 97595890
Aircraft Charter Services
N.A.I.C.S.: 481219

Chapman Freeborn Australia   (1)
Hangar 5 228 Wirraway Road, Essendon Fields, Victoria, 2031, Australia
Tel.: (61) 3 9351 0328
Aircraft Charter Services
N.A.I.C.S.: 481219

Chapman Freeborn Aviation Services FZE   (1)
Block 7W Office 2056, Dubai Airport Free Zone (DAFZA), Dubai, United Arab Emirates
Tel.: (971) 4 2067300
Aircraft Charter Services
N.A.I.C.S.: 481219

Chapman Freeborn Handcarry Ltd   (1)
Unit 1702 Tung Che Commercial Centre, 246 Des Voeux Road West, Hong Kong, China (Hong Kong)
Tel.: (852) 2148 9068
Web Site: http://www.chapman-freeborn.com
Aircraft Charter Services
N.A.I.C.S.: 481219

Chapman Freeborn Havacilik Tasimacilik Tic. Ltd. Sti.   (1)
Buyukehir Mahallesi Cumhuriyet Caddesi Ekinoks Residence E-1 Blok, Buyukehir Mahallesi Cumhuriyet Caddesi Ekinoks Residence E-1 Blok D, Istanbul, Turkiye
Tel.: (90) 212 663
Aircraft Charter Services
N.A.I.C.S.: 481219

Chapman Freeborn c/o Covio SA   (1)
Kloten Chapman Freeborn c/o Covio SA Oberfeldstrasse 12d, 8302, Kloten, Switzerland
Tel.: (41) 44 803 90 90
Aircraft Charter Services
N.A.I.C.S.: 481219

CHAPMANS LIMITED
Level 10 52 Phillip Street, Sydney, 2000, NSW, Australia
Tel.: (61) 2 9300 3630   AU
Web Site:
  http://www.chapmansltd.com
Year Founded: 1922
Rev.: $1,306,090
Assets: $3,225,095
Liabilities: $454,836
Net Worth: $2,770,259
Earnings: ($7,787,262)

Fiscal Year-end: 12/31/17
Investment Services
N.A.I.C.S.: 523999
Peter James Dykes (Chm)

CHAPPAL ENERGIES MAURITIUS LIMITED
5th Floor Nexsky Building, Ebene, Mauritius
Web Site:
  https://chappalenergies.com
NICH—(OTC)
Energy Services
N.A.I.C.S.: 213112
Ufoma Joseph Immanuel (Mng Dir)

Subsidiaries:

Equinor Nigeria Energy Company Limited   (1)
Petroleum & Natural Gas Exploration, Drilling & Extraction
N.A.I.C.S.: 211120

CHAPS HOLDING SAS
4 rue du Port aux Vins, 92150, Suresnes, France
Tel.: (33) 157326060
Web Site: https://www.chapsvision.fr
Emp.: 100
Holding Company
N.A.I.C.S.: 551112
Olivier Dellenbach (CEO)

Subsidiaries:

ChapsVision SASU   (1)
4 rue du Port aux Vins, 92150, Suresnes, France
Tel.: (33) 15732606
Web Site: https://www.chapsvision.fr
Software Publr
N.A.I.C.S.: 513210

Subsidiary (Domestic):

SYSTRAN S.A.   (2)
5 rue Feydeau, 75002, Paris, France
Tel.: (33) 144824900
Web Site: https://www.systransoft.com
Sales Range: $10-24.9 Million
Emp.: 52
Language Translation Software Developer, Publisher & Whslr
N.A.I.C.S.: 513210

Subsidiary (US):

SYSTRAN Software, Inc.   (3)
4445 Eastgate Mall Ste 310, San Diego, CA 92121
Tel.: (858) 457-1900
Web Site: http://www.systransoft.com
Emp.: 30
Language Translation Software Developer, Publisher & Whslr
N.A.I.C.S.: 513210

CHAR TECHNOLOGIES LTD.
895 Don Mills Road Suite 400, Toronto, M3C 1W3, ON, Canada   ON
Web Site:
  https://chartechnologies.com
Year Founded: 2013
YES—(TSXV)
Rev.: $1,510,478
Assets: $14,247,884
Liabilities: $9,011,937
Net Worth: $5,235,947
Earnings: ($6,972,682)
Fiscal Year-end: 09/30/23
Investment Services
N.A.I.C.S.: 523999
Andrew J. White (Co-Founder & CEO)

Subsidiaries:

CharTech Solutions Inc.   (1)
789 Don Mills Rd Ste 403, Toronto, M3C 1T5, ON, Canada
Tel.: (416) 467-5555
Web Site: http://www.chartechsolutions.com
Renewable Environmental Services

N.A.I.C.S.: 541620

CHARAN INSURANCE PUBLIC COMPANY LIMITED
408/1 Ratchadaphisek, Huaykwang, Bangkok, 10310, Thailand
Tel.: (66) 22761024
Web Site:
  https://charaninsurance.co.th
Year Founded: 1949
CHARAN—(THA)
Rev.: $9,085,107
Assets: $26,747,054
Liabilities: $10,417,289
Net Worth: $16,329,765
Earnings: $787,382
Emp.: 64
Fiscal Year-end: 12/31/23
Insurance Management Services
N.A.I.C.S.: 524298
Kittipong Charanvas (Asst Mng Dir)

CHARBONE HYDROGEN CORPORATION
5005 Boul Lapiniere suite 1080, Brossard, J4Z 0N5, QC, Canada
Tel.: (450) 678-7171   Ca
Web Site: https://www.charbone.com
Year Founded: 2018
CHHYF—(OTCQB)
Rev.: $16,771
Assets: $3,293,737
Liabilities: $3,344,369
Net Worth: ($50,632)
Earnings: ($5,508,119)
Fiscal Year-end: 12/31/22
Hydrogen Fuel Mfr
N.A.I.C.S.: 325120
Benoit Veilleux (CFO)

CHARCOL LIMITED
5th Floor Cutlers Exchange 123 Houndsditch, London, EC3A 7BU, United Kingdom
Tel.: (44) 2076117000
Web Site:
  http://www.johncharcol.co.uk
Sales Range: $10-24.9 Million
Emp.: 150
Mortgage Services
N.A.I.C.S.: 522310
Walter Avrili (Dir-Product & Mortgage Technical)

CHARDAN METROPOL ACQUISITION CORP.
13 Donskaya Ulitsa, 119049, Moscow, Russia
Tel.: (7) 495 933 3310   VG
Year Founded: 2011
Investment Services
N.A.I.C.S.: 523999
Alexis O. Rodzianko (Co-Chm & CFO)

CHARGEPANEL AB
Skeppsbron 34, 111 30, Stockholm, Sweden
Tel.: (46) 812032500
Web Site:
  https://www.chargepanel.com
Year Founded: 2009
CHARGE—(OMX)
Rev.: $869,617
Assets: $643,278
Liabilities: $1,034,407
Net Worth: ($391,129)
Earnings: ($1,533,742)
Emp.: 9
Fiscal Year-end: 12/31/23
Software Development Services
N.A.I.C.S.: 541511

CHARGEPOINT TECHNOLOGY LTD.
Venture Point Business Park 58 Ev-

ans Rd, Liverpool, L24 9PB, United Kingdom
Tel.: (44) 1517284500
Web Site:
  http://www.thechargepoint.com
Year Founded: 2009
Containment Equipment & Other Transfer Services
N.A.I.C.S.: 484110
Chris Eccles (CEO)

Subsidiaries:

Terracon Corporation   (1)
1376 W Central St Ste 130, Franklin, MA 02038-7100
Tel.: (508) 429-9950
Web Site: http://www.terracon-solutions.com
All Other Plastics Product Mfr
N.A.I.C.S.: 326199
John Miersma (Treas)

CHARGER METALS NL
Unit 32 L3 22 Railway Road, Subiaco, 6008, WA, Australia
Tel.: (61) 861465325   AU
Web Site:
  https://www.chargermetals.com.au
Year Founded: 2020
CHR—(ASX)
Rev.: $582
Assets: $5,868,282
Liabilities: $195,893
Net Worth: $5,672,389
Earnings: ($1,317,650)
Fiscal Year-end: 06/30/22
Metal Exploration Services
N.A.I.C.S.: 213114
Aidan Platel (CEO)

CHARGEURS NV
112 avenue Kleber, 75116, Paris, France
Tel.: (33) 147041360
Web Site: http://www.chargeurs.fr
Year Founded: 1872
Rev.: $655,734,807
Assets: $716,126,919
Liabilities: $444,819,931
Net Worth: $271,306,988
Earnings: $30,424,814
Emp.: 2,072
Fiscal Year-end: 12/31/18
Wool & Textile Product Mfr
N.A.I.C.S.: 313310
Michael Fribourg (Chm & CEO)

Subsidiaries:

Chargeurs Entretelas (Iberica)   (1)
Rua Sao Gemil 175, Pedroucos, 4425-692, Maia, Portugal
Tel.: (351) 220423735
Web Site: http://www.chargeurs.pt
Footwear Product Mfr
N.A.I.C.S.: 316210
Antonio Martins (Dir Gen)

CHARGEURS SA
7 Rue Kepler, FR-75116, Paris, France
Tel.: (33) 147041340
Web Site: https://www.chargeurs.com
CRI—(EUR)
Rev.: $904,721,584
Assets: $1,145,088,152
Liabilities: $817,393,720
Net Worth: $327,694,432
Earnings: $37,829,792
Emp.: 2,500
Fiscal Year-end: 12/31/21
Wool, Textiles & Protective Surfacing Mfr
N.A.I.C.S.: 314999
Laurent Derolez (CEO)

Subsidiaries:

Chargeurs Entretelas (Portugal) Ltd   (1)

Rua de Sangemil 175, Aguas Santas, 4425-692, Maia, Portugal
Tel.: (351) 229783140
Textile Products Mfr
N.A.I.C.S.: 314999
Antonio Martins *(Gen Mgr)*

Chargeurs Fabrics **(1)**
38 rue Marbeuf, 09301, Paris, Cedex 1, France **(100%)**
Tel.: (33) 149531000
Web Site: http://www.chargeurs.fr
Garment Fabric Mfr
N.A.I.C.S.: 313320

Subsidiary (Domestic):

Avelana **(2)**
Saint Nestor, PO Box 105, 9301, Villeneuve d'Olmes, Lavelanet, France **(100%)**
Tel.: (33) 561032222
Web Site: http://www.avelana.com
Sales Range: $25-49.9 Million
Emp.: 250
Wool-Lycra Blend Fabric Mfr
N.A.I.C.S.: 315990

Lepoutre Ternynck **(2)**
Zi De La Martinoire 1 Rue Jacquard, BP 40039, 59392, Wattrelos, Cedex, France
Tel.: (33) 320233030
Web Site: http://www.lepoutre.fr
Sales Range: $25-49.9 Million
Emp.: 12
Stretch Fabric Mfr
N.A.I.C.S.: 315990

Roudiere SA **(2)**
1 Bis Chemin De La Coume, PO Box 38, 9300, Lavelanet, France **(100%)**
Tel.: (33) 561032000
Web Site: http://www.roudiere.com
Woolen Fabric Mfr
N.A.I.C.S.: 315990

Chargeurs Fashion Technologies **(1)**
Buire-Courcelles, BP 70112, 80202, Peronne, Cedex, France
Tel.: (33) 322734000
Sales Range: $150-199.9 Million
Interlinings Mfr
N.A.I.C.S.: 313310
Bernard Vossart *(Mng Dir)*

Subsidiary (US):

Precision Textiles LLC **(2)**
200 Maltese Dr, Totowa, NJ 07512
Tel.: (973) 890-3873
Web Site: https://precisiontextiles-usa.com
Fabric Coating Mills
N.A.I.C.S.: 313320
Jack Higgins *(Controller)*

Chargeurs Interfodere Italia S.p.A. **(1)**
Via Oratorio 48, 20016, Pero, Milan, Italy
Tel.: (39) 0235371521
Web Site: http://www.chargeurs-interfodere.com
Sales Range: $25-49.9 Million
Emp.: 3
Textile Interlining Mfr
N.A.I.C.S.: 314999

Chargeurs Interlining **(1)**
Route De Peronne, BP 89, Buires Courcelles, Peronne, 80200, France **(100%)**
Tel.: (33) 322734000
Web Site: http://www.chargeurs.fr
Sales Range: $100-124.9 Million
Emp.: 170
Garment Interlinings Mfr
N.A.I.C.S.: 313320
Henri Mazeau *(Mgr-Pur)*

Subsidiary (Non-US):

Chargeurs Interlining (HK) Limited **(2)**
Unit 1501 COL Tower Wharf T & T Square 123 Hoi Bun Road, Kwun Tong, Kowloon, China (Hong Kong)
Tel.: (852) 27556788
Textile Products Mfr
N.A.I.C.S.: 314999

Subsidiary (Domestic):

DHJ International **(2)**

1 Rue de Morat, Meyer, Selestat, 67600, France **(100%)**
Tel.: (33) 388850777
Web Site: http://www.dhjinternational.com
Sales Range: $25-49.9 Million
Emp.: 80
Garment Interlining & Technical Fabric Mfr
N.A.I.C.S.: 315990

Subsidiary (Non-US):

Interlana S.r.o **(2)**
Svermova 21, 460 10, Liberec, 10, Czech Republic
Tel.: (420) 488055555
Web Site: http://www.chargeurs-interlining.com
Garment Interlining Mfr
N.A.I.C.S.: 315990

Subsidiary (Domestic):

Lainiere de Picardie BC **(2)**
BP 20089, 80202, Peronne, Cedex, France
Tel.: (33) 322838383
Garment Interlining Mfr
N.A.I.C.S.: 315990

Subsidiary (Non-US):

Lainiere de Picardie Argentina S.A. **(3)**
Avda Brasil 2543, 1260, Buenos Aires, Argentina **(100%)**
Tel.: (54) 43080096
Web Site: http://www.entamer.com.ar
Sales Range: $25-49.9 Million
Emp.: 50
Garment Interlining Mfr
N.A.I.C.S.: 315990

Lainiere de Picardie Deutschland GmbH **(3)**
Rossdorfer Strasse 48, Messel, 64409, Germany **(100%)**
Tel.: (49) 61599173
Web Site: http://www.lpger.de
Emp.: 7
Garment Interlining Mfr
N.A.I.C.S.: 315990
Urs Wandeler *(Gen Mgr)*

Lainiere de Picardie Golaplast Brazil Textil Ltda **(3)**
450 Rua Urbano Santos Cumbica, Sao Paulo, CEP 07183-280, Cumbica Garhulhos, Brazil **(100%)**
Tel.: (55) 1164325008
Web Site: http://www.lainieredepicardie.com
Sales Range: $25-49.9 Million
Emp.: 44
Garment Interlining Mfr
N.A.I.C.S.: 315990

Lainiere de Picardie Korea Co. Ltd **(3)**
4 F Sebang Bldg 935-40 Bangbae-dong, Seocho-ku, Seoul, Korea (South)
Tel.: (82) 25847311
Emp.: 22
Textile Products Mfr
N.A.I.C.S.: 314999
Ko Yoong-Sik *(Mgr)*

Lainiere de Picardie UK Ltd **(3)**
5 Danbury Ct, Linford Wood, Milton Keynes, MK14 6PQ, Buckinghamshire, United Kingdom **(100%)**
Tel.: (44) 8701213160
Web Site: http://www.lainieredepicardie.com
Sales Range: $25-49.9 Million
Emp.: 4
Garment Interlining Mfr
N.A.I.C.S.: 315990
Leclmaca Cei *(CEO)*

Lainiere de Picardie Uruguay S.A. **(3)**
Lainiere De Picadie Argentina S A, Avda Brasil 2543, 1260, Buenos Aires, Argentina **(100%)**
Tel.: (54) 43080096
Web Site: http://www.lainieredepicardie.com
Garment Interlining Mfr
N.A.I.C.S.: 315990

Subsidiary (US):

Lainiere de Picardie, Inc. **(3)**

835 Wheeler Way Ste A, Langhorne, PA 19047
Tel.: (215) 702-9090
Sales Range: $25-49.9 Million
Emp.: 70
Garment Interlining Mfr
N.A.I.C.S.: 424310
John Suhuss *(Gen Mgr)*

Subsidiary (Non-US):

Stroud Riley (Pty) Ltd **(2)**
12 Lindsay Rd, Korsten, Port Elizabeth, 6001, Eastern Cape, South Africa **(100%)**
Tel.: (27) 414531990
Web Site: http://www.chargeurs-interlining.com
Sales Range: $25-49.9 Million
Emp.: 11
Garment Interlining Mfr
N.A.I.C.S.: 315990
Anthony Allen *(Mng Dir)*

Chargeurs Protective Films **(1)**
27 Rue Du Dr Emile Bataille, PO Box 4, Deville les Rouen, 76250, Rouen, France **(100%)**
Tel.: (33) 232827232
Web Site: http://www.chargeurs-protective.com
Sales Range: $50-74.9 Million
Emp.: 250
Mfr of Temporary Protective Films
N.A.I.C.S.: 322220
Laurent Derolez *(Mng Dir)*

Subsidiary (Non-US):

Boston Tapes S.p.A **(2)**
S P Cellole-Piedimonte, Sessa Aurunca, 81037, Caserta, Italy **(100%)**
Tel.: (39) 082 368 0211
Web Site: https://www.bostontapes.com
Mfr of Protective Coatings
N.A.I.C.S.: 325510

Subsidiary (US):

Main Tape Company, Inc. **(2)**
1 Capital Dr, Cranbury, NJ 08512
Tel.: (609) 395-1704
Web Site: https://www.maintape.com
Supplier of Protective Films
N.A.I.C.S.: 322220

Subsidiary (Domestic):

Novacel **(2)**
27 Rue Du Docteur Emile Bataille, PO Box 4, Deville Les Rouen, 76250, Rouen, France **(100%)**
Tel.: (33) 23 282 7232
Web Site: https://www.novacel.world
Sales Range: $50-74.9 Million
Emp.: 200
Mfr of Protective Coatings
N.A.I.C.S.: 325510

Subsidiary (Non-US):

Novacel GmbH **(2)**
Normandiestrasse 3, 50259, Pulheim, Germany **(100%)**
Tel.: (49) 22 349 8740
Web Site: http://www.novacel.de
Sales Range: $25-49.9 Million
Emp.: 20
Mfr of Protective Coatings
N.A.I.C.S.: 325510
Karl-Friedrich Boehle *(Mng Dir)*

Novacel Iberica S.p.A. **(2)**
Polig Ind Pla d En Coll C/del Mig esq C/Segre s/n, Montcada i Reixac, 08110, Barcelona, Spain
Tel.: (34) 93 575 2252
Web Site: http://www.chargeurs-protective.com
Mfr of Protective Coatings
N.A.I.C.S.: 325510

Novacel Italia S.R.L **(2)**
Via Machiavelli 6/8, 20025, Legnano, MI, Italy
Tel.: (39) 033 193 6601
Web Site: http://www.novacel.it
Mfr of Protective Coatings
N.A.I.C.S.: 325510

Novacel Shanghai **(2)**
N 179 Jiugang Road Sector 2, Sijing Indus-

trial Park Songjiang District, Shanghai, 201601, China **(100%)**
Tel.: (86) 215 761 7568
Web Site: http://www.chargeursprotective.com
Sales Range: $25-49.9 Million
Emp.: 17
Mfr of Protective Coatings
N.A.I.C.S.: 325510

Novacel UK Ltd **(2)**
Unit 6 Sundon Business Park, Dencora Way, Luton, LU3 3HP, Bedfordshire, United Kingdom **(100%)**
Web Site: http://www.novacel.co.uk
Sales Range: $25-49.9 Million
Emp.: 20
Mfr of Protective Coatings
N.A.I.C.S.: 325510

Subsidiary (US):

Novacel, Inc. **(2)**
21 3rd St, Palmer, MA 01069-1542
Tel.: (413) 283-3468
Web Site: http://www.novacel.com
Sales Range: $50-74.9 Million
Emp.: 200
Mfr of Protective Coatings
N.A.I.C.S.: 322220

Unit (Domestic):

Troy Laminating & Coating, Inc. **(3)**
421 S Union St, Troy, OH 45373-4151
Tel.: (937) 335-5611
Web Site: http://www.troylaminatingandcoating.com
Sales Range: $25-49.9 Million
Emp.: 100
Mfr of Coated & Laminated Products
N.A.I.C.S.: 322120
Dave Bullard *(Mng Dir)*

Subsidiary (Non-US):

S.A Novacel Belgium NV **(2)**
Generaal de Wittelaan 17 bus 36, 28000, Mechelen, Belgium
Tel.: (32) 1 556 9666
Web Site: http://www.chargeurs-protective.com
Mfr of Protective Coatings
N.A.I.C.S.: 325510

Chargeurs Wool **(1)**
159 Ave Delamarne Parc De La, Marcqren Baroeul, 59700, Wattrelos, France **(100%)**
Tel.: (33) 320996868
Web Site: http://www.chargeurs.fr
Sales Range: $25-49.9 Million
Emp.: 10
Wool Tops Mfr
N.A.I.C.S.: 313310

Subsidiary (Non-US):

Chargeurs Wool (Argentina) SA **(2)**
Avenida De Mayo 605 Piso 11, C1084 AAB, Buenos Aires, Argentina **(100%)**
Tel.: (54) 143457983
Web Site: http://www.chargeurs.fr
Wool Tops Mfr
N.A.I.C.S.: 313310

Chargeurs Wool (South Africa) (Pty) Ltd **(2)**
163 Main Road Warmer, Port Elizabeth, 6070, Eastern Cape, South Africa
Tel.: (27) 415810081
Emp.: 2
Textile Wool Distr
N.A.I.C.S.: 424350

Subsidiary (US):

Chargeurs Wool (USA) Inc. **(2)**
178 Wool Rd, Jamestown, SC 29453
Tel.: (843) 257-2212
Web Site: https://chargeurswoolusa.com
Emp.: 80
Protective Fabric Mfr
N.A.I.C.S.: 313210
Martin Doldan *(Controller)*

Subsidiary (Non-US):

Chargeurs Wool Sales (Europe) SRL **(2)**
Via Candelo 60, 13900, Biella, Italy
Tel.: (39) 0152528400

Chargeurs SA—(Continued)

Web Site: http://www.chargeurs.com
Emp.: 9
Textile Products Mfr
N.A.I.C.S.: 314999

DHJ (Malaysia) Sdn Bhd (1)
27 Lebuh Perusahaan Kelebang 11, Perak
Darul Ridzuan, Chemor, 31200, Malaysia
Tel.: (60) 52912345
Textile Products Mfr
N.A.I.C.S.: 314999

DHJ Interlining Limited (1)
No 2680 Zhulu West Rd, Qingpu Xujing,
Shanghai, China
Tel.: (86) 2169762683
Sales Range: $25-49.9 Million
Emp.: 20
Textile Products Mfr
N.A.I.C.S.: 314999
Chuck Lai *(Gen Mgr)*

Intissel SAS (1)
Rue Jacquard - ZI de la Martinoire, BP 107,
59393, Wattrelos, France
Tel.: (33) 320116050
Web Site: http://www.intissel.com
Textile Non Woven Fabric Mfr
N.A.I.C.S.: 313230

Lanas Trinidad SA (1)
Calle Miami 2047, 11500, Montevideo, Uru-
guay
Tel.: (598) 26010024
Web Site: http://www.lanastrinidad.com
Rev.: $50,000,000
Wool Tops Mfr & Distr
N.A.I.C.S.: 313310

Leach Colour Limited (1)
Dyson Wood Way, Bradley, Huddersfield,
HD2 1GN, West Yorkshire, United Kingdom
Tel.: (44) 1484551200
Web Site: https://www.weareleach.com
Publishing & Broadcasting Services
N.A.I.C.S.: 519290
James Lavin *(Mng Dir)*

**Ningbo Chargeurs Yak Textile Trading
Co. Ltd** (1)
No 501 Yayuan S Rd Shigan St, Yinzhou
Dist, Ningbo, 315153, China
Tel.: (86) 57488251123
Sales Range: $150-199.9 Million
Emp.: 800
Textile Products Mfr
N.A.I.C.S.: 314999
Chuck Lai *(Gen Mgr)*

Novacel Korea Ltd. (1)
8F Fire Service Benefit Society Bldg
Garabon-Dong, Songpa-Ku, Seoul, 05719,
Korea (South)
Tel.: (82) 23 402 2477
Web Site: http://www.novacel.co.uk
Self-Adhesive Plastic Film Mfr
N.A.I.C.S.: 326112

Omma S.r.l. (1)
Via Dell'Artigianato 13/11, 20812, Limbiate,
MB, Italy
Tel.: (39) 029964634
Web Site: https://www.omma.com
Emp.: 20
Industrial Machinery Mfr
N.A.I.C.S.: 333248

Senfa SAS (1)
1 rue de Morat, BP 8, 67601, Selestat, Ce-
dex, France
Tel.: (33) 388850777
Web Site: https://senfa-coating.com
Coated Fabric Mfr
N.A.I.C.S.: 313320

Skira Editore S.p.A. (1)
Via Torino 61, Milan, 20123, Italy
Tel.: (39) 02724441
Web Site: http://www.skira.net
Sales Range: $25-49.9 Million
Emp.: 40
Book Publishers
N.A.I.C.S.: 513130

Walco Machines Company Inc. (1)
9017 Arrow Rte, Rancho Cucamonga, CA
91730
Tel.: (909) 483-3333
Web Site: https://www.walcomachine.com

Emp.: 360
Lamination Machinery Mfr
N.A.I.C.S.: 333248

**CHARILAOS APOSTOLIDES
PUBLIC LTD.**
75 Athalassa Avenue 1st Floor Chapo
Tower, Strovolos, 2012, Nicosia, Cy-
prus
Tel.: (357) 22312000   CY
Web Site:
http://www.chapogroup.com
Year Founded: 1949
Sales Range: $75-99.9 Million
Emp.: 583
Building & Civil Engineering Services
N.A.I.C.S.: 541330

Subsidiaries:

Chapomed Ltd (1)
75 Athalassis Ave Chapo Bldg, PO Box
24765, 1303, Nicosia, Cyprus   (100%)
Tel.: (357) 22497874
Web Site: http://www.chapogroup.com
Sales Range: $25-49.9 Million
Emp.: 40
Engineeering Services
N.A.I.C.S.: 541330

Getian General Services Ltd (1)
Tseriou Avenue, Strovolos Municipality,
Nicosia, Cyprus   (100%)
Tel.: (357) 22323533
Web Site: http://www.ggs.com.cy
Sales Range: $25-49.9 Million
Emp.: 10
Concrete Contractor
N.A.I.C.S.: 238110
Andreas Phociou *(Gen Mgr)*

CHARIOT CARRIERS INC.
105 5760 9th Street SE, Calgary,
T2H 1Z9, AB, Canada
Tel.: (403) 640-0822
Web Site:
http://www.chariotcarriers.com
Year Founded: 1992
Rev.: $32,054,292
Emp.: 180
Child Carrier Products Mfr
N.A.I.C.S.: 339930

CHARIOT LIMITED
Oak House Hirzel Street, Saint Peter
Port, GY1 2NP, Guernsey
Tel.: (44) 2084342754   GY
Web Site:
https://www.chariotenergygroup.com
CHAR—(AIM)
Rev.: $80,000
Assets: $74,645,000
Liabilities: $5,767,000
Net Worth: $68,878,000
Earnings: ($15,571,000)
Fiscal Year-end: 12/31/23
Oil & Gas Exploration Services
N.A.I.C.S.: 211120
Adonis Pouroulis *(Founder & CEO-
Acting)*

Subsidiaries:

Chariot Brasil Petroleo e Gas
Ltda.   (1)
Praia de Botafogo 501 Sala 207 Torre
Corcovado, Botafogo, 22250-0040, Rio de
Janeiro, Brazil
Tel.: (55) 2125469911
Oil & Gas Exploration Services
N.A.I.C.S.: 213112

Chariot Oil & Gas Statistics
Limited   (1)
19-21 Old Bond Street, London, W1S 4PX,
United Kingdom
Tel.: (44) 2073180450
Oil & Gas Exploration Services
N.A.I.C.S.: 213112

**CHARISMA ENERGY SER-
VICES LIMITED**

8 Wilkie Road 03-01 Wilkie Edge,
Singapore, 228095, Singapore
Tel.: (65) 65947849   SG
Web Site:
https://www.charismaenergy.com
Year Founded: 1997
5QT—(CAT)
Rev.: $5,842,000
Assets: $32,400,000
Liabilities: $82,177,000
Net Worth: ($49,777,000)
Earnings: ($421,000)
Emp.: 251
Fiscal Year-end: 12/31/23
Investment Holding Company
N.A.I.C.S.: 551112
Wee Sin Tan *(Co-Sec)*

Subsidiaries:

Yew Hock Marine Engineering Pte.
Ltd.   (1)
1 Kaki Bukit Av 3, 02-17 KB-1 Bldg, Singa-
pore, 416087, Singapore   (51%)
Tel.: (65) 64482181
Emp.: 50
Electricity Plant Construction Services
N.A.I.C.S.: 237130

CHARKHESHGAR CO.
No 170 Shahid Vahid Dastgerdi Zafar
St, Tehran, Iran
Tel.: (98) 2122253039
Web Site: https://www.sschar.com
Year Founded: 1969
CHAR—(THE)
Sales Range: Less than $1 Million
Transmission & Steering Mfr
N.A.I.C.S.: 336350

CHARLE CO., LTD.
7-7-1 Minatojima Nakamachi, Chuo-
ku, Kobe, 654-0192, Hyogo, Japan
Tel.: (81) 787927000
Web Site: https://www.charle.co.jp
Year Founded: 1975
9885—(TKS)
Rev.: $87,040,480
Assets: $141,414,340
Liabilities: $20,325,750
Net Worth: $121,088,590
Earnings: $3,866,850
Emp.: 204
Fiscal Year-end: 03/31/24
Apparel Product Whslr
N.A.I.C.S.: 424350

**CHARLES RUSSELL SPEECH-
LYS LLP**
5 Fleet Place, London, EC4M 7RD,
United Kingdom
Tel.: (44) 20 7203 5000   UK
Web Site:
http://www.charlesrussell.com
Year Founded: 1760
Sales Range: $200-249.9 Million
Emp.: 600
Law firm
N.A.I.C.S.: 541110
David Berry *(Partner)*

CHARLES TYRWHITT LLP.
13 Silver Road, London, W12 7RR,
United Kingdom
Tel.: (44) 20 7839 6060
Web Site: http://www.ctshirts.co.uk
Year Founded: 1986
Sales Range: $150-199.9 Million
Emp.: 480
Jean Apparel Mfr
N.A.I.C.S.: 315250
Nick Wheeler *(Owner)*

CHARLESGLEN LTD.
7687 110 Ave NW, Calgary, T3R
1R8, AB, Canada
Tel.: (403) 241-0888

Web Site:
http://www.charlesglentoyota.com
Year Founded: 1987
Rev.: $90,976,282
Emp.: 90
New & Used Car Dealers
N.A.I.C.S.: 441110
John Perri *(Mgr-Quality Control)*

**CHARLWOOD PACIFIC
GROUP**
1199 West Pender Street Suite 900,
Vancouver, V6E 2R1, BC, Canada
Tel.: (604) 718-2612
Web Site:
http://www.charlwoodpacific.com
Holding Company; Travel, Real Es-
tate & Mortgage Brokerage Franchi-
sor
N.A.I.C.S.: 551112
U. Gary Charlwood *(Founder, Chm &
CEO)*

Subsidiaries:

Centum Financial Group Inc. (1)
1199 W Pender St Ste 700, Vancouver,
V6E 2R1, BC, Canada
Tel.: (604) 257-3940
Web Site: http://www.centum.ca
Emp.: 10
Mortgage Brokerage Agency Franchisor
N.A.I.C.S.: 533110
U. Gary Charlwood *(Chm & CEO)*

Century 21 Canada Limited
Partnership   (1)
500-1285 West Pender St, Vancouver, V6E
4B1, BC, Canada
Tel.: (604) 606-2100
Web Site: https://www.c21.ca
Real Estate Agency Franchisor
N.A.I.C.S.: 533110
U. Gary Charlwood *(Chm)*

UNIGLOBE Travel International Lim-
ited Partnership   (1)
1199 West Pender Street Suite 900, Van-
couver, V6E 2R1, BC, Canada
Tel.: (604) 718-2600
Web Site: http://www.uniglobetravel.com
Travel Agency Franchisor
N.A.I.C.S.: 533110
U. Gary Charlwood *(Founder, Chm & CEO)*

**CHARM CARE CORPORATION
K.K.**
3-6-32 Nakanoshima, 21F Daibiru
Main Building, Osaka, 530-0005, Ja-
pan
Tel.: (81) 664453389
Web Site: https://www.charmcc.jp
Year Founded: 1984
6062—(TKS)
Rev.: $281,407,280
Assets: $361,596,400
Liabilities: $241,002,960
Net Worth: $120,593,440
Earnings: $28,565,680
Emp.: 254
Fiscal Year-end: 06/30/22
Residential Care Services
N.A.I.C.S.: 623990
Takahiko Shimomura *(Pres)*

**CHARM COMMUNICATIONS
INC.**
CN01 Laijin Cultural Industrial Park,
Beijing, 100025, China
Tel.: (86) 10 8556 2666   Ky
Web Site: http://www.charmgroup.cn
Year Founded: 2008
Television Advertising Services
N.A.I.C.S.: 541810
He Dang *(Founder, Chm & CEO)*

Subsidiaries:

O'Master Communications (Hong
Kong) Ltd.   (1)
Rm C 22/F Derrick Indl Bldg, Wong Chuk
Hang, Hong Kong, China (Hong Kong)

Tel.: (852) 28936552
Television Advertising Services
N.A.I.C.S.: 541810

CHARM ENGINEERING CO., LTD.

5 Hyeongje-ro Namsa-eup, Cheoin-gu, Yongin, 449-884, Gyeonggi-do, Korea (South)
Tel.: (82) 313308500
Web Site: https://www.charmeng.com
Year Founded: 1973
009310—(KRS)
Rev.: $130,839,734
Assets: $567,323,506
Liabilities: $501,275,607
Net Worth: $66,047,899
Earnings: ($1,739,814)
Emp.: 164
Fiscal Year-end: 12/31/22
Semiconductor Product Mfr
N.A.I.C.S.: 334413
Kyunghee Lee *(CEO)*

CHARMACY PHARMACEUTI-CAL CO., LTD.

No 235 Songshan North Road, Longhu District, Shantou, 515041, Guangdong, China
Tel.: (86) 75488206420   CN
Web Site: https://www.chmyy.com
Year Founded: 2000
2289—(HKG)
Rev.: $586,209,177
Assets: $402,370,274
Liabilities: $318,904,957
Net Worth: $83,465,317
Earnings: $12,689,400
Emp.: 817
Fiscal Year-end: 12/31/22
Holding Company
N.A.I.C.S.: 551112
Chuanglong Yao *(Chm, CEO & Exec Dir)*

CHARMS INDUSTRIES LTD.

108 B/109 Sampada Building Mithakhali Six Roads, Opp Hare Krishna Complex B/H Kiran Motors, Ahmedabad, 380009, Gujarat, India
Tel.: (91) 7926422081
Web Site:
https://www.charmsindustries.co.in
531327—(BOM)
Rev.: $8,080
Assets: $83,778
Liabilities: $14,164
Net Worth: $69,615
Earnings: ($38,514)
Emp.: 3
Fiscal Year-end: 03/31/21
Foreign Currency Trading Services
N.A.I.C.S.: 523160
Shivkumar Raghunandan Chauhan *(Mng Dir)*

CHARMT, INC.

Hobujaama 4, Tallinn, 10151, Estonia
Tel.: (372) 2512629446   NV
Year Founded: 2018
CHMT—(OTCIQ)
Liabilities: $5,080
Net Worth: ($5,080)
Earnings: ($16,619)
Emp.: 1
Fiscal Year-end: 12/31/22
Software Development Services
N.A.I.C.S.: 541511
Gediminas Knyzelis *(Founder, Pres, Treas & Sec)*

CHARMWELL HOLDINGS LTD.

Rm1520 Ginza Plaza No 2a Sai Yeung Choi Street South, Mongkok, Kowloon, China (Hong Kong)
Tel.: (852) 27826128

Web Site:
http://www.dinson.chinaexporter.com
Holding Company
N.A.I.C.S.: 551112

Subsidiaries:

Woodland Pulp, LLC   **(1)**
144 Main St, Baileyville, ME 04694   **(100%)**
Tel.: (207) 427-3311
Web Site: http://www.woodlandpulp.com
Sales Range: $125-149.9 Million
Emp.: 300
Pulp Mill
N.A.I.C.S.: 322110
Scott Beal *(Mgr-Environmental & Security)*

CHARMZONE GLOBAL CO., LTD.

736 Suinro Sangnok-gu, Ansan, 426220, Gyeonggi-do, Korea (South)
Tel.: (82) 3180850700
Web Site: http://interbulls.co.kr
Year Founded: 1998
158310—(KRS)
Rev.: $2,960,599
Assets: $17,890,994
Liabilities: $2,635,954
Net Worth: $15,255,040
Earnings: ($5,238,282)
Emp.: 17
Fiscal Year-end: 12/31/22
Printed Circuit Board Processing Machine Mfr
N.A.I.C.S.: 333242
Gang Se Lee *(CEO)*

CHARN ISSARA DEVELOP-MENT PUBLIC COMPANY LIMITED

2922/200 10th FL Charn Issara Tower II New Petch buri Road, Bangkapi Huay Kwang, Bangkok, 10310, Thailand
Tel.: (66) 23082020
Web Site:
https://www.charnissara.com
Year Founded: 1989
CI—(THA)
Rev.: $65,664,988
Assets: $374,243,052
Liabilities: $297,885,875
Net Worth: $76,357,177
Earnings: ($8,938,817)
Emp.: 79
Fiscal Year-end: 12/31/23
Real Estate Development Services
N.A.I.C.S.: 531390
Srivara Issara *(Chm)*

Subsidiaries:

Charn Issara Viphapol Company Limited   **(1)**
2922/181 New Phetchaburi Road, Huai Khwang, Bangkok, 10310, Thailand
Tel.: (66) 2 308 2016
Real Estate Development Services
N.A.I.C.S.: 531390

Sri panwa Management Co., Ltd. **(1)**
Phuket 88 Moo 8 Sakdidej Road Vichit, Muang, Phuket, 83000, Thailand
Tel.: (66) 7 637 1000
Web Site: https://www.sripanwa.com
Hotel Operator
N.A.I.C.S.: 721110

CHARNIC CAPITAL TBK PT

Menara Sudirman 8th floor Jl Jend Sudirman Kav 60, Jakarta, 12190, Indonesia
Tel.: (62) 215226528
Web Site: https://charnic.com
Year Founded: 2007
NICK—(INDO)
Rev.: $192,977
Assets: $12,746,731
Liabilities: $83,541
Net Worth: $12,663,190

Earnings: ($4,444,661)
Emp.: 9
Fiscal Year-end: 12/31/23
Real Estate Development Services
N.A.I.C.S.: 531390
Nicholas Santoso *(Sec)*

CHAROEN AKSORN HOLDING GROUP CO. LTD.

1 Charoenrat Road Thung Wat Don Sathon, Bangkok, 10120, Thailand
Tel.: (66) 2210 8888
Web Site: http://www.cas-group.com
Year Founded: 1971
Sales Range: $75-99.9 Million
Printing Supplies & Equipment Distr
N.A.I.C.S.: 424110
Surapol D ararattanaroj *(CEO)*

Subsidiaries:

C.A.S. Asset Co., Ltd.   **(1)**
30/1 moo 2 Chetsadawithi Road Khok Kham, Muang, Samut Sakhon, 74000, Thailand
Tel.: (66) 34452222
Web Site: http://www.sinsakhon.com
Asset Management Services
N.A.I.C.S.: 531390

CAS Paper Mill Co.   **(1)**
10th Floor Vibulthani Tower I 3195/15 Rama IV Road Klongton, Klongtoey District, Bangkok, 10110, Thailand
Tel.: (66) 2 661 3486
Sales Range: $125-149.9 Million
Emp.: 50
Newsprint Mfr
N.A.I.C.S.: 322120
Torpong Thongcharoen *(Gen Mgr)*

CHAROEN AKSORN TRADING CO., LTD.   **(1)**
2589 Soi Ladprao 91, Wangthonglang, 10310, Bangkok, Thailand
Tel.: (66) 25420511
Web Site: http://www.cas-trading.com
Printing Paper Mfr & Distr
N.A.I.C.S.: 322120

STAR PAPER INTERNATIONAL CO., LTD.   **(1)**
939 Rama 3 Rd Bang Phong Pang, Yannawa, Bangkok, 10120, Thailand
Tel.: (66) 26831700
Web Site: http://www.starpaperinter.com
Printing Paper Mfr & Distr
N.A.I.C.S.: 322120

Thai Nippon Rubber Industry Co., Ltd. - Si Racha Factory   **(1)**
Pinthong Industrial Estate 789/139 Moo 1 Nongkham, Si Racha, 20110, Chonburi, Thailand
Tel.: (66) 38317999
Web Site: http://www.tnrcondom.com
Rubber Products Mfr
N.A.I.C.S.: 326299

CHAROEN POKPHAND FOODS PUBLIC COMPANY LIMITED

313 C P Tower Silom Road, Bangrak, Bangkok, 10500, Thailand
Tel.: (66) 27668000   TH
Web Site:
https://www.cpfworldwide.com
Year Founded: 1978
CPF—(THA)
Rev.: $17,624,936,438
Assets: $28,078,118,258
Liabilities: $18,510,718,283
Net Worth: $9,567,399,975
Earnings: $469,104,217
Emp.: 48,695
Fiscal Year-end: 12/31/21
Food Products Mfr
N.A.I.C.S.: 551112
Dhanin Chearavanont *(Co-Chm)*

Subsidiaries:

AHM Lifestyles-Creative Hospitality Joint Stock Company   **(1)**

230 Nguyen Van Huong Street, Thao Dien Ward Thu Duc City, Ho Chi Minh City, Vietnam
Tel.: (84) 2836363695
Web Site: https://ahm-lifestyles.com
Restaurant Services
N.A.I.C.S.: 722511

Asia Aquaculture (M) Sdn. Bhd.   **(1)**
Batu 22 Kg Sg Hj Muhammad, 36200, Selekoh, Perak, Malaysia
Tel.: (60) 56486481
Web Site: http://www.cp-malaysia.com
Sales Range: $10-24.9 Million
Emp.: 29
Shrimp Farming Services
N.A.I.C.S.: 112512

B.P. Food Products Co., Ltd.   **(1)**
57 Moo 5 Pahonyothin Road Nongkhainam, Nongkae, Saraburi, Thailand
Tel.: (66) 3637 1885
Livestock & Animal Feed Mfr
N.A.I.C.S.: 311119

Bangkok Agro-Industrial Products Public Company Limited   **(1)**
64 Navathani Village Soi 3 Sukhaphiban 2 Khwang, Khlong Kum Khet Buengkum, Bangkok, Thailand
Tel.: (66) 26804500
Animal Feed Mfr
N.A.I.C.S.: 311111

Bangkok Food Products Co., Ltd.   **(1)**
Ramkhamhaeng 24 Rd Hua Mak, Bang Kapi, Bangkok, 10240, Thailand
Tel.: (66) 26759859
Animal Feed Mfr
N.A.I.C.S.: 311111

Bangkok Produce Merchandising Plc   **(1)**
18th Floor C P Tower 313 Silom Road, Bangkok, 10500, Thailand
Tel.: (66) 26258000
Web Site: http://www.thaifishmeal.com
Animal Feed Raw Material Distr
N.A.I.C.S.: 424590

Bangkok Produce Merchandising Public Company Limited   **(1)**
313 Silom Road, Bang Rak, Bangkok, Thailand
Tel.: (66) 26258000
Animal Food Distr
N.A.I.C.S.: 424910

Bellisio Foods, Inc.   **(1)**
701 N Washington St Ste 400, Minneapolis, MN 55401
Tel.: (612) 758-8400
Web Site: https://www.bellisiofoods.com
Frozen Food Specialties
N.A.I.C.S.: 311412
Joel Conner *(Chm)*

Subsidiary (Domestic):

Overhill Farms, Inc.   **(2)**
2727 E Vernon Ave, Vernon, CA 90058
Tel.: (323) 582-9977
Web Site: https://www.overhillfarms.com
Prepared Frozen Meals Mfr
N.A.I.C.S.: 311412

Berice LLC   **(1)**
113 Attwood Dr E, Dublin, GA 31027
Tel.: (404) 764-0609
Web Site: https://www.bernicefood.com
Restaurant Services
N.A.I.C.S.: 722511

C.P. Aquaculture (Beihai) Co., Ltd.   **(1)**
Hong Kong Road Bei Hai Industrial Zone, Beihai, 536005, Guangxi, China
Tel.: (86) 7792084362
Aquatic Feeds Mfr & Distr
N.A.I.C.S.: 311119

C.P. Aquaculture (Dongfang) Co., Ltd.   **(1)**
Laocheng Development Zone, Chengmai, Haikou, 570125, Hainan, China
Tel.: (86) 898 3696 3928
Shrimp Hatching Services
N.A.I.C.S.: 112512

Charoen Pokphand Foods Public Company
Limited—(Continued)

C.P. Cambodia Co., Ltd. (1)
K M 23 National Road No 4, Bek Chan
Commune, Phnom Penh, Kandal, Cambo-
dia
Tel.: (855) 397339
Web Site: http://www.cpcambodia.com.kh
Emp.: 1,500
Animal Feed Mfr
N.A.I.C.S.: 311111

C.P. Food Products Co., Ltd. (1)
1 CP Tower II 18th Floor Ratchadapisek
Road, Dindaeng, 10320, Bangkok, Thailand
Tel.: (66) 2641 1333
Restaurant Management Services
N.A.I.C.S.: 722511

C.P. Land Plc (1)
1 3 5 7 Fortune Town 29th Floor Ratchada-
phisek Road, Din Daeng Subdistrict Din
Daeng District, Bangkok, 10400, Thailand
Tel.: (66) 2 070 8888
Web Site: https://www.cplandproperty.com
Property Development Services
N.A.I.C.S.: 531390

C.P. Laos Co., Ltd. (1)
363/4-5 34 Kamphengmeuang St Phonth-
anNeua, Vientiane, Lao People's Democratic
Republic
Tel.: (856) 21453508
Livestock Farming & Animal Feeds Mfr
N.A.I.C.S.: 115210

C.P. Merchandising Co., Ltd. (1)
313 C P Tower Silom Road, Bangrak,
Bangkok, 10500, Thailand
Tel.: (66) 784 9000
Web Site: http://www.cpmerchandising.com
Sales Range: $25-49.9 Million
Emp.: 100
Animal Feed Mfr
N.A.I.C.S.: 311119

C.P. Pokphand Co. Ltd. (1)
21/F Far East Finance Centre 16 Harcourt
Road, Central, China (Hong Kong) (74%)
Tel.: (852) 25201601
Web Site: http://www.cpp.hk
Rev.: $6,960,836,000
Assets: $5,345,838,000
Liabilities: $3,378,800,000
Net Worth: $1,967,038,000
Earnings: $467,704,000
Emp.: 42,000
Fiscal Year-end: 12/31/2019
Investment Holding Company
N.A.I.C.S.: 551112
Adirek Sripratak (Vice Chm)

Subsidiary (Non-US):

**Pucheng Chia Tai Biochemistry Co.,
Ltd.** (2)
No 56 Dashixi, Putan Village Pucheng
County, Nanping, 353400, Fujian Province,
China (69.5%)
Tel.: (86) 400 600 8169
Web Site: https://www.ct-bio.cn
Sales Range: $200-249.9 Million
Emp.: 600
Antibiotics Mfr & Marketer
N.A.I.C.S.: 325411

**C.P. Standart Gida Sanayi ve Ticaret
A.S.** (1)
Buyukdere Cad Akinci Bayiri Sok No 6, Me-
cidiyekoy, 34394, Istanbul, Turkiye
Tel.: (90) 212 274 8536
Web Site: https://www.cpturkiye.com
Emp.: 60
Poultry & Cattle Feeds Mfr
N.A.I.C.S.: 311119
Nezih Gencer (Mng Dir-Sls)

CP HiLai Harbour Co., Ltd. (1)
6th Floor Charoen Nakorn Road, Khlong
Ton Sai Sub-district Klongsan District,
Bangkok, 10600, Thailand
Tel.: (66) 20551888
Web Site: http://www.cphilai.com
Restaurant Operators
N.A.I.C.S.: 722511

CPF (India) Private Ltd. (1)
841/1 Binnamangala 1st Stage 100ft Road
Indiranagar, Bengaluru, 560038, Karnataka,
India

Tel.: (91) 8066746300
Web Site: https://cpbrandindia.com
N.A.I.C.S.: 311119
Dhanin Chearavanont (Founder)

CPF Denmark A/S (1)
Tomrervej 10A, PO Box 67, 6800, Varde,
Denmark (52%)
Tel.: (45) 75261330
Web Site: http://www.cpf.co.th
Processed Meat & Food Products Importer
& Distr
N.A.I.C.S.: 424470

CPF Distribution GmbH (1)
Rothenbaumchaussee 80C, 20148, Ham-
burg, Germany
Tel.: (49) 40238064101
Web Site: https://cpf-distribution.com
Restaurant Services
N.A.I.C.S.: 722511

CPF Europe S.A. (1)
Avenue Belle Vue 17, Waterloo, 1410,
Belgium (99.99%)
Tel.: (32) 23575380
Web Site: http://www.cpfeurope.com
Sales Range: $25-49.9 Million
Emp.: 13
Processed Meat & Food Products Importer
& Distr
N.A.I.C.S.: 424470

Subsidiary (Non-US):

CP Foods (UK) Limited (2)
Avon House Hartlebury Trading Estate,
Hartlebury, Kidderminster, DY10 4JB,
Worcs, United Kingdom (100%)
Tel.: (44) 1299253131
Web Site: http://www.cpfoods.co.uk
Sales Range: $25-49.9 Million
Emp.: 50
Processed Meat & Food Products Importer
& Distr
N.A.I.C.S.: 424470

CPF Food Products Co., Ltd. (1)
252/129-132 Muang Thai-Phatra Office
Tower 2 29-3, 10310, Bangkok, Thailand
Tel.: (66) 2 6944466
Sales Range: $25-49.9 Million
Emp.: 100
Processed Meat Mfr
N.A.I.C.S.: 311612

CPF Hong Kong Co., Ltd. (1)
39 Wang Kwong Rd, Kowloon Bay, Kow-
loon, China (Hong Kong)
Tel.: (852) 35079100
Web Site: http://www.cpbrand.com
Property Development Services
N.A.I.C.S.: 531390

CPF IT Center Co., Ltd. (1)
313 CP Tower 16 Fl, Silom, 10500, Bang-
kok, Thailand
Tel.: (66) 26258000
Information Technology Services
N.A.I.C.S.: 541511

CPF Japan Co., Ltd. (1)
Tokyo Garden Terrace Kioicho 28th Floor
Kioi Tower 1-3, Kioicho Chiyoda-ku, Tokyo,
102-0094, Japan
Tel.: (81) 354012231
Web Site: https://www.su-cpi.co.jp
N.A.I.C.S.: 424470

CPF Logistics Co., Ltd. (1)
38 Q-House Tower Convent 5 AB 5th Floor
Convent Road, Silom, Bangkok, Thailand
Tel.: (66) 27845713
Logistic Services
N.A.I.C.S.: 541614

CPF Premium Foods Co., Ltd (1)
26/3 Moo 7 Suwinthawong Road Tambol
Klongnakornnueng, 24000, Chachoengsao,
Thailand
Tel.: (66) 38593046
Food Processing Services
N.A.I.C.S.: 311710

CPF Tokyo Co., Ltd. (1)
8 Floor Shibanishii Building No 9-1 Shiba
4-Chome, Minato-Ku, Tokyo, 108-0014,
Japan
Tel.: (81) 354012231
Web Site: http://www.su-cpi.co.jp

Sales Range: $25-49.9 Million
Emp.: 11
Processed Meats Distr
N.A.I.C.S.: 311119
Kittiya Kongmanmana (Asst VP)

CPF Trading Co., Ltd. (1)
28/F Muang Thai-Phatra Office Tower 2
252/115-116, Huaykwang, Bangkok, 10310,
Thailand
Tel.: (66) 26930583
Animal Food Products Whslr
N.A.I.C.S.: 424490

CPF Training Center Co., Ltd. (1)
1 Fl 14 th CP Tower 2 Ratchadapisek
Road, Din Daeng, Bangkok, 10400, Thai-
land
Tel.: (66) 26421491
Web Site: http://www.cpftc.cpf.co.th
Training Center Services
N.A.I.C.S.: 611519

Calibre Nature (M) Sdn. Bhd. (1)
Unit 06-01 6th Floor Lee Kay Huan Lot
14408 Jalan Genting Kelang, Setapak,
Kuala Lumpur, 53200, Malaysia
Tel.: (60) 3 4027 1800
Web Site: http://www.cp-malaysia.com
Aquaculture Integration Services
N.A.I.C.S.: 112519

**Charoen Pokphand (India) Private
Limited** (1)
104 G N T Road Sholavaram Post Red
Hills, Nallur Vijaynallur Village, Chennai,
600 067, Tamil Nadu, India
Tel.: (91) 442 447 4166
Web Site: http://www.mycpindia.com
Sales Range: $50-74.9 Million
Emp.: 6
Livestock Feed Mfr
N.A.I.C.S.: 424520

**Charoen Pokphand (Taiwan) Co.,
Ltd.** (1)
17 Floor 87 Sung Chiang Road, 10466, Tai-
pei, Taiwan
Tel.: (886) 2 25060567
Web Site: http://www.cpfoods.com.tw
Vaccines Whslr
N.A.I.C.S.: 424210

**Charoen Pokphand Enterprise (Tai-
wan) Co., Ltd.** (1)
17th Floor No 87 Songjiang Road, 10486,
Taipei, Taiwan
Tel.: (886) 22 507 7071
Web Site: https://www.cptwn.com.tw
Sales Range: $25-49.9 Million
Emp.: 100
Chicken Poultry Farming Services
N.A.I.C.S.: 311615
Cheng Wu Yueh (Pres)

**Charoen Pokphand Foods (Malaysia)
Sdn. Bhd.** (1)
6th Floor Wisma Lee Kay Huan Jalan
Genting Kelang, Setapak, 53200, Kuala
Lumpur, Malaysia
Tel.: (60) 340271800
Web Site: http://www.cp-malaysia.com
Poultry Processing Services
N.A.I.C.S.: 311615

**Charoen Pokphand Foods (Over-
seas) LLC** (1)
Pushkina Street 8th km, Lukhovitsy, Mos-
cow, Russia
Tel.: (7) 4966361255
Web Site: https://www.cpfrussia.ru
Sales Range: $25-49.9 Million
Emp.: 3
Convenience Foods Mfr
N.A.I.C.S.: 311710

**Charoen Pokphand Foods Canada
Inc.** (1)
7030 Woodbine Ave Suite 203, Markham,
L3R 6G2, ON, Canada
Tel.: (905) 604-4993
Web Site: http://www.cpfcanada.com
Food Product Whslr
N.A.I.C.S.: 424490

**Charoen Pokphand Foods Philippines
Corporation** (1)
Unit 1C-1D LSC Building Lazatin Boulevard,
Dolores Homesite Exit 2, San Fernando,
2000, Pampanga, Philippines

Tel.: (63) 344320994
Sales Range: $25-49.9 Million
Emp.: 55
Shrimp Hatching Services
N.A.I.C.S.: 112512
Wichet Kaewpa (Asst VP)

**Charoen Pokphand Northeastern
Public Company Limited** (1)
Bangkok 313 C P Tower 15th Floor Silom
Road, Bangrak, 10500, Bangkok, Thailand
Tel.: (66) 26804500
Livestock & Animal Feed Mfr
N.A.I.C.S.: 311111

**Chia Tai Enterprises International
Ltd.** (1)
21/F Far East Finance Centre 16 Harcourt
Road, Hong Kong, China (Hong Kong)
Tel.: (852) 25201601
Web Site: https://www.ctei.com.hk
Rev.: $159,239,000
Assets: $350,585,000
Liabilities: $94,833,000
Net Worth: $255,752,000
Earnings: ($4,259,000)
Emp.: 1,000
Fiscal Year-end: 12/31/2022
Chemical Product Mfr & Distr
N.A.I.C.S.: 325998
Phityaisarakul Thirayut (CEO-Biochemical
Div)

**Chia Tai Yongji Enterprise Co.,
Ltd.** (1)
Yongji Economic Development Zone, Jilin,
132200, China
Tel.: (86) 43265021199
Seafood Product Distr
N.A.I.C.S.: 424460

Chozen Holdings Ltd. (1)
Park House Park Terrace, Worcester Park,
London, KT4 7JZ, Surrey, United Kingdom
Tel.: (44) 208 337 0643
Web Site: https://www.chozen.co.uk
Restaurant Operators
N.A.I.C.S.: 722511
Keith English (Mgr-Ops)

Dzine Food Solutions Co., Ltd. (1)
230 Nguyen Van Huong Street, Thao Dien
Ward Thu Duc City, Ho Chi Minh City, Viet-
nam
Tel.: (84) 2862706273
Web Site: https://dzinefs.vn
Restaurant Services
N.A.I.C.S.: 722511

Food Trac Ltd. (1)
2nd Floor 27-29 Scottish Mutual House
North Street, Hornchurch, RM11 1RS, Es-
sex, United Kingdom
Tel.: (44) 170 845 8824
Web Site: https://www.foodtrac.co.uk
Food Product Whslr
N.A.I.C.S.: 424490

**Fujian Sumpo Foods Holdings Com-
pany Limited** (1)
No 110 Industrial And Commercial District
Donggongxia, Xinluo Region, Longyan,
364000, China
Tel.: (86) 59 7231 6719
Investment Management Service
N.A.I.C.S.: 523999

Hefei Chia Tai Co., Ltd. (1)
No 228 Fanhua Avenue The ETDA, Hefei,
230601, Anhui, China
Tel.: (86) 5513811050
Seafood Product Distr
N.A.I.C.S.: 424460

Homegrown Shrimp (USA), LLC (1)
21125 SW Farm Rd, Indiantown, FL 34956
Tel.: (772) 597-8484
Web Site: https://homegrownshrimp-
usa.com
Seafood Retailer
N.A.I.C.S.: 445250

International Pet Food Co., Ltd. (1)
127/4 Panjathani Tower 4th Floor Nonsi
Road, Chongnonsi Yannawa, Bangkok,
10120, Thailand
Tel.: (66) 2 036 4683
Web Site: https://www.jerhigh.com
Sales Range: $25-49.9 Million
Emp.: 40
Pet Food Mfr & Distr

N.A.I.C.S.: 311119

Jiangsu Huai Yin Chia Tai Co., Ltd. (1)
118 Zhengda Road, Huai'an, 223003, Jiangsu, China
Tel.: (86) 51783805005
Seafood Product Distr
N.A.I.C.S.: 424460

Klang Co., Ltd. (1)
313 CP Tower Silom Road Bangrak, Bangkok, 10500, Thailand
Tel.: (66) 26258000
Web Site: http://www.cpfworldwide.com
Shrimp Processing Services
N.A.I.C.S.: 112512

Lianyungang Chia Tai Feed Co., Ltd. (1)
Lianyungang Development Zone, Lianyungang, Jiangsu, China
Tel.: (86) 51882342558
Animal Feed Mfr
N.A.I.C.S.: 311119

Norfolk Foods (Private) Limited (1)
No 142 Katuwana Industrial Estate, Homagama, 10200, Sri Lanka
Tel.: (94) 11 285 7340
Web Site: https://www.crescentfoods.lk
Food Production Mfr
N.A.I.C.S.: 311999
Mohammed Ziauddin *(Founder & Mng Dir)*

Paulsen Food GmbH (1)
Rothenbaumchaussee 80C, 20148, Hamburg, Germany
Tel.: (49) 4023 806 4100
Web Site: https://www.paulsen-food.com
Food Product Import & Export Services
N.A.I.C.S.: 522299

Pet Republic Sp. z o.o. (1)
Ul Nasienna 22, 95-040, Koluszki, Poland
Tel.: (48) 222759210
Web Site: https://petrepublic.pl
Pet Food Retailer
N.A.I.C.S.: 459910

Pucheng Chia Tai Biochemistry Ltd. (1)
No 56 Dashixi Group, Putan Village Pucheng County, Nanping, Fujian, China
Tel.: (86) 4006008169
Web Site: http://www.pcfdata.com
Chlortetracycline Product Mfr
N.A.I.C.S.: 325411

Qingdao Chia Tai Agricultural Development Co., Ltd. (1)
Rd Zheng Da, Fu An 2nd Industrial Park, Jiaozhou, 266314, Shandong, China
Tel.: (86) 53283228008
Seafood Product Distr
N.A.I.C.S.: 424460

Rajburi Foods Co., Ltd. (1)
80/3 Moo 8 Donkrabueng, Banpong, Ratchaburi, 70110, Thailand
Tel.: (66) 3236 8181
Animal Feed Mfr
N.A.I.C.S.: 311119

Russia Baltic Pork Invest ASA (1)
JSC Pravdinsk Pig Production, PO Box 5179, Kaliningrad, 236006, Russia
Tel.: (7) 4012307700
Web Site: http://www.rbpi.no
Seafood Product Distr
N.A.I.C.S.: 424460

Seafoods Enterprise Co., Ltd (1)
82/12-13 Moo 4 Thonburi-Paktor Road, Bangkok, Thailand
Tel.: (66) 26258000
Shrimp Mfr
N.A.I.C.S.: 112512

Shenyang Chia Tai Livestock Co., Ltd. (1)
Bakeshu Street, Qianjin Village Dongling District, Shenyang, 110044, China
Tel.: (86) 2488010411
Emp.: 166
Seafood Product Distr
N.A.I.C.S.: 424460

Shijiazhuang Chia Tai Co., Ltd. (1)
Luquan Pingnan, Shijiazhuang, 050225, Hebei, China

Tel.: (86) 31182262794
Seafood Product Distr
N.A.I.C.S.: 424460

Star Feedmills (M) Sdn. Bhd. (1)
No PT 12007 Jalan Perindustrian Mahkota 2, Kawasan Perindustrian Mahkota, 43700, Beranang, Selangor Darul Ehsan, Malaysia
Tel.: (60) 389218299
Web Site: http://www.cp-malaysia.com
Emp.: 200
Aquatic Feeds Mfr & Distr
N.A.I.C.S.: 311119

The Foodfellas Ltd. (1)
6-9 The Square Stockley Park, Uxbridge, UB11 1FW, Middlesex, United Kingdom
Tel.: (44) 2086223064
Web Site: http://www.thefoodfellas.co.uk
Food Product Import & Export Services
N.A.I.C.S.: 522299

Tops Foods NV (1)
Lammerdries - Oost 26, 2250, Olen, Belgium
Tel.: (32) 1 428 5560
Web Site: https://www.topsfoods.com
Prepared Food Mfr & Whslr
N.A.I.C.S.: 311991

Westbridge Foods (Thailand) Ltd. (1)
8 The Horizon Building 3rd Floor, Sukhumvit 63 Prakanong Nua Wattana, Bangkok, 10110, Thailand
Tel.: (66) 27269898
Food Product Development Services
N.A.I.C.S.: 541715

Wuhan Chia Tai Co., Ltd. (1)
East Lake New High Technology Development Zone, Guannan Village, Wuhan, 430074, Hubei, China
Tel.: (86) 27878008703
Seafood Product Distr
N.A.I.C.S.: 424460

Yichang Chia Tai Co., Ltd. (1)
Yichang Hubei Xiao Ting Road No 188, Yichang, 443007, China
Tel.: (86) 7176514405
Food Product Whslr
N.A.I.C.S.: 424490

CHAROEN POKPHAND GROUP CO., LTD.
CP Tower 313 Silom Road, Bangrak, Bangkok, 10500, Thailand
Tel.: (66) 26258000   TH
Web Site:
   http://www.cpgroupglobal.com
Year Founded: 1921
Sales Range: $25-49.9 Billion
Emp.: 280,000
Diversified Holding Company
N.A.I.C.S.: 551112
Suphachai Chearavanont *(CEO)*

Subsidiaries:

Allianz C.P. General Insurance Co., Ltd. (1)
CP Twr 19 Fl 313 Silom Rd Bangrak, Bangkok, 10500, Thailand
Tel.: (66) 26389000
Web Site: http://www.allianzcp.com
Sales Range: $50-74.9 Million
Emp.: 100
Insurance Services; Owned by Allianz AG & by Charoen Pokphang Group
N.A.I.C.S.: 524298
Pakit Iamopus *(Pres & CEO)*

C.P. BANGLADESH Co., Ltd. (1)
House 28 Alaol Avenue, Sector 6 Uttara, Dhaka, 1230, Bangladesh
Tel.: (880) 2 8919479
Web Site: http://www.cpbangladesh.com
Livestock Breeding Services
N.A.I.C.S.: 112990
Navee Permpeerapet *(VP-Hatchery & Breeder)*

C.P. Lotus Corporation (1)
21st Floor Far East Finance Centre, 16 Harcourt Road, Hong Kong, China (Hong Kong) **(100%)**
Tel.: (852) 2520 1601

Web Site: http://www.cplotuscorp.com
Rev.: $1,471,640,779
Assets: $1,033,829,762
Liabilities: $829,241,461
Net Worth: $204,588,301
Earnings: ($41,924,515)
Emp.: 10,900
Fiscal Year-end: 12/31/2018
Grocery Stores
N.A.I.C.S.: 445110
Soopakij Chearavanont *(Co-Chm)*

C.P. Products, Inc. (1)
7135 Minstrel Way Ste 203, Columbia, MD 21045
Tel.: (800) 720-6668
Food Products Mfr
N.A.I.C.S.: 311999
Terry Goodman *(Pres & CEO)*

CP Intertrade Company Limited (1)
202 Le Concorde Tower 19th Floor Ratchadapisek Road, Huaykwang, Bangkok, 10310, Thailand
Tel.: (66) 2 646 7000
Business Support Services
N.A.I.C.S.: 561499

CP Vietnam Corporation (1)
So 2 duong 2A KCN Bien Hoa 2, Bien Hoa, T Dong Nai, Vietnam
Tel.: (84) 613 836 251
Web Site: http://www.cp.com.vn
Livestock Breeding Services
N.A.I.C.S.: 112990

CPPC Public Company Limited (1)
313 CP Tower 18th Floor Silom Road, Bangrak, 10500, Thailand
Tel.: (66) 2 6258075
Web Site: http://www.cppcnet.com
Plastics & Packaging Mfr
N.A.I.C.S.: 326199
Prasert Poongkumarn *(Chm, Pres & CEO)*

Charoen Pokphand Intertrade Singapore (Pte) Ltd. (1)
315 Outram Road Tan Boon Liat Building 12-08B, Singapore, Singapore
Tel.: (65) 6538 7020
Business Support Services
N.A.I.C.S.: 561499

Chia Tai Company Limited (1)
299-301 Songsawad Road, Samphantawong District, 10100, Bangkok, Thailand
Tel.: (66) 2 233 8191
Web Site: http://www.chiataigroup.com
Business Support Services
N.A.I.C.S.: 561499

EK Chor China Motorcycle Co., Ltd. (1)
21st Fl Far E Finance Ctr, 16 Harcourt Rd, Hong Kong, China (Hong Kong) **(68%)**
Tel.: (852) 25201601
Web Site: http://www.ekchor-china.com
Sales Range: $1-4.9 Billion
Emp.: 3,000
Holding Company; Motorcycle Mfr
N.A.I.C.S.: 551112

Freewill Solutions Company Limited (1)
29 th Floor Lumpini Tower 1168/86-88 Rama IV Road Tungmahamek, Sathorn, Bangkok, 10120, Thailand
Tel.: (66) 2679 8556
Web Site: http://www.freewillsolutions.com
Software Development Services
N.A.I.C.S.: 541511
Orachat Rakphongphairoj *(Dir-HR)*

Myanmar C.P Livestock Co., Ltd (1)
No 135 Pyay Road 8 miles, Mayangone Township, Yangon, Myanmar
Tel.: (95) 1 651324
Web Site: http://www.myanmarcp.com
Livestock Breeding Services
N.A.I.C.S.: 112990

Perfect Companion Group Company Limited (1)
195 Empire Tower 14th Fl South Rd Yannawa, Sathorn, Bangkok, 10120, Thailand
Tel.: (66) 2 670 9600
Web Site: http://www.perfectcompanion.com
Food Products Mfr
N.A.I.C.S.: 311999

True Corporation Public Company Limited (1)

18 True Tower Ratchadapisek Road, Huai Khwang, Bangkok, 10310, Thailand
Tel.: (66) 28591111
Web Site: https://www.true.th
Rev.: $6,081,344,462
Assets: $21,739,897,904
Liabilities: $19,235,837,865
Net Worth: $2,504,060,038
Earnings: ($453,551,259)
Emp.: 10,777
Fiscal Year-end: 12/31/2023
Cable Television, Internet & Mobile Services
N.A.I.C.S.: 516120
Suphachai Chearavanont *(Chm)*

Subsidiary (Domestic):

Cineplex Company Limited (2)
Tipco Tower 118/1 Rama VI Road, Samsennai Phyathai, Bangkok, 10400, Thailand **(99.99%)**
Tel.: (66) 26159000
Sales Range: $25-49.9 Million
Emp.: 12
Motion Picture & Video Producer
N.A.I.C.S.: 512110

Total Access Communication Public Co., Ltd. (2)
319 Chamchuri Square Building 22nd - 41st Floors Phayathai Road, Pathumwan, Bangkok, 10330, Thailand
Tel.: (66) 22028000
Web Site: http://www.dtac.co.th
Telecommunication Servicesb
N.A.I.C.S.: 517111
Boonchai Bencharongkul *(Chm)*

Subsidiary (Domestic):

DTAC Network Co., Ltd. (3)
333/3 Moo 14 Phayathai Road, Pathum Wan, Bangkok, 10900, Thailand
Tel.: (66) 22028000
Telecommunication Servicesb
N.A.I.C.S.: 517810

TAC Property Co., Ltd. (3)
319 Chamchuri Square Building 41st Fl Phayathai Rd, Pathumwan, Bangkok, 10330, Thailand
Tel.: (66) 2 202 8000
Asset Management Services
N.A.I.C.S.: 523940

TeleAssets Co., Ltd. (3)
319 Chamchuri Square Building 41st Fl Phayathai Rd, Pathumwan, Bangkok, 10330, Thailand
Tel.: (66) 2 202 8000
Telecommunications Equipment Leasing Services
N.A.I.C.S.: 532490

United Communication Industry Public Company Limited (3)
499 Moo 3 Benchachinda Bldg, Vibhavadi Rangsit Road, Ladyao Chatuchak, Bangkok, 10900, Thailand **(99.8%)**
Tel.: (66) 29531111
Web Site: http://www.ucom.co.th
Sales Range: $100-124.9 Million
Telecommunication Servicesb
N.A.I.C.S.: 517111

Subsidiary (Domestic):

United Information Highway Co., Ltd. (4)
99 Moo 3 Benchachinda Bldg Vibhavadi Rangsit Rd Ladyao, Chatuchak, Bangkok, 10900, Thailand
Tel.: (66) 283148881
Web Site: http://www.uih.co.th
Data Communication Services
N.A.I.C.S.: 517112

Subsidiary (Domestic):

UBC Cable Network Public Company Limited (2)
Tipco Tower 118/Rama VI Road, Samsennai Phyathai, Bangkok, 10400, Thailand **(99.02%)**
Tel.: (66) 26159000
Sales Range: $350-399.9 Million
Emp.: 1,016
Cable Television Broadcasting Services
N.A.I.C.S.: 516120

Charoen Pokphand Group Co., Ltd.—(Continued)

CHAROENRUT KARNTAW CO., LTD.
361/1 Soi Anamaingamjarean 25
Rama 2 Road, Thakham Bangkun-
tien, Bangkok, 10150, Thailand
Tel.: (66) 864657777   TH
Web Site:
  https://www.charoenrutkarntaw.com
Cotton & Synthetic Fiber Mfr
N.A.I.C.S.: 313110

CHARRIER SA
53 rue de la Jominere, 49300, Cho-
let, Maine Et Loire, France
Tel.: (33) 241710485
Web Site: http://www.charrier-
concessionaire.fr
Rev.: $26,200,000
Emp.: 21
New & Used Car Dealers
N.A.I.C.S.: 441110
Laurent Pignon *(Mgr)*

CHARTER HALL LIMITED
Level 20 No1 Martin Place, Sydney,
2000, NSW, Australia
Tel.: (61) 286519000   AU
Web Site:
  https://www.charterhall.com.au
Year Founded: 1991
CHC—(ASX)
Rev.: $774,924,566
Assets: $2,516,704,293
Liabilities: $594,486,821
Net Worth: $1,922,217,472
Earnings: $379,723,764
Emp.: 270
Fiscal Year-end: 06/30/21
Real Estate Investment Trust
N.A.I.C.S.: 525990
David Harrison *(CEO & Mng Dir)*

Subsidiaries:

Charter Hall Long WALE REIT   **(1)**
Level 20 No 1 Martin Place, Sydney, 2000,
NSW, Australia   **(10.7%)**
Tel.: (61) 286519000
Web Site: https://www.charterhall.com.au
Rev.: $146,817,997
Assets: $3,507,287,656
Liabilities: $1,257,134,066
Net Worth: $2,250,153,591
Earnings: ($341,133,676)
Emp.: 191
Fiscal Year-end: 06/30/2024
Real Estate Investment Trust
N.A.I.C.S.: 525990

Joint Venture (Domestic):

ALE Property Group   **(2)**
Level 10 6 O Connell Street, Sydney, 2000,
NSW, Australia   **(50%)**
Tel.: (61) 2 8231 8588
Web Site: http://www.alegroup.com.au
Rev.: $164,113,301
Assets: $1,026,675,445
Liabilities: $457,408,534
Net Worth: $569,266,911
Earnings: $137,279,028
Emp.: 11
Fiscal Year-end: 06/30/2021
Owner of Pubs
N.A.I.C.S.: 531390
Andrew Frederick Osborne Wilkinson *(CEO
& Mng Dir)*

Subsidiary (Domestic):

Australian Leisure & Entertainment
Property Management Limited   **(3)**
Level 10 Norwich House 6 O'Connell St,
Sydney, 2000, NSW, Australia
Tel.: (61) 282318588
Web Site: http://www.alegroup.com.au
Sales Range: $25-49.9 Million
Emp.: 6
Investment Property Management Services
N.A.I.C.S.: 541618

Australian Leisure & Entertainment
Property Trust   **(3)**
Level 10 Norwich House 6 O'Connell St,
Sydney, 2000, NSW, Australia
Tel.: (61) 282318588
Web Site: http://www.alegroup.com.au
Sales Range: $25-49.9 Million
Emp.: 6
Investment Property Management Services
N.A.I.C.S.: 541618
Andrew Wilkinson *(Mng Dir)*

Charter Hall Real Estate Inc.   **(1)**
155 N Wacker Dr Ste 1680, Grayslake, IL
60606
Tel.: (312) 546-7610
Real Estate Management Services
N.A.I.C.S.: 531390

Charter Hall Real Estate Manage-
ment Services (NSW) Pty
Limited   **(1)**
11/333 George Street, Sydney, 2000, NSW,
Australia
Tel.: (61) 289084000
Property Management Services
N.A.I.C.S.: 531311

Charter Hall Real Estate Manage-
ment Services (QLD) Pty Limited   **(1)**
L 13 1 Martin Pl, Sydney, 2000, NSW, Aus-
tralia
Tel.: (61) 263525311
Property Management Services
N.A.I.C.S.: 531311

Charter Hall Real Estate Management Services (VIC) Pty Limited   **(1)**
101 Collins St, Melbourne, 3000, VIC, Australia
Tel.: (61) 396639986
Real Estate Management Services
N.A.I.C.S.: 531390

Charter Hall Retail Management Pty
Limited   **(1)**
PO Box 2704, Sydney, 2001, NSW, Austra-
lia
Tel.: (61) 2 8232 3333
Real Estate Management Services
N.A.I.C.S.: 531390

Charter Hall Retail REIT   **(1)**
Level 20 No 1 Martin Place, Sydney, 2000,
NSW, Australia   **(10.7%)**
Tel.: (61) 286519000
Web Site: http://www.charterhall.com.au
Rev.: $144,030,448
Assets: $2,535,790,588
Liabilities: $787,259,612
Net Worth: $1,748,530,976
Earnings: $11,485,043
Fiscal Year-end: 06/30/2024
Supermarket Operator
N.A.I.C.S.: 445110
David Harrison *(Exec Dir)*

Charter Hall Social Infrastructure
REIT   **(1)**
Level 20 No 1 Martin Place, Sydney, 2000,
NSW, Australia   **(8.7%)**
Tel.: (61) 399036157
Web Site: https://www.charterhall.com.au
Rev.: $78,959,379
Assets: $1,477,277,173
Liabilities: $505,705,157
Net Worth: $972,552,015
Earnings: $38,273,456
Fiscal Year-end: 06/30/2023
Real Estate Investment Trust
N.A.I.C.S.: 525990
Nick Anagnostou *(CEO)*

Folkestone Limited   **(1)**
Level 10 60 Carrington Street, Sydney,
2000, NSW, Australia
Tel.: (61) 2 8667 2800
Web Site: http://folkestone.com.au
Rev.: $43,200,687
Assets: $140,291,255
Liabilities: $20,482,277
Net Worth: $119,808,978
Earnings: $10,127,520
Fiscal Year-end: 06/30/2017
Property Development & Construction Ser-
vices
N.A.I.C.S.: 531311

Subsidiary (Domestic):

Access Constructions Pty Ltd   **(2)**

57 Roberts Ave, Mulgrave, 3170, VIC, Aus-
tralia
Tel.: (61) 385589500
Web Site:
  http://www.accessconstructions.com.au
Building Construction Services
N.A.I.C.S.: 236220

CHARTER PACIFIC CORPO-RATION LIMITED
Level 12 50 Cavill Avenue, PO Box
40, Surfers Paradise, 4217, QLD,
Australia
Tel.: (61) 755382558
Web Site: http://www.charpac.com.au
Year Founded: 1988
Sales Range: Less than $1 Million
Emp.: 20
Financial Services
N.A.I.C.S.: 523940
Steven Allan Cole *(Sec)*

CHARTERED CAPITAL & IN-VESTMENT LTD.
711 Mahakant Opp VS Hospital, Ellis-
bridge, Ahmedabad, 380 006, India
Tel.: (91) 7926577571
Web Site:
  https://www.charteredcapital.net
511696—(BOM)
Rev.: $294,804
Assets: $7,299,922
Liabilities: $151,945
Net Worth: $7,147,977
Earnings: $61,507
Emp.: 6
Fiscal Year-end: 03/31/21
Financial Investment Services
N.A.I.C.S.: 523999
Amrit Lal Sanghvi *(Vice Chm)*

CHARTERED LOGISTICS LTD.
6 Chartered House Sanand Road
Sarkhej, Sardar Patel Ring Road
Bakrol Cross Road Bakrol, Ahmeda-
bad, 382210, India
Tel.: (91) 9879209040
Web Site: https://www.chartered.co.in
Year Founded: 1995
531977—(BOM)
Rev.: $18,191,273
Assets: $14,205,528
Liabilities: $8,266,167
Net Worth: $5,939,361
Earnings: ($323,000)
Emp.: 91
Fiscal Year-end: 03/31/21
Food Transportation Services
N.A.I.C.S.: 488490
Lalit Kumar Gandhi *(Mng Dir)*

Subsidiaries:

Chartered Motors Pvt Ltd   **(1)**
Opposite Viraj Farm Navagam Rajkot High-
way, Vartej, Bhavnagar, 364 060, India
Tel.: (91) 278 2541101
Sales Range: $25-49.9 Million
Emp.: 35
Motor Vehicle Whslr
N.A.I.C.S.: 423110
Nirav Dave *(Gen Mgr)*

CHARTERHOUSE CAPITAL PARTNERS LLP
Warwick Court 7th Floor, Paternoster
Square, London, EC4M 7DX, United
Kingdom
Tel.: (44) 2073345300   UK
Web Site:
  http://www.charterhouse.co.uk
Year Founded: 1982
Emp.: 50
Privater Equity Firm
N.A.I.C.S.: 523999
James Simon Edward Arnell *(Partner)*

Subsidiaries:

Acromas Holdings Ltd.   **(1)**
Enbrook Park, Folkestone, CT20 3SE,
Kent, United Kingdom
Tel.: (44) 1303776023
Web Site: http://www.acromas.co.uk
Sales Range: $1-4.9 Billion
Emp.: 31,302
Holding Company; Financial, Insurance,
Travel, Healthcare & Lifestyle Products &
Services
N.A.I.C.S.: 551112
John Andrew Goodsell *(Chm & CEO)*

Subsidiary (Domestic):

Saga Group Limited   **(2)**
Enbrook Park, Middleburg Square, Folke-
stone, CT20 3SE, Kent, United Kingdom
Tel.: (44) 1303771111
Web Site: http://www.saga.co.uk
Sales Range: $125-149.9 Million
Emp.: 6,000
Holding Company; Insurance, Travel, Finan-
cial & Lifestyle Products & Services
N.A.I.C.S.: 551112
Roger Ramsden *(CEO-Saga Svcs)*

Subsidiary (Domestic):

Acromas Holidays Limited   **(3)**
Enbrook Park, Middleburg Square, Folke-
stone, CT20 3SE, Kent, United Kingdom
Tel.: (44) 1303 771 111
Web Site: http://www.travel.saga.co.uk
Vacation & Tour Travel Agency
N.A.I.C.S.: 561510
Susan Hooper *(CEO)*

Acromas Shipping Limited   **(3)**
Enbrook Park, Middleburg Square, Folke-
stone, CT20 3SE, Kent, United Kingdom
Tel.: (44) 1303 771 111
Web Site: http://www.saga.co.uk
Cruise Vacation Travel Agency
N.A.I.C.S.: 561510

Allied Healthcare   **(3)**
Beaconsfield Court Beaconsfield Road, Hat-
field, AL10 8HU, Herts, United Kingdom
Tel.: (44) 8458501435
Web Site: http://www.alliedhealthcare.com
Holding Company; Health & Social Care
Staffing
N.A.I.C.S.: 551112
John Rennocks *(Chm)*

Subsidiary (Domestic):

Nestor Primecare Services Ltd.   **(4)**
Beaconfields Court Beaconsfield Road, Hat-
field, AL10 8HU, Herts, United Kingdom
Tel.: (44) 1707 286800
Web Site: http://www.nestor-
healthcare.co.uk
Sales Range: $10-24.9 Million
Health Care Srvices
N.A.I.C.S.: 621999

Subsidiary (US):

Allied Healthcare International
Inc.   **(3)**
245 Park Ave 39th Fl, New York, NY 10167
Tel.: (212) 750-0064
Web Site: http://www.alliedhealthcare.com
Sales Range: $250-299.9 Million
Emp.: 1,160
Holding Company; Healthcare Staffing
N.A.I.C.S.: 551112

Subsidiary (Non-US):

Allied Healthcare Group Holdings
Limited   **(4)**
Stone Business Park, Brooms Road, Stone,
ST15 0TL, Staffs, United Kingdom
Tel.: (44) 1785810600
Web Site: http://www.alliedhealthcare.co.uk
Holding Company
N.A.I.C.S.: 551112

Subsidiary (Domestic):

Allied Healthcare Holdings
Limited   **(5)**
Stone Business Park, Brooms Road, Stone,
ST15 0TL, Staffs, United Kingdom
Tel.: (44) 1785810600

Web Site: http://www.alliedhealthcare.co.uk
Sales Range: $150-199.9 Million
Emp.: 200
Holding Company; Healthcare Staffing Services
N.A.I.C.S.: 551112

Subsidiary (Domestic):

Allied Healthcare Group Limited (6)
Stone Business Park, Brooms Road, Stone, ST15 OTL, Staffordshire, United Kingdom
Tel.: (44) 1785810600
Web Site: http://www.alliedhealthcare.co.uk
Sales Range: $25-49.9 Million
Nursing & Healthcare Services
N.A.I.C.S.: 621610

Subsidiary (Domestic):

Saga Services Limited (3)
Enbrook Park, Middleburg Square, Folkestone, CT20 1AZ, Kent, United Kingdom
Tel.: (44) 1303771111
Web Site: http://www.saga.co.uk
Financial Information & Advisory Services
N.A.I.C.S.: 525990
Andrew Goodsell (CEO)

Subsidiary (Domestic):

The Automobile Association Limited (2)
Fanum House Basingview, Basingstoke, RG21 4EA, Hants, United Kingdom
Tel.: (44) 8705448866
Web Site: http://www.theaa.com
Sales Range: $300-349.9 Million
Automobile Services Club
N.A.I.C.S.: 561599
Michael Cutbill (Dir-Mktg & Sls)

BARTEC Top Holding GmbH (1)
Max-Eyth-Strasse 16, 97980, Bad Mergentheim, Germany
Tel.: (49) 7931 597 0
Web Site: http://www.bartec.de
Sales Range: $350-399.9 Million
Industrial Safety Products Mfr
N.A.I.C.S.: 551112
Ralf Koster (Chm-Mgmt Bd & CEO)

Subsidiary (Non-US):

BARTEC AB (2)
Lyckeaborg, S-371 93, Karlskrona, Sweden
Tel.: (46) 455 687 400
Web Site: http://www.bartec.se
Industrial Safety Products Mfr
N.A.I.C.S.: 334519
Joakim Gerser (Mng Dir)

BARTEC Belgium NV/SA (2)
H Hartlaan 26 Industriepark Schoonhees Zone 1, B-3980, Tessenderlo, Belgium
Tel.: (32) 13 6723 08
Web Site: http://www.bartec.be
Industrial Safety Products Mfr
N.A.I.C.S.: 334519
Caroline Fonteyn (Engr-Sls)

BARTEC Elektrotechnik GmbH (2)
Brown Boveri Strasse 8/2/1, A-2351, Wiener Neudorf, Austria
Tel.: (43) 2236 21204 0
Web Site: http://www.bartec.at
Industrial Safety Products Mfr
N.A.I.C.S.: 334519

BARTEC Engineering + Services AG (2)
Hinterbergstrasse 28, CH-6330, Cham, Switzerland
Tel.: (41) 41 74727 27
Web Site: http://www.bartec.ch
Industrial Safety Products Mfr
N.A.I.C.S.: 334519
Harald Lumetzberger (Mng Dir)

Subsidiary (Domestic):

BARTEC GmbH (2)
Max-Eyth-Strasse 16, Bad Mergentheim, 97980, Germany
Tel.: (49) 7931 597 0
Web Site: http://www.bartec.de
Industrial Safety Products Mfr
N.A.I.C.S.: 334519
Ewald Warmuth (Gen Mgr)

Subsidiary (Non-US):

BARTEC Hungary Kft. (2)
Budafoki ut 187-189, 1117, Budapest, Hungary
Tel.: (36) 1 204 0864
Web Site: http://www.bartec.hu
Industrial Safety Products Mfr
N.A.I.C.S.: 334519
Attila Major (Mgr-Technical)

BARTEC NEDERLAND b.v. (2)
Boelewerf 25, 2987 VD, Ridderkerk, Netherlands
Tel.: (31) 180 410588
Web Site: http://www.bartec.nl
Emp.: 30
Industrial Safety Products Mfr
N.A.I.C.S.: 334519
Rob Veth (Mng Dir)

BARTEC PIXAVI AS (2)
Domkirkeplassen 2, NO-4006, Stavanger, Norway
Tel.: (47) 90 94 31 56
Web Site: http://www.bartec-pixavi.com
Industrial Safety Technology Mfr
N.A.I.C.S.: 334220
Christian Rokseth (CEO)

BARTEC Polska Sp. z o.o. (2)
ul. Murarska 28, 43-100, Tychy, Poland
Tel.: (48) 32 32644.00
Web Site: http://www.bartec.pl
Industrial Safety Products Mfr
N.A.I.C.S.: 334519
Mieczyslaw Kolek (Mng Dir)

BARTEC S.A. (2)
Crta. de L'Hospitalet, 66-68 Nave D Poligono Industrial Almeda, E-08940, Cornella de Llobregat, Spain
Tel.: (34) 93 3314 258
Web Site: http://www.bartec.es
Industrial Safety Products Mfr
N.A.I.C.S.: 334519
Adam Segales (Mng Dir)

BARTEC S.r.l. (2)
Via per Carpiano 8/10, I-20077, Melegnano, Italy
Tel.: (39) 0298 2319 91
Web Site: http://www.bartec.it
Industrial Safety Products Mfr
N.A.I.C.S.: 334519

BARTEC TECHNOR AS (2)
PO Box 418, 4067, Stavanger, Norway
Tel.: (47) 51844100
Web Site: http://www.bartec-technor.no
Industrial Safety Equipment Mfr
N.A.I.C.S.: 334513
Halvor Lunde (Mng Dir)

BARTEC UK Ltd. (2)
Arundel House Little 66 Hollins Brook Park, Pilsworth, Bury, BL9 8RN, United Kingdom
Tel.: (44) 8444 992 710
Web Site: http://www.bartec.co.uk
Emp.: 12
Industrial Safety Products Mfr
N.A.I.C.S.: 334519
Kevin Morris (Mng Dir)

BARTEC VODEC Ltd. (2)
No 5 Centurion Business Park Dabell Avenue Blenheim Industrial Estate, Nottingham, NG6 8WA, United Kingdom
Tel.: (44) 115 96752 40
Web Site: http://www.bartec-vodec.com
Wired Telecommunication System Mfr
N.A.I.C.S.: 334290
William Dudeney (Mgr-Design & Dev)

BARTEC Varnost, d.o.o. (2)
Cesta 9 avgusta 59, SLO-1410, Zagorje ob Savi, Slovenia
Tel.: (386) 3 5664 366
Web Site: http://www.bartec.si
Industrial Safety Products Mfr
N.A.I.C.S.: 334519
Sasha Pablec (Product Mgr)

BARTEC s.a.r.l. (2)
20 rue de l'industrie, BP 80420, F-67412, Illkirch-Graffenstaden, France
Tel.: (33) 388 590305
Web Site: http://www.bartec.fr
Industrial Safety Products Mfr
N.A.I.C.S.: 334519
Yves Bossler (Mgr-Sls Support)

BARTEC s.r.o. (2)
Jana Palacha 743, CZ-278 01, Kralupy nad Vltavou, Czech Republic
Tel.: (420) 221 220 005
Web Site: http://www.bartec.cz
Industrial Safety Products Mfr
N.A.I.C.S.: 334519

OOO "BARTEC Rus" (2)
3 Proezd Perova Polya 8 Bld 11, 111141, Moscow, Russia
Tel.: (7) 495 646 24 10
Web Site: http://www.bartec-russia.ru
Industrial Safety Products Mfr
N.A.I.C.S.: 334519

OOO "BARTEC SB" (2)
3 Proezd Perova Polya 8 Bld 11, 111141, Moscow, Russia
Tel.: (7) 495 726 46 37
Mining Safety Products Mfr
N.A.I.C.S.: 334519

H.A. Bruno LLC (1)
210 E Rte 4 Ste 204, Paramus, NJ 07652
Tel.: (201) 226-1130
Web Site: http://www.habruno.com
Sales Range: $1-9.9 Million
Emp.: 40
Event Marketing & Exhibits/Trade Shows
N.A.I.C.S.: 541810
Stephen Ianuzzi (Pres)

Holding Bercy Investissement SCA (1)
61/69 rue de Bercy, 75589, Paris, Cedex 12, France
Tel.: (33) 140195000
Holding Company
N.A.I.C.S.: 551112

Holding (Domestic):

Elior SCA (2)
Tour Egee 11 allee de lArche, 92032, Paris, Cedex, France
Tel.: (33) 171067000
Web Site: https://www.eliorgroup.com
Food Catering & Contract Services
N.A.I.C.S.: 722320
Philip Guillemot (CEO-Elior France)

Subsidiary (Non-US):

Avenance Italia S.p.A (3)
Via Venezia Giulia 5/A, Milan, 20157, Italy
Tel.: (39) 02 39039630
Catering Services
N.A.I.C.S.: 722320

Subsidiary (Domestic):

Gemeaz Cusin S.p.A. (4)
Via Privata Venezia Giulia 5A, Milan, 20157, Italy
Tel.: (39) 02 390391
Web Site: http://www.gemeaz.it
Sales Range: $400-449.9 Million
Catering Services
N.A.I.C.S.: 722320

Subsidiary (US):

Corporate Chefs Inc. (3)
22 Parkridge Rd, Haverhill, MA 01835
Tel.: (978) 372-7400
Web Site: http://www.corporatechefs.com
Provider of Contract Food Services
N.A.I.C.S.: 722310
Shawn Bramble (Mng Dir)

Preferred Meals, Inc. (3)
5240 St Charles Rd, Berkeley, IL 60163
Web Site: http://www.preferredmeals.com
Emp.: 5,000
Institutional Food Services
N.A.I.C.S.: 722310
George Chivari (Pres & CEO)

TrustHouse Services Group, Inc. (3)
2201 Water Ridge Pkwy Ste 320, Charlotte, NC 28217
Tel.: (704) 424-1071
Web Site:
    http://www.trusthouseservices.com
Sales Range: $450-499.9 Million
Holding Company; Food Management Outsourcing Services
N.A.I.C.S.: 551112
Michael Bailey (Chm)

Subsidiary (Domestic):

A'viands, LLC (4)
1751 County Rd B W Ste 300, Roseville, MN 55113
Tel.: (651) 631-0940
Web Site: http://www.aviands.com
Sales Range: $75-99.9 Million
Food Service Management Contractor
N.A.I.C.S.: 722310
William J. Benzick (Founder & Chm)

Aladdin Food Management Services, LLC (4)
21 Armory Dr, Wheeling, WV 26003
Tel.: (304) 242-6200
Web Site: http://www.aladdinfood.com
Sales Range: $75-99.9 Million
Contract Food Services
N.A.I.C.S.: 722310
Wayne F. Burke (Pres & CEO)

Subsidiary (Domestic):

AmeriServe Food Management Services (5)
200 E Walnut St, Columbia, MO 65203
Tel.: (573) 499-1500
Web Site: http://www.ameriservefood.com
Sales Range: $10-24.9 Million
Contract Food Services
N.A.I.C.S.: 722310
Richard Liebman (Founder)

Subsidiary (Domestic):

Fitz, Vogt & Associates, Ltd. (4)
28 Main St, Walpole, NH 03608
Tel.: (603) 756-4578
Web Site: http://www.fitzvogt.com
Sales Range: $25-49.9 Million
Contract Food Services
N.A.I.C.S.: 722310

Lindley Food Service Corporation (4)
201 Wallace St, New Haven, CT 06511
Tel.: (203) 777-3598
Web Site: http://www.lindleyfoodservice.com
Sales Range: $10-24.9 Million
Emp.: 225
Contract Food Services
N.A.I.C.S.: 722310
Mark Cerreta (Co-Owner)

Valley Services, Inc. (4)
4400 Mangum Dr, Flowood, MS 39232-2113 (100%)
Tel.: (601) 664-3100
Web Site: http://www.valleyinc.com
Sales Range: $350-399.9 Million
Emp.: 2,750
Food Contracting Services
N.A.I.C.S.: 722310
Jim Walt (Pres & CEO)

SLR Consulting Ltd. (1)
7 Wornal Park Menmarsh Road, Worminghall, Aylesbury, HP18 9PH, Bucks, United Kingdom
Tel.: (44) 1844 337380
Web Site: http://www.slrconsulting.com
Sales Range: $150-199.9 Million
Emp.: 1,100
Environmental Consulting Services
N.A.I.C.S.: 541620
Neil Penhall (CEO)

Subsidiary (Domestic):

Corporate Citizenship Limited (2)
Greencoat House Francis Street, London, SW1P 1DH, United Kingdom
Tel.: (44) 20 7861 1616
Web Site: http://www.corporate-citizenship.com
Public Relation Agency Services
N.A.I.C.S.: 541611
Amanda Jordan (Dir)

Subsidiary (US):

E.Vironment, LLC (2)
14011 Park Dr Ste 100, Tomball, TX 77377-6288
Tel.: (281) 351-2856
Web Site: http://www.evironmentgroup.com
Environmental Management Services
N.A.I.C.S.: 541620
John Turley (Mng Partner)

Charterhouse Capital Partners LLP—(Continued)

Subsidiary (Non-US):

HFP Acoustical Consultants Corp. (2)
10201 Southport Road SW Suite 1140, Calgary, T2W 4X9, AB, Canada
Tel.: (403) 259-6600
Web Site: http://www.hfpacoustical.com
Acoustical Engineering Consulting Services
N.A.I.C.S.: 541620
Leslie Frank (Pres)

Subsidiary (US):

Milone & Mac Broom (2)
99 Realty Dr, Cheshire, CT 06410
Tel.: (203) 271-1773
Web Site:
   http://www.miloneandmacbroom.com
Engineeering Services
N.A.I.C.S.: 541330

Subsidiary (Domestic):

HTE Northeast (3)
2 Cote Ln # 1, Bedford, NH 03110
Tel.: (603) 668-1654
Web Site: http://www.htenortheast.com
Rev.: $1,264,000
Emp.: 8
Engineeering Services
N.A.I.C.S.: 541330
Charles E. Teale (Owner)

Subsidiary (Non-US):

SLR Consulting (Canada) Ltd (3)
1620 W 8th Ave Ste 200, Vancouver, V6J 1V4, BC, Canada
Tel.: (604) 738-2500
Web Site: http://www.slrconsulting.com
Environmental Consulting Services
N.A.I.C.S.: 541620
Kevin Rattue (Pres)

SLR Consulting (Ireland) Ltd (2)
7 Dundrum Business Park Windy Arbour, Dundrum, Dublin, D14 N2Y7, Ireland
Tel.: (353) 1 296 4667
Web Site: http://www.slrconsulting.com
Emp.: 28
Environmental Consulting Services
N.A.I.C.S.: 541620

SLR Consulting (South Africa) Pty Ltd (2)
Metago House Block 7 Fourways Manor Office Park, Cnr Roos and Macbeth Streets, Johannesburg, 2191, South Africa
Tel.: (27) 11 467 0945
Web Site: http://www.slrconsulting.com
Environmental Consulting Services
N.A.I.C.S.: 541620
Kevin Pietersen (Mng Dir)

SLR Consulting Australia Pty Ltd (2)
2 Lincoln Street, Lane Cove, 2066, NSW, Australia
Tel.: (61) 2 9427 8100
Web Site:
   http://www.slrconsultingaustralia.com.au
Environmental Consulting Services
N.A.I.C.S.: 541620
Peter Georgiou (Mng Dir)

Subsidiary (US):

SLR International Corporation (2)
22118 20th Ave SE Ste G202, Bothell, WA 98021
Tel.: (425) 402-8800
Web Site: http://www.slrconsulting.com
Sales Range: $1-9.9 Million
Emp.: 64
Environmental Consulting Services
N.A.I.C.S.: 541620
Andrew Dimitriou (Mgr-Seattle)

Sagemcom Broadband SAS (1)
250 route de l'Empereur, 92848, Rueil-Malmaison, Cedex, France
Tel.: (33) 157611000
Web Site: http://www.sagemcom.com
Emp.: 4,000
Communications Systems & Products Mfr
N.A.I.C.S.: 517112
Patrick Sevian (Pres)

Subsidiary (Non-US):

Sagemcom Broadband Germany GmbH (2)
Ludwig-Erhard-Str 1a, D-65760, Eschborn, Germany
Tel.: (49) 619695450
Web Site: http://www.sagemcom.com
Communications Systems & Products Mfr
N.A.I.C.S.: 517112
Michael Schnurbusch (Mng Dir)

Sagemcom Magyarorszag Elektronikai Kft. (2)
Montevideo u 16/a, H-1037, Budapest, Hungary
Tel.: (36) 13991020
Web Site: http://www.sagem.hu
Electronic Equipment Wholesaler
N.A.I.C.S.: 334511
Zoltan Dubi (Mng Dir)

SkillSoft Limited (1)
Belfield Office Park, Clonskeagh, Dublin, Ireland
Tel.: (353) 1 218 1000
Web Site: http://www.skillsoft.com
Sales Range: $300-349.9 Million
Interactive Software Developer
N.A.I.C.S.: 513210
Charles E. Moran (Founder)

Group (Non-US):

SkillSoft - EMEA Headquarters (2)
1st Floor 5 Arlington Square Downshire Way, Bracknell, RG12 1WA, United Kingdom
Tel.: (44) 1276401950
Web Site: http://www.skillsoft.com
Sales Range: $10-24.9 Million
In-House Course Ware Development Center Mfr
N.A.I.C.S.: 334610
Kevin Young (Mng Dir)

Subsidiary (Non-US):

SkillSoft Deutschland GmbH (3)
Niederkasseler Lohweg 191, 40547, Dusseldorf, Germany
Tel.: (49) 21116433
Web Site: http://www.skillsoft.de
Sales Range: $10-24.9 Million
Online Business Training & Certification Programs
N.A.I.C.S.: 334610

Subsidiary (Domestic):

SkillSoft UK Limited (3)
Compass House 2nd Fl 207-215 London Rd, Camberley, GU15 3EY, United Kingdom
Tel.: (44) 01276401950
Web Site: http://www.skillsoft.com
Sales Range: $10-24.9 Million
Interactive Software Designed to Meet Businesses' Information Technology Education & Training Needs
N.A.I.C.S.: 334610
Kevin Young (Mng Dir & VP)

Subsidiary (Non-US):

SkillSoft Asia Pacific Pty. Limited (2)
Level 27 101 Collins Street, Melbourne, 3000, VIC, Australia
Tel.: (61) 299416333
Web Site: http://www.skillsoft.com
Sales Range: $10-24.9 Million
Emp.: 35
Interactive Software Designed to Meet Businesses' Information Technology Education & Training Needs
N.A.I.C.S.: 334610
Melissa Ries (Mng Dir & VP)

Subsidiary (US):

SkillSoft Corporation (2)
107 Northeastern Blvd, Nashua, NH 03062-1916
Tel.: (603) 324-3000
Web Site: http://www.skillsoft.com
Sales Range: $100-124.9 Million
Holding Company
N.A.I.C.S.: 551112
Colm M. Darcy (VP)

Subsidiary (Domestic):

Books24x7.com, Inc. (3)
100 River Rdg Dr Ste 102, Norwood, MA 02062
Tel.: (781) 440-0550
Web Site: http://www.books24x7.com
Sales Range: $10-24.9 Million
Web-Based Digital Technical & Business Reference Content
N.A.I.C.S.: 541511
Douglas King (VP-Sls)

Element K Press LLC (3)
500 Canal View Blvd, Rochester, NY 14623-2800
Tel.: (585) 240-7500
Sales Range: $10-24.9 Million
Newsletters for Users of Various PC Software
N.A.I.C.S.: 513199

Subsidiary (Non-US):

SkillSoft Canada Limited (3)
20 Knowledge Park Drive, Fredericton, E3C, 2P5, NB, Canada
Tel.: (506) 457-1285
Web Site: http://www.skillsoft.com
Sales Range: $75-99.9 Million
Emp.: 310
Interactive Software Designed to Meet Businesses' Information Technology Education & Training Needs
N.A.I.C.S.: 334610

Subsidiary (Domestic):

SkillSoft Ireland Limited (2)
Block 7 Belfield Office Park Clonskeagh, Dublin, 4, Ireland
Tel.: (353) 12181000
Web Site: http://www.skillsoft.com
Sales Range: $25-49.9 Million
Emp.: 90
Interactive Software Designed to Meet Businesses' Information Technology Education & Training Needs
N.A.I.C.S.: 334610
Kate McCarthy (VP-Accessibility)

Tarsus Group plc (1)
15 Harcourt Street, Dublin, 2, Ireland
Tel.: (353) 14794209
Web Site: http://www.tarsus.com
Rev.: $126,554,289
Assets: $414,510,155
Liabilities: $285,245,240
Net Worth: $129,264,915
Earnings: $13,705,416
Emp.: 541
Fiscal Year-end: 12/31/2018
Exhibitions & Conferences Marketing Services
N.A.I.C.S.: 561499
Lisa Milburn (Mng Dir-Labelexpo Global Series)

Subsidiary (US):

Tarsus Expositions Inc (2)
175 N Patrick Blvd 3180, Brookfield, WI 53045
Tel.: (262) 782-1900
Web Site: http://www.tarsus.com
Sales Range: $25-49.9 Million
Emp.: 18
Exhibitions & Conferences Marketing Services
N.A.I.C.S.: 561920

Subsidiary (Non-US):

Tarsus France (2)
2 rue des Bourets, 92 150, Suresnes, France
Tel.: (33) 141188618
Web Site: http://www.tarsus.fr
Sales Range: $10-24.9 Million
Exhibitions & Conferences Marketing Services
N.A.I.C.S.: 561920
Gadrat Romuald (Pres)

CHARTRAND FORD
1610 boul Saint Martin Est, Laval, H7G 4W6, QC, Canada
Tel.: (450) 669-6110

Rev.: $74,366,650
Emp.: 95
New & Used Car Dealers
N.A.I.C.S.: 441110
Marc Dubuc (Gen Mgr-Sls)

CHARTRES POIDS LOURDS (LECHEVALIER-DOURS) S.A.
ZI 3 av Laennec Rocade Sud 19 rue Rene Cassin, 28000, Chartres, France
Tel.: (33) 237910931
Sales Range: $10-24.9 Million
Emp.: 62
New & Used Car Sales
N.A.I.C.S.: 441110
Christian Dours (Pres)

CHARTWELL RETIREMENT RESIDENCES
7070 Derrycrest Drive, Mississauga, L5W 0G5, ON, Canada
Tel.: (905) 501-9219
Web Site: https://www.chartwell.com
Year Founded: 2003
CSH.UN—(TSX)
Rev.: $709,112,569
Assets: $2,673,248,677
Liabilities: $2,026,998,564
Net Worth: $646,250,113
Earnings: $7,926,061
Emp.: 15,589
Fiscal Year-end: 12/31/21
Real Estate Investment Services
N.A.I.C.S.: 523999
Michael Deane Harris (Chm)

CHASE ASIA PUBLIC COMPANY LIMITED
8/9-10 Soi Vibhavadi Rangsit 44, Ladyao Chatuchak, Bangkok, 10900, Thailand
Tel.: (66) 28558285
Web Site: https://www.chase.co.th
Year Founded: 1998
CHASE—(THA)
Rev.: $14,401,393
Assets: $113,132,425
Liabilities: $14,472,486
Net Worth: $98,659,939
Earnings: $3,883,324
Emp.: 538
Fiscal Year-end: 12/31/23
Investment Management Service
N.A.I.C.S.: 523999
Pradit Leosirikul (Chm)

CHASE BRIGHT STEEL LTD.
D-115 Steel Chamber Tower Plot No - 514 Steel Market Complex, Rabale, Kalamboli, 410218, Maharashtra, India
Tel.: (91) 9820211194
Web Site:
   https://www.chasebrightsteel.com
504671—(BOM)
Rev.: $331,871
Assets: $106,975
Liabilities: $1,808,044
Net Worth: ($1,701,069)
Earnings: $63,439
Emp.: 2
Fiscal Year-end: 03/31/24
Steel Bars Mfr & Distr
N.A.I.C.S.: 331110
Avinash Jajodia (Chm & Mng Dir)

CHASE SCIENCE CO., LTD.
Room 1707 Rongqiao Center No 100 Jiangbin West Avenue, Taijiang District, Fuzhou, 350004, Fujian, China
Tel.: (86) 59187580735
Web Site: https://www.echase.cn
Year Founded: 1995

300941—(SSE)
Rev.: $55,480,464
Assets: $196,818,336
Liabilities: $19,901,700
Net Worth: $176,916,636
Earnings: $15,517,008
Fiscal Year-end: 12/31/22
Information Technology Services
N.A.I.C.S.: 541512
Gengsheng Zhang *(Chm & Gen Mgr)*

CHASEN HOLDINGS LIMITED
18 Jalan Besut, Singapore, 619571,
Singapore
Tel.: (65) 62665978
Web Site:
https://www.chasen.com.sg
Year Founded: 1999
5NV—(SES)
Rev.: $121,552,427
Assets: $155,322,712
Liabilities: $101,544,276
Net Worth: $53,778,436
Earnings: $1,520,563
Emp.: 1,607
Fiscal Year-end: 03/31/23
Logistic Services
N.A.I.C.S.: 541614
Dorothy Beng Geok Yap *(Head-Corp Admin)*

Subsidiaries:

Chasen (Shanghai) Hi Tech Machinery Services Pte Ltd (1)
Unit 1011 Block 5 XIZI International Centre 898 XiuWen Road, Minhang District, Shanghai, 201199, China **(100%)**
Tel.: (86) 2157774827
Web Site: http://www.chasen.com.cn
Machinery & Equipment Transportation Services
N.A.I.C.S.: 488999
Tuck Nang Cheong *(Gen Mgr)*

Chasen (USA), Inc. (1)
19925 Stevens Creek Blvd Ste 100, Cupertino, CA 95014
Tel.: (669) 255-5179
Web Site: https://www.chasen-usa.com
Logistic Services
N.A.I.C.S.: 541614

Chasen Engineering Sdn. Bhd. (1)
No 30 Lorong Nagasari 11 Taman Nagarasi, 13600, Perai, Penang, Malaysia
Tel.: (60) 45050600
Logistics Consulting Servies
N.A.I.C.S.: 541614

Chasen Logistics Sdn Bhd (1)
Block 5 Lot 247 Lorong Perusahaan 10 Prai Industrial Estate, 13600, Prai, Penang, Malaysia
Tel.: (60) 4 380 0600
Sales Range: $25-49.9 Million
Emp.: 100
Warehousing & Logistics Services
N.A.I.C.S.: 493110

Chasen Logistics Services Limited (1)
Tel.: (65) 62665978
Web Site: http://www.chasen.com.sg
Sales Range: $50-74.9 Million
Emp.: 150
Warehousing & Logistics Services
N.A.I.C.S.: 493110

Chasen Sino-Sin (Beijing) Hi Tech Services Pte Ltd (1)
Lugu Road No 74, Shijingshan District, Beijing, 100040, China
Tel.: (86) 106 860 8392
Web Site: https://www.chasen.com.sg
Machinery & Equipment Transportation Services
N.A.I.C.S.: 483211

Chasen Transport Logistics Co., Ltd. (1)
7th Floor Arror Building 40 Hoang Viet Street, Ward 4 Tan Binh District, Ho Chi Minh City, Vietnam
Tel.: (84) 2838488275
Logistics Consulting Servies

N.A.I.C.S.: 541614
Swee Meng Kang *(Country Mgr)*

City Zone Express (Shanghai) Co., Ltd. (1)
Logistics Consulting Servies
N.A.I.C.S.: 541614

City Zone Express Worldwide Co., Ltd. (1)
900/31 Lot 33 SV River Mall LG Floor Rama III Road Bangpongpang, Yannawa, Bangkok, 10120, Thailand
Tel.: (66) 74809202
Logistics Consulting Servies
N.A.I.C.S.: 541614

DNKH Logistics Pte Ltd (1)
27 Penjuru Lane 02-02, Singapore, 609195, Singapore
Tel.: (65) 6 846 8485
Web Site: https://www.dnkh-logistics.com
Emp.: 130
Logistics & Warehousing Services
N.A.I.C.S.: 541614

Goh Kwang Heng Pte Ltd (1)
31 Jurong Port Road 07-32 Jurong Logistic Hub South Wing Lobby, Singapore, 619115, Singapore
Tel.: (65) 6 893 7797
Web Site: https://www.gkh.com.sg
Sales Range: $50-74.9 Million
Emp.: 100
Scaffolding Services
N.A.I.C.S.: 238190

HLE Construction & Engineering Sdn. Bhd. (1)
B-3A-2 Jalan Dataran SD2 Dataran SD PJU 9, Bandar Sri Damansara, 52200, Kuala Lumpur, Malaysia
Tel.: (60) 362729967
Logistics Consulting Servies
N.A.I.C.S.: 541614

Hup Lian Engineering Pte Ltd (1)
56 Senoko Road, Woodlands East Industrial Estate, Singapore, 758120, Singapore **(66%)**
Tel.: (65) 63822180
Web Site: http://www.1991huplian.com
Steel Fabrication Services
N.A.I.C.S.: 331110

Liten Logistics Services Pte Ltd (1)
6 Tuas Avenue 20, Singapore, 638820, Singapore
Tel.: (65) 68973551
Sales Range: $25-49.9 Million
Emp.: 50
General Warehouse & Logistics Management Services
N.A.I.C.S.: 493110

REI Promax Technologies Pte Ltd (1)
Blk 11 Kallang Place 02-09, Kallang Basin Industrial Estate, Singapore, 339155, Singapore
Tel.: (65) 62995758
Web Site: https://www.rei-promax.com
Sales Range: $25-49.9 Million
Emp.: 40
Precision Moldings & Assemblies Mfr
N.A.I.C.S.: 333511

REI Technologies Pte Ltd (1)
31 Jurong Port Road 04-20/21 Jurong Logistics Hub, Singapore, 619115, Singapore
Tel.: (65) 6 268 5700
Web Site: https://www.reitech.com.sg
Sales Range: $25-49.9 Million
Emp.: 50
Industrial Engineering Services
N.A.I.C.S.: 541330

Subsidiary (Non-US):

REI Hi-Tech Sdn Bhd (2)
30 Lorong Nagasari 11 Taman Nagasari, 13600, Prai, Penang, Malaysia
Tel.: (60) 4 399 8425
Web Site: https://www.reitech.com.sg
Industrial Engineering Services
N.A.I.C.S.: 541330

Team Glass Engineering Pte. Ltd. (1)
No 56 Senoko Road, Woodlands East In-

dustrial Estate, Singapore, 758120, Singapore
Tel.: (65) 62685700
Logistic Services
N.A.I.C.S.: 541614

Towards Green Sdn. Bhd. (1)
No 530-A Tingkat 1 Jalan Kenanga 29/17, Bandar Indahpura Kulai, 81000, Johor, Malaysia
Tel.: (60) 76633515
Logistics Consulting Servies
N.A.I.C.S.: 541614

CHASHMA SUGAR MILLS LIMITED
Kings Arcade 20 A Markaz F7, Islamabad, Pakistan
Tel.: (92) 966750090
Web Site:
https://www.chashmasugarmills.com
Year Founded: 1991
CHAS—(PSX)
Rev.: $112,127,574
Assets: $93,981,854
Liabilities: $46,350,645
Net Worth: $47,631,209
Earnings: $4,562,506
Emp.: 926
Fiscal Year-end: 09/30/20
Sugar Mfr
N.A.I.C.S.: 311313

CHASSAY AUTOMOBILES SAS
11 Boulevard Abel Gance, 37 100, Tours, Indre-et-Loire, France
Tel.: (33) 247406060   FR
Web Site: http://www.chassay.fr
Sales Range: $10-24.9 Million
New & Used Car Dealers
N.A.I.C.S.: 441110
Christian Chassay *(Pres)*

CHASWOOD RESOURCES HOLDINGS LTD.
Unit 6 01 Level 6 Work Clearwater Jalan Changkat Semantan, Bukit Damansara, Kuala Lumpur, 50490, Malaysia
Tel.: (60) 3 2715 8688   SG
Web Site:
http://www.chaswood.com.my
Rev.: $671,177
Assets: $672,636
Liabilities: $15,518,532
Net Worth: ($14,845,896)
Earnings: ($5,096,080)
Emp.: 1,500
Fiscal Year-end: 12/31/19
Holding Company; Casual Dining Restaurant Operator
N.A.I.C.S.: 551112
Andrew Roach Reddy *(Mng Dir)*

CHASYS CO., LTD
528 Iryeon-ro Jillyang-eup, Gyeongsan, 38488, Gyeongsangbuk-do, Korea (South)
Tel.: (82) 538518511
Web Site: https://www.chasys.com
Year Founded: 1989
033250—(KRS)
Rev.: $30,191,739
Assets: $69,841,974
Liabilities: $43,496,831
Net Worth: $26,345,143
Earnings: ($4,318,794)
Emp.: 129
Fiscal Year-end: 06/30/22
Automobile Parts Mfr
N.A.I.C.S.: 336390
Myeong-Gon Lee *(Chm & CEO)*

Subsidiaries:

Shandong Kangtai Chasys Automobile Parts Co., Ltd (1)
No 98 Chushan East Rd, Zhaoyuan, 265400, Shandong, China

Tel.: (86) 5358243910
Automotive Products Mfr
N.A.I.C.S.: 336390

CHATEAU INTERNATIONAL DEVELOPMENT CO., LTD.
No 451 Kenting Rd, Hengchun Township, Ping-tung, 94644, Taiwan
Tel.: (886) 88862345
Web Site: https://www.chateau-hotels.com.tw
Year Founded: 1995
2722—(TAI)
Rev.: $25,013,080
Assets: $99,940,674
Liabilities: $26,518,983
Net Worth: $73,421,692
Earnings: $2,589,424
Emp.: 290
Fiscal Year-end: 12/31/23
Hotels, Amusement Parks & Restaurant Owner & Operator
N.A.I.C.S.: 721110

CHATHAM ROCK PHOSPHATE LIMITED
Level 1 93 The Terrace, PO Box 231, Takaka, Wellington, 7142, New Zealand
Tel.: (64) 21558185   NZ
Web Site:
https://www.rockphosphate.co.nz
NZP—(TSXV)
Rev.: $304
Assets: $5,801,011
Liabilities: $427,583
Net Worth: $5,373,428
Earnings: ($1,308,205)
Fiscal Year-end: 03/31/23
Phosphate Rock Mining
N.A.I.C.S.: 212390
Chris D. Castle *(CEO & Mng Dir)*

CHAUDRONNERIE DE L'EST
BP 161, Langres, Cedex, France
Tel.: (33) 325875587
Web Site: http://www.cdesas.fr
Rev.: $22,700,000
Emp.: 111
Fabricated Plate Work
N.A.I.C.S.: 332313
Delphine Lamotte *(Dir-Pur)*

CHAUX ET ENDUITS DE SAINT ASTIER
Lieu Dit La Jarthe, 24110, Perigueux, Saint-Astier, France
Tel.: (33) 553540660
Web Site: http://www.c-e-s-a.fr
Rev.: $23,900,000
Emp.: 120
Plumbing Fixtures, Equipment & Supplies
N.A.I.C.S.: 423720
Alain Stipal *(Pres)*

CHAVDA INFRA LIMITED
Binori B Square 1 Office No 304 - 307 406 & 407, Hathisingh Wadi Ambli - Bopal Road, Ahmedabad, 380058, India
Tel.: (91) 7948926087
Web Site:
https://www.chavdainfra.com
Year Founded: 1990
CHAVDA—(NSE)
Rev.: $19,703,298
Assets: $18,756,070
Liabilities: $15,058,993
Net Worth: $3,697,078
Earnings: $1,464,818
Emp.: 217
Fiscal Year-end: 03/31/23
Construction Engineering Services
N.A.I.C.S.: 541330
Jeet Chavda *(Mng Dir)*

Chavda Infra Limited—(Continued)

CHAYO GROUP PUBLIC COM-PANY LIMITED

44/543-544 Phahonyothin Rd,
Khwaeng Anusawari Khet Bang
Khen, Bangkok, 10220, Thailand
Tel.: (66) 20164411   TH
Web Site: https://www.chayo555.com
Year Founded: 1997
CHAYO—(THA)
Rev.: $43,081,650
Assets: $272,402,293
Liabilities: $147,007,479
Net Worth: $125,394,814
Earnings: $13,102,290
Emp.: 226
Fiscal Year-end: 12/31/23
Commercial Banking Services
N.A.I.C.S.: 522110
Wutisak Lapcharoensap *(Chm)*

CHC HEALTHCARE GROUP

No 88 Xingai Rd, Neihu Dist, Taipei,
114067, Taiwan
Tel.: (886) 266081999
Web Site: https://www.chengyeh.com
Year Founded: 1977
4164—(TAI)
Rev.: $92,997,905
Assets: $401,178,782
Liabilities: $200,975,675
Net Worth: $200,203,108
Earnings: $12,151,768
Emp.: 55
Fiscal Year-end: 12/31/22
Medical Product Distr
N.A.I.C.S.: 423450
Pei-Lin Lee *(Pres & Gen Mgr)*

Subsidiaries:

CHC (Guangzhou) Medical Technol-
ogy Co., Ltd.   **(1)**
Unit 09 10F GIE Tower No 403 HuangShi
Rd East, Yuexiu Dist, Guangzhou, 510095,
China
Tel.: (86) 2083282215
Medical Instrument Distr
N.A.I.C.S.: 423450

Chiu Ho (China) Medical Technology
Co., Ltd.   **(1)**
Unit 01 15F Fangheng Times Center Build-
ing B No 10 Courtyard, Wangjing Street,
Chaoyang District, Beijing, 100102, China
Tel.: (86) 1065888563
Health Care Management Services
N.A.I.C.S.: 621999

Neusoft CHC Medical Service Co.,
Ltd.   **(1)**
No Neusoft Park C1 177-1 Chuangxin
Road, Hunna District, Shenyang, 110167,
China
Tel.: (86) 2083282215
Health Care Management Services
N.A.I.C.S.: 621999

PT CHC Medika Indonesia   **(1)**
Radiation Oncology Department Floor B1
Lots 29 Lebak Bulus 1 Rd, RT 6/RW 4
Lebak Bulus Cilandak West Cilandak Cilan-
dak, South Jakarta, 12440, Jakarta, Indone-
sia
Tel.: (62) 81287546978
Health Care Management Services
N.A.I.C.S.: 621999

CHD CHEMICALS LTD.

SCF 214 Motor Market Manimajra,
Chandigarh, 160101, India
Tel.: (91) 9814811155
Web Site:
    https://www.chdchemicals.com
539800—(BOM)
Rev.: $4,308,841
Assets: $5,459,782
Liabilities: $3,639,513
Net Worth: $1,820,268
Earnings: $69,629
Emp.: 10

Fiscal Year-end: 03/31/22
Chemical Products Distr
N.A.I.C.S.: 424690
Divya Kothari *(Mng Dir)*

CHECK POINT SOFTWARE TECHNOLOGIES LTD.

5 Shlomo Kaplan Street, Tel Aviv,
6789159, Israel
Tel.: (972) 37534599   ii
Web Site:
    https://www.checkpoint.com
Year Founded: 1993
CHKP—(NASDAQ)
Rev.: $2,414,700,000
Assets: $5,695,500,000
Liabilities: $2,874,500,000
Net Worth: $2,821,000,000
Earnings: $840,300,000
Emp.: 6,450
Fiscal Year-end: 12/31/23
Internet Security Solutions Including
VPN & Firewall
N.A.I.C.S.: 513210
Dorit Dor *(VP-Products)*

Subsidiaries:

Check Point Software Technologies,
Inc.   **(1)**
959 Skyway Rd Ste 300, San Carlos, CA
94070   **(100%)**
Tel.: (650) 628-2000
Web Site: http://www.checkpoint.com
Sales Range: $50-74.9 Million
Emp.: 200
Develops, Markets & Supports Network Se-
curity Software Products Which Enable
Connectivity with Security & Manageability
N.A.I.C.S.: 513210

Subsidiary (Non-US):

Check Point Holding (Singapore) PTE
Ltd.   **(2)**
100 Beach Rd 20-04 Shaw Tower, Singa-
pore, 189702, Singapore
Tel.: (65) 64351318
Sales Range: $25-49.9 Million
Emp.: 15
Information Technology Consulting Services
N.A.I.C.S.: 541512
S. Raj *(Gen Mgr)*

Check Point Holding AB   **(2)**
Luntmakargatan 22, Stockholm; 111 37,
Sweden
Tel.: (46) 8 459 54 00
Web Site: http://www.checkpoint.com
Sales Range: $50-74.9 Million
Emp.: 25
Investment Management Service
N.A.I.C.S.: 523999

Check Point Software Technologies
(Austria) GmbH   **(2)**
Vienna Twin Tower A1504 Wienerberg-
strasse 11, Vienna, 1100, Austria
Tel.: (43) 1 99460 6701
Web Site: http://www.checkpoint.com
Computer Software Development Services
N.A.I.C.S.: 541512

Check Point Software Technologies
(Belgium) S.A.   **(2)**
Imperiastraat 10 - Bus 4, 1930, Zaventem,
Belgium
Tel.: (32) 2 416 27 80
Web Site: http://www.checkpoint.com
Sales Range: $25-49.9 Million
Emp.: 10
Security Software Development Services
N.A.I.C.S.: 541511

Check Point Software Technologies
(Brazil) LTDA   **(2)**
Rua Samuel Morse 120, 04576-060, Sao
Paulo, Brazil
Tel.: (55) 11 5501 2040
Web Site: http://www.checkpoint.com
Security Software Development Services
N.A.I.C.S.: 541511

Check Point Software Technologies
(Czech Republic) s.r.o.   **(2)**
IBC Building Pobrezni 3/620, 186 00,

Prague, Czech Republic
Tel.: (420) 222 311 495
Web Site: http://www.checkpoint.com
Sales Range: $25-49.9 Million
Emp.: 6
Software Development Services
N.A.I.C.S.: 541511

Check Point Software Technologies
(Denmark) ApS   **(2)**
Ragnagade 7, 2100, Copenhagen, Den-
mark
Tel.: (45) 70219219
Computer Software Whslr
N.A.I.C.S.: 423430

Check Point Software Technologies
(Finland) Oy   **(2)**
Stella Business Park / Solaris-house Lars
Sonckin kaari 12, PL 20, 02600, Espoo,
Finland
Tel.: (358) 467121390
Sales Range: $25-49.9 Million
Emp.: 11
Information Technology Consulting Services
N.A.I.C.S.: 541512
Petra Nyman *(Acct Mgr)*

Check Point Software Technologies
(Greece) SA   **(2)**
27 Andrea Papandreou Str, Marousi, 151
24, Maroussi, Greece
Tel.: (30) 2108105590
Cyber Security Solution Services
N.A.I.C.S.: 541511

Check Point Software Technologies
(Hong Kong) Ltd.   **(2)**
Unit 1507B-08 AIA Tower North Point 183
Electric Road, Hong Kong, China (Hong
Kong)
Tel.: (852) 85222163966
Sales Range: $25-49.9 Million
Emp.: 10
Computer Software Development Services
N.A.I.C.S.: 541511
Calvin Ng *(Country Mgr)*

Check Point Software Technologies
(Hungary) Ltd.   **(2)**
Bajza u 24, 1062, Budapest, Hungary
Tel.: (36) 302642642
Cyber Security Solution Services
N.A.I.C.S.: 541511

Check Point Software Technologies
(India) Private Limited   **(2)**
33/1 4th Floor Vittal Mallya Road, Benga-
luru, 560 001, India
Tel.: (91) 80 3079 1400
Web Site: http://www.checkpoint.com
Computer Software Development Services
N.A.I.C.S.: 541512
Bhaskar Bakthavatsalu *(Mng Dir-India &
SAARC)*

Check Point Software Technologies
(Italia) Srl   **(2)**
Via M Vigano De Vizzi 93/95, 20092, Cini-
sello Balsamo, Milan, Italy
Tel.: (39) 026659981
Web Site: http://www.checkpoint.com
Software Publishing Services
N.A.I.C.S.: 513210

Check Point Software Technologies
(Japan) Ltd.   **(2)**
6F Kensei Shinjuku Bldg 5-5-3 Shinjuku,
Shinjuku Ku, Tokyo, 160 0022,
Japan   **(100%)**
Tel.: (81) 353672500
Web Site: http://www.checkpoint.co.jp
Sales Range: $25-49.9 Million
Emp.: 40
N.A.I.C.S.: 449210

Check Point Software Technologies
(Korea) Ltd.   **(2)**
7th Floor Dongsung Building 17-8 Yeouido-
Dong Yeongdeungpo-Gu, Youngdeungpo-
Ku, Seoul, 150-874, Korea (South)
Tel.: (82) 2 786 2320
Web Site: http://www.checkpoint.com
Sales Range: $25-49.9 Million
Emp.: 6
Security Software Development Services
N.A.I.C.S.: 541511

Check Point Software Technologies
(Poland) Sp. z o. o,   **(2)**

Bagno 2/221, 00-112, Warsaw, Poland
Tel.: (48) 22 403 30 93
Web Site: http://www.checkpoint.pl
Sales Range: $25-49.9 Million
Emp.: 10
Security Software Development Services
N.A.I.C.S.: 541511

Check Point Software Technologies
(RMN) SRL.   **(2)**
Str Burdujeni 1 Bucharest Sector 3, Bucha-
rest, Romania
Tel.: (40) 721275492
Software Development Services
N.A.I.C.S.: 541511

Check Point Software Technologies
(Russia) OOO   **(2)**
Nikoloyamskaya St 13 bld 17, Moscow,
108249, Russia
Tel.: (7) 495 967 7444
Web Site: http://www.checkpoint.com
Retail Software Publisher
N.A.I.C.S.: 423430

Check Point Software Technologies
(Singapore) Ltd.   **(2)**
78 Shenton Way 09-01 Tower 1, Singapore,
079120, Singapore   **(100%)**
Tel.: (65) 64351318
Sales Range: $25-49.9 Million
Emp.: 15
N.A.I.C.S.: 449210
Darric Hor *(Reg Dir)*

Check Point Software Technologies
(Switzerland) A.G.   **(2)**
Otto Schutz-Weg 9, 8050, Zurich, Switzer-
land
Tel.: (41) 44 316 64 44
Web Site: http://www.checkpoint.com
Emp.: 21
Network Security Software Development
Services
N.A.I.C.S.: 561621

Check Point Software Technologies
(UK) Ltd.   **(2)**
6th Floor 4 Chiswell Street, London, EC1Y
4UP, United Kingdom   **(100%)**
Tel.: (44) 207 628 4211
Web Site: http://www.checkpoint.com
Sales Range: $25-49.9 Million
Emp.: 27
Software Mfr
N.A.I.C.S.: 513210

Check Point Software Technologies
Australia Pty Ltd   **(2)**
202 657 Pacific Highway, Saint Leonards,
2065, NSW, Australia   **(100%)**
Tel.: (61) 294936000
Web Site: http://www.checkpoint.com.au
Sales Range: $25-49.9 Million
Emp.: 18
N.A.I.C.S.: 449210

Check Point Software Technologies
B.V.   **(2)**
Hoofdveste 7A, Houten, 3992 DH, Nether-
lands
Tel.: (31) 30 5112110
Web Site: http://www.checkpoint.com
Emp.: 12
Computer Software Whslr
N.A.I.C.S.: 423430

Check Point Software Technologies
GmbH   **(2)**
Fraunhofer Strasse 7, D 85737, Ismaning,
Germany   **(100%)**
Tel.: (49) 899998190
Web Site: http://www.checkpoint.com
Sales Range: $25-49.9 Million
Emp.: 30
Security System Sales
N.A.I.C.S.: 449210

Check Point Software Technologies
Ltd.   **(2)**
Couodezome 1 Plz Dlaze Zictol Hugo,
92411, Puteaux, France   **(100%)**
Tel.: (33) 155491200
Web Site: http://www.checkpoint.com
Sales Range: $25-49.9 Million
Emp.: 30
Security Solutions Sales
N.A.I.C.S.: 449210

Check Point Software Technologies
Mexico S.A. de C.V.   **(2)**

Paseo de Tamarindos N 400 Torre A 5 Piso
Colonia Bosque de las Lomas, Mexico,
05120, Mexico
Tel.: (52) 5515178736
Software Development Services
N.A.I.C.S.: 541511

Check Point Software Technologies
Norway A.S. (2)
St Olavs Plass 2, 0165, Oslo, Norway
Tel.: (47) 23 30 80 50
Web Site: http://www.checkpoint.com
Computer Software Development Services
N.A.I.C.S.: 541511

Pointsec Mobile Technologies AB (2)
Luntmakargatan 22, 111 37, Stockholm,
Sweden
Tel.: (46) 84595400
Web Site: http://www.pointsec.com
Emp.: 40
Security Software & Technology Services
N.A.I.C.S.: 513210

Subsidiary (Non-US):

Pointsec Mobile Technologies
Limited (3)
Unit 4 Lindenwood Crockford Lane, Chine-
ham Business Park, Basingstoke, RG24
8QY, Hants, United Kingdom
Tel.: (44) 2077636970
Mobile Technology Mfr
N.A.I.C.S.: 517810

Subsidiary (Domestic):

Zone Labs LLC (2)
959 Skwy Rd Ste 300, San Carlos, CA
94070
Tel.: (877) 966-5221
Web Site: http://www.zonealarm.com
Security Software Mfr
N.A.I.C.S.: 541511

RM Source, Inc. (1)
1225 Crescent Green, Cary, NC 27518
Web Site: http://www.rmsource.com
Computer System Design Services
N.A.I.C.S.: 541512

CHECK-CAP LTD.
29 Abba Hushi Ave, PO Box 1271,
Isfiya, 3009000, Haifa, 3009000, Is-
rael
Tel.: (972) 48303401 II
Web Site: https://www.check-
cap.com
CHEK—(NASDAQ)
Rev.: $1,719,000
Assets: $25,017,000
Liabilities: $1,330,000
Net Worth: $23,687,000
Earnings: ($17,568,000)
Fiscal Year-end: 12/31/23
Medical Imaging Products Mfr
N.A.I.C.S.: 334510
Yoav Kimchy (Founder & CTO)

CHECKIT PLC
Broers Building JJ Thomson Avenue,
Cambridge, CB3 0FA, United King-
dom
Tel.: (44) 1252406340 UK
Web Site: https://www.checkit.net
CKT—(AIM)
Rev.: $18,057,676
Assets: $50,642,956
Liabilities: $8,553,636
Net Worth: $42,089,320
Earnings: ($9,232,496)
Emp.: 183
Fiscal Year-end: 01/31/22
Engineered Products Mfr
N.A.I.C.S.: 334118
Keith Antony Daley (Chm)

Subsidiaries:

Cross Technologies plc (1)
5 Lakeside Business Park, Swan Lane,
Sandhurst, GU47 9DN, Berkshire, United
Kingdom
Tel.: (44) 01252749500
Web Site: http://www.qados.co.uk

Sales Range: $25-49.9 Million
Emp.: 25
Digital Radiography Systems, Medical La-
sers, Aesthetic Lasers & Skin Cooling De-
vices Mfr
N.A.I.C.S.: 423450

Division (Domestic):

QADOS (2)
5 Lakeside Business Park, Swan Lane,
Sandhurst, GU47 9DN, Berkshire, United
Kingdom
Tel.: (44) 1252878999
Web Site: http://www.qados.co.uk
Sales Range: $25-49.9 Million
Emp.: 20
Radiotherapy & X-Ray Imaging Equipment
Mfr
N.A.I.C.S.: 423450

Elektron Components
Corporation (1)
11849 Telegraph Rd, Santa Fe Springs, CA
90670 (100%)
Tel.: (760) 343-3650
Web Site: http://www.arcoelectric.com
Switches, Indicator Lights & Fuse Holders
Mfr & Distr
N.A.I.C.S.: 335313

Elektron Components Ltd. (1)
29 Central Avenue, West Molesey, KT8
2RF, Surrey, United Kingdom
Tel.: (44) 2089793232
Web Site: http://www.arcoelectric.co.uk
Sales Range: $25-49.9 Million
Emp.: 40
Appliance Switches & Indicator Lights Mfr &
Distr
N.A.I.C.S.: 335313
John Wilson (Mng Dir)

Elektron Components Tunisie
Sarl (1)
13 Rue 62128 Zone Industrielle Ibn Khal-
doun Citie Ettahir, 2042, Tunis, Tunisia
Tel.: (216) 71 923 600
Electromechanical Component Mfr
N.A.I.C.S.: 334419

Hartest Precision Instruments India
Private Limited (1)
304 Plot No 7 Mahajan Tower Shreshtha
Vihar, New Delhi, 110092, India
Tel.: (91) 1122152150
Sales Range: $25-49.9 Million
Emp.: 2
Industrial Control & Precision Measurement
Machinery Mfr
N.A.I.C.S.: 334519

Hartest Precision Instruments
Limited (1)
Broers Bldg JJ Thomson Ave, Cambridge,
CB3 0FA, United Kingdom
Tel.: (44) 1737 649300
Web Site: http://www.elektron-
technology.com
Sales Range: $25-49.9 Million
Emp.: 70
Industrial Control & Precision Measurement
Machinery Mfr
N.A.I.C.S.: 334519
Nigel Rose (Mng Dir)

Titman Tip Tools Limited (1)
Valley Road, Clacton-on-Sea, CO15 6PP,
Essex, United Kingdom
Tel.: (44) 1255220123
Web Site: http://www.titman.co.uk
Sales Range: $25-49.9 Million
Emp.: 60
Machine Tools Mfr
N.A.I.C.S.: 333517
Martin Newnham (Mgr-Bus Dev)

Subsidiary (Non-US):

Titman Tip Tools GmbH (2)
Messingweg 33, Wolbeck, 48308, Senden,
Germany
Tel.: (49) 25973659742
Web Site: https://www.titman.de
Tungsten Carbide Component Whslr
N.A.I.C.S.: 424990

Titman Tip Tools Ltd (1)
31-315 Plantation Dr, Thousand Palms, CA
92276

Tel.: (760) 799-5668
Tungsten Carbide Component Mfr
N.A.I.C.S.: 339999

**CHECKPOINT TRENDS LIM-
ITED**
604 6th floor Meghdoot Gulmohar
Cross Road No 6 JVPD Scheme,
Mumbai, 400049, India
Tel.: (91) 9167469649
Web Site: https://www.rubramed.com
531099—(BOM)
Rev.: $66,206
Assets: $123,486
Liabilities: $39,181
Net Worth: $84,305
Earnings: $766
Fiscal Year-end: 03/31/21
Pharmaceuticals Product Mfr
N.A.I.C.S.: 325412
Sunil Khandalwal (Mng Dir)

CHEE CORP.
Guo Fu Center No 18 Qin Ling Road,
Laoshan District, Qingdao, 266000,
China
Tel.: (86) 318 497 4394 NV
Web Site: http://www.corpchee.com
Year Founded: 2016
ECRP—(OTCIQ)
Rev.: $745
Assets: $1,126,730
Liabilities: $93,304
Net Worth: $1,033,426
Earnings: ($482,018)
Emp.: 3
Fiscal Year-end: 01/31/21
Electronics Goods & Accessories
Distr
N.A.I.C.S.: 423620
Aaron Klusman (Chm & CEO)

**CHEE WAH CORPORATION
BERHAD**
6428 Lorong Mak Mandin Tiga Mak
Mandin Industrial Estate, 13400, But-
terworth, Malaysia
Tel.: (60) 43329299 MY
Web Site: http://www.campap.com
Year Founded: 1959
CHEEWAH—(KLS)
Sales Range: $10-24.9 Million
Stationery & Printing Material Mfr
N.A.I.C.S.: 327110
Eng Sheng Lee (Dir-Fin)

CHEER HOLDING, INC.
No 8 Tuofangying South Road, 22Nd
Floor Block B Xinhua Technology
Building, Beijing, 100016, China
Tel.: (86) 1087700500 Ky
Web Site:
http://www.yaoshixinghui.com
Year Founded: 2018
GSMG—(NASDAQ)
Rev.: $157,079,000
Assets: $205,963,000
Liabilities: $33,460,000
Net Worth: $172,503,000
Earnings: $26,890,000
Emp.: 138
Fiscal Year-end: 12/31/22
Investment Services
N.A.I.C.S.: 523999

**CHEER TIME ENTERPRISES
CO., LTD.**
No 311 Qionglin S Rd, Xinzhuang
Dist, New Taipei City, 24264, Taiwan
Tel.: (886) 222052032
Web Site: https://www.cheer-
time.com.tw
Year Founded: 1987
3229—(TAI)
Rev.: $30,352,103
Assets: $30,085,384

Liabilities: $9,865,790
Net Worth: $20,219,594
Earnings: ($829,491)
Emp.: 200
Fiscal Year-end: 12/31/23
Single, Double & Multi-Layer Printed
Circuit Boards Mfr
N.A.I.C.S.: 334412

Subsidiaries:

Cheer Time Enterprises Co., Ltd -
Kuei-Shan Plant (1)
No 8 Cha Juan Rd Gueishan Shiang,
Taoyuan, 333, Taiwan
Tel.: (886) 3350 9199
Web Site: http://www.cheer-time.com
Printed Circuit Board Mfr
N.A.I.C.S.: 334412

CHEERWIN GROUP LIMITED
No 2 Luju Road, Liwan District,
Guangzhou, Guangdong, China Ky
Web Site: https://www.cheerwin.com
Year Founded: 2006
6601—(HKG)
Rev.: $220,958,543
Assets: $547,408,299
Liabilities: $115,391,337
Net Worth: $432,016,962
Earnings: $9,818,463
Emp.: 904
Fiscal Year-end: 12/31/22
Personal Care Product Retailer
N.A.I.C.S.: 456199
Danxia Chen (Chm)

**CHEETAH CANYON RE-
SOURCES CORP.**
3920 Delbrook Ave N, Vancouver,
V7N 3Z8, BC, Canada
Tel.: (604) 505-4380
Oil & Gas Exploration Services
N.A.I.C.S.: 211130
Jatinder Singh Bal (Pres & CEO)

**CHEETAH HOLDINGS BER-
HAD**
Suite 11 1A Level 11 Menara Weld 76
Jalan Raja Chulan, 50200, Kuala
Lumpur, Malaysia
Tel.: (60) 320311988
Web Site:
http://www.cheetah.com.my
CHEETAH—(KLS)
Rev.: $35,987,603
Assets: $36,792,706
Liabilities: $2,388,186
Net Worth: $34,404,520
Earnings: ($1,754,047)
Fiscal Year-end: 06/30/22
Sports Apparel Retailer
N.A.I.C.S.: 315210
Kee Foo Chia (Chm & Mng Dir)

CHEETAH OIL & GAS LTD.
17 Victoria Road, Nanaimo, V9R
4N9, BC, Canada
Tel.: (250) 714-1101
Year Founded: 1992
Oil & Energy Services
N.A.I.C.S.: 213112
Georgina Martin (Pres, CEO & CFO)

CHEIL BIO CO., LTD.
Room 1601 767 Sinsu-ro Knowledge
Industry Center, Suji-gu, Yongin,
16827, Gyeonggi-do, Korea (South)
Tel.: (82) 314272861
Web Site: https://www.cheilbio.com
Year Founded: 1977
052670—(KRS)
Rev.: $11,772,373
Assets: $26,330,540
Liabilities: $995,964
Net Worth: $25,334,576
Earnings: ($1,309,910)
Emp.: 57

Cheil Bio Co., Ltd.—(Continued)

Fiscal Year-end: 12/31/22
Veterinary Drug Mfr
N.A.I.C.S.: 325412
Kim Jung A. *(Gen Mgr)*

CHEIL ELECTRIC CO., LTD.
555 Euleukdo Daoro, Saha Gu, Busan, Korea (South)
Tel.: (82) 512059111
Web Site: https://www.cheilelec.com
Year Founded: 1955
199820—(KRS)
Rev.: $101,362,610
Assets: $129,980,772
Liabilities: $37,854,064
Net Worth: $92,126,708
Earnings: $5,670,559
Emp.: 269
Fiscal Year-end: 12/31/22
Electrical Products Mfr
N.A.I.C.S.: 335313
Sang-Bum Park *(Mng Dir & Exec Dir)*

CHEIL GRINDING WHEEL IND. CO., LTD.
34 Daesong-ro 101beon-gil, Nam-Gu, Pohang, Gyeongsangbuk-do, Korea (South)
Tel.: (82) 542858401
Web Site: https://www.grinding.co.kr
Year Founded: 1955
001560—(KRS)
Rev.: $63,994,830
Assets: $79,858,411
Liabilities: $9,166,421
Net Worth: $70,691,990
Earnings: $1,692,820
Emp.: 57
Fiscal Year-end: 12/31/22
Grinding Wheel Product Mfr
N.A.I.C.S.: 327910
Yu-In Oh *(CEO)*

Subsidiaries:

Dongil Metal Co., Ltd. - Dasan Factory (1)
70 Dasansandan-ro Dasan-myeon, Goryeong-gun, Dasan, 40113, Gyeongsangbuk-do, Korea (South)
Tel.: (82) 549545501
Construction Machinery & Equipment Parts Mfr
N.A.I.C.S.: 333120

Keum Sung Grinding Wheel Co., Ltd. (1)
4 3B/14L 122 Street Mongnae-ro, Danwon-gu, Ansan, Kyeonggido, Korea (South)
Tel.: (82) 3149425557
Web Site: https://www.ksabrasive.com
Abrasive Product Mfr
N.A.I.C.S.: 327910

Semyung Industrial Co., Ltd. (1)
20 Gongdan 4-ro Jillyang-eup, PO Box 715-838, Gyeongsan, 712-838, Gyeongsangbuk, Korea (South)
Tel.: (82) 53 856 5101
Web Site: https://smautoparts.com
Damper & Other Rubber Mfr
N.A.I.C.S.: 326299
Oh Yu-in *(CEO)*

CHEIL TECHNOLOGY CORP.
No 8 Tzu Chiang Street, Tucheng Dist, New Taipei City, Taiwan
Tel.: (886) 222696669
5452—(TPE)
Rev.: $173,487,411
Assets: $128,844,571
Liabilities: $54,138,714
Net Worth: $74,705,857
Earnings: $5,459,782
Fiscal Year-end: 12/31/20
Electronic Components Mfr
N.A.I.C.S.: 334419
Kang-Hwa Ma *(Chm)*

CHELLARAMS PLC
110/114 Oshodi-Apapa Expressway, Isolo, Lagos, Nigeria
Tel.: (234) 17733838
Web Site:
https://www.chellaramsplc.com
Year Founded: 1923
Rev.: $17,789,000
Assets: $21,031,072
Liabilities: $33,500,605
Net Worth: ($8,569,533)
Earnings: ($10,257,444)
Emp.: 416
Fiscal Year-end: 03/31/20
Diversified Trading Services
N.A.I.C.S.: 425120
Suresh Murli Chellaram *(Mng Dir)*

Subsidiaries:

United Technical & Allied Services Limited (1)
110/114 Oshodi-Apapa Expressway Isolo, Lagos, Nigeria
Tel.: (234) 8088888827
Web Site: http://www.utasnigeria.com
Industrial Equipment Distr
N.A.I.C.S.: 423830

CHELSEA LOGISTICS AND INFRASTRUCTURE HOLDINGS CORP.
Stella Hizon Reyes Road Bo Pampanga, Davao, 8000, Philippines
Tel.: (63) 284034015 PH
Web Site:
https://www.chelsealogistics.ph
Year Founded: 2016
C—(PHI)
Rev.: $92,946,124
Assets: $709,747,330
Liabilities: $592,221,952
Net Worth: $117,525,378
Earnings: ($81,229,553)
Emp.: 2,041
Fiscal Year-end: 12/31/21
Logistics Management Services
N.A.I.C.S.: 483113
Dennis A. Uy *(Founder & Chm)*

Subsidiaries:

Chelsea Shipping Corporation (1)
12th Floor Udenna Tower Rizal Drive Corner 4th Avenue, Bonifacio Global City, Taguig, Philippines
Tel.: (63) 284034015
Web Site: https://www.chelseashipping.ph
Cargo Services
N.A.I.C.S.: 481112

Subsidiary (Domestic):

Fortis Tugs Corporation (2)
Salong, Calaca, Batangas, 4212, Philippines
Tel.: (63) 24034015
Shipping Logistics Services
N.A.I.C.S.: 488510

Subsidiary (Domestic):

Davao Gulf Marine Services, Inc. (3)
2nd Floor Lagura Bldg JP Cabaguio Avenue, Davao, 8000, Philippines
Tel.: (63) 823218503
Shipping Logistics Services
N.A.I.C.S.: 488510

Starlite Ferries, Inc. (1)
Rizal Avenue Corner P Dandan St, Batangas, Philippines
Tel.: (63) 437239965
Web Site: https://www.starliteferries.com
Travel Agency Services
N.A.I.C.S.: 561510
Shane Anthony G. Arante *(Gen Mgr)*

Trans-Asia Shipping Lines, Incorporated (1)
Cor MJ Cuenco Ave & Osmena Blvd, Cebu, Philippines
Tel.: (63) 322546491
Web Site:
https://www.transasiashipping.com

Emp.: 300
Cargo Services
N.A.I.C.S.: 481112

Worklink Services, Inc. (1)
A1 Do-Well Compound 700 M Lerma St, Brgy Old Zaniga, Mandaluyong, Philippines
Tel.: (63) 285333888
Web Site: https://wsi.ph
Freight Forwarding Services
N.A.I.C.S.: 488510
Dexter A. Silva *(Gen Mgr)*

CHELSEA OIL AND GAS LTD.
127 10th Ave NW, Calgary, T2M 0B4, AB, Canada
Tel.: (403) 457-1959
Web Site:
http://www.chelseaoilandgas.com
COGLF—(OTCBB)
Sales Range: Less than $1 Million
Oil & Gas Exploration Services
N.A.I.C.S.: 213112
Jesse Meidl *(CEO)*

CHELSFIELD PARTNERS LLP
50 Hans Crescent, London, SW1X 0NA, United Kingdom
Tel.: (44) 20 7290 2388 UK
Web Site: http://www.chelsfield.com
Year Founded: 2005
Real Estate Investment & Development Services
N.A.I.C.S.: 531390
Elliott Bernerd *(Co-Founder & Chm)*

Subsidiaries:

Chelsfield France Ltd (1)
54 Avenue Montaigne, 75008, Paris, France
Tel.: (33) 1 83 75 47 10
Web Site: http://www.chelsfield.com
Real Estate Investment Services
N.A.I.C.S.: 531390
Stephanie Vinot *(Office Mgr)*

CHELVERTON GROWTH TRUST PLC
23 Cathedral Yard, Exeter, EX1 1HB, United Kingdom
Tel.: (44) 2072228989
CGW—(LSE)
Rev.: $28,855
Assets: $4,037,105
Liabilities: $828,931
Net Worth: $3,208,174
Earnings: ($1,124,041)
Fiscal Year-end: 08/31/19
Investment Management Service
N.A.I.C.S.: 525990
Kevin Allen *(Mgr-Fund)*

CHELVERTON UK DIVIDEND TRUST PLC
Hamilton Centre Rodney Way, Chelmsford, CM1 3BY, United Kingdom
Tel.: (44) 1392412122
SDV—(LSE)
Rev.: $33,698,610
Assets: $86,907,657
Liabilities: $22,633,192
Net Worth: $64,274,465
Earnings: $31,743,494
Fiscal Year-end: 04/30/21
Investment Management Service
N.A.I.C.S.: 525990

CHELYABINSK FORGE & PRESS PLANT PJSC
st Gorelova 12, Chelyabinsk, 454012, Russia
Tel.: (7) 3512594550 RU
Web Site: http://www.chkpz.ru
Year Founded: 1941
CHKZ—(MOEX)
Sales Range: Less than $1 Million
Metal Product Mfr & Distr
N.A.I.C.S.: 331110

Andrey Gartung *(Gen Dir)*

CHELYABINSK PLANT OF THE PROFILED STEEL DECKING PJSC
ul Valdai 7, Chelyabinsk, 454081, Russia
Tel.: (7) 3517710909
PRFN—(MOEX)
Sales Range: Less than $1 Million
Construction Material Mfr & Distr
N.A.I.C.S.: 331110

CHELYABINSK ZINC PLANT JSC
Sverdlovski Trakt 24, Chelyabinsk, 454084, Russia
Tel.: (7) 3517990009
Web Site: https://www.zinc.ru
Zinc & Zinc Alloy Product Mfr
N.A.I.C.S.: 212230
Natalia Vasilieva *(Head-PR Dept)*

CHELYABINVESTBANK PJSC
8 Revolution Square, 454113, Chelyabinsk, Russia
Tel.: (7) 3512680088
Web Site: http://www.chelinvest.ru
Sales Range: Less than $1 Million
Commercial Banking Services
N.A.I.C.S.: 522110

CHEM-DRY FRANCHISING LIMITED
Belprin Road, Beverley, HU17 0LP, Yorkshire, United Kingdom
Tel.: (44) 1482888195
Web Site: http://www.chemdry.co.uk
Sales Range: $25-49.9 Million
Emp.: 200
Polish & Sanitation Good Mfr
N.A.I.C.S.: 325612
Andrew Lloyd-Jones *(Mng Dir)*

Subsidiaries:

Chem-Dry UK Limited (1)
Belprin Road, Swinemoor Lane, Beverley, HU17 0LP, Yorkshire, United Kingdom (100%)
Tel.: (44) 1482872770
Web Site: http://www.chemdry.co.uk
Piece Goods Notions & Dry Goods Whslr
N.A.I.C.S.: 424310
Nick Houton *(Mgr-Fin)*

CHEMANEX PLC
No 199 Kew Road, 2, Colombo, 02, Sri Lanka
Tel.: (94) 1123268458
Web Site: https://www.chemanex.lk
Year Founded: 1974
CHMX—(COL)
Rev.: $3,540,644
Assets: $9,327,286
Liabilities: $445,085
Net Worth: $8,882,201
Earnings: $591,026
Emp.: 14
Fiscal Year-end: 03/31/23
Textile Products Mfr
N.A.I.C.S.: 314999
S. Fernando *(CEO)*

CHEMBOND CHEMICALS LTD
Chembond Centre EL-71 MIDC Mahape, Navi Mumbai, 400 710, Maharastra, India
Tel.: (91) 2262643000
Web Site:
https://www.chembondindia.com
CHEMBOND—(NSE)
Rev.: $39,554,520
Assets: $48,337,421
Liabilities: $8,145,692
Net Worth: $40,191,729
Earnings: $2,785,815
Emp.: 107

Fiscal Year-end: 03/31/21
Chemicals Mfr
N.A.I.C.S.: 325998
Nirmal V. Shah *(Vice Chm & Mng Dir)*

Subsidiaries:

Chembond Chemicals Ltd - BADDI
Plant **(1)**
Khasra No 77/2 Village Theda Lodhimajra
Tehsil Nalagarh, Baddi, Solan, 174101, Himachal Pradesh, India
Tel.: (91) 92184 44550
Sales Range: $25-49.9 Million
Emp.: 25
Chemicals Mfr
N.A.I.C.S.: 325520
D. N. Sharma *(Plant Mgr)*

Chembond Chemicals Ltd - BALAS-
ORE Plant **(1)**
Near Ramuna Golai Opp Gurudwara Gati
Courier Office, Beside Rajesh Chemicals,
Baleshwar, 756019, Orissa, India
Tel.: (91) 93380 13422
Web Site: http://www.chembondindia.com
Sales Range: $25-49.9 Million
Emp.: 3
Chemicals Mfr
N.A.I.C.S.: 325998
Nirmal V. Shah *(Vice Chm & Mng Dir)*

Chembond Chemicals Ltd - CHEN-
NAI Plant **(1)**
No S-50 Sipcot Industrial Complex Phase -
III, Ranipet, Chennai, 632 405, Tamil Nadu,
India
Tel.: (91) 4172299119
Web Site: http://www.chembondindia.com
Sales Range: $25-49.9 Million
Chemicals Mfr
N.A.I.C.S.: 325520

Chembond Chemicals Ltd - Construc-
tion Chemical Division **(1)**
Chembond Centre EL-71 Mahape MIDC,
Navi Mumbai, 400 710, India
Tel.: (91) 2262643000
Web Site: http://chembondconschem.com
Sales Range: $250-299.9 Million
Construction Chemical Mfr & Whslr
N.A.I.C.S.: 424690

Chembond Chemicals Ltd -
DUDHWADA Plant **(1)**
404/B/P-1 Village Dudhawada ECP Road,
Tal Padra Dist, Vadodara, 391 450, Gujarat,
India
Tel.: (91) 2662613700
Web Site: http://www.chembondindia.com
Construction Chemicals Mfr
N.A.I.C.S.: 325998

Chembond Chemicals Ltd - Manufac-
turing Plant **(1)**
Khasra No 177/2, Village Theda PO Lo-
dhimajra Tehsil Nalagarh Baddi Dist, Solan,
174 101, Himachal Pradesh, India
Tel.: (91) 9218444550
Web Site: http://www.chembondindia.com
Sales Range: $50-74.9 Million
Construction Chemical Mfr & Whslr
N.A.I.C.S.: 424690

Chembond Chemicals Ltd - Manufac-
turing Plant **(1)**
Opp Gurudwara Gati Courier Ofc, Beside
Rajesh Chem, Baleshwar, 756019, Orissa,
India
Tel.: (91) 9338013422
Web Site: http://www.chembondbsnl.com
Sales Range: $50-74.9 Million
Emp.: 100
Industrial Chemical Mfr & Whslr
N.A.I.C.S.: 424690

Chembond Chemicals Ltd - TARA-
PUR Plant **(1)**
E-6/4 Tarapur MIDC, Dist Palghar, Palghar,
401 506, Maharashtra, India
Tel.: (91) 2525 272615
Web Site: http://www.chembondindia.com
Chemicals Mfr
N.A.I.C.S.: 325520

Phiroze Sethna Private Limited **(1)**
Royal Insurance Building 14 J Tata Road,
Mumbai, 400020, India
Tel.: (91) 222 282 1845

Web Site: https://www.phirol.com
Automobile Mfr
N.A.I.C.S.: 336110

CHEMCEL BIO-TECH LIMITED
16-130/12 JRD Tata Industrial Estate
Kanuru, Vijayawada, 520007, Andhra
Pradesh, India
Tel.: (91) 8662544996
Web Site:
http://www.chemcelbiotechltd.com
Year Founded: 1995
Sales Range: $10-24.9 Million
Agrochemical Mfr
N.A.I.C.S.: 325320
Kanuparthi Trinatha Vijay Kumar
(Mng Dir)

**CHEMCLIN DIAGNOSTICS
CO., LTD.**
Beike modern manufacturing park No
7 Fengxian Middle Road, Yongfeng
Base Haidian District, Beijing,
100094, China
Tel.: (86) 1058717511
Web Site: https://www.chemclin.com
Year Founded: 2007
688468—(SHG)
Rev.: $65,323,922
Assets: $223,399,763
Liabilities: $29,566,990
Net Worth: $193,832,772
Earnings: $21,428,648
Fiscal Year-end: 12/31/22
Medical Product Mfr & Distr
N.A.I.C.S.: 339112
Lin Li *(Chm & Gen Mgr)*

**CHEMCO ELECTRICAL CON-
TRACTORS LTD.**
9220 39 Ave NW, Edmonton, T6E
5T9, AB, Canada
Tel.: (780) 436-9570
Web Site: http://www.chemco-
elec.com
Year Founded: 1963
Sales Range: $150-199.9 Million
Emp.: 1,300
Electrical Contractor
N.A.I.C.S.: 238210
Brian Halina *(Pres)*

**CHEMCON SPECIALITY
CHEMICALS LIMITED**
9th Floor Onyx Business Center Ak-
shar Chowk Old Padra Road, Vado-
dara, 390020, Gujarat, India
Tel.: (91) 2652981195
Web Site: https://www.cscpl.com
Year Founded: 1988
543233—(BOM)
Rev.: $36,354,714
Assets: $67,975,348
Liabilities: $11,029,978
Net Worth: $56,945,370
Earnings: $8,566,276
Emp.: 207
Fiscal Year-end: 03/31/22
Chemicals Mfr
N.A.I.C.S.: 325998
Shahilkumar Maheshbhai Kapatel
(Sec & Compliance Officer)

**CHEMCRUX ENTERPRISES
LIMITED**
330 TRIVIA Complex Natubhai Circle,
Racecourse, Vadodara, 390 007, Gu-
jarat, India
Tel.: (91) 2652988903 In
Web Site: https://www.chemcrux.com
Year Founded: 1983
540395—(BOM)
Rev.: $13,140,691
Assets: $11,296,549
Liabilities: $3,818,533
Net Worth: $7,478,016

Earnings: $2,036,430
Emp.: 91
Fiscal Year-end: 03/31/22
Chemical Product Mfr & Distr
N.A.I.C.S.: 325194
Girish Champaklal Shah *(Chm)*

**CHEMEMAN PUBLIC COM-
PANY LIMITED**
195/11-12 Lake Rajada Office Com-
plex 2 10th-11th Floor Rajadapisek
Rd, Klongtoey, Bangkok, 10110,
Thailand
Tel.: (66) 266197348 TH
Web Site:
https://www.chememan.com
Year Founded: 2003
CMAN—(THA)
Rev.: $104,321,911
Assets: $186,669,048
Liabilities: $116,034,586
Net Worth: $70,634,463
Earnings: $3,287,417
Emp.: 555
Fiscal Year-end: 12/31/23
Mineral Lime Product Mfr & Distr
N.A.I.C.S.: 327410
Adisak Lowjun *(CEO)*

Subsidiaries:

Chememan Australia Pty Ltd. **(1)**
11 Sparks Road, Henderson, 6166, WA,
Australia
Tel.: (61) 894374800
Limestone Distr
N.A.I.C.S.: 423320

CHEMFAB ALKALIS LIMITED
Team House GST Salai Vandalur,
Chennai, 600 048, India
Tel.: (91) 4466799595 In
Web Site:
https://www.chemfabalkalis.com
541269—(BOM)
Rev.: $37,850,344
Assets: $48,073,075
Liabilities: $7,395,829
Net Worth: $40,677,246
Earnings: $3,923,938
Emp.: 192
Fiscal Year-end: 03/31/22
Specialty Chemicals Mfr
N.A.I.C.S.: 325180
V. M. Srinivasan *(CEO)*

CHEMFAB INDUSTRIES INC.
466 Polymoore Drive, PO Box 3200,
Corunna, N0N 1G0, ON, Canada
Tel.: (519) 862-1433
Web Site: http://www.cii-
chemfab.com
Year Founded: 1980
Rev.: $40,891,176
Emp.: 300
Mechanical Contractor
N.A.I.C.S.: 238220
Jeff DeVlugt *(Pres & Gen Mgr)*

**CHEMI DAROU INDUSTRIAL
COMPANY**
Abali Rd Km 3, 16575 361, Tehran,
Iran
Tel.: (98) 21 77330291
Web Site:
http://www.chemidarou.com
Year Founded: 1965
Emp.: 478
Pharmaceutical Preparation Mfr
N.A.I.C.S.: 325412

**CHEMICAL INDUSTRIES (FAR
EAST) LTD.**
3 Jalan Samulun, Singapore, 629127,
Singapore
Tel.: (65) 62650411 SG
Web Site: http://www.cil.sg
Year Founded: 1962

C05—(SES)
Rev.: $53,785,106
Assets: $109,081,141
Liabilities: $8,610,597
Net Worth: $100,470,545
Earnings: $3,814,005
Emp.: 200
Fiscal Year-end: 03/31/24
Holding Company; Chemical Mfr &
Distr; Real Estate Services
N.A.I.C.S.: 551112
Cecil Yew Khang Lim *(Exec Dir)*

**CHEMICAL INDUSTRIES
HOLDING COMPANY**
5 Tolombat Street, Garden City,
Cairo, Egypt
Tel.: (20) 227954006 EG
Web Site: http://www.cihc-eg.com
Sales Range: $100-124.9 Million
Nitogenous Fertilizers, Paper, Chemi-
cals, Plastics, Leathers, Cement,
Cigarettes & Tobacco Mfr
N.A.I.C.S.: 325998
Emad Eldeen M. Khalid *(Chm &
CEO)*

Subsidiaries:

Eastern Company **(1)**
450 Al-Ahram st, Giza, Egypt
Tel.: (20) 2 35724711
Web Site: http://www.easternegypt.com
Cigarette Mfr
N.A.I.C.S.: 312230

Egyptian Chemical Industries Co.
(Kima) **(1)**
12 Talaat Harb Street, Cairo, Egypt
Tel.: (20) 225740774
Web Site: https://www.kimaegypt.com
Sales Range: $200-249.9 Million
Emp.: 2,400
Chemicals Mfr
N.A.I.C.S.: 325130

Egyptian Co. for shoes (BATA) **(1)**
61 Ekhshidi Str Qabbary, Alexandria, Egypt
Tel.: (20) 3 4409333
Footwear Mfr
N.A.I.C.S.: 316210

El Mex Salines Co. **(1)**
Wadi Al Kamar-Max, Alexandria, Egypt
Tel.: (20) 3 4440946
Web Site: http://www.mexsalines.com
Industrial Salt Mfr
N.A.I.C.S.: 325998
Mahmoud El-Sherif *(Chm & CEO)*

El Nasr Company for Fertilizers &
Chemical Industries **(1)**
Etaka, Suez, Egypt
Tel.: (20) 62 336 0041
Web Site: http://www.semadco.com
Fertilizer Mfr & Distr
N.A.I.C.S.: 325314
Mohamed Kamal Eldien Nasser *(Chm &
Mng Dir)*

El Nasser Electric & Electronic Appa-
ratus CO. **(1)**
Canal El Mahmudia-nozha, Alexandria,
21553, Egypt
Tel.: (20) 3 3815181
Web Site: http://www.neeasae.com.eg
Emp.: 1,000
Lamp Mfr
N.A.I.C.S.: 335139
Ahamad Youins *(Chm)*

El Nassr Company For Rubber Prod-
ucts (Narubeen) **(1)**
22 Soliman El Halaby St, Cairo, Egypt
Tel.: (20) 3504824
Web Site: http://www.naroben.com
Rubber Products Mfr
N.A.I.C.S.: 326220
Ibrahim Al-Zayat *(Chm & Mng Dir)*

El-Delta Company **(1)**
PO Box 35691, Talkha, Dakahlia, Egypt
Tel.: (20) 502525834
Web Site: http://www.el-deltafert.com.eg
Producer of Nitrogen Fertilizers
N.A.I.C.S.: 325311

Chemical Industries Holding Company—(Continued)

El-Nasr Saline Company (1)
2 El Horreya Ave, Alexandria, Egypt
Tel.: (20) 3 4837493
Web Site: http://www.nasrsalines.net
Salt Mfr
N.A.I.C.S.: 311942
Samia Mohamed Ebrahim Zien El (Chm)

**General Company for Paper Industry
(RAKTA)** (1)
Tabia-Rashid, Alexandria, Egypt
Tel.: (20) 3 5615860
Web Site: http://www.rakta-eg.com
Paper Product Mfr & Distr
N.A.I.C.S.: 322120

**General Trading & Chemicals
Co.** (1)
Immobilia Bldg 26 Sherif St, Cairo,
Egypt (100%)
Tel.: (20) 23933347
Import & Export of Chemicals
N.A.I.C.S.: 325998

Moharram Press Company (1)
Canal Elmahmoudia St, Alexandria, Egypt
Tel.: (20) 3 3813295
Corrugated Board Mfr
N.A.I.C.S.: 322211

National Cement Company (1)
Al-Tebbin-South Helwan Governorate, PO
Box 18, Helwan, Egypt
Tel.: (20) 25434797
Web Site: http://www.ncc-eg.com
Cement Product Mfr
N.A.I.C.S.: 327420
Mahmoud Ibrahim Abdelfatah Sadon (Mng
Dir)

National Plastics Company (1)
72 Gameat El Dowel Al Arabia St, Mo-
handessen, Giza, Egypt
Tel.: (20) 3389151
Mfr of Lead Acid Batteries; Urea Trays;
Melamine Sets; Toilet Seats
N.A.I.C.S.: 335910

Nile Match Company (1)
Canal EL-mahmoudia Rd Moharram Bey,
Alexandria, Egypt
Tel.: (20) 3 3816527
Safety Match Distr
N.A.I.C.S.: 424990

Sinai Manganese Company (1)
1 Kasr El Nile Str, Cairo, Egypt
Tel.: (20) 2 25740005
Cement Product Mfr
N.A.I.C.S.: 327420
Mohamed Sayed (Chm)

**Sprig & Transport needs Manufactur-
ing Co** (1)
8 EL Massanea St-Amerya, Cairo, Egypt
Tel.: (20) 2 22842333
Automotive Components Mfr
N.A.I.C.S.: 336390

**The Egyptian Company For Pipes &
Cement Products Co.
(SIEGWART)** (1)
Maasara-Helwan 15 Shreef St, Cairo, Egypt
Tel.: (20) 2 23690032
Web Site: http://www.siegwarteg.com
Concrete Pipe Mfr
N.A.I.C.S.: 327332
Esam El-deen Mohammed Moharam (Chm)

The Tractors & Engineering Co. (1)
18 Emad El Din St, Cairo, Egypt
Tel.: (20) 2 5743594
Web Site: http://www.almaharees.com
Industrial Supplies Whslr
N.A.I.C.S.: 423840

Transport & Engineering Co (1)
38th St Semouha, PO Box 668, Alexandria,
Egypt
Tel.: (20) 3 427 4277
Web Site: http://www.trenco-tire.com.eg
Tiles Mfr
N.A.I.C.S.: 326211
Taher Mahmoud Salama (Chm & Co-Mng
Dir)

CHEMICAL WORKS OF GEDEON RICHTER PLC

Gyomroi ut 19-21, 1103, Budapest,
Hungary
Tel.: (36) 14314000
Web Site: https://www.richter.hu
Year Founded: 1901
RICHTER—(LUX)
Rev.: $2,199,810,917
Assets: $3,672,829,661
Liabilities: $767,118,821
Net Worth: $2,905,710,841
Earnings: $430,930,067
Emp.: 12,167
Fiscal Year-end: 12/31/22
Pharmaceuticals Product Mfr
N.A.I.C.S.: 325412
Erik Bogsch (Chm & Member-Exec
Bd)

Subsidiaries:

Gedeon Richter KZ LLP (1)
St Tole bi 187, 050008, Almaty, Kazakhstan
Tel.: (7) 7272582622
Web Site: https://www.g-richter.kz
Pharmaceuticals Mfr
N.A.I.C.S.: 325412

Gedeon Richter UA TOV (1)
17-B Turgenevska str, 01054, Kiev, Ukraine
Tel.: (380) 443893950
Pharmaceuticals Mfr
N.A.I.C.S.: 325412

Gedeon Richter Vietnam Ltd. (1)
2A Nguyen Van Huong St, Thao Dien Thu
Duc City, Ho Chi Minh City, Vietnam
Tel.: (84) 2837442655
Healtcare Services
N.A.I.C.S.: 621999

**Richter-Helm BioLogics Manage-
ment GmbH** (1)
Suhrenkamp 59, 22335, Hamburg, Ger-
many
Tel.: (49) 4055290801
Web Site: http://www.richter-helm.eu
Biotechnology Products Mfr
N.A.I.C.S.: 325414
Kai Pohlmeyer (Mng Dir)

CHEMIE TECHNIK GMBH

Robert Bosch Strasse 19, 72189,
Vohringen, Germany
Tel.: (49) 745496520
Web Site: http://elkalub.com
Year Founded: 1956
Rev.: $10,026,859
Emp.: 30
Automotive Lubricant Mfr
N.A.I.C.S.: 324191
Joachim Hof (CEO)

CHEMIESYNTH (VAPI) LTD.

B-401 402 4th Floor Neelkanth Busi-
ness Park Vidyavihar West, Mumbai,
400 086, India
Tel.: (91) 2225144402
Web Site:
https://www.chemiesynth.com
Year Founded: 1986
Rev.: $1,614,505
Assets: $2,132,614
Liabilities: $1,618,042
Net Worth: $514,572
Earnings: $168,305
Emp.: 41
Fiscal Year-end: 03/31/19
Organic Chemical Product Mfr
N.A.I.C.S.: 325199
Sandip Satishbhai Zaveri (Mng Dir)

CHEMINVEST AS

Sokolovska 2, 6674, Humenne, 066
74, Slovakia
Tel.: (421) 577721738
Web Site: https://www.cheminvest.sk
1CHI01AE—(BRA)
Sales Range: Less than $1 Million
Heating Equipment Installation Ser-
vices
N.A.I.C.S.: 238220

Viera Furyova (Chm-Mgmt Bd)

CHEMIPLASTICA S.P.A.

Via Dante 60, Carbonate, 22070,
Como, Italy
Tel.: (39) 033183651
Web Site:
http://www.chemiplastica.com
Year Founded: 1955
Sales Range: $100-124.9 Million
Emp.: 200
Chemicals Mfr
N.A.I.C.S.: 325998
Claudio Colombo (Chm & CEO)

Subsidiaries:

Chemiplastica AB (1)
Perstorp Industrial Park, 284 80, Perstorp,
Sweden
Tel.: (46) 43537000
Sales Range: $50-74.9 Million
Emp.: 110
Amino Polymers Engineering Materials Mfr
N.A.I.C.S.: 326199
Gabriel Munck (Gen Mgr)

Chemiplastica Inc. (1)
238 Nonotuck St, Florence, MA 01062-2671
Tel.: (413) 584-2472
Web Site: http://www.thermosets.com
Sales Range: $25-49.9 Million
Emp.: 28
Amino Polymers Engineering Materials Mfr
N.A.I.C.S.: 326199

**Chemiplastica Pls.Mel.Tic.ve San.
A.S.** (1)
Buyukcavuslu Merkez Mah Cerkezkoy Cad
No 583, Silivri, Istanbul, Turkiye
Tel.: (90) 212 745 35 18
Plastic Mold & Resin Distr
N.A.I.C.S.: 424610

Chemiplastica S.A. (1)
Via Motta 12, 6900, Lugano, Switzerland
Tel.: (41) 91 9102430
Plastic Mold & Resin Distr
N.A.I.C.S.: 424610

Chemiplastica SA de CV (1)
Carretera Panamericana km 291 7 Tramo
Celaya, Salamanca, Villagran, 38260,
Mexico
Tel.: (52) 411 155 3131
Plastic Mold & Resin Distr
N.A.I.C.S.: 424610

CHEMIPRO KASEI KAISHA LTD.

14th floor Sannomiya Century Build-
ing 83 Kyomachi, Chuo-ku, Kobe,
650-0034, Hyogo, Japan
Tel.: (81) 783932530
Web Site: https://www.chemipro.co.jp
Year Founded: 1982
4960—(TKS)
Sales Range: $50-74.9 Million
Emp.: 200
Chemical Mfr & Distr
N.A.I.C.S.: 325992
Naohiko Fukuoka (Chm, Pres &
CEO)

Subsidiaries:

**Chemipro Kasei Kaisha Ltd. - Aioi
Plant** (1)
5377-5 Aza-komaru, Hyogo, Japan
Tel.: (81) 791233869
Chemical Agent Mfr
N.A.I.C.S.: 325992

**Chemipro Kasei Kaisha Ltd. - Akashi
Plant** (1)
22-31 Minamifutami Futami-cho, Akashi,
Hyogo, Japan
Tel.: (81) 789422111
Chemical Agent Mfr
N.A.I.C.S.: 325992

**Chemipro Kasei Kaisha Ltd. - Fuku-
shima Plant** (1)
12 Aza-amagasaku Sugaya Takinemachi,
Tamura, Fukushima, Japan
Tel.: (81) 247681130

Chemical Agent Mfr
N.A.I.C.S.: 325992

**Chemipro Kasei Kaisha Ltd. - Himeji
Plant** (1)
1611 Hamada Aboshi-ku, Himeji, Hyogo,
Japan
Tel.: (81) 792735152
Chemical Agent Mfr
N.A.I.C.S.: 325992

**Chemipro Kasei Kaisha Ltd. - Osaka
Plant** (1)
1-48 2-chome Umemachi Konohana-ku,
Osaka, Japan
Tel.: (81) 664610431
Chemical Agent Mfr
N.A.I.C.S.: 325992

CHEMISOL ITALIA S.R.L.

Via Sempione 13, 21053, Castel-
lanza, Varese, Italy
Tel.: (39) 0331523111
Web Site: http://www.chemisol.it
Rev.: $42,140,080
Emp.: 50
Plant Protective Services
N.A.I.C.S.: 213112
Gianluca Bagatti (Owner)

CHEMISTREE TECHNOLOGY, INC.

Suite 810-609 Granville Street, PO
Box 10322, Vancouver, V7Y 1G5,
BC, Canada
Tel.: (604) 689-7422
Web Site: https://www.chemistree.ca
CHMJF—(CNSX)
Rev.: $67,941
Assets: $2,928,414
Liabilities: $7,159,896
Net Worth: ($4,231,482)
Earnings: ($3,546,840)
Fiscal Year-end: 06/30/21
Cannabis Product Distr
N.A.I.C.S.: 459999
Karl Kottmeier (Pres & CEO)

CHEMITALIC DENMARK A/S

Egebjergvej 128, 8700, Horsens,
Denmark
Tel.: (45) 2496 1350
Sales Range: $25-49.9 Million
Emp.: 120
Printed Circuit Board Mfr
N.A.I.C.S.: 334412
Palle Morthorst (Dir-Sls)

Subsidiaries:

Chemitalic Suzhou Ltd. (1)
Unit 3 Genway Ready Build Factory, SIP
Export Processing Zone Dis, 215021, Su-
zhou, Jiangsu, China
Tel.: (86) 51262823088
Bare Printed Circuit Board Mfr
N.A.I.C.S.: 334412

CHEMO PHARMA LABORATO-RIES LTD

Empire House 3rd Floor 214 Dr D N
Road, Fort, Mumbai, 400001, India
Tel.: (91) 2222078382
Web Site:
https://www.thechemopharma.com
Year Founded: 1942
506365—(BOM)
Rev.: $91,185
Assets: $1,508,765
Liabilities: $7,978
Net Worth: $1,500,788
Earnings: $34,135
Fiscal Year-end: 03/31/21
Pharmaceuticals Product Mfr
N.A.I.C.S.: 325412
Ashok Govindlal Somani (CFO)

CHEMOFORM AG

Heinrich-Otto-Str 28, 73240, Wendlingen am Neckar, Germany

Tel.: (49) 702440480
Web Site: http://www.chemoform.com
Year Founded: 1962
Rev.: $11,862,840
Emp.: 25
Chemical Products Mfr
N.A.I.C.S.: 325998
Gerhard Mayer-Klenk *(Founder)*

Subsidiaries:

Chemoform Austria GmbH (1)
Tragosser Strasse 109, 8600, Bruck an der
Mur, Austria
Tel.: (43) 386281390
Swimming Pool Equipments Distr
N.A.I.C.S.: 423910

Chemoform CZ s.r.o. (1)
Nad Safinou 348, 252 42, Vestec, Czech
Republic
Tel.: (420) 244913137
Swimming Pool Equipments Distr
N.A.I.C.S.: 423910

Chemoform Polska Sp. z o.o. (1)
Ul Gacka 1, 41-218, Sosnowiec, Poland
Tel.: (48) 322977138
Swimming Pool Equipments Distr
N.A.I.C.S.: 423910

Chemoform Romania s.r.l. (1)
Punct de lucru Pipera Soseaua Pipera Tu-
nari Nr 2 A, 077190, Bucharest, Ilfov, Ro-
mania
Tel.: (40) 212420594
Swimming Pool Equipments Distr
N.A.I.C.S.: 423910

CHEMOLAK

Tovarenska 7, 919 04, Trnava, Slova-
kia
Tel.: (421) 335560111
Web Site: http://www.chemolak.sk
Sales Range: Less than $1 Million
Chemical Products Mfr
N.A.I.C.S.: 325998
Roman Sustek *(Chm & CEO)*

CHEMOMAB THERAPEUTICS LTD.

Kiryat Atidim Building 7, Tel Aviv,
6158002, Israel
Tel.: (972) 773310156   DE
Web Site:
    https://www.chemomab.com
Year Founded: 2011
CMMB—(NASDAQ)
Rev.: $353,000
Assets: $43,063,000
Liabilities: $6,840,000
Net Worth: $36,223,000
Earnings: ($27,646,000)
Emp.: 37
Fiscal Year-end: 12/31/22
Cancer Cell Prevention Products Mfr
& Researcher
N.A.I.C.S.: 325412
Adi Mor *(Chief Scientific Officer)*

Subsidiaries:

BioCancell Therapeutics Israel
Ltd. (1)
1 3 High Tech Village Givat Ram, Jerusa-
lem, 9139102, Israel
Tel.: (972) 25486555
Web Site: http://www.biocancell.com
Sales Range: $10-24.9 Million
Emp.: 5
Health Care Therapeutic Services
N.A.I.C.S.: 621340
Aris Wind *(CEO)*

Chemomab Therapeutics Inc. (1)
Kiryat Atidim Building 7, Tel Aviv, 6158002,
Israel
Tel.: (972) 773310156
Web Site: http://www.chemomab.com
Assets: $64,353,000
Liabilities: $2,887,000
Net Worth: $61,466,000
Earnings: ($12,478,000)
Emp.: 20
Fiscal Year-end: 12/31/2021

Biotechnology Research & Developement
N.A.I.C.S.: 541714
Mitchell L. Jones *(VP-Corp Dev & Strategy)*

CHEMOMETEC A/S

Gydevang 43, 3450, Allerod, Den-
mark
Tel.: (45) 48131020
Web Site:
    https://www.chemometec.com
Year Founded: 1997
CHEMM—(CSE)
Rev.: $63,994,733
Assets: $95,205,684
Liabilities: $18,077,296
Net Worth: $77,128,388
Earnings: $25,852,180
Emp.: 164
Fiscal Year-end: 06/30/23
Laboratory Analytical Instruments Mfr
N.A.I.C.S.: 334516
Preben Konig *(Chm)*

CHEMOPROJEKT, A.S.

Trebohosticka 14, 100 31, Prague,
10, Czech Republic
Tel.: (420) 261 305 111   CZ
Web Site:
    http://www.chemoprojekt.cz
Year Founded: 1950
Sales Range: $25-49.9 Million
Emp.: 200
Engineering & Procurement Services
N.A.I.C.S.: 541330
Tomas Plachy *(Chm)*

CHEMOS A.D.

Horgoski put 97, 24413, Palic, Serbia
Tel.: (381) 24656500
Web Site: https://www.chemos.rs
Year Founded: 1958
CHMS—(BEL)
Rev.: $1,580,091
Assets: $3,017,316
Liabilities: $412,889
Net Worth: $2,604,428
Earnings: $62,083
Emp.: 61
Fiscal Year-end: 12/31/23
Plastic Packaging Products Mfr
N.A.I.C.S.: 326112
Zoran Rajak *(Exec Dir)*

CHEMOXY INTERNATIONAL LIMITED

All Saints Refinery Cargo Fleet Road,
Middlesbrough, TS3 6AF, Cleveland,
United Kingdom
Tel.: (44) 1642248555   UK
Web Site: http://www.chemoxy.com
Year Founded: 1868
Emp.: 171
Solvents & Specialty Chemicals Mfr
N.A.I.C.S.: 325998
Martyn Bainbridge *(COO)*

CHEMRING DEFENCE UK LTD

Wilne Mill Draycott, Derby, DE72
3QJ, United Kingdom
Tel.: (44) 1332871100
Web Site:
    http://www.chemringdefence.com
Sales Range: $10-24.9 Million
Emp.: 200
Chemical Product & Preparation Mfr
N.A.I.C.S.: 325998

CHEMRING GROUP PLC

Roke Manor Old Salisbury Lane,
Romsey, SO51 0ZN, Hampshire,
United Kingdom
Tel.: (44) 1794463401   UK
Web Site: https://www.chemring.com
CMGMF—(OTCIQ)
Rev.: $601,198,416
Assets: $841,922,172
Liabilities: $274,259,440

Net Worth: $567,662,732
Earnings: $64,355,928
Emp.: 2,300
Fiscal Year-end: 10/31/22
Electronic, Engineering & Chemical
Products Mfr for Military & Marine
Safety
N.A.I.C.S.: 325998
Sarah Ellard *(Sec & Dir-Legal)*

Subsidiaries:

Alloy Surfaces Company, Inc. (1)
121 N Commerce Dr, Chester, PA
19014   **(100%)**
Tel.: (610) 497-7979
Sales Range: $25-49.9 Million
Emp.: 100
Ordnance & Accessories Mfr
N.A.I.C.S.: 332994

CHG Group, Inc. (1)
2 Wortley Road Deepcar, Sheffield, S36
2UZ, Yorkshire, United Kingdom
Tel.: (44) 1142180470
Web Site: http://www.chg-group.co.uk
Electrical Engineering Services
N.A.I.C.S.: 541330

Chemring Australia Pty Ltd (1)
230 Staceys Road, Lara, 3212, VIC,
Australia   **(100%)**
Tel.: (61) 352208500
Web Site: https://www.chemring.com
Sales Range: $25-49.9 Million
Emp.: 85
Navigational Services to Shipping
N.A.I.C.S.: 488330

Chemring Countermeasures Ltd (1)
High Post, Salisbury, SP4 6AS, Wiltshire,
United Kingdom   **(100%)**
Tel.: (44) 1722411611
Web Site: https://www.chemring.com
Sales Range: $100-124.9 Million
Emp.: 450
Small Arms Ammunition Mfr
N.A.I.C.S.: 332992

Chemring Defence Germany
GmbH (1)
Vielander Weg 147, 27574, Bremerhaven,
Germany   **(100%)**
Tel.: (49) 4713930
Semiconductor & Related Device Mfr
N.A.I.C.S.: 334413

Chemring Defence Spain S.L. (1)
Carretera Mendi S/N, Galar, 31191, Na-
varra, Spain
Tel.: (34) 948317862
Sales Range: $25-49.9 Million
Emp.: 18
Explosives Mfr
N.A.I.C.S.: 325920
Maitane Arana *(Gen Mgr)*

Chemring EOD Limited (1)
Ordnance House Blackhill Rd, Holton Heath
Poole, Dorset, BH16 6LW, United
Kingdom   **(100%)**
Tel.: (44) 1202628155
Web Site: http://www.chemringeod.com
Sales Range: $25-49.9 Million
Emp.: 49
Semiconductor & Related Device Mfr
N.A.I.C.S.: 334413
David McDonald *(Mng Dir)*

Chemring Energetic Devices,
Inc. (1)
2525 Curtiss St, Downers Grove, IL 60515
Tel.: (630) 969-0620
Web Site: https://www.chemring.com
Sales Range: $10-24.9 Million
Emp.: 100
Energetic Materials Mfr
N.A.I.C.S.: 334419
John Fair *(VP-Sls & Mktg)*

Chemring Energetics UK Limited (1)
Leafield Way Wiltshire, Corsham,
SN139SS, United Kingdom   **(100%)**
Tel.: (44) 1225810771
Web Site:
    http://www.chemringenergetics.co.uk
Sales Range: $25-49.9 Million
Emp.: 10
Engineering Services

N.A.I.C.S.: 541330

Chemring Nobel AS (1)
Engeneveien, 3475, Saetre, Norway
Tel.: (47) 32278600
Web Site: https://www.chemring.com
Sales Range: $25-49.9 Million
Emp.: 95
Explosives Mfr
N.A.I.C.S.: 325920

Chemring Sensors & Electronic Sys-
tems, Inc. (1)
23031 Ladbrook Dr, Dulles, VA 20166
Tel.: (703) 661-0283
Detection System & Sensor Product Mfr
N.A.I.C.S.: 334511

Kilgore Flares (1)
155 Kilgore Dr, Toone, TN 38381
Tel.: (731) 228-5200
Web Site: http://www.kilgoreflares.com
Sales Range: $125-149.9 Million
Emp.: 300
Mfr of Military & Commercial Flares & Pyro-
technics
N.A.I.C.S.: 336413

Non-Intrusive Inspection Technology,
Inc. (1)
23031 Ladbrook Dr, Dulles, VA 20166
Tel.: (703) 661-0283
Web Site: https://www.chemring.com
Sales Range: $75-99.9 Million
Emp.: 250
Landmine Detection System Mfr
N.A.I.C.S.: 334511
Juan Hernandez *(VP-Bus Dev)*

Plant (Domestic):

Non-Intrusive Inspection Technology,
Inc. - Charlottesville Facility (2)
1725 Discovery Dr, Charlottesville, VA
22911
Tel.: (434) 964-4800
Web Site: http://www.niitek.com
Landmine Detection System Mfr
N.A.I.C.S.: 334511

Richmond Eei Ltd (1)
Thetford Armtec Estate North Lopham, Nor-
folk, IP222LR, United Kingdom   **(100%)**
Tel.: (44) 1379686800
Sales Range: $25-49.9 Million
Emp.: 9
Electrical Equipment & Component Mfr
N.A.I.C.S.: 335999
Robert Gilbert *(Mng Dir)*

Roke Manor Research Ltd (1)
Old Salisbury Lane, Romsey, SO51 0ZN,
Hampshire, United Kingdom
Tel.: (44) 1794833000
Technology Consulting Services
N.A.I.C.S.: 541690

CHEMSPEC INTERNATIONAL LIMITED

No 200 Wu Wei Road, Shanghai,
200331, China
Tel.: (86) 2163639090   Ky
Web Site:
    http://www.chemspec.com.cn
Sales Range: $150-199.9 Million
Emp.: 1,794
Specialty Chemicals Mfr
N.A.I.C.S.: 325998
Jianhua Yang *(Chm & CEO)*

CHEMTECH INDUSTRIAL VALVES LIMITED

503 5th Floor Sunrise Business Park
Plot no B 68 Road no 16, Wagle Es-
tate Thane W, Mumbai, 400604, Ma-
harashtra, India
Tel.: (91) 2225839500
Web Site:
    https://www.chemtechvalves.com
Year Founded: 1997
537326—(BOM)
Rev.: $1,593,671
Assets: $3,660,106
Liabilities: $2,403,366
Net Worth: $1,256,739

Chemtech Industrial Valves Limited—(Continued)

Earnings: ($76,541)
Emp.: 37
Fiscal Year-end: 03/31/22
Industrial Valve Mfr
N.A.I.C.S.: 332911
Harsh Pradeep Badkur *(Mng Dir)*

CHEMTRADE LOGISTICS IN-COME FUND

155 Gordon Baker Road Suite 300,
Toronto, M2H 3N5, ON, Canada
Tel.: (416) 496-4177
Web Site:
   https://www.chemtradelogistics.com
Year Founded: 2001
CHE.UN—(TSX)
Rev.: $1,079,263,997
Assets: $1,955,955,023
Liabilities: $1,482,038,065
Net Worth: $473,916,958
Earnings: ($131,014,690)
Emp.: 1,474
Fiscal Year-end: 12/31/20
Holding Company
N.A.I.C.S.: 551112
Mark Davis *(Pres & CEO)*

Subsidiaries:

Aglobis GmbH **(1)**
Friedrichstrasse 47, 45128, Essen, Germany
Tel.: (49) 20180987100
Web Site:
   http://www.chemtradelogistics.com
Sales Range: $25-49.9 Million
Emp.: 16
Chemical Products Mfr & Sales
N.A.I.C.S.: 325180

Chemtrade Electrochem Inc. **(1)**
Suite 2100 144 - 4th Avenue SW, Calgary,
T2P 3N4, AB, Canada
Tel.: (416) 496-4177
Rev.: $496,294,688
Assets: $541,188,907
Liabilities: $292,125,485
Net Worth: $249,063,423
Earnings: $39,619,997
Fiscal Year-end: 12/31/2017
Specialty Chemicals Mfr
N.A.I.C.S.: 325998
Mark Davis *(Pres & CEO)*

Chemtrade Logistics, Inc. **(1)**
155 Gordon Baker Road Suite 300, Toronto,
M2H 3N5, ON, Canada
Tel.: (416) 496-5856
Web Site:
   https://www.chemtradelogistics.com
Sales Range: $450-499.9 Million
Emp.: 100
Supplier of Sulphuric Acid, Liquid Sulphur
Dioxide & Sodium Hydrosulphite: Spent
Acid Processing Services
N.A.I.C.S.: 325998
Leon Aarts *(Grp VP-Corp Dev & Strategy)*

Subsidiary (US):

Chemtrade Logistics (US), Inc. **(2)**
7680 Ottawa Rd, Elida, OH 45820
Tel.: (419) 641-4151
Chemical Products Mfr
N.A.I.C.S.: 325998

Subsidiary (Domestic):

Chemtrade Performance Chemicals
US, LLC **(3)**
814 Tyvola Rd Ste 126, Charlotte, NC
28217-3539
Tel.: (704) 369-2489
Chemical Products Mfr
N.A.I.C.S.: 325998

Chemtrade Refinery Services
Inc. **(3)**
140 Goes In Lodge Rd, Riverton, WY
82501-9100
Tel.: (307) 856-9217
Chemical Products Mfr & Distr
N.A.I.C.S.: 325180

Chemtrade Pulp Chemicals Trust **(1)**

111 Gordon Baker Rd, Toronto, M2H 3R1,
ON, Canada
Tel.: (416) 496-5856
Web Site:
   http://www.chemtradelogistics.com
Emp.: 150
Investment Management Service
N.A.I.C.S.: 523999

CHEMTRONICS CO., LTD.

31 Baeil-gil Jeondong-myeon,
Bundang-gu, Sejong, Gyeonggi-do,
Korea (South)
Tel.: (82) 317767690
Web Site:
   https://www.chemtronics.co.kr
Year Founded: 1997
089010—(KRS)
Rev.: $476,278,923
Assets: $360,123,335
Liabilities: $245,936,915
Net Worth: $114,186,420
Earnings: $4,605,916
Emp.: 510
Fiscal Year-end: 12/31/22
Sensor Product Mfr
N.A.I.C.S.: 334413
Bo-Gyun Kim *(Pres & CEO)*

Subsidiaries:

Beyond_i Co., Ltd. **(1)**
Floor 7 DTC Tower 49 Daewangpangyo-ro
644beon-gil, Bundang-gu, Seongnam,
13493, Gyeonggi-do, Korea (South)
Tel.: (82) 704 499 7514
Web Site: https://www.beyondi.co.kr
Automotive Electronics Services
N.A.I.C.S.: 541715
Eungsoo Kim *(Pres & CEO)*

CHEMTRONICS China **(1)**
No 5 1st Branch Road Saida Xiqing Economic Development Area, Tianjin, China
Tel.: (86) 2223888555
Electronic Components Distr
N.A.I.C.S.: 423690

CHEMTRONICS Europe s.r.o **(1)**
Feriencikova 18, 811 08, Bratislava, Slovakia
Tel.: (421) 317883421
Electronic Components Distr
N.A.I.C.S.: 423690

Chemtronics Co., Ltd. - Pyeongtaek
Plant **(1)**
45 Poseunggongdan-ro 118beon-gil
Poseung-eup, Pyeongtaek, Gyeonggi-do,
Korea (South)
Tel.: (82) 316837461
Sensor Product Mfr
N.A.I.C.S.: 334413

Chemtronics Co., Ltd. - Sejong
Plant **(1)**
31 Baeil-gil Jeondong-myeon, Sejong, Korea (South)
Tel.: (82) 448683011
Sensor Product Mfr
N.A.I.C.S.: 334413

Chemtronics Co., Ltd. - Yongin
Plant **(1)**
35 Hyeongje-ro Namsa-eup, Cheoin-gu,
Yongin, Gyeonggi-do, Korea (South)
Tel.: (82) 313213800
Sensor Product Mfr
N.A.I.C.S.: 334413

Chemtronics USA Inc **(1)**
7841 Balboa Ave Ste 205, San Diego, CA
92111
Tel.: (858) 874-6883
Electronic Components Distr
N.A.I.C.S.: 423690

Chemtrovina Co. Ltd. **(1)**
Nhon Trach II - Loc Khang IP, Nhon Trach,
Dong Nai, Vietnam
Tel.: (84) 61 356 0414
Chemical Product Mfr & Distr
N.A.I.C.S.: 325998

PT Chemtronics Indonesia **(1)**
Jl jababeka IV C Blok T-11 Kawsan Industri
Jababeka Pasirgombong, Cikarang Utara,

Bekasi, 17530, Jawa Barat, Indonesia
Tel.: (62) 21 8984 534
Electronic Components Distr
N.A.I.C.S.: 423690

WITS Co., Ltd. **(1)**
Floor 3 Block B9 Maeyoung-ro, Yongtong-gu, Suwon, Gyeonggi, Korea (South)
Tel.: (82) 704 925 9511
Web Site: https://www.ewits.co.kr
Communication Equipment Mfr
N.A.I.C.S.: 334290
Kim Bogyun *(Pres & CEO)*

Witsvina Company Limited **(1)**
Lot Cn7 Diem Thuy IP A Area, Hong Tien
Commune Pho Yen Town, Thai Nguyen,
Vietnam
Tel.: (84) 96 602 5656
Chemical Product Mfr & Distr
N.A.I.C.S.: 325998

CHEMTROS CO., LTD.

7 Neungan-ro, Danwon-gu, Ansan,
15427, Korea (South)
Tel.: (82) 314910653
Web Site: https://chemtros.com
Year Founded: 2015
220260—(KRS)
Rev.: $43,738,393
Assets: $74,750,881
Liabilities: $29,536,560
Net Worth: $45,214,321
Earnings: $2,923,167
Emp.: 143
Fiscal Year-end: 12/31/22
Financial Investment Management
Services
N.A.I.C.S.: 523940
Dong-Hoon Lee *(Pres & CEO)*

CHEN FULL INTERNATIONAL CO., LTD.

9F No 99 Sec 1 Nankan Rd, Luzhu,
Taoyuan, 33859, Taiwan
Tel.: (886) 33220022
Web Site:
   https://www.chenfull.com.tw
Year Founded: 1982
8383—(TAI)
Industrial Equipment Distr
N.A.I.C.S.: 423830
Chiung-Ju Chang *(Chm)*

CHEN HSONG HOLDINGS LTD.

13-15 Dai Wang St Tai Po Industrial
Estate, Tai Po, China (Hong Kong)
Tel.: (852) 2 665 3888   CN
Web Site: http://www.chenhsong.com
Year Founded: 1958
0057—(HKG)
Rev.: $304,464,126
Assets: $564,730,933
Liabilities: $176,108,260
Net Worth: $388,622,673
Earnings: $26,418,329
Emp.: 2,300
Fiscal Year-end: 03/31/21
Holding Company; Manufacturer of
Injection Moulding Machines
N.A.I.C.S.: 551112
Chen Chiang *(Founder)*

Subsidiaries:

Asian Plastic Machinery Co. Ltd. **(1)**
No1 Sung Chian North Road, Chung Li Industrial District, Chung-li, 320, Taoyuan,
Taiwan
Tel.: (886) 34522288
Web Site: http://www.asianplastic.com.tw
Plastic Injection Molding Machine Mfr
N.A.I.C.S.: 333248

Chen Hsong (Middle East) FZE **(1)**
PO Box 18161, Jafza South Jebel Ali,
Dubai, United Arab Emirates
Tel.: (971) 48806658
Web Site:
   http://www.chenhsongmiddleeast.com
Injection Molding Machine Mfr

N.A.I.C.S.: 333248

Chen Hsong Europe B.V. **(1)**
Hulostraat 2, Pannerden, 6911 KX, Zevenaar, Netherlands
Tel.: (31) 316240718
Web Site: http://en.chenhsongeurope.eu
Injection Molding Machine Mfr
N.A.I.C.S.: 333248

Chen Hsong Germany GmbH **(1)**
Hooghe Weg 4, 47906, Kempen, Germany
Tel.: (49) 15201604760
Web Site: http://de.chenhsongeurope.eu
Injection Molding Machine Mfr
N.A.I.C.S.: 333248

Chen Hsong Machinery Co. Ltd. **(1)**
13-15 Dai Wang Street, Tai Po Industrial
Estate, Tai Po, NT, China (Hong
Kong) **(100%)**
Tel.: (852) 26653888
Web Site: http://www.chenhsong-machinery.com.hk
Sales Range: $25-49.9 Million
Emp.: 100
Mfr of Plastic Injection Moulding Machines
N.A.I.C.S.: 333248

Chen Hsong Machinery Taiwan Co.
Ltd. **(1)**
No1 Sung Chian North Ro, Chung Li Industrial District, Chung-li, 320, Taoyuan,
Taiwan **(100%)**
Tel.: (886) 3 4522288
Web Site: http://www.asianplastic.com.tw
Sales Range: $100-124.9 Million
Emp.: 300
Mfr & Sales of Plastic Injection Molding
Machines
N.A.I.C.S.: 333248

Chen Hsong Middle East Makine Ticaret Anonim Sirketi **(1)**
Ikitelli Organize Sanayii Mahallesi Bedrettin,
Dalan Bulvari Bina No 39 1 Kat no 71 Basaksehir, Istanbul, 34490, Türkiye
Tel.: (90) 5333901054
Injection Molding Machine Mfr
N.A.I.C.S.: 333248

Chen Hsong Precision Mould Co.,
Ltd. **(1)**
13-15 Dai Want St, Tai Po Indus Estate, Tai
Po, China (Hong Kong) **(100%)**
Tel.: (852) 26653888
Web Site: http://www.chenhsong.com.hk
Sales Range: $25-49.9 Million
Emp.: 100
Mfr & Sales of Moulds & Dies
N.A.I.C.S.: 333514
Chen Chiang *(Chm)*

Chen Hsong South America Importacao, Exportacao e Comercio de Equipamentos Ltda. **(1)**
Av Cesar Simoes 331 Bairro Jardim Henriqueta, Sao Paulo, 06764-480, SP, Brazil
Tel.: (55) 1143417478
Injection Molding Machine Mfr
N.A.I.C.S.: 333248

Productive Heat Treatment Co.
Ltd. **(1)**
13-15 Dai Wang St, Tai Po Industrial Estate,
Tai Po, China (Hong Kong) **(100%)**
Tel.: (852) 24238433
Sales Range: $25-49.9 Million
Emp.: 100
Heating Equipment
N.A.I.C.S.: 333414
Chen Chiang *(Chm)*

Shenzhen Chen Hsong Machinery
Co. Ltd. **(1)**
Chen Hsong Industrial Park Kengzi Town,
Longgang, Shenzhen, 518122, Guangdong,
China **(100%)**
Tel.: (86) 75584139999
Web Site: http://www.chenhsong.com.hk
Sales Range: $400-449.9 Million
Mfr & Sales of Plastic Injection Moulding
Machines & Related Components
N.A.I.C.S.: 333248

CHEN KE MING FOOD MANU-FACTURING CO., LTD

No 28 Zhenhua Road Environmental
Protection Technology Industrial Park,
Yuhua District, Changsha, 410116,
Hunan, China
Tel.: (86) 7375213069
Web Site: http://www.kemen.net.cn
Year Founded: 1997
002661—(SSE)
Rev.: $704,779,920
Assets: $618,748,416
Liabilities: $254,667,348
Net Worth: $364,081,068
Earnings: $21,736,728
Emp.: 1,840
Fiscal Year-end: 12/31/22
Noodle Mfr & Distr
N.A.I.C.S.: 311999
Chen Hong *(Chm & Gen Mgr)*

CHEN LIN EDUCATION GROUP HOLDINGS LIMITED

No 001 Lianfu Avenue, Xinjian District, Nanchang, China
Tel.: (86) 79183652111   Ky
Web Site: https://www.chenlin-edu.com
Year Founded: 2018
1593—(HKG)
Rev.: $78,896,409
Assets: $517,153,920
Liabilities: $392,888,507
Net Worth: $124,265,414
Earnings: ($5,819,682)
Emp.: 2,356
Fiscal Year-end: 08/31/22
Holding Company
N.A.I.C.S.: 551112
Anne Yu *(Sec)*

CHEN XING DEVELOPMENT HOLDINGS LIMITED

18 Anning Street, Yuci District, Jinzhong, Shanxi, China
Tel.: (86) 3543990366   Ky
Web Site: http://www.chen-xing.cn
Year Founded: 1997
2286—(HKG)
Rev.: $167,901,552
Assets: $1,781,815,979
Liabilities: $1,534,308,469
Net Worth: $247,507,510
Earnings: $7,146,922
Emp.: 237
Fiscal Year-end: 12/31/22
Real Estate Manangement Services
N.A.I.C.S.: 531210
Xuankui Bai *(Chm)*

CHENAVARI TORO INCOME FUND LIMITED

Old Bank Chambers La Grande Rue
St Martins, Saint Peter Port, GY4
6RT, United Kingdom
Tel.: (44) 2072593600
Web Site: http://www.torolimited.gg
TORO—(LSE)
Rev.: $56,056,990
Assets: $306,185,946
Liabilities: $42,410,852
Net Worth: $263,775,094
Earnings: $50,491,870
Fiscal Year-end: 09/30/21
Investment Services
N.A.I.C.S.: 525910

CHENBRO MICOM CO., LTD.

19F No 558 Zhongyuan Rd, Xinzhuang Dist, New Taipei City,
242030, Taiwan
Tel.: (886) 282265500
Web Site:
  https://www.chenbro.com.tw
Year Founded: 1983
8210—(TAI)
Rev.: $367,809,856
Assets: $457,408,139

Liabilities: $275,000,774
Net Worth: $182,407,364
Earnings: $36,202,621
Emp.: 1,304
Fiscal Year-end: 12/31/23
Computer Related Products Mfr
N.A.I.C.S.: 334118
Frank Chen *(Co-Founder)*

Subsidiaries:

ChenPower Information Technology
(Shanghai) Co., Ltd.   **(1)**
No 9 Lane 1188 Shenhong Road Henderson Xu Hui Center, Ming Hang Dist, Shanghai, China
Tel.: (86) 213 323 2288
Barebone Server System Mfr
N.A.I.C.S.: 334111

Chenbro Europe B.V.   **(1)**
Avignonlaan 35, Eindhoven, 5627GA, Netherlands
Tel.: (31) 40 295 2045
Web Site: http://www.chenbro.com
Sales Range: $25-49.9 Million
Emp.: 10
Chassis Product Mfr
N.A.I.C.S.: 336110

Chenbro GmbH   **(1)**
Carl-Friedrich-Benz-Str 13, 47877, Willich,
Germany
Tel.: (49) 21548142730
Barebone Server System Mfr
N.A.I.C.S.: 334111

Chenbro Micom (Shenzhen) Co.,
Ltd.   **(1)**
Room 2109 Hua Rong Building 178 Mintian
Road, Futian CBD, Shenzhen, 518048,
China
Tel.: (86) 755 2382 4355
Chassis Product Mfr
N.A.I.C.S.: 336110

Chenbro Micom (USA) Inc.   **(1)**
2800 E Jurupa St, Ontario, CA 91761
Tel.: (909) 937-0100
Computer Terminal Mfr
N.A.I.C.S.: 334118
Bronson Peng *(Project Mgr)*

Chenbro UK Ltd.   **(1)**
Crossford Court Dane Road, Sale, M33
7BZ, Manchester, United Kingdom
Tel.: (44) 1614255341
Computer Peripheral Equipment Whslr
N.A.I.C.S.: 423430

CHENG EUI PRECISION INDUSTRY CO., LTD.

No 18 Zhongshan Rd, Tu Cheng Dist,
New Taipei City, 23680, Taiwan
Tel.: (886) 222699888
Web Site: http://www.foxlink.com
Sales Range: $25-49.9 Million
Emp.: 10,000
Networking Products Communications Connectors & Cablings Mfr
N.A.I.C.S.: 334417
T. C. Gou *(Chm & Pres)*

Subsidiaries:

Dongguan Fuqiang Electronics Co.,
Ltd.   **(1)**
Chenguei Industry District, Dong Keng,
Dongguan, Guang Dong, China
Tel.: (86) 76983697203
Energy Wire Mfr & Distr
N.A.I.C.S.: 335929

FIT Holding Co., Ltd.   **(1)**
No 49 Section 4 Zhongyang Road, Tucheng
District, New Taipei City, 236, Taiwan
Tel.: (886) 222699866
Web Site: https://www.fit-holding.com
Display Instruments Mfr
N.A.I.C.S.: 334513

Foxlink Automotive Technology (Kunshan) Co., Ltd.   **(1)**
No 6 Zheng Wei West Road, Jin Xi Town,
Kunshan, Jiangsu, China
Tel.: (86) 51257235288
Energy Wire Mfr & Distr

N.A.I.C.S.: 335929

Foxlink Automotive Technology Co.,
Ltd.   **(1)**
No 18 Zhongshan Rd, Tu-Cheng Dist, New
Taipei City, 23680, Taiwan
Tel.: (886) 222699888
Energy Wire Mfr & Distr
N.A.I.C.S.: 335929

Foxlink International Inc   **(1)**
925 W Lambert Rd Ste C, Brea, CA 92821-2943
Tel.: (714) 256-1777
Web Site: http://www.foxlink.com
Rev.: $38,164,520
Emp.: 45
Communications Connectors
N.A.I.C.S.: 335931

Fugang Electric (Kunshan) Co.,
Ltd.   **(1)**
No 6 Zheng Wei West Road, Jin Xi Town,
Kunshan, Jiangsu, China
Tel.: (86) 51257235288
Energy Wire Mfr & Distr
N.A.I.C.S.: 335929

Fugang Electric (Maanshan) Co.,
Ltd.   **(1)**
No 2161 Chenguei Rd, Economic and Technical Development Zone, Ma'anshan, Anhui,
China
Tel.: (86) 5555238888
Energy Wire Mfr & Distr
N.A.I.C.S.: 335929

Fugang Electric (Nan Chang) Co.,
Ltd.   **(1)**
No 189 Torch 3 Road, High-Tech Zone,
Nanchang, Jiangxi, China
Tel.: (86) 79188165508
Energy Wire Mfr & Distr
N.A.I.C.S.: 335929

Fugang Electric (Xuzhou) Co.,
Ltd.   **(1)**
North Side of Shenda Road, Economic and
Technological Development Zone, Xuzhou,
China
Tel.: (86) 51687982688
Energy Wire Mfr & Distr
N.A.I.C.S.: 335929

Fugang Electronic (Dong Guan) Co.,
Ltd.   **(1)**
Industry Street, Dong-Keng, Dongguan,
Guangdong, China
Tel.: (86) 76983882225
Energy Wire Mfr & Distr
N.A.I.C.S.: 335929

Glory Science Co., Ltd.   **(1)**
No 22 Houke S Rd, Houli Dist, Taichung,
42152, Taiwan
Tel.: (886) 425587889
Web Site: https://www.glorytek.com.tw
Optical Instrument Mfr
N.A.I.C.S.: 333310

Glorytek (Yancheng) Co., Ltd.   **(1)**
No 18 Xiwang Avenue South Rd,
Yancheng, Jiangsu, China
Tel.: (86) 51588310168
Energy Wire Mfr & Distr
N.A.I.C.S.: 335929

Shinfox Co., Ltd.   **(1)**
No 49 Sec 4 Zhongyang Rd, Tucheng Dist,
New Taipei City, 236040, Taiwan
Tel.: (886) 222699888
Web Site: https://www.shinfox.com.tw
Wind Power Generation Services
N.A.I.C.S.: 221115
Hu Hui-sen *(Pres)*

Studio A Inc   **(1)**
7F No 260 Sec 2 Bade Rd, Songshan Dist,
Taipei, 105, Taiwan
Tel.: (886) 227118838
Energy Wire Mfr & Distr
N.A.I.C.S.: 335929

Studio A Technology Limited   **(1)**
Room 3906 Cable TV Tower 9 Hoi Shing
Road, Tsuen Wan, New Territories, China
(Hong Kong)
Tel.: (852) 23312902
Energy Wire Mfr & Distr
N.A.I.C.S.: 335929

Wei Hai Fu Kang Electric Co.,
Ltd.   **(1)**
No 26 Jiashan Road, Chucun County Gao
District, Weihai, Shandong, China
Tel.: (86) 6313659328
Energy Wire Mfr & Distr
N.A.I.C.S.: 335929

CHENG LOONG CORP.

No 1 Sec 1 Min Sheng Rd, Panchiao
Dist, New Taipei City, 220, Taiwan
Tel.: (886) 222225131
Web Site: https://www.clc.com.tw
Year Founded: 1959
1904—(TAI)
Rev.: $1,378,902,626
Assets: $2,309,650,228
Liabilities: $1,338,350,419
Net Worth: $971,299,810
Earnings: $30,509,924
Emp.: 6,798
Fiscal Year-end: 12/31/23
Corrugated Paper Box Mfr
N.A.I.C.S.: 322211
Feng-Chih Yeh *(Head-Auditing Div)*

Subsidiaries:

Cheng Loong (Gwangtung) Paper
Co., Ltd.   **(1)**
No3 HouJie DongYie Road, HouJie Town,
Dongguan, GuangDong, China
Paper Products Mfr
N.A.I.C.S.: 322211

Cheng Loong Binh Duong Container
Co., Ltd.   **(1)**
Lot CN 8 Road N6 Song Than 3 Industrial
Park, Thu Dau Mot, Binh Duong, Vietnam
Tel.: (84) 2743636900906
Paper Products Mfr
N.A.I.C.S.: 322211

Cheng Loong Binh Duong Paper Co.,
Ltd.   **(1)**
Zone No 4 Singapore Ascendas-Protrade
Industrial Zone An Tay Ward, Ben Cat, Binh
Duong, Vietnam
Paper Products Mfr
N.A.I.C.S.: 322211

Cheng Loong Corp. - Chupei Mill   **(1)**
No 300 Sec 2 Chiang Ching Rd Ta-I Li,
Chupei, Hsinchu, Taiwan
Tel.: (886) 35561226
Paper Products Mfr
N.A.I.C.S.: 322211

Cheng Loong Corp. - Houli Mill   **(1)**
No 2 Sec 3 Sanfeng Rd Guangfu Li Houli
Dist, Taichung, 421, Taiwan
Tel.: (886) 425565160
Paper Products Mfr
N.A.I.C.S.: 322211

Cheng Loong Corp. - Hsinchu
Mill   **(1)**
No 308 Nioupu Rd Jungpu Li, Hsinchu,
300, Taiwan
Tel.: (886) 35388193
Paper Products Mfr
N.A.I.C.S.: 322211

Cheng Loong Corp. - Los Angeles
Branch   **(1)**
1160 E Slauson Ave, Los Angeles, CA
90010
Tel.: (323) 231-9183
Paper Products Mfr
N.A.I.C.S.: 322211

Cheng Loong Corp. - Miaoli
Plant   **(1)**
No 10 Zhonglong 3rd Rd Jungping Tsuen,
Tongluo, 366, Miaoli, Taiwan
Tel.: (886) 37230661
Paper Products Mfr
N.A.I.C.S.: 322211

Cheng Loong Corp. - New Jersey
Branch   **(1)**
277 Fairfield Rd 332, Fairfield, NJ 07004
Tel.: (973) 882-7728
Paper Products Mfr
N.A.I.C.S.: 322211

Cheng Loong Corp.—(Continued)

Cheng Loong Corp. - Taichung Plant (1)
No 532 Zili Rd Wuqi Dist, Taichung, 435, Taiwan
Tel.: 886) 426301919
Paper Products Mfr
N.A.I.C.S.: 322211

Cheng Loong Corp. - Talin Plant (1)
No 20 Linzitou Sanho Li Dalin Township, Chiayi, 622, Taiwan
Tel.: (886) 52953110
Paper Products Mfr
N.A.I.C.S.: 322211

Cheng Loong Corp. - Taoyuan Mill (1)
No 116 Dagung Rd Beigang Li Dayuan Dist, Taoyuan, 337, Taiwan
Tel.: (886) 33868311
Paper Products Mfr
N.A.I.C.S.: 322211

Cheng Loong Corp. - Taoyuan Plant (1)
No 36 Ln 511 Sec 2 Zhongzheng E Rd Wuchuan Li, Dayuan Dist, Taoyuan, 337, Taiwan
Tel.: (886) 33811911
Paper Products Mfr
N.A.I.C.S.: 322211

Cheng Loong Corp. - Taoyuan Plant II (1)
No.82 Aly 29 Ln 536 Sec 3 Zhongzheng E Rd Wuchuan Li, Dayuan Dist, Taoyuan, 337, Taiwan
Tel.: (886) 33810062
Paper Products Mfr
N.A.I.C.S.: 322211

Cheng Loong Corp. - Taoyuan Plant, Form & Packaging Materials (1)
No 280 Chaoyin N Rd Lin 14 Beigang Li, Dayuan Dist, Taoyuan, 337, Taiwan
Tel.: (886) 33866100
Paper Products Mfr
N.A.I.C.S.: 322211

Cheng Loong Corp. - Yenchao Plant (1)
No 130 Zhong an Rd Anjau Li Yanchao Dist, Kaohsiung, 824, Taiwan
Tel.: (886) 76161511
Paper Products Mfr
N.A.I.C.S.: 322211

Cheng Loong Long An Container Co., Ltd. (1)
Lo C7 Duong So2 Khu Cong Nghiep Hai Son Xa Duc Hoa Ha Huyen, Duc Hoa, Long An, Vietnam
Tel.: (84) 2723774519529
Paper Products Mfr
N.A.I.C.S.: 322211

Chengdu Cheng Loong Packing Products Co., Ltd. (1)
NO1 Tengfei 11Rd Southwest Air Harbor Development, Economic Zone, Chengdu, Sichuan, China
Tel.: (86) 2869286846
Paper Products Mfr
N.A.I.C.S.: 322211

Chong Qing Cheng Loong Paper Co., Ltd. (1)
Luohuang Industrial Park B District Road No 19 Jiangjin District, Chongqing, China
Tel.: (86) 2361089666
Paper Products Mfr
N.A.I.C.S.: 322211

Chung Loong Paper Holdings Limited (1)
No 399 Xiupu Road, Pudong New District, Shanghai, China
Tel.: (86) 2158128666
Paper Products Mfr
N.A.I.C.S.: 322211

CorAsia Corp. (1)
363 Fairview Way, Milpitas, CA 95035
Tel.: (408) 649-3472
Web Site: https://www.corasiacorp.com
Paper Products Mfr
N.A.I.C.S.: 322211

Dongguang City Ming Loong Paper Co., Ltd. (1)
No 3 North 4 Lane Hetian Dadao Houjie Town, Dongguan, GuangDong, China
Tel.: (86) 76988632888
Paper Products Mfr
N.A.I.C.S.: 322211

Gemtech Optoelectronics Corp. (1)
5-2 Chi-Lin Rd Chung-Li Industrial Park, Tao-Yuan Hsien, Chung-li, 320, Taiwan
Tel.: (886) 34342538
Web Site: http://www.gem-tech.com.tw
Glass Products Mfr
N.A.I.C.S.: 327215

Henan Cheng Loong Packing Products Co., Ltd. (1)
Tel.: (86) 37122710661
Paper Products Mfr
N.A.I.C.S.: 322211

Kunfu Paper (Kunsan) Co., Ltd. (1)
No 18 Qianhua Road Dianshan Lake Town, Kunshan, Jiangsu, China
Tel.: (86) 51257498808
Paper Products Mfr
N.A.I.C.S.: 322211

Long Fu Paper (Kunshan) Co., Ltd. (1)
No 18 Qianhua Road Dianshan Lake Town, Kunshan, Jiangsu, China
Tel.: (86) 51257498808
Paper Products Mfr
N.A.I.C.S.: 322211

Loong Fu Paper (Kunsan) Co., Ltd. (1)
No 18 Qianhua Road Dianshan Lake Town, Kunshan, Jiangsu, China
Tel.: (86) 51257498808
Paper Products Mfr
N.A.I.C.S.: 322211

Ming Fong Plastic (Dong Guan) Co., Ltd. (1)
Yinhe Road Xinan District Shijie Town, Dongguan, GuangDong, China
Tel.: (86) 76986322156
Paper Products Mfr
N.A.I.C.S.: 322211

Qingdao Chung Loong Paper Co., Ltd. (1)
No 144Taiguang Road, Jiangshan Town, Qingdao, China
Tel.: (86) 53286491461
Paper Products Mfr
N.A.I.C.S.: 322211

Shan Fu Paper (Kunson) Co., Ltd. (1)
No 98 B Zone Gui Lin Road KunShan, Comprehensive Bonded Zone, Kunshan, Jiang Su, China
Tel.: (86) 51257721188
Paper Products Mfr
N.A.I.C.S.: 322211

Shanghai Chung Hao Paper Co., Ltd. (1)
No 399 Xiupu Road, Pudong New District, Shanghai, China
Tel.: (86) 2158128866
Paper Products Mfr
N.A.I.C.S.: 322211

Subsidiary (Non-US):

Dongguan Ming Loong Paper Co., Ltd. (2)
Tel.: (86) 76988632888
Paper Products Mfr
N.A.I.C.S.: 322211

Subsidiary (Domestic):

Zhengzhou Cheng Loong Packing Products Co., Ltd. (2)
Third Factory building Shenzhou Rd and Yanhe Rd Intersection south, Hezhuang Town, Xinzheng, Henan, China
Tel.: (86) 37162535152
Paper Products Mfr
N.A.I.C.S.: 322211

Shanghai Chung Loong Paper Co., Ltd. (1)
No 489 Xiupu Road Pudong New District,
Shanghai, China
Tel.: (86) 2158129798
Paper Products Mfr
N.A.I.C.S.: 322211

Sun Favorite Co., Ltd. (1)
20th Floor No 3 Section 1 Minsheng Road, Banqiao District, New Taipei City, Taiwan
Tel.: (886) 229599788
Web Site: https://www.sunfavorite.com
Beverage Distr
N.A.I.C.S.: 424490

Suzhou Cheng Loong Paper Co., Ltd. (1)
No 162 Taisan Road, Suzhou New District, Suzhou, Jiangsu, China
Tel.: (86) 51266654808
Paper Products Mfr
N.A.I.C.S.: 322211

Tianjin Chung Loong Paper Co., Ltd. (1)
No 51 XinHuan East Road West District TainjinDevelopement Zone, Tianjin, China
Tel.: (86) 2266879966
Paper Products Mfr
N.A.I.C.S.: 322211

Vina Tawana Container Co., Ltd. (1)
Nhon Trach III Industrial Zone, Nhon Trach, Dong Nai, Vietnam
Tel.: (84) 2513560445
Paper Products Mfr
N.A.I.C.S.: 322211

Yamahatsu Nihon Co., Ltd. (1)
104-0061 4-6 Ginza 3-Chome Chuo-Ku Cheng Loong Ginza Bldg 7F, Tokyo, Japan
Tel.: (81) 352500928
Paper Products Mfr
N.A.I.C.S.: 322211

Zhangzhou Cheng Loong Paper Co., Ltd. (1)
Third Factory building Shenzhou Rd and Yanhe Rd Intersection south, Hezhuang Town, Xinzheng, Henan, China
Tel.: (86) 37162535152
Paper Products Mfr
N.A.I.C.S.: 322211

CHENG MEI MATERIALS TECHNOLOGY CORPORATION
No13 Muzhagang W Rd, Shanhua Town, T'ainan, 74148, Taiwan
Tel.: (886) 65889988
Web Site: https://www.cmmt.com.tw
4960—(TAI)
Rev.: $302,091,718
Assets: $464,784,246
Liabilities: $164,595,958
Net Worth: $300,188,288
Earnings: ($18,998,560)
Emp.: 716
Fiscal Year-end: 12/31/23
Optoelectronics
N.A.I.C.S.: 334419
Jau-Yang Ho (Chm & Gen Mgr)

Subsidiaries:

Hengmei Optoelectronic Corporation (1)
No 111 Jianhu Road Economic Development Zone, Kunshan, Jiangsu, China
Tel.: (86) 51257169988
Web Site: https://en.cnhmo.cn
Polarizer Product Mfr
N.A.I.C.S.: 334516

CHENG SHIN RUBBER (XIAMEN) IND., LTD.
No 15 Xi Bin Road, Xing Lin Industrial District, Xiamen, 361022, China
Tel.: (86) 5926211606
Web Site: http://www.csttires.com
Year Founded: 1989
Sales Range: $100-124.9 Million
Emp.: 20,000
Tire & Tube Distr
N.A.I.C.S.: 441340
Marx Lee (Mgr-Sls)

Subsidiaries:

Cheng Shin Holland BV. (1)
Noorddammerweg 1c, 1424 NV, De Kwakel, Netherlands
Tel.: (31) 206402620
Tire Mfr & Distr
N.A.I.C.S.: 326211
Dean Sullivan (VP)

Cheng Shin Rubber Ind. Co., Ltd. (1)
8th Fl World Trade Building 50 Sec 1 Shin-Sheng S Rd, Taipei, Taiwan
Tel.: (886) 223937451
Web Site: https://www.csttires.com
Rev.: $3,083,603,070
Assets: $4,561,286,277
Liabilities: $1,922,796,611
Net Worth: $2,638,489,666
Earnings: $156,091,048
Emp.: 20,000
Fiscal Year-end: 12/31/2022
Tiles Mfr
N.A.I.C.S.: 326211

Subsidiary (US):

Cheng Shin Rubber USA, Inc. (2)
545 Old Peachtree Rd, Suwanee, GA 30024
Tel.: (678) 407-6700
Web Site: http://www.maxxis.com
Tiles Mfr
N.A.I.C.S.: 326211

Subsidiary (Non-US):

Maxxis International - UK plc (2)
Carr Road, Felixstowe, IP11 3RX, Suffolk, United Kingdom
Tel.: (44) 843 504 2881
Web Site: http://maxxis.co.uk
Tire & Tube Mfr
N.A.I.C.S.: 423130
Rachel Franklin (Coord-Mktg Comm)

Maxxis Tech Center Europe B.V. (2)
Weverstraat 5, 5405, Uden, Netherlands
Tel.: (31) 413245801
Web Site: http://www.maxxistce.nl
Sales Range: $10-24.9 Million
Emp.: 6
Tire & Tubes Mfr
N.A.I.C.S.: 423130
R. Versteeg (Gen Mgr)

Cheng Shin Tire (Xiamen) Co., Ltd. (1)
15 Xiyuan Road, Haicang Area, Xiamen, Fujian, China
Tel.: (86) 592 6885333
Web Site: http://www.csttires.com
Tiles Mfr
N.A.I.C.S.: 326211

New Pacific Industry Co., Ltd. (1)
44 Sec 1 Chung Shan Rd, Chung Chuang Vlg Hua Tan, Chang-Hua, Taiwan
Tel.: (886) 47869711
Sales Range: $50-74.9 Million
Emp.: 120
Mfr of Automotive Parts
N.A.I.C.S.: 336340

Xiamen Cheng Shin Enterprise Co., Ltd. (1)
Haicang Investment Area, Xinyang Industrial Area, Xiamen, China
Tel.: (86) 5926809900
Tire Mfr & Distr
N.A.I.C.S.: 326211

CHENG UEI PRECISION INDUSTRY CO., LTD.
No 18 Zhongshan Rd, Tu Cheng Dist, New Taipei City, 23680, Taiwan
Tel.: (886) 222699888
Web Site: https://www.foxlink.com
Year Founded: 1986
2392—(TAI)
Emp.: 29,382
Storage Battery Mfr
N.A.I.C.S.: 335910
T. C. Gou (Chm & Pres)

CHENGBANG ECO-

ENVIRONMENT CO., LTD.
No 599 Zhijiang Road, Shangcheng District, Hangzhou, 310008, Zhejiang, China
Tel.: (86) 57187832006
Web Site: https://www.cbgfcn.com
Year Founded: 1996
603316—(SHG)
Rev.: $112,282,780
Assets: $422,850,093
Liabilities: $299,044,081
Net Worth: $123,806,012
Earnings: ($7,777,023)
Fiscal Year-end: 12/31/22
Landscaping Architectural Services
N.A.I.C.S.: 541320
Fang Liqiang *(Chm)*

CHENGDA PHARMACEUTI-CALS CO., LTD.
No 36 Huanghe Road Huimin Street, Jiashan, 314100, Zhejiang, China
Tel.: (86) 57384601188
Web Site:
https://www.chengdapharm.com
Year Founded: 1999
301201—(CHIN)
Rev.: $58,352,366
Assets: $345,820,421
Liabilities: $24,845,493
Net Worth: $320,974,929
Earnings: $12,814,127
Fiscal Year-end: 12/31/23
Pharmaceutical Product Mfr & Distr
N.A.I.C.S.: 325412
Jianli Ge *(Chm)*

CHENGDA TECHNOLOGY CO., LTD.
8 Derech Hameshi St, Ganei Tikva, 5591179, Israel
Tel.: (972) 507844477   DE
Year Founded: 2017
SKMT—(OTCIQ)
Liabilities: $18,550
Net Worth: ($18,550)
Earnings: ($61,193)
Emp.: 1
Fiscal Year-end: 12/31/20
Portfolio Management Services
N.A.I.C.S.: 523940
Xin Jiang *(Chm, Pres, CEO, CFO & Sec)*

CHENGDU ALD AVIATION MANUFACTURING CORPORA-TION
Antai 2nd Road West Hi-Tech Zone, Chengdu, 611730, Sichuan, China
Tel.: (86) 2887866448
Web Site: https://www.cdald.com
Year Founded: 2004
300696—(CHIN)
Rev.: $49,257,175
Assets: $308,058,838
Liabilities: $42,023,245
Net Worth: $266,035,593
Earnings: $9,698,339
Fiscal Year-end: 12/31/23
Aerospace Component Mfr
N.A.I.C.S.: 336413
Xie Peng *(Chm)*

CHENGDU B-RAY MEDIA CO., LTD.
23F 25F Building A Borui Creative Chengdu No 38 Sanse Road, Creative Industry Business District Jinji-ang District, Chengdu, 610063, Sich-uan, China
Tel.: (86) 2887651183
Web Site: https://www.b-raymedia.com
Year Founded: 1988
600880—(SHG)
Rev.: $71,176,763

Assets: $542,251,771
Liabilities: $92,177,781
Net Worth: $450,073,990
Earnings: $5,650,595
Fiscal Year-end: 12/31/22
Newspaper & Commercial Printing Services
N.A.I.C.S.: 323111
Mu Tao *(Chm)*

CHENGDU BRIGHT EYE HOS-PITAL CO., LTD.
No 215 North 4th Section Yihuang Road, Jinniu District, Chengdu, 610084, Sichuan, China
Tel.: (86) 2152990538
Web Site: https://www.purui.cn
Year Founded: 2000
301239—(CHIN)
Rev.: $376,311,669
Assets: $666,675,953
Liabilities: $345,700,529
Net Worth: $320,975,424
Earnings: $37,094,802
Fiscal Year-end: 12/31/23
Ophthalmic General Medical Services
N.A.I.C.S.: 622310
Xuyang Xu *(Chm)*

CHENGDU CORPRO TECH-NOLOGY CO., LTD.
No 1 Gao Peng Avenue Hi-Tech Zone, Chengdu, 610041, Sichuan, China
Tel.: (86) 2865557557
Web Site: https://www.corpro.cn
300101—(CHIN)
Rev.: $166,004,748
Assets: $365,864,148
Liabilities: $125,315,424
Net Worth: $240,548,724
Earnings: $42,136,848
Emp.: 120
Fiscal Year-end: 12/31/22
Electronic Component & Equipment Mfr
N.A.I.C.S.: 334419

CHENGDU DAHONGLI MA-CHINERY CO., LTD.
24th Floor Building B AVIC Interna-tional Exchange Center, No 777 North Section of Yizhou Avenue High-tech Zone, Chengdu, 611300, Sich-uan, China
Tel.: (86) 2888266821
Web Site: http://www.dhljq.com
Year Founded: 2004
300865—(SSE)
Rev.: $69,816,708
Assets: $173,066,868
Liabilities: $45,891,144
Net Worth: $127,175,724
Earnings: $2,855,736
Fiscal Year-end: 12/31/22
Mining Equipment Mfr & Distr
N.A.I.C.S.: 333131
Dehong Gan *(Chm)*

CHENGDU EASTON BIOPHAR-MACEUTICALS CO., LTD.
No 8 Ankang Road Tianfu Interna-tional Bio-town, Hi-tech District, Chengdu, 611731, Sichuan, China
Tel.: (86) 2887827191
Web Site:
https://www.eastonpharma.cn
Year Founded: 2009
688513—(SHG)
Rev.: $164,340,011
Assets: $423,662,644
Liabilities: $80,460,502
Net Worth: $343,202,142
Earnings: $34,611,520
Emp.: 1,000
Fiscal Year-end: 12/31/22

Pharmaceutical Product Mfr & Distr
N.A.I.C.S.: 325412
Ying Wang *(CEO)*

Subsidiaries:

Chengdu Shuode Pharmaceutical Co., Ltd.   (1)
No 5 Keyuan Road South, Hi-Tech District, Chengdu, China
Tel.: (86) 2867585098
Construction Services
N.A.I.C.S.: 236220

Chengdu Unovel Pharmaceutical Co., Ltd.   (1)
Lake Road Tianfu New Area, Free Trade Pilot Zone, Chengdu, Sichuan, China
Tel.: (86) 2867585098
Biopharmaceutical Research & Develop-ment Services
N.A.I.C.S.: 541714

Sichuan Qingmu Pharmaceutical Co., Ltd.   (1)
No 55 South Shunjiang Avenue, East Eco-nomic Development Zone, Meishan, 062100, Sichuan, China
Tel.: (86) 2838591060
Pharmaceutical Preparation Mfr
N.A.I.C.S.: 325412

Sichuan Sunheal Pharmaceutical Co., Ltd.   (1)
No 8 Xiyuan Ave, Hi-tech District, Chengdu, 611731, China
Tel.: (86) 2867585098
Pharmaceutical Products Distr
N.A.I.C.S.: 424210

Xizang Runhe Pharmaceutical Co., Ltd.   (1)
Zangqing Industrial Park, Golmud, Qinghai, China
Tel.: (86) 2867585098
Pharmaceutical Products Distr
N.A.I.C.S.: 424210

CHENGDU EOPTOLINK TECH-NOLOGY INC.
No 127 West Wulian Street, Shuang-liu District, Chengdu, 610213, Sich-uan, China
Tel.: (86) 2867087983
Web Site: https://www.eoptolink.com
Year Founded: 2008
300502—(CHIN)
Rev.: $436,297,777
Assets: $907,071,690
Liabilities: $137,188,618
Net Worth: $769,883,072
Earnings: $96,955,661
Emp.: 2,500
Fiscal Year-end: 12/31/23
Optical Communication Equipment Mfr & Distr
N.A.I.C.S.: 334220
Gao Guangrong *(Chm)*

CHENGDU EXPRESSWAY CO., LTD.
9/F Youyi Data Building No 28 Jingyuan East Road, Deyuan Town Pidu District, Chengdu, China
Tel.: (86) 28886056063   CN
Web Site: http://www.chengdugs.com
Year Founded: 1998
1785—(HKG)
Rev.: $364,565,868
Assets: $1,281,448,560
Liabilities: $590,962,274
Net Worth: $690,486,285
Earnings: $81,005,435
Emp.: 2,190
Fiscal Year-end: 12/31/22
Highway Construction Services
N.A.I.C.S.: 237310
Dapan Ding *(Deputy Gen Mgr)*

CHENGDU FUSEN NOBLE-HOUSE INDSTRL CO LTD
No 189 Tianhe West Second Street

High-tech Zone, Chengdu, 610041, Sichuan, China
Tel.: (86) 2867670333
Web Site: http://www.fsmjj.cn
Year Founded: 2000
002818—(SSE)
Rev.: $208,175,292
Assets: $992,282,616
Liabilities: $131,118,156
Net Worth: $861,164,460
Earnings: $109,940,220
Fiscal Year-end: 12/31/22
Online Household Product Distr
N.A.I.C.S.: 444110
Bing Liu *(Chm)*

CHENGDU GALAXY MAGNET CO., LTD.
No 608 Baicao Road, Western Hi-tech Area, Chengdu, 611731, Sich-uan, China
Tel.: (86) 2887824321
Web Site:
https://www.galaxymagnets.com
Year Founded: 1993
300127—(CHIN)
Rev.: $139,293,648
Assets: $212,995,224
Liabilities: $16,384,680
Net Worth: $196,610,544
Earnings: $24,071,580
Emp.: 1,200
Fiscal Year-end: 12/31/22
Magnetic Components Mfr
N.A.I.C.S.: 334610
Li Gang *(Chm)*

CHENGDU GAS GROUP CO., LTD.
No 19 Shaoling Road, Wuhou Dis-trict, Chengdu, 610041, Sichuan, China
Tel.: (86) 28962777
Web Site: https://www.cdgas.com
Year Founded: 1986
603053—(SHG)
Rev.: $678,895,930
Assets: $1,010,791,927
Liabilities: $390,662,789
Net Worth: $620,129,138
Earnings: $69,013,620
Emp.: 2,000
Fiscal Year-end: 12/31/22
Oil & Gas Distribution Services
N.A.I.C.S.: 221210
Wang Biaohao *(Chm)*

CHENGDU GUIBAO
No 16 Xinyuan Road Hi-Tech Zone, Chengdu, 610041, China
Tel.: (86) 2885311860
Web Site: https://www.cnguibao.com
300019—(SSE)
Rev.: $358,542,949
Assets: $443,151,541
Liabilities: $107,597,446
Net Worth: $335,554,094
Earnings: $43,366,946
Fiscal Year-end: 12/31/23
Industrial Adhesives Mfr
N.A.I.C.S.: 325520
Youzhi Wang *(Chm & Sec-Interim)*

CHENGDU HAONENG TECH-NOLOGY CO., LTD.
No 288 Nan Er Road Chengdu, Eco-nomic And Technological Develop-ment Zone, Chengdu, 610100, Sich-uan, China
Tel.: (86) 2886216855
Web Site: https://www.cdhntech.com
Year Founded: 2006
603809—(SHG)
Rev.: $206,629,572
Assets: $661,690,416
Liabilities: $365,154,005

Chengdu Haoneng Technology Co., Ltd.—(Continued)

Net Worth: $296,536,411
Earnings: $29,680,307
Emp.: 2,200
Fiscal Year-end: 12/31/22
Auto Parts Mfr & Distr
N.A.I.C.S.: 336350
Hou Fan *(Sec)*

Subsidiaries:

Chongqing Haoneng Xingfu Synchronizer Co., Ltd. (1)
No 898 Baiyun Avenue Qinggang Street, Bishan District, Chongqing, 402761, China
Tel.: (86) 2341787822
Web Site: https://www.cqhnxf.com
Emp.: 230
Auto Parts Mfr
N.A.I.C.S.: 332119

Chongqing Qingzhu Machinery Manufacturing Co., Ltd. (1)
No 898 Baiyun Avenue Qinggang Street, Bishan District, Chongqing, China
Tel.: (86) 2341786022
Web Site: https://www.cqqingz.com
Automobile Equipment Mfr & Distr
N.A.I.C.S.: 336320

Luzhou Changjiang Machinery Co., Ltd. (1)
No 18 4 section of wine Valley Road, Jiangyang Distr, Luzhou, Sichuan, China
Tel.: (86) 830 896 1304
Web Site: https://www.cjmp.com.cn
Steel Ring Mfr
N.A.I.C.S.: 332119

CHENGDU HI-TECH DEVELOPMENT CO., LTD.
No 8 Jiuxing Avenue High-Tech Industrial Development Zone, Chengdu, 610041, Sichuan, China
Tel.: (86) 2885137070
Web Site: http://www.cdgxfz.com
Year Founded: 1992
000628—(SSE)
Rev.: $922,512,240
Assets: $1,920,372,948
Liabilities: $1,642,966,416
Net Worth: $277,406,532
Earnings: $27,949,428
Fiscal Year-end: 12/31/22
Real Estate Support Services
N.A.I.C.S.: 531390
Ren Zheng *(Chm)*

CHENGDU HONGQI CHAIN CO., LTD.
No 7 Dikang Avenue High-tech Zone, West District, Chengdu, 611731, Sichuan, China
Tel.: (86) 2887825762
Web Site: http://www.hqls.com.cn
Year Founded: 2000
002697—(SSE)
Rev.: $1,406,820,636
Assets: $1,150,214,364
Liabilities: $567,478,548
Net Worth: $582,735,816
Earnings: $68,188,068
Emp.: 13,230
Fiscal Year-end: 12/31/22
Convenience Store Owner & Operator
N.A.I.C.S.: 445131
Shiru Cao *(Chm & Gen Mgr)*

CHENGDU HUASUN TECHNOLOGY GROUP INC., LTD.
No 1168 Shuxin Avenue Hightech, West District, Chengdu, 611731, Sichuan, China
Tel.: (86) 2867692806
Web Site: https://www.huasungrp.com
Year Founded: 1988

000790—(SSE)
Rev.: $122,583,240
Assets: $235,459,224
Liabilities: $94,287,024
Net Worth: $141,172,200
Earnings: $5,787,288
Fiscal Year-end: 12/31/22
Pharmaceuticals Product Mfr
N.A.I.C.S.: 005412
Huang Mingliang *(Chm & Pres)*

CHENGDU HUAZE COBALT & NICKEL MATERIAL CO., LTD.
Room 1512 Gemini International Office West No 666, North Section of Fengxi Avenue Wenjiang District, Chengdu, 611130, Sichuan, China
Tel.: (86) 28 86758751
Web Site: http://www.hznc.com.cn
Sales Range: $1-4.9 Billion
Non-ferrous Metal Smelting Services
N.A.I.C.S.: 331410
Tao Wang *(Chm)*

CHENGDU INFORMATION TECHNOLOGY OF CHINESE ACADEMY OF SCIENCES CO., LTD.
No 1369 Kezhi Road Xinglong Street, New District, Chengdu, 610213, Sichuan, China
Tel.: (86) 2885135151
Web Site: http://www.casit.com.cn
Year Founded: 2001
300678—(CHIN)
Rev.: $83,299,014
Assets: $177,899,790
Liabilities: $56,124,669
Net Worth: $121,775,121
Earnings: $5,417,852
Fiscal Year-end: 12/31/23
Public Relations Consulting Services
N.A.I.C.S.: 541820
Shi Zhiming *(Chm)*

CHENGDU JIAFAANTAI EDUCATION TECHNOLOGY CO., LTD.
Jiafa Technology Building No 188 Wukexi 2nd Road, Wuhou District, Chengdu, 610041, Sichuan, China
Tel.: (86) 2865293708
Web Site: http://www.jf-r.com
Year Founded: 2002
300559—(CHIN)
Rev.: $85,126,162
Assets: $201,337,497
Liabilities: $29,404,508
Net Worth: $171,932,989
Earnings: $18,456,702
Fiscal Year-end: 12/31/23
Software Development Services
N.A.I.C.S.: 513210
Yuan Bin *(Chm)*

CHENGDU JOUAV AUTOMATION TECHNOLOGY CO., LTD.
Room 801-805 8th Floor Block A Building 3 No 200 Tianfu 5th Street, Hi-tech Zone, Chengdu, 610094, Sichuan, China
Tel.: (86) 2885223959
Web Site: http://www.jouav.com
Year Founded: 2010
688070—(SHG)
Rev.: $40,337,987
Assets: $133,339,607
Liabilities: $38,944,854
Net Worth: $94,394,753
Earnings: $(3,678,157)
Emp.: 700
Fiscal Year-end: 12/31/22
Automobile Product Mfr & Distr
N.A.I.C.S.: 336390
Peter Wang *(Co-Founder)*

CHENGDU KANGHONG PHARMACEUTICALS GROUP CO., LTD.
108 Shuxi Road, Jinniu District, Chengdu, 610036, Sichuan, China
Tel.: (86) 2887502055
Web Site: https://www.cnkh.com
Year Founded: 1996
002773—(SSE)
Rev.: $475,819,812
Assets: $1,083,990,492
Liabilities: $114,264,540
Net Worth: $969,725,952
Earnings: $125,892,468
Emp.: 4,045
Fiscal Year-end: 12/31/22
Pharmaceutical Product Mfr & Distr
N.A.I.C.S.: 325412
Zunhong Ke *(Chm)*

CHENGDU LEEJUN INDUSTRIAL CO., LTD.
No 5 Wukedong 2nd Road, Wuhou District, Chengdu, 610045, Sichuan, China
Tel.: (86) 2885368611
Web Site: https://www.cdleejun.com
002651—(SSE)
Rev.: $143,198,172
Assets: $486,748,548
Liabilities: $122,124,132
Net Worth: $364,624,416
Earnings: $30,843,072
Emp.: 800
Fiscal Year-end: 12/31/22
Roll Presses Mfr
N.A.I.C.S.: 333248

CHENGDU M&S ELECTRONICS TECHNOLOGY CO., LTD.
No 350 Tongzizu South Street Xinglong Street, Tianfu New District, Chengdu, 610299, Sichuan, China
Tel.: (86) 2861773081
Web Site: http://www.microwave-signal.com
Year Founded: 2013
688311—(SHG)
Rev.: $67,237,223
Assets: $368,630,267
Liabilities: $119,046,985
Net Worth: $249,583,281
Earnings: $3,648,743
Fiscal Year-end: 12/31/22
Electronic Product Mfr & Distr
N.A.I.C.S.: 334419
Rong Xiang *(Chm)*

CHENGDU OLYMVAX BIO-PHARMACEUTICALS, INC.
No 99 Tianxin Road Hi-Tech Zone, Hi-Tech Zone West, Chengdu, 611731, Sichuan, China
Tel.: (86) 2869361111
Web Site: https://www.olymvax.com
Year Founded: 2009
688319—(SHG)
Rev.: $76,866,290
Assets: $207,633,516
Liabilities: $82,417,959
Net Worth: $125,215,557
Earnings: $3,731,425
Emp.: 440
Fiscal Year-end: 12/31/22
Pharmaceutical Product Mfr & Distr
N.A.I.C.S.: 325412
Hongguang Li *(Dir-Quality)*

CHENGDU QINCHUAN IOT TECHNOLOGY CO., LTD.
No 931 South Fourth Road, Economic Development Zone Longquanyi District, Chengdu, 610100, Sichuan, China
Tel.: (86) 2884879878
Web Site: https://www.cdqckj.com

Year Founded: 2001
688528—(SHG)
Rev.: $51,653,314
Assets: $146,456,786
Liabilities: $41,165,771
Net Worth: $105,291,014
Earnings: $192,516
Fiscal Year-end: 12/31/22
Measuring Instruments Mfr
N.A.I.C.S.: 334513
Zehua Shao *(Chm & Gen Mgr)*

CHENGDU QUSHUI SCIENCE & TECHNOLOGY CO., LTD.
No 8 7th Floor Building 1 No 1268 MiddleSection of Tianfu Avenue, High-tech Zone Pilot Free Trade Zone, Chengdu, 610041, Sichuan, China
Tel.: (86) 2886645940
Year Founded: 2014
301336—(CHIN)
Rev.: $45,307,080
Assets: $121,841,928
Liabilities: $11,744,460
Net Worth: $110,097,468
Earnings: $5,179,356
Fiscal Year-end: 12/31/22
Furniture Product Mfr & Distr
N.A.I.C.S.: 337126

CHENGDU RAINBOW APPLIANCE (GROUP) SHARES CO., LTD.
No 73 Shunjiang Section Wuhou Avenue, Wuhou District, Chengdu, 610045, Sichuan, China
Tel.: (86) 2885362392
Web Site: http://www.rainbow.com.cn
Year Founded: 1994
003023—(SSE)
Rev.: $165,214,296
Assets: $278,138,016
Liabilities: $75,713,508
Net Worth: $202,424,508
Earnings: $13,290,264
Fiscal Year-end: 12/31/22
Household Appliance Mfr & Distr
N.A.I.C.S.: 335220
Rongfu Liu *(Chm & Dir)*

CHENGDU RML TECHNOLOGY CO., LTD.
No 19 Section 4 Huafu Avenue Gongxing Street, Shuangliu District, Chengdu, 610200, Sichuan, China
Tel.: (86) 2885870001
Web Site: https://www.rml138.com
Year Founded: 2007
301050—(CHIN)
Rev.: $120,783,312
Assets: $544,780,080
Liabilities: $216,315,684
Net Worth: $328,464,396
Earnings: $38,923,092
Fiscal Year-end: 12/31/22
Electronic Component Mfr & Distr
N.A.I.C.S.: 334419
Jieru Deng *(Chm)*

CHENGDU ROAD & BRIDGE ENGINEERING CO., LTD.
No 1777 North Section of Tianfu Avenue High tech Zone, Chengdu, 610045, Sichuan, China
Tel.: (86) 2885003000
Web Site: https://www.cdlq.com
Year Founded: 1988
002628—(SSE)
Rev.: $187,950,672
Assets: $1,078,447,500
Liabilities: $646,245,756
Net Worth: $432,201,744
Earnings: $1,283,256
Fiscal Year-end: 12/31/22

Road & Bridge Construction & Engineering Services
N.A.I.C.S.: 237310
Lin Xiaoqing *(Chm)*

CHENGDU SHENGBANG SEALS CO., LTD.
No 1388 Konggang 2nd Road, Airport Economic Development Zone Shuangliu District, Chengdu, 610207, Sichuan, China
Tel.: (86) 2884266688
Web Site: https://www.cdsbs.com
Year Founded: 2004
301233—(CHIN)
Rev.: $47,077,246
Assets: $142,014,123
Liabilities: $19,520,270
Net Worth: $122,493,852
Earnings: $8,865,488
Fiscal Year-end: 12/31/23
Rubber Products Mfr
N.A.I.C.S.: 326220
Kai Lai *(Chm)*

CHENGDU SHENGNUO BIO-PHARMACEUTICAL CO., LTD.
258 Industrial Avenue Section, Dayi County, Chengdu, 611330, China
Tel.: (86) 2888203606   CN
Web Site:
    https://www.snbiopharm.com
Year Founded: 2001
688117—(SHG)
Rev.: $55,558,639
Assets: $155,564,407
Liabilities: $39,490,491
Net Worth: $116,073,917
Earnings: $9,053,610
Fiscal Year-end: 12/31/22
Pharmaceutical Product Mfr & Distr
N.A.I.C.S.: 325412
Yongjun Wen *(Chm & Gen Mgr)*

CHENGDU SIWI SCIENCE AND TECHNOLOGY COMPANY LIMITED
No 18 Xinhang Road the West park of the Hi-tech Development Zone, Chengdu, 611731, Sichuan, China
Tel.: (86) 2887877008   CN
Web Site: http://www.cdc.com.cn
Year Founded: 1994
1202—(HKG)
Rev.: $42,683,511
Assets: $142,926,555
Liabilities: $24,487,856
Net Worth: $118,438,700
Earnings: $222,798
Emp.: 528
Fiscal Year-end: 12/31/22
Telecommunication Cable Mfr & Distr
N.A.I.C.S.: 332618
Li Tao *(Chm)*

Subsidiaries:

Nanjing Putian Telege Intelligent Building Ltd.   (1)
No 18 Songgang Street, Jiangning Economic and Technological Development Zone, Nanjing, 211102, China
Tel.: (86) 2566675222
Web Site: https://www.telege.cn
Electronic Products Mfr
N.A.I.C.S.: 335999

CHENGDU SPACEON ELECTRONICS CO., LTD.
No 2 Building Guobin Base Jinke East Rd, Jinniu District, Chengdu, China
Tel.: (86) 2861070147
Web Site: https://www.elecspn.com
Year Founded: 2004
002935—(SSE)
Rev.: $170,010,360
Assets: $361,409,256

Liabilities: $150,605,676
Net Worth: $210,803,580
Earnings: $15,795,000
Emp.: 600
Fiscal Year-end: 12/31/22
Satellite Equipment Mfr & Distr
N.A.I.C.S.: 334511
Zhao Xiaohu *(Chm)*

CHENGDU TANGYUAN ELECTRIC CO., LTD.
No 9 Wukexi 1st Road, Wuhou, Chengdu, 610046, Sichuan, China
Tel.: (86) 2885003300
Web Site: http://www.cdtye.com
Year Founded: 2010
300789—(SSE)
Rev.: $60,874,632
Assets: $180,283,428
Liabilities: $54,273,024
Net Worth: $126,010,404
Earnings: $12,808,692
Fiscal Year-end: 12/31/22
Electrical Equipment Mfr & Distr
N.A.I.C.S.: 335999
Tanglong Chen *(Chm)*

CHENGDU TECHCENT ENVIRONMENT INDUSTRY CO., LTD.
No 188 Datong Road, Qingbaijiang, Chengdu, 610300, China
Tel.: (86) 2883625802   CN
Web Site: http://www.tbhic.cn
300362—(CHIN)
Rev.: $58,660,268
Assets: $605,801,601
Liabilities: $851,561,283
Net Worth: ($245,759,682)
Earnings: ($262,381,864)
Emp.: 700
Fiscal Year-end: 12/31/19
Large Energy Saving, Environmental Protection & Clean Energy Equipment Mfr
N.A.I.C.S.: 333248
Ye Peng *(Chm)*

Subsidiaries:

Centrisys Corporation   (1)
9586 58th Pl, Kenosha, WI 53144   (80%)
Tel.: (262) 654-6006
Web Site: http://www.centrisys.com
Centrifuge Mfr
N.A.I.C.S.: 333998
Michael Kopper *(Founder, Pres & CEO)*

CHENGDU TIANJIAN TECHNOLOGY CO., LTD.
No 333 Hemao Street Hightech Zone, Science & Technology Incubation Park Chengdu High-tech Zone, Chengdu, 610212, Sichuan, China
Tel.: (86) 2885331008
Web Site: https://www.cdtjkj.com
Year Founded: 2005
002977—(SSE)
Rev.: $48,123,504
Assets: $187,838,352
Liabilities: $38,270,232
Net Worth: $149,568,120
Earnings: $10,212,696
Fiscal Year-end: 12/31/22
Power Distribution Equipment Mfr & Distr
N.A.I.C.S.: 335311
Jiyong Lou *(Chm)*

CHENGDU TIANQI INDUSTRY (GROUP) CO., LTD.
No 10 East Gaopeng Road, Hi-Tech Development Zone, Chengdu, 610041, Sichuan, China
Tel.: (86) 28 8514 0380   CN
Web Site: http://www.tianqigroup.cn
Year Founded: 1997

Holding Company
N.A.I.C.S.: 551112

Subsidiaries:

Chengdu Tianqi Machinery, Metals & Minerals Import & Export Co., Ltd.   (1)
No 10 East Gaopeng Road, Hi-Tech Development Zone, Chengdu, Sichuan, China
Tel.: (86) 28 8515 9223
Web Site: http://www.tqmmm.com.cn
Resource Minerals & Large-Scale Machinery Wholesale Trade Distr
N.A.I.C.S.: 425120

Tianqi Lithium Corporation   (1)
No 166 Hongliang West 1st Street, Tianfu New District, Chengdu, Sichuan, China
Tel.: (86) 2885146615
Web Site: http://www.tianqilithium.com
Rev.: $5,600,396,406
Assets: $10,380,077,121
Liabilities: $2,632,568,952
Net Worth: $7,747,508,169
Earnings: $3,550,638,984
Emp.: 2,864
Fiscal Year-end: 12/31/2023
Lithium Chemical Mfr
N.A.I.C.S.: 325998
Weiping Jiang *(Founder & Chm)*

Joint Venture (Non-US):

Talison Lithium Pty. Ltd.   (2)
Level 15 216 St Georges Terrace, Perth, 6000, WA, Australia
Tel.: (61) 892635555
Web Site: https://www.talisonlithium.com
Sales Range: $125-149.9 Million
Emp.: 140
Lithium Mining Services
N.A.I.C.S.: 212290
Lorry Mignacca *(CEO & Mng Dir)*

CHENGDU WINTRUE HOLDING CO., LTD.
4-5 / F Huijing building No 969 Shulong Avenue, Xindu District, Chengdu, 610500, Sichuan, China
Tel.: (86) 2883961041
Web Site: https://www.shindoo.com
Year Founded: 1995
002539—(SSE)
Rev.: $2,878,448,508
Assets: $2,626,153,920
Liabilities: $1,536,742,584
Net Worth: $1,089,411,336
Earnings: $209,469,780
Emp.: 10,000
Fiscal Year-end: 12/31/22
Fertilizer, Soda Ash, Ammonium Chloride, Anhydrous Sodium Sulphate, Edible Salt, Industrial Salt & Other Chemical Products Mfr
N.A.I.C.S.: 325998
Mu Jiayun *(Chm)*

Subsidiaries:

YingCheng Shindoo Import & Export Trading Co., Ltd.   (1)
Chengzhong Private Economy Zone, Yingcheng City, Xiaogan, Hubei, China
Tel.: (86) 7123221947
Soda Ash Whslr
N.A.I.C.S.: 424690

CHENGDU XGIMI TECHNOLOGY CO., LTD.
Building 4 Area A No 1129, Chengdu Hitech Zone, Chengdu, 610000, Sichuan, China
Tel.: (86) 2867599894
Web Site: http://www.xgimi.com
Year Founded: 2013
688696—(SHG)
Rev.: $592,816,719
Assets: $742,163,091
Liabilities: $301,465,560
Net Worth: $440,697,531
Earnings: $70,406,107
Fiscal Year-end: 12/31/22

Electrical Equipment Mfr & Distr
N.A.I.C.S.: 335999
Bo Zhong *(Chm)*

CHENGDU XILING POWER SCIENCE & TECHNOLOGY INCORPORATED COMPANY
No 298 Tengfei Avenue, Qingyang Industrial Development Zone, Chengdu, 610091, Sichuan, China
Tel.: (86) 13438053702
Web Site: https://cdxldl.com
Year Founded: 1999
300733—(CHIN)
Rev.: $214,037,012
Assets: $427,456,918
Liabilities: $202,032,000
Net Worth: $225,424,918
Earnings: ($14,884,887)
Fiscal Year-end: 12/31/23
Automotive Parts Mfr & Distr
N.A.I.C.S.: 336350
Xiaolin Wei *(Chm & Gen Mgr)*

CHENGDU XINGRONG ENVIRONMENT CO., LTD.
No 1000 Jincheng Road Gaoxin District, Chengdu, 610041, China
Tel.: (86) 2885293300
Web Site: http://www.cdxrec.com
000598—(SSE)
Rev.: $1,071,207,072
Assets: $5,382,740,844
Liabilities: $3,173,479,452
Net Worth: $2,209,261,392
Earnings: $227,143,332
Fiscal Year-end: 12/31/22
Tap Water Supply Services
N.A.I.C.S.: 221310
Liu Ai *(Chm)*

CHENGDU XINZHU ROAD & BRIDGE MACHINERY CO., LTD.
No 99 Xingyuan 3rd Road Xinjin Industrial Park, Sichuan, 611430, Sichuan, China
Tel.: (86) 2882556968
Web Site: https://www.xinzhu.com
Year Founded: 2001
002480—(SSE)
Rev.: $231,578,568
Assets: $1,652,708,772
Liabilities: $1,253,324,124
Net Worth: $399,384,648
Earnings: ($79,547,832)
Emp.: 1,300
Fiscal Year-end: 12/31/22
Road & Bridge Machinery Mfr
N.A.I.C.S.: 333120
Xiao Guanghui *(Chm)*

Subsidiaries:

Shanghai Aowei Technology Development Co., Ltd.   (1)
No 188 Guoshoujing Rd Hi-Tech Park, Pudong, Shanghai, China
Tel.: (86) 2150802888
Web Site: https://www.aowei.com
Electrical Equipment Mfr & Distr
N.A.I.C.S.: 335999
Jiang Qi *(Mgr-Trade Dept)*

CHENGDU XUGUANG ELECTRONICS CO., LTD.
318 Xingong Avenue, Xindu district, Chengdu, 610500, Sichuan, China
Tel.: (86) 2883967045
Web Site:
    https://www.xuguang.com.cn
Year Founded: 1965
600353—(SHG)
Rev.: $160,230,307
Assets: $386,328,908
Liabilities: $139,727,723
Net Worth: $246,601,185

Chengdu Xuguang Electronics Co., Ltd.—(Continued)

Earnings: $14,056,174
Emp.: 1,500
Fiscal Year-end: 12/31/22
Electron & Vacuum Tube Mfr
N.A.I.C.S.: 334419
Liu Bo *(Dir-Import & Export Dept)*

CHENGDU YUNDA TECHNOL-OGY CO., LTD.

No 11 Xinda Road West Park High-tech Zone, Chengdu, 611731c, Sich-uan, China
Tel.: (86) 2882839999
Web Site: https://www.yd-tec.com
Year Founded: 2006
300440—(CHIN)
Rev.: $127,919,844
Assets: $359,296,236
Liabilities: $165,002,292
Net Worth: $194,293,944
Earnings: $5,738,148
Emp.: 1,000
Fiscal Year-end: 12/31/22
Railway Transportation Security System Mfr
N.A.I.C.S.: 336999
Hongyun He *(Chm & Gen Mgr)*

CHENGDU ZHIMINGDA ELEC-TRONICS CO., LTD.

No 51 Tengfei Avenue, Qingyang, Chengdu, 610073, Sichuan, China
Tel.: (86) 2861509199
Web Site: http://www.zmdde.com
Year Founded: 2002
688636—(SHG)
Rev.: $75,937,643
Assets: $211,559,564
Liabilities: $73,627,529
Net Worth: $137,932,035
Earnings: $10,583,731
Fiscal Year-end: 12/31/22
Electronic Product Mfr & Distr
N.A.I.C.S.: 334419
Yong Wang *(Chm)*

CHENGHE ACQUISITION CO.

38 Beach Road 29-11 South Beach Tower, Singapore, 189767, Singapore
Tel.: (65) 98518611 Ky
Year Founded: 2021
CHEA—(NASDAQ)
Rev.: $1,632,704
Assets: $120,939,257
Liabilities: $124,485,543
Net Worth: ($3,546,286)
Earnings: $982,840
Emp.: 2
Fiscal Year-end: 12/31/22
Investment Services
N.A.I.C.S.: 523999
Richard Qi Li *(Chm)*

CHENGTUN MINING GROUP CO., LTD.

33F Building A Tefang Portman Fortune Center No 81 Zhanhong Road, Xiamen, 361000, Fujian, China
Tel.: (86) 5925891697
Web Site: http://www.600711.com
Year Founded: 1997
600711—(SHG)
Rev.: $3,560,059,255
Assets: $4,486,204,878
Liabilities: $2,130,468,182
Net Worth: $2,355,736,697
Earnings: ($13,413,605)
Fiscal Year-end: 12/31/22
Mining Services
N.A.I.C.S.: 212230
Dong Chen *(Board of Directors & Chm)*

Subsidiaries:

Nzuri Copper Limited **(1)**
Unit 13 100 Railway Road Daglish, Perth, 6008, WA, Australia
Tel.: (61) 8 6424 8100
Web Site: http://www.nzuricopper.com.au
Rev.: $91,285
Assets: $37,782,769
Liabilities: $5,492,823
Net Worth: $32,289,945
Earnings: ($2,484,459)
Fiscal Year-end: 06/30/2018
Copper Exploration Services
N.A.I.C.S.: 212230
Hannah Hudson *(CFO & Sec)*

CHENGUANG BIOTECH GROUP CO., LTD.

No 1 Chenguang Road, Quzhou County, Handan, 057250, Hebei, China
Tel.: (86) 3108859030
Web Site: https://www.cn-cg.com
Year Founded: 2000
300138—(CHIN)
Rev.: $883,940,148
Assets: $972,093,096
Liabilities: $520,836,264
Net Worth: $451,256,832
Earnings: $60,937,812
Emp.: 100
Fiscal Year-end: 12/31/22
Flavoring Syrups & Food Extracts Mfr
N.A.I.C.S.: 311930
Zhou Jing *(Sec)*

Subsidiaries:

Handan Chenguang Precious Oil Co., Ltd **(1)**
No 1 Chenguang Road, Quzhou County, Handan, 057250, Hebei Province, China
Tel.: (86) 310 8852088
Web Site: http://www.hdcgzp.com
Edible Oil Mfr
N.A.I.C.S.: 311225

Yingkou Chenguang Foods Co Ltd **(1)**
Qinglongshan St, Bayuquan District, Yingkou, 115007, Liaoning, China
Tel.: (86) 417 6237628
Edible Oil Mfr
N.A.I.C.S.: 311225

CHENGXIN LITHIUM GROUP CO., LTD.

56F Block A Shenye Shangcheng Office Building, Futian District, Shenzhen, 518038, China
Tel.: (86) 75582557707
Web Site: https://www.cxlithium.com
Year Founded: 2001
002240—(SSE)
Rev.: $1,690,307,892
Assets: $2,587,675,896
Liabilities: $762,720,192
Net Worth: $1,824,955,704
Earnings: $779,565,384
Emp.: 2,400
Fiscal Year-end: 12/31/22
Fiberboard Mfr & Sales
N.A.I.C.S.: 325220
Zhou Wei *(Chm)*

Subsidiaries:

Guangdong Weihua Corporation (Meizhou Medium-density Fiberboard Factory) **(1)**
Longkeng Vlg Xiyang Town Dongsheng Industrial Zone, Mei County, 514031, Meizhou, Guangdong, China
Tel.: (86) 753 2886815
Sales Range: $50-74.9 Million
Emp.: 200
Fibreboard Mfr
N.A.I.C.S.: 321219

Qingyuan Weilibang Wood Co., Ltd. **(1)**
Bldg Material & Ceramic Industrial Ctr Yu-

antan Town, Qingcheng District, 511533, Qingyuan, Guangdong, China
Tel.: (86) 7633296269
Sales Range: $50-74.9 Million
Emp.: 200
Medium Density Fiberboards Mfr
N.A.I.C.S.: 321219

CHENGZHI CO., LTD.

Jiangxi Huajiang Building TusPark No 299 Yuping East Avenue, Economic Development Zone, Nanchang, 330013, Jiangxi, China
Tel.: (86) 79183826898
Web Site: http://www.chengzhi.com.cn
Year Founded: 1998
000990—(SSE)
Rev.: $1,645,106,112
Assets: $3,443,406,876
Liabilities: $844,178,868
Net Worth: $2,599,228,008
Earnings: $7,424,352
Fiscal Year-end: 12/31/22
Pharmaceuticals Product Mfr
N.A.I.C.S.: 325412
Zhu Yujie *(Chm-Supervisory Bd)*

CHENMING ELECTRONIC TECH. CORP.

No 27 Sec 6 Mincyuan E Rd, Neihu District, Taipei, 114, Taiwan
Tel.: (886) 227973999
Web Site: https://www.uneec.com
3013—(TAI)
Rev.: $211,307,164
Assets: $213,322,632
Liabilities: $106,764,082
Net Worth: $106,558,549
Earnings: $8,278,361
Emp.: 3,160
Fiscal Year-end: 12/31/23
Computer Equipment Mfr
N.A.I.C.S.: 518210
Mu-Ho Lin *(Chm)*

Subsidiaries:

Chenming Electronic (Dongguan) Co., Ltd. **(1)**
No 442 Zhenan Middle Road, Changan Town, Dongguan, 523873, Guangdong, China
Tel.: (86) 7698 541 9999
Web Site: http://www.uneec.com
Electronics Metal Parts Mfr
N.A.I.C.S.: 334419

Chenming Electronic Technology USA, Inc. **(1)**
8101 Sandy Spring Rd Ste 250, Laurel, MD, 20707
Tel.: (651) 239-8263
Electronic Computer Mfr
N.A.I.C.S.: 334111

Chenming Mold Ind. Corp. - Keelung Plant **(1)**
23 Wu Shuin Street, Keelung, Taiwan
Tel.: (886) 2 2432 4032
Web Site: http://www.uneec.com
Sales Range: $25-49.9 Million
Emp.: 40
Metal Stamping Mfr
N.A.I.C.S.: 332119

Chenming USA Inc. **(1)**
788 Sandoval Way, Hayward, CA 94544
Tel.: (510) 429-3882
Web Site: https://www.chenmingusa.com
Sales Range: $50-74.9 Million
Emp.: 9
Computer Peripheral Equipment Distr
N.A.I.C.S.: 423430
Walter Yeung *(Exec VP)*

CHENNAI FERROUS INDUS-TRIES LIMITED

No 180-183 Periya Obulapuram Village Nagaraja Kandigai, Madharapakkam Road, Gummidipoondi, 601 201, India

Tel.: (91) 4427991450
Web Site: https://www.chennaiferrous.com
Year Founded: 2010
539011—(BOM)
Rev.: $13,097,716
Assets: $7,804,188
Liabilities: $2,076,975
Net Worth: $5,727,213
Earnings: $3,453,939
Emp.: 10
Fiscal Year-end: 03/31/22
Construction Material Mfr & Distr
N.A.I.C.S.: 331110
Natarajan R. *(Chm & Mng Dir)*

CHENNAI MEENAKSHI MULTI-SPECIALITY HOSPITAL LIM-ITED

New No 70 Old No 149 Luz Church Road, Mylapore, Chennai, 600 004, Tamil Nadu, India
Tel.: (91) 4442938938
Web Site: https://www.cmmh.in
523489—(BOM)
Rev.: $2,730,127
Assets: $2,620,979
Liabilities: $3,272,122
Net Worth: ($651,143)
Earnings: ($170,587)
Emp.: 231
Fiscal Year-end: 03/31/21
Hospital Management Services
N.A.I.C.S.: 622310
R. Deenadayalu *(Compliance Officer & Sec)*

CHENZHOU CITY JINGUI SIL-VER INDUSTRY CO., LTD.

No 1 Fucheng Avenue Industry Park, Chenzhou, 423038, China
Tel.: (86) 7352659899
Web Site: http://www.jingui-silver.com
002716—(SSE)
Rev.: $476,479,692
Assets: $577,372,536
Liabilities: $319,002,840
Net Worth: $258,369,696
Earnings: ($23,451,012)
Emp.: 370
Fiscal Year-end: 12/31/22
Silver & Other Metals Producer
N.A.I.C.S.: 331410
Yong Gui Cao *(Chm & Gen Mgr)*

CHEONGBO INDUSTRIAL CO., LTD.

208 Namdong-daero, Namdong-gu, 405-817, Incheon, Korea (South)
Tel.: (82) 328163550
Web Site: http://www.cheongbo.co.kr
Year Founded: 1979
013720—(KRS)
Rev.: $27,630,663
Assets: $57,040,509
Liabilities: $24,340,598
Net Worth: $32,699,911
Earnings: ($22,776,849)
Emp.: 50
Fiscal Year-end: 12/31/22
Valve Tappet Mfr & Distr
N.A.I.C.S.: 332911
Sang-Wook An *(Pres & CEO)*

CHEONGHO ICT CO., LTD.

2700 Hagun-ri Yangchon-Eup, Gangnam Gu, Gimpo, 135-819, Gyeonggi-do, Korea (South)
Tel.: (82) 2367077002
Web Site: http://www.chunghocomnet.com
Year Founded: 1977
012600—(KRS)
Rev.: $17,259,473
Assets: $22,984,474
Liabilities: $7,474,690

Net Worth: $15,509,785
Earnings: ($3,327,619)
Emp.: 53
Fiscal Year-end: 12/31/22
Automatic Teller Machine & Office
Automation Equipment Mfr
N.A.I.C.S.: 334118
Jung Woo Sung (Deputy Gen Mgr)

Subsidiaries:

Chungho ComNet Co., Ltd. - Gimpo
Factory **(1)**
185 Hwanggeum 1 Ro Yangchon Eub,
Gimpo, Gyeonggi Do, Korea (South)
Tel.: (82) 2 851 6700
Office Automation Equipment Mfr
N.A.I.C.S.: 334118

CHEOPS TECHNOLOGY FRANCE SA

37 Rue Thomas Edison, 33610, Meri-
gnac, France
Tel.: (33) 556188383
Web Site: http://www.cheops.fr
MLCHE—(EUR)
Sales Range: $125-149.9 Million
Emp.: 500
Computer Services
N.A.I.C.S.: 541519
Nicholas Fleuriot (Chm & CEO)

CHEPRI HOLDING B.V.

Karolusguldenstraat 6, 's-
Hertogenbosch, Netherlands
Tel.: (31) 736400715
Web Site: http://www.chepriplant.nl
Investment Company
N.A.I.C.S.: 523940

Subsidiaries:

ECF Group B.V. **(1)**
Hooge Zijde 32, PO Box 8565, Eindhoven,
5605, Netherlands
Tel.: (31) 402380480
Web Site: http://www.ecfgroup.com
Sales Range: $100-124.9 Million
Emp.: 150
Investment Company
N.A.I.C.S.: 523940

Subsidiary (Domestic):

Bakker Continental B.V. **(2)**
Marinus Van Meelweg 19, 5657 EN, Eind-
hoven, Hooge Zegde, Netherlands **(100%)**
Tel.: (31) 402380482
Sales Range: $25-49.9 Million
Emp.: 70
Direct Marketing & Sales Promotion Ser-
vices
N.A.I.C.S.: 541860

MediaMotion **(2)**
10 Fortranweg, 3802 RE, Amersfoort,
Netherlands **(100%)**
Tel.: (31) 334502811
Web Site: http://www.media-motion.nl
Sales Range: $50-74.9 Million
Emp.: 150
N.A.I.C.S.: 512110

CHEQUEFECTIVO, S.A.

Carrera 13 No 96-67 Of 507 Edificio
Akori, Bogota, Colombia
Tel.: (57) 1 3099898
Web Site:
http://www.chequefectivo.com
CHEF—(PAN)
Sales Range: Less than $1 Million
Investment Advisory Services
N.A.I.C.S.: 523940
Juan Hernan Ortiz Zambrano (Gen
Mgr)

CHEQUERS SA

5 Rue Francois 1er, 75008, Paris,
France
Tel.: (33) 153576100 FR
Web Site:
https://www.chequerscapital.com

Year Founded: 1972
Private Investment Firm
N.A.I.C.S.: 523940
Denis Metzger (Chm)

Subsidiaries:

Alkern SAS **(1)**
ZI Parc de la Motte au Bois, BP 59, Rue
Andre Bigotte, 62440, Harnes,
France **(87%)**
Tel.: (33) 3 21 79 34 30
Web Site: http://www.alkern.fr
Sales Range: $200-249.9 Million
Emp.: 803
Concrete Products Mfr
N.A.I.C.S.: 327390

Subsidiary (Domestic):

Beton 06 SA **(2)**
Route de Levens, 06730, Saint-Andre-de-
la-Roche, France
Tel.: (33) 4 93 27 70 70
Web Site: http://www.beton06.com
Stone Pavements & Concrete Block Mfr
N.A.I.C.S.: 327331

Novadal Privat SAS **(2)**
6 Blvd de l'Industrie, 85170, Belleville-sur-
Vie, France **(100%)**
Tel.: (33) 2 51 41 06 00
Web Site: http://www.novadal.fr
Brick & Clay Tile Mfr
N.A.I.C.S.: 327331

Biolchim S.p.A. **(1)**
Via San Carlo 2130, 40059, Medicina, Bolo-
gna, Italy
Tel.: (39) 051 6971811
Web Site: http://www.biolchim.it
Sales Range: $50-74.9 Million
Specialty Fertilizers & Biostimulants Mfr &
Distr
N.A.I.C.S.: 325314
Leonardo Valenti (Mng Dir)

EMVIA Living GmbH **(1)**
Suderstrasse 77, 20097, Hamburg, Ger-
many
Tel.: (49) 40 3688 133 0
Web Site: http://www.emvia.de
Nursing Home Operator
N.A.I.C.S.: 623110
Volker Feldkamp (Chm-Mgmt Bd)

Spandex AG **(1)**
Aegertweg 4, 8305, Dietlikon,
Switzerland **(100%)**
Tel.: (41) 44 818 86 86
Web Site: http://www.spandex.com
Commercial Art & Graphic Design; Signs &
Advertising Services
N.A.I.C.S.: 541430
Rodney Larson (CEO)

Subsidiary (Non-US):

H. Brunner GmbH **(2)**
Am Risisee 13, 77855, Achern, Germany
Tel.: (49) 7841 685 200
Web Site: http://www.brunner-folien.de
Digital Imaging Services
N.A.I.C.S.: 541430
Rodney Larson (Mng Dir)

Spandex Belgium NV **(2)**
Excelsiorlaan 55, 1930, Zaventem, Belgium
Tel.: (32) 2 725 73 70
Web Site: http://www.spandex.be
Digital Printing & Graphic Production; Sign
Systems, Display & Equipment Distr
N.A.I.C.S.: 323111

Spandex Ltd **(2)**
1600 Park Avenue, Aztec West, Almonds-
bury, BS32 4UA, Bristol, United Kingdom
Tel.: (44) 800772633
Web Site: http://www.spandex.co.uk
Digital Printing, Cutting & Routing Services
N.A.I.C.S.: 323111
Leon Watson (Gen Mgr)

CHERAT CEMENT COMPANY LIMITED

Modern Motors House Beaumont
Road, Karachi, 75530, Pakistan
Tel.: (92) 2135683566
Web Site: https://www.gfg.com.pk

Year Founded: 1981
CHCC—(KAR)
Rev.: $156,534,296
Assets: $212,341,772
Liabilities: $127,950,654
Net Worth: $84,391,118
Earnings: $19,903,398
Emp.: 966
Fiscal Year-end: 06/30/21
Cement Mfr
N.A.I.C.S.: 325520
Yasir Masood (CFO)

Subsidiaries:

Faruque (Pvt) Ltd **(1)**
Modern Motors House Beaumont Road,
Karachi, 75530, Pakistan
Tel.: (92) 21111000009
Web Site: https://gfg.com.pk
Investment Management Service
N.A.I.C.S.: 523940

Greaves Pakistan (Pvt) Ltd **(1)**
Modern Motors House Beaumont Road,
Karachi, 75530, Pakistan
Tel.: (92) 2135682565
Web Site: https://gfg.com.pk
Construction Machinery Mfr
N.A.I.C.S.: 333120

Unicol Ltd. **(1)**
3rd Floor Modern Motors-House Beaumont
Road, Karachi, Pakistan
Tel.: (92) 2111 135 4111
Web Site: https://www.unicol.com.pk
Ethanol Product Mfr
N.A.I.C.S.: 325193
Asif Qadir (Chm)

CHERAT PACKAGING LIMITED

Modern Motors House Beaumont
Road, Karachi, 75530, Pakistan
Tel.: (92) 2135683566
Web Site: http://www.gfg.com.pk
CPPL—(LAH)
Rev.: $58,110,662
Assets: $81,503,361
Liabilities: $49,435,772
Net Worth: $32,067,589
Earnings: $4,041,428
Emp.: 229
Fiscal Year-end: 06/30/19
Packaging Mfr
N.A.I.C.S.: 322299
Akbarali Pesnani (Chm)

Subsidiaries:

Greaves Airconditioning (Pvt.)
Ltd **(1)**
Modern Motors House Beaumont Road,
Karachi, 75530, Pakistan
Tel.: (92) 2135682565
Web Site: https://gfg.com.pk
Airconditioning & Refrigeration Parts Distr
N.A.I.C.S.: 423740

CHEREPOVETS PLYWOOD & FURNITURE PLANT, JSC

4 Proezjaya Str, Vologda Region,
Cherepovets, 162604, Russia
Tel.: (7) 8202556823
Web Site: http://www.cfmk.ru
Year Founded: 1958
Sales Range: Less than $1 Million
Furniture Product Mfr
N.A.I.C.S.: 337122
Anna Borisova (Head-Export Sls
Dept-Birch Plywood & Sawnwood)

CHERISH SUNSHINE INTER-NATIONAL LIMITED

Unit 1802 18/F No 88 Gloucester
Road, Wanchai, China (Hong Kong)
Tel.: (852) 21140101 BM
Web Site: http://www.cpphk1094.cn
1094—(HKG)
Rev.: $12,066,724
Assets: $46,433,058
Liabilities: $20,059,743
Net Worth: $26,373,314

Earnings: $28,505
Emp.: 120
Fiscal Year-end: 12/31/20
Information Technology Services
N.A.I.C.S.: 541512
Jinwei Zheng (Chm & CEO)

CHERKASYOBLENERGO PJSC

285 Gogolya str, Cherkasy, 18136,
Ukraine
Tel.: (380) 72 36 02 63
Web Site:
http://www.cherkasyoblenergo.com
Eletric Power Generation Services
N.A.I.C.S.: 221118

CHERNAN METAL INDUS-TRIAL CORP.

18F-1 No 161 Sec 1 Wanshou Rd,
Gueishan Dist, Taoyuan, 333, Taiwan
Tel.: (886) 282092883
3631—(TPE)
Rev.: $3,876,872
Assets: $89,486,446
Liabilities: $37,790,045
Net Worth: $51,696,401
Earnings: ($1,684,926)
Fiscal Year-end: 12/31/22
Nonferrous Metal Product Distr
N.A.I.C.S.: 423510
Wei Su-Zhu (Chm & CEO)

CHERNG TAY TECHNOLOGY CO., LTD.

No 1 Luke 3rd Rd, Luzhu, Kaohsiung,
821, Taiwan
Tel.: (886) 76955222
Web Site: https://www.chetay.com.tw
Year Founded: 1983
4767—(TPE)
Rev.: $44,583,310
Assets: $43,692,555
Liabilities: $16,564,112
Net Worth: $27,128,443
Earnings: $2,106,713
Fiscal Year-end: 12/31/22
Adhesive Product Mfr
N.A.I.C.S.: 325520
Sheng Yi Wang (Chm)

Subsidiaries:

Cherng Tay Technology (India) Pri-
vate Limited **(1)**
Plot No 851 2nd Floor Udyog Vihar Phase
5, Gurgaon, 122016, Haryana, India
Tel.: (91) 1244296255
Waterproofing Product Mfr
N.A.I.C.S.: 313320

PT Cherng Tay Indonesia **(1)**
Jl West Outer Circle No 5-i Rt 009 Rw 007
Kel, Uri Kosambi Kec Cengkareng West,
Jakarta, 11520, Indonesia
Tel.: (62) 2156945257
Waterproofing Product Mfr
N.A.I.C.S.: 313320

Thanh Thai Viet Nam Industry Tech-
nology Company Limited **(1)**
Floor M- No 74C Nguyen Van Cu Street,
Dist 1, Ho Chi Minh City, Vietnam
Tel.: (84) 2838389663
Waterproofing Material Mfr
N.A.I.C.S.: 313320

Vietnam Cherng Tay Technology Co.,
Ltd. **(1)**
No 74C Nguyen Van Cu Street, P Nguyen
Cu Trinh District 1, Ho Chi Minh City, Viet-
nam
Tel.: (84) 2838389662
Waterproofing Product Mfr
N.A.I.C.S.: 313320

CHERNIGIVOBLENERGO PJSC

Horkoho St 40, Chernigov, 14000,
Ukraine
Tel.: (380) 462772901

Chernigivoblenergo PJSC—(Continued)

Web Site:
https://chernihivoblenergo.com.ua
Year Founded: 1893
Eletric Power Generation Services
N.A.I.C.S.: 221118

CHERNOMORSKI HOLDING AD

Alexander Malinov Blvd No 80A,
1712, Sofia, Bulgaria
Tel.: (359) 898448869
CHL—(BUL)
Sales Range: Less than $1 Million
Insurance Services
N.A.I.C.S.: 524210

CHERRY SE

Rosental 7 c/o Mindspace, 80331,
Munich, Germany
Tel.: (49) 964320610
Web Site: https://www.cherry-
world.com
Year Founded: 1953
C3RY—(MUN)
Rev.: $139,595,400
Assets: $263,328,188
Liabilities: $128,534,623
Net Worth: $134,793,566
Earnings: ($140,059,026)
Emp.: 476
Fiscal Year-end: 12/31/23
Computer Product Mfr
N.A.I.C.S.: 334118
Mathias Dahn (CFO)

Subsidiaries:

Active Key GmbH (1)
Rosental 7 Mindspace, D-80331, Munich,
Germany
Tel.: (49) 924148337
Web Site: https://www.activekey.de
Keyboard Mfr & Distr
N.A.I.C.S.: 334118

Cherry Electronics (Hong Kong) Co.,
Ltd. (1)
Room 19 Unit 509 511 5/F Silvercord Tower
2 30 Canton Road, Tsim Sha Tsui, Kow-
loon, China (Hong Kong)
Tel.: (852) 39598252
Electrical Product Mfr & Distr
N.A.I.C.S.: 335999

Cherry Europe GmbH (1)
Cherrystrasse 2, D-91275, Auerbach, Ger-
many
Tel.: (49) 964320610
Web Site: https://www.cherry.de
Emp.: 500
Computer Input Device Mfr & Distr
N.A.I.C.S.: 334112

Zhuhai Cherry Electronics Co.,
Ltd. (1)
No 8 Plant Jinyuan 1st Road High Tech In-
dustrial Zone, Tangjiawan Town, Zhuhai,
519060, Guangdong, China
Tel.: (86) 7563689088
Electrical Product Mfr & Distr
N.A.I.C.S.: 335999

CHERRYBRO CO., LTD.

1770 Saenggeojincheon-ro, Iwol-
myeon, Jincheon, 27820,
Chungcheongbuk-do, Korea (South)
Tel.: (82) 435303200
Web Site: https://www.cherrybro.com
Year Founded: 1991
066360—(KRS)
Rev.: $308,633,147
Assets: $212,254,563
Liabilities: $147,655,934
Net Worth: $64,598,629
Earnings: $7,014,296
Emp.: 318
Fiscal Year-end: 12/31/22
Farm Management Services
N.A.I.C.S.: 115116
Jong-Geol Park (Vice Chm)

CHERRYPICK GAMES SA

Tel.: (48) 570650151
Web Site:
https://www.cherrypickgames.com
Year Founded: 2014
Software Development Services
N.A.I.C.S.: 541511
Michael Sroczynski (Founder & Dir-
Game)

CHERVON HOLDINGS LIMITED

No 99 West Tian-Yuan Rd, Jiangning
Economic & Technical Development
Zone, Nanjing, 211106, Jiangsu
Sheng, China
Tel.: (86) 2584994002
Web Site:
https://global.chervongroup.com
2285—(HKG)
Holding Company; Power Tools &
Outdoor Power Equipment Mfr &
Whslr
N.A.I.C.S.: 551112
Longquan Pan (Founder, Chm &
CEO)

CHERY AUTOMOBILE CO., LTD.

8 Changchun Rd Economic & Tech-
nological Development Zone, Wuhu,
241009, China
Tel.: (86) 5535922993
Web Site:
http://www.cheryinternational.com
Year Founded: 1997
Sales Range: $1-4.9 Billion
Emp.: 20,000
Motor Vehicles Mfr
N.A.I.C.S.: 336110
Tongyao Yin (Chm)

Subsidiaries:

Chery South Africa (1)
Cnr Madeley and Rietfontein Road, Boks-
burg, 1459, South Africa
Tel.: (27) 118945889
Web Site: http://www.cheryauto.co.za
Motor Vehicle Distr
N.A.I.C.S.: 423110

CHERYONG INDUSTRIAL CO LTD

GaRam Bldg 628 Achasan-ro,
Gwangjin, Seoul, 143-810, Korea
(South)
Tel.: (82) 222043700
Web Site: http://www.cheryong.co.kr
Year Founded: 2011
147830—(KRS)
Rev.: $46,852,979
Assets: $65,450,689
Liabilities: $7,199,194
Net Worth: $58,251,495
Earnings: $7,208,862
Emp.: 51
Fiscal Year-end: 12/31/22
Power Transmission Product Mfr
N.A.I.C.S.: 221121
Jong Tae Park (CEO)

Subsidiaries:

Cheryong Electric Co., Ltd (1)
21 Sinilseo-ro Daedeok-gu, Daejeon, 306-
230, Korea (South)
Tel.: (82) 42 930 3000
Web Site: http://www.cheryong.co.kr
Power Transmission Equipment Whslr
N.A.I.C.S.: 423840

Cheryong Industrial Co Ltd - Daejeon
Factory (1)
1686-2 Sinil-dong, Daedeok-gu, Daejeon,
Chungcheong, Korea (South)
Tel.: (82) 429303000
Web Site: http://www.cheryongelec.com
Power Transmission Equipment Whslr
N.A.I.C.S.: 423840

CHESAPEAKE GOLD CORPORATION

201 - 1512 Yew Street, Vancouver,
V6K 3E4, BC, Canada
Tel.: (778) 731-1362
BC
Web Site:
https://www.chesapeakegold.com
Year Founded: 2002
CKG—(OTCIQ)
Rev.: $340,292
Assets: $135,264,817
Liabilities: $8,318,766
Net Worth: $126,946,052
Earnings: ($5,789,654)
Emp.: 28
Fiscal Year-end: 12/31/21
Gold & Silver Mining Services
N.A.I.C.S.: 212220
Alberto Galicia (VP-Exploration)

Subsidiaries:

Minerales El Prado S.A. de C.V. (1)
Cerro Blanco 410 Fraccion Lomas de Sa-
huatoba, Durango, 34108, Mexico
Tel.: (52) 6181302326
Gold Ore Mining Services
N.A.I.C.S.: 212220

CHESHER EQUIPMENT LTD.

6599 Kitimat Rd Unit 2, Mississauga,
L5N 4J4, ON, Canada
Tel.: (905) 363-0309
Web Site: http://www.chesher.com
Year Founded: 1967
Sales Range: Less than $1 Million
Emp.: 10
Food Machinery & Equipment Distr
N.A.I.C.S.: 423850
Chris Koehler (Pres)

CHESNARA PLC

2nd floor Building 4 West Strand
Business Park West Strand Road,
Preston, PR1 8UY, United Kingdom
Tel.: (44) 1772972050
UK
Web Site:
https://www.chesnara.co.uk
Year Founded: 2004
CSN—(LSE)
Rev.: $400,728,351
Assets: $14,331,421,358
Liabilities: $13,910,925,271
Net Worth: $420,496,087
Earnings: ($124,126,483)
Emp.: 419
Fiscal Year-end: 12/31/22
Holding Company; Life Insurance
N.A.I.C.S.: 551112
David Rimmington (Dir-Fin)

Subsidiaries:

City of Westminster Assurance Com-
pany Limited (1)
Arndale House Arndale Ctr, PO Box 1023,
LU12TG, Luton, United Kingdom
Tel.: (44) 1582742800
Fire Insurance Services
N.A.I.C.S.: 524113

Countrywide Assured Plc (1)
83 School Road Sale, Chester, M33 7XA,
United Kingdom (100%)
Tel.: (44) 1619736248
Sales Range: $50-74.9 Million
Emp.: 4
Financial Investment Activities
N.A.I.C.S.: 523999

Moderna Forsakringar Liv AB (1)
Sveavagen 167, PO Box 7830, 103 98,
Stockholm, Sweden
Tel.: (46) 856200600
Web Site:
http://www.modernaforsakringar.se
Sales Range: $10-24.9 Million
Emp.: 30
Fire Insurance Services
N.A.I.C.S.: 524210

Subsidiary (Domestic):

Movestic Kapitalforvaltning AB (2)
Birgerjarlsgatan 57 B, PO Box 7853, Stock-
holm, 103 99, Sweden
Tel.: (46) 812039200
Web Site: http://www.movestic.se
General Insurance Services
N.A.I.C.S.: 524210

Scildon N.V. (1)
Laapersveld 68, 1213 VB, Hilversum, Neth-
erlands
Tel.: (31) 356252525
Web Site: https://www.scildon.nl
Insurance Management Services
N.A.I.C.S.: 524298

Waard Verzekeringen B.V. (1)
Geert Scholtenslaan 11, 1687 CL, Wognum,
Netherlands
Tel.: (31) 883741000
Web Site:
https://www.waardverzekeringen.nl
Insurance Services
N.A.I.C.S.: 524210

CHESSWOOD GROUP LIMITED

41 Scarsdale Road Suite 5, Toronto,
M3B 2R2, ON, Canada
Tel.: (416) 386-3099
Web Site:
https://www.chesswoodgroup.com
Year Founded: 2006
CHW—(TSX)
Rev.: $91,570,568
Assets: $647,286,634
Liabilities: $537,129,094
Net Worth: $110,157,540
Earnings: ($6,668,937)
Emp.: 103
Fiscal Year-end: 12/31/20
Investment Management Service
N.A.I.C.S.: 523999
Lisa Stevenson (Fin Dir)

Subsidiaries:

Acura Sherway (1)
2000 The Queensway, Etobicoke, M9C
5H5, ON, Canada
Tel.: (416) 620-1987
Web Site: https://www.acurasherway.com
Automobile Dealership
N.A.I.C.S.: 441110

Chesswood GP Limited (1)
156 Duncan Mill Rd Ste 15, Toronto, M3B
3N2, ON, Canada
Tel.: (416) 386-3099
Web Site: http://www.chesswoodgroup.com
Emp.: 5
Financial Management & Investment Ser-
vices
N.A.I.C.S.: 523999
Barry Shafran (Pres & CEO)

Pawnee Leasing Corporation (1)
3801 Automation Way Ste 207, Fort Collins,
CO 80525
Tel.: (970) 482-2556
Web Site: https://www.pawneeleasing.com
Equipment Leasing Services
N.A.I.C.S.: 532490
Gary H. Souverein (Pres)

Rifco Inc. (1)
Millennium Centre Suite 702 4909 49th
Street, Red Deer, T4N 1V1, AB, Canada
Tel.: (403) 314-1288
Web Site: http://www.rifco.net
Rev.: $27,237,425
Assets: $157,921,993
Liabilities: $139,557,970
Net Worth: $18,364,023
Earnings: ($3,747,121)
Emp.: 100
Fiscal Year-end: 03/31/2021
Financial Lenders
N.A.I.C.S.: 525990
Doug Decksheimer (CMO & VP)

Tandem Finance Inc. (1)
3801 Automation Way Ste 207, Fort Collins,
CO 80525
Web Site: https://www.tandemfinance.com

Finance Leasing Services
N.A.I.C.S.: 522220
Mike Sheehan (Pres)

Vault Credit Corporation (1)
41 Scarsdale Road Suite 5, Toronto, M3B
2R2, ON, Canada
Tel.: (416) 499-8466
Web Site: https://vaultcredit.com
Financial Services
N.A.I.C.S.: 523999
Daniel Wittlin (CEO & Founder)

Vault Payment Systems LLC (1)
41 Scarsdale Road Suite 5, Toronto, M3B
2R2, ON, Canada
Financial Services
N.A.I.C.S.: 523999

CHESTER CARTAGE LTD.
1995 Markham Rd, Toronto, M1B
2W3, ON, Canada
Tel.: (416) 754-7720
Web Site:
　http://www.chestercartage.com
Year Founded: 1945
Sales Range: $10-24.9 Million
Transportation & Warehousing Services
N.A.I.C.S.: 493110
Bill Beighton (Mgr-Ops)

CHESTERFIELD RESOURCES PLC
6 Heddon Street, London, W1B 4BT,
United Kingdom
Web Site:
　https://www.chesterfieldplc.com
Year Founded: 2017
CHF—(LSE)
Assets: $3,578,038
Liabilities: $172,521
Net Worth: $3,405,518
Earnings: ($4,619,272)
Emp.: 9
Fiscal Year-end: 12/31/22
Mineral Exploration Services
N.A.I.C.S.: 213115

CHETTINAD GROUP OF COMPANIES
Rani Seethai Hall 5th Floor 603,
Anna Salai, Chennai, 600 006, India
Tel.: (91) 44 2829 2727
Web Site: http://www.chettinda.com
Year Founded: 1962
Holding Company
N.A.I.C.S.: 551112
M.A.M.R. Muthiah (Vice Chm & Mng Dir)

Subsidiaries:

**Chettinad Cements Corporation
Limited** (1)
Rani Seethai Hall 5th Floor 603, Anna
Salai, Chennai, 600 006, India
Tel.: (91) 4428292727
Web Site: http://www.chettinad.com
Cement & Construction Materials Mfr
N.A.I.C.S.: 327310
M. A. M. R. Muthiah (Mng Dir)

Plant (Domestic):

**Chettinad Cements Corp. Ltd. - Karik-
kali Plant** (2)
Rani Meyyammai Nagar Vedasandur Taluk,
Karikkali Post, Vedasandur, 624 703, Tamil
Nadu, India
Tel.: (91) 4551 234441
Web Site: http://www.chettinad.com
Emp.: 25
Cement Mfr
N.A.I.C.S.: 327310
Alex West (Sr VP)

**Chettinad Cements Corp. Ltd. - Pu-
liyur Plant** (2)
Kumara Rajah Muthiah Nagar Puliyur CF
Post, Karur, 639 114, Tamil Nadu, India
Tel.: (91) 4324 251354
Web Site: http://www.chettinadcement.com

Emp.: 300
Cement Mfr
N.A.I.C.S.: 327310
C. Sudhakar (CEO)

CHEUK NANG (HOLDINGS) LIMITED
Suite 4901 49/ FCentral Plaza 18
Harbour Road, Wanchai, China
(Hong Kong)
Tel.: (852) 25267799　　　　　HK
Web Site:
　https://www.cheuknang.com.hk
Year Founded: 1963
0131—(HKG)
Rev.: $7,318,067
Assets: $1,205,916,309
Liabilities: $320,011,633
Net Worth: $885,904,676
Earnings: ($19,247,943)
Emp.: 75
Fiscal Year-end: 06/30/22
Property Management Services
N.A.I.C.S.: 237210
Connie Sau Fun Ho (Sec)

Subsidiaries:

**Cheuk Nang Property Management
Company** (1)
4901 49th Fl Central Plaza 18 Harbour
Road, Wanchai, China (Hong Kong)
Tel.: (852) 25267799
Property Development Services
N.A.I.C.S.: 531190

**Lo & Son Land Investment Company
Limited** (1)
30-32 F Cheuk Nang 21st Century Plz,
Wanchai, China (Hong Kong)
Tel.: (852) 25267799
Property Management Services
N.A.I.C.S.: 531312

Martego Sdn Bhd (1)
No 5 Changkat Perak Off Lorong Perak,
Jalan P Ramlee, 50250, Kuala Lumpur,
Malaysia
Tel.: (60) 321611188
Web Site: https://martego.com.my
Property Investment & Development Services
N.A.I.C.S.: 531312
Karen Haw (Exec Sec)

Yorksbon Development Limited (1)
30-33 F Cheuk Nang Plz 250 Hennessy Rd,
Wanchai, China (Hong Kong)
Tel.: (852) 25267799
Property Investment & Development Services
N.A.I.C.S.: 531312
Howald Cho (Mgr-Mktg)

CHEUNG HO ELECTRIC CO., LIMITED
Lead On Industrial Building 18 Ng
Fong Street, Unit FP, 2/F San Po
Kong, China (Hong Kong)
Tel.: (852) 29842617
Year Founded: 1997
Engineeering Services
N.A.I.C.S.: 541330

CHEUNG WOH TECHNOLO-GIES LTD.
23 Tuas South Street 1, Singapore,
638033, Singapore
Tel.: (65) 68618036
Web Site:
　http://www.cheungwoh.com.sg
Year Founded: 1972
C50—(SES)
Rev.: $36,211,359
Assets: $67,482,279
Liabilities: $11,283,857
Net Worth: $56,198,423
Earnings: ($3,754,615)
Emp.: 2,000
Fiscal Year-end: 02/28/20
Computer Component Mfr
N.A.I.C.S.: 334118

Kung Ming Law (Exec Dir)

Subsidiaries:

**Cheung Woh Precision (Zhuhai) Co.,
Ltd** (1)
163 Zhu Feng Way Xin Qing Science &
Technology Park, Doumen, Zhuhai, 519180,
China
Tel.: (86) 7565212268
Web Site: http://www.cheungwoh.com.sg
Precision Tools & Die Mfr
N.A.I.C.S.: 332216

**Cheung Woh Technologies (Malay-
sia) Sdn. Bhd.** (1)
1059 MK 6 Lorong Perusahaan Maju 2,
13600, Prai, Penang, Malaysia
Tel.: (60) 45077820
Hard Disk Drive Component Mfr & Distr
N.A.I.C.S.: 332721
Loh Yut Chai (Asst Gen Mgr)

**Cheung Woh Technologies (Johor)
Sdn. Bhd.** (1)
Plo 107 and 108 Jalan Cyber 5 Kawasan
Perindustrian Senai Phase 3, 81400, Senai,
Johor, Malaysia
Tel.: (60) 75980557
Hard Disk Drive Component Mfr & Distr
N.A.I.C.S.: 332721
Hai Ting Tan (Mgr-Admin)

**Cheung Woh Technologies (Zhuhai)
Co., Ltd** (1)
163 Zhu Feng Way Xin Qing Science &
Technology Park, Doumen, Zhuhai, 519180,
China
Tel.: (86) 7565212268
Web Site: http://www.cheungwoh.com.sg
Sales Range: $200-249.9 Million
Precision Tools & Die Mfr
N.A.I.C.S.: 332216

CHEVAL QUANCARD
La Mouline 4 Rue Du Carbouney,
Carbon Blanc, 33560, Bordeaux,
France
Tel.: (33) 557778888
Web Site:
　http://www.chevalquancard.com
Rev.: $21,200,000
Emp.: 43
Wine & Distilled Beverages
N.A.I.C.S.: 424820
Roland Quancard (Pres & Member-
Exec Bd)

CHEVALIER INTERNATIONAL HOLDINGS LIMITED
22/F Chevalier Commercial Centre 8
Wang Hoi Road, Kowloon Bay, China
(Hong Kong)
Tel.: (852) 2 318 1818　　　　　BM
Web Site: http://www.chevalier.com
0025—(HKG)
Rev.: $1,113,669,168
Assets: $2,607,317,157
Liabilities: $1,159,311,192
Net Worth: $1,448,005,965
Earnings: $89,341,093
Emp.: 3,700
Fiscal Year-end: 03/31/22
Holding Company; Coffee & Other
Beverage Products Mfr & Distr
N.A.I.C.S.: 551112
Chung Leung Ho (Exec Dir)

Subsidiaries:

**CPC Construction Hong Kong
Limited** (1)
22/F Chevalier Commercial Centre 8 Wang
Hoi Road, Kowloon Bay, China (Hong
Kong)
Tel.: (852) 27984255
General Construction Services
N.A.I.C.S.: 236220

**Chevalier (Aluminium Engineering)
Limited** (1)
22/F Chevalier Commercial Centre 8 Wang
Hoi Road, Kowloon Bay, China (Hong
Kong)

Tel.: (852) 21114988
Aluminium Window Distr
N.A.I.C.S.: 444110

**Chevalier (Building Supplies & Engi-
neering) Limited** (1)
22/F Chevalier Commercial Centre 8 Wang
Hoi Road, Kowloon Bay, China (Hong
Kong)
Tel.: (852) 21114725
Building Materials Distr
N.A.I.C.S.: 423320

**Chevalier (Construction) Company
Limited** (1)
22/F Chevalier Commercial Centre 8 Wang
Hoi Road, Kowloon Bay, China (Hong
Kong)
Tel.: (852) 23181818
Building Construction & Maintenance Services
N.A.I.C.S.: 561790

**Chevalier (E & M Contracting)
Limited** (1)
22/F Chevalier Commercial Centre 8 Wang
Hoi Road, Kowloon Bay, China (Hong
Kong)
Tel.: (852) 21114811
Electrical & Mechanical Equipment Installation Services
N.A.I.C.S.: 238290

Chevalier (Envirotech) Limited (1)
22/F Chevalier Commercial Centre 8 Wang
Hoi Road, Kowloon Bay, China (Hong
Kong)
Tel.: (852) 23316317
Engineeering Services
N.A.I.C.S.: 541330

**Chevalier (Insurance Brokers)
Limited** (1)
22/F Chevalier Commercial Centre 8 Wang
Hoi Road, Kowloon Bay, China (Hong
Kong)
Tel.: (852) 28816481
Insurance Services
N.A.I.C.S.: 524210

**Chevalier (Network Solutions)
Limited** (1)
22/F Chevalier Commercial Centre 8 Wang
Hoi Road, Kowloon Bay, China (Hong
Kong)
Tel.: (852) 29533330
Network Solution Services
N.A.I.C.S.: 541512

Chevalier Automobiles Inc. (1)
4334 Kingston Road, Scarborough, M1E
2M8, ON, Canada
Tel.: (416) 281-1234
Automotive Distr
N.A.I.C.S.: 441110

**Chevalier Cold Storage & Logistics
Limited** (1)
124-130 Kwok Shui Road, Kwai Chung,
China (Hong Kong)
Tel.: (852) 24230170
Web Site: http://www.chevalier-
logistics.com.hk
Cold Storage & Logistics Services
N.A.I.C.S.: 493120

**Chevalier Insurance Company
Limited** (1)
22/F Chevalier Commercial Centre 8 Wang
Hoi Road, Kowloon Bay, China (Hong
Kong)
Tel.: (852) 23121818
Insurance Services
N.A.I.C.S.: 524210

**Chevalier International (USA),
Inc.** (1)
430 E Grand Ave, South San Francisco, CA
94080
Tel.: (650) 877-8118
Sales Range: $10-24.9 Million
Groceries, General Line
N.A.I.C.S.: 424410

**Chevalier Property Management
Limited** (1)
22/F Chevalier Commercial Centre 8 Wang
Hoi Road, Kowloon Bay, China (Hong
Kong)
Tel.: (852) 27588632

Chevalier International Holdings Limited—(Continued)

Real Estate Services
N.A.I.C.S.: 531390

Chevalier iTech Services Limited (1)
22/F Chevalier Commercial Centre 8 Wang
Hoi Rd, Kowloon Bay, China (Hong Kong)
Tel.: (852) 27984483
Web Site: https://www.chevalier-itech.com
Printing Machinery Distr
N.A.I.C.S.: 423830

Chevalier iTech Thai Limited (1)
540 Bamrungmuang Rd, Watdebsirin Pom-
prabsuttupai, Bangkok, 10100, Thailand
Tel.: (66) 22264300
Automation & Computer Product Distr
N.A.I.C.S.: 423690

Macleh (Chevalier) Limited (1)
3100 Steeles Avenue East Suite 301 Gate-
way Centre, Markham, L3R 8T3, ON,
Canada
Tel.: (905) 940-2373
Real Estate Services
N.A.I.C.S.: 531390

Shanghai Chevalier Trading Co.,
Ltd. (1)
Room 2106 21/F Ascendas Plaza 333 Tian
Yao Qiao Road, Xuhui District, Shanghai,
200030, China
Tel.: (86) 2161196969
Escalator & Mechanical Equipment Mfr
N.A.I.C.S.: 333921

CHEVALLIER SUD
2 Boulevard De Sarrians, 84170,
Monteux, Vaucluse, France
Tel.: (33) 490662014
Sales Range: $10-24.9 Million
Emp.: 29
Local Trucking without Storage
N.A.I.C.S.: 484110
Dominique Chevallier (Mng Dir, Mng
Dir & Chm)

CHEVIOT BRIDGE LIMITED
Level 9 564 St Kilda Rd, Melbourne,
3000, VIC, Australia
Tel.: (61) 386567000
Sales Range: $10-24.9 Million
Emp.: 28
Wine Mfr & Sales
N.A.I.C.S.: 312130
Maurice Dean (Mng Dir)

Subsidiaries:

Kirribilly Vineyards Pty Limited (1)
318 Main N Rd, PO Box 771, Clare, 5453,
South Australia, Australia
Tel.: (61) 8 88421849
Vineyards & Wineries Services
N.A.I.C.S.: 312130
Robert Ian Stanway (Mng Dir)

Kirribilly Viticulture Pty Limited (1)
318 Main N Rd, PO Box 771, Clare, 5453,
South Australia, Australia
Tel.: (61) 888421122
Sales Range: $10-24.9 Million
Vineyard Cultivation Services
N.A.I.C.S.: 111332

CHEVIOT COMPANY LIMITED
24 Park Street Celica House 9th
Floor Celica Park, Kolkata, 700 016,
West Bengal, India
Tel.: (91) 8232087911
Web Site:
   https://www.cheviotgroup.com
CHEVIOT—(NSE)
Rev.: $81,520,557
Assets: $82,729,333
Liabilities: $7,245,352
Net Worth: $75,483,981
Earnings: $10,831,098
Emp.: 4,127
Fiscal Year-end: 03/31/22
Jute Products Mfr
N.A.I.C.S.: 313210

Harsh Vardhan Kanoria (Chm, CEO
& Mng Dir)

Subsidiaries:

Cheviot Agro Industries Pvt, Ltd. (1)
Magma House 9th Floor 24 Park Street,
Kolkata, 700016, India
Tel.: (91) 8232087911
Tea Leaf Mfr
N.A.I.C.S.: 311920

Cheviot International Ltd. (1)
DLF Tower A 12th Floor 1210, Jasola, New
Delhi, 110025, India
Tel.: (91) 1146706580
Tea Leaf Mfr
N.A.I.C.S.: 311920

CHEVITA GMBH
Raiffeisenstrasse 2, Pfaffenhofen,
85276, Germany
Tel.: (49) 84418530   De
Web Site: http://www.chevita.com
Year Founded: 1968
Sales Range: $10-24.9 Million
Emp.: 50
Animal Health Products Mfr
N.A.I.C.S.: 311119
Ludwig Schrag (Mng Dir)

**CHEVRILLON & ASSOCIES
SCA**
4-6 rond-point des Champs-Elysees,
75008, Paris, France
Tel.: (33) 1 53 93 91 00   FR
Web Site:
   http://www.groupechevrillon.com
Year Founded: 1992
Venture Capital & Private Equity Firm
N.A.I.C.S.: 523999
Cyrille Chevrillon (CEO)

**CHEVRILLON PHILIPPE IN-
DUSTRIE**
98-102 rue de Paris, 92100,
Boulogne-Billancourt, Cedex, France
Tel.: (33) 155605590
Web Site: http://www.cpibooks.com
Year Founded: 1996
Sales Range: $500-549.9 Million
Emp.: 3,700
Monochrome Book Mfr, Owned by
CVC Capital Partners & by Cognetas
LLP
N.A.I.C.S.: 323117
Pierre-Francois Catte (Mng Dir)

Subsidiaries:

CPI BLACKPRINT IBERICA,
S.L. (1)
Torre Bovera 19-25, Sant Andreu de la
Barca, 08740, Barcelona, Spain
Tel.: (34) 93 681 0899
Book Printing Services
N.A.I.C.S.: 323117

CPI Group (UK) Ltd (1)
108-110 Beddington Lane, Croydon, CR0
4YY, Surrey, United Kingdom
Tel.: (44) 20 8612 3400
Book Printing Services
N.A.I.C.S.: 323117
Francois Golicheff (CEO)

Subsidiary (Domestic):

Bookmarque (2)
110 Beddington Lane, Croydon, CR0 4TD,
Surrey, United Kingdom
Tel.: (44) 2086123400
Web Site: http://www.fulmar.com
Paperback Book Printing
N.A.I.C.S.: 323117
Keith Marley (Mng Dir)

CPI Colour (2)
108-110 Beddington Lane, Croydon, CR0
4YY, Surrey, United Kingdom
Tel.: (44) 20 8612 3400
Web Site: http://cpibooks.com
Book Publishers
N.A.I.C.S.: 513130

Royle Corporate Print Ltd. (2)
Royle House, 110 Beddington Lane, Croy-
don, CR0 4TD, Surrey, United Kingdom
Tel.: (44) 2086882300
Web Site: http://www.royle-print.co.uk
Emp.: 100
Printing of Corporate & Marketing Literature
N.A.I.C.S.: 323111
Allison Kaye (Mng Dir)

Royle Financial Print Ltd (2)
141-143 Shoreditch High Street, London,
E1 6JE, United Kingdom
Tel.: (44) 2075533500
Web Site: http://www.roylefinancial.com
Domestic & International Corporate Finance
Printing
N.A.I.C.S.: 323111
John Cullender (Mng Dir)

The White Quill Press (2)
The Orion Centre, 108 Beddington Lane,
Croydon, CR0 4YY, Surrey, United Kingdom
Tel.: (44) 2086888300
Emp.: 300
Book Jacket Mfr
N.A.I.C.S.: 323111

CPI Moravia Books s.r.o. (1)
Brnenska 1024, 691 23, Pohorelice, Czech
Republic
Tel.: (420) 519 440 111
Book Printing Services
N.A.I.C.S.: 323117
Jurgen Heisters (Mng Dir)

Clausen & Bosse GmbH (1)
Birkstrasse 10, 25917, Leck, Germany
Tel.: (49) 4662830
Web Site: http://www.clausenbosse.de
Sales Range: $200-249.9 Million
Emp.: 600
Books Printing
N.A.I.C.S.: 513130
Sven Lincoln (Dir-Sls)

Koninklijke Wohrmann B.V. (1)
Estlandsestraat 1, PO Box 92, 7202 CP,
Zutphen, Netherlands
Tel.: (31) 575 58 21 21
Book Printing Services
N.A.I.C.S.: 323117

**CHEVRON LUBRICANTS
LANKA PLC**
Tel.: (94) 114524524
Web Site: https://www.chevron.lk
Year Founded: 1992
LLUB.N0000—(COL)
Rev.: $81,803,967
Assets: $43,386,361
Liabilities: $22,883,945
Net Worth: $20,502,416
Earnings: $12,203,504
Emp.: 73
Fiscal Year-end: 12/31/22
Lubricant Oil Mfr & Distr
N.A.I.C.S.: 324191

CHEWATHAI PLC
1168/80 Lumpini Tower 27th Floor
Rama4 Road Tungmahamek Area,
Sathorn District, Bangkok, 10120,
Thailand
Web Site: http://www.chewathai.com
CHEWA—(THA)
Rev.: $54,850,559
Assets: $172,420,308
Liabilities: $116,938,634
Net Worth: $55,481,674
Earnings: ($2,017,559)
Emp.: 228
Fiscal Year-end: 12/31/23
Real Estate Development
N.A.I.C.S.: 531390
Sunantra Mahaprasitchai (Exec VP-
Fin & Acctg)

CHEYNET S.A.S
30 Route du Fau, 43240, Saint-Just-
Malmont, France
Tel.: (33) 477356043
Web Site: http://www.cheynet.fr

Holding Company Fabric & Medical
Support Services
N.A.I.C.S.: 551112

Subsidiaries:

Bertheas & Cie (1)
Parc d Activites de Stelytec, BP 28, 42401,
Saint-Chamond, Cedex, France
Tel.: (33) 477 29 33 33
Web Site: http://www.bertheas.com
Emp.: 70
Elastic Bandage Mfr
N.A.I.C.S.: 339113
Eric Bahon (Mgr)

Cheynet Asia (Co.) Ltd. (1)
304 Industrial Park 324 Moo 7 Tambol Tha
Toom, Amphur, Prachin Buri, 25140, Thai-
land
Tel.: (66) 837 414 101
Apparels Mfr
N.A.I.C.S.: 315250

Cheynet Elastics (1)
BP 7, 43240, Saint-Just-Malmont, France
Tel.: (33) 4 77 35 60 43
Emp.: 500
Apparel Accessory Mfr
N.A.I.C.S.: 315990

Cheynet Tunisie (1)
Rue Ibn Khaldoun, BP 151, 4022, Akouda,
Tunisia
Tel.: (216) 73 256 755
Apparels Mfr
N.A.I.C.S.: 315250

Narrow Fabric Industries Corp. (1)
701 W Reading Ave, Reading, PA 19611
Tel.: (610) 376-2891
Sales Range: $25-49.9 Million
Emp.: 100
Mfr of Narrow Elastics for Use in Lingerie &
Foundation Trades
N.A.I.C.S.: 313220

CHHABRA SPINNERS LIMITED
Tel.: (91) 7291222531
531653—(BOM)
Yarn Spinning Services
N.A.I.C.S.: 313110
Mandeep Singh Chhabra (Mng Dir)

CHI & PARTNERS LIMITED
7-9 Rathbone Street, London, W1T
1LY, United Kingdom
Tel.: (44) 20 7462 8500   UK
Web Site:
   http://www.chiandpartners.com
Year Founded: 2001
Emp.: 200
Advetising Agency
N.A.I.C.S.: 541810
Micky Tudor (Exec Dir-Creaitve)

Subsidiaries:

Halpern Ltd. (1)
7-9 Rathbone Street, London, W1T 1LY,
United Kingdom (50.1%)
Tel.: (44) 20 7462 8500
Emp.: 20
Public Relations Agency
N.A.I.C.S.: 541820
Jenny Halpern Prince (Founder & CEO)

Rapier Communications Limited (1)
The Network Bldg 97 Tottenham Court Rd,
London, WIT 4TP, United Kingdom
Tel.: (44) 2073698000
Web Site: http://www.rapieruk.com
Rev.: $269,407,050
Emp.: 9
Advetising Agency
N.A.I.C.S.: 541810

**CHI CHENG ENTERPRISE CO.,
LTD.**
No 111 Jian 2nd Rd, Zonghe Dist,
New Taipei City, Taiwan
Tel.: (886) 222226638
Web Site:
   https://www.chicheng.com.tw
Year Founded: 1973

3095—(TPE)
Rev.: $13,463,559
Assets: $27,299,597
Liabilities: $26,061,470
Net Worth: $1,238,127
Earnings: ($1,000,657)
Fiscal Year-end: 12/31/22
Hardware Product Mfr
N.A.I.C.S.: 332510
Zheng-Kuang Chang *(Founder, Chm & Pres)*

CHI HO DEVELOPMENT HOLDINGS LIMITED

Unit B1 8/F Yip Fung Industrial Building 28-36 Kwai Fung Cresent, Kwai Chung, New Territories, China (Hong Kong)
Tel.: (852) 2 893 5917   Ky
Web Site: http://www.chdev.com.hk
8423—(HKG)
Rev.: $33,174,817
Assets: $38,267,076
Liabilities: $20,741,403
Net Worth: $17,525,673
Earnings: $1,034,678
Emp.: 49
Fiscal Year-end: 03/31/22
Building Renovation Services
N.A.I.C.S.: 236220
Raymond Ka Ho Leung *(Chm & Compliance Officer)*

CHI HUA FITNESS CO., LTD.

No 231 Dexing Rd, Hukou Township, Hsinchu, Taiwan
Tel.: (886) 36992860
Web Site: http://www.chihua.com.tw
Year Founded: 1997
1593—(TPE)
Rev.: $27,354,845
Assets: $65,887,315
Liabilities: $22,695,151
Net Worth: $43,192,165
Earnings: $6,222,962
Fiscal Year-end: 12/31/22
Fitness Equipment Distr
N.A.I.C.S.: 423910
Chia-Jung Lee *(Chm)*

CHI KAN HOLDINGS LIMITED

1008 10/F China Shipbuilding Tower No 650 Cheung Sha Wan Road, Cheung Sha Wan, Kowloon, China (Hong Kong)
Tel.: (852) 23806861   Ky
Web Site: http://www.chikanck.com
Year Founded: 1989
9913—(HKG)
Holding Company
N.A.I.C.S.: 551112
Hon Kwong Lo *(Chm)*

CHI MEI GROUP

59-1 San Chia Tsun Jen Te, T'ainan, 71710, Hsien, Taiwan
Tel.: (886) 62663000
Web Site: http://www.chimeicorp.com
Year Founded: 1960
Sales Range: $5-14.9 Billion
Emp.: 36,000
Holding Company
N.A.I.C.S.: 551112
Chiang Siang Liao *(Chm)*

Subsidiaries:

Chi Mei Corporation   (1)
No 59-1 San Chia Jen Te, T'ainan, 71702, Hsien, Taiwan
Tel.: (886) 62663000
Web Site: http://www.chimeicorp.com
Plastics Processing Services
N.A.I.C.S.: 326199

Plant (Domestic):

Chi Mei Corp - PRP Tree Valley Plant   (2)

18 Wangjia Road, Xinshi District, T'ainan, 74148, Taiwan
Tel.: (886) 6 5889966
Plastics Product Mfr
N.A.I.C.S.: 326199

Subsidiary (Non-US):

Zhenjiang Chimei Chemical Co., Ltd.   (2)
18 Hanfeng Road, Zhenjiang Dagang Development Area, Zhenjiang, Jiangsu, China
Tel.: (86) 511 83121300
Plastic Product Distr
N.A.I.C.S.: 424610

LINSHINE Engineering Plastics (Suzhou) Co., Ltd.   (1)
No 8 Qiye Road, Suzhou Industrial Park, Jiangsu, China
Tel.: (86) 51265073088
Polymer Material Mfr
N.A.I.C.S.: 325211

Zhangzhou CHIMEI Chemical Co., Ltd.   (1)
No 516 Shugang Avenue South, Gulei Town Gulei Port Economic Development Zone, Zhangzhou, Fujian, China
Tel.: (86) 5963808757
Polymer Material Mfr
N.A.I.C.S.: 325211

CHI SHENG PHARMA & BIO-TECH CO., LTD.

No 3 Shih Chen Road Hsin Chu Industrial Park, Hukou, 30352, Hsin Chu, Taiwan
Tel.: (886) 35983811
Web Site: https://www.cscp.com.tw
Year Founded: 1962
4111—(TPE)
Rev.: $35,740,018
Assets: $56,296,376
Liabilities: $18,084,013
Net Worth: $38,212,363
Earnings: $4,815,246
Fiscal Year-end: 12/31/22
Medical Equipment Mfr & Distr
N.A.I.C.S.: 339112

CHIA CHANG CO., LTD.

No 45 Ln 205 Sec 2 Nanshan Rd, Luzhou Dist, Taoyuan, 338, Taiwan
Tel.: (886) 33228175
Web Site:
https://www.chiachang.com
Year Founded: 1985
4942—(TAI)
Rev.: $198,648,346
Assets: $346,418,706
Liabilities: $67,396,217
Net Worth: $279,022,489
Earnings: $20,039,471
Emp.: 161
Fiscal Year-end: 12/31/23
Metal Stamping & Injection Molds
N.A.I.C.S.: 332119
L. C. Cheng *(CFO)*

Subsidiaries:

Chia Chang Technology (Chong Qing) Co., Ltd.   (1)
No 449 MaLingYan Road, ChengGong Industrial Park, Chongqing, China
Tel.: (86) 2342599018
Closure & Metal Stamping Mfr
N.A.I.C.S.: 332119

Chia Chang Technology (Suzhou) Co., Ltd.   (1)
No 1 Dongjin Road, Hedong Industrial Zone Wuzhong Economic Development Zone, Suzhou, Jiang Su, China
Tel.: (86) 51265978860
Closure & Metal Stamping Mfr
N.A.I.C.S.: 332119

Nanjing Chia-Chan Precious Electronics Co., Ltd.   (1)
No 5 HengTai Road, Nanjing Economic and Technological Development Zone, Nanjing, Jiang Su, China

Tel.: (86) 2552686099
Closure & Metal Stamping Mfr
N.A.I.C.S.: 332119

Ning Bo Chia Chang Electroinc Hardware Co., Ltd.   (1)
No 35 Yan Shan He North Road, Da Gan Township Beilun District, Ningbo, Zhejiang, China
Tel.: (86) 57486113898
Closure & Metal Stamping Mfr
N.A.I.C.S.: 332119

Ningbo Chia chang Electronics Hardware Co., Ltd.   (1)
No 35 Yan Shan He North Road, Da Gan Township Beilun District, Ningbo, Zhejiang, China
Tel.: (86) 57486113898
Metal Stamping Parts Mfr & Distr
N.A.I.C.S.: 332119

Quan Rui (Dongguan) Industrial Co., Ltd.   (1)
No 26 Wei Jian Rd, Cha Shan Town, Dongguan, Guangdong, China
Tel.: (86) 76985315642
Closure & Metal Stamping Mfr
N.A.I.C.S.: 332119

CHIA HER INDUSTRIAL CO., LTD.

7th F No 102 Dunhua North Road, Taipei, 105, Taiwan
Tel.: (886) 227123998
Web Site: https://www.chgtex.com
1449—(TAI)
Rev.: $86,881,582
Assets: $199,696,484
Liabilities: $143,788,804
Net Worth: $55,907,680
Earnings: $2,465,777
Fiscal Year-end: 12/31/23
Fabric Product Mfr
N.A.I.C.S.: 313310

Subsidiaries:

Chia Her Industrial Co., Ltd. - Tainan Mill   (1)
No 102 Dunhua North Road 7th Floor, 105, Taipei, Taiwan
Tel.: (886) 227123998
Fashion Design Services
N.A.I.C.S.: 541490

CHIA HSIN CEMENT CORP.

No 96 Sec 2 Zhongshan N Rd, Zhongshan Dist, Taipei, 00104, Taiwan
Tel.: (886) 225515211
Web Site:
https://www.chcgroup.com.tw
Year Founded: 1954
Cement Mfr
N.A.I.C.S.: 327310
Jason K. L. Chang *(Chm)*

CHIA TA WORLD CO., LTD.

No 16 Lane 317 Chung Cheng North Road, Yong Kang District, T'ainan, Taiwan
Tel.: (886) 62533117
Web Site: https://www.ctworld.com.tw
2033—(TAI)
Rev.: $19,212,106
Assets: $40,686,254
Liabilities: $7,047,222
Net Worth: $33,639,032
Earnings: ($101,769)
Emp.: 150
Fiscal Year-end: 12/31/23
Steel Product Mfr & Distr
N.A.I.C.S.: 331110
Da-Ho Wu *(Chm)*

CHIA YI STEEL CO., LTD.

No 21 Chenggong 2nd St, Minxiong Township, Chiayi, 62155, Taiwan
Tel.: (886) 52211411
Web Site: https://www.cysteel.com.tw

Year Founded: 1974
2067—(TPE)
Rev.: $38,713,410
Assets: $62,045,368
Liabilities: $47,398,305
Net Worth: $14,647,063
Earnings: ($1,425,288)
Fiscal Year-end: 12/31/22
Additive Mfr
N.A.I.C.S.: 333248
Kuang-Chao Tsao *(Chm)*

Subsidiaries:

Chia Yi Steel (Yan Cheng) Co., Ltd.   (1)
No 888 Zhongshan Road, Caiqiao Town Binhai, Yancheng, Jiangsu, China
Tel.: (86) 5158086588
Steel Casting Mfr
N.A.I.C.S.: 331513

Chung Yo Materials Co., Ltd.   (1)
No 6 Wenxing Rd, Gangshan Dist, Kaohsiung, 820110, Taiwan
Tel.: (886) 76955677
Web Site: https://www.cymaterials.com.tw
Metal Powder Mfr & Distr
N.A.I.C.S.: 331492

Yow Bell Casting (Tai Cang) Co., Ltd.   (1)
Xingang Road, Xintang District Liuhe Town, Taicang, Jiangsu, China
Tel.: (86) 51253623380
Hydraulic Component Mfr & Distr
N.A.I.C.S.: 333996

CHIALIN PRECISION INDUSTRIAL CO., LTD.

No 110 Section 2 West Ho-ping Tayuan, Tao-Yuan, Hsien, Taiwan
Tel.: (886) 33858181
Web Site: https://www.chialin.com.tw
Year Founded: 1988
3310—(TPE)
Rev.: $48,335,053
Assets: $191,500,610
Liabilities: $146,439,577
Net Worth: $45,061,032
Earnings: $4,173,842
Fiscal Year-end: 12/31/22
Machine Component Mfr & Distr
N.A.I.C.S.: 332721
Po-Chen Lin *(Chm)*

Subsidiaries:

Dongguan Jiahong Electronics Co., Ltd.   (1)
Factory Building E No 8 Lane 10 Minchang Road Nanzha Sixth Area, Meishida Industrial Park Humen Town, Dongguan, China
Tel.: (86) 76986639850
Connector Terminal Product Mfr
N.A.I.C.S.: 334417

Dongguan Jinnjixing Precision Optical Co., Ltd.   (1)
1 Fuxing Road, Xiagang Neighborhoods Chang'an Town, Dongguan, Guangdong, China
Tel.: (86) 76981587588
Die Set Mfr
N.A.I.C.S.: 333514

Kunshan Jinnji Precision Mold Co., Ltd.   (1)
150 North Binjiang Road, ZhangpuTown, Kunshan, Jiangsu, China
Tel.: (86) 51257448881
Die Set Mfr
N.A.I.C.S.: 333514

Newtech Scientific Technology Corp.   (1)
No 1-6 Ln 1010 Zhongshan Rd, Shengang Dist, Taichung, 429, Taiwan
Tel.: (886) 425626560
Connector Terminal Product Mfr
N.A.I.C.S.: 334417

Suzhou Chialin Precision Industrial Co., Ltd.   (1)
Zhujia Workshop Building A4, Weiting Town Suzhou Industrial Park, Jiangsu, China

CHIALIN Precision Industrial Co., Ltd.—(Continued)

Tel.: (86) 51262625188
Connector Terminal Product Mfr
N.A.I.C.S.: 334417

Techwin Opto-Electronics Co., Ltd.   **(1)**
4F No 48-1 Zhongshan Rd, Tucheng Dist, New Taipei City, 236, Taiwan
Tel.: (886) 222682338
Web Site: http://www.techwin.com.tw
Electronic Component Mfr & Distr
N.A.I.C.S.: 334419

CHIAN HSING FORGING INDUSTRIAL CO., LTD.
No 3-1 Xiehe South Lane, Xitun District, Taichung, 407108, Taiwan
Tel.: (886) 423592000
Web Site: https://www.ch-forging.com.tw
Year Founded: 1971
4528—(TPE)
Rev.: $76,005,816
Assets: $137,827,846
Liabilities: $65,355,595
Net Worth: $72,472,251
Earnings: $5,630,522
Emp.: 527
Fiscal Year-end: 12/31/22
Automobile Parts Mfr
N.A.I.C.S.: 336390
Mu-Shan Chiang (Pres)

Subsidiaries:

Chian Hsing (Huai'an) Auto Parts Co., Ltd.   **(1)**
No 188 Shenzhen East Road, Nanmachang Township Huaian Economic & Technology Development Zone, Huainan, China
Tel.: (86) 51783718028
Automotive Parts Mfr & Distr
N.A.I.C.S.: 336390

Chian Hsing (Taicang) Metal Products Co., Ltd.   **(1)**
No 48 Zhenghe Middle Road, Ludu Town, Taicang, China
Tel.: (86) 51253450111
Automotive Parts Mfr & Distr
N.A.I.C.S.: 336390

CHIANG MAI RAM MEDICAL BUSINESS PCL
8 Boonruangrit Rd Amphur Mueang, Chiang Mai, 50200, Thailand
Tel.: (66) 53999777
Web Site: http://www.lanna-hospital.com
CMR—(THA)
Rev.: $153,092,032
Assets: $361,476,867
Liabilities: $233,755,576
Net Worth: $127,721,291
Earnings: $6,356,551
Fiscal Year-end: 12/31/23
Hospital Management Services
N.A.I.C.S.: 622110
Varaphan Unachak (Chm)

CHIANGMAI FROZEN FOODS PUBLIC COMPANY LIMITED
149/34 Soi Anglo Plaza Surawongse Road, Bangrak, Bangkok, 10500, Thailand
Tel.: (66) 26340061
Web Site: https://www.cmfrozen.com
Year Founded: 1988
CM—(THA)
Rev.: $36,601,787
Assets: $44,586,471
Liabilities: $4,545,587
Net Worth: $40,040,884
Earnings: $2,931,451
Emp.: 1,425
Fiscal Year-end: 12/31/23
Frozen Vegetables & Fruits Processing & Export Services
N.A.I.C.S.: 311411

Prayoon Pholpipattanaphong (Chm)

Subsidiaries:

Chiangmai Frozen Foods Public Company Limited - Chiangmai Factory 1   **(1)**
92 Moo 3 Tumbol Nongjom Amphur Sansai, Chiang Mai, 50210, Thailand
Tel.: (66) 538449614
Frozen Vegetable Mfr
N.A.I.C.S.: 311411

Chiangmai Frozen Foods Public Company Limited - Chiangmai Factory 2   **(1)**
299 Moo 14 Tumbol Maefak mai Amphur Sansai, Chiang Mai, 50290, Thailand
Tel.: (66) 5384808894
Frozen Vegetable Mfr
N.A.I.C.S.: 311411

CHIANGMAI RIMDOI PCL
164/34-36 Changklan Road, Changklan Muang, Chiang Mai, 50100, Thailand
Tel.: (66) 53271420
Web Site: https://www.cmrd.co.th
Year Founded: 1990
CRD—(THA)
Rev.: $23,573,100
Assets: $24,574,676
Liabilities: $16,797,643
Net Worth: $7,777,033
Earnings: $(2,223,552)
Fiscal Year-end: 12/31/23
Construction Services
N.A.I.C.S.: 236220
Prawat Siripatrodom (Chm & Vice Chm)

CHIBOUGAMAU DRILLING LTD
527 Road 167 CP 4, Chibougamau, G8P 2K5, QC, Canada
Tel.: (418) 748-3977
Web Site: http://www.chibougamaudrilling.ca
Year Founded: 1968
Rev.: $12,520,073
Emp.: 180
Diamond Drilling Services
N.A.I.C.S.: 339910
Lynda Desgagne (Controller)

CHIBOUGAMAU INDEPENDENT MINES INC.
86-14th Street, Rouyn-Noranda, J9X 2J1, QC, Canada
Tel.: (819) 797-5242
Web Site: https://www.chibougamaumines.com
CLL1—(DEU)
Rev.: $6,384
Assets: $462,513
Liabilities: $168,193
Net Worth: $294,320
Earnings: $(692,899)
Fiscal Year-end: 12/31/19
Metal Mining
N.A.I.C.S.: 212290
Jack Stoch (Pres & CEO)

CHIC REPUBLIC PUBLIC COMPANY LIMITED
Pradit Manutham Road Khlong Chan, Bang Kapi District, Bangkok, 10240, Thailand
Tel.: (66) 25147111
Web Site: https://www.chicrepublicthai.com
CHIC—(THA)
Rev.—$20,138,882
Assets: $47,141,185
Liabilities: $22,348,414
Net Worth: $24,792,772
Earnings: $415,001
Emp.: 246

Fiscal Year-end: 12/31/23
Furnishing Product Distr
N.A.I.C.S.: 423220
Paiboon Sareewiwatthana (Chm)

CHICHIBU RAILWAY CO., LTD.
1-1 Akebono-cho, Tokyo, 360-0033, Saitama, Japan
Tel.: (81) 485233311
Web Site: http://www.chichibu-railway.co.jp
Year Founded: 1899
9012—(TKS)
Rev.: $32,461,174
Assets: $108,708,262
Liabilities: $76,141,373
Net Worth: $32,566,889
Earnings: $607,862
Fiscal Year-end: 03/31/24
Rail Transportation Services
N.A.I.C.S.: 488210
Takao Otani (Pres)

CHICONY ELECTRONICS CO., LTD.
No 69 Sec 2 Guangfu Rd, Sanchong Dist, New Taipei City, 24158, Taiwan
Tel.: (886) 266266788
Web Site: https://www.chicony.com
Year Founded: 1983
2385—(TAI)
Rev.: $3,215,361,565
Assets: $2,970,423,545
Liabilities: $1,459,136,215
Net Worth: $1,511,287,330
Earnings: $294,310,267
Emp.: 27,535
Fiscal Year-end: 12/31/23
Input Devices (Keyboards), Power Supplies & Digital Image Products Mfr & Marketer
N.A.I.C.S.: 334118
Kun-Tai Hsu (Chm)

Subsidiaries:

CHICONY ELECTRONICS CEZ S.R.O   **(1)**
Tovarni 1553, 535 01, Prelouc, Czech Republic
Tel.: (420) 46 977 5555
Web Site: http://www.chicony.com.tw
Sales Range: $25-49.9 Million
Emp.: 55
Computer Peripherals Mfr
N.A.I.C.S.: 334118

Chicony America Inc.   **(1)**
53 Parker, Irvine, CA 92618
Tel.: (949) 380-0928
Web Site: https://www.chicony.com.tw
Emp.: 10
Input Devices (keyboards), Power Supplies & Digital Image Products Mfr & Marketer
N.A.I.C.S.: 334118

Chicony Electronics (DongGuan) Co., Ltd.   **(1)**
Jingsheng Road Niushan Industrial Part, Dongcheng District, Dongguan, Guangdong, China
Tel.: (86) 76988775888
Computer Peripheral Product Mfr
N.A.I.C.S.: 334118

Chicony Electronics (Mainland China II) Co., Ltd.   **(1)**
San Zhong Gong Ye Qu, Qingxi, Dongguan, China
Tel.: (86) 769 7311688
Web Site: http://www.chicony.com.tw
Input Devices, Power Supplies & Digital Image Products Mfr & Marketer
N.A.I.C.S.: 334118

Chicony Electronics (SU Zou, Mainland China III) Co., Ltd.   **(1)**
No 2379 Zhongshan North Road, Songling Town, Wujiang, Jiangsu, China
Tel.: (86) 5126 340 8988
Web Site: http://www.chicony.com.tw
Computer Peripheral Equipment Distr
N.A.I.C.S.: 423430

Chicony Electronics GmbH   **(1)**
Borsteler Chaussee, 85-99A, Hamburg, Germany
Tel.: (49) 405144000
Web Site: http://www.chicony.de
Sales Range: $25-49.9 Million
Emp.: 20
Input Devices, Power Supplies & Digital Image Products Mfr & Marketer
N.A.I.C.S.: 334118

Chicony Electronics Japan Co., Ltd.   **(1)**
5F Aobadai Tower Annex 3-1-18 Aobadai, Meguro-Ku, Tokyo, 153-0042, Kanagawa, Japan
Tel.: (81) 36 455 0908
Web Site: http://www.chicony.com.tw
Sales Range: $50-74.9 Million
Emp.: 7
Computer Peripheral Equipment Distr
N.A.I.C.S.: 423430

Chicony Power Technology (Thailand) Co., Ltd.   **(1)**
210 Moo 3 Laemchabang Industrial Estate, Tungsukla Siracha, Chon Buri, 20230, Thailand
Tel.: (66) 38197188
Power Switching Equipment Mfr
N.A.I.C.S.: 335313

CHICONY POWER TECHNOLOGY CO., LTD.
30F No 69 Sec 2 Guangfu Rd, Sanchong Dist, New Taipei City, 241, Taiwan
Tel.: (886) 266260678
Web Site: https://www.chiconypower.com
Year Founded: 2008
6412—(TAI)
Rev.: $1,283,998,061
Assets: $857,213,520
Liabilities: $460,286,215
Net Worth: $396,927,305
Earnings: $101,510,083
Emp.: 8,104
Fiscal Year-end: 12/31/22
Electronic & Computer Parts & Components Mfr
N.A.I.C.S.: 334419
Peter Tseng (Pres)

Subsidiaries:

Chicony Power Technology Hong Kong Limited   **(1)**
Room 301-307 5 Science Park West Avenue HK Science Park N T, Sha Tin, China (Hong Kong)
Tel.: (852) 21918133
Power Supply & Adapter Product Mfr
N.A.I.C.S.: 334118

CHIEFTAIN METALS INC.
2 Bloor Street West, Suite 2000, Toronto, M4W 3E2, ON, Canada
Tel.: (416) 479-5410
Year Founded: 2009
Zinc, Copper, Lead, Gold & Silver Mining Services
N.A.I.C.S.: 212290
Pompeyo Gallardo (CFO)

CHIEFTEK PRECISION CO., LTD.
NO 3 Dali 1st Rd, Xinshi Dist Southern Taiwan Science Park, Tainan City, 744-093, Taiwan
Tel.: (886) 65055858
Web Site: https://www.chieftek.com
Year Founded: 1998
1597—(TAI)
Electronic Components Mfr
N.A.I.C.S.: 334419
Angelika Chen (CEO)

CHIEN KUO CONSTRUCTION CO., LTD.
20th Floor No 67 Section 2 Dunhua

South Road, Taipei, Taiwan
Tel.: (886) 27849730
Web Site:
https://www.ckgroup.com.tw
5515—(TAI)
Rev.: $136,903,066
Assets: $264,646,022
Liabilities: $106,048,493
Net Worth: $158,597,528
Earnings: $11,070,113
Emp.: 266
Fiscal Year-end: 12/31/23
Construction & Engineering Services
N.A.I.C.S.: 236220
Chi-Te Chen (Vice Chm)

Subsidiaries:

WeBIM Services Co., Ltd.   (1)
11F No 207 Songjiang Rd, Zhongshan Dist,
Taipei, 104, Taiwan
Tel.: (886) 225069906
Web Site: http://www.webim.com.tw
Smart Construction & Planning Services
N.A.I.C.S.: 541310
Mark Lee (Pres)

**CHIEN SHING HARBOUR SER-
VICE CO., LTD.**
No 68 Sec 3 Lingang Rd, Wuqi Dist,
Taichung, 435, Taiwan
Tel.: (886) 426399666
Web Site:
http://www.chienshing.com.tw
8367—(TAI)
Rev.: $75,886,390
Assets: $496,300,612
Liabilities: $360,340,939
Net Worth: $135,959,673
Earnings: $11,184,473
Fiscal Year-end: 12/31/23
Freight Forwarding & Logistics Con-
sulting Services
N.A.I.C.S.: 488510
Albert Chen (Chm)

**CHIEN SHING STAINLESS
STEEL CO., LTD.**
No 222 Industry Road Hsiao Pyi Li,
Madou Dist, T'ainan, Taiwan
Tel.: (886) 65703271
Web Site: https://www.csssc.com.tw
Year Founded: 1978
2025—(TAI)
Rev.: $24,156,806
Assets: $59,025,048
Liabilities: $3,284,705
Net Worth: $55,740,343
Earnings: $7,463,226
Emp.: 69
Fiscal Year-end: 12/31/23
Stainless Steel Mfr
N.A.I.C.S.: 331110
Shuo-Tang Yeh (Chm)

**CHIEN WEI PRECISE TECH-
NOLOGY CO., LTD.**
No 20-16 Chen Pei N Lane, Feng-
shan, Kaohsiung, 83041, Taiwan
Tel.: (886) 77313911
Web Site:
https://www.chienwei.com.tw
Year Founded: 1981
8092—(TPE)
Rev.: $13,114,905
Assets: $24,837,351
Liabilities: $15,045,712
Net Worth: $9,791,639
Earnings: $172,560
Fiscal Year-end: 12/31/22
Grinding Machine Mfr
N.A.I.C.S.: 333517
Cheng Chang-Chuang (VP)

Subsidiaries:

ACM-Service Company LLC   (1)
st Zemledelcheskaya 5A, Saint Petersburg,
Russia

Tel.: (7) 8127401163
Web Site: https://acm-service.ru
Milling Equipment Mfr & Distr
N.A.I.C.S.: 333519

Dynamic Tooling Services (Private)
Limited   (1)
33/S Quaid-e-Azam Industrial Estate, Kot
Lakhpat, Lahore, Pakistan
Tel.: (92) 4235213737
Web Site: https://dts.com.pk
Industrial Equipment Whsr
N.A.I.C.S.: 423830

EUROMECCANICA S.p.A.   (1)
Via Giuseppe Righi 12 -ZI, Moletolo, 43100,
Parma, Italy
Tel.: (39) 0521771071
Industrial Machinery Distr
N.A.I.C.S.: 333248

I Machine Technology LLC   (1)
Mira Avenue 95 office 80, Moscow, Russia
Tel.: (7) 4956406615
Web Site: https://i-machine.ru
Industrial Machinery Distr
N.A.I.C.S.: 333248

James Precision Engineering Pte
Ltd   (1)
02-06 Hiangkie Industrial Building Lobby A,
27 Woodlands Industrial Park E1, Singa-
pore, 757718, Singapore
Tel.: (65) 63673789
Web Site: https://www.cmm.com.sg
Test & Measuring Instrument Distr
N.A.I.C.S.: 423830

Jazon Sp. z o.o.   (1)
ul Wysockiego 164A, 15-167, Bialystok,
Poland
Tel.: (48) 856544620
Web Site: https://jazon.com.pl
Industrial Machinery Mfr & Distr
N.A.I.C.S.: 333248

Kula Makina Imalat San. Tic. Ltd.
Sti.   (1)
Ivedik OSB 1483 Sokak No 1, Ostim, An-
kara, Turkiye
Tel.: (90) 3123951818
Web Site: https://kula.com.tr
Grinding Machinery Mfr & Distr
N.A.I.C.S.: 333248

PT Trimitra Tehnik   (1)
Jl Goa 1 No 12 Perumnas 3, Karawaci,
Tangerang, 15810, Banten, Indonesia
Tel.: (62) 2191926106
Machining Equipment Mfr & Distr
N.A.I.C.S.: 332710

Sipcon Instrument Industries Pvt.
Ltd.   (1)
116-B HSIDC Industrial Estate, Ambala,
133006, Haryana, India
Tel.: (91) 8222929966
Web Site: https://www.sipconinstrument.com
Measuring Equipment Mfr
N.A.I.C.S.: 333914

Tat Ee Metrology Sdn Bhd   (1)
PS 3-25B 1St Floor Jalan Desa 2/4 Desa
Aman Puri, Kepong, 52100, Kuala Lumpur,
Malaysia
Tel.: (60) 362773823
Cutting Equipment Mfr & Distr
N.A.I.C.S.: 333515

CHIERU CO., LTD.
Tennozu Central Tower 3F 2-2-24
Higashi-shinagawa Shinagawa-ku,
Tokyo, 140-0002, Japan
Tel.: (81) 67129721   JP
Web Site: https://www.chieru.co.jp
Year Founded: 2006
3933—(TKS)
Rev.: $30,544,810
Assets: $40,446,590
Liabilities: $22,520,270
Net Worth: $17,926,320
Earnings: $2,306,890
Emp.: 189
Fiscal Year-end: 03/31/24
Educational Software Development
Services
N.A.I.C.S.: 541511

Mutsumi Kawai (Chm & Pres)

CHIESI FARMACEUTICI SPA
Via Palermo 26 A ingresso Via G
Chiesi 1, 43122, Parma, Italy
Tel.: (39) 05212791
Web Site:
http://www.chiesigroup.com
Year Founded: 1935
Sales Range: $1-4.9 Billion
Emp.: 4,800
Pharmaceuticals Mfr
N.A.I.C.S.: 325412
Alessandro Chiesi (Head-Europe
Reg)

Subsidiaries:

Amryt Pharma plc   (1)
Dept 920A 196 High Road Wood Green,
London, N22 8HH, United Kingdom
Tel.: (44) 35315180200
Web Site: http://www.amrytpharma.com
Rev.: $222,543,000
Assets: $816,057,000
Liabilities: $459,396,000
Net Worth: $356,661,000
Earnings: $1,000,000
Emp.: 289
Fiscal Year-end: 12/31/2021
Pharmaceuticals Mfr
N.A.I.C.S.: 325412
Alan Mooney (Sec)

Subsidiary (US):

Aegerion Pharmaceuticals, Inc.   (2)
1 Main St Ste 800, Cambridge, MA 02142
Tel.: (617) 500-7867
Proprietary Pharmaceutical Product Mfr
N.A.I.C.S.: 325411
William H. Lewis (Co-Founder)

Subsidiary (Non-US):

Aegerion Pharmaceuticals S.A.S. (3)
3 rue Progin, 39300, Champagnole, France
Tel.: (33) 686112497
Pharmacies & Drug Retailer
N.A.I.C.S.: 456110

Subsidiary (US):

Chiasma, Inc.   (2)
140 Kendrick St Bldg C E, Needham, MA
02494
Tel.: (617) 928-5300
Web Site: http://www.chiasma.com
Rev.: $1,826,000
Assets: $176,338,000
Liabilities: $84,553,000
Net Worth: $91,785,000
Earnings: ($74,779,000)
Emp.: 85
Fiscal Year-end: 12/31/2020
Biopharmaceutical Mfr
N.A.I.C.S.: 325412
David M. Stack (Chm)

Subsidiary (Non-US):

Chiasma (Israel) Ltd.   (3)
5 Golda Meir Street 5th Floor, PO Box
4086, Ness Ziona, Israel
Tel.: (972) 89393888
Pharmaceuticals Product Mfr
N.A.I.C.S.: 325412

Asche Chiesi GmbH   (1)
Gasstrasse 6, 22761, Hamburg, Germany
Tel.: (49) 40897240
Web Site: http://www.asche.de
Sales Range: $125-149.9 Million
Emp.: 392
Mfr of Pharmaceuticals
N.A.I.C.S.: 325412

Chiesi Australia Pty Ltd   (1)
Suite 3 22 Gillman Street, Hawthorn East,
3123, VIC, Australia
Tel.: (61) 39 077 4486
Web Site: https://www.chiesi.com.au
Emp.: 90
Pharmaceuticals Product Mfr
N.A.I.C.S.: 325412

Chiesi Espana S.A.   (1)
Berlin 38-48 7a Planta, 08029, Barcelona,
Spain

Tel.: (34) 93494800
Web Site: http://www.chiesigroup.com
Pharmaceuticals Mfr
N.A.I.C.S.: 325412

Chiesi Farmaceutica Ltda.   (1)
Dr Rubens Gomes Bueno Street 691 14
Floor Varzea de Baixo, Sao Paulo, 04730-
000, Brazil
Tel.: (55) 113 095 2300
Web Site: https://www.chiesi.com.br
Pharmaceuticals Product Mfr
N.A.I.C.S.: 325412
Rodrigo Lorca (Pres)

Chiesi Farmaceutical Italia   (1)
Via Palermo 26/A, 43122, Parnell, Italy
Tel.: (39) 05212791
Sales Range: $25-49.9 Million
Pharmaceuticals Mfr
N.A.I.C.S.: 325412

Chiesi Hellas A.E.B.E.   (1)
Renou Poggi 1, Alimos, 174 55, Athens,
Greece
Tel.: (30) 210 617 9763
Web Site: https://www.chiesi.gr
Pharmaceuticals Product Mfr
N.A.I.C.S.: 325412

Chiesi Hellas S.A.   (1)
89 Karamanli K 30 Anapafseos Av, Vrilissia,
15235, Athens, Greece
Tel.: (30) 210 6179763
Web Site: http://www.chiesi.gr
Pharmaceutical Products Distr
N.A.I.C.S.: 424210
Stavros Theodorakis (Gen Mgr)

Chiesi Ilac Ticaret A.S.   (1)
Buyukdere Cad No 126 Ozsezen Is Merkezi
C Blok Kat 3 Esentepe, Sisli, 34394, Istan-
bul, Turkiye
Tel.: (90) 212 370 91 00
Web Site: http://www.chiesi.com.tr
Pharmaceutical Products Distr
N.A.I.C.S.: 424210

Chiesi Italia S.p.A.   (1)
Via Giacomo Chiesi 1, 43122, Parma, Italy
Tel.: (39) 0521 2791
Web Site: https://www.chiesi.it
Pharmaceuticals Product Mfr
N.A.I.C.S.: 325412
Monica Pigato (Comm Mgr)

Chiesi Ltd.   (1)
Cheadle Royal Business Park, Highfield,
Cheadle, SK8 3GY, United Kingdom
Tel.: (44) 1614885555
Web Site: http://www.chiesi.uk.com
Emp.: 250
Pharmaceuticals Mfr
N.A.I.C.S.: 325412
Ugo Di Francesco (CEO)

Chiesi Mexico, SA de CV   (1)
Av Coyoacan No 1622 Edificio 2 Piso 1 Ofi-
cina 208 Col Del Valle, Del Benito Juarez,
Mexico, Mexico
Tel.: (52) 55 4040 7244
Web Site: http://www.chiesi.mx
Pharmaceutical Products Distr
N.A.I.C.S.: 424210
Mario Muniz (Gen Mgr)

Chiesi Pharma AB   (1)
Klara Norra kyrkogata 34, 111 22, Stock-
holm, Sweden
Tel.: (46) 8 753 3520
Web Site: https://www.chiesipharma.se
Pharmaceuticals Product Mfr
N.A.I.C.S.: 325412
Olav Fromm (Gen Mgr)

Chiesi Pharmaceutical (Shanghai)
Co., Ltd   (1)
Unit 2603-2606 City Point No 666 West
Huaihai Road, Shanghai, 200052, China
Tel.: (86) 21 52588899
Web Site: http://www.chiesigroup.com
Pharmaceutical Products Distr
N.A.I.C.S.: 424210
Davide Dalle Fusine (Gen Mgr)

Chiesi Pharmaceuticals (Pvt)
Limited   (1)
57-A Block G Gulberg III, Lahore, Pakistan
Tel.: (92) 425838174
Web Site: http://www.chiesigroup.com
Pharmaceuticals Mfr

Chiesi Farmaceutici SpA—(Continued)

N.A.I.C.S.: 325412

Chiesi Pharmaceuticals BV (1)
Gebouw Glasgow Lange Kleiweg 52J, 2288
GK, Rijswijk, Netherlands
Tel.: (31) 70 413 2080
Web Site: http://www.chiesi.nl
Pharmaceutical Products Distr
N.A.I.C.S.: 424210
Maurits Huigen (Gen Mgr)

Chiesi Pharmaceuticals Inc. (1)
9605 Metical Central Dr, Rockville, MD
20850
Tel.: (301) 424-2661
Web Site: http://www.chiesi.com
Sales Range: $25-49.9 Million
Emp.: 10
Pharmaceuticals Mfr
N.A.I.C.S.: 325412

Chiesi Pharmaceuticals LLC (1)
Lesnaya str 43, 127055, Moscow, Russia
Tel.: (7) 4959671212
Web Site: http://www.chiesi.ru
Pharmaceutical Products Distr
N.A.I.C.S.: 424210
Yury Litvishchenko (Gen Mgr)

Chiesi Poland Sp. z o.o. (1)
Al Solidarnosci 117, 00-140, Warsaw, Po-
land
Tel.: (48) 22 620 14 21
Web Site: http://www.chiesi.pl
Pharmaceutical Products Distr
N.A.I.C.S.: 424210
Lokaj Krzysztof (Gen Mgr)

Chiesi Romania S.r.l. (1)
10 Venezuela Str, District 1, 01183, Bucha-
rest, Romania
Tel.: (40) 21 202 3642
Web Site: https://www.chiesi.ro
Pharmaceuticals Product Mfr
N.A.I.C.S.: 325412

Chiesi S.A. (1)
17 Avenue de l Europe Immeuble Djinn,
92277, Bois-Colombes, France
Tel.: (33) 147688899
Web Site: http://www.chiesi.fr
Sales Range: $50-74.9 Million
Emp.: 150
Pharmaceuticals Mfr
N.A.I.C.S.: 325412
Francesco Zangiacomi (Dir-Fin)

Chiesi Slovakia s.r.o. (1)
Sulekova 14, 811 06, Bratislava, Slovakia
Tel.: (421) 2 59 30 00 60
Web Site: http://www.chiesi.sk
Pharmaceutical Products Distr
N.A.I.C.S.: 424210
Jana Chovancova (Office Mgr)

Chiesi Slovenija, d.o.o (1)
Trdinova ulica 4, 1000, Ljubljana, Slovenia
Tel.: (386) 1 43 00 901
Web Site: http://www.chiesi.si
Emp.: 11
Pharmaceutical Products Distr
N.A.I.C.S.: 424210
Lucija Strmsnik (Mgr-Mktg & Field Force)

Chiesi USA Inc. (1)
175 Regency Woods Pl Ste 600, Cary, NC
27518
Web Site: https://www.chiesiusa.com
Pharmaceuticals Product Mfr
N.A.I.C.S.: 325412
Jon Zwinski (CEO & Gen Mgr)

Cornerstone Therapeutics, Inc. (1)
1255 Crescent Green Dr Ste 250, Cary, NC
27518
Tel.: (919) 678-6611
Web Site: http://www.crtx.com
Rev.: $116,084,000
Assets: $369,375,000
Liabilities: $203,202,000
Net Worth: $166,173,000
Earnings: ($11,888,000)
Emp.: 105
Fiscal Year-end: 12/31/2012
Asthma Prevention & Therapeutic Products
Mfr
N.A.I.C.S.: 325412
Kenneth McBean (Pres)

Subsidiary (Domestic):

Cornerstone BioPharma, Inc. (2)
1255 Crescent Green Dr Ste 250, Cary, NC
27518-8123
Tel.: (919) 678-6507
Pharmaceuticals Product Mfr
N.A.I.C.S.: 325412

**Farmalab Industrias Quiimicas e Far-
maceuticas Ltda** (1)
Alexandre Dumas 1658 1213 floor, Chacara
Santo Antonio, 04717-004, Sao Paulo, Bra-
zil
Tel.: (55) 01130952300
Web Site: http://www.farmalabchiesi.com.br
Pharmaceuticals Mfr
N.A.I.C.S.: 325412

Nh.Co Nutrition S.A.S. (1)
400 Avenue Roumanille, BP 309, 06906,
Sophia-Antipolis, France
Tel.: (33) 49 200 7680
Web Site: https://nhco-nutrition.com
Pharmaceuticals Product Mfr
N.A.I.C.S.: 325412

Torrex Chiesi Pharma GmbH (1)
Gonzagagasse 16/16, 10101, Vienna, Aus-
tria
Tel.: (43) 140739190
Web Site: http://www.chiesi-cee.com
Sales Range: $25-49.9 Million
Emp.: 80
Pharmaceuticals Mfr
N.A.I.C.S.: 325412

Subsidiary (Non-US):

Chiesi Bulgaria Ltd. (2)
Ofiice 104 Business Centre Serdika 83
Gyueshevo Str, 1330, Sofia, Bulgaria
Tel.: (359) 2 920 12 05
Web Site: http://www.chiesi.bg
Pharmaceutical Products Distr
N.A.I.C.S.: 424210
George Krastev (Country Mgr)

Chiesi CZ s.r.o. (2)
Na Kvetnici 33, 140 00, Prague, Czech
Republic
Tel.: (420) 261 221 745
Web Site: http://www.chiesi.cz
Pharmaceutical Products Distr
N.A.I.C.S.: 424210
Libor Pocta (Country Mgr)

CHIFENG JILONG GOLD MIN-
ING CO., LTD.
No 7 Xiaojingjia Wanfeng Road, Bei-
jing, 100080, China
Tel.: (86) 1053232323
Web Site: https://cfgold.com
600988—(SHG)
Rev.: $879,856,937
Assets: $2,463,218,948
Liabilities: $1,423,093,221
Net Worth: $1,040,125,727
Earnings: $63,336,602
Emp.: 4,000
Fiscal Year-end: 12/31/22
Gold Ore Mining Services
N.A.I.C.S.: 212220
Xiaozhao Lu (Chm)

CHIGO HOLDING LIMITED
Chigo Industrial Park Lishui, Nanhai,
Foshan, 528244, Guangdong, China
Tel.: (86) 757 85668114   Ky
Web Site: http://www.chigogroup.com
Rev.: $1,333,157,240
Assets: $1,448,834,612
Liabilities: $1,187,417,431
Net Worth: $261,417,181
Earnings: ($69,850,735)
Emp.: 11,454
Fiscal Year-end: 12/31/18
Air Conditioner Mfr
N.A.I.C.S.: 333415

CHIH LIEN INDUSTRIAL CO.,
LTD.
480 Chung Shing Road, Shin Wu
District, Taoyuan, 32749, Taiwan

Tel.: (886) 34772797
Web Site:
https://www.chihlien.com.tw
Year Founded: 1973
2024—(TAI)
Rev.: $29,969,226
Assets: $60,060,072
Liabilities: $24,063,343
Net Worth: $35,996,728
Earnings: ($1,791,654)
Emp.: 180
Fiscal Year-end: 12/31/23
Steel Wire & Steel Bar Mfr
N.A.I.C.S.: 331110
Hsieh Ren-Ho (Founder)

Subsidiaries:

**Chih Lien Industrial Co., Ltd. - Dong
Guan Factory** (1)
Chih Lien Industrial Zone Wu Sha Sec
Zhen An Road, Chang An Town, Dongguan,
Guangdong, China
Tel.: (86) 76985312723
Sales Range: $25-49.9 Million
Emp.: 96
Steel Wire & Bar Mfr
N.A.I.C.S.: 331110

**Chih Lien Industrial Co., Ltd. - Shin
Wu Factory** (1)
No 480 Chung Shing Road, Shin Wu
Hsiang, 327, Taoyuan, Taiwan
Tel.: (886) 34772797
Sales Range: $50-74.9 Million
Emp.: 155
Steel Wire & Bar Mfr
N.A.I.C.S.: 331110
Chun Shin Liu (Gen Mgr)

CHIIKISHINBUNSHA CO., LTD.
679-1 Takatsu, Chiba, Yachiyo, 276-
0036, Japan
Tel.: (81) 474803377
Web Site:
https://www.chiikinews.co.jp
Year Founded: 1984
2164—(TKS)
Rev.: $31,537,440
Assets: $13,222,880
Liabilities: $12,080,640
Net Worth: $1,142,240
Earnings: ($3,213,760)
Fiscal Year-end: 08/31/20
Newspaper Publisher; Advertising
Services
N.A.I.C.S.: 513110
Jun Yamada (Pres)

CHIKARANOMOTO HOLDINGS
CO., LTD.
1-13-14 Daimyo, Chuo-ku, Fukuoka,
810-0041, Japan
Tel.: (81) 927624445
Web Site:
https://www.chikaranomoto.com
Year Founded: 1986
3561—(TKS)
Rev.: $210,039,360
Assets: $113,883,690
Liabilities: $52,615,600
Net Worth: $61,268,090
Earnings: $14,449,460
Emp.: 581
Fiscal Year-end: 03/31/24
Restaurant Operators
N.A.I.C.S.: 722511
Shigemi Kawahara (Founder, Chm &
Pres)

CHILDREN'S HOSPITAL
TRUST
Ground Floor Nurses Residence 1
Milner Service Road, Rondebosch,
Cape Town, 7700, South Africa
Tel.: (27) 216867860
Web Site:
https://www.childrenshospital.org.za
Year Founded: 1994

Health Care Srvices
N.A.I.C.S.: 621610

CHILDRENS HOSPITAL FOUN-
DATION
Level 14 199 Grey Street, South Bris-
bane, Brisbane, 4101, QLD, Australia
Tel.: (61) 736066100
Web Site:
https://www.childrens.org.au
Year Founded: 1985
Health Care Srvices
N.A.I.C.S.: 621610

CHILE MINING TECHNOLO-
GIES INC.
Jorge Canning 1410, Nunoa, San-
tiago, Chile
Tel.: (56) 2 8131087   NV
Copper Mining Services
N.A.I.C.S.: 212230
Jorge Osvaldo Orellana (CEO)

CHILIME HYDROPOWER COM-
PANY LIMITED
Maharajgunj kapan Marga, Kath-
mandu, Nepal
Tel.: (977) 14370773
Web Site: https://www.chilime.com.np
Year Founded: 1996
CHCL—(NEP)
Rev.: $9,616,068
Assets: $402,846,547
Liabilities: $249,771,845
Net Worth: $153,074,702
Earnings: $4,177,638
Fiscal Year-end: 07/16/22
Hydro Power Generation Services
N.A.I.C.S.: 221111
Man Ghising Kul (Chm)

Subsidiaries:

**Chilime Engineering & Services Com-
pany Limited** (1)
Maharajgunj, Kathmandu, Nepal
Tel.: (977) 14016276
Web Site: https://www.chesco.com.np
Hydroelectric Power Generation Services
N.A.I.C.S.: 221111
Prajesh Bikram Thapa (CEO)

**Madhya Bhotekoshi Jalavidhyut Com-
pany Limited** (1)
Nabil Bank Tower 1st Floor Maharajgunj,
PO Box 23599, Kathmandu, Nepal
Tel.: (977) 14721641
Web Site: http://www.mbjcl.com.np
Hydroelectric Power Generation Services
N.A.I.C.S.: 221111

**Rasuwagadhi Hydropower Company
Limited** (1)
Chakrapath Maharajgunj, Kathmandu, Ne-
pal
Tel.: (977) 14371744
Web Site: https://www.rghpcl.com.np
Hydroelectric Power Generation Services
N.A.I.C.S.: 221111

**Sanjen Jalavidhyut Company
Limited** (1)
Maharajgunj Kapan Marga, Kathmandu,
Nepal
Tel.: (977) 14374275
Web Site: https://www.sjcl.com.np
Hydroelectric Power Generation Services
N.A.I.C.S.: 221111

CHILL BRANDS GROUP PLC
5 St Helen's Place, London, EC3A
6AB, United Kingdom
Tel.: (44) 2033285656
Web Site:
https://chillbrandsgroup.com
Year Founded: 2015
Industrial Gas Manufacturing
N.A.I.C.S.: 325120
Antonio Russo (Co-CEO)

CHILLED & FROZEN LOGIS-

TICS HOLDING CO., LTD.

33-8 Wakamatsucho, Shinjuku-ku,
Tokyo, 162-0056, Japan
Tel.: (81) 352918100   JP
Web Site: https://www.cflogi.co.jp
Year Founded: 2015
9099—(TKS)
Rev.: $1,073,202,240
Assets: $857,251,120
Liabilities: $414,904,160
Net Worth: $442,346,960
Earnings: $32,098,880
Emp.: 3,497
Fiscal Year-end: 03/31/22
Holding Company; Freight Forward-
ing, Logistics Services & Warehous-
ing
N.A.I.C.S.: 551112
Hiromasa Aya *(Pres)*

Subsidiaries:

Hutech Norin Co., Ltd.   (1)
33-8 Wakamatsucho, Shinjuku-ku,
162-0056, Japan
Tel.: (81) 352918111
Web Site: https://www.hutechnorin.co.jp
Emp.: 1,536
Automobile Freight Transportation Services
N.A.I.C.S.: 484110

Meito Transportation Co., Ltd.   (1)
33-8 Wakamatsu-cho, Shinjuku-ku, Tokyo,
162-0056, Japan
Web Site: http://www.meiun.co.jp
Freight Transportation Services
N.A.I.C.S.: 484110

CHILTERN CAPITAL LLP

Lion Court 25 Procter Street, London,
WC1V 6NY, United Kingdom
Tel.: (44) 2036375620
Web Site: http://chilterncapital.co.uk
Privater Equity Firm
N.A.I.C.S.: 523999
Ryan Robson *(Chm)*

Subsidiaries:

Hanmere Polythene Ltd   (1)
Blackhorse Road, Letchworth, SG6 1HD,
Herts, United Kingdom
Tel.: (44) 1462474777
Packaging Services
N.A.I.C.S.: 333993

Subsidiary (Non-US):

Amerplast Ltd.   (2)
Vestonkatu 24, PO Box 33, 33731, Tam-
pere, Finland
Tel.: (358) 10 214 200
Web Site: http://www.amerplast.com
Flexible Packaging Products Mfr
N.A.I.C.S.: 326112
Iska Nirvio *(CFO)*

Subsidiary (Non-US):

Amerplast AB   (3)
Lindovagen 72, 602 28, Norrkoping, Swe-
den
Tel.: (46) 707 46 27 22
Flexible Packaging Products Sales
N.A.I.C.S.: 424610

Amerplast Sp. z o.o.   (3)
Graniczna Street 57, 05 825, Grodzisk Ma-
zowiecki, Poland
Tel.: (48) 227385900
Sales Range: $75-99.9 Million
Flexible Packaging Products Mfr
N.A.I.C.S.: 326112
Ari Olkinuora *(Plant Mgr)*

OOO Amerplast   (3)
Moskovsky pr 22-L 41-n, 190013, Saint Pe-
tersburg, Russia
Tel.: (7) 8126002133
Sales Range: $50-74.9 Million
Emp.: 8
Flexible Packaging Products Sales
N.A.I.C.S.: 424610
Kouhta Olga *(Mng Dir)*

Strata Products Limited   (1)
Plymouth Avenue, Brookhill Industrial Es-

tate, Pinxton, NG16 6NS, Nottinghamshire,
United Kingdom
Tel.: (44) 1773510520
Web Site: http://www.strataproducts.co.uk
Emp.: 234
Plastic Packaging Product Mfr & Distr
N.A.I.C.S.: 326199
Jay Ilsen *(CEO)*

CHIMCOMPLEX S.A. BORZ-ESTI

Industriilor Street no 3, Onesti,
601124, Bacau, Romania
Tel.: (40) 234302250
Web Site: https://chimcomplex.com
Year Founded: 1954
CHOB—(BUC)
Rev.: $321,958,420
Assets: $305,346,826
Liabilities: $211,096,279
Net Worth: $94,250,547
Earnings: $23,960,402
Emp.: 1,926
Fiscal Year-end: 12/31/20
Organic Products & Chemical Pro-
ducer
N.A.I.C.S.: 324110
Stefan Vuza *(Chm)*

CHIME BALL TECHNOLOGY CO., LTD.

No 33 Ln 277 Sec 3 Changxing Rd,
Luzhu Dist, Taoyuan, Taiwan
Tel.: (886) 33249948
Web Site: https://www.cbtech.com.tw
Year Founded: 1999
1595—(TPE)
Rev.: $56,146,171
Assets: $159,633,336
Liabilities: $76,217,459
Net Worth: $83,415,877
Earnings: $7,024,107
Emp.: 81
Fiscal Year-end: 12/31/22
Hardware Product Mfr
N.A.I.C.S.: 332510
Hung-Ming Chang *(Chm)*

CHIMERA INVESTMENTS LLC

Office 410 Royal Group Headquarters
Building Khalifa Park, Abu Dhabi,
United Arab Emirates
Tel.: (971) 28886666
Web Site:
   https://chimerainvestment.com
Year Founded: 2007
Privater Equity Firm
N.A.I.C.S.: 523940
Syed Basar Shueb *(Chm)*

Subsidiaries:

Belton Financial Holding   (1)
Nile City Towers North Tower 33rd Floor
Corniche El-Nil 2005C, 11221, Cairo,
Egypt   (55.9%)
Tel.: (20) 224616300
Web Site: https://www.beltoneholding.com
Rev.: $33,093,572
Assets: $347,066,110
Liabilities: $5,871,106
Net Worth: $341,195,004
Earnings: $17,937,001
Emp.: 2,300
Fiscal Year-end: 12/31/2023
Holding Company
N.A.I.C.S.: 551112
Ahmed Abdel Gaber *(CIO)*

Subsidiary (Domestic):

Beltone Asset Management   (2)
Nile City Towers South Tower 7th Floor Cor-
niche El-Nil 2005 A, Cairo, 11221, Egypt
Tel.: (20) 2 3308 1900
Web Site: http://www.beltonefinancial.com
Sales Range: $1-9.9 Million
Asset Management Services
N.A.I.C.S.: 523940
Wael Mohamed Sayed El Mahgary *(Gen Mgr & Head-Asset Mgmt)*

Beltone Investment Banking   (2)
Nile City Towers South Tower 7th Floor Cor-
niche El-Nil 2005 A, Cairo, 11221, Egypt
Tel.: (20) 2 3308 1900
Web Site: http://www.beltonefinancial.com
Sales Range: $1-9.9 Million
Investment Banking Services
N.A.I.C.S.: 523150
Rania Afifi *(Dir-Investment Banking)*

Beltone Private Equity   (2)
Nile City Towers South Tower 7th Floor Cor-
niche El-Nil 2005 A, Cairo, 11221, Egypt
Tel.: (20) 2 2461 0300
Web Site: http://www.beltonepe.com
Sales Range: $10-24.9 Million
Privater Equity Firm
N.A.I.C.S.: 523999

Beltone Securities Brokerage   (2)
Liberty Tower 2 Wadi El-Nil Street, Mo-
handessin, Giza, Egypt
Tel.: (20) 2 3308 1800
Web Site: http://www.beltonefinancial.com
Emp.: 250
Securities Brokerage Services
N.A.I.C.S.: 523150
Amr Mosaad *(Gen Mgr & Head-Brokerage)*

CHIMERIC THERAPEUTICS LIMITED

Level 3 62 Lygon Street, Carlton,
3053, VIC, Australia
Tel.: (61) 398245254   AU
Web Site:
   https://www.chimerictherapy.com
Year Founded: 2020
CHM—(ASX)
Rev.: $2,937,816
Assets: $14,589,283
Liabilities: $10,898,395
Net Worth: $3,690,889
Earnings: ($16,898,279)
Fiscal Year-end: 06/30/23
Biotechnology Research & Develop-
ment Services
N.A.I.C.S.: 541714
Jason B. Litten *(Chief Medical Offi-
cer)*

CHIMIMPORT AD

2 Stefan Karadja Str, Sofia, 1000,
Bulgaria
Tel.: (359) 29801611   BG
Web Site: http://www.chimimport.bg
CHIM—(BUL)
Rev.: $242,581,070
Assets: $6,528,752,211
Liabilities: $5,604,995,087
Net Worth: $923,757,124
Earnings: $27,298,970
Emp.: 4,534
Fiscal Year-end: 12/31/22
Investment Holding Company
N.A.I.C.S.: 551112
Alexander Kerezov *(Deputy Chm-
Mgmt Bd)*

Subsidiaries:

Bulgaria Air AD   (1)
1 Brussels Blvd Sofia Airport, Sofia, 1540,
Bulgaria
Tel.: (359) 29373254
Web Site: http://www.air.bg
Oil Transportation Services
N.A.I.C.S.: 481111

CCB Group EAD   (1)
103 GS Rakovski Str, 1086, Sofia,
Bulgaria   (100%)
Tel.: (359) 2 926 6107
Bank Holding Company; Banking & Insur-
ance Products & Services
N.A.I.C.S.: 551111

Subsidiary (Domestic):

Central Cooperative Bank Plc   (2)
87 Tsarigradsko Shose Blvd, 1086, Sofia,
Bulgaria   (68.56%)
Tel.: (359) 29266214
Web Site: https://www.ccbank.bg
Rev.: $73,901

Assets: $4,269,557
Liabilities: $3,915,707
Net Worth: $353,850
Earnings: $20,893
Emp.: 1,783
Fiscal Year-end: 12/31/2022
Retail & Commercial Banking
N.A.I.C.S.: 522110
Ivo Kamenov *(Chm-Supervisory Bd)*

Subsidiary (Non-US):

Centralna kooperativna Banka
AD   (3)
Ul 1732 no 2, 1000, Skopje, North Macedo-
nia
Tel.: (389) 23249300
Web Site: https://www.ccbank.mk
Rev.: $11,410,521
Assets: $222,577,790
Liabilities: $198,087,713
Net Worth: $24,490,077
Earnings: $980,006
Fiscal Year-end: 12/31/2023
Commercial Banking Services
N.A.I.C.S.: 522110
Tihomir Angelov Atanasov *(Chm-
Supervisory Bd)*

TatInvestBank ZAO   (3)
ul Vishnevskogo 24, Tatarstan Republic,
420043, Kazan, Russia   (55.91%)
Tel.: (7) 843 238 0339
Web Site: http://www.tib.ru
Retail, Commercial & Investment Banking
N.A.I.C.S.: 522110

Oil and Gas Exploration and Produc-
tion Plc   (1)
2 Stefan Karadja Str, 1080, Sofia, Bulgaria
Tel.: (359) 29801611
Web Site: https://www.ogep-bg.com
Sales Range: Less than $1 Million
Oil & Gas Exploration Services
N.A.I.C.S.: 213112
Lyubomir Todorov Chakarov *(Exec Dir)*

Subsidiary (Domestic):

Bulgarian Petroleum Refinery Ltd (2)
West Industrial Zone, PO Box 81, Pleven,
5800, Bulgaria
Tel.: (359) 64 98 22 06
Web Site: http://www.bpr-bg.com
Petroleum Refining Services
N.A.I.C.S.: 324110
Isai Lazarov *(Co-Mng Dir)*

CHIMIN HEALTH MANAGE-MENT CO., LTD.

No 888 Huangyan Beiyuan Road,
Huangyan District, Taizhou, China
Tel.: (86) 57684066800
Web Site: https://www.chimin.cn
Year Founded: 1996
603222—(SHG)
Rev.: $117,547,962
Assets: $381,054,080
Liabilities: $131,925,147
Net Worth: $249,128,933
Earnings: $4,839,448
Emp.: 2,073
Fiscal Year-end: 12/31/22
Medical Instrument Mfr & Distr
N.A.I.C.S.: 339112
Lisha Li *(Chm)*

CHIMIREC

1 Rue Luzerniere, Dugny, 93440,
Saint Denis, France
Tel.: (33) 149929765
Web Site: http://www.chimirec.fr
Rev.: $20,200,000
Emp.: 70
Scrap & Waste Mats
N.A.I.C.S.: 423930
Jean Fixot *(Pres)*

Subsidiaries:

CHIMIREC AVRASYA Endustriyel Atik
San. ve Tic. Ltd.   (1)
Karadenizliler Mah Basyigit Cad No 186,
Basiskele, Kocaeli, Turkiye
Tel.: (90) 262 349 53 76

Chimirec—(Continued)

Web Site: http://www.chimirec.com.tr
Recyclable Material Distr
N.A.I.C.S.: 423930

Chimirec Polska Sp. z o.o. **(1)**
ul Chelmzynska 180 C, 04-464, Warsaw,
Poland
Tel.: (48) 22 437 97 00
Web Site: http://www.chimirec.pl
Recyclable Material Distr
N.A.I.C.S.: 423930

CHIMPHARM JSC

Rashidova Street 81, 160019, Shymkent, Kazakhstan
Tel.: (7) 72525610120
Web Site: http://www.santo.kz
Emp.: 1,000
Pharmaceuticals Mfr
N.A.I.C.S.: 325412
Jiri Urbanec *(CEO)*

CHIN CHIN AGRO-INDUSTRIAL COMPANY

Km 2nd Of Fariman Rd First Subway-Beside Sugar Factory,
Mashhad, Razavi Khorasan, Iran
Tel.: (98) 5113920229
Year Founded: 1974
CHCH1—(THE)
Sales Range: Less than $1 Million
Emp.: 117
Food Products Mfr
N.A.I.C.S.: 311999

CHIN HIN GROUP BERHAD

A-1-9 Pusat Perdagangan Kuchai, No
2 Jalan 1/127 off Jalan Kuchai Lama,
58200, Kuala Lumpur, Wilayah
Persekutuan, Malaysia
Tel.: (60) 379817878
Web Site:
https://www.chinhingroup.com
Year Founded: 1974
CHINHIN—(KLS)
Rev.: $344,900,539
Assets: $434,238,870
Liabilities: $292,373,841
Net Worth: $141,865,029
Earnings: $21,369,779
Emp.: 1,734
Fiscal Year-end: 12/31/22
Building Materials Distributor
N.A.I.C.S.: 444180
Chiau Beng Teik *(Deputy Chm)*

Subsidiaries:

Chin Hin Concrete (KL) Sdn Bhd **(1)**
A-1-9 Pusat Perdagangan Kuchai No 2
Jalan 1/127 Off Jalan, Kuchai Lama, 58200,
Kuala Lumpur, Wilayah Persekutuan, Malaysia
Tel.: (60) 379815828
Mixed Concrete Mfr
N.A.I.C.S.: 327320
K. C. Kua *(Gen Mgr-Sls & Mktg-Central Region)*

Chin Hin Concrete (North) Sdn
Bhd **(1)**
No 46A Jalan Raja Uda Pusat Perniagaan
Raja Uda, 12300, Butterworth, Pulau
Pinang, Malaysia
Tel.: (60) 43102788
Mixed Concrete Mfr
N.A.I.C.S.: 327320
Mohd Fairus *(Engr-QC)*

Chin Hin Group Property Berhad **(1)**
No 2 Jalan 1/127 off Jalan Kuchai Lama,
Kuala Lumpur Wilayah Persekutuan, 58200,
Kuala Lumpur, Penang, Malaysia **(50.8%)**
Tel.: (60) 79817878
Web Site: https://www.chinhingroup.com
Rev.: $69,209,573
Assets: $164,359,015
Liabilities: $112,933,113
Net Worth: $51,425,901
Earnings: $2,253,502
Emp.: 474

Fiscal Year-end: 12/31/2022
Commercial Vehicles Mfr
N.A.I.C.S.: 336390
Li Ling Foo *(Co-Sec)*

Subsidiary (Non-US):

BKCV Sdn Bhd **(2)**
Tel.: (60) 45931504
Investment Services
N.A.I.C.S.: 523999

Subsidiary (Domestic):

BKGM Industries Sdn Bhd **(2)**
1177 Jalan Dato Keramat, Seberang Perai
Selatan, 14300, Nibong Tebal, Penang,
Malaysia
Tel.: (60) 45931504
Investment Services
N.A.I.C.S.: 523999

Boon Koon Fleet Management Sdn
Bhd **(2)**
No 998 Ground Floor Jalan Tok Kangar,
Juru, 14100, Simpang Empat, Penang, Malaysia
Tel.: (60) 4 351 7699
Auto Fleet Management Services
N.A.I.C.S.: 423110

Boon Koon Services & Parts Sdn
Bhd **(2)**
No 998 Ground Flor Jalan Tok Kangar,
Juru, 14100, Simpang Empat, Penang, Malaysia
Tel.: (60) 4 501 7177
Automotive Parts & Services
N.A.I.C.S.: 423120

Boon Koon Vehicles industries Sdn
Bhd **(2)**
1177 Jalan Dato Keramat, Nibong Tebal,
Seberang Perai Selatan, 14300, Nibong
Tebal, Penang, Malaysia
Tel.: (60) 45931504
Vehicle Mfr
N.A.I.C.S.: 336110

CNMY Trucks Sdn Bhd **(2)**
No 1767 Jalan Titi Timbul, Seberang Perai
Selatan, 14300, Nibong Tebal, Penang,
Malaysia
Tel.: (60) 4 593 1212
Truck Mfr & Sales
N.A.I.C.S.: 336120

First Peninsula Credit Sdn Bhd **(2)**
No 998 1st Floor Jalan Tok Kangar Auto
Link, Suru Seberang Perai Tengah, 14100,
Simpang Empat, Malaysia
Tel.: (60) 4 508 0877
Renting Services
N.A.I.C.S.: 522291

G-Cast UHPC Sdn Bhd **(1)**
A-1-3A Pusat Perdagangan Kuchai No 2
Jalan 1/127 off Jalan, Kuchai Lama, 58200,
Kuala Lumpur, Malaysia
Tel.: (60) 378316399
Web Site: https://www.g-castuhpc.com.my
Mixed Concrete Mfr
N.A.I.C.S.: 327320

Metex Steel Sdn Bhd **(1)**
A-1-1 & A-2-1 Pusat Perdagangan Kuchai
No 2 1/127 Off Jalan, 58200, Kuala Lumpur, Malaysia
Tel.: (60) 37 984 9168
Web Site: https://www.metex.com.my
Steel Products Mfr
N.A.I.C.S.: 331110
Kent Khong *(Sls Mgr)*

Midah Industries Sdn Bhd **(1)**
36-3 Jalan 10/116B Kuchai Entrepreneurs
Park Off Jalan, Kuchai Lama, 58200, Kuala
Lumpur, Malaysia
Tel.: (60) 379833391
Web Site: http://www.midah.com.my
Wood Product Mfr & Distr
N.A.I.C.S.: 321999
William Tan *(Mgr-Bus Dev)*

Subsidiary (Domestic):

Epic Diversity Sdn Bhd **(2)**
36-2 Jalan Kuchai Maju 11 Kuchai Entrepreneurs Park Off Jalan, Kuchai Lama,
58200, Kuala Lumpur, Malaysia
Tel.: (60) 379813223

Web Site: http://www.epicloc.com
Door Security Lock Mfr
N.A.I.C.S.: 332510

Starken AAC Sdn Bhd **(1)**
No A-1-3A Pusat Perdagangan Kuchai No 2
1/127 Off Jalan, Kuchai Lama, 58200,
Kuala Lumpur, Malaysia
Tel.: (60) 379838068
Web Site: https://www.starken.com.my
Mixed Concrete Mfr
N.A.I.C.S.: 327320

Subsidiary (Domestic):

G-Cast Concrete Sdn Bhd **(2)**
A-1-3A Pusat Perdagangan Kuchai No 2
Jalan 1/127 Off Jalan, Kuchai Lama, 58200,
Kuala Lumpur, Wilayah Persekutuan, Malaysia
Tel.: (60) 379828168
Web Site: https://www.g-cast.com.my
Mixed Concrete Mfr
N.A.I.C.S.: 327320
Jun Hoe Wong *(Sls Mgr)*

MI Polymer Concrete Pipes Sdn
Bhd **(2)**
Lot PLO 285 PTD 34300 Jalan Wawasan 9,
Sri Gading Industrial Area Batu Pahat,
83300, Johor, Malaysia
Tel.: (60) 74558393
Web Site: https://www.mipipes.net
Concrete Pipe Mfr
N.A.I.C.S.: 327332

Starken Drymix Solutions Sdn
Bhd **(2)**
A-1-3A Pusat Perdagangan Kuchai No 2
Jalan 1/127 Off Jalan, Kuchai Lama, 58200,
Kuala Lumpur, Malaysia
Tel.: (60) 379828066
Web Site:
https://www.starkendrymix.com.my
Cement Mfr
N.A.I.C.S.: 327310
Natasha Hue *(Mktg Mgr)*

Starken Paint Sdn Bhd **(2)**
A-1-3A Pusat Perdagangan Kuchai No 2
Jalan 1/127 Off Jalan, Kuchai Lama, 58200,
Kuala Lumpur, Malaysia
Tel.: (60) 377341355
Web Site: https://www.starkenpaint.com
Paint Product Mfr & Distr
N.A.I.C.S.: 325510

Stradaverse Sdn. Bhd. **(1)**
A-16-07 Tower A Pinnacle Petaling Jaya
Lorong Utara C, 46200, Petaling Jaya, Malaysia
Tel.: (60) 379323376
Web Site: https://www.stradaverse.ai
Information Technology Services
N.A.I.C.S.: 541519

CHIN HUAY PUBLIC COMPANY LIMITED

181 Tha Kham Rd Samae Dam Bang
Khun Thian, Bangkok, 10150, Thailand
Tel.: (66) 24160708
Web Site: https://www.chinhuay.com
Year Founded: 1925
CH—(THA)
Rev.: $53,336,613
Assets: $51,413,804
Liabilities: $14,522,986
Net Worth: $36,890,818
Earnings: $1,646,331
Emp.: 1,287
Fiscal Year-end: 12/31/23
Packaged Food Product Mfr
N.A.I.C.S.: 311991

CHIN POON INDUSTRIAL CO., LTD.

No 46 Nei-Tsuoh St 3rd Lin, Nei-
Tsuoh Village Lu-Chu, Taoyuan,
Hsien, Taiwan
Tel.: (886) 33222226
Web Site: https://www.chinpoon.com
2355—(TAI)
Rev.: $547,742,384
Assets: $743,697,967

Liabilities: $217,112,520
Net Worth: $526,585,447
Earnings: $24,943,686
Emp.: 5,651
Fiscal Year-end: 12/31/21
Printed Circuit Board Mfr
N.A.I.C.S.: 334412
Vincent Huang *(Chm, Pres & CEO)*

Subsidiaries:

Draco PCB Public Company
Limited **(1)**
Bangkadi Industrial Park Mu 5 152 Tiwanon
Road, Amphur Muang, Pathumthani, 12000,
Thailand
Tel.: (66) 25011241
Web Site: https://www.dracopcb.com
Emp.: 550
Printed Circuit Board Mfr
N.A.I.C.S.: 334418
Jittima Neoythong *(Sr Mgr-Mktg & Sls)*

CHIN TECK PLANTATIONS BERHAD

Suite 2B-3A-2 Block 2B Level 3A
Plaza Sentral Jalan Stesen Sentral 5,
Kuala Lumpur Sentral, 50470, Kuala
Lumpur, Malaysia
Tel.: (60) 322614633
Web Site:
https://www.chinteck.com.my
CHINTEK—(KLS)
Rev.: $43,528,894
Assets: $192,874,018
Liabilities: $11,114,708
Net Worth: $181,759,310
Earnings: $11,295,162
Fiscal Year-end: 08/31/23
Oil Palms Cultivation & Palm Oil Mfr
N.A.I.C.S.: 115115
Kok Tiong Gan *(CFO & Sec)*

CHIN WELL HOLDINGS BERHAD

1586 MK 11 Lorong Perusahaan
Utama 1 Bukit Tengah Industrial
Park, Bukit Mertajam, 14000, Penang,
Malaysia
Tel.: (60) 45075858 **MY**
Web Site:
https://www.chinwell.com.my
CHINWEL—(KLS)
Rev.: $96,603,606
Assets: $161,031,845
Liabilities: $16,619,491
Net Worth: $144,412,354
Earnings: $8,336,197
Emp.: 600
Fiscal Year-end: 06/30/23
Fastener Mfr
N.A.I.C.S.: 339993
Yung Chuan Tsai *(Mng Dir)*

Subsidiaries:

Chin Herr Industries (M) Sdn.
Bhd. **(1)**
1500 MK 11 Lorong Perusahaan Utama
Satu, Bukit Tengah Industrial Estate, 14000,
Bukit Mertajam, Penang, Malaysia
Tel.: (60) 45076888
Web Site: https://www.chinherr.com
Iron & Wire Product Mfr
N.A.I.C.S.: 331110

CHINA 21ST CENTURY EDUCATION GROUP LTD.

Zhongdian Information Building 8th
Floor No 356 Zhongshan West Road,
Qiaoxi District, Shijiazhuang, 050000,
China
Tel.: (86) 31166036112 **Ky**
Web Site:
http://www.21centuryedu.com
1598—(HKG)
Rev.: $43,791,883
Assets: $274,546,865
Liabilities: $172,635,980
Net Worth: $101,910,884

Earnings: $3,751,207
Emp.: 1,202
Fiscal Year-end: 12/31/22
Educational Support Services
N.A.I.C.S.: 611710
Yunong Li *(Founder & Chm)*

CHINA 33 MEDIA GROUP LIMITED

Unit 2001 Tower A Haiyunxuan 99
Lianhui Road Xizhimen North Road,
Haidian District, Beijing, China
Tel.: (86) 31506788   Ky
Web Site:
http://www.china33media.com
8087—(HKG)
Rev.: $9,975,280
Assets: $51,229,012
Liabilities: $39,431,902
Net Worth: $11,797,110
Earnings: ($8,074,123)
Emp.: 27
Fiscal Year-end: 12/31/22
Advertising Services
N.A.I.C.S.: 541850
Deqing Ruan *(Chm & Officer-Compliance)*

CHINA 9D CONSTRUCTION GROUP, INC.

4F Jia De Plaza 118 Qing Chun
Road, Hangzhou, 310000, Zhejiang,
China
Tel.: (86) 571 8722 0222   NV
Sales Range: $50-74.9 Million
Architectural & Construction Services
N.A.I.C.S.: 541310
Zheng Ying *(Chm & CEO)*

CHINA AEROSPACE INTERNATIONAL HOLDINGS LIMITED

Room 1103-1107A 11/F One Harbourfront, 18 Tak Fung Street Hunghom,
Kowloon, China (Hong Kong)
Tel.: (852) 21938888   HK
Web Site: http://www.casil-group.com
0031—(HKG)
Rev.: $573,945,330
Assets: $1,946,393,070
Liabilities: $698,848,538
Net Worth: $1,247,544,533
Earnings: ($32,222,055)
Emp.: 5,715
Fiscal Year-end: 12/31/22
Aerospace Equipment Mfr
N.A.I.C.S.: 334511
Ken Ka Kin Chan *(Sec)*

Subsidiaries:

CASIL Optoelectronic Product Development Limited   (1)
18/F China Aerospace Centre 143 Hoi Bun
Road Kwun Tong, Kowloon, China (Hong
Kong)
Tel.: (852) 23307800
Web Site: http://www.casil-module.com.hk
Liquid Crystal Display Mfr & Distr
N.A.I.C.S.: 334419

Chee Yuen Plastic Products (Huizhou) Company Limited   (1)
Zhongkai Avenue, Aerospace Technology
Industrial Park, Huizhou, 516001, Guangdong, China
Tel.: (86) 7522606090
Plastics Product Mfr
N.A.I.C.S.: 326199

Plant (Domestic):

Chee Yuen Plastic Products (Huizhou) Company Limited - Battery
Factory   (2)
Building 1 Aerospace Technology Huizhou
Industrial Park, Zhongkai Avenue, Huizhou,
516001, Guangdong, China
Tel.: (86) 7522606099
Battery Mfr
N.A.I.C.S.: 335910

Cheefat Metal Products & Plastic
Plating Co., Ltd.   (1)
Building 404 Longxi Electroplating Base,
Boluo County, Huizhou, Guangdong, China
Tel.: (86) 752 260 6595
Web Site: https://en.cheefat.com
Emp.: 1,800
Mold Product Mfr
N.A.I.C.S.: 333511

Cheeyuen Electronics Technology
(Huizhou) Co., Ltd.   (1)
Qing Cao Wo Industrial Zone Zhen Long
HuiYang District, Huizhou, Guangdong,
China
Tel.: (86) 7523086888
Packaging Products Mfr
N.A.I.C.S.: 339991

Cheeyuen Surface Treament (Huizhou) Co., Ltd.   (1)
Building 404 Plating Industrial Base Longxi
Town Boluo County, Huizhou, Guangdong,
China
Tel.: (86) 7526292765
Mold Product Mfr
N.A.I.C.S.: 333511

Conhui (Huizhou) Semiconductor
Company Limited   (1)
Block 8 No 49 Zhong Kai Road, China
Aerospace Industrial Park, Huizhou, Guangdong, China
Tel.: (86) 7522609600
Emp.: 1,500
Liquid Crystal Display Mfr & Distr
N.A.I.C.S.: 334419

Hong Yuen Electronics Limited   (1)
Room 401 4th Floor No 143 Hoi Bun Road,
Kwun Tong, Kowloon, China (Hong Kong)
Tel.: (852) 2 363 9241
Web Site: https://www.pcb.com.cn
Printed Circuit Board Mfr & Distr
N.A.I.C.S.: 334412

Subsidiary (Non-US):

Dong guan Hong Yuen Electronics
Ltd.   (2)
The 4th Industrial Area of Nanzha, Humen,
Dongguan, Guangdong, China
Tel.: (86) 76988628888
Web Site: https://www.pcb.com.cn
Emp.: 1,800
Printed Circuit Board Mfr
N.A.I.C.S.: 334412

Huizhou Jeckson Electric Company
Limited   (1)
China Aerospace Industrial Park 49 Zhong
kai NO 2 Road, Huizhou, 516006, Guangdong, China
Tel.: (86) 7522609015
Electronic Products Mfr
N.A.I.C.S.: 335999

Shenzhen Chee Yuen Plastic Products Company Limited   (1)
Shenkeng Industrial Village Henggang
Town, Shenzhen, 516001, Guangdong,
China
Tel.: (86) 75528638966
Plastic Product Mfr & Distr
N.A.I.C.S.: 326199

CHINA AEROSPACE SCIENCE AND INDUSTRY CORPORATION LIMITED

china Aerospace Building NO 8A
Fucheng Road, Haidian District, Beijing, China
Tel.: (86) 1068373522
Web Site: https://www.casic.com
Sales Range: Less than $1 Million
Emp.: 145,987
Aerospace Development Services
N.A.I.C.S.: 541715

CHINA AEROSPACE SCIENCE AND TECHNOLOGY CORPORATION

16 Fucheng Road, Haidian District,
Beijing, 100048, China
Tel.: (86) 1068767492

Web Site:
https://www.spacechina.com
Year Founded: 1999
Sales Range: Less than $1 Million
Space Research & Development Services
N.A.I.C.S.: 541715
Chen Mingbo *(Chm)*

Subsidiaries:

China Satellite Communications Co.,
Ltd.   (1)
Building A China Satellite Communications
Tower No 65 Zhichun Road, Haidian District, Beijing, 100190, China
Tel.: (86) 1062586600
Web Site: http://www.chinasatcom.com
Rev.: $383,760,768
Assets: $3,148,906,869
Liabilities: $453,104,061
Net Worth: $2,695,802,808
Earnings: $129,270,660
Fiscal Year-end: 12/31/2022
Telecommunication Servicesb
N.A.I.C.S.: 517810
Zhongbao Li *(Chm)*

CHINA AEROSPACE TIMES ELECTRONICS CO., LTD.

No1 Fengying East Road, Haidian
District, Beijing, 100094, China
Tel.: (86) 1088106362
Web Site: http://www.catec-ltd.cn
Year Founded: 1986
600879—(SHG)
Rev.: $2,453,581,471
Assets: $6,210,572,940
Liabilities: $3,517,270,712
Net Worth: $2,693,302,228
Earnings: $85,718,468
Fiscal Year-end: 12/31/22
Aerospace Equipment Mfr & Distr
N.A.I.C.S.: 334220
Jiang Liang *(Chm)*

CHINA AGRI PRODUCTS EXCHANGE LIMITED

Suite 3202 32/F Skyline Tower 39
Wang Kwong Road, Kowloon Bay,
Kowloon, China (Hong Kong)
Tel.: (852) 2 312 8329
Web Site: http://www.cnagri-products.com
0149—(HKG)
Rev.: $112,042,991
Assets: $708,240,530
Liabilities: $404,939,933
Net Worth: $303,300,597
Earnings: $4,776,903
Emp.: 1,115
Fiscal Year-end: 03/31/22
Agricultural Products Development
N.A.I.C.S.: 484220
Raymond Sui Wah Leung *(CEO & Sec)*

CHINA AGRI-BUSINESS, INC.

Building 2 Unit 1 15th Floor Ling Xian
Xin Cheng, 86 Gaoxin Road, Hi-Tech
Industrial Devel Zone, Xi'an, 710065,
Shaanxi, China
Tel.: (86) 29 6859 6556   MD
Web Site: http://www.chinaagri-business.com
Sales Range: $10-24.9 Million
Emp.: 138
Biochemical Agricultural Products Developer & Mfr
N.A.I.C.S.: 325320
Liping Deng *(Pres & CEO)*

CHINA AIRCRAFT LEASING GROUP HOLDINGS LIMITED

32/F Far East Finance Centre 16
Harcourt Road, Admiralty, Hong
Kong, China (Hong Kong)
Tel.: (852) 37598428   Ky
Web Site: https://www.calc.com.hk

Year Founded: 2006
1848—(HKG)
Rev.: $531,802,755
Assets: $7,054,840,200
Liabilities: $6,257,172,533
Net Worth: $797,667,668
Earnings: $27,499,710
Emp.: 169
Fiscal Year-end: 12/31/22
Aircraft Leasing
N.A.I.C.S.: 532411
Richard Luo *(Head-Technical & Asset Mgmt)*

Subsidiaries:

Universal Asset Management,
Inc.   (1)
5350 Poplar Ave Ste 390, Memphis, TN
38119-0931
Tel.: (901) 682-4064
Web Site: https://www.uaminc.com
Aviation Asset Management, Aircraft Disassembly Services & Commercial Aviation Aftermarket Component Whslr
N.A.I.C.S.: 488190
Jeff Sabo *(Sr VP)*

CHINA AIRLINES LTD.

No 1 Hangzhan S Rd, Dayuan Dist,
Taoyuan, 33758, Taiwan
Tel.: (886) 33998888   TW
Web Site: http://www.china-airlines.com
Year Founded: 1959
2610—(TAI)
Rev.: $6,043,911,934
Assets: $9,524,262,402
Liabilities: $6,990,534,449
Net Worth: $2,533,727,953
Earnings: $244,324,560
Emp.: 11,429
Fiscal Year-end: 12/31/23
Passenger & Cargo Air Transportation Services
N.A.I.C.S.: 481111
Su-Chien Hsieh *(Chm & Pres)*

Subsidiaries:

Abacus Distribution Systems Taiwan
Ltd.   (1)
15th Floor No 57 Fu-Hsin North Road, Taipei, Taiwan   **(93.93%)**
Tel.: (886) 227516988
Web Site: http://www.abacus.com.tw
Sales Range: $25-49.9 Million
Emp.: 110
Computer System Design Services
N.A.I.C.S.: 541512

CAL-Dynasty International, Inc.   (1)
200 Continental Blvd, El Segundo, CA
90245   **(100%)**
Tel.: (310) 322-2888
Web Site: https://www.china-airlines.com
Scheduled Passenger Air Transportation &
Various Travel Services
N.A.I.C.S.: 481111

Subsidiary (Domestic):

Dynasty Hotel of Hawaii, Inc   (2)
1830 Ala Moana Blvd Rm 212, Honolulu, HI
96815-1602
Tel.: (808) 955-0088
Web Site:
http://www.ramadaplazawaikiki.com
Home Management Services
N.A.I.C.S.: 721110
Roger Chang *(Gen Mgr)*

Dynasty Properties Co., Ltd.   (2)
750 N 43rd St Apt 47, Grand Forks, ND
58203-1903   **(100%)**
Tel.: (701) 741-2574
Real Estate Agency
N.A.I.C.S.: 531210

Ramada Waikiki   (2)
1830 Ala Moana Blvd, Honolulu, HI
96815-1602   **(100%)**
Tel.: (808) 955-1111
Sales Range: $10-24.9 Million
Emp.: 50
Hotel

China Airlines Ltd.—(Continued)

N.A.I.C.S.: 721110
Christine Wang (Gen Mgr)

Cal Hotel Co. Ltd. (1)
2008 Shattuck Ave, Berkeley, CA
94704-1117 **(100%)**
Tel.: (510) 849-9479
Sales Range: $10-24.9 Million
Emp.: 1
Hotels & Motels
N.A.I.C.S.: 721110
Albert Ho (Gen Mgr)

**China Pacific Catering Services
Ltd.** (1)
No 22 Lane 156 Section 2 Haishan Road,
Luzhu District, 338, Taoyuan,
Taiwan **(51%)**
Tel.: (886) 3 354 1000
Web Site: https://www.cpcs.com.tw
Sales Range: $150-199.9 Million
Emp.: 800
Airline Kitchen Services; Catering Services
N.A.I.C.S.: 722330

**Dynasty Aerotech International
Corp.** (1)
337 Hang Qin Taoyuan City Park Road on
the 6th No 6 Hangqin S Rd, Taiwan
Taoyuan International Airport Dayuan Dist,
Taoyuan, Taiwan
Tel.: (886) 33833242
Web Site: http://www.dynasty-aerotech.com
Aircraft Maintenance & Repair Services
N.A.I.C.S.: 488190

Dynasty Holidays, Inc. (1)
You Ginza Dai Ni Bldg 5Fl 197, Chuo-ku,
Tokyo, 104 0061, Japan **(51%)**
Tel.: (81) 355240880
Web Site: http://www.dynasty-holidays.com
Sales Range: $10-24.9 Million
Emp.: 30
Travel Agencies
N.A.I.C.S.: 561510
Scott Shih (Pres)

Hwa Hsia Company Ltd. (1)
HangZhan S Rd Dayuan Township,
Taoyun, 33758, Taiwan **(100%)**
Tel.: (886) 33833242
Web Site: http://www.hh-cal.com.tw
Emp.: 500
Airport Terminal Ground Service-Airline
Cabin Cleaning, Cargo Container Mainte-
nance & Aircraft Accessory Cleaning
N.A.I.C.S.: 488190
Jerry Chih-Yuan Yang (Gen Mgr)

Mandarin Airlines (1)
13F 134 Sec 3 Minsheng E Rd, Taipei,
Taiwan **(93.99%)**
Tel.: (886) 227171230
Web Site: http://www.mandarin-airlines.com
Sales Range: $125-149.9 Million
Emp.: 300
Scheduled Passenger Air Transportation
N.A.I.C.S.: 481111

Taiwan Air Cargo Terminal Ltd. (1)
No 10-1 Hangqin N Rd, Dayuan Dist,
Taoyuan, 33758, Taiwan **(54%)**
Tel.: (886) 3 398 7877
Web Site: https://www.tactl.com
Sales Range: $350-399.9 Million
Emp.: 600
Aviation Cargo Transportation Services
N.A.I.C.S.: 488190
S. C. Hsieh (CEO)

**Taiwan Aircraft Maintenance & Engi-
neering Co., Ltd.** (1)
No 7 Hangqin S Rd, Dayuan Dist, Taoyuan,
33758, Taiwan
Tel.: (886) 33833521
Web Site: http://www.taiwan-tameco.com
Aircraft Maintenance & Repair Services
N.A.I.C.S.: 488190

CHINA ALL ACCESS (HOLD-INGS) LIMITED

Room 805 8/F Greenfield Tower Con-
cordia Plaza 1 Science Museum
Road, T S T, Kowloon, China (Hong
Kong)
Tel.: (852) 3579 2368

Web Site:
http://www.chinaallaccess.com
Year Founded: 2003
Rev.: $721,859,221
Assets: $593,861,566
Liabilities: $510,911,218
Net Worth: $82,950,348
Earnings: ($380,799,403)
Emp.; 1,991
Fiscal Year-end: 12/31/19
Integrated Information Communica-
tion Application Solutions Designer &
Developer
N.A.I.C.S.: 334290
Yuen Ming Chan (Chm)

Subsidiaries:

**All Access Communication Technol-
ogy (Shenzhen) Limited** (1)
6th Fl North Building Wandelai Tower Sci-
ence and Technology Park, Shenzhen,
China
Tel.: (86) 75586360009
Communication Equipment Whslr
N.A.I.C.S.: 423690

**Beijing All Access Noter Communica-
tion Technology Co., Limited** (1)
No 22 Wanyuan Street BDA, Beijing, China
Tel.: (86) 1087123500
Communication Equipment Whslr
N.A.I.C.S.: 423690

**Guangdong All Access Noter Com-
munication Technology Co.,
Limited** (1)
Suite 1604 R and F Yingxin Building 28
Hua Xia Road, Tianhe, Guangzhou, China
Tel.: (86) 2085601670
Communication Equipment Whslr
N.A.I.C.S.: 423690

**Hebei Noter Communication Technol-
ogy Co., Limited** (1)
7/F Digital Building No 60 West Avenue,
Shijiazhuang, Hebei, China
Tel.: (86) 31186685582
Communication Equipment Whslr
N.A.I.C.S.: 423690

**Shanghai All Access Noter Communi-
cation Technology Co., Limited** (1)
No 1403 Minsheng Road, Pudong New
Area, Shanghai, China
Tel.: (86) 2133927568
Communication Equipment Whslr
N.A.I.C.S.: 423690

CHINA ALUMINUM CANS HOLDINGS LIMITED

Unit G 20/F Golden Sun Centre
59/67 Bonham Strand West, Sheung
Wan, China (Hong Kong)
Tel.: (852) 25482780
Web Site: http://www.6898hk.com
6898—(HKG)
Rev.: $26,840,535
Assets: $50,156,333
Liabilities: $3,959,895
Net Worth: $46,196,438
Earnings: $2,660,543
Emp.: 237
Fiscal Year-end: 12/31/22
Aluminum Aerosol Cans Mfr
N.A.I.C.S.: 332431
Wan Tsang Lin (Founder, Chm & Gen
Mgr)

Subsidiaries:

**Euro Asia Packaging (Guangdong)
Co., Ltd.** (1)
No 5 Yabai South Road National Health
Technology Industrial Base, Torch Develop-
ment Zone, Zhongshan, 528437, Guang-
dong, China
Tel.: (86) 76085288589
Web Site: https://www.euroasia-p.com
Aluminum Aerosol Cans Mfr
N.A.I.C.S.: 332431

**Guangzhou Botny Chemical Co.,
Ltd.** (1)

No 628 North Jufeng Road, Aotou Con-
ghua, Guangzhou, 510940, Guangdong,
China
Tel.: (86) 2087879888
Web Site: https://www.botny.com
Automotive Maintenance Product Mfr &
Whslr
N.A.I.C.S.: 333310

CHINA ALUMINUM INTERNA-TIONAL ENGINEERING COR-PORATION LIMITED

Building C 99 No Xingshikou Road,
Haidian District, Beijing, 100093,
China
Tel.: (86) 1082406806
Web Site: http://www.chalieco.com.cn
Year Founded: 2003
2068—(HKG)
Rev.: $3,327,104,980
Assets: $6,653,736,918
Liabilities: $5,185,846,879
Net Worth: $1,467,890,040
Earnings: $28,764,735
Emp.: 12,219
Fiscal Year-end: 12/31/22
Nonferrous Metals
N.A.I.C.S.: 331529
Jian Zhang (CFO)

Subsidiaries:

**China Aluminum Great Wall Con-
struction Co., Ltd.** (1)
81 Runan Road, Shangjie District,
Zhengzhou, 450041, China
Tel.: (86) 37168923623
Emp.: 800
Nonferrous Metal Foundry Mfr
N.A.I.C.S.: 331529
Zhang Zhongwei (Gen Mgr)

**China Nonferrous Metals Industry's
Twelfth Metallurgical Construction
Co., Ltd.** (1)
No 239 Aluminum Avenue Aluminum Base,
Hejin, 43304, Shanxi, China
Tel.: (86) 3598880201
Nonferrous Metal Foundry Mfr
N.A.I.C.S.: 331529

**China Nonferrous Metals Processing
Technology Co., Ltd.** (1)
No 1 Xiyuan Road, Luoyang, 471039,
Henan, China
Tel.: (86) 3796 487 6691
Web Site: https://www.cnpt.com.cn
Nonferrous Metal Foundry Mfr
N.A.I.C.S.: 331529

**Henan Ninth Metallurgical Construc-
tion Co., Ltd.** (1)
No 39 Changchun Road, High and New
Technology Industries Development Zone,
Zhengzhou, 450001, Henan, China
Tel.: (86) 37160995066
Web Site: http://www.hnjyjs.com
Nonferrous Metal Foundry Mfr
N.A.I.C.S.: 331529

**Sixth Metallurgical Construction Com-
pany of China Nonferrous Metals In-
dustry Co., Ltd.** (1)
No 36 Huaihe Road, Zhengzhou, 450006,
Henan, China
Tel.: (86) 37167178509
Nonferrous Metal Foundry Mfr
N.A.I.C.S.: 331529

CHINA ANCHU ENERGY STORAGE GROUP LIMITED

Fordoo Industrial Zone E12 Xunmei
Industrial Zone, Fengze District,
Quanzhou, Fujian, China
Tel.: (86) 59522137999
Web Site: http://www.fordoo.cn
2399—(HKG)
Rev.: $84,789,104
Assets: $187,244,741
Liabilities: $126,120,758
Net Worth: $61,123,982
Earnings: ($12,445,477)
Emp.: 133

Fiscal Year-end: 12/31/22
Men's Clothing Mfr
N.A.I.C.S.: 315250
Kin Sun Kwok (Founder & Chm)

CHINA ANIMAL HEALTHCARE LTD.

6 Kangding Street Beijing Economic-
Technological Development Area,
Beijing, 100176, China
Tel.: (86) 10 51571908 BM
Web Site:
http://www.chinanimalhealthcare.com
Sales Range: $125-149.9 Million
Emp.: 2,600
Animal Drug Mfr
N.A.I.C.S.: 325412
Yangang Wang (Chm & CEO)

CHINA ANIMAL HUSBANDRY INDUSTRY CO., LTD.

Building 16-17 Area 8 ABP 188 South
Fourth Ring West Road, Fengtai Dis-
trict, Beijing, 100070, China
Tel.: (86) 1063701111
Web Site: https://www.cahic.com
Year Founded: 1998
600195—(SHG)
Rev.: $827,170,110
Assets: $1,114,411,830
Liabilities: $224,060,934
Net Worth: $890,350,896
Earnings: $77,229,589
Fiscal Year-end: 12/31/22
Animal Drug Product Mfr
N.A.I.C.S.: 325412
Hou Shizhong (Chm-Supervisory Bd)

Subsidiaries:

QYH Biotech Co., Ltd. (1)
Building No 20 Part 11 ABP No 188 South-
west 4th Ring Road, Fengtai District, Bei-
jing, 100070, China
Tel.: (86) 1083672069
Web Site: https://bioqyh.cnadc.com.cn
Veterinary Biological Product Mfr & Distr
N.A.I.C.S.: 325412

**Shandong Shengli Bio-Engineering
Co., Ltd.** (1)
2906 Building 1-B Jinan Pharm Valley
Gangxingsan road High-tech Zone, Jinan,
250000, Shandong, China
Tel.: (86) 53188725615
Web Site: https://shenglibio.cnadc.com.cn
Veterinary Biological Product Mfr & Distr
N.A.I.C.S.: 325412

CHINA AOYUAN GROUP LIM-ITED

Aoyuan Tower No 48 Wanhui Yi
Road, Panyu District, Guangzhou,
511445, Guangdong, China
Tel.: (86) 2038686666 Ky
Web Site: https://en.aoyuan.com.cn
Year Founded: 1996
3883—(HKG)
Rev.: $2,627,034,509
Assets: $32,913,394,254
Liabilities: $35,389,614,452
Net Worth: ($2,476,220,198)
Earnings: ($1,192,842,050)
Emp.: 9,002
Fiscal Year-end: 12/31/22
Real Estate Development Services
N.A.I.C.S.: 531390
Zi Wen Guo (Founder & Chm)

CHINA APEX GROUP LIMITED

Suite 510 Chater House 8 Connaught
Road, Central, China (Hong Kong)
Tel.: (852) 75785682111 Ky
Web Site: http://www.kee.com.cn
Year Founded: 1992
2011—(HKG)
Rev.: $27,486,195
Assets: $38,978,280
Liabilities: $12,660,368

Net Worth: $26,317,913
Earnings: $83,895
Emp.: 637
Fiscal Year-end: 12/31/22
Holding Company; Zipper Mfr
N.A.I.C.S.: 339993

Subsidiaries:

KEE (Guangdong) Garment Accessories Limited　　　　　　　　　　　　　　(1)
Xiahengtian Industrial Zone Shachong, Lishui Nanhai, Foshan, Guangdong, China
Tel.: (86) 75785682111
Web Site: http://www.kee.com.cn
Zipper Mfr
N.A.I.C.S.: 339993

KEE (Jingmen) Garment Accessories Limited　　　　　　　　　　　　　　(1)
KEE Accessories Garden Longjing Road, High-tech Industrial Zone, Jingmen, Hubei, China
Tel.: (86) 7242458778
Web Site: http://www.kee.com.cn
Zipper Mfr
N.A.I.C.S.: 339993

KEE (Zhejiang) Garment Accessories Limited　　　　　　　　　　　　　　(1)
116 Jinjia Road Jiashan Economic Development Zone, Jiashan, Jiaxing, Zhejiang, China
Tel.: (86) 57384633222
Web Site: http://www.kee.com.cn
Zipper Mfr
N.A.I.C.S.: 339993

KEE Zippers Corporation Limited　(1)
Unit B16/F YHC Tower 1 Sheung Yuet Road, Kowloon Bay, Kowloon, China (Hong Kong)
Tel.: (852) 23692288
Web Site: https://www.kee.com.cn
Zipper Mfr
N.A.I.C.S.: 339993

CHINA ARCHITECTURE DESIGN & RESEARCH GROUP
No 19 Chegongzhuang Street, Beijing, 100044, China
Tel.: (86) 10 68302001　　　　CN
Web Site: http://en.cadreg.com
Year Founded: 2001
Engineering Project Consultation, Planning, Design, Project Management & Surveying
N.A.I.C.S.: 541310
Xiu Long (Pres)

Subsidiaries:

CPG Corporation Pte Ltd.　　　　(1)
238B Thomson Rd 18-00, Tower B Novena Square, 307685, Singapore, Singapore　　　　　　　　　(100%)
Tel.: (65) 63574888
Web Site: http://www.cpgcorp.com.sg
Sales Range: $350-399.9 Million
Emp.: 2,000
Engineeering Services
N.A.I.C.S.: 541330
Sin Khoon Khew (CEO)

Subsidiary (Non-US):

CPG Advisory (Shanghai) Co. Ltd.　　　　　　　　　　　　　　(2)
9th Fl Golden Bridge Plz No 585 Xi Zang Rd, 200003, Shanghai, China　　(100%)
Tel.: (86) 2163517888
Web Site: http://www.cpgcorp.com.sg
Sales Range: $25-49.9 Million
Emp.: 70
Engineeering Services
N.A.I.C.S.: 541330

CPG Consultants India Pvt Ltd　(2)
21/30 Prestige Craig House Craig Park Layout Mahatma Gandhi Road, Bengaluru, 560 001, India
Tel.: (91) 80 2559 0281
Web Site: http://www.cpgindia.com
Sales Range: $25-49.9 Million
Emp.: 85
Engineering Design Services
N.A.I.C.S.: 541490

Subsidiary (Domestic):

CPG Consultants Pte Ltd.　　　　(2)
238B Thomson Road 18-00, Tower B Novena Square, Singapore, 307685, Singapore　　　　　　　　　(100%)
Tel.: (65) 63574888
Web Site: http://www.cpgcorp.com.sg
Sales Range: $300-349.9 Million
Emp.: 2,000
Engineeering Services
N.A.I.C.S.: 541330
Jess Wong (Mgr-Fin)

CPG Facilities Management Pte Ltd.　　　　　　　　　　　　　　(2)
plot 125A Lor 2 Toa Payoh 02-136, Singapore, 311125, Singapore　　　　(100%)
Tel.: (65) 63258880
Web Site: http://www.cpgfm.com.sg
Sales Range: $25-49.9 Million
Emp.: 100
Services to Buildings & Dwellings
N.A.I.C.S.: 561790
Seng Joo How (Mng Dir)

CPG Investments Pte Ltd.　　　(2)
238B Thomson Road #18-00, Tower B Novena Square, 307685, Singapore, Singapore
Tel.: (65) 63574888
Web Site: http://www.cpgcorp.com.sg
Sales Range: $600-649.9 Million
Emp.: 1,007
Financial Investment Activities
N.A.I.C.S.: 523999

Subsidiary (Non-US):

CPG Vietnam Co Ltd　　　　　　(2)
Levels 12 and 16 Saigon Riverside Office Center, No 2A-4A Ton Duc Thang Street District 1, Ho Chi Minh City, Vietnam
Tel.: (84) 2838217000
Web Site: http://www.cpgcorp.com.sg
Sales Range: $25-49.9 Million
Emp.: 130
Consulting Engineering Services
N.A.I.C.S.: 541330
Jimmy Tsen (Gen Dir)

Subsidiary (Domestic):

PM Link Pte Ltd　　　　　　　　(2)
70 Bendemeer Road 03-01 Luzerne, Singapore, 339940, Singapore
Tel.: (65) 6391 7088
Web Site: http://www.pmlink.com.sg
Project Management Services
N.A.I.C.S.: 541618
Annie Lai (Mgr-Admin)

Zhong Xu Architecture Design Co., Ltd.　　　　　　　　　　　　　　(1)
No 6 Baiwangzhuang Street, Xicheng District, Beijing, 100037, China
Tel.: (86) 1068365151
Engineeering Services
N.A.I.C.S.: 541330

CHINA ART FINANCIAL HOLDINGS LIMITED
Room 1907 19/F China Evergrande Centre 38 Gloucester Road, Wanchai, China (Hong Kong)
Tel.: (852) 35895189　　　　Ky
Web Site: http://www.cnartfin.com.hk
1572—(HKG)
Rev.: $3,838,255
Assets: $155,639,858
Liabilities: $2,090,556
Net Worth: $153,549,302
Earnings: $2,049,278
Emp.: 28
Fiscal Year-end: 12/31/22
Art Finance Services
N.A.I.C.S.: 522220
Zhijun Fan (Founder, Chm & CEO)

CHINA ASIA VALLEY GROUP LIMITED
1237-1240 Sun Hung Kai Centre 30 Harbour Road, Wanchai, China (Hong Kong)
Tel.: (852) 38990300　　　　BM

Web Site: http://www.chngraphene.com
Year Founded: 1996
0063—(HKG)
Rev.: $5,084,063
Assets: $47,439,945
Liabilities: $30,713,348
Net Worth: $16,726,598
Earnings: ($5,993,393)
Emp.: 149
Fiscal Year-end: 12/31/22
Real Estate Investment Holding Company
N.A.I.C.S.: 551112
Huang Binghuang (Chm)

CHINA ASSET MANAGEMENT CO., LTD.
12/F Building B Tongtai Plaza No 33 Jinrong Street, Xicheng District, Beijing, 100033, China
Tel.: (86) 10 8806 6688　　　　CN
Web Site: http://www.chinaamc.com
Year Founded: 1998
Rev.: $50,600,000,000
Investment Management & Advisory Services
N.A.I.C.S.: 523940
Tianming Teng (Exec VP)

Subsidiaries:

China Asset Management (Hong Kong) Limited　　　　　　　　　(1)
37/F Bank of China Tower 1 Garden Road, Hong Kong, China (Hong Kong)　(100%)
Tel.: (852) 34068688
Web Site: https://www.chinaamc.com.hk
Investment Management & Advisory Services
N.A.I.C.S.: 523940
Iris Chen (CEO)

CHINA ASSETS (HOLDINGS) LIMITED
19/F Wing On House 71 Des Voeux Road, Central, China (Hong Kong)
Tel.: (852) 25219888　　　　HK
Web Site: http://www.chinaassets.com
Year Founded: 1978
Sales Range: Less than $1 Million
Financial Investment Services
N.A.I.C.S.: 523999
Yuen Yat Lo (Mng Dir)

CHINA ASSURANCE FINANCE GROUP LIMITED
Room 2204 22/F Leighton Centre 77 Leighton Road, Causeway Bay, Hong Kong, China (Hong Kong)
Tel.: (852) 3157 0001
Web Site: http://www.cafgroup.hk
Investment Holding Company; Corporate Credit Financial Services
N.A.I.C.S.: 551112
Nixon Man Kin Pang (Founder & Chm)

Subsidiaries:

China Assurance Finance Group Limited　　　　　　　　　　　　(1)
13/F Liaohai International Building 6 Wei San Road, Zhangjiakou, Hebei, China
Tel.: (86) 313 5911313
Corporate Credit Financial Services
N.A.I.C.S.: 522390

China Assurance Finance Group Limited　　　　　　　　　　　　(1)
23/F Office Tower Zhongxin Huiyang Building 59 Hubin Road North, Siming District, Xiamen, China
Tel.: (86) 592 5360307
Corporate Credit Financial Services
N.A.I.C.S.: 522390

CHINA AUTO ELECTRONICS GROUP LIMITED

233 East Part Qibin Road, Qibin District, Hebi, 458030, Henan, China
Tel.: (86) 3923314522
Web Site: http://www.thb.com.cn
Sales Range: $400-449.9 Million
Electrical & Electronics Systems Mfr
N.A.I.C.S.: 334515

Subsidiaries:

Hebi Haichang Special Equipment Co Ltd　　　　　　　　　　　　(1)
215 Qibin Road, Qibin District, Hebi, 458030, Henan, China
Tel.: (86) 3923357155
Web Site: http://www.thbhc.com.cn
Industrial Machinery Mfr
N.A.I.C.S.: 333515

CHINA AUTO SYSTEM TECHNOLOGIES LIMITED
Room 1613 16/F Leighton Centre, 77 Leighton Road, Causeway Bay, China (Hong Kong)
Tel.: (852) 2881 5300
Web Site: http://www.chinaautosystem.com
Sales Range: $150-199.9 Million
Emp.: 300
Automobile Air-Conditioning Compressors Mfr
N.A.I.C.S.: 336390
Yichen Zhang (Chm)

CHINA AUTOMATION GROUP LIMITED
Unit 3205B - 3206 32/F Office Tower Convention Plaza No 1 Harbour Road, Wanchai, China (Hong Kong)
Tel.: (852) 25980088
Web Site: http://www.cag.com.hk
Rev.: $274,946,157
Assets: $709,967,576
Liabilities: $510,524,481
Net Worth: $199,443,094
Earnings: $1,059,602
Emp.: 2,307
Fiscal Year-end: 12/31/18
Engineeering Services
N.A.I.C.S.: 541330
Benson Chiu Chi Chow (Sec & Controller-Fin)

Subsidiaries:

Beijing Consen Automation Control Company Limited　　　　　　　(1)
1117 1119 High-Tech Buidling No 229 Beishuan Middle Road, Hai Dian District, Beijing, China
Tel.: (86) 1082884888
Web Site: http://www.consen.net
Emp.: 200
Security Control System Mfr & Distr
N.A.I.C.S.: 334515

FireBus Systems, Inc.　　　　　(1)
109 Magellan Cir, Webster, TX 77598
Tel.: (832) 519-8008
Web Site: http://www.firebus.net
Fire Protection & Safety Services
N.A.I.C.S.: 922160

Nanjing Huashi Electronic Scientific Company Limited　　　　　　　(1)
No 26 Fengyi Road Yuhua Economic Development Zone, Nanjing, Jiangsu, China
Tel.: (86) 2557931977
Web Site: http://www.huashi.cc
Emp.: 330
Vehicle Electrical Equipment Mfr & Distr
N.A.I.C.S.: 336320
Tian Lei (Chm)

Tri-control Automation Company Limited　　　　　　　　　　　　(1)
Rm 3205b-06 32/F Convention Plz Office Twr, Wanchai, China (Hong Kong)
Tel.: (852) 25980020
Automation Control System Distr
N.A.I.C.S.: 423830

Tri-sen Systems Corporation　　(1)
109 Magellan Cir, Webster, TX 77598

CHINA AUTOMATION GROUP LIMITED

China Automation Group Limited—(Continued)
Tel.: (832) 632-1211
Web Site: http://tri-sen.com
Turbomachinery Control Mfr & Distr
N.A.I.C.S.: 334513

Trisen Asia Control Pte. Limited **(1)**
56 Kallang Pudding Road 06-10 HH Kallang, Singapore, 349328, Singapore
Tel.: (65) 60019100
Control Product Distr
N.A.I.C.S.: 423610
Ian Tan (Mgr-Project Mgmt)

Wuzhong Instrument Company Limited **(1)**
China Automation Industrial Zone Kaiyuan Avenue, Litong District, Wuzhong, 751100, Ningxia, China
Tel.: (86) 9532239025
Web Site: http://www.wzyb.com.cn
Control Valve Product Mfr & Distr
N.A.I.C.S.: 332912
Yu Shan Ma (Chm)

CHINA AUTOMOBILE NEW RETAIL (HOLDINGS) LIMITED

Workshop 06 & 07 36th Floor King Palace Plaza No 52A Sha Tsui Road, Tsuen Wan, New Territories, China (Hong Kong)
Tel.: (852) 2 411 7895 **BM**
Web Site:
http://www.lisigroup.com.hk
0526—(HKG)
Rev.: $283,443,096
Assets: $785,287,201
Liabilities: $767,013,231
Net Worth: $18,273,970
Earnings: ($390,837,638)
Emp.: 1,940
Fiscal Year-end: 03/31/21
Holding Company; Plastic & Metal Household Products Mfr
N.A.I.C.S.: 551112
Jianhe Cheng (Exec Dir)

Subsidiaries:

Falton Investment Limited **(1)**
Flat A 2 F Yeung Yiu Chung No 6 Indus Bldg 19 Cheung Shun St, Kowloon, New Territories, China (Hong Kong)
Tel.: (852) 24117878
Plastics Product Mfr
N.A.I.C.S.: 325510

Grandmate Industrial Company Limited **(1)**
Za 2 Fl Yeung Yiu Chung 6 Industrial Unit 19 Cheung Shun St, Cheung Sha Wan, Kowloon, China (Hong Kong)
Tel.: (852) 24117878
Sales Range: $25-49.9 Million
Emp.: 30
Cookware Distr
N.A.I.C.S.: 423220

Magicgrand Development Limited **(1)**
Rm E-H 24 F Superluck Indus Ctr Ph 2 57 Sha Tsui Rd, Tsuen Wan, New Territories, China (Hong Kong)
Tel.: (852) 24117878
Plastic & Metal Products Mfr & Sales
N.A.I.C.S.: 326220

Magician Industrial Company Limited **(1)**
Workshop 06 & 07 36th FloorKing Palace Plaza No 52A Sha Tsui Road, Tsuen Wan, Hong Kong, China (Hong Kong)
Tel.: (852) 24111110
Web Site: http://www.lisigroup.com.hk
Emp.: 20
Plastics & Metal Products Sales
N.A.I.C.S.: 423940

Magician Lifestyle Limited **(1)**
Flat A 2 F Yeung Yiu Chung No 6 Indus Bldg 19 Cheung Shun St, Cheung Sha Wan, Kowloon, China (Hong Kong)
Tel.: (852) 24117896
Sales Range: $25-49.9 Million
Emp.: 22
Cooking Utensil Distr

N.A.I.C.S.: 423220
More Concept Limited **(1)**
36 4 King Place Plaza No 52A Sha Tsui Rd, Cheung Sha Wan, Tsuen Wan, New Territory, China (Hong Kong)
Tel.: (852) 24117878
Plastics & Metal Products Sales
N.A.I.C.S.: 423940

Well Harbour Development Limited **(1)**
Workshop 06 & 07 36th Fl King Pl Plz 52 A Sha Tsui Rd, Tsuen Wan, New Territory, China (Hong Kong)
Tel.: (852) 24117878
Web Site: http://www.lisigroup.com
Paper Products & Housewares Whslr
N.A.I.C.S.: 423220

CHINA AUTOMOBILE PARTS HOLDINGS LIMITED

No 2-1 Jalan Sri Hartamas 8 Sri Hartamas, Wilayah Persekutuan, Kuala Lumpur, 50480, Malaysia
Tel.: (60) 3 6201 1120
Holding Company; Motor Vehicle Chassis Components & Other Motor Vehicle Parts Mfr
N.A.I.C.S.: 551112

Subsidiaries:

QuanZhou FenSun Automobile Parts Co., Ltd. **(1)**
Neikeng industrial Area Shangfang Village, Neikeng Town, Jinjiang, 362200, Fujian, China
Tel.: (86) 595 68585535
Emp.: 500
Motor Vehicle Parts Mfr
N.A.I.C.S.: 336390
Zhang Martin (Mgr-Sls)

CHINA AUTOMOBILE TRADING CO., LTD.

F 22 23 Millennium Plaza Tower A No 72 North Xisanhuan Road, Haidian District, Beijing, China
Tel.: (86) 10 88422222
Web Site: http://www.ctcai.com
Year Founded: 1993
Motor Vehicle Importing
N.A.I.C.S.: 423110

Subsidiaries:

Spyker of China Ltd. **(1)**
West Third Ring North Road, Beijing Economic & Trade Build, Beijing, Haidian, China
Tel.: (86) 1068484266
Automobile Mfr; Sportscars
N.A.I.C.S.: 336110
Martyn Schilte (Mng Dir)

CHINA AUTOMOTIVE ENGINEERING RESEARCH INSTITUTE CO., LTD.

No 9 Jinyu Avenue Northern, Chongqing, 401122, China
Tel.: (86) 2368825531
Web Site: http://www.caeri.com.cn
Year Founded: 1965
601965—(SHG)
Rev.: $462,000,043
Assets: $1,128,901,672
Liabilities: $258,255,986
Net Worth: $870,645,686
Earnings: $96,755,705
Fiscal Year-end: 12/31/22
Technical Consulting Services
N.A.I.C.S.: 541690
Zhou Yulin (Chm)

Subsidiaries:

Guangdong Automotive Test Center Co., Ltd. **(1)**
Chanxiu Road Luoge Industrial Park, Chancheng Distrit, Foshan, Guangdong, China
Tel.: (86) 75788735368

Engineering Research & Development Services
N.A.I.C.S.: 541715

Suzhou CAERI Automobile Test & Development Co., Ltd. **(1)**
Lu Shan Road No 699 High-tech Zone, Suzhou, Jiangsu, China
Tel.: (86) 51269370775
Engineering Research & Development Services
N.A.I.C.S.: 541715

CHINA AUTOMOTIVE INTERIOR DECORATION HOLDINGS LIMITED

No 28 Xinfeng Road Xinfeng Industrial Park, Fangqian Town New District, Wuxi, Jiangsu, China
Tel.: 51088278561 **Ky**
Web Site: http://www.joystar.com.hk
Year Founded: 2003
0048—(HKG)
Rev.: $25,838,654
Assets: $43,133,267
Liabilities: $26,051,360
Net Worth: $17,081,906
Earnings: ($11,029,543)
Emp.: 96
Fiscal Year-end: 12/31/22
Automotive Interiors Mfr
N.A.I.C.S.: 336360
Yuejin Zhuang (Founder, Chm & CEO)

CHINA AUTOMOTIVE SYSTEMS, INC.

No 88 Jingsha Avenue, Shashi District, Jingzhou, 434000, Hubei, China
Tel.: (86) 7164127901 **DE**
Web Site: https://www.caasauto.com
Year Founded: 1999
CAAS—(NASDAQ)
Rev.: $529,551,000
Assets: $714,352,000
Liabilities: $387,519,000
Net Worth: $326,833,000
Earnings: $21,181,000
Emp.: 4,093
Fiscal Year-end: 12/31/22
Power Steering Systems & Components Mfr
N.A.I.C.S.: 336211
Hanlin Chen (Chm)

Subsidiaries:

Henglong USA Corporation **(1)**
Web Site: http://www.caas-usa.com
Automobile Parts Mfr
N.A.I.C.S.: 336390

Jingzhou Henglong Automotive Parts Co., Ltd. **(1)**
No 1 Henglong Road Yuqiao Development Zone, Jingzhou, 434000, China **(80%)**
Tel.: (86) 7168327809
Automobile Parts Mfr
N.A.I.C.S.: 336110

Jingzhou Hengsheng Automotive System Co., Ltd. **(1)**
Cross Of Shacen Road Dongfang Ave Development Zone, Jingzhou, 434000, Hubei, China
Tel.: (86) 7168304756
Sales Range: $50-74.9 Million
Emp.: 22
Auto Steering System Mfr & Distr
N.A.I.C.S.: 336330

Shashi Jiulong Power Steering Gears Co., Ltd. **(1)**
1 Henglong Road, Yu Qiao Development Zone, Shashi District, Jinzhou, 434000, Hubei, China **(81%)**
Tel.: (86) 7168327777
Sales Range: $200-249.9 Million
Emp.: 700
Power Steering Components Mfr
N.A.I.C.S.: 336330

Shenyang Jinbei Henglong Automotive Steering System Co., Ltd. **(1)**
No 15 Yunhai Road, Development Zone, 110141, Shenyang, Liaoning, China **(70%)**
Tel.: (86) 2425377031
Motor Vehicle Parts Mfr
N.A.I.C.S.: 336390

Universal Sensors, Inc. **(1)**
Henglong Group Building No 1 Guan Shan 1 Road, East Lake Hi-Tech Zone, Wuhan, 430073, Hubei, China **(60%)**
Tel.: (86) 13476067938
Web Site: http://www.usisensor.com
Measuring & Controlling Device Mfr
N.A.I.C.S.: 334519

CHINA BANKING CORPORATION

China Bank Building, 8745 Paseo de Roxas Corner Villar Street, Makati, 1226, Philippines
Tel.: (63) 288855555
Web Site: https://www.chinabank.ph
Year Founded: 1920
CHIB—(PHI)
Rev.: $951,090,691
Assets: $23,136,246,141
Liabilities: $20,658,491,485
Net Worth: $2,477,754,656
Earnings: $314,209,438
Emp.: 9,747
Fiscal Year-end: 12/31/21
International & Commercial Banking Services
N.A.I.C.S.: 522110
Gilbert U. Dee (Vice Chm)

Subsidiaries:

CBC Properties & Computer Center, Inc. **(1)**
4/F and 15/F China Bank Building, 8745 Paseo de Roxas cor Villar St, Makati, Philippines
Tel.: (63) 28855555
Computer Related Services
N.A.I.C.S.: 541519

China Bank Capital Corporation **(1)**
28F BDO Equitable Tower 8751 Paseo de Roxas, Makati, Philippines
Tel.: (63) 28855798
Financial Advisory Services
N.A.I.C.S.: 523940
Ricardo R. Chua (Chm)

China Bank Securities Corporation **(1)**
28th Floor BDO Equitable Tower 8751 Paseo de Roxas, Bgy Bel-Air, Makati, 1226, Philippines
Tel.: (63) 283337388
Web Site:
https://www.chinabankseconline.ph
Brokerage Services
N.A.I.C.S.: 523150
Marisol M. Teodoro (Pres & CEO)

ChinaBank Properties & Computer Center, Inc. **(1)**
4/F & 15/F China Bank Building 8745 Paseo de Roxas cor Villar St, Makati, 1226, Philippines **(100%)**
Tel.: (63) 2 885 5555
Web Site: https://www.chinabank.ph
Computer-Related Services Solely to China Bank
N.A.I.C.S.: 541513
Phillip M. Tan (Gen Mgr)

ChinaBank Savings, Inc. **(1)**
314 Sen Gil Puyat Avenue, Makati, 1226, Philippines
Tel.: (63) 288847878
Web Site: https://www.cbs.com.ph
Banking Services
N.A.I.C.S.: 522110
Ricardo R. Chua (Chm)

Chinabank Insurance Brokers, Inc. **(1)**
8/F VGP Center 6772 Ayala Ave, Makati, 1226, Philippines **(100%)**
Tel.: (63) 8855762

Web Site: https://www.chinabank.ph
Full-Service Insurance Brokerage
N.A.I.C.S.: 524210
Julieta P. Guanlao *(Pres)*

CHINA BAOAN GROUP CO., LTD.

Floor 28 & 29 Building A Baoan Plaza
No 1002 Sungang East Road, Shenzhen, 518020, Guangdong, China
Tel.: (86) 75525170336
Web Site:
  http://www.chinabaoan.com
Year Founded: 1983
000009—(SSE)
Rev.: $4,497,410,736
Assets: $7,341,980,724
Liabilities: $4,696,486,704
Net Worth: $2,645,494,020
Earnings: $162,383,832
Fiscal Year-end: 12/31/22
Real Estate Development Services
N.A.I.C.S.: 531110
Zhengli Chen *(Chm & Pres)*

Subsidiaries:

IPE Group Limited   **(1)**
Units 5-6 23/F Enterprise Square Three No
39 Wang Chiu Road, Kowloon, China
(Hong Kong)   **(50.48%)**
Tel.: (852) 26885920
Web Site: http://www.ipegroup.com
Rev.: $122,727,165
Assets: $297,901,838
Liabilities: $54,110,873
Net Worth: $243,790,965
Earnings: $3,536,978
Emp.: 1,977
Fiscal Year-end: 12/31/2022
High Precision Metal Components Mfr
N.A.I.C.S.: 332216
Ng Hoi Ping *(Exec Dir)*

Subsidiary (Non-US):

Genex Infosys Ltd.   **(2)**
Nitol Niloy Tower Level 8 Nikunja C/A Airport Road, Dhaka, 1229, Bangladesh
Tel.: (880) 9612111000
Web Site: https://www.genexinfosys.com
Rev.: $14,148,853
Assets: $36,553,263
Liabilities: $14,778,487
Net Worth: $21,774,776
Earnings: $4,427,454
Emp.: 3,248
Fiscal Year-end: 06/30/2022
Financial Consulting Services
N.A.I.C.S.: 541611
Prince Mojumder *(Founder & CEO)*

CHINA BAOFENG (INTERNATIONAL) LTD.

Suites 3401 34/F Two Pacific Place
88 Queensway, Hong Kong, China
(Hong Kong)
Tel.: (852) 2115 2137
Web Site: http://www.baofengintl.com
Rev.: $126,701,742
Assets: $619,759,947
Liabilities: $385,183,844
Net Worth: $234,576,103
Earnings: $42,482,240
Emp.: 192
Fiscal Year-end: 12/31/19
Household Furnitures & Accessories
Designer, Developer & Marketer
N.A.I.C.S.: 337126
Yingchen Jiao *(Sec)*

Subsidiaries:

Couture Lamps, Inc.   **(1)**
3506 Airport Rd, Jonesboro, AR 72401
Web Site: http://www.couturelamps.com
Lighting Fixture Distr
N.A.I.C.S.: 423610
Dale Earls *(CFO)*

Mastercraft International Limited   **(1)**
Unit 503 5th Floor Tower B Hunghom Commercial Centre, 37 Ma Tau Wai Road Hunghom, Kowloon, China (Hong Kong)

Tel.: (852) 27658362
Web Site: http://www.mastercraft-i.com
Home Decor Accessory Retailer
N.A.I.C.S.: 449129

Ningxia Baofeng Energy Group Co., Ltd.   **(1)**
Baofeng Circular Economy Industrial Park,
Ningdong Energy Chemical Base Ningxia,
Yinchuan, 750411, China
Tel.: (86) 9515558031
Web Site: http://www.baofengenergy.com
Rev.: $4,034,048,405
Assets: $9,917,797,311
Liabilities: $4,582,077,218
Net Worth: $5,335,720,093
Earnings: $782,373,574
Fiscal Year-end: 12/31/2023
Chemical Product Mfr & Distr
N.A.I.C.S.: 325998

CHINA BAOLI TECHNOLO-GIES HOLDINGS LTD.

Suites 3401-3413 34/F Two Pacific
Place, 88 Queensway, Hong Kong,
China (Hong Kong)
Tel.: (852) 2807 8255   **BM**
Sales Range: $10-24.9 Million
Emp.: 305
Holding Company
N.A.I.C.S.: 551112
Zhang Yi *(Chm)*

CHINA BAOWU STEEL GROUP CORP., LTD.

Building No 11859 Shibo Avenue
Baowu Tower, Pudong New Area,
Shanghai, 200126, China
Tel.: (86) 2120658888   **CN**
Web Site:
  https://www.baowugroup.com
Year Founded: 1978
Sales Range: $25-49.9 Billion
Emp.: 130,000
Holding Company; Iron & Steel Products Mfr & Whslr
N.A.I.C.S.: 551112
Chen Derong *(Chm & Sec)*

Subsidiaries:

Aquila Resources Pty Limited   **(1)**
Level 14 225 St Georges Terrace, Perth,
6000, WA, Australia   **(85%)**
Tel.: (61) 894230111
Web Site:
  http://www.aquilaresources.com.au
Sales Range: $500-549.9 Million
Emp.: 78
Iron Ore & Metalurgical Coal Exploration &
Mining Services
N.A.I.C.S.: 212210
Martin Alciaturi *(CFO)*

Bao Island Enterprises Limited   **(1)**
Add: 29/F Harbour Centre, 25 Harbour
Road, Hong Kong, China (Hong Kong)
Tel.: (852) 28333223
Steel Importer Exporter & Whslr
N.A.I.C.S.: 331110

Bao-Trans Enterprises Ltd.   **(1)**
50F Flat L Office Tower Convention Plaza 1
Harbour Road, Hong Kong, China (Hong
Kong)
Tel.: (852) 25285766
Web Site: http://www.baotrans.com.hk
Steel Importer Exporter & Whslr
N.A.I.C.S.: 327910

Baoshan Iron & Steel Co., Ltd.   **(1)**
Baosteel Command Center No 885 Fujin
Road, Baoshan District, Shanghai, 201900,
China
Tel.: (86) 2126647000
Web Site: https://www.baosteel.com
Rev.: $51,099,065,103
Assets: $55,140,791,856
Liabilities: $25,250,955,458
Net Worth: $29,889,836,398
Earnings: $1,687,368,562
Emp.: 37,383
Fiscal Year-end: 12/31/2022
Steel Products Mfr
N.A.I.C.S.: 331110

Jixin Zou *(Chm)*

Subsidiary (Domestic):

Baosteel Desheng Stainless Steel
Co., Ltd.   **(2)**
JinGang Industrial Zone LuoYuan Bay Development Zone, Luoyuan, Beijing, 350601,
Fujian, China
Tel.: (86) 59162586013
Stainless Steel Products Mfr
N.A.I.C.S.: 332999

Baosteel Development Co., Ltd.   **(2)**
No 889 Baoyang Road, Shanghai, 201900,
China
Tel.: (86) 21 56125101
Iron & Steel Product Distr
N.A.I.C.S.: 423390

Subsidiary (Non-US):

Baosteel Europe GmbH   **(2)**
Nonnensteig 1, Hamburg, 20149, Germany
Tel.: (49) 40419940
Web Site: http://www.baosteel.eu
Sales Range: $25-49.9 Million
Emp.: 30
Steel Importer Exporter & Whslr
N.A.I.C.S.: 331110
Chang Zheng Zou *(Pres)*

Subsidiary (Domestic):

Baosteel Group Finance Co.,
Ltd.   **(2)**
9th Floor Baosteel Tower 370 Pudian Road,
Pudong New District, Shanghai, 200122,
China
Tel.: (86) 21 58358888
Iron & Steel Product Distr
N.A.I.C.S.: 423390

Baosteel Group Shanghai Ergang
Co., Ltd.   **(2)**
221 Huangxing Road, Yangpu District,
Shanghai, 200090, China
Tel.: (86) 21 6543 2629
Iron & Steel Product Distr
N.A.I.C.S.: 423390

Baosteel Group Xinjiang Bayi Iron &
Steel Co., Ltd.   **(2)**
Bayi Road, Toutunhe District, Urumqi,
830022, Xinjiang, China
Tel.: (86) 9913893418
Iron & Steel Product Mfr
N.A.I.C.S.: 332999

Subsidiary (Non-US):

Baosteel Italia Distribution Center
S.p.A.   **(2)**
Via XII Ottobre 214, Genoa, 16121, Italy
Tel.: (39) 0105308872
Web Site: http://www.baosteel.com
Steel Distr
N.A.I.C.S.: 331110

Subsidiary (Domestic):

Baosteel Metal Co., Ltd   **(2)**
Building 2 Alley 803 Shuangcheng Road,
Baoshan District, Shanghai, 200940, China
Tel.: (86) 2161805678
Packaging Services
N.A.I.C.S.: 561910

Subsidiary (Non-US):

Baosteel Singapore Pte. Ltd.   **(2)**
7 Temasek Blvd, Suntec Tower 1 40 02/03,
Singapore, 38987, Singapore
Tel.: (65) 63336818
Web Site: http://www.baosteel.sg
Sales Range: $25-49.9 Million
Emp.: 20
Steel Importer Exporter & Whslr
N.A.I.C.S.: 331110
Xie Weidong *(Gen Mgr)*

Subsidiary (Domestic):

Baosteel Special Material Co.,
Ltd.   **(2)**
No 1269 Shuichan Road, Baoshan District,
Shanghai, 200940, China
Tel.: (86) 2126032603
Stainless Steel Products Mfr
N.A.I.C.S.: 332999

Subsidiary (Non-US):

Baosteel Trading Europe GmbH **(2)**
Nonnensteig 1 20149, Hamburg, Germany
Tel.: (49) 40 41994101
Steel Importer Exporter & Whslr
N.A.I.C.S.: 331110

Baosteel do Brasil Ltda.   **(2)**
Av Rio branco No 277 Sala 1210, Sala
3103, 20040-009, Rio de Janeiro, Brazil
Tel.: (55) 2125311363
Web Site: http://www.baosteel.com
Sales Range: $25-49.9 Million
Emp.: 4
Steel Importer Exporter & Whslr
N.A.I.C.S.: 331110
Yonghong Zhao *(Gen Mgr)*

Joint Venture (Domestic):

Baosteel-Nippon Steel Automotive
Steel Sheets Co., Ltd.   **(2)**
Cold Rolling Complex Weiwu Rd Baoshan
Steel, Baoshan Dist, Shanghai,
China   **(50%)**
Tel.: (86) 21 2664 3800
Automotive Steel Sheet Products Mfr
N.A.I.C.S.: 332322

Subsidiary (Domestic):

Wuhan Iron & Steel Co., Ltd.   **(2)**
3 Yangang Road, Qingshan District, Wuhan, 430083, Hubei, China
Tel.: (86) 27 86807870
Web Site: http://english.wisco.com.cn
Sales Range: $5-14.9 Billion
Emp.: 27,328
Iron & Steel Producer
N.A.I.C.S.: 332111

Subsidiary (Domestic):

Guangxi Iron & Steel Group Co.,
Ltd.   **(3)**
5F Huarong Assets Mansion 38-3 Minzu
Boulevard, Nanning, 530022, Guangxi
Zhuang, China
Tel.: (86) 771 5889552
Iron & Steel Production
N.A.I.C.S.: 331110

WISCO Echeng Iron & Steel Co.,
Ltd.   **(3)**
105 Wuchang Boulevard, Ezhou, 436002,
Hubei, China
Tel.: (86) 711 3233321
Web Site: http://www.ecsteel.com.cn
Iron & Steel Production
N.A.I.C.S.: 331110

Subsidiary (Non-US):

WISCO Tailored Blanks GmbH **(3)**
Mannesmannstrasse 101, 47259, Duisburg,
Germany
Tel.: (49) 203 52752 75
Web Site: http://www.tailored-blanks.com
Sales Range: $900-999.9 Million
Emp.: 950
Steel Products Mfr
N.A.I.C.S.: 332999
Lars Krause *(Member-Mgmt Bd)*

Baosteel America Inc.   **(1)**
Continental Plz Ste 1 401 Hackensack Ave,
Hackensack, NJ 07601-6404   **(100%)**
Tel.: (201) 457-1144
Web Site: http://www.baosteelusa.com
Sales Range: $25-49.9 Million
Emp.: 16
Steel Importer Exporter & Whslr
N.A.I.C.S.: 331110

Howa Trading Co., Ltd.   **(1)**
Howa Bldg 15 Banchi, Ichiban-Cho
Chiyoda-Ku, Tokyo, 102-0082, Japan
Tel.: (81) 3 3237 9121
Web Site: http://www.howa-trading.com
Iron & Steel Product Distr
N.A.I.C.S.: 423390
Zhao Fanglin *(Chm)*

Maanshan Iron & Steel Company
Limited   **(1)**
No 8 Jiuhuaxi Road, Ma'anshan, Anhui,
China   **(57.18%)**
Tel.: (86) 5552888158

China Baowu Steel Group Corp.,
Ltd.—(Continued)

Web Site: https://www.magang.com.hk
Rev.: $12,504,104,103
Assets: $12,365,754,032
Liabilities: $7,369,394,231
Net Worth: $4,996,359,802
Earnings: $394,972,179
Emp.: 22,145
Fiscal Year-end: 12/31/2020
Iron & Steel Products Mfr
N.A.I.C.S.: 332111
Wang Qiangmin *(Gen Mgr)*

Affiliate (Domestic):

Anhui BRC & Ma Steel Weldmesh
Co. Ltd.   **(2)**
Hunan Xi Rd 1500 Caishihe Rd, Economic
& Development Zone, 243002, Wuhu, An-
hui, China   **(50%)**
Tel.: (86) 5557119320
Web Site: http://www.mgbrc.com.cn
Prefabricated Steel Reinforcement Mfr
N.A.I.C.S.: 331110

Subsidiary (Non-US):

MG Trading and Development
GmbH   **(2)**
Am Dreieck 9, Kaarst, 41564, Germany
Tel.: (49) 2131967070
Web Site: http://www.mg-trading.de
Sales Range: $25-49.9 Million
Emp.: 3
Industrial Machinery Mfr
N.A.I.C.S.: 333248
Yi Ting *(Chm)*

Subsidiary (Domestic):

Ma Steel (Wuhu) Processing and Dis-
tribution Co., Ltd.   **(2)**
No 1 Yuexiu Road, Economic Tech Devel-
opment Zone, Wuhu, 241009, China
Tel.: (86) 553 222 9188
Sales Range: $50-74.9 Million
Emp.: 160
Processing & Sale of Metal Products
N.A.I.C.S.: 332111

Ma Steel International Trade and
Economic Corporation   **(2)**
8 West Jiuhua Road, Yushan District,
Ma'anshan, 243003, Anhui, China
Tel.: (86) 5552882092
Web Site: http://www.masteeltrade.com
Machinery & Raw Materials Importer; Steel
Products Export
N.A.I.C.S.: 423510

Subsidiary (Non-US):

Maanshan Iron & Steel (HK)
Limited   **(2)**
Rm 4308 44th Fl China Resources Bldg,
Wanchai, China (Hong Kong)
Tel.: (852) 28027338
Trading of Steel & Iron Ores; Metal Whslr
N.A.I.C.S.: 423510
Jianguo Gu *(Chm)*

Magang (Group) Holding Company
Limited   **(1)**
No 8 Jiuhuaxi Road, Ma'anshan, 243003,
Anhui, China
Tel.: (86) 555 2883492
Web Site: http://www.magang.com.cn
Holding Company: Iron & Steel
N.A.I.C.S.: 551112
Wei Yao *(Chm & Sec)*

Subsidiary (Non-US):

Maanshan Iron and Steel (Australia)
Proprietary Limited   **(2)**
Level 20 77 St Georges Terrace, Perth,
6831, WA, Australia
Tel.: (61) 892217958
Metal Mining Services
N.A.I.C.S.: 212290

Nantong Baosteel Steel & Iron Co.,
Ltd.   **(1)**
161 Northeast Tangzhahe Rd, Nantong,
226002, China
Tel.: (86) 51385549470
Iron & Steel Product Mfr
N.A.I.C.S.: 332999

Ningbo Baoxin Stainless Steel Co.,
Ltd.   **(1)**
Ningbo Economic & Technical Development
Zone, Beilun Xiapu, Ningbo, 315807, Zheji-
ang, China
Tel.: (86) 574 86718888
Stainless Steel Products Mfr
N.A.I.C.S.: 331110

Ningbo Iron & Steel Co., Ltd.   **(1)**
No 168 Lin'gang Road No 2, Xiapu Beilun
District, Ningbo, 315807, Zhejiang, China
Tel.: (86) 57486859000
Stainless Steel Products Mfr
N.A.I.C.S.: 332999

Shanghai Baohua International Ten-
dering Co., Ltd.   **(1)**
No 1813 Mudanjiang Road, Baoshan Dis-
trict, Shanghai, 201900, China
Tel.: (86) 2126642577
Stainless Steel Products Mfr
N.A.I.C.S.: 332999

Shanghai Baosight Software Co.,
Ltd.   **(1)**
515 Guoshoujing Road Zhangjiang Hi-Tech
Park, Shanghai, 201203, Pudong, China
Tel.: (86) 21 50801155
Web Site: http://www.baosight.com
Software Devolopment
N.A.I.C.S.: 513210

Shanghai Baosteel Chemical Co.,
Ltd.   **(1)**
Shengqiao Road, Baoshan District, Shang-
hai, 200942, China   **(100%)**
Tel.: (86) 2126648409
Web Site: http://www.baosteel.com
Sales Range: $450-499.9 Million
Emp.: 1,500
Chemicals Mfr
N.A.I.C.S.: 325998

Shanghai Huagongbao E-commerce
Co., Ltd.   **(1)**
Rm 503 9th building 803Shuangcheng Rd,
Shanghai, 200940, China
Tel.: (86) 4008206662
Web Site: http://www.b-chem.com
Iron & Steel Product Distr
N.A.I.C.S.: 423390

Shanghai Krupp Stainless Co.,
Ltd.   **(1)**
21 Tong Yao Road Pudong New Area,
Shanghai, 200126, China   **(40%)**
Tel.: (86) 2138874887
Web Site: http://ww.skschina.com
Cold Rolled Steel Mfr
N.A.I.C.S.: 331221

Shanghai Meishan Iron & Steel Co.,
Ltd.   **(1)**
Zhong Hua Men Wai, Xinjian, Nanjing,
210039, Jiangsu, China
Tel.: (86) 25 86363114
Iron & Steel Product Distr
N.A.I.C.S.: 423390

Xinjiang Ba Yi Iron & Steel Co.,
Ltd.   **(1)**
Xingang Road, Touhunhe District, Urumqi,
830022, Xinjiang, China
Tel.: (86) 9913890166
Web Site: http://www.bygt.com.cn
Rev.: $3,235,421,994
Assets: $4,169,215,459
Liabilities: $3,749,802,863
Net Worth: $419,412,596
Earnings: ($191,935,617)
Fiscal Year-end: 12/31/2022
Iron & Steel Product Mfr & Distr
N.A.I.C.S.: 331110
Wu Bin *(Chm)*

Yantai Lubao Steel Pipe Co.,
Ltd.   **(1)**
No1030 Yongda Street, Fushan District,
Yantai, 265503, Shandong, China
Tel.: (86) 5356310555
Web Site: http://www.en.lubaosteelpipe.com
Steel Pole Mfr
N.A.I.C.S.: 331210

**CHINA BCT PHARMACY
GROUP, INC.**

No 102 Chengzhan Road, Liuzhou,
545007, Guangxi, China
Tel.: (86) 7723638318   **DE**
Web Site: http://www.china-bct.com
Year Founded: 2006
CNBI—(OTCIQ)
Sales Range: $200-249.9 Million
Emp.: 1,677
Pharmaceuticals & Medicines Mfr &
Retailer
N.A.I.C.S.: 325412
Huitian Tang *(Chm & CEO)*

**CHINA BEIDAHUANG INDUS-
TRY GROUP HOLDINGS LTD.**

Room 225, 2/F Mega Cube 8 Wang
Kwong Road, Kowloon Bay, Kowloon,
China (Hong Kong)
Tel.: (852) 28805033
0039—(HKG)
Rev.: $118,610,190
Assets: $247,984,185
Liabilities: $147,815,850
Net Worth: $100,168,335
Earnings: ($28,355,873)
Emp.: 167
Fiscal Year-end: 12/31/22
Ethanol Product Mfr
N.A.I.C.S.: 325193
Li Jiehong *(Chm)*

**CHINA BEST GROUP HOLD-
ING LIMITED**

26th Fl World-Wide House 19 Des
Voeux Road, Central, China (Hong
Kong)
Tel.: (852) 28778838
Web Site: http://www.cbgroup.com.hk
0370—(HKG)
Rev.: $153,006,910
Assets: $267,359,031
Liabilities: $119,068,532
Net Worth: $148,290,499
Earnings: ($4,696,033)
Emp.: 402
Fiscal Year-end: 03/31/21
Coal & Coke Manufacturing
N.A.I.C.S.: 423520
Yu Ho *(Sec)*

Subsidiaries:

Jet Air (Singapore) Private
Limited   **(1)**
02-222 Air freight terminal 2 95 Airport
Cargo Rd, Singapore, 918101, Singapore
Tel.: (65) 65427966
Sales Range: $25-49.9 Million
Emp.: 3
Air Freight Forwarding Services
N.A.I.C.S.: 481212
Katherine Sim *(Mgr-Admin)*

Jet Dispatch Limited   **(1)**
15615 146th Ave Ste 213, Jamaica, NY
11434-4211
Tel.: (718) 949-8325
Freight Forwarding Services
N.A.I.C.S.: 488510
Raymond Sgeto *(Office Mgr)*

**CHINA BESTER GROUP TELE-
COM CO., LTD.**

No 1 Jiangxing Road Jianghan Eco-
nomic Development Zone, Wuhan,
430023, China
Tel.: (86) 2783510888
Web Site:
    https://www.chinabester.com
Year Founded: 1992
603220—(SHG)
Rev.: $371,095,073
Assets: $650,267,163
Liabilities: $388,685,045
Net Worth: $261,582,118
Earnings: $15,274,228
Fiscal Year-end: 12/31/22
Telecommunication Servicesb
N.A.I.C.S.: 517112

Li Liubing *(Chm)*

Subsidiaries:

Polywin Computer Limited   **(1)**
Room C3 26th Floor TML Plaza 3 Hoi
Shing Road, New Territories, Tsuen Wan,
China (Hong Kong)
Tel.: (852) 31681684
Web Site: https://polywin.com.hk
Telecommunication Engineering Services
N.A.I.C.S.: 541618

**CHINA BESTSTUDY EDUCA-
TION GROUP**

35/F Tower B China International
Center No 33 Zhongshansan Road,
Yuexiu District, Guangzhou, China
Tel.: (86) 2038970000   **Ky**
Web Site: http://www.beststudy.com
Year Founded: 1997
3978—(HKG)
Rev.: $68,955,214
Assets: $122,103,353
Liabilities: $65,116,397
Net Worth: $56,986,956
Earnings: $7,591,849
Emp.: 1,022
Fiscal Year-end: 12/31/22
Educational Support Services
N.A.I.C.S.: 611710
Junjing Tang *(Co-Founder, Chm &
CEO)*

**CHINA BILLS FINANCE COR-
PORATION**

4F No 99 Sec 2 Tiding Blvd, Neihu
Dist, Taipei, 114, Taiwan
Tel.: (886) 227991177
Web Site: http://www.cbf.com.tw
Year Founded: 1978
2820—(TAI)
Rev.: $102,510,935
Assets: $7,271,521,325
Liabilities: $6,456,150,546
Net Worth: $815,370,779
Earnings: $42,137,478
Emp.: 155
Fiscal Year-end: 12/31/23
Financial Services
N.A.I.C.S.: 523999
Cheng-Ching Wu *(Chm)*

**CHINA BIOLOGIC PRODUCTS
HOLDINGS, INC.**

18th Floor Jialong International Build-
ing 19 Chaoyang Park Road, Chaoy-
ang District, Beijing, 100125, China
Tel.: (86) 1065983177   **Ky**
Web Site:
    http://www.chinabiologic.com
Year Founded: 2002
Rev.: $503,744,922
Assets: $1,937,858,497
Liabilities: $163,006,640
Net Worth: $1,774,851,857
Earnings: $138,807,748
Emp.: 2,269
Fiscal Year-end: 12/31/19
Biological Product Mfr
N.A.I.C.S.: 325414

Subsidiaries:

Beijing Tianxinfu Medical Appliance
Co., Ltd.   **(1)**
30 Huoju Street Science and Technology
Park, Changping District, Beijing, 47993,
China
Tel.: (86) 1084513557
Web Site: http://www.tyfmedical.com
Surgical Instrument Mfr & Distr
N.A.I.C.S.: 339112

Shandong Taibang Biological Prod-
ucts Co. Ltd.   **(1)**
No 14 Hushan Rd, Taishan District,
Taishan, 271000, Shandong, China
Tel.: (86) 5386203897
Web Site: http://www.ctbb.com.cn

Biopharmaceutical Whslr
N.A.I.C.S.: 456110

CHINA BIOTECH SERVICES HOLDINGS LIMITED

26/F Times Tower 391-407 Jaffe
Road, Wan Chai, Hong Kong, China
(Hong Kong)
Tel.: (852) 21492588   Ky
Web Site: http://www.ruikang.com.hk
Year Founded: 1996
8037—(HKG)
Rev.: $236,070,330
Assets: $187,487,603
Liabilities: $82,106,303
Net Worth: $105,381,300
Earnings: $89,959,920
Emp.: 260
Fiscal Year-end: 12/31/22
Holding Company
N.A.I.C.S.: 551112
Anson Pak Hou Leung (CEO & Officer-Compliance)

Subsidiaries:

Fortstone International (Hong Kong)
Limited   (1)
Room 1512-13 15th Floor Ocean Center,
Tsim Sha Tsui, Kowloon, China (Hong
Kong)
Tel.: (852) 25919878
Web Site: https://www.fortstone.hk
Wealth Management Services
N.A.I.C.S.: 523940

Genezone International Health Man-
agement Limited   (1)
Room 1904-5A Sino Plaza 255-257 Glouc-
ester Road, Causeway Bay, China (Hong
Kong)
Tel.: (852) 69562469
Web Site: http://www.genezonehealth.com
Medical Equipment Retailer
N.A.I.C.S.: 423450

PHC Medical Diagnostic Centre
Limited   (1)
Room 1618 16/F Vanta Industrial Centre No
21-33 Tai Lin Pai Road, Kwai Chung, New
Territories, China (Hong Kong)
Tel.: (852) 27718299
Web Site: https://www.phclab.com.hk
Medical Diagnostic Services
N.A.I.C.S.: 621511

Precision Health Care Services
Limited   (1)
Room 2301-02 23/F Hang Lung Centre
2-20 Paterson Street, Causeway Bay,
China (Hong Kong)
Tel.: (852) 27857011
Web Site: https://www.v-care.hk
Health Care Srvices
N.A.I.C.S.: 621610

ProGene Molecular Diagnostic Center
Limited   (1)
4/F Town Health Technology Centre 10-12
Yuen Shun Circuit NT, Siu Lek Yuen, Sha
Tin, China (Hong Kong)
Tel.: (852) 26132369
Web Site: http://www1.progene.com.hk
Medical Diagnostic Services
N.A.I.C.S.: 621511

CHINA BLUECHEMICAL LTD.

65/F Bank of China Tower No 1 Gar-
den Road, Central, China (Hong
Kong)
Tel.: (852) 84527343   CN
Web Site:
https://www.chinabluechem.com.cn
Year Founded: 2006
CBLUF—(OTCIQ)
Rev.: $1,977,051,119
Assets: $3,253,441,931
Liabilities: $792,128,517
Net Worth: $2,461,313,414
Earnings: $249,049,070
Emp.: 4,191
Fiscal Year-end: 12/31/22
Natural Gas Mfr & Sales

N.A.I.C.S.: 211130
Sau Mei Ng (Co-Sec)

CHINA BOHAI BANK CO., LTD.

No 218 Haihe East Road, Hedong
District, Tianjin, 300012, China
Tel.: (86) 4008888811   CN
Web Site: https://www.cbhb.com.cn
Year Founded: 2005
9668—(HKG)
Rev.: $8,655,141,556
Assets: $233,154,116,231
Liabilities: $217,705,995,954
Net Worth: $15,448,120,277
Earnings: $858,100,238
Emp.: 13,286
Fiscal Year-end: 12/31/22
Commercial Banking Services
N.A.I.C.S.: 522110
Hongzhi Qu (Pres)

CHINA BOQI ENVIRONMEN-TAL HOLDING CO., LTD.

11F Beijing R&F Center Office 63
East 3rd Ring Middle Rd Cha, Bei-
jing, 100022, China
Tel.: (86) 1058782222
2377—(HKG)
Rev.: $266,794,819
Assets: $663,432,682
Liabilities: $263,443,190
Net Worth: $399,989,491
Earnings: $21,854,383
Emp.: 1,459
Fiscal Year-end: 12/31/22
Solid Waste Treatment & Disposal
Services
N.A.I.C.S.: 562212
Cheng Liquan Richard (Chm)

CHINA BOTON GROUP COM-PANY LIMITED

Room 2101-02 21st Floor Wing On
House 71 Des Voeux Road, Central,
China (Hong Kong)
Tel.: (852) 28380095
Web Site: http://www.chinaffl.com
3318—(HKG)
Rev.: $326,402,903
Assets: $905,721,242
Liabilities: $447,719,594
Net Worth: $458,001,648
Earnings: $11,861,132
Emp.: 1,464
Fiscal Year-end: 12/31/22
Flavors & Fragrance Sales & Mfr
N.A.I.C.S.: 456120
Ming Fan Wang (Chm & CEO)

Subsidiaries:

Dongguan Boton Flavor & Fra-
grances Company Limited   (1)
NO 8 Dajin Road, Xixi Village Liaobu Town,
Dongguan, 523425, Guangdong, China
Tel.: (86) 76983308999
Web Site: https://www.dbff.com
Emp.: 300
Food Flavor Mfr & Distr
N.A.I.C.S.: 325190

Dongguan Boton Flavors & Fra-
grances Company Limited   (1)
NO 8 Dajin Road, Liangbian Village Liaobu
Town, Dongguan, 523402, Guangdong,
China
Tel.: (86) 7698 330 8999
Web Site: https://www.dbff.com
Fragrance Mfr
N.A.I.C.S.: 325620

Shenzhen Huachang Industrial Co.,
Ltd.   (1)
F16 Building A Boton Technology Park Cha-
guang Road Xili, Nanshan District, Shen-
zhen, China
Tel.: (86) 75529686095
Web Site: http://www.neworiginsmoke.com
Emp.: 1,500
Tobacco & Vape Device Mfr
N.A.I.C.S.: 312230

Jennifer Zhang (Sls Mgr)

CHINA BOZZA DEVELOPMENT HOLDINGS LIMITED

Room 1901 19F Dachong Interna-
tional Centre Tonggu Road, Nanshan
District, Shenzhen, Guangdong,
China
Tel.: (86) 755 82793080   Ky
Web Site: http://www.chinacaflc.com
Rev.: $7,763,747
Assets: $84,215,209
Liabilities: $48,120,094
Net Worth: $36,095,115
Earnings: ($48,723,260)
Emp.: 27
Fiscal Year-end: 12/31/19
Holding Company
N.A.I.C.S.: 551112

CHINA BPIC SURVEYING IN-STRUMENTS AG

Room 313 Unit 2 Building 3 ZhuJi-
angmoer International, ChangPing
District, Beijing, China
Tel.: (86) 10 57227983   De
Web Site: http://www.bpicsurvey.com
Year Founded: 2012
Holding Company; Surveying Instru-
ments Mfr
N.A.I.C.S.: 551112

Subsidiaries:

Beijing Precise Instruments Co.,
Ltd.   (1)
Room 313 Unit 2 Building 3 ZhuJiangmoer
International, ChangPing District, Beijing,
China
Tel.: (86) 10 5722 7983
Web Site: http://www.bpicsurvey.com
Surveying Instruments Mfr
N.A.I.C.S.: 334519
Wei Xie (Mng Dir)

CHINA BRIGHT CULTURE GROUP

Yard 4 Wan Hui.No 2 Guangbai East
Road, Chaoyang, Beijing, China
Tel.: (86) 1088135018   Ky
Web Site: http://www.sinozswh.com
Year Founded: 2014
1859—(HKG)
Rev.: $42,532,916
Assets: $216,998,870
Liabilities: $51,945,613
Net Worth: $165,053,257
Earnings: $6,945,448
Emp.: 84
Fiscal Year-end: 12/31/21
Television Broadcasting Services
N.A.I.C.S.: 516120
Mu Liu (Chm & CEO)

CHINA BRIGHT STONE IN-VESTMENT MANAGEMENT GROUP

Unit 2209 22/F Wu Chung House 213
Queens Road East, Wanchai, China
(Hong Kong)
Tel.: (852) 39737725
Web Site:
   http://www.chinabrightstone.com
Investment Management Service
N.A.I.C.S.: 523999
Feng Gao (Chm)

CHINA BRILLIANT GLOBAL LIMITED

DD125 Lot 1998 RP othersShek Po
Road, Hong Kong, China (Hong
Kong)
Tel.: (852) 28388873   Ky
Web Site: https://www.cbg.com.hk
Year Founded: 1989
8026—(HKG)
Rev.: $10,035,418
Assets: $21,771,953

Liabilities: $12,080,525
Net Worth: $9,691,428
Earnings: ($5,952,943)
Emp.: 24
Fiscal Year-end: 03/31/22
Holding Company; Medical, Pharma-
ceutical & Healthcare Food Products
Mfr & Distr; Money Lending Services;
Jewelry Retail & Wholesale
N.A.I.C.S.: 551112
Koon Fat Chan (CFO & Sec)

Subsidiaries:

Prosten Technology Company
Limited   (1)
Unit 802 8th Floor Dominion Centre, 43-59
Queen's Road East, Wanchai, China (Hong
Kong)   (100%)
Tel.: (852) 28388873
Web Site: http://www.prosten.com
Computer Equipment Trader; Software De-
veloper; System Integrator; System Devel-
opment Consulting Services
N.A.I.C.S.: 423430
Luyi Li (Exec Dir & CEO-Grp Ops)

CHINA BUILDING MATERIAL TEST & CERTIFICATION GROUP CO., LTD

Guanzhuang Dongli 1 Chaoyang Dist,
Beijing, 100024, China
Tel.: (86) 1051167681
Web Site: http://www.ctc.ac.cn
Year Founded: 1950
603060—(SHG)
Rev.: $340,832,049
Assets: $616,727,667
Liabilities: $278,585,836
Net Worth: $338,141,831
Earnings: $35,514,110
Emp.: 1,600
Fiscal Year-end: 12/31/22
Construction Engineering Services
N.A.I.C.S.: 541330

CHINA CALXON GROUP CO., LTD.

56 Building 1 Room 318 Huimin
Road, Hangzhou, 310002, Zhejiang,
China
Tel.: (86) 57187376666
Web Site: http://www.calxon-
   group.com
918—(SSE)
Rev.: $236,398,338
Assets: $2,722,478,087
Liabilities: $2,200,866,294
Net Worth: $521,611,792
Earnings: $6,274,262
Fiscal Year-end: 12/31/19
Real Estate Support Services
N.A.I.C.S.: 531390
Yonghua Qian (Chm & Gen Mgr)

CHINA CARBON NEUTRAL DEVELOPMENT GROUP LIM-ITED

Room 1001 10/F Wing On Centre
111 Connaught Road, Central, China
(Hong Kong)
Tel.: (852) 37288700   Ky
Web Site: http://www.bisu-tech.com
Year Founded: 2013
1372—(HKG)
Rev.: $90,436,515
Assets: $40,103,595
Liabilities: $46,449,143
Net Worth: ($6,345,548)
Earnings: ($25,377,345)
Emp.: 329
Fiscal Year-end: 12/31/22
Holding Company; Automotive En-
gines Developer & Mfr; Civil Engi-
neering Works & Building Construc-
tion & Maintenance
N.A.I.C.S.: 551112
Artem Matyushok (CEO)

China Carbon Neutral Development Group Limited—(Continued)

CHINA CASTSON 81 FINANCE COMPANY LIMITED"

Rm 18 9/F Block B Focal Industrial Centre, 21 Man Lok Street Hunghom, Kowloon, China (Hong Kong)
Tel.: (852) 35896710   BM
0810—(HKG)
Rev.: $62,858
Assets: $7,661,348
Liabilities: $570,435
Net Worth: $7,090,913
Earnings: ($3,568,853)
Emp.: 16
Fiscal Year-end: 12/31/22
Investment Management Service
N.A.I.C.S.: 523940
Yiu Wah Leung (Co-Sec)

CHINA CBM GROUP COMPANY LIMITED

Room 20 19/F Fortune Commercial Building 362 Sha Tsui Road, Tsuan Wan, Hong Kong, China (Hong Kong)
Tel.: (852) 23661613   BM
8270—(HKG)
Rev.: $45,841,864
Assets: $65,169,328
Liabilities: $30,910,183
Net Worth: $34,259,144
Earnings: $17,144,384
Emp.: 238
Fiscal Year-end: 12/31/22
Holding Company
N.A.I.C.S.: 551112
Zhong Sheng Wang (Chm & Compliance Officer)

CHINA CENTURY DRAGON MEDIA, INC.

Room 801 7 Wenchanger Road, Jiangbei, Huizhou, Guangdong, China
Tel.: (86) 752 3138789   DE
Sales Range: $50-74.9 Million
Emp.: 98
Television Advertising Services
N.A.I.C.S.: 541890
HaiMing Fu (CEO)

CHINA CGAME, INC.

105 Baishi Road Jiuzhou West Avenue, Zhuhai, 519070, China
Tel.: (86) 7568538908   DE
Web Site: http://www.caebuilding.com
Year Founded: 2004
Sales Range: $25-49.9 Million
Emp.: 416
Designs, Engineers & Installs Curtain Wall Systems Including Wooden & Metal Curtain Walls
N.A.I.C.S.: 541330

Subsidiaries:

Techwell Engineering Ltd.   (1)
Room 403 Lu Plaza 2 Wing Yip Street, Kwun Tong, Kowloon, China (Hong Kong)   (100%)
Tel.: (852) 2793 1083
Manufactures & Constructs External Building Facades Including Roofing Systems for Buildings & Curtain Walls
N.A.I.C.S.: 541330

CHINA CHEMICAL & PHARMACEUTICAL CO., LTD.

No 23 Hsiang Yang Rd, Taipei, 10046, Taiwan
Tel.: (886) 223124200
Web Site: https://www.ccpc.com.tw
Year Founded: 1952
1701—(TAI)
Rev.: $275,005,770
Assets: $416,989,749

Liabilities: $175,379,905
Net Worth: $241,609,844
Earnings: $15,586,771
Emp.: 1,783
Fiscal Year-end: 12/31/22
Pharmaceutical Products Mfr & Distr
N.A.I.C.S.: 325412
Hsun-Sheng Wang (Chm)

Subsidiaries:

China Chemical & Pharmaceutical Co., Ltd. - Hsinfong Plant   (1)
No 182-1 Keng Tze Kou Hsinfong Shiang, Xinfeng Township, Hsinchu, 30444, Taiwan
Tel.: (886) 3 559 9866
Web Site: http://www.ccpc.com.tw
Pharmaceuticals Product Mfr
N.A.I.C.S.: 325412

China Chemical & Pharmaceutical Co., Ltd. - Taichung Plant   (1)
No 10 Keng-yeh 15th Rd Industrial Zone, Taichung, 40755, Taiwan
Tel.: (886) 42 359 6818
Web Site: http://www.ccpc.com.tw
Pharmaceuticals Product Mfr
N.A.I.C.S.: 325412

Chunghwa Yuming Healthcare Co., Ltd.   (1)
No 23 Xiangyang Rd, Zhongzheng Dist, Taipei, 10046, Taiwan
Tel.: (886) 282538769
Web Site: https://www.cyh365.com.tw
Sales Range: $550-599.9 Million
Emp.: 1,200
Pharmaceutical Products Mfr & Distr
N.A.I.C.S.: 424210

Phermpep Biotechnology Co., Ltd.   (1)
3F 23 Keya Rd, Daya Dist, Taichung, 42881, Taiwan
Tel.: (886) 422870998
Pharmaceuticals Product Mfr
N.A.I.C.S.: 325412

Tai Rung Development Co., Ltd.   (1)
No 26 Dongxing St, Shulin Dist, Taipei, 238, Taiwan
Tel.: (886) 286863079
Ampoules & Plastic Containers Mfr
N.A.I.C.S.: 326160

CHINA CHEMICAL CORP.

1 Electric Power Plant Rd, Zhou Cun District, Zibo, 255330, SD, China
Tel.: (86) 5336168699   DE
Web Site: https://www.chinachemicalcorp.com
Year Founded: 2008
CHCC—(OTCIQ)
Sales Range: $75-99.9 Million
Emp.: 176
Chemical Products
N.A.I.C.S.: 325998
Feng Lu (Chm, Pres & CEO)

CHINA CHENGTONG DEVELOPMENT GROUP LIMITED

Suite 6406 64/F Central Plaza 18 Harbour Road, Wanchai, China (Hong Kong)
Tel.: (852) 21601600   HK
Web Site: https://www.hk217.com
Year Founded: 2020
0217—(HKG)
Rev.: $162,867,225
Assets: $1,276,241,213
Liabilities: $901,996,838
Net Worth: $374,244,375
Earnings: $9,854,220
Emp.: 269
Fiscal Year-end: 12/31/22
Marine Travelling Services
N.A.I.C.S.: 483111
Tsz Kin Poon (Sec)

CHINA CHUNLAI EDUCATION GROUP CO., LTD.

No 66 Beihai East Road, Shangqiu, Henan, China
Tel.: (86) 370 355 5128   Ky
Web Site: http://www.chunlaiedu.com
Year Founded: 2004
1969—(HKG)
Rev.: $159,644,667
Assets: $774,353,982
Liabilitioo: $168,826,667
Net Worth: $315,527,415
Earnings: $92,986,979
Emp.: 2,352
Fiscal Year-end: 08/31/21
Educational Support Services
N.A.I.C.S.: 611710
Chunlai Hou (Founder & Chm)

CHINA CIFCO INVESTMENT CO., LTD.

No 8 1F Block 1 No 14 Guanghua Road, Jianguomenwai Chaoyang District, Beijing, 100020, China
Tel.: (86) 1065807596
Web Site: http://www.cifco996.com
000996—(SSE)
Rev.: $4,461,912
Assets: $98,264,556
Liabilities: $30,779,892
Net Worth: $67,484,664
Earnings: ($477,360)
Fiscal Year-end: 12/31/22
Logistics & Automotive Services
N.A.I.C.S.: 541614
Xin Jiang (Chm & Gen Mgr)

CHINA CINDA ASSET MANAGEMENT CO., LTD.

No 1 Building 9 Naoshikou Street, Xicheng District, Beijing, 100031, China
Tel.: (86) 1063080000   CN
Web Site: https://www.cinda.com.cn
Year Founded: 1999
1359—(HKG)
Rev.: $15,341,533
Assets: $232,585,596
Liabilities: $202,703,147
Net Worth: $29,882,449
Earnings: $2,257,898
Emp.: 13,067
Fiscal Year-end: 12/31/20
Asset Management Services
N.A.I.C.S.: 523999
Zhenhong Luo (Chief Risk Officer)

Subsidiaries:

China Cinda (HK) Holdings Co., Ltd.   (1)
12 / F AIA Central 1 Connaught Road, Central, China (Hong Kong)
Tel.: (852) 25276686
Web Site: https://www.cindahk.com
Asset Management & Financial Services
N.A.I.C.S.: 523940

China Cinda (Macau) Asset Management Co., Ltd.   (1)
Rua Pequim No 126 Edificio Comercial I Tak 23Andar, Macau, China (Macau)
Tel.: (853) 28786409
Investment Management Service
N.A.I.C.S.: 523940

China Jingu International Trust Co., Ltd.   (1)
10th Floor Tower C Tongtai Building No 33 Financial Street, Xicheng District, Beijing, China
Tel.: (86) 1088086686
Asset Management & Financial Services
N.A.I.C.S.: 523940

Cinda Capital Management Co., Ltd.   (1)
4 and 6/F Tower B East Gate Plaza 29 Dongzhong Street, Dongcheng District, Beijing, 100027, China
Tel.: (86) 1086376800
Asset Management & Financial Services
N.A.I.C.S.: 523940

Cinda Financial Leasing Co., Ltd.   (1)
2nd Floor Building B Donghuan Plaza No 29 Dongzhong Street, Dongcheng District, Beijing, 100027, China
Tel.: (86) 1064198135
Web Site: https://www.cindaflc.com
Asset Management & Financial Services
N.A.I.C.S.: 523940

Cinda Futures Co., Ltd.   (1)
Floor 19-20 Tianren Building No 188 Liyi Road Ningwei Street, Xiaoshan District, Hangzhou, 311215, Zhejiang, China
Tel.: (86) 4006728728
Web Site: https://www.cindaqh.com
Asset Management & Financial Services
N.A.I.C.S.: 523940

Cinda Innovation Investment Co., Ltd.   (1)
Building 1 Court 9 Naoshikou Street, Xicheng District, Beijing, 100031, China
Tel.: (86) 1063081248
Investment Management Service
N.A.I.C.S.: 523940

Cinda Investment Co., Ltd.   (1)
16-19/F Block C Beijing International Building, A18 Zhongguancun South Street Haidian District, Beijing, 100081, China
Tel.: (86) 1062157302
Asset Management & Financial Services
N.A.I.C.S.: 523940

Cinda Real Estate Co., Ltd.   (1)
Tower A Beijing International Building No 18 Zhongguancun South Street, Haidian District, Beijing, 100081, China
Tel.: (86) 1082190959
Web Site: http://www.cindare.com
Rev.: $2,562,032,608
Assets: $12,412,215,836
Liabilities: $8,888,619,051
Net Worth: $3,523,596,785
Earnings: $77,276,708
Fiscal Year-end: 12/31/2022
Real Estate Manangement Services
N.A.I.C.S.: 531110
Deng Lixin (Chm & Sec-Party Committee)

Cinda Securities Co., Ltd.   (1)
Building 1 No 9 Naoshikou Street, Xicheng District, Beijing, 100031, China
Tel.: (86) 95321
Web Site: https://www.cindasc.com
Securities Brokerage Services
N.A.I.C.S.: 523150

First State Cinda Fund Management Co., Ltd.   (1)
24/F China Merchants Bank Building 7088 Shen Nan Road, Shenzhen, 518040, China
Tel.: (86) 75583172666
Web Site: http://www.fscinda.com
Asset Management & Financial Services
N.A.I.C.S.: 523940

Happy Life Insurance Co., Ltd.   (1)
8/F Tower B East Gate Plaza 29 Dongzhong Street, Dongcheng District, Beijing, 100027, China   (50.99%)
Tel.: (86) 1066271800
Investment Management Service
N.A.I.C.S.: 523940
Jiabao Ma (Portfolio Mgr)

Nanyang Commercial Bank Limited   (1)
151 Des Voeux Road, Central, China (Hong Kong)   (100%)
Tel.: (852) 2 852 0888
Web Site: https://www.ncb.com.hk
Commercial Banking Services
N.A.I.C.S.: 522110

Xinfeng Investment Management Co., Ltd.   (1)
Room 201-2 2nd Floor Building 1 Yard No 35 Jinshifang Street, Xicheng District, Beijing, 100032, China
Tel.: (86) 1083252212
Web Site: http://www.xinfenginvestment.com
Asset Management & Financial Services
N.A.I.C.S.: 523940

Zhongrun Economic Development Co., Ltd.   (1)
9/F China Commerce Tower 5 Sanlihe East

Road, Xicheng District, Beijing, 100045, China
Tel.: (86) 1068535368
Asset Management & Financial Services
N.A.I.C.S.: 523940

CHINA CITIC FINANCIAL AS-SET MANAGEMENT CO., LTD.
No 8 Financial Street, Xicheng District, Beijing, 100033, China
Tel.: (86) 1059618888   CN
Web Site: https://www.chamc.com.cn
Year Founded: 1999
2799—(HKG)
Rev.: $16,121,146,438
Assets: $243,987,275,299
Liabilities: $220,593,790,724
Net Worth: $23,393,484,574
Earnings: $324,729,961
Emp.: 10,947
Fiscal Year-end: 12/31/19
Financial Investment Services
N.A.I.C.S.: 523999
Zhanfeng Wang *(Chm)*

Subsidiaries:

China Huarong (Macau) International
Company Limited   **(1)**
32/F Bank of China Building No 323
Avenida Doutor Mario Soares, Macau, China (Macau)
Tel.: (853) 82968000
Financial Services
N.A.I.C.S.: 541611

China Huarong Financial Leasing Co
Ltd   **(1)**
6-7/F Building A Zhejiang World Trade Ctr
122 Shugua, Hangzhou, 310007, Zhejiang, China   **(79.92%)**
Tel.: (86) 57187950988
Financial Lending Services
N.A.I.C.S.: 532490

D'Long International Strategic Investment Co., Ltd.   **(1)**
1155 Yuanshen Road, Pudong New Area, Shanghai, 200135, China
Tel.: (86) 2168624600
Web Site: http://www.d-long.com
Holding Company
N.A.I.C.S.: 551112

Subsidiary (Domestic):

Shenyang Hejin Holding Investment
Co., Ltd.   **(2)**
No 55 New Century Road Hunnan, Shenyang, Liaoning, China
Tel.: (86) 24 62336790
Web Site: http://www.hjinv.com
Holding Company: Non-Ferrous Metal Alloy Material Smelting, Processing, Manufacture & Marketing
N.A.I.C.S.: 551112

Huarong (HK) International Holdings
Limited   **(1)**
Unit 1504-1506 No 1 Harbor Road Convention Center Office Building, Hong Kong, China (Hong Kong)
Tel.: (852) 28775838
Holding Company
N.A.I.C.S.: 551112
Kate Yu *(Accountant)*

Huarong Capital Management Co.,
Ltd.   **(1)**
7-8/F Block C No 8 Financial Street, Xicheng District, Beijing, 100033, China
Tel.: (86) 1059619057
Financial Services
N.A.I.C.S.: 541611

Huarong Financial Leasing Co.,
Ltd.   **(1)**
6-7F Office Building A World Trade Center Grand Hotel No 122, 122 Shuguang Road, Hangzhou, 310007, Zhejiang, China
Tel.: (86) 57187950988
Web Site: http://www.hrflc.com
Financial Lending Services
N.A.I.C.S.: 533110

Huarong Futures Co., Ltd.   **(1)**
Building 3 No 53-1 Kunbei Road, Haikou,

570105, Hainan, China
Tel.: (86) 89866779160
Financial Investment Services
N.A.I.C.S.: 523940

Huarong Huitong Asset Management
Co., Ltd.   **(1)**
Block 2 2A Baiwanzhuang Street, Xicheng District, Beijing, 100037, China
Tel.: (86) 1057809334
Financial Services
N.A.I.C.S.: 541611

Huarong Industrial Investment &
Management Co., Ltd.   **(1)**
Jia No 2 Baiwanzhuang Street, Xicheng District, Beijing, 100037, China
Tel.: (86) 1057649123
Financial Services
N.A.I.C.S.: 541611

Huarong International Financial Holdings Limited   **(1)**
Unit A 16/F and Unit A 17/F Two Pacific Place 88 Queensway, Hong Kong, China (Hong Kong)   **(51%)**
Tel.: (852) 39653965
Web Site: http://www.hrif.com.hk
Rev.: $35,270,325
Assets: $730,824,135
Liabilities: $824,266,590
Net Worth: ($93,442,455)
Earnings: ($284,073,315)
Emp.: 42
Fiscal Year-end: 12/31/2022
Holding Company; Investment & Financial Services
N.A.I.C.S.: 551112
Mei Ming *(Deputy CEO)*

Subsidiary (Non-US):

Huarong Financial (Shenzhen) Equity
Investment Fund Management Co.,
Ltd.   **(2)**
1604 unit Tower2 Huanggang Business Center Jin tian road, Futian District, Shenzhen, China
Tel.: (86) 75583320332
Investment Banking Services
N.A.I.C.S.: 523150

Subsidiary (Domestic):

Huarong International Asset Management Limited   **(2)**
29/F One Pacific Place 88 Queensway, Hong Kong, China (Hong Kong)
Tel.: (852) 39653965
Investment Banking Services
N.A.I.C.S.: 523150
Leo Xu *(Sr VP)*

Huarong International Securities
Limited   **(2)**
19/F Bank Centre 636 Nathan Rd, Mong Kok, Kowloon, China (Hong Kong)
Tel.: (852) 29286028
Web Site: http://sec.unitedsimsen.com
Securities Brokerage & Dealing Services
N.A.I.C.S.: 523150

Huarong Investment Stock Corporation Limited   **(2)**
Room 3201 32/F Two Pacific Place, 88 Queensway, Hong Kong, China (Hong Kong)   **(100%)**
Tel.: (852) 3908 7777
Web Site: http://www.hriv.com.hk
Rev.: $65,641,908
Assets: $815,428,412
Liabilities: $650,759,151
Net Worth: $164,669,260
Earnings: ($119,033,759)
Emp.: 33
Fiscal Year-end: 12/31/2019
Foundation & Substructure Construction
N.A.I.C.S.: 238190
Yang Rungui *(Chm)*

Subsidiary (Non-US):

Huarong Tianhai (Shanghai) Investment Management Company
Limited   **(2)**
Unit 2506 Block 1 No1198 Century Avenue, Pudong, Shanghai, China
Tel.: (86) 2168980188
Investment Banking Services

N.A.I.C.S.: 523150

Huarong International Trust Co.,
Ltd.   **(1)**
12th Floor Tower B Tongtai Building No 33 Financial Street, Xicheng District, Beijing, 100033, China
Tel.: (86) 4006109969
Web Site: http://www.huarongtrust.com.cn
Financial Services
N.A.I.C.S.: 541611

Huarong Real Estate Co., Ltd.   **(1)**
Jia No 2 Baiwanzhuang Street, Xicheng District, Beijing, 100037, China
Tel.: (86) 1057649191
Web Site: http://www.hrzy.cc
Real Estate Management Services
N.A.I.C.S.: 531390

Huarong Rongtong (Beijing) Technology Co., Ltd.   **(1)**
6/F Hesheng Wealth Square 13 Deshengmenwai Street, Xicheng District, Beijing, 100088, China
Tel.: (86) 1059618249
Financial Services
N.A.I.C.S.: 541611

Huarong Ruitong Equity Investment
Management Co., Ltd.   **(1)**
6/F No 8 Financial Street, Xicheng District, Beijing, 100033, China
Tel.: (86) 1059618585
Financial Services
N.A.I.C.S.: 541611

Huarong Securities Co., Ltd.   **(1)**
Tower A No 8 Financial Street, Xicheng District, Beijing, 100033, China
Tel.: (86) 1058568065
Web Site: http://www.hrsec.com.cn
Securities Brokerage Services
N.A.I.C.S.: 523150

Huarong Tianze Investment Co.,
Ltd.   **(1)**
3/F Block 1 1 South Yuetan Road, Xicheng District, Beijing, 200002, China
Tel.: (86) 107326656
Financial Services
N.A.I.C.S.: 541611

Huarong Xiangjiang Bank Co.,
Ltd.   **(1)**
No 828 Section 1 Furong South Road, Changsha, 410004, Hunan, China
Tel.: (86) 73189828811
Web Site: http://www.hrxjbank.com.cn
Commercial Banking Services
N.A.I.C.S.: 522110

Huarong Yufu Equity Investment
Fund Management Co., Ltd.   **(1)**
9/F Block C No 8 Financial Street, Xicheng District, Beijing, 100033, China
Tel.: (86) 1059619161
Financial Services
N.A.I.C.S.: 541611

Huarong Zhiyuan Investment & Management Co., Ltd.   **(1)**
Block C No 8 Financial Street, Xicheng District, Beijing, 100033, China
Tel.: (86) 1059618866
Financial Services
N.A.I.C.S.: 541611

Huarong Zhongguancun Distressed
Asset Exchange Co., Ltd.   **(1)**
12/F Zhongguancun Capital Building No 62 South Xueyuan Road, Haidian District, Beijing, 100081, China
Tel.: (86) 1057780808
Financial Services
N.A.I.C.S.: 541611

Rongde Asset Management Co.,
Ltd.   **(1)**
F3/9 Zhuozhu Center No 6 Wudinghou Street, Xicheng District, Beijing, 100033, China
Tel.: (86) 1059400399
Financial Services
N.A.I.C.S.: 541611

CHINA CITY INFRASTRUCTURE GROUP LIMITED
Suite 6208 62/F Central Plaza 18

Harbour Road, Wanchai, China (Hong Kong)
Tel.: (852) 28270088
Web Site: http://www.city-infrastructure.com
2349—(HKG)
Rev.: $8,363,108
Assets: $178,793,888
Liabilities: $77,754,728
Net Worth: $101,039,160
Earnings: ($14,562,540)
Emp.: 141
Fiscal Year-end: 12/31/22
Investment Holding Company
N.A.I.C.S.: 551112
Li Chao Bo *(Chm)*

Subsidiaries:

Hangzhou Niagra Real Estates Company Limited   **(1)**
Room 501 Unit 3 No 1 Linping City Harbor, Yuhang District, Hangzhou, 311100, Zhejiang, China
Tel.: (86) 57186237218
Property Development Services
N.A.I.C.S.: 531390

Wuhan Future City Hotel Management Company Limited   **(1)**
147 South Luoshi Road, Hongshan District, Wuhan, 430070, China
Tel.: (86) 2787578708
Property Development Services
N.A.I.C.S.: 531390

Wuhan Future City Property Management Company Limited   **(1)**
147 Luoshi South Road, Hongshan District, Wuhan, 430070, China
Tel.: (86) 2787571389
Property Development Services
N.A.I.C.S.: 531390

CHINA CLEAN ENERGY INC.
Jiangyin Industrial Zone, Jiangyin Town, Fuqing, 350309, Fujian, China
Tel.: (86) 59185782596   DE
Web Site:
http://www.chinacleanenergyinc.com
Year Founded: 2006
CCGY—(OTCEM)
Sales Range: $50-74.9 Million
Emp.: 120
Biodiesel Fuel & Chemicals Mfr
N.A.I.C.S.: 324199
Ri-Wen Xue *(COO)*

Subsidiaries:

Fujian Zhongde Technology Co.,
Ltd.   **(1)**
Fulu Industry District, Longtian Town, Fuqing, 350315, China
Tel.: (86) 59185773387
Web Site: http://www.fj-zd.com
Sales Range: $50-74.9 Million
Industrial Chemicals Mfr
N.A.I.C.S.: 325180
Kiaming Ou *(Gen Mgr)*

CHINA CLEAN ENERGY TECHNOLOGY GROUP LIMITED
5th Floor Block C Zhongtian Building No 38 Shandongtou Road, Laoshan District, Qingdao, Shandong, China
Tel.: (86) 53288833918   Ky
Year Founded: 2003
Rev.: $9,712,626
Assets: $218,468,624
Liabilities: $160,489,512
Net Worth: $57,979,112
Earnings: $9,219,218
Emp.: 17
Fiscal Year-end: 12/31/19
Software Development Services
N.A.I.C.S.: 541511

CHINA COAL ENERGY COMPANY LIMITED
No 1 Huangsidajie, Chaoyang Dis-

China Coal Energy Company Limited—(Continued)

trict, Beijing, 100120, China
Tel.: (86) 1082236028   CN
Web Site:
  https://en.chinacoalenergy.com
Year Founded: 2006
601898—(SHG)
Rev.: $26,718,103,816
Assets: $48,371,721,173
Liabilities: $23,064,047,685
Net Worth: $25,307,673,488
Earnings: $2,704,647,901
Emp.: 47,122
Fiscal Year-end: 12/31/23
Minneral Mining Services
N.A.I.C.S.: 212114
Yi Peng *(Vice Chm)*

Subsidiaries:

China Coal Energy Shandong Co., Ltd.   (1)
No 135 Tianjin Road, Rizhao, 276826, Shandong, China
Tel.: (86) 633 8333626
Web Site: http://www.chinacoalenergy.com
Coal Mining & Distr
N.A.I.C.S.: 213113

China Coal Handan Design Engineering Co.,Ltd.   (1)
No 114 Fu He Bei Dajie, Handan, 56031, Hebei, China
Tel.: (86) 310 7106407
Web Site: http://www.chinacoalenergy.com
Coal Mining & Distr
N.A.I.C.S.: 213113

China Coal Pingshuo Industry Coal Limited Liability Corporation   (1)
PO Box 1, Shuozhou, 036006, Shanxi, China
Tel.: (86) 3492208501
Coal Mining Equipment Mfr
N.A.I.C.S.: 333131

China Coal Xi'an Engineering Design Co., Ltd.   (1)
North Tanta Road No 66, Xi'an, Shaanxi, China
Tel.: (86) 2987870114
Web Site: http://www.en.cxms.com.cn
Engineeering Services
N.A.I.C.S.: 541330
Binxue Shen *(CEO)*

China National Coal Import & Export (Tianjin) Co., Ltd.   (1)
No 41 Munan Road, Heping District, Tianjin, 300050, China
Tel.: (86) 2223141268
Coal Mining Services
N.A.I.C.S.: 213113

China National Coal Industry Qinhuangdao Imp. & Exp. Co., Ltd.   (1)
No 252 Minzu Road, Qinhuangdao, 066000, Hebei, China
Tel.: (86) 3353878888
Web Site: http://www.chinacoalenergy.com
Coal Mining Services
N.A.I.C.S.: 213113

China National Coal Mining Equipment Co., Ltd.   (1)
No 192 Anwai Dajie, Dongcheng, Beijing, 100011, China
Tel.: (86) 10 64268372
Web Site: http://www.chinacoal-cme.com
Coal Mining Machinery Mfr & Leasing Services
N.A.I.C.S.: 333131

Shanghai ChinaCoal East China Co., Ltd.   (1)
6th Floor No 899 Orient Road, Pudong New District, Shanghai, 200122, China
Tel.: (86) 21 68764227
Web Site: http://www.chinacoalenergy.com
Coal Mining & Whslr
N.A.I.C.S.: 213113

Shanghai Datun Energy Resources Technology Development Company Limited   (1)
Pei Xian, Xuzhou, 211611, Jiangsu, China

Tel.: (86) 51689025204
Energy Saving Equipments Mfr
N.A.I.C.S.: 333414

Sunfield Resources Pty. Limited   (1)
Suite 1602 447 Kent Street, Sydney, 2000, NSW, Australia
Tel.: (61) 292838889
Web Site: http://www.sunfieldresources.com
Emp.: 6
Coal Trading
N.A.I.C.S.: 324199

Xi an Engineering Design Co., Ltd.   (1)
No 64 Yanta Beiduan Heping Men Wai, Xi'an, 710054, Shaanxi, China
Tel.: (86) 29 87857449
Web Site: http://www.chinacoalenergy.com
Coal Mining & Distr
N.A.I.C.S.: 213113

CHINA COAL XINJI ENERGY CO., LTD.
Xinji Energy Office Park Minhui Street, Shannan New District, Huainan, 232001, Anhui, China
Tel.: (86) 5548661819
Web Site: https://en.chinacoal.com
Year Founded: 1997
601918—(SHG)
Rev.: $1,685,201,825
Assets: $4,732,312,740
Liabilities: $2,989,817,649
Net Worth: $1,742,495,091
Earnings: $289,828,633
Emp.: 18,000
Fiscal Year-end: 12/31/22
Coal Mining Services
N.A.I.C.S.: 212114
Wang Zhigen *(Chm)*

CHINA COME RIDE NEW ENERGY GROUP LIMITED
Unit E 33/F Legend Tower 7 Shing Yip Street Kwun Tong, Kowloon, China (Hong Kong)
Tel.: (852) 31877009   Ky
Web Site: http://www.knk.com.hk
8039—(HKG)
Rev.: $5,319,909
Assets: $1,702,149
Liabilities: $1,981,133
Net Worth: ($278,984)
Earnings: ($1,694,926)
Emp.: 26
Fiscal Year-end: 03/31/21
Architectural Engineering Consulting Services
N.A.I.C.S.: 541310
Joe Kai Kit Poon *(Founder & Compliance Officer)*

CHINA COMMUNICATIONS CONSTRUCTION COMPANY LIMITED
No 85 Deshengmenwai Street, Xicheng District, Beijing, 100088, China
Tel.: (86) 1082016655   CN
Web Site: https://en.ccccltd.cn
Year Founded: 2006
1800—(HKG)
Rev.: $95,678,878,950
Assets: $199,811,732,490
Liabilities: $144,992,581,650
Net Worth: $54,819,150,840
Earnings: $3,007,359,090
Emp.: 133,294
Fiscal Year-end: 12/31/20
Construction Engineering Services
N.A.I.C.S.: 237990
Wang Haihuai *(Pres)*

Subsidiaries:

CCCC Dredging (Group) Co., Ltd.   (1)
CCCC Building Block A Desheng International No 85 Deshengmenwai Street,

Xicheng District, Beijing, China
Tel.: (86) 108 201 7839
Web Site: https://www.cccc-cdc.com
Emp.: 10,000
Civil Engineering Construction Services
N.A.I.C.S.: 237990

CCCC Financial Leasing Co., Ltd.   (1)
18th Floor Block B No 3261 Dongfang Road, Pudong New Area, Shanghai, China
Tel.: (86) 216 838 6860
Web Site: https://www.ccclc.com
Bridge Construction Services
N.A.I.C.S.: 237310

CCCC First Harbour Consultants Co., Ltd.   (1)
Fdine Tower 18 Dongting Road, Hexi District, Tianjin, 300222, China
Tel.: (86) 222 816 0808
Web Site: https://en.fdine.com.cn
Construction Engineering Services
N.A.I.C.S.: 541330
Feng Zhongwu *(Pres)*

CCCC First Harbour Engineering Co., Ltd.   (1)
Building No 8 Shipping Services Center Yuejin Road, Tianjin Port Bonded Zone, Tianjin, 300461, China
Tel.: (86) 222 560 0500
Web Site: https://www.ccccyhj.com
Bridge Construction Services
N.A.I.C.S.: 237310

CCCC Fourth Harbour Engineering Co., Ltd.   (1)
Building No 368 Lijiao Road, Haizhu District, Guangzhou, 510290, China
Tel.: (86) 28126575
Web Site: http://www.cccc4.com
Bridge Construction Services
N.A.I.C.S.: 237310

CCCC Fourth Highway Engineering Co., Ltd.   (1)
27th Floor Block A Jindi Center 91 Jianguo Road, Chaoyang District, Beijing, 100022, China
Tel.: (86) 1057673399
Web Site: http://www.ccfourth.com
Emp.: 7,500
Bridge Construction Services
N.A.I.C.S.: 237310

CCCC Fund Management Co., Ltd.   (1)
9th Floor Office Building Block A Donghuan Plaza No 9 Dongzhong Street, Dongcheng District, Beijing, 100027, China
Tel.: (86) 106 414 5888
Web Site: https://www.cccc-fund.com
Fund Management Services
N.A.I.C.S.: 525190

CCCC Guangzhou Dredging Co., Ltd.   (1)
362 Binjiang Road Binjiangzhong Road, Guangzhou, 510221, Guangdong, China
Tel.: (86) 2089004418
Web Site: http://www.ccgdc.com
Dredging Contractors
N.A.I.C.S.: 237990

CCCC Highway Consultants Co., Ltd.   (1)
No 85 Deiwai Street, Xicheng District, Beijing, 100088, China
Tel.: (86) 1082017100
Web Site: http://www.hpdi.com.cn
Emp.: 800
Bridge Construction Services
N.A.I.C.S.: 237310

CCCC International Holding Limited   (1)
28th Floor Room 2805 Office Tower Convention Plaza 1 Harbour Road, Wan Chai, Wanchai, China (Hong Kong)
Tel.: (852) 2 359 8888
Web Site: https://www.ccci.hk
Investment Management Service
N.A.I.C.S.: 523940
Lu Jianzhong *(Chm)*

CCCC Investment Co., Ltd.   (1)
Moutai Building Building 3 No 29 North Third Ring Middle Road, Xicheng District,

Beijing, 100029, China
Tel.: (86) 108 209 7600
Web Site: https://www.ccccic.com.cn
Investment Management Service
N.A.I.C.S.: 523999

CCCC Second Harbour Engineering Co., Ltd.   (1)
No 11 Jinyinhu Road, Dongxihu District, Wuhan, 430040, China
Tel.: (86) 2783920888
Web Site: http://www.sneb.com.cn
Emp.: 7,945
Bridge Construction Services
N.A.I.C.S.: 237310
Jiang Chengshuang *(Chm)*

CCCC Second Highway Consultants Co., Ltd.   (1)
18 Chuangye Road Wuhan Economic and Technological Development Zone, Wuhan, Hubei, China
Tel.: (86) 2784214000
Web Site: http://www.cchcc.cn
Bridge Construction Services
N.A.I.C.S.: 237310
Cheng Ping *(Deputy Gen Mgr)*

CCCC Second Highway Engineering Co., Ltd.   (1)
No 33 Science & Technology Sixth Road, Xi'an, 710065, China
Tel.: (86) 2989560118
Web Site: http://www.seberbc.com
Bridge Construction Services
N.A.I.C.S.: 237310

CCCC Shanghai Equipment Engineering Co., Ltd.   (1)
12F 3456 Pu Dong Nan Road, Shanghai, 200125, China
Tel.: (86) 2150390000
Web Site: http://www.ccccsh.com
Sales Range: $25-49.9 Million
Emp.: 30
Port Machinery Installation & Mfr
N.A.I.C.S.: 333120
Yang Tian *(Gen Mgr)*

CCCC Third Harbour Engineering Co., Ltd.   (1)
No 139 Pingjiang Road, Shanghai, 200032, China
Tel.: (86) 216 403 0607
Web Site: https://www.ccshj.com
Bridge Construction Services
N.A.I.C.S.: 237310

CCCC Xi'an Road Construction Machinery Co., Ltd.   (1)
No 8 West Section of Jinggao South Road, Jingwei Industrial Park, Xi'an, 710200, Shaanxi, China
Tel.: (86) 298 696 6888
Web Site: https://en.rm.com.cn
Emp.: 1,000
Road Construction Machinery Mfr & Sales
N.A.I.C.S.: 333120

China Harbour Engineering Company Ltd.   (1)
9 Chun Xiu Rd, Dong Zhi Men Wai, Beijing, 100027, China
Tel.: (86) 1064175744
Web Site: http://www.chec.bj.cn
Sales Range: $1-4.9 Billion
Emp.: 6,000
Marine Engineering, Dredging, Reclamation & Road & Bridge Design Services
N.A.I.C.S.: 541330
Bo Wang *(VP)*

China Road & Bridge Corporation   (1)
No 88 C Andingmenwai Avenue, Beijing, 100011, China
Tel.: (86) 1064280055
Web Site: http://www.crbc.com
Bridge Construction Services
N.A.I.C.S.: 237310
Lu Shan *(Chm)*

Chuwa Bussan Co., Ltd.   (1)
No 8-14 Higashi Kanda 2-chome, Chiyoda-ku, Tokyo, 101-0031, Japan
Tel.: (81) 35 821 6011
Web Site: http://www.chuwabussan.com
Industrial Machinery Distr
N.A.I.C.S.: 423810

John Holland Group Pty. Ltd. (1)
Level 9 180 Flinders Street, Melbourne, 3000, VIC, Australia
Tel.: (61) 38 698 9400
Web Site: https://www.johnholland.com.au
Engineering, Commercial & Industrial Construction Services
N.A.I.C.S.: 236220
Darryn Alfred Ray (CFO)

Subsidiary (Domestic):

John Holland Constructions Pty Ltd. (2)
70 Trenerry Crescent, Abbotsford, 3067, VIC, Australia
Tel.: (61) 399345209
Web Site: http://www.johnholland.com.au
Engineering, Contracting & Construction Services
N.A.I.C.S.: 236220

Shanghai Zhenhua Heavy Industry Co., Ltd (1)
No 3261 Dongfang Road Pudong New Area, Shanghai, 200125, China
Tel.: (86) 2158396666
Web Site: https://www.zpmc.com
Rev.: $4,238,927,737
Assets: $10,981,128,885
Liabilities: $8,436,751,676
Net Worth: $2,544,377,210
Earnings: $52,219,983
Fiscal Year-end: 12/31/2022
Large Port Loading Equipment & Steel Bridge Mfr
N.A.I.C.S.: 333248
Bin Chen (VP)

Zhenhua Logistics Group Co., Ltd. (1)
No 158 Jingmen Avenue, Xingang, Tianjin, 300461, China
Tel.: (86) 2225762168
Web Site: http://www.eng.zh-logistics.com.cn
Logistics Consulting Servies
N.A.I.C.S.: 541614

CHINA COMMUNICATIONS MULTIMEDIA GROUP CO., LTD.
16F No 508 Section 5 Zhongxiao East Road, Xinyi District, Taipei, 11083, Taiwan
Tel.: (886) 227276801
Web Site: https://www.ccmg.mobi
Year Founded: 2013
6404—(TPE)
Rev.: $1,157,483
Assets: $1,272,054
Liabilities: $878,686
Net Worth: $393,369
Earnings: ($1,179,288)
Fiscal Year-end: 12/31/21
Telecommunication Servicesb
N.A.I.C.S.: 517111

CHINA CONCH ENVIRONMENT PROTECTION HOLDINGS LIMITED
No 1005 South Jiuhua Road, Yijiang District, Wuhu, 241070, Anhui, China   Ky
Web Site: https://www.conchenviro.com
Year Founded: 2020
0587—(HKG)
Rev.: $264,991,710
Assets: $1,307,887,583
Liabilities: $788,868,178
Net Worth: $519,019,405
Earnings: $55,226,536
Emp.: 3,686
Fiscal Year-end: 12/31/22
Holding Company
N.A.I.C.S.: 551112

CHINA CONCH VENTURE HOLDINGS LIMITED
No 1011 South Jiuhua Road, Yijiang District, Wuhu, 241070, China

Tel.: (86) 5538398080   Ky
Web Site: https://www.conchventure.com
Year Founded: 2013
586—(HKG)
Sales Range: $700-749.9 Million
Emp.: 3,941
Holding Company; Energy Preservation, Environmental Protection Solutions & Building Materials
N.A.I.C.S.: 551112
Jingbin Guo (Chm)

Subsidiaries:

Conch Venture Environmental Protection Technology (Shanghai) Co., Ltd. (1)
No 18 Lane 928 Yumin South Road, Jiading District, Shanghai, China
Tel.: (86) 2131083192
Web Site: https://en.conchventure-ep.com
Construction Engineering Services
N.A.I.C.S.: 541330

CHINA CONSTRUCTION BANK (RUSSIA) LIMITED
Lubyanskiy proezd 11/1 bldg 1, 101000, Moscow, Russia
Tel.: (7) 4956759800
Web Site: http://ru.ccb.com
Year Founded: 2013
Sales Range: Less than $1 Million
Commercial Banking Services
N.A.I.C.S.: 522110

CHINA CONSTRUCTION BANK CORPORATION
No 25 Finance Street, Xicheng, Beijing, 100033, China
Tel.: (86) 1066215533   CN
Web Site: https://www.ccb.com
Year Founded: 1954
CICHF—(OTCIQ)
Rev.: $175,685,351,586
Assets: $5,397,862,800,708
Liabilities: $4,951,091,816,133
Net Worth: $446,770,984,575
Earnings: $46,825,351,972
Emp.: 376,871
Fiscal Year-end: 12/31/23
State-Owned Commercial Bank
N.A.I.C.S.: 522110
Gengsheng Zhang (Exec VP)

Subsidiaries:

CCB Futures Co., Ltd. (1)
5F CCB Building 99 Yincheng Road, Pudong District, Shanghai, 200120, China
Tel.: (86) 2160636320
Web Site: http://www.ccbfutures.com
Asset Management Services
N.A.I.C.S.: 523940

CCB International (Holdings) Limited (1)
12th Floor China Construction Bank Tower 3 Connaught Road Central, Central, China (Hong Kong)
Tel.: (852) 39118000
Web Site: https://www.ccbintl.com.hk
Emp.: 100
Investment Services
N.A.I.C.S.: 523999

CCB Trust Co., Ltd. (1)
10th Floor Chang'an Xingrong Center Building 4 No 1, Courtyard Naoshikou Street Xicheng District, Beijing, China
Tel.: (86) 4006495533
Web Site: http://www.ccbtrust.com.cn
Financial Investment Services
N.A.I.C.S.: 523999

China Construction Bank (Asia) Corporation Limited (1)
16F York House The Landmark 15 Queens Road, Central, China (Hong Kong)
Tel.: (852) 27795533
Web Site: http://www.asia.ccb.com

Sales Range: $200-249.9 Million
Personal & Commercial Banking Services
N.A.I.C.S.: 522110

China Construction Bank (Brasil) Banco Multiplo S/A (1)
Web Site: http://www.br.ccb.com
Sales Range: $1-4.9 Billion
Emp.: 920
Banking Services
N.A.I.C.S.: 522110

China Construction Bank (Europe) S.A. (1)
1 Boulevard Royal, 2449, Luxembourg, Luxembourg
Web Site: http://eu.ccb.com
Financial Investment Services
N.A.I.C.S.: 523999

China Construction Bank (London) Limited (1)
111 Old BRoad Street, London, EC2N 1AP, United Kingdom
Tel.: (44) 2070386000
Web Site: http://uk.ccb.com
Financial Investment Services
N.A.I.C.S.: 523999

China Construction Bank (Malaysia) Berhad (1)
Level 20 Menara CCB Quill 6 No6, Leboh Ampang City Centre, 50100, Kuala Lumpur, Malaysia
Tel.: (60) 60321601888
Web Site: http://my.ccb.com
Financial Investment Services
N.A.I.C.S.: 523999

China Construction Bank (New Zealand) Limited (1)
Level 29 Vero Centre 48 Shortland Street, Auckland, 1010, New Zealand
Tel.: (64) 93388200
Web Site: https://nz.ccb.com
Financial Investment Services
N.A.I.C.S.: 523999

PT Bank China Construction Bank Indonesia Tbk (1)
Sahid Sudirman Center Lt 15, Jl Jend Sudirman Kav 68, Jakarta, 10220, Indonesia   (60%)
Tel.: (62) 50821000
Web Site: https://idn.ccb.com
Rev.: $109,760,159
Assets: $1,808,705,373
Liabilities: $1,383,961,602
Net Worth: $424,743,772
Earnings: $15,669,438
Emp.: 1,137
Fiscal Year-end: 12/31/2023
Foreign Exchange Banking Services
N.A.I.C.S.: 523160
You Wen Nan (Chm)

CHINA CONTAINER TERMINAL CORP.
No 275 Section 3 Datong Road, Xizhi District, New Taipei City, 221, Taiwan
Tel.: (886) 286482211
Web Site: https://www.cctcorp.com.tw
Year Founded: 1969
2613—(TAI)
Rev.: $102,956,797
Assets: $336,935,270
Liabilities: $232,826,441
Net Worth: $104,108,829
Earnings: $3,334,903
Fiscal Year-end: 12/31/23
Marine Port Operator
N.A.I.C.S.: 488310

Subsidiaries:

CCTC Friend Stevedore Co., Ltd. (1)
No 275 Sec 3 Datong Rd Xizhi District, New Taipei City, 221, Taiwan
Tel.: (886) 86482211
Logistics Management Services
N.A.I.C.S.: 541614

CHINA COSCO SHIPPING CORPORATION LIMITED
5299 Binjiang Dadao, Pudong New

District, Shanghai, 200080, China
Tel.: (86) 21 6596 6666   CN
Web Site: http://www.coscoshipping.com
Year Founded: 2016
Sales Range: Less than $1 Million
Holding Company; Deep Sea & Coastal Freight Shipping, Logistics & Support Services
N.A.I.C.S.: 551112
Lirong Xu (Chm)

Subsidiaries:

COSCO (H.K.) Shipping Co., Limited (1)
50-51/F COSCO Tower 183 Queens Road, Central, China (Hong Kong)
Tel.: (852) 28098888
Freight Transportation Services
N.A.I.C.S.: 488510

COSCO Anqing Container Shipping Agency Co., Ltd. (1)
Suite 1506 15th Floor Anqing Xinglida Mansion South Jixian Road, Anqing, Anhui, China
Tel.: (86) 556 5563642
Web Site: http://lines.coscoshipping.com
Freight Transportation Services
N.A.I.C.S.: 488510

COSCO Chongqing International Freight Co., Ltd. (1)
22F JinGang Bldg No 3 Buxingjie, Jiangbei District, Chongqing, China
Tel.: (86) 2367989983
Web Site: http://lines.coscoshipping.com
Freight Transportation Services
N.A.I.C.S.: 488510
Yu Jian (Gen Mgr-Customer Svc Dept)

COSCO Finance Co., Ltd. (1)
F19 Yuetan Commercial Plaza A No 2 Yuetan Beijie, Xicheng District, Beijing, 100045, China
Tel.: (86) 10 68083199
Financial Management Services
N.A.I.C.S.: 523999

COSCO Hebei International Freight Co., Ltd. (1)
No 589 Heping Road W, Shijiazhuang, Hebei, China
Tel.: (86) 311 8733 2028
Web Site: http://lines.coscoshipping.com
Freight Transportation Services
N.A.I.C.S.: 488510
Lixin Gu (Mgr-Sls Dept)

COSCO Hunan International Freight Co., Ltd. (1)
23 Floor Room 023 Bofu International Building No 416, Middle Furong Road, Changsha, Hunan, China
Tel.: (86) 731 825 60471
Web Site: http://lines.coscoshipping.com
Freight Transportation Services
N.A.I.C.S.: 488510
Nie Zhang (Deputy Mgr-Sls Dept)

COSCO Huzhou International Freight Co., Ltd. (1)
No 2767 North Secend Ring Road, Huzhou, China
Tel.: (86) 572 2105929
Web Site: http://lines.coscoshipping.com
Freight Transportation Services
N.A.I.C.S.: 488510
Xiaoli Yang (Deputy Mgr-Customer Svc Div)

COSCO Jiangxi International Freight Co., Ltd. (1)
Unit B&C 11F Center No 1368 Honggu Middle Road, Nanchang, Jiangxi, China
Tel.: (86) 791 86491400
Web Site: http://lines.coscoshipping.com
Freight Transportation Services
N.A.I.C.S.: 488510
Zhi Chen (Sls Mgr)

COSCO Manning Cooperation Inc. (1)
6th Floor Building 3 Triumph Center No 170 Beiyuan Road, Chaoyang District, Beijing, 100101, China
Tel.: (86) 10 59639300
Web Site: http://www.coscoman.com
Freight Transportation Services
N.A.I.C.S.: 488510

China COSCO Shipping Corporation
Limited—(Continued)

Subsidiary (Domestic):

**Shenzhen Cosco International Ship-
management Co., Ltd.** (2)
Room 3021 Top Office Glittery City No 3027
Shennan Road Central, Shenzhen, 518033,
China
Tel.: (86) 755 83289181
Web Site: http://www.coscoman.com
Freight Transportation Services
N.A.I.C.S.: 488510

**COSCO Neimenggu International
Freight Co., Ltd.** (1)
No 28 City Building Room 1008, Zhongshan
Lu hui District, Hohhot, Neimenggu, China
Tel.: (86) 471 6673199
Web Site: http://lines.coscoshipping.com
Freight Transportation Services
N.A.I.C.S.: 488510

**COSCO Ningxia International Freight
Co., Ltd.** (1)
4/1/301 Xinnengyuan Garden Huanghe
Dong Road, Jinfeng District, Yinchuan,
China
Tel.: (86) 951 6710768
Web Site: http://lines.coscoshipping.com
Freight Transportation Services
N.A.I.C.S.: 488510
Li Na Yang *(Mgr-Sls Dept)*

**COSCO Qingdao International
Freight Co., Ltd.** (1)
Room 303 3F No 6 HanCheng Road,
Qingdao, Shandong, China
Tel.: (86) 532 55 713 883
Web Site: http://lines.coscoshipping.com
Freight Transportation Services
N.A.I.C.S.: 488510
Peng Liu *(Mgr-Customer Svc Div)*

**COSCO Qinghai International Freight
Co., Ltd.** (1)
28-2-212 No 16 Nanshan Road, Xining,
Qinghai, China
Tel.: (86) 971 5500357
Web Site: http://lines.coscoshipping.com
Freight Transportation Services
N.A.I.C.S.: 488510
Hao Huang *(Mgr)*

**COSCO SHIPPING (Hong Kong) Co.,
Limited** (1)
52/F 47/F COSCO Tower Queen's Road,
183 Queen's Road, Central, China (Hong
Kong) (66.12%)
Tel.: (852) 28098888
Web Site: https://hk.coscoshipping.com
Holding Company
N.A.I.C.S.: 551112
Xianghao Liu *(VP & Controller-Fin)*

Subsidiary (Non-US):

**Beijing COSCO SHIPPING Invest-
ment Co., Ltd.** (2)
Rm 909 Block A Lucky Tower No 3 East
Third-Ring Road, Chaoyang District, Beijing,
100027, China
Tel.: (86) 10 6466 6426
Web Site: http://www.coscointl.com
Financial Management Services
N.A.I.C.S.: 523940

Subsidiary (Domestic):

Beijing Ocean Hotel Co., Ltd. (3)
189 Dong Si South Street, Dong Cheng
District, Beijing, 100005, China
Tel.: (86) 10 6522 8888
Web Site: http://www.coscointl.com
Hotel Operator
N.A.I.C.S.: 721110

**COSCO (Beijing) Enterprises Co.,
Ltd.** (3)
No 6 East Chang An Avenue, Dongcheng
District, Beijing, China
Tel.: (86) 10 6512 1188
Web Site: http://www.coscointl.com
Property Management Services
N.A.I.C.S.: 531390

Subsidiary (Domestic):

**COSCO (HK) Freight Service Hold-
ings Ltd.** (2)

Rm 4007-9 40/F COSCO Tower 183
Queen's Road, Central, China (Hong Kong)
Tel.: (852) 2559 1996
Holding Company
N.A.I.C.S.: 551112

**COSCO SHIPPING (Hong Kong)
Property Development Limited** (2)
Rm 4208 42/F COSCO Tower 183 Queen's
Road, Central, China (Hong Kong)
Tel.: (852) 2809 6326
Web Site: http://www.coscointl.com
Real Estate Development Services
N.A.I.C.S.: 531390

Subsidiary (Domestic):

**COSCO International Travel (HK)
Co., Ltd.** (3)
Rm 4013 40/F COSCO Tower 183 Queen's
Road, Central, China (Hong Kong)
Tel.: (852) 2559 0666
Web Site: http://www.coscointl.com
Travel Agency
N.A.I.C.S.: 561510

**Hong Kong COSCO Hotel Manage-
ment Co., Ltd.** (3)
20-21 Kennedy Town Praya Road, Hong
Kong, China (Hong Kong)
Tel.: (852) 2816 2358
Web Site: http://www.coscointl.com
Hotel Management Services; Hotels
N.A.I.C.S.: 721110

Subsidiary (Non-US):

**Jiang Men Yuan Hui Property Co.,
Ltd.** (3)
No 13 Gangkou 1st Road No 2 COSCO
Tower, Jiangmen, 529051, Guangdong,
China
Tel.: (86) 750 3383 328
Web Site: http://www.coscointl.com
Real Estate Development Services
N.A.I.C.S.: 531390

Subsidiary (Domestic):

**COSCO Shipping International (Hong
Kong) Co., Ltd.** (2)
52/F & 47/F COSCO Tower, Queens Road,
Central, China (Hong Kong) (66.12%)
Tel.: (852) 28097888
Web Site: http://www.coscointl.com
Rev.: $505,223,723
Assets: $1,177,397,858
Liabilities: $141,896,408
Net Worth: $1,035,501,450
Earnings: $46,779,368
Emp.: 850
Fiscal Year-end: 12/31/2022
Diversified Investment & Holding Company;
Ship Trading; Supplying Services; Property
Investment & Development; Infrastructure
Investment; Building Construction
N.A.I.C.S.: 551112
Jianhui Zhu *(Chm & Mng Dir)*

Subsidiary (Domestic):

**COSCO SHIPPING (Hong Kong) In-
surance Brokers Limited** (3)
Rm 4701 14/F COSCO Tower, 183 Queens
Road, Central, China (Hong Kong)
Tel.: (852) 2809 6696
Web Site: http://www.coscointl.com
Insurance Brokerage Services
N.A.I.C.S.: 524210

**COSCO SHIPPING (Hong Kong)
Ship Trading Company Limited** (3)
Rm 4802 48/F COSCO Tower, 183 Queens
Road, Central, China (Hong Kong)
Tel.: (852) 28098388
Web Site: http://www.coscointl.com
Freight Transportation Services
N.A.I.C.S.: 488510

Subsidiary (Non-US):

**COSCO (Beijing) Marine Electronic
Equipment Limited** (4)
13/F Qiancun Commercial Mansion Anzhen
Xili, Chaoyang District, Beijing, 100029,
China
Tel.: (86) 10 5834 1558
Web Site: http://www.coscointl.com
Marine Equipment & Spare Parts Trading
N.A.I.C.S.: 423690

**Coscoship Beijing Company
Limited** (4)
Rm 1108 Lucky Tower A 3 Dong San Huan
Bei Road, Chaoyang District, Beijing,
100027, China
Tel.: (86) 10 6466 6411
Web Site: http://www.coscointl.com
Freight Transportation Services
N.A.I.C.S.: 488510

Joint Venture (Non-US):

**Tianjin Cosco Kansai Paint & Chemi-
cals Co., Ltd.** (3)
42 5th Avenue, TEDA, Tianjin, 300457,
China
Tel.: (86) 22 2529 2004
Web Site: http://www.kansai.com.cn
Paint & Chemical Mfr
N.A.I.C.S.: 325510

Subsidiary (Non-US):

Xing Yuan (Singapore) Pte. Ltd. (3)
7 Soon Lee Street #02-38 Ispace, Singa-
pore, 627608, Singapore
Tel.: (65) 62783368
Web Site: http://www.coscointl.com
Freight Transportation Services; Marine
Equipment & Spare Parts Trading
N.A.I.C.S.: 488510

Subsidiary (Domestic):

**Yuantong Marine Service Co.
Limited** (3)
Units 3-9 Level 27 Tower 2 Kowloon Com-
merce Centre, 51 Kwai Cheong Road Kwai
Chung, Central, New Territories, China
(Hong Kong)
Tel.: (852) 2851 2011
Web Site: http://www.coscointl.com
Marine Equipment Installation Services; Ma-
rine Equipment & Spare Parts Trading
N.A.I.C.S.: 336611

Subsidiary (US):

**Yuan Hua Technical & Supply
Corporation** (4)
100 Lighting Way, Secaucus, NJ
07094-3681 (51%)
Tel.: (201) 422-8994
Web Site: http://www.coscointl.com
Marine Equipment & Spare Parts Supply;
Vessel Management Services
N.A.I.C.S.: 336611

Subsidiary (Non-US):

**Yuantong Marine Trade (Shanghai)
Co. Limited** (3)
Room 801 Block B Hopson Fortune Plaza
No 839 Dalian Road, Hong Kou District,
Shanghai, 200086, China
Tel.: (86) 21 6590 9061
Web Site: http://www.coscointl.com
Ship Building & Repairing Services
N.A.I.C.S.: 336611

**COSCO SHIPPING (South East Asia)
Pte. Ltd.** (1)
30 Cecil St #26-01 Prudential Tower, Singa-
pore, 049712, Singapore
Tel.: (65) 68850888
Holding Company
N.A.I.C.S.: 551112

Subsidiary (Domestic):

**COSCO SHIPPING International
(Singapore) Co., Ltd.** (2)
30 Cecil Street 26-01 Prudential Tower, Sin-
gapore, 049712, Singapore
Tel.: (65) 68850858
Web Site:
https://www.coscoshipping.com.sg
Rev.: $135,355,601
Assets: $648,593,501
Liabilities: $276,691,661
Net Worth: $371,901,840
Earnings: $1,990,457
Emp.: 841
Fiscal Year-end: 12/31/2023
Shipping, Ship Repair & Other Shipping Re-
lated Services
N.A.I.C.S.: 483111
Zhu Jian Dong *(Chm & Pres)*

Subsidiary (Non-US):

**COSCO (Shanghai) Shipyard Co.,
Ltd** (3)
2600 Longwu Road, Shanghai, 200231,
China
Tel.: (86) 21 5482 1256
Ship Building & Repairing Services
N.A.I.C.S.: 336611

Subsidiary (Domestic):

**COSCO Marine Engineering (Singa-
pore) Pte Ltd.** (3)
52 Penjuru Lane, Singapore, 609213,
Singapore (90%)
Tel.: (65) 6261 8009
Ship Building & Repairing Services
N.A.I.C.S.: 336611

Cogent Holdings Limited (3)
Cogent 1 Logistics Hub 1 Buroh Crescent
#6M-01, Singapore, 627545, Singapore
Tel.: (65) 62666161
Web Site: http://www.cogentholdingsltd.com
Holding Company; Freight Transportation,
Warehousing & Other Logistics Services
N.A.I.C.S.: 551112

**COSCO SHIPPING Development
Co., Ltd.** (1)
No 5299 Binjiang Avenue, Pudong New
Area, Shanghai, 200127, China
Tel.: (86) 2165966666
Web Site:
http://en.development.coscoshipping.com
Rev.: $3,598,983,793
Assets: $17,991,800,906
Liabilities: $3,598,983,793
Net Worth: $4,056,760,745
Earnings: $550,586,659
Emp.: 7,964
Fiscal Year-end: 12/31/2022
Container Shipping ervices
N.A.I.C.S.: 488510
Chong Liu *(Gen Mgr, Gen Mgr, Exec Dir &
Exec Dir)*

Subsidiary (Domestic):

**China Shipping Investment Co.,
Ltd** (2)
24F No 1050 Dongda Ming Road, Shang-
hai, 200080, China
Tel.: (86) 21 6596 8084
Web Site: http://www.csinvest.com.cn
Ship Building & Repair Services
N.A.I.C.S.: 336611

Subsidiary (Non-US):

**Florens Asset Management Company
Limited** (2)
50/F COSCO Tower 183 Queens Road,
Central, China (Hong Kong)
Tel.: (852) 2866 9959
Web Site: http://www.florens.com
Holding Company; Container Management
Services
N.A.I.C.S.: 551112
Peter Su *(CEO)*

Subsidiary (US):

**Florens Asset Management (USA),
Limited** (3)
100 Lighting Way, Secaucus, NJ 07094
Tel.: (973) 890-5050
Web Site: http://www.florens.com
Storage Containers Leasing Services
N.A.I.C.S.: 532490
Lisa Hall *(Mktg Mgr-US East Coast & East-
ern Canada)*

**COSCO SHIPPING Energy Transpor-
tation Co., Ltd.** (1)
No 670 Dongdaming Road, Hongkou Dis-
trict, Shanghai, 200080, China
Tel.: (86) 2165967678
Web Site: https://energy.coscoshipping.com
Rev.: $2,492,450,462
Assets: $10,105,709,691
Liabilities: $4,651,074,260
Net Worth: $5,454,635,431
Earnings: $403,163,535
Emp.: 7,398
Fiscal Year-end: 12/31/2020
Oil, Coal & Dry Bulk Cargo Shipping
N.A.I.C.S.: 488510
Liu Hanbo *(CEO & Exec Dir)*

COSCO SHIPPING Financial Holdings Co., Limited **(1)**
32/F China Merchants Tower Shun Tak Centre 168-200 Connaught Road, Central, China (Hong Kong)
Tel.: (852) 28150338
Web Site: http://www.cnshipping.com.hk
Holding Company
N.A.I.C.S.: 551112

Subsidiary (Non-US):

Ningbo Pacific Container Co., Ltd. **(2)**
No 101 Qihang North Road, Zhanqi Yinzhou, Ningbo, 315145, China
Tel.: (86) 57488194618
Container Mfr
N.A.I.C.S.: 332439

Qidong Singamas Energy Equipment Co., Ltd. **(2)**
No 1 Taiping Road, Huiping, Qidong, 226262, Jiangsu, China
Tel.: (86) 51383681333
Container Mfr
N.A.I.C.S.: 332439
Danny Guo *(Mktg Mgr)*

Qingdao Pacific Container Co., Ltd. **(2)**
No 373 Maoshan Road Qingdao Economic And Technical Development Zone, Qingdao, Shandong, China
Tel.: (86) 53286916160
Web Site: http://www.qpclcontainer.com
Bulk Container Mfr
N.A.I.C.S.: 332420
Benson Ji *(Mgr-Mktg)*

Subsidiary (Domestic):

Qidong Pacific Port Co., Ltd. **(3)**
No 1 Taiping Road, Huiping, Qidong, 226262, Jiangsu, China
Tel.: (86) 51383613333
Container Mfr
N.A.I.C.S.: 332439

COSCO SHIPPING Korea Co., Ltd. **(1)**
11F Dong-Woo Bldg 708-1 Yeogsam-Dong, Kangnam-gu, Seoul, 135 080, Korea (South)
Tel.: (82) 2 5656710
Web Site: http://lines.coscoshipping.com
Freight Transportation Services
N.A.I.C.S.: 488510

COSCO SHIPPING Lines (France) S.A.S. **(1)**
1 rue Mozart, 92110, Clichy, France
Tel.: (33) 147585975
Web Site: http://lines.coscoshipping.com
Freight Transportation Services
N.A.I.C.S.: 488510

COSCO SHIPPING Lines (Oceania) Pty. Ltd. **(1)**
Level 2 101 Sussex Street, Sydney, 2000, NSW, Australia
Tel.: (61) 293739588
Web Site: http://www.coscoshipping.com.au
Freight Transportation Services
N.A.I.C.S.: 488510

COSCO SHIPPING Lines (Spain) S.A. **(1)**
2 Casanova Street 6th floor, 08011, Barcelona, Spain
Tel.: (34) 933047126
Web Site: http://coscospain.com
Freight Transportation Services
N.A.I.C.S.: 488510
Cunxun Huang *(Mng Dir)*

COSCO SHIPPING Logistics Co., Ltd. **(1)**
No 220 Balizhuang Beili Block, Chaoyang District, Beijing, 100025, China
Tel.: (86) 10 51568000
Web Site: http://www.cosco-logistics.com.cn
Freight Transportation Services
N.A.I.C.S.: 488510
Jun Han *(Chm & Pres)*

Subsidiary (Domestic):

COSCO SHIPPING Logistics (Beijing) Co., Ltd. **(2)**

10F Towercrest Plaza No 3 Maizidian West Road, Chaoyang District, Beijing, 100125, China
Tel.: (86) 84688800
Web Site: http://www.cosco-logistics.com.cn
Freight Transportation Services
N.A.I.C.S.: 488510

Subsidiary (Non-US):

COSCO SHIPPING Logistics (Hong Kong) Co., Ltd. **(2)**
Rm 4008-4009 COSCO Tower 183 Queen's Road, Central, China (Hong Kong)
Tel.: (852) 25591996
Web Site: http://www.cosco-logistics.com.cn
Container Shipping ervices
N.A.I.C.S.: 488510

Subsidiary (Domestic):

COSCO SHIPPING Logistics (Nanjing) Co., Ltd. **(2)**
No 330 North Zhongshan Road, Nanjing, 210003, China
Tel.: (86) 25 58779068
Web Site: http://www.coscologistics.sh.cn
Freight Transportation Services
N.A.I.C.S.: 488510

COSCO SHIPPING Logistics (Ningbo) Co., Ltd. **(2)**
No 58 Dazha Road North Shore Fortune Center, Ningbo, 315020, China
Tel.: (86) 574 87032288
Web Site: http://www.cosco-logisticsnb.com.cn
Freight Transportation Services
N.A.I.C.S.: 488510
Yansong Zhang *(Gen Mgr)*

COSCO SHIPPING Logistics (Qingdao) Co., Ltd. **(2)**
21 Wuxia Road, Qingdao, 266002, China
Tel.: (86) 532 82916666
Web Site: http://www.cosco-logisticsqd.com
Emp.: 2,133
Freight Transportation Services
N.A.I.C.S.: 488510

Subsidiary (Non-US):

COSCO SHIPPING Logistics (West Asia) L.L.C. **(2)**
PO Box 122997, Dubai, 999041, United Arab Emirates
Tel.: (971) 4 3687142
Web Site: http://www.cosco-logistics.com.cn
Deep Sea Freight Transportation Services
N.A.I.C.S.: 483111

Subsidiary (Domestic):

Cosco Logistics (Dalian) Co Ltd. **(2)**
Floor 10-12 Seaview Hotel No 2 Gangwan Street, Zhongshan District, Dalian, 116001, China
Tel.: (86) 411 82513888
Web Site: http://www.cosco-logisticsdl.com
Freight Transportation Services
N.A.I.C.S.: 488510

Rizhao COSCO Logistics Limited **(2)**
106 Huanghai Road 1, Rizhao, 276826, Shandong, China
Tel.: (86) 633 8320765
Web Site: http://www.penavicorz.com
Freight Transportation Services
N.A.I.C.S.: 488510

Shenzhen COSCO Logistics Co., Ltd. **(2)**
25/F Liantai Building Zhuzilin, Futian District, Shenzhen, 518040, China
Tel.: (86) 755 23955000
Web Site: http://www.cosco-logistics.gz.cn
Freight Forwarding Services
N.A.I.C.S.: 488510

Zhanjiang COSCO Logistics Co., Ltd. **(2)**
No 7 Renmin East Road, Xiashan District, Zhanjiang, 524001, Guangdong, China
Tel.: (86) 759 2381001
Web Site: http://www.cosco-logistics.gz.cn
Container Shipping ervices
N.A.I.C.S.: 488510

COSCO SHIPPING Network Limited **(1)**

Rm 4206 42/F COSCO Tower 183 Queen's Road, Central, China (Hong Kong)
Tel.: (852) 2809 7178
Web Site: http://www.coscointl.com
Freight Transportation Services
N.A.I.C.S.: 488510

COSCO SHIPPING Specialized Carriers Co., Ltd. **(1)**
15F-26F COSCO Guangzhou Building No 20 Huacheng Avenue, Zhujiang New Town, Guangzhou, 510623, Guangdong, China
Tel.: (86) 2038161888
Web Site: http://www.coscol.com.cn
Rev.: $1,713,895,766
Assets: $3,542,819,736
Liabilities: $2,038,511,377
Net Worth: $1,504,308,359
Earnings: $115,232,093
Fiscal Year-end: 12/31/2022
Ocean Shipping Services
N.A.I.C.S.: 483111
Zhang Wei *(Chm)*

Subsidiary (Domestic):

COSCO Guangzhou Marine Service Co., Ltd. **(2)**
2/F 404-4 Huan Shi Dong Road, Guangzhou, 510061, China
Tel.: (86) 20 37634623
Web Site: http://www.coscol.com.cn
Freight Transportation Services; Shipping Mechanical Instalation & Maintenance
N.A.I.C.S.: 488510

Subsidiary (Non-US):

COSCO SHIPPING Heavy Transport (Europe) B.V. **(2)**
Otto Reuchlinweg 1142, 3072 MD, Rotterdam, Netherlands
Tel.: (31) 10 24 04 777
Web Site: http://www.coscoht.com
Freight Transportation Services
N.A.I.C.S.: 488510
Cai Guo Jun *(CFO)*

COSCO SHIPPING Technology Co., Ltd. **(1)**
No 600 Minsheng Road, Pudong New Area, Shanghai, 200135, China
Tel.: (86) 2165969398
Web Site: http://tech.coscoshipping.com
Rev.: $245,921,832
Assets: $439,890,048
Liabilities: $238,031,352
Net Worth: $201,858,696
Earnings: $25,541,568
Fiscal Year-end: 12/31/2022
Intelligent Transportation Systems & Industrial Automation Products Mfr
N.A.I.C.S.: 334513
Liang Yanfeng *(Chm)*

COSCO Shanxi International Freight Co., Ltd. **(1)**
No 11 Building Hongyeli, Yifenyuan Community, Taiyuan, Shanxi, China
Tel.: (86) 351 6260 106
Web Site: http://lines.coscoshipping.com
Freight Transportation Services
N.A.I.C.S.: 488510
Guo Hong Jia *(Asst Mgr-Sls Dept)*

COSCO Shaoxing International Freight Co., Ltd. **(1)**
11/F Tianma Building South of City Jiefang South Road, Shaoxing, Zhejiang, China
Tel.: (86) 575 88319318
Web Site: http://lines.coscoshipping.com
Freight Transportation Services
N.A.I.C.S.: 488510

COSCO Shenzhen International Freight Co., Ltd. **(1)**
2/F China Merchants Development Center Nanhai Road, Nanshan District, Shenzhen, 518067, China
Tel.: (86) 755 26839999
Web Site: http://lines.coscoshipping.com
Freight Transportation Services
N.A.I.C.S.: 488510
Pei Deng *(Mgr-Foreign Trade Div)*

COSCO Shipping (UK) Company Limited **(1)**
COSCO House Vicarage Drive, Essex, Barking, IG11 7NA, United Kingdom

Tel.: (44) 2085948688
Freight Transportation Services
N.A.I.C.S.: 488510

COSCO Shipping Guangxi International Freight Co., Ltd. **(1)**
28/F T2 Shangdong International Building No 166 Minzu Avenue, Nanning, Guangxi, China
Tel.: (86) 771 5582820
Web Site: http://lines.coscoshipping.com
Freight Forwarding Services
N.A.I.C.S.: 488510
Kun Jiang *(Mgr-Domestic Trade Div)*

COSCO Shipping Guangzhou International Freight Co., Ltd. **(1)**
4F No Yanjiang Dong Road, Guangzhou, 510100, China
Tel.: (86) 20 830 51398
Web Site: http://lines.coscoshipping.com
Freight Transportation Services
N.A.I.C.S.: 488510
Bryant Chen *(Mgr-Foreign Trade Div)*

COSCO Shipping Guizhou International Freight Co., Ltd. **(1)**
B-9-4 9-5 Empark Shopping Center, Guiyang, Guizhou, China
Tel.: (86) 851 6813403
Web Site: http://www.coscoshipping.com
Freight Transportation Services
N.A.I.C.S.: 488510

COSCO Shipping International Trading Company Limited **(1)**
12A/F Qiancun Mansions A 5th Block Anzhen Xili, Chaoyang District, Beijing, China
Tel.: (86) 10 58341 688
Web Site: http://www.coscotrading.com.cn
Trade & Supply Chain Services
N.A.I.C.S.: 541614
Min Li *(Gen Mgr)*

COSCO Shipping Jiangsu International Freight Co., Ltd. **(1)**
20F Block A New Century Plaza No 288 East Zhongshan Road, Nanjing, China
Tel.: (86) 25 52335908
Web Site: http://lines.coscoshipping.com
Freight Transportation Services
N.A.I.C.S.: 488510
Bo Li *(Gen Mgr-Jiangsu & Anhui Sls Unit)*

COSCO Shipping Jiangsu International Freight Co., Ltd. **(1)**
7/F No 109 West Shazhou Road, Zhangjiagang, Jiangsu, China
Tel.: (86) 512 58 33 11 76
Web Site: http://lines.coscoshipping.com
Freight Transportation Services
N.A.I.C.S.: 488510
Jia You *(Deputy Gen Mgr-Sls Unit)*

COSCO Shipping Lines (Canada) Inc. **(1)**
Suite 2288 Four Bentall Centre 1055 Dunsmuir, PO Box 49208, Vancouver, V7X 1K8, BC, Canada
Tel.: (604) 689-8989
Web Site: http://lines.coscoshipping.com
Container Shipping & Freight Transportation Services
N.A.I.C.S.: 488510

COSCO Shipping Lines (North America) Inc. **(1)**
100 Lighting Way 3rd Fl, Secaucus, NJ 07094-3681
Tel.: (201) 422-0500
Web Site: http://lines.coscoshipping.com
Holding Company; Regional Managing Office
N.A.I.C.S.: 551112

Subsidiary (Domestic):

COSCO Agencies (Los Angeles) Inc. **(2)**
588 Harbor Scenic Way 3rd Fl, Long Beach, CA 90802
Tel.: (213) 689-6700
Web Site: http://www.lines.coscoshipping.com
Marine Cargo Handling
N.A.I.C.S.: 488510

Subsidiary (Non-US):

COSCO Brasil S.A. **(2)**

China COSCO Shipping Corporation Limited—(Continued)

Av Paulista 1337 - 18 Andar, CEP 01311-200, Sao Paulo, Brazil
Tel.: (55) 11 3177 2888
Web Site: http://www.cosco.com.br
Freight Transportation Services
N.A.I.C.S.: 488510
Edison Santana (Mgr)

COSCO Chile S.A. (2)
Alonso de Cordova #5670 9th Floor 904 Office, Las Condes, Santiago, Chile
Tel.: (56) 2 222 92 492
Web Site:
    http://www.lines.coscoshipping.com
Freight Transportation Services
N.A.I.C.S.: 488510

COSCO Peru S.A. (2)
Av Republica de Panama 3418 Oficina 401, San Isidro, Lima, Peru
Tel.: (51) 1 421 5014
Web Site:
    http://www.lines.coscoshipping.com
Freight Transportation Services
N.A.I.C.S.: 488510

COSCO SHIPPING Argentina (2)
Av Paseo Colon 221 1st Floor, Buenos Aires, 1063, Argentina
Tel.: (54) 1143430607
Web Site: http://lines.coscoshipping.com
Freight Transportation Services
N.A.I.C.S.: 488510

Subsidiary (Domestic):

Sea Trade International, Inc. (2)
100 Lighting Way, Secaucus, NJ 07094
Tel.: (201) 422-8688
Web Site: http://www.seatrade-usa.com
Deep Sea Freight Transportation
N.A.I.C.S.: 483111
Kelly Mao (Acct Mgr)

COSCO Shipping Lines Co., Ltd. (1)
No 378 Dong Da Ming Road, Shanghai, 200080, China
Tel.: (86) 2135124888
Sales Range: $5-14.9 Billion
Deep Sea Freight Container Transportation Services
N.A.I.C.S.: 483111

Subsidiary (US):

COSCO Container Lines North America Inc. (2)
100 Lighting Way 3rd Floor, Secaucus, NJ 07094
Tel.: (201) 422-0500
Web Site: http://lines.coscoshipping.com
Deep Sea Freight Container Transportation Services
N.A.I.C.S.: 483111
Frank Grossi (Exec VP)

Subsidiary (Non-US):

COSCO Container Lines Vietnam Company Ltd. (2)
209 Nguyen Van Thu St, Da Kao Ward District 1, Ho Chi Minh City, Vietnam
Tel.: (84) 8 3829 0000
Web Site: http://www.coscoshipping.com
Freight Transportation Services
N.A.I.C.S.: 488510

COSCO SHIPPING Lines (Central Europe) s.r.o. (2)
Karolinska 650/1, 186 00, Prague, Czech Republic
Tel.: (420) 227 355 333
Web Site: http://lines.coscoshipping.com
Freight Forwarding Services
N.A.I.C.S.: 488510

COSCO SHIPPING Lines (Japan) Co., Ltd. (2)
3-2-1 Kasumigaseki 33rd Floor Kasumigaseki Common Gate Western Hall, Chiyoda-ku, Tokyo, 100013, Japan
Web Site: http://www.cosco.co.jp
Freight Transportation Services
N.A.I.C.S.: 488510

COSCO SHIPPING Lines (Malaysia) Sdn. Bhd. (2)
Suite 19.03 & 19.04B The Pinnacle Persi-aran Lagoon, Bandar Sunway, 46150, Petaling Jaya, Selangor, Malaysia (100%)
Tel.: (60) 3 5624 4188
Web Site: http://www.coscoshipping.com.my
Emp.: 214
Freight Transportation Services
N.A.I.C.S.: 488510
Tian Hua (Mng Dir)

COSCO SHIPPING Lines (New Zealand) Ltd (2)
Level 2 9 Nelson Street, Auckland, 1010, New Zealand
Tel.: (64) 9 3027393
Web Site: http://www.cosco.co.nz
Freight Transportation Services
N.A.I.C.S.: 488510
Fleur Seretis (Mgr-Sls & Mktg)

COSCO SHIPPING Lines (Romania) Co. Ltd. Srl (2)
Splaiul Unirii St No 86 1st-2nd Floors, District 4, 040038, Bucharest, Romania
Tel.: (40) 21 210 95 19
Web Site: http://www.csromania.ro
Freight Transportation Services
N.A.I.C.S.: 488510
Catalin Petre (Deputy Gen Mgr)

Cosco Lanka (Pvt) Ltd. (2)
3rd Floor Sayuru Sevena 46/12 Nawam Mw, Colombo, Sri Lanka
Tel.: (94) 112 167 300
Web Site: http://lines.coscoshipping.com
Freight Transportation Services
N.A.I.C.S.: 488510

Coskor Shipping Co., Ltd. (2)
11F Dongwoo Building 328 Teheranro, Gangnam-gu, Seoul, 16212, Korea (South)
Tel.: (82) 2 5671171
Web Site: http://coscoshipping.co.kr
Freight Transportation Services
N.A.I.C.S.: 488510

New Golden Sea Shipping Pte., Ltd. (2)
30 Cecil Street #25-01 Prudential Tower, Singapore, 049712, Singapore
Tel.: (65) 6812 8288
Web Site: http://lines.coscoshipping.com
Container Shipping ervices
N.A.I.C.S.: 488510
Ramon Zhu (Gen Mgr-Global Sls Dept)

Subsidiary (Domestic):

Shanghai Pan Asia Shipping Company Limited (2)
No 658 Dongda Ming Road, Shanghai, China
Tel.: (86) 21 3540 4688
Web Site: http://www.panasiashipping.com
Container Shipping ervices
N.A.I.C.S.: 488510

Tangshan COSCO SHIPPING Lines Logistics Co., Ltd. (2)
No 9 Haibin Road, Tangshan Seaport Economic Development Zone, Tangshan, China
Web Site: http://lines.coscoshipping.com
Freight Transportation Services
N.A.I.C.S.: 488510
Zhenmin Zhu (Deputy Gen Mgr)

COSCO Shipping Lines Emirates LLC (1)
Citadel Tower 30th Floor Sheikh Zayed Road Business Bay, PO Box 28732, Dubai, United Arab Emirates
Tel.: (971) 4 4526 868
Web Site: http://lines.coscoshipping.com
Freight Transportation Services
N.A.I.C.S.: 488510
C. C. Appachu (Deputy Gen Mgr)

COSCO Shipping Yunnan International Freight Co., Ltd. (1)
Room 2808 28th Floor Block B Linlan Plaza Xinxin Road, Panlong District, Kunming, Yunnan, China
Tel.: (86) 871 651 20 518
Web Site: http://lines.coscoshipping.com
Freight Transportation Services
N.A.I.C.S.: 488510
Ming Liu (Deputy Mgr-Mktg & Sls Div)

COSCO Taicang International Freight Co., Ltd. (1)
7F No 309 Zhenghe Zhong Road, Taicang,
Jiangsu, China
Tel.: (86) 512 53562718
Web Site: http://lines.coscoshipping.com
Freight Transportation Services
N.A.I.C.S.: 488510
Yun Li (Deputy Gen Mgr-Sls Unit)

COSCO Tianjin International Freight Co., Ltd. (1)
Rm 302 Building 14 No 1 Dongfeng Zhong Road, Hangu, Tianjin, China
Tel.: (86) 22 6711 9319
Web Site: http://lines.coscoshipping.com
Freight Transportation Services
N.A.I.C.S.: 488510
Yingjian Zhou (Mgr-Sls)

COSCO Wenzhou International Freight Co., Ltd. (1)
Room 1101 Hengjiu Building No 525 ShiFu Road, Wenzhou, Zhejiang, China
Tel.: (86) 577 8895 9605
Web Site: http://lines.coscoshipping.com
Freight Transportation Services
N.A.I.C.S.: 488510
Li Zhou (Mgr-Mktg & Sls)

COSCO Wuxi International Freight Co., Ltd. (1)
9/F No 800 Yinxiu Road, Binhu District, Wuxi, Jiangsu, China
Tel.: (86) 510 82711282
Web Site: http://lines.coscoshipping.com
Freight Transportation Services
N.A.I.C.S.: 488510
Yanqing Xia (Mgr-Customer Svc Div)

COSCO Yangpu Shipping Agency Ltd. (1)
Rm 901 Xinpu Building Yangpu Development Zone, Yangpu, Hainan, China
Tel.: (86) 898 28823711
Web Site: http://lines.coscoshipping.com
Freight Transportation Services
N.A.I.C.S.: 488510

COSCO Yangzhou international Freight Co., Ltd. (1)
Room 718-720 Block 7 Building A Huayuan International Mansion, 215 West Wenhui, Yangzhou, China
Tel.: (86) 514 877 82 805
Web Site: http://lines.coscoshipping.com
Freight Transportation Services
N.A.I.C.S.: 488510
Jianhua Dong (Mgr-Customer Svc Dept)

COSCO Zhejiang International Freight Co., Ltd. (1)
Floor 10 Kaixuanmen Plaza No 11 Qingchun Road, Hangzhou, Zhejiang, China
Tel.: (86) 571 87239628
Web Site: http://lines.coscoshipping.com
Freight Transportation Services
N.A.I.C.S.: 488510
Weijiang Chen (Gen Mgr)

COSCO Zhenjiang International Freight Co., Ltd. (1)
11/F No 61 Nanshan Rd, Zhenjiang, Jiangsu, China
Tel.: (86) 511 85 21 30 19
Web Site: http://lines.coscoshipping.com
Freight Transportation Services
N.A.I.C.S.: 488510
Xiang Ai (Mgr-Customer Svc Div)

China Shipping Agency Co., Ltd. (1)
10-11F No 118 Yuanshen Road, Pudong New Area, Shanghai, 200120, China
Tel.: (86) 21 6596 6898
Web Site: http://www.csagency.com.cn
Emp.: 1,600
Shipping Agency Services
N.A.I.C.S.: 488510

China Shipping Bulk Carrier Co., Ltd. (1)
308th Bin Jiang Zhong Road, Guangzhou, China
Tel.: (86) 20 84100338
Web Site: http://www.csbulk.com
Freight Transportation Services
N.A.I.C.S.: 488510
Qiu Guoxuan (Mng Dir)

Cosco Shipping Agency (Greece) S.A. (1)
85 Akti Miaouli & 2 Flessa Str, 185 38, Pi-raeus, Greece
Tel.: (30) 210 4290810
Web Site: http://lines.coscoshipping.com
Container Shipping ervices
N.A.I.C.S.: 488510
Varvara Skavatsou (Mgr-Control-Rail Tower)

Cosco Shipping Lines (Belgium) NV (1)
Madrasstraat 70, Bus 301, 2000, Antwerp, Belgium
Tel.: (32) 3 222 17 11
Web Site: http://www.coscoshippinglines.be
Freight Forwarding Services
N.A.I.C.S.: 488510

Cosco Shipping Lines (India) Pvt. Ltd. (1)
ICICI Venture House 2nd Floor, Appasaheb Marathe Marg Prabhadevi, Mumbai, 400 025, India
Tel.: (91) 22 61247300
Web Site:
    http://www.coscoshippinglinesindia.com
Freight Transportation Services
N.A.I.C.S.: 488510
Ashok Rajbhar (Head-Import Dept)

Cosco Shipping Lines (Myanmar) Co., Ltd. (1)
Room 1813 Sule Square Office Tower No 221 Sule Pagoda Road, Kyauktada Township, Yangon, Myanmar
Tel.: (95) 1 9255 082
Web Site: http://lines.coscoshipping.com
Freight Transportation Services
N.A.I.C.S.: 488510

Cosco Shipping Lines (Poland) Sp. z oo (1)
ul Slaska 21, 81-319, Gdynia, Poland
Tel.: (48) 586609300
Web Site: http://www.cosco.pl
Freight Transportation Services
N.A.I.C.S.: 488510
Guo ZhenDong (Mng Dir)

Cosco Shipping Lines (Pty) Ltd (1)
3rd Floor Bedford Centre Smith Street, Bedfordview, 2007, South Africa
Tel.: (27) 11 622 5658
Web Site: http://lines.coscoshipping.com
Ship Building & Repairing Services
N.A.I.C.S.: 336611

Cosco Shipping Lines Pakistan Pvt. Ltd. (1)
8th Floor Plot# BC-10 Block-4 Clifton Diamond Building, Clifton, 756000, Karachi, Pakistan
Tel.: (92) 21 351 80 630
Web Site: http://www.coscosaeed.com
Freight Transportation Services
N.A.I.C.S.: 488510

Cosco Shipping Uruguay (1)
Rincon 477 Oficina 402 Edificio Presidente, Montevideo, Uruguay
Tel.: (598) 2 9168000
Web Site: http://lines.coscoshipping.com
Freight Transportation Services
N.A.I.C.S.: 488510

Cosco Suzhou International Freight Forwarding Co., Ltd. (1)
3 Floor HongYun Building No 280 Renmin Road, Suzhou, Jiangsu, China
Tel.: (86) 512 65132158
Web Site: http://lines.coscoshipping.com
Freight Transportation Services
N.A.I.C.S.: 488510
Weikang Jin (Mgr-Customer Svc)

Hanyuan Technical Service Center GmbH (1)
Herrengraben 74, 20459, Hamburg, Germany
Tel.: (49) 40 369881 0
Web Site: http://www.hanyuan.de
Ship Building & Repairing Services
N.A.I.C.S.: 336611
Jun Xiong (Mng Dir)

Hop Hing Marine Industrial (Hong Kong) Limited (1)
3/F 81 Hing Wah Street West Lai Chi Kok, Kowloon, China (Hong Kong)
Tel.: (852) 2307 5088
Web Site: http://www.coscointl.com

Ship Building & Repairing Services
N.A.I.C.S.: 336611

Jiangmen Cosco Shipping Aluminium Co., Ltd. (1)
No 22 Gaosha Zhong Road, Jiangmen, Guangdong, China **(100%)**
Tel.: (86) 750 3112016
Web Site: http://www.coscoal.com
Emp.: 750
Aluminum Extrusions Mfr
N.A.I.C.S.: 331318

New Century Decal (Shenzhen) Limited (1)
1/F & 2/F Building 10 Block 3 Yangbei Industrial Park Huangtian, Xixiang Town Baoan District, Shenzhen, 518128, China
Tel.: (86) 755 8606 3708
Web Site: http://www.coscointl.com
Marine Transportation Signs Marking & Container Mfr
N.A.I.C.S.: 332439

Orient Overseas (International) Limited (1)
31/F Harbour Centre 25 Harbour Road, Wanchai, China (Hong Kong) **(88.53%)**
Tel.: (852) 283338888
Web Site: http://www.ooilgroup.com
Rev.: $8,191,304,000
Assets: $10,644,553,000
Liabilities: $5,002,059,000
Net Worth: $5,642,494,000
Earnings: $903,018,000
Emp.: 10,552
Fiscal Year-end: 12/31/2020
Container Transport & Logistical Services; Ports & Terminals; Property Development & Investment
N.A.I.C.S.: 488999
Erxin Yao (Dir-Corporate Planning)

Subsidiary (Domestic):

Orient Overseas Container Line Limited (2)
31/F Harbour Centre 25 Harbour Road, Wanchai, China (Hong Kong) **(100%)**
Tel.: (852) 28333888
Web Site: http://www.oocl.com
Sales Range: $750-799.9 Million
Container Transportation, Logistics & Terminal Services
N.A.I.C.S.: 488320
Steve Siu (CIO)

Subsidiary (Domestic):

OOCL (Asia Pacific) Ltd (3)
31st Floor 25 Harbour Centre, 25 Harbour Road, Wanchai, China (Hong Kong)
Tel.: (852) 28333888
Web Site: http://www.oocl.com
Container Transportation, Logistics & Terminal Services
N.A.I.C.S.: 488510

Subsidiary (Non-US):

OOCL (India) Private Ltd (4)
ICC Chambers 5th Floor Saki Vihar Road Opp Santogen Silk Mills, Powai, Mumbai, 400072, India
Tel.: (91) 2266511100
Web Site: http://www.oocl.com
Liner Agency; Container Transportation, Logistics & Terminal Services
N.A.I.C.S.: 488510

OOCL (Korea) Ltd (4)
Room 730 Royal Building Saemunan-ro 5-gil 19 Dangju-dong, Jongno-gu, Seoul, 03173, Korea (South)
Tel.: (82) 23982300
Web Site: http://www.oocl.com
Liner Agency; Container Transportation, Logistics & Terminal Services
N.A.I.C.S.: 483111
Jennifer Hyun Jung Kim (Pres)

OOCL (Philippines) Inc. (4)
11th Floor Two-Ecom Centre-Tower B Bayshore Ave, Mall of Asia Complex, Pasay, 1300, Philippines
Tel.: (63) 2 554 8000
Web Site: http://www.oocl.com
Liner Agency; Container Transportation, Logistics & Terminal Services
N.A.I.C.S.: 483111

Leah Ramos (Reg Mgr-Ops)

Subsidiary (Domestic):

OOCL Logistics Philippines Inc. (5)
11th Floor Two-Ecom Center Tower B Bayshore Ave, Mall of Asia Complex, Pasay, 1300, Philippines
Tel.: (63) 25548100
Web Site: http://www.oocllogistics.com
Supply Chain Management & Logistics Services; Domestic Warehousing & Transportation
N.A.I.C.S.: 541614

Subsidiary (Non-US):

OOCL (Singapore) Pte Ltd (4)
79 Anson Road #14-00, Singapore, 079906, Singapore
Tel.: (65) 64383383
Web Site: http://www.oocl.com
Liner Agency, Container Transportation, Logistics & Terminal Services.
N.A.I.C.S.: 483111
Eddie Leong (Asst Gen Mgr)

OOCL (Taiwan) Co Ltd (4)
No 15 Chinan Road Section 1, Taipei, Taiwan
Tel.: (886) 2 2397 8168
Web Site: http://www.oocl.com
Liner Agency; Container Transportation, Logistics & Terminal Services
N.A.I.C.S.: 483111

OOCL Australia Pty Ltd (4)
Level 3 107 Mount Street, Sydney, 2060, NSW, Australia
Tel.: (61) 289128888
Web Site: http://www.oocl.com
Liner Agency; Container Transportation, Logistics & Terminal Services
N.A.I.C.S.: 488510
Eddy Declercq (Mng Dir)

OOCL China Domestics Ltd (4)
21st Floor OOCL Plaza, No 841 Yan'an Road (M), Shanghai, 200040, China
Tel.: (86) 2123018888
Web Site: http://www.oocl.com
Freight Agency & Cargo Consolidation Services
N.A.I.C.S.: 488510

Orient Overseas Container Line (China) Co. Ltd - Guangzhou Branch (4)
Unit 04-07 13th Floor Jinlilai Digital Network Building No 138, East Tiyu Road Tianhe District, Guangzhou, 510620, China
Tel.: (86) 20 3815 5128
Web Site: http://www.oocl.com
Liner Agency; Container Transportation, Logistics & Terminal Services
N.A.I.C.S.: 483111

Orient Overseas Container Line (Malaysia) Sdn. Bhd. (4)
Unit 10.2 Level 10 Menara Axis, No 2 Jalan 51A/223, 46100, Petaling Jaya, Selangor, Malaysia
Tel.: (60) 377113333
Web Site: http://www.oocl.com
Liner Agency; Container Transportation, Logistics & Terminal Services
N.A.I.C.S.: 483111
Dennis Ng (Mng Dir)

Overseas Container Line Limited - Japan Branch (4)
1-11-2 Osaki 8/F Gate City Osaki East Tower, Shinagawa-ku, Tokyo, 141 0032, Japan
Tel.: (81) 3 3493 6001
Web Site: http://www.oocl.com
Liner Agency; Container Transportation, Logistics & Terminal Services
N.A.I.C.S.: 483111

Subsidiary (Non-US):

OOCL (Canada) Inc. (3)
703 Evans Avenue Suite 300, Toronto, M9C 5E9, ON, Canada
Tel.: (416) 620-4040
Web Site: http://www.oocl.com
Container Transportation & Logistics Services
N.A.I.C.S.: 488510

Robert Wiltshire (Reg Sls Mgr)

OOCL (Europe) Ltd (3)
OOCL House Bridge Road, Levington, Ipswich, IP10 0NE, Suffolk, United Kingdom
Tel.: (44) 1473 659 000
Web Site: http://www.oocl.com
Investment Holding & Liner Territorial Office; Container Transportation, Logistics & Terminal Services
N.A.I.C.S.: 551112
Richard Hew (Mng Dir & Sls Mgr-UK)

Subsidiary (Non-US):

OOCL (Benelux) NV (4)
Theater Building Italielei 124 Bus 74, B-2000, Antwerp, Belgium
Tel.: (32) 32348811
Web Site: http://www.oocl.com
Liner Agency; Container Transportation, Logistics & Terminal Services
N.A.I.C.S.: 483111
Danny Van den Bosch (Gen Mgr)

OOCL (Denmark) A/S (4)
Store Torv 3 3 sal, DK-8000, Arhus, C, Denmark
Tel.: (45) 86762880
Web Site: http://www.oocl.com
Emp.: 12
Liner Agency; Container Transportation, Logistics & Terminal Services
N.A.I.C.S.: 488510
Finn Nielsen (Country Mgr)

OOCL (Deutschland) GmbH (4)
Hillmannstrasse 2a, 28195, Bremen, Germany
Tel.: (49) 42130180
Web Site: http://www.oocl.com
Liner Agency; Container Transportation, Logistics & Terminal Services
N.A.I.C.S.: 488510
Astrid Keller (Gen Mgr)

OOCL (Finland) Ltd Oy (4)
Energiakuja 3, FIN-00180, Helsinki, Finland
Tel.: (358) 942428000
Web Site: http://www.oocl.com
Liner Agency; Container Transportation, Logistics & Terminal Services
N.A.I.C.S.: 488510
Nina Bredenberg (Country Mgr)

OOCL (France) S.A. (4)
Franklin Building, BP 147, 32 rue Pierre Brossolette, 76051, Le Havre, Cedex, France
Tel.: (33) 2 35 19 59 00
Web Site: http://www.oocl.com
Liner Agency; Container Transportation, Logistics & Terminal Services
N.A.I.C.S.: 488510
Philippe Varlet (Country Mgr)

OOCL (Italy) S.r.l. (4)
Via De Marini 53 Torre Shipping Scala A 12 Floor, 16145, Genoa, Italy
Tel.: (39) 0108598301
Web Site: http://www.oocl.com
Liner Agency; Container Transportation, Logistics & Terminal Services
N.A.I.C.S.: 483111
Alfredo Floro (Office Mgr)

OOCL (Portugal) Lda (4)
Rua Dr Jose Domingues Oliveira 69, Leca da Palmeira, 4450-710, Porto, Portugal
Tel.: (351) 229998460
Web Site: http://www.oocl.com
Liner Agency; Container Transportation, Logistics & Terminal Services
N.A.I.C.S.: 483111
Carmo Lobo (Country Mgr)

OOCL (Russia) Ltd (4)
4th Floor Business Center Imperial Prospect Stachek 48 Building 2, 198097, Saint Petersburg, Russia
Tel.: (7) 8123357915
Web Site: http://www.oocl.com
Liner Agency; Container Transportation, Logistics & Terminal Services
N.A.I.C.S.: 483111

OOCL (Sweden) AB (4)
Stampgatan 14, 411 01, Gothenburg, Sweden
Tel.: (46) 313355900
Web Site: http://www.oocl.com

Liner Agency; Container Transportation, Logistics & Terminal Services
N.A.I.C.S.: 483111
Bjarne Wesenlund (Sr Coord-Ops)

Subsidiary (Domestic):

OOCL (UK) Ltd (4)
OOCL House Bridge Road, Levington, Ipswich, IP10 0NE, Suffolk, United Kingdom
Tel.: (44) 1473659000
Web Site: http://www.oocl.com
Liner Agency; Container Transportation, Logistics & Terminal Services
N.A.I.C.S.: 483111
Richard Hew (Mng Dir & Sls Mgr-UK)

Subsidiary (Non-US):

Orient Overseas Container Line (Spain) S. L. (4)
Avenida Drassanes 6 Planta 10 Pta 4, 08001, Barcelona, Spain
Tel.: (34) 93 481 4260
Web Site: http://www.oocl.com
Liner Agency; Container Transportation, Logistics & Terminal Services
N.A.I.C.S.: 483111
Pedro Estevez (Country Mgr)

Subsidiary (Non-US):

OOCL (UAE) LLC (3)
16th Floor Unit 1601 The H Hotel, PO Box 23230, Sheikh Zayed Road, Dubai, United Arab Emirates
Tel.: (971) 4 520 3000
Web Site: http://www.oocl.com
Supply Chain Management & Logistics Services; Domestic Warehousing & Transportation
N.A.I.C.S.: 541614
John Knight (Reg Head)

Subsidiary (US):

OOCL (USA) Inc. (3)
10913 S River Front Pkwy Ste 200, South Jordan, UT 84095-5641
Tel.: (801) 302-6625
Web Site: http://www.oocl.com
Container Transportation, Logistics & Terminal Services
N.A.I.C.S.: 488510
Paul Devine (Pres)

Subsidiary (Domestic):

Global Terminal & Container Services Inc. (4)
302 Port Jersey BLVD, Jersey, NJ 07305
Tel.: (201) 451-5200
Web Site: http://www.global-terminal.com
Terminal Operation & Container Services
N.A.I.C.S.: 488320

Long Beach Container Terminal LLC (4)
1171 Pier F Ave, Long Beach, CA 90802
Tel.: (562) 951-6000
Web Site: http://www.lbct.com
Terminal Operations
N.A.I.C.S.: 488310
Anthony Otto (Pres)

Subsidiary (Domestic):

OOCL Logistics Limited (3)
12/F One Harbour Square 181 Hoi Bun Road Kwun Tong, Kowloon, China (Hong Kong)
Tel.: (852) 2506 6888
Web Site: http://www.oocllogistics.com
Logistics & Supply Chain Services
N.A.I.C.S.: 541614

Subsidiary (Non-US):

OLL Logistics (Malaysia) Sdn. Bhd. (4)
Unit 10.2 Level 10 Menara Axis No 2 Jalan 51A/223, 46100, Petaling Jaya, Selangor Darul Ehsan, Malaysia
Tel.: (60) 377113200
Web Site: http://www.oocllogistics.com
Supply Chain Management & Logistics Services; Domestic Warehousing & Transportation
N.A.I.C.S.: 541614

China COSCO Shipping Corporation
Limited—(Continued)

**OOCL Logistics (Australia) Pty.
Ltd.** (4)
Level 3 107 Mount Street, Sydney, 2060,
NSW, Australia
Tel.: (61) 289128877
Web Site: http://www.oocllogistics.com
Supply Chain Management & Logistics Ser-
vices; Domestic Warehousing & Transporta-
tion
N.A.I.C.S.: 541614

OOCL Logistics (China) Ltd (4)
8 9/F Tower B Zhenhua Enterprise Plaza,
3261 Dong Fang Road, Shanghai, 200125,
China
Tel.: (86) 21 2301 88 99
Web Site: http://www.oocllogistics.com
Supply Chain Management & Logistics Ser-
vices; Domestic Warehousing & Transporta-
tion
N.A.I.C.S.: 541614

OOCL Logistics (Europe) Ltd (4)
OOCL House Bridge Road, Levington Suf-
folk, London, IP10 0NE, United Kingdom
Tel.: (44) 1473 659000
Web Site: http://www.oocllogistics.com
Supply Chain Management & Logistics Ser-
vices; Domestic Warehousing & Transporta-
tion
N.A.I.C.S.: 541614

Branch (Non-US):

**OOCL Logistics (Europe) Ltd -
Bremen Branch** (5)
Hillmannstrasse 2a, 28195, Bremen, Ger-
many
Tel.: (49) 421160580
Web Site: http://www.oocllogistics.com
Supply Chain Management & Logistics Ser-
vices; Domestic Warehousing & Transporta-
tion
N.A.I.C.S.: 541614

**OOCL Logistics (Europe) Ltd - Rot-
terdam Branch** (5)
Weena Zuid 134 6th Floor, 3012 NC, Rot-
terdam, Netherlands
Tel.: (31) 10 224 8290
Web Site: http://www.oocllogistics.com
Supply Chain Management & Logistics Ser-
vices; Domestic Warehousing & Transporta-
tion
N.A.I.C.S.: 541614

Subsidiary (Non-US):

**OOCL Logistics (India) Private
Limited** (4)
AR Complex 2nd Floor 1090 Poonamallee
High Road, Chennai, 600 084, India
Tel.: (91) 44 6625 1121
Web Site: http://www.oocllogistics.com
Supply Chain Management & Logistics Ser-
vices; Domestic Warehousing & Transporta-
tion
N.A.I.C.S.: 541614

OOCL Logistics (Japan) Ltd (4)
2-3-14 Higashi Shinagawa 12/F Tokyo Front
Terrace, Shinagawa-ku, Tokyo, 140-0002,
Japan
Tel.: (81) 3 68725480
Web Site: http://www.oocllogistics.com
Supply Chain Management & Logistics Ser-
vices; Domestic Warehousing & Transporta-
tion
N.A.I.C.S.: 541614

OOCL Logistics (Korea) Ltd. (4)
Room 730 Royal Building 19 Saemunan-ro
5-gil, Jongno-gu, Seoul, 03173, Korea
(South)
Tel.: (82) 2 39 82 389
Web Site: http://www.oocllogistics.com
Supply Chain Management & Logistics Ser-
vices; Domestic Warehousing & Transporta-
tion
N.A.I.C.S.: 541614

**OOCL Logistics (Singapore) Pte.
Ltd.** (4)
79 Anson Road #14-00, Singapore, 079906,
Singapore
Tel.: (65) 64381808
Web Site: http://www.oocllogistics.com

Supply Chain Management & Logistics Services; Domestic Warehousing & Transportation
N.A.I.C.S.: 541614

OOCL Logistics (Taiwan) Ltd (4)
6F No 15 Sec 1 Chi-Nan Road, Taipei, Taiwan
Tel.: (886) 2 239 781 66
Web Site: http://www.oocllogistics.com
Supply Chain Management & Logistics Services; Domestic Warehousing & Transportation
N.A.I.C.S.: 541614

OOCL Logistics (Thailand) Ltd (4)
75/76 Ocean Tower II 31st Fl Sukhumvit 19,
Klongtoey Nua Wattana, Bangkok, 10110,
Thailand
Tel.: (66) 26469590
Web Site: http://www.oocllogistics.com
Supply Chain Management & Logistics Ser-
vices; Domestic Warehousing & Transporta-
tion
N.A.I.C.S.: 541614

Subsidiary (US):

OOCL Logistics (USA) Inc. (4)
17F Wall St Plz 88 Pine St, New York, NY
10005
Tel.: (212) 269-9010
Web Site: http://www.oocllogistics.com
Supply Chain Management & Logistics Services; Domestic Warehousing & Transportation
N.A.I.C.S.: 541614

Subsidiary (Non-US):

PT. OOCL Logistics Indonesia (4)
Wisma 46 Kota BNI 22nd Floor Suite #2202
Jl Jend Sudirman Kav 1, Jakarta, 10220,
Indonesia
Tel.: (62) 21 30405153
Web Site: http://www.oocllogistics.com
Supply Chain Management & Logistics Ser-
vices; Domestic Warehousing & Transporta-
tion
N.A.I.C.S.: 541614

PT Ocean Global Shipping (1)
Jl Ir H Juanda III No 23 C-D-E, Jakarta,
10120, Indonesia
Tel.: (62) 21 381 0338
Web Site: http://www.gpi-g.com
Freight Deep Sea Transportation Services
N.A.I.C.S.: 483111

Piraeus Port Authority S.A. (1)
10 Akti Miaouli street, 18538, Piraeus,
Greece (51%)
Tel.: (30) 2104550000
Web Site: https://www.olp.gr
Rev.: $209,979,864
Assets: $618,782,512
Liabilities: $279,374,444
Net Worth: $339,408,068
Earnings: $57,075,791
Emp.: 960
Fiscal Year-end: 12/31/2022
Coastal Freight Transportation Services
N.A.I.C.S.: 483113
Zhang Anming (CEO-Acting)

**Shanghai Ocean Shipping Co.,
Ltd.** (1)
No 1555 Changyang Road, Shanghai,
200090, China
Tel.: (86) 2165701888
Web Site: http://www.coscoshanghai.com
Freight Transportation Services
N.A.I.C.S.: 488510
Jiangping Qin (Gen Mgr)

**Shanghai Pudong New Area Newcen-
tury Decal Co., Ltd.** (1)
No 990 Shixin Road, Ji Chang Village Pu-
dong New Area, Shanghai, China
Tel.: (86) 21 6896 2258
Web Site: http://www.coscoind.com.hk
Container Mfr; Transportation & Marine
Transport Signs Marking
N.A.I.C.S.: 332439

Subsidiary (Domestic):

**COSCO Jiaxing International Freight
Co., Ltd.** (2)
Floor 3 No 985 Ji Yang Road, Jiaxing, Ji-

angsu, China
Tel.: (86) 573 82112209
Web Site: http://lines.coscoshipping.com
Freight Transportation Services
N.A.I.C.S.: 488510
Qinli Cao (Mgr-Customer Svc)

**COSCO SHIPPING Heavy Industry
Co., Ltd.** (2)
No 118 Yuanshen Road, Pudong New Dis-
trict, Shanghai, 200120, China
Tel.: (86) 21 58600111
Web Site: http://chi.coscoshipping.com
Freight Transportation Services
N.A.I.C.S.: 488510
Yangfeng Liang (Pres)

Smart Watch Assets Limited (1)
Rm 4202 42F COSCO Tower 183 Queens
Road, Central, China (Hong Kong)
Tel.: (852) 2809 7293
Web Site: http://www.cosco.com.hk
Financial Management Services
N.A.I.C.S.: 523999

CHINA CREATIVE DIGITAL EN-
TERTAINMENT LIMITED

Unit C 8/F D2 Place Two 15 Cheung
Shun Street Cheung Sha Wan, Kow-
loon, China (Hong Kong)
Tel.: (852) 28927807
Web Site:
http://www.china3d8078.com
8078—(HKG)
Rev.: $2,729,991
Assets: $6,143,575
Liabilities: $159,563,093
Net Worth: ($153,419,517)
Earnings: ($69,920,832)
Emp.: 34
Fiscal Year-end: 06/30/21
Film Production Services
N.A.I.C.S.: 512110
Albert Wing Ho Lee (Exec Dir)

Subsidiaries:

**China 3D Digital Distribution
Limited** (1)
1/F Morrison Plaza 9 Morrison Hill Road,
Wanchai, China (Hong Kong)
Tel.: (852) 2882 1816
Motion Picture Distr
N.A.I.C.S.: 512120

CHINA CREATIVE GLOBAL
HOLDINGS LIMITED

Unit 913 9/F China Merchants Tower,
Shun Tak Centre 200 Connaught Rd
Central, Sheung Wan, China (Hong
Kong)
Tel.: (852) 2395 0838   Ky
Web Site: http://www.cchome.hk
Sales Range: $200-249.9 Million
Emp.: 1,631
Fireplace Equipment Mfr & Distr
N.A.I.C.S.: 333414
Fanglin Chen (Chm)

CHINA CRYSTAL NEW MATE-
RIAL HOLDINGS CO., LTD

Chemical industry district, Zhutang
town, Jiangyin, Jiangsu, China
Tel.: (86) 27830623
Web Site:
https://www.crystalnewmaterial.com
Year Founded: 2012
900250—(KRS)
Rev.: $58,977,842
Assets: $320,319,200
Liabilities: $20,116,811
Net Worth: $300,202,389
Earnings: $11,673,400
Emp.: 278
Fiscal Year-end: 12/31/22
Holding Company
N.A.I.C.S.: 551112
Yue lun He (CEO)

CHINA CULTURE INDUSTRIAL

INVESTMENT FUND MANAGE-
MENT CO., LTD.

12/F No 28 Fengsheng Hutong,
Xicheng District, Beijing, China
Tel.: (86) 10 57503518
Web Site: http://www.chinacf.com
Privater Equity Firm
N.A.I.C.S.: 523999
Hang Chen (Mng Dir)

CHINA CUSTOMER RELA-
TIONS CENTERS, INC.

1366 Zhongtianmen Dajie Xinghuo
Science & Technology Park, High-
tech Zone, Tai'an, 271000, Shan-
dong, China
Tel.: (86) 538 691 8899   VG
Web Site: http://www.ccrc.com
CCRC—(NASDAQ)
Rev.: $240,316,024
Assets: $143,957,860
Liabilities: $48,442,062
Net Worth: $95,515,798
Earnings: $24,860,799
Emp.: 14,057
Fiscal Year-end: 12/31/20
Call Center Business Process Out-
sourcing Services
N.A.I.C.S.: 561422
Gary Wang (Founder, Chm & CEO)

CHINA CYTS TOURS HOLD-
ING CO., LTD.

CYTS Building No 5 Dongzhimen
South Street, Dongcheng District,
Beijing, 100007, China
Tel.: (86) 1058158717
Web Site: http://www.aoyou.com
Year Founded: 1997
600138—(SHG)
Rev.: $900,924,589
Assets: $2,466,091,209
Liabilities: $1,328,454,565
Net Worth: $1,137,636,644
Earnings: ($46,830,659)
Fiscal Year-end: 12/31/22
Holding Company
N.A.I.C.S.: 551112
Ni Yangping (Chm)

CHINA DATANG CORPORA-
TION

No 1 Guangningbo Str, Xicheng Dis-
trict, 10032, Beijing, China
Tel.: (86) 1066586666
Web Site: http://www.china-cdt.com
Year Founded: 2002
Sales Range: $25-49.9 Billion
Emp.: 99,132
Extra Large Scaled Power Genera-
tion Services
N.A.I.C.S.: 221122
Jinhang Chen (Pres)

Subsidiaries:

**China Datang Corporation Renew-
able Power Co., Limited** (1)
Block B Building 1 Court 6 Yinhe Street,
Shijingshan District, Beijing, 100040, China
Tel.: (86) 1081130702
Web Site: http://www.cdt-re.com
Rev.: $1,754,891,752
Assets: $13,695,777,670
Liabilities: $8,884,279,638
Net Worth: $4,811,498,032
Earnings: $546,327,990
Emp.: 4,174
Fiscal Year-end: 12/31/2022
Wind Power Generation
N.A.I.C.S.: 221118
Li Kai (Chm)

**Datang Environment Industry Group
Co., Ltd.** (1)
No 120 Zizhuyuan Road Haidian District,
Beijing, 100097, China
Web Site: http://www.dteg.com.cn
Rev.: $747,310,169
Assets: $2,576,095,283

Liabilities: $1,607,791,723
Net Worth: $968,303,560
Earnings: $33,432,469
Emp.: 1,008
Fiscal Year-end: 12/31/2022
Environmental Protection Services
N.A.I.C.S.: 924110
Zhu Liming *(Chm)*

Datang International Power Generation Co., Ltd.   **(1)**
No 9 Guangningbo Street, Xicheng District, Beijing, 100033, China   **(34.77%)**
Tel.: (86) 1088008678
Web Site: http://www.dtpower.com
Rev.: $14,649,020,940
Assets: $42,971,032,846
Liabilities: $28,950,888,244
Net Worth: $14,020,144,602
Earnings: $804,812,130
Emp.: 33,340
Fiscal Year-end: 12/31/2020
Power Distr
N.A.I.C.S.: 335311
Xuejun Ying *(Sec & Deputy Gen Mgr)*

Subsidiary (Domestic):

Shanxi Datang International Shentou Power Generation Company Limited   **(2)**
Zhenhua St Shentou Town, Shuocheng District, Shentou, 036011, Shanxi, China
Tel.: (86) 3492045495
Power Generation Services
N.A.I.C.S.: 221111

Guangxi Guiguan Electric Power Co., Ltd.   **(1)**
No 126 Minzu Avenue, Qingxiu District, Nanning, 530029, Guangxi, China
Tel.: (86) 7716118888
Web Site: http://www.ggep.com.cn
Rev.: $1,491,709,832
Assets: $6,350,491,747
Liabilities: $3,264,465,714
Net Worth: $3,086,026,033
Earnings: $450,557,865
Fiscal Year-end: 12/31/2022
Electric Power Generation & Distribution Services
N.A.I.C.S.: 221118
Zhao Dabin *(Chm)*

CHINA DAYE NON-FERROUS METALS MINING LIMITED
No 10B 16/F Tower 3 China Hong Kong City China Ferry Terminal, 33 Canton Road, Kowloon, China (Hong Kong)
Tel.: (852) 28682101
Web Site: http://www.hk661.com
0661—(HKG)
Rev.: $4,725,655,646
Assets: $3,260,614,360
Liabilities: $2,660,599,796
Net Worth: $600,014,563
Earnings: ($900,806)
Emp.: 5,434
Fiscal Year-end: 12/31/22
Investment Services
N.A.I.C.S.: 523940
Zhong Long *(CEO)*

CHINA DEMETER FINANCIAL INVESTMENTS LIMITED
Tel.: (852) 21161218   BM
Web Site:
http://www.chinademeter.com
Year Founded: 2000
8120—(HKG)
Rev.: $18,092,633
Assets: $31,668,578
Liabilities: $15,173,775
Net Worth: $16,494,803
Earnings: ($2,418,293)
Emp.: 185
Fiscal Year-end: 12/31/22
Investment Services; Consumer Goods & Agricultural Products
N.A.I.C.S.: 523999
Chun Kei Lam *(Exec Dir)*

CHINA DESIGN GROUP CO., LTD.
No 9 Ziyun Avenue, Qinhuai District, Nanjing, 210014, Jiangsu, China
Tel.: (86) 2584202066
Web Site: http://www.jsjty.com
Year Founded: 1966
603018—(SHG)
Rev.: $819,785,393
Assets: $1,663,060,661
Liabilities: $1,033,713,547
Net Worth: $629,347,114
Earnings: $95,981,512
Emp.: 6,300
Fiscal Year-end: 12/31/22
Construction Engineering Services
N.A.I.C.S.: 541330

CHINA DEVELOPMENT BANK CORPORATION
No 18 Fuxingmennei Street, Xicheng District, Beijing, 100031, China
Tel.: (86) 1068306688   CN
Web Site: http://www.cdb.com.cn
Year Founded: 1994
Sales Range: $1-4.9 Billion
Bank Holding Company; Commercial & Investment Banking
N.A.I.C.S.: 551111
Zhijie Zheng *(Vice Chm & Pres)*

Subsidiaries:

BAZHONG CDB VILLAGE BANK CO., LTD.   **(1)**
23 Xihua Road, Bazhou District, Bazhong, 636000, China
Tel.: (86) 827 3333655
Commercial Banking Services
N.A.I.C.S.: 522110

BEILUN CDB VILLAGE BANK CO., LTD.   **(1)**
837-847 Xinda Road, Beilun District, Ningbo, 315800, China
Tel.: (86) 574 86856785
Commercial Banking Services
N.A.I.C.S.: 522110

CDB LEASING CO., LTD.   **(1)**
49-52F New World Centre 6009 Yitian Road, Futian District, Shenzhen, 518026, Guangdong, China
Tel.: (86) 755 23980999
Commercial Banking Services
N.A.I.C.S.: 522110

CHINA DEVELOPMENT BANK CAPITAL CO., LTD.   **(1)**
10/F Winland International Finance Centre 7 Financial Street, Xicheng District, Beijing, 100033, China
Tel.: (86) 10 88308477
Commercial Banking Services
N.A.I.C.S.: 522110

CHINA DEVELOPMENT BANK SECURITIES CO., LTD.   **(1)**
25/F Raffles City Beijing Office Tower 1 Dongzhimen South Street, Dongcheng District, Beijing, 1000007, China
Tel.: (86) 10 51789101
Commercial Banking Services
N.A.I.C.S.: 522110

China Development Bank International Investment Limited   **(1)**
Tel.: (852) 39791500
Web Site: https://www.cdb-intl.com
Investment Services
N.A.I.C.S.: 523999
Zhe Bai *(Chm)*

DALATE CDB VILLAGE BANK CO., LTD.   **(1)**
Ground Floor 2 Dongdajiayuan Xiyuan Rd, Shulinzhao Town Dalate County, Ordos, 014300, Inner Mongolia, China
Tel.: (86) 477 3969785
Commercial Banking Services
N.A.I.C.S.: 522110

DATONG CDB VILLAGE BANK CO., LTD.   **(1)**
70-4 Renmin Road, Qiaotou Town, Datong,

810100, Qinghai, China
Tel.: (86) 971 7830961
Commercial Banking Services
N.A.I.C.S.: 522110

DAYE CDB VILLAGE BANK CO., LTD.   **(1)**
104 Daye Road, Daye, 435100, Hubei, China
Tel.: (86) 714 8725699
Commercial Banking Services
N.A.I.C.S.: 522110

LONGKOU NANSHAN CDB VILLAGE BANK CO., LTD.   **(1)**
3 Nanshanzhong Road, Nanshan Industrial Park, Longkou, 265706, Shandong, China
Tel.: (86) 535 8808508
Commercial Banking Services
N.A.I.C.S.: 522110

MILUO CDB VILLAGE BANK CO., LTD.   **(1)**
1 Dazhong South Road, Miluo, Yueyang, 414400, Hunan, China
Tel.: (86) 730 5559999
Commercial Banking Services
N.A.I.C.S.: 522110

PI COUNTY CDB VILLAGE BANK CO., LTD.   **(1)**
1/F R&D Building of 19MCC, Pitong, 611730, Sichuan, China
Tel.: (86) 28 61410770
Commercial Banking Services
N.A.I.C.S.: 522110

PINGLIANG JINGCHUAN HUITONG VILLAGE BANK CO., LTD.   **(1)**
18 Anding Street, Jingchuan, 744300, Gansu, China
Tel.: (86) 933 3321929
Commercial Banking Services
N.A.I.C.S.: 522110

TONGZHOU CDB VILLAGE BANK CO., LTD.   **(1)**
Jia 66 Yangzhuang Nanli, Tongzhou District, Beijing, 101121, China
Tel.: (86) 10 52998500
Commercial Banking Services
N.A.I.C.S.: 522110

Taurus Mineral Limited   **(1)**
Room 1901 CG Wu Bldg 302 Hennessy Road, Wanchai, China (Hong Kong)   **(40%)**
Investment Holding Company
N.A.I.C.S.: 551112

Subsidiary (Non-US):

Kalahari Minerals Plc   **(2)**
1B 38 Jermyn Street, London, SW1Y 6DN, United Kingdom   **(98%)**
Tel.: (44) 20 7292 9110
Web Site: http://www.kalahari-minerals.com
Sales Range: $1-9.9 Million
Emp.: 7
Holding Company; Metal Ore Exploration & Mining Services
N.A.I.C.S.: 551112
Mark Hohnen *(Founder)*

XIQING CDB VILLAGE BANK CO., LTD.   **(1)**
Ground Floor Jin Sha Shui Yu Hua Cheng South of Zhongbei Street, Zhongbei Town Xiqing District, Tianjin, 300112, China
Tel.: (86) 22 58967002
Commercial Banking Services
N.A.I.C.S.: 522110

YICHENG CDB VILLAGE BANK CO., LTD.   **(1)**
Yiyang Gallery Street, Yicheng, 441400, Hubei, China
Tel.: (86) 710 4221000
Commercial Banking Services
N.A.I.C.S.: 522110

ZHENLAI CDB VILLAGE BANK CO., LTD.   **(1)**
480 Xinxing South Street, Zhenlai Baicheng, Jilin, 137300, China
Tel.: (86) 436 5077104
Commercial Banking Services
N.A.I.C.S.: 522110

CHINA DEVELOPMENT BANK

FINANCIAL LEASING CO., LTD.
CDB Financial Center Building Fuzhong 3rd Road, Futian District, Shenzhen, 518038, China
Tel.: (86) 75523980999   CN
Web Site: https://www.cdb-leasing.com
Year Founded: 1984
1606—(HKG)
Rev.: $3,185,353,761
Assets: $56,725,590,247
Liabilities: $51,563,616,388
Net Worth: $5,161,973,859
Earnings: $574,621,871
Emp.: 571
Fiscal Year-end: 12/31/23
Financial Investment Services
N.A.I.C.S.: 532411
Xuedong Wang *(Chm)*

Subsidiaries:

CDB Aviation Lease Finance Designated Activity Company   **(1)**
1GQ George's Quay, Dublin, D02 Y098, Ireland
Tel.: (353) 15681000
Web Site: https://www.cdbaviation.aero
Lease & Manage Commercial Aircraft Services
N.A.I.C.S.: 532411
Xuedong Wang *(Chm)*

CHINA DIGITAL CULTURE (GROUP) LIMITED
Unit 17B 17/F United Centre 95 Queensway, Hong Kong, China (Hong Kong)
Tel.: (852) 28015562   Ky
Year Founded: 2002
8175—(HKG)
Rev.: $7,269,055
Assets: $59,974,152
Liabilities: $68,489,025
Net Worth: ($8,514,873)
Earnings: ($46,682,247)
Emp.: 67
Fiscal Year-end: 12/31/20
Internet Publishing Services
N.A.I.C.S.: 516210
Tung Chi Hsu *(Co-CEO & Compliance Officer)*

CHINA DIGITAL MEDIA CORPORATION
2505-06 25th Floor Stelux House, 698 Prince Edward Road East, Kowloon, China (Hong Kong)
Tel.: (852) 23908600   NV
Web Site:
http://www.chinadigimedia.com
Year Founded: 1987
Sales Range: $1-9.9 Million
Emp.: 3
Cable Television Operations
N.A.I.C.S.: 516210
Daniel Chi Shing Ng *(Chm & CEO)*

CHINA DIGITAL TV HOLDING CO., LTD.
Jingmeng High-Tech Building B 4th Floor No, 5 Shangdi East Road Haidian District, Beijing, 100085, China
Tel.: (86) 10 62971199   Ky
Web Site: http://www.novel-supertv.com
Year Founded: 2004
Rev.: $6,201,000
Assets: $33,784,000
Liabilities: $4,802,000
Net Worth: $28,982,000
Earnings: $4,099,000
Emp.: 131
Fiscal Year-end: 12/31/17
Conditional Access Systems to Digital Television Market
N.A.I.C.S.: 334220

China Digital TV Holding Co., Ltd.—(Continued)

CHINA DIGITAL VIDEO HOLD-INGS LIMITED
China Digital Video Technical Plaza
No 131 West Fourth Ring Road
North, Haidian District, Beijing,
100195, China
Tel.: (86) 1062586666　　　Ky
Web Site: http://www.cdv.com
8280—(HKG)
Rev.: $36,550,472
Assets: $76,846,536
Liabilities: $56,881,235
Net Worth: $19,965,301
Earnings: ($15,268,079)
Emp.: 388
Fiscal Year-end: 03/31/23
Broadcasting Equipment Mfr & Distr
N.A.I.C.S.: 334220
Fushuang Zheng *(Founder, Chm & CEO)*

CHINA DILI GROUP
No 279 Xuefu Road, Nangang District, Harbin, 150090, Heilongjiang, China
Tel.: (86) 45182716666　　　Ky
Web Site:
http://www.renhebusiness.com
1387—(HKG)
Rev.: $244,938,330
Assets: $2,817,378,158
Liabilities: $845,745,311
Net Worth: $1,971,632,848
Earnings: $35,332,222
Emp.: 2,651
Fiscal Year-end: 12/31/21
Investment Holding Company; Developer of Underground Shopping Malls
N.A.I.C.S.: 551112
Bin Dai *(CEO)*

Subsidiaries:

China Dili Group Management
Limited　　　　　　　　　(1)
Room 4205-10 42/F China Resources Building 26 Harbour Road, Wanchai, 999077, China (Hong Kong)
Tel.: (852) 36657777
Web Site: https://www.diligrp.com.
Food Distr
N.A.I.C.S.: 424490

CHINA DING YI FENG HOLD-INGS LIMITED
Unit 6602-03 Level 66 International Commerce Centre 1 Austin Road West, Kowloon, China (Hong Kong)
Tel.: (852) 28389806　　　Ky
Web Site: http://www.cifund.com.hk
Year Founded: 2001
0612—(HKG)
Rev.: $950,000
Assets: $1,428,338,000
Liabilities: $319,128,000
Net Worth: $1,109,210,000
Earnings: $330,237,000
Emp.: 35
Fiscal Year-end: 12/31/20
Investment Management Service
N.A.I.C.S.: 523150
Hammond Hong Man Luk *(CEO & Controller-Financial)*

CHINA DISTANCE EDUCATION HOLDINGS LIMITED
18th Floor Xueyuan International Tower, 1 Zhichun Road Haidian District, Beijing, 100083, China
Tel.: (86) 1082319999　　　Ky
Web Site: http://www.cdeledu.com
Year Founded: 2000
DL—(NYSE)
Rev.: $209,558,000
Assets: $398,139,000
Liabilities: $271,195,000

Net Worth: $126,944,000
Earnings: $10,430,000
Emp.: 2,457
Fiscal Year-end: 09/30/20
Online Education & Test Preparation Courses & Other Related Services & Products
N.A.I.C.S.: 923110
Zhongdong Zhu *(Co-Founder, Chm & CEO)*

Subsidiaries:

China Distance Education
Limited　　　　　　　　　(1)
18th Floor Xue Yuan International Towers No 1 Zhichun Road, Hai Dian District, Beijing, 100083, China
Tel.: (86) 10 8231 9999
Online Educational Support Services
N.A.I.C.S.: 611710

CHINA DIVE COMPANY LIM-ITED
Changbu Village Xinxu Town Huiyang District, Huizhou, 516223, Guangdong, China
Tel.: (86) 75583571281
Web Site: http://www.china-dive.com
300526—(SSE)
Rev.: $25,563,089
Assets: $100,381,660
Liabilities: $43,105,634
Net Worth: $57,276,026
Earnings: ($28,993,460)
Fiscal Year-end: 12/31/20
Marine Diving Equipment Mfr & Distr
N.A.I.C.S.: 332999

CHINA DONGSHENG INTER-NATIONAL, INC.
Jifeng East Road, Gaoxin District, Jilin, China
Tel.: (86) 4324566702　　　DE
CDSG—(OTCIQ)
Sales Range: Less than $1 Million
Pharmaceuticals Product Mfr
N.A.I.C.S.: 325412
Aidong Yu *(Chm, Pres, CEO & CFO)*

CHINA DONGXIANG (GROUP) COMPANY LIMITED
Building 21 No 2 Jingyuanbei Street, Beijing Economic and Technology Development Zone, Beijing, 100176, China
Tel.: (86) 1067836666
Web Site: http://www.dxsport.com
3818—(HKG)
Rev.: $232,459,570
Assets: $1,464,447,414
Liabilities: $126,187,417
Net Worth: $1,338,259,997
Earnings: $15,922,270
Emp.: 471
Fiscal Year-end: 03/31/23
Sportswear Products Mfr
N.A.I.C.S.: 314999
Yihong Chen *(Founder & Chm)*

CHINA DREDGING ENVIRON-MENTAL PROTECTION HOLD-ING LIMITED
Rooms 1501-02 15/F Siu On Plaza 482 Jaffe Road, Causeway Bay, China (Hong Kong)
Tel.: (852) 25877366
Web Site: http://www.cdep.com.hk
0871—(OTCIQ)
Rev.: $54,120,269
Assets: $265,166,741
Liabilities: $147,544,675
Net Worth: $117,622,066
Earnings: ($44,244,954)
Emp.: 471
Fiscal Year-end: 12/31/22
Dredging Services

N.A.I.C.S.: 238910
Kaijin Liu *(Founder & Chm)*

CHINA DU KANG CO., LTD.
Town of Dukang Baishui County A 28 Van Metropolis 35 Tangyan Road, Xi'an, 710065, Shaanxi, China
Tel.: (86) 2988830106822　　　NV
Sales Range: $1 0.0 Million
Emp.: 192
White Wines Mfr, Licensor, Distr & Sales
N.A.I.C.S.: 312130
Yongsheng Wang *(Pres & CEO)*

CHINA E-INFORMATION TECH-NOLOGY GROUP LIMITED
Unit 2609-10 26/F Office Tower Convention Plaza 1 Harbour Road, Wanchai, China (Hong Kong)
Tel.: (852) 28581938　　　Ky
8055—(HKG)
Rev.: $7,849,981
Assets: $15,758,003
Liabilities: $3,453,697
Net Worth: $12,304,305
Earnings: ($4,250,278)
Emp.: 37
Fiscal Year-end: 12/31/20
Learning Services
N.A.I.C.S.: 611710
Wei Yuan *(CEO & Compliance Officer)*

CHINA E-WALLET PAYMENT GROUP LIMITED
Room 626-629 Corporation Park 11 On Lai Street, Siu Lek Yuen, Sha Tin, NT, China (Hong Kong)
Tel.: (852) 26372800　　　BM
Web Site: http://www.rcg.tv
Year Founded: 1999
0802—(HKG)
Rev.: $11,359,485
Assets: $50,965,830
Liabilities: $4,550,093
Net Worth: $46,415,738
Earnings: ($8,759,633)
Emp.: 45
Fiscal Year-end: 12/31/22
Radio Frequency Identification Technologies
N.A.I.C.S.: 334220
Poon Chun Yin *(Exec Dir)*

CHINA EAST EDUCATION HOLDINGS LIMITED
No 1009 Xuelin Road, Vocational Education Town Xinzhan District, Hefei, Anhui, China　　　Ky
Web Site:
https://www.chinaeastedu.com
Year Founded: 1988
0667—(HKG)
Rev.: $550,876,994
Assets: $1,286,432,903
Liabilities: $510,020,215
Net Worth: $776,412,688
Earnings: $37,746,732
Emp.: 10,881
Fiscal Year-end: 12/31/23
Holding Company
N.A.I.C.S.: 551112
Guoqing Xiao *(Deputy Chm)*

CHINA EASTERN AIRLINES CORPORATION LTD.
The Board Office Block A2 CEA Building 36 Hongxiang sanlu Road, Northern District Minhang District, Shanghai, 200335, China
Tel.: (86) 2122330932　　　CN
Web Site: https://www.ceair.com
Year Founded: 1957
600115—(SHG)
Rev.: $10,284,527,670

Assets: $44,245,515,900
Liabilities: $35,489,257,980
Net Worth: $8,756,257,920
Earnings: ($2,035,241,640)
Emp.: 80,321
Fiscal Year-end: 12/31/21
Airline Transport Services
N.A.I.C.S.: 481111
Yangmin Li *(Pres & Vice Chm)*

CHINA ECAPITAL CORPORA-TION
China Resources Building 19th Floor, 8 Jian Guo Men Bei Avenue, Beijing, 100005, China
Tel.: (86) 10 8519 2080
Web Site: http://www.china-ecapital.com
Year Founded: 2000
Private Investment Firm
N.A.I.C.S.: 523999
Ran Wang *(Co-Founder, Partner & CEO)*

CHINA ECO-FARMING LIM-ITED
Room 2002 20/F OTB Building 160 Gloucester Road, Wanchai, China (Hong Kong)
Tel.: (852) 31060388　　　BM
Web Site: http://www.chinaeco-farming.com
Year Founded: 2000
8166—(HKG)
Rev.: $9,341,543
Assets: $30,435,908
Liabilities: $13,965,458
Net Worth: $16,470,450
Earnings: ($6,709,050)
Emp.: 52
Fiscal Year-end: 12/31/21
Investment Management Service
N.A.I.C.S.: 523940
David Tat Man So *(Compliance Officer)*

Subsidiaries:

Inno-Bag Limited　　　　　(1)
Room 1709 17th Floor Fortune Commercial Building 362 Sha Tsui Road, Tsuen Wan, Hong Kong, China (Hong Kong)
Tel.: (852) 81132378
Web Site: https://www.inno-bag.com
Emp.: 2
Investment Management Service
N.A.I.C.S.: 523940

CHINA ECO-MATERIALS GROUP CO., LIMITED
No 200 Liu Gang Tou Qinglin Community, Tangshan Township, Nanjing, 211131, Jiangsu, China
Tel.: (86) 2584100618　　　Ky
Year Founded: 2019
Rev.: $7,016,512
Assets: $12,318,145
Liabilities: $3,839,007
Net Worth: $8,479,138
Earnings: $1,358,888
Emp.: 29
Fiscal Year-end: 02/28/19
Holding Company
N.A.I.C.S.: 551112
Jinru Lin *(Chm & CEO)*

CHINA ECOTOURISM GROUP LIMITED
Unit 3308 33/F Office Tower Convention Plaza 1 Harbour Road, Wanchai, China (Hong Kong)
Tel.: (852) 21366618
Web Site:
http://www.chinalotsynergy.com
1371—(HKG)
Rev.: $16,112,182
Assets: $73,932,110
Liabilities: $61,004,702

Net Worth: $12,927,407
Earnings: ($36,231,901)
Emp.: 201
Fiscal Year-end: 12/31/21
Lottery Products Distr
N.A.I.C.S.: 561499
Jingwei Wu *(Pres)*

CHINA EDUCATION ALLI-ANCE, INC.

58 Heng Shan Road Kun Kun Shopping Mall, Harbin, 150090, China
Tel.: (86) 45182335794　　　　NC
Web Site:
　http://www.chinaeducation.com
Year Founded: 1996
Sales Range: Less than $1 Million
Emp.: 1,071
Educational Services Including On-Line Portal, Training Centers, Software & Media
N.A.I.C.S.: 611519
Xiqun Yu *(Chm, Pres & CEO)*

CHINA EDUCATION GROUP HOLDINGS LIMITED

Suite 1504 Two Exchange Square 8 Connaught Place, Central, China (Hong Kong)
Tel.: (852) 2 111 8468　　　　Ky
Web Site:
　http://www.chinaeducation.hk
Year Founded: 1999
0839—(HKG)
Rev.: $564,186,632
Assets: $4,097,900,822
Liabilities: $2,296,637,664
Net Worth: $1,801,263,158
Earnings: $225,488,656
Emp.: 11,034
Fiscal Year-end: 08/31/21
Education Training Services
N.A.I.C.S.: 611210
Guo Yu *(Co-Chm)*

CHINA EDUCATION RESOURCES INC.

Suite 300 515 West Pender Street, Vancouver, V6B 6H5, BC, Canada
Tel.: (604) 331-2388　　　　BC
Web Site:
　https://www.chinaeducation.com
Year Founded: 2000
CHNUF—(OTCEM)
Rev.: $7,425,335
Assets: $7,218,025
Liabilities: $6,933,421
Net Worth: $284,604
Earnings: $359,449
Emp.: 35
Fiscal Year-end: 12/31/20
Educational Products Including Textbooks & Software
N.A.I.C.S.: 923110
Chengfeng F. Zhou *(CEO & Chm)*

Subsidiaries:

CEN China Education Network
Ltd.　　　　　　　　　　　　　**(1)**
Suite 300 515 West Pender Street, 925 West Georgia Street, Vancouver, V6B 6H5, BC, Canada
Tel.: (604) 683-6865
Sales Range: $10-24.9 Million
Emp.: 2
Educational Products & Services
N.A.I.C.S.: 611710

CHINA EDUCATION, INC.

Suite 2504 China World Tower 1 China World Trade Center, 1 Jian Guo Men Wai Avenue, Beijing, 100004, China
Tel.: (86) 1065059478　　　　Ky
Sales Range: $10-24.9 Million
Emp.: 1,170

Elementary & High Schools Owner & Operator
N.A.I.C.S.: 611110
Lawrence Lee *(Co-Chm)*

CHINA ELECTRIC MFG. CORPORATION

2F No 124 Xingshan Road, Taipei, Taiwan
Tel.: (886) 227191188
Web Site:
　http://www.chinaelectric.com.tw
1611—(TAI)
Rev.: $44,523,789
Assets: $178,808,980
Liabilities: $37,252,983
Net Worth: $141,555,997
Earnings: $4,890,938
Emp.: 130
Fiscal Year-end: 12/31/23
Lighting Product Mfr
N.A.I.C.S.: 335131

CHINA ELECTRIC MOTOR, INC.

Sunna Motor Industry Park Fuyuan 2nd Road, Fuyong High and New Technology Development Zone Baoan District, Shenzhen, China
Tel.: (86) 75581499969　　　　DE
Sales Range: $75-99.9 Million
Emp.: 920
Micro-Motor Products Designer, Mfr, Marketer & Sales
N.A.I.C.S.: 335312
Xiaohui Li *(Chm, Pres & CEO)*

CHINA ELECTRONICS CORPORATION

Tower-A CEC Great Wall Building No 3 Kefa Road, Nanshan District, Shenzhen, 100846, Guangdong, China
Tel.: (86) 1083026500　　　　CN
Web Site: https://www.cec.com.cn
Year Founded: 1989
Sales Range: Less than $1 Million
Holding Company; Information Technology Products Mfr & Services
N.A.I.C.S.: 551112
Lu Zhipeng *(VP & Deputy Gen Mgr)*

Subsidiaries:

Bridgelux, Inc.　　　　　　　　**(1)**
46430 Fremont Boulevard, Fremont, CA 94538
Tel.: (925) 583-8400
Web Site: http://www.bridgelux.com
Light Emitting Diode Technologies Developer & Mfr
N.A.I.C.S.: 335139
Timothy Lester *(Co-CEO)*

China Electronics Huada Technology
Company Limited　　　　　　**(1)**
Room 3403 China Resources Building 26 Harbour Road, Wanchai, China (Hong Kong)　　　　　　　　　**(74.98%)**
Tel.: (852) 25989088
Web Site: http://www.cecholding.com
Electronic Products Mfr
N.A.I.C.S.: 327110
Hongzhou Liu *(Mng Dir)*

China National Software & Service
Co., Ltd　　　　　　　　　　**(1)**
Chinasoft Software Park No 18 Changsheng Road, Changping District, Beijing, 102200, China
Tel.: (86) 4001601670
Web Site: https://www.css.com.cn
Rev.: $1,353,482,030
Assets: $1,442,659,266
Liabilities: $942,819,584
Net Worth: $499,839,683
Earnings: $6,364,669
Emp.: 10,554
Fiscal Year-end: 12/31/2022
Software Development, Distribution & Services
N.A.I.C.S.: 513210
Zhou Zailong *(Gen Mgr)*

Subsidiary (Domestic):

Great Wall Computer Software &
Systems Co., Ltd　　　　　　**(2)**
5/F Gaode Building 10 Huayuan Dong Road, Haidian District, Beijing, 100083, China
Tel.: (86) 1082038899
Web Site: http://www.gwssi.com.cn
Software Equipment Services
N.A.I.C.S.: 541513

Dalian Pactera Technology International Co., Ltd.　　　　　　**(1)**
Room 106 1st Floor Building C4 Building C4 No 66, Zhongguancun Dongsheng Science Park Haidian District, Beijing, 100085, China
Tel.: (86) 10 5987 5000
Web Site: http://www.pactera.com
Information Technology Consulting & Outsourcing Services
N.A.I.C.S.: 541519
Lu Zhequn *(CEO)*

Subsidiary (Non-US):

Lifewood Data Technology
Limited　　　　　　　　　　　**(2)**
Wharf Telecommunications Center 7 CantonRoad, Kowloon, Tsim Sha Tsui, China (Hong Kong)
Tel.: (852) 28511033
Web Site: http://www.lifewood.com
Business Process Outsourcing Services
N.A.I.C.S.: 561499

Pactera Technology Japan Co.,
Ltd.　　　　　　　　　　　　　**(2)**
Toyuso Hulic 7 3 Nihonbashi Odenmacho, Chuo ku, Tokyo, 163-0222, Japan
Tel.: (81) 3 352 379865
Web Site: http://www.pactera.com
Information Technology Consulting Services
N.A.I.C.S.: 541512

Subsidiary (US):

Pactera Technology NA, Inc.　　**(2)**
14980 NE 31st Way Ste 100, Redmond, WA 98052
Tel.: (425) 233-8578
Web Site: http://www.pactera-edge.com
Custom Computer Programming Services
N.A.I.C.S.: 541511

Subsidiary (Domestic):

Blue Fountain Media Inc.　　　　**(3)**
102 Madison Ave 2nd Fl, New York, NY 10016
Tel.: (212) 260-1978
Web Site:
　http://www.bluefountainmedia.com
Website Design Provider
N.A.I.C.S.: 518210
Brian Byer *(Gen Mgr)*

Great Wall Technology Co., Ltd.　**(1)**
No 2 Keyuan Road Technology & Industry Park, Nanshan District, Shenzhen, 518057, China
Tel.: (86) 75526728686
Web Site: http://www.greatwalltech.com
Sales Range: $10-24.9 Million
Emp.: 59,000
Computer Mfr & Computer Services
N.A.I.C.S.: 334111
Man Chi Tam *(Exec Dir)*

Subsidiary (Domestic):

China Greatwall Technology Group
Co., Ltd.　　　　　　　　　　　**(2)**
China Electronics Great Wall Building Science and Technology Park, Nanshan District, Shenzhen, 518057, China
Tel.: (86) 75526634759
Web Site: http://www.greatwall.com.cn
Rev.: $1,969,438,536
Assets: $4,755,561,408
Liabilities: $2,670,871,320
Net Worth: $2,084,690,088
Earnings: $16,887,312
Emp.: 1,000
Fiscal Year-end: 12/31/2022
Computer Parts & Products Mfr
N.A.I.C.S.: 334111
Liding Song *(Chm)*

Shenzhen Kaifa Technology Co.,
Ltd.　　　　　　　　　　　　　**(2)**
7006 Caitian Road, Futian District, Shenzhen, 518035, Guangdong, China
Tel.: (86) 75583032000
Web Site: https://www.kaifa.com.cn
Rev.: $2,263,020,552
Assets: $3,904,936,776
Liabilities: $2,225,411,604
Net Worth: $1,679,525,172
Earnings: $92,530,620
Emp.: 16,000
Fiscal Year-end: 12/31/2022
Computer & Video Equipment Mfr
N.A.I.C.S.: 334111
James Zhou *(Chm)*

Subsidiary (Domestic):

Shenzhen Kafia Magnetic Recording
Co., Ltd　　　　　　　　　　　**(3)**
Caitian Rd 7006, Futian Distric, Shenzhen, 518035, China
Tel.: (86) 75583275000
Disk Mfr
N.A.I.C.S.: 334118

CHINA ELECTRONICS HOLDINGS, INC.

Building 3 Longhe East Road, Binhi District, Lu'an, 237000, Anhui, China
Tel.: (86) 5643224888　　　　NV
Web Site:
　http://www.chinacrazybuy.com
Year Founded: 2002
CEHD—(OTCIQ)
Sales Range: $25-49.9 Million
Emp.: 66
Consumer Electronics & Appliances Retailer
N.A.I.C.S.: 449210
Hailong Liu *(Chm, Pres, CEO & CFO)*

CHINA ELECTRONICS TECHNOLOGY CO., LTD.

No 381 Xingang Middle Road, Haizhu District, Guangzhou, 510310, Guangdong, China
Tel.: (86) 2084118000
Web Site: https://www.chinagci.com
Year Founded: 2003
002544—(SSE)
Rev.: $993,403,008
Assets: $1,379,747,304
Liabilities: $832,532,688
Net Worth: $547,214,616
Earnings: $29,959,956
Fiscal Year-end: 12/31/22
Communication, Electronic & Information Products Mfr
N.A.I.C.S.: 334220
Pu Yuan *(Chm)*

CHINA ELECTRONICS TECHNOLOGY GROUP CORPORATION

No 27 Wanshou Road Haidian District, Beijing, China
Tel.: (86) 1068200821
Web Site: http://www.cetc.com.cn
Year Founded: 2002
Sales Range: Less than $1 Million
Emp.: 150,000
Electronics & Communication Equipment Mfr & Distr
N.A.I.C.S.: 334210
Li Shouwu *(VP)*

CHINA EMEDIA HOLDINGS CORPORATION

Suite 2302 Seaview Commercial Building, 21 Connaught Road West, Sheung Wan, China (Hong Kong)
Tel.: (852) 90099119　　　　DE
Web Site:
　http://eb623346.eserviceweb.net
Year Founded: 2009
Internet Marketing Solutions

China eMedia Holdings Corporation—(Continued)
N.A.I.C.S.: 541613
Kai Lun Ng (Chm)

CHINA ENERGINE INTERNATIONAL (HOLDINGS) LIMITED
Unit 2301 23rd Floor Office Tower
Convention Plaza, 1 Harbour Road,
Wanchai, China (Hong Kong)
Tel.: (852) 25861185
Web Site: http://www.energine.hk
Year Founded: 1997
Rev.: $4,919,002
Assets: $402,175,882
Liabilities: $447,220,441
Net Worth: ($45,044,559)
Earnings: ($135,534,058)
Emp.: 354
Fiscal Year-end: 12/31/19
Wind Energy Related Products Mfr
N.A.I.C.S.: 333921
Jun Xu (Controller-Fin)

Subsidiaries:

Beijing Wanyuan-Henniges Sealing
Systems Co., Ltd   (1)
No 1 Nan Da Hong Men Road, Fengtai District, Beijing, 100076, China
Tel.: (86) 68384743
Web Site:
  http://www.hennigesautomotive.com
Vehicle Sealing Systems & Anti-Vibration
Products Mfr
N.A.I.C.S.: 336390

CHINA ENERGY DEVELOPMENT HOLDINGS LIMITED
Units 5611-12 56th Floor The Center
99 Queen's Road Central, Central,
China (Hong Kong)
Tel.: (852) 21693382   Ky
Web Site:
  http://www.cnenergy.com.hk
Year Founded: 2001
0228—(HKG)
Rev.: $41,186,070
Assets: $326,413,898
Liabilities: $106,270,103
Net Worth: $220,143,795
Earnings: $10,577,783
Emp.: 41
Fiscal Year-end: 12/31/22
Oil & Gas Exploration Services
N.A.I.C.S.: 213112
Guoqiang Zhao (CEO)

CHINA ENERGY ENGINEERING CORPORATION LIMITED
Building 1 No 26 XIDAWANG Road,
Chaoyang District, Beijing, 100022,
China
Tel.: (86) 1059098831   CN
Web Site: https://en.ceec.net.cn
Year Founded: 2014
3996—(HKG)
Rev.: $56,218,410,501
Assets: $108,434,342,185
Liabilities: $82,369,200,543
Net Worth: $26,065,141,643
Earnings: $1,558,416,454
Emp.: 117,039
Fiscal Year-end: 12/31/23
Construction Engineering Services
N.A.I.C.S.: 541330
Hougui Zhou (VP)

CHINA ENERGY RECOVERY INC.
Building 26 No 1388 Zhangdong
Road Zhangjiang Hi-Tech Park,
Shanghai, 201203, China
Tel.: (86) 2120281866   DE
Web Site:
  http://www.chinaenergyrecovery.com
Year Founded: 1998
CGYV—(OTCEM)

Sales Range: $75-99.9 Million
Emp.: 420
Waste Energy Management Services
N.A.I.C.S.: 562998
Qinghuan Wu (Chm & CEO)

CHINA ENERGY RESERVE & CHEMICALS GROUP CO., LTD.
Rongbao Building 26 Gulouwai
Street, Dongcheng District, Beijing,
100120, China
Tel.: (86) 1082809064   CN
Web Site: http://www.cercg.com
Holding Company; Oil, Natural Gas &
Related Chemical Products & Services
N.A.I.C.S.: 551112
Yihe Chen (Chm)

CHINA ENERGY TECHNOLOGY CORP. LTD.
No 1122 South Yanan Street, New
District, Bengbu, Anhui, China
Tel.: (86) 552 411 6868   NV
Web Site: http://www.rrjtyn.com
Year Founded: 2012
Sales Range: $1-9.9 Million
Emp.: 270
Solar Powered Water Heater Systems Mfr
N.A.I.C.S.: 333415
Quan Ji (Pres, CEO, CFO, Treas &
Sec)

CHINA ENTERPRISE COMPANY LIMITED
Floor 4-7 No 1388 Puming Road, Pudong New Area, Shanghai, 200127,
China
Tel.: (86) 2120772222
Web Site: http://www.cecl.com.cn
Year Founded: 1993
600675—(SHG)
Rev.: $365,229,470
Assets: $8,242,967,019
Liabilities: $5,933,441,044
Net Worth: $2,309,525,974
Earnings: $3,236,852
Fiscal Year-end: 12/31/22
Real Estate Manangement Services
N.A.I.C.S.: 531311
Li Zhong (Chm)

CHINA ENTERPRISES LIMITED
21 F Catic Plaza 8 Causeway Road,
Causeway Bay, China (Hong Kong)
Tel.: (852) 31510300   BM
Web Site:
  http://www.chinaenterprisesltd.com
Year Founded: 1993
CSHEF—(OTCEM)
Sales Range: Less than $1 Million
Holding Company; Tire Mfr
N.A.I.C.S.: 551112
Lien Kait Long (CFO)

CHINA ENVIRONMENT LTD.
65 Chulia Street 46-00 OCBC Centre,
Singapore, 049513, Singapore
Tel.: (65) 66706641   SG
Web Site: http://www.chinaenv.net
Year Founded: 2003
5OU—(SES)
Sales Range: $75-99.9 Million
Waste Gas Treatment Services
N.A.I.C.S.: 562998
Min Huang (Chm)

CHINA ENVIRONMENTAL ENERGY INVESTMENT LIMITED
Room 910 9/F Harbour Centre 25
Harbour Road, Wanchai, China
(Hong Kong)
Tel.: (852) 2 536 0288   BM
Web Site: http://www.986.com.hk
Year Founded: 1965

0986—(HKG)
Rev.: $14,046,825
Assets: $54,312,317
Liabilities: $6,054,063
Net Worth: $48,258,254
Earnings; $77,904
Emp.: 50
Fiscal Year-end: 03/31/22
Holding Company; Elcctro Dopooitod
Copper Foil, Copper Clad Laminates
& Printed Circuit Boards Mfr
N.A.I.C.S.: 551112
Yaying Zhou (Chm)

Subsidiaries:

Nam Hing Circuit Board Company
Limited   (1)
Unit 704 Yuen Long Trading Centre 33
Wang Yip Street West, PO Box 267, Yuen
Long, New Territories, China (Hong Kong)
Tel.: (852) 24716438
Web Site: https://www.namhing-pcb.com.hk
Sales Range: $100-124.9 Million
Emp.: 300
Printed Circuit Board Mfr
N.A.I.C.S.: 334412
Lau Kwai (Founder)

Nam Hing Industrial Laminate
Limited   (1)
Unit 4 7/F Yuen Long Trading Ctr 33 Wang
Yip St W Yuen Long, PO Box 267, Yuen
Long, New Territories, China (Hong Kong)
Tel.: (852) 24759105
Web Site: http://www.nh-laminate.com.hk
Sales Range: $25-49.9 Million
Copper Clad Laminates Mfr
N.A.I.C.S.: 326130
Lau Pheriok (Mng Dir)

Zhongshan Nam Hing Insulating Material Limited   (1)
Dongsheng Indus Dev Estate, Lan Wang,
Zhongshan, Guangdong, China
Tel.: (86) 76085601415
Industrial Laminates Mfr
N.A.I.C.S.: 326130

CHINA ENVIRONMENTAL RESOURCES GROUP LIMITED
Room 2811 28/F West Tower Shun
Tak Centre 200 Connaught Road,
Central, China (Hong Kong)
Tel.: (852) 39043300   Ky
Web Site:
  http://www.cergroup.com.hk
1130—(HKG)
Rev.: $12,019,388
Assets: $100,669,922
Liabilities: $31,476,150
Net Worth: $69,193,772
Earnings: ($1,912,515)
Emp.: 60
Fiscal Year-end: 06/30/22
Fertilizer Mfr
N.A.I.C.S.: 325314
Kwong Choi Leung (Exec Dir)

Subsidiaries:

Power Asia Motorsport Company
Limited   (1)
RM 3-5 G/F Po Hong Centre 2 Wang Tung
Street, Main entrance at Sheung Yee Road
Kowloon Bay, Kowloon, China (Hong Kong)
Tel.: (852) 37920298
Web Site:
  http://www.powerasiamotorsport.com
Motorcycle Parts & Accessory Distr
N.A.I.C.S.: 441227

CHINA ENVIRONMENTAL TECHNOLOGY & BIOENERGY HOLDINGS LIMITED
Unit 1610 16/F The Metropolis Tower
10 Metroplis Drive, Hunghom, Kowloon, China (Hong Kong)
Tel.: (852) 39041866   Ky
Web Site:
  http://www.merrygardenholdings.com
Year Founded: 1995

1237—(HKG)
Rev.: $65,291,195
Assets: $142,729,376
Liabilities: $19,124,446
Net Worth: $123,604,931
Earnings: ($952,474)
Emp.: 149
Fiscal Year-end: 12/31/22
Wood Processing Services
N.A.I.C.S.: 321999
Zheyan Wu (CEO)

Subsidiaries:

Fujian Zhangping Kimura Forestry
Products Co., Ltd.   (1)
Fushan Industrial Zone, Zhangping,
364400, China
Tel.: (86) 59 7783 1258
Web Site: http://www.kimura.co.cn
Household Mfr & Distr
N.A.I.C.S.: 337122

Merry Garden (US) Inc.   (1)
1297 Babcock Ct, Brentwood, CA 94513
Tel.: (925) 634-4821
Household Product Mfr & Distr
N.A.I.C.S.: 337122

CHINA ENVIRONMENTAL TECHNOLOGY HOLDINGS LIMITED
Unit 1003-5 10/F Shui On Centre 6-8
Harbour Road, Wanchai, China
(Hong Kong)
Tel.: (852) 25111870   Ky
Web Site: http://www.cethl.com
Year Founded: 2001
0646—(HKG)
Rev.: $4,896,000
Assets: $4,447,073
Liabilities: $77,876,363
Net Worth: ($73,429,290)
Earnings: ($3,190,433)
Emp.: 49
Fiscal Year-end: 12/31/22
Sewage Treatment Services
N.A.I.C.S.: 221320
Zhong Ping Xu (Chm)

CHINA ERZHONG GROUP DEYANG HEAVY INDUSTRIES CO., LTD.
460 West Zhujiang Road, Deyang,
618013, Sichuan, China
Tel.: (86) 8382343088
Web Site: http://www.china-erzhong.com
Emp.: 12,650
Heavy Technical Equipment Mfr;
Steel Products Casting & Forging
N.A.I.C.S.: 333248

CHINA ESSENCE GROUP LTD.
Unit 2607 26/F Inspring Space 25
Ganluyuan Nanli, Qingnian Road
Chaoyang Area, Beijing, China
Tel.: (86) 1085590127
Web Site:
  http://www.chinaessence.com
Sales Range: $1-9.9 Million
Potato Starch Mfr
N.A.I.C.S.: 311221
Guolin Wu (Chief R&D Officer)

CHINA EVER GRAND FINANCIAL LEASING GROUP CO., LTD.
Room 2203 22/F Kwan Chart Tower
No 6 Tonnochy Road, Wanchai,
China (Hong Kong)
Tel.: (852) 25737899
Web Site: http://www.egichk.com
0379—(HKG)
Rev.: $9,917,715
Assets: $102,170,213
Liabilities: $33,746,190
Net Worth: $68,424,023

Earnings: $5,560,658
Emp.: 65
Fiscal Year-end: 12/31/22
Investment Holding Services
N.A.I.C.S.: 523999
Lik Ping Wong *(Chm)*

Subsidiaries:

Fook Cheong Ho International
Limited **(1)**
Rm D 5 F Unison Indust Ctr 27 31, Au Pui
Wan St Fotan, Sha Tin, New Territories,
China (Hong Kong)
Tel.: (852) 26908484
Web Site: http://www.pme8.com
Sales Range: $25-49.9 Million
Industrial Abrasive Products Whslr
N.A.I.C.S.: 423840
Bannie Cheng *(Mng Dir)*

CHINA EVERBRIGHT GROUP LIMITED

17/F China Overseas International
Centre No 28 Ping An Li West Street,
Xicheng District, Beijing, 100034,
China
Tel.: (86) 1088009000 **CN**
Web Site: https://www.everbright.com
Year Founded: 1983
Sales Range: Less than $1 Million
Holding Company
N.A.I.C.S.: 551112

Subsidiaries:

Ambrx, Inc. **(1)**
10975 N Torrey Pines Rd, La Jolla, CA
92037
Tel.: (858) 875-2400
Web Site: http://www.ambrx.com
Biopharmaceutical Developer
N.A.I.C.S.: 325412
Feng Tian *(Chm, Pres & CEO)*

China Everbright Bank Co., Ltd. **(1)**
Everbright Center No 25 Taipingqiao Ave,
Xicheng District, Beijing, 100033,
China **(23.69%)**
Tel.: (86) 1063636363
Web Site: https://www.cebbank.com
Rev.: $33,932,184,750
Assets: $822,448,133,100
Liabilities: $752,737,889,520
Net Worth: $69,710,243,580
Earnings: $5,807,425,050
Emp.: 46,316
Fiscal Year-end: 12/31/2020
Commercial Banking Services
N.A.I.C.S.: 522110
Xiaopeng Li *(Chm)*

Subsidiary (Domestic):

Shanghai Everbright Convention and
Exhibition Centre Limited **(2)**
5F B Block 66 Caobao Road, Xuhui District,
Shanghai, 200235, China
Tel.: (86) 21 64753288
Web Site: http://www.secec.com
Exhibition & Convention Center Operating
Services
N.A.I.C.S.: 561591

China Everbright Environment Group
Limited **(1)**
Rm 2703 27/F Far East Finance Centre, 16
Harcourt Road, Hong Kong, China (Hong
Kong) **(41.39%)**
Tel.: (852) 28041886
Web Site: https://www.cebenvironment.com
Rev.: $4,769,668,997
Assets: $24,358,479,942
Liabilities: $16,358,314,696
Net Worth: $8,000,165,246
Earnings: $704,814,753
Emp.: 12,400
Fiscal Year-end: 12/31/2022
Construction Services
N.A.I.C.S.: 237990
Yunge Cai *(Chm)*

Subsidiary (Non-US):

China Everbright Water Limited **(2)**
26/F Block A Oriental Xintiandi Plaza No
1003 Shennan Avenue, Futian District,

Shenzhen, 518000, China **(74%)**
Tel.: (86) 75582999100
Web Site: https://www.ebwater.com
Rev.: $730,451,402
Assets: $3,470,533,735
Liabilities: $1,999,406,042
Net Worth: $1,471,127,694
Earnings: $140,119,229
Emp.: 2,231
Fiscal Year-end: 12/31/2020
Waste & Waste Water Treatment Services
N.A.I.C.S.: 562998
Yuexing Wang *(VP)*

NOVAGO Sp. z o.o. **(2)**
al Niepodleglosci 124 room 6, 02-577, War-
saw, Poland
Tel.: (48) 22 300 50 43
Web Site: http://www.novago.pl
Solid Waste Treatment Services
N.A.I.C.S.: 562212
Piotr Jeromin *(COO)*

Plant (Domestic):

NOVAGO Sp. z o.o. - Kosiny
Plant **(3)**
Kosiny Bartosowe 57, 06-521, Wisniowa,
Poland
Tel.: (48) 603900501
Web Site: http://en.novago.pl
Solid Waste Treatment Services
N.A.I.C.S.: 562212

NOVAGO Sp. z o.o. - Rozanki
Plant **(3)**
Rozanki 13, 14-240, Susz, Poland
Tel.: (48) 552211295
Web Site: http://en.novago.pl
Solid Waste Treatment Services
N.A.I.C.S.: 562212

NOVAGO Sp. z o.o. - Zlotow
Plant **(3)**
Szpitalna 38, 77-400, Zlotow, Poland
Tel.: (48) 672633011
Web Site: http://www.en.novago.pl
Solid Waste Treatment Services
N.A.I.C.S.: 562212

NOVAGO Sp. z o.o. - Znin Plant **(3)**
Wawrzynki 35, 88-400, Znin, Poland
Tel.: (48) 525513575
Web Site: http://en.novago.pl
Solid Waste Treatment Services
N.A.I.C.S.: 562212

China Everbright Greentech Ltd. **(1)**
Room 3602 36/F Far East Finance Centre
16 Harcourt Road, Hong Kong, China
(Hong Kong)
Tel.: (852) 22591238
Web Site: https://www.ebgreentech.com
Rev.: $1,026,141,803
Assets: $4,992,437,940
Liabilities: $3,266,816,603
Net Worth: $1,725,621,338
Earnings: $43,987,500
Emp.: 3,580
Fiscal Year-end: 12/31/2022
Solar & Wind Power Structure Services
N.A.I.C.S.: 237130
Wing Chow *(Sec)*

China Everbright Limited **(1)**
46/F Far East Finance Centre 16 Harcourt
Road, Hong Kong, China (Hong
Kong) **(49.74%)**
Tel.: (852) 25289882
Web Site: http://www.everbright.com
Rev.: $982,735,575
Assets: $10,770,767,903
Liabilities: $5,941,437,525
Net Worth: $4,829,330,378
Earnings: ($981,790,163)
Emp.: 273
Fiscal Year-end: 12/31/2022
Investment Holding Company
N.A.I.C.S.: 551112
Lianchen Yin *(Co-Chief Investment Officer)*

Holding (US):

Burke E. Porter Machinery
Company **(2)**
730 Plymouth Ave NE, Grand Rapids, MI
49505
Tel.: (616) 234-1200
Web Site: http://www.bepco.com
Electrical Equipment Mfr & Distr

N.A.I.C.S.: 334290
Jon Lawrence *(Dir-Bus-New Product Dev)*

Holding (Non-US):

Tirana International Airport
SHPK **(2)**
Administration Building, Rinas, Tirana,
Albania **(100%)**
Tel.: (355) 42381600
Web Site: http://www.tirana-airport.com
Airport Operator
N.A.I.C.S.: 488119
Rolf Castro-Vasquez *(CEO)*

Everbright Securities Co., Ltd. **(1)**
No 1508 Xinzha Road Jingan District,
Shanghai, 200040, China
Tel.: (86) 2122169914
Web Site: https://www.ebscn.com
Rev.: $2,074,563,598
Assets: $36,448,405,391
Liabilities: $26,915,892,775
Net Worth: $9,532,512,616
Earnings: $603,804,942
Emp.: 8,064
Fiscal Year-end: 12/31/2023
Securities Brokerage Services
N.A.I.C.S.: 523150
Jian Mei *(VP)*

Sun Life Everbright Life Insurance
Company Limited **(1)**
4th Floor Tianjin International Building 75
Nanjing Road, Heping District, Tianjin,
300050, China **(50%)**
Tel.: (86) 22 2339 1188
Web Site: http://www.sunlife-everbright.com
Life Insurance Products & Services
N.A.I.C.S.: 524113

CHINA EVERGRANDE GROUP

No 78 Huangpu Avenue West, Tianhe
District, Guangzhou, 510620, Guang-
dong, China
Tel.: (86) 85222879229 **Ky**
Web Site:
https://mobilesite.evergrande.com
Year Founded: 1996
EGRNQ—(OTCIQ)
Sales Range: $75-99.9 Million
Real Estate Manangement Services
N.A.I.C.S.: 551112
Miaoling He *(Exec Dir)*

Subsidiaries:

China Evergrande New Energy Ve-
hicle Group Limited **(1)**
28th Floor Evergrande International Center
No 78 Huangpu Avenue West, Guangzhou,
510620, Guangdong, China **(74.99%)**
Tel.: (86) 2098657431
Web Site: http://www.evergrandehealth.com
Rev.: $2,372,705,816
Assets: $22,991,418,815
Liabilities: $23,885,938,771
Net Worth: ($894,519,956)
Earnings: ($1,174,340,401)
Emp.: 8,796
Fiscal Year-end: 12/31/2020
Media & Healthcare Services
N.A.I.C.S.: 561499
Shawn Siu *(Chm)*

CHINA EVERGREEN ACQUISITION CORPORATION

B-2102 CaiZhi Tower Zhongguancun
Rd E, Haidian, Beijing, 100083,
China
Tel.: (86) 13901174642 **Ky**
Year Founded: 2007
Sales Range: $25-49.9 Million
Emp.: 5
Investment Services
N.A.I.C.S.: 523999
Gui Fa Cao *(Chm)*

CHINA EXECUTIVE EDUCATION CORP.

c/o Hangzhou MYL Business Administration Consulting Co. Ltd., Room
307 Hualong Business Bldg, 110 Mo-

ganshan Road, Hangzhou, 310005,
China
Tel.: (86) 57188808109 **NV**
Web Site: http://www.myl101.com
Year Founded: 2008
Sales Range: $10-24.9 Million
Emp.: 294
Executive Management Training Ser-
vices
N.A.I.C.S.: 611430
Kaien Liang *(Chm & CEO)*

CHINA EXPRESS AIRLINES CO., LTD.

2nd 3rd Floor Annex Building of Air-
port Hotel Longdongbao Airport, Nan-
ming District, Guiyang, 401120,
Guizhou, China
Tel.: (86) 2367153222
Web Site:
https://www.chinaexpressair.com
Year Founded: 2006
002928—(SSE)
Rev.: $371,099,664
Assets: $2,586,910,716
Liabilities: $2,123,552,808
Net Worth: $463,357,908
Earnings: ($277,172,064)
Emp.: 5,000
Fiscal Year-end: 12/31/22
Air Freight Transportation Services
N.A.I.C.S.: 481212
Wu Longjiang *(CEO & Dir)*

CHINA FANGDA GROUP CO., LTD.

Fangda building Keji South 12th
Road Shenzhen high tech Zone,
Nanshan District, Shenzhen, 518055,
China
Tel.: (86) 75526788571
Web Site: https://www.fangda.com
000055—(SSE)
Rev.: $540,115,992
Assets: $1,789,424,676
Liabilities: $972,241,920
Net Worth: $817,182,756
Earnings: $39,723,372
Fiscal Year-end: 12/31/22
Curtain Wall Product Mfr
N.A.I.C.S.: 332323
Jian Ming Xiong *(Chm & Pres)*

CHINA FAW GROUP CORPORATION

No 288 TianFu Road, Jingyue Devel-
opment Zone, Changchun, 130011,
Jilin, China
Tel.: (86) 43181121510
Web Site: https://www.faw.com
Year Founded: 1953
Sales Range: $25-49.9 Billion
Emp.: 118,000
Automobile & Commercial Truck Mfr
N.A.I.C.S.: 336110
Qiu Xiandong *(Chm)*

Subsidiaries:

Changchun Faway Automobile Com-
ponents Co., Ltd. **(1)**
No 1399 Dongfeng South Street Automobile
Industry Development Zone, Changchun,
130011, Jilin, China
Tel.: (86) 43185765685
Web Site: http://www.fawfw.com.cn
Rev.: $2,804,018,621
Assets: $2,832,134,297
Liabilities: $1,515,689,141
Net Worth: $1,316,445,156
Earnings: $76,375,452
Emp.: 18,000
Fiscal Year-end: 12/31/2022
Automobile Parts Mfr & Distr
N.A.I.C.S.: 336390
Hu Hanjie *(Chm)*

China FAW Group Import & Export
Corporation **(1)**

China FAW Group Corporation—(Continued)

No 3025 Dongfeng Street, Changchun,
130011, China
Tel.: (86) 43185123405
Automotive Components Mfr
N.A.I.C.S.: 336110

China Railway Materials Company
Limited (1)
Building 2 No 5 Fenghuangzui Street,
Fengtai District, Beijing, 100073, China
Tel.: (86) 1051895000
Web Site: https://www.crmsc.com.cn
Rev.: $7,649,699,616
Assets: $3,882,617,388
Liabilities: $2,554,198,920
Net Worth: $1,328,418,468
Earnings: $97,739,460
Fiscal Year-end: 12/31/2022
Automobile Parts Mfr
N.A.I.C.S.: 336390
Zhao Xiaohong (Chm & Sec-Party)

FAW Jiefang Group Co., Ltd. (1)
No 2259 Dongfeng Avenue Automobile De-
velopment Zone, Changchun, 130011, Jilin,
China
Tel.: (86) 43180918881
Web Site: http://www.fawcar.com.cn
Rev.: $8,848,102,085
Assets: $9,120,706,123
Liabilities: $5,730,315,200
Net Worth: $3,390,390,923
Earnings: $105,647,015
Emp.: 7,836
Fiscal Year-end: 12/31/2023
Automobiles Parts Mfr & Distr
N.A.I.C.S.: 336110

FAW Vehicle Manufacturers SA (Pty)
Ltd (1)
45 Brabazon Road Islando, Johannesburg,
South Africa
Tel.: (27) 877020800
Web Site: http://www.faw.co.za
Automotive Components Mfr
N.A.I.C.S.: 336110

FAW-EASTERN EUROPE LLC (1)
Varshavskoe sh 138, 117519, Moscow,
Russia
Tel.: (7) 4953139106
Web Site: http://www.wib-faw.ru
Automotive Components Mfr
N.A.I.C.S.: 336110

FAW-Volkswagen Automotive Co.,
Ltd. (1)
Dongfeng Street, Changchun, 130011, Jilin,
China (60%)
Tel.: (86) 431 85990151
Web Site: http://www.faw-volkswagen.com
Sales Range: $1-4.9 Billion
Emp.: 9,800
Motor Vehicle Mfr & Distr
N.A.I.C.S.: 336110

FAWorit-AUTO Company (1)
Bayzakova st 303, Almaty, Kazakhstan
Tel.: (7) 3272740549
Web Site: http://www.faw.kz
Automotive Components Mfr
N.A.I.C.S.: 336110

Myanmar FAW Intl. (1)
350 Strand RD, Latha Township, Yangon,
Myanmar
Tel.: (95) 1246626
Automotive Components Mfr
N.A.I.C.S.: 336110

Qiming Information Technology Co.,
Ltd. (1)
No 1009 Baihe Street Jingyue Hightech In-
dustrial Development Zone, Changchun,
130117, Jilin, China
Tel.: (86) 43189603547
Web Site: http://www.qm.cn
Rev.: $216,373,248
Assets: $312,367,536
Liabilities: $118,275,768
Net Worth: $194,091,768
Earnings: $10,271,664
Fiscal Year-end: 12/31/2022
Software Development Services
N.A.I.C.S.: 513210
Zhang Zhigang (Chm)

Tianjin FAW Toyota Motor Co.,
Ltd. (1)

No 2 Liuli Road, Yangliuqing Village, Tianjin,
300380, Xiqing, China
Tel.: (86) 2227944050
Web Site: http://en.tjfaw.com
Motor Vehicles Mfr
N.A.I.C.S.: 336390

CHINA FEIHE LIMITED
Star City Int'l Bldg 10 Jiuxianqiao Rd
C-16th FL, Chaoyang District, Beijing,
100016, China
Tel.: (86) 1084574688 Ky
Web Site:
https://www.chinafeiheir.com
Year Founded: 1962
6186—(HKG)
Rev.: $2,704,392,307
Assets: $5,011,447,441
Liabilities: $1,365,243,132
Net Worth: $3,646,204,309
Earnings: $455,575,986
Emp.: 178
Fiscal Year-end: 12/31/23
Dairy Products Mfr
N.A.I.C.S.: 311514
Youbin Leng (Chm & CEO)

Subsidiaries:

Canada Royal Milk ULC (1)
1680 Venture Dr, Kingston, K7P 0E9, ON,
Canada
Tel.: (613) 817-1228
Web Site: https://www.canadaroyalmilk.com
Milk Powder Mfr & Distr
N.A.I.C.S.: 311514
Carey Bidtnes (Mgr-Human Resource De-
partment)

Vitamin World USA Corporation (1)
8447 Wilshire Blvd Ste 206, Beverly Hills,
CA 90211
Web Site: https://www.vitaminworld.com
N.A.I.C.S.: 325412

CHINA FIBER OPTIC NET-
WORK SYSTEM GROUP LTD.
Room 1511 15th Floor New World
Tower 1, 16-18 Queen's Road, Cen-
tral, China (Hong Kong)
Tel.: (852) 28778033
Web Site:
http://www.chinafiberoptic.com
Sales Range: $250-299.9 Million
Emp.: 734
Fiber Optic Cord Mfr
N.A.I.C.S.: 335921
Bing Zhao (Chm)

CHINA FIBRETECH LTD.
Wubao Industrial Zone, Shishi,
362700, Fujian, China
Tel.: (86) 595 88904838
Web Site: http://www.china-
fibretech.com
Year Founded: 1995
Sales Range: $10-24.9 Million
Emp.: 510
Fabric Processing Services
N.A.I.C.S.: 313310
Eric Choo Han Kiat (CEO)

CHINA FILM CO., LTD.
No 10 Fenghe First Park Fengxiang
Technology Development Zone,
Yangsong Town Huairou District, Bei-
jing, 100044, China
Tel.: (86) 1088321280
Web Site: http://www.zgdygf.com
Year Founded: 2010
600977—(SHG)
Rev.: $409,946,828
Assets: $2,413,072,139
Liabilities: $830,510,310
Net Worth: $1,582,561,829
Earnings: ($30,175,470)
Fiscal Year-end: 12/31/22
Film Production Services
N.A.I.C.S.: 512110
Fu Ruoqing (Chm & Gen Mgr)

CHINA FILMS TECHNOLOGY
INC.
Yunmeng Economic and Technologi-
cal Development Zone, Firsta Road,
Yunmeng, 432500, Hubei, China
Tel.: (86) 7124326146 NV
Web Site:
http://www.debangtech.com
Sales Range: $25-49.9 Million
Emp.: 145
Flexible Film Mfr
N.A.I.C.S.: 322220
Zhian Zhang (Chm)

CHINA FINANCE INVESTMENT
HOLDINGS LIMITED
Suite 1510 15/F Ocean Centre Har-
bour City 5 Canton Road, Tsim Sha
Tsui West, Kowloon, China (Hong
Kong)
Tel.: (852) 37000200 BM
Web Site: http://www.cfih.hk
Year Founded: 1992
0875—(HKG)
Rev.: $127,417,890
Assets: $144,552,488
Liabilities: $83,973,158
Net Worth: $60,579,330
Earnings: $5,108,798
Emp.: 60
Fiscal Year-end: 12/31/22
Holding Company; Agricultural & Inte-
grated Financial Services
N.A.I.C.S.: 551112
Yuhao Lin (Chm)

Subsidiaries:

Golden Rich Securities Limited (1)
22/F Siu On Centre 188 Lockhart Road,
Wanchai, China (Hong Kong)
Tel.: (852) 2 377 6800
Web Site: https://www.grsl.hk
Security Brokerage Services
N.A.I.C.S.: 523150

CHINA FINANCE ONLINE CO.
LIMITED
17th Floor of Fuzhuo Plaza A No 28
Xuanwai Street, Xicheng District, Bei-
jing, 100052, China
Tel.: (86) 1083363100 HK
Web Site: http://www.jrj.com.cn
JRJC—(NASDAQ)
Rev.: $40,033,097
Assets: $77,957,306
Liabilities: $73,318,256
Net Worth: $4,639,050
Earnings: ($10,558,169)
Emp.: 441
Fiscal Year-end: 12/31/20
Chinese Financial & Market Informa-
tion Services
N.A.I.C.S.: 523999
Zhiwei Zhao (Chm & CEO)

Subsidiaries:

China Finance Online (1)
No 690 Pibo Rd Bldg 8 3F, Shanghai,
201203, China
Tel.: (86) 2150819999
Web Site: http://www.stockstar.com
Sales Range: $200-249.9 Million
Emp.: 1,000
Online Comprehensive, Timely & Profes-
sional Financial Information & Data Ser-
vices
N.A.I.C.S.: 517810

China Finance Online (Beijing) Co.,
Ltd. (1)
Corporate Square 35 Financial St, Xicheng
District, Beijing, 100032, China
Tel.: (86) 1086325288
Chinese Financial & Market Information
Services
N.A.I.C.S.: 523999

Daily Growth Securities Limited (1)
Room 3705 The Center 99 Queen's Road,

Central, China (Hong Kong)
Tel.: (852) 3900 1701
Securities Brokerage Services
N.A.I.C.S.: 523150
Kiwi Wong (Mgr-Admin)

Fortune Software (Beijing) Co.,
Ltd (1)
9th Floor Tower C Corporate Square No 35
Financial St, 100033, Beijing, Xicheng Dis-
trict, China
Tel.: (86) 10 5832 5388
Web Site:
http://www.chinafinanceonline.com
Online Information Storage & Retrieval Ser-
vices
N.A.I.C.S.: 561499

Shenzhen Genius Information Tech-
nology Co., Ltd. (1)
11/F Aolin Pike Building Shangbao Lu Futian Qu, Shenzhen, 518034, China
Tel.: (86) 21 5081 9999
Software Development Services
N.A.I.C.S.: 541511

CHINA FINANCIAL INTERNA-
TIONAL INVESTMENTS LIM-
ITED
Suite 6504 65th Floor Central Plaza
18 Harbour Road, Wanchai, China
(Hong Kong)
Tel.: (852) 35425373 Ky
0721—(HKG)
Rev.: $288,141
Assets: $78,195,157
Liabilities: $4,316,832
Net Worth: $73,878,325
Earnings: ($27,755,851)
Emp.: 11
Fiscal Year-end: 06/30/22
Holding Company
N.A.I.C.S.: 551112
Lin Dong Du (Chm & CEO)

CHINA FINANCIAL LEASING
GROUP LIMITED
11th Floor Club Centre 55 Connaught
Road West, Hong Kong, China (Hong
Kong)
Tel.: (852) 26360888
Web Site: https://www.cflg.com.hk
2312—(HKG)
Rev.: $19,763
Assets: $8,788,703
Liabilities: $101,235
Net Worth: $8,687,468
Earnings: ($2,614,005)
Emp.: 2
Fiscal Year-end: 12/31/22
Financial Lending Services
N.A.I.C.S.: 551112
Hang Chi Chan (Exec Dir)

CHINA FINANCIAL SERVICES
HOLDINGS LIMITED
Suite 5606 56/F Central Plaza 18
Harbour Road, Wanchai, China
(Hong Kong)
Tel.: (852) 25986183
Web Site: http://www.cfsh.com.hk
Rev.: $98,276,025
Assets: $768,270,738
Liabilities: $276,281,178
Net Worth: $491,989,560
Earnings: $27,473,320
Emp.: 300
Fiscal Year-end: 12/31/19
Holding Company; Supermarket
Chain Operations; Financial Services
N.A.I.C.S.: 551112
Siu Lam Cheung (Founder)

Subsidiaries:

Access (UK) Education Limited (1)
Room 25 Citibase 95 Ditchling Road, Brigh-
ton, BN1 4ST, United Kingdom
Tel.: (44) 1273987719
Web Site: http://www.access-edu.co.uk

Emp.: 6
Education Recruiting & Guardianship Services
N.A.I.C.S.: 611710

K.P.A. Company Limited (1)
Rm 5606 56 F Cent Plz 18 Harbour Rd, Wanchai, China (Hong Kong)
Tel.: (852) 25986183
Web Site: http://www.cfsh.com.hk
Sales Range: $50-74.9 Million
Emp.: 20
Property Investment Services
N.A.I.C.S.: 531110

KP Credit Gain Finance Company Limited (1)
Room 2803 28/F Tung Wai Commercial Building 109-111 Gloucester Road, Hong Kong, China (Hong Kong)
Tel.: (852) 39984025
Financial Credit Services
N.A.I.C.S.: 522320

Qian Long Assets Management Company Limited (1)
Room 5606 56/F Central Plaza No 18 Harbor Road, Wanchai, China (Hong Kong)
Tel.: (852) 25986183
Wealth Management Services
N.A.I.C.S.: 523940

Qianlong Asset Management Limited (1)
Room 5606 56/F Central Plaza No 18 Harbor Road, Wanchai, China (Hong Kong)
Tel.: (852) 2 598 6183
Wealth Management Services
N.A.I.C.S.: 523940

CHINA FINEBLANKING TECHNOLOGY CO., LTD.
No 40 Xinggong Rd, Changhu, Shengang, 509, Taiwan
Tel.: (886) 47980339
Web Site: https://www.cftc.tw
1586—(TPE)
Rev.: $79,407,216
Assets: $133,611,293
Liabilities: $85,393,334
Net Worth: $48,217,960
Earnings: $1,348,654
Fiscal Year-end: 12/31/22
Automobile Equipment Mfr
N.A.I.C.S.: 336110
I-Hsiang Huang (Chm)

Subsidiaries:

CFTC Precision (HuiAn) Limited (1)
Kaiming South Road No 11, Economic-Technological Development Area, Huai'an, Jiangsu, China
Tel.: (86) 51783565028
Hard Drive Mfr
N.A.I.C.S.: 334118

CFTC Precision Sdn. Bhd. (1)
Plo 346 Lot 84769 Jalan Perak, 81700, Pasir Gudang, Johor, Malaysia
Tel.: (60) 72524299
Emp.: 66
Precision Stamping Machine Mfr
N.A.I.C.S.: 333248

CHINA FIRST CAPITAL GROUP LIMITED
Unit 4501-02 & 12-13 45/F The Central, 99 Queen's Road Center, Central, China (Hong Kong)
Tel.: (852) 31666888
Web Site: http://en.cfcg.com.hk
1269—(HKG)
Rev.: $168,467,645
Assets: $386,268,199
Liabilities: $530,438,220
Net Worth: ($144,170,021)
Earnings: ($58,908,470)
Emp.: 1,752
Fiscal Year-end: 12/31/22
Investment Services
N.A.I.C.S.: 523999
Zhijun Zhao (Co-CEO)

Subsidiaries:

First Capital International Finance Limited (1)
Units 4513 45/F The Center 99 Queen's Road, Central, China (Hong Kong)
Tel.: (852) 3 166 6888
Financial Advisory Services
N.A.I.C.S.: 523940
Larry Chan (Mng Dir)

First Capital Securities Limited (1)
Units 4512 45/F The Center 99 Queen's Road, Central, China (Hong Kong)
Tel.: (852) 3 166 6832
Dealing & Underwriting Security Services
N.A.I.C.S.: 523150

Nanyang Cijan Auto Shock Absorber Co., Ltd. (1)
No 76 Laojie Rd, Xichuan County, Nanyang, 474450, Henan, China
Tel.: (86) 37769219933
Web Site: http://www.china-shock-absorber.com
Sales Range: $400-449.9 Million
Emp.: 150
Automobile Parts Mfr
N.A.I.C.S.: 336390
Chun Zhi Zhao (Gen Mgr)

CHINA FIRST HEAVY INDUSTRIES CO., LTD.
No 9 Changqian Road Hongbao Office, Fulaerji District, Qiqihar, 161042, Heilongjiang, China
Tel.: (86) 4526810123
Web Site: http://www.cfhi.com
Year Founded: 1954
601106—(SHG)
Rev.: $3,353,582,157
Assets: $5,793,019,044
Liabilities: $4,127,054,504
Net Worth: $1,665,964,540
Earnings: $14,496,005
Fiscal Year-end: 12/31/22
Heavy Steel Machinery Mfr
N.A.I.C.S.: 333248
Liu Mingzhong (Chm)

CHINA FLEXIBLE PACKAGING HOLDINGS LIMITED
No 689 Xiguan Road, Rongcheng District, Jieyang, 522000, Guangdong, China
Tel.: (86) 6638811898 BM
Flexible Packaging Material Mfr
N.A.I.C.S.: 326112
Hanming Zeng (Chm & CEO)

CHINA FOOD COMPANY PLC
17 Hanover Square, London, W1S 1HU, United Kingdom
Tel.: (44) 2079308888
Web Site:
http://www.chinafoodcompany.com
Sales Range: $25-49.9 Million
Emp.: 1,082
Cooking Sauces & Animal Feed Mfr
N.A.I.C.S.: 311111
John McLean (Chm)

Subsidiaries:

Full Fortune Holdings Pte Ltd (1)
36 Robinson Road, Singapore, Singapore
Tel.: (65) 65360880
Investment Management Service
N.A.I.C.S.: 523940

CHINA FOOD PACKING INC., LTD.
Flat RM 1407 City Landmark 1 69 Chung On Street, Tsuen Wan, Hong Kong, China (Hong Kong)
Tel.: (852) 29407730
Web Site:
http://www.chinafoodpack.co.kr
Year Founded: 2007
Sales Range: $125-149.9 Million
Metal Tank Mfr

N.A.I.C.S.: 332431
Man Chan (CEO & Exec Dir)

CHINA FOODS HOLDINGS LTD.
Suite 3102 Everbright Center 108 Gloucester Road, Wanchai, 0000, China (Hong Kong)
Tel.: (852) 36188608 BC
Year Founded: 1972
CFOO—(OTCEM)
Rev.: $158,475
Assets: $365,181
Liabilities: $755,996
Net Worth: ($390,815)
Earnings: ($403,700)
Fiscal Year-end: 12/31/23
Holding Company
N.A.I.C.S.: 551112
Xiao Jun Kong (CEO & CFO)

CHINA FORTUNE HOLDINGS LIMITED
Room 1505-6 15/F Tower A Regent Centre 63 Wo Yi Hop Road, Kwai Chung, New Territories, China (Hong Kong)
Tel.: (852) 24220811
Web Site: http://www.fortunetele.com
0110—(HKG)
Rev.: $10,273,440
Assets: $2,007,743
Liabilities: $3,199,868
Net Worth: ($1,192,125)
Earnings: ($2,599,598)
Emp.: 23
Fiscal Year-end: 12/31/22
Telecommunication & Investment Services
N.A.I.C.S.: 541618
Steve Siu Ying Lau (Founder, Chm & CEO)

CHINA FORTUNE INVESTMENTS (HOLDING) LIMITED
Shop 212-213 2nd Floor Shun Tak Centre, 168-200 Connaught Road, Central, China (Hong Kong)
Tel.: (852) 3641 3988 Ky
Web Site: http://www.cfihk.com.hk
Rev.: $249,033,000
Assets: $388,192,000
Liabilities: $42,050,998
Net Worth: $7,517,238
Earnings: ($342,467,000)
Emp.: 45
Fiscal Year-end: 12/31/18
Holding Company
N.A.I.C.S.: 551112
Chun Tak Cheng (Chm)

Subsidiaries:

Queensway Golf International Limited (1)
Shop 219-222 Shun Tak Centre 168-200 Connaught Road C Sheung Wan, Hong Kong, China (Hong Kong)
Tel.: (852) 28660306
Web Site: http://www.qw.com.hk
Golf Product Distr
N.A.I.C.S.: 423910

CHINA FORTUNE LAND DEVELOPMENT CO., LTD.
Jiacheng Plaza No 18 Xiaguang Lane East Third Ring North Road, Chaoyang District, Beijing, 100027, China
Tel.: (86) 1059115055
Web Site: https://www.cfldcn.com
Year Founded: 1998
600340—(SHG)
Rev.: $4,484,619,678
Assets: $57,367,814,573
Liabilities: $53,950,983,901
Net Worth: $3,416,830,672
Earnings: $222,230,666
Fiscal Year-end: 12/31/22

Real Estate Development Services
N.A.I.C.S.: 531390
Wenxue Wang (Chm)

CHINA FUTEX HOLDINGS LIMITED
Xiawei Village, Fugong Town, Longhai, Fujian, China
Tel.: (86) 5966841968
Web Site: http://www.kx-machine.com
Rev.: $16,373,931
Assets: $29,869,692
Liabilities: $9,791,761
Net Worth: $20,077,932
Earnings: $2,377,463
Emp.: 91
Fiscal Year-end: 12/31/19
Textile Machinery Mfr
N.A.I.C.S.: 333248
Yuan Yuan (Chm & CEO)

CHINA GALAXY SECURITIES COMPANY LIMITED
Add Building 1 No 8 Xiying Street Qinghai Financial Building, Fengtai District, Beijing, 100073, China
Tel.: (86) 4008888888 CN
Web Site:
https://www.chinastock.com.cn
Year Founded: 2007
601881—(SSE)
Rev.: $6,061,842,462
Assets: $86,566,200,155
Liabilities: $72,358,610,157
Net Worth: $14,207,589,998
Earnings: $1,074,639,455
Emp.: 13,165
Fiscal Year-end: 12/31/22
Financial Investment Services
N.A.I.C.S.: 523999
Chen Gongyan (Chm)

Subsidiaries:

China Galaxy International Financial Holdings Company Limited (1)
20/F Wing On Centre 111 Connaught Road, Sheung Wan, Central, 999077, China (Hong Kong)
Tel.: (852) 3 698 6888
Web Site: https://www.chinastock.com.hk
Investment Banking Services
N.A.I.C.S.: 523150

Galaxy Futures Company Limited (1)
Floor 9th SOHO Century Plaza 1501 Century Avenue, Pudong New Area, Shanghai, 200122, China (100%)
Tel.: (86) 2160329581
Web Site: http://www.yhqh.com.cn
Risk Managemeng Srvices
N.A.I.C.S.: 541611
Chen Youan (Chm)

CHINA GAOXIAN FIBRE FABRIC HOLDINGS LTD.
Industrial Area of Balidian Town, Wuxing District, Huzhou, 313002, Zhejiang, China
Tel.: (86) 5722573333
Web Site:
http://www.chinagaoxian.com
AZZ—(SES)
Sales Range: $350-399.9 Million
Emp.: 1,100
Polyester Yarn & Knit Fabric Mfr
N.A.I.C.S.: 313110
Lin Xingdi (CEO-Interim)

CHINA GAS HOLDINGS LIMITED
1601 Capital Centre 151 Gloucester Road, Wanchai, China (Hong Kong)
Tel.: (852) 28770800
Web Site:
https://www.chinagasholdings.com.hk

China Gas Holdings Limited—(Continued)

0384—(HKG)
Rev.: $10,404,250,004
Assets: $19,003,633,067
Liabilities: $11,240,095,232
Net Worth: $7,763,537,835
Earnings: $492,400,615
Emp.: 100,000
Fiscal Year-end: 03/31/24
Holding Company
N.A.I.C.S.: 551112
Ming Hui Liu *(Co-Founder, Chm, Co-Pres & Mng Dir)*

Subsidiaries:

Rich Legend International
Limited **(1)**
Room 101 Building A Lishui Eastern Industrial Zone, He Lang Sha Lishui Town Nanhai District, Foshan, Guangdong, China
Tel.: (86) 75785632770
Emp.: 600
Textile Product Mfr & Distr
N.A.I.C.S.: 314999

CHINA GAS INDUSTRY INVESTMENT HOLDINGS CO., LTD.
No 9 Binhe Road, Lubei District, Tangshan, Hebei, China
Tel.: (86) 3152702346 Ky
Web Site: https://en.cgiihldgs.com
Year Founded: 2004
1940—(HKG)
Rev.: $206,462,393
Assets: $342,401,599
Liabilities: $132,854,874
Net Worth: $209,546,725
Earnings: $17,733,200
Emp.: 323
Fiscal Year-end: 12/31/23
Holding Company
N.A.I.C.S.: 551112
Li Yao *(Chm)*

CHINA GEM HOLDINGS LIMITED
Room 2606B 26th Floor Bank of America Tower 12 Harcourt Road, Central, China (Hong Kong)
Tel.: (852) 21399500 BM
Web Site: http://www.1191hk.com
Rev.: $13,346,679
Assets: $122,651,967
Liabilities: $110,282,232
Net Worth: $12,369,735
Earnings: ($51,686,951)
Emp.: 28
Fiscal Year-end: 12/31/19
Property Development & Installation Services
N.A.I.C.S.: 531312
Li Tie Han *(CFO)*

CHINA GENERAL PLASTICS CORPORATION
12Fl No 37 JiHu Road, Nei-Hu District, Taipei, 11492, Taiwan
Tel.: (886) 287516888
Web Site: https://www.cgpc.com.tw
Year Founded: 2012
1305—(TAI)
Rev.: $448,258,755
Assets: $580,471,282
Liabilities: $246,010,128
Net Worth: $334,461,154
Earnings: $12,873,998
Emp.: 862
Fiscal Year-end: 12/31/23
Polyvinyl Chloride Resins Mfr
N.A.I.C.S.: 325211
Yi-Gui Wu *(Chm & CEO)*

Subsidiaries:

CGPC America Corporation **(1)**
4 Latitude Way Ste 108, Corona, CA 92881

Tel.: (951) 332-4100
Upholstery Fabric Distr
N.A.I.C.S.: 424310

China General Plastics Corporation - Toufen Plant **(1)**
No 571 Minzu Rd, Toufen, 351, Miaoli, Taiwan
Tel.: (886) 37623391
Polyvinyl Chloride Resins Mfr
N.A.I.C.S.: 325211

CHINA GENERAL TECHNOLOGY (GROUP) HOLDING CO., LTD.
90 West Third Ring Road, Fengtai District, Beijing, 100055, China
Tel.: (86) 10 6334 8889 CN
Web Site: http://www.genertec.com.cn
Year Founded: 1998
Sales Range: Less than $1 Million
Holding Company; Wholesale Trade
Brokerage Services
N.A.I.C.S.: 551112

CHINA GENGSHENG MINERALS, INC.
No 88 Gengsheng Road, Dayugou Town, Gongyi, 451271, Henan, China
Tel.: (86) 37164059818 NV
Web Site: http://www.gengsheng.com
Year Founded: 1986
CHGS—(OTCEM)
Sales Range: $50-74.9 Million
Emp.: 1,200
Mineral Products Mfr
N.A.I.C.S.: 327999
Shunqing Zhang *(Chm, Pres & CEO)*

CHINA GERUI ADVANCED MATERIALS GROUP LIMITED
1 Shuanghu Development Zone, Xinzheng City, Zhengzhou, 451191, Henan, China
Tel.: (86) 37162568634 VG
Web Site: http://www.geruigroup.com
Sales Range: $150-199.9 Million
Emp.: 1,100
Cold-Rolled Specialty Steel Products Mfr
N.A.I.C.S.: 331221
Mingwang Lu *(Chm & CEO)*

CHINA GEWANG BIOTECHNOLOGY, INC.
Floor 29 No 334 Huanshi E Rd, Yuexiu District, Guangzhou, 510623, Guangdong, China
Tel.: (86) 2423974663 NV
Year Founded: 2009
CGWB—(OTCBB)
Sales Range: $25-49.9 Million
Bio Technology Services
N.A.I.C.S.: 325412
Li Wang *(CEO)*

CHINA GEZHOUBA GROUP COMPANY LIMITED
Tower F Ocean International Center 208 Ciyunsi Beili, Chaoyang District, Beijing, 100025, China
Tel.: (86) 1059525952
Web Site: http://www.gzbgj.com
Year Founded: 1970
600068—(SHG)
Rev.: $15,733,229,226
Assets: $33,551,708,619
Liabilities: $24,073,980,797
Net Worth: $9,477,727,822
Earnings: $939,252,519
Emp.: 40,000
Fiscal Year-end: 12/31/19
Construction Engineering Services
N.A.I.C.S.: 541330
Xiaohua Chen *(Chm & Pres)*

CHINA GINGKO EDUCATION GROUP COMPANY LIMITED
31/F 148 Electric Road, North Point, China (Hong Kong)
Tel.: (852) 36190956 Ky
Web Site: http://www.chinagingkoedu.com
Year Founded: 2002
1851—(HKG)
Rev.: $40,181,497
Assets: $197,808,296
Liabilities: $108,419,828
Net Worth: $89,388,468
Earnings: $11,935,123
Emp.: 830
Fiscal Year-end: 12/31/22
Educational Support Services
N.A.I.C.S.: 611710
Gongyu Fang *(Founder, Chm & CEO)*

CHINA GINSENG HOLDINGS, INC.
64 Jie Fang Da Road Ji Yu Building A Suite 1208, Changchun, 130022, China
Tel.: (86) 43185790039 NV
Web Site: http://www.chinaginsengs.com
Year Founded: 2004
Sales Range: Less than $1 Million
Emp.: 48
Ginseng Mfr, Distr & Marketer
N.A.I.C.S.: 325411
Jiankun Song *(Chm & CEO)*

CHINA GLASS HOLDINGS LIMITED
Room 2608 26/F West Tower Shun Tak Centre 168-200 Connaught Road, Central, China (Hong Kong)
Tel.: (852) 25592996
Web Site: http://www.chinaglassholdings.com
3300—(HKG)
Rev.: $607,538,318
Assets: $1,865,256,541
Liabilities: $1,403,214,322
Net Worth: $462,042,220
Earnings: $14,289,210
Emp.: 4,151
Fiscal Year-end: 12/31/22
Glass Products Mfr & Sales
N.A.I.C.S.: 327215
Xiangdong Cui *(Exec Dir)*

Subsidiaries:

Beijing CNG SINGYES Green Building Technology Co., Ltd. **(1)**
Room 0304 A Tower Mingren Flat No 101 Anli Road, Chaoyang District, Beijing, China
Tel.: (86) 1056226168
Flat Glass Mfr
N.A.I.C.S.: 327211

Dongtai China Glass Special Glass Company Limited **(1)**
Weijiu Road Economic Development Zone, Dongtai, Jiangsu, China
Tel.: (86) 51585030068
Web Site: http://www.dtcg.cn
Emp.: 500
Glass Product Mfr & Distr
N.A.I.C.S.: 327215
Hongfu Yang *(Chm)*

Linyi CNG Glass Company Limited **(1)**
Fuzhuang Subdistrict Office Luozhuang District, Linyi, Shandong, China
Tel.: (86) 5398508060
Emp.: 600
Glass Product Mfr & Distr
N.A.I.C.S.: 327215
Xiangdong Cui *(Chm)*

Olivotto Glass Technologies S.p.A. **(1)**
Viale Gandhi 22, 10051, Avigliana, Italy **(100%)**
Tel.: (39) 0119343511

Web Site: http://www.olivotto.it
Sales Range: $25-49.9 Million
Mfr of Hollow Glass Forming Machinery
N.A.I.C.S.: 333248
Sergio Sarvia *(Pres & CEO)*

Shaanxi CNG New Technology Co., Ltd. **(1)**
Xianhong Road Dongjiao Weicheng Town, Xianyang, Shaanxi, China
Tel.: (86) 2932865086
Emp.: 750
Glass Product Mfr & Distr
N.A.I.C.S.: 327215

Suqian CNG Electronic Glass Company Limited **(1)**
No 86 Jinghang road, High-tech Development Zone, Suqian, Jiangsu, China
Tel.: (86) 52788278111
Web Site: http://www.sqcngglass.com
Glass Product Mfr & Distr
N.A.I.C.S.: 327211

Suqian CNG New Materials Company Limited **(1)**
No 288 Yunhe Beilu, Suqian, Jiangsu, China
Tel.: (86) 52784212875
Emp.: 1,000
Glass Product Mfr & Distr
N.A.I.C.S.: 327215
Xiangdong Cui *(Chm)*

Weihai CNG Coated Glass Company Limited **(1)**
No 516 qishan road, lingang district, Weihai, Shandong, China
Tel.: (86) 6315990082
Web Site: https://en.lanxing.com
Emp.: 1,100
Glass Product Mfr & Distr
N.A.I.C.S.: 327215
Xiangdong Cui *(Chm)*

Weihai China Glass Solar Company Limited **(1)**
HuanShan Road, Eco and Tech Devlopment Zone, Weihai, 264205, Shandong, China
Tel.: (86) 631 596 0532
Web Site: https://www.cgsolar.com
Solar Module Mfr & Distr
N.A.I.C.S.: 334413

Wuhai CNG Special Glass Company Limited **(1)**
Qianli Mountain Industrial Zone Haibo Wan District, Wuhai, Inner Mongolia, China
Tel.: (86) 4732093050
Emp.: 480
Glass Product Mfr & Distr
N.A.I.C.S.: 327215

CHINA GLAZE CO., LTD.
136 Sec 4 Chung Hsing Road, Chutung, Hsinchu, 31061, Taiwan
Tel.: (886) 35824128
Web Site: https://www.china-glaze.com.tw
Year Founded: 1974
1809—(TAI)
Rev.: $77,085,808
Assets: $150,618,491
Liabilities: $41,667,188
Net Worth: $108,951,302
Earnings: ($1,820,759)
Fiscal Year-end: 12/31/23
Glaze & Ceramic Products Mfr & Distr
N.A.I.C.S.: 327212
Xianzong Cai *(VP)*

Subsidiaries:

Guangdong Sanshui T&H glaze Co., Ltd. **(1)**
Industrial Zone of Da-Busha Datang, Sanshui, Foshan, 528143, Guagndong, China
Tel.: (86) 7578 729 3010
Web Site: http://www.china-glaze.com.tw
Sales Range: $100-124.9 Million
Emp.: 300
Ceramic Glazing Services
N.A.I.C.S.: 238150

PT. China Glaze Indonesia **(1)**

Kawasan Industri Suryacipta Jl Surya Lestari Kav 1-17C Kutameker, Ciampel, Karawang, 41361, Jawa Barat, Indonesia
Tel.: (62) 26 744 0938
Web Site: http://www.china-glaze.com.tw
Ceramic Mfr
N.A.I.C.S.: 327120

Shandong T&H glaze Co., Ltd.　　**(1)**
Economic Development Zone, Gaoqing, Zibo, 256300, Shandong, China
Tel.: (86) 533 625 8888
Web Site: http://www.china-glaze.com.tw
Ceramic Glazing Services
N.A.I.C.S.: 238150

Shanghai T&H glaze Co., Ltd.　　**(1)**
Waldo Road 538 Westgate, Minhang District, Shanghai, 200237, China
Tel.: (86) 216 497 5566
Web Site: http://www.china-glaze.com.tw
Ceramic Glazing Services
N.A.I.C.S.: 238150

CHINA GOLD INTERNATIONAL RESOURCES CORP. LTD.

Suite 660 One Bentall Centre 505 Burrard Street, PO Box 27, Vancouver, V7X 1M4, BC, Canada
Tel.: (604) 609-0598　　　　　BC
Web Site:
　　https://www.chinagoldintl.com
JINFF—(OTCIQ)
Rev.: $1,104,949,000
Assets: $3,194,911,000
Liabilities: $1,291,481,000
Net Worth: $1,903,430,000
Earnings: $225,401,000
Emp.: 2,089
Fiscal Year-end: 12/31/22
Gold & Nonferrous Metal Mining & Production Services
N.A.I.C.S.: 212220
Jerry Quan Xie *(Sec & Exec VP)*

CHINA GOLDEN CLASSIC GROUP LIMITED

Flat B 19/F Times Media Centre 133 Wan Chai Road, Wanchai, China (Hong Kong)
Tel.: (852) 31523579　　　　　Ky
Web Site:
　　http://www.goldenclassicbio.com
Year Founded: 2015
8281—(HKG)
Rev.: $45,304,044
Assets: $54,085,428
Liabilities: $16,087,050
Net Worth: $37,998,378
Earnings: $1,967,982
Emp.: 268
Fiscal Year-end: 12/31/21
Household Product Mfr & Distr
N.A.I.C.S.: 325611
Qiuyan Li *(Chm & Compliance Officer)*

CHINA GRAPHITE GROUP LIMITED

No 1 Building 1 Graphite Development Zone, Yanjun Farm Luobei County, Hegang, Heilongjiang, China
Tel.: (86) 4686970222　　　　Ky
Web Site:
　　https://www.chinagraphite.com.hk
Year Founded: 2020
2237—(HKG)
Rev.: $27,967,712
Assets: $79,699,961
Liabilities: $17,558,706
Net Worth: $62,141,255
Earnings: $2,951,650
Emp.: 198
Fiscal Year-end: 12/31/23
Graphite Product Mfr
N.A.I.C.S.: 335991
Cherie Mak Po Man *(Sec)*

CHINA GREAT LAND HOLDINGS LTD.

Longzhu Building 22nd Floor No 2 Longkunbei Road, Haikou, Hainan, China
Tel.: (86) 898 665 01875
D50—(SES)
Sales Range: $1-9.9 Million
Holding Company
N.A.I.C.S.: 551112
Zhangjiang De Malca Li *(Chm & Mng Dir)*

CHINA GREAT STAR INTERNATIONAL LIMITED

Grand Pavilion Hibiscus Way 802 West Bay Road, PO Box 31119, Georgetown, KY1-1205, Cayman Islands
Tel.: (345) 86 595 8673 2222
Web Site:
　　http://www.chinagreatstar.co.kr
Rev.: $3,274,231,087
Assets: $4,008,657,871
Liabilities: $434,414,785
Net Worth: $3,574,243,086
Earnings: $228,252,620
Emp.: 1,145
Fiscal Year-end: 12/31/18
Holding Company
N.A.I.C.S.: 551112
Youzhi Wu *(CEO)*

CHINA GREAT WALL ASSET MANAGEMENT CORPORATION

Floors 9-12 Yuetan DaSha Office Bldg A, No 2 YueTan Beijie Xichengqu, Beijing, 100 045, China
Tel.: (86) 1068054068
Web Site: http://www.gwamcc.com
Year Founded: 2016
Financial Assets Management Services
N.A.I.C.S.: 523940
Dongping Zhao *(CEO)*

Subsidiaries:

Great Wall Pan Asia Holdings Limited　　　　　　　　　**(1)**
21st Floor Bank of America Tower, 12 Harcourt Road, Central, China (Hong Kong)
Tel.: (852) 31208204
Web Site: http://www.gwpaholdings.com
Rev.: $16,798,226
Assets: $1,011,051,391
Liabilities: $670,454,678
Net Worth: $340,596,712
Earnings: ($41,219,428)
Emp.: 21
Fiscal Year-end: 12/31/2020
Holding Company; Property Investment Services
N.A.I.C.S.: 551112
Xuefeng Meng *(Deputy CEO)*

Nissay-Greatwall Life Insurance Co., Ltd.　　　　　　　　　　**(1)**
37th Floor United Plaza 1468, Nanjing Road West, Shanghai, 200 040, China
Tel.: (86) 38999888
Web Site: http://www.nissay.co.jp
Life Insurance Products & Services; Owned 50% by Nippon Life Insurance Co. & 50% by China Great Wall Asset Management Corporation
N.A.I.C.S.: 524113

CHINA GREAT WALL SECURITIES CO., LTD.

16-17F Shenzhen Special Zone Press Tower No 6008, Shennan Boulevard, Shenzhen, 518034, Guangdong, China
Tel.: (86) 4006666888
Web Site: https://www.cgws.com
Year Founded: 1995
002939—(SSE)
Rev.: $438,998,508
Assets: $14,073,811,128
Liabilities: $10,131,812,964

Net Worth: $3,941,998,164
Earnings: $126,194,328
Emp.: 3,000
Fiscal Year-end: 12/31/22
Asset Management Services
N.A.I.C.S.: 523999

CHINA GREEN AGRICULTURE, INC.

3/F Borough A Block A No 181 South Taibai Road, Xi'an, 710065, Shaanxi, China
Tel.: (86) 2988266368　　　　NV
Web Site: https://www.cgagri.com
CGA—(NYSE)
Rev.: $124,140,355
Assets: $186,681,364
Liabilities: $61,313,507
Net Worth: $125,367,857
Earnings: ($13,281,985)
Emp.: 424
Fiscal Year-end: 06/30/23
Organic Liquid Compound Fertilizer Researcher & Mfr
N.A.I.C.S.: 325314
Richard Zhuoyu Li *(Chm & Co-CEO)*

Subsidiaries:

Beijing Tianjuyuan Fertilizer Co., Ltd.　　　　　　　　　　**(1)**
East High Town South Zhang Dai Village South, Pinggu, Beijing, 101203, China
Tel.: (86) 1060997511
Web Site: http://www.bjtjy.com
Fertilizer Mfr
N.A.I.C.S.: 325311

Shaanxi TechTeam Jinong Humic Acid Product Co., Ltd　　　　**(1)**
3/F Borough A Block A No181 South Tai Bai Road, Xi'an, 710065, China
Tel.: (86) 2988266408
Fertilizer Mfr
N.A.I.C.S.: 325311
Ethan Lu *(Mgr-Sls)*

CHINA GREEN ELECTRICITY INVESTMENT OF TIANJIN CO., LTD.

10F No 5 Chaowai Avenue, Chaoyang District, Beijing, 100020, China
Tel.: (86) 1085727717
Web Site:
　　http://www.gyfz000537.com
Year Founded: 1986
000537—(SSE)
Rev.: $481,545,029
Assets: $5,270,693,276
Liabilities: $2,788,159,557
Net Worth: $2,482,533,720
Earnings: $88,830,968
Fiscal Year-end: 12/31/22
Real Estate Development Services
N.A.I.C.S.: 531390
Nian Jianjun *(Chm)*

CHINA GREEN MATERIAL TECHNOLOGIES, INC.

1 Yantai Third Road Centralism Area Haping Road, Harbin Economic and Technological Development Zone, Harbin, 150060, Heilongjiang, China
Tel.: (86) 451 5175 0888　　　NV
Web Site:
　　http://www.sinogreenmaterial.com
Sales Range: $10-24.9 Million
Emp.: 245
Starch-Based Biodegradable & Disposable Food Trays, Containers, Tableware & Packaging Materials
N.A.I.C.S.: 325998
Zhonghao Su *(CEO)*

Subsidiaries:

Harbin ChangFangYuan Hi-Tech Environment-Friendly Industrial Co., Ltd　　　　　　　　　　　　**(1)**
No 172 Zhongshan Road, Harbin, 150040,

Heilongjiang, China
Tel.: (86) 45182811855
Disposable Tableware Distr
N.A.I.C.S.: 424990

CHINA GREENFRESH GROUP CO., LTD.

8Floor Building No 10 Business Center, Siming District, Xiamen, China
Tel.: (86) 5922999800　　　　Ky
Web Site: http://www.china-greenfresh.com
Year Founded: 1995
Rev.: $146,414,418
Assets: $321,120,567
Liabilities: $16,517,031
Net Worth: $304,603,536
Earnings: $21,407,660
Emp.: 651
Fiscal Year-end: 12/31/18
Edible Fungi Product Mfr & Distr
N.A.I.C.S.: 311421
Songhui Zheng *(Founder, Chm & CEO)*

Subsidiaries:

Singapore Cambo Biological Technology Pte. Ltd.　　　　　**(1)**
60 Paya Lebar Rd 09-06 Paya Lebar Square, Singapore, 409051, Singapore
Tel.: (65) 91005813
Web Site: http://www.cambosg.com
Health Care Product Mfr & Distr
N.A.I.C.S.: 325412

CHINA GREENLAND BROAD GREENSTATE GROUP CO., LTD.

Floor 8 Block D3 5th Building Hongqiao World Center 1588 Lane, Zhuguang Road, Shanghai, China
Tel.: (86) 2152751811
1253—(HKG)
Rev.: $15,342,210
Assets: $412,662,697
Liabilities: $329,636,736
Net Worth: $83,025,961
Earnings: ($59,297,519)
Emp.: 102
Fiscal Year-end: 12/31/22
Landscape Architectural Services
N.A.I.C.S.: 541320
Zhengping Wu *(Chm & CEO)*

CHINA GRENTECH CORPORATION LIMITED

15th Floor Block A Guoren Building, Keji Central 3rd Road, Hi-Tech Park Nanshan District, Shenzhen, 518057, China
Tel.: (86) 755 8350 1796　　　Ky
Year Founded: 1999
Sales Range: $250-299.9 Million
Emp.: 4,443
Designer & Mfr of Wireless Telecommunications Equipment
N.A.I.C.S.: 517112
Yingjie Gao *(Chm, Pres & CEO)*

Subsidiaries:

Coc Rf Technology & Information Plc　　　　　　　　　　　**(1)**
201 room BeDesta building in front of Dember city, Addis Ababa, Ethiopia
Tel.: (251) 944155527
Wireless Telecommunication Services
N.A.I.C.S.: 517111

GrenTech India Pvt Ltd　　　　**(1)**
B 506 5TH Floor Galleria Hiranandani Business Park, Powai, Mumbai, 400 076, India
Tel.: (91) 2240154812
Wireless Telecommunication Services
N.A.I.C.S.: 517112
Moreshwar Sawant *(Reg Mgr)*

GrenTech Pakistan (Pvt.) Ltd　　**(1)**
1st Floor West-76 Umer plaza Blue Area Jinnah Avenue, Islamabad, Pakistan

China GrenTech Corporation Limited—(Continued)

Tel.: (92) 512605933
Wireless Telecommunication Services
N.A.I.C.S.: 517112
Rahat Ullah Khan (Mgr-Project & Implementations)

GrenTech RF communication Nigeria Ltd (1)
Cluster D Block D1 Flat 105 1004 Estate
Victoria Island, Lagos, Nigeria
Tel.: (234) 7056568617
Wireless Telecommunication Services
N.A.I.C.S.: 517112

Grentech RF Communication Nigeria Limited (1)
Cluster D Block D1 Flat 105, 1004 estate
Victoria Island, Lagos, Nigeria
Tel.: (234) 7055535642
Wireless Telecommunication Services
N.A.I.C.S.: 517111

Grentech SA (Pty) Ltd (1)
No 38 Third Ave Complex 18A Stigligh
Road, Rivonia, Johannesburg, 2191, Gauteng, South Africa
Tel.: (27) 743803948
Wireless Telecommunication Services
N.A.I.C.S.: 517111

PT.GRENTECH INDONESIA (1)
Wsima Argo Manunggal 17th Floor Jl Jend
Gatot Subroto Kav 22, Jakarta, 12930, Indonesia
Tel.: (62) 212522259
Wireless Telecommunication Services
N.A.I.C.S.: 517112
Wahyudi Yudi (Project Mgr)

Quanzhou Lake Communication Co., Ltd. (1)
1306 Tower A Tiancheng Square 324, Longkou East Tianhe North, Guangzhou,
518040, China
Tel.: (86) 20 85266957
Designer & Mfr of Wireless Telecommunications Equipment
N.A.I.C.S.: 517112

Shenzhen GrenTech Co., Ltd. (1)
Tower B Zhongyin Building, Caitian Road
North, Futian District, Shenzhen, China
Tel.: (86) 75526503007
Web Site: http://www.grentech.com
Designer & Mfr of Wireless Telecommunications Equipment
N.A.I.C.S.: 517112

CHINA GUANGDONG NUCLEAR POWER HOLDING CO., LTD.
Keji Building No 1001 ShangbuZhong
Road, Futian District, Shenzhen,
518028, Guangdong, China
Tel.: (86) 55 8367 1581   CN
Year Founded: 1994
Sales Range: $1-4.9 Billion
Holding Company; Nuclear Power
Plant Developer & Operator
N.A.I.C.S.: 551112
Zhimin Qian (Chm)

Subsidiaries:

CGNPC Uranium Resources Co., Ltd. (1)
30/F Bldg A The International Center of
Times, No 101 Shaoyaoju Beili, Chaoyang
District, Beijing, 100031, China   (100%)
Tel.: (86) 10 6811 8820
Web Site: http://www.cgnpc.com.cn
Holding Company; Uranium Exploration,
Development, Mining, Trading & Power
Plant Supplier
N.A.I.C.S.: 551112

Joint Venture (Non-US):

Taurus Mineral Limited (2)
Room 1901 CC Wu Bldg 302 Hennessy
Road, Wanchai, China (Hong
Kong)   (60%)
Investment Holding Company
N.A.I.C.S.: 551112

Subsidiary (Non-US):

Kalahari Minerals Plc (3)
1B 38 Jermyn Street, London, SW1Y 6DN,
United Kingdom   (98%)
Tel.: (44) 20 7292 9110
Web Site: http://www.kalahari-minerals.com
Sales Range: $1-9.9 Million
Emp.: 7
Holding Company; Metal Ore Exploration &
Mining Services
N.A.I.C.S.: 551112
Mark Hohnen (Founder)

CHINA GUANGFA BANK CO., LTD.
CGB Building No 713 Dongfengdong
Road, Yuexiu District, Guangzhou,
510080, Guangdong, China
Tel.: (86) 2087311722
Web Site:
    http://www.cgbchina.com.cn
Year Founded: 1988
Rev.: $13,482,140,170
Assets: $376,753,371,763
Liabilities: $346,764,731,165
Net Worth: $29,988,640,598
Earnings: $1,800,330,224
Emp.: 35,429
Fiscal Year-end: 12/31/19
Commercial Banking Services
N.A.I.C.S.: 522110
Xiaolong Zheng (VP)

CHINA GUODIAN CORPORATION
6-8 Fuchengmeng Bei Street,
Xicheng District, Beijing, 100034,
China
Tel.: (86) 1058682001   CN
Web Site: http://www.cgdc.com.cn
Holding Company; Power Generation
& Distribution
N.A.I.C.S.: 551112
Baoping Qiao (Chm, Sec-Party Grp &
Deputy Gen Mgr)

Subsidiaries:

**Fujian Dongshan Aozishan Wind
Power Development Co., Ltd.** (1)
No 410 Gongyuan Road Dongpu Street,
Xipu Town Dongshan, Zhangzhou, Fujian,
China
Tel.: (86) 5965832377
Power Generation Services
N.A.I.C.S.: 221111

GD Power Development Co., Ltd. (1)
No 19 Anyuan Anhui North, Chaoyang District, Beijing, 100101, China   (53.42%)
Tel.: (86) 1058685000
Rev.: $27,052,361,365
Assets: $57,964,404,710
Liabilities: $42,482,292,470
Net Worth: $15,482,112,240
Earnings: $396,582,432
Fiscal Year-end: 12/31/2022
Holding Company; Power Generation &
Distribution
N.A.I.C.S.: 551112
Guolin Zhang (Deputy Gen Mgr)

**Guodian Chongqing Hengtai Power
Generation Co., Ltd.** (1)
Guanba Town, Wansheng District,
Chongqing, 400800, China
Tel.: (86) 2348296252
Power Generation Services
N.A.I.C.S.: 221111

**Guodian Jingmen Jiangshan Power
Generation Co., Ltd.** (1)
No 80 Baimiao Road, Jingmen, 448040,
China
Tel.: (86) 7242227380
Power Generation Services
N.A.I.C.S.: 221111

**Guodian Yuyuan Power Generation
Co., Ltd.** (1)
No 31 Nanhuan w Rd, Jiyuan, 454650,
China

Tel.: (86) 3916919888
Power Generation Services
N.A.I.C.S.: 221111

**Xinjiang Tianfeng Power Generation
Co., Ltd** (1)
Hexing Building Xiba m Rd, Urumqi,
830063, China
Tel.: (86) 9915913701
Power Generation Services
N.A.I.C.S.: 221111

**Yichun Xinganling Wind Power Co.,
Ltd.** (1)
38 Xizhinan Road, Suihua, 152061, China
Tel.: (86) 455 8702 896
Power Generation Services
N.A.I.C.S.: 221111

CHINA HAIDA LTD.
420 North Bridge Road No 04-06
North Bridge Centre, Singapore,
188727, Singapore
Tel.: (65) 65336360
Web Site: http://www.haida.com.sg
C92—(SES)
Rev.: $4,698,644
Assets: $5,808,957
Liabilities: $7,164,100
Net Worth: ($1,355,142)
Earnings: ($27,795,205)
Emp.: 231
Fiscal Year-end: 12/31/20
Aluminium Products Mfr
N.A.I.C.S.: 331318
Youcai Xu (CEO)

Subsidiaries:

**Jiangyin Litai Decorative Materials
Co., Ltd.** (1)
Huashi Town, 214421, Wuxi, Jiangsu, China
Tel.: (86) 51086213931
Laminated Plastics & Sheets Mfr
N.A.I.C.S.: 326130
Zou Chenghui (Mgr)

**Jiangyin Litai Ornamental Materials
Co., Ltd.** (1)
8 Huannan Road Huashi, Jiangyin, 214421,
Jiangsu, China
Tel.: (86) 51086213931
Web Site: http://www.aluminum-composite-
material.com
Aluminum Composite Panel Mfr
N.A.I.C.S.: 331315

CHINA HAINAN RUBBER INDUSTRY GROUP CO., LTD.
4th Floor Fortune Plaza No 103 Binhai Avenue, Haikou, 570105, Hainan,
China
Tel.: (86) 89831669317
Web Site: http://www.hirub.cn
Year Founded: 2005
601118—(SHG)
Rev.: $2,158,126,462
Assets: $3,163,383,330
Liabilities: $1,770,374,530
Net Worth: $1,393,008,800
Earnings: $9,588,099
Emp.: 16,000
Fiscal Year-end: 12/31/22
Rubber Product Mfr & Whslr
N.A.I.C.S.: 326299
Yilun Ai (Chm)

Subsidiaries:

Halcyon Agri Corporation Ltd. (1)
180 Clemenceau Avenue No 05-02, Haw
Par Centre, Singapore, 239922,
Singapore   (68.1%)
Tel.: (65) 64600200
Web Site: https://www.halcyonagri.com
Rev.: $1,708,786,000
Assets: $1,963,991,000
Liabilities: $1,214,886,000
Net Worth: $749,105,000
Earnings: ($60,613,000)
Emp.: 16,458
Fiscal Year-end: 12/31/2020
Rubber Mfr
N.A.I.C.S.: 326299

Pascal Demierre (Chief Corp Officer)

Subsidiary (Domestic):

GMG Global Limited (2)
180 Clemenceau Avenue 05-02 Haw Par
Centre, Singapore, 239922,
Singapore   (100%)
Tel.: (65) 64600200
Web Site: http://www.halcyonagri.com
Investment Holding Company
N.A.I.C.S.: 551112
Dino Ma Deyou (VP)

CHINA HAISHENG JUICE HOLDINGS CO., LTD.
Room B 3rd Floor Eton Buildi 288
Des Voeux Road Central, Central,
China (Hong Kong)
Tel.: (852) 2988109553   Ky
Web Site:
    http://www.chinahaisheng.com
Year Founded: 1996
0359—(HKG)
Rev.: $183,105,254
Assets: $1,639,087,309
Liabilities: $1,303,343,375
Net Worth: $335,743,934
Earnings: ($16,472,986)
Emp.: 2,940
Fiscal Year-end: 12/31/20
Food Product Mfr & Distr
N.A.I.C.S.: 311411

CHINA HANKING HOLDINGS LIMITED
No 227 Qingnian Street, Shenhe District, Shenyang, 110016, Liaoning,
China
Tel.: (86) 2431298912
Web Site: http://www.hanking.com
3788—(HKG)
Rev.: $479,033,740
Assets: $583,869,368
Liabilities: $343,594,415
Net Worth: $240,274,953
Earnings: $101,027,134
Emp.: 1,725
Fiscal Year-end: 12/31/21
Iron Ore Mining
N.A.I.C.S.: 212210

Subsidiaries:

Liaoning Hanking Green Building Materials Co., Ltd. (1)
Lagu Industrial Park, Shenfu New District,
Shenyang, Liaoning, China
Tel.: (86) 2454024703
Web Site: http://www.lnhwisjc.com
Green Building Material Mfr & Whslr
N.A.I.C.S.: 332311

PT Konutara Sejati (1)
Jl Bahagia No 31, Kendari, Indonesia
Tel.: (62) 4013190911
Nickel Ore Product Distr
N.A.I.C.S.: 423510

CHINA HAO RAN RECYCLING CO., LTD.
Suite 3201 Jardine House 1 Connaught, Central, China (Hong Kong)
Tel.: (852) 2533 3618
Web Site: http://www.china-haoran.com
Rev.: $359,747,281
Assets: $227,100,967
Liabilities: $78,938,621
Net Worth: $148,162,346
Earnings: ($92,507,664)
Emp.: 940
Fiscal Year-end: 12/31/17
Holding Company
N.A.I.C.S.: 551112
Haorong Zhang (Chm & CEO)

CHINA HARMONY AUTO HOLDING LIMITED
15A 16 World Trade Center, business

district Zheng Dong New District, Zhengzhou, 450000, China
Tel.: (86) 37163910000   Ky
Web Site: http://www.hexieauto.com
Year Founded: 2005
3836—(HKG)
Rev.: $2,291,560,924
Assets: $1,516,679,003
Liabilities: $670,529,340
Net Worth: $846,149,663
Earnings: ($227,841,682)
Emp.: 3,779
Fiscal Year-end: 12/31/22
Automotive Distr
N.A.I.C.S.: 423110

CHINA HARZONE INDUSTRY CO., LTD.
No 5 Sunshine Avenue, Jiangxia District Economic Developement Zone, Wuhan, 430223, Hubei, China
Tel.: (86) 2787970446
Web Site: https://www.china-huazhou.com
Year Founded: 1967
300527—(CHIN)
Rev.: $84,948,551
Assets: $551,471,061
Liabilities: $192,732,210
Net Worth: $358,738,851
Earnings: ($30,632,283)
Fiscal Year-end: 12/31/23
Emergency Engineering Equipment Mfr & Distr
N.A.I.C.S.: 334511
Wang Xiaofeng (Chm)

CHINA HEALTH GROUP INC.
Haitong Commercial Center No.11 North West 3rd Ring Road, Haidian District, Beijing, 100089, China
Tel.: (86) 1088500088   Ky
Web Site: http://www.chgi.net
8225—(HKG)
Rev.: $1,837,836
Assets: $25,078,950
Liabilities: $5,158,577
Net Worth: $19,920,373
Earnings: ($2,221,970)
Emp.: 47
Fiscal Year-end: 12/31/22
Pharmaceuticals Product Mfr
N.A.I.C.S.: 325412
William Xia Guo (Founder & Chm)

CHINA HEALTH INDUSTRIES HOLDINGS, INC.
3199-1 Longxiang Road, Songbei District, Harbin, 150028, Heilongjiang, China
Tel.: (86) 45188100688   DE
Web Site:
   http://www.chinahealthindustry.com
CHHE—(OTCQB)
Rev.: $267
Assets: $50,747,518
Liabilities: $7,944,799
Net Worth: $42,802,719
Earnings: ($353,950)
Emp.: 45
Fiscal Year-end: 06/30/22
Medical Drug Mfr & Sales
N.A.I.C.S.: 325412
Xin Sun (Chm, CEO, CFO & Treas)

CHINA HEALTH RESOURCE, INC.
343 Sui Zhou Zhong Road, Suining, 629000, Sichuan, China
Tel.: (86) 8252391788   DE
Web Site:
   http://www.chinahealthresource.com
Year Founded: 2002
Sales Range: $10-24.9 Million
Emp.: 230
Pharmaceuticals Mfr

N.A.I.C.S.: 325412
Jiayin Wang (Pres & CEO)

CHINA HEALTHCARE LIMITED
20 Jalan Afifi CERTIS CISCO Centre II 06-02/03/04/05, Singapore, 409179, Singapore
Tel.: (65) 64478788   SG
Web Site:
   http://www.econhealthcare.com
Year Founded: 1987
Sales Range: $10-24.9 Million
Nursing Home Services
N.A.I.C.S.: 623312
Chu Poh Ong (Chm & CEO)

Subsidiaries:

Econ Ambulance Services Pte Ltd   (1)
10 Buangkok View, Singapore, 539747, Singapore
Tel.: (65) 63856860
Web Site: http://www.econhealthcare.com
Sales Range: $10-24.9 Million
Emp.: 10
Ambulance Service
N.A.I.C.S.: 621910
Janneth Goh (Gen Mgr)

Econ Careskill Training Centre Pte Ltd   (1)
260 Sims Ave No 04-01, Singapore, 387604, Singapore
Tel.: (65) 67418640
Web Site: http://www.econcareskill.com
Sales Range: $10-24.9 Million
Emp.: 4
Healthcare Training Services
N.A.I.C.S.: 621999

Econ Healthcare (M) Sdn Bhd   (1)
6th & 7th Fl Chinese Maternity Hospital, 106 Jln Pudu, Kuala Lumpur, 55100, Malaysia
Tel.: (60) 320267118
Web Site: http://www.econhealthcare.com
Sales Range: $10-24.9 Million
Emp.: 80
Nursing Home Services
N.A.I.C.S.: 623110
Yong Lailatun (Sr Mgr-Ops)

Econ Medicare Centre Pte Ltd   (1)
58 Braddell Rd, Singapore, 359905, Singapore
Tel.: (65) 64931336
Nursing Home
N.A.I.C.S.: 623110

Econ Medicare Centre Sdn Bhd   (1)
6th & 7th Fl Chinese Maternity Hospital, 106 Jalan Pudu, 55100, Kuala Lumpur, Malaysia
Tel.: (60) 320267118
Web Site: http://www.econhelpcare.com
Sales Range: $10-24.9 Million
Emp.: 50
Nursing Home
N.A.I.C.S.: 623110

Sunnyville Nursing Home (1996) Pte Ltd   (1)
10 Ama Keng Rd, Singapore, 709828, Singapore
Tel.: (65) 67937009
Web Site: http://www.econhealthcare.com
Sales Range: $10-24.9 Million
Emp.: 20
Nursing Home
N.A.I.C.S.: 623110
Iris Koh (Mgr)

West Point Hospital Pte Ltd   (1)
235 Corporation Dr, Singapore, 619771, Singapore
Tel.: (65) 62625858
Web Site: http://www.westpointhospital.com
Sales Range: $10-24.9 Million
Emp.: 50
Hospital
N.A.I.C.S.: 622110

CHINA HEALTHWISE HOLDINGS LIMITED
Unit 1209 Shun Tak Centre West

Tower 168-200 Connaught Road, Central, China (Hong Kong)
Tel.: (852) 2 268 8248   Ky
Web Site:
   http://www.healthwisehk.com
0348—(HKG)
Rev.: $21,936,789
Assets: $40,511,973
Liabilities: $15,610,578
Net Worth: $24,901,395
Earnings: ($13,290,873)
Emp.: 100
Fiscal Year-end: 12/31/21
Investment Holding Company
N.A.I.C.S.: 551112
Hong Wai Lei (Chm)

Subsidiaries:

Kid Galaxy Inc.   (1)
150 Dow St Tower 2 Unit 425b, Manchester, NH 03101
Tel.: (603) 645-6252
Sales Range: $1-9.9 Million
Emp.: 12
Toy Mfr
N.A.I.C.S.: 339930
James Marotta (VP-Sls)

Nam Pei Hong Sum Yung Drugs Company Limited   (1)
Flat B 1 / F Chi Lun Cheong Industrial Building 11 Rising Sun Street, To Kwa Wan, Kowloon, China (Hong Kong)
Tel.: (852) 27429811
Web Site: http://www.nampeihong.com
Seafood Product Distr
N.A.I.C.S.: 424460

New Mind (Hong Kong) Limited   (1)
Unit C 20/F Nathan Commercial Building 430-436 Nathan Road, Yau Ma Tei, Kowloon, China (Hong Kong)
Tel.: (852) 36210809
Web Site: https://www.newmindhk.com
Paper Products Mfr
N.A.I.C.S.: 322299

CHINA HEFENG RESCUE EQUIPMENT, INC.
88 Taishan Street Beijing Industrial Zone, Longgang District, Huludao, 125000, Liaoning, China
Tel.: (86) 4293181998   DE
Web Site:
   http://www.hefengrescue.com
Year Founded: 2010
Sales Range: $1-9.9 Million
Emp.: 90
Mining Equipment Distr
N.A.I.C.S.: 423810
Baoyuan Zhu (Chm)

CHINA HI-TECH GROUP CO., LTD.
No 1-118 Longtai Road Lisul Town, Shunyi District, Beijing, 100871, China
Tel.: (86) 15600730280
Web Site:
   http://www.chinahitech.com.cn
Year Founded: 1992
600730—(SHG)
Rev.: $17,278,031
Assets: $298,095,708
Liabilities: $47,686,635
Net Worth: $250,409,072
Earnings: ($12,146,088)
Fiscal Year-end: 12/31/22
Trading Services
N.A.I.C.S.: 522299
Tao Lan (VP & Deputy Gen Mgr)

Subsidiaries:

CHTC Heavy Industry Co., Ltd.   (1)
No 258 Wutong Street, Zhengzhou, 450053, China
Tel.: (86) 37185516721
Web Site: https://en.zzfj.com
Textile Machinery Mfr & Distr
N.A.I.C.S.: 333248

CHTC Holdings Co., Ltd.   (1)
8/F 22-28 Cheung Tat Road, Tsing Yi, China (Hong Kong)
Tel.: (852) 24973300
Textile Machinery Mfr & Distr
N.A.I.C.S.: 333248

CHTC Investment Management Co., Ltd.   (1)
Office D 19/F Yonghua Mansion, No 138 PuDong Ave Pudong New Area, Shanghai, 200120, China
Tel.: (86) 2158793228
Textile Machinery Mfr & Distr
N.A.I.C.S.: 333248

CHTC KAMA Co., Ltd.   (1)
6 Floor No 1958 Zhongshan North Road, Putuo District, Shanghai, 200063, China
Tel.: (86) 2162035587
Web Site: https://www.kama.com.cn
Truck Mfr & Distr
N.A.I.C.S.: 336120

CHTC Real Estate Co., Ltd.   (1)
20/F China Garments Mansion 99 Jianguo Road, Chaoyang District, Beijing, 100020, China
Tel.: (86) 1065838555
Textile Machinery Mfr & Distr
N.A.I.C.S.: 333248

China National Garments Group Corporation   (1)
27/F China Garments Mansion 99 Jianguo Road, Chaoyang District, Beijing, 100020, China
Tel.: (86) 1065813501
Textile Machinery Mfr & Distr
N.A.I.C.S.: 333248

China Textile Science & Technology Co., Ltd.   (1)
No 19 Yongchang Southern Road, Beijing Economic & Technical Development Zone, Beijing, 100176, China
Tel.: (86) 1067856990
Textile Machinery Mfr & Distr
N.A.I.C.S.: 333248

Hantrong Investment Co., Ltd.   (1)
Building 5 Yard 6 Jingshun East Street, Chaoyang District, Beijing, 100015, China
Tel.: (86) 1084536170
Textile Machinery Mfr & Distr
N.A.I.C.S.: 333248

Hi-Tech Fiber Group Corporation   (1)
China Garment Mansion 99 Jianguo Road, Beijing, 100020, China
Tel.: (86) 1065838003
Web Site: https://www.htfiber.com
Spun Yarn Mfr & Distr
N.A.I.C.S.: 313110

CHINA HI-TECH GROUP CORPORATION
China Garments Mansion 99 Jianguo Road, Chaoyang District, Beijing, 100020, China
Tel.: (86) 1065838033
Web Site: http://www.chtgc.com
Year Founded: 1998
Emp.: 60,000
Holding Company
N.A.I.C.S.: 551112
Jie Zhang (Chm)

Subsidiaries:

CHTC Fong's International Company Limited   (1)
Level 13 Tower 2 Kowloon Commerce Centre 51 Kwai Cheong Road, Kwai Chung, China (Hong Kong)
Tel.: (852) 24973300
Web Site: http://www.fongs.com
Rev.: $317,307,720
Assets: $505,460,745
Liabilities: $328,866,615
Net Worth: $176,594,130
Earnings: ($31,585,703)
Emp.: 2,800
Fiscal Year-end: 12/31/2022
Dyeing & Finishing Machines Mfr
N.A.I.C.S.: 339999
Maoxin Ye (Chm)

China Hi-Tech Group Corporation—(Continued)

China Garments Co., Ltd.   (1)
17/F Zhejiang Mansion, Chaoyang District, Beijing, 100029, China
Tel.: (86) 1064428234
Textile Machinery Mfr & Distr
N.A.I.C.S.: 314999

China National Chemical Fiber Corporation   (1)
23/F China Garments Mansion 99 Jianguo Road, Chaoyang District, Beijing, 100020, China
Tel.: (86) 1065813481
Textile Machinery Mfr & Distr
N.A.I.C.S.: 314999

China Silk Industrial Corporation   (1)
No 56 North 8 Tiao, Xisi Xicheng District, Beijing, 100034, China
Tel.: (86) 1066180642
Textile Machinery Mfr & Distr
N.A.I.C.S.: 314999

China Texmatech Co., Ltd.   (1)
18th Floor China Garments Mansion 99 Jianguo Road, Beijing, 100020, China
Tel.: (86) 1065838200
Web Site: https://www.ctmtc.com
Textile Machinery Mfr
N.A.I.C.S.: 314999

China Textile Industrial Corporation for Foreign Economic & Technical Cooperation   (1)
18/F China Garments Mansion 99 Jianguo Road, Chaoyang District, Beijing, 100020, China
Tel.: (86) 1065815588
Textile Machinery Mfr & Distr
N.A.I.C.S.: 314999

Jingwei Textile Machinery Company, Ltd.   (1)
7F C Block First Shanghai Center No 39 Liangmaqiao Rd, Chaoyang District, Beijing, 100125, China
Tel.: (86) 1084534078
Web Site: http://www.jwgf.com
Rev.: $1,668,895,488
Assets: $5,509,064,340
Liabilities: $2,048,516,028
Net Worth: $3,460,548,312
Earnings: $63,792,144
Fiscal Year-end: 12/31/2022
Textile Machinery Mfr
N.A.I.C.S.: 333248
Yuming Yao (Gen Mgr)

Kama Co., Ltd.   (1)
6 Floor No 1958 Zhongshan North Road, Putuo District, Shanghai, 200063, China
Tel.: (86) 2162035587
Web Site: https://www.kama.com.cn
Rev.: $401,752,578
Assets: $517,425,653
Liabilities: $428,228,550
Net Worth: $89,197,103
Earnings: ($24,953,545)
Emp.: 3,500
Fiscal Year-end: 12/31/2022
Trucks Mfr
N.A.I.C.S.: 333924

Subsidiary (Domestic):

Heilongjiang Fujin Kama Vehicle Wheel Manufacturing Co., Ltd.   (2)
North of Xinkai Road, Fujin, Heilongjiang, China
Tel.: (86) 454 2346090
Web Site: http://www.hlj-kmcl.com
Wheel Mfr
N.A.I.C.S.: 336390

Nanchang Kama Co., Ltd.   (2)
Economic & Technical Development Zone, Nanchang, China
Tel.: (86) 791 83950651
Web Site: http://www.nckama.cn
Construction Machinery Mfr
N.A.I.C.S.: 333120
Jackson Wang (Mgr-Overseas)

Shandong Huayuan Laidong Internal Combustion Engine Co., Ltd.   (2)
40 Wulong North Road, Laiyang, Shandong, China
Tel.: (86) 535 7215050

Web Site: http://www.chinalaidong.com
Emp.: 3,570
Automotive Spare Parts Mfr & Distr
N.A.I.C.S.: 333618

Shandong KAMA Automobile Manufacturing Co., Ltd.
288 Guangchang East Street, Shouguang, Shandong, China
Tel.: (00) 500 5202020
Web Site: http://www.kamaqc.com
Emp.: 3,500
Trucks Mfr
N.A.I.C.S.: 333924

Shanghai Kaining Import & Export Co., Ltd.   (2)
10/F 1958 Zhongshan North Road, Shanghai, China
Tel.: (86) 21 52046620
Automotive Spare Parts Mfr & Distr
N.A.I.C.S.: 333618

Wuxi Worldbest Kama Power Co., Ltd.   (2)
Room 209 No 1958 The Zhongshan North Road, Shanghai, 200063, China
Tel.: (86) 21 62035586
Web Site: http://www.wxkama.com
Emp.: 350
Automotive Spare Part Mfr & Distr
N.A.I.C.S.: 333618

Shandong Helon Co., Ltd.   (1)
No 555 Hailong Road, Hanting District, Weifang, 261100, Shandong, China
Tel.: (86) 5362275216
Textile Machinery Mfr & Distr
N.A.I.C.S.: 314999

Swan Fiber Co., Ltd.   (1)
No 1369 Shengxing West Road, Baoding, 071055, Hebei, China
Tel.: (86) 3123322161
Textile Machinery Mfr & Distr
N.A.I.C.S.: 314999

CHINA HIGH PRECISION AUTOMATION GROUP LIMITED
Room 703 Jubilee Centre 18 Fenwick Street, Wanchai, China (Hong Kong)
Tel.: (852) 28771809
Web Site: http://www.chpag.net
Sales Range: $25-49.9 Million
Emp.: 844
High Precision Industrial Automation Instrument Mfr
N.A.I.C.S.: 334513
Fun Chung Wong (Chm & CEO)

Subsidiaries:

Fujian Wide Plus Precision Instruments Co., Ltd.   (1)
No 1 Chashan Rd Mawei Hi-tech Dev Zone, Fuzhou, 350015, Fujian, China
Tel.: (86) 59183969908
Web Site: http://www.wideplus.com
Sales Range: $400-449.9 Million
Precision Tools Mfr & System Integration Services
N.A.I.C.S.: 332216

CHINA HIGH-SPEED RAILWAY TECHNOLOGY CO., LTD.
No 59 Gaoliangqiao Xiejie 16 / F Zhongkun PLAZA, Haidian District, Beijing, 100044, China
Tel.: (86) 1056500505
Web Site: https://www.shenzhou-gaotie.com
Year Founded: 1997
000008—(SSE)
Rev.: $248,922,180
Assets: $1,579,230,432
Liabilities: $950,215,968
Net Worth: $629,014,464
Earnings: ($118,814,904)
Emp.: 2,700
Fiscal Year-end: 12/31/22
Rail Transit System Maintenance Services
N.A.I.C.S.: 485119

Kong Lingsheng (Chm & Sec-Party Committee)

CHINA HOLDINGS, INC.
Suite 601 110 Dai-Hou-Bei-Li, Hai-Dian-District, Beijing, 100091, China
Tel.: (86) 7789950789
Medicinal & Botanical Instrument Mfr
N.A.I.C.S.: 325411
Julianna Lu (Pres, CEO & COO)

CHINA HONGBAO HOLDINGS LIMITED
5/F Shum Tower No 268 Des Voeux Road Central, Sheung Wan, China (Hong Kong)
Tel.: (852) 27806888   Ky
Web Site: http://www.pakwingc.com
Year Founded: 2011
8316—(HKG)
Rev.: $12,926,715
Assets: $13,478,918
Liabilities: $16,591,703
Net Worth: ($3,112,785)
Earnings: ($2,427,728)
Emp.: 73
Fiscal Year-end: 03/31/23
Foundation Piling Services
N.A.I.C.S.: 238910
Hobby Hon Ming Lau (Gen Mgr)

CHINA HONGGUANG HOLDINGS LIMITED
Eastside of Middle of Rongchi Road, Xianqiao Rongcheng, Jieyang, Guangdong, China
Tel.: (86) 34683496   Ky
Web Site: http://www.hongguang.hk
Year Founded: 1992
8646—(HKG)
Rev.: $29,295,302
Assets: $57,196,573
Liabilities: $19,384,607
Net Worth: $37,811,966
Earnings: $4,852,224
Emp.: 66
Fiscal Year-end: 12/31/22
Holding Company
N.A.I.C.S.: 551112
Jiakun Wei (CEO)

CHINA HONGQIAO GROUP LIMITED
Weiqiao aluminum building Huixian 1st Road, Zouping Economic Development Zone, Zouping, Shandong, China
Tel.: (86) 28151080   Ky
Web Site:
    https://en.hongqiaochina.com
Year Founded: 1994
1378—(HKG)
Rev.: $18,501,278,245
Assets: $27,735,944,423
Liabilities: $13,023,875,720
Net Worth: $14,712,068,703
Earnings: $1,730,415,374
Emp.: 48,908
Fiscal Year-end: 12/31/23
Aluminium Products Mfr
N.A.I.C.S.: 331318
Shuliang Zheng (Vice Chm)

Subsidiaries:

PT Well Harvest Winning Alumina Refinery   (1)
Panin Senayan Bank Building 2nd Floor Jl Gen Sudirman Kav 1, Jakarta, 10270, Indonesia
Tel.: (62) 2125675440
Web Site: https://www.whwalumina.com
Alumina Refining Mfr & Distr
N.A.I.C.S.: 331313
Zang Jinjun (CEO)

CHINA HONGXING SPORTS LIMITED

Jiangnan Torch Development Area Licheng District, 362000, Quanzhou, Fujian, China
Tel.: (86) 59522462620
Web Site:
    http://www.chinahongxing.org
Sales Range: $250-299.9 Million
Footwear Mfr
N.A.I.C.S.: 316210
Jeffrey Li (Mgr-Intl Market Dev)

Subsidiaries:

Hongrong Light Industry Co., Ltd.   (1)
Jiangnan Hi Tec Area, Licheng, Quanzhou, 362000, China
Tel.: (86) 15960221545
Sports Apparels Mfr
N.A.I.C.S.: 316210

Hongxing Erke Sports Goods Co., Ltd   (1)
Jiangnan Torch Development Area, Licheng District, Quanzhou, 362000, Fujian, China
Tel.: (86) 5922951388
Sports Goods Mfr
N.A.I.C.S.: 316210

CHINA HOUSING & LAND DEVELOPMENT, INC.
1008 Liuxue Road, Baqiao District, Xi'an, 710038, Shaanxi, China
Tel.: (86) 2983328813
Web Site: http://www.chldinc.com
Year Founded: 1999
Sales Range: $125-149.9 Million
Emp.: 677
Real Estate Development
N.A.I.C.S.: 525990
Pingji Lu (Chm & CEO)

CHINA HUADIAN CORPORATION LTD.
No 2 Xuanwumennei Street Xicheng District, Beijing, 100031, China
Tel.: (86) 10 8356 6666
Web Site: http://www.chd.com.cn
Year Founded: 2002
Sales Range: Less than $1 Million
Emp.: 105,006
Eletric Power Generation Services
N.A.I.C.S.: 221115
Jianguo Zhao (Chm)

Subsidiaries:

Huadian Energy Company Limited   (1)
No 209 Dacheng Street, Nangang District, Harbin, 150001, Heilongjiang, China
Tel.: (86) 45158681820
Web Site: https://www.hdenergy.com
Eletric Power Generation Services
N.A.I.C.S.: 221118

Huadian Fuxin Energy Corporation Limited   (1)
Floor 9th Block B Huadian Mansion No 2 Xuanwumennei Street, Xicheng District, Beijing, 100031, China
Tel.: (86) 1083567377
Rev.: $2,829,932,864
Assets: $16,057,343,013
Liabilities: $10,569,266,259
Net Worth: $5,488,076,754
Earnings: $385,153,078
Emp.: 9,045
Fiscal Year-end: 12/31/2019
Eletric Power Generation Services
N.A.I.C.S.: 221118

CHINA HUAJUN GROUP LIMITED
36/F Champion Tower 3 Garden Road, Central, China (Hong Kong)
Tel.: (852) 22909222   BM
Web Site:
    http://www.chinahuajungroup.com
0377—(HKG)
Rev.: $5,381,406,260
Assets: $2,410,874,258

Liabilities: $2,540,316,484
Net Worth: ($129,442,226)
Earnings: ($273,354,984)
Emp.: 2,557
Fiscal Year-end: 12/31/21
Printing, Packaging & Paper Products Mfr
N.A.I.C.S.: 322130
Guang Bao Meng *(Chm)*

Subsidiaries:

Dongguan New Island Printing Co., Ltd. (1)
Da Ling Shan Science and Industrial Park, Da Ling Shan, Dongguan, China
Tel.: (86) 7698 562 5222
Paper Packaging Mfr
N.A.I.C.S.: 322220

New Island Printing (Liaoning) Company Limited (1)
No 17 Xinmin Street, West District, Yingkou, Liaoning, China
Tel.: (86) 417 338 1888
Paper Packaging Mfr
N.A.I.C.S.: 322220

New Island Printing (US) Inc. (1)
226 E 54th St Ste 300, New York, NY 10022
Tel.: (212) 355-1652
Web Site: http://www.newisland.com
Commercial Printing Services
N.A.I.C.S.: 323111

New Island Printing Company Limited (1)
Room 1701 17/F Billion Plaza 8 Cheung Yue Street, Cheung Sha Wan, Kowloon, China (Hong Kong)
Tel.: (852) 24428282
Web Site: http://www.newisland.com
Commercial Printing Services
N.A.I.C.S.: 323111

Shanghai New Island Packaging Printing Co., Ltd. (1)
No 1550 East Rongle Road, Songjiang, Shanghai, China
Tel.: (86) 215 774 2828
Paper Packaging Mfr
N.A.I.C.S.: 322220

CHINA HUANCHI BEARING GROUP CO., LTD.
No 12 Hengpeng Road Henghe Industry Zone, Cixi City, Ningbo, 315318, China
Tel.: (86) 574 63198088
Web Site: http://www.hchbearing.com
Year Founded: 1973
Emp.: 2,500
Ball & Roller Bearing Mfr
N.A.I.C.S.: 332991
Chengjiang Hu *(Chm)*

Subsidiaries:

HCH BEARING ITALY Srl (1)
Via G Garibaldi 46, 20861, Brugherio, Italy
Tel.: (39) 0398964570
Pump Distr
N.A.I.C.S.: 423830
Marco Ganatea *(Engr-Sls)*

HCH Bearing Americas (1)
14476-406 Duval Pl W, Jacksonville, FL 32218
Tel.: (904) 374-7471
Web Site:
  http://www.hchbearingamericas.com
Emp.: 5
Ball & Roller Bearing Mfr
N.A.I.C.S.: 332991
Douglas Robbie *(Gen Mgr)*

HCH Bearing Germany GmbH (1)
Ferdinand- Lassalle-Strasse 24, 72770, Reutlingen, Germany
Tel.: (49) 71219631982
Pump Distr
N.A.I.C.S.: 423830

CHINA HUANENG GROUP CO., LTD.

No 6 Fuxingmennei Street, Xicheng District, Beijing, 100031, China
Tel.: (86) 1063228800 CN
Web Site: https://www.chng.com.cn
Year Founded: 1985
Sales Range: Less than $1 Million
Holding Company; Power Generation
N.A.I.C.S.: 551112
Wen Shugang *(Chm)*

Subsidiaries:

Great Wall Securities Co., Ltd. (1)
Room 201-C220 Building 4-7 Anbailijing Park Jingtian Section, Shennandadao Road Futian District, Shenzhen, 518034, China
Tel.: (86) 755 33966012
Web Site: http://www.cgws.com
Financial Management Services
N.A.I.C.S.: 523999

Huaneng Capital Services Co., Ltd. (1)
9F West Wing Bldg C Tianyin Mansion 2C Fu Xing Men South Street, Xicheng District, Beijing, 100031, China (100%)
Tel.: (86) 10 63081800
Web Site: http://www.hncapital.com.cn
Financial Management Services
N.A.I.C.S.: 523999
Guo Junming *(Chm)*

Subsidiary (Domestic):

Alltrust Insurance Company of China Limited (2)
2F Huaneng Union Tower No 958 Lu Jia Zui Ring Road, Pudong, Shanghai, 200120, China
Tel.: (86) 21 51105888
Web Site: http://www.alltrust.com.cn
Property & Casualty Insurance Services
N.A.I.C.S.: 524126

Baocheng Futures Co., Ltd. (2)
3F-5F South Podium Building Gongyuan Building No 8 Qiu Shi Road, Hangzhou, 310013, China
Tel.: (86) 571 85151166
Web Site: http://www.bcqhgs.com
Securities Brokerage Services
N.A.I.C.S.: 523150

China Huaneng Finance Co., Ltd. (2)
3F Huashi Mansion No 26B Financial Street, Xicheng District, Beijing, 100140, China
Tel.: (86) 10 66217799
Web Site: http://www.hnf.com.cn
Financial Management Services
N.A.I.C.S.: 523999

Huaneng Guicheng Trust Co., Ltd. (2)
14F Xindu Fortune Building No 27 Beijing Road, Yunyan District, Guiyang, 550001, China
Tel.: (86) 851 6827188
Web Site: http://www.hngtrust.com
Financial Management Services
N.A.I.C.S.: 523999
Ding Yi *(Chm)*

Huaneng Invesco WLR Investment Consulting Co., Ltd. (2)
Suite 628 Winland International Center No 7 Financial Street, Xicheng District, Beijing, 100140, China
Tel.: (86) 10 6655 5358
Investment Advisory Services
N.A.I.C.S.: 523940
Ding Yi *(Chm)*

Huaneng Lancang River Hydropower Co., Ltd. (1)
No 1 Middle Road of Shijicheng Huaneng Lancang River Building, Guandu District, Kunming, 650214, China
Tel.: (86) 87 1721 6533
Eletric Power Generation Services
N.A.I.C.S.: 221118

Huaneng Power International, Inc. (1)
Huaneng Building 6 Fuxingmennei Street, Xicheng District, Beijing, 100031, China
Tel.: (86) 1063226999

Web Site: https://www.hpi.com.cn
Rev.: $35,830,520,315
Assets: $77,509,297,373
Net Worth: $25,261,194,009
Earnings: $1,235,128,024
Emp.: 57,038
Fiscal Year-end: 12/31/2023
Electricity Distribution Services
N.A.I.C.S.: 221112
Chaoquan Huang *(VP)*

Subsidiary (Domestic):

Shandong Rizhao Power Company Limited (2)
36 Yuhan Road, Rizhao, Shandong, China
Tel.: (86) 1066491999
Thermal Power Plants Developer
N.A.I.C.S.: 221111
Yu Zhiqiang *(Plant Mgr)*

Huaneng Renewables Corporation Limited (1)
10-11 Floor Huaneng Build No 23A, Fuxing Road District, Beijing, 100036, China (100%)
Tel.: (86) 10 68221618
Web Site: http://www.hnr.com.cn
Rev.: $1,693,835,808
Assets: $12,891,945,750
Liabilities: $8,789,978,733
Net Worth: $4,101,967,017
Earnings: $454,846,799
Emp.: 2,614
Fiscal Year-end: 12/31/2018
Wind Power, Solar Energy, Marine Energy, Hydrogen Power & Other Renewable Energies
N.A.I.C.S.: 221118
Gang Lin *(Chm)*

CHINA HUARONG ENERGY CO. LTD.
Room 2201 22nd Floor China Evergrande Centre, 38 Gloucester Road, Wanchai, China (Hong Kong)
Tel.: (852) 39001888 Ky
Web Site:
  http://www.huarongenergy.com.hk
1101—(HKG)
Rev.: $14,439,438
Assets: $199,587,305
Liabilities: $1,394,434,969
Net Worth: ($1,194,847,664)
Earnings: ($94,192,114)
Emp.: 149
Fiscal Year-end: 12/31/22
Construction, Engineering & Ship Building Services
N.A.I.C.S.: 237990
Qiang Chen *(Chm & CEO)*

Subsidiaries:

Hefei Rong An Power Machinery Co., Ltd. (1)
No 9166 Susong Road, Anhui Hefei Economic and Technological Development zone, Hefei, Anhui, China
Tel.: (86) 5518788888
Web Site: https://www.ronganpower.com
Marine Engine Mfr
N.A.I.C.S.: 333618

CHINA HUIRONG FINANCIAL HOLDINGS LIMITED
22F Cultural and Creative Building No 345 East Baodai Road, Suzhou, Jiangsu, China
Tel.: (86) 51265131585 Ky
Web Site: http://www.cnhuirong.com
Year Founded: 2011
1290—(HKG)
Rev.: $41,255,776
Assets: $434,533,436
Liabilities: $113,752,450
Net Worth: $320,780,986
Earnings: $15,430,392
Emp.: 141
Fiscal Year-end: 12/31/21
Holding Company
N.A.I.C.S.: 551112

Min Wu *(Chm & CEO)*

CHINA HUISHAN DAIRY HOLDINGS COMPANY LIMITED
Huishan Building No 111A South Huanghe Street Huanggu District, Shenghe, 110000, China
Tel.: (86) 25277974 Ky
Web Site:
  http://www.huishandairy.com
Dairy Products Producer.
N.A.I.C.S.: 112120
Kai Yang *(Chm & CEO)*

CHINA INDEX HOLDINGS LIMITED
Tower A No 20 Guogongzhuang Middle Street, Fengtai District, Beijing, 100070, China
Tel.: (86) 1056319106 Ky
Web Site:
  http://www.chinaindexholdings.com
Year Founded: 2007
CIH—(NASDAQ)
Rev.: $95,136,209
Assets: $73,662,908
Liabilities: $71,999,814
Net Worth: $1,663,095
Earnings: $42,773,474
Emp.: 858
Fiscal Year-end: 12/31/21
Holding Company
N.A.I.C.S.: 551112
Vincent Tianquan Mo *(Founder & Chm)*

CHINA INDUSTRIAL SECURITIES FINANCIAL GROUP
32/F 25/F 23/F Infinitus Plaza 199 Des Voeux Road Central, Sheung Wan, China (Hong Kong)
Tel.: (852) 35095999 Ky
Web Site: https://www.xyzq.com.hk
Year Founded: 2015
6058—(HKG)
Rev.: $69,440,952
Assets: $2,115,355,601
Liabilities: $1,588,314,028
Net Worth: $527,041,573
Earnings: $6,973,339
Emp.: 230
Fiscal Year-end: 12/31/23
Financial Investment Services
N.A.I.C.S.: 523999
Xiang Wang *(Deputy CEO)*

Subsidiaries:

China Industrial Securities International Asset Management Limited (1)
32/F 25/F & 23/F Infinitus Plaza 199 Des Voeux Road Central, Sheung Wan, China (Hong Kong)
Tel.: (852) 35095999
N.A.I.C.S.: 523940

China Industrial Securities International Brokerage Limited (1)
32/F 25/F & 23/F Infinitus Plaza 199 Des Voeux Road Central, Sheung Wan, China (Hong Kong)
Tel.: (852) 35095999
N.A.I.C.S.: 523999

China Industrial Securities International Capital Limited (1)
32/F 25/F & 23/F Infinitus Plaza 199 Des Voeux Road Central, Sheung Wan, China (Hong Kong)
Tel.: (852) 35090099
N.A.I.C.S.: 523150

China Industrial Securities International Futures Limited (1)
32/F 25/F & 23/F Infinitus Plaza 199 Des Voeux Road Central, Sheung Wan, China (Hong Kong)
Tel.: (852) 35095999
N.A.I.C.S.: 523999

China Industrial Securities Financial Group—(Continued)

China Industrial Securities International Wealth Management Limited (1)
32/F and 25/F Infinitus Plaza 199 Des Voeux Road, Sheung Wan, Central, China (Hong Kong)
Tel.: (852) 35095850
Wealth Management Services
N.A.I.C.S.: 523940

CHINA INDUSTRIAL WASTE MANAGEMENT, INC.
No 1 Huaihe West Road E-T-D Zone, Dalian, 116600, China
Tel.: (86) 41182595139　　NV
Year Founded: 1987
CIWT—(OTCEM)
Sales Range: $25-49.9 Million
Emp.: 570
Industrial Waste Collection, Treatment, Disposal & Recycling Services
N.A.I.C.S.: 562211
Jun Li (COO)

Subsidiaries:

Dalian Lipp Environmental Energy Engineering & Technology Co., Ltd (1)
1th Huaihexi 3rd Rd Development District, Dalian, Liaoning, China
Tel.: (86) 411 87305560
Web Site: http://www.lipp-system.cn
Waste Disposals & Sewage Treatment Services
N.A.I.C.S.: 221320
Jinqing Dong (Chm & CEO)

CHINA INFRASTRUCTURE & LOGISTICS GROUP LTD.
Suite 2101 21/F Two Exchange Square, Central, China (Hong Kong)
Tel.: (852) 31580603　　Ky
Web Site: http://www.cilgl.com
1719—(HKG)
Rev.: $31,944,606
Assets: $217,196,774
Liabilities: $94,772,182
Net Worth: $122,424,592
Earnings: $3,247,716
Emp.: 389
Fiscal Year-end: 12/31/21
Port Operation & Construction Services
N.A.I.C.S.: 488310
Bingmu Xie (CEO & Compliance Officer)

Subsidiaries:

Wuhan International Container Company Limited (1)
8 Pingjiang Road Yangluo Economic Development Zone, Wuhan, 430415, Hubei, China
Tel.: (86) 2786983333
Web Site: http://www.witport.com
Rev.: $13,465,396
Port Construction Services
N.A.I.C.S.: 237990
Bingmu Xie (Gen Mgr)

CHINA INFRASTRUCTURE CONSTRUCTION CORPORATION
Shidai Caifu Tiandi Building Suite 1906-09, 1 Hangfeng Road, Fengtai District, Beijing, 100070, China
Tel.: (86) 1051709287　　CO
Year Founded: 2003
CHNC—(OTCIQ)
Rev.: $296,000
Assets: $127,000
Liabilities: $189,000
Net Worth: $(62,000)
Earnings: $(91,000)
Emp.: 25
Fiscal Year-end: 05/31/20

Ready-Mix Concrete & Cement Mfr
N.A.I.C.S.: 327320
David J. Cutler (CEO)

CHINA INFRASTRUCTURE INVESTMENT LIMITED
Suite 607 6/F Ocean Centre 5 Canton Road, Tsim Sha Tsui, Kowloon, China (Hong Kong)
Tel.: (852) 23836868　　Ky
Web Site: http://www.china-infrastructure.com
Year Founded: 1992
0600—(HKG)
Rev.: $21,228,585
Assets: $624,237,684
Liabilities: $3,580,515,575
Net Worth: $(2,956,277,891)
Earnings: ($1,793,748,971)
Emp.: 14
Fiscal Year-end: 12/31/22
Investment Management Service
N.A.I.C.S.: 523940
De Chao Ye (Exec Dir)

CHINA INNOVATION INVESTMENT LIMITED
26/F No 9 Des Voeux Road West, Sheung Wan, China (Hong Kong)
Tel.: (852) 21119988　　Ky
Web Site: http://www.1217.com.hk
Year Founded: 2002
1217—(HKG)
Rev.: $57,534,248
Assets: $71,913,443
Liabilities: $98,175
Net Worth: $71,815,268
Earnings: $733,890
Emp.: 21
Fiscal Year-end: 12/31/22
Investment Management Service
N.A.I.C.S.: 523940
Xin Xiang (Chm & CEO)

CHINA INTEGRATED ENERGY, INC.
10F Western International Square, 2 Gaoxin Road, Xi'an, 710043, Shaanxi, China
Tel.: (86) 29 8268 3920　　DE
Web Site: http://www.chinaintegrated.com
Year Founded: 1998
Sales Range: $400-449.9 Million
Emp.: 373
Oil & Gasoline Exploration, Production & Distribution Services
N.A.I.C.S.: 211120
Xincheng Gao (Chm, Pres & CEO)

CHINA INTELLIGENCE INFORMATION SYSTEMS, INC.
11th Floor Tower B1 Yike Industrial Base, Shunhua, Jinan, 250101, China
Tel.: (86) 53155585742　　NV
IICN—(OTCIQ)
Sales Range: $1-9.9 Million
Emp.: 90
VoIP Software Products & Services
N.A.I.C.S.: 513210
Kunwu Li (Pres, CEO & Interim CFO)

CHINA INTELLIGENT LIGHTING AND ELECTRONICS, INC.
29 & 31 Huanzhen Road, Shuikou Town, Huizhou, 516005, Guangdong, China
Tel.: (86) 7523138511　　DE
Year Founded: 2007
Sales Range: $25-49.9 Million
Emp.: 645
LED & Other Lighting Products Designer, Mfr & Sales
N.A.I.C.S.: 335139
Xuemei Li (Chm, Pres & CEO)

CHINA INTERNATIONAL CAPITAL CORPORATION LIMITED
28th Floor China World Office 2 No 1 Jianguomenwai Avenue, Beijing, 100004, China
Tel.: (86) 1065051166　　CN
Web Site: https://en.cicc.com
Year Founded: 1995
001995—(33E)
Rev.: $4,678,709,588
Assets: $86,440,322,702
Liabilities: $71,916,425,113
Net Worth: $14,523,897,590
Earnings: $853,406,119
Emp.: 15,327
Fiscal Year-end: 12/31/23
Asset Management Services
N.A.I.C.S.: 523999
King Fung Wong (CFO)

Subsidiaries:

CICC ALPHA (Beijing) Investment Fund Management Co., Ltd (1)
Unit 05 52 Floor China World Tower A No 1 Jian Guo Men Wai Avenue, Chaoyang District, Beijing, 100004, China
Tel.: (86) 108 587 5300
Web Site: https://www.ciccalpha.com
Investment Management Service
N.A.I.C.S.: 523940
Joseph Liang (Chm)

CICC Europe (1)
Neue Mainzer Strasse 52-58, 60311, Frankfurt am Main, Germany
Tel.: (49) 69244373560
Financial Investment Services
N.A.I.C.S.: 523999

CICC Zhide Capital Corporation Limited (1)
32nd Floor Azia Center 1233 Lujiazui Ring Road Pudong New Are, Shanghai, 200120, China
Tel.: (86) 2158796226
Investment Management Service
N.A.I.C.S.: 523940

China International Capital Corporation (Hong Kong) Limited (1)
29th Floor One International Finance Centre 1 Harbour View Street, Central, China (Hong Kong)
Tel.: (852) 2872 2000
Financial Services
N.A.I.C.S.: 523940

Subsidiary (US):

CICC US Securities, Inc. (2)
280 Park Ave 32F, New York, NY 10017
Tel.: (646) 794-8800
Web Site: https://en.cicc.com
Security Brokerage Services
N.A.I.C.S.: 523150

Subsidiary (Non-US):

China International Capital Corporation (Singapore) Pte. Limited (2)
33-01 6 Battery Road, Singapore, 049909, Singapore
Tel.: (65) 6572 1999
Financial Services
N.A.I.C.S.: 523940

China International Capital Corporation (UK) Limited (2)
25th Floor 125 Old Broad Street, London, EC2N 1AR, United Kingdom
Tel.: (44) 2073675718
Security Brokerage Services
N.A.I.C.S.: 523150

China International Capital Corporation Hong Kong Asset Management Limited (1)
29th Floor One International Finance Centre 1 Harbour View Street, Central, China (Hong Kong)
Tel.: (852) 28722000
Web Site: https://cicchkam.com
N.A.I.C.S.: 523999
David Lee (COO)

China Investment Securities Company Limited (1)

Yi Tian Road Shenzhen-wing ultra 6003 Business Center A, 4th floor 18-21 layers Futian District, Shenzhen, 518048, China
Tel.: (86) 75582026809
Web Site: http://www.china-invs.cn
Security Brokerage Services
N.A.I.C.S.: 523150

CHINA INTERNATIONAL DEVELOPMENT CORPORATION LIMITED
Level 26 39 Queen's Road Central, Central, China (Hong Kong)
Tel.: (852) 23293678　　Ky
Web Site: http://www.irasia.com
Year Founded: 2004
0264—(HKG)
Rev.: $7,145,355
Assets: $3,899,205
Liabilities: $9,766,245
Net Worth: $(5,867,040)
Earnings: $(2,414,340)
Emp.: 142
Fiscal Year-end: 12/31/22
Leather Accessories Design & Mfr
N.A.I.C.S.: 315990
Jingfei Zhao (Chm)

Subsidiaries:

Sun Ray Manufactory, Limited (1)
3/F Victory Industrial Building 151-157 Wo Yi Hop Road, Victory Industrial Building, Kwai Chung, New Territories, China (Hong Kong)
Tel.: (852) 2 424 0392
Web Site: https://www.sunraymfg.com
Leather Wallet Mfr
N.A.I.C.S.: 316990

CHINA INTERNATIONAL HOLDINGS LIMITED
Room 806 8/F Kai Tak Commercial Building, 317 and 319 Des Voeux Road, Central, China (Hong Kong)
Tel.: (852) 28511008　　BM
Web Site: https://www.cihgrp.net
BEH—(SES)
Rev.: $14,344,816
Assets: $110,434,620
Liabilities: $37,322,497
Net Worth: $73,112,123
Earnings: $8,653,218
Fiscal Year-end: 12/31/22
Holding Company
N.A.I.C.S.: 551112
Chang Shan (Co-Founder & Chm)

CHINA INTERNATIONAL MARINE CONTAINERS (GROUP) CO., LTD.
CIMC R D Center No 2 Gangwan Avenue, Shekou Industrial Park Nanshan District, Shenzhen, 518067, Guangdong, China
Tel.: (86) 75526691130　　HK
Web Site: https://www.cimc.com
Year Founded: 1980
000039—(SSE)
Rev.: $12,280,175,297
Assets: $24,628,586,255
Liabilities: $16,752,651,603
Net Worth: $7,875,934,652
Earnings: $359,197,170
Emp.: 49,715
Fiscal Year-end: 12/31/19
Shipping Related Equipment Mfr & Distr
N.A.I.C.S.: 332439
Yinhui Li (VP)

Subsidiaries:

Albert Ziegler GmbH (1)
Albert-Ziegler-Strasse 1, 89537, Giengen an der Brenz, Germany
Tel.: (49) 73229510
Web Site: https://www.ziegler.de

Sales Range: $250-299.9 Million
Emp.: 1,000
Fire Service Vehicle Pump & Hose Mfr
N.A.I.C.S.: 336999

Beheermaatschappij Burg B.V   **(1)**
Katwijkerlaan 75, Pijnacker, 2641 PD, Zuid-Holland, Netherlands
Tel.: (31) 153694340
Web Site: https://bedrijveninformatiegids.nl
Management Consulting Services
N.A.I.C.S.: 541618

Burg Carrosserie B.V.   **(1)**
Lakenblekerstraat 26, North Holland, 1431 GG, Aalsmeer, Netherlands
Tel.: (31) 850227700
Web Site: http://www.burgers-carrosserie.nl
Sales Range: $25-49.9 Million
Emp.: 40
Automobile Body Mfr
N.A.I.C.S.: 336211

Burg Service B.V.   **(1)**
Middenweg 6, PO Box 299, 4782 PM, Moerdijk, Netherlands
Tel.: (31) 88 00 30 800
Web Site: http://www.burgservice.nl
Sales Range: $25-49.9 Million
Emp.: 65
Stainless Steel Storage Tank Mfr
N.A.I.C.S.: 331210
Hans Van Wijngaarden *(Mgr-Workshop-Trailerhal)*

C&C Trucks Co., Ltd.   **(1)**
Lianhe Building No 2 Eqiao Road, Sanshan Economic Development Zone, Wuhu, Anhui, China
Tel.: (86) 5537527000
Truck Parts Mfr & Distr
N.A.I.C.S.: 336390

CIMC Australia Pty Ltd.   **(1)**
20 Whitfield Blvd Cranbourne West, Dandenong, 3977, VIC, Australia   **(100%)**
Web Site: http://www.cimc.com.au
Sales Range: $50-74.9 Million
Emp.: 150
Metal Container Mfr
N.A.I.C.S.: 332439

CIMC Burg B.V.   **(1)**
Tel.: (31) 153694340
Sales Range: $25-49.9 Million
Emp.: 25
Transportation Services
N.A.I.C.S.: 488999

CIMC ENRIC Holdings Limited   **(1)**
CIMC R&D Center No 2 Gangwan Avenue Shekou Industrial Zone, Nanshan District, Shenzhen, Guangdong, China
Tel.: (86) 75526691130
Web Site: http://www.enricgroup.com
Rev.: $2,752,087,244
Assets: $3,118,912,150
Liabilities: $1,781,250,167
Net Worth: $1,337,661,983
Earnings: $152,325,295
Emp.: 10,500
Fiscal Year-end: 12/31/2022
Investment Management Service
N.A.I.C.S.: 523999

Subsidiary (Non-US):

CIMC Enric Tank & Process B.V.   **(2)**
Kapitein Grantstraat 8, 7821 AR, Emmen, Netherlands
Tel.: (31) 591 61 48 88
Web Site: http://www.cimc-enric.nl
Emp.: 65
Holding Company; Industrial Tank & Process Equipment Mfr & Whslr
N.A.I.C.S.: 551112

Subsidiary (Non-US):

Ziemann Holvrieka A/S   **(3)**
Kulholmsvej 24, 8930, Randers, Denmark
Tel.: (45) 86 428400
Web Site: http://www.holvrieka.com
Sales Range: $25-49.9 Million
Emp.: 65
Industrial Tank & Process Equipment Mfr
N.A.I.C.S.: 332420
Bo Mortensen *(Mng Dir)*

Subsidiary (Domestic):

Ziemann Holvrieka B.V.   **(3)**

Kapitein Grantstraat 8, 7821 AR, Emmen, Netherlands
Tel.: (31) 591 614888
Web Site: http://www.ziemann-holvrieka.com
Sales Range: $25-49.9 Million
Emp.: 60
Stainless Steel Tank Mfr
N.A.I.C.S.: 331210

Subsidiary (Non-US):

Ziemann Holvrieka GmbH   **(3)**
Schwieberdinger Strasse 86, 71636, Ludwigsburg, Germany   **(100%)**
Tel.: (49) 7141 408 0
Web Site: http://www.ziemann.com
Brewery Tanks & Process Equipment Mfr
N.A.I.C.S.: 332420
Klaus Gehrig *(Mng Dir)*

Subsidiary (Domestic):

Ziemann Holvrieka International B.V.   **(3)**
Lorentzstraat 7, 8606 JP, Sneek, Netherlands
Tel.: (31) 515 43 53 73
Web Site: http://www.holvrieka.com
Emp.: 100
Stainless Steel Tank Mfr
N.A.I.C.S.: 331210

Subsidiary (Non-US):

Ziemann Holvrieka N.V.   **(3)**
Wervikstraat 350, PO Box 19, 8930, Menen, Belgium
Tel.: (32) 56 514251
Web Site: http://www.holvrieka.com
Sales Range: $25-49.9 Million
Emp.: 50
Stainless & Fabrication Steel Container Mfr
N.A.I.C.S.: 332439
Anton Dirven *(Mng Dir)*

CIMC Finance Company Limited   **(1)**
11th Floor China Merchants Plaza No 1166 Wanghai Road Shekou, Nanshan District, Shenzhen, China
Tel.: (86) 75526807000
Web Site: https://www.cimcfinance.com
Financial Services
N.A.I.C.S.: 541611

CIMC Financing & Leasing Co., Ltd.   **(1)**
Floor 20 Building 1 China Merchants Plaza 1166 Wanghai Road Shekou, Nanshan District, Shenzhen, 518067, Guangdong, China
Tel.: (86) 75526806668
Financial Services
N.A.I.C.S.: 541611

CIMC Holdings Australia Pty Ltd   **(1)**
U 2 14 Monterey Rd, Dandenong, 3175, VIC, Australia
Tel.: (61) 397972100
Investment Management Service
N.A.I.C.S.: 523999

CIMC Jidong (Qinhuangdao) Vehicles Manufacture Co., Ltd.   **(1)**
No 9 Weihai Ave East Side Of Zhejiang North Road East Area, Qinhuangdao, 066004, Hebei, China
Tel.: (86) 3355181939
Automobile Mfr
N.A.I.C.S.: 336110

CIMC Modern Logistic Development Co., Ltd.   **(1)**
F9 Building MSD-B1 No 62 Second Street, Economic and Technological Development Zone, Tianjin, China
Tel.: (86) 2260977770
Freight Transportation Services
N.A.I.C.S.: 488510

CIMC Modern Logistics Development Co., Ltd.   **(1)**
F9 Building MSD-B1 No 62 Second Street, Tianjin Economic Technological Development Zone, Tianjin, China
Tel.: (86) 2260977770
Logistics & Transportation Services
N.A.I.C.S.: 541614

CIMC Offshore Engineering Holdings Co., Ltd.   **(1)**
Tel.: (86) 41139968185

---

33 High Tech Zone, Yantai, Shandong, China
Tel.: (86) 5354879999
N.A.I.C.S.: 922160

CIMC Raffles Offshore (Singapore) Limited   **(1)**
No 1 Claymore Drive 08-04 Orchard Towers, Singapore, 229594, Singapore
Tel.: (65) 6735 8690
Web Site: http://www.yantai-raffles.com
Emp.: 10
Oil & Gas Offshore Services
N.A.I.C.S.: 213112

CIMC Security Technology Co., Ltd.   **(1)**
22F Shenzhen Free Trade Center Shekou Industrial Zone, Shenzhen, Guangdong, China
Tel.: (86) 75526816681
N.A.I.C.S.: 922160

CIMC TransPack Technology Co., Ltd.   **(1)**
31/F New Times Plaza No 1 Taizi Road, Nanshan District, Shenzhen, Guangdong, China
Tel.: (86) 75526818020
N.A.I.C.S.: 922160

CIMC USA Inc.   **(1)**
289 E Water Tower Dr, Monon, IN 47959
Tel.: (219) 253-2054
Web Site: http://www.cimc.com
Sales Range: $100-124.9 Million
Emp.: 500
Industrial Equipment Mfr
N.A.I.C.S.: 333248

CIMC Vehicle (Guangxi) Co., Ltd.   **(1)**
3 Xiuxiang Ave Xixiangtang, Nanning, 530003, Guangxi, China
Tel.: (86) 771 3213559
Heavy Trailer & Truck Mfr
N.A.I.C.S.: 336120

CIMC Vehicle (Liaoning) Co., Ltd.   **(1)**
No 88 Binhai South Road, Yingkou, Liaoning, China
Tel.: (86) 417 3286900
Auto Parts & Accessories Mfr
N.A.I.C.S.: 336390

CIMC Vehicle (Shandong) Co., Ltd.   **(1)**
No 8001 Jingshi Highway, Mingshui Economical Development Zone, Jinan, 250200, Shandong, China   **(87.01%)**
Tel.: (86) 53185833021
Web Site: https://www.cimc-sd.com
Sales Range: $25-49.9 Million
Emp.: 10
Nonmetallic Mineral Product Mfr
N.A.I.C.S.: 327999

CIMC Vehicle Australia Pty Ltd   **(1)**
20 Whitfield Blvd Cranbourne West, Dandenong, 3977, VIC, Australia
Tel.: (61) 397972100
Emp.: 50
Transportation Equipment Mfr
N.A.I.C.S.: 336999
Sven Liao *(Gen Mgr)*

Caspian Driller Pte. Ltd.   **(1)**
08-04 Orchard Towers, Singapore, 229594, Singapore
Tel.: (65) 6735 8690
Metal Container Mfr
N.A.I.C.S.: 332439

China International Marine Containers (Hong Kong) Limited   **(1)**
Rm 3101-2 31th Fl Vicwood Plz, Central District, Central, China (Hong Kong)   **(100%)**
Tel.: (852) 28051268
Web Site: http://www.cinc.com
Sales Range: $75-99.9 Million
Emp.: 200
Industrial Supplies Whslr
N.A.I.C.S.: 423840

Dalian CIMC Container Co., Ltd   **(1)**
IIIB-2 Dalian Free Trade Zone, 116-600, Dalian, China   **(100%)**
Tel.: (86) 41139968185

Web Site: http://www.palletcenter.com
Sales Range: $200-249.9 Million
Emp.: 1,000
Power Boiler & Heat Exchanger Mfr
N.A.I.C.S.: 332410

Dalian CIMC Logistics Equipment Co., Ltd.   **(1)**
20/F Building 1 China Merchants Tower No 1166 Wanghai Road, Shekou, Shenzhen, Guangdong, China   **(100%)**
Tel.: (86) 75526806668
Web Site: http://www.cimc.com
Sales Range: $5-14.9 Billion
Emp.: 50,000
Metal Container Mfr
N.A.I.C.S.: 332439

Dalian CIMC Railway Equipment Co., Ltd.   **(1)**
Free Trade Zone IIIB-2, Dalian, 116600, Liaoning, China
Tel.: (86) 411 3921 6026
Railroad Rolling Stock Mfr
N.A.I.C.S.: 336510

Direct Chassis LLC   **(1)**
700 Rockmead Dr Ste 250, Kingwood, TX 77339-2106
Tel.: (281) 812-3462
Web Site: http://www.directchassis.com
Chassis Distr
N.A.I.C.S.: 423110

Donghwa Container Transportation Service Co., Ltd.   **(1)**
5th Floor No 500 Changjiang Road, Shanghai, 200431, China
Tel.: (86) 21 66151717
Web Site: http://www.donghwa.com.cn
Sales Range: $125-149.9 Million
Emp.: 500
Container Transportation Services
N.A.I.C.S.: 488999

Enric (Bengbu) Compressor Co., Ltd.   **(1)**
No 2001 South Outer Ring Road, Bengbu, 233052, Anhui, China
Tel.: (86) 5523073687
Web Site: https://www.enriccompressor.com
Sales Range: $200-249.9 Million
Emp.: 640
Compressor Machinery Mfr
N.A.I.C.S.: 333912

Enric (Lang fang) Energy Equipment integration Co., Ltd.   **(1)**
Web Site: http://www.cimc.com
Industrial Equipment Mfr
N.A.I.C.S.: 333248

Exploitatiemaatschappij Intraprogres B.V   **(1)**
Katwijkerlaan 75, 2641 PD, Pijnacker, Netherlands
Tel.: (31) 153694340
Freight Trucking Services
N.A.I.C.S.: 484121

Gansu CIMC Huajun Vehicle Co., Ltd.   **(1)**
No 26 Changan Road, Baiyin District, Baiyin, 730900, Gansu, China
Tel.: (86) 943 8250666
Web Site: http://www.gszjhj.com
Motor Vehicles Mfr
N.A.I.C.S.: 336110

Immoburg N.V.   **(1)**
Kanaallaan 54, Bree, 3960, Limburg, Belgium
Tel.: (32) 89469111
Real Estate Development Services
N.A.I.C.S.: 531390

Jiaxing CIMC Wood Co., Ltd.   **(1)**
177 Xiangjia Road, Lize Weitang Industrial Park, Jiashan, Zhejiang, China
Tel.: (86) 57384616851
Web Site: http://www.jxcimc.com
Container Wood Floor Mfr & Distr
N.A.I.C.S.: 321920
Guanjun Han *(Sls Mgr)*

Jingmen Hongtu Special Aircraft manufacturing Co., Ltd   **(1)**
Seaplanes Supplies Pressure Vessel Mfr
N.A.I.C.S.: 332439

China International Marine Containers (Group) Co., Ltd.—(Continued)

LAG Trailers N.V. (1)
Kanaallaan 54, 3960, Bree, Belgium
Tel.: (32) 89469111
Web Site: https://www.lag.eu
Sales Range: $100-124.9 Million
Emp.: 450
Truck Tankers Mfr
N.A.I.C.S.: 336120

Liangshan Dongyue CIMC Vehicle Co., Ltd. (1)
Quanpu Industrial Park, Liangshan County, Jining, Shandong, China
Tel.: (86) 5375108018
Web Site: https://www.lsdongyue.com
Emp.: 1,000
Automobile Mfr
N.A.I.C.S.: 336212

Luoyang CIMC Lingyu Automobile CO., LTD. (1)
No 966 Guanlin Road, Luolong District, Luoyang, Henan, China
Tel.: (86) 37965937666
Web Site: https://www.lingyu.com
Sales Range: $200-249.9 Million
Emp.: 1,000
Trailer & Container Mfr
N.A.I.C.S.: 336212

Luoyang Linyu Automobile Co., Ltd (1)
West Section of Guanlin Road, Luolong District, Luoyang, 471004, Henan, China
Tel.: (86) 37965937678
Web Site: http://www.lingyu.com
Sales Range: $200-249.9 Million
Emp.: 100
Automobile Mfr
N.A.I.C.S.: 336110
Yonghua Guo (Gen Mgr)

Marshall Lethlean Industries Pty Ltd (1)
20 Whitfield Blvd, Cranbourne West, Dandenong, 3977, VIC, Australia
Tel.: (61) 397972100
Web Site: https://www.mli.com.au
Emp.: 10
Transporting Equipment Mfr
N.A.I.C.S.: 336999

Nanjing Yangzi Petrochemical Design & Engineering Co., Ltd. (1)
Tel.: (86) 2557785888
Web Site: http://www.ypdi.com
Construction Engineering Services
N.A.I.C.S.: 541330

Nantong CIMC Special Transportation Equipment Manufacture Co., Ltd. (1)
NO 169 Chenggang Road, Gangzha District, Nantong, 226000, Jiangsu, China
Tel.: (86) 51385066067
Web Site: https://www.cimcnt.com
Transportation Equipment Mfr
N.A.I.C.S.: 336999

Nantong CIMC Tank Equipment Co., Ltd. (1)
No159 Cheng Gang Road, Nantong, Jiangsu, China (100%)
Tel.: (86) 51385066888
Web Site: https://www.cimctank.com
Sales Range: $1-4.9 Billion
Emp.: 5,000
Nonmetallic Mineral Product Mfr
N.A.I.C.S.: 327999

Ningbo CIMC Container Service Co., Ltd. (1)
No 255 Zhujiang Road Beilun Zone, Ningbo, China
Tel.: (86) 574 26883553
Container Trucking Services
N.A.I.C.S.: 484110
Huang Lupeng (Gen Mgr)

Ningbo CIMC Logistics Equipment Co., Ltd. (1)
Ningbo Export-Processing Zone, Ningbo, Zhejiang, China
Tel.: (86) 574 8682 5122
Logistic Metal Container Mfr
N.A.I.C.S.: 332439

Noordkoel B.V. (1)

Kapitein Grantstraat 8, Emmen, 7821 AR, Drenthe, Netherlands
Tel.: (31) 591614888
Business Support Services
N.A.I.C.S.: 561499

Qingdao CIMC Container Manufacture Co., Ltd (1)
No 1 East Kaifa Road E&T Development Zone, Qingdao, 266500, China
Tel.: (86) 532 86935706
Metal Container Mfr
N.A.I.C.S.: 332439

Qingdao CIMC Eco - Equipment Co., Ltd. (1)
No 1 Huanghedong Road Economic Technological Development Zone, Qingdao, China
Tel.: (86) 532 86935712
Web Site: http://www.cimc.com
Automobile Spare Parts Mfr
N.A.I.C.S.: 336390

Qingdao CIMC Reefer Container Manufacture Co., Ltd. (1)
Reefer Container Mfr
N.A.I.C.S.: 332439

Qingdao CIMC Special Reefer Co., Ltd. (1)
12 Dongwaihuan Road, 266300, Jinan, Shandong, China (100%)
Tel.: (86) 53282279978
Nonmetallic Mineral Product Mfr
N.A.I.C.S.: 327999

Qingdao Kooll Logistics Co., Ltd. (1)
Qingdao Economic and Technological Development Zone, The former Bay Port Road 115, Qingdao, 266510, Shandong, China
Tel.: (86) 532 86828666
Web Site: http://www.kooll.cn
Logistics Consulting Servies
N.A.I.C.S.: 541614

Shanghai CIMC Baowell Industries Co. Ltd (1)
No 1881 Yueluo Road, Baoshan District, Shanghai, 201908, China
Tel.: (86) 2156860000
Wood Container & Pallet Mfr
N.A.I.C.S.: 321920

Shanghai CIMC Reefer Containers Co., Ltd. (1)
No 6888 Hutai Rd, Baoshan Dist, Shanghai, China (100%)
Tel.: (86) 2156010088
Fabricated Structural Metal Mfr
N.A.I.C.S.: 332312

Shanghai CIMC Special Vehicle Co., Ltd. (1)
No 1771 Fuyuan Road, Baoshan District, Shanghai, China
Tel.: (86) 21 56861100
Automobile Mfr
N.A.I.C.S.: 336110

Shanghai CIMC Yangshan Container Service Co., Ltd. (1)
5th Floor No 500 Changjiang Road, Shanghai, 200431, China
Tel.: (86) 21 66151717
Warehousing & Logistics Services
N.A.I.C.S.: 493110

Shenzhen CIMC Industry & City Development Co., Ltd. (1)
Block B Building T1 CIMC Qianhai International Center No 401, Qianwan 1st Road Nanshan District, Shenzhen, Guangdong, China
Tel.: (86) 75526868181
N.A.I.C.S.: 922160

Shenzhen CIMC Investment Holding Company (1)
17 Floor Times Plaza Building No 1 Taizi Road, Shekou Industrial Zone, Shenzhen, 518067, Guangdong, China
Tel.: (86) 755 26808080
Web Site: http://www.cimc-scih.com
Container Leasing Services
N.A.I.C.S.: 532411

Shenzhen CIMC Tianda Airport Equipment Co., Ltd. (1)
No 4 Gongye 4th Rd Shekou, Shenzhen,

518067, Guangdong, China
Tel.: (86) 75526688488
Web Site: http://web.cimc.com
Airport Support & Logistics Equipment Mfr
N.A.I.C.S.: 336212

Subsidiary (Domestic):

Xinfa Airport Equipment Ltd. (2)
Jingchang High-tech Information Industrial Park No 97 Changping Road, Shahe Changping, Beijing, China
Tel.: (86) 10 80722951
Web Site: http://www.xinfa-china.com
Apron Bus Mfr
N.A.I.C.S.: 336110
Henry Qiu (Mgr)

Shenzhen CIMC Wood Co., Ltd. (1)
5/F No 2 Gangwan Avenue Shekou Industrial Zone, Nanshan District, Shenzhen, 518067, China
Tel.: (86) 75526691129
Transportation Equipment Mfr & Distr
N.A.I.C.S.: 336999

Shenzhen CIMC Yantian Port Container Service Co., Ltd (1)
Mingzhu 3rd Street, Yantian Road, Shenzhen, China (55%)
Tel.: (86) 75525283836
Web Site: http://www.cimc-services.com
Sales Range: $50-74.9 Million
Emp.: 200
Nonmetallic Mineral Product Mfr
N.A.I.C.S.: 327999

Shenzhen Southern CIMC Containers Service Co., Ltd. (1)
Qianhaiwan Logistics Zone Yue Liang Wan Avenue, Shenzhen, 518067, China
Tel.: (86) 755 26691131
Web Site: http://www.cimc.com
Metal Container Mfr
N.A.I.C.S.: 332439

Shenzhen Southern CIMC Eastern Logistics Equipment Manufacturing Co., Ltd. (1)
3th Jinglong Avenue Pingshan Town, Longgang District, Shenzhen, 518118, China
Tel.: (86) 755 89663666
Web Site: http://www.cimcsouth.com
Logistic Conatiner Equipment Mfr
N.A.I.C.S.: 332439

Shijiazhuang Enric Gas Equipment Co., Ltd. (1)
No 169 Yuxiang Street Equipment Manufacture Base, Shijiazhuang, 051430, Hebei, China
Tel.: (86) 31181663810
Web Site: https://www.cimc-enric.com
Gas Equipment Mfr
N.A.I.C.S.: 332420
George Zhao (Mgr-Sls)

TGE Gas Engineering GmbH (1)
Mildred-Scheel-Strasse 1, 53175, Bonn, Germany
Tel.: (49) 228 60448 0
Web Site: http://www.tge-gas.com
Engineeering Services
N.A.I.C.S.: 541330
Xiaohu Yang (Chm-Supervisory Bd)

Tacoba Consultant Forestry N.V (1)
Mataal Straal 16, Paramaribo, Suriname
Tel.: (597) 401485
Emp.: 10
Forestry Consulting Services
N.A.I.C.S.: 115310
Yuan Gun (Gen Mgr)

Taicang CIMC Containers Co., Ltd. (1)
No 96 Binjiang Avenue Gangkou Development Zone, Taicang, Jiangsu, China
Tel.: (86) 512 53782629
Sales Range: $50-74.9 Million
Emp.: 200
Freight Forwarding Services
N.A.I.C.S.: 488510

Technodyne International Limited (1)
Black Horse House 8-10 Leigh Road, Eastleigh, SO50 9FH, Hampshire, United Kingdom
Tel.: (44) 2380629929
Web Site: https://technodyne.com

Emp.: 40
Cryogenic Storage Equipment Mfr
N.A.I.C.S.: 332420

Tianjin CIMC Logistics Equipments Co., Ltd. (1)
Tel.: (86) 2259887105
Logistics Equipment & Container Mfr
N.A.I.C.S.: 332439

Tianjin CIMC North Ocean Container Co., Ltd. (1)
No 510 Xiamen Road Hi-Tech Development Zone, Tanggu, Tianjin, China
Tel.: (86) 2225601900
Container Mfr & Distr
N.A.I.C.S.: 332420

Vanguard National Trailer Corporation (1)
289 E Water Tower Dr, Monon, IN 47959 (100%)
Tel.: (219) 253-2000
Web Site: https://www.vanguardtrailer.com
Sales Range: $25-49.9 Million
Emp.: 100
Trailer Mfr
N.A.I.C.S.: 336212

Wuhu CIMC RuiJiang Automobile CO LTD (1)
National High-tech Industrial Development Zone, Wuhu, 241002, Anhui, China
Tel.: (86) 5533002555
Web Site: https://www.cimc-whrj.com
Heavy Vehicle & Automobile Mfr
N.A.I.C.S.: 336110

Xinhui CIMC Container Co., Ltd. (1)
Xinhui Zhongji Industrial Park Da Ao Town, Xinhui District, Jiangmen, 529144, Guangdong, China
Tel.: (86) 7506248888
Fabricated Metal Container Mfr
N.A.I.C.S.: 332439

Xinhui CIMC Special Transportation Equipment Co., Ltd. (1)
Da Ao Town, Xinhui Dist, Jiangmen, 529144, Guangdong, China
Tel.: (86) 7506248888
Web Site: http://www.cimc.com
Transportation Equipment Mfr
N.A.I.C.S.: 336999

Xinhui CIMC Wood Co., Ltd. (1)
Xinhui Cimc Industrial Park Da Ao Town, Xinhui District, Jiangmen, 529144, Guangdong, China
Tel.: (86) 7506248906
Industrial Timber Products Distr
N.A.I.C.S.: 423990

Yangzhou CIMC Tong Hua Special Vehicles Co., Ltd. (1)
No 9 Linjiang Road, Yangzhou, 225009, Jiangsu, China
Tel.: (86) 51487877888
Web Site: https://www.chinatrailer.com
Heavy Trailer Mfr
N.A.I.C.S.: 336212

Yangzhou Runyang Logistics Equipments Co., Ltd. (1)
39 Yangwei Road, Dev Zone, Yangzhou, 225102, Jiangsu, China
Tel.: (86) 51480382888
Web Site: http://www.yzryc.com
Logistic Metal Container Mfr
N.A.I.C.S.: 332439

Yangzhou Tonglee Reefer Container Co., Ltd. (1)
(51%)
Tel.: (86) 51480383111
Web Site: http://www.tlc-yz.com
Sales Range: $450-499.9 Million
Emp.: 1,800
Nonmetallic Mineral Product Mfr
N.A.I.C.S.: 327999

Yangzhou Tonglee Reefer Equipment Co.,Ltd (1)
(100%)
Tel.: (86) 51480383130
Web Site: http://www.tlc-yz.com
Emp.: 1,200
Nonmetallic Mineral Product Mfr
N.A.I.C.S.: 327999

Yantai CIMC Raffles Ship Co., Ltd. (1)
No 70 Zhifu Island East Road, Zhifu District, Yantai, 264000, China
Tel.: (86) 5356801451
Ship Building Services
N.A.I.C.S.: 336611
Shao Yong Qiang *(Gen Mgr)*

Yantai Tiezhongbao steel processing Co., Ltd. (1)
No 70 Zhifu East Road, Zhifu District, Yantai, Shandong, China
Tel.: (86) 18615022388
Metal Products Mfr
N.A.I.C.S.: 332999

Zhangjiagang CIMC Sanctum Cryogenic Equipment Machinery Co., Ltd. (1)
Xizhong Road Nanshagang, Jingang Town, Zhangjiagang, 215632, Jiangsu, China
Tel.: (86) 51258391235
Web Site: https://en.sdy-cn.com
Cryogenic Tank Mfr
N.A.I.C.S.: 332420

Zhangzhou CIMC Container Co., Ltd. (1)
China Merchants Zhangzhou Development Zone, Zhangzhou, China
Tel.: (86) 596 685 6179
Fabricated Metal Container Mfr
N.A.I.C.S.: 332439
Tony Chang *(Gen Mgr)*

Zhumadian CIMC Huajun Vehicle Co.,Ltd (1)
Zhumadian yicheng area Middle section of Xuesong Rd, 463000, Zhengzhou, Henan, China (75%)
Tel.: (86) 3963810953
Web Site: http://www.hjcl.com
Sales Range: $1-4.9 Billion
Emp.: 3,500
Nonmetallic Mineral Product Mfr
N.A.I.C.S.: 327999
Fapei Wu *(VP)*

Zhumadian CIMC Huajun Vehicle Trading Co., Ltd (1)
Tel.: (86) 3963810953
Truck & Trailer Distr
N.A.I.C.S.: 423120
Guo Yonghua *(Gen Mgr)*

CHINA INVESTMENT AND FINANCE GROUP LIMITED
Room 1104 Crawford House 70 Queen's Road, Central, China (Hong Kong)
Tel.: (852) 2 165 4759
Web Site: http://www.chnif.com
1226—(HKG)
Rev.: $583,119
Assets: $26,215,959
Liabilities: $999,595
Net Worth: $25,216,364
Earnings: $460,330
Emp.: 11
Fiscal Year-end: 03/31/21
Investment Holding Services
N.A.I.C.S.: 523940

CHINA INVESTMENT CORPORATION
New Poly Plaza No 1 Chaoyangmen Beidajie, Dongcheng District, Beijing, 100010, China
Tel.: (86) 10 8409 6277   CN
Web Site: http://www.china-inv.cn
Year Founded: 2007
Investment Management Service
N.A.I.C.S.: 523940
Guo Xiangjun *(Exec VP)*

Subsidiaries:

Asciano Limited (1)
Level 4 476 St Kilda Road, Melbourne, 3004, VIC, Australia
Tel.: (61) 3 92487000
Web Site: http://www.asciano.com.au

Sales Range: $1-4.9 Billion
Ports & Rail Assets Management
N.A.I.C.S.: 485112
Roger Burrows *(CFO)*

Joint Venture (Non-US):

C3 Limited (2)
58 Cross Road Sulphur Point, Tauranga, 3110, New Zealand
Tel.: (64) 75728972
Web Site: https://www.c3.co.nz
Emp.: 800
Marine Cargo Handling Services
N.A.I.C.S.: 488320
Chris Sutherland *(Gen Mgr-Logistics-New Zealand)*

Central Huijin Investment Ltd. (1)
New Poly Plaza 1 Chaoyangmen Beidajie, Dongcheng District, Beijing, 100010, China
Tel.: (86) 10 6408 6638
Web Site: http://www.huijin.cn
Investment Management Service
N.A.I.C.S.: 523999
Chun Peng *(Pres)*

Subsidiary (Domestic):

China Jianyin Investment Limited (2)
Building C No 28 JianGuoMenNei Street, Dongcheng District, Beijing, 100005, China (100%)
Tel.: (86) 10 6627 6114
Web Site: http://en.jic.cn
Sales Range: $1-4.9 Billion
Emp.: 14,000
Investment Services
N.A.I.C.S.: 523999

Subsidiary (Non-US):

SGD S.A. (3)
Immeuble Le Bellini 14 bis terrasse Bellini, 92807, Puteaux, Cedex, France
Tel.: (33) 140903600
Web Site: http://www.sgd-pharma.com
Sales Range: $300-349.9 Million
Emp.: 2,750
Glass Container Mfr
N.A.I.C.S.: 327213
Jurgen Sackhoff *(CEO)*

Subsidiary (Non-US):

SGD Kipfenberg GmbH (4)
Altmuhlstrasse 2, D-85110, Kipfenberg, Germany
Tel.: (49) 84651710
Web Site: http://www.sgd-kipfenberg.de
Pharmaceutical Industry Glass Bottles Mfr
N.A.I.C.S.: 327213
Bernd Schulda *(Mng Dir)*

CHINA INVESTMENTS HOLDINGS LIMITED
Unit 501 Wing On Plaza 62 Mody Road, Tsimshatsui, Kowloon, China (Hong Kong)
Tel.: (852) 23012128   BM
0132—(HKG)
Rev.: $97,873,080
Assets: $1,134,101,535
Liabilities: $867,271,448
Net Worth: $266,830,088
Earnings: $5,460,060
Emp.: 1,189
Fiscal Year-end: 12/31/22
Holding Company
N.A.I.C.S.: 551112
Xiangming He *(Chm)*

CHINA ITS (HOLDINGS) CO., LTD.
Building 204 No 10 Electronic City of IT Industrail Park, Beijing Jiuxianqiao North Road Chaoyang District, Beijing, 100015, China
Tel.: (86) 1059330088
Web Site: http://www.its.cn
1900—(HKG)
Rev.: $100,305,130
Assets: $398,903,076
Liabilities: $132,770,243
Net Worth: $266,132,833

Earnings: $13,164,606
Emp.: 228
Fiscal Year-end: 12/31/22
Transportation Infrastructure Technology Services
N.A.I.C.S.: 541512
Hailin Jiang *(CEO)*

CHINA JICHENG HOLDINGS LIMITED
Yonghe Industrial Section Yonghe Town, Jinjiang, Fujian, China
Tel.: (86) 59588071660   Ky
Web Site: http://www.china-jicheng.cn
1027—(HKG)
Rev.: $49,694,299
Assets: $65,768,976
Liabilities: $19,182,571
Net Worth: $46,586,405
Earnings: ($4,132,393)
Emp.: 571
Fiscal Year-end: 12/31/22
Holding Company; Umbrella Mfr
N.A.I.C.S.: 551112
Wenji Huang *(Chm)*

CHINA JISHAN HOLDINGS LIMITED
112 Robinson Road 05-01, Singapore, 068902, Singapore
Tel.: (65) 62276660
Web Site: http://www.jishangroup.com
J18—(SES)
Rev.: $5,397,875
Assets: $121,552,574
Liabilities: $95,846,949
Net Worth: $25,705,625
Earnings: ($6,564,999)
Fiscal Year-end: 12/31/19
Textile Svcs
N.A.I.C.S.: 313310
Priscilla Wai Teng Chan *(Sec)*

Subsidiaries:

Handan Jishan Real Estate Development Co., Ltd. (1)
No 115 Eastern Renmin Road, Handan, 056000, Hebei, China
Tel.: (86) 3103125678
Textile Products Distr
N.A.I.C.S.: 423830

Quzhou Jishan Real Estate Development Co., Ltd. (1)
No 23 Nankai Street, Quzhou, 057250, Hebei, China
Tel.: (86) 3108816877
Textile Products Distr
N.A.I.C.S.: 423830

Shaoxing Jishan Zhiye Co., Ltd. (1)
No 168 Second Ring Road, Shaoxing, 312000, China
Tel.: (86) 57585099001
Textile Products Distr
N.A.I.C.S.: 423830

Zhejiang Jishan Holdings Ltd. (1)
2nd Floor Building A Xiandai Mansion, 276 Middle Zhongxing Road, Shaoxing, 312000, China
Tel.: (86) 57585202628
Textile Products Distr
N.A.I.C.S.: 423830

Zhejiang Jishan Printing & Dyeing Co., Ltd. (1)
Kebei Industrial Zone, Shaoxing, 312081, Zhejiang, China
Tel.: (86) 57584608755
Web Site: http://www.jishantextile.com
Textile Product Mfr & Distr
N.A.I.C.S.: 313310
Micky Ling *(Mgr-Sls)*

CHINA JO-JO DRUGSTORES, INC.
4th Floor Building 5 Renxin Yaju,

Gong Shu District, Hangzhou, 310014, Zhejiang, China
Tel.: (86) 57188219579   NV
Web Site: https://www.jiuzhou360.com
Year Founded: 2006
CJJD—(NASDAQ)
Rev.: $154,541,077
Assets: $95,057,090
Liabilities: $80,763,953
Net Worth: $14,293,137
Earnings: ($4,234,242)
Emp.: 939
Fiscal Year-end: 03/31/24
Drug Store & Pharmacy Owner & Operator
N.A.I.C.S.: 456110
Lei Liu *(Chm & CEO)*

Subsidiaries:

Hangzhou Jiuzhou Grand Pharmacy Chain Co., Ltd. (1)
Rm 507-513 5/f Suite A Meidu Pla, Hangzhou, 310011, China
Tel.: (86) 57188078
Health Care Srvices
N.A.I.C.S.: 622110

CHINA JUSHI CO., LTD.
No 669 South Wenhua Road Economic Development Zone, Tongxiang, 314500, Zhejiang, China
Tel.: (86) 57388181222
Web Site: https://www.jushi.com
Year Founded: 1999
600176—(SHG)
Rev.: $2,059,675,786
Assets: $7,210,062,874
Liabilities: $3,056,563,788
Net Worth: $4,153,499,086
Earnings: $421,527,747
Emp.: 12,850
Fiscal Year-end: 12/31/23
Fiberglass Mfr & Whslr
N.A.I.C.S.: 327212
Wang Yuan *(VP & Controller)*

Subsidiaries:

Jushi Canada Fiberglass Co. Ltd. (1)
1350 Rodick Rd Unit 3, Markham, L3R 5X4, ON, Canada
Tel.: (905) 477-7628
Insulation Fiberglass Mfr & Distr
N.A.I.C.S.: 327993

Jushi Group (BZ) Sinosia Composite Materials Co., Ltd. (1)
Rua Jaime Reis n 86 CEP 80, Curitiba, 510-010, Brazil
Tel.: (55) 1938781033
Insulation Fiberglass Mfr & Distr
N.A.I.C.S.: 327993

Jushi Group (HK) Sinosia Composite Materials Co., Ltd. (1)
Room 901 Bonham Centre 79-85 Bonham Strand East, Central, China (Hong Kong)
Tel.: (852) 25456068
Web Site: https://jushisinosiahk.com
Insulation Fiberglass Distr
N.A.I.C.S.: 424310

Jushi Group (SA) Sinosia Composite Materials Co., Ltd. (1)
162 Main Reef Road, Johannesburg, South Africa
Tel.: (27) 116145122
Web Site: https://www.jushisinosia.co.za
Insulation Fiberglass Mfr & Distr
N.A.I.C.S.: 327993

Jushi Group Chengdu Co., Ltd. (1)
899 Oucheng Road, Qingquan Town Qingbaijiang District, Chengdu, 610300, China
Tel.: (86) 2889302060
Insulation Fiberglass Mfr & Distr
N.A.I.C.S.: 327993

Jushi Group Hong Kong Co., Limited (1)
Unit B 12/F Chinaweal Centre 414-424

China Jushi Co., Ltd.—(Continued)

Jaffe Road, Wanchai, Hong Kong, China
(Hong Kong)
Tel.: (852) 23263183
Fiber Glass Mfr & Distr
N.A.I.C.S.: 326199

Jushi Group Jiujiang Co., Ltd.   (1)
6 Jinxiu Avenue Export Processing Zone,
Jiujiang, 332005, Jiangxi, China
Tel.: (86) 7928258776
Emp.: 1,500
Fiber Glass Mfr
N.A.I.C.S.: 327212

Jushi India Fiberglass Pvt Ltd.   (1)
G-19-20 Sitaram Mill Compound, Creative
Industrial Estate N M Joshi Marg Lower
Parel, Mumbai, 400011, India
Tel.: (91) 67218006
Web Site: https://www.jushifiberglass.com
Emp.: 8,000
Insulation Fiberglass Mfr
N.A.I.C.S.: 327993

Jushi Italy SRL   (1)
Via Adige 10/12, Castiglione Olona Varese,
21043, Milan, Italy
Tel.: (39) 0331857918
Insulation Fiberglass Mfr & Distr
N.A.I.C.S.: 327993

Jushi Japan Co., Ltd.   (1)
1-6-3 Yurakucho, Chiyoda, Tokyo, 100-
0006, Japan
Tel.: (81) 362688508
Web Site: https://www.jushijapan.co.jp
Construction Materials Distr
N.A.I.C.S.: 423320

Jushi Korea Co., Ltd.   (1)
Rm No 810 Life Office 61-3 Yoido-Dong,
Youngdeungpo-Gu, Seoul, 150-731, Korea
(South)
Tel.: (82) 221683288
Insulation Fiberglass Mfr & Distr.
N.A.I.C.S.: 327993

Jushi Spain.S.A.   (1)
Avd de Barajas 24 Planta 2 Edificio Gamma,
Parque Empresarial Omega, Alcobendas,
28108, Madrid, Spain
Tel.: (34) 917678817
Fiber Glass Mfr & Distr
N.A.I.C.S.: 326199

CHINA KANGDA FOOD COM-
PANY LIMITED
No Boulevard Binhai 8399 Huangdao
District, Qingdao, Shandong, China
Tel.: (86) 53286171115
Web Site:
  http://www.kangdafood.com
0834—(HKG)
Rev.: $245,108,495
Assets: $187,280,543
Liabilities: $108,414,774
Net Worth: $78,865,769
Earnings: ($2,119,900)
Emp.: 1,998
Fiscal Year-end: 12/31/22
Food Mfr & Distr
N.A.I.C.S.: 311999
Yanxu Gao *(Exec Dir)*

Subsidiaries:

Shandong Kaijia Food Company
Limited   (1)
No 138 Zone A Xiazhuang Industrial Park,
Gaomi, 261505, Shandong, China
Tel.: (86) 5362129828
Web Site: https://www.sdkaijiafood.com
Frozen Food & Slaughtering Mfr
N.A.I.C.S.: 311999

CHINA KELI ELECTRIC COM-
PANY LTD.
Suite 850 - 1095 West Pender Street,
Vancouver, V6E 2M, BC, Canada
Tel.: (525) 138-1632
Web Site: http://www.zkl.cc
Year Founded: 2005
Rev.: $8,744,654
Assets: $25,572,300

Liabilities: $28,686,314
Net Worth: ($3,114,014)
Earnings: ($4,994,378)
Fiscal Year-end: 04/30/17
Holding Company
N.A.I.C.S.: 551112

Subsidiaries:

Zhuhai Keli Electronic Co., Ltd.   (1)
No 32 Jinfeng West Road Jinding Technol-
ogy Industrial Park Xi, Zhuhai, 519085,
China
Tel.: (86) 75 6338 2666
Electrical Equipment & Component Mfr
N.A.I.C.S.: 335999

CHINA KEPEI EDUCATION
GROUP LIMITED
Qifu Road, Gaoyao District, Zha-
oqing, Guangdong, China
Tel.: (86) 7588387888   Ky
Web Site:
  http://www.chinakepeiedu.com
Year Founded: 2000
1890—(HKG)
Rev.: $202,135,705
Assets: $1,035,293,594
Liabilities: $508,573,588
Net Worth: $526,720,007
Earnings: $98,873,892
Emp.: 3,583
Fiscal Year-end: 08/31/22
Educational Support Services
N.A.I.C.S.: 611710
Nianqiao Ye *(Founder, Chm, CEO & Gen Mgr)*

CHINA KINGHO ENERGY
GROUP CO., LTD.
Floor 36 Middle Tower China Over-
seas Plaza No 8 Yard Guanghua
Dongli, Jianguomenwai Chaoyang
District, Beijing, 100020, China
Tel.: (86) 10 5630 7890   CN
Web Site:
  http://www.chinakingho.com
Year Founded: 2011
Emp.: 20,000
Holding Company; Coal Mining, Pro-
cessing & Wholesale Distribution
N.A.I.C.S.: 551112
Qinghua Huo *(Chm)*

CHINA KINGS RESOURCES
GROUP CO., LTD.
Room 2301 South Building Anno Do-
mini Mansion No 8 Qiushi Road,
Hangzhou, 310013, Zhejiang, China
Tel.: (86) 57188380819
Web Site:
  https://www.chinesekings.com
Year Founded: 2001
603505—(SHG)
Rev.: $147,439,375
Assets: $429,417,935
Liabilities: $206,694,226
Net Worth: $222,723,708
Earnings: $31,229,677
Emp.: 700
Fiscal Year-end: 12/31/22
Fluorite Mine Development Services
N.A.I.C.S.: 212390
Wang Jinhua *(Chm)*

CHINA KINGSTONE MINING
HOLDINGS LIMITED
Unit 14 8/F Seapower Tower Concor-
dia Plaza No 1 Science Museum
Road, Kowloon, China (Hong Kong)
Tel.: (852) 25274999
Web Site:
  http://www.kingstonemining.com
1380—(HKG)
Rev.: $10,149,376
Assets: $41,030,917
Liabilities: $12,782,297

Net Worth: $28,248,620
Earnings: ($8,688,514)
Emp.: 28
Fiscal Year-end: 12/31/22
Marble Mining Services
N.A.I.C.S.: 212390
Cuiwei Zhang *(Exec Dir)*

CHINA KUNDA TECHNOLOGY
HOLDINGS LIMITED
4 Shenton Way 17-01 SGX Centre 2,
Singapore, 068807, Singapore
Tel.: (65) 68178944   SG
Web Site:
  https://www.chinakunda.com
Year Founded: 2007
GU5—(CAT)
Rev.: $3,681,547
Assets: $4,182,525
Liabilities: $2,038,672
Net Worth: $2,143,852
Earnings: ($1,380,884)
Emp.: 85
Fiscal Year-end: 03/31/23
Holding Company; Precision Molds,
Plastic Injection Parts & In-Mold
Decoration Products Mfr & Whslr
N.A.I.C.S.: 551112
Kaoqun Cai *(CEO & Chm)*

Subsidiaries:

Yick Kwan Tat Enterprises Company
Limited   (1)
6 South Bantian Rd, Shenzhen, 518129,
Guangdong, China
Tel.: (86) 755 28778999
Web Site: http://www.kundamould.com
Sales Range: $200-249.9 Million
Emp.: 900
Plastic Injection & IMD Products Mfr
N.A.I.C.S.: 326199

CHINA LEADSHINE TECHNOL-
OGY CO., LTD.
Floor 9 11 Building A3 Nanshan
Zhiyuan No 1001 Xueyuan Road,
Taoyuan Street Nanshan, Shenzhen,
518052, Guangdong, China
Tel.: (86) 75526400242
Web Site: http://www.leadshine.com
Year Founded: 2007
002979—(SSE)
Rev.: $187,835,544
Assets: $307,989,864
Liabilities: $137,139,912
Net Worth: $170,849,952
Earnings: $30,931,524
Emp.: 1,400
Fiscal Year-end: 12/31/22
Electrical Equipment Mfr & Distr
N.A.I.C.S.: 335999
Weiping Li *(Chm & Gen Mgr)*

Subsidiaries:

Leadshine America Inc.   (1)
26050 Towne Ctr Dr, Foothill Ranch, CA
92610
Tel.: (949) 608-7270
Web Site: https://www.leadshineusa.com
Motion Control Product Mfr & Distr
N.A.I.C.S.: 335314

CHINA LEON INSPECTION
HOLDING LIMITED
11/F Sanyuan Building 18 Xibahe
East Lane, Chaoyang District, Beijing,
100028, China
Tel.: (86) 1084603113   Ky
Web Site:
  http://www.huaxialihong.com
Year Founded: 2009
1586—(HKG)
Rev.: $120,361,785
Assets: $96,911,220
Liabilities: $34,815,533
Net Worth: $62,095,688
Earnings: $13,365,570

Emp.: 2,528
Fiscal Year-end: 12/31/22
Coal Testing & Inspection Services
N.A.I.C.S.: 213113
Xiangli Li *(Chm & CEO)*

Subsidiaries:

Leon Inspection & Testing India Pri-
vate Limited   (1)
No 4 3rd Floor 5th Cross Street Dr Radhak-
riahnan Salai, Mylapore, Chennai, 600004,
India
Tel.: (91) 4442185033
Geophysical Surveying & Mapping Services
N.A.I.C.S.: 213113
G. Krishnakumar *(Deputy Gen Mgr)*

Leon Inspection Testing Services
Sdn. Bhd   (1)
No 46 Jalan Gebeng 1/24 Bandar Industri
Gebeng Jaya, 26100, Kuantan, Pahang,
Malaysia
Tel.: (60) 95838955
Geophysical Surveying & Mapping Services
N.A.I.C.S.: 213113
Mohamad Ridzuan Lee Abdullah *(Gen Mgr)*

Leon Overseas Pte. Ltd   (1)
51 Science Park Road 04-25 The Aries,
Singapore Science Park II, Singapore,
117586, Singapore
Tel.: (65) 64600290
Inspection, Surveying, Certification, Testing
& Tank Calibration Services
N.A.I.C.S.: 541380

Subsidiary (Domestic):

Saybolt (Singapore) Pte Ltd.   (2)
50 Science Park Road 04-06/10, Science
Park II, Singapore, 117406, Singapore
Tel.: (65) 67752922
Bunker Surveying Services
N.A.I.C.S.: 488390

Pt. Leon Testing & Consultancy   (1)
Citra Towers Office North Tower 20th Floor -
20E, Jl Benyamin Suaeb KavA6 Kemay-
oran, Jakarta, 10630, Indonesia
Tel.: (62) 2122605900
Geophysical Surveying & Mapping Services
N.A.I.C.S.: 213113
Sanggit Sugiarto *(Gen Mgr-ops)*

CHINA LESSO GROUP HOLD-
INGS LIMITED
Liansu Industrial Estate, Longjiang
Town Shunde District, Foshan,
528318, Guangdong, China
Tel.: (86) 75729223015   Ky
Web Site: http://www.lesso.com
Year Founded: 1996
2128—(HKG)
Rev.: $4,319,716,424
Assets: $8,276,945,602
Liabilities: $5,105,338,384
Net Worth: $3,171,607,218
Earnings: $353,091,960
Emp.: 19,690
Fiscal Year-end: 12/31/22
Plastic Pipes & Pipe Fittings Mfr
N.A.I.C.S.: 326122
Luen Hei Wong *(Founder & Chm)*

CHINA LIBERAL EDUCATION
HOLDINGS LIMITED
Room 1618 Zhongguangcun MOOC
Times Building 18 Zhongguangcun
Street, Haidian District, Beijing,
100190, China
Tel.: (86) 1065978118   Ky
Web Site:
  http://www.chinaliberal.com
Year Founded: 2019
CLEU—(NASDAQ)
Rev.: $5,023,099
Assets: $12,773,914
Liabilities: $1,132,985
Net Worth: $11,640,929
Earnings: $1,208,696
Emp.: 41
Fiscal Year-end: 12/31/20

Holding Company
N.A.I.C.S.: 551112
Jianxin Zhang *(Chm & CEO)*

CHINA LIFE INSURANCE COMPANY LIMITED

No 16 Financial Street, Xicheng District, Beijing, 100033, China
Tel.: (86) 1063633333   CN
Web Site: https://www.e-chinalife.com
Year Founded: 1949
601628—(SHG)
Rev.: $116,008,390,563
Assets: $815,307,792,424
Liabilities: $750,226,655,959
Net Worth: $65,081,136,464
Earnings: $2,922,851,130
Emp.: 102,238
Fiscal Year-end: 12/31/23
Investment Management Service
N.A.I.C.S.: 523999
Hong Yang *(VP)*

Subsidiaries:

China Life AMP Asset Management
Company   **(1)**
Floor 10 11 12 Building 2 No 28 Financial
Street, Yingtai Business Center Xicheng
District, Beijing, 100033, China
Tel.: (86) 1050850888
Web Site: http://www.gsfunds.com.cn
Asset Management Services
N.A.I.C.S.: 523940

China Life Asset Management Company Limited   **(1)**
China Life Insurance Center No 17 Financial Street, Xicheng District, Beijing,
100033, China
Tel.: (86) 1066221188
Web Site: https://www.clamc.com
N.A.I.C.S.: 523940

China Life Insurance Asset Management Company Limited   **(1)**
9/F Suite A Tongtai Mansion No 33 Jinrong
Street, Xicheng District, Beijing, 100032,
China   **(60%)**
Tel.: (86) 1088088866
Web Site: http://www.clamc.com
Asset Management Services
N.A.I.C.S.: 524298

China Life Pension Company
Limited   **(1)**
No 12 Financial Street, Xicheng District,
Beijing, 100033, China
Tel.: (86) 1063635888
Web Site: http://www.clpc.com.cn
Insurance Services
N.A.I.C.S.: 524210

China Life Wealth Management Company Limited   **(1)**
12th Floor Xidan Joy City Office Building No
131 Xidan North Street, Xicheng District,
Beijing, China
Tel.: (86) 1059250539
Web Site: http://www.clwmc.com.cn
Asset Management Services
N.A.I.C.S.: 523940

CHINA LILANG LIMITED

200 Chang Xing Road, Jinjiang,
362200, Fujian, China
Tel.: (86) 59585622666   Ky
Web Site: http://www.lilanz.com
Year Founded: 1987
1234—(HKG)
Rev.: $517,770,131
Assets: $767,237,990
Liabilities: $204,438,215
Net Worth: $562,799,775
Earnings: $71,721,738
Emp.: 3,942
Fiscal Year-end: 12/31/21
Apparels Mfr
N.A.I.C.S.: 315990
Dong Xing Wang *(Chm)*

CHINA LINEN TEXTILE INDUSTRY, LTD.

Chengdong Street, Lanxi, Heilongjiang, China
Tel.: (86) 4555635885   Ky
Year Founded: 2000
Sales Range: $50-74.9 Million
Emp.: 1,408
Linen Textile Products Mfr & Sales
N.A.I.C.S.: 314999
Ren Gao *(Chm, Pres & CEO)*

CHINA LITERATURE LTD.

6 Building 690 BiBo Road Pudong
New Area, Shanghai, 201203, China
Tel.: (86) 2161870500
Web Site: http://www.yuewen.com
0772—(HKG)
Rev.: $1,070,637,329
Assets: $3,191,920,711
Liabilities: $671,077,742
Net Worth: $2,520,842,969
Earnings: $85,310,971
Emp.: 1,800
Fiscal Year-end: 12/31/22
Online Book Publisher
N.A.I.C.S.: 513130
Wenhui Wu *(Vice Chm)*

CHINA LOGISTICS GROUP, INC.

23F Gutai Beach Building No 969
Zhongshan Road South, Shanghai,
200011, China
Tel.: (86) 21 63355100   FL
Web Site:
   http://www.chinalogisticsinc.com
Sales Range: $10-24.9 Million
Emp.: 126
International Freight Forwarding &
Logistics Services
N.A.I.C.S.: 488510

Subsidiaries:

Shandong Jiajia International Freight
& Forwarding Co., Ltd.   **(1)**
F1618B North Golden Plaza 20 Middle
Hongkong Road, Qingdao, 266071, China
Tel.: (86) 53285021713
Web Site: http://www.jiajia.com.cn
Emp.: 87
Freight Transportation Arrangement Services
N.A.I.C.S.: 488510
Hui Liu *(Founder)*

CHINA LOGISTICS PROPERTY HOLDINGS COMPANY LIMITED

No 1899 Shenkun Road, Minhang
District, Shanghai, 201106, China
Tel.: (86) 2166277577   Ky
Web Site:
   http://www.cnlpholdings.com
1589—(HKG)
Sales Range: $50-74.9 Million
Emp.: 155
Logistics Consulting Servies
N.A.I.C.S.: 541614
Shifa Li *(Founder, Chm & Pres)*

CHINA LONGEVITY GROUP COMPANY LIMITED

Room 617 6/F Seapower Tower Concordia Plaza 1 Science Museum
Road, Tsimshatsui East, Kowloon,
China (Hong Kong)
Tel.: (852) 24773799   Ky
Web Site:
   http://www.chinalongevity.hk
Rev.: $220,777,908
Assets: $213,174,862
Liabilities: $127,418,475
Net Worth: $85,756,387
Earnings: $16,268,604
Emp.: 471

Fiscal Year-end: 12/31/21
Polyester Fabric & Other Reinforced
Composite Materials Mfr
N.A.I.C.S.: 313110
Shengxiong Lin *(Chm)*

CHINA LONGYI GROUP INTERNATIONAL HOLDINGS LIMITED

8/F East Area Century Golden Resources Business Center 69 Banjing
Road, Haidian District, Beijing,
100089, China
Tel.: (86) 1088452568   NY
Web Site:
   http://www.jiuzhoushengjiu.com
CGYG—(OTCBB)
Sales Range: $1-9.9 Million
Emp.: 47
Holding Company
N.A.I.C.S.: 551112
Changde Li *(Chm)*

CHINA LONGYUAN POWER GROUP CORP LTD.

Room 2006 20th Floor Block c 6
Fuchengmen North Stree, Xicheng
District, Beijing, China
Tel.: (86) 1066579988
Web Site: https://www.clypg.com.cn
Year Founded: 1993
CLPXF—(OTCIQ)
Rev.: $5,519,169,113
Assets: $30,906,532,593
Liabilities: $19,865,428,666
Net Worth: $11,041,103,927
Earnings: $848,642,833
Emp.: 8,842
Fiscal Year-end: 12/31/22
Wind Electric Power Generation Services
N.A.I.C.S.: 221115
Yongping Yu *(Chm-Supervisory Bd)*

Subsidiaries:

Hero Asia Investment Limited   **(1)**
Room 3901 Hong Kong Plaza 39th Floor
186-191 Connaught Road, West Sai Ying
Pun, Hong Kong, China (Hong Kong)
Tel.: (852) 2858 9336
Wind Electric Power Generation Services
N.A.I.C.S.: 221115

Jiangsu Longyuan Wind Power Generation Co., Ltd.   **(1)**
14F Huali Building 6 Gongnong Road, Nantong, 226007, Jiangsu, China
Tel.: (86) 513 8501 0086
Wind Electric Power Generation Services
N.A.I.C.S.: 221115

CHINA LSOTOPE & RADIATION CORPORATION

66 Changwa Zhongjie, Haidian District, Beijing, 100089, China
Tel.: (86) 1068517560   CN
Web Site: http://www.circ.com.cn
Year Founded: 1983
1763—(HKG)
Rev.: $722,174,638
Assets: $1,470,545,107
Liabilities: $623,738,232
Net Worth: $846,806,875
Earnings: $94,494,395
Emp.: 3,120
Fiscal Year-end: 12/31/21
Medical Product Mfr & Distr
N.A.I.C.S.: 325412
Wendy Mei Ha Kam *(Co-Sec)*

CHINA LUDAO TECHNOLOGY COMPANY LIMITED

Unit 02-03 28/F China Merchants
Tower Shun Tak Centre, No 168-200
Connaught Road, Central, China
(Hong Kong)
Tel.: (852) 28732023

Web Site: http://www.ludaocn.com
2023—(HKG)
Rev.: $75,072,020
Assets: $161,491,309
Liabilities: $108,928,076
Net Worth: $52,563,233
Earnings: $3,095,960
Emp.: 383
Fiscal Year-end: 12/31/22
Cleaning & Personal Care Products
Mfr
N.A.I.C.S.: 325611
Yuerong Yu *(Founder & Chm)*

Subsidiaries:

Zhejiang Ludao Technology Co.,
Ltd.   **(1)**
No 5 Industrial Avenue Sanmen Industrial
Zone, Taizhou, 317100, Zhejiang, China
Tel.: (86) 57683232779
Web Site: http://www.ludaocn.com
Emp.: 400
Aerosol Product Mfr & Distr
N.A.I.C.S.: 325612
Xiaobing Wang *(Gen Mgr)*

CHINA MACHINERY ENGINEERING CORPORATION

CMEC Mansion No 178 Guanganmenwai Street, Xicheng District, Beijing, 100055, China
Tel.: (86) 10 63451188   CN
Web Site: http://www.cmec.com
Year Founded: 1978
Rev.: $4,049,147,154
Assets: $7,693,262,493
Liabilities: $5,123,416,169
Net Worth: $2,569,846,325
Earnings: $312,137,734
Emp.: 5,322
Fiscal Year-end: 12/31/19
Construction Engineering Services
N.A.I.C.S.: 237990
Wei Ai *(VP-Import & Export Trading Bus)*

Subsidiaries:

Ausino Pty Ltd.   **(1)**
129-131 McEwan Road, Heidelberg, 3081,
VIC, Australia
Tel.: (61) 3 9459 6011
Engineeering Services
N.A.I.C.S.: 541330

CMEC (Beijing) International Economic & Legal Advisors Inc.   **(1)**
Room 1301 CMEC Building No 178
Guang'anmenwai Street, Xicheng District,
Beijing, 100055, China
Tel.: (86) 10 6347 7391
Legal Advisory Services
N.A.I.C.S.: 541199

CMEC Beijing Property Development
Co., Ltd.   **(1)**
CMEC Building No 178 Guanganmenwai
Street, Xicheng District, Beijing, 100055,
China
Tel.: (86) 1063317391
Machinery Equipment Product Mfr & Distr
N.A.I.C.S.: 333248

CMEC Comtrans International Co.,
Ltd.   **(1)**
Room 1206 No 178 Guang An Men Wai
Street, Xicheng District, Beijing, China
Tel.: (86) 1063323527
Web Site: http://www.en.comtrans.com.cn
Logistic Services
N.A.I.C.S.: 488510

CMEC Engineering C.A.   **(1)**
Parque Cristal 10-4 Av Francisco de Miranda, Los Palos Grandes, Caracas, Venezuela
Tel.: (58) 426 3110826
Engineeering Services
N.A.I.C.S.: 541330

CMEC Engineering Machinery Import
& Export Co., Ltd.   **(1)**
CMEC Building No 178 Guanganmenwai

China Machinery Engineering
Corporation—(Continued)

Street, Xicheng District, Beijing, 100055,
China
Tel.: (86) 1063474525
Machinery Equipment Product Mfr & Distr
N.A.I.C.S.: 333248

**CMEC General Machinery Import &
Export Co., Ltd.** (1)
CMEC Building No 178 Guanganmenwai
Street, Xicheng District, Beijing, 100055,
China
Tel.: (86) 1063479212
Machinery Equipment Product Mfr & Distr
N.A.I.C.S.: 333248

**CMEC Group Shanghai International
Forwarding Co., Ltd.** (1)
No 1 Yin gao Road, Baoshan District,
Shanghai, 200439, China
Tel.: (86) 2165911961
Machinery Equipment Product Mfr & Distr
N.A.I.C.S.: 333248

CMEC Guinea Equatorial, S.L. (1)
Paseo Maritimo, Bata, Equatorial Guinea
Tel.: (240) 222783802
Machinery Equipment Product Mfr & Distr
N.A.I.C.S.: 333248

**CMEC International Engineering Co.,
Ltd.** (1)
CMEC Building No 178 Guanganmenwai
Street, Xicheng District, Beijing, 100055,
China
Tel.: (86) 1063365805
Machinery Equipment Product Mfr & Distr
N.A.I.C.S.: 333248

**CMEC International Exhibition Co.,
Ltd.** (1)
No 178 Guanganmenwai Street, Beijing,
China
Tel.: (86) 1063452258
Web Site: http://www.cmecexpo.com
Other Commercial Services
N.A.I.C.S.: 561499

CMEC Japan Company Ltd. (1)
204 Okamoto Bldg 2-8 Yotsuya, Shinjuku-
Ku, Tokyo, 160-0004, Japan
Tel.: (81) 3 3358 0521
Web Site: http://www.cmecjapan.com
Electrical Equipment Distr
N.A.I.C.S.: 423610

CMEC Lanka (Private) Limited (1)
25 East Tower World Trade Center Echelon
Square, Colombo, Sri Lanka
Tel.: (94) 718728508
Machinery Equipment Product Mfr & Distr
N.A.I.C.S.: 333248

CMEC Middle East FZE (1)
Jebel Ali Free Zone, Dubai, United Arab
Emirates
Tel.: (971) 13701281967
Machinery Equipment Product Mfr & Distr
N.A.I.C.S.: 333248

**CMEC Namibia (Proprietary)
Limited** (1)
No 122 Uhland Street, Windhoek, 90408,
Namibia
Tel.: (264) 61 233396
Emp.: 3
Engineeering Services
N.A.I.C.S.: 541330
Frank W. (Mng Dir)

CMEC Nigeria Development Ltd. (1)
Block 1 Plot 1B Crown Court Mabushi,
Abuja, Nigeria
Tel.: (234) 8141838633
Engineeering Services
N.A.I.C.S.: 541330

**CMEC Petrochemical-General Ma-
chinery Co., Ltd.** (1)
CMEC Building No 178 Guanganmenwai
Street, Xicheng District, Beijing, 100055,
China
Tel.: (86) 1063448252
Machinery Equipment Product Mfr & Distr
N.A.I.C.S.: 333248
Dongming Fan (Mgr-Mktg)

**CMEC Saudi for Construction
LLC** (1)

Level 6 Akaria Plaza North Wing Olaya
Street, Riyadh, 11481, Saudi Arabia
Tel.: (966) 543711631
Machinery Equipment Product Mfr & Distr
N.A.I.C.S.: 333248

CMEC Senegal S.A. (1)
22 Rue Saint-Michel, BP 24515, Dakar,
Senegal
Tel.: (221) 3382 9705 0
Engineeering Services
N.A.I.C.S.: 541330

**CMEC Zambia Development
Limited** (1)
Plot No E 100 Ibex hill, Lusaka, Zambia
Tel.: (260) 961005810
Machinery Equipment Product Mfr & Distr
N.A.I.C.S.: 333248

CMIC Enmei Co., Ltd. (1)
6F Shinanomachi Sanmo Buliding 12 Shi-
nanomachi, Shinjuku-ku, Tokyo, 160-0016,
Japan
Tel.: (81) 333597621
Machinery Equipment Product Mfr & Distr
N.A.I.C.S.: 333248

**CMIC International Exhibition Co.,
Ltd.** (1)
Machinery Mansion No 248
Guang'anmenwai Street, Xicheng District,
Beijing, 100055, China
Tel.: (86) 10 6331 7661
Web Site: http://www.cmecexpo.com
Event Management Services
N.A.I.C.S.: 711310

**China Equipment International Trad-
ing Co., Ltd.** (1)
CMEC Building No 178 Guanganmenwai
Street, Xicheng District, Beijing, 100055,
China
Tel.: (86) 1063452245
Machinery Equipment Product Mfr & Distr
N.A.I.C.S.: 333248

**China Everbest Development Interna-
tional Limited** (1)
Rm 804 Tower 1 South Seas Center T S T
East, Kowloon, China (Hong Kong)
Tel.: (852) 23116028
Machinery Equipment Product Mfr & Distr
N.A.I.C.S.: 333248

**China JiKan Research Institute of
Engineering Investigations & Design,
Co., Ltd.** (1)
51 Xianning Middle Road Xian, Shaanxi,
710043, China
Tel.: (86) 2962658800
Machinery Equipment Product Mfr & Distr
N.A.I.C.S.: 333248

**China Machinery & Equipment (HK)
Co., Ltd.** (1)
Rm 804 Tower 1 South Seas Center T S T
East, Kowloon, China (Hong Kong)
Tel.: (852) 2311 6028
Industrial Machinery & Equipment Distr
N.A.I.C.S.: 423830

**China Machinery & Equipment Inter-
national Tendering Co., Ltd.** (1)
CMEC Building No 178 Guanganmenwai
Street, Xicheng District, Beijing, 100055,
China
Tel.: (86) 1063452250
Machinery Equipment Product Mfr & Distr
N.A.I.C.S.: 333248

**China Machinery Engineering Argen-
tina SA** (1)
Room E 8th Floor Esmeralda 1375 Retiro,
Buenos Aires, Argentina
Tel.: (54) 9 1141 9250 69
Industrial Machinery & Equipment Distr
N.A.I.C.S.: 423830

**China Machinery Engineering Co.,
Hubei Ltd.** (1)
7A Floor East Building A No 10 Wenxiu
Street, Hongshan District, Wuhan, Hubei,
China
Tel.: (86) 27 87454115
Web Site: http://www.sino-boat.com
Industrial Machinery & Equipment Distr
N.A.I.C.S.: 423830

**China Machinery Engineering Corpo-
ration (PNG) Limited** (1)

Unit 5 Ixia Apartment Savannah Heights
Section 531 Hohola, National Capital Dis-
trict, Port Moresby, Papua New Guinea
Tel.: (675) 72570306
Machinery Equipment Product Mfr & Distr
N.A.I.C.S.: 333248

**China Machinery Engineering Henan
Co., Ltd.** (1)
16-1 Jinshui Road, Zhengzhou, 450003,
Henan, China
Tel.: (86) 37165866090
Web Site: http://www.cmec-henan.com
Machinery Equipment Product Mfr
N.A.I.C.S.: 333248

**China Machinery Engineering Suzhou
Co., Ltd.** (1)
No 659 Jinmen Road, Suzhou, 215004, Ji-
angsu, China
Tel.: (86) 512 6532 1256
Industrial Machinery & Equipment Mfr
N.A.I.C.S.: 333310

**China Machinery Engineering Wuxi
Co., Ltd.** (1)
15-16 Fl A10 Building 777 Jianzhu West
Road, Wuxi, 214000, Jiangsu, China
Tel.: (86) 51082305188
Machinery Equipment Product Mfr & Distr
N.A.I.C.S.: 333248

**China Machinery Engineering Yinch-
uan Free Trade Zone Co., Ltd.** (1)
Block I-06 Free Trade Zone Ningxia, Yinch-
uan, 750403, China
Tel.: (86) 13895186565
Web Site: http://www.cmecsrip.com
Logistic Services
N.A.I.C.S.: 488510

**China Machinery Industrial Products
Co., Ltd.** (1)
501 No 178 Guang Anmen Wai Street,
Xicheng District, Beijing, China
Tel.: (86) 1063396908
Web Site: http://www.cmecipc.com
Fabrication & Finish Machine Part Mfr
N.A.I.C.S.: 332322

**China Machinery International Engi-
neering Design & Research Institute
Co., Ltd.** (1)
No 18 Shaoshan Middle Road, Changsha,
410007, Hunan, China
Tel.: (86) 731 8538 3000
Industrial Research & Development Ser-
vices
N.A.I.C.S.: 541715

**China National Complete Engineering
Corporation** (1)
F7 Zhuyu Guoji Block 4 No 9 Shouti Nanlu,
Haidian District, Beijing, 100044, China
Tel.: (86) 1068739900
Web Site: http://www.cmcec.com
Machinery Equipment Product Mfr & Distr
N.A.I.C.S.: 333248
Huang Fuwei (Chm)

**China National Electric Engineering
Co., Ltd.** (1)
CNEEC Bldg 9 South Shouti Rd, Haidian
District, Beijing, 100048, China
Tel.: (86) 1068798899
Web Site: http://www.cheec.com.cn
Engineering & Construction Services
N.A.I.C.S.: 541330
Zhang Yanfei (Chm)

**China Power Construction Engineer-
ing Consulting Corporation** (1)
No 668 Minzhu Road, Wuchang, Wuhan,
430071, Hubei, China
Tel.: (86) 27 6781 9528
Construction Engineering Services
N.A.I.C.S.: 237990

**China-East Resources Import & Ex-
port Co., Ltd.** (1)
Machinery Mansion No 248 Guanganmen-
wai Street, Xicheng District, Beijing,
100055, China
Tel.: (86) 1063317852
Machinery Equipment Product Mfr & Distr
N.A.I.C.S.: 333248

Euro M.E.C. GmbH (1)
Schlesierweg 13, Lohmar, 53797, Germany

Tel.: (49) 224610110
Machinery Equipment Product Mfr & Distr
N.A.I.C.S.: 333248

**Fujian Zhongshe Machinery & Equip-
ment Imp. & Exp. Co., Ltd.** (1)
23A Ping An Building No 88 Wuyi Road,
Fuzhou, 350005, China
Tel.: (86) 59183227379
Web Site: http://www.cmecfi.com
Industrial Machinery & Equipment Mfr
N.A.I.C.S.: 333310

**Henan Machinery & Electric Import &
Export Co., Ltd.** (1)
No 16-1 Jinshui Road, Zhengzhou, 450003,
Henan, China
Tel.: (86) 37165866072
Web Site: http://www.cmec-henan.com
Electrical Equipment Distr
N.A.I.C.S.: 423610

**Shanghai Zhong Jing Import & Export
Corporation** (1)
2Floor No 1 Yin Gao Road, Baoshan,
Shanghai, 200439, China
Tel.: (86) 2165919255
Web Site: http://www.shzj-machinery.com.cn
Emp.: 50
Industrial Machinery & Equipment Distr
N.A.I.C.S.: 423830

**Shenzhen CMEC Industry Co.,
Ltd.** (1)
No 1028 Buji Road, Luohu District, Shen-
zhen, Guangdong, China
Tel.: (86) 755 2578 0566
Engineeering Services
N.A.I.C.S.: 541330

Sinland Development Pte, Ltd. (1)
20 Collyer Quay 19-02, Singapore, 049319,
Singapore
Tel.: (65) 65321108
Web Site:
http://www.sinlanddevelopment.com
Machinery Equipment Product Mfr & Distr
N.A.I.C.S.: 333248

**Sino American Machinery
Corporation** (1)
23282 Mill Creek Dr Ste 235, Laguna Hills,
CA 92653
Tel.: (949) 305-3800
Industrial Machinery Equipment Distr
N.A.I.C.S.: 423830
Jason Jiang (Mgr)

**Zhongshe M&E Import & Export Co.,
Ltd.** (1)
10/F CMEC Building No 178 Guanganmen-
wai Street, Xicheng District, Beijing,
100055, China
Tel.: (86) 1063448258
Machinery Equipment Product Mfr & Distr
N.A.I.C.S.: 333248

**CHINA MAGNESIUM CORPO-
RATION LIMITED**
Seabank Building Level 10 12-14 Ma-
rine Parade, PO Box 3767, South-
port, 4215, QLD, Australia
Tel.: (61) 7 55311808
Web Site:
http://www.chinamagnesium.com
Rev.: $229,408
Assets: $15,744,568
Liabilities: $7,918,144
Net Worth: $7,826,424
Earnings: ($2,419,626)
Emp.: 49
Fiscal Year-end: 06/30/18
Magnesium Mining Services
N.A.I.C.S.: 212290
Guicheng Jia (Gen Mgr & Dir-CMC
China)

**CHINA MAN-MADE FIBER
CORPORATION**
10-11F No 50 Sec 1 Xinsheng S Rd,
Taipei, 100, Taiwan
Tel.: (886) 223937111
Web Site: https://www.cmfc.com.tw
Year Founded: 1955

1718—(TAI)
Rev.: $695,721,972
Assets: $29,503,577,191
Liabilities: $26,904,209,259
Net Worth: $2,599,367,932
Earnings: $118,246,374
Emp.: 557
Fiscal Year-end: 12/31/23
Timber Product Mfr
N.A.I.C.S.: 313110
K. S. Wang (Chm)

CHINA MAPLE LEAF EDUCATIONAL SYSTEMS LIMITED

No 9 Central Street Jinshitan, Dalian, 116650, China
Tel.: (86) 41187906822   Ky
Web Site:
http://www.mapleleafschools.com
Year Founded: 1995
1317—(HKG)
Rev.: $144,172,908
Assets: $1,207,482,023
Liabilities: $994,695,242
Net Worth: $212,786,781
Earnings: ($478,571,352)
Emp.: 1,890
Fiscal Year-end: 08/31/21
Education Training Services
N.A.I.C.S.: 611110
Sherman Shu Liang Jen (Pres, Founder & Chm)

Subsidiaries:

Maple Leaf Education Asi Pacific
Ltd   (1)
Unit 1302 13 F Tai Tung Building 8 Fleming Road, Wanchai, China (Hong Kong)
Tel.: (852) 3955 1012
School Operator
N.A.I.C.S.: 611699
Grace Jen (Fin Mgr)

Subsidiary (Non-US):

Kingsley EduGroup Ltd.   (2)
LG5 Kingsley International School Persiaran Kingsley, Kingsley Hills Putra Heights, 47650, Subang Jaya, Selangor, Malaysia
Tel.: (60) 354816090
Web Site: http://www.kingsley.edu.my
Rev.: $7,538,094
Assets: $42,363,415
Liabilities: $23,817,049
Net Worth: $18,546,366
Earnings: $503,139
Fiscal Year-end: 06/30/2019
Educational Support Services
N.A.I.C.S.: 611710
Goh Ming Choon (Chm)

Subsidiary (Domestic):

Kingsley International Sdn. Bhd.   (3)
Persiaran Kingsley Kingsley Hills Putra Heights, 47650, Subang Jaya, Selangor, Malaysia
Tel.: (60) 54816090
School Management Services
N.A.I.C.S.: 611430
Ellis Lee (CEO)

Maple Leaf Education North America
Limited   (1)
8771 Lansdowne Road, Richmond, V6X 3X7, BC, Canada
Tel.: (604) 599-2639
Emp.: 30
School Operator
N.A.I.C.S.: 611110
Stuart McIlmoyle (Pres)

CHINA MARINE FOOD GROUP, LTD.

Da Bao Industrial Zone, Shishi, 362700, Fujian, China
Tel.: (86) 59588987588   NV
Year Founded: 1999
CMFO—(OTCEM)
Sales Range: $150-199.9 Million
Emp.: 517

Seafood Products Processor, Distr & Sales
N.A.I.C.S.: 311710
Pengfei Liu (Chm, CEO & Sec)

CHINA MARINE INFORMATION ELECTRONICS COMPANY LIMITED

No 72 Kunming South Road, Haidian District, Beijing, 100097, China
Tel.: (86) 1088010561
Web Site: http://www.cecgt.com
Year Founded: 1993
600764—(SHG)
Rev.: $602,531,921
Assets: $1,498,592,731
Liabilities: $406,256,849
Net Worth: $1,092,335,882
Earnings: $82,130,588
Fiscal Year-end: 12/31/22
Computer System Integration Services
N.A.I.C.S.: 541512
Li Xiaochun (Chm)

CHINA MASS MEDIA CORP.

6/F Tower B Corporate Square 35 Finance Street, Xicheng District, Beijing, 100033, China
Tel.: (86) 1088091099   Ky
Web Site: http://www.chinammia.com
Year Founded: 2003
Sales Range: $25-49.9 Million
Emp.: 151
Television Advertising Services
N.A.I.C.S.: 541890
Shengcheng Wang (Chm & CEO)

CHINA MASTER LOGISTICS CO., LTD.

23/F CML Tower No 169 ShenZhen Road, Qingdao, 266100, China
Tel.: (86) 53283879655
Web Site: https://www.cmlog.com.cn
Year Founded: 2006
603967—(SHG)
Rev.: $1,664,926,464
Assets: $534,581,761
Liabilities: $206,918,614
Net Worth: $327,663,147
Earnings: $34,234,996
Fiscal Year-end: 12/31/22
Logistics Consulting Servies
N.A.I.C.S.: 541614
Songqing Li (Chm)

Subsidiaries:

CML (Dalian) Logistics Co., Ltd.   (1)
Rm 1402 Hongyu Bldg No 68 Renmin Street, Zhongshan District, Dalian, China
Tel.: (86) 41182531019
Logistic Services
N.A.I.C.S.: 541614

CML (Lianyungang) Logistics Co.,
Ltd.   (1)
Rm 506 and 508 Navigation Mark Dept Bldg 2 No 48 Haitang South Rd, Lianyun District, Lianyungang, China
Logistic Services
N.A.I.C.S.: 541614

CML (Ninbo) Logistics Co., Ltd.   (1)
Depot No 2 Beijixing Rd, Beilun District, Ningbo, Zhejiang, China
Tel.: (86) 5742 766 3818
Logistic Services
N.A.I.C.S.: 541614

CML (Ningbo) Logistics Co., Ltd.   (1)
Tel.: (86) 57427663818
Logistic Services
N.A.I.C.S.: 541614

CML (Qingdao) Bonded Logistics
Co., Ltd.   (1)
Qingdao Bonded Logistics Park No 68 Qianwangang Road, Economic-Technological Development Zone, Qingdao, China
Logistic Services

N.A.I.C.S.: 541614
CML (Rizhao) Logistics Co., Ltd.   (1)
Logistic Services
N.A.I.C.S.: 541614

CML (Rongcheng) Logistics Co.,
Ltd.   (1)
No 19 Haigang Road, Weihai, Shandong, China
Logistic Services
N.A.I.C.S.: 541614

CML (Shaanxi) Logistics Co.,
Ltd.   (1)
Rm 604 Floor Building D Van Metroplis No 35 Tangyan Road, Hi-Tech Zone, Xi'an, China
Tel.: (86) 2988455895
Logistic Services
N.A.I.C.S.: 541614

CML (Tianjin) Binhai Logistics Co.,
Ltd.   (1)
No 478 Two Road Xingang, Tanggu New Binhai District, Tianjin, China
Tel.: (86) 2225607273
Shipping Agency & Commodity Logistics Services
N.A.I.C.S.: 541614

CML (Tianjin) Logistics Co., Ltd.   (1)
Logistic Services
N.A.I.C.S.: 541614

CML (Tianjin) Maritime Co., Ltd.   (1)
Logistic Services
N.A.I.C.S.: 541614

CML (Weihai) Logistics Co., Ltd.   (1)
2F No 288 Haibu Rd, Eco and Tech Develop Zone, Weihai, Shandong, China
Logistic Services
N.A.I.C.S.: 541614

CML (Yantai) Logistics Co., Ltd.   (1)
Rm 808 Qili Bldg No 80 Chaoyang Street, Yantai, China
Tel.: (86) 5356860085
Logistic Services
N.A.I.C.S.: 541614

CML Airport International Logistics
Co., Ltd.   (1)
Prologistics Park Zhongcheng South Rd, Liuting Town Chengyang District, Qingdao, China
Tel.: (86) 53289227106
Logistic Services
N.A.I.C.S.: 541614

CML Changxing (Tianjin) International
Logistics Co., Ltd.   (1)
No 530 Dongsan Road North Port, Binhai New Area, Tianjin, China
Tel.: (86) 2225607275
Logistic Services
N.A.I.C.S.: 541614

CML Global Logistics Co., Ltd.   (1)
Logistic Services
N.A.I.C.S.: 541614

CML Grand Journey Logistics Shang-
hai Co., Ltd.   (1)
988 Shenchang Road Hongqiao Vanke Center, Building 2 Suite 602B-603A Minhang, Shanghai, China
Tel.: (86) 2163390109
Logistic Services
N.A.I.C.S.: 541614

CML GrandRail International Logistics
Co., Ltd.   (1)
22nd Floor CMLTower 169 Shenzhen Road, Laoshan District, Qingdao, Shandong, China
Tel.: (86) 53288990168
Logistic Services
N.A.I.C.S.: 541614

CML Grandtrust Logistics Co.,
Ltd.   (1)
5th Floor CMLTower 169 Shenzhen Road, Laoshan District, Qingdao, Shandong, China
Logistic Services
N.A.I.C.S.: 541614

CML Grandwill Logistics Co.,
Ltd.   (1)

22nd Floor CMLTower 169 Shenzhen Road, Laoshan District, Qingdao, Shandong, China
Logistic Services
N.A.I.C.S.: 541614

CML Supply Chain Management
(Zhengzhou) Co., Ltd.   (1)
Room 1103 Shenglong Plaza No 11 Building No 288 Jinshui Road, Jinshui District, Zhengzhou, China
Tel.: (86) 37189916680
Logistic Services
N.A.I.C.S.: 541614

CML Supply Chain Management Co.,
Ltd.   (1)
2nd Floor CMLTower 169 Shenzhen Road, Laoshan District, Qingdao, Shandong, China
Logistic Services
N.A.I.C.S.: 541614

CML Zhenghai Logistics Co.,
Ltd.   (1)
403 Building 2 No 2 Poly Daming Lake No 787 Minghu East Road, Lixia District, Jinan, China
Tel.: (86) 18806391717
Shipping Agency & Commodity Logistics Services
N.A.I.C.S.: 541614

CML(Longkou)Logistics Co., Ltd.   (1)
18 HuanhaiRd, Longkou, Shandong, China
Tel.: (86) 5358841639
Logistic Services
N.A.I.C.S.: 541614

CML-Reefer (Qingdao) Container
Technical Co., Ltd.   (1)
No 667 Hengshan Road, Economic-Technological Development Zone, Qingdao, China
Logistic Services
N.A.I.C.S.: 541614

Cmlog Tianchi Smart Cold Chain
(QingDao) Co., Ltd.   (1)
No 6 Xiangjiang Branch Road Shangde Avenue, Jiaozhou city, Qingdao, Shandong, China
Tel.: (86) 1396 966 9182
Logistic Services
N.A.I.C.S.: 541614

Dalian Port Bulk Logistics Center Co.,
Ltd.   (1)
Dalian Port Ore Terminal Building, Xingang Jinzhou District, Dalian, China
Logistic Services
N.A.I.C.S.: 541614

Fujian Kemen Port Supply Chain
Management Co., Ltd.   (1)
13 1005Room No 70 Jiang Bin East Road, Mawei District, Fuzhou, China
Tel.: (86) 59183690557
Logistic Services
N.A.I.C.S.: 541614

NANJING CML GrandLink Logistics
Co., Ltd.   (1)
Room 710 Building 1 Longhu Shidai Shangcheng Yunlongshan Road, Jianye District, Nanjing, China
Tel.: (86) 2586613188
Container Technical Services
N.A.I.C.S.: 811310

Ningbo CML Grandcorp Logistics
Co., Ltd.   (1)
9-6 Room Global Shipping Plaza No 269 Ningdong Road, Yinzhou District, Ningbo, China
Tel.: (86) 57428906493
Logistic Services
N.A.I.C.S.: 541614

Qingdao GLX Logistics Co., Ltd.   (1)
No 10 Fenjin Road, Economic-Technological Development Zone, Qingdao, China
Tel.: (86) 53286900517
Logistic Services
N.A.I.C.S.: 541614

Qingdao Grand Ocean Maritime Co.,
Ltd.   (1)
22/F CML Tower No 169 ShenZhen Road,

China Master Logistics Co., Ltd.—(Continued)

Qingdao, China
Tel.: (86) 53283892856
Logistic Services
N.A.I.C.S.: 541614

Qingdao Port Dongjiakou Bulk Logistics Center Co., Ltd. (1)
No 88 Gangrun Road, Boli Town Huangdao District, Qingdao, China
Tel.: (86) 53266789888
Logistic Services
N.A.I.C.S.: 541614

Rizhao Landbridge Port Supply Chain Management Co., Ltd. (1)
The Cross of Shenglan East Road and Dashan Road, Lanshan, Rizhao, Shandong, China
Tel.: (86) 6338389357
Logistic Services
N.A.I.C.S.: 541614

Shanghai Smart Cold SCM Co., Ltd. (1)
Room 201 Building B NO 9 Lane 368 Cenglin Road Lin-Gang Special Area, China Shanghai Pilot Free Trade Zone, Shanghai, China
Tel.: (86) 2161096490
Container Technical Services
N.A.I.C.S.: 811310

Tianjin Port Master Logistics Co., Ltd. (1)
No 64 Three Road, Xingang Tanggu New Binhai District, Tianjin, China
Tel.: (86) 2225607270
Logistic Services
N.A.I.C.S.: 541614

WUHAN CML GrandLink Logistics Co., Ltd. (1)
5706 57/F China Minsheng Bank Building, Jianghan District, Wuhan, China
Tel.: (86) 2783901677
Shipping Agency & Commodity Logistics Services
N.A.I.C.S.: 541614

Zhongchuang Ships Management Co., Ltd. (1)
23/F CML Tower No 169 ShenZhen Road, Qingdao, Shandong, China
Tel.: (86) 53283896212
Logistic Services
N.A.I.C.S.: 541614

CHINA MEDIA GROUP

Global Trade Window Guoxing Avenue, Meilan District, Haikou, 570203, Hainan, China
Tel.: (86) 89866196114
Web Site: https://www.000793.com
Year Founded: 1991
000793—(SSE)
Rev.: $106,581,852
Assets: $764,160,696
Liabilities: $421,267,392
Net Worth: $342,893,304
Earnings: ($95,961,996)
Fiscal Year-end: 12/31/22
Advertisement Publishing Services
N.A.I.C.S.: 513110
Gong Yuguo (Chm)

CHINA MEDIA INC.

Room 10128 No 269-5-1 Taibai South Road, Yanta District, Xi'an, 710068, Shaan'Xi, China
Tel.: (86) 2987651114   NV
Web Site: http://www.xatvm.com
Year Founded: 2007
CHND—(OTCEM)
Assets: $14,000
Liabilities: $1,607,000
Net Worth: ($1,593,000)
Earnings: ($143,000)
Emp.: 6
Fiscal Year-end: 06/30/22
Holding Company; Television Broadcasting
N.A.I.C.S.: 551112

Dean Li (Pres, CEO & Sec)

CHINA MEDICAL & HEALTH-CARE GROUP LIMITED

47/F China Online Centre 333 Lockhart Road, Wanchai, China (Hong Kong)
Tel.: (852) 31028500
Web Site: http://www.cmhg.com.hk
0383—(HKG)
Rev.: $183,327,533
Assets: $412,148,085
Liabilities: $210,843,563
Net Worth: $201,304,523
Earnings: ($15,190,988)
Emp.: 2,577
Fiscal Year-end: 12/31/22
Healtcare Services
N.A.I.C.S.: 621399
Sok Un Chong (Deputy Chm)

Subsidiaries:

Kunming Tongren Hospital Co., Ltd. (1)
No 1099 Guangfu Road, Kunming, Yunnan, China
Tel.: (86) 87164562222
Web Site: https://www.kmtrh.org
Emp.: 800
Hospital Management Services
N.A.I.C.S.: 622110

Nanjing Tongren Hospital Co., Ltd. (1)
No 2007 Jiyin Street, Jiangning Economic and Technological Development Zone, Nanjing, 211102, Jiangsu, China
Tel.: (86) 2566989999
Web Site: http://www.njtrh.com
Hospital Management Services
N.A.I.C.S.: 622110

CHINA MEDICAL (INTERNA-TIONAL) GROUP LIMITED

26 Boon Lay Way 01 80 2nd Level, Singapore, 609970, Singapore
Tel.: (65) 6262 6211
Web Site:
http://www.cmigmedical.com
Sales Range: $10-24.9 Million
Aesthetic Medical Products Mfr
N.A.I.C.S.: 325412

Subsidiaries:

Albedo Corporation Pte. Ltd. (1)
360 Orthar Road 04-08, Singapore, 238999, Singapore
Tel.: (65) 68624272
Web Site: http://www.albedo.com
Sales Range: $50-74.9 Million
Emp.: 10
Industrial Supplies Distr
N.A.I.C.S.: 423510

Albedo Sdn. Bhd. (1)
27-2 Jalan Pu 7/3 Taman Puchong Utama, 47140, Puchong, Selangor, Malaysia
Tel.: (60) 380652558
Customer Care Services
N.A.I.C.S.: 561422

CHINA MEDICAL SYSTEM HOLDINGS LTD.

6F-8F Block B Majialong Chuangxin Building 198 Daxin Road, Nanshan District, Shenzhen, 518052, Guangdong, China
Tel.: (86) 75582416868
Web Site: http://www.cms.net.cn
0867—(HKG)
Rev.: $1,284,708,719
Assets: $2,492,596,876
Liabilities: $423,511,265
Net Worth: $2,069,085,611
Earnings: $459,977,778
Emp.: 5,647
Fiscal Year-end: 12/31/22
Pharmaceuticals Mfr
N.A.I.C.S.: 325412
Kong Lam (Chm, Pres & CEO)

Subsidiaries:

Blueberry Therapeutics Limited (1)
Blueberry Therapeutics Mereside Alderley Park, Nether Alderley Macclesfield, Alderley Edge, SK10 4TG, Cheshire, United Kingdom
Tel.: (44) 1625238776
Pharmaceuticals Product Mfr
N.A.I.C.E.: 325412
John Ridden (CEO)

Sky United Trading Limited (1)
Rm 2106 21F Island Pl Tower 510 Kings Rd, North Point, China (Hong Kong)
Tel.: (852) 23693889
Sales Range: $25-49.9 Million
Emp.: 5
Pharmaceuticals Mfr
N.A.I.C.S.: 325412

CHINA MEDICAL TECHNOLO-GIES, INC.

24 Yong Chang North Road, Beijing Economic-Technological, Development Area, Beijing, 100176, China
Tel.: (86) 1067871166   Ky
Year Founded: 1999
Sales Range: $125-149.9 Million
Emp.: 897
Medical Device Developer, Mfr & Distr
N.A.I.C.S.: 339112
Xioadong Wu (Founder, Chm & CEO)

CHINA MEDICINE CORPORA-TION

2/F Guangri Tower No 9 Siyounan Road 1st Street, Yuexiu District, Guangzhou, China
Tel.: (86) 2087372102   NV
Web Site: http://www.cmc621.com
Year Founded: 2005
CHME—(OTCIQ)
Sales Range: $25-49.9 Million
Emp.: 281
Pharmaceutical & Medical Products Developer & Distr
N.A.I.C.S.: 325412
Senshan Yang (CEO)

Subsidiaries:

Konzern US Holding Corporation (1)
Rm 702 Guangri Mansion No 9 Siyou Nan Rd, Wuyang Xincheng, Guangzhou, 510600, Guangdong, China
Tel.: (86) 2087391718
Web Site:
http://www.chinamedicinecorp.com
Sales Range: $50-74.9 Million
Emp.: 100
Pharmaceutical Services
N.A.I.C.S.: 424210

CHINA MEHECO GROUP CO., LTD.

Apartment B General Times Center Building 1 Zone 1 Yard 1, Xiying Street Fengtai District, Beijing, 100061, China
Tel.: (86) 1081167788
Web Site: https://www.meheco.com
Year Founded: 1984
600056—(SHG)
Rev.: $5,278,007,990
Assets: $5,040,165,209
Liabilities: $3,190,663,780
Net Worth: $1,849,501,429
Earnings: $103,293,010
Fiscal Year-end: 12/31/22
Pharmaceutical Product Mfr & Distr
N.A.I.C.S.: 325412
Yang Guang (Chm & Sec)

Subsidiaries:

Beijing Meheco Baitai Pharmaceutical Technology Co., Ltd. (1)
Building 4 No 23 Beiwucun Road, North Area of Beiwucun Innovation Park Haidian District, Beijing, 100095, China

Tel.: (86) 1088850068
Pharmaceuticals Product Mfr
N.A.I.C.S.: 325412

Beijing Meheco Yonstron Pharmaceutical Co., Ltd. (1)
Storey 2 Building 5 Area C Yiyuan Cultural Innovation Industry Park, Xingshikou Road Haidian District, Beijing, 100095, China
Tel · (86) 1062047332
Pharmaceuticals Product Mfr
N.A.I.C.S.: 325412

China General Technology (Group) Pharmaceutical Holding Co., Ltd. (1)
No 18 Guangming Zhongjie, Dongcheng District, Beijing, 100061, China
Tel.: (86) 1067107699
Pharmaceuticals Product Mfr
N.A.I.C.S.: 325412

China Meheco Beijing Baitai Pharma Co., Ltd. (1)
Building 4 Beiwu Innovation Park 23 Beiwucun Road, Haidian District, Beijing, 100195, China
Tel.: (86) 1088850068
Medical & Medical Equipment Distr
N.A.I.C.S.: 423450

China Meheco Beijing Pharma Co., Ltd. (1)
F2 Building 5 Zone B of Yiyuan Wenchuang Base Xingtaikou Road, Haidian District, Beijing, 100195, China
Tel.: (86) 62047332
Medical & Medical Equipment Distr
N.A.I.C.S.: 423450

China Meheco Co., Ltd. - Tanggu Processing Plant (1)
11940 Xijintang Road Babaocun Village Hujiayuan Street, Binhai New District, Tianjin, 300454, China
Tel.: (86) 2225362338
Pharmaceuticals Product Mfr
N.A.I.C.S.: 325412

China Meheco Great Wall Pharma Co., Ltd. (1)
63 West 4th Ring South Road, Fengtai District, Beijing, 100071, China
Tel.: (86) 1051218507
Pharmaceuticals Product Mfr
N.A.I.C.S.: 325412

China Meheco Guangdong Pharma Co., Ltd. (1)
F14 410-412 Dongfeng Middle Road, Yuexiu District, Guangzhou, 510030, China
Tel.: (86) 2083486333
Medical & Medical Equipment Distr
N.A.I.C.S.: 423450

China Meheco Heilongjiang Pharma Co., Ltd. (1)
F16 398 Changjiang Road, Nangang District, Harbin, 150090, China
Tel.: (86) 45185520729
Medical & Medical Equipment Distr
N.A.I.C.S.: 423450

China Meheco Henan Pharma Co., Ltd. (1)
149 Huozhan Street, Guancheng Hui District, Zhengzhou, 450004, China
Tel.: (86) 37166328997
Medical & Medical Equipment Distr
N.A.I.C.S.: 423450

China Meheco Hubei Pharma Co., Ltd. (1)
F5 Xingchang Industrial Park 16 Sandao Street, Wuchang District, Wuhan, 430060, China
Tel.: (86) 2788851822
Emp.: 200
Medical & Medical Equipment Distr
N.A.I.C.S.: 423450

China Meheco International Co., Ltd. (1)
No 18 Guangming Middle Street, Dongcheng District, Beijing, 100061, China
Tel.: (86) 1067107218
Web Site: http://en.mehecointl.com
Pharmaceuticals Product Mfr
N.A.I.C.S.: 325412

China Meheco Jiangxi Nanhua Pharma Co., Ltd. (1)

228 Liyushan South Road, Urumqi, 830054, China
Tel.: (86) 9914320095
Medical & Medical Equipment Distr
N.A.I.C.S.: 423450

China Meheco Jiangxi Pharma Co., Ltd. (1)
104 Beijing West Road, Nanchang, 330046, Jiangxi, China
Tel.: (86) 79186270334
Medical & Medical Equipment Distr
N.A.I.C.S.: 423450

China Meheco Kangli Pharma Co., Ltd. (1)
269 Nanhai Road, Haikou, 570311, Hainan, China
Tel.: (86) 89868689839
Pharmaceuticals Product Mfr
N.A.I.C.S.: 325412

China Meheco Keyi Pharma Co., Ltd. (1)
8 Huanglongshan South Road Donghu New Technology Development Zone, Wuhan, 430000, Hubei, China
Tel.: (86) 2787402251
Pharmaceuticals Product Mfr
N.A.I.C.S.: 325412

China Meheco Med-Tech Service Co., Ltd. (1)
The 11th Floor Block C No 43 of Yonggui Center Guanggumennei Street, Dongcheng District, Beijing, 100062, China
Tel.: (86) 1067107566
Pharmaceuticals Product Mfr
N.A.I.C.S.: 325412

China Meheco Sanyang Pharma Co., Ltd. (1)
8 Haili Road, Xiuying District, Haikou, 570310, China
Tel.: (86) 89868711786
Pharmaceuticals Product Mfr
N.A.I.C.S.: 325412

China Meheco Topfond Pharma Co., Ltd. (1)
2 Guangming Road, Zhumadian, 463000, Henan, China
Tel.: (86) 3963832729
Macrolides Mfr
N.A.I.C.S.: 325411

China Meheco Topfond Traditional Chinese Medicine Co., Ltd. (1)
15 Yulan Street High-tech Development Zone, Zhengzhou, 450001, China
Tel.: (86) 37167983620
Pharmaceuticals Product Mfr
N.A.I.C.S.: 325412

China Meheco Xinjiang Pharma Co., Ltd. (1)
86 East 6th Road Shihezi Development Zone, Xinjiang, 832000, China
Tel.: (86) 9932816730
Pharmaceuticals Product Mfr
N.A.I.C.S.: 325412

Genertec Meheco Tibet Zhongjian Co., Ltd. (1)
Zangqing Industrial Park, Golmud, Qinghai, China
Tel.: (86) 1067093166
Medical Device Mfr & Distr
N.A.I.C.S.: 325412

Hainan General Sanyang Pharmaceutical Co., Ltd. (1)
Xiuying Yonggui Industrial Zone, Haikou, 570316, China
Tel.: (86) 89868711786
Pharmaceuticals Product Mfr
N.A.I.C.S.: 325412

Henan Province Pharmaceutical Co., Ltd. (1)
No 149 Huozhan Street, Zhengzhou, China
Tel.: (86) 37166328997
Pharmaceuticals Product Mfr
N.A.I.C.S.: 325412

Hubei Keyi Pharmaceutical Co., Ltd. (1)
No 3-3 Guangdong Industrial Park, East Lake New Technology Develpment Zone,

Wuhan, 430074, China
Tel.: (86) 2787561258
Pharmaceuticals Product Mfr
N.A.I.C.S.: 325412

Jiangxi Province Pharmaceutical Group Corporation (1)
No 104 Beijing West Road, Nanchang, 330046, Jiangxi, China
Tel.: (00) 70100270004
Pharmaceuticals Product Mfr
N.A.I.C.S.: 325412

Shanghai Pukang Pharmaceutical Co., Ltd. (1)
No 200 Peikun Road Minhang Development Zone, Shanghai, 201111, China
Tel.: (86) 2164098830
Pharmaceuticals Product Mfr
N.A.I.C.S.: 325412

Topfond Pharmaceutical Co., Ltd. (1)
No 2 Guangming Road, Zhumadian, 463000, Henan, China
Tel.: (86) 3963836688
Pharmaceuticals Product Mfr
N.A.I.C.S.: 325412

Xinjiang Tianshan Pharmaceuticals Industry Co., Ltd. (1)
No 228 Li Yushan South Road, Urumqi, 830054, China
Tel.: (86) 9914323595
Web Site: http://www.tszhiyao.com
Emp.: 87
Pharmaceuticals Product Mfr
N.A.I.C.S.: 325412

Xinjiang Topfond Hengde Pharmaceutical Co., Ltd. (1)
No 244 North Road, Shihezi, 832000, Xinjiang, China
Tel.: (86) 9932816732
Pharmaceuticals Product Mfr
N.A.I.C.S.: 325412

CHINA MEIDONG AUTO HOLDINGS LIMITED
Room 2404 24th Floor World-Wide House 19 Des Voeux Road, Central, China (Hong Kong)
Tel.: (852) 26685038　　　　Ky
Web Site:
　http://www.meidongauto.com
1268—(HKG)
Rev.: $4,023,124,654
Assets: $1,999,212,181
Liabilities: $1,376,709,469
Net Worth: $622,502,712
Earnings: $78,053,414
Emp.: 4,689
Fiscal Year-end: 12/31/22
Holding Company
N.A.I.C.S.: 551112
Fan Ye *(Founder & Chm)*

Subsidiaries:

Beijing Huibaohang Auto Sales & Services Co., Ltd. (1)
Jingzhou Road South Yancun Bridge East Yancun Town Fangshan District, Beijing, China
Tel.: (86) 1059943555
Web Site: http://www.bjhbh.nbmw.com
Automobile Dealers
N.A.I.C.S.: 441110

Changsha Meidong Lexus Auto Sales & Services Co., Ltd. (1)
Room 1497 14/F Yannong Building Junction of Luquan Road and, Lusong Road High-tech Industrial Development Zone, Changsha, China
Tel.: (86) 73183868777
Web Site: http://www.cs-lexus.com
Automobile Dealers
N.A.I.C.S.: 441110

Chengde Meibaohang Auto Sales & Services Co., Ltd. (1)
South of Dantazi Songshi Line Road Shuangtashan Town, Shuangluan District, Changde, China
Tel.: (86) 3142528808

Automobile Dealers
N.A.I.C.S.: 441110

Dongguan Dongbu Toyota Auto Sales & Services Co., Ltd. (1)
A0201 International Automobile City Tangchun Section, Guanzhang Road Liaobu Town, Dongguan, China
Tel.: (86) 76983267666
Web Site: http://www.toyota-db.com
Automobile Dealers
N.A.I.C.S.: 441110

Dongguan Dongmei Toyota Auto Sales & Services Co., Ltd. (1)
A9 Lindong Road Three Lincun Village Tangxia Town, Dongguan, China
Tel.: (86) 76982087777
Web Site: http://www.toyota-dm.com
Automobile Dealers
N.A.I.C.S.: 441110

Dongguan Guanfeng Auto Co., Ltd. (1)
Dongguan International Automobile City Liaobu Town Guanzhang Highway, Dongguan, China
Tel.: (86) 76983267333
Web Site: http://www.gfxd.net
Automobile Dealers
N.A.I.C.S.: 441110

Foshan Meixin Lexus Auto Sales & Services Co., Ltd. (1)
No 2 Luocun Avenue Luocun Village Shishan Town Nanhai District, Foshan, Guangdong, China
Tel.: (86) 75763227777
Automobile Dealers
N.A.I.C.S.: 441110

Guangzhou Meibaohang Auto Sales & Services Co., Ltd. (1)
No 515 Zengcheng Avenue, Zengcheng District, Guangzhou, China
Tel.: (86) 2032833777
Web Site: https://www.gzmbh.bmw.com.cn
Automobile Dealers
N.A.I.C.S.: 441110

Hengyang Meibaohang Auto Sales & Services Co., Ltd. (1)
No 1 Phase 2 Yangliu Automobile City Waihuan West Road, Zhengxiang District, Hengyang, 610036, China
Tel.: (86) 7342828777
Web Site: https://www.hymbh.bmw.com.cn
Automobile Dealers
N.A.I.C.S.: 441110

Heyuan Guanfenghang Auto Co., Ltd. (1)
Lijiang Industrial Zone Eastern Ring Road, Heyuan, China
Tel.: (86) 7627992777
Web Site: http://www.hygfh.com
Automobile Dealers
N.A.I.C.S.: 441110

Jiujiang Dongbu Toyota Auto Sales & Services Co., Ltd. (1)
No 171 Jiurui Avenue, Jiujiang, Jiangxi, China
Tel.: (86) 7928502222
Automobile Dealers
N.A.I.C.S.: 441110

Lanzhou Meidong Lexus Auto Sales & Services Co., Ltd. (1)
1 101 Jiuzhou Boulevard, Chengguan District, Lanzhou, China
Tel.: (86) 9318337777
Web Site: http://www.lzmdlexus.com
Automobile Dealers
N.A.I.C.S.: 441110

Liuyang Meibaohang Auto Sales & Services Co., Ltd. (1)
800 meters from West Bus Station Jili Street towards Taiping Bridge, Liuyang, Hunan, China
Tel.: (86) 73183220777
Web Site: https://www.lymbh.bmw.com.cn
Automobile Dealers
N.A.I.C.S.: 441110

Longyan Meidong Lexus Auto Sales & Services Co., Ltd. (1)
Room 301 3/F Kaotang Village Office Long-

men Town Xinluo District, Longyan, China
Tel.: (86) 5973307777
Automobile Dealers
N.A.I.C.S.: 441110

Qingyuan Meidong Lexus Auto Sales & Services Co., Ltd. (1)
4-2 Building No 38 Renmin 4th Road Henghe District, Qingyuan, Guangdong, China
Tel.: (86) 763688777
Automobile Dealers
N.A.I.C.S.: 441110

Quanzhou Meidong Toyota Auto Sales & Services Co., Ltd. (1)
No 1210-1218 Southern Ring Road Licheng District, Quanzhou, China
Tel.: (86) 59536617777
Web Site: http://qzmd.ftms-dlr.com.cn
Automobile Dealers
N.A.I.C.S.: 441110

Xiamen Meidong Auto Sales & Services Co., Ltd. (1)
No 1289 Maqing Road Haicang District, Xiamen, China
Tel.: (86) 5926207777
Web Site: http://www.xmlexus.com
Automobile Dealers
N.A.I.C.S.: 441110

Xinyu Dongbu Toyota Auto Sales & Services Co., Ltd. (1)
Next to Central Bus Terminal Xinxin North Avenue, Development Zone High Tech Industrial Park, Xinyu, Guangdong, China
Tel.: (86) 7906652256
Automobile Dealers
N.A.I.C.S.: 441110

Yangjiang Meibaohang Auto Sales & Services Co., Ltd. (1)
No 67 Yudong 1st Road Dongcheng Town Yangdong County, Yangjiang, Guangdong, China
Tel.: (86) 6626626777
Automobile Dealers
N.A.I.C.S.: 441110

Yiyang Dongxin Auto Sales & Services Co., Ltd. (1)
Ningcheng Intercity Road West Gaoxin District, Yiyang, China
Tel.: (86) 7376600777
Automobile Dealers
N.A.I.C.S.: 441110

Yueyang Meibaohang Auto Sales & Services Co., Ltd. (1)
Liangang Road Chenglingji Lingang Industrial New District, Yueyang, Hunan, China
Tel.: (86) 7308888866
Automobile Dealers
N.A.I.C.S.: 441110

Zhuhai Meidong Lexus Auto Sales & Services Co., Ltd. (1)
No 311 Huayu Road Xiangzhou District, Zhuhai, Guangdong, China
Tel.: (86) 7568985577
Automobile Dealers
N.A.I.C.S.: 441110

Zhuzhou Meibaohang Auto Sales & Services Co., Ltd. (1)
No 688 Zhuzhou Avenue, Liyu Industrial Park, Zhuzhou, Hunan, China
Tel.: (86) 73122220000
Web Site:
　https://www.meibaohang.bmw.com.cn
Automobile Dealers
N.A.I.C.S.: 441110

CHINA MENGNIU DAIRY COMPANY LIMITED
32nd Floor COFCO Tower 262 Gloucester Road, Causeway Bay, China (Hong Kong)
Tel.: (852) 21809050
Web Site: https://www.mengniuir.com
Year Founded: 1999
2319—(HKG)
Rev.: $13,655,300,316
Assets: $15,953,138,984
Liabilities: $8,939,997,785
Net Worth: $7,013,141,200

China Mengniu Dairy Company
Limited—(Continued)

Earnings: $676,641,421
Emp.: 46,064
Fiscal Year-end: 12/31/23
Dairy Product Mfr & Distr
N.A.I.C.S.: 311514
Chris Kwok *(Sec & Controller-Fin)*

Subsidiaries:

Bellamy's Australia Limited **(1)**
115 Cimitiere Street, PO Box 96, Launceston, 7250, TAS, Australia
Tel.: (61) 363329200
Web Site:
http://www.bellamysorganic.com.au
Sales Range: $250-299.9 Million
Organic Food Mfr
N.A.I.C.S.: 311999
Henry Jiong Ou Hong *(Gen Mgr-Hong Kong)*

China Modern Dairy Holdings
Ltd. **(1)**
Economic and Technological Development
Zone, Danyang Town Bowang District,
Ma'anshan, 243121, Anhui, China**(60.77%)**
Tel.: (86) 5557167700
Web Site: http://www.moderndairyir.com
Rev.: $1,726,230,776
Assets: $4,046,517,961
Liabilities: $2,411,798,641
Net Worth: $1,634,719,320
Earnings: $81,469,346
Emp.: 8,455
Fiscal Year-end: 12/31/2022
Raw Milk Production & Dairy Farming
N.A.I.C.S.: 112120
Lina Gao *(Vice Chm & CEO)*

Mengniu Dairy (Dengkou Bayan
Gaole) Co., Ltd. **(1)**
Inside Mengniu Indus Park Zone, Hohhot,
Inner Mongolia, China
Tel.: (86) 4782207888
Dairy Products Mfr & Sales
N.A.I.C.S.: 112120

Yashili International Holdings
Ltd. **(1)**
11/F East Tower Skyline Plaza 832 Yuejiang
Road Central, Haizhu District, Guangzhou,
Guangdong, China **(89.82%)**
Tel.: (86) 2037795190
Web Site: http://www.yashili.hk
Rev.: $524,844,965
Assets: $995,144,249
Liabilities: $248,776,726
Net Worth: $746,367,523
Earnings: ($32,392,667)
Emp.: 2,434
Fiscal Year-end: 12/31/2022
Holding Company; Food Products Mfr
N.A.I.C.S.: 551112
Zhiyuan Yan *(CEO)*

Yashili New Zealand Dairy Co.,
Ltd. **(1)**
1 Yashili Drive, Pokeno, Auckland, 2471,
New Zealand
Tel.: (64) 96005800
Web Site: http://www.yashili.co.nz
Dairy Products Mfr
N.A.I.C.S.: 311511
Nick Zhang *(Mgr-Sls, Ops & Plng)*

CHINA MERCHANTS BANK
CO LTD

No 7088 Shennan Avenue, Futian
District, Shenzhen, 518040, Guangdong, China
Tel.: (86) 75583198888
Year Founded: 1987
600036—(SHG)
Rev.: $52,902,816,743
Assets: $1,553,307,460,129
Liabilities: $1,400,387,883,123
Net Worth: $152,919,577,006
Earnings: $20,845,915,430
Emp.: 116,529
Fiscal Year-end: 12/31/23
Commercial Banking Services
N.A.I.C.S.: 522110

CHINA MERCHANTS GROUP
LIMITED

Shun Tak Centre 168-200 Connaught
Road 40th Floor, China Merchants
Building, Central, China (Hong Kong)
Tel.: (852) 25428288 **HK**
Web Site: https://www.cmhk.com
Year Founded: 1872
Sales Range: $100-124.9 Million
Emp.: 1,000
Holding Company; Transportation,
Financial Investment, Property Development & Management Services
N.A.I.C.S.: 551112
Jianhong Li *(Pres)*

Subsidiaries:

China Merchants Bank Co., Ltd. **(1)**
19 /F China Merchants Bank Tower No
7088 Shennan Boulevard, Shenzhen,
518040, China **(18.03%)**
Tel.: (86) 75583198888
Web Site: https://english.cmbchina.com
Rev.: $52,006,258,307
Assets: $1,526,983,135,800
Liabilities: $1,376,655,128,489
Net Worth: $150,328,007,311
Earnings: $20,492,634,027
Emp.: 116,529
Fiscal Year-end: 12/31/2023
Commercial Banking Services
N.A.I.C.S.: 522110
Jianhong Li *(Chm)*

Subsidiary (Non-US):

CMB International Capital Corporation Limited **(2)**
Unit 1803 18 F Bank of America Tower 12
Harcourt Road, Central, China (Hong Kong)
Tel.: (852) 37618888
Web Site: http://www.cmbi.com.hk
Securities Brokerage Services
N.A.I.C.S.: 523150
Shako Zuocheng *(Pres)*

Subsidiary (Domestic):

China Merchants Fund Management
Co., Ltd. **(2)**
23 Floor China Merchants Bank Tower 7088
Shennan Blvd, Shenzhen, 518040,
China **(55%)**
Tel.: (86) 755 8319 6666
Web Site: http://www.cmfchina.com
Rev.: $9,503,400,000
Emp.: 179
Asset Management Services
N.A.I.C.S.: 523940
Yuhui Chen *(Dir-Equity Res)*

Subsidiary (Non-US):

Wing Lung Bank Limited **(2)**
45 Des Voeux Road, Central, China (Hong Kong)
Tel.: (852) 23095555
Web Site: http://www.winglungbank.com
Rev.: $952,445,342
Assets: $38,227,213,979
Liabilities: $33,395,800,100
Net Worth: $4,831,413,879
Earnings: $493,972,087
Emp.: 1,836
Fiscal Year-end: 12/31/2017
Commercial Banking Services
N.A.I.C.S.: 522110
Hao Li *(Vice Chm)*

Subsidiary (Domestic):

Wing Lung Bank (Trustee) Ltd. **(3)**
45 Des Voeux Road, Central, China (Hong Kong)
Tel.: (852) 28268404
Web Site: http://www.winglungbank.com
Rental Agency & Financial Property Management Services
N.A.I.C.S.: 525990

Wing Lung Finance Ltd. **(3)**
45 Des Voeux Road 4th Floor, Central,
China (Hong Kong)
Tel.: (852) 28268333
Web Site: http://www.winglungbank.com
Hire Purchase, Stocking Loan & Leasing
Financial Services

Wing Lung Futures Limited **(3)**
45 Des Voeux Road, Central, China (Hong Kong)
Tel.: (852) 28268333
Web Site: http://www.winglungbank.com
Sales Range: $50-74.9 Million
Emp.: 50
Futures & Options Trading Services
N.A.I.C.S.: 523160

Wing Lung Insurance Co. Ltd. **(3)**
10th Floor Wing Lung Bank Building, 45
Des Voeux Road, Central, China (Hong Kong)
Tel.: (852) 28268229
Web Site: http://www.winglungbank.com
Sales Range: $75-99.9 Million
Emp.: 100
Insurance Services
N.A.I.C.S.: 524113

Wing Lung Property Management
Limited **(3)**
45 Des Voeux Road, Central, China (Hong Kong)
Tel.: (852) 28268333
Web Site: http://www.winglungbank.com
Property Management & Rental Agency
Services
N.A.I.C.S.: 531390

Wing Lung Securities Ltd. **(3)**
BFF Bank Center 636 Nathan Rd, Mongkok, Kowloon, China (Hong Kong)
Tel.: (852) 21714987
Web Site: http://www.winglungsec.com
Securities Brokerage
N.A.I.C.S.: 523150

China Merchants Capital Investment
Co., Ltd. **(1)**
20/F Tower B East Pacific International
Center 7888 Shennan Avenue, Futian District, Shenzhen, 518040, China
Tel.: (86) 755 88326300
Web Site: http://www.cmcapital.com.cn
Investment Management Service
N.A.I.C.S.: 523940

China Merchants China Direct Investments Limited **(1)**
1609 Three Pacific Place 1 Queen s Road
East, Hong Kong, China (Hong
Kong) **(24.65%)**
Tel.: (852) 28589089
Web Site: http://www.cmcdi.com.hk
Sales Range: $10-24.9 Million
Security Management Services
N.A.I.C.S.: 525990
Yue Kit Tse *(Exec Dir)*

China Merchants Energy Shipping
Co., Ltd. **(1)**
32/F China Merchants Tower Shun Tak
Centre, 168-200 Connaught Road Central,
Hong Kong, China (Hong Kong)
Tel.: (852) 25172128
Web Site:
https://www.cmenergyshipping.com
Rev.: $3,299,829,170
Assets: $7,955,319,341
Net Worth: $4,760,732,853
Earnings: $616,713,242
Fiscal Year-end: 12/31/2023
Marine Transportation Services
N.A.I.C.S.: 483111
Yongxin Wang *(Pres & Mng Dir)*

China Merchants Expressway Network & Technology Holdings Co.,
Ltd. **(1)**
31 Floor China Merchants Office Building
118 Jianguo Road, Chaoyang District, Beijing, 100022, China
Tel.: (86) 1056529000
Web Site: http://www.cmexpressway.com
Rev.: $1,347,385,218
Assets: $21,804,696,583
Liabilities: $10,431,990,613
Net Worth: $11,372,705,970
Earnings: $936,897,541
Fiscal Year-end: 12/31/2023
Construction Services
N.A.I.C.S.: 236220
Wang Xiufeng *(Chm)*

China Merchants Huajian Highway
Investment Co., Ltd. **(1)**

31F-China Merchants Tower No 118 Jian
Guo Road, Chaoyang District, Beijing,
100022, China **(98.5%)**
Tel.: (86) 10 56529000
Web Site: http://www.hj.net.cn
Highway Construction Services
N.A.I.C.S.: 237310
Luo Huilai *(Mng Dir)*

Subsidiary (Non-US):

China Merchants Holdings (Pacific)
Limited **(2)**
50 Raffles Place #32-01 Singapore Land
Tower, 048623, Singapore, Singapore
Tel.: (65) 68360200
Holding Company; Real Estate Investment
& Development
N.A.I.C.S.: 551112
Yuan Jun Chen *(Deputy Gen Mgr)*

China Merchants Industry Holdings
Co., Ltd. **(1)**
NO 1-7 Sai Tso Wan Road Tsing Yi Island,
New Territories, Hong Kong, China (Hong
Kong)
Tel.: (852) 24367800
Web Site: http://www.cmindustry.com.hk
Offshore Engineering Services
N.A.I.C.S.: 541330
Zhou Zhiyu *(Chm)*

Subsidiary (Non-US):

AVIC International Maritime Holdings
Limited **(2)**
8 Robinson Road 13-00 ASO Building, Singapore, 048544, Singapore
Tel.: (65) 66325688
Web Site: http://www.avicintl.com.sg
Rev.: $85,439,887
Assets: $451,695,035
Liabilities: $414,954,837
Net Worth: $36,740,198
Earnings: $5,642,731
Fiscal Year-end: 12/31/2018
Integrated Maritime Services
N.A.I.C.S.: 541330
Weicheng Diao *(Chm)*

Subsidiary (Non-US):

AVIC International Ship Development
(China) Co., Ltd. **(3)**
27-28th Floor CATIC Mansion 212 Jiangning Rd, Shanghai, 200041, China
Tel.: (86) 21 5289 5588
Ship Whslr
N.A.I.C.S.: 423860
Ying Chen *(Project Mgr)*

Subsidiary (Domestic):

AVIC International Offshore (Xiamen)
Co., Ltd. **(4)**
E Unit 18th Floor Hongxiang Mansion 258
Hubin South Rd Siming District, Xiamen,
361004, China
Tel.: (86) 5925186100
Ship Whslr
N.A.I.C.S.: 423860
Vera Yu *(Asst VP)*

Subsidiary (Non-US):

Deltamarin Ltd. **(3)**
Postikatu 2, 20250, Turku, Finland
Tel.: (358) 2 4336 300
Web Site: http://www.deltamarin.com
Emp.: 400
Ship Building Services
N.A.I.C.S.: 336611
Janne Uotila *(Mng Dir)*

Subsidiary (Non-US):

Deltamarin (China) Co., Ltd. **(4)**
JingAn China Tower Room 1801-1802 1701
West Beijing Road, Shanghai, 200040,
China
Tel.: (86) 2162887901
Engineering Consulting Services
N.A.I.C.S.: 541330
Shi Yun *(Gen Mgr)*

Deltamarin Sp.z o.o. **(4)**
Ul Azymutalna 9, 80-298, Gdansk, Poland
Tel.: (48) 587106269
Web Site: http://www.deltamarin.com
Emp.: 120

Ship Building Services
N.A.I.C.S.: 336611
Andrzej Rachwalik *(Architect-Naval-Concept Dev)*

China Merchants Insurance Company Limited　　　　　**(1)**
18/F China Merchants Tower Shun Tak Centre, 168-200 Connaught Road Centre, Hong Kong, China (Hong Kong)
Tel.: (852) 2890 5940
Web Site: http://www.cmihk.net
General Insurance Services
N.A.I.C.S.: 524210

China Merchants Port Holdings Company Limited　　　　　**(1)**
38/F China Merchants Tower Shun Tak Centre, 168-200 Connaught Road, Central, China (Hong Kong)　　**(55.82%)**
Tel.: (852) 21028888
Web Site: http://cmport.com.hk
Rev.: $1,467,404,501
Assets: $22,021,802,753
Liabilities: $6,577,760,170
Net Worth: $15,444,042,583
Earnings: $943,806,152
Emp.: 7,749
Fiscal Year-end: 12/31/2023
Shipping Services & Port Operations
N.A.I.C.S.: 488320
Gangfeng Fu *(Exec Dir)*

Subsidiary (Non-US):

China Merchants Port Group Co., Ltd.　　　　　**(2)**
25th Floor China Merchants Port Plaza 1 Gongye 3rd Road, Nanshan District, Shenzhen, 518067, Guangdong, China
Tel.: (86) 75526828888
Web Site: https://www.szcwh.com
Rev.: $2,180,781,427
Assets: $27,491,872,046
Liabilities: $10,105,693,708
Net Worth: $17,386,178,338
Earnings: $1,037,828,435
Emp.: 14,450
Fiscal Year-end: 12/31/2023
Holding Company
N.A.I.C.S.: 551112
Xiufeng Wang *(Vice Chm)*

Hempel-Hai Hong Coatings (Kunshan) Co., Ltd　　　　　**(2)**
No 1 HaiHong Road, Zhangpu, Kunshan, 215321, Jiangsu, China
Tel.: (86) 51257440886
Web Site: http://www.hempel.com
Sales Range: $50-74.9 Million
Emp.: 200
Chemical & Allied Product Mfr
N.A.I.C.S.: 424690
Shan Gang Zhang *(Mgr)*

Shekou Container Terminals (Phase III) Co., Ltd　　　　　**(2)**
Jetty Three Harbour Road, Shekou, 518069, Shenzhen, China
Tel.: (86) 75526822199
Web Site: http://www.sctcn.com
Security System Services
N.A.I.C.S.: 561621
Erik Yim *(Mng Dir)*

Shenzhen Cyber-Harbour Network Co. Limited　　　　　**(2)**
7th Floor Finance Centre No 22, Taizi Road, Shenzhen, China
Tel.: (86) 75526856200
Web Site: http://www.chnetcn.com
Sales Range: $25-49.9 Million
Emp.: 100
Security System Services
N.A.I.C.S.: 561621

China Merchants Securities Co., Ltd.　　　　　**(1)**
No 111 Fuhua Yi Road Futian Street, Futian District, Shenzhen, 518026, Guandong, China
Tel.: (86) 75526951111
Web Site: https://www.newone.com.cn
Rev.: $2,744,408,105
Assets: $96,346,503,974
Liabilities: $79,449,498,505
Net Worth: $16,897,005,469
Earnings: $1,213,441,405
Emp.: 9,230

Fiscal Year-end: 12/31/2023
Asset Management Services
N.A.I.C.S.: 523150
Jiantao Xiong *(Pres & CIO)*

China Merchants Shekou Industrial Zone Co., Ltd.　　　　　**(1)**
1 New Times Plaza Room 2901, Prince Edward Road, Shekou Industrial Zone, Shenzhen, 518080, Guangdong, China
Tel.: (86) 755 2681 8928
Web Site: http://skiz.shekou.com
Real Estate Investment Trust
N.A.I.C.S.: 525990
Zheng Hu *(Exec Dir)*

Subsidiary (Domestic):

China Merchants Property Development Co., Ltd.　　　　　**(2)**
No 3 Building Nanhai E Cool Park No 6 Xinghua Road Shekou, Nanshan District, Shenzhen, 518067, China　　**(51.89%)**
Tel.: (86) 75526818600
Web Site: http://www.cmpd.cn
Sales Range: $5-14.9 Billion
Emp.: 16,720
Real Estate Management & Development Services
N.A.I.C.S.: 531390

Subsidiary (Non-US):

China Merchants Land Limited　　**(3)**
Room 2603-2606 26/F China Merchants Tower Shun Tak Centre, No 168-200 Connaught Road, Central, China (Hong Kong)　　**(70.18%)**
Tel.: (852) 39765300
Web Site: http://www.cmland.hk
Rev.: $4,193,937,119
Assets: $18,373,909,320
Liabilities: $13,779,141,714
Net Worth: $4,594,767,606
Earnings: $242,895,650
Emp.: 799
Fiscal Year-end: 12/31/2022
Investment Holding Company
N.A.I.C.S.: 523999
Shu So *(Exec Dir)*

China Merchants Technology Holdings Co., Ltd.　　　　　**(1)**
5/F Innovation Centre Nanhai Road North Branch No 1077, Shekou Industrial Zone, Shenzhen, Guangdong, China
Tel.: (86) 75526888600
Web Site: http://www.cmtech.net
Sales Range: $50-74.9 Million
Emp.: 20
Holding Company
N.A.I.C.S.: 551112
Liji Gu *(Chm)*

China Merchants Zhangzhou Development Zone Co., Ltd.　　　　　**(1)**
Zhangzhou China Merchants Economic and Technological Development Zone, Zhangzhou, China
Tel.: (86) 596 6851001
Web Site: http://www.cmzd.com
Construction Engineering Services
N.A.I.C.S.: 541330

Hoi Tung Marine Machinery Suppliers Limited　　　　　**(1)**
27/F China Merchants Tower Shun Tak Centre, 168-200 Cannaught Road, Central, China (Hong Kong)
Tel.: (852) 2544 7511
Web Site: http://www.hoitung.com.hk
Marine Equipment Transportation Services
N.A.I.C.S.: 423860

Subsidiary (US):

Amtoon Incorporation　　　　　**(2)**
9420 Telstar Ave Ste 168, El Monte, CA 91731
Tel.: (626) 279-6611
Industrial Supplies Whslr
N.A.I.C.S.: 423840

Subsidiary (Non-US):

China Communications Import & Export Corporation　　　　　**(2)**
6F China Merchants Tower 118 Jianguo Road, Chaoyang District, Beijing, 100022, China

Tel.: (86) 10 56529777
Web Site: http://www.ciesco.com.cn
Logistics Consulting Servies
N.A.I.C.S.: 541614
He Yulong *(Gen Mgr)*

Subsidiary (Domestic):

Hai Luen Trading Co., Ltd.　　　　　**(2)**
17/F No 9 Des Voeux Road West, Hong Kong, China (Hong Kong)
Tel.: (852) 2545 0956
Web Site: http://www.hailuen.com
Liquor Distr
N.A.I.C.S.: 424820
W. K. Chung *(Mgr-Dept)*

Subsidiary (Non-US):

Hoi Tung (Shanghai) Limited　　　　　**(2)**
5th Floor China Merchants Tower 161 LuJiaZui (E) Road, 200120, Shanghai, China
Tel.: (86) 21 58785353
Industrial Supplies Whslr
N.A.I.C.S.: 423840

Hoi Tung (Shenzhen) Co., Ltd.　　　　　**(2)**
Room 603 B&H Plaza 27 Nan Hai Ave, Shekou, Shenzhen, 518067, China
Tel.: (86) 755 26815128
Web Site: http://www.hoitungsz.com
Electrical Equipment Distr
N.A.I.C.S.: 423610

Merchants Japan Company Limited　　　　　**(2)**
No 6 Shin Osaka Building 1002 7-3 Nishinakagima 6-Chome, Yodogawa-ku, Osaka, 532-0011, Japan
Tel.: (81) 6 68866083
Marine Equipment Distr
N.A.I.C.S.: 423860

P.T. Loscam Indonesia　　　　　**(2)**
Kawasan Industri KIMU JI Raya Kalimalang, Bekasi, 17520, Indonesia
Tel.: (62) 21 883 72050
Web Site: http://www.loscam.com
Emp.: 30
Pallet Distr
N.A.I.C.S.: 423830,
Zulhizar Hasibuan *(Gen Mgr)*

Hong Kong Ming Wah Shipping Co., Ltd.　　　　　**(1)**
Room 3102 31/F China Merchants Tower Shun Tak Centre, Connaught Road, Central, China (Hong Kong)
Tel.: (852) 25172128
Web Site: http://www.hkmw.com.hk
Sales Range: $50-74.9 Million
Emp.: 100
Deep Sea Freight Transportation Services
N.A.I.C.S.: 483111

Loscam (Hong Kong) Limited　　**(1)**
Unit 3103-6 31/F Infinitus Plaza 199 Des Voeux Road, Central, China (Hong Kong)
Tel.: (852) 2200 0688
Web Site: http://www.loscam.com
Pallet Mfr & Distr
N.A.I.C.S.: 321920
Raymond Yu *(Chm)*

Subsidiary (Domestic):

China Merchants Loscam (Asia Pacific) Co., Limited　　　　　**(2)**
3302 Citicorp Centre 18 Whitfield Road, Causeway Bay, China (Hong Kong)
Tel.: (852) 2200 0688
Pallet Distr
N.A.I.C.S.: 423830

Subsidiary (Non-US):

Loscam (Malaysia) Sdn. Bhd.　　　**(2)**
Lot 7 Jalan Lada Sulah 16/11 Seksyen 16, 40000, Shah Alam, Selangor, Malaysia
Tel.: (60) 3 5511 7066
Pallet Distr
N.A.I.C.S.: 423830

Loscam (New Zealand) Limited　　**(2)**
PO Box 112240, Penrose, 1642, Auckland, New Zealand
Tel.: (64) 21756339
Pallet Distr
N.A.I.C.S.: 423830
Naiome Jones *(Mgr-Fin)*

Loscam (Philippines), Inc　　　　　**(2)**
No 6 bldg B Diode Street Light Industry & Science Park 1, Brgy Pulo, Cabuyao, Laguna, Philippines
Tel.: (63) 2 396 4051
Pallet Distr
N.A.I.C.S.: 423830

Loscam (Singapore) Private Limited　　　　　**(2)**
37 Joo Koon Circle, Jurong, 629062, Singapore
Tel.: (65) 6863 0316
Pallet Distr
N.A.I.C.S.: 423830

Loscam (Thailand) Limited　　　　　**(2)**
255 Moo 5 Phaholyothin KM 61 Road Tombon Lamsai, Wangnoi District, Ayutthaya, 13170, Thailand
Tel.: (66) 3527 6888
Pallet Distr
N.A.I.C.S.: 423830
Daniel Bunnett *(Exec VP)*

Loscam Australia Pty Ltd.　　　　　**(2)**
Level 1/37-41 Prospect Street, PO Box 605, Box Hill, 3128, VIC, Australia
Tel.: (61) 3 9843 3700
Pallet Distr
N.A.I.C.S.: 423830
Daniel Bunnett *(Exec VP)*

Loscam Packaging Equipment Leasing (Shanghai) Co., Ltd.　　　　　**(2)**
508 Sino Life Tower No707 Zhangyang Rd, Pudong, Shanghai, 200120, China
Tel.: (86) 21 6104 8156
Pallet Distr
N.A.I.C.S.: 423830

Loscam Vietnam Co., Ltd.　　　　　**(2)**
Mapletree Logistics Center No 1 VSIP St 10, Singapore Industrial Park, Thuan An, Binh Duong, Vietnam
Tel.: (84) 650 3 769 199
Pallet Distr
N.A.I.C.S.: 423830

SINOTRANS & CSC Holdings Co., Ltd.　　　　　**(1)**
Sinotrans Plaza A A43 Xizhimen Beidajie, Beijing, 100029, China
Tel.: (86) 1052296903
Web Site: http://www.sinotrans-csc.com
Logistics & Transportation Services
N.A.I.C.S.: 541614

Subsidiary (Domestic):

SINOTRANS & CSC Shipbuilding Industry Corporation　　　　　**(2)**
Room 2411 Chang Hang Building No 69 Yan Jiang Ave, Wuhan, 430021, Hubei, China
Tel.: (86) 27 82767575
Web Site: http://sbico.sinotrans-csc.com
Logistics Consulting Servies
N.A.I.C.S.: 541614

Plant (Domestic):

SINOTRANS & CSC Shipbuilding Industry Corporation - China Changjiang National Shipping Group Motor Factory　　　　　**(3)**
No 5 Jiufeng Street Canglongdao Hi-Tech Park, Jiangxia District, Wuhan, 430205, Hubei, China
Tel.: (86) 27 87801308
Web Site: http://www.chmoto.com
Electric Motor Mfr
N.A.I.C.S.: 335312

SINOTRANS & CSC Shipbuilding Industry Corporation - Hongguang Port Machinery Plant　　　　　**(3)**
No 385 Jiangnan Road, Yichang, 443004, Hubei, China
Tel.: (86) 717 6675376
Industrial Machinery Mfr
N.A.I.C.S.: 333924

Subsidiary (Non-US):

SINOTRANS CANADA INC.　　　　　**(2)**
1580 Harbour Centre 555 West Hastings Street, Vancouver, V6B4N6, BC, Canada
Tel.: (604) 685-1500
Freight Forwarding Services

China Merchants Group Limited—(Continued)

N.A.I.C.S.: 488510

Sinotrans (Germany) GmbH (2)
Deichstr 1, 20459, Hamburg, Germany
Tel.: (49) 40 36155 0
Web Site: http://www.sinotrans.de
Emp.: 10
Shipping Agency Services
N.A.I.C.S.: 488510
Zhiqiang Chang (Mng Dir)

Subsidiary (Non-US):

Sinotrans Netherlands B.V. (3)
Westfrankelandsedijk 1, 3115 HG,
Schiedam, Netherlands
Tel.: (31) 10 487 7166
Shipping Agency Services
N.A.I.C.S.: 488510

Subsidiary (Non-US):

**Sinotrans (Hong Kong) Holdings
Ltd.** (2)
21/F Great Eagle Centre 23 Harbour Road,
Wanchai, China (Hong Kong)
Tel.: (852) 2827 0013
Holding Company
N.A.I.C.S.: 551112

Sinotrans Agencies (S) PTE Ltd. (2)
No 1 Shenton Way 16-05, Singapore,
68803, Singapore
Tel.: (65) 6323 7390
Shipping Agency Services
N.A.I.C.S.: 488510

Subsidiary (Domestic):

**Sinotrans Container Lines Company
Limited** (2)
Sinotrans Mansion 20F-25F No 188 Fujian
Road C, Shanghai, 200001, China
Tel.: (86) 21 63757000
Web Site: http://www.sinolines.com
Marine Transportation Services
N.A.I.C.S.: 483111

Subsidiary (Non-US):

Sinotrans Japan Co., Ltd. (3)
3F New Nishi-Shinbashi Bldg 2-11-6 Nishi-
Shinbashi, Minato-Ku, Tokyo, Japan
Tel.: (81) 3 3595 6321
Web Site: http://www.sinotrans.co.jp
Logistics Consulting Servies
N.A.I.C.S.: 541614

**Sinotrans Korea Shipping Co.,
Ltd.** (3)
116 5F Sogong-ro, Jung-gu, Seoul, Korea
(South)
Tel.: (82) 2 3788 8200
Web Site: http://www.sinotrans.co.kr
Shipping Agency Services
N.A.I.C.S.: 488510

Subsidiary (Domestic):

Sinotrans Limited (2)
Building 10/Sinotrans Tower B No 5 Anding
Road, Chaoyang District, Beijing, 100029,
China
Tel.: (86) 1052296666
Web Site: https://www.sinotrans.com
Rev.: $12,951,889,468
Assets: $10,084,082,827
Liabilities: $5,142,941,053
Net Worth: $4,941,141,774
Earnings: $440,097,385
Emp.: 34,628
Fiscal Year-end: 12/31/2020
Shipping & Transportation
N.A.I.C.S.: 488210
Rong Song (VP)

Subsidiary (Domestic):

China Marine Shipping Agency Company Limited (3)
Rm718 Tower A Sinotrans Plaza A 43 Xizhi-
men Beidajie, Beijing, 100082, China
Tel.: (86) 10 52295703
Web Site: http://www.sinoagent.com
Shipping Agency Services
N.A.I.C.S.: 488510
Wu Xueming (Chm)

Subsidiary (Domestic):

China Marine Shipping Agency Zhenjiang Co., Ltd. (4)
12/F Foreign Trade Bldg No 98 Zhongshan
Road West, Zhenjiang, 212004, Jiangsu,
China
Tel.: (86) 511 85242330
Shipping Agency Services
N.A.I.C.S.: 488510
Dai Meng (Gen Mgr)

China Marine Shipping Agency, Jiangsu Company Limited (4)
5/F Sinotrans Mansion 129 Zhonghua
Road, Nanjing, 210001, China
Tel.: (86) 25 52377808
Shipping Agency Services
N.A.I.C.S.: 488510
Zhu Jun (Gen Mgr)

China Marine Shipping Agency, Nantong Company Limited (4)
125 West Qing Nian Road, Nantong,
226006, Jiangsu, China
Tel.: (86) 513 83519134
Shipping Agency Services
N.A.I.C.S.: 488510
Gao Haiyan (Gen Mgr)

China Marine Shipping Agency, Taicang Company Limited (4)
3rd floor no 1 dongting Road N, Taicang,
215400, Taicang, China
Tel.: (86) 512 53515957
Shipping Agency Services
N.A.I.C.S.: 488510
Yang Jianming (Gen Mgr)

China Marine Shipping Agency, Taizhou Company Limited (4)
88 Gongren West Road, Jiaojiang, Taizhou,
318000, Zhejiang, China
Tel.: (86) 576 88881092
Shipping Agency Services
N.A.I.C.S.: 488510
Cai Deqing (Gen Mgr)

China Marine Shipping Agency, Zhangjiagang Company Limited (4)
45 Changjiang Mid - Road, Jingang Town,
Zhangjiagang, 215633, Jiangsu, China
Tel.: (86) 512 58332515
Shipping Agency Services
N.A.I.C.S.: 488510
Liang Maozhong (Gen Mgr)

Subsidiary (Non-US):

**Keppel Logistics (Hong Kong)
Ltd** (3)
17th Floor Hua Fu Commercial Buiding No
111 Queen's Road West, Victoria, China
(Hong Kong) **(70%)**
Tel.: (852) 2894 8388
Web Site: http://www.keppellog.com
Freight Forwarding Services
N.A.I.C.S.: 488510

Sinotrans (HK) Logistics Limited (3)
Unit F & G 20/F MG Tower 133 Hoi Bun
Road, Kwun Tong, China (Hong Kong)
Tel.: (852) 25597911
Web Site: http://www.sinotrans-logistics.com
Logistics Consulting Servies
N.A.I.C.S.: 541614
Jessica Lau (Asst Mgr-Forwarding)

Subsidiary (Non-US):

PT. Sinotrans CSC Indonesia (4)
Kawasan CBD Pluit Blok S no 5 Jl Pluit Se-
latan Raya, Jakarta, 14440, Indonesia
Tel.: (62) 21 66675444
Logistics Consulting Servies
N.A.I.C.S.: 541614
Mike Mei (Project Mgr-Logistics)

**Shanghai Well-Trans International
Logistics Co., Ltd.** (4)
Rm 11A-B Jiu An Plaza 258 Tong Ren
Road, Shanghai, China
Tel.: (86) 21 62891222
Logistics Consulting Servies
N.A.I.C.S.: 541614
Jacky Yan (Deputy Gen Mgr-Mktg)

**Sinotrans Logistics (Cambodia) Co.
Ltd.** (4)
Room 089 Building F Phnom Penh Center

Sihanouk Blvd Sangkat Tonle Bass, Phnom
Penh, Cambodia
Tel.: (855) 23 217781
Logistics Consulting Servies
N.A.I.C.S.: 541614
Charlie Lin (Gen Mgr-Mktg)

**Sinotrans Logistics (M) Sdn.
Bhd.** (4)
Suite 517 Centre Building No 8 Jalan Batu
Tiga Lama, 41300, Klang, Selangor, Malaysia
Tel.: (60) 3 33431296
Logistics Consulting Servies
N.A.I.C.S.: 541614
Willy Chen (Gen Mgr-Mktg)

**Sinotrans Thai Logistics Company
Limited** (4)
193/69-70 Lake Rajada Office Complex
17th Floor Rachadapisek Road, Klongtoey,
Bangkok, 10110, Thailand
Tel.: (66) 2 6618090
Logistics Consulting Servies
N.A.I.C.S.: 541614
Mervyn Yan (Gen Mgr-Mktg)

**Well Transportation Myanmar Co.,
Ltd.** (4)
East Point Condo C Room No 1103 11th
Floor, Pazundaung Township, Yangon,
Myanmar
Tel.: (95) 9 73098536
Logistics Consulting Servies
N.A.I.C.S.: 541614
Pacino Zou (Gen Mgr-Mktg)

Subsidiary (Domestic):

Sinotrans Air Transportation Development Co., Ltd. (3)
5/FNo 1Bldg No 20 Tianzhu Rd Area A, Bei-
jing Tianzhu Airport Economic Development
Zone, Beijing, 101312, Shunyi,
China **(100%)**
Tel.: (86) 1080418808
Web Site: http://www.sinoair.com
Air Freight Forwarding & Logistics Services
N.A.I.C.S.: 484122

Affiliate (Domestic):

DHL-Sinotrans International Air Courier Ltd. (4)
No 18 Ronghua Nanlu, BDA, 100176, Bei-
jing, China
Tel.: (86) 10 8785 2000
Web Site: http://www.cn.dhl.com
Sales Range: $25-49.9 Million
Emp.: 160
Express Mail Services
N.A.I.C.S.: 492110

Subsidiary (Domestic):

**Sinotrans Changjiang Company
Limited** (3)
Sinotrans Jiangsu Mansion 129 Zhonghua
Rd, Nanjing, 210001, China
Tel.: (86) 25 52377502
Web Site: http://www.sinotrans-cj.com
Logistics Consulting Servies
N.A.I.C.S.: 541614

Subsidiary (Domestic):

China Marine Shipping Agency Rugao Co., Ltd. (4)
Room 103 Customs Building No 25 Huaji-
ang Road M, Rugao, 226532, China
Tel.: (86) 513 83558109
Shipping Agency Services
N.A.I.C.S.: 488510

Sinotrans Jiangxi Co., Ltd. (4)
2F Sinotrans Mansion No 191 Lushan
Road, Jiujiang, Jiangxi, China
Tel.: (86) 792 2162503
Logistics Consulting Servies
N.A.I.C.S.: 541614

Sinotrans Nanchang Co., Ltd. (4)
Rm1906 Changqing International Trade
Building No 8 Hongcheng Road, Nanchang,
Jiangxi, China
Tel.: (86) 791 86426923
Logistics Consulting Servies
N.A.I.C.S.: 541614

**Sinotrans Nanjing Export Processing
Zone Logistics Co., Ltd.** (4)
6 Xingzhi Rd Qixla, Nanjing, 210064, Ji-
angsu, China
Tel.: (86) 25 8566 3880
Logistics Consulting Servies
N.A.I.C.S.: 541614
Yao Haipng (Gen Mgr)

Subsidiary (Domestic):

**Sinotrans Chongqing Company
Limited** (3)
No 9 Qiaobeiyuan, Jiangbei, Chongqing,
China
Tel.: (86) 23 67852927
Freight Forwarding Services
N.A.I.C.S.: 488510

**Sinotrans Eastern Company
Limited** (3)
13F Sinotrans Mansion No188 Fujian Road,
Shanghai, China
Tel.: (86) 21 63757885
Web Site: http://www.sinotransproject.com
Logistics Consulting Servies
N.A.I.C.S.: 541614
Gu Yu (Gen Mgr)

**Sinotrans Guangdong Company
Limited** (3)
13/F No 97 Haiyuan Rd, Huangpu,
Guangzhou, 510700, China
Tel.: (86) 20 61892810
Web Site: http://www.gd.sinotrans.com
Freight Forwarding Services
N.A.I.C.S.: 488510
Zhanfa Liu (Gen Mgr)

Subsidiary (Domestic):

**China Marine Shipping Agency
Guangdong Co., Ltd.** (4)
17/F Sinotrans Bldg No 97 Haiyuan Rd,
Huangpu, Guangzhou, Guangdong, China
Tel.: (86) 20 61892100
Freight Forwarding Services
N.A.I.C.S.: 488510

**Guangdong Changtong Warehouse &
Terminal Co., Ltd.** (4)
No 363 Longjiao Rd, Shijing Town Baiyun,
Guangzhou, Guangdong, China
Tel.: (86) 20 61898814
Warehousing & Freight Forwarding Services
N.A.I.C.S.: 493110

**Guangdong Eternal Way International
Freight Co., Ltd.** (4)
5/F Sinotrans Bldg No 233 Guangyuan
Zhong Rd, Guangzhou, Guangdong, China
Tel.: (86) 20 61892956
Freight Forwarding Services
N.A.I.C.S.: 488510

Subsidiary (Non-US):

Guangdong Transport Co., Ltd. (4)
10/F Tung Hip Comm Bldg No 244-248 Des
Voeux Rd, Central, China (Hong Kong)
Tel.: (852) 28153398
Freight Forwarding Services
N.A.I.C.S.: 488510

Sinomart Transport Co., Ltd. (4)
DD130 Lot 759 RP South-West Portion
Lam Tei, Tuen Mun, Hong Kong, China
(Hong Kong)
Tel.: (852) 29509661
Freight Forwarding Services
N.A.I.C.S.: 488510

Subsidiary (Domestic):

**Sinotrans Dongguan Logistics Co.,
Ltd.** (4)
Water & Rail Terminal, Shilong, Dongguan,
China
Tel.: (86) 769 89066166
Logistics Consulting Servies
N.A.I.C.S.: 541614

**Sinotrans Foshan Express Management and Custom Brokerage Co.,
Ltd.** (4)
No 15 Gangkou Rd, Chancheng, Foshan,
Guangdong, China
Tel.: (86) 757 66637336
Freight Forwarding Services
N.A.I.C.S.: 488510

Sinotrans Foshan Logistics Co., Ltd. **(4)**
No 10 JiangNan Rd, Ronggui Town Shunde, Foshan, Guangdong, China
Tel.: (86) 757 29915258
Logistics Consulting Servies
N.A.I.C.S.: 541614

Sinotrans Foshan Shipping Co., Ltd. **(4)**
1/F Block 4 Foreign Trade New Village No 18 Qingshui Rd, Chancheng, Foshan, Guangdong, China
Tel.: (86) 757 83311365
Freight Forwarding Services
N.A.I.C.S.: 488510

Sinotrans Foshan Warehouse & Terminal Co., Ltd. **(4)**
No 63 Shakou Shang Street, Jiujiang Town Nanhai, Foshan, Guangdong, China
Tel.: (86) 757 66863151
Warehousing & Freight Forwarding Services
N.A.I.C.S.: 493110

Sinotrans Guangdong Customs Broker Co., Ltd. **(4)**
No 1 Liucun North Luogang East, Guangzhou, Guangdong, China
Tel.: (86) 20 61892280
Freight Forwarding Services
N.A.I.C.S.: 488510

Sinotrans Guangdong Dongjiang Warehouse & Terminal Co., Ltd. **(4)**
No 66-68 Dongjiang Avenue Guangzhou Economic & Technological, Guangzhou, Guangdong, China
Tel.: (86) 20 61897831
Warehousing & Freight Forwarding Services
N.A.I.C.S.: 493110

Sinotrans Guangdong Huangpu Warehouse & Terminal Co., Ltd. **(4)**
No 713 Gangqian Rd, Huangpu, Guangzhou, Guangdong, China
Tel.: (86) 20 61893666
Warehousing & Freight Forwarding Services
N.A.I.C.S.: 493110

Sinotrans Guangdong International Freight Forwarding Co., Ltd. **(4)**
8/F Sinotrans Bldg No 233 Guangyuan Zhong Rd, Guangzhou, Guangdong, China
Tel.: (86) 20 61898039
Freight Forwarding Services
N.A.I.C.S.: 488510

Sinotrans Guangdong Property Management Co., Ltd. **(4)**
1/F Sinotrans Bldg No 97 Haiyuan Rd, Huangpu, Guangzhou, Guangdong, China
Tel.: (86) 20 61892236
Freight Forwarding Services
N.A.I.C.S.: 488510

Sinotrans Guangdong Shipping Co., Ltd. **(4)**
7/F Sinotrans Bldg No 2 Haiyuan Rd, Huangpu, Guangzhou, Guangdong, China
Tel.: (86) 20 61892559
Freight Forwarding Services
N.A.I.C.S.: 488510

Sinotrans Jiangmen Warehouse & Terminal Co., Ltd. **(4)**
Zhonghua Avenue, Waihai Town, Jiangmen, Guangdong, China
Tel.: (86) 750 7365768
Warehousing & Freight Forwarding Services
N.A.I.C.S.: 493110

Subsidiary (Non-US):

Sinotrans Macao Co., Ltd. **(4)**
Block E 5/F Yide Commercial Centre No 126 Beijing Street, Macau, China (Macau)
Tel.: (853) 853 66187157
Freight Forwarding Services
N.A.I.C.S.: 488510

Subsidiary (Domestic):

Sinotrans Shenzhen Customs Broker Co., Ltd. **(4)**
D Block 20/F Seaview Square No 18 Taizi Rd Shekou, Shenzhen, Guangdong, China
Tel.: (86) 755 61896866
Freight Forwarding

N.A.I.C.S.: 488510

Sinotrans Shenzhen Logistics Co., Ltd. **(4)**
Liyuan Road No 333, Luohu District, Shenzhen, 518023, Guangdong, China
Tel.: (86) 755 61896333
Web Site: http://szlc.transgd.com.cn
Warehousing & Freight Forwarding Services
N.A.I.C.S.: 493110

Sinotrans Zhongshan Customs Broker Co., Ltd. **(4)**
Room A1 No 3 Warehouse No 17 the 1st East Yanjiang Rd Torch, Hi-Tech Industrial Development Zone, Zhongshan, Guangdong, China
Tel.: (86) 760 28188515
Freight Forwarding Services
N.A.I.C.S.: 488510

Sinotrans Zhongshan Logistics Co., Ltd. **(4)**
Sinotrans Zhongshan Logistics Center No 39 the 4th East Yanjiang Rd, Torch Hi-Tech Industrial Development Zone, Zhongshan, Guangdong, China
Tel.: (86) 760 28185093
Logistics Consulting Servies
N.A.I.C.S.: 541614

Sinotrans Zhongshan Warehouse & Terminal Co., Ltd. **(4)**
Foreign Trade Terminal No 17 the 1st East Yanjiang Rd Torch Hi-Tech, Industrial Development Zone, Zhongshan, Guangdong, China
Tel.: (86) 760 28185168
Warehousing & Freight Forwarding Services
N.A.I.C.S.: 493110

Subsidiary (Domestic):

Sinotrans Heavy-lift Logistics Company Limited **(3)**
Room 802 Building 13 Zhongrun Century Square No 13777 Jingshi Road, Lixia District, Jinan, 250014, Shandong, China
Tel.: (86) 531 62339090
Web Site: http://www.sinotrans-heavylift.com
Freight Forwarding Services
N.A.I.C.S.: 488510

Sinotrans Landbridge Transportation Company Limited **(3)**
No 6 Zhongshan W RD, Xugou Town Lianyungang, Lianyungang, Jiangsu, China
Tel.: (86) 518 8231 3264
Freight Forwarding Services
N.A.I.C.S.: 488510

Sinotrans Shandong Company Limited **(3)**
Waiyun Mansion 5 Henan Road Shinan District, Qingdao, 266001, China
Tel.: (86) 532 8289 5555
Web Site: http://www.sd.sinotrans.com
Freight Forwarding Services
N.A.I.C.S.: 488510

Subsidiary (Domestic):

Sinotrans Shantou Co. Ltd. **(2)**
9 Jinsha Road, Shantou, 515031, China
Tel.: (86) 754 88679065
Web Site: http://www.sinotrans-st.com
Freight Forwarding Services
N.A.I.C.S.: 488510

Subsidiary (Non-US):

Sun Yee Godown&Transportation Co. Ltd
RM 1908 Hong Kong Plaza 186-191 Connaught Rd West, Hong Kong, China (Hong Kong)
Tel.: (852) 2559 8480
Marine Transportation Services
N.A.I.C.S.: 483111

Wide Shine Development Limited **(2)**
32/F Chinachem Century Tower 178 Gloucester Road, Wanchai, China (Hong Kong)
Tel.: (852) 2853 9668
Web Site: http://www.wsd.com.hk
Container Leasing Services
N.A.I.C.S.: 532490
Samuel Cheuk *(Deputy Mgr)*

Sinotrans Shipping Limited **(1)**
21st Floor Great Eagle Centre 23 Harbour Road, Wanchai, China (Hong Kong)
Tel.: (852) 28271108
Web Site: http://www.sinotranship.com
Sales Range: $1-4.9 Billion
Emp.: 648
Shipping Company
N.A.I.C.S.: 813910
Shaohua Xie *(Controller-Fin)*

Subsidiary (Domestic):

Creative Enterprise Holdings Ltd. **(2)**
Unit E and F 25/F Block 2 Vigor Building 49-53 Ta Chuen Ping Street, Kwai Chung, Hong Kong, New Territories, China (Hong Kong) **(53.51%)**
Tel.: (852) 26678638
Web Site: http://www.cpsc.hk
Rev.: $114,514,635
Assets: $56,098,343
Liabilities: $12,027,840
Net Worth: $44,070,503
Earnings: $7,239,450
Emp.: 5,092
Fiscal Year-end: 03/31/2021
Property Management Services
N.A.I.C.S.: 531312
Poon Kin Leung *(Chm & Exec Dir)*

Zhanjiang Port (Group) Co., Ltd. **(1)**
8 Baogang Road, Xiashan, Zhanjiang, 524068, China
Tel.: (86) 75 9225 5516
Web Site: http://www.zjport.com
Freight Transportation Services
N.A.I.C.S.: 483111
Enhuai Liu *(CEO)*

CHINA MERCHANTS SHEKOU INDUSTRIAL ZONE HOLDINGS CO., LTD.
No 3 Nanhai Yiku No 6 Xinghua Road Shekou, Nanshan District, Shenzhen, 518067, China
Tel.: (86) 75526819600
Web Site:
　https://www.cmsk1979.com
Year Founded: 1979
001979—(SSE)
Rev.: $25,693,573,464
Assets: $124,460,581,752
Liabilities: $84,525,138,360
Net Worth: $39,935,443,392
Earnings: $598,676,832
Fiscal Year-end: 12/31/22
Holding Company
N.A.I.C.S.: 551112
Yongjun Xu *(Chm)*

CHINA METAL PRODUCTS CO., LTD.
4F No 85 Section 4 Renai Rd, Daian Dist, Taipei, 106, Taiwan
Tel.: (886) 227112831
Web Site: https://www.cmp.com.tw
Year Founded: 1972
1532—(TAI)
Rev.: $576,194,196
Assets: $1,770,809,606
Liabilities: $1,208,750,960
Net Worth: $562,058,646
Earnings: $42,824,878
Emp.: 1,354
Fiscal Year-end: 12/31/23
Automobile Parts Mfr
N.A.I.C.S.: 336390

Subsidiaries:

CMJ Co., Ltd. **(1)**
Third FL Crescendo BL, Shinyokohama 2-3-4, Yokohama, Japan
Tel.: (81) 454705158
Web Site: https://www.c-m-j.co.jp
Machine Parts Mfr & Distr
N.A.I.C.S.: 333248

CMW (Tianjin) Industry Co., Ltd. **(1)**
No 55 Guanghua St Tianjin Economic-Technological Development Area West, Tianjin, 300462, China
Tel.: (86) 2266320600

Iron Casting Mfr
N.A.I.C.S.: 331511

China Metal Automotive International Co. **(1)**
Rm s 907 and 908 Holiday Inn Shanghai Pudong Bldg No 899 Dong Fang Rd, Shanghai, Pudong, China
Tel.: (86) 2158208377
Iron Casting Mfr
N.A.I.C.S.: 331511

China Metal International Holdings Inc. **(1)**
Rm 1502 The Chinese Bank Bldg 61-65 Des Voeux Road, Central, China (Hong Kong)
Tel.: (852) 2 2868 9939
Metal Casting Mfr & Distr
N.A.I.C.S.: 331511

China Metal Japan Co., Ltd. **(1)**
3-4 Shin-Yokohama 2 Chome, Kohoku-ku, Yokohama, 222-0033, Kanagawa ken, Japan
Tel.: (81) 454705158
Web Site: http://www.china-metal-japan.jp
Emp.: 12
Logistics Management Services
N.A.I.C.S.: 541614

China Metal Products Co., Ltd. - Hsinchu Plant **(1)**
No 488 Shangkeng Vlg Xinfeng Township, Hsinchu, 304, Taiwan
Tel.: (886) 35591126
Iron Casting Mfr
N.A.I.C.S.: 331511

China Metal Products Co., Ltd. - Pingzhen Plant **(1)**
12F No 85 Sec 4 Renai Rd Daan Dist, Taipei, 106, Taiwan
Tel.: (886) 227112831
Iron Casting Mfr
N.A.I.C.S.: 331511

China Metal Products Co., Ltd. - Plymouth Branch **(1)**
15035 Pilot Dr, Plymouth, MI 48170
Tel.: (734) 207-0077
Iron Casting Mfr
N.A.I.C.S.: 331511

Cmai Industries, Inc. **(1)**
15035 Pilot Dr, Plymouth, MI 48170
Tel.: (248) 217-8827
Vehicle Parts Retailing Services
N.A.I.C.S.: 541715

PUJEN Land Development Co., Ltd. **(1)**
11F No 85 Sec 4 Ren'ai Rd, Da'an Dist, Taipei, 106, Taiwan
Tel.: (886) 227417335
Property Development Services
N.A.I.C.S.: 531390

Suzhou CMB Machinery Co., Ltd. **(1)**
No 96 Zhenbei Rd, Tongan Township Gaoxin Dist, Suzhou, 215153, Jiangsu, China
Tel.: (86) 51268097900
Metal Products Mfr
N.A.I.C.S.: 331511

Suzhou CMS Machinery Co., Ltd. **(1)**
No 151 Jinfeng Rd New Dist, Suzhou, 2105011, Jiangsu, China
Tel.: (86) 51268099929
Iron Casting Mfr
N.A.I.C.S.: 331511

Tianjin CMT Industry Co., Ltd. **(1)**
No's 0-10 Tanghan Rd, Tanggu Dist, Tianjing, 300451, China
Tel.: (86) 2225211445
Metal Products Mfr
N.A.I.C.S.: 331511

CHINA METAL RECYCLING (HOLDINGS) LIMITED
Rm 3003A-5 30/F The Centrium 60 Wyndham Street 1 Harbour Road, Central, China (Hong Kong)
Tel.: (852) 25474725　　　　　　　**Ky**

China Metal Recycling (Holdings)
Limited—(Continued)

Web Site:
http://www.chinametalrecycle.com
Sales Range: $1-4.9 Billion
Emp.: 600
Scrap Metal Recycling Services
N.A.I.C.S.: 423510
Chi Wai Chun (Chm & CEO)

Subsidiaries:

Guangzhou Asia Steel Co., Ltd. **(1)**
15 F Yagang Mansion No 3401, Huangpu
Dist, Guangzhou, 510735, Guangdong,
China
Tel.: (86) 2082221668
Web Site: http://www.cmr773.com
Scrap Metal Recycling Services
N.A.I.C.S.: 423930

CHINA METAL RESOURCES UTILIZATION LTD.

She Nos 1 3 and 8 Shunhe Village
Xiaojiangou Town, Youxian District,
Mianyang, Sichuan, China
Tel.: (86) 8168386777   Ky
Web Site: http://www.cmru.com.cn
1636—(HKG)
Rev.: $1,083,810,499
Assets: $945,453,460
Liabilities: $705,454,121
Net Worth: $239,999,339
Earnings: ($13,404,971)
Emp.: 592
Fiscal Year-end: 12/31/21
Recycled Copper Product Mfr
N.A.I.C.S.: 331529
Jianqiu Yu (Founder, Chm & CEO)

Subsidiaries:

Mianyang Science Technology City
Development Investment (Group)
Co., Ltd. **(1)**
268 Jiuzhou Avenue, Mianyang, China
Tel.: (86) 8166336160
Web Site: http://www.mysdic.com
Real Estate Construction Services
N.A.I.C.S.: 236220

CHINA METRO-RURAL HOLDINGS LIMITED

Suite 2204 22 F Sun Life Tower The
Gateway 15 Canton Road, Tsimshatsui, Kowloon, China (Hong Kong)
Tel.: (852) 21113815   HK
Web Site:
http://www.chinametrorural.com
Holding Company; Agricultural Logistics Services; Jewelry Mfr
N.A.I.C.S.: 551112

Subsidiaries:

Man Sang International Limited **(1)**
Unit WF 25th Floor Eight Commercial Tower
8 Sun Yip Street, Chai Wan, China (Hong
Kong)
Tel.: (852) 3 595 6500
Web Site: http://www.msil.com.hk
Rev.: $15,046,291
Assets: $432,375,527
Liabilities: $407,848,819
Net Worth: $24,526,708
Earnings: ($48,446,178)
Emp.: 393
Fiscal Year-end: 03/31/2022
Pearl Processor & Distr
N.A.I.C.S.: 339910
Xingrong Hu (Chm)

CHINA MING YANG WIND POWER GROUP LIMITED

Jianye Road Mingyang Industry Park,
National Hi-Tech Industrial Development Zone, Zhongshan, 528437,
Guangdong, China
Tel.: (86) 760 28138888   Ky
Web Site: http://www.mywind.com.cn
Sales Range: $1-4.9 Billion
Emp.: 4,379

Wind Turbine Mfr
N.A.I.C.S.: 333611
Chuanwei Zhang (Chm & CEO)

Subsidiaries:

RENergy Electric Tianjin Ltd. **(1)**
Xinghua 7 Rd 1 XEDA, Tianjin, China
Tel.: (86) 2259585788
Wind Electric Power Generation Services
N.A.I.C.S.: 221115

Zhongshan Ruike New Energy Co.,
Ltd. **(1)**
13th Torch Road Torch Development Zone,
Zhongshan, Guangdong, China
Tel.: (86) 76028112299
Web Site: http://www.rksolar.com.cn
Thin Film Photovoltaic Product Mfr
N.A.I.C.S.: 334413
Zhang Chuanwei (Chm)

CHINA MINING INTERNATIONAL LIMITED

5th Floor Zhong Chuang Building,
Intersection of Zhong Wang Road
and Zheng Guang North Street, Singapore, 450000, Singapore
Tel.: (65) 63208485   Ky
Web Site: https://www.chinamining-international.com
Year Founded: 1999
BHD—(SES)
Rev.: $1,196,056
Assets: $25,998,873
Liabilities: $11,830,422
Net Worth: $14,168,451
Earnings: ($11,905,915)
Emp.: 23
Fiscal Year-end: 12/31/23
Holding Company; Iron Ore Mining;
Property Development Services
N.A.I.C.S.: 551112
Bin Li (CEO)

CHINA MINING UNITED FUND

22/F IFC Building No 8 Jianguomenwai Avenue, Chao Yang District, Beijing, 100020, China
Tel.: (86) 10 85660017
Web Site: http://www.cmufund.com
Mining & Related Assets Closed-End
Investment Fund
N.A.I.C.S.: 525990
Zhi Zheng (Chm)

CHINA MINSHENG BANKING CORPORATION LTD.

No 2 Fuxingmennei Street, Xicheng
District, Beijing, China
Tel.: (86) 95568
Web Site: https://www.cmbc.com.cn
Year Founded: 1996
CGMBF—(OTCIQ)
Rev.: $43,908,913,530
Liabilities: $981,920,591,850
Net Worth: $82,924,606,080
Earnings: $5,377,977,420
Emp.: 59,262
Fiscal Year-end: 12/31/20
Commercial Banking Services
N.A.I.C.S.: 522110
Wanchun Zheng (Pres)

Subsidiaries:

Minsheng Financial Leasing Co.,
Ltd. **(1)**
Unit 402 Building 3 Financial Center No 158
West 3rd Road, Tianjin Airport Economic
Zone, Tianjin, 300308, China
Tel.: (86) 2224891248
Web Site: https://www.msfl.com.cn
Financial Services
N.A.I.C.S.: 541611

Minsheng Royal Fund Management
Co., Ltd. **(1)**
13/F Minsheng Financial Building No 2005
FuZhong No 3 Road, Futian District, Shenzhen, 518038, China

Tel.: (86) 4008888388
Web Site: https://www.msjyfund.com.cn
Financial Services
N.A.I.C.S.: 541611

CHINA MINSHENG INVESTMENT GROUP CORP., LTD.

23F 100 South Zhongshan Street,
Shanghai, 200010, China
Tel.: (86) 0213335300   CN
Web Site: https://www.cm-inv.com
Year Founded: 2014
Investment Holding Company
N.A.I.C.S.: 551112
Yang Xiaoping (Vice Chm)

Subsidiaries:

China Minsheng Jiaye Investment
Co., Ltd. **(1)**
7F The Bund International Plaza, 100 South
Zhongshan Rd, Shanghai, 200010, China
Tel.: (86) 21 333 55 333
Web Site: http://www.cm-inv.com
Real Estate & Industrial Investment Firm
N.A.I.C.S.: 523999
Chen Donghui (Pres)

Subsidiary (Domestic):

Yida China Holdings Limited **(2)**
Block 4 Yida Plaza 93 Northeast Road,
Shahekou District, Dalian, 200010,
China   **(61.11%)**
Tel.: (86) 02161160755
Web Site: http://www.yidachina.com.cn
Rev.: $636,422,389
Assets: $5,571,642,586
Liabilities: $3,970,285,535
Net Worth: $1,601,357,051
Earnings: ($103,403,617)
Emp.: 614
Fiscal Year-end: 12/31/2022
Holding Company
N.A.I.C.S.: 551112
Xiuwen Jiang (Chm & CEO)

CHINA MOBILE COMMUNICATIONS CORPORATION

Tel.: (852) 31218888   HK
Sales Range: $25-49.9 Billion
Emp.: 127,959
Holding Company; Mobile Telecommunications
N.A.I.C.S.: 551112
Yuejia Sha (VP)

Subsidiaries:

China Mobile Group Beijing Company
Limited **(1)**
58 Dongzhong St, Dong Cheng District,
Beijing, 100027, China
Tel.: (86) 10 6554 6699
Mobile Communications Services
N.A.I.C.S.: 541618

China Mobile Group Hebei Company
Limited **(1)**
136 Dongfeng Road, Qiaodong District, Shijiazhuang, 050021, China
Tel.: (86) 31180998848
Mobile Communications Services
N.A.I.C.S.: 541618

China Mobile Group Heilongjiang
Company Limited **(1)**
No 168 Xinwan Road, songbei District, Harbin, 150090, China
Tel.: (86) 45186309075
Mobile Communications Services
N.A.I.C.S.: 541618

China Mobile Group Neimenggu
Company Limited **(1)**
39-A Tengfei South Road, Saihan District,
Hohhot, 010011, China
Tel.: (86) 4712301806
Mobile Communications Services
N.A.I.C.S.: 541618

China Mobile Group Ningxia Company Limited **(1)**
217 Xinchang East Road, Jinfeng District,
Yinchuan, 750002, China
Tel.: (86) 13629580010

Mobile Communications Services
N.A.I.C.S.: 541618

China Mobile Group Tianjin Company
Limited **(1)**
99 Center Avenue, Airport Economic District, Tianjin, 300450, China
Tel.: (86) 13920039966
Mobile Communications Services
N.A.I.C.S.: 541618

China Mobile Limited **(1)**
60th Floor The Center 99 Queen s Road,
Central, China (Hong Kong)   **(74.08%)**
Tel.: (852) 31218888
Web Site: https://www.chinamobileltd.com
Rev.: $139,747,036,996
Assets: $275,899,562,472
Liabilities: $89,536,996,012
Net Worth: $186,362,566,460
Earnings: $18,267,473,416
Emp.: 451,830
Fiscal Year-end: 12/31/2023
Cellular Telecommunications Services
N.A.I.C.S.: 517112
Jie Yang (Chm)

CHINA MOBILE IOT COMPANY LIMITED

Building D2A Phase II D Zone Hightech Park Development, No 8 Yangliu
North Road Yubei, Chongqing, China
Tel.: (86) 4001100868
Web Site: https://iot.10086.cn
Year Founded: 2012
Emp.: 3,000
Telecommunication Servicesb
N.A.I.C.S.: 517810

CHINA MODERN AGRICULTURAL INFORMATION, INC.

No A09 Wuzhou Sun Town Limin Avenue, Limin Development District,
Harbin, 150000, Heilongjiang, China
Tel.: (86) 45184800733   NV
Year Founded: 2008
CMCI—(OTCIQ)
Sales Range: $100-124.9 Million
Emp.: 172
Agricultural Services
N.A.I.C.S.: 112120
Youliang Wang (CEO & Gen Mgr)

CHINA MOTOR BUS COMPANY LIMITED

26th Floor Island Place Tower 510
Kings Road, North Point, 2606-08,
China (Hong Kong)
Tel.: (852) 25151331   HK
0026—(HKG)
Rev.: $9,413,347
Assets: $1,026,950,755
Liabilities: $12,244,587
Net Worth: $1,014,706,168
Earnings: $9,331,316
Emp.: 14
Fiscal Year-end: 06/30/22
Property Management Services
N.A.I.C.S.: 531311
Henry Ngan (Chm)

CHINA MOTOR CORPORATION

No 618 Xiucai Rd Yangmei Dist,
Taoyuan, 326, Taiwan
Tel.: (886) 34783191
Web Site: https://www.mitsubishi-motors.com.tw
Year Founded: 1969
2204—(TAI)
Rev.: $1,259,250,059
Assets: $1,647,027,506
Liabilities: $355,366,153
Net Worth: $1,291,661,353
Earnings: $193,738,277
Emp.: 2,200
Fiscal Year-end: 12/31/23
Commercial Vehicle Mfr
N.A.I.C.S.: 336211

Chao-Wen Chen *(Pres)*

Subsidiaries:

China Engine Corporation   (1)
No 3 Lin 30 Heng Fong Chun Tayuan
Hsiang, Taoyuan, Taiwan
Tel.: (886) 33818001
Motor Vehicle Body Mfr
N.A.I.C.S.: 336211

China Motor Corporation - Hsin-Chu
Plant   (1)
No 2 Kwan Fu Rd Hsin Chu Industrial Park
Hu Kou Hsiang Hsin Chu Hsien, Hsin-chu,
Taiwan
Tel.: (886) 35985841
Automobile Parts Mfr
N.A.I.C.S.: 336110

China Motor Corporation - Yang-Mei
Plant   (1)
No 618 Sioucai Rd Yang Mei, Taoyuan,
326, Taiwan
Tel.: (886) 34783191
Automobile Parts Mfr
N.A.I.C.S.: 336110

China Motor Corporation - Yu-Shih
Plant   (1)
No 3 Chin Lan Rd Youth Industry Park
Yang Mei, Taoyuan, 326, Taiwan
Tel.: (886) 34642151
Automobile Parts Mfr
N.A.I.C.S.: 336110

Gatetech Technology Inc.   (1)
No 1-1 Tatung 1st Rd, Guan-Yin Industry
Park, Taoyuan, Taiwan
Tel.: (886) 34831689
Web Site: https://www.gatetech.com.tw
Emp.: 600
Alloy Parts Distr
N.A.I.C.S.: 423510
P. C. Paul Cheng *(Founder)*

Greentrans Corporation   (1)
No 618 Xiucai Rd, Yangmei, Taoyuan, 326,
Taiwan
Tel.: (886) 34783191
Web Site: https://www.greentrans.com.tw
Motorcycle Mfr
N.A.I.C.S.: 336991

**CHINA NATIONAL ACCORD
MEDICINES CORP., LTD.**
Yizhi Pharmaceutical Building No 15
Bagua 4th Road, Futian District,
Shenzhen, 518029, China
Tel.: (86) 75525875195
Web Site:
   http://www.szaccord.com.cn
Year Founded: 1993
200028—(SSE)
Rev.: $10,311,416,856
Assets: $7,003,564,776
Liabilities: $4,182,341,904
Net Worth: $2,821,222,872
Earnings: $208,734,084
Fiscal Year-end: 12/31/22
Pharmaceutical Product Mfr & Distr
N.A.I.C.S.: 325412
Wu Yijian *(Chm)*

**CHINA NATIONAL AVIATION
FUEL GROUP CORPORATION**
CNAF Plaza No 2 Madian Road,
Haidian District, Beijing, 100088,
China
Tel.: (86) 1059890000
Web Site: http://www.cnaf.com
Sales Range: $25-49.9 Billion
Emp.: 9,300
Air Transportation Logistics Services
N.A.I.C.S.: 488190
Qiang Zhou *(Chm)*

Subsidiaries:

China Aviation Oil (Singapore) Corpo-
ration Ltd.   (1)
8 Temasek Boulevard 31-02 Suntec Tower
Three, Singapore, 038988,
Singapore   **(51%)**
Tel.: (65) 63348979

Web Site: http://www.caosco.com
Rev.: $14,429,573,000
Assets: $1,787,514,000
Liabilities: $835,167,000
Net Worth: $952,347,000
Earnings: $58,373,000
Emp.: 152
Fiscal Year-end: 12/31/2023
Jet Fuel Distribution
N.A.I.C.S.: 457210
Doreen Nah *(Sec)*

**CHINA NATIONAL AVIATION
HOLDING COMPANY**
25-28F Air China Plaza No 36 Xi-
aoyun Road, Beijing, 100027, Chaoy-
ang, China
Tel.: (86) 1084488888   HK
Web Site:
   http://www.airchinagroup.com
Year Founded: 2002
Sales Range: $5-14.9 Billion
Emp.: 100
Holding Company; Passenger Trans-
portation
N.A.I.C.S.: 551112
Jianjiang Cai *(Chm)*

Subsidiaries:

Air China Cargo Co., Ltd.   (1)
No 29 Tianzhu Road Tianzhu Airport Eco-
nomic Development Zone, Beijing, 101318,
China
Tel.: (86) 10 61465599
Web Site: http://www.airchinacargo.com
Air Cargo Services
N.A.I.C.S.: 488119

Air China Ltd.   (1)
No 30 Tianzhu Road, Shunyi District, Bei-
jing, 101312, China
Tel.: (86) 1061461959
Web Site: http://www.airchina.com.cn
Rev.: $7,426,820,794
Assets: $41,419,591,434
Liabilities: $38,392,541,320
Net Worth: $3,027,050,114
Earnings: ($5,422,177,660)
Emp.: 87,190
Fiscal Year-end: 12/31/2022
Provider of Commercial Air Line Services
N.A.I.C.S.: 481111
Zhiyong Song *(Vice Chm)*

Joint Venture (Domestic):

Aircraft Maintenance & Engineering
Corp.   (2)
Beijing Capital International Airport, Beijing,
100621, China
Tel.: (86) 10645611224
Web Site: http://www.ameco.com.cn
Sales Range: $800-899.9 Million
Aircraft Maintenance, Repair & Overhaul
Services; Owned 60% by China National
Aviation Holding Company & 40% by Deut-
sche Lufthansa AG
N.A.I.C.S.: 488190
Sun Wei *(Reg Dir)*

Air Macau Co., Ltd.   (1)
398 Alameda Drive Carlos D'Assumpcao,
12-18 andar, Macau, China
(Macau)   **(51%)**
Tel.: (853) 3966888
Web Site: http://www.airmacau.com.mo
Sales Range: $5-14.9 Billion
Regional Airline Services
N.A.I.C.S.: 481111

China Air Express Co., Limited   (1)
No 1670-1 Sec 1 huanzhong Rd, Xitun, Tai-
chung, 40761, Taiwan
Tel.: (886) 911887777
Web Site: http://www.cae-tw.com
Air Cargo Services
N.A.I.C.S.: 488119

**CHINA NATIONAL BUILDING
MATERIAL GROUP CO., LTD.**
Building 2 Guohai Plaza No 17 Fux-
ing Road, Haidian District, Beijing,
100036, China
Tel.: (86) 1068138199   CN
Web Site: https://www.cnbm.com.cn

Year Founded: 1984
Sales Range: $25-49.9 Billion
Emp.: 100,000
Holding Company; Building Materials
Mfr & Distr
N.A.I.C.S.: 551112
Zhiping Song *(Chm)*

Subsidiaries:

BNBM PNG Limited   (1)
Boroko Kennedy Road, PO Box 466, Gor-
don, Port Moresby, Papua New Guinea
Tel.: (675) 323 3379
Web Site: http://www.bnbmpng.com
Emp.: 500
Construction Materials Distr
N.A.I.C.S.: 423390

Beijing New Building Materials Public
Limited Company   (1)
Block A Beixin Center No 9 Qibei Road Fu-
ture Science City, Beijing, 102209, China
Tel.: (86) 1082945588
Web Site: http://www.bnbm.com.cn
Rev.: $2,798,777,124
Assets: $4,016,077,416
Liabilities: $1,005,393,168
Net Worth: $3,010,684,248
Earnings: $440,350,560
Fiscal Year-end: 12/31/2022
Building Materials Mfr
N.A.I.C.S.: 423320
Xue Zhongmin *(Chm)*

Beixin New Building Material (Group)
Co., Ltd.   (1)
Building 4 Interwest Business Center No 9
Shouti South Road, Haidian District, Beijing,
100048, China
Tel.: (86) 1068799800
Web Site: http://www.bnbmg.com.cn
Construction Materials Distr
N.A.I.C.S.: 423390

CNBM GERMANY GMBH.   (1)
Landshuter Allee 8-10, 80637, Munich, Ger-
many
Tel.: (49) 89 54558192
Construction Materials Distr
N.A.I.C.S.: 423390

CNBM INDIA PRIVATE LIMITED   (1)
3-6-540/C Second Floor Saraswathi Chambers Street No 7, Himayatnagar, Hyderabad, 500029, Andhra Pradesh, India
Tel.: (91) 40 27611800
Construction Materials Distr
N.A.I.C.S.: 423390

CNBM International (Jordan)
Company   (1)
No 18 AlFayhaa, Shmeisani, Amman, Jor-
dan
Tel.: (962) 779889152
Construction Materials Distr
N.A.I.C.S.: 423390

CNBM VIETNAM COMPANY
LIMITED   (1)
SO 115 TT3 KDT My Dinh-Song Da, Tu
Liem District, Hanoi, Vietnam
Tel.: (84) 4 37878481
Construction Materials Distr
N.A.I.C.S.: 423390

CNBM in Ukraine, LLC.   (1)
40richchya Zhovtnya avenue 93 office 325,
Kiev, 03127, Ukraine
Tel.: (380) 442584859
Construction Materials Distr
N.A.I.C.S.: 423390

CNBMIT Co., Ltd   (1)
14/F International Trade Building No 3002
Renmin South Road, Luohu District, Shen-
zhen, 518014, China
Tel.: (86) 755 82211330
Web Site: http://www.cnbmit.com
Electronic Equipment Distr
N.A.I.C.S.: 423690

China Composites Group Corporation
Ltd.   (1)
12th Floor Tower 2 Guohai Plaza No 17
Fuxing Road, Haidian District, Beijing,
100036, China
Tel.: (86) 10 68138899
Web Site: http://www.ccgc.com.cn

Fiber Glass Mfr
N.A.I.C.S.: 327212

Subsidiary (Domestic):

Lianyungang Zhongfu Lianzhong
Composites Group Co., Ltd.   (2)
195 Hailian East Road, Lianyungang,
222006, Jiangsu, China
Tel.: (86) 518 85150330
Web Site: http://www.lzfrp.com
Emp.: 2,000
Industrial Pipe Mfr
N.A.I.C.S.: 326122

China National Building Material
Company Limited   (1)
21st floor Building 2 Guohai Plaza No 17
Fuxing Road, Haidian District, Beijing,
100036, China
Tel.: (86) 1068138300
Web Site: https://www.cnbmltd.com
Rev.: $29,607,948,362
Assets: $68,858,862,329
Liabilities: $41,603,357,199
Net Worth: $27,255,505,130
Earnings: $1,464,880,277
Emp.: 145,277
Fiscal Year-end: 12/31/2023
Building Product Mfr
N.A.I.C.S.: 327310
Shou Peng *(Bd of Dirs & Pres)*

Subsidiary (Domestic):

China Triumph International Engi-
neering Co., Ltd.   (2)
2000 Zhongshanbei Road, Shanghai, China
Tel.: (86) 21 62030071
Web Site: http://www.ctiec.net
Engineeering Services
N.A.I.C.S.: 541330

Subsidiary (Non-US):

CTF Solar GmbH   (3)
Manfred-von-Ardenne-Ring 20 Haus F,
01099, Dresden, Germany
Tel.: (49) 6195 6796 0
Web Site: http://www.ctf-solar.com
Solar Module Mfr
N.A.I.C.S.: 334413
Michael Harr *(Gen Mgr)*

Subsidiary (Domestic):

China United Cement
Corporation   (2)
16 Floor 11 Sanlihe Road, Haidian, Beijing,
100037, China
Tel.: (86) 10 8808 3366
Construction Materials Distr
N.A.I.C.S.: 423320

China United Cement Group Corpo-
ration Limited   (2)
16/F Jia No 11 Sanlihe Rd, Haidian District,
Beijing, China
Tel.: (86) 10 8808 3366
Construction Materials Distr
N.A.I.C.S.: 423390

China National Building Material
Group FZE   (1)
Plot No S30408 JAFZA South, Jebel Ali
Free Zone, Dubai, United Arab Emirates
Tel.: (971) 4 8806686
Construction Materials Distr
N.A.I.C.S.: 423390

China National United Equipment
Group Corp.   (1)
No 33 West Huangchenggen South Str,
Xicheng Dist, Beijing, China
Tel.: (86) 10 66014182
Industrial Machinery & Equipment Distr
N.A.I.C.S.: 423830

Jushi Canada Co., Ltd.   (1)
1350 Rodick Road Unit 3, Markham, L3R
5X4, ON, Canada
Tel.: (905) 477-7628
Web Site: http://www.jushicanada.com
Fiber Glass Mfr
N.A.I.C.S.: 327212
James Gardiner *(Mng Dir)*

Jushi Group Co., Ltd.   (1)
669 Wenhua Road South, Tongxiang Economic Development Zone, Tongxiang, Zheji-

China National Building Material Group Co., Ltd.—(Continued)

ang, China
Tel.: (86) 57388136219
Web Site: http://www.jushi.com
Emp.: 8,000
Fiber Glass Mfr
N.A.I.C.S.: 327212
James Wang (Gen Mgr-Sls & Mktg-Intl)

Subsidiary (Non-US):

Jushi France SAS (2)
ZI du Champ Dolin Parc Technoland 3 Allée du Lazio Batiment C, 69800, Saint Priest, France
Tel.: (33) 789380396
Web Site: http://www.jushi.fr
Emp.: 4
Fiber Glass Fabric Distr
N.A.I.C.S.: 424310
Dany Mougenot (Mgr-Sls)

Subsidiary (US):

Jushi USA Fiberglass Co Ltd (2)
3130 Bluff Rd Ste B, Irwindale, CA 29209
Tel.: (626) 960-2038
Web Site: https://www.jushiusa.com
Fiber Glass Fabric Distr
N.A.I.C.S.: 424310
Jason Takac (Mgr-Sls-Northeast Reg)

Jushi Singapore Pte. Ltd. (1)
10 Ubi Crescent, Singapore, 408564, Singapore
Tel.: (65) 6742 5118
Web Site: http://www.jushigroup.com
Emp.: 5
Fiber Glass Mfr & Distr
N.A.I.C.S.: 327212
Seng Han Song (Gen Mgr)

PT. CNBM INTERNATIONAL INDONESIA (1)
Jalan Prof Dr Satrio Kav 1, Jakarta, 12940, Indonesia
Tel.: (62) 21 522 5217
Construction Materials Distr
N.A.I.C.S.: 423390

SINOI GmbH (1)
Kohnsteinbrucke 10, 99734, Nordhausen, Germany
Tel.: (49) 36331 9 03 00
Web Site: http://www.sinoi.de
Emp.: 100
Windmill Equipment Mfr
N.A.I.C.S.: 333111
Ren Guifang (Mng Dir)

Sinoma Energy Conservation Ltd. (1)
Sinoma Energy Conservation Building, Beichen District, Tianjin, 300400, China
Tel.: (86) 222778815
Web Site: https://www.sinoma-ec.cn
Rev.: $452,008,197
Assets: $699,108,265
Liabilities: $356,523,294
Net Worth: $342,584,972
Earnings: $22,022,765
Fiscal Year-end: 12/31/2022
Waste Heat Power Generation Services
N.A.I.C.S.: 562213
Qi Zhang (Chm)

Tangshan Senpu Mine Equipment Co., Ltd. (1)
No 138 Gongyuandao, Fengrun, Tangshan, 063034, Hebei, China
Tel.: (86) 315 3080608
Construction Materials Distr
N.A.I.C.S.: 423390

CHINA NATIONAL CHEMICAL CORPORATION

No 62 North Fourth Ring Road West, Haidian District, Beijing, 100080, China
Tel.: (86) 10826775304 CN
Web Site: https://www.chemchina.cn
Year Founded: 2004
Holding Company; Chemicals Mfr
N.A.I.C.S.: 551112

Subsidiaries:

ADAMA Ltd. (1)

6F A7 Office Building No 10 Courtyard, Chaoyang Park South Road Chaoyang District, Beijing, China (78.9%)
Tel.: (86) 1056718100
Web Site: https://www.adama.com
Rev.: $5,248,421,568
Assets: $8,140,460,796
Liabilities: $4,893,759,936
Net Worth: $3,246,700,860
Earnings: $85,558,356
Emp.: 9,000
Fiscal Year-end: 12/31/2022
Agricultural Chemical Product Mfr
N.A.I.C.S.: 325320
An Liru (Sr VP-China)

Subsidiary (Non-US):

ADAMA Agricultural Solutions Ltd. (100%)
Golan Street, Airport City, 7015103, Israel
Tel.: (972) 73 232 1000
Web Site: http://www.adama.com
Crop Protection Product Mfr
N.A.I.C.S.: 325320
Xingqiang Yang (Chm)

Subsidiary (Non-US):

ADAMA Agriculture España, S.A. (3)
Principe de Vergara 110 5, 28002, Madrid, Spain
Tel.: (34) 91 585 2380
Web Site: http://www.aragro.es
Agricultural Chemical Mfr
N.A.I.C.S.: 325320

ADAMA Andina B.V. Sucursal Colombia (3)
Carrera 11 No 87-51 Piso 4, Bogota, 29611, Colombia
Tel.: (57) 1 6446730
Web Site: http://www.adama.com
Agricultural Chemical Mfr
N.A.I.C.S.: 325320

ADAMA Argentina S.A. (3)
Cerrito 1186 8th Floor, Buenos Aires, C1010AAX, Argentina
Tel.: (54) 1148136040
Web Site: http://www.adama.com
Agricultural Chemical Mfr
N.A.I.C.S.: 325320

ADAMA France S.A.S (3)
31/33 rue de Verdun, 92156, Suresnes, Cedex, France
Tel.: (33) 1 41 47 33 33
Web Site: http://www.adama.com
Agricultural Chemical Mfr
N.A.I.C.S.: 325998

Adama Agricultural Solutions S.R.L. (3)
Sosea Bucuresti Nord nr 10 Global City Business Park Cladirea O21 Et 6, Voluntari Jud Ilfov, Bucharest, 077190, Romania
Tel.: (40) 213077612
Web Site: http://www.adama.com
Agricultural Chemical Mfr
N.A.I.C.S.: 325320

Adama Agricultural Solutions UK Ltd. (3)
Third Floor East 1410 Arlington Business Park, Theale, RG19 4LW, Berks, United Kingdom
Tel.: (44) 1635860555
Web Site: http://www.adama.com
Agricultural Chemical Mfr
N.A.I.C.S.: 325320

Adama Brasil S.A. (3)
Rua Pedron Antonio Souza 400, Jardim Eucaliptos Londrina Site, Londrina, 86031610, PR, Brazil
Tel.: (55) 4333719000
Web Site: http://www.adama.com
Agricultural Chemical Mfr
N.A.I.C.S.: 325320

Adama Italia S.R.L. (3)
Via Zanica 19, 24050, Milan, Italy
Tel.: (39) 035 328 811
Web Site: http://www.adama.com
Agricultural Chemical Mfr
N.A.I.C.S.: 325320

Subsidiary (Domestic):

Adama Makhteshim Ltd. (3)

PO Box 60, Industrial Zone, Beersheba, 84100, Israel
Tel.: (972) 86296611
Web Site: http://www.adama.com
Agricultural Chemical Mfr
N.A.I.C.S.: 325320

Subsidiary (US):

Control Solutions Inc. (3)
5903 Genoa-Red Bluff Rd, Pasadena, TX 77507
Tel.: (281) 892-2500
Web Site:
   http://www.controlsolutionsinc.com
Pest Control & Animal Health Solutions & Services
N.A.I.C.S.: 561710

Subsidiary (Domestic):

Bonide Products, Inc. (4)
6301 Sutliff Rd, Oriskany, NY 13424-4326
Tel.: (315) 736-8231
Web Site: http://www.bonide.com
Pesticides & Home Gardening Products
N.A.I.C.S.: 325998

Subsidiary (Non-US):

MAGAN Korea Co. Ltd. (3)
275-5 8th FL Yangjae-Dong, Seocho-Gu, Seoul, 137-943, Korea (South)
Tel.: (82) 234446883
Web Site: http://www.adama.com
Agricultural Chemical Mfr
N.A.I.C.S.: 325320

Subsidiary (Non-US):

Alfa Agricultural Supplies S.A. (2)
73 Ethnikis Antistasseos, Chalandri, 152 31, Athens, Greece (100%)
Tel.: (30) 2111205555
Web Site: http://www.alfagro.gr
Agricultural Chemical Mfr
N.A.I.C.S.: 325320

Cangzhou Dahua Group Co., Ltd. (1)
No 20 Yongji East Road, Cangzhou, 061000, Hebei, China
Tel.: (86) 3713556486
Web Site: https://www.czdh.chemchina.com
Rev.: $689,866,464
Assets: $989,504,914
Liabilities: $392,654,321
Net Worth: $596,850,593
Earnings: $58,981,815
Fiscal Year-end: 12/31/2022
Chemical Products Mfr
N.A.I.C.S.: 325998
Liu Zeng (Chm & Gen Mgr)

Subsidiary (Domestic):

Cangzhou Mingzhu Plastic Co., Ltd. (2)
Mingzhu Building HiTech Zone, Cangzhou, 061000, Hebei, China
Tel.: (86) 3172075225
Web Site: https://www.cz-mz.com
Rev.: $397,980,648
Assets: $984,545,172
Liabilities: $250,480,620
Net Worth: $734,064,552
Earnings: $39,452,400
Emp.: 2,000
Fiscal Year-end: 12/31/2022
Plastic Tank Mfr
N.A.I.C.S.: 326122
Hongwei Chen (Chm)

ChemChina Guilin Tire Co, Ltd (1)
80 Hengtang Road, Qixing District Guangxi Zhuang, Guilin, 541004, China
Tel.: (86) 773 5883569
Web Site: http://www.gllt.chemchina.com
Tiles Mfr
N.A.I.C.S.: 326211

ChemChina Petrochemical Co., Ltd (2)
The West Beisihuan Avenue No 62, Haidian District, Beijing, 100080, China
Tel.: (86) 10 82677233
Web Site:
   http://www.chemchinapetro.com.cn
Crude Oil Refining Services
N.A.I.C.S.: 324110
Wu Hong (Gen Mgr)

Subsidiary (Non-US):

ChemChina (Singapore) Pte. Ltd (2)
6 Battery Road 16-06, Singapore, 049909, Singapore
Tel.: (65) 6426 7617
Petroleum Product Distr
N.A.I.C.S.: 424720

Subsidiary (Domestic):

ChemChina Logistics Co Ltd (2)
Sanshandao Industrial Park, Laizhou, 261442, Shandong, China
Tel.: (86) 535 2783418
Logistics Consulting Servies
N.A.I.C.S.: 541614

Daqing Zhonglan Petrochemical Co Ltd (2)
Lahua East Road, Ranghulu District, Daqing, 163713, Heilongjiang, China
Tel.: (86) 459 6728362
Petrochemical Products Mfr
N.A.I.C.S.: 324110

Qingdao Anbang Petrochemical Co Ltd (2)
Jihongtan Neighborhood Office, Yangcheng District, Qingdao, 266111, Shandong, China
Tel.: (86) 532 87803838
Petrochemical Products Mfr
N.A.I.C.S.: 324110

China Haohua Chemical Group Co., Ltd. (1)
No 19 Xiaoyinglu, Chaoyang District, Beijing, 100101, China
Web Site: http://www.chinahaohua.com.cn
Holding Company; Chemicals Mfr
N.A.I.C.S.: 551112

Affiliate (Domestic):

Haohua Chemical Science & Technology Corp. (2)
87 Jindu Section Wainan Airport Road, Chengdu, 610225, Sichuan, China
Tel.: (86) 2885961516
Web Site: http://www.tkgf.chemchina.com
Rev.: $1,273,081,170
Assets: $2,165,656,943
Liabilities: $1,011,114,300
Net Worth: $1,154,542,643
Earnings: $163,550,051
Fiscal Year-end: 12/31/2022
Scientific Research & Development Services
N.A.I.C.S.: 541715
Gongwei Gu (Pres)

China National Bluestar (Group) Co., Ltd. (1)
No 19 East Road North No 3 Ring Road, ChaoYang District, Beijing, 100029, China
Tel.: (86) 1064429448
Web Site: http://www.china-bluestar.com
Sales Range: $1-4.9 Billion
Emp.: 37,000
Petroleum Products, Organic & Inorganic Chemicals Developer & Mfr
N.A.I.C.S.: 325998
Michael Keonig (CEO)

Subsidiary (Non-US):

Adisseo France S.A.S. (2)
Immeuble Antony Parc 2 10 Place du General de Gaulle, 92160, Antony, France
Tel.: (33) 1467470000
Web Site: http://www.adisseo.com
Sales Range: $750-799.9 Million
Emp.: 1,200
Animal Vitamin & Nutritional Food Additive Developer & Mfr
N.A.I.C.S.: 311119
Francois Pellet (Exec Dir-SBU Specialties)

Affiliate (Domestic):

China Haohua Engineering Co., Ltd. (2)
No 1 Zhongle Building Yard 15 Xiaoying Road, Chaoyang District, Beijing, 100101, China
Tel.: (86) 64893721
Web Site: http://www.hhgc.chemchina.com
Environmental Engineering & Consulting Services
N.A.I.C.S.: 541330

Subsidiary (Non-US):

Elkem ASA (2)
Drammensveien 169, 0277, Oslo, Norway
Tel.: (47) 22450100
Web Site: http://www.elkem.com
Sales Range: $1-4.9 Billion
Emp.: 6,200
Development & Production of Advanced
Ceramics & Environmental Technology Mfr
N.A.I.C.S.: 331524
Karin Aslaksen *(Sr VP-HR)*

Division (Domestic):

Elkem ASA - Materials Division (3)
Siskoveien 100, PO Box 8126, Vaagsbygd,
Kristiansand, 4621, Norway
Tel.: (47) 38017500
Web Site: http://www.materials.elkem.com
Sales Range: $25-49.9 Million
Emp.: 80
Microsilica Products, Cement Building Prod-
ucts, Silicon Metal Powders & Silicon Ni-
tride Mfr
N.A.I.C.S.: 327310
Helge Aasen *(Mng Dir)*

Division (Non-US):

Elkem Japan K.K. (4)
Nikko Sanno Bldg, 401 5 3 Akasaka 2
Chome, Tokyo, 107-0052, Japan
Tel.: (81) 335847711
Web Site: http://www.elkem.co.jp
Sales Range: $25-49.9 Million
Emp.: 12
Construction Materials Mfr
N.A.I.C.S.: 423390

Division (Domestic):

Elkem ASA - Silicon Division (3)
PO Box 334, NO 0213, Oslo, Norway
Tel.: (47) 22450100
Web Site: http://www.elkem.com
Sales Range: $50-74.9 Million
Emp.: 120
Silicon Products
N.A.I.C.S.: 331524
Halge Aasin *(Pres)*

Subsidiary (Non-US):

Elkem Iceland (4)
Grundartangi, Skilmannahreppur, IS-301,
Akranes, Iceland
Tel.: (354) 04320200
Sales Range: $25-49.9 Million
Emp.: 120
Ferrosilicon Mfr
N.A.I.C.S.: 331110

Division (Domestic):

Elkem Marnes Kvartsittbrudd (4)
Elkem Marnes, N 8130, Sandhorney, Nor-
way
Tel.: (47) 75758502
Web Site: http://www.elkem.no
Silicone Products Mfr
N.A.I.C.S.: 331524

Division (US):

Elkem Silicon Materials USA (4)
Airport Ofc Park Bldg 2 400 Rouser Rd,
Moon Township, PA 15108-2749
Tel.: (412) 299-7200
Web Site: http://www.elkem.com
Silicon Metal & Calcium Carbide Mfr
N.A.I.C.S.: 331524

Division (Domestic):

Elkem Tana (4)
Austertana, NO-9845, Tana, Norway
Tel.: (47) 78926140
Web Site: http://www.elkem.no
Rev.: $2,145,000
Emp.: 20
Quartzite Quarrying
N.A.I.C.S.: 212319
Rune Martinussen *(Gen Mgr)*

Elkem Thamshavn (4)
PO Box 10, NO-7301, Orkanger, Norway
Tel.: (47) 72488200
Web Site: http://www.elkem.no

Sales Range: $25-49.9 Million
Ferrosilicon Mfr
N.A.I.C.S.: 331110
Steinar Talle *(Plant Mgr)*

Division (Domestic):

Elkem ASA-Carbon Division (3)
Sisaadeien 100, PO Box 8040, Kristian-
sand, 4621, Norway
Tel.: (47) 38017500
Web Site: http://www.elkem.nl
Sales Range: $100-124.9 Million
Emp.: 400
Carbon Products Mfr
N.A.I.C.S.: 335991
Johannes Toste *(Gen Mgr)*

Subsidiary (Non-US):

Carboderivados S.A. (4)
Rua Atalydes, Moreira De Souza, n245 CI-
VIT I, CEP 29168 060, Serra, Espirito
Santo, Brazil
Tel.: (55) 27 2123 200
Sales Range: $25-49.9 Million
Emp.: 34
Carbon Products Mfr
N.A.I.C.S.: 325180

Division (Domestic):

Elkem Bjolvefossen (3)
Hoffsveien 65B, Majorstua, 5614, Alvik,
Norway
Tel.: (47) 56550800
Web Site: http://www.elkem.com
Sales Range: $50-74.9 Million
Emp.: 110
Foundry Products
N.A.I.C.S.: 331524
Sroda Nummetal *(Mng Dir)*

Subsidiary (Non-US):

Elkem Ltd. (3)
305 Glossop Rd, Sheffield, S10 2HL, South
Yorkshire, United Kingdom
Tel.: (44) 42700334
Web Site: http://www.elkem.com
Sales Range: $25-49.9 Million
Emp.: 10
Foundry Products
N.A.I.C.S.: 331523

Elkem Metal Canada Inc. (3)
1685 Main Street West Suite 303, Hamilton,
L8S 1G5, ON, Canada
Tel.: (905) 572-6722
Web Site: http://www.elkem.com
Sales Range: $25-49.9 Million
Emp.: 80
Ferrosilicon Mfr
N.A.I.C.S.: 331110

Division (Domestic):

**Elkem Metals Canada
Inc.-Hamilton** (4)
1685 Main St W Ste 303, Hamilton, L8S
1G5, ON, Canada
Tel.: (905) 572-6722
Web Site: http://www.elkem.com
Sales Range: $50-74.9 Million
Emp.: 4
Metals Sales & Distr
N.A.I.C.S.: 522110
Chris Lisso *(Dir-Sls & Mktg)*

Subsidiary (Non-US):

Euro Nordic Logistics B.V. (3)
Klompenmakerstraat 3, 2984 BB, Rid-
derkerk, Netherlands
Tel.: (31) 180441144
Web Site: http://www.euronordic.nl
Sales Range: $25-49.9 Million
Emp.: 55
Logistic Services
N.A.I.C.S.: 541614
Kees Groeneveld *(Mng Dir)*

Subsidiary (Domestic):

REC Solar Holdings AS (3)
Fiskaveien 100, 4621, Kristiansand, Norway
Tel.: (47) 46633606
Web Site: https://www.recgroup.com
Sales Range: $750-799.9 Million
Emp.: 2,000

Holding Company; Solar Cells & Modules
Mfr
N.A.I.C.S.: 551112
Soon Kim Ter *(COO)*

Subsidiary (US):

REC Americas, LLC (4)
1820 Gateway Dr Ste #170, San Mateo, CA
94404
Tel.: (877) 332-4087
Solar Panel Mfr
N.A.I.C.S.: 334419
Zony A. Chen *(VP-Sls & Mktg)*

Subsidiary (Non-US):

REC Site Services Pte Ltd (4)
20 Tuas South Avenue 14, Singapore,
637312, Singapore
Tel.: (65) 64959228
Wafers Mfr
N.A.I.C.S.: 334413

REC Solar EMEA GmbH (4)
Leo Pold Strasse 175, 80804, Munich, Ger-
many
Tel.: (49) 8944238590
Solar Cell & Module Mfr
N.A.I.C.S.: 334419

REC Solar Pte. Ltd. (4)
20 Tuas South Avenue 14, Singapore,
637312, Singapore
Tel.: (65) 64959228
Wafers Mfr
N.A.I.C.S.: 334413

**Chonche Group Nanjing No.7425
Factory** (1)
Pioneer Park No 7, Qixia district, Nanjing,
210028, Jiangsu, China
Tel.: (86) 25 83130808
Web Site: www.nj7425.com
Hose Mfr
N.A.I.C.S.: 326220

**Deyang Haohua Qingping Linkuang
Co., Ltd.** (1)
Hanwang, Mianzhu, 618200, Sichuan,
China
Tel.: (86) 838 6102926
Emp.: 2,700
Chemical Mining Services
N.A.I.C.S.: 212390

**Dezhou Shihua Chemical Co.,
Ltd.** (1)
New park area Tianqu Industrial Park,
Decheng district, Dezhou, 253000, Shan-
dong, China
Tel.: (86) 534 2622704
Web Site: http://www.hhdz.chemchina.com
Emp.: 1,600
Petrochemical Products Mfr
N.A.I.C.S.: 324110

**Double Happiness Tyre Industrial Co,
Ltd** (1)
9 Fengyi St, Qingxu county, Taiyuan,
030400, Shanxi, China
Tel.: (86) 351 579 6799
Web Site: http://www.rubber.chemchina.com
Tiles Mfr
N.A.I.C.S.: 326211

**Fujian Sanming Double-wheel Chemi-
cal Machinery Co. Ltd** (1)
Jinsha Park Sanming New and High-tech
Industry Development Zone, Sanming,
365500, Fujian, China
Tel.: (86) 598 5066366
Web Site: http://www.smhj.chemchina.com
Industrial Automation Equipments Mfr
N.A.I.C.S.: 334513

**Guangxi Hechi Chemical Co.,
Ltd.** (1)
No 40 Liujia Town, Jinchengjiang District,
Hechi, 547007, Guangxi, China
Tel.: (86) 7782266882
Web Site:
https://www.hechihuagong.com.cn
Rev.: $22,549,644
Assets: $40,254,084
Liabilities: $26,993,304
Net Worth: $13,260,780
Earnings: ($14,101,776)
Fiscal Year-end: 12/31/2022
Chemical Fertiliser Mfr

N.A.I.C.S.: 325312
Weiguang Shi *(Chm)*

**Guizhou Crystal Organic Chemical
(Group) Co., Ltd.** (1)
Dongping Road, Qingzhen, 551402,
Guizhou, China
Tel.: (86) 851 2561355
Web Site: http://www.hhsj.chemchina.com
Emp.: 2,500
Chemical Products Mfr
N.A.I.C.S.: 325199

Subsidiary (Domestic):

**Guizhou Crystal Chemical Co
Ltd** (2)
3F Torch Software Park Gaoxin Dev Area,
Wudang Dist, Guiyang, 551402, China
Tel.: (86) 851 2561 085
Chemical Products Mfr
N.A.I.C.S.: 325199

**Haohua East China Chemical Co.,
Ltd.** (1)
9th floor Zhongda Square No 989 Dongfang
Road, Pudong New Area District, Shanghai,
China
Tel.: (86) 21 68763143
Web Site: http://www.easthaohua.com
Chemical Products Mfr
N.A.I.C.S.: 325199

**Haohua Hitone Investment Manage-
ment Co., Ltd.** (1)
Floor 9 Building C Zhongji Wealth Garden
No 19 Xiaoying Road, Chaoyang District,
Beijing, 100101, China
Tel.: (86) 10 58650066
Web Site: http://www.hhht.chemchina.com
Financial Investment Management Services
N.A.I.C.S.: 523940
Chu Jianting *(Pres, Member-Mgmt Bd &
Gen Mgr)*

Subsidiary (Domestic):

**Oriental Chemical Industrial Corp
Ltd,** (2)
16F Tower C Caifujiayuan 19 Xiaoying Rd
Yayuncun, Chaoyang District, Beijing,
100101, China
Tel.: (86) 10 5865 0187
Fertilizer Mfr
N.A.I.C.S.: 325311

**Shenzhen Tongda Chemical
Corporation** (2)
11F West Tower Xincheng Building 13
Shennan Middle Rd, Shenzhen, 518031,
Guangdong, China
Tel.: (86) 755 2598 5566
Chemical Products Distr
N.A.I.C.S.: 424690

Taian Haohua Plastic Co., Ltd (2)
NO 44 TianZhuFeng Road, Tai'an, Shan-
Dong, China
Tel.: (86) 538 6136990
Web Site: http://www.haohua.cc
Emp.: 800
Plastics Product Mfr
N.A.I.C.S.: 326199

**Zhonghao Alkali Industry Co.,
Ltd.** (2)
Rm 804 Building1 180 Beiyuan Rd, Chaoy-
ang District, Beijing, 100101, China
Tel.: (86) 10 6494 4761
Chemical Products Mfr
N.A.I.C.S.: 325199

**Haohua Honghe Chemical Co.,
Ltd.** (1)
Hongheba, Zigong, 643000, Sichuan, China
Tel.: (86) 813 4662900
Web Site: http://www.hhhh.chemchina.com
Chemical Products Mfr
N.A.I.C.S.: 325199
Xie Xueduan *(Chm & Gen Mgr)*

Haohua Junhua Group Co., Ltd. (1)
No 439 Zhonghua avenue, Zhumadian,
463000, Henan, China
Tel.: (86) 396 3821121
Web Site: http://www.hhjh.chemchina.com
Emp.: 4,000
Petrochemical Products Mfr
N.A.I.C.S.: 324110

China National Chemical Corporation—(Continued)

Haohua Yuhang Chemical Co., Ltd. (1)
No 279 Jiefang East Rd, Jiaozuo, 454002, Henan, China
Tel.: (86) 391 3970000
Web Site: http://www.haohuayuhang.com
Chemical Products Mfr
N.A.I.C.S.: 325199
Jiang Zhenghui (Exec Dir)

Hebei Shenghua Chemical Co., Ltd. (1)
No 10 Shenghua Dongdajie, Qiaodong district, Zhangjiakou, 075000, Hebei, China
Tel.: (86) 313 4036191
Web Site: http://www.hhsh.chemchina.com
Chemical Products Mfr
N.A.I.C.S.: 325199
Liu Wenxian (Gen Mgr)

Heilongjiang Chemical Group Co., Ltd. (1)
2 Xiangyangdajie, Fulaerji district, Qiqihar, 161061, Heilongjiang, China
Tel.: (86) 452 8927437
Petrochemical Products Mfr
N.A.I.C.S.: 324110

Heilongjiang Haohua Chemical Co., Ltd. (1)
Yushutun, Angangxi District, Qiqihar, 161033, Heilongjiang, China
Tel.: (86) 452 6200521
Web Site: http://www.hhhlj.chemchina.com
Emp.: 1,867
Chemical Products Mfr
N.A.I.C.S.: 325199

Hunan Haohua Chemical Co Ltd. (1)
No 18 Dingshan Rd, Shifeng district, Zhuzhou, 412005, Hunan, China
Tel.: (86) 731 22969099
Web Site: http://www.hn-haohua.com
Agrochemical Mfr
N.A.I.C.S.: 325320

Hunan Petrochemical Supply & Marketing Corporation (1)
No 135 Yuejin Rd, Changsha, Hunan, China
Tel.: (86) 731 85163689
Petrochemical Product Distr
N.A.I.C.S.: 424690

KraussMaffei Company Limited (1)
No 3 Jinling Industrial Park, Jihongtan Town Chengyang district, Qingdao, 100029, Shandong, China
Tel.: (86) 1061958651
Web Site: https://www.kraussmaffei.ltd
Rev.: $1,464,314,801
Assets: $2,817,257,457
Liabilities: $2,327,027,031
Net Worth: $490,230,426
Earnings: $227,156,558)
Fiscal Year-end: 12/31/2022
Tiles Mfr
N.A.I.C.S.: 326211
Zhang Chi (Chm & Gen Mgr)

KraussMaffei Technologies GmbH (1)
Krauss-Maffei-Strasse 2, 80997, Munich, Germany
Tel.: (49) 8988990
Web Site: http://www.kraussmaffei.de
Holding Company
N.A.I.C.S.: 551112
Karlheinz Bourdon (Sr VP-Integration)

Holding (Domestic):

KraussMaffei Group GmbH (2)
Krauss-Maffei-Strasse 2, 80997, Munich, Germany
Tel.: (49) 89 88 990
Web Site: http://www.kraussmaffeigroup.com
Emp.: 4,500
Plastic & Rubber Machinery & Equipment Mfr
N.A.I.C.S.: 333248
Frank Stieler (CEO)

Subsidiary (Domestic):

KraussMaffei Berstorff GmbH (3)
An der Breiten Wiese 3 5, Hannover, 30625, Germany
Tel.: (49) 51157020
Web Site: http://www.kraussmaffeiberstorff.com
Rubber & Plastic Processing & Converting Services
N.A.I.C.S.: 333248
Paul Eberhard Kortmann (Mng Dir)

Subsidiary (Non-US):

KraussMaffei Group France SAS (3)
5 Allee Des Barbanniers, 92632, Gennevilliers, France
Tel.: (33) 146852525
Web Site: http://www.kraussmaffeigroup.fr
Injection Molding Machinery Mfr & Whslr
N.A.I.C.S.: 333248
Faredh Djaziri (Dir-Bus Dev-Maghreb & Francophone Africa)

KraussMaffei Group UK Ltd. (3)
410 Europa Boulevard Gemini Business Park, Warrington, WA5 7TR, Chesire, United Kingdom
Tel.: (44) 1925 644100
Web Site: http://www.kraussmaffeigroup.uk
Injection Molding Machinery Whslr
N.A.I.C.S.: 333248
Mike Bate (Mng Dir)

Pirelli & C. S.p.A. (1)
Viale Piero e Alberto Pirelli n 25, 20126, Milan, Italy
Tel.: (39) 0264421
Web Site: https://www.pirelli.com
Rev.: $5,660,275,259
Assets: $16,900,603,280
Liabilities: $11,309,839,036
Net Worth: $5,590,764,244
Earnings: $52,412,686
Emp.: 30,510
Fiscal Year-end: 12/31/2020
Tires, Tubes, Synthetic Rubber & Specialty Polymers Mfr
N.A.I.C.S.: 326211
Francesco Sala (Exec VP-Europe-Reg)

Subsidiary (Domestic):

Pirelli Ambiente S.r.l. (2)
Viale Piero e Alberto Pirelli n 25, 20126, Milan, Italy (100%)
Tel.: (39) 02 64421
Web Site: http://www.pirelli.com
Automotive & Industrial Tire Mfr
N.A.I.C.S.: 326211

Pirelli Servizi Finanziari S.p.A. (2)
Viale Piero e Alberto Pirelli n 25, 20126, Milan, Italy
Tel.: (39) 0264421
Web Site: http://www.pirelli.com
Financial Services
N.A.I.C.S.: 525990

Pirelli Sistemi Informativi S.r.l. (2)
Viale Piero e Alberto Pirelli n 25, 20126, Milan, Italy (100%)
Tel.: (39) 0264421
Web Site: http://www.pirelli.com
Data Storage Services
N.A.I.C.S.: 518210

Pirelli Tyre S.p.A. (2)
Viale Piero e Alberto Pirelli n 25, 20126, Milan, Italy (100%)
Tel.: (39) 0264421
Web Site: http://www.pirelli.com
Pneumatic Tires Mfr & Distr
N.A.I.C.S.: 326211
Ayhan Guven (CTO & Head-Change Mgmt)

Subsidiary (Non-US):

Deutsche Pirelli Reifen Holding GmbH (3)
Hochster Strasse 48-60, 64747, Breuberg, Germany
Tel.: (49) 6163710
Web Site: http://www.pirelli.com
Tire Mfr & Distr
N.A.I.C.S.: 326211

Subsidiary (Domestic):

Pirelli Deutschland GmbH (4)
Hochster Strasse 48-60, 64747, Breuberg, Germany (100%)
Tel.: (49) 6163 71 0
Web Site: http://www.pirelli.com
Tires & Rims Mfr & Distr
N.A.I.C.S.: 326211
Michael Wendt (Chm-Mgmt Bd)

Pirelli Personal Service GmbH (4)
Hochster Strasse 48-60, 64747, Breuberg, Germany (100%)
Tel.: (49) 6163 710
Web Site: http://www.pirelli.com
Automotive Tire Repair & Maintenance Services
N.A.I.C.S.: 811198

Subsidiary (Domestic):

Driver Italia S.p.A. (3)
Viale Piero e Alberto Pirelli n 25, 20126, Milan, Italy
Tel.: (39) 02 64421
Web Site: http://www.pirelli.com
Tire Mfr & Distr
N.A.I.C.S.: 326211

Subsidiary (Non-US):

Elastika Pirelli C.S.A. (3)
Vouliagmenis Avenue 580, Argyroupoli, 164 52, Athens, Greece (99.9%)
Tel.: (30) 210 519 1000
Web Site: http://www.pirelli.com
Tiles Mfr
N.A.I.C.S.: 326211

Subsidiary (Domestic):

Driver Hellas C.S.A. (4)
Vouliagmenis Avenue 580, Argyroupoli, 164 52, Athens, Greece (72.8%)
Tel.: (30) 210 5191000
Web Site: http://www.pirelli.com
Tiles Mfr
N.A.I.C.S.: 326211

Subsidiary (Non-US):

Pirelli China Tyre N.V. (3)
Weena 737, 3013 AM, Rotterdam, Netherlands (100%)
Tel.: (31) 900 3344 550
Web Site: http://www.pirelli.com
Tiles Mfr
N.A.I.C.S.: 326211

Subsidiary (Non-US):

Pirelli Tyre Co., Ltd (4)
Floor 16 Huahong Business Center No 5 Lane 388 Daduhe Road, Putuo District, Shanghai, China (90%)
Tel.: (86) 5373653319
Web Site: http://www.pirelli.com
Tire Mfr & Distr
N.A.I.C.S.: 326211

Subsidiary (Non-US):

Pirelli Comercial de Pneus Brasil Ltda (3)
Av Brigadeiro Faria Lima 4221-14 A, Itaim Bibi, 04538-133, Sao Paulo, Brazil (85%)
Tel.: (55) 11 4322 2000
Web Site: http://www.pirelli.com
Automotive & Industrial Tire Mfr
N.A.I.C.S.: 326211

Subsidiary (Domestic):

Comercial e Importadora de Pneus Ltda (4)
Av Brigadeiro Faria Lima 4221-14 A, Itaim Bibi, Sao Paulo, 04538-133, Brazil (100%)
Tel.: (55) 11 4322 2000
Web Site: http://www.pirelli.com
Automotive Tire Mfr & Distr
N.A.I.C.S.: 326211

Subsidiary (Domestic):

Pirelli Industrie Pneumatici S.r.l. (3)
Viale Piero e Alberto Pirelli n 25, 20126, Milan, Italy (100%)
Tel.: (39) 0264421
Web Site: http://www.pirelli.com
Automotive & Industrial Tire Mfr & Distr
N.A.I.C.S.: 326211

Subsidiary (Non-US):

Pirelli Japan K.K. (3)
3-5-5 Shiba 7F Shiba Koen Building, Minato-Ku, Tokyo, Japan (100%)
Tel.: (81) 120 29 3332

Web Site: http://www.pirelli.com
Tiles Mfr
N.A.I.C.S.: 326211

Pirelli Motorsport Services Ltd (3)
Derby Road, Burton-on-Trent, DE13 0BH, Staffs, United Kingdom (100%)
Tel.: (44) 1283525252
Tire Mfr & Distr
N.A.I.C.S.: 326211

Pirelli Neumaticos S.A. (3)
Plaza Europa 21-23 pl 7-9, L'Hospitalet del Llobregat, 08908, Barcelona, Spain (100%)
Tel.: (34) 933663500
Web Site: http://www.pirelli.com
Automotive & Industrial Tire Mfr
N.A.I.C.S.: 326211
Javier Caballero (Dir-Mktg)

Subsidiary (Domestic):

Omnia Motor S.A. (4)
Plaza Europa N 21-23 9th Floor, L'Hospitalet del Llobregat, 08908, Barcelona, Spain (100%)
Tel.: (34) 933663555
Web Site: http://www.omniamotor.com
Automotive & Industrial Tire Mfr
N.A.I.C.S.: 326211

Subsidiary (Non-US):

Pirelli Neumaticos S.A. de C.V. (3)
Boulevard Mineral de Penafiel 402 Puerto Interior, CP 36275, Silao, Guanajuato, Mexico (99.4%)
Tel.: (52) 5591382336
Web Site: http://www.pirelli.com
Tiles Mfr
N.A.I.C.S.: 326211

Pirelli Neumaticos S.A.I.C (3)
Cervantes 1901, 1722, Merlo, Argentina (66.5%)
Tel.: (54) 1144896600
Web Site: http://www.pirelli.com
Automotive & Industrial Tire Mfr
N.A.I.C.S.: 326211

Pirelli Neumaticos de Mexico S.A. de C.V. (3)
Boulevard Mineral de Penafiel 402 Puerto Interior, CP 36275, Silao, Guanajuato, Mexico (99.98%)
Tel.: (52) 55 9138 2345
Web Site: http://www.pirelli.com
Automotive Tire Mfr
N.A.I.C.S.: 326211

Subsidiary (US):

Pirelli North America Inc. (3)
100 Pirelli Dr, Rome, GA 30161-7000 (100%)
Tel.: (706) 368-5800
Web Site: http://www.us.pirelli.com
Holding Company; Regional Managing Office
N.A.I.C.S.: 551112

Subsidiary (Domestic):

Pirelli Tire LLC (4)
100 Pirelli Dr, Rome, GA 30161-7000 (100%)
Tel.: (706) 368-5800
Web Site: http://www.us.pirelli.com
Tires, Tubes, Synthetic Rubber & Specialty Polymers Mfr
N.A.I.C.S.: 326211
Pierluigi Dinelli (Chm/CEO-NAFTA)

Subsidiary (Non-US):

Pirelli Pneus Ltda (3)
Av Alexandre de Gusmao 397-Homero Thom, Santo Andre, 09111-310, SP, Brazil (85%)
Tel.: (55) 11 4998 5522
Tire Mfr & Distr
N.A.I.C.S.: 326211

Pirelli Polska Sp. z.o.o. (3)
Ul Klimczaka 1, 02-797, Warsaw, Poland (100%)
Tel.: (48) 225171000
Web Site: http://www.pirelli.com
Automotive & Industrial Tire Mfr

N.A.I.C.S.: 326211

Pirelli Slovakia S.R.O. **(3)**
Mileticova 23, 821 09, Bratislava,
Slovakia **(100%)**
Tel.: (421) 2 529 62 594
Web Site: http://www.pirelli.com
Tiles Mfr
N.A.I.C.S.: 326211

Pirelli Tyre (Suisse) SA **(3)**
Saint Jakobs-Strasse 54, CH 4052, Basel,
Switzerland **(100%)**
Tel.: (41) 613164111
Web Site: http://www.pirelli.com
Tiles Mfr
N.A.I.C.S.: 326211

Subsidiary (Non-US):

Pirelli Asia Pte. Limited **(4)**
77 Robinson #23-01, Singapore, 068896,
Singapore **(100%)**
Tel.: (65) 6709 3106
Web Site: http://www.pirelli.com
Tiles Mfr
N.A.I.C.S.: 326211

Pirelli GmbH **(4)**
Lembockgasse 47a A, 1230, Vienna,
Austria **(100%)**
Tel.: (43) 1250820
Web Site: http://www.pirelli.com
Automotive & Industrial Tire Mfr
N.A.I.C.S.: 326211

Pirelli Tire, Inc. **(4)**
1111 Blvd Dr Frederik-Philips Suite 506,
Saint Laurent, H4M 2X6, QC,
Canada **(100%)**
Tel.: (514) 331-4241
Web Site: http://www.pirelli.com
Tire Whslr
N.A.I.C.S.: 423130

Pirelli Tyre (Pty) Ltd **(4)**
Cambridge Park - Unit E 5 Bauhinia Street
Highveld Technopark, Centurion, South
Africa **(100%)**
Tel.: (27) 12 6655676
Web Site: http://www.pirelli.com
Automotive Tire Mfr
N.A.I.C.S.: 326211

Pirelli Tyre (Suisse) S.A. - Czech **(4)**
Na Pankraci 1062/58, 14000, Prague,
Czech Republic
Tel.: (420) 261215055
Web Site: http://www.pirelli.com
Tire Mfr & Distr
N.A.I.C.S.: 326211

Pirelli Tyres Australia Pty. Ltd. **(4)**
Level 10 37 York Street, Sydney, 2000,
NSW, Australia **(100%)**
Tel.: (61) 299886000
Web Site: http://www.pirelli.com
Automotive & Industrial Tire Mfr
N.A.I.C.S.: 326211

Pirelli Tyres Belux S.A. **(4)**
Lenniksebaan 451 Route de Lennik, 1070,
Brussels, Belgium **(100%)**
Tel.: (32) 2 510 10 00
Web Site: http://www.pirelli.com
Automotive & Industrial Tire Mfr
N.A.I.C.S.: 326211

Pirelli Tyres Nederland B.V. **(4)**
Weena 737, 3013 AM, Rotterdam,
Netherlands **(100%)**
Tel.: (31) 900 3344550
Web Site: http://www.pirelli.com
Automotive & Industrial Tire Mfr
N.A.I.C.S.: 326211

Subsidiary (Non-US):

Pirelli Tyre Nordic AB **(3)**
Gustavslundsvagen 141, PO Box 14147,
Bromma, 16714, Stockholm,
Sweden **(100%)**
Tel.: (46) 86220850
Web Site: http://www.pirelli.com
Automotive & Industrial Tire Mfr
N.A.I.C.S.: 326211

Pirelli Tyres Alexandria Co. **(3)**
Km 36 Alexandria Cairo Desert Rd El
Nahda Rd El Ameria, Alexandria, Egypt
Tel.: (20) 3 45 40 454

Web Site: http://www.pirelli.com
Tiles Mfr
N.A.I.C.S.: 326211

Pirelli UK Tyres Limited **(3)**
Derby Road, Burton-on-Trent, DE13 0BH,
Staffs, United Kingdom **(100%)**
Tel.: (44) 1283525252
Web Site: http://www.pirelli.com
Tiles Mfr
N.A.I.C.S.: 326211
Wayne Nickless *(Dir-Mktg)*

Subsidiary (Domestic):

Pirelli Tyres Ltd **(4)**
Derby Road, Burton-on-Trent, DE13 0BH,
Staffs, United Kingdom **(100%)**
Tel.: (44) 1 283 525252
Web Site: http://www.pirelli.com
Automotive Tire Mfr
N.A.I.C.S.: 326211

Subsidiary (Non-US):

Pneus Pirelli SAS **(3)**
Immeuble le Rameau Paris Nord 2-22 av-
enue des Nations, BP 43021, Villepinte
Roissy, 95911, Paris, Cedex,
France **(100%)**
Tel.: (33) 149897777
Web Site: http://www.pirelli.com
Automotive & Industrial Tire Mfr
N.A.I.C.S.: 326211

**S.C. Pirelli Tyres Romania
S.R.L.** **(3)**
Str Draganesti nr 35, 230150, Slatina, Olt,
Romania **(100%)**
Tel.: (40) 249 507349
Web Site: http://www.pirelli.com
Automotive & Industrial Tire Mfr
N.A.I.C.S.: 326211

Subsidiary (Non-US):

Pirelli UK Limited **(2)**
Derby Road, Burton-on-Trent, DE13 0BH,
Staffs, United Kingdom **(100%)**
Tel.: (44) 1283525252
Web Site: http://www.pirelli.com
Holding Company; Regional Managing Of-
fice
N.A.I.C.S.: 551112

Subsidiary (Domestic):

Servizi Aziendali Pirelli S.C.p.A. **(2)**
Viale Piero e Alberto Pirelli n 25, 20126,
Milan, Italy **(91.32%)**
Tel.: (39) 02 64421
Web Site: http://www.pirelli.com
Office Services
N.A.I.C.S.: 561110

T.P. Industrial Holding S.p.A. **(2)**
Viale Piero e Alberto Pirelli n 25, 20126,
Milan, Italy
Tel.: (39) 0264421
Web Site: http://www.pirelli.com
Holding Company
N.A.I.C.S.: 551112

Subsidiary (Domestic):

Prometeon Tyre Group S.r.l. **(3)**
Viale Sarca 222, 20126, Milan,
Italy **(52%)**
Tel.: (39) 01189561
Web Site: http://www.prometeon.com
Emp.: 7,300
Tire Mfr & Distr
N.A.I.C.S.: 326211

**Qingdao Rubber Six Conveyor Belt
Co, LTD** **(1)**
Hua YangLu 36, Qingdao, China
Tel.: (86) 532 83848888
Web Site: http://www.rubber6.com
Rubber Products Mfr
N.A.I.C.S.: 326299

**Sichuan BlueStar Machinery Co,
Ltd** **(1)**
678 Jinsha West Rd Deyang Economic &
Technological Development Zone, Deyang,
618000, Sichuan, China
Tel.: (86) 838 2607800
Web Site: http://www.sc-bluestar.com.cn
Emp.: 1,000
Industrial Machinery Mfr

N.A.I.C.S.: 333998

**Siping Haohua Chemical Co.,
Ltd.** **(1)**
No 936 North Second Street, Tiedong Dis-
trict, Siping, 136001, Jilin, China
Tel.: (86) 434 3536029
Web Site: http://www.hhsp.chemchina.com
Emp.: 3,000
Chemical Products Mfr
N.A.I.C.S.: 325199

Syngenta AG **(1)**
Schwarzwaldalle 215, 4058, Basel, Switzer-
land
Tel.: (41) 61 323 1111
Web Site: http://www.syngenta.com
Sales Range: $5-14.9 Billion
Emp.: 49,000
Agribusiness Holding Company
N.A.I.C.S.: 325311
Jeff Rowe *(Pres-Global Seeds)*

Subsidiary (Non-US):

Maribo Seed International ApS **(2)**
Hojbygardvej 31, 4960, Holeby, Denmark
Tel.: (45) 5446 0700
Web Site: http://www.mariboseed.com
Emp.: 350
Sugar Beet Seed Production Services
N.A.I.C.S.: 111991
Thomas Hansen *(Dir-Sls)*

O.O.O. Syngenta **(2)**
2 Letnikovskaya street bldg 3, 115114, Mos-
cow, Russia **(100%)**
Tel.: (7) 4956281687
Web Site: http://www.syngenta.ru
Soil Preparation, Planting & Cultivating
N.A.I.C.S.: 115112

**Syngenta (China) Investment Com-
pany Limited** **(2)**
6F FuHui Mansion No 3 Lane 26th QiXia
Road, 200120, Shanghai, China
Tel.: (86) 21 3865 1800
Investment Management Service
N.A.I.C.S.: 523999

Subsidiary (Domestic):

Syngenta Agro AG **(2)**
Rudolf-Maag-Strasse, 8157, Dielsdorf, Swit-
zerland
Tel.: (41) 448558877
Crop Protection Chemical Mfr
N.A.I.C.S.: 325320

Subsidiary (Non-US):

Syngenta Agro GmbH **(3)**
Am Technologiepark 1-5, 63477, Maintal,
Germany
Tel.: (49) 6181 9081 0
Web Site: http://www.syngenta.de
Crop Protection Agents Distr
N.A.I.C.S.: 424690

Syngenta Agro S.A **(3)**
Calle de la Ribera de Loira 8-10 3rd Floor,
28042, Madrid, Spain
Tel.: (34) 91 387 6410
Web Site: http://www.syngenta.es
Agricultural Chemical Mfr
N.A.I.C.S.: 325320

Syngenta Agro Services AG **(3)**
77 Lotissement Mohamed Saidoun, Kouba,
Algiers, Algeria
Tel.: (213) 21 28 64 64
Agrochemical Products Distr
N.A.I.C.S.: 424690

Syngenta Agro d.o.o. **(3)**
Samoborska 147, 10000, Zagreb, Croatia
Tel.: (385) 1 388 76 70
Web Site: http://www.syngenta.hr
Emp.: 21
Agriculture Product Distr
N.A.I.C.S.: 424910

Syngenta Agro, S.A. de C.V. **(3)**
Avenida Insurgentes Sur #1431 12th floor,
Col Insurgantes, Mexico, CP 03920, Mexico
Tel.: (52) 5591839199
Web Site: http://www.syngenta.com.mx
Agricultural Chemical Mfr
N.A.I.C.S.: 325199

Syngenta Polska Sp. z o.o **(3)**

Gyneju g 16, LT-01109, Vilnius, Lithuania
Tel.: (370) 52 420 013
Agricultural Chemical Distr
N.A.I.C.S.: 424690
Arnoldas Cepele *(Mgr-Product Dev)*

Syngenta Polska Sp. z o.o **(3)**
Atmodas 19-213, Jelgava, 3007, Latvia
Tel.: (371) 6 30 25626
Web Site: http://www.syngenta.lv
Agricultural Chemical Distr
N.A.I.C.S.: 424690
Oridigus Caplikas *(Gen Mgr)*

Subsidiary (Non-US):

Syngenta Asia Pacific Pte. Ltd. **(2)**
1 Harbourfront Ave 03-03/10 Keppel Bay
Tower, Singapore, 098632, Singapore
Tel.: (65) 6333 6400
Agricultural Farm Crop Distr
N.A.I.C.S.: 424910

Syngenta Bangladesh Limited **(2)**
5th Floor Green Rawshan Ara Tower 755
Satmasjid Road, Dhanmondi, Dhaka, 1205,
Bangladesh
Tel.: (880) 2 9142581 3
Web Site: http://www.syngenta.com.bd
Agricultural Chemical Distr
N.A.I.C.S.: 424910

Syngenta Bulgaria EOOD **(2)**
Tsarigradsko Shose blvd 115 M Hermes
Park building D floor 6, 1784, Sofia, Bul-
garia
Tel.: (359) 28004000
Web Site: http://www.syngenta.bg
Agricultural Chemical Mfr
N.A.I.C.S.: 325320

Syngenta Canada Inc. **(2)**
140 Research Lane Research Park,
Guelph, N1G 4Z3, ON, Canada **(100%)**
Tel.: (519) 836-5665
Web Site: http://www.syngenta.ca
Emp.: 350
Crop Protection Chemicals Distr
N.A.I.C.S.: 424910

Subsidiary (US):

Syngenta Corporation **(2)**
3411 Silverside Rd Ste 100, Wilmington, DE
19809
Tel.: (302) 425-2000
Web Site: http://www.syngenta-us.com
Holding Company; Regional Managing Of-
fice; Agricultural Products Mfr & Distr
N.A.I.C.S.: 551112
Laure Roberts *(Head-HR)*

Subsidiary (Domestic):

Ag Connections, LLC **(3)**
111 Poplar St Ste 212, Murray, KY 42071
Tel.: (270) 435-4369
Web Site: http://www.agconnections.com
Computer System Design Services
N.A.I.C.S.: 541512
Joe Bogle *(Mgr-Product)*

GreenLeaf Genetics LLC **(3)**
1330 Lagoon Ave, Minneapolis, MN 55408
Tel.: (612) 656-8600
Web Site: http://www.syngenta-us.com
Scientific Information Services
N.A.I.C.S.: 519290
Dave Treinen *(Head)*

Syngenta Crop Protection, LLC **(3)**
3411 Silverside Rd Ste 100, Wilmington, DE
19810
Tel.: (336) 632-6000
Web Site:
  http://www.syngentacropprotection.com
Agricultural Chemical Mfr
N.A.I.C.S.: 325320
Mark Coffelt *(Head-Technical Svcs-
Greensboro)*

Subsidiary (Domestic):

Syngenta Crop Protection, Inc. **(4)**
3905 Hwy 75 River Rd PO Box 1, Saint Gabriel, LA 70776
Tel.: (225) 642-1100
Web Site:
  http://www.syngentacropprotection.com
Pesticides, Seed Production & Other Agricultural Chemicals Mfr

China National Chemical Corporation—(Continued)

N.A.I.C.S.: 325320

Subsidiary (Domestic):

Syngenta Seeds, LLC (3)
1330 Lagoon Ave, Minneapolis, MN 55408
Tel.: (612) 656-8600
Web Site: http://www.syngenta.com
Brooding, Production, Conditioning & Marketing of Field Crop Seeds
N.A.I.C.S.: 424910
David Hollinrake (Head-Strategy & Portfolio Mgmt-Global)

Subsidiary (Domestic):

Syngenta Crop Protection AG (2)
Rosentalstrasse 67, 4002, Basel, Switzerland
Tel.: (41) 613231111
Crop Protection Chemical Mfr
N.A.I.C.S.: 325320
Alexandra Brand (Reg Dir-Europe, Africa & Middle East)

Subsidiary (Non-US):

Syngenta Crop Protection - Finland Office (3)
Loukkutie 4, 21110, Naantali, Finland
Tel.: (358) 2 436 7151
Web Site: http://www.syngenta.fi
Agricultural Chemicals & Seed Distr
N.A.I.C.S.: 424690

Syngenta Crop Protection A/S (3)
Strandlodsvej 44, 2300, Copenhagen, Denmark
Tel.: (45) 3287 1100
Web Site: http://www.syngenta.dk
Agricultural Chemical Distr
N.A.I.C.S.: 424690

Syngenta Crop Protection B.V. (3)
Jacob Obrechtlaan 7a, 4611 AP, Bergen-op-Zoom, Netherlands (100%)
Tel.: (31) 164225500
Web Site: http://www.syngenta.nl
Plant Breeding, Seed Merchants
N.A.I.C.S.: 115112

Syngenta Crop Protection Limited (3)
25 th Fl Tower A Cyberworld Tower 90 Ratchadapisek Road, Huai Khwang, Bangkok, 10310, Thailand
Tel.: (66) 2 201 4999
Web Site: http://www.syngenta.co.th
Plant Protection Chemicals Mfr
N.A.I.C.S.: 325320

Subsidiary (Domestic):

Syngenta Crop Protection Monthey SA (3)
Route de l Ile-au-Bois, 1870, Monthey, Switzerland
Tel.: (41) 244752111
Web Site: http://www.syngenta.ch
Agricultural Chemical Distr
N.A.I.C.S.: 424910

Syngenta Crop Protection Munchwilen AG (3)
Breitenloh 5, 4333, Munchwilen, Switzerland
Tel.: (41) 628685111
Web Site: http://www.syngenta.com
Agricultural Chemical Mfr
N.A.I.C.S.: 325320

Subsidiary (Non-US):

Syngenta Crop Protection S.A. (3)
Sucursal Peru Calle Rene Descartes 170 Urb Santa Raquel II, Ate, Peru
Tel.: (51) 13484834
Agricultural Chemical Product Mfr
N.A.I.C.S.: 325320

Syngenta Crop Protection Sdn Bhd (3)
MR1-02-02 Sri Acappella Commercial Annex, No 1 Jalan Lompat Tinggi 13/33 Seksyen 13, 40100, Shah Alam, Selangor Darul Ehsan, Malaysia
Tel.: (60) 3 55109878
Plant Protection Chemicals Distr
N.A.I.C.S.: 424910

Syngenta Polska Sp. z o.o. (3)
Szamocka 8, 01-797, Warsaw, Poland
Tel.: (48) 22 32 606 01
Web Site: http://www.syngenta.pl
Crop Protection Products Distr
N.A.I.C.S.: 424910

Syngenta Protecao de Cultivos Ltda. (3)
Avenida Das Nacoes Unidas 17007 Torre Sigma 11 andar, Varzea de Baixo, Sao Paulo, 04730-000, Brazil (100%)
Tel.: (55) 56432322
Web Site: http://www.syngenta.com.br
Mfr & Sale of Herbicides, Fungicides, Insecticides, Rodenticides, Colors, Reactives, Vats, Coriacids, Sodium Silicate & Merchanting of ICI & Other Products
N.A.I.C.S.: 325320
Wellington Ribeiro (Mgr-Mktg Comm)

Syngenta UK Limited (3)
CPC4 Capital Park, Fulbourn, Cambridge, CB21 5XE, United Kingdom
Tel.: (44) 1223 883400
Web Site: http://www.syngenta-crop.co.uk
Crop Protection Chemicals Distr
N.A.I.C.S.: 424690

Subsidiary (Non-US):

Syngenta Czech s.r.o. (2)
Bucharova 1314/8 building D floor 12, Prague, 158 00, Czech Republic
Tel.: (420) 2 220 90 411
Web Site: http://www.syngenta.cz
Agricultural Chemical Distr
N.A.I.C.S.: 424910

Syngenta Finance N.V. (2)
Westeinde 62, 1601 BK, Enkhuizen, Netherlands
Tel.: (31) 28366411
Financial Management Services
N.A.I.C.S.: 523999

Syngenta Grangemouth (2)
Centre Earls Road, Grangemouth, FK3 8XG, United Kingdom (100%)
Tel.: (44) 1324662100
Web Site: http://www.syngenta.co.uk
Emp.: 350
Chemicals Mfr
N.A.I.C.S.: 325998

Syngenta Ireland Limited (2)
Block 6 Cleaboy Business Park Old Kilmeaden Road, Waterford, Ireland
Tel.: (353) 51 377203
Web Site: http://www.syngenta.ie
Agricultural Chemical Distr
N.A.I.C.S.: 424690

Syngenta Japan Co., Ltd. (2)
21st Floor Office Tower X 1-8-10 Harumi, Chuo-ku, Tokyo, 104-6021, Japan
Tel.: (81) 3 6221 1001
Web Site: http://www.syngenta.co.jp
Crops & Commercial Seed Distr
N.A.I.C.S.: 424910
Minoru Matoba (Pres & CEO)

Syngenta LAN (2)
5 Ave 5-55 Zona 14 Europlaza Torre 3 Nivel 8 Ofi 802, Guatemala, Guatemala
Tel.: (502) 2 312 7000
Web Site: http://www.syngenta.com.gt
Agricultural Chemical Distr
N.A.I.C.S.: 424910

Syngenta Ltd. (2)
CPC4 Capital Park Fulbourn, Cambridge, CB21 5XE, United Kingdom (100%)
Tel.: (44) 1223 883400
Web Site: http://www.syngenta.co.uk
Plant Breeding, Seed Merchants
N.A.I.C.S.: 115112

Syngenta S.A. (2)
Costa Del Este Av La Rotonda Edificio Torre V piso 12, PO Box 832-0063, WTC, Panama, Panama
Tel.: (507) 2708200
Web Site: http://www.syngenta.com.pa
Agriculture Product Distr
N.A.I.C.S.: 424910

Syngenta Seedco (Pty) Limited (2)
Block 10 Thornhill Office Park 94 Bekker Street, PO Box X60, Halfway House, Midrand, 1685, South Africa

Tel.: (27) 115414000
Web Site: http://www.syngenta.co.za
Agricultural Products & Services
N.A.I.C.S.: 115112
Clara Mohashoa (Mgr)

Syngenta Seeds A/S (2)
Strandlodsvej 44, 2300, Copenhagen, Denmark
Tel.: (45) 32871100
Web Site: http://www.syngenta.dk
Agricultural & Horticultural Products Distr
N.A.I.C.S.: 424930
Carsten Lundsteen (Head-Seeds)

Syngenta Seeds B.V. (2)
Westeinde 62, 1601 BK, Enkhuizen, Netherlands
Tel.: (31) 228366411
Web Site: http://www.syngenta.nl
Nursery & Tree Production
N.A.I.C.S.: 111421

Syngenta Seeds Co. Ltd. (2)
18 floor Cheil Bank HQ Buil 100 Gongpyong-dong, Chongro-gu, Seoul, 110-702, Korea (South)
Tel.: (82) 2 3985 650
Web Site: http://www.syngenta.co.kr
Agricultural & Horticultural Products Distr
N.A.I.C.S.: 424910

Syngenta Seeds GmbH (2)
Zum Knipkenbach 20, 32107, Bad Salzuflen, Germany
Tel.: (49) 3940891390
Agricultural & Horticultural Services
N.A.I.C.S.: 115112

Syngenta Seeds N.V. (2)
Technologiepark 30, 9052, Gent, Belgium
Tel.: (32) 9 210 17 60
Web Site: http://www.syngenta.com
Agriculture Product Distr
N.A.I.C.S.: 424510

Syngenta Slovakia s.r.o. (2)
Prievozska 4/d, 821 09, Bratislava, Slovakia
Tel.: (421) 2 49 10 80 11
Web Site: http://www.syngenta.sk
Plant Protection Products Distr
N.A.I.C.S.: 424910

Syngenta South Africa (Pty) Limited (2)
Block 10 Thornhill Office Park 94 Bekker Street, PO Box X60, Halfway House, Midrand, 1685, South Africa
Tel.: (27) 11 541 4000
Web Site: http://www.syngenta.co.za
Agriculture Product Distr
N.A.I.C.S.: 424510
Antonie Delport (Mng Dir & Head)

Syngenta Taiwan Ltd (2)
District B 11th Floor No 2 Section 1 Dunhua South Road, Songshan District, Taipei, 105, Taiwan
Tel.: (886) 2 2559 2901
Web Site: http://www.syngenta.com.tw
Agricultural Chemical Distr
N.A.I.C.S.: 424910

Syngenta Treasury N.V. (2)
Westeinde 62, Enkhuizen, 1601 BK, Netherlands
Tel.: (31) 228366411
Investment Management Service
N.A.I.C.S.: 523999

Tianjin Univtech Co., Ltd. (1)
West Anshan Road No 171, Nankai District, Tianjin, 300072, China
Tel.: (86) 22 27404420
Web Site: http://www.hhjt.chemchina.com
Chemical Products Mfr
N.A.I.C.S.: 325199

Xingtai Hengyuan Chemical Group Co., Ltd. (1)
3 km north to Neiqiu, Xingtai, 054200, Hebei, China
Tel.: (86) 319 686 2248
Web Site: http://www.hhhy.chemchina.com
Emp.: 450
Chemical Products Mfr
N.A.I.C.S.: 325199
Yang Zhenlin (Chm)

Yiyang Rubber & Plastics Machinery Group Co, Ltd (1)

180 Huilong Rd, Yiyang, 413000, Hunan, China
Tel.: (86) 737 620 5808
Web Site: http://www.yyxj.chemchina.com
Plastic Injection Molding Machine Mfr
N.A.I.C.S.: 333248

Subsidiary (Domestic):

Yiyang Zhonghai Shipyard Co, Ltd (2)
No 128 Zhixi Road, Yiyang, 413000, China
Tel.: (86) 737 4260939
Web Site: http://www.yyzhs.com
Emp.: 700
Ship Building Services
N.A.I.C.S.: 336611

CHINA NATIONAL CHEMICAL ENGINEERING CO., LTD.
No 2 Dongzhimennei Street, Dongcheng District, Beijing, 100007, China
Tel.: (86) 1059765575　　CN
Web Site: https://www.cncec.com.cn
Year Founded: 1953
601117—(SSE)
Rev.: $25,159,093,423
Assets: $30,763,790,892
Liabilities: $21,768,059,339
Net Worth: $8,995,731,553
Earnings: $844,982,051
Fiscal Year-end: 12/31/23
Construction Engineering Services
N.A.I.C.S.: 541330
Xiangong Wu (Deputy Gen Mgr)

Subsidiaries:

China Chemical Engineering Second Construction Corporation (1)
Huajian Building No 9 Xieyuan Road, Changfeng Business District, Taiyuan, 030021, Shanxi, China
Tel.: (86) 3516599047
Web Site: http://www.ccescc.com
Engineeering Services
N.A.I.C.S.: 541330

China Chemical Guilin Engineering Co., Ltd. (1)
77 Qixing Road, Guilin, 541004, China
Tel.: (86) 7735833005
Web Site: http://www.cgec.com.cn
Engineeering Services
N.A.I.C.S.: 541330

China Eleventh Chemical Construction Co., Ltd. (1)
No 53 Bianjing Road, Kaifeng, 475002, Henan, China
Tel.: (86) 37122905559
Web Site: http://www.en.eleco.com.cn
Engineeering Services
N.A.I.C.S.: 541330
Han Changen (Gen Mgr & Sr Engr)

China National Chemical Engineering No.14 Construction Co., Ltd. (1)
No 148 Xinhua Road, Jiangbei New District, Nanjing, Jiangsu, China
Tel.: (86) 2558380761
Web Site: https://www.14hj.com
Engineeering Services
N.A.I.C.S.: 541330

China National Chemical Engineering No.16 Construction Company (1)
No 79 Xiling 2nd Road, Xiling District, Yichang, 443000, Hubei, China
Tel.: (86) 7176835664
Web Site: https://www.cncec16.com.cn
Engineeering Services
N.A.I.C.S.: 541330
Wang Songbai (Deputy Gen Mgr)

China National Chemical Engineering No.7 Construction Company Ltd. (1)
No 537 Longdunan Road, Longquanyi District, Chengdu, 610100, Sichuan, China
Tel.: (86) 2868897777
Web Site: http://www.cnce7.com
Engineeering Services
N.A.I.C.S.: 541330

China National Chemical Engineering Sixth Construction Co., Ltd. (1)

No 1 Nanshan Road, Dongjin New District, Xiangyang, 441100, Hubei, China
Tel.: (86) 7102695685
Web Site: https://en.scccnce.com.cn
Fine Chemical Engineering Services
N.A.I.C.S.: 541330

China Tianchen Engineering Corporation　　(1)
No 1 Jingjin Road, Beichen Disrict, Tianjin, 300400, China
Tel.: (86) 2223408999
Web Site: http://www.china-tcc.com
Emp.: 2,000
Engineeering Services
N.A.I.C.S.: 541330

Hualu Engineering & Technology Co., Ltd.　　(1)
Hualu Building No 7 South Tangyan Road, Hi-tech Development Zone, Xi'an, 710065, Shaanxi, China
Tel.: (86) 2987988000
Web Site:
　https://www.en.chinahualueng.com
Engineeering Services
N.A.I.C.S.: 541330

Sedin Engineering Co., Ltd.　　(1)
No 1 Saiding Rd Jinyang St, Xuefu District, Taiyuan, 030032, Shanxi, China
Tel.: (86) 3512179092
Engineeering Services
N.A.I.C.S.: 541330

The Fourth Construction Corporation　　(1)
No 356 Zhongshan West Rd, Shijiazhuang, 050051, Hebei, China
Tel.: (86) 31166033500
Web Site: http://www.cefoc.com
Automation Engineering Services
N.A.I.C.S.: 541330

Wuhuan Engineering Co., Ltd.　　(1)
No 1019 Minzu Avenue, East Lake New Technology Development Zone, Wuhan, 430223, China
Tel.: (86) 2781927319
Web Site: https://www.cwcec.com
Engineeering Services
N.A.I.C.S.: 541330

CHINA NATIONAL COMPLETE PLANT IMPORT & EXPORT CORPORATION

Complant Mansion 9 Xi Bin He Lu An Ding Men, Beijing, 100011, China
Tel.: (86) 1064253388
Web Site: http://www.complant.com
Year Founded: 1959
Construction & Engineering Services
N.A.I.C.S.: 237990
Liu Yan *(Chm)*

Subsidiaries:

Hua Lien International (Holding) Company Limited　　(1)
Room 1701 17/F World-Wide House 19 Des Voeux Road, Central, China (Hong Kong)
Tel.: (852) 27952608
Rev.: $18,211,463
Assets: $13,647,600
Liabilities: $147,921,930
Net Worth: ($134,274,330)
Earnings: ($5,799,848)
Emp.: 137
Fiscal Year-end: 12/31/2022
Holding Company
N.A.I.C.S.: 551112
Xueyi Liu *(Exec Dir)*

CHINA NATIONAL CULTURE GROUP LTD.

Office Unit 403 4th Floor Wing Tuck Commercial Centre, 177-183 Wing Lok Street, Sheung Wan, China (Hong Kong)
Tel.: (852) 5 802 5231　　Ky
Web Site: http://www.cncg-media.com
0745—(HKG)
Rev.: $10,072,693

Assets: $13,130,938
Liabilities: $4,637,605
Net Worth: $8,493,333
Earnings: ($7,263,767)
Emp.: 22
Fiscal Year-end: 03/31/21
Movie Production & Distribution Services
N.A.I.C.S.: 512110

CHINA NATIONAL ELECTRIC APPARATUS RESEARCH INSTITUTE CO., LTD.

No 204 West Xingang Road, Guangzhou, 510300, China
Tel.: (86) 2089050888
Web Site: https://www.cei1958.com
Year Founded: 1987
688128—(SHG)
Rev.: $532,752,195
Assets: $877,335,816
Liabilities: $501,580,418
Net Worth: $375,755,398
Earnings: $51,009,342
Emp.: 150
Fiscal Year-end: 12/31/22
Electrical Equipment Mfr & Distr
N.A.I.C.S.: 335999
Xiaobin Zhang *(Chm)*

Subsidiaries:

Guangzhou Kinte Desheng Intelligent Equipment Co., Ltd.　　(1)
No 16 Yufeng Road, Shiling Town Huadu District, Guangzhou, 510860, China
Tel.: (86) 18926128992
Web Site: https://www.kinteconveyor.com
Automation Electrical Appliance Mfr

Guangzhou Kinte Electric Industrial Co., Ltd.　　(1)
No 16 Yufeng Road, Shiling Town Huadu District, Guangzhou, 510860, China
Tel.: (86) 2086985899
Web Site: https://www.kinte.com.cn
Home Appliance & Mold Mfr
N.A.I.C.S.: 333511

Guangzhou Kinte Industrial Co., Ltd.　　(1)
No 16 Yufeng Road, Shiling Town Huadu District, Guangzhou, China
Tel.: (86) 2086985888
Web Site: https://www.kinte-ind.com
Battery Testing Equipment Mfr & Distr
N.A.I.C.S.: 334515

Guangzhou Kinte Material Technology Co., Ltd.　　(1)
No 16 Yufeng Road, Shiling Town Huadu District, Guangzhou, 510850, China
Tel.: (86) 2086985856
Electronic & Electrical Equipment Services
N.A.I.C.S.: 811310

CHINA NATIONAL GOLD GROUP GOLD JEWELLERY CO., LTD.

No 1 Liuyin Park South Street Anwai Street, Dongcheng, Beijing, 100011, China
Tel.: (86) 1084115629
Web Site:
　http://www.chnau99999.com
Year Founded: 2010
600916—(SHG)
Rev.: $6,616,247,087
Assets: $1,632,890,301
Liabilities: $649,835,798
Net Worth: $983,054,503
Earnings: $107,452,753
Fiscal Year-end: 12/31/22
Jewelry Product Distr
N.A.I.C.S.: 458310
Xiongwei Chen *(Chm)*

CHINA NATIONAL MACHIN-

ERY INDUSTRY CORPORA-TION

No 3 Danling Street, Haidian District, Beijing, 100080, China
Tel.: (86) 1082688888
Web Site:
　https://www.sinomach.com.cn
Year Founded: 1997
Sales Range: $25-49.9 Billion
Emp.: 140,000
Investment Management Service
N.A.I.C.S.: 523940
Ding Hongxiang *(VP)*

Subsidiaries:

Changchun Research Institute for Mechanical Science Co., Ltd.　　(1)
No 1118 Yueda Road High-Tech Zone Changchun, Jilin, 130103, China
Tel.: (86) 43185187033
Web Site: http://www.ccss.com.cn
Automobile Parts Distr
N.A.I.C.S.: 423110
Xie Jianyu *(Project Mgr-HR)*

China CAMC Engineering Co., Ltd.　　(1)
SINOMACH Plaza NO 3 Danling Street, Haidian District, Beijing, 100080, China
Tel.: (86) 1082688866
Web Site: https://www.camce.com.cn
Rev.: $1,364,300,496
Assets: $3,067,897,248
Liabilities: $1,509,808,248
Net Worth: $1,558,089,000
Earnings: $46,896,408
Emp.: 10,000
Fiscal Year-end: 12/31/2022
Construction Engineering Services
N.A.I.C.S.: 541330
Bo Wang *(Chm)*

China Cmiic Engineering & Construction Corp.　　(1)
5 Building 5 South Alley San Li He Road, Xicheng District, Beijing, 100045, China
Tel.: (86) 1068595600
Web Site: http://www.sinoconst.com.cn
Automobile Parts Distr
N.A.I.C.S.: 423110

China National Automation Control System Corp.　　(1)
No 2 in Tuanjiehu Beilu Road, Beijing, 100026, China
Tel.: (86) 1065823388
Web Site: http://www.cacs.com.cn
Automobile Parts Distr
N.A.I.C.S.: 423110

China National Automotive Industry International Corp.　　(1)
Tower A No 3 Danling Street, Haidian District, Beijing, 100080, China
Tel.: (86) 10 82606899
Web Site: http://www.en.cnaico.com.cn
Automobile Parts Distr
N.A.I.C.S.: 423110

China National Erzhong Group Co.　　(1)
No 460 West Zhujiang Road, Deyang, 618013, Sichuan, China
Tel.: (86) 2862338767
Web Site: http://www.china-erzhong.com
Automobile Parts Distr
N.A.I.C.S.: 423110
Wang Lichuan *(Mgr-Sls)*

China National General Machinery Engineering Corp　　(1)
A2 Taiping St, Xuanwu District, Beijing, 100050, China
Tel.: (86) 1063133888
Web Site: http://www.cgme.com.cn
Automobile Parts Distr
N.A.I.C.S.: 423110
Jin Huang *(Pres)*

China National Heavy Machinery Corporation　　(1)
No Jia 23 Fuxing Road, Gongzhufen, Beijing, 100036, China
Tel.: (86) 1068211861
Web Site: http://www.chmc2003.com
Automobile Parts Distr

N.A.I.C.S.: 423110

China National Machinery & Equipment I/E Corp　　(1)
11-12/FL JINHE Bldg 1008 Jiefangeast Rd, Wuxi, China
Tel.: (86) 51082301550
Web Site: http://www.cmecwuxi.com
Automobile Parts Distr
N.A.I.C.S.: 423110

China Ocean Aviation Group Incorporation　　(1)
No 36 Cuiwei Road, Haidian District, Beijing, 100036, China
Tel.: (86) 1063984671
Web Site: http://www.coagi.com.cn
Automobile Parts Distr
N.A.I.C.S.: 423110

China Perfect Machinery Industry Corp., Ltd.　　(1)
North Road 24th Floor Block D 1759, Zhongshan, Shanghai, 200061, China
Tel.: (86) 2161397700
Web Site: http://www.chinaperfect.com.cn
Automobile Parts Distr
N.A.I.C.S.: 423110

China Sinomach Heavy Industry Corporation Ltd.　　(1)
Av Guangshunbei No16 Palacio Huacai Barrio, Chaoyang, Beijing, 100102, China
Tel.: (86) 1057387927
Automobile Parts Distr
N.A.I.C.S.: 423110

SINOMACH Capital Management Corporation　　(1)
11th Floor Huapu International Plaza No19 Chaowai Dajie, Chaoyang Dist, Beijing, 100020, China
Tel.: (86) 1065802288
Web Site: http://www.sino-capital.com.cn
Automobile Parts Distr
N.A.I.C.S.: 423110

Sinomach Automobile Co., Ltd.　　(1)
2-1605 No 2 Rongyuan Road Huayuan Industrial Zone, Binhai High-tech Zone, Tianjin, 100190, China
Tel.: (86) 1082169288
Web Site: https://www.sinomach-auto.com
Rev.: $5,555,503,409
Assets: $4,564,393,147
Liabilities: $2,992,827,207
Net Worth: $1,571,565,940
Earnings: $44,727,621
Fiscal Year-end: 12/31/2022
Automobile Whslr
N.A.I.C.S.: 423110
Dai Min *(Chm)*

Sinomach Precision Industry Co., Ltd.　　(1)
Building A Jian Ye Zongbugang No18 Dirun Road, Zheng Dong New District, Zhengzhou, 450018, Henan, China
Tel.: (86) 37167617777
Web Site: http://www.sinomach-pt.com
Automobile Parts Distr
N.A.I.C.S.: 423110

Sumec Corporation Limited　　(1)
SUMEC Building No 198 Changjiang Road, Xuanwu District, Nanjing, 210018, China　　**(41.6%)**
Tel.: (86) 2584511888
Web Site: https://www.sumec.com
Rev.: $20,451,849,671
Assets: $7,678,004,554
Liabilities: $5,737,535,806
Net Worth: $1,940,468,748
Earnings: $132,706,708
Emp.: 16,593
Fiscal Year-end: 12/31/2022
Automobile Parts Distr
N.A.I.C.S.: 423110

Subsidiary (US):

Berkshire Blanket Incorporated　　(2)
44 E Main St, Ware, MA 01082
Web Site: http://www.berkshireblanket.com
Sales Range: $25-49.9 Million
Blankets & Manmade Fiber Mfr
N.A.I.C.S.: 313210
Scott Maddalene *(Pres)*

CHINA NATIONAL MATERIALS

CHINA NATIONAL MATERIALS —(CONTINUED)

COMPANY LIMITED

8th Floor Building 2 Guohai Plaza No
17 Fuxing Road, Haidian District, Bei-
jing, 100036, China
Tel.: (86) 1068139666 **CN**
Web Site: http://en.sinoma-ltd.cn
Year Founded: 2007
Cement & Engineering Equipment &
Materials
N.A.I.C.S.: 333120
Mingqing Yu *(VP)*

Subsidiaries:

CTG International Inc. **(1)**
1268 E Edna Pl, Covina, CA 91724-2509
Tel.: (626) 332-0800
Web Site: http://www.ctgnf.com
Sales Range: $25-49.9 Million
Emp.: 5
Glass Fiber Distr
N.A.I.C.S.: 327212
Bob Zhang *(Pres)*

Jiangxi Sinoma New Solar Materials
Co., Ltd. **(1)**
No 1859 Economic Development Zone,
Xinyu, Jiangxi, China
Tel.: (86) 7906863333
Web Site: http://www.sinomasolar.com
Silica Crucibles Mfr & Distr
N.A.I.C.S.: 327120

Ningxia Building Materials Group Co.,
Ltd. **(1)**
No 219 East Street Peoples Square, Jin-
feng, Yinchuan, 750002, Ningxia, China
Tel.: (86) 2136741127
Web Site:
https://www.ningxiabuildingmaterials.com
Rev.: $1,215,530,550
Assets: $1,414,558,319
Liabilities: $370,665,744
Net Worth: $1,043,892,575
Earnings: $74,264,903
Fiscal Year-end: 12/31/2022
Cement Mfr & Distr
N.A.I.C.S.: 327310
Zibo Yin *(Chm)*

Sinoma Advanced Materials Co.
Ltd. **(1)**
16 Wangjing North Road, Chaoyang Dis-
trict, Beijing, 100102, China
Tel.: (86) 10 64390145
Web Site: http://www.sinoma-zoomber.cn
Quartz Crystals Mfr & Engineering Services
N.A.I.C.S.: 334419

Sinoma Jinjing Fiber Glass Co.,
Ltd. **(1)**
No 122 Yumin Road Zibo National New Hi-
Tech Industrial Park, Zibo, 255086, Shan-
dong, China
Tel.: (86) 5333919112
Web Site: http://www.sinoma-fiberjj.cn
Fiber Glass Products Mfr
N.A.I.C.S.: 326191

Sinoma Science & Technology Co.,
Ltd. **(1)**
Building 1 Lu Xun Cultural Park Creation
and Exhibition Center, Yuanda South Street
Haidian District, Beijing, 100097, China
Tel.: (86) 1088433966
Web Site: https://www.sinomatech.com
Rev.: $3,104,096,580
Assets: $6,583,153,824
Liabilities: $3,417,810,552
Net Worth: $3,165,343,272
Earnings: $492,965,460
Fiscal Year-end: 12/31/2022
Fiber Material Mfr
N.A.I.C.S.: 313110
Huang Zaiman *(Chm & Pres)*

Subsidiary (Domestic):

Beijing Composite Material Co.,
Ltd. **(2)**
261 Kangxi Rd Badaling Industry Develop-
ment Zone, Yanqing, 102101, Beijing, China
Tel.: (86) 10 61161236
Web Site: http://www.sinoma-composite.cn
Water Tanks & Pipes Mfr
N.A.I.C.S.: 332420

Jianwu Long *(Mgr-Mktg)*

Taishan Fiberglass Inc. **(2)**
Economic Development Zone, Tai'an,
271000, Shandong, China
Tel.: (86) 5386627910
Web Site: http://www.ctgf.com
Fiberglass Products Mfr & Distr
N.A.I.C.S.: 327212
Zhiyao Tang *(Chm & Pres)*

Sinoma Yanzhou Mining Engineering
Co., Ltd. **(1)**
No 136 Zhongqiao North Street, Yanzhou,
272100, Shandong, China
Tel.: (86) 5373413645
Web Site: http://old.sinoma.cn
Engineeering Services
N.A.I.C.S.: 541330

Suzhou Tianshan Cement
Co.,Ltd. **(1)**
North End of Gaodian Bridge, Chefang
Town, Suzhou, 215125, Jiangsu, China
Tel.: (86) 51265922579
Portland Cement Mfr
N.A.I.C.S.: 327310

Taishan Fiberglass Zoucheng Co.,
Ltd. **(1)**
Liyan Industrial Park, Taiping Town,
Zoucheng, 273517, Shandong, China
Tel.: (86) 5375463988
Fiber Glass Mfr
N.A.I.C.S.: 327212

Xiamen ISO Standard Sand Co.,
Ltd. **(1)**
No 45 Yanghe Road Xinyang Industrial
Zone, Haicang Investment Zone, 361022,
Xiamen, Fujian, China
Tel.: (86) 592 6516879
Web Site: http://www.isosand.com
Sand Distr
N.A.I.C.S.: 423320

CHINA NATIONAL NUCLEAR
CORPORATION

No 1 Nansanxiang Sanlihe, Xicheng
district, Beijing, 100822, China
Tel.: (86) 1068512211 **CN**
Web Site: https://en.cnnc.com.cn
Year Founded: 1955
Sales Range: $25-49.9 Billion
Emp.: 100,000
Nuclear Technology Industries Hold-
ing Company
N.A.I.C.S.: 551112
Jianfeng Yu *(Chm & Sec)*

Subsidiaries:

CNNC International Limited **(1)**
Unit 3009 30th Floor No 118 Connaught
Road West, Hong Kong, China (Hong
Kong)
Tel.: (852) 2598 1010
Web Site: http://www.cnncintl.com
Rev.: $407,038,641
Assets: $147,304,761
Liabilities: $104,297,427
Net Worth: $43,007,334
Earnings: ($28,163,266)
Emp.: 22
Fiscal Year-end: 12/31/2019
Holding Company
N.A.I.C.S.: 551112
Philip Sau Yan Li *(Sec & Controller-Fin)*

China Isotope & Radiation
Corporation **(1)**
66 Changwa Zhongjie, Haidian Distric, Bei-
jing, 100089, China
Tel.: (86) 1068522774
Web Site: https://www.circ.com.cn
Radio Pharmaceutical Product Mfr & Distr
N.A.I.C.S.: 325412

China National Nuclear Power Co
Ltd. **(1)**
Building 10 East District No 9 Linglong
Road, Haidian District, Beijing, 100097,
China
Tel.: (86) 1081920188
Web Site: https://en.cnnc.com.cn
Rev.: $9,870,071,001
Assets: $64,330,413,062
Liabilities: $43,856,686,600

Net Worth: $20,473,726,462
Earnings: $1,247,484,160
Fiscal Year-end: 12/31/2022
Electricity Distribution Services
N.A.I.C.S.: 221114

China Nuclear Energy Industry
Corporation **(1)**
No 9 Huayuan Street, Beijing, 100032,
China
Tel.: (86) 10 66297162
Web Site: http://www.cneic.com.cn
Chemical Products Distr
N.A.I.C.S.: 424690

China Zhongyuan Engineering
Corporation **(1)**
No B3 South Building Huayuan Road, Haid-
ian District, Beijing, China
Tel.: (86) 10 62355635
Web Site: http://www.czec.com.cn
Civil Engineering Services
N.A.I.C.S.: 541330
Shi Yue *(VP & Sr Engr)*

Cnnc Sufa Technology Industry Co
Ltd. **(1)**
501 Zhujiang Road, Suzhou, China
Tel.: (86) 51266672341
Web Site: https://www.chinasufa.com.cn
Industrial Valve Mfr & Distr
N.A.I.C.S.: 332911

Langer Heinrich Uranium (Pty)
Ltd. **(1)**
3981 B Ext 10 New Indus Area, PO Box
156, Swakopmund, Erongo,
Namibia **(25%)**
Tel.: (264) 64 410 6450
Web Site: https://www.lhupl.com
Sales Range: $200-249.9 Million
Emp.: 674
Uranium Mining Services
N.A.I.C.S.: 212290

Rossing Uranium Ltd. **(1)**
28 Hidipo Hamuntenya Avenue, Private Bag
5005, Swakopmund, 9000,
Namibia **(68.62%)**
Tel.: (264) 645209111
Web Site: http://www.rossing.com
Emp.: 950
Uranium Mining
N.A.I.C.S.: 212290
Glynis Labuschagne *(Sec)*

CHINA NATIONAL OFFSHORE
OIL CORP.

No 25 Chaoyangmen North Street,
Box 4705, Dongcheng District, Bei-
jing, 100010, China
Tel.: (86) 1084521331 **CN**
Web Site: https://www.cnooc.com.cn
Year Founded: 1982
Sales Range: $75-99.9 Billion
Oil Production Services
N.A.I.C.S.: 211120
Zhou Xinhuai *(Vice Chm, Pres &
CEO)*

Subsidiaries:

CNOOC Energy Technology & Ser-
vices Ltd. **(1)**
No 6 Dongzhimenwai Street, Dongcheng,
Beijing, 100027, China
Tel.: (86) 1084528003
Web Site: http://cenertech.cnooc.com.cn
Rev.: $6,708,941,905
Assets: $5,710,190,429
Liabilities: $2,475,461,210
Net Worth: $3,234,729,219
Earnings: $339,239,197
Fiscal Year-end: 12/31/2022
Petroleum Product Distr
N.A.I.C.S.: 424720
Lei Zhu *(Chm)*

CNOOC Limited **(1)**
65th Floor Bank of China Tower One Gar-
den Road, Central, China (Hong
Kong) **(66%)**
Tel.: (852) 22132500
Web Site: https://www.cnoocltd.com
Rev.: $37,706,666,310
Assets: $120,510,236,490
Liabilities: $46,666,693,530

Net Worth: $73,843,542,960
Earnings: $10,771,735,470
Emp.: 18,887
Fiscal Year-end: 12/31/2021
Offshore Oil & Gas Exploration & Produc-
tion Services
N.A.I.C.S.: 211120
Weizhi Xie *(CFO)*

Subsidiary (Non-US):

CNOOC Uganda Ltd **(2)**
Plot 22 Simba Towers John Babiha Acacia
Ave, Kampala, Uganda
Tel.: (256) 204 500000
Petroleum Exploration Services
N.A.I.C.S.: 211120

China Offshore Oil (Singapore) Inter-
national Pte. Ltd. **(2)**
12 Marina Boulevard #34-02 Marina Bay,
Financial Centre Tower 3, Singapore,
018982, Singapore **(100%)**
Tel.: (65) 65356995
Oil Exploration & Drilling Services
N.A.I.C.S.: 213111

Subsidiary (US):

OOGC America LLC **(2)**
945 Bunker Hill Rd Ste 1000, Houston, TX
77024
Tel.: (713) 380-4800
Petroleum Exploration Services
N.A.I.C.S.: 211120

China Oilfield Services Limited **(1)**
(54.74%)
Tel.: (86) 1084521685
Web Site: https://www.cosl.com.cn
Rev.: $5,006,508,956
Assets: $10,836,646,320
Liabilities: $5,234,955,327
Net Worth: $5,601,690,994
Earnings: $330,308,564
Emp.: 15,151
Fiscal Year-end: 12/31/2022
Holding Company; Offshore Oil & Gas Drill-
ing, Well & Marine Support Services
N.A.I.C.S.: 551112
Qi Meisheng *(Chm & CEO)*

Subsidiary (Non-US):

COSL (Australia) Pty Ltd. **(2)**
Level 1 1 Preston Street, Como, 6152, WA,
Australia
Tel.: (61) 8 6436 1488
Oil Drilling Services
N.A.I.C.S.: 213111

COSL (Middle East) FZE **(2)**
Office 624 Bldg 5WA, PO Box 293606,
Dubai Airport Free Zone, Dubai, United
Arab Emirates
Tel.: (971) 46091165
Oil Drilling Services
N.A.I.C.S.: 213111
Colin Ren *(Mgr-Engrg & Tech)*

Subsidiary (Domestic):

COSL Chemicals (Tianjin), Ltd. **(2)**
600 County Rd, Binhai, Tianjin, China
Tel.: (86) 22 66909932
Web Site: http://www.coslchemicals.com
Oil Drilling Services
N.A.I.C.S.: 213111

Subsidiary (Non-US):

COSL Drilling Pan-Pacific Ltd. **(2)**
3 Benoi Road, Singapore, 629877, Singa-
pore
Tel.: (65) 6513 6701
Web Site: http://www.cosl.com.sg
Oil Drilling Services
N.A.I.C.S.: 213111
Qing Yong Jin *(VP-Mktg)*

COSL Holding AS **(2)**
Beddingen 8, Aker brygge, Oslo, 0118, Nor-
way
Tel.: (47) 22 01 42 00
Holding Company
N.A.I.C.S.: 551112

COSL Mexico S.A.de C.V **(2)**
Edificio de Oficinas Takin Avenida Isla de
Tris 28 Kilometro 5, Fraccionamiento San
Miguel, 24157, Ciudad del Carmen,

Campeche, Mexico
Tel.: (52) 938 1182398
Oil Drilling Services
N.A.I.C.S.: 213111
Domingo Cabrera *(Mgr-Maintenance)*

COSL Norwegian AS (2)
Vestre Svanholmen 4, Sandnes, 4313, Norway
Tel.: (47) 51 95 09 04
Web Site: http://www.cosl.no
Emp.: 45
Holding Company
N.A.I.C.S.: 551112
Jorgen Arnesen *(Pres & CEO)*

Joint Venture (Domestic):

Eastern Marine Services Limited (2)
Room 1008-1010 10F Building B, No 317
Xianxia Road, Shanghai, 200051, China
Tel.: (86) 62706737
Web Site: http://www.emsl.com.cn
Sales Range: $250-299.9 Million
Offshore Oil & Gas Exploration, Production
Support & Pipeline Construction Services;
Owned 51% by China Oilfield Services Limited & 49% by Trico Marine Services, Inc.
N.A.I.C.S.: 213112

Subsidiary (Non-US):

PT. COSL INDO (2)
Prudential Tower 21st Floor Jl Jend
Sudirman Kav 79, Jakarta, 12910, Indonesia
Tel.: (62) 21 57932563
Oil Drilling Services
N.A.I.C.S.: 213111
Tarmono Lastchild *(Engr-Cementing)*

CHINA NATIONAL PETRO-LEUM CORPORATION
9 Dongzhimen North Street,
Dongcheng District, Beijing, 100007,
China
Tel.: (86) 1062094114   CN
Web Site: https://www.cnpc.com.cn
Year Founded: 1988
000617—(SSE)
Rev.: $396,592,337,052
Assets: $606,134,697,372
Liabilities: $266,469,706,854
Net Worth: $339,664,990,518
Earnings: $8,527,453,497
Fiscal Year-end: 12/31/19
Holding Company; Oil & Gas Products & Services
N.A.I.C.S.: 551112
Houliang Dai *(Chm)*

Subsidiaries:

CNPC Capital Company Limited (1)
No 11966 Jingshi West Road, Jinan,
250306, Shandong, China
Tel.: (86) 53187422326
Web Site: http://www.cnpc.com.cn
Rev.: $5,398,774,396
Assets: $148,676,321,015
Liabilities: $123,099,021,738
Net Worth: $25,577,299,277
Earnings: $682,096,478
Fiscal Year-end: 12/31/2023
Investment Management Service
N.A.I.C.S.: 523999
Jiang Shangjun *(Vice Chm & Pres)*

Kunlun Energy Co. Ltd. (1)
39/F 118 Connaught Road West, Hong
Kong, China (Hong Kong)
Tel.: (852) 25222282
Web Site: https://www.kunlun.com.hk
Rev.: $23,807,044,750
Assets: $19,230,726,628
Liabilities: $8,056,878,600
Net Worth: $11,173,848,028
Earnings: $1,135,772,043
Emp.: 30,916
Fiscal Year-end: 12/31/2022
Crude Oil & Natural Gas Exploration, Development & Production
N.A.I.C.S.: 211130
Yongqi Zhao *(CEO)*

PetroChina Company Limited (1)
No 9 Dongzhimen North Street, Dongcheng

District, Beijing, 100007, China   **(86.42%)**
Tel.: (86) 1059982622
Web Site: https://www.petrochina.com.cn
Rev.: $416,899,091,715
Assets: $381,135,079,752
Liabilities: $155,362,344,927
Net Worth: $225,772,734,825
Earnings: $22,311,696,943
Emp.: 398,440
Fiscal Year-end: 12/31/2023
Oil & Gas Distribution Services
N.A.I.C.S.: 221210
Liangwei Duan *(Pres)*

Joint Venture (Non-US):

Arrow Energy Pty. Ltd. (2)
Level 39 111 Eagle Street, Brisbane, 4000,
QLD, Australia
Tel.: (61) 730124000
Web Site: https://www.arrowenergy.com.au
Sales Range: $50-74.9 Million
Coal Seam Gas Extraction Services
N.A.I.C.S.: 211130
Qian Mingyang *(CEO)*

Subsidiary (Domestic):

CH4 Operations Pty Ltd (3)
Level 19 42-60 Albert St, Brisbane, 4000,
Queensland, Australia
Tel.: (61) 732282300
Sales Range: $75-99.9 Million
Emp.: 200
Oil & Gas Supplier
N.A.I.C.S.: 213112

Joint Venture (Domestic):

BP PetroChina Jiangmen Fuels Co.
Ltd. (2)
Room 1101 11th Flr CTS Ctr No 219
Zhongshan Wu Rd, Guangzhou, 510030,
China   **(50%)**
Tel.: (86) 2083966988
Sales Range: $75-99.9 Million
Emp.: 200
Petroleum & Petroleum Products Whslr
N.A.I.C.S.: 424720

Subsidiary (Domestic):

PetroChina International Co. Ltd. (2)
No 27 Chengfang Street, Xicheng District,
Beijing, 100033, China
Tel.: (86) 1066227001
Web Site: http://www.petrochinaintl.com.cn
Sales Range: $150-199.9 Million
Petroleum Producer
N.A.I.C.S.: 211120

Subsidiary (Non-US):

CNPC - AMG JSC (3)
158 Nekrasov str, 030006, Aktobe, Kazakhstan
Tel.: (7) 3132 96 68 10
Web Site: http://www.cnpc-amg.kz
Sales Range: Less than $1 Million
Oil & Gas Transportation Services
N.A.I.C.S.: 213112
Wang Zhong Cai *(CEO & Gen Dir)*

Subsidiary (US):

PetroChina International (America)
Inc. (3)
Plaza Ten Ste 302 #3 2nd St, Jersey City,
NJ 07311
Tel.: (201) 716-1818
Oil & Natural Gas Producer
N.A.I.C.S.: 211120

Subsidiary (Non-US):

PetroChina International
(Indonesia) (3)
Menara Kuningan 17th-27th floor, Jl Hr Rasuna Said Blok X-7 Kav 5, Jakarta, 12940,
Indonesia
Tel.: (62) 21 579 45300
Web Site: http://www.petrochina.co.id
Sales Range: $900-999.9 Million
Petroleum Producer
N.A.I.C.S.: 211120

PetroChina International (Japan) Co.
Ltd. (3)
21F Shiodome Sumitomo Bldg 1-9-2,
Higashi-Shimbashi Minato-ku, Tokyo, 105-0021, Japan

Tel.: (81) 3 3575 8881
Web Site: http://www.petrochina.com
Oil & Natural Gas Producer
N.A.I.C.S.: 211120

PetroChina International (Kazakhstan) Co., Ltd (3)
110 Str Furmanov, Almaty, Kazakhstan
Tel.: (7) 3272 596315
Oil & Natural Gas Producer
N.A.I.C.S.: 327910

PetroChina International (London)
Co., Limited (3)
8th Floor Marble Arch Tower, 55 Bryanston
Street, London, W1H 7AA, United Kingdom
Tel.: (44) 2078680856
Sales Range: $75-99.9 Million
Emp.: 7
Petroleum & Natural Gas
N.A.I.C.S.: 221210

PetroChina International (Middle
East) Company Limited (3)
Office 102-104 The Gate Village 04, PO
Box 506728, Dubai International Financial
Centre, Dubai, United Arab Emirates
Tel.: (971) 44407800
Web Site: http://www.petrochina.com
Oil & Natural Gas Producer
N.A.I.C.S.: 211120
Qianlan Wu *(Mng Dir)*

PetroChina International (Rus) Co.,
Ltd (3)
117198 E303-305, Leninsky Prospekt
113/1, Moscow, Russia
Tel.: (7) 95 9565771
Oil & Natural Gas Producer
N.A.I.C.S.: 211120

PetroChina International (Turkmenistan) Ltd. (3)
48 Garashizlik Street, Ashgabat, Turkmenistan
Tel.: (993) 9312 48176
Oil & Natural Gas Producer
N.A.I.C.S.: 327910

Singapore Petroleum Company
Limited (3)
One Temasek Avenue 27-00 Millenia Tower,
Singapore, 039192, Singapore   **(96.2%)**
Tel.: (65) 62766006
Web Site: http://www.spc.com.sg
Sales Range: $75-99.9 Million
Emp.: 180
Oil & Gas Field Development & Production
Services; Petroleum Refining; Petroleum
Production & Distr
N.A.I.C.S.: 211120

Subsidiary (Non-US):

Singapore Petroleum Co. (HK)
Ltd. (4)
1205 18 Harbour Road, Wanchai, Hong
Kong, China (Hong Kong)   **(100%)**
Tel.: (852) 36782296
Web Site: http://www.spc.com.sg
Petroleum Product Distr
N.A.I.C.S.: 424720

Joint Venture (Domestic):

Singapore Refining Co. Pte. Ltd. (4)
1 Merlimau Rd, Singapore, 628260,
Singapore   **(50%)**
Tel.: (65) 63570100
Web Site: https://www.src.com.sg
Petroleum Refiner
N.A.I.C.S.: 324110

PetroKazakhstan Inc. (1)
Sun Life Plz N Tower, Calgary, T2P 3N3,
AB, Canada
Tel.: (403) 221-8435
Web Site: http://www.petrokazakhstan.com
Sales Range: $1-4.9 Billion
Oil & Gas Exploration, Acquisition & Refinement; Owned 67% by China National Petroleum Corporation & 33% by JSC KazMunayGas Exploration
N.A.I.C.S.: 211120

CHINA NATIONAL PHARMACEUTICAL GROUP CORPORATION

Sinopharm Plaza No 20 Zhichun
Road, Haidian District, Beijing,
100191, China
Tel.: (86) 1082287727
Web Site:
   https://www.sinopharm.com
Year Founded: 1998
Rev.: $84,023,882,142
Assets: $53,999,273,641
Liabilities: $37,052,971,579
Net Worth: $16,946,302,062
Earnings: $2,114,060,275
Fiscal Year-end: 12/31/23
Pharmaceuticals Mfr
N.A.I.C.S.: 325412
Dong Zenghe *(Gen Mgr & Deputy*
Gen Mgr)

Subsidiaries:

Beijing Tiantan Biological Products
Corporation Limited (1)
No 2 Shuangqiao Road, Chaoyang District,
Beijing, 100024, China
Tel.: (86) 1065434018
Web Site: https://www.tiantanbio.com
Rev.: $598,287,166
Assets: $1,816,875,586
Liabilities: $222,445,534
Net Worth: $1,594,430,052
Earnings: $123,696,472
Fiscal Year-end: 12/31/2022
Biological Product Mfr
N.A.I.C.S.: 325414
Xue Zhongmin *(Chm)*

China National Group Corporation of
Traditional & Herbal Medicine (1)
Floor 12 Machinery Building No 248,
Guang'an Men Wai Street, Beijing, 100055,
China
Tel.: (86) 10 633 172 20
Web Site: http://www.sino-tcm.com
Sales Range: $100-124.9 Million
Medicinal Products Developer, Mfr & Distr
N.A.I.C.S.: 325411

China National Medical Equipment
Industry Corporation (1)
20 Zhichun Road, Haidian District, Beijing,
100088, China
Tel.: (86) 1082029999
Web Site: http://www.cmic.com.cn
Medical Equipment Mfr & Distr
N.A.I.C.S.: 339112

Subsidiary (Domestic):

CMICS Medical Electronic Instrument
Co., Ltd. (2)
45 Huifeng 4 Road Zhongkai Hi-tech Development Zone, Guangdong, Huizhou,
516006, China
Tel.: (86) 7522775520
Web Site: http://www.cmics.com.cn
Sales Range: $25-49.9 Million
Emp.: 120
Medical Electronic Instruments
N.A.I.C.S.: 339112
Zhu Ai Cheng *(Gen Mgr)*

China National Medicines Corporation
Ltd. (1)
12A Sanyuan Xi Xiang Yongwai, Chongwen
District, Beijing, 10007, China
Tel.: (86) 10 672 544 49
Web Site: http://www.cncm.com.cn
Pharmaceutical Distribution
N.A.I.C.S.: 424210

China National Pharmaceutical Foreign Trade Corporation (1)
F/3-4 Sinopharm Building 20 Zhichun Road,
Haidian District, Beijing, 100088, China
Tel.: (86) 1062026699
Web Site: http://www.sino-pharm.com
Sales Range: $100-124.9 Million
Pharmaceutical Wholesale Trade Agency
Distr
N.A.I.C.S.: 425120

China Pharmaceutical Advertising
Limited Company (1)
7th Floor 20 Zhichun Rd, Haidian District,
Beijing, 100088, China
Tel.: (86) 1082074512
Web Site: http://www.spadv.com

China National Pharmaceutical Group Corporation—(Continued)

Advetising Agency
N.A.I.C.S.: 541810

China Traditional Chinese Medicine Holdings Co. Ltd. (1)
Room 1601 Emperor Group Centre 288 Hennessy Road, Wanchai, China (Hong Kong) **(56.97%)**
Tel.: (852) 28543393
Web Site: https://www.china-tcm.com.cn
Rev.: $2,008,315,577
Assets: $5,001,039,716
Liabilities: $1,779,336,796
Net Worth: $3,221,702,921
Earnings: $101,193,581
Emp.: 17,662
Fiscal Year-end: 12/31/2022
Pharmaceuticals Mfr
N.A.I.C.S.: 325412
Xian Wu *(Chm)*

Subsidiary (Non-US):

Foshan Dezhong Pharmaceutical Co., Ltd. (2)
No 89 Foping Rd, Foshan, 528000, Guangdong, China
Tel.: (86) 757 82286 327
Web Site: http://www.dezhong.com
Pharmaceuticals Mfr
N.A.I.C.S.: 325412

HM Science Inc. (1)
Room 719/706 20 Zhichun Road, Haidian District, Beijing, 100088, China
Tel.: (86) 1062362317
Web Site: http://www.hm-science.com
Sales Range: $50-74.9 Million
Emp.: 8
Medicinal Wholesale Trade Agency; Owned by Kracie Holdings, Ltd. & by China National Pharmaceutical Group Corporation (SINOPHARM)
N.A.I.C.S.: 425120

Qingdao Huazhong Pharmaceuticals Co., Ltd. (1)
202 Chong Qing Nan Road, Qingdao, 266100, Shangdong, China
Tel.: (86) 53284961075
Web Site: http://www.phm-huazhong.com
Traditional Chinese Medicinal Mfr; Owned by Kracie Holdings, Ltd. & by China National Pharmaceutical Group Corporation (SINOPHARM)
N.A.I.C.S.: 325411

Reed Sinopharm Exhibitions Co., Ltd. (1)
15th Floor Tower B Ping An International Finance Center, No 1-3 Xinyuan South Rd, Beijing, 100027, China
Tel.: (86) 1084556677
Web Site: http://www.reed-sinopharm.com
Pharmaceutical Medical & Health Care Exhibition Trade Show Organizer Services
N.A.I.C.S.: 561920

SINOPHARM Medicine Holding Co., Ltd. (1)
Floor 42 Bund Center, Shanghai, 200002, China
Tel.: (86) 21 63351899
Pharmaceutical Products Distr
N.A.I.C.S.: 424210

SINOPHARM United Engineering Company Ltd. (1)
8 Daping Zheng Street, Yuzhong District, Chongqing, 400042, China
Tel.: (86) 23 688 108 52
Web Site: http://www.cpidi.com
Emp.: 50
Engineering & Project Design Services
N.A.I.C.S.: 541330

Sichuan Industrial Institute of Antibiotics (1)
18 Shanbanqiao Road, Chengdu, 610051, Sichuan, China
Tel.: (86) 28 438 46 63
Medicinal Research & Development
N.A.I.C.S.: 541715

Sino-Swed Pharmaceutical Corp., Ltd. (1)
Unit 1801-1805 China Resources Building,

No 8 Jianguomenbei Avenue, Beijing, 100005, China
Tel.: (86) 1065189090
Web Site: http://www.sspc.com.cn
Sales Range: $250-299.9 Million
Emp.: 1,000
Parenteral Nutrition, Enteral Nutrition & Application Device Mfr; Owned 51% by Fresenius SE & 49% by China National Pharmaceutical Group Corporation (SINOPHARM)
N.A.I.C.S.: 325411

CHINA NATIONAL RAILWAY SIGNAL & COMMUNICATION CORP.
CRSC Mansion Courtyard No 1 South Beijing Auto Museum Road, Fengtai District, Beijing, 100070, China
Tel.: (86) 10 50809077
Web Site: http://www.crsc.com.cn
Year Founded: 1953
Rev.: $5,701,677,259
Assets: $11,401,998,502
Liabilities: $7,070,063,567
Net Worth: $4,331,934,934
Earnings: $543,169,106
Emp.: 19,215
Fiscal Year-end: 12/31/18
Railway Signal & Communication Equipment Mfr & Distr
N.A.I.C.S.: 334290
Zhiliang Zhou *(Chm)*

Subsidiaries:

Beijing Railway Signal Co., Ltd. (1)
No 2 Sicun Langfa Huangcun, Daxing, Beijing, 102613, China
Tel.: (86) 10 51214022
Web Site: http://www.brsf.com.cn
Traffic Signal System & Equipment Mfr
N.A.I.C.S.: 334290

CASCO Signal Ltd. (1)
11F Building 2 Shibei One Center No 21 Lane 1401 Jiangchang Road, Jing'an District, Shanghai, 200070, China
Tel.: (86) 2156637080
Web Site: https://www.casco.com.cn
Sales Range: $25-49.9 Million
Emp.: 2,000
Engineeering Services
N.A.I.C.S.: 541330

Jiazuo Railway Cable Co., Ltd. (1)
No 8 ZhanQian Road, Jiaozuo, 454001, Henan, China
Tel.: (86) 391 2632223
Web Site: http://www.jzrcw.com
Cable & Wire Mfr
N.A.I.C.S.: 332618
Wang Ge *(Chm)*

Jinxin Company (1)
No 1199 Xunhai Road, Dongli, Tianjin, China
Tel.: (86) 22 60403811
Web Site: http://www.trsc.com.cn
Rail Electrical System & Equipment Mfr
N.A.I.C.S.: 336320

Shenyang Railway Signal Co., Ltd. (1)
No 16 Beisan Middle Road, Tiexi, 110025, Shenyang, China
Tel.: (86) 24 62136269
Web Site: http://www.syrsc.cn
Rail Electrical System & Equipment Mfr
N.A.I.C.S.: 336320

CHINA NATURAL RESOURCES, INC.
Room 2205 Shun Tak Centre, 200 Connaught Road Central, Hong Kong, China (Hong Kong)
Tel.: (852) 28107205
Web Site: https://www.chnr.net
Year Founded: 1986
CHNR—(NASDAQ)
Rev.: $2,870,389
Assets: $51,087,568
Liabilities: $23,197,679
Net Worth: $27,889,889

Earnings: ($8,422,107)
Emp.: 75
Fiscal Year-end: 12/31/21
Holding Company; Mining Services
N.A.I.C.S.: 551112
Wenlie Peng *(VP)*

Subsidiaries:

Feishang Mining Holding Limited (1)
Room 2105 West Tower Shun Tak Centre, 200 Connaught Road C, Sheung Wan, China (Hong Kong)
Tel.: (852) 2810 7205
Holding Company
N.A.I.C.S.: 551112
Feilie Li *(CEO)*

Subsidiary (Non-US):

Wuhu Feishang Mining Development Co., Ltd. (2)
Fanxin Road, Fanchang, Wuhu, 243601, China **(100%)**
Tel.: (86) 5537337566
Zinc, Iron & Other Minerals Mining
N.A.I.C.S.: 212230

CHINA NEPSTAR CHAIN DRUGSTORE LTD.
25F Neptunus Yinhe Keji Building No 1 Kejizhong 3rd Road, Nanshan District, Shenzhen, 518057, Guangdong, China
Tel.: (86) 755 2643 5319
Web Site: http://www.nepstar.cn
Sales Range: $450-499.9 Million
Drug Store Owner & Operator
N.A.I.C.S.: 456110

Subsidiaries:

Guangzhou Nepstar Chain Co., Ltd. (1)
No 281 Chigang E Rd, Haizhu Dist, Guangzhou, 510310, Guangdong, China
Tel.: (86) 2034029301
Pharmaceutical Product Retailer
N.A.I.C.S.: 456110

Shenzhen Nepstar Chain Co., Ltd. (1)
Haiwang Xingchen 7 F Fumin Plaza Qifeng Road, Guancheng District, Dongguan, 523000, Guangdong, China
Tel.: (86) 76922366079
Drug Store
N.A.I.C.S.: 456110

CHINA NETCOM TECHNOLOGY HOLDINGS LIMITED
Unit 1006 10/F Tower One Lippo Centre 89 Queensway, Hong Kong, China (Hong Kong)
Tel.: (852) 28336142
Web Site:
http://www.chinanetcomtech.com
8071—(HKG)
Rev.: $3,478,455
Assets: $5,273,910
Liabilities: $1,738,718
Net Worth: $3,535,193
Earnings: ($1,422,135)
Emp.: 55
Fiscal Year-end: 12/31/22
Holding Company
N.A.I.C.S.: 551112
Haitao Sun *(Chm)*

CHINA NETWORKS INTERNATIONAL HOLDING LTD.
801 Block C Central International Trade 6A Jianguomenwai Avenue, Beijing, 100022, China
Tel.: (86) 1085911829
Year Founded: 2008
CNWHF—(OTCIQ)
Sales Range: Less than $1 Million
Television Broadcasting Services
N.A.I.C.S.: 516120
Shuangqing Li *(Chm, CEO & CFO)*

CHINA NEW BORUN CORPORATION
Bohai Industrial Park, Yangkou Town, Shouguang, 262715, Shandong, China
Tel.: (86) 5365451199
Web Site:
http://www.chinanewborun.com
BORN—(NYSE)
Sales Range: $250-299.9 Million
Emp.: 1,109
Corn-Based Edible Alcohol Mfr & Distr
N.A.I.C.S.: 325998
Jinmiao Wang *(Chm, Pres & CEO)*

Subsidiaries:

Daqing Borun Biotechnology Co., Ltd. (1)
Corn Industrial Park, Jubao Zhusan Township Datong, Daqing, 163515, Heilongjiang, China
Tel.: (86) 4596989708
Emp.: 563
Edible Alcohol Product Mfr & Distr
N.A.I.C.S.: 311221
Shunliang Hu *(Gen Mgr)*

CHINA NEW CITY COMMERCIAL DEVELOPMENT LIMITED
Room 1201 12th Floor Building 2 Highlong Plaza North Ganjie Road, Xiaoshan, Hangzhou, Zhejiang, China
Tel.: (86) 57183737878
Web Site:
http://www.chinanewcity.com.cn
1321—(HKG)
Sales Range: $25-49.9 Million
Emp.: 1,272
Commercial Property Development Services
N.A.I.C.S.: 531312
Ni Jin *(Vice Chm & VP)*

CHINA NEW ECONOMY FUND LIMITED
Unit 702 7/F 135 Bonham Strand Trade Centre 135 Bonham Strand, Sheung Wan, Hong Kong, China (Hong Kong)
Tel.: (852) 27069536
Web Site:
http://www.chinaneweconomy.com
Year Founded: 2010
0080—(HKG)
Rev.: $397,304
Assets: $19,049,435
Liabilities: $909,398
Net Worth: $18,140,036
Earnings: ($6,724,997)
Emp.: 6
Fiscal Year-end: 12/31/22
Closed-End Investment Fund
N.A.I.C.S.: 525990
Xu Gu *(Exec Dir)*

CHINA NEW ENERGY LIMITED
8/F Zone B Energy Saving Environmental Protection Building of GIEC, No 2 Nengyuan Road Tianhe District, Guangzhou, 510640, China
Tel.: (86) 20 8705 9371
Web Site:
http://www.chinanewenergy.co.uk
Year Founded: 2006
Rev.: $57,033,650
Assets: $57,387,536
Liabilities: $38,723,003
Net Worth: $18,664,533
Earnings: $8,466,941
Emp.: 86
Fiscal Year-end: 12/31/19
Bioethanol, Biobutanol & Biogas Plant & Equipment Mfr & Engineering
N.A.I.C.S.: 237990
Weijun Yu *(Chm)*

Subsidiaries:

Guangdong Zhongke Tianyuan New
Energy Technology Co., Ltd. **(1)**
8/F Technology Integration Building of GIEC
No 4 Nengyuan Road, Wushan Tianhe District, Guangzhou, 510640, China
Tel.: (86) 20 8705 7185
Web Site: http://www.zkty.com.cn
Emp.: 80
Bio-Energy Technologies Developer, Mfr &
Installation Services
N.A.I.C.S.: 333248

Subsidiary (Domestic):

Guangdong Boluo Jiuneng High-New
Technology Engineering Co., Ltd. **(2)**
Zhouji High & New Technology Industrial
Zone, Boluo County, Huizhou, 516100,
Guangdong, China
Tel.: (86) 7526221499
Web Site: http://www.zkty.com.cn
Sales Range: $25-49.9 Million
Emp.: 20
Environmental Engineering Services
N.A.I.C.S.: 541330

CHINA NEW HIGHER EDUCATION GROUP LIMITED

25F Tower A Global Trade Center No
36 North 3rd Ring East Road,
Dongcheng District, Beijing, China
Tel.: (86) 105 260 1271   Ky
Web Site: http://www.xingaojiao.com
Year Founded: 1999
2001—(HKG)
Rev.: $229,425,081
Assets: $1,215,280,565
Liabilities: $726,187,209
Net Worth: $489,093,355
Earnings: $90,669,218
Emp.: 8,647
Fiscal Year-end: 08/31/21
Education Training Services
N.A.I.C.S.: 611310
Xiaoxuan Li *(Founder & Chm)*

CHINA NEW TOWN DEVELOPMENT COMPANY LIMITED

2/F Palm Grove House, PO Box
3340, Road Town, Tortola, Virgin Islands (British)
Tel.: (284) 4946004   VG
Web Site: http://www.china-newtown.com
1278—(HKG)
Rev.: $60,195,634
Assets: $1,109,769,715
Liabilities: $452,005,773
Net Worth: $657,763,942
Earnings: $21,303,662
Emp.: 128
Fiscal Year-end: 12/31/23
Holding Company; Commercial Real
Estate Developer & Property Manager
N.A.I.C.S.: 551112
Janson Bing Shi *(Exec Dir)*

Subsidiaries:

China New Town Development Company Limited - Corporate Office **(1)**
2503 Convention Plaza Office Tower No 1
Harbour Road, Wanchai, China (Hong
Kong)
Tel.: (852) 3 965 9000
Web Site: https://www.china-newtown.com
Corporate Office; Commercial Real Estate
Developer & Property Manager
N.A.I.C.S.: 551114
Yao Min Li *(Vice Chm)*

CHINA NONFERROUS GOLD LIMITED

Kryso Resources Limited Unit 2 24
The Plaza 535 Kings Road, London,
SW10 0SZ, United Kingdom
Tel.: (44) 2073499160
Web Site: http://www.cnfgold.com

Year Founded: 2004
CNG—(LSE)
Rev.: $68,525,000
Assets: $88,841,000
Liabilities: $402,272,000
Net Worth: ($313,431,000)
Earnings: ($287,043,000)
Emp.: 701
Fiscal Year-end: 12/31/22
Mineral Exploration Services
N.A.I.C.S.: 213115
Xiang Wu *(Chm)*

Subsidiaries:

Kryso Resources Limited **(1)**
Unit 2 24 The Plaza 535 Kings Road, London, SW10 0SZ, United Kingdom
Tel.: (44) 2073499160
Gold Mining Services
N.A.I.C.S.: 212220

LLC Pakrut **(1)**
130 Karin Mann Street, Dushanbe, 734012,
Tajikistan
Tel.: (992) 887756666
Gold Mining Services
N.A.I.C.S.: 212220

CHINA NONFERROUS METAL MINING (GROUP) CO., LTD.

CNMC Building No 10 Anding Road,
Chaoyang District, Beijing, 100029,
China
Tel.: (86) 10 84426666   CN
Web Site: http://www.cnmc.com.cn
Year Founded: 1983
Sales Range: $15-24.9 Billion
Emp.: 27,798
Mineral Exploration Services
N.A.I.C.S.: 212290
Zhang Keli *(Pres)*

Subsidiaries:

CNMC (Guangxi) Pinggui PGMA Co.,
Ltd. **(1)**
1 South Dian Chang Road, Pinggui District
Guangxi, Hezhou, 542800, China
Tel.: (86) 774 8832755
Web Site: http://www.pgma.com.cn
Mineral Exploration Services
N.A.I.C.S.: 212290
Li Zhiming *(Chm & Mng Dir)*

Plant (Domestic):

CNMC (Guangxi) Pinggui PGMA Co.,
Ltd. - Titanium Dioxide Plant **(2)**
Shuiyanba Mine Area, Huangtian Town,
Hezhou, 542800, Guangxi, China
Tel.: (86) 774 8838123
Chemical Products Mfr
N.A.I.C.S.: 325998

Subsidiary (Domestic):

Hezhou Pinggui PGMA Cement Co.
Ltd **(2)**
26 Dianchang Rd, Pinggui District, Hezhou,
542601, Guangxi, China
Tel.: (86) 15278452018
Mineral Exploration Services
N.A.I.C.S.: 212290

Hezhou Pinggui PGMA Transportation Co. Ltd **(2)**
9 Xiwan Rd, Pinggui District, Hezhou,
542800, Guangxi, China
Tel.: (86) 774 8836513
Logistics Consulting Servies
N.A.I.C.S.: 541614

CNMC (Ningxia) Orient Group Co.,
Ltd. **(1)**
No 105 Youse road, dawukou District, Shizuishan, 753000, Ningxia, China
Tel.: (86) 952 2098888
Web Site: http://www.cnmnc.com
Metal Products Mfr
N.A.I.C.S.: 332117
Zhang Chuangqi *(Chm)*

Subsidiary (Domestic):

Ningxia Orient Tantalum Industry Co.,
Ltd. **(2)**

Yejin Road, Dawukou District, Shizuishan,
753000, Ningxia, China
Tel.: (86) 9522098563
Web Site: http://www.otic.com.cn
Rev.: $138,465,288
Assets: $280,690,488
Liabilities: $69,217,200
Net Worth: $211,473,288
Earnings: $23,945,220
Fiscal Year-end: 12/31/2022
Metal Product Smelting Services
N.A.I.C.S.: 331492
Wang Kai *(Chm)*

CNMC (Shenyang) Mining Investment
Co., Ltd. **(1)**
China Nonferrous Building 58 Wei 13 Road,
Shenhe District, Shenyang, Liaoning, China
Tel.: (86) 24 22718786
Web Site: http://www.sykytz.com
Investment Management Service
N.A.I.C.S.: 523940

CNMC Albetter Albronze Co.,
Ltd. **(1)**
East Second Ring Road Industrial Estate,
Linqing, 252600, Shandong, China
Tel.: (86) 635 2411066
Web Site: http://www.albetter.com
Copper Product Mfr
N.A.I.C.S.: 331420

China Non-ferrous Metal Industry's
Foreign Engineering & Construction
Co., Ltd. **(1)**
China Nonferrous Building South Building
No 10 Anding Road, Chaoyang, Beijing,
100029, China
Tel.: (86) 1084427227
Web Site: http://www.nfc.com.cn
Rev.: $1,035,086,364
Assets: $2,815,076,160
Liabilities: $1,677,103,272
Net Worth: $1,137,972,888
Earnings: $20,605,104
Fiscal Year-end: 12/31/2022
Non-ferrous Metal Mining Services
N.A.I.C.S.: 331410
Junman Qin *(Chm, Gen Mgr & Dir)*

Subsidiary (Domestic):

China Nerin Engineering Co. Ltd **(2)**
888 Qianhu Avenue, Hongjiaozhou, Nanchang, 330031, Jiangxi, China
Tel.: (86) 79186757666
Web Site: http://www.nerin.com
Engineering Consulting Services
N.A.I.C.S.: 541330
Zhang Xiaobo *(Chm)*

China Nonferrous Mining Corporation
Limited **(1)**
China Nonferrous Metal Building No 10
Anding Road, Chaoyang District, Beijing,
China **(74.52%)**
Tel.: (86) 85295197870
Web Site: https://www.cnmcl.net
Rev.: $4,094,716,000
Assets: $4,021,016,000
Liabilities: $1,688,080,000
Net Worth: $2,332,936,000
Earnings: $382,129,000
Emp.: 9,115
Fiscal Year-end: 12/31/2022
Copper Mining
N.A.I.C.S.: 212230
Kaishou Xie *(VP)*

Xincheng Construction Supervision &
Consulting Co., Ltd. **(1)**
Room 630-633 Jingmen Building Sanduan
NO.9 Yangfangdian Road, Haidian District,
Beijing, 100038, China
Tel.: (86) 10 63971469
Web Site: http://www.xchjl.com
Construction Engineering Services
N.A.I.C.S.: 541330

CHINA NORTH INDUSTRIES GROUP CORPORATION

No 46 Sanlihe Road, Xicheng District,
Beijing, 100821, China
Tel.: (86) 1063529988   CN
Web Site:
https://www.norincogroup.com.cn
Sales Range: $50-74.9 Billion
Emp.: 280,000

Holding Company; Military, Industrial,
Chemical & Opto-Electronic Information Technology Products Mfr
N.A.I.C.S.: 551112
Liu Dashan *(Pres)*

Subsidiaries:

Beijing North Vehicle Group
Corporation **(1)**
No 5 Wuli Zhu Jia Fen Chang Xin Dian,
Fengtai District, Beijing, China
Tel.: (86) 10 83807000
Web Site: http://www.bj-north.com.cn
Emp.: 4,000
Military Vehicle Mfr
N.A.I.C.S.: 336992

China Wuzhou Engineering Corporation Ltd. **(1)**
85 Xibianmennei Street, PO Box 55, Beijing, 100053, China
Tel.: (86) 10 83196688
Web Site: http://www.wuzhou.com.cn
Engineeering Services
N.A.I.C.S.: 541330
Yu Yaming *(Chm)*

Hubei Jiangshan Heavy Industries
Co., Ltd. **(1)**
No 6 Xinxing Road, Hi-tech District, Xiangyang, 441000, Hubei, China
Tel.: (86) 710 3085323
Web Site: http://www.jszgjt.net
Emp.: 200
Military Vehicle Mfr
N.A.I.C.S.: 336992

Jinxi Industries Group Co., Ltd. **(1)**
No 5 North Lane, Taiyuan, 030027, China
Tel.: (86) 35 1626 2649
Web Site: http://www.jxgc.com
Emp.: 15,000
Automobile Parts Mfr
N.A.I.C.S.: 336390

Subsidiary (Domestic):

Jinxi Axle Co., Ltd. **(2)**
No 5 North Alley Heping North Road,
Taiyuan, 030 027, Shanxi, China
Tel.: (86) 3516629027
Web Site: http://en.jinxiaxle.com
Rev.: $174,834,687
Assets: $554,189,730
Liabilities: $99,445,166
Net Worth: $454,744,565
Earnings: $1,476,755
Emp.: 1,200
Fiscal Year-end: 12/31/2022
Railway Transportation Device Mfr
N.A.I.C.S.: 336350
Wu Zhenguo *(Chm)*

Liaoshen Industrial Group Co.,
Ltd. **(1)**
New road no 42, Shenyang, Liaoning,
China
Tel.: (86) 24 88279440
Military Vehicle Mfr
N.A.I.C.S.: 336992

North Lingyun Industrial Group Co.,
Ltd. **(1)**
Songlindian, Zhuozhou, 072761, Hebei,
China
Tel.: (86) 31 2367 6616
Web Site: http://www.lyig.com.cn
Plastic Automotive Components Mfr
N.A.I.C.S.: 336390

Subsidiary (Non-US):

Kiekert AG **(2)**
Hoeseler Platz 2, 42579, Heiligenhaus, Germany
Tel.: (49) 2056150
Web Site: http://www.kiekert.de
Sales Range: $650-699.9 Million
Emp.: 3,380
Automotive Latching Systems Mfr
N.A.I.C.S.: 336390
Karl Krause *(CEO)*

Subsidiary (US):

Keykert USA, Inc. **(3)**
46941 Liberty Dr, Wixom, MI 48393
Tel.: (248) 960-4100
Web Site: http://www.kiekert.com

China North Industries Group
Corporation—(Continued)

Sales Range: $25-49.9 Million
Emp.: 100
Automotive Latching Systems Mfr
N.A.I.C.S.: 336390

Subsidiary (Non-US):

Kiekert CS s.r.o. (3)
Jaselska 593, CZ-535 01, Prelouc, Czech
Republic
Tel.: (420) 468 88 1111
Web Site: http://www.kiekert.cz
Automotive Latching Systems Mfr
N.A.I.C.S.: 336390
Lukas Hlava *(Gen Mgr)*

**North Night Vision Technology Co.,
Ltd.** (1)
No 53 Keyi Rd, Hi-tech Development Zone,
Kunming, 650106, China
Tel.: (86) 87168320634
Web Site: http://www.nvir.cn
Navigation Systems Mfr
N.A.I.C.S.: 334511

**Northeast Industries Group Co.,
Ltd.** (1)
2555 Chaoran Street, High-Tech Zone,
Changchun, Jilin, China
Tel.: (86) 43185157778
Web Site: http://www.dgjt.com
Motor Vehicle Component Mfr
N.A.I.C.S.: 551112

Subsidiary (Domestic):

**Jilin Dahua Machine Manufacturing
Co., Ltd.** (2)
2555 Chaoran Street, High-New Technology
Development Zone, Changchun, 130103,
Jilin, China
Tel.: (86) 431 85157888
Web Site: http://www.dahuajl.com
Emp.: 1,000
Automobile Parts Mfr
N.A.I.C.S.: 336310

Sichuan Nitrocell Corporation (1)
Gaoba, Luzhou, 646605, Sichuan, China
Tel.: (86) 8302796927
Web Site: http://en.sn-nc.com
Rev.: $359,235,864
Assets: $663,194,844
Liabilities: $237,089,268
Net Worth: $426,105,576
Earnings: $13,061,412
Fiscal Year-end: 12/31/2022
Nitrocellulose Product Mfr
N.A.I.C.S.: 325998
Shang Hong *(Fin Dir)*

**Sun Life Everbright Life Insurance
Company Limited** (1)
4th Floor Tianjin International Building 75
Nanjing Road, Heping District, Tianjin,
300050, China (12.5%)
Tel.: (86) 22 2339 1188
Web Site: http://www.sunlife-everbright.com
Life Insurance Products & Services
N.A.I.C.S.: 524113

CHINA NT PHARMA GROUP COMPANY LIMITED
28th Floor The Wellington 198 Wellington Street, Sheung Wan, China
(Hong Kong)
Tel.: (852) 28081606
Web Site: http://www.ntpharma.com
1011—(HKG)
Rev.: $29,075,717
Assets: $141,202,807
Liabilities: $175,131,590
Net Worth: ($33,928,783)
Earnings: ($9,323,262)
Emp.: 130
Fiscal Year-end: 12/31/22
Pharmaceuticals Mfr
N.A.I.C.S.: 325412
Tit Ng *(Founder, Chm & CEO)*

Subsidiaries:

Guangdong NT Pharma Co., Ltd. (1)
Room 1006 10/F Eastern Tower of Tianyu
Square No 625 Tianhe Road, Tianhe Dis-

trict, Guangzhou, 510630, Guangdong,
China
Tel.: (86) 2087598141
Pharmaceutical Product Mfr & Distr
N.A.I.C.S.: 325412

**NT Biopharmaceuticals Changsha
Co., Ltd.** (1)
323 Kangning Road Liuyang Industrial
Park, Liuyang, Hunan, China
Tel.: (86) 73182721399
Pharmaceutical Product Mfr & Distr
N.A.I.C.S.: 325412

**NT Biopharmaceuticals Jiangsu Co.,
Ltd.** (1)
No 825 Yaocheng Avenue, Taizhou,
225300, China
Tel.: (86) 52386200680
Prescription Medicine Mfr & Whslr
N.A.I.C.S.: 325412

NT Pharma (Jiangsu) Co., Ltd. (1)
No 825 Yaocheng Avenue, Taizhou,
225300, China
Tel.: (86) 52386200680
Pharmaceutical Product Mfr & Distr
N.A.I.C.S.: 325412

NT Tong Zhou (Beijing) Pharmaceuticals Co., Ltd. (1)
Room 603 Block F Fu Hua Mansion No 8
Chaotianmen Street North, Dongcheng District, Beijing, 100027, China
Tel.: (86) 1065543193
Pharmaceutical Product Mfr & Distr
N.A.I.C.S.: 325412

**NTP (China) Investment Co.,
Ltd.** (1)
11/F S2 The Bund Finance Center No 600
Zhongshan East 2nd Road, Huangpu District, Shanghai, 200020, China
Tel.: (86) 2123159999
Financial Investment Services
N.A.I.C.S.: 523999

**Suzhou First Pharmaceutical Co.,
Ltd.** (1)
No 1 Hualing Street Suhong Road East Suzhou Industrial Park, Suzhou, 215008, Jiangsu, China
Tel.: (86) 51287169555
Pharmaceutical Product Mfr & Distr
N.A.I.C.S.: 325412
Weizhong Wu *(Chm & Gen Mgr)*

CHINA NUCLEAR ENERGY TECHNOLOGY CORPORATION LIMITED
Room 2801 28/F China Resources
Building, 26 Harbour Road, Wanchai,
China (Hong Kong)
Tel.: (852) 39830923 BM
Web Site: http://www.cnetcl.com
Year Founded: 1983
0611—(HKG)
Rev.: $272,656,455
Assets: $1,200,911,663
Liabilities: $984,999,338
Net Worth: $215,912,325
Earnings: $12,540,135
Emp.: 278
Fiscal Year-end: 12/31/22
Home Management Services
N.A.I.C.S.: 721110
Chi Shing Chung *(Exec Dir)*

CHINA NUCLEAR ENGINEERING CORPORATION LIMITED
No 12 Chegongzhuang Avenue
Xicheng District, Beijing, 100037,
China
Tel.: (86) 1088306639
Web Site: http://www.en.cnecc.com
601611—(SHG)
Rev.: $13,918,946,881
Assets: $27,711,290,098
Liabilities: $22,785,132,989
Net Worth: $4,926,157,110
Earnings: $246,341,249
Fiscal Year-end: 12/31/22
Construction Engineering Services

N.A.I.C.S.: 541330

CHINA NUCLEAR POWER CO., LTD.
No 1 Nansanxiang Sanlihe, Beijing,
100045, China
Tel.: (86) 1068555920
Web Site: http://www.cnnp.com.cn
601985—(SHG)
Rev.: $10,008,498,352
Assets: $65,232,644,532
Liabilities: $44,471,774,875
Net Worth: $20,760,869,657
Earnings: $1,264,980,076
Emp.: 18,000
Fiscal Year-end: 12/31/22
Nuclear Electric Power Generation
Services
N.A.I.C.S.: 221113

CHINA NUTRIFRUIT GROUP LIMITED
5th Floor Chuangye Building Chuangye Plaza Industrial Zone 3,
Daqing Hi-Tech Indus Dev Zone,
Daqing, 163316, Heilongjiang, China
Tel.: (86) 4598972870 NV
Sales Range: $75-99.9 Million
Emp.: 516
Holding Company: Specialty Fruit-Based Products Developer, Processor, Marketer & Distr
N.A.I.C.S.: 551112
Changjun Yu *(Chm, Pres & CEO)*

CHINA OCEAN GROUP DEVELOPMENT LIMITED
Room 03 22/F China Resources
Building 26 Harbour Road, Wan Chai,
Hong Kong, China (Hong Kong)
Tel.: (852) 3702 3115 BM
Web Site:
http://www.chinaoceangroup.com.hk
Year Founded: 2001
8047—(HKG)
Rev.: $80,189,833
Assets: $199,221,734
Liabilities: $61,239,059
Net Worth: $137,982,675
Earnings: ($49,046,967)
Emp.: 61
Fiscal Year-end: 03/31/21
Holding Company
N.A.I.C.S.: 551112
Rongsheng Liu *(Chm & CEO)*

CHINA OCEAN INDUSTRY GROUP LIMITED
Unit D 16/F MG Tower 133 Hoi Bun
Road, Kwun Tong, Kowloon, China
(Hong Kong)
Tel.: (852) 2587 8628 BM
Rev.: $1,268,691
Assets: $175,807,030
Liabilities: $590,523,947
Net Worth: ($414,716,917)
Earnings: ($141,345,638)
Emp.: 350
Fiscal Year-end: 12/31/19
Ship Building Services
N.A.I.C.S.: 336611
Ming Li *(Chm)*

CHINA OCEANWIDE HOLDINGS GROUP CO., LTD.
22/F Tower C, Minsheng Fincl Center, Beijing, China
Tel.: (86) 10 85259988 CN
Web Site:
http://en.chinaoceanwide.com
Year Founded: 1985
Holding Company
N.A.I.C.S.: 551112
Zhiqiang Lu *(Founder & Chm)*

Subsidiaries:

International Data Group, Inc. (1)
140 Kendrick St Blg B, Needham, MA
01701
Tel.: (508) 879-0700
Web Site: http://www.idg.com
Holding Company; Technology Industry
Trade Journal, Internet & Mobile Application
Publisher, Marketer & Convention Organizer
N.A.I.C.S.: 551112
Mohamad S. Ali *(CEO)*

Subsidiary (Domestic):

IDG Enterprise (2)
140 Kendrick St Bldg B, Needham, MA
02494
Tel.: (508) 879-0700
Web Site: https://www.idg.com
Publishing Services
N.A.I.C.S.: 513120
Genevieve Juillard *(CEO)*

Subsidiary (Non-US):

CW Fachverlag GmbH (3)
Sandleitengasse 15-17 Stiege 1 1st floor
TOP 19, 1160, Vienna, Austria
Tel.: (43) 650 3347035
Web Site: http://www.computerwelt.at
IT & Telecommunications
N.A.I.C.S.: 519290

Subsidiary (Domestic):

Computerworld, Inc. (3)
265 Worthington St, Springfield, MA 01103
Tel.: (508) 875-5000
Web Site: http://www.computerworld.com
Magazine Publisher
N.A.I.C.S.: 513120

Connell Communications Inc. (3)
360 Fee Fee Rd, Maryland Heights, MO
63043
Tel.: (314) 298-8727
Web Site: http://www.connellcom.com
Provider of Publishing Services
N.A.I.C.S.: 513120

Subsidiary (Non-US):

IDC Asean (3)
The Pinnacle Suite 7-03 Level 7 Persiaran
Lagoon Bandar Sunway, Subang Jaya,
Subang Jaya, 47500, Malaysia
Tel.: (60) 37663 2288
Web Site: http://www.idc.com
Provider of Business Information & Data
N.A.I.C.S.: 561499

IDC Asia & Pacific (3)
Unit 801A, Tower B Manulife Finance Centre, 223-231 Wai Yip Street, Kwun Tong,
Kowloon, China (Hong Kong)
Tel.: (852) 25303831
Web Site: http://www.idc.com
Telecommunications Products & Services
N.A.I.C.S.: 517810

IDC Asia Pacific (Singapore) (3)
Fuji Xerox Tower 80 Anson Road 38th
Floor, Singapore, 079907, Singapore
Tel.: (65) 62260330
Web Site: http://www.idc.com
Publisher
N.A.I.C.S.: 513120
Eva Au *(Mng Dir)*

IDC Australia (3)
11/160-166 Sussex Street, North Sydney,
2000, NSW, Australia
Tel.: (61) 2 9925 2298
Web Site: http://www.idc.com
Information Technology Services
N.A.I.C.S.: 519290

IDC Benelux (3)
Suikersilo Oost 1, 1165 MS, Halfweg, Netherlands
Tel.: (31) 20 333 0650
Web Site: http://www.idcbenelux.com
Publishing
N.A.I.C.S.: 513120
Martin Canning *(Grp VP-Consulting)*

IDC Brazil (3)
Av Eng Luiz Carlos Berrini 1645 - 8andar,
04571-000, Sao Paulo, Brazil
Tel.: (55) 1155083400

Web Site: http://www.idc.com
International Fund to Assist Entrepreneurs
with Business Expansion
N.A.I.C.S.: 523150
Denis Arcieri *(Country Mgr)*

IDC Central Europe GmbH   **(3)**
Karntner Ring 5-7, A 1090, Vienna, Austria
Tel.: (43) 2051160 1103
Web Site: http://www.idc.com
Computer Newspapers, Magazines & Books
N.A.I.C.S.: 513120

IDC Central Europe GmbH   **(3)**
Hanauer Landstr 182 D, Frankfurt, 60314,
Germany
Tel.: (49) 69905020
Web Site: http://www.idc.com
Market Analysis, Intelligence & Tactical Sup-
port to Users in IT & Telecommunications
N.A.I.C.S.: 513120
Wafa Moussavi-Amin *(Mng Dir-Northern
Europe & Grp VP)*

IDC China   **(3)**
Room 901 Tower E Global Trade Center 36
North 3rd Ring Road, Beijing, 100013,
China
Tel.: (86) 10 5889 1666
Web Site: http://www.idc.com
Provider of Business Information & Data
N.A.I.C.S.: 561499
Xi Wang *(Mgr-Res)*

IDC Columbia   **(3)**
Carrera 13 A 89 38 Nippon Ctr Oficina 627,
Bogota, Colombia
Tel.: (57) 16914356
Web Site: http://www.idccolombia.com.co
Market Analysis, Intelligence & Tactical Sup-
port to Users in IT & Telecommunications
N.A.I.C.S.: 517810
Carlos Villate *(Partner-Consulting)*

IDC France   **(3)**
13 rue Paul Valery, 75116, Paris, Cedex,
France
Tel.: (33) 156262666
Web Site: http://www.idc.fr
Publishing
N.A.I.C.S.: 513120
Helen Fily *(Sls Dir)*

IDC India Ltd.   **(3)**
Unit no.221-223 Vipul Plaza 2nd Floor Sec-
tor 54 Golf Course Road, Gurgaon, 122002,
India
Tel.: (91) 124 476 2300
Web Site: http://www.idc.com
Provider of Business Information & Data
N.A.I.C.S.: 561499

IDC Israel   **(3)**
11 Tuval St - 5th Floor, Ramat Gan,
5252226, Israel
Tel.: (972) 36871727
Web Site: http://www.idc.com
IT Consulting Services
N.A.I.C.S.: 541618
Gideon Lopez *(Country Mgr)*

IDC Italy   **(3)**
Viale Monza 14, 20127, Milan, Italy
Tel.: (39) 02284571
Web Site: http://www.idcitalia.com
Market Analysis, Intelligence & Tactical Sup-
port to Users in IT & Telecommunications
N.A.I.C.S.: 517810
Barbara Cambieri *(Mng Dir & Grp VP)*

IDC Japan Co., Ltd.   **(3)**
1 13 5 Kudankita Chiyoda, Tokyo, 102-
0073, Japan
Tel.: (81) 335564760
Web Site: http://www.idc.com
Market Analysis, Intelligence & Tactical Sup-
port to Users in IT & Telecommunications
N.A.I.C.S.: 517810
Masato Takeuchi *(Pres & CEO)*

IDC Korea Ltd.   **(3)**
Suite 406 Trade Tower 511 Yeongdong-
daero, Gangnam-gu, Seoul, 06164, Korea
(South)
Tel.: (82) 25514380
Web Site: http://www.idc.com
Business Information & Data Services
N.A.I.C.S.: 561499

Subsidiary (Domestic):

IDC Latin America   **(3)**

4090 NW 97 Ave Ste 350, Miami, FL
33178-6204
Tel.: (305) 351-3020
Web Site: http://www.idc.com
Internet Connectivity Services
N.A.I.C.S.: 517810
Eric Prothero *(Sr VP-Worldwide Tracker
Res & Corp Dev)*

Subsidiary (Non-US):

IDC Mexico   **(3)**
Manuel Avila Camacho 32 - 1102 piso 11,
Col Lomas de Chapultepec, Mexico, 11000,
Distrito Federal, Mexico
Tel.: (52) 5550101400
Web Site: http://www.idc.com
Market Analysis, Intelligence & Tactical Sup-
port to Users in IT & Telecommunications
N.A.I.C.S.: 517810

IDC Nordic (Denmark) A/S   **(3)**
Predgate 23 A, K 1260, Copenhagen, Den-
mark
Tel.: (45) 39162222
Web Site: http://www.nordic.idc.com
Sales Range: $10-24.9 Million
Emp.: 16
Provider of Business Information & Data
N.A.I.C.S.: 561499
Johnny Cederlund *(Mgr-Global Acct)*

IDC Nordic (Sweden)   **(3)**
Magnus Ladulasgatan 65, 106 78, Stock-
holm, Sweden
Tel.: (46) 8 444 15 90
Web Site: http://www.nordic.idc.com
Provider of Business Information & Data
N.A.I.C.S.: 561499
Jan Larsen *(VP-EMEA)*

IDC Philippines   **(3)**
Unit 1803 Trade and Financial Tower 7th
Avenue corner 32nd Street, Bonifacio
Global City, Taguig, 1201, Philippines
Tel.: (63) 24787260
Web Site: http://www.idc.com
Provider of Business Information & Data
N.A.I.C.S.: 561499

IDC Polska   **(3)**
Godara 9, Warsaw, 02 626, Poland
Tel.: (48) 225484050
Web Site: http://www.idc.com
Business Information & Data
N.A.I.C.S.: 561499

IDC Portugal   **(3)**
Centro Empresarial Torres de Lisboa Rua
Tomas da Fonseca Torre G, Lisbon, 1600-
209, Portugal
Tel.: (351) 21 723 06 22
Web Site: http://www.idc.pt
Information Technology Services
N.A.I.C.S.: 519290

Subsidiary (Domestic):

IDC Research, Inc.   **(3)**
5 Speen St, Framingham, MA 01701-4674
Tel.: (508) 872-8200
Web Site: http://www.idc.com
Market Intelligence, Advisory & Marketing
Event Organizing Services
N.A.I.C.S.: 561499
Leif Eriksen *(VP-Res-Future of Ops)*

Subsidiary (Non-US):

IDC Russia   **(3)**
Timiryazevskaya Street 1 Building 5, Mos-
cow, 127422, Russia
Tel.: (7) 495 9 747 747
Web Site: http://www.idc.com
Market Analysis, Intelligence & Tactical Sup-
port to Users in IT & Telecommunications
N.A.I.C.S.: 517810
Robert Farish *(VP-IDC Russia & CIS)*

IDC Spain   **(3)**
C/Serrano 41 - 3A planta, Madrid, 28001,
Spain
Tel.: (34) 917872150
Web Site: http://www.idcspain.com
International Fund to Assist Entrepreneurs
with Business Expansion
N.A.I.C.S.: 523150
Jorge Gil *(Gen Mgr)*

IDC Taiwan   **(3)**
E-1 4F No 89 Sungren Rd, Xinyi District,

Taipei, 110, Taiwan
Tel.: (886) 287580800
Web Site: http://www.idc.com
Provider of Business Information & Data
N.A.I.C.S.: 561499

IDC Turkey   **(3)**
Nispetiye Mahallesi Cahit Aybar Sokak Zin-
cirlikuyu Harp Akademileri, 4 Daire 74 Be-
siktas, 34340, Istanbul, Turkiye
Tel.: (90) 2123560282
Web Site: http://www.idc.com
Provider of Business Information
N.A.I.C.S.: 513120
Nevin Cizmeciogullari *(Country Dir)*

IDC UK Ltd.   **(3)**
5th floor Ealing Cross 85 Uxbridge Road,
London, W5 5TH, United Kingdom
Tel.: (44) 2089877100
Web Site: http://www.uk.idc.com
IT Consulting Services
N.A.I.C.S.: 541618
Dan Timberlake *(Mng Dir-UK & Ireland)*

IDC Venezuela   **(3)**
Lomas de La Trinidad Calle del Sauce
Quinta El Sauce No 1, Caracas, 1080, Ven-
ezuela
Tel.: (58) 212 945 2314
Web Site: http://www.idc.com
Market Analysis, Intelligence & Tactical Sup-
port to Users in IT & Telecommunications
N.A.I.C.S.: 513120

IDG Business Verlag GmbH   **(3)**
YonelSeinengir Strasse 26, Munich, 80807,
Germany
Tel.: (49) 89 360 86 0
Web Site: http://www.idg.de
Magazine Publisher
N.A.I.C.S.: 513120

IDG China Co., Ltd.   **(3)**
Room 901m Tower E Global Trade Center
36 North 3rd Ring Road, 100013, Beijing,
China
Tel.: (86) 10 5889 1666
Web Site: http://www.idc.com
Magazine Publisher
N.A.I.C.S.: 513120
Xi Wang *(Mgr-Res)*

IDG Communications Italia Srl   **(3)**
S.S. Del Sempione 28, 20017, Milan, Italy
Tel.: (39) 02 4997 7209
Web Site: http://www.fieramilano.it
Market Analysis, Intelligence & Tactical Sup-
port to Users in IT & Telecommunications
N.A.I.C.S.: 517810

IDG Communications Media AG   **(3)**
Lyonel-Feininger-Strasse 26, 80807, Mu-
nich, Germany
Tel.: (49) 89 360 86 0
Web Site: http://www.idg.de
Marketing Consulting Services
N.A.I.C.S.: 541910
Kevin Krull *(Chm)*

IDG Communications Media AG   **(3)**
Lyonel-Feininger-Str 26, 80807, Munich,
Germany
Tel.: (49) 89360860
Web Site: http://www.idg.de
Computer Magazine Publisher
N.A.I.C.S.: 513120
Kevin Krull *(Chm)*

IDG Communications Norge AS   **(3)**
PO Box 171 City Center, 0102, Oslo, Nor-
way
Tel.: (47) 22053000
Publishing Services
N.A.I.C.S.: 513120
Morten Hansen *(CEO)*

IDG Communications Pty. Ltd.   **(3)**
Level 10 15 Blue St, Sydney, 2060, NSW,
Australia
Tel.: (61) 294395133
Web Site: http://www.idg.com.au
Media & Research Publishing Services
N.A.I.C.S.: 513120
Barbara Simon *(Pres)*

**IDG Communications Publishing
Group SRL**   **(3)**
8 10 Maresal Averescu Fl 7 Rm 705 715,
Bucharest, 71316, Romania
Tel.: (40) 212242621

N.A.I.C.S.: 513120
Gineta Rosca *(Mgr-Sls)*

IDG Communications UK, Ltd.   **(3)**
101 Euston Road, London, NW1 2RA,
United Kingdom
Tel.: (44) 20 7756 2800
Web Site: http://www.idg.co.uk
Magazine Publisher
N.A.I.C.S.: 513120
Kit Gould *(Pres-B2C)*

IDG Communications, S.A.U.   **(3)**
Velazquez 105 Floor 5, 28006, Madrid,
Spain
Tel.: (34) 913496600
Web Site: http://www.idg.es
Market Analysis, Intelligence & Tactical Sup-
port to Users in IT & Telecommunications
N.A.I.C.S.: 513120

IDG Computerworld do Brazil   **(3)**
Avenida Chedid Jafet 222 Via Olimpia, Sao
Paulo, Brazil
Tel.: (55) 11 3823 6600
Magazine Publisher
N.A.I.C.S.: 513120

IDG Czech Republic, a.s.   **(3)**
Seydlerova 2451, Prague, 158 00, Czech
Republic
Tel.: (420) 775 210 150
Web Site: http://www.idg.com
Newspaper & Magazines Publisher
N.A.I.C.S.: 513120
Jana Pelikanova *(Mng Dir)*

IDG Denmark A/S   **(3)**
Horkaer 18, 2730, Herlev, Denmark
Tel.: (45) 77300300
Market Analysis, Intelligence & Tactical Sup-
port to Users in IT & Telecommunications
N.A.I.C.S.: 517810

IDG Entertainment Media GmbH   **(3)**
Lyonel-Feininger-Str 26, Munich, 80807,
Germany
Tel.: (49) 89 360 86 0
Magazine Publisher
N.A.I.C.S.: 513120

IDG Entertainment Verlag GmbH   **(3)**
Lyonel Feininger Street 26, Munich, 80807,
Germany
Tel.: (49) 89360860
Web Site: http://www.idg.de
International Fund to Assist Entrepreneurs
with Business Expansion
N.A.I.C.S.: 523150

IDG Global Solutions   **(3)**
Lionel Feininger Strasse 26, Munich, D
80807, Germany
Tel.: (49) 89 360 86 0
Web Site: http://www.idg.com
International Fund to Assist Entrepreneurs
with Business Expansion
N.A.I.C.S.: 523150

IDG Global Solutions APAC   **(3)**
80 Anson Road #31-05 Fuji Xerox Tower,
Singapore, 077907, Singapore
Tel.: (65) 98337294
Web Site: http://www.idg.com
International Fund to Assist Entrepreneurs
with Business Expansion
N.A.I.C.S.: 523150

IDG Japan, Inc.   **(3)**
4-3-12 Toranomon, Minato-ku, Tokyo, 105-
8308, Japan
Tel.: (81) 358003111
Web Site: http://www.idg.co.jp
Magazine Publisher
N.A.I.C.S.: 513120

IDG Magazines Norge AS   **(3)**
PO Box 171 City Center, 0102, Oslo, Nor-
way
Tel.: (47) 2205 3000
Web Site: http://www.cw.no
Magazine Publisher
N.A.I.C.S.: 513120
Morten Hansen *(Mng Dir)*

IDG Media Private Limited   **(3)**
35/2 Langford Rd Cross Bheemanna
Garde, Sampangi Rama Nagara, Benga-
luru, 560025, India
Tel.: (91) 96063 93030
Web Site: http://www.idg.com

China Oceanwide Holdings Group Co.,
Ltd.—(Continued)

Magazine Publisher
N.A.I.C.S.: 513120

IDG Netherlands (3)
Joop Geesinkweg 701 51, 1114 AB, Amsterdam, Netherlands
Tel.: (31) 207585955
Web Site: http://www.idg.nl
Publisher of News & Business Information
N.A.I.C.S.: 513120

IDG Poland S.A. (3)
Twarda 18 Spektrum Tower, Warsaw, 2092, Poland
Tel.: (48) 223217800
Web Site: http://www.idg.com.pl
Market Analysis, Intelligence & Tactical Support to Users in IT & Telecommunications
N.A.I.C.S.: 513120
Marcin Tyborowski (Dir-Sls)

IDG Sweden AB (3)
Magnus Ladulasgatan 65, Stockholm, 106
78, Sweden
Tel.: (46) 84536000
Web Site: http://www.idgsverige.se
Marketing Publisher
N.A.I.C.S.: 513120

IDG Taiwan (3)
19F NO15-1 Sec 1 Hang Chou S Road,
Taipei, Taiwan
Tel.: (886) 2 23214335
Magazine Publisher
N.A.I.C.S.: 513120

**International Data Corporation
(Canada) Ltd** (3)
33 Yonge Street Suite 902, Toronto, M5E
1G4, ON, Canada
Tel.: (416) 369-0033
Web Site: http://www.idc.com
Market Research on Information Technology
Industry
N.A.I.C.S.: 541910
Lars Goransson (Mng Dir)

Inviarco SAS (3)
Carrera 90 No 154A 75 Piso 4, Bogota, DC,
Colombia
Tel.: (57) 1 686 2462
Web Site: http://www.computerworld.co
Computer Magazine Publisher
N.A.I.C.S.: 513120

Media Trans Asia Limited (3)
Ocean Tower 2 No 75-8 Suksumbit Rd,
Suksumbit Soi 19 Wattana Dist, Bangkok,
10110, Thailand
Tel.: (66) 22042370
Web Site: http://www.mediatransasia.com
Market Analysis, Intelligence & Tactical Support to Users in IT & Telecommunications
N.A.I.C.S.: 513120

Mediateam Ltd. (3)
55 Spruce Avenue Stillorgan Industrial Estate Sandyford, Leopardstown, Dublin, Ireland
Tel.: (353) 1 294 7777
Web Site: http://www.mediateam.ie
Technology Magazine Publisher
N.A.I.C.S.: 513120
Paul Byrne (Dir-Sls)

Subsidiary (Domestic):

Network World, Inc. (3)
5 Speen St, Framingham, MA 01701
Tel.: (508) 875-5000
Web Site: http://www.networkworld.com
Publisher of Computer Magazines
N.A.I.C.S.: 513120

Subsidiary (Non-US):

PT Prima Infosarana Media (3)
Gramedia Majalah Building Unit 13th Floor,
JI Panjang No 8A Kebon Jeruk, Jakarta,
11530, Indonesia
Tel.: (62) 215330150
Web Site: http://www.infokomputer.com
IT Magazine Publisher
N.A.I.C.S.: 513120
Dahlan Dahi (Grp Dir)

Subsidiary (Domestic):

IDG World Expo Corporation (2)

492 Old Connecticut Path Ste 420,
Framingham, MA 01701
Tel.: (508) 879-6700
Web Site: http://www.idgworldexpo.com
Organizes Trade Shows
N.A.I.C.S.: 561920

MEMSIC, Inc. (2)
1 Tech Dr Ste 325, Andover, MA 01810
Tel.: (978) 738-0900
Web Site: http://www.memsic.com
Semiconductor Sensor & System Solutions
Based on Integrated Micro Electro-Mechanical Systems (MEMS), Technology
& Mixed Signal Circuit Design
N.A.I.C.S.: 334413

Oceanwide Holdings Co., Ltd. (1)
22F Tower C Minsheng Financial Center 28
Jianguomennei Street, Dongcheng District,
Beijing, 100005, China
Tel.: (86) 1085259698
Web Site: http://www.fhkg.com
Rev.: $1,835,106,624
Assets: $14,768,734,968
Liabilities: $14,643,165,420
Net Worth: $125,569,548
Earnings: ($1,619,728,812)
Fiscal Year-end: 12/31/2022
Holding Company; Real Estate Investment
& Property Management Services
N.A.I.C.S.: 551112
Guosheng Liu (CFO)

Subsidiary (Non-US):

China Oceanwide Holdings Ltd. (2)
64th Floor Bank of China Tower 1 Garden
Road, Hong Kong, China (Hong
Kong) **(71.58%)**
Tel.: (852) 39595500
Web Site: http://www.oceanwide.hk
Rev.: $3,573,060
Assets: $2,108,827,433
Liabilities: $1,900,067,348
Net Worth: $208,760,085
Earnings: ($309,431,918)
Emp.: 56
Fiscal Year-end: 12/31/2022
Holding Company
N.A.I.C.S.: 551112
Xiaosheng Han (Chm)

CHINA OIL & GAS GROUP LIMITED

Suite 2805 28th Floor Sino Plaza
255-257 Gloucester Road, Causeway
Bay, China (Hong Kong)
Tel.: (852) 22002222
Web Site: https://www.hk603.hk
0603—(HKG)
Rev.: $2,221,115,280
Assets: $2,925,830,858
Liabilities: $1,780,899,983
Net Worth: $1,144,930,875
Earnings: $179,275,965
Emp.: 4,837
Fiscal Year-end: 12/31/22
Oil & Gas Exploration
N.A.I.C.S.: 213112
Tie-Liang Xu (Chm & CEO)

Subsidiaries:

Accelstar Pacific Limited (1)
C/o Overseas Mgmt Company Trust BVI Ltd
2nd FI RG Hodge Plz, Road Town, VG1110,
Tortola, Virgin Islands (British)
Tel.: (284) 4944693
Investment Holding Services
N.A.I.C.S.: 523999

CHINA OIL HBP SCIENCE & TECHNOLOGY CO., LTD.

Floor 12/16 Floor No 17 Madian East
Road, Haidian District, Beijing,
100088, China
Tel.: (86) 1062071047
Web Site: http://www.china-hbp.com
Year Founded: 1998
002554—(SSE)
Rev.: $278,962,164
Assets: $703,270,620
Liabilities: $345,308,184
Net Worth: $357,962,436

Earnings: $22,351,680
Emp.: 1,300
Fiscal Year-end: 12/31/22
Oil & Gas Field Equipment Mfr
N.A.I.C.S.: 333132
Pan Qing (Chm)

CHINA OILFIELD TECHNOLOGY SERVICES GROUP LIMITED

28 Xin Fa Street Hi-Tech Development Zone, Daqing, 163316, Heilongjiang, China
Tel.: (86) 4596030223
Web Site:
    http://www.chinaoilfieldtech.com
Sales Range: Less than $1 Million
Crude Oil Producer
N.A.I.C.S.: 324199
Vincent Bock Hui Lim (Sec)

CHINA ORAL INDUSTRY GROUP HOLDINGS LIMITED

Units 1903-04 19/F Tamson Plaza
161 Wai Yip Street, Kwun Tong, Kowloon, China (Hong Kong)
Tel.: (852) 21111325   Ky
Web Site: http://www.alpha-era.co
Year Founded: 2003
8406—(HKG)
Rev.: $29,837,668
Assets: $26,794,778
Liabilities: $9,504,799
Net Worth: $17,289,979
Earnings: ($4,893,080)
Emp.: 571
Fiscal Year-end: 12/31/22
Rubber Products Mfr
N.A.I.C.S.: 326299
Xiaodong Huang (Chm)

Subsidiaries:

Swiftech Company Limited (1)
Dongcheng Industrial Zone Xinping Road,
Minzhong Town, Zhongshan, Guangdong,
China
Tel.: (86) 76028108960
Rubber Products Mfr
N.A.I.C.S.: 326299
Becky Lam (Mgr-Exporting Dept)

Swiftech International Limited (1)
Unit 1902 19/F Tamson Plaza 161 Wai Yip
Street, Kwun Tong, Kowloon, China (Hong
Kong)
Tel.: (852) 76028108960
Construction Product Whslr
N.A.I.C.S.: 444180

CHINA ORIENTAL GROUP COMPANY LIMITED

Suites 901-2 and 10 Great Eagle
Centre, 23 Harbour Road, Wanchai,
China (Hong Kong)
Tel.: (852) 25111369   BM
Web Site:
    http://www.chinaorientalgroup.com
0581—(HKG)
Rev.: $6,826,294,613
Assets: $6,742,512,036
Liabilities: $3,192,547,597
Net Worth: $3,549,964,439
Earnings: $113,914,242
Emp.: 11,500
Fiscal Year-end: 12/31/22
Iron & Steel Mfr
N.A.I.C.S.: 331110
Hao Zhu (Exec Dir)

Subsidiaries:

**China Oriental Singapore Pte.
Ltd.** (1)
600 North Bridge Road 04-02 Parkview
Square, Singapore, 188778, Singapore
Tel.: (65) 65928122
Web Site: http://www.chinaoriental.com
Emp.: 10
Iron & Steel Whslr

N.A.I.C.S.: 423510
Hou Li Wei (Gen Mgr)

**Foshan Jinxi Jinlan Cold Rolled
Sheets Co., Ltd.** (1)
Yanghe's Jurisdiction Cangjiang Industrial
Zone, Gaoming, Foshan, Guangdong,
China
Tel.: (86) 75788911133
Web Site: https://www.jxjl.cn
Steel Products Mfr
N.A.I.C.S.: 331221

**Hebei Jinxi Iron & Steel Group Co.,
Ltd.** (1)
Room 2901-3 Ful Building No 9 East Third
Ring Middle Road, Chaoyang District, Beijing, 100020, China
Tel.: (86) 1085910207
Web Site: https://www.hbjxgtjt.com.cn
Iron & Steel Mfr
N.A.I.C.S.: 331110
Jingyuan Han (Chm & Pres)

Jinxi Vodar Engineering Co., Ltd. (1)
No 7 Liaoning Road Ziya Circular Economy
Industrial Park, Tianjin, China
Tel.: (86) 2258607755
Web Site: http://www.jinxivodar.com
Iron & Steel Whslr
N.A.I.C.S.: 423510
Zhou Carson (CEO)

CHINA ORIENTED INTERNATIONAL HOLDINGS LIMITED

Baililiu Village, Zhutang Township
Suiping County, Zhumadian, Henan,
China   Ky
Web Site: https://www.china-oriented.com
Year Founded: 2012
1871—(HKG)
Rev.: $5,522,264
Assets: $39,924,679
Liabilities: $13,677,309
Net Worth: $26,247,369
Earnings: ($1,169,002)
Emp.: 209
Fiscal Year-end: 12/31/23
Holding Company
N.A.I.C.S.: 551112
Xiangzhong Qi (Founder)

CHINA OUHUA WINERY HOLDINGS LIMITED

No 3 North Wolong Road, Yantai,
Shan Dong, China
Tel.: (86) 5356019888
Web Site:
    https://www.ouhuazhuangyuan.com
5188—(KLS)
Rev.: $2,024,119
Assets: $23,334,487
Liabilities: $716,382
Net Worth: $22,618,105
Earnings: ($3,591,604)
Emp.: 110
Fiscal Year-end: 12/31/22
Wine Producer & Distr
N.A.I.C.S.: 312130
Wang Chao (CEO, Founder & Chm)

CHINA OUTFITTERS HOLDINGS LTD.

Room 1303 13/F New East Ocean
Centre 9 Science Museum Road,
Tsim Sha Tsui East, Kowloon, China
(Hong Kong)
Tel.: (852) 24196989   Ky
Web Site: http://www.cohl.hk
Year Founded: 1999
1146—(HKG)
Rev.: $28,994,846
Assets: $206,303,620
Liabilities: $28,129,280
Net Worth: $178,174,339
Earnings: ($35,613,583)
Emp.: 273
Fiscal Year-end: 12/31/22
Holding Company

N.A.I.C.S.: 551112
Yongli Zhang *(Chm & CEO)*

CHINA OVERSEAS NUOXIN INTERNATIONAL HOLDINGS LIMITED

Office 810 Unit 1908 19 F 9 Queen s Road Central, Kwai Chung, New Territories, China (Hong Kong)
Tel.: (852) 3 892 5999 **Ky**
Web Site: http://www.co-nuoxin.com
Year Founded: 1984
0464—(HKG)
Rev.: $34,277,467
Assets: $23,347,057
Liabilities: $14,262,350
Net Worth: $9,084,706
Earnings: ($1,478,885)
Emp.: 776
Fiscal Year-end: 03/31/22
Electrical Appliance Mfr & Whslr
N.A.I.C.S.: 335210
Patrick Pak Chuen Kwong *(Sr Mgr-Engrg)*

CHINA OVERSEAS PROPERTY HOLDINGS LTD.

19th Floor China Overseas Building No 139 Hennessy Road, No 138 Lockhart Road, Wanchai, China (Hong Kong)
Tel.: (852) 28237088 **Ky**
Web Site: http://www.copl.com.hk
2669—(HKG)
Rev.: $1,617,843,420
Assets: $1,290,477,863
Liabilities: $823,447,530
Net Worth: $467,030,333
Earnings: $163,286,573
Emp.: 57,425
Fiscal Year-end: 12/31/22
Holding Company
N.A.I.C.S.: 551112
Yuk Fai Kam *(Deputy CFO)*

CHINA PACIFIC INSURANCE (GROUP) CO., LTD.

No 1 Zhongshan South Road, Huangpu, Shanghai, 200010, China
Tel.: (86) 2158767282
Web Site: https://www.cpic.com.cn
Year Founded: 1991
601601—(SSE)
Rev.: $45,626,056,201
Assets: $330,135,491,967
Liabilities: $292,430,703,348
Net Worth: $37,704,788,619
Earnings: $3,931,126,749
Emp.: 98,732
Fiscal Year-end: 12/31/23
Life & Property Insurance Services
N.A.I.C.S.: 524113
Fan Fu *(Pres)*

Subsidiaries:

China Pacific Property Insurance Co., Ltd. **(1)**
190 Cent Yincheng Rd, Shanghai, 200120, China
Tel.: (86) 2158776688
Web Site: http://www.cpic.com.cn
Property Insurance Services
N.A.I.C.S.: 524126
Zongmin Wu *(Pres)*

CHINA PAPER HOLDINGS LIMITED

South Part Jianshe Road, Linyi, Shandong, China
Tel.: (86) 5398500106
Web Site: http://www.chinapaper-holdings.com
Sales Range: $125-149.9 Million
Paper Mfr
N.A.I.C.S.: 313110

CHINA PARENTING NETWORK HOLDINGS LIMITED

Gu Yang Building 19th Floor No 600 Zhujiang Road, Nanjing, 210018, China
Tel.: (86) 2586884590 **Ky**
Web Site: http://www.ci123.com
1736—(HKG)
Rev.: $11,929,788
Assets: $23,436,410
Liabilities: $9,220,489
Net Worth: $14,215,921
Earnings: ($5,897,502)
Emp.: 92
Fiscal Year-end: 12/31/22
Marketing Consulting Services
N.A.I.C.S.: 541613
Li Cheng *(CEO)*

CHINA PARTYTIME CULTURE HOLDINGS LIMITED

No 3 Chunchao Road Yichun Economic and Technological Development Zone, Yichun, Jiangxi, China
Tel.: (86) 4000002783 **Ky**
Web Site: http://www.partytime.com.cn
Year Founded: 2004
1532—(HKG)
Rev.: $42,276,265
Assets: $69,923,272
Liabilities: $13,903,952
Net Worth: $56,019,319
Earnings: ($2,051,384)
Emp.: 567
Fiscal Year-end: 12/31/22
Lingerie Mfr & Distr
N.A.I.C.S.: 315250
Xin Fu Lin *(Chm & CEO)*

CHINA PENGFEI GROUP LIMITED

Benjiaji Northern Suburb, Haian, Nantong, Jiangsu, China
Tel.: (86) 51388758898 **Ky**
Web Site: http://www.pengfeichina.com.cn
Year Founded: 1994
3348—(HKG)
Rev.: $222,872,926
Assets: $421,685,222
Liabilities: $308,697,480
Net Worth: $112,987,742
Earnings: $17,137,224
Emp.: 1,100
Fiscal Year-end: 12/31/22
Grinding Equipment Mfr
N.A.I.C.S.: 325411
Jiaan Wang *(Chm)*

CHINA PETROCHEMICAL CORPORATION

22 Chaoyangmen North Street, Chaoyang District, Beijing, 100728, China
Tel.: (86) 1059960114 **CN**
Web Site: https://www.sinopecgroup.com
Year Founded: 1998
Rev.: $452,424,646,530
Assets: $285,447,041,397
Liabilities: $150,425,210,816
Net Worth: $135,021,830,581
Earnings: $9,558,309,830
Emp.: 368,009
Fiscal Year-end: 12/31/23
Petrochemicals Extraction Services
N.A.I.C.S.: 551112
Zhao Dong *(Chm-Supervisory Bd)*

Subsidiaries:

China Petroleum & Chemical Corporation **(1)**
22 Chaoyangmen North Street, Chaoyang District, Beijing, 100728, China
Tel.: (86) 1059969999
Rev.: $444,757,282,898
Assets: $280,335,622,508

Liabilities: $147,996,095,481
Net Worth: $132,339,527,027
Earnings: $9,396,322,552
Emp.: 368,009
Fiscal Year-end: 12/31/2023
Holding Company; Petroleum Production & Refining Services & Petrochemical Mfr
N.A.I.C.S.: 551112
Yongsheng Ma *(Pres)*

Joint Venture (Domestic):

BASF-YPC Company Limited **(2)**
No 8 East Xinhua Road, Jiangbei New Area, Nanjing, 210048, Jiangsu, China **(50%)**
Tel.: (86) 2558569966
Web Site: https://www.basf-ypc.com.cn
Petrochemical Products Mfr
N.A.I.C.S.: 325110

Affiliate (Domestic):

Petro-CyberWorks Information Technology Co., Ltd. **(2)**
ten A 22 Nan Xin Cang Business Building 12th floor, Dongcheng District, Beijing, 100007, China
Tel.: (86) 1084191188
Web Site: http://www.pcitc.com
Information Technology Services
N.A.I.C.S.: 541512

Joint Venture (Domestic):

Shanghai Gaoqiao BASF Dispersions Co., Ltd. **(2)**
No 99 Ln 1929 Pudong Bei Road, Pudong New Area, Shanghai, 200137, China
Tel.: (86) 2158670303
Web Site: http://www.sgbd.com.cn
Sales Range: $50-74.9 Million
Emp.: 200
Adhesive Raw Material Mfr
N.A.I.C.S.: 325520

Shanghai SECCO Petrochemical Co., Ltd. **(2)**
30/31F A Building Far East International Plaza No 319 Xian Xia Road, No 299 Xian Xia Road, Shanghai, 200051, China
Tel.: (86) 2152574688
Web Site: https://www.secco.com.cn
Emp.: 500
Petrochemical Products Mfr
N.A.I.C.S.: 325110

Subsidiary (Non-US):

Sinopec (Hong Kong) Limited **(2)**
12/F Office Tower Convention Plaza 1 Harbour Road, Wanchai, China (Hong Kong)
Tel.: (852) 2824 2638
Fuel Oil Distr
N.A.I.C.S.: 424720

Subsidiary (Domestic):

Sinopec Beijing Yanhua Petrochemical Company Limited **(2)**
No 1 Gangnan, Yanshan Fangshan District, Beijing, 102500, China
Tel.: (86) 1069342295
Emp.: 16,000
Provider of Petrochemical Products
N.A.I.C.S.: 325110

Sinopec Chemical Sales Company **(2)**
A6 Huixin East Street, Chaoyang District, 100029, Beijing, China
Tel.: (86) 10 8464 5788
Chemical Products Sales
N.A.I.C.S.: 424690

Affiliate (Domestic):

Sinopec Fujian Refining & Chemical Co., Ltd. **(2)**
Quangang District, Quanzhou, China
Tel.: (86) 59587789188
Chemical Processing Services
N.A.I.C.S.: 325110

Subsidiary (Domestic):

Sinopec Guangzhou Company **(2)**
No 239 Shihua Road, Huangpu District, Guangzhou, 510726, China
Tel.: (86) 2082123888

Web Site: http://english.sinopec.com
Petrochemical Mfr
N.A.I.C.S.: 325110

Sinopec Qilu Petrochemical Co., Ltd. **(2)**
15 Huangong Road Linzi, Zibo, 255408, Shandong, China
Tel.: (86) 5337180777
Web Site: http://english.sinopec.com
Petrochemical Processing Services
N.A.I.C.S.: 325110

Joint Venture (Domestic):

Qilu Eastman Specialty Chemicals Ltd. **(3)**
6-1 Xinhua Road Linzi, Zibo, 255400, Shandong, China
Tel.: (86) 533 7512705
Web Site: http://www.eastmanchemical.com
Sales Range: $25-49.9 Million
Emp.: 70
Chemical Products Mfr
N.A.I.C.S.: 325998

Subsidiary (Domestic):

Sinopec Sales Company, Ltd. **(2)**
No A6 Huisingong Street, Chaoyan District, Beijing, China
Tel.: (86) 1064998828
Petrochemical Sales Services
N.A.I.C.S.: 424690

Sinopec Shanghai Petrochemical Company Limited **(2)**
No 48 Jinyi Road, Jinshan District, Shanghai, 200540, PRC, China **(55.56%)**
Tel.: (86) 2157941941
Web Site: http://www.spc.com.cn
Rev.: $12,631,115,931
Assets: $6,302,556,412
Liabilities: $2,264,651,246
Net Worth: $4,037,905,165
Earnings: ($435,468,783)
Emp.: 8,007
Fiscal Year-end: 12/31/2022
Mfr of Ethylene, Deisel Fuel, Gasoline, Synthetic Fibers & Petrochemicals
N.A.I.C.S.: 325211
Zemin Guan *(Pres & VP)*

Subsidiary (Non-US):

Amodaimi Oil Company, Ltd. **(3)**
Av 12 de Octubre N24 593 & Francisco Salazar 1 - 3 Edificio Plaza, 2000 Ofic 3 A, Quito, Ecuador **(100%)**
Tel.: (593) 2 2976600
Sales Range: $200-249.9 Million
Emp.: 400
Oil & Gas Exploration Services
N.A.I.C.S.: 213112
Luis Garcia *(Gen Mgr)*

Subsidiary (Domestic):

China Jinshan Associated Trading Corp. **(3)**
4 F Information Ctr Bldg Weier Rd, Shanghai, 200540, China **(67.33%)**
Tel.: (86) 2157940433
Web Site: http://www.cjatc.com
Sales Range: $25-49.9 Million
Emp.: 60
Import & Export Technology, Equipment & Spare Parts of Petrochemical, Synthetic Fiber & Plastic
N.A.I.C.S.: 325110
Wu Huili *(Mgr-Trading Mgmt)*

Subsidiary (Domestic):

Sinopec Shengli Oilfield Co., Ltd. **(2)**
258 Jinan Road, Dongying District, Dongying, 257001, Shandong, China
Tel.: (86) 5468552074
Petrochemical Products Mfr
N.A.I.C.S.: 325110

Sinopec Taishan Oil Products Co., Ltd. **(2)**
No 104 Dongyue Street, Tai'an, 27100, Shandong, China
Tel.: (86) 3588265105
Petrochemical Products Mfr
N.A.I.C.S.: 325110

China Petrochemical Corporation—(Continued)

Sinopec Wuhan Phoenix Co., Ltd. (2)
Changqing Road, Qingshan District, Wuhan, 430082, Hubei, China
Tel.: (86) 2786515662
Web Site: http://english.sinopec.com
Petrochemical Products Mfr
N.A.I.C.S.: 325110

Sinopec Zhenhai Refining & Chemical Co., Ltd. (2)
Ahenhai District, Ningbo, 315207, Zhejiang, China
Tel.: (86) 444238
Sales Range: $25-49.9 Million
Emp.: 6
Petrochemical Products Mfr
N.A.I.C.S.: 325110

Subsidiary (Domestic):

Zhenhai Petrochemical Engineering Co., Ltd. (3)
High-Tech zones No 36 Xinghai South Road, Ningbo, 315042, Zhejiang, China
Tel.: (86) 57487917820
Web Site: http://www.izpec.com
Rev.: $80,655,490
Assets: $198,096,397
Liabilities: $73,011,945
Net Worth: $125,084,452
Earnings: $14,468,473
Emp.: 350
Fiscal Year-end: 12/31/2022
Petrochemical Construction Management Services
N.A.I.C.S.: 237120
Zheng Zhen (Chm)

Subsidiary (Non-US):

UNIPEC Asia Co. Ltd. (2)
Room 1202 12th Floor Convention Plaza Office Tower 1, Harbour Road, Wanchai, China (Hong Kong)
Tel.: (852) 28796688
Sales Range: $50-74.9 Million
Emp.: 40
Petrochemical Trading Services
N.A.I.C.S.: 213112

UNIPEC UK Co. Ltd. (2)
20th Floor Marble Arch Tower, 55 Bryanston Street, London, W1H 7AA, United Kingdom
Tel.: (44) 2076169888
Web Site: http://www.sinopec.com
Petrochemical Trading Services
N.A.I.C.S.: 213112

Sinopec Engineering (Group) Co. Ltd. (1)
Tower B No 19 Anhuibeili, Chaoyang District, Beijing, 100101, China
Tel.: (86) 1064998000
Web Site: https://www.segroup.cn
Rev.: $8,020,939,395
Assets: $10,949,202,750
Liabilities: $6,620,095,168
Net Worth: $4,329,107,582
Earnings: $364,977,781
Emp.: 17,301
Fiscal Year-end: 12/31/2020
Engineering Services
N.A.I.C.S.: 541330
Lili Sun (Exec Dir)

Sinopec Fuel Oil Sales Co., Ltd (1)
F7-8 Building 1 No Jia 6 of HuiXin East Street, Chao Yang District, Beijing, 100029, China
Tel.: (86) 10 69166666
Web Site: http://fuel.sinopec.com
Petroleum Product Distr
N.A.I.C.S.: 424720

Subsidiary (Non-US):

Sinopec Fuel Oil (Singapore) Pte. Ltd. (2)
1 Temasek Avenue 20-04, Millenia Tower, Singapore, 039192, Singapore
Tel.: (65) 66028766
Petroleum Product Distr
N.A.I.C.S.: 424720

Sinopec International Petroleum Exploration & Production Corporation (1)

No 263 North Fourth Ring Road, Haidian District, Beijing, 100083, China
Tel.: (86) 1082310862
Web Site: https://sipc.sinopec.com
Holding Company; Petroleum Upstream & Downstream Properties Investment & Management
N.A.I.C.S.: 551112

Joint Venture (Non-US):

Mansarovar Energy Colombia Ltd. (2)
Calle 100 No 13 - 76 Piso 11, Bogota, Colombia
Tel.: (57) 1 485 1212
Web Site: https://www.mansarovar.com.co
Crude Petroleum Production & Transportation Services Owned by Oil & Natural Gas Corporation & by China Petrochemical Services
N.A.I.C.S.: 211120
Sidhartha Sur (Mgr-Ops)

Subsidiary (Non-US):

Sinopec Daylight Energy Ltd. (2)
Sun Life Plaza East Tower Suite 2700 112 - 4th Avenue SW, 112 4th Avenue SW, Calgary, T2P 0H3, AB, Canada
Tel.: (403) 266-6900
Web Site: http://www.sinopeccanada.com
Sales Range: $650-699.9 Million
Emp.: 233
Oil & Natural Gas Exploration & Production Services
N.A.I.C.S.: 211120
Randy Ford (VP)

Sinopec Oilfield Equipment Corporation (1)
No 5 Huagong Park First Road Eastlake New tech Development Zone, Wuhan, 430205, Hubei, China
Tel.: (86) 2751005600
Web Site: https://www.sofe.sinopec.com
Rev.: $1,088,368,164
Assets: $1,395,755,712
Liabilities: $966,999,384
Net Worth: $428,756,328
Earnings: $7,241,832
Emp.: 6,342
Fiscal Year-end: 12/31/2022
Petroleum Drilling & Mining Equipment Mfr
N.A.I.C.S.: 333132
Xuejun Liu (Pres)

Sinopec Oilfield Service Corporation (1)
No 9 Jishikou Road, Chaoyang District, Beijing, 100728, China (72.01%)
Tel.: (86) 1059965998
Web Site: http://ssc.sinopec.com
Rev.: $10,357,685,395
Assets: $9,996,552,587
Liabilities: $8,953,756,999
Net Worth: $1,042,795,588
Earnings: $65,119,486
Emp.: 70,000
Fiscal Year-end: 12/31/2022
Oil Field Services
N.A.I.C.S.: 213112
Jianqiang Yuan (Gen Mgr)

CHINA PETROCHEMICAL DEVELOPMENT CORP.
No 1 Jingjian Road, Dashe District, Kaohsiung, 815, Taiwan
Tel.: (886) 73513521
Web Site: https://www.cpdc.com.tw
Year Founded: 1969
CPDC—(LUX)
Rev.: $863,803,689
Assets: $4,764,886,670
Liabilities: $2,189,062,117
Net Worth: $2,575,824,554
Earnings: ($35,359,755)
Emp.: 1,117
Fiscal Year-end: 12/31/23
Resins & Plastics Products Distr
N.A.I.C.S.: 325211
Chien-Hsien Lee (Asst VP)

Subsidiaries:

CPDC Green Technology Corp. (1)
No 421 Beishanwei 2nd Rd, Annan Dist,

T'ainan, 709, Taiwan
Tel.: (886) 62842730
Engineering Services
N.A.I.C.S.: 541330

Chemax International Corporation (1)
8F No 12 Dongsing Rd, Songshan District, Taipei, 105, Taiwan
Tel.: (886) 287878677
Web Site: http://www.chemax.com.tw
Sales Range: $50-74.9 Million
Emp.: 10
Petrochemicals Import & Distr
N.A.I.C.S.: 424690

China Petrochemical Development Corp. - Dashe Plant (1)
No 1 Jingjian Road, Dashe District, Kaohsiung, 815, Taiwan
Tel.: (886) 7 351 3521
Web Site: http://www.cpdc.com.tw
Petrochemical Mfr
N.A.I.C.S.: 324110

China Petrochemical Development Corp. - Hsiaokang Plant (1)
No 34 Zhonglin Road, Xiaogang District, Kaohsiung, 812, Taiwan
Tel.: (886) 78711160
Web Site: http://www.cpdc.com.tw
Petrochemical Mfr
N.A.I.C.S.: 324110

China Petrochemical Development Corp. - Tou-Fen Plant (1)
No 217 Sec 2 Ziqiang Road, Miaoli County, Toufen, 351, Taiwan
Tel.: (886) 37623381
Web Site: http://www.cpdc.com.tw
Petrochemical Mfr
N.A.I.C.S.: 324110

Ding-Yue Development Co., Ltd. (1)
8F No 12 Dongxing Road, Songshan District, Taipei, Taiwan
Tel.: (886) 287873099
Commercial Building Services
N.A.I.C.S.: 236220

Eternal Chemical Co., Ltd. - Lu-Chu Plant (1)
No 22 Changxing Rd, Luzhu Dist, Kaohsiung, 821, Taiwan
Tel.: (886) 76963331
Web Site: http://www.eternal-group.com
Sales Range: $1-4.9 Billion
Unsaturated Polyester Resins Mfr
N.A.I.C.S.: 325211

Jiangsu Weiming New Material Co., Ltd. (1)
Complex building intersection of Jingyi Road and Zhongxin Road, Yangkou Gang Rudong County, Changsha, 226413, China
Tel.: (86) 51369881266
Web Site: https://en.cpdcwm.com
Electronic Grade Chemical Mfr
N.A.I.C.S.: 325199

Praxair Chemax Semiconductor Materials Co., Ltd. (1)
6th Floor No 145 Zhengjiu Road, Zhubei, Hsin-chu, 30251, Taiwan (50%)
Tel.: (886) 35543538
Gas, Chemical & Delivery System Solutions for Semiconductor Production
N.A.I.C.S.: 334413

Taivex Therapeutics Inc. (1)
2F NO 12 Dongxing Rd, Songshan Dist, Taipei, 105, Taiwan
Tel.: (886) 22 748 6200
Web Site: https://www.taivex.com
Anti-Cancer Drug Mfr
N.A.I.C.S.: 325412
Janson Yu (Gen Mgr)

Taiwan Chlorine Industries Ltd. (1)
25 Chungchih Street, Hsiaokang District, Kaohsiung, 812, Taiwan (40%)
Tel.: (886) 7 871 5171
Web Site: https://www.tciwestlake.com.tw
Chlorine Mfr
N.A.I.C.S.: 325180

Tsou Seen Chemical Industries Corporation (1)
8F 12 Tunghsing Rd, Taipei, 105, Taiwan
Tel.: (886) 28 787 8510

Web Site: https://www.cpdc.com.tw
Dicalcium Phosphate & Liquid Fertilizers Mfr
N.A.I.C.S.: 325312

Weihua (Rudong) Trade Co., Ltd. (1)
Sunshine Island Rudong Country, Nantong, Jiangsu, China
Tel.: (86) 51300000200
Chemical Raw Material Whslr
N.A.I.C.S.: 424690

Weiqiang International Trade (Shanghai) Co., Ltd. (1)
Siu Fung Road on the 18th Asia Pacific Plaza Building 5 Room, Huaqiao Town, Kunshan, Jiangsu, China
Tel.: (86) 51250328900
Chemical Raw Material Whslr
N.A.I.C.S.: 424690

CHINA PHARMA HOLDINGS, INC.
Second Floor No 17 Jinpan Road, Haikou, 570216, Hainan, China
Tel.: (86) 89866811730   DE
Web Site:
https://www.chinapharmaholding.com
CPHI—(NYSE)
Rev.: $7,011,299
Assets: $16,469,200
Liabilities: $9,014,579
Net Worth: $7,454,621
Earnings: ($3,078,818)
Emp.: 231
Fiscal Year-end: 12/31/23
Holding Company; Pharmaceutical Mfr
N.A.I.C.S.: 551112
Zhilin Li (Chm, Pres & CEO)

CHINA PIPE GROUP LIMITED
12th Floor Phase 1 Austin Tower, 22-26A Austin Avenue Tsim Sha Tsui, Kowloon, China (Hong Kong)
Tel.: (852) 27287237
Web Site: http://www.softpower.hk
0380—(HKG)
Rev.: $64,141,109
Assets: $105,213,113
Liabilities: $32,826,700
Net Worth: $72,386,414
Earnings: $1,922,318
Emp.: 168
Fiscal Year-end: 12/31/20
Pipes & Fittings Mfr & Sales
N.A.I.C.S.: 332996
Ben Ansheng Yu (CEO)

CHINA POLY GROUP CORPORATION
28th Floor New Poly Plaza No 1 Chaoyangmen North Street, Dongcheng District, Beijing, 100010, Dongcheng, China
Tel.: (86) 1064082288   CN
Web Site: https://www.poly.com.cn
Year Founded: 1993
Sales Range: $700-749.9 Million
Real Estate Developments, International Trade of Military & Civil Products, Culture & Arts & Mineral Resources Investments
N.A.I.C.S.: 531390
Liu Hualong (Chm & Sec)

Subsidiaries:

Beijing Poly Artist Management Co., Ltd. (1)
Poly Plaza 14 Dongzhimen Nandajie, Dongcheng District, Beijing, 100027, China
Tel.: (86) 10 64157662
Web Site: http://www.polyagency.com
Culture & Art Management Services
N.A.I.C.S.: 711320
Julia Pang (Dir-Mktg)

Beijing Poly Forbidden City Theatre Management Co., Ltd. (1)

Forbidden City Concert Hall, Zhongshan Park, Beijing, 100031, China
Tel.: (86) 10 65598285
Theatre Management Services
N.A.I.C.S.: 541611

Beijing Polystar Digidisc Co., Ltd. (1)
No 26 Yuhua Road Section B, Airport Industrial Park, Beijing, 101300, China
Tel.: (86) 10 80498488
Web Site: http://www.polydisc.com
Disk Drives Mfr
N.A.I.C.S.: 334112

Chongqing Poly International Cinema (1)
No 59 Minquan Road Jiaochangkou, Yuzhong District, Chongqing, 400010, China
Tel.: (86) 23 63729191
Theatre Management Services
N.A.I.C.S.: 541611

Chongqing Poly Wanhe Cinema Chain Co., Ltd. (1)
8th Floor Building A Dushi Plaza No 39 Wusi Road, Yuzhong District, Chongqing, 400010, China
Tel.: (86) 23 63782339
Theatre Management Services
N.A.I.C.S.: 541611

Eastern Dragon Film Co., Ltd (1)
5G Building A Guomen Building No 1 Zuojiazhuang, Chaoyang District, Beijing, 100028, China
Tel.: (86) 10 64653866
Theatre Management Services
N.A.I.C.S.: 541611

Guangdong Poly Auction Co., Ltd (1)
EFG 8/F Ming Yue Ge 20 Ming Yue Yi Road, Guangzhou, 510600, China
Tel.: (86) 20 22264188
Web Site: http://www.poly-auction.com
Art Auction Services
N.A.I.C.S.: 459920

Guangdong Poly Pharmaceutical Co., Ltd (1)
5 Changxin Road, Tianhe District, Guangzhou, 510650, China
Tel.: (86) 20 37091688
Pharmaceuticals Product Mfr
N.A.I.C.S.: 325412

Guangxi Poly Yuanchen Real Estate Development Co., Ltd (1)
23/F East Manhattan 52-1 Jinhu Road, Nanning, 530028, Guangxi, China
Tel.: (86) 771 5569263
Real Estate Development Services
N.A.I.C.S.: 531390

Guangzhou Poly Southen Culture Promulgation Co., Ltd (1)
1801 Citic Plaza Tianhebei Road, Guangzhou, 510613, China
Tel.: (86) 20 83589482
Culture & Art Management Services
N.A.I.C.S.: 711320

Harbin Poly Real Estate Comprehensive Development Co., Ltd (1)
10/F Poly Technologies Plaza 93 Zhongshan Road, Harbin, 150036, China
Tel.: (86) 451 82393185
Real Estate Development Services
N.A.I.C.S.: 531390

Helongjiang Poly Aoyu Real Estate Development Co., Ltd (1)
2/F Poly Technologies Plaza 93 Zhongshan Road, Harbin, 150036, China
Tel.: (86) 451 82393168
Real Estate Development Services
N.A.I.C.S.: 531390

Liaoning Poly Armor Vehicle Co., Ltd. (1)
No 6 Dongduan Hunhenan Road, Dongzhou District, Fushun, 113105, Liaoning, China
Tel.: (86) 413 4072092
Defense Equipment Distr
N.A.I.C.S.: 423860

Poly (Baotou) Real Estate Development Co., Ltd. (1)

17 Gangtie street, Baotou, 014030, China
Tel.: (86) 472 5900001
Real Estate Development Services
N.A.I.C.S.: 531390

Poly (Beijing) Real Estate Development Co., Ltd. (1)
8F Haijian Building 8 Changwaxi Rd, Haidian, Beijing, 100089, China
Tel.: (86) 10 82644665
Real Estate Development Services
N.A.I.C.S.: 531390

Poly (Chongqing) Golf Management Co., Ltd. (1)
1 Longhuai Street, Jingkai North New Area, Chongqing, 401122, China
Tel.: (86) 731 67883339
Golf Management Services
N.A.I.C.S.: 541611

Poly (Chongqing) Investment Industry Co., Ltd. (1)
1 Liuyun Rd Jinyu Street, Jingkai North New Area, Chongqing, 401122, China
Tel.: (86) 23 67465506
Financial Investment Services
N.A.I.C.S.: 523999

Poly (Guangzhou) International Trade Investment Co., Ltd. (1)
2205 Zhongzhou Center North Tower 1068 Xingang East Rd, Haizhu District, Guangzhou, 510320, China
Tel.: (86) 20 89231992
Financial Investment Services
N.A.I.C.S.: 523999

Poly (Guangzhou) Property Management Co., Ltd. (1)
Poly Lily Business Center 381 Industry Strict, Haizhu District, Guangzhou, 510280, China
Tel.: (86) 20 89604931
Real Estate Development Services
N.A.I.C.S.: 531390

Poly (Guangzhou) Real Estate Club Management Co., Ltd. (1)
Poly Mountain Villa 68 Congyun Rd, Baiyun District, Guangzhou, 510420, China
Tel.: (86) 20 36640989
Real Estate Development Services
N.A.I.C.S.: 531390

Poly (Guangzhou) Real Estate Development Co., Ltd. (1)
20F Poly International Plaza North Tower 688 Yuejiang Middle Rd, Haizhu District, Guangzhou, 510308, China
Tel.: (86) 20 87519031
Real Estate Development Services
N.A.I.C.S.: 531390

Poly (Hong Kong) Holdings Limited (1)
2503 Admiralty Centre Tower 1 18 Harcourt Road, Hong Kong, China (Hong Kong)
Tel.: (852) 28106216
Financial Investment Services
N.A.I.C.S.: 523999

Poly (Hu'nan) Real Estate Development Co., Ltd. (1)
27F Hu'nan Culture Building 139 Shaoshan North Rd, Changsha, 410011, China
Tel.: (86) 731 2767311
Web Site: http://www.polyhn.com
Real Estate Development Services
N.A.I.C.S.: 531390

Poly (Science City, Guangzhou) Real Estate Development Co., Ltd. (1)
Poly Forest Whisper Villadom Kaichuang Rd, Science City, Guangzhou, 510630, China
Tel.: (86) 20 32079888
Real Estate Development Services
N.A.I.C.S.: 531390

Poly (Shanghai) Real Estate Development Co., Ltd. (1)
24F Jianke Building 75 Wanping South Rd, Shanghai, 200032, China
Tel.: (86) 21 64693515
Real Estate Development Services
N.A.I.C.S.: 531390
Shuai Sun *(Mgr-Investment)*

Poly (Shenyang) Real Estate Development Co., Ltd. (1)

4F Chenyu Building South Sijing street, Heping, Shenyang, 110003, China
Tel.: (86) 24 23270616
Real Estate Development Services
N.A.I.C.S.: 531390

Poly (Wuhan) Real Estate Development Co., Ltd. (1)
27F Guanggu International Building 2-2 Guandongyuan Rd, Donghu District, Wuhan, 480074, China
Tel.: (86) 27 87775000
Real Estate Development Services
N.A.I.C.S.: 531390

Poly Building Corporation (1)
18/F Wanshang Plaza 22 Shi Jing Shan Road, Shi Jing Shan District, Beijing, 100043, China
Tel.: (86) 10 52632912
Web Site: http://www.polybuilding.com.cn
Construction Engineering Services
N.A.I.C.S.: 541330

Poly Explosives Co., Ltd. (1)
No 12 Chegongzhuang Street, Xicheng District, Beijing, 100037, China
Tel.: (86) 10 88 305 888
Web Site: http://www.polyexplosives.com
Chemical Product Mfr & Distr
N.A.I.C.S.: 325199

Poly Guizhou Real Estate Development Co., Ltd (1)
23/F B Shimao Plaza 56 Yan'an Road, Guiyang, 550001, Guizhou, China
Tel.: (86) 851 5285111
Web Site: http://www.polyguizhou.com
Real Estate Development Services
N.A.I.C.S.: 531390

Poly Jilin Ammunition Manufacturing Co., Ltd. (1)
Factory 3305, Dunhua, Jilin, 133700, China
Tel.: (86) 433 6161050
Defense Equipment Distr
N.A.I.C.S.: 423860

Poly Property Services Co., Ltd. (1)
Floor 48-49 Poly Development Plaza No 832 Yuejiang Middle Road, Haizhu District, Guangzhou, Guangdong, China
Tel.: (86) 2089899959
Web Site: https://www.polywuye.com
Rev.: $1,231,372,671
Assets: $1,446,943,124
Liabilities: $489,874,114
Net Worth: $957,069,011
Earnings: $106,651,779
Emp.: 44,351
Fiscal Year-end: 12/31/2020
Property Management Services
N.A.I.C.S.: 531311
Jiahe Li *(Exec Dir)*

Poly Sagawa Logistic Co., Ltd. (1)
G 14/F Shenzhen Development Bank Plaza No 5047 Shennandong Rd, Shenzhen, 518001, China
Tel.: (86) 755 61307010
Logistics Consulting Servies
N.A.I.C.S.: 541614

Poly South China Industry Co., Ltd. (1)
8F Nanfang Building Haiwu Rd, Nanhai District, Foshan, 528200, China
Tel.: (86) 20 87789010
Real Estate Development Services
N.A.I.C.S.: 531390

Poly Southern Group Co., Ltd. (1)
1801 Office Building CITIC Plaza, 233 Tianhe Rd (N), Guangzhou, 1801, P.C., China
Tel.: (86) 20 38911822
Web Site: http://www.poly.com.cn
Real Estate Development
N.A.I.C.S.: 531190

Subsidiary (Domestic):

Poly Developments and Holdings Group Co., Ltd. (2)
30-33/F North Tower Poly International Square No 688, Yuejiang Middle Road Haizhu District, Guangzhou, 510308, Haizhu, China (100%)
Tel.: (86) 2089898000

Web Site: http://www.poly.com.cn
Rev.: $39,467,596,657
Assets: $206,453,202,953
Liabilities: $161,217,515,258
Net Worth: $45,235,687,695
Earnings: $2,575,893,458
Emp.: 110,000
Fiscal Year-end: 12/31/2022
Real Estate Services
N.A.I.C.S.: 531190
Ping He *(Co-Chm)*

Shanghai Poly Sagawa Logistic Co., Ltd. (1)
Room 1570 Gangtai Plaza 700 Yan'andong Rd, Huangpu Area, Shanghai, 200001, China
Tel.: (86) 21 65957860
Logistics Consulting Servies
N.A.I.C.S.: 541614

Shanghai Poly Technologies Co., Ltd. (1)
8th fl Itaili Plaza 446 Zhaojiabang Rd, Shanghai, 200031, China
Tel.: (86) 21 64665050
Defense Equipment Distr
N.A.I.C.S.: 423860
Charles Qi Jun *(Mgr-Import)*

Shanxi Poly Xingchen Coking Co., Ltd. (1)
Yunyi Village Duanchun Town, Lingshi, Jinzhong, 031303, Shanxi, China
Tel.: (86) 354 7625498
Coal Mining Services
N.A.I.C.S.: 212115

Shenzhen Poly Culture Plaza Co., Ltd (1)
26/F Shenzhen Poly Plaza Chuangye Road, Nanshan District, Shenzhen, 518054, China
Tel.: (86) 755 61381007
Web Site: http://www.szpoly.com.cn
Theatre Management Services
N.A.I.C.S.: 541611

Tianjin Poly Sagawa Trading Co., Ltd. (1)
48 Dongfang Dadao Tianjin Bonded Zone, Tianjin, 300461, China
Tel.: (86) 22 25700488
Defense Equipment Distr
N.A.I.C.S.: 423860

Zhengzhou Poly International Cinema (1)
No 47 Nongye East Road, Jinshui District, Zhengzhou, 450008, He'nan, China
Tel.: (86) 371 69528101
Theatre Management Services
N.A.I.C.S.: 541611

CHINA POLYPEPTIDE GROUP, INC.
No 11 Jianda Road, Jianghan Economical Development Zone, Wuhan, 430023, China
Tel.: (86) 27 8351 8396   DE
Year Founded: 2007
Sales Range: $25-49.9 Million
Polypeptide-Based Nutritional Supplements & Health Food Research, Development & Sales
N.A.I.C.S.: 111419
Shengfan Yan *(Pres)*

CHINA POST GROUP CORPORATION LIMITED
No 3 Financial Street, Beijing, 100808, Xicheng District, China
Tel.: (86) 10 6885 9944
Web Site:
http://www.chinapost.com.cn
Sales Range: $25-49.9 Billion
Emp.: 927,800
Newspaper Distribution, Postal Remittances, Stamp Distribution, Logistics & Postal Services
N.A.I.C.S.: 491110
Li Guohua *(Pres)*

Subsidiaries:

China Post Life Insurance Co., Ltd. (1)

China Post Group Corporation Limited—(Continued)

Block B Jinding Building No 3 Financial Street, Xicheng District, Beijing, 100808, China
Tel.: (86) 1068856880
Web Site: http://www.chinapost-life.com
Financial Investment Services
N.A.I.C.S.: 523999

CHINA POWER CLEAN ENERGY DEVELOPMENT COMPANY LIMITED

Room 01-05 38/F China Resources Building No 26 Harbour Road, Wanchai, China (Hong Kong)
Tel.: (852) 36078888   BM
Web Site:
https://cpnewenergy.todayir.com
Rev.: $690,503,378
Assets: $3,674,682,624
Liabilities: $2,420,490,948
Net Worth: $1,254,191,677
Earnings: $27,040,475
Emp.: 1,901
Fiscal Year-end: 12/31/18
Construction & Power Generation Services
N.A.I.C.S.: 236210
Lianhui He (Exec Dir)

CHINA POWER EQUIPMENT, INC.

Yongle Industry Zone Jingyang Industry Concentration Area, Xi'an, 713702, Shaanxi, China
Tel.: (86) 2962619758   MD
Year Founded: 2006
CPQQ.OB—(OTCBB)
Sales Range: $25-49.9 Million
Emp.: 75
Electrical Power Transformer Products Mfr
N.A.I.C.S.: 334416
Yongxing Song (Chm, Pres & CEO)

CHINA POWER INTERNATIONAL DEVELOPMENT LIMITED

Suite 6301 63/F Central Plaza 18 Harbour Road, Wanchai, China (Hong Kong)
Tel.: (852) 28023861   HK
Web Site: https://www.chinapower.hk
Year Founded: 2004
2380—(HKG)
Rev.: $6,214,352,087
Assets: $42,935,271,772
Liabilities: $29,594,363,807
Net Worth: $13,340,907,965
Earnings: $636,567,282
Emp.: 14,254
Fiscal Year-end: 12/31/23
Hydroelectric Power Generation
N.A.I.C.S.: 221111
Siu Cheung (Sec)

Subsidiaries:

Wu Ling Power Corporation   (1)
No 188 Wuling Road, Tianxin District, Changsha, 410004, Hunan, China
Tel.: (86) 73185893188
Web Site: https://www.wldl.com.cn
Emp.: 2,385
Electric Power Generation & Distribution Services
N.A.I.C.S.: 221118

CHINA POWERPLUS LIMITED

80 Robinson Road 02-00, Jurong, Singapore, 068898, Singapore
Tel.: (65) 62663502
Web Site:
http://www.chinapowerplus.com
Sales Range: $50-74.9 Million
Portable Power Tools Mfr
N.A.I.C.S.: 332999
Min-Li Tan (Sec)

CHINA PRECISION STEEL, INC.

18th Floor Teda Building 87 Wing Lok Street, Sheungwan, Hong Kong, China (Hong Kong)
Tel.: (852) 25432290   CO
Web Site:
http://www.chinaprecisionsteel.com
Sales Range: $25-49.9 Million
Emp.: 177
Cold-Rolled Steel Products Mfr
N.A.I.C.S.: 331221
Hai Sheng Chen (CEO & CFO)

Subsidiaries:

OraLabs, Inc.   (1)
18685 E Plz Dr, Parker, CO 80134
Tel.: (303) 783-9499
Web Site: http://www.oralabs.com
Sales Range: $75-99.9 Million
Emp.: 150
Oral Care Products Retailer
N.A.I.C.S.: 423450
Mark Hayes (Dir-Mfg)

CHINA PRIMARY ENERGY HOLDINGS LIMITED

Suite 701 Ocean Centre 5 Canton Road Tsim Sha Tsui, Kowloon, China (Hong Kong)
Tel.: (852) 2807 1800   Ky
Web Site: http://www.china-p-energy.etnet.com.hk
Year Founded: 2001
8117—(HKG)
Rev.: $11,379,003
Assets: $78,447,571
Liabilities: $34,893,475
Net Worth: $43,554,095
Earnings: $1,173,976
Emp.: 156
Fiscal Year-end: 12/31/20
Holding Company
N.A.I.C.S.: 551112
Zheng Ma (Chm)

CHINA PROPERTIES GROUP LTD

14th Fl Wheelock House 20 Pedder St, Central, China (Hong Kong)
Tel.: (852) 23116788
Web Site: http://www.cpg-group.com
Rev.: $75,672,013
Assets: $7,910,700,618
Liabilities: $3,125,299,080
Net Worth: $4,785,401,538
Earnings: ($36,338,104)
Emp.: 382
Fiscal Year-end: 12/31/19
Property Development in Residential & Commercial Sectors
N.A.I.C.S.: 531210

CHINA PROPERTIES INVESTMENT HOLDINGS LIMITED

Room 4303 43/F China Resources Building 26 Harbour Road, Wanchai, China (Hong Kong)
Tel.: (852) 25360991
Web Site: http://www.736.com.hk
0736—(HKG)
Rev.: $9,189,567
Assets: $112,538,275
Liabilities: $27,902,630
Net Worth: $84,635,644
Earnings: $4,665,078
Emp.: 35
Fiscal Year-end: 03/31/21
Investment Holding Company
N.A.I.C.S.: 523940
Tat On Au (Exec Dir)

Subsidiaries:

Lok Wing group Limited   (1)
1B Kai Yee Ct 58 Battery St, Yau Ma Tei, Kowloon, China (Hong Kong)
Tel.: (852) 81022703

Real Estate Property Management Services
N.A.I.C.S.: 531311

CHINA PROSPEROUS CLEAN ENERGY CORPORATION

West Side Public Transportation Gas Filling Center, Angang Avenue-Middle Part, Yindu, Anyang, 455000, Henan, China
Tel.: (86) 3723166864   NV
Web Site: http://www.otcpb.com
Year Founded: 2006
Sales Range: $25-49.9 Million
Emp.: 260
Natural & Liquefied Petroleum Gas Distr & Retailer; Gas Filling Stations Construction Services
N.A.I.C.S.: 221210
Wei Wang (Chm, CEO, Treas & Sec)

CHINA PUBLISHING & MEDIA HOLDINGS CO., LTD.

Jia No 55 Chaoyangmennei Street, Dongcheng District, Beijing, 100010, China
Tel.: (86) 1058110824
Web Site: http://www.cnpubc.com
Year Founded: 2011
601949—(SHG)
Rev.: $862,231,332
Assets: $2,086,652,318
Liabilities: $792,820,913
Net Worth: $1,293,831,405
Earnings: $91,373,485
Fiscal Year-end: 12/31/22
Books Publishing Services
N.A.I.C.S.: 513130
Huang Zhijian (Chm)

CHINA PUTIAN FOOD HOLDING LIMITED

Room 3312 33/F West Tower Shun Tak Centre 200 Connaught Road, Central, China (Hong Kong)
Tel.: (852) 35824666
Web Site: http://www.putian.com.hk
1699—(HKG)
Rev.: $97,551,105
Assets: $192,429,921
Liabilities: $86,343,334
Net Worth: $106,086,587
Earnings: $1,150,607
Emp.: 486
Fiscal Year-end: 12/31/20
Hog Farming, Slaughtering & Sales
N.A.I.C.S.: 112210
Chenyang Cai (Chm & CEO)

CHINA QINBA PHAMACEUTICALS, INC.

24th Floor Building A Zhengxin Mansion Hi-Tech Development Zone, 5 of 1st Gaoxin Road, Xi'an, China
Tel.: (86) 2982098912   DE
Web Site:
http://www.chinapharmainc.com
Sales Range: $10-24.9 Million
Emp.: 486
Pharmaceuticals Mfr
N.A.I.C.S.: 325412
Wang Guozhu (Chm & CEO)

CHINA QINFA GROUP LIMITED

Unit Nos 2201-2208 Level 22 South Tower, Poly International Plaza No 1 Pazhou Avenue East Haizhu District, Guangzhou, China
Tel.: (86) 2089898239   Ky
Web Site: http://www.qinfagroup.com
Year Founded: 1996
00866—(HKG)
Sales Range: $450-499.9 Million
Emp.: 2,027
Coal Mining Services
N.A.I.C.S.: 213113
Da Xu (Chm & Exec Dir)

CHINA QUANJUDE (GROUP) CO., LTD.

No 217 Xiheyan Qianmen, Xicheng District, Beijing, 100051, China
Tel.: (86) 1083156608
Web Site:
http://www.quanjude.com.cn
Year Founded: 1994
002186—(SSE)
Rev.: $100,919,520
Assets: $211,539,276
Liabilities: $104,051,844
Net Worth: $107,487,432
Earnings: ($38,906,616)
Fiscal Year-end: 12/31/22
Restaurant Operators
N.A.I.C.S.: 722511
Wu Jinmei (Chm)

CHINA RAILWAY CONSTRUCTION CORPORATION LIMITED

No 40 Fuxing Road, Haidian District, Beijing, 100855, China
Tel.: (86) 1051888114
Web Site: https://www.crcc.cn
Year Founded: 2007
601186—(SHG)
Rev.: $139,470,856,939
Assets: $190,408,284,735
Liabilities: $142,355,639,756
Net Worth: $48,052,644,979
Earnings: $3,430,828,925
Emp.: 286,242
Fiscal Year-end: 12/31/20
Construction Engineering Services
N.A.I.C.S.: 237990
Shangbiao Zhuang (Pres)

Subsidiaries:

CRCC Finance Company Limited   (1)
10th Floor China Railway Construction Building No 40 Fuxing Road, Haidian District, Beijing, 100855, China
Tel.: (86) 4006011866
Web Site: https://crfc.crcc.cn
Construction Finance Services
N.A.I.C.S.: 522292

CRCC Harbour & Channel Engineering Bureau Group Co., Ltd.   (1)
No 189 Cuifeng Street, Qianshan District, Zhuhai, Guangdong, China
Tel.: (86) 7566157966
Web Site: http://hceb.crcc.cn
Heavy Construction Services
N.A.I.C.S.: 237990
Tan Shilin (VP)

China Civil Engineering Construction Corporation   (1)
4 Beifengwo, Haidian District, Beijing, China
Tel.: (86) 1052108888
Web Site: https://www.ccecc.com.cn
Engineering & Construction Services
N.A.I.C.S.: 541330

Subsidiary (Non-US):

CCECC (Botswana) (Pty) Ltd.   (2)
Plot 153 Commerce Park, Private Bag T08, Tlokweng, Gaborone, Botswana
Tel.: (267) 3925332
Civil Engineering Services
N.A.I.C.S.: 541330

Subsidiary (Domestic):

CCECC International Trading Co. Ltd.   (2)
11/f Dacheng Plaza No 28 Xuanwumen West Avenue Xuanwu District, Beijing, 100053, China
Tel.: (86) 1063600935
Civil Engineering Services
N.A.I.C.S.: 541330

Subsidiary (Non-US):

CCECC Nigeria Ltd.   (2)
46 Nnamdi Azikiwe Drive Ebute Metta Lagos Minland, Lagos, Nigeria
Tel.: (234) 8033154680

Civil Engineering Services
N.A.I.C.S.: 541330

China Civil Engineering Construction Company(Macau) Ltd.. (2)
Assumpcao No 263 22 Andar C H Edif China Civil Plaza, Macau, China (Macau)
Tel.: (853) 28781160
Sales Range: $10-24.9 Million
Emp.: 30
Civil Engineering Services
N.A.I.C.S.: 541330
Cong Yu (Mgr)

Subsidiary (Domestic):

Shanghai CCECC Enterprises Company Ltd. (2)
27/F Shanghai CCECC Mansion No 666 Gonghexin Road, Shanghai, 200070, China
Tel.: (86) 2166531726
Civil Engineering Services
N.A.I.C.S.: 541330

China Railway 11th Bureau Group Co., Ltd. (1)
No 277 Zhongshan Road, Wuchang District, Wuhan, 430061, Hubei, China
Tel.: (86) 2788710611
Web Site: https://cr11g.crcc.cn
N.A.I.C.S.: 541330

China Railway 12th Bureau Group Co., Ltd. (1)
No 130 Xikuang Street, Taiyuan, 030024, Shanxi, China
Tel.: (86) 3512653240
Web Site: http://cr12g.crcc.cn
Heavy Construction Services
N.A.I.C.S.: 237990

China Railway 14th Bureau Group Co., Ltd. (1)
No 2666 Aoti West Road, Lixia District, Jinan, 250101, Shandong, China
Tel.: (86) 53188385114
Web Site: https://cr14g.crcc.cn
Heavy Construction Services
N.A.I.C.S.: 237990

China Railway 16th Bureau Group Co., Ltd. (1)
No 2 Hongsongyuan North Lane, Chaoyang District, Beijing, 100018, China
Tel.: (86) 1084311177
Web Site: http://www.cr16g.com.cn
Heavy Construction Services
N.A.I.C.S.: 237990

China Railway 17th Bureau Group Co., Ltd. (1)
No 84 Pingyang Road, Taiyuan, 030006, Shanxi, China
Tel.: (86) 3517257114
Web Site: https://cr17g.crcc.cn
Heavy Construction Services
N.A.I.C.S.: 237990

China Railway 18th Bureau Group Co., Ltd. (1)
China Railway No 18 Bureau, Liulindong Hexi District, Tianjin, 300222, China
Tel.: (86) 2260282114
Web Site: https://cr18g.crcc.cn
Heavy Construction Services
N.A.I.C.S.: 237990

China Railway 19th Bureau Group Co., Ltd. (1)
No 137 Nanjiao Street, Liaoyang, 111000, Liaoning, China
Tel.: (86) 4192326114
Construction Engineering Services
N.A.I.C.S.: 237990

China Railway 20th Bureau Group Co., Ltd. (1)
89 Taihua North Road, Xi'an, 710016, Shaanxi, China
Tel.: (86) 2982153600
Web Site: http://cr20g.crcc.cn
Heavy Construction Services
N.A.I.C.S.: 237990

China Railway 21st Bureau Group Co., Ltd. (1)
No 921 Beibinhe West Road, Anning District, Lanzhou, 730070, China
Tel.: (86) 9314539822

Web Site: https://cr21g.crcc.cn
Emp.: 14,000
Heavy Construction Services
N.A.I.C.S.: 237990

China Railway 22nd Bureau Group Co., Ltd. (1)
No 35 Shijingshan Road, Shijingshan District, Beijing, 100043, China
Tel.: (86) 1051889839
Web Site: https://cr22g.crcc.cn
Emp.: 10,800
Heavy Construction Services
N.A.I.C.S.: 237990

China Railway 23rd Bureau Group Co., Ltd. (1)
Section 2 West Second Ring Road, Chengdu, 610072, Sichuan, China
Tel.: (86) 1052688535
Web Site: https://cr23g.crcc.cn
N.A.I.C.S.: 541330
Xiao Hongwu (Chm)

China Railway Construction (HK) Limited (1)
Unit A 10th Fl MG Tower, 133 Hoi Bun Road, Kwun Tong, Kowloon, China (Hong Kong)
Tel.: (852) 27749886
Web Site: http://www.crcc.cn
Sales Range: $25-49.9 Million
Emp.: 15
Railway Construction Services
N.A.I.C.S.: 237990

China Railway Construction Bridge Engineering Bureau Group Co., Ltd. (1)
No 32 Zhonghuan West Road, Airport Economic Zone, Tianjin, 300300, China
Tel.: (86) 2288958900
Bridge Construction Services
N.A.I.C.S.: 237310

China Railway Construction Heavy Industry Corporation Limited (1)
No 88 Dongqi Road, National Economic Technical Development Zone, Changsha, 410100, Hunan, China
Tel.: (86) 73184071702
Web Site: https//en.crchi.com
Construction Machinery Mfr
N.A.I.C.S.: 333517

China Railway Construction Investment Group Co., Ltd. (1)
Block B China Railway Construction Building No 40 Fuxing Road, Haidian District, Beijing, 100855, China
Tel.: (86) 1052689500
Web Site: http://crci.crcc.cn
Investment Services
N.A.I.C.S.: 523999

China Railway Construction Real Estate Group Co., Ltd. (1)
Tower B China Railway Construction Building No 40 Fuxing Road, Haidian District, Beijing, 100039, China
Tel.: (86) 1052689999
Web Site: https://crccre.crcc.cn
Real Estate Services
N.A.I.C.S.: 531210

China Railway Electrification Bureau (Group) Co., Ltd. (1)
Baoman Road Mancheng County, Baoding, 072150, Hebei, China
Tel.: (86) 3127065872
Web Site: http://www.eeb.cn
Railway Road Construction Services
N.A.I.C.S.: 236220

China Railway Fifth Survey & Design Institute Group Co., Ltd. (1)
No 9 Kangzhuang Road, Daxing District, Beijing, 102600, China
Tel.: (86) 1051011629
Web Site: http://t5y.crcc.cn
Emp.: 1,700
Civil Construction Consulting Services
N.A.I.C.S.: 541330

China Railway First Survey & Design Institute Group Co., Ltd. (1)
No 2 Xiying Road, Xi'an, 710043, China
Tel.: (86) 2982365030
Web Site: https://fsdi.crcc.cn

Civil Construction Consulting Services
N.A.I.C.S.: 541330

China Railway Fourth Survey and Design Institute Group Co., Ltd (1)
Room B 5 F Building B Huifangyuan, Nanshan District, Shenzhen, 518052, China
Tel.: (86) 75526530649
Engineering Consulting Services
N.A.I.C.S.: 541330

China Railway Material Group Co., Ltd. (1)
No 19 West Fourth Ring Middle Road, Beijing, 100143, China
Tel.: (86) 1051881000
Web Site: http://crmg.crcc.cn
Emp.: 2,000
Logistic Services
N.A.I.C.S.: 488510
Wang Hui (Chm & Sec)

China Railway Shanghai Design Institute Group Co., Ltd. (1)
No 1265 Gonghe New Road, Shanghai, 200070, China
Tel.: (86) 2163818855
Web Site: http://sty.crcc.cn
Civil Construction Consulting Services
N.A.I.C.S.: 541330

Corriente Resources, Inc. (1)
Unit S209-5811 Cooney Road, Richmond, V6X 3M1, BC, Canada
Tel.: (604) 282-7212
Web Site: https://www.corriente.com
Sales Range: $200-249.9 Million
Emp.: 252
Copper & Gold Mining Services
N.A.I.C.S.: 212230
Shouhua Jin (Chm & Mng VP)

CHINA RAILWAY GROUP LIMITED
China Railway Plaza No 69 Fuxing Road, Haidian District, Beijing, 100039, China
Tel.: (86) 1051878413　　CN
Web Site: https://www.crecg.com
Year Founded: 1950
601390—(CHIN)
Rev.: $149,341,262,116
Assets: $183,870,708,473
Liabilities: $135,886,215,899
Net Worth: $47,984,492,575
Earnings: $3,859,021,306
Emp.: 285,405
Fiscal Year-end: 12/31/20
Construction Engineering Services
N.A.I.C.S.: 551112
Yun Chen (Pres)

Subsidiaries:

China Railway Development & Investment Co., Ltd. (1)
No 68 Qingyuan Road, Xishan District, Kunming, 650118, Yunnan, China
Tel.: (86) 87168107718
Web Site: http://www.cqtz.crec.cn
Construction & Asset Management Services
N.A.I.C.S.: 561110

China Railway Engineering Consulting Group Co., Ltd. (1)
No 15 Guangan Rd, Fengtai District, Beijing, 100055, China
Tel.: (86) 1051835097
Web Site: https://zx.crec.cn
Engineering Consulting Services
N.A.I.C.S.: 541330

China Railway Guangzhou Engineering Group Co. Ltd. (1)
No 582 Jingang Avenue, Nansha District, Guangzhou, 511457, China
Tel.: (86) 2061996691
Web Site: http://www.e.crecgz.cn
Emp.: 6,000
Construction Services
N.A.I.C.S.: 236220

China Railway Huatie Engineering Designing Group Co., Ltd. (1)
China Railway Huatie Building No 36 Fengtaibei Road, Fengtai District, Beijing,

100071, China
Tel.: (86) 1063319661
Web Site: https://ztht.crec.cn
Engineering Consulting Services
N.A.I.C.S.: 541330

China Railway Investment Group Co., Ltd. (1)
No 3 Automobile Museum South Road, Fengtai District, Beijing, China
Tel.: (86) 1083920866
Web Site: https://www.zttzjt.com.cn
Construction & Asset Management Services
N.A.I.C.S.: 561110

China Railway Liuyuan Group Co., Ltd. (1)
No 36 Zhonghuan West Road, Airport Economic Zone, Tianjin, 300308, China
Tel.: (86) 2258173500
Web Site: https://www.crlgc.com
Railroad Equipment Mfr
N.A.I.C.S.: 336510

China Railway Major Bridge Engineering Group Co., Ltd. (1)
No 6 Sixin Avenue, Hanyang District, Wuhan, 430050, Hubei, China
Tel.: (86) 2784596411
Web Site: https://www.ztmbec.com
Construction Engineering Services
N.A.I.C.S.: 237210
Liu Ziming (Chm)

China Railway Major Bridge Reconnaissance & Design Institute Co., Ltd. (1)
No 8 Boxue Road, Wuhan Economic and Technological Development Zone, Wuhan, Hubei, China
Tel.: (86) 2784957629
Web Site: https://www.brdi.cn
Construction Engineering Services
N.A.I.C.S.: 541330

China Railway No 8 Engineering Group Co., Ltd. (1)
Tel.: (86) 2887518338
Web Site: http://www.cr8gc.com
Emp.: 11,300
Construction Services
N.A.I.C.S.: 236220

China Railway Real Estate Group Co Ltd (1)
9 F No 15 Guangan Road, Fengtai District, Beijing, 100055, China
Tel.: (86) 1058095852
Real Estate Development Services
N.A.I.C.S.: 236116

China Railway Shanhaiguan Bridge Group Co., Ltd. (1)
35 Nanhaixi Road, Shanhaiguan District, Qinhuangdao, 066205, Hebei, China
Tel.: (86) 3357940128
Web Site: http://www.crsbg.com
Sales Range: $400-449.9 Million
Emp.: 1,300
Railway Steel Structure Mfr
N.A.I.C.S.: 332312
Liu Enguo (CEO)

China Railway Southwest Research Institute Co., Ltd. (1)
No 97 Gunan Street, High-tech West District, Chengdu, 611731, Sichuan, China
Tel.: (86) 2867582907
Web Site: http://www.swi.com.cn
Sales Range: $150-199.9 Million
Emp.: 1,000
Engineering Consulting Services
N.A.I.C.S.: 541330

CHINA RAILWAY HI-TECH INDUSTRY CORPORATION
No 5 Yard No 10 Auto Museum West Road, Fengtai District, Beijing, 100070, Sichuan, China
Tel.: (86) 1083777888
Web Site: http://www.crec.com.cn
Year Founded: 1999
600528—(SHG)
Rev.: $4,045,920,629
Assets: $7,512,500,034
Liabilities: $4,066,926,224
Net Worth: $3,445,573,810

China Railway Hi-Tech Industry Corporation—(Continued)

Earnings: $262,144,631
Fiscal Year-end: 12/31/22
Railway Construction Services
N.A.I.C.S.: 237990
Zhang Wei *(Chm)*

CHINA RAILWAY MATERIALS CO., LTD.

No 11 Huayuan Street, Xicheng District, Beijing, 100032, China
Tel.: (86) 10 51895188
Web Site: http://www.crmsc.com.cn
Railway Material Whslr
N.A.I.C.S.: 423390
Li Wenke *(Pres)*

Subsidiaries:

CRM (Hong Kong) Holdings Limited   (1)
Science Museum Rd, Tsim Sha Tsui East, Hong Kong, China (Hong Kong)
Tel.: (852) 27217333
Steel Product Distr
N.A.I.C.S.: 423390

CRM Beijing Taibo Real Estate Co., Ltd.
12A Fuhua Building A No 8 Chaoyangmen North Street, Dongcheng District, Beijing, 100027, China
Tel.: (86) 1065541432
Steel Product Distr
N.A.I.C.S.: 423390

CRM Chaohu Railway Cement Co., Ltd.   (1)
Lintou Town, Lintou, 238103, Anhui, China
Tel.: (86) 5654721201
Steel Product Distr
N.A.I.C.S.: 423390

CRM Taiyuan Rail Sleepers Co., Ltd.   (1)
No 112 Xinlan Road, Taiyuan, 030041, Shanxi, China
Tel.: (86) 3512643130
Steel Product Distr
N.A.I.C.S.: 423390

CRM Wuhan Wood Preservation Co., Ltd.   (1)
No 1 Hexi Road, Liuzhou, 545007, Guangxi Zhuang, China
Tel.: (86) 7723616642
Steel Product Distr
N.A.I.C.S.: 423390

CRM Yingtan Wood Preservation Co., Ltd.   (1)
No 6 Junmin Road, Yingtan, 335002, Jiangxi, China
Tel.: (86) 7016221981
Steel Product Distr
N.A.I.C.S.: 423390

CRM Zhenlai Wood Preservation Co., Ltd.   (1)
Nenxi Road, Zhenlai, 137300, Jilin, China
Tel.: (86) 4366175061
Steel Product Distr
N.A.I.C.S.: 423390

China Railway Leasing Co., Ltd.   (1)
R2001 Citibank Building No 33 Huayuanshiqiao Road, Pudong District, Shanghai, 200120, China
Tel.: (86) 21 61050100
Steel Product Distr
N.A.I.C.S.: 423390

China Railway Material Trading Co., Ltd.   (1)
19th Building 3rd Section Headquarter Base No 188 Southwest, Fengtai District, Beijing, 100070, China
Tel.: (86) 1051864311
Steel Product Distr
N.A.I.C.S.: 423390

China Railway Materials Beijing Company   (1)
17-19/F Gate 1 No 28 Xuanwumen West Street, Xuanwu District, Beijing, 100053, China

Tel.: (86) 1063600174
Steel Product Distr
N.A.I.C.S.: 423390

China Railway Materials Co., Ltd. - CRM Harbin Wood Preservation Factory   (1)
No 130 Xianfeng Road, Daowai District, Harbin, 150056, Heilongjiang, China
Tel.: (86) 45182400010
Steel Product Distr
N.A.I.C.S.: 423390

China Railway Materials Co., Ltd. - CRM Longchang Railway Works Equipment Factory   (1)
No 75 Waizhan Road, Longchang, 642150, Sichuan, China
Tel.: (86) 8323944559
Steel Product Distr
N.A.I.C.S.: 423390

China Railway Materials Development Holding Co., Ltd.   (1)
No 25 B Nanbinhe Road, Xuanwu District, Beijing, 100055, China
Tel.: (86) 1051920695
Steel Product Distr
N.A.I.C.S.: 423390

China Railway Materials Guangzhou Company   (1)
No 65 Zhongshan-yi Road, Guangzhou, 510600, Guangdong, China
Tel.: (86) 2087662843
Steel Product Distr
N.A.I.C.S.: 423390

China Railway Materials Harbin Company   (1)
No 117 Xidazhi Street, Nangang District, Harbin, 150006, Heilongjiang, China
Tel.: (86) 45186247760
Steel Product Distr
N.A.I.C.S.: 423390

China Railway Materials Import & Export Co., Ltd.   (1)
16/F Gate 1 No 28 Xuanwumen West Street, Xuanwu District, Beijing, 100053, China
Tel.: (86) 1063601712
Web Site: http://www.sinorails.com
Steel Product Distr
N.A.I.C.S.: 423390

China Railway Materials Shanghai Company   (1)
No 88 Huiwen Road, Zhabei District, Shanghai, 200071, China
Tel.: (86) 2156635647
Steel Product Distr
N.A.I.C.S.: 423390
Suyang Zhang *(Asst Mgr-Steel Trade Dept)*

China Railway Materials Shenyang Company   (1)
No 18 South Shengli Street, Heping District, Shenyang, 110001, Liaoning, China
Tel.: (86) 2423506494
Steel Product Distr
N.A.I.C.S.: 423390

China Railway Materials Tianjin Company   (1)
No 21 Jintang Road, Hedong District, Tianjin, 300171, China
Tel.: (86) 2224250086
Steel Product Distr
N.A.I.C.S.: 423390

China Railway Materials Wuhan Company   (1)
No 169 Ziyang Road, Wuchang District, Wuhan, 430060, Hubei, China
Tel.: (86) 2788043129
Steel Product Distr
N.A.I.C.S.: 423390

China Railway Modern Logistic Technology Co., Ltd.   (1)
R 508 Satellite Building No 63 Zhichun Road, Haidian District, Beijing, 100080, China
Tel.: (86) 1062568104
Web Site: http://www.crml.com.cn
Steel Product Distr
N.A.I.C.S.: 423390
Jitka Bednarikova *(Accountant)*

PetroChina & CRM Oil Marketing Co., Ltd.   (1)
R 811-812 Ideal International Building No 58 Northwest 4th Ring Road, Haidian District, Beijing, 100080, China
Tel.: (86) 1082607538
Steel Product Distr
N.A.I.C.S.: 423390

Pingdingshan Rail Sleeper Company   (1)
Shuiku Road, Pingdingshan, 467001, Henan, China
Tel.: (86) 3752712227
Steel Product Distr
N.A.I.C.S.: 423390

SINOPEC & CRM Oil Marketing Co., Ltd.   (1)
R 1901 Building A Horizon International Tower No 6 Zhichun Road, Haidian District, Beijing, 100080, China
Tel.: (86) 1082800678
Steel Product Distr
N.A.I.C.S.: 423390

Shenzhen Sunray (Group) Co., Ltd.   (1)
R 1901 Pacific Commerce Mansion No 4028 Jiabin Rd, Shenzhen, 518001, Guangdong, China
Tel.: (86) 75582138980
Steel Product Distr
N.A.I.C.S.: 423390

Transgoods America Inc.   (1)
33320 9th Ave S Ste 260, Federal Way, WA 98003
Tel.: (253) 661-0440
Steel Product Distr
N.A.I.C.S.: 423390

CHINA RAILWAY PREFABRICATED CONSTRUCTION CO., LTD.

No 86-5 Changyang Wanxing Road, Fangshan District, Beijing, 102444, China
Tel.: (86) 1057961616
Web Site: http://www.htcxms.com
Year Founded: 2006
300374—(CHIN)
Rev.: $210,703,825
Assets: $461,180,704
Liabilities: $339,678,353
Net Worth: $121,502,351
Earnings: ($22,920,591)
Fiscal Year-end: 12/31/23
Wallboard Mfr & Distr
N.A.I.C.S.: 327420
Zhiqiang Sun *(Board of Directors & Chm)*

CHINA RAILWAY SIGNAL & COMMUNICATION CORPORATION LTD.

Block No 1 Qichebowuguan Nanlu Fengtai Science Park, Beijing, 100070, China
Tel.: (86) 1051846108   CN
Web Site: http://www.crsc.cn
3969—(HKG)
Rev.: $5,568,732,630
Assets: $16,172,815,752
Liabilities: $9,626,828,960
Net Worth: $6,545,986,791
Earnings: $567,767,482
Emp.: 19,649
Fiscal Year-end: 12/31/22
Railways Transportation Services
N.A.I.C.S.: 551112
Zhiliang Zhou *(Chm)*

Subsidiaries:

Beijing National Railway Research & Design Institute of Signal & Communication Co., Ltd.   (1)
Building No 18 Huayuan Yili Fengtai District, Beijing, 100073, China
Tel.: (86) 1051841588
Web Site: http://qlth.crsc.cn

Engineering Design Services
N.A.I.C.S.: 541330

CRSC Research & Design Institute Group Co., Ltd.   (1)
Building No 18 Huayuan Yili, Fengtai District, Beijing, 100073, China
Tel.: (86) 1051841588
Web Site: http://www.qlth.crsc.cn
Emp.: 1,500
Railroad Mfr
N.A.I.C.S.: 336510

CRSC Wanquan Signal Equipment Co., Ltd.   (1)
Haiyun International Building Building Nanxing Street, Shangcheng District, Hangzhou, China
Tel.: (86) 57186699948
Web Site: http://www.thwq.crsc.cn
Tram Signal Equipment & System Mfr
N.A.I.C.S.: 334290

CHINA RAILWAY SPECIAL CARGO LOGISTICS CO., LTD.

China Railway Business Building No 24 Yaziqiao Road, Xuanwu, Beijing, 100055, China
Tel.: (86) 4008016799
Web Site: https://www.crscl.com.cn
Year Founded: 2003
001213—(SSE)
Rev.: $1,328,967,432
Assets: $2,793,467,196
Liabilities: $220,791,636
Net Worth: $2,572,675,560
Earnings: $58,357,260
Fiscal Year-end: 12/31/22
Cargo Logistics Services
N.A.I.C.S.: 541614
Yu Yongli *(Chm)*

CHINA RAILWAY TIELONG CONTAINER LOGISTICS CO., LTD.

No 1 Xinan Street, Zhongshan District, Dalian, 116001, Liaoning, China
Tel.: (86) 41182808013
Web Site: https://www.chinacrt.com
Year Founded: 1993
600125—(SHG)
Rev.: $1,685,095,528
Assets: $1,321,440,405
Liabilities: $381,602,089
Net Worth: $939,838,316
Earnings: $47,383,371
Fiscal Year-end: 12/31/22
Railway Transportation Services
N.A.I.C.S.: 482111
Jianmin Wang *(Chief Admin Officer)*

CHINA RARE EARTH HOLDINGS LIMITED

Room 2509 Harcourt House 39 Gloucest Road, Wanchai, China (Hong Kong)
Tel.: (852) 28696283
Web Site: http://www.creh.com.hk
0769—(HKG)
Rev.: $143,466,647
Assets: $378,235,527
Liabilities: $19,081,817
Net Worth: $359,153,710
Earnings: $2,658,020
Emp.: 400
Fiscal Year-end: 12/31/20
Holding Company; Rare Earth Materials Processor & Distr
N.A.I.C.S.: 551112
Cainan Jiang *(Exec Dir)*

Subsidiaries:

Yixing Xinwei Leeshing Rare Earth Company Limited   (1)
Dingshu, Yixing, 214226, Jiangsu, China
Tel.: (86) 51087454950
Sales Range: $125-149.9 Million
Emp.: 500
Rare Earth Materials Processor & Distr

N.A.I.C.S.: 327120
Jiang Dawei *(Exec Dir)*

CHINA RARE EARTH RESOURCES AND TECHNOLOGY CO., LTD.

TowerA Minmetals Plaza No3 Chao Yangmen North Avenue, Dongcheng District, Beijing, 100010, China
Tel.: (86) 1060169000   CN
Web Site:
  https://www.minmetals.com
Year Founded: 1950
Sales Range: Less than $1 Million
Emp.: 240,000
Minerals & Metals Production & Trading Services
N.A.I.C.S.: 213114
Jiao Jian *(Sr VP)*

Subsidiaries:

ALBUM TRADING COMPANY
LIMITED   (1)
16th Floor CMA Building 32 to 26 Malaysia Command Street, Macau, China (Macau)
Tel.: (853) 28717421
Metal Mining Services
N.A.I.C.S.: 212290

Cheeminmet Finance Limited   (1)
16/F China Minmetals Tower 79 Chatham Road, Tsimshatsui, Kowloon, China (Hong Kong)
Tel.: (852) 26136000
Sales Range: $50-74.9 Million
Emp.: 20
Financial Services
N.A.I.C.S.: 525990

Cheerglory Traders Limited   (1)
11 F China Minmetals Tower 79 Chatham Road S, Tsimshatsui, Kowloon, China (Hong Kong)
Tel.: (852) 26136000
Web Site: http://www.cheerglory.com
Sales Range: $75-99.9 Million
Emp.: 200
Metal Distr
N.A.I.C.S.: 423510

China Antimony Technology Co., Ltd.   (1)
No 2 East 13 Road New & High-Tech Industrial Development Zone, Nanning, 530221, Guangxi, China
Tel.: (86) 771 3810422
Metal Mining Services
N.A.I.C.S.: 213114

China Expand Development Ltd.   (1)
79 Chathan Rd S Tsimshatsui, Kowloon, China (Hong Kong)
Tel.: (852) 26136000
Web Site: http://www.minmetals.com
Sales Range: $25-49.9 Million
Emp.: 40
Real Estate Services
N.A.I.C.S.: 531390
Qian Zigang *(Gen Mgr)*

China International Engineering & Materials Corp.   (1)
Minmetals Plaza 5 Sanlihe Road, Haidian District, Beijing, 100044, China
Tel.: (86) 10 68495194
Web Site: http://www.minmetals.com
Metal Distr
N.A.I.C.S.: 423510

China Metallurgical Group
Corporation   (1)
No 28 Shuguang Xili, Chaoyang District, Beijing, 100028, China   **(100%)**
Tel.: (86) 10 5986 8666
Web Site: http://www.mcc.com.cn
Holding Company
N.A.I.C.S.: 551112
Wenqing Guo *(Pres)*

Subsidiary (Domestic):

Metallurgical Corporation of China
Limited   (2)
28 Shuguang Xili, Chaoyang District, Beijing, 100028, China   **(64.18%)**
Tel.: (86) 1059869999

Web Site: http://www.mcc.com.cn
Rev.: $82,059,851,573
Assets: $81,051,228,124
Liabilities: $58,633,593,404
Net Worth: $22,417,634,720
Earnings: $1,789,913,602
Emp.: 98,385
Fiscal Year-end: 12/31/2022
Construction Engineering Services
N.A.I.C.S.: 551112
Wenqing Guo *(Chm)*

Subsidiary (Domestic):

CCTEC Engineering Co., Ltd.   (3)
51 Guanggu Ave, Wuhan, 430073, Hubei, China
Tel.: (86) 2781628177
Web Site: http://www.cctec.cn
Sales Range: $150-199.9 Million
Emp.: 1,000
Metallurgical Engineering Services
N.A.I.C.S.: 541330

Zhongye Changtian International Engineering Co., Ltd.   (3)
No 1 Laodong Middle Rd, Changsha, 410007, Hunan, China
Tel.: (86) 73182760423
Web Site: http://www.cie-cn.com
Sales Range: $100-124.9 Million
Emp.: 650
Engineeering Services
N.A.I.C.S.: 541330
Shuguang Yi *(Chm)*

China Minmet Investment
Limited   (1)
79 Chatham Road South Tsimshatsui, Kowloon, China (Hong Kong)
Tel.: (852) 26136000
Web Site: http://www.chinaminmetals.com
Sales Range: $100-124.9 Million
Emp.: 150
Investment Services
N.A.I.C.S.: 523999

China Minmetals H.K. (Holding)
Limited   (1)
19/F China Minmetals Tower 79 Chatham Road South, Tsimshatsui, Kowloon, China (Hong Kong)
Tel.: (852) 26136000
Web Site: http://www.minmetals.com.cn
Sales Range: $25-49.9 Million
Emp.: 20
Metal Distr
N.A.I.C.S.: 423510

China Minmetals Hainan Trading Development Corp.   (1)
16th Floor Shenfa Building 22 Jinlong Road, Finance and Trade District, 570125, Haikou, China
Tel.: (86) 89868520885
Web Site: http://www.minmetals.com
Trading in Metals, Minerals & Electrical Products
N.A.I.C.S.: 213114

China Minmetals NZ Ltd.   (1)
Level 15 99 Albert St, PO Box 5922, Wellesley St, Auckland, New Zealand
Tel.: (64) 9 3778955
Web Site: http://www.minmetals.co.nz
Metal Mining Services
N.A.I.C.S.: 213114
Luo Jiaxiang *(Gen Mgr)*

China Minmetals Non-Ferrous Metals Co. Ltd.   (1)
Block A Minmetals Building 6 Sanlihe Road, Haidian District, Beijing, 100044, China   **(82.23%)**
Tel.: (86) 1068495202
Web Site: http://www.cmnltd.com
Sales Range: $1-4.9 Billion
Copper, Aluminum, Tungsten, Tin, Antimony, Lead, Zinc, Precious Metals & Rare Earth Metals Distr
N.A.I.C.S.: 423510

Subsidiary (Non-US):

MMG Limited   (2)
Unit 1208 12/F China Minmetals Tower, 79 Chatham Road South Tsimshatsui, Kowloon, China (Hong Kong)   **(72%)**
Tel.: (852) 22169688

Web Site: http://www.mmg.com
Rev.: $3,254,200,000
Assets: $12,535,500,000
Liabilities: $8,307,000,000
Net Worth: $4,228,500,000
Earnings: $243,500,000
Emp.: 4,296
Fiscal Year-end: 12/31/2022
Holding Company; Zinc, Copper & Other Metals Exploration, Development & Mining
N.A.I.C.S.: 551112
Lucia Suet Kam Leung *(Sec)*

Corporate Headquarters (Non-US):

MMG Limited - Corporate Office   (3)
Level 23 28 Freshwater Place, Southbank, 3006, VIC, Australia
Tel.: (61) 392880888
Web Site: http://www.mmg.com
Rev.: $3,670,200,000
Assets: $13,255,400,000
Liabilities: $10,359,100,000
Net Worth: $2,896,300,000
Earnings: $137,400,000
Emp.: 3,491
Fiscal Year-end: 12/31/2018
Corporate Office; Zinc, Copper & Other Metals Exploration, Development & Mining
N.A.I.C.S.: 551114
Wenqing Guo *(Chm)*

Subsidiary (Domestic):

MMG Australia Limited   (4)
Level 23 28 Freshwater Place, Southbank, 3006, VIC, Australia   **(100%)**
Tel.: (61) 3 9288 0888
Web Site: http://www.mmg.com
Sales Range: $100-124.9 Million
Emp.: 200
Metallic Mineral & Metal Ore Exploration Development & Mining Service
N.A.I.C.S.: 213114
Andrew Gordon Michelmore *(CEO)*

Subsidiary (Non-US):

MMG Canada   (4)
2600-1177 West Hastings Street, Vancouver, V6E 2K3, BC, Canada
Tel.: (778) 373-5600
Web Site: http://www.mmg.com
Metallic Mineral Exploration & Development Services
N.A.I.C.S.: 213114

Xstrata Las Bambas S.A.   (4)
Pasaje Los Delfines 159 Urbanizacion Las Gardenias, Santiago de Surco, Lima, Peru
Tel.: (51) 1 2177070
Copper Mining Services
N.A.I.C.S.: 212230

China Minmetals South America (Holding) Ltd.   (1)
Rua Assembleia 10-S 3420, CEP 20011-901, Rio de Janeiro, RJ, Brazil
Tel.: (55) 2125312321
Sales Range: $50-74.9 Million
Emp.: 2
Metal Distr
N.A.I.C.S.: 423510
Dai Baolong *(Mng Dir)*

China Minmetals Zhuhai Import and Export Trading Co., Ltd.   (1)
Room 2703 Bright Intl Trade Center, 47 Haibin Rd S Jida, Zhuhai, 519015, China   **(100%)**
Tel.: (86) 7563222358
Web Site: http://www.minmetals.com
Metal Distr
N.A.I.C.S.: 423510

China National Metal Products Imp/Exp Company   (1)
Minmetals Plz 5 Sanlihe Rd, Beijing, 100044, China
Tel.: (86) 1068494508
Web Site: http://www.minmetals.com
Sales Range: $50-74.9 Million
Emp.: 50
Metal & Electrical Products Importer & Exporter
N.A.I.C.S.: 423510
Fang Gang *(Gen Mgr)*

China National Metals & Minerals Imp. & Exp. Shanghai Pudong

Corp.   (1)
16A Bao Ding Building 550 Xujiahui Road, Shanghai, 200025, China
Tel.: (86) 2164739872
Metal & Mineral Importer & Exporter
N.A.I.C.S.: 423510

China National Metals & Minerals Imp/Exp Shenzhen Corp.   (1)
15 Fl Times Financial Ctr 4001 Shen Nan Rd, Shenzhen, 518034, China
Tel.: (86) 75582389287
Sales Range: $50-74.9 Million
Emp.: 20
Metal & Mineral Importer & Exporter
N.A.I.C.S.: 423510

China National Metals & Minerals Import & Export Corporation   (1)
Room 304 Dom 3 UL, Profsoyuznaya, Moscow, 117036, Russia
Tel.: (7) 495 1245128
Metal Mining Services
N.A.I.C.S.: 212290
Wang Dijun *(Gen Mgr)*

China National Minerals Co., Ltd.   (1)
5 Sanlihe Road Haidian District, Beijing, 100044, China
Tel.: (86) 1068494481
Web Site:
  http://www.minerals.minmetals.com.cn
Sales Range: $1-4.9 Billion
Emp.: 250
Iron Ore, Billets, Pig Iron, Steel Scraps, Demo-Vessel, Coke, Coal, Ferroalloys, Refractory Raw Materials, Barite, Fluorspars & Talc Importer & Exporter
N.A.I.C.S.: 423510
Jinzeng He *(Mng Dir)*

China Palace International Travel Service   (1)
15 Garden Road, Haidian District, Beijing, 100088, China
Tel.: (86) 1062052214
Travel Services
N.A.I.C.S.: 561599

China Rare Earth Resources & Technology Co., Ltd.   (1)
Floor 15 Building A Haode Ginza No 18 Zhangjiang South Avenue, Ganzhou, 341000, Jiangxi, China
Tel.: (86) 7978398390
Web Site: https://www.cmreltd.com
Rev.: $531,548,784
Assets: $474,509,880
Liabilities: $36,428,184
Net Worth: $438,081,696
Earnings: $58,355,856
Fiscal Year-end: 12/31/2022
Aluminum Product Smelting Services
N.A.I.C.S.: 331314
Yang Guo'an *(Chm)*

Ganzhou Gannan Tungsten Co., Ltd.   (1)
4/F Huangjin Mansion Huangjin Avenue, Ganzhou, 341000, Jiangxi, China
Tel.: (86) 797 8381158
Metal Mining Services
N.A.I.C.S.: 212290
Kong Fanzhi *(Gen Mgr)*

Hanxing Metallurgical Mine Administration   (1)
No 54 Northern Zhainghua Road, Handan, Hebei, China
Tel.: (86) 31030233951
Web Site: http://www.hxks.com
Metals, Minerals & Electrical Products
N.A.I.C.S.: 213114

ICBC-AXA-Minmetals Assurance Co., Ltd.   (1)
12/F China Merchants Tower 161 Lu Jai Zui Road, Pudong New District, Shanghai, 200120, China   **(12.5%)**
Tel.: (86) 2158792288
Web Site: http://www.icbc-axa.com
Sales Range: $10-24.9 Million
Insurance Services in Life, Education, Retirement, Health & Wealth Management
N.A.I.C.S.: 524113

Janfair Pty. Ltd.   (1)
Level 15 215 Adelaide Street, Brisbane, 4000, QLD, Australia

China Rare Earth Resources And Technology Co.,
Ltd.—(Continued)

Tel.: (61) 738326755
Web Site: http://www.janfair.com
Sales Range: $50-74.9 Million
Emp.: 5
Real Estate Services
N.A.I.C.S.: 531390

**Minerals Ganzhou Rare Earth Co.,
Ltd**   (1)
8th Floor Tianjihuating Building NO 2
Changzheng Road, Ganzhou, 341000, Ji-
angxi, China
Tel.: (86) 797 8398389
Metal Mining Services
N.A.I.C.S.: 212290

**Minmetals (Guizhou) Ferro-Alloys Co.
Ltd.**   (1)
No 301 Hongqibei Rd, Hongfenghu,
Qingzhen, 551400, Guizhou, China
Tel.: (86) 851 2551827
Metal Mining Services
N.A.I.C.S.: 212290

**Minmetals (Hunan) Ferroalloys Co.
Ltd.**   (1)
Xinxiang W Rd, Xiangtan, 410011, Hunan,
China
Tel.: (86) 73156806847
Metal Mining Services
N.A.I.C.S.: 212290
Deng Chuping *(Mng Dir)*

Minmetals (UK) Ltd.   (1)
Mimet House 5A Praed Street, London, W2
1NJ, United Kingdom
Tel.: (44) 2074114012
Web Site: http://www.minmetals.co.uk
Sales Range: $50-74.9 Million
Emp.: 8
Metal Distr
N.A.I.C.S.: 423510

Minmetals Australia Pty. Ltd.   (1)
Level 8 564 Saint Kilda Road, Melbourne,
3004, VIC, Australia   **(100%)**
Tel.: (61) 395206800
Web Site:
   http://www.australia.minmetals.com.cn
Sales Range: $25-49.9 Million
Emp.: 25
Metal Distr
N.A.I.C.S.: 423510
Zhilong Liu *(Mng Dir)*

Minmetals Capital Co., Ltd.   (1)
No 69 Lufeng Road Hi-tech Development
Zone, Changsha High-Tech Industrial Dev
Zone, Changsha, 100027, Hunan, China
Tel.: (86) 73188657382
Web Site: http://www.king-ray.com.cn
Rev.: $1,549,533,122
Assets: $21,464,976,541
Liabilities: $13,269,981,774
Net Worth: $8,194,994,767
Earnings: $355,219,427
Emp.: 3,060
Fiscal Year-end: 12/31/2022
Electronic & Super Hard Mineral Research
& Development Services
N.A.I.C.S.: 327999
Ligong Zhao *(Chm & Pres)*

**Minmetals Capitals & Securities,
Inc.**   (1)
16 F China Minmetals Tower 79 Chatham
Rd S, Kowloon, China (Hong Kong)
Tel.: (852) 26136000
Web Site: http://www.minmetals.com
Sales Range: $25-49.9 Million
Emp.: 50
Metal Investments
N.A.I.C.S.: 331512

**Minmetals Development Co.,
Ltd.**   (1)
Block B No 5 Sanlihe Road, Haidian Dis-
trict, Beijing, 100044, China
Tel.: (86) 1068494206
Web Site: https://www.minlist.com.cn
Rev.: $11,041,890,706
Assets: $3,204,707,459
Liabilities: $2,505,892,657
Net Worth: $698,814,801
Earnings: $47,680,402
Emp.: 4,100
Fiscal Year-end: 12/31/2022

Freight Transportation, Logistics, Storage &
Mineral Trading Services; Hotel Manage-
ment & Technology Services
N.A.I.C.S.: 488510
Wei Tao *(Chm)*

Minmetals Engineering Co. Ltd.   (1)
Room 2011 Tengda Building 168 Xizhimen-
wai Dajie, Haidian, Beijing, 100044, China
Tel.: (86) 10 8857 6455622
Metal Mining Services
N.A.I.C.S.: 212290
He Liu *(Mng Dir)*

**Minmetals Environmental Technology
co., LTD**   (1)
No 58 Chaozhang Xincun, Wuxi, 214023,
China
Tel.: (86) 510 5057890
Metal Mining Services
N.A.I.C.S.: 212290
Gao Jianqi *(Gen Mgr)*

Minmetals Finance Company   (1)
Minmetals Plaza 5 Sanlihe Road, Haidian
District, Beijing, China
Tel.: (86) 1068495359
Financial Services
N.A.I.C.S.: 523999

Minmetals Germany GmbH   (1)
Kaiserswerther Strasse 22, Dusseldorf,
40477, Germany   **(100%)**
Tel.: (49) 21149680
Web Site: http://www.minmetals.de
Sales Range: $150-199.9 Million
Emp.: 20
Metal Distr
N.A.I.C.S.: 423510
Jianxun Yan *(Gen Mgr)*

**Minmetals International Tendering
Co., Ltd.**   (1)
5 D Block 2nd floor Sanlihe Road, Haidian
District, Beijing, China
Tel.: (86) 1068494375
Web Site: http://mitc.minmetals.com
Loan Broker
N.A.I.C.S.: 522310
Xiao Jian *(Pres)*

Minmetals Japan Corporation   (1)
2-7-15 Fukagawa Koto-Ku, Tokyo, 135-
0033, Japan
Tel.: (81) 356399555
Sales Range: $50-74.9 Million
Emp.: 10
Metal Distr
N.A.I.C.S.: 423510

Minmetals Korea Co., Ltd.   (1)
Room 1103 Hyoryung Building 1 Mugyo-
Dong Jung-Gu, Seoul, 100170, Korea
(South)
Tel.: (82) 27794741
Web Site: http://www.minmetals.com
Sales Range: $50-74.9 Million
Emp.: 6
Metal Distr
N.A.I.C.S.: 423510
Fujun Sun *(Gen Mgr)*

Minmetals Land Limited   (1)
18th Floor China Minmetals Tower 79
Chatham Road South, Tsimshatsui, Kow-
loon, China (Hong Kong)
Tel.: (852) 26136363
Web Site: http://www.minmetalsland.com
Rev.: $1,283,227,448
Assets: $8,591,845,688
Liabilities: $6,448,303,193
Net Worth: $2,143,542,495
Earnings: ($173,428,560)
Emp.: 1,211
Fiscal Year-end: 12/31/2022
Real Estate Services
N.A.I.C.S.: 531390
Jianbo He *(Chm)*

**Minmetals Materials (Changshu)
Management Co., Ltd.**   (1)
No 1 Kehong Road Changshu Riverside
Industrial Park, Changshu, 215536, Ji-
angsu, China
Tel.: (86) 512 52109999
Steel Plate Mfr
N.A.I.C.S.: 331221
Xu Huizhong *(Gen Mgr)*

**Minmetals Nanjing International Trad-
ing Co., Ltd.**   (1)

Room 1509 Longsheng Building, 23
Hongwu Road, Nanjing, 210005, China
Tel.: 2586899367
Web Site: http://www.minmetals.com.cn
Sales Range: $50-74.9 Million
Emp.: 24
International Metal Wholesale Trading Ser-
vices
N.A.I.C.S.: 423510
Weidong Liu *(Gen Mgr)*

Minmetals North Europe AB   (1)
Arenavagen 41, PO Box 10114, 121 28,
Stockholm, Sweden
Tel.: (86) 86699001
Web Site: http://www.minmetals.se
Sales Range: $50-74.9 Million
Emp.: 5
Metal Distr
N.A.I.C.S.: 423510
J. Hong Li *(Gen Mgr)*

Minmetals R.S.A. (PTY) Ltd.   (1)
EOH Business Park Bld A 1st Floor, Os-
borne Lane, Bedfordview, 2007, South Af-
rica
Tel.: (27) 116150029
Web Site: http://www.minmetals.co.za
Sales Range: $50-74.9 Million
Emp.: 5
Metal Distr
N.A.I.C.S.: 423510
Jingbo Li *(Gen Mgr)*

Minmetals Real Estate Company   (1)
Minmetals Plaza 5 Sanlihe Rd, Haidian Dis-
trict, Beijing, 100044, China
Tel.: (86) 1068495117
Web Site: http://www.minmetals.com
Real Estate Services
N.A.I.C.S.: 531390

**Minmetals Securities Brokerage Co.
Ltd.**   (1)
NF-A Haiwaizhuangshi Bldg Huafu Rd, Fu-
tian, Shenzhen, 518031, China
Tel.: (86) 755 83343496
Securities Brokerage Services
N.A.I.C.S.: 523150

**Minmetals Shipping (Singapore) Pte.
Ltd.**   (1)
24 Raffles Place 19-05, Clifford Centre, Sin-
gapore, 048621, Singapore
Tel.: (65) 5385090
Cargo Shipping Services
N.A.I.C.S.: 488510
Wang Qi *(Gen Mgr)*

**Minmetals South-East Asia Corpora-
tion Pte. Ltd.**   (1)
19-04 Clifford Ctr 24 Raffles Pl, Singapore,
048621, Singapore
Tel.: (65) 356566
Web Site: http://www.minmetals.com.sg
Sales Range: $50-74.9 Million
Emp.: 10
Metal Distr
N.A.I.C.S.: 423510

Minmetals Spain S.A.   (1)
1 Piso 4 Numero 128-130 Plaza, P Taulat,
08005, Barcelona, Spain
Tel.: (34) 933072007
Web Site: http://www.minmetals.com
Metal Distr
N.A.I.C.S.: 423510

**Minmetals Tongling Gem Stone Co.,
Ltd.**   (1)
Minmetals Plaza 5 Sanlihe Road, Haidian
District, Beijing, 100044, China
Tel.: (86) 1068495057
Gem Stone Distr
N.A.I.C.S.: 423940

**Minmetals Xiamen Enterprises Co.,
Ltd.**   (1)
11/F Huicheng Commercial Centre, Xiamen,
China
Tel.: (86) 898 58566930
Metal Distr
N.A.I.C.S.: 423510

**Minmetals Xinjiang Ala-Shankou
Trading Co., Ltd.**   (1)
Zhungeer Road, Ala-Shankou, Xinjiang,
833418, China
Tel.: (86) 9096993966
Metal Distr

Minmetals Yantai Co., Ltd.   (1)
Room 1005 1010 Qili Mansion, Yantai,
264100, China
Tel.: (86) 5356627672
Web Site: http://www.minmetal-yantai.com
Sales Range: $25-49.9 Million
Emp.: 19
Metal Distr
N.A.I.C.S.: 423510
Chang Seng *(Gen Mgr)*

**Minmetals Yingkou Medium-Heavy
Plate Co., Ltd.**   (1)
Yejin Street Fanrong Road No 1, Laobian,
Yingkou, Liaoning, China
Tel.: (86) 417 3256011
Steel Plate Mfr
N.A.I.C.S.: 331221

**Minmetals Zhejiang International
Trading Co., Ltd.**   (1)
Floor 17 Zhijun Building No 96 Fengqui
Road, Hangzhou, 315009, China
Tel.: (86) 57185802380
International Metal Wholesale Trading Ser-
vices
N.A.I.C.S.: 423510

**Minmetals Zhenjiang Import and Ex-
port Trading Co., Ltd.**   (1)
F/15 Zhongshan Bldg No 381 Zhongshan
Dong Rd, Zhenjiang, 212001, Jiangsu,
China
Tel.: (86) 511 5220522
Metal Mining Services
N.A.I.C.S.: 212290

Minmetals, Inc.   (1)
1200 Harbor Blvd, Weehawken, NJ
07086   **(100%)**
Tel.: (201) 809-1898
Web Site: http://www.minmetalsusa.com
Sales Range: $50-74.9 Million
Emp.: 20
Metal Products Mfr
N.A.I.C.S.: 423520
Caojing Liu *(Pres)*

Subsidiary (Domestic):

Minmetals, Inc. (L.A.)   (2)
1037 Walnut Ave, Pomona, CA 91766
Tel.: (909) 627-8258
Web Site: http://www.minmetalsusa.com
Metal Distr
N.A.I.C.S.: 423510

Minnat Resources Pte. Ltd.   (1)
24 Raffles Place, #19-03 Clifford Centre,
048621, Singapore, Singapore
Tel.: (65) 65357406
Web Site: http://www.minmetals.com.sg
Administration & Metal Mining Services
N.A.I.C.S.: 213114

Shanghai Oriental Futures Co.,   (1)
Room 704 22 417 Street Lancun Road,
Shanghai, 200122, China
Tel.: (86) 2168401560
Futures Trading Services; Owned by China
Minmetals Corporation & by Huadong Sup-
ply Company of China Non-Ferrous Metals
Industrial Corporation
N.A.I.C.S.: 523210

**Shangri-La International Hotel Mar-
keting Ltd.**   (1)
The Kerry Centre Hotel No 1 Guang Hua
Road, Chao Yang District, Beijing, 100020,
China
Tel.: (86) 1065618833
Sales Range: $100-124.9 Million
Emp.: 700
Hotel Operations
N.A.I.C.S.: 721110

**CHINA REDSTONE GROUP,
INC.**
239 Jianxin Road, Jiangbei District,
Chongqing, 400000, China
Tel.: (86) 2340251111   DE
Web Site:
   http://www.chinaredstone.com
Sales Range: $25-49.9 Million
Emp.: 43

Funeral Services & Cemeteries; Hospitality Services
N.A.I.C.S.: 812220
Yiyou Ran *(Chm, Pres & CEO)*

CHINA REFORM CULTURE HOLDINGS CO., LTD.
2F North Side China Culture Building No 57 Honglian South Road, Xicheng District, Beijing, 100055, China
Tel.: (86) 1068313202
Web Site: http://www.sh3f.com
Year Founded: 1992
600636—(SHG)
Rev.: $65,802,925
Assets: $399,168,404
Liabilities: $22,164,822
Net Worth: $377,003,582
Earnings: $18,766,861
Emp.: 600
Fiscal Year-end: 12/31/22
Inorganic Chemical Mfr
N.A.I.C.S.: 325180
Zhixue Wang *(Chm)*

CHINA REFORM HEALTH MANAGEMENT AND SERVICES GROUP CO., LTD.
Room 703 Junhua Haiyi Hotel No 18 Wenhua Road, Longhua District, Haikou, 570105, Hainan, China
Tel.: (86) 1057825201
Web Site: http://www.crhms.cn
Year Founded: 1986
000503—(SSE)
Rev.: $43,675,632
Assets: $155,099,880
Liabilities: $54,996,084
Net Worth: $100,103,796
Earnings: ($11,859,588)
Fiscal Year-end: 12/31/22
Pharmaceutical Products Distr
N.A.I.C.S.: 325412
Li Yonghua *(Chm)*

CHINA REGENERATIVE MEDICINE INTERNATIONAL CO., LTD.
Room 3006-10 30th Fl China Resources Building 26 Harbour Road, Wanchai, China (Hong Kong)
Tel.: (852) 3966 8388   HK
Web Site: http://www.crmi.hk
Year Founded: 2001
8158—(HKG)
Rev.: $23,905,024
Assets: $19,668,289
Liabilities: $26,781,536
Net Worth: ($7,113,247)
Earnings: ($56,600,035)
Emp.: 172
Fiscal Year-end: 12/31/20
Holding Company
N.A.I.C.S.: 551112
Chuang Wang *(Chm & Compliance Officer)*

Subsidiaries:

BioCell Technology Limited   **(1)**
Science Park 15 W7 Floor, Hong Kong, China (Hong Kong)
Tel.: (852) 396 6852
Clinical Cell Operation Services
N.A.I.C.S.: 541714

Shaanxi Aierfu Activtissue Engineering Company Limited   **(1)**
No 4 Dengling No 1 Road, High-tech District, Xi'an, Shanxi, China
Tel.: (86) 298 129 7536
Skin Related Product Mfr & Distr
N.A.I.C.S.: 325620

Shanghai Hesidi Cosmetics Company Limited   **(1)**
3F Bldg A 11 Keyuan Rd, Nanshan District, Shenzhen, Guangdong, China
Tel.: (86) 7558 661 8580

Medical Equipment Distr
N.A.I.C.S.: 423450

Shenzhen AiNear Cornea Engineering Company Limited   **(1)**
No 12 Ganli No 6 Road Buji Street Block B Building 1 101-102, Zhonghaixin Science and Technology Park, Shenzhen, China
Tel.: (86) 7558 935 0161
Cornea Product Mfr & Distr
N.A.I.C.S.: 339115

Tianjin Weikai Bioeng Ltd.   **(1)**
Starfish Plaza Binhai Tanggu Marine Hi-Tech Development Area, Tianjin, China
Tel.: (86) 226 537 8916
Medical Equipment Distr
N.A.I.C.S.: 423450

CHINA REINSURANCE (GROUP) CORPORATION
China Reinsurance Building No 11 Jinrong Avenue, Xicheng District, Beijing, 100033, China
Tel.: (86) 1066576666   CN
Web Site: https://eng.chinare.com.cn
Year Founded: 1949
1508—(HKG)
Rev.: $15,146,609,299
Assets: $63,653,022,126
Liabilities: $49,505,520,326
Net Worth: $14,147,501,800
Earnings: $801,754,680
Emp.: 63,914
Fiscal Year-end: 12/31/23
Investment Management Service
N.A.I.C.S.: 523999
Hong Zhang *(Chm-Supervisory Bd)*

Subsidiaries:

Chaucer Holdings Limited   **(1)**
Plantation Place 30 Fenchurch Street, Plantation Place, London, EC3M 3AD, United Kingdom
Tel.: (44) 2073979700
Web Site: http://www.chaucerplc.com
Insurance & Reinsurance Underwriting Services
N.A.I.C.S.: 524210
John Fowle *(CEO)*

Subsidiary (Non-US):

Chaucer Latin America S.A   **(2)**
Av Cordoba 1131 8 Piso, 1055, Buenos Aires, Argentina
Tel.: (54) 11 5353 3400
Web Site: http://www.chaucer.com
Insurance Related Activities
N.A.I.C.S.: 524298

Chaucer Singapore Pte Limited   **(2)**
138 Market Street 04-03 CapitaGreen, Singapore, 048946, Singapore
Tel.: (65) 6 499 0820
Web Site: http://www.chaucerplc.com
Sales Range: $25-49.9 Million
Emp.: 18
Insurance Related Activities
N.A.I.C.S.: 524298

Subsidiary (Domestic):

Chaucer Syndicates Limited   **(2)**
Plantation Place 30 Fenchurch Street, London, EC3M 3AD, United Kingdom
Tel.: (44) 2073979700
Web Site: http://www.chaucerplc.com
Sales Range: $75-99.9 Million
Emp.: 350
Management of Insurance Underwriting
N.A.I.C.S.: 541611

Subsidiary (Non-US):

Chaucer Labuan Limited   **(3)**
Brighton Place Ground Floor U0215, Jalan Bahasa, Labuan, 87014, Malaysia
Tel.: (60) 87442899
Asset Management Services
N.A.I.C.S.: 525920

Chaucer MENA Limited   **(3)**
Office 106 Tower 1 Al Fattan Currency House DIFC, Dubai International Financial Centre, Dubai, United Arab Emirates
Tel.: (971) 44019633

Reinsurance Carrier Services
N.A.I.C.S.: 524130

Subsidiary (Non-US):

Chaucer Underwriting A/S   **(2)**
Kongens Nytorv 5, Copenhagen, 1050, Denmark   **(100%)**
Tel.: (45) 3 314 6022
Web Site: http://www.chaucerplc.com
Sales Range: $25-49.9 Million
Emp.: 15
Insurance Agencies & Brokerages
N.A.I.C.S.: 524210

China Continent Property & Casualty Insurance Company Ltd.   **(1)**
Floor 6 7 8 9 10 Building 1 Lane 1199 Minsheng Road, Pilot Free Trade Zone, Shanghai, 200120, China
Tel.: (86) 2168577777
Web Site: https://www.ccic-net.com.cn
N.A.I.C.S.: 524126

China Life Reinsurance Company Ltd.   **(1)**
Floors 9 15 and 16 China Re Building No 11 Jinrong Avenue, Xicheng District, Beijing, 100033, China
Tel.: (86) 106 657 6366
Web Site: https://www.chinalifere.cn
Reinsurance Services
N.A.I.C.S.: 524130

China Re New York Liaison Office Inc.   **(1)**
45 Broadway Ste 1410, New York, NY 10006
Tel.: (212) 248-0810
Reinsurance Services
N.A.I.C.S.: 524130

China Re UK Limited   **(1)**
Upper Ground Floor 1 Minster Court, London, EC3R 7AA, United Kingdom
Tel.: (44) 2072839711
Property & Casualty Reinsurance Services
N.A.I.C.S.: 524130

China Re Underwriting Agency Limited   **(1)**
Upper Ground Floor 1 Minster Court, London, EC3R 7AA, United Kingdom
Tel.: (44) 2072839711
N.A.I.C.S.: 524210

Huatai Insurance Agency & Consultant Service Limited   **(1)**
15/F China Reinsurance Center No 18 Luomashi Avenue, Xicheng District, Beijing, 100052, China
Tel.: (86) 1056533627
Insurance Services
N.A.I.C.S.: 524210
Cunqiang Li *(Chief Strategy Officer & Exec Deputy Gen Mgr)*

Subsidiary (Domestic):

Huatai Surveyors & Adjusters Company Limited   **(2)**
15F China Re Center No 18 Luomashi Avenue, Xicheng District, Beijing, 100052, China
Tel.: (86) 1056533269
Web Site: https://www.htsurveyor.com
N.A.I.C.S.: 524210
Yong Luo *(Chm)*

CHINA RENAISSANCE HOLDINGS LTD.
Pacific Century Place Gate 1 Space 8 No 2A Workers Stadium North Road, Chaoyang District, Beijing, 100027, China
Tel.: (86) 1085679988   Ky
Web Site: http://www.huaxing.com
1911—(HKG)
Rev.: $267,272,240
Assets: $2,170,091,873
Liabilities: $958,581,500
Net Worth: $1,211,510,373
Earnings: $252,089,436
Emp.: 737
Fiscal Year-end: 12/31/21
Financial Investment Management Services

N.A.I.C.S.: 523940
Fan Bao *(Co-Founder, Chm & CEO)*

Subsidiaries:

China Renaissance Securities (US) Inc.   **(1)**
600 5Th Ave 21st Fl Rockefeller Plz, New York, NY 10020
Tel.: (212) 554-2960
Investment Banking Services
N.A.I.C.S.: 523150
Jonathan J. D. Hong *(Pres & Mng Dir)*

CHINA RENEWABLE ENERGY INVESTMENT LTD.
9th Floor Tower 1 South Seas Centre 75 Mody Road Tsimshatsui East, Kowloon, China (Hong Kong)
Tel.: (852) 27311000   Ky
Web Site: http://www.cre987.com
Year Founded: 2002
00987—(HKG)
Rev.: $26,585,616
Assets: $374,601,644
Liabilities: $127,811,441
Net Worth: $246,790,203
Earnings: $11,100,793
Emp.: 97
Fiscal Year-end: 12/31/20
Wind Power Generation Services
N.A.I.C.S.: 221115
Samuel Wing Sum Leung *(CFO)*

CHINA RESOURCES (HOLDINGS) CO., LTD.
49th Floor China Resources Building, 26 Harbour Road, Wanchai, China (Hong Kong)
Tel.: (852) 28797888   HK
Web Site: http://www.crc.com.hk
Year Founded: 1938
Sales Range: $15-24.9 Billion
Emp.: 80,000
Holding Company
N.A.I.C.S.: 551112
Bin Wei *(CFO)*

Subsidiaries:

CRE Properties (Hong Kong) Ltd.   **(1)**
Yuen Fat Administration Building 89 Yen Chow Street West, West Kowloon Reclamation, Kowloon, China (Hong Kong) **(100%)**
Tel.: (852) 28277333
Sales Range: $50-74.9 Million
Emp.: 50
Commercial Property Investment, Development & Management Services
N.A.I.C.S.: 531390
PakShing Lau *(Chm & Gen Mgr)*

China Resources Beer (Holdings) Company Limited   **(1)**
Rooms 2301 2310 23rd Floor China Resources Building, 26 Harbour Road, Wanchai, China (Hong Kong) **(51.69%)**
Tel.: (852) 23609722
Web Site: https://www.crbeer.com.hk
Rev.: $5,390,451,927
Assets: $9,903,079,309
Liabilities: $5,171,411,165
Net Worth: $4,731,668,144
Earnings: $721,920,691
Emp.: 27,232
Fiscal Year-end: 12/31/2023
Holding Company; Beer Brewer
N.A.I.C.S.: 551112
Tomakin Po Sing Lai *(CFO & Sec)*

Subsidiary (Non-US):

China Resources Snow Breweries Ltd.   **(2)**
Room 306 China Resources Bldg 8 Jianguomen N Ave, Dongcheng District, Beijing, 100005, China **(100%)**
Tel.: (86) 1065179898
Web Site: http://www.snowbeer.com.cn
Sales Range: $650-699.9 Million
Emp.: 2,000
Holding Company; Beer Breweries & Whslr
N.A.I.C.S.: 551112

China Resources (Holdings) Co., Ltd.—(Continued)

China Resources Chemicals Holdings Ltd. (1)
49/F China Resources Building, 26 Harbour Road, Wanchai, China (Hong Kong) **(100%)**
Tel.: (852) 28797888
Web Site: http://www.crc.com.hk
Sales Range: $25-49.9 Million
Emp.: 20
Chemical Products Distr
N.A.I.C.S.: 424690
Chu Tan (Gen Mgr)

China Resources Gas Group Limited (1)
Room 1901-02 China Resources Building No 26 Harbour Road, Wanchai, China (Hong Kong) **(74.94%)**
Tel.: (852) 25938200
Web Site: https://www.crcgas.com
Rev.: $12,056,478,715
Assets: $14,320,249,978
Liabilities: $7,605,555,996
Net Worth: $6,714,693,982
Earnings: $806,231,421
Emp.: 56,114
Fiscal Year-end: 12/31/2022
Investment Holding Company
N.A.I.C.S.: 551112
Bin Ge (Vice Chm)

Holding (Non-US):

BP Fujian Limited (2)
17E Metropolitan Financial Plaza, 43 Dongjie Road Gulou District, Fuzhou, Fujian, China
Tel.: (86) 5917676007
Sales Range: $125-149.9 Million
Emp.: 300
Liquefied Petroleum Gas Distr
N.A.I.C.S.: 457210

Subsidiary (Domestic):

China Resources Gas (Holdings) Ltd. (2)
19/F China Resources Building, 26 Harbour Road, Wanchai, China (Hong Kong) **(100%)**
Tel.: (852) 25937375
Web Site: http://www.crcgas.com
Liquefied Petroleum Gas Distr
N.A.I.C.S.: 457210
Baofeng Shi (Dir-Ops)

Holding (Non-US):

Zhengzhou China Resources Gas Co., Ltd. (2)
352 Longhai Road West, Zhengzhou, 450006, Henan, China **(56.87%)**
Tel.: (86) 371 6885 5777
Web Site: http://www.hnzzgas.com
Sales Range: $200-249.9 Million
Emp.: 1,656
Holding Company; Natural Gas Distr, Pressure Control Equipment Mfr & Gas Pipeline Construction Services
N.A.I.C.S.: 551112
Guoqi Yan (Chm & Compliance Officer)

China Resources Land Limited (1)
48/F Block E China Resources Land Building 18 Dachong 1st Road, Nanshan District, Wanchai, China (Hong Kong) **(67.3%)**
Tel.: (852) 28772330
Web Site: https://www.crland.com.hk
Rev.: $28,669,295,387
Assets: $149,719,193,204
Liabilities: $102,407,073,964
Net Worth: $47,312,119,240
Earnings: $4,481,856,585
Emp.: 55,311
Fiscal Year-end: 12/31/2022
Commercial & Residential Property Investment, Development & Management
N.A.I.C.S.: 525990
Dawei Zhang (Vice Chm)

China Resources Microelectronics Ltd. (1)
Room 510 IC Development Centre Hongkong Science Park, Sha Tin, China (Hong Kong) **(60.11%)**
Tel.: (852) 22999188
Web Site: http://www.crmicro.com

Sales Range: $450-499.9 Million
Emp.: 7,751
Holding Company; Semiconductors Developer & Mfr
N.A.I.C.S.: 551112
Nan-xiang Chen (Deputy Gen Mgr)

Co-Headquarters (Non-US):

China Resources Microelectronics Ltd. (2)
No 14 Liangxi Road, Wuxi, 214061, Jiangsu, China
Tel.: (86) 51085807123
Web Site: http://www.crmicro.com
Electronic Information Services
N.A.I.C.S.: 334417
Guoping Wang (CEO)

Subsidiary (Domestic):

ANST, China Resources Micro-Assembly Technology Co., Ltd. (3)
B-27 Ximei Road Wuxi New-High Technology, Industrial Development Zone, Wuxi, 214028, Jiangsu, China **(100%)**
Tel.: (86) 51082990111
Web Site: http://www.anst.com.cn
Integrated Circuit Testing & Packaging Services
N.A.I.C.S.: 541380
Xiaojian Zhang (Gen Mgr)

Division (Domestic):

CSMC Technologies Corporation (3)
8 Xinzhou Road, Wuxi, 214028, Jiangsu, China **(100%)**
Tel.: (86) 51088118888
Web Site: http://www.csmc.com.cn
Semiconductor Mfr
N.A.I.C.S.: 334413
Howard Ko (VP)

Subsidiary (Domestic):

Wuxi China Resources Huajing Microelectronics Co., Ltd. (3)
No 14 Liangxi Road, Wuxi, 214061, Jiangsu, China **(100%)**
Tel.: (86) 510 8580 7228
Web Site: http://www.crhj.com.cn
Power Transistor Chips Mfr
N.A.I.C.S.: 334413

Wuxi China Resources Semico Co., Ltd. (3)
180-22 Linghu Road, Wuxi, Jiangsu, China **(100%)**
Tel.: (86) 510 8581 0118
Web Site: http://www.semico.com.cn
Integrated Circuit Design Services
N.A.I.C.S.: 541490

China Resources Ng Fung Limited (1)
8/F China Resources Building, 26 Harbour Road, Wanchai, China (Hong Kong) **(100%)**
Tel.: (852) 25938777
Web Site: http://www.nfh.com.hk
Fresh, Live & Frozen Seafood, Meat, Poultry & Other Foodstuffs Distr
N.A.I.C.S.: 424420
Weiyong Wang (CEO & Gen Mgr)

China Resources Pharmaceutical Group Limited (1)
4101-05 41/F China Resources Building 26 Harbour Road, Wanchai, China (Hong Kong)
Tel.: (852) 25938991
Web Site: https://www.crpharm.com
Rev.: $25,850,561,507
Assets: $27,004,769,605
Liabilities: $16,682,571,918
Net Worth: $10,322,197,687
Earnings: $686,643,216
Emp.: 64,000
Fiscal Year-end: 12/31/2020
Pharmaceutical Product Mfr & Distr
N.A.I.C.S.: 325412
Peter Chi Lik Lo (Sec)

China Resources Power Holdings Co., Ltd. (1)
Rooms 2001-2002 20th Floor China Resources Building 26 Harbour Road, Wanchai, China (Hong Kong) **(65.3%)**
Tel.: (852) 25937530

Web Site: https://www.cr-power.com
Rev.: $8,970,663,603
Assets: $33,487,327,234
Liabilities: $19,821,858,572
Net Worth: $13,665,468,662
Earnings: $1,119,073,688
Emp.: 21,611
Fiscal Year-end: 12/31/2020
Holding Company; Electric Power Plant Investment, Development, Operation & Management Services
N.A.I.C.S.: 551112
Xiao Wang (CFO & Sec)

China Resources Retail (Group) Co., Ltd. (1)
4/F Yuen Fat Bldg 89 Yen Chow Street West, West Kowloon Reclamation, Kowloon, China (Hong Kong) **(100%)**
Tel.: (852) 28391888
Web Site: http://www.crcretail.com
Holding Company; Arts & Crafts Retail & Pharmacy Stores Operator
N.A.I.C.S.: 551112

China Resources Textiles (Holdings) Co., Ltd. (1)
11/F China Resources Building, 26 Harbour Road, Wanchai, China (Hong Kong) **(100%)**
Tel.: (852) 25938111
Web Site: http://www.crlintex.com
Sales Range: $600-649.9 Million
Emp.: 1,000
Holding Company; Textiles Processing & Garments Mfr & Distr
N.A.I.C.S.: 551112

Subsidiary (Non-US):

China Resources Textiles Co., Ltd. (2)
China Resources Building 10th FL 5001 Shennan Road East, Luohu District, Shenzhen, China **(100%)**
Tel.: (86) 755 8269 1888
Web Site: http://www.crlintex.com
Emp.: 40
Textiles Processing & Garments Mfr & Distr
N.A.I.C.S.: 313110

China Resources Vanguard Co., Ltd. (1)
No 27 Water Bay Road, Luohu District, Shenzhen, 518020, Guangdong, China **(100%)**
Tel.: (86) 75525685001
Web Site: http://www.crvanguard.com.cn
Supermarkets Owner & Operator
N.A.I.C.S.: 445110
Shuo Chen (CEO)

Subsidiary (Non-US):

China Resources Vanguard (Hong Kong) Co., Ltd. (2)
B 84 Paksik Godown No 2, 15 29 Wo Shui St, Hong Kong, China (Hong Kong) **(100%)**
Tel.: (852) 28278333
Web Site: http://www.crvanguard.com.hk
Sales Range: $150-199.9 Million
Emp.: 1,000
Supermarkets Owner & Operator
N.A.I.C.S.: 445110

Genesis Care Pty. Ltd. (1)
Buildings 1&11 The Mill 41-43 Bourke Road, Sydney, 2015, NSW, Australia
Tel.: (61) 2 8236 3300
Web Site: http://www.genesiscare.com.au
Medical Facility Operator
N.A.I.C.S.: 621399
Dan Collins (Founder, CEO & Mng Dir)

CHINA RESOURCES AND TRANSPORTATION GROUP LIMITED
Unit Nos 11-12 Level 10 Tower 1 Millennium City, No 388 Kwun Tong Road Kwun Tong, Kowloon, China (Hong Kong)
Tel.: (852) 31767100
Web Site: http://www.crtg.com.hk
0269—(HKG)
Rev.: $75,804,314
Assets: $805,215,658

Liabilities: $2,436,591,476
Net Worth: ($1,631,375,818)
Earnings: $261,748,969
Emp.: 378
Fiscal Year-end: 03/31/24
Expressway & Toll Road Construction Services
N.A.I.C.S.: 237310
David Kam Ching Tsang (Dir-Fin)

CHINA RESOURCES BOYA BIO-PHARMACEUTICAL GROUP CO., LTD.
No 333 Huiquan Road High-tech Industrial park, Fuzhou, 344000, Jiangxi, China
Tel.: (86) 7948224549
Web Site: https://www.china-boya.com
Year Founded: 1993
300294—(CHIN)
Sales Range: $125-149.9 Million
Blood Products Researcher, Developer, Mfr & Distr
N.A.I.C.S.: 325414
Qiu Kai (Chm)

Subsidiaries:

Green Cross HK Holdings Limited (1)
Room 1808 18/F Tower II Admiralty Centre Harcourt Road, Admiralty, Hong Kong, China (Hong Kong)
Tel.: (852) 3153 5651
Holding Company
N.A.I.C.S.: 551112

CHINA RESOURCES BUILDING MATERIALS TECHNOLOGY HOLDINGS LIMITED
Rm 3001-05 China Resources Building 26 Harbour Road, Wanchai, China (Hong Kong)
Tel.: (852) 31186800 **HK**
Web Site: http://www.crcement.com
Year Founded: 2003
1313—(OTCIQ)
Rev.: $4,117,551,727
Assets: $10,302,473,322
Liabilities: $3,805,065,370
Net Worth: $6,497,407,952
Earnings: $238,048,615
Emp.: 19,046
Fiscal Year-end: 12/31/22
Cement Mfr
N.A.I.C.S.: 327310
Liang Zhang (Sr VP & Gen Mgr-Guangdong)

Subsidiaries:

China Resources Cement (Fengkai) Limited (1)
Changgang Industrial Park, Changgang Town, Zhaoqing, 526541, Guangdong Fengkai, China
Tel.: (86) 7586882666
Cement Mfr & Whslr
N.A.I.C.S.: 327310

China Resources Cement (Shangsi) Limited (1)
Zhonghua Road, Siyang Town, Fangcheng, Shangsi Guangxi, China
Tel.: (86) 7708518658
Cement Mfr & Whslr
N.A.I.C.S.: 327310

China Resources Concrete (Nanning) Limited (1)
8 Kilometres Nanwu Road, Santang Town Xingning District, Nanning, 530024, Guangxi, China
Tel.: (86) 7715661518
Concrete Mix Mfr
N.A.I.C.S.: 327320

DongGuan Universal Classical Material Ltd. (1)
Hengjiangxia, Changping Town, Dongguan, Guangdong, China

Tel.: (86) 76982831813
Web Site: https://www.uniplususa.com
Quartz Compound Stone Distr
N.A.I.C.S.: 423320

Quality Control Consultants
Limited (1)
7b Block 3 Tai Ping Industrial Centre 53
Ting Kok Road, Tai Po, China (Hong Kong)
Tel.: (852) 26657131
Testing & Calibration Services
N.A.I.C.S.: 541380

**CHINA RESOURCES DEVEL-
OPMENT INC.**
1402 China Resources Bldg, Wan-
chai, China (Hong Kong)
Tel.: (852) 25042333 Ky
Web Site:
http://www.sscmandarin.com
Year Founded: 2010
Sales Range: $25-49.9 Million
Emp.: 4
Investment Services
N.A.I.C.S.: 523999
Xiaona Ma (VP-Bus Dev, Asst Treas
& Asst Sec)

**CHINA RESOURCES DOUBLE-
CRANE PHARMACEUTICAL
CO., LTD.**
No 1 Lizhe East 2nd Road Wangjing,
Chaoyang District, Beijing, 100102,
China
Tel.: (86) 1064742227
Web Site: https://www.dcpc.com
Year Founded: 1939
600062—(SHG)
Rev.: $1,326,348,312
Assets: $2,033,348,153
Liabilities: $526,905,896
Net Worth: $1,506,442,256
Earnings: $163,376,404
Emp.: 12,000
Fiscal Year-end: 12/31/22
Pharmaceutical Product Mfr & Distr
N.A.I.C.S.: 325412
Xin Li (Chm & Pres)

**CHINA RESOURCES MEDICAL
HOLDINGS CO., LTD.**
41/F China Resources Building, 26
Harbour Road, Wanchai, China
(Hong Kong)
Tel.: (852) 2593 7782 Ky
Web Site: http://www.phg.com.cn
Year Founded: 2013
1515—(HKG)
Rev.: $421,427,087
Assets: $1,373,250,800
Liabilities: $401,829,842
Net Worth: $971,420,957
Earnings: $49,076,380
Emp.: 4,903
Fiscal Year-end: 12/31/20
Healtcare Services
N.A.I.C.S.: 622110
Libing Cheng (CEO)

**CHINA RESOURCES MIXC
LIFESTYLE SERVICES LIM-
ITED**
30/F China Resources Land Building
Tower B No 9668 Shennan Avenue,
Nanshan District, Shenzhen, China
Tel.: (86) 28772330 Ky
Web Site:
https://www.crmixclifestyle.com.cn
Year Founded: 1994
1209—(HKG)
Rev.: $2,044,604,564
Assets: $3,846,848,970
Liabilities: $1,626,527,470
Net Worth: $2,220,321,500
Earnings: $407,432,432
Emp.: 40,977
Fiscal Year-end: 12/31/23

Property Management Services
N.A.I.C.S.: 531311

**CHINA RESOURCES SANJIU
MEDICAL & PHARMACEUTI-
CAL CO., LTD.**
No 1 Guanqing Road Guanlan Hight-
ech Park Guanhu Street, Longhua
District, Shenzhen, 518110, Guang-
dong, China
Tel.: (86) 75583360999
Web Site: https://www.999.com.cn
000999—(SSE)
Rev.: $2,538,356,184
Assets: $3,808,038,312
Liabilities: $1,346,347,548
Net Worth: $2,461,690,764
Earnings: $343,811,520
Fiscal Year-end: 12/31/22
Pharmaceuticals Product Mfr
N.A.I.C.S.: 325412
Huawei Qiu (Pres)

Subsidiaries:

Kunming Shenghuo Pharmaceutical
(Group) Co., Ltd., (1)
No 2 Jing You Road Kunming National
Economy & Technology Developing, Kun-
ming, 650217, China (100%)
Tel.: (86) 87167282619
Web Site: http://www.shenghuo.com.cn
Pharmaceuticals Mfr
N.A.I.C.S.: 325412

CHINA RISUN GROUP LTD.
Building 4 Section 5 188 Western
Road of South Loop 4 ABP Area,
Fengtai District, Beijing, 100070,
China
Tel.: (86) 1063701616
Web Site: http://www.risun.com
Year Founded: 1995
1907—(HKG)
Rev.: $3,031,239,320
Assets: $3,709,924,994
Liabilities: $2,441,897,291
Net Worth: $1,268,027,704
Earnings: $260,595,349
Emp.: 4,407
Fiscal Year-end: 12/31/20
Coal Product Mfr
N.A.I.C.S.: 324199
Zhang Yingwei (Exec Dir)

CHINA RITAR POWER CORP.
Room 405 Tower C Huahan Building
16 Langshan Road, North High-Tech
Indus Park, Nanshan District, Shen-
zhen, 518057, China
Tel.: (86) 75583475380 NV
Web Site: http://www.ritarpower.com
Sales Range: $75-99.9 Million
Emp.: 1,700
Lead Acid Battery Mfr
N.A.I.C.S.: 335910
Jiada Hu (Pres)

**CHINA RONGZHONG FINAN-
CIAL HOLDINGS CO. LTD.**
Room 1306 13/F Tai Yau Building No
181 Johnston Road, Wanchai, China
(Hong Kong)
Tel.: (852) 28992682 Ky
Web Site: http://www.chinarzfh.com
Year Founded: 2008
3963—(HKG)
Rev.: $2,040,593
Assets: $109,241,804
Liabilities: $123,428,314
Net Worth: ($14,186,510)
Earnings: ($15,655,979)
Emp.: 23
Fiscal Year-end: 03/31/21
Holding Company
N.A.I.C.S.: 551112
Emilie Hoi Yan Wong (CEO)

**CHINA RUIFENG RENEWABLE
ENERGY HOLDINGS LIMITED**
Room 1801 18/F Great Eagle Centre
No 23 Harbour Road, Wanchai,
China (Hong Kong)
Tel.: (852) 25985188 Ky
Web Site: http://www.c-ruifeng.com
0527—(HKG)
Rev.: $53,072,097
Assets: $474,765,156
Liabilities: $377,749,060
Net Worth: $97,016,096
Earnings: ($31,250,703)
Emp.: 125
Fiscal Year-end: 12/31/20
Wind Power Generation Services
N.A.I.C.S.: 221115
Zhixiang Zhang (CEO)

Subsidiaries:

Hebei Hongsong Wind Power Co.,
Ltd. (1)
173 Wulie Road, Chengde, Hebei, China
Tel.: (86) 3142385122
Web Site: http://www.hsfd.net
Wind Power Services
N.A.I.C.S.: 221115

**CHINA RUITAI INTERNA-
TIONAL HOLDINGS CO., LTD.**
Wenyang Town, Feicheng, 271603,
Shandong, China
Tel.: (86) 538 3850 703 DE
Web Site: http://www.rutocel.com
Sales Range: $25-49.9 Million
Emp.: 530
Chemical Products Mfr
N.A.I.C.S.: 325998
Dian Min Ma (Chm, CEO & Sec)

CHINA RUNJI CEMENT, INC.
Xian Zhong, Han Shan County, Hefei,
23181, China
Tel.: (86) 5654219871 DE
CRJI—(OTCIQ)
Sales Range: Less than $1 Million
Construction Materials Distr
N.A.I.C.S.: 423390
Xinshui Xuan (Chm, Pres & CEO)

**CHINA RUYI HOLDINGS LIM-
ITED**
23rd Floor China Evergrande Centre
38 Gloucester Road, Wanchai, China
(Hong Kong)
Tel.: (852) 21521621 BM
Web Site: http://www.htmimi.com
0136—(HKG)
Rev.: $185,317,891
Assets: $1,855,943,248
Liabilities: $736,192,735
Net Worth: $1,119,750,512
Earnings: $110,572,301
Emp.: 374
Fiscal Year-end: 12/31/22
Investment Management Service
N.A.I.C.S.: 523940

Subsidiaries:

Sun Materials Technology Co.,
Ltd. (1)
2F No 12 Ln 181 Sec 2 Jiuzong Rd, Neihu
Dist, Taipei, 114709, Taiwan
Tel.: (886) 226579077
Semiconductor Equipment Mfr
N.A.I.C.S.: 334413

**CHINA SAFTOWER INTERNA-
TIONAL HOLDING GROUP
LIMITED**
9 Huaide Road Economic & Technical
Development Zone, Guanghan, Sich-
uan, China
Tel.: (86) 8393308536 Ky
Web Site: http://www.saftower.com
Year Founded: 2004

8623—(HKG)
Holding Company
N.A.I.C.S.: 551112
Fei Dang (Chm & CEO)

**CHINA SAITE GROUP COM-
PANY LIMITED**
Unit 6105 61/F The Center 99
Queens Road, Central, China (Hong
Kong)
Tel.: (852) 2126 7434 Ky
Web Site:
http://www.chinasaite.com.cn
Year Founded: 1998
Rev.: $218,275,606
Assets: $481,722,286
Liabilities: $98,987,328
Net Worth: $382,734,959
Earnings: $20,210,955
Emp.: 591
Fiscal Year-end: 12/31/18
Steel Structure Construction
N.A.I.C.S.: 238120
Jianqiang Jiang (Founder & Chm)

**CHINA SANDI HOLDINGS LIM-
ITED**
Room 3405 34/F China Merchant
Tower, Shun Tak Center Sheung
Wan, Hong Kong, China (Hong Kong)
Tel.: (852) 2 587 7786
Web Site:
http://www.chinasandi.com.cn
0910—(HKG)
Rev.: $448,530,548
Assets: $4,594,568,421
Liabilities: $3,812,330,099
Net Worth: $782,238,322
Earnings: $31,472,092
Emp.: 490
Fiscal Year-end: 12/31/21
Forestry Business Services
N.A.I.C.S.: 115310
Jiadi Guo (Chm)

Subsidiaries:

Yunnan ShenYu New Energy Com-
pany Limited (1)
Building No 8 Floor 9 Hongxing Interna-
tional Plaza Guangfu Rd, Kunming, 650051,
Yunnan, China
Tel.: (86) 871 63131938
Web Site: http://www.syxny.cn
Biodiesel Fuel Research
N.A.I.C.S.: 221112
Gouging Ping Pou (Gen Mgr)

**CHINA SANJIANG FINE
CHEMICALS COMPANY LIM-
ITED**
Pinghai Road, Jiaxing, Zhejiang,
China
Tel.: (86) 57385286861 Ky
Web Site:
http://www.chinasanjiang.com
2198—(HKG)
Rev.: $1,275,123,318
Assets: $1,688,168,439
Liabilities: $954,033,461
Net Worth: $734,134,978
Earnings: $186,027,122
Emp.: 1,037
Fiscal Year-end: 12/31/20
Chemicals Mfr
N.A.I.C.S.: 325998
Jianzhong Guan (Co-Founder &
Chm)

**CHINA SCE GROUP HOLD-
INGS LIMITED**
No 2 Lane 1688 Shenchang Road,
Minhang District, Shanghai, China
Tel.: (86) 02152636666 Ky
Web Site: http://www.sce-re.com
Year Founded: 1987
1966—(HKG)
Rev.: $4,990,448,812

China SCE Group Holdings Limited—(Continued)

Assets: $26,139,835,441
Liabilities: $20,141,263,450
Net Worth: $5,998,571,991
Earnings: $681,114,359
Emp.: 9,414
Fiscal Year-end: 12/31/20
Holding Company; Residential Property Developer; Construction Machinery & Electric Power Equipment Mfr & Sales
N.A.I.C.S.: 551112
Chiu Yeung Wong (Co-Founder & Chm)

CHINA SCIENCE PUBLISHING & MEDIA LTD.

16 Donghuangchenggen North Street, Beijing, 100717, China
Tel.: (86) 1064010643
Web Site: https://www.cspm.com.cn
Year Founded: 1954
601858—(SHG)
Rev.: $380,340,315
Assets: $953,110,932
Liabilities: $267,098,027
Net Worth: $686,012,905
Earnings: $65,806,182
Fiscal Year-end: 12/31/22
Books Publishing Services
N.A.I.C.S.: 513130
Hu Huaqiang (Chm)

Subsidiaries:

Beijing Zhongke I/E Company Ltd. (1)
Room 801 Building B 8th Floor Huangcheng International Building, No 138 Andingmenwai Street Dongcheng District, Beijing, 100011, China
Tel.: (86) 1084039343
Web Site: https://bjzhongke.com.cn
Electronic Equipment Import Services
N.A.I.C.S.: 532210

CHINA SECURITY & SURVEILLANCE TECHNOLOGY, INC.

13/F Shenzhen Special Zone Press Tower, Shennan Road, Shenzhen, 518034, Futian, China
Tel.: (86) 755 8351 0888   DE
Web Site: http://www.csst.com
Sales Range: $650-699.9 Million
Emp.: 3,500
Security & Surveillance Solutions
N.A.I.C.S.: 561621
Guoshen Tu (Chm & CEO)

Subsidiaries:

Changzhou Minking Electronics Co., Ltd. (1)
No 65-12 Xinggang Road Zhonglou Economic Development Zone, Changzhou, 213000, Jiangsu, China
Tel.: (86) 519 86666112
Web Site: http://www.minking.cc
Sales Range: $100-124.9 Million
Emp.: 300
Surveillance Equipment Mfr
N.A.I.C.S.: 334419

China Security & Surveillance Distribution (PRC), Inc (1)
Building 6th Tong Fuyu, Gongming Town, 518107, Shenzhen, China
Tel.: (86) 755 33265722
Security & Surveillance Equipment Distr
N.A.I.C.S.: 423690

China Security & Surveillance Manufacturing (PRC), Inc. (1)
Floor 1 Sector 6 Tong Fu Yu CSST Science & Tech Park, Guang Ming New District, Shenzhen, China
Tel.: (86) 75533265694
Web Site: http://www.hts.cn
Surveillance Equipment Mfr
N.A.I.C.S.: 334419

Guangdong Stonesonic Digital Technique Co., Ltd. (1)
Stonesonic Digital Zone North Chaozhou Avenue, Chaozhou, 521000, China
Tel.: (86) 7682802892
Web Site: http://www.stonesonic.com
Sales Range: $100-124.9 Million
Emp.: 300
Surveillance Systems Mfr
N.A.I.C.S.: 334419
Lzxiu Fang (Gen Mgr)

Shenzhen Coson Electronic Co. Ltd. (1)
01 17th Floor Yinglong Building 6025 Shennan Mid Road, Shenzhen, 518040, China
Tel.: (86) 755 33358689
Web Site: http://www.coson.com
Sales Range: $50-74.9 Million
Emp.: 250
Security Equipment Mfr
N.A.I.C.S.: 334419

Shenzhen Longhorn Security Technology Co., Ltd. (1)
The 4th Building New and High Technology Industrial Park, Guangming Wandaiheng Baoan, Shenzhen, 518106, China
Tel.: (86) 75533265561
Web Site: http://www.securitychina.com.cn
Sales Range: $200-249.9 Million
Emp.: 600
Security Device Mfr
N.A.I.C.S.: 334419
Helen Peng (Mgr)

CHINA SECURITY CO., LTD.

Building 5 Huazhong Xiaogui Mountain Financial Culture Park, 203 Zisha Road Wuchang District, Wuhan, 430000, Hubei, China
Tel.: (86) 2161070029
Web Site: https://www.600654.com
Year Founded: 1987
600654—(SHG)
Rev.: $356,931,072
Assets: $605,714,368
Liabilities: $400,743,860
Net Worth: $204,970,508
Earnings: ($47,222,515)
Emp.: 11,000
Fiscal Year-end: 12/31/22
Security Systems & Security Products Mfr
N.A.I.C.S.: 561621
Wu Bowen (Chm)

Subsidiaries:

Australian Security Group Pty Ltd. (1)
11 Compark Circuit, Mulgrave, 3170, VIC, Australia
Tel.: (61) 385278888
Web Site: buvm
Smart Healthcare & Cyber Security Services
N.A.I.C.S.: 561621

Changzhou Mingjing IoT Sensing Co., Ltd. (1)
No 65-12 Xinggang Road Zhonglou Economic Development Zone, Changzhou, 213000, Jiangsu, China
Tel.: (86) 51986699912
Web Site: https://www.minking.cc
Video Storage & Platform Software Services
N.A.I.C.S.: 513210

China Security & Fire IOT Sensing (Shenzhen) Co., Ltd. (1)
The 4th Building WanDaiHeng Technology Industrial Park Gongchang Road, Guangming District, Shenzhen, China
Tel.: (86) 7553 326 5055
Web Site: https://www.ihorn-tech.com
Communication Equipment Mfr & Distr
N.A.I.C.S.: 334290

China Security &Fire Xulong Electronic & Technology Co., Ltd. (1)
Room 705 D Tower No 1 of First Zhangba Road, Huiqin International Business Center High-tech District, Xi'an, 710065, China
Tel.: (86) 298 825 9898
Intelligent Security Product Mfr

N.A.I.C.S.: 334290

Guardforce (Macau) Limited (1)
Av Venceslau De Morais Edf Ind Keck Seng Fase III 2N, Macau, China (Macau)
Tel.: (853) 2 848 1236
Emp.: 600
Security Services
N.A.I.C.S.: 561612

Guardforce Limited (1)
1/F Guardforce Center 3 Hok Yuen Street East, Hung Hom, Kowloon, China (Hong Kong)
Tel.: (852) 2 765 7654
Web Site: https://www.guardforce.com.hk
Emp.: 1,400
Security Services
N.A.I.C.S.: 561612

Hong Kong Wei (1)
1st Floor Wei On Centre, 3 Hok Yuen East Street Hung Hom, Kowloon, China (Hong Kong)
Tel.: (852) 27657654
Information Technology Services
N.A.I.C.S.: 541519

Jiangsu Zhongke Intelligent System Co., Ltd. (1)
No 336 Labor Road, Suzhou, 215004, China
Tel.: (86) 51268365923
Web Site: https://www.scsic.cn
Construction & Maintenance Services
N.A.I.C.S.: 212321

Macau Wei An Co., Ltd. (1)
Block N 2nd Floor Phase 3, Industrial Building Muras Avenue, Macau, China (Macau)
Tel.: (853) 28481236
Information Technology Services
N.A.I.C.S.: 541519

Shanghai Hu Gong Auto-electric Co., Ltd. (1)
1288 Xie Chun Rd Huangdu Industry Zone, Jiading, Shanghai, 201804, China
Tel.: (86) 21 69592666
Web Site: http://www.hg-china.com
Motor Vehicle Electronic Component Mfr
N.A.I.C.S.: 336320

Shanghai Qingtian Electronic Technology Co., Ltd. (1)
7th Floor No 318 Wuning South Road, Jing an District, Shanghai, 200042, China
Tel.: (86) 2162560980
Web Site: https://www.ksetg.com
Digital Software Research & Consulting Services
N.A.I.C.S.: 541512

Shenzhen Coson Technology Co., Ltd. (1)
4th Floor Building 5 Almes Robot Base, Guangming District, Shenzhen, China
Tel.: (86) 7553 326 5777
Web Site: https://www.coson.com
Security System Services
N.A.I.C.S.: 561621

Shenzhen Haoen Safety Technology Co., Ltd. (1)
Building 4 & Building 5 first floor, Guangming High tech Industrial Park Wandaiheng Guangming New District, Shenzhen, China
Tel.: (86) 75533265555
Smart Healthcare & Cyber Security Services
N.A.I.C.S.: 561621

Shenzhen Kesong Technology Co., Ltd. (1)
Building 4 Wandaiheng High-tech Industrial Park, Guangming New District, Shenzhen, China
Tel.: (86) 75533265777
Web Site: https://www.coson.com
Access Control System Mfr
N.A.I.C.S.: 333921

Shenzhen Weida Medical System Engineering Co., Ltd. (1)
12 F South Building of The Cangsong Building The Sixth Road, Shatou Street Futian District, Shenzhen, China
Tel.: (86) 75586660022
Smart Healthcare & Cyber Security Services

N.A.I.C.S.: 561621

Thailand Wei An Co., Ltd. (1)
1780 Teo Hong Bangna Building Bangna-Trad Road, Bangna, Bangkok, 10260, Thailand
Tel.: (66) 27467000
System Integration Services
N.A.I.C.S.: 541512

Zhejiang Huahe Wanrun Information Technology Co., Ltd. (1)
25F Building A Chengnan Business Building, No 115 Huifeng West Road, Yinzhou District, Ningbo, 315000, Zhejiang, China
Tel.: (86) 57487171269
Web Site: https://www.hirun.net.cn
Emp.: 130
Software Development Services
N.A.I.C.S.: 541511

Zhong'an Xiaoxulong Electronic Technology Co., Ltd. (1)
705 Building IBC-D Huixin No 1, Zhangbayi Road High tech Zone, Xi'an, 710065, China
Tel.: (86) 2988259898
Information Technology Services
N.A.I.C.S.: 541519

Zhuhai Luckystar Electronics Co., Ltd. (1)
Number 20 Second Road Pingbei Nanping Scientific Zone, Zhuhai, 519060, China
Tel.: (86) 75 6868 2088
Electronic Components Mfr
N.A.I.C.S.: 336320

CHINA SENIOR LIVING INDUSTRY INTERNATIONAL HOLDING CORPORATION

No 28 Xi Hua South Rd High-tech Zone, Xianyang, Shaan'xi, China
Tel.: (86) 2933257666   NV
Year Founded: 1986
CHYL—(OTCIQ)
Sales Range: Less than $1 Million
Emp.: 55
Senior Living Facilities Management Services
N.A.I.C.S.: 623312
Zhongyang Shang (Chm & Pres)

CHINA SHANSHUI CEMENT GROUP LTD.

Sunnsy Industrial Park Gushan Town, Changqing District, Jinan, 250307, Shandong, China
Tel.: (86) 852 2525 7918
Web Site: http://www.shanshuigroup.com
Sales Range: $1-4.9 Billion
Emp.: 21,759
Cement Mfr & Sales
N.A.I.C.S.: 327310
Heping Li (CEO)

Subsidiaries:

Shandong Shanshui Cement Group Ltd. (SUNNSY) (1)
Shanshui Industrial Park Gushan Town, Jinan, 250307, P.C., China
Tel.: (86) 531 8207 0036
Web Site: http://en.shanshuigroup.com
Cement Mfr & Distr
N.A.I.C.S.: 327310
Zhangli Chang (Chm)

Yantai Shanshui Cement Co.,Ltd (1)
Qixia Economic Dev Zone, Yantai, 264000, Shandong, China
Tel.: (86) 5355571036
Cement Mfr
N.A.I.C.S.: 327310

Zibo Shuangfeng Shanshui Cement Co., Ltd. (1)
Shuanggou Town Zichuan District, Zibo, China
Tel.: (86) 53382070036
Cement Plant Construction Services
N.A.I.C.S.: 236210

CHINA SHENGDA PACKAGING GROUP INC.

No 2 Beitang Road Xiaoshan Economic & Technological Development Zone, Hangzhou, 311215, Zhejiang, China
Tel.: (86) 571 82838805　　NV
Year Founded: 2007
Sales Range: $150-199.9 Million
Corrugated Paperboards, Flexo-Printed & Color-Printed Paper Cartons Mfr
N.A.I.C.S.: 322211
Daliang Teng *(CEO)*

Subsidiaries:

Zhejiang Great Shengda Packaging Co., Ltd.　　　　　　　　　(1)
No 2 Beitang Road Xiaoshan Economic and Technological Development Zone, Hangzhou, 311215, China
Tel.: (86) 57182838411
Corrugated & Solid Fiber Box Mfr
N.A.I.C.S.: 322211

CHINA SHENGHAI GROUP LIMITED

5/F Block 5 Huli Industrial Park Meixi Road, Tongan District, Xiamen, Fujian, China
Tel.: (86) 5927116336　　Ky
Web Site: http://www.xmwofan.com
Year Founded: 2005
1676—(HKG)
Rev.: $24,930,025
Assets: $76,573,132
Liabilities: $8,177,584
Net Worth: $68,395,549
Earnings: ($4,941,789)
Emp.: 486
Fiscal Year-end: 12/31/20
Food Product Mfr & Distr
N.A.I.C.S.: 311710
Rongru Liu *(Founder, Co-Chm & CEO)*

CHINA SHENGHUO PHARMACEUTICAL HOLDINGS, INC.

Kunming National Economy & Technology Dev District, No 2 Jing You Road, Kunming, 650217, China
Tel.: (86) 871 728 2628　　DE
Sales Range: $25-49.9 Million
Emp.: 416
Pharmaceuticals Mfr
N.A.I.C.S.: 325412
Gui Hua Lan *(Chm & CEO)*

CHINA SHENGMU ORGANIC MILK LIMITED

Unit 1303 13/F Hua Fu Commercial Building 111 Queens Road West, Hong Kong, China (Hong Kong)
Tel.: (852) 37582932　　Ky
Web Site: http://www.youjimilk.com
1432—(HKG)
Rev.: $407,664,692
Assets: $1,030,371,875
Liabilities: $506,466,297
Net Worth: $523,905,578
Earnings: $70,625,060
Emp.: 2,589
Fiscal Year-end: 12/31/20
Dairy Farming Services
N.A.I.C.S.: 112120
Tongshan Yao *(Founder)*

CHINA SHENSHAN ORCHARD HOLDINGS CO., LTD.

Guanghua RD Chi Ma Port Industrial Zone, Jinshui District, Chibi, Hubei, China
Tel.: (86) 37188886800　　BM
Web Site: https://www.ddhlimited.com
Year Founded: 2008
BKV—(SES)
Rev.: $17,363,443

Assets: $195,474,051
Liabilities: $50,577,685
Net Worth: $144,896,366
Earnings: ($11,327,428)
Emp.: 743
Fiscal Year-end: 06/30/20
Distilled Wine Producer & Marketer
N.A.I.C.S.: 312130

CHINA SHESAYS MEDICAL COSMETOLOGY INC.

New No 83 Xinnan Road, Wuhou District, Chengdu, 610041, Sichuan, China
Tel.: (86) 2885482277　　NV
Year Founded: 2005
CSAY—(OTCIQ)
Sales Range: $10-24.9 Million
Professional Medical Beauty, Cosmetic Surgery & Cosmetic Dentistry Services
N.A.I.C.S.: 622110
Yixiang Zhang *(Chm, CEO & CFO)*

CHINA SHINEWAY PHARMACEUTICAL GROUP LTD.

Suite 3109 31/F Central Plaza 18 Harbour Road, Wanchai, China (Hong Kong)
Tel.: (852) 35210816
Web Site:
http://www.shineway.com.hk
2877—(OTCIQ)
Rev.: $546,997,674
Assets: $1,139,768,083
Liabilities: $256,055,466
Net Worth: $883,712,616
Earnings: $100,073,798
Emp.: 4,131
Fiscal Year-end: 12/31/22
Mfr & Trading Of Chinese Medicines
N.A.I.C.S.: 524114
Randy King Kuen Hung *(Dir-IR)*

CHINA SHIPBUILDING INDUSTRY COMPANY LIMITED

No 72 Kunming Hunan Road, Haidian District, Beijing, 100097, China
Tel.: (86) 1088010555
Web Site: https://www.csic.com.cn
Year Founded: 1999
601989—(CHIN)
Rev.: $6,199,352,832
Assets: $26,521,191,380
Liabilities: $14,715,721,220
Net Worth: $11,805,470,160
Earnings: ($317,415,520)
Emp.: 150,000
Fiscal Year-end: 12/31/22
Ship Repairer, Refitter & Mfr; Ship Equipment & Engineering Services
N.A.I.C.S.: 336611
Wang Yongliang *(Chm)*

Subsidiaries:

Afai Southern Shipyard (Panyu Guangzhou) Ltd.　　　　　　(1)
No 40 Xining Road Luopu Street, Panyu District, Guangzhou, 511431, Guangdong, China　　　　　　　　　　　(51%)
Tel.: (86) 20 84581902
Web Site: http://www.afaisouth.com
Emp.: 290
Aluminum Alloy Mfr & Distr
N.A.I.C.S.: 331314

China Ship Design & Research Centre Co., Ltd.　　　　　　(1)
10th Floor Tower C New Logo International Building No A 18, Zhongguancun South Street Haidian District, Beijing, 100081, China
Tel.: (86) 1062100550
Web Site: http://www.csdc.csic.com.cn
Ship Building & Repairing Services
N.A.I.C.S.: 336611

China Shipbuilding Mansion Science Research Center Company

Limited　　　　　　　　　　(1)
No 222 Shanshui East Road, Wuxi, Jiangsu, China
Tel.: (86) 501085558639
Web Site: https://www.cssrc.com
Emp.: 1,800
Marine Cargo Mfr
N.A.I.C.S.: 336611

Dalian Marine Diesel Co., Ltd.　(1)
No 1-1 Haifang Street, Xigang District, Dalian, 116021, Liaoning, China
Tel.: (86) 41184417273
Web Site: http://www.dmd.com.cn
Ship Building & Repairing Services
N.A.I.C.S.: 336611

Dalian Shipbuilding Industry Co., Ltd.　　　　　　　　　(1)
1 Yanhai Street, Dalian, Liaoning, China
Tel.: (86) 41184482888
Web Site: https://www.dsic.cn
Ship Building & Repairing Services
N.A.I.C.S.: 336611

Qingdao Beihai Shipbuilding Heavy Industry Co., Ltd.　　　　(1)
No 369 Lijiang East Rd, Economic Technical Development Zone, Qingdao, 266520, China
Tel.: (86) 53286756187
Web Site: https://www.bhshipyard.com.cn
Ship Building & Repairing Services
N.A.I.C.S.: 336611

Shanhaiguan Shipbuilding Industry Co., Ltd.　　　　　　(1)
No 1 of Shipyard Road, Economic and Technological Development Area, Qinhuangdao, 066206, Hebei, China
Tel.: (86) 3355088528
Web Site: https://www.shgsic.com
Ship Building & Repairing Services
N.A.I.C.S.: 336611
Yao Hong Shan *(Pres)*

Tianjin Xingang Shipbuilding Heavy Industry Co., Ltd.　　　　(1)
No 2999 Huanghe Street, Harbor Economic Area Binhai New Area, Tianjin, 300452, China
Tel.: (86) 2225310610
Web Site: http://www.xgsic.com.cn
Ship Building & Repairing Services
N.A.I.C.S.: 336611

Wuchang Shipbuilding Industry Co., Ltd.　　　　　　　　(1)
No 66 Xinggu Avenue Shuangliu Street, Xinzhou District, Wuhan, 430416, Hubei, China
Tel.: (86) 2768887022
Web Site: https://www.wuchuan.com.cn
Ship Building & Repairing Services
N.A.I.C.S.: 336611

CHINA SHIPBUILDING INDUSTRY GROUP POWER CO., LTD.

No 72 Kunming Hunan Road, Haidian District, Beijing, 100097, Hebei, China
Tel.: (86) 1088010590
Web Site: http://www.sail.com.cn
Year Founded: 2000
600482—(SHG)
Rev.: $5,377,044,353
Assets: $12,055,838,095
Liabilities: $5,645,857,450
Net Worth: $6,409,980,645
Earnings: $46,709,269
Emp.: 22,000
Fiscal Year-end: 12/31/22
Storage Battery Mfr & Distr
N.A.I.C.S.: 335910
Hongguang Zhu *(VP & Deputy Gen Mgr)*

CHINA SHOUGUAN INVESTMENT HOLDING GROUP CORPORATION

Suite 2606 Office Building Great China International Exchange Square, North Fuhua Road Futian

District, Shenzhen, China
Tel.: (86) 75582520008　　NV
Web Site:
http://www.chinashouguan.com
Year Founded: 2010
CHSO—(OTCIQ)
Gold Mining Services
N.A.I.C.S.: 212220
Feize Zhang *(CEO)*

CHINA SHUIFA SINGYES ENERGY HOLDINGS LIMITED

No 8 Hongda Road Nanping Technology Park, Zhuhai, China
Tel.: (86) 7566916369
Web Site:
http://www.singyessolar.com
0750—(OTCIQ)
Rev.: $827,487,057
Assets: $2,042,344,456
Liabilities: $1,355,369,354
Net Worth: $686,975,102
Earnings: $49,202,779
Emp.: 1,400
Fiscal Year-end: 12/31/20
Holding Company; Curtain Walls Designer, Mfr, Supplier & Installer
N.A.I.C.S.: 551112
Qingtao Zheng *(Chm)*

Subsidiaries:

Zhuhai Singyes Curtain Wall Engineering Co., Ltd　　　　　(1)
Zhuhai Singyes Curtain Wall Engineering Co., Ltd, Nanping Technology Park, Zhuhai, 519060, Guangdong, China
Tel.: (86) 7568682222
Curtain Walls Design & Mfr
N.A.I.C.S.: 322220

Zhuhai Singyes Renewable Energy Technology Co., Ltd.　　(1)
No 8 Hongda Rd, Nanping Technology Park, Zhuhai, Guangdong, China
Tel.: (86) 7568911890
Curtain Walls Design & Mfr
N.A.I.C.S.: 322220

CHINA SILVER GROUP LIMITED

Unit 1416 China Merchants Tower Shun Tak Centre, Connaught Road Central Sheung Wan, Central, 168-200, China (Hong Kong)
Tel.: (852) 31062608
Web Site: http://www.chinasilver.hk
Year Founded: 2002
815—(HKG)
Rev.: $729,176,949
Assets: $691,866,944
Liabilities: $133,151,747
Net Worth: $558,715,197
Earnings: $31,528,013
Emp.: 914
Fiscal Year-end: 12/31/20
Silver Ingot & Other Non-Ferrous Metal Products Mfr
N.A.I.C.S.: 332999
Wantian Chen *(Founder & Chm)*

Subsidiaries:

C SMall Group Limited　　　　(1)
Unit 1417 China Merchants Tower Shun Tak Centre, 168-200 Connaught Road Central, Sheung Wan, China (Hong Kong)
Tel.: (852) 3106 2608
Web Site: http://www.csmall.com
Rev.: $53,281,535
Assets: $241,961,795
Liabilities: $27,924,667
Net Worth: $214,037,128
Earnings: ($5,454,736)
Emp.: 204
Fiscal Year-end: 12/31/2020
Jewelry Product Retailer
N.A.I.C.S.: 423940
He Chen *(Chm & Co-CEO)*

CHINA SILVER TECHNOLOGY

CHINA SILVER TECHNOLOGY —(CONTINUED)

HOLDINGS LIMITED

Unit E 30/F Tower B Billion Centre, 1
Wang Kwong Road Kowloon Bay,
Kowloon, China (Hong Kong)
Tel.: (852) 24131189 — Ky
Web Site: http://www.tatchun.com
0515—(HKG)
Rev.: $33,172,823
Assets: $89,935,950
Liabilities: $87,539,715
Net Worth: $2,396,235
Earnings: ($5,573,663)
Emp.: 367
Fiscal Year-end: 12/31/22
PCB Business & LED Lighting Mfr
N.A.I.C.S.: 335132
Ming Xu *(CEO)*

Subsidiaries:

Tat Chun Printed Circuit Board Company Limited — (1)
31F Aitken Vanson Ctr No 61 Hoi Yuen Rd,
Kwun Tong, Kowloon, China (Hong Kong)
Tel.: (852) 24131189
Web Site: http://www.tatchunpcb.com.hk
Emp.: 100
Printed Circuit Board Mfr
N.A.I.C.S.: 334412

Zhongshan Tat Chun Printed Circuit
Board Company Limited — (1)
No 91 Gaoping Ave Gaoping Indus Zone,
Sanjiao Town, Zhongshan, 528445, Guangdong, China
Tel.: (86) 76085546388
Printed Circuit Board Mfr
N.A.I.C.S.: 334412

CHINA SINGYES NEW MATERIALS HOLDINGS LIMITED

No 9 Jinzhu Road Technology Innovation Coast High-tech, Development
Zone Jinding Town, Zhuhai, 519000,
Guangdong, China
Tel.: (86) 7566916205 — BM
Web Site: http://www.syeamt.com
Year Founded: 2010
8073—(HKG)
Rev.: $15,402,048
Assets: $48,423,093
Liabilities: $11,430,232
Net Worth: $36,992,861
Earnings: $9,346
Emp.: 129
Fiscal Year-end: 12/31/20
Electronic Parts Mfr & Distr
N.A.I.C.S.: 334419
Hongwei Liu *(Co-Founder)*

Subsidiaries:

Zhuhai Singyes New Materials Technology Co. Ltd. — (1)
No 9 Jinzhu Road Science and Technology
Innovation Coast, High-tech Zone, Zhuhai,
519000, Guangdong, China
Tel.: (86) 4006023918
Web Site: https://www.syeamt.com
Electronic Components Mfr
N.A.I.C.S.: 334419

CHINA SINOSTAR GROUP COMPANY LIMITED

Suites 2602-2603 26/F Tower 1, The
Harbourfront 18 Tak Fung Street
Hunghom, Kowloon, China (Hong
Kong)
Tel.: (852) 2 286 0728
Web Site: http://www.00485.hk
0485—(HKG)
Rev.: $3,810,327
Assets: $50,653,671
Liabilities: $10,276,997
Net Worth: $40,376,673
Earnings: ($1,989,903)
Emp.: 21
Fiscal Year-end: 03/31/21

Holding Company; Electronic Products Mfr & Real Estate Investment
Services
N.A.I.C.S.: 551112

CHINA SKY CHEMICAL FIBRE CO., LTD.

Jiangnan Industrial Garden Licheng,
362000, Quanzhou, Fujian, China
Tel.: (86) 59522463111 — Ky
Year Founded: 2005
E90—(SES)
Textile & Garment Mfr
N.A.I.C.S.: 316990

CHINA SKY ONE MEDICAL, INC.

No 2158 North Xiang An Road, Song
Bei District, Harbin, 150001, China
Tel.: (86) 45187032617 — NV
Web Site: http://www.cski.com.cn
Year Founded: 1986
Sales Range: $125-149.9 Million
Emp.: 2,279
Pharmaceuticals Mfr
N.A.I.C.S.: 325412
Yan-Qing Liu *(Chm, Pres & CEO)*

Subsidiaries:

Harbin Tian Di Ren Medical Science
and Technology Company — (1)
Rm 1706 Diwang Bldg 30 Ganshui Rd,
Nangang Heilongjiang, 150090, Harbin,
China
Tel.: (86) 45153994064
Chinese Herbal Medicines Research & Development Services
N.A.I.C.S.: 541715

CHINA SKYRISE DIGITAL SERVICE INC.

Tel.: (86) 5386202306 — NV
Web Site:
http://www.chinaskyrise.com
Year Founded: 2006
CSKD—(OTCIQ)
Sales Range: $10-24.9 Million
Emp.: 145
Digital Residential Safety & Video
Surveillance Products
N.A.I.C.S.: 334310
Mingchun Zhou *(Pres & CEO)*

CHINA SLP FILTRATION TECHNOLOGY, INC.

Shishan Industrial Park, Nanhai District, Foshan, Guangdong, China
Tel.: (86) 75786683197 — DE
Web Site: http://www.silepu.com
Sales Range: $10-24.9 Million
Emp.: 176
Nonwoven Fabric Mfr
N.A.I.C.S.: 313230
Jie Li *(CEO)*

CHINA SMARTER ENERGY GROUP HOLDINGS LTD.

Room 3205-08 32/F Harbour Centre
25 Harbour Road, Wanchai, China
(Hong Kong)
Tel.: (852) 2823 5988 — BM
Web Site: http://www.cse1004.com
Rev.: $44,258,161
Assets: $666,623,211
Liabilities: $419,438,141
Net Worth: $247,185,070
Earnings: ($30,312,507)
Emp.: 48
Fiscal Year-end: 03/31/18
Investment Services in Fur, Mining &
Solar Energy Businesses
N.A.I.C.S.: 523999
Xu David Hua *(Chm)*

CHINA SMARTPAY GROUP HOLDINGS LIMITED

Room 3101 31/F Hong Kong Plaza
188 Connaught Road West, Hong
Kong, China (Hong Kong)
Tel.: (852) 25468808 — Ky
Web Site:
http://www.chinasmartpay.com
Year Founded: 2007
8325—(HKG)
Rev.: $6,776,057
Assets: $107,000,389
Liabilities: $83,309,988
Net Worth: $23,690,402
Earnings: ($15,125,614)
Emp.: 192
Fiscal Year-end: 03/31/21
Holding Company
N.A.I.C.S.: 551112
Song Xiangping *(Exec Dir)*

Subsidiaries:

Oriental City Group (Thailand) Company Limited — (1)
24/F TST Tower 21 Viphavadi-Rangsit
Road, Jomphol Jatujak, Bangkok, 10900,
Thailand
Tel.: (66) 2 273 8320
Web Site: https://www.ocgt.co.th
Financial Transaction Processing Services
N.A.I.C.S.: 522320

Oriental Payment Group Holdings
Ltd. — (1)
2606 West Tower Shun Tak Centre 200
Connaught Road Central, Hong Kong,
China (Hong Kong)
Tel.: (852) 3 582 3088
Web Site: http://www.ocg.com.hk
Rev.: $1,595,354
Assets: $10,662,390
Liabilities: $4,542,547
Net Worth: $6,119,843
Earnings: ($3,953,882)
Emp.: 29
Fiscal Year-end: 03/31/2021
Electronic Payment Services
N.A.I.C.S.: 522320
Chun Fai Yu *(Chm)*

CHINA SOAR INFORMATION TECHNOLOGY, INC.

Room 803 8/F K Wah Centre 191
Java Road, North Point, 02910,
China (Hong Kong)
Tel.: (852) 852 6688 3925 — DE
Year Founded: 2013
Rev.: $1
Assets: $1,227
Liabilities: $29,063
Net Worth: ($27,836)
Earnings: ($54,139)
Fiscal Year-end: 07/31/18
Mobile Internet Software Development Services
N.A.I.C.S.: 541511
Mu Chun Lin *(Pres, CEO, CFO, Treas & Sec)*

CHINA SOLAR & CLEAN ENERGY SOLUTIONS, INC.

3/F West Wing Dingheng Plaza, 45A
North Fengtai Road, Beijing, 100071,
China
Tel.: (86) 1063860500 — NV
Web Site: http://www.delisolar.com
CSOL—(OTCIQ)
Sales Range: $25-49.9 Million
Emp.: 700
Renewable Energy Services
N.A.I.C.S.: 221118
Deli Du *(Founder)*

Subsidiaries:

Beijing Ailiyang Solar Energy Technology Co. Ltd. — (1)
No 45 North Road, Fengtai, Beijing, China
Tel.: (86) 13311318578
Web Site: http://www.ailiyang.cn
Solar Heating Products Mfr
N.A.I.C.S.: 333414

Beijing Deli Solar Technology Development Co., Ltd. — (1)
28 Fengtai N Rd Fengtai, Beijing, China
Tel.: (86) 1063869399
Solar Energy Heating Products Mfr
N.A.I.C.S.: 333414

CHINA SOLAR ENERGY HOLDINGS LIMITED

Room 2502 25/F 148 Electric Road,
North Point, China (Hong Kong)
Tel.: (852) 31042820
Web Site: http://www.chinasolar-energy.com
Sales Range: $10-24.9 Million
Emp.: 114
Solar Cell Mfr
N.A.I.C.S.: 334413
Xin Ye Xie *(Exec Dir)*

Subsidiaries:

Terra Solar North America, Inc. — (1)
522 SW 5th Ave Ste 915, Portland, OR
97204
Tel.: (503) 227-2023
Photovoltaic Module Mfr
N.A.I.C.S.: 334413

CHINA SOUTH CITY HOLDINGS LIMITED

Suites 3306-08 33/F Tower 5 The
Gateway 15 Canton Road, Tsim Sha
Tsui, Kowloon, China (Hong Kong)
Tel.: (852) 31883118
Web Site:
https://www.chinasouthcity.com
Year Founded: 2002
1668—(HKG)
Rev.: $1,329,993,779
Assets: $16,043,489,948
Liabilities: $10,227,785,359
Net Worth: $5,815,704,589
Earnings: $97,911,814
Emp.: 2,816
Fiscal Year-end: 03/31/22
Large Scale Integrated Logistics &
Trade Centers Developer & Operator
N.A.I.C.S.: 236220
Chung Hing Cheng *(Co/Co-Founder, Co-Chm, Chm & Exec Dir)*

CHINA SOUTH INDUSTRIES GROUP CORPORATION

69 Zizhuyuan Road, Haidian District,
Beijing, China
Tel.: (86) 1068963980 — CN
Web Site: http://www.csgc.com.cn
Year Founded: 1999
Sales Range: $25-49.9 Billion
Automobile Mfr
N.A.I.C.S.: 336110
Bin Xu *(Pres)*

CHINA SOUTH PUBLISHING & MEDIA GROUP CO., LTD.

No 38 Yingpan East Road, Changsha, 410005, Hunan, China
Tel.: (86) 73184405077
Web Site: https://www.zncmjt.com
Year Founded: 2008
601098—(SHG)
Rev.: $1,750,031,932
Assets: $3,484,552,935
Liabilities: $1,315,778,902
Net Worth: $2,168,774,033
Earnings: $196,452,131
Fiscal Year-end: 12/31/22
Books Publishing Services
N.A.I.C.S.: 513130
Shuguang Gong *(Chm)*

Subsidiaries:

Hunan Children & Juvenile's Publishing House Co., Ltd. — (1)
No 89 Evening News Avenue, Changsha,
Hunan, China
Tel.: (86) 73182196320

Books Publishing Services
N.A.I.C.S.: 513130

Hunan Education Television Media Co., Ltd. (1)
The new Road 77, Yuhua District, Changsha, Hunan, China
Tel.: (86) 73185392288
Newspaper Publishing & Media Services
N.A.I.C.S.: 541890

Hunan Electronic & Audio-Visual Publishing House Co., Ltd. (1)
Camp Road on the 3rd, Changsha, Hunan, China
Tel.: (86) 73184456374
Audio & Video Publishing Services
N.A.I.C.S.: 512290

Hunan Literature & Art Publishing House Co., Ltd. (1)
508 East Second Ring Road Section, Yuhua District, Changsha, Hunan, China
Tel.: (86) 73185983077
Art Publishing Services
N.A.I.C.S.: 513120

Hunan People's Publishing House Co., Ltd. (1)
Publishing Building No 3 Yingpan East Road, Kaifu District, Changsha, Hunan, China
Tel.: (86) 73182683330
Book & Literature Publishing Services
N.A.I.C.S.: 513130

Hunan Publishing Investment Holding Group Financial Co., Ltd. (1)
3/F Electronic Building No 38 Yingpan East Road, Kaifu District, Changsha, Hunan, China
Tel.: (86) 73189937890
Investment Publication Services
N.A.I.C.S.: 523940

Hunan Science & Technology Press Co., Ltd. (1)
40 41f BOFU international financial center No 416 Section 1, Furong Middle Road Kaifu District, Changsha, Hunan, China
Tel.: (86) 73184375806
Web Site: https://www.hnstp.com
Books Publishing Services
N.A.I.C.S.: 513130

Hunan Tianwen Xinhua Printing Co., Ltd. (1)
No 8 Yinxing Road LeiFeng Street, Changsha, 410219, China
Tel.: (86) 73188387675
Emp.: 1,200
Books Publishing Services
N.A.I.C.S.: 513130
Tom Thong *(Mgr)*

Hunan Xiaoxiang Morning Herald Media Management Co., Ltd. (1)
No 258 Lushan South Road, Tianxin District, Changsha, Hunan, China
Tel.: (86) 73185015691
Newspaper Publishing Services
N.A.I.C.S.: 513110

Hunan Yuelu Publishing House Co., Ltd. (1)
No 47 Aimin Road Hexi, Changsha, Hunan, China
Tel.: (86) 73188884136
Books Publishing Services
N.A.I.C.S.: 513130

Tianwen Digital Media Technology (Beijing) Co., Ltd. (1)
Deshengmen Avenue 83 Desheng International Center Block B 5th Floor, Xicheng District, Beijing, China
Tel.: (86) 73188732836
Digital Media Services
N.A.I.C.S.: 541890

CHINA SOUTHERN AIRLINES CO., LTD.
No 68 Qixin Road, Baiyun District, Guangzhou, 510403, China
Tel.: (86) 2086122480
Web Site: https://www.csair.com
600029—(SHG)
Rev.: $22,143,470,315

Assets: $42,814,853,788
Liabilities: $35,615,446,389
Net Worth: $7,199,407,399
Earnings: $4,268,525,698
Emp.: 90,000
Fiscal Year-end: 12/31/23
Oil Transportation Services
N.A.I.C.S.: 481111
Zheng Rong Zhang *(Exec VP)*

Subsidiaries:

Chongqing Airlines Company Limited (1)
Jiangbei Airport Shuangfengqiao Street, Yubei District, Chongqing, China
Tel.: (86) 2367150023
Airline Transportation Services
N.A.I.C.S.: 481111

Guangzhou Baiyun International Logistic Company Limited (1)
Airport Logistics Zone West Side North Exit Avenue, Baiyun International Airport, Guangzhou, 510470, China
Tel.: (86) 2036062166
Web Site: http://www.airlog.cn
Oil Transportation Services
N.A.I.C.S.: 481112

Guangzhou Nanland Air Catering Company Limited (1)
Nanlian Catering Building Konggang 6th Road, Guangzhou Baiyun International Airport, Guangzhou, China
Tel.: (86) 86123218
Airline Catering Services
N.A.I.C.S.: 722310

Guizhou Airlines Company Limited (1)
No 1 Longdongbao Airport Road, Guiyang, Guizhou, China
Tel.: (86) 8515362032
Airline Transportation Services
N.A.I.C.S.: 481111

Shantou Airlines Company Limited (1)
8 Chunjiang Road Longsheng Industry Region, Shantou, China
Tel.: (86) 75488392699
Oil Transportation Services
N.A.I.C.S.: 481112

Xiamen Airlines Co., Ltd. (1)
321 Donghuang Road, Xiamen, 361000, Fujian, China (60%)
Tel.: (86) 5925739888
Web Site: https://www.xiamenair.com
Commercial Aviation Services
N.A.I.C.S.: 481111

Zhuhai Airlines Company Limited (1)
West of Jingshan Road, Jida, Zhuhai, China
Tel.: (86) 7566838687
Oil Transportation Services
N.A.I.C.S.: 481112

Zhuhai Xiang Yi Aviation Technology Company Limited (1)
No 32 Land, Free Trade Zone, Zhuhai, 519030, Guangdong, China
Tel.: (86) 7563213388
Web Site: http://www.zhftc.com
Flight Simulation Services
N.A.I.C.S.: 611512

CHINA SOUTHERN POWER GRID CO., LTD.
No 11 Kexiang Road Science City, Guangzhou, 510530, Guangdong, China
Tel.: (86) 2038121080
Web Site: http://www.eng.csg.cn
Year Founded: 2002
Sales Range: $25-49.9 Billion
Emp.: 130,000
Construction & Power Network Services
N.A.I.C.S.: 237130
Zhenping Meng *(Chm)*

Subsidiaries:

Guangzhou Power Supply Co., Ltd (1)

No 2 Nan Er Rd, Tianhe District, Guangzhou, 510620, Guangdong, China
Tel.: (86) 20 38122925
Web Site: http://www.guangzhou.csg.cn
Electric Power Transmission Services
N.A.I.C.S.: 221121

Hainan Power Grid Company (1)
No 34 Haifu Road, Haikou, 570203, China
Tel.: (86) 89865343312
Electric Power Generation
N.A.I.C.S.: 221122

CHINA SOUTHERN POWER GRID ENERGY EFFICIENCY & CLEAN ENERGY CO., LTD.
No 6 Huasui Road, Tianhe District, Guangzhou, 510623, Guangdong, China
Tel.: (86) 2038122705
Web Site: http://www.ny.csg.cn
Year Founded: 2010
003035—(SSE)
Rev.: $405,490,644
Assets: $2,157,532,416
Liabilities: $1,167,480,756
Net Worth: $990,051,660
Earnings: $77,704,380
Fiscal Year-end: 12/31/22
Energy Distribution Services
N.A.I.C.S.: 221122
Hua Qin *(Chm)*

CHINA SPACESAT CO., LTD.
Floor 12 Shenzhou Building Zhongguancun South Street, Haidian District, Beijing, 100081, China
Tel.: (86) 1068118118
Web Site:
https://www.spacesat.com.cn
Year Founded: 1997
600118—(SHG)
Rev.: $1,081,498,665
Assets: $2,006,919,239
Liabilities: $790,972,671
Net Worth: $1,215,946,569
Earnings: $35,734,700
Emp.: 3,000
Fiscal Year-end: 12/31/21
Satellite & Satellite Application System Mfr
N.A.I.C.S.: 334419
Ge Ge Yujun *(Pres)*

CHINA SPORTS INDUSTRY GROUP CO., LTD.
No 225 Chaowai Street, Chaoyang District, Beijing, 100020, China
Tel.: (86) 1085160999
Web Site: https://www.csig158.com
Year Founded: 1998
600158—(SHG)
Rev.: $232,122,343
Assets: $854,351,051
Liabilities: $311,944,753
Net Worth: $542,406,299
Earnings: $8,414,293
Fiscal Year-end: 12/31/21
Sports Real Estatte Management Services
N.A.I.C.S.: 711211
Single Iron *(Chm)*

Subsidiaries:

China Sports International Co., Ltd. (1)
Floor 4 No 5 Tiyuguan Road, Dongcheng District, Beijing, China
Tel.: (86) 106 711 2235
Web Site: https://www.chinasportscoltd.com
Sporting & Athletic Good Mfr
N.A.I.C.S.: 339920

China Sports Management Group Co., Ltd. (1)
NO 50 Tiantan East Road, Dongcheng District, Beijing, China
Tel.: (86) 106 710 0101
Web Site: www.csmg.com.cn

Sporting & Athletic Good Mfr
N.A.I.C.S.: 339920

CHINA SPORTS INTERNATIONAL LIMITED
Clarendon House 2 Church Street, Hamilton, HM 11, Bermuda
Tel.: (441) 295 5950
Web Site:
http://www.chinasportsintl.com
Rev.: $31,718,619
Assets: $81,884,232
Liabilities: $13,604,817
Net Worth: $68,279,415
Earnings: ($1,792,932)
Fiscal Year-end: 12/31/16
Sport Shoe Mfr
N.A.I.C.S.: 316210
Shaoxiong Lin *(Chm & CEO)*

CHINA STAR ENTERTAINMENT LIMITED
Unit 3409 Shun Tak Centre West Tower 168 200 Connaught Road, Central, China (Hong Kong)
Tel.: (852) 2 313 1888 BM
0326—(HKG)
Rev.: $479,419
Assets: $681,776,543
Liabilities: $286,584,918
Net Worth: $395,191,624
Earnings: ($20,187,305)
Emp.: 66
Fiscal Year-end: 12/31/21
Motion Picture Producer & Distr
N.A.I.C.S.: 512110
Wah Keung Heung *(Chm)*

Subsidiaries:

China Star Entertainment Holding Company (1)
Unit 3409 Shun Tak Centre West Tower 1682-200 Connaught Road, Central, China (Hong Kong)
Tel.: (852) 23131888
Web Site: http://www.chinastar.com.hk
Sales Range: $25-49.9 Million
Emp.: 30
Television Show Production Services
N.A.I.C.S.: 512110

China Star HK Distribution Limited (1)
Rm 3409 Shun Tak Ctr W Tower, 168 Connaught Rd C, Hong Kong, China (Hong Kong)
Tel.: (852) 23131888
Web Site: http://www.chinastar.com.hk
Sales Range: $25-49.9 Million
Emp.: 50
Motion Picture Distr
N.A.I.C.S.: 512110

China Star International Distribution Limited (1)
Ste 503 C Miramar Tower, 132 Nathan Rd TST, Kowloon, China (Hong Kong)
Tel.: (852) 23131888
Sales Range: $25-49.9 Million
Emp.: 30
Television Show Production Services
N.A.I.C.S.: 512110
Charles Heung *(Chm)*

CHINA STARCH HOLDINGS LTD.
Suite 3312 Tower 1 Times Square 1 Matheson Street, Causeway Bay, China (Hong Kong)
Tel.: (852) 28666390 Ky
3838—(HKG)
Rev.: $1,362,383,308
Assets: $699,785,449
Liabilities: $219,604,932
Net Worth: $480,180,517
Earnings: $31,720,445
Emp.: 2,316
Fiscal Year-end: 12/31/20
Holding Company
N.A.I.C.S.: 551112

China Starch Holdings Ltd.—(Continued)

Qixiang Tian *(Chm)*

CHINA STATE CONSTRUC-TION ENGINEERING CORPORATION LIMITED

CSC Fortune International Center
Building 3 Courtyard 5 Anding Road,
Chaoyang District, Beijing, 100029,
China
Tel.: (86) 1086498181
Web Site: https://www.cscec.com.cn
Year Founded: 1982
601668—(CHIN)
Rev.: $288,529,310,628
Assets: $372,467,624,162
Liabilities: $276,941,301,998
Net Worth: $95,526,322,164
Earnings: $7,153,422,260
Emp.: 382,492
Fiscal Year-end: 12/31/22
Construction & Engineering Services
N.A.I.C.S.: 236210
Xuexuan Zheng *(Pres)*

Subsidiaries:

CSC & EC (Pty) Ltd.   (1)
PO Box 00335, Gaborone, Botswana
Tel.: (267) 301 427
Construction Services
N.A.I.C.S.: 236210

CSCEC Xinjiang Construction & Engineering (Group) Co., Ltd.   (1)
NO 239 Qingnian Road, Urumqi, 830002,
Xinjiang, China
Tel.: (86) 9918855621
Web Site: https://www.xjco.cscec.com
Real Estate Services
N.A.I.C.S.: 531390

China Construction (South Pacific) Development Co. Pte. Ltd.   (1)
182 Cecil Street 31-01, Frasers Towers,
Singapore, 069547, Singapore
Tel.: (65) 6 227 4537
Web Site:
    https://en.chinaconstruction.cscec.com
Sales Range: $25-49.9 Million
Emp.: 100
Construction Services
N.A.I.C.S.: 236210
Chen Guo Cai *(CEO)*

China Construction American Co.   (1)
525 Washington Blvd 31st Fl, Jersey City,
NJ 07310
Tel.: (201) 876-2788
Web Site: https://www.chinaconstruction.us
Emp.: 50
Construction Services
N.A.I.C.S.: 236210
Ning Yuan *(Chm & Pres)*

China Construction Decoration Engineering Co.   (1)
6th Floor B Building CSCEC Mansion 15
Sanlihe Rd, Haidian District, Beijing,
100037, China
Tel.: (86) 1088082736
Web Site: http://www.cscec-zs.com
Emp.: 200
Engineeering Services
N.A.I.C.S.: 541330

China Construction First Building (Group) Corporation Ltd.   (1)
Beijing Fengtai District No 52 West Fourth
Ring Road, Beijing, 100161, China
Tel.: (86) 10 8398 2099
Web Site: http://www.cscec1b.net
Heavy Construction Services
N.A.I.C.S.: 236210

China Construction Import & Export Co.   (1)
14 Fuwai Avenue, Xincheng District, Beijing,
100037, China
Tel.: (86) 10 8603 6253
Import & Export Services
N.A.I.C.S.: 561499

China Overseas Holding Ltd.   (1)

10/F Three Pacific Place 1 Queen's Road
East, Central, China (Hong Kong)
Tel.: (852) 28 237 8888
Web Site: https://www.cohl.com
Construction Services
N.A.I.C.S.: 236210

Subsidiary (Domestic):

China Overseas Grand Oceans Group Ltd.   (2)
Suites 701-702 7/F Three Pacific Place 1
Queen's Road East, Hong Kong, China
(Hong Kong)
Tel.: (852) 29880600
Web Site: https://www.cogogl.com.hk
Rev.: $7,960,237,317
Assets: $25,030,714,305
Liabilities: $19,852,220,730
Net Worth: $5,178,493,576
Earnings: $423,145,215
Emp.: 3,061
Fiscal Year-end: 12/31/2022
Real Estate Development Services
N.A.I.C.S.: 531190
Paul Man Kwan Wang *(CFO)*

Branch (Domestic):

China Overseas Holding Ltd.   (2)
27th Floor China Overseas Mansion, 139
Hennessy Road, Wanchai, China (Hong
Kong)
Tel.: (852) 2823 7888
Web Site: http://www.cscec.com
Construction Services
N.A.I.C.S.: 236210

Subsidiary (Domestic):

China Overseas Land & Investment Limited   (2)
10/F Three Pacific Place 1 Queen's Road
East, Hong Kong, China (Hong Kong)
Tel.: (852) 29880666
Web Site: https://www.cohl.com
Rev.: $24,966,987,290
Assets: $126,447,459,570
Liabilities: $74,789,032,316
Net Worth: $51,658,427,254
Earnings: $3,400,001,661
Emp.: 4,351
Fiscal Year-end: 12/31/2022
Property Development & Investment Services
N.A.I.C.S.: 531390
Jianguo Yan *(Chm)*

China State Construction International Co.   (1)
12th Floor Beijing Sunflower Tower 37
Maizzidian St, Chaoyang District, Beijing,
100026, China
Tel.: (86) 1085276299
Web Site: http://www.cscec.com
Emp.: 200
Heavy Construction Services
N.A.I.C.S.: 236210

CHINA STATE CONSTRUCTION INTERNATIONAL HOLDINGS LIMITED

28/F China Overseas Building 139
Hennessy Road, Wanchai, China
(Hong Kong)
Tel.: (852) 28237888
Web Site: https://www.csci.com.hk
CCOHF—(OTCIQ)
Rev.: $13,032,482,395
Assets: $29,247,144,172
Liabilities: $20,582,728,411
Net Worth: $8,664,415,760
Earnings: $1,082,401,114
Emp.: 15,312
Fiscal Year-end: 12/31/22
Professional & Management Services
N.A.I.C.S.: 541330
Wenbin Zhou *(VP)*

Subsidiaries:

China State Construction Development Holdings Limited   (1)
16/F Eight Commercial Tower 8 Sun Yip
Street, Chai Wan, China (Hong
Kong)   (74.2%)
Tel.: (852) 2 557 3121

Web Site: http://www.cscd.com.hk
Rev.: $811,906,786
Assets: $1,136,265,948
Liabilities: $931,825,168
Net Worth: $204,440,781
Earnings: $36,618,325
Emp.: 4,434
Fiscal Year-end: 12/31/2021
Construction & Engineering Services
N.A.I.C.S.: 237000
Alan Sai Ying Lau *(Dir-Mktg Far East Aluminium Works)*

Subsidiary (Non-US):

Far East Aluminium Works (Singapore) Pte. Ltd.   (2)
No 10 Jalan Besar 12-01 Sim Lim Tower,
Singapore, Singapore
Tel.: (65) 62971638
Aluminum Window & Cladding Installation
Services
N.A.I.C.S.: 238350

Far East Aluminium Works Canada Corporation   (2)
Unit 2001 1700 Langstaff Road, Concord,
L4K 3S3, ON, Canada
Tel.: (905) 695-6996
Aluminum Windows & Claddings Installation
Services
N.A.I.C.S.: 238350
Rebecca Tock *(Mgr-Admin)*

Subsidiary (Domestic):

Far East Aluminium Works Company Limited   (2)
16/F Eight Commercial Tower 8 Sun Yip
Street, Chai Wan, China (Hong Kong)
Tel.: (852) 2 557 3121
Web Site: https://www.fareastglobal.com
Sales Range: $25-49.9 Million
Emp.: 100
Aluminum Window & Curtain Walls Installation Services
N.A.I.C.S.: 238150

Subsidiary (US):

Far East Aluminum Works (U.S.) Corporation   (2)
353 Pilot Rd Ste B, Las Vegas, NV 89119
Tel.: (702) 796-8818
Sales Range: $25-49.9 Million
Emp.: 4
Aluminium Forgings Mfr
N.A.I.C.S.: 332112

Far East Facade, Inc.   (2)
353 Pilot Rd Ste B, Las Vegas, NV 89119
Tel.: (702) 796-8818
Sales Range: $25-49.9 Million
Emp.: 6
Aluminum Window & Curtain Walls Installation Services
N.A.I.C.S.: 238150

Subsidiary (Non-US):

Gamma Windows and Walls International Inc.   (2)
1700 Langstaff Road Suite 2001, Concord,
L4K 3S3, ON, Canada
Tel.: (905) 695-6996
Curtain Wall & Aluminium Window Installation Services & Mfr
N.A.I.C.S.: 238150
Harry Wang *(Pres)*

Netfortune (Shanghai) Aluminium Works Co. Ltd.   (2)
Room 1906 Golden Magnolia Plaza No 1
Dapu Road, Luwan District, Shanghai,
200023, China
Tel.: (86) 215 396 0151
Web Site: http://www.fareastglobal.com
Emp.: 100
Aluminum Window & Claddings Installation
Services
N.A.I.C.S.: 238350

CHINA STATE SHIPBUILDING CORPORATION

Tel.: (86) 2133116666
Web Site: https://www.cssc.net.cn
Year Founded: 1999
600150—(CHIN)

Shipbuilding, Ship Repair, Shipboard
Equipment Mfg, Marine Design & Research Services
N.A.I.C.S.: 336611
Wen Gang *(Chm & Sec-Party)*

Subsidiaries:

CSSC (Hong Kong) Shipping Company Limited   (1)
Room 1802 18th Floor World-wide House
19 Des Voeux Road, Central, China (Hong
Kong)
Tel.: (852) 22385299
Web Site: https://csscshipping.com
Rev.: $327,998,204
Assets: $5,273,119,650
Liabilities: $3,969,845,626
Net Worth: $1,303,274,025
Earnings: $178,978,065
Emp.: 81
Fiscal Year-end: 12/31/2021
Ship Leasing Services
N.A.I.C.S.: 532411
Kai Hu *(Gen Mgr)*

China CSSC Holdings Limited   (1)
Room 12803 No 1 Pudong Avenue, Pudong
New District, Shanghai, 200129, China
Tel.: (86) 2168861666
Web Site: http://csscholdings.cssc.net.cn
Rev.: $10,361,999,391
Assets: $24,622,309,565
Liabilities: $17,357,061,309
Net Worth: $7,265,248,255
Earnings: $409,475,659
Fiscal Year-end: 12/31/2023
Ship Building & Maintenance Services
N.A.I.C.S.: 336611
Jincheng Yang *(Gen Mgr)*

Subsidiary (Domestic):

CSSC Science and Technology Co., Ltd   (2)
13th Floor Jiangnan Shipyard Building No
600 Luban Road, Shanghai, 200023, China
Tel.: (86) 2153023456
Web Site: https://cssckj.com
Rev.: $470,263,019
Assets: $1,057,056,900
Liabilities: $446,550,863
Net Worth: $610,506,037
Earnings: $15,436,573
Emp.: 900
Fiscal Year-end: 12/31/2022
Steel Structures Mfr & Sales
N.A.I.C.S.: 332312
Zuojun Tan *(Chm)*

China Shipbuilding NDRI Engineering Co., Ltd   (1)
303 Wu Ning Rd, Shanghai, 200063, China
Tel.: (86) 21 62549700
Web Site: http://www.ndri.sh.cn
Emp.: 700
Marine Engineering Services
N.A.I.C.S.: 541330

China Shipbuilding Trading Co., Ltd.   (1)
8th-12th Floor Bldg 1 No 9 Shouti South
Road, Haidian District, Beijing, 100048,
China
Tel.: (86) 10 88573688
Web Site: http://www.cstc.com.cn
Cargo Transportation Services
N.A.I.C.S.: 488510

CHINA STATIONERY LIMITED

Donglou Village Wuli Ting, Jiangkou
Town Hangjiang District, Putian, Fujian, China
Tel.: (86) 594 369 7883   BM
Web Site: http://www.cstationery.com
Year Founded: 2007
Rev.: $72,005,433
Assets: $410,145,243
Liabilities: $11,231,934
Net Worth: $398,913,309
Earnings: $4,322,523
Emp.: 344
Fiscal Year-end: 12/31/16
Stationery Products
N.A.I.C.S.: 322230
Fung Chan *(Founder, Chm & CEO)*

CHINA STEEL CORPORATION
1 Chung Kang Rd Hsiao Kang, Kaohsiung, 81233, Taiwan
Tel.: (886) 78021111   TW
Web Site: https://www.csc.com.tw
Year Founded: 1971
2002—(TAI)
Rev.: $11,196,842,017
Assets: $22,625,461,532
Liabilities: $11,132,546,218
Net Worth: $11,492,915,314
Earnings: $80,311,120
Emp.: 9,961
Fiscal Year-end: 12/31/20
Iron & Steel Product Mfr
N.A.I.C.S.: 331110
Chien-Chih Hwang (Exec VP)

Subsidiaries:

C.S. Aluminium Corporation   (1)
No 17 Tung Lin Rd, Siaogang District, Kaohsiung, 81260, Taiwan   (98%)
Tel.: (886) 78718666
Web Site: http://www.csalum.com.tw
Sales Range: $100-124.9 Million
Emp.: 600
Mfr of Aluminum Alloy Ingot, Aluminum Plate, Aluminum Sheet/Coil & Aluminum Foil
N.A.I.C.S.: 331524

CHC RESOURCES
CORPORATION   (1)
22F No 88 Chenggong 2nd Road, Qianzhen District, Kaohsiung, 806, Taiwan
Tel.: (886) 73368377
Web Site: https://www.chc.com.tw
Rev.: $405,340,316
Assets: $401,299,439
Liabilities: $195,762,869
Net Worth: $205,536,570
Earnings: $28,058,896
Emp.: 278
Fiscal Year-end: 12/31/2023
Porland Cement Mfr & Distr
N.A.I.C.S.: 327310
Zhi Lin Yang (Asst Gen Mgr-Resource Reutilization Div)

CHINA STEEL CHEMICAL CO.,
LTD.   (1)
25F No 88 Chenggong 2nd Rd, Qianzhen Dist, Kaohsiung, 80661, Taiwan
Tel.: (886) 73383515
Web Site: https://www.cscc.com.tw
Rev.: $272,006,203
Assets: $372,296,595
Liabilities: $103,665,518
Net Worth: $268,631,077
Earnings: $46,969,389
Emp.: 331
Fiscal Year-end: 12/31/2023
Petroleum Product Mfr
N.A.I.C.S.: 324199
Ming-Dar Fang (Pres)

CSC Solar Corporation   (1)
9F 88 Chenggong 2rd Rd, Qianzhen, Kaohsiung, 80661, Taiwan
Tel.: (886) 75368156
N.A.I.C.S.: 221114

CSC Sonoma Pty. Ltd.   (1)
Level 23 240 Queen Street, Brisbane, 4000, QLD, Australia
Tel.: (61) 730019222
Mining Exploration Services
N.A.I.C.S.: 213114

CSC Steel Sdn. Bhd.   (1)
180 Kawasan Industri Ayer Keroh, 75450, Melaka, Malaysia   (70%)
Tel.: (60) 6 231 0169
Web Site: http://www.cscmalaysia.com
Sales Range: $200-249.9 Million
Emp.: 600
Mfr of Cold Rolled Steel Products
N.A.I.C.S.: 331221

CSGT (Shanghai) Co., Ltd.   (1)
Room 1907 No 501 Daming Road, Hongkou District, Shanghai, 200080, China
Tel.: (86) 2162896898
Automobile Material Distr
N.A.I.C.S.: 441330

CSGT (Shenzhen) Co., Ltd.   (1)

NO 02 Floor 38 Building 1 Excellence Century Center Jintian Road, Futian Street Futian District, Shenzhen, China
Tel.: (86) 75582520312
Steel Product Distr
N.A.I.C.S.: 423510

CSGT (Singapore) Pte. Ltd.   (1)
1 Raffles Place 23-02 One Raffles Place, Singapore, 048616, Singapore
Tel.: (65) 62238777
Steel Material Mfr
N.A.I.C.S.: 331210
Y. K. Wong (Reg Sls Mgr)

CSGT Hong Kong Limited   (1)
1407-19 Des Voeux Road Central, Central, China (Hong Kong)
Tel.: (852) 25231488
Steel Corp Product Distr
N.A.I.C.S.: 423510

CSGT Metals Vietnam Joint Stock
Company   (1)
Lot VI - 1A The 6th Road, Ho Nai Industrial Zone Trang Bom District, Ho Chi Minh City, Dong Nai, Vietnam
Tel.: (84) 61 367 1151
Web Site: https://www.csmv.vn
Flat Metal Product Distr
N.A.I.C.S.: 423510
Nee Lung Yuan (Chm & CEO)

CSGT Trading India Private
Limited   (1)
215 Atrium Unit No 101-102 1st Floor A-Wing Andheri-Kurla Road, Andheri-E, Mumbai, 400059, India
Tel.: (91) 2266979580
Steel & Aluminium Product Distr
N.A.I.C.S.: 423510
Rolen Wu (Mng Dir)

Changchun CECK Auto. Parts Co.,
Ltd.   (1)
No 2299 Chaoyue Street High-tech Development Zone, Changchun, Jilin, China
Tel.: (86) 43181105600
Web Site: http://www.cc-ceck.com
Automobile Parts Mfr
N.A.I.C.S.: 336390

Changzhou China Steel Precision
Materials Co., Ltd.   (1)
No 18 Changyang Road, Wujin Economic Development Zone, Changzhou, 213149, Jiangsu, China
Tel.: (86) 51989616168
Web Site: https://www.cscpm.com.cn
Stainless Steel Material Mfr
N.A.I.C.S.: 331210

China Ecotek Corporation   (1)
No 88 Chenggong 2nd Rd, Qianzhen Dist, Kaohsiung, 806, Taiwan   (50%)
Tel.: (886) 73306138
Web Site: http://www.ecotek.com.tw
Sales Range: Less than $1 Million
Emp.: 250
Environment Protection Industries, Steel & Related Industries, Waste Treatment & Facility Maintenance, Co-Generation Plant Planning, Design, Construction & Feasibility Study
N.A.I.C.S.: 562219

China Hi-Ment Corp.   (1)
22F No 88 Chenggong 2nd Rd, Qian-Zhen, Kaohsiung, 80661, Taiwan   (35%)
Tel.: (886) 73368377
Web Site: http://www.chc.com.tw
Sales Range: $50-74.9 Million
Emp.: 200
Mfr & Sales of Cement & Slag Powder, Waste Treatment & International Trade
N.A.I.C.S.: 327310

China Prosperity Development
Corporation   (1)
23F No 88 Chenggong 2nd Rd, Qianzhen Dist, Kaohsiung, 806, Taiwan   (100%)
Tel.: (886) 5362500
Web Site: https://www.cpdc-csc.com.tw
Sales Range: $50-74.9 Million
Emp.: 9
Real Estate Development
N.A.I.C.S.: 531390
Yi-Chih Hsu (VP)

China Steel Chemical Corp.   (1)

25F No 88 Chenggong 2nd Rd, Qianzhen Dist, Kaohsiung, 80661, Taiwan   (31%)
Tel.: (886) 7 338 3515
Web Site: https://www.cscc.com.tw
Sales Range: $1-4.9 Billion
Emp.: 140
Mfr of Coal Tar, Coke, Coke Breeze, Coal Chemical, Anti-Corrosion & Water Proof Coating Material for Construction
N.A.I.C.S.: 324199

China Steel Corporation India Pvt.
Ltd.   (1)
Office No 204 2nd Floor ISCON Atria-2 Gotri Road, Vadodara, 390021, Gujarat, India
Tel.: (91) 922 798 9880
Web Site: https://www.csci.co.in
Electric Steel Product Mfr
N.A.I.C.S.: 331110
Kuei-Sung Tseng (Chm)

China Steel Express Corporation   (1)
24th Floor No 88 Chenggong 2nd Road, Qianzhen District, Kaohsiung, 806, Taiwan   (100%)
Tel.: (886) 73378888
Web Site: https://www.csebulk.com.tw
Sales Range: $25-49.9 Million
Emp.: 55
Bulk & General Cargo, Shipping & Chartering Service
N.A.I.C.S.: 481212

China Steel Global Trading
Corporation   (1)
10F 88 Chenggong 2nd Rd, Qianzhen, Kaohsiung, 80661, Taiwan   (100%)
Tel.: (886) 73322168
Web Site: http://www.csgt.com.tw
Sales Range: $125-149.9 Million
Emp.: 70
Steel Product Trading Business, Industrial Materials Trading Business & Sales Agent for Steel & Aluminium Products
N.A.I.C.S.: 425120

China Steel Machinery
Corporation   (1)
No 3 Taiji Rd, Xiaogang Dist, Kaohsiung, Taiwan
Tel.: (886) 78020111
Emp.: 600
Industrial Steel Machinery Mfr
N.A.I.C.S.: 333248

China Steel Power Corporation   (1)
30F No 68 Sec 5 Zhongxiao E Rd, Xinyi Dist, Taipei, 11065, Taiwan
Tel.: (886) 223450128
N.A.I.C.S.: 221115

China Steel Precision Metals Kunshan Co., Ltd.   (1)
No 168 Shuanghua Road Huaqiao, Kunshan, Jiangsu, China
Tel.: (86) 51257601373
Electric Equipment Mfr
N.A.I.C.S.: 335311

China Steel Precision Metals
Qingdao Co., Ltd.   (1)
No 500 Fenjin Road, Economic Technological District, Qingdao, 266555, China
Tel.: (86) 53258718558
Web Site: https://www.cscmq.com
Steel Material Mfr
N.A.I.C.S.: 331210

China Steel Resources
Corporation   (1)
No 38 Yanhai 3rd Rd, Xiaogang Dist, Kaohsiung, 812, Taiwan
Tel.: (886) 73371111
N.A.I.C.S.: 327999

China Steel Security Corporation   (1)
17F No 247 Minsheng 1st Rd, Sinsing District, Kaohsiung, 80046, Taiwan   (100%)
Tel.: (886) 72299678
Web Site: http://www.cscess.com.tw
Sales Range: Less than $1 Million
Emp.: 1,147
Security Services & Systems
N.A.I.C.S.: 561621

China Steel Structure Co., Ltd.   (1)
500 Zhongxing Rd, Yanchao District, Kaohsiung, 82447, Taiwan   (19%)
Tel.: (886) 7 616 8688

Web Site: https://www.cssc.com.tw
Emp.: 354
Build-Up Steel Sections & Other Steel Structures
N.A.I.C.S.: 332312

China Steel and Nippon Steel Vietnam Joint Stock Company   (1)
My Xuan A2 Industrial Zone, My Xuan Ward, Phu My, Vietnam
Tel.: (84) 2543931168
Web Site: https://www.csvc.com.vn
Emp.: 800
Steel Sheet Mfr
N.A.I.C.S.: 331221

ChinaSteel Management Consulting
Corporation   (1)
24F-6 No 31 HaiBian Road Lingya, Kaohsiung, 80248, Taiwan
Tel.: (886) 78051088
Management Consulting Services
N.A.I.C.S.: 541618
C. T. Wong (Chm)

Chung Hung Steel Corporation   (1)
317 Yu Liao Road Chiao Tou District, Kaohsiung, 82544, Taiwan
Tel.: (886) 76117171
Web Site: http://www.chsteel.com.tw
Rev.: $1,234,971,928
Assets: $1,078,931,971
Liabilities: $547,227,848
Net Worth: $531,704,123
Earnings: $5,208,836
Emp.: 1,081
Fiscal Year-end: 12/31/2023
Rolled Steel Pipes Mfr
N.A.I.C.S.: 331110
Min-Hsiung Liu (Bd of Dirs & Chm)

Dragon Steel Corporation   (1)
No 100 Longchang Rd, Longjing Dist, Taichung, 434, Hsien, Taiwan   (30%)
Tel.: (886) 426306088
Web Site: https://www.dragonsteel.com.tw
Sales Range: $100-124.9 Million
Emp.: 3,206
H-Sections & Hot Rolled Steel Coils
N.A.I.C.S.: 331110

Dyna Rechi (Jiujiang) Co., Ltd.   (1)
No 15 Riverside Road West of Port Development Zone, Jiujiang, Jiangxi, China
Tel.: (86) 7922131888
Brushless DC Motor Mfr
N.A.I.C.S.: 335312

Formosa Ha Tinh Steel
Corporation   (1)
Vung Ang Economic Zone, Ky Long Ward Ky Anh Town, Ha Tinh, Vietnam
Tel.: (84) 2393722123
Web Site: https://www.fhs.vn
N.A.I.C.S.: 331110

Gains Investment Corporation   (1)
26F No 88 Chenggong 2nd Road, Qianzhen, Kaohsiung, 806, Taiwan   (100%)
Tel.: (886) 73382288
Web Site: https://gains.com.tw
Sales Range: $1-9.9 Million
Emp.: 20
Direct Investments Focusing on Industrial Materials, Electronic Related Industries, Telecommunication Industries & Other High-Tech Industries
N.A.I.C.S.: 523940

Group Steel Corporation (M) Sdn.
Bhd.   (1)
180 Kawasan Industri Ayer Keroh, Melaka, 75450, Malaysia   (90%)
Tel.: (60) 62319990
Web Site: http://www.cscmalaysia.com
Sales Range: $100-124.9 Million
Emp.: 600
Mfr of Hot-Dip Galvanized Steel Coils & Color Steel Sheets
N.A.I.C.S.: 331110

HIMAG Magnetic Corporation   (1)
24 1 Chien Kuo Rd, Nei Pu Industrial District, Ping-tung, Taiwan   (50%)
Tel.: (886) 87780222
Web Site: http://www.himag.com.tw
Sales Range: $1-9.9 Million
Emp.: 30
Mfr of Ferrite Materials Such As Iron Oxide, Ferrite Powder & Ferrite Core

China Steel Corporation—(Continued)

N.A.I.C.S.: 327110

InfoChamp Systems Corporation (1)
19F No 88 Chenggong 2nd Rd, Qianzhen
Dist, Kaohsiung, 806, Taiwan (100%)
Tel.: (886) 75350101
Web Site: https://www.icsc.com.tw
Sales Range: $75-99.9 Million
Emp.: 300
Enterprise Resource Planning; Supply
Chain Management; Information System
Design,
N.A.I.C.S.: 541512
Liang Chi-Hsiou *(Chm)*

MagnPower Corporation (1)
No 36 Jingjian Rd, Pingtung County, Ping-
tung, 900, Taiwan
Tel.: (886) 87510333
Web Site: https://en.magnpower.com.tw
N.A.I.C.S.: 332117

**Ningbo Huayang Aluminium-Tech
Co., Ltd.** (1)
High-Tech Development Zone Siming East
Road No 288, Fenghua, Zhejiang, China
Tel.: (86) 5748 895 1888
Web Site: http://www.nhac.com.cn
Aluminium Products Mfr
N.A.I.C.S.: 331313

OIDC (1)
12F No 760 Bade Rd Sec 4, Taipei, 105,
Taiwan (20%)
Tel.: (886) 227626360
Web Site: http://www.oidc.com.tw
Sales Range: $1-9.9 Million
Emp.: 15
Oversea Investments
N.A.I.C.S.: 523150

**Rechi Refrigeration (Dongguan) Co.,
Ltd.** (1)
No 48 Gaokersan Road Xinlian Administra-
tive Division, Humen Town, Dongguan,
Guangdong, China
Tel.: (86) 76985528857
Brushless DC Motor Mfr
N.A.I.C.S.: 335312

**Sing Da Marine Structure
Corporation** (1)
No 201 Sec 1 Dongfang Rd, Qieding Dist,
Kaohsiung, 85243, Taiwan
Tel.: (886) 76080088
Web Site: https://www.sdms.com.tw
N.A.I.C.S.: 221115
Hung Bao-Tuan *(Chm)*

Tang Eng Iron Works Co., Ltd. (1)
458 Hsin Hsing Road Feng-Shan Village,
Hu Kou Hsiang, Hsin-chu, 300,
Taiwan (8%)
Tel.: (886) 35981721
Sales Range: $400-449.9 Million
Emp.: 1,848
Stainless Steel & Construction
N.A.I.C.S.: 331513

**United Steel Engineering & Construc-
tion Corp.** (1)
500 Zhongxing Rd, Yanchao District, Kaoh-
siung, 82477, Taiwan
Tel.: (886) 76167677
Web Site: http://www.usec.com.tw
Construction Engineering Services
N.A.I.C.S.: 237990

Wuhan InfoChamp I.T. Co., Ltd. (1)
15F Quanta Building No1 Friendship Ave,
Wuchang District, Wuhan, China
Tel.: (86) 2787611330
N.A.I.C.S.: 541512

**CHINA STEEL STRUCTURE
CO., LTD.**
500 Zhongxing Rd, Yanchao District,
Kaohsiung, 82447, Taiwan
Tel.: (886) 76168688
Web Site: https://www.cssc.com.tw
Year Founded: 1978
2013—(TAI)
Rev.: $616,081,994
Assets: $471,678,454
Liabilities: $295,169,811
Net Worth: $176,508,643

Earnings: $17,513,587
Emp.: 354
Fiscal Year-end: 12/31/23
Structural Steel Mfr
N.A.I.C.S.: 331110

Subsidiaries:

**China Steel Structure Co., Ltd. -
Tainan Guantlan Factory** (1)
No 2 Gongye S Rd Guantian Industrial Park
Service Center, Tainan City, 720, Taiwan
Tel.: (886) 66986651
Steel Products Mfr
N.A.I.C.S.: 331511

**CHINA SUCCESS FINANCE
GROUP HOLDINGS LIMITED**
604 6 Floor Tesbury Centre 28
Queens Road East, Wanchai, China
(Hong Kong)
Tel.: (852) 21807189
Web Site:
http://www.chinasuccessfinance.com
3623—(HKG)
Rev.: $136,379,422
Assets: $183,679,486
Liabilities: $110,153,547
Net Worth: $73,525,939
Earnings: ($12,954,825)
Emp.: 61
Fiscal Year-end: 12/31/20
Financial Loans
N.A.I.C.S.: 522310
Tiewei Zhang *(Founder & Chm)*

Subsidiaries:

**Anli Financial Communications
Limited** (1)
Room 1901-02 19th Floor Shanghai Indus-
trial Building, 48-62 Hennessy Road, Wan-
chai, China (Hong Kong)
Tel.: (852) 23256661
Investment & Financial Services
N.A.I.C.S.: 523999
Judith Cheung *(Mgr-Fin Comm & IR)*

**CHINA SUN BIO-CHEM TECH-
NOLOGY GROUP COMPANY
LTD.**
32nd Fl The Space Intl Centr No 8
Dongdaqiao Road, Beijing, China
Tel.: (86) 1058700700
Corn Starch Mfr
N.A.I.C.S.: 311221
Sun Guiji *(Founder, Chm & CEO)*

**CHINA SUN GROUP HIGH-
TECH CO.**
1 Hutan Street Zhongshan District,
Dalian, 116015, PRC, China
Tel.: (86) 41182897752 NC
Year Founded: 2004
CSGH—(OTCBB)
Sales Range: $25-49.9 Million
Emp.: 264
Cobaltosic Oxide & Lithium Iron
Phosphate Mfr
N.A.I.C.S.: 325998
Guosheng Fu *(CEO & VP)*

CHINA SUNERGY CO., LTD.
No 123 Focheng West Road Jiangn-
ing, Jiangning Economic & Technical
Development Zone, Nanjing, 211100,
Jiangsu, China
Tel.: (86) 2552766666 Ky
Web Site: http://www.csun-solar.com
Year Founded: 2004
Emp.: 2,627
Solar Cell Products Mfr
N.A.I.C.S.: 335999

Subsidiaries:

**CEEG (Shanghai) Solar Science
Technology Co., Ltd.** (1)
No 5999 Guangfulin Road Songjiang Dis-
trict, Shanghai, 201616, China

Tel.: (86) 2160291899
Solar Cell Mfr
N.A.I.C.S.: 334413
Jenny Jin *(Mgr-Overseas Sls)*

**CSUN - China Sunergy (South Africa)
Co., Ltd.** (1)
25 Birmingham Road Benoni Industrial
Sites, Johannesburg, Gauteng, South Africa
Tel.: (27) 114200030
Solar Cell Mfr
N.A.I.C.S.: 334413

**CSUN - China Sunergy Clean Tech
Inc.** (1)
2880 Zanker Rd Ste 203, San Jose, CA
95134
Tel.: (408) 954-7392
Solar Cell Mfr
N.A.I.C.S.: 334413

**CSUN - China Sunergy Europe
GmbH** (1)
Schillerstrasse 42-44, 60313, Frankfurt,
Germany
Tel.: (49) 6996869766
Solar Cell Mfr
N.A.I.C.S.: 334413
Melissa Meng *(Mgr-Acct)*

CSUN Australia Pty. Ltd. (1)
Level 57 Mlc Centre 19-29 Martin Place,
Sydney, 2000, NSW, Australia
Tel.: (61) 292382024
Solar Cell Mfr
N.A.I.C.S.: 334413
Florence Zhu *(Mgr-Sls & Mktg)*

**CSUN Eurasia Energy Systems In-
dustry & Trade Inc.** (1)
Istanbul Industrial & Free Trade Zone Akif
Kopuz St, No T-10 B Block 1st floor Aydinli-
Tuzla, 34957, Istanbul, Turkiye
Tel.: (90) 2163940820
Solar Cell Mfr
N.A.I.C.S.: 334413
Attila Akarsu *(Mgr-Production)*

**CSUN Japan Solar Energy Co.,
Ltd.** (1)
5F 2-2-10 Minamishinagawa Shinagawa-ku,
Tokyo, 140-0004, Japan
Tel.: (81) 367129581
Solar Cell Mfr
N.A.I.C.S.: 334413

**CSUN Renewable Energy (France)
S.a.r.l.** (1)
2405 Route Des Dolines, PO Box 65,
Sophia-Antipolis, France
Tel.: (33) 489829278
Solar Cell Mfr
N.A.I.C.S.: 334413

Korea Sunergy Co., Ltd (1)
171 Majung-ro Seo-gu, Incheon, Korea
(South)
Tel.: (82) 7041337012
Web Site: http://www.koreasunergy.com
Solar Cell Mfr
N.A.I.C.S.: 334413

**Nanjing Renewable Energy Co.,
Ltd.** (1)
NO 6 Shuige Road Jiangning Economic &
Development District, Nanjing City Prac,
211100, Nanjing, China
Tel.: (86) 2552095678
Solar Cell Mfr
N.A.I.C.S.: 334413

**CHINA SUNSHINE PAPER
HOLDINGS COMPANY LIM-
ITED**
Changle Economic Developed Zone,
Weifang, 262400, China
Tel.: (86) 5366856166 Ky
Web Site:
http://www.sunshinepaper.com.cn
Year Founded: 2000
2002—(HKG)
Rev.: $1,022,436,976
Assets: $1,437,179,970
Liabilities: $911,411,665
Net Worth: $525,768,306
Earnings: $78,748,255
Emp.: 4,520

Fiscal Year-end: 12/31/20
Paper Products Mfr
N.A.I.C.S.: 322299
Dongxing Wang *(Chm & Gen Mgr)*

Subsidiaries:

**Century Sunshine Paper (USA)
Inc.** (1)
1000 Lakes Dr Ste 430, West Covina, CA
91790-2928
Tel.: (626) 502-1360
Paper Product Distr
N.A.I.C.S.: 424130

**Shandong Century Sunshine Paper
Group Co., Ltd.** (1)
Changle Economic Development Zone, Wei-
fang, 262400, Shandong, China
Tel.: (86) 5366856167
Emp.: 150
Paper Products Mfr
N.A.I.C.S.: 322299

**CHINA SUNSINE CHEMICAL
HOLDINGS LTD**
112 Robinson Road 11-01, Singa-
pore, 068902, Singapore
Tel.: (65) 62209070
Web Site:
https://www.chinasunsine.com
QES—(SES)
Rev.: $491,614,787
Assets: $617,720,280
Liabilities: $64,684,225
Net Worth: $553,036,055
Earnings: $52,459,859
Emp.: 2,116
Fiscal Year-end: 12/31/23
Rubber Chemical Products Mfr
N.A.I.C.S.: 326211
Cheng Qiu Xu *(Chm)*

**CHINA SUNTIEN GREEN EN-
ERGY CORPORATION LTD.**
Suite 2103 21st Floor Prudential
Tower The Gateway Harbour City,
Kowloon, China (Hong Kong)
Tel.: (852) 21530956 CN
Web Site: https://www.suntien.com
Year Founded: 2010
0956—(HKG)
Rev.: $1,916,792,739
Assets: $2,318,010,139
Liabilities: $751,707,174
Net Worth: $1,566,302,965
Earnings: $296,113,817
Emp.: 2,388
Fiscal Year-end: 12/31/20
Natural Gas Distribution Services
N.A.I.C.S.: 221210
Hong Jun Wang *(Exec Dir)*

**CHINA SUPPLY CHAIN HOLD-
INGS LIMITED**
Room 2606 26/F Shing Kai Commer-
cial Centre, 144-151 Connaught
Road West, Hong Kong, China (Hong
Kong)
Tel.: (852) 23860066
Web Site: http://www.yat-sing.com.hk
3708—(HKG)
Rev.: $49,077,535
Assets: $32,525,660
Liabilities: $13,123,973
Net Worth: $19,401,688
Earnings: ($1,871,371)
Emp.: 93
Fiscal Year-end: 06/30/20
Building Maintenance & Renovation
Services
N.A.I.C.S.: 561210
Ming Dai *(Exec Dir)*

**CHINA SXT PHARMACEUTI-
CALS, INC.**
178 Taidong Rd N, Taizhou, 225300,
Jiangsu, China

Tel.: (86) 52386299087   VG
Web Site: https://www.sxtchina.com
Year Founded: 2005
SXTC—(NASDAQ)
Rev.: $1,928,497
Assets: $23,127,057
Liabilities: $9,196,611
Net Worth: $13,930,446
Earnings: ($3,098,532)
Emp.: 75
Fiscal Year-end: 03/31/24
Pharmaceutical Product Mfr & Distr
N.A.I.C.S.: 325412
Feng Zhou *(Pres, CEO, Founder & Chm)*

CHINA SYNTHETIC RUBBER CORPORATION

8F No 113 Chung Shan N Rd Sec 2,
Taipei, 104, Taiwan
Tel.: (886) 225316556   TW
Web Site: http://www.csrcgroup.com
Year Founded: 1973
Sales Range: $350-399.9 Million
Carbon Black & Gelatine Mfr
N.A.I.C.S.: 325180

Subsidiaries:

Continental Carbon Company   (1)
16850 Park Row, Houston, TX
77084-5023   **(66.67%)**
Tel.: (281) 647-3700
Web Site: http://www.continentalcarbon.com
Sales Range: $150-199.9 Million
Emp.: 259
Carbon Black Developer & Mfr
N.A.I.C.S.: 325180

Continental Carbon India Ltd.   (1)
A-14 Industrial Area 1 South Side of GT Rd,
Ghaziabad, 201 001, India   **(66.7%)**
Tel.: (91) 1202840505
Web Site: http://www.continentalcarbon.com
Sales Range: $50-74.9 Million
Emp.: 156
Mfr & Marketer of Carbon Black
N.A.I.C.S.: 325180

Synpac-Kingdom Pharmaceutical Co., Ltd.   (1)
7th Fl 113 Zhong Shan N Rd Section 2, Taipei, 104, Taiwan   **(60%)**
Tel.: (886) 225818887
Web Site: http://www.sking.com.tw
Sales Range: $50-74.9 Million
Emp.: 146
Generic Pharmaceutical Mfr & Marketer
N.A.I.C.S.: 325412

CHINA TAIFENG BEDDINGS HOLDINGS LIMITED

Rm 911 9/F Blk A Hunghom Commercial Ctr, 39 Ma Tau Wai Road,
Hung Hom, China (Hong Kong)
Tel.: (852) 2230 8913   Ky
Web Site: http://www.taifeng.cc
Year Founded: 2009
Sales Range: $300-349.9 Million
Emp.: 5,384
Cotton Yarns & Bedding Products Mfr & Distr
N.A.I.C.S.: 325220
Chunwei Liu *(CEO)*

CHINA TAIPING INSURANCE HOLDINGS COMPANY LIMITED

25/F China Taiping Finance Centre
18 King Wah Road, North Point,
China (Hong Kong)
Tel.: (852) 28546100
Web Site:
https://www.ctih.cntaiping.com
CINSF—(OTCIQ)
Rev.: $38,132,817,233
Assets: $180,117,520,927
Liabilities: $167,505,384,999
Net Worth: $12,612,135,929
Earnings: $707,804,261
Emp.: 68,386

Fiscal Year-end: 12/31/22
Capital Management Services
N.A.I.C.S.: 551112
Sidong Wang *(Chm)*

Subsidiaries:

China Taiping Insurance (HK) Company Limited   (1)
15/F China Taiping Finance Centre 18 King Wah Road, North Point, China (Hong Kong)
Tel.: (852) 28151551
Web Site: https://www.hk.cntaiping.com
Property & Casualty Insurance Services
N.A.I.C.S.: 524126
Huang Zhao Hui *(Deputy CEO)*

China Taiping Insurance (Singapore) Pte. Ltd.   (1)
3 Anson Road 16-00 Springleaf Tower, Singapore, 079909, Singapore
Tel.: (65) 63896111
Web Site: https://sg.cntaiping.com
General Insurance Services
N.A.I.C.S.: 524113
Bo Hong *(Chm)*

China Taiping Insurance (UK) Company Limited   (1)
2 Finch Lane, London, EC3V 3NA, United Kingdom
Tel.: (44) 2078391888
Web Site: https://www.uk.cntaiping.com
Property & Casualty Insurance Services
N.A.I.C.S.: 524126

PT China Taiping Insurance Indonesia   (1)
The Tower 16th Floor Jl Jend Gatot Subroto Kav 12, Setiabudi, Jakarta Selatan, 12930, Indonesia
Tel.: (62) 2180600910
Web Site: https://www.id.cntaiping.com
Property & Casualty Insurance Services
N.A.I.C.S.: 524126

Taiping Financial Holdings Company Limited   (1)
19/F 20/F China Taiping Finance Centre 18 King Wah Road, North Point, China (Hong Kong)
Tel.: (852) 36691888
Web Site: https://www.tpfh.cntaiping.com
Holding Company
N.A.I.C.S.: 551112
Bo Hong *(Chm)*

Taiping Fund Management Company Limited   (1)
7th Floor Taiping Financial Building No 488 Yincheng Middle Road, Pudong New District, Shanghai, 200120, China
Tel.: (86) 2138556666
Web Site: https://www.taipingfund.com.cn
Investment Fund Management Services
N.A.I.C.S.: 523940

Taiping Reinsurance (China) Company Limited   (1)
Unit 08 09 11-19 Floor 5 No 16 Luomashi Avenue, Xicheng District, Beijing, 100052, China
Tel.: (86) 1057098588
Web Site: https://cntpre.cntaiping.com
Reinsurance Services
N.A.I.C.S.: 524130

Taiping Reinsurance Brokers Limited   (1)
Room 1201 China Taiping Finance Centre 18 King Wah Road, North Point, China (Hong Kong)
Tel.: (852) 31902001
Web Site: https://www.tprb.cntaiping.com
Reinsurance Services
N.A.I.C.S.: 524130
Liheng Wen *(Gen Mgr & Exec Dir)*

Taiping Reinsurance Company Limited   (1)
17/F China Taiping Finance Centre 18 King Wah Road, North Point, China (Hong Kong)
Tel.: (852) 28653838
Web Site: https://www.tpre.cntaiping.com
Reinsurance Services
N.A.I.C.S.: 524130
Yin Zhaojun *(Chm)*

CHINA TAISAN TECHNOLOGY

GROUP HOLDINGS LIMITED

Zhengdong Development Area
Dongcheng, Dongshi Town, 362271,
Jingjiang, Fujian, China
Tel.: (86) 59585507565
Sports & Leisure Apparel Mfr
N.A.I.C.S.: 315250
Wen Chang Lin *(Co-Founder & CEO)*

CHINA TANGSHANG HOLDINGS LIMITED

Unit 1201 12/F 29 Austin Road Tsim Sha Tsui, Kowloon, China (Hong Kong)
Tel.: (852) 2 331 1500   BM
Web Site: http://www.ts674.com
Year Founded: 1991
0674—(HKG)
Rev.: $33,133,711
Assets: $252,583,941
Liabilities: $175,147,927
Net Worth: $77,436,013
Earnings: $2,022,175
Emp.: 53
Fiscal Year-end: 03/31/22
Holding Company; Investment Management Services
N.A.I.C.S.: 551112
Weiwu Chen *(Chm)*

CHINA TECHFAITH WIRELESS COMMUNICATION TECHNOLOGY LIMITED

Tower D Mfox Plaza Ke Chuang 12th Street, Beijing Economic-Technological Development Area Yi Zhuang, Beijing, 101111, China
Tel.: (86) 10 5822 8888
Web Site:
http://www.techfaithwireless.com
Year Founded: 2002
CNTFY—(OTCIQ)
Sales Range: $25-49.9 Million
Emp.: 115
Mobile Handset Software & Design Solutions
N.A.I.C.S.: 541990
Defu Dong *(CEO)*

Subsidiaries:

TechFaith (Shanghai)   (1)
6F No 8 Building 3000 LongDong Avenue, RiverFront Harbor, Shanghai, 201203, China
Tel.: (86) 2161005656
Mobile Handset Software & Design Solutions
N.A.I.C.S.: 517112

TechFaith (Shenzhen)   (1)
A Block 6 Floor Building B1 Cyber Tech Zone Gaoxin Ave 7 s, Hi-tech Industrial District, Shenzhen, 518057, China
Tel.: (86) 755 3330 0202
Mobile Handset Software & Design Solutions
N.A.I.C.S.: 517112

TechFaith Intelligent Handset Technology Limited   (1)
No 10A Tower D2 IT Park Electronoic Town Jiun Xian Qiao North Road, Chao Yang District, Beijing, 0100015, China
Tel.: (86) 1058229999
Sales Range: $25-49.9 Million
Emp.: 100
Mobile Phones & Related Products Development
N.A.I.C.S.: 517112

CHINA TECHNOLOGY DEVELOPMENT GROUP CORPORATION

Unit 1712 13, Tower 1, Admiralty Centre, No 18 Harcourt Road, Hong Kong, China
Tel.: (86) 85231128461
Web Site: http://www.chinactdc.com

CTDC—(NASDAQ)
Rev.: $1,172,000
Assets: $8,297,000
Liabilities: $1,808,000
Net Worth: $6,489,000
Earnings: ($14,371,000)
Emp.: 68
Fiscal Year-end: 12/31/06
N.A.I.C.S.:

CHINA TECHNOLOGY INDUSTRY GROUP LIMITED

Room 1801 18th floor Kai Tak Commercial Building, 317 & 319 Des Voeux Road, Central, China (Hong Kong)
Tel.: (852) 26822308   Ky
Web Site:
http://www.chinatechsolar.com
8111—(HKG)
Rev.: $11,064,060
Assets: $25,425,046
Liabilities: $12,465,012
Net Worth: $12,960,034
Earnings: ($571,320)
Emp.: 28
Fiscal Year-end: 03/31/22
Holding Company
N.A.I.C.S.: 551112
Tung Ping Chiu *(Chm & CEO)*

Subsidiaries:

Truth Honour Electronic Limited   (1)
Room 1104 SUP Tower 75 Kings Road, North Point, China (Hong Kong)
Tel.: (852) 28026881
Solar Power Structure Construction Services
N.A.I.C.S.: 237130

CHINA TELECOMMUNICATIONS CORPORATION

31 Jinrong Street, Xicheng District,
Beijing, 100033, China
Tel.: (852) 28779777   CN
Web Site:
http://www.chinatelecom.com.cn
Year Founded: 2000
Telecommunication Servicesb
N.A.I.C.S.: 551112
Liang Baojun *(Pres & COO)*

Subsidiaries:

China Telecom Corporation Limited   (1)
31 Jinrong Street, Xicheng District, Beijing, 100033, China   **(70.89%)**
Tel.: (86) 1058501508
Web Site: http://www.chinatelecom-h.com
Rev.: $67,595,299,200
Assets: $52,126,448,400
Net Worth: $61,274,350,800
Earnings: $3,885,710,400
Emp.: 280,683
Fiscal Year-end: 12/31/2022
Wire-Line Telecommunications Services
N.A.I.C.S.: 551112
Zhongyue Chen *(Exec VP)*

Subsidiary (Domestic):

China Communications Services Corporation Limited   (2)
Block No 1 Compound No 1 Fenghuangzui Street, Fengtai District, Beijing, 100073, China
Tel.: (86) 1058502290
Web Site: https://www.chinaccs.com.hk
Rev.: $20,576,910,168
Assets: $16,862,781,070
Liabilities: $10,816,632,837
Net Worth: $6,046,148,233
Earnings: $516,681,020
Emp.: 3,576
Fiscal Year-end: 12/31/2023
Telecommunication Servicesb
N.A.I.C.S.: 517810
Furong Si *(Co-Pres)*

Subsidiary (Non-US):

China Telecom (Australia) Pty Ltd   (2)

China Telecommunications Corporation—(Continued)

Suite 2 Level 10 50 Pitt Street, Sydney,
2000, NSW, Australia
Tel.: (61) 292528821
Telecommunication Servicesb
N.A.I.C.S.: 517810
Xuan Ye Anthea (Pres)

China Telecom (Canada) ULC (2)
175 Commerce Valley Drive W Unit 210,
Markham, L3T 7P6, ON, Canada
Tel.: (289) 597-8338
Web Site: http://www.chinatelecom.ca
Telecommunication Servicesb
N.A.I.C.S.: 517810
Kenneth Ma (Country Mgr)

China Telecom (Europe) Limited (2)
11th Floor Exchange Tower 1 Harbour Ex-
change Square, London, E14 9GE, United
Kingdom
Tel.: (44) 20 7537 7156
Web Site: http://www.cteurope.net
Emp.: 100
Telecommunication Servicesb
N.A.I.C.S.: 517810
Meng Li (Dir-Mobile Bus Dept)

Subsidiary (Non-US):

**China Telecom (Deutschland)
GmbH** (3)
Bockenheimer Landstrasse 77, 60325,
Frankfurt am Main, Germany
Tel.: (49) 69 240 032 901
Telecommunication Servicesb
N.A.I.C.S.: 517810
Yue Zhang (Mgr-HR & Admin)

China Telecom (France) Ltd. (3)
9 av Franklin D Roosevelt, 75008, Paris,
France
Tel.: (33) 1 45 61 22 49
Telecommunication Servicesb
N.A.I.C.S.: 517810

Subsidiary (Non-US):

**China Telecom (India) Private
Limited** (2)
1002 Ablock Iris Tech Park Sohna Road,
Gurgaon, 122 018, Haryana, India
Tel.: (91) 9582290196
Telecommunication Servicesb
N.A.I.C.S.: 517810
Alen Wang (Mng Dir)

**China Telecom (Kazakhstan) Limited
Liability Partnership** (2)
19 Al-Farabi Ave, Nurly Tau 1B Office 205,
050059, Almaty, Kazakhstan
Tel.: (7) 727 330 89 02
Emp.: 5
Telecommunication Servicesb
N.A.I.C.S.: 517810
Olzhan Kassym (Gen Mgr)

**China Telecom (Malaysia) Sdn.
Bhd.** (2)
Level 11 Quill 7 No 9 Jalan Stesen Sentral
5 Kuala Lumpur Central, 50470, Kuala
Lumpur, Malaysia
Tel.: (60) 6339 0080
Telecommunication Servicesb
N.A.I.C.S.: 517810

**China Telecom (Singapore) Pte.
Ltd.** (2)
250 North Bridge Road Ste 36-01A/02
Raffles City Tower, Singapore, 179101,
Singapore
Tel.: (65) 6339 0080
Telecommunication Servicesb
N.A.I.C.S.: 517810
Lynn Dai (Pres)

Subsidiary (US):

China Telecom Americas (2)
607 Herndon Pkwy Ste 201, Herndon, VA
20170
Tel.: (703) 787-0088
Web Site: http://www.ctamericas.com
Sales Range: $25-49.9 Million
Emp.: 20
Telecommunication Servicesb
N.A.I.C.S.: 517111
Luis E. Fiallo (Mng Dir-Bus Dev)

Subsidiary (Non-US):

**China Telecom Information Technol-
ogy (Vietnam) Co., Ltd.** (2)
V407 Pacific Place 83B Ly Thuong Kiet,
Hoan Kiem, Hanoi, Vietnam
Tel.: (84) 4 39461883
Telecommunication Servicesb
N.A.I.C.S.: 517810

China Telecom Korea Limited (2)
Seoul Finance Center 7F Taepyeongno
1-ga, Jung-Gu, Seoul, Korea (South)
Tel.: (82) 2 3789 1628
Telecommunication Servicesb
N.A.I.C.S.: 517810

China Telecom Middle East (2)
Office 7 1st Floor Building 12 Dubai Internet
City, PO Box 73030, Dubai, United Arab
Emirates
Tel.: (971) 4 3756 989
Telecommunication Servicesb
N.A.I.C.S.: 517810

**China Telecom South Africa (Pty)
Ltd** (2)
Ground Floor Building 16 The Woodlands
Office Park Cnr Woodlands, Kelvin Drive
Woodmead, Sandton, 2196, South Africa
Tel.: (27) 11 656 3196
Web Site:
http://www.chinatelecomglobal.com
Emp.: 5
Telecommunication Servicesb
N.A.I.C.S.: 517810
Donald Nxumalo (Bus Mgr)

China Telecom do Brasil Ltda. (2)
Rua Dom Jose de Barros 177 8o Andar
Conjunto 801, Vila Buarque, 01038-100,
Sao Paulo, Brazil
Tel.: (55) 11 975839318
Telecommunication Servicesb
N.A.I.C.S.: 517810
Yi Wang (Gen Mgr)

Subsidiary (Domestic):

**Jiangsu Telecom Company
Limited** (2)
268 Hanzhong Road, Nanjing, 210029,
China (100%)
Tel.: (86) 256588577
Web Site: http://www.telecomjs.com
Telecommunication Servicesb
N.A.I.C.S.: 517111

Subsidiary (Non-US):

**Limited Liability Company China
Telecom** (2)
Office 601 Block 1 Lubyanskiy Proezd 11/1,
101000, Moscow, Russia
Tel.: (7) 91 9970 0669
Telecommunication Servicesb
N.A.I.C.S.: 517810

Subsidiary (Non-US):

China Telecom Global Ltd (3)
28/F Everbright Centre 108 Gloucester
Road, Wanchai, China (Hong Kong)
Tel.: (852) 31000000
Web Site:
http://www.chinatelecomglobal.com
Telecommunication Servicesb
N.A.I.C.S.: 517810
Kate Lui (Sr Acct Mgr)

Subsidiary (Non-US):

PT China Telecom Indonesia (2)
Suite 3110 31st Floor Wisma 46-Kota BNI
Jl Jend Sudirman Kav 1, Jakarta, 10220,
Indonesia
Tel.: (62) 21 572 1385
Telecommunication Servicesb
N.A.I.C.S.: 517810
Michael Yu (Mng Dir)

Joint Venture (Domestic):

**Yangtze Optical Fibre & Cable Joint
Stock Limited Company** (2)
No 9 Optics Valley Avenue, Wuhan,
430073, China
Tel.: (86) 2768789088
Web Site: http://www.yofc.com
Rev.: $1,259,622,143

Assets: $2,429,236,476
Liabilities: $991,280,957
Net Worth: $1,437,955,519
Earnings: $83,297,213
Emp.: 7,000
Fiscal Year-end: 12/31/2020
Fiber Optic Cable Mfr
N.A.I.C.S.: 335921
Frank Franciscus Dorjee (Exec Dir)

CHINA TELETECH HOLDING,
INC.
Guanlan Area Xintian Jun xin Indus-
trial Zone Building, Bao an District,
Shenzhen, Guangdon, China
Tel.: (86) 2150917695 FL
Web Site:
http://www.chinateletech.com
Year Founded: 1999
CNCT—(OTCEM)
Emp.: 1
Holding Company; Prepaid Calling
Card & Mobile Phone Distr & Ser-
vices
N.A.I.C.S.: 551112
Yan-Ping Sheng (Pres, CEO & CFO)

Subsidiaries:

China Teletech Limited (1)
Room A 20/F International Trade Residen-
tial and Commercial Building, Nanhu Road,
Shenzhen, China (100%)
Tel.: (86) 75582204422
Sales Range: $10-24.9 Million
Emp.: 18
Prepaid Calling Card & Mobile Phone Distr
& Services
N.A.I.C.S.: 423610

CHINA TELEVISION COMPANY
118 Chung Yang Road, Taipei, Tai-
wan
Tel.: (886) 227838308
Web Site: http://new.ctv.com.tw
9928—(TAI)
Rev.: $32,294,449
Assets: $118,802,082
Liabilities: $104,483,007
Net Worth: $14,319,075
Earnings: ($278,884)
Emp.: 6,000
Fiscal Year-end: 12/31/23
Color Television Production & Broad-
casting Services
N.A.I.C.S.: 516120
Hu Hsueh Chu (Chm & Gen Mgr)

CHINA TELEVISION MEDIA,
LTD.
22F Building B Winterland Center No
1 Xida Wang Road, Chaoyang Dis-
trict, Beijing, 100026, China
Tel.: (86) 1065999000
Web Site: https://www.ctv-
media.com.cn
Year Founded: 1997
600088—(SHG)
Rev.: $161,388,705
Assets: $219,019,226
Liabilities: $72,186,239
Net Worth: $146,832,988
Earnings: ($9,166,716)
Fiscal Year-end: 12/31/22
Television Program Production Ser-
vices
N.A.I.C.S.: 512110
He Fang (Sec)

CHINA THREE GORGES COR-
PORATION
No 1 Liuhe Road, Jiang'an District,
Wuhan City, Hubei, China
Tel.: (86) 1057081588
Web Site: https://www.ctg.com.cn
Year Founded: 1993
Emp.: 100
Hydroelectric Power Generation
N.A.I.C.S.: 221111

Subsidiaries:

**China Three Gorges Brasil Energia
Ltda.** (1)
Rua Funchal 418 3 floor, 04551-060, Sao
Paulo, Brazil
Tel.: (55) 11 5632 3200
Web Site: http://www.ctgbr.com.br
Emp.: 1,064
Holding Company; Hydroelectric, Wind &
Solar Power Plant Operator
N.A.I.C.S.: 551112
Yinsheng Li (CEO)

Subsidiary (Domestic):

**Rio Paranapanema Participacoes
S.A.** (2)
Avenida das Nacoes Unidas 12 901 Torre
Norte 30th andar, 04578-000, Sao Paulo,
SP, Brazil
Tel.: (55) 1155013400
Holding Company; Hydroelectric Power
Plant Operator
N.A.I.C.S.: 551112

Subsidiary (Domestic):

Rio Paranapanema Energia S.A. (3)
Avenida das Nacoes Unidas 12 901 30th
andar, 04578-910, Sao Paulo, SP,
Brazil (94.28%)
Tel.: (55) 1155013400
Web Site:
http://www.paranapanemaenergia.com.br
Rev.: $244,801,302
Assets: $664,441,269
Liabilities: $329,872,251
Net Worth: $334,568,912
Earnings: $43,478,843
Emp.: 329
Fiscal Year-end: 12/31/2022
Hydroelectric Power Generation & Distribu-
tion
N.A.I.C.S.: 221111
Yinsheng Li (Chm & CEO)

**China Three Gorges Renewables
(Group) Co., Ltd.** (1)
Room 206-23 2nd Floor Building 1 No. 1
Gongyuan Street, Tongzhou District, Beijing,
101199, China
Tel.: (86) 1057680278
Web Site: https://www.ctg.com.cn
Rev.: $3,667,128,988
Assets: $43,158,446,071
Liabilities: $29,937,779,935
Net Worth: $13,220,666,136
Earnings: $994,279,838
Fiscal Year-end: 12/31/2023
Wind Electric Power Generation
N.A.I.C.S.: 221115
Zhang Long (Exec Chm & Gen Mgr)

China Yangtze Power Co., Ltd. (1)
Building B Fukai Building No 19 Financial
Street, Xicheng District, Beijing, 100032,
China
Tel.: (86) 1058688999
Web Site: https://www.cypc.com.cn
Rev.: $7,309,291,757
Assets: $45,948,467,214
Liabilities: $18,464,590,282
Net Worth: $27,483,876,932
Earnings: $2,991,788,374
Emp.: 7,750
Fiscal Year-end: 12/31/2022
Hydroelectric Power Generation
N.A.I.C.S.: 221111
Zhenbo Ma (Vice Chm)

Subsidiary (Domestic):

**China Yangtze Power International
(Hong Kong) Co., Ltd.** (2)
21F Focus Place B 19 Financial Street,
Xicheng District, Beijing, 100033, China
Tel.: (86) 1058688933
Web Site: http://www.cypi.hk
Eletric Power Generation Services
N.A.I.C.S.: 221111
Qin Guobin (Pres)

Subsidiary (Non-US):

**Los Andes Servicios Corporativos
S.A.C.** (2)
Av Calango s/n, San Juan de Miraflores,
15842, Lima, Peru
Tel.: (51) 17002800

Web Site: https://www.andes.com.pe
Electrical Equipment & Mining Sector Transportation Services
N.A.I.C.S.: 561910

Tecsur S.A.   (2)
Pasaje Calango 158, San Juan de Miraflores, Peru
Tel.: (51) 17000000
Web Site: https://www.tecsur.com.pe
Emp.: 1,000
Electronic Services
N.A.I.C.S.: 238210

CHINA TIAN YUAN HEALTHCARE GROUP LIMITED

Room Nos 1120-1126 11/F Sun Hung Kai Centre, 30 Harbour Road, Wanchai, China (Hong Kong)
Tel.: (852) 25681008   Ky
Web Site: http://www.tianyuanhealthcare.com
Rev.: $21,905,986
Assets: $90,056,182
Liabilities: $16,506,614
Net Worth: $73,549,568
Earnings: ($5,113,601)
Emp.: 84
Fiscal Year-end: 12/31/18
Business Consulting Services
N.A.I.C.S.: 541611
Jiang Yulin *(Chm)*

CHINA TIANBAO GROUP DEVELOPMENT COMPANY LIMITED

No 33 Guanyun East Road,
Zhuozhou, Hebei, China
Tel.: (86) 3123650258   Ky
Web Site: http://www.chinatbjt.com
Year Founded: 1998
1427—(HKG)
Rev.: $516,216,735
Assets: $989,831,590
Liabilities: $788,224,849
Net Worth: $201,606,741
Earnings: $50,815,314
Emp.: 428
Fiscal Year-end: 12/31/20
Real Estate Development Services
N.A.I.C.S.: 531390
Baotian Li *(Chm & CEO)*

CHINA TIANFEIHONG WINE, INC.

1849 Licheng Middle Avenue,
Chengxiang District, Putian, 351100,
Fujian, China
Tel.: (86) 549 6258386   DE
Year Founded: 2005
Sales Range: $1-9.9 Million
Emp.: 27
Fruit Wine Distr
N.A.I.C.S.: 424820
Zhiliang Fang *(Chm & CEO)*

CHINA TIANRUI AUTOMOTIVE INTERIORS CO., LTD.

No 6 Weihua Road North Jingwei Xincheng, Xi An Economic & Technological Development Zone, Xi'an, Shaanxi, China
Tel.: (86) 298 696 2279   Ky
Web Site: http://www.trqcns.com
6162—(HKG)
Rev.: $45,315,841
Assets: $87,684,534
Liabilities: $46,827,717
Net Worth: $40,856,817
Earnings: $1,122,876
Emp.: 507
Fiscal Year-end: 12/31/21
Automotive Parts Mfr & Distr
N.A.I.C.S.: 335139
Jianli Hou *(Founder, Chm, CEO & Gen Mgr)*

CHINA TIANRUI GROUP CEMENT COMPANY LIMITED

No 63 Guangcheng East Road, Ruzhou, 467500, Henan, China
Tel.: (86) 3756056006   Ky
Web Site: http://www.trcement.com
1252—(HKG)
Rev.: $1,864,681,220
Assets: $4,970,055,948
Liabilities: $2,699,039,746
Net Worth: $2,271,016,203
Earnings: $301,892,645
Emp.: 7,787
Fiscal Year-end: 12/31/20
Cement Mfr
N.A.I.C.S.: 327310
Liufa Li *(Founder)*

Subsidiaries:

Tianrui Group Nanzhao Cement
Company Limited   (1)
231 Provincial Road Nanzhao, Nanyang,
Henan, China
Tel.: (86) 377 6663 3333
Cement Product Mfr & Distr
N.A.I.C.S.: 327310

Tianrui Group Zhoukou Cement Company Limited   (1)
West Side End Of Zhouluo Road, Guanpo
Village Nanjiao, Zhoukou, 466060, Henan,
China
Tel.: (86) 3948301536
Cement Product Mfr & Distr
N.A.I.C.S.: 327310

Tianrui Xindeng Zhengzhou Cement
Company Limited   (1)
Qingshigou, Xuanhua Town Dengfeng,
Henan, China
Tel.: (86) 3716 297 5868
Web Site: https://www.xdcem.com
Cement Mfr
N.A.I.C.S.: 327310

CHINA TIANYF HOLDINGS GROUP LIMITED

No 18 Keyan Road Science City
High-tech Industrial Development
Zone, Guangzhou, China
Tel.: (86) 2032016868   Ky
Web Site:
http://www.greatwater.com.cn
Year Founded: 2001
8196—(HKG)
Rev.: $36,047,560
Assets: $46,514,520
Liabilities: $36,538,679
Net Worth: $9,975,841
Earnings: ($1,621,199)
Emp.: 69
Fiscal Year-end: 12/31/22
Waste Treatment Services
N.A.I.C.S.: 221310
Yang Xie *(Chm & CEO)*

Subsidiaries:

Guangzhou Great Water Environmental Protection Co., Ltd.   (1)
Ke Yan Lu No 18 Guangzhou Science City,
Guangzhou, China
Tel.: (86) 2032016868
Web Site: https://www.greatwater.com.cn
Environmental Remediation Services
N.A.I.C.S.: 562910

Shanghai Great Water Environmental
Protection Co., Ltd.   (1)
Room 1088 Xiangyian No 1808 Cadillac
Building, Yangpu, Shanghai, China
Tel.: (86) 2165116528
Environmental Remediation Services
N.A.I.C.S.: 562910

Vietnam Great Water Environmental
Protection Co., Ltd.   (1)
Vinaconex 9 tower HH2-2 area Pham Hung
Road, Me Tri ward NamTuLiem District, Hanoi, Vietnam
Tel.: (84) 432004001
Environmental Remediation Services
N.A.I.C.S.: 562910

CHINA TIANYING INC.

No 268 Huanghai Avenue West, Haian County, Nantong, 226600, Jiangsu, China
Tel.: (86) 51380688810
Web Site: http://www.ctyi.com.cn
Year Founded: 1994
000035—(SSE)
Rev.: $941,620,680
Assets: $3,716,074,908
Liabilities: $2,250,567,072
Net Worth: $1,465,507,836
Earnings: $17,337,996
Emp.: 7,787
Fiscal Year-end: 12/31/22
Communication Equipment Mfr
N.A.I.C.S.: 334220
Shengjun Yan *(Chm)*

Subsidiaries:

Aplas Ltd.   (1)
359 Terry Fox Dr, Kanata, K2K 2E7, ON,
Canada
Tel.: (613) 271-0668
Waste Treatment Services
N.A.I.C.S.: 562211

Europe TianYing BVBA   (1)
Pastoor Cooremansstraat 3 Groot-Bijgaarden, 1702, Brussels, Belgium
Tel.: (32) 28937311
Web Site: http://www.ctyi.com.cn
Emp.: 12
Waste Treatment Services
N.A.I.C.S.: 562211
Jingwen Xu *(Project Engr)*

Firion Investments SL   (1)
Calle de Claudio Coello 124, 28006, Madrid, Spain
Financial Investment Services
N.A.I.C.S.: 523999
Maria Lorena Salamanca Cuevas *(Dir)*

CHINA TIME SHARE MEDIA CO. LTD.

Chuanban Dayu Building 312 Long
Zhua Shu Xiao Hong M, Chaoyang
District, Beijing, 100078, China
Tel.: (86) 1087695559   Ky
Web Site: http://www.dytsm.com
Sales Range: $25-49.9 Million
Emp.: 586
Advertising Services
N.A.I.C.S.: 541890
Jilun He *(Chm & CEO)*

CHINA TING GROUP HOLDINGS LIMITED

27/F King Palace Plaza 55 King Yip
Street, Kwun Tong, Kowloon, China
(Hong Kong)
Tel.: (852) 22737800   Ky
Web Site:
https://www.chinating.com.hk
Year Founded: 1992
3398—(HKG)
Rev.: $207,563,129
Assets: $514,093,514
Liabilities: $164,047,211
Net Worth: $350,046,303
Earnings: ($42,846,382)
Emp.: 3,660
Fiscal Year-end: 12/31/21
Holding Company; Apparel Mfr &
Retailer
N.A.I.C.S.: 551112
Raymond Ho Lung Cheng *(Sec & Controller-Fin)*

Subsidiaries:

China Ting Garment Mfg (Group)
Limited   (1)
27th Floor King Palace Plaza 55 King Yip
Street, Kwun Tong, Kowloon, China (Hong
Kong)   (100%)
Tel.: (852) 29509788
Web Site: https://www.chinating.com.hk
Emp.: 70
Finished Garment International Trade Whslr
N.A.I.C.S.: 425120

CHINA TITANS ENERGY TECHNOLOGY GROUP CO., LTD.

Titans Industrial Park shihuaxilu, Zhuhai, 519015, China
Tel.: (86) 7563325899   Ky
Web Site: http://www.titans.com.cn
Year Founded: 1992
2188—(HKG)
Rev.: $42,223,450
Assets: $126,618,872
Liabilities: $49,264,216
Net Worth: $77,354,657
Earnings: ($4,628,627)
Emp.: 410
Fiscal Year-end: 12/31/20
Power Electronics & Automation Control Mfr
N.A.I.C.S.: 334416
Wei An *(CEO)*

CHINA TMK BATTERY SYSTEMS INC.

Rm 2406 Greater China International
Trade Plaza Fuhua Rd, Futian District, Shenzhen, 518046, China
Tel.: (86) 75582865777   NV
Year Founded: 2006
DFEL—(OTCIQ)
Sales Range: $10-24.9 Million
Emp.: 80
Nickel Metal Hydride Cell (Ni-MH)
Rechargeable Batteries Mfr & Sales
N.A.I.C.S.: 335910
Henian Wu *(Chm, CEO & CFO)*

CHINA TOBACCO INTERNATIONAL (HK) COMPANY LIMITED

Room 1002 10/F Tower A China Life
Center One Harbour Gate, 18 Hung
Luen Road Hung Hom, Kowloon,
China (Hong Kong)   HK
Web Site: https://www.ctihk.com.hk
Year Founded: 1989
6055—(HKG)
Rev.: $1,073,655,972
Assets: $821,669,752
Liabilities: $533,065,443
Net Worth: $288,604,309
Earnings: $59,867,166
Emp.: 246
Fiscal Year-end: 12/31/22
Tobacco Leaf Product Distr
N.A.I.C.S.: 424940
Chengrui Wang *(Sec)*

Subsidiaries:

China Brasil Tabacos Exportadora
S.A.   (1)
Street Silveira Martins 1733, Venancio Aires, CEP 95800-000, Brazil
Tel.: (55) 37934500
Web Site: https://www.cbtexport.com
Emp.: 200
Tobacco Leaves Mfr
N.A.I.C.S.: 312230

CHINA TONTINE WINES GROUP LIMITED

Room 1703 17th Floor COFCO
Tower, No 262 Gloucester Road
Causeway Bay, Hong Kong, China
(Hong Kong)
Tel.: (852) 2 521 1628   BM
Web Site: http://www.tontine-wines.com.hk
0389—(HKG)
Rev.: $31,924,521
Assets: $98,948,993
Liabilities: $10,279,778
Net Worth: $88,669,215
Earnings: $2,637,663
Emp.: 318
Fiscal Year-end: 12/31/21
Wine Producer & Distr

China Tontine Wines Group Limited—(Continued)
N.A.I.C.S.: 312130
Guangyuan Wang (CEO & Chm)

CHINA TOPREACH INC.
6th Floor San Shan Tower 59 Dongjie Street, Fuzhou, 350001, China
Tel.: (86) 5918 831 0920 **Ky**
Web Site:
  http://www.chinatopreach.com
CGSXF—(OTCIQ)
Sales Range: $75-99.9 Million
Emp.: 1,070
Newpaper & Online Publisher
N.A.I.C.S.: 513110
Zhi Chen (CEO)

CHINA TOURISM AND CULTURE INVESTMENT GROUP CO., LTD.
19th Floor Jianglv Industrial Building No 169 Fuzhou Road, Donghu District, Nanjing, 330006, Jiangxi, China
Tel.: (86) 79182263019
Web Site: http://www.cutc.com.cn
Year Founded: 1998
600358—(SHG)
Rev.: $79,266,849
Assets: $66,658,986
Liabilities: $40,947,674
Net Worth: $25,711,312
Earnings: $1,049,350
Fiscal Year-end: 12/31/22
Resort Operator
N.A.I.C.S.: 721110
Shi Liang (Vice Chm)

CHINA TOURISM GROUP DUTY FREE CORPORATION LIMITED
Room 418 Building A Zhengdong International Building No 2-1, Dongzhimenwai Xiaojie Dongcheng District, Beijing, China
Tel.: (86) 4000500180
Web Site:
  https://www.ctgdutyfree.com.cn
Year Founded: 1984
1880—(HKG)
Rev.: $9,351,476,601
Assets: $10,920,110,517
Liabilities: $2,725,931,976
Net Worth: $8,194,178,542
Earnings: $929,564,508
Fiscal Year-end: 12/31/23
Alcoholic Beverage Distr
N.A.I.C.S.: 424820
Hui Peng (Chm)

Subsidiaries:

CITS Group Shanghai Co., Ltd. **(1)**
16th Floor Building 1 Chang an Building No 1001 Chang an Road, Shanghai, 200070, China
Tel.: (86) 2163178705
Web Site: http://www.citssh.com
Tour Operator
N.A.I.C.S.: 561520

China Duty Free Group Corporation **(1)**
Room 418 Building A Zhengdong International Mansion, No A 2-1 Dongzhimenwai Xiaojie Road Dongcheng District, Beijing, 100027, China
Tel.: (86) 4000500180
Web Site: https://www.cdfg.com.cn
Tour Operator
N.A.I.C.S.: 561520
Charles Chen (Pres)

China International Travel Service (Qingdao) Co., Ltd. **(1)**
Qingdao Wanda Plaza Commercial Building Central Business District, Block B 5 Layer Lianyungang Road 33 525, Qingdao, 266034, China
Tel.: (86) 53266067001
Web Site: http://www.citsqd.net

Tour Operator
N.A.I.C.S.: 561520

China International Travel Service Dalian Co., Ltd. **(1)**
No 9 Liberation Street Wanda Building 4 Layer, Zhongshan District, Dalian, China
Tel.: (86) 4006781954
Web Site: http://www.citsdl.com.cn
Tour Operator
N.A.I.C.S.: 561520

Chongqing China International Travel Service Co., Ltd. **(1)**
10th Floor No 177 Bayi Road, Yuzhong District, Chongqing, China
Tel.: (86) 2363821162
Web Site: http://www.citscq.com
Tour Operator
N.A.I.C.S.: 561520

Dandong China International Travel Service Co., Ltd. **(1)**
20-2 Shiwe Road, Dandong, China
Tel.: (86) 4152132237
Web Site: http://www.ddcits.com
Travel Management Services
N.A.I.C.S.: 561510

Guizhou China International Travel Service Co., Ltd. **(1)**
No 53 East Yingpan Road, Kaili, Guizhou, China
Tel.: (86) 8558222506
Web Site: http://www.guizhoucits.com
Tour Operator
N.A.I.C.S.: 561520

Heilongjiang China International Travel Service Limited **(1)**
East Straight Street No 261 Building 18 Layer Industry, Nangang District, Harbin, China
Tel.: (86) 4000561000
Web Site: http://www.en.hlj-cits.com
Tour Operator
N.A.I.C.S.: 561520

Huangshan China International Travel Service Co., Ltd. **(1)**
Room 810 Building a of Tiandu Mansion No 9 Tiandu Road, Tunxi District, Huangshan, 245000, Anhui, China
Tel.: (86) 5592542110
Web Site: http://www.huangshantour.com
Tour Operator
N.A.I.C.S.: 561520
Johnson Yeh (Dir-Individual Travelers Dept)

Kunming China International Travel Service Co., Ltd. **(1)**
No 1118 South Ring Road, Kunming, 650011, China
Tel.: (86) 87163566660
Web Site: http://www.kmcits.cn
Tour Operator
N.A.I.C.S.: 561520

Lijiang China International Travel Service Co., Ltd. **(1)**
Lifang Commercial Building Shangri-La Avenue, Lijiang, 674100, Yunnan, China
Tel.: (86) 8885160370
Web Site: http://www.ljcits.cn
Travel Management Services
N.A.I.C.S.: 561510

Wuyishan China International Travel Service Co., Ltd. **(1)**
CITS Building SanGu Street WuYiShan City Holiday Resort, Fuzhou, 354302, Fujian, China
Tel.: (86) 5995301390
Web Site: http://www.wuyishanguide.com
Tour Guide & Other Travel Services
N.A.I.C.S.: 561510

Xian China International Travel Service Co., Ltd. **(1)**
48 Changan North Road, Beilin District, Xi'an, Shaanxi, China
Tel.: (86) 2962889999
Web Site: http://www.citsxa.com
Tour Operator
N.A.I.C.S.: 561520

Zhangjiajie China International Travel Service Co., Ltd. **(1)**
Office Building 4th Floor Guolv Building No

631 Ziwu Road, Zhangjiajie, China
Tel.: (86) 7442200001
Web Site: http://www.zjjvip.com
Travel Agency Services
N.A.I.C.S.: 561510

Zhejiang China International Travel Service Co., Ltd. **(1)**
12/15th Floor Xincheng Building No 639 Qianjiang Road, Hangzhou, 010000, China
Tel.: (86) 57185059000
Web Site: http://www.zjcits1954.com
Emp.: 200
International Travel Agency Services
N.A.I.C.S.: 561510

Zhuhai China International Travel Service Co., Ltd. **(1)**
Fenghuang Road South 1034, Zhuhai, China
Tel.: (86) 7562120028
Web Site: http://www.zhcits.com
Tour Operator
N.A.I.C.S.: 561520

CHINA TOWER CORPORATION LIMITED
Room 3401 34/F China Resources Building 26 Harbour Road, Wanchai, China (Hong Kong)
Tel.: (852) 28114566 **CN**
Web Site: https://ir.china-tower.com
Year Founded: 2014
0788—(HKG)
Rev.: $12,761,685,866
Assets: $42,307,266,283
Liabilities: $15,503,018,387
Net Worth: $26,804,247,895
Earnings: $1,216,631,591
Emp.: 1,503
Fiscal Year-end: 12/31/22
Telecommunication Servicesb
N.A.I.C.S.: 517112
Jilu Tong (Chm)

CHINA TRAVEL INTERNATIONAL INVESTMENT HONG KONG LTD
12/F CTS House 78-83 Connaught Road, Central, China (Hong Kong)
Tel.: (852) 28533888
Web Site: http://www.ctg.cn
0308—(HKG)
Rev.: $470,496,984
Assets: $3,328,767,174
Liabilities: $862,509,639
Net Worth: $2,466,257,535
Earnings: ($11,812,891)
Emp.: 5,199
Fiscal Year-end: 12/31/21
Tour Operations, Hotels, Theme Parks, Passenger & Freight Transportation, Golf Club & Infrastructure Investment Services
N.A.I.C.S.: 561520
Qiang Wu (Chm, Deputy Gen Mgr & Exec Dir)

Subsidiaries:

Agencia De Viagens E Turismo Grand, Limitada **(1)**
Rua de Pequim n s 202-246 Edifcio Macau Finance Centre 17andar M, Macau, China (Macau)
Tel.: (853) 28700044
Travel Management Services
N.A.I.C.S.: 561510

China Heaven Creation International Performing Arts Co., Ltd. **(1)**
yabao road 18th floor hua sheng electronic international building, Chaoyang District, Beijing, 100020, China
Tel.: (86) 5 120 6688
Web Site: https://www.heaven-creation.com
Performing Art Services
N.A.I.C.S.: 711190

China Travel & Trading (Deutschland) GmbH **(1)**
Dusseldorfer Strasse 14, 60329, Frankfurt am Main, Germany

Tel.: (49) 699705260
Web Site: http://www.chinatravelservice.de
Travel Management Services
N.A.I.C.S.: 561510
Yuhong Zhang (Mng Dir)

China Travel Hi-Tech Computer Hong Kong Ltd. **(1)**
11/F China Travel Group Building 78-83 Connaught Road, Central, China (Hong Kong)
Tel.: (852) 2 853 3200
Web Site: https://www.ctseb.com
Travel Management Services
N.A.I.C.S.: 561510

China Travel Service (Australia) Pty. Ltd. **(1)**
Suite 3-7 Level 1 650 George St World Square, Sydney, 2000, NSW, Australia
Tel.: (61) 29 372 0000
Web Site: https://www.chinatravel.com.au
Travel Management Services
N.A.I.C.S.: 561510

China Travel Service (Canada) Inc. **(1)**
100 Sheppard Avenue East Suite 780, Toronto, M2N 6N5, ON, Canada
Tel.: (416) 979-8993
Web Site: https://www.canadacts.com
Tour Operator
N.A.I.C.S.: 561520

China Travel Service (Hong Kong) Ltd. **(1)**
Ground Floor CTS House 78-83 Connaught Road, Central, China (Hong Kong)
Tel.: (852) 2 998 7888
Web Site: https://w1.ctshk.com
Travel Management Services
N.A.I.C.S.: 561510

China Travel Service (Korea) Co., Ltd. **(1)**
No 403 Da Dong B/D 92 Da-Dong, Chung-ku, Seoul, 100180, Korea (South)
Tel.: (82) 27523399
Web Site: http://www.ctshk.com
Travel Management Services
N.A.I.C.S.: 561510

China Travel Service (N.Z.) Ltd. **(1)**
Level 2 CTS House 175 Queen Street, PO Box 105516, Auckland, New Zealand
Tel.: (64) 93096458
Web Site: http://www.kiwiyou.co.nz
Travel Management Services
N.A.I.C.S.: 561510

China Travel Service (U.K.) Ltd. **(1)**
CTS House 7 Upper St Martins Lane, London Wall, London, WC2H 9DL, United Kingdom
Tel.: (44) 1718369911
Web Site: http://www.ctshk.com
Travel Management Services
N.A.I.C.S.: 561510

China Travel Service (U.S.A.) Inc. **(1)**
388 E Valley Blvd Ste 210-211, Alhambra, CA 91801
Tel.: (626) 457-8668
Web Site:
  https://www.chinatravelservice.com
Travel Management Services
N.A.I.C.S.: 561510

CHINA TREASURE MINE TECHNOLOGY HOLDINGS CO., LTD.
Oxford Commercial Building 18F 494-496 Nathan Road, Kowloon, China (Hong Kong)
Tel.: (852) 277 18608
Web Site: http://www.bomkon.com
Sales Range: $1-9.9 Million
Internet & Mobile Application Software
N.A.I.C.S.: 513210

CHINA TREASURES NEW MATERIALS GROUP LTD.
Room 1910 19/F C C Wu

Building302-308 Hennessy Road, Wanchai, China (Hong Kong)
Tel.: (852) 4318256933   Ky
Web Site: https://www.jl-ks.cn
Year Founded: 2014
2439—(HKG)
Rev.: $45,930,673
Assets: $46,705,302
Liabilities: $16,369,110
Net Worth: $30,336,193
Earnings: $8,730,978
Emp.: 159
Fiscal Year-end: 12/31/22
Plastic Product Mfr & Distr
N.A.I.C.S.: 326199
Peng Li (VP)

CHINA TRENDS HOLDINGS LIMITED

26/F No 9 Des Voeux Road West, Sheung Wan, China (Hong Kong)
Tel.: (852) 3106 2200   Ky
Web Site: http://www.8171.com.hk
Rev.: $11,114,138
Assets: $15,282,705
Liabilities: $323,694
Net Worth: $14,959,011
Earnings: ($683,525)
Emp.: 11
Fiscal Year-end: 12/31/18
Holding Company
N.A.I.C.S.: 551112
Xin Xiang (Chm & CEO)

Subsidiaries:

Boss Systems Limited   (1)
4 Lockhart Place Mount Wellington, 1060, Auckland, North Island, New Zealand
Tel.: (64) 92703615
Investment Holding Services
N.A.I.C.S.: 551112

CHINA TRUSTFUL GROUP LIMITED

Units 2610-2611 26/F China Merchants Tower Shun Tak Centre, 168-200 Connaught Road, Central, China (Hong Kong)
Tel.: (852) 2528 1280   BM
Web Site: http://www.china-trustful.com
Rev.: $27,542,222
Assets: $92,208,269
Liabilities: $9,384,704
Net Worth: $82,823,565
Earnings: $1,185,091
Emp.: 98
Fiscal Year-end: 12/31/18
Holding Company
N.A.I.C.S.: 551112
Jie Fei (Chm)

CHINA U-TON FUTURE SPACE INDUSTRIAL GROUP HOLDINGS LTD.

Room 2404 24th Floor Great Eagle Centre, 23 Harbour Road, Wanchai, China (Hong Kong)
Tel.: (852) 3 460 3561
Web Site: http://www.chinauton.com.hk
Rev.: $12,718,112
Assets: $119,102,586
Liabilities: $91,893,406
Net Worth: $27,209,180
Earnings: ($21,016,351)
Emp.: 196
Fiscal Year-end: 12/31/19
Underground Fiber Optic Cable Mfr
N.A.I.C.S.: 335921
Changqing Jiang (Founder & Chm)

CHINA UNION HOLDINGS LTD.

16th Floor Hualian Building No 2008 Shennan Middle Road, Futian District, Shenzhen, 518031, Guangdong, China
Tel.: (86) 75583667257
Web Site: http://www.udcgroup.com
Year Founded: 1994
000036—(SSE)
Rev.: $329,090,580
Assets: $1,296,721,764
Liabilities: $417,872,520
Net Worth: $878,849,244
Earnings: $61,179,300
Fiscal Year-end: 12/31/22
Holding Company
N.A.I.C.S.: 551112
Gong Zemin (Chm)

CHINA UNITED INSURANCE SERVICE, INC.

7F No 311 Section 3 Nan-King East Road, Taipei, 105405, Taiwan
Tel.: (886) 287126958   DE
Year Founded: 2010
CUII—(OTCQB)
Rev.: $131,930,218
Assets: $138,892,796
Liabilities: $62,360,340
Net Worth: $76,532,456
Earnings: $11,101,163
Emp.: 310
Fiscal Year-end: 12/31/22
Fire Insurance Services
N.A.I.C.S.: 524113
Yi Hsiao Mao (CEO)

Subsidiaries:

Joint Insurance Broker Co., Ltd.   (1)
7th Floor No 311 Section 3 Nanjing East Road, Songshan District, Taipei, Taiwan
Tel.: (886) 227138086
Web Site: https://www.jib.com.tw
Insurance Brokerage Services
N.A.I.C.S.: 524210

Prime Financial Asia Ltd.   (1)
2106 Technology Plaza 651 King's Road, Hong Kong, China (Hong Kong)
Tel.: (852) 25909896
Web Site: https://www.prime-fa.com
Insurance Brokerage Services
N.A.I.C.S.: 524210

Uniwill Insurance Broker Co., Ltd.   (1)
37th & 38th Floors No 386 Zhengzheng Road, Xitun District, Taichung, Taiwan
Tel.: (886) 422597555
Web Site: https://www.unibroker.com.tw
Insurance Broker Services
N.A.I.C.S.: 524210

CHINA UNITED NETWORK COMMUNICATIONS GROUP COMPANY LIMITED

No 21 Financial Street, Xicheng District, Beijing, 100140, China
Tel.: (86) 1066259550
Web Site: https://www.chinaunicom.com.hk
600050—(SHG)
Rev.: $49,834,120,640
Assets: $90,514,058,675
Liabilities: $41,756,722,624
Net Worth: $48,757,336,051
Earnings: $1,024,848,340
Fiscal Year-end: 12/31/22
Holding Company
N.A.I.C.S.: 551112
Wang Xiaochu (Chm)

Subsidiaries:

China Unicom (Hong Kong) Limited   (1)
75th Floor The Center 99 Queens Road Central, Hong Kong, China (Hong Kong)
Tel.: (852) 21262018
Web Site: http://www.chinaunicom.com.hk
Rev.: $51,589,083,961
Assets: $91,527,885,467
Liabilities: $42,527,830,084
Net Worth: $49,000,055,383

Earnings: $2,619,904,741
Emp.: 241,735
Fiscal Year-end: 12/31/2023
Telecommunications & Internet Services
Jacky Shun Loy Yung (Sec)

Subsidiary (US):

China Netcom (USA) Operations Limited   (2)
707 Wilshire Blvd Ste 3088, Los Angeles, CA 90017
Tel.: (213) 489-5636
Web Site: http://www.chinunicomamericas.com
Sales Range: $25-49.9 Million
Emp.: 30
Telecommunications
N.A.I.C.S.: 517810

Subsidiary (Domestic):

China Netcom Group Corporation (Hong Kong) Limited   (2)
46 Floor Cheung Kong Centre, 2 Queens Road, Central, China (Hong Kong)
Tel.: (852) 2626 8888
Web Site: http://www.china-netcom.com
Sales Range: $5-14.9 Billion
Emp.: 142,110
Broadband Internet Access & Telecom Services
N.A.I.C.S.: 517111

Subsidiary (Non-US):

China Unicom (Europe) Operations Limited   (2)
Level 32 25 Canada Square, London, E14 5LQ, Canary Wharf, United Kingdom
Tel.: (44) 2077151999
Telecommunication Servicesb
N.A.I.C.S.: 517111

China Unicom (Japan) Operations Corporation   (2)
2403-B Mita Kokusai Building 1428 Minato-ku, 1-4-28 Mita Minato-ku, Tokyo, 108-0073, Japan
Tel.: (81) 354396698
Telecommunication Servicesb
N.A.I.C.S.: 517111

Subsidiary (US):

China Unicom USA Corporation   (2)
624 S Grant Ave Ste 900, Los Angeles, CA 90017
Tel.: (213) 624-1038
Telecommunications
N.A.I.C.S.: 517810

Subsidiary (Non-US):

Unicom New Century Telecommunications Corporation Limited   (2)
No 133A Xidan North St, Xicheng District, Beijing, 100032, China
Tel.: (86) 1066505588
Sales Range: $100-124.9 Million
Emp.: 400
Telecommunication Servicesb
N.A.I.C.S.: 517111

China United Network Communications Limited   (1)
29th Floor No 1033 Changning Road, Changning District, Shanghai, 200050, China
Tel.: (86) 21 527 322 28
Web Site: http://eng.chinaunicom.com
Telecommunications
N.A.I.C.S.: 517810

CHINA UNITED VENTURE INVESTMENT LIMITED

Unit 802 Level 8 Admiralty Centre Tower 2 18 Harcourt Road, Admiralty, Hong Kong, China (Hong Kong)
Tel.: (852) 27635048   Ky
Web Site: http://www.glorymark.com.tw
Year Founded: 2002
8159—(HKG)
Rev.: $43,255,013
Assets: $53,182,035
Liabilities: $31,110,765

Net Worth: $22,071,270
Earnings: $6,340,065
Fiscal Year-end: 12/31/22
Holding Company
N.A.I.C.S.: 551112
Kuo-Shi Pang (Co-Founder)

Subsidiaries:

Glory Mark Electronic Limited   (1)
3F No 6 Lane 148 Li Der Street Chung Ho City, Taipei, Taiwan
Tel.: (886) 222227133
Web Site: http://www.glorymark.com.tw
Emp.: 30
Computer Products Distr
N.A.I.C.S.: 423430
Steve Pang (Gen Mgr)

CHINA UPTOWN GROUP COMPANY LIMITED

Suite 1501 15/F Tower 1 Silvercord 30 Canton Road, Tsimshatsui, Kowloon, China (Hong Kong)
Tel.: (852) 35824878   Ky
Web Site: http://www.chinauptown.com.hk
2330—(HKG)
Rev.: $42,215,637
Assets: $167,990,322
Liabilities: $54,127,254
Net Worth: $113,863,067
Earnings: ($1,104,797)
Emp.: 41
Fiscal Year-end: 12/31/20
Investment Holding Services
N.A.I.C.S.: 551112
Anthony Sai Chung Lau (CEO)

CHINA VALVES TECHNOLOGY, INC.

93 West Xinsong Road, Kaifeng, 475002, Henan, China
Tel.: (86) 371 8601877   NV
Year Founded: 1997
Sales Range: $150-199.9 Million
Emp.: 1,900
Metal Valve Mfr
N.A.I.C.S.: 332919
Siping Fang (Chm, Pres & Sec)

CHINA VANADIUM TITANO-MAGNETITE MINING COMPANY LIMITED

31/F Tower Two Times Square 1 Matheson Street, Causeway Bay, China (Hong Kong)
Tel.: (852) 288 843 3449   Ky
Web Site: http://www.chinavtmmining.com
0893—(HKG)
Rev.: $109,508,380
Assets: $177,970,881
Liabilities: $35,464,591
Net Worth: $142,506,290
Earnings: $1,164,090
Emp.: 127
Fiscal Year-end: 12/31/21
Iron Ore Mining Services
N.A.I.C.S.: 212210
Zhong Ping Jiang (CEO)

CHINA VANKE CO., LTD.

Vanke Center No 33 Huanmei Road Dameisha, Yantian District, Shenzhen, 518083, Guangdong, China
Tel.: (86) 75525606666
Web Site: https://cnold.vanke.com
Year Founded: 1984
000002—(SSE)
Rev.: $64,485,361,750
Assets: $208,358,741,153
Liabilities: $152,569,317,844
Net Worth: $55,789,423,308
Earnings: $1,684,022,541
Emp.: 131,817
Fiscal Year-end: 12/31/23
Real Estate Manangement Services

China Vanke Co., Ltd.—(Continued)

N.A.I.C.S.: 531190
Liang Yu *(Chm)*

Subsidiaries:

Changchun Vanke Real Estate Development Company Limited **(1)**
Office Building Vanke Blue Mountain 666 Dongsheng Avenue, Erdao District, Changchun, 130033, China
Tel.: (86) 43189607800
N.A.I.C.S.: 531210

Chengdu Vanke Real Estate Company Limited **(1)**
Hi-Tech Vanke Tower 50 Yunhua Rd, Hi-Tech Zone, Chengdu, 610049, Sichuan, China
Tel.: (86) 2884781999
Real Estate Manangement Services
N.A.I.C.S.: 531390

Dalian Vanke Property Company Limited **(1)**
6C Zhoushuizi Plaza, Ganjingzi District, Dalian, 116000, China
Tel.: (86) 41184375601
N.A.I.C.S.: 531210

Dongguan Vanke Real Estate Company Limited **(1)**
8th Floor Business Tower GF Financial Building 3 Shizhu Road New City, Nancheng District, Dongguan, 523000, Guangdong, China
Tel.: (86) 76922306868
Real Estate Manangement Services
N.A.I.C.S.: 531390

Foshan Vanke Property Company Limited **(1)**
30th Floor Rural Commercial Bank Building No 26 Nanhai Avenue North, Nanhai District, Foshan, 528000, China
Tel.: (86) 75782365000
N.A.I.C.S.: 531210

Guangzhou Vanke Real Estate Company Limited **(1)**
42 Yanyu Road Ersha Isle, Yuexiu District, Guangzhou, 510105, Guangdong, China
Tel.: (86) 2087351866
Property Management Services
N.A.I.C.S.: 531390

Guiyang Vanke Real Estate Company Limited **(1)**
Guiyang Vanke Vanke Linglong Bay Shuidong Road, Yunyan District, Guiyang, 5500081, Guizhou, China
Tel.: (86) 8518599996
N.A.I.C.S.: 531210

Jiangxi Vanke Yida Property Investment Company Limited **(1)**
501 Section A Taihao Business Building 807 Huoju Avenue High-Tech Zone, Nanchang, 330000, China
Tel.: (86) 79188189090
N.A.I.C.S.: 531210

Qingdao Vanke Real Estate Company Limited **(1)**
Vanke Real Estate 12th Floor Huayin Building 5A Donghai West Road, South District, Qingdao, 266071, China
Tel.: (86) 53288257555
N.A.I.C.S.: 531210

Tangshan Vanke Real Estate Development Company Limited **(1)**
Vanke Section A Building A Longxin Courtyard 118 Torch Road, High-Tech Development Zone Lubei District, Tangshan, 063000, China
Tel.: (86) 3152522600
N.A.I.C.S.: 531210

Tianjin Vanke Real Estate Company Limited **(1)**
19th-20th Floor Meijiang Center Building Huandao West Road, South Meijiang Hexi District, Tianjin, 300221, China
Tel.: (86) 2288155666
N.A.I.C.S.: 531210

Vanke Holdings USA LLC **(1)**
130 W 42nd St Fl 16, New York, NY 10036

Tel.: (646) 650-2888
Web Site: https://www.vanke.us
Real Estate Services
N.A.I.C.S.: 531210
Trey Clark *(Sr VP-Investments)*

Vanke Overseas Investment Holding Company Limited **(1)**
55/F Bank of China Tower 1 Garden Road, Central, China (Hong Kong) **(73.9%)**
Tel.: (852) 2 309 8888
Web Site: http://www.vankeoverseas.com
Rev.: $59,486,221
Assets: $767,594,934
Liabilities: $212,951,655
Net Worth: $554,643,278
Earnings: $54,776,774
Emp.: 105
Fiscal Year-end: 12/31/2021
Holding Company; Commercial Property Investment, Development & Management
N.A.I.C.S.: 551112
Dongwu Que *(CEO)*

Vanke Real Estate (Hong Kong) Co., Ltd. **(1)**
55th Floor Bank of China Tower 1 Garden Road, Central, China (Hong Kong)
Tel.: (852) 2309 8888
Rev.: $1,631,316,120
Assets: $15,559,541,970
Liabilities: $13,131,455,490
Net Worth: $2,428,086,480
Earnings: $200,209,620
Fiscal Year-end: 12/31/2016
Holding Company; Real Estate Investment, Development & Sales
N.A.I.C.S.: 551112
Dongwu Que *(Mng Dir)*

Wuhan Vanke Real Estate Company Limited **(1)**
2nd Floor 8 Hong Kong Road, Jiang an District, Wuhan, 430015, China
Tel.: (86) 2782450700
N.A.I.C.S.: 531210

Wuhu Vanke Real Estate Company Limited **(1)**
Wuhu Vanke 899 Zhongjiang Avenue, Jiujiang District, Wuhu, Anhui Province, China
Tel.: (86) 5532111168
N.A.I.C.S.: 531210

CHINA VAST INDUSTRIAL URBAN DEVELOPMENT COMPANY LIMITED
3707-08 37/F West Tower Shun Tak Centre, 168-200 Connaught Road, Central, 999077, China (Hong Kong)
Tel.: (852) 29126300
Web Site: http://www.vastiud.com
6166—(HKG)
Rev.: $367,493,796
Assets: $2,263,108,728
Liabilities: $1,305,885,129
Net Worth: $957,223,599
Earnings: $129,403,617
Emp.: 838
Fiscal Year-end: 12/31/20
Industrial Building Development
N.A.I.C.S.: 236210
Jianjun Wang *(Chm & Pres)*

CHINA VERED FINANCIAL HOLDING CORPORATION LIMITED
22nd Floor China Taiping Tower 8 Sunning Road, Causeway Bay, Hong Kong, China (Hong Kong)
Tel.: (852) 39783888 **HK**
Web Site:
https://www.chinavered.com
0245—(HKG)
Rev.: $31,079,018
Assets: $569,191,365
Liabilities: $39,403,365
Net Worth: $529,788,000
Earnings: ($79,408,020)
Emp.: 51
Fiscal Year-end: 12/31/22
Financial Services
N.A.I.C.S.: 561499

Subsidiaries:

CM Securities (Hongkong) Company Limited **(1)**
24/F China Taiping Tower 8 Sunning Road, Causeway Bay, Hong Kong, China (Hong Kong)
Tel.: (852) 38993900
Web Site: https://www.veredsec.com
Financial Brokerage Services
N.A.I.C.S.: 523150

CHINA VITUP HEALTH CARE HOLDINGS, INC.
108-1 Nashan Road, Zhongshan District, Dalian, China
Tel.: (86) 41182653668 **NV**
Year Founded: 2003
Sales Range: $1-9.9 Million
Emp.: 107
Holding Company; Medical Clinics Owner & Operator
N.A.I.C.S.: 551112
ShuBin Wang *(Chm & Pres)*

CHINA VOCATIONAL EDUCATION HOLDINGS LIMITED
No 11 Huali Road, Zengcheng, Guangzhou, Guangdong, China
Tel.: (86) 2082901822 **Ky**
Web Site:
http://www.hualiuniversity.com
Year Founded: 2000
1756—(HKG)
Rev.: $135,078,516
Assets: $969,700,869
Liabilities: $558,269,969
Net Worth: $411,430,900
Earnings: $21,979,353
Emp.: 2,157
Fiscal Year-end: 08/31/21
Educational Support Services
N.A.I.C.S.: 611710
Zhang Zhifeng *(Founder & Chm)*

CHINA VTV LIMITED
315-321 Lockhart Road 23 Floor Flat C 393 Jaffe Road, Wanchai, China (Hong Kong)
Tel.: (852) 67353339 **NV**
Year Founded: 2015
CVTV—(OTCIQ)
Rev.: $16,000
Assets: $673,000
Liabilities: $1,259,000
Net Worth: ($586,000)
Earnings: ($785,000)
Emp.: 96
Fiscal Year-end: 02/28/21
Online Apparel Retailer
N.A.I.C.S.: 458110
Yatao Wang *(Co-Founder)*

CHINA WAFER LEVEL CSP CO., LTD.
No 29 Tinglan Lane Suzhou Industrial Park, Suzhou, 215026, China
Tel.: (86) 51267730001
Web Site: https://www.wlcsp.com
Year Founded: 2005
603005—(SHG)
Rev.: $155,292,368
Assets: $644,060,907
Liabilities: $79,574,817
Net Worth: $564,486,090
Earnings: $31,990,182
Emp.: 2,000
Fiscal Year-end: 12/31/22
Holding Company
N.A.I.C.S.: 551112
Wang Wei *(Chm & CEO)*

Subsidiaries:

Optiz Inc. **(1)**
2225 E Bayshore Rd, Palo Alto, CA 94303
Tel.: (650) 320-1648
Web Site: https://www.optiztech.com

Semiconductor Product Mfr & Distr
N.A.I.C.S.: 334413
Vage Oganesian *(Co-Founder & Pres)*

CHINA WAH YAN HEALTHCARE LTD.
36th Floor Times Tower 391-407 Jaffe Road, Wanchai, China (Hong Kong)
Tel.: (852) 2187 3085
Web Site:
http://www.chinawahyan.com
Rev.: $25,031,856
Assets: $112,659,913
Liabilities: $71,430,709
Net Worth: $41,229,204
Earnings: ($40,134,799)
Emp.: 1,001
Fiscal Year-end: 12/31/16
Consultancy Services For Medical Equipment
N.A.I.C.S.: 334510
Ka Chung Chan *(Chm)*

CHINA WAN TONG YUAN (HOLDINGS) LTD.
Unit 3508 35th Floor West Tower Shun Tak Centre, 168-200 Connaught Road, Central, China (Hong Kong)
Tel.: (852) 39967597 **Ky**
Web Site: http://www.chinawty.com
Year Founded: 2007
6966—(HKG)
Rev.: $6,733,426
Assets: $42,766,886
Liabilities: $13,938,586
Net Worth: $28,828,300
Earnings: $2,779,229
Emp.: 57
Fiscal Year-end: 12/31/21
Landscaping Services
N.A.I.C.S.: 561730
Xingying Li *(Exec Dir)*

CHINA WANTIAN HOLDINGS LIMITED
Workshop A & B 1/F Sunking Factory Building No 1-7 Shing Chuen Road, Tai Wai, Sha Tin, New Territories, China (Hong Kong)
Tel.: (852) 39291088 **HK**
Web Site: http://www.cyfood.com.hk
Year Founded: 2005
1854—(HKG)
Rev.: $13,762,940
Assets: $18,777,166
Liabilities: $6,747,073
Net Worth: $12,030,094
Earnings: ($1,063,311)
Emp.: 81
Fiscal Year-end: 03/31/21
Food Product Mfr & Distr
N.A.I.C.S.: 311411
Chi Ching Liu *(Chm & Exec Dir)*

Subsidiaries:

C.Y. Food Trading (HK) Company Limited **(1)**
Workshop A B 1/F Sunking Factory Building No 1-7 Shing Chuen Road, Tai Wai, Sha Tin, New Territories, China (Hong Kong)
Tel.: (852) 39291088
Web Site: https://www.cyfood.com.hk
Fruit & Vegetable Whslr
N.A.I.C.S.: 424480
Joey Chang *(Mgr-Quality Assurance)*

CHINA WASTE CORPORATION LIMITED
Level 31 1 O'Connell Street, Sydney, 2000, NSW, Australia
Tel.: (61) 2 9276 2000 **AU**
Web Site:
http://www.chinawastecorp.com
Sales Range: Less than $1 Million
Waste Management Services

N.A.I.C.S.: 562998
Peter Harrison *(Chm)*

CHINA WATER AFFAIRS GROUP LTD

Suite 6408 64/F Central Plaza 18 Harbour Road, Wanchai, China (Hong Kong)
Tel.: (852) 39686666
Web Site:
http://www.chinawatergroup.com
CWAFF—(OTCIQ)
Rev.: $1,809,856,508
Assets: $7,798,446,720
Liabilities: $5,098,999,635
Net Worth: $2,699,447,085
Earnings: $393,763,988
Emp.: 11,400
Fiscal Year-end: 03/31/23
Utilities Supplying Services
N.A.I.C.S.: 221310
Chuan Liang Duan *(Chm)*

Subsidiaries:

Ming Hing Waterworks Engineering
(PRC) Limited **(1)**
Units 1809-1812 Telford House 16 Wang Hoi Road, Kowloon Bay, Kowloon, China (Hong Kong)
Tel.: (852) 23808265
Web Site: http://www.minghing.com.hk
Sales Range: $50-74.9 Million
Water & Sewer System Construction Services
N.A.I.C.S.: 237110

CHINA WATER INDUSTRY GROUP LIMITED

Room 1207 12th Floor West Tower Shun Tak Centre 168-200 Connaught Road, Central, Sheung Wan, China (Hong Kong)
Tel.: (852) 2 547 6382
Web Site:
http://www.chinawaterind.com
1129—(HKG)
Rev.: $142,109,003
Assets: $498,103,606
Liabilities: $249,705,409
Net Worth: $248,398,197
Earnings: $3,295,052
Emp.: 1,022
Fiscal Year-end: 12/31/21
Water Supply & Sewage Treatment Services
N.A.I.C.S.: 221320
Feng Liu *(Exec Dir)*

Subsidiaries:

Shenzhen City New China Water
Electric Power Limited **(1)**
BC 20/F A Zhong Tou International Business Centre 1061 Xiangmei Road, Shenzhen, China
Tel.: (86) 75523638888
Investment & Operation Water Project Services
N.A.I.C.S.: 551112

CHINA WEAVING MATERIALS HOLDINGS LIMITED

Fengtian Development Zone, Fengxin County, Nanchang, Jiangxi, China
Tel.: (86) 7954509997
Web Site:
http://www.weavingmaterials.com
3778—(HKG)
Rev.: $217,723,207
Assets: $231,125,558
Liabilities: $134,720,464
Net Worth: $96,405,094
Earnings: $9,622,201
Emp.: 3,046
Fiscal Year-end: 12/31/20
Yarn & Cotton Mfr
N.A.I.C.S.: 313110
Hong Zheng *(Chm)*

CHINA WEST CONSTRUCTION CO., LTD.

25/26th Floor China Construction Building No 989 Hahzhou Road, Shuangliu District, Chengdu, 610017, Sichuan, China
Tel.: (86) 2883335219
Web Site: https://cwcg.cscec.com
002302—(SSE)
Rev.: $3,441,533,493
Assets: $4,611,187,902
Liabilities: $3,166,864,131
Net Worth: $1,444,323,770
Earnings: $76,231,364
Fiscal Year-end: 12/31/22
Concrete Products Mfr
N.A.I.C.S.: 327999

CHINA WESTERN POWER INDUSTRIAL CO., LTD.

No 66 Rongchuan Road, Hi-Tech Industrial Park, Zigong, 643001, Sichuan, China
Tel.: (86) 8136666666
Web Site: https://www.cwpc.com.cn
Year Founded: 1983
002630—(SSE)
Rev.: $120,623,256
Assets: $1,426,843,080
Liabilities: $1,279,042,596
Net Worth: $147,800,484
Earnings: ($106,294,032)
Fiscal Year-end: 12/31/22
Boiler Mfr
N.A.I.C.S.: 332410
Renchao Li *(Chm)*

CHINA WIND POWER INTERNATIONAL CORP.

150 York Street Ste 818, Toronto, M5H 3S5, ON, Canada
Tel.: (416) 916-4205 ON
Web Site:
http://www.chinawindpower.com
Year Founded: 1987
Sales Range: $1-9.9 Million
Emp.: 35
Wind Power Generation & Development Services
N.A.I.C.S.: 221118
Jun Liu *(Chm & CEO)*

CHINA WIRE & CABLE CO., LTD.

4th Floor No 58 Section 3 Zhongshan North Road, Zhongshan District, Taipei, Taiwan
Tel.: (886) 25993456
Web Site: https://www.cwco.com.tw
1603—(TAI)
Rev.: $108,389,613
Assets: $288,653,410
Liabilities: $103,961,167
Net Worth: $184,692,243
Earnings: $10,302,723
Fiscal Year-end: 12/31/22
Wire & Cable Mfr
N.A.I.C.S.: 335929

CHINA WOOD OPTIMIZATION (HOLDINGS) LIMITED

Room 2204 22/F Harbour Centre, 25 Harbour Road, Wanchai, China (Hong Kong)
Tel.: (852) 3579 4507
Web Site:
http://www.chinawood.com.hk
Rev.: $30,287,831
Assets: $108,685,738
Liabilities: $14,613,801
Net Worth: $94,071,937
Earnings: $10,030,022
Emp.: 198
Fiscal Year-end: 12/31/19
Processed Wood Products Mfr & Distr

N.A.I.C.S.: 321999
Tsun Yim *(Co-Founder & Chm)*

CHINA WOOD, INC.

Daizhuang Industry Zone, Yitang Town, Lanshan District, Linyi, 276000, Shandong, China
Tel.: (86) 5398566168 NV
Sales Range: $25-49.9 Million
Emp.: 430
Plywood Mfr
N.A.I.C.S.: 321211
Xiaoling Ye *(Chm)*

CHINA WORLD TRADE CENTER CO., LTD.

No 1 Jian Guo Men Wai Avenue, Chaoyang District, Beijing, 100004, China
Tel.: (86) 1065052288
Web Site: https://www.cwtc.com
Year Founded: 1985
600007—(SHG)
Rev.: $483,295,649
Assets: $1,800,951,558
Liabilities: $516,434,991
Net Worth: $1,284,516,567
Earnings: $156,668,260
Fiscal Year-end: 12/31/22
Commercial & Residential Buildings & Facilities Operation & Management
N.A.I.C.S.: 531312
Huang Guoxiang *(Chm)*

CHINA WUYI CO., LTD.

4th Floor Landmark Plaza No 89 Wusi Road, Fuzhou, 350001, Fujian, China
Tel.: (86) 59188323721
Web Site:
http://www.chinawuyi.com.cn
Year Founded: 1988
000797—(SSE)
Rev.: $1,027,054,080
Assets: $3,216,064,176
Liabilities: $2,415,893,688
Net Worth: $800,170,488
Earnings: $4,275,180
Fiscal Year-end: 12/31/22
Real Estate Support Services
N.A.I.C.S.: 531390
Zengzhong Lin *(Chm)*

CHINA XD ELECTRICITY CO., LTD.

Block A No 7 Tangxing Road, High-tech District, Xi'an, 710075, Shaanxi, China
Tel.: (86) 2988832083
Web Site: http://www.xdect.com.cn
Year Founded: 2008
601179—(SHG)
Rev.: $2,557,157,906
Assets: $5,734,401,384
Liabilities: $2,513,068,908
Net Worth: $3,221,332,475
Earnings: $85,979,500
Emp.: 15,800
Fiscal Year-end: 12/31/22
Power Transmission, Distribution & Control Equipment Mfr & Sales
N.A.I.C.S.: 335311
Zhao Qi *(Chm)*

CHINA XD PLASTICS COMPANY LTD.

No 9 Dalian North Road Haping Road Centralized Industrial Park, Harbin Development Zone, Harbin, 150060, Heilongjiang, China
Tel.: (86) 45184346600 NV
Web Site: http://www.chinaxd.net
CXDC—(NASDAQ)
Rev.: $1,311,901,681
Assets: $2,923,926,000
Liabilities: $2,156,711,763

Net Worth: $767,214,237
Earnings: ($181,802,265)
Emp.: 967
Fiscal Year-end: 12/31/20
Modified Plastic Products Mfr & Distr
N.A.I.C.S.: 326199
Jie Han *(Chm, Pres & CEO)*

Subsidiaries:

Al Composites Materials FZE **(1)**
RA07BB01 North Jebel Ali Free Zone, Dubai, United Arab Emirates
Tel.: (971) 48876070
Plastics Product Mfr
N.A.I.C.S.: 325211
Yizihaerjiang Aisikaer *(Bus Mgr-Intl)*

CHINA XIANGTAI FOOD CO., LTD.

27F Samsung Hub 3 Church Street, Singapore, 049483, Singapore
Tel.: (86) 2386330158 Ky
Year Founded: 2018
BTOG—(NASDAQ)
Rev.: $2,888,482
Assets: $6,684,745
Liabilities: $5,775,162
Net Worth: $909,583
Earnings: ($18,284,958)
Emp.: 5
Fiscal Year-end: 06/30/24
Meat Product Mfr & Distr
N.A.I.C.S.: 311611
Zeshu Dai *(Chm & CEO)*

CHINA XINHUA EDUCATION GROUP LTD.

No 555 West Wangjiang Road High-tech Development Zone, Hefei, 230088, Anhui, China
Tel.: (86) 5516 587 2223 Ky
Web Site:
http://www.chinaxhedu.com
Year Founded: 1999
2779—(HKG)
Rev.: $86,622,789
Assets: $607,475,045
Liabilities: $137,408,840
Net Worth: $470,066,206
Earnings: $54,310,187
Emp.: 1,995
Fiscal Year-end: 12/31/21
Educational Support Services
N.A.I.C.S.: 611710
Junbao Wu *(Founder & Chm)*

CHINA XLX FERTILISER LTD

Xinxiang Economic Development Zone, Henan, 453731, China
Tel.: (86) 3735592888 SG
Web Site: http://www.chinaxlx.com.hk
Year Founded: 2006
1866—(HKG)
Rev.: $1,600,235,858
Assets: $3,210,529,645
Liabilities: $2,226,251,305
Net Worth: $984,278,341
Earnings: $80,304,715
Emp.: 8,267
Fiscal Year-end: 12/31/20
Fertilizer Mfr
N.A.I.C.S.: 325314
Xingxu Liu *(Chm)*

Subsidiaries:

Henan Xinlianxin Blue Environmental
Protection Technology Co., Ltd. **(1)**
East Section of Qinglong Road, Xinxiang Economic Development Zone, Xinxiang, Henan, China
Tel.: (86) 3737082972
Web Site: https://www.cynsxlx.com
Automotive Urea Mfr
N.A.I.C.S.: 325311

Jiujiang Xinlianxin Fertiliser Co.,
Ltd. **(1)**
Jishan Industrial Park, Pengze, Jiujiang,

China XLX Fertiliser Ltd—(Continued)

Jiangxi, China
Tel.: (86) 7922333333
Compound Fertilizer & Synthetic Ammonia
Mfr
N.A.I.C.S.: 325311

**Xinjiang Xinlianxin Energy Chemical
Co., Ltd.** (1)
Taxi River Industrial Park, Manas, Changji,
Xinjiang, China
Tel.: (86) 9946866668
Web Site: http://www.xjxlx.com.cn
Urea & Compound Fertilizer Mfr.
N.A.I.C.S.: 325311

**Xinxiang Ruicheng Technology Co.,
Ltd.** (1)
East Section of Qinglong Road, Xinxiang
Economic Development Zone, Henan,
China
Tel.: (86) 1383 908 1833
Web Site: https://www.ruichengchem.com
Chemical Product Mfr & Distr
N.A.I.C.S.: 325998

CHINA YIBAI UNITED GUAR-
ANTEE INTERNATIONAL
HOLDING, INC.
205 Xingsha Ave Ste 3106, Chang-
sha, 410100, Hunan, China
Tel.: (86) 73186886588
Year Founded: 1987
Financial Services
N.A.I.C.S.: 523999
Minle Zheng (CEO)

CHINA YIDA HOLDING, CO.
28/F Yifa Building No 111 Wusi Road,
Fuzhou, 350003, Fujian, China
Tel.: (86) 7188389552　　　　　　　　NV
Web Site: http://www.yidacn.net
Sales Range: $10-24.9 Million
Emp.: 635
Holding Company; Advertising Ser-
vices; Tourism
N.A.I.C.S.: 551112
Minhua Chen (Co-Owner, Chm, Pres
& CEO)

CHINA YONGDA AUTOMO-
BILES SERVICES HOLDINGS
LIMITED
299 Ruijin Road S, Shanghai,
200023, China
Tel.: (86) 2163026789　　　　　　　　Ky
Web Site: http://www.ydauto.com.cn
3669—(HKG)
Rev.: $10,500,071,159
Assets: $5,322,130,996
Liabilities: $3,429,120,481
Net Worth: $1,893,010,515
Earnings: $265,525,953
Emp.: 16,177
Fiscal Year-end: 12/31/20
Car Retail, Rental, Insurance & In-
spection Services
N.A.I.C.S.: 441110
Tak On Cheung (Chm)

Subsidiaries:

**Anhui Yongda Baoyi Automobile
Sales and Services Co., Ltd.** (1)
No 49 Changchun Street Baohe Industrial
Area, Hefei, China
Tel.: (86) 5513663911
Automobile Dealers
N.A.I.C.S.: 441110

**Beijing Baozen Baiwang Automobile
Sales and Services Co., Ltd.** (1)
In Baiwang Green Valley Auto Park, Haidian
District, Beijing, China
Tel.: (86) 1062826789
New Car Dealers
N.A.I.C.S.: 441110

**Changshu Yongda Lujie Automobile
Sales & Services Co., Ltd.** (1)
188 Qingduntang Road Car Market Lan-
drover and Jaguar Exhibition Hall, Chang-

shu, Jiangsu, China
Tel.: (86) 51252936789
Automotive Retailer
N.A.I.C.S.: 441120

**Changzhi Baozen Lufu Automobile
Sales and Services Co., Ltd.** (1)
No 101 Zhenzhang Village on West 1st
Ring RD, Changzhi, China
Tel.: (86) 3556016789
New Car Dealers
N.A.I.C.S.: 441110
Wang Yi Jong (Mgr-Sls)

**Changzhou Baozun Automobile Sales
& Services Co., Ltd.** (1)
No 225 South Ring 2nd Road, Jintan Dis-
trict, Changzhou, China
Tel.: (86) 51982685050
Automotive Retailer
N.A.I.C.S.: 441120

**Fujian Baitai Automobile Sales & Ser-
vices Co., Ltd.** (1)
No 26 Liang'an Road 80 Meters Away From
Lanpu Highway Exit, Shanggan Town Min-
hou County, Fuzhou, China
Tel.: (86) 59122260911
Automotive Retailer
N.A.I.C.S.: 441120

**Fujian Yongda Automobile Sales and
Services Co., Ltd.** (1)
Crossing of Qingrong Ave and Fuyu Rd
Rongqiao Development Zone, Fuqing,
China
Tel.: (86) 591 85366789
Automobile Dealers
N.A.I.C.S.: 441110

**Fuzhou Yongda Automobile Sales
and Services Co., Ltd.** (1)
No 10 Gaoshi Rd Gaishan Investment Area,
Cangshan, Fuzhou, China
Tel.: (86) 591 88036789
Automobile Dealers
N.A.I.C.S.: 441110

**Handan Baohe Automobile Sales and
Service Co., Ltd.** (1)
No 570 Yinxin North Street, Congtai, Han-
dan, China
Tel.: (86) 310 7055000
New Car Dealers
N.A.I.C.S.: 441110

**Huzhou Yongda Aocheng Automobile
Sales and Services Co., Ltd.** (1)
No 211 Shushan Road Balidian Town, Wux-
ing, Huzhou, China
Tel.: (86) 572 2756789
New Car Dealers
N.A.I.C.S.: 441110

**Huzhou Yongda Automobile Sales
and Services Co., Ltd.** (1)
No 215 Songxue Rd Balidian Town, Hu-
zhou, China
Tel.: (86) 572 2676789
New Car Dealers
N.A.I.C.S.: 441110

**Huzhou Yongda Lubao Automobile
Sales and Services Co., Ltd.** (1)
No 188 Zhumuyang Road, Huzhou, Zheji-
ang, China
Tel.: (86) 572 2356789
New Car Dealers
N.A.I.C.S.: 441110

**Jiangxi Yongda Rongjian Automobile
Sales and Services Co., Ltd.** (1)
Cross of Jinlingxi Road & Zhanggongwang
Road Development Zone, Ganzhou, China
Tel.: (86) 797 2139789
New Car Dealers
N.A.I.C.S.: 441110

**Jiangyin Baozen Automobile Sales
and Services Co., Ltd.** (1)
No 77 Chengyang Rd, Jiangyin, China
Tel.: (86) 510 80111678
New Car Dealers
N.A.I.C.S.: 441110

**Jiangyin Leichi Automobile Sales &
Services Co., Ltd.** (1)
No 202 Chengyang Road, Jiangyin, China
Tel.: (86) 51086776789

Automotive Retailer
N.A.I.C.S.: 441120

**Jiaxing Yongda Tongcheng Auto
Sales and Service Co., Ltd.** (1)
No 1699 Chengbei Road, Jiaxing, Zhejiang,
China
Tel.: (86) 5738 279 6789
Web Site: http://www.ydauto.com.cn
New Car Dealers
N.A.I.C.S.: 441110

**Jiaxing Zhibao Automobile Sales and
Service Co., Ltd.** (1)
Intersection of Changsheng South Road &
Huayan Road, Jiaxing, China
Tel.: (86) 57389897888
New Car Dealers
N.A.I.C.S.: 441110

**Kunshan Baozen Automobile Sales
and Services Co., Ltd.** (1)
No 208 North Huangpujiang RD, Kunshan,
China
Tel.: (86) 512 50356789
New Car Dealers
N.A.I.C.S.: 441110

**Linfen Baozen Automobile Sales and
Services Co., Ltd.** (1)
About 180 meters north of Yaodu Rural
Commercial Bank Delong Branch, Qinshu
Road Yaodou District, Linfen, China
Tel.: (86) 357 259 6789
Web Site: http://www.ydauto.com.cn
New Car Dealers
N.A.I.C.S.: 441110

**Linhai Baozen Automobile Sales and
Services Co., Ltd.** (1)
No 116 South Jingjiang Rd, Linhai, China
Tel.: (86) 576 8579 6789
New Car Dealers
N.A.I.C.S.: 441110

**Linyi Yubaohang Automobile Sales
and Service Company Limited** (1)
Luo Zhuang YiHe road & HuDong road in-
terchange, Linyi, China
Tel.: (86) 5397091111
New Car Dealers
N.A.I.C.S.: 441110

**Lishui Jiacheng Automobile Sales
Co., Ltd.** (1)
Yanquan Automobile Market 4S Area P
Plots, Lishui, Zhejiang, China
Tel.: (86) 5782228888
New Car Dealers
N.A.I.C.S.: 441110

**Mianyang Xinjincheng Automobile
Sales & Services Co., Ltd.** (1)
B-10 Liaoning Road West Yongxing, Hi-
Tech District, Mianyang, China
Tel.: (86) 8168010911
Automotive Retailer
N.A.I.C.S.: 441120

**Nantong Baozen Automobile Sales
and Services Co., Ltd.** (1)
No 277 East Qingnian Road, Nantong,
China
Tel.: (86) 51385331678
Web Site: http://www.ntpmw.com.cn
Emp.: 150
New Car Dealers
N.A.I.C.S.: 441110
Taiyan wang Wang (Mgr)

**Rui'an Yongda Nanyang Lujie Auto-
mobile Sales & Services Co.,
Ltd.** (1)
Tangxia International Automobile and Motor-
cycle Parts, Ruian, Zhejiang, China
Tel.: (86) 57766086789
Automotive Retailer
N.A.I.C.S.: 441120

**Shanghai Baozen Automobile Sales
and Services Co., Ltd.** (1)
No 2777 Longdong Ave Pudong New Area,
Shanghai, China
Tel.: (86) 2158966789
New Car Dealers
N.A.I.C.S.: 441110

**Shanghai Baozen Zhonghuan Auto-
mobile Sales and Services Co.,**

Ltd. (1)
No 999 West Changjiang Road, Baoshan,
Shanghai, China
Tel.: (86) 2156996789
New Car Dealers
N.A.I.C.S.: 441110

**Shanghai Huangpu Baozen Automo-
bile Sales Co., Ltd** (1)
No 523 Huaihai Zhong Road, Shanghai,
China
Tel.: (86) 21 31166789
Passenger Vehicle Distr
N.A.I.C.S.: 441110

**Shanghai Putuo Baozen Automobile
Sales and Services Co., Ltd.** (1)
No 638 West Yunling Rd, Putuo, Shanghai,
China
Tel.: (86) 21 52696789
New Car Dealers
N.A.I.C.S.: 441110

**Shanghai West Shanghai Jiawo Auto-
mobile Sales & Services Co.,
Ltd.** (1)
No 3 2018 Yongsheng Road, Jiading Dis-
trict, Shanghai, China
Tel.: (86) 2159523399
Automotive Retailer
N.A.I.C.S.: 441120

**Shanghai West Shanghai Shenjie
Automobile Sales & Services Co.,
Ltd.** (1)
No 325 Hong Liu Road, Putuo District,
Shanghai, 200331, China
Tel.: (86) 2166271575
Automotive Retailer
N.A.I.C.S.: 441120

**Shanghai Yongda Automobile Nanhui
Sales and Services Co., Ltd.** (1)
No 3113 Dachuang Rd Pudong New Area,
Shanghai, China
Tel.: (86) 21 68091888
New Car Dealers
N.A.I.C.S.: 441110

**Shanghai Yongda Automobile Pudong
Sales and Services Co., Ltd.** (1)
No 2178 Hunan Rd Pudong New Area,
Shanghai, China
Tel.: (86) 2150856789
New Car Dealers
N.A.I.C.S.: 441110

**Shanghai Yongda Automobile Pudong
Trade Co., Ltd.** (1)
No 2761 Zhangyang Rd Pudong New Area,
Shanghai, China
Tel.: (86) 21 58216789
New Car Dealers
N.A.I.C.S.: 441110

**Shanghai Yongda Automobile Puxi
Sales and Services Co., Ltd.** (1)
No 818 Wubao Rd Dickhead New Area,
Minhang, Shanghai, China
Tel.: (86) 21 64016789
Passenger Vehicle Distr
N.A.I.C.S.: 423110
Huang Vei Bei (Mng Dir)

**Shanghai Yongda Automobile Sales
Co., Ltd.** (1)
No 1441 Yuqiao Rd Pudong New Area,
Shanghai, China
Tel.: (86) 21 58956789
New Car Dealers
N.A.I.C.S.: 441110

**Shanghai Yongda Automobile Songji-
ang Sales and Services Co., Ltd.** (1)
No 588 Fangta North Road, Songjiang Dis-
trict, Shanghai, China
Tel.: (86) 216 774 1088
Web Site: http://www.ydauto.com.cn
New Car Dealers
N.A.I.C.S.: 441110

**Shanghai Yongda Automobile Trade
Center Co., Ltd.** (1)
No 1600 Longwu Rd, Minhang, Shanghai,
China
Tel.: (86) 2154366789
New Car Dealers
N.A.I.C.S.: 441110

Shanghai Yongda Baoyunlai Automobile Sales and Services Co., Ltd.　**(1)**
No 2711 Longdong Ave Pudong New Area, Shanghai, China
Tel.: (86) 21 58960011
New Car Dealers
N.A.I.C.S.: 441110

Shanghai Yongda Bashi Automobile Sales and Services Co., Ltd.　**(1)**
No 1682 Hongmei Rd, Minhang, Shanghai, China
Tel.: (86) 21 64853030
New Car Dealers
N.A.I.C.S.: 441110

Shanghai Yongda Haojie Automobile Sales and Services Co., Ltd.　**(1)**
No 1391 Yuqiao Rd Pudong New Area, Shanghai, 201204, China
Tel.: (86) 21 58516789
Emp.: 100
New Car Dealers
N.A.I.C.S.: 441110
Tan Yuseng *(Gen Mgr)*

Shanghai Yongda Infiniti Automobile Sales and Services Co., Ltd.　**(1)**
2755 Longdong Avenue, Pudong New Area, Shanghai, China
Tel.: 216 856 5678
Web Site: http://www.ydauto.com.cn
New Car Dealers
N.A.I.C.S.: 441110

Shanghai Yongda Infiniti Qibao Automobile Sales and Services Co., Ltd.　**(1)**
No 789 Wubao Rd, Minhang District, Shanghai, 201105, China
Tel.: (86) 216 421 6789
Web Site: http://www.infiniti-pxyd.com.cn
New Car Dealers
N.A.I.C.S.: 441110

Shanghai Yongda Lujie Automobile Sales and Services Co., Ltd.　**(1)**
No 2711 Longdong Ave, Pudong New Area, Shanghai, China
Tel.: (86) 21 20236789
New Car Dealers
N.A.I.C.S.: 441110

Shanghai Yongda Qidong Automobile Sales and Services Co., Ltd.　**(1)**
No 6 Qingnian Road, Chengbei Industrial Park, Qidong, Jiangsu, China
Tel.: 5138 092 6789
Web Site: http://www.ydauto.com.cn
New Car Dealers
N.A.I.C.S.: 441110

Shanghai Yongda Qiming Automobile Sales & Services Co., Ltd.　**(1)**
No 1447 Luoshan Rd, Pudong New District, Shanghai, 200135, China
Tel.: (86) 2150336789
Automotive Retailer
N.A.I.C.S.: 441120

Shanghai Yongda Shenlong Automobile Sales and Services Co., Ltd.　**(1)**
No 1110 North Songwei Rd, Songjiang District, Shanghai, China
Tel.: (86) 21 57706789
Web Site: http://www.ydauto.com.cn
New Car Dealers
N.A.I.C.S.: 441110

Shanghai Yongda Tongbao Automobile Sales and Services Co., Ltd.　**(1)**
No 977 Changjiang West Road, Baoshan District, Shanghai, China
Tel.: 216 620 8666
Web Site: http://www.ydauto.com.cn
New Car Dealers
N.A.I.C.S.: 441110

Shanghai Yongda Tongning Automobile Sales and Services Co., Ltd.　**(1)**
No 3099 Dachuan Rd Pudong New Area, Huinan, Shanghai, China
Tel.: (86) 21 68009789
New Car Dealers
N.A.I.C.S.: 441110

Shanghai Yongda Tongsheng Automobile Sales and Services Co., Ltd.

No 555 Yutang Rd, Songjiang, Shanghai, China
Tel.: (86) 21 67761088
New Car Dealers
N.A.I.C.S.: 441110

Shanghai Yongda Toyota Automobile Sales and Services Co., Ltd.　**(1)**
No 2865 Longdong Ave Cunt New Area, Shanghai, China
Tel.: (86) 21 58965678
New Car Dealers
N.A.I.C.S.: 441110

Shanghai Yongda Weirong Automobile Sales and Services Co., Ltd.　**(1)**
No 1461 Yuqiao Rd Pudong New Area, Shanghai, China
Tel.: (86) 21 50836789
New Car Dealers
N.A.I.C.S.: 441110

Shanghai Yongda Zhongxin Automobile Sales and Services Co., Ltd.　**(1)**
No 9568 North Tsing Highway, Qingpu, Shanghai, China
Tel.: (86) 21 69226789
New Car Dealers
N.A.I.C.S.: 441110

Shaoxing Hecheng Haichang Automobile Sales and Service Co., Ltd.　**(1)**
Xihutou Doumen Town Paojiang, Shaoxing, China
Tel.: (86) 575 88222288
New Car Dealers
N.A.I.C.S.: 441110
Chusiong Ing Cen *(Mgr)*

Shaoxing Yongda Wuxian Automobile Sales and Services Co., Ltd.　**(1)**
Crossing of Zhongxing Ave & National Highway 329, Paojiang West Lake, Shaoxing, China
Tel.: (86) 575 88976789
New Car Dealers
N.A.I.C.S.: 441110

Shengzhou Baozen Auto Sales & Services Co., Ltd.　**(1)**
No 1777-2 Shengzhou Avenue South Sanjiang Street, Shengzhou, Zhejiang, China
Tel.: (86) 5758 313 6789
Web Site: http://www.ydauto.com.cn
New Car Dealers
N.A.I.C.S.: 441110

Shijiazhuang Baohe Automotive Sales & Service Co., Ltd.　**(1)**
No 86 Beierhuan East Road, ChangAn, Shijiazhuang, China
Tel.: (86) 31185663000
New Car Dealers
N.A.I.C.S.: 441110

Taicang Baozen Automobile Sales and Services Co., Ltd.　**(1)**
No 8 Beijing West Road, Taicang, Jiangsu, China
Tel.: (86) 5125 377 6789
Web Site: http://www.ydauto.com.cn
New Car Dealers
N.A.I.C.S.: 441110

Taixing Yongda Zhongcheng Automobile Sales & Services Co., Ltd.　**(1)**
No 158 Jiang Ping Road, Taixing, Jiangsu, China
Tel.: (86) 52387986789
Automotive Retailer
N.A.I.C.S.: 441120

Taiyuan Baozen Automobile Sales and Services Co., Ltd.　**(1)**
No 101 Taiyu RD, Taiyuan, China
Tel.: (86) 3517826789
New Car Dealers
N.A.I.C.S.: 441110

Taizhou Baozen Automobile Sales and Services Co., Ltd.　**(1)**
No 707 East Ring Jiaojiang Ave, Taizhou, China
Tel.: (86) 576 8189 6789
New Car Dealers
N.A.I.C.S.: 441110

Taizhou Yongda Aocheng Automobile Sales and Services Co., Ltd.　**(1)**

No 998 Huanghai Road, Jiaojiang, Taizhou, China
Tel.: (86) 576 88696789
New Car Dealers
N.A.I.C.S.: 441110

Wenzhou Baozen Automobile Sales and Services Co., Ltd.　**(1)**
No 2111 Liule Road Yueqing City Xiamen Section of National Highway 104, Wenzhou, Zhejiang, China
Tel.: (86) 5772 777 6789
Web Site: http://www.ydauto.com.cn
New Car Dealers
N.A.I.C.S.: 441110

Wenzhou Yongda Lujie Automobile Sales and Services Co., Ltd.　**(1)**
300m North of Entrance of Tudutang Village 104 national highway, Tiancheng Neighbourhood Leqing, Wenzhou, China
Tel.: (86) 577 27876789
New Car Dealers
N.A.I.C.S.: 441110

Wuxi Baozen Automobile Sales and Services Co., Ltd.　**(1)**
No 91-99 Taiwan Joy City, Qingyan Road, Wuxi, China
Tel.: (86) 51085029966
New Car Dealers
N.A.I.C.S.: 441110

Wuxi Yicheng Automobile Sales & Services Co., Ltd.　**(1)**
No 23-6 Xianfeng Road, Xishan District, Wuxi, China
Tel.: (86) 51089116789
Automotive Retailer
N.A.I.C.S.: 441120

Wuxi Yongda Oriental Automobile Sales and Services Co., Ltd.　**(1)**
No 290 Jincheng East Road, Wuxi, China
Tel.: (86) 5108 877 0911
Web Site: http://www.porsche-wuxi.com
Emp.: 130
New Car Dealers
N.A.I.C.S.: 441110

Yancheng Baozen Automobile Sales and Services Co., Ltd.　**(1)**
Economic Development Zone Taishan Road No 11, Yancheng, China
Tel.: (86) 515 88151678
New Car Dealers
N.A.I.C.S.: 441110

Yongjia Baozen Automobile Sales and Services Co., Ltd.　**(1)**
No 10 Luopu West Road, Oubei Town Yongjia County, Wenzhou, Zhejiang, China
Tel.: (86) 5772 189 6789
Web Site: http://www.ydauto.com.cn
New Car Dealers
N.A.I.C.S.: 441110

Yuncheng Baozen Automobile Sales and Services Co., Ltd.　**(1)**
No 34 Kangjie North Road, Airport New District, Yuncheng, Shanxi, China
Tel.: (86) 359 248 6789
Web Site: http://www.ydauto.com
Car Repair & Maintenance Services
N.A.I.C.S.: 811114

Zhengzhou Yongda Hexie Automobile Sales and Services Co., Ltd.　**(1)**
The East Side of 500 Meters to the North of Huayuan North Road, Lianhuo Highway, Zhengzhou, China
Tel.: (86) 371 86670691
New Car Dealers
N.A.I.C.S.: 441110

CHINA YOUNGMAN AUTOMOBILE GROUP CO., LTD.
No 501 BaDa Street, Jinhua, 321016, Zhejiang, China
Tel.: (86) 57989186133　　　CN
Web Site: http://www.young-man.cn
Emp.: 4,000
Holding Company; Motor Vehicle & Motor Vehicle Components Mfr & Distr
N.A.I.C.S.: 551112
Qingnian Pang *(Chm)*

Subsidiaries:

Zhejiang Youngman Lotus Automobile Co., Ltd.　**(1)**
No 501 BaDa Street, Jinhua, 321016, Zhejiang, China
Tel.: (86) 57989186388
Web Site: http://www.youngmanlotus.com
Car & Sport Utility Vehicle Mfr & Distr
N.A.I.C.S.: 336110

CHINA YOURAN DAIRY GROUP LIMITED
No 169 Hexi Road, Saihan District Inner Mongolia, Hohhot, China
Tel.: (86) 4713353607　　　Ky
Web Site:
　https://www.yourandairy.com
Year Founded: 1984
9858—(HKG)
Rev.: $2,588,321,887
Assets: $6,396,727,957
Liabilities: $4,583,107,139
Net Worth: $1,813,620,819
Earnings: ($201,164,710)
Emp.: 12,373
Fiscal Year-end: 12/31/23
Dairy Product Mfr & Distr
N.A.I.C.S.: 333241
Jiping Dong *(VP)*

CHINA YOUZAN LIMITED
Unit 2708 27/F The Center 99 Queens Road, Central, China (Hong Kong)
Tel.: (852) 2979 5223　　　BM
Web Site:
　http://www.chinayouzan.com
8083—(HKG)
Rev.: $278,952,971
Assets: $1,871,074,061
Liabilities: $1,161,696,593
Net Worth: $709,377,468
Earnings: ($83,599,496)
Emp.: 3,603
Fiscal Year-end: 12/31/20
Financial Payment Services
N.A.I.C.S.: 522320
Guisen Guan *(Chm)*

CHINA YUAN HONG FIRE CONTROL GROUP HOLDINGS LTD
Baisha Meilin Industrial Area, Nan'an, 362300, Fujian, China
Tel.: (86) 595 86278200　　　Ky
Web Site:
　http://www.en.baishafire.com
Sales Range: $50-74.9 Million
Emp.: 350
Fire Safety Products Mfr
N.A.I.C.S.: 922160
Zhuge Zhuang *(Chm, Founder & CEO)*

CHINA YUANBANG PROPERTY HOLDINGS LIMITED
9th Floor Yuanbang Building No 599 Huangshi West Road, Baiyun District, Guangzhou, 510430, China
Tel.: (86) 2026272116
Web Site: http://www.yuanbang.com
BCD—(SES)
Rev.: $12,131,168
Assets: $462,140,039
Liabilities: $321,160,794
Net Worth: $140,979,246
Earnings: ($19,558,789)
Emp.: 255
Fiscal Year-end: 06/30/22
Property Development Services
N.A.I.C.S.: 531312
Jiangtao Zhou *(VP)*

CHINA YUHUA EDUCATION CORPORATION LIMITED
No. 21 4/F Block 10 3 Mazhuang

CHINA YUHUA EDUCATION CORPORATION
LIMITED—(Continued)

Street, Zhengdong New District,
Zhengzhou, China
Tel.: (86) 3716 067 3938   Ky
Web Site:
 http://www.yuhuachina.com
6169—(HKG)
Rev.: $340,037,501
Assets: $1,365,143,692
Liabilities: $785,615,223
Net Worth: $579,528,469
Earnings: $130,653,811
Emp.: 7,002
Fiscal Year-end: 08/31/21
Education Services
N.A.I.C.S.: 611310
Guangyu Li (Chm)

CHINA YURUN FOOD GROUP LIMITED

10 Yurun Road, Jianye District, Nan-
jing, 210041, China
Tel.: (86) 2556677150   BM
Web Site: http://www.yurun.com.hk
Year Founded: 1993
1068—(DEU)
Rev.: $276,360,755
Assets: $150,410,239
Liabilities: $213,619,436
Net Worth: ($63,209,197)
Earnings: ($3,237,057)
Emp.: 1,400
Fiscal Year-end: 12/31/22
Processed Meat Mfr
N.A.I.C.S.: 311612
Linwei Yang (VP & Exec Dir-
Downstream Processed Meat Bus)
Subsidiaries:

Anhui Furun Meat Processing Co.,
Ltd   (1)
No16 Fuhu Road, Fuyang, 236022, China
Tel.: (86) 5582318806
Meat Product Distr
N.A.I.C.S.: 424470

Jinan Wanrun Meat Processing Co.,
Ltd.   (1)
No 8 Yongshen Road, Jinan, 251600,
Shanghe County, China
Tel.: (86) 53182336611
Meat Product Distr
N.A.I.C.S.: 424470

Nanjing Yurun Food Co., Ltd.   (1)
No 17 Yurun Road, Jianye District, Nanjing,
210000, China
Tel.: (86) 2586781030
Meat Product Distr
N.A.I.C.S.: 424470

Suzhou Furun Meat Processing Co.,
Ltd.   (1)
18 Huaihe Rd, Yongqiao, Suzhou, 234000,
Anhui, China
Tel.: (86) 5573324286
Meat Product Distr
N.A.I.C.S.: 424470

Zhongxiang Panlong Meat Process-
ing Co., Ltd.   (1)
West Ring Road 2 Zhongxiang Industrial
Park, Jingmen, HuBei, China
Tel.: (86) 7244288555
Meat Product Distr
N.A.I.C.S.: 424470

CHINA YUTIAN HOLDINGS LIMITED

East side of 328 Provincial Road and
North of Metallurgical Avenue,
Hongze County, Huai'an, 223100,
Jiangsu, China
Tel.: (86) 85236202070   Ky
Web Site: http://www.hkgg.hk
Year Founded: 2013
Glass Product Mfr & Distr
N.A.I.C.S.: 327215
Xuemei Wang (Founder, Chm &
Compliance Officer)

CHINA ZENITH CHEMICAL GROUP LIMITED

Room 4007 40/F China Resources
Building 26 Harbour Road, Wanchai,
China (Hong Kong)
Tel.: (852) 28453131   Ky
Web Site:
 http://www.xinyangmaojian.com.hk
Year Founded: 1913
0362—(HKG)
Rev.: $29,539,129
Assets: $267,163,110
Liabilities: $255,721,423
Net Worth: $11,441,687
Earnings: ($59,277,402)
Emp.: 632
Fiscal Year-end: 06/30/21
Organic Products Mfr
N.A.I.C.S.: 325199
Yuk Foebe Chan (Chm & CEO)

CHINA ZHENGTONG AUTO SERVICES HOLDINGS LIMITED

No 59 West Third Ring South Road,
FengTai District, Beijing, China
Tel.: (86) 106 382 9393   Ky
Web Site:
 http://www.zhengtongauto.com
Year Founded: 1999
1728—(HKG)
Rev.: $3,215,192,898
Assets: $4,003,344,513
Liabilities: $3,920,515,970
Net Worth: $82,828,543
Earnings: ($579,251,312)
Emp.: 7,468
Fiscal Year-end: 12/31/21
Car Dealership Owner & Operator
N.A.I.C.S.: 441110
Kunpeng Wang (Vice Chm)

Subsidiaries:

Baoding Aoze Automobile Sales Ser-
vices Co., Ltd.   (1)
No 1399 South 2nd Ring, Lianchi, Baoding,
071000, Hebei, China
Tel.: (86) 3126782080
Car Dealer Services
N.A.I.C.S.: 441120

Baotou Luze Automobile Sales Ser-
vices Co., Ltd.   (1)
Xitu Road, Xitu, Baotou, 014030, China
Tel.: (86) 4726196988
Car Dealer Services
N.A.I.C.S.: 441120

Baotou Zhongrui Automobile Sales
Service Co., Ltd.   (1)
Hope Industrial, Kun, Baotou, China
Tel.: (86) 4726166868
Car Dealer Services
N.A.I.C.S.: 441120

Beijing Zhengtong Baozehang Auto-
mobile Sales Services Co., Ltd.   (1)
1st Floor Tower B Donghuicuiyuán Garden
Damazhuang Village Liyuan Town,
Tongzhou, Beijing, 101121, China
Tel.: (86) 1080556366
Car Dealer Services
N.A.I.C.S.: 441120

Beijing Zhengtong Dingwo Automo-
bile Sales Services Co., Ltd.   (1)
Tower No 1 Huicuiyuan Garden Da-
mazhuang Villiage Liyuan Town, Tongzhou,
Beijing, 101101, China
Tel.: (86) 4008105220
Car Dealer Services
N.A.I.C.S.: 441120

Chengdu Qibao Automobile Sales
Services Co., Ltd.   (1)
No 968 Chengshuang Avenue, Wuhou,
Chengdu, China
Tel.: (86) 2885176666
Car Dealer Services
N.A.I.C.S.: 441120

Dongguan Aoze Automobile Sales
Services Co., Ltd.   (1)

Front of Tongsha Garden Guanchang Road,
East District, Dongguan, 523330, Guang-
dong, China
Tel.: (86) 76989890000
Car Dealer Services
N.A.I.C.S.: 441120

Dongguan Liaobu SCAS Automobile
Sales Services Co., Ltd.   (1)
Liaochong Mid Road Motortown, Liaobu,
Dongguan, 523415, Guangdong, China
Tel.: (86) 76981192777
Car Dealer Services
N.A.I.C.S.: 441120

Dongguan SCAS Automobile Sales
Services Co., Ltd.   (1)
Baima Block Guantai Raod, Nancheng,
Dongguan, 523072, China
Tel.: (86) 76986225988
Car Dealer Services
N.A.I.C.S.: 441120

Dongguan Zhengtong Kaidi Automo-
bile Sales Services Co., Ltd.   (1)
Huanchang West Road, Changping, Dong-
guan, 523572, China
Tel.: (86) 76982801666
Car Dealer Services
N.A.I.C.S.: 441120

Foshan Dingbaohang Automobile
Sales Services Co., Ltd.   (1)
No 49 Xingye Road, Chancheng, Foshan,
China
Tel.: (86) 75782503338
Car Dealer Services
N.A.I.C.S.: 441120

Fujian SCAS Automobile Sales Ser-
vices Co., Ltd.   (1)
Huluzhen Village Zexu Road, Cangshan,
Fuzhou, 350000, China
Tel.: (86) 59183488910
Car Dealer Services
N.A.I.C.S.: 441120

Fuzhou Dingwo Automobile Sales
Services Co., Ltd.   (1)
No 85 Jingan Road, Fuzhou, 350011, China
Tel.: (86) 59183488910
Car Dealer Services
N.A.I.C.S.: 441120

Ganzhou Baoze Automobile Sales
Services Co., Ltd.   (1)
East Side of Jintan Avenue Ganzhou Devel-
opment Zone, Ganzhou, Jiangxi, China
Tel.: (86) 7978336699
Car Dealer Services
N.A.I.C.S.: 441120

Guangdong SCAS Automobile Sales
Services Co., Ltd.   (1)
2 Suite No 57 Daguan South Road, Tianhe,
Guangzhou, China
Tel.: (86) 2028857488
Car Dealer Services
N.A.I.C.S.: 441120

Guangzhou Baotaihang Automobile
Sales Services Co., Ltd.   (1)
No 1 Xingye Avenue, Panyu, Guangzhou,
China
Tel.: (86) 2031191999
Car Dealer Services
N.A.I.C.S.: 441120

Guangzhou Baoze Automobile Sales
Services Co., Ltd.   (1)
No 146-1 Fangcun Avenue East, Liwan Dis-
trict, Guangzhou, Guangdong Province,
China
Tel.: (86) 208 189 9999
Web Site: https://www.gzbaoze.bmw.com.cn
Car Dealer Services
N.A.I.C.S.: 441120

Hainan SCAS Automobile Sales Ser-
vices Co., Ltd.   (1)
Gaoxin Garden Crosspoint of Nahai Road
and Yongwan Road, Haikou, 570216,
Hainan, China
Tel.: (86) 89831918888
Car Dealer Services
N.A.I.C.S.: 441120

Henan Jintangsheng Automobile Co.,
Ltd.   (1)

No 86 Zhenghua Road, Jinshui,
Zhengzhou, 450000, China
Tel.: (86) 37160221800
Car Dealer Services
N.A.I.C.S.: 441120

Hengyang Luze Automobile Sales
Services Co., Ltd.   (1)
2nd Yangliu Automobile Sale Garden
Huaxin Dovelopment Zone, Hengyang,
421000, Hunan, China
Tel.: (86) 7348185678
Car Dealer Services
N.A.I.C.S.: 441120

Hubei Aoze Automobile Sales Ser-
vices Co., Ltd.   (1)
No 6 Huangpu Science and Technology
Park, Wuhan, Hubei, China
Tel.: (86) 2759201111
Car Dealer Services
N.A.I.C.S.: 441120

Hubei Changze Automobile Sales
Services Co., Ltd.   (1)
No 10 Zhihu West Rd, Hongshan District,
Wuhan, 430070, Hubei, China
Tel.: (86) 2787888657
Car Dealer Services
N.A.I.C.S.: 441120

Hunan SCAS Automobile Sales Ser-
vices Co., Ltd.   (1)
125 Xiangfu Rd Central, Tianxin, Changsha,
Hunan, China
Tel.: (86) 73182176888
Car Dealer Services
N.A.I.C.S.: 441120

Jiangxi Zhengtong Zetian Automobile
Sales Services Co., Ltd.   (1)
Huanqiu Garden Side Back of Baoze BMW
Showroom Yuping East Street, Changbei,
Nanchang, 330000, China
Tel.: (86) 79183970011
Car Dealer Services
N.A.I.C.S.: 441120

Jieyang Dingjie Automobile Sales
Services Co., Ltd.   (1)
National Avenue 206 No 3 Road Jiedong
Test Zone, Jieyang, China
Tel.: (86) 6638550000
Car Dealer Services
N.A.I.C.S.: 441120

Jieyang Luze Automobile Sales Ser-
vices Co., Ltd.   (1)
206 National Highway No 3 Road Jiedong
Experiment Zone, Jieyang, 515500, China
Tel.: (86) 6688553666
Car Dealer Services
N.A.I.C.S.: 441120

Jingmen Baoze Automobile Sales
Services Co., Ltd.   (1)
No 48 Moon Lake Road, Caodao District,
Jingmen, Hubei, China
Tel.: (86) 7248653123
Web Site: http://www.jmbaoze.bmw.com.cn
Car Dealer Services
N.A.I.C.S.: 441120

Qingdao Aoze Automobile Sales Ser-
vices Co., Ltd.   (1)
No 909 East Huanghe Road, Huangdao,
Qingdao, 266599, Shangdong, China
Tel.: (86) 53255710111
Car Dealer Services
N.A.I.C.S.: 441120

Shanghai Aohui Automobile Sales
Services Co., Ltd.   (1)
No 1610-A Husong Rd, Songjiang District,
Shanghai, China
Tel.: (86) 2133736666
Car Dealer Services
N.A.I.C.S.: 441120

Shanghai Dongzheng Automotive Fi-
nance Co., Ltd.   (1)
Unit ABC 30F Mirae Asset Tower 166 Luji-
azuihuan Road, Shanghai, 200120, China
Tel.: (86) 2120689938
Web Site: http://www.dongzhengafc.com
Rev.: $113,888,960
Assets: $960,437,026
Liabilities: $337,705,788
Net Worth: $622,731,238

Earnings: $8,424,252
Emp.: 218
Fiscal Year-end: 12/31/2020
Financial Consulting Services
N.A.I.C.S.: 541611
Fan Lin *(Chm)*

Shanghai Luda Automobile Sales Services Co., Ltd. (1)
No 829 Zhennan Road, Shanghai, China
Tel.: (86) 2152840077
Car Dealer Services
N.A.I.C.S.: 441120

Shanghai Qize Automobile Sales Services Co., Ltd. (1)
No 2996-1 Longwu Rd, Xuhui, Shanghai, 200231, China
Tel.: (86) 2133883677
Car Dealer Services
N.A.I.C.S.: 441120

Shanghai Shenxie Automobile Trading Co., Ltd. (1)
No 9998 Zhongchun Road, Minhang, Shanghai, China
Tel.: (86) 2164796928
Car Dealer Services
N.A.I.C.S.: 441120

Shangrao Baoze Automobile Sales Services Co., Ltd. (1)
No 58 Sanqingshan Av Moon Bay Auto City, Shangrao, Jiangxi, China
Tel.: (86) 7936099999
Car Dealer Services
N.A.I.C.S.: 441120

Shantou Baoze Automobile Sales Services Co., Ltd. (1)
No 257 Daxue Road, Jinping, Shantou, 515000, Guangdong, China
Tel.: (86) 75488883368
Car Dealer Services
N.A.I.C.S.: 441120

Shantou Hongxiang Materials Co., Ltd. (1)
No 52 Zhujiang Road, Longhu, Shantou, China
Tel.: (86) 75488880000
Car Dealer Services
N.A.I.C.S.: 441120

Shengzhou Aoze Automobile Sales Services Co., Ltd. (1)
No 1801 South Shengzhou Road Sanjiang Street, Shengzhou, 312400, Zhejiang, China
Tel.: (86) 57583176666
Car Dealer Services
N.A.I.C.S.: 441120

Shenzhen Aoze Automobile Sales Services Co., Ltd. (1)
No 42 Meilin Road, Futian, Shenzhen, 518049, China
Tel.: (86) 75583102001
Car Dealer Services
N.A.I.C.S.: 441120

Shenzhen Baotaihang Automobile Sales Services Co., Ltd. (1)
No 5071 Luosha Road, Luohu, Shenzhen, China
Tel.: (86) 75522238951
Car Dealer Services
N.A.I.C.S.: 441120

Shenzhen Baoze Automobile Sales Services Co., Ltd. (1)
1F Zhenhua Times Square No 21 Heping Road, Longhua New District, Shenzhen, 518109, Guangdong, China
Tel.: (86) 7552 527 0100
Web Site: http://www.szbz.bmw.com.cn
Car Dealer Services
N.A.I.C.S.: 441120

Shenzhen Dingwo Automobile Sales Services Co., Ltd. (1)
East Side First Floor Printing Plant Jingtian Commercial Newspaper, Lianhua Street Futian District, Shenzhen, 518000, China
Tel.: (86) 75588695668
Car Dealer Services
N.A.I.C.S.: 441120

Shenzhen Huashunbao Automobile Sales Services Co., Ltd. (1)

1F Building A Nitta Industrial Plant No 101 Fuyong Street, Baoan, Shenzhen, China
Tel.: (86) 75522238881
Car Dealer Services
N.A.I.C.S.: 441120

Shenzhen Huashunbao Automobile Services Co., Ltd. (1)
Liyuan Exhibition Hall No 218 Baogang Road, Luohu, Shenzhen, China
Tel.: (86) 75522238811
Car Dealer Services
N.A.I.C.S.: 441120

Suzhou Anzhixing Automobile Sales Services Co., Ltd. (1)
200meters North from DMV Jinhai South Road Economic Develop Zone, Suzhou, 234000, Anhui, China
Tel.: (86) 5573959999
Car Dealer Services
N.A.I.C.S.: 441120

Tianjin SCAS Automobile Sales Services Co., Ltd. (1)
No 62 Huanhe North Road Tianjin Airport Economic Area, Tianjin, 300308, China
Tel.: (86) 2284909001
Car Dealer Services
N.A.I.C.S.: 441120

Weihai Luze Automobile Sales Services Co., Ltd. (1)
Weihai Land Rover 4S Shop east of Qingdao-Weihai Express, north of Zhejiang Road 4 Goldern Sunshine Motor Expo Town, Weihai, 264201, Shandong, China
Tel.: (86) 6313636666
Car Dealer Services
N.A.I.C.S.: 441120

Wuhan Baoze Automobile Sales Services Co., Ltd. (1)
No 6 Huangpu Science and Technology Park, Jiang'an District, Wuhan, China
Tel.: (86) 275 920 1111
Web Site: https://www.baoze.bmw.com.cn
Car Dealer Services
N.A.I.C.S.: 441120

Wuhan Luze Automobile Sales Services Co., Ltd. (1)
No 6 Shiqiao 2nd Road Huangpu Science and Technology Park, Jiang an District, Wuhan, China
Tel.: (86) 2759335888
Web Site: http://www.whe.landrover.com.cn
Car Dealer Services
N.A.I.C.S.: 441120

Wuhan Zhengtong Yuechi Automobile Sales Services Co., Ltd. (1)
Tieji Automobile Garden Erhuan Road Side Xudongtuanjie Road, Wuhan, 430000, China
Tel.: (86) 2759605500
Car Dealer Services
N.A.I.C.S.: 441120

Xiangtan Baoze Automobile Sales Services Co., Ltd. (1)
No 5 Xiangwang Road Jiuhua Economic Zone, Xiangtan, Hunan, China
Tel.: (86) 73152827777
Car Dealer Services
N.A.I.C.S.: 441120

Xiangyang Baoze Automobile Sales Services Co., Ltd. (1)
A39 Shenzhen Industrial Garden Economy Development Area, Xiangyang, 441002, China
Tel.: (86) 7102177778
Car Dealer Services
N.A.I.C.S.: 441120

Yichang Baoze Automobile Sales Services Co., Ltd. (1)
No 49 Development Avenue East Mountain Development Zone, Yichang, Hubei, China
Tel.: (86) 7176900777
Car Dealer Services
N.A.I.C.S.: 441120

Yichun Baoze Automobile Sales Services Co., Ltd. (1)
No 754 Yichun Road Economic and Techonological Development Zone, Yuanzhou District, Yichun, Jiangxi, China

Tel.: (86) 7953935666
Web Site:
　http://www.yichnbaoze.bmw.com.cn
Car Dealer Services
N.A.I.C.S.: 441120

Zhanjiang Zhengtong Kaidi Automobile Sales Services Co., Ltd. (1)
Haitian International Automobile Town Haitian Road, Chikan, Zhanjiang, 524043, China
Tel.: (86) 7593370111
Car Dealer Services
N.A.I.C.S.: 441120

Zhengzhou Dingwo Automobile Sales Services Co., Ltd. (1)
No 136 Eighth Street and Jingbei 1st Road, Economic and Technological Development Zone, Zhengzhou, Henan, China
Tel.: (86) 37155195555
Car Dealer Services
N.A.I.C.S.: 441120

Zhuhai Baoze Automobile Sales Services Co., Ltd. (1)
No 200 North Jinfeng Road High-tech Zone, Xiangzhou, Zhuhai, Guangdog, China
Tel.: (86) 7563912888
Car Dealer Services
N.A.I.C.S.: 441120

Zhuhai SCAS Automobile Sales Services Co., Ltd. (1)
No 1 Pingxi 3rd Nanping Science & Technology Garden Nanping, Zhuhai, Guangdong, China
Tel.: (86) 7568818222
Car Dealer Services
N.A.I.C.S.: 441120

CHINA ZHENHUA (GROUP) SCIENCE & TECHNOLOGY CO., LTD.
No 268 North Section of Xintian Avenue, Wudang District, Guiyang, 550018, Guizhou, China
Tel.: (86) 85186302675
Web Site: https://www.czst.com.cn
Year Founded: 1997
000733—(SSE)
Rev.: $1,020,268,548
Assets: $1,903,849,272
Liabilities: $534,563,172
Net Worth: $1,369,286,100
Earnings: $334,497,384
Fiscal Year-end: 12/31/22
Electronic Products Mfr
N.A.I.C.S.: 334419
Yang Liming *(Chm & Sec-Party Committee)*

CHINA ZHESHANG BANK CO., LTD.
No 1 Minxin Road, Shangcheng District, Hangzhou, 310020, Zhejiang, China
Tel.: (86) 57188268966　　　CN
Web Site: https://www.czbank.com
Year Founded: 2004
601916—(SHG)
Rev.: $8,820,336,730
Assets: $435,295,608,108
Liabilities: $409,047,131,148
Net Worth: $26,248,476,961
Earnings: $2,083,517,944
Emp.: 19,907
Fiscal Year-end: 12/31/23
Commercial Banking Services
N.A.I.C.S.: 522110
Renkang Shen *(Chm)*

CHINA ZHONG QI HOLDINGS LIMITED
1602 Phase A Science & Technology Innovation Plaza, Shenzhen, 331111, China
Tel.: (86) 5612953898　　　NJ
Web Site: https://shanxiindustrial.com
Year Founded: 2004
CHZQ—(OTCIQ)

Sales Range: Less than $1 Million
Metal Mining Services
N.A.I.C.S.: 213114
Daniel J. Sobolewski *(CEO)*

CHINA ZHONGDI DAIRY HOLDINGS COMPANY LIMITED
10th Floor Block A Times Fortune Compound No A6 Shuguang Xili, Chaoyang District, Beijing, 100028, China
Tel.: (86) 58677300　　　Ky
Web Site: http://www.zhongdidairy.hk
Rev.: $214,561,421
Assets: $761,794,281
Liabilities: $437,767,799
Net Worth: $324,026,482
Earnings: $14,649,576
Emp.: 1,426
Fiscal Year-end: 12/31/19
Holding Company
N.A.I.C.S.: 551112
Jianshe Zhang *(Chm & Exec Dir)*

CHINA ZHONGHUA GEOTECHNICAL ENGINEERING CO., LTD.
No 13 Keyuan Road, Daxing District, Beijing, 102600, China
Tel.: (86) 1061271720
Web Site: https://www.cge.com.cn
002542—(SSE)
Rev.: $301,391,380
Assets: $1,173,750,194
Liabilities: $759,762,475
Net Worth: $413,987,719
Earnings: ($97,953,035)
Emp.: 210
Fiscal Year-end: 12/31/22
Dynamic Consolidation Foundation Treatment Services
N.A.I.C.S.: 236210
Yanwei Wu *(Chm)*

CHINA ZHONGWANG HOLDINGS LIMITED
No 299 Wensheng Road, Liaoyang, Liaoning, China
Tel.: (86) 4193688888
Web Site:
　http://www.zhongwang.com
Rev.: $3,374,827,327
Assets: $17,647,599,146
Liabilities: $12,511,889,829
Net Worth: $5,135,709,317
Earnings: $454,813,013
Emp.: 46,334
Fiscal Year-end: 12/31/19
Aluminium Products Mfr
N.A.I.C.S.: 331318
Changqing Lu *(Chm & Pres)*

Subsidiaries:

Aluminiumwerk Unna AG (1)
Uelzener Weg 36, 59425, Unna, Germany
Tel.: (49) 23032060
Web Site: http://www.alunnatubes.com
Aluminium Alloy & Rolling Mfr
N.A.I.C.S.: 331315

Tianjin Zhongwang Aluminium Company Limited (1)
No 1156 Wuning Road Auto Parts Industrial Park, Wuqing District, Tianjin, 301700, China
Tel.: (86) 2259667711
Web Site: http://www.zhongwangtj.com
Aluminium Alloy & Rolling Mfr & Distr
N.A.I.C.S.: 331315
Young Lee *(Product Mgr)*

CHINA-ASEAN CAPITAL ADVISORY COMPANY
67/F Two International Finance Centre 8 Finance Street, Central, China
(Hong Kong)

China-ASEAN Capital Advisory Company—(Continued)

Tel.: (852) 6297 5019
Web Site: http://www.china-asean-fund.com
Private Investment Firm
N.A.I.C.S.: 523999
Patrick Ip (Mng Dir)

CHINA-BIOTICS, INC.

No 26 Orient Global Headquarter Lane 118 Yonghe Road, Zhabei District, Shanghai, 200072, China
Tel.: (86) 2158349748   DE
Web Site: http://www.chn-biotics.com
Sales Range: $75-99.9 Million
Emp.: 341
Probiotic Products Developer for Dietary Supplements & Food Additives
N.A.I.C.S.: 325414
Jinan Song (Chm, Pres, CEO, Treas & Sec)

CHINA-HONG KONG PHOTO PRODUCTS HOLDINGS LIMITED

8th Floor Tsuen Wan Industrial Centre 220-248 Texaco Road, Tsuen Wan, China (Hong Kong)
Tel.: (852) 2 408 8663   BM
Web Site:
http://www.chinahkphoto.com.hk
Year Founded: 1968
1123—(HKG)
Rev.: $130,945,655
Assets: $114,494,127
Liabilities: $30,523,246
Net Worth: $83,970,881
Earnings: $2,264,502
Emp.: 530
Fiscal Year-end: 03/31/22
Holding Company; Photographic Equipment & Supplies Distr
N.A.I.C.S.: 551112
Dennis Tai Lun Sun (Chm)

Subsidiaries:

Emmy Technology Development Limited   (1)
8/F Tsuen Wan Ind Centre 220 Texaco Rd, Tsuen Wan, China (Hong Kong)
Tel.: (852) 23660238
Web Site: https://emmy.com.hk
Electronic Product Distr
N.A.I.C.S.: 449210

Fotomax (F.E.) Ltd.   (1)
Unit 02-04 West Wing 8/F Tsuen Wan Ind Centre 220 Texaco Road, Tsuen Wan, China (Hong Kong)   (100%)
Tel.: (852) 31891648
Web Site: https://www.fotomax.com
Retail Photographic Developing & Processing Services & Supplies Stores Operator
N.A.I.C.S.: 449210

Fuji Life Science Products Limited   (1)
8/F Tsuen Wan Industrial Centre 220 Texaco Road, Tsuen Wan, China (Hong Kong)
Tel.: (852) 29426333
Anti Aging Product Distr
N.A.I.C.S.: 456120

Fuji Photo Products Company, Limited   (1)
8 /F 8/F Tsuen Wan Ind Centre 220 Texaco Rd, Tsuen Wan, China (Hong Kong)   (100%)
Tel.: (852) 24088663
Web Site: https://www.fujifilm.com.hk
Sales Range: $50-74.9 Million
Emp.: 60
Photographic Developing & Processing Supplies Marketer & Distr
N.A.I.C.S.: 423410

YCY International Limited   (1)
8/F Tsuen Wan Ind Centre 220 Texaco Rd, Tsuen Wan, China (Hong Kong)
Tel.: (852) 21978200

Electronic Product Distr
N.A.I.C.S.: 449210

CHINA-SINGAPORE SUZHOU INDUSTRIAL PARK DEVELOPMENT GROUP CO., LTD.

48th Floor Zhongxin Building No 15 Yueliangwan Road, Suzhou Industrial Park, Suzhou, 215123, Jiangsu, China
Tel.: (86) 51266609999
Web Site: https://www.cssd.com.cn
Year Founded: 1994
601512—(SHG)
Rev.: $665,761,665
Assets: $4,556,630,768
Liabilities: $2,025,146,434
Net Worth: $2,531,484,334
Earnings: $225,729,392
Fiscal Year-end: 12/31/22
Construction Services
N.A.I.C.S.: 236220
Zhao Zhisong (Chm & CEO)

CHINACACHE INTERNATIONAL HOLDINGS LTD.

No 8 Zhuyuan 3rd Street Area 3 Tianzhu Comprehensive Bonded Zone, Shunyi District, Beijing, China
Tel.: (86) 1064085088   Ky
Web Site:
http://www.chinacache.com
Year Founded: 1998
Rev.: $51,376,982
Assets: $201,074,796
Liabilities: $304,414,634
Net Worth: ($103,339,839)
Earnings: ($11,108,797)
Emp.: 74
Fiscal Year-end: 12/31/20
Holding Company; Internet Content & Application Delivery Services
N.A.I.C.S.: 551112
Bang Zhang (Chm)

Subsidiaries:

ChinaCache Networks (Hong Kong) Limited   (1)
Room C 18/F Wing Hang Insurance Building 11 Wing Kut Street, Central, China (Hong Kong)
Tel.: (852) 2524 8268
Internet Service Provider
N.A.I.C.S.: 517111

CHINACAST EDUCATION CORPORATION

Suite 08 20th Floor 1 International Financial Centre, 1 Harbour View Street, Central, China (Hong Kong)
Tel.: (852) 39606506   DE
Sales Range: $75-99.9 Million
Emp.: 1,600
E-Learning, Post Secondary Education Long Distance, K-12 Education, Vocational Training, Career Training, Enterprise Training & Government Training Services
N.A.I.C.S.: 611710
Derek Feng (Chm & Interim CEO)

Subsidiaries:

ChinaCast Technology (HK) Limited   (1)
Rm C 16/F Hamilton Coml Bldg 558 560 Nathan Rd, Mongkok, Kowloon, China (Hong Kong)
Tel.: (852) 28112389
Telecommunication Network Services
N.A.I.C.S.: 517111

CHINACHEM GROUP

35-38/F Nina Tower 8 Yeung Uk Road, Tsuen Wan, Hong Kong, China (Hong Kong)
Tel.: (852) 2739 8811

Web Site:
https://www.chinachemgroup.com
Emp.: 100
Real Estate Manangement Services
N.A.I.C.S.: 531210

Subsidiaries:

Pine Care Group Limited   (1)
G/F I Koon Wah Lane 68-72 Yuk Wah Street Tsz Wan Shan, Kowloon, China (Hong Kong)   (56.2%)
Tel.: (852) 2 771 2229
Web Site: http://www.pinecaregroup.com
Rev.: $31,752,683
Assets: $119,568,845
Liabilities: $93,232,806
Net Worth: $26,336,039
Earnings: $414,542
Emp.: 466
Fiscal Year-end: 03/31/2021
Women Healthcare Services
N.A.I.C.S.: 623110

Subsidiary (Domestic):

Patina Wellness Limited   (2)
18 Junction Road, Kowloon City, Kowloon, China (Hong Kong)
Tel.: (852) 3 890 3188
Web Site: https://www.patina.com.hk
Elder Care Services
N.A.I.C.S.: 624120

CHINAEDU HOLDINGS LTD.

4th Floor-A GeHua Building No 1 Qinglong Hutong, Dongcheng District, Beijing, 100007, China
Tel.: (86) 10 8418 6655   Ky
Web Site: http://www.chinaedu.net
Holding Company; Online Educational Services
N.A.I.C.S.: 551112
Julia Huang (Chm)

Subsidiaries:

ChinaEdu Corporation   (1)
4th Floor-A GeHua Building No 1 Qinglong Hutong, Dongcheng District, Beijing, 100007, China
Tel.: (86) 10 84186655
Web Site: http://www.chinaedu.net
Sales Range: $75-99.9 Million
Online Education Services
N.A.I.C.S.: 923110
Julia Huang (Chm)

CHINAETEK SERVICE & TECHNOLOGY CO., LTD.

Floor 11-12 Building 3 Poly Qiyue Metropolis No 10, Auto Museum East Road Fengtai District, Beijing, 100071, China
Tel.: (86) 1081377099
Web Site: https://www.ce-service.com.cn
Year Founded: 2005
301208—(SSE)
Rev.: $185,986,476
Assets: $258,949,548
Liabilities: $67,945,176
Net Worth: $191,004,372
Earnings: $19,869,408
Fiscal Year-end: 12/31/22
Information Technology Services
N.A.I.C.S.: 541512
Li Dongping (Chm)

CHINALIN SECURITIES CO., LTD.

Floor 32-33 Building C China Resources Land Building, No 9668 Shennan Avenue Yuehai Street Nanshan District, Shenzhen, 518052, China
Tel.: (86) 75582707766
Web Site: https://www.chinalions.com
Year Founded: 1997
002945—(SSE)
Rev.: $196,234,272
Assets: $2,912,286,312

Liabilities: $2,018,252,808
Net Worth: $894,033,504
Earnings: $65,239,668
Fiscal Year-end: 12/31/22
Investment Banking Services
N.A.I.C.S.: 523150
Qin Xiang (CEO)

CHINANETCENTER CO., LTD.

Floor 6 Weishi Building No 39 Xueyuan Road, Haidian District, Beijing, 100191, China
Tel.: (86) 4000100617   CN
Web Site:
http://www.chinanetcenter.com
Year Founded: 2000
300017—(CHIN)
Rev.: $700,937,282
Assets: $1,619,964,403
Liabilities: $265,748,873
Net Worth: $1,354,215,530
Earnings: $25,316,420
Fiscal Year-end: 12/31/21
Online Business Solutions
N.A.I.C.S.: 518210

Subsidiaries:

CDNetworks, Inc.   (1)
1840 Enterprise Way, Monrovia, CA 91016
Web Site: https://www.cdnetworks.com
Software Developer
N.A.I.C.S.: 513210

CHINASOFT INTERNATIONAL LTD.

Room 4607-8 46/F Cosco Tower 183 Queens Road, Central, China (Hong Kong)
Tel.: (852) 2 915 2830
Web Site: http://www.chinasofti.com
0354—(HKG)
Rev.: $2,818,769,224
Assets: $2,589,600,311
Liabilities: $808,295,206
Net Worth: $1,781,305,104
Earnings: $174,152,275
Emp.: 92,039
Fiscal Year-end: 12/31/21
Information Technology Outsourcing Services & Software
N.A.I.C.S.: 541519
Simon Chung (COO)

Subsidiaries:

Beijing Chinasoft International Education Technology Co., Ltd.   (1)
12/F North Building of Tower C Raycom Infotech Park, 2 Kexueyuan South Road Zhongguancun Haidian District, Beijing, 100190, China
Tel.: (86) 400 183 1066
Training & Outsourcing Services
N.A.I.C.S.: 611710

CS&S Cyber Resources Software Technology (Tianjin) Co., Ltd.   (1)
4 F Xinzheng Bldg 1 Changwa Zhonglu, Haidian, Beijing, 100089, China
Tel.: (86) 1059715666
Web Site: http://www.chinasoftinc.com
IT Outsourcing Services
N.A.I.C.S.: 541613

Chinasoft International (Guang Zhou) Information Technology Limited   (1)
Unit B F 16 Gaosheng Bldg No 109 Tiyu W Rd, Guangzhou, 510620, China
Tel.: (86) 2038792990
Sales Range: $25-49.9 Million
Emp.: 50
IT Consulting & Training Services
N.A.I.C.S.: 541613

Chinasoft International Inc.   (1)
2535 152nd Ave NE Ste B2, Redmond, WA 98052
Tel.: (425) 296-6253
Sales Range: $25-49.9 Million
Emp.: 35
IT Outsourcing Services
N.A.I.C.S.: 541613

Chinasoft Resource (International)
Limited   **(1)**
Unit 333 1st FL Core Bldg 2, Central, China
(Hong Kong)
Tel.: (852) 24432790
Web Site: http://www.chinasoft-
resource.com
Sales Range: $25-49.9 Million
Emp.: 10
IT Outsourcing Services
N.A.I.C.S.: 541613

Dalian Xinhua Infotech Co., Ltd   **(1)**
601 No 5 Software Park East Rd, Dalian,
116023, China
Tel.: (86) 41184760101
Web Site: http://www.digittime.com
Sales Range: $150-199.9 Million
Emp.: 1,000
Business & Engineering Process Outsourc-
ing Services
N.A.I.C.S.: 561499

Shanghai Chinasoft Resources Infor-
mation Technology Services
Limited   **(1)**
Ln 879 Zhongjiang Rd 4th Fl Bldg 15,
Shanghai, 200333, China
Tel.: (86) 2152829078
Web Site: http://www.chinasoft-
resource.com
Sales Range: $150-199.9 Million
Emp.: 1,300
IT Training & Outsourcing Services
N.A.I.C.S.: 611710

Shanghai Huateng Software Systems
Co., Ltd.   **(1)**
11 F No 481 Hongcao Rd, Shanghai,
200233, China   **(91.22%)**
Tel.: (86) 2151751660
Web Site: http://www.huateng.com
Application Software Development Services
N.A.I.C.S.: 541511

CHINESE ENERGY HOLDINGS LIMITED
Unit 3517 35/F West Tower Shun Tak
Centre 168-200 Connaught Road,
Central, China (Hong Kong)
Tel.: (852) 2 537 8881   HK
Web Site: http://www.chinese-
energy.com
8009—(HKG)
Rev.: $55,392,783
Assets: $53,485,942
Liabilities: $936,653
Net Worth: $52,549,290
Earnings: ($1,298,958)
Emp.: 18
Fiscal Year-end: 03/31/21
Holding Company
N.A.I.C.S.: 551112
Haining Chen (Chm, CEO & Compli-
ance Officer)

CHINESE ESTATES HOLDINGS LIMITED
21st Floor Chubb Tower Windsor
House 311 Gloucester Road Cause-
way Bay, Wanchai, China (Hong
Kong)
Tel.: (852) 28666999   HK
Web Site:
https://www.chineseestates.com
CESTF—(OTCIQ)
Rev.: $183,392,335
Assets: $2,483,739,313
Liabilities: $694,170,000
Net Worth: $1,789,569,313
Earnings: $147,266,988
Emp.: 498
Fiscal Year-end: 12/31/22
Real Estate Investment, Brokerage &
Development Services
N.A.I.C.S.: 525990
Ming-wai Lau (Chm & Chm)

Subsidiaries:

Chinese Estates (Harcourt House)
Limited   **(1)**

Various Portions and Carpark 39 Gloucester
Road, 38 Gloucester Rd, Wanchai, 52,
China (Hong Kong)
Tel.: (852) 28655266
Web Site: https://www.chineseestates.com
Real Estate Prorperty Leasing Services
N.A.I.C.S.: 531110

Chinese Estates Limited   **(1)**
26 F Macomutual Tower 38 Gloucester Rd,
Hong Kong, China (Hong Kong)
Tel.: (852) 28666999
Web Site: https://www.chineseestates.com
Sales Range: $100-124.9 Million
Emp.: 250
Property Investment Managing Services
N.A.I.C.S.: 525990
Matthew Cheong (Mng Dir)

Dollar Union Limited   **(1)**
26 F MassMutual Tower 38 Gloucester Rd,
Wanchai, China (Hong Kong)
Tel.: (852) 28666999
Web Site: http://www.chineseestate.com
Real Estate Agency & Brokerage Services
N.A.I.C.S.: 531210

Fair Eagle Securities Company
Limited   **(1)**
Room 1901 19/F Chubb Tower Windsor
House 311 Gloucester Road, Causeway
Bay, China (Hong Kong)
Tel.: (852) 25262538
Web Site: https://www.faireagle.com.hk
Financial Services
N.A.I.C.S.: 523999

Speed Win Limited   **(1)**
26 F MassMutual Tower 38 Gloucester Rd,
Wanchai, China (Hong Kong)
Tel.: (852) 28666999
Web Site: https://www.chineseestate.com
Sales Range: $150-199.9 Million
Emp.: 300
Property Development Services
N.A.I.C.S.: 531311

The House of Kwong Sang Hong
Limited   **(1)**
3/F MassMutual Tower 38 Gloucester Rd,
Wanchai, China (Hong Kong)
Tel.: (852) 28615808
Web Site: https://www.twogirls.hk
Emp.: 10
Cosmetics Distr
N.A.I.C.S.: 456120
Sue Chan (Mgr)

CHINESE FOOD & BEVERAGE GROUP LIMITED
Unit 2101 21/F Yue Xiu Building 160-
174 Lockhart Road, Wanchai, China
(Hong Kong)
Tel.: (852) 3106 6950   Ky
Web Site:
http://www.cfbgroup.com.hk
Rev.: $10,880,720
Assets: $7,334,131
Liabilities: $4,894,485
Net Worth: $2,439,645
Earnings: $10,859,141
Emp.: 60
Fiscal Year-end: 12/31/18
Holding Company
N.A.I.C.S.: 551112
Eric Todd (Exec Dir)

CHINESE GAMER INTERNA-TIONAL CORP.
4/F 2 Lane 47 Nan-Kang Road Sec-
tion 3, Taipei, Taiwan
Tel.: (886) 226522689
Web Site:
https://www.chinesegamer.net
3083—(TPE)
Rev.: $11,454,867
Assets: $39,596,786
Liabilities: $4,280,493
Net Worth: $35,316,293
Earnings: ($709,502)
Fiscal Year-end: 12/31/22
Software Development Services
N.A.I.C.S.: 541511
Wang Chun-Po (Chm)

CHINESE GLOBAL INVES-TORS GROUP LTD.
3 Shenton Way 11-10 Shenton
House, Singapore, 068805, Singa-
pore
Tel.: (65) 6438 2286   SG
Web Site:
http://www.chineseinvestors.com
Year Founded: 1966
Building Protection, Restoration &
Waterproofing Systems Mfr
N.A.I.C.S.: 561790
Kim Khuan Ng (Dir-Ops-Malaysia)

CHINESE MARITIME TRANS-PORT LTD.
Chinese Maritime Building 15 JiNan
Road Sect 1, Taipei, 10051, Taiwan
Tel.: (886) 223963282
Web Site: https://www.cmt.tw
Year Founded: 1946
2612—(TAI)
Rev.: $131,295,721
Assets: $765,677,985
Liabilities: $384,717,766
Net Worth: $380,960,220
Earnings: $10,591,190
Emp.: 64
Fiscal Year-end: 12/31/23
Inland Container Transportation Ser-
vices
N.A.I.C.S.: 488510
William Shih-Hsiao Peng (Chm)

Subsidiaries:

CMT Logistics Co., Ltd.   **(1)**
9F 15 Jinan Road Section 1, Puhsin, Taipei,
10051, Taiwan
Tel.: (886) 223936242
Web Site: http://www.agcnt.com.tw
Sales Range: $25-49.9 Million
Emp.: 100
Warehousing & Logistics Services
N.A.I.C.S.: 493110
Y. M. Wang (Gen Mgr)

China Ace Shipping Pte. Ltd.   **(1)**
20 Cecil Street 21-04 Equity Plaza, Singa-
pore, 049705, Singapore
Tel.: (65) 63252533
Marine Transportation Services
N.A.I.C.S.: 561910

Chinese Maritime Transport (S) Pte.
Ltd.   **(1)**
111 North Bridge Road 20-05 Peninsula
Plaza, Singapore, 179098, Singapore
Tel.: (65) 63376556
Marine Shipping Services
N.A.I.C.S.: 488330

CHINESE PEOPLE HOLDINGS COMPANY LIMITED
Unit 1101 11th Floor Tung Ning Build-
ing 2 Hillier Street, Central, China
(Hong Kong)
Tel.: (852) 2 902 2008
Web Site: http://www.681hk.com
0681—(HKG)
Rev.: $418,508,589
Assets: $548,428,065
Liabilities: $98,431,909
Net Worth: $449,996,155
Earnings: $28,658,390
Emp.: 5,000
Fiscal Year-end: 12/31/21
Natural Gas Sales
N.A.I.C.S.: 211130
Fun Replen Li (Sec)

CHINESE PETROLEUM ENGI-NEERING CORPORATION
No 2 Daqing East Road, Dushanzi
District, Karamay, 102200, Xinjiang,
China
Tel.: (86) 1080163999
600339—(SHG)
Rev.: $11,735,983,238
Assets: $15,031,065,980

Liabilities: $11,447,327,661
Net Worth: $3,583,738,319
Earnings: $101,191,980
Fiscal Year-end: 12/31/22
Petrochemical Product Mfr & Distr
N.A.I.C.S.: 325110
Yu Guofeng (Sec)

CHINESE STRATEGIC HOLD-INGS LIMITED
Unit 1 21/F Yue Xiu Building Nos
160-174 Lockhart Road, Wanchai,
China (Hong Kong)
Tel.: (852) 2504 0838   BM
Web Site:
http://www.chinarailwaylogistics.com
Rev.: $531,617
Assets: $45,405,262
Liabilities: $33,669,744
Net Worth: $11,735,518
Earnings: ($23,182,243)
Emp.: 33
Fiscal Year-end: 12/31/19
Holding Company
N.A.I.C.S.: 551112
Ivy Shui Sheung Chan (Exec Dir)

CHINESE UNIVERSE PUB-LISHING AND MEDIA GROUP CO., LTD.
No 95 Lijing Road, Honggutan Dis-
trict, Nanchang, 330038, Jiangxi,
China
Tel.: (86) 79185896008
Web Site: http://www.600373.com.cn
Year Founded: 1998
600373—(SHG)
Rev.: $1,641,577,738
Assets: $4,070,351,519
Liabilities: $1,512,116,820
Net Worth: $2,558,234,700
Earnings: $313,072,378
Fiscal Year-end: 12/31/21
Books Publishing Services
N.A.I.C.S.: 513130
Dongliang Zhao (Chm)

CHINESEWORLDNET.COM INC.
Appleby Clifton House 75 Fort Street,
PO Box 190, Grand Cayman,
Georgetown, E9 KY1-1104, Cayman
Islands
Tel.: (345) 9494900   Ky
Web Site:
http://www.chineseworldnet.com
Year Founded: 2000
CWNOF—(OTCIQ)
Assets: $122,018
Liabilities: $242,109
Net Worth: ($120,091)
Earnings: ($61,991)
Fiscal Year-end: 12/31/23
Online Financial Services
N.A.I.C.S.: 519290
Chi Cheong Liu (Pres, CEO, CFO,
Treas & Sec)

CHING CHAN OPTICAL TECH-NOLOGY CO., LTD.
No 58 Lane 110 Zhongxiao St, Hu-
Nei Dist, 82945, Kaohsiung, 82945,
Taiwan
Tel.: (886) 76937937
Web Site: https://www.ccm3s.com
Year Founded: 1992
2070—(TPE)
Rev.: $18,871,619
Assets: $38,904,793
Liabilities: $11,396,992
Net Worth: $27,507,801
Earnings: $2,595,660
Fiscal Year-end: 12/31/22
Inspection Machinery Mfr & Distr
N.A.I.C.S.: 334519
Alex Wu (Chm)

Ching Chan Optical Technology Co.,
Ltd.—(Continued)

CHING FENG HOME FASH-IONS CO., LTD.

373 Sec 4 Yen-Hai Rd Fu-Nan Vil-
lage, Fu Hsien Chang-Hwa, Taipei,
Taiwan
Tel.: (886) 47801967
Web Site: https://www.chingfeng.com
9935—(TAI)
Rev.: $165,308,945
Assets: $223,355,689
Liabilities: $152,108,526
Net Worth: $71,247,163
Earnings: $6,897,133
Emp.: 1,871
Fiscal Year-end: 12/31/22
Home Decoration Equipment Design
Services
N.A.I.C.S.: 811411

CHING LEE HOLDINGS LIM-ITED

Room 203-204 2nd Floor Hang Bong
Commercial Centre 28 Shanghai
Street, Jordan, Kowloon, China
(Hong Kong)
Tel.: (852) 2 376 0720   **Ky**
Web Site:
  http://www.chingleeholdings.com
Year Founded: 1998
3728—(HKG)
Rev.: $69,198,028
Assets: $41,505,635
Liabilities: $27,996,786
Net Worth: $13,508,849
Earnings: ($2,342,406)
Emp.: 94
Fiscal Year-end: 03/31/22
Building Repair & Maintenance Ser-
vices
N.A.I.C.S.: 236118
Choi Wah Ng (Founder, Chm &
Officer-Compliance)

CHINHUNG INTERNATIONAL (INC.)

807 69 Convensia-daero, Yeonsu-gu,
Incheon, Korea (South)
Tel.: (82) 324320658
Web Site: https://www.chinhung.co.kr
Year Founded: 1959
002780—(KRS)
Rev.: $482,393,949
Assets: $346,489,856
Liabilities: $174,119,730
Net Worth: $172,370,126
Earnings: $38,012,963
Emp.: 487
Fiscal Year-end: 12/31/22
Construction Engineering Services
N.A.I.C.S.: 541330
Jae-Bong Ro (CEO)

CHINLINK INTERNATIONAL HOLDINGS LIMITED

Suites 5-6 40/F One Exchange
Square, 8 Connaught Place, Central,
China (Hong Kong)
Tel.: (852) 2 126 6333   **BM**
Web Site: http://www.chinlinkint.com
0997—(HKG)
Rev.: $24,003,823
Assets: $718,380,680
Liabilities: $463,521,488
Net Worth: $254,859,192
Earnings: ($42,866,374)
Emp.: 252
Fiscal Year-end: 03/31/22
Holding Company
N.A.I.C.S.: 551112
Wai Yip Siu (Exec Dir)

Subsidiaries:

Chinlink Finance Lease Company
Limited   (1)

Room A1404 Kerry B Xi'an Industrial De-
sign Industrial Park, 166 Mingguang Road
Xi'an Economic Technological Development
Zone Xi'an, Shaanxi, 710000,
China   (62.5%)
Tel.: (86) 2987303640
Financial Services
N.A.I.C.S.: 523940

Chinlink Supply Chain Services
(Shaanxi) Company Limited   (1)
Room D101 Qinfengge Xian Software Park
No 68 Keji Second Road, Hi-Tech Industries
Development Zone Xian, Shaanxi, 710075,
China
Tel.: (86) 2988233731
Financial Services
N.A.I.C.S.: 523940

Chinlink Tian Hui Company
Limited   (1)
Suites 5-6 40/F One Exchange Square 8
Connaught Place, Central, China (Hong
Kong)
Tel.: (852) 21266333
Web Site: http://www.chinlinkint.com
Financial Services
N.A.I.C.S.: 523940

MCM Asia Limited   (1)
Tel.: (852) 22100888
Commercial Banking Services
N.A.I.C.S.: 522110

Shaanxi Chinlink Financial Guarantee
Limited   (1)
20/F Chinlink International Centre
Fengcheng Tenth Road North, Xi'an Eco-
nomic and Technological Development
Zone, Shaanxi, 710016, China
Tel.: (86) 2981889278
Financial Services
N.A.I.C.S.: 523940

CHINNEY ALLIANCE GROUP LIMITED

23/F Wing On Centre 111 Connaught
Road, Sheung Wan, Central, China
(Hong Kong)
Tel.: (852) 28773307   **BM**
Web Site: http://www.chinney-
  alliance.com
0385—(HKG)
Rev.: $877,040,913
Assets: $636,580,274
Liabilities: $344,107,161
Net Worth: $292,473,113
Earnings: $12,171,843
Emp.: 1,640
Fiscal Year-end: 12/31/21
Plastic Product Whslr
N.A.I.C.S.: 424990
James Sai-Wing Wong (Chm)

Subsidiaries:

Chinney Alliance Engineering
Limited   (1)
Units 901-903 9/F Laford Centre 838 Lai
Chi Kok Road, Kowloon, China (Hong
Kong)
Tel.: (852) 2 563 6128
Web Site: https://www.chinney-eng.com
Engineering Product Distr
N.A.I.C.S.: 423690
K. K. Wong (Mng Dir)

Chinney Construction Company,
Limited   (1)
Block A&B 9th Floor Hong Kong Spinners
Industrial Building Phase VI, 481-483 Castle
Peak Road, Kowloon, China (Hong Kong)
Tel.: (852) 23710100
Engineering Product Distr
N.A.I.C.S.: 423490
Wong Wing Chung (Asst Mgr-Plng)

Chinney Kin Wing Holdings Ltd. (1)
Room 2308 23/F Wing On Centre 111 Con-
naught Road, Central, China (Hong Kong)
Tel.: (852) 2877 3307
Web Site:
  http://www.chinneykinwing.com.hk
Rev.: $200,348,632
Assets: $147,961,471
Liabilities: $82,524,371
Net Worth: $65,437,100

Earnings: $9,954,676
Emp.: 621
Fiscal Year-end: 12/31/2020
Holding Company
N.A.I.C.S.: 551112
Yuen-Keung Chan (Chm)

Driltech Geotechnical Engineering
Limited   (1)
Blocko A&B 0th Floor Hong Kong Spinners
Industrial Building Phase 6, 481-483 Castle
Peak Road, Kowloon, China (Hong Kong)
Tel.: (852) 23710008
Engineering Product Distr
N.A.I.C.S.: 423490

Jacobson (Shenzhen) Trading Com-
pany Limited   (1)
Unit 3608 Futian Street 3031 Shennan
Zhong Road, Hon Kwok Commercial Center
Funan Community Futian District, Shen-
zhen, China
Tel.: (86) 75582762314
Engineering Plastic & Pigment Distr
N.A.I.C.S.: 424690

Jacobson van den Berg (Hong Kong)
Limited   (1)
Flat A 7/F Cheung Lung Industrial Building
10 Cheung Yee Street, Cheung Sha Wan,
Kowloon, China (Hong Kong)
Tel.: (852) 2 828 9328
Web Site: https://www.jvdb.com
Engineering Plastic Distr
N.A.I.C.S.: 424610
Joseph Wong (Sr Mgr-Product Dev)

Kin Wing Foundations Limited   (1)
Blocks A&B 9th Floor Hong Kong Spinners
Industrial Building, Phase VI 481-483 Castle
Peak Road, Kowloon, China (Hong Kong)
Tel.: (852) 24156509
Engineering Product Distr
N.A.I.C.S.: 423490

Westco Chinney Limited   (1)
Blk C 9/F Hong Kong Spinners Ind Bldg
Phase VI 481-483 Castle Peak Rd, Kow-
loon, China (Hong Kong)
Tel.: (852) 23624301
Web Site: http://www.westcochinney.com
Air Conditioner Whslr
N.A.I.C.S.: 423730
Alex Ho (Project Mgr)

CHINNEY INVESTMENTS, LIM-ITED

23rd Floor Wing On Centre 111 Con-
naught Road, Central, China (Hong
Kong)
Tel.: (852) 28773307   **HK**
0216—(HKG)
Rev.: $143,490,379
Assets: $2,817,584,867
Liabilities: $1,191,175,959
Net Worth: $1,626,408,908
Earnings: $12,322,878
Emp.: 370
Fiscal Year-end: 03/31/22
Holding Company
N.A.I.C.S.: 551112
James Sai Wing Wong (Chm)

CHINO CORPORATION

32-8 Kumano-Cho, Itabashi-Ku, To-
kyo, 173-8632, Japan
Tel.: (81) 339562171
Web Site: https://www.chino.co.jp
Year Founded: 1913
6850—(TKS)
Rev.: $181,279,250
Assets: $241,463,300
Liabilities: $88,170,790
Net Worth: $153,292,510
Earnings: $11,607,160
Emp.: 1,095
Fiscal Year-end: 03/31/24
Controlling Equipment Mfr & Whslr
N.A.I.C.S.: 334513
Mikio Toyoda (Pres & CEO)

Subsidiaries:

ADVANCE RIKO, Inc.   (1)

4388 Ikonobe-cho, Tsuzuki-ku, Yokohama,
224-0053, kanagawa, Japan
Tel.: (81) 45 931 2221
Web Site: http://www.advance-riko.com
Emp.: 88
Measuring Equipment Distr
N.A.I.C.S.: 423830
Narishi Gonohe (Pres & CEO)

AR'S Co., Ltd.   (1)
13F Yokohama Creation Square 5-1 Sa-
kaecho, Kanagawa-ku, Yokohama, 221-
0052, Kanagawa, Japan
Tel.: (81) 45 440 1123
Web Site: http://www.arsjp.com
Electronic Equipment Distr
N.A.I.C.S.: 423690
Noriyuki Saito (Auditor)

ASAKAWA Lens Works Co., Ltd. (1)
18-18 Kawarai-cho Kuki Shobu Industrial
Park No 4-2, Kuki, 346-0028, Saitama, Ja-
pan
Tel.: (81) 480 26 1800
Web Site: http://www.asakawalens.co.jp
Emp.: 18
Optical Instrument Mfr
N.A.I.C.S.: 333310

CHINO Corporation (Thailand)
Limited   (1)
No 65 42 Tower 10th Floor Soi Sukhumvit
42 Kluaynamthai Sukhumvit Road, Pra-
kanong Klongtoey, Bangkok, 10110, Thai-
land
Tel.: (66) 27122630
Web Site: https://www.chinothailand.com
Emp.: 10
Measuring Equipment Distr
N.A.I.C.S.: 423830

CHINO Corporation India Pvt.
Ltd.   (1)
PAP-A235-240 South Central Road MIDC
Mahape, TTC Industrial Area, Navi Mumbai,
400 710, India
Tel.: (91) 22 4129 3000
Web Site: http://www.chinoindia.com
Emp.: 40
Measuring Equipment Mfr & Distr
N.A.I.C.S.: 334513
Takao Kariya (Chm)

CHINO Softex Corporation   (1)
1 Mori, Fujioka, 375-8505, Gunma, Japan
Tel.: (81) 274426601
Software Development Services
N.A.I.C.S.: 541511

Cascade Automation Systems
B.V.   (1)
Tinstraat 37-39, 2984 AN, Ridderkerk, Neth-
erlands
Tel.: (31) 18 046 3870
Web Site: https://www.cascade.net
Temperature Control Sensor Mfr
N.A.I.C.S.: 334513
Patrick Braams (Mng Dir)

Che Scientific Company (H.K.)
Limited   (1)
Unit D 18/F Roxy Industrial Centre 58-66
Tai Lin Pai Road, Kwai Chung, China (Hong
Kong)
Tel.: (852) 2 481 1323
Web Site: https://www.chescientific.com
Industrial Testing Equipment Distr
N.A.I.C.S.: 423830

Chino Instrumentation (Kunshan) Co.,
Ltd.   (1)
No 449-10 Xiangshi Road Shipai, Bacheng
Town, Kunshan, Jiangsu, China
Tel.: (86) 5125 788 1727
Web Site: https://www.chino-cik.com
Emp.: 70
Measuring Device System Mfr & Distr
N.A.I.C.S.: 334515

Chino Works America, Inc.   (1)
22301 S Western Ave Ste 105, Torrance,
CA 90501
Tel.: (310) 787-8899
Web Site: http://www.chinoamerica.com
Measuring Equipment Distr
N.A.I.C.S.: 423830
Hideki Negishi (Pres)

Dakin Engineering Pte Ltd   (1)
3791 Jalan Bukit Merah 03-02 e-centre Re-

dhill, Singapore, 159471, Singapore
Tel.: (65) 6 270 9116
Temperature Control Sensor Mfr
N.A.I.C.S.: 334513

Import, Building & Trading Co., **(1)**
Ltd.
12 Hacharoshet St, Kfar Saba, 4464010,
Israel
Tel.: (972) 3 687 9901
Web Site: https://www.ibt.co.il
Electronic Instrumentation Mfr & Distr
N.A.I.C.S.: 334515

Inovativni Technologie S.R.O. **(1)**
Cernokostelecka 1168/90, Strasnice, 10000,
Prague, Czech Republic
Tel.: (420) 22 030 3951
Web Site: https://www.inovatec.cz
Agricultural Waste Treatment Services
N.A.I.C.S.: 562219

Korea CHINO Corporation **(1)**
9 Dongtan-daero 17-gil, Dongtan-myeon,
Hwaseong, 18481, Gyeonggi-do, Korea
(South)
Tel.: (82) 313793700
Web Site: http://www.chinokorea.com
Measuring Equipment Mfr & Distr
N.A.I.C.S.: 334513

Mawi-Therm Temperatur-
Prozesstechnik GmbH **(1)**
Keunefeld 9, 45355, Essen, Germany
Tel.: (49) 2013 655 8866
Web Site: https://mawi-therm.com
Pressure Measurement Instrument Mfr &
Distr
N.A.I.C.S.: 334513

Meiyo Electric Co., Ltd. **(1)**
485 Nanatsushinya, Shimizu-ku, Shizuoka,
424-0066, Japan
Tel.: (81) 54 345 2211
Web Site: https://www.meiyoelc.co.jp
Measurement Equipment Mfr & Distr
N.A.I.C.S.: 334515
Yasuko Sugino (Pres)

Phuc Loc Engineering & Trading Co., **(1)**
Ltd.
16 Street No 16 Lu Gia Apartment Building,
Ward 15 District 11, Ho Chi Minh City,
700000, Vietnam
Tel.: (84) 83 868 4301
Web Site: https://phuc-loc.com
Electrical Equipment Distr
N.A.I.C.S.: 423610

Precision Control Sdn Bhd **(1)**
No 43 Jalan Kota Raja F27/F Hicom Town
Centre Section 27, 40400, Shah Alam, Se-
langor, Malaysia
Tel.: (60) 35 191 8113
Web Site: https://precisioncontrol.com.my
Engineeering Services
N.A.I.C.S.: 541330

Sanki Keiso Co., Ltd. **(1)**
32-8 Kumano-cho, Itabashi-ku, Tokyo, 173-
8632, Saitama, Japan
Tel.: (81) 359170345
Web Site: https://www.sankikeiso.co.jp
Emp.: 20
Refrigeration & Heating Equipment Distr
N.A.I.C.S.: 423740

Sedem S.A. **(1)**
Alts Forns 52, 08038, Barcelona, Spain
Tel.: (34) 93 223 0708
Web Site: https://www.sedemsa.com
Pressure Measurement Instrument Mfr &
Distr
N.A.I.C.S.: 334513
Eduardo Junyent (Mng Dir)

Shanghai DAHUA-CHINO Instrument
Co., Ltd. **(1)**
615 Ning Qiao Road, Jin Qiao Economic
Technological Development Zone Pudong
New Area, Shanghai, 201206, China
Tel.: (86) 2150325111
Web Site: http://www.dh-chino.com
Emp.: 50
Measuring Equipment Mfr & Distr
N.A.I.C.S.: 334513

Tai Yu & Co., Ltd. **(1)**
7th Fl 57 Sec 3 Chung Shan North Rd, Taipei, 10461, Taiwan

Tel.: (886) 22 595 3355
Temperature Control Sensor Mfr
N.A.I.C.S.: 334513

Tangko Prima PT **(1)**
Angkasa Dalam 1 No 50 D, Jakarta Pusat,
10610, Indonesia
Tel.: (62) 21 425 7844
Electronic Instrumentation Mfr & Distr
N.A.I.C.S.: 334515

Westcon Instrumentacao Industrial
Ltda **(1)**
Rua Alvaro Rodrigues 257, Sao Paulo,
04582-000, Brazil
Tel.: (55) 11 561 7488
Web Site: https://www.wii.com.br
Automation Machinery Mfr
N.A.I.C.S.: 333998

CHINOOK INDUSTRIAL LTD.
516 60 Avenue SE, Calgary, T2H
0P9, AB, Canada
Tel.: (403) 253-8291 **Ca**
Web Site: https://www.chinook.ca
Year Founded: 1970
Sales Range: $1-9.9 Million
Industrial Component Parts & Marine
Engines
N.A.I.C.S.: 333618
Mark Drossos (Controller)

CHINT GROUP CORPORATION
Station Road No 168 Liushi Urban
Zhejiang Yueqing, Zhoushan, Zheji-
ang, China
Tel.: (86) 2167777777
Web Site: http://www.cccme.org.cn
Year Founded: 1984
Holding Company; Power & Trans-
mission Products Mfr
N.A.I.C.S.: 551112
Cunhui Nan (Chm & CEO)

Subsidiaries:

Astronergy **(1)**
1335 Binan Road, Binjiang District,
Hangzhou, 310053, Zhejiang, China
Tel.: (86) 571 5603 2092
Web Site: http://www.astronergy.com
Solar Cell Mfr
N.A.I.C.S.: 334413
Cunhui Nan (Chm)

Subsidiary (Non-US):

Astronergy GmbH **(2)**
Karlstr 8, 88212, Ravensburg, Germany
Tel.: (49) 751 295096 10
Solar Cell Distr
N.A.I.C.S.: 423690

Astronergy Solar Company Co.,
Ltd. **(2)**
21 Block-A Diamond District Old Airport
Road, Bengaluru, 560 008, India
Tel.: (91) 80 2521 6293
Solar Cell Distr
N.A.I.C.S.: 423690

Astronergy Solar Korea Co., Ltd. **(2)**
5th Fl Cowell Bldg 66-1, Banpo-Dong
Seocho-Gu, Seoul, 06577, Korea (South)
Tel.: (82) 2 2226 3911
Web Site: http://www.astronergy.co.kr
Emp.: 50
Solar Cell Distr
N.A.I.C.S.: 423690
Jyh Ping Chang (CEO)

Astronergy Solar Thailand Co.,
Ltd **(2)**
184/88 Forum Tower 18 FL Ratchadapised
Rd, Huay-Kwang, Bangkok, 10320, Thai-
land
Tel.: (66) 2 645 4155
Solar Cell Distr
N.A.I.C.S.: 423690

Subsidiary (US):

Astronergy Solar, Inc. **(2)**
851 Burlway Rd Ste 301, Burlingame, CA
94010
Tel.: (415) 802-7399
Solar Cell Distr

N.A.I.C.S.: 423690

Subsidiary (Non-US):

Chint Energy SLU **(2)**
Paseo de Gracia 78 2-1a, 08008, Barce-
lona, Spain
Tel.: (34) 9346 73778
Solar Cell Distr
N.A.I.C.S.: 423690

CHINT ELECTRICS EUROPE
S.R.L **(1)**
Viale Ancona 26, 30172, Mestre, Venice,
Italy
Tel.: (39) 041 532 2064
Electrical Equipment Distr
N.A.I.C.S.: 423610

CHINT ELETRICOS AMERICA DO
SUL LTDA **(1)**
Avenida Paulista no 2073 - Conjunto Nacio-
nal - Edificio Horsa 1, Conjunto 1407/1408,
Bela Vista, Brazil
Tel.: (55) 11 3266 7654
Electrical Equipment Distr
N.A.I.C.S.: 423610

CHINT West Asia & Africa FZE **(1)**
Office NO LB182406, PO Box 263174,
Jebel Ali, Dubai, United Arab Emirates
Tel.: (971) 48848286
Electrical Equipment Distr
N.A.I.C.S.: 423610

Noark Electric (USA) Inc, **(1)**
15302 E Valley Blvd, City of Industry, CA
91746
Tel.: (626) 330-7007
Web Site: http://www.noarkusa.com
Electrical Equipment Distr
N.A.I.C.S.: 423610

Subsidiary (Non-US):

Noark Electric (Europe) S.R.O. **(2)**
Sezemicka 2757/2, 193 00, Prague, Czech
Republic
Tel.: (420) 226 203 120
Web Site: http://www.noark-electric.eu
Electrical Equipment Mfr & Distr
N.A.I.C.S.: 334416

Noark Electric (Romania) S.R.O. **(2)**
Iride Business Park 9-9a Dimitrie Pompei
Blvd Sector 2, 020335, Bucharest, Romania
Tel.: (40) 720 560 812
Electrical Equipment Distr
N.A.I.C.S.: 423610

Noark Electric (Shanghai) Co.,
Ltd. **(2)**
3857 Sixian Road, Songjiang District,
Shanghai, 201614, China
Tel.: (86) 21 37791111
Electrical Equipment Distr
N.A.I.C.S.: 423610

Zhejiang CHINT Electrics Co.,
Ltd. **(1)**
No 1 CHINT Road CHINT Industrial Zone
North Baixiang, Yueqing, 325603, Zhejiang,
China
Tel.: (86) 4001177797
Rev.: $6,454,796,115
Assets: $14,648,552,821
Liabilities: $8,816,089,520
Net Worth: $5,832,463,301
Earnings: $564,866,153
Emp.: 40,000
Fiscal Year-end: 12/31/2022
Power Transmission & Distribution Products
Mfr
N.A.I.C.S.: 335311
Cunhui Nan (Chm & Pres)

Subsidiary (Non-US):

Sunlight Electrical Pte Ltd **(2)**
1 Third Chin Bee Road, Singapore, 618679,
Singapore
Tel.: (65) 67419055
Web Site: http://www.sunlightgroup.com
Electrical Components Mfr & Whslr
N.A.I.C.S.: 335313

Subsidiary (Non-US):

Sunlight Electrical (Vietnam) Co.,
Ltd. **(3)**

20 Doc Lap VSIP 1, Thuan An, Binh Duong,
Vietnam
Tel.: (84) 6503743505
Web Site: http://www.sunlightgroup.com
Emp.: 100
Power Transmission Equipment Mfr
N.A.I.C.S.: 333612

Sunlight Switchgear Sdn. Bhd. **(3)**
PTD 37437 Off Perindustrian Senai 3 Ka-
wasan, Perindustrian Senai FASA 2, 81400,
Senai, Johor, Malaysia
Tel.: (60) 75999600
Web Site: http://www.sunlightgroup.com
Emp.: 100
Power Products Mfr & Distr
N.A.I.C.S.: 335999

CHINTZ & COMPANY
1720 Store St, Victoria, V8W 1V5,
BC, Canada
Tel.: (250) 388-0996
Web Site: http://www.chintz.com
Rev.: $14,615,598
Emp.: 200
Home Furnishings Stores
N.A.I.C.S.: 449129
Nicole Degoutiere (Owner)

CHINVEST SAS
Route de Marthon, 16380, Chazelles-
sur-Lyon, France
Tel.: (33) 545235050 **FR**
Web Site: http://www.chazelles.com
Year Founded: 1979
Sales Range: $10-24.9 Million
Emp.: 130
Fireplaces, Inserts, Stoves & Barbe-
cues Mfr & Distr
N.A.I.C.S.: 333414
Dominique Combeau (Chm & Pres)

CHINYANG CHEMICAL COR-
PORATION
93 Jangsaengpo-ro, Namgu, Ulsan,
Korea (South)
Tel.: (82) 522780701
Web Site: https://www.chinyang.co.kr
Year Founded: 1963
051630—(KRS)
Rev.: $39,825,209
Assets: $35,197,950
Liabilities: $9,801,025
Net Worth: $25,396,925
Earnings: $760,013
Emp.: 83
Fiscal Year-end: 12/31/20
Polyvinyl Chloride Product Mfr
N.A.I.C.S.: 325211
Sang-Yong Kim (CEO)

CHINYANG HOLDINGS COR-
PORATION
73 Saessak-Ro, Busanjin-gu, Busan,
Korea (South)
Tel.: (82) 518098813
Web Site: http://www.cyholdings.kr
Year Founded: 2008
100250—(KRS)
Rev.: $185,300,506
Assets: $471,697,357
Liabilities: $153,620,197
Net Worth: $318,077,160
Earnings: $22,031,843
Emp.: 9
Fiscal Year-end: 12/31/22
Holding Company
N.A.I.C.S.: 551112
Kyu-Ho Lim (Vice Chm & CEO)

Subsidiaries:

Chin Yang Industry Co., Ltd. **(1)**
42 Yusangongdan 7-gil, Yangsan,
Gyeongsangnam-do, Korea (South)
Tel.: (82) 553828981
Web Site: http://www.cyc1963.com
Rev.: $64,177,353
Assets: $63,446,205
Liabilities: $24,153,201

Chinyang Holdings Corporation—(Continued)

Net Worth: $39,293,005
Earnings: $4,706,425
Emp.: 81
Fiscal Year-end: 12/31/2022
Plastics Product Mfr
N.A.I.C.S.: 326199
Kyu-Mo Yang (Founder & Chm)

CHINYANG POLY URETHANE CO LTD
85 Segyo Industrial Complex Road, Pyeongtaek, Gyeonggi-do, Korea (South)
Tel.: (82) 316572545
Web Site:
https://www.chinyangpoly.kr
Year Founded: 1975
010640—(KRS)
Rev.: $40,436,616
Assets: $35,346,827
Liabilities: $11,792,531
Net Worth: $23,554,296
Earnings: $2,679,158
Emp.: 64
Fiscal Year-end: 12/31/22
Polyurethane Plastic Mfr & Distr
N.A.I.C.S.: 326150
YoungTae Cho (Pres)

CHIOME BIOSCIENCE INC.
Sumitomo Fudosan Nishi-shinjuku Bldg No 6 3-12-1 Honmachi, Shibuya-ku, Tokyo, 151-0071, Japan
Tel.: (81) 363833561
Web Site: https://www.chiome.co.jp
Year Founded: 2005
4583—(TKS)
Rev.: $4,517,100
Assets: $15,881,550
Liabilities: $3,047,250
Net Worth: $12,834,300
Earnings: ($8,905,140)
Emp.: 68
Fiscal Year-end: 12/31/22
Pharmaceuticals Mfr
N.A.I.C.S.: 325412
Shigeru Kobayashi (Pres & CEO)

CHIORINO S.P.A.
Via Sant'Agata 9, 13900, Biella, Italy
Tel.: (39) 015 84891   IT
Web Site: http://www.chiorino.com
Year Founded: 1906
Sales Range: $100-124.9 Million
Emp.: 850
Industrial Belting Products Mfr & Whslr
N.A.I.C.S.: 326220

Subsidiaries:

Chiorino, Inc.   (1)
Harmony Business Park 125 Ruthar Dr, Newark, DE 19711
Tel.: (302) 292-1906
Web Site: http://www.chiorino.us
Mechanical Belting Products Whslr
N.A.I.C.S.: 423840
Kenneth Denaker (Reg Sls Mgr)

CHIP ENG SENG CORPORATION LTD.
171 Chin Swee Road 12-01 CES Centre, Singapore, 169877, Singapore
Tel.: (65) 68010088
Web Site:
http://www.chipengseng.com.sg
Year Founded: 1998
C29—(SES)
Rev.: $509,327,676
Assets: $2,416,214,293
Liabilities: $1,799,188,636
Net Worth: $617,025,656
Earnings: ($59,257,595)
Emp.: 680
Fiscal Year-end: 12/31/20

Building Construction & Real Estate Management
N.A.I.C.S.: 236220
Siang Thong Yeo (Mng Dir-Building Construction Div)

Subsidiaries:

CEL Australia Pty Ltd   (1)
Level 8 420 St Kilda Hd, Melbourne, 3004, VIC, Australia
Tel.: (61) 390089010
Web Site: http://www.celaustralia.com.au
Property Development Services
N.A.I.C.S.: 531390
Carman Choke (Fin Mgr)

CEL Development Pte. Ltd.   (1)
171 Chin Swee Road 11-01 CES Center, Singapore, 169877, Singapore
Tel.: (65) 6 801 0188
Web Site:
https://www.celdevelopment.com.sg
Emp.: 40
Residential Property Development Services
N.A.I.C.S.: 236116
Sock Joo Lim (Exec Dir)

CES Education Pte. Ltd.   (1)
171 Chin Swee Road CES Centre, Singapore, 169877, Singapore
Tel.: (65) 68010088
Web Site: http://www.ceseducation.com.sg
Holding Company
N.A.I.C.S.: 551112
Koh Thiam Seng (Exec VP)

Subsidiary (Domestic):

White Lodge Education Group Services Pte. Ltd.   (2)
970 Toa Payoh N 06-01, Singapore, 318992, Singapore
Tel.: (65) 62554230
Web Site: http://www.whitelodge.education
Holding Company
N.A.I.C.S.: 551112
Wang Hong (Head-Mandarin)

CES Engineering & Construction Pte. Ltd   (1)
69 Ubi Crescent 06-01 Ces Bldg, Singapore, 408561, Singapore
Tel.: (65) 68480848
Web Site: http://www.chipengseng.com
Property Development Services
N.A.I.C.S.: 236116

CES Land Pte. Ltd.   (1)
69 Ubi Crescent 06-01 Ces Building, Singapore, 408561, Singapore
Tel.: (65) 65000065
Web Site: http://www.chipengseng.com.sg
Property Development Services
N.A.I.C.S.: 236220

CES-Precast Pte. Ltd.   (1)
11 Tuas Basin Close, Singapore, 638806, Singapore
Tel.: (65) 65828488
Web Site: http://www.chipengseng.com.sg
Sales Range: $25-49.9 Million
Emp.: 25
Precast Products Mfr & Distr
N.A.I.C.S.: 327390

Chip Eng Seng Contractors (1988) Pte Ltd   (1)
69 Ubi Cres No 06-01 CES Bldg, Singapore, 408561, Singapore
Tel.: (65) 68480848
Web Site: http://www.chipengseng.com.sg
Building Construction
N.A.I.C.S.: 236220

Subsidiary (Domestic):

CES Building and Construction Pte Ltd   (2)
69 Ubi Crescent 06-01 Ces Bldg, Singapore, 408561, Singapore
Tel.: (65) 68480848
Commercial Property Development Services
N.A.I.C.S.: 236220

Sembcorp Design and Construction Pte Ltd   (2)
167 Jalan Bukit Merah 13-10 Tower 5, Singapore, 150167, Singapore
Tel.: (65) 6305 2788

Web Site: http://www.sembcorpdc.com
Construction Engineering Services
N.A.I.C.S.: 541330
Ching Khiang Tay (Deputy CEO)

Excelsior Education Management Sdn Bhd   (1)
No 8 Jalan Purnama, Bandar Seri Alam, 81750, Johor Bahru, Johor, Malaysia
Tel.: (60) 73888999
Educational Support Services
N.A.I.C.S.: 611710
Ravi Shankar Raman (VP-IT Mgmt)

Invictus International School (Hong Kong) Limited   (1)
Monterey Place 23 Tong Chun St New Territories, Tseung Kwan O, China (Hong Kong)
Tel.: (852) 36431868
Web Site: http://www.tko.invictusschool.hk
Educational Support Services
N.A.I.C.S.: 611710
Christopher Jackson (Principal)

Invictus International School Pte. Ltd.   (1)
73 Loewen Road 01-21, Singapore, 248843, Singapore
Tel.: (65) 62593877
Web Site: http://www.invictus.school
Education Services
N.A.I.C.S.: 611710
Tina Cooper (Principal)

Invictus Junior Schools Pte. Ltd. (1)
171 Chin Swee Road 10-09, Singapore, 169877, Singapore
Tel.: (65) 80569520
Educational Support Services
N.A.I.C.S.: 611710

Invictus School (Chai Wan) Limited   (1)
188 Tai Tam Road Hong Kong Island, Chai Wan, China (Hong Kong)
Tel.: (852) 36431868
Web Site:
http://www.chaiwan.invictusschool.hk
Educational Support Services
N.A.I.C.S.: 611710
Lee Harvey (Principal-Chaiwan Campus)

Sing-Ed Global Schoolhouse Pte. Ltd.   (1)
171 Chin Swee Road CES Centre 10-01 Sing-Ed Global Schoolhouse, Singapore, 169877, Singapore
Tel.: (65) 68010088
Web Site:
https://www.singedglobalschools.com.sg
Educational Support Services
N.A.I.C.S.: 611710

Swallows & Amazons Pte. Ltd.   (1)
The Grandstand South Carpark 200 Turf Club Road, Singapore, 287994, Singapore
Tel.: (65) 6 762 8158
Web Site:
https://www.swallowsandamazons.com.sg
Educational Support Services
N.A.I.C.S.: 611710
Jackie Barkham (Principal)

The Perse School (Singapore) Pte. Ltd.   (1)
191 Upper Bukit Timah Road, Singapore, 588180, Singapore
Tel.: (65) 69718210
Web Site: http://www.perse.edu.sg
Education Services
N.A.I.C.S.: 611710
Claire Bell (Principal)

White Lodge Bangsar South Childcare Centre Sdn. Bhd.   (1)
South Unit 2-1 Level 2 Nexus Bangsar South No 7 Jalan Kerinchi, 59200, Kuala Lumpur, Malaysia
Tel.: (60) 322422663
Education Services
N.A.I.C.S.: 611710
Yvonne Khong (Principal)

White Lodge Kindergarten, East Coast Pte. Ltd.   (1)
102 Guillemard Road 02-01 Former Badminton Hall Kindergarten, East Coast, Singapore, 399719, Singapore

Tel.: (65) 64406690
Education Services
N.A.I.C.S.: 611710
Heather Yew (Principal)

White Lodge Kindergarten, Phoenix Park Pte. Ltd.   (1)
310 Tanglin Road Kindergarten Phoenix Park, Singapore, 247975, Singapore
Tel.: (65) 62353310
Education Services
N.A.I.C.S.: 611710
Kathy Bolouri (Principal)

White Lodge Mont Kiara Childcare Centre Sdn. Bhd.   (1)
B-G-10 & B-G-11 Gateway Kiaramas No 1 Jalan Desa Kiara, Mont Kiara, 50480, Kuala Lumpur, Malaysia
Tel.: (60) 362010314
Education Services
N.A.I.C.S.: 611710
Kimbery Lee (Principal)

White Lodge Preschool River Valley Pte. Ltd.   (1)
262 River Valley RoadÂ, Singapore, 238308, Singapore
Tel.: (65) 69026906
Education Services
N.A.I.C.S.: 611710
Wong Yiun Swan (Principal)

White Lodge School of Arts, Loewen Gardens Pte. Ltd.   (1)
75E Loewen Road Dempsey Road, Singapore, 248845, Singapore
Tel.: (65) 64757262
Education Services
N.A.I.C.S.: 611710

White Lodge, Bukit Timah Pte. Ltd.   (1)
39 Linden Dr Kindergarten, Bukit Timah, Singapore, 288712, Singapore
Tel.: (65) 64688846
Education Services
N.A.I.C.S.: 611710
Jesika Thakkar (Principal)

White Lodge, Upper Bukit Timah Pte. Ltd.   (1)
1 Jln Siap Kindergarten, Upper Bukit Timah, Singapore, 678541, Singapore
Tel.: (65) 63145481
Education Services
N.A.I.C.S.: 611710
Patricia Lyn (Principal)

White Lodge, Upper East Coast Pte. Ltd.   (1)
36 Toh DriveÂ, Singapore, 507889, Singapore
Tel.: (65) 65431802
Education Services
N.A.I.C.S.: 611710

White Lodge, West Coast Pte. Ltd.   (1)
9 South Buona Vista Road, Singapore, 118141, Singapore
Tel.: (65) 67798465
Education Services
N.A.I.C.S.: 611710
Guganeshwari Rangaswamy (Principal)

CHIP HOPE CO., LTD.
9/F-1 258 Lian-Cheng Rd, Zhonghe, Taiwan
Tel.: (886) 282271166
Web Site:
http://www.chiphope.com.tw
8084—(TPE)
Rev.: $36,241,316
Assets: $36,676,953
Liabilities: $23,757,903
Net Worth: $12,919,051
Earnings: $1,674,483
Fiscal Year-end: 12/31/22
Integrated Circuit Mfr & Distr
N.A.I.C.S.: 334413
Yueh-Ching Cheng (Chm & CEO)

CHIPBOND TECHNOLOGY CORPORATION
No 3 Li Hsin 5th Rd Hsinchu Science

Park, Hsinchu, 30078, Taiwan
Tel.: (886) 35678788
Web Site:
  https://www.chipbond.com.tw
Year Founded: 1997
6147—(TPE)
Rev.: $655,887,611
Assets: $1,796,318,942
Liabilities: $210,863,951
Net Worth: $1,585,454,991
Earnings: $130,633,371
Emp.: 2,624
Fiscal Year-end: 12/31/23
Semiconductor Product Mfr
N.A.I.C.S.: 334413
Fei-Jain Wu *(Chm)*

CHIPITA S.A.
12th km National Road Athens - La-
mia, 144 52, Metamorfosis, Attica,
Greece
Tel.: (30) 210 288 5000   **GR**
Web Site: http://www.chipita.com
Year Founded: 1973
Emp.: 4,700
Cakes, Pastries, Cookies & Bread
Chips Mfr & Marketer
N.A.I.C.S.: 311999
Spyros Theodoropoulos *(CEO)*

Subsidiaries:

Chipita America, Inc.   **(1)**
1 Westbrook Corporate Ctr Ste 640,
Westchester, IL 60154-5701
Tel.: (708) 731-2430
Web Site: http://www.chipita.us.com
Sales Range: $25-49.9 Million
Emp.: 60
Soft Croissant Mfr
N.A.I.C.S.: 311812

Unit (Domestic):

Chipita America, Inc. - Tulsa   **(2)**
601 S Boulder Ave Ste 900, Tulsa, OK
74119
Tel.: (918) 560-4100
Web Site: http://www.chipita.us.com
Soft Croissant Mfr
N.A.I.C.S.: 311812

Chipita Bulgaria S.A.   **(1)**
6 Seraphim Stoev Str, Kazichene Village
Pancharevo, 1532, Sofia, Bulgaria
Tel.: (359) 2 9761600
Food Products Distr
N.A.I.C.S.: 424420
Vili Ramcheva *(Mgr-Mktg)*

Chipita CZ s.r.o   **(1)**
Evropska 423/178, Vokovice, 160 00,
Prague, Czech Republic
Tel.: (420) 2 4144 4800
Food Products Distr
N.A.I.C.S.: 424420

Chipita Germany GmbH   **(1)**
Franz - Rennefeld - Weg 2-6, 40472, Dus-
seldorf, Germany
Tel.: (49) 211 2398370
Food Products Distr
N.A.I.C.S.: 424420

Chipita Gida Uretim A.S.   **(1)**
Inonu Mah Plastics 1st Avenue 11th Street
No 5, Industrial Area of Gebze Geposb,
41400, Gebze, Kocaeli, Turkiye
Tel.: (90) 262 75 11 555
Food Products Distr
N.A.I.C.S.: 424420
Georgios Lampousis *(Country Mgr)*

Chipita Hungary Kft.   **(1)**
Vasut Ut 11, 2040, Budaors, Hungary
Tel.: (36) 23 33 80 23
Web Site: http://www.chipita.com
Food Products Distr
N.A.I.C.S.: 424420

Chipita India Pvt Ltd.   **(1)**
A-178 TTC Industrial Estate MIDC, Kopar
Khairane, Mumbai, 400710, India
Tel.: (91) 22 27788610
Food Products Distr
N.A.I.C.S.: 424420
Bafna Mangatmal *(CFO)*

Chipita Lefco LLC   **(1)**
Timiryazeva Street 72-49 k Office 1204,
220035, Minsk, Belarus
Tel.: (375) 173363355
Salty Snack Mfr
N.A.I.C.S.: 311919

Chipita Poland S.p. z.o.o.   **(1)**
Al Niepodleglosci 18, 02653, Warsaw, Po-
land
Tel.: (48) 22 4895 500
Food Products Distr
N.A.I.C.S.: 424420
Piotr Nowosielski *(Dir-Fin)*

Chipita Romania S.R.L.   **(1)**
Drumul Mare 8, Clinceni, 077060, Ilfov,
Romania
Tel.: (40) 21 3520290
Food Products Distr
N.A.I.C.S.: 424420
Gianina Stancu *(Sr Accountant)*

Chipita Saint-Petersburg LLC   **(1)**
Svobody Str 50D Krasnoe Selo, 198320,
Saint Petersburg, Russia
Tel.: (7) 8479435678
Food Products Distr
N.A.I.C.S.: 424420
Irina Reshetnik *(Coord-Import Pur)*

Chipita Slovakia s.r.o.   **(1)**
Stefanikova 43, 811 04, Bratislava, Slovakia
Tel.: (421) 2 5262 0273
Food Products Distr
N.A.I.C.S.: 424420
Antonin Fiala *(Country Mgr)*

Chipita Ukraine Trade LLC   **(1)**
23 Baggovutivska str, 04107, Kiev, Ukraine
Tel.: (380) 44 5035550
Food Products Distr
N.A.I.C.S.: 424420

Chipita YU a.d.   **(1)**
Bulevar Mihaila Pupina 10v, 11070, Bel-
grade, Serbia
Tel.: (381) 11 630 46 80
Web Site: http://www.chipita.com
Emp.: 4
Food Products Distr
N.A.I.C.S.: 424420

**CHIPLUN FINE CHEMICALS
LTD.**
E 25 Lote MIDC Taluka Khed, Rat-
nagiri, 415722, Maharashtra, India
Tel.: (91) 2356272480
530417—(BOM)
Chemical Products Mfr
N.A.I.C.S.: 325199
Chhabildas Muchhala *(Vice Chm &
Compliance Officer)*

**CHIPMOS TECHNOLOGIES
INC.**
No 1 R and D Road 1 Hsinchu Sci-
ence Park, Hsin-chu, Taiwan
Tel.: (886) 35770055   **CN**
Web Site: https://www.chipmos.com
IMOS—(NASDAQ)
Rev.: $667,736,860
Assets: $1,443,281,868
Liabilities: $669,020,636
Net Worth: $774,261,233
Earnings: $61,519,088
Emp.: 5,396
Fiscal Year-end: 12/31/23
Semiconductor Devices Mfr
N.A.I.C.S.: 334413
Shih-Jye Cheng *(Pres & Chm)*

Subsidiaries:

ChipMOS Assembly Fab   **(1)**
No 5 Nan-Ko Rd 7 Southern Taiwan Sci-
ence Pk, Taipei, Taiwan
Tel.: (886) 65052388
Sales Range: $800-899.9 Million
Emp.: 3,000
Semiconductor & Related Device Mfr
N.A.I.C.S.: 334413
S. J. Cheng *(Chm)*

ChipMOS Gold Bumping Fab   **(1)**
No 37 Hsin Tai Road, Jhubei, Hsin-chu,

302, Taiwan
Tel.: (886) 36562078
Web Site: http://www.chipmos.com
Sales Range: $200-249.9 Million
Emp.: 600
Semiconductor & Related Device Mfr
N.A.I.C.S.: 334413

ChipMOS Japan Inc.   **(1)**
Robot FA Bldg 1-9-1 Nakasa, Mihama-Ku,
Chiba, 261-0023, Japan
Tel.: (81) 43 299 6914
Web Site: http://www.chipmos.com.tw
Semiconductor & Related Device Mfr
N.A.I.C.S.: 334413

ChipMOS Testing Fab   **(1)**
No 1 R and D Road 1, Hsinchu Science
Park, Hsin-chu, Taiwan
Tel.: (886) 35770055
Semiconductor & Related Device Mfr
N.A.I.C.S.: 334413

ChipMOS U.S.A., Inc.   **(1)**
2890 N 1st St, San Jose, CA
95134   **(100%)**
Tel.: (408) 922-2777
Web Site: https://www.chipmos-usa.com
Sales Range: $25-49.9 Million
Emp.: 4
Semiconductor & Related Device Mfr
N.A.I.C.S.: 334413
Steve Cheng *(Pres)*

**CHIPONE TECHNOLOGY (BEI-
JING) CO., LTD.**
Building 56 No 2 Jingyuan North
Street, Economic-Technological De-
velopment Area, Beijing, China
Tel.: (86) 10 8200 4128   **CN**
Web Site: http://www.chiponeic.com
Semiconductor Mfr
N.A.I.C.S.: 334413

CHIPS&MEDIA, INC.
7~8F NC Tower I 509 Teheran-ro,
Gangnam-gu, Seoul, Korea (South)
Tel.: (82) 25683767
Web Site:
  https://www.chipsnmedia.com
Year Founded: 2003
094360—(KRS)
Rev.: $18,479,133
Assets: $48,379,077
Liabilities: $16,187,410
Net Worth: $32,191,667
Earnings: $7,641,543
Emp.: 66
Fiscal Year-end: 12/31/22
Semiconductor Devices Mfr
N.A.I.C.S.: 334413
Steve Sang-Hyun Kim *(Pres & CEO)*

**CHIPSEA TECHNOLOGIES
(SHENZHEN) CORP.**
3rd Floor Building T1 Shenzhen Bay
Innovation and Technology Center,
Keyuan Avenue Yuehai Street Nan-
shan District, Shenzhen, 518000,
Guangdong, China
Tel.: (86) 75586169257
Web Site: https://www.chipsea.com
Year Founded: 2003
688595—(SHG)
Rev.: $86,721,219
Assets: $238,782,366
Liabilities: $84,753,260
Net Worth: $154,029,105
Earnings: $392,474
Fiscal Year-end: 12/31/22
Semiconductor Product Mfr & Distr
N.A.I.C.S.: 334413
Guojian Lu *(Chm & Gen Mgr)*

Subsidiaries:

Chengdu Xinhai Chuangxin Technol-
ogy Co., Ltd.   **(1)**
1201 Taihe International Finance Center No
619 3rd Tianfu Street, Wuhou District,
Chengdu, Sichuan, China
Tel.: (86) 2863917307

Information Technology Services
N.A.I.C.S.: 541519

Hefei Xinhai Electronic Technology
Co., Ltd.   **(1)**
Floor 8 Block A Building G3 Phase II Inno-
vation Industrial Park, Hefei High tech
Zone, Anhui, China
Tel.: (86) 75586169257
Information Technology Services
N.A.I.C.S.: 541519

Shanghai Chipsea Innovation Tech-
nology Co., Ltd.   **(1)**
901 Floor 9 Building A Building 1 No 199
Jinwan Road, Pilot Free Trade Zone,
Shanghai, China
Tel.: (86) 75586169257
Information Technology Services
N.A.I.C.S.: 541519

Xi'an Xinhai Microelectronics Technol-
ogy Co., Ltd.   **(1)**
Room 1002 10th Floor T1 Building Phase II,
Taiwei Smart Chain Center No 8 Tangyan
South Road Yanta District, Xi'an, Shaanxi,
China
Tel.: (86) 75586169257
Electric Equipment Mfr
N.A.I.C.S.: 334419

CHIRANA T. INJECTA, A.S.
Nam Dr A Schweitzera 194, 916 01,
Stara Tura, Slovakia
Tel.: (421) 327752801
Web Site: http://www.t-injecta.sk
Year Founded: 1947
Sales Range: $10-24.9 Million
Emp.: 470
Medical Instrument Mfr
N.A.I.C.S.: 339112
Gabriela Vdoviakova *(Asst Gen Dir)*

CHIRIPAL INDUSTRIES LTD.
Chiripal House Shivranjani Cross
Roads Satellite, Ahmedabad, 380
015, Gujarat, India
Tel.: (91) 7926734660
Web Site:
  http://www.chiripalgroup.com
Year Founded: 1972
Sales Range: $200-249.9 Million
Emp.: 1,470
Fabric & Textile Mfr & Exporter
N.A.I.C.S.: 313310
Vedprakash Chiripal *(Chm & Mng Dir)*

Subsidiaries:

Chiripal Industries Ltd. - Fabric
Division   **(1)**
Saijpur-Gopalpur Pirana road, Piplej,
Ahmedabad, 382 405, Gujarat, India
Tel.: (91) 79 25714568
Garments Mfr
N.A.I.C.S.: 315250

Chiripal Industries Ltd. - Petrochemi-
cal Division   **(1)**
Survey No 199 & 200/1-2 Saijpur-Gopalpur
Pirana road, Piplej, Ahmedabad, 382 405,
Gujarat, India
Tel.: (91) 79 98258 00199
Garments Mfr
N.A.I.C.S.: 315250

Nandan Denim Limited   **(1)**
Chirpal House Shivranjani Cross Road Sat-
ellite, Ahmedabad, 380015, Gujarat, India
Tel.: (91) 7926473301
Web Site: http://www.nandandenim.com
Rev.: $152,027,667
Assets: $161,509,107
Liabilities: $97,214,099
Net Worth: $64,295,008
Earnings: ($2,555,062)
Emp.: 3,027
Fiscal Year-end: 03/31/2021
Denim Fabric Mfr
N.A.I.C.S.: 314999
Deepak J. Chiripal *(CEO)*

Subsidiary (Domestic):

CIL Nova Petrochemicals
Limited   **(2)**

Chiripal Industries Ltd.—(Continued)

Chiripal House Shivranjani Cross Road Satellite, Ahmedabad, 380 015, Gujarat, India
Tel.: (91) 7926734660
Web Site: https://www.cnpcl.com
Rev.: $21,268,420
Assets: $22,531,113
Liabilities: $10,866,328
Net Worth: $11,664,785
Earnings: $727,709
Emp.: 419
Fiscal Year-end: 03/31/2021
Petrochemical Products Mfr
N.A.I.C.S.: 325110
Pradeep Khandelwal (CEO)

CHIRISA CAPITAL MANAGE-MENT LTD.
15 Pembroke Street Lower, Dublin, D02 DD35, Ireland
Tel.: (353) 1 547 5511
Web Site: http://www.chirisa.com
Year Founded: 2011
Private Investment Firm
N.A.I.C.S.: 523999
Colm Piercy (Chm)

CHISON MEDICAL TECH-NOLOGIES CO., LTD.
No 3 Changjiang South Road, Xinwu District, Wuxi, 214028, Jiangsu, China
Tel.: (86) 51085270304
Web Site: https://www.chison.com
Year Founded: 1996
688358—(SHG)
Rev.: $53,470,399
Assets: $212,555,295
Liabilities: $28,138,743
Net Worth: $184,416,551
Earnings: $14,860,329
Fiscal Year-end: 12/31/22
Medical Product Mfr & Distr
N.A.I.C.S.: 339112
Shanjue Mo (Chm)

Subsidiaries:

Chison Deutschland GmbH   (1)
Ungelsheimer Weg 7, 40472, Dusseldorf, Germany
Tel.: (49) 21143791728
Medical Device Mfr & Distr
N.A.I.C.S.: 339112

Chison USA Inc.   (1)
2700 Richards Rd Ste 104, Bellevue, WA 98005
Tel.: (425) 454-2421
Ultrasound System Mfr & Distr
N.A.I.C.S.: 339113

CHITA KOGYO CO., LTD.
2-12-4 Maenamicho, Kasugai, 486-0903, Aichi, Japan
Tel.: (81) 568277771
Web Site: https://www.chitakogyo.co.jp
59930—(NGO)
Rev.: $130,476,720
Assets: $227,605,840
Liabilities: $42,543,600
Net Worth: $185,062,240
Earnings: $14,026,320
Emp.: 500
Fiscal Year-end: 03/31/22
Hardware Product Mfr
N.A.I.C.S.: 332510
Osamu Yoshida (Chm)

CHITEC TECHNOLOGY CO., LTD.
16F No 51 Sec 2 Keelung Rd, Taipei, 110502, Taiwan
Tel.: (886) 227006678
Web Site: https://www.chitec.com
Year Founded: 1998
3430—(TAI)
Chemical Products Mfr
N.A.I.C.S.: 325998

Ching-Fan Chu (Chm)

CHITOGENX INC
16667 Hymus Blvd, Kirkland, H9H 4R9, QC, Canada
Tel.: (514) 782-0951
Web Site: http://www.orthorti.com
CHNXF—(OTCIQ)
Assets: $403,232
Liabilities: $5,068,338
Net Worth: ($4,665,106)
Earnings: ($1,173,450)
Fiscal Year-end: 01/31/24
Medical Instrument Mfr
N.A.I.C.S.: 339112
Michael Atkin (Chm)

CHITRCHATR COMMUNICA-TIONS INC.
76 Marlyn Court NE, Calgary, T2A 7H5, AB, Canada
Tel.: (702) 475-5636   BC
Web Site: http://www.chitrchatr.com
Year Founded: 2013
Software Publisher
N.A.I.C.S.: 513210
Rahim Mohamed (Pres & CEO)

CHITTAGONG CAPITAL LIM-ITED
Crown Chamber 3rd Floor 325 Asadgonj, Chittagong, 4000, Bangladesh
Tel.: (880) 31610926
Web Site: http://www.ctgcap.com
Year Founded: 2005
Security Brokerage Services
N.A.I.C.S.: 523150
Mohammed Jahangir Alam (Mng Dir)

CHITTAGONG STOCK EX-CHANGE LTD.
CSE Bldg 1080 Sk Mujib Rd, 4100, Chittagong, Agrabad, Bangladesh
Tel.: (880) 31714632
Web Site: http://www.cse.com.bd
Sales Range: $25-49.9 Million
Emp.: 80
Stock Exchange Services
N.A.I.C.S.: 523150
Al Maruf Khan (Pres)

CHIU TING MACHINERY CO., LTD.
No 78 Yuang Feng road, Taiping Dist, Taichung, Taiwan
Tel.: (886) 422700258
Web Site: https://www.geetech.com.tw
Year Founded: 1981
1539—(TAI)
Rev.: $50,148,270
Assets: $82,379,277
Liabilities: $30,637,103
Net Worth: $51,742,174
Earnings: $2,060,172
Emp.: 128
Fiscal Year-end: 12/31/23
Machinery & Hardware Components Mfr
N.A.I.C.S.: 238290

Subsidiaries:

Chiu Ting Industrial (Huizhou) Co., Ltd.   (1)
Yu Fang Industrial Park Chenjian, Chenjian, Huizhou, 516000, Guang Dong, China
Tel.: (86) 752 308 9556
Web Site: http://www.cnc-geetech.com
Industrial Machinery Mfr
N.A.I.C.S.: 333517

Oliver Machinery Co.   (1)
921 Thomas Ave SW, Renton, WA 98057
Tel.: (253) 867-0334
Web Site: https://olivermachinery.net
Emp.: 4
Woodworking Machinery Mfr
N.A.I.C.S.: 333243

CHIYODA CO., LTD.
5F Fujisawa Building 4-30-16 Ogikubo, Suginami-ku, Tokyo, 167-8505, Japan
Tel.: (81) 353354131
Web Site: https://www.chiyodagrp.co.jp
Year Founded: 1948
8185—(TKS)
Rev.: $661,638,800
Assets: $600,962,580
Liabilities: $233,324,810
Net Worth: $367,637,770
Earnings: $13,123,590
Emp.: 1,156
Fiscal Year-end: 02/29/24
Shoe Mfr & Distr
N.A.I.C.S.: 316210
Masao Funahashi (Chm)

CHIYODA CORPORATION
Minato Mirai Grand Central Tower 4-6-2 Minatomirai, Nishi-ku, Yokohama, 220-8765, Japan
Tel.: (81) 452257734
Web Site: http://www.chiyoda-corp.com
Year Founded: 1948
CHYCF—(OTCIQ)
Rev.: $3,344,534,410
Assets: $2,822,251,870
Liabilities: $2,782,082,900
Net Worth: $40,168,970
Earnings: ($104,642,910)
Emp.: 3,496
Fiscal Year-end: 03/31/24
Construction & Engineering Services
N.A.I.C.S.: 236210
Masaji Santo (Pres, COO & Chief Sustainability Officer)

Subsidiaries:

Arrow Business Consulting Corporation   (1)
432-1 Tsurumichuo 4-Chome, Tsurumi-Ku, Yokohama, 230-0051, Kanagawa, Japan
Tel.: (81) 455025774
Financial & Accounting Consulting Services
N.A.I.C.S.: 541219

Arrowhead International Corporation   (1)
2nd Azuma bldg 3-18-21 Shibaura, Minato-Ku, Tokyo, 108-0023, Japan
Tel.: (81) 334544120
Web Site: http://www.arrowhead.co.jp
Sales Range: $25-49.9 Million
Emp.: 54
Air Cargo Services
N.A.I.C.S.: 481212
Masataka Kanakugi (Auditor)

Chiyoda & Public Works Co., Ltd.   (1)
201-206 Prime Hill Business Square No 60 Shwe Dagon Pagoda Road, Dagon Township, Yangon, Myanmar
Tel.: (95) 18382710
Web Site: https://www.cpw.com.mm
Sales Range: $25-49.9 Million
Emp.: 40
Industrial Facilities Design & Construction Services
N.A.I.C.S.: 236210
Daniel Tin Ko Htwe (Mng Exec Officer)

Chiyoda (Thailand) Limited   (1)
140/42 ITF Tower II 20th Floor Silom Road Kwaeng Suriyawong, Khet Bangrak, Bangkok, 10500, Thailand
Tel.: (66) 22316441
Web Site: http://www.chiyoda-corp.com
Sales Range: $25-49.9 Million
Emp.: 10
Industrial Facilities Design & Construction Services
N.A.I.C.S.: 237130
Monbuhiko Kono (Mng Dir)

Chiyoda Advanced Solutions Corporation   (1)
Technowave 100 Building 1-25 Shin-Urashima-Cho 1-chome, Kanagawa-Ku, Yo-

kohama, 221-0031, Kanagawa, Japan
Tel.: (81) 454411260
Web Site: http://www.chiyoda-as.co.jp
Engineering Consulting Services
N.A.I.C.S.: 541330
Masahiro Watanabe (Pres & CEO)

Chiyoda Almana Engineering LLC   (1)
Markaz Almana Building 2nd Floor Al Malaa Street, PO Box 22961, Najma, Doha, Qatar
Tel.: (974) 44074666
Web Site: https://www.chiyoda-almana.com
Sales Range: $75-99.9 Million
Emp.: 300
Construction Engineering Services
N.A.I.C.S.: 541330
Koichi Tanemura (Deputy Mng Dir-Bus Ops)

Chiyoda Corporation (Shanghai)   (1)
Room 606 UC Tower No 500 Fushan Road Pu Dong New Area, Shanghai, 200122, China
Tel.: (86) 2168761500
Emp.: 6
Industrial Facilities Design & Construction Services
N.A.I.C.S.: 237130
Sato Akihiro (Gen Mgr)

Chiyoda International Corporation   (1)
2050 W Sam Houston Pkwy S Ste 850, Houston, TX 77042
Tel.: (713) 965-9005
Sales Range: $25-49.9 Million
Emp.: 2
Construction & Engineering Services
N.A.I.C.S.: 236210
Koji Okamoto (Dir-Sls & Mktg)

Chiyoda Keiso Co., Ltd.   (1)
3-13 Moriya-Cho Kanagawa-Ku Yokohama-Shi, Yokohama, 221-0022, Kanagawa, Japan
Tel.: (81) 45 441 9600
Web Site: http://www.cst.chiyoda.co.jp
Oil & Gas Field Construction Services
N.A.I.C.S.: 213112

Chiyoda Kosho Co., Ltd.   (1)
34-26 Tsurumichuo 4-Chome, Tsurumi-Ku Yokohama, Yokohama, 230 0051, Kanagawa, Japan
Tel.: (81) 455067662
Construction Engineering Services
N.A.I.C.S.: 541330

Chiyoda Malaysia Sdn. Bhd.   (1)
9 06 Level 9 Menara Raja Laut 288 Jalan Raja Laut, 50350, Kuala Lumpur, Malaysia
Tel.: (60) 326037000
Web Site: http://www.chiyoda.com.my
Construction Engineering Services
N.A.I.C.S.: 541330

Chiyoda Philippines Corporation.   (1)
15th Flr Sun Plaza Building 1507 Shaw Boulevard cor Princeton Street, Barangay Wack-Wack, Mandaluyong, 1555, Philippines
Tel.: (63) 85717580
Web Site: https://www.chiyodaphil.com.ph
Sales Range: $150-199.9 Million
Emp.: 625
Civil Engineering Services
N.A.I.C.S.: 541330
Toshiaki Saito (Pres & CEO)

Chiyoda Singapore (Pte) Limited   (1)
14 International Business Park, Jurong East, Singapore, 609922, Singapore
Tel.: (65) 65633488
Web Site: http://www.chiyoda.com.sg
Sales Range: $50-74.9 Million
Emp.: 300
Construction & Engineering Services
N.A.I.C.S.: 236210
Takahiro Teraoka (Mng Dir)

Chiyoda System Technologies Corporation   (1)
Technowave 100 Building 1-1-25 Shinurashima-cho, Kanagawa-Ku, Yokohama, 221-0031, Japan
Tel.: (81) 454411433
Web Site: https://www.cst.chiyoda.co.jp
Emp.: 284
Electrical & Instrumentation Facilities Engineering, Designing & Construction; Information Technology Consulting Services

N.A.I.C.S.: 541330
Hiroshi Kojima *(Exec Officer)*

Chiyoda TechnoAce Co., Ltd. **(1)**
3-13 Moriya-cho, Kanagawa-ku, Yokohama,
221-0022, Kanagawa, Japan
Tel.: (81) 454419600
Web Site: https://www.cta.chiyoda.co.jp
Sales Range: $25-49.9 Million
Emp.: 100
Construction Engineering Services
N.A.I.C.S.: 541330
Ishiwatari Takao *(Pres)*

Chiyoda U-Tech Co., Ltd. **(1)**
13 Moriya-cho 3-chome, Kanagawa-Ku, Yo-
kohama, 221-0022, Japan
Tel.: (81) 454411818
Web Site: http://www.utc-yokohama.com
Emp.: 200
Software Consulting Services
N.A.I.C.S.: 541512

Chiyoda do Brasil Representacoes
Ltda. **(1)**
Praia de Botafogo 228 Sala 501, 22250-
040, Botafogo, Rio de Janeiro, Brazil
Tel.: (55) 2137388280
Web Site: http://www.chiyoda-corp.com
Sales Range: $50-74.9 Million
Emp.: 2
Oil & Gas Field Engineering Services
N.A.I.C.S.: 213112
Tomoyuki Tsukamoto *(Mgr)*

L&T-Chiyoda Limited **(1)**
5th Floor West Block 1 L T Knowledge City
Gate no 1, Ajwa-Waghodia Crossing NH 8,
Vadodara, 390 019, Gujarat, India **(50%)**
Tel.: (91) 2652442000
Web Site: https://www.lntchiyoda.com
Sales Range: $200-249.9 Million
Emp.: 600
Engineering Consulting Services; Owned
50% by Larsen & Toubro Limited & 50% by
Chiyoda Corporation
N.A.I.C.S.: 541690
Anand C. Ghaisas *(CEO)*

PT. Chiyoda International
Indonesia **(1)**
9th Floor Mid-Plaza Building Jalan Jenderal
Sudirman Kav 10-11, 10220, Jakarta, Indo-
nesia
Tel.: (62) 215704693
Web Site: http://www.chiyoda-corp.com
Sales Range: $25-49.9 Million
Emp.: 9
Construction Engineering Services
N.A.I.C.S.: 541330

PlantStream Inc. **(1)**
Nippon Gas Hatchobori Bldg 8F Hatchobori
2-10-7, Chuo City, Tokyo, 104-0032, Japan
Tel.: (81) 362228808
Web Site: https://plantstream3d.com
Building Design Services
N.A.I.C.S.: 541310

TIS Chiyoda Systems Inc. **(1)**
Technowave 100 Building 1-1-25
Shinurashima-cho, Kanagawa-ku, Yoko-
hama, 221-0031, Japan
Tel.: (81) 454419736
Web Site: http://www.tc-systems.co.jp
IT System Consulting Services
N.A.I.C.S.: 541611
Fumiyasu Mase *(Pres)*

CHIYODA INTEGRE CO., LTD.
1-1 Nibancho, Chiyoda-ku, Tokyo,
102-0084, Japan
Tel.: (81) 335423410
Web Site: https://www.chiyoda-i.co.jp
Year Founded: 1955
6915—(TKS)
Rev.: $282,297,240
Assets: $343,005,630
Liabilities: $71,915,100
Net Worth: $271,090,530
Earnings: $19,538,250
Emp.: 2,997
Fiscal Year-end: 12/31/22
Office Automation Equipment Mfr &
Whslr
N.A.I.C.S.: 333310
Mitsuaki Koike *(Chm & Pres)*

Subsidiaries:

CHIYODA INTEGRE (PHILIPPINES)
CORPORATION **(1)**
Lot 4-B First Philippine Industrial Park II
Brgy, Santo Tomas, Batangas, 4234, Philip-
pines
Tel.: (63) 437798080
Office Automation Equipment Whslr
N.A.I.C.S.: 423420

CHIYODA INTEGRE DE BAJA CALI-
FORNIA, S. A. DE C. V. **(1)**
Ave Universidad 2550 Parque Industrial In-
ternacional, 22424, Tijuana, Mexico
Tel.: (52) 6646231800
Office Automation Equipment Whslr
N.A.I.C.S.: 423420

CHIYODA INTEGRE DE MEXICO,
S.A. DE C.V. **(1)**
Paseo de las Colinas Circuit Lots 1-12,
Colinas de Leon Ind Park, 37668, Leon,
Guanajuato, Mexico
Tel.: (52) 4771043087
Web Site: https://www.ci-mx.com
Office Automation Equipment Whslr
N.A.I.C.S.: 423420

Chiyoda Integre (Dalian) CO.,
LTD. **(1)**
No Building17-2 DD Port Shuzi No 3 Road,
E T Development Zone, Dalian, 116620,
China
Tel.: (86) 41187654010
Office Automation Equipment Whslr
N.A.I.C.S.: 423420

Chiyoda Integre (Dong Guan) CO.,
LTD. **(1)**
XingYuan Street DaLingShan Section79,
DaLingShan Town, Dongguan, 523811,
GuangDong, China
Tel.: (86) 76988961122
Office Automation Equipment Whslr
N.A.I.C.S.: 423420

Chiyoda Integre (Guangzhou) CO.,
LTD. **(1)**
No C21 Lingxing Industry Park Shilou Town,
Panyu District, Guangzhou, 511447, Guang-
dong, China
Tel.: (86) 20 3913 4622
Office Automation Equipment Whslr
N.A.I.C.S.: 423420

Chiyoda Integre (HK) LTD. **(1)**
Room 804 Greenfield Tower Concordia
Plaza 1 Science Museum Road, Tsimshat-
sui, Kowloon, China (Hong Kong)
Tel.: (852) 27548383
Office Automation Equipment Whslr
N.A.I.C.S.: 423420

Chiyoda Integre (Shandong) CO.,
LTD. **(1)**
Building F No 7 Shaoxing Road, Economic-
Technical Development Area, Yantai,
264006, Shandong, China
Tel.: (86) 5356350111
Office Automation Equipment Whslr
N.A.I.C.S.: 423420

Chiyoda Integre (Shanghai) Co.,
Ltd. **(1)**
709B CITIC Square No 1168 West Nanjing
Road, Shanghai, 200040, China
Tel.: (86) 2162265707
Automobile Equipment Mfr
N.A.I.C.S.: 336320

Chiyoda Integre (Shenzhen) CO.,
LTD. **(1)**
7/F 7DE Laifu Bldg Left saide of Goverment
Office Blk2 Fuyong Road, Baoan, Shen-
zhen, 518103, Guandong, China
Tel.: (86) 755 2960 1835
Office Automation Equipment Whslr
N.A.I.C.S.: 423420

Chiyoda Integre (Suzhou) CO.,
LTD. **(1)**
No 79 Ta-yuan Road, New District, Suzhou,
215009, Jiangsu, China
Tel.: (86) 51268084778
Office Automation Equipment Whslr
N.A.I.C.S.: 423420

Chiyoda Integre (Thailand) CO.,
LTD. **(1)**

61 Moo2 Banpo Bang Pa-in, Ayutthaya,
13160, Thailand
Tel.: (66) 3535070713
Web Site: https://www.ci-th.com
Office Automation Equipment Whslr
N.A.I.C.S.: 423420

Chiyoda Integre (Tian Jin) CO.,
LTD. **(1)**
No 40 Huang Hai First Street Teda, Tianjin,
300457, China
Tel.: (86) 22 5983 8666
Office Automation Equipment Whslr
N.A.I.C.S.: 423420

Chiyoda Integre (Zhong Shan) CO.,
LTD. **(1)**
8 Qin Ye Street Torch High-tech Industry
DevelopmentZone, Development Zone,
Zhongshan, 528437, Guangdong, China
Tel.: (86) 76085592747
Office Automation Equipment Whslr
N.A.I.C.S.: 423420

Chiyoda Integre Co. (M) Sdn.
Bhd. **(1)**
Lot PT 506 Persiaran Sabak Bernam
Seksyen 26, Kaw Perindustrian Hicom,
40000, Shah Alam, Selangor, Malaysia
Tel.: (60) 3 51912800
Web Site: http://www.ci-m.com
Emp.: 200
Office Automation Equipment Whslr
N.A.I.C.S.: 423420

Subsidiary (Domestic):

Chiyoda Integre Co. (Penang) Sdn.
Bhd. **(2)**
No 1556 Lorong Perusahaan Maju 6, Ka-
wasan Perindustrian Perai, 13600, Prai,
Penang, Malaysia
Tel.: (60) 4 5078585
Web Site: http://www.cipenang.com
Emp.: 130
Electrical Products Distr
N.A.I.C.S.: 423610
Shinzo Yamasaki *(Mng Dir)*

Chiyoda Integre Co. (S) Pte. Ltd. **(1)**
2 Venture Drive 11-09 Vision Exchange,
Singapore, 608526, Singapore
Tel.: (65) 62727020
Office Automation Equipment Whslr
N.A.I.C.S.: 423420

Subsidiary (Non-US):

Chiyoda Integre Co. (Johor) Sdn.
Bhd. **(2)**
27 Jalan Firma 2 Kawasan Perindustrian
Tebrau IV, 81000, Johor Bahru, Johor, Ma-
laysia
Tel.: (60) 73548716
Office Automation Equipment Whslr
N.A.I.C.S.: 423420

Chiyoda Integre Slovakia, s.r.o. **(1)**
Udernicka 9, 851 01, Bratislava, Slovakia
Tel.: (421) 263532125
Web Site: https://www.chiyoda.sk
Plastic Product Distr
N.A.I.C.S.: 424610

Chiyoda Integre Vietnam CO.,
LTD. **(1)**
C-4 Thang Long Industrial Park, Kim Chung
Commune Dong Anh Dist, Hanoi, Vietnam
Tel.: (84) 439515537
Office Automation Equipment Whslr
N.A.I.C.S.: 423420

Chiyoda Integre of America (San Di-
ego), Inc. **(1)**
9335 Airway Rd Ste 106, San Diego, CA
92154
Tel.: (619) 420-8383
Web Site: https://www.chiyodausa.com
Emp.: 6
Office Automation Equipment Whslr
N.A.I.C.S.: 423430

PT. Chiyoda Integre Indonesia **(1)**
Kawasan Industri Suryacipta Jl Surya Nusa
I Blok B29-32 Desa, Kutamekar Kec Ciam-
pel, Karawang, 41363, Jawa Barat, Indone-
sia
Tel.: (62) 267440785
Office Automation Equipment Whslr
N.A.I.C.S.: 423420

Sunfelt Co., Ltd. **(1)**
2-1-4 Kotobuki, Taito-ku, Tokyo, 111-0042,
Japan
Tel.: (81) 338425562
Web Site: https://www.sunfelt.co.jp
Emp.: 40
Non-Woven Felt Mfr
N.A.I.C.S.: 313230
Noboru Harashima *(Pres)*

CHIYODA UTE CO., LTD.
928 Takamatsu Kawagoe-cho Mie-
gun, Mie, 510-8570, Japan
Tel.: (81) 593635555
Web Site: http://www.chiyoda-
ute.co.jp
Year Founded: 1948
53870—(TKS)
Rev.: $243,994,080
Assets: $308,288,640
Liabilities: $175,798,480
Net Worth: $132,490,160
Earnings: $6,388,800
Fiscal Year-end: 03/31/21
Construction Material Mfr & Distr
N.A.I.C.S.: 327120
Haruhisa Hirata *(Pres & CEO)*

Subsidiaries:

Chiyoda Ute Co., Ltd. - Chiba
Plant **(1)**
12 Kitasode, Sodegaura, Chiba, Japan
Tel.: (81) 438632511
Gypsum Product Recycling Services
N.A.I.C.S.: 327420

Chiyoda Ute Co., Ltd. - Kaizuka
Plant **(1)**
16-1 Minato, Kaizuka, Osaka, Japan
Tel.: (81) 724315211
Gypsum Product Recycling Services
N.A.I.C.S.: 327420

Chiyoda Ute Co., Ltd. - Muroran
Plant **(1)**
Sakimori-cyo389-12, Muroran, Hokkaido,
Japan
Tel.: (81) 143591100
Gypsum Product Recycling Services
N.A.I.C.S.: 327420

Chiyoda Ute Co., Ltd. - Okayama
Plant **(1)**
6-9-1 Tai, Tamano, Okayama, Japan
Tel.: (81) 863323551
Gypsum Product Recycling Services
N.A.I.C.S.: 327420

Chiyoda Ute Co., Ltd. - Shimonoseki
Plant **(1)**
7-1-1 Hikoshima-sakomachi, Shimonoseki,
Yamaguchi, Japan
Tel.: (81) 832676464
Gypsum Product Recycling Services
N.A.I.C.S.: 327420

CHK OIL LIMITED
Suites 1905-07 19th Floor Tower 6
The Gateway, Harbour City, Kowloon,
China (Hong Kong)
Tel.: (852) 25222898　　　　**BM**
Web Site: http://www.chkoilltd.com
0632—(HKG)
Rev.: $197,089,824
Assets: $79,650,309
Liabilities: $18,784,002
Net Worth: $60,866,307
Earnings: $19,065,824
Emp.: 36
Fiscal Year-end: 12/31/21
Oil & Gas Production; Recycling Pro-
cessor & Distr
N.A.I.C.S.: 324199
Liu Gui Feng *(Chm)*

CHL LIMITED
Hotel The Suryaa New Delhi New
Friends Colony, New Delhi, 110 025,
India
Tel.: (91) 1126835070
Web Site: https://www.chl.co.in
Year Founded: 1979

CHL LIMITED

CHL LIMITED—(Continued)
532992—(BOM)
Rev.: $8,708,727
Assets: $41,929,183
Liabilities: $47,972,652
Net Worth: ($6,043,469)
Earnings: ($2,025,373)
Fiscal Year-end: 03/31/22
Home Management Services
N.A.I.C.S.: 721110
Gagan Malhotra *(Exec Dir)*

CHL S.P.A.

Via G Marconi 128, 50131, Florence,
Italy
Tel.: (39) 05550517211　　　IT
Web Site: http://www.chl.it
Year Founded: 1993
Sales Range: $25-49.9 Million
Emp.: 45
Products & Services for Information
Technology, Multi-Media & Telecom-
munications
N.A.I.C.S.: 449210
Sauro Landi *(Chm & CEO)*

Subsidiaries:

Nexta Ltd. (1)
1 Purley Place, Islington, London, N1 1QA,
United Kingdom
Tel.: (44) 2071531046
Web Site: http://www.nextaltd.uk
Telecom Services
N.A.I.C.S.: 517810

CHLITINA HOLDING LIMITED

10F No 107 Songren Rd, Xinyi Dist,
Taipei, 110, Taiwan
Tel.: (886) 227238666　　　Ky
Web Site:
　　https://www.chlitinaholding.com
Year Founded: 2012
4137—(TAI)
Rev.: $148,296,898
Assets: $291,213,240
Liabilities: $122,836,615
Net Worth: $168,376,625
Earnings: $33,799,469
Emp.: 874
Fiscal Year-end: 12/31/23
Beauty & Skin Care Products
N.A.I.C.S.: 325620
Joanna Pi-Hua Chen *(Chm)*

CHN ENERGY CHANGYUAN ELECTRIC POWER CO., LTD.

National Energy Building No 63 Xu-
dong Street, Hongshan District, Wu-
han, 430066, Hubei, China
Tel.: (86) 2788717135
Web Site: https://www.cydl.com.cn
Year Founded: 1995
000966—(SSE)
Rev.: $2,058,533,568
Assets: $4,329,102,024
Liabilities: $2,945,749,248
Net Worth: $1,383,352,776
Earnings: $17,332,332
Fiscal Year-end: 12/31/22
Electric Power Generation & Distribu-
tion Services
N.A.I.C.S.: 221122
Wang Dong *(Chm)*

CHO PHARMA, INC.

7F Building C No 99 Ln 130 Sec 1
Academia Rd, Nangang Dist, Taipei,
115202, Taiwan
Tel.: (886) 226558059
Web Site:
　　https://www.chopharma.com
Year Founded: 2013
6586—(TAI)
Pharmaceuticals Product Mfr
N.A.I.C.S.: 325412
Chao-Long Chen *(Chm)*

CHO THAVEE PUBLIC COMPANY LIMITED

265 M 4 Klang Mueng Road Mueang
Kao, Muang, Khon Kaen, 40000,
Thailand
Tel.: (66) 43043888　　　TH
Web Site: https://www.cho.co.th
Year Founded: 1994
CHO—(THA)
Rev.: $11,866,186
Assets: $95,690,168
Liabilities: $80,258,884
Net Worth: $15,431,284
Earnings: ($16,711,848)
Fiscal Year-end: 12/31/23
Truck Bodies & Trailers Mfr
N.A.I.C.S.: 336120
Siriwat Taveesangskulthai *(Exec Dir)*

Subsidiaries:

Cho Thavee Thermotech Company
Limited (1)
Tel.: (66) 4304387778
Web Site: https://www.ctvthermotech.com
Refrigeration Material Mfr
N.A.I.C.S.: 333415

CHO-A PHARM. CO., LTD.

ACE Techno Tower 1F 12
Dangsan-ro 2-gil, Youngdungpo-Ku,
Seoul, 07299, Korea (South)
Tel.: (82) 266709200
Web Site: http://www.choa.co.kr
Year Founded: 1988
034940—(KRS)
Rev.: $52,830,701
Assets: $65,685,427
Liabilities: $26,255,332
Net Worth: $39,430,095
Earnings: $430,051
Emp.: 234
Fiscal Year-end: 12/31/22
Pharmaceuticals Mfr
N.A.I.C.S.: 325412

Subsidiaries:

CHO-A Pharm. Co., Ltd. - Haman
Factory (1)
318 Gwangjeong-ro, Haman, 52052,
Gyeongsangnam-do, Korea (South)
Tel.: (82) 555805200
Pharmaceuticals Product Mfr
N.A.I.C.S.: 325412

CHOA PHARMACEUTICAL CO., LTD.

ACE Techno-Tower 1F 12
Dangsan-ro 2-gil, Yeongdeungpo-gu,
Seoul, 07299, Korea (South)
Tel.: (82) 266709200
Web Site: https://www.choa.co.kr
Year Founded: 1988
034940—(KRS)
Rev.: $52,830,701
Assets: $65,685,427
Liabilities: $26,255,332
Net Worth: $39,430,095
Earnings: $430,051
Emp.: 234
Fiscal Year-end: 12/31/22
Pharmaceuticals Product Mfr
N.A.I.C.S.: 325412

CHOBI COMPANY LIMITED

28 Hyoryeong-ro 77-gil, Seocho-Gu,
Seoul, 06627, Korea (South)
Tel.: (82) 234885800
Web Site: https://www.chobi.co.kr
Year Founded: 1955
001550—(KRS)
Rev.: $113,941,622
Assets: $99,742,030
Liabilities: $52,586,629
Net Worth: $47,155,401
Earnings: $6,625,390
Emp.: 108
Fiscal Year-end: 12/31/22

Fertilizer Mfr
N.A.I.C.S.: 325314

CHOCOLADEFABRIKEN LINDT & SPRUNGLI AG

Seestrasse 204, CH-8802, Kilchberg,
Switzerland
Tel.: (41) 447162233　　　CH
Web Site: https://www.lindt-
　　spruengli.com
Year Founded: 1845
LISN—(SWX)
Rev.: $5,541,130,820
Assets: $8,808,314,856
Liabilities: $3,929,600,887
Net Worth: $4,878,713,969
Earnings: $631,596,452
Emp.: 14,466
Fiscal Year-end: 12/31/22
Holding Company; Chocolate &
Chocolate Confection Mfr & Marketer
N.A.I.C.S.: 551112
Adalbert Lechner *(Grp CEO)*

Subsidiaries:

Chocoladefabriken Lindt & Sprüngli
(Schweiz) AG (1)
Seestrasse 204, 8802, Kilchberg,
Switzerland (100%)
Tel.: (41) 447162233
Web Site: http://www.lindt-spruengli.com
Sales Range: $150-199.9 Million
Emp.: 900
Mfr & Distr of Chocolate Products
N.A.I.C.S.: 311352

Chocoladefabriken Lindt & Sprüngli
GmbH (1)
Susterfeldstr 130, 52072, Aachen,
Germany (100%)
Tel.: (49) 24188810
Sales Range: $350-399.9 Million
Emp.: 2,000
Mfr & Distr of Chocolate Products
N.A.I.C.S.: 311352
Adalbert Lechner *(CEO)*

Lindt & Sprüngli (Asia Pacific)
Ltd. (1)
Room 3428 Sun Hung Kai Centre, 30 Har-
bour Road, Wanchai, China (Hong
Kong) (100%)
Tel.: (852) 25265829
Sales Range: $50-74.9 Million
Emp.: 8
Sales & Distributor of Candy & Other Con-
fectionery Products
N.A.I.C.S.: 424450
David Leuenberger *(Reg Dir)*

Lindt & Sprüngli (Australia) Pty.
Ltd. (1)
16 Hollinsworth Road Marsden Park, Syd-
ney, 2765, NSW, Australia (100%)
Tel.: (61) 298542500
Web Site: http://www.lindt.com.au
Sales Range: $25-49.9 Million
Emp.: 50
Sales & Distribution of Candy & Other Con-
fectionery Products
N.A.I.C.S.: 424450

Lindt & Sprüngli (Austria) GmbH (1)
Hietzinger Hauptstrasse 1A, 1130, Vienna,
Austria (100%)
Tel.: (43) 1601820
Web Site: http://www.lindt.at
Sales Range: $25-49.9 Million
Emp.: 35
Mfr & Distr of Chocolate Products
N.A.I.C.S.: 311352

Lindt & Sprüngli (Brazil) Holding
Ltda. (1)
Rua Professor Atilio Innocenti 165 12th
Floor, Itaim, Sao Paulo, 04538-000, Brazil
Tel.: (55) 1146898180
N.A.I.C.S.: 311352

Lindt & Sprüngli (CEE) s.r.o. (1)
Karolinska 650/1, 186 00, Prague, Czech
Republic
Tel.: (420) 222316488
Web Site: http://www.lindt.cz
Chocolate Mfr

N.A.I.C.S.: 311351

Lindt & Sprüngli (Canada), Inc. (1)
181 University Ave Ste 900, Toronto, M5H
3M7, ON, Canada (100%)
Tel.: (416) 351-8566
Web Site: http://www.lindt.ca
Sales Range: $50-74.9 Million
Emp.: 100
Sales & Distribution of Candy & Other Con-
fectionery Products
N.A.I.C.S.: 424450

Lindt & Sprüngli (China) Ltd. (1)
Unit 1901 & 1906 No 429 North Nanquan
Road, Free Trade Zone, Shanghai, 200120,
China
Tel.: (86) 2158311998
Web Site: https://www.lindt.cn
N.A.I.C.S.: 311352

Lindt & Sprüngli (España) SA (1)
Torre Mapfre Planta 37, Marina 16-18,
08005, Barcelona, Spain (100%)
Tel.: (34) 934590200
Web Site: http://www.lindt.es
Sales Range: $50-74.9 Million
Emp.: 40
Sales & Distribution of Candy & Other Con-
fectionery Products
N.A.I.C.S.: 424450

Lindt & Sprüngli (Nordic) AB (1)
PO Box 3048, 169 03, Solna, Sweden
Tel.: (46) 854614000
Web Site: http://www.lindt-nordic.com
Chocolate Mfr
N.A.I.C.S.: 311351

Lindt & Sprüngli (North America)
Inc. (1)
4717 Grand Ave Ste 700, Kansas City, MO
64112
Tel.: (816) 731-1900
N.A.I.C.S.: 311352

Lindt & Sprüngli (Poland) Sp. z
oo (1)
ul Franciszek Klimczak 1, 02-797, Warsaw,
Poland (100%)
Tel.: (48) 226422829
Web Site: http://www.lindt.pl
Sales Range: $50-74.9 Million
Emp.: 70
Sales & Distribution of Candy & Other Con-
fectionery Products
N.A.I.C.S.: 424450

Lindt & Sprüngli (South Africa) (Pty)
Ltd. (1)
18th Floor Portside 4 Bree Street, PO Box
576, Cape Town, 8001, South Africa
Tel.: (27) 218310310
Web Site: http://www.lindt.co.za
Chocolate Mfr
N.A.I.C.S.: 311351

Lindt & Sprüngli (UK) Ltd. (1)
Top Floor 4 New Square Bedfont Lakes,
Feltham, TW14 8HA, Middlesex, United
Kingdom (100%)
Tel.: (44) 20 8602 4100
Web Site: http://www.lindt.co.uk
Sales Range: $75-99.9 Million
Emp.: 80
Sales & Distribution of Chocolates & Other
Confectionery Products
N.A.I.C.S.: 424450

Lindt & Sprüngli (USA) Inc. (1)
1 Fine Chocolate Pl, Stratham, NH 03885
Tel.: (603) 778-8100
Web Site: https://www.lindtusa.com
Sales Range: $50-74.9 Million
Emp.: 250
Chocolate Products Mfr & Distr
N.A.I.C.S.: 311351

Subsidiary (Domestic):

Ghirardelli Chocolate Company (2)
1111 139th Ave, San Leandro, CA
94578-2631 (100%)
Tel.: (510) 483-6970
Web Site: https://www.ghirardelli.com
Chocolate Mfr
N.A.I.C.S.: 311351

Russell Stover Candies, LLC (2)
4900 Oak St, Kansas City, MO 64112
Tel.: (816) 842-9240

Web Site: http://www.russellstover.com
Candy Mfr
N.A.I.C.S.: 311352
Darrin Buehler *(VP-Pur)*

Lindt & Sprungli Japan Co., Ltd. (1)
313 Minamiaoyama 3rd Floor 3-13-18 Minamiaoyama, Minato-ku, Tokyo, 107-0062, Japan
Tel.: (81) 120313045
Web Site: https://www.lindt.jp
N.A.I.C.S.: 311352

Lindt & Sprungli S.p.A. (1)
Largo Edoardo Bulgheroni 1, Induno Olona, 21056, Varese, Italy (100%)
Tel.: (39) 0332209111
N.A.I.C.S.: 311352

Subsidiary (Domestic):

Caffarel S.p.A. (2)
Via Gianavello 41, 10062, Luserna San Giovanni, TO, Italy (100%)
Tel.: (39) 0121958251
Web Site: http://www.caffarel.com
Sales Range: $100-124.9 Million
Emp.: 500
Mfr, Sales & Distribution of Chocolate Products & Hard Candies
N.A.I.C.S.: 311352

Lindt & Sprungli SA (1)
5 Boulevard de la Madeleine, 75001, Paris, France (100%)
Tel.: (33) 158623636
Web Site: http://www.lindt.fr
Sales Range: $25-49.9 Million
Emp.: 60
Mfr & Distr of Chocolate Products
N.A.I.C.S.: 311352

Lindt & Sprungli de Mexico SA de CV (1)
Torre Reforma Av Paseo De La Reforma 483 Floor 21 Of 2102, Cuauhtemoc, 06500, Mexico, Mexico
Tel.: (52) 5547774005
Web Site: https://www.lindt.com.mx
N.A.I.C.S.: 311352

CHOCOLATS CAMILLE BLOCH S.A.

Grand Rue 21, CH 2608, Courtelary, Switzerland
Tel.: (41) 329451200
Web Site: http://www.camillebloch.ch
Year Founded: 1929
Sales Range: $25-49.9 Million
Emp.: 180
Chocolate Product Mfr
N.A.I.C.S.: 311352
Daniel Bloch *(CEO)*

CHODAI CO., LTD.

20-4 1-chome Nihonbashi-Kakigaracho, Chuo-Ku, Tokyo, 103-0014, Japan
Tel.: (81) 3 3639 3411
Web Site: http://www.chodai.co.jp
Year Founded: 1968
Rev.: $265,939,170
Assets: $230,827,240
Liabilities: $97,422,080
Net Worth: $133,405,160
Earnings: $17,028,690
Emp.: 777
Fiscal Year-end: 09/30/19
Construction Engineering Services
N.A.I.C.S.: 541330
Yasuji Nagaya *(Pres)*

Subsidiaries:

Chodai & Kiso - Jiban Vietnam Co., Ltd. (1)
6-Floor TID Building 4, Lieu Giai Ba Dinh Dist, Hanoi, Vietnam
Tel.: (84) 2437624555
Web Site: http://www.ckjvn.vn
Construction Consultancy Services
N.A.I.C.S.: 541611
Hung Ho Thai *(Pres)*

Chodai-Tec Co., Ltd. (1)
1-20-4 Kakigara-cho Nihonbashi, Chuo-ku,

Tokyo, 103-0014, Japan
Tel.: (81) 336393411
Web Site: https://www.chodai-tec.co.jp
Emp.: 126
Construction Consultancy Services
N.A.I.C.S.: 541611

Junpuzi. Co., Ltd. (1)
1F Toshin Higashiikebukuro Building 5-44-15 Higashiikebukuro, Toshima-ku, Tokyo, 170-0013, Japan
Tel.: (81) 362716061
Web Site: https://www.jpz.co.jp
Emp.: 15
Highway Road Services
N.A.I.C.S.: 237310

Kiso-Jiban Consultants Co., Ltd. (1)
12Floor 1-5-7, Kameido Koto-ku, Tokyo, 136-8577, Japan
Tel.: (81) 368618800
Web Site: http://www.kisojiban.com
Emp.: 590
Civil Engineering Services
N.A.I.C.S.: 541330
Yoshiyuki Yaguira *(Pres)*

CHOFU SEISAKUSHO CO., LTD.

2-1 Ogimachi Chofu, Yamaguchi, Shimonoseki, 752-8555, Japan
Tel.: (81) 832481111   JP
Web Site: https://www.chofu.co.jp
Year Founded: 1954
5946—(TKS)
Rev.: $343,907,540
Assets: $1,006,886,350
Liabilities: $64,568,630
Net Worth: $942,317,720
Earnings: $28,345,820
Emp.: 1,400
Fiscal Year-end: 12/31/23
Air Conditioners, Boilers, Water Heaters & Other Related Appliances Mfr & Distr
N.A.I.C.S.: 423730
Kiyotaka Taneda *(Pres & CEO)*

Subsidiaries:

Osaka Technocrat. Co., Ltd. (1)
1-3-4 Jodori, Sakai-ku, Sakai, 590-0045, Osaka, Japan
Tel.: (81) 722210426
Web Site: https://www.osaka-techno.com
Emp.: 23
HVAC System Mfr
N.A.I.C.S.: 333415

CHOICE DEVELOPMENT, INC.

9F 288 Sec 6 Civic Blvd, Taipei, 11087, Taiwan
Tel.: (886) 287681999
Web Site:
    https://www.choiceprintgroup.com
Year Founded: 1946
9929—(TAI)
Rev.: $22,934,300
Assets: $71,458,711
Liabilities: $43,782,889
Net Worth: $27,675,822
Earnings: ($4,611,269)
Fiscal Year-end: 12/31/23
Commercial Printing Services
N.A.I.C.S.: 323120
Lin Chiu Yu *(Founder)*

Subsidiaries:

Choice Development, Inc. - Linkou Factory (1)
No 71 Wunhua 1st Rd, Gueishan, 333, Taoyuan, Taiwan
Tel.: (886) 33283950
Commercial Printing Services
N.A.I.C.S.: 323111

Choice Development, Inc. - Tainan Factory (1)
No 13 Sinsin Rd Anping Industrial Park, South District, Tainan City, 702, Taiwan
Tel.: (886) 62613121
Commercial Printing Services
N.A.I.C.S.: 323111

CHOICE INTERNATIONAL LIMITED

Sunil Patodia Tower J B Nagar, Andheri East, Mumbai, 400 099, India
Tel.: (91) 2267079999
Web Site:
    https://www.choiceindia.com
CHOICEIN—(NSE)
Rev.: $39,032,980
Assets: $133,443,192
Liabilities: $77,370,166
Net Worth: $56,073,026
Earnings: $7,317,014
Emp.: 1,164
Fiscal Year-end: 03/31/22
Investment Banking Services
N.A.I.C.S.: 523150
Kamal Poddar *(Mng Dir)*

Subsidiaries:

Choice Capital Advisors Private Limited (1)
Shree Shakambhari Corporate Park Plot No 156-158 Chakravarti Ashok, Society JB Nagar Andheri East, Mumbai, 400 099, India
Tel.: (91) 2267079999
Sales Range: $200-249.9 Million
Financial Management Services
N.A.I.C.S.: 523940

Choice Consultancy Services Pvt. Ltd. (1)
Shree Shakambhari Corporate Park Plot No 156 - 158, Chakravarti Ashok Complex J B Nagar Andheri E, Mumbai, 400 099, India
Tel.: (91) 226 707 9999
Web Site: https://choiceconsultancy.co.in
Business Management Consulting Services
N.A.I.C.S.: 541611
Arun Poddar *(CEO)*

Choice Equity Broking Private Limited (1)
Sunil Patodia Tower J B Nagar, Andheri East, Mumbai, 400 099, India
Tel.: (91) 2267079999
Security Brokerage Services
N.A.I.C.S.: 523150
Sandeep B. Jhunjhunwala *(VP)*

CHOICE N.V.

Geldenaaksevest 2, 3000, Leuven, Belgium
Web Site:
    https://www.corp.watchchoice.tv
Year Founded: 2020
MLTV—(EUR)
Assets: $83,322,573
Liabilities: $396,722
Net Worth: $82,925,852
Earnings: ($1,526,702)
Fiscal Year-end: 12/31/21
Video Broadcasting Services
N.A.I.C.S.: 516120
Bart Van Coppenolle *(CEO)*

CHOICES MARKETS LTD.

8188 River Way, Delta, V4G 1K5, BC, Canada
Tel.: (604) 952-2266
Web Site:
    http://www.choicesmarket.com
Year Founded: 1990
Sales Range: $25-49.9 Million
Grocery Stores
N.A.I.C.S.: 445110
Wayne Lockhart *(Owner)*

CHOIL ALUMINUM CO., LTD.

98 Gongdan 6-ro, Jillyang-eup, Gyeongsan, 38467, Gyeongsangbuk-do, Korea (South)
Tel.: (82) 538565252
Web Site: https://www.choilal.co.kr
Year Founded: 1975
018470—(KRS)
Rev.: $431,349,512
Assets: $282,011,013
Liabilities: $138,648,837

Net Worth: $143,362,176
Earnings: $13,674,751
Emp.: 387
Fiscal Year-end: 12/31/22
Aluminum Products Mfr & Sales
N.A.I.C.S.: 331315
Seong Won-mo *(VP)*

CHOKSI ASIA PRIVATE LIMITED

57 Nehru Road Parle East, Mumbai, 400057, India
Tel.: (91) 9870356789
Web Site: http://www.choksi-asia.com
Photosensitized Materials Mfr
N.A.I.C.S.: 334510
Samir Choksi *(Dir)*

CHOKSI IMAGING LTD.

163/164 Choksi Bhuvan Nehru Road, Vile Parle East, Mumbai, 400057, India
Tel.: (91) 9821669911
Web Site:
    https://www.choksiworld.com
530427—(BOM)
Rev.: $2,148,428
Assets: $2,895,766
Liabilities: $516,721
Net Worth: $2,379,045
Earnings: $260,442
Emp.: 32
Fiscal Year-end: 03/31/21
Photographic Product Mfr & Distr
N.A.I.C.S.: 326113
Anil V. Choksi *(Exec Dir)*

CHOKSI LABORATORIES LIMITED

Survey No 9/1 Balaji Tulsiyana Industrial Park, Kumedi, Indore, 452010, MP, India
Tel.: (91) 7313501112
Web Site: https://www.choksilab.com
Year Founded: 1982
526546—(BOM)
Rev.: $4,117,072
Assets: $8,799,623
Liabilities: $6,355,918
Net Worth: $2,443,705
Earnings: $28,256
Fiscal Year-end: 03/31/22
Pharmaceuticals Product Mfr
N.A.I.C.S.: 325412
Sunil Choksi *(Mng Dir & Chm)*

CHOKWANG LEATHER CO., LTD.

Songjeong-dong, Heungdeok-gu, Cheongju, Chungbuk, Korea (South)
Tel.: (82) 432705311
Web Site: http://www.chokwang.co.kr
Year Founded: 1966
004700—(KRS)
Rev.: $93,578,436
Assets: $339,040,750
Liabilities: $49,083,855
Net Worth: $289,956,895
Earnings: $4,649,000
Emp.: 151
Fiscal Year-end: 12/31/22
Leather Mfr & Whlsr
N.A.I.C.S.: 316110
Yeon-Seok Lee *(Board of Directors, Pres & CEO)*

CHOKWANG PAINT CO., LTD.

148 Samdeok-ro 5 beon-gil, Sasang-gu, Busan, 46909, Korea (South)
Tel.: (82) 513047701
Web Site: https://www.ckpc.co.kr
Year Founded: 1947
004910—(KRS)
Rev.: $199,781,056
Assets: $296,144,999
Liabilities: $165,959,816

Chokwang Paint Co., Ltd.—(Continued)

Net Worth: $130,185,182
Earnings: ($5,561,574)
Emp.: 489
Fiscal Year-end: 12/31/22
Paint Product Mfr & Whlsr
N.A.I.C.S.: 325510
Sung Ah Yang (CEO)

Subsidiaries:

Chokwang Vina Co., Ltd.　　　　　(1)
Lot A-5E-CN My Phuoc Industrial Zone, Lot
A-5E-CN My Phuoc III Industrial Zone, Ho
Chi Minh City, Binh Duong, Vietnam
Tel.: (84) 2743848750
Coating Paint Mfr
N.A.I.C.S.: 325510

CHOLAMANDALAM FINAN-CIAL HOLDINGS LIMITED

Dare House No 234 N S C Bose
Road, Chennai, 600 001, India
Tel.: (91) 44421777705
Web Site: https://www.cholafhl.com
Year Founded: 1949
CHOLAHLDNG—(NSE)
Rev.: $1,898,018,850
Assets: $12,096,023,940
Liabilities: $11,360,843,130
Net Worth: $735,180,810
Earnings: $240,816,030
Fiscal Year-end: 03/31/21
Holding Company
N.A.I.C.S.: 551112
M.M. Murugappan (Chm)

CHONBANG CO., LTD.

13th F Chungjung Tower Building 464
Chungjeongno 3, Seodaemun-Ku,
Seoul, Korea (South)
Tel.: (82) 221226000
Web Site:
　　https://www.chonbang.co.kr
Year Founded: 1953
000950—(KRS)
Rev.: $95,809,076
Assets: $233,767,294
Liabilities: $72,192,612
Net Worth: $161,574,682
Earnings: $51,736,715
Emp.: 236
Fiscal Year-end: 12/31/22
Yarns & Fabrics Mfr
N.A.I.C.S.: 313110
Gyu Ok Cho (Chm & CEO)

Subsidiaries:

Chonbang Auto Co., Ltd.　　　　(1)
191 Pyeongongsandan-ro, Gwangsan-gu,
Gwangju, Gyeonggi, Korea (South)
Tel.: (82) 62 716 6707
Web Site: http://www.chonbangauto.co.kr
Automobile Sales & Services
N.A.I.C.S.: 423110

Chonbang Co., Ltd. - Gwangju
Factory　　　　　　　　　　　(1)
No 100 Im-dong, Buk-gu, Gwangju, Korea
(South)
Tel.: (82) 62 520 3300
Cotton Yarn Mfr
N.A.I.C.S.: 115111

Chonbang Co., Ltd. - Youngam
Factory　　　　　　　　　　　(1)
10 Sinbukgongdan-ro, Shinbuk-myeon, Yeon-
gam, Jeollanam-do, Korea (South)
Tel.: (82) 614729191
Fabrics Mfr
N.A.I.C.S.: 313210

Jeonsantex Co., Ltd.　　　　　　(1)
357 Gangseo-gu, Gangseo-ro, Seoul, Ko-
rea (South)
Tel.: (82) 23 664 3423
Web Site: https://www.jeonsantex.co.kr
Emp.: 43
Textile & Fabric Mfr
N.A.I.C.S.: 313310
Deokhyeon Cho (CEO)

Qingdao Tracon Electronic Co.,
Ltd.　　　　　　　　　　　　(1)
266-100 He-Ma-Shi, Billage Subdistrict Of-
fice of Fu-Shan-Hou Shi-bei Distric,
Qingdao, 266-100, China
Tel.: (86) 5328 569 2388
Web Site: http://www.chonbang.co.kr
Film Condenser Mfr
N.A.I.C.S.: 326113

Samdong Industry Co., Ltd.　　　(1)
1122-27 Seongjin-ro ipjang-myeon, Seobuk-
gu, Cheonan, Chungcheongnam-do, Korea
(South)
Tel.: (82) 41 589 9560
Web Site: https://www.samdong.co.kr
Plastics Product Mfr
N.A.I.C.S.: 325211
Byungjo Jeong (CEO)

CHONBURI CONCRETE PRODUCT PUBLIC COMPANY LIMITED

39/1 Moo1 Sukhumvit Road Huaykapi
sub-district Mueang District, Chon
Buri, 20000, Thailand
Tel.: (66) 14098877　　　　　　TH
Web Site: https://www.ccp.co.th
Year Founded: 1983
CCP—(THA)
Rev.: $87,819,079
Assets: $92,366,312
Liabilities: $50,171,363
Net Worth: $42,194,949
Earnings: $3,377,803
Fiscal Year-end: 12/31/23
Concrete Product Mfr & Distr
N.A.I.C.S.: 327390
Prathip Thipakornsukhasem (Chm)

Subsidiaries:

Chonburi Kanyong Co., Ltd.　　　(1)
39/1-4 Moo 1 Sukhumvit Road Huai Kapi,
Muang, Chon Buri, 20000, Thailand
Tel.: (66) 3826540099
Web Site: https://www.kanyongh.com
Construction Material Retailer
N.A.I.C.S.: 444180

CHONG FAI JEWELLERY GROUP HOLDINGS COMPANY LIMITED

No 6-13 Faerie Court 80 Ko Shan
Road, Hung Hom, Kowloon, China
(Hong Kong)　　　　　　　　　Ky
Web Site:
　　https://www.chongfaiholdings.com
Year Founded: 1997
8537—(HKG)
Rev.: $13,845,229
Assets: $16,660,089
Liabilities: $7,250,998
Net Worth: $9,409,091
Earnings: ($990,953)
Emp.: 85
Fiscal Year-end: 03/31/22
Holding Company
N.A.I.C.S.: 551112
Chun Keung Fu (Chm)

CHONG HONG CONSTRUC-TION CO., LTD.

11th Floor No 30 Beiping East Road,
Zhongzheng District, Taipei, 100, Tai-
wan
Tel.: (886) 223963280
Web Site:
　　https://www.chonghong.com.tw
5534—(TAI)
Rev.: $320,420,407
Assets: $1,492,337,397
Liabilities: $834,053,665
Net Worth: $658,283,732
Earnings: $60,038,815
Fiscal Year-end: 12/31/23
Construction Engineering Services
N.A.I.C.S.: 541330

CHONG KIN GROUP HOLD-INGS LIMITED

Rm 6807-8 68/F Central Plaza 18
Harbour Road, Wanchai, China
(Hong Kong)
Tel.: (852) 2123 8400　　　　　Ky
Web Site:
　　http://www.chongkin.com.hk
Year Founded. 2010
1609—(HKG)
Rev.: $66,597,407
Assets: $117,637,428
Liabilities: $30,511,885
Net Worth: $87,125,543
Earnings: ($31,582,953)
Emp.: 350
Fiscal Year-end: 03/31/20
Concrete Placing Services
N.A.I.C.S.: 238110
Zhang Jinbing (Co-Chm)

CHONG KUN DANG HOLD-INGS CORP.

8 Chungjeong-ro, Seodaemun-gu,
Seoul, Korea (South)
Tel.: (82) 263730600
Web Site: https://www.ckd-
　　holdings.com
Year Founded: 1941
001630—(KRS)
Rev.: $697,174,440
Assets: $1,055,678,068
Liabilities: $443,194,861
Net Worth: $612,483,207
Earnings: $824,109
Emp.: 41
Fiscal Year-end: 12/31/22
Pharmaceuticals Product Mfr
N.A.I.C.S.: 325412
Choi Hee-Nam (CEO)

Subsidiaries:

CKD Venture Capital Corp.　　　(1)
29 Teheran-ro 87-gil, Gangnam-gu, Seoul,
Korea (South)
Tel.: (82) 2 3453 3331
Web Site: http://www.ckdvc.co.kr
Financial Investment Services
N.A.I.C.S.: 523910

Chong Kun Dang Bio Co., Ltd.　　(1)
Chonggeundang Building 8 Chungjeong-ro,
Seodaemun-gu, Seoul, Korea (South)
Tel.: (82) 21940555
Web Site: https://www.ckdbio.com
Pharmaceuticals Product Mfr
N.A.I.C.S.: 325412

Plant (Domestic):

Chong Kun Dang Bio Co., Ltd. - An-
san Plant　　　　　　　　　　(2)
292 Shinwon-ro, Danwon-gu, Ansan,
Gyeonggi-do, Korea (South)
Tel.: (82) 31 489 1000
Pharmaceuticals Product Mfr
N.A.I.C.S.: 325412

Chong Kun Dang Healthcare
Corp.　　　　　　　　　　　(1)
Chongkeundang Building Floor 5 6
Chungpa-ro, Yongsan-gu, Seoul, Korea
(South)
Tel.: (82) 25750100
Web Site: http://www.ckdhc.com
Pharmaceuticals Product Mfr
N.A.I.C.S.: 325412

Plant (Domestic):

Chong Kun Dang Healthcare Corp. -
Dangjin-gun Factory　　　　　(2)
30 Bogun 1-gil, Songak-eup, Dangjin,
Chungcheongnam-do, Korea (South)
Tel.: (82) 41 357 6699
Pharmaceuticals Product Mfr
N.A.I.C.S.: 325412

Chong Kun Dang Pharmaceutical
Corp. - Cheonan Factory　　　(1)
15-20 Osaedang-li seonggeo-eup, seobuk-
gu, Cheonan, Chungnam, Korea (South)
Tel.: (82) 41 529 3100

Pharmaceuticals Product Mfr
N.A.I.C.S.: 325412

Chong Kun Dang pharmaceutical
Corp.　　　　　　　　　　　(1)
8 Chungjeong-ro, Seodaemun-gu, Seoul,
Korea (South)
Tel.: (82) 22 194 0300
Medicine Product Mfr & Distr
N.A.I.C.S.: 325412
Young-Joo Kim (Pres)

Chong Kundang Industrial Co.,
Ltd.　　　　　　　　　　　　(1)
8 th Floor Chong Kundang Building 8
Chungjeong-ro, Seodaemun-gu, Seoul, Ko-
rea (South)
Tel.: (82) 2 362 3111
Web Site: https://www.ckdi.co.kr
Real Estate Lending Services
N.A.I.C.S.: 522292

CHONG SING HOLDINGS FIN-TECH GROUP LIMITED

Rooms 3533-39 Level 35, Two Pa-
cific Place 88 Queensway, Hong
Kong, China (Hong Kong)
Tel.: (852) 3102 1327　　　　　Ky
Web Site: http://www.creditchina.hk
Year Founded: 2003
Financial Services
N.A.I.C.S.: 522310
Xiuren Hu (Chm, CEO & Chief Com-
pliance Officer)

CHONG WAH PLASTICS SDN BHD

Lot 1503 Batu 8 1/2 Jalan Kelang
Lama, 46000, Petaling Jaya, Selan-
gor Darul Ehsan, Malaysia
Tel.: (60) 3 78767066
Web Site:
　　http://www.chongwahgroup.com
Year Founded: 1966
Emp.: 300
Plastics Product Mfr
N.A.I.C.S.: 326199

Subsidiaries:

Chong-Wah NTIA Sdn. Bhd.　　　(1)
Lot No 1503 Batu 8 1/2 Jalan Klang Lama,
Petaling Jaya, 46000, Selangor Darul Eh-
san, Malaysia
Tel.: (60) 378767066
Web Site: http://www.chongwahgroup.com
Sales Range: $75-99.9 Million
Mfr & Distributor of Anti-Rust Products
N.A.I.C.S.: 325998

CHONGHERR INVESTMENTS LTD.

Lot 50 Goldmine Road, Helidon, Bris-
bane, 4344, QLD, Australia
Tel.: (61) 7 3711 2088
Web Site:
　　http://www.chongherr.com.au
Rev.: $803,391
Assets: $1,539,562
Liabilities: $357,299
Net Worth: $1,182,263
Earnings: $47,506
Emp.: 12
Fiscal Year-end: 12/31/18
Sandstone Mining, Mfr & Exporter
N.A.I.C.S.: 212319
De-Hui Liu (Chm & Mng Dir)

Subsidiaries:

Australian Sandstone Industries Pty.
Ltd.　　　　　　　　　　　　(1)
Level 34 Central Plz One 345 Queen St,
Brisbane, 4000, QLD, Australia
Tel.: (61) 732218999
Web Site: http://www.asisandstone.com.au
Sales Range: $50-74.9 Million
Emp.: 10
Sandstone Quarrying & Processing Ser-
vices
N.A.I.C.S.: 212311

CHONGQING BAIYA SANI-TARY PRODUCTS CO., LTD.
Baiya International Industrial Park
Maliu Yanjiang Development Zone,
Banan District, Chongqing, 400042,
China
Tel.: (86) 2368825666
Web Site: https://www.baiya.cn
Year Founded: 2010
003006—(SSE)
Rev.: $226,344,456
Assets: $243,116,640
Liabilities: $63,333,036
Net Worth: $179,783,604
Earnings: $26,295,516
Fiscal Year-end: 12/31/22
Sanitary Product Mfr & Distr
N.A.I.C.S.: 322291
Yonglin Feng *(Chm & Gen Mgr)*

CHONGQING BREWERY CO., LTD
13th Floor Kingold International Fi-
nancial Center No 62 Jinsui Road,
Tianhe District, Guangzhou, 510627,
Guangdong, China
Tel.: (86) 2389139399
Web Site:
  http://www.chongqingbeer.com
Year Founded: 1993
600132—(SHG)
Rev.: $1,866,575,815
Assets: $1,766,941,820
Liabilities: $1,287,654,977
Net Worth: $479,286,843
Earnings: $181,140,183
Fiscal Year-end: 12/31/21
Beer Mfr & Distr
N.A.I.C.S.: 312120
Joao Abecasis *(Chm)*

CHONGQING CASIN GROUP CO., LTD.
25/F Financial Information Industrial
Building No 1 Yellow Road, Jianbei
District, Chongqing, China
Tel.: (86) 23 6767 5999   CN
Web Site: http://www.cqcasin.com
Year Founded: 1997
Investment Holding Company
N.A.I.C.S.: 551112
Shengju Lu *(Founder & Chm)*

CHONGQING CHANGAN AU-TOMOBILE COMPANY LTD.
No 260 Jianxin East Rd, Jiangbei
District, Chongqing, China
Tel.: (86) 2367594008   CN
Web Site:
  https://www.globalchangan.com
200625—(SSE)
Rev.: $17,023,901,544
Assets: $20,505,217,824
Liabilities: $11,667,206,304
Net Worth: $8,838,011,520
Earnings: $1,094,902,380
Emp.: 150,000
Fiscal Year-end: 12/31/22
Automobile Mfr & Whslr
N.A.I.C.S.: 336110

Subsidiaries:

Chongqing Changan Suzuki Automo-
bile Co., Ltd.   (1)
Inside Dajiang Industrial Park Yudong Town,
Banan Dist, Chongqing, 401321,
China   (100%)
Tel.: (86) 2366288607
Web Site: http://www.changansuzuki.com
Automotive Mfr & Distr
N.A.I.C.S.: 336110

CHONGQING CHANGJIANG RIVER MOULDING MATERIAL (GROUP) CO., LTD.
6 Wu Xing Middle Road, Tong Jia Xi

Beibei, Chongqing, 400709, China
Tel.: (86) 2368256374
Web Site: https://www.ccrmm.com.cn
Year Founded: 1993
001296—(SSE)
Rev.: $132,888,600
Assets: $264,679,272
Liabilities: $43,349,904
Net Worth: $221,329,368
Earnings: $10,066,680
Fiscal Year-end: 12/31/22
Industrial Sand Mining Services
N.A.I.C.S.: 212322
Xiong Ying *(Chm)*

Subsidiaries:

Chongqing Changjiang River Mould-
ing Material Changzhou Co., Ltd. (1)
17 Xumen Road, Jintan, Jiangsu, 213200,
China
Tel.: (86) 51968082171
Foundry Sand Mfr & Distr
N.A.I.C.S.: 327999

Chongqing Changjiang River Mould-
ing Material Chengdu Co., Ltd. (1)
259 Tonggang South Road South Zone of
Modern industrial Port, Chengdu, 611730,
China
Tel.: (86) 2866316168
Foundry Sand Mfr & Distr
N.A.I.C.S.: 327999

Chongqing Changjiang River Moulding Material Kunshan Co., Ltd. (1)
238 Weishanhu Road Economic Development Zone, Kunshan, 215333, China
Tel.: (86) 51257618890
Foundry Sand Mfr & Distr
N.A.I.C.S.: 327999

Chongqing Changjiang River Moulding Material Shiyan Co., Ltd. (1)
89 Bailang Eaast Road Economic Development Zone, Shiyan, 442013, China
Tel.: (86) 7198314168
Foundry Sand Mfr & Distr
N.A.I.C.S.: 327999

Chongqing Changjiang River Mould-
ing Material Xiantao Co., Ltd. (1)
Mao Zui Inductrial Park, Xiantao, 433008,
China
Tel.: (86) 15727286771
Foundry Sand Mfr & Distr
N.A.I.C.S.: 327999

CHONGQING CHUANYI AUTO-MATION CO., LTD.
No 61 Middle Section of Huangshan
Avenue, Liangjiang New District,
Chongqing, 401121, China
Tel.: (86) 2367033458
Web Site: http://www.cqcy.com
Year Founded: 1999
603100—(SHG)
Rev.: $894,373,005
Assets: $1,046,572,404
Liabilities: $566,042,116
Net Worth: $480,530,288
Earnings: $81,295,714
Fiscal Year-end: 12/31/22
Automatic Industrial Control System
Mfr
N.A.I.C.S.: 332911
Tian Shanbin *(Chm)*

Subsidiaries:

Chongqing Chuanyi Metallic Func-
tional Materials Co., Ltd. (1)
Sanhuashi Beibei, Chongqing, China
Tel.: (86) 236 822 4320
Web Site: https://www.cqcy01.com
Emp.: 420
Electrical Contact Material & Alloy Mfr
N.A.I.C.S.: 331492

CHONGQING CONSTRUCTION ENGING GRP CO LTD
No 1596 Jinkai Avenue Liangjiang

New District, Chongqing, 401122,
China
Tel.: (86) 2363511570
Web Site: https://www.ccegc.cn
Year Founded: 1998
600939—(SHG)
Rev.: $6,925,896,366
Assets: $11,522,402,855
Liabilities: $10,223,345,607
Net Worth: $1,299,057,248
Earnings: $21,257,739
Emp.: 13,000
Fiscal Year-end: 12/31/22
Construction Engineering Services
N.A.I.C.S.: 541330
Sun Lidong *(Chm & Sec-Party)*

CHONGQING DEPARTMENT STORE CO., LTD.
10-11F and 14F No 18 Qingnian
Road, Yuzhong District, Chongqing,
400010, China
Tel.: (86) 2363843197
Web Site: http://www.e-cbest.com
Year Founded: 1992
600729—(SHG)
Rev.: $2,569,837,557
Assets: $2,415,457,563
Liabilities: $1,679,149,054
Net Worth: $736,308,509
Earnings: $124,026,959
Fiscal Year-end: 12/31/22
Departmental Store Operator
N.A.I.C.S.: 455110
Zhang Wenzhong *(Chm)*

CHONGQING DIMA INDUSTRY CO., LTD.
No 8 Changdian Road Chayuan In-
dustrial Park, Nanan District,
Chongqing, 400060, China
Tel.: (86) 2361521553
Web Site: https://wap.dima-
  industry.com
Year Founded: 1997
600565—(SHG)
Rev.: $3,199,601,995
Assets: $9,880,058,256
Liabilities: $8,133,362,369
Net Worth: $1,746,695,888
Earnings: ($490,996,238)
Fiscal Year-end: 12/31/22
Real Estate Property Development
Services
N.A.I.C.S.: 531390

CHONGQING FULING ELEC-TRIC POWER INDUSTRIAL CO., LTD.
No 20 Wangzhou Road, Fuling Dis-
trict, Chongqing, 408000, China
Tel.: (86) 2372286777
Web Site: http://www.flepc.com
Year Founded: 1999
600452—(SHG)
Rev.: $500,124,947
Assets: $980,764,397
Liabilities: $334,145,303
Net Worth: $646,619,094
Earnings: $86,083,087
Fiscal Year-end: 12/31/22
Electric Power Distribution Services
N.A.I.C.S.: 221122
Zuoxiang Yang *(Chm)*

CHONGQING FULING ZHACAI GROUP CO., LTD.
Er Du Village First Group Jiangbei
Street, Fuling District, Chongqing,
408000, China
Tel.: (86) 2372222635
Web Site: http://www.flzc.com
002507—(SSE)
Rev.: $357,784,128
Assets: $1,207,689,912
Liabilities: $118,864,044

Net Worth: $1,088,825,868
Earnings: $126,190,116
Emp.: 900
Fiscal Year-end: 12/31/22
Mustards & Sauces Mfr
N.A.I.C.S.: 311941
Binquan Zhou *(Chm)*

CHONGQING GAS GROUP CORPORATION LTD.
No 7 Hongen Road, Jiangbei District,
Chongqing, 400020, China
Tel.: (86) 2367952837
Web Site: http://www.cqgas.cn
Year Founded: 1995
600917—(SHG)
Rev.: $1,196,536,394
Assets: $1,391,178,974
Liabilities: $607,538,934
Net Worth: $783,640,040
Earnings: $69,915,851
Fiscal Year-end: 12/31/21
Gas Distribution & Gas Equipment
Installation Services
N.A.I.C.S.: 221210
Li Jinlu *(Chm)*

CHONGQING HELICOPTER INVESTMENT CO. LTD.
6th Floor Building C1 No 68 Uranus
Building, Avenue of the Stars,
401121, Chongqing, China
Tel.: (86) 23 67886800
Web Site: http://www.cqhic.cn
Sales Range: $500-549.9 Million
Holding Company
N.A.I.C.S.: 551112
Huang Yong *(Chm)*

Subsidiaries:

The Enstrom Helicopter Corp. (1)
2209 22nd St, Menominee, MI 49858
Tel.: (906) 863-1200
Web Site: http://www.enstromhelicopter.com
Sales Range: $10-24.9 Million
Emp.: 100
Helicopter Mfr
N.A.I.C.S.: 336411
Steve Sanders *(Dir-Mfg)*

CHONGQING HONGJIU FRUIT CO., LTD.
22nd Floor Block B Zhongtiefenghui
No 3 Donghu South Road, Yubei Dis-
trict, Chongqing, China
Tel.: (86) 2367064616   CN
Web Site: https://www-en.hjfruit.com
Year Founded: 2002
6689—(HKG)
Rev.: $2,310,490,453
Assets: $1,495,758,128
Liabilities: $518,563,605
Net Worth: $977,194,523
Earnings: $222,850,993
Emp.: 2,607
Fiscal Year-end: 12/31/22
Fruit & Vegetable Distr
N.A.I.C.S.: 445230
Jiang Zongying *(Gen Mgr)*

CHONGQING IRON & STEEL CO LTD
No 2 Jiangnan Avenue Jiangnan
Street, Changshou District,
Chongqing, 401258, China
Tel.: (86) 2368983482
Web Site: https://www.cqgt.cn
601005—(SHG)
Rev.: $5,133,238,980
Assets: $5,526,817,976
Liabilities: $2,530,412,731
Net Worth: $2,996,405,245
Earnings: ($143,125,080)
Emp.: 6,215
Fiscal Year-end: 12/31/22
Iron & Steel Mfr
N.A.I.C.S.: 331222

Chongqing Iron & Steel Co Ltd—(Continued)

Yongxiang Li *(Vice Chm & Gen Mgr)*

CHONGQING JIANSHE VE-HICLE SYSTEM CO., LTD.
No 1 Jianshe Road Huaxi Industrial Zone, Banan District, Chongqing, 400054, China
Tel.: (86) 2366295333
Web Site: http://www.jianshe.com.cn
200054—(SSE)
Rev.: $66,565,044
Assets: $125,926,164
Liabilities: $110,329,128
Net Worth: $15,597,036
Earnings: ($5,578,092)
Fiscal Year-end: 12/31/22
Motorcycle Accessory Distr
N.A.I.C.S.: 441227
Hongxian Lu *(Chm)*

CHONGQING LIFAN INDUS-TRY (GROUP) IMP. & EXP. CO., LTD.
Lifan Mansion No 16 FengXi Road, Caijiagang Beibei, Chongqing, 400707, China
Tel.: (86) 23 61663253
Web Site: http://www.lifan.com
Year Founded: 1992
Sales Range: $1-4.9 Billion
Emp.: 13,200
Engine, Motorcycle & Automobile Mfr, Marketer, Exporter & Importer
N.A.I.C.S.: 336310
Minshan Yin *(Chm)*

CHONGQING LUMMY PHAR-MACEUTICAL CO., LTD.
15th and 16th Floor Bldg B
Chongqing Academy of Science & Technology, No 2 Yangliu Road
Huangshan Avenue Yubei District, Chongqing, 401121, China
Tel.: (86) 2367300395
Web Site: https://www.cqlummy.com
Year Founded: 1999
300006—(CHIN)
Rev.: $126,144,232
Assets: $407,180,392
Liabilities: $108,273,311
Net Worth: $298,907,081
Earnings: ($1,257,410)
Emp.: 2,069
Fiscal Year-end: 12/31/23
Pharmaceutical Product Mfr & Distr
N.A.I.C.S.: 325412
Yu Qiu *(Chm & Gen Mgr)*

Subsidiaries:

Sichuan Hezheng Pharmacy Co., Ltd. **(1)**
No 68 Jinke South Road High-tech Industrial Development Zone, Jinniu District, Chengdu, Sichuan, China
Tel.: (86) 2887500832
Web Site: http://www.hygien.cn
Pharmaceutical Product Mfr & Distr
N.A.I.C.S.: 325412

CHONGQING MACHINERY & ELECTRONICS HOLDING (GROUP) CO., LTD.
60 Mid-Section Huangshan Avenue, New North Zone, Chongqing, 401123, China
Tel.: (86) 23 6307 6836
Web Site: http://www.cme-cq.com
Holding Company
N.A.I.C.S.: 551112
Yuxiang Wang *(Chm)*

Subsidiaries:

Chongqing Machinery & Electric Co., Ltd. **(1)**
No 60 Middle Section of Huangshan Av-

enue, New North Zone, Chongqing, China **(52.22%)**
Tel.: (86) 2363075707
Web Site: http://www.chinacqme.com
Rev.: $975,482,835
Assets: $2,546,997,699
Liabilities: $1,401,637,689
Net Worth: $1,145,360,010
Earnings: $33,220,182
Emp.: 8,233
Fiscal Year-end: 12/31/2020
Motor Vehicle Parts Mfr
N.A.I.C.S.: 336310
Yuxiang Wang *(Chm)*

Subsidiary (Domestic):

Chongqing CAFF Automotive Braking & Steering System Co., Ltd. **(2)**
10 West Chang'an-Ford Road Jinkai Avenue, Yubei District, Chongqing, 401122, China
Tel.: (86) 23 89053836
Web Site: http://www.cqcaff.com
Emp.: 1,500
Automotive Products Mfr
N.A.I.C.S.: 336330

Chongqing Gas Compressor Factory Co., Ltd. **(2)**
No 1 Shangqiao, Dongfeng Xinsi Village Shapingba District, Chongqing, 400037, China **(64.21%)**
Tel.: (86) 2365237515
Web Site: http://www.cqcompressor.com
Compressor & Accessory Equipment Mfr
N.A.I.C.S.: 333912

Chongqing General Industry (Group) Co., Ltd **(2)**
No 18 Jidian Road, Nan'an District, Chongqing, 401336, China
Tel.: (86) 2367661176
Web Site: http://www.cqgic.com
Emp.: 2,000
Air Compressor Mfr & Distr
N.A.I.C.S.: 333912

Chongqing Machine Tools (Group) Co., Ltd. **(2)**
6 Jiangxi Road, Nan'an District, Chongqing, China
Tel.: (86) 23 62555280
Web Site: http://www.en.chmti.com
Industrial Machinery Mfr
N.A.I.C.S.: 333517

Chongqing Pigeon Electric Wires & Cables Co., Ltd. **(2)**
998 Airport Avenue, YuBei District, Chongqing, China
Tel.: (86) 23 67166111
Web Site: http://www.cq-cable.com
Cable Products Mfr
N.A.I.C.S.: 332618

Chongqing Pump Industry Co., Ltd. **(2)**
No 8 Jingsheng Road Jingkou Industrial Park, Shapingba District, Chongqing, 400033, China
Tel.: (86) 2361727350
Web Site: http://www.english.cqpump.com
Exporting Pump Mfr
N.A.I.C.S.: 333914

Subsidiary (Non-US):

Holroyd Precision Ltd. **(2)**
Harbour Lane North Milnrow, Rochdale, OL16 3LQ, Lancashire, United Kingdom
Tel.: (44) 1706526590
Web Site: http://www.holroyd.com
Metalworking Mfr
N.A.I.C.S.: 333517

PTG Deutschland GmbH **(2)**
Pilsener Strasse 9, 86199, Augsburg, Germany
Tel.: (49) 8219089830
CNC Machine Tool Mfr
N.A.I.C.S.: 333517

PTG Heavy Industries Limited **(2)**
Bays 5 and 6 Rosemount Works Huddersfield Road, Elland, HX5 0EE, West Yorkshire, United Kingdom
Tel.: (44) 1422379222
Textile Machinery Mfr
N.A.I.C.S.: 333248

Subsidiary (Domestic):

Qijiang Gear Transmission Co., Ltd. **(2)**
Western Gear City Of China, Qijiang, Chongqing, 401421, China
Tel.: (86) 2348609892
Web Site: http://en.qjgt.com
Emp.: 1,400
Automobile Parts Mfr
N.A.I.C.S.: 336350

CHONGQING MAS SCI. & TECH. CO., LTD.
No 28 Fuyuan Road, Jiulongpo District, Chongqing, 400039, China
Tel.: (86) 4000239989
Web Site: https://www.cqmas.com
300275—(CHIN)
Rev.: $52,781,976
Assets: $170,291,160
Liabilities: $61,236,864
Net Worth: $109,054,296
Earnings: $5,243,940
Fiscal Year-end: 12/31/22
Coal Mine Safety & Security Monitoring Systems
N.A.I.C.S.: 213113
Yan Ma *(Chm)*

Subsidiaries:

Chongqing MAS Geyi Science & Technology Co., Ltd. **(1)**
6/F C2 High-tech Business Park No 105 Erlang Chuangye Road, Jiulongpo District, Chongqing, China
Tel.: (86) 2360367617
Safety System Mfr
N.A.I.C.S.: 334290

Liupanshui MAS Technology Co., Ltd. **(1)**
Department B Building 6 Minshang Technology Park, No 2 Hongqiao Road Hongqiao District, Liupanshui, China
Tel.: (86) 8586239008
Safety System Mfr
N.A.I.C.S.: 334290

MAS Zhongtai (Beijing) Technology Co., Ltd. **(1)**
Room 308 Building 10 Zhongguancun Software Center, No 8 Northeast Wangxi Road Haidian District, Beijing, China
Tel.: (86) 1082826762
Safety System Mfr
N.A.I.C.S.: 334290

MAS metamap (Beijing) Software Technology Co., Ltd. **(1)**
Room 308 Building 10 Zhongguancun Software Center, No 8 Northeast Wangxi Road Haidian District, Beijing, China
Tel.: (86) 4006556646
Safety System Mfr
N.A.I.C.S.: 334290

CHONGQING PHARSCIN PHARMACEUTICAL CO., LTD.
No 89 Middle Section of Huangshan-Avenue, Yubei District, Chongqing, 401120, China
Tel.: (86) 2367622999
Web Site: https://www.pharscin.com
Year Founded: 1996
002907—(SSE)
Rev.: $110,239,272
Assets: $262,080,468
Liabilities: $35,981,712
Net Worth: $226,098,756
Earnings: $13,815,360
Emp.: 1,300
Fiscal Year-end: 12/31/22
Pharmaceutical Product Mfr & Distr
N.A.I.C.S.: 325412
Hongtao You *(Founder & Chm)*

CHONGQING PORT CO., LTD.
No 298 Haier Road, Jiangbei Distict, Chongqing, 400025, China
Tel.: (86) 2363100561

Web Site: https://www.cqggf.com.cn
Year Founded: 1999
600279—(SHG)
Rev.: $839,871,174
Assets: $1,892,696,588
Liabilities: $848,956,527
Net Worth: $1,043,740,061
Earnings: $10,314,097
Fiscal Year-end: 12/31/21
Cargo Handling Services
N.A.I.C.S.: 488320
Qu Hong *(Chm)*

CHONGQING QIN'AN M&E PLC.
No 58 Sendi Avenue, Xipeng Town Jiulongpo District, Chongqing, 401326, China
Tel.: (86) 9923812993
Web Site: http://www.qamemc.com
Year Founded: 1995
603758—(SHG)
Rev.: $217,426,439
Assets: $471,453,216
Liabilities: $65,152,553
Net Worth: $406,300,663
Earnings: $15,705,557
Fiscal Year-end: 12/31/21
Powertrain Parts Mfr & Distr
N.A.I.C.S.: 336310
Yuanming Tang *(Chm & Pres)*

CHONGQING ROAD & BRIDGE CO., LTD.
No 11 Danlong Road, Nanping Economic & Technological Development Zone, Chongqing, 400060, China
Tel.: (86) 2362803632
Web Site: https://www.cqrb.com.cn
600106—(SHG)
Rev.: $17,033,946
Assets: $969,223,994
Liabilities: $342,355,853
Net Worth: $626,868,141
Earnings: $28,487,357
Fiscal Year-end: 12/31/22
Toll Road & Bridge Construction Services
N.A.I.C.S.: 237310
Jiang Jin *(Chm)*

CHONGQING RURAL COM-MERCIAL BANK CO., LTD.
36 jinmen road, jiangbei district, Chongqing, 400023, China
Tel.: (86) 2361111637
Web Site: https://www.cqrcb.com
COGQF—(OTCIQ)
Rev.: $6,907,269,467
Assets: $199,590,450,820
Liabilities: $182,429,707,853
Net Worth: $17,160,742,966
Earnings: $1,540,367,745
Emp.: 15,017
Fiscal Year-end: 12/31/23
Commercial Banking Services
N.A.I.C.S.: 522110

Subsidiaries:

CQRC Financial Leasing Co., Ltd. **(1)**
Annex No 11 & 12 No 99 Jinkai Avenue, Liangjiang New District, Chongqing, 401121, China
Tel.: (86) 2363569568
N.A.I.C.S.: 522220

Fujian Fu'an CQRC Village & Township Bank Co., Ltd. **(1)**
1 Guanhang Road, Cheng Bei, Fu'an, 355000, Fujian, China
Tel.: (86) 5938988916
Commercial Banking Services
N.A.I.C.S.: 522110

Fujian Pingtan CQRC Village & Township Bank Co., Ltd. **(1)**
A3-A6 19th Pai Kangde Huayuan Villa, Tancheng Town Pingtan County, Fuzhou,

350400, Fujian, China
Tel.: (86) 59186175991
Commercial Banking Services
N.A.I.C.S.: 522110

Fujian Shaxian CQRC Village &
Township Bank Co., Ltd.   (1)
Floor 1 and 2 North Tower of Yongshun
Building Xincheng Central Road, Sha
County, Sanming, 365050, Fujian, China
Tel.: (86) 5985758880
Commercial Banking Services
N.A.I.C.S.: 522110

Fujian Shishi CQRC Village & Town-
ship Bank Co., Ltd.   (1)
No 2454 2456 2458 Hong Xing Interna-
tional Building Baqi Road, Shishi, 362700,
Fujian, China
Tel.: (86) 59582269866
Commercial Banking Services
N.A.I.C.S.: 522110

Guangxi Luzhai CQRC Village &
Township Bank Co., Ltd.   (1)
8 Guiyuan Road, Nanxin District Luzhai
County, Liuzhou, 545600, Guangxi, China
Tel.: (86) 7726822818
Commercial Banking Services
N.A.I.C.S.: 522110

Jiangsu Zhangjiagang CQRC Village
& Township Bank Co., Ltd.   (1)
No 487 and 489 Changan Road, Zhangjia-
gang, 215600, Jiangsu, China
Tel.: (86) 51258918959
Commercial Banking Services
N.A.I.C.S.: 522110

Sichuan Dazhu CQRC Village &
Township Bank Co., Ltd.   (1)
Block H8/9 Huangge Commercial Plaza
Xinhua Road East, Zhuyang Town Dazhu
County, Chengdu, 635100, Sichuan, China
Tel.: (86) 8186256123
Commercial Banking Services
N.A.I.C.S.: 522110

Yunnan Dali CQRC Village & Town-
ship Bank Co., Ltd.   (1)
No 176 Yangbi Road Economic Develop-
ment Zone, Dali, 671000, Yunnan, China
Tel.: (86) 8722188319
Commercial Banking Services
N.A.I.C.S.: 522110

Yunnan Heqing CQRC Village &
Township Bank Co., Ltd.   (1)
15 Xinghe Road, Yunhe Town Hexing
County, Dali, 671500, Yunnan, China
Tel.: (86) 8724125480
Commercial Banking Services
N.A.I.C.S.: 522110

Yunnan Shangri-La CQRC Village &
Township Bank Co., Ltd.   (1)
3AS-1-1 No 7 Huajun Plaza Changzheng
Da Road, Xianggelila County, Kunming,
674499, Yunnan, China
Tel.: (86) 8878980066
Commercial Banking Services
N.A.I.C.S.: 522110

Yunnan Xishan CQRC Village &
Township Bank Co., Ltd.   (1)
No 924 926 928 Dianchi Road Dianchi Na-
tional Tourist Resort, Kunming, 650000,
Yunnan, China
Tel.: (86) 87168183750
Commercial Banking Services
N.A.I.C.S.: 522110

Yunnun Xiangyun CQRC Village &
Township Bank Co., Ltd.   (1)
No 16 Block 11 Xiangyun Yinxiang Garden
Wenyuan Road North Side, Xiangcheng
Town Xiangyun County, Dali, 672100, Yun-
nan, China
Tel.: (86) 8723997552
Commercial Banking Services
N.A.I.C.S.: 522110

CHONGQING SANFENG ENVI-
RONMENT GROUP CORP.,
LTD.
No 3 Jianqiao Avenue Area A Ji-
anqiao Industrial Park, Dadukou Dis-
trict, Chongqing, 400084, China

Tel.: (86) 2388055666
Web Site: https://www.cseg.cn
Year Founded: 2009
601827—(SHG)
Rev.: $845,666,013
Assets: $3,315,248,843
Liabilities: $1,873,182,893
Net Worth: $1,442,065,950
Earnings: $159,956,976
Emp.: 7,279
Fiscal Year-end: 12/31/22
Waste Management Services
N.A.I.C.S.: 562998
Qinping Lei (Chm)

CHONGQING SANXIA PAINTS
CO., LTD.
Degan Industrial Park, Jiangjin Dis-
trict, Chongqing, 402284, China
Tel.: (86) 2347262501
Web Site: https://www.sanxia.com
Year Founded: 1931
000565—(SSE)
Rev.: $65,825,136
Assets: $226,074,888
Liabilities: $43,671,420
Net Worth: $182,403,468
Earnings: $7,363,980
Emp.: 700
Fiscal Year-end: 12/31/22
Paint & Coating Mfr
N.A.I.C.S.: 325510
Jiang Wei (Chm)

CHONGQING SHUNBO ALUMI-
NUM CO., LTD.
Caojie Expansion Park, Hechuan,
Chongqing, 401572, China
Tel.: (86) 2342466969
Year Founded: 2003
002996—(SSE)
Rev.: $1,553,709,924
Assets: $828,223,812
Liabilities: $461,758,752
Net Worth: $366,465,060
Earnings: $28,046,304
Fiscal Year-end: 12/31/22
Aluminium Products Mfr
N.A.I.C.S.: 331313

CHONGQING SIFANG NEW
MATERIAL CO., LTD.
No 306 Nanhu Road Nanpeng Street,
Banan District, Chongqing, 401307,
China
Tel.: (86) 2386129888
Web Site: https://www.cqsifang.com
Year Founded: 2003
605122—(SHG)
Rev.: $232,143,636
Assets: $611,137,894
Liabilities: $300,910,517
Net Worth: $310,227,377
Earnings: ($13,688,214)
Fiscal Year-end: 12/31/22
Cement Product Mfr & Distr
N.A.I.C.S.: 327310
Dezhi Li (Chm & Gen Mgr)

CHONGQING SKYMAN INDUS-
TRY (GROUP) CO., LTD.
Cuntan Area C Gangcheng Industrial
Park, Jiangbei District, Chongqing,
400026, China
Tel.: (86) 2367783888   CN
Web Site: http://www.skyman.com.ch
Year Founded: 1992
Emp.: 600
Auto Parts Mfr
N.A.I.C.S.: 336390
Gong Liangliang (Pres)

Subsidiaries:

Skyman Auto Chassis (Wuhu) Co.,
Ltd   (1)
No 2 Plant 81 Feixiang Road, Jiaojiang

Economic Development Zone, Wuhu,
400026, China
Tel.: (86) 55359688888
Web Site: http://www.skychassis.com
Emp.: 150
Auto Parts Mfr
N.A.I.C.S.: 336211

CHONGQING TAIJI INDUSTRY
(GROUP) CO., LTD.
No 1 Taiji Avenue, Fuling District,
Chongqing, 401123, China
Tel.: (86) 2372800072
Web Site: http://www.taiji.com
Year Founded: 1993
600129—(SHG)
Rev.: $1,972,712,580
Assets: $2,064,890,557
Liabilities: $1,653,905,443
Net Worth: $410,985,114
Earnings: $49,098,273
Fiscal Year-end: 12/31/22
Pharmaceutical Mfr & Drug Store
Operator
N.A.I.C.S.: 325412
Yu Min (Chm & Gen Mgr)

CHONGQING THREE GORGES
WATER CONSERVANCY AND
ELECTRIC POWER CO., LTD.
No 85 Gaosuntang, Wanzhou District,
Chongqing, 401120, China
Tel.: (86) 2363801161
Web Site: http://www.cqsxsl.com
Year Founded: 1994
600116—(SHG)
Rev.: $1,557,459,166
Assets: $3,069,202,547
Liabilities: $1,483,162,083
Net Worth: $1,586,040,464
Earnings: $66,861,288
Emp.: 4,000
Fiscal Year-end: 12/31/22
Hydraulic Power Generation & Distri-
bution Services
N.A.I.C.S.: 221111
Zeyong Zhou (Pres)

CHONGQING VDL ELECTRON-
ICS CO., LTD.
Building 1-4 Puli Industrial New Area
Zhaojia Street, Kaizhou District,
Chongqing, 405401, China
Tel.: (86) 2352862502
Web Site: https://www.gdvdl.com
Year Founded: 2007
301121—(CHIN)
Rev.: $134,603,110
Assets: $346,644,703
Liabilities: $118,618,119
Net Worth: $228,026,584
Earnings: $3,271,475
Fiscal Year-end: 12/31/23
Battery Mfr
N.A.I.C.S.: 335910
Chuanqin Zhu (Chm)

CHONGQING WANLI NEW EN-
ERGY CO., LTD.
No 26 Chuangye Road Shuangfu
Street, Jiangjin District, Chongqing,
402247, China
Tel.: (86) 2385532408
Web Site: https://www.cqwanli.com
Year Founded: 1943
600847—(SHG)
Rev.: $65,921,844
Assets: $106,588,268
Liabilities: $9,933,862
Net Worth: $96,654,407
Earnings: ($4,588,721)
Fiscal Year-end: 12/31/22
Lead Storage Battery Mfr
N.A.I.C.S.: 335910
Dai Jiangong (Chm & Sec)

CHONGQING WATER GROUP
CO., LTD.
No 1 Longjiawan, Yuzhong District,
Chongqing, 400015, China
Tel.: (86) 2363860827
Web Site: https://www.cncqsw.com
601158—(SHG)
Rev.: $1,092,153,615
Assets: $4,486,835,850
Liabilities: $2,076,274,470
Net Worth: $2,410,561,380
Earnings: $268,035,632
Fiscal Year-end: 12/31/22
Water Supply Management Services
N.A.I.C.S.: 221310
Shian Wang (Chm)

CHONGQING YUKAIFA CO.,
LTD.
No 128 Zhongshan 3rd Road, Yu-
zhong District, Chongqing, 400015,
China
Tel.: (86) 2363855506
Web Site: http://www.cqukf.com
Year Founded: 1992
000514—(SSE)
Rev.: $125,736,624
Assets: $1,034,760,636
Liabilities: $451,053,252
Net Worth: $583,707,384
Earnings: $22,855,716
Fiscal Year-end: 12/31/22
Real Estate Support Services
N.A.I.C.S.: 531390
Anjin Wang (Gen Mgr)

CHONGQING YUXIN PINGRUI
ELECTRONIC CO., LTD.
No 992 Gaoteng Avenue, Hangu
Town Jiulongpo District, Chongqing,
401329, China
Tel.: (86) 2365828790
Web Site: https://www.cqyx.com.cn
Year Founded: 2003
301107—(SSE)
Rev.: $78,652,080
Assets: $145,267,668
Liabilities: $18,396,612
Net Worth: $126,871,056
Earnings: $9,225,684
Fiscal Year-end: 12/31/22
Electronic Component Mfr & Distr
N.A.I.C.S.: 334419
Hu Yunping (Chm)

CHONGQING ZAISHENG
TECHNOLOGY CORP., LTD.
No 1 Chanyi Road Huixing Street,
Yubei District, Chongqing, 401120,
China
Tel.: (86) 2367183329
Web Site: https://www.cqzskj.com
Year Founded: 2007
603601—(SHG)
Rev.: $227,222,349
Assets: $479,803,030
Liabilities: $165,458,662
Net Worth: $314,344,368
Earnings: $21,197,536
Fiscal Year-end: 12/31/22
Fiberglass Product Mfr & Distr
N.A.I.C.S.: 313210
Guo Mao (Chm)

CHONGQING ZHENGCHUAN
PHARMACEUTICAL PACKAG-
ING CO., LTD.
Zhengchuan Glass Industrial Park
Longfeng Street, Beibei District,
Chongqing, 400700, China
Tel.: (86) 2368349898
Web Site: http://www.cqzcjt.com
Year Founded: 1988
603976—(SHG)
Rev.: $111,786,241
Assets: $281,875,562

Chongqing Zhengchuan Pharmaceutical Packaging Co., Ltd.—(Continued)

Liabilities: $115,614,514
Net Worth: $166,261,048
Earnings: $9,093,006
Fiscal Year-end: 12/31/22
Glass Bottle Mfr
N.A.I.C.S.: 327215
Deng Yong (Chm & Pres)

Subsidiaries:

Chongqing Zhengchuan Yongcheng Pharmaceutical Material Co., Ltd. **(1)**
No 5B33 Yunhang Road Shuitu High Technology Industrial Zone, Beibei, Chongqing, China
Tel.: (86) 2368349810
Pharmaceutical Glass Mfr & Distr
N.A.I.C.S.: 327213

CHONGQING ZHIFEI BIOLOGICAL PRODUCTS CO.,LTD
F50/ F51 Building T1 IFS No 1 Qingyun Road, Jiangbei District, Chongqing, China
Tel.: (86) 2386358685
Web Site:
https://en.zhifeishengwu.com
Year Founded: 1995
300122—(CHIN)
Rev.: $5,372,267,004
Assets: $5,335,723,692
Liabilities: $1,932,959,808
Net Worth: $3,402,763,884
Earnings: $1,058,475,600
Emp.: 4,500
Fiscal Year-end: 12/31/22
Pharmaceuticals Product Mfr
N.A.I.C.S.: 325412

CHONGYI ZHANGYUAN TUNGSTEN CO., LTD.
Chongyi County, Ganzhou, 341300, Jiangxi, China
Tel.: (86) 7973820789
Web Site: https://www.zy-tungsten.com
Year Founded: 1990
002378—(SSE)
Rev.: $449,753,148
Assets: $672,760,296
Liabilities: $391,165,632
Net Worth: $281,594,664
Earnings: $28,548,936
Fiscal Year-end: 12/31/22
Tungsten Mining & Production Services
N.A.I.C.S.: 212290
Huang Zelan (Chm)

Subsidiaries:

Ganzhou Achteck Tool Technology Co., Ltd. **(1)**
Economic Development Area, Ganzhou, 341000, Jiangxi, China
Tel.: (86) 7978086879
Web Site: https://www.achtecktool.com
Metal Ore Mining Services
N.A.I.C.S.: 212290

CHOO BEE METAL INDUSTRIES BERHAD
Wisma Soon Teik Aun Jalan Bendahara, 31650, Ipoh, Perak, Malaysia
Tel.: (60) 52558111
Web Site: https://www.choobee.com
CHOOBEE—(KLS)
Rev.: $104,362,328
Assets: $139,710,899
Liabilities: $7,550,265
Net Worth: $132,160,635
Earnings: $1,721,693
Emp.: 300
Fiscal Year-end: 12/31/22
Steel Pole Mfr
N.A.I.C.S.: 331110

Sieng Tzi Lee (Exec Dir)

Subsidiaries:

Choo Bee Hardwares Sdn. Berhad **(1)**
No 11 Jalan SKI 1/KU7 Kawasan Perindustrian Hi-Tech Sungai Kapar Indah, 42200, Klang, Selangor, Malaysia
Tel.: (60) 332918922
Steel Pole Mfr
N.A.I.C.S.: 331210

Subsidiary (Domestic):

Choo Bee Hardware (Sabah) Sdn. Bhd. **(2)**
25 1/2km Jalan Tuaran, Tamparuli, 89257, Kota Kinabalu, Sabah, Malaysia
Tel.: (60) 88491992
Steel Pole Mfr
N.A.I.C.S.: 331210

CHOO CHIANG HOLDINGS LTD.
10 Woodlands Loop, Singapore, 738388, Singapore
Tel.: (65) 63685922   SG
Web Site:
https://www.choochiang.com
Year Founded: 1977
42E—(CAT)
Rev.: $68,928,274
Assets: $61,863,970
Liabilities: $13,914,262
Net Worth: $47,949,708
Earnings: $7,983,792
Emp.: 138
Fiscal Year-end: 12/31/23
Electrical Products Distr
N.A.I.C.S.: 423610
Thomas Teck Chuan Lim (Chm & CEO)

CHOONGANG VACCINE LABORATORY CO., LTD.
1476-37 YuSeongdaero, Yuseonggu, Daejeon, 34055, Korea (South)
Tel.: (82) 428639308
Web Site: https://www.cavac.co.kr
Year Founded: 1968
072020—(KRS)
Rev.: $30,142,455
Assets: $88,096,533
Liabilities: $14,998,020
Net Worth: $73,098,513
Earnings: $3,102,098
Emp.: 180
Fiscal Year-end: 12/31/22
Biological Product Mfr
N.A.I.C.S.: 325412
InJoong Yoon (CEO)

CHOPARD & CIE S.A.
Rue de Veyrot 8, PO Box 85, 1217, Meyrin, Geneva, Switzerland
Tel.: (41) 227193131
Web Site: http://www.chopard.com
Sales Range: $450-499.9 Million
Emp.: 800
Watch & Jewelry Distr
N.A.I.C.S.: 458310
Karl Friedrich Scheufele (Pres)

Subsidiaries:

CHOPARD (ASIA) PTE LTD **(1)**
7 Temasek Boulevard 39-02 Suntec Tower One, Singapore, 038987, Singapore
Tel.: (65) 6333 0801
Watch Distr
N.A.I.C.S.: 423940
Bruce Wagner (Reg Mgr-Cus Svc)

CHOPARD (GREAT BRITAIN) LTD **(1)**
28 Welbeck Street, London, W1G 8EW, United Kingdom
Tel.: (44) 20 7467 4200
Watch & Jewelery Distr
N.A.I.C.S.: 423940
Chris Proffitt (Mng Dir)

CHOPARD DEUTSCHLAND GMBH **(1)**
Carl - Benz - Strasse 1, Birkenfeld, 75217, Pforzheim, Germany
Tel.: (49) 7231 4867
Web Site: http://www.chopard.de
Jewelry Mfr
N.A.I.C.S.: 339910

CHOPARD HONG KONG LTD **(1)**
20/F 8 Observatory Road, Causeway Bay, China (Hong Kong)
Tel.: (852) 3406 9300
Web Site: http://www.chopard.com
Watch & Jewelery Distr
N.A.I.C.S.: 423940
Ricky Law (Dir-Wholesales)

CHOPARD IBERICA S,L **(1)**
Passeig de Gracia 86 6PL, 08008, Barcelona, Spain
Tel.: (34) 93 414 6920
Watch & Jewelery Distr
N.A.I.C.S.: 423940

CHOPARD ITALIA S.R.L **(1)**
Lungarno Vespucci 8, 50123, Florence, Italy
Tel.: (39) 055 21 31 15
Web Site: http://www.chopard.com
Emp.: 10
Watch & Jewelery Distr
N.A.I.C.S.: 423940
Simona Zito (Mgr)

CHOPARD JAPAN LTD **(1)**
Chopard Building 2-4-14 Ginza, Chuo-Ku, Tokyo, 104-0061, Japan
Tel.: (81) 3 5524 8975
Watch & Jewelery Distr
N.A.I.C.S.: 423940
Takato Nakajima (Mgr-IT & Logistics)

CHOPARD MALAYSIA SDN BHD **(1)**
Suite 4 2 4th floor - Manera Keck Seng 203, Jalan Bukit Bintang, 55100, Kuala Lumpur, Malaysia
Tel.: (60) 3 2148 6843
Emp.: 10
Watch & Jewelery Distr
N.A.I.C.S.: 423940
Joanne Lum (Mgr-Fin)

CHOPARD MARKETING SERVICES, INC **(1)**
75 Valencia Ave Ste 1200, Coral Gables, FL 33134
Tel.: (305) 774-3898
Watch & Jewelry Distr
N.A.I.C.S.: 423940
Rudolf Lang (Mng Dir)

CHOPARD TRADING (Shanghai) Co. LTD **(1)**
Room 1805-1811 Plaza 66 Office Tower 1 1266 Nanjing Road West, Shanghai, China
Tel.: (86) 21 6136 7800
Watch & Jewelery Distr
N.A.I.C.S.: 423940
Matthew Sun (Dir-Sls)

CHOPARD UHRENHANDELS GMBH **(1)**
Am Kohlmarkt 16, 1010, Vienna, Austria
Tel.: (43) 1 533 7197
Web Site: http://www.chopard.at
Emp.: 18
Watch & Jewelery Distr
N.A.I.C.S.: 423940
Koblmueller Thomas (CEO)

Chopard USA Ltd. **(1)**
21 E 63rd St, New York, NY 10065
Tel.: (212) 821-0300
Web Site: http://www.chopard.com
Sales Range: $50-74.9 Million
Emp.: 55
Watches, Jewelry & Accessories Sales
N.A.I.C.S.: 423940

LE PETIT-FILS DE L.U. CHOPARD FRANCE SAS **(1)**
100 rue du Faubourg Saint-Honore, 75008, Paris, France
Tel.: (33) 1 42 68 80 30
Watch & Jewelery Distr
N.A.I.C.S.: 423940

CHOPARD AUTOMOBILES SAS

The Trigone 6 Rue Gerard Mantion, 25000, Besancon, France
Tel.: (33) 3 81 47 50 50
Web Site:
http://www.groupechopard.com
Automobile Dealers
N.A.I.C.S.: 441110
Muriel Ranieri (Mgr-HR)

Subsidiaries:

Mercedes-Benz Lyon SAS **(1)**
89-91 rue Marietton, 69009, Lyon, France
Tel.: (33) 472857800
Web Site:
http://www.groupechopard.mercedes-benz.fr
New & Used Car Dealer
N.A.I.C.S.: 441110

CHOPPIES ENTERPRISES LTD.
Choppies Distribution Center Plot 169 GICP, Gaborone, Botswana
Tel.: (267) 3186657
Web Site:
https://www.choppies.co.bw
Year Founded: 1986
CHOP—(BOT)
Rev.: $473,147,459
Assets: $158,810,055
Liabilities: $155,746,196
Net Worth: $3,063,860
Earnings: $10,942,356
Emp.: 9,740
Fiscal Year-end: 06/30/23
Food Products Mfr
N.A.I.C.S.: 311999

Subsidiaries:

Choppies Enterprises Kenya Limited **(1)**
Central Business Park Road C Off Enterprise Road, Nairobi, Kenya
Tel.: (254) 791334455
Web Site: https://choppies.co.ke
All Grocery Product Distr
N.A.I.C.S.: 445110

Choppies Supermarket Mozambique Limitada **(1)**
Mall de Tete Corner of EN7 & Avinada Da Visao Mundial Bairro Matema, Tete, Mozambique
Tel.: (258) 25220170
All Grocery Product Distr
N.A.I.C.S.: 445110

Choppies Supermarkets Limited **(1)**
Warehouse 4 Plot, Makeni, 29389, Lusaka, Zambia
Tel.: (260) 950551720
All Grocery Product Distr
N.A.I.C.S.: 445110

Choppies Supermarkets Namibia (Pty) Ltd **(1)**
ERF 499 Silver Street Prosperita Windhoek, PO Box 21491, Windhoek, Namibia
Tel.: (264) 61246301
All Grocery Product Distr
N.A.I.C.S.: 445110

Choppies Supermarkets Tanzania Limited **(1)**
Harbour View Towers 5th Floor Samora Avenue, PO Box 10295, Dar es Salaam, Tanzania
Tel.: (255) 689680197
All Grocery Product Distr
N.A.I.C.S.: 445110

Nanavac Investments (Pvt) Ltd **(1)**
12273a Falcon Street And Phoenix Road, Belmont, Bulawayo, Zimbabwe
Tel.: (263) 772804253
Web Site: https://nanavac-investments-ta-choppies.business.site
All Grocery Product Distr
N.A.I.C.S.: 445110

CHORDIA FOOD PRODUCTS LTD.
Plot No 399 400 Survey, Village San-

gavi Shirwal Tal- Khandala, Satara,
412801, Maharashtra, India
Tel.: (91) 919881107000
Web Site:
https://www.chordiafoods.com
Year Founded: 1960
519475—(BOM)
Rev.: $11,015,768
Assets: $7,989,400
Liabilities: $3,680,136
Net Worth: $4,309,264
Earnings: ($650,573)
Emp.: 152
Fiscal Year-end: 03/31/22
Processed Food Mfr
N.A.I.C.S.: 311411
Pradeep Hukmichand Chordia *(Mng Dir)*

CHORI CO., LTD.
4-2-13 Awajimachi, Chuo-ku, Osaka,
540-8603, Japan
Tel.: (81) 662285000   JP
Web Site: https://www.chori.co.jp
Year Founded: 1948
8014—(TKS)
Rev.: $2,033,890,390
Assets: $947,543,500
Liabilities: $404,882,330
Net Worth: $542,661,170
Earnings: $63,614,640
Emp.: 1,304
Fiscal Year-end: 03/31/24
Trading House; Import; Export & Brokerage of Textile Materials & Products; Metal Products, Plastic Resins, Chemicals, Fertilizers
N.A.I.C.S.: 314999
Shigemasa Yabu *(Bd of Dirs, Mng Exec Officer & Mng Exec Officer)*

Subsidiaries:

Asada U Co., Ltd.   **(1)**
1-16-7 Nishiki, Naka-ku, Nagoya, 460-0003,
Aichi, Japan
Tel.: (81) 522183040
Web Site: https://asada-u.co.jp
Packaging Material Distr
N.A.I.C.S.: 423840

Beijing Chostar Equipment Engineering Technology Co., Ltd.   **(1)**
No 5 Xingye Street BDA, Beijing, 100176,
China
Tel.: (86) 1058082004
Web Site:
https://www.chostar.chemchina.com
Chemical Product Mfr & Distr
N.A.I.C.S.: 325998

Business Anchor Corporation   **(1)**
Awajicho 1-7-3 Nichichi Sasuji Building 9F,
Chuo-ku, Osaka, 540-8603, Japan
Tel.: (81) 662285528
Web Site: https://www.chori-bac.co.jp
Emp.: 71
Business Support Services
N.A.I.C.S.: 561499

Chori (China) Co., Ltd.   **(1)**
Room 1201 Shanghai International Trade
Center No 2201 Yan'an Road West, Shanghai, China
Tel.: (86) 2162787890
Industrial Product Whslr
N.A.I.C.S.: 423840

Chori (Dalian) Commercial Import
Export Co., Ltd.   **(1)**
5th Floor SenMao Bldg No 147 Zhongshan
Road, Xigang District, Dalian, China
Tel.: (86) 41183699674
Textile Products Distr
N.A.I.C.S.: 424310

Chori (Dalian) Trading Co., Ltd. **(1)**
5th Floor SenMao Bldg No 147 Zhongshan
Road, Xigang District, Dalian, China
Tel.: (86) 41183691785
Sales Range: $25-49.9 Million
Textile Products Distr
N.A.I.C.S.: 424350

Chori (Tianjin) Co., Ltd.   **(1)**

Room 1603 The Exchange South Tower
189 Nanjing Road, Heping District, Tianjin,
300051, China
Tel.: (86) 22 8319 1606
Web Site: http://www.chori.co.jp
Textile Products Mfr
N.A.I.C.S.: 314999

Chori America, Inc.   **(1)**
30 Montgomery St Ste 1230, Jersey City,
NJ 07302-3834   **(100%)**
Tel.: (201) 324-1030
Web Site: https://www.chori.co.jp
Sales Range: $25-49.9 Million
Trading House
N.A.I.C.S.: 424310

Chori Analysis & Technology Service
(Suzhou)Co., Ltd.   **(1)**
B2-603 Bio Bay, Suzhou Industrial Park,
Suzhou, China
Tel.: (86) 51287662970
Chemical Analysis Services
N.A.I.C.S.: 541380

Chori Co. (Hong Kong) Ltd.   **(1)**
Unit605 6/F Tower2 Silvercord No 30 Canton Road, Tsim Sha Tsui, Kowloon, China
(Hong Kong)
Tel.: (852) 27242333
Web Site: http://www.chori.co.jp
Foreign Currency Exchange Services
N.A.I.C.S.: 523160

Chori Comercial De Mexico S.A. DE
C.V.   **(1)**
Av Ejercito Nacional 843 B Corporativo Antara I Piso 5 Col Granada, Delegacion
Miguel Hidalgo, 11520, Mexico, Mexico
Tel.: (52) 5576787707
Industrial Product Whslr
N.A.I.C.S.: 423840

Chori Europe GmbH   **(1)**
Hugenottenallee 175, 63263, Neu-Isenburg,
Germany   **(100%)**
Tel.: (49) 6102798010
Sales Range: $25-49.9 Million
Emp.: 3
Trading House; Import; Export & Brokerage
of Textile Materials & Products; Metal Products, Plastic Resins, Chemicals, Fertilizers
N.A.I.C.S.: 314999

Chori Fashion Network Co., Ltd. **(1)**
Rm 606 6/F Mirror Tower 61 Mody Rd,
Hong Kong, China (Hong Kong)
N.A.I.C.S.: 523160

Chori Glex Co., Ltd.   **(1)**
Tower C Shinagawa Intercity 15-3 Konan
2-Chome, Minato-ku, Tokyo, 108-6216, Japan
Tel.: (81) 35 715 4350
Web Site: https://www.c-glex.co.jp
Emp.: 24
Industrial Product Whslr
N.A.I.C.S.: 423840
Nobuo Mori *(Pres)*

Chori Imaging Corporation   **(1)**
3-13-6 Shinyokohama, Kouhoku-ku, Yokohama, Japan
Tel.: (81) 45 476 2260
Web Site: http://www.chori-imaging.com
Image Processing Apparatus Distr
N.A.I.C.S.: 423610

Chori Korea Co., Ltd.   **(1)**
Shinsong Bldg Rm 1404 67 Yeouinaru-Ro,
Yeongdeungpo-gu, Seoul, 07327, Korea
(South)
Tel.: (82) 27614127
Industrial Product Whslr
N.A.I.C.S.: 423840

Chori MODA Co., Ltd.   **(1)**
11th Floor Yoyogi 1-chome Building 1-22-22
Yoyogi, Shibuya-ku, Tokyo, 151-0053, Japan
Tel.: (81) 368598261
Web Site: https://www.chori-moda.com
Apparel Retailer
N.A.I.C.S.: 458110

Chori Machinery Co., Ltd.   **(1)**
Tower C Shinagawa Intercity 15-3 Konan
2-Chome, Minato-ku, Tokyo, 108-6216, Japan
Tel.: (81) 357816431
Web Site: https://www.chori-machinery.com

Transportation Equipment Whslr
N.A.I.C.S.: 423860

Chori Middle East FZE   **(1)**
Jafza View 18 15th Floor Office No 1503,
PO Box 17334, Jebel Ali, Dubai, United
Arab Emirates
Tel.: (971) 4 8814742
Web Site: http://www.chori.co.jp
Chemical & Textile Products Mfr
N.A.I.C.S.: 325998

Chori Shanghai Ltd.   **(1)**
Room 1201 Shanghai International Trade
Center No 2201 Yan'an Road West, Shanghai, 200336, China   **(100%)**
Tel.: (86) 216 278 7890
Web Site: http://www.chori.com.cn
Sales Range: $50-74.9 Million
Emp.: 90
Financial Services
N.A.I.C.S.: 523940
Mao Inoue *(Gen Mgr)*

Chori Singapore Pte. Ltd.   **(1)**
1 Harbourfront Avenue 13-03 Keppel Bay
Tower, Singapore, 098632,
Singapore   **(100%)**
Tel.: (65) 62088802
Web Site: http://www.chori.co.jp
Sales Range: $25-49.9 Million
Emp.: 9
Trading House; Import; Export & Brokerage
of Textile Materials & Products; Metal Products, Plastic Resins, Chemicals, Fertilizers
N.A.I.C.S.: 314999

Chori Trading India PTE. LTD. **(1)**
Office No 505 5th Floor Centre Point Andheri Kurla Road J B Nagar, Andheri East,
Mumbai, 400059, Maharashtra, India
Tel.: (91) 2242955722
Industrial Product Whslr
N.A.I.C.S.: 423840

Chori Trading Malaysia Sdn Bhd **(1)**
Lot No 5F-2A 5th Floor Tower5 Puchong
Financial Corporate Centre, Jalan Puteri 1/2
Bandar Puteri Puchong, 47100, Puchong,
Selangor, Malaysia
Tel.: (60) 380665773
Web Site: http://www.chori.com.my
Sales Range: $25-49.9 Million
Emp.: 5
Trading House; Import; Export & Brokerage
of Textile Materials & Products; Metal Products, Plastic Resins, Chemicals & Fertilizers
N.A.I.C.S.: 314999

Chori Urban Development Co.,
Ltd.   **(1)**
2-4-3 Horidomecho Nihonbashi, Chuo-ku,
Tokyo, Japan
Tel.: (81) 3 3665 2527
Web Site: http://www.cud.co.jp
Real Estate Manangement Services
N.A.I.C.S.: 531390

Chori Vietnam Co., Ltd.   **(1)**
Unit 1705-1706 17th Floor Saigon Riverside
Office Center, 2A-4A Ton Duc Thang street
Ben Nghe Ward District 1, Ho Chi Minh
City, Vietnam
Tel.: (84) 2838220348
Industrial Product Whslr
N.A.I.C.S.: 423840

Dalian Anchor Business Service Co.,
Ltd.   **(1)**
Central Plaza Hotel Dalian Rm No 904 No
145 Zhongshan Road, Xigang District, Dalian, China
Tel.: (86) 411 83700273
Office Outsourcing Services
N.A.I.C.S.: 561499

Dijion Co., Ltd   **(1)**
23-3 Sakuragaoka, Shibuya-ku, Tokyo, Japan
Tel.: (81) 3 3780 0891
Web Site: http://www.dijion.co.jp
Ladies Apparel Whslr
N.A.I.C.S.: 424350

Kozakura Shokai Co.,Ltd.   **(1)**
3-3-1 Nishi-Shimbashi, Minato-ku, Tokyo,
105-0003, Japan
Tel.: (81) 334324703
Web Site: https://kozakura.co.jp
Petroleum Product Distr

N.A.I.C.S.: 424720

MCC Industry Company Limited **(1)**
Unit 605 6/F Tower 2 Silvercord No 30 Canton Road, Tsim Sha Tsui, Kowloon, China
(Hong Kong)
Tel.: (852) 31521428
Textile Products Distr
N.A.I.C.S.: 424310

Miyako Kagaku Co., Ltd.   **(1)**
6F Chiyoda Hall 1-6-17 Kudanminami,
Chiyoda-ku, Tokyo, 102-0074, Japan
Tel.: (81) 366850385
Web Site: https://www.miyakokagaku.co.jp
Emp.: 101
Industrial Product Whslr
N.A.I.C.S.: 423840

P.T. Chori Indonesia   **(1)**
Wisma Keiai 22nd Floor, Jl Jend Sudirman
Kav 3, Jakarta Pusat, 10220, Indonesia
Tel.: (62) 215723375
Web Site: http://www.chori.co.jp
Sales Range: $25-49.9 Million
Emp.: 14
Provider of Trading & Import & Export Services
N.A.I.C.S.: 561990

Qingdao Red Butterfly Precision Materials Co., Ltd.   **(1)**
No 1 Haiwan Road, Xinhe Ecological
Chemical Technology Industry Base,
Pingdu, Qingdao, China
Tel.: (86) 53282850182
Web Site: https://en.qingdaohongdie.com
Salt Mfr & Distr
N.A.I.C.S.: 311942

Red Butterfly Strontium Industry Co.,
Ltd.   **(1)**
29 Pinhe Street Long Shui Town, Longshui
Town, Chongqing, 43648968, Dazu, China
Tel.: (86) 23 67961322
Web Site: http://www.hxsz.cn
Emp.: 300
Carbonic Strontium Mfr & Distr
N.A.I.C.S.: 327999
Cassie Dhang *(Office Mgr)*

Shanghai Xindie Tanaka Garments
Co., Ltd.   **(1)**
No.1678, Liyue Lu, Pujiang Zhen, Minhang,
201114, Shanghai, China
Mfr of Knitted Garments
N.A.I.C.S.: 315120

Taiwan Chori Merchandise Cooperation LTD.   **(1)**
5 Fl-8 No 188 Sec 5 Nanjing E Road,
Songshan Dist, Taipei, 10571, Taiwan
Tel.: (886) 227472251
Industrial Product Whslr
N.A.I.C.S.: 423840

Thai Chori Co., Ltd.   **(1)**
Thaniya Plaza Bldg 11th Floor Zone C D
No 52 Silom Road Suriyawong, Bangrak,
Bangkok, 10500, Thailand
Tel.: (66) 22670231
Sales Range: $25-49.9 Million
Emp.: 31
Trading House; Import; Export & Brokerage
of Textile Materials & Products; Metal Products, Plastic Resins, Chemicals, Fertilizers
N.A.I.C.S.: 314999
Kotalo Moai *(Pres)*

Tohcho Co., Limited   **(1)**
1-2-2 Yuraku-cho, Chiyoda-ku, Tokyo, 103-
8652, Japan
Tel.: (81) 336652472
Web Site: https://www.toho.co.jp
Emp.: 357
Chemical Product Whslr
N.A.I.C.S.: 424690

Tokyo Kutsushita Co., Ltd.   **(1)**
1-1-6 Saga, Koto-ku, Tokyo, Japan
Tel.: (81) 3 5639 9570
Web Site: http://www.k-tk.com
Inner Socks Mfr & Distr
N.A.I.C.S.: 315120

CHOROKBAEM COMPANY
CO., LTD.
19 Eonju-ro 148-gil, Gangnam-gu,
Seoul, Korea (South)

Chorokbaem Company Co., Ltd.—(Continued)
Tel.: (82) 262379784
Web Site: http://www.mmcorp.com
Year Founded: 2002
052300—(KRS)
Rev.: $164,687,211
Assets: $513,024,990
Liabilities: $183,754,292
Net Worth: $329,270,698
Earnings: ($109,002,283)
Emp.: 20
Fiscal Year-end: 12/31/22
Logistic Services
N.A.I.C.S.: 541614

CHORUS AVIATION INC.
3 Spectacle Lake Drive Suite 380,
Dartmouth, B3B 1W8, NS, Canada
Tel.: (902) 873-5000
Web Site:
　https://www.chorusaviation.com
Year Founded: 2005
CHR—(TSX)
Rev.: $800,487,567
Assets: $2,488,054,839
Liabilities: $1,947,914,749
Net Worth: $540,140,089
Earnings: ($16,025,006)
Emp.: 4,426
Fiscal Year-end: 12/31/21
Holding Company
N.A.I.C.S.: 551112
Joseph D. Randell (Pres & CEO)

Subsidiaries:

Jazz Aviation LP　　　　　　　(1)
310 Goudey Drive, Enfield, B2T 1M6, NS,
Canada　　　　　　　　　　(100%)
Tel.: (902) 873-5000
Web Site: https://www.flyjazz.ca
Emp.: 5,000
Oil Transportation Services
N.A.I.C.S.: 481111
Steve Linthwaite (VP-Flight Ops)

Division (Domestic):

Air Canada Express　　　　　　(2)
5520 Miller Road, Richmond, V7B 1L9, BC,
Canada
Tel.: (604) 244-2600
Web Site: http://www.flyjazz.ca
Sales Range: $400-449.9 Million
Emp.: 1,200
Airline Services
N.A.I.C.S.: 481111

Air Canada Express　　　　　　(2)
1000 Air Ontario Dr, London, N5V 3S4, ON,
Canada
Tel.: (519) 457-8071
Web Site: http://www.flyjazz.ca
Airline Services
N.A.I.C.S.: 481111

Voyageur Airways Limited　　　(1)
1500 Airport Road, North Bay, P1B 8G2,
ON, Canada
Tel.: (705) 476-1750
Web Site: https://www.voyav.com
Emp.: 250
Oil Transportation Services
N.A.I.C.S.: 481111
Cory Cousineau (VP-Comml Svcs)

Voyageur Aviation Corp.　　　　(1)
1500 Airport Road, North Bay, P1B 8G2,
ON, Canada
Tel.: (705) 476-1750
Web Site: https://www.voyav.com
Aviation Services
N.A.I.C.S.: 488190
Scott Tapson (Pres)

CHORUS LIMITED
Level 10 1 Willis Street, Wellington,
6140, New Zealand
Tel.: (64) 800600100
Web Site: https://www.chorus.co.nz
Year Founded: 2011
CHRYY—(OTCIQ)
Rev.: $586,124,402
Assets: $3,687,200,957

Liabilities: $3,051,435,407
Net Worth: $635,765,550
Earnings: $14,952,153
Emp.: 846
Fiscal Year-end: 06/30/23
Telecommunication Servicesb
N.A.I.C.S.: 517111
Jonathan Peter Hartley (Deputy Chm)

CHOSA ONCOLOGY AB
Scheeletorget 1, Medicon Village,
223 81, Lund, Sweden
Tel.: (46) 737517278
Web Site:
　https://www.chosaoncology.com
Year Founded: 2007
Biotechnology Research & Development Services
N.A.I.C.S.: 541714
Anders Mansson (CEO)

CHOTHANI FOODS LIMITED
408 B Wing Damji Shamji Corporate
Square Laxmi Nagar, Ghatkopar
East, Mumbai, 400 075, Maharashtra,
India
Tel.: (91) 8452928889　　　　　In
Web Site:
　https://www.chothanifoodsltd.com
Year Founded: 1975
540681—(BOM)
Rev.: $541,707
Assets: $1,227,521
Liabilities: $329,250
Net Worth: $898,271
Earnings: $12,049
Emp.: 15
Fiscal Year-end: 03/31/21
Food Product Mfr & Distr
N.A.I.C.S.: 311942
Neeraj Ashok Chothani (Chm, Mng
Dir & CFO)

CHOTIWAT MANUFACTURING PUBLIC COMPANY LIMITED
1069 Asia Highway Kho Hong, Hat
Yai, Songkhla, 90110, Thailand
Tel.: (66) 7 420 0999
Web Site: https://www.chotiwat.com
Year Founded: 1960
CMCF—(THA)
Seafood Product Mfr
N.A.I.C.S.: 311710
Kitipong Urapeepatanapong (Chm)

CHOU ASSOCIATES MANAGEMENT INC.
110 Sheppard Avenue East Suite
301, Box 18, Toronto, M2N 6Y8, ON,
Canada
Tel.: (416) 214-0675
Web Site: http://www.choufunds.com
Investment Fund Management Services
N.A.I.C.S.: 523940
Francis S. M. Chou (Pres, CEO &
Portfolio Mgr)

CHOUSHIMARU CO., LTD.
2-39 Hamada, Mihama-ku, Chiba,
261-0025, Japan
Tel.: (81) 433501266
Web Site:
　https://www.choushimaru.co.jp
Year Founded: 1977
30750—(TKS)
Sales Range: Less than $1 Million
Restaurant Services
N.A.I.C.S.: 722511
Mitsuru Ishida (Pres & CEO)

CHOW ENERGY PUBLIC COMPANY LIMITED
2525 FYI Center Tower 2 10th Floor
Unit2/1006-1008 Rama 4 Road, Khlongtoei, Bangkok, 10110, Thailand

Tel.: (66) 2033091014
Web Site:
　https://www.chowenergy.co.th
Year Founded: 2014
Emp.: 100
Holding Company
N.A.I.C.S.: 551112
Anavin Jiratomsiri (CEO)

CHOW SANG SANG HOLDINGS INTERNATIONAL LIMITED
27/F 9 Wing Hong Street Cheung
Sha Wan, Kowloon, China (Hong
Kong)
Tel.: (852) 21923123　　　　　BM
Web Site:
　https://www.chowsangsang.com
Year Founded: 1934
116—(HKG)
Rev.: $1,689,343,926
Assets: $2,170,277,714
Liabilities: $620,052,390
Net Worth: $1,550,225,324
Earnings: $70,224,967
Emp.: 10,109
Fiscal Year-end: 12/31/20
Jewelry Mfr & Whslr
N.A.I.C.S.: 339910
Vincent Wing Shing Chow (Chm &
Gen Mgr)

CHOW STEEL INDUSTRIES PUBLIC COMPANY LIMITED
2525 FYI CenterTower 2 10th Floor
Unit2/1006-1008 Rama 4 Road, Kh-
longtoei, Bangkok, 10110, Thailand
Tel.: (66) 20330901
Web Site: https://www.chowsteel.com
Year Founded: 2000
CHOW—(THA)
Rev.: $113,757,831
Assets: $98,618,857
Liabilities: $33,092,791
Net Worth: $65,526,065
Earnings: $13,437,158
Emp.: 269
Fiscal Year-end: 12/31/23
Steel Billets Mfr
N.A.I.C.S.: 331110
Pruchya Piumsomboon (Chm)

Subsidiaries:

Captain Cash Holding Company
Limited　　　　　　　　　　(1)
2525 FYI Center Tower 2 10th Floor Unit
2/1006-1008 Rama 4 Road, Klongtoei,
Bangkok, 10110, Thailand
Tel.: (66) 20330921
Financial Services
N.A.I.C.S.: 523999

Chow International Co., Ltd.　　(1)
2525 FYI Center Tower 2 10th Floor
Unit2/1006-1008 Rama 4 Road, Khlongtoei
Khlongtoei, Bangkok, 10110, Thailand
Tel.: (66) 2033091516
Web Site: http://www.chow-
　international.co.th
Renewable Energy Services
N.A.I.C.S.: 221112

Chow Shining Energy Company
Limited　　　　　　　　　　(1)
2525 FYI Center Tower 2 10th Floor Unit
2/1006-1008 Rama 4 Road, Khlongtoei,
Bangkok, 10110, Thailand
Tel.: (66) 20330924
Renewable Energy Services
N.A.I.C.S.: 221114

Premier Solution Co., Ltd.　　　(1)
2525 FYI Center Tower 2 10th Floor
Unit2/1007-1008 Rama 4 Road, Khlongtoei
Khlongtoei, Bangkok, 10110, Thailand
Tel.: (66) 2033091928
Web Site: https://www.ps-cl.com
Investment Advisory Services
N.A.I.C.S.: 523940

S.R.G.A. Company Limited　　　(1)

2525 FYI Center Tower 2 10th Floor Unit
2/1006-1008 Rama 4 Road, Klongtoei,
Bangkok, 10110, Thailand
Tel.: (66) 20330925
Renewable Energy Services
N.A.I.C.S.: 221114

CHOW TAI FOOK ENTERPRISES LIMITED
38/F New World Tower 16-18
Queen's Road, Central, China (Hong
Kong)
Tel.: (852) 25268649　　　　　HK
Year Founded: 1966
Investment Holding Company
N.A.I.C.S.: 551112
Henry Kar-Shun Cheng (Chm)

Subsidiaries:

Chow Tai Fook Jewellery Group
Limited　　　　　　　　　　(1)
38/F New World Tower, 16-18 Queens
Road, Central, China (Hong Kong)
Tel.: (852) 21383399
Web Site: https://www.ctfjewellerygroup.com
Rev.: $9,049,726,924
Assets: $8,294,471,636
Liabilities: $4,222,882,588
Net Worth: $4,071,589,048
Earnings: $796,593,378
Emp.: 27,900
Fiscal Year-end: 03/31/2021
Holding Company; Jewelry & Watch Retailer
N.A.I.C.S.: 551112
Henry Kar-Shun Cheng (Chm)

Subsidiary (Domestic):

CTF Watch Limited　　　　　　(2)
38/F New World Tower 16-18 Queen's
Road, Central, China (Hong Kong)
Tel.: (852) 2526 8649
Web Site: http://watch.chowtaifook.com
Watch Retailer
N.A.I.C.S.: 458310

Chow Tai Fook Jewellery Co.,
Ltd.　　　　　　　　　　　　(2)
38/F New World Tower 16-18 Queen's
Road, Central, China (Hong Kong)
Tel.: (852) 25268649
Web Site: http://www.chowtaifook.com
Jewelry Mfr & Retail Stores Operator
N.A.I.C.S.: 458310
Bobby Chun-Wai Liu (Exec Dir)

Subsidiary (US):

Hearts on Fire Company LLC　　(2)
99 Summer St, Boston, MA 02110
Tel.: (617) 523-5588
Web Site: http://www.heartsonfire.com
Diamond Jewelry Mfr & Distr
N.A.I.C.S.: 339910
Glenn Rothman (Founder & CEO)

New World Development Company
Limited　　　　　　　　　　(1)
30/F New World Tower 18 Queen's Road,
Central, China (Hong Kong)
Tel.: (852) 25231056
Web Site: http://www.nwd.com.hk
Rev.: $8,798,074,046
Assets: $82,016,305,422
Liabilities: $44,857,322,198
Net Worth: $37,158,983,224
Earnings: $554,846,164
Emp.: 28,000
Fiscal Year-end: 06/30/2022
Property Management Services
N.A.I.C.S.: 531311
Henry Kar-Shun Cheng (Chm)

Subsidiary (Domestic):

NWS Holdings Limited　　　　　(2)
21/F NCB Innovation Centre 888 Lai Chi
Kok Road Cheung Sha Wan, Kowloon,
China (Hong Kong)　　　　　(60%)
Tel.: (852) 21310600
Web Site: https://www.nws.com.hk
Rev.: $4,016,256,628
Assets: $19,188,457,784
Liabilities: $12,238,099,626
Net Worth: $6,950,358,158
Earnings: $281,731,014

Emp.: 13,800
Fiscal Year-end: 06/30/2022
Holding Company; Infrastructure & Facilities Support Services
N.A.I.C.S.: 551112
Henry Kar-Shun Cheng *(Chm & Exec Dir)*

Subsidiary (Domestic):

FTLife Insurance Company Limited   **(3)**
28th Floor Wing On Centre 111 Connaught Road, Central, China (Hong Kong)
Tel.: (852) 2591 8888
Web Site: http://www.ftlife.com.hk
Life, Property & Casualty Insurance Products & Services
N.A.I.C.S.: 524113
Fang Lin *(Chm)*

Subsidiary (Domestic):

New World China Land Limited   **(2)**
9/F New World Tower 1 18 Queen's Road, Central, China (Hong Kong)   **(100%)**
Tel.: (852) 21310201
Web Site: http://www.nwcl.com.hk
Sales Range: $1-4.9 Billion
Emp.: 10,742
Investment Property for Lease, Develop & Manage Resort & Hotel Projects
N.A.I.C.S.: 523999
Henry Kar-Shun Cheng *(Chm & Mng Dir)*

Subsidiary (Domestic):

Dalian New World Hotel Co., Ltd.   **(3)**
Hong Kong Corporate Office 36/F New World Tower 1, 18 Queen's Road, Central, China (Hong Kong)   **(100%)**
Tel.: (852) 21382222
Web Site: http://www.rosewoodhotelgroup.com
Sales Range: $10-24.9 Million
Emp.: 60
Hotels & Motels
N.A.I.C.S.: 721110

New World China Land Investments Company Limited   **(3)**
9th Floor New World Twr I, 18 Queens Rd, Central, China (Hong Kong)   **(100%)**
Tel.: (852) 21382222
Web Site: http://www.newworldhospality.com
Sales Range: $25-49.9 Million
Emp.: 30
Real Estate Property Lessors
N.A.I.C.S.: 531190

Subsidiary (Domestic):

New World Department Store China Limited   **(2)**
7th Floor 88 Hing Fat Street, Causeway Bay, China (Hong Kong)   **(83.9%)**
Tel.: (852) 27533988
Web Site: http://www.nwds.com.hk
Rev.: $249,519,162
Assets: $1,613,978,590
Liabilities: $1,097,638,631
Net Worth: $516,339,959
Earnings: ($62,346,481)
Emp.: 2,412
Fiscal Year-end: 06/30/2022
Department Stores
N.A.I.C.S.: 455110
Henry Kar-Shun Cheng *(Chm)*

New World Hotels (Holdings) Limited   **(2)**
36/F New World Tower 1, 18 Queen's Road, Central, China (Hong Kong)   **(64%)**
Tel.: (852) 2138 2222
Web Site: http://www.newworldhotels.com
Sales Range: $25-49.9 Million
Emp.: 50
Holding Company; Hotel Owner & Operator
N.A.I.C.S.: 551112
Henry Kar-Shun Cheng *(Mng Dir)*

Subsidiary (Domestic):

New World Hotel Management Limited   **(3)**
36/F New World Tower 1, 18 Queen's Road, Central, China (Hong Kong)   **(70%)**
Tel.: (852) 2138 2222

Web Site:
http://www.newworldhospality.com
Emp.: 50
Hotel Developer & Operator
N.A.I.C.S.: 721110
Symon Bridle *(COO)*

Subsidiary (US):

Rosewood Hotels & Resorts LLC   **(3)**
500 Crescent Ct Ste 300, Dallas, TX 75201
Tel.: (214) 880-4200
Web Site: http://www.rosewoodhotels.com
Sales Range: $10-24.9 Million
Emp.: 55
Hotel Owner & Operator
N.A.I.C.S.: 721110
Susan Aldridge *(Gen Counsel & Sr VP-Legal)*

Subsidiary (Non-US):

Al Faisaliah Hotel   **(4)**
King Fahad Rd, PO Box 4148, Olaya, Riyadh, 11491, Saudi Arabia
Tel.: (966) 12732000
Web Site: http://www.alfaisaliahhotel.com
Hotel
N.A.I.C.S.: 721110
Oliver Braun *(Dir-Mktg)*

Subsidiary (Domestic):

Caneel Bay   **(4)**
Route 20 N Shore Rd, Saint John, VI 00831
Tel.: (340) 776-6111
Web Site: http://www.caneelbay.com
Hotel
N.A.I.C.S.: 721110
Nikoley Hotze *(Mng Dir)*

Subsidiary (Non-US):

Hotel Al Khozama   **(4)**
Olaya Rd, PO Box 4148, Riyadh, 11491, Saudi Arabia
Tel.: (966) 1462732000
Web Site: http://www.al-khozama.com
Hotel
N.A.I.C.S.: 721110

Subsidiary (Domestic):

Hotel Crescent Court   **(4)**
400 Crescent Ct, Dallas, TX 75201
Tel.: (214) 871-3200
Web Site: http://www.rosewoodhotels.com
Sales Range: $10-24.9 Million
Hotel
N.A.I.C.S.: 721110
Jennifer Kukulski *(Mgr-Sls)*

Subsidiary (Non-US):

Jumba Bay   **(4)**
PO Box 243, Saint John's, Antigua & Barbuda
Tel.: (268) 4626000
Web Site: http://www.rosewoodhotels.com
Sales Range: $10-24.9 Million
Emp.: 230
Hotel
N.A.I.C.S.: 721110
Andrew Hedley *(Reg VP-Caribbean)*

King Pacific Lodge   **(4)**
4850 Cowley Crescent, Richmond, V7B 1C1, BC, Canada
Tel.: (604) 503-5474
Web Site: http://www.kingpacificlodge.com
Sales Range: $10-24.9 Million
Emp.: 40
Hotel
N.A.I.C.S.: 721110

Subsidiary (Domestic):

Little Dix Bay   **(4)**
Cruz Bay, Saint John, VI 00831-0720
Tel.: (284) 495-5555
Web Site: http://www.littledixbay.com
Hotel
N.A.I.C.S.: 721110
Lily Carr *(Mgr-Sls)*

The Carlyle, A Rosewood Hotel   **(4)**
35 E 76th St, New York, NY 10021
Tel.: (212) 744-1600
Web Site: http://www.rosewoodhotels.com
Hotel
N.A.I.C.S.: 812930

Stephanie Caldwell *(Mgr-HR)*

Subsidiary (Non-US):

The Dharmawangsa   **(4)**
Jalan Brawijawa Raya No 26, Jakarta, 12160, Indonesia
Tel.: (62) 217258181
Web Site: http://www.the-dharmawangsa.com
Hotel
N.A.I.C.S.: 721110

Subsidiary (Domestic):

The Mansion on Turtle Creek   **(4)**
2821 Turtle Creek Blvd, Dallas, TX 75219
Tel.: (214) 559-2100
Hotel
N.A.I.C.S.: 722511
Duncan Grham *(Mng Dir)*

CHOW TAI SENG JEWELLERY COMPANY LIMITED
Floor 19-23 Block A Shuibei No 1 No 3033 Buxin Road Cuizhu Street, Luohu District, Shenzhen, 518020, China
Tel.: (86) 75582288871
Web Site:
http://www.chowtaiseng.com
Year Founded: 2007
002867—(SSE)
Rev.: $1,560,978,432
Assets: $1,068,057,900
Liabilities: $218,793,744
Net Worth: $849,264,156
Earnings: $153,120,240
Fiscal Year-end: 12/31/22
Jewelry Design Services
N.A.I.C.S.: 541490
Zongwen Zhou *(Chm & Pres)*

CHOWGULE & COMPANY PVT. LTD.
Chowgule House Mormugao Harbour, Goa, 403 803, India
Tel.: (91) 832 2525000   In
Web Site: http://www.chowgule.co.in
Year Founded: 1941
Sales Range: $400-449.9 Million
Holding Company; Activities in Mining, Transportation, Export of Iron Ore, Shipbuilding & Material Handling & Construction Equipment
N.A.I.C.S.: 551112
Vijay Vishwasrao Chowgule *(Chm & CEO)*

Subsidiaries:

Chowgule & Company (Salt) Private Limited   **(1)**
Chowgule House Mormugao Harbour, Goa, 403 803, India
Tel.: (91) 832 252 5047
Web Site: http://www.chowgule.co.in
Industrial Salt Production & Export
N.A.I.C.S.: 327999
Nathan Ramesh Chowgule *(Exec Dir)*

Chowgule Brothers Pvt. Ltd   **(1)**
Chowgule House Mormugao Harbour, Goa, 403 803, India
Tel.: (91) 8322525107
Web Site: http://www.chowgulebrothers.com
Sales Range: $1-9.9 Million
Emp.: 98
Shipping, Insurance, Freight Forwarding, Warehousing & Custom Broking
N.A.I.C.S.: 488510
Jaywant Yeshwantrao Chowgule *(Exec Dir)*

Chowgule Construction Technologies Pvt. Ltd.   **(1)**
Bakhtawar 4th Floor, Nariman Point, Mumbai, 400 021, Maharashtra, India
Tel.: (91) 22 6620 2500
Web Site: http://www.chowguletech.com
Chemical Products Distr
N.A.I.C.S.: 424690
Sujit Varghese *(Mgr-Mktg)*

Chowgule Industries Pvt. Ltd.   **(1)**

Chowgule House, Mormugao Harbour, Goa, 403 803, India
Tel.: (91) 832 2525000
Web Site:
http://www.chowguleindustries.com
Trading Services; Motor Vehicle Sales, Marketing of Pipes, Chemicals & Waste Water Systems
N.A.I.C.S.: 423110

Chowgule Koster (India) Construction Chemicals Pvt. Ltd.   **(1)**
Bakhtawar 4th Floor Namiman Point, Mumbai, 400021, Maharashtra, India
Tel.: (91) 22 66202500
Web Site: http://www.chowgulekoster.com
Waterproofing Products Mfr & Distr
N.A.I.C.S.: 325998

Chowgule Mediconsult Private Limited   **(1)**
204 Sukh Sagar N S Patkar Marg Chowpathy, Mumbai, 400007, India
Tel.: (91) 22 4342 2121
Web Site:
http://www.chowgulemediconsult.com
Emp.: 27
Healthcare Software Development Services
N.A.I.C.S.: 541511
Bhavesh Thakker *(VP)*

Chowgule Steamships Limited   **(1)**
503 5th floor Gabmar Apartment, Goa, 403 802, India
Tel.: (91) 8322514100
Web Site:
https://www.chowgulesteamships.co.in
Rev.: $5,603,871
Assets: $15,691,248
Liabilities: $15,691,381
Net Worth: ($132)
Earnings: $477,204
Emp.: 6
Fiscal Year-end: 03/31/2021
Bulk Cargo Shipping Services
N.A.I.C.S.: 483111
Darshan Karekar *(Compliance Officer & Sec)*

Deccan Alloy Metal Industries Pvt. Ltd.   **(1)**
2095 E Ward Vikram Nagar near Tembalai Hill, Kolhapur, 416 005, India
Tel.: (91) 2312655115
Web Site: http://www.chowgule.co.in
Industrial & Medical Oxygen Mgr
N.A.I.C.S.: 325120

Keltech Energies Ltd.   **(1)**
3 Embassy Icon Infantry Road, Crescent Road, Bengaluru, 560 001, India
Tel.: (91) 8022257900
Web Site: http://www.keltechenergies.com
Emp.: 100
Explosives Mfr
N.A.I.C.S.: 325920
Deepak Joshi *(Sr Gen Mgr)*

Kolhapur Oxygen and Acetylene Private Limited   **(1)**
2095 E Ward Vikram Nagar near Tembalai Hill, Kolhapur, 416 005, India
Tel.: (91) 2312655115
Web Site: http://www.chowgule.co.in
Industrial & Medical Oxygen & Nitrogen Mfr
N.A.I.C.S.: 325120

CHRISTCHURCH CITY HOLDINGS LTD.
Level 1 151 Cambridge Terrace, Christchurch, 8013, New Zealand
Tel.: (64) 3 941 8475
Web Site: http://www.cchl.co.nz
Year Founded: 1993
Holding Company
N.A.I.C.S.: 551112
Therese Arseneau *(Chm)*

Subsidiaries:

Christchurch International Airport Ltd   **(1)**
Car Park Building 30 Durey Road, Christchurch, New Zealand
Tel.: (64) 3 358 5029
Web Site:
http://www.christchurchairport.co.nz
Airport Management Services

Christchurch City Holdings Ltd.—(Continued)
N.A.I.C.S.: 488119

City Care Ltd (1)
226 Antigua Street, Christchurch, 8011, New Zealand
Tel.: (64) 3 941 7200
Web Site: http://www.citycare.co.nz
Emp.: 1,500
Construction Services
N.A.I.C.S.: 236220
Onno Mulder (CEO)

Subsidiary (Domestic):

Command Building Services Limited (2)
8/5 Bouverie Street, Petone, Wellington, 5012, New Zealand
Tel.: (64) 45688002
Construction Engineering Services
N.A.I.C.S.: 541330
Anusheel Chandra (Gen Mgr)

Eco Central Ltd (1)
Level 1 9 Baigent Way, Middleton, Christchurch, New Zealand
Tel.: (64) 39417513
Web Site: http://www.ecocentral.co.nz
Waste Recycling Services
N.A.I.C.S.: 562920
Craig Downie (CEO)

Enable Services Ltd (1)
Enable House 2nd Floor 106 Wrights Road, 1143, Christchurch, New Zealand
Tel.: (64) 800 434 273
Web Site: http://www.enable.net.nz
Telecommunication Servicesb
N.A.I.C.S.: 517111
Steve Fuller (CEO)

Subsidiary (Domestic):

Connetics Limited (2)
12 Chapmans Road, Woolston, Christchurch, 8022, New Zealand
Tel.: (64) 33537200
Web Site: http://www.connetics.co.nz
Logistics Consulting Servies
N.A.I.C.S.: 541614
Jono Brent (CEO)

Lyttelton Port Company Limited (1)
Waterfront House 37-39 Gladstone Quay, Lyttelton, Christchurch, 8082, New Zealand
Tel.: (64) 33288198
Web Site: http://www.lpc.co.nz
Rev.: $112,087,138
Assets: $392,641,027
Liabilities: $45,235,017
Net Worth: $347,406,009
Earnings: $28,342,035
Emp.: 525
Fiscal Year-end: 06/30/2019
Port Supply & Marine Cargo Terminal Services
N.A.I.C.S.: 488320
Paul Monk (Gen Mgr-Bulk Cargo & Marine Svcs & Mgr-Ops)

Orion New Zealand Ltd (1)
565 Wairakei Road, PO Box 13896, Christchurch, 8141, New Zealand
Tel.: (64) 33639898
Web Site: http://www.oriongroup.co.nz
Electricity Distribution Services
N.A.I.C.S.: 221122
Vaughan Hartland (CFO)

Red Bus Ltd (1)
120 Ferry Road, PO Box 10 171, Christchurch, New Zealand
Tel.: (64) 33794260
Web Site: http://www.redbus.co.nz
Bus Transportation Services
N.A.I.C.S.: 485113
Nic Aitken (Mgr-Workshop)

CHRISTIAN BERNER TECH TRADE AB
Designvagen 1, SE-435 33, Molnlycke, Sweden
Tel.: (46) 313366900
Web Site:
    https://www.christianberner.com
Year Founded: 1897

CBTT.B—(OMX)
Rev.: $85,120,158
Assets: $62,641,079
Liabilities: $41,136,077
Net Worth: $21,505,002
Earnings: $3,798,641
Emp.: 198
Fiscal Year-end: 12/31/20
Technical Solutions
N.A.I.C.S.: 541990
Joachim Berner (Chm)

Subsidiaries:

A/S Christian Berner (1)
Ostensjoveien 14A, 0661, Oslo, Norway
Tel.: (47) 23348400
Filling Machine Equipment Mfr
N.A.I.C.S.: 333993

AB GF Swedenborg (1)
Method path 2D, 43533, Molnlycke, Sweden
Tel.: (46) 313368780
Web Site: https://swedenborg.se
Industrial Component Mfr
N.A.I.C.S.: 333248

Bullerbekamparen AB (1)
Hantverksvagen 25, 443 61, Stenkullen, Sweden
Tel.: (46) 30223320
Web Site: https://bullerbekamparen.se
Fighter Jet Engine Mfr
N.A.I.C.S.: 336412

Christian Berner AS (1)
Maglebjergvej 5A, 2800, Kongens Lyngby, Denmark
Tel.: (45) 70254242
Filling Machine Equipment Mfr
N.A.I.C.S.: 333993

Christian Berner OY (1)
Jaakonkatu 2, 01620, Vantaa, Finland
Tel.: (358) 92766830
Web Site: https://www.christianberner.fi
Filling Machine Equipment Mfr
N.A.I.C.S.: 333993

Empakk AS (1)
Sivlokka 5, 1664, Rolvsoy, Norway
Tel.: (47) 69326911
Web Site: https://empakk.no
Food Packaging Services
N.A.I.C.S.: 624210

Zander & Ingestrom AB (1)
Matslingan 19A, 187 66, Taby, Sweden
Tel.: (46) 8809000
Web Site: https://www.zeta.se
Filling Machine Equipment Mfr
N.A.I.C.S.: 333993

CHRISTIAN DIOR S.A.
30 Avenue Montaigne, 75008, Paris, France
Tel.: (33) 144132222
Web Site: https://www.dior-finance.com
Year Founded: 1946
CHDRF—(OTCIQ)
Rev.: $73,505,158,400
Assets: $121,737,992,600
Liabilities: $71,627,896,200
Net Worth: $50,110,096,400
Earnings: $5,348,312,200
Emp.: 196,006
Fiscal Year-end: 12/31/22
Mfr & Distr of Apparel, Luggage & Fine Leather Goods, Perfumes & Beauty Products, Champagne, Brandy, Wines, Watches & Jewelry
N.A.I.C.S.: 316990
Delphine Arnault (CEO)

Subsidiaries:

CD INVESTISSEMENTS SARL (1)
Suite 2 Espace de Comboire, Echirolles, 38130, France
Tel.: (33) 4 76 09 72 12
Investment Management Service
N.A.I.C.S.: 523999

CHRISTIAN LOUBOUTIN SAS

19 Rue Jean-Jacques Rousseau, Paris, 75001, France
Tel.: (33) 142360531
Web Site:
    http://www.christianlouboutin.fr
Year Founded: 1992
Sales Range: $10-24.9 Million
Emp.: 15
Shoe Mfr & Retailer
N.A.I.C.S.: 316210
Bruno Chambelland (Pres)

CHRISTIAN MAYR GMBH & CO. KG
Eichenstrasse 1, 87665, Mauerstetten, Germany
Tel.: (49) 8341 804 0
Web Site: http://www.mayr.com
Year Founded: 1987
Sales Range: $125-149.9 Million
Emp.: 800
Industrial Equipment Mfr
N.A.I.C.S.: 333248
Gunther Klingler (CEO)

Subsidiaries:

Mayr Corp. (1)
4 N St Ste 300, Waldwick, NJ 07463
Tel.: (201) 445-7210
Web Site: http://www.mayr.com
Industrial Machinery Mfr
N.A.I.C.S.: 333248
Hans Eberle (Pres)

Mayr France S.A. (1)
Z A L du Minopole Rue Nungesser et Coli, 62160, Bully-les-Mines, France
Tel.: (33) 321729191
Emp.: 50
Industrial Equipment Distr
N.A.I.C.S.: 423840

Mayr Italia S.r.l. (1)
Viale Veneto 3, 35020, Saonara, Italy
Tel.: (39) 0498791020
Industrial Equipment Distr
N.A.I.C.S.: 423840

Mayr Korea Co. Ltd. (1)
SK Technopark 77-1 Room No 1002, Seongsan-gu, Changwon, Korea (South)
Tel.: (82) 552624024
Web Site: http://www.mayrkorea.com
Industrial Equipment Distr
N.A.I.C.S.: 423840

Mayr Kupplungen AG (1)
Tobelackerstrasse 11, 8212, Neuhausen am Rheinfall, Switzerland
Tel.: (41) 526740870
Industrial Equipment Distr
N.A.I.C.S.: 423840

Mayr Polska sp. z o.o. (1)
Rojow ul Hetmanska 1, 63-500, Ostrzeszow, Poland
Tel.: (48) 627322800
Industrial Equipment Distr
N.A.I.C.S.: 423840

Mayr Power Transmission (Zhangjiagang) Co., Ltd. (1)
16 Chang Xing Development Zone Hale No 3, 215600, Zhangjiagang, China
Tel.: (86) 51258917567
Industrial Equipment Distr
N.A.I.C.S.: 423840

Mayr Transmission (S) Pte Ltd. (1)
8 Boon Lay Way 03-06 TradeHub21, Singapore, 609964, Singapore
Tel.: (65) 65601230
Industrial Equipment Distr
N.A.I.C.S.: 423840

Mayr Transmissions Ltd. (1)
Units 10-11 Valley Road Business Park, Keighley, BD21 4L, West Yorkshire, United Kingdom
Tel.: (44) 1535 663900
Web Site: http://www.mayr.co.uk
Industrial Machinery Mfr
N.A.I.C.S.: 333248

CHRISTIAN POTIER S.A.
1819 chemin de Beauchamp,

CS2008 Monteux, 84207, Carpentras, Cedex, France
Tel.: (33) 4 90 60 67 00
Web Site: http://www.christian-potier.fr
Year Founded: 1985
Sales Range: $10-24.9 Million
Sauces & Spreads Mfr
N.A.I.C.S.: 311042

CHRISTIANI & NIELSEN (THAI) PUBLIC COMPANY LIMITED
727 La Salle Road, Bangna-Tai Subdistrict Bangna, Bangkok, 10260, Thailand
Tel.: (66) 23388000
Web Site: https://www.cn-thai.co.th
Year Founded: 1930
CNT—(THA)
Rev.: $211,617,013
Assets: $189,354,427
Liabilities: $140,406,671
Net Worth: $48,947,755
Earnings: $577,089
Emp.: 746
Fiscal Year-end: 12/31/23
Construction Services
N.A.I.C.S.: 236210
Kirit Shah (Bd of Dirs & Vice Chm)

CHRISTIE & SON SALES LTD
24 Forest Hills Parkway, Dartmouth, B2W 6E4, NS, Canada
Tel.: (902) 462-6107
Year Founded: 1976
Rev.: $11,998,403
Emp.: 100
Automotive Parts & Accessories Stores
N.A.I.C.S.: 441330
Archie Christie (Pres)

CHRISTIE GROUP PLC
Whitefriars House 6 Carmelite Street, London, EC4Y 0BS, United Kingdom
Tel.: (44) 2072270707
Web Site:
    https://www.christiegroup.com
CTG—(AIM)
Rev.: $83,857,121
Assets: $37,491,912
Liabilities: $33,290,780
Net Worth: $4,201,131
Earnings: ($4,837,666)
Fiscal Year-end: 12/31/23
Software Sector
N.A.I.C.S.: 334610
David B. Rugg (Chm & CEO)

Subsidiaries:

Christie & Co Austria GmbH (1)
Stallburggasse 2/3a, 1010, Vienna, Austria
Tel.: (43) 189053570
Hotel Real Estate Services
N.A.I.C.S.: 531390

Christie & Co S.A.S. (1)
10 Rue La Fayette, 75009, Paris, France
Tel.: (33) 153967272
Hotels & Restaurant Services
N.A.I.C.S.: 561599

Christie + Co GmbH (1)
Schillerstrasse 12, 60313, Frankfurt, Germany
Tel.: (49) 699074570
Web Site: http://www.christie.com
Sales Range: $25-49.9 Million
Emp.: 4
Business Valuing & Surveying Services
N.A.I.C.S.: 561499

Christie + Co OY (1)
Technopolis Ruoholahti 2 Energiakuja 2, 00180, Helsinki, Finland
Tel.: (358) 941378500
Web Site: http://www.christiecorporate.com
Sales Range: $25-49.9 Million
Emp.: 3
Business Valuers & Surveying Services
N.A.I.C.S.: 561110

Christie + Co SARL (1)
10 rue La Fayette, 75009, Paris, France
Tel.: (33) 153967272
Web Site: http://www.christie.com
Sales Range: $25-49.9 Million
Emp.: 10
Business Valuing & Surveying Services
N.A.I.C.S.: 561110

Christie Group Central Services
Limited (1)
Pinder House 249 Upper Third Street, Milton Keynes, MK9 1DS, United Kingdom
Tel.: (44) 190 892 0550
Professional Business Services
N.A.I.C.S.: 541990

Christie, Owen & Davies Ltd. (1)
Whitefriars House 6 Carmelite Street, London, EC4Y 0BS, United Kingdom
Tel.: (44) 2072270700
Web Site: http://www.christie.com
Sales Range: $50-74.9 Million
Emp.: 80
Professional Brokerage & Advisory Services
N.A.I.C.S.: 524210

Christie, Owen & Davies SL (1)
Paseo de Gracia 11 Esc B 4 3, 08007, Barcelona, Spain
Tel.: (34) 933436161
Web Site: http://www.christie.com
Sales Range: $25-49.9 Million
Emp.: 3
Business Valuers & Surveying Services
N.A.I.C.S.: 561499

Pinders Professional & Consultancy
Services Ltd. (1)
Pinder House 249 Upper Third St, Milton Keynes, MK9 1DS, Buckinghamshire, United Kingdom
Tel.: (44) 1908350500
Web Site: http://www.pinders.co.uk
Emp.: 30
Business Appraising & Surveying Services
N.A.I.C.S.: 531320

RCC Business Mortgage Brokers
Ltd. (1)
39 Victoria St, London, SW1H 0EU, United Kingdom
Tel.: (44) 207 227 0774
Web Site: http://www.christiefinance.com
Sales Range: $50-74.9 Million
Emp.: 5
Business Mortgage Broker Services
N.A.I.C.S.: 522310

RCC Insurance Brokers PLC (1)
2 Minster Court Mincing Lane, London, EC3R 7PD, United Kingdom
Tel.: (44) 3330107189
Web Site: https://www.christieinsurance.com
Sales Range: $50-74.9 Million
Emp.: 20
Commercial Insurance Brokerage Services
N.A.I.C.S.: 524210

Venners Ltd. (1)
3 Essex House Astra Ctr Edinburgh Way, Harlow, CM20 2BN, Essex, United Kingdom
Tel.: (44) 1279620820
Web Site: http://www.venners.com
Sales Range: $25-49.9 Million
Emp.: 200
Stocktake & Auditing Services
N.A.I.C.S.: 561990
Scott Hulme (Mng Dir)

Venners Systems & Services
Corporation (1)
200-1920 Yonge St, Toronto, M4S 3E2, ON, Canada
Tel.: (416) 572-7784
Web Site: http://www.vennersys.com
Sales Range: $25-49.9 Million
Emp.: 4
Software Development & Consulting Services
N.A.I.C.S.: 541511

Vennersys Limited (1)
249 Upper Third St Witan Gate W, Milton Keynes, MK9 1DS, Buckinghamshire, United Kingdom
Tel.: (44) 1908735274
Web Site: https://www.vennersys.co.uk
Sales Range: $25-49.9 Million
Emp.: 10
Leisure & Hospitality Solutions

N.A.I.C.S.: 541611

Vennersys Ltd. (1)
Centre House, Walsall, Aldridge, WS9 8LT, United Kingdom
Tel.: (44) 192 247 2044
Web Site: https://www.vennersys.co.uk
Information Technology Services
N.A.I.C.S.: 541519
Paul Harding (Mng Dir)

CHRISTIE INNOMED, INC.
516, Dufour Street Saint-Eustache, J7R 0C3, QC, Canada
Tel.: (450) 472-9120
Web Site:
  https://www.christieinnomed.com
Year Founded: 1954
Medical Imaging Solutions
N.A.I.C.S.: 621512
Martin Roy (Pres & CEO)

Subsidiaries:

Comp-Ray, Inc. (1)
205 W Deer Valley Rd, Phoenix, AZ 85027
Tel.: (602) 861-2159
Web Site: http://www.compray.com
Sales Range: $1-9.9 Million
Emp.: 41
Medical, Dental & Hospital Equipment & Supplies Whslr
N.A.I.C.S.: 423450
Gary J. Walton (Pres)

CHRISTIE LITES INC.
100 Carson St Unit A, Toronto, M8W 3R9, ON, Canada
Tel.: (416) 644-1010
Web Site: http://www.christielites.com
Year Founded: 1985
Sales Range: $10-24.9 Million
Emp.: 65
Stage Lighting Services
N.A.I.C.S.: 423490
Ken Alexander (VP-Rentals-Vancouver)

CHRISTINA LAKE CANNABIS CORP.
1890 1075 West Georgia Street, Vancouver, V6E 3C9, BC, Canada
Tel.: (604) 687-2038
Web Site:
  https://www.christinalakecorp.com
CLCFF—(OTCQB)
Rev.: $7,879,949
Assets: $14,702,497
Liabilities: $5,989,494
Net Worth: $8,713,003
Earnings: ($1,586,246)
Emp.: 15
Fiscal Year-end: 11/30/22
Cannabis Product Distr
N.A.I.C.S.: 424210
Ryan Smith (CFO)

CHRISTINE INTERNATIONAL HOLDINGS LIMITED
No 33 Jinshajiang Road, Putuo District, Shanghai, China
Tel.: (86) 2162866666   Ky
Web Site:
  http://www.christine.com.cn
Year Founded: 2008
1210—(HKG)
Rev.: $44,742,529
Assets: $68,700,743
Liabilities: $100,267,672
Net Worth: ($31,566,929)
Earnings: ($26,064,851)
Emp.: 2,018
Fiscal Year-end: 12/31/21
Bakery Product Mfr & Whslr
N.A.I.C.S.: 311813
Liao Weilun (VP-Fin & Acctg)

Subsidiaries:

Hangzhou Danbi Food Co., Ltd. (1)

Jianhua Village Pengbu Town Jianggan, Hangzhou, 310021, Zhejiang, China
Tel.: (86) 571 85107777
Bakery Products Mfr
N.A.I.C.S.: 424490

Shanghai Christine Foodstuff Co., Ltd. (1)
No 17 Chang'An S Rd, Zhangjiagang, 215600, Jiangsu, China
Tel.: (86) 51258978371
Bakery Products Mfr
N.A.I.C.S.: 424490

CHRISTOF HOLDING AG
Glacisstrasse 37, 8051, Graz, Austria
Tel.: (43) 506610
Web Site: http://www.christof-group.at
Year Founded: 1966
Sales Range: $400-449.9 Million
Emp.: 2,700
Holding Company
N.A.I.C.S.: 551112
Stefan Christof (Chm-Mgmt Bd & CEO)

Subsidiaries:

Ferrostaal Christof Romania SRL (1)
Strada Trandafirilor 49 A, 107084, Brazii, Romania
Tel.: (40) 344 401027
Plant Design & Construction Services
N.A.I.C.S.: 541420

Greentech Energiesysteme
GmbH (1)
Plabutscherstrasse 115, 8051, Graz, Austria
Tel.: (43) 316 685500 3730
Web Site: http://www.greentech.co.at
Biomass Heating System Mfr
N.A.I.C.S.: 333414

J. Christof E & P Services S.R.L. (1)
Strada Trandafirilor 49 A, 107084, Brazii, Romania
Tel.: (40) 344 401027
Oil & Gas Equipment Maintenance & Support Services
N.A.I.C.S.: 811310

J. Christof Gesellschaft m.b.H. (1)
Plabutscherstrasse 115, 8051, Graz, Austria
Tel.: (43) 316 685500 0
Web Site: http://www.christof-group.com
Plant Design & Construction Services
N.A.I.C.S.: 541420

J. Christof Romania S.R.L. (1)
Strada Trandafirilor 49 A, 107084, Brazii, Romania
Tel.: (40) 344 401027
Management Services
N.A.I.C.S.: 541618
Markus Gran (Mng Dir)

JCR-Christof Consulting S.R.L. (1)
Strada Trandafirilor 49 A, 107084, Brazii, Romania
Tel.: (40) 344 401027
Plant Design & Construction Services
N.A.I.C.S.: 541420

PMS Elektro- und Automationstechnik
GmbH (1)
PMS - Strasse 1, 9431, Sankt Stefan im Lavanttal, Austria
Tel.: (43) 507670
Web Site: http://www.pms.at
Engineeering Services
N.A.I.C.S.: 541330

PMSR Electro si Automatizare
S.R.L. (1)
Strada Trandafirilor 49 A/1, 107084, Brazii, Romania
Tel.: (40) 344 802048 0
Electrical Instrumentation & Control Mfr
N.A.I.C.S.: 335314

Quality-Safety-Engineering
GmbH (1)
Plabutscherstrasse 115, 8051, Graz, Austria
Tel.: (43) 316 686300 0
Web Site: http://www.qse.co.at
Quality, Safety & Environmental Consulting Services

N.A.I.C.S.: 541690
Manfred Strecker (Mng Dir)

RIA Rohr- und Industrieanlagenbau
GmbH (1)
Glacisstrasse 37, 8010, Graz, Austria
Tel.: (43) 316 327643
Technical Staffing Services
N.A.I.C.S.: 561311

Renewable Energy Products
GmbH (1)
Concept Strasse 1, 8101, Gratkorn, Austria
Tel.: (43) 316 685500 3471
Wood Gas Power Station Engineering Services
N.A.I.C.S.: 541420

SC Dinafit SRL (1)
Strada Trandafirilor 49 A, 107084, Brazil, Romania
Tel.: (40) 344 401027
Rotating Equipment Repair & Maintenance Services
N.A.I.C.S.: 811310
Wolfgang Koch (Mng Dir)

Schoeller-Bleckmann Nitec
GmbH (1)
Hauptstrasse 2, Ternitz, 2630, Austria (100%)
Tel.: (43) 26303190
Web Site: http://www.christof-group.com
Sales Range: $25-49.9 Million
Emp.: 140
High-Pressure Equipment Mfr
N.A.I.C.S.: 332420
Othmar Posch (CEO)

ace Apparatebau construction & engineering GmbH (1)
Hans Thalhammer Strasse 18, 8501, Lieboch, Austria
Tel.: (43) 3136 63600 0
Web Site: http://www.christof-group.com
Emp.: 100
Industrial Equipment Mfr
N.A.I.C.S.: 333248
Markus Fuchsbichler (Mng Dir)

apb Apparatebau Schweisstechnik
GmbH (1)
Gustav-Kramer-Strasse 5b, 8605, Kapfenberg, Austria
Tel.: (43) 3862 25025
Industrial Equipment Mfr
N.A.I.C.S.: 333248

CHROMA ATE INC.
88 Wenmao Road Guishan, Taoyuan, 33383, Taiwan
Tel.: (886) 33279999
Web Site:
  https://www.chromaate.com
2360—(TAI)
Rev.: $610,747,320
Assets: $1,094,919,609
Liabilities: $358,568,383
Net Worth: $736,351,226
Earnings: $133,937,468
Emp.: 3,442
Fiscal Year-end: 12/31/23
Test & Measurement Instruments Mfr
N.A.I.C.S.: 334515
Leo Huang (Chm & CEO)

Subsidiaries:

Chroma ATE (Suzhou) Co., Ltd. (1)
Building 7 ShiShan Industrial Gallery No 855 Zhu Jiang Road, New District, Suzhou, Jiangsu, China
Tel.: (86) 51268245425
Measurement Equipment Distr
N.A.I.C.S.: 423830

Chroma ATE Europe B.V. (1)
Morsestraat 32, 6716 AH, Ede, Netherlands
Tel.: (31) 318648282
Sales Range: $50-74.9 Million
Emp.: 11
Measuring & Testing Equipments Distr
N.A.I.C.S.: 423830

Subsidiary (Non-US):

Chroma Germany GmbH (2)
Sudtiroler Str 9, 86165, Augsburg, Germany

Chroma ATE Inc.—(Continued)

Tel.: (49) 8217909670
Electronic Test & Measurement Equipment Distr
N.A.I.C.S.: 423830

Chroma ATE Inc. (1)
7 Chrysler, Irvine, CA 92618
Tel.: (949) 421-0355
Web Site: https://www.chromaus.com
Sales Range: $25-49.9 Million
Emp.: 15
Automatic Testing Equipments Distr
N.A.I.C.S.: 423830

Subsidiary (Domestic):

Chroma Systems Solutions, Inc. (2)
19772 Pauling, Foothill Ranch, CA 92610
Tel.: (949) 600-6400
Web Site: https://www.chromausa.com
Sales Range: $25-49.9 Million
Emp.: 50
Power Supplies Distr
N.A.I.C.S.: 423610

Chroma ATE Inc. - Lin-Kou Factory (1)
66 Huaya 1st Road Guishan, Kuei-ShanHsiang, Taoyuan, 33383, Taiwan
Tel.: (886) 33279999
Sales Range: $450-499.9 Million
Emp.: 2,000
Measuring & Testing Equipments Mfr
N.A.I.C.S.: 334513
Leo Huang (Gen Mgr)

Chroma Electronics (Shanghai) Co., Ltd. (1)
3F Building 40 No 333 Qin Jiang Road, Shanghai, 200233, Guangdong, China
Tel.: (86) 2164959900
Web Site: http://www.chroma.com.cn
Sales Range: $25-49.9 Million
Emp.: 50
Measuring & Testing Equipments Distr
N.A.I.C.S.: 423830
Emma Chan (Mng Dir)

Chroma Electronics (Shenzhen) Co., Ltd. (1)
8F No 4 Nanyou Tian An Industrial Estate, Shenzhen, 518052, Guangdong, China
Tel.: (86) 75526644598
Web Site: https://www.chroma.com.cn
Sales Range: $50-74.9 Million
Emp.: 100
Measuring & Testing Equipments Distr
N.A.I.C.S.: 423830

Chroma Japan Corp. (1)
888 Nippa-cho, Kouhoku-ku, Yokohama, 223-0057, Kanagawa, Japan
Tel.: (81) 455421118
Web Site: https://www.chromaate.com
Emp.: 59
Measuring & Testing Equipments Distr
N.A.I.C.S.: 423830

Chroma New Material Corporation (1)
4F No 68 Huaya 1st Road, Guishan, Taoyuan, 33383, Taiwan
Tel.: (886) 33279998
Web Site: http://www.chromanmc.com.tw
Sales Range: $550-599.9 Million
Emp.: 2,000
Wiring Supplies Distr
N.A.I.C.S.: 423610

Chroma Systems Solutions, Inc. (1)
2757 Galleon Crescent, Mississauga, L5M5T9, ON, Canada
Tel.: (905) 821-1094
Measuring & Testing Equipments Distr
N.A.I.C.S.: 423830

EVT Technology Co., Ltd. (1)
No 88 Wenmao Rd, Guishan Dist, Taoyuan, 333001, Taiwan
Tel.: (886) 33970022
Web Site: https://www.evt.com.tw
Motor Controller & Electric Drive System Mfr
N.A.I.C.S.: 335314

Environmental Stress Systems, Inc. (1)

20071 Soulsbyville Rd, Soulsbyville, CA 95372
Tel.: (209) 588-1993
Web Site: http://www.essproducts.com
Microwave Components Supplier
N.A.I.C.S.: 423610

Innovative Nanotech Incorporated (1)
5F No 6-2 Duxing Road, East District, Hsin-chu, 30078, Taiwan
Tel.: (886) 35632880
Web Site: https://www.i-nanotech.com
Semiconductor Mfr
N.A.I.C.S.: 334413
Leo Huang (Chm)

Mas Automation Corp. (1)
No 6 Lane 17 Niupu Street Road, Hsinchu, 30091, Taiwan
Tel.: (886) 35386189
Web Site: https://www.mas-automation.com
Automation Equipment Mfr
N.A.I.C.S.: 333998

Neworld Electronics Ltd. (1)
Unit 6 6F Shui Hing Centre No13 Sheung Yuet Road, Kowloon Bay, Kowloon, China (Hong Kong)
Tel.: (852) 23319350
Sales Range: $50-74.9 Million
Emp.: 6
Measuring & Testing Equipments Distr
N.A.I.C.S.: 423830

Quantel Private Ltd. (1)
25 Kallang Avenue 05-02, Singapore, 339416, Singapore
Tel.: (65) 67453200
Web Site: https://quantel-global.com
Measurement Equipment Distr
N.A.I.C.S.: 423830

Sajet System Technology (Suzhou) Co., Ltd. (1)
503-1 4th Floor Genway, Lohas Town 88 Building 999 Xinghu Road SiP, Suzhou, China
Tel.: (86) 51268071889
Precision Tool Mfr & Distr
N.A.I.C.S.: 332613

Testar Electronic Corporation (1)
68 Hwa-Ya 1st Road, Hwa-Ya Technology Park, Taoyuan, 333, Hsien, Taiwan
Tel.: (886) 33279600
Web Site: https://www.testar.com.tw
Emp.: 127
Electronic Testing Equipment Mfr
N.A.I.C.S.: 334515

Testar Electronics Corporation (1)
68 Hwa-Ya 1st Road, Hwa-Ya Technology Park Taoyuan, Hsien, 333, Taiwan
Tel.: (886) 33279600
Web Site: https://www.testar.com.tw
Testing Instrument Distr
N.A.I.C.S.: 423450

Touch Cloud Inc. (1)
7F -2 No 142 Section 4 Zhongxiao East Road, Da'an District, Taipei, 106, Taiwan
Tel.: (886) 227788611
Web Site: https://www.touchcloud.com.tw
Software Development Services
N.A.I.C.S.: 541511

Wei Kuang Automatic Equipment (Xiamen) Co., Ltd. (1)
Unit 101 and 102 No 20 Jinhui Road, Houxi Jimei District, Xiamen, 361024, China
Tel.: (86) 5923755410
Automation Equipment Mfr
N.A.I.C.S.: 333998

Weikuang Mech. Eng. (NANJING) Co., Ltd. (1)
811 Hushan Road, Jiangning District, Nanjing, 211100, Jiangsu, China
Tel.: (86) 255 217 8501
Web Site: http://www.chromaate.com
Measuring & Testing Equipments Distr
N.A.I.C.S.: 423830

CHROMATIC INDIA LIMITED
207 Vardhaman Complex Premises co-op Soc Ltd LBS Marg, Vikhroli W, Mumbai, 400083, India
Tel.: (91) 22 61369800

Web Site: http://www.chromatic.in
Rev.: $1,165,074
Assets: $62,685,211
Liabilities: $13,531,132
Net Worth: $49,154,079
Earnings: ($60,088)
Emp.: 39
Fiscal Year-end: 03/31/19
Specialty Chemicals Mfr
N.A.I.C.S.: 325998

CHROMETCO LIMITED
Unit 25 Sunninghill Office Park 4 Peltier Drive, Sunninghill, Johannesburg, 2054, Gauteng, South Africa
Tel.: (27) 112398800 ZA
Web Site:
https://www.chrometco.co.za
Year Founded: 2003
CMO—(JSE)
Rev.: $75,136,989
Assets: $84,570,919
Liabilities: $74,798,477
Net Worth: $9,772,442
Earnings: ($13,343,772)
Fiscal Year-end: 02/28/21
Mineral Exploration Services
N.A.I.C.S.: 212290
Marcel Naude (CFO)

CHROMOGENEX TECHNOLO-GIES LTD.
Unit 1-2 Heol Rhosyn Dafen Ind Est, Llanelli, SA14 8QG, Carmarthenshire, United Kingdom
Tel.: (44) 1554 755444
Web Site:
http://www.chromogenex.com
Year Founded: 1985
Sales Range: $10-24.9 Million
Emp.: 36
Medical Equipment Mfr
N.A.I.C.S.: 339112
Peter McGuinness (CEO)

CHROMOGENICS AB
Ullforsgatan 15, 75228, Uppsala, Sweden
Tel.: (46) 184300430
Web Site:
https://www.chromogenics.com
Year Founded: 2003
CHRO—(OMX)
Rev.: $1,710,266
Assets: $15,126,397
Liabilities: $8,524,169
Net Worth: $6,602,227
Earnings: ($5,336,855)
Emp.: 31
Fiscal Year-end: 12/31/22
Glass Material Mfr
N.A.I.C.S.: 327215
Jerker Lundgren (CEO)

CHRYSALIS INVESTMENTS LIMITED
1 Royal Plaza Royal Avenue, Saint Peter Port, GY1 2HL, Guernsey, United Kingdom UK
Web Site:
https://www.chrysalisinvestment.uk
Year Founded: 2018
CHRY—(LSE)
Rev.: $1,438,574
Assets: $1,022,345,007
Liabilities: $2,168,046
Net Worth: $1,020,176,961
Earnings: ($99,596,436)
Fiscal Year-end: 09/30/23
Investment Management Service
N.A.I.C.S.: 523999
Andrew Haining (Chm)

CHRYSCAPITAL INVESTMENT ADVISORS (INDIA) PRIVATE LIMITED

Suite 101 The Oberoi Dr Zakir Hussain Marg, New Delhi, 110003, India
Tel.: (91) 1141291000 In
Web Site:
http://www.chryscapital.com
Rev.: $2,500,000,000
Emp.: 20
Privater Equity Firm
N.A.I.C.S.: 523000

Subsidiaries:

Infogain Corporation (1)
485 Alberto Way Ste 100, Los Gatos, CA 95032
Tel.: (408) 355-6000
Web Site: http://www.infogain.com
Emp.: 4,000
Computer Related Consulting Services
N.A.I.C.S.: 541512
Kapil K. Nanda (Founder & Chm)

Subsidiary (Domestic):

Revel Consulting Inc. (2)
4020 Lake Washington Blvd NE Ste 210, Kirkland, WA 98033
Tel.: (206) 407-3173
Web Site: http://www.revelconsulting.com
Business Services & Consulting
N.A.I.C.S.: 541611
Brett Alston (Mng Partner)

Subsidiary (Domestic):

Two Shea Consulting, Inc. (3)
1009 Oak Hill Rd Ste 202, Lafayette, CA 94549
Tel.: (925) 962-7432
Web Site: http://www.twoshea.com
Sales Range: $1-9.9 Million
Emp.: 15
Computer System Design Services
N.A.I.C.S.: 541512
Maureen Shea (Pres & CEO)

CHRYSCAPITAL MANAGE-MENT CO.
IFS Court TwentyEight, Cybercity, Ebene, 72201, Mauritius
Tel.: (230) 4673000
Web Site:
http://www.chryscapital.com
Investment Firm
N.A.I.C.S.: 523999
Sudip Nandy (Mng Dir)

Subsidiaries:

GeBBS Healthcare Solutions Inc. (1)
600 Corporate Pointe Ste 1250, Culver City, CA 90230
Tel.: (201) 227-0088
Web Site: http://www.gebbs.com
Medical Coding & Collections for Medical Practices
N.A.I.C.S.: 561440
Vijay Singh (Chm)

Subsidiary (Domestic):

Aviacode Incorporated (2)
515 E 100 S Ste 700, Salt Lake City, UT 84102
Tel.: (801) 858-8100
Web Site: http://www.aviacode.com
Health Care Srvices
N.A.I.C.S.: 621999
David Jensen (Founder & Chm)

Medical Record Associates Inc (2)
3 Boulevard St, Milton, MA 02186
Tel.: (617) 698-4411
Web Site: http://www.mrahis.com
Rev.: $5,000,000
Emp.: 45
Administrative Management & General Management Consulting Service
N.A.I.C.S.: 541611
Terry Conway (VP-Ops)

Xoriant Corporation (1)
1248 Reamwood Ave, Sunnyvale, CA 94089
Tel.: (408) 743-4400
Web Site: http://www.xoriant.com
Sales Range: $25-49.9 Million
Emp.: 800

Information Technology & Computer Related Services
N.A.I.C.S.: 541512
Girish Gaitonde *(Founder & CEO)*

Subsidiary (Non-US):

Xoriant Canada **(2)**
440 Laurier Ave W Ste 200, Ottawa, K1R 7X6, ON, Canada
Tel.: (613) 788-2782
Web Site: http://www.xoriant.com
Information Technology Services
N.A.I.C.S.: 541511

Xoriant India **(2)**
4th Fl Winchester High St, Powai, Mumbai, 400 076, India
Tel.: (91) 2230511000
Web Site: http://www.xoriant.com
Sales Range: $25-49.9 Million
Emp.: 300
Information Technology Services
N.A.I.C.S.: 541511
Arun Tendulkar *(COO)*

CHRYSOS CORPORATION LIMITED
Tel.: (61) 870927979 **AU**
Web Site: https://www.chrysos.com.au
Year Founded: 2016
C79—(ASX)
Rev.: $18,522,527
Assets: $106,546,261
Liabilities: $25,548,021
Net Worth: $80,998,240
Earnings: $288,844
Emp.: 200
Fiscal Year-end: 06/30/23
Software Development Services
N.A.I.C.S.: 541511
Brett Anthony Coventry *(CFO)*

CHS CONTAINER HANDEL GMBH
Tillmannstrasse 19, 28239, Bremen, Germany
Tel.: (49) 421643960
Web Site: http://www.chs-container.de
Year Founded: 1986
Sales Range: $10-24.9 Million
Emp.: 58
Containers Rental & Leasing Services
N.A.I.C.S.: 532490
Carsten Leopold *(Mng Dir)*

Subsidiaries:

CHS CONTAINER SERVIS LTD STI **(1)**
Kemankes mah Mumhane cad Nuribey is han1 No 17 K 4, Karakoy, 34425, Istanbul, Turkiye
Tel.: (90) 2122920705
Web Site: http://www.chs-container.com.tr
Container Distr
N.A.I.C.S.: 423840
Ayca Turkantos *(Gen Mgr)*

CHS Container Bulgaria Ltd. **(1)**
32 Tzar Simeon I Str, 9000, Varna, Bulgaria
Tel.: (359) 52609075
Web Site: http://www.chs-container.bg
Container Distr
N.A.I.C.S.: 423840

CHS Container Handel B.V. **(1)**
Van Maasdijkweg 55, 3088 ED, Rotterdam, Netherlands
Tel.: (31) 108209783
Container Distr
N.A.I.C.S.: 423840
George Krebbers *(Mgr-Sls)*

CHS SUDCON GmbH **(1)**
Posthalterring 5, 85599, Vaterstetten, Germany
Tel.: (49) 8921752500
Web Site: http://www.chs-suedcon.de
Container Distr
N.A.I.C.S.: 423840

CHS-Container A/S **(1)**
Nordlandsvej 88A, 8240, Risskov, Denmark
Tel.: (45) 86761700
Web Site: http://www.chs-container.dk
Container Distr
N.A.I.C.S.: 423840

CHTC HELON CO., LTD.
Building 1 No 13 Deshengmenwai Street, Xicheng District, Beijing, 100088, China
Tel.: (86) 5367530007
Web Site: http://www.helon.cn
Year Founded: 1988
000677—(SSE)
Rev.: $139,130,784
Assets: $163,926,828
Liabilities: $31,035,420
Net Worth: $132,891,408
Earnings: $6,958,224
Fiscal Year-end: 12/31/22
Textile Product Mfr & Distr
N.A.I.C.S.: 325220
Changbin Ji *(Chm)*

CHU KAI PUBLIC COMPANY LIMITED
44/88 Moo 1 Srisachorakheyai Bangna-Trad Road K 22, Bangsaothong, Samut Prakan, 10570, Thailand
Tel.: (66) 27150000 **TH**
Web Site: https://www.chukai.co.th
Year Founded: 1990
CRANE—(THA)
Rev.: $16,874,418
Assets: $54,410,621
Liabilities: $30,172,820
Net Worth: $24,237,801
Earnings: $2,734,704
Fiscal Year-end: 12/31/23
Repair & Maintenance Services
N.A.I.C.S.: 811198
Junjira Pairrungsri *(Member-Exec Bd & Exec VP)*

Subsidiaries:

The Crane Laem Chabang Co., Ltd. **(1)**
195/95 Moo 5 Nhongkham, Si Racha, 20230, Chonburi, Thailand
Tel.: (66) 38 481 888
Crane Rental Services
N.A.I.C.S.: 532490

The Crane Rayong Co., Ltd. **(1)**
4/2 Village No 4, Nikom Pattana, 21180, Rayong, Thailand
Tel.: (66) 386061745
Web Site: http://www.chukai.co.th
Crane Rental Services
N.A.I.C.S.: 532490

The Crane Service Co., Ltd. **(1)**
42/51 Moo 14 Bangna-Trad Rd Km 7, Bangkaew, Bang Phli, 10540, Samutprakarn, Thailand
Tel.: (66) 2 720 9933
Web Site: http://www.chukai.co.th
Crane Rental Services
N.A.I.C.S.: 532490

CHU KONG PETROLEUM AND NATURAL GAS STEEL PIPE HOLDINGS LIMITED
2/F 3-5 Golden Dragon City Yayun Avenue, Panyu District, 511450, Guangzhou, Guangdong, China
Tel.: (86) 2084558888 **Ky**
Web Site: http://pck.todayir.com
1938—(HKG)
Rev.: $331,626,906
Assets: $920,313,155
Liabilities: $789,609,319
Net Worth: $130,703,836
Earnings: $22,889,974
Emp.: 824
Fiscal Year-end: 12/31/22
Steel Pole Mfr
N.A.I.C.S.: 331210

Chang Chen *(Founder, Chm & CEO)*

Subsidiaries:

Crown Central Holdings Limited **(1)**
Suite 1-2 19 15/ F Tower 3 China Hong Kong City 33 Canton Road, Tsim Sha Tsui, Kowloon, China (Hong Kong)
Tel.: (852) 26261833
Steel Pipe Distr
N.A.I.C.S.: 423510

Ningbo Sanhe Steel Pipe Co., Ltd. **(1)**
Wulipai Jiaochuan Streets, Zhenhai District, Ningbo, 315200, Zhejiang, China
Tel.: (86) 57486300333
Welded Steel Pipe Mfr & Distr
N.A.I.C.S.: 331210

PT. Chu Kong Steel Indonesia **(1)**
6th Floor Tower 1 MD Place Jl Setiabudi Selatan No 7, Jakarta, 12910, Indonesia
Tel.: (62) 2129029888
Rolled Coil Mfr & Distr
N.A.I.C.S.: 331210

Panyu Chu Kong Steel Pipe (Lianyungang) Co., Ltd. **(1)**
No 396 Jiangsu Road, Xuwei District, Lianyungang, 222006, Jiangsu, China
Tel.: (86) 51880687776
Welded Pipe Mfr & Distr
N.A.I.C.S.: 331210

Panyu Chu Kong Steel Pipe (Zhuhai) Co., Ltd. **(1)**
Furnishment Manufacture Area Gaolanport Economic Zone, Zhuhai, 519050, Guangdong, China
Tel.: (86) 7566250888
Welded Pipe Mfr & Distr
N.A.I.C.S.: 331210

Sino Richfield Pte. Ltd. **(1)**
13-02 Goldhill Plaza No 51 Newton Road, Singapore, 308900, Singapore
Tel.: (65) 68049106
Web Site: http://www.pck.com.cn
Emp.: 4
Steel Product Distr
N.A.I.C.S.: 423510

CHU KONG SHIPPING ENTERPRISES (HOLDING) CO. LTD.
Chu Kong Shipping Tower, 143 Connaught Road Central, Hong Kong, China (Hong Kong)
Tel.: (852) 25471528
Web Site: http://www.cks.com.hk
Holding Company
N.A.I.C.S.: 551112
Weiqing Liu *(Chm)*

Subsidiaries:

Chu Kong Shipping Enterprises (Group) Company Limited **(1)**
24th Floor Chu Kong Shipping Tower 143 Connaught Road, Central, China (Hong Kong) **(71%)**
Tel.: (852) 25479947
Web Site: https://www.cksd.com
Rev.: $369,691,988
Assets: $582,646,950
Liabilities: $136,995,308
Net Worth: $445,651,643
Earnings: $13,773,188
Emp.: 2,231
Fiscal Year-end: 12/31/2022
Cargo Shipping & Port Operation Services
N.A.I.C.S.: 488320
Jie Chen *(Deputy Gen Mgr)*

CHUAN HOLDINGS LIMITED
20 Senoko Drive, Singapore, 758207, Singapore
Tel.: (65) 63834925 **Ky**
Web Site: https://chuanholdingsltd.com
Year Founded: 1996
1420—(HKG)
Rev.: $91,518,594
Assets: $92,164,659
Liabilities: $22,416,875
Net Worth: $69,747,785

Earnings: $2,457,775
Emp.: 574
Fiscal Year-end: 12/31/23
General Construction Services
N.A.I.C.S.: 236220
Alan Kui Teng Lim *(Founder, Chm & Mng Dir)*

CHUAN HUAT RESOURCES BERHAD
Wisma Lim Kim Chuan Lot 50A Jalan 1/89B 3 1/2 Miles, off Jalan Sungei Besi, 57100, Kuala Lumpur, Malaysia
Tel.: (60) 379833333
Web Site: https://chuanhuat.com.my
7016—(KLS)
Rev.: $150,725,673
Assets: $155,595,155
Liabilities: $73,394,879
Net Worth: $82,200,275
Earnings: $1,690,811
Emp.: 512
Fiscal Year-end: 06/30/22
Computer Diskettes Mfr
N.A.I.C.S.: 334610
Mark Loong Heng Lim *(Deputy Mng Dir)*

Subsidiaries:

Keyline Consulting Sdn. Bhd. **(1)**
Ground Floor Wisma Pineapple Lot 135 Jalan 1/89B 3 1/2 Mile Off Jalan, Sungai Besi, 57100, Kuala Lumpur, Malaysia
Tel.: (60) 379878266
Web Site: https://www.keyline.com.my
Security Door Hardware Consultation Mfr
N.A.I.C.S.: 332510

Subsidiary (Domestic):

CH Sweestdoor Door Sdn. Bhd. **(2)**
No 6 Jalan 3 Hi-Tech 5 Industrial Park, 43500, Semenyih, Selangor, Malaysia
Tel.: (60) 379878266
Web Site: http://www.sweesdor.com
Security Door Hardware Consultation Mfr
N.A.I.C.S.: 332510

CHUAN HUP HOLDINGS LIMITED
8 Eu Tong Sen Street 24-90 The Central, Singapore, 059818, Singapore
Tel.: (65) 65599700
Web Site: https://www.chuanhup.com.sg
C33—(SES)
Rev.: $4,914,000
Assets: $244,551,000
Liabilities: $10,909,000
Net Worth: $233,642,000
Earnings: $5,787,000
Emp.: 14
Fiscal Year-end: 06/30/23
Marine Transportation Services
N.A.I.C.S.: 483111
Valerie May Wei Tan *(Sec & Head-Legal & Corp Secretarial)*

Subsidiaries:

Beauford Marine Pte Ltd **(1)**
390 Jalan Ahmad Ibrahim, Singapore, 629155, Singapore
Tel.: (65) 6559 9700
Web Site: http://www.Chuanhup.com.sg
Sales Range: $25-49.9 Million
Emp.: 20
Cruise Line Services
N.A.I.C.S.: 483114
William Chan *(Mgr-Ops)*

Cresta Investment Pte Ltd **(1)**
390 Jalan Ahmad Ibrahim, Jurong, Singapore
Tel.: (65) 68611711
Investment Management Service
N.A.I.C.S.: 523940

CHUAN SENG LEONG PTE. LTD.

Chuan Seng Leong Pte. Ltd.—(Continued)

21 Benoi Sector 03-03 Mapletree Benoi Logistics Hub, Singapore, 629853, Singapore
Tel.: (65) 65651225   SG
Web Site: http://www.csl.com.sg
Year Founded: 1976
Sales Range: $10-24.9 Million
Emp.: 45
Household & Personal Care Product Distr
N.A.I.C.S.: 424490
Amos Chong How Lee (Gen Mgr)

CHUANG'S CHINA INVESTMENTS LIMITED

25F Alexandra House 18 Chater Road Central, Central, China (Hong Kong)
Tel.: (852) 25222013   BM
Web Site: https://www.chuangs-china.com
CUG—(DEU)
Rev.: $229,539,773
Assets: $942,239,529
Liabilities: $356,241,599
Net Worth: $585,997,930
Earnings: $53,578,163
Emp.: 143
Fiscal Year-end: 03/31/21
Real Estate Development Services
N.A.I.C.S.: 531390
Albert Ka Pun Chuang (Chm)

Subsidiaries:

Chuang's Properties (Central Plaza) Sdn. Bhd.   (1)
CP01 Suite 16 05 16th Floor Wisma Chuang 34 Jalan Sultan Ismail, 50250, Kuala Lumpur, Malaysia
Tel.: (60) 321481555
Web Site: https://www.wismachuang.com
Security Services
N.A.I.C.S.: 561612

CHUANG'S CONSORTIUM INTERNATIONAL LIMITED

25/F Alexandra House 18 Chater Road, Central, China (Hong Kong)
Tel.: (852) 25222013   BM
Web Site: https://www.chuangs-consortium.com
0367—(HKG)
Rev.: $271,732,355
Assets: $2,775,265,498
Liabilities: $1,089,122,211
Net Worth: $1,686,143,287
Earnings: $25,745,827
Emp.: 342
Fiscal Year-end: 03/31/21
Investment Management Service
N.A.I.C.S.: 523940
Albert Ka Pun Chuang (Chm & Mng Dir)

Subsidiaries:

Sav Hospitality Limited   (1)
83 Wuhu Street, Hunghom, Kowloon, China (Hong Kong)
Tel.: (852) 2275 8888
Web Site: http://www.savhospitality.com
Hotel Operator
N.A.I.C.S.: 721110
Edwin Chuang (CEO & Founder)

Sintex Nylon and Cotton Products (Pte) Limited   (1)
245 Jln Ahmad Ibrahim, Singapore, 629144, Singapore
Tel.: (65) 62652633
Emp.: 10
Cotton Product Distr
N.A.I.C.S.: 424990
Irene Lim (Mgr)

Yuen Sang Watch Industries Limited   (1)
Unit A 1/F 100 Texaco Road, Tsuen Wan, New Territories, China (Hong Kong)

Tel.: (852) 2342 0165
Web Site: http://www.yuensang.com.hk
Watch Mfr & Distr
N.A.I.C.S.: 339910
David Yeung (Gen Mgr)

CHUANGLIAN HOLDINGS LIMITED

Room 905 06 9F China Evergrande Tower, 38 Gloucester Road, Wanchai, China (Hong Kong)
Tel.: (852) 35825200   Ky
Web Site: http://www.chinahrt.com
2371—(HKG)
Rev.: $45,717,048
Assets: $78,019,859
Liabilities: $23,186,358
Net Worth: $54,833,501
Earnings: $1,528,114
Emp.: 484
Fiscal Year-end: 12/31/22
Education Services
N.A.I.C.S.: 611710
Xing Lu (Chm)

CHUBB LIMITED

Baerengasse 32, CH-8001, Zurich, Switzerland
Tel.: (41) 434567600   CH
Web Site: https://www.chubb.com
Year Founded: 1985
CB—(NYSE)
Rev.: $49,735,000,000
Assets: $230,682,000,000
Liabilities: $166,991,000,000
Net Worth: $63,691,000,000
Earnings: $9,028,000,000
Emp.: 40,000
Fiscal Year-end: 12/31/23
Fire Insurance Services
N.A.I.C.S.: 551112
Evan G. Greenberg (Chm, Pres & CEO)

Subsidiaries:

ACE American Insurance Company   (1)
436 Walnut St, Philadelphia, PA 19106
Tel.: (215) 640-1000
General Insurance Services
N.A.I.C.S.: 524210

ACE Capital Title Reinsurance Company   (1)
1133 Ave, New York, NY 10036
Tel.: (215) 640-1000
N.A.I.C.S.: 524298

ACE European Holdings Limited   (1)
Ace Building 100 Leadenhall St, London, EC3A 3BP, United Kingdom   (100%)
Tel.: (44) 2071737000
Emp.: 60
Holding Company; Investment Management Services
N.A.I.C.S.: 551112

Subsidiary (Non-US):

Chubb Underwriting (DIFC) Limited   (2)
Dubai International Financial Centre Currency House Tower 1 Level 7, PO Box 482028, Dubai, United Arab Emirates
Tel.: (971) 44172700
Insurance Management Services
N.A.I.C.S.: 524298
Mike Jones (Sr Mgr-Comm-Europe, Eurasia & Africa)

Subsidiary (Non-US):

Chubb Insurance Hong Kong Limited   (3)
25th Floor Shui On Centre, No 6-8 Harbour Road, Wanchai, China (Hong Kong)   (99.99%)
Tel.: (852) 3191 6222
Web Site: http://www.chubb.com
Insurance Brokerage Services
N.A.I.C.S.: 524210

Chubb Peru S.A. Compania de Seguros y Reaseguros   (3)
Calle Amador Merino Reyna No 267 Floor 4, San Isidro, Lima, Peru   (99.99%)
Tel.: (51) 14175000
Web Site: http://www.chubb.com
Insurance Brokerage Services
N.A.I.C.S.: 524210

Chubb Soguros Moxioo, S.A.   (3)
Av Paseo de la Reforma No 250 Torre Niza Piso 15, Colonia Juarez, 06600, Mexico, Mexico
Tel.: (52) 15552585800
Web Site: https://www.chubb.com
Insurance Brokerage Services
N.A.I.C.S.: 524210
Fernando de la Garza (VP-Agents & Fin)

Subsidiary (Non-US):

Chubb Underwriting (DIFC) Limited   (2)
Currency House Tower 1 Level 7, PO Box 482028, Dubai, United Arab Emirates
Tel.: (971) 44172700
Property & Casualty Insurance Services
N.A.I.C.S.: 524126

ACE Fianzas Monterrey, S.A.   (1)
Ruben Dario No 38, Mexico, 11580, DF, Mexico   (99.95%)
Tel.: (52) 83191820
Web Site: http://www.chubb.com
Rev.: $36,157,308
Assets: $222,879,574
Liabilities: $152,615,434
Net Worth: $70,264,140
Earnings: $25,021,255
Fiscal Year-end: 12/31/2017
Surety Bonding Services
N.A.I.C.S.: 522390

ACE Fire Underwriters Insurance Company   (1)
436 Walnut St. Philadelphia, PA 19106
Tel.: (215) 640-1000
N.A.I.C.S.: 524298

ACE Servicios S.A.   (1)
Av Leandro N Alem 855 Piso 19, Buenos Aires, C1001AAD, Argentina
Tel.: (54) 1141144000
Web Site: http://www.acelimited.com
General Insurance Services
N.A.I.C.S.: 524210

Atlantic Employers Insurance Company   (1)
55 Haddonfield Rd Ste 210, Cherry Hill, NJ 19106   (100%)
Tel.: (215) 640-1000
Web Site: http://www.chubb.com
General Insurance Services
N.A.I.C.S.: 524210

Bankers Standard Insurance Company   (1)
436 Walnut St, Philadelphia, PA 19106
Tel.: (215) 640-1000
N.A.I.C.S.: 524298

Century Indemnity Company   (1)
436 Walnut St, Philadelphia, PA 19106
Tel.: (215) 640-1000
N.A.I.C.S.: 524298

Chubb Alternative Risk Ltd.   (1)
Chubb Building 17 Woodbourne Avenue, Hamilton, HM08, Bermuda
Tel.: (441) 2955200
N.A.I.C.S.: 524298

Chubb Arabia Cooperative Insurance Company   (1)
8th Floor Southern Tower Khobar Business Gate, King Faisal Bin Abdulaziz Street Coastal Road, Al Khobar, Saudi Arabia
Tel.: (966) 138047600
Web Site: https://www.chubb.com
Emp.: 100
General Insurance Services
N.A.I.C.S.: 524126
Abdullah Abdulaziz El Khereiji (Chm)

Chubb Asia Pacific Services Pte. Ltd.   (1)
138 Market Street #11-01 CapitaGreen, Singapore, 048946, Singapore   (100%)
Tel.: (65) 6398 8000

Web Site: http://www.chubb.com
Insurance Management Services
N.A.I.C.S.: 524298

Chubb European Group Limited   (1)
Karntner Ring 5-7, 1010, Vienna, Austria
Tel.: (43) 171093550
Web Site: http://www.chubb.com
Insurance Management Services
N.A.I.C.S.: 524298
Kerstin Hartung Alexandre (Head-Mktg & Comm)

Chubb Group Management & Holdings Ltd.   (1)
17 Woodbourne Ave, Hamilton, HM08, Bermuda   (100%)
Tel.: (441) 2955200
Web Site: http://www.chubb.com
Holding Company; Insurance Programs
N.A.I.C.S.: 551112
Samantha Froud (Chief Admin Officer-Ops)

Subsidiary (Domestic):

Chubb Bermuda Insurance Ltd.   (2)
Chubb Building 17 Woodbourne Avenue, Hamilton, HM08, Bermuda
Tel.: (441) 2955200
Insurance Services
N.A.I.C.S.: 524128
James Paugh (Gen Counsel)

Subsidiary (Domestic):

Paget Reinsurance Ltd   (3)
Chubb Building 17 Woodbourne Avenue, Hamilton, HM08, Bermuda
Tel.: (441) 2955200
General Insurance Services
N.A.I.C.S.: 524210

Sovereign Risk Insurance Limited   (3)
17 Woodbourne Avenue, Hamilton, HM 08, Bermuda
Tel.: (441) 2964279
Web Site: https://www.sovereignbermuda.com
Risk Insurance Services
N.A.I.C.S.: 524298
Price Lowenstein (Pres-Div)

Subsidiary (US):

Chubb INA Holdings Inc.   (2)
436 Walnut St, Philadelphia, PA 19106
Tel.: (215) 640-1000
Web Site: http://www.chubb.com
Holding Company; Insurance Products & Services
N.A.I.C.S.: 551112

Subsidiary (Domestic):

ACE Insurance Company of the Midwest   (3)
120 N 9th St, Richmond, IN 47374   (100%)
Tel.: (215) 640-1000
Web Site: http://www.chubb.com
Property & Casualty Insurance Services
N.A.I.C.S.: 524126

ACE Property and Casualty Insurance Company   (3)
436 Walnut St, Philadelphia, PA 19106   (100%)
Tel.: (215) 640-1000
Web Site: http://www.chubb.com
Property & Casualty Insurance Services
N.A.I.C.S.: 524126

Subsidiary (Domestic):

Chubb Tempest Re USA LLC   (4)
281 Tresser Blvd Ste 500, Stamford, CT 06901-3264
Tel.: (203) 328-7033
Property & Casualty Insurance Services
N.A.I.C.S.: 524126

Subsidiary (Domestic):

Bellemead Development Corporation   (3)
15 Mountain View Rd, Warren, NJ 07059
Tel.: (908) 903-7400
Commercial & Industrial Real Estate Developer
N.A.I.C.S.: 236115

Chubb Asset Management Inc. **(3)**
1133 Ave of The Americas Fl 44, New York, NY 10036
Tel.: (212) 827-4400
Wealth Management Services
N.A.I.C.S.: 525910

Chubb Asset Managers, Inc. **(3)**
15 Mountain View Rd, Warren, NJ 07061
Tel.: (908) 903-3764
Web Site: http://www2.chubb.com
Sales Range: $800-899.9 Million
Emp.: 2,000
Asset Management Services
N.A.I.C.S.: 561499

Subsidiary (Non-US):

Chubb Atlantic Indemnity, Ltd. **(3)**
Belvedere Building 4th Floor 69 Pitts Bay Road, Pembroke, HM 08, Bermuda **(100%)**
Tel.: (441) 292 7343
Web Site: http://www.chubb.com
Property & Casualty Insurance Services
N.A.I.C.S.: 524126

Subsidiary (US):

DHC Corporation **(4)**
202B Halls Mill Rd, Whitehouse Station, NJ 08889
Tel.: (908) 572-2000
Web Site: http://www.chubb.com
Health & Medical Insurance Services
N.A.I.C.S.: 524114

Subsidiary (Domestic):

Chubb Computer Services, Inc. **(3)**
202B Halls Mill Rd, Whitehouse Station, NJ 08889
Tel.: (908) 572-2000
Web Site: http://www.chubb.com
Computer Training & Staffing Services
N.A.I.C.S.: 611519

Chubb Custom Market, Inc. **(3)**
15 Mtn View Rd, Warren, NJ 07059
Tel.: (908) 903-2100
Web Site: http://www.chubb.com
Property & Casualty Insurance Underwriting Services
N.A.I.C.S.: 524298

Chubb Financial Solutions, Inc. **(3)**
202B Halls Mill Rd, Whitehouse Station, NJ 08889
Tel.: (908) 572-2000
Web Site: http://www.chubb.com
Financial Services
N.A.I.C.S.: 523999

Chubb Indemnity Insurance Company **(3)**
202B Halls Mill Rd, Whitehouse Station, NJ 08889
Tel.: (908) 572-2000
Web Site: http://www.chubb.com
Property & Casualty Insurance Services
N.A.I.C.S.: 524128

Chubb Insurance Solutions Agency Inc. **(3)**
202 Halls Mill Rd, Whitehouse Station, NJ 08889
Tel.: (908) 572-2000
Insurance Agency Services
N.A.I.C.S.: 524210

Chubb Re, Inc. **(3)**
4 Essex Ave Ste 300, Bernardsville, NJ 07924
Tel.: (908) 630-2700
Web Site: http://www.chubb.com
Emp.: 4
Reinsurance Services
N.A.I.C.S.: 524130

Chubb US Holdings Inc. **(3)**
1601 Chestnut St, Philadelphia, PA 19192-0003
Tel.: (215) 640-1000
Property & Casualty Insurance Services
N.A.I.C.S.: 524126

Combined Insurance Company of America **(3)**
8750 W Bryn Mawr Ave 7th Fl, Chicago, IL 60631
Supplemental Accident, Disability, Health & Life Insurance Products & Services
N.A.I.C.S.: 524113
Jasmin Zamora *(Mgr-Comm & Community Rels Program)*

Branch (Non-US):

Combined Insurance Company of America - Canada **(4)**
7300 Warden Ave Ste 300, Markham, L3R OX3, ON, Canada
Tel.: (905) 305-1922
Web Site: http://www.combined.ca
Supplemental Accident, Disability, Health & Life Insurance Services
N.A.I.C.S.: 524114
Vincent Iozzo *(CFO & VP)*

Branch (Domestic):

Combined Insurance Company of America - Chicago **(4)**
111 E Wacker Dr Ste 700, Chicago, IL 60601
Tel.: (800) 428-5466
Web Site: http://www.combinedinsurance.com
Supplemental Accident, Disability, Health & Life Insurance Products & Services
N.A.I.C.S.: 524113

Subsidiary (Non-US):

Combined Life Insurance Company of Australia, Ltd. **(4)**
Level 18 101 Miller Street, North Sydney, 2060, NSW, Australia
Tel.: (61) 1300300480
Web Site: http://www.combined.com.au
Supplemental Accident, Disability, Health & Life Insurance Services
N.A.I.C.S.: 524114

Subsidiary (Domestic):

Combined Life Insurance Company of New York **(4)**
13 Cornell Rd, Latham, NY 12110
Supplemental Accident, Disability, Health & Life Insurance Products & Services
N.A.I.C.S.: 524113

Subsidiary (Domestic):

ESIS, Inc. **(3)**
436 Walnut St, Philadelphia, PA 19106 **(100%)**
Tel.: (215) 640-1000
Web Site: https://www.esis.com
Workers Compensation Claims Management Services
N.A.I.C.S.: 524298
Stephen Craig *(Sr VP & Mng Dir-Health Safety & Environmental)*

Subsidiary (Non-US):

ESIS Academy PTE. Ltd. **(4)**
1010 Dover Road 03-17, Singapore, 139658, Singapore
Tel.: (65) 63988660
Web Site: http://www.esisacademy.com
Environmental Consulting Services
N.A.I.C.S.: 541620
Lim Say Thiam *(Principal)*

Subsidiary (Domestic):

Executive Risk Indemnity Inc. **(3)**
82 Hopmeadow St, Simsbury, CT 06070
Tel.: (908) 572-2000
Web Site: http://www.chubb.com
Emp.: 13
Insurance Services
N.A.I.C.S.: 524210

Executive Risk Specialty Insurance Company **(3)**
202B Halls Mill Rd, Whitehouse Station, NJ 08889
Web Site: http://www.chubb.com
Insurance Services
N.A.I.C.S.: 524126

Federal Insurance Company **(3)**
202B Hall's Mill Rd, Whitehouse Station, NJ 08889
Tel.: (908) 903-2000
Insurance Services
N.A.I.C.S.: 524210

Subsidiary (Non-US):

Chubb Insurance Company Limited **(4)**
Room 1301-1312 Citic Square 1168 Nanjing Road West, Shanghai, 200041, China
Tel.: (86) 2123256688
Insurance Agency Services
N.A.I.C.S.: 524210

Chubb Seguros Argentina S.A. **(4)** **(99.2%)**
Tel.: (54) 1141144000
Web Site: http://www.chubb.com
Property & Casualty Insurance Services
N.A.I.C.S.: 524126
Fernando Mendez *(Pres)*

Subsidiary (US):

Chubb Insurance Company Of New Jersey **(2)**
202B Halls Mill Rd, Whitehouse Station, NJ 08889
Tel.: (908) 903-2000
Property & Casualty Insurance Services
N.A.I.C.S.: 524126

Division (Domestic):

Chubb & Son Inc. **(3)**
202 Halls Mill Rd, Whitehouse Station, NJ 08889
Tel.: (908) 572-2000
Web Site: http://www.chubb.com
Insurance Products & Services
N.A.I.C.S.: 524126

Subsidiary (Domestic):

Chubb Services Corporation **(4)**
202B Halls Mill Rd, Whitehouse Station, NJ 08889
Tel.: (908) 903-2000
Web Site: http://www.chubb.com
Consulting & Claims Administration Services
N.A.I.C.S.: 524298

Subsidiary (Domestic):

Chubb Custom Insurance Company **(3)**
202B Hall's Mill Rd, Whitehouse, NJ 08889
Tel.: (908) 572-2000
Property & Casualty Insurance Services
N.A.I.C.S.: 524128

Chubb Group of Insurance Company **(3)**
330 E Kilbourn Ave Ste 1450, Milwaukee, WI 53202-3146
Tel.: (414) 221-7600
Web Site: http://www.chubb.com
Insurance Products & Services
N.A.I.C.S.: 524210
Walter Cane *(COO & Sr VP-Midwest Reg)*

Subsidiary (Domestic):

Chubb Group of Insurance Company - Oregon **(4)**
Pioneer Tower Ste 1120 888 SW 5th Ave, Portland, OR 97204
Tel.: (503) 221-4240
Web Site: http://www.chubb.com
Insurance Products & Services
N.A.I.C.S.: 524210

Subsidiary (Non-US):

Chubb Insurance Company of Canada **(3)**
199 Bay St Ste 2500, PO Box 139, Commerce Court Postal Station, Toronto, M5L 1A9, ON, Canada
Tel.: (416) 359-3222
Web Site: http://www.chubb.com
Property & Casualty Insurance Services
N.A.I.C.S.: 524128
Ellin Moore *(Reg Exec Officer-Canadian Chubb Companies)*

Subsidiary (Domestic):

Chubb Insurance Company of New Jersey **(3)**
202 HallS Mill Rd, Whitehouse Station, NJ 08889
Tel.: (908) 572-2000

Web Site: http://www.chubb.com
Property & Casualty Insurance Services
N.A.I.C.S.: 524126

Affiliate (Domestic):

Chubb Lloyds Insurance Company of Texas **(3)**
2001 Bryan St Ste 3400, Dallas, TX 75201-2068
Tel.: (908) 903-2525
Insurance Services
N.A.I.C.S.: 524126

Subsidiary (Domestic):

Chubb National Insurance Company **(3)**
202B Hall's Mill Rd, Whitehouse, NJ 08889
Web Site: http://www.chubb.com
Property & Casualty Insurance Services
N.A.I.C.S.: 524126

Subsidiary (Non-US):

Chubb de Mexico, Compania Afianzadora, S.A. de C.V. **(3)**
Ava Santa Fe 505 Fl 17 Cruise Mamca Santa Fe, Mexico, 05349, DF, Mexico
Tel.: (52) 5550815600
Web Site: http://www.chubb.com
Assets: $809,142,295
Liabilities: $488,121,180
Net Worth: $321,021,115
Earnings: $50,370,382
Fiscal Year-end: 12/31/2017
Guaranty Insurance Services
N.A.I.C.S.: 524127

Subsidiary (Domestic):

Great Northern Insurance Company **(3)**
202B Hall's Mill Rd, Whitehouse Station, NJ 08889
Tel.: (908) 903-2000
Property & Casualty Insurance Services
N.A.I.C.S.: 524126

Subsidiary (Non-US):

Vigilant Insurance Company **(3)**
Web Site: http://www.chubb.com
Property & Casualty Insurance Services
N.A.I.C.S.: 524126

Group (Domestic):

Chubb Tempest Re Group **(2)**
Chubb Building 17 Woodbourne Avenue, Hamilton, HM08, Bermuda
Tel.: (441) 2955200
Reinsurance Products & Services
N.A.I.C.S.: 524130
James E. Wixtead *(Pres)*

Subsidiary (Domestic):

Chubb Tempest Life Reinsurance Limited **(3)**
Chubb Building 17 Woodbourne Avenue, Hamilton, HM 08, Bermuda
Tel.: (441) 2955200
Web Site: http://www.chubb.com
Life & Annuity Reinsurance Products & Services
N.A.I.C.S.: 524130

Subsidiary (Domestic):

Chubb Tempest Reinsurance Ltd. **(4)**
Chubb Building 17 Woodbourne Avenue, Hamilton, HM08, Bermuda
Tel.: (441) 295 5200
Web Site: http://www.chubb.com
Reinsurance Products & Services
N.A.I.C.S.: 524130

Unit (Non-US):

Chubb Tempest RE Canada, Inc. **(5)**
1800 McGill College Avenue Suite 910, Montreal, H3A 3J6, QC, Canada
Tel.: (514) 798-7284
Web Site: http://www.chubb.com
Property & Casualty Reinsurance Underwriting Services
N.A.I.C.S.: 524298

Chubb Limited—(Continued)

Subsidiary (US):

Chubb Tempest Re USA LLC (5)
2 Stamford Plz 281 Tresser Blvd Ste 500,
Stamford, CT 06901-3264
Tel.: (203) 328-7033
Web Site: http://www.chubb.com
Reinsurance Products & Services
N.A.I.C.S.: 524130
Michael O'Donnell (Pres-Div)

Unit (Domestic):

Chubb Tempest Life Re - USA (6)
10 Exchange Pl 13th Fl, Jersey City, NJ
07302
Tel.: (201) 479-6485
Web Site: http://www.chubb.com
Life & Annuity Reinsurance Products & Services
N.A.I.C.S.: 524130

Subsidiary (US):

Rain & Hail LLC (2)
9200 Northpark Dr Ste 300, Johnston, IA
50131
Tel.: (515) 559-1000
Web Site: https://www.rainhail.com
Group Insurance Services
N.A.I.C.S.: 524210

Division (Domestic):

**Rain and Hail Insurance Service,
Inc.** (3)
9200 Northpark Dr Ste 300, Johnston, IA
50131
Tel.: (515) 559-1000
Web Site: http://www.railhail.com
Insurance Management Services
N.A.I.C.S.: 524126

Subsidiary (Domestic):

**Agri General Insurance
Company** (4)
9200 Northpark Dr Ste 350, Johnston, IA
50131 (100%)
Tel.: (515) 559-1100
Web Site: http://www.rainhail.com
Agricultural Insurance Services
N.A.I.C.S.: 524126

Division (Domestic):

Chubb Agribusiness (5)
72 N Franklin St, Wilkes Barre, PA 18773-
0016
Web Site:
   https://www.chubbagribusiness.com
Commercial Agricultural Insurance Services
N.A.I.C.S.: 524126

Division (Non-US):

**Rain and Hail Insurance Service,
Ltd.** (3)
4303 Albert Street Suite 200, Regina, S4S
3R6, SK, Canada (100%)
Tel.: (306) 584-8844
General Insurance Services
N.A.I.C.S.: 524210

Subsidiary (US):

**Westchester Fire Insurance
Company** (2)
11575 Great Oaks Way Ste 200, Alpharetta,
GA 30022
Web Site: http://www.westchester.com
Commercial Property, Casualty Insurance &
Reinsurance Products & Services
N.A.I.C.S.: 524126
David Lupica (COO)

**Chubb Holdings Australia Pty
Limited** (1)
Level 38 Grosvenor Place 225 George
Street, Sydney, 2000, NSW,
Australia (100%)
Tel.: (61) 293353200
Web Site: http://www.chubb.com
Holding Company; General Insurance Services
N.A.I.C.S.: 551112

Subsidiary (Domestic):

**Chubb Insurance Australia
Limited** (2)
Grosvenor Place Level 38 225 George
Street, Sydney, 2000, NSW, Australia
Tel.: (61) 293353200
Web Site: https://www.chubb.com
Emp.: 800
Insurance Services
N.A.I.C.S.: 524113
Robin Moore (Head-Mktg & Comm-New
Zealand)

**Chubb Insurance (Switzerland)
Limited** (1)
Barengasse 32, 8001, Zurich, Switzerland
Tel.: (41) 434567600
Emp.: 95
Insurance Management Services
N.A.I.C.S.: 524298
Erwin Soland (Mgr-Property)

Subsidiary (Non-US):

**Chubb Reinsurance (Switzerland)
Limited** (2)
Tel.: (41) 434567600
Web Site: http://www.chubb.com
Reinsurance Services
N.A.I.C.S.: 524130

**Chubb Insurance Company of Puerto
Rico** (1)
1445 FD Roosevelt Ave 33 Resolucion St Fl
5th, San Juan, PR 00920-2717
Tel.: (787) 274-4700
General Insurance Services
N.A.I.C.S.: 524113
Judith Hernandez (Pres)

Chubb Insurance Egypt S.A.E. (1)
3 Abou El Feda Street 5th Floor, Zamalek,
Cairo, 11211, Egypt
Tel.: (20) 227360006
Web Site: http://www.chubb.com
Insurance Management Services
N.A.I.C.S.: 524298
Mike Jones (Sr Mgr-Comm-Europe, Eurasia
& Africa)

Chubb Insurance Japan (1)
Garden City Shinagawa Gotenyama 6-7-29
Kita-shinagawa, Shinagawa-ku, Tokyo, 141-
8679, Japan
Tel.: (81) 363647000
Web Site: http://www.chubb.com
Rev.: $490,442,400
Assets: $556,953,600
Earnings: $200,776,800
Fiscal Year-end: 03/31/2018
Insurance Products & Services
N.A.I.C.S.: 524113
Brad Bennett (Pres, CEO & Pres-Far East)

**Chubb Insurance Malaysia
Berhad** (1)
Wisma Chubb 38 Jalan Sultan Ismail,
50250, Kuala Lumpur, Malaysia (100%)
Tel.: (60) 320583000
Rev.: $206,093,527
Assets: $485,730,721
Liabilities: $315,146,830
Net Worth: $170,583,890
Earnings: $19,342,996
Fiscal Year-end: 12/31/2017
General Insurance Services
N.A.I.C.S.: 524210
Leo Moggie (Chm)

**Chubb Insurance New Zealand
Limited** (1)
CU1-3 Shed 24 Princes Wharf, Auckland,
1010, New Zealand
Tel.: (64) 93771459
Insurance Services
N.A.I.C.S.: 524113

Chubb Insurance S.A.-N.V. (1)
Chaussee de la hulpe 166, 1170, Brussels,
Belgium (99.94%)
Tel.: (32) 25169711
Web Site: http://www.chubb.com
Holding Company; Insurance Management
Services
N.A.I.C.S.: 551112

**Chubb Insurance Solutions Agency
Inc.** (1)

436 Walnut St, Philadelphia, PA
19106 (100%)
Tel.: (215) 640-1000
Web Site: http://www.chubb.com
Insurance Management Services
N.A.I.C.S.: 524298

**Chubb Insurance South Africa
Limited** (1)
Ground Floor The Bridle Hunts End Office
Park 38 Wierda Road West, Wierda Valley,
Sandton, 1926, South Africa
Tel.: (27) 117225700
General Insurance Services
N.A.I.C.S.: 524126
Gary Jack (Pres)

**Chubb Insurance Vietnam Company
Limited** (1)
Saigon Finance Center 9 Dinh Tien Hoang
St 8/F, DaKao Ward Dist 1, Ho Chi Minh
City, Vietnam
Tel.: (84) 839107227
Web Site: https://www.chubb.com
Insurance Brokerage Services
N.A.I.C.S.: 524210

Chubb Life Assurance Public Company Limited (1)
130-132 Sindhorn Building Tower 3 21st
22nd Floor Wireless Road, Lumpini Pa-
thumwan, Bangkok, 10330,
Thailand (75.01%)
Tel.: (66) 26156860
Rev.: $137,514,420
Assets: $345,454,840
Liabilities: $291,073,720
Net Worth: $54,381,120
Earnings: $6,338,340
Fiscal Year-end: 12/31/2017
Insurance Agency Services
N.A.I.C.S.: 524210

**Chubb Life Insurance Company of
Canada** (1)
199 Bay Street Suite 2500, PO Box 139,
Commerce Court Postal Station, Toronto,
M5L 1E2, ON, Canada (100%)
Tel.: (416) 359-3222
Web Site: http://www.chubb.com
General Insurance Services
N.A.I.C.S.: 524210
Ellen J. Moore (Exec Officer-Canadian
Chubb Companies Reg)

Chubb Life Insurance Vietnam Company Limited (1)
21st Floor Sun Wah Tower 115 Nguyen Hue
St, Dist 1, Ho Chi Minh City, Vietnam
Tel.: (84) 2838278989
Fire Insurance Services
N.A.I.C.S.: 524113

**Chubb Resseguradora Brasil
S.A.** (1)
Avenida Reboucas No 3974 25th Floor B,
Sao Paulo, 05402-600, Brazil (99.99%)
Tel.: (55) 1145044400
Web Site: http://www.chubb.com
Insurance Management Services
N.A.I.C.S.: 524298

Chubb Seguradora Macau S.A. (1)
Avenida Comercial De Macau, No 5 Edifi-
cio FIT Centre 5 Andar, Macau, China
(Macau) (99.9%)
Tel.: (853) 82964321
Insurance Brokerage Services
N.A.I.C.S.: 524210

Chubb Seguros Chile SA (1)
Miraflores 222 Piso 11, Santiago Centro,
Santiago, Chile
Tel.: (56) 25498300
Rev.: $112,544,366
Assets: $321,805,427
Liabilities: $275,188,676
Net Worth: $46,616,751
Earnings: $715,337
Fiscal Year-end: 12/31/2017
General Insurance Services
N.A.I.C.S.: 524210
Paola Pizarro (Dir-HR)

Chubb Seguros Colombia S.A. (1)
Carrera 7 No 71-21 Torre B Piso 7, Bogota,
Colombia (99.99%)
Web Site: http://www.chubb.com
Rev.: $146,375,301
Assets: $309,126,903

Liabilities: $261,070,773
Net Worth: $48,056,130
Earnings: $1,439,788
Fiscal Year-end: 12/31/2017
Property & Casualty Insurance Services
N.A.I.C.S.: 524126
Manuel Obregon (Pres)

Chubb Seguros Ecuador S.A. (1)
Corporate Center Ekopark Tower 4 Floor 4,
Quito, Ecuador (99.99%)
Tel.: (593) 43731810
Web Site: http://www.chubb.com
General Insurance Services
N.A.I.C.S.: 524210
Edwin Astudillo (Pres & CEO)

Chubb Seguros Panama S.A. (1)
Business Park Torre V Piso 14 Ave La Ro-
tonda, Costa del Este, Panama, Panama
Tel.: (507) 2050400
Web Site: http://www.chubb.com
Rev.: $18,320,863
Assets: $45,262,201
Liabilities: $25,981,761
Net Worth: $19,280,440
Earnings: $4,731,390
Fiscal Year-end: 12/31/2017
General Insurance Services
N.A.I.C.S.: 524210
Oscar Perez Nation (Pres)

**Chubb Seguros de Vida Chile
S.A.** (1)
Miraflores 222 Piso 11, Santiago,
Chile (97.9%)
Tel.: (56) 225498300
Web Site: http://www.chuub.com
Insurance Brokerage Services
N.A.I.C.S.: 524210

Chubb Services UK Limited (1)
100 Leadenhall Street, London, EC3A 3BP,
United Kingdom
Tel.: (44) 2071737000
General Insurance Services
N.A.I.C.S.: 524126
Eileen Castolene (Dir-European Ops)

**Cigna Worldwide Life Insurance
Company Limited** (1)
15/F 28 Hennessy Road, Wan Chai, Hong
Kong, China (Hong Kong)
Tel.: (852) 25601990
Web Site: http://www.cigna.com.hk
Insurance Management Services
N.A.I.C.S.: 524298

ESIS Canada, Inc. (1)
199 Bay Street Suite 2500, PO Box 139
Commerce Court Postal Station, Toronto,
M5L 1E2, ON, Canada (100%)
Tel.: (416) 368-2911
Web Site: http://www.chubb.com
Property & Casualty Insurance Services
N.A.I.C.S.: 524126

LLC Chubb Insurance Company (1)
Savvinskaya embankment 23 building 1, vn
ter g Khamovniki municipal district, 119435,
Moscow, Russia (100%)
Tel.: (7) 4955892227
Web Site: http://www.chubb-insurance.ru
General Insurance Services
N.A.I.C.S.: 524210
Nikolay Dmitriev (Reg Dir-Property & Liability Insurance-Eurasia & Africa)

PT Asuransi Cigna (1)
Tempo Pavilion 2 Jl H R Rasuna Said Kav
10, South Jakarta, 12950, Indonesia
Tel.: (62) 1500033
Web Site: http://www.cigna.co.id
Fire Insurance Services
N.A.I.C.S.: 524113

**PT Chubb General Insurance
Indonesia** (1)
Chubb Square 6th Floor Jl MH Thamrin No
10, Jakarta, 10230, Indonesia (80%)
Tel.: (62) 2123568888
General Insurance Services
N.A.I.C.S.: 524210
Budi Tatawidjaja (Dir-Compliance)

Subsidiary (Domestic):

**PT Asuransi Chubb Syariah
Indonesia** (2)

the Indonesian Stock Exchange Building Tower II 10th Floor Suite 1001, JI Gen Sudirman Kav 52-53, Jakarta, 12190, Indonesia
Tel.: (62) 29498555
Web Site: https://chubbsyariah.co.id
General Insurance Services
N.A.I.C.S.: 524210

PT Chubb General Insurance Indonesia (1)
JI Landasan Pacu Barat Blok B10 Kav No 2 Kemayoran, Jakarta, 10610, Indonesia
Tel.: (62) 2165703977
Insurance Agency Services
N.A.I.C.S.: 524210

PT Chubb Life Insurance Indonesia (1)
Plaza Bank Index 1st Floor JI MH Thamrin No 57, Jakarta, 10350, Indonesia **(98.21%)**
Tel.: (81) 21 2356 8887
Web Site: http://www.chubb.com
Rev.: $87,036,390
Assets: $183,863,330
Liabilities: $148,163,960
Net Worth: $35,699,370
Earnings: $8,710,730
Fiscal Year-end: 12/31/2017
General Insurance Services
N.A.I.C.S.: 524210
Enni Agustiningsih *(Head-Mktg-Surabaya Reg)*

Pacific Employers Insurance Company (1)
436 Walnut St, Philadelphia, PA 19106
Tel.: (215) 640-1000
Property & Casualty Insurance Services
N.A.I.C.S.: 524126

Subsidiary (Domestic):

Illinois Union Insurance Company (2)
525 W Monroe St Ste 400, Chicago, IL 60661
Tel.: (312) 775-3100
Web Site: http://www.chubb.com
Insurance Brokerage Services
N.A.I.C.S.: 524210

Recovery Services International, Inc. (1)
436 Walnut St, Philadelphia, PA 19106 **(100%)**
Tel.: (215) 640-1000
Web Site: http://www.chubb.com
Emp.: 5
Insurance Management Services
N.A.I.C.S.: 524298

Westchester Surplus Lines Insurance Company (1)
11575 Great Oaks Way Ste 200, Alpharetta, GA 30022 **(100%)**
Web Site: https://www.westchester.com
Insurance Agencies & Brokerage Services
N.A.I.C.S.: 524210
David Lupica *(COO)*

CHUBU ELECTRIC POWER CO., INC.

1 Higashi-shincho, Higashi-ku, Nagoya, 461-8680, Aichi, Japan
Tel.: (81) 529518211 JP
Web Site: https://www.chuden.co.jp
Year Founded: 1951
9502—(TKS)
Rev.: $23,864,836,540
Assets: $46,987,958,370
Liabilities: $29,173,539,060
Net Worth: $17,814,419,310
Earnings: $2,664,755,400
Emp.: 3,180
Fiscal Year-end: 03/31/24
Electricity Distribution Services
N.A.I.C.S.: 221122
Kingo Hayashi *(Pres)*

Subsidiaries:

Aoyama-Kogen Wind Farm Co., Ltd. (1)
12-19 Okura, Tsu, 514-0834, Mie, Japan
Tel.: (81) 592287773
Web Site: https://www.awf.co.jp

N.A.I.C.S.: 221111
Atsuya Yoshida *(CEO)*

Asahi Synchrotech Co., Ltd. (1)
2-13-34 Konan, Minato-ku, Tokyo, 108-0075, Japan
Tel.: (81) 357152550
Web Site: https://www.synchrotech.co.jp
Emp.: 214
Engineeering Services
N.A.I.C.S.: 541330
Mitsunobu Kato *(Pres & CEO)*

CD Energy Direct Co., Ltd. (1)
4-5-1 Nihonbashi Muromachi, Chuo-ku, Tokyo, 103-0022, Japan
Tel.: (81) 120811792
Web Site: https://www.cdedirect.co.jp
Electric Power Supply & Gas Supply Services
N.A.I.C.S.: 221121

CEPO Handa Biomass Power Generation Co., Inc. (1)
4-1 Nitocho, Handa, 475-0033, Aichi, Japan
Tel.: (81) 569840030
Web Site: https://cepohanda.com
N.A.I.C.S.: 221111
Osamu Nakagawa *(CEO)*

Centrair Energy Supply Co., Ltd. (1)
1-1 Centrair, Tokoname, 479-0881, Aichi, Japan
Tel.: (81) 569387200
N.A.I.C.S.: 221111

Chubu Cable Network Company, Incorporated (1)
3 9 27 Masaki NFC Kanayama Building 2nd Floor, Naka-ku, Nagoya, Aichi, Japan
Tel.: (81) 120441061
Web Site: http://www.ccnw.co.jp
Cable TV Services
N.A.I.C.S.: 516210

Chubu Electric Power Co., Inc. - UK Office (1)
2nd Floor 210 High Holborn, London, WC1V 7EP, United Kingdom
Tel.: (44) 207 409 0142
Web Site: http://www.chuden.co.jp
Sales Range: $75-99.9 Million
Emp.: 4
Electric Utility Services
N.A.I.C.S.: 221122
Masaya Kawaguchi *(Gen Mgr)*

Chubu Electric Power Company U.S.A. Inc. (1)
900 17th St NW Ste 1220, Washington, DC 20006-2514
Tel.: (202) 775-1960
Web Site: http://www.chuden.co.jp
Sales Range: $75-99.9 Million
Emp.: 6
Electric Utility Services
N.A.I.C.S.: 221118
Akihiro Niwa *(Gen Mgr)*

Chubu Liquid Oxygen Co., Ltd. (1)
27 Minamihama-Cho, Chita, 478-0045, Aichi, Japan
Tel.: (81) 562561231
Web Site: https://www.chueki.co.jp
N.A.I.C.S.: 325120

Chubu Plant Service Co., Ltd. (1)
11-22 Gohonmatsu-cho, Atsuta-ku, Nagoya, 456-8516, Japan
Tel.: (81) 526791200
Web Site: https://home.chubuplant.co.jp
Emp.: 1,499
Civil Engineering & Construction Services
N.A.I.C.S.: 237990

Chubu Seiki Co., Ltd. (1)
5177 7 Hiyoshi cho, Mizunami-shi, Gifu, 509-6251, Japan
Tel.: (81) 572691025
Web Site: http://chukoh-seiki.com
Electric Equipment Mfr
N.A.I.C.S.: 335999
Yoshikatsu Kudo *(Pres)*

Chuden Auto Lease Co., Ltd. (1)
4-5 Shioyacho, Minami-ku, Nagoya, 457-8580, Japan
Tel.: (81) 528232441
Web Site: https://www.chuden-al.co.jp
Emp.: 193

Leasing Services
N.A.I.C.S.: 531210

Chuden CTI Co., Ltd. (1)
1-10-10 Higashisakura, Higashi-ku, Nagoya, 461-0005, Aichi, Japan
Tel.: (81) 527406201
Web Site: http://www.cti.co.jp
Information Technology Services
N.A.I.C.S.: 541519
Yujun Naito *(Pres & CEO)*

Chuden Real Estate Co., Ltd. (1)
2-2-5 Sakae, Naka-ku, Nagoya, 460-0008, Japan
Tel.: (81) 522041383
Web Site: https://www.chudenfudosan.co.jp
Emp.: 546
Real Estate Services
N.A.I.C.S.: 531210

Chuden Transportation Service Co., Ltd. (1)
3-12 Oe-Cho, Minato-ku, Nagoya, 455-0024, Japan
Tel.: (81) 526136265
Web Site: https://ctps.co.jp
N.A.I.C.S.: 532120
Yasunobu Aketa *(CEO)*

Chuden Wing Co., Ltd. (1)
Tel.: (81) 528190621
Web Site: http://www.chuden-wing.co.jp
Electric Power Supply Services
N.A.I.C.S.: 221121

Community Network Center Inc. (1)
10th floor Higashizakura Daiichi Building 1-3-10 Higashizakura, Higashi-ku, Nagoya, 461-0005, Aichi, Japan
Tel.: (81) 529555161
Web Site: https://www.cnci.co.jp
Emp.: 109
Technology & Communication Services
N.A.I.C.S.: 541519

Diamond Power Corporation (1)
11F Sakura Muromachi Building 4-5-1 Nihonbashi Muromachi, Chuo-ku, Tokyo, 103-0022, Japan **(80%)**
Tel.: (81) 362140902
Web Site: https://www.diapwr.co.jp
Sales Range: $75-99.9 Million
Emp.: 12
Electric Power Distr
N.A.I.C.S.: 221122

GTS Japan Co., Ltd. (1)
Kashiwa Building 3F 2-16-3 Takadanobaba, Shinjuku-ku, Tokyo, 169-0075, Japan
Tel.: (81) 351553166
Web Site: https://www.gts-japan.com
N.A.I.C.S.: 541390
Masashi Kanazawa *(Dir)*

Greenway Grid Global Pte. Ltd. (1)
6 Temasek Boulevard 42 02 Suntec Tower 4, Singapore, 038986, Singapore
Tel.: (65) 69093083
Web Site: http://www.greenwaygrid.global
Iota Infrastructure Services
N.A.I.C.S.: 517111
Kazuhiko Shiba *(Pres)*

Jera Co., Ltd. (1)
Nihonbashi Takashimaya Mitsui Building 25th Floor 2 5 1 Nihonbashi, Chuo-ku, Tokyo, Japan
Tel.: (81) 33 272 4631
Web Site: https://www.jera.co.jp
Emp.: 4,907
Engineeering Services
N.A.I.C.S.: 541330
Toshihiro Sano *(Chm)*

Nagoya City Energy Co., Ltd. (1)
3 20 17 Marunouchi KDX Sakuradori Building 11F, Naka-ku, Nagoya, 460-0002, Japan
Tel.: (81) 527372100
Web Site: http://www.nc-energy.co.jp
Electric Power Supply Services
N.A.I.C.S.: 221121

Necolico LLC (1)
6th floor Akihabara Crossside 2-1-8 Higashikanda, Chiyoda-ku, Tokyo, 101-0031, Japan
Tel.: (81) 356876775
Web Site: https://www.necolico.co.jp
Iota Infrastructure Services
N.A.I.C.S.: 517111

Omaezaki Cable Television (1)
7563-17 Ikeshinden, Omaezaki, 437-1612, Shizuoka, Japan
Tel.: (81) 537868882
Web Site: https://maotv.jp
Cable TV Services
N.A.I.C.S.: 516210

PT. Asahi Synchrotech Indonesia (1)
Wisma Keiai 8th floor JI Jend Sudirman Kav 3, Jakarta, 10220, Indonesia
Tel.: (62) 215724011
Engineeering Services
N.A.I.C.S.: 541330
Sugeng Rusdianto *(Sr Mgr-Construction)*

Shin-Nihon Helicopter Co., Ltd. (1)
3rd Floor Toyo Central Building 1-13 Toyo 4-Chome, Koto-ku, Tokyo, 135-0016, Japan
Tel.: (81) 356177131
Web Site: https://snkk-net.com
N.A.I.C.S.: 541614
Takashi Oshima *(CEO)*

Techno Chubu Co., Ltd. (1)
3 12 Oecho, Minato Ward, Nagoya, 455-8512, Japan
Tel.: (81) 526147171
Web Site: http://www.techno-chubu.co.jp
Electric Equipment Mfr
N.A.I.C.S.: 335999

Tokai Concrete Industries Co., Ltd. (1)
55 1 Kitadakase Shichijo Kamiita-cho, Itano-gun, Tokushima, 771-1302, Japan
Tel.: (81) 886942222
Web Site: http://toukai-con.jp
Ready-mixed Concrete Mfr & Whslr
N.A.I.C.S.: 327320

Yonago Biomass Power Generation LLC (1)
3153-1 Oshinotsucho, Yonago, 683-0101, Tottori, Japan
Tel.: (81) 859212081
Web Site: https://www.yonago-biomass.co.jp
N.A.I.C.S.: 221111

e-Kurashi Co., Ltd. (1)
3-30-9 Uchiyama, Chikusa-ku, Nagoya, 464-0075, Aichi, Japan
Tel.: (81) 120667539
Web Site: https://www.e-kurashi.co.jp
Living Facility Services
N.A.I.C.S.: 623312

CHUBU SHIRYO CO., LTD.

Takisada Nagoya Building 5F 13-19 Nishiki 2-chome, Naka-ku, Nagoya, 460-0003, Aichi, Japan
Tel.: (81) 522043050
Web Site:
https://www.chubushiryo.co.jp
Year Founded: 1949
2053—(TKS)
Rev.: $1,548,240,470
Assets: $686,276,640
Liabilities: $252,250,820
Net Worth: $434,025,820
Earnings: $21,991,470
Emp.: 487
Fiscal Year-end: 03/31/24
Animal Feed Mfr & Distr
N.A.I.C.S.: 311111
Hirano Harunobu *(Pres & CEO)*

CHUBU STEEL PLATE CO., LTD.

5-1 Kousudori, Nakagawa-Ku, Nagoya, 454-8506, Aichi, Japan
Tel.: (81) 526613811
Web Site:
https://www.chubukohan.co.jp
Year Founded: 1950
5461—(NGO)
Rev.: $447,869,052
Assets: $618,090,346
Liabilities: $106,071,989
Net Worth: $512,018,357
Earnings: $47,485,946
Emp.: 500
Fiscal Year-end: 03/31/24
Plate Product Mfr

Chubu Steel Plate Co., Ltd.—(Continued)
N.A.I.C.S.: 332313
Daigou Kaneko *(Mng Dir)*

Subsidiaries:

CK Clean Ad Co., Ltd. (1)
2F CK Building 1-2-1 Kowaridori, Minato-ku, Nagoya, 455-0077, Japan
Tel.: (01) 520541715
Web Site: https://www.ck-clean-ad.co.jp
Emp.: 42
Thick Plate Mfr
N.A.I.C.S.: 332313

CHUBU SUISAN CO., LTD.
2-22 Kawanamicho, Atsuta-Ku, Nagoya, 456-0072, Aichi, Japan
Tel.: (81) 526833000
Web Site: https://www.nagoya-chusui.co.jp
Year Founded: 1946
8145—(NGO)
Sales Range: Less than $1 Million
Marine Products Distr
N.A.I.C.S.: 423990
Tsuyoshi Wakisaka *(Pres & CEO)*

CHUBU-NIPPON BROADCAST-ING CO., LTD.
1-2-8 Shinsakae, Naka-Ku, Nagoya, 460-8405, Aichi, Japan
Tel.: (81) 522418111
Web Site: https://www.hicbc.com
Year Founded: 1950
Holding Company
N.A.I.C.S.: 551112

CHUCO CO., LTD.
27 Toko-cho, Gifu, 500-8137, Japan
Tel.: (81) 582472511
Web Site: https://www.chuco.co.jp
2139—(NGO)
Rev.: $67,637,906
Assets: $34,258,332
Liabilities: $20,977,860
Net Worth: $13,280,472
Earnings: $1,268,582
Emp.: 290
Fiscal Year-end: 03/31/24
Newspaper, Magazine & Internet Publisher
N.A.I.C.S.: 513120
Kazutoshi Goto *(Pres)*

CHUDENKO CORPORATION
6-12 Koamicho, Naka-ku, Hiroshima, 730-0855, Japan
Tel.: (81) 822917411   JP
Web Site:
   https://www.chudenko.co.jp
Year Founded: 1944
1941—(TKS)
Rev.: $1,328,775,250
Assets: $1,854,382,620
Liabilities: $440,364,810
Net Worth: $1,414,017,810
Earnings: $52,463,570
Emp.: 3,577
Fiscal Year-end: 03/31/24
Electric Power, Communications, Water & Civil Infrastructure Engineering, Construction & Facilities Contracting Services
N.A.I.C.S.: 541330
Hirofumi Obata *(Chm)*

Subsidiaries:

Berryne Co., Ltd. (1)
735 Shichijoi Kinjo-cho, Hamada, 697-0123, Japan
Tel.: (81) 855422515
Web Site: https://www.berryne.co.jp
Fresh Fruit Distr
N.A.I.C.S.: 424480

Chudenko Eletech Yamaguchi Co., Ltd. (1)
789-7 Kurashita Ogori Shimogo, Yamagu-

chi, 754-0002, Japan
Tel.: (81) 839760350
Web Site: https://www.eletech-ya.co.jp
Emp.: 88
Electrical Contracting Services
N.A.I.C.S.: 238210

Chudenko World Farm Co., Ltd. (1)
6-12 Koamicho, Naka-ku, Hiroshima, 730-0855, Japan
Tel.: (81) 822333137
Agricultural Services
N.A.I.C.S.: 115112

Chuo Kaihatsu Corporation (1)
3-13-5 Nishiwaseda, Shinjuku-ku, Tokyo, 169-8612, Japan
Tel.: (81) 332083111
Web Site: https://www.ckcnet.co.jp
Construction Services
N.A.I.C.S.: 541330

Eapec Hiroshima Co., Ltd. (1)
24-1 Funairisaiwai-cho, Naka-ku, Hiroshima, 730-0844, Japan
Tel.: (81) 825326167
Electrical Contracting Services
N.A.I.C.S.: 238210

Hayamizudenki Co., Ltd. (1)
2-5-11 Kaiun-cho, Nagata-ku, Kobe, 653-0052, Japan
Tel.: (81) 787319301
Web Site: https://www.hayamizudenki.co.jp
Lighting Design Services
N.A.I.C.S.: 541490

Sugiyamakankousetubi Co., Ltd. (1)
Kaiji Building 4th Floor 1-3 Kaigan-dori, Naka-ku, Yokohama, 231-0002, Kanagawa, Japan
Tel.: (81) 452288300
Web Site: https://www.sugisetu.com
Emp.: 26
Plumbing Services
N.A.I.C.S.: 238220

CHUETSU PULP & PAPER CO., LTD.
282 Yoneshima, Takaoka, 933-8533, Toyama, Japan
Tel.: (81) 766262401
Web Site: https://www.chuetsu-pulp.co.jp
Year Founded: 1947
3877—(TKS)
Rev.: $712,729,860
Assets: $852,181,030
Liabilities: $484,658,420
Net Worth: $367,522,610
Earnings: $24,463,610
Emp.: 781
Fiscal Year-end: 03/31/24
Paper Product Mfr & Distr
N.A.I.C.S.: 322299
Hisashi Uematsu *(Chm)*

CHUGAI MINING CO. LTD.
Marunouchi Bldg 12F 2-4-1 Marunouchi, Chiyoda-ku, Tokyo, 100-6312, Japan
Tel.: (81) 332011541
Web Site:
   https://www.chugaikogyo.co.jp
Year Founded: 1932
1491—(TKS)
Rev.: $751,940,380
Assets: $80,212,350
Liabilities: $33,235,080
Net Worth: $46,977,270
Earnings: $1,440,980
Emp.: 129
Fiscal Year-end: 03/31/24
Precious Metals
N.A.I.C.S.: 331410
Atsushi Ohara *(Gen Dir)*

Subsidiaries:

Chugai Mining Co. Ltd. - Mochikoshi Plant (1)
892 41 Yugashima Izu, Shizuoka, Japan
Tel.: (81) 558850762
Web Site: http://www.chugaikogyo.co.jp

Gold & Silver Products Mfr
N.A.I.C.S.: 332813

Chugai Mining Co. Ltd. - Tokyo Plant (1)
2-12-16 Keihinjima, Ota-ku, Tokyo, 143-0003, Japan
Tel.: (81) 3 3790 7130
Web Site: http://www.chugaikogyo.co.jp
Gold Mining Services
N.A.I.C.S.: 212220

CHUGAI RO CO., LTD.
3-6-1 Hiranomachi, Chuo-ku, Osaka, 541-0046, Japan
Tel.: (81) 662211251
Web Site: https://www.chugai.co.jp
Year Founded: 1945
1964—(TKS)
Rev.: $193,560,630
Assets: $322,984,430
Liabilities: $139,437,950
Net Worth: $183,546,480
Earnings: $14,522,170
Emp.: 450
Fiscal Year-end: 03/31/24
Industrial Furnaces, Incinerators & Ovens Mfr
N.A.I.C.S.: 333994
Isamu Ikeda *(Exec Officer & Gen Mgr-Thermo Sys Dept & Plant Div)*

Subsidiaries:

CR Co., Ltd. (1)
2-4-7 Kyomachibori Nishi-ku, Osaka, 550-0003, Japan
Tel.: (81) 664477253
Life & Non-Life Insurance Agent; Parking Lot Operator; Temporary Employment Services
N.A.I.C.S.: 524298

Chugai Air System Co., Ltd. (1)
94-7 Ishizunishimachi Nichi-ku Sakai-city, Osaka, 592-8332, Japan
Tel.: (81) 722801661
Sales Range: $25-49.9 Million
Emp.: 12
Wet & Dry Type Dehumidifiers, Clean Dryers, Environmental Testing Systems, Aging Systems & Air Conditioners
N.A.I.C.S.: 333415

Chugai Engineering Co.,Ltd. (1)
94-7 Ishizu Nishimachi, Nishi-ku, Sakai, 592-8332, Osaka, Japan
Tel.: (81) 722800791
Web Site: http://chugai.co.jp
Sales Range: $25-49.9 Million
Emp.: 64
Industrial Furnace Mfr
N.A.I.C.S.: 333994

Chugai Plant Co., Ltd. (1)
2-4 ChikkoShinmachi, Nishi-ku, Sakai, 592-8331, Osaka, Japan
Tel.: (81) 722471360
Sales Range: $50-74.9 Million
Emp.: 200
Industrial Furnace Designer, Mfr, Operator, Maintenance & Sales
N.A.I.C.S.: 333994

Chugai Ro (Thailand) Co., Ltd. (1)
No 1 MD Tower 8th Floor Room F Soi Bangna-Trad 25, Bangna Nuea Sub-District Bang Na District, Bangkok, 10260, Thailand
Tel.: (66) 2 186 4950
Web Site: https://chugairothailand.com
Industrial Stove Mfr & Distr
N.A.I.C.S.: 333994

Chugai Ro Aluminum (Shandong) Co., Ltd. (1)
South of Road 10 High-New Technology, Industrial Development Zone, Tai'an, Shandong, China
Tel.: (86) 5386928799
Web Site: http://www.chugai.co.jp
Sales Range: $25-49.9 Million
Emp.: 50
Industrial Furnaces & Ovens
N.A.I.C.S.: 333994
Suiguo Zong *(Pres)*

Chugai Ro Co., Ltd. - Kokura Factory (1)

2-2-1 Higashiminato, Kokura-Kita-ku, Kita-kyushu, 803-0802, Japan
Tel.: (81) 935715788
Industrial Furnace Mfr
N.A.I.C.S.: 333994

Chugai Ro Co., Ltd. - Sakai Works (1)
2-4 Chikko-Shinmachi, Nishi-ku, Sakai, 592-9331, Japan
Tel.: (81) 722472501
Web Site: http://www.chugai.co.jp
Sales Range: $100-124.9 Million
Emp.: 469
Industrial Furnace Mfr
N.A.I.C.S.: 333994

Chugai Ro Shanghai Co., Ltd. (1)
Tel.: (86) 2162950081
Web Site: http://www.chugai.com
Sales Range: $25-49.9 Million
Emp.: 60
Industrial Furnaces & Ovens
N.A.I.C.S.: 333994

Chugai Ro Thermal Engineering (Shanghai) Co., Ltd. (1)
No 333 Chi Hua Road, Huqiao Lin Hai Industrial Zone Zhelin Town Fengxian, Shanghai, 201417, China
Tel.: (86) 213 361 8366
Industrial Stove Mfr & Distr
N.A.I.C.S.: 333994

PT. Chugai Ro Indonesia (1)
6th Floor Menara Global Kav 27 Jalan Gatot Subroto No 3, Kuningan Kota Jakarta Selatan Daerah Khusus Ibukota, Jakarta, 10340, Indonesia
Tel.: (62) 21 527 9652
Web Site: https://chugairoindonesia.com
Heating Equipment Distr
N.A.I.C.S.: 423720
Tetsuya Kawanaka *(Pres)*

Taiwan Chugai Ro Co., Ltd. (1)
No 6 Siwei 3rd Road Room A1 21st Floor Siwei Financial Building, Lingya District, Kaohsiung, 802, Taiwan
Tel.: (886) 75357898
Web Site: https://chugairo.com.tw
Sales Range: $25-49.9 Million
Emp.: 7
Industrial Furnaces & Ovens
N.A.I.C.S.: 333994
M Michicu *(Pres)*

CHUGIN FINANCIAL GROUP, INC.
1-15-20 Marunouchi, Okayama, Japan
Tel.: (81) 862233111   JP
Web Site: https://www.chugin-fg.co.jp
Year Founded: 2022
5832—(TKS)
Rev.: $1,220,609,210
Assets: $71,148,744,440
Liabilities: $67,307,574,290
Net Worth: $3,841,170,150
Earnings: $211,520
Emp.: 3,009
Fiscal Year-end: 03/31/24
Bank Holding Company
N.A.I.C.S.: 551111
Masato Miyanaga *(Chm)*

Subsidiaries:

The Chugoku Bank, Limited (1)
1-15-20 Marunouchi, Kita-ku, Okayama, Japan
Tel.: (81) 862233111
Web Site: https://www.chugin.co.jp
Rev.: $1,244,509,200
Assets: $98,815,463,120
Liabilities: $93,468,095,600
Net Worth: $5,347,367,520
Earnings: $177,860,320
Emp.: 2,792
Fiscal Year-end: 03/31/2022
Banking Services
N.A.I.C.S.: 522110

Subsidiary (Domestic):

Chugin Asset Management Company, Limited (2)

2-11-23 Yanagimachi, Kita-ku, Okayama, 700-0823, Japan
Tel.: (81) 862245310
Web Site: http://www.chugin-am.jp
Asset Management Services
N.A.I.C.S.: 561110

Chugin Securities Co., Ltd. **(2)**
2-5 Honmachi Chugin Station Building, Kita-ku, Okayama, 700-0822, Japan
Tel.: (81) 862353441
Web Site: http://www.chugin-sec.co.jp
Emp.: 107
Securities Brokerage Services
N.A.I.C.S.: 523150

The Chugin Credit Guarantee Co., Limited **(2)**
2-10-17 Marunouchi, Kita-ku, Okayama, 700-0823, Japan
Tel.: (81) 862311266
Emp.: 20
Credit Guarantee Services
N.A.I.C.S.: 561450
Yutaka Toda *(Pres)*

The Chugin Lease Company, Limited **(2)**
Chugoku Ginko Honten Bekkan Nai, Okayama, Japan
Tel.: (81) 862327060
Sales Range: $25-49.9 Million
Emp.: 50
Equipment Rental & Leasing
N.A.I.C.S.: 532420

The Chugin Operation Center, Co., Limited **(2)**
1-15-20 Marunouchi, Kita-ku, Okayama, 700-0823, Japan
Tel.: (81) 862346539
Web Site: http://www.chugin.co.jp
Deposit & Bank Remittances & Valuation of Collateralized Real Estate
N.A.I.C.S.: 522320

CHUGOKU MARINE PAINTS, LTD.

Tokyo Club Building 2-6 Kasumigaseki 3-chome, Chiyoda-ku, Tokyo, 100-0013, Japan
Tel.: (81) 335063971
Web Site: https://www.cmp.co.jp
Year Founded: 1917
4617—(TKS)
Rev.: $767,910,140
Assets: $875,190,440
Liabilities: $371,673,690
Net Worth: $503,516,750
Earnings: $65,386,120
Emp.: 2,104
Fiscal Year-end: 03/31/24
Marine Paints & Adhesives Mfr & Sales
N.A.I.C.S.: 325510
Masataka Uetake *(Chm & CEO)*

Subsidiaries:

CMP Coatings Inc **(1)**
1610 Engineers Rd, Belle Chasse, LA 70037
Tel.: (504) 392-4817
Sales Range: $25-49.9 Million
Emp.: 24
Paint Varnish & Supplies Whslr
N.A.I.C.S.: 424950

CMP Planning Ltd. **(1)**
1-15-2 Yoshijimahigashi, Naka-Ku, Hiroshima, 730-0822, Japan
Tel.: (81) 822419188
Web Site: http://www.cmp.co.jp
Urban Planning & Community & Rural Development Administration
N.A.I.C.S.: 925120

Charter Chemical & Coating Corporation **(1)**
1 Mercedes Ave, San Miguel Metro Manila, 1600, Pasig, Philippines
Tel.: (63) 26417101
Web Site: http://www.csp.co.kr
Sales Range: $50-74.9 Million
Emp.: 200
Paint & Coating Mfr

N.A.I.C.S.: 325510

Chugoku Marine Paints (Guangdong) Ltd **(1)**
Industrial Development Area, Lunjiao Shunde, Foshan, 528308, Guangdong, China
Tel.: (86) 75727733451
Other Chemical & Allied Products Merchant Whslr
N.A.I.C.S.: 424690

Chugoku Marine Paints (Hellas) S.A. **(1)**
str Kanari 8, 18538, Piraeus, Greece
Tel.: (30) 2104535089
Web Site: https://www.cmphellas.gr
Sales Range: $25-49.9 Million
Emp.: 14
Paint Varnish & Supplies Whslr
N.A.I.C.S.: 424950

Chugoku Marine Paints (Hongkong) Ltd **(1)**
Room 01 22nd Floor Island Place Tower 510 King s Road, North Point, China (Hong Kong)
Tel.: (852) 25766376
Web Site: http://www.cmp.com
Sales Range: $25-49.9 Million
Emp.: 15
Paint Varnish & Supplies Whslr
N.A.I.C.S.: 424950

Chugoku Marine Paints (Nagasaki), Ltd. **(1)**
1-16 Saiwaimachi, Nagasaki, 850-0046, Japan
Tel.: (81) 958260256
Marine Coating Mfr
N.A.I.C.S.: 325510

Chugoku Marine Paints (Shanghai), Ltd. **(1)**
4677 Jiasong Road, Jiading, Shanghai, China
Tel.: (86) 2152357799
Paint Mfr & Distr
N.A.I.C.S.: 325510

Plant (Domestic):

Chugoku Marine Paints (Shanghai), Ltd. - Factory & Technical Center **(2)**
4677 Jiasong Road North, Jiading, Shanghai, 201814, China
Tel.: (86) 21 59501000
Web Site: http://www.csp.co.kr
Paints Mfr
N.A.I.C.S.: 325510

Chugoku Marine Paints (Singapore) Pte. Ltd. **(1)**
22 Tuas Street, Singapore, 638459, Singapore
Tel.: (65) 68616500
Sales Range: $50-74.9 Million
Emp.: 10
Paint & Adhesive Mfr & Distr
N.A.I.C.S.: 325510
Y. Nagakawa *(Mng Dir)*

Chugoku Marine Paints (Taiwan) Ltd **(1)**
5F-2 Shen Hsiang Tang Building No 146 Sung Chiang Road, Taipei, 10458, Taiwan
Tel.: (886) 225110106
Sales Range: $50-74.9 Million
Emp.: 10
Other Chemical & Allied Products Merchant Whslr
N.A.I.C.S.: 424690

Chugoku Marine Paints, Ltd. - Kyushu Factory **(1)**
2783 Tade Yoshinogari -Cho, Kanzaki-Gun, Saga, 842-0035, Japan
Tel.: (81) 952 52 1313
Web Site: http://www.cmp.co.jp
Industrial Equipment Mfr
N.A.I.C.S.: 333248

Chugoku Marine Paints, Ltd. - Shiga Factory **(1)**
2306-7 Mikami, Yasu, 520-2323, Shiga, Japan.
Tel.: (81) 77 587 0488
Web Site: http://www.cmp.co.jp
Industrial Machinery Mfr

N.A.I.C.S.: 333248

Chugoku Paints (Germany) GmbH **(1)**
Johannisbollwerk 19, 20459, Hamburg, Germany
Tel.: (49) 4022630490
Web Site: http://www.germany.chugoku.nl
Sales Range: $25-49.9 Million
Emp.: 6
Other Chemical & Allied Products Merchant Whslr
N.A.I.C.S.: 327910
Wols Ruedigern *(Mng Dir)*

Chugoku Paints (India) Private Limited **(1)**
104 Jolly Maker Chamber No 2 10th Floor 225 Nariman Point, Mumbai, 400 021, Maharashtra, India
Tel.: (91) 2243550600
Web Site: http://www.cmp.co.jp
Sales Range: $25-49.9 Million
Emp.: 18
Paint & Coating Mfr
N.A.I.C.S.: 325510
K. L. Batra *(Mng Dir)*

Chugoku Paints (Malaysia) Sdn. Bhd. **(1)**
902 Menara PJ AMCORP Trade Center No 18 Persiaran Barat, No 18 Persiaran Barat, 46050, Petaling Jaya, Selangor Darul Ehsan, Malaysia
Tel.: (60) 379564373
Sales Range: $25-49.9 Million
Emp.: 20
Painting & Wall Covering Contractors
N.A.I.C.S.: 238320
Y. Nishimora *(Mng Dir)*

Plant (Domestic):

Chugoku Paints (Malaysia) Sdn. Bhd. - Johor Factory **(2)**
PLO 430 Jalan Emas Dua, Pasir Gudang Industrial Estate, Pasir Gudang, 81700, Johor, Malaysia
Tel.: (60) 7 2511502
Web Site: http://www.cmp.co.jp
Paints Mfr
N.A.I.C.S.: 325510

Chugoku Paints (UK) Limited **(1)**
Godliman House 21 Godliman Street, London, EC4V 5BD, United Kingdom
Tel.: (44) 77780021
Web Site: http://www.cmp.co.jp
Sales Range: $50-74.9 Million
Emp.: 8
Paint Varnish & Supplies Whslr
N.A.I.C.S.: 424950

Chugoku Paints BV **(1)**
Sluisweg 12, 4794 SW, Heijningen, Netherlands
Tel.: (31) 167526100
Web Site: http://www.chugoku.com
Sales Range: $25-49.9 Million
Emp.: 60
Paint Varnish & Supplies Whslr
N.A.I.C.S.: 424950
Kenichi Date *(Mng Dir)*

Chugoku Samhwa Paints Ltd. **(1)**
Sales Range: $25-49.9 Million
Emp.: 240
Paint & Coating Mfr
N.A.I.C.S.: 325510
Masuda Hiroshi *(Pres)*

Plant (Domestic):

Chugoku-Samhwa Paints Ltd. - Gyeongnam Factory **(2)**
322 Gimhae-daero 927beon-gil Hallim-myeon, Gimhae, 50850, Gyeongsangnam-do, Korea (South)
Tel.: (82) 55 340 0777
Web Site: http://www.csp.co.kr
Emp.: 10
Paint & Coating Mfr
N.A.I.C.S.: 325510

Chugoku Soft Development Co. Ltd. **(1)**
1-7 Meijishinkai Otake-Shi, Hiroshima, 739-0652, Japan
Tel.: (81) 827578569
Paint & Coating Mfr

N.A.I.C.S.: 325510
T. Yamazumi *(Mng Dir)*

Global Engineering Service Co., Ltd. **(1)**
1-7 Meijishinkai, Otake, 739-0652, Hiroshima, Japan
Tel.: (81) 827578555
Web Site: http://www.gmp.company.jp
Sales Range: $25-49.9 Million
Emp.: 40
Engineeering Services
N.A.I.C.S.: 541330
Hisashi Nakamura *(Mng Dir)*

Kobe Paints, Ltd. **(1)**
1321-1 Rokubuichi Aza Hyakuchobu, Inami-Cho Kako-Gun, Hyogo, 675-1112, Japan
Tel.: (81) 794950301
Web Site: http://www.cmp.co.jp
Sales Range: $25-49.9 Million
Emp.: 70
Paint & Coating Mfr
N.A.I.C.S.: 325510

Ohtake-Meishin Chemical Co., Ltd. **(1)**
1-7 Meijishingai, Otake, 739-0652, Hiroshima, Japan
Tel.: (81) 827577955
Web Site: http://www.cmp.co.jp
Sales Range: $25-49.9 Million
Emp.: 25
Other Chemical & Allied Products Merchant Whslr
N.A.I.C.S.: 424690

P.T. Chugoku Paints Indonesia **(1)**
MidPlaza I 8th Floor Jl Jend Sudirman Kav 10-11, Jalan Jendral Sudirman Kav 10, Jakarta Pusat, 10220, Indonesia
Tel.: (62) 215700515
Web Site: https://www.chugoku.co.id
Paint & Coating Mfr
N.A.I.C.S.: 325510
Kamine Ainaho *(Mng Dir)*

Sanyo Kosan Co., Ltd. **(1)**
352-2 Noji, Sukumo, Kouchi, Japan
Tel.: (81) 880630892
Marine Paint Mfr & Distr
N.A.I.C.S.: 325510

Shipping, Trading & Lighterage Co. LLC **(1)**
6th floor Shipping Tower Building Opposite Port Rashid, PO Box 464, Bur Dubai, Dubai, United Arab Emirates
Tel.: (971) 43934666
Web Site: http://www.stalco.ae
Sales Range: $25-49.9 Million
Emp.: 75
Navigational Services to Shipping
N.A.I.C.S.: 488330

Wen Trading Co., Ltd. **(1)**
1-6-18 Hikoshimaenoura-Cho, Shimonoseki-Shi, 750-0075, Yamaguchi, Japan
Tel.: (81) 83 266 5271
Web Site: http://www.cmp.co.jp
Adhesive Mfr
N.A.I.C.S.: 325520

CHUKONG HOLDINGS LIMITED

3A-20 Focus Square 6 Futong East Avenue, Beijing, 100102, China
Tel.: (86) 10 84783860 Ky
Web Site: http://en.chukong-inc.com
Year Founded: 2010
Sales Range: $75-99.9 Million
Mobile Entertainment Platform
N.A.I.C.S.: 513210
Haozhi Chen *(Co-Founder & CEO)*

CHUKYO IYAKUHIN CO., LTD.

2-15-1 Kamezaki Kitaura-cho, Handa, 475-8541, Aichi, Japan
Tel.: (81) 569290202
Web Site:
https://chukyoiyakuhin.co.jp
Year Founded: 1978
4558—(TKS)
Sales Range: $50-74.9 Million
Household Medicine Distr
N.A.I.C.S.: 456110

CHUKYO IYAKUHIN CO., LTD.—(Continued)

Masayuki Yamada (Chm & Co-CEO)

CHULARAT HOSPITAL PUBLIC COMPANY LIMITED

Chularat 3 International Hospital
88/8-9 Moo 11 Theparak Road KM
145, Bangpla Bangplee, Samut Pra-
kan, 10540, Thailand
Tel.: (66) 20332900   TH
Web Site: http://www.chularat.com
Year Founded: 1986
CHG—(THA)
Rev.: $233,956,503
Assets: $299,632,849
Liabilities: $68,116,970
Net Worth: $231,515,880
Earnings: $31,155,277
Emp.: 6,071
Fiscal Year-end: 12/31/23
Hospital Owner & Operator
N.A.I.C.S.: 622110
Kriengsak Plussind (Chm)

CHUM MINING GROUP INC.

14727 129th Street, Edmonton, T6V
1C4, AB, Canada
Tel.: (780) 887-4998   NV
Year Founded: 2012
Uranium & Other Metal Mining
N.A.I.C.S.: 212290
Wayne Cadence (Pres, CEO, CFO,
Treas & Sec)

CHUMPORN PALM OIL INDUS-TRY PUBLIC COMPANY LIM-ITED

1168/91 Lumpini Tower Building, 30th
Floor Rama IV Road Thung Maha
Mek Subdistrict Sathon District,
Bangkok, 10120, Thailand
Tel.: (66) 26799166
Web Site: https://www.cpi-th.com
Year Founded: 1979
CPI—(THA)
Rev.: $153,826,794
Assets: $130,672,015
Liabilities: $53,616,307
Net Worth: $77,055,708
Earnings: $4,414,702
Emp.: 915
Fiscal Year-end: 12/31/23
Palm Oil Mfr
N.A.I.C.S.: 311224
Rachoj Tawintermsup (Deputy CEO)

Subsidiaries:

CPI Agrotech Co., Ltd.   (1)
1168/91 30th Floor Lumpini Tower Rama IV
Rd, Thung Maha Mek Sathorn, Bangkok,
10120, Thailand
Tel.: (66) 26799166
Web Site: https://www.cpiagrotech.com
Soybean Oil Mfr
N.A.I.C.S.: 311224

CHUN CAN CAPITAL GROUP

Grosvenor Business Tower Sheikh
Zayed Road, PO Box 410550, Dubai,
United Arab Emirates   NV
Web Site:
   http://www.chuncangroup.com
Year Founded: 1996
Precious Metal Mining & Production
Enterprises
N.A.I.C.S.: 212290
Clara J. Gomez (CEO & CFO)

CHUN YU WORKS & CO., LTD.

No 100 Tapao St, Kangshan, 82063,
Kaohsiung, Taiwan
Tel.: (886) 76224111
Web Site: https://www.chunyu.com.tw
Year Founded: 1949
2012—(TAI)
Rev.: $276,681,405

Assets: $397,931,114
Liabilities: $231,833,930
Net Worth: $166,097,185
Earnings: $11,794,957
Emp.: 2,000
Fiscal Year-end: 12/31/23
Aerospace Fasteners & Medical
Equipment Mfr
N.A.I.C.S.: 334511
Chen Chi-Tai (Chm)

Subsidiaries:

Chun Yu (DongGuan) Metal Products
Co., Ltd.   (1)
Song Mu Shan Administration Zone, Da-
lang, Dongguan, 523795, Guangdong,
China
Tel.: (86) 76983310921
Structured Steel Products Mfr
N.A.I.C.S.: 331221

Chun Yu Bio-Tech Co., Ltd.   (1)
No 269 Jiahua Rd, Gangshan Dist, Kaohsi-
ung, 820, Taiwan
Tel.: (886) 76218318
Web Site: https://www.chunyubio.com
Sales Range: $25-49.9 Million
Emp.: 25
Industrial Fastener Mfr
N.A.I.C.S.: 332722

Chun Yu Metal Products Co.,
Ltd.   (1)
Songmushan, Dalang Town Yongfeng Man-
agement District, Dongguan, 523795,
Guangdong, China
Tel.: (86) 7698 331 0921
Web Site: https://www.chunyu.com.cn
Automobile Parts Mfr
N.A.I.C.S.: 336390

Chun Yu Works & Co., Ltd. - Chiash-
ing Plant   (1)
No 1 Chiashing Road, Kangshan, Kaohsi-
ung, 82057, Taiwan
Tel.: (886) 76214121
Fastener Mfr
N.A.I.C.S.: 332722

Chun Yu Works & Co., Ltd. - Kang-
shan Plant   (1)
No 100 Tapao Street, Kangshan Town, Ka-
ohsiung, 82063, Taiwan
Tel.: (886) 7 622 4111
Web Site: https://www.chunyu.com.tw
Industrial Fastener Mfr
N.A.I.C.S.: 331110

Chun Zu Machinery Ind. Co.,
Ltd.   (1)
No 50 Dapao Street, Gangshan, Kaohsi-
ung, 82063, Taiwan
Tel.: (886) 76212196
Web Site: https://www.chunzu.com.tw
Rev.: $67,000,000
Emp.: 214
Metal Parts Forming Machinery Mfr
N.A.I.C.S.: 333517

Chun Zu Machinery Industry Co.,
Ltd.   (1)
6639 Jihe Road, Baihe Town Qingpu Dis-
trict, Shanghai, 201709, China
Tel.: (86) 215 974 2888
Web Site: https://chunzu.com.cn
Bolt Former & Nut Former Mfr
N.A.I.C.S.: 332722

Hi-Ace Trading Co., Ltd.   (1)
No 28 Dabao St, Gangshan Dist, Kaohsi-
ung, 820, Taiwan
Tel.: (886) 762141067
Industrial Fasteners Distr
N.A.I.C.S.: 423710

PT. Moonlion Industries
Indonesia   (1)
Jl Rawa Bali No 8 Industrial Estate, Puloga-
dung, Jakarta, 13920, Indonesia
Tel.: (62) 214602888
Web Site: http://www.chunyu.com.tw
Hardware Mfr
N.A.I.C.S.: 332722

Shanghai Chun Zu Machinery Industry Co., Ltd.   (1)
6639 Jihe Road Baihe Town, Qingpu Dis-

trict, Shanghai, 201709, China
Tel.: (86) 2159742888
Sales Range: $50-74.9 Million
Emp.: 220
Hardware Mfr
N.A.I.C.S.: 332722

Shanghai Tongsheng Trading Co.,
Ltd.   (1)
No 9088 Hutai Rd, Luojing Town, Shanghai,
200949, China
Tel.: (86) 2166877015
Web Site: http://www.chunyu.com.tw
Emp.: 40
Fastener Distr
N.A.I.C.S.: 423710

Shanghai Uchee Hardware Products
CO., LTD   (1)
No 5 Minying Road, Luojing Town Baoshan
District, Shanghai, 200949, China
Tel.: (86) 2166877022
Web Site: https://www.uchee.com.cn
Fastener Distr
N.A.I.C.S.: 423710

USI Corporation - Kaohsiung
Plant   (1)
330 Feng Jen Road Jen Wu Hsiang, Kaoh-
siung, 814, Taiwan
Tel.: (886) 73711721
Polyethylene Resins Mfr
N.A.I.C.S.: 325211

CHUN YUAN STEEL INDUS-TRY CO., LTD.

4th F No 502 Fuhsing North Road,
Chungshan District, Taipei, Taiwan
Tel.: (886) 225018111   TW
Web Site: https://www.cysco.com.tw
Year Founded: 1965
2010—(TAI)
Rev.: $693,110,867
Assets: $663,963,218
Liabilities: $269,551,447
Net Worth: $394,411,771
Earnings: $29,128,551
Fiscal Year-end: 12/31/23
Steel Pole Mfr
N.A.I.C.S.: 332322
Chun-Yung Huang (VP-Sales)

Subsidiaries:

Chun Yuan Construction Co.,
Ltd.   (1)
3rd Floor No 502 Fuxing North Road,
Zhongshan District, Taipei, 10364, Taiwan
Tel.: (886) 22 501 8111
Web Site: https://www.chunyuan.com.tw
Commercial Building Construction & Archi-
tectural Services
N.A.I.C.S.: 236220

Chun Yuan Steel Industry Co., Ltd. -
Automated Storage System
Division   (1)
No 236 Bade Sec Shengting Rd, Longtan
Dist, Taoyuan, 32542, Taiwan
Tel.: (886) 3 489 2131
Web Site: http://www.cysco.com.tw
Global Logistics Engineering & Steel Mate-
rial Processing, Stamping Technology &
Steel Racks Mfr
N.A.I.C.S.: 541614

Chun Yuan Steel Industry Co., Ltd. -
Kaohsiung plant   (1)
No 5 Shchiuan Rd, Hsiao-Kang District, Ka-
ohsiung, 812, Taiwan
Tel.: (886) 7 802 2187
Web Site: http://www.cysco.com.tw
Fabricated Steel Product Mfr
N.A.I.C.S.: 332313

Chun Yuan Steel Industry Co., Ltd. -
Shi Tsu Plant   (1)
No 565 Sec 3 Datong Rd, Xizhi Dist, New
Taipei City, 10476, Taiwan
Tel.: (886) 28 648 6111
Web Site: https://www.cysco.com.tw
Metal Stamping Mfr
N.A.I.C.S.: 332119

Chun Yuan Steel Industry Co., Ltd. -
Special Steel Kao Hsiung Plant   (1)

No 10 Yenhai 2nd Road, Hsiao Kang Dis-
trict, Kaohsiung, 81249, Taiwan
Tel.: (886) 78060888
Metal Stamping Mfr
N.A.I.C.S.: 332119

Chun Yuan Steel Industry Co., Ltd. -
Special Steel Strip Division   (1)
No 236 Bate Section Shang Ting Road,
Longtan Hsiang, Taoyuan, 32671, Taiwan
Tel.: (886) 34892131
Stainless Steel Products Mfr
N.A.I.C.S.: 331110

Chun Yuan Steel Industry Co., Ltd. -
Special Steel Tai Chung Plant   (1)
No 501-1 Wuguang Road, Wu Jih Hsiang,
Taichung, 414, Taiwan
Tel.: (886) 4 2338 4688
Steel Strips Mfr
N.A.I.C.S.: 331110

Chun Yuan Steel Industry Co., Ltd. -
Taichung plant   (1)
No 13 25th Road Industrial Zone, Taichung,
40850, Taiwan
Tel.: (886) 423592111
Web Site: http://www.cysco.com.tw
Motor & Ceiling Fan Blades Mfr
N.A.I.C.S.: 332216

Qingdao Chun Yuan Precision
Mechatronic Co., Ltd.   (1)
No 199 Qianshan South Road Qingdao De-
velopment Area, Qingdao, 266500, Shan-
dong, China
Tel.: (86) 53286990599
Industrial Component Mfr
N.A.I.C.S.: 333248

Shanghai Chun Yuan Steel Industry
Co., LTD   (1)
No 3030 Tanglu Road, Tangzhen Town Pu-
dong, Shanghai, 201203, New Teritories,
China
Tel.: (86) 215 896 1652
Web Site: https://www.cysco.com.tw
Container Angles Mfr
N.A.I.C.S.: 339999

Shanghai Huateng Metal Processing
Co., Ltd.   (1)
No 1131 Yecheng Road, Jiading, Shanghai,
201821, China
Tel.: (86) 2159161089
Punching Machine Mfr
N.A.I.C.S.: 333517

CHUNBO CO., LTD.

312 Jungwonsaneop-ro, Judeok-eup,
Cheongju, 27459, Chungcheongbuk-
do, Korea (South)
Tel.: (82) 7048652525
Web Site:
   https://www.chunbochem.com
Year Founded: 1997
278280—(KRS)
Rev.: $252,234,811
Assets: $627,909,094
Liabilities: $325,066,475
Net Worth: $302,842,619
Earnings: $28,657,494
Emp.: 134
Fiscal Year-end: 12/31/22
Chemical Material Mfr & Distr
N.A.I.C.S.: 334413
Sang-Yul Lee (Board of Directors &
CEO)

Subsidiaries:

Chunbo Advanced Materials Co.
Ltd.   (1)
163 Jungwonsaneop-ro Judeok-eup, Chun-
gju, Chungcheongbuk, Korea (South)
Tel.: (82) 438422802
Semiconductor Product Mfr & Distr
N.A.I.C.S.: 334413

Chunbo Fine Chem Co., Ltd.   (1)
97-8 Haengje-gil 76beon-gil, Samseong-
myeon, Eumseong, Chungcheongbuk-do,
Korea (South)
Tel.: (82) 438824452
Semiconductor Product Mfr & Distr
N.A.I.C.S.: 334413

CHUNG FU CO., LTD

2F No 666 Jingping Road, Zhonghe District, New Taipei City, 23559, Taiwan
Tel.: (886) 282422881
Web Site:
https://www.chungfutex.com.tw
Year Founded: 1960
1435—(TAI)
Rev.: $277,969
Assets: $50,040,320
Liabilities: $6,014,912
Net Worth: $44,025,408
Earnings: ($1,367,572)
Fiscal Year-end: 12/31/23
Electric Component Whslr
N.A.I.C.S.: 423690

CHUNG HWA CHEMICAL IN-DUSTRIAL WORKS LTD.

No 15 Gongye 5th Rd, Guanyin Dist, Taoyuan, 328, Taiwan
Tel.: (886) 34761266
Web Site:
https://www.chciworld.com.tw
Year Founded: 1956
1727—(TAI)
Rev.: $72,121,721
Assets: $89,259,325
Liabilities: $39,888,660
Net Worth: $49,370,666
Earnings: $3,974,612
Fiscal Year-end: 12/31/22
Chemical Products Mfr
N.A.I.C.S.: 325998
Yuen Ken Wen *(Chm & Gen Mgr)*

CHUNG HWA FOOD INDUS-TRIAL CO., LTD.

110-6 Lung-Mu Road, Tashu District, Kaohsiung, Taiwan
Tel.: (886) 76515511
Web Site:
http://www.chunghwa.com.sg
4205—(TPE)
Rev.: $57,584,092
Assets: $71,538,505
Liabilities: $12,456,305
Net Worth: $59,082,200
Earnings: $11,028,609
Fiscal Year-end: 12/31/22
Food Products Mfr
N.A.I.C.S.: 311999
Min-Chuan Chen *(Chm)*

CHUNG HWA PULP CORP.

12th Floor No 51 Section 2 Chongqing South Road, Taipei, Taiwan
Tel.: (886) 223962998
Web Site: https://www.chp.com.tw
Year Founded: 1968
1905—(TAI)
Rev.: $688,370,065
Assets: $1,158,612,959
Liabilities: $586,851,510
Net Worth: $571,761,449
Earnings: ($18,133,261)
Emp.: 2,845
Fiscal Year-end: 12/31/23
Pulp & Paper Product Mfr
N.A.I.C.S.: 322299
Kirk Hwang *(Chm & CEO)*

Subsidiaries:

Chung Hwa Pulp Corp. - Chiutang Mill   **(1)**
112 Chiutang Rd Chiutang Village Tahsu District, Kaohsiung, 84041, Taiwan
Tel.: (886) 76512611
Pulp & Paper Product Mfr
N.A.I.C.S.: 333243

Chung Hwa Pulp Corp. - Hualien Mill   **(1)**
100 Kuang Hwa St Chi-An, Hua-lien, 97313, Taiwan
Tel.: (886) 38421171

Pulp & Paper Product Mfr
N.A.I.C.S.: 333243

Chung Hwa Pulp Corp. - Taitung Mill   **(1)**
371 Sec 4 Chung Hsing Rd, Taitung, 95060, Taiwan
Tel.: (886) 89382250
Pulp & Paper Product Mfr
N.A.I.C.S.: 333243

CHUNG LIEN TRANSPORTA-TION CO., LTD.

Industrial Park First Road No 7, Taichung, Taiwan
Tel.: (886) 423598181
5604—(TPE)
Rev.: $5,248,471
Assets: $89,431,469
Liabilities: $17,279,930
Net Worth: $72,151,539
Earnings: $2,937,343
Fiscal Year-end: 12/31/23
Motor Freight Transportation Services
N.A.I.C.S.: 484210
Nanzhou Su *(Chm)*

CHUNG-HSIN ELECTRIC & MACHINERY MANUFACTUR-ING CORP.

No 25 Wende Road, Guishan Dist, Taoyuan, 33383, Taiwan
Tel.: (886) 33284170
Web Site: https://www.chem.com.tw
Year Founded: 1956
1513—(TAI)
Rev.: $578,565,759
Assets: $1,114,912,937
Liabilities: $599,715,011
Net Worth: $515,197,927
Earnings: $51,855,683
Emp.: 2,284
Fiscal Year-end: 12/31/23
Electric Equipment Mfr
N.A.I.C.S.: 335999
Hui-Chuan Kuo *(Pres)*

Subsidiaries:

CHEM Energy SA (Pty) Ltd.   **(1)**
27 Umkhomazi Drive Dube TradeZone, La Mercy, Durban, 4399, KwaZulu-Natal, South Africa
Tel.: (27) 32 815 3220
Web Site: https://www.chemenergysa.com
Fuel Cell Product Mfr
N.A.I.C.S.: 335999

CHEM USA Corp.   **(1)**
8356 Central Ave, Newark, CA 94560-4743
Tel.: (510) 608-8818
Web Site: https://www.chemusa.com
Sales Range: $10-24.9 Million
Emp.: 30
Notebook Computers Sales
N.A.I.C.S.: 423430

Chung - Hsin Power Systems (Jiangsu) Corp.   **(1)**
Huolong Industrial Park, Haimen, 226144, Jiangsu, China
Tel.: (86) 51382398888
Emp.: 180
Gas-Insulated Switchgear Mfr
N.A.I.C.S.: 335313

Chung Hsin Power Systems (Shenyang) Inc.   **(1)**
No 58 Hong Hai road, Shenyang, Liao Ning, China
Tel.: (86) 242 532 1700
Web Site: http://www.chem.com.tw
Aluminum Casting Parts Mfr & Distr
N.A.I.C.S.: 331315

Chung-Hsin Precision Machinery Co., Ltd.   **(1)**
Industrial Park, Huolong Town, Haimen, 226144, Jiang-Su, China
Tel.: (86) 5138 239 8888
Web Site: http://www.chem.com.tw
Electrical Equipment Mfr & Distr
N.A.I.C.S.: 335999

Etrovision Technology Co., Ltd.   **(1)**
2F 19-5 Sanchong Road, Nankang District, Taipei, 115, Taiwan
Tel.: (886) 226551518
Web Site: www.etrovision.com
Sales Range: $25-49.9 Million
Emp.: 50
Semiconductor & Device Mfr
N.A.I.C.S.: 334413

Global-Entech Co., Ltd   **(1)**
8F-5 No 238 Jinhua North Rd, North District 404, Taichung, Taiwan   **(99.77%)**
Tel.: (886) 42 238 0408
Web Site: https://www.chem.com.tw
Professional, Scientific & Technical Services
N.A.I.C.S.: 541990

H2 Power Tech, LLC   **(1)**
746 SE Glenwood Dr, Bend, OR 97702
Tel.: (541) 383-3390
Web Site: https://www.h2powertech.com
Fuel Cell Product Mfr
N.A.I.C.S.: 335999
Harol Hal Koyama *(CEO)*

Jiangsu Chung - Hsin Precision Machinery Co., Ltd.   **(1)**
Industrial Park, Huolong Town, Haimen, 226144, Jiangsu, China
Tel.: (86) 51382398888
Gas-Insulated Switchgear Product Mfr & Distr
N.A.I.C.S.: 335313

Nantong Shengyi Precision Machinery Co., Ltd.   **(1)**
Industrial & Trading Park Area, Huolong Hanmen, Nantong, 226144, Jiangsu, China
Tel.: (86) 51382398901
Bearing Mfr & Distr
N.A.I.C.S.: 336310

Parktron Malaysia Sdn Bhd   **(1)**
No 3-16 Jalan USJ Sentral 3 USJ Sentral Persiaran Subang 1, 47600, Subang Jaya, Selangor, Malaysia
Tel.: (60) 3 8023 0024
Parking Meter Mfr
N.A.I.C.S.: 334514

Parktron Technology Co., Ltd   **(1)**
9F -3 No 16 Jian 8th Rd, Zhonghe Dist, New Taipei City, 235, Taiwan
Tel.: (886) 28 227 6186
Web Site: https://www.parktron.com
Sales Range: $25-49.9 Million
Emp.: 25
Automatic Vending Machine Mfr
N.A.I.C.S.: 333310

Shandong Grad Group   **(1)**
No 6 Grad Road Tianqu Industrial Park, Dezhou, Shandong, China
Tel.: (86) 5342730845
Web Site: http://www.gradgroup.com
Emp.: 2,000
Air Conditioning Equipment Mfr & Distr
N.A.I.C.S.: 333415

Tone Zoom Industry Co., Ltd.   **(1)**
No13-1 Szu-hu-wei, Chang-liang-tsun Hukou, Hsin-chu, Taiwan
Tel.: (886) 35990397
Plastic Product Mfr & Distr
N.A.I.C.S.: 325211

WHA Dun Building Management Service Co., Ltd.   **(1)**
2F No 19-5 San-Chong Road, Nankang Software Park, Taipei, 115, Taiwan
Tel.: (886) 226551350
Electrical & Mechanical Equipment Maintenance Services
N.A.I.C.S.: 811310

CHUNG-KANG STEEL STRUC-TURE (KUNSHAN) CO., LTD.

No 168 Shuanghua Rd Huaciao Township, Kunshan, Jiangsu, China
Tel.: (86) 51257605788
Steel Products Mfr
N.A.I.C.S.: 331511

CHUNGDAHM LEARNING, INC.

21F Parnas Tower 521 Teheran-ro, Gangnam-gu, Seoul, 06164, Korea (South)

Tel.: (82) 234299407
Web Site: https://creverse.com
Year Founded: 1998
096240—(KRS)
Rev.: $174,492,179
Assets: $171,923,372
Liabilities: $135,940,327
Net Worth: $35,983,045
Earnings: $3,782,268
Emp.: 1,162
Fiscal Year-end: 12/31/22
Online Education Services
N.A.I.C.S.: 611710

Subsidiaries:

CMS Edu Co., Ltd.   **(1)**
Bumyang Building 2nd 7th Floor 208 Bangbae-ro, Seocho-gu, Seoul, Korea (South)
Tel.: (82) 25528500
Web Site: http://www.cmsedu.co.kr
Rev.: $73,654,076
Assets: $83,159,811
Liabilities: $50,069,345
Net Worth: $33,090,466
Earnings: $5,618,250
Emp.: 1,083
Fiscal Year-end: 12/31/2021
Education Services
N.A.I.C.S.: 611710

Chungdahm Philippines, Inc.   **(1)**
15F Wilcon IT Hub 2251 1231 Chino Roces Ave, Makati, Metro Manila, Philippines
Tel.: (63) 28227988
Web Site: https://www.chungdahm.com.ph
Emp.: 500
Educational Support Services
N.A.I.C.S.: 611691

CHUNGDAM GLOBAL CO., LTD.

Centroad Bldg B-2401 incheon towerdaero, Yeonsu-gu, Incheon, Korea (South)
Tel.: (82) 327218211
Web Site:
https://www.chungdamgroup.com
Year Founded: 2017
362320—(KRS)
Cosmetic Product Distr
N.A.I.C.S.: 456120

CHUNGHSIN TECHNOLOGY GROUP CO., LTD

618-2 Gongren West Road, Jiaojiang Area, Taizhou, 318000, China
Tel.: (86) 5768 832 2668
Web Site: http://www.cncoptronics.cn
603996—(SHG)
Rev.: $20,182,353
Assets: $135,183,311
Liabilities: $435,468,783
Net Worth: ($300,285,472)
Earnings: ($200,132,095)
Fiscal Year-end: 12/31/20
Television & Computer Mfr & Distr
N.A.I.C.S.: 334310

CHUNGHWA CHEMICAL SYN-THESIS & BIOTECH CO., LTD.

1 Tung-Hsing St, Shu-Lin, 23850, Taipei, 23850, Taiwan
Tel.: (886) 286843318
Web Site: https://www.ccsb.com.tw
Year Founded: 1964
1762—(TAI)
Rev.: $68,231,169
Assets: $169,124,262
Liabilities: $59,564,274
Net Worth: $109,559,988
Earnings: $8,663,102
Emp.: 330
Fiscal Year-end: 12/31/23
Chemical, Pharmaceutical & Biotechnology Mfr
N.A.I.C.S.: 325998

Chunghwa Chemical Synthesis & Biotech Co., Ltd.—(Continued)

Subsidiaries:

Chunghwa Biomedical Technology Co., Ltd. **(1)**
8F No 73 Zhouzi Street, Neihu District, Taipei, 114, Taiwan
Tel.: (886) 226599070
Health Care Products Mfr
N.A.I.C.S.: 325611

Pharmaports LLC **(1)**
1 E Uwchlan Ave Ste 116, Exton, PA 19341
Tel.: (610) 524-7888
Web Site: https://pharmaports.com
Emp.: 4
Pharmaceutical Products Distr
N.A.I.C.S.: 424210

CHUNGHWA TELECOM CO., LTD.
No 21-3 Sec 1 Xinyi Rd, Zhongzheng Dist, Taipei, Taiwan
Tel.: (886) 223445488
Web Site: https://www.cht.com.tw
Year Founded: 1996
CHT—(NYSE)
Rev.: $6,978,676,172
Assets: $16,375,605,791
Liabilities: $4,096,613,826
Net Worth: $12,278,991,964
Earnings: $1,190,038,458
Emp.: 32,383
Fiscal Year-end: 12/31/23
Telecommunication Servicesb
N.A.I.C.S.: 517112
Hong-Chan Ma (Sr Exec VP-Bus)

Subsidiaries:

CHT Security Co., Ltd. **(1)**
8F No 26 Sec 1 Hangzhou S Rd, Taipei, 10052, Taiwan
Tel.: (886) 223431628
Web Site: http://www.chtsecurity.com
System Security Services
N.A.I.C.S.: 561621

Chief Telecom Inc. **(1)**
(69%)
Tel.: (886) 226576688
Web Site: http://www.chief.com.tw
International Telecommunications Services
N.A.I.C.S.: 517111

Subsidiary (Domestic):

Unigate Telecom Inc. **(2)**
No 250 Yuang Guang St Neihu Chiu, Taipei, 11483, Taiwan
Tel.: (886) 2 2657 6688
Web Site: http://www.unigate.net.tw
Sales Range: $50-74.9 Million
Emp.: 160
Telecommunication Servicesb
N.A.I.C.S.: 517810

Chunghwa Leading Photonics Tech Co., Ltd. **(1)**
No 6 Ziqiang 7th Rd, Zhongli Dist, Taoyuan, 32063, Taiwan
Tel.: (886) 34353888
Web Site: https://en.clpt.com.tw
Short-Wave Infrared Device Mfr
N.A.I.C.S.: 334413

Chunghwa Precision Test Tech. Co., Ltd **(1)**
2F No 15 Gongye 3rd Rd, Pingjhen, 324, Taoyuan, Taiwan
Tel.: (886) 3 469 1234
Web Site: http://www.cht-pt.com.tw
Sales Range: $50-74.9 Million
Emp.: 250
Test Board Mfr
N.A.I.C.S.: 335999

Chunghwa Precision Test Tech. USA Corporation **(1)**
2047 Zanker Rd Ste 10, San Jose, CA 95131
Tel.: (408) 380-0008
Semiconductors & Equipment Mfr
N.A.I.C.S.: 334413

Chunghwa System Integration Co., Ltd. **(1)**
No 2-1 Aly 8 Ln 85 Sec 3 Muzha Rd, Wenshan Dist, Taipei, 116, Taiwan
Tel.: (886) 223454666
Information Technology Consulting Services
N.A.I.C.S.: 541512

Chunghwa Telecom (Thailand) Co., Ltd. **(1)**
65/131 16th Floor Chamnan Phenjati Business Centre Rama 9 Rd, Huay Kwang District, Bangkok, 10310, Thailand
Tel.: (66) 224871012
Network Telecommunication Services
N.A.I.C.S.: 517810
Yang Wen-Jang (Gen Dir)

Chunghwa Telecom Global, Inc. **(1)**
2107 N 1st St Ste 580, San Jose, CA 95131 **(100%)**
Tel.: (408) 988-1898
Sales Range: $25-49.9 Million
Emp.: 20
International Telecommunications Services
N.A.I.C.S.: 517112

Chunghwa Telecom Japan Co., Ltd **(1)**
Asakawa Building 5F 2-1-17 Shibadaimon, Minato-Ku, Tokyo, 105-0012, Japan **(100%)**
Tel.: (81) 334365988
Telecommunication Servicesb
N.A.I.C.S.: 517112

Chunghwa Telecom Singapore Pte Ltd **(1)**
331 North Bridge Road 03-05 Odeon Towers, Singapore, 188720, Singapore **(100%)**
Tel.: (65) 63372010
Telecommunication Servicesb
N.A.I.C.S.: 517112

Chunghwa Telecom Vietnam Co., Ltd. **(1)**
Room 703 7th Floor 3D Viet Nam Duy Tan St, Dich Vong Hau Ward Cau Giay Dist, Hanoi, Vietnam
Tel.: (84) 24379511502
Internet Hosting Services
N.A.I.C.S.: 518210

Donghwa Telecom Co. Ltd **(1)**
Unit A 7/F Tower A Billion Centre No 1 Wang Kwong Road, Kowloon Bay, Kowloon, China (Hong Kong) **(100%)**
Tel.: (852) 35862600
International Telecommunications Services
N.A.I.C.S.: 517112
Michael Lu (Mgr-Project)

Light Era Development Co., Ltd. **(1)**
4th Floor Business Building No 31 Alguo East Road, Zhongzheng District, Taipei, 100, Taiwan
Tel.: (886) 227039789
Web Site: https://www.light-era.com.tw
Real Estate Development Services
N.A.I.C.S.: 531390

Senao International Co., Ltd. **(1)**
2F No 531 Zhongzheng Rd, Xindian Dist, New Taipei City, 231, Taiwan **(31%)**
Tel.: (886) 033289289
Computer Communication Based Consumer Electronics
N.A.I.C.S.: 423430

Subsidiary (Domestic):

Senao Networks, Inc. **(2)**
No 500 Fusing 3rd Road, Linkou Huaya Science and Technology Park Guishan District, Taoyuan, Kuei-shan Hsiang, Taiwan
Tel.: (886) 33289289
Web Site: https://www.senaonetworks.com
Data Networking & Wireless Voice Communication Products
N.A.I.C.S.: 518210

Smartfun Digital Co., Ltd. **(1)**
8th Floor No 88 Section 4 Xinyi Road, Da'an District, Taipei, Taiwan
Tel.: (886) 223257188
Web Site: http://www.smartfun.com.tw
Software Development Services
N.A.I.C.S.: 541511

Spring House Entertainment Tech Inc. **(1)**

10th Floor No 106 Zhouzi Street, Neihu, Taipei, 114, Taiwan
Tel.: (886) 287518399
Web Site: https://www.springhouse.com.tw
Mobile Application Software Development Services
N.A.I.C.S.: 541511

CHUNGKWANG CONSTRUCTION CO., LTD.
550 Eonju-ro Gangnam-gu, Seoul, Korea (South)
Tel.: (82) 2 34616393
Highway & Street Construction
N.A.I.C.S.: 237310
Soong Huh (CEO)

CHUNGNAM NATIONAL UNIVERSITY
99 Daehak-ro, Yuseong-gu, Daejeon, 34134, Korea (South)
Tel.: (82) 428215114
Web Site: https://plus.cnu.ac.kr
Year Founded: 1952
Educational Support Services
N.A.I.C.S.: 611710

CHUNICHI SHIMBUN CO., LTD.
1-6-1 Sannomaru, Naka-Ku, Nagoya, 460-0001, Aichi, Japan
Tel.: (81) 522018811
Web Site: http://www.chunichi.co.jp
Year Founded: 1886
Sales Range: $1-4.9 Billion
Emp.: 3,500
Newspaper Publishing & News Distribution
N.A.I.C.S.: 513110
Bungo Shirai (Chm)

Subsidiaries:

Chunichi Dragons Co., Inc. **(1)**
Chunichi Bldg 6th FL 4-1-1 Sakae, Naka-ku, Nagoya, 460-0008, Aichi, Japan
Tel.: (81) 522618811
Web Site: http://www.dragons.co.jp
Sales Range: $75-99.9 Million
Emp.: 100
Professional Basketball Team
N.A.I.C.S.: 711211
Takao Sasaki (Pres)

CHUNIL EXPRESS CO., LTD.
11-9 Choryang-dong, Dong-gu, Busan, Korea (South)
Tel.: (82) 512549111
Web Site:
http://www.chunilexpress.com
Year Founded: 1949
000650—(KRS)
Rev.: $28,918,339
Assets: $42,066,620
Liabilities: $21,652,338
Net Worth: $20,414,282
Earnings: ($4,607,385)
Emp.: 311
Fiscal Year-end: 12/31/22
Bus Transportation Services
N.A.I.C.S.: 485210
Jae-Myung Park (Chm)

CHUNTEX ELECTRONIC CO., LTD.
1F No 136 Lane 235, Baoqiao Rd, New Taipei City, 231, Xindian, Taiwan
Tel.: (886) 289121889 **TW**
Web Site: http://www.ctx.com.tw
Year Founded: 1981
Computer Terminal Mfr
N.A.I.C.S.: 334118

CHUO ELECTRONICS CO., LTD.
Hachioji Sq Bldg 7 Fl 3-20-6 Myojin Cho, Tokyo, 192-0046, Japan
Tel.: (81) 426565811
Web Site: http://www.cec.co.jp
Year Founded: 1960

Sales Range: $50-74.9 Million
Emp.: 70
Electronic Components Mfr
N.A.I.C.S.: 423690
Hitoshi Miyata (Gen Mgr)

CHUO GYORUI CO., LTD.
6-6-2 Toyosu, Koto-ku, Tokyo, 135-8108, Japan
Tel.: (81) 366333000
Web Site:
https://www.chuogyorui
Year Founded: 1947
8030—(TKS)
Rev.: $909,456,680
Assets: $518,323,150
Liabilities: $313,419,760
Net Worth: $204,903,390
Earnings: $14,105,740
Fiscal Year-end: 03/31/24
Marine Product Whslr
N.A.I.C.S.: 424460
Hiroyasu Ito (Chm & CEO)

Subsidiaries:

Chiba Chuo Gyorui Co., Ltd. **(1)**
2-1 Takahama 2-chome, Mihama-ku, Chiba, 261-0003, Japan
Tel.: (81) 432483418
Seafood Product Distr
N.A.I.C.S.: 424460

Chuo Foods Co., Ltd. **(1)**
HOHSUI CORP 8F 6-3 Toyosu 6-chome, Koto-ku, Tokyo, 135-0061, Japan
Tel.: (81) 366333420
Seafood Product Distr
N.A.I.C.S.: 424460
Yuen Kan Wen (Chm)

Chuo Koage Co., Ltd. **(1)**
Fisheries wholesale market Bldg 6-2 Toyosu 6-chome, Koto-ku, Tokyo, 135-0061, Japan
Tel.: (81) 366333456
Web Site: http://www.chuo-koage.co.jp
Seafood Product Distr
N.A.I.C.S.: 424460

Kashiwa Uoichiba Co., Ltd. **(1)**
69-1 Wakashiba, Kashiwa, 277-8545, Chiba, Japan
Tel.: (81) 471324761
Web Site: https://www.kashiwa-marunaka.jp
Seafood Product Distr
N.A.I.C.S.: 424460

Ocean Stage Inc. **(1)**
3-2-5 5F Tsukiji, Chuo-Ku, Tokyo, 104-0045, Japan
Tel.: (81) 355500051
Web Site: https://www.oceanstage.jp
Seafood Product Distr
N.A.I.C.S.: 424460

Tokyo Kitauo Co., Ltd. **(1)**
50 Senjuhashido-machi, Adachi-ku, Tokyo, 120-0038, Japan
Tel.: (81) 338705100
Seafood Product Distr
N.A.I.C.S.: 424460

CHUO MALLEABLE IRON CO., LTD.
1-300 Asadahirako, Nisshin, 4700128, Japan
Tel.: (81) 528058601
Web Site: https://chuokatan.co.jp
Year Founded: 1944
5607—(TKS)
Rev.: $321,327,600
Assets: $382,631,040
Liabilities: $153,011,760
Net Worth: $229,619,280
Earnings: $7,589,120
Fiscal Year-end: 03/31/22
Steel Furniture Mfr & Distr
N.A.I.C.S.: 337214
Yutaka Takeyama (Pres & Dir)

CHUO SEISAKUSHO LTD.
24-1 Uchihama-cho, Mizuho-Ku, Nagoya, 467-8563, Japan
Tel.: (81) 8216111

Web Site: https://www.chuo-
seisakusho.co.jp
6846—(NGO)
Rev.: $39,889,500
Assets: $41,393,380
Liabilities: $20,540,800
Net Worth: $20,852,580
Earnings: $348,460
Fiscal Year-end: 03/12/20
Electrical Equipment Mfr & Distr
N.A.I.C.S.: 335999
Kuniyuki Goto *(Pres)*

CHUO SENKO ADVERTISING CO., LTD.
6-1 Ginza 2-Chome, Chuo-ku, Tokyo,
104-8211, Japan
Tel.: (81) 335620151   JP
Web Site: http://www.chusen.co.jp
Year Founded: 1954
Emp.: 630
Advetising Agency
N.A.I.C.S.: 541810
Shigeru Ohsawa *(Chm & Pres)*

Subsidiaries:

CS Advertising SDN. BHD.   **(1)**
25G & 25M Medan Setia 1 Plaza, Damansara Heights, 50490, Kuala Lumpur, Malaysia
Tel.: (60) 3 2093 3611
N.A.I.C.S.: 541810

Chuo Senko (Cambodia) Holding Co.,
Ltd.   **(1)**
No 35-37 Samdech Pan (St. 214) 1st Fl
Room B5, T&C Coffee, Phnom Penh, Cam-
bodia
Tel.: (855) 23 991 116
Emp.: 3
N.A.I.C.S.: 541810

Chuo Senko (Thailand) Public Co.,
Ltd.   **(1)**
18th Fl Emporium Tower 622 Sukhumvit
Rd, Klongton Klongtoey, Bangkok, 10110,
Thailand
Tel.: (66) 2 664 9700
Web Site: http://www.chuosenko.co.th
N.A.I.C.S.: 541810

Chuo Senko Advertising (HK)
Ltd.   **(1)**
17 Flr Winsan Tower 98 Thomson Rd, Wan-
chai, China (Hong Kong)
Tel.: (852) 2375 4194
N.A.I.C.S.: 541810
Menehiro Sagawa *(Pres)*

Chuo Senko Advertising (S) Pte.
Ltd.   **(1)**
10 Genting Road Level 4, 34973, Singa-
pore, Singapore
Tel.: (65) 6225 3511
N.A.I.C.S.: 541810

Chuo Senko Advertising (Taiwan)
Co., Ltd.   **(1)**
12F No 102 Dunhua N Rd, Songshan Dis-
trict, Taipei, 105, Taiwan
Tel.: (886) 2 2547 2818
N.A.I.C.S.: 541810

Chuo Senko Advertising Co.,
Ltd.   **(1)**
Nagahori Plz Bldg 2-4-8 Minami-Senba,
Chuo-ku, Osaka, 542-0081, Japan
Tel.: (81) 6 6262 5991
Web Site: http://www.chusen.co.jp
Emp.: 7
N.A.I.C.S.: 541810

Chuo Senko Advertising Co.,
Ltd.   **(1)**
3th Floor Kiku Building 1-19-26 Aoi,
Higashi-ku, Nagoya, 461-0004, Aichi, Japan
Tel.: (81) 52 937 6361
Web Site: http://www.chusen.co.jp
N.A.I.C.S.: 541810

Chuo Senko Advertising Co.,
Ltd.   **(1)**
6-1 Ginza 2-chome, Chuo-ku, Sapporo,
104-8211, Japan
Tel.: (81) 11 241 2495

Web Site: http://www.chusen.co.jp
N.A.I.C.S.: 541810

Chuo Senko Advertising Co.,
Ltd.   **(1)**
6-1 Ginza 2-chome, Chuo-ku, Tokyo, 104
8211, Japan
Tel.: (81) 92 733 6191
Web Site: http://www.chusen.co.jp
N.A.I.C.S.: 541810

Chuo Senko Advertising Co.,
Ltd.   **(1)**
2th Floor Kanagaki Building Nakahiro-cho,
Nishi-ku, Hiroshima, 733-0012, Japan
Tel.: (81) 82 294 4547
Web Site: http://www.chusen.co.jp
N.A.I.C.S.: 541810

Chuo Senko Advertising Co.,
Ltd.   **(1)**
Ekinan Building 1-10-19 Ekinan, Takaoka-
ku, Toyama, 933-0871, Japan
Tel.: (81) 766 22 3631
Web Site: http://www.chusen.co.jp
N.A.I.C.S.: 541810

Chuo Senko Advertising Co.,
Ltd.   **(1)**
5th Floor Saseigaiyo Building 3-6-12
Kokubu-cho, Aoba-ku, Sendai, 980-0803,
Miyagi, Japan
Tel.: (81) 22 267 5996
Web Site: http://www.chusen.co.jp
N.A.I.C.S.: 541810

Chuo Senko Advertising Co.,
Ltd.   **(1)**
C/O Fujidenso 2-4-6 Awacha, Urasoe, 900-
0034, Okinawa, Japan
Tel.: (81) 98 877 4991
Web Site: http://www.chusen.co.jp
N.A.I.C.S.: 541810

Chuo Senko Vietnam Representative
Office   **(1)**
OSIC Building 7th Floor Unit F 8 Nguyen
Hue Boulevard, District 1, Ho Chi Minh City,
Vietnam
Tel.: (84) 8 824 5231 3
N.A.I.C.S.: 541810

P.T. Chuo Senko Indonesia   **(1)**
Sentral Senayan1 8th Floor Jl Asia Afrika
No 8, Jakarta, 10270, Indonesia
Tel.: (62) 21 572 5845
Web Site: http://www.chuosenko.co.id
N.A.I.C.S.: 541810

CHUO SPRING CO., LTD.
68 Aza Kamishiota Narumi-cho,
Midori-ku, Nagoya, 458-8505, Aichi,
Japan
Tel.: (81) 526231111
Web Site: https://www.chkk.co.jp
Year Founded: 1925
5992—(TKS)
Rev.: $667,444,750
Assets: $1,015,110,920
Liabilities: $404,379,970
Net Worth: $610,730,950
Earnings: $13,153,900
Emp.: 4,291
Fiscal Year-end: 03/31/24
Spring Product Mfr & Distr
N.A.I.C.S.: 332613
Satoshi Suzuki *(Mng Officer)*

Subsidiaries:

ACK CONTROLS Inc.   **(1)**
2600 Happy Vly Rd, Glasgow, KY 42141
Tel.: (270) 678-6200
Emp.: 260
Cable Mfr
N.A.I.C.S.: 335921
Carrol Knicely *(Gen Mgr)*

CEPLUS Co., Ltd.   **(1)**
41-1 Miyashita Fukuta- cho, Miyoshi, 470-
0225, Aichi, Japan
Tel.: (81) 561 34 2285
Web Site: http://www.ceplus.co.jp
Emp.: 35
Plating Services
N.A.I.C.S.: 332813

Chuhatsu (Thailand) Co., Ltd.   **(1)**
17/3 Moo2 Tambon, Bankhai Amphur
Bankhai, Rayong, 21120, Thailand
Tel.: (66) 38017870
Web Site: https://www.chuo.co.th
Emp.: 550
Cable & Spring Mfr
N.A.I.C.S.: 332613
Vijit Katanyuta *(Pres)*

Plant (Domestic):

Chuhatsu (Thailand) Co., Ltd. - He-
maraj Plant   **(2)**
349 Moo3 Nonglalok Sub-Distric, Bankhai
Distric, Rayong, 21120, Thailand
Tel.: (66) 38 892044
Spring & Cable Mfr
N.A.I.C.S.: 332613

Chuhatsu Hanbai Co., Ltd.   **(1)**
2-114 Naruo, Minami-ku, Nagoya, 457-
0066, Japan
Tel.: (81) 526143653
Web Site: http://www.yukidouraku.com
Sales Range: $50-74.9 Million
Emp.: 120
Automobile Parts Distr
N.A.I.C.S.: 441330

Chuhatsu North America, Inc.   **(1)**
2600 Happy Valley Rd, Glasgow, KY 42141
Tel.: (270) 678-6200
Web Site: https://www.chuosna.com
Emp.: 231
Automotive Parts Mfr & Distr
N.A.I.C.S.: 336390

Chuhatsu Seikou Co., Ltd.   **(1)**
13 Fukuda Miyoshi-cho, Miyoshi, 470-0225,
Aichi, Japan
Tel.: (81) 561323671
Web Site: https://www.chkk-csk.co.jp
Emp.: 55
Spring Mfr
N.A.I.C.S.: 332613

Chuhatsu Unyu Co., Ltd.   **(1)**
4-3 Yashiki-cho, Hekinan, 447-0077, Aichi,
Japan
Tel.: (81) 566 48 1021
Emp.: 37
Logistics Consulting Servies
N.A.I.C.S.: 541614

Chuhatsu-Techno Co., Ltd.   **(1)**
1-3-79 Kita-Inter-Kogyodanchi, Hachinohe,
039-2245, Aomori, Japan
Tel.: (81) 178 21 2166
Emp.: 14
Automobile Parts Mfr
N.A.I.C.S.: 336390

Chuo Spring Co., Ltd. - Fujioka
Plant   **(1)**
1071-1 Mukaihora Fukami-cho, Toyota, 470-
0441, Aichi, Japan
Tel.: (81) 565 76 0621
Emp.: 553
Control Cable & Spring Mfr
N.A.I.C.S.: 332613

Chuo Spring Co., Ltd. - Hekinan
Plant   **(1)**
1-21Yashiki-cho, Hekinan, 447-0077, Aichi,
Japan
Tel.: (81) 566 48 1111
Emp.: 132
Spring Mfr
N.A.I.C.S.: 332613

Chuo Spring Co., Ltd. - Miyoshi
Plant   **(1)**
29-5 Gongenyama Fukuta-cho, Miyoshi,
470-0225, Aichi, Japan
Tel.: (81) 561 34 1111
Emp.: 377
Spring Mfr
N.A.I.C.S.: 332613

FEC Chain Corporation   **(1)**
337 Kanorimachi, Chuo-ku, Hamamatsu,
435-0026, Shizuoka, Japan
Tel.: (81) 534254117
Web Site: https://www.fecchain.co.jp
Emp.: 130
Automotive Parts Mfr & Distr
N.A.I.C.S.: 336110

FUJIOKA-CHUHATSU Co., Ltd.   **(1)**

1077-4 Mukaihora Fukami-cho, Toyota, 470-
0441, Aichi, Japan
Tel.: (81) 565 76 7260
Emp.: 10
Cable Mfr
N.A.I.C.S.: 335921

GIFU-CHUHATSU Co., Ltd.   **(1)**
1265-6 Taniguminare, Ibigawa-cho Ibi-gun,
Gifu, 501-1314, Japan
Tel.: (81) 585563021
Emp.: 111
Control Cable Production Services
N.A.I.C.S.: 335921

Kunshan Chuho Spring Co., Ltd.   **(1)**
No 176 Xiong Ying Road Kunshan Eco-
nomic Technical, Development Zone, Kun-
shan, 215300, Jiangsu, China
Tel.: (86) 51236691668
Emp.: 116
Spring & Cable Mfr
N.A.I.C.S.: 332613

NAGASAKI-CHUHATSU Co.,
Ltd.   **(1)**
147-48 Masuragahara-machi, Oomura-shi,
Nagasaki, 856-0022, Japan
Tel.: (81) 957532512
Emp.: 62
Spring & Cable Mfr
N.A.I.C.S.: 332613

P.T. Chuhatsu Indonesia   **(1)**
Jalan K H Noer Ali Desa Cibuntu, Cibitung,
Bekasi, 17520, Jawa Barat, Indonesia
Tel.: (62) 21 88330010
Web Site: http://www.chuhatsu.co.id
Emp.: 453
Chassis Spring Mfr
N.A.I.C.S.: 332613
A. Hefri Kurnia *(Mgr-Sls)*

REELEX CO., LTD.   **(1)**
141 Hachiken-cho, Handa, 475-0807, Aichi,
Japan
Tel.: (81) 569 23 7723
Emp.: 8
Reel Mfr
N.A.I.C.S.: 334310

Taiwan Chuhatsu Factory Co.,
Ltd.   **(1)**
No 3 Su Wei Road Houkou Hsiang, Hsin-
chu, Taiwan
Tel.: (886) 35 98 3224
Emp.: 70
Spring & Cable Mfr
N.A.I.C.S.: 332613

Tianjin Chuhatsu Huaguan Machinery
Co., Ltd.   **(1)**
65 Yujian Road, Hexi District, Tianjin,
300221, China
Tel.: (86) 2288253342
Emp.: 143
Cable Mfr
N.A.I.C.S.: 335921

Tianjin Longxing Co., Ltd.   **(1)**
Emp.: 119
Spring Mfr
N.A.I.C.S.: 332613

Tianjin Zhongxing Automotive Com-
ponents Co., Ltd.   **(1)**
No 89 Xinye 2nd Avenue the west zone of
TEDA, Tianjin, China
Tel.: (86) 22 5982 5980
Emp.: 55
Spring Mfr
N.A.I.C.S.: 332613

Togo Cable Co., Ltd.   **(1)**
23-3 Hara Azabu-cho, Miyoshi, 470-0206,
Aichi, Japan
Tel.: (81) 561343166
Emp.: 61
Cable Mfr
N.A.I.C.S.: 335921

Xiaogan Chuhatsu Lioho Automotive
Components Co., Ltd.   **(1)**
3 Road Liuhe Industrial Park, High-Tech
District, Xiaogan, China
Tel.: (86) 7122859933
Emp.: 28
Chassis Spring Mfr
N.A.I.C.S.: 332613

Chuo Spring Co., Ltd.—(Continued)

Xiaogan Zhongxing Automotive Components Co., Ltd. (1)
3 Road Liuhe Industrial Park, High-Tech District, Xiaogan, China
Tel.: (86) 712 285 9933
Emp.: 4
Spring Mfr
N.A.I.C.S.: 332613

CHUO WAREHOUSE CO., LTD.
41 Uchihatacho Suzaku, Shimogyo Ward, Kyoto, 600-8843, Japan
Tel.: (81) 753136151
Web Site: https://www.chuosoko.co.jp
Year Founded: 1927
9319—(TKS)
Rev.: $175,244,320
Assets: $383,485,760
Liabilities: $82,063,150
Net Worth: $301,422,610
Earnings: $11,223,780
Fiscal Year-end: 03/31/24
Warehousing Services
N.A.I.C.S.: 493110
Masakazu Kimura (Pres)

CHUOKEIZAI-SHA HOLDINGS, INC.
1-35 Jinbocho Kanda, Chiyoda-ku, Tokyo, 101-0051, Japan
Tel.: (81) 332933371
Web Site:
https://www.chuokeizai.co.jp
Year Founded: 1948
9476—(TKS)
Rev.: $21,489,790
Assets: $42,050,790
Liabilities: $11,868,660
Net Worth: $30,182,130
Earnings: $382,860
Emp.: 90
Fiscal Year-end: 09/30/23
Books Publishing Services
N.A.I.C.S.: 513130
Norio Yamamoto (Pres)

CHUONG DUONG BEVERAGES JOINT STOCK COMPANY
606 Vo Van Kiet Cau Kho Ward, District 1, Ho Chi Minh City, Vietnam
Tel.: (84) 838367518
Web Site:
https://www.cdbeco.com.vn
SCD—(HOSE)
Rev.: $5,202,654
Assets: $28,331,551
Liabilities: $28,814,950
Net Worth: ($483,400)
Earnings: ($4,913,182)
Fiscal Year-end: 12/31/23
Beverages Mfr
N.A.I.C.S.: 312111

CHUONG DUONG CORPORATION
328 Vo Van Kiet, District 1, Ho Chi Minh City, Vietnam
Tel.: (84) 2838367734
Web Site:
https://www.chuongduongcorp.vn
Year Founded: 1977
CDC—(HOSE)
Rev.: $53,712,811
Assets: $74,402,338
Liabilities: $60,463,802
Net Worth: $13,938,537
Earnings: $439,027
Fiscal Year-end: 12/31/23
Civil Engineering Services
N.A.I.C.S.: 237990
Tran Mai Cuong (Chm)

CHUOU INTERNATIONAL GROUP CO., LTD.

2-12-101 Tojin 2-chome, Yubinbango, Saga, 840-0813, Japan
Tel.: (81) 952376231
Web Site: https://www.cig-ins.co.jp
Year Founded: 1992
7170—(TKS)
Rev.: $4,707,760
Assets: $12,329,510
Liabilities: $7,621,750
Net Worth: $4,707,760
Earnings: $14,180
Fiscal Year-end: 12/31/23
Insurance Agency Services
N.A.I.C.S.: 524210

CHURCH INTERNATIONAL LTD
1 Tolherst Court Turkey Mill Ashford Road, Maidstone, ME14 5SF, Kent, United Kingdom
Tel.: (44) 1622675126
Web Site: http://www.church-int.com
Year Founded: 1984
Management Consultancy Services
N.A.I.C.S.: 541611
Chriss Andrews (Founder & CEO)

CHURCHILL CHINA PLC
No 1 Marlborough Way, Tunstall, Stoke-on-Trent, ST6 5NZ, United Kingdom
Tel.: (44) 1782577566
Web Site:
http://www.churchill1795.com
Year Founded: 1795
CHH—(LSE)
Rev.: $104,823,680
Assets: $102,546,149
Liabilities: $26,236,792
Net Worth: $76,309,357
Earnings: $9,824,316
Emp.: 700
Fiscal Year-end: 12/31/23
China Dishes & Tableware Mfr
N.A.I.C.S.: 327110
David J. S. Taylor (Sec & Dir-Fin)

Subsidiaries:

Furlong Mills Limited (1)
Furlong Lane, Stoke-on-Trent, ST6 3LE, United Kingdom (55.6%)
Tel.: (44) 1782838428
Web Site: http://www.furlongmills.co.uk
Sales Range: $10-24.9 Million
Emp.: 50
Clay Supplier & Miller
N.A.I.C.S.: 327120
Michael Roper (Mng Dir)

CHURCHILL RESOURCES INC.
133 Richmond St W Suite 505, Toronto, M5H 2L3, ON, Canada
Tel.: (647) 988-0930
Web Site:
https://www.churchillresources.com
CRICF—(OTCIQ)
Rev.: $530,905
Assets: $2,121,766
Liabilities: $519,037
Net Worth: $1,602,730
Earnings: ($2,292,134)
Fiscal Year-end: 08/31/23
Business Consulting Services
N.A.I.C.S.: 522299
William J. Fisher (Chm)

CHUTIAN DRAGON CO., LTD.
Room 1508 15th Floor Office Building B, Jinyuan Times Shopping Center Yuanda Road Haidian District, Beijing, 100097, China
Tel.: (86) 1068967666
Web Site: https://www.ctdcn.com
Year Founded: 2002
003040—(SSE)
Rev.: $241,403,760
Assets: $310,807,692

Liabilities: $98,461,116
Net Worth: $212,346,576
Earnings: $23,304,996
Fiscal Year-end: 12/31/22
Software Development Services
N.A.I.C.S.: 541511
Fangyang Mao (Chm)

CHUYING AGRO-PASTORAL GROUP CO., LTD.
Century Avenue Xuedian Town, Xinzheng City, Zhengzhou, 451162, Henan, China
Tel.: (86) 371 62583588
Web Site: http://www.chu-ying.com
Year Founded: 1988
Rev.: $517,006,840
Assets: $3,062,931,130
Liabilities: $2,691,895,850
Net Worth: $371,035,280
Earnings: ($603,368,500)
Fiscal Year-end: 12/31/18
Livestock Breeding Services
N.A.I.C.S.: 112210
Jianfang Hou (Chm & CEO)

CHUZHOU DUOLI AUTOMOTIVE TECHNOLOGY CO., LTD.
No 109 Maan East Road, Chuzhou, 239000, Anhui, China
Tel.: (86) 5503978376
Year Founded: 2010
001311—(SSE)
Rev.: $538,375,932
Assets: $744,397,803
Liabilities: $154,715,305
Net Worth: $589,682,499
Earnings: $68,329,423
Fiscal Year-end: 12/31/23
Automobile Parts Mfr & Distr
N.A.I.C.S.: 336110
Liqin Deng (Chm)

CHYANG SHENG DYEING & FINISHING CO., LTD.
6F No 63 Sec 1 Dihua St, Datong Dist, Taipei, 103, Taiwan
Tel.: (886) 225556866
Web Site:
https://www.csgroup.com.tw
Year Founded: 1983
1463—(TAI)
Rev.: $11,364,269
Assets: $96,139,733
Liabilities: $18,367,147
Net Worth: $77,772,586
Earnings: $3,509,009
Fiscal Year-end: 12/31/23
Dyeing & Pigment Mfr
N.A.I.C.S.: 325130
Chen Renfa (Chm)

CHYY DEVELOPMENT GROUP LIMITED
8/F Chung Hing Commercial Building 62-63 Connaught Road Central, Central, China (Hong Kong)
Tel.: (852) 37539800
Web Site:
http://www.cgsenergy.com.hk
Year Founded: 1999
8128—(HKG)
Rev.: $22,808,178
Assets: $201,935,215
Liabilities: $146,708,559
Net Worth: $55,226,656
Earnings: ($13,198,136)
Emp.: 475
Fiscal Year-end: 12/31/21
Holding Company
N.A.I.C.S.: 551112
Katherine Wai Kay Chan (Deputy Chm)

Subsidiaries:

Ever Source Science & Technology Development Group Co., Limited (1)

No 102 Xingshikou Street, Haidian District, Beijing, 100093, China
Tel.: (86) 106 259 5998
Web Site: http://www.hyy.com.cn
Ground Source Equipment Mfr & Distr
N.A.I.C.S.: 334512
Manquan Wang (Gen Mgr)

CI COM SA
Tel.: (41) 227374000
Web Site: https://www.cicomsa.com
CIE—(SWX)
Sales Range: Less than $1 Million
Financial Brokerage Services
N.A.I.C.S.: 523160
Michel Rethoret (Vice Chm & CFO)

CI FINANCIAL CORPORATION
15 York Street Second Floor, Toronto, M5J 0A3, ON, Canada
Tel.: (416) 364-1145
Web Site: https://www.cifinancial.com
Year Founded: 1965
CIXXF—(OTCIQ)
Rev.: $2,073,562,540
Assets: $7,537,308,057
Liabilities: $6,751,954,563
Net Worth: $785,353,495
Earnings: $4,597,926
Emp.: 2,390
Fiscal Year-end: 12/31/23
Holding Company; Investment & Wealth Management Services
N.A.I.C.S.: 551112
William T. Holland (Chm)

Subsidiaries:

Assante Wealth Management (Canada) Ltd. (1)
199 Bay Street Suite 2700, Toronto, M5L 1E2, ON, Canada
Tel.: (416) 348-9994
Web Site: http://www.assante.com
Emp.: 830
Investment Advisory & Wealth Management Services
N.A.I.C.S.: 523940
Sean Etherington (Pres)

Balasa Dinverno Foltz LLC (1)
500 Park Blvd Ste 1400, Itasca, IL 60143
Tel.: (630) 875-4900
Web Site: http://www.bdfllc.com
Investment Management Service
N.A.I.C.S.: 541611
Heather L. Locus (Mgr-Wealth)

Barrett Asset Management, LLC (1)
90 Park Ave 34th Fl, New York, NY 10016
Tel.: (212) 983-5080
Web Site: http://www.barrettasset.com
Sales Range: $10-24.9 Million
Emp.: 20
Investment Advisory Services
N.A.I.C.S.: 523940
Peter H. Shriver (CEO)

Bowling Portfolio Management LLC (1)
4030 Smith Rd, Cincinnati, OH 45209-1957
Tel.: (513) 871-7776
Web Site: http://www.bowlport.com
Investment Advice
N.A.I.C.S.: 523940
Kathy Wayner (Pres, CEO & Mng Partner)

CI Investment Services Inc. (1)
199 Bay St Suite 2600, Toronto, M5L 1E2, ON, Canada
Tel.: (416) 235-0200
Web Site:
https://www.ciinvestmentservices.com
Financial Investment Services
N.A.I.C.S.: 523999

CI Investments Inc. (1)
15 York Street 2nd Floor, Toronto, M5J 0A3, ON, Canada
Tel.: (416) 364-1145
Web Site: https://www.cifinancial.com
Sales Range: $700-749.9 Million
Investment Fund Management Services
N.A.I.C.S.: 523940
Douglas J. Jamieson (Pres)

Affiliate (Domestic):

Skylon All Asset Trust (2)
2 Queen Street East Twentieth Floor, Toronto, M5C 3G7, ON, Canada
Tel.: (416) 364-1145
Web Site: http://www.skyloncapital.com
Sales Range: Less than $1 Million
Closed-End Investment Fund
N.A.I.C.S.: 525990

Skylon International Advantage Yield Trust (2)
2 Queen Street East 20th Floor, Toronto, M5C 3G7, ON, Canada
Tel.: (416) 364-1145
Web Site: http://www.skyloncapital.com
Rev.: $1,988
Assets: $8,437,242
Liabilities: $666,988
Net Worth: $7,770,254
Earnings: ($62,623)
Fiscal Year-end: 12/31/2012
Closed-End Investment Fund
N.A.I.C.S.: 525990

Yield Advantage Income Trust (2)
2 Queen Street East Twentieth Floor, Toronto, M5C 3G7, ON, Canada
Tel.: (416) 364-1145
Web Site: http://www.skyloncapital.com
Rev.: $840,473
Assets: $9,361,329
Liabilities: $787,003
Net Worth: $8,574,326
Earnings: $751,914
Fiscal Year-end: 12/31/2014
Closed-End Investment Fund
N.A.I.C.S.: 525990

CI Private Counsel LP (1)
15 York Street 2nd Floor, Toronto, M5J 0A3, ON, Canada
Tel.: (416) 681-7171
Financial Investment Services
N.A.I.C.S.: 523999
James E. Ross *(Pres)*

Division (Domestic):

CI Private Wealth (2)
15 York Street 2nd Floor, Toronto, M5J 0A3, ON, Canada
Tel.: (416) 681-7171
Web Site: http://www.cifinancial.com
Wealth Management Services
N.A.I.C.S.: 523999
James E. Ross *(Pres)*

Subsidiary (US):

Matrix Capital Advisors LLC (3)
200 S Wacker Dr Ste 726, Chicago, IL 60606
Tel.: (312) 612-6100
Web Site: http://www.matrixcapital.com
Professional, Scientific & Technical Services
N.A.I.C.S.: 541990
Kimberly L. Lundgren *(Mgr-Ops)*

Dowling & Yahnke, LLC (1)
12265 El Camino Real Ste 300, San Diego, CA 92130
Tel.: (858) 509-9500
Web Site: http://www.dywealth.com
Emp.: 23
Investment Management Service
N.A.I.C.S.: 523940
William G. Beamer *(Pres & CIO)*

GSFM Pty Limited (1)
Level 19 Governor Macquarie Tower 1 Farrer Place, Sydney, 2000, NSW, Australia
Tel.: (61) 29 324 4356
Web Site: https://www.gsfm.com.au
Investment Management Service
N.A.I.C.S.: 523940
Andrew Koolman *(Acct Mgr-New South Wales)*

Marret Asset Management Inc. (1)
15 York Street 2nd Floor, Toronto, M5J 0A3, ON, Canada (65%)
Tel.: (416) 214-5800
Web Site: http://marret.com
Investment Management Service
N.A.I.C.S.: 523940
Paul Sandhu *(Pres & CEO)*

Affiliate (Domestic):

Marret High Yield Strategies Fund (2)

2 Queen Street East Suite 1200, Toronto, M5C 3G7, ON, Canada
Tel.: (416) 214-5800
Web Site: http://www.marret.com
Rev.: $2,774
Assets: $13,257,461
Liabilities: $83,855
Net Worth: $13,173,606
Earnings: ($33,794)
Fiscal Year-end: 12/31/2020
Closed-End Investment Fund
N.A.I.C.S.: 525990
Paul Sandhu *(Pres & CEO-Marret Asset Management Inc)*

Marret Multi-Strategy Income Fund (2)
2 Queen Street East 12th Floor, Toronto, M5C 3G7, ON, Canada
Tel.: (416) 214-5800
Web Site: http://marret.ca
Rev.: $119,378
Assets: $761,431
Liabilities: $151,065
Net Worth: $610,365
Earnings: $51,702
Fiscal Year-end: 12/31/2021
Closed-End Investment Fund
N.A.I.C.S.: 525990
Paul Sandhu *(Pres & CEO-Marret Asset Management Inc)*

RGT Wealth Advisors, LLC (1)
5950 Sherry Ln Ste 600, Dallas, TX 75225
Tel.: (214) 360-7000
Web Site: https://www.rgtadvisors.com
Investment Advisory Services
N.A.I.C.S.: 523940
Adam Goldenberg *(Mng Dir)*

Sentry Investments Inc. (1)
Commerce Court West 199 Bay St Ste 2700, PO Box 108, Toronto, M5L 1E2, ON, Canada
Tel.: (416) 364-8788
Web Site: http://www.ci.com
Sales Range: $25-49.9 Million
Emp.: 100
Asset Management Company
N.A.I.C.S.: 523999
James Dutkiewicz *(CIO)*

The Roosevelt Investment Group, Inc. (1)
570 Lexington Ave Ste 1800, New York, NY 10022
Tel.: (646) 452-6700
Web Site: https://www.rooseveltinvestments.com
Investment Management Service
N.A.I.C.S.: 523940
Adam Sheer *(Co-CEO)*

Wealthbar Financial Services Inc. (1)
Suite 900-625 Howe St, Vancouver, V6C 2T6, BC, Canada
Web Site: https://www.cidirectinvesting.com
Financial Investment Services
N.A.I.C.S.: 523999

WisdomTree Asset Management Canada, Inc. (1)
161 Bay Street 27th Floor, Toronto, M5J 2S1, ON, Canada
Tel.: (866) 893-8733
Web Site: http://www.wisdomtree.ca
Global Market Investment Services
N.A.I.C.S.: 523910

CI GAMES S.A.
Rondo Daszynskiego 2B, 00-843, Warsaw, Poland
Tel.: (48) 227183500
Web Site: https://www.cigames.com
Year Founded: 2002
CIG—(WAR)
Rev.: $62,241,616
Assets: $69,866,362
Liabilities: $29,145,325
Net Worth: $40,721,036
Earnings: $3,675,559
Emp.: 191
Fiscal Year-end: 12/31/23
Game Software Publsihers
N.A.I.C.S.: 513210
Marek Tyminski *(CEO)*

Subsidiaries:

United Label S.A. (1)
Ul Marszalkowska 126/134, 00-008, Warsaw, Poland
Tel.: (48) 22 718 3500
Web Site:
https://www.unitedlabelgames.com
Game Development Services
N.A.I.C.S.: 713120

CI MEDICAL CO., LTD.
2-6 Asahigaoka, Hakusan, 924-0004, Ishikawa, Japan
Tel.: (81) 762788802
Web Site: https://www.ci-medical.co.jp
Year Founded: 2000
3540—(TKS)
Rev.: $323,502,520
Assets: $294,277,540
Liabilities: $151,492,030
Net Worth: $142,785,510
Earnings: $14,761,380
Emp.: 900
Fiscal Year-end: 12/31/23
Dental Care Product Mfr & Distr
N.A.I.C.S.: 339114
Kiyoto Shimizu *(Pres & CEO)*

CI RESOURCES LIMITED
6 Thorogood Street, Burswood, 6100, WA, Australia
Tel.: (61) 6 250 4900
Web Site:
http://www.ciresources.com.au
Year Founded: 1987
Rev.: $112,188,605
Assets: $192,939,667
Liabilities: $45,481,805
Net Worth: $147,457,863
Earnings: $5,207,027
Fiscal Year-end: 06/30/21
Phosphate & Chalk Mining, Processing & Sales
N.A.I.C.S.: 212390
Lip Sin Tee *(Exec Dir)*

Subsidiaries:

Phosphate Resources (Singapore) Pte Ltd (1)
8 Liang Seah Street 02-06 Liang Seah Court, Singapore, 189029, Singapore
Tel.: (65) 6 332 0961
Rental & Leasing Space Services
N.A.I.C.S.: 531190

Phosphate Resources Limited (1)
6 Thorogood Street, Burswood, 6100, WA, Australia
Tel.: (61) 8 6250 4900
Web Site: http://www.cirp.com
Sales Range: $100-124.9 Million
Phosphate Rock Mining
N.A.I.C.S.: 212390
Kevin Edwards *(COO & Sec)*

CI SYSTEMS (ISRAEL) LTD.
PO Box 147, Migdal Ha'Emeq, 2306990, Israel
Tel.: (972) 46448888
Web Site: https://www.ci-systems.com
Year Founded: 1977
CISY—(TAE)
Rev.: $36,799,000
Assets: $39,968,000
Liabilities: $14,767,000
Net Worth: $25,201,000
Earnings: $5,046,000
Emp.: 150
Fiscal Year-end: 09/30/23
Semiconductor Product Mfr & Distr
N.A.I.C.S.: 334413
Graham Jackson *(Co-Chm)*

CI-CO S.A.
Aleea Campul Mosilor 5, Bucharest, Romania

Tel.: (40) 212522952
Web Site: https://www.ci-co.ro
CICO—(BUC)
Rev.: $3,426,161
Assets: $14,169,076
Liabilities: $801,225
Net Worth: $13,367,850
Earnings: $947,130
Emp.: 32
Fiscal Year-end: 12/31/23
Real Estate Investment Services
N.A.I.C.S.: 531390
Florentina-Adriana Tudor *(Pres)*

CIA DE INVERSIONES LA ESPANOLA SA
Prat 887 4th Floor, Valparaiso, Chile
Tel.: (56) 256738
Year Founded: 1977
ESPANOLA—(SGO)
Sales Range: Less than $1 Million
Investment Holding Company Services
N.A.I.C.S.: 551112
Carmen Garcia Dominguez *(Pres)*

CIA DE TECIDOS DO NORTE DE MINAS - COTEMINAS
Avenida Lincoln Alves dos Santos No 955 Distrito Industrial, Montes Claros, 39404-005, Minas Gerais, Brazil
Tel.: (55) 3840095000
Year Founded: 1967
CTNM4—(BRAZ)
Rev.: $271,885,908
Assets: $636,413,526
Liabilities: $506,918,347
Net Worth: $129,495,179
Earnings: ($119,664,107)
Fiscal Year-end: 12/31/22
Textile Mfr
N.A.I.C.S.: 313310
Josue Christiano Gomes Da Silva *(Chm, CEO & Member-Exec Bd)*

CIA DE TRANSMISSAO DE ENERGIA ELETRICA PAULISTA
Av das Nacoes Unidas 14 171-Torre Crystal-6 andar, Vila Gertrudes, Sao Paulo, 04794-000, SP, Brazil
Tel.: (55) 31387000
Web Site: http://www.isacteep.com.br
Year Founded: 1999
TRPL4—(BRAZ)
Rev.: $710,638,283
Assets: $4,727,880,826
Liabilities: $2,012,264,601
Net Worth: $2,715,616,225
Earnings: $650,314,463
Emp.: 1,400
Fiscal Year-end: 12/31/20
Electric Power Distribution Services
N.A.I.C.S.: 221122
Rui Chammas *(Co-CEO & Member-Exec Bd)*

Subsidiaries:

Interligacao Eletrica Garanhuns S.A. (1)
Rua Joao Cauas n 51 Sala 308 Empresarial Casa Forte Poco da Panela, Recife, 52061-390, Brazil
Tel.: (55) 8130497171
Web Site: http://www.iegaranhuns.com.br
Eletric Power Generation Services
N.A.I.C.S.: 221118

CIA DISTRIB DE GAS DO RIO DE JANEIRO - CEG
Avenida Pedro Segundo 68 Sao Cristovao, Rio de Janeiro, 20941-070, Brazil
Tel.: (55) 2131156565
Web Site: https://www.naturgy.com.br
CEGR3—(BRAZ)
Rev.: $1,001,449,000

CIA Distrib de Gas do Rio de Janeiro - CEG—(Continued)

Assets: $810,352,314
Liabilities: $562,024,797
Net Worth: $248,327,517
Earnings: $106,709,387
Fiscal Year-end: 12/31/23
Natural Gas Distribution Services
N.A.I.C.S.: 221210
Bruno Armbrust *(CEO & Member-Exec Bd)*

CIA ELECTRICA DEL LITORAL SA
San Sebastian N 2952 2 Piso Oficina 202, Las Condes, Santiago, Chile
Tel.: (56) 223621436
Web Site: https://www.litoral.cl
Year Founded: 1949
LITORAL—(SGO)
Sales Range: Less than $1 Million
Electric Power Distribution Services
N.A.I.C.S.: 221122
Francisco Mualim Tietz *(Chm & Pres)*

CIA ENERGETICA DE PERNAMBUCO - CELPE
Avenida Joao de Barros 111 Boa Vista Recife, Boa Vista, 50050-902, PE, Brazil
Tel.: (55) 8132175116
Web Site: http://www.servicos.celpe.com.br
CEPE6—(BRAZ)
Sales Range: Less than $1 Million
Electric Power Distribution Services
N.A.I.C.S.: 221122
Antonio Carlos Sanches *(CEO)*

CIA ESTADUAL GER.TRANS.ENER.ELET-CEEE-GT
Av Joaquim Porto Villanova 201 - Building A Bairro Jardim Carvalho, 91410-400, Porto Alegre, Rio Grande do Sul, Brazil
Tel.: (55) 5133825715
Web Site: http://www.ceee.com.br
Year Founded: 1943
EEEL3—(BRAZ)
Rev.: $64,320,294
Assets: $1,281,133,162
Liabilities: $700,981,177
Net Worth: $580,151,986
Earnings: ($24,138,060)
Fiscal Year-end: 03/31/20
Electricity Provision
N.A.I.C.S.: 221118
Tassiara Schmitt *(Head-Mgmt & Strategic Planning Div)*

CIA IGUACU DE CAFE SOLUVEL
BR 369 - Rodovia Mello Peixoto Km 88, 86300-000, Cornelio Procopio, Parana, Brazil
Tel.: (55) 43 3401 1211
Web Site: http://www.iguacu.com.br
Year Founded: 1967
Coffee Mfr & Whslr
N.A.I.C.S.: 311920
Edivaldo Barrancos *(Dir-IR)*

CIA MARITIMA CHILENA SA
Plaza de la Justicia 59 Casillas 1410 210-V, Valparaiso, Chile
Tel.: (56) 32259001
Cargo Transportation Services
N.A.I.C.S.: 488490
Marcelo Ramos De Aguirre *(CEO)*

CIA SANEAMENTO DO PARANA-SANEPAR
Rua Engenheiros Reboucas 1376,

Reboucas, Curitiba, 80215-900, PR, Brazil
Tel.: (55) 33303929   BR
Web Site: http://www.ite.sanepar.com.br
Year Founded: 1963
SAPR11—(BRAZ)
Sales Range: Less than $1 Million
Solid Waste Management Services
N.A.I.C.S.: 562111
Claudio Stabile *(CEO)*

CIA SEGUROS ALIANCA DA BAHIA
Rua Pinto Martins 11, Comercio, Salvador, Brazil
Tel.: (55) 7136161055
Web Site: http://www.alba.com.br
CSAB4—(BRAZ)
Sales Range: Less than $1 Million
General Insurance Services
N.A.I.C.S.: 524210
Paulo Sergio Freire de Carvalho Goncalves Tourinho *(Chm, CEO & Member-Exec Bd)*

CIA TECIDOS SANTANENSE
Av Osmane Barbosa 1235 JK, Montes Claros, 39404-006, Minas Gerais, Brazil
Tel.: (55) 3133499820
CTSA4—(BRAZ)
Rev.: $73,277,201
Assets: $111,807,973
Liabilities: $56,151,122
Net Worth: $55,656,851
Earnings: $1,105,629
Fiscal Year-end: 12/31/22
Women's Clothing Mfr
N.A.I.C.S.: 315250
Josue Christiano Gomes Da Silva *(Chm & CEO)*

CIAAT CO., LTD.
40 Pyeongdongsandan-ro 169beon-gil, Gwangsan-gu, Gwangju, 62419, Korea (South)
Tel.: (82) 629407200
Web Site: https://www.mydigicube.com
Year Founded: 2006
Ink Ribbon Mfr & Distr
N.A.I.C.S.: 325992
Koo Sang-Jun *(Mgr-Mgmt Support)*

CIAN AGRO INDUSTRIES & INFRASTRUCTURE LIMITED
4th Floor Gupta Tower Science college Road, Civil Lines, Nagpur, 440001, Maharashtra, India
Tel.: (91) 7122551144
Web Site: https://www.cianindustries.com
Year Founded: 1985
519477—(BOM)
Rev.: $36,553,622
Assets: $43,217,156
Liabilities: $36,374,179
Net Worth: $6,842,977
Earnings: $359,282
Emp.: 71
Fiscal Year-end: 03/31/21
Grocery Product Mfr & Distr
N.A.I.C.S.: 311225
Gauri Dilip Chandrayan *(Chm)*

CIAN HEALTHCARE LIMITED
5th Floor Sacred World 508-511 Vitthal Rao Shivarkar Rd, Above McDonald 's Wanowrie, Pune, 411040, India
Tel.: (91) 9049233757
Web Site: https://www.cian.co
Year Founded: 2003
542678—(BOM)
Rev.: $10,702,501

Assets: $22,650,141
Liabilities: $15,080,274
Net Worth: $7,569,867
Earnings: ($755,323)
Fiscal Year-end: 03/31/22
Pharmaceutical Preparation Mfr
N.A.I.C.S.: 325412
Suraj Zanwar *(Chm & Mng Dir)*

CIAN PLC
64 Agiou Georgiou Makri Anna Maria Lena Court Flat 201, 6037, Larnaca, 6037, Cyprus
Tel.: (357) 22418200   CY
Web Site: https://investor.cian.ru
Year Founded: 2017
CIAN—(MOEX)
Rev.: $111,343,020
Assets: $93,939,780
Liabilities: $26,468,550
Net Worth: $67,471,230
Earnings: $6,465,600
Emp.: 812
Fiscal Year-end: 12/31/22
Investment Services
N.A.I.C.S.: 523999
Alexey Chekanov *(CTO)*

CIBOX INTERACTIVE SA
17 Allee Jean-Baptiste Preux, 94140, Alfortville, France
Tel.: (33) 146701834
Web Site: https://www.ciboxcorp.com
Year Founded: 1995
CIB—(EUR)
Sales Range: $1-9.9 Million
Computer Peripheral Distr
N.A.I.C.S.: 423430
Ming Lun Sung *(Chm & CEO)*

CIBRASEC-COMPANHIA BRASILEIRA DE SECURITIZACAO
Av Paulista 1439-2 Sobreloja, 01311-200, Sao Paulo, Brazil
Tel.: (55) 1132663223
Web Site: http://www.cibrasec.com.br
Emp.: 100
Financial Investment Services
N.A.I.C.S.: 523940
Onivaldo Scalco *(CEO & Dir-IR)*

CIBUS NORDIC REAL ESTATE AB
Tel.: (46) 761444888
Web Site: https://www.cibusnordic.com
CIBUS—(OMX)
Rev.: $115,175,912
Assets: $2,082,587,956
Liabilities: $1,329,503,561
Net Worth: $753,084,395
Earnings: $86,326,354
Emp.: 9
Fiscal Year-end: 12/31/22
Real Estate Management Services
N.A.I.C.S.: 531390
Sverker Kallgarden *(CEO)*

CIC HOLDINGS LIMITED
Tuscany Office Park, PO Box 3581, 2128, Rivonia, South Africa
Tel.: (27) 118070109
Web Site: http://www.cicholdings.com
CCI—(JSE)
Sales Range: $300-349.9 Million
Holding Company; Business Support Services
N.A.I.C.S.: 551112
Trevor P. Rogers *(CEO)*

Subsidiaries:

CIC Marketing (Pty) Limited   (1)
Tuscany Block 5 Coonbe Pl, Johannesburg, 2128, Gauteng, South Africa
Tel.: (27) 118070109

Consumer Goods Distr
N.A.I.C.S.: 423620

Commercial Investment Corporation (Pty) Limited   (1)
Corner Iscor & Solingen St Northern Indus Area, Windhoek, Namibia
Tel.: (264) 612855800
Sales Range: $100-124.9 Million
Emp.: 250
Insurance Underwriting Services
N.A.I.C.S.: 524114

Global Holdings (Botswana) (Pty) Limited   (1)
Plot 20774 Old Hyundai Plant Broadhurst Industrial, Gaborone, Botswana
Tel.: (267) 3904941
Sales Range: $150-199.9 Million
Emp.: 600
General Warehousing & Distribution Services
N.A.I.C.S.: 493110
Autash Arora *(Mng Dir)*

CIC INSURANCE GROUP LIMITED
CIC Plaza Upper Hill Mara Road, PO Box 59485, 00200, Nairobi, Kenya
Tel.: (254) 202823000   KE
Web Site: https://ke.cicinsurancegroup.com
CIC—(NAI)
Rev.: $193,045,311
Assets: $382,269,653
Liabilities: $324,417,563
Net Worth: $57,852,090
Earnings: $10,957,706
Emp.: 793
Fiscal Year-end: 12/31/23
General Insurance Services
N.A.I.C.S.: 524210
Japheth Anavila Magomere *(Chm)*

CIC MINING RESOURCES LIMITED
802 Office Tower The St Regis Beijing, No 21 Jianguomenwai Dajie, Beijing, 100020, China
Tel.: (86) 10 8532 2861   Ca
Web Site: http://www.cicresources.com
Year Founded: 2003
Sales Range: Less than $1 Million
Mining Investment & Royalty Services
N.A.I.C.S.: 213114
Stuart J. Bromley *(Chm & CEO)*

CIC39 CORP.
45A Nguyen Van Tiet, Lai Thieu Ward, Thuan An, Binh Duong, Vietnam
Tel.: (84) 2743759446
Web Site: https://www.cic39.vn
Year Founded: 1993
C32—(HOSE)
Rev.: $20,357,579
Assets: $35,617,812
Liabilities: $13,537,414
Net Worth: $22,080,398
Earnings: ($1,111,658)
Emp.: 222
Fiscal Year-end: 12/31/23
Concrete Products Mfr
N.A.I.C.S.: 327390

CICCOLELLA SPA
Parasacco Indl Zone San Nicola, Melfi, 85025, Italy
Tel.: (39) 0972255200   IT
Web Site: http://www.ciccolella.eu
Sales Range: $450-499.9 Million
Emp.: 1,225
Production & marketing of cut flowers & potted plants.
N.A.I.C.S.: 424930
Corrado Ciccolella *(Chm & CEO)*

CICLAD SA

22 Avenue Franklin Roosevelt, 75008, Paris, France
Tel.: (33) 156597733   FR
Web Site: http://www.ciclad.com
Year Founded: 1988
Privater Equity Firm
N.A.I.C.S.: 523999
Stephane Billon *(Mng Partner)*

Subsidiaries:

Edeis S.A.S.   **(1)**
19 boulevard Paul Vaillant Couturier, 94200, Ivry-sur-Seine, France
Tel.: (33) 1 5620 5000
Web Site: http://www.edeis.com
Emp.: 1,000
Engineering & Infrastructure Management Services
N.A.I.C.S.: 237990
Melanie Henou *(Dir-HR & Comm Mgr)*

CICLET HOLDINGS INC.
B11 L12 Woodpecker Street Bougainvillea Village Agus, Lapu-Lapu, 66015, Philippines
Tel.: (63) 905 420 1506   NV
Year Founded: 2016
Rev.: $2
Assets: $3,498
Liabilities: $81,324
Net Worth: ($77,826)
Earnings: ($20,295)
Fiscal Year-end: 01/31/22
Software Development Services
N.A.I.C.S.: 541511
Eugenio L. Jumawan Jr. *(Chm, Pres, CEO, CFO, Treas & Sec)*

CICOR TECHNOLOGIES LTD.
Route de l Europe 8, 2017, Boudry, Switzerland
Tel.: (41) 328430500
Web Site: https://www.cicor.com
CICN—(SWX)
Rev.: $347,220,621
Assets: $406,579,823
Liabilities: $241,512,195
Net Worth: $165,067,627
Earnings: $4,235,033
Emp.: 2,074
Fiscal Year-end: 12/31/22
Printed Circuit Board Mfr
N.A.I.C.S.: 334412
Robert Demuth *(Chm)*

Subsidiaries:

Axis Electronics Limited   **(1)**
Bedford Heights Manton Lane, Bedford, MK41 7NY, Bedfordshire, United Kingdom
Tel.: (44) 1234342932
Web Site: https://www.axis-electronics.com
Electronic Equipment Mfr & Distr
N.A.I.C.S.: 335999

Cicor Americas Inc.   **(1)**
185 Alewife Brook Pkwy Ste 210, Cambridge, MA 02138
Tel.: (617) 576-2005
Printed Circuit Board Mfr
N.A.I.C.S.: 334412

Cicor Anam Ltd.   **(1)**
15 VSIP St 4, Thuan An, Binh Duong, Vietnam
Tel.: (84) 650 75 6623
Web Site: http://www.cicor.com
Electronic Products Assembling Services
N.A.I.C.S.: 334418

Cicor Asia Pte. Ltd.   **(1)**
7 North Coast Avenue 03-66/67/68/69, Singapore, 737664, Singapore
Tel.: (65) 65461600
Printed Circuit Board Mfr
N.A.I.C.S.: 334412

Cicor Deutschland GmbH   **(1)**
An d Priessnitzaue 22, 01328, Dresden, Germany
Tel.: (49) 351266130
Electronic Components Mfr
N.A.I.C.S.: 334419

Cicor Digital Elektronik GmbH   **(1)**
Am Schunkenhofe 7, 99848, Wutha-Farnroda, Germany
Tel.: (49) 369212010
Web Site: https://cicor-digitalelektronik.de
Emp.: 125
Electronic Equipment Mfr & Distr
N.A.I.C.S.: 335999

Cicor Ecotool Pte Ltd.   **(1)**
45 Changi South Ave 2# 04-00, Singapore, 486133, Singapore
Tel.: (65) 65 455 030
Web Site: http://www.cicor.com
Sales Range: $25-49.9 Million
Emp.: 100
Electronic Components & Systems Mfr
N.A.I.C.S.: 334419

Cicor Electronic Solutions Division   **(1)**
Industriestrasse 8, Bronschhofen, 9552, Saint Gallen, Switzerland
Tel.: (41) 71 913 7373
Web Site: http://www.cicor.com
Circuit Board Mfr
N.A.I.C.S.: 334412

Cicor Management AG   **(1)**
World Trade Ctr Leutschenbachstrasse 95, 8050, Zurich, Switzerland
Tel.: (41) 438114405
Web Site: http://www.cicor.com
Sales Range: $25-49.9 Million
Emp.: 1,900
Business Management Services
N.A.I.C.S.: 561110

Cicor Reinhardt Microtech AG   **(1)**
Tel.: (41) 817200456
Sales Range: $25-49.9 Million
Emp.: 48
Thin Film Circuits Mfr
N.A.I.C.S.: 334413

Cicor Vietnam Company Ltd.   **(1)**
No 3 VSIP Street 6 Vietnam-Singapore Industrial Park, Thuan Giao Ward, Thuan An, Binh Duong, Vietnam
Tel.: (84) 2743756623
Electronic Components Mfr
N.A.I.C.S.: 334419

Cicorel SA   **(1)**
Route de l Europe 8, 2017, Boudry, Neuchatel, Switzerland
Tel.: (41) 328430500
Web Site: https://www.cicorel.ch
Sales Range: $25-49.9 Million
Emp.: 100
Flexible Printed Circuit Board Mfr
N.A.I.C.S.: 334412

PT Cicor Panatec   **(1)**
J1 Beringin Lot 322-324 BIP Muka Kuning, Batam, Indonesia
Tel.: (62) 770612233
Printed Circuit Board Mfr
N.A.I.C.S.: 334412

PT ESG Panatec   **(1)**
Batamindo Indus Park Lot 338 Jalan Beringin Muka Kuning, Batam, 29433, Riau Islands, Indonesia
Tel.: (62) 770612233
Sales Range: $100-124.9 Million
Emp.: 300
Electronic Products Assembling Services
N.A.I.C.S.: 334419

Photochemie AG   **(1)**
Gewerbestrasse 1, 6314, Unterageri, Zug, Switzerland
Tel.: (41) 417544545
Sales Range: $25-49.9 Million
Emp.: 80
Circuit Board Mfr
N.A.I.C.S.: 334412

RHe Microsystems GmbH   **(1)**
Heidestrasse 70, 01454, Radeburg, Saxony, Germany
Tel.: (49) 352841990
Web Site: http://www.cicor.com
Sales Range: $25-49.9 Million
Emp.: 80
Semiconductor Integrated Circuits Mfr
N.A.I.C.S.: 334413

Reinhardt Microtech GmbH   **(1)**
Seebahnstrasse 14, 89077, Ulm, Germany

Tel.: (49) 73179035213
Sales Range: $25-49.9 Million
Emp.: 36
Thin Film Circuits Mfr
N.A.I.C.S.: 334413

Suzhou Cicor Technology Co., Ltd.   **(1)**
No 11 Building No 666 Jianlin Road SND-EPZ Sub-industrial Park, Suzhou, 215151, China
Tel.: (86) 51266672033
Printed Circuit Board Mfr
N.A.I.C.S.: 334412

Swisstronics Contract Manufacturing AG   **(1)**
Gebenloostrasse 15, 9552, Bronschhofen, Switzerland
Tel.: (41) 719137373
Sales Range: $50-74.9 Million
Emp.: 180
Circuit Board Mfr
N.A.I.C.S.: 334412

Systel SA   **(1)**
Via Luserte Sud 7, 6572, Quartino, Ticino, Switzerland
Tel.: (41) 918503811
Web Site: http://www.systel.ch
Sales Range: $25-49.9 Million
Emp.: 50
Circuit Board Mfr
N.A.I.C.S.: 334412
Andre Bermann *(Gen Mgr)*

Systronics S.R.L.   **(1)**
Str III -Zona Industriala Arad Vest Nr 14, 310580, Arad, Romania
Tel.: (40) 257285944
Sales Range: $100-124.9 Million
Emp.: 300
Printed Circuit Board Mfr
N.A.I.C.S.: 334412
Cosmin Popa *(Mng Dir)*

TT Electronics IOT Solutions Limited   **(1)**
Fourth Floor St Andrews House, West Street, Woking, GU21 6EB, United Kingdom
Tel.: (44) 1932 825 300
Web Site: http://www.ttelectronics.com
Printed Circuit Board Mfr
N.A.I.C.S.: 334412

Subsidiary (Non-US):

Stadium Asia   **(2)**
Unit A 3/F Bamboos Centre 52 Hung To Road, Kwun Tong, Kowloon, Hong Kong, China (Hong Kong)
Tel.: (852) 23891271
Electronics Mfr
N.A.I.C.S.: 334220

Subsidiary (Domestic):

Stadium Electronics Limited   **(2)**
Fourth Floor St Andrews House, West Street, Woking, GU21 6EB, United Kingdom   **(100%)**
Tel.: (44) 1932 825 300
Printed Circuit Board Mfr
N.A.I.C.S.: 334412

Stadium Power Limited   **(2)**
Fourth Floor St Andrews House, West Street, Woking, GU21 6EB, United Kingdom   **(100%)**
Tel.: (44) 1932 825 300
Power Units Mfr
N.A.I.C.S.: 334220

CID ADRIATIC INVESTMENTS GMBH
Teinfaltstrasse 8/4, 1010, Vienna, Austria
Tel.: (43) 1 319 4058   AT
Web Site: http://www.cid-adriatic.at
Financial Investment Services
N.A.I.C.S.: 523999
Alexander Walther *(Mng Dir)*

Subsidiaries:

Fabrika duhana Sarajevo d.d.   **(1)**
Pofalicka 5, 71000, Sarajevo, Bosnia & Herzegovina
Tel.: (387) 33 278 800

Web Site: http://www.fds.ba
Cigarette Mfr; Banking & Financial Services
N.A.I.C.S.: 312230
Edin Mulahasanovic *(Dir)*

Subsidiary (Domestic):

UPI Poslovni Sistem d.d. Sarajevo   **(2)**
ul Branilaca Sarajeva br 20, 71 000, Sarajevo, Bosnia & Herzegovina
Tel.: (387) 33 444174
Sales Range: $75-99.9 Million
Property Management Services
N.A.I.C.S.: 531311
Tarik Solakovic *(Dir & Member-Mgmt Bd)*

Vakufska Banka d.d. Sarajevo   **(2)**
Marsala Tita 13, 71000, Sarajevo, Bosnia & Herzegovina   **(73.21%)**
Tel.: (387) 33280100
Web Site: http://www.vakuba.ba
Sales Range: $1-9.9 Million
Emp.: 172
Banking Services
N.A.I.C.S.: 523150
Elma Zukic *(Member-Mgmt Bd)*

CID GROUP
19F Tower B CCIG International Plaza 333 Cao Xi North Road, Shanghai, China
Tel.: (86) 21 3397 3678
Web Site: http://www.cidgroup.com
Year Founded: 1998
Privater Equity Firm
N.A.I.C.S.: 523999
Steven Chang *(Mng Partner)*

CIE AMENAGEMENT COTEAUX DE GASCOGNE
Chemin De Lalette, 65000, Tarbes, Hautes Pyrenees, France
Tel.: (33) 562517149
Rev.: $23,500,000
Emp.: 209
Engineeering Services
N.A.I.C.S.: 541330
Henri Tardieu *(Dir)*

CIE AUTOMOTIVE S.A.
Alameda Mazarredo 69 8, 48009, Bilbao, Biscay, Spain
Tel.: (34) 946054835
Web Site:
https://www.cieautomotive.com
CIE—(BIL)
Rev.: $4,543,883,431
Assets: $6,257,864,004
Liabilities: $4,424,058,948
Net Worth: $1,833,805,056
Earnings: $383,947,456
Emp.: 25,182
Fiscal Year-end: 12/31/23
Automotive Components Supplier
N.A.I.C.S.: 336350
Goizalde Egana Garitagoitia *(Vice Chm)*

Subsidiaries:

Advanced Comfort Systems France, S.A.S.   **(1)**
Moulin Jacquet Business Park 5 7 rue du Moulin Jacquet, BP 59, 79302, Bressuire, Cedex, France
Tel.: (33) 549740622
Web Site: https://group-acs.com
Automobile Parts Mfr
N.A.I.C.S.: 336390

Advanced Comfort Systems Iberica, S.L.U.   **(1)**
Rua A Coruna 7-11 Parque Tecnoloxico de Galicia, San Cibrao das Vinas, 32900, Orense, Spain
Tel.: (34) 988608086
Automobile Parts Mfr
N.A.I.C.S.: 336390

Advanced Comfort Systems Romania, S.R.L.   **(1)**
Str Garii nr 1, Pogoanele, 125200, Buzau, Romania

Cie Automotive S.A.—(Continued)
Tel.: (40) 238402231
Automobile Parts Mfr
N.A.I.C.S.: 336390

Advanced Comfort Systems Shanghai Co. Ltd. (1)
Lot 3-4 No 579 Dongxing Rd, Songjiang District, Shanghai, China
Tel.: (86) 2167743655
Automobile Parts Mfr
N.A.I.C.S.: 336390

Alcasting Legutiano, S.L.U. (1)
Zabaldea 2, Pol Ind Goiain, 01170, Legutiano, Alava, Spain
Tel.: (34) 945465375
Automobile Parts Mfr
N.A.I.C.S.: 336390

Alurecy, S.A.U. (1)
Barrio Torrezar S N, 48410, Orozko, Vizcaya, Spain
Tel.: (34) 946610019
Automobile Parts Mfr
N.A.I.C.S.: 336390

Autocom Componentes Automotivos do Brasil Ltda. (1)
Av Eurico Ambrogi Santos 1200, Distrito Industrial de Piracangagua, Taubate, 12042-010, Sao Paulo, Brazil
Tel.: (55) 1236272000
Automobile Parts Mfr
N.A.I.C.S.: 336390

Autoforjas, Ltda. (1)
Av Prefeito Alberto Moura n 900, Distrito Industrial, Sete Lagoas, 35702-383, MG, Brazil
Tel.: (55) 3121068603
Automobile Parts Mfr
N.A.I.C.S.: 336390

Autometal S.A. (1)
Av Fagundes de Oliveira 1650, Diadema, 09950-905, Sao Paulo, Brazil
Tel.: (55) 1140708200
Web Site: http://www.autometal.com.br
Sales Range: $1-4.9 Billion
Automotive Segment Supplier
N.A.I.C.S.: 423110

Autometal SBC Injecao e Pintura de Plasticos Ltda. (1)
Estrada Particular Eiji Kikuti 300 Galpao 1 Cooperativa, Sao Bernardo do Campo, SP, Brazil
Tel.: (55) 1143556700
Automotive Component Mfr & Distr
N.A.I.C.S.: 336390

CIE Automotive Maroc, s.a.r.l. d'au (1)
Zone Franche d Exportation De Tanger Ilot 26 B Lot N 2, 90100, Tangiers, Morocco
Tel.: (212) 539394163
Plastic Molding Product Mfr
N.A.I.C.S.: 333248

CIE Automotive Parts (Shanghai) Co., Ltd. (1)
500 Sheng Xin Nan Lu, Nanxiang Town Jiading District, Shanghai, 201802, China
Tel.: (86) 2169978218
Automobile Parts Mfr
N.A.I.C.S.: 336390

CIE Automotive, USA Inc. (1)
15030 23 Mile Rd, Shelby, MI 48315
Tel.: (586) 566-3900
Automobile Parts Mfr
N.A.I.C.S.: 336390

CIE Celaya, S.A.P.I. de C.V. (1)
Av Norte Cuatro 100, Ciudad Industrial, 38010, Celaya, Gto, Mexico
Tel.: (52) 4616185600
Automobile Parts Mfr
N.A.I.C.S.: 336390

CIE Compiegne, S.A.S. (1)
12 Rue du Four St Jacques, 60203, Compiegne, France
Tel.: (33) 344235678
Automobile Parts Mfr
N.A.I.C.S.: 336390

CIE Deutschland, GmbH (1)

Waldauer Weg 82, 34253, Lohfelden, Germany
Tel.: (49) 56153242
Automobile Parts Mfr
N.A.I.C.S.: 336390

CIE Forjas Minas, Ltda. (1)
Av Prefeito Alberto Moura n 900, Distrito Industrial, Sete Lagoas, 35702-383, MG, Brazil
Tel.: (55) 3121068603
Automotive Component Mfr & Distr
N.A.I.C.S.: 336390

CIE Galfor, S.A.U. (1)
Rua 2 3, Poligono, San Cibrao, 32901, Orense, Spain
Tel.: (34) 988011000
Automotive Component Mfr & Distr
N.A.I.C.S.: 336390

CIE Mecauto, S.A.U. (1)
C/Medigorritxu 140, Poligono Industrial Jundiz, 01015, Vitoria, Alava, Spain
Tel.: (34) 945030500
Automobile Parts Mfr
N.A.I.C.S.: 336390

CIE Metal CZ, s.r.o. (1)
Hranicka 328 Prumyslova zona Lesna, 757 01, Valasske Mezirici, Czech Republic
Tel.: (420) 722965432
Web Site: https://www.ciemetal.cz
Automobile Parts Mfr
N.A.I.C.S.: 336390

CIE Plasticos Mexico, S.A. de C.V. (1)
Servidumbre de Paso 851-A1-PM3, Parque Industrial Santa Monica, 25300, Saltillo, Coahuila, Mexico
Tel.: (52) 8449860060
Automobile Parts Mfr
N.A.I.C.S.: 336390

CIE Plasty CZ, s.r.o. (1)
Hranicka 328, 75701, Valasske Mezirici, Czech Republic
Tel.: (420) 571752588
Web Site: https://www.cieplasty.cz
Automotive Part Mfr & Distr
N.A.I.C.S.: 336390

CIE Praga Louny, a.s. (1)
Husova 552, 440 01, Louny, Czech Republic
Tel.: (420) 415635222
Metal Fabricate Mfr
N.A.I.C.S.: 332312

CIE Stratis-Tratamentos, Ltda. (1)
Lotes 10 a 15, Zona Industrial da Varzea, 4755-439, Barcelos, Portugal
Tel.: (351) 253830160
Web Site: https://www.ciestratis.pt
Automobile Parts Mfr
N.A.I.C.S.: 336390

CIE Udalbide, S.A.U. (1)
Barrio Lejarza 6 Etxano, 48213, Izurtza, Vizcaya, Spain
Tel.: (34) 946217600
Automotive Stamping Part Mfr
N.A.I.C.S.: 336370

CIE Unitools Press CZ, a.s. (1)
Hranicka 328, 75701, Valasske Mezirici, Czech Republic
Tel.: (420) 722965432
Web Site: https://www.cieunitools.cz
Automotive Stamping Part Mfr
N.A.I.C.S.: 336370

CIE Zdanice, s.r.o. (1)
Nadrazni 418, Zdanice, 69632, Hodonin, Czech Republic
Tel.: (420) 518305451
Automobile Parts Mfr
N.A.I.C.S.: 336390

Componentes Automotivos Taubate, Ltda. (1)
Av Eurico Ambrogi Santos 1200, Distrito Industriale Piracangagua, Taubate, Sao Paulo, Brazil
Tel.: (55) 1236276001
Automobile Parts Mfr
N.A.I.C.S.: 336390

Componentes de Automocion Recytec, S.L.U. (1)

San Bartolome 15, Poligono Industrial Gojain, 01171, Legutiano, Alava, Spain
Tel.: (34) 945465429
Automobile Parts Mfr
N.A.I.C.S.: 336390

Componentes de Direccion Recylan, S.L.U. (1)
Parque Empresarial La Muga 1B Navarra, 31160, Orkoion, Spain
Tel.: (34) 948321404
Automobile Parts Mfr
N.A.I.C.S.: 336390

Denat 2007, S.L.U. (1)
Rua B n 3, Poligono Industrial A Granxa, 36475, Porrino, Pontevedra, Spain
Tel.: (34) 986342320
Automobile Parts Mfr
N.A.I.C.S.: 336390

Durametal, S.A. (1)
Avenida Parque Norte II, 170 Distrito Industrial, Maracanau, 61939-180, CE, Brazil
Tel.: (55) 8540080400
Web Site: https://www.durametal.com.br
Automobile Parts Mfr
N.A.I.C.S.: 336390

Egana 2, S.L. (1)
Pol Okango s/n, 48240, Berriz, Bizkaia, Spain
Tel.: (34) 946056100
Automobile Parts Mfr
N.A.I.C.S.: 336390

Forjas de Celaya, S.A. de C.V. (1)
Carretera Celaya-Salamanca Km 5 A-9, 38020, Celaya, Guanajuato, Mexico
Tel.: (52) 4611076802
Automobile Parts Mfr
N.A.I.C.S.: 336390

Gameko Fabricacion de Componentes, S.A. (1)
C/San Antolin 6, P I Gojain, 01171, Legutiano, Alava, Spain
Tel.: (34) 636466830
Automobile Parts Mfr
N.A.I.C.S.: 336390

Golde Auburn Hills, LLC (1)
4000 Pinnacle Ct, Auburn Hills, MI 48326
Tel.: (248) 606-1912
Automobile Parts Mfr
N.A.I.C.S.: 336390

Golde Changchun Co., Ltd. (1)
No 8755 Xihu Road, Changchun Automotive Industries Development Area, Jilin, China
Tel.: (86) 43187075618
Automotive Components Mfr
N.A.I.C.S.: 336390

Golde Lozorno, Spol, s.r.o. (1)
APP Hala A 1006, 90055, Lozorno, Slovakia
Tel.: (421) 232256221
Automotive Components Mfr
N.A.I.C.S.: 336390

Golde Oradea, SRL (1)
Calea Ogorului 214, Bihor, 410554, Oradea, 410554, Romania
Tel.: (40) 372421478
Automotive Components Mfr
N.A.I.C.S.: 336390

Golde Shandong Co., Ltd. (1)
No 1029-2 Yongda Street, Fushan District, Yantai, 265500, Shandong, China
Tel.: (86) 5352138000
Automotive Components Mfr
N.A.I.C.S.: 336390

Golde Shanghai Co., Ltd. (1)
Building 44 No255 Riying N Road, Waigaoqiao Free Trade Zone, Shanghai, 200131, China
Tel.: (86) 2150462223
Emp.: 707
Automotive Components Mfr
N.A.I.C.S.: 336390

Golde Tianjin Co., Ltd. (1)
Plant 1 No 3 West Haihang Road Xiandai Industry Zone, Ninghe District, Tianjin, 301510, China
Tel.: (86) 2269481251
Automotive Components Mfr
N.A.I.C.S.: 336390

Golde Wuhan Co., Ltd. (1)
Building No 1 Liancun Industrial Park, Caidian Economic Development Area, Wuhan, Hubei, China
Tel.: (86) 2784971925
Automotive Components Mfr
N.A.I.C.S.: 336390

Grupo Componentes Vilanova, S.L. (1)
Ronda d Europa 24, 08800, Vilanova i la Geltru, Spain
Tel.: (34) 938142801
Automobile Parts Mfr
N.A.I.C.S.: 336390

Industrias Amaya Telleria, S.A.U. (1)
Zubieta s/n, Poligono Industrial, 48340, Amorebieta-Etxano, Bizkaia, Spain
Tel.: (34) 946300696
Automobile Parts Mfr
N.A.I.C.S.: 336390

Inyectametal, S.A. (1)
Arzubia 13, 48220, Abadino, Vizcaya, Spain
Tel.: (34) 946811950
Automobile Parts Mfr
N.A.I.C.S.: 336390

Jardim Sistemas Automotivos e Industriais, S.A. (1)
Rua Waldemar Rigout n 105, Vila Carlina, Maua, 09370-830, SP, Brazil
Tel.: (55) 1145468600
Web Site: http://www.jardimsistemas.com.br
Automobile Parts Mfr
N.A.I.C.S.: 336390

MAR SK, s.r.o. (1)
Ulica priemyselna 1940/14, Sucany, 038 52, Zilina, Slovakia
Tel.: (421) 434260413
Web Site: http://www.ciemarsk.sk
Automobile Parts Mfr
N.A.I.C.S.: 336390

Maquinados de Precision de Mexico S. de R.L. de C.V. (1)
Avenida El Laurel No 209, Fraccionamiento Industrial El Vergel, 38110, Celaya, Guanajuato, Mexico
Tel.: (52) 4611613193
Automotive Component Mfr & Distr
N.A.I.C.S.: 336390

Mecanizaciones del Sur-Mecasur, S.A. (1)
Pe Aeropolis C/Hispano Aviacion 5, La Rinconada, 41300, Seville, Spain
Tel.: (34) 954115081
Web Site: https://www.mecanisur.es
Tool Product Mfr
N.A.I.C.S.: 333517

Metalurgica Nakayone, Ltda. (1)
Via Francisco Botti 105, Pinhal Cabreuva, Sao Paulo, 13317-286, Brazil
Tel.: (55) 1145291600
Web Site: https://www.nakayone.com.br
Automotive Stamping Part Mfr
N.A.I.C.S.: 336370

Newcor, Inc. (1)
1021 N Shiawassee St, Corunna, MI 48817
Tel.: (989) 743-3936
Holding Company; Machine Tools, Automotive Camshafts, Gears & Driveshafts Mfr
N.A.I.C.S.: 551112

Subsidiary (Domestic):

Blackhawk Engineering, Inc. (2)
118 Blackhawk Ln, Cedar Falls, IA 50613
Tel.: (319) 266-2681
Web Site: https://www.blackhawkengineering.com
Precisioned Machined Products Mfr
N.A.I.C.S.: 333517
Leslie DeGroote (Controller)

Machine Tool & Gear, Inc. (2)
1021 N Shiawassee St, Corunna, MI 48817
Tel.: (989) 743-3936
Web Site: http://www.cieautomotive.com
Automotive Components & Machine Tools Mfr
N.A.I.C.S.: 336390

Rochester Gear, Inc. (2)
9900 Main St, Clifford, MI 48727
Tel.: (989) 761-7521

Emp.: 100
Gears, Shafts & Screw Machine Products
Mfr
N.A.I.C.S.: 336390

Nova Recyd, S.A.U. (1)
C/San Bartolome 13, Poligono Industrial
Gojain, 01170, Legutiano, Alava, Spain
Tel.: (34) 945465380
Automobile Parts Mfr
N.A.I.C.S.: 336390

Nugar, S.A. de C.V. (1)
Avenida 4 No 12, Parque Industrial, 54900,
Tultitlan, Mexico, Mexico
Tel.: (52) 5558992503
Automobile Parts Mfr
N.A.I.C.S.: 336390

Orbelan Plasticos, S.A. (1)
Ama Candida 13, 20140, Andoain, Spain
Tel.: (34) 943591151
Automobile Parts Mfr
N.A.I.C.S.: 336390

**Pintura, Estampado y Montaje,
S.A.P.I. de C.V.** (1)
Avenida Concepcion Beistegui numero
2007, 38024, Celaya, Guanajuato, Mexico
Tel.: (52) 4614716601
Automobile Parts Mfr
N.A.I.C.S.: 336390

**Recogida de Aceites y Grasas
Maresme, S.L.U.** (1)
Pasaje Oeste 6 nave 6, Pol Industrial Bo-
visa, 8329, Barcelona, Spain
Tel.: (34) 935550780
Web Site: https://www.maresmerecicla.com
Oil Recycling Services
N.A.I.C.S.: 423930

Recyde, S.A.U. (1)
Elorrio Bide S N, Pol Ind Pagatza Elgeta,
20690, Guipuzcoa, Spain
Tel.: (34) 943788000
Automobile Parts Mfr
N.A.I.C.S.: 336390

SC CIE Matricon, S.A. (1)
Street Gheorghe Doja Nr 155, 540394,
Tirgu Mures, 540394, Romania
Tel.: (40) 372659700
Automobile Parts Mfr
N.A.I.C.S.: 336390

Somaschini Automotive, SRL (1)
Via Enrico Mattei 42, 24060, Entratico, BG,
Italy
Tel.: (39) 0354256811
Automobile Parts Mfr
N.A.I.C.S.: 336390

**Transformaciones Metalurgicas
Norma, S.A.** (1)
Parcela 7, P I Itziar Itziar-Deba, 20829, Gui-
puzcoa, Spain
Tel.: (34) 943606030
Automobile Parts Mfr
N.A.I.C.S.: 336390

CIE FINANCIERE DE L'OUEST AFRICAIN SA
18 rue Parchappe, 3195, Dakar, Sen-
egal
Tel.: (221) 338897770
FOAF—(EUR)
Sales Range: Less than $1 Million
Holding Company
N.A.I.C.S.: 551112
Francois Bakou *(Chm & CEO)*

CIE IMPORT PRODUITS ALI-MENTAIRES
Les Neufs Arpents 394 Rue De Flins,
Bouafle, 78410, Paris, France
Tel.: (33) 130904600
Web Site: http://www.delicemer.fr
Sales Range: $10-24.9 Million
Emp.: 21
Fish & Seafoods
N.A.I.C.S.: 424460
Jean-Luc Paviot *(Gen Mgr)*

CIE INTL ANDRE TRIGANO
Num 111-113 111 Reuilly, 75012,
Paris, France
Tel.: (33) 144681747
Rev.: $21,500,000
Emp.: 429
Fabricated Textile Products
N.A.I.C.S.: 314999
Andre Trigano *(Pres)*

CIEL LTD.
5th Floor Ebene Skies Rue de l Insti-
tut, Ebene, Mauritius
Tel.: (230) 4042200
Web Site: https://www.cielgroup.com
Year Founded: 1912
CIEL—(MAU)
Rev.: $763,178,773
Assets: $2,113,501,752
Liabilities: $1,465,891,172
Net Worth: $647,610,580
Earnings: $92,723,628
Emp.: 37,500
Fiscal Year-end: 06/30/23
Apparel Trim & Packaging Product
Mfr
N.A.I.C.S.: 315990
Arnaud Dalais *(Chm)*

Subsidiaries:

International Medical Centres
Limited (1)
Plot 37 Yusuf Lule Road Nakasero, Kam-
pala, Uganda
Tel.: (256) 312188800
Web Site: http://www.imc.img.co.ug
Medical Clinic Services
N.A.I.C.S.: 622110
Joel Oroni *(Gen Mgr)*

Long Beach Resort Ltd. (1)
Matara Road, Koggala, Colombo, Sri Lanka
Tel.: (94) 912283332
Web Site:
http://www.thelongbeachresort.com
Resort & Spa Services
N.A.I.C.S.: 721110

MITCO Group Ltd. (1)
4th Floor Ebene Skies Rue de L'Institut,
Ebene, Mauritius
Tel.: (230) 4048000
Web Site: https://www.mitcoworld.com
Emp.: 35,000
Financial Services
N.A.I.C.S.: 523999
Jerome De Chasteauneuf *(Chm)*

CIELO S.A.
Alameda Xingu 512 Alphaville Ba-
rueri, Sao Paulo, 06455-030, Brazil
Tel.: (55) 1125968453
Web Site: https://www.cielo.com.br
Year Founded: 1995
CIOXY—(OTCIQ)
Rev.: $1,895,050,986
Assets: $19,267,120,204
Liabilities: $16,588,431,657
Net Worth: $2,678,688,547
Earnings: $441,262,390
Emp.: 6,376
Fiscal Year-end: 12/31/23
Electronic Payment Solutions
N.A.I.C.S.: 425120
Dilson Tadeu da Costa Ribeiro
*(Member-Exec Bd-Products & Bus
Dev Area)*

Subsidiaries:

BRASPAG Tecno. em Pagto.
Ltda. (1)
Av Marechal Camara-160 9 Andar-Centro,
20020-080, Rio de Janeiro, Brazil
Tel.: (55) 11985410288
Web Site: http://www.braspag.com.br
Ecommerce Services
N.A.I.C.S.: 522320

Cateno Gestao de Contas de Pagto
S.A. (1)
Alameda Xingu 512-16 Andar Alphaville,
Barueri, 06455-030, Sao Paulo, Brazil
Tel.: (55) 20247380
Web Site: http://www.cateno.com.br
Debit & Credit Management Services
N.A.I.C.S.: 522390
Fernando Travencolo *(Mgr-Infrastructure)*

Merchant e-Solutions, Inc. (1)
3400 Bridge Pkwy Ste 100, Redwood City,
CA 94065
Tel.: (650) 628-6850
Web Site: http://www.merchante-
solutions.com
Sales Range: $100-124.9 Million
Electronic Payment Software Developer
N.A.I.C.S.: 513210
Sharif M. Bayyari *(Pres-US)*

CIELO WASTE SOLUTIONS CORP.
605 5th Avenue S W Suite 2500, Cal-
gary, T2P 3H5, AB, Canada
Tel.: (403) 348-2972   BC
Web Site: https://www.cielows.com
Year Founded: 2011
CWSFF—(OTCIQ)
Assets: $35,352,997
Liabilities: $16,183,014
Net Worth: $19,169,983
Earnings: ($31,063,536)
Fiscal Year-end: 04/30/21
Materials Recovery, Renewable Die-
sel & Landfill Reduction Services
N.A.I.C.S.: 562998
Don Allan *(Chm)*

CIEM S.P.A.
Via Cerro Tartari, 03043, Cassino,
Frosinone, Italy
Tel.: (39) 0776 46681   IT
Web Site: http://www.ciemgroup.com
Year Founded: 1984
Automobile Parts Mfr
N.A.I.C.S.: 811310
Alessandro Damiani *(Project Mgr)*

Subsidiaries:

FATA Automation Limited (1)
Elgar House, Shrub Hill Road, Worcester,
WR4 9EE, United Kingdom
Tel.: (44) 1905 613931
Web Site: http://www.fataautomation.co.uk
Sales Range: $25-49.9 Million
Emp.: 8
Designer, Supplier & Installer of Automated
Handling Systems
N.A.I.C.S.: 333922
Nicola Cipolletta *(Mng Dir)*

MADA S.p.A. (1)
Viale delle Industrie Strada Statale 8,
81020, San Marco Evangelista, CE, Italy
Tel.: (39) 0823 226 111
Web Site: http://www.madacaserta.com
Emp.: 40
Material Handling Equipment Mfr
N.A.I.C.S.: 333922
Antonio D'Amico *(Dir-Technical)*

CIFI EVER SUNSHINE SER-VICES GROUP LIMITED
6 / F Xuhui Center No 20 Lane 1188
Shenhong Road, Minhang District,
Shanghai, 200335, China
Tel.: (86) 2161208582   Ky
Web Site:
http://www.ysservice.com.cn
Year Founded: 2002
1995—(HKG)
Rev.: $720,518,439
Assets: $1,113,299,239
Liabilities: $394,478,060
Net Worth: $718,821,179
Earnings: $106,103,287
Emp.: 16,709
Fiscal Year-end: 12/31/21
Residential Property Management
Services
N.A.I.C.S.: 531311
Zhong Lin *(Chm)*

CIFI HOLDINGS (GROUP) CO. LTD.
No 39 Lane 1088 Shenhong Road,
Minhang District, Shanghai, 201106,
China
Tel.: (86) 21561316
Web Site: http://www.cifi.com.cn
Year Founded: 2000
0884—(HKG)
Rev.: $10,085,290,862
Assets: $42,271,757,237
Liabilities: $33,206,294,909
Net Worth: $9,065,462,328
Earnings: ($1,218,523,597)
Emp.: 28,023
Fiscal Year-end: 12/31/23
Holding Company
N.A.I.C.S.: 551112
Zhong Lin *(Founder & Chm)*

Subsidiaries:

Shanghai Xuyu Property Co. Ltd. (1)
Siying Park XiaoKunShan Town Song Jiang
County, Shanghai, China
Tel.: (86) 216 4090198
Real Estate Development Services
N.A.I.C.S.: 531390

CIFIN S.R.L.
Via Archimede n 10, 41019, Soliera,
MO, Italy
Tel.: (39) 059 895411   IT
Web Site: http://www.emmegi.com
Year Founded: 1972
Holding Company; Aluminum, PVC,
Light Alloy & Glass Working Machin-
ery Mfr & Whslr
N.A.I.C.S.: 551112

Subsidiaries:

CIPI S.p.A (1)
Via Lorenteggio 259, 20152, Milan, Italy
Tel.: (39) 024832981
Web Site: http://www.cipi.it
Commercial Printing Services
N.A.I.C.S.: 323111

Emmegi S.p.A. (1)
Via Archimede n 10, Frazione Limidi,
41019, Soliera, MO, Italy
Tel.: (39) 059 895411
Web Site: http://www.emmegi.com
Aluminium Cutting Machines Mfr
N.A.I.C.S.: 811310
Alberto Geremia *(Mgr-Sls)*

Subsidiary (Non-US):

Emmegi (Suzhou) Co., Ltd. (2)
No 9 Guanshan Road Yangshan Science &
Technology Park Snd, 215151, Suzhou,
China
Tel.: (86) 51266167398
Steel Product Distr
N.A.I.C.S.: 423510
Hong Yang *(Deputy Gen Mgr)*

Emmegi (UK) Ltd. (2)
Unit 14 Spitfire Close Coventry Business
Park, Coventry, CV5 6UR, United Kingdom
Tel.: (44) 2476676192
Steel Product Distr
N.A.I.C.S.: 423510
Ian Latimer *(Mng Dir)*

Emmegi Deutschland GmbH (2)
Zeppelinstrasse 4, 73119, Zell unter Aichel-
berg, Germany
Tel.: (49) 716494000
Steel Product Distr
N.A.I.C.S.: 423510

Emmegi Iberica, S.A. (2)
Pol Ind Can Canals C/ Menorca 27-29,
Sant Quirze del Valles, 08192, Barcelona,
Spain
Tel.: (34) 937213630
Steel Product Distr
N.A.I.C.S.: 423510

Emmegi Scandinavia AB (2)
Vestby, PO Box 64, 3282, Kvelde, Norway
Tel.: (47) 33179270
Steel Product Distr

Cifin S.r.l.—(Continued)

N.A.I.C.S.: 423510

Emmegi Scandinavia AB (2)
Mattlaggargatan 3, PO Box 123, 57521,
Eksjo, Sweden
Tel.: (46) 38114380
Steel Product Distr
N.A.I.C.S.: 423510

Emmegi Suisse SA (2)
Via G B Pioda 9, 6900, Lugano, Switzerland
Tel.: (41) 919109940
Steel Product Distr
N.A.I.C.S.: 423510

Emmegi Turk (2)
Organize Sanayi Bolgesi Ataturk Oto Sanayi
Sitesi Unal Is Merkezi 22, No 21 Ikitelli Basaksehir, 34365, Istanbul, Turkiye
Tel.: (90) 2124852440
Steel Product Distr
N.A.I.C.S.: 423510

Emmegi do Brasil Ltda (2)
Av Vitoria Rossi Martini 592, 13347-650,
Indaiatuba, Brazil
Tel.: (55) 1939356512
Steel Product Distr
N.A.I.C.S.: 423510
Emilio Rizzi (Dir-Comml)

Subsidiary (Domestic):

Emmegisoft srl. (2)
Via Carpi-Ravarino 300, Soliera, 41019,
Modena, Italy
Tel.: (39) 059566273
Web Site: http://www.emmegisoft.com
Software Development Services
N.A.I.C.S.: 541511
Federico Pelloni (Project Mgr)

Keraglass Industries S.r.l. (1)
Via Sassogattone 13/A, Baiso, 42031, Reggio Emilia, Italy
Tel.: (39) 0522993027
Web Site: http://www.keraglass.com
Glass Products Mfr
N.A.I.C.S.: 327215

elumatec AG (1)
Pinacher Strasse 61, 75417, Muhlacker,
Germany
Tel.: (49) 7041140
Web Site: http://www.elumatec.com
Emp.: 720
Industrial Cutting Machines Mfr
N.A.I.C.S.: 333515
Ralf Haspel (CEO)

Subsidiary (Non-US):

OOO elumatec Rus (2)
ul Flotskaya 76, 125413, Moscow, Russia
Tel.: (7) 4996410400
Web Site: http://www.elumatec.ru
Industrial Machinery & Equipment Distr
N.A.I.C.S.: 423830

P&N Homag Importacao e Comercio Ltda. (2)
Wolsir Antonini 120, 95700-000, Bento Goncalves, Rio Grande do Sul, Brazil
Tel.: (55) 5421025400
Web Site: http://www.pnhomag.com.br
Industrial Machinery & Equipment Distr
N.A.I.C.S.: 423830

elumatec Asia pte Ltd. (2)
7 Kian Teck Way, 628734, Singapore, Singapore
Tel.: (65) 62641182
Web Site: http://www.elumatec.com
Industrial Machinery & Equipment Distr
N.A.I.C.S.: 423830

elumatec Australia Pty. Ltd. (2)
Unit 1/14 Centre Place Wetherill Park, Sydney, 2164, NSW, Australia
Tel.: (61) 297252100
Web Site: http://www.elumatec.com.au
Industrial Machinery & Equipment Distr
N.A.I.C.S.: 423830
Kevin Maton (Mgr-Warehouse)

elumatec Austria GmbH (2)
Ziegelweg 1, 4481, Asten, Austria
Tel.: (43) 7224670530
Web Site: http://www.elumatec.com

Industrial Machinery & Equipment Distr
N.A.I.C.S.: 423830

elumatec Benelux b.v. (2)
Hoogeveenenweg 204, 2913 LV,
Nieuwerkerk, Netherlands
Tel.: (31) 180315858
Web Site: http://www.elumatec.com
Industrial Machinery & Equipment Distr
N.A.I.C.S.: 423830
Bas Ladestein (Mng Dir)

elumatec Bulgaria EOOD (2)
Dejan Belischki Str 52, 1404, Sofia, Bulgaria
Tel.: (359) 29580810
Web Site: http://www.elumatec.com
Industrial Machinery & Equipment Distr
N.A.I.C.S.: 423830

elumatec CZ s.r.o. (2)
Na Salajce 1004, 696 81, Bznec, Czech
Republic
Tel.: (420) 513035900
Web Site: http://www.elumatec.com
Industrial Machinery & Equipment Distr
N.A.I.C.S.: 423830

elumatec Chile Limitada (2)
Avenida Nueva Tajamar 481 Torre Sur, Las
Condes, Chile
Tel.: (56) 97 303 28 14
Web Site: http://www.elumatec.com
Industrial Machinery & Equipment Distr
N.A.I.C.S.: 423830

elumatec France S.A.S. (2)
Route de Soufflenheim, 67660, Betschdorf,
France
Tel.: (33) 388545710
Web Site: http://www.elumatec.com
Industrial Machinery & Equipment Mfr
N.A.I.C.S.: 333998

elumatec India Private Limited (2)
Electronic Zone Near Larsen and Toubro
Infotech EL 123, MIDC Industrial Area Mahape, Navi Mumbai, 400710, Maharashtra,
India
Tel.: (91) 2227626601
Web Site: http://www.elumatec.com
Industrial Machinery & Equipment Distr
N.A.I.C.S.: 423830
Deelip Rane (Mgr-Svc)

elumatec Italia S.r.l. (2)
Via G Rivani 99, 40138, Bologna, Italy
Tel.: (39) 051531908
Web Site: http://www.elumatec.com
Industrial Machinery & Equipment Distr
N.A.I.C.S.: 423830
Marco Di Giovanni (Dir-Tech)

elumatec Korea Co. Ltd. (2)
RM802 Hyundai office B/D 9-4, Sunae-dong
Bundang-gu, Seongnam, Gyeonggi-do, Korea (South)
Tel.: (82) 317198523
Industrial Machinery & Equipment Distr
N.A.I.C.S.: 423830

elumatec Lithuania UAB (2)
Naujoji str 140, 62175, Alytus, Lithuania
Tel.: (370) 52715388
Web Site: http://www.glastech.lt
Industrial Machinery & Equipment Distr
N.A.I.C.S.: 423830

elumatec Machinery Shanghai Co. Ltd. (2)
NO 258-1 Fang Dong Road, Jiuting Town
Songjiang District, Shanghai, 201615, China
Tel.: (86) 2167639570
Web Site: http://www.elumatec.com
Industrial Machinery & Equipment Distr
N.A.I.C.S.: 423830

elumatec Makine ve Servis San. Ve Tic. Ltd. Sti. (2)
Mahmutbey Merkez Mah Kucukhalkali Cad
No 10-Z1, Bagcilar, Istanbul, Turkiye
Tel.: (90) 2126544461
Web Site: http://www.elumatec.com
Industrial Machinery & Equipment Distr
N.A.I.C.S.: 423830

elumatec Malaysia SDN BHD (2)
No 7 Jalan 7/155 Bukit Jalil Integrated Business Park, 58200, Kuala Lumpur, Malaysia
Tel.: (60) 377857330
Web Site: http://www.elumatec.com

Industrial Machinery & Equipment Distr
N.A.I.C.S.: 423830

elumatec Maschinen d.o.o. (2)
El-Gazalije 3, 77000, Bihac, Bosnia & Herzegovina
Tel.: (387) 37312640
Web Site: http://www.elumatec.com
Industrial Machinery & Equipment Distr
N.A.I.C.S.: 423830
Amra Babic (Officer-Pur & Admin)

elumatec Maschinen sh.p.k. (2)
Lidhja e Lezhes No 86, 42000, Vushtrri,
Kosovo, Serbia
Tel.: (381) 28573085
Web Site: http://www.elumatec.com
Industrial Machinery & Equipment Distr
N.A.I.C.S.: 423830
Qemajl Behrami (Mng Dir)

elumatec Middle East LLC (2)
Waha Community Block F Office 1007 Nad
Al Hamar Street, PO Box 215623, Dubai,
United Arab Emirates
Tel.: (971) 42393932
Web Site: http://www.elumatec.com
Industrial Machinery & Equipment Distr
N.A.I.C.S.: 423830
Mohannad Othman (Mgr-Svc)

elumatec Norge AS (2)
Risoyaveien 7, 3290, Stavern, Norway
Tel.: (47) 33190730
Web Site: http://www.elumatec.com
Industrial Machinery & Equipment Distr
N.A.I.C.S.: 423830

Subsidiary (US):

elumatec North America Inc. (2)
4320 Ralph Jones Ct, South Bend, IN
46628
Tel.: (574) 273-1790
Web Site:
http://www.elumatecnorthamerica.com
Industrial Machinery & Equipment Distr
N.A.I.C.S.: 423830
Steve VanTongeren (Pres)

Subsidiary (Non-US):

elumatec Polska Sp. z o. o. (2)
ul Przemysowa 10, 62-300, Wrzesnia, Poland
Tel.: (48) 614377000
Web Site: http://www.elumatec.pl
Industrial Machinery & Equipment Distr
N.A.I.C.S.: 423830

elumatec Romania srl.. (2)
Str Polona Nr 86 Sect 1, Bucharest, Romania
Tel.: (40) 212106917
Web Site: http://www.elumatec.com
Industrial Machinery & Equipment Distr
N.A.I.C.S.: 423830

elumatec Shenzhen Co. Ltd. (2)
Flat 710 International Culture Building No
3039 Shenzhen South Road, 518033,
Shenzhen, China
Tel.: (86) 75583297555
Web Site: http://www.elumatec.com
Industrial Machinery & Equipment Distr
N.A.I.C.S.: 423830

elumatec Skandinavien AB (2)
Backa Bergogatan 18, 422 46, Hisings
Backa, Sweden
Tel.: (46) 317424880
Web Site: http://www.elumatec.com
Industrial Machinery & Equipment Distr
N.A.I.C.S.: 423830

elumatec Slovensko, s.r.o. (2)
Pribinova 79, 92001, Hlohovec, Slovakia
Tel.: (421) 337330671
Web Site: http://www.elumatec.com
Industrial Machinery & Equipment Distr
N.A.I.C.S.: 423830

elumatec South Africa (Pty) Ltd. (2)
Branch Office Johannesburg 39 Kelly Road,
The Palisades Jet Park, 1459, Johannesburg, South Africa
Tel.: (27) 114521214
Web Site: http://www.elumatec.co.za
Industrial Machinery & Equipment Distr
N.A.I.C.S.: 423830

elumatec South Africa (Pty) Ltd. (2)
Unit 4 Drill Park 3 Drill Ave Montague, Cape
Town, 7441, South Africa
Tel.: (27) 215514420
Web Site: http://www.elumatec.com
Industrial Machinery & Equipment Distr
N.A.I.C.S.: 423830

elumatec Swiss AG (2)
Talstr 31, 8808, Pfaffikon, Switzerland
Tel.: (41) 554101340
Web Site: http://www.elumatec.com
Industrial Machinery & Equipment Distr
N.A.I.C.S.: 423830

elumatec United Kingdom Ltd. (2)
Unit 2 Europa Business Park Maidstone
Road, Kingston, Milton Keynes, MK10 OBD,
United Kingdom
Tel.: (44) 1908580800
Web Site: http://www.elumatec.com
Industrial Machinery & Equipment Distr
N.A.I.C.S.: 423830
Bryan Dando (Reg Mgr-Sls)

elumatec d.o.o. (2)
IX Juzna obala 22, 10020, Zagreb, Croatia
Tel.: (385) 16520008
Web Site: http://www.elumatec.com
Industrial Machinery & Equipment Distr
N.A.I.C.S.: 423830

elumatec d.o.o. (2)
Str Trgovacka 16a apartman G2, Zarkovo,
11030, Belgrade, Serbia
Tel.: (381) 112394831
Web Site: http://www.elumatec.de
Industrial Machinery & Equipment Distr
N.A.I.C.S.: 423830
Bojan Dejanovic (Engr-Electronics)

elumatec de America Latina S.A. (2)
Recyba. 2790 C1653MUO 3669 Villa Ballester,
B1653MUO, Buenos Aires, Argentina
Tel.: (54) 1147679806
Web Site: http://www.elumatec.com
Industrial Machinery & Equipment Distr
N.A.I.C.S.: 423830
Adriana Costa (Head-Fin)

Subsidiary (Domestic):

elusoft GmbH (2)
Industriegebiet Breitwasen Breitwasenring
4, 72135, Dettenhausen, Baden-
Wurttemberg, Germany
Tel.: (49) 7157 526 65 00
Web Site: http://www.elusoft.de
Software Development Services
N.A.I.C.S.: 541511
Ralf Haspel (Mng Dir)

CIG SHANGHAI CO., LTD.
Building 8 2388 Chenhang Road 5th
Floor, Minhang District, Shanghai,
201114, China
Tel.: (86) 2180233300
Web Site: https://www.cigtech.com
603083—(SHG)
Rev.: $531,499,714
Assets: $734,550,813
Liabilities: $464,184,190
Net Worth: $270,366,623
Earnings: $24,074,177
Fiscal Year-end: 12/31/22
Communication Equipment Mfr &
Distr
N.A.I.C.S.: 334210

Subsidiaries:

CIG Photonics Japan Limited (1)
4-1-55 Oyama, Chuo-ku, Sagamihara, 252-
5250, Kanagawa, Japan
Tel.: (81) 428610047
Software Publishing Services
N.A.I.C.S.: 541511

CIGTech Japan Limited (1)
Keio Hachioji Myojincho Bldg 5F 4-9-8
Myojin-cho, Hachioji, 192-0046, Tokyo, Japan
Tel.: (81) 345777711
Software Publishing Services
N.A.I.C.S.: 541511

Cambridge Industries Group, Ltd. (1)

Suite 0301 3/F Fontaine Building 18 Mody Road, Tsim Sha Tsui, Kowloon Bay, China (Hong Kong)
Tel.: (852) 35202145
Software Publishing Services
N.A.I.C.S.: 541511

Cambridge Industries USA, Inc. (1)
2445 Augustine Dr 6th Fl, Santa Clara, CA 95054
Tel.: (408) 606-2200
Software Publishing Services
N.A.I.C.S.: 541511

CIGALAH TRADING ESTAB-LISHMENT
Cigalah Yousfia Building Ali Bin Abi Taleb Street, Sharafiyah District, Jeddah, Saudi Arabia
Tel.: (966) 126148001   SA
Web Site: https://cigalah.com
Financial Services
N.A.I.C.S.: 523999

CIGLANA A.D.
Ledine br 1, 21240, Titel, Serbia
Tel.: (381) 212960174
Web Site: https://www.ciglanatitel.rs
Year Founded: 1991
CGLT—(BEL)
Rev.: $17,491
Assets: $447,111
Liabilities: $408,193
Net Worth: $38,917
Earnings: ($30,003)
Emp.: 5
Fiscal Year-end: 12/31/23
Construction Product Mfr
N.A.I.C.S.: 327331
Radoslav Mitric (Exec Dir)

CIGNITI TECHNOLOGIES LTD.
6th Floor Orion Block International Tech Park Plot No 17, Software Units Layout Madhapur, Hyderabad, 500081, India
Tel.: (91) 4040382255   In
Web Site: https://www.cigniti.com
534758—(BOM)
Rev.: $199,304,406
Assets: $101,433,859
Liabilities: $30,772,903
Net Worth: $70,660,956
Earnings: $20,181,116
Emp.: 3,949
Fiscal Year-end: 03/31/23
Software Testing Services
N.A.I.C.S.: 541512
Subramanyam C. V. (Chm & Mng Dir)

Subsidiaries:

Cigniti Technologies Canada Inc. (1)
2000 Argentia Road Plaza 4 Suite 302, Mississauga, L5N 1W1, ON, Canada
Tel.: (647) 951-5943
Software Development Services
N.A.I.C.S.: 541511

Cigniti Technologies Inc. (1)
433 E Las Colinas Blvd Ste 1300, Irving, TX 75039
Tel.: (469) 673-3443
Software Testing Services
N.A.I.C.S.: 541511

Cigniti, Inc. (1)
433 E Las Colinas Blvd Ste 1300, Irving, TX 75039
Tel.: (469) 673-3443
Web Site: https://www.cigniti.com
Sales Range: $10-24.9 Million
Emp.: 155
Computer System Design Services
N.A.I.C.S.: 541512

CII BRIDGES AND ROAD IN-VESTMENT JOINT STOCK COMPANY
4th Floor 70 Lu Gia Ward 15 District 11, Ho Chi Minh City, Vietnam

Tel.: (84) 838688239
Web Site: https://www.ciibr.com.vn
Year Founded: 1978
LGC—(HOSE)
Rev.: $65,797,389
Assets: $944,044,564
Liabilities: $730,469,614
Net Worth: $213,574,950
Earnings: $28,493,714
Emp.: 22
Fiscal Year-end: 12/31/23
Construction Services
N.A.I.C.S.: 237310

CIKER A.D.
Atile Jozefa 1, Cantavir, Serbia
Tel.: (381) 24 782 281
Year Founded: 1990
Sales Range: Less than $1 Million
Emp.: 2
Grocery Store Operator
N.A.I.C.S.: 445110

CIL GROUP SL
Avda Manoteras 50, 28050, Madrid, Spain
Tel.: (34) 913023140
Web Site: http://www.cilmd.com
Emp.: 1,000
Direct Mail Marketing Services
N.A.I.C.S.: 541860
Silvia Reiris Rico (CEO)

Subsidiaries:

Club Internacional del Libro, Marketing Directo, S.L. (1)
Avda. Manoteras 50, 28050, Madrid, Spain
Tel.: (34) 902 11 30 11.
Direct Mail Marketing Services
N.A.I.C.S.: 541860

Gratisfilm Photocolor Club SA (1)
Calle Bravo Murillo 359, Portal 8 1', Madrid, 28020, Spain
Tel.: (34) 913842030
Web Site: http://www.gratisfilm.es
Emp.: 500
Books Publishing Services
N.A.I.C.S.: 513130
Ramon Martin (Mgr-Fin)

Oy Valitut Palat - Reader's Digest AB (1)
Petajanmaentae 14 Pl 106, 00380, Helsinki, Finland
Tel.: (358) 1066778
Web Site: http://www.valitutpalat.fi
Sales Range: $25-49.9 Million
Emp.: 70
Magazine Publisher
N.A.I.C.S.: 513120

Reader's Digest AB (1)
Hornsbruksgatan 28, Stockholm, 117 34, Sweden
Tel.: (46) 858710900
Web Site: http://www.readersdigest.se
Sales Range: $25-49.9 Million
Emp.: 15
Magazine Publisher
N.A.I.C.S.: 513120

S.A. De Promociones Y Ediciones (1)
Avda Manoteras 50, 28050, Madrid, Spain
Tel.: (34) 902 11 30 11
Direct Mail Marketing Services
N.A.I.C.S.: 541860

Selection du Reader's Digest S.A. (1)
1 Avenue Louis Pasteur, Bagneux, 92220, France
Tel.: (33) 146748484
Web Site: http://www.rd.com
Sales Range: $50-74.9 Million
Emp.: 400
Magazine Publisher
N.A.I.C.S.: 513120

CIL HOLDINGS LIMITED
Workshop 607 6/F Sun Cheong Industrial Building 1 Cheung Shun

Street, Kowloon, China (Hong Kong)
Tel.: (852) 3521 1226   BM
Web Site:
    http://www.capitalfp.com.hk
Rev.: $17,253,856
Assets: $20,712,467
Liabilities: $20,818,450
Net Worth: ($105,983)
Earnings: ($7,234,277)
Emp.: 24
Fiscal Year-end: 06/30/19
Holding Company
N.A.I.C.S.: 551112
Wilson Wong (Deputy Chm)

CIM FINANCIAL SERVICES LIMITED
33 Edith Cavell Street, Port Louis, Mauritius
Tel.: (230) 2137676
Web Site: https://www.cim.mu
Year Founded: 1987
CIM—(MAU)
Rev.: $75,327,290
Assets: $465,182,493
Liabilities: $339,831,710
Net Worth: $125,350,783
Earnings: $20,712,903
Emp.: 1,000
Fiscal Year-end: 09/30/23
Financial Services
N.A.I.C.S.: 523999
Gyaneshwarnath Gowrea (Mng Dir-Cim Tax Svcs)

Subsidiaries:

International Management (Mauritius) Limited (1)
Lescascades Bldg, Edith Cavell Str, Port Louis, Mauritius
Tel.: (230) 2129800
Web Site:
    http://www.cimglobalbusiness.com
Sales Range: $50-74.9 Million
Emp.: 250
Financial & Corporate Services
N.A.I.C.S.: 525990
Graham Sheward (Mng Dir)

TheBrandHouse Ltd (1)
Industrial Park 1, Riche Terre, Mauritius
Tel.: (230) 2071700
Web Site: https://www.thebrandhouse.mu
Emp.: 350
Home Appliances & Consumer Electronics Distr & Retailer
N.A.I.C.S.: 423620
Clovis Wong (CEO)

CIM INTERNATIONAL GROUP, INC.
55 Commerce Valley Drive W Unit 502, Markham, L3T 7V9, ON, Canada
Tel.: (905) 597-8858
Web Site:
    http://www.cimintgroup.com
Rev.: $88,355
Assets: $2,620,058
Liabilities: $10,864,001
Net Worth: ($8,243,944)
Earnings: ($16,579,398)
Fiscal Year-end: 12/31/19
Real Estate Manangement Services
N.A.I.C.S.: 531210
Jerry Feng (CEO)

CIMB GROUP HOLDINGS BERHAD
Level 13 Menara CIMB Jalan Stesen Sentral 2, Kuala Lumpur Sentral, 50470, Kuala Lumpur, Malaysia
Tel.: (60) 322618888   MA
Web Site: https://www.cimb.com
Year Founded: 1974
CIMB—(KLS)
Rev.: $5,013,896,720
Assets: $155,253,365,503
Liabilities: $140,472,647,831

Net Worth: $14,780,717,672
Earnings: $1,515,787,302
Emp.: 33,632
Fiscal Year-end: 12/31/23
Holding Company
N.A.I.C.S.: 551111
Hamidah Naziadin (Chief People Officer & CEO-CIMB Foundation)

Subsidiaries:

CIMB Bank (Cambodia) Plc (1)
No 60 Preah Monivong Blvd Phum 10, Sangkat Voat Phnum Khan Doun Penh, Phnom Penh, 120211, Cambodia
Tel.: (855) 23988388
Web Site: https://www.cimbbank.com.kh
N.A.I.C.S.: 522110

CIMB Bank Bhd. (1)
Level 19 Menara Bumiputera-Commerce No 11 Jalan Raja Laut, 50350, Kuala Lumpur, Malaysia
Tel.: (60) 362047788
Web Site: http://www.cimb.my
Online Transaction & Banking Services
N.A.I.C.S.: 522320
Alice Chong (VP)

Subsidiary (Non-US):

CIMB Bank (Vietnam) Limited (2)
Level 2 CornerStone Building 16 Phan Chu Trinh, Hoan Kiem District, Hanoi, Vietnam
Tel.: (84) 2432663388
Web Site: http://www.cimbbank.com.vn
Investment Banking Services
N.A.I.C.S.: 523150
Loan Huynh (Mgr-Treasury)

Subsidiary (Domestic):

CIMB Bank (I) Ltd. (2)
Level 14 A Main Office Tower Financial Park Labuan Jalan Merdeka, 87000, Labuan, Malaysia
Tel.: (60) 87597500
Investment Banking Services
N.A.I.C.S.: 523150

iCIMB (Malaysia) Sdn. Bhd. (2)
19th Floor Tower 5 Avenue 7 Bangsar South No 8 Jalan Kerinchi, 59200, Kuala Lumpur, Malaysia
Tel.: (60) 321807198
Investment Banking Services
N.A.I.C.S.: 523150

CIMB Group Sdn. Bhd. (1)
10th Floor Bangunan CIMB Jalan Semantan, 50490, Kuala Lumpur, Malaysia
Tel.: (60) 320848888
Web Site: http://www.cimb.com.my
Sales Range: $50-74.9 Million
Emp.: 3,000
Investment Holding
N.A.I.C.S.: 551111

Subsidiary (Non-US):

Armada Investment Holding Ltd (2)
30 Shotover Street Queenstown Town Centre, Queenstown-Lakes, Queenstown, Otago, New Zealand
Tel.: (64) 34412100
Investment Management Service
N.A.I.C.S.: 523999

Subsidiary (Domestic):

CIMB Private Equity Sdn Bhd (2)
Level 33 Menara Bumiputra Commerce 11, Jalan Raja Laut, 50350, Kuala Lumpur, Malaysia
Tel.: (60) 326192827
Sales Range: $50-74.9 Million
Emp.: 25
Commercial Banking Services
N.A.I.C.S.: 522110

Subsidiary (Non-US):

CIMB Securities International Pte Ltd (2)
Tel.: (65) 62251228
Web Site: http://www.itrade.com.sg
Commercial Banking Services
N.A.I.C.S.: 522110

CIMB Group Holdings Berhad—(Continued)

Subsidiary (Non-US):

CGS-CIMB Securities (Singapore) Pte. Ltd　　　(3)
Tel.: (65) 65389889
Web Site: http://www.cimbsecurities.com
Emp.: 500
Security Brokerage Services
N.A.I.C.S.: 523150

CGS-CIMB Securities (UK) Limited　　　(3)
Tel.: (44) 2072012199
Web Site: https://www.cgs-cimb.com
Emp.: 15
Financial Security Services
N.A.I.C.S.: 523999

CIMB Securities (HK) Ltd　　　(3)
Tel.: (852) 28680380
Commercial Banking Services
N.A.I.C.S.: 522110

PT CIMB Securities Indonesia　　　(3)
Tel.: (62) 215151330
Web Site: http://www.cimb.com
Emp.: 300
Commercial Banking Services
N.A.I.C.S.: 522110

Subsidiary (Non-US):

CIMB Thai Bank Public Company Limited　　　(2)
44 Langsuan Road, Lumpini Pathum Wan, Bangkok, 10330, Thailand　　　**(93.15%)**
Tel.: (66) 26267777
Web Site: https://www.cimbthai.com
Rev.: $489,718,097
Assets: $14,858,022,198
Liabilities: $13,486,625,832
Net Worth: $1,371,396,366
Earnings: $46,861,020
Emp.: 2,485
Fiscal Year-end: 12/31/2023
Banking & Financial Services
N.A.I.C.S.: 522110
Robert Dau Meng Cheim *(Chm)*

Subsidiary (Domestic):

CIMB Principal Asset Management Company Limited　　　(3)
44 Cimb Thai Bank Building 16th Floor Langsuan Road, Lumpini Pathumwan, Bangkok, 10330, Thailand
Tel.: (66) 26869595
Web Site: https://www.principal.th
Sales Range: $50-74.9 Million
Emp.: 70
Asset Management Services
N.A.I.C.S.: 523999
Shahul Hamid *(Chm)*

Joint Venture (Domestic):

CIMB-Principal Asset Management Berhad　　　(2)
10th Floor Bangunan CIMB Jalan Semantan, Damansara Heights, Kuala Lumpur, 50490, Malaysia
Tel.: (60) 3 2084 2000
Web Site: http://www.cimb-principal.com.my
Emp.: 185
Asset Management
N.A.I.C.S.: 523940
Munirah Khairuddin *(CEO)*

Subsidiary (Domestic):

CIMB Wealth Advisors Berhad　　　(3)
50 52 54 Jalan ss 21/39 Damansara Utama, 47400, Petaling Jaya, Selangor, Malaysia
Tel.: (60) 3 7718 3000
Web Site:
　http://www.cwealthadvisors.com.my
Financial Advisory Services
N.A.I.C.S.: 523999

Subsidiary (Non-US):

CIMB-Principal Asset Management (Singapore) Pte Ltd　　　(3)
50 Raffles Place 22-03A Singapore Land Tower, Singapore, 48623, Singapore
Tel.: (65) 6210 8488
Web Site: http://www.principal.com.sg

Emp.: 1
Asset Management Services
N.A.I.C.S.: 523940

CIMB-Principal Asset Management Company Limited　　　(3)
44 CIMB THAI Bank Building 16th Floor Langsuan Road, Lumpini Pathumwan, Bangkok, 10330, Thailand
Tel.: (66) 26860505
Web Site: http://www.principal.th
Emp.: 100
Financial Management Services
N.A.I.C.S.: 523999

Subsidiary (Domestic):

Commerce Asset Ventures SDN BHD　　　(2)
6 Commerce House 22-24 Jalan Sri Semantan Satu, 50490, Kuala Lumpur, Malaysia
Tel.: (60) 0327325577
Web Site: http://www.cinb.com
Sales Range: $25-49.9 Million
Emp.: 30
Investment Management Service
N.A.I.C.S.: 541611

Goodmaid Chemical Corporation Sdn Bhd　　　(2)
Suite C-12-12 Plaza Mont Kiara No 2 Jalan Kiara, Mont Kiara, 70450, Kuala Lumpur, Malaysia
Tel.: (60) 362039558
Web Site: http://www.goodmaid.net
Household Cleaning Product Mfr
N.A.I.C.S.: 325612

Goodmaid Marketing Sdn Bhd　　　(2)
Ste C 12 12 Plz Mont Kiara No 2, Jalan Kiara Mont Kiara, 50480, Kuala Lumpur, Malaysia
Tel.: (60) 362039558
Household Cleaning Product Mfr
N.A.I.C.S.: 325612

Subsidiary (Non-US):

PT Bank CIMB Niaga Tbk　　　(2)
Jl Jend Sudirman Kav 58, Jakarta, 12190, Indonesia
Tel.: (62) 212505252
Web Site: https://www.cimbniaga.co.id
Banking Services
N.A.I.C.S.: 522110

Joint Venture (Non-US):

PT Principal Asset Management　　　(2)
Revenue Tower District 8 5th Floor Jl Jend Sudirman No 52-53, Sudirman No 28, Jakarta, 12190, Indonesia
Tel.: (62) 215 088 9988
Web Site: https://www.principal.co.id
Commercial Banking Services
N.A.I.C.S.: 522110
Priyanto Soedarsono *(CIO)*

PT Bank CIMB Niaga Tbk　　　(1)
Graha Niaga Jl Jend Sudirman Kav 58, Jakarta, 12190, Indonesia
Tel.: (62) 212505252
Investment Banking Services
N.A.I.C.S.: 523150
Samuel Charles *(Mgr-Payment)*

PT Kencana Internusa Artha Finance　　　(1)
Gedung Kita Finance Jl R S Fatmawati No 16, Jakarta, 12420, Indonesia
Tel.: (62) 21 7590 8899
Web Site: http://www.kitafinance.com
Automobile Financing Services
N.A.I.C.S.: 525990
Eiichiro Ito *(VP)*

Principal Islamic Asset Management Sdn. Bhd.　　　(1)
10th floor Bangunan CIMB Jalan Semantan, Damansara Heights, 50490, Kuala Lumpur, Malaysia
Tel.: (60) 320848888
Web Site: https://www.principalislamic.com
Asset Management Services
N.A.I.C.S.: 523940

Touch 'N Go Sdn. Bhd.
Level 9 Tower 6 Avenue 5 Bangsar South

No 8, Jalan Kerinchi, 59200, Kuala Lumpur, Malaysia
Tel.: (60) 327148888
Web Site: https://www.touchngo.com.my
Digital Payment Services
N.A.I.C.S.: 522320

iCIMB (MSC) Sdn Bhd　　　(1)
19th Floor Menara Atlas 5 Jalan 4/83a, Kuala Lumpur, 59200, Malaysia
Tel.: (60) 322960000
Financial Management Services
N.A.I.C.S.: 523999

CIMC VEHICLE (GROUP) CO., LTD.
CIMC R&D Center No 2 Gangwan Avenue Shekou Industrial Zone, Shenzhen, 518067, Guangdong, China
Tel.: (86) 75526802955
Web Site:
　https://www.cimcvehiclesgroup.com
Year Founded: 2002
1839—(HKG)
Rev.: $3,316,333,983
Assets: $3,119,299,101
Liabilities: $1,243,487,583
Net Worth: $1,875,811,518
Earnings: $156,350,432
Emp.: 11,975
Fiscal Year-end: 12/31/22
Truck Trailer Mfr & Distr
N.A.I.C.S.: 336212
David Li *(Pres)*

Subsidiaries:

Burg Trailer Service B.V.
Katwijkerlaan 75, 2641 PD, Pijnacker, Netherlands
Tel.: (31) 15 369 4340
Web Site: https://www.burgtrailerservice.nl
Transportation Maintenance Services
N.A.I.C.S.: 485999

CIMC Intermodal Equipment LLC　　　(1)
10530 Sessler St, South Gate, CA 90280
Web Site:
　https://www.ciemanufacturing.com
Intermodal Chassis Container Trailer Mfr
N.A.I.C.S.: 336212

CIMC Trailer Poland Sp. z o.o.
UI Handlowa 21, 81-061, Gdynia, Poland
Tel.: (48) 58 760 2600
Web Site: https://www.cimc-vehicles.pl
Transportation Equipment Mfr & Distr
N.A.I.C.S.: 336999

CIMC Vehicle Europe GmbH　　　(1)
Apothekerstrasse 3, 89257, Illertissen, Germany
Tel.: (49) 730 392 8200
Web Site: https://www.cimc-vehicles.eu
Intermodal Chassis Container Trailer Mfr
N.A.I.C.S.: 336212
Wolfgang Schuster *(Mng Dir)*

CIMC Vehicles South Africa (Pty) Ltd.　　　(1)
Cnr of Lamp and Lantern Road, Germiston, 1428, South Africa
Tel.: (27) 11 824 2208
Web Site: https://www.cimc.co.za
Transportation Equipment Mfr & Distr
N.A.I.C.S.: 336999

General Transport Equipment Pty. Ltd.　　　(1)
159 McDowell St, Kewdale, 6105, WA, Australia
Tel.: (61) 89 352 4000
Web Site: https://www.gtetrailers.com.au
Transportation Equipment Distr
N.A.I.C.S.: 423860

LAG Service Polska Sp. z o.o.　　　(1)
ul Z Nalkowskiej 32, 41-922, Radzionkow, Poland
Tel.: (48) 32 271 0925
Transportation Equipment Mfr & Distr
N.A.I.C.S.: 336999
Jaroslaw Rojek *(Mgr)*

Liangshan CIMC Dongyue Vehicles Co., Ltd.　　　(1)

Quanpu Industrial Zone, Liangshan County, Jining, Shandong, China
Web Site: https://www.cimcchina.com
Automotive Trailer Mfr & Distr
N.A.I.C.S.: 336212
Zengcai Yue *(Founder)*

Liaoning CIMC Vehicle Logistics Equipments Co., Ltd.　　　(1)
No 264 Northeast Road, Dadong, Shenyang, 110044, China
Tel.: (86) 24 88902000
Logistics Container Equipment Mfr
N.A.I.C.S.: 332439

Qingdao CIMC Reefer Trailer Co., Ltd.　　　(1)
Yunhai Road, Jiaozhou, Qingdao, Shandong, China
Tel.: (86) 5328 112 1501
Web Site: https://en.cimcreefertrailer.com
Intermodal Chassis Container Trailer Mfr
N.A.I.C.S.: 336212
Katie Yuan *(Sls Dir)*

Qingdao CIMC Special Vehicle Co., Ltd.　　　(1)
No 2 Huaihedong Road, Economy and Technology Development Zone, Qingdao, 266500, Shandong, China
Tel.: (86) 5325 557 1622
Web Site:
　https://www.cimcvehiclesqingdao.com
Transportation Equipment Mfr & Distr
N.A.I.C.S.: 336999

SDC Trailers Ltd.　　　(1)
116 Deerpark Rd, Toomebridge, Antrim, BT41 3SS, United Kingdom
Tel.: (44) 287 965 0765
Web Site: https://www.sdctrailers.com
Transportation Equipment Mfr & Distr
N.A.I.C.S.: 336999

Shenzhen CIMC Vehicle Sales Co., Ltd.　　　(1)
5th Floor CIMC R&D Center No 2 Gang-Wan Avenue, Nanshan, Shenzhen, 518067, China
Tel.: (86) 18823579670
Automobile Parts Distr
N.A.I.C.S.: 327910

Yangzhou CIMC Tonghua Tank Equipment Co., Ltd.　　　(1)
No 139 Yangzijiang M Rd, Yangzhou, China
Tel.: (86) 51487872332
Motor Truck Trailer Mfr
N.A.I.C.S.: 336212

CIMC-TIANDA HOLDINGS COMPANY LIMITED
Units A-B 16/F China Overseas Building No 139 Hennessy Road, Wanchai, China (Hong Kong)
Tel.: (852) 075523362689　　　HK
Web Site: http://www.cimc-tianda.com
Rev.: $852,541,289
Assets: $1,386,971,994
Liabilities: $883,483,373
Net Worth: $503,488,621
Earnings: $34,925,272
Emp.: 5,257
Fiscal Year-end: 12/31/19
Fire Engines, Fire & Safety Equipment Mfr & Sales
N.A.I.C.S.: 922160
Xiong Jiang *(Exec Dir)*

Subsidiaries:

Pteris Global Limited　　　(1)
28 Quality Road, Singapore, 618828, Singapore　　　**(99.4%)**
Tel.: (65) 68612828
Web Site: http://www.pterisglobal.com
Airport Baggage Handling Services
N.A.I.C.S.: 488119
Fucheng Yan *(Mng Dir, Exec VP & Gen Mgr-Intralogistics Div)*

Subsidiary (Non-US):

IR (Middle East) LLC　　　(2)
Saraya Ave Building Block A A306, Al Garhoud, Dubai, United Arab Emirates

Tel.: (971) 42834839
Web Site: http://www.pterisglobal.com
Airport Logistics Services
N.A.I.C.S.: 488119

Pteris Global (Beijing) Ltd. (2)
Room 1609A Zhao Lin Building No 15 of
Rong Hua Middle Road, Yi Zhuang Busi-
ness Development Area Daxing District,
Beijing, 100176, China
Tel.: (86) 1081502963
Web Site: http://www.pterisglobal.com
Airport Logistics Services
N.A.I.C.S.: 488119

Pteris Global Sdn Bhd (2)
PTD 2447 Kayu Ara Pasong Mukim Api-Api,
82010, Pontian Kecil, Johor Darul Takzim,
Malaysia
Tel.: (60) 76952828
Web Site: http://www.pterisglobal.com
Airport Baggage Handling Services
N.A.I.C.S.: 488119

**Shung Ching Beijing Huasheng
Emergency Equipment Systems Co.,
Ltd.** (1)
Beiqijia Hongxiang Hung Industrial Incuba-
tor Base 3, Beijing, 102209, Changping Dis-
trict, China
Tel.: (86) 10 81784090
Web Site: http://www.czhs.com.cn
Fire Fighting Equipments Mfr
N.A.I.C.S.: 922160

**Wanyou Fire Engineering Group
Company Limited** (1)
51 N Rd Fuzhou City No 158 Eight-story
High-King Trade Ctr, Fuzhou, China
Tel.: (86) 59187562228
Web Site: http://www.wanyoufire.com
Fire Fighting Equipments Mfr
N.A.I.C.S.: 922160

CIMCO MARINE AB
Metallgatan 6, 262 72, Angelholm,
Sweden
Tel.: (46) 431371130
Web Site:
https://www.oxemarine.com
Year Founded: 2012
5LK—(DEU)
Power Transmission Equipment Mfr
N.A.I.C.S.: 333613
Anders Berg *(Chm)*

CIMENTAS IZMIR CIMENTO
FABRIKASI TURK A.S.
Isiklar Mah Eski Kemalpasa Cad Ci-
mentas Block No 4B Bornova, 35070,
Izmir, Turkiye
Tel.: (90) 2324721050
Web Site:
https://www.cimentas.com.tr
Year Founded: 1950
CMENT—(IST)
Rev.: $363,789,376
Assets: $458,895,138
Liabilities: $115,089,674
Net Worth: $343,805,463
Earnings: $24,192,325
Emp.: 763
Fiscal Year-end: 12/31/23
Cement Mfr
N.A.I.C.S.: 327310
Taha Aksoy *(Chm)*

Subsidiaries:

Recydia AS (1)
Tel.: (90) 2324722350
Web Site: https://www.recydia.com
Waste Management Services
N.A.I.C.S.: 562119

CIMINO & ASSOCIATI PRIVATE
EQUITY S.P.A.
Via Monte Rosa 88, The Private Eq-
uity House, 20149, Milan, Italy
Tel.: (39) 027636131   IT
Web Site: http://www.cape.it
Year Founded: 1999
Rev.: $730,056,000

Emp.: 7,000
Privater Equity Firm
N.A.I.C.S.: 523999
Simone Cimino *(Founder)*

Subsidiaries:

Cape-Natixis S.G.R. S.p.A. (1)
Monte Rosa No 88, I-20149, Milan, Italy
Tel.: (39) 027636131
Web Site: http://www.cape.it
Sales Range: $125-149.9 Million
Emp.: 25
Private Equity Funds Management Services
N.A.I.C.S.: 523999

CIMPRESS PLC
First Floor Building 3 Finnabair Busi-
ness and Technology Park, Dundalk,
A91 H9N9, Co Louth, Ireland
Tel.: (353) 429388500   IE
Web Site: https://www.cimpress.com
Year Founded: 1994
CMPR—(NASDAQ)
Rev.: $3,291,856,000
Assets: $1,892,157,000
Liabilities: $2,441,669,000
Net Worth: ($549,512,000)
Earnings: $177,808,000
Emp.: 15,000
Fiscal Year-end: 06/30/24
Offices of Other Holding Companies
N.A.I.C.S.: 551112
Robert S. Keane *(Chm & CEO)*

Subsidiaries:

AlbumPrinter Services B.V. (1)
Stationsplein 53-57, 1012 AB, Amsterdam,
Netherlands
Tel.: (31) 205218950
Web Site: http://www.allbelle.nl
Photo Album Software Publisher
N.A.I.C.S.: 513210

Araprint B.V. (1)
Arnhem Street 10, 7418 CL, Deventer,
Netherlands
Tel.: (31) 888855222
Web Site: http://www.araprint.nl
Apparels Mfr
N.A.I.C.S.: 315990

Build A Sign LLC (1)
11525B Stonehollow Dr, Austin, TX
78758   **(99%)**
Tel.: (512) 685-6821
Web Site: http://www.buildasign.com
Broom, Brush & Mop Mfr
N.A.I.C.S.: 339994
Bryan Kranik *(CEO)*

Cimpress Australia Pty Ltd (1)
66 Paramount Bvd, Derrimut, 3030, VIC,
Australia
Tel.: (61) 1800021631
Apparels Mfr
N.A.I.C.S.: 315990

Cimpress India Private Limited (1)
C' Block Voltas Premises T B Kadam Marg,
Chinchpokli, Mumbai, 400 033, Maharash-
tra, India
Tel.: (91) 2267186718
Apparels Mfr
N.A.I.C.S.: 315990
Nishant Raj *(Engr-Mfg)*

Cimpress Japan Co., Ltd. (1)
Pacific Century Place 8F 1-11-1
Marunouchi, Chiyoda-ku, Tokyo, 100-6208,
Japan
Tel.: (81) 5038206600
Web Site: http://www.cimpressjapan.com
Online Printing Services
N.A.I.C.S.: 323111

**Druck.at Druck- und Handelsgesell-
schaft GmbH** (1)
Aredstrasse 7, 2544, Leobersdorf, Austria
Tel.: (43) 225664131
Apparels Mfr
N.A.I.C.S.: 315990

Drukwerkdeal.nl Productie B.V. (1)
Keulenstraat 4, 7418 ET, Deventer, Nether-
lands
Tel.: (31) 888855222

Web Site: https://www.drukwerkdeal.nl
Commercial Printing Services
N.A.I.C.S.: 323111

Exagroup SAS (1)
159 rue de Thor Business Plaza bat 2,
34000, Montpellier, France
Tel.: (33) 467223655
Web Site: https://www.exaprint.fr
Apparels Mfr
N.A.I.C.S.: 315990

FotoKnudsen AS (1)
Hjalmar Brantingsvei 2, 5143, Bergen, Nor-
way
Tel.: (47) 153000
Web Site: http://www.fotoknudsen.no
Apparels Mfr
N.A.I.C.S.: 315990

Grafica Editora Aquarela S.A. (1)
Rua Joao Ferreira de Camargo 714, 06460-
060, Barueri, Brazil
Tel.: (55) 1141669600
Web Site: http://www.grafica-
aquarela.com.br
Commercial Printing Services
N.A.I.C.S.: 323111

Litotipografia Alcione S.r.l. (1)
V Galilei 47, 38015, Lavis, Trentino, Italy
Tel.: (39) 04611732000
Web Site: https://www.alcione-tn.it
Commercial Printing Services
N.A.I.C.S.: 323111

National Pen Co., LLC (1)
12121 Scripps Summit Dr, San Diego, CA
92131
Tel.: (858) 675-3000
Web Site: http://www.pens.com
Pen & Mechanical Pencil Mfr
N.A.I.C.S.: 339940
Sarah Garvey *(Comm Mgr-Global)*

**National Pen Promotional Products
Limited** (1)
Building D Xerox Technology Park Dublin
Road, Co Louth, Dundalk, Ireland
Tel.: (353) 429388554
Stationery Product Retailer
N.A.I.C.S.: 459410

Pixartprinting S.p.A. (1)
Via 1 Maggio 8, Quarto d'Altino, 30020,
Venice, Italy
Tel.: (39) 0422823301
Apparels Mfr
N.A.I.C.S.: 315990
Rodrigo Padovan *(CIO)*

Tradeprint Distribution Limited (1)
2 Fulton Road, Dundee, DD2 4SW, United
Kingdom
Tel.: (44) 3300240020
Web Site: https://www.tradeprint.co.uk
Printing Services
N.A.I.C.S.: 323111

VistaPrint B.V. (1)
Hudsonweg 8, 5928 LW, Venlo,
Netherlands   **(100%)**
Tel.: (31) 778507700
Web Site: https://www.vistaprint.co.uk
Sales Range: $25-49.9 Million
Emp.: 22
Online Printing Services
N.A.I.C.S.: 323111
Annie Drapeau *(Chief People Officer)*

VistaPrint Jamaica Limited (1)
Data Entry Building #4, 1 Mangrove Way,
Montego Bay, St. James, Jamaica
Web Site: http://www.vistaprint.com
Online Printing Services
N.A.I.C.S.: 323111

**VistaPrint North American Services
Corp.** (1)
447 Advance Blvd, Windsor, N8N 5G8, ON,
Canada   **(100%)**
Tel.: (519) 727-0008
Sales Range: $125-149.9 Million
Emp.: 400
Online Printing Services
N.A.I.C.S.: 323111

Subsidiary (Domestic):

VistaPrint Canada Limited (2)
447 Advance Boulevard, Windsor, N8N

5G8, ON, Canada
Tel.: (519) 727-0008
Web Site: http://www.vistaprint.com
Online Printing Services
N.A.I.C.S.: 323111

VistaPrint USA, Incorporated (1)
275 Wyman Strt, Waltham, MA
02451   **(100%)**
Tel.: (781) 652-6300
Web Site: http://www.vistaprint.com
Sales Range: $50-74.9 Million
Emp.: 900
Online Printing Services
N.A.I.C.S.: 323111
Trynka Shineman *(Pres-North America)*

Subsidiary (Domestic):

99designs Inc. (2)
2201 Broadway Ste 815 8th Fl, Oakland,
CA 94612
Tel.: (800) 513-1678
Web Site: http://www.99designs.com
Professional, Scientific & Technical Services
N.A.I.C.S.: 541990

Vistaprint Australia Pty Ltd (1)
66 Paramount Boulevard, Derrimut, Mel-
bourne, 3030, VIC, Australia
Tel.: (61) 1800864973
Web Site: https://www.vistaprint.com.au
Stationery Printing Service
N.A.I.C.S.: 323113

**Vistaprint Corporate Solutions
Incorporated** (1)
275 Wyman St, Waltham, MA 02451
Web Site:
https://www.vistaprintcorporate.com
Ecommerce Services
N.A.I.C.S.: 323111

Vistaprint Espana S.L. (1)
Calle Bac De Roda Ed Metrovacesa Park
22 64, Barcelona, 08019, Spain
Tel.: (34) 935450800
Web Site: http://www.vistaprint.es
Commercial Printing Services
N.A.I.C.S.: 323111

Vistaprint Netherlands B.V. (1)
Hudsonweg 8, 5928 LW, Venlo, Nether-
lands
Tel.: (31) 778507700
Commercial Lithographic Printing Services
N.A.I.C.S.: 323111

Vistaprint Tunisie SARL (1)
Immeuble Lac 8 Les Jardins Du Lac Les
Berges Du Lac Ii, Tunis, Tunisia
Tel.: (216) 71799688
Online Publishing Services
N.A.I.C.S.: 513199

WIRmachenDRUCK GmbH (1)
Muhlbachstr 7, 71522, Backnang, Germany
Tel.: (49) 71199598220
Web Site: https://www.wir-machen-druck.de
Digital Printing Services
N.A.I.C.S.: 323111

Webs, Inc. (1)
1100 Wayne Ave Ste 801, Silver Spring,
MD 20910
Tel.: (301) 960-9000
Web Site: http://www.webs.com
Internet Publishing Services
N.A.I.C.S.: 513199
Haroon Mokhtarzada *(Founder & CEO)*

CIMS S.A.
Av Bartolomeu Mitre 336 - Parte,
22431002, Rio de Janeiro, Brazil
Tel.: (55) 2132622500
CMSA4—(BRAZ)
Assets: $1,874
Liabilities: $310
Net Worth: $1,564
Earnings: ($46,338)
Fiscal Year-end: 12/31/23
Financial Investment Services
N.A.I.C.S.: 523999
Jose Guilherme Cruz Souza
(Member-Exec Bd)

CINCO INVESTMENTS PLC
3rd Floor 14 Hanover Street Hanover

CINCO Investments Plc—(Continued)

Square, London, W1S1 YH, United Kingdom
Tel.: (44) 2075145872
Web Site:
http://www.cincoinvestments.eu
Oil Refineries
N.A.I.C.S.: 324110
Wasslm Ashl *(Chm)*

CINCON ELECTRONICS CO., LTD.
14F No 306 Section 4 Hsin Yi Rd, Taipei, Taiwan
Tel.: (886) 227086210
Web Site: https://www.cincon.com
Year Founded: 1991
3332—(TPE)
Rev.: $53,497,608
Assets: $72,519,495
Liabilities: $21,053,841
Net Worth: $51,465,654
Earnings: $6,854,423
Fiscal Year-end: 12/31/22
Power Conversion Product Distr
N.A.I.C.S.: 423610
Cheng Chen-San *(Chm)*

Subsidiaries:

Harmon & Sullivan Associates, Inc.   (1)
2117 Buffalo Rd Ste 307, Rochester, NY 14624
Tel.: (585) 235-3030
Web Site: https://hsa-sales.com
Electrical Apparatus Distr
N.A.I.C.S.: 423610

CINDA INTERNATIONAL HOLDINGS LIMITED
45th Floor COSCO Tower 183 Queens Road, Central, China (Hong Kong)
Tel.: (852) 22357888
Web Site: http://www.cinda.com.hk
0111—(HKG)
Rev.: $17,375,828
Assets: $212,378,025
Liabilities: $91,493,618
Net Worth: $120,884,408
Earnings: ($2,857,020)
Emp.: 105
Fiscal Year-end: 12/31/22
Securities & Commodities Brokerage Services; Investment Advisory Services
N.A.I.C.S.: 523150
Mun Lau *(Deputy CEO & Sec)*

CINDRELLA FINANCIAL SERVICES LIMITED
9 Mangoe Lane 3rd Floor, Kolkata, 700 001, West Bengal, India
Tel.: (91) 3322001338
Web Site:
https://www.cindrellafinancial.com
Year Founded: 1994
531283—(BOM)
Rev.: $31,918
Assets: $646,348
Liabilities: $30,142
Net Worth: $616,206
Earnings: $31,807
Fiscal Year-end: 03/31/22
Financial Services
N.A.I.C.S.: 523999
Sangita Devi Baid *(Chm & Mng Dir)*

CINDRELLA HOTELS LTD.
The Cindrella Hotel 3rd Mile Sevoke Road, Siliguri, 734008, West Bengal, India
Tel.: (91) 3532544130
Web Site:
https://www.cindrellahotels.com

526373—(BOM)
Rev.: $744,949
Assets: $1,460,164
Liabilities: $268,449
Net Worth: $1,191,714
Earnings: $50,198
Emp.: 83
Fiscal Year-end: 03/31/22
Hotel Services
N.A.I.C.S.: 721120
Sangita Devi Baid *(Chm)*

CINEMA TRUSTS INVESTMENTS IN MOVIES LP
Sha'ul Hameleh 16, Tel Aviv, 46712, Israel
Tel.: (972) 99581422
Motion Picture Production & Distribution Services
N.A.I.C.S.: 512110

CINEMEDIA AG
Muhlenstrasse 52-54, 12249, Berlin, Germany
Tel.: (49) 30 76787 0
Web Site: http://cinemedia.de
Studio & Film Setting Services
N.A.I.C.S.: 512110

CINEOPTIC A.D.
Koce Kapetana 12-14, Belgrade, Serbia
Tel.: (381) 11 24496 92
Year Founded: 1952
Sales Range: Less than $1 Million
Emp.: 17
Medical & Dental Instrument Mfr
N.A.I.C.S.: 339112

CINEPLEX INC.
1303 Yonge St, Toronto, M4T 2Y9, ON, Canada
Tel.: (416) 323-6600
Web Site: https://corp.cineplex.com
CGX—(TSX)
Rev.: $327,198,780
Assets: $1,825,739,824
Liabilities: $1,806,782,050
Net Worth: $18,957,774
Earnings: ($492,017,353)
Emp.: 10,000
Fiscal Year-end: 12/31/20
Holding Company
N.A.I.C.S.: 551112
Ellis Jacob *(Pres & CEO)*

Subsidiaries:

Cineplex Digital Media Inc.   (1)
Suite 200 6940 Fisher Road SE, Calgary, T2H 0W3, AB, Canada
Tel.: (403) 264-4420
Outdoor Advertising ServicesOutdoor Advertising Services
N.A.I.C.S.: 541850

Cineplex Digital Networks Inc.   (1)
369 York Street Suite 2C, London, N6B 3R4, ON, Canada
Tel.: (519) 438-0111
Emp.: 150
Digital Advertising Services
N.A.I.C.S.: 541850
Fab Stanghieri *(Gen Mgr)*

Cineplex Entertainment LP   (1)
1303 Yonge Street, Toronto, M4T 2Y9, ON, Canada   (76%)
Tel.: (416) 323-6600
Web Site: http://www.cineplex.com
Sales Range: $500-549.9 Million
Emp.: 130
Movie Theatre Operator
N.A.I.C.S.: 512131
Richard Wood *(VP-Lease Admin)*

Galaxy Entertainment Inc.   (1)
4750 Rutherford Rd Suite 213, Nanaimo, V9T 4K6, BC, Canada
Tel.: (250) 729-8012
Movie Theatre Operator
N.A.I.C.S.: 512131

CINEPLEX S.A.
Av Paseo de la Republica cuadra 1, Piso 4 Edificio Centro Civico, Lima, Peru
Tel.: (51) 6194400
Web Site:
http://www.cineplanet.com.pe
Year Founded: 1999
CINEP2BC1A—(LIM)
Sales Range: Less than $1 Million
Movie Theatre Operator
N.A.I.C.S.: 512132

CINER GROUP
Pasalimani Caddesi No 41, Uskudar, 34674, Istanbul, Turkiye
Tel.: (90) 2165312444
Web Site:
http://www.cinergroup.com.tr
Year Founded: 1978
Emp.: 10,500
Holding Company Services
N.A.I.C.S.: 551112
Turgay Ciner *(Chm)*

CINERAD COMMUNICATIONS LIMITED
80 Burtolla Street, Kolkata, 700 007, West Bengal, India
Tel.: (91) 7719913351
Web Site:
https://www.cineradcomm.com
Year Founded: 1986
530457—(BOM)
Rev.: $7,777
Assets: $170,290
Liabilities: $3,014
Net Worth: $167,276
Earnings: ($10,739)
Fiscal Year-end: 03/31/22
Advertising & Promotional Film Production Services
N.A.I.C.S.: 512110
Vinita Daga *(CEO & Mng Dir)*

CINESE INTERNATIONAL GROUP HOLDINGS LIMITED
15 Kern Road, Toronto, M3B 1S9, ON, Canada
Tel.: (416) 929-0888
Web Site: http://www.toureast.com
Year Founded: 1976
1620—(HKG)
Rev.: $13,250,977
Assets: $18,153,236
Liabilities: $11,716,316
Net Worth: $6,436,920
Earnings: $373,424
Emp.: 71
Fiscal Year-end: 12/31/23
Travel & Ticketing Services
N.A.I.C.S.: 561510
Rita Pik Fong Tsang *(Founder & Chm)*

CINESYSTEM S.A.
Avenue Getulio Vargas 266 Sala 504 Zona 01, Maringa, 87013-919, PR, Brazil
Tel.: (55) 1145675500
Web Site:
http://www.cinesystem.com.br
CNSY3—(BRAZ)
Sales Range: Less than $1 Million
Movie Theatre Operator
N.A.I.C.S.: 512131
Ricardo Eugenio Rossini *(COO)*

CINEVISTA LTD
1 Silver Croft Off T P S III Corner of 16th & 33rd Road, Bandra West, Mumbai, 400 050, India
Tel.: (91) 2262516537
Web Site:
https://www.cinevistaas.com

532324—(BOM)
Rev.: $196,821
Assets: $25,337,786
Liabilities: $9,282,232
Net Worth: $16,055,554
Earnings: ($2,248,315)
Emp.: 16
Fiscal Year-end: 03/31/22
Media & Entertainment Services
N.A.I.C.S.: 512199
K. B. Nair *(CFO)*

CINEWORLD GROUP PLC
Cineworld Investor Relations 8th Floor Vantage London Great West Road, Brentford, TW8 9AG, United Kingdom
Tel.: (44) 2074133333   UK
Web Site:
https://www.cineworldplc.com
Year Founded: 2004
CINE—(LSE)
Rev.: $852,300,000
Assets: $10,625,200,000
Liabilities: $10,398,900,000
Net Worth: $226,300,000
Earnings: ($26,651,500,000)
Emp.: 30,432
Fiscal Year-end: 12/31/20
Motion Picture Theaters (except Drive-Ins)
N.A.I.C.S.: 512131
Anthony Herbert Bloom *(Chm)*

Subsidiaries:

Adelphi-Carlton Limited   (1)
Parnell Ctr Parnell St, Co Dublin, Dublin, 1, Ireland
Tel.: (353) 18728895
Movie Theaters
N.A.I.C.S.: 512131
Lorraine Pierce *(Mgr)*

All Job Poland Sp. z o.o.   (1)
ul Woloska 12, 02-675, Warsaw, Poland
Tel.: (48) 22 456 6542
Web Site: https://www.alljob.pl
Theater Services
N.A.I.C.S.: 512131

Cineworld Cinema Properties Limited   (1)
Power Rd Studios, London, W4 5PY, United Kingdom
Tel.: (44) 2089875000
Web Site: http://www.cineworld.co.uk
Sales Range: $75-99.9 Million
Emp.: 150
Film Production Services
N.A.I.C.S.: 711510

Forum Film Czech s.r.o.   (1)
Arkalycka 951/3, 149 00, Prague, Czech Republic
Tel.: (420) 91 433 7912
Web Site: https://www.forumfilm.cz
Theater Services
N.A.I.C.S.: 512131

Forum Film Slovakia s.r.o.   (1)
Eurovea Pribinova 8, 81109, Bratislava, Slovakia
Tel.: (421) 249113116
Web Site: http://www.forumfilm.sk
Theater Services
N.A.I.C.S.: 512131

New Age Media Romania SRL   (1)
13 Ana Davila Street 1st Floor near the Cotroceni Palace, 050491, Bucharest, Romania
Tel.: (40) 21 306 7074
Web Site: http://www.newagemedia.eu
Theater Services
N.A.I.C.S.: 512131

Picturehouse Cinemas Limited   (1)
7th Floor St Vincent House 30 Orange Street, London, WC2H 7HH, United Kingdom
Tel.: (44) 207 326 2649
Web Site: https://www.picturehouses.com
Theater Services
N.A.I.C.S.: 512131

Regal Cinemas, Inc. (1)
101 E Blount Ave, Knoxville, TN
37920 (100%)
Tel.: (865) 922-1123
Web Site: http://www.regmovies.com
Holding Company; Motion Picture Theater
Owner & Operator
N.A.I.C.S.: 551112

Subsidiary (Domestic):

Digital Cinema Implementation Part-
ners, LLC (2)
100 Enterprise Dr Ste 505, Rockaway, NJ
07866
Tel.: (201) 252-4141
Web Site: http://www.dcip.com
Motion Picture Theater Operator
N.A.I.C.S.: 512131
Rich Manzione (Pres & CEO)

Great Escape Theatres of New Al-
bany, LLC (2)
300 Professional Ct, New Albany, IN 47150
Tel.: (844) 462-7342
Motion Picture Theater Operator
N.A.I.C.S.: 512131

Great Escape of Nitro, LLC (2)
12 Jw Dr, Nitro, WV 25143
Tel.: (844) 462-7342
Web Site: http://www.regmovies.com
Building Rental & Leasing Services
N.A.I.C.S.: 531120

R.C.Cobb, Inc. (2)
101 E Blount Ave, Knoxville, TN 37918-
5803
Tel.: (865) 922-1123
Motion Picture Theater Operator
N.A.I.C.S.: 512131

Ragains Enterprises LLC (2)
300 Professional Ct Ste 200, New Albany,
IN 47150-8407
Tel.: (844) 462-7342
Web Site: http://www.regmovies.com
Motion Picture Theater Operator
N.A.I.C.S.: 512131

Regal Cinemas Corporation (2)
101 E Blount Ave, Knoxville, TN 37920
Tel.: (865) 922-1123
Web Site: http://www.regmovies.com
Holding Company; Motion Picture Theatre
Operator
N.A.I.C.S.: 551112

Subsidiary (Domestic):

United Artists Theatre Circuit,
Inc. (3)
101 E Blount Ave, Knoxville, TN 37918
Tel.: (865) 922-1123
Web Site: http://www.regmovies.com
Motion Picture Theater Operator
N.A.I.C.S.: 512131

CINIS FERTILIZER AB
Djuphamnsvagen 9, Kopmanholmen,
893 40, Ornskoldsvik, Sweden
Web Site: https://www.cinis-
fertilizer.com
Year Founded: 2018
CINIS—(OMX)
Rev.: $355,915
Assets: $73,683,816
Liabilities: $35,778,846
Net Worth: $37,904,971
Earnings: ($3,053,378)
Emp.: 11
Fiscal Year-end: 12/31/23
Mineral Exploration Services
N.A.I.C.S.: 212390
Henrik Andersson (CFO)

CINKARNA CELJE D.D.
Kidriceva 26, 3001, Celje, Slovenia
Tel.: (386) 34276000 SI
Web Site: https://www.cinkarna.si
Year Founded: 1873
CICG—(LJU)
Rev.: $194,794,446
Assets: $286,914,297
Liabilities: $42,703,614
Net Worth: $244,210,683

Earnings: $13,967,775
Emp.: 731
Fiscal Year-end: 12/31/23
Titanium Dioxide Pigment Mfr
N.A.I.C.S.: 325998
Nikolaja Podgorsek Selic (Member-
Mgmt Bd & Mgr-Technical)

CINT GROUP AB
Luntmakargatan 18 1tr, 111 37,
Stockholm, Sweden
Tel.: (46) 854563300
Web Site: https://www.cint.com
Year Founded: 1998
CINT—(OMX)
Rev.: $287,651,630
Assets: $675,518,023
Liabilities: $280,553,637
Net Worth: $394,964,386
Earnings: ($483,717,893)
Emp.: 1,018
Fiscal Year-end: 12/31/23
Software Development Services
N.A.I.C.S.: 541511
Bridget Bidlack (Chief Product Offi-
cer)

Subsidiaries:

Cint Australia Pty. Ltd. (1)
Cint WeWork 64 York St, Sydney, 2000,
NSW, Australia
Tel.: (61) 415447759
Consumer Research Services
N.A.I.C.S.: 541910

Cint UK Ltd. (1)
1 Finsbury Market, Hackney, London, EC2A
2BN, United Kingdom
Tel.: (44) 2035142100
Market Research Technology Services
N.A.I.C.S.: 541910

Gap Fish GmbH (1)
Uhlandstrasse 175, 10719, Berlin, Germany
Tel.: (49) 30809520679
Web Site: https://gapfish.com
Emp.: 40
Online Market Research Services
N.A.I.C.S.: 541910

Lucid Czech Republic s.r.o. (1)
Liberecka 85, 466 01, Jablonec nad Nisou,
Czech Republic
Tel.: (420) 483570127
Web Site: https://www.lucid.cz
Jewellery Design Mfr
N.A.I.C.S.: 339910

CINVEN LIMITED
21 St. James's Sq, London, SW1Y
4JZ, United Kingdom
Tel.: (44) 2076613333 UK
Web Site: http://www.cinven.com
Year Founded: 1977
Private Equity Firm
N.A.I.C.S.: 523999
Peter Catterall (Partner-Consumer &
Fin Svcs)

Subsidiaries:

Barentz International B.V. (1)
Saturnusstraat 15, 2132 HB, Hoofddorp,
Netherlands
Tel.: (31) 23 567 34 56
Web Site: http://www.barentz.com
Ingredients Mfr & Distr
N.A.I.C.S.: 325998
Pavel Kratochvil (Exec VP)

Subsidiary (Non-US):

Additive Solutions Pty Ltd (2)
43-45 Renver Road, Clayton, 3168, VIC,
Australia
Tel.: (61) 398061250
Web Site:
http://www.additivesolutions.com.au
Food Ingredient Distr
N.A.I.C.S.: 424490

Barentz (Romania) S.R.L. (2)
12th Opanez Street 3rd Floor, 023776, Bucharest, Romania

Tel.: (40) 21 260 3065
Web Site: http://www.barentz.com
Capsule Mfr
N.A.I.C.S.: 325412

Barentz ApS (2)
Englandsgade 22, 5000, Odense, Denmark
Tel.: (45) 31665035
Pharmaceutical Products Distr
N.A.I.C.S.: 424210

Barentz Asia Pacific Pte. Ltd. (2)
1 Senoko Avenue 01-06/07 Food Axis, Sin-
gapore, 758297, Singapore
Tel.: (65) 66900300
Food Ingredient Distr
N.A.I.C.S.: 424490

Subsidiary (Domestic):

Barentz B.V. (2)
Saturnsstraat 15, 2132 HB, Hoofddorp,
Netherlands
Tel.: (31) 23 567 3456
Web Site: http://www.barentz.com
Life Sciences Ingredients Mfr
N.A.I.C.S.: 325412

Subsidiary (Non-US):

Barentz Gida ve Kimya Tic. Ltd.
Sti. (2)
EGS Business Park Blocks World Trade
Center B-2 Blok F 9 D 308-309, Yesilkoy,
34149, Istanbul, Turkiye
Tel.: (90) 2124658055
Food Ingredient Distr
N.A.I.C.S.: 424490

Barentz Hungary Kft. (2)
Devai u 26-28, 1134, Budapest, Hungary
Tel.: (36) 13231918
Pharmaceutical Products Distr
N.A.I.C.S.: 424210

Barentz Ireland Limited (2)
PRL Building Block S Grants View
Greenogue Business Park, Dublin, D24
XN60, Ireland
Tel.: (353) 14039518
Pharmaceutical Products Distr
N.A.I.C.S.: 424210

Barentz N.V. (2)
Excelsiorlaan 7, Box 2, 1930, Zaventem,
Belgium
Tel.: (32) 27252430
Pharmaceutical Products Distr
N.A.I.C.S.: 424210

Barentz Sarl (2)
45 rue de la Milletiere Batiment Guillaumet,
37100, Tours, France
Tel.: (33) 247490970
Food Ingredient Distr
N.A.I.C.S.: 424490

Barentz UA LLC (2)
Pavlivska street 29 5th Floor, Kiev, Ukraine
Tel.: (380) 503585870
Pharmaceutical Products Distr
N.A.I.C.S.: 424210

Barentz d.o.o. (2)
Bulevar oslobodjenja 111, 11000, Belgrade,
Serbia
Tel.: (381) 113112125
Pharmaceutical Products Distr
N.A.I.C.S.: 424210

Barentz spol. s.r.o. (2)
Za Trati 752, 339 01, Klatovy, Czech Re-
public
Tel.: (420) 376370011
Pharmaceutical Products Distr
N.A.I.C.S.: 424210

Barentz spol. s.r.o. (2)
Nizovec 8936 2a, 960 01, Zvolen, Slovakia
Tel.: (421) 455324351
Human Nutrition Product Distr
N.A.I.C.S.: 456191

Barentz-Sander AG (2)
Hinterbergstrasse 18, 6312, Steinhausen,
Switzerland
Tel.: (41) 417106141
Web Site: http://www.barentz-sander.ch
Food Ingredient Distr
N.A.I.C.S.: 424490

Subsidiary (US):

Ingredients, Inc. (2)
1130 W Lake Cook Rd, Buffalo Grove, IL
60089-1986
Tel.: (847) 419-9595
Web Site: http://www.ingredientsinc.com
Sales Range: $1-9.9 Million
Emp.: 9
Food Preparations Mfr
N.A.I.C.S.: 311999
Debbie Stewart (CFO)

Subsidiary (Non-US):

PT Barentz (2)
Menara Satu Sentra Kelapa Gading 8th
Floor Unit 808, Jl Boulevard Kelapa Gading
Kav LA3 No 1 Summarecon Kelapa Gad-
ing, Jakarta, 14240, Indonesia
Tel.: (62) 2129385877
Pharmaceutical Products Distr
N.A.I.C.S.: 424210

SK Chemtrade Services Pty Ltd (2)
8 Platinum Crescent Montague Gardens,
Cape Town, South Africa
Tel.: (27) 215510681
Web Site: http://www.skchemtrade.co.za
Food Flavor Ingredient Mfr & Distr
N.A.I.C.S.: 311999

Vita Barentz Co. Ltd. (2)
22 Soi Sukhumvit 42 Sukhumvit Road, Prakanong Klongteoy, Bangkok, 10110, Thailand
Tel.: (66) 2712104477
Food Ingredient Distr
N.A.I.C.S.: 424490

Cinven Capital Management (V) Gen-
eral Partner Limited (1)
3rd Floor Tudor House Le Bordage, Saint
Peter Port, GY1 3PP, Guernsey
Tel.: (44) 1481 74970
Investment Advisory Services
N.A.I.C.S.: 523940

Cinven GmbH (1)
Main Tower Neue Mainzer Str 52, 60311,
Frankfurt am Main, Germany
Tel.: (49) 69 90027 0
Investment Advisory Services
N.A.I.C.S.: 523940

Cinven HK Limited (1)
Suite 5812-14 Two International Finance
Centre 8 Finance Street, Central, Hong
Kong, China (Hong Kong)
Tel.: (852) 3665 2880
Investment Advisory Services
N.A.I.C.S.: 523940

Cinven Luxembourg S.a r.l (1)
Ballade B2 Building 4 Rue Albert Bor-
schette, 1246, Luxembourg, Luxembourg
Tel.: (352) 2609 5200
Investment Advisory Services
N.A.I.C.S.: 523940

Cinven Partners LLP (1)
Warwick Court Paternoster Square, London,
EC4M 7AG, United Kingdom
Tel.: (44) 20 7661 3333
Investment Advisory Services
N.A.I.C.S.: 523940

Cinven S.r.l. (1)
Via Manzoni 30, 20121, Milan, Italy
Tel.: (39) 02 3211 1700
Web Site: http://www.cinven.com
Investment Advisory Services
N.A.I.C.S.: 523940

Compre Group Holdings Ltd. (1)
4th Floor Victoria Place 31 Victoria Street,
Hamilton, HM 10, Bermuda
Tel.: (441) 704 0106
Web Site: https://compre-group.com
Insurance Services
N.A.I.C.S.: 524210

Coor Service Management Holding
AB (1)
Knarrarnasgatan 7, 164 99, Kista, Sweden
Tel.: (46) 105595000
Web Site: https://www.coor.com
Rev.: $1,104
Assets: $667
Liabilities: $485
Net Worth: $182

Cinven Limited—(Continued)

Earnings: $24
Emp.: 10,267
Fiscal Year-end: 12/31/2022
Integrated Facilities Management Services
N.A.I.C.S.: 561210
Rikard Wannerholt (Sr VP-Ops)

Subsidiary (Non-US):

Coor Service Management A/S (2)
Bregnerodvej 133, 3460, Birkerod, Denmark
Tel.: (45) 44 77 88 88
Web Site: http://www.coor.dk
Facilities Support Services
N.A.I.C.S.: 561210

Coor Service Management AS (2)
Vollsveien 6, 1366, Lysaker, Norway
Tel.: (47) 405 55 000
Web Site: http://www.coor.no
Facilities Support Services
N.A.I.C.S.: 561210
Nikolai Utheim (CFO)

Coor Service Management NV (2)
Pantserschipstraat 181/5, 9000, Gent, Belgium
Tel.: (32) 9 223 19 99
Facilities Support Services
N.A.I.C.S.: 561210

Coor Service Management Oy (2)
Mannerheimintie 117, 00280, Helsinki, Finland
Tel.: (358) 10 234 3400
Facilities Support Services
N.A.I.C.S.: 561210
Anne-May Asplund (Dir-HR & Comm)

Eurovita Holding S.p.A. (1)
Via Fra Riccardo Pampuri 13, 20141, Milan, Italy
Tel.: (39) 0358032572
Web Site: http://www.eurovita.it
Holding Company; Health & Life Insurance Services
N.A.I.C.S.: 551112
Davide Croff (Chm)

Subsidiary (Domestic):

Eurovita S.p.A. (2)
Via Pampuri 13, 20141, Milan, Italy
Tel.: (39) 0358032572
Web Site: http://www.eurovita.it
Life Insurance Policies to Individuals, Families & Businesses
N.A.I.C.S.: 524298
Davide Croff (Chm)

Subsidiary (Domestic):

Eurovita Assicurazioni S.p.A (3)
Via dei Maroniti 12, 187, Rome, Italy (96.88%)
Tel.: (39) 06 474821
Web Site: http://www.eurovita.it
Fire Insurance Services
N.A.I.C.S.: 524113

Friends Provident International Limited (1)
5th Floor Building 6 Emaar Square Burj Dubai Business Hub, PO Box 215113, Dubai, United Arab Emirates
Tel.: (971) 44362800
Web Site: http://www.fpinternational.com
General Insurance Services
N.A.I.C.S.: 524210
Steve Weston (Exec Dir & Dir-Customer Svc)

Helix Industries Ltd. (1)
2B Sidings Court, Doncaster, DN4 5NU, South Yorkshire, United Kingdom
Tel.: (44) 1302762700
Holding Company
N.A.I.C.S.: 551112

Subsidiary (Domestic):

K.J.P. Ltd. (2)
93-103 Drummond Street, London, NW1 2HJ, United Kingdom
Agricultural, Photographic & Technical Services
N.A.I.C.S.: 541990

Hotelbeds Group, S.L.U. (1)
Camino de Son Fangos 100 Complejo Mi-

rall Balear Tower A 5 andar 6A-7A, 07007, Palma de Mallorca, Spain
Tel.: (34) 971 178 800
Web Site: http://group.hotelbeds.com
Holding Company; Online Wholesale & Retail Travel Agency
N.A.I.C.S.: 561520
Sam Turner (Dir-Wholesale Sls & Sourcing)

Subsidiary (Non-US):

HotelBeds Hong Kong Limited (2)
Room 1029-1032 Star House 3 Salisbury Road, Tsim Sha Tsui, Kowloon, China (Hong Kong)
Tel.: (852) 21129998
Web Site: http://www.hotelbeds.com
Travel & Tour Accommodation Services
N.A.I.C.S.: 561520
Annie Cheung (Mgr-Fin)

Hotelbeds Pte. Ltd. (2)
101 Thomson Road #16-01 United Square, Singapore, 307591, Singapore
Tel.: (65) 63306666
Web Site: http://www.pacificworld.com
Travel & Tour Accommodation Services
N.A.I.C.S.: 561520

Subsidiary (Domestic):

Hotelbeds Spain, S.L.U. (2)
Complejo Mirall Balear Cami de Son Fangos 100 Torre A 5 Planta, 07007, Palma de Mallorca, Spain
Tel.: (34) 971 211601
Web Site: http://checkpickup.com
Travel & Tour Accommodation Services
N.A.I.C.S.: 561599

Hotelopia SL (2)
Complex Mirall Balear Cami de Son Fangos 100 Torre A 5a Planta, CP 07007, Palma de Mallorca, Spain
Tel.: (34) 902 430 419
Web Site: http://www.hotelopia.com
Hotel Operator
N.A.I.C.S.: 721110

Subsidiary (US):

Intercruises Shoreside & Port Services Inc. (2)
711 12th Ave, New York, NY 10019
Tel.: (212) 459-9263
Web Site: http://www.intercruises.com
Ground Handling & Port Agency Services
N.A.I.C.S.: 488310
Simon O'Sullivan (Pres-North America)

Subsidiary (Non-US):

Intercruises Shoreside & Port Services Pty Ltd (2)
Suite 101 Level 1 72 Pitt Street, Sydney, 2000, NSW, Australia
Tel.: (61) 295500047
Web Site: http://www.intercruises.com
Tour Operating Services
N.A.I.C.S.: 561520
Martin Bidgood (Reg Dir)

MicronNexus GmbH (2)
Humboldthaus Am Sandtorkai 37, 20457, Hamburg, Germany
Tel.: (49) 40 18 88 98 0
Web Site: http://www.carnect.com
Information Technology Consulting Services
N.A.I.C.S.: 541512
Christopher Paul Leonard (Mng Dir)

Subsidiary (US):

Tourico Holidays, Inc. (2)
220 E Central Pkwy Ste 4000, Altamonte Springs, FL 32701
Tel.: (407) 667-8700
Web Site: http://login.touricoholidays.com
Travel Tour Operator
N.A.I.C.S.: 561520
Uri Argov (CEO)

INSEEC Executive Education SASU (1)
27 Avenue Claude Vellefaux, 75010, Paris, France
Tel.: (33) 1 42 09 99 17
Web Site: http://www.inseec-bs.com
Educational Institution
N.A.I.C.S.: 923110
Catherine Lespine (CEO)

JLA Limited (1)
Meadowcroft Lane Halifax Road, Rippon-den, HX6 4AJ, W Yorks, United Kingdom - England
Tel.: (808) 239-7578
Web Site: https://jla.com
Laundry & Catering Equipment Distr
N.A.I.C.S.: 423440

JOST-Werke GmbH (1)
Siemensstrasse 2, 63263, Neu-Isenburg, Germany
Tel.: (49) 61022950
Web Site: http://www.jost-werke.com
Sales Range: $450-499.9 Million
Emp.: 500
Commercial Vehicle Component Mfr
N.A.I.C.S.: 336390

Kurt Geiger Limited (1)
24 Britton Street, London, EC1M 5UA, United Kingdom
Tel.: (44) 207 781 7480
Web Site: http://www.kurtgeiger.com
Footwear Designer & Retailer
N.A.I.C.S.: 458210
Rebecca Farrar-Hockley (Chief Creative Officer)

Subsidiary (Domestic):

Shoeaholics Limited (2)
24 Britton Street, London, EC1M 5UA, United Kingdom
Tel.: (44) 207 781 7481
Web Site: http://www.shoeaholics.com
Online Shoe Store Operator
N.A.I.C.S.: 316990

Medpace, Inc. (1)
5375 Medpace Way, Cincinnati, OH 45227 (80%)
Tel.: (513) 579-9911
Web Site: http://www.medpace.com
Sales Range: $150-199.9 Million
Emp.: 1,000
Pharmaceutical Research & Development Services
N.A.I.C.S.: 541715
August James Troendle (Chm, Pres & CEO)

Subsidiary (Non-US):

Beijing Medpace Medical Science & Technology Ltd. (2)
No 23 East Business Tower Sheng Shi Long Yuan, No 1005 Gao Bei Dian Xiang Xi Dian, Beijing, 100022, China
Tel.: (86) 10 87706500
Pharmaceutical Research & Development Services
N.A.I.C.S.: 541715
Kathy Ma (Gen Mgr)

Subsidiary (Domestic):

Imaging Core Lab LLC (2)
5375 Medpace Way, Cincinnati, OH 45227
Tel.: (513) 366-3266
Medical Laboratories
N.A.I.C.S.: 621511
Mike Brown (Dir-Ops)

Subsidiary (Non-US):

Medpace Australia Pty. Ltd. (2)
Omnico Business Centre Suite 1 Building 26 270 Ferntree Gully Road, Notting Hill, 3168, VIC, Australia
Tel.: (61) 3 9541 2100
Pharmaceutical Research & Development Services
N.A.I.C.S.: 541715

Medpace Belgium BVBA (2)
Technologielaan 19, B-3001, Leuven, Belgium
Tel.: (32) 16 391870
Web Site: http://www.medpace.com
Pharmaceutical Research & Development Services
N.A.I.C.S.: 541715

Medpace Brazil Ltda. (2)
Av Maria Coelho Aguiar 215 Bloco C 3 Andar Jd Sao Luiz, 05804-900, Sao Paulo, Brazil
Tel.: (55) 11 3741 3662
Pharmaceutical Research & Development Services

N.A.I.C.S.: 541715
Priscilla Capone (Country Mgr)

Medpace Clinical Research India Pvt. Ltd. (2)
Office No 1416 14th Floor Rupa Solitaire Building No A-1 Sector-1, Millenium Business Park Next to DAKC Mahape, Navi Mumbai, 400701, India
Tel.: (91) 22 412 83900
Pharmaceutical Research & Development Services
N.A.I.C.S.: 541715
Preeti Kabra (Gen Mgr)

Medpace Europe B.V. (2)
Rivium 2e Straat 55, 2909 LG, Capelle aan den IJssel, Netherlands
Tel.: (31) 10 2667711
Web Site: http://www.medpace.com
Emp.: 2
Pharmaceutical Research & Development Services
N.A.I.C.S.: 541715
Dieter Seitz-Tutter (VP-Europe)

Medpace Germany GmbH (2)
Theresienhoehe 30, 80339, Munich, Germany
Tel.: (49) 89 89 55 718 0
Pharmaceutical Research & Development Services
N.A.I.C.S.: 541715
Christopher Peterson (Project Coord)

Medpace Hong Kong Ltd. (2)
Unit 320 3F Core Building 2 No 1 Science Park West Avenue, Hong Kong Science Park Shatin New Territories, Hong Kong, China (Hong Kong)
Tel.: (852) 3173 0700
Pharmaceutical Research & Development Services
N.A.I.C.S.: 541715
Main-Fong Ang (Dir-Clinical Ops)

Medpace Hungary Kft. (2)
Andrassy ut 100, 1062, Budapest, Hungary
Tel.: (36) 1 580 2230
Pharmaceutical Research & Development Services
N.A.I.C.S.: 541715

Medpace Italy Srl (2)
Via Giuseppe Sacchi 3, 20121, Milan, Italy
Tel.: (39) 02 83413400
Pharmaceutical Research & Development Services
N.A.I.C.S.: 541715
Vincenzo Lopreiato (Country Mgr)

Subsidiary (Domestic):

Medpace Reference Laboratories LLC (2)
5365 Medpace Way, Cincinnati, OH 45227
Tel.: (513) 366-3270
Web Site: http://www.medpace.com
Medical Laboratories
N.A.I.C.S.: 621511

Subsidiary (Non-US):

Medpace Russia LLC (2)
Pereulok Grivtsova 4 St, 190000, Saint Petersburg, Russia
Tel.: (7) 8123209587
Pharmaceutical Research & Development Services
N.A.I.C.S.: 541715
Svetlana Timofeeva (Country Mgr)

Medpace South Africa Pty. Ltd. (2)
6 Griswold Road, Saxonwold, 2196, Johannesburg, South Africa
Tel.: (27) 11 447 7494
Web Site: http://www.medpace.com
Emp.: 8
Pharmaceutical Research & Development Services
N.A.I.C.S.: 541715
Carolyn Glashagen (Mng Dir)

Medpace Taiwan Ltd. (2)
12/F East Site No 51 Hengyang Road Zhongzheng Dist, Taipei, 10045, Taiwan
Tel.: (886) 2 2370 1000
Pharmaceutical Research & Development Services
N.A.I.C.S.: 541715

Partner in Pet Food Hungaria Kft. **(1)**
Puskas Tivadar u 14, 2040, Budaors, Hungary
Tel.: (36) 1 801 02 03
Web Site: http://www.ppfeurope.com
Pet Food Mfr
N.A.I.C.S.: 311119
Attila Balogh *(Chm & CEO)*

Subsidiary (Non-US):

Partner in Pet Food CZ S.R.O **(2)**
Office Park Building B 6th Floor Bucharova 1423/6, Nove Butovice, 158 00, Prague, Czech Republic
Tel.: (420) 234 111 111
Web Site: http://www.partnerinpetfood.com
Pet Food Mfr
N.A.I.C.S.: 311119

Partner in Pet Food SK S.R.O **(2)**
Dunajsky Klatov 141, 930 21, Dunajska Streda, Slovakia
Tel.: (421) 31 559 13 65
Pet Food Distr
N.A.I.C.S.: 424490

Premium Credit Limited **(1)**
Ermyn House Ermyn Way, Leatherhead, KT22 8UX, Surrey, United Kingdom
Tel.: (44) 3447369836
Web Site: http://www.premiumcredit.com
Emp.: 300
Third Party Insurance Premium Financing Services
N.A.I.C.S.: 524292
Roger Brown *(Dir-Comml)*

STADA Arzneimittel AG **(1)**
Stadastrasse 2-18, 61118, Bad Vilbel, Germany
Tel.: (49) 61016030
Web Site: http://www.stada.de
Rev.: $2,665,973,183
Assets: $4,072,036,518
Liabilities: $2,724,669,054
Net Worth: $1,347,367,463
Earnings: $355,183,396
Emp.: 10,416
Fiscal Year-end: 12/31/2018
Pharmaceuticals Mfr
N.A.I.C.S.: 325412
Jens Steegers *(Deputy Chm-Supervisory Bd)*

Subsidiary (Domestic):

ALIUD PHARMA GmbH **(2)**
Gottlieb-Daimler-Str 19, 89150, Laichingen, Germany
Tel.: (49) 73 33 96 51 0
Web Site: http://www.aliud.de
Emp.: 70
Pharmaceutical & Health Care Products Mfr
N.A.I.C.S.: 325412
Incrid Blumenthal *(Mgr)*

ALIUD PHARMA Verwaltungs-GmbH **(2)**
Gottlieb-Daimler-Str 19, Laichingen, 89150, Germany
Tel.: (49) 7333 965 10
Web Site: http://www.aliud.de
Sales Range: $25-49.9 Million
Emp.: 40
Pharmaceutical & Health Care Products Mfr
N.A.I.C.S.: 325412
Ingrid Blumbnthao *(Mng Dir)*

Subsidiary (Non-US):

Britannia Pharmaceuticals Ltd. **(2)**
200 Longwater Ave Queen Park, Reading, RG2 6GP, Berks, United Kingdom
Tel.: (44) 1635 568400
Web Site: http://www.britannia-pharm.co.uk
Pharmaceutical & Health Care Products Mfr
N.A.I.C.S.: 325412
Robert Wood *(Mng Dir)*

Centrafarm B.V. **(2)**
Nieuwe Donk 3, 4879 AC, Etten-Leur, Netherlands
Tel.: (31) 76 508 10 00
Web Site: http://www.centrafarm.nl
Sales Range: $50-74.9 Million
Emp.: 60
Pharmaceutical Products Distr
N.A.I.C.S.: 424210

Hans Stols *(Gen Mgr)*

Subsidiary (Domestic):

Centrafarm Nederland B.V. **(3)**
Nieuwe Donk 3, Etten-Leur, 4879 AC, Netherlands
Tel.: (31) 765081000
Web Site: http://www.centrafarm.nl
Emp.: 60
Pharmaceutical Products Mfr & Distr
N.A.I.C.S.: 325412

Subsidiary (Domestic):

Neocare B.V. **(4)**
Nieuwe Donk 3, Postbus 289, 4879 AC, Etten-Leur, Netherlands
Tel.: (31) 765081700
Web Site: http://www.neocare.nl
Sales Range: $25-49.9 Million
Emp.: 3
Pharmaceutical & Health Care Products Mfr
N.A.I.C.S.: 325412

Subsidiary (Domestic):

Centrafarm Pharmaceuticals B.V. **(3)**
Postbus 289, 4870 AG, Etten-Leur, Netherlands
Tel.: (31) 765081000
Pharmaceutical & Health Care Products Mfr
N.A.I.C.S.: 325412

HTP Huisapotheek B.V. **(3)**
Nieuwe Donk 3, Etten-Leur, 4879 AC, North Brabant, Netherlands
Tel.: (31) 765081000
Web Site: http://www.centrafarm.nl
Emp.: 50
Pharmaceutical & Health Care Products Mfr
N.A.I.C.S.: 325412

Healthypharm B.V. **(3)**
Nieuwe Donk 3, Postbus 289, 4879 AC, Etten-Leur, Netherlands
Tel.: (31) 765012045
Pharmaceutical & Health Care Products Mfr
N.A.I.C.S.: 325412

Subsidiary (Non-US):

Clonmel Healthcare Limited **(2)**
Waterford Road, E91 D768, Clonmel, Ireland
Tel.: (353) 52617 7777
Web Site: http://www.clonmel-health.ie
Pharmaceutical & Health Care Products Mfr
N.A.I.C.S.: 325412
Kieran Mulhall *(Dir-Ops)*

Croma Medic, Inc. **(2)**
Suite 301 Alegria Bldg 2229 Chino Roces Avenue, Makati, 1231, Philippines
Tel.: (63) 2 817 8541
Web Site: https://www.stada-apac.com
Pharmaceutical Products Mfr & Distr
N.A.I.C.S.: 325412

Crosspharma Ltd. **(2)**
22-26 Duncrue Road, Belfast, BT3 9BP, United Kingdom
Tel.: (44) 2890 776 877
Pharmaceutical & Health Care Products Mfr
N.A.I.C.S.: 325412

EG Labo SAS - Laboratoires Eurogenerics SAS **(2)**
Central Park 9-15 rue Maurice Mallet, 92130, Issy-les-Moulineaux, France
Tel.: (33) 146948686
Web Site: https://www.eglabo.fr
Pharmaceuticals Product Mfr
N.A.I.C.S.: 325412

EG S.A. **(2)**
Heizel Esplanade B 22, Brussels, 1020, Belgium
Tel.: (32) 2 479 78 78
Web Site: https://www.eg.be
Emp.: 170
Pharmaceuticals Product Mfr
N.A.I.C.S.: 325412

EG S.p.A. **(2)**
Via Pavia 6, Milan, 20136, Italy
Tel.: (39) 028310371
Web Site: http://www.eglab.it
Pharmaceutical & Health Care Products Mfr
N.A.I.C.S.: 325412

Forum Bioscience Holdings Ltd. **(2)**

Betchworth House 57-65 Station Rd, Redhill, RH1 1DL, Surrey, United Kingdom
Tel.: (44) 1737 857700
Web Site: http://www.forum.co.uk
Sales Range: $100-124.9 Million
Emp.: 125
Holding Company; Pharmaceutical Sales
N.A.I.C.S.: 551112

Genus Pharmaceuticals Ltd. **(2)**
Linthwaite Manchester Road, Huddersfield, HD7 5QH, United Kingdom
Tel.: (44) 1484 842217
Pharmaceutical & Health Care Products Mfr
N.A.I.C.S.: 325412

Hemofarm Koncern A.D. **(2)**
Beogradski Put BB, Vrsac, 26300, Serbia
Tel.: (381) 13803100
Web Site: http://www.hemofarm.com
Sales Range: $1-4.9 Billion
Emp.: 2,500
Pharmaceuticals Mfr
N.A.I.C.S.: 325412

Subsidiary (Domestic):

Hemofarm A.D. **(3)**
Beogradski put bb, 26300, Vrsac, Serbia
Tel.: (381) 13 803 100
Web Site: http://www.hemofarm.com
Emp.: 3,600
Pharmaceutical & Health Care Products Mfr
N.A.I.C.S.: 325412
Ronald Seeliger *(Gen Mgr)*

Subsidiary (Non-US):

Hemofarm Banja Luka d.o.o. **(3)**
Novakovici b b, Banja Luka, 78000, Bosnia & Herzegovina
Tel.: (387) 51 331 650
Web Site: https://www.hemofarm.ba
Emp.: 200
Pharmaceutical & Health Care Products Mfr
N.A.I.C.S.: 325412
Sasa Urosevic *(Dir)*

Hemomont d.o.o. **(3)**
8 Marta 55a, 20000, Podgorica, Montenegro
Tel.: (382) 81 662 322
Web Site: https://www.hemofarm.com
Pharmaceuticals Mfr
N.A.I.C.S.: 325412

Hemopharm GmbH **(3)**
Theodor-Heuss-Strasse 52, 61118, Bad Vilbel, Germany
Tel.: (49) 6101985740
Web Site: http://www.hemopharm.de
Pharmaceutical Mfr & Distr
N.A.I.C.S.: 325412
Christos Gallis *(Mng Dir)*

OOO Hemofarm **(3)**
Kiyevskoye shosse 62, 249030, Obninsk, Russia
Tel.: (7) 4843990500
Web Site: https://www.stada.ru
Pharmaceutical & Health Care Products Mfr
N.A.I.C.S.: 325412

STADA Hemofarm S.R.L. **(3)**
Calea Torontalului km 6, 300633, Timisoara, Romania
Tel.: (40) 256203922
Web Site: http://www.hemofarm.com
Pharmaceutical Mfr & Distr
N.A.I.C.S.: 325412

Subsidiary (Non-US):

IZGRADNJA d.o.o. **(2)**
Kralja Zvonimira 45, 51260, Crikvenica, Croatia
Tel.: (385) 51241424
Web Site: http://www.izgradnja-ck.hr
Sales Range: $25-49.9 Million
Emp.: 59
Construction Engineering Services
N.A.I.C.S.: 541330
Goran Rubcic *(Dir-Tech)*

Laboratorio STADA, S.L **(2)**
Calle Frederic Mompou 5 Sant Just Desvern, Barcelona, 08960, Spain
Tel.: (34) 934738889
Web Site: http://www.stada.es
Pharmaceutical Mfr & Distr
N.A.I.C.S.: 325412

Subsidiary (Domestic):

ProtoPharma Gesellschaft fur Engineering und Consulting mbH **(2)**
Hessenring 107, 61348, Bad Homburg, Germany
Tel.: (49) 6172 27909 10
Web Site: http://www.protopharma.de
Sales Range: $25-49.9 Million
Emp.: 30
Pharmaceutical Industry Plant Design, Engineering & Consulting Services
N.A.I.C.S.: 541330

Subsidiary (Non-US):

STADA Arzneimittel Gesellschaft m.b.H. **(2)**
Muthgasse 36, 1190, Vienna, Austria
Tel.: (43) 1 367 85 85
Web Site: http://www.stada.at
Pharmaceutical & Health Care Products Mfr
N.A.I.C.S.: 325412
Martin Spatz *(Mng Dir)*

Subsidiary (Domestic):

STADA Consumer Health & STADAPHARM GmbH **(2)**
Stadastrasse 2 18, 61118, Bad Vilbel, Germany
Tel.: (49) 61016030
Web Site: http://www.stada.de
Pharmaceutical & Health Care Products Mfr
N.A.I.C.S.: 325412

STADA GmbH **(2)**
Stadastr 2-18, 61118, Bad Vilbel, Germany
Tel.: (49) 61016030
Pharmaceutical & Health Care Products Mfr
N.A.I.C.S.: 325412

Subsidiary (Non-US):

STADA PHARMA Bulgaria EOOD **(2)**
29 Atanas Dukov Street Floor 5 Rainbow Center, Sofia, 1407, Bulgaria
Tel.: (359) 29624626
Web Site: https://www.stada.com
Pharmaceutical & Health Care Products Mfr
N.A.I.C.S.: 325412

STADA PHARMA CZ, s.r.o. **(2)**
Siemensova 2717/4, 155 00, Prague, Czech Republic
Tel.: (420) 257 888 111
Web Site: http://www.stada-pharma.cz
Pharmaceuticals Product Mfr
N.A.I.C.S.: 325412

STADA Pharmaceuticals (Asia) Ltd. **(2)**
Room 13-18, 37/F Tower 1 Millennium City 1 388 Kwun Tong Road, Kwun Tong, Kowloon, China (Hong Kong)
Tel.: (852) 3156 7800
Web Site: https://www.stada-apac.com
Pharmaceutical & Health Care Products Mfr
N.A.I.C.S.: 325412
Zhou Fan *(Gen Mgr-Greater China)*

Subsidiary (Non-US):

STADA Pharmaceuticals (Beijing) Ltd. **(3)**
No 15 Yunteng Rd Industrial Development Zone, Beijing, 101500, China **(83.35%)**
Tel.: (86) 10 6907 6655
Web Site: https://www.stada.com
Pharmaceutical & Health Care Products Mfr
N.A.I.C.S.: 325412

Subsidiary (Domestic):

STADA R&D GmbH **(2)**
Stadastrasse 2 18, 61118, Bad Vilbel, Germany
Tel.: (49) 61016030
Pharmaceutical & Health Care Products Research & Development
N.A.I.C.S.: 325412

Subsidiary (Non-US):

STADA Service Holding B.V. **(2)**
Van de Reijtstraat 31-E, Breda, 4814, NE, Netherlands
Tel.: (31) 765081000
Web Site: http://www.centrafarm.nl

Cinven Limited—(Continued)

Pharmaceutical & Health Care Products Mfr
N.A.I.C.S.: 325412

Subsidiary (Domestic):

STADApharm GmbH **(2)**
Stadastrasse 2-18, 61118, Bad Vilbel, Germany
Tel.: (49) 61016030
Web Site: http://www.stada.de
Pharmaceutical & Health Care Products Mfr
N.A.I.C.S.: 325412

Subsidiary (Non-US):

Stada Nordic ApS **(2)**
Marielundvej 46 A, 2730, Herlev, Denmark
Tel.: (45) 44859999
Web Site: https://stada.dk
Pharmaceuticals Product Mfr
N.A.I.C.S.: 325412

Thornton & Ross Limited **(2)**
Linthwaite, Huddersfield, HD7 5QH, United Kingdom
Tel.: (44) 1484842217
Web Site: http://www.thorntonandross.co.uk
Pharmaceuticals Mfr
N.A.I.C.S.: 325412

Subsidiary (Domestic):

cell pharm Gesellschaft fur pharmazeutische und diagnostische Praparate mbH **(2)**
Theodor-Heuss-Str 52, 61118, Bad Vilbel, Germany
Tel.: (49) 610130420
Web Site: http://www.cellpharm.com
Sales Range: $25-49.9 Million
Emp.: 20
Pharmaceutical & Health Care Products Mfr
N.A.I.C.S.: 325412
Anne Demberg (Pres)

SYNLAB International GmbH **(1)**
Moosacher Strasse 88, 80809, Munich, Germany
Tel.: (49) 89 307602 0
Web Site: http://www.synlab.com
Emp.: 17,000
Holding Company; Human & Veterinary Medicine Laboratory Diagnostic & Environmental Analysis Services
N.A.I.C.S.: 551112
Bartl Wimmer (CEO & Mng Dir)

Subsidiary (Non-US):

Genon Laboratories Limited **(2)**
Unit 6a Top Land Country Business Park, Cragg Vale Hebden Bridge, Halifax, HX7 5RU, W Yorks, United Kingdom
Tel.: (44) 1422884287
Food Allergen Testing Services
N.A.I.C.S.: 541380
Lucy Caistor (Gen Mgr)

Subsidiary (Domestic):

SYNLAB Holding Deutschland GmbH **(2)**
Gubener Strasse 39, 86156, Augsburg, Germany
Tel.: (49) 821 52157 0
Web Site: http://www.synlab.de
Human & Veterinary Medicine Laboratory Diagnostic & Environmental Analysis Services
N.A.I.C.S.: 621511
Martin Beer (COO & Mng Dir)

Subsidiary (Non-US):

Institut fur medizinische und chemische Labordiagnostik GmbH **(3)**
Rosensteingasse 49-51, 1170, Vienna, Austria
Tel.: (43) 1 545 31 82
Web Site: http://www.synlab.at
Emp.: 100
Human & Veterinary Medicine Diagnostic Laboratory Services
N.A.I.C.S.: 621511
Renee Tauffer (Dir-Medical)

Subsidiary (Non-US):

SYNLAB Laboratory Services Limited **(2)**

4th Floor 1 Kingdom Street, London, W2 6BD, United Kingdom
Tel.: (44) 1873 856688
Web Site: http://www.synlab.co.uk
Food, Drug & Alcohol Testing Services
N.A.I.C.S.: 621511

TK Elevator GmbH **(1)**
thyssenkrupp Allee 1, 45143, Essen, Germany
Tel.: (49) 2018440
Web Site: http://www.thyssenkrupp-elevator.com
Sales Range: $5-14.9 Billion
Emp.: 39,501
Holding Company; Elevator & Lift Developr, Mfr & Distr
N.A.I.C.S.: 551112
Uday Yadav (CEO)

Subsidiary (US):

Braun Thyssenkrupp Elevator, LLC **(2)**
2829 Royal Ave, Madison, WI 53713
Tel.: (608) 221-4400
Web Site: http://www.braun-corp.com
Sales Range: $1-9.9 Million
Emp.: 100
Building Equipment Contractors
N.A.I.C.S.: 238290
Darrell Braun (CEO)

O'Keefe Elevator Company Inc. **(2)**
1402 Jones St, Omaha, NE 68102
Tel.: (402) 345-4056
Web Site: http://www.okeefe-elevator.com
Sales Range: $10-24.9 Million
Elevators
N.A.I.C.S.: 423830
Denny B. Wychulis (CEO)

Subsidiary (Non-US):

Sun Rhine Enterprises Ltd. **(2)**
10F-1 No 18 Sec 1 Chang-An E Road, Taipei, 104, Taiwan
Tel.: (886) 2 25618310
Web Site: http://www.thyssenkrupp-elevator.com.tw
Sales Range: $25-49.9 Million
Emp.: 100
Lift Repair & Installation Services
N.A.I.C.S.: 238290

TK Elevator **(2)**
Andropov Ave 18 bldg 7, 115432, Moscow, Russia
Tel.: (7) 4959358517
Web Site: http://tkelevator.ru
Sales Range: $50-74.9 Million
Emp.: 150
Elevator Mfr
N.A.I.C.S.: 333921

ThyssenKrupp Accessibility B.V. **(2)**
Van Utrechtweg 99, 2921 LN, Krimpen aan de Ijssel, Netherlands
Tel.: (31) 180 530 900
Web Site: http://www.tkacc.nl
Elevator & Stair Lift Mfr
N.A.I.C.S.: 333921

Subsidiary (Domestic):

ThyssenKrupp Accessibility Holding GmbH **(2)**
Hatzper Strasse 36, 45149, Essen, Germany
Tel.: (49) 2017995911
Web Site: http://www.tk-access4all.com
Sales Range: $25-49.9 Million
Emp.: 11
Holding Company; Wheel Chair Lift Mfr
N.A.I.C.S.: 551112

ThyssenKrupp Aufzuge GmbH **(2)**
Bernhaeuser Strasse 45, PO Box 230370, 73765, Neuhausen, Germany
Tel.: (49) 711652220
Web Site: http://www.thyssenkrupp-elevator.com
Sales Range: $1-4.9 Billion
Emp.: 3,000
Elevator Mfr
N.A.I.C.S.: 331513

Subsidiary (Non-US):

ThyssenKrupp Elevadores S.A. **(2)**

Fonrouge 1561, C1440CYO, Buenos Aires, Argentina
Tel.: (54) 1146301600
Web Site: http://www.thyssenkrupp.com
Elevator Mfr
N.A.I.C.S.: 333921

ThyssenKrupp Elevadores S.A. **(2)**
Carrera 85K 46 A 66 Torre 2 of 401, Centro Logistico San Cayetano 666 Santa Fe, Bogota, Colombia
Tel.: (57) 16700070
Web Site: http://www.thyssenkrupp.com
Sales Range: $100-124.9 Million
Emp.: 270
Elevator Mfr
N.A.I.C.S.: 333921

ThyssenKrupp Elevadores S.A. **(2)**
Via Porras San Francisco Local 65, Panama, Panama
Tel.: (507) 3881111
Web Site: http://www.thyssenkrupp.com
Elevator Mfr
N.A.I.C.S.: 333921

ThyssenKrupp Elevadores S.A. **(2)**
Alcantara 200 Piso 6, Las Condes, Santiago, Chile
Tel.: (56) 2 370 2932
Elevator Mfr
N.A.I.C.S.: 333921

ThyssenKrupp Elevadores S.A.C. **(2)**
Av San Borja Sur 1180 - 1182, San Borja, Lima, Peru
Tel.: (51) 16250400
Web Site: http://www.thyssenkrupp.com
Elevator Mfr
N.A.I.C.S.: 333921

ThyssenKrupp Elevadores, S.A. **(2)**
Sintra Business Park Building 4 2B, 2710-089, Sintra, Portugal
Tel.: (351) 21 430 81 00
Sales Range: $100-124.9 Million
Emp.: 500
Elevator & Escalator Installation Services
N.A.I.C.S.: 238290
Ricardo Malheiro (CEO)

ThyssenKrupp Elevadores, S.A. **(2)**
4th avenue 17-09 - zone 14, Guatemala, Guatemala
Tel.: (502) 2 368 2020
Web Site: http://www.thyssenkrupp.com
Sales Range: $25-49.9 Million
Emp.: 40
Elevator Mfr
N.A.I.C.S.: 333921

ThyssenKrupp Elevadores, S.A. **(2)**
Rua Santa Maria 1000, 92500-000, Guaiba, Portoalegre, Brazil
Tel.: (55) 51 2129 7241
Elevator Mfr
N.A.I.C.S.: 333921

ThyssenKrupp Elevadores, S.A. de C.V. **(2)**
General Mendez 19 Col Daniel Garza Extension, 11840, Mexico, Mexico
Tel.: (52) 55 5344 4571
Web Site: http://www.thyssenkrupp.com
Sales Range: $25-49.9 Million
Emp.: 100
Elevator Mfr
N.A.I.C.S.: 333921

ThyssenKrupp Elevadores, S.L. **(2)**
Calle Cifuentes s / n, 28021, Madrid, Spain
Tel.: (34) 901020909
Web Site: http://www.thyssenkrupp-elevator.com
Installation, Modernization & Maintenance of Elevators, Escalators, Moving Walks, Platform & Scenic Equipment
N.A.I.C.S.: 333921

ThyssenKrupp Elevadores, S.R.L. **(2)**
Democracia N 1893, 11800, Montevideo, Uruguay
Tel.: (598) 51 48 07 206
Elevator Mfr
N.A.I.C.S.: 333921

ThyssenKrupp Elevator & Escalator (Shanghai) Co.Ltd. **(2)**

Room 2603 Wisdom Plaza 518 Wuning South Road, Shanghai, 200042, China
Tel.: (86) 21 5298 8958
Web Site: http://www.thyssenkrupp-elevator.com.cn
Elevator Mfr
N.A.I.C.S.: 333921

ThyssenKrupp Elevator (BD) Pvt. Ltd. **(2)**
AncAnchor Tower 7th Floor 108 Bir Uttam C R Dutta Road, 1205, Dhaka, Bangladesh
Tel.: (880) 2448620013
Web Site: http://www.thyssenkrupp-elevator.com.bd
Sales Range: $25-49.9 Million
Emp.: 70
Elevator Mfr
N.A.I.C.S.: 333921

ThyssenKrupp Elevator (HK) Ltd. **(2)**
31st Floor Enterprise Plaza 3 39 Wang Chiu Road, Kowloon Bay, Kowloon, China (Hong Kong)
Tel.: (852) 2766 0218
Web Site: http://www.thyssenkrupp-elevator.com.hk
Emp.: 250
Elevator Mfr
N.A.I.C.S.: 333921

ThyssenKrupp Elevator (India) Private Limited **(2)**
A-24 Vardhan House Street no 3 MIDC, Andheri East, Mumbai, 400 093, Maharashtra, India
Tel.: (91) 2266902300
Web Site: http://www.thyssenkrupp-elevator.com
Sales Range: $100-124.9 Million
Emp.: 500
Elevator Mfr
N.A.I.C.S.: 333921

ThyssenKrupp Elevator (Korea) Ltd. **(2)**
201 Mokdongseo-ro, Yangcheon-gu, Seoul, 158-719, Korea (South)
Tel.: (82) 2 2610 7777
Web Site: http://www.thyssenkrupp-elevator.co.kr
Elevator Mfr
N.A.I.C.S.: 333921

Plant (Domestic):

ThyssenKrupp Elevator (Korea) Ltd. - Cheonan Plant **(3)**
115-24 Sindu-ri Ipjang-myeon, Seobuk-gu, Cheonan, 330-826, Chungcheongnam-do, Korea (South)
Tel.: (82) 41 589 4000
Web Site: http://www.thyssenkrupp-elevator.co.kr
Emp.: 1,000
Elevator Mfr
N.A.I.C.S.: 333921

Subsidiary (Non-US):

ThyssenKrupp Elevator (Singapore) Pte.Ltd. **(2)**
3 International Business Park 06-01 Nordic European Centre, Singapore, 609927, Singapore
Tel.: (65) 68901640
Web Site: http://www.thyssenkrupp-elevator.com.sg
Emp.: 70
Elevator & Escalator Installation Services
N.A.I.C.S.: 238290

ThyssenKrupp Elevator A/S **(2)**
Erhvervsvej 4, 2600, Glostrup, Denmark
Tel.: (45) 70130808
Web Site: http://www.thyssenkrupp-elevator.dk
Sales Range: $25-49.9 Million
Emp.: 231
Elevator Mfr
N.A.I.C.S.: 333921

ThyssenKrupp Elevator A/S **(2)**
Brobekkveien 38, PO Box 6877, Rodelokka, 504, Oslo, Norway
Tel.: (47) 23173700
Sales Range: $25-49.9 Million
Emp.: 30
Elevator Mfr
N.A.I.C.S.: 333921

ThyssenKrupp Elevator Almoayyed W.L.L. (2)
Suite 2703 Almoayyed Tower Building 2504 Road 2832, PO Box 60059, Al Seef District, 428, Manama, Bahrain
Tel.: (973) 17311515
Web Site: http://www.thyssenkrupp-elevator-seame.com
Elevator Installation & Maintenance Services
N.A.I.C.S.: 811310

Subsidiary (US):

ThyssenKrupp Elevator Americas Corp. (2)
2500 Northwinds Pkwy, Alpharetta, GA 30004
Tel.: (678) 319-3245
Web Site: http://www.thyssenkruppelevator.com
Elevator & Lift Product Mfr & Maintenance
N.A.I.C.S.: 333921

Subsidiary (Domestic):

Computerized Elevator Control Corp. (3)
24 Empire Blvd, Moonachie, NJ 07074-1303
Tel.: (201) 508-2300
Web Site: http://www.swiftcec.com
Sales Range: $25-49.9 Million
Emp.: 85
Elevators & Equipment Mfr
N.A.I.C.S.: 333921

National Wheel-O-Vator Co. Inc. (3)
509 W Font St, Roanoke, IL 61561
Tel.: (309) 923-7803
Web Site: http://www.wheelovator.com
Sales Range: $25-49.9 Million
Emp.: 150
Wheelchair Lift & Home Elevator Mfr & Distr
N.A.I.C.S.: 333921

Plant (Domestic):

ThyssenKrupp Elevator (3)
700 Hicksville Rd, Bethpage, NY 11714
Tel.: (631) 491-3111
Web Site: http://www.thyssenkruppelevator.com
Sales Range: $50-74.9 Million
Emp.: 215
Elevator Installation & Conversion
N.A.I.C.S.: 238290

ThyssenKrupp Elevator (3)
1650 Shelby Oaks Dr N Ste 6, Memphis, TN 38134
Tel.: (901) 377-1993
Web Site: http://www.thyssenkruppelevator.com
Sales Range: $25-49.9 Million
Emp.: 100
Passenger & Freight Elevators & Stage Lifts Mfr
N.A.I.C.S.: 333921

Subsidiary (Domestic):

ThyssenKrupp Elevator Capital Corp. (3)
3965 Mendenhall Rd Ste 10, Memphis, TN 38115
Tel.: (901) 365-5100
Web Site: http://www.thyssenkrupp.com
Elevator Mfr
N.A.I.C.S.: 333921

ThyssenKrupp Elevator Corp. (3)
15141 E Whittier Blvd Ste 505, Whittier, CA 90603
Tel.: (901) 365-5600
Web Site: http://www.thyssenkrupp.com
Elevator Mfr
N.A.I.C.S.: 333921

ThyssenKrupp Elevator Inc. (3)
1650 Shelby Oaks Dr Ste 6, Memphis, TN 38134
Tel.: (901) 377-1993
Web Site: http://www.thyssenkrupp.com
Emp.: 260
Elevator Mfr
N.A.I.C.S.: 333921

ThyssenKrupp Elevator Manufacturing Inc. (3)

9280 Crestwyn Hills Dr, Collierville, TN 38125
Tel.: (901) 261-1800
Elevator Mfr
N.A.I.C.S.: 333921

Subsidiary (Non-US):

ThyssenKrupp Elevator Asia Pacific Ltd. (2)
7/F Sun Hung Kai Center 30 Habour Road, Wanchai, China (Hong Kong)
Tel.: (852) 3511 0688
Web Site: http://www.thyssenkrupp-elevator-ap.com
Sales Range: $25-49.9 Million
Emp.: 40
Elevator Installation & Maintenance Services
N.A.I.C.S.: 811310

ThyssenKrupp Elevator B.V. (2)
Fascinatio Boulevard 806-808, 2909 VA, Capelle aan den IJssel, Netherlands
Tel.: (31) 88 4479 200
Web Site: http://www.thyssenkruppliften.nl
Sales Range: $25-49.9 Million
Emp.: 60
Elevator Installation Services
N.A.I.C.S.: 238290

ThyssenKrupp Elevator Canada Ltd. (2)
2075 Kennedy Rd Suite 600, Scarborough, M1T 3V3, ON, Canada
Tel.: (416) 291-2000
Sales Range: $25-49.9 Million
Emp.: 1,800
Elevator & Lift Mfr & Distr
N.A.I.C.S.: 333921

ThyssenKrupp Elevator Holding France S.A.S. (2)
8 Rue Parmentier, 92816, Puteaux, France
Tel.: (33) 1 573265 58
Web Site: http://www.thyssenkrupp.com
Elevator Installation & Maintenance Services
N.A.I.C.S.: 811310

ThyssenKrupp Elevator Innovation Center, S.A. (2)
La Laboral Ciudad de la Cultura, '33203, Gijon, Asturias, Spain
Tel.: (34) 98 519 67 92
Elevator Mfr
N.A.I.C.S.: 333921

ThyssenKrupp Elevator Ireland, Ltd. (2)
Unit 11 Seatown Business Campus Seatown Road, Swords, Dublin, Ireland
Tel.: (353) 1 8956903
Web Site: http://www.thyssenkrupp.com
Sales Range: $25-49.9 Million
Emp.: 20
Elevator Installation Services
N.A.I.C.S.: 238290

ThyssenKrupp Elevator Italia S.p.A. (2)
Via A Volta 16, 20093, Cologno Monzese, Italy
Tel.: (39) 02 89 69 63 00
Web Site: http://www.thyssenkrupp-elevator.com
Elevator Installation Services
N.A.I.C.S.: 238290

ThyssenKrupp Elevator Malaysia Sdn. Bhd. (2)
Level 18 The Pinnacle Persiaran Lagoon Bandar Sunway, 46150, Petaling Jaya, Selangor Darul Ehsen, Malaysia
Tel.: (60) 356229988
Web Site: http://www.thyssenkrupp-elevator.com.my
Emp.: 200
Elevator Installation & Maintenance Services
N.A.I.C.S.: 811310

ThyssenKrupp Elevator Manufacturing France S.A.S. (2)
Rue de Champfleur Z I Saint-Barthelemy, BP 10746, 49007, Angers, France
Tel.: (33) 2 41 33 36 75
Web Site: http://www.thyssenkrupp-ascenseurs.fr

Elevator & Escalator Mfr
N.A.I.C.S.: 333921

ThyssenKrupp Elevator Manufacturing Spain S.L. (2)
C/ Federico Cantero Villamil 4 Parque Tecnologico, 28935, Mostoles, Madrid, Spain
Tel.: (34) 91 481 7700
Web Site: http://www.thyssenkrupp-elevator-manufacturing-spain.com
Elevator Mfr
N.A.I.C.S.: 333921
Elena Mozo (Mgr-Comm)

ThyssenKrupp Elevator Queensland Pty. Ltd. (2)
303 Cleveland Street, PO Box 16, Surry Hills, 2010, NSW, Australia
Tel.: (61) 2 8303 9000
Web Site: http://www.thyssenkrupp.com
Elevator Installation Services
N.A.I.C.S.: 238290

ThyssenKrupp Elevator SRL (2)
Preziei no 11 floor 3 sector 6, 6th District, Bucharest, 62202, Romania
Tel.: (40) 21 3180879
Web Site: http://www.thyssenkrupp-elevator-romania.com
Sales Range: $25-49.9 Million
Emp.: 32
Elevator Installation Services
N.A.I.C.S.: 238290

ThyssenKrupp Elevator Saudi Co. Ltd. (2)
Salah Eddin Al-Ayoubi Street, PO Box 9812, Jarir Bookstore Al Bawani Tower 6th Floor, 11423, Riyadh, Saudi Arabia
Tel.: (966) 114868900
Web Site: http://www.thyssenkrupp.com
Elevator Installation & Maintenance Services
N.A.I.C.S.: 811310

ThyssenKrupp Elevator Southern Europe, Africa & Middle East, S.L.U. (2)
Paseo de la Castellana 259C Floor 23, Madrid, 28046, Spain
Tel.: (34) 912028000
Web Site: http://www.thyssenkrupp-elevator-seame.com
Elevator Mfr
N.A.I.C.S.: 333921

ThyssenKrupp Elevator Sp. z o.o. (2)
Aleje Jerozolimskie 179, 02-222, Warsaw, Poland
Tel.: (48) 22 530 99 00
Web Site: http://www.thyssenkruppelevator.pl
Emp.: 50
Elevator Installation & Maintenance Services
N.A.I.C.S.: 811310

ThyssenKrupp Elevator Sverige AB (2)
Storsatragrand 12, 127 39, Skarholmen, Sweden
Tel.: (46) 8 449 2250
Web Site: http://www.thyssenkrupp.com
Sales Range: $25-49.9 Million
Emp.: 100
Elevator Installation Services
N.A.I.C.S.: 238290

ThyssenKrupp Elevator UK Ltd. (2)
4 Bull Close Road, Nottingham, NG7 2UL, United Kingdom
Tel.: (44) 115 986 8213
Web Site: http://www.thyssenkrupp-elevator.com
Elevator Installation Services
N.A.I.C.S.: 238290

ThyssenKrupp Elevator Vietnam Co., Ltd. (2)
198 Truong Chinh, Khuong Thuong Ward Dong Da District, 10200, Hanoi, Vietnam
Tel.: (84) 437282116
Web Site: http://www.thyssenkrupp.com.vn
Elevator Installation Services
N.A.I.C.S.: 238290

ThyssenKrupp Elevatori d.o.o. (2)

Bulevar Mihaila Pupina 10z/1, Belgrade, 11000, Serbia
Tel.: (381) 11 21 29 612
Web Site: http://www.thyssenkrupp-elevator.rs
Sales Range: $25-49.9 Million
Emp.: 20
Elevator Installation & Maintenance Services
N.A.I.C.S.: 811310
Igor Tanaskovic (Mng Dir)

ThyssenKrupp Elevators (Shanghai) Co., Ltd. (2)
No 2 Xunye Rd Sheshan Subarea Songjiang Industrial Area, Shanghai, 201602, China
Tel.: (86) 2157076888
Web Site: http://www.thyssenkrupp-elevator.com.cn
Elevator Mfr
N.A.I.C.S.: 333921

ThyssenKrupp Elevators Hellas S.A. (2)
37 Sepolion Str, 104 45, Athens, Greece
Tel.: (30) 210 825 2766
Web Site: http://www.thyssenkrupp.com
Sales Range: $25-49.9 Million
Emp.: 52
Elevator Installation Services
N.A.I.C.S.: 238290

ThyssenKrupp Northern Elevator Ltd. (2)
410 Passmore Avenue Unit 1, Scarborough, M1V 5C3, ON, Canada
Tel.: (416) 291-2000
Sales Range: $75-99.9 Million
Emp.: 300
Elevator Mfr
N.A.I.C.S.: 333921

Subsidiary (Domestic):

Thyssen Dover Elevator (Canada) Ltd. (3)
410 Passmore Ave, Scarborough, M1V 5C3, ON, Canada
Tel.: (416) 291-2000
Web Site: http://www.thyssenkrupp.com
Elevator Mfr
N.A.I.C.S.: 333921

Subsidiary (Non-US):

ThyssenKrupp Tailored Blanks (Wuhan) Ltd. (2)
Yinguang Av Guannan Industry Park, 430074, Wuhan, China
Tel.: (86) 27 8756 1616
Web Site: http://www.thyssenkrupp.com
Automotive Tailored Blank Mfr
N.A.I.C.S.: 336390

Truvo NV/SA (1)
Uitbreidingstraat 80 bus 3, 2600, Berchem, Belgium
Tel.: (32) 32856411
Web Site: http://www.truvo.com
Sales Range: $500-549.9 Million
Online & Print Directory Publisher
N.A.I.C.S.: 513140
Wim van Neutegem (VP-Tax & Treasury)

Subsidiary (Non-US):

Gouden Gids B.V. (2)
Harkerbergweg 88, 1101 CM, Amsterdam, Zuidoost, Netherlands
Tel.: (31) 205676767
Web Site: http://www.truvo.nl
Sales Range: $100-124.9 Million
Business & Services Contact Information Directory
N.A.I.C.S.: 513140

Paginas Amarelas S.A. (2)
Ave D Joao II No 1 17 01 74 Piso, 1990 083, Lisbon, Portugal
Tel.: (351) 218989500
Web Site: http://www.paginasamarelas.pt
Sales Range: $50-74.9 Million
Emp.: 200
Yellow Pages for Telephone Directories
N.A.I.C.S.: 517810

Publitec B.V. (2)
Herikerberweg 88, 1101 CM, Amsterdam, Netherlands

Cinven Limited—(Continued)

Tel.: (31) 205676869
Web Site: http://www.publitec.nl
Sales Range: $25-49.9 Million
Emp.: 100
Marketing, Media Measurement, Business &
Directory Information
N.A.I.C.S.: 513140

Viridium Holding AG (1)
Dornhofstrasse 36, 63263, Neu-Isenburg,
Germany
Tel.: (49) 61 025 9950
Web Site: https://www.viridium-gruppe.com
Holding Company; Insurance Services
N.A.I.C.S.: 551112
Heinz-Peter Ross (CEO)

Holding (Domestic):

Generali Lebensversicherung AG (2)
Oeder Weg 151, 60318, Frankfurt am Main,
Germany (89.9%)
Tel.: (49) 6915022000
Web Site: http://www.generali.de
Sales Range: $100-124.9 Million
Emp.: 250
Insurance Services
N.A.I.C.S.: 524128

Subsidiary (US):

Beacon Capital Strategic L.P. (3)
200 State St 5th Fl, Boston, MA 02109
Tel.: (617) 457-0400
Real Estate Management Services
N.A.I.C.S.: 531390

Subsidiary (Domestic):

GLL Real Estate Partners GmbH
(GLL) (3)
Lindwurmstrasse 76, 80337, Munich, Ger-
many
Tel.: (49) 89 726 103 930
Web Site: http://www.gll-partners.com
Real Estate Fund Manager Investments
N.A.I.C.S.: 523999
Rainer Gobel (Co-Founder & Mng Dir)

Generali Partner GmbH (3)
Adenauerring 7, 81737, Munich, Germany
Tel.: (49) 89 51210
General Insurance Services
N.A.I.C.S.: 524210

Generali Pensionsmanagement
GmbH (3)
Besenbinderhof 43, 20097, Hamburg, Ger-
many
Tel.: (49) 4028654050
Pension Fund Services
N.A.I.C.S.: 525110

Generali Properties Fund I GmbH &
Co. KG. (3)
Lindwurmstr 76, 80337, Munich, Germany
Tel.: (49) 89 726103930
Web Site: http://www.gll-partners.com
Sales Range: $25-49.9 Million
Emp.: 70
Property Management Services
N.A.I.C.S.: 531311

Thuringia Generali 1. Immobilien AG
& Co. KG (3)
Adenauerring 7, 81737, Munich, Germany
Tel.: (49) 8951210
Real Estate Rental Services
N.A.I.C.S.: 531390

Thuringia Generali 2. Immobilien AG
& Co. KG (3)
Sonnenstrasse 31, 80331, Munich, Ger-
many
Tel.: (49) 892103760
General Insurance Services
N.A.I.C.S.: 524210

Volksfursorge 1. Immobilien AG & Co.
KG (3)
Besenbinderhof 43, 20097, Hamburg, Ger-
many
Tel.: (49) 40 2865 0
Financial Management Services
N.A.I.C.S.: 523999

Volksfursorge Fixed Asset GmbH (3)
Besenbinderhof 43, 20097, Hamburg, Germany

Tel.: (49) 40 380781454
Asset Management Services
N.A.I.C.S.: 523940

Holding (Domestic):

Heidelberger Lebensversicherung
AG (2)
Dornhofstrasse 36, 63263, Neu-Isenburg,
Germany
Tel.: (49) 4021 995 6900
Web Site: https://www.heidelberger-leben.de
Sales Range: $75-99.9 Million
Life Insurance Products & Services
N.A.I.C.S.: 524113
Michael Sattler (Member-Exec Bd & CFO)

Subsidiary (Domestic):

Skandia Retail Europe Holding
GmbH (3)
Kaiserin Augusta Allee 108, Berlin, 10553,
Germany
Tel.: (49) 30310070
Web Site: http://www.skandia.de
Holding Company; Life Insurance Products
& Services
N.A.I.C.S.: 551112
Rolf-Peter Hoenen (Chm-Supervisory Bd)

Subsidiary (Non-US):

Skandia Lebensversicherung AG (4)
Tel.: (49) 6102 833 9910
Web Site: https://www.ska-lv.de
Life Insurance Products & Services
N.A.I.C.S.: 524113
Michael Sattler (Chm)

Subsidiary (Domestic):

Skandia Versicherung Management &
Service GmbH (4)
Kaiserin Augusta Allee, Berlin, 10553, Ger-
many
Tel.: (49) 30310072835
Web Site: http://www.skandia.de
Insurance & Investment Products Services
N.A.I.C.S.: 524113
Heinz-Peter Ross (Mng Dir)

Visma AS (1)
Karenlyst Alle 56, 0277, Oslo,
Norway (31.3%)
Tel.: (47) 46404000
Web Site: http://www.visma.com
Rev.: $1,706,404,419
Assets: $4,273,388,164
Liabilities: $2,705,806,114
Net Worth: $1,567,582,050
Earnings: $112,499,095
Emp.: 11,175
Fiscal Year-end: 12/31/2019
Business Software Developer
N.A.I.C.S.: 513210
Oystein Moan (Chm & Co-CEO)

Subsidiary (Domestic):

Visma Mamut AS (2)
Karenslyst Alle 56, 0277, Oslo, Norway
Tel.: (47) 46404000
Web Site: http://www.visma.no
Integrated Customer Relationship Manage-
ment Accounting Personnel & E-commerce
Software Mfr
N.A.I.C.S.: 513210
Kenneth Lovold (Mng Dir)

Subsidiary (Non-US):

Mamut AB (3)
Kungsgatan 24, Stockholm, Sweden
Tel.: (46) 084116190
Sales Range: $25-49.9 Million
Emp.: 30
Software Reproducing
N.A.I.C.S.: 334610

Mamut Aps (3)
Arne Jacobsens Alle 15, 2300, Copenha-
gen, Denmark
Tel.: (45) 80390002
Web Site: http://www.mamut.dk
Sales Range: $25-49.9 Million
Emp.: 15
Computer & Computer Peripheral Equip-
ment & Software Merchant Whslr
N.A.I.C.S.: 423430
Michael Brahe (Pres)

Subsidiary (Domestic):

Mamut Norge AS (3)
Pilestredet 75 C, Oslo, Norway
Tel.: (47) 23203500
Web Site: http://www.mamut.com
Computer & Computer Peripheral Equip-
ment & Software Merchant Whslr
N.A.I.C.S.: 423430

Subsidiary (Non-US):

Mamut Software Ltd. (3)
90 Long Acre Covent Garden, London,
WC2E 9RZ, United Kingdom
Tel.: (44) 2071530900
Web Site: http://www.visma.co.uk
Computer & Computer Peripheral Equip-
ment & Software Merchant Whslr
N.A.I.C.S.: 423430

CIP MERCHANT CAPITAL LIM-
ITED
3rd Floor 1 Le Truchot, Saint Peter
Port, GY1 1WD, Guernsey
Tel.: (44) 1481 749 360 GY
Web Site:
http://www.cipmerchantcapital.com
Year Founded: 2017
CIP—(AIM)
Sales Range: Less than $1 Million
Emp.: 403
Investment Management Service
N.A.I.C.S.: 523940

CIPHER PHARMACEUTICALS
INC.
5750 Explorer Drive Suite 404, Mis-
sissauga, L4W 0A9, ON, Canada
Tel.: (905) 602-5840 ON
Web Site:
https://www.cipherpharma.com
CPH—(TSX)
Rev.: $22,451,000
Assets: $46,455,000
Liabilities: $18,444,000
Net Worth: $28,011,000
Earnings: $3,242,000
Emp.: 6
Fiscal Year-end: 12/31/19
Drug Developer
N.A.I.C.S.: 325412
Craig Mull (Chm & CEO-Interim)

CIPHERLAB CO., LTD.
12F 333 Dunhua S Rd Sec 2, Taipei,
106033, Taiwan
Tel.: (886) 286471166
Web Site: https://www.cipherlab.com
Year Founded: 1988
6160—(TPE)
Rev.: $39,332,208
Assets: $42,919,520
Liabilities: $17,739,705
Net Worth: $25,179,814
Earnings: $975,331
Emp.: 12
Fiscal Year-end: 12/31/22
Automatic Identification Device Mfr
N.A.I.C.S.: 334519
Steven Liau (Chm & CEO)

Subsidiaries:

CipherLab Electronics Trading
(Shanghai) Co., Ltd. (1)
J Room 4F No 728 West Yan an Road,
Changning District, Shanghai, 200050,
China
Tel.: (86) 2133680288
Electrical & Mechanical Equipment Mfr
N.A.I.C.S.: 333248
Shun Ume (Mgr-HR)

CipherLab USA Inc. (1)
2552 Summit Ave Ste 400, Plano, TX
75074
Tel.: (469) 241-9779
Electrical & Mechanical Equipment Mfr
N.A.I.C.S.: 333248

MPLUS TECHNOLOGY Co.,
Ltd. (1)
2F No.105 Minquan Rd, Xindian, New Tai-
pei City, 23141, Taiwan
Tel.: (886) 222180606
Web Site: https://www.mplustech.com
Business Consulting Services
N.A.I.C.S.: 541618

CIPIA VISION LTD.
Sapir St 5, Herzliya, Israel
Tel.: (972) 775047760
Web Site: https://www.cipia.com
CPIA—(TAE)
Rev.: $5,351,000
Assets: $11,874,000
Liabilities: $4,746,000
Net Worth: $7,128,000
Earnings: ($9,128,000)
Fiscal Year-end: 06/30/23
Software Development Services
N.A.I.C.S.: 541511
David Tolub (CEO)

CIPIO PARTNERS GMBH
Palais am Lenbachplatz, Ottostrasse
8, Munich, 80333, Germany
Tel.: (49) 8955 06 960
Web Site:
http://www.cipiopartners.com
Year Founded: 2003
Capital Investment Management &
Advisory Firm
N.A.I.C.S.: 523940
Roland Dennert (Mng Partner)

CIPLA LTD.
Cipla House Peninsula Business Park
Ganpatrao Kadam Marg Lower Parel,
Mumbai, 400013, India
Tel.: (91) 2224826000 In
Web Site: https://www.cipla.com
CIPLA—(LUX)
Rev.: $3,009,040,125
Assets: $3,699,302,880
Liabilities: $816,780,510
Net Worth: $2,882,522,370
Earnings: $347,617,725
Emp.: 25,927
Fiscal Year-end: 03/31/22
Pharmaceuticals Mfr
N.A.I.C.S.: 325412
Umang Vohra (Mng Dir & CEO-
Global)

Subsidiaries:

Breathe Free Lanka (Private)
Limited (1)
345- 4/1 Galle Road, Colpetty, Colombo, Sri
Lanka
Tel.: (94) 112577731
Web Site: https://srilanka.cipla.com
Emp.: 120
Healtcare Services
N.A.I.C.S.: 621999
Azam Jaward (Head-Country)

Celeris d.o.o. (1)
Vukovarska 284 C, 10000, Zagreb, Croatia
Tel.: (385) 1 2444 644
Web Site: http://www.cipla.com
Emp.: 16
Medical Equipment Mfr & Distr
N.A.I.C.S.: 334510
Dario Naletilic (Gen Mgr)

Cipla (EU) Limited (1)
3rd Floor 364-366 Kensington High Street,
W14 8NS, London, United Kingdom
Tel.: (44) 2073994882
Web Site: https://uk.cipla.com
Pharmaceuticals Product Mfr
N.A.I.C.S.: 325412

Joint Venture (Non-US):

Cipla Maroc SA (2)
1st Floor Building B Residence Ben
Mahyou, ibnou Toufail street and Abdelhak
Ben Mahyou street corner, Casablanca,
Morocco (75.1%)
Tel.: (212) 522454610

Web Site: https://www.cipla.com
Emp.: 66
Pharmaceutical Products Distr
N.A.I.C.S.: 424210

Cipla Australia Pty Limited   (1)
Level 1 132 Albert Road, South Melbourne,
3205, VIC, Australia
Tel.: (61) 396964438
Emp.: 50
Pharmaceutical Products Distr
N.A.I.C.S.: 424210

Cipla Europe NV   (1)
Uitbreidingstraat 84-3rd floor, 2600, Antwerp, Belgium   (100%)
Tel.: (32) 80026564
Pharmaceuticals Product Mfr
N.A.I.C.S.: 325412

Cipla Health Limited   (1)
Art Guild House B-Wing 4th Floor Phoenix
MarketCity, Kurla West, Mumbai, 400070,
India
Tel.: (91) 2262453800
Web Site: https://www.ciplahealth.in
Healtcare Services
N.A.I.C.S.: 621999
Shivam Puri (CEO)

Cipla Kenya Limited   (1)
Nivina Towers 4th Floor Museum Hill Westlands Road, 46986, Nairobi, Kenya
Tel.: (254) 207767000
Web Site: https://www.cipla.co.ke
Healtcare Services
N.A.I.C.S.: 621999
Martin Sweeney (VP & Head-Comml)

Cipla Malaysia Sdn. Bhd.   (1)
Unit 1101 Amcorp Tower Amcorp Trade
Centre No 18 Jln Persiaran Barat, 46050,
Petaling Jaya, Selangor, Malaysia
Tel.: (60) 379562677
Pharmaceutical Products Distr
N.A.I.C.S.: 424210
Nishant Saxena (CEO)

Cipla Medpro South Africa
Limited   (1)
Parc du Cap Office Park Building 9, Mispel
Street, Bellville, 7530, South Africa
Tel.: (27) 219140520
Web Site: http://www.cipla.co.za
Sales Range: $250-299.9 Million
Emp.: 696
Pharmaceuticals Mfr & Distr
N.A.I.C.S.: 325412
Jacques van Staden (COO)

Subsidiary (Domestic):

Cipla Agrimed (Pty) Ltd.   (2)
North Highway Business Park 41 Park Avenue, PO Box 26822, Monument Park, Pretoria, 0105, Centurion, South Africa
Tel.: (27) 12 661 4076
Web Site: http://www.ciplaagrimed.co.za
Veterinary Medicines Developer, Mfr & Supplier
N.A.I.C.S.: 325412
Basie Hattingh (Mgr-Sls-Natl)

Cipla Medpro (Pty) Limited   (2)
Parc du Cap Office Park Building 9, Mispel
Street, Bellville, 7530, Western Cape, South
Africa
Tel.: (27) 21 914 0520
Web Site: http://www.ciplamedpro.co.za
Sales Range: $100-124.9 Million
Emp.: 400
Pharmaceuticals Product Mfr
N.A.I.C.S.: 325412
Jacques van Staden (COO)

Cipla Medpro Distribution Centre
(Pty) Limited   (2)
Unit 3 Durbanville Industrial Park, Lilie
Street, Durbanville, 7550, Western Cape,
South Africa
Tel.: (27) 21 975 1901
Web Site: http://www.cipla.co.za
Sales Range: $25-49.9 Million
Emp.: 60
Pharmaceutical Products Distr
N.A.I.C.S.: 424210
Joseph Ludorf (Mng Dir)

Cipla Medpro Manufacturing (Pty)
Limited   (2)

1474 South Coast Road, Mobeni, Durban,
4060, South Africa
Tel.: (27) 314513800
Web Site: http://www.ciplamedpro.co.za
Sales Range: $100-124.9 Million
Emp.: 460
Pharmaceuticals Product Mfr
N.A.I.C.S.: 325412

Cipla Vet (Pty) Limited   (2)
Rosen Heights Rosen Park, Bellville, 7530,
Western Cape, South Africa
Tel.: (27) 219434220
Web Site: http://www.ciplavet.co.za
Sales Range: $25-49.9 Million
Emp.: 9
Veterinary Medicine Mfr
N.A.I.C.S.: 325412
Craig Mincher (Mng Dir)

Cipla USA Inc.   (1)
9100 S Dadeland Blvd Ste 1500, Miami, FL
33156
Tel.: (786) 497-7276
Web Site: https://www.ciplausa.com
Emp.: 3
Pharmaceutical Product Mfr & Distr
N.A.I.C.S.: 325412

Subsidiary (Domestic):

Exelan Pharmaceuticals, Inc.   (2)
370 W Camino Gardens Blvd Ste 204,
Boca Raton, FL 33432   (100%)
Tel.: (561) 287-6631
Web Site: https://www.exelanpharma.com
Generic Pharmaceutical Marketer & Whslr
N.A.I.C.S.: 424210
Brian Christensen (Pres & Head-Ops)

InvaGen Pharmaceuticals Inc.   (2)
Ste B 7 Oser Ave, Hauppauge, NY
11788   (100%)
Tel.: (631) 231-3233
Web Site: http://www.invagen.com
Emp.: 500
Pharmaceutical Preparation Mfr
N.A.I.C.S.: 325412

Goldencross Pharma Pvt. Ltd.   (1)
Plot 17/18 Golden Ind Estate Somnath
Road, Dabhel, Daman, 396215, India
Tel.: (91) 2602241902
Pharmaceuticals Product Mfr
N.A.I.C.S.: 325412

Madison Pharmaceuticals Inc.   (1)
375 S End Ave MS 22G, New York, NY
10280
Tel.: (212) 513-0048
Web Site: https://www.madisonpharm.com
Pharmaceutical Products Distr
N.A.I.C.S.: 424210

Mirren (Pty) Ltd.   (1)
18 Golden Drive Morehill, Benoni, 1501,
South Africa
Tel.: (27) 114254026
Pharmaceutical Product Mfr & Distr
N.A.I.C.S.: 325412

Sitec Labs Pvt. Ltd.   (1)
Plot No Gen 40 TTC Industrial Area MIDC
Near Nelco Bus Stop, Behind Millennium
Business Park Mahape, Navi Mumbai, 400
710, India
Tel.: (91) 2269416200
Web Site: https://www.siteclabs.com
Emp.: 400
Laboratory Testing Services
N.A.I.C.S.: 621512
Ratnakar Jadhav (Head-Ops-Bioclinical)

CIRATA PLC.
47 Esplanade, Saint Helier, JE1
OBD, Jersey
Tel.: (44) 1143039985
Web Site: https://cirata.com
Year Founded: 2005
CRTA—(AIM)
Rev.: $9,685,000
Assets: $25,599,000
Liabilities: $9,036,000
Net Worth: $16,563,000
Earnings: ($29,605,000)
Emp.: 177
Fiscal Year-end: 12/31/22
Software Publisher

N.A.I.C.S.: 513210
David Richards (Co-Founder, Chm,
Pres & CEO)

Subsidiaries:

WANdisco International Limited   (1)
Wizu Workspace 5th floor - Castleton Suite
32 Eyre St, Sheffield City Centre, Sheffield,
S1 4QZ, United Kingdom
Tel.: (44) 1143039985
Web Site: https://www.wandisco.com
Software Publishing Services
N.A.I.C.S.: 513210

WANdisco Software (Chengdu)
Ltd.   (1)
Suite 19 11th Floor Building E2 No 1268
Mid Tianfu Avenue, Tianfu Software Park
Chengdu Hi-Tech Industrial Development
Zone, Chengdu, Sichuan, China
Tel.: (86) 1084053411
Cloud Data Migration Services
N.A.I.C.S.: 518210

WANdisco, Inc.   (1)
5000 Executive Pkwy Ste 270, San Ramon,
CA 94583
Tel.: (925) 380-1728
Web Site: https://cirata.com
Software Development Services
N.A.I.C.S.: 541511
Stephen Kelly (CEO)

WANdisco, Pty Ltd   (1)
Level 25 88 Phillip Street, Sydney, 2000,
NSW, Australia
Tel.: (61) 282110620
Cloud Data Migration Services
N.A.I.C.S.: 518210

CIRCA GROUP AS
Karenslyst Alle 53, 0279, Oslo, Norway
Tel.: (47) 47684244
Web Site: https://www.circa-group.com
Year Founded: 2006
CIRCA—(OSL)
Rev.: $1,812,001
Assets: $39,880,207
Liabilities: $7,437,945
Net Worth: $32,442,262
Earnings: ($6,450,464)
Emp.: 17
Fiscal Year-end: 12/31/23
Renewable Gas Services
N.A.I.C.S.: 221210
Tone Leivestad (CFO)

CIRCHEM AB
Malderistvagen 3, 46830, Vargon,
Sweden
Tel.: (46) 708611780
Web Site: https://www.circhem.com
Year Founded: 2013
CRB—(DEU)
Chemical Product Mfr & Distr
N.A.I.C.S.: 325199
Andreas Wadstedt (COO)

CIRCIO HOLDING ASA
Vollsveien 19, N-1366, Lysaker, Norway
Tel.: (47) 21398810
Web Site: https://www.circio.com
TA50—(DEU)
Rev.: $923,887
Assets: $9,275,263
Liabilities: $9,038,241
Net Worth: $237,022
Earnings: ($39,986,883)
Emp.: 22
Fiscal Year-end: 12/31/22
Biotechnology Research & Development Services
N.A.I.C.S.: 541714
Oystein Soug (Interim CFO)

**CIRCLE INTERNATIONAL
HOLDINGS LIMITED**
Unit E-03A-3 Block E Setiawalk Per-

siaran Wawasan Pusat Bandar, Puchong, 47160, Selangor Darul Ehsan,
Malaysia
Tel.: (60) 386001931   Ky
Web Site:
http://www.circlecorpgroup.com
Year Founded: 2009
Rev.: $3,175,169
Assets: $6,993,077
Liabilities: $5,092,972
Net Worth: $1,900,105
Earnings: $813,808
Fiscal Year-end: 12/31/17
Investment Holding Company
N.A.I.C.S.: 551112
Brian Tan (Founder)

CIRCLE OIL PLC
58 South Mall, Cork, Ireland
Tel.: (353) 61319366   IE
Web Site: http://www.circleoil.net
Sales Range: $75-99.9 Million
Emp.: 31
Oil & Gas Exploration Services
N.A.I.C.S.: 213112
Stephen Ian Jenkins (Chm)

Subsidiaries:

Circle Oil Oman Limited   (1)
Al Khuwair 25 College Street Way No 4927
Villa No 2084, PO Box No 270, 134, Muscat, Oman
Tel.: (968) 24483006
Sales Range: $50-74.9 Million
Emp.: 3
Oil & Gas Exploration Services
N.A.I.C.S.: 213112
Hassan Husain Al Lawati (Gen Mgr)

CIRCLE PROPERTY PLC
15 Duke Street St Jamess, London,
SW1Y 6DB, United Kingdom
Tel.: (44) 2079308503   JE
Web Site:
http://www.circleproperty.co.uk
Year Founded: 2002
CRC—(AIM)
Rev.: $13,430,121
Assets: $194,601,285
Liabilities: $89,507,897
Net Worth: $105,093,388
Earnings: ($3,442,253)
Fiscal Year-end: 03/31/21
Real Estate Investment Services
N.A.I.C.S.: 531210
John Arnold (CEO)

**CIRCLE RING NETWORK SDN
BHD**
No 8 & 10 Jalan Jurutera U1/23
Seksyen U1, Shah Alam, 40150, Selangor, Malaysia
Tel.: (60) 378054441   MY
Year Founded: 1995
Electronic Water Meters Mfr & Distr
N.A.I.C.S.: 334419
Hamidon Abdullah (Chm)

CIRCLE S.P.A.
Via Bombrini 13/3, 16149, Genoa,
Italy
Tel.: (39) 0108691015
Web Site: http://www.circletouch.eu
Year Founded: 2012
CIRC—(ITA)
Sales Range: Less than $1 Million
Logistics Consulting Servies
N.A.I.C.S.: 541614
Luca Abatello (Owner, Pres & CEO)

**CIRCLEPRINTERS HOLDING
BV**
Sprendlingenstraat 48, Oisterwijk,
5061KN, Netherlands
Tel.: (31) 13 440 02 13
Web Site: http://circleprinters.nl
Printing Services

CirclePrinters Holding BV—(Continued)

N.A.I.C.S.: 323120

Subsidiaries:

Antok Nyomdaipari Kft   **(1)**
Epitok Utja 1, Celldomolk, Gyor, 9500, Hungary
Tel.: (36) 95 525 060
Web Site: http://www.antok.hu
Commercial Printing Mfr
N.A.I.C.S.: 323111
Paul Hochbaum (Mng Dir)

Senefelder Misset B.V.   **(1)**
Mercuriusstraat 35, Doetinchem, 7006 RK, Netherlands
Tel.: (31) 4355500
Web Site: http://www.senefelder.nl
Book Periodical & Newspaper Merchant Whslr
N.A.I.C.S.: 424920
Tim Pott (Sls Mgr)

CIRCUIT FABOLOGY MICRO-ELECTRONICS EQUIPMENT CO., LTD.

789 Changning Avenue, High-Tech District, Hefei, 230000, Anhui, China
Tel.: (86) 55163823652
Web Site: https://www.cfmee.com
Year Founded: 2015
688630—(SHG)
Rev.: $91,579,635
Assets: $217,151,275
Liabilities: $69,856,961
Net Worth: $147,294,314
Earnings: $19,176,534
Fiscal Year-end: 12/31/22
Electronic Product Mfr & Distr
N.A.I.C.S.: 334419
Zhuo Cheng (Chm)

CIRCUIT SYSTEMS (INDIA) LIMITED

B-24 GIDC Electronics Estate Sector-25, Gandhinagar, 382044, Gujarat, India
Tel.: (91) 79 2328 7086
Web Site: http://www.mycsil.com
Rev.: $3,515,273
Assets: $4,908,253
Liabilities: $1,723,705
Net Worth: $3,184,549
Earnings: $242,552
Emp.: 65
Fiscal Year-end: 03/31/16
Printed Circuit Board Mfr
N.A.I.C.S.: 334412
Paresh N. Vasani (Founder & CEO)

CIRCULAR WATERS SOLUTIONS S.R.L

Str. Emil Racovita 26B Vila 41, Parter Biroul nr. 7 Voluntari, Ilfov, 77190, Romania
Tel.: (40) 726313279
Year Founded: 2024
Waste Treatment Services
N.A.I.C.S.: 221310

Subsidiaries:

WABAG Water Services SRL   **(1)**
Dimitrie Pompeiu Blv No 6E 13th floor, 2nd District, 020337, Bucharest, Romania
Tel.: (40) 371604200
Web Site: http://www.wabag.ro
Emp.: 100
Water Treatment Plant Construction Services
N.A.I.C.S.: 221310

CIRCUTECH INTERNATIONAL HOLDINGS LIMITED

Unit 1001 10/F Houston Centre 63 Mody Road Tsim Sha Tsui East, Kowloon, China (Hong Kong)
Tel.: (852) 34687748   **Ky**
Web Site: https://www.circutech.com

8051—(HKG)
Rev.: $46,940,400
Assets: $22,106,588
Liabilities: $1,700,978
Net Worth: $20,405,610
Earnings: $691,178
Emp.: 32
Fiscal Year-end: 12/31/22
Surveillance Equipment Mfr & Distr
N.A.I.C.S.: 334511
Han Chun-Wei (CFO & Exec Dir)

Subsidiaries:

Signal Communications Limited   **(1)**
Units 1905-1906 19/F Tins Enterprises Centre 777 Lai Chi Kok Road, Kowloon, China (Hong Kong)
Tel.: (852) 29955992
Web Site: https://www.teleeye.com
Video Equipment Distr
N.A.I.C.S.: 423410

CIRKEL GMBH & CO.KG

Flaesheimer Strasse 605, 45721, Recklinghausen, Germany
Tel.: (49) 236493810
Web Site: http://www.cirkel.de
Year Founded: 1898
Rev.: $70,349,400
Emp.: 120
Construction Product Mfr
N.A.I.C.S.: 423320
Attila Dal (Co-Mng Dir)

CIRMAKER TECHNOLOGY CORPORATION

No 8 Lane 377 Chung Cheng Road Feng Yeh Li Yang Mei, Taoyuan, 326, Taiwan
Tel.: (886) 32821006
CRKT—(OTCIQ)
Sales Range: Less than $1 Million
Electronic Components Mfr
N.A.I.C.S.: 334419
Kam Kwan Chu (Pres & CEO)

CIRRUS NETWORKS HOLDINGS LIMITED

Level 28 108 St Georges Tce, Perth, 6000, WA, Australia
Tel.: (61) 861804222
Web Site: http://www.cirrusnetworks.com.au
CNW—(ASX)
Rev.: $79,769,874
Assets: $31,534,446
Liabilities: $18,733,065
Net Worth: $12,801,381
Earnings: $361,158
Emp.: 203
Fiscal Year-end: 06/30/22
IT Infrastructure Building & Management Services
N.A.I.C.S.: 541519
Matthew Sullivan (CEO & Mng Dir)

CIRTEK HOLDINGS LIMITED

1 F Wing Ming Industrial Centre 15 Cheung Yue Street Lai Chi Kok, Kowloon, China (Hong Kong)
Tel.: (852) 24878865   **Ky**
Web Site: https://www.cirtek.com
Year Founded: 2019
1433—(HKG)
Rev.: $52,092,930
Assets: $50,371,043
Liabilities: $19,865,393
Net Worth: $30,505,650
Earnings: $1,601,145
Emp.: 1,164
Fiscal Year-end: 12/31/22
Holding Company
N.A.I.C.S.: 551112
Barry Sing Ming Chan (Chm)

Subsidiaries:

Charming Printing Limited   **(1)**

Room H01 10/F Universal Industrial Centre 19-25 Shan Mei St, Fotan, China (Hong Kong)
Tel.: (852) 21361430
Printing Product Mfr & Distr
N.A.I.C.S.: 323111

CIRTEK HOLDINGS PHILIPPINES CORP.

116 East Main Avenue Phase V SEZ Laguna Technopark, Binan, Laguna, Philippines
Tel.: (63) 49 5412310
Web Site: http://www.cirtekholdings.com
Year Founded: 1984
Holding Company; Electronics
N.A.I.C.S.: 551112
Jerry Liu (Chm)

Subsidiaries:

Cirtek Electronics Corporation   **(1)**
116 East Main Avenue Phase V SEZ Laguna Technopark, Binan, 4024, Laguna, Philippines
Tel.: (63) 495412310
Web Site: http://www.cirtek-electronics.com
Semiconductor Mfr
N.A.I.C.S.: 334413
Jorge S. Aguilar (Pres)

Quintel Technology Ltd.   **(1)**
1200 Ridgeway Ave Ste 132, Rochester, NY 14615
Tel.: (585) 420-8720
Web Site: http://www.quintelsolutions.com
Wireless Communication Product Mfr
N.A.I.C.S.: 517112
David Barker (CTO & Dir-Tech Applications)

CIS CO., LTD.

88 Uisadang-daero, Yeongdeungpo-gu, Seoul, Korea (South)
Tel.: (82) 232765871
Year Founded: 2015
222080—(KRS)
Financial Investment Management Services
N.A.I.C.S.: 523940
Dong-Jin Kim (CEO)

Subsidiaries:

Creative & Innovative System Co., Ltd.   **(1)**
37 Palgong-ro 47-gil, Dong-gu, Daegu, 701170, Korea (South)
Tel.: (82) 53 593 1552
Web Site: http://www.cisro.co.kr
Electrode, Battery & Other Related Equipment Mfr
N.A.I.C.S.: 335999
Soo-ha Kim (CEO)

CIS PROMOTION

116 Quai Charles Roissard, Chambery, 73000, Savoie, France
Tel.: (33) 479691645
Web Site: http://www.cis-promotion.com
Rev.: $20,500,000
Emp.: 25
Real Estate Agents & Managers
N.A.I.C.S.: 531210
Jean-Jacques Bellemin Comte (Gen Mgr)

CISALFA SPORT S.P.A.

Via Lega Lombarda Curno,, 24035, Lombardia, Italy
Tel.: (39) 07461736143
Web Site: https://www.cisalfasport.it
Emp.: 1,543
Sports Apparel
N.A.I.C.S.: 458110

CISCAR

77-81 ter Rue Marcel Dassault, 92100, Paris, France
Tel.: (33) 180052323
Web Site: http://www.ciscar.fr

Industrial Machinery & Equipment Whslr
N.A.I.C.S.: 423830
Jean-Claude Noyer (Chm)

CISCOM CORP.

20 Bay Street Suite 1110, Toronto, M5J 2N8, ON, Canada
Tel.: (416) 366-9727
Web Site: https://ciscomcorp.com
Year Founded: 2020
CISC—(CNSX)
Emp.: 100
Holding Company
N.A.I.C.S.: 551112
Drew A. Reid (Exec Chm & CEO)

Subsidiaries:

Prospect Media Group Ltd.   **(1)**
300-129 Spadina Ave Ste 300, Toronto, M5V 2L3, ON, Canada
Tel.: (416) 348-7386
Web Site: http://www.prospectmedia.com
Sales Range: $25-49.9 Million
Emp.: 35
Marketing & Promotional Services
N.A.I.C.S.: 541613
David G. Maples (Pres)

CISEN PHARMACEUTICAL CO., LTD.

Tongji Sci-Tech Industrial Park High-Tech Industrial DevelopmentZone, Jining, 272073, Shandong, China
Tel.: (86) 5372989199
Web Site: https://www.cisen-pharma.com
Year Founded: 1998
603367—(SHG)
Rev.: $570,878,811
Assets: $956,836,263
Liabilities: $204,878,672
Net Worth: $751,957,591
Earnings: $49,150,207
Emp.: 4,000
Fiscal Year-end: 12/31/22
Pharmaceuticals Product Mfr
N.A.I.C.S.: 325412

Subsidiaries:

Cisen Pharmaceuticals India Private Limited   **(1)**
Plot No S-86 Phase II-C Verna Industrial Estate, Verna, Goa, 403722, India
Tel.: (91) 8322783282
Web Site: https://www.cisenindia.com
Pharmaceutical Services
N.A.I.C.S.: 621610

CISTOCA A.D.

Brace Podgornika 2, Banja Luka, Bosnia & Herzegovina
Tel.: (387) 51 304 477
Web Site: http://www.cistocabl.com
Year Founded: 1955
CIST—(BANJ)
Sales Range: Less than $1 Million
Emp.: 241
Waste Collection Services
N.A.I.C.S.: 562119
Miodrag Kaurin (Chm-Mgmt Bd)

CITA MINERAL INVESTINDO TBK

Panin Bank Building 2nd Floor Jl Jend Sudirman Kav 1, Senayan, Jakarta Pusat, 10270, Indonesia
Tel.: (62) 217251344
Web Site: https://www.citamineral.com
Year Founded: 1992
CITA—(INDO)
Rev.: $213,828,972
Assets: $404,206,484
Liabilities: $45,646,850
Net Worth: $358,559,634
Earnings: $46,666,195
Emp.: 436

Fiscal Year-end: 12/31/23
Metal Mining Services
N.A.I.C.S.: 213114
Harry Kesuma Tanoto *(Chm)*

CITADEL CAPITAL S.A.E.
1089 Corniche El-Nil Four Seasons
Nile Plaza Office Building, Garden
City, 11519, Cairo, Egypt
Tel.: (20) 227914440   EG
Web Site: https://qalaaholdings.com
Year Founded: 2004
Privater Equity Firm
N.A.I.C.S.: 523999
Ahmed Hassanein Heikal *(Co-Founder & Chm)*

Subsidiaries:

ASEC Cement Co.   **(1)**
Kafr El Elw-Helwan z, PO Box 11421,
Cairo, Egypt
Tel.: (20) 250107719
Web Site: http://www.asec-egypt.com
Cement Manufacturing
N.A.I.C.S.: 327310

Rally Energy Limited   **(1)**
444 5th Ave SW Ste 1120, Calgary, T2P
2T8, AB, Canada
Tel.: (403) 538-0000
Sales Range: $50-74.9 Million
Emp.: 65
Oil & Gas Exploration Services
N.A.I.C.S.: 211120

CITADEL REALTY & DEVELOPERS LTD.
Marathon FutureX, N M Joshi Marg
Lower Parel West, Mumbai, 400 013,
India
Tel.: (91) 2262638200
Web Site: https://www.citadelrealty.in
502445—(BOM)
Rev.: $343,734
Assets: $3,979,876
Liabilities: $2,613,279
Net Worth: $1,366,597
Earnings: $59,173
Fiscal Year-end: 03/31/22
Civil Engineering Services
N.A.I.C.S.: 237990
Sundaram Ramamurthi *(CEO)*

CITAGLOBAL BERHAD
Tingkat 9 Blok 4 Menara TH Plaza
Sentral Jalan Stesen Sentral 5,
50470, Kuala Lumpur, 50470, Malaysia
Tel.: (60) 327738800   MY
Web Site: https://www.wzs.my
Year Founded: 2004
CITAGLB—(KLS)
Rev.: $45,594,921
Assets: $101,388,571
Liabilities: $34,110,265
Net Worth: $67,278,307
Earnings: ($8,782,011)
Emp.: 369
Fiscal Year-end: 12/31/22
Holding Company; Steel Producer
N.A.I.C.S.: 551112
Uzir Ubaidillah *(Vice Chm)*

Subsidiaries:

Citaglobal Capital Sdn. Bhd.   **(1)**
3B-3-5 Tingkat 3 Blok 3B, Menara TH Plaza
Sentral Jalan Stesen Sentral 5, 50470,
Kuala Lumpur, Wilayah Persekutuan, Malaysia
Tel.: (60) 327738800
Web Site: https://citaglobalcapital.my
Financial Services
N.A.I.C.S.: 523999

WZS BinaRaya Sdn Bhd   **(1)**
No 28-3 Jalan PJU 5/17 Dataran Sunway
Kota Damansara, 47810, Petaling Jaya,
Selangor Darul Ehsan, Malaysia
Tel.: (60) 361568693
Web Site: http://www.wzsbinaraya.com

Civil Engineering Services
N.A.I.C.S.: 541330
Choi Chee Ken *(Co-Founder)*

WZS Misi Setia Sdn Bhd   **(1)**
A-1-5 Endah Promenade Jalan 3/149E Taman Sri Endah, Bandar Baru Sri Petaling,
57000, Kuala Lumpur, Malaysia
Tel.: (60) 390589000
Web Site: http://www.msog.com.my
Oil & Gas Pipeline Construction Services
N.A.I.C.S.: 237120

CITAIR INC.
73 Mill Street, Hensall, N0M 1X0,
ON, Canada
Tel.: (519) 262-2600
Web Site:
    http://Www.generalcoachcan.com
Year Founded: 1950
Sales Range: $25-49.9 Million
Emp.: 120
Mobile Home Mfr
N.A.I.C.S.: 321992
Roger W. Faulkner *(Pres)*

CITATION RESOURCES LIMITED
Level 1 Wesley Central 8-12 Market
Street, Fremantle, 6160, WA, Australia
Tel.: (61) 8 9431 9888   AU
Web Site: http://www.citation.net.au
Sales Range: $1-9.9 Million
Coal Mining & Processing Services
N.A.I.C.S.: 213113

CITECH CO., LTD.
11F 932Yangjae-daero Songpa-gu,
Seoul, Korea (South)
Web Site: http://www.citech.kr
Year Founded: 2006
004920—(KRS)
Rev.: $43,505,339
Assets: $72,638,273
Liabilities: $31,836,320
Net Worth: $40,801,954
Earnings: ($504,431)
Emp.: 67
Fiscal Year-end: 12/31/22
Information Technology Services
N.A.I.C.S.: 541512
Kim Jong-Seo *(Pres)*

CITI PROPERTIES REIT
Bul Dzheyms Baucher 23, Sofia,
1164, Bulgaria
Tel.: (359) 24224947
CITP—(BUL)
Sales Range: Less than $1 Million
Real Estate Services
N.A.I.C.S.: 531390

CITIBASE HOLDINGS PLC
Mount Manor House 16 The Mount
Guildford, Surrey, GU2 4HN, United
Kingdom
Tel.: (44) 2078087444
Web Site: http://www.citibase.co.uk
Sales Range: $25-49.9 Million
Emp.: 75
Holding Company; Office Leasing
Services
N.A.I.C.S.: 551112
David Joseph *(Co-Founder)*

CITIC GROUP CORPORATION
CITIC Tower Guanghualu, Chaoyang
District, Beijing, 100020, China
Tel.: (86) 1064660088   CN
Web Site: https://www.group.citic
Year Founded: 1979
Sales Range: Less than $1 Million
Holding Company
N.A.I.C.S.: 551112
Jiong Wang *(Vice Chm & Pres)*

Subsidiaries:

Asia Satellite Telecommunications
Holdings Limited   **(1)**
12/F Harbour Centre 25 Harbour Road,
Wanchai, China (Hong Kong)
Tel.: (852) 25000888
Web Site: http://www.asiasat.com
Rev.: $184,072,286
Assets: $921,704,344
Liabilities: $457,659,986
Net Worth: $464,044,358
Earnings: $54,814,891
Emp.: 133
Fiscal Year-end: 12/31/2018
Satellite Telecommunication Services
N.A.I.C.S.: 517410
Sue Ching Yeung *(CFO & Sec)*

Subsidiary (Domestic):

Asia Satellite Telecommunications
Co., Ltd.   **(2)**
15 Dai Kwai Street, Tai Po Industrial Estate,
Hong Kong, New Territories, China (Hong
Kong)
Tel.: (852) 25000888
Web Site: http://www.asiasat.com
Sales Range: $25-49.9 Million
Emp.: 50
Satellite Telecommunication Services
N.A.I.C.S.: 517410
Sabrina Cubbon *(Gen Mgr-Mktg)*

Bohai Aluminium Industries Ltd.   **(1)**
95 Beihuan Rd, Halgang District, Qinhuangdao, Hebei, China
Tel.: (86) 335302000000
Web Site: http://www.bail.com.cn
Aluminium Whslr
N.A.I.C.S.: 331313

CITIC Assets Management Corporation Ltd.   **(1)**
3/F Office Tower A Donghuan Plaza 9
Dongzhongjie, Dongcheng District, Beijing,
100027, China
Tel.: (86) 10 64196666
Web Site: http://amc.ecitic.com
Private Equity Investment & Asset Management Services
N.A.I.C.S.: 523940
Zhiqiang Liu *(Chm)*

CITIC Automobile Co., Ltd.   **(1)**
8 Fangyuan Nanjie St, Chaoyang District,
Lanzhou, 471039, China   **(100%)**
Tel.: (86) 64359780
Web Site: http://www.citic.com
Sales Range: $25-49.9 Million
Emp.: 50
N.A.I.C.S.: 336340

CITIC Bohai Aluminium Industries
Holding Company Ltd.   **(1)**
89 Beihuanlu, Haigang District, Qinhuangdao, 066003, Hebei, China **(100%)**
Tel.: (86) 3353181757
Web Site: http://www.bolv.citic
Fabricated Aluminum Mfr
N.A.I.C.S.: 331315

CITIC Capital Holdings Limited   **(1)**
28/F CITIC Tower 1 Tim Mei Avenue, Central, China (Hong Kong)
Tel.: (852) 37106888
Web Site: http://www.citiccapital.com
Privater Equity Firm
N.A.I.C.S.: 523999
Annie Fung *(Sr Mng Dir & COO)*

Subsidiary (Domestic):

Amoy Food Ltd.   **(2)**
11-15 Dai Fu Street Tai Po Estate, Tai Po
Industrial Estate, Tai Po, NT, China (Hong
Kong)   **(90.4%)**
Tel.: (852) 26656633
Web Site: http://www.amoy.com
Asian Sauces & Frozen Dim Sum Mfr
N.A.I.C.S.: 311941

Holding (Non-US):

AsiaInfo, Inc.   **(2)**
East Area No 10, Xibeiwang East Road,
Beijing, 100193, China
Tel.: (86) 10 82166688
Web Site: http://www.asiainfo.com

Sales Range: $500-549.9 Million
Emp.: 11,246
Holding Company; Telecom Network Integration & Software Solution Services
N.A.I.C.S.: 551112
Edward Suning Tian *(Chm)*

Subsidiary (Non-US):

AsiaInfo International Pte. Ltd.   **(3)**
51 Goldhill Plaza #12-06, Singapore,
308900, Singapore
Tel.: (65) 6355 0248
Information Technology Consulting Services
N.A.I.C.S.: 541512

Subsidiary (US):

Lenovo-AsiaInfo Technologies,
Inc   **(3)**
2137 Hwy Rt 35, Holmdel, NJ 07733
Tel.: (732) 383-9066
Web Site: http://www.lenovoai.com
Computer Equipment & Software Whslr
N.A.I.C.S.: 423430
Jian Qi *(Chm)*

Subsidiary (US):

CITIC Capital Partners LLC   **(2)**
1120 Avenue Of The Americas Ste 1501,
New York, NY 10022
Tel.: (212) 395-9767
Web Site: http://www.citiccapital.com
Sales Range: $50-74.9 Million
Emp.: 10
Privater Equity Firm
N.A.I.C.S.: 523999
Marjorie Miller *(Office Mgr)*

Holding (Domestic):

Erno Laszlo, Inc.   **(3)**
129 W 29th St, New York, NY 10001
Tel.: (212) 373-4700
Web Site: http://www.ernolaszlo.com
Dermatological Skincare Products Mfr
N.A.I.C.S.: 325412
Charles Denton *(Chm & CEO)*

Joint Venture (Domestic):

OmniVision Technologies, Inc.   **(3)**
4275 Burton Dr, Santa Clara, CA 95054
Tel.: (408) 567-3000
Web Site: https://www.ovt.com
Sales Range: $1-4.9 Billion
Emp.: 2,176
Image Sensors Mfr
N.A.I.C.S.: 334413
Anson Chan *(CFO & VP-Fin)*

Subsidiary (Non-US):

OmniVision Technologies (Shanghai)
Co., Ltd.   **(4)**
No 88 Shangke Road, Pudong District,
Shanghai, 201210, China
Tel.: (86) 216 175 9888
Web Site: http://www.ovt.com
Electronic Parts Whslr
N.A.I.C.S.: 423690

OmniVision Technologies Singapore
Pte. Ltd   **(4)**
3A International Business Park 06-07/08
Tower A ICON IBP, 06-07/08 Tower A ICON
IBP, Singapore, 609935, Singapore
Tel.: (65) 6 933 1933
Web Site: http://www.ovt.com
Digital Imaging Sensor Chip Mfr
N.A.I.C.S.: 334413

Joint Venture (Domestic):

The Colibri Group, Inc.   **(3)**
25 Fairmount Ave, East Providence, RI
02914
Tel.: (401) 943-2100
Web Site: http://www.colibri.com
Sales Range: $100-124.9 Million
Mfr & Distr of Jewelry, Lighters, Accessories
& Clocks; Owned by Founders Equity Inc.,
Main Street Resources & CITIC Group
N.A.I.C.S.: 423940
Yazir Phelps *(CMO)*

Subsidiary (Domestic):

Western Schools, Inc.   **(4)**
PO Box 1930, Brockton, MA 02303-1930

CITIC Group Corporation—(Continued)

Tel.: (508) 638-7000
Web Site: http://www.westernschools.com
Home Study Continuing Education (for Nurses)
N.A.I.C.S.: 611710

Holding (Non-US):

Trilogy International Limited (2)
Level 6 Chelsea House 85 Fort Street, Auckland, 1010, New Zealand
Tel.: (64) 9 367 9486
Web Site: http://www.trilogyproducts.com
Fragrances, Soaps, Skincare & Candles Whslr & Mfr
N.A.I.C.S.: 325620

CITIC Development Co., Ltd. (1)
Capital Mansion 6 Xinyuan Nanlu, Beijing, 100004, China
Tel.: (86) 10 646 62243
Financial Services
N.A.I.C.S.: 523999

CITIC GSI Tomida Group Co., Ltd. (1)
The Business Building Second Happiness Village, Chayang District, Beijing, China
Tel.: (86) 1064673002
Textiles Mfr & Distr
N.A.I.C.S.: 313310

CITIC Guoan Group Co., Ltd. (1)
Guoan Mansion 7th Floor One Guoan Dong Dian Street, Dong Da Qiao, Chao Yang District, Beijing, 100020, China (50%)
Tel.: (86) 10 695 3760
Web Site: http://www.guoan.citic.com
Sales Range: $1-4.9 Billion
Emp.: 11,059
Industrial Development Services
N.A.I.C.S.: 925120

Subsidiary (Domestic):

CITIC Guoan Information Industry Co., Ltd. (2)
Guoan Mansion 1 Guoan Dong Beije, Chaoyang District, Beijing, 100020, China (100%)
Tel.: (86) 10 6501 0855
Web Site: http://www.guoan.citic.com
Sales Range: $50-74.9 Million
Emp.: 60
Investment Holdings; Industrial Development Services
N.A.I.C.S.: 523999

Subsidiary (Non-US):

Guoan International Limited (2)
15th Floor of Tower II Admiralty Centre, 18 Harcourt Road, Hong Kong, China (Hong Kong)
Tel.: (852) 35858700
Web Site: http://www.guoanintl.com
Rev.: $26,682,828
Assets: $132,362,203
Liabilities: $91,803,391
Net Worth: $40,558,812
Earnings: ($5,982,365)
Emp.: 108
Fiscal Year-end: 12/31/2019
Mobile Product Whslr
N.A.I.C.S.: 423690
Jun Du (Chm)

CITIC Heavy Machinery Co., Ltd. (1)
206 Jianshe Road, Jianxi District Luoyang, Guangzhou, 471039, Henan, China
Tel.: (86) 379 6408 8888
Web Site: http://www.chmc.citic.com
Heavy Machinery Mfr
N.A.I.C.S.: 333248

CITIC Hong Kong (Holdings) Ltd. (1)
32nd Fl Citic Tower 1 Tim Mei Ave, Central, China (Hong Kong)
Tel.: (852) 28202111
Sales Range: $100-124.9 Million
Emp.: 200
Holding Company
N.A.I.C.S.: 551112
Chang Ming (Chm)

CITIC Institute of Architecture & Design Research (1)
Capital Mansion 6 Xinyuannanlu, 100004, Beijing, China (100%)

Tel.: (86) 10 6466 0088
Web Site: http://www.whadi.com.cn
Sales Range: $25-49.9 Million
Emp.: 200
Contract Engineering Services
N.A.I.C.S.: 541330

CITIC International Contracting Inc. (1)
22/F Tower A TYG Center C2 Dongsanhuanbeilu, Chaoyang District, Beijing, 100027, China
Tel.: (86) 10 59660133
Construction Engineering Services
N.A.I.C.S.: 541330

CITIC Investment Holdings Ltd. (1)
15/F Capital Mansion 6 Xinyuannanlu, Chaoyang District, Beijing, 100004, China
Tel.: (86) 10 84861511
Web Site: http://www.invest.citic.com
Holding Company
N.A.I.C.S.: 551112

CITIC Ltd. (1)
32nd Floor CITIC Tower 1 Tim Mai Avenue, Central, China (Hong Kong) (77.9%)
Tel.: (852) 28202111
Web Site: https://www.citic.com
Rev.: $71,319,362,020
Net Worth: $130,094,645,160
Earnings: $10,438,093,440
Emp.: 135,304
Fiscal Year-end: 12/31/2020
Holding Company; Telecommunications, Power Generation, Property Investment & Industrial Manufacturing
N.A.I.C.S.: 551112
Jiong Wang (Vice Chm & Co-Pres)

Subsidiary (Non-US):

CITIC Australia Pty. Ltd. (2)
CITIC House Level 7 99 King St, Melbourne, 3000, VIC, Australia (100%)
Tel.: (61) 396148000
Sales Range: $50-74.9 Million
Emp.: 45
Investment & Trading Services
N.A.I.C.S.: 523999
Chen Zeng (Mng Dir)

Subsidiary (Domestic):

CITIC Australia Trading Limited (3)
Level 7 CITIC House 99 King St, 3000, Melbourne, VIC, Australia
Tel.: (61) 396148000
Aluminium & Alumina Mfg
N.A.I.C.S.: 331313
Tinghu Guo (Mng Dir)

Subsidiary (Non-US):

CITIC Envirotech Ltd (2)
10 Science Park Road 01-01 The Alpha, Singapore, 117684, Singapore
Tel.: (65) 6774 7298
Web Site: http://www.unitedenvirotech.com
Rev.: $727,292,764
Assets: $2,769,408,327
Liabilities: $1,764,468,182
Net Worth: $1,004,940,145
Earnings: $82,771,599
Emp.: 1,740
Fiscal Year-end: 12/31/2018
Holding Company; Engineering Services
N.A.I.C.S.: 551112
Lin Fong Ngoo (CFO)

Subsidiary (Non-US):

Dataran Tenaga (M) Sdn. Bhd. (3)
No 88 Jalan Mutiara Emas 7/5 Taman Mount Austin, Johor Bahru, 81100, Johor, Malaysia (100%)
Tel.: (60) 73534062
Web Site: http://www.datarantenaga.com.my
Pump Distr
N.A.I.C.S.: 423830

Subsidiary (Domestic):

Memstar Pte. Ltd. (3)
11 Kian Teck Drive, Singapore, 628828, Singapore
Tel.: (65) 67752512
Web Site: http://www.memstar.com.sg
Water Filter & Membrane Products Mfr
N.A.I.C.S.: 325211
Hailin Ge (CEO-Mfg)

Subsidiary (Non-US):

NOVO Envirotech (Tianjin) Co. Ltd (3)
Tianjin Hedong Hung Xin Road, Datong Shishang Garden, Tianjin, 300160, China
Tel.: (86) 22 24587890
Web Site: http://www.unitedenvirotech.com
Environmental Engineering Services
N.A.I.C.S.: 237110

Novo Envirotech (Guangzhou) Co. Ltd (3)
5th Floor Building 7 Huangzhou Idustrial Park Chebei Road, Tianhe District, Guangzhou, 510660, China
Tel.: (86) 2038796430
Web Site: http://www.novoet.com
Environmental Engineering Services
N.A.I.C.S.: 562998

UE NOVO (Malaysia) Sdn. Bhd. (3)
No 125A Jalan Sutera Tanjung 8/2 Taman Sutera Utama, Skudai, 81300, Johor Bahru, Johor, Malaysia
Tel.: (60) 75575718
Web Site: http://www.unitedenvirotech.com
Environmental Engineering Services
N.A.I.C.S.: 541330

Subsidiary (Non-US):

CITIC Industrial Investment Group Corp., Ltd. (2)
1085 Pudong Avenue, Shanghai, 200135, China (100%)
Tel.: (86) 21 6105 3788
Sales Range: $50-74.9 Million
Holding Company; Infrastructure & Industrial Platform Investment & Asset Management Services
N.A.I.C.S.: 551112
Jiong Wang (Chm)

CITIC Metal Co., Ltd. (2)
Capital Mansion Room 1903 6 Xinyuan Nanlu, Chaoyang District, Beijing, 100004, China
Tel.: (86) 10 6443 6509
Web Site: http://www.citicmetal.com.cn
Metal Ore & Coal Mining & Resource Trading
N.A.I.C.S.: 212290

CITIC New Zealand Ltd. (2)
Level 24 ASB Bank Ct 135 Albert St, PO Box 7348, Auckland, 1015, New Zealand (100%)
Tel.: (64) 93091528
Lumber Production Services
N.A.I.C.S.: 113110

Subsidiary (Domestic):

CITIC Resources Holdings Limited (2)
Suites 6701-02 08B 67/F International Commerce Centre, 1 Austin Road West, Kowloon, China (Hong Kong) (54%)
Tel.: (852) 28998200
Web Site: http://www.citicresources.com
Rev.: $749,697,752
Assets: $1,589,781,972
Liabilities: $597,323,731
Net Worth: $992,458,241
Earnings: $178,936,189
Emp.: 206
Fiscal Year-end: 12/31/2022
Forest Products
N.A.I.C.S.: 113310
Sun Yang (Vice Chm)

CITIC Telecom International CPC Limited (2)
20th Fl Lincoln House Taikoo Pl, 979 King's Road, Quarry Bay, China (Hong Kong)
Tel.: (852) 21707101
Web Site: http://www.citictel-cpc.com
Network Communications & Security Solutions
N.A.I.C.S.: 519290
Stephen Ho (CEO)

CITIC Telecom International Holdings Limited (2)
25/F CITIC Telecom Tower 93 Kwai Fuk Road, Kwai Chung, New Territories, China (Hong Kong)
Tel.: (852) 23778888

Web Site: https://www.citictel.com
Rev.: $1,289,152,500
Assets: $2,318,077,500
Liabilities: $983,025,000
Net Worth: $1,335,052,500
Earnings: $156,060,000
Emp.: 2,530
Fiscal Year-end: 12/31/2022
Telecommunication Servicesb
N.A.I.C.S.: 517010
Yue Jiang Xin (Chm)

Joint Venture (Non-US):

Cherry Valley Farms Ltd. (2)
Cherry Valle House Laceby Business Park Grimsby Road, Grimsby, DN37 7DP, United Kingdom
Tel.: (44) 1472808400
Web Site: http://www.cherryvalley.co.uk
Duck Meat Production
N.A.I.C.S.: 112390
Richard Bird (Mng Dir)

Subsidiary (Non-US):

China CITIC Bank Corporation Limited (2)
Floors 6-30 & 32-42 Building 1 No 10 Guanghua Road, Chaoyang District, Beijing, 100020, China (67.13%)
Rev.: $29,834,736,510
Net Worth: $85,803,421,980
Earnings: $7,504,225,800
Emp.: 1,767
Fiscal Year-end: 12/31/2020
Banking Services
N.A.I.C.S.: 522110
Heying Fang (Chm, Pres & CFO)

Subsidiary (Non-US):

CITIC International Financial Holdings Limited (3)
Ste 2701 2709 CITIC Tower, 1 Tim Mei Avenue, Central, China (Hong Kong) (100%)
Tel.: (852) 36073000
Web Site: http://www.citicifh.com
Sales Range: $500-549.9 Million
Emp.: 1,500
Financial Services Holding Company
N.A.I.C.S.: 551111
Zhenming Chang (Vice Chm)

Subsidiary (Domestic):

China CITIC Bank International Limited (4)
61-65 Des Voeux Road, Central, Hong Kong, China (Hong Kong)
Tel.: (852) 36036633
Web Site: https://www.cncbinternational.com
Rev.: $1,561,982,450
Assets: $46,384,453,072
Liabilities: $40,419,786,228
Net Worth: $5,964,666,843
Earnings: $360,870,751
Emp.: 2,051
Fiscal Year-end: 12/31/2019
Commericial Banking
N.A.I.C.S.: 522110
Helen Chau Yuk Kan Ng (Head-Personal & Bus Banking)

Branch (US):

China CITIC Bank International Ltd. - Los Angeles Branch (5)
323 W Valley Blvd, Alhambra, CA 91803-3339
Tel.: (626) 282-9820
Web Site: http://www.cncbinternational.com
Sales Range: $50-74.9 Million
Emp.: 12
Banking Services
N.A.I.C.S.: 522110

China CITIC Bank International Ltd. - New York Branch (5)
410 Park Ave 18th Fl, New York, NY 10022
Tel.: (212) 588-7000
Web Site: http://www.cncbinternational.com
Commercial & International Banking
N.A.I.C.S.: 522110

Subsidiary (Domestic):

Dah Chong Hong Holdings Ltd. (2)
8/F DCH Building, 20 Kai Cheung Road, Kowloon, China (Hong Kong) (100%)

Tel.: (852) 2768 3388
Web Site: http://www.dch.com.hk
Rev.: $6,496,611,820
Assets: $3,481,212,470
Liabilities: $2,103,054,300
Net Worth: $1,378,158,170
Earnings: $120,922,430
Emp.: 17,596
Fiscal Year-end: 12/31/2018
Holding Company
N.A.I.C.S.: 551112
Ying Ha Wu *(Chief Corp Officer)*

Subsidiary (Non-US):

Nanjing Iron & Steel Co., Ltd. **(2)**
No 8 Xingfu Road Xiejiadian, Jiangbei New
Area, Nanjing, 210035, Jiangsu,
China **(55.2%)**
Tel.: (86) 2584671237
Web Site: https://www.njsteel.com
Rev.: $10,044,137,766
Assets: $10,131,881,480
Liabilities: $6,208,896,281
Net Worth: $3,922,985,199
Earnings: $294,264,233
Fiscal Year-end: 12/31/2023
Iron & Metal Product Mfr
N.A.I.C.S.: 331110
Ruirong Zhu *(Vice Chm & Pres)*

Subsidiary (Domestic):

New Hong Kong Tunnel Company
Limited **(2)**
The Administration Building NKIL 6047, Cha
Kwo Ling East Kwun Tong, Kowloon, China
(Hong Kong)
Tel.: (852) 23480011
Web Site:
    http://www.easternharbourtunnel.com.hk
Sales Range: $50-74.9 Million
Emp.: 200
Eastern Harbour Tunnel Construction &
Maintenance
N.A.I.C.S.: 488490

Sims Trading Company Ltd. **(2)**
7th Floor DCH Building, 20 Kai Cheung
Road, Kowloon, China (Hong Kong)
Tel.: (852) 22621798
Web Site: http://www.simshk.com
Sales Range: $25-49.9 Million
Emp.: 100
Consumer & Healthcare Products Importer,
Distributor & Wholesaler
N.A.I.C.S.: 424490
Glenn Robert Sturrock Smith *(CEO)*

Affiliate (Domestic):

South Manganese Investment
Limited **(2)**
23/F 28 Hennessy Road, Wanchai, China
(Hong Kong) **(43.46%)**
Tel.: (852) 21791310
Web Site: http://www.dameng.citic.com
Rev.: $563,328,276
Assets: $1,168,391,513
Liabilities: $839,354,117
Net Worth: $329,037,396
Earnings: ($59,054,009)
Emp.: 7,258
Fiscal Year-end: 12/31/2020
Manganese Mining Services
N.A.I.C.S.: 212290
Weijian Li *(Vice Chm)*

Subsidiary (Non-US):

Guangxi Start Manganese Materials
Co., Ltd. **(3)**
Hurun Town, Jingxi County, Hurun, 533803,
China
Tel.: (86) 776 6189108
Web Site: http://www.gxsdt.com
Manganese Mining Services
N.A.I.C.S.: 212290

CITIC Machinery Manufacturing Co.,
Ltd. **(1)**
Jianxi District, Luoyang, 471039, Henan,
China **(100%)**
Tel.: (86) 357 391 3008
Web Site: http://www.machine.citic.com
Sales Range: $25-49.9 Million
Emp.: 20
Heavy Machinery Mfr
N.A.I.C.S.: 333248

CITIC Networks Management Co.,
Ltd. **(1)**
1/F Capital Mansion 6 Xinyuannanlu, Cha-
oyang District, Beijing, 100004,
China **(100%)**
Tel.: (86) 10 8486 8800
Sales Range: $25-49.9 Million
Emp.: 50
Digital Network Development & Marketing
Services
N.A.I.C.S.: 541519
Wang Jiong *(Vice Chm & Pres)*

Subsidiary (Domestic):

CITIC Networks Co., Ltd. **(2)**
1/F Capital Mansion 6 Xinyuannanlu, Cha-
oyang District, Beijing, 100004, China
Tel.: (86) 10 84868800
Information Technology Services
N.A.I.C.S.: 541512

Joint Venture (Domestic):

Great Wall Broadband Network Ser-
vice Co., Ltd. **(2)**
68 ZijinBuilding Floor 17th Wanquan Road,
Haidian District, Beijing, 100086,
China **(50%)**
Tel.: (86) 1082659931
Computer Storage Technology Mfr
N.A.I.C.S.: 334112

CITIC Ningbo Group **(1)**
29 Jiangdong Road N Citic Mansion,
Ningbo, 315040, Zhejiang, China
Tel.: (86) 574 8657 3176
Real Estate Services
N.A.I.C.S.: 531390

Affiliate (Domestic):

Ningbo Daxie Development Zone **(2)**
Daxie Island Beilun District, Ningbo Devel-
opment Zone, Ningbo, 315812, Zhejiang,
China
Tel.: (86) 574 7332022
Web Site: http://www.daxie.gov.cn
Sales Range: $75-99.9 Million
Emp.: 150
Land Development Services
N.A.I.C.S.: 531390

CITIC Ocean Helecopter Co.,
Ltd. **(1)**
19th Fl Agricultural Bank Tower, 188 Jiefang
Rd W Shinzhen, Guangzhou, Guangjong,
China **(100%)**
Tel.: (86) 7555590796
Web Site: http://www.china-cohc.com
Harbor Pilot Delivery Services
N.A.I.C.S.: 532411

CITIC Private Equity Funds Manage-
ment Co., Ltd. **(1)**
11/F Jinbao Tower No 89 Jinbao Street
Dongcheng District, Beijing, 100005, China
Tel.: (86) 10 8507 9000
Web Site: http://www.citicpe.com
Privater Equity Firm
N.A.I.C.S.: 523999
Lefei Liu *(Chm & CEO)*

CITIC Publishing House **(1)**
Ta Yuan Diplomatic Office Bldg 14 Liang-
mahe St, Chaoyang District, Beijing,
100600, China
Tel.: (86) 1085323366
Web Site: http://www.publish.citic.com
Publishing Services
N.A.I.C.S.: 513199

CITIC Qinhuangdao Co., Ltd. **(1)**
Don Wang Ling Haigang District, Qin-
huangdao, 66003, Hebei, China
Tel.: (86) 353100888
Aluminum Curtain Wall, Doors & Windows
Mfr
N.A.I.C.S.: 332321

CITIC South China Group Co.,
Ltd. **(1)**
75th Fl CITIC Plz 233 Tianhe Beilu,
Guangzhou, 510613, China
Tel.: (86) 2038770068
Web Site: http://www.citicsouth.com.cn
Sales Range: $50-74.9 Million
Emp.: 50
Real Estate Investment & Property Manage-
ment Services

N.A.I.C.S.: 531390

CITIC Tianjin Investment Holding Co.,
Ltd. **(1)**
249 Huanghailu Tianjin Economic-
Technological Development Area, Tianjin,
300457, China
Tel.: (86) 22 66233996
Web Site: http://www.tianjin.citic.com
Holding Company
N.A.I.C.S.: 551112

CITIC Travel Co., Ltd. **(1)**
7th Fl Ste 2 Bld CITIC Bldg, 19 Jian-
guomenwai Dajie, Beijing, 100004,
China **(100%)**
Tel.: (86) 85263636
Web Site: http://www.citictravel.com
Sales Range: $25-49.9 Million
Emp.: 120
Provider of Travel & Tourism Services
N.A.I.C.S.: 561510

China International Economic Consul-
tants Co., Ltd. **(1)**
13th Fl Capital Mansion 6 Xinyuan Nanlu,
Chaoyang District, Beijing, 100004,
China **(100%)**
Tel.: (86) 1084861313
Web Site: http://www.ciec.cc
Consulting Services
N.A.I.C.S.: 541618

Jiangyin Xingcheng Special Steel
Works Co., Ltd. **(1)**
No 297 Binjiang East Road, 214400, Ji-
angyin, Jiangsu, China
Tel.: (86) 51086271692
Web Site: http://www.jyxc.com
Special Steel Manufacturing
N.A.I.C.S.: 331110

Macao Cement Manufacturing Co.,
Ltd. **(1)**
Estrada De Nossa Senhora De Ka Ho, PO
Box 1106, Coloane, Macau, China
(Macau) **(100%)**
Tel.: (853) 28870511
Web Site: http://www.mocement.com.mo
Cement Mfr
N.A.I.C.S.: 327310

CITIC GUOAN WINE CO., LTD.
No 39 Hongshan Road, Urumqi,
830002, Xinjiang, China
Tel.: (86) 9918881238
Web Site: http://www.guoanwine.com
Year Founded: 1997
600084—(SHG)
Rev.: $20,553,675
Assets: $193,739,294
Liabilities: $21,838,799
Net Worth: $171,900,495
Earnings: ($123,673,306)
Fiscal Year-end: 12/31/22
Wine Mfr & Distr
N.A.I.C.S.: 312130
Wang Yi *(Chm)*

CITIC HEAVY INDUSTRIES CO., LTD.
206 Jianshe Road, Jianxi District, Lu-
oyang, 471039, Henan, China
Tel.: (86) 37964088999
Web Site:
    https://citicheavyindustries.com
Year Founded: 1956
601608—(SHG)
Rev.: $1,239,310,196
Assets: $2,738,146,676
Liabilities: $1,637,082,252
Net Worth: $1,101,064,424
Earnings: $20,430,573
Fiscal Year-end: 12/31/22
Industrial Machinery Mfr & Distr
N.A.I.C.S.: 333248
Wuhan Qi *(Chm)*

Subsidiaries:

CITIC HIC Australia Pty. Ltd. **(1)**
Level 2 Small Tower Gateway Business
Park 63 Parramatta Road, Silverwater,
2128, NSW, Australia

N.A.I.C.S.: 531390

Tel.: (61) 297355600
Industrial Machinery & Equipment Distr
N.A.I.C.S.: 423830

CITIC HIC Gandara Censa
S.A.U. **(1)**
36400 Porrino, Pontevedra, Spain
Tel.: (34) 986346000
Web Site: http://www.citic-censa.com
Mining Machinery & Equipment Mfr
N.A.I.C.S.: 333131

CITIC HIC North America Co.,
Ltd. **(1)**
6500 Trans Canada Ste 320, Pointe-Claire,
H9R 0A5, QC, Canada
Tel.: (514) 447-6111
Industrial Machinery Mfr
N.A.I.C.S.: 333248

CITIC Heavy Industries Chile
SpA. **(1)**
Av Isidora Goyenechea 2939 7th Floor - of
702, Las Condes, Santiago, Chile
Tel.: (56) 223039390
Industrial Machinery & Equipment Distr
N.A.I.C.S.: 423830

CITIC Heavy Industries South Africa
Pty Ltd. **(1)**
8th Floor Convention Towers Cnr Heeren-
gracht and Coen Steytler Rd, Cape Town,
South Africa
Tel.: (27) 214014560
Industrial Machinery & Equipment Distr
N.A.I.C.S.: 423830

CITIC SMCC Process Technology Pty
Ltd. **(1)**
Cnr Coonan St and Riverview Tce Unit 201
167 Connan Street, Indooroopilly, Brisbane,
4068, QLD, Australia
Tel.: (61) 737203200
Industrial Machinery & Equipment Distr
N.A.I.C.S.: 423830

CITIC-Heavy Industries Co., Ltd. **(1)**
6500 Trans Canada Suite 320, Pointe-
Claire, H9R 0A5, QC, Canada
Tel.: (514) 447-6111
Industrial Machinery & Equipment Distr
N.A.I.C.S.: 423830

Citic Heavy Industries Brasil **(1)**
Rua Ministro Orozimbo Nonato no 102 sala
2003 Torre B, Vila da Serra, Nova Lima,
34006-053, Minas Gerais, Brazil
Tel.: (55) 3135895600
Web Site: http://citicbrasil.com.br
Construction Machinery Mfr & Distr
N.A.I.C.S.: 333120

CITIC OFFSHORE HELICOP-TER CO., LTD.
Shenzhen Helicopter Field No 3533
Nanhai Avenue, Nanshan District,
Shenzhen, 518052, Guangdong,
China
Tel.: (86) 75526723146
Web Site: http://www.cohc.citic
Year Founded: 1999
000099—(SSE)
Rev.: $252,454,644
Assets: $907,503,480
Liabilities: $188,482,788
Net Worth: $719,020,692
Earnings: $27,269,892
Fiscal Year-end: 12/31/22
Aviation Transportation & Mainte-
nance Services
N.A.I.C.S.: 488119
Yang Wei *(Chm)*

CITIC PACIFIC SPECIAL STEEL GROUP CO., LTD.
CITIC Special Steel Building No 1
Changshan Avenue, Wuxi, Jiangyin,
214422, Jiangsu, China
Tel.: (86) 7146297373
Web Site: http://en.citicsteel.com
Year Founded: 1993
000708—(SSE)
Rev.: $13,807,597,284
Assets: $12,744,756,648

CITIC Pacific Special Steel Group Co., Ltd.—(Continued)

Liabilities: $7,628,954,112
Net Worth: $5,115,802,536
Earnings: $997,595,352
Emp.: 40,000
Fiscal Year-end: 12/31/22
Steel Products Mfr
N.A.I.C.S.: 331221
Qian Gang (Chm)

CITIC PRESS CORPORATION
3rd 5th 6th 9th 18th Floor Building A
Jiaming Center, No 27 North East
Third Ring Road Chaoyang District,
Beijing, 100029, China
Tel.: (86) 1084156171
Web Site: http://www.press.citic
Year Founded: 1993
300788—(SSE)
Rev.: $252,822,492
Assets: $448,323,876
Liabilities: $160,765,020
Net Worth: $287,558,856
Earnings: $17,703,036
Fiscal Year-end: 12/31/22
Books Publishing Services
N.A.I.C.S.: 513130
Bin Wang (Chm)

CITIC SECURITIES CO., LTD.
10F CITIC Securities Tower No 48
Liangmaqiao Road, Chaoyang District, Beijing, 100026, China
Tel.: (86) 1060836030   CN
Web Site: https://www.cs.ecitic.com
Year Founded: 1995
CIIHF—(OTCIQ)
Rev.: $9,141,234,523
Assets: $183,683,815,151
Liabilities: $147,408,380,945
Net Worth: $36,275,434,205
Earnings: $2,992,966,091
Emp.: 19,012
Fiscal Year-end: 12/31/22
Holding Company; Securities & Commodities Futures Brokerage, Dealing & Investing Services
N.A.I.C.S.: 551112
Minghui Yang (Pres)

Subsidiaries:

CITIC Securities (Zhejiang) Co., Ltd. (1)
19-20/F Hengxin Tower 588 Jiangnandadao, Binjiang District, Hangzhou, 310052, Zhejiang, China
Tel.: (86) 571 8578 3737
Web Site: http://www.bigsun.com.cn
Securities Brokerage, Investment Advisory & Dealing Services
N.A.I.C.S.: 523150

CITIC Securities Brokerage (HK) Limited (1)
26/F CITIC Tower 1 Tim Mei Avenue, Central, China (Hong Kong)
Tel.: (852) 22376899
Web Site: https://www.citics.com.hk
Investment Services
N.A.I.C.S.: 523999

CITIC Securities International Co., Ltd. (1)
26/F CITIC Tower 1 Tim Mei Avenue, Central, China (Hong Kong)   (100%)
Tel.: (852) 22376899
Web Site: http://www.citics.com.hk
Sales Range: $100-124.9 Million
Emp.: 200
Investment Banking, Securities Brokerage & Asset Management Services
N.A.I.C.S.: 523150

CITIC Securities Investment Limited (1)
17/F CITIC Securities Tower No 48 Liangmaqiao Road, Chaoyang District, Beijing, China
Tel.: (86) 1060833811
Financial Advisory Services

CITIC Securities South China Company Limited (1)
Room 901 No 395 Linjiang Avenue Room 1001, Tianhe District, Guangzhou, China
Tel.: (86) 2088836999
Web Site: https://www.gzs.com.cn
Investment & Life Insurance Services
N.A.I.C.S.: 524113

CITIC Wantong Securities Co., Ltd. (1)
21/F Tower 1 Qingdao International Finance Center 222 Shenzhen Road, Laoshan District, Qingdao, 266061, China   (96%)
Tel.: (86) 532 8502 2313
Web Site: http://www.zxwt.com.cn
Securities Brokerage, Investment Advisory & Dealing Services
N.A.I.C.S.: 523150

CITICS Futures Co., Ltd. (1)
1301-1305 13F and 14F North Block Times Square Excellence Phase II, No 8 Zhongxin 3rd Road Futian District, Shenzhen, 518048, China   (100%)
Tel.: (86) 4009908826
Web Site: https://www.citicsf.com
Commodities Futures Broker & Dealer
N.A.I.C.S.: 523160

CLSA Australia Holdings Pty .Ltd. (1)
Level 35 Grosvenor Place 225 George Street, Sydney, 2000, NSW, Australia
Tel.: (61) 285714200
Investment Banking Services
N.A.I.C.S.: 523150

CLSA Europe B.V. (1)
World Trade Center Amsterdam Tower 8 Level 7 Strawinskylaan 729, 1077 XX, Amsterdam, Netherlands
Tel.: (31) 202048300
Investment Services
N.A.I.C.S.: 523999

CLSA Fund Services (Asia) Limited (1)
18/F One Pacific Place 88, Queensway, Hong Kong, China (Hong Kong)
Tel.: (852) 26008888
Asset Management Services
N.A.I.C.S.: 531390

CLSA Limited (1)
18/F One Pacific Place 88 Queensway, Queensway, Hong Kong, China (Hong Kong)
Tel.: (852) 2 600 8888
Web Site: http://www.clsa.com
Emp.: 1,500
Securities Brokerage Services
N.A.I.C.S.: 523150
Jonathan Slone (CEO)

Subsidiary (Domestic):

CLSA Capital Partners (HK) Limited (2)
Room 809-810 8F One Pacific Place 88 Queensway, 89 Queensway, Hong Kong, China (Hong Kong)
Tel.: (852) 26008888
Web Site: https://www.clsacapital.com
Privater Equity Firm
N.A.I.C.S.: 523999

CLSA Premium Ltd (1)
Suites 7501 & 7508 75/F International Commerce Centre, 1 Austin Road West, Kowloon, China (Hong Kong)   (59.04%)
Tel.: (852) 26007670
Web Site: http://www.clsapremium.com
Rev.: $5,487,728
Assets: $36,249,525
Liabilities: $6,822,525
Net Worth: $29,427,000
Earnings: ($3,959,130)
Emp.: 8
Fiscal Year-end: 12/31/2022
Financial Investment Services
N.A.I.C.S.: 523999
Stephen Gregory McCoy (Exec Dir)

Subsidiary (Non-US):

KVB Kunlun New Zealand Limited (2)

Level 10 The National Bank Tower 205 Queen Street, Auckland, 1010, New Zealand
Tel.: (64) 9 359 8988
Web Site: http://www.kvbkunlun.com
Emp.: 54
Financial Investment Management Services
N.A.I.C.S.: 523940

KVB Kunlun Pty Limited (2)
Level 18 Citigroup Centre 2 Park Street, Sydney, 2000, NSW, Australia
Tel.: (61) 2 8263 0188
Web Site: http://www.kvbkunlun.com
Financial Investment Management Services
N.A.I.C.S.: 523940

Clsa B.V. (1)
World Trade Center Amsterdam Tower 8 Level 7 Strawinskylaan 729, 1077 XX, Amsterdam, Netherlands
Tel.: (31) 202048300
Investment Banking Services
N.A.I.C.S.: 523150

Goldstone Investment Co., Ltd. (1)
Room 1601 16/F Building 1 No 6 Xinyuan South Road, Chaoyang District, Beijing, 100026, China   (100%)
Tel.: (86) 1060837800
Web Site: https://www.goldstone-investment.com
Privater Equity Firm
N.A.I.C.S.: 523999

Joint Venture (US):

OmniVision Technologies, Inc. (2)
4275 Burton Dr, Santa Clara, CA 95054
Tel.: (408) 567-3000
Web Site: https://www.ovt.com
Sales Range: $1-4.9 Billion
Emp.: 2,176
Image Sensors Mfr
N.A.I.C.S.: 334413
Anson Chan (CFO & VP-Fin)

Subsidiary (Non-US):

OmniVision Technologies (Shanghai) Co., Ltd. (3)
No 88 Shangke Road, Pudong District, Shanghai, 201210, China
Tel.: (86) 216 175 9888
Web Site: http://www.ovt.com
Electronic Parts Whslr
N.A.I.C.S.: 423690

OmniVision Technologies Singapore Pte. Ltd. (3)
3A International Business Park 06-07/08 Tower A ICON IBP, 06-07/08 Tower A ICON IBP, Singapore, 609935, Singapore
Tel.: (65) 6 933 1933
Web Site: http://www.ovt.com
Digital Imaging Sensor Chip Mfr
N.A.I.C.S.: 334413

Guangzhou Securities Co., Ltd. (1)
19th Floor 20th Floor Main Tower, Guangzhou International Finance Center No 5 Zhujiang West Road, Guangzhou, 510623, China   (100%)
Tel.: (86) 2088836999
Web Site: http://www.gzs.com.cn
Financial Management Services
N.A.I.C.S.: 551112

CITICORE ENERGY REIT CORPORATION
11th Floor Rockwell Santolan Town Plaza 276 Bonny Serrano Avenue, Little Baguio, San Juan, Philippines
Tel.: (63) 288265698
Web Site: https://www.creit.com.ph
CREIT—(PHI)
Rev.: $32,467,039
Assets: $175,552,354
Liabilities: $94,858,225
Net Worth: $80,694,129
Earnings: $25,243,231
Emp.: 6
Fiscal Year-end: 12/31/23
Real Estate Investment Services
N.A.I.C.S.: 531190

CITIGOLD CORPORATION LIMITED

Level 1 1024 Ann Street, PO Box 1133, Fortitude Valley, 4006, QLD, Australia
Tel.: (61) 738394041   AU
Web Site: https://www.citigold.com
CTO—(ASX)
Rev.: $113,962
Assets: $75,857,578
Liabilities: $11,397,051
Net Worth: $64,460,527
Earnings: ($1,543,027)
Fiscal Year-end: 06/30/24
Gold Mining
N.A.I.C.S.: 212220
Sibasis Acharya, (Dir)

Subsidiaries:

Charters Towers Gold Pty Ltd (1)
Clermont Hwy, Charters Towers, 4820, QLD, Australia
Tel.: (61) 747877550
Web Site: http://www.citigold.com
Sales Range: $50-74.9 Million
Emp.: 55
Mining & Agriculture
N.A.I.C.S.: 212220
Danny Stanford (Gen Mgr)

CITIPORT FINANCIAL SERVICES LIMITED
House No 8-3-678/42/5 1st Floor Santoshi Manor Navodaya Colony, Yellareddyguda, Hyderabad, 500073, Telangana, India
Tel.: (91) 4066461811
Web Site: http://www.citiportfinancialservice.com
531235—(BOM)
Rev.: $69,151
Assets: $517,062
Liabilities: $99,659
Net Worth: $417,403
Earnings: $3,140
Emp.: 9
Fiscal Year-end: 03/31/22
Financial Investment Services
N.A.I.C.S.: 523999
Enjamuri Pardha Saradhi (Mng Dir)

CITIPOST GROUP
51 Hailey Road, Erith, DA18 4AA, Kent, United Kingdom
Tel.: (44) 2032600100
Web Site: http://www.citipost.co.uk
Year Founded: 1985
Sales Range: $50-74.9 Million
Emp.: 400
Business-to-Business Mail Services
N.A.I.C.S.: 491110
Kim Michael (Mng Dir)

Subsidiaries:

13ten Limited (1)
Unit 1 Langham Park Berristow Lane, Normanton, DE55 2JL, Derbyshire, United Kingdom
Tel.: (44) 8700948032
Web Site: http://www.13-ten.com
Courier Service
N.A.I.C.S.: 492110
Rob Bradford (Mng Dir)

Citipost AMP Ltd. (1)
51 Hailey Road, Erith, DA18 4AA, Kent, United Kingdom
Tel.: (44) 02032600100
Web Site: http://www.citipost.com
Sales Range: $10-24.9 Million
Emp.: 50
Catalogue & Directory Delivery Services
N.A.I.C.S.: 492210
Kim Michael (Mng Dir)

Citipost DSA Ltd. (1)
51 Hailey Rd, Erith, DA18 4AA, Kent, United Kingdom
Tel.: (44) 2032600100
Web Site: http://www.citipost.com
Sales Range: $10-24.9 Million
Emp.: 50
Postal Delivery Services

N.A.I.C.S.: 491110
Rob Bradford *(Mng Dir)*

Citipost Direct Distribution Ltd. **(1)**
51 Hailey Rd, Erith, DA18 4AA, Kent,
United Kingdom
Tel.: (44) 2032600100
Web Site: http://www.citipost.com
Sales Range: $10-24.9 Million
Emp.: 30
Magazine, Newspaper & Journal Fulfillment
& Distribution Services
N.A.I.C.S.: 491110
John Payne *(Mng Dir)*

Citipost UK Ltd **(1)**
Russelsheimer Strasse 22, 60326, Frank-
furt, Germany
Tel.: (49) 69 97390252
Web Site: http://www.citipost.com
Business-to-Business Mail Services
N.A.I.C.S.: 491110
FRon Christopher *(Gen Mgr)*

HomeMoveBox Ltd. **(1)**
6 Hailey Road, Erith, DA18 4AP, Kent,
United Kingdom
Tel.: (44) 2032600192
Web Site: http://www.homemovebox.com
Paper Packaging Services
N.A.I.C.S.: 561910

**CITITEC ASSOCIATES LIM-
ITED**
50 Featherstone Street, London,
EC1Y 8RT, United Kingdom
Tel.: (44) 207 608 5858
Web Site: http://www.cititec.com
Year Founded: 1998
Sales Range: $75-99.9 Million
Emp.: 50
Employee Recruitment Services
N.A.I.C.S.: 561311
Stephen Grant *(Dir-Ops)*

CITIUS RESOURCES PLC
167-169 Great Portland Street Fifth
Floor, London, W1W 5PF, United
Kingdom   UK
Web Site:
  https://www.citiusresources.co.uk
Year Founded: 2020
CRES—(LSE)
Assets: $1,055,190
Liabilities: $54,329
Net Worth: $1,000,861
Earnings: ($352,592)
Emp.: 3
Fiscal Year-end: 04/30/22
Investment Management Service
N.A.I.C.S.: 523999
Cameron Pearce *(CEO)*

CITIZEN INFOLINE LIMITED
411 Sakar-II Ellisbridge Ashram road,
Ahmedabad, 380 006, Gujarat, India
Tel.: (91) 7926585555
Web Site:
  http://www.citizeninfoline.com
538786—(BOM)
Rev.: $159,174
Assets: $636,181
Liabilities: $10,454
Net Worth: $625,727
Earnings: ($8,722)
Fiscal Year-end: 03/31/22
Online Information Services
N.A.I.C.S.: 513140
Omprakash L. Jain *(Founder, Chm &
CEO)*

CITIZEN WATCH CO., LTD.
6-1-12 Tanashi-cho, Nishitokyo, 188-
8511, Tokyo, Japan
Tel.: (81) 424661231   JP
Web Site: https://www.citizen.co.jp
Year Founded: 1930
7762—(TKS)
Rev.: $2,067,806,300
Assets: $2,746,091,450
Liabilities: $1,053,045,710

Net Worth: $1,693,045,740
Earnings: $151,752,380
Emp.: 800
Fiscal Year-end: 03/31/24
Holding Company; Watch & Watch
Parts Mfr & Whslr
N.A.I.C.S.: 551112
Toshihiko Sato *(Pres, Pres & CEO)*

Subsidiaries:

**Brasciti Industria e Comercio de
Relogios da Amazonia, S.A.** **(1)**
Av Abiurana No 1799, Distrio Industrial,
Manaus, AM, Brazil
Tel.: (55) 926152169
Assembler of Watches
N.A.I.C.S.: 334519

Bulova Corporation **(1)**
Empire State Building 350 5th Ave, New
York, NY 10118
Tel.: (212) 497-1875
Web Site: http://www.bulova.com
Sales Range: $150-199.9 Million
Emp.: 210
Mfr & Retailer of Watches & Clocks
N.A.I.C.S.: 334519
Jeffrey Cohen *(Pres)*

Subsidiary (Non-US):

Bulova de Mexico, SRL **(2)**
Magdalena 211 Piso 2, Col de Valle, 03100,
Mexico, Mexico
Tel.: (52) 5555435800
Web Site: http://www.bulova.ch
Sales Range: $25-49.9 Million
Emp.: 30
Watch & Clock Mfr & Distr
N.A.I.C.S.: 334519
Carolina Sepulveda *(Gen Mgr)*

C-E (Hong Kong) Ltd. **(1)**
Unit 718 7/F Chevalier Commercial Centre
8 Wang Hoi Road, Kowloon Bay, Kowloon,
China (Hong Kong)
Tel.: (852) 2 793 0613
Web Site: http://www.c-e.co.jp
Sales Range: $25-49.9 Million
Emp.: 10
Electronic Components Mfr
N.A.I.C.S.: 334419

C-E (Singapore) Pte. Ltd. **(1)**
96 Somerset Rd, 9 7 8 UOL Bldg, Singa-
pore, 238163, Singapore
Tel.: (65) 67341398
Web Site: http://www.c-e.co.jp
Sales Range: $10-24.9 Million
Emp.: 8
Provider of Electronic Equipment
N.A.I.C.S.: 449210

Cincom Miyano Taiwan Co., Ltd. **(1)**
10th Floor No 174 Fuxing North Road,
Zhongshan District, Taipei, Taiwan
Tel.: (886) 227150598
CNC Lathe & Peripheral Parts Distr
N.A.I.C.S.: 423690

**Citizen (China) Precision Machinery
Co., Ltd.** **(1)**
3010 Sichou Road of Zhoucun, Zibo, Shan-
dong, China
Tel.: (86) 5336150560
Watch Mfr & Distr
N.A.I.C.S.: 339910

**Citizen (Shanghai) Trading Co.,
Ltd.** **(1)**
Room 1306 Harbour Ring Plaza 18 XI Zang
Zhong Road, Huangpu District, Shanghai,
200001, China
Tel.: (86) 2133660606
Watch Mfr & Distr
N.A.I.C.S.: 339910

Citizen America Corp. **(1)**
Ste 404 363 Van Ness Way, Torrance, CA
90501-6282
Tel.: (949) 428-3700
Web Site: http://www.citizen-america.com
Sales Range: $25-49.9 Million
Emp.: 25
Sale of Information Equipment
N.A.I.C.S.: 423430

Citizen Business Expert Co., Ltd. **(1)**

6-1-12 Tanashi-Cho, Nishi-Tokyo, 188-8511,
Tokyo, Japan
Tel.: (81) 42 461 1211
Watch & Parts Mfr
N.A.I.C.S.: 334519

**Citizen Customer Service Co.,
Ltd.** **(1)**
5-7-3 Takenotsuka, Adachi-ku, Tokyo, 121-
0813, Japan
Tel.: (81) 366312760
Watch Mfr & Distr
N.A.I.C.S.: 339910

Citizen Electronics Co., Ltd. **(1)**
1-23-1 Kamikurechi, Fujiyoshida, 403-0001,
Yamanashi, Japan
Tel.: (81) 555234121
Emp.: 2,361
Watch Parts, Buzzers, LEDs, Sensors,
Electronic Thermometers & Electronic Blood
Pressure Monitors Mfr
N.A.I.C.S.: 334519
Tokio Ito *(Officer-Operating)*

Subsidiary (Non-US):

C-E (Deutschland) GmbH **(2)**
Stephanstrasse 3, 60313, Frankfurt am
Main, Germany
Tel.: (49) 692992480
Web Site: http://cede.citizen.co.jp
Sales Range: $50-74.9 Million
Emp.: 1
Electronic Components Distr
N.A.I.C.S.: 423690
Atsuro Ijichi *(Mng Dir)*

Subsidiary (US):

CECOL, Inc. **(2)**
10 N Martingale Rd Ste 400, Schaumburg,
IL 60173
Tel.: (847) 619-6700
Web Site: http://www.cecol.com
Electronic Product Distr
N.A.I.C.S.: 423690
Ryuzo Kondo *(Pres)*

Subsidiary (Non-US):

**Citizen Electronics (China) Co.,
Ltd.** **(2)**
Room 2710 27F New Town Center Building
83 Loushanguan Road, Changning District,
Shanghai, 200336, China
Tel.: (86) 2162955510
Sales Range: $25-49.9 Million
Emp.: 8
Electronic Components Mfr
N.A.I.C.S.: 334419
Shingo Yamata *(Mng Dir)*

Subsidiary (Domestic):

**Citizen Electronics Timel Co.,
Ltd.** **(2)**
1-27-8 Mukaihara, Fujiyoshida, 403-0018,
Yamanashi, Japan
Tel.: (81) 555234351
Emp.: 215
Light Emitting Diode Mfr
N.A.I.C.S.: 334419
Yasuki Kuwabara *(Gen Mgr)*

**Citizen Financial Service Co.,
Ltd.** **(1)**
6-1-12 Tanashi-Cho, Nishi-Tokyo, 188-8511,
Tokyo, Japan
Tel.: (81) 424 68 4934
Financial Management Services
N.A.I.C.S.: 523999
Toshio Tokura *(Gen Mgr)*

Citizen Finedevice Co., Ltd. **(1)**
6663-2 Funatsu Fujikawaguchiko-Machi,
Minamitsuru-gun, Yamanashi, 401-0395,
Japan
Tel.: (81) 555231231
Web Site: https://cfd.citizen.co.jp
Emp.: 902
Watch Parts, Cases, Dials, Watch Glass,
Liquid Crystal Cells, Gauges & Plastic Parts
Molds Mfr
N.A.I.C.S.: 334519
Tamotsu Shiga *(Operating Officer)*

Subsidiary (Domestic):

Citizen Chiba Precision Co., Ltd. **(2)**

1811-3 Yoshihashi, Yachiyo, 276-0047,
Chiba, Japan
Tel.: (81) 47 458 7935
Web Site: http://ccj.citizen.co.jp
Sales Range: $50-74.9 Million
Emp.: 10
Electric Motor Mfr
N.A.I.C.S.: 335312

Subsidiary (Non-US):

**Citizen Precision Guangzhou
Ltd.** **(2)**
Wang-ting Road Xinhua Street Huadu Re-
gion, Guangzhou, 510812, Guang Dong,
China
Tel.: (86) 20 8687 6014
Electronic Components Mfr
N.A.I.C.S.: 334419

Subsidiary (Domestic):

**Citizen Precision Hachinohe Co.,
Ltd.** **(2)**
1-1-39 Kita-inter-kogyodanchi, Hachinohe,
039-2245, Aomori, Japan
Tel.: (81) 178 28 1211
Electronic Components Mfr
N.A.I.C.S.: 334419

**Citizen Finedevice Philippines
Corp.** **(1)**
Lot 9-A Special Economic Zone FPIP II-
SEZ Sta Anastacia Sto Tomas, First Philip-
pine Industrial Park II, Batangas, 4234,
Philippines
Tel.: (63) 25555256
Watch Mfr & Distr
N.A.I.C.S.: 339910

Citizen Finetech Miyota Co. **(1)**
4107-5 Miyota Miyota-Machi, Kitasaku-Gun,
Nagano, 389-0295, Japan
Tel.: (81) 267 32 3232
Web Site: http://cfm.citizen.co.jp
Sales Range: $200-249.9 Million
Emp.: 539
Electronic Components Mfr
N.A.I.C.S.: 334419
Toshihiko Sato *(Pres)*

Plant (Domestic):

**Citizen Finetech Miyota Co., Ltd. -
Kitamimaki Works** **(2)**
353 Yaehara, Tomi, 389-0406, Nagano-ken,
Japan
Tel.: (81) 268 67 1800
Web Site: http://cfm.citizen.co.jp
Electronic Components Mfr
N.A.I.C.S.: 334419

Subsidiary (US):

**Miyota Development Center of
America, Inc.** **(2)**
2602 Clover Basin Dr, Longmont, CO
80503
Tel.: (303) 774-2221
Web Site: https://www.miyotadca.com
Sales Range: $25-49.9 Million
Emp.: 20
Microdisplays Mfr
N.A.I.C.S.: 334413

Citizen Jewelry Co., Ltd. **(1)**
3F Homat Horizon Bldg 6-2 Gobancho,
Chiyoda-Ku, Tokyo, 102-0076, Japan
Tel.: (81) 3 5215 2136
Jewelry & Precious Metal Mfr
N.A.I.C.S.: 339910

Citizen Latinamerica Corp. **(1)**
Sales Range: $25-49.9 Million
Emp.: 20
Retailer of Watches & Clocks
N.A.I.C.S.: 458310

**Citizen Logistics Service Co.,
Ltd.** **(1)**
6-9 Hachiman, Hiki-gun Kawajima-Machi,
Saitama, 350-0151, Japan
Tel.: (81) 492973323
Watch Mfr & Distr
N.A.I.C.S.: 339910

Citizen Macchine Italia S.r.l. **(1)**
Via Guglielmo Marconi 47, Comun Nuovo,
24040, Bergamo, Italy
Tel.: (39) 035877738

Citizen Watch Co., Ltd.—(Continued)

Machine Tools Mfr
N.A.I.C.S.: 333517

Citizen Machinery Asia Co., Ltd. (1)
199 Mu 1 Phahon Yothin Road, Sanap
Tuep Sub-District Wang Noi District Phra
Nakhon Si, Ayutthaya, 13170, Thailand
Tel.: (66) 35902640
Web Site: https://cma.citizen.co.th
Sales Range: $25-49.9 Million
Emp.: 160
Watches & Clocks
N.A.I.C.S.: 334519

Citizen Machinery Co., Ltd. (1)
4107-6 Miyota, Miyota-machi Kitasaku-gun,
Nagano, 389-0206, Japan
Tel.: (81) 267325961
Web Site: http://www.cmj.citizen.co.jp
Emp.: 770
CNC Lathe Mfr
N.A.I.C.S.: 332721
Keiichi Nakajima (Pres)

Citizen Machinery Europe GmbH (1)
Mettinger Strasse 11, D-73728, Esslingen,
Germany
Tel.: (49) 7113906100
Web Site: http://www.citizen.de
Sales Range: $50-74.9 Million
Emp.: 100
Holding Company; Commercial Printing
Equipment Mfr & Distr
N.A.I.C.S.: 551112

Subsidiary (Domestic):

Citizen Systems Europe GmbH (2)
Otto-Hirsch-Brucken 17, 70329, Stuttgart,
Germany
Tel.: (49) 711490320
Web Site: https://www.citizen-systems.com
Sales Range: $25-49.9 Million
Emp.: 50
Printers & Calculators Mfr & Whslr
N.A.I.C.S.: 333248
Mark Moore (Mng Dir)

**Citizen Machinery Miyano Co.,
Ltd.** (1)
4107-6 Miyota, Miyota-machi Kitasaku-gun,
Karuizawa, 389-0206, Nagano, Japan
Tel.: (81) 267325980
Web Site: https://cmj.citizen.co.jp
Sales Range: $200-249.9 Million
Emp.: 800
Machine Tool Mfr & Distr
N.A.I.C.S.: 333517
Keiichi Nakajima (Pres & CEO)

Affiliate (Domestic):

Alps Tool Co., Ltd. (2)
10070 Sakaki, Sakaki-cho Hanishina-gun,
Nagano, 389-0601, Japan
Tel.: (81) 268822511
Sales Range: $1-9.9 Million
Emp.: 320
Tools & Accessories; Bar Feeders
N.A.I.C.S.: 332216

Subsidiary (Non-US):

**Citizen (China) Precision Machinery
Co., Ltd. - Shanghai Branch** (2)
Room 101, Building B The Rainbow Centre
No 3051 Hechuan Rd, Shanghai, 201103,
China
Tel.: (86) 2158681740
Sales Range: $25-49.9 Million
Emp.: 30
Precision Instruments Distr
N.A.I.C.S.: 423990
Yoshiharu Saito (Pres & CEO)

Citizen Machinery Europe GmbH (2)
Mettinger Strasse 11, 73728, Esslingen,
Germany
Tel.: (49) 7113906100
Sales Range: $25-49.9 Million
Emp.: 15
Industrial Machinery
N.A.I.C.S.: 423830

**Citizen Machinery Philippines
Inc,** (2)
First Philippine Industrial Park FPIP Lot No
29 Barangay Ulango, Tanauan, 4232, Batangas, Philippines

Tel.: (63) 434056241
Sales Range: $100-124.9 Million
Emp.: 30
Casting & Machine Tool Mfr
N.A.I.C.S.: 333517

**Citizen Machinery United Kingdom,
Ltd.** (2)
1 Park Avenue, Bushey, WD23 2DA, United
Kingdom
Tel.: (44) 1923691500
Web Site:
https://www.citizenmachinery.co.uk
Emp.: 58
Automatic Lathe Machinery Distr
N.A.I.C.S.: 423840
Darren Wilkins (Deputy Mng Dir)

Affiliate (Domestic):

Mectron Japan, Inc. (2)
11240 Oaza Shomotakeshi, Nagano,
3852507, Japan
Tel.: (81) 268852345
Sales Range: $25-49.9 Million
Emp.: 80
Drilling & Tapping Machines & Equipment
N.A.I.C.S.: 332216

Ocean Machinery (2)
1263 Oaza-Shomotakeshi, Takeshi-mura,
Chiisagata-gun, Nagano, Japan
Tel.: (81) 268853431
Lathes Mfr
N.A.I.C.S.: 333517

**Citizen Machinery Service Co.,
Ltd.** (1)
4107-6 Miyota, Miyota-machi Kitasaku-gun,
Nagano, 389-0206, Japan
Tel.: (81) 267325900
Watch Mfr & Distr
N.A.I.C.S.: 339910

**Citizen Machinery Vietnam Co.,
Ltd.** (1)
J2 J3 J4 JAPAN Hai Phong industrial Zone,
An hung Commune An Duong district, Hai-
phong, Vietnam
Tel.: (84) 313743232
Watch Mfr & Distr
N.A.I.C.S.: 339910

Citizen Micro Co., Ltd. (1)
712 Komahongo, Hidaka, 350-1251, Sai-
tama, Japan
Tel.: (81) 429820271
Web Site: http://mic.citizen.co.jp
Sales Range: $100-124.9 Million
Emp.: 161
Precision Electronic Equipment Mfr
N.A.I.C.S.: 334419

Subsidiary (Non-US):

**Citizen Micro Devices (Suzhou) Co.,
Ltd.** (2)
No 388 South-Jinfeng Road Mudu Town,
Wuzhong District, 215101, Suzhou, Ji-
angsu, China
Tel.: (86) 512 6655 3232
Web Site: http://www.citizen.co.jp
Electronic Components Mfr
N.A.I.C.S.: 334419
Jin Wang (Mgr)

Subsidiary (Domestic):

Citizen Yubaril Co., Ltd. (2)
4-107-6 Chome Minami Shimizusawa, Yu-
bari, 068-0536, Hokkaido, Japan
Tel.: (81) 1235 9 6221
Web Site: http://www.citizen-yubari.jp
Wrist Watch Parts Mfr
N.A.I.C.S.: 334519

Citizen Plaza Co., Ltd. (1)
4-29-27 Takadanobaba, Shinjuku-ku, Tokyo,
169-0075, Japan
Tel.: (81) 3 3363 2211
Web Site: http://www.citizen-plaza.co.jp
Emp.: 58
Shopping Mall Management Services
N.A.I.C.S.: 531120
Junji Nagasawa (Pres)

Citizen Retail Planning., Ltd. (1)
4F Hundred Circus East Tower 2-27-7,
HyakuninCho Shinjuku-Ku, Tokyo, 169-
0073, Japan

Tel.: (81) 366327850
Watch Mfr & Distr
N.A.I.C.S.: 339910

Citizen Sakae Trading Co., Ltd. (1)
7F Yushima Sakae Bldg 3-39-3 Yushima,
Bunkyo-Ku, Tokyo, 113-0034, Japan
Tel.: (81) 3 3833 3811
Electronic Components Distr
N.A.I.C.S.: 423690

**Citizen Seimitsu (Thailand) Co.,
Ltd.** (1)
34 Moo 1 tambol, Ban-Chang Amphur
U-Thai, Ayutthaya, 13210, Thailand
Tel.: (66) 3 520 0565
Web Site: http://www.citizen-seimitsu-
thailand-coltd.business.site
Fabricated Metal Products Mfr
N.A.I.C.S.: 332312

**Citizen Systems (Dongguan) Co.,
Ltd.** (1)
Bubugao Road No 220, Jiangbei Village
Wusha Changan Town, Dongguan, Guang
Dong, China
Tel.: (86) 76985325301
Watch Mfr & Distr
N.A.I.C.S.: 339910

Citizen Systems (H.K.) Ltd. (1)
4/F Hung To Road, Kwun Tong, Kowloon,
China (Hong Kong)
Tel.: (852) 23575603
Watch Mfr & Distr
N.A.I.C.S.: 339910

**Citizen Systems America
Corporation** (1)
363 Van Ness Way Ste 404, Torrance, CA
90501-6282
Tel.: (310) 781-1460
Web Site: https://www.citizen-systems.com
Sales Range: $25-49.9 Million
Emp.: 14
Business Machines, Citizen Dot Matrix
Printers, Thermal Printers, Calculators, Au-
dio Products LCD Products & Portable
Hand-Held Televisions Distr & Mfr
N.A.I.C.S.: 423420
Victor Barczyk (Exec VP)

Citizen Systems Europe GmbH (1)
Mettinger Strasse 11, Esslingen, 73728,
Taden Wuerttempeg, Germany
Tel.: (49) 7113906400
Web Site: http://www.citizen-systems.com
Sales Range: $25-49.9 Million
Emp.: 11
Mfr of Precision Industrial Machinery
N.A.I.C.S.: 333517
Mark Beauchamp (Mgr-Mktg-Europe)

Citizen Systems Japan Co., Ltd. (1)
6-1-12 Tanashi-cho, Nishi-Tokyo, 188-8511,
Tokyo, Japan
Tel.: (81) 424684771
Web Site: http://csj.citizen.co.jp
Sales Range: $50-74.9 Million
Emp.: 1,265
Electronic Component Mfr & Distr
N.A.I.C.S.: 334419

Subsidiary (Non-US):

**Citizen Systems (Jiangmen) Co.,
Ltd.** (2)
Block C N0 399 Jinxing Road Jianghai
Area, Jiangmen, 529040, Guangdong,
China
Tel.: (86) 7503870833
Electric Equipment Mfr
N.A.I.C.S.: 335999

**Citizen Systems Europe
Corporation** (2)
Otto-Hirsch-Brucken 17, 70329, Stuttgart,
Germany
Tel.: (49) 711490320
Web Site: http://www.citizen-systems.com
Sales Range: $25-49.9 Million
Emp.: 12
Printer & Electronic Component Mfr
N.A.I.C.S.: 334118
Mark Moore (Mng Dir)

Citizen T.I.C. Co., Ltd. (1)
5-16-12 Maehara-Cho, Koganei, 184-0013,
Japan
Tel.: (81) 423862261

Web Site: https://tic.citizen.co.jp
Emp.: 167
Timing Device Mfr
N.A.I.C.S.: 334514
Takada Yoshio (Mgr)

Citizen Techno Co., Ltd. (1)
3 Floor Homat Horizon Bldg 6-2, Tokyo, 024
0051, Iwate, Japan
Tel.: (81) 352152136
Mfr of IC Packaging
N.A.I.C.S.: 334519

Citizen Tokorozawa Works (1)
840 Shimotomi, Tokorozawa, 359-8511, Sai-
tama, Japan
Tel.: (81) 429901117
Web Site: https://www.citizen.co.jp
Sales Range: $25-49.9 Million
Emp.: 200
Mfr of Precision Industrial Machinery
N.A.I.C.S.: 334519

Citizen Watch (China) Co., Ltd. (1)
No 7 Tianzhu Road, Tianzhu Airport Indus-
trial Zone Shunyi District, Beijing, 101312,
China
Tel.: (86) 1080486655
Web Site: http://www.citizen.com.cn
Mfr of Watches
N.A.I.C.S.: 334519

Citizen Watch (Switzerland) AG (1)
Zurich Strasse 17, 2504, Biel/Bienne, Swit-
zerland
Tel.: (41) 323424931
Web Site: http://www.citizenwatch.ch
Sales Range: $25-49.9 Million
Emp.: 3
Mfr of Watches & Clocks
N.A.I.C.S.: 334519

Citizen Watch (U.K.) Ltd. (1)
Citizen House 19 Business Centere Molly
Millars Lane, Wokingham, RG41 2QY, Berk-
shire, United Kingdom
Tel.: (44) 1189890333
Web Site: http://www.citizenwatch.co.uk
Sales Range: $25-49.9 Million
Emp.: 35
Retailer of Watches & Clocks
N.A.I.C.S.: 458310
Brian Gillingham (CFO & COO)

**Citizen Watch Co. of America,
Inc.** (1)
1000 W 190th St Dept R, Torrance, CA
90502-1040
Tel.: (212) 497-9732
Web Site: https://www.citizenwatch.com
Watch Retailer
N.A.I.C.S.: 423940

**Citizen Watch Co. of Canada,
Ltd.** (1)
380 Bentley Street, Markham, L3R 3L2,
ON, Canada
Tel.: (905) 415-1100
Web Site: http://www.citizenwatch.com
Sales Range: $25-49.9 Million
Emp.: 25
Mfr of Watches
N.A.I.C.S.: 334519

Citizen Watch Espana S.A. (1)
Ctra de L' Hospitalet 147-149 London build-
ing, Cornella de Llobregat, 08940, Barce-
lona, Spain
Tel.: (34) 936333202
Web Site: https://www.citizen.es
Sales Range: $25-49.9 Million
Emp.: 12
Retailer of Watches & Clocks
N.A.I.C.S.: 334519

Citizen Watch Europe GmbH (1)
Hans-Duncker Str 8, 21035, Hamburg, Ger-
many
Tel.: (49) 40734620
Sales Range: $25-49.9 Million
Emp.: 100
Retailer of Watches, Clocks & Jewelry
N.A.I.C.S.: 458310

Citizen Watch Iberica S.a.u. (1)
Ctra de L'Hospitalet 147-149 London build-
ing, Cornella de Llobregat, 08940, Barce-
lona, Spain
Tel.: (34) 936333202
Web Site: https://citizen.es

Watch Mfr & Distr
N.A.I.C.S.: 339910

Citizen Watch Italy S.p.A. (1)
Tel.: (39) 0295311100
Web Site: http://www.citizen.it
Sales Range: $25-49.9 Million
Emp.: 27
Retailer of Watches & Clocks
N.A.I.C.S.: 458310

Citizen Watch Manufacturing (Thailand) Co., Ltd. (1)
49 Moo 4 Sambundit, Rojana Industrial
Park Uthai, Ayutthaya, 13210, Thailand
Tel.: (66) 35200796
Watch Mfr & Distr
N.A.I.C.S.: 339910

Citizen Watch Manufacturing Co., Ltd (1)
840 Shimotomi, Tokorozawa, 359-8511, Saitama, Japan
Tel.: (81) 429901117
Web Site: https://cwmj.citizen.co.jp
Emp.: 2,092
Watch Mfr
N.A.I.C.S.: 334519
Katsuhiro Miwa (Mng Dir & Exec Officer)

Citizen Watch United Kingdom, Ltd. (1)
Citizen House 19 The Business Centre
Molly Millars Lane, Wokingham, RG41 2QY,
Berkshire, United Kingdom
Tel.: (44) 1189368855
Web Site: https://www.citizenwatch.co.uk
Watch Mfr & Distr
N.A.I.C.S.: 339910

Citizen Watch do Brasil S.A. (1)
Av Marques De Sao Vicente 121-Bloco B
CJ 1 702 17 Andar-Barra Funda, 01139-
001, Sao Paulo, Brazil
Tel.: (55) 1133922820
Watch Mfr
N.A.I.C.S.: 334519

Citizen Watches (H.K.) Ltd. (1)
2/F 64 Hung To Road, Kwun Tong, Kowloon, China (Hong Kong)
Tel.: (852) 23034223
Web Site: https://www.citizen.com.hk
Sales Range: $25-49.9 Million
Emp.: 100
Retailer of Watches & Clocks
N.A.I.C.S.: 458310

Subsidiary (Non-US):

Citizen Watches (Malaysia) Sdn. Bhd. (2)
Suite A605 West Wing 6th Floor Wisma
Consplant 2 No 7 Jalan SS 16/1, 47500,
Subang Jaya, Selangor, Malaysia
Tel.: (60) 3 5637 9811
Web Site: http://www.citizen.com.my
Sales Range: $25-49,9 Million
Emp.: 7
Watch Mfr
N.A.I.C.S.: 334519

Citizen Watches (India) Pvt. Ltd. (1)
Tel.: (91) 8043473777
Web Site: http://www.citizenwatches.co.in
Sales Range: $25-49.9 Million
Emp.: 55
Watches Assembler & Retailer
N.A.I.C.S.: 334519

Citizen Watches (N.Z.) Ltd. (1)
10 Eden Street, Private Bag 99902, Newmarket, Auckland, 1149, New Zealand
Tel.: (64) 95233393
Web Site: http://www.citizen.co.nz
Sales Range: $25-49.9 Million
Emp.: 8
Watches & Clocks Mfr
N.A.I.C.S.: 334519

Citizen Watches Australia Pty. Ltd. (1)
475 Victoria Avenue, Chatswood, 2067,
NSW, Australia
Tel.: (61) 294527300
Sales Range: $25-49.9 Million
Emp.: 100
Mfr of Watches & Clocks
N.A.I.C.S.: 458310

Citizen Watches Gulf Co. (1)
Road No 628 Jebel Ali Fz Factory units
FC2 3 4 5 and 6, PO Box 16772, Rd No
628, 16772, Dubai, United Arab Emirates
Tel.: (971) 48815171
Web Site: http://www.citizen-ne.com
Emp.: 25
Mfr of Watches & Clocks
N.A.I.C.S.: 334519

Citizen de Mexico, S.A. de C.V. (1)
Insurgentes Sur 730 14th floor, Col del
Valle, 03100, Mexico, DF, Mexico
Tel.: (52) 5550611840
Sales Range: $50-74.9 Million
Emp.: 130
Mfr of Watches & Cases
N.A.I.C.S.: 339910

Civis Manufacturing Ltd. (1)
601 Prince's Bldg Charter Road, Central,
China (Hong Kong)
Tel.: (852) 31232300
Watch Mfr & Distr
N.A.I.C.S.: 339910

Egasca, S.A. (1)
Poligono Industrial Erisono 2, Eibar, 20600,
Tolosa, Gipuzkoa, Spain
Tel.: (34) 943200300
Web Site: http://www.egasca.com
Machine Tool Distr
N.A.I.C.S.: 423830

Farbest Industries Ltd. (1)
64 Hung To Rd, Kwun Tong, Kowloon,
Hong Kong, China (Hong Kong)
Tel.: (852) 23442618
Web Site: http://www.citizen.co.jp
Sales Range: $25-49.9 Million
Emp.: 14
Mfr of Watches & Watch Accessories
N.A.I.C.S.: 423940

Firstcome Electronics Ltd. (1)
Unit 717 7/F Chevalier Commercial Centre
8 Wang Hoi Road, Kowloon Bay, Kowloon,
China (Hong Kong)
Tel.: (852) 2 341 6221
Web Site: http://www.citizen.co.jp
Sales Range: $25-49.9 Million
Emp.: 10
Electric Equipment Mfr
N.A.I.C.S.: 334419

Frederique Constant Holding S.A. (1)
Chemin du Champ-des-Filles 32, 1228,
Plan-les-Ouates, Switzerland
Tel.: (41) 22 860 0440
Web Site:
    https://www.frederiqueconstant.com
Watch Mfr & Distr
N.A.I.C.S.: 339910

Funehiki Seimitsu Co., Ltd. (1)
6-2 Koyodai Funehiki Cho, Tamura Gun,
Fukushima, 963 4000, Japan
Tel.: (81) 247611160
Parts for Watches & Electronic Equipment
Mfr
N.A.I.C.S.: 334519

Goodrington Co., Ltd. (1)
64 Hung To Road, Kwun Tong, Kowloon,
China (Hong Kong)
Tel.: (852) 23640251
Web Site: http://www.citizen.co.hk
Assembler of Watches & Manufacturer of
Watch Cases
N.A.I.C.S.: 334519

Guangzhou Most Crown Electronics Limited (1)
No 59 Punan Road, Yun Pu Industrial Zone
Huangpu, Guangzhou, China
Tel.: (86) 2082253555
Watch Mfr & Distr
N.A.I.C.S.: 339910

Heiwa Tokei Manufacturing Co., Ltd. (1)
435 Shimotonooka, Iida, 395 0195, Nagano, Japan
Tel.: (81) 265281500
Web Site: http://www.heiwatokei.co.jp
Sales Range: $75-99.9 Million
Emp.: 500
Assembler of Watches & Manufacturer of
Automation, Information & Electronic Equipment

N.A.I.C.S.: 334519

Hestika France S.A.S (1)
1385 Avenue du Mole ZAE des Lacs 3,
Ayse, 74130, Bonneville, France
Tel.: (33) 450985269
Web Site: http://www.hestika-citizen.fr
CNC Lathe Mfr
N.A.I.C.S.: 332721

Hi-Mecha Co., Ltd. (1)
2534-6 Kubota Kubota-machi, Yonezawa,
992-0003, Yamagata, Japan
Tel.: (81) 238372905
Sales Range: $25-49.9 Million
Emp.: 136
Mfr of Watch Parts
N.A.I.C.S.: 334519
Toshihiro Kamemori (Chm & CEO)

Jiang Xing Electronics Ltd. (1)
1F/2F/3F Building 7 399 Jinxing Road, Jianghai District, Jiangmen, Guangdong,
China
Tel.: (86) 7503809733
Watch Mfr & Distr
N.A.I.C.S.: 339910

Manufacture la Joux-Perret S.A. (1)
Boulevard des Eplatures 38, 2300, La
Chaux-de-Fonds, Switzerland
Tel.: (41) 329679797
Watch Making Component Mfr
N.A.I.C.S.: 339910

Marubeni Citizen-Cincom Inc. (1)
40 Boroline Rd Ste 6, Allendale, NJ 07401-
1613
Tel.: (201) 818-0100
Sales Range: $25-49.9 Million
Emp.: 25
Mfr of Precision Industrial Machinery
N.A.I.C.S.: 423830
John Antignani (Pres)

Master Crown Electronics (Wuzhou) Ltd. (1)
No 8 Building 137 Xinxing 2nd Road, Wuzhou, Guangxi, China
Tel.: (86) 13877413333
Watch Mfr & Distr
N.A.I.C.S.: 339910

Most Crown Industries Ltd. (1)
2/F 64 Hung to Road, Kwun Tong, Kowloon,
China (Hong Kong)
Tel.: (852) 26996000
Web Site: http://cfm.citizen.co.jp
Sales Range: $25-49.9 Million
Emp.: 20
Assembler of Watches & Manufacturer of
Quartz Oscillators
N.A.I.C.S.: 334519

Shiang Pao Precision Co., Ltd. (1)
No 5 Lane 108 An Her Road, Tantzu, Taichung, Taiwan
Tel.: (886) 425339674
Mfr of Molds, Watch Parts & Plastic Mold
Parts
N.A.I.C.S.: 334519

Silver Denken Co., Ltd. (1)
1-14-11 Shimoigusa, Suginami-Ku, Tokyo,
167 0022, Japan
Tel.: (81) 333102700
Web Site: http://www.silver-denken.co.jp
Sales Range: $25-49.9 Million
Emp.: 20
Retailer of Game Machines
N.A.I.C.S.: 459110

Sunciti Manufacturers Ltd. (1)
64 Hung To Road, Kwun Tong, Kowloon,
China (Hong Kong)
Tel.: (852) 27903188
Web Site: https://www.citizen.co.jp
Sales Range: $25-49.9 Million
Emp.: 90
Assembler of Watches & Mfr of Watch
Cases
N.A.I.C.S.: 423940

Sunciti PVD (Jiangmen) Ltd. (1)
106B Yamen, Electroplating Industrial Base
Xin hui District, Jiangmen, Guangdong,
China
Tel.: (86) 7503689801
Watch Mfr & Distr
N.A.I.C.S.: 339910

T.I.C.-Citizen Co., Ltd. (1)
5-6-12 Maehara-cho, Koganei, 184-0013,
Tokyo, Japan
Tel.: (81) 423862379
Emp.: 140
Mfr of Institutional & Outdoor Clocks & Indicators
N.A.I.C.S.: 334519
Masayuki Yoshimuta (Pres & CEO)

The Grace Limited (1)
3 4 33 Kokubun Cho, Sendai, 980 0803,
Miyagi Aoba Ku, Japan
Tel.: (81) 222636801
Jewelry Whslr
N.A.I.C.S.: 458310

Tokyo Bijutsu Co., Ltd. (1)
3-31-15 Ikebukuro Honmachi, Toshima-ku,
Tokyo, 170-0011, Japan
Tel.: (81) 339841741
Sales Range: $50-74.9 Million
Emp.: 186
Video Planning & Production; Commercial
Printing & Publishing
N.A.I.C.S.: 512110
Akihiro Kamata (Pres)

Tokyo Citizen Corporation (1)
Citizen Ueno Bldg 2 18 5 Higashi Ueno,
Taito Ku, Tokyo, 110 0015, Japan
Tel.: (81) 338334915
Sales Range: $25-49.9 Million
Emp.: 25
Watches, Clocks & Jewelry Whslr
N.A.I.C.S.: 458310

Walop Ltd. (1)
1st Fl 64 Hung PO Rd Kwun Tong, Kowloon, China (Hong Kong)
Tel.: (852) 26932056
Sales Range: $25-49.9 Million
Emp.: 12
Mfr of Watch Parts, Cases, Watch Glass,
Dials & Liquid Crystal Panels
N.A.I.C.S.: 334519

CITIZEN YARNS LIMITED
UL-10 Ankur Complex B/h Town Hall,
Opp X-Ray House Ellisbridge,
Ahmedabad, 380006, Gujarat, India
Tel.: (91) 9998848345
Web Site:
    http://www.citizenyarns1990.com
Year Founded: 1990
Rev.: $11,561
Assets: $27,041
Liabilities: $37,718
Net Worth: ($10,677)
Earnings: ($2,692)
Fiscal Year-end: 03/31/18
Yarn & Thread Mill Operator
N.A.I.C.S.: 313110
Hariprasad G. Khetan (Exec Dir)

CITIZENS BANK INTERNATIONAL LIMITED
Narayanhiti Path, Kathmandu, 44600,
Nepal
Tel.: (977) 14427842
Web Site: https://www.ctznbank.com
Year Founded: 2007
CZBIL—(NEP)
Rev.: $91,189,494
Assets: $1,415,086,367
Liabilities: $1,254,762,015
Net Worth: $160,324,352
Earnings: $15,709,142
Emp.: 1,458
Fiscal Year-end: 07/15/21
Financial Services
N.A.I.C.S.: 523999
Bal Krishna Prasai (Chm)

Subsidiaries:

Nepal Housing & Merchant Finance Ltd. (1)
NH&MF Building Dillibazar, Kathmandu,
Nepal
Tel.: (977) 1 4430528
Web Site: http://www.nhmf.com.np

Citizens Bank International Limited—(Continued)

Sales Range: Less than $1 Million
Financial Services
N.A.I.C.S.: 523999

Shrijana Finance (Financial Institution) Ltd. (1)
College Road Bhanu Tole, Morang, Biratnagar, Nepal
Tel.: (977) 21517510
Web Site: http://www.srijanafinance.com
Rev.: $7,445,478
Assets: $68,819,712
Liabilities: $62,500,348
Net Worth: $6,319,364
Earnings: $1,311,151
Emp.: 140
Fiscal Year-end: 07/16/2019
Financial Management Services
N.A.I.C.S.: 522110
Suyesh Pyakurel (Chm)

Tinau Mission Development Bank Limited (1)
Hospital Line Rupandehi, Butwal, 08, Nepal
Tel.: (977) 71545576
Web Site: http://www.tinaubank.com
Banking Services
N.A.I.C.S.: 522110
Rajendra Prasad Ojha (Chm)

CITRA NUSA HOLDINGS BERHAD
Wisma CNI No 2 Jalan Perunding U1/17 Hicom Glenmarie Industrial Park, Seksyen U1, 40150, Shah Alam, Selangor, Malaysia
Tel.: (60) 355694000
Web Site: https://www.citranusaholdings.com
Year Founded: 1989
CNH—(KLS)
Rev.: $16,327,527
Assets: $18,344,802
Liabilities: $3,514,886
Net Worth: $14,829,916
Earnings: ($473,957)
Emp.: 298
Fiscal Year-end: 12/31/22
Management Services
N.A.I.C.S.: 561110
Yoke Kwai Chin (Sec)

Subsidiaries:

CNI Enterprise (M) Sdn. Bhd. (1)
Wisma CNI No 2 Jalan Perunding U1/17, Hicom Glenmarie Industrial Park, 40150, Shah Alam, Selangor, Malaysia
Tel.: (60) 355694000
Web Site: https://www.cni.my
Wellness Product Distr
N.A.I.C.S.: 456199

Exclusive Mark (M) Sdn. Bhd. (1)
No 2 Jalan U1/17 Seksyen U1, Hicom-Glenmarie Industrial Park, 40000, Shah Alam, Selangor, Malaysia
Tel.: (60) 355692641
Food & Beverage Mfr
N.A.I.C.S.: 311999

Lotus Supplies Sdn. Bhd. (1)
No 2 Jalan U1/17 Section U1, Hicom-Glenmarie Industrial Park, 40000, Shah Alam, Selangor, Malaysia
Tel.: (60) 35 569 4948
Web Site: https://www.lotussupplies.com.my
Food Products Mfr
N.A.I.C.S.: 311999

Q-Pack (M) Sdn Bhd (1)
No 2 Jalan Perunding U1/17, Hicom-Glenmarie Industrial Park, 40000, Shah Alam, Selangor Darul Ehsan, Malaysia
Tel.: (60) 355692635
Web Site: https://www.qpack.com.my
Home Care Product Mfr
N.A.I.C.S.: 325620

Symplesoft Sdn. Bhd. (1)
Wisma CNI No 2 Jalan U1/17 Seksyen U1, Glenmarie Industrial Park, 40000, Shah Alam, Selangor, Malaysia
Tel.: (60) 35 569 1107
Web Site: https://www.symplesoft.com.my

Internet Marketing Services
N.A.I.C.S.: 541890

CITRINE GLOBAL CORP.
2 Jabotinsky St Atrium Tower, Ramat Gan, Tel Aviv, 5250501, Israel
Tel.: (972) 737600341   DE
Web Site: http://www.citrine-global.com
Year Founded: 2010
CTGL—(OTCQB)
Assets: $1,309,000
Liabilities: $3,780,000
Net Worth: ($2,471,000)
Earnings: ($2,645,000)
Emp.: 18
Fiscal Year-end: 12/31/22
Investment Services
N.A.I.C.S.: 523999
Ora Elharar Soffer (Chm, Pres & CEO)

CITROEN UK LIMITED
221 Bath Rd, Slough, SL1 4BA, Berks, United Kingdom
Tel.: (44) 8444630010
Web Site: http://www.citroen.co.uk
Year Founded: 1919
Sales Range: $75-99.9 Million
Emp.: 500
Automobiles Mfr & Distr
N.A.I.C.S.: 441227
Linda Jackson (CEO)

CITRUS LEISURE PLC
Tel.: (94)-115755055
Web Site: https://www.citrusleisure.com
REEF—(COL)
Rev.: $2,633,028
Assets: $46,853,494
Liabilities: $24,656,058
Net Worth: $22,197,436
Earnings: ($3,805,440)
Emp.: 31
Fiscal Year-end: 03/31/21
Hotel Owner & Operator
N.A.I.C.S.: 721110
Prema Cooray (Chm)

Subsidiaries:

HVA Foods PLC (1)
118 Braybrooke Place, 00200, Colombo, Sri Lanka
Tel.: (94) 114427600
Tea Product Mfr
N.A.I.C.S.: 311920
B. S. M. De Selva (Chm)

Hikkaduwa Beach Resort PLC (1)
No 56/1 Kynsey Road, 08, Colombo, Sri Lanka
Tel.: (94) 115755055
Rev.: $3,993,552
Assets: $32,303,539
Liabilities: $18,069,390
Net Worth: $14,234,149
Earnings: ($4,226,440)
Emp.: 133
Fiscal Year-end: 03/31/2023
Tourist Hotel Management Services
N.A.I.C.S.: 721110
P. C. B. Talwatte (CEO)

CITY & LAND DEVELOPERS, INC.
3/F Cityland Condominium 10 Tower 2 154 H V Dela Costa St, Makati, Philippines
Tel.: (63) 28161574
Web Site: https://www.cityland.info
Year Founded: 1988
LAND—(PHI)
Rev.: $51,567,187
Assets: $353,097,572
Liabilities: $77,712,763
Net Worth: $275,384,809
Earnings: $18,949,980
Emp.: 252

Fiscal Year-end: 12/31/21
Real Estate Development Services
N.A.I.C.S.: 531390
Stephen C. Roxas (Chm)

CITY BUICK CHEVROLET CADILLAC GMC
1900 Victoria Park Ave, Toronto, M1R 1T6, ON, Canada
Tel.: (416) 288-5492
Web Site: http://www.citybuick.com
Rev.: $74,685,712
Emp.: 147
New & Used Car Dealers
N.A.I.C.S.: 441110
Dean Fera (Gen Mgr-Sls)

CITY CEMENT COMPANY
PO Box 3070, 11471, Riyadh, 11471, Saudi Arabia
Tel.: (966) 920004324
Web Site: https://www.citycement.sa 3003—(SAU)
Rev.: $115,019,790
Assets: $517,593,943
Liabilities: $32,568,614
Net Worth: $485,025,329
Earnings: $30,665,358
Emp.: 550
Fiscal Year-end: 12/31/22
Cement Mfr
N.A.I.C.S.: 327310
Abdulaziz Mishal Abdulaziz Al Saud (Chm)

CITY CHIC COLLECTIVE LIMITED
151-163 Wyndham Street, Alexandria, 2015, NSW, Australia
Tel.: (61) 290594300   AU
Web Site: https://www.citychiccollective.com
Year Founded: 1998
CCX—(ASX)
Rev.: $88,350,026
Assets: $94,107,238
Liabilities: $70,656,383
Net Worth: $23,450,855
Earnings: ($25,647,035)
Emp.: 546
Fiscal Year-end: 06/30/24
Women's Clothing Store
N.A.I.C.S.: 458110
Phil Ryan (CEO)

Subsidiaries:

Millers Fashion Club (QLD) Pty Limited (1)
151-163 Wyndham St, Alexandria, 2015, NSW, Australia
Tel.: (61) 283039800
Sales Range: $50-74.9 Million
Emp.: 200
Women's Apparel Retailer
N.A.I.C.S.: 458110

Millers Fashion Club (VIC) Pty Limited (1)
Shop 13 Croydon Market, Croydon, 3136, Victoria, Australia
Tel.: (61) 397249327
Women's Apparel Retailer
N.A.I.C.S.: 458110

Millers Fashion Club (WA) Pty Limited (1)
166 Murry St, Perth, 6000, WA, Australia
Tel.: (61) 892256169
Web Site: http://www.millers.net.au
Women's Apparel Retailer
N.A.I.C.S.: 458110

CITY DEVELOPMENT ENVIRONMENT CO., LTD.
16F Investment Building No 41 Nongye Road, Zhengzhou, 450008, Henan, China
Tel.: (86) 37169158399
Web Site: http://www.tlcement.com

Year Founded: 1998
000885—(SSE)
Rev.: $892,352,916
Assets: $3,581,237,556
Liabilities: $2,539,643,652
Net Worth: $1,041,593,904
Earnings: $148,289,076
Fiscal Year-end: 12/31/22
Cement Mfr
N.A.I.C.S.: 327310
Yang Bai (Chm)

CITY FORD SALES LTD.
14750 Mark Messier Trail, Edmonton, T6V 1H5, AB, Canada
Tel.: (780) 454-2000
Web Site: https://www.cityfordsales.com
Year Founded: 1985
Rev.: $51,341,268
Emp.: 100
New & Used Car Dealers
N.A.I.C.S.: 441110
Ray McMillan (Mgr-Fleet Sls)

CITY GENERAL INSURANCE COMPANY LIMITED
Baitul Hossain Building 4th Floor 27 Dilkusha Commercial Area, Dhaka, 1000, Bangladesh
Tel.: (880) 2223387296
Web Site: https://www.cityinsurance.com.bd
CITYGENINS—(DHA)
Rev.: $2,886,986
Assets: $19,527,725
Liabilities: $6,811,504
Net Worth: $12,716,221
Earnings: $1,880,047
Emp.: 227
Fiscal Year-end: 12/31/23
Insurance Services
N.A.I.C.S.: 524298
Hossain Ahktar (Exec Dir)

CITY GROUP COMPANY KSCP
Sulaibia Industrial Area Block No 2 Building No 800100, Kuwait, Kuwait
Tel.: (965) 188 2211
Web Site: http://www.citygroupco.com
Rev.: $71,983,339
Assets: $128,390,251
Liabilities: $46,064,690
Net Worth: $82,325,561
Earnings: $15,005,148
Emp.: 1,500
Fiscal Year-end: 12/31/19
Passenger & Cargo Transportation Services; Warehousing Services
N.A.I.C.S.: 488999
Hany Shawky (Vice Chm)

Subsidiaries:

Boodai Aviation Agencies Co WLL (1)
PO Box 5798, Kuwait, 13058, Kuwait
Tel.: (965) 22413716
Web Site: http://www.boodaiaviation.com
Sales Range: $25-49.9 Million
Emp.: 146
Travel Agency Services
N.A.I.C.S.: 561510

Boodai Aviation Co. WLL (1)
PO Box 787, Safat, Kuwait, 13008, Kuwait
Tel.: (965) 24841314
Web Site: http://www.boodaicorp.com
Travel Agency Services
N.A.I.C.S.: 561510

CITY INVEST BANK AO
2/4 Liter A Shpalernaya ul, 191123, Saint Petersburg, Russia
Tel.: (7) 8123240690
Web Site: http://www.cibank.ru
Year Founded: 1994
Sales Range: Less than $1 Million

Mortgage Banking Services
N.A.I.C.S.: 522292
Goldfarb Mikhail Wolfowich *(Chm-Supervisory Bd)*

CITY LODGE HOTELS LIMITED

The Lodge Bryanston Gate Office ParkCorner Homestead Avenue Main Road, Bryanston, 2060, South Africa
Tel.: (27) 115572600
CLH—(JSE)
Rev.: $90,554,875
Assets: $170,119,509
Liabilities: $111,078,750
Net Worth: $59,040,759
Earnings: $8,647,588
Emp.: 1,199
Fiscal Year-end: 06/30/23
Hotel Owner & Operator
N.A.I.C.S.: 721110
Andrew C. Widegger *(CEO)*

Subsidiaries:

City Lodge Bryanston (Pty) Limited   (1)
Cnr Main Road and Peter Place, Bryanston West, Sandton, Gauteng, South Africa
Tel.: (27) 11 706 7800
Web Site: http://www.citylodge.co.za
Sales Range: $25-49.9 Million
Emp.: 30
Home Management Services
N.A.I.C.S.: 561110
Jason Viljoen *(Gen Mgr)*

City Lodge Holdings (Share Block) (Pty) Ltd   (1)
R2 305 Herman St, Germiston, 1429, Gauteng, South Africa
Tel.: (27) 114445300
Home Management Services
N.A.I.C.S.: 561110

CITY OF LONDON GROUP PLC

6th Floor 60 Gracechurch Street, London, EC3V 0HR, United Kingdom
Tel.: (44) 20 37952680   UK
Web Site:
http://www.cityoflondongroup.com
Year Founded: 1985
CIN—(LSE)
Rev.: $2,579,668
Assets: $146,546,866
Liabilities: $93,071,706
Net Worth: $53,475,160
Earnings: ($17,486)
Emp.: 76
Fiscal Year-end: 03/31/21
Equity Investment Firm
N.A.I.C.S.: 523999
Paul Milner *(Exec Dir)*

Subsidiaries:

City of London Financial Services Limited   (1)
30 Cannon St, London, EC4M 6XH, United Kingdom
Tel.: (44) 2076285518
Web Site: http://www.cityoflondongroup.com
Sales Range: $50-74.9 Million
Emp.: 3
Investment Management Service
N.A.I.C.S.: 523999

Living Plus Limited   (1)
Stanley House The Boulevard, Clarence Dock, Leeds, LS10 1PZ, West Yorkshire, United Kingdom
Tel.: (44) 177 289 7251
Web Site: https://www.livingplus.co.uk
Real Estate Services
N.A.I.C.S.: 531390
Greg Reed *(CEO)*

Recognise Bank Limited   (1)
The Royal Exchange First Floor 1 Royal Exchange Steps, London, EC3V 3DG, United Kingdom
Tel.: (44) 345 872 7888
Web Site: https://www.recognisebank.co.uk
Financial Services

N.A.I.C.S.: 523999
David Jenkins *(CFO)*

Tavernier Limited   (1)
17 Albemarle St, London, W1S 4HP, United Kingdom
Tel.: (44) 2074933322
Web Site: http://www.tavernier.co.uk
Investment Holding Services
N.A.I.C.S.: 523999

CITY OF LONDON INVESTMENT GROUP PLC

77 Gracechurch Street, London, EC3V 0AS, United Kingdom
Tel.: (44) 2077110771   UK
Web Site: https://clig.com
Year Founded: 1991
CLIG—(LSE)
Rev.: $69,453,000
Assets: $178,971,000
Liabilities: $25,327,000
Net Worth: $153,644,000
Earnings: $17,115,000
Emp.: 121
Fiscal Year-end: 06/30/24
Asset Management & Investment Services
N.A.I.C.S.: 523999
Barry Martin Olliff *(Founder)*

Subsidiaries:

City of London Investment Management (Singapore) Pte. Ltd.   (1)
20 Collyer Quay 10-04, Singapore, 049319, Singapore
Tel.: (65) 6 236 9139
Fund Management Services
N.A.I.C.S.: 523940

City of London Investment Management Company Limited   (1)
77 Grace Church St, London, EC3V 0AS, United Kingdom
Tel.: (44) 2077110771
Web Site: http://www.citlon.co.uk
Sales Range: $50-74.9 Million
Emp.: 25
Investment Management Service
N.A.I.C.S.: 523940
Barry Olliss *(Gen Mgr)*

City of London US Investments Limited   (1)
77 Grace Church St, London, EC3V 0AS, United Kingdom
Tel.: (44) 2077110771
Web Site: http://www.citlon.co.uk
Sales Range: $50-74.9 Million
Emp.: 25
Unit Trust Brokerage & Managing Services
N.A.I.C.S.: 523150

CITY OFFICE REIT, INC.

666 Burrard Street Suite 3210, Vancouver, V6C 2X8, BC, Canada
Tel.: (604) 806-3366   MD
Web Site: https://cioreit.com
CIO—(NYSE)
Rev.: $179,096,000
Assets: $1,511,376,000
Liabilities: $738,743,000
Net Worth: $772,633,000
Earnings: ($2,035,000)
Emp.: 20
Fiscal Year-end: 12/31/23
Real Estate Investment Trust
N.A.I.C.S.: 523999
Anthony Maretic *(CFO, Treas & Sec)*

Subsidiaries:

CIO San Tan II, Limited Partnership   (1)
3100 W Ray Rd, Chandler, AZ 85226
Tel.: (480) 899-2504
Real Estate Services
N.A.I.C.S.: 531390

City Center STF, LP   (1)
2701 Maitland Center Pkwy Ste 225, Maitland, FL 32751-7409
Tel.: (727) 822-3395

Nonresidential Building Leasing Services
N.A.I.C.S.: 531120

CITY ONLINE SERVICES LTD.

701 7th Floor Aditya Trade Center, Ameerpet, Hyderabad, 500 038, India
Tel.: (91) 4068218888
Web Site:
https://www.cityonlines.com
Year Founded: 1999
Rev.: $2,017,413
Assets: $1,610,179
Liabilities: $1,286,844
Net Worth: $323,335
Earnings: ($129,976)
Emp.: 48
Fiscal Year-end: 03/31/19
Internet Service Provider
N.A.I.C.S.: 517111
Raghava Rao Suryadevara *(Chm & Mng Dir)*

CITY PARK D.D.

ul Mula Mustafe Baseskije 5, 71000, Sarajevo, Bosnia & Herzegovina
Tel.: (387) 33203877
Web Site: http://www.citypark.ba
CTPSR—(SARE)
Rev.: $987,714
Assets: $5,783,360
Liabilities: $2,032,416
Net Worth: $3,750,944
Earnings: $493,548
Emp.: 16
Fiscal Year-end: 12/31/21
Food Transportation Services
N.A.I.C.S.: 488490
Hajrudin Mulic *(Pres)*

CITY PHARMACY LTD

Lot 01 Section 38 Waigani Dr, PO Box 1663, Port Moresby, Papua New Guinea
Tel.: (675) 325 9044
Web Site: http://www.cpl.com.pg
Year Founded: 1986
Sales Range: $10-24.9 Million
Emp.: 240
Pharmaceutical Retailer
N.A.I.C.S.: 456110
Mahesh Patel *(Co-Founder & Chm)*

CITY PUB GROUP PLC

2nd Floor Essel House 29 Foley Street, London, W1W 7TH, United Kingdom
Tel.: (44) 2075595106
Web Site:
http://www.citypubcompany.com
CPC—(LSE)
Rev.: $35,049,542
Assets: $202,748,328
Liabilities: $75,034,396
Net Worth: $127,713,932
Earnings: ($8,774,944)
Emp.: 984
Fiscal Year-end: 12/27/20
Restaurant Operators
N.A.I.C.S.: 722511
Clive Watson *(Chm)*

CITY PULSE MULTIPLEX LIMITED

10 Acres Mall Nr Raipur Gate Raipur, Swastik Cross Road C G Road, Ahmedabad, 380009, India
Tel.: (91) 917925451536
Web Site: https://www.citypulse.co.in
Year Founded: 2000
542727—(BOM)
Rev.: $64,387
Assets: $1,274,678
Liabilities: $543,912
Net Worth: $730,766
Earnings: ($53,740)
Fiscal Year-end: 03/31/22
Filmmakers Services

N.A.I.C.S.: 512110
Arpit Mehta *(CEO)*

CITY REFRIGERATION HOLDINGS (UK) LIMITED

Caledonia House Lawmoor Street, Glasgow, G5 0US, United Kingdom
Tel.: (44) 141 418 9000
Web Site: http://www.cityfm.com
Year Founded: 1985
Sales Range: $550-599.9 Million
Emp.: 10,707
Investment Management Service
N.A.I.C.S.: 523940
William Haughey *(Founder)*

Subsidiaries:

City Holdings (Aus) Pty Ltd   (1)
Level 1 350 Wellington Road, Mulgrave, 3170, VIC, Australia
Tel.: (61) 385620700
Web Site: http://www.cityholdings.com.au
Holding Company
N.A.I.C.S.: 551112

CITY SERVICE SE

Ozo Str 12A, 08200, Vilnius, Lithuania
Tel.: (370) 52394900
Web Site: https://www.cityservice.eu
CTS—(WAR)
Rev.: $91,069,501
Assets: $83,858,191
Liabilities: $64,411,828
Net Worth: $19,446,363
Earnings: ($5,586,013)
Emp.: 1,594
Fiscal Year-end: 12/31/22
Property Management Services
N.A.I.C.S.: 523940
Andrius Janukonis *(Chm-Supervisory Bd)*

Subsidiaries:

Atrium 21 Sp. z o.o.   (1)
ul Stefana Batorego 20, 02-591, Warsaw, Poland
Tel.: (48) 698648969
Web Site: http://www.agencja.atrium21.pl
Real Estate Manangement Services
N.A.I.C.S.: 531311

City Service Polska Sp. z o.o.   (1)
ul 17 Stycznia 48, 02-146, Warsaw, Poland
Tel.: (48) 225725570
Building Management & Administration Services
N.A.I.C.S.: 541611

EnergiaOK Sp. z o.o.   (1)
street Cybernetyki 10, 02-677, Warsaw, Poland
Tel.: (48) 691476172
Web Site: https://www.energiaok.pl
Electric Power Distribution Services
N.A.I.C.S.: 221122

Home Rent sp. z o.o.   (1)
Ul Stefana Batorego 20, 02-591, Warsaw, Poland
Tel.: (48) 22 257 8795
Web Site: https://www.homerent.pl
Apartment Rental Agency Services
N.A.I.C.S.: 531110

OAO City Service   (1)
Kondratievsky Ave 15 Bldg 3, 195197, Saint Petersburg, Russia
Tel.: (7) 8126111004
Web Site: http://www.cityservice.spb.ru
Building Management & Administration Services
N.A.I.C.S.: 541611

SIA City Service Engineering   (1)
Brivibas iela 155A, Riga, LV-1012, Latvia
Tel.: (371) 22124444
Web Site: https://cse.lv
Building Management & Administration Services
N.A.I.C.S.: 541611
Michail Cerniavskij *(Dir Gen)*

SIA Latvijas Namsaimnieks   (1)

City Service SE—(Continued)

Brivibas iela 155A, Riga, LV-1012, Latvia
Tel.: (371) 22124444
Web Site:
https://www.latvijasnamsaimnieks.lv
Building Renovation Services
N.A.I.C.S.: 236118

SIA Namu Serviss APSE (1)
Zivju iela 11/13-7N, Liepaja, Latvia
Tel.: (371) 22124444
Web Site: https://www.apse.lv
Building Renovation Services
N.A.I.C.S.: 236118
Gints Locmelis (Project Mgr)

UAB Acta Iuventus (1)
AJ Povilaicio st 18, LT-04340, Vilnius, Lithuania
Tel.: (370) 870035555
Web Site: http://www.stebit.lt
Internet Communication Services
N.A.I.C.S.: 517810
Raimondas Dagelis (CEO)

UAB City Service Engineering (1)
Ozo 12A, 08200, Vilnius, Lithuania
Tel.: (370) 70055966
Web Site: https://cse.lt
Commercial Building Maintenance Services
N.A.I.C.S.: 561790
Sarunas Setikas (Sls Mgr)

UAB Economus (1)
Ozo 12A-1, Vilnius, LT-08200, Lithuania
Tel.: (370) 870055966
Web Site: http://www.economus.lt
Outdoor Playground Maintenance Services
N.A.I.C.S.: 713990

UAB Karoliniskiu Turgus (1)
Loretos Asanaviciutes g 35, LT-04314, Vilnius, Lithuania
Tel.: (370) 869980819
Web Site: http://www.karoliniskiu-turgus.mozello.com
Supermarket Operator
N.A.I.C.S.: 445110

UAB Mano Aplinka (1)
Elektrines st 3, Vilnius, Lithuania
Tel.: (370) 861659938
Web Site: http://www.manoaplinka.eu
Building Cleaning Services
N.A.I.C.S.: 561720
Diana Lube (COO)

UAB Mano Bustas (1)
Freedom Ave 77B, LT-08200, Vilnius, Lithuania
Tel.: (370) 70055966
Web Site: https://www.manobustas.lt
Building Renovation Services
N.A.I.C.S.: 236118

UAB Mano Bustas Alytus (1)
New st 3, Alytus, Lithuania
Tel.: (370) 70055966
Building Renovation Services
N.A.I.C.S.: 236118

UAB Mano Bustas Kaunas (1)
Butrimonio str 5A, Kaunas, Lithuania
Tel.: (370) 70055966
Building Renovation Services
N.A.I.C.S.: 236118

UAB Mano Bustas Klaipeda (1)
Kuosu str 18-1, Klaipeda, Lithuania
Tel.: (370) 70055966
Building Renovation Services
N.A.I.C.S.: 236118

UAB Mano Bustas Siauliai (1)
Tilzes str 122, Siauliai, Lithuania
Tel.: (370) 70055966
Building Renovation Services
N.A.I.C.S.: 236118

UAB Mano Bustas Vilnius (1)
Ozo g 12A, Vilnius, Lithuania
Tel.: (370) 870055966
Building Renovation Services
N.A.I.C.S.: 236118

UAB Mano Sauga LT (1)
Elektrines g 3, Vilnius, Lithuania
Tel.: (370) 870055966
Web Site: http://www.manosauga.lt
Security System Services
N.A.I.C.S.: 561621

UAB Pastatu Prieziura (1)
Verkiu st 48, LT-44489, Kaunas, Lithuania
Tel.: (370) 865610853
Web Site: http://www.pup.lt
Construction Contracting Services
N.A.I.C.S.: 236220

UAB Pastatu Valdymas (1)
Kedru st 4-101, Vilnius, Lithuania
Tel.: (370) 61633026
Web Site: http://www.pastatuvaldymas.com
Building Management & Administration Services
N.A.I.C.S.: 541611

UAB PortalPRO (1)
Ozo str 12A-1, LT-08200, Vilnius, Lithuania
Tel.: (370) 62333715
Web Site: https://www.portalpro.lt
Site Preparation Contracting Services
N.A.I.C.S.: 238910

ZAO City Service (1)
Korablestroiteley Str 31 Bldg 2, 199397, Saint Petersburg, Russia
Tel.: (7) 8123036520
Building Management & Administration Services
N.A.I.C.S.: 541611

CITY SITE ESTATES PLC
145 St Vincent Street, Glasgow, G2 5JF, United Kingdom
Tel.: (44) 1412482534
Web Site: http://www.cseplc.co.uk
Residential Property Management Services
N.A.I.C.S.: 531311
Louis M. Goodman (Mng Dir)

CITY SPORTS AND RECREATION PUBLIC COMPANY LIMITED
22 Navatanee Road Ramintra Khannayao, Bangkok, 10230, Thailand
Tel.: (66) 23761693
Web Site: http://www.navatanee.com
CSR—(THA)
Rev.: $5,435,253
Assets: $39,072,576
Liabilities: $4,247,140
Net Worth: $34,825,436
Earnings: $1,533,162
Fiscal Year-end: 12/31/23
Golf Course & Clubs
N.A.I.C.S.: 713910
Maevdi Navapan (Chm & CEO)

CITY STEEL PUBLIC COMPANY LIMITED
88/3 Moo 4 Bypass Rd Nongmaidaeng, Muang, Chon Buri, 20000, Thailand
Tel.: (66) 813596942
Web Site: http://www.citysteelpcl.com
Year Founded: 1995
CITY—(THA)
Rev.: $2,870,160
Assets: $36,029,631
Liabilities: $346,671
Net Worth: $35,682,960
Earnings: ($834,982)
Emp.: 185
Fiscal Year-end: 07/31/23
Metal Products Mfr
N.A.I.C.S.: 332999
Charoenpong Ongwongsakul (Chm & CEO)

Subsidiaries:

City Steel Products Company Limited (1)
88/20 Moo 10 Bypass Road Napa Muang, Chon Buri, 20000, Thailand
Tel.: (66) 3878206468
Metal Product Mfr & Distr
N.A.I.C.S.: 332312

Mark Worldwide Company Limited (1)
41/58-61 Moo 1 Bypass Road Bansuan,

Muang, Chon Buri, 20000, Thailand
Tel.: (66) 38287111
Web Site: https://www.citysteelpcl.com
Metal Product Mfr & Distr
N.A.I.C.S.: 332312

CITY UNION BANK LTD
Narayana No 24B Gandhi Nagar, Kumbakonam, 612001, Tamilnadu, India
Tel.: (91) 4352402322
Web Site:
https://www.cityunionbank.com
Year Founded: 1904
CUB—(NSE)
Rev.: $660,585,130
Assets: $7,277,044,743
Liabilities: $6,479,546,742
Net Worth: $797,498,001
Earnings: $88,828,563
Emp.: 5,843
Fiscal Year-end: 03/31/21
Banking Services
N.A.I.C.S.: 522110
N. Kamakodi (CEO & Mng Dir)

Subsidiaries:

City Union Bank Ltd - International Banking Division (1)
No 706 Mount Rd Thousand Lights, Chennai, 600006, Tamil Nadu, India
Tel.: (91) 4428297202
Web Site: http://www.cityunionbank.com
Sales Range: $50-74.9 Million
Emp.: 32
Banking Services
N.A.I.C.S.: 522110
S Balasubramanian (Chm)

CITY VIEW GREEN HOLDINGS INC.
1173 Dundas Street East Suite 132, Toronto, M4M 3P1, ON, Canada
Tel.: (416) 722-4994   BC
Web Site: https://cityviewgreen.ca
Year Founded: 2008
CVY—(DEU)
Rev.: $197,568
Assets: $1,251,313
Liabilities: $2,295,215
Net Worth: ($1,043,901)
Earnings: ($1,784,751)
Fiscal Year-end: 12/31/22
Gold & Other Precious Metals Mining
N.A.I.C.S.: 212220
Roberto Fia (CEO)

Subsidiaries:

Grupo Mineros del Caribe, S. A. S. (1)
Carrera 43 A 1 Sur 188, Medellin, Colombia
Tel.: (57) 43213577
Gold Mining Services
N.A.I.C.S.: 212220

CITY WINDMILLS LTD.
Suite 72 Carioca Business Park, 2 Sawley Road, Manchester, M40 8BB, Lancs, United Kingdom
Tel.: (44) 22 310 8603   UK
Web Site:
http://www.citywindmills.com
Year Founded: 2010
Windmill Mfr
N.A.I.C.S.: 335311
David Mapley (CEO & CFO)

CITYA IMMOBILIER SAS
8 10 12 Rue du Docteur Herpin, 370000, Tours, France
Tel.: (33) 247315000
Web Site: http://www.citya.com
Real Estate Services & Administration
N.A.I.C.S.: 531190
Martine Cohade (Project Mgr)

Subsidiaries:

Century 21 France SAS (1)

3 rue des Cevennes, 91090, Lisses, France
Tel.: (33) 169111221
Web Site: http://www.century21.fr
Real Estate Rental Services
N.A.I.C.S.: 531390

CITYCHAMP DARTONG CO., LTD.
Block C Building 1 Crown City Datong Plaza No 5 Puxiazhou Road, Cangshan, Fuzhou, 350007, Fujian, China
Tel.: (86) 59183350013
Web Site: https://www.gcdt.net
600067—(SHG)
Rev.: $1,564,027,906
Assets: $3,282,717,616
Liabilities: $2,110,870,083
Net Worth: $1,171,847,533
Earnings: $9,860,264
Emp.: 1,100
Fiscal Year-end: 12/31/22
Real Estate Developer; Enameled Wire Mfr
N.A.I.C.S.: 237210

CITYCHAMP WATCH & JEWELLERY GROUP LIMITED
Units 1902-04 Level 19 International Commerce Centre, 1 Austin Road West, Kowloon, China (Hong Kong)
Tel.: (852) 22753700
Web Site:
http://www.citychampjewellery.com
0256—(HKG)
Rev.: $204,941,970
Assets: $2,060,048,483
Liabilities: $1,527,243,705
Net Worth: $532,804,778
Earnings: ($15,228,218)
Emp.: 3,850
Fiscal Year-end: 12/31/22
Watches & Timepieces Mfr
N.A.I.C.S.: 339910
Chi Fong (CFO & Sec)

Subsidiaries:

Bendura Bank AG (1)
Schaaner Strasse 27, Bendern, 9487, Gamprin, Liechtenstein (84.69%)
Tel.: (423) 2655656
Web Site: https://www.bendura.li
Rev.: $57,442,112
Emp.: 133
Fiscal Year-end: 12/31/2019
Banking Services
N.A.I.C.S.: 522110
Andreas Insam (CEO & Member-Mgmt Bd)

Subsidiary (Domestic):

Bendura Fund Management Alpha AG (2)
Schaaner Strasse 27, Bendern, 9487, Gamprin, Liechtenstein
Tel.: (423) 3881000
Investment Fund Services
N.A.I.C.S.: 525910

Bendura Fund Management Beta AG (2)
Schaaner Strasse 27, Bendern, 9487, Gamprin, Liechtenstein
Tel.: (423) 3994000
Web Site: https://www.bendurafunds-beta.li
Investment Fund Services
N.A.I.C.S.: 525910

Corum Deutschland GmbH (1)
Heinrich-Heine-Allee 4, 40213, Dusseldorf, Germany
Tel.: (49) 2111306390
Web Site: http://www.corum-watches.de
Watch Mfr
N.A.I.C.S.: 334519

Corum Italia Srl (1)
Via Senato 12, 20121, Milan, Italy
Tel.: (39) 0286984188
Watch Mfr
N.A.I.C.S.: 334519

EBOHR Luxuries International Co., Limited (1)
7 Fl Ste B Xinnengyuan Mansion Nanhai Rd, Nanshan Dist, Shenzhen, 518054, Guangdong, China
Tel.: (86) 755 266 45031
Web Site: http://www.chinahaidian.com
Sales Range: $100-124.9 Million
Emp.: 300
Design, Manufacture & Marketer of Watches
N.A.I.C.S.: 423940

Ernest Borel Holdings Limited (1)
Unit 1612-18 Level 16 Tower 1 Grand Century Place, 193 Prince Edward Road West Mongkok, Kowloon, China (Hong Kong)
Tel.: (852) 36285511
Web Site: http://www.ernestborel.ch
Rev.: $17,514,420
Assets: $43,694,505
Liabilities: $29,944,650
Net Worth: $13,749,855
Earnings: ($1,538,670)
Emp.: 146
Fiscal Year-end: 12/31/2022
Holding Company
N.A.I.C.S.: 551112
Wei Xiong *(Exec Dir)*

Subsidiary (Non-US):

Boillat Les Bois S.A. (2)
Rue de l Ouest 7, 2340, Le Noirmont, Switzerland
Tel.: (41) 329532260
Web Site: http://www.blbwatch.ch
Watch Mfr & Distr
N.A.I.C.S.: 339910

Ernest Borel (Guangzhou) Co., Ltd. (2)
Suite 701 Taikoo Hui Tower 1 385 Tianhe Road Tianhe District, Guangzhou, 510620, China
Tel.: (86) 4008303865
Watch Distr
N.A.I.C.S.: 423940

Ernest Borel S.A. (2)
Rue Des Perrieres 8, Case Postale 234, 2340, Le Noirmont, Switzerland
Tel.: (41) 329261726
Watch Mfr & Distr
N.A.I.C.S.: 339910

Subsidiary (Domestic):

Top Win International Trading Limited (2)
33/F Sunshine Plaza 353 Lockhart Rd, Wanchai, China (Hong Kong)
Tel.: (852) 28157988
Watch Distr
N.A.I.C.S.: 423940
Yau Chiu Sit *(Founder)*

Eterna AG (1)
Schutzengasse 46, 2540, Grenchen, Switzerland
Tel.: (41) 32 938 2382
Web Site: https://www.eterna.com
Watch Mfr
N.A.I.C.S.: 334519

Montres Corum S.A.R.L. (1)
Rue du Petit-Chateau 1, 2300, La Chaux-de-Fonds, Switzerland
Tel.: (41) 329670670
Web Site: https://www.corum-watches.com
Watch & Clock Parts Mfr
N.A.I.C.S.: 334519

Rotary Watches Limited (1)
Elm Yard 13-16 Elm Street, London, WC1X 0BJ, United Kingdom
Tel.: (44) 2074345500
Web Site: https://www.rotarywatches.com
Watch Mfr
N.A.I.C.S.: 334519

Zhuhai Rossini Glasses Industry Limited (1)
No 12 Jingle Rd Jida, Xiangzhou Dist, Zhuhai, Guangdong, China
Tel.: (86) 7563956303
Web Site: http://www.rossini.com.cn
Sales Range: $50-74.9 Million
Emp.: 100
Eyeglasses Distr

N.A.I.C.S.: 423460

Zhuhai Rossini Watch Industry Limited (1)
No 12 Jingle Rd Jida, Xiangzhou Dist, Zhuhai, 519015, Guangdong, China
Tel.: (86) 7563333805
Web Site: http://www.rossini.com.cn
Sales Range: $125-149.9 Million
Emp.: 400
Watches Mfr & Distr
N.A.I.C.S.: 334519

Subsidiary (Domestic):

Guangzhou Five Goat Watch Co., Limited (2)
14 Shiliugang Rd, Guangzhou, 510315, China
Tel.: (86) 2084225149
Web Site: http://www.dixmont.com.cn
Watch Mfr
N.A.I.C.S.: 334519

CITYCON OYJ
Iso Omena Piispansilta 9 A, FI-02230, Espoo, Finland
Tel.: (358) 207664400
Web Site: https://www.citycon.com
Year Founded: 1988
CTY1S—(HEL)
Rev.: $346,260,712
Assets: $5,131,534,478
Liabilities: $2,527,636,006
Net Worth: $2,603,898,472
Earnings: $9,966,754
Emp.: 234
Fiscal Year-end: 12/31/19
Real Estate Sector
N.A.I.C.S.: 531390
Chaim K. Katzman *(Chm)*

Subsidiaries:

Citycon AB (1)
Box 47 203, 100 74, Stockholm, Sweden
Tel.: (46) 8 522 80 317
Real Estate Lending Services
N.A.I.C.S.: 531190

Subsidiary (Domestic):

Citycon Development AB (2)
Liljeholmstorget 7, PO Box 47203, Stockholm, 117 63, Sweden
Tel.: (46) 852280310
Web Site: http://www.citycon.se
Commercial Building Construction Services
N.A.I.C.S.: 236220

Citycon Jakobsbergs Centrum AB (2)
Tornerplatsen 30, PO Box 47203, 177 30, Stockholm, Sweden
Tel.: (46) 858430470
Shopping Mall Operator
N.A.I.C.S.: 531120

Citycon Liljeholmstorget Galleria AB (2)
Nybohovsbacken 38, Stockholm, 117 63, Sweden
Tel.: (46) 852280310
Shopping Mall Operator
N.A.I.C.S.: 531120

Stenungs Torg Fastighets AB (2)
Vastanvindsgatan 8, 444 30, Stenungsund, Sweden
Tel.: (46) 856253200
Web Site: https://www.stenungstorg.se
Emp.: 100
Shopping Mall Operator
N.A.I.C.S.: 531120

Strompilen AB (2)
Stroempilsplatsen 10, 907 43, Umea, Sweden
Tel.: (46) 90 71 96 10
Shopping Mall Operator
N.A.I.C.S.: 531120

Citycon Estonia OU (2)
Paldiski Mnt 102, Tallinn, 13522, Estonia
Tel.: (372) 6659100
Web Site: http://www.roccaalmare.ee

Sales Range: $10-24.9 Million
Emp.: 10
Home Management Services
N.A.I.C.S.: 721110

Subsidiary (Domestic):

Kristiine Keskus OU (2)
Endla 45, Tallinn, 10615, Estonia
Tel.: (372) 665 9100
Web Site: http://www.kristiine.com
Sales Range: $50-74.9 Million
Emp.: 9
Shopping Mall Operator
N.A.I.C.S.: 531120

Rocca al Mare Kaubanduskeskuse AS (2)
Paldiski mnt 102, 13522, Tallinn, Estonia
Tel.: (372) 6659345
Web Site: https://www.roccaalmare.ee
Emp.: 9
Shopping Mall Operator
N.A.I.C.S.: 531120

Citycon Finland Oy (1)
Iso Omena Piispansilta 9 A, 02230, Espoo, Finland
Tel.: (358) 207664400
Rental & Leasing Space Services
N.A.I.C.S.: 531190

Citycon Norway AS (1)
Verkstedveien 1, Skoyen, 0277, Oslo, Norway
Tel.: (47) 23282700
Shipping Services
N.A.I.C.S.: 492110

Forssan Hameentie 3 Koy (1)
Haemeentie 3, 31100, Forssa, Finland
Tel.: (358) 207 664 510
Shopping Mall Operator
N.A.I.C.S.: 531120

Heikintori Oy (1)
Kauppamiehentie 1, Tapiola, Espoo, 2130, Finland
Tel.: (358) 207664641
Web Site: http://www.heikonteri.fi
Emp.: 5
Shopping Mall Leasing Services
N.A.I.C.S.: 531120
Ismo Korhonen *(Gen Mgr)*

Jyvaskylan Kauppakatu 31 Koy (1)
Kauppakatu 31 3 krs, 40100, Jyvaskyla, Finland
Tel.: (358) 400 783 811
Shopping Mall Operator
N.A.I.C.S.: 531120

Kauppakeskus Isokarhu Oy (1)
Saaristenkatu 3, 13100, Hameenlinna, Finland
Tel.: (358) 10 228 70 47
Shopping Mall Operator
N.A.I.C.S.: 531120

Koskikeskuksen Huolto Oy (1)
Koskikeskus 2 krs Hatanpaan valtatie 1, 33100, Tampere, Finland
Tel.: (358) 505296555
Web Site: http://www.koskikeskus.fi
Real Estate Management Services
N.A.I.C.S.: 531390

Lahden Trio Koy (1)
Aleksanterinkatu 18, 15140, Lahti, Finland
Tel.: (358) 400150586
Real Estate Management Services
N.A.I.C.S.: 531390

Lappeenrannan Villimiehen Vitonen Oy (1)
Saaristenkatu 3, 13100, Hameenlinna, Finland
Tel.: (358) 10 228 7047
Real Estate Management Services
N.A.I.C.S.: 531390

Myyrmanni Koy (1)
Iskoskuja 3 A 1, PO Box 33, 01600, Vantaa, Finland
Tel.: (358) 406705927
Web Site: https://www.myyrmanni.fi
Real Estate Management Services
N.A.I.C.S.: 531390

Oulun Galleria Koy (1)
Isokatu 23, Oulu, 90100, Finland

Tel.: (358) 20 766 4474
Web Site: http://www.citycon.com
Emp.: 1
Shopping Mall Operator
N.A.I.C.S.: 531120

Porin Asema-Aukio Koy (1)
Satakunnankatu 23 B, 28130, Pori, Finland
Tel.: (358) 2 633 7046
Real Estate Management Services
N.A.I.C.S.: 531390

Porin Isolinnankatu 18 Koy (1)
Isolinnankatu 18, 28100, Pori, Finland
Tel.: (358) 10 228 7047
Shopping Mall Operator
N.A.I.C.S.: 531120

Tampereen Suvantokatu Koy (1)
Pohjoisesplanadi 35 A b, 00100, Helsinki, Finland
Tel.: (358) 102287047
Real Estate Management Services
N.A.I.C.S.: 531390

UAB Prekybos Centras Mandarinas (1)
Ateities G 91, Vilnius, 06324, Lithuania
Tel.: (370) 52794177
Web Site: http://www.mandarinas.lt
Sales Range: $50-74.9 Million
Emp.: 2
Shopping Mall Operator
N.A.I.C.S.: 531120

CITYLAND DEVELOPMENT CORPORATION
2F Cityland Condominium 10 Tower 1 156 HV Dela Costa St, Salcedo Village, Makati, 1226, Philippines
Tel.: (63) 28936060
Web Site: https://cityland.info
CDC—(PHI)
Rev.: $54,837,083
Assets: $250,747,458
Liabilities: $41,482,807
Net Worth: $209,264,651
Earnings: $17,409,788
Fiscal Year-end: 12/31/23
Real Estate Services
N.A.I.C.S.: 531210
Josef C. Gohoc *(Pres)*

CITYMAN LIMITED
153 Old No 43/35 2nd Floor Promenade Road 2nd Cross, Frazer Town, Bengaluru, 560 005, India
Tel.: (91) 8025540183
Web Site: https://www.cityman.in
Year Founded: 1992
521210—(BOM)
Rev.: $1,528,800
Assets: $1,051,719
Liabilities: $1,857,315
Net Worth: ($805,596)
Earnings: $408,026
Emp.: 3
Fiscal Year-end: 03/31/23
Readymade Garments Mfr & Distr
N.A.I.C.S.: 315250
Santhosh Joseph Karimattom *(Chm, CEO & Mng Dir)*

CITYNEON HOLDINGS LIMITED
Cityneon Building 25 Tai Seng Avenue 06-01, Singapore, 534104, Singapore
Tel.: (65) 65716338
Web Site: http://www.cityneon.net
Sales Range: $75-99.9 Million
Event & Exhibition Services
N.A.I.C.S.: 711310
Form Po Cho *(Sec)*

Subsidiaries:

Animax Designs Inc. (1)
PO Box 100893, Nashville, TN 37224-0893
Tel.: (615) 889-1248
Web Site: http://www.animaxdesigns.com
Emp.: 150

Cityneon Holdings Limited—(Continued)

Hobby, Toy & Game Stores
N.A.I.C.S.: 459120
Chuck Fawcett *(Pres & CEO)*

**Cityneon DAG India Private
Limited** (1)
D-236 Sector 63, Noida, 201307, Uttar
Pradesh, India
Tel.: (91) 1204273319
Web Site: http://www.cityneonindia.com
Interior Design Services
N.A.I.C.S.: 541410

**CITYON SYSTEMS (INDIA)
LTD.**
215 Delhi Chambers Delhi Gate, New
Delhi, 110 002, Delhi, India
Tel.: (91) 1141563395
Web Site:
http://www.cityonsystems.in
Year Founded: 2004
Commercial Goods Trading Services
N.A.I.C.S.: 523160
Ashok Kumar Sharma *(CFO)*

CITYSPRINT (UK) LIMITED
58-62 Scrutton Street, London, EC2A
4PH, United Kingdom
Tel.: (44) 2078801111 UK
Web Site: http://www.citysprint.co.uk
Sales Range: $50-74.9 Million
Emp.: 268
Courier Service
N.A.I.C.S.: 492110
Gerard Keenan *(Dir-Fin)*

Subsidiaries:

CYC Logistics Ltd (1)
Units 3-4 221 New Kent Road, London,
SE1 4AG, United Kingdom
Tel.: (44) 20 7939 7000
Web Site: http://www.cycplc.com
Courier Delivery Services
N.A.I.C.S.: 492110

Crisis Courier Solutions Ltd (1)
6 Scotia Close Brackmills Ind Est,
Northampton, NN4 7HR, United Kingdom
Tel.: (44) 1604674110
Web Site: http://www.crisiscouriers.com
Courier Delivery Services
N.A.I.C.S.: 492110
Helen O'Keeffe *(Mng Dir)*

Dash-It Ltd (1)
Unit 15 Majestic Road Nursling Industrial
Estate, Southampton, SO16 0YT, Hants,
United Kingdom
Tel.: (44) 2380226879
Web Site: http://www.dash-it.co.uk
Logistics Consulting Services
N.A.I.C.S.: 541614

Letchworth Couriers Ltd. (1)
Unit 4 Green Lane 1 Industrial Estate,
Letchworth, SG6 1HB, United Kingdom
Tel.: (44) 1462483583
Web Site:
http://www.letchworthcouriers.co.uk
Courier Delivery Services
N.A.I.C.S.: 492110
Dave Northfield *(Mng Dir)*

Network Logistics UK Ltd (1)
Unit 1 Lawford Terrace Lawford Close, Bir-
mingham, B7 4HJ, United Kingdom
Tel.: (44) 8453452248
Web Site: http://www.networklogistics.uk.net
Courier Delivery Services
N.A.I.C.S.: 492110

Sky Blue Couriers Ltd (1)
The Barn Grove Hill, Suckley, Worcester,
WR6 5EE, United Kingdom
Tel.: (44) 1212280107
Courier Delivery Services
N.A.I.C.S.: 492110

**CITYSTATE SAVINGS BANK,
INC.**
Citystate Centre Building 2nd floor
Shaw Boulevard, Metro Manila,
Pasig, 1600, Philippines

Tel.: (63) 284703333 PH
Web Site:
https://citystatesavings.com
Year Founded: 1997
CSB—(PHI)
Rev.: $8,311,544
Assets: $102,061,910
Liabilities: $81,404,429
Net Worth: $20,657,481
Earnings: ($1,740,987)
Emp.: 322
Fiscal Year-end: 12/31/23
Banking Services
N.A.I.C.S.: 522110
Emerson G. Igarta *(VP)*

**CITYWIDE SERVICE SOLU-
TIONS PTY LTD**
294 Arden Street, North Melbourne,
3051, VIC, Australia
Tel.: (61) 392615000
Web Site: http://www.citywide.com.au
Rev.: $165,419,847
Assets: $125,091,586
Liabilities: $45,650,933
Net Worth: $79,440,654
Earnings: $3,338,185
Emp.: 1,000
Fiscal Year-end: 06/30/19
Environmental, Civil Infrastructure,
Engineering & Maintenance Services
N.A.I.C.S.: 541330
John M. Brumby *(Chm)*

Subsidiaries:

Sterling Group Services Pty Ltd (1)
41 Huntingwood Drive, Huntingwood, 2148,
NSW, Australia
Tel.: (61) 2 9672 7499
Web Site: http://www.sterlinggroup.com.au
Landscaping Services
N.A.I.C.S.: 561730
Ian George *(Head-Gardner)*

CITYWIRE HOLDINGS LTD.
87 Vauxhall Walk, London, SE11
5HJ, United Kingdom
Tel.: (44) 2078402250
Web Site: http://www.citywire.co.uk
Sales Range: $50-74.9 Million
Emp.: 250
Holding Company; Internet & Maga-
zine Publisher
N.A.I.C.S.: 551112
Lawrence Lever *(Chm)*

Subsidiaries:

Citywire Financial Publishers Ltd. (1)
87 Vauxhall Walk, London, SE11 5HJ,
United Kingdom
Tel.: (44) 2078402250
Web Site: http://www.citywire.co.uk
Sales Range: $75-99.9 Million
Emp.: 150
Financial Information Publisher
N.A.I.C.S.: 513120

CITYXPRESS CORPORATION
200-1727 West Broadway, Vancou-
ver, V6J 4W6, BC, Canada
Tel.: (604) 638-3820
Web Site: http://www.cityxpress.com
Year Founded: 1997
Sales Range: $1-9.9 Million
Emp.: 50
Software Developer for Online Auc-
tions, Marketplaces & E-Commerce
Classifieds for Newspapers
N.A.I.C.S.: 513210
Phil Dubois *(Pres & CEO)*

CIVIC MOTORS HONDA
1171 St Laurent Blvd, Ottawa, K1K
3B7, ON, Canada
Tel.: (855) 842-5306
Web Site: http://www.civicmotors.com
Year Founded: 1975
New & Used Car Dealers

N.A.I.C.S.: 441110
Luis Castillo *(Mgr-Parts)*

CIVIL BANK LIMITED
Civil Trade Centre Sundhara, PO Box
9799, Kathmandu, 11, Nepal
Tel.: (977) 14251015
Web Site:
http://www.civilbank.com.np
CBL—(NEP)
Rev.: $53,683,734
Assets: $656,378,510
Liabilities: $569,371,651
Net Worth: $87,007,054
Earnings: $4,856,706
Fiscal Year-end: 07/15/20
Commercial Banking Services
N.A.I.C.S.: 522110
Govinda Gurung *(CEO)*

Subsidiaries:

Unique Finance Limited (1)
New Plaza Putalisadak, PO Box 25263,
Kathmandu, Nepal
Tel.: (977) 14440955
Financial Services
N.A.I.C.S.: 523999

**CIVIL MERCHANT BITTIYA
SANSTHA LIMITED**
Kuleshwor MM Complex, Kathmandu,
Nepal
Tel.: (977) 1 4289524
Web Site:
http://www.civilmbsl.com.np
Year Founded: 2005
Sales Range: Less than $1 Million
Financial Services
N.A.I.C.S.: 523999

**CIVIL PENSION FUND INVEST-
MENT CO.**
No 11 Next to Golestan Junction Zar-
toshtian St West Shiraz Ave, Tehran,
Iran
Tel.: (98) 2141237000
Web Site: https://www.cpfic.com
Year Founded: 2014
SAND1—(THE)
Sales Range: Less than $1 Million
Investment Services
N.A.I.C.S.: 525910
Omid Shahbazi *(Chm)*

CIVITANAVI SYSTEMS SPA
Via della Tecnologia 2/4, Pedaso,
63827, Ascoli Piceno, FM, Italy
Tel.: (39) 0733773648 IT
Web Site: https://www.civitanavi.com
Year Founded: 2012
CNS—(ITA)
Rev.: $37,137,848
Assets: $91,342,476
Liabilities: $40,932,867
Net Worth: $50,409,608
Earnings: $7,527,465
Emp.: 148
Fiscal Year-end: 12/31/22
Aircraft Part Mfr
N.A.I.C.S.: 336413
Andrea Pizzarulli *(CEO & Co-
Founder)*

Subsidiaries:

Civitanavi Systems UK Ltd. (1)
Building 20A1 Southmead Road, Filton,
Bristol, BS34 7RR, United Kingdom
Tel.: (44) 1174625818
Navigational System Distr
N.A.I.C.S.: 488330

**CIVITAS INTERNATIONAL
MANAGEMENT CONSUL-
TANTS GMBH**
Possartstrasse 12, D-81679, Munich,
Germany
Tel.: (49) 893838590

Web Site: http://www.civitas.com
Year Founded: 1971
Rev.: $19,311,600
Emp.: 35
Business Consulting Services
N.A.I.C.S.: 541618
Klaus Ewerth *(Mng Dir)*

**CIVITAS SOCIAL HOUSING
PLC**
51 New North Road Exeter, Devon,
London, EX4 4EP, United Kingdom
Tel.: (44) 2037094624
Web Site:
http://www.civitassocialhousing.com
CSH—(LSE)
Rev.: $66,555,434
Assets: $1,405,928,564
Liabilities: $491,506,859
Net Worth: $914,421,705
Earnings: $48,979,749
Fiscal Year-end: 03/31/21
Real Estate Manangement Services
N.A.I.C.S.: 531210
Paul Bridge *(CEO)*

CIVMEC LIMITED
16 Nautical Drive, Henderson, 6166,
WA, Australia
Tel.: (61) 894376288 SG
Web Site: https://www.civmec.com.au
Year Founded: 2009
CVL—(ASX)
Rev.: $690,091,261
Assets: $607,855,074
Liabilities: $281,852,386
Net Worth: $326,002,687
Earnings: $43,008,466
Emp.: 2,198
Fiscal Year-end: 06/30/24
Construction Engineering Services
N.A.I.C.S.: 237990
Justine Campbell *(CFO)*

CIWEN MEDIA CO., LTD.
Susan Cultural and Creative Industry
Park No 129 Nangao Road,
Cuigezhuang Chaoyang District, Bei-
jing, 100015, China
Tel.: (86) 1084409922
Web Site: http://www.ciwen.com.cn
Year Founded: 1998
002343—(SSE)
Rev.: $65,486,772
Assets: $227,811,636
Liabilities: $91,568,880
Net Worth: $136,242,756
Earnings: $6,911,892
Fiscal Year-end: 12/31/22
Investment Services
N.A.I.C.S.: 523999
Hua Yuping *(Chm)*

CJ BIOSCIENCE, INC.
Chunlab Tower 34 Samseong-Ro 85-
Gil, Gangnam-Gu, Seoul, 06194, Ko-
rea (South)
Tel.: (82) 234522520
Web Site:
http://www.cjbioscience.com
Year Founded: 2009
311690—(KRS)
Rev.: $4,013,985
Assets: $107,046,824
Liabilities: $26,221,991
Net Worth: $80,824,834
Earnings: ($17,730,555)
Emp.: 76
Fiscal Year-end: 12/31/21
Biotechnology Research & Develop-
ment Services
N.A.I.C.S.: 541714

**CJ CENTURY LOGISTICS
HOLDINGS BERHAD**
No 12 Persiaran Astana, KU2 Bandar

Bukit Raja, 41050, Port Klang, Selangor Darul Ehsan, Malaysia
Tel.: (60) 333855888
Web Site: https://www.cjcentury.com
Year Founded: 1997
7117—(KLS)
Rev.: $196,909,206
Assets: $162,594,074
Liabilities: $68,415,450
Net Worth: $94,178,624
Earnings: $5,960,423
Emp.: 1,100
Fiscal Year-end: 12/31/22
Freight Forwarding, Transportation & Warehousing Services
N.A.I.C.S.: 493110
Edwin Khoo Soon Yeap *(Exec Dir)*

Subsidiaries:

CJ Century Technology Sdn. Bhd.   **(1)**
Lot 4A Jalan Sultan Mohamed 3, Kawasan Perindustrian Bandar Sultan Suleiman, 42000, Port Klang, Selangor Darul Ehsan, Malaysia
Tel.: (60) 333222488
Procurement Logistics Services
N.A.I.C.S.: 541614

Century Logistics Sdn. Bhd.   **(1)**
No 12 Persiaran Astana / KU2 Bandar Bukit raja, 41050, Klang, Selangor Darul Ehsan, Malaysia
Tel.: (60) 333755888
Procurement Logistics Services
N.A.I.C.S.: 541614

CJ CGV CO., LTD.
I Park Mall 6th FL 55 Hangang-Daero 23-gil, Yongsan-gu, Seoul, 04377, Korea (South)
Tel.: (82) 23716660
Web Site: http://www.cgv.co.kr
Year Founded: 1999
079160—(KRS)
Rev.: $982,761,736
Assets: $2,762,326,252
Liabilities: $2,460,826,728
Net Worth: $301,499,524
Earnings: ($127,442,769)
Emp.: 1,185
Fiscal Year-end: 12/31/22
Theater Operator
N.A.I.C.S.: 711110
Jay-Hyun Lee *(Chm)*

CJ CORPORATION
CJ CheilJedang Center 330 Dongho-ro, Jung-Gu, Seoul, Korea (South)
Tel.: (82) 27268114
Web Site: https://en.cj.net
Year Founded: 1953
001040—(KRS)
Rev.: $29,439,174,711
Assets: $36,822,967,863
Liabilities: $22,658,439,874
Net Worth: $14,164,527,989
Earnings: $187,687,174
Emp.: 53
Fiscal Year-end: 12/31/20
Food Product Mfr & Distr
N.A.I.C.S.: 551112
Hong Ki Kim *(Co-CEO & VP)*

Subsidiaries:

Amoeba Culture Co., Ltd.   **(1)**
8-3 Nonhyeon-ro 146-gil, Gangnam-gu, Seoul, Korea (South)
Tel.: (82) 2344517978
Web Site: https://www.amoebaculture.com
Music Concert Services
N.A.I.C.S.: 711310

Anipark Co., Ltd.   **(1)**
7th FL Mario Tower 28 digital-ro 30-gil, Guro-gu, Seoul, 152-741, Korea (South)
Tel.: (82) 1588 5180
Web Site: http://www.ani-park.com
Online Game Development Services
N.A.I.C.S.: 541511

Honggyu Kim *(CEO)*

Batavia Biosciences B.V.   **(1)**
Bioscience Park Leiden Zernikedreef 16, 2333 CL, Leiden, Netherlands
Tel.: (31) 889950600
Web Site: https://bataviabiosciences.com
Biotechnology Research & Development Services
N.A.I.C.S.: 541714

Batavia Biosciences Inc.   **(1)**
300 Trade Ctr Ste 6650, Woburn, MA 01801
Tel.: (781) 305-3921
Biotechnology Research & Development Services
N.A.I.C.S.: 541714

CJ (Changchun) Feed Co., Ltd.   **(1)**
No 1958 Xingbei Road, Economic and Technological Development Zone, Changchun, China
Tel.: (86) 43189368896
Corrugated Carton & Textile Tube Mfr
N.A.I.C.S.: 322211

CJ (Chengdu) Feed Co., Ltd.   **(1)**
No 12 Hongda Road, Liucheng Town Wenjiang District, Chengdu, 611130, Sichuan, China
Tel.: (86) 2882782154
Corrugated Carton & Textile Tube Mfr
N.A.I.C.S.: 322211

CJ (Nanjing) Feed Co., Ltd.   **(1)**
Zhujiang Road, Nanjing zhujiang Industrial Area Pukou District, Nanjing, 211800, Jiangsu, China
Tel.: (86) 1051087711
Corrugated Carton & Textile Tube Mfr
N.A.I.C.S.: 322211

CJ (Shenyang) Feed Co., Ltd.   **(1)**
Shenyang New and High-tech Agricultural Development Zone, huishan street No 127, Shenyang, 110164, Liaoning, China
Tel.: (86) 5328491140
Corrugated Carton & Textile Tube Mfr
N.A.I.C.S.: 322211

CJ 4DPLEX Co., Ltd.   **(1)**
8F 55 Hangang-daero 23-gil, Yongsan-gu, Seoul, Korea (South)
Tel.: (82) 23715615
Web Site: https://www.cj4dx.com
Theater Operator
N.A.I.C.S.: 512131
Theodore T. Y. Kim *(Chief Bus Officer)*

CJ America, Inc.   **(1)**
300 S Grand Ave Ste 1100, Los Angeles, CA 90071
Tel.: (213) 338-2700
Web Site: https://cjamerica.com
Sales Range: $25-49.9 Million
Emp.: 50
Public Relations Services
N.A.I.C.S.: 541820

Subsidiary (Domestic):

CJ E&M America Inc.   **(2)**
5700 Wilshire Blvd Ste 550, Los Angeles, CA 90036
Tel.: (213) 406-8600
Emp.: 60
Media Advertising Services
N.A.I.C.S.: 541840

CJ Entertainment America Corp.   **(2)**
5700 Wilshire Blvd Ste 550, Los Angeles, CA 90036
Tel.: (213) 406-8600
Sales Range: $25-49.9 Million
Emp.: 20
Entertainers & Entertainment Groups
N.A.I.C.S.: 711410

CJ Internet Inc.   **(2)**
1298 Kifer Rd Ste 507, Sunnyvale, CA 94086-5321
Tel.: (408) 232-5487
Internet Publishing & Broadcasting
N.A.I.C.S.: 516210

CJ Omni, Inc.   **(2)**
6305 Alondra Blvd, Paramount, CA 90723
Tel.: (562) 531-3854
Food Products Mfr
N.A.I.C.S.: 311999

CJ Pacific Corporation   **(2)**
141 W Jackson Blvd Ste 2194, Chicago, IL 60604
Tel.: (503) 223-6555
Web Site: http://www.cjpis.co.kr
Food Mfr
N.A.I.C.S.: 311999

TMI Trading Corp.   **(2)**
7 Bushwick Pl, Brooklyn, NY 11206
Tel.: (718) 386-6868
Web Site: https://www.twinmarquis.com
Food Products Distr
N.A.I.C.S.: 424420

CJ CheilJedang Corp.   **(1)**
CJ CheilJedang Center 330 Dongho-ro, Jung-gu, Seoul, 04560, Korea (South)
Tel.: (82) 267401114
Web Site: https://www.cj.co.kr
Rev.: $21,542,592,305
Assets: $21,975,178,919
Liabilities: $13,231,549,442
Net Worth: $8,743,629,478
Earnings: $415,259,190
Emp.: 8,612
Fiscal Year-end: 12/31/2023
Food Products Mfr
N.A.I.C.S.: 311999
Kyung Shik Sohn *(Chm & CEO-CJ Corp)*

Subsidiary (Non-US):

CJ (Haerbin) Feed Co., Ltd.   **(2)**
Bohaidong Road Haping Road, Haerbin city Development zone Jizhong District, Harbin, 150060, Heilongjiang, China
Tel.: (86) 4518 678 6068
Web Site: https://china.cj.net
Animal Feed Mfr
N.A.I.C.S.: 311119

CJ (Shenyang) Biotech Co., Ltd.   **(2)**
Shenbei Hui Shan Shen North Road Economic Development Zone No 157, Shenyang, Liaoning, China
Tel.: (86) 24 31410076
Biotechnology Research & Development Services
N.A.I.C.S.: 541714

CJ Beijing Foods Co., Ltd.   **(2)**
Songlanpu, Shahe Town Changping District, Beijing, 102206, China
Tel.: (86) 108 072 3171
Web Site: https://english.cj.net
Food Mfr
N.A.I.C.S.: 311999

Subsidiary (Domestic):

CJ Beijing Bakery Co., Ltd.   **(3)**
Songlanpu, Shahe Town Changping District, Beijing, 102206, China
Tel.: (86) 105 108 7711
Web Site: https://www.english.cj.net
Sales Range: $750-799.9 Million
Cookie & Cracker Mfr
N.A.I.C.S.: 311821

Subsidiary (US):

CJ Bio America Inc.   **(2)**
1946 Harvest Ave, Fort Dodge, IA 50501
Tel.: (515) 302-8028
Bioscience Product Mfr & Distr
N.A.I.C.S.: 325411
Jeffrey Booth *(Mgr-HR)*

Subsidiary (Non-US):

CJ Changsha Feed Co., Ltd   **(2)**
No 8 Renhe Rd Gaotangling Town Wangcheng Xian, Changsha, 410200, Hunan, China
Tel.: (86) 731 82963000
Animal Feed Mfr
N.A.I.C.S.: 311119

Subsidiary (US):

CJ Foods, Inc.   **(2)**
5801 S Malt Ave, Los Angeles, CA 90040
Tel.: (323) 278-5200
Sales Range: $1-9.9 Million
Emp.: 11
Groceries, General Line Whslr
N.A.I.C.S.: 424410
Shin Sung *(Pres)*

Subsidiary (Domestic):

CJ Bakery, Inc.   **(3)**
3530 Wilshire Blvd Ste 1220, Los Angeles, CA 90010-2341
Tel.: (213) 427-5566
Sales Range: $10-24.9 Million
Emp.: 50
Commercial Bakeries
N.A.I.C.S.: 311812

Subsidiary (Non-US):

CJ Qingdao Feed Co., Ltd.   **(2)**
Laixi Economic & Technical Development Zone, Qingdao, 266601, Shandong, China
Tel.: (86) 532 8849 3851
Animal Feed Mfr
N.A.I.C.S.: 311119

Subsidiary (Domestic):

CJ Seafood Corporation   **(2)**
388Bungil 32 Dunchondearo, Jungwon-gu, Seongnam, Gyeonggi-do, Korea (South)
Tel.: (82) 317309114
Web Site: http://www.cjseafood.net
Rev.: $117,122,029
Assets: $109,994,769
Liabilities: $51,941,092
Net Worth: $58,053,677
Earnings: $5,691,033
Emp.: 382
Fiscal Year-end: 12/31/2022
Food Product Whslr
N.A.I.C.S.: 424460
In-Duk Lee *(CEO)*

Subsidiary (Non-US):

CJ Tianjin Feed Co., Ltd.   **(2)**
Jin-Hai Road East Jing-Hai Economy Development Zone New Borough, Tianjin, 301600, China
Tel.: (86) 22 6860 9931
Animal Feed Mfr
N.A.I.C.S.: 311119

CJ Vina Agri Co., Ltd.   **(2)**
National Highway 1A, My Yen Commune Ben Luc District, Ho Chi Minh City, Long An, Vietnam
Tel.: (84) 272 387 0366
Web Site: https://cjvina.com
Sales Range: $75-99.9 Million
Animal Feed Mfr
N.A.I.C.S.: 311119

CJ Zhengzhou Feed Co., Ltd.   **(2)**
Hehuan west street No 3, Zhengzhou, 450001, Henan, China
Tel.: (86) 371 6784 8493
Animal Feed Mfr
N.A.I.C.S.: 311119

Subsidiary (US):

Kahiki Foods, Inc.   **(2)**
1100 Morrison Rd, Gahanna, OH 43230-3230
Web Site: http://www.kahiki.com
Asian-inspired Frozen Food Mfr
N.A.I.C.S.: 311412

Subsidiary (Non-US):

PT. CJ Feed Jombang   **(2)**
Jl Raya Mojoagung-Jombang Km 2, Desa Gambiran-Mojoagung Jomban, Bali, Jawa Timur, Indonesia
Tel.: (62) 321497200
Sales Range: $25-49.9 Million
Animal Feed Mfr
N.A.I.C.S.: 311119

PT. CheilJedang Indonesia (Pasuruan)   **(2)**
DS Arjosari Kec Rejoso, 67 181, Pasuruan, East Java, Indonesia
Tel.: (62) 343401349
Food Additives Mfr
N.A.I.C.S.: 325199

PT. CheilJedang Superfeed   **(2)**
Jl Lanud Gorda Desa Julang Kec Cikande Kab, Serang, 42101, Banten, Indonesia
Tel.: (62) 254400660
Animal Feed Mfr
N.A.I.C.S.: 311119

CJ Corporation—(Continued)

Subsidiary (Domestic):

Youngwoo Frozen Foods Co., Ltd. (2)
4F FI B/D 40 munjeong-dong, Songpa-gu, Seoul, Korea (South)
Tel.: (82) 2 3403 9684 5
Web Site: http://www.young-woo.com
Frozen Food Mfr
N.A.I.C.S.: 311412
Kyung Yeol Yoo (CEO)

CJ China Ltd. (1)
Suite 3003 30/FI Central Plaza 18 Harbour Road, Wanchai, China (Hong Kong)
Tel.: (852) 28029909
Web Site: http://www.cjpis.co.kr
Sales Range: $25-49.9 Million
Emp.: 50
Chemical & Allied Products Merchant Whslr
N.A.I.C.S.: 424690

CJ Corp. (1)
Saigon Trade Center 28th FI Unit 2805 37 Ton Duc Thang Street, District 1, Ho Chi Minh City, Vietnam
Tel.: (84) 89100720
Corrugated Carton & Textile Tube Mfr
N.A.I.C.S.: 322211

CJ Corp. (Beijing) (1)
13/F ONE INDIGO 20 Jiuxianqiao Road, Chaoyang District, Beijing, 100016, China
Tel.: (86) 1056396000
Convenience Foods Mfr
N.A.I.C.S.: 311999

CJ Corp. (Moscow) (1)
ul Ordjonikidz 11 block 1/2, Moscow, 117-198, Russia
Tel.: (7) 4959373457
Web Site: http://www.cj.com
Sales Range: $25-49.9 Million
Emp.: 5
Chemicals Mfr
N.A.I.C.S.: 325411
Kim Seong Min (Mng Dir)

CJ DCH Guangdong Frozen Food Co., Ltd. (1)
10 Jiang Yu Road, Jinguzhou Xinhui District, Jiangmen, 529100, China
Tel.: (86) 7506396660
Food & Beverage Mfr & Distr
N.A.I.C.S.: 311999

CJ ENM Co., Ltd. (1)
870-13 Gwacheon-daero, Seocho-gu, Seoul, Korea (South)
Tel.: (82) 221070114
Web Site: http://www.cjenm.com
Rev.: $3,675,646,384
Assets: $7,924,833,177
Liabilities: $4,592,733,774
Net Worth: $3,332,099,403
Earnings: ($135,617,130)
Emp.: 3,366
Fiscal Year-end: 12/31/2022
Television Home Shopping Services
N.A.I.C.S.: 459999
Heo Min Heoi (CEO)

Subsidiary (US):

CJ CGV America LA LLC (2)
1801 Century Park E Ste 1901, Los Angeles, CA 90067
Tel.: (310) 557-3050
Home Shopping Services
N.A.I.C.S.: 516210

Subsidiary (Domestic):

CJ E&M Corporation (2)
CJ E&M Center 66 Sangamsan-ro, Mapo-gu, Seoul, 121-904, Korea (South)
Tel.: (82) 2 371 5501
Web Site: http://www.cjenm.com
Sales Range: $1-9.9 Million
Television Broadcasting Services
N.A.I.C.S.: 516120
Sung Su Kim (CEO)

Subsidiary (Domestic):

CJ Olive Young Co., Ltd. (3)
24th floor KDB Tower 372 Hangang-daero, Yongsan-gu, Seoul, 04323, Korea (South)
Tel.: (82) 1 577 4887

Web Site: https://www.oliveyoung.co.kr
Beauty Product Distr
N.A.I.C.S.: 456120

CJ Telenix Co., Ltd. (3)
10th/11th floor Daeryung Post Tower 288 Digital-ro, Guro-gu, Seoul, 8390, Korea (South)
Tel.: (82) 220269900
Web Site: https://www.cjtelenix.com
Television Broadcasting Services
N.A.I.C.S.: 516120

Subsidiary (Domestic):

StudioDragon Corp. (2)
75 Maebongsan-ro 17th Floor, Mapo-gu, Seoul, Korea (South)
Tel.: (82) 23718502
Web Site: https://www.studiodragon.net
Rev.: $535,324,446
Assets: $836,541,117
Liabilities: $329,760,305
Net Worth: $506,780,812
Earnings: $38,783,352
Emp.: 141
Fiscal Year-end: 12/31/2022
Drama Studio Contract Services
N.A.I.C.S.: 611610
Si Kwon Lee (Auditor)

CJ ENM Japan Inc. (1)
10F CJ Bldg 2-7-4 Nishishinbashi, Minato-ku, Tokyo, 105-0003, Japan
Tel.: (81) 335194551
Food & Beverage Mfr & Distr
N.A.I.C.S.: 311999

CJ Educations Corporation (1)
9F CJ Cheiljedang Center 330 dongho-ro, Jung-gu, Seoul, 100-400, Korea (South)
Tel.: (82) 1577 0801
Web Site: http://www.cjeducations.com
Educational Support Services
N.A.I.C.S.: 611710

CJ Engineering & Construction Corp (1)
Seogun Bldg Kyonggi-Do, Anyang, 431-810, Korea (South)
Tel.: (82) 27269504
Construction Engineering Services
N.A.I.C.S.: 541330

CJ Europe GmbH (1)
Ober Der Roeth 4, 65824, Schwalbach, Germany
Tel.: (49) 6196590126
Web Site: http://www.cjpis.co.kr
Sales Range: $25-49.9 Million
Emp.: 21
Farm Supplies Whslr
N.A.I.C.S.: 424910
Seong-Jin Bae (Mng Dir)

CJ Foods Manufacturing, Corporation (1)
500 S State College Blvd, Fullerton, CA 92831
Tel.: (714) 888-8200
Food Products Mfr
N.A.I.C.S.: 311999

CJ Foods Myanmar Co., Ltd. (1)
No 57/60 Lower Mingalardon Road, Danyingone Insein Township, Yangon, Myanmar
Tel.: (95) 9454339179
Food & Beverage Mfr & Distr
N.A.I.C.S.: 311999

CJ Foods USA Inc. (1)
4 Centerpointe Dr Ste 100, La Palma, CA 90623
Tel.: (714) 367-7200
Web Site: https://cjfoods.com
Food Product Mfr & Distr
N.A.I.C.S.: 311991

CJ Foods Vietnam Co., Ltd. (1)
Lot III/21 - Road 19/5A, Tan Binh Industrial Park Tay Thanh Ward Tan Phu District, Ho Chi Minh City, Vietnam
Tel.: (84) 873006054
Food Product Mfr & Distr
N.A.I.C.S.: 311991

CJ Foodville Corp. (1)
3 9-11F KT&G Eulji-ro Tower 34 106-9 Chodong Mareunnae-ro, Jung-gu, 04555, Seoul, Korea (South)
Tel.: (82) 1 577 0700

Web Site: https://www.cjfoodville.co.kr
Restaurant Operators
N.A.I.C.S.: 722511

Subsidiary (US):

Tous Les Jours International Corp. (2)
3530 Wilshire Blvd, Los Angeles, CA 90010-2020
Tel.: (213) 427-5566
Food Products Mfr
N.A.I.C.S.: 311999

CJ Foodville USA Inc. (1)
6834 E Slauson Ave, Commerce, CA 90040
Tel.: (323) 480-9100
Food Service
N.A.I.C.S.: 722310

CJ Freshway America Corporation (1)
300 S Grand Ave Ste 1100, Los Angeles, CA 90071
Tel.: (714) 494-1299
Food & Beverage Mfr & Distr
N.A.I.C.S.: 311999

CJ Freshway Qingdao Corporation (1)
Unit 505 SIIC T3 No 195 HongKong Road, Laoshan District, Qingdao, China
Tel.: (86) 53255716600
Food & Beverage Mfr & Distr
N.A.I.C.S.: 311999

CJ Grand, S.A. De C.V. (1)
AV Mariano Escobedo 555 Piso 1 Col, Bosque de Chapultepec, 11580, Mexico, Mexico
Tel.: (52) 8008898989
Food & Beverage Mfr & Distr
N.A.I.C.S.: 311999

CJ ICM (UK) Ltd. (1)
22-24 Red lion Court Fleet Street, London, EC4A 3EB, United Kingdom
Tel.: (44) 2034758008
Logistic Services
N.A.I.C.S.: 541614

CJ ICM Austria GmbH (1)
Wagramerstrasse 4 Top Nr ZW61-01-08, 1220, Vienna, Austria
Tel.: (43) 1263234213
Logistic Services
N.A.I.C.S.: 541614

CJ ICM FZCO (1)
Plot Mo-0425 N303, PO Box 61280, Jebel Ali Free Zone, Dubai, United Arab Emirates
Tel.: (971) 48055000
Web Site: https://www.cj-icm.com
Logistics Consulting Servies
N.A.I.C.S.: 541614

CJ ICM Italia S.R.L (1)
Via di Campo Marzio 14, 34123, Trieste, Italy
Tel.: (39) 0403173526
Logistic Services
N.A.I.C.S.: 541614

CJ ICM Logistics Espana S.L. (1)
Dr Fleming Nbr 1 1st Floor, 28036, Madrid, Spain
Tel.: (34) 913949130
Logistic Services
N.A.I.C.S.: 541614

CJ ICM Logistics GmbH (1)
Hammerbrookstr 90, 20097, Hamburg, Germany
Tel.: (49) 406077190
Logistic Services
N.A.I.C.S.: 541614

CJ ICM Logistics LLC (1)
37m Ilia Chavchavadze Avenue Axis Towers Floor 12, 179, Tbilisi, Georgia
Tel.: (995) 322259595
Logistic Services
N.A.I.C.S.: 541614

CJ ICM Tashkent MchJ (1)
4A 1-st Nukus Street, 100060, Tashkent, Uzbekistan
Tel.: (998) 712540019
Logistic Services
N.A.I.C.S.: 541614

CJ International Trading Co., Ltd. (1)
Rm 2501-2502 Maxdo Centre No 8 Xingyi Road, Hongqiao Development Zone, Shanghai, China
Tel.: (86) 2152080281
Logistic Services
N.A.I.C.S.: 541614

CJ Japan Corp. (1)
6th floor of CJ Building 2-7-4 Nishi-Shimbashi, Minato-ku, Tokyo, 105-0003, Japan
Tel.: (81) 33 580 1050
Web Site: https://www.cjjapan.net
Sales Range: $25-49.9 Million
Emp.: 25
Durable Goods Whslr
N.A.I.C.S.: 423990

Subsidiary (Domestic):

CJ E&M Japan Inc. (2)
3rd floor of CJ Building 2-7-4 Nishi-Shimbashi, Minato-Ku, Tokyo, 105-0003, Japan
Tel.: (81) 33 502 3141
Web Site: https://mnetjp.com
Sales Range: $25-49.9 Million
Radio Broadcasting Stations
N.A.I.C.S.: 334220

CJ Internet Japan Corp. (2)
2-7-4 Nishishinbashi, Minatoku, Tokyo, 105-0003, Japan
Tel.: (81) 351577430
Internet Services
N.A.I.C.S.: 517121

CJ Liao Cheng Biotech Co., Ltd. (1)
Liaohe Road, Liaocheng Economic and Development Zone, Liaocheng, 252022, Shandong, China
Tel.: (86) 6358519696
Organic Chemical Mfr
N.A.I.C.S.: 325199

CJ Logistics Asia Pte. Ltd. (1)
20 Toh Guan Rd, Singapore, 608839, Singapore
Tel.: (65) 64102800
Logistic Services
N.A.I.C.S.: 541614

CJ Logistics Corporation (1)
7, Jong-ro 5-gil, Jongno-gu, Seoul, Seoul, 03157, Korea (South)
Tel.: (82) 237820114
Web Site: https://www.cjlogistics.com
Rev.: $9,304,256,765
Assets: $7,434,760,961
Liabilities: $4,340,446,465
Net Worth: $3,094,314,496
Earnings: $139,250,807
Emp.: 7,442
Fiscal Year-end: 12/31/2022
Logistic Services
N.A.I.C.S.: 541614
Sin-Ho Ho Kang (CEO)

Subsidiary (Domestic):

CJ GLS Corporation (2)
2-5F CJ Korea Express Bldg 58-12 Seosomun-dong, Jung-gu, Seoul, Korea (South)
Tel.: (82) 2 870 6185
Web Site: http://www.cjgls.com
Third Party Logistics Services
N.A.I.C.S.: 488510

Subsidiary (US):

CJ GLS America, Inc. (3)
5801 S Malt Ave, Commerce, CA 90040
Tel.: (323) 278-5280
Web Site: http://www.cjgls.com
Third Party Logistics Services
N.A.I.C.S.: 488510

Subsidiary (Non-US):

CJ GLS Asia Pte. Ltd. (3)
20 Toh Guan Road #08-00 CJ GLS Building, Singapore, 608839, Singapore
Tel.: (65) 64102800
Web Site: http://www.cjgls.com
Logistics Consulting Servies
N.A.I.C.S.: 541614
Cheong Kwok Weng (Mng Dir)

Subsidiary (Non-US):

CJ GLS (Hong Kong) Ltd. (4)
Room 2503-4 EW International Tower 120
Texaco Road, Tsuen Wan, Hong Kong,
China (Hong Kong)
Tel.: (852) 2429 6788
Logistics Consulting Servies
N.A.I.C.S.: 541614

Subsidiary (Domestic):

CJ GLS (S) Airfreight Pte. Ltd. (4)
119 Airport Cargo Road, 02-07/08 Changi
Cargo Agents, Singapore, 918109, Singa-
pore
Tel.: (65) 430338
Web Site: http://www.cjgls.com
Sales Range: $25-49.9 Million
Emp.: 25
Scheduled Freight Air Transportation
N.A.I.C.S.: 481112
Tommy Lin *(Mgr-Ops)*

Subsidiary (Non-US):

CJ GLS (S) Infotech Pte. Ltd. (4)
Tel.: (65) 64102800
Web Site: http://m.cj.net
Logistics Consulting Servies
N.A.I.C.S.: 541614

Subsidiary (Domestic):

CJ GLS (S) Shipping Pte. Ltd. (4)
20 Toh Guan Road, 08-00 CJ GLS Building,
Singapore, 608839, Singapore
Tel.: (65) 64102800
Web Site: http://www.cjkoreaexpress.com
Sales Range: $125-149.9 Million
Navigational Services to Shipping
N.A.I.C.S.: 488330
Lee Joon *(Gen Mgr)*

Subsidiary (Non-US):

CJ GLS (Shenzhen) Co., Ltd. (4)
Rm 231 2nd floor Bonded Market Builiding
No88 Xiangyu Road, Huli District, Xiamen,
China
Tel.: (86) 592 291 2217
Logistics Consulting Servies
N.A.I.C.S.: 541614

CJ GLS (Thailand) Co., Ltd. (4)
598 Q House Phloenchit Khwang Lumphini
Khet, Pathumwan, Bangkok, 10330, Thai-
land
Tel.: (66) 26273925 8
Logistics Consulting Servies
N.A.I.C.S.: 541614

CJ GLS Malaysia Sdn. Bhd. (4)
Lot D23 Cargo Forwarders Building Malay-
sia Airlines Freight, Kuala Lumpur, 64000,
Selangor, Malaysia
Tel.: (60) 3 8787 1388
Web Site: http://www.cjgls.com
Emp.: 5
Logistics Consulting Servies
N.A.I.C.S.: 541614
Bruce Lee *(Gen Mgr)*

Subsidiary (Domestic):

**CJ GLS Forwarding Malaysia Sdn.
Bhd.** (5)
No 68 Jln Batai Laut 4 Taman Intan, 10050,
Penang, Malaysia
Tel.: (60) 333411818
Freight Forwarding Services
N.A.I.C.S.: 488510

Subsidiary (Non-US):

PT CJ GLS Indonesia (4)
Graha Kirana Building Lt 2 Unit 201 Jalan
Yos Sudarso Kav 88, Jakarta, Indonesia
Tel.: (62) 21 6531 1202
Logistics Consulting Servies
N.A.I.C.S.: 541614

Qingdao CJ GLS Inc. (4)
Qingdao Guangdong Development bank
B/D 1803 No 40, Shangdong Road,
Qingdao, Shangdong, China
Tel.: (86) 53285015660
Logistics Consulting Servies
N.A.I.C.S.: 541614

Subsidiary (Non-US):

**CJ GLS Central America, S.A. DE
C.V.** (3)
Manufactura 502 Parque Industrial Quere-
taro, Santa Rosa Jauregui, 76220, Quere-
taro, Mexico
Tel.: (52) 4422409301
Web Site: http://www.cjgls.com
Emp.: 33
Logistics Consulting Servies
N.A.I.C.S.: 541614
Jim Young Kim *(Gen Mgr)*

CJ GLS Philippines Inc. (3)
6/F TM Kalaw Center 667 TM Kalaw Er-
mita, Manila, Philippines
Tel.: (63) 63 567 1320
Logistics Consulting Servies
N.A.I.C.S.: 541614

Subsidiary (Domestic):

**CJ GLS Philippines VMI Warehouse
Inc.** (4)
36 Burgos St Calamba City Dental Care
Clinic, Calamba, 4027, Philippines
Tel.: (63) 2 567 1320
Logistics Consulting Servies
N.A.I.C.S.: 541614

Subsidiary (Domestic):

**CJ Korea Express Busan Container
Terminal Corporation** (2)
294 Sinseon-ro, Nam-gu, Busan, 608-741,
Korea (South)
Tel.: (82) 51 620 0200
Web Site: http://www.kbct.co.kr
Logistics Consulting Servies
N.A.I.C.S.: 541614
Sung-Ho Choi *(Pres)*

Subsidiary (US):

CJ Logistics America, LLC (2)
1750 S Wolf Rd, Des Plaines, IL
60018-1924 (90%)
Tel.: (800) 372-1960
Web Site: https://america.cjlogistics.com
Warehousing, Storage & Distribution Ser-
vices
N.A.I.C.S.: 493110
Ken Heller *(COO)*

CJ Logistics USA Corporation (2)
18805 S Laurel Park Rd, Rancho
Dominguez, CA 90220
Tel.: (814) 994-1200
Logistic Services
N.A.I.C.S.: 541614

Subsidiary (Non-US):

Korea Express Europe GmbH (2)
Cargo City Sued Geb 558E, 60549, Frank-
furt am Main, Germany
Tel.: (49) 69 6860 3991
Web Site: http://www.koreaexpress.de
Freight Forwarding Services
N.A.I.C.S.: 488510

**Korea Express Hong Kong Co.,
Ltd.** (2)
Unit A 9/F Dynamic Cargo Centre 188 Ye-
ung UK Road, Tsuen Wan, New Territories,
China (Hong Kong)
Tel.: (852) 3126 9640
Freight Forwarding Services
N.A.I.C.S.: 488510
Young-Ho Jang *(Mgr)*

Korea Express Japan Co., Ltd. (2)
Tel.: (81) 335005841
Web Site: http://www.korex.co.jp
Sales Range: $25-49.9 Million
Emp.: 27
Freight Forwarding Services
N.A.I.C.S.: 488510
Han-Bok Woo *(Pres & CEO)*

**Korea Express Shanghai Co.,
Ltd.** (2)
RM 1205-1209 No 1118 South Pudong
Road Pudong New District, Shanghai,
200122, China
Tel.: (86) 21 6859 5000
Web Site: http://www.korex.co.kr
Warehousing & Freight Forwarding Services
N.A.I.C.S.: 493110

Jae-Kyoon Kim *(Mgr)*

Korea Express Tianjin Co., Ltd. (2)
Room No 806 8/F Tower C City Center Bldg
Xigang Street, Heping District, Tianjin,
China
Tel.: (86) 22 2351 1009
Freight Forwarding Services
N.A.I.C.S.: 488510
Kwan-Sik Yun *(Mgr)*

Subsidiary (US):

Korea Express U.S.A. Inc. (2)
11 Commerce Ct W S, New Brunswick, NJ
08810
Tel.: (609) 860-3070
Web Site: http://www.korex.co.kr
Logistics & Parcel Delivery Services
N.A.I.C.S.: 492110

CJ Logistics Europe GmbH (1)
Rhonestr 7, 60528, Frankfurt am Main, Ger-
many
Tel.: (49) 6968603990
Food & Beverage Mfr & Distr
N.A.I.C.S.: 311999

CJ Logistics Japan Corporation (1)
CJ Bldg 2-7-4 Nishishinbashi, Minato-ku,
Tokyo, 105-0003, Japan
Tel.: (81) 335005841
Logistic Services
N.A.I.C.S.: 541614

CJ Logistics PH Corp. (1)
8/F iMet BPO Tower, Metropolitan Park Bay
Area Roxas Boulevard, Pasay, Philippines
Tel.: (63) 25413904
Logistic Services
N.A.I.C.S.: 541614

CJ Mainfrost Foods GmbH (1)
Siemenstrasse 13-17, 61130, Nidderau,
Germany
Tel.: (49) 618792920
Web Site: https://blbigo.eu
Packaging Food Product Mfr & Distr
N.A.I.C.S.: 311999

CJ N City Co., Ltd. (1)
2nd Floor Seoul Tower Mountain 1-3
Yongsan-dong 2-ga, Yongsan-gu, Seoul,
Korea (South)
Tel.: (82) 2 3455 9277
Food Products Mfr
N.A.I.C.S.: 311999

CJ Nutracon Pty. (1)
49-71 Hermitage Road, PO Box 730, Too-
woomba, 4350, QLD, Australia
Tel.: (61) 74 698 6999
Web Site: https://www.cjnutracon.net
Veal Product Mfr
N.A.I.C.S.: 311612

**CJ Olive Young (Shanghai)
Corporation** (1)
705 Tower 7 No 988 Shenchang Road,
Shanghai, China
Tel.: (86) 2153292383
Food & Beverage Mfr & Distr
N.A.I.C.S.: 311999

CJ Olivenetworks Vina Co., Ltd. (1)
Twin City 366 Hangang-daero, Yongsan-gu,
Seoul, Korea (South)
Tel.: (82) 262520000
Web Site: https://en.cjolivenetworks.co.kr
Software Development Services
N.A.I.C.S.: 541511

CJ Philippines Inc. (1)
Barangay Sampaioc, San Rafael, Bulacan,
Philippines
Tel.: (63) 44 766 6235
Web Site: http://english.cj.net
Animal Feed Mfr
N.A.I.C.S.: 311119

CJ Powercast Inc. (1)
Vision World Building 2F 19 Seohyeon-ro
180beon-gil, Bundang-gu, Seongnam,
Gyeonggi-do, Korea (South)
Tel.: (82) 31 780 0001
Web Site: http://www.cjpowercast.com
Emp.: 200
Digital Broadcasting Services
N.A.I.C.S.: 516120
Hyun Sang Pil *(CEO)*

CJ Qingdao Foods Co., Ltd. (1)
Laixi Economic and Technical Development
Zone, Qingdao, 266601, China
Tel.: (86) 2152080289
Food Service
N.A.I.C.S.: 722310

CJ Raviollo Rus LLC (1)
Petergofskoe Shosse 73 Building 2 Letter
A, Saint Petersburg, 198206, Russia
Tel.: (7) 8123038877
Web Site: https://www.cjraviollo.ru
Food Product Mfr & Distr
N.A.I.C.S.: 311991

**CJ Speedex Logistics Deqing Co.,
Ltd.** (1)
2nd Floor TCL Industrial Building No 6 Eling
South Road, Huicheng District, Huizhou,
Guangdong, China
Tel.: (86) 7522562013
Web Site: https://www.cjspd.com
Ecommerce Services
N.A.I.C.S.: 459999

CJ Systems Co., Ltd. (1)
256 Vision World B/D 2FL Seohyeon-dong,
Bundang-gu, Seongnam, 463-824, Korea
(South)
Tel.: (82) 3 1776 5999
Construction Engineering Services
N.A.I.C.S.: 541330

**CJ Tur Yem Sanayi ve Ticaret
Anonim Sirketi** (1)
Organize Sanayi Bolgesi 1 Cad No 9 In-
egol, Bursa, Turkiye
Tel.: (90) 2247148731
Sales Range: $25-49.9 Million
Emp.: 30
Food Processing Services
N.A.I.C.S.: 311423

CJ Vietnam Company Limited (1)
CJ Building 2bis-4-6 Le Thanh Ton, Ben
Nghe Ward District 1, Ho Chi Minh City,
Vietnam
Tel.: (84) 862556800
Food Product Mfr & Distr
N.A.I.C.S.: 311991

CJ do Brasil Ltda. (1)
Av das Nacoes Unidas 12901-9 ANDAR-
CONJ 902 Skyscraper, Brooklin Novo, Sao
Paulo, 04578- 910, Brazil
Tel.: (55) 113 717 8700
Web Site: http://www.cjbio.net
Sales Range: $25-49.9 Million
Emp.: 30
Lysine Mfr
N.A.I.C.S.: 334516

**Cofeed Feedmill (Changchun) Co.,
Ltd.** (1)
2158 Huaguang Street, High Technology
Industrial Development Area, Changchun,
China
Tel.: (86) 43187013159
Food & Beverage Mfr & Distr
N.A.I.C.S.: 311999

Conpac Warehousing Pte. Ltd. (1)
20 Toh Guan Road 08-00 CJ GLS Building,
Singapore, 608839, Singapore
Tel.: (65) 64102800
Logistic Services
N.A.I.C.S.: 541614

Eccho Rights AB (1)
Kungsgatan 48, 111 35, Stockholm, Swe-
den
Tel.: (46) 855609380
Web Site: https://ecchorights.com
Media Production Services
N.A.I.C.S.: 512110

Ezbiome, Inc. (1)
704 Quince Orchard Rd, Gaithersburg, MD
20878
Tel.: (301) 798-9222
Web Site: https://ezbiome.com
Biotechnology Laboratory Services
N.A.I.C.S.: 541714

**Gemadept Hai Phong One Member
Company Limited** (1)
Floor 21 - No 6 Le Thanh Ton, Ben Nghe
Ward District 1, Ho Chi Minh City, Vietnam
Tel.: (84) 2838236236
Web Site: https://www.gemadept.com.vn

CJ Corporation—(Continued)

Freight Transportation Services
N.A.I.C.S.: 488510

Gemadept Logistics One Member
Company Limited **(1)**
11th Floor CJ Tower 6 Le Thanh Ton Str,
District 1, Ho Chi Minh City, Vietnam
Tel.: (84) 2838279288
Web Site:
https://www.gemadeptlogistics.com.vn
Logistic Services
N.A.I.C.S.: 541614

Goodconcert Co., Ltd. **(1)**
97-1 Cheongdam-dong, Gangnam-gu,
Seoul, 135-100, Korea (South)
Tel.: (82) 2 575 3003
Media Advertising Services
N.A.I.C.S.: 541840

Gyoza Keikaku Co., Ltd. **(1)**
8F No 2-7-4 Nishi-Shimbashi, Minato-ku,
Tokyo, 105-0003, Japan
Tel.: (81) 358609426
Web Site: https://www.gyozakeikaku.com
Emp.: 150
Packaging Food Product Mfr & Distr
N.A.I.C.S.: 311999

H&S Productions, LLC **(1)**
16200 Addison Rd Ste 155, Addison, TX
75001
Tel.: (972) 407-0058
Web Site: https://hspi.net
Oil Exploration Services
N.A.I.C.S.: 213112

Liaocheng Lantian Cogeneration
Plant Co., Ltd. **(1)**
Liaohe Road, Liaocheng Economic and Development
Zone, Liaocheng, 252022, Shandong,
China
Tel.: (86) 6358518888
Organic Chemical Mfr
N.A.I.C.S.: 325199

Mezzomedia Inc. **(1)**
4F 330 Dongho-ro, Jung-gu, Seoul, 463-
824, Gyeonggi-do, Korea (South)
Tel.: (82) 26 484 3000
Web Site: https://www.mezzomedia.co.kr
Media Advertising Services
N.A.I.C.S.: 541840

N2play Co., Ltd. **(1)**
Guro 3-dong Mario Tower, Guro-gu, Seoul,
152-741, Korea (South)
Tel.: (82) 10 4390 6864
Web Site: http://www.n2play.co.kr
Game Development Services
N.A.I.C.S.: 541511

On Game Network Inc. **(1)**
266-1 First tower 4th Floor Seohyeon-dong,
Bundang-gu, Seongnam, 463-824, Korea
(South)
Tel.: (82) 2 371 9009
Web Site: http://www.ongamenet.com
Television Broadcasting Services
N.A.I.C.S.: 516120

PT CJ Feed & Care Indonesia **(1)**
Menara Jamsostek Lt 15 Jl Jend Gatot
Subroto No 38, Kuningan Barat, South Jakarta,
Indonesia
Tel.: (62) 2152995106
Web Site: https://cj.co.id
Animal Feed Mfr & Distr
N.A.I.C.S.: 311119

PT CJ Logistics Indonesia **(1)**
Gd Kirana Iii-Lt 17 Jl Boulevard Raya Kav 1
Kelapa Gading, Jakarta Utara, Indonesia
Tel.: (62) 2165311202
Logistic Services
N.A.I.C.S.: 541614

PT. Super Unggas Jaya **(1)**
JL Lanud Gorda, Desa Julang Kec Cikande
Kab, Serang, 42186, Banten, Indonesia
Tel.: (62) 2152995152
Corrugated Carton & Textile Tube Mfr
N.A.I.C.S.: 322211

PT.Cheil Jedang Indonesia **(1)**
Desa Arjosari, Kecamatan Rejoso, Pasuruan,
67181, Indonesia
Tel.: (62) 343482333
Organic Chemical Mfr

N.A.I.C.S.: 325199

Sam Hae Commercial Co., Ltd. **(1)**
H Business Park A-1405 25 Beopwon-ro
11-gil, Songpa-gu, Seoul, Korea (South)
Tel.: (82) 24312345
Web Site: https://www.samhae.co.kr
Seaweed Product Mfr & Retailer
N.A.I.C.S.: 311710

Shanghai SMG-CJ Homeshopping
Co., Ltd. **(1)**
400 Guo Ding Road, Yangpu District,
Shanghai, China
Tel.: (86) 2151119910
Home Shopping Services
N.A.I.C.S.: 455219

SongLim Food Co., Ltd. **(1)**
687-33 Ideok-ro, Deoksan-myeon, Jincheon,
Chungcheongbuk, Korea (South)
Tel.: (82) 435369730
Web Site: https://www.songlim-food.com
Food & Beverage Mfr
N.A.I.C.S.: 311999

Suntron Investments Limited **(1)**
7th Floor Nation Centre Kimathi Street, Nairobi,
Kenya
Tel.: (254) 724257024
Web Site: https://suntra.co.ke
Stock Brokerage Services
N.A.I.C.S.: 523150

Tiantian CJ Home Shopping Co.,
Ltd. **(1)**
SanJia Shopping Channel Tianjin TV No
143 Weijin Road, Heping Dis, Tianjin, China
Tel.: (86) 2223601000
Home Shopping Services
N.A.I.C.S.: 455219

Ulsan Port Operating Co., Ltd. **(1)**
139-2 Maeam-dong, Nam-gu, Ulsan, Korea
(South)
Tel.: (82) 52 226 3300
Cost Management Services
N.A.I.C.S.: 488310

CJ DARCL LOGISTICS LIMITED

M-2 Himland House Karampura Commercial
Complex, Delhi, 110 015,
India
Tel.: (91) 1125920610
Web Site: http://www.darcl.com
Sales Range: $300-349.9 Million
Emp.: 3,000
Integrated Logistics Services
N.A.I.C.S.: 541614
Krishan Kumar Agarwal *(Chm & Mng Dir)*

CJ FRESHWAY CORPORATION

25 World Cup buk-ro 54-gil, Mapo-gu,
Seoul, Korea (South)
Tel.: (82) 221496114
Web Site:
https://www.cjfreshway.com
Year Founded: 1988
051500—(KRS)
Rev.: $2,107,479,497
Assets: $1,138,785,527
Liabilities: $828,874,806
Net Worth: $309,910,721
Earnings: $37,657,129
Emp.: 7,065
Fiscal Year-end: 12/31/22
Catering Services
N.A.I.C.S.: 722320
Lee Geon-Il *(CEO)*

Subsidiaries:

CJ Olive Networks Co., Ltd. **(1)**
10th floor Twin City 366 Hangang-daero,
Yongsan-gu, Seoul, Korea (South)
Tel.: (82) 262520000
Web Site: https://www.cjolivenetworks.co.kr
Information Technology Services
N.A.I.C.S.: 541519
Cha In-Hyok *(CEO)*

CJS PLV

119 Grand-Rue, 92310, Sevres,
France
Tel.: (33) 141140440
Web Site: http://www.cjs-plv.fr
Advertising Material Distr
N.A.I.C.S.: 541890
Jean-Francois Lendais *(Chm & CEO)*

CJSC DONETSKSTEEL METALLURGICAL PLANT

House 106A Torgivelna Street,
Donetsk Region, 85300, Pokrovsk,
Ukraine
Tel.: (380) 62 388 04 39
Web Site: http://www.dmz.com.ua
Year Founded: 2002
DOMZ—(UKR)
Sales Range: Less than $1 Million
Iron & Steel Product Mfr
N.A.I.C.S.: 331110
Andriy Ivanovych Nykytenko *(Gen Mgr)*

CJSC GLORIA JEANS CORPORATION

184 Stachki Str, 344090, Rostov-na-
Donu, Russia
Tel.: (7) 8005008282
Web Site: http://www.gloria-jeans.ru
Year Founded: 1988
Sales Range: $25-49.9 Million
Emp.: 200
Denim Garments Mfr & Distr
N.A.I.C.S.: 315210
Vladimir Melnikov *(Gen Dir)*

CJSC RUSSIAN STANDARD CORPORATION

World Trade Center Office 1503a
Krasnopresnenskaya Emb 12,
123610, Moscow, Russia
Tel.: (7) 4957771777
Web Site:
http://www.russianstandard.com
Year Founded: 1992
Sales Range: $5-14.9 Billion
Emp.: 12,000
Holding Company; Banking, Insurance
& Distilled Beverages
N.A.I.C.S.: 551112
Roustam V. Tariko *(Founder & Chm)*

Subsidiaries:

Fratelli Gancia & C. S.p.A. **(1)**
Corso Liberta 66, Canelli, 14053, Asti, Italy
Tel.: (39) 0141 8301
Web Site: http://www.gancia.it
Emp.: 100
Wine Mfr & Distr
N.A.I.C.S.: 312130

JSC Russian Standard Bank **(1)**
36 Tkatskaya Street, Moscow, 105187,
Russia
Tel.: (7) 495 797 8402
Web Site:
http://www.russianstandardbank.com
Sales Range: $1-4.9 Billion
Emp.: 24,921
Commercial & Investment Banking
N.A.I.C.S.: 522110
Roustam V. Tariko *(Chm)*

JSC Russian Standard
Insurance **(1)**
st Malaya Semenovskaya 9 building 3 Business,
107023, Moscow, Russia
Tel.: (7) 4959807760
Web Site: http://www.rsins.ru
Life & Other Insurance Products & Services
N.A.I.C.S.: 524113

Roust Inc. **(1)**
World Trade Center Office 1507 Krasno-
presnenskaya Nab 12, 123610, Moscow,
Russia
Tel.: (7) 495 727 1075
Distilled Spirits Distr
N.A.I.C.S.: 424820

Subsidiary (US):

Central European Distribution
Corporation **(2)**
3000 Atrium Way Ste 265, Mount Laurel,
NJ 08054
Tel.: (856) 273-6980
Web Site: http://www.cedc.com
Rev.: $1,745,315,000
Assets: $1,767,552,000
Liabilities: $1,964,461,000
Net Worth: ($196,909,000)
Earnings: ($363,238,000)
Emp.: 4,067
Fiscal Year-end: 12/31/2012
Holding Company; Distilled Beverages Mfr
& Distr
N.A.I.C.S.: 551112
Grant Winterton *(CEO)*

Subsidiary (Non-US):

Agis SA **(3)**
Szosa Chelminska 26, Torun, 87 100, Poland
Tel.: (48) 566225658
Web Site: http://www.agis.com.pl
Sales Range: $150-199.9 Million
Distributes Wines, Beers & other Beverages
N.A.I.C.S.: 445320

Bols Hungary, Kft **(3)**
Alkotas Point Irodahaz Alkotas u 50, 1123,
Budapest, 1123, Hungary
Tel.: (36) 13252500
Alcoholic Beverages Mfr
N.A.I.C.S.: 312140

Russian Standard Credit Bureau
LLC **(1)**
st Shcherbakovskaya 3 floor 10
office 1001, 105318, Moscow, Russia
Tel.: (7) 4956096424
Web Site: http://www.rs-cb.ru
Consumer Credit Services
N.A.I.C.S.: 561450

Russian Standard Vodka **(1)**
World Trade Center Office 1507 Entrance 3
12 Krasnopresenskaya NAB, 123610, Moscow,
Russia
Tel.: (7) 495 967 0990
Web Site:
http://www.russianstandardvodka.com
Distillery
N.A.I.C.S.: 312140
Roustam V. Tariko *(Chm & CEO)*

CJSC S7 GROUP

ul Petrovka 7 4th floor BC Geneva
House, 107031, Moscow, Russia
Tel.: (7) 4957777110
Web Site: http://www.s7space.ru
Holding Company; Air & Space
Transportation
N.A.I.C.S.: 551112
Dzhuraeva Ranokhon Frunzevna
(CEO)

Subsidiaries:

Siberia Airlines PJSC **(1)**
Mozzherina Prospect 10 Office 201, Town
of Ob, 633104, Novosibirsk, Russia
Tel.: (7) 495 783 0707
Web Site: http://www.s7.ru
Oil Transportation Services
N.A.I.C.S.: 481111

CJSC SBERBANK CIB

st Vavilova d 19, 117312, Moscow,
Russia
Tel.: (7) 4952450500
Web Site: https://sbrf-cib.ru
Financial Investment Services
N.A.I.C.S.: 523999
Svetlana Fedotova *(Mng Dir & Head-
Transport & Vehicle Mfg)*

CK ASSET HOLDINGS LIMITED

7th Floor Cheung Kong Center 2
Queens Road, Central, China (Hong
Kong)
Tel.: (852) 21288888

Web Site: http://www.ckah.com
Year Founded: 2015
1113—(HKG)
Rev.: $9,084,309,942
Assets: $65,035,720,219
Liabilities: $13,987,628,919
Net Worth: $51,048,091,301
Earnings: $2,239,574,680
Emp.: 57,000
Fiscal Year-end: 12/31/23
Holding Company
N.A.I.C.S.: 551112
Victor Tzar Kuoi Li *(Chm & Mng Dir)*

Subsidiaries:

Accipiter Holdings Designated Activity
Company   **(1)**
28-29 Sir John Rogersons Quay, Dublin,
Ireland
Tel.: (353) 15170100
Web Site: http://www.accipiter.aero
Aircraft Leasing Services
N.A.I.C.S.: 532411

Albany Investments Limited   **(1)**
48 Dover Street Mayfair, London, W1S 4FF,
United Kingdom
Tel.: (44) 7917750170
Web Site: http://www.albanyinvestment.com
Investment Advisory Services
N.A.I.C.S.: 523940
Andrew Smith *(Founder & Mng Dir)*

Citybase Property Management
Limited   **(1)**
Unit No 1 6/F Hampton Loft 11 Hoi Fan
Road, Tai Kok Tsui, Kowloon, China (Hong
Kong)
Tel.: (852) 2 388 7786
Web Site: https://www.citybaseltd.com
Sales Range: $650-699.9 Million
Emp.: 2,000
Property Management Services
N.A.I.C.S.: 531311

Goodwell Property Management
Limited   **(1)**
2/F New Treasure Centre 10 Ng Fong
Street, San Po Kong, Kowloon, China
(Hong Kong)
Tel.: (852) 2 960 0982
Web Site: https://www.goodwell.com.hk
Emp.: 2,600
Property Management Services
N.A.I.C.S.: 531311
Dicto Leung *(Gen Mgr)*

Greene King plc   **(1)**
Westgate Brewery, Bury Saint Edmunds,
IP33 1QT, Suffolk, United Kingdom
Tel.: (44) 1284763222
Web Site: https://www.greeneking.co.uk
Rev.: $2,813,290,438
Assets: $6,577,838,268
Liabilities: $3,902,871,010
Net Worth: $2,674,967,258
Earnings: $152,790,008
Emp.: 38,000
Fiscal Year-end: 04/29/2019
Holding Company; Breweries, Pubs & Inns
Owner, Developer & Operator
N.A.I.C.S.: 551112
Richard Smothers *(CFO)*

Subsidiary (Domestic):

Greene King Brewing & Retailing
Limited   **(2)**
Limited Westgate Brewery Bury St, PO Box
337, Edmunds, Bury Saint Edmunds, IP33
1QT, Suffolk, United Kingdom   **(100%)**
Tel.: (44) 128 484 3200
Web Site:
    https://www.greenekingpubs.co.uk
Emp.: 22,550
Breweries & Retail Assets Operator
N.A.I.C.S.: 312120
Ben Melrose *(Partner-Recruitment Bus)*

Subsidiary (Domestic):

Belhaven Brewery Company
Limited   **(3)**
Brewery Lane, Belhaven, Dunbar, EH42
1PE, E Lothian, United Kingdom
Tel.: (44) 136 886 2734
Web Site: https://www.belhaven.co.uk

Sales Range: $125-149.9 Million
Emp.: 300
Beer & Ale Brewer & Whslr
N.A.I.C.S.: 312120
Chris Houlton *(Mng Dir)*

Greene King Retailing Limited   **(3)**
Westgate Brewery, Bury Saint Edmunds,
IP33 1QT, United Kingdom
Tel.: (44) 1284763222
Web Site: http://www.findaproperpub.co.uk
Sales Range: $100-124.9 Million
Emp.: 800
Pubs, Restaurants & Hotels Operator
N.A.I.C.S.: 722410

Subsidiary (Domestic):

Greene King Retail Services
Limited   **(4)**
Sunrise HouseNinth Avenue, PO Box 337,
Burton-on-Trent, DE14 3JZ, Suffolk, United
Kingdom   **(100%)**
Tel.: (44) 1284763222
Web Site: http://www.greeneking.co.uk
Emp.: 600
Office Administrative Services
N.A.I.C.S.: 561110
Nick MacKenzie *(CEO)*

Premium Dining Restaurants & Pubs
Limited   **(4)**
Westgate Brewery, PO Box 337, Bury Saint
Edmunds, IP33 1QT, Suffolk, United King-
dom
Tel.: (44) 8456080713
Web Site:
    https://www.lochfyneseafoodandgrill.co.uk
Sales Range: $100-124.9 Million
Restaurant & Pub Management Services
N.A.I.C.S.: 722511
Johnny Noble *(Co-Founder)*

Subsidiary (Domestic):

Greene King Services Limited   **(2)**
Abbot House Westgate Brewery, PO Box
337, Bury Saint Edmunds, IP33 1QT, Suf-
folk, United Kingdom   **(100%)**
Tel.: (44) 1284763222
Web Site: https://www.greeneking.co.uk
Emp.: 1,000
Office Administrative Services
N.A.I.C.S.: 561110
Clive Chasser *(Mng Dir)*

Harbour Plaza Degrees Limited   **(1)**
199 Kowloon City Road, Tokwawan Kowloon, Hong Kong, China (Hong Kong)
Tel.: (852) 21261988
N.A.I.C.S.: 721110

Harbour Plaza Hotel Management
Limited   **(1)**
8/F 813 Two Harbourfront 22 Tak Fung
Street Hunghom, Kowloon, China (Hong
Kong)
Tel.: (852) 21231845
Web Site: https://www.harbour-plaza.com
Hotel Operator
N.A.I.C.S.: 721110
Poh Chan Koh *(Dir-Fin)*

Subsidiary (Domestic):

Harbour Grand Hong Kong
Limited   **(2)**
MTR Fortress Hill Station Exit A 23 Oil
Street North Point, Hong Kong, China
(Hong Kong)
Tel.: (852) 21212688
Web Site: https://www.harbourgrand.com
Hotel Operator
N.A.I.C.S.: 721110

Subsidiary (Non-US):

Harbour Plaza Chongqing Company
Limited   **(2)**
No 68 Zou-Rong Road Yuzhong District,
Chongqing, 400010, China
Tel.: (86) 2363700888
Hotel Operator
N.A.I.C.S.: 721110

Subsidiary (Domestic):

Harbour Plaza Metropolis
Limited   **(2)**

7 Metropolis Drive Hunghom, Kowloon,
China (Hong Kong)
Tel.: (852) 31606888
Web Site: https://www.harbour-plaza.com
Hotel Operator
N.A.I.C.S.: 721110

Harbour Plaza Resort City
Limited   **(2)**
18 Tin Yan Road, Tin Shui Wai, New Terri-
tories, China (Hong Kong)
Tel.: (852) 21806688
Hotel Operator
N.A.I.C.S.: 721110

Hutchison Hotel Hong Kong
Limited   **(2)**
20 Tak Fung Street Whampoa Garden Hun-
ghom, Kowloon, China (Hong Kong)
Tel.: (852) 26213188
Web Site: https://www.harbourgrand.com
Hotel Operator
N.A.I.C.S.: 721110

Randash Investment Limited   **(2)**
665 King s Road North Point, Hong Kong,
China (Hong Kong)
Tel.: (852) 21878888
Hotel Operator
N.A.I.C.S.: 721110

Sino China Enterprises Limited   **(2)**
8 Hung Luen Road Hunghom Bay, Kow-
loon, China (Hong Kong)
Tel.: (852) 21869036
Hotel Operator
N.A.I.C.S.: 721110

The Kowloon Hotel Limited   **(2)**
19-21 Nathan Road Tsimshatsui, Kowloon,
China (Hong Kong)
Tel.: (852) 29292888
Web Site: https://www.harbour-plaza.com
Hotel Operator
N.A.I.C.S.: 721110
Victor Chan *(Gen Mgr)*

Hutchison Whampoa Properties
(Chengdu) Limited   **(1)**
20/F Tower A Times Plaza No 2 Zongfu
Road, Chengdu, 610016, Sichuan, China
Tel.: (86) 2886660066
Property Development Services
N.A.I.C.S.: 531210

Hutchison Whampoa Properties
(Chongqing Nanan) Limited   **(1)**
10/F Metropolitan Tower No 68 Zourong
Road, Chongqing, 400010, China
Tel.: (86) 2363813800
Property Development Services
N.A.I.C.S.: 531210

Hutchison Whampoa Properties
(Qingdao) Limited   **(1)**
16 Guan Xian Road Shi Bei District,
Qingdao, 266011, Shandong, China
Tel.: (86) 53282816688
Property Development Services
N.A.I.C.S.: 531210

Hutchison Whampoa Properties (Wu-
han Jianghan South) Limited   **(1)**
16/F Changhang Building 69 Yanjiang Av-
enue Hankou, Wuhan, 430021, Hubei,
China
Tel.: (86) 2785682288
Property Development Services
N.A.I.C.S.: 531210

Matrica Limited   **(1)**
1 Tsing Yi Road, Tsing Yi, Hong Kong,
China (Hong Kong)
Tel.: (852) 21299988
Web Site: https://www.ramblerhotels.com
N.A.I.C.S.: 721110

Ocean Century Investments
Limited   **(1)**
32 City Garden Road North Point, Hong
Kong, China (Hong Kong)
Tel.: (852) 38932888
Web Site:
    https://www.hotelalexandrahk.com
N.A.I.C.S.: 721110

Reliance Comfort Limited
Partnership   **(1)**
PO Box 2305, Oshawa, L1H 7V5, ON,
Canada

Tel.: (416) 499-7600
Web Site:
    http://www.reliancehomecomfort.com
Heating, Ventilation & Air Conditioning
Equipment Rental & Sales & Home Security
Services
N.A.I.C.S.: 423730

Shanghai Westgate Mall Co.,
Ltd.   **(1)**
No 1038 Nanjing West Road, Shanghai,
China
Tel.: (86) 2162187878
Web Site: https://www.westgatemall.com.cn
Mall Operator
N.A.I.C.S.: 531120
Yi Cai *(Officer-Mktg)*

Shenzhen Hutchison Whampoa
CATIC Properties Limited   **(1)**
3/F Le Parc Shopping Centre 1280 Fu-
zhong 3rd Road Futian District, Shenzhen,
518028, China
Tel.: (86) 75582963300
Property Development Services
N.A.I.C.S.: 531210

ista International GmbH   **(1)**
Luxemburger Str 1, 45131, Essen, Ger-
many
Tel.: (49) 20145902
Web Site: https://www.ista.com
Energy & Water Metering Equipment Mfr
N.A.I.C.S.: 334515

Subsidiary (Non-US):

S.A. ista N.V.   **(2)**
Square Marie Curie 50, 1070, Brussels,
Belgium
Tel.: (32) 2 523 4060
Web Site: http://www.ista.com
Emp.: 70
Energy & Water Metering Equipment Mfr
N.A.I.C.S.: 334515

ista Brasil Servicos de Energia
Ltda.   **(2)**
Alameda Joaquim Eugenio de Lima 696 cj
131, Jardim Paulista, Sao Paulo, 01403-
000, Brazil
Tel.: (55) 11 3285 6040
Web Site: http://www.ista.com.br
Energy & Water Metering Equipment Mfr
N.A.I.C.S.: 334515
Thomas Kunzmann *(COO)*

ista CIS   **(2)**
27 avenue Carnot, 91300, Massy, France
Tel.: (33) 16 919 5300
Web Site: https://www.ista.com
Energy & Water Metering Equipment Mfr
N.A.I.C.S.: 334515
Laurent Sireix *(Pres)*

ista Ceska republica s.r.o.   **(2)**
Jeremiasova 947, 15500, 155 00, Prague,
Czech Republic
Tel.: (420) 296337511
Web Site: https://www.ista.com
Energy & Water Metering Equipment Mfr
N.A.I.C.S.: 334515
Veronika Budilova *(Mgr-Fin)*

ista Danmark A/S   **(2)**
Borupvang 5B, 2750, Ballerup, Denmark
Tel.: (45) 7 732 3232
Web Site: https://www.ista.com
Energy & Water Metering Equipment Mfr
N.A.I.C.S.: 334515

Subsidiary (Domestic):

ista Deutschland GmbH   **(2)**
Luxemburger Strasse 1, 45131, Essen,
Germany   **(100%)**
Tel.: (49) 2 014 5902
Web Site: https://www.ista.com
Sales Range: $450-499.9 Million
Energy & Water Metering Equipment Mfr
N.A.I.C.S.: 334515
Dieter Hackenberg *(CFO)*

Subsidiary (Non-US):

ista Energy Solutions Limited   **(2)**
The Officers' Mess Royston Road, Duxford,
Cambridge, CB22 4QH, United Kingdom
Tel.: (44) 122 387 4974
Web Site: https://www.ista.com
Energy & Water Metering Equipment Mfr

CK Asset Holdings Limited—(Continued)

N.A.I.C.S.: 334515
Oliver Sporrer (Dir-Ops)

ista Enerji Hizmetleri Tic. Ltd. Sti. (2)
Kisikli Caddesi Sarkuysan Ak Is Merkezi No
4 A Blok D 1-A, Altunizade, 34662, Istanbul,
Turkiye
Tel.: (90) 2164742222
Web Site: https://www.ista.com.tr
Energy & Water Metering Equipment Mfr
N.A.I.C.S.: 334515

ista Italia S.R.L. (2)
Via Lepetit 40, 20020, Lainate, Italy
Tel.: (39) 02 962 8831
Web Site: https://www.ista.com
Energy & Water Metering Equipment Mfr
N.A.I.C.S.: 334515

ista Luxemburg GmbH (2)
23 rue des Bruyeres, 1274, Howald, Lux-
embourg
Tel.: (352) 495 2221
Web Site: https://www.ista.com
Energy & Water Metering Equipment Mfr
N.A.I.C.S.: 334515

**ista Magyarorszag Merestechnika
Szerviz Kft.** (2)
Mazsa ter 2-6, H-1107, Budapest, Hungary
Tel.: (36) 1 8890 562
Energy & Water Metering Equipment Mfr
N.A.I.C.S.: 334515

**ista Measurement Technology Ser-
vices (Beijing) Co., Ltd.** (2)
Ling Hang Int 3-1-806, ChongWen District,
100061, Beijing, China
Tel.: (86) 10 6710 1976
Web Site: http://www.ista.com.cn
Energy & Water Metering Equipment Mfr
N.A.I.C.S.: 334515
Richard Wang (Gen Mgr)

**ista Metering Services Espana,
S.A.** (2)
Avda de la Albufera 319 4th Floor, 28031,
Madrid, Spain
Tel.: (34) 91 701 2470
Web Site: https://www.ista.com
Energy & Water Metering Equipment Mfr
N.A.I.C.S.: 334515

ista Middle East FZE (2)
Unit 204 Cayan Business Centre Tecom C
Al Sufouh Third, PO Box 293861, Dubai,
United Arab Emirates
Tel.: (971) 800478263
Web Site: https://www.ista.com
Energy & Water Metering Equipment Mfr
N.A.I.C.S.: 334515

ista Nederland B.V. (2)
Tel.: (31) 10 245 5700
Web Site: https://www.ista.com
Energy & Water Metering Equipment Mfr
N.A.I.C.S.: 334515
Steven Ossewaarde (Mgr-Ops)

ista Norge AS (2)
Trollasveien 34, 1414, Trollasen, Norway
Tel.: (47) 2 288 5900
Web Site: https://www.ista.com
Energy & Water Metering Equipment Mfr
N.A.I.C.S.: 334515
Espen Karlsholmen (Country Mgr)

ista Osterreich GmbH (2)
Leopold-Bohm-Strasse 12, 1030, Vienna,
Austria
Tel.: (43) 502302300
Energy & Water Metering Equipment Mfr
N.A.I.C.S.: 334515

ista Polska Sp.z.o.o. (2)
Al 29 Listopada 155C, 31-406, Krakow,
Poland
Tel.: (48) 12 651 0100
Web Site: https://www.ista.com
Energy & Water Metering Equipment Mfr
N.A.I.C.S.: 334514

ista Romania SRL (2)
Splaiul Independentei nr 294 corp O2 et 1
Sector 6, 060031, Bucharest, Romania
Tel.: (40) 21 315 9824
Web Site: https://www.ista.com
Energy & Water Metering Equipment Mfr
N.A.I.C.S.: 334515

ista Rus o.o.o. (2)
101 Prospekt Mira c 2, 129085, Moscow,
Russia
Tel.: (7) 95 9 80 51 12
Web Site: http://www.ista-rus.ru
Energy & Water Metering Equipment Mfr
N.A.I.C.S.: 334515

ista Slovakia s.r.o. (2)
Podunajska ulica 25, 02100, Dratislava,
Slovakia
Tel.: (421) 240240999
Web Site: https://www.ista.com
Emp.: 20
Energy & Water Metering Equipment Mfr
N.A.I.C.S.: 334515
Jane Macava (Gen Mgr)

ista Swiss AG (2)
Zofingerstrasse 61, 4665, Oftringen, Swit-
zerland
Tel.: (41) 62 746 9900
Web Site: https://www.ista.com
Emp.: 35
Energy & Water Metering Equipment Mfr
N.A.I.C.S.: 334515

CK BIRLA GROUP

8th Floor Birla Tower 25, Bara-
khamba Road, New Delhi, 110 001,
India
Tel.: (91) 1142092100
Web Site:
http://www.ckbirlagroup.com
Holding Company
N.A.I.C.S.: 551112
Chandra Kant Birla (CEO)

Subsidiaries:

HIL Limited (1)
Office No 1 and 2 Level 7 SLN Terminus
SY No 133, Near Botanical Gardens Gachi-
bowli, Hyderabad, 500032, Telangana, India
Tel.: (91) 4068249000
Web Site: https://www.hil.in
Rev.: $417,921,641
Assets: $288,489,611
Liabilities: $152,635,610
Net Worth: $135,854,000
Earnings: $35,455,807
Emp.: 1,556
Fiscal Year-end: 03/31/2021
Cement & Roofing Materials Mfr & Distr
N.A.I.C.S.: 327310
C. K. Birla (Chm)

**National Engineering Industries
Ltd** (1)
Khatipura Road, Rajasthan, 302006, Jaipur,
India
Tel.: (91) 1412223221
Bearing Exporter & Mfr
N.A.I.C.S.: 811310
Gourav Chaturvedi (CFO)

Subsidiary (Non-US):

KINEX BEARINGS, a.s. (2)
ul 1 maja 71/36, 014 83, Bytca, Slovakia
Tel.: (421) 41 5556 201
Web Site: http://www.kinex.sk
Ball Bearing Mfr
N.A.I.C.S.: 332991

CK COMPANY CO., LTD.

2nd floor Yeonggyeong BD 68gil 45
Samsung-dong 124 Bongeunsa-ro,
Gangnam-gu, Seoul, Korea (South)
Tel.: (82) 15443058
Web Site: http://www.ckcompany.net
Year Founded: 2012
Ice Making Machine Mfr & Distr
N.A.I.C.S.: 333415
Yong-Tae Won (CEO)

CK HUTCHISON HOLDINGS
LIMITED

48th Floor Cheung Kong Center 2
Queen's Road, Central, China (Hong
Kong)
Tel.: (852) 21281188
Web Site: https://www.ckh.com.hk
Year Founded: 2014

CKHUF—(OTCIQ)
Rev.: $34,359,756,080
Assets: $161,817,792,080
Liabilities: $80,552,266,340
Net Worth: $81,265,525,740
Earnings: $4,823,465,060
Emp.: 300,000
Fiscal Year-end: 12/31/20
Holding Company
N.A.I.C.S.: 551112
Canning Kin Ning Fok (Co-Mng Dir)

Subsidiaries:

A.S. Watson Retail (HK) Ltd (1)
Watson House 1-5 Wo Liu Hang Road, Fo
Tan, Sha Tin, New Territories, China (Hong
Kong) (100%)
Tel.: (852) 26068833
Web Site: http://www.aswatson.com
Beauty Product Retailer
N.A.I.C.S.: 456120

Subsidiary (Non-US):

Kruidvat Retail BV (2)
Nijborg 17, Renswoude, 3927 DA, Nether-
lands
Tel.: (31) 318579111
Web Site: http://www.kruidvat.nl
Sales Range: $800-899.9 Million
Emp.: 3,900
Health & Beauty Supplies
N.A.I.C.S.: 456120
Gerard Panbreen (CEO)

Superdrug Stores PLC (2)
51 Sydenham Road, Croydon, CR0 2EU,
Surrey, United Kingdom
Tel.: (44) 3456710709
Web Site: https://hutchisonports.com
Rev.: $1,497,400,064
Emp.: 300
Retail Drugs & Sundries
N.A.I.C.S.: 456110

The Perfume Shop Limited (2)
Hutchison House 5 Hester Road, Battersea,
London, SW11 4AN, United Kingdom
Tel.: (44) 333 344 2646
Web Site: https://www.theperfumeshop.com
Sales Range: $125-149.9 Million
Emp.: 2,000
Perfume Store Operator
N.A.I.C.S.: 456199

AVR-Afvalverwerking B.V. (1)
Prof Gerbrandyweg 10 Havennummer
4506, Botlek, 3197 KK, Rotterdam, Nether-
lands
Tel.: (31) 181275275
Web Site: https://www.avr.nl
Waste Recycling Services
N.A.I.C.S.: 562998

**Alexandria International Container
Terminals Company S.A.E.** (1)
Dekheila Port Gate 3 or 5 Quay No 98,
Agamy, Alexandria, Egypt
Tel.: (20) 34881015
Web Site: https://www.aict.com.eg
Port Operation Services
N.A.I.C.S.: 488310

**Beijing Net-Infinity Technology Devel-
opment Co. Ltd.** (1)
Room 708 Tower W3 The Towers Oriental
Plaza No 1 East Chang An Avenue, Dong
Cheng District, Beijing, 100738, China
Tel.: (86) 10 5815 0088
Web Site: http://www.net-infinity.net
Internet Access Services
N.A.I.C.S.: 517810

**CK Infrastructure Holdings
Limited** (1)
12/F Cheung Kong Centre, 2 Queens
Road, Central, China (Hong Kong)
Tel.: (852) 21223133
Web Site: https://www.cki.com.hk
Rev.: $5,014,377,548
Assets: $21,197,873,401
Liabilities: $4,662,798,574
Net Worth: $16,535,074,827
Earnings: $1,044,512,889
Emp.: 2,361
Fiscal Year-end: 12/31/2022
Infrastructure Developer & Investor
N.A.I.C.S.: 531390

Canning Kin Ning Fok (Deputy Chm)

Joint Venture (Domestic):

**Alliance Construction Materials
Ltd.** (2)
1901A One Harbourfront 18 Tak Fung
Street, Hung Hom, China (Hong
Kong) (50%)
Tel.: (852) 2 862 2200
Web Site: https://www.concrete.hk
Sales Range: $75-99.9 Million
Emp.: 240
Construction Materials Mfr & Distr
N.A.I.C.S.: 238110

Joint Venture (Non-US):

CitiPower (2)
PO Box 14090, Melbourne, 8001, VIC,
Australia (50%)
Tel.: (61) 1300301101
Web Site: http://www.citipower.com.au
Sales Range: $650-699.9 Million
Emp.: 1,500
Electric Power Distr
N.A.I.C.S.: 221122
Peter Tulloch (Chm)

Subsidiary (Non-US):

DUET Group (2)
Level 15 55 Hunter Street, Sydney, 2000,
NSW, Australia (100%)
Tel.: (61) 282242701
Web Site: http://www.duet.net.au
Energy Utility Services & Gas Pipeline &
Distribution Businesses
N.A.I.C.S.: 221210

Subsidiary (Domestic):

**DBNGP (WA) Nominees Pty
Limited** (3)
Level 6 12-14 The Esp, Perth, 6000, WA,
Australia
Tel.: (61) 892234300
Natural Gas Transmission Services
N.A.I.C.S.: 486210

**DBNGP (WA) Transmission Pty
Limited** (3)
Level 6 12-14 The Esplanade, Perth, 6000,
WA, Australia
Tel.: (61) 892234300
Natural Gas Pipeline Construction Services
N.A.I.C.S.: 237120

DBNGP Holdings Pty Limited (3)
Level 6 12-14 The Esplanade, Perth, 6000,
WA, Australia (100%)
Tel.: (61) 892234300
Web Site: http://www.dbp.net.au
Oil & Gas Exploration Services
N.A.I.C.S.: 213112

**DUET Investment Holdings
Limited** (3)
Level 11 1 Martin Pl, Sydney, 2000, NSW,
Australia
Tel.: (61) 282324491
Investment Management Service
N.A.I.C.S.: 523940

Energy Developments Limited (3)
Waterfront Place Level 6 1 Eagle Street,
Brisbane, 4000, QLD, Australia (100%)
Tel.: (61) 7 3275 5555
Web Site:
http://www.energydevelopments.com
Renewable Energy Services (through Land-
fill Gas Power Generation), Coal Mine
Methane Power Generation & Remote Area
Power Generation
N.A.I.C.S.: 221118
Glen Marshall (Sec)

Subsidiary (Domestic):

EDL Group Operations Pty Ltd (4)
Waterfront Place Level 6 1 Eagle Street,
Brisbane, 4000, QLD, Australia
Tel.: (61) 732755555
Web Site: http://edlenergy.com
Other Business Service Centers
N.A.I.C.S.: 561439

EDL NGD (WA) Pty Ltd (4)
Waterfront Place Level 6 1 Eagle Street,
Brisbane, 4000, QLD, Australia
Tel.: (61) 732755555

Web Site:
http://www.energydevelopments.com
Industrial Machinery Mfr
N.A.I.C.S.: 333248

Subsidiary (Non-US):

Energy Developments (UK)
Limited   **(4)**
Chancery House 199 Silbury Boulevard,
Milton Keynes, MK 9 1JL, United Kingdom
Tel.: (44) 1908953350
Web Site:
http://www.energydevelopments.com
Other Electric Power Generation
N.A.I.C.S.: 221118
Lorraine Lanigan (Controller-Fin)

Subsidiary (US):

Energy Developments, Inc.   **(4)**
608 S Washington Ave, Lansing, MI 48933
Tel.: (517) 208-0743
Web Site:
http://www.energydevelopments.com
Renewable Energy Services through Land-
fill Gas Power Generation, Coal Mine Meth-
ane Power Generation & Remote Area
Power Generation
N.A.I.C.S.: 221118
Chris Eastgate (CFO)

Subsidiary (Domestic):

United Energy Distribution Pty
Limited   **(3)**
43-45 Centreway, PO Box 449, Mount Wa-
verley, Melbourne, 3149, VIC, Australia
Tel.: (61) 300 131 689
Web Site: http://www.unitedenergy.com.au
Electricity Distribution Services
N.A.I.C.S.: 221122
Garrick Rollason (CFO)

Subsidiary (Non-US):

EnviroWaste Services Limited   **(2)**
Level 1 345 Neilson St Onehunga, 1642,
Auckland, New Zealand
Tel.: (64) 9 636 0350
Web Site: http://www.envirowaste.co.nz
Emp.: 100
Waste Management Services
N.A.I.C.S.: 562998

Northumbrian Water Group Plc   **(2)**
Northumbria House Abbey Road, Pity Me,
Durham, DH1 5FJ, United Kingdom
Tel.: (44) 3456047468
Web Site: http://www.nwl.co.uk
Sales Range: $1-4.9 Billion
Water Supply & Waste Water Services
N.A.I.C.S.: 924110

Subsidiary (Non-US):

AquaGib Limited   **(3)**
Suite 10b Leanse Place 50 Town Range,
Gibraltar, Gibraltar   **(66.67%)**
Tel.: (350) 2 007 3659
Web Site: https://www.aquagib.gi
Sales Range: $50-74.9 Million
Emp.: 28
Water Supply Services
N.A.I.C.S.: 221310

Subsidiary (Domestic):

Ayr Environmental Services
Limited   **(3)**
Meadowhead Road Works & Sludge Treat-
ment Centre, Irvine, KA11 5AY, United
Kingdom   **(75%)**
Tel.: (44) 1913016836
Sales Range: $10-24.9 Million
Emp.: 20
Waste Water Treatment Services
N.A.I.C.S.: 562998

Ayr Environmental Services Opera-
tions Limited   **(3)**
Meadowhead Road Works & Sludge Treat-
ment Centre, Irvine, KA11 5AY, Ayrshire,
United Kingdom
Tel.: (44) 1294278871
Waste Treatment Services
N.A.I.C.S.: 562219
Geroge Mitchell (Mgr-Facilities)

Northumbrian Services Limited   **(3)**
Northumbria House Abbey Road, Pity Me,

Durham, DH1 5FJ, United
Kingdom   **(100%)**
Tel.: (44) 8706084820
Web Site: http://www.riwl.co.uk
Sales Range: $350-399.9 Million
Emp.: 1,000
Water Supply Services
N.A.I.C.S.: 221310
Heidi Mottram (CEO)

Northumbrian Water Limited   **(3)**
Northumbria House Abbey Road, Durham,
DH1 5FJ, United Kingdom   **(100%)**
Tel.: (44) 345 717 1100
Web Site: https://www.nwl.co.uk
Sales Range: $350-399.9 Million
Emp.: 600
Water Supply & Irrigation Systems
N.A.I.C.S.: 221310
Heidi Mottram (CEO)

Subsidiary (Domestic):

Essex & Suffolk Water Ltd   **(4)**
PO Box 292, Durham, DH1 9TX, United
Kingdom
Tel.: (44) 8457820999
Waste Treatment Services
N.A.I.C.S.: 221310
Heidi Mottram (CEO)

Division (Domestic):

Northumbrian Water Scientific Ser-
vices (NWSS)   **(4)**
Northumberland Dock Road, Howdon,
Wallsend, NE28 0QD, United
Kingdom   **(100%)**
Tel.: (44) 333 321 4932
Web Site: https://www.nwss-labs.co.uk
Emp.: 100
Analysis & Sampling of Waters, Air Emis-
sions & Soils
N.A.I.C.S.: 541380

Subsidiary (Non-US):

Northumbrian Water Projects
Limited   **(3)**
Nli Carrigrennan Wwtp, Little Island, Cork,
NE48 1BX, Ireland
Tel.: (353) 214976200
Web Site: http://www.nwg.co.uk
Operation & Maintenance of Waste Water
Treatment Assets
N.A.I.C.S.: 562998

Joint Venture (Non-US):

Powercor Australia Limited   **(2)**
40 Market St, Melbourne, 3000, VIC,
Australia   **(50%)**
Tel.: (61) 396834444
Web Site: http://www.powercor.com.au
Sales Range: $75-99.9 Million
Emp.: 80
Electric Power Distr
N.A.I.C.S.: 221122

SA Power Networks   **(2)**
1 ANZAC Highway, Keswick, 5035, SA,
Australia   **(50%)**
Tel.: (61) 131261
Web Site:
https://www.sapowernetworks.com.au
Sales Range: $1-4.9 Billion
Emp.: 2,000
Electricity Distr
N.A.I.C.S.: 221122
Peter Peace Tulloch (Chm)

Subsidiary (Non-US):

TransAlta Power, L.P.   **(2)**
110 12th Ave SW, Calgary, T2P 2M, AB,
Canada   **(100%)**
Tel.: (403) 267-2520
Web Site: http://www.transaltapower.com
Sales Range: $1-4.9 Billion
Electric Power Generation & Distr
N.A.I.C.S.: 221122

CK Life Sciences International, (Hold-
ings) Inc.   **(1)**
2 Dai Fu Street Tai Po Industrial Estate, Tai
Po, China (Hong Kong)   **(45.32%)**
Tel.: (852) 21261212
Web Site: http://www.ck-lifesciences.com
Rev.: $672,637,725
Assets: $1,436,512,155

Liabilities: $906,692,280
Net Worth: $529,819,875
Earnings: $16,823,880
Emp.: 1,856
Fiscal Year-end: 12/31/2022
Holding Company
N.A.I.C.S.: 551112
Hing Lam Kam (Pres & Co-CEO)

Subsidiary (Non-US):

Cheetham Salt Limited   **(2)**
Level 6 565 Bourke Street, Melbourne,
3000, VIC, Australia   **(100%)**
Tel.: (61) 38 624 6800
Web Site: https://www.cheethamsalt.com.au
Salt Product Mfr
N.A.I.C.S.: 327999
Andrew Speed (CEO)

Subsidiary (Non-US):

PT Cheetham Garam Indonesia   **(3)**
Jl Australia I Kav I 3/1 Kawasan Industri
KIEC, Cilegon, 42443, Banten, Indonesia
Tel.: (62) 25 431 0317
Web Site:
https://www.cheethamindonesia.com
Sales Range: $25-49.9 Million
Emp.: 40
Salt Product Mfr
N.A.I.C.S.: 325998
Arthur Tanudaja (Pres)

Subsidiary (Non-US):

Lipa Pharmaceuticals Limited   **(2)**
21 Reaghs Farm Road, Minto, 2566, NSW,
Australia
Tel.: (61) 28 796 1400
Web Site: https://www.lipa.com.au
Sales Range: $75-99.9 Million
Emp.: 380
Vitamin & Nutritional Pharmaceutical Mfr
N.A.I.C.S.: 325412

Eversholt UK Rails Limited   **(1)**
Ground Floor WeWork 1 Waterhouse
Square 138-142, Holborn, London, EC1N
2ST, United Kingdom
Tel.: (44) 2073805040
Web Site: https://eversholtrail.co.uk
Freight Rolling Stock Services
N.A.I.C.S.: 488210

HUD Group   **(1)**
TYTL 108RP Sai Tso Wan Road, Tsing Yi,
New Territories, China (Hong
Kong)   **(50%)**
Tel.: (852) 2 431 2828
Web Site: https://www.hud.com.hk
Ship Building, Maintenance & Repair Ser-
vices
N.A.I.C.S.: 336611

Subsidiary (Domestic):

HongKong Salvage & Towage   **(2)**
2/F HUD Administration Building Sai Tso
Wan Road, Sai Tso Wan Road, Tsing Yi,
New Territories, China (Hong Kong)
Tel.: (852) 2 427 7477
Web Site: http://www.hud.com.hk
Sales Range: $25-49.9 Million
Emp.: 50
Shipbuilding & Repair Services
N.A.I.C.S.: 336611

HUTCHMED (CHINA) LIMITED   **(1)**
48th Floor Cheung Kong Center, 2 Queen s
Road Central, Hong Kong, China (Hong
Kong)   **(60.49%)**
Tel.: (852) 21218200
Rev.: $426,409,000
Assets: $1,029,445,000
Liabilities: $392,575,000
Net Worth: $636,870,000
Earnings: ($360,835,000)
Emp.: 2,025
Fiscal Year-end: 12/31/2022
Holding Company; Pharmaceutical Mfr
N.A.I.C.S.: 551112
Simon To (Chm)

Harbour Plaza 8 Degrees
Limited   **(1)**
199 Kowloon City Road, Tokwawan, Kow-
loon, China (Hong Kong)
Tel.: (852) 2 126 1988
Web Site: https://www.harbour-plaza.com
Emp.: 200

Home Management Services
N.A.I.C.S.: 721110

Harwich International Port
Limited   **(1)**
Parkeston, Harwich, CO12 4SR, Essex,
United Kingdom
Tel.: (44) 1255242000
Web Site: https://www.harwich.co.uk
Port Operation Services
N.A.I.C.S.: 488310

Hutchison 3G Austria GmbH   **(1)**
Brunner Strasse 52, 1210, Vienna, Austria
Tel.: (43) 660303030
Web Site: http://www.drei.at
Mobile Telecommunications Services
N.A.I.C.S.: 517112
Jan Trionow (CEO)

Subsidiary (Domestic):

Orange Austria Telecommunication
GmbH   **(2)**
Brunner Strasse 52, 1210, Vienna,
Austria   **(100%)**
Tel.: (43) 1 277728 0
Web Site: http://www.orange.at
Mobile Telecommunications Services
N.A.I.C.S.: 517112

Hutchison Ajman International Termi-
nals Limited - F.Z.E   **(1)**
Department of Port and Customs, PO Box
388, Ajman, United Arab Emirates
Tel.: (971) 67470111
Web Site:
https://www.hutchisonportsajman.com
Port Operation Services
N.A.I.C.S.: 488310

Hutchison Korea Terminals
Limited   **(1)**
314 Chungjang-daero, Dong-gu, Busan,
Korea (South)
Tel.: (82) 516308200
Web Site: https://www.hktl.com
Port Operation Services
N.A.I.C.S.: 488310

Hutchison Laemchabang Terminal
Limited   **(1)**
88 Moo 3, Tungsukhla Siracha District,
Bangkok, Chonburi, Thailand
Tel.: (66) 38408700
Web Site: https://hutchisonports.co.th
Port Operation Services
N.A.I.C.S.: 488310

Hutchison Port Holdings Limited   **(1)**
Terminal 4 Container Port Road South,
Kwai Chung, NT, China (Hong Kong)
Tel.: (852) 26197888
Web Site: https://hutchisonports.com
Sales Range: $400-449.9 Million
Emp.: 30,000
Operator of Ports & Terminals
N.A.I.C.S.: 488310
Eric S. C. Ip (Exec Dir)

Subsidiary (Non-US):

Europe Containers Terminals
B.V.   **(2)**
Reeweg 25, 3199 LJ, Rotterdam,
Netherlands   **(100%)**
Tel.: (31) 104916911
Web Site: https://www.ect.nl
Sales Range: $200-249.9 Million
Emp.: 1,000
Container Terminal Operator
N.A.I.C.S.: 488320

Hutchison Ports Sweden AB   **(1)**
Norvikvagen 18, 149 45, Nynashamn, Swe-
den
Tel.: (46) 760230500
Web Site:
https://hutchisonportsstockholm.se
Port Operation Services
N.A.I.C.S.: 488310

Hutchison Telecommunications (Aus-
tralia) Limited   **(1)**
Level 27 Tower Two International Towers
Sydney 200 Barangaroo Avenue, Baranga-
roo, 2000, NSW, Australia   **(87.87%)**
Tel.: (61) 290155088
Web Site: https://www.hutchison.com.au
Rev.: $583,746

CK Hutchison Holdings Limited—(Continued)

Assets: $148,013,895
Liabilities: $908,654
Net Worth: $147,105,241
Earnings: ($84,493,933)
Emp.: 2
Fiscal Year-end: 12/31/2023
Telecommunication Servicesb
N.A.I.C.S.: 517112
Canning Kin Ning Fok (Chm)

Joint Venture (Domestic):

TPG Telecom Limited (2)
Level 1 177 Pacific Highway, Saint Leonards, 2060, NSW, Australia
Tel.: (61) 299644646
Web Site: http://www.vodafone.com.au
Rev.: $3,768,816,838
Assets: $13,396,907,567
Liabilities: $5,483,958,858
Net Worth: $7,912,948,709
Earnings: $33,376,473
Emp.: 6,000
Fiscal Year-end: 12/31/2023
Mobile Telecommunications Services
N.A.I.C.S.: 517112

Subsidiary (Domestic):

TPG Corporation Limited (3)
65 Waterloo Road, North Ryde, Sydney, 2113, NSW, Australia
Tel.: (61) 298500800
Web Site: http://www.tpg.com.au
Rev.: $1,947,478,648
Assets: $4,207,075,247
Liabilities: $2,034,034,989
Net Worth: $2,173,040,258
Earnings: $310,635,020
Emp.: 5,056
Fiscal Year-end: 07/31/2018
Telecommunications & Multi Media Services
N.A.I.C.S.: 517121

Subsidiary (Domestic):

TPG Holdings Limited (4)
Level 24 200 Barangaroo Ave, Sydney, 2000, NSW, Australia
Tel.: (61) 290073023
Web Site: https://www.tpg.com.au
Sales Range: $125-149.9 Million
Holding Company; Internet, Internet-Based Telecommunications & Information Technology Networking Services
N.A.I.C.S.: 551112

Subsidiary (Domestic):

AAPT Limited (5)
680 George Street Level 23, Sydney, 2000, NSW, Australia
Tel.: (61) 2 8277 5405
Web Site: http://www.aapt.com.au
Sales Range: $350-399.9 Million
Emp.: 1,000
Telecommunication Servicesb
N.A.I.C.S.: 517111

Chariot Limited (5)
Level 1 5 Leigh Street, Adelaide, 5000, SA, Australia
Tel.: (61) 1300147425
Web Site: https://www.chariot.net.au
Sales Range: $10-24.9 Million
Internet Services
N.A.I.C.S.: 517810

Subsidiary (Non-US):

Kooee Pty Ltd (5)
Tel.: (61) 249265007
Telecommunication Servicesb
N.A.I.C.S.: 517810

Subsidiary (Non-US):

Kooee Communications Pty Ltd (6)
Tel.: (61) 249265007
Web Site: http://www.kooee.com.au
Emp.: 50
Telecommunication Servicesb
N.A.I.C.S.: 517810

Subsidiary (Domestic):

PIPE Transmission Pty Ltd (5)
L 17 Pipe Networks House 127 Creek St, Brisbane, 4000, QLD, Australia
Tel.: (61) 732339800

Web Site: http://www.pipenetworks.com
Emp.: 80
Telecommunication Servicesb
N.A.I.C.S.: 517810

SPT Telecommunications Pty Ltd (5)
11-17 Mosbri Crescent, Newcastle, 2300, NSW, Australia
Tel.: (61) 249265007
Sales Range: $25-49.9 Million
Emp.: 20
Telecommunication Servicesb
N.A.I.C.S.: 517810
Mik Watts (Gen Mgr)

Soul Communications Pty. Limited (5)
Level 14 201 Kent Street, GPO Box N800, Grosvenor Place, Sydney, 2000, NSW, Australia
Tel.: (61) 282206000
Web Site: http://www.soulaustralia.com.au
Sales Range: $350-399.9 Million
Emp.: 100
Mobile, Wired, Internet & Broadband Telecommunications Reseller
N.A.I.C.S.: 517121

Soul Pattinson Telecommunications Pty Ltd (5)
L 14 201 Kent St, Sydney, 2000, NSW, Australia
Tel.: (61) 282206000
Telecommunication Servicesb
N.A.I.C.S.: 517810

TPG Internet Pty. Ltd. (5)
65 Waterloo Rd, Macquarie Park, North Ryde, 2113, NSW, Australia
Tel.: (61) 298500800
Web Site: http://www.tpg.com.au
Emp.: 150
Internet & Internet-Based Telecommunications Services
N.A.I.C.S.: 517810

TPG Network Pty Ltd (5)
65 Waterloo Rd, North Ryde, 2113, NSW, Australia
Tel.: (61) 298500800
Network Systems Integration Services
N.A.I.C.S.: 541512

TPG Research Pty Ltd (5)
53 Dundas Ct, Phillip, Canberra, 2606, ACT, Australia
Tel.: (61) 262851711
Software Development Services
N.A.I.C.S.: 541511

iiNet Limited (5)
65 Waterloo Road, Macquarie Park, 2113, NSW, Australia
Tel.: (61) 8 9214 2222
Web Site: http://www.iinet.net.au
Internet Services
N.A.I.C.S.: 517810
Michael M. Malone (Founder)

Subsidiary (Domestic):

Westnet Ltd (6)
Locked Bag 16, Cloisters Square, Perth, 6850, WA, Australia
Tel.: (61) 131960
Web Site: https://www.westnet.com.au
Internet Broadband Services
N.A.I.C.S.: 517810

Hutchison Telecommunications International Ltd. (1)
20/F Hutchison Telecom Tower 99 Cheung Fai Rd, Tsing Yi, China (Hong Kong)
Tel.: (852) 21283222
Web Site: http://www.htil.com
Sales Range: $200-249.9 Million
Emp.: 2,200
Telecommunication Servicesb
N.A.I.C.S.: 517111

Joint Venture (Non-US):

Hutchison Essar Limited (2)
Hutch House Peninsula Corporate Park, Ganpatrao Kdam Marg, Lower Parel, Mumbai, 400 013, India
Tel.: (91) 2256661200
Wireless Telecommunication Services
N.A.I.C.S.: 517112

Subsidiary (Domestic):

Hutchison Telecommunications Hong Kong Holdings Limited (2)
15/F Hutchison Telecom Tower 99 Cheung Fai Road, Tsing Yi, Hong Kong, China (Hong Kong) (100%)
Tel.: (852) 21286828
Web Site: http://www.hthkh.com
Rev.: $823,921,684
Assets: $1,911,383,184
Liabilities: $599,000,601
Net Worth: $1,312,382,583
Earnings: ($20,192,467)
Emp.: 1,066
Fiscal Year-end: 12/31/2022
Telecommunication Servicesb
N.A.I.C.S.: 517112
Edith Shih (Sec)

Maritime Transport Services Limited (1)
Maritime House Clickett Hill Road, Felixstowe, IP11 4AX, Suffolk, United Kingdom
Tel.: (44) 1394617300
Web Site: https://www.maritimetransport.com
Logistic Services
N.A.I.C.S.: 541614

Oman International Container Terminal L.L.C. (1)
Terminal-C Sohar Port and Free zone, PO Box 82, Sohar, Oman
Tel.: (968) 26865600
Web Site: https://oict.com.om
Port Operation Services
N.A.I.C.S.: 488310

Panama Ports Company, S.A. (1)
Arnulfo Arias Madrid Avenue Building 1501, PO Box 0843-00574, Panama, Panama
Tel.: (507) 2075100
Web Site: https://www.ppc.com.pa
Port Operation Services
N.A.I.C.S.: 488310

Parknshop (HK) Limited (1)
Watson House 1-5 Wo Liu Hang Road, Fo Tan Sha Tin New Territories, Hong Kong, China (Hong Kong)
Tel.: (852) 26068833
Web Site: https://www.pns.hk
Hardware & Grocery Product Retailer
N.A.I.C.S.: 424410

Port of Felixstowe Limited (1)
Tomline House The Dock, Felixstowe, IP11 3SY, Suffolk, United Kingdom
Tel.: (44) 1394604500
Web Site: https://www.portoffelixstowe.co.uk
Port Operation Services
N.A.I.C.S.: 488310

TOM Group Limited (1)
Room 1601-05 16/F China Resources Building, 26 Harbour Road, Wanchai, China (Hong Kong) (36.73%)
Tel.: (852) 21217838
Web Site: http://www.tomgroup.com
Rev.: $105,840,428
Assets: $408,283,305
Liabilities: $526,249,620
Net Worth: ($117,966,315)
Earnings: $23,612,108
Emp.: 1,700
Fiscal Year-end: 12/31/2022
News & Reference Web Sites, Advertising & Marketing Services & Magazine Publisher
N.A.I.C.S.: 541890
Kwok Mung Yeung (CEO)

Subsidiary (Non-US):

TOM Online Inc. (2)
Rm 801-802 8/F Tower W3 Oriental Plaza No1 Dong Chang An Avenue, Dong Cheng District, Beijing, 100738, China
Tel.: (86) 1085180006
Web Site: http://www.tom.com
Wireless Internet Services; Website Operator
N.A.I.C.S.: 334118

Three Ireland (Hutchison) Limited (1)
28/29 Sir John Rogerson's Quay, Dublin, 2, Ireland (100%)
Tel.: (353) 15426300
Web Site: https://www.three.ie

Emp.: 1,300
Mobile Communications Services
N.A.I.C.S.: 517112
Elaine Carey (Chief Commt Officer)

WEX Pharmaceuticals Inc. (1)
Suite 1150 - 1100 Melville Street, Vancouver, V6E 4A6, BC, Canada
Tel.: (604) 683-8880
Web Site: http://www.wexpharma.com
Sales Range: Less than $1 Million
Emp.: 26
Pharmaceutical Development Services
N.A.I.C.S.: 541715
Christopher C. Gallen (CEO)

Watsons Personal Care Stores Sdn. Bhd. (1)
Level 7 Arena Watsons Exchange 106 Lingkaran Trx Tun Razak Exchange, Wilayah Persekutuan Kuala Lumpur, 55188, Kuala Lumpur, Malaysia
Tel.: (60) 327076688
Web Site: https://www.watsons.com.my
Emp.: 800
Luxury Product Retailer
N.A.I.C.S.: 423940

Winchesto Finance Company Limited (1)
7-12/F Cheung Kong Ctr 2 Queens Rd C, Central District, Hong Kong, China (Hong Kong)
Tel.: (852) 25266911
Financial Management Services
N.A.I.C.S.: 523999

iMarkets Limited (1)
12/F Cheung Kong Center 2 Queen's Road, Central, China (Hong Kong)
Tel.: (852) 2 122 3028
Web Site: https://www.imarkets.com.hk
Electronic Platform Financial Investment Services
N.A.I.C.S.: 523999
Edmond Tak Chuen Ip (Chm)

CK POWER PUBLIC COMPANY LIMITED

587 Viriyathavorn Building 19th Floor Sutthisarn Winitchai Road, Ratchadaphisek Subdistrict Dindaeng District, Bangkok, 10400, Thailand
Tel.: (66) 26919720
Web Site: https://www.ckpower.co.th
Year Founded: 2011
CKP—(THA)
Rev.: $319,552,544
Assets: $2,007,393,921
Liabilities: $871,302,487
Net Worth: $1,136,091,434
Earnings: $56,290,408
Emp.: 266
Fiscal Year-end: 12/31/23
Electric Power
N.A.I.C.S.: 221122
Michael Eric Reader (Deputy Mng Dir-Engrg)

Subsidiaries:

Bangpa-in Cogeneration Limited (1)
No 587 Sutthisarnvinijchai Road, Dindaeng District, Bangkok, 10400, Thailand (65%)
Tel.: (66) 22750026
Electric Power & Steam Generation & Distribution Services
N.A.I.C.S.: 221118
Woravuth Anuruxwonpsri (Mng Dir)

CK SAN-ETSU CO., LTD.

2121 Shugocho, Takaoka, 933-0983, Japan
Tel.: (81) 766280025
Web Site: https://www.cksanetu.co.jp
5757—(TKS)
Rev.: $736,572,130
Assets: $509,895,400
Liabilities: $155,546,520
Net Worth: $354,348,880
Earnings: $25,217,150
Emp.: 1,000
Fiscal Year-end: 03/31/24
Brass Product Mfr & Distr

N.A.I.C.S.: 331420

Subsidiaries:

CK Trading Co., Ltd. **(1)**
099 St 598 S K Chrang Chanress II Khan
Russekeo, Phnom Penh, Cambodia
Tel.: (855) 12833378
Brass Material Distr
N.A.I.C.S.: 423720

SAN-ETSU Metals Co., Ltd. **(1)**
1892 Ota, Tonami, 939-1315, Toyama, Japan
Tel.: (81) 763331212
Web Site: https://www.sanetu.co.jp
Emp.: 530
Brass Material Mfr & Distr
N.A.I.C.S.: 331523
Hiroyuki Tsuriya *(Mng Dir)*

Subsidiary (Domestic):

SAN-ETSU Metals Co., Ltd. - Shin
Nitto Plant **(2)**
4-1 Kashiwabara, Ishioka, 315-8536, Ibaraki, Japan
Tel.: (81) 299237161
Web Site: https://www.sanetu.co.jp
Brass Material Mfr & Distr
N.A.I.C.S.: 331523

SAN-ETSU Metals Co., Ltd. -
Takaoka Plant **(2)**
1-4-1 Yoshihisa, Takaoka, 933-0002,
Toyama, Japan
Tel.: (81) 766848300
Web Site: https://www.sanetu.co.jp
Brass Material Mfr & Distr
N.A.I.C.S.: 331523

San-Etsu Metals (Shanghai) Co.,
Ltd. **(1)**
Room No 1111 New Town Centre 83 Lou
Shan Guan Road, Shanghai, 200336,
China
Tel.: (86) 2162368345
Web Site: http://www.sanetu.co.jp
Brass Material Distr
N.A.I.C.S.: 423720

Taiwan San-Etsu Co., Ltd. **(1)**
No 765 Section 2 Taiwan Boulevard, Xitun
District, Taichung, Taiwan
Tel.: (886) 424379052
Web Site: http://www.sanetu.co.jp
Brass Material Distr
N.A.I.C.S.: 423720

Yashima Co., Ltd. **(1)**
Kabutocho Heiwa Bldg No 6 6-5, Nihonbashi Kabutocho Chuo-ku, Tokyo, 103-0026, Japan
Tel.: (81) 367582559
Web Site: http://www.yashima-co.co.jp
Emp.: 267
Industrial Machinery Distr
N.A.I.C.S.: 423830
Atsushi Sato *(Chm)*

CKD BIO CORP.
CKD Building 8 Chungjeong-ro,
Seodaemun-gu, Seoul, 03742, Korea
(South)
Tel.: (82) 221940555
Web Site: https://www.ckdbio.com
Year Founded: 2001
063160—(KRS)
Rev.: $119,684,465
Assets: $239,757,293
Liabilities: $126,395,103
Net Worth: $113,362,190
Earnings: ($12,810,906)
Emp.: 558
Fiscal Year-end: 12/31/22
Pharmaceuticals Product Mfr
N.A.I.C.S.: 325412
Jeong-Jin Lee *(CEO)*

CKD CORPORATION
2-250 Ouji, Komaki, 485-8551, Aichi,
Japan
Tel.: (81) 568771111
Web Site: https://www.ckd.co.jp
Year Founded: 1943

6407—(NGO)
Rev.: $888,172,860
Assets: $1,376,180,652
Liabilities: $523,204,346
Net Worth: $852,976,306
Earnings: $55,090,834
Emp.: 4,645
Fiscal Year-end: 03/31/24
Automatic Machinery, Labor-Saving
Components, Pneumatic Valves &
Cylinders & Auxiliary Components,
Fluid Control Components Mfr &
Sales
N.A.I.C.S.: 333995
Kiyoshi Miura *(Auditor)*

Subsidiaries:

CDK Korea Corporation **(1)**
3rd Floor 44 Sinsu-ro, Mapo-gu, Seoul,
121-856, Korea (South)
Tel.: (82) 27835201
Web Site: http://www.ckdkorea.co.kr
Pharmaceutical Preparation Products Mfr
N.A.I.C.S.: 325412

CKD (China) Corporation **(1)**
No 21 Xinhua Road, Xinwu District, Wuxi,
214028, Jiangsu, China
Tel.: (86) 5108 534 5300
Web Site: https://www.ckd.com.cn
Emp.: 777
Develops, Manufactures & Sells Fluid
Power Cylinders
N.A.I.C.S.: 333995

CKD (SHANGHAI)
CORPORATION **(1)**
Room 601 6th Floor Yuanzhongkeyan
Building No 1905 Hongmei Road, Xuhui
District, Shanghai, 200233, China
Tel.: (86) 216 191 1888
Web Site: http://www.ckd.sh.cn
Electrical Component Mfr
N.A.I.C.S.: 334419

CKD Corporation **(1)**
3940 Olympic Blvd Ste 380, Erlanger, KY
41018-3973
Tel.: (859) 283-2776
Web Site: https://www.ckdusa.com
Sales Range: $25-49.9 Million
Emp.: 3
Pneumatic Cylinder Developer, Mfr & Whslr
N.A.I.C.S.: 444140

CKD Corporation **(1)**
595 Round Rock W Dr, Round Rock, TX
78681
Tel.: (512) 339-3035
Web Site: http://www.ckd.com
Sales Range: $50-74.9 Million
Emp.: 2
Develops, Manufactures & Sells Fluid
Power Cylinders
N.A.I.C.S.: 423690

CKD Corporation **(1)**
2450 Scott Blvd Ste 302, Santa Clara, CA
95050
Tel.: (408) 327-9000
Web Site: https://www.ckdusa.com
Sales Range: $50-74.9 Million
Emp.: 8
Develops, Manufactures & Sells Fluid
Power Cylinders
N.A.I.C.S.: 423990

CKD Corporation - Kasugai Plant **(1)**
1-850 Horinouchi-cho-kita, Kasugai, 486-8530, Aichi, Japan
Tel.: (81) 568816221
Sales Range: $200-249.9 Million
Emp.: 900
Semiconductor Equipment Mfr
N.A.I.C.S.: 334413

CKD Corporation - Yokkaichi
Plant **(1)**
2800 Takayama Komaki-cho, Yokkaichi,
512-1303, Mie, Japan
Tel.: (81) 593392140
Automated Industrial Machinery Mfr
N.A.I.C.S.: 333248

CKD Europe B.V. **(1)**
Beechavenue 125A, 1119 RB, Schiphol-
Rijk, Netherlands

Tel.: (31) 235541490
Web Site: http://www.ckdeu.info
Automation Machinery & Component Mfr &
Distr
N.A.I.C.S.: 333998

CKD Field Engineering
Corporation **(1)**
2-250 Oji, Komaki, 485-8551, Aichi Prefecture, Japan
Tel.: (81) 568741384
Automatic Machinery Maintenance Services
N.A.I.C.S.: 811310

CKD Global Service Corporation **(1)**
250 Ouji 2-chome, Komaki, 485-8551, Aichi,
Japan
Tel.: (81) 568741121
Insurance Services
N.A.I.C.S.: 524298

CKD Global Services
Corporation **(1)**
250 Ouji 2-chome, Komaki, 485-8551, Aichi,
Japan
Tel.: (81) 568741121
Fluid Control Component Mfr & Distr
N.A.I.C.S.: 332912

CKD India Private Limited **(1)**
Unit No 607 6th Floor Welldone Tech Park
Sector 48 Sohna Road, Gurgaon, 122018,
Haryana, India
Tel.: (91) 1244188212
Web Site: http://www.ckdin.co.in
Emp.: 28
Industrial Electrical Component Mfr & Distr
N.A.I.C.S.: 335999
Masanori Takeda *(Pres)*

CKD Korea Corporation **(1)**
44 Sinsu-ro 3rd Floor, Mapo-gu, Seoul, 121-856, Korea (South)
Tel.: (82) 27835201
Web Site: https://www.ckdkorea.co.kr
Emp.: 43
Fluid Control Component Mfr & Distr
N.A.I.C.S.: 332912

CKD Mexico, S. de R.L. de C.V. **(1)**
Cerrada la Noria No 200 Int A-01 Queretaro
Park II, Parque Industrial Queretaro Santa
Rosa Jauregui, 76220, Queretaro, Mexico
Tel.: (52) 4421610624
Web Site: http://www.ckdmex.com.mx
Machinery Equipment Mfr & Whslr
N.A.I.C.S.: 333248

CKD Nikki Denso Co., Ltd. **(1)**
2-8-24 Arima, Miyamae-ku, Kawasaki, 216-0003, Kanagawa, Japan
Tel.: (81) 448554311
Web Site: http://www.nikkidenso.co.jp
Emp.: 230
Industrial Machinery Mfr & Retailer
N.A.I.C.S.: 333248
Shigeru Kawamura *(CEO)*

CKD Shikoku Seiko Corporation **(1)**
3661-53 Hiratachohenai 2-Chome, Sukumo,
788-0783, Kouchi, Japan
Tel.: (81) 880661566
Automated Pharmaceutical & Food Packaging Machine Mfr
N.A.I.C.S.: 333993

CKD Singapore Pte Ltd **(1)**
33 Tannery Lane 04-01 Hoesteel Industrial
Building, Singapore, 347789,
Singapore **(100%)**
Tel.: (65) 6 744 2623
Web Site: https://www.ckdsing.com.sg
Sales Range: $25-49.9 Million
Emp.: 22
Develops, Manufactures & Sells Fluid
Power Cylinders
N.A.I.C.S.: 333995

CKD Thai Corporation Ltd. **(1)**
700/58 Moo1 Bangna-Trad Rd Km 58,
Bankao, Phan Thong, 20160, Chon Buri,
Thailand **(100%)**
Tel.: (66) 2 267 6300
Web Site: https://www.ckdthai.com
Sales Range: $100-124.9 Million
Emp.: 500
Develops, Manufactures & Sells Fluid
Power Cylinders
N.A.I.C.S.: 333995

CKD USA Corporation **(1)**

1605 Penny Ln, Schaumburg, IL
60173 **(100%)**
Tel.: (847) 648-4400
Web Site: https://www.ckdusa.com
Sales Range: $500-549.9 Million
Emp.: 18
Develops, Manufactures & Sells Fluid
Power Cylinders
N.A.I.C.S.: 332911
Tim Cochrane *(Treas & Sec)*

CKD Vietnam Engineering Co.,
Ltd. **(1)**
18th Floor CMC Tower Duy Tan Street, Cau
Giay District, Hanoi, Vietnam
Tel.: (84) 2437957633
Automation Machinery Mfr & Distr
N.A.I.C.S.: 333248

M-CKD Precision Sdn. Bhd. **(1)**
Lot No 6 Jalan Modal 23/2 Seksyen 23 Kawasan MIEL Fasa 8, 40300, Shah Alam,
Selangor, Malaysia **(100%)**
Tel.: (60) 35 541 1468
Web Site: https://www.mckd.com.my
Sales Range: $1-9.9 Million
Emp.: 54
Develops, Manufacures & Sells Fluid Power
Cylinders
N.A.I.C.S.: 333995
Kok Choy Wong *(Gen Mgr)*

Nikki Denso International Korea Co.,
Ltd. **(1)**
D311 Centroad 323 Incheon Tower-Daero,
Yeonsu-gu, Incheon, 22007, Korea (South)
Tel.: (82) 328312133
Servo Motor Mfr & Distr
N.A.I.C.S.: 335312

PT CKD Trading Indonesia **(1)**
Bidakara Tower 2 18th Floor Jl Gen Gatot
Subroto Kav 71-73, Pancoran, Jakarta,
12870, Indonesia
Tel.: (62) 2129386601
Web Site: https://www.ckdti.co.id
Emp.: 10
Automatic Machinery Distr
N.A.I.C.S.: 423830
Andy Yulius Canser *(Pres)*

Taiwan CKD Corporation **(1)**
16F-3 No 7 Sec 3 New Taipei Blvd, Xin-
zhuang Dist, New Taipei City, 242,
Taiwan **(100%)**
Tel.: (886) 28 522 8198
Web Site: https://www.ckdtaiwan.com.tw
Sales Range: $25-49.9 Million
Emp.: 19
Develops, Manufactures & Sells Fluid
Power Cylinders
N.A.I.C.S.: 333995

CKF, INC.
48 Prince St, Hantsport, B0P 1P0,
NS, Canada
Tel.: (902) 684-3231
Web Site: http://www.ckfinc.com
Year Founded: 1933
Sales Range: $75-99.9 Million
Pulp Fibre Tableware Products Mfr
N.A.I.C.S.: 337126
Brad Dennis *(VP-Sls Mktg)*

CKM APPLIED MATERIALS
CORP.
No 9 Gongye Road, Guantian Dist,
Tainan City, 720008, Taiwan
Tel.: (886) 66986623
Web Site: https://www.ckm.com.tw
Year Founded: 1982
8930—(TPE)
Rev.: $41,003,940
Assets: $75,214,239
Liabilities: $33,727,605
Net Worth: $41,486,634
Earnings: $5,427,884
Fiscal Year-end: 12/31/22
Building Material Mfr & Distr
N.A.I.C.S.: 327120
Chen Yuan-Teng *(Chm & CEO)*

CKP LEISURE LIMITED

CKP Leisure Limited—(Continued)

3 Second Floor xth Central Mall Near
Dmart Mahavir Nagar, KandiVali
West, Mumbai, 400067, India
Tel.: (91) 7710044458
Web Site: http://www.ckpleisure.com
Entertainment Services
N.A.I.C.S.: 713990

CKP PRODUCTS LIMITED
Shop 223 2nd Floor Powai Plaza A
Premises CSL A S Marg, Hiranandani
Gardens Powai, Mumbai, 400076,
India
Tel.: (91) 7710044458
Web Site: http://www.ckpproducts.in
Rev.: $34,970,966
Assets: $5,418,334
Liabilities: $3,278,453
Net Worth: $2,139,880
Earnings: $90,657
Emp.: 8
Fiscal Year-end: 03/31/19
Pharmaceuticals Product Mfr
N.A.I.C.S.: 325412
Prafulla Bhat (Chm)

CL ASSET HOLDINGS, LIMITED
Level 2 28 34 Clarke Street, Crows
Nest, 2065, NSW, Australia
Tel.: (61) 294323999
Web Site: http://www.cl.com.au
Sales Range: $25-49.9 Million
Emp.: 3
Property Investor, Developer, Operator & Manager
N.A.I.C.S.: 531390
Peter Mitropoulos (Exec Dir)

CL EDUCATE LIMITED
A-45 First Floor Mohan Co-operative
Industrial Estate, New Delhi, 110 044,
India
Tel.: (91) 1141281100
Web Site: https://www.cleducate.com
Year Founded: 1996
540403—(BOM)
Rev.: $29,506
Assets: $47,472
Liabilities: $11,759
Net Worth: $35,713
Earnings: $1,882
Emp.: 446
Fiscal Year-end: 03/31/22
Professional Development Services
N.A.I.C.S.: 611430
Satya Narayanan R. (Chm)

Subsidiaries:

Kestone CL Asia Hub Pte. Ltd. (1)
120 Robinson Road 15-01, Singapore,
068913, Singapore
Tel.: (65) 90554959
Digital Marketing Services
N.A.I.C.S.: 541613

Kestone CL US Limited (1)
5201 Great America Pkwy Ste 350, Santa
Clara, CA 95054
Tel.: (408) 772-2262
Digital Marketing Services
N.A.I.C.S.: 541613

Kestone Integrated Marketing Services Private Limited (1)
37 7th Cross RMJ Mandoth Towers, Vasanthnagar, Bengaluru, 560052, Karnataka,
India
Tel.: (91) 9716299360
Digital Marketing Services
N.A.I.C.S.: 541613

CL FINANCIAL LIMITED
1 Herbert Street, Saint Claire, Port of
Spain, Trinidad & Tobago
Tel.: (868) 6287589
Emp.: 5
Holding Company

N.A.I.C.S.: 551112
Marlon Holder (CEO)

CL GROUP (HOLDINGS) LIMITED
Unit B 16/F Bank of East Asia Harbour View Center 56 Gloucester
Road, Wanchai, China (Hong Kong)
Tel.: (852) 3 426 2664
Web Site:
  http://www.cheongleesec.com.hk
8098—(HKG)
Rev.: $6,407,666
Assets: $35,790,253
Liabilities: $9,855,187
Net Worth: $25,935,066
Earnings: ($1,033,541)
Fiscal Year-end: 03/31/22
Security Trading Services
N.A.I.C.S.: 523150
Kin Chung Kwok (CEO)

CL HOLDINGS INC.
11th Floor Minami Aoyama Bright
Square 2-26-1 Minamiaoyama,
Minato-ku, Tokyo, 107-0062, Japan
Tel.: (81) 334083090
Web Site:
  https://www.clholdings.co.jp
Year Founded: 1988
4286—(TKS)
Rev.: $211,793,855
Assets: $140,878,758
Liabilities: $63,548,067
Net Worth: $77,330,690
Earnings: $2,405,021
Fiscal Year-end: 12/31/22
Marketing Consulting Services
N.A.I.C.S.: 541613
Satoshi Yamashita (Pres)

Subsidiaries:

LEGS (SHANGHAI) TRADING COMPANY, LTD. (1)
8F-806 ChunQiu International Building
No699 ZhaoHua Rd, ChangNing Section,
Shanghai, China
Tel.: (86) 216 230 0596
Web Site: http://www.legs-sh.com
Novelty Product Mfr & Distr
N.A.I.C.S.: 339999
Junichiro Uchikawa (Chm)

Legs (Shanghai) Cultural & Creative
Company, Ltd. (1)
8F-806 ChunQiu International Building No
699 ZhaoHua Rd, Changing Section,
Shanghai, China
Tel.: (86) 216 230 0596
Business Construction Support Services
N.A.I.C.S.: 561990
Satoshi Nishijima (Mng Dir)

M&I Co., Ltd. (1)
3F Kusumoto 2nd Building 1-2-8, Chiyoda-
ku, Tokyo, 101-0047, Japan
Tel.: (81) 33 292 1247
Web Site: https://www.m-i.co.jp
Emp.: 172
Software Development Services
N.A.I.C.S.: 541511

CL INTERNATIONAL CO., LTD.
12F Woolim Lion's Valley Bldg 311-3,
Sangdaewon-Dong Jungwon-gu,
Seongnam, 462-806, Gyeonggi-do,
Korea (South)
Tel.: (82) 31 777 7330
Year Founded: 1996
Sales Range: $10-24.9 Million
Emp.: 81
Communication Equipment Mfr
N.A.I.C.S.: 334220
Gwang Hyeok Park (CEO)

CLAAS KGAA MBH
Muhlenwinkel 1, 33428, Harsewinkel,
Germany
Tel.: (49) 52 4712 1743

Web Site: http://www.claas-
  group.com
Year Founded: 1913
Rev.: $4,365,170,605
Assets: $3,955,263,770
Liabilities: $2,368,057,076
Net Worth: $1,587,206,694
Earnings: $107,409,132
Emp.: 11,448
Fiscal Year-end: 09/30/19
Holding Company; Agricultural Machinery Mfr & Distr
N.A.I.C.S.: 551112
Jan-Hendrik Mohr (Member-Exec Bd-
Grain Harvest Div)

Subsidiaries:

Brotje Automation GmbH (1)
Am Autobahnkreuz 14, 26180, Rastede, **(100%)**
Germany
Tel.: (49) 44029660
Web Site: http://www.broetje-automation.de
Sales Range: $75-99.9 Million
Emp.: 250
N.A.I.C.S.: 238210

CLAAS Agricultural Machinery Private
Limited (1)
487/B1 14th Cross 2nd Stage 4th Phase,
Peenya Industrial Area, 560058, Bengaluru,
Karnataka, India
Tel.: (91) 8067167000
Agricultural Machinery Mfr
N.A.I.C.S.: 333111
Bhimashankar Gujari (Sr Mgr-Spare Parts)

CLAAS Agrosystems KGaA mbH &
Co KG
Backerkamp 19, 33330, Gutersloh, Germany
Tel.: (49) 52 41 300 6 0
Web Site: http://www.claas-
  agrosystems.com
Software Development Services
N.A.I.C.S.: 541511

CLAAS America Latina Representacao Ltda. (1)
Rua Dom Pedro II, 90550-140, Porto
Alegre, Brazil
Tel.: (55) 5133941900
Web Site: http://www.claas.com.br
Agricultural Machinery & Equipment Mfr
N.A.I.C.S.: 333111

CLAAS Anlagemanagement
GmbH (1)
Munsterstr 33, Harsewinkel, 33428,
Nordrhein-Westfalen, Germany
Tel.: (49) 524 7120
Web Site: http://www.claas.com
Agricultural Equipment Mfr
N.A.I.C.S.: 333111

CLAAS E-Systems GmbH (1)
Sommerkampen 11, Dissen am Teutoburger
Wald, 49201, Osnabruck, Germany
Tel.: (49) 542193110
Web Site: http://www.claas-e-systems.com
Agricultural Engineering Equipment Mfr
N.A.I.C.S.: 333111
Stephan Vormbrock (Mng Dir)

CLAAS Eastern Ltd. (1)
London Road, Sleaford, NG34 8NX, Lincolnshire, United Kingdom
Tel.: (44) 1529303093
Web Site: http://www.eastern.claas-
  dealer.co.uk
Agricultural Machinery Mfr
N.A.I.C.S.: 333111
Nicholas Pearson (Mgr-Svcs)

CLAAS Italia S.p.A. (1)
Via Torino 9/11, 13100, Vercelli, Italy
Tel.: (39) 01 61 29 84 11
Web Site: http://www.claas.it
Agricultural Equipment Mfr
N.A.I.C.S.: 333111

Subsidiary (Domestic):

CLAAS Agricoltura S.R.L. (2)
Via Brescia 60, 25024, Leno, Italy
Tel.: (39) 030 9038411
Web Site: http://www.claas.it
Emp.: 70

Agricultural Equipment Mfr
N.A.I.C.S.: 333111

CLAAS Manns Ltd. (1)
Saxham, Bury Saint Edmunds, IP28 6QZ,
Suffolk, United Kingdom
Tel.: (44) 1284777700
Web Site: http://www.manns.claas-
  dealer.co.uk
Emp.: 100
Agricultural Machinery Mfr
N.A.I.C.S.: 333111
Alastair McCallum (Mgr-Used Machinery)

CLAAS Middle East - FZE (1)
Dubai Silicon Oasis, 341351, Dubai, United
Arab Emirates
Tel.: (971) 503061090
Agricultural Machinery & Equipment Mfr
N.A.I.C.S.: 333111

CLAAS North America Holdings
Inc. (1)
8401 S 132nd St, Omaha, NE 68138
Tel.: (402) 861-1000
Holding Company
N.A.I.C.S.: 551112

Subsidiary (Domestic):

Nebraska Harvest Center Inc. (2)
925 280th Rd, Seward, NE 68434
Tel.: (402) 643-4050
Web Site: http://www.nebharv.com
Agricultural Equipment Distr
N.A.I.C.S.: 424910

CLAAS Service and Parts GmbH (1)
Kranstrasse 40, 59071, Hamm, Germany
Tel.: (49) 52 47 12 0
Logistics Consulting Servies
N.A.I.C.S.: 541614
Kerstin Finke (Mgr-HR)

CLAAS Western Ltd. (1)
Cotswold Agricultural Centre Spine Road
Junction, Cirencester, GL7 5QA, Gloucestershire, United Kingdom
Tel.: (44) 1285863190
Web Site: http://www.western.claas-
  dealer.co.uk
Agricultural Machinery Mfr
N.A.I.C.S.: 333111
Will Greenway (Sls Dir)

Canada West Harvest Centre
Inc. (1)
8 Industrial Drive West Emerald Park, Regina, S4L 1C6, SK, Canada
Tel.: (306) 525-2300
Web Site: http://www.cawhc.com
Farming Services
N.A.I.C.S.: 111998
Don Schultz (Mgr-Territory Acct)

Claas Argentina S.A. (1)
Ruta 34 km 255, Sunchalez, 2322, Santa
Fe, Argentina **(100%)**
Tel.: (54) 3493427700
Web Site: http://www.claas.com.ar
Harvesting Machinery & Equipment Mfr
N.A.I.C.S.: 333111

Claas Bordesholm GmbH (1)
Dieselstrasse 3, Wattenbek, 24582, Bordesholm, Germany **(74.4%)**
Tel.: (49) 4322754961
Web Site: http://www.claas-bordesholm.de
Farm & Garden Machinery & Equipment
Whslr
N.A.I.C.S.: 333111

Claas France Holding S.A.S. (1)
Avenue Du Parc Medicis, 94260, Fresnes,
France **(100%)**
Tel.: (33) 146748181
Web Site: http://www.claas.fr
Sales Range: $50-74.9 Million
Emp.: 80
Holding Company
N.A.I.C.S.: 551112

Subsidiary (Domestic):

CLAAS Tractor S.A.S. (2)
7 rue Dewoitine, 78141, Velizy-Villacoublay,
Cedex, France
Tel.: (33) 1 34 65 56 56
Agricultural Equipment Mfr
N.A.I.C.S.: 333111

Claas France S.A.S. (2)
Ave du Parc Medicis, 94832, Fresnes, Cedex, France (100%)
Tel.: (33) 146748181
Web Site: http://www.claas.fr
Sales Range: $50-74.9 Million
Emp.: 180
Lawn & Garden Tractor & Home Lawn & Garden Equipment Mfr
N.A.I.C.S.: 333112

Subsidiary (Domestic):

Claas Reseau Agricole S.A.S. (3)
Route De Joinville Zone Artisanale, Rupt-sur-Moselle, France (100%)
Tel.: (33) 325949500
Web Site: http://www.claas.fr
Sales Range: $50-74.9 Million
Emp.: 69
Industrial Machinery & Equipment Whslr
N.A.I.C.S.: 423830

Subsidiary (Domestic):

Usines CLAAS France S.A.S. (2)
Saint Remy, 57140, Woippy, France
Tel.: (33) 3 87 34 41 00
Web Site: http://www.claasfrance.com
Emp.: 351
Agricultural Equipment Mfr
N.A.I.C.S.: 333111

Claas Hungaria Kft. (1)
Kombajn utca 1, 5200, Torokszentmiklos, Hungary (100%)
Tel.: (36) 56597600
Web Site: http://www.claashungaria.hu
Farm Machinery & Equipment Mfr
N.A.I.C.S.: 333111

Claas Iberica S.A. (1)
C/Zeus N 5, Avenida de la Constitucion N 2, 28880, Madrid, Spain (100%)
Tel.: (34) 918307950
Web Site: http://www.claas.com
Farm & Garden Machinery & Equipment Whslr
N.A.I.C.S.: 333111

Claas India Ltd. (1)
15/3 Mathura Road, Faridabad, 121003, Haryana, India (100%)
Tel.: (91) 1294297000
Web Site: http://www.claas.com
Sales Range: $25-49.9 Million
Emp.: 50
Farm Machinery & Equipment Mfr
N.A.I.C.S.: 333111

Claas Industrietechnik GmbH (1)
Halberstadter Str 15-19, 33106, Paderborn, Germany (100%)
Tel.: (49) 52517050
Web Site: http://www.claas-cit.com
Sales Range: $150-199.9 Million
Emp.: 500
Industrial Machinery & Equipment Whslr
N.A.I.C.S.: 423830
Uwe Bolweg (Mng Dir-Comml & Mgr-Comml)

Claas Omaha Inc. (1)
8401 S 132nd St, Omaha, NE 68138-5600 (100%)
Tel.: (402) 861-1000
Web Site: http://www.claasofamerica.com
Emp.: 275
Farm Machinery & Equipment Mfr
N.A.I.C.S.: 333111

Claas Saulgau GmbH (1)
Zeppelinstr 2, 88348, Saulgau, Germany (100%)
Tel.: (49) 75812030
Web Site: http://www.claas.com
Sales Range: $25-49.9 Million
Emp.: 50
Farm Machinery & Equipment Mfr
N.A.I.C.S.: 333111

Claas Selbstfahrende Erntemaschinen GmbH (1)
Munsterstr 33, Harsewinkel, 33428, Gutersloh, Germany (100%)
Tel.: (49) 5247120
Web Site: http://www.claas.de
Sales Range: $400-449.9 Million
Emp.: 2,000
Farm Machinery & Equipment Mfr

N.A.I.C.S.: 333111

Claas U.K. Ltd. (1)
Saxham Business Park, Bury Saint Edmunds, IP28 6QZ, Suffolk, United Kingdom (100%)
Tel.: (44) 1284763100
Web Site: http://www.claas.co.uk
Sales Range: $25-49.9 Million
Emp.: 100
Farm & Garden Machinery & Equipment Whslr
N.A.I.C.S.: 333111

Subsidiary (Domestic):

Anglia Harvesters Ltd. (2)
Leicester Road, Market Harborough, LE16 7QT, Leicestershire, United Kingdom
Tel.: (44) 1858 466660
Agricultural Equipment Mfr
N.A.I.C.S.: 333111

CLAAS Holdings Ltd. (2)
Saxham Business Park Little Saxham, Suffolk, Bury Saint Edmunds, IP28 6QZ, United Kingdom
Tel.: (44) 1284 763 100
Holding Company
N.A.I.C.S.: 551112

Eastern Harvesters Ltd. (2)
The Forge Markham Moor, Retford, DN22 0QU, Nottinghamshire, United Kingdom
Tel.: (44) 1777 838888
Web Site: http://www.eastern.claas-dealer.co.uk
Emp.: 12
Agricultural Equipment Mfr
N.A.I.C.S.: 333111
Richard Sharman (Sls Mgr-Field)

Southern Harvesters Ltd. (2)
Horse Pond Road Cane End, Reading, RG4 9HJ, Berkshire, United Kingdom
Tel.: (44) 1189 723741
Web Site: http://www.southern.claas-dealer.co.uk
Agricultural Equipment Mfr
N.A.I.C.S.: 333111

Western Harvesters Ltd. (2)
Old Walls, Cirencester, GL7 5NX, Gloucestershire, United Kingdom
Tel.: (44) 1285 740408
Agricultural Equipment Mfr
N.A.I.C.S.: 333111

Claas Vertriebsgesellschaft mbH (1)
Muhlenwinkel 1, 33428, Harsewinkel, Germany (100%)
Tel.: (49) 5247120
Web Site: http://www.claas.com
Sales Range: $400-449.9 Million
Emp.: 1,500
Farm Machinery & Equipment Mfr
N.A.I.C.S.: 333111

Subsidiary (Domestic):

BLT Brandenburger Landtechnik GmbH (2)
Gorlsdorfer Strasse 4A, 16278, Angermunde, Germany
Tel.: (49) 3331 26380
Agricultural Equipment Mfr
N.A.I.C.S.: 333111
Helmut Rothe (Gen Mgr)

CLAAS Braunschweig GmbH (2)
Waller See, 38179, Schwulper, Germany
Tel.: (49) 531 310 233 0
Web Site: http://www.claas-braunschweig.de
Agricultural Equipment Mfr
N.A.I.C.S.: 333111

CLAAS Thuringen GmbH (2)
Hinter den Garten 4, 99869, Schwabhausen, Germany
Tel.: (49) 36256 8600 0
Web Site: http://www.claas-thueringen.de
Agricultural Equipment Mfr
N.A.I.C.S.: 333111

CLAAS Weser Ems GmbH (2)
Ermker Weg 15, 49696, Molbergen, Germany
Tel.: (44) 4475 918 72 0
Web Site: http://www.claas-weser-ems.de
Agricultural Equipment Mfr
N.A.I.C.S.: 333111

Mecklenburger Landtechnik GmbH (2)
Tarnower Landweg 8, Muhlengeez, 18276, Gulzow-Pruzen, Germany
Tel.: (49) 38450 301 0
Web Site: http://www.mecklenburger-lt.de
Agricultural Equipment Mfr
N.A.I.C.S.: 333111

CLABO S.P.A.
Viale dell 'Industria 15, Jesi, 60035, Ancona, Italy
Tel.: (39) 073161531
Web Site: https://www.clabo.it
CLA—(ITA)
Sales Range: Less than $1 Million
Food Industry Refrigerated Showcases & Furniture Mfr
N.A.I.C.S.: 333241
Alessandro Francinella (Dir-Operation & Supply Chain)

CLABUCET ESTIVAL 2002 S.A.
Hotel Clabucet, Neptun, Constanta, Romania
Tel.: (40) 241491073
UCET—(BUC)
Assets: $1,062,768
Liabilities: $38,160
Net Worth: $1,024,608
Earnings: ($17,300)
Emp.: 1
Fiscal Year-end: 12/31/23
Restaurant & Hotel Operator
N.A.I.C.S.: 722511
Mircea-Mihai Vere (Pres)

CLAIMPICKER AG
1st Floor 9 Building Shilong Road, Shanghai, China
Tel.: (86) 21 51699668
Web Site: http://www.claimpicker.de
Photo & Video Filing Sharing Services
N.A.I.C.S.: 516210
Andre Muller (Chm)

CLAIMSECURE INC.
City Centre Plaza 1 City Centre Drive Suite 620, Mississauga, L5B 1M2, ON, Canada
Tel.: (905) 949-2322
Web Site: http://www.claimsecure.com
Year Founded: 1982
Rev.: $218,753,494
Emp.: 300
Health Care Management Services
N.A.I.C.S.: 621610
Dave Wowchuk (VP-Sls)

CLAIRGUIL
RN 165 Zac Kervidanou 3, Mellac, 29300, Quimper, France
Tel.: (33) 298719191
Rev.: $20,300,000
Emp.: 61
Grocery Stores
N.A.I.C.S.: 445110
Xavier Le Jouan (Mng Dir)

CLAIRVEST GROUP INC.
22 St Clair Avenue East Suite 1700, Toronto, M4T 2S3, ON, Canada
Tel.: (416) 925-9270 ON
Web Site: https://www.clairvest.com
CVG—(TSX)
Rev.: $278,194,414
Assets: $1,058,536,706
Liabilities: $136,160,528
Net Worth: $922,376,178
Earnings: $258,314,332
Emp.: 43
Fiscal Year-end: 03/31/22
Merchant Banking Services
N.A.I.C.S.: 523150
Kenneth B. Rotman (CEO & Mng Dir)

Subsidiaries:

Discovery Air Inc. (1)
170 Attwell Drive Suite 370, Etobicoke, M9W 5Z5, ON, Canada
Tel.: (416) 246-2684
Web Site: http://www.discoveryair.com
Rev.: $130,248,120
Assets: $226,831,454
Liabilities: $186,989,106
Net Worth: $39,842,348
Earnings: ($13,742,470)
Emp.: 850
Fiscal Year-end: 01/31/2017
Aviation & Aviation Related Services
N.A.I.C.S.: 488119
Paul Bouchard (CEO)

Subsidiary (Domestic):

Air Tindi Ltd. (2)
23 Mitchell Drive, Yellowknife, X1A 2P3, NT, Canada
Tel.: (867) 669-8200
Web Site: http://www.airtindi.com
Sales Range: $50-74.9 Million
Emp.: 180
Aircraft Charter Services
N.A.I.C.S.: 481219

Discovery Air Defence Services Inc. (2)
52 Hymus Boulevard Suite 200, Pointe-Claire, H9R 1C9, QC, Canada
Tel.: (514) 694-5565
Web Site: http://www.discoveryair-ds.com
Military Air Combat Training Services
N.A.I.C.S.: 611512
Paul Bouchard (Pres)

Discovery Mining Services Ltd. (2)
101-487 Range Lake Road, PO Box 2248, Yellowknife, X1A 2P7, NT, Canada
Tel.: (867) 920-4600
Web Site: http://www.discoverymining.ca
Sales Range: $50-74.9 Million
Emp.: 70
Mining Support Services
N.A.I.C.S.: 213115

Great Slave Helicopters Ltd. (2)
106 Dickins Street, Yellowknife, X1A 3T2, NT, Canada
Tel.: (867) 873-2081
Web Site: http://www.gsheli.com
Sales Range: $50-74.9 Million
Emp.: 200
Helicopter Operation Services
N.A.I.C.S.: 481111
Jonathan Talon (Dir-Ops)

Durante Rentals, LLC (1)
717 Hutchinson River Pkwy, Bronx, NY 10465
Tel.: (718) 239-6969
Web Site: http://www.duranterentals.com
Sales Range: $10-24.9 Million
Emp.: 112
Tools & Construction Equipment Rental Services
N.A.I.C.S.: 532412
John Durante (Co-Founder)

Subsidiary (Domestic):

Iron Source, LLC (2)
25113 Dupont Blvd, Georgetown, DE 19947
Web Site: http://www.ironsourcede.com
Construction, Mining & Forestry Machinery & Equipment Rental & Leasing
N.A.I.C.S.: 532412
Chess Hedrick (Mgr)

CLAMART AUTOMOBILES
185 Avenue Victor Hugo, 92140, Clamart, France
Tel.: (33) 141331919
Web Site: http://www.clamartautomobiles.fr
Rev.: $20,700,000
Emp.: 33
New & Used Car Dealers
N.A.I.C.S.: 441110
Jean-Claude Jacquetin (Dir)

CLANCY CONSULTING LTD
2 Dunham Court, Altrincham, WA14 4NX, Cheshire, United Kingdom

Clancy Consulting Ltd—(Continued)

Tel.: (44) 1616136000
Web Site: http://www.clancy.co.uk
Year Founded: 1972
Rev.: $11,525,866
Emp.: 110
Building Consulting Services
N.A.I.C.S.: 541618
Alan Bramwell (CEO)

CLARA INDUSTRIES LIMITED

127/1 Simbhalka Junardar Janta
Road, Saharanpur, 247001, Uttar
Pradesh, India
Tel.: (91) 8171884399
Web Site: https://www.clara.co.in
Year Founded: 2008
543435—(BOM)
Emp.: 75
Flexible Plastic Packaging Mfr
N.A.I.C.S.: 326112
Nikhil Kukreja (Chm & Mng Dir)

CLARANET LIMITED

21 Southampton Row, London,
WC1B 5HA, United Kingdom
Tel.: (44) 3303900500   UK
Web Site: http://www.claranet.co.uk
Year Founded: 1996
Sales Range: $25-49.9 Million
Emp.: 1,800
Internet Access Services
N.A.I.C.S.: 541512
Charles Costandi Nasser (CEO)

Subsidiaries:

Claranet Benelux BV   (1)
Science Park 5630, 5692 EN, Son, Nether-
lands
Tel.: (31) 40 239 33 63
Web Site: http://www.claranet.nl
Web Hosting Services
N.A.I.C.S.: 518210
Wiebe Nauta (Mng Dir)

Claranet GmbH   (1)
Hanauer Landstrasse 196, 60314, Frank-
furt, Germany
Tel.: (49) 69 40 80 18 0
Web Site: http://www.claranet.de
Web Hosting Services
N.A.I.C.S.: 518210
Markus Bach (Dir-Ops & Customer Svc)

Claranet Portugal   (1)
Ed Parque Expo Av D Joao II 1 07 - 2 1,
1998-014, Lisbon, Portugal
Tel.: (351) 21 319 92 00
Web Site: http://www.claranet.pt
Web Hosting Services
N.A.I.C.S.: 518210

Claranet S.A.U.   (1)
Juan Gris 10-18 Planta 4 Torres Cerda,
08014, Barcelona, Spain
Tel.: (34) 934 452 650
Web Site: http://www.claranet.es
Web Hosting Services
N.A.I.C.S.: 518210

Claranet SAS   (1)
18-20 rue du Faubourg du Temple, 75011,
Paris, France
Tel.: (33) 1 70 13 70 00
Web Site: http://www.claranet.fr
Web Hosting Services
N.A.I.C.S.: 518210

Claranet SOHO   (1)
Dallam Court Dallam Lane, Warrington,
WA2 7LT, Cheshire, United Kingdom
Tel.: (44) 1925 855 800
Web Site: http://www.claranetsoho.co.uk
Internet Service Provider
N.A.I.C.S.: 517810

Netscalibur Ltd.   (1)
21 Southampton Row, London, WC1B 5HA,
United Kingdom
Tel.: (44) 8708878800
Web Site: http://www.netscalibur.co.uk
Online Business Services
N.A.I.C.S.: 561499

CLARANOVA SA

89-91 Bulevard National, Immeuble
Vision La Defense, 92257, La
Garenne-Colombes, France
Tel.: (33) 141271970
Web Site: http://www.claranova.com
Year Founded: 1984
Rev.: $184,722,085
Assets: $92,075,095
Liabilities: $75,718,898
Net Worth: $16,356,197
Earnings: ($9,379,078)
Emp.: 294
Fiscal Year-end: 06/30/18
Communications Software Mfr
N.A.I.C.S.: 513210
Roger Bloxberg (CEO-North America
& Mgmt Bd)

Subsidiaries:

Avanquest China   (1)
Huitong Building Room 1201 569 East Jin-
Ling Lu, Shanghai, 200021, China
Tel.: (86) 2153066033
Software Publishing Services
N.A.I.C.S.: 513210

Avanquest Deutschland GmbH   (1)
Sckellstrasse 6, 81667, Munich, Germany
Tel.: (49) 897909790
Web Site: http://www.avanquest.de
Software Distr
N.A.I.C.S.: 423430

Avanquest France   (1)
89-91 Boulevard National Immeuble Vision
La Defense, 92250, La Garenne-Colombes,
France
Tel.: (33) 156765800
Web Site: http://www.avanquest.fr
Sales Range: $25-49.9 Million
Emp.: 90
Computer Softwares Mfr
N.A.I.C.S.: 513210

Avanquest Iberica S.L.   (1)
C Peru 6 EdificiosTwin Golf Bloque B Ofi-
cina 4 2a Pl, Las Matas, 28290, Madrid,
Spain
Tel.: (34) 916307023
Web Site: http://www.avanquest.es
Sales Range: $50-74.9 Million
Emp.: 2
Software Distr
N.A.I.C.S.: 423430

Avanquest Italia Srl   (1)
Via E Sacchi 8, 26100, Cremona, Italy
Tel.: (39) 0372 38791
Web Site: http://www.avanquest.it
Computer Softwares Mfr
N.A.I.C.S.: 513210

Avanquest Publishing USA   (1)
7031 Koll Center Pkwy Ste 150, Pleasan-
ton, CA 94566
Tel.: (925) 474-1700
Web Site: http://www.avanquestusa.com
Sales Range: $25-49.9 Million
Emp.: 23
Computer Softwares Mfr
N.A.I.C.S.: 513210

Avanquest Software USA   (1)
1333 W 120th Ave Ste 314, Westminster,
CO 80234
Tel.: (720) 330-1400
Web Site: http://www.avanquest.com
Computer Softwares Mfr
N.A.I.C.S.: 513210

Avanquest UK Ltd   (1)
Sheridan House, 40-43 Jewry Street, Win-
chester, SO23 8RY, Hants, United Kingdom
Tel.: (44) 01962835000
Web Site: http://www.avanquest.co.uk
Sales Range: $25-49.9 Million
Emp.: 80
Computer Softwares Mfr
N.A.I.C.S.: 513210

Nova Development Corp.   (1)
23801 Calabasas Rd Ste 2005, Calabasas,
CA 91302
Tel.: (818) 591-9600
Web Site: http://www.novadevelopment.com

Sales Range: $25-49.9 Million
Emp.: 60
Computer Software Developer
N.A.I.C.S.: 541511
Roger Bloxberg (CEO)

PlanetArt, LLC   (1)
23801 Calabasas Rd Ste 2005, Calabasas,
CA 91302   (92.27%)
Tel.: (818) 591-9600
Web Site: http://www.planetart.com
Digital Personalized Design Services
N.A.I.C.S.: 541490
Roger Bloxberg (CEO)

Subsidiary (Domestic):

CafePress, Inc.   (2)
11909 Shelbyville Rd, Louisville, KY 40243
Tel.: (919) 323-4480
Web Site: http://www.cafepressinc.com
Online Service for Designing & Selling Cus-
tom Merchandise
N.A.I.C.S.: 518210

Personal Creations Inc.   (2)
4840 Eastgate Mall, San Diego, CA 92121
Web Site: http://www.personalcreations.com
Mail Order Catalog & E-Commerce Ser-
vices
N.A.I.C.S.: 425120

CLAREN ENERGY CORP.

880-580 Hornby Street, Vancouver,
V6C 4B6, BC, Canada
Tel.: (604) 639-4529
Web Site: http://clarenenergy.com
CEN.H—(TSXV)
Assets: $2,007
Liabilities: $378,903
Net Worth: ($376,896)
Earnings: $40,641
Fiscal Year-end: 07/31/24
Oil & Gas Exploration Services
N.A.I.C.S.: 211120
Matthew J. Anderson (CFO)

CLARIANE SE

21-25 rue Balzac, 75008, Paris,
France
Tel.: (33) 155375200   FR
Web Site: https://www.clariane.com
Year Founded: 2003
KORI—(EUR)
Rev.: $4,893,238,722
Assets: $15,727,996,978
Liabilities: $11,553,728,686
Net Worth: $4,174,268,293
Earnings: $33,820,419
Emp.: 57,518
Fiscal Year-end: 12/31/22
Retirement Home & Elder Care Ser-
vices
N.A.I.C.S.: 623110
Christian Chautard (Chm)

Subsidiaries:

Alpheide-Seniorenzentrum
GmbH   (1)
Am Exerzierplatz 26, 31582, Nienburg, Ger-
many
Tel.: (49) 50214747
Home Care Services
N.A.I.C.S.: 621610

Alten-Pflegeheim Veitsbronn
GmbH   (1)
Nurnberger Strasse 7, 90587, Veitsbronn,
Germany
Tel.: (49) 911743880
Home Care Services
N.A.I.C.S.: 621610

Arche de Vie SA   (1)
Rue Charbonnel 115A Ransart, 6043,
Charleroi, Belgium
Tel.: (32) 71370149
Healtcare Services
N.A.I.C.S.: 621610

Bellevue SA   (1)
Avenue du Roi 157, Forest, 1190, Brussels,
Belgium
Tel.: (32) 25330100

Healtcare Services
N.A.I.C.S.: 621610

Casa Reha Seniorenpflegeheim
GmbH   (1)
Berkersheimer Weg 195, 60433, Frankfurt
am Main, Germany
Tel.: (49) 695870080
Home Care Services
N.A.I.C.S.: 621610

Centro Medico Specialistico Srl   (1)
Via Berruti 34, 10034, Chivasso, TO, Italy
Tel.: (39) 0116982080
Web Site:
    http://www.centromedicospecialistico.com
Health Care Services
N.A.I.C.S.: 621610

Claire de Vie Sprl   (1)
Rue Hubert Goffin 312 Glain, 4000, Liege,
Belgium
Tel.: (32) 42399540
Healtcare Services
N.A.I.C.S.: 621610

Croce Di Malta Srl   (1)
Via Brusa 20, Canzo, 22035, Como, Italy
Tel.: (39) 0316731
Health Care Srvices
N.A.I.C.S.: 621610

De Nootelaer Plc   (1)
Papestraat 4, 3140, Keerbergen, Belgium
Tel.: (32) 15516805
Healtcare Services
N.A.I.C.S.: 621610

Evergreen Pflege- Und Betreuung-
szentrum Bergneustädt GmbH   (1)
Bahnstrasse 7, 51702, Bergneustadt, Ger-
many
Tel.: (49) 2261501180
Home Care Services
N.A.I.C.S.: 621610

Evergreen Pflege- Und Betreuung-
szentrum Butzbach GmbH   (1)
Hinter der Burg 2, 35510, Butzbach, Ger-
many
Tel.: (49) 6033973280
Home Care Services
N.A.I.C.S.: 621610

Evergreen Pflege- Und Betreuung-
szentrum Landscheid GmbH   (1)
Burger Strasse 9, 54526, Landscheid, Ger-
many
Tel.: (49) 6575902690
Home Care Services
N.A.I.C.S.: 621610

Evergreen Pflege- Und Betreuung-
szentrum Paderborn GmbH   (1)
Bahnhofstrasse 27-33, 66538, Neunkirchen,
Germany
Tel.: (49) 682140250
Home Care Services
N.A.I.C.S.: 621610

Evergreen Pflege- Und Betreuung-
szentrum Recklinghausen GmbH   (1)
August-Cohaupt-Strasse 21, 45659, Reck-
linghausen, Germany
Tel.: (49) 2361306790
Home Care Services
N.A.I.C.S.: 621610

Evergreen Pflege- Und Betreuung-
szentrum Saarburg GmbH   (1)
Bruckenstrasse 2a, Saarburg, 54439, Trier,
Germany
Tel.: (49) 658199961900
Home Care Services
N.A.I.C.S.: 621610

Evergreen Pflegezentrum Am Alten
Poststadion GmbH   (1)
Lievelingsweg 90, 53119, Bonn, Germany
Tel.: (49) 2289263780
Home Care Services
N.A.I.C.S.: 621610

Golden Morgen BVBA   (1)
Kettenisser Strasse 68, Lontzen, 4711,
Liege, Belgium
Tel.: (32) 87557222
Healtcare Services
N.A.I.C.S.: 621610

Haus Amselhof Seniorenresidenz GmbH **(1)**
Amselweg 2-6, 59556, Lippstadt, Germany
Tel.: (49) 294194020
Home Care Services
N.A.I.C.S.: 621610

Hausliche Krankenpflege Charlotte Konig GmbH & Co. **(1)**
Limburger Str 85, Lommersum, 53919, Weilerswist, Germany
Tel.: (49) 225152429
Web Site: http://www.koenig-pflegedienst.de
Outpatient Care Services
N.A.I.C.S.: 621498

Helvita Seniorenzentren GmbH **(1)**
Hauptstrasse 27, Niedersteinbach, 56593, Altenkirchen, Germany
Tel.: (49) 26877943100
Home Care Services
N.A.I.C.S.: 621610

Heydeveld Bvba **(1)**
Ringlaan 28, Opwijk, 1745, Leuven, Belgium
Tel.: (32) 52353900
Healtcare Services
N.A.I.C.S.: 621610

Home Residence Du Plateau Sprl **(1)**
Chaussee d'Ottembourg 221, 1300, Wavre, Belgium
Tel.: (32) 10226056
Healtcare Services
N.A.I.C.S.: 621610

Huyse Elckerlyc NV **(1)**
Trinellestraat 23, Riemst, 3770, Hasselt, Belgium
Tel.: (32) 12241450
Healtcare Services
N.A.I.C.S.: 621610

Karen Sprl **(1)**
Laakstraat 20 Koersel, 03582, Beringen, Belgium
Tel.: (32) 11434312
Healtcare Services
N.A.I.C.S.: 621610

Kinetika Sardegna Srl **(1)**
Viale Marconi 160, Quartu Sant'Elena, Cagliari, CA, Italy
Tel.: (39) 07086053
Web Site: http://www.kinetikasardegna.it
Health Care Srvices
N.A.I.C.S.: 621610

Korian Deutschland AG **(1)**
Zirkus-Krone-Strasse 10, 80335, Munich, Germany **(100%)**
Tel.: (49) 89 242065 0
Holding Company
N.A.I.C.S.: 551112
Yann Coleou *(Chm-Mgmt Bd)*

Subsidiary (Domestic):

Curanum AG **(2)**
Zirkus-Krone-Strasse 10, 80335, Munich, Germany
Tel.: (49) 892420650
Web Site: http://www.curanum.de
Sales Range: $400-449.9 Million
Emp.: 7,102
Nursing Care Services
N.A.I.C.S.: 623110
Walther Wever *(Chm-Mgmt Bd & CEO)*

Subsidiary (Domestic):

Alten-und Pflegeheim Sieglar GmbH **(3)**
Rathausstrasse 1, 53844, Troisdorf, Germany
Tel.: (49) 22414940
Nursing Home Services
N.A.I.C.S.: 623110

Subsidiary (Non-US):

CB Seniorenresidenz Armbrustergasse GmbH **(3)**
Armbrustergasse 6-8, Vienna, 1190, Austria
Tel.: (43) 1379050
Web Site: http://www.bonifatius.at
Senior Citizen Homes Operation Services
N.A.I.C.S.: 623312

Subsidiary (Domestic):

CURANUM Bad Hersfeld GmbH **(3)**
Gotzbertstrasse 92, 36251, Bad Hersfeld, Germany
Tel.: (49) 66211820
Web Site: http://www.korian.de
Nursing Home Services
N.A.I.C.S.: 623110

CURANUM Franziskushaus GmbH **(3)**
Hagenstrasse 16-18, Gelsenkirchen, 45894, Nordrhein-Westfalen, Germany
Tel.: (49) 2099331440
Senior Residential Home Care Services
N.A.I.C.S.: 623110

CURANUM Seniorenpflegezentrum Am Spessart **(3)**
Ludwig-Straub-Str 10, 63856, Bessenbach, Bavaria, Germany
Tel.: (49) 6095 998 0
Web Site: http://www.curanum-seniorenpflegezentrum-bessenbach.de
Senior Residential Home Care Services
N.A.I.C.S.: 623110
Markus Thumm *(Mgr-Facility Mgmt)*

CURANUM Westfalen GmbH **(3)**
Am Ochsenkamp 60, 58332, Schwelm, Nordrhein-Westfalen, Germany
Tel.: (49) 2336929100
Web Site: http://www.Curanum.com
Senior Citizens Nursing Home Services
N.A.I.C.S.: 623110

ELISA Seniorenstift GmbH **(3)**
Maximilianstr 35c, 80539, Munich, Bavaria, Germany
Tel.: (49) 892420650
Sales Range: $450-499.9 Million
Emp.: 5,000
Senior Citizens Residential Homes
N.A.I.C.S.: 623312
Judith Barth *(CFO)*

Subsidiary (Domestic):

Elisa Seniorenstift Aschaffenburg GmbH **(4)**
Goldbacher Strasse 13, 63739, Aschaffenburg, Bavaria, Germany
Tel.: (49) 60213840
Web Site: http://www.elisa-seniorenstift-aschaffenburg.de
Adult Home Care Services
N.A.I.C.S.: 623312

Subsidiary (Domestic):

Krankenheim Ruhesitz am Wannsee-Seniorenheimstatt GmbH **(3)**
Am Sandwerder 43, 14109, Berlin, Germany
Tel.: (49) 30 8 04 74 91 0
Senior Residential Home Care Services
N.A.I.C.S.: 623110

Residenz Lobberich GmbH **(3)**
Burgstrasse 9, Lobberich, 41334, Nettetal, Nordrhein-Westfalen, Germany
Tel.: (49) 215395730
Sales Range: $10-24.9 Million
Emp.: 60
Nursing Homes Management Services
N.A.I.C.S.: 623110

Seniorenzentrum Hennef GmbH **(3)**
Kurhausstrasse 45, 53773, Hennef, Germany
Tel.: (49) 22429300
Senior Residential Home Care Services
N.A.I.C.S.: 623110

Wascherei Ellerich GmbH **(3)**
Wilhelm-Conrad-Rontgen-Str 1, Kaisersesch, 56759, Rhineland-Palatinate, Germany
Tel.: (49) 265398980
Web Site: http://www.curanum.de
Sales Range: $25-49.9 Million
Emp.: 140
Laundry & Dry Cleaning Services
N.A.I.C.S.: 812320

Korian Les Oliviers JSC **(1)**
Avenue du Cours, Le-Puy-Sainte-Reparade, 13610, Le Puy, France
Tel.: (33) 442617800

Residential Health Care Services
N.A.I.C.S.: 623990

Korian Les Trois Tours JSC **(1)**
517 Chemin de Grand Pre, La Destrousse, 13112, Marseille, France
Tel.: (33) 442183737
Residential Health Care Services
N.A.I.C.S.: 623990

Le Colvert Sprl **(1)**
Rue Chapelle Notre-Dame 10 Ceroux-Mousty, 1341, Ottignies, Belgium
Tel.: (32) 10620511
Healtcare Services
N.A.I.C.S.: 621610

Les Charmilles SA **(1)**
Rue d'Eghezee 54, Auvelais, 5060, Namur, Belgium
Tel.: (32) 71266190
Healtcare Services
N.A.I.C.S.: 621610

Les Flots LLC **(1)**
257 Route de Toulouse, Talence, 33400, Gironde, France
Tel.: (33) 557011515
Residential Health Care Services
N.A.I.C.S.: 623990

Les Recollets SA **(1)**
Rue de Merbes 333, Buvrinnes, 7133, Binche, Belgium
Tel.: (32) 64369150
Healtcare Services
N.A.I.C.S.: 621610

Les Sitelles Sa **(1)**
Route Provinciale 121, Chastre, 1450, Wavre, Belgium
Tel.: (32) 10654800
Healtcare Services
N.A.I.C.S.: 621610

Mafi Srl **(1)**
Viale delle Industrie 7, Busnago, 20874, Monza, MB, Italy
Tel.: (39) 0399374039
Web Site: http://www.mafi-srl.com
Industrial Building Construction Services
N.A.I.C.S.: 236210

Maison de XX Aout SA **(1)**
Rue du Mery 2, 4000, Liege, Belgium
Tel.: (32) 42224677
Web Site: http://www.maisons-de-repos.be
Healtcare Services
N.A.I.C.S.: 621610

Marienia SA **(1)**
34 Avenue de Navarre, Cambo-les-Bains, 64250, Bayonne, France
Tel.: (33) 559936800
Web Site: http://www.marienia.fr
Clinical Services
N.A.I.C.S.: 621999

Onafhankelijke Thuiszorg Vlaanderen CVBA **(1)**
Overwinningsstraat 133-135, 2830, Willebroek, Belgium
Tel.: (32) 38607000
Web Site: http://www.otvhomecare.be
Healtcare Services
N.A.I.C.S.: 621610

Petits-Fils Developpement JSC **(1)**
42 rue Eugene, 75018, Paris, France
Tel.: (33) 404040404
Web Site: http://franchise.petits-fils.com
Personal Care Services
N.A.I.C.S.: 812199
Florence Laurent-Bellue *(Office Mgr)*

Pflege Aus Einer Hand GmbH **(1)**
Bahnhofstr 44, 57258, Freudenberg, Germany
Tel.: (49) 273447500
Web Site: http://www.pflege-aus-einer-hand.de
Outpatient Care Services
N.A.I.C.S.: 621498

Phonix - Haus Roggenberg - Pflegeheim GmbH **(1)**
Veit-Stoss-Weg 15, Lichtenau, 91586, Paderborn, Germany
Tel.: (49) 982792920
Home Care Services

Phonix - Haus Silberdistel - Alten-U.Pflegeheim GmbH **(1)**
Laupenweg 8, Sipplingen, 78354, Tubingen, Germany
Tel.: (49) 75519518100
Home Care Services
N.A.I.C.S.: 621610

Phonix - Seniorenzentrum Graf Tilly GmbH **(1)**
Munchener Str 133, 85051, Ingolstadt, Germany
Tel.: (49) 8418813110
Home Care Services
N.A.I.C.S.: 621610

Phonix - Seniorenzentrum Hessenallee GmbH **(1)**
Hessenallee 71, 34613, Schwalmstadt, Germany
Tel.: (49) 6691806700
Home Care Services
N.A.I.C.S.: 621610

Phonix Seniorenresidenz Elstertalblick GmbH **(1)**
Elstertalblick 2, 08527, Plauen, Germany
Tel.: (49) 374170110
Home Care Services
N.A.I.C.S.: 621610

Phonix Sozialzentrum Windsbach GmbH **(1)**
Ansbacher Strasse 36, Windsbach, 91575, Ansbach, Germany
Tel.: (49) 987167810
Home Care Services
N.A.I.C.S.: 621610

Phonix-Haus Am Steinsgraben Senioren- Und Pflegezentrum GmbH **(1)**
Am Steinsgraben 17, 37085, Gottingen, Germany
Tel.: (49) 551488560
Home Care Services
N.A.I.C.S.: 621610

Phonix-Haus Rosmarin Senioren-Und Pflegezentrum GmbH **(1)**
Rosmarinstrasse 12, 40235, Dusseldorf, Germany
Tel.: (49) 21190940
Home Care Services
N.A.I.C.S.: 621610

Phonix-Seniorenresidenz Am Teichberg GmbH **(1)**
Eichenstrasse 43, 34466, Wolfhagen, Germany
Tel.: (49) 5692997730
Home Care Services
N.A.I.C.S.: 621610

Phonix-Seniorenzentrum Ahornhof GmbH **(1)**
Darmstadter Strasse 21-25, Langen, 63225, Darmstadt, Germany
Tel.: (49) 6103301170
Home Care Services
N.A.I.C.S.: 621610

Phonix-Seniorenzentrum Am Bodenseering GmbH **(1)**
Am Bodenseering 18, 95445, Bayreuth, Germany
Tel.: (49) 9211627180
Home Care Services
N.A.I.C.S.: 621610

Phonix-Seniorenzentrum Am Muppberg GmbH **(1)**
Heidestrasse 21, 96465, Neustadt, Germany
Tel.: (49) 9568891880
Home Care Services
N.A.I.C.S.: 621610

Phonix-Seniorenzentrum Am Schlossteich GmbH **(1)**
Saarbrucker Platz 6, 65510, Idstein, Germany
Tel.: (49) 6126224660
Home Care Services
N.A.I.C.S.: 621610

Phonix-Seniorenzentrum Evergreen GmbH **(1)**
Auf der Loh 8, Schnaittenbach, 92253, Am-

Clariane SE—(Continued)

berg, Germany
Tel.: (49) 9622703370
Home Care Services
N.A.I.C.S.: 621610

Phonix-Seniorenzentrum Evergreen Maxhutte GmbH (1)
Ernst-von-Fromm-Str 6, 93142, Maxhutte-Haidhof, Germany
Tel.: (49) 9471308520
Home Care Services
N.A.I.C.S.: 621610

Phonix-Seniorenzentrum Gartenstadt GmbH (1)
Franz-Schubert-Str 13, 97421, Schweinfurt, Germany
Tel.: (49) 9721475990
Home Care Services
N.A.I.C.S.: 621610

Phonix-Seniorenzentrum Herzog Albrecht GmbH (1)
Hartackerstr 31, Vohburg, 85088, Pfaffenhofen, Germany
Tel.: (49) 8457936870
Home Care Services
N.A.I.C.S.: 621610

Phonix-Seniorenzentrum Im Bruhl GmbH (1)
Placidus- Muth- Str 2, 99084, Erfurt, Germany
Tel.: (49) 361663880
Home Care Services
N.A.I.C.S.: 621610

Phonix-Seniorenzentrum Mainparksee GmbH (1)
Albert-Einstein-Strasse 1-5 Mainaschaff, 63814, Aschaffenburg, Germany
Tel.: (49) 6021447760
Home Care Services
N.A.I.C.S.: 621610

Phonix-Seniorenzentrum Neuperlach GmbH (1)
Friedrich-Engels-Bogen 4, 81735, Munich, Germany
Tel.: (49) 8918914850
Home Care Services
N.A.I.C.S.: 621610

Phonix-Seniorenzentrum St Hedwig GmbH (1)
Werstener Feld 231, 40591, Dusseldorf, Germany
Tel.: (49) 2113026500
Home Care Services
N.A.I.C.S.: 621610

Phonix-Seniorenzentrum Taunusblick GmbH (1)
Darmstadter Landstrasse 106, 60598, Frankfurt am Main, Germany
Tel.: (49) 699688540
Home Care Services
N.A.I.C.S.: 621610

Phonix-Seniorenzentrum Ulmenhof GmbH (1)
Ulmenstr 35, 63303, Dreieich, Germany
Tel.: (49) 6103706560
Home Care Services
N.A.I.C.S.: 621610

Phonix-Seniorenzentrum Zwei Linden GmbH (1)
Ludwig-Pfeuffer-Ring 8, Giebelstadt, 97232, Wurzburg, Germany
Tel.: (49) 9334970050
Home Care Services
N.A.I.C.S.: 621610

Poort Van Wijk BV (1)
Groenewoudseweg 13, 3945 BC, Cothen, Netherlands
Tel.: (31) 343565187
Healtcare Services
N.A.I.C.S.: 621610

RVT Dellebron BVBA (1)
Mountstraat 21, Kortenaken, 3470, Leuven, Belgium
Tel.: (32) 11888900
Healtcare Services
N.A.I.C.S.: 621610

Residence Au Bon Vieux Temps Plc (1)
Rue de Corbais 18A, 1435, Mont-Saint-Guibert, Belgium
Tel.: (32) 10659117
Healtcare Services
N.A.I.C.S.: 621610

Residence Aux Deux Parcs SA (1)
Duysburghstraat 21, Jotto, 1000, Brussels, Belgium
Tel.: (32) 24754080
Healtcare Services
N.A.I.C.S.: 621610

Residence La Passerinette Sa (1)
Rue des Deux Tilleuls 69, Soumagne, 4630, Liege, Belgium
Tel.: (32) 43774392
Healtcare Services
N.A.I.C.S.: 621610

Residence Le Progres Plc (1)
Chaussee de Jolimont 88, Haine-Saint-Paul, 7100, La Louviere, Belgium
Tel.: (32) 64232700
Healtcare Services
N.A.I.C.S.: 621610

Residence Melopee Plc (1)
Rue Melopee 50, 1080, Brussels, Belgium
Tel.: (32) 24105101
Healtcare Services
N.A.I.C.S.: 621610

Residence Reine Astrid SA (1)
Rue Reine Astrid 236-238 Maurage, 7110, La Louviere, Belgium
Tel.: (32) 64662865
Healtcare Services
N.A.I.C.S.: 621610

Residence Ry Du Chevreuil Sprl (1)
Rue de Rhion 4, Eghezee, 5310, Namur, Belgium
Tel.: (32) 81512656
Healtcare Services
N.A.I.C.S.: 621610

Residence Seigneurie Du Val Sa (1)
Rue du Congo 52, 7700, Mouscron, Belgium
Tel.: (32) 56344220
Healtcare Services
N.A.I.C.S.: 621610

Residencias Familiares Para Mayores SL (1)
Urb Alicante Playa s/n, 29604, Marbella, Malaga, Spain
Tel.: (34) 952859958
Web Site: http://www.seniorsresidencias.es
Personal Care Services
N.A.I.C.S.: 812199

Residentie Boneput Plc (1)
Boneputstraat 5, 3960, Bree, Belgium
Tel.: (32) 89466647
Healtcare Services
N.A.I.C.S.: 621610

Residentie Edelweis Plc (1)
Liersesteenweg 165-171, Beglijnendijk, 3130, Leuven, Belgium
Tel.: (32) 16536911
Healtcare Services
N.A.I.C.S.: 621610

Residentie Paloke NV (1)
Palokestraat 40, 1080, Sint-Jans-Molenbeek, Belgium
Tel.: (32) 25241009
Healtcare Services
N.A.I.C.S.: 621610

Residentie Prinsenpark NV (1)
D'Ierdstraat 11, 3600, Genk, Belgium
Tel.: (32) 89320000
Healtcare Services
N.A.I.C.S.: 621610

Residenza Villa Carla Srl (1)
Viale Italia 1, 04011, Aprilia, Latina, Italy
Tel.: (39) 069286351
Web Site: http://www.villa-carla.it
Health Care Srvices
N.A.I.C.S.: 621610

Rooierheide NV (1)
Rooierheidestraat 96, Diepenbeek, 3590, Hasselt, Belgium

Tel.: (32) 11299100
Healtcare Services
N.A.I.C.S.: 621610

Rsa Fratesole Srl (1)
Via San Romolo 109, Figline e Incisa Valdarno, 50063, Florence, Italy
Tel.: (39) 055915301
Health Care Srvices
N.A.I.C.S.: 621610

Rustoord de Vlaamse Ardennen LLC (1)
Kromstraat 5, Horebeke, 9667, Sint-Truiden, Belgium
Tel.: (32) 55480211
Healtcare Services
N.A.I.C.S.: 621610

SAS La Louisiane (1)
2 Rue Pierre Gilles de Gennes, 22600, Loudeac, France
Tel.: (33) 296661919
Web Site: http://en.mobilhomelouisiane.com
Mobile Home Services
N.A.I.C.S.: 321991

SAS La Villa Du Parc (1)
49 route de Ria, Pyrenees-Orientales, 66500, Prades, France
Tel.: (33) 468053679
Web Site: http://www.villa-du-parc.com
Hospitality Services
N.A.I.C.S.: 721110

Sarl Clinique Maison Blanche (1)
14 Allee Henri Dunant, 28500, Vernouillet, France
Tel.: (33) 826960017
Healtcare Services
N.A.I.C.S.: 621999

Schauinsland Pflegebetrieb GmbH (1)
Luginsland 37, 75181, Pforzheim, Germany
Tel.: (49) 723195550
Home Care Services
N.A.I.C.S.: 621610

Sci Korian Le Grand Parc Immobilier (1)
1-3 rue Aime Cesaire, 78280, Guyancourt, France
Tel.: (33) 134823482
Residential Health Care Services
N.A.I.C.S.: 623990

Sci Korian Les Catalaunes Immobilier (1)
6 rue de l'Hopital Militaire, 51000, Chalons-en-Champagne, France
Tel.: (33) 359919191
Residential Health Care Services
N.A.I.C.S.: 623990

Sci Korian Mornay Immobilier (1)
216 Route de Ribemont Mornay, Saint-Pierre-de-l'Isle, 17330, Saint-Pierre, France
Tel.: (33) 546595700
Residential Health Care Services
N.A.I.C.S.: 623990

Segesta Spa (1)
Viale Cassala 16, 20143, Milan, Italy
Tel.: (39) 02831271
Health Care Srvices
N.A.I.C.S.: 621610
Antonella Ferioli (*Mktg Mgr*)

Senior Living Group NV (1)
Satenrozen 1b, 2550, Kontich, Belgium
Tel.: (32) 34437651
Healtcare Services
N.A.I.C.S.: 621610

Senioren- Und Fachpflegezentrum GmbH (1)
Feldstrasse 39, 63110, Rodgau, Germany
Tel.: (49) 61068210
Home Care Services
N.A.I.C.S.: 621610

Senioren-Domizil Familie Wohnsiedler GmbH (1)
Saline Theodorshalle 28, 55543, Bad Kreuznach, Germany
Tel.: (49) 67133653
Home Care Services
N.A.I.C.S.: 621610

Seniorenpflege Hassloch GmbH (1)

Schillerstrasse 18a, 67454, Hassloch, Germany
Tel.: (49) 632487000
Home Care Services
N.A.I.C.S.: 621610

Seniorenresidenz Dettelbach GmbH (1)
Schillerstrasse 1, 97337, Dettelbach, Germany
Tel.: (49) 93243050
Home Care Services
N.A.I.C.S.: 621610

Seniorenwohnanlage Oettingen GmbH (1)
Lange-Mauer Str 4, 86732, Oettingen, Germany
Tel.: (49) 90827030
Home Care Services
N.A.I.C.S.: 621610

Seniorheim An Der Paar GmbH (1)
Franz-Beck-Str 6, 86551, Aichach, Germany
Tel.: (49) 825186740
Home Care Services
N.A.I.C.S.: 621610

Seniorie de Maretak NV (1)
Ziekenhuislaan 10, 1500, Halle, Belgium
Tel.: (32) 23590300
Healtcare Services
N.A.I.C.S.: 621610

Sentivo Eitorf GmbH (1)
Leienbergstrasse 18, 53783, Eitorf, Germany
Tel.: (49) 22438453100
Home Care Services
N.A.I.C.S.: 621610

Sentivo Monchengladbach GmbH (1)
Giesenkirchener Str 88, 41238, Monchengladbach, Germany
Tel.: (49) 21669458800
Home Care Services
N.A.I.C.S.: 621610

Sentivo Rhondorf GmbH (1)
Rhondorfer Strasse 80 b, Rhondorf, 53604, Bad Honnef, Germany
Tel.: (49) 22249810100
Home Care Services
N.A.I.C.S.: 621610

Sentivo Solingen GmbH (1)
Friedrichstr 36, 42655, Solingen, Germany
Tel.: (49) 21223392100
Home Care Services
N.A.I.C.S.: 621610

Smeralda Rsa Di Padru Srl (1)
Via Antonio Vivaldi, Padru, 07020, Sassari, OT, Italy
Tel.: (39) 0789481011
Health Care Srvices
N.A.I.C.S.: 621610

Sogemi Srl (1)
Via G di Capi 26, 46100, Mantua, Italy
Tel.: (39) 0376302810
Web Site: http://www.sogemisrl.it
Industrial Vehicle Mfr
N.A.I.C.S.: 336110

Sotec GmbH (1)
Gewerbestr 14, 77694, Kehl, Germany
Tel.: (49) 7851955800
Web Site: https://www.sotec4u.com
Mechanical Equipment Mfr
N.A.I.C.S.: 332991
Steffen Olshausen (*Mng Dir*)

Sozialkonzept Barbarahof GmbH (1)
Lange Wanne 95, 38259, Salzgitter, Germany
Tel.: (49) 53418080
Home Care Services
N.A.I.C.S.: 621610

Sozialkonzept Cacilienhof mbH (1)
Bruno-Rappel-Weg 1, Berenbostel, 30827, Garbsen, Germany
Tel.: (49) 51314660
Home Care Services
N.A.I.C.S.: 621610

Sozialkonzept Dorotheenhof GmbH (1)

Im Moorgartenfeld 4, 29690, Schwarmstedt, Germany
Tel.: (49) 50719610
Home Care Services
N.A.I.C.S.: 621610

Sozialkonzept Friederikenhof GmbH **(1)**
Adelbyheck 28-30, 24943, Flensburg, Germany
Tel.: (49) 461670470
Home Care Services
N.A.I.C.S.: 621610

Sozialkonzept Helenenhof GmbH **(1)**
Johann-Schroth-Strasse 2, Bad Bodenteich, 29389, Uelzen, Germany
Tel.: (49) 58249530
Home Care Services
N.A.I.C.S.: 621610

Sozialkonzept Im Rosenpark GmbH **(1)**
Berliner Strasse 16, 30966, Hemmingen, Germany
Tel.: (49) 51141080
Home Care Services
N.A.I.C.S.: 621610

Sozialkonzept Katharinenhof mbH **(1)**
Matthaeikirchstrasse 9, 30519, Hannover, Germany
Tel.: (49) 51187060
Home Care Services
N.A.I.C.S.: 621610

Sozialkonzept Lorettahof GmbH **(1)**
Bruhlstr 7, Herrstein, 55756, Birkenfeld, Germany
Tel.: (49) 67859980
Home Care Services
N.A.I.C.S.: 621610

Sozialkonzept Luisenhof GmbH **(1)**
Schwimmbadstrasse 8, 78147, Vohrenbach, Germany
Tel.: (49) 77279280
Home Care Services
N.A.I.C.S.: 621610

Sozialkonzept Magdalenenhof mbH **(1)**
Friedrichstr 43, 39218, Schonebeck, Germany
Tel.: (49) 39287895
Home Care Services
N.A.I.C.S.: 621610

Sozialkonzept Marienhof GmbH **(1)**
Ringstrasse 27, Glan Muenchweiler, 66907, Kusel, Germany
Tel.: (49) 63839260
Home Care Services
N.A.I.C.S.: 621610

Sozialkonzept Mariettenhof GmbH **(1)**
Schlossstrasse 25, Dahn, 66994, Pirmasens, Germany
Tel.: (49) 63919920
Home Care Services
N.A.I.C.S.: 621610

Sozialkonzept Schulze-Kathrinhof GmbH **(1)**
Viktoriastrasse 22, Saarwellingen, 66793, Saarlouis, Germany
Tel.: (49) 68389800
Home Care Services
N.A.I.C.S.: 621610

Sozialkonzept Sophienhof GmbH **(1)**
Hauptstrasse 61, 32457, Porta Westfalica, Germany
Tel.: (49) 57197480
Home Care Services
N.A.I.C.S.: 621610

Studio Serenissima Srl **(1)**
Via Tor De'Schiavi 354, 00171, Rome, RM, Italy
Tel.: (39) 0694801417
Web Site: http://roma38.tecnorete.it
Real Estate Services
N.A.I.C.S.: 531210

Ten Prins Plc **(1)**
Boulevard Prince de Liege 38, Anderlecht, 1070, Brussels, Belgium
Tel.: (32) 25206947

Healtcare Services
N.A.I.C.S.: 621610

Vii Voyes Sprl **(1)**
Rue des VII Voyes 9, Vedrin, 5020, Namur, Belgium
Tel.: (32) 81210313
Healtcare Services
N.A.I.C.S.: 621610

Villa Astra BV **(1)**
Bas Backerlaan 12, 7316 DZ, Apeldoorn, Netherlands
Tel.: (31) 555266820
Healtcare Services
N.A.I.C.S.: 621610

Villa Delle Terme Spa **(1)**
Via Giovan Battista Amici 1, 50131, Florence, Italy
Tel.: (39) 0550750641
Health Care Srvices
N.A.I.C.S.: 621610

Villa Oosterveld BV **(1)**
65 West Highway, 6842 BB, Arnhem, Netherlands
Tel.: (31) 263898330
Healtcare Services
N.A.I.C.S.: 621610

Villa San Clemente Srl **(1)**
Via G Garibaldi 77, 20852, Villasanta, MB, Italy
Tel.: (39) 0392052393
Health Care Srvices
N.A.I.C.S.: 621610

Villa Silvana Spa **(1)**
Viale Europa 1/3, 04011, Aprilia, Latina, Italy
Tel.: (39) 06921401
Web Site: http://www.villa-silvana.it
Health Care Srvices
N.A.I.C.S.: 621610

Villa Spes Nostra BV **(1)**
Hindersteinlaan 30, 3451 EZ, Vleuten, Netherlands
Tel.: (31) 306778788
Healtcare Services
N.A.I.C.S.: 621610

Villa de Horsting BV **(1)**
Badhuislaan 1, Laag-Soeren, 6957 DB, Rheden, Netherlands
Tel.: (31) 313610061
Healtcare Services
N.A.I.C.S.: 621610

Vittoria Srl **(1)**
Corso Porta Nuova 127, 37122, Verona, Italy
Tel.: (39) 0452057707
Web Site: http://www.vittoriasrl.com
Real Estate Services
N.A.I.C.S.: 531390

WBW GmbH **(1)**
Lippestr 18, 44579, Castrop-Rauxel, Germany
Tel.: (49) 2305972270
Web Site: http://www.wbw-gmbh.de
Plant & Industrial Construction Services
N.A.I.C.S.: 236210

CLARIANT AG
Rothausstrasse 61, CH 4132, Muttenz, Switzerland
Tel.: (41) 614695111 CH
Web Site: https://www.clariant.com
Year Founded: 1995
CLN—(SWX)
Rev.: $5,202,044,234
Assets: $6,354,884,743
Liabilities: $3,763,964,837
Net Worth: $2,590,919,907
Earnings: $253,149,514
Emp.: 10,198
Fiscal Year-end: 12/31/23
Offices of Other Holding Companies
N.A.I.C.S.: 551112
Hariolf Kottmann *(Chm)*

Subsidiaries:

Beraca Ingredientes Naturais S.A. **(1)**
Rod BR 316 S/N Km 08 QD 03 LT 03

Galpao-2 Levilancia, Ananindeua, 67030-000, PA, Brazil
Tel.: (55) 1156837233
Web Site: https://beraca.com
Beauty Product Distr
N.A.I.C.S.: 424210

Clariant (Argentina) S.A. **(1)**
Av Jose Garibaldi No 2401, Lomas De Zamora, 1836, Buenos Aires, Argentina **(100%)**
Tel.: (54) 1142390600
Web Site: http://www.clariant.com.ar
Sales Range: $50-74.9 Million
Emp.: 120
Mfr of Dyes & Paints
N.A.I.C.S.: 325130

Clariant (Australia) Pty. Ltd. **(1)**
100 Heales Road, Lara, 3212, VIC, Australia **(100%)**
Tel.: (61) 385623301
Sales Range: $100-124.9 Million
Emp.: 65
Mfr of Dyes & Paints
N.A.I.C.S.: 325130

Clariant (Canada), Inc. **(1)**
4600 Rue Cousens, Saint Laurent, H41X3, QC, Canada **(100%)**
Tel.: (514) 334-1117
Sales Range: $25-49.9 Million
Emp.: 52
Mfr of Dyes & Paints
N.A.I.C.S.: 325130
Allen Ferguson *(Mgr-Oil Svcs)*

Subsidiary (Domestic):

Phostech Lithium Inc. **(2)**
280 Avenue Liberte, Candiac, J5R 6X1, QC, Canada
Tel.: (514) 906-1359
Lithium Product Mfr
N.A.I.C.S.: 325199
Michel Parent *(Mgr-Sls & Mktg-North America)*

Prairie Petro-Chem Ltd. **(2)**
738-6th St, Estevan, S4A 1A4, SK, Canada
Tel.: (306) 634-5808
Chemical Product Mfr & Distr
N.A.I.C.S.: 325998
Clinton Lund *(Mgr-Laboratory)*

Clariant (Chile) Ltda. **(1)**
Camino a Melipilla No 15170, Maipu, Santiago, Chile
Tel.: (56) 223734100
Chemicals Mfr
N.A.I.C.S.: 325998

Clariant (China) Ltd. **(1)**
5/F Sandoz Center 178-182 Texaco Road, Tsuen Wan, NT, China (Hong Kong) **(100%)**
Tel.: (852) 24064189
Web Site: http://www.clariant.com
Sales Range: $50-74.9 Million
Emp.: 150
Mfr of Dyes & Paints
N.A.I.C.S.: 325130

Subsidiary (Non-US):

Clariant (Tianjin) Ltd. **(2)**
7 Sanwei Rd Dong Li Economic Development Zone, Dongli District, Tianjin, 300300, China **(100%)**
Tel.: (86) 2224994288
Web Site: http://www.clariant.com
Sales Range: $100-124.9 Million
Mfr of Dyes & Paints
N.A.I.C.S.: 325130

Subsidiary (Domestic):

Clariant (Tianjin) Pigments Co. Ltd. **(3)**
Ji An St Zhanggui Zhuang Rd, Dongli District, 300163, Tianjin, China **(100%)**
Tel.: (86) 2224722778
Mfr of Dyes & Paints
N.A.I.C.S.: 325130

Clariant Pigments (Tianjin) Ltd **(3)**
Guihua No 2 Rd Bohai Fine Chemical Industrial Park Dagang, Petrochemical Industrial Park, Tianjin, 300270, China
Tel.: (86) 22 6323 3737
Chemical Products Mfr

N.A.I.C.S.: 325998

Subsidiary (Non-US):

Clariant Chemicals (China) Ltd. **(2)**
No 288 Chunde Road, Minhang District, Shanghai, 201108, China **(100%)**
Tel.: (86) 2122483000
Sales Range: $25-49.9 Million
Mfr of Dyes & Paints
N.A.I.C.S.: 325130

Clariant Chemicals (Guangzhou) Ltd. **(2)**
No 2 Nan Yun San Road Science City Guangzhou Hi-Tech Indus Dev Zone, 510665, Guangzhou, China **(100%)**
Tel.: (86) 20 2820 2222
Web Site: http://www.clariant.masterbatches.com
Mfr of Dyes & Paints
N.A.I.C.S.: 325130

Clariant Masterbatches (Beijing) Ltd **(2)**
2 Yan Qi North No 2 Street Yan Qi Industrial Development Zone, Huai Rou, Beijing, 101407, China
Tel.: (86) 10 6166 5500
Web Site: http://www.clariant.in
Plastic Colorant Mfr & Distr
N.A.I.C.S.: 325998

Subsidiary (Non-US):

Clariant Masterbatches (Malaysia) Sdn Bhd **(3)**
No 79 & 80 Hicom Sector B Jalan Teluk Gadung 27/93A, 40000, Shah Alam, Selangor Darul Ehsan, Malaysia
Tel.: (60) 3 5101 2888
Web Site: http://www.seap.clariant.com
Sales Range: $25-49.9 Million
Chemical Products Distr
N.A.I.C.S.: 424690
Alex Lin *(Mgr-Mktg)*

Clariant Masterbatches (Saudi Arabia) Ltd **(3)**
Al Kharj Road 201, PO Box 5882, Riyadh, 11432, Saudi Arabia
Tel.: (966) 1 265 2828
Sales Range: $75-99.9 Million
Emp.: 125
Chemical Product Mfr & Distr
N.A.I.C.S.: 325998

Subsidiary (Domestic):

Clariant Masterbatches (Shanghai) Ltd **(3)**
No 88 Lane 4377 Jin Du Road, Ming Hang District, Shanghai, 201108, China
Tel.: (86) 21 5442 6515
Chemical Product Mfr & Distr
N.A.I.C.S.: 424690

Subsidiary (Non-US):

Clariant Masterbatches Thailand Ltd **(3)**
700/848 Amata Nakorn Industrial Estate Phase 8 Moo 1, Tambol Phan Thong Chonburi, Bangkok, 20160, Amphur Phan Thong, Thailand **(100%)**
Tel.: (66) 38 939 599
Web Site: http://www.seap.clariant.com
Sales Range: $50-74.9 Million
Emp.: 215
Mfr of Dyes & Paints. Testing Laboratories & Warehousing
N.A.I.C.S.: 325130

Clariant (Colombia) S.A. **(1)**
Calle 18 Nr 43 A 72, Bogota, Colombia **(100%)**
Tel.: (57) 15781200
Web Site: http://www.clariant.com.co
Sales Range: $50-74.9 Million
Emp.: 140
Mfr of Dyes & Paints
N.A.I.C.S.: 325130

Clariant (Denmark) A/S **(1)**
Naverland 8, DK 2600, Glostrup, Denmark **(100%)**
Tel.: (45) 43241700
Mfr of Dye & Paint
N.A.I.C.S.: 325130

Clariant AG—(Continued)

Clariant (Egypt) S.A.E. (1)
19 Khalil El Arousi Street, Heliopolis, 11757,
Cairo, Egypt
Tel.: (20) 2 774 7065
Sales Range: $25-49.9 Million
Emp.: 50
Mfr of Dyes & Paints
N.A.I.C.S.: 325130

Unit (Domestic):

**Clariant (Egypt)
S.A.E.-EGCODAR** (2)
23 Alexandria Cairo Desert Rd, 21311, Al-
exandria, Egypt (100%)
Tel.: (20) 34701149
Web Site: http://www.clariant.com
Sales Range: $25-49.9 Million
Dyes & Paints Mfr
N.A.I.C.S.: 325130

Clariant (Finland) Oy (1)
Ayritie 8 D, 01510, Vantaa, Finland (100%)
Tel.: (358) 984554200
Web Site: http://www.clariant.com
Sales Range: $25-49.9 Million
Emp.: 20
Mfr of Dyes & Paints
N.A.I.C.S.: 325130

Clariant (France) (1)
52 Ave Deschamps Pierreuh, 92000, Pu-
teaux, France (100%)
Tel.: (33) 146969600
Web Site: http://www.clariant.fr
Sales Range: $25-49.9 Million
Emp.: 100
Mfr of Dyes & Paints
N.A.I.C.S.: 325130

Subsidiary (Domestic):

Airsec S.A.S. (2)
6 Rue Louise Michel, Choisy-le-Roi, 94600,
France
Tel.: (33) 1 41 76 20 00
Web Site: http://www.clariant.com
Emp.: 50
Chemical Product Mfr & Distr
N.A.I.C.S.: 325998

Clariant Huningue (2)
Ave De Bale, 68331, Huningue,
France (100%)
Tel.: (33) 389896000
Web Site: http://www.clariant.fr
Sales Range: $100-124.9 Million
Mfr of Dyes & Paints
N.A.I.C.S.: 325130

K.J. Quinn S.A.S. (2)
14/16 Boulevard du Docteur Pontier Zone
Ind De Rieutord, 81304, Graulhet, France
Tel.: (33) 5 63428374
Leather Product Mfr
N.A.I.C.S.: 316990

Clariant (Gulf) FZE (1)
Dubai Science Park North Tower Office No
1601, PO Box 2326, Jebel Ali Free Zone,
9712, Dubai, United Arab Emirates
Tel.: (971) 42484949
Sales Range: $25-49.9 Million
Emp.: 20
Chemical Product Mfr & Distr
N.A.I.C.S.: 325998
Rachid Rouchdi (Mgr-Mktg)

Clariant (Hellas) S.A. (1)
67 Lelas Karagianni Street 33 Amarousiou
Street, Lykovrisi, 14123, Athens,
Greece (100%)
Tel.: (30) 2102896100
Sales Range: $10-24.9 Million
Emp.: 9
Mfr of Dyes & Paints
N.A.I.C.S.: 325130
Kostas Mavros (Mng Dir)

Clariant (India) Ltd. (1)
Paville House 3rd Fl Of Veer Savarkar Marg
Opposite Siddhivinayak Temp, Mumbai,
400025, Maharashtra, India (51%)
Tel.: (91) 2224323434
Web Site: http://www.clariantindia.com
Sales Range: $75-99.9 Million
Emp.: 400
Mfr of Dyes & Paints
N.A.I.C.S.: 325130

Achala Danait (Mng Dir)

Subsidiary (Domestic):

**Clariant Chemicals (India)
Limited** (2)
Gut no 31 TTC Reliable Tech Park Behind
Reli Village Elthan, Off Thane-Belapur Road
Airoli, Navi Mumbai, 400 708, Maharashtra,
India
Tel.: (91) 2271251000
Web Site: https://www.clariant.com
Rev.: $101,768,285
Assets: $88,593,441
Liabilities: $33,008,416
Net Worth: $55,585,025
Earnings: $29,997,841
Emp.: 499
Fiscal Year-end: 03/31/2021
Paint & Coatings Mfr
N.A.I.C.S.: 325510
Kewal Handa (Chm)

Clariant (Italia) S.p.A. (1)
Via A Manzoni, 20030, Milan, Italy
Tel.: (39) 0299181
Web Site: http://www.clariant.com
Sales Range: $125-149.9 Million
Emp.: 300
Mfr of Dyes & Paints
N.A.I.C.S.: 325130

Clariant (Japan) K.K. (1)
2-28-8 Bunkyo Green Court / Center Office
9F Honkomagome, Bunkyo-ku, Tokyo, 113-
8662, Japan (100%)
Tel.: (81) 359777900
Web Site: http://www.clariant.co.jp
Sales Range: $125-149.9 Million
Emp.: 450
Mfr of Dyes & Paints
N.A.I.C.S.: 325130

Clariant (Korea) Ltd. (1)
78 Cheolgang-ro 492 beon-gilDaesong-
myeon, Nam-gu, Pohang, 37872,
Gyeongsangbuk-do, Korea (South)
Tel.: (82) 542782141
Chemical Product Mfr & Distr
N.A.I.C.S.: 325998

Clariant (Malaysia) Sdn. Bhd. (1)
No 79&80 Hicom Sector B, 40000, Shah
Alam, Selangor, Malaysia (100%)
Tel.: (60) 351012888
Web Site: https://www.clariant.com
Sales Range: $25-49.9 Million
Emp.: 40
Mfr of Dyes & Paints
N.A.I.C.S.: 325130
Walter Mohr (Mng Dir)

Clariant (Maroc) S.A. (1)
Tel.: (212) 522862660
Sales Range: $25-49.9 Million
Emp.: 40
Mfr of Dyes & Paints
N.A.I.C.S.: 325130

Clariant (Mexico) S.A. de C.V. (1)
Av Eje 5 Norte N 990 Edificio E PB Frac-
cion E, Delegacion Azcapotzalco, 02230,
Santa Barbara, Edo De Mexico,
Mexico (100%)
Tel.: (52) 5552295500
Sales Range: $150-199.9 Million
Emp.: 750
Mfr of Dyes & Paints
N.A.I.C.S.: 325130

Subsidiary (Domestic):

**Clariant Productos Quimicos S.A. de
C. V.** (2)
Plasticos 28, Morelos, 54540, Naucalpan,
Mexico (100%)
Tel.: (52) 5552295500
Web Site: http://www.clariant.com.mx
Sales Range: $100-124.9 Million
Emp.: 345
Mfr of Dyes & Paints
N.A.I.C.S.: 325130

Clariant (New Zealand) Ltd. (1)
4 Rothwell Ave Albany Industrial Ests, PO
Box 300009, Auckland, 1310, New
Zealand (100%)
Tel.: (64) 99145566
Web Site: http://www.clariant.com

Sales Range: $25-49.9 Million
Emp.: 60
Mfr of Dyes & Paints
N.A.I.C.S.: 325130
Roy Grave (Mng Dir)

Clariant (Norge) AS (1)
Solheimsviken, PO Box 2313, Bergen,
5008, Norway (100%)
Tel.: (47) 55363450
Web Site: http://www.clariant.com
Sales Range: $25-49.9 Million
Emp.: 25
Mfr of Dyes & Paints
N.A.I.C.S.: 325130

Subsidiary (Domestic):

**Clariant Oil Services Scandinavia
AS** (2)
Thormohlensgate 53C, Hordaland, 5006,
Bergen, Norway
Tel.: (47) 55363450
Emp.: 32
Chemical Products Distr
N.A.I.C.S.: 424690
Frode Bekkestad (Pres)

Clariant (Osterreich) GmbH (1)
Neustiftgasse 3/2, 1070, Vienna,
Austria (100%)
Tel.: (43) 1205050
Web Site: http://www.clariant.at
Sales Range: $1-9.9 Million
Emp.: 70
Mfr of Dyes & Paints
N.A.I.C.S.: 325130

Clariant (Peru) S.A. (1)
Av Los Frutales 245 Ate Casilla, 4620,
Lima, Peru (100%)
Tel.: (51) 12072280
Synthetic Dyes & Paints Mfr
N.A.I.C.S.: 325130

Clariant (RUS) LLC (1)
Block 6 office 3-15, Prospekt Andropova 18,
115432, Moscow, Russia
Tel.: (7) 4957875050
Chemicals Mfr
N.A.I.C.S.: 325998

Clariant (Singapore) Pte. Ltd. (1)
1 International Business Park 08-03-04 The
Synergy, Singapore, 609917,
Singapore (100%)
Tel.: (65) 65630288
Web Site: http://www.seap.clariant.com
Sales Range: $50-74.9 Million
Emp.: 112
Mfr of Dyes & Paints
N.A.I.C.S.: 325130

Clariant (Sverige) AB (1)
Fogelbergs 1C, PO Box 5415, Molndal,
43135, Sweden (100%)
Tel.: (46) 31678500
Web Site: http://www.clariant.com
Sales Range: $25-49.9 Million
Emp.: 15
Mfr of Dyes & Paints
N.A.I.C.S.: 325130
Catharina Ericsson (Gen Mgr)

Clariant (Taiwan) Co. Ltd. (1)
5th Fl No 96 Chien Kuo N Rd Sec 1, Taipei,
00104, Taiwan (100%)
Tel.: (886) 225166886
Web Site: http://www.clariant.com
Sales Range: $25-49.9 Million
Emp.: 100
Mfr of Dyes & Paints
N.A.I.C.S.: 325130
Jennifer Yu (Mng Dir)

Clariant (Thailand) Ltd. (1)
3195/11 6th floor Vibulthani Tower Rama IV
Road, Klongton Klongtoey, Bangkok, 10110,
Thailand
Tel.: (66) 20798350
Chemical Product Mfr & Distr
N.A.I.C.S.: 325998

Subsidiary (Domestic):

**Clariant Chemicals (Thailand)
Ltd.** (2)
No 3195 Flat 11 6th Fl Vibulthani Tower 1
Klongtoey, Rama 4 Rd Klongton, Bangkok,
10110, Thailand (100%)
Tel.: (66) 26615360

Web Site: http://www.clariant.co.th
Sales Range: $25-49.9 Million
Emp.: 300
Mfr of Dyes & Paints
N.A.I.C.S.: 325130
Danial Hug (Pres)

Clariant (Turkiye) A.S. (1)
Tahsin Tekoglu Caddesi No 1 3, Sefakoy,
TR 34620, Istanbul, Turkiye (100%)
Tel.: (90) 2124134100
Web Site: http://www.clariant.com
Sales Range: $125-149.9 Million
Emp.: 200
Mfr of Dyes & Paints
N.A.I.C.S.: 325130

Clariant (Uruguay) SA (1)
Zonamerica Of 704 A Ruta 8 - Km 17, 500
San Isidro, Montevideo, 91600, Uruguay
Tel.: (598) 2 518 2261
Chemical Product Mfr & Distr
N.A.I.C.S.: 325998

Clariant (Venezuela) S.A. (1)
Zona Industrial San Vicente I Av Anton
Philips, Maracay, 2104, Edo Aragua,
Venezuela (100%)
Tel.: (58) 2435503111
Web Site: https://www.clariant.com
Sales Range: $50-74.9 Million
Emp.: 249
Mfr of Dyes & Paints
N.A.I.C.S.: 325130

Clariant Benelux SA/NV (1)
Parc Scientifique Fleming Fond Jean
Paques 1, Louvain-la-Neuve, 1348,
Belgium (100%)
Tel.: (32) 0010480511
Sales Range: $100-124.9 Million
Emp.: 200
Mfr of Dyes & Paints
N.A.I.C.S.: 325130

**Clariant Bentonite (Jiangsu) Co.,
Ltd.** (1)
No 408 Yinhe Road, Zhenjiang New District,
Zhenjiang, 212132, Jiangsu, China
Tel.: (86) 51183378578
Chemicals Mfr
N.A.I.C.S.: 325998

Clariant Catalysts (Japan) K.K. (1)
2-28-8 Bunkyo Green Court / Center Office
9F Honkomagome, Bunkyo-ku, Tokyo, 113-
8662, Kanto, Japan
Tel.: (81) 359777300
Chemicals Mfr
N.A.I.C.S.: 325998

**Clariant Chemicals (Huizhou)
Ltd.** (1)
No 34 Bihai Road, Daya Bay Petrochemical
Industrial Park, Huizhou, 516082, Guang-
dong, China
Tel.: (86) 7523142700
Chemicals Mfr
N.A.I.C.S.: 325998

**Clariant Chemicals (Taiwan) Co.,
Ltd** (1)
5/F No 96 Chien Kuo N Road Sec 1, Taipei,
10489, Taiwan
Tel.: (886) 2 25166886
Chemical Product Mfr & Distr
N.A.I.C.S.: 325998

**Clariant Chemicals Technology
(Shanghai) Ltd.** (1)
No 288 Chunde Road, Xinzhuang Industrial
Zone Minhang District, Shanghai, 201100,
China
Tel.: (86) 2122483000
Chemicals Mfr
N.A.I.C.S.: 325998

**Clariant Colorquimica (Chile)
Ltda.** (1)
Camino A Melipilla 15 170, Santiago,
9260075, Chile (100%)
Tel.: (56) 23734100
Web Site: http://www.clariant.com.cl
Sales Range: $50-74.9 Million
Emp.: 120
Mfr of Dyes & Paints
N.A.I.C.S.: 325130

Clariant Consulting AG (1)
Novocheryomushkinskaya street 61,

117418, Moscow, Russia
Tel.: (7) 4957875050
Chemical Products Distr
N.A.I.C.S.: 424690

Clariant Corporation **(1)**
500 E Morehead St Ste 400, Charlotte, NC
28202
Tel.: (704) 331-7000
Web Site: http://www.clariant-northamerica.com
Sales Range: $1-4.9 Billion
Emp.: 200
Specialty Chemicals Mfr
N.A.I.C.S.: 325199
Kenneth Golder *(CEO)*

Division (Domestic):

Clariant Corporation **(2)**
Ste 100 7855 National Tpke, Louisville, KY
40214-4901
Tel.: (502) 363-3099
Web Site: http://www.clariant.com
Catalyst & Specialty Chemical Mfr
N.A.I.C.S.: 325180

Joint Venture (Domestic):

Scientific Design Company, Inc. **(3)**
49 Industrial Ave, Little Ferry, NJ
07643-1922 **(50%)**
Tel.: (201) 641-0500
Web Site: https://www.scidesign.com
Sales Range: $25-49.9 Million
Emp.: 70
Process Technology Licensor
N.A.I.C.S.: 325180
Darren S. Adams *(Pres & CEO)*

Division (Domestic):

Sud-Chemie Inc.-Air Purification **(3)**
32 Fremont St, Needham, MA
02494-2933 **(100%)**
Tel.: (781) 444-5188
Web Site: http://www.sud-chemieinc.com
Sales Range: $25-49.9 Million
Emp.: 35
Precious Metal Based Catalyst Mfr
N.A.I.C.S.: 325180

Division (Domestic):

Clariant-Masterbatches Division **(2)**
85 Industrial Dr, Holden, MA 01520
Tel.: (508) 829-6321
Web Site:
    http://www.clariant.masterbatches.com
Sales Range: $1-4.9 Billion
Emp.: 3,500
Color & Additive Masterbatches & Specialty
Compounding
N.A.I.C.S.: 325991

Unit (Domestic):

Clariant Corporation **(3)**
926 Elliot Rd Albion Industrial Park, Albion,
MI 49224
Tel.: (517) 629-9101
Web Site: http://www.clariant.com
Sales Range: $25-49.9 Million
Emp.: 90
Chemicals, Catalysis & Plastics & Coatings
N.A.I.C.S.: 325211
Denise Richardson *(Mgr-Environmental)*

Clariant Corporation **(3)**
3023 Mayo St, Dalton, GA 30720
Tel.: (706) 275-8567
Web Site: http://www.clariant.com
Chemicals, Catalysis & Plastics & Coatings
N.A.I.C.S.: 325211

Subsidiary (Domestic):

Octagon Process, L.L.C. **(2)**
625 E Catawba Ave, Mount Holly, NC
28012
Tel.: (704) 822-2677
Web Site: http://www.octagonprocess.com
Emp.: 150
Aircraft Runway De-icing & Anti-icing Prod-uct Mfr
N.A.I.C.S.: 325998
Angela Modica *(Mgr-HR)*

Clariant Finance (Luxembourg)
S.A. **(1)**

12 Rue Guillaume Kroll, Luxembourg, 1882,
Luxembourg
Tel.: (352) 26189020
Financial Management Services
N.A.I.C.S.: 523999

Clariant GmbH **(1)**
Am Unisyspark 1, Sulzbach, 65843, Hellen,
Germany
Tel.: (49) 619675760
Web Site: http://www.clariant.de
Sales Range: $300-349.9 Million
Emp.: 400
Mfr of Printing Inks & Pigments for Paints,
Lacquers, Plastics & Specialty Applications
N.A.I.C.S.: 325130
Ulrich Ott *(Head-Germany)*

Subsidiary (Domestic):

Clariant (Deutschland) GmbH **(2)**
Benzstrasse 11, 70771, Leinfelden,
Germany **(100%)**
Tel.: (49) 71190320
Sales Range: $200-249.9 Million
Emp.: 120
Mfr of Dyes & Paints
N.A.I.C.S.: 325130
Martin Wissner *(Mgr-Site)*

Subsidiary (Domestic):

Clariant Advanced Materials
GmbH **(3)**
Am Unisys Park 1, 65843, Sulzbach, Ger-many
Tel.: (49) 6196 757 7893
Web Site:
    http://www.advancedmaterials.clariant.com
Sales Range: $250-299.9 Million
Plastic Material Mfr & Distr
N.A.I.C.S.: 325211

Clariant Masterbatch GmbH & Co.
OHG **(3)**
Hohenrhein 1, 56112, Lahnstein, Rheinland
Tfalz, Germany **(100%)**
Tel.: (49) 2621140
Web Site:
    http://www.clariant.masterbaches.com
Sales Range: $125-149.9 Million
Mfr of Dyes & Paints
N.A.I.C.S.: 325130

Subsidiary (Non-US):

Clariant Masterbatch Iberica **(4)**
Carretera N II Km 592 4, 08740, Barcelona,
Spain **(100%)**
Tel.: (34) 936356100
Web Site:
    http://www.clariant.masterbatches.com
Sales Range: $25-49.9 Million
Emp.: 75
N.A.I.C.S.: 325998

Subsidiary (Domestic):

Clariant Masterbatches (Deutschland)
GmbH **(4)**
Andrea Heser Hohenrhein 1, 56112, Lahn-stein, Germany
Tel.: (49) 2621 14 213
Chemical Products Distr
N.A.I.C.S.: 424690

Subsidiary (Non-US):

Clariant Masterbatches (Finland)
Oy **(4)**
Ayritie 8 D, Vantaa, 100, Finland
Tel.: (358) 10 680 8500
Chemical Product Mfr & Distr
N.A.I.C.S.: 325998

Clariant Masterbatches (Italia)
S.p.A. **(4)**
Via Bergamo 77, 23807, Merate, Lecco,
Italy
Tel.: (39) 02 9918 4326
Web Site:
    http://www.colorworks.clariant.com
Chemical Product Mfr & Distr
N.A.I.C.S.: 325998

Clariant Masterbatches Benelux
SA **(4)**
Parc Scientifique Fleming Fond Jean
Paques 1, 1348, Louvain-la-Neuve, Belgium
Tel.: (32) 10480677

Web Site:
    http://www.clariant.masterbatches.com
Emp.: 95
Chemical Product Mfr & Distr
N.A.I.C.S.: 325998
Gordi Zanberkum *(Mgr-Sls)*

Clariant Masterbatches Ireland
Limited **(4)**
Monread Industrial Estate Monread Road,
Naas, Co Kildare, Ireland **(100%)**
Tel.: (353) 45866565
Sales Range: $25-49.9 Million
Emp.: 40
Chemical Preparation
N.A.I.C.S.: 325998
Peter Joyce *(Gen Mgr)*

Clariant Masterbatches Norden
AB **(4)**
Jarnyxegatan 7, PO Box 905, 200 39,
Malmo, Sweden
Tel.: (46) 40 671 72 00
Chemical Product Mfr & Distr
N.A.I.C.S.: 325998

Subsidiary (Domestic):

Clariant Verwaltungsgesellschaft
mbH **(4)**
Am Unisys Park 1, Hellen, 65843, Schwal-bach am Taunus, Germany **(100%)**
Tel.: (49) 619675760
Web Site: https://www.clariant.com
Sales Range: $125-149.9 Million
Emp.: 350
Mfr of Dyes & Paints
N.A.I.C.S.: 325130
Ulrich Ott *(Mng Dir)*

Clariant Huajin Catalysts (Panjin)
Ltd. **(1)**
Hongqi Street, Shuangtaizi District, Panjin,
124021, Liaoning, China
Tel.: (86) 4275855154
Chemicals Mfr
N.A.I.C.S.: 325998

Clariant Iberica Produccion S.A. **(1)**
Avinguda Baix Llobregat 3 - 5, 08970, Sant
Joan Despi, Barcelona, Spain
Tel.: (34) 934798200
Chemicals Mfr
N.A.I.C.S.: 325998

Clariant Iberica S.A. **(1)**
Via Augusta 252 260, 8017, Barcelona,
Spain **(100%)**
Tel.: (34) 933068121
Web Site: http://www.clariant.es
Sales Range: $25-49.9 Million
Emp.: 100
Mfr of Dyes & Paints
N.A.I.C.S.: 325130

Subsidiary (Domestic):

Clariant Iberica Servicios S.L. **(2)**
Sucursal en Espana Avda Baix Llobregat
3-5, Sant Joan Despi, 08970, Barcelona,
Spain
Tel.: (34) 934798200
Web Site: https://www.clariant.com
Chemical Product Mfr & Distr
N.A.I.C.S.: 325998

Subsidiary (Non-US):

Clariant Quimicos (Portugal) Ltd. **(2)**
Estrada Nacional 249 Km 15, 2725 397,
Mem Martins, Portugal **(100%)**
Tel.: (351) 219269762
Web Site: http://www.clariant.com
Sales Range: $25-49.9 Million
Emp.: 50
Mfr of Dyes & Paints
N.A.I.C.S.: 325130

Clariant Industries (Korea) Ltd. **(1)**
84-7 Chungdam-dong, Kangnam-ku, Seoul,
Korea (South) **(100%)**
Tel.: (82) 2 510 8000
Web Site: http://www.clariant.com
Sales Range: $25-49.9 Million
Emp.: 75
Mfr of Dyes & Paints
N.A.I.C.S.: 325130

Clariant Pakistan (private) limited **(1)**
Office 707 Plot No 31-1-A Parsa Tower

Block -6, P E C H S Main Shahrah-e-Faisal,
Karachi, 74200, Sindh, Pakistan
Tel.: (92) 213437233334
Chemical Products Mfr
N.A.I.C.S.: 325199

Clariant Plastics & Coatings (Japan)
K.K. **(1)**
2-28-8 Bunkyo Green Court / Center Office
9F Honkomagome, Bunkyo-ku, Tokyo, 113-8662, Kanto, Japan
Tel.: (81) 359777924
Chemicals Mfr
N.A.I.C.S.: 325998

Clariant Plastics & Coatings Mexico,
S.A. de C.V. **(1)**
Calle Plasticos 28, Santa Clara Coatitla,
55540, Ecatepec, Morelos, Mexico
Tel.: (52) 5552295500
Chemicals Mfr
N.A.I.C.S.: 325998

Clariant Plastics & Coatings Southern
Africa (Pty) Ltd. **(1)**
19 Van Eck Street, Chamdor, Krugersdorp,
1739, Gauteng, South Africa
Tel.: (27) 110400206
Chemicals Mfr
N.A.I.C.S.: 325998

Clariant Poland Spolka z.o.o. **(1)**
ul Sniezna 6, 80-554, Gdansk, Pomerania,
Poland
Tel.: (48) 587687394
Chemicals Mfr
N.A.I.C.S.: 325998

Clariant Polska Sp. z.o.o. **(1)**
Ul Pulawska 303, 02785, Warsaw,
Poland **(100%)**
Tel.: (48) 225494200
Web Site: http://www.clariant.pl
Sales Range: $25-49.9 Million
Emp.: 23
Mfr of Dyes & Paints
N.A.I.C.S.: 325130

Subsidiary (Domestic):

COLEX Spolka z o.o. **(2)**
Ul Kolorowa 14, Zgierz, 95-100, Poland
Tel.: (48) 42 714 0200
Web Site: http://www.colex.com.pl
Chemical Products Mfr
N.A.I.C.S.: 325998
Andrzej Chojnacki *(Dir-R&D)*

Clariant Prodotti (Italia) S.p.A. **(1)**
Building 23 3rd and 4th floor Via A Manzoni
37, Palazzolo Milanese, 20030, Milan, Italy
Tel.: (39) 02363141
Chemicals Mfr
N.A.I.C.S.: 325998

Clariant Products (Schweiz) AG **(1)**
Rothausstrasse 61, 4132, Muttenz,
Switzerland **(100%)**
Tel.: (41) 61 469 5111
Web Site: http://www.clariant.com
Sales Range: $125-149.9 Million
Emp.: 1,000
Specialty Chemicals
N.A.I.C.S.: 325998
Hariolf Kottmann *(CEO)*

Clariant Produkte (Deutschland)
GmbH **(1)**
Stroofstrasse 27, 65933, Frankfurt am
Main, Germany
Tel.: (49) 6938000
Chemicals Mfr
N.A.I.C.S.: 325998

Clariant Qatar W.L.L. **(1)**
Al Mesaieed Industrial Area Inside MIC
Gate No 1, 50240, Mesaieed, Doha, Qatar
Tel.: (974) 44902348
Chemicals Mfr
N.A.I.C.S.: 325998

Clariant S.A. **(1)**
Av das Nacoes Unidas 18 001, Sao Paulo,
04795-900, SP, Brazil **(100%)**
Tel.: (55) 115 683 7233
Web Site: http://www.clariant.com.br
Sales Range: $450-499.9 Million
Emp.: 1,900
Mfr of Dyes & Paints
N.A.I.C.S.: 325130

Clariant AG—(Continued)

Clariant SE - Branch Muttenz (1)
Rothausstrasse 61, 4132, Muttenz, Switzerland
Tel.: (41) 61 469 51 11
Web Site: http://www.clariant.com
Emp.: 1,000
Chemical Products Mfr & Distr
N.A.I.C.S.: 325998

Clariant Sangho Ltd. (1)
84 7 Chungdam Dong, Kangnam Ku,
Seoul, 135 100, Korea (South) (80%)
Tel.: (82) 2510800
Web Site: http://www.clariantsangho.co.kr,
Sales Range: $75-99.9 Million
Emp.: 120
N.A.I.C.S.: 325998

Clariant Sasol Catalysts Ltd. (1)
Eugene Houdry Street, Northern Industries,
Sasolburg, 1947, Free State, South Africa
Tel.: (27) 169511000
Specialty Chemicals Mfr
N.A.I.C.S.: 325998

Clariant Services (France) SAS (1)
6 rue Louise Michel Val-de-Marne, 94600,
Choisy-le-Roi, France
Tel.: (33) 141762000
Chemicals Mfr
N.A.I.C.S.: 325998

**Clariant Services (Poland) SP. z
o.o.** (1)
Dr Stefana Kopcinskiego 62, 90-032, Lodz,
Voivodeship, Poland
Tel.: (48) 539999960
Chemicals Mfr
N.A.I.C.S.: 325998

**Clariant Southern Africa (Pty)
Ltd.** (1)
Unit 10 Ground Floor Greenstone Hill Office
Park 24 Emerald Boulevard, Greenstone
Hill, 1609, Gauteng, South Africa
Tel.: (27) 169511110
Chemical Products Mfr
N.A.I.C.S.: 325998

Clariant Specialty Chemicals (Zhenjiang) Co., Ltd. (1)
No 39 West Lin Jiang Road, Zhenjiang New
District, Zhenjiang, 212132, Jiangsu, China
Tel.: (86) 51185966612
Chemicals Mfr
N.A.I.C.S.: 325998

Clariant Tunisie S.A. (1)
19 rue de l'Artisanat, BP 2, TN-1080, Tunis,
Cedex, Tunisia (100%)
Tel.: (216) 70 837 667
Mfr of Dyes & Paints
N.A.I.C.S.: 325130

Clariant UK Ltd. (1)
Clariant House Unit 2 Rawdon Park,
Yeadon, Leeds, LS19 7BA, United
Kingdom (100%)
Tel.: (44) 113 239 7936
Web Site: http://www.clariant.co.uk
Sales Range: $400-449.9 Million
Emp.: 250
Dyes & Paints Mfr
N.A.I.C.S.: 325130

Subsidiary (Domestic):

Clariant Distribution UK Limited (2)
Unit 2 Rawdon Park Yeadon, Leeds, LS19
7BA, United Kingdom
Tel.: (44) 1454411789
Chemical Products Distr
N.A.I.C.S.: 424690

Clariant Holdings UK Ltd. (2)
Clariant House Unit 2 Rawdon Park,
Yeadon Leeds, Leeds, LS19 7BA, United
Kingdom (100%)
Tel.: (44) 1132397936
Web Site: http://www.clariant.com
Sales Range: $25-49.9 Million
Emp.: 80
Holding Company
N.A.I.C.S.: 551112

Clariant Oil Services UK Ltd. (2)
Howe Moss Place, Kirkhill Industrial Estate
Dyce, Aberdeen, BD5 8FJ, ABD, United
Kingdom (100%)

Tel.: (44) 1224797400
Web Site: http://www.clariant.co.uk
Sales Range: $50-74.9 Million
Emp.: 80
N.A.I.C.S.: 325998

Clariant Services UK Ltd (2)
Airedale House 423 Kirkstall Road, Leeds,
LS4 2EW, West Yorkshire, United Kingdom
Tel.: (44) 1132397936
Chemical Products Distr
N.A.I.C.S.: 424690

Clariant Ukraine LLC (1)
Soborna str 2-B office 52, Region v
Petropavlivska Borshchagovka, 08130,
Kiev, Lugansk, Ukraine
Tel.: (380) 504251396
Chemicals Mfr
N.A.I.C.S.: 325998

Clearwater Technologies Ltd (1)
Welsh Road East, Road Town, Virgin Islands (British)
Tel.: (284) 4944742
Financial Management Services
N.A.I.C.S.: 523999

**Colorants Solutions (Argentina)
S.A.** (1)
Parque Industrial Camino de la Costa Brava
s/n, B2800DDX, Buenos Aires, Zarate, Argentina
Tel.: (54) 3487429400
Chemicals Mfr
N.A.I.C.S.: 325998

Colorants Solutions (Brazil) Ltda. (1)
Av Jorge Bey Maluf 2163 Vila Theodoro,
Sao Paulo, Suzano, 08686-000, Piaui, Brazil
Tel.: (55) 1147458200
Chemicals Mfr
N.A.I.C.S.: 325998

**Colorants Solutions (Thailand)
Ltd.** (1)
851 Bangpoo Industrial Estate Soi 11 Mu4
Sukhumvit Road, Tambol Praeksa, 10280,
Amphur Muang, Samutprakan, Thailand
Tel.: (66) 27093131
Chemicals Mfr
N.A.I.C.S.: 325998

**Companhia Brasileira de Bentonita
Ltda.** (1)
Estrada da Fazenda Santa Helena s/n, Distrito Pradoso Vitoria da Conquista, Salvador, 45050-355, Bahia, Brazil
Tel.: (55) 7734024094
Chemicals Mfr
N.A.I.C.S.: 325998

EBITO Chemiebeteiligungen AG (1)
Rothausstrasse 61, 4132, Muttenz, Switzerland
Tel.: (41) 614695111
Chemical Products Mfr
N.A.I.C.S.: 325998

**Lucas Meyer Cosmetics Canada
Inc.** (1)
2590 Boul Laurier Place de la Cite Tour
Belle Cour Bureau 650, Quebec, G1V 4M6,
QC, Canada
Tel.: (418) 653-6888
Web Site:
http://www.lucasmeyercosmetics.com
Cosmetic Product Distr
N.A.I.C.S.: 424210

Subsidiary (Non-US):

Lucas Meyer Cosmetics (2)
Campus Eiffel - Batiment Edison 13 rue Ella
Maillart, 91300, Massy, France
Tel.: (33) 169106969
Web Site:
http://www.lucasmeyercosmetics.com
Cosmetic Product Mfr & Distr
N.A.I.C.S.: 325620

**Southern Cross Botanicals Pty.
Ltd.** (2)
226 Hinterland Way, Knockrow, 2479,
NSW, Australia
Tel.: (61) 266878828
Web Site:
http://www.lucasmeyercosmetics.com
Cosmetics Products Mfr

N.A.I.C.S.: 325620

Navigance GmbH (1)
Rundfunkplatz 2, 80335, Munich, Germany
Tel.: (49) 895110126
Web Site: https://www.navigance.com
Software Development Services
N.A.I.C.S.: 541511

P.T. Clariant Indonesia (1)
Jl Raya Bojonegoro - Cepu Km 22 Cengungklung - Kalitidu, Bojonegoro, East
Java, 62152, Indonesia (100%)
Tel.: (62) 215538589
Sales Range: $125-149.9 Million
Emp.: 500
Mfr of Dyes & Paints
N.A.I.C.S.: 325130

**P.T. Colorants Solutions
Indonesia** (1)
Gatot Subroto km 4 Jl Kali Sabi No 1 Kec,
Cibodas, 15138, Tangerang, Banten, Indonesia
Tel.: (62) 215538589
Chemicals Mfr
N.A.I.C.S.: 325998

**PT. Clariant Adsorbents
Indonesia** (1)
Jl Raya Lengkong Km 45 Desa Neglasari
Kec, Cimapag, 43174, Sukabumi, 43174,
Jawa Barat, Indonesia
Tel.: (62) 2666461014
Chemicals Mfr
N.A.I.C.S.: 325998

Sud-Chemie India Pvt. Ltd. (1)
401/402 Office Block Plot A-4, DLF Place
District Centre Saket, New Delhi, 110 017,
India
Tel.: (91) 1146460100
Web Site: https://www.sud-chemie-india.com
Chemicals Mfr
N.A.I.C.S.: 325998
Stefan Christof Johannes Heuser (Chm)

swissnovaChem Ltd. (1)
c/o Novac AG Uferstrasse 90, CH 4051,
Basel, Switzerland
Tel.: (41) 23417730305
Web Site: http://www.clariant.com
Mfr of Dyes & Paints
N.A.I.C.S.: 325130

CLARIDGE HOMES INC.
2001 210 Gladstone Avenue, Ottawa,
K2P 0Y6, ON, Canada
Tel.: (613) 233-6030
Web Site:
http://www.claridgehomes.com
Rev.: $25,669,350
Emp.: 90
Residential Construction
N.A.I.C.S.: 236116
Subhash Malhotra (Pres)

CLARIDGE PUBLIC LIMITED
Georgiou Genathiou Street 10 Agathangelos Court 3rd floor, 3041, Limassol, Cyprus
Tel.: (357) 25820920
Web Site:
https://www.claridgepublic.com
CLA—(CYP)
Rev.: $496,439
Assets: $7,334,438
Liabilities: $3,355,351
Net Worth: $3,979,087
Earnings: ($647,873)
Fiscal Year-end: 12/31/21
Home Management Services
N.A.I.C.S.: 721110
Platon E. Lanitis (Chm)

CLARINS S.A.
12 Ave Porte Ternes, PO Box 174,
92203, Paris, France
Tel.: (33) 147381212   FR
Web Site: http://www.clarins.com
Year Founded: 1954
Sales Range: $1-4.9 Billion
Emp.: 6,200

Perfume, Cosmetic & Skin Care
Products Mfr, Distr & Marketer
N.A.I.C.S.: 325620
Christian Courtin-Clarins (Pres)

Subsidiaries:

Clarins (U.K.) Ltd. (1)
10 Cavendish Place, London, W1G 9DN,
United Kingdom (100%)
Tel.: (44) 2073076700
Web Site: http://www.clarins.com.uk
Sales Range: $25-49.9 Million
Emp.: 100
Distribution & Sales of Cosmetics
N.A.I.C.S.: 456120
Peter Cooke (Dir-Fin)

Clarins BV (1)
Kanalpad 61, Apeldoorn, 7321 AN,
Netherlands (100%)
Tel.: (31) 555428842
Sales Range: $50-74.9 Million
Emp.: 30
Perfumes & Toiletries Distr
N.A.I.C.S.: 424210
Renee Depree (Gen Mgr)

Clarins Belgique (1)
Waterloo Atrium - 4th floor Dreve Richelle
167, 1410, Waterloo, Belgium
Tel.: (32) 23850280
Web Site: http://www.clarins.com
Sales Range: $25-49.9 Million
Emp.: 40
Distr of Cosmetics
N.A.I.C.S.: 456120

Clarins Canada Inc. (1)
815 desserte St, Laval, H7W 5N4, QC,
Canada (100%)
Tel.: (450) 688-0144
Sales Range: $25-49.9 Million
Emp.: 100
Cosmetics & Perfumes Distr
N.A.I.C.S.: 456120

Clarins GmbH (1)
Petersbrunner Strasse 13, 82319, Starnberg, Germany (100%)
Tel.: (49) 815126030
Web Site: http://www.clarins.de
Sales Range: $25-49.9 Million
Emp.: 70
Cosmetics Distr
N.A.I.C.S.: 456120
Stephan Seidel-Jarleton (Mng Dir)

Clarins K.K. (1)
6-8-10 Roppongi, Tokyo, 106 0032,
Japan (100%)
Tel.: (81) 334708554
Web Site: http://www.jp.clarins.com
Sales Range: $100-124.9 Million
Emp.: 40
Cosmetic Product Distribution
N.A.I.C.S.: 456120
Olivier Tallot (Mgr-Brand-Fragrance Grp-
Asia Pacific)

Clarins Korea Ltd. (1)
A Fl Daedong Bldg 823 -21, Kangnam Ku
Yeoksam-Dong, Seoul, 135 933, Korea
(South) (100%)
Tel.: (82) 25429045
Web Site: http://kr.clarins.com
Perfumes & Cosmetics Distr
N.A.I.C.S.: 456120

Clarins Ltd. (1)
Unit 12 K World Tech Ctr 95 How Ming St,
Kwun Tong, Kowloon, China (Hong
Kong) (100%)
Tel.: (852) 27901883
Rev.: $6,814,493
Emp.: 170
Skin Care, Makeup Product & Perfume Distribution
N.A.I.C.S.: 456120

Clarins Paris SA (1)
Edificio Bruselas Avenida De Europa 4 3rd
Fl, 28108, Alcobendas, Moraleja,
Spain (100%)
Tel.: (34) 916572159
Web Site: http://www.clarins.es
Sales Range: $25-49.9 Million
Emp.: 60
Distr of Perfumes & Cosmetics
N.A.I.C.S.: 456120

Julio Quiroga *(Mng Dir)*

Clarins Pte. Ltd. **(1)**
302 Orchard Rd 05 01 Tong Bldg, Singapore, 238 862, Singapore **(100%)**
Tel.: (65) 68386334
Web Site: http://www.clarins.com.sg
Sales Range: $50-74.9 Million
Emp.: 200
Skin Care, Makeup Products & Perfumes Distribution
N.A.I.C.S.: 456120
Larry Soo *(Gen Mgr)*

Clarins SA **(1)**
2 Rte De La Galaise, Plan-les-Ouates, 1228, Switzerland **(100%)**
Tel.: (41) 228841212
Web Site: http://www.clarins.com
Sales Range: $50-74.9 Million
Emp.: 180
Distr of Skin Care, Make-up & Perfume
N.A.I.C.S.: 456120

Clarins Sdn Bhd **(1)**
Unit 6 05 6 07 Level 6 Amoda, 22 Jalan Imbi, Kuala Lumpur, 55100, Malaysia **(100%)**
Tel.: (60) 321414076
Web Site: http://www.clarins.com
Rev.: $2,847,328
Emp.: 20
Skin Care & Makeup Products & Perfume Distribution
N.A.I.C.S.: 456120
Tan Seong Teck *(COO)*

Clarins USA Inc. **(1)**
1 Park Ave 19th Fl, New York, NY 10016 **(100%)**
Tel.: (212) 980-1800
Web Site: http://www.clarinsusa.com
Sales Range: $75-99.9 Million
Emp.: 150
Skin Care, Make-up Products & Perfume Distribution
N.A.I.C.S.: 424210
Marc Rosenblum *(Pres-Ops Svcs)*

Laboratoires Clarins **(1)**
5 Rue Ampere, Pontoise, 95300, France **(100%)**
Tel.: (33) 134351515
Web Site: http://www.claris.net
Sales Range: $125-149.9 Million
Emp.: 500
Mfr of Perfumes & Cosmetics
N.A.I.C.S.: 325620

Monarimport S.p.A. **(1)**
Via Di Vittorio 13, 40050, Castenaso, BO, Italy **(100%)**
Tel.: (39) 0516055111
Sales Range: $50-74.9 Million
Emp.: 119
Cosmetics Distr
N.A.I.C.S.: 456120
Loretta Varani *(Mgr-Mktg-Clarins)*

Nevinar Cosmetics Ltd. **(1)**
92 Upper Georges St, Dun Laoghaire, S Dublin, Ireland **(100%)**
Tel.: (353) 12846477
Web Site: http://www.clarins.com
Sales Range: $25-49.9 Million
Emp.: 15
Cosmetics Distr
N.A.I.C.S.: 424210
Jerry Hickey *(Mng Dir)*

Talboom B.V. **(1)**
Laan Van Westenenk 64, 7336 AZ, Apeldoorn, Netherlands **(100%)**
Tel.: (31) 555428842
Sales Range: $25-49.9 Million
Emp.: 40
Distr of Cosmetics
N.A.I.C.S.: 424210
Beatrice Heudier *(Gen Mgr)*

CLARION S.A. AGROINDUSTRIAL
Rua Frei Egidio Laurent 308, 06298-020, Osasco, SP, Brazil
Tel.: (55) 11 3604 8111
Web Site:
http://www.clarionsa.com.br
Edible Oil Whslr
N.A.I.C.S.: 424490

CLARIS LIFESCIENCES LTD.
Nr Parimal Crossing Ellisbridge, Ahmedabad, 380 006, India
Tel.: (91) 79 26563331 In
Web Site:
http://www.clarislifesciences.com
Year Founded: 1999
Sales Range: $100-124.9 Million
Emp.: 959
Holding Company; Pharmaceutical Products Mfr
N.A.I.C.S.: 551112
Arjun S. Handa *(Vice Chm & Mng Dir)*

Subsidiaries:

PT Claris Lifesciences Indonesia **(1)**
Jl Johar No 5 Menteng, Jakarta, 10350, Indonesia **(100%)**
Tel.: (62) 213149338
Pharmaceuticals Mfr
N.A.I.C.S.: 325412

CLARITY GOLD CORP.
915-1055 W Hastings St, Vancouver, V6E 2E9, BC, Canada
Tel.: (604) 283-2997
Web Site:
http://www.claritygoldcorp.com
Year Founded: 2019
CMET—(CNSX)
Assets: $658,727
Liabilities: $460,128
Net Worth: $198,599
Earnings: ($1,703,398)
Fiscal Year-end: 12/31/23
Mining Services
N.A.I.C.S.: 212290
James Rogers *(CEO)*

CLARITY MEDICAL GROUP HOLDING LIMITED
1302 13/F 9 Queen's Road Central, Hong Kong, China (Hong Kong)
Tel.: (852) 34290031 Ky
Web Site:
https://www.claritymedic.com
Year Founded: 2005
1406—(HKG)
Rev.: $29,051,068
Assets: $37,422,773
Liabilities: $4,474,703
Net Worth: $32,948,070
Earnings: $1,740,069
Emp.: 99
Fiscal Year-end: 03/31/22
Holding Company
N.A.I.C.S.: 551112
Po Yu Chan *(Sec)*

CLARITY PHARMACEUTICALS LIMITED
4 Cornwallis Street National Innovation Centre, Eveleigh, Sydney, 2015, NSW, Australia
Tel.: (61) 292094037 AU
Web Site:
https://www.claritypharma.com
Year Founded: 2010
CU6—(ASX)
Rev.: $7,605,670
Assets: $50,137,841
Liabilities: $5,034,060
Net Worth: $45,103,780
Earnings: ($16,041,238)
Emp.: 40
Fiscal Year-end: 06/30/23
Pharmaceutical Product Mfr & Distr
N.A.I.C.S.: 325412
David Green *(CFO)*

CLARIVATE PLC
70 St Mary Axe, London, EC3A 8BE, United Kingdom
Tel.: (44) 2074334000 JE
Web Site: https://www.clarivate.com

Year Founded: 1864
CLVT—(NYSE)
Rev.: $2,628,800,000
Assets: $12,706,800,000
Liabilities: $6,714,500,000
Net Worth: $5,992,300,000
Earnings: ($986,600,000)
Emp.: 12,000
Fiscal Year-end: 12/31/23
Scientific Information Research & Publishing Services
N.A.I.C.S.: 541990
Matitiahu Shem Tov *(CEO)*

Subsidiaries:

CPA Global Limited **(1)**
Liberation House Castle Street, Saint Helier, JE1 1BL, Jersey
Tel.: (44) 1534 888 711
Web Site: http://www.cpaglobal.com
Emp.: 1,800
Holding Company; Intellectual Property Management, Software & Legal Advisory Services
N.A.I.C.S.: 551112

Subsidiary (Non-US):

CPA Global (Asia) Limited **(2)**
Units 2301-2303 23/F Tai Tung Building No 8 Fleming Road, Wanchai, China (Hong Kong)
Tel.: (852) 3177 3488
Web Site: http://www.cpaglobal.com
Intellectual Property Management, Software & Legal Advisory Services
N.A.I.C.S.: 541199

Subsidiary (US):

CPA Global North America LLC **(2)**
2318 Mill Rd 12th Fl, Alexandria, VA 22314
Tel.: (703) 739-2234
Web Site: http://www.cpaglobal.com
Holding Company; Regional Managing Office; Intellectual Property Management, Software & Legal Advisory Services
N.A.I.C.S.: 551112

Subsidiary (Domestic):

CPA Global (Landon IP), Inc. **(3)**
2318 Mill Rd 12th Fl, Alexandria, VA 22314
Tel.: (703) 739-2234
Web Site: http://www.cpaglobal.com
Patent-Related Research & Support Services
N.A.I.C.S.: 541199

CPA Global Patent Research LLC **(3)**
2318 Mill Rd 12th Fl, Alexandria, VA 22314
Tel.: (703) 739-2234
Web Site: http://www.cpaglobal.com
Intellectual Property Management & Legal Advisory Services
N.A.I.C.S.: 541199

Subsidiary (Domestic):

CPA Global Patent Research Limited **(2)**
Liberation House Castle Street, Saint Helier, JE1 1BL, Jersey
Tel.: (44) 1534888711
Web Site: http://www.cpaglobal.com
Intellectual Property Management & Legal Advisory Services
N.A.I.C.S.: 541199

Subsidiary (Non-US):

CPA Global Software Solutions Australia Pty. Ltd. **(2)**
Level 4 10 Barrack Street, Sydney, 2000, NSW, Australia
Tel.: (61) 299933000
Web Site: http://www.cpaglobal.com
Intellectual Property Management Software Developer, Publisher & Outsourced Legal Advisory Services
N.A.I.C.S.: 513210

CPA Global Support Services India Pvt. Limited **(2)**
LGF GF 1st 2nd & 3rd Floor Tower-B, Tech Boulevard Plot no 6 Sector-127, Noida, 201 301, India

Tel.: (91) 120 406 7000
Web Site: http://www.cpaglobal.com
Intellectual Property Management & Legal Consulting Services
N.A.I.C.S.: 541199

Decision Resources, LLC **(1)**
100 District Ave Ste 213, Burlington, MA 01803-5007
Tel.: (781) 993-2500
Web Site:
http://www.decisionresourcesgroup.com
Sales Range: $25-49.9 Million
Emp.: 200
Market Analysis, Business & Economic Research Services
N.A.I.C.S.: 541910
Ken McLaren *(Chief Strategy & Exec Officer)*

Subsidiary (Domestic):

Activate Networks Inc. **(2)**
1 Newton Executive Park Ste 100, Newton, MA 02462
Tel.: (617) 558-0210
Web Site: http://www.activatenetworks.net
Business Network Analytics Software Developer
N.A.I.C.S.: 513210
Larry Miller *(Pres & CEO)*

ProQuest, LLC **(1)**
789 E Eisenhower Pkwy, Ann Arbor, MI 48106
Tel.: (734) 761-4700
Web Site: http://www.proquest.com
Sales Range: $100-124.9 Million
Emp.: 1,550
Creates Specialized Information Resources & Technologies
N.A.I.C.S.: 513140
Andrew M. Snyder *(Chm)*

Subsidiary (Domestic):

Dialog, LLC **(2)**
2250 Perimeter Park Dr Ste 300, Morrisville, NC 27560 **(100%)**
Tel.: (919) 804-6400
Web Site: http://www.dialog.com
Sales Range: $25-49.9 Million
Emp.: 1,100
Business, Finance, Science & Legal Information Services
N.A.I.C.S.: 519290
Libby Trudell *(VP-Mktg)*

Subsidiary (Non-US):

Ex Libris Ltd. **(2)**
Bldg 8 4th Floor Malcha Technological Park, Jerusalem, 9695809, Israel
Tel.: (972) 26499100
Web Site: http://www.exlibrisgroup.com
Emp.: 520
Library & Information Center Software Developer
N.A.I.C.S.: 513210
Sarit Olamy *(VP-HR)*

Subsidiary (Non-US):

Ex Libris (Australia) Pty Ltd **(3)**
Level 2 229 Greenhill Road, Dulwich, 5065, SA, Australia
Tel.: (61) 881391500
Web Site: http://www.exlibrisgroup.com
Library & Information Center Software Developer
N.A.I.C.S.: 513210

Ex Libris (UK) Limited **(3)**
8th Floor 70 St Mary Axe, London, EC3A 8BE, United Kingdom
Tel.: (44) 2078321700
Web Site: http://www.exlibrisgroup.com
Library & Information Center Software Developer
N.A.I.C.S.: 513210

Subsidiary (US):

Ex Libris (USA) Inc. **(3)**
1350 E Touhy Ave Ste 150 W, Des Plaines, IL 60018
Tel.: (847) 296-2200
Web Site: http://www.exlibrisgroup.com
Library & Information Center Software Developer
N.A.I.C.S.: 513210

Clarivate PLC—(Continued)

Subsidiary (Non-US):

Ex Libris Asia Pte Ltd. (3)
Just Office Ste #31 3 Church St Level 25
Samsung Hub, Singapore, 049483, Singapore
Tel.: (65) 66922381
Web Site: http://www.exlibrisgroup.com
Library & Information Center Software Developer
N.A.I.C.S.: 513210
Ziv BenZvi (VP-Asia Pacific)

Ex Libris Italy S.r.l. (3)
Via Cartiera 4 Borgonuovo di Pontecchio, 40037, Sasso Marconi, Bologna, Italy
Tel.: (39) 0510418019
Web Site: http://www.exlibrisgroup.com
Library & Information Center Software Developer
N.A.I.C.S.: 513210

Skillsoft Corporation (1)
300 Innovative Way Ste 201, Nashua, NH 03062
Tel.: (603) 324-3000
Web Site: https://www.skillsoft.com
Rev.: $555,124,000
Assets: $1,642,687,000
Liabilities: $1,110,931,000
Net Worth: $531,756,000
Earnings: ($724,964,000)
Emp.: 2,324
Fiscal Year-end: 01/31/2023
Investment Holding Company
N.A.I.C.S.: 551112
Ron Hovsepian (Chm)

CLARK COMMUNICATIONS LIMITED

19 Thistle Street, Belfast, EH2 1DF, United Kingdom
Tel.: (44) 131 225 9596
Web Site:
   http://www.clarkcommunications.uk
Year Founded: 2012
Emp.: 7
Public Relation Agency Services
N.A.I.C.S.: 541820
Lesley Brydon (Mng Dir)

CLARK CONTRACTS LTD

23 McFarlane Street, Paisley, PA3 1RY, United Kingdom
Tel.: (44) 1418478787
Web Site:
   http://www.clarkcontracts.com
Year Founded: 1978
Rev.: $46,973,614
Emp.: 186
Construction Services
N.A.I.C.S.: 236220
Gordon Cunningham (Mng Dir)

CLARK ORIENT (BVI) LTD.

Room 2906 29/F China Online Centre 333 Lockhart Road, Wanchai, Hong Kong, China (Hong Kong)
Tel.: (852) 2877 7308   VG
Investment Services
N.A.I.C.S.: 523999

Subsidiaries:

Ecomax, Inc. (1)
630 5th Ave Ste 2338, New York, NY 10111   (85%)
Tel.: (929) 923-2740
Rev.: $424,391
Assets: $168,506
Liabilities: $466,116
Net Worth: ($297,610)
Earnings: ($89,920)
Emp.: 1
Fiscal Year-end: 06/30/2023
Investment Services
N.A.I.C.S.: 523999

CLARKE INC.

168 Hobsons Lake Drive Suite 300, Halifax, B3S 0G4, NS, Canada
Tel.: (902) 442-3000   Ca

Web Site: https://www.clarkeinc.com
Year Founded: 1921
CK5A—(DEU)
Rev.: $58,506,698
Assets: $298,370,566
Liabilities: $124,172,688
Net Worth: $174,197,878
Earnings: $2,585,531
Emp.: 550
Fiscal Year-end: 12/31/23
Investment Holding Company
N.A.I.C.S.: 551112
George Armoyan (Chm)

Subsidiaries:

Holloway Lodging Corporation (1)
145 Hobsons Lake Drive Suite 106, Halifax, B3SOH9, NS, Canada   (100%)
Tel.: (902) 404-3499
Web Site: http://www.hlcorp.ca
Rev.: $79,100,656
Assets: $228,511,460
Liabilities: $142,436,594
Net Worth: $86,074,866
Earnings: $15,814,561
Emp.: 1,000
Fiscal Year-end: 12/31/2018
Real Estate Investment Services
N.A.I.C.S.: 523999
Felix Seiler (CEO & Interim & COO)

Unit (Domestic):

Airlane Hotel & Conference Centre Thunder Bay (2)
698 Arthur St West, Thunder Bay, P7E 5R8, ON, Canada
Tel.: (807) 473-1600
Web Site: http://www.airlanehotel.com
Sales Range: $10-24.9 Million
Emp.: 100
Hotel Operations
N.A.I.C.S.: 721110

Hilton London (2)
300 King Street, London, N6B 1S2, ON, Canada
Tel.: (519) 439-1661
Web Site: http://www.hiltonlondon.com
Emp.: 200
Hotel Operations
N.A.I.C.S.: 721110

Holiday Inn Oakville Centre Hotel (2)
590 Argus Road, Oakville, L6J 3J3, ON, Canada
Tel.: (905) 842-5000
Web Site: http://www.hioakville.com
Sales Range: $10-24.9 Million
Emp.: 100
Hotel Operations
N.A.I.C.S.: 721110

Super 8 Motel Timmins (2)
730 Algonquin Blvd East, Timmins, P4N 7G2, ON, Canada
Tel.: (705) 302-0324
Web Site: http://www.wyndhamhotels.com
Sales Range: $10-24.9 Million
Emp.: 40
Hotel Operations
N.A.I.C.S.: 721110

The Chimo Hotel (2)
1199 Joseph Cyr Street, Ottawa, K1J 7T4, ON, Canada
Tel.: (613) 744-1060
Web Site: https://chimo.ontariocahotel.com
Sales Range: $10-24.9 Million
Emp.: 40
Hotel Operations
N.A.I.C.S.: 721110
Jean-Pierre Benjamin (Gen Mgr)

Travelodge Barrie on Bayfield (2)
300 Bayfield Street, Barrie, L4M 3B9, ON, Canada
Tel.: (705) 996-0702
Web Site:
   http://www.travelodgebarrieonbay.com
Sales Range: $10-24.9 Million
Emp.: 30
Hotel Operations
N.A.I.C.S.: 721110

Travelodge Hotel Belleville (2)
11 Bay Bridge Road, Belleville, K8P 3P6,

ON, Canada
Tel.: (613) 968-3411
Web Site: http://www.travelodge.ca
Sales Range: $10-24.9 Million
Emp.: 50
Hotel Operations
N.A.I.C.S.: 721110

Travelodge Ottawa West (2)
1376 Carling Avenue, Ottawa, K1Z 7L5, ON, Canada
Tel.: (613) 722-7600
Web Site: http://www.travelodge.ca
Emp.: 100
Hotel Operations
N.A.I.C.S.: 721110

Travelodge Timmins (2)
1136 Riverside Drive, Timmins, P4R 1A2, ON, Canada
Tel.: (750) 360-1122
Web Site: http://www.travelodge.com
Hotel Operations
N.A.I.C.S.: 721110

Yellowknife Inn (2)
49 Street & Franklin Ave, PO Box 490, Yellowknife, X1A 2N4, NT, Canada
Tel.: (867) 873-2601
Web Site: http://www.yellowknifeinn.com
Sales Range: $10-24.9 Million
Emp.: 65
Hotel Operations
N.A.I.C.S.: 721110

CLARKE REAL ESTATE LTD.

117 Columbus Drive, Carbonear, A1Y 1A6, NL, Canada
Tel.: (709) 596-4444
Web Site: http://www.barryclarke.ca
Rev.: $11,427,000
Emp.: 10
Real Estate Services
N.A.I.C.S.: 531390
Barry Clarke (Founder & Owner)

CLARKSON PLC

Commodity Quay St Katharine Docks, London, E1W 1BF, United Kingdom
Tel.: (44) 2073340000   UK
Web Site: https://www.clarksons.com
Year Founded: 1852
CKN—(LSE)
Rev.: $762,181,267
Assets: $1,050,618,531
Liabilities: $529,033,072
Net Worth: $521,585,458
Earnings: $100,479,677
Emp.: 1,847
Fiscal Year-end: 12/31/22
Integrated Shipping Services
N.A.I.C.S.: 488510
Jeff Woyda (CFO & COO)

Subsidiaries:

Clarkson (Deutschland) GmbH (1)
Johannisbollwerk 20 5 Fl, Hamburg, Germany
Tel.: (49) 40319766110
Sales Range: $50-74.9 Million
Emp.: 8
Chemical Products Distr
N.A.I.C.S.: 424690

Clarkson Asia Ltd. (1)
1706-1713 32 Fl Sun Hung Kai Centre, 30 Harbour Road, Wanchai, China (Hong Kong)
Tel.: (852) 28663111
Web Site: http://www.clarksons.com.hk
Sales Range: $25-49.9 Million
Emp.: 20
Freight Transportation Arrangement
N.A.I.C.S.: 488510

Clarkson Asia Pte Ltd. (1)
29-01 Asia Square Tower 2 12 Marina View, Singapore, 018961, Singapore
Tel.: (65) 6 339 0036
Web Site: http://www.clarkson.com
Sales Range: $25-49.9 Million
Emp.: 100
Freight Transportation Arrangement
N.A.I.C.S.: 488510

Clarkson Australia (Pty) Limited (1)
11th Floor 157 Walker Street North, Sydney, 2000, NSW, Australia
Tel.: (61) 299540200
Web Site: http://www.clarksonaustralia.com
Sales Range: $25-49.9 Million
Emp.: 11
Freight Transportation Arrangement
N.A.I.C.S.: 488510

Subsidiary (Domestic):

Clarkson Melbourne Pty Limited (2)
Level 12 636 St Kilda Road, Melbourne, 3004, VIC, Australia
Tel.: (61) 398676800
Emp.: 12
Marine Shipping Services
N.A.I.C.S.: 483111
David Mullin (Mng Dir)

Clarkson Australia Holdings Pty Ltd (1)
Tel.: (61) 299540200
Sales Range: $50-74.9 Million
Emp.: 15
Ship Broking Services
N.A.I.C.S.: 523910

Clarkson Investment Services (DIFC) Limited (1)
Liberty House C/o Dubai International Financial Center, PO Box 506827, Office No 615 616 & 617, Dubai, United Arab Emirates
Tel.: (971) 4 4037000
Web Site: http://www.clarksons.com
Emp.: 15
Cargo Handling Services
N.A.I.C.S.: 488320

Clarkson Italia Srl (1)
Piazza Rossetti 3A, 16129, Genoa, Italy
Tel.: (39) 0105 5401
Web Site: https://www.clarksons.com
Sales Range: $25-49.9 Million
Emp.: 20
Freight Transportation Arrangement
N.A.I.C.S.: 488510

Clarkson Norway AS (1)
Godt Haab Strandveien 50, Lysaker, 1366, Norway
Tel.: (47) 67 10 23 00
Petrochemical Gas Broking Services
N.A.I.C.S.: 213112

Subsidiary (Domestic):

Clarksons Platou AS (2)
Munkedamsveien 62c, 0270, Oslo, Norway
Tel.: (47) 2 311 2000
Web Site: http://www.clarksons.com
Sales Range: $200-249.9 Million
Emp.: 364
Ship Brokerage & Chartering Services
N.A.I.C.S.: 488390

Subsidiary (Domestic):

Clarksons Platou Securities AS (3)
Munkedamsveien 62c, 0270, Oslo, Norway
Tel.: (47) 2 201 6389
Web Site: https://securities.clarksons.com
Sales Range: $50-74.9 Million
Emp.: 82
Securities Brokerage
N.A.I.C.S.: 523150
Erik Helverd (Mng Dir)

Clarkson Overseas Shipbroking Limited (1)
Tel.: (44) 2073343440
Ship Brokerage Services
N.A.I.C.S.: 488390

Subsidiary (Non-US):

Clarkson (Hellas) Limited (2)
62 Kisissias Ave Marousi, Maroussi, 15125, Athens, Greece
Tel.: (30) 210 458 6700
Emp.: 39
Cargo Handling Services
N.A.I.C.S.: 488320
Savvas Athanasiadis (Mgr-Sls & Pur)

Clarkson Shipping Services India Private Limited (2)
Tel.: (91) 1147774444

Sales Range: $25-49.9 Million
Emp.: 1
Marine Shipping Transportation Services
N.A.I.C.S.: 483111

Clarkson Paris SAS (1)
90 Avenue Des Champs Elysees, 75008,
Paris, France
Tel.: (33) 1 74 31 11 16
Marine Shipping Services
N.A.I.C.S.: 488390

**Clarkson Research Holdings
Limited** (1)
Commodity Quay St Katharine Docks, London, E1W 1BF, United Kingdom
Tel.: (44) 1531634561
Sales Range: $25-49.9 Million
Emp.: 16
Shipping Agency Services
N.A.I.C.S.: 488510

Subsidiary (Domestic):

**Clarkson Research Services
Limited** (2)
Commodity Quay St Katharine Docks, London, E1W 1BF, United Kingdom
Tel.: (44) 2073343134
Emp.: 50
Shipping Related Services
N.A.I.C.S.: 488390

Clarkson Securities Limited (1)
St Magnus House 3 Lower Thames Street,
London, EC3R 6HE, United Kingdom
Tel.: (44) 207 334 3151
Web Site: http://www.clarksonsecurities.com
Financial & Brokerage Services
N.A.I.C.S.: 523150
Alex Gray (CEO)

**Clarkson Shipbroking (Shanghai) Co.
Limited** (1)
2203-04 Shanghai Huadian Tower 839
Guozhan Road, Pudong New Area, Shanghai, 200126, China
Tel.: (86) 216 103 0100
Shipping Services
N.A.I.C.S.: 488510

**Clarkson Shipping Services USA
Inc.** (1)
1333 W Loop S Ste 1100, Houston, TX
77027
Tel.: (713) 235-7400
Web Site: http://www.clarksons-houston.com
Sales Range: $25-49.9 Million
Emp.: 75
Freight Transportation Arrangement
N.A.I.C.S.: 488510
Roger Horten (Mng Dir)

**Clarkson South Africa (Pty)
Limited** (1)
23 Hallifax, Bryanston, 2191, Johannesburg, South Africa
Tel.: (27) 11 803 0008
Emp.: 2
Shipping Services
N.A.I.C.S.: 488330

Clarkson Valuations Limited (1)
Commodity Quay St Katharine Docks, London, E1W 1BF, United Kingdom
Tel.: (44) 2073343134
Web Site: https://www.clarksons.net
Sales Range: $75-99.9 Million
Emp.: 350
Offshore Unit Valuation Services
N.A.I.C.S.: 541990

Clarksons Brasil Ltda. (1)
16th floor Manhattan Tower Av Rio Branco
89, Centro, Rio de Janeiro, 20040-004,
Brazil
Tel.: (55) 2139238800
Shipbroking Distr
N.A.I.C.S.: 423860

Clarksons DMCC (1)
14th Floor Gold Tower Cluster I Jumeirah
Lakes Towers, PO Box 102929, Dubai,
United Arab Emirates
Tel.: (971) 44509400
Logistic Services
N.A.I.C.S.: 541614

Clarksons Denmark ADS (1)

Philip Heymans Alle 29 2 Th, 2900, Hellerup, Denmark
Tel.: (45) 32740303
Shipbroking Distr
N.A.I.C.S.: 423860

Clarksons Deutschland GmbH (1)
Johannisbollwerk 20 5 fl, 20459, Hamburg,
Germany
Tel.: (49) 40319766110
Logistic Services
N.A.I.C.S.: 541614

Clarksons ESG Core Plus AS (1)
Munkedamsveien 62c, 0270, Oslo, Norway
Tel.: (47) 23112000
Shipbroking Distr
N.A.I.C.S.: 423860

Clarksons Japan K.K. (1)
15Fl Otemachi Financial City South Tower
1-9-7 Otemachi, Chiyoda-ku, Tokyo, 100-
0004, Japan
Tel.: (81) 335109880
Logistic Services
N.A.I.C.S.: 541614

Clarksons Korea Limited (1)
6F Shin-A Building 50 Seosomun-ro 11-gil,
Jung-gu, Seoul, 04515, Korea (South)
Tel.: (82) 261371400
Logistic Services
N.A.I.C.S.: 541614

Clarksons Martankers, S.L.U. (1)
Paseo del Pintor Rosales 38, 28008, Madrid, Spain
Tel.: (34) 913091335
Ship Broking Services
N.A.I.C.S.: 488510

Clarksons Netherlands B.V. (1)
Westerlaan 11, 3016 CK, Rotterdam, Netherlands
Tel.: (31) 107422827
Logistic Services
N.A.I.C.S.: 541614

Clarksons Norway AS (1)
Munkedamsveien 62c, 0270, Oslo, Norway
Tel.: (47) 23112000
Logistic Services
N.A.I.C.S.: 541614

**Clarksons Platou (Australia) Pty
Limited** (1)
Level 9 16 St Georges Terrace, Perth,
6000, WA, Australia
Tel.: (61) 86 210 8700
Ship Broking Services
N.A.I.C.S.: 488510

Clarksons Platou (Brasil) Ltda. (1)
16th Floor Manhattan Tower Av Rio Branco
89 Sala 1601, Centro, Rio de Janeiro,
20040-004, Brazil
Tel.: (55) 213 923 8800
Ship Broking Services
N.A.I.C.S.: 488510

Clarksons Platou (Denmark) ApS (1)
Strandvejen 70 2, 2900, Hellerup, Denmark
Tel.: (45) 3 274 0303
Ship Broking Services
N.A.I.C.S.: 488510

**Clarksons Platou (Korea) Company
Limited** (1)
6F Shin-A Building 50 Seosomun-ro 11-gil,
Jung-gu, Seoul, 04515, Korea (South)
Tel.: (82) 26 137 1400
Ship Broking Services
N.A.I.C.S.: 488510

**Clarksons Platou (Nederland)
B.V.** (1)
De Coopvaert Blaak 522, 3011 TA, Rotterdam, Netherlands
Tel.: (31) 10 742 2827
Ship Broking Services
N.A.I.C.S.: 488510

**Clarksons Platou (South Africa) (Pty)
Limited** (1)
PO Box 5890, Rivona, Johannesburg,
2128, South Africa
Tel.: (27) 11 803 0008
Ship Broking Services
N.A.I.C.S.: 488510

Clarksons Platou (Sweden) AB (1)

Dragarbrunnsgatan 55, 753 20, Uppsala,
Sweden
Tel.: (46) 1 850 2075
Ship Broking Services
N.A.I.C.S.: 488510

Clarksons Platou (USA) Inc. (1)
280 Park Ave 21st Fl, New York, NY 10017
Tel.: (212) 317-7080
Ship Broking Services
N.A.I.C.S.: 488510

Clarksons Platou Asia Limited (1)
3209-3214 Sun Hung Kai Centre 30 Harbour Road, Wanchai, China (Hong Kong)
Tel.: (852) 2 866 3111
Shipping Services
N.A.I.C.S.: 488510

**Clarksons Platou Asia Pte.
Limited** (1)
29-01 Asia Square Tower 2 12 Marina View,
Singapore, 018961, Singapore
Tel.: (65) 6 339 0036
Shipping Services
N.A.I.C.S.: 488510

Clarksons Platou DMCC (1)
Jumeirah Lakes Towers, PO Box 102929,
Dubai, United Arab Emirates
Tel.: (971) 4 450 9400
Shipping Services
N.A.I.C.S.: 488510

Clarksons Platou GmbH (1)
Johannisbollwerk 20 5 Fl, 20459, Hamburg,
Germany
Tel.: (49) 4031 976 6110
Shipping Services
N.A.I.C.S.: 488510

Clarksons Platou Japan K.K. (1)
15Fl Otemachi Financial City South Tower
1-9-7 Otemachi, Chiyoda-ku, Tokyo, 100-
0004, Japan
Tel.: (81) 33 510 9880
Shipping Services
N.A.I.C.S.: 488510

Clarksons Platou Shipbroking (Switzerland) SA (1)
Rue de la Fontaine 1, 1204, Geneva, Switzerland
Tel.: (41) 22 308 9900
Shipping Services
N.A.I.C.S.: 488510

**Clarksons Securities Canada
Inc.** (1)
Sun Life Plaza 144-4 Avenue SW Suite
1600, Calgary, T2P 3N4, AB, Canada
Tel.: (403) 440-1114
Shipbroking Distr
N.A.I.C.S.: 423860

Clarksons Securities Inc. (1)
1230 6th Ave 16th Fl, New York, NY 10020
Tel.: (212) 314-0980
Shipbroking Distr
N.A.I.C.S.: 423860

**Clarksons Singapore Pte.
Limited** (1)
29-01 Asia Square Tower 2 12 Marina View,
Singapore, 018961, Singapore
Tel.: (65) 63390036
Logistic Services
N.A.I.C.S.: 541614

Clarksons South Africa (Pty.) Ltd. (1)
PO Box 5890, Rivona, Johannesburg,
2128, South Africa
Tel.: (27) 118030008
Logistic Services
N.A.I.C.S.: 541614

Clarksons Sweden AB (1)
Dragarbrunnsgatan 55, 75320, Uppsala,
Sweden
Tel.: (46) 18502075
Logistic Services
N.A.I.C.S.: 541614

Clarksons Switzerland S.A. (1)
Rue du Prince 9, 1204, Geneva, Switzerland
Tel.: (41) 223089900
Logistic Services
N.A.I.C.S.: 541614

Genchem Holdings Limited (1)

Tel.: (44) 1473297300
Web Site: http://www.clarkson.com
Sales Range: $25-49.9 Million
Emp.: 16
Integrated Shipping Services
N.A.I.C.S.: 488330

Gibb Group (Netherlands) B.V. (1)
Scheepmakersweg 5, 1786 PD, Den
Helder, Netherlands
Tel.: (31) 852731910
Logistic Services
N.A.I.C.S.: 541614

Gibb Group Ltd. (1)
Tel.: (44) 1224620940
Web Site: https://gibbgroupltd.com
Oil & Gas Distr
N.A.I.C.S.: 424720

H Clarkson & Company Limited (1)
St Magnus House 3 Lower Thames St, London, EC3R 6HE, United Kingdom
Tel.: (44) 2073340000
Web Site: http://www.clarksons.com
Sales Range: $125-149.9 Million
Emp.: 350
Integrated Shipping Services
N.A.I.C.S.: 488330

Subsidiary (Non-US):

Clarkson Port Services Limited (2)
Tel.: (44) 1375859711
Web Site: http://www.clarksons.com
Sales Range: $25-49.9 Million
Emp.: 2
Integrated Shipping Services
N.A.I.C.S.: 488330

HC Shipping and Chartering Ltd (1)
6 Prince Street Dagger Lane, Hull, HU1
2LJ, United Kingdom
Tel.: (44) 148 258 6760
Web Site: https://www.hcshipping.com
Emp.: 7
Ship Chartering Services
N.A.I.C.S.: 483111
Mark Collins (Dir-Chartering)

Overseas Wiborg Chartering Co. (1)
7 Mount Lassen Dr Ste A-121, San Rafael,
CA 94903 (50%)
Tel.: (415) 479-2706
Freight Transportation Arrangement
N.A.I.C.S.: 488510

CLARO PRODUCTS GMBH
Sonystrasse 20, 5081, Anif, Austria
Tel.: (43) 623226260
Web Site: https://www.claro.at
Year Founded: 1995
Soap & Detergent Product Mfr
N.A.I.C.S.: 325611

CLAS OHLSON AB
Clas Ohlson AB, 793 85, Insjon, Sweden
Tel.: (46) 24744000
Web Site:
https://www.clasohlson.com
CLAS—(OMX)
Rev.: $845,233,078
Assets: $478,584,207
Liabilities: $343,963,959
Net Worth: $134,620,248
Earnings: $16,915,339
Emp.: 3,066
Fiscal Year-end: 04/30/23
Retail Trading Company
N.A.I.C.S.: 449129
Tina Englyst (Head-Legal & Sustainability)

Subsidiaries:

Clas Ohlson AS (1)
PO Box 485, Sentrum, 0105, Oslo, Norway
Tel.: (47) 23214000
Web Site: http://www.clasohlson.com
Sales Range: $25-49.9 Million
Emp.: 25
Department Stores
N.A.I.C.S.: 455110

Clas Ohlson Ltd. (1)
Aquilla House First Floor 1 Becketts Wharf

Clas Ohlson AB—(Continued)

Lower Teddington Road, Hampton Wick,
Kingston upon Thames, KT1 4ER, United
Kingdom
Tel.: (44) 2082479300
Web Site: http://www.clasohlson.co.uk
Electrical & Hardware Online Retailer
N.A.I.C.S.: 423620

Clas Ohlson OY　　　　　　　　　　**(1)**
Kaivokatu 10 B, 00100, Helsinki,
Finland　　　　　　　　　　　　**(100%)**
Tel.: (358) 201112222
Web Site: http://www.clasohlson.com
Sales Range: $125-149.9 Million
Emp.: 500
Department Stores
N.A.I.C.S.: 455110

CLASQUIN S.A.
235 cours Lafayette, 69006, Lyon,
France
Tel.: (33) 472831700
Web Site: https://www.clasquin.com
ALCLA—(EUR)
Rev.: $620,475,770
Assets: $276,237,995
Liabilities: $205,763,329
Net Worth: $70,474,666
Earnings: $22,017,883
Emp.: 1,520
Fiscal Year-end: 12/31/23
Logistic Services
N.A.I.C.S.: 488510
Yves Revol *(Chm)*

Subsidiaries:

Art Shipping International SAS　**(1)**
5 Rue Blanche 18 Rue Soleillet, 75009,
Paris, France
Tel.: (33) 142022575
Logistic Services
N.A.I.C.S.: 488510

Cargolution Inc.　　　　　　　　**(1)**
2100 Reverchon Avenue Suite 100, Dorval,
H9P 2S7, QC, Canada
Tel.: (514) 636-2576
Web Site: https://www.cargolution.com
Logistics & Transport Services
N.A.I.C.S.: 541614
Michael Buckley *(Gen Mgr)*

Clasquin Australia Pty Ltd.　　**(1)**
Unit 25 Noble St Allawah, 2218, Sydney,
NSW, Australia
Tel.: (61) 289866600
Web Site: http://www.clasquin.com
Freight Transportation Arrangement
N.A.I.C.S.: 488510

Clasquin Burkina Faso Ltd.　　**(1)**
Port Sec-Batiment Multiservices Bureau N 8
Batiment Mutiservices, BP 290, Bobo-
Dioulasso, Burkina Faso
Tel.: (226) 20975882
Logistic Services
N.A.I.C.S.: 488510

Clasquin Chile Spa　　　　　　**(1)**
Edificio Plaza Bucarest Calle bucarest N150
oficina 604, 7500000, Providencia, San-
tiago, Chile
Tel.: (56) 232102843
Logistic Services
N.A.I.C.S.: 488510
Jose Luis Quezada Venegas *(Mgr-Comml)*

Clasquin Espana S.L.　　　　　**(1)**
Centro de Carga Aerea Oficina 208,
Madrid-Barajas, 28042, Madrid, Spain
Tel.: (34) 917478586
Sales Range: $25-49.9 Million
Emp.: 2
Freight Transportation Arrangement
N.A.I.C.S.: 488510
Jean Christophe *(Dir-Ops)*

Clasquin Far East Ltd.　　　　**(1)**
Units 05-09 12/F Metroloft 38 Kwai Hei
Street, New Territories, Hong Kong,
999077, China (Hong Kong)
Tel.: (852) 27587832
Logistic Services
N.A.I.C.S.: 488510
Matthew Chan *(Sls Mgr)*

Clasquin India Pvt. Ltd.　　　　**(1)**
Unit 4-5 Ground Floor Palm Court Sector
14, Gurgaon, 122001, New Delhi, India
Tel.: (91) 1244024900
Logistic Services
N.A.I.C.S.: 488510
Ashish Bangera *(Country Mgr)*

**Clasquin International Taiwan
Ltd.**　　　　　　　　　　　　　　**(1)**
4th Floor No 16 Lane 345 Yangkuang St,
Neihu District, 11491, Taipei, Taiwan
Tel.: (886) 226595840
Web Site: http://www.clasquin.com
Freight Transportation Arrangement
N.A.I.C.S.: 488510

Clasquin Italia S.R.L.　　　　　**(1)**
London Street 1/3, 20 090 Limito de Piol-
tello, Segrate, Italy
Tel.: (39) 0226952189
Freight Transportation Arrangement
N.A.I.C.S.: 488510

Clasquin Japan Co. Ltd.　　　　**(1)**
Gotanda Koyo Building 4F, 1-9-4 Higashi
Gotanda, Shinagawa-ku, Tokyo, 141-0022,
Japan
Tel.: (81) 332807951
Freight Transportation Arrangement
N.A.I.C.S.: 488510

Clasquin Korea Co. Ltd.　　　　**(1)**
4F Inwoo Building 11, Tojeong-ro, Seoul,
04166, Korea (South)
Tel.: (82) 23223500
Sales Range: $25-49.9 Million
Emp.: 13
Freight Transportation Arrangement
N.A.I.C.S.: 488510
Namtyo Kim *(Gen Mgr)*

Clasquin Malaysia Sdn Bhd　　**(1)**
Suite 9 01 Level 9 Menara Summit, Persi-
aran Kewajipan, 47600, Kuala Lumpur, Se-
langor Darul Ehsan, Malaysia
Tel.: (60) 380248772
Web Site: https://www.clasquin.com
Sales Range: $25-49.9 Million
Emp.: 10
Freight Transportation Arrangement
N.A.I.C.S.: 488510

Clasquin Portugal Lda.　　　　**(1)**
Rua Barao Sao Januario Loja 29, nr 33 of-
fice 4 5 Barao S Januario Loja, 4470-473,
Porto, Portugal
Tel.: (351) 1223253000
Logistic Services
N.A.I.C.S.: 488510
Joao Moreira *(Mng Dir)*

Clasquin Shanghai Ltd.　　　　**(1)**
Room 203 Qingke Mansion No 138 Fen
Yang Road, Shanghai, 200031, China
Tel.: (86) 2164451452
Logistics Consulting Management Services
N.A.I.C.S.: 541614

Subsidiary (Domestic):

Clasquin (Far East) Ltd.　　　　**(2)**
Room 1232 Bloc A International Culture
Mansion Shennan Avenue, Shenzhen,
China
Tel.: (86) 755 835 535 85
Web Site: http://www.clasquin.com
Freight Transportation Arrangement
N.A.I.C.S.: 488510

Clasquin Singapore Pte. Ltd.　**(1)**
No 19 Tai Seng Avenue 05-6 Home-Fix
Building, PO Box 625, Singapore, 534054,
Singapore
Tel.: (65) 64267129
Sales Range: $25-49.9 Million
Emp.: 20
Freight Transportation Arrangement
N.A.I.C.S.: 488510

Clasquin Thailand (Co.) Ltd.　　**(1)**
14th Floor Unit F-G 163 Ocean Insurance
Building Surawongse RD, Suriyawongse,
Bangkok, 10500, Thailand
Tel.: (66) 2 634 2360
Web Site: http://www.clasquin.com
Sales Range: $25-49.9 Million
Emp.: 20
Freight Transportation Arrangement
N.A.I.C.S.: 488510

Clasquin USA Inc.　　　　　　　**(1)**
10 5th St Ste 401, Valley Stream, NY 11581
Tel.: (516) 823-0000
Sales Range: $25-49.9 Million
Emp.: 20
Freight Transportation Services
N.A.I.C.S.: 488510
Didier Vanderperre *(Pres & Mng Dir)*

Clasquin Vietnam Ltd.　　　　　**(1)**
Golden Link Building 132A Nguyen Trong
Tuyen Street, Ward 8 Phu Nhuan Dist, Ho
Chi Minh City, Vietnam
Tel.: (84) 2838121174
Logistic Services
N.A.I.C.S.: 488510

Clasquind India Pvt. Ltd.　　　　**(1)**
Office No-211 B Sagar Tech Plaza Sakinaka
Junction Andheri Kurla Road, Mumbai,
400072, India
Tel.: (91) 2228528090
Freight Transportation Management Ser-
vices
N.A.I.C.S.: 541614

Cosmos Consultants SA　　　　**(1)**
355 rue Albert Einstein Le Myaris - Bat E,
Le Myaris, 13290, Aix-en-Provence, France
Tel.: (33) 41 357 0425
Web Site: http://www.cosmos-consulting.fr
Information Technology Services
N.A.I.C.S.: 541511

Cvi International Sas　　　　　　**(1)**
3 Rue Escarfait, 11000, Dakar, Senegal
Tel.: (221) 338238779
Freight Transportation Management Ser-
vices
N.A.I.C.S.: 541614

Lci Clasquin SA　　　　　　　　**(1)**
400 Rue Joseph Leon Jacquemaire, 69400,
Villefranche-sur-Saone, France
Tel.: (33) 474621719
Logistic Services
N.A.I.C.S.: 488510

Log System Sarl　　　　　　　　**(1)**
235 Cours Lafayette, 69006, Lyon, France
Tel.: (33) 472831740
Web Site: http://www.logsystem.fr
Software Publishing Services
N.A.I.C.S.: 513210

Timar SA　　　　　　　　　　　**(1)**
Immeuble N1 Rue N 1 Quartier Oukacha
Ain Sebba, Casablanca, Morocco
Tel.: (212) 522676000
Web Site: http://www.timar.ma
Sales Range: $50-74.9 Million
Transportation Services
N.A.I.C.S.: 488510
Jean Charles Puech *(Founder)*

CLASS 1 NICKEL & TECH-NOLOGIES LIMITED
82 Richmond Street East, Toronto,
M5C 1P1, ON, Canada
Tel.: (416) 454-0166
Web Site:
　https://www.class1nickel.com
NICO—(CNSX)
Assets: $3,145,799
Liabilities: $405,881
Net Worth: $2,739,918
Earnings: ($1,356,671)
Fiscal Year-end: 12/31/20
Mineral Exploration & Mining Ser-
vices
N.A.I.C.S.: 213115
Tony Donaghy *(Principal-Geological)*

CLASS EDITORI S.P.A.
5 Via Marco Burigozzo, 20122, Milan,
Italy
Tel.: (39) 02582191
Web Site: https://www.classeditori.it
Year Founded: 1986
CLE—(ITA)
Sales Range: $150-199.9 Million
Emp.: 299
Newspaper, Magazine & Electronic
Publisher; Radio, TV & Satellite
Broadcasting Services

N.A.I.C.S.: 513110
Viktor Ukmar *(Chm)*

Subsidiaries:

MF Dow Jones News S.r.l.　　　**(1)**
Via Marco Burigozzo 5, 20122, Milan,
Italy　　　　　　　　　　　　　**(50%)**
Tel.: (39) 0258219715
Web Site: http://www.dowjones.com
Newspaper Publishers
N.A.I.C.S.: 513110

Telesia S.p.A.　　　　　　　　　**(1)**
via Ottavio Gasparri 13/17, 00152, Rome,
Italy
Tel.: (39) 06594651
Web Site: https://www.telesia.it
Sales Range: Less than $1 Million
Media Broadcasting Services
N.A.I.C.S.: 516120
Gianalberto Zapponini *(CEO)*

CLASSIC DREAM PROPER-TIES LTD.
2F Shui On Garden Office Guang Fo
Road, Huangqi Dali Town Nanhai
District, Foshan, 528248, Guang-
dong, China
Tel.: (86) 75785999390　　　**VG**
Year Founded: 2002
Real Estate Development
N.A.I.C.S.: 531210
Zhu Bang Shen *(Exec Chm)*

CLASSIC ELECTRICALS LIM-ITED
1301 13th Floor Peninsula Business
Park Tower B Senapati Bapat Marg,
Lower Parel W, Mumbai, 400 013,
India
Tel.: (91) 2230036565
Web Site:
　https://classicelectricals.co.in
512213—(BOM)
Rev.: $623,402
Assets: $1,599,752
Liabilities: $86,397
Net Worth: $1,513,355
Earnings: $489,989
Emp.: 2
Fiscal Year-end: 03/31/21
Financial Services
N.A.I.C.S.: 523999
Rajesh Hirji Shah *(Mng Dir)*

CLASSIC FILAMENTS LIMITED
Plot No 1 Priyanka House Umiyad-
ham Road Varachha, Surat, 395 006,
India
Tel.: (91) 2612540570
Web Site:
　https://www.classicfilamentsltd.com
Year Founded: 1990
540310—(BOM)
Rev.: $43,242
Assets: $1,089,655
Liabilities: $258,352
Net Worth: $831,302
Earnings: ($12,479)
Fiscal Year-end: 03/31/21
Textile Product Mfr & Distr
N.A.I.C.S.: 313240
Jayantilal Gaudani *(Mng Dir)*

CLASSIC GLOBAL FINANCE & CAPITAL LTD.
Office No 8 IInd Floor Sodhi Com-
plex, Opp Ramgarhia School Miller
Ganj, Ludhiana, 141 003, India
Tel.: (91) 11329319296
Web Site:
　https://www.classicgfcl.com
538433—(BOM)
Rev.: $48,154
Assets: $1,039,473
Liabilities: $228,762
Net Worth: $810,711
Earnings: $2,497

Emp.: 1
Fiscal Year-end: 03/31/21
Financial Support Services
N.A.I.C.S.: 523999
Nand Kishore (Exec Dir)

CLASSIC LEASING & FI-NANCE LTD.
16A Everest House 46C Jawaharlal
Nehru Road, Kolkata, 700 071, India
Tel.: (91) 3322883104
Web Site:
https://www.classicleasing.net
540481—(BOM)
Rev.: $36,349
Assets: $288,199
Liabilities: $952,571
Net Worth: ($664,372)
Earnings: ($1,064,550)
Fiscal Year-end: 03/31/22
Financial Consulting Services
N.A.I.C.S.: 541611
Surya Prakash (CFO)

CLASSIC MINERALS LIMITED
71 Furniss Road, Landsdale, 6065,
WA, Australia
Tel.: (61) 863050221   AU
Web Site:
https://www.classicminerals.com.au
CLZ—(ASX)
Rev.: $53,329
Assets: $6,564,462
Liabilities: $11,347,907
Net Worth: ($4,783,445)
Earnings: ($15,417,719)
Fiscal Year-end: 06/30/23
Metal Mining
N.A.I.C.S.: 212290
Dean Goodwin (CEO)

CLASSIC SCENIC BERHAD
Lot 12 Jalan RP3 Taman Rawang
Perdana, 48000, Rawang, Selangor
Darul Ehsan, Malaysia
Tel.: (60) 360917477
Web Site:
https://www.classicscenic.com
CSCENIC—(KLS)
Rev.: $16,685,945
Assets: $37,159,370
Liabilities: $3,121,694
Net Worth: $34,037,676
Earnings: $4,019,941
Emp.: 391
Fiscal Year-end: 12/31/22
Wooden Picture Frame Mfr
N.A.I.C.S.: 321999
Richard Chee Keong Lim (Chm)

Subsidiaries:

Lim Ket Leng Timber Sdn. Bhd.   (1)
Lot 12 Jalan RP3 Taman Rawang Perdana,
Rawang Industrial Estate, 48000, Rawang,
Selangor, Malaysia
Tel.: (60) 360917477
Web Site: http://www.limketlengtimber.com
Wooden Pallet & Stillage Mfr
N.A.I.C.S.: 321920

CLASSIFIED GROUP
2/F Cheung Tak Industrial Building 30
Wong Chuk Hang Road, Wong Chuk
Hang, Hong Kong, China (Hong
Kong)
Tel.: (852) 21274922   Ky
Web Site:
https://www.classifiedgroup.com.hk
Year Founded: 2006
8232—(HKG)
Rev.: $7,725,644
Assets: $10,020,714
Liabilities: $4,764,650
Net Worth: $5,256,064
Earnings: ($2,135,006)
Emp.: 92
Fiscal Year-end: 12/31/21

Restaurant Operators
N.A.I.C.S.: 722511
Arnold Chi Chiu Wong (Co-Founder,
Chm & Compliance Officer)

CLASSITA HOLDINGS BER-HAD
Wisma Caely Lot 2661 3rd Miles
Jalan Maharaja Lela, 36000, Teluk
Intan, Perak, Malaysia
Tel.: (60) 56218888   MY
Web Site:
https://classitaholdings.com
Year Founded: 1986
CLASSITA—(KLS)
Rev.: $9,727,926
Assets: $44,505,424
Liabilities: $21,328,645
Net Worth: $23,176,779
Earnings: ($2,030,918)
Emp.: 451
Fiscal Year-end: 06/30/23
Holding Company
N.A.I.C.S.: 551112
Sau Leng Chan (Co-Sec)

Subsidiaries:

Classita (M) Sdn. Bhd.   (1)
Wisma Caely Lot 2661 3rd Mile Jalan Ma-
haraja Lela, 36000, Teluk Intan, Perak, Ma-
laysia
Tel.: (60) 5 621 8888
Web Site: https://www.classita.com.my
Women Innerwear Mfr
N.A.I.C.S.: 315250

CLASSYS INC.
Classis 208 Teheran-ro, Gangnam-
gu, Seoul, Korea (South)
Tel.: (82) 15443481
Web Site: https://www.classys.co.kr
Year Founded: 2007
214150—(KRS)
Rev.: $108,763,087
Assets: $254,192,320
Net Worth: $176,067,808
Earnings: $57,815,422
Emp.: 350
Fiscal Year-end: 12/31/22
Medical Device Mfr
N.A.I.C.S.: 339112

CLAUSAL COMPUTING OY
Kutojantie 3, 02630, Espoo, Finland
Tel.: (358) 9 278 2200
Web Site: http://www.clausal.com
Computer Software Developer
N.A.I.C.S.: 513210
Tatu Ylonen (Owner)

CLAVIS TECHNOLOGIES IN-TERNATIONAL CO., LTD.
1564-1 Seojin Bldg 3rd Floor,
Seocho3-Dong, Seocho-Gu, Seoul,
137-874, Korea (South)
Tel.: (82) 234719340   NV
Year Founded: 2003
Sales Range: Less than $1 Million
Emp.: 7
Radio Frequency Identification (RFID)
Products & Solutions
N.A.I.C.S.: 334220
Hwan Sup Lee (Pres & CEO)

CLAVISTER HOLDING AB
Sjogatan 6 J, SE-891 60, Ornskolds-
vik, Sweden
Tel.: (46) 660299200
Web Site: https://www.clavister.com
CLAV—(OMX)
Rev.: $15,943,972
Assets: $29,717,971
Liabilities: $52,439,396
Net Worth: ($22,721,425)
Earnings: ($6,487,383)
Emp.: 109

Fiscal Year-end: 12/31/23
Network Security Products
N.A.I.C.S.: 513210
John Vestberg (Pres & CEO)

Subsidiaries:

PhenixID AB   (1)
Soder Malarstrand 71, 118 25, Stockholm,
Sweden
Tel.: (46) 86677555
Web Site: https://www.phenixid.se
Software Development Services
N.A.I.C.S.: 541511
Johan Edlund (CEO)

CLAXSON INTERACTIVE GROUP, INC.
Avenida Melian 2752, Buenos Aires,
C1430EYH, Argentina
Tel.: (54) 3058943500
Year Founded: 2001
Software Development Services
N.A.I.C.S.: 513210
Roberto Vivo-Chaneton (CEO)

CLAYMORE SILVER BULLION TRUST
200 University Avenue 13th Floor,
Toronto, M5H 3C6, ON, Canada
Tel.: (416) 813-2006   Ca
Web Site:
http://www.claymoreinvestments.ca
Year Founded: 2009
Financial Services
N.A.I.C.S.: 523991

CLAYTON CONSTRUCTION CO. LTD.
PO Box 11577, Lloydminster, T9V
38B, AB, Canada
Tel.: (306) 344-4649
Web Site:
http://www.claytonconstruction.ca
Rev.: $11,919,728
Emp.: 25
Oil Field Services
N.A.I.C.S.: 213112
Glenn Clayton (Pres)

CLAYTON GLASS LTD.
Harelaw Industrial Estate, North
Road, Durham, DH9 8UX, Stanley,
United Kingdom
Tel.: (44) 207 288200
Web Site: http://claytonglass.co.uk
Year Founded: 1956
Roof Glass Mfr
N.A.I.C.S.: 327215
Ryan Green (Mng Dir)

Subsidiaries:

Romag Ltd.   (1)
Leadgate Industrial Estate, Durham, DH8
7RS, United Kingdom
Tel.: (44) 1207500000
Web Site: http://www.romag.co.uk
Glass Processors & Solar Photovoltaic Mfr
N.A.I.C.S.: 332216
Kevin Webster (Dir-Tech & QA)

CLC INDUSTRIES LIMITED
A-60 Okhla Industrial Area Phase-II,
New Delhi, 110020, India
Tel.: (91) 2406608636
Web Site: https://www.clcindia.com
Year Founded: 1991
SPENTEX—(NSE)
Sales Range: $75-99.9 Million
Yarn & Thread Mfr
N.A.I.C.S.: 313110
Ajay Kumar Choudhary (Chm)

Subsidiaries:

Amit Spinning Industries Limited   (1)
Gat No 47 & 48 Sangawade Village Kol-
hapur Hupari Road Taluka Karveer, New
Delhi, 110 020, India
Tel.: (91) 7038094545

Web Site: https://www.girnarspintex.com
Cotton Yarn Mfr
N.A.I.C.S.: 313110
I. B. Maner (Mng Dir)

Schoeller Litvinov K.S.   (1)
Nadrazni 557, 436 57, Litvinov, Czech Re-
public
Tel.: (420) 476 769 111
Web Site: http://www.schoeller-litvinov.cz
Sales Range: $25-49.9 Million
Emp.: 20
Yarn & Thread Mfr
N.A.I.C.S.: 313110
Ivo Horin (Head-Sls Dept)

Schoeller Textile (Netherlands),
B.V.   (1)
De entree 99, 1017 CA, Amsterdam, Neth-
erlands
Tel.: (31) 20 5554466
Yarn Product Mfr
N.A.I.C.S.: 313110

Spentex Industries Limited - Baramati
Unit   (1)
D-48 MIDC, Pune, Baramati, 413 133, Ma-
harashtra, India
Tel.: (91) 2112 243745
Web Site: http://www.spentex.net
Cotton Yarn Mfr
N.A.I.C.S.: 313110
K. Shankar Mani (Sr VP)

Spentex Industries Limited - Solapur
Unit   (1)
B -1 MIDC Chincholi-Kondi, Sholapur, 413
255, Maharashtra, India
Tel.: (91) 217 2357249
Emp.: 50
Cotton Yarn Mfr
N.A.I.C.S.: 313110
Mukund Choudhary (Mng Dir)

Spentex Tashkent Toytepa LLC   (1)
Zie Said Street 2A, Tashkent, 700042, Uz-
bekistan
Tel.: (998) 711204800
Sales Range: $350-399.9 Million
Emp.: 200
Cotton Yarn Mfr
N.A.I.C.S.: 313110

CLEAN & CARBON ENERGY S.A.
Ul Mila 2, 00-180, Warsaw, Poland
Tel.: (48) 915610011
Web Site: https://www.ccenergy.pl
CCE—(WAR)
Assets: $37,131,606
Liabilities: $13,140,244
Net Worth: $23,991,362
Earnings: ($2,014,736)
Fiscal Year-end: 12/31/23
Real Estate Development Services
N.A.I.C.S.: 531390
Jozef Boguslaw Mikolajczyk (Chm &
Pres)

CLEAN & SCIENCE CO., LTD.
67 3-gil Buk-myeon 3-sandan, Jeong-
eup 3 Industrial Complex Block 15,
Jeongeup, Jeollabuk-do, Korea
(South)
Tel.: (82) 25500900
Web Site: https://www.cands.co.kr
Year Founded: 1973
045520—(KRS)
Rev.: $65,988,511
Assets: $72,498,173
Liabilities: $51,651,783
Net Worth: $20,846,390
Earnings: ($12,503,154)
Emp.: 142
Fiscal Year-end: 12/31/22
Filter Paper Mfr
N.A.I.C.S.: 322299
Alex Kwag (CEO)

Subsidiaries:

Clean & Science Co., Ltd. - Hanam
Factory   (1)
28-13 Deokpungbuk-ro 6beon-gil, Hanam,

CLEAN & SCIENCE Co., Ltd.—(Continued)
Gyeonggi-do, Korea (South)
Tel.: (82) 25500907
Filtration Paper Mfr
N.A.I.C.S.: 322299

Clean & Science Co., Ltd. - Jeong-eup Factory (1)
67 3-gil Buk-myeon 3-sandan, Jeong-eup 3 Industrial Complex Block 15, Jeongeup, Jeollabuk-do, Korea (South)
Tel.: (82) 25500900
Filtration Paper Mfr
N.A.I.C.S.: 322299

CLEAN AIR METALS, INC.
217 Queen Street West Suite 401, Toronto, M5J 2Y1, ON, Canada
Tel.: (416) 263-9200
Web Site:
   http://www.cleanairmetals.ca
Platinum Exploration Services
N.A.I.C.S.: 212290

CLEAN BIOENERGY INC.
3352 11215 Jasper Ave, Edmonton, T5K 0L5, AB, Canada
Tel.: (780) 669-6604
Web Site:
   http://www.cleanbioenergyinc.com
Year Founded: 2010
Zero Emissions Sanitary Combustion & Incinerator Mfr
N.A.I.C.S.: 562213
Bruce Youb (CEO)

CLEAN COAL POWER R&D CO., LTD.
102-3 Iwamamachi-Kawada, Iwaki-City, Fukushima, 974-8222, Japan
Tel.: (81) 246773111
Web Site: http://www.ccpower.co.jp
Year Founded: 2001
Sales Range: $10-24.9 Million
Emp.: 63
Energy Research & Development
N.A.I.C.S.: 541715
Tsutomu Watamabe (Pres & CEO)

CLEAN LINEN SERVICES LIMITED
CLEAN House Grove Business Park Waltham Road White Waltham, Maidenhead, SL6 3TN, Berkshire, United Kingdom
Tel.: (44) 3332414250
Web Site:
   http://www.cleanservices.co.uk
Sales Range: $25-49.9 Million
Emp.: 1,400
Laundry Services
N.A.I.C.S.: 812320
Jason Miller (CEO)

Subsidiaries:

CLEAN Linen Services Limited - Banbury Plant (1)
Unit 2 Beaumont Road, Banbury, OX16 1RH, Oxfordshire, United Kingdom
Tel.: (44) 1295268480
Laundry Services
N.A.I.C.S.: 812332

CLEAN Linen Services Limited - Camberley Plant (1)
40 Glebeland Road, Camberley, GU15 3DB, Surrey, United Kingdom
Tel.: (44) 1276854160
Laundry Services
N.A.I.C.S.: 812332

CLEAN Linen Services Limited - Reading Plant (1)
1 Darwin Close, Reading, RG2 0TB, Berkshire, United Kingdom
Tel.: (44) 1189314672
Laundry Services
N.A.I.C.S.: 812332

CLEAN MOTION AB
Seglarvagen 3, 444 30, Lerum, Sweden
Tel.: (46) 735320273
Web Site:
   https://www.cleanmotion.se
Year Founded: 2009
Automobile Equipment Mfr
N.A.I.C.S.: 336320
Goran Folkesson (CEO)

CLEAN POWER HYDROGEN PLC
Unit D Parkside Business Park Spinners Road, Doncaster, DN2 4BL, United Kingdom
Tel.: (44) 1302328075
Web Site: https://www.cph2.com
Year Founded: 2012
CPH2—(LSE)
Rev.: $268,229
Assets: $36,474,150
Liabilities: $5,216,802
Net Worth: $31,257,348
Earnings: ($4,276,759)
Emp.: 26
Fiscal Year-end: 12/31/22
Natural Gas Distribution
N.A.I.C.S.: 221210

Subsidiaries:

Clean Power Hydrogen Group Limited (1)
Unit D Parkside Business Park Spinners Road, Doncaster, DN2 4BL, United Kingdom
Tel.: (44) 1302328075
Web Site: https://www.cph2.com
Unique Membrane-Free Electrolyser Mfr & Distr
N.A.I.C.S.: 325120

CLEAN R SIA
Vietalvas iela 5, 1009, Riga, Latvia
Tel.: (371) 67111001
Web Site: http://www.cleanr.lv
Sales Range: $10-24.9 Million
Emp.: 950
Waste Management Services
N.A.I.C.S.: 562998
Ieva Jansone (Chm)

CLEAN SCIENCE & TECHNOLOGY LIMITED
Office No 603 & 604 6th Floor Tower No 15 Cybercity Magarpatta City, Hadapsar, Pune, 411013, Maharashtra, India
Tel.: (91) 912041264761
Web Site:
   https://www.cleanscience.co.in
Year Founded: 2003
CLEAN—(NSE)
Rev.: $97,578,254
Assets: $126,217,865
Liabilities: $21,324,576
Net Worth: $104,893,289
Earnings: $31,189,568
Emp.: 438
Fiscal Year-end: 03/31/22
Chemical Mfr & Distr
N.A.I.C.S.: 325199
Ashok Boob (Mng Dir)

CLEAN SEAS SEAFOOD LTD.
7 Frederick Road, Royal Park, 5014, SA, Australia
Tel.: (61) 1800870073
Web Site:
   https://www.cleanseas.com.au
Year Founded: 2000
CSS—(OSL)
Rev.: $50,694,195
Assets: $76,203,725
Liabilities: $14,340,012
Net Worth: $61,863,713
Earnings: $6,647,464
Fiscal Year-end: 06/30/22

Seafood Producer
N.A.I.C.S.: 424420
Robert Gratton (CEO)

CLEAN SEED CAPITAL GROUP LTD.
14 - 7541 Conway Avenue, Burnaby, V5E 2P7, BC, Canada
Tel.: (604) 566 0805
Web Site:
   https://www.cleanseedcapital.com
Year Founded: 2010
CLGPF—(OTCEM)
Rev.: $5,782
Assets: $10,130,356
Liabilities: $2,888,398
Net Worth: $7,241,959
Earnings: ($2,558,872)
Emp.: 16
Fiscal Year-end: 06/30/21
Investment Services; Agriculture
N.A.I.C.S.: 523999
Graeme Lempriere (Founder, Chm & CEO)

CLEAN TEQ WATER LIMITED
12/21 Howleys Rd, Notting Hill, 3168, VIC, Australia
Tel.: (61) 397976700
Web Site:
   https://www.cleanteqwater.com
Year Founded: 2021
CNQ—(ASX)
Rev.: $8,044,742
Assets: $8,167,573
Liabilities: $2,958,301
Net Worth: $5,209,272
Earnings: ($3,576,831)
Fiscal Year-end: 06/30/23
Waste Treatment Services
N.A.I.C.S.: 562211
Anita Addorisio (Sec)

Subsidiaries:

NematiQ Pty. Ltd. (1)
2/21 Howleys Rd, Notting Hill, 3168, VIC, Australia
Tel.: (61) 397976700
Web Site: https://www.nematiq.com
Graphene Filtration Product Distr
N.A.I.C.S.: 423720

CLEAN TRANSPORTATION GROUP, INC.
7810 Marchwood Place, Vancouver, V5S 4A6, BC, Canada
Tel.: (604) 202-3212
Web Site: http://www.ctginc.com
Year Founded: 1978
Sales Range: Less than $1 Million
Automotive Engine Maintenance Service Products Mfr
N.A.I.C.S.: 336310

CLEANAWAY COMPANY LIMITED
1F No 308 Zhongshan S Rd, Gangshan District, Kaohsiung, 820, Taiwan
Tel.: (886) 76228422
Web Site: http://www.cleanaway.tw
Year Founded: 1999
8422—(TAI)
Rev.: $139,483,496
Assets: $500,525,832
Liabilities: $277,987,988
Net Worth: $222,537,844
Earnings: $32,026,520
Fiscal Year-end: 12/31/23
Hazardous & Non-Hazardous Industrial Waste Treatment & Disposal
N.A.I.C.S.: 562211
Ching-Hsiang Yang (Chm)

Subsidiaries:

Cleanaway Enterprise Company Limited (1)
Add 1F No 308 Zhongshan S Rd Gangshan

Dist, Kaohsiung, 820, Taiwan
Tel.: (886) 76228422
Web Site: http://www.cleanaway.tw
Emp.: 150
Metal Solidification Services
N.A.I.C.S.: 532490

Top-Comment Resources Company Limited (1)
1F No 308 Zhongshan S Rd, Gangshan Dist, Kaohsiung, 820111, Taiwan
Tel.: (886) 522115268
Web Site: https://www.topcomm.com.tw
Pipe Paper Mfr & Distr
N.A.I.C.S.: 326122

CLEANAWAY WASTE MANAGEMENT LIMITED
Level 4 441 St Kilda Road, Melbourne, 3004, VIC, Australia
Tel.: (61) 383975100
Web Site:
   https://www.cleanaway.com.au
Year Founded: 1987
CWY—(ASX)
Rev.: $2,509,481,827
Assets: $4,255,141,542
Liabilities: $2,250,868,046
Net Worth: $2,004,273,496
Earnings: $105,635,683
Fiscal Year-end: 06/30/24
Waste & Environmental Services
N.A.I.C.S.: 562998
Mark Chellew (Chm)

Subsidiaries:

ASP Plastics Pty Limited (1)
17 Harris Street, Saint Marys, 2760, NSW, Australia
Tel.: (61) 288819400
Web Site: https://www.aspplastics.com.au
Plastics Product Mfr
N.A.I.C.S.: 326199

Australian Pollution Engineering Pty Ltd (1)
PO Box 200, Bendigo, 3539, VIC, Australia
Tel.: (61) 354422444
Web Site: http://www.auspolleng.com.au
Waste Management Services
N.A.I.C.S.: 562998

Australian Terminal Services Pty Ltd (1)
L 1 159 Coronation Dr, Milton, 4064, QLD, Australia
Tel.: (61) 733677800
Sales Range: $25-49.9 Million
Emp.: 230
Waste Management Services
N.A.I.C.S.: 562998
Stewart Cummins (CFO)

Baxter Business Pty Ltd (1)
L 1 159 Coronation Dr, Milton, 4064, QLD, Australia
Tel.: (61) 733677800
Web Site: http://www.transpacific.com.au
Waste Management Services
N.A.I.C.S.: 562998
Robert Boucher (CEO)

Baxter Recyclers Pty Ltd (1)
PO Box 3233, Albury, 2640, NSW, Australia
Tel.: (61) 260401304
Waste Management Services
N.A.I.C.S.: 562998

Cleanaway Daniels NSW Pty Ltd (1)
2 Wiblin St, Silverwater, 2128, NSW, Australia
Tel.: (61) 1300667787
Waste Management Services
N.A.I.C.S.: 562998

Cleanaway Daniels VIC Pty Ltd (1)
34-36 Cahill St, Dandenong South, 3175, VIC, Australia
Tel.: (61) 387964484
Web Site: https://www.danielshealth.com.au
Waste Management Services
N.A.I.C.S.: 562998

Cleanaway Industries Pty Ltd. (1)
Level 1 159 Coronation Drive, Milton, 4064, QLD, Australia

Tel.: (61) 733677800
Sales Range: $350-399.9 Million
Waste Management Services
N.A.I.C.S.: 562111

Subsidiary (Domestic):

Tox Free (Australia) Pty Ltd (2)
Level 4 441 St Kilda Road, Melbourne,
3004, VIC, Australia
Tel.: (61) 83975100
Web Site: https://www.cleanaway.com.au
Hazardous Waste Treatment & Disposal
Services
N.A.I.C.S.: 562211

Tox Free (Henderson) Pty Ltd (2)
24 Stuart Drv, Henderson, 6166, WA, Australia
Tel.: (61) 1300869373
Hazardous Waste Treatment & Disposal
Services
N.A.I.C.S.: 562211

Tox Free (Kwinana) Pty Ltd (2)
4 Mason Rd, Kwinana, 6167, WA, Australia
Tel.: (61) 894392362
Emp.: 20
Hazardous Waste Treatment & Disposal
Services
N.A.I.C.S.: 562211
Steve Gostlow (Gen Mgr)

Tox Free (New South Wales) Pty Ltd (2)
66 Links Rd, Saint Marys, 2760, NSW, Australia
Tel.: (61) 2 9623 2122
Hazardous Waste Treatment & Disposal
Services
N.A.I.C.S.: 562211
Adam Greenwood (Mgr-Tech)

Tox Free (Queensland) Pty Ltd (2)
168 Musgrave Road, Coopers Plains, 4108,
QLD, Australia
Tel.: (61) 7 3277 2474
Web Site: http://www.toxfree.com
Emp.: 15
Hazardous Waste Treatment & Disposal
Services
N.A.I.C.S.: 562211
Angela Horner (Mgr-Admin)

Waste Services Australia Pty Ltd (2)
Se 1a 1050 Hay St, West Perth, 6005, WA,
Australia
Tel.: (61) 862167000
Hazardous Waste Treatment & Disposal
Services
N.A.I.C.S.: 562211

Cleanaway Superior Pak Pty Ltd (1)
335 Fision Avenue East, PO Box 1327,
Eagle Farm, 4009, QLD, Australia
Tel.: (61) 736382200
Web Site: https://www.superiorpak.com.au
Emp.: 300
Waste Collection Machinery & Equipment
Mfr
N.A.I.C.S.: 333310

ERS Singapore Pte Ltd (1)
2 Venture Drive Unit No 12 30 Vision Exchange, Singapore, 608526, Singapore
Tel.: (65) 68616757
Web Site: http://www.ers.com
Waste Management Services
N.A.I.C.S.: 562998
Jenniffer Lim (Sr Mgr)

Enviroguard Pty Ltd (1)
50 Quarry Rd, Erskine Park, 2759, NSW,
Australia
Tel.: (61) 298343411
Web Site: http://www.transpacific.com.au
Sales Range: $25-49.9 Million
Emp.: 11
Waste Management Services
N.A.I.C.S.: 562998
Eric Le Provost (Bus Mgr)

Grasshopper Environmental Pty. Ltd. (1)
200 Walters Road Arndell Park, Sydney,
2148, NSW, Australia
Tel.: (61) 1300147277
Web Site: https://grasshopper.net.au
Industrial Waste Management Services
N.A.I.C.S.: 562910

L V Rawlinson & Associates Pty Ltd (1)
19 Riverly Ave, Gerroa, 2534, NSW, Australia
Tel.: (61) 242344444
Web Site:
http://www.cleanawaymanagement.com
Sales Range: $25-49.9 Million
Emp.: 12
Waste Management Services
N.A.I.C.S.: 562998
Susin Patterson (Office Mgr)

Mann Waste Management Pty Ltd (1)
109 Potassium Street, Narangba, Brisbane,
4504, QLD, Australia (100%)
Tel.: (61) 732931000
Web Site: http://www.cleanaway.com.au
Emp.: 20
Water Supply & Irrigation Systems
N.A.I.C.S.: 221310
Mark Smith (Gen Mgr)

NQ Resource Recovery Pty Ltd (1)
L 1 159 Coronation Dr, Milton, 4064, QLD,
Australia
Tel.: (61) 733677800
Web Site: http://www.transpacific.com.au
Sales Range: $25-49.9 Million
Emp.: 200
Waste Management Services
N.A.I.C.S.: 562998

Nationwide Oil Pty Ltd (1)
159 Coronation Dr, Milton, 4064, QLD, Australia
Tel.: (61) 733677800
Web Site: http://www.transpacific.com.au
Waste Management Services
N.A.I.C.S.: 562998

Quantum Environmental Services Pty Ltd. (1)
Homebush Business Village Unit 50/11-21
Underwood Road, Homebush, 2140, NSW,
Australia
Tel.: (61) 733677800
Web Site: http://www.transpacific.com.au
Waste Management Services
N.A.I.C.S.: 562998

Rubus Holdings Pty Ltd (1)
L 1 159 Coronation Dr, Milton, 4064, QLD,
Australia
Tel.: (61) 733677800
Waste Management Services
N.A.I.C.S.: 562998

Transpacific Industries Pty Ltd (1)
L 1 159 Coronation Dr, Milton, 4064, QLD,
Australia
Tel.: (61) 733677800
Waste Management Services
N.A.I.C.S.: 562998

Subsidiary (Domestic):

Associated Oils Pty Ltd (2)
L 1 Caroma Bldg 159 Coronation Dr, Milton,
4064, QLD, Australia
Tel.: (61) 733677800
Waste Management Services
N.A.I.C.S.: 562998

Australian Resource Recovery Pty Ltd (2)
L 1 Caroma Bldg 159 Coronation Dr, Milton,
4064, QLD, Australia
Tel.: (61) 733677800
Web Site: http://www.transpac.com.au
Sales Range: $1-4.9 Billion
Emp.: 7,000
Waste Management Services
N.A.I.C.S.: 562998

ERS Australia Pty Ltd (2)
L 1 159 Coronation Dr, Milton, 4064, QLD,
Australia
Tel.: (61) 733677800
Web Site: http://www.transpacific.com.au
Waste Management Services
N.A.I.C.S.: 562998

Transpacific Bituminous Products Pty Ltd (2)
L 1 159 Coronation Dr, Milton, 4064, QLD,
Australia
Tel.: (61) 733677800
Web Site: http://www.transpacific.com.au

Bituminous Products & Surface Coatings
Mfr
N.A.I.C.S.: 327991
Chris Unin (Gen Mgr-HR)

Transpacific Cleanaway Pty. Ltd. (2)
Level 1 159 Coronation Drive, Milton, 4064,
QLD, Australia (100%)
Tel.: (61) 733677800
Sales Range: $25-49.9 Million
Emp.: 200
Solid Waste Collection Services
N.A.I.C.S.: 562111
Tony Roderick (COO)

Transpacific Manufacturing Systems Pty Ltd (2)
L 1 159 Coronation Dr, 4064, QLD,
Australia
Tel.: (61) 733677800
Cleaning Machinery Mfr
N.A.I.C.S.: 333310

Transpacific Paramount Services Pty Ltd (2)
1 Chester Rd, Altona, 3018, VIC, Australia
Tel.: (61) 393981211
Sales Range: $10-24.9 Million
Emp.: 50
Waste Management Services
N.A.I.C.S.: 562998

Transpacific Recycling Pty Ltd (2)
1/6 Hereford St, Berkeley Vale, 2261, NSW,
Australia
Tel.: (61) 243883900
Sales Range: $75-99.9 Million
Emp.: 270
Waste Paper Disposal Services
N.A.I.C.S.: 562211

Transpacific Resources Pty Ltd (2)
L 1/159 Coronation Dr, Milton, 4064, QLD,
Australia
Tel.: (61) 733677800
Web Site: http://www.transpacific.com.au
Sales Range: $25-49.9 Million
Emp.: 200
Waste Management Services
N.A.I.C.S.: 562998

Transpacific Superior Pak Pty Ltd (2)
181 Fisson Avenue West, Eagle Farm,
4009, QLD, Australia
Tel.: (61) 732687244
Web Site: http://superiorpak.com.au
Sales Range: $25-49.9 Million
Emp.: 60
Waste Processing Equipment Mfr
N.A.I.C.S.: 333248
Rob Wrigley (Mng Dir)

Transpacific Waste Management Pty Ltd (2)
Level 1 159 Coronation Dr, Milton, 4064,
QLD, Australia
Tel.: (61) 733677800
Sales Range: $75-99.9 Million
Emp.: 270
Waste Management Services
N.A.I.C.S.: 562998

Transwaste Technologies Pty Ltd (2)
88-90 Ordish Rd, Dandenong, 3175, VIC,
Australia
Tel.: (61) 397947211
Web Site: http://www.cleanaway.com.au
Emp.: 30
Waste Management Services
N.A.I.C.S.: 562998
Rosy Jack (Mgr-Admin)

Waste Management Pacific Pty. Limited (1)
PO Box 274, Beecroft, Sydney, 2119, NSW,
Australia (100%)
Tel.: (61) 298735785
Air & Water Resource & Solid Waste Management Programs Administration
N.A.I.C.S.: 924110

CLEANBNB SPA
via Giuseppe Frua 20, 20146, Milan,
Italy
Web Site: https://www.cleanbnb.net
Hotel & Restaurant Management
Services
N.A.I.C.S.: 721110

Francesco Zorgno (Chm & CEO)

CLEANSPACE HOLDINGS LIMITED
Unit 5 39 Herbert St, Saint Leonards,
2065, NSW, Australia
Tel.: (61) 284364000   AU
Web Site:
https://www.cleanspacetech.com
Year Founded: 2009
CSX—(ASX)
Rev.: $7,884,618
Assets: $18,892,407
Liabilities: $4,577,040
Net Worth: $14,315,367
Earnings: ($5,301,945)
Emp.: 63
Fiscal Year-end: 06/30/23
Holding Company
N.A.I.C.S.: 551112
Graham A. McLean (CEO)

Subsidiaries:

CleanSpace Technology Pty Limited (1)
Unit 5 39 Herbert St, Saint Leonards, 2065,
NSW, Australia
Tel.: (61) 284364000
Web Site: https://cleanspacetechnology.com
Medical Respirator Mfr & Distr
N.A.I.C.S.: 339113

CLEANTECH LITHIUM PLC
De Carteret House 7 Castle Street,
Saint Helier, JE2 3BT, Jersey
Tel.: (44) 1534668321   JE
Web Site: https://www.ctlithium.com
Year Founded: 2017
CTLHF—(OTCQX)
Assets: $22,676,112
Liabilities: $799,982
Net Worth: $21,876,130
Earnings: ($4,797,446)
Emp.: 13
Fiscal Year-end: 12/31/22
Mining Services
N.A.I.C.S.: 212390

CLEANTECH POWER CORP.
1890 - 1075 West Georgia Street,
Vancouver, V6C 3C9, BC, Canada
Tel.: (647) 531-8264   BC
Web Site:
https://www.cleantechpower.ca
Year Founded: 1987
PWWRF—(OTCIQ)
Renewable Energy Services
N.A.I.C.S.: 221210
Frank Carnevale (CEO)

CLEANTEK INDUSTRIES INC.
1210, 520 5th Ave SW, Calgary, T2P
3R7, AB, Canada
Tel.: (403) 567-8700   AB
Web Site: https://cleantekinc.com
Year Founded: 1994
CTEK—(TSXV)
Rev.: $842,242
Assets: $2,102,422
Liabilities: $2,621,177
Net Worth: ($518,755)
Earnings: ($7,368,615)
Fiscal Year-end: 12/31/19
Oil & Gas Services Including Wellsite
Gas Detection & Artificial Lift Solutions
N.A.I.C.S.: 213112

Subsidiaries:

Southwest Oilfield Products, Inc. (1)
10340 Wallisville Rd, Houston, TX 77013
Tel.: (713) 675-7541
Web Site: http://www.glb-energy.com
Sales Range: $25-49.9 Million
Emp.: 160
Oil & Gas Pump Products Mfr
N.A.I.C.S.: 333914

CLEANTEK Industries Inc.—(Continued)

Mark Johns (Mgr-Pur)

CLEANUP CORPORATION
6-22-22 Nishi-nippori, Arakawa-ku, Tokyo, 116-8587, Japan
Tel.: (81) 338944771
Web Site: https://cleanup.jp
Year Founded: 1949
7955—(TKS)
Rev.: $845,961,020
Assets: $602,779,120
Liabilities: $228,197,030
Net Worth: $374,582,090
Earnings: $9,703,480
Emp.: 3,469
Fiscal Year-end: 03/31/24
Household Equipment Mfr & Whslr
N.A.I.C.S.: 337126
Kyoichi Inoue (Chm)

Subsidiaries:

Cleanup (Shanghai) Co., Ltd. (1)
Room A8673 7/F Block A8 JBC Plaza No 808 Hong Qiao Road, Shanghai, 200030, China
Tel.: (86) 2164480400
Web Site: https://www.cleanup-sh.com.cn
Emp.: 13
Household Equipment Whslr
N.A.I.C.S.: 423210

Cleanup Career Service Co., Ltd. (1)
6 Hosoya Emukai Yotsukura-cho, Iwaki, 979-0204, Fukushima, Japan
Tel.: (81) 246340241
Web Site: https://www.cleanup-careerservice.jp
Emp.: 176
Household Equipment Mfr
N.A.I.C.S.: 337126

Cleanup Corporation - Crete Factory (1)
28-11 Hebinami Joban-shimofunao-machi, Iwaki, 972-8312, Fukushima, Japan
Tel.: (81) 246446398
Household Equipment Mfr
N.A.I.C.S.: 337126

Cleanup Corporation - Kashima Factory (1)
73-3 Nishikizawa Joban-Mizunoya-machi, Iwaki, 972-8311, Fukushima, Japan
Tel.: (81) 246437620
Household Equipment Mfr
N.A.I.C.S.: 337126

Cleanup Corporation - Kashima System Factory (1)
85-13 Kameno-o Joban-Mizunoya-machi, Iwaki, 972-8311, Fukushima, Japan
Tel.: (81) 246441115
Household Equipment Mfr
N.A.I.C.S.: 337126

Cleanup Corporation - Project Sales Division (1)
Urbannet Kanda Bldg 3-6-2 Uchikanda, Chiyoda-ku, Tokyo, 101-0047, Japan
Tel.: (81) 3 3258 6070
Household Equipment Mfr
N.A.I.C.S.: 337126

Cleanup Corporation - Yotsukura Factory (1)
52 Aza-Kobashimae Hosoya Yotsukura-machi, Iwaki, 979-0204, Fukushima, Japan
Tel.: (81) 246343333
Household Equipment Mfr
N.A.I.C.S.: 337126

Cleanup Corporation - Yumoto Factory (1)
20-2 Sawame Joban-Iwagaoka-machi, Iwaki, 972-8313, Fukushima, Japan
Tel.: (81) 246342331
Household Equipment Mfr
N.A.I.C.S.: 337126

Cleanup Heartful Co., Ltd. (1)
6-25-3 Nishi-nippori, Arakawa-ku, Tokyo, 116-0013, Japan
Tel.: (81) 338108363

Web Site: https://cleanup.jp
Emp.: 58
Fabricated Metal Products Mfr
N.A.I.C.S.: 332312

Cleanup Logistics Co., Ltd. (1)
1-2-17 Negishi Sumitomo Fudosan Ueno Building No 7 3F, Taito-ku, Tokyo, 110-0003, Japan
Tel.: (81) 368590660
Web Site: https://cleanup-logistics.co.jp
Emp.: 101
Kitchen Cleaning Equipment Mfr
N.A.I.C.S.: 325612

Cleanup Okayama Industrial Co., Ltd. (1)
30 Taiheidai Shoo-cho, Katsuta-gun, Okayama, 709-4321, Japan
Tel.: (81) 868385121
Household Equipment Mfr
N.A.I.C.S.: 337126

Plant (Domestic):

Cleanup Okayama Industrial Co., Ltd. - Tsuyama Factory (2)
558-3 Kanai, Tsuyama, 708-0855, Okayama, Japan
Tel.: (81) 868 26 1007
Household Equipment Mfr
N.A.I.C.S.: 337126

Cleanup Steel Processing Co., Ltd. (1)
85-4 Kameno-o Joban-Mizunoya-machi, Iwaki, 972-8311, Fukushima, Japan
Tel.: (81) 246443011
Household Equipment Mfr
N.A.I.C.S.: 337126

Plant (Domestic):

Cleanup Steel Processing Co., Ltd. - Noda Factory (2)
15-12 Aza-Kitatsubo Onahamanoda, Fukushima, 971-8126, Fukushima, Japan
Tel.: (81) 246 58 6140
Fabricated Metal Products Mfr
N.A.I.C.S.: 332312

Cleanup Techno Service Co., Ltd. (1)
2-1-1 Sumiyoshi, Soka, 340-0014, Saitama, Japan
Tel.: (81) 489264771
Web Site: https://cleanup-techno.jp
Emp.: 247
Household Equipment Mfr
N.A.I.C.S.: 337126

Inoue Kosan Co., Ltd. (1)
6-22-22 Nishi-nippori, Arakawa-ku, Tokyo, 116-0013, Japan
Tel.: (81) 338107820
Kitchen Cleaning Equipment Mfr
N.A.I.C.S.: 325612

Shenyang Cleanbiz Co., Ltd. (1)
No 15 Hunhe 20th Street Eco-Tech Zone, Shenyang, 110141, China
Tel.: (86) 24 8810 5588
Household Equipment Mfr
N.A.I.C.S.: 337126

CLEAR BLUE TECHNOLOGIES INTERNATIONAL, INC.
30 Lesmill Road Unit 7, Toronto, M3B 2T6, ON, Canada
Tel.: (647) 748-4822
Web Site:
https://www.clearbluetech.com
Year Founded: 2014
CBUTF—(OTCIQ)
Rev.: $3,147,747
Assets: $6,569,724
Liabilities: $5,595,607
Net Worth: $974,116
Earnings: ($2,991,610)
Fiscal Year-end: 12/31/20
Solar Equipment Distr
N.A.I.C.S.: 423690
John Tuerk (Co-Founder & Chief Power Officer)

CLEAR GOLD RESOURCES, INC.
1066 Heywood St, Vancouver, V7L 1H3, BC, Canada
Tel.: (604) 428-6128
CFA.H—(TSXV)
Assets: $5,218
Liabilities: $1,653,294
Net Worth: ($1,648,075)
Earnings: ($134,472)
Fiscal Year-end: 06/30/24
Application Software Development Services
N.A.I.C.S.: 541511
Jeremy Ford (CEO)

CLEAR MEDIA LIMITED
Room 1202 12/F The Lee Gardens 33 Hysan Avenue, Causeway Bay, China (Hong Kong)
Tel.: (852) 29601229
Web Site: http://www.clear-media.net
Rev.: $158,683,274
Assets: $697,892,080
Liabilities: $382,476,355
Net Worth: $315,415,725
Earnings: ($42,424,309)
Emp.: 807
Fiscal Year-end: 12/31/20
Outdoor Media Company
N.A.I.C.S.: 541890
Zi Jing Han (CEO)

CLEARBELL CAPITAL LLP
2 Harewood Place, London, W1S 1BX, United Kingdom
Tel.: (44) 20 7494 7620   UK
Web Site: http://www.clearbell.com
Real Estate Investment Firm
N.A.I.C.S.: 531390
Manish Chande (Sr Partner)

CLEARBRIDGE HEALTH LIMITED
37 Jalan Pemimpin Mapex 08-05, Singapore, 577177, Singapore
Tel.: (65) 62510136   SG
Web Site:
https://www.clearbridgehealth.com
1H3—(SES)
Rev.: $25,761,841
Assets: $62,452,628
Liabilities: $19,185,298
Net Worth: $43,267,331
Earnings: ($13,699,686)
Emp.: 91
Fiscal Year-end: 12/31/21
Medical Diagnostic Services
N.A.I.C.S.: 621511
Johnson Chen (Founder)

Subsidiaries:

Clearbridge Lifestyle Pte. Ltd. (1)
37 Jalan Pemimpin 08-05 Mapex, Singapore, 577177, Singapore
Tel.: (65) 62510136
Web Site: http://www.clearbridgelifeasia.com
Medical Laboratory Services
N.A.I.C.S.: 621511

Clearbridge Medica Sdn Bhd (1)
E-1-02 Block E Level 1 Unit No 2 Plaza Arkadia No 3, Jalan Intisari Perdana Desa ParkCity, 52200, Kuala Lumpur, Malaysia
Tel.: (60) 170 081 7880
Web Site:
https://www.clearbridgemedical.com.my
Healtcare Services
N.A.I.C.S.: 621999

Clearbridge Medical Group Pte. Ltd. (1)
37 Jalan Pemimpin 08-05 Mapex, Singapore, 577177, Singapore
Tel.: (65) 6 251 0136
Web Site:
https://www.clearbridgemedical.com
Medical Laboratory Services
N.A.I.C.S.: 621511
Loo Han Woen (Dir-Medical)

Subsidiary (Non-US):

Clearbridge Medical Hong Kong Corporation Limited (2)
Unit 2A 19th Floor East Point Centre 555 Hennessy Road, Hong Kong, China (Hong Kong)
Tel.: (852) 2 155 1951
Web Site:
https://www.clearbridgemedical.com.hk
Medical Laboratory Services
N.A.I.C.S.: 621511

Clearbridge Medical Philippines, Inc. (1)
33 V Luna Avenue Brgy Pinyahan, Quezon City, 1100, Philippines
Tel.: (63) 916 276 7459
Web Site:
https://www.clearbridgemedical.com.ph
Healtcare Services
N.A.I.C.S.: 621999

Dental Focus (Bendemeer) Pte. Ltd. (1)
Blk 30 Bendemeer Road 01 - 883, Singapore, 330030, Singapore
Tel.: (65) 62966848
Dental Health Care Services
N.A.I.C.S.: 621210

Dental Focus (People's Park) Pte. Ltd. (1)
101 Upper Cross Street 02-69 People's Park Centre, Singapore, 058357, Singapore
Tel.: (65) 65320477
Dental Health Care Services
N.A.I.C.S.: 621210

Dental Focus (Pioneer) Pte. Ltd. (1)
638A Jurong West St 61 02-05 Pioneer Mall, Singapore, 640638, Singapore
Tel.: (65) 68610148
Dental Health Care Services
N.A.I.C.S.: 621210

PT Indo Genesis Medika (1)
Infinia Park Warehousing Complex Blok B-81 Jl Dr Saharjo No 45, Kebayoran Baru, Jakarta, 12850, Indonesia
Tel.: (62) 218 378 1125
Web Site: https://www.igmlabs.com
Medical Device Distr
N.A.I.C.S.: 423450
Putri Ramasari Hamid (COO)

Sam Laboratory Pte. Ltd. (1)
37 Jalan Pemimpin Mapex 04-13, Singapore, 577177, Singapore
Tel.: (65) 67373867
Web Site: http://www.samlaboratory.com
Medical Laboratory Services
N.A.I.C.S.: 621511

CLEARDEBT GROUP PLC
Nelson House Park Road, Timperley, Manchester, WA14 5BZ, Cheshire, United Kingdom
Tel.: (44) 1619692030
Web Site:
http://www.cleardebtgroup.co.uk
Sales Range: $10-24.9 Million
Emp.: 135
Holding Company; Financial Services
N.A.I.C.S.: 551112
David Emanuel Merton Mond (CEO & Sec)

Subsidiaries:

Abacus (Financial Consultants) Limited (1)
Nelson House Park Rd, Timperley, Altrincham, WA14 5BZ, Cheshire, United Kingdom
Tel.: (44) 1619058810
Web Site: http://www.abacusfinance.co.uk
Debt Management Services
N.A.I.C.S.: 561440
David E. Mond (CEO)

ClearCash Limited (1)
1st Floor Charter House Woodlands Road, Timperley, Altrincham, WA14 1HF, Cheshire, United Kingdom
Tel.: (44) 1619686838
Web Site: http://www.icount.co.uk

Prepaid Cash Card & Online Bill Payment Services
N.A.I.C.S.: 522320
Samuel Mond *(Mng Dir)*

ClearDebt Limited   (1)
Nelson House Park Rd, Timperley, Altrincham, WA14 5BZ, Cheshire, United Kingdom
Tel.: (44) 1619692030
Web Site: http://www.cleardebt.co.uk
Emp.: 100
Debt Management Services
N.A.I.C.S.: 523999
Jacqueline Cohen *(Mgr-Mktg)*

The Debt Advice Portal Limited   (1)
Nelson House Park Road, Timperley, Altrincham, WA14 5BZ, Cheshire, United Kingdom
Tel.: (44) 20 7193 4143
Debt Management Services
N.A.I.C.S.: 561440

CLEARFORD WATER SYSTEMS INC.
300-1545 Carling Ave, Ottawa, K1Z 8P9, ON, Canada
Tel.: (613) 599-6474   Ca
Web Site: https://www.clearford.com
Year Founded: 2000
CLI—(TSXV)
Rev.: $11,485,225
Assets: $14,013,340
Liabilities: $55,013,038
Net Worth: ($40,999,698)
Earnings: ($6,971,114)
Emp.: 44
Fiscal Year-end: 12/31/20
Waste Water Management Services
N.A.I.C.S.: 562219
Glenn Gold *(Chm)*

Subsidiaries:

Clearford - Koester Canada, Inc.   (1)
294 Fifty Road, Stoney Creek, L8E 5L1, ON, Canada
Tel.: (519) 751-2228
Web Site: http://www.koestercanada.ca
Water Supply System Services
N.A.I.C.S.: 221310
Richard H. Nie *(Pres)*

Subsidiary (Domestic):

Team Aquatic Inc.   (2)
704 Mara Street Suite 212, Point Edward, N7V 1X4, ON, Canada
Tel.: (519) 542-7900
Web Site: http://www.teamaquatic.com
Water Supply System Services
N.A.I.C.S.: 221310

UV Pure Technologies Inc.   (1)
60 Venture Drive Unit 7, Toronto, M1B 3S4, ON, Canada
Tel.: (416) 208-9884
Web Site: http://www.uvpure.com
Water Supply System Services
N.A.I.C.S.: 221310
Maryam Eyvazi *(Mng Dir)*

CLEARMIND MEDICINE INC.
101-1220 W 6 Ave, Vancouver, V6H 1A5, BC, Canada
Tel.: (778) 400-5347
Web Site:
https://www.clearmindmedicine.com
CMND—(NASDAQ)
Rev.: $59,174
Assets: $5,953,288
Liabilities: $4,969,816
Net Worth: $983,472
Earnings: ($8,620,837)
Emp.: 3
Fiscal Year-end: 10/31/23
Mineral Exploration & Mining Services
N.A.I.C.S.: 213115
Alan Rootenberg *(CFO)*

CLEARSPEED TECHNOLOGY PLC
130 Aztec West, Park Avenue, Bristol, BS32 4UB, United Kingdom
Tel.: (44) 1454629623   UK
Web Site: http://www.clearspeed.com
Year Founded: 2001
Sales Range: $1-9.9 Million
Emp.: 6
Semiconductor Products Developer & Mfr
N.A.I.C.S.: 334413
Russell David *(COO)*

CLEARSPRING CAPITAL PARTNERS
333 Bay Street Ste 640, Toronto, M5H 2R2, ON, Canada
Tel.: (416) 868-4900
Web Site: http://www.cscap.ca
Year Founded: 2002
Privater Equity Firm
N.A.I.C.S.: 523999
Marie-Claude Boisvert *(Partner)*

Subsidiaries:

Demers, Manufacturier d'Ambulances Inc.   (1)
28 Richelieu, Beloeil, J3G 4N5, QC, Canada
Tel.: (450) 467-4683
Web Site: http://www.demers-ambulances.com
Sales Range: $10-24.9 Million
Ambulances Designer & Mfr
N.A.I.C.S.: 336211
Benoit R. Lafortune *(Exec VP)*

Subsidiary (US):

Braun Industries, Inc.   (2)
1170 Production Dr, Van Wert, OH 45891
Tel.: (419) 232-7020
Web Site: http://www.braunambulances.com
Customized Ambulance Mfr
N.A.I.C.S.: 336211
Kim Braun *(Pres)*

Subsidiary (Domestic):

Crestline Coach Ltd.   (2)
126 Wheeler Street, Saskatoon, S7P 0A9, SK, Canada
Tel.: (306) 934-8844
Web Site: http://www.crestlinecoach.com
Sales Range: $10-24.9 Million
Ambulance & Emergency Vehicle Mfr
N.A.I.C.S.: 336110
Steven Hoffrogge *(Pres & CEO)*

Subsidiary (US):

Medix Specialty Vehicles, Inc.   (2)
3008 Mobile Dr, Elkhart, IN 46514-5524
Tel.: (574) 266-0911
Web Site: http://www.medixambulance.com
Rev.: $6,500,000
Emp.: 57
Light Truck & Utility Vehicle Mfr
N.A.I.C.S.: 336110
Art Brown *(Mgr-Warranty & Svc-Electrical Product Dev)*

CLEARVIEW WEALTH LIMITED
Level 15 20 Bond Street, Sydney, 2000, NSW, Australia
Tel.: (61) 280951300
Web Site:
http://www.clearview.com.au
CVW—(ASX)
Rev.: $222,964,075
Assets: $1,889,097,882
Liabilities: $1,653,279,240
Net Worth: $235,818,642
Earnings: $4,674,145
Fiscal Year-end: 06/30/24
Financial Investment & Life Insurance Services
N.A.I.C.S.: 523999
Justin McLaughlin *(Chief Investment Officer)*

Subsidiaries:

ClearView Financial Advice Pty Limited   (1)

Level 14 20 Bond Street, Sydney, 2000, NSW, Australia
Tel.: (61) 1800290813
Web Site:
http://www.clearviewadvice.com.au
Financial Advisory Services
N.A.I.C.S.: 523940
Todd Kardash *(Gen Mgr)*

Lavista Licensee Solutions Pty Limited   (1)
Level 13 Corporate Centre One 2 Corporate Court, Bundall, 4217, QLD, Australia
Tel.: (61) 1300557598
Web Site: https://www.lavista.com.au
Financial Advisory Services
N.A.I.C.S.: 523940

Matrix Planning Solutions Limited   (1)
Level 13 Corporate Centre One 2 Corporate Court, Bundall, 4217, QLD, Australia
Tel.: (61) 1300557598
Web Site: https://www.matrixplan.com.au
Financial Advisory Services
N.A.I.C.S.: 523940
Tony Mantineo *(Head-Bus Growth)*

CLEARVISE AG
Unter den Eichen 7, 65195, Wiesbaden, Germany
Tel.: (49) 61195011780
Web Site: https://www.clearvise.de
Year Founded: 2010
ABO—(MUN)
Rev.: $228,502
Assets: $154,518,490
Liabilities: $8,825,036
Net Worth: $145,693,454
Earnings: $6,027,155
Emp.: 13
Fiscal Year-end: 12/31/23
Eletric Power Generation Services
N.A.I.C.S.: 221115
Manuel Sieth *(CFO)*

CLEARVUE TECHNOLOGIES LIMITED
Suite 7 567 Newcastle Street, West Perth, 6005, WA, Australia
Tel.: (61) 892209020
Web Site:
https://www.clearvuepv.com
Year Founded: 1996
CPV—(ASX)
Rev.: $1,079,831
Assets: $13,457,606
Liabilities: $848,743
Net Worth: $12,608,863
Earnings: ($2,916,235)
Fiscal Year-end: 06/30/22
Other Electric Power Generation
N.A.I.C.S.: 221118
Victor Rosenberg *(Founder & Chm)*

Subsidiaries:

Clearvue (Asia) Pte.Ltd.   (1)
12-02 Raffles City Tower 250 North Bridge Rd, Singapore, 179101, Singapore
Tel.: (65) 8004922408
Solar Glass Energy Product Mfr & Distr
N.A.I.C.S.: 333414

CLEARWATER FINE FOODS INCORPORATED
c/o Clearwater Seafood 757 Bedford Highway, Bedford, B4A 3Z7, NS, Canada
Tel.: (902) 443-0550   ON
Investment Holding Company
N.A.I.C.S.: 551112
John C. Risley *(Pres)*

CLEEN ENERGY AG
Hollriglstrasse 8A, Haag, 3350, Amstetten, Austria
Tel.: (43) 743493080400
Web Site: https://www.cleen-energy.com
CLEN—(VIE)

Sales Range: Less than $1 Million
Lighting Equipment Mfr
N.A.I.C.S.: 335132
Lukas Scherzenlehner *(CEO & Member-Mgmt Bd)*

CLEEVE TECHNOLOGY INCORPORATED
716 Colonel Sam Drive, Oshawa, L1H 7Y2, ON, Canada
Tel.: (905) 579-9502
Web Site: http://www.cleevetech.com
Year Founded: 1998
Electrical Products Supplier
N.A.I.C.S.: 423610
Paul Church *(Pres)*

CLEGHORN MINERALS LTD.
152 Chemin de la Mine Ecole, Val d'Or, J9P 7B6, QC, Canada
Tel.: (819) 824-2808   BC
Web Site:
https://www.cleghornminerals.com
Year Founded: 2010
CZZ—(TSXV)
Assets: $28,052
Liabilities: $2,751
Net Worth: $25,301
Earnings: ($128,829)
Fiscal Year-end: 03/31/23
Investment Services
N.A.I.C.S.: 523999
Glenn J. Mullan *(CEO)*

CLEMENGER HARVIE EDGE
658 Church St, Richmond, Melbourne, 3121, VIC, Australia
Tel.: (61) 3 8416 6888
Year Founded: 1974
Emp.: 100
N.A.I.C.S.: 541810
Martin Griffin *(Chm)*

CLEMEX TECHNOLOGIES INC.
800 Guimond, Longueuil, J4G 1T5, QC, Canada
Tel.: (450) 651-6573   QC
Web Site: http://www.clemex.com
Year Founded: 1990
Image Analysis Solutions
N.A.I.C.S.: 334513
Caroline Trudel *(Treas, Sec & VP-Fin & Admin)*

CLEMONDO GROUP AB
Estrids Vag 23 A, Kristianstad, 291 65, Sweden
Tel.: (46) 38221980
CLEM—(OMX)
Rev.: $27,686,780
Assets: $18,642,167
Liabilities: $7,584,331
Net Worth: $11,057,836
Earnings: $988,743
Emp.: 54
Fiscal Year-end: 12/31/23
Renewable Energy Consulting Services
N.A.I.C.S.: 541690
Jesper Svensson *(CEO)*

CLENERGY (XIAMEN) TECHNOLOGY CO., LTD.
999-1009 Minan Rd Huoju Hi-tech Ind Dev Zone, Xiang an District, Xiamen, 361101, Fujian, China
Tel.: (86) 5923110088
Web Site:
https://www.clenergy.com.cn
Year Founded: 2007
603628—(SHG)
Rev.: $202,447,281
Assets: $317,579,142
Liabilities: $162,209,104
Net Worth: $155,370,038
Earnings: $15,357,064

Clenergy (Xiamen) Technology Co.,
Ltd.—(Continued)

Emp.: 500
Fiscal Year-end: 12/31/22
Solar Roof Mfr & Distr
N.A.I.C.S.: 335131

Subsidiaries:

Clean Energy (Thailand) Co.,
Ltd. (1)
9/2 5th Floor Vorasin Building Soi Yasoob 2
Viphavadee-rungsit Road, Chomphon Sub-
district Chatucha, Bangkok, 10900, Thailand
Tel.: (66) 632280200
Web Site: http://www.clenergythailand.com
Solar Mounting System Distr
N.A.I.C.S.: 423720

Clenergy America Inc (1)
400 Continental Blvd 6th Fl, El Segundo,
CA 90245
Tel.: (310) 426-2617
Web Site: http://www.clenergy.us
Solar Mounting System Distr
N.A.I.C.S.: 423720

Clenergy Europe Limited (1)
3 Old Rectory Mews Church Hill, Wootton,
Northampton, NN4 6LQ, United Kingdom
Tel.: (44) 1604877573
Web Site: http://www.clenergy.uk.com
Solar Mounting System Distr
N.A.I.C.S.: 423720

Clenergy Pty Ltd (1)
Ground Floor Unit 1 10 Duerdin Street,
Clayton, 3168, VIC, Australia
Tel.: (61) 392398088
Web Site: http://www.clenergy.com.au
Solar Mounting System Distr
N.A.I.C.S.: 423720

CLEOPATRA HOSPITALS

39 41 Cleopatra St, Heliopolis, Cairo,
Egypt
Tel.: (20) 224143931
Web Site:
   https://www.cleopatrahospitals.com
Year Founded: 2014
CLHO.CA—(EGX)
Rev.: $75,821,724
Assets: $94,648,575
Liabilities: $43,059,298
Net Worth: $51,589,277
Earnings: $9,987,011
Emp.: 4,600
Fiscal Year-end: 12/31/23
Healthcare Technology Services
N.A.I.C.S.: 621999
Ahmed Adel Badreldin *(Chm)*

Subsidiaries:

Al-Shorouk Hospital Company
S.A.E (1)
3 5 Bahr El Ghazal St Mohandiseen, Giza,
Egypt
Tel.: (20) 233044901
Hospital Operator
N.A.I.C.S.: 622110

CLEOPATRA INTERNATIONAL GROUP, INC.

No 12 Ying Chun Road 9th Floor, Hai
Wai Lian Yi Building, Luo Hu District,
Shenzhen, Guangdong, China
Tel.: (86) 755 8230 9541   NV
Sales Range: $1-9.9 Million
Emp.: 225
Beauty, Hair & Spa Services
N.A.I.C.S.: 812112
Yongping Xu *(CEO)*

CLERE AG

Bergkircherner Strasse 228, 32549,
Bad Oeynhausen, Germany
Tel.: (49) 5734 922 0   De
Web Site: http://www.clere.de
Holding Company
N.A.I.C.S.: 551112
Thomas van Aubel *(Chm-Supervisory Bd)*

CLERHP ESTRUCTURAS SA

Europa Avenue 3B Mezzanine 1,
30007, Murcia, Spain
Tel.: (34) 868481604
Web Site: https://www.clerhp.com
Building Construction Services
N.A.I.C.S.: 236220
Juan Andres Romero Hernandez
(Founder, Chm & CEO)

CLERMONT LEISURE (UK) LIMITED

60 Chiswell Street, London, EC1Y
4AG, United Kingdom
Tel.: (44) 2071380000
Year Founded: 2005
Gambling & Casinos
N.A.I.C.S.: 713210
Vanthan Hout *(Dir)*

CLESTRA HAUSERMAN S.A.

1 Route Du Docteur Albert
Schweitzer, PO Box 40309, 67411,
Illkirch-Graffenstaden, Cedex, France
Tel.: (33) 388309200
Web Site: http://www.en.clestra.com
Sales Range: $125-149.9 Million
Emp.: 1,000
Furniture Systems Mfr
N.A.I.C.S.: 337215
Xavier P. Negiar *(Chm, Pres & CEO)*

Subsidiaries:

CLESTRA CLEANROOM SA (1)
56 rue Jean Giraudoux, 67200, Strasbourg,
France
Tel.: (33) 388308730
Web Site: http://www.clestra-cleanroom.com
Industrial Construction Services
N.A.I.C.S.: 236210

Clestra B.V (1)
Weg en Bos 80 A, 2661 GZ, Bergschen-
hoek, Netherlands
Tel.: (31) 105210012
Furniture Whslr
N.A.I.C.S.: 423210

Clestra GmbH (1)
Dreieich Plaza 2a, Dreieich, 63303, Ger-
many
Tel.: (49) 61039960
Furniture Whslr
N.A.I.C.S.: 423210

Clestra Hauserman (100%)
Via San Giorgio 2, Parabiago, 20015, Milan,
Italy
Tel.: (39) 0331495201
Web Site: http://www.ipsclestra.com
Office Furniture Sale & Distr
N.A.I.C.S.: 449110

Clestra Hauserman Korea (1)
9th Fl Kotef Bldg 35 3 Yeido Dong, Yong-
dungpo Po Gu, 150 704, Seoul, Korea
(South) (50%)
Tel.: (82) 27846274
Web Site: http://www.clestra.co.kr
Sales Range: $25-49.9 Million
Emp.: 30
Provider of Furniture; Joint Venture of
Posco, Korea & Clestra Hauserman S.A.
N.A.I.C.S.: 337211

Clestra Hauserman Switzerland (1)
Ctr De Construction Crissier Chemin Du
Closalet 4, 1023, Cressier,
Switzerland (100%)
Tel.: (41) 216376622
Sales Range: $25-49.9 Million
Emp.: 30
Furniture Systems Mfr
N.A.I.C.S.: 337215
Niteo Migile *(Mng Dir)*

Clestra Hauserman, Inc. (1)
259 Veterans Ln Ste 201, Doylestown, PA
18901
Tel.: (267) 880-3700
Web Site: http://www.clestra.com
Sales Range: $25-49.9 Million
Emp.: 14
Movable Walls & Partitions Mfr, Designer &
Installer

N.A.I.C.S.: 238990
Remyi Cole *(Mgr-Sls-Houston)*

Clestra K.K. (1)
3-53-3 Sendagaya Yfl Bldg 3 4f, Shibuya,
Tokyo, 151-0051, Japan
Tel.: (81) 334234681
Furniture Whslr
N.A.I.C.S.: 423210

Clestra Limited (1)
Hamilton House 3 North Street, Carshalton,
SM5 2HZ, United Kingdom
Tel.: (44) 2087732121
Furniture Whslr
N.A.I.C.S.: 423210

Clestra Limited (1)
28 Yee Wo Street 13/F Hang Seng Cause-
way Bay Bldg, Causeway Bay, Hong Kong,
China (Hong Kong)
Tel.: (852) 25061681
Furniture Whslr
N.A.I.C.S.: 423210

CLEVELAND MINING COMPANY LIMITED

Suite 1 41 Walters Drive, Osborne
Park, 6017, WA, Australia
Tel.: (61) 86 389 6000
Web Site:
   http://www.clevelandmining.com.au
CDG—(ASX)
Sales Range: Less than $1 Million
Gold Mining & Exploration Services
N.A.I.C.S.: 212220
David Mendelawitz *(Mng Dir)*

CLEVER GLOBAL SA

Glorieta Fernando Quinones,
Tomares, Sevilla, Spain
Tel.: (34) 902105018
Web Site: https://www.clever-
   global.com
CLE—(MAD)
Sales Range: Less than $1 Million
Pharmaceutical Product Mfr & Distr
N.A.I.C.S.: 325412
Fernando Gutierrez Huerta *(Chm & CEO)*

CLEVO COMPANY

35F No 555 Siyuan Rd, Xinzhuang
Dist, New Taipei City, 242, Taiwan
Tel.: (886) 222789696
Web Site: http://www.clevo.com.tw
2362—(TAI)
Rev.: $797,271,071
Assets: $3,087,909,920
Liabilities: $1,741,123,974
Net Worth: $1,346,785,946
Earnings: $34,667,254
Emp.: 2,328
Fiscal Year-end: 12/31/23
Laptop Computers Mfr
N.A.I.C.S.: 334111
Kun-Tai Hsu *(Chm)*

CLICKDEALER ASIA PTE LTD.

Herengracht 124-128, Amsterdam,
Netherlands
Tel.: (31) 20 240 44 59
Web Site: http://www.clickdealer.com
Year Founded: 2012
Advertising Services
N.A.I.C.S.: 541810

Subsidiaries:

Fiksu, Inc. (1)
31 St James Ave Ste 1150, Boston, MA
02116
Tel.: (855) 463-4578
Web Site: http://www.fiksu.com
Sales Range: $10-24.9 Million
Emp.: 130
Mobile Application Marketing Solutions
N.A.I.C.S.: 541890
Micah Adler *(Founder, Pres & CEO)*

CLICKS GROUP LIMITED

Cnr Searle and Pontac Streets, PO

Box 5142, Cape Town, 8000, South
Africa
Tel.: (27) 214601911
Web Site:
   https://www.clicksgroup.co.za
Year Founded: 1968
CLCGY—(OTCIQ)
Rev.: $2,353,242,641
Assets: $1,005,231,044
Liabilities: $690,229,090
Net Worth: $315,001,954
Earnings: $134,006,908
Emp.: 17,865
Fiscal Year-end: 08/31/23
Health & Beauty Products Retailer;
DVDs, CDs & Gaming Software Re-
tailer
N.A.I.C.S.: 456120
Vikesh Ramsunder *(CEO)*

Subsidiaries:

Clicks Direct Medicines (Proprietary)
Limited (1)
PO Box 30480, Wibsey, Johannesburg,
1717, South Africa
Tel.: (27) 102103300
Web Site:
   http://www.clicksdirectmedicines.co.za
Pharmaceutical Product Whslr
N.A.I.C.S.: 424210

Kalahari Medical Distributors (Propri-
etary) Limited (1)
Unit 1-3 Plot 25001 Makgadigau Rd,
G/West Industrial, Gaborone, Botswana
Tel.: (267) 3934750
Web Site: https://kalaharimedical.com
Sales Range: $25-49.9 Million
Emp.: 60
Pharmaceutical Products Distr
N.A.I.C.S.: 424210

New Clicks South Africa (Proprietary)
Limited (1)
14 Tamar Avenue, Florida, 1709, Western
Cape, South Africa
Tel.: (27) 114701000
Pharmaceuticals Product Mfr
N.A.I.C.S.: 325412

United Pharmaceutical Distributors
(Proprietary) Limited (1)
14 Tamar Avenue, Roodepoort, 1709, South
Africa
Tel.: (27) 114701000
Web Site: https://upd.co.za
Sales Range: $75-99.9 Million
Emp.: 1,500
Pharmaceutical Product Whslr
N.A.I.C.S.: 424210
Vikash Singh *(Mng Dir)*

CLIENT SERVICE INTERNA-TIONAL, INC.

A1601 Fenglian Plaza No 18 Cha-
owai Street, Chaoyang District, Bei-
jing, 100020, China
Tel.: (86) 1065880766
Web Site: http://www.csii.com.cn
Year Founded: 1999
300663—(SSE)
Rev.: $165,138,480
Assets: $410,302,152
Liabilities: $228,513,636
Net Worth: $181,788,516
Earnings: $3,035,448
Fiscal Year-end: 12/31/22
Software Product Development Ser-
vices
N.A.I.C.S.: 541511
Wang Anjing *(Chm & Gen Mgr)*

CLIENTELE LIMITED

Clientele Office Park Corner Rivonia
& Alon Road, Morningside, Sandton,
2196, South Africa
Tel.: (27) 113203000   ZA
Web Site: https://www.clientele.co.za
CLI—(JSE)
Rev.: $117,231,382
Assets: $642,058,957

Liabilities: $580,114,809
Net Worth: $61,944,148
Earnings: $25,880,026
Emp.: 3,663
Fiscal Year-end: 06/30/23
Holding Company; Insurance & Investment Products & Services
N.A.I.C.S.: 551112
Brenda-Lee Du Toit *(Dir-Strategic Ops)*

Subsidiaries:

Clientele Life Assurance Company Limited   (1)
Clientele Office Park Corner Rivonia and Alon Roads, Morningside, Sandton, 2196, Gauterng, South Africa
Tel.: (27) 113203000
Web Site: https://www.clientele.co.za
Life Insurance Products & Services
N.A.I.C.S.: 524113
Basil William Reekie *(Mng Dir)*

CLIFFMONT RESOURCES LTD.
1305 - 1090 West Georgia Street, Vancouver, V6E 3V7, BC, Canada
Tel.: (604) 808-4686
Year Founded: 2006
CMO.H—(TSXV)
Assets: $45,728
Liabilities: $521,483
Net Worth: ($475,755)
Earnings: $27,438
Emp.: 25
Fiscal Year-end: 09/30/22
Mineral Exploration Services
N.A.I.C.S.: 213115

CLIFFORD MODERN LIVING HOLDINGS LIMITED
8 Shiguang Road Panyu, Guangzhou, 511496, Guangdong, China
Tel.: (86) 2084771409   Ky
Web Site:
  http://www.cliffordmodernliving.com
3686—(HKG)
Rev.: $53,756,633
Assets: $118,371,521
Liabilities: $28,712,502
Net Worth: $89,659,019
Earnings: $13,357,656
Emp.: 630
Fiscal Year-end: 12/31/22
Residential Property Management Services
N.A.I.C.S.: 531311
Lai Hung Man *(Founder, Chm & CEO)*

CLIFFSIDE LTD.
11 Church Street Suite 200, Toronto, M5E 1W1, ON, Canada
Tel.: (647) 226-4894   Ca
Year Founded: 2024
Investment Services
N.A.I.C.S.: 523999
Michael Stein *(Owner)*

Subsidiaries:

Cliffside Capital Ltd.   (1)
11 Church St Suite 200, Toronto, M5E 1W1, ON, Canada
Tel.: (647) 226-4894
Web Site: https://www.cliffsidecapital.ca
Rev.: $12,422,975
Assets: $93,668,842
Liabilities: $86,483,600
Net Worth: $7,185,243
Earnings: $611,929
Fiscal Year-end: 12/31/2023
Holding Company
N.A.I.C.S.: 551112

CLIFTON ASSET MANAGEMENT PLC
The Pavilions Eden Park, Ham

Green, Bristol, BS20 0DD, United Kingdom
Tel.: (44) 1275 813 700
Web Site: http://www.clifton-asset.co.uk
Year Founded: 1986
Sales Range: $1-9.9 Million
Emp.: 90
Financial & Consulting Services
N.A.I.C.S.: 525990
Adam Tavener *(Chm)*

Subsidiaries:

Clifton Consulting Ltd   (1)
The Pavilions Ham Green, Bristol, BS20 0DD, United Kingdom
Tel.: (44) 1275 813700
Web Site: http://www.cliftonasset.co.uk
Emp.: 10
Business & Exit Strategy Planning
N.A.I.C.S.: 541611
Neil Greenaway *(Mng Dir)*

Clifton Wealth Ltd   (1)
The Pavilions Eden Park Ham Green, Bristol, BS20 0DD, United Kingdom
Tel.: (44) 1275 813700
Web Site: http://www.clifton-wealth.com
Emp.: 20
Wealth Management, Employee Benefits & Protection
N.A.I.C.S.: 523940
Jo Purcell *(Gen Mgr)*

Morgan Lloyd Administration Ltd   (1)
The Outlook Ham Green, Bristol, BS20 0DD, United Kingdom
Tel.: (44) 8431781272
Web Site: http://www.morgan-lloyd.co.uk
Investment Management Consulting Services
N.A.I.C.S.: 541611

CLIMALEVEL ENERGIESYSTEME GMBH
Kolner Strasse 60 Loevenich, 50859, Cologne, Germany
Tel.: (49) 22198880300
Web Site: http://www.climalevel.com
Surface Heating & Cooling System Mfr
N.A.I.C.S.: 334512

CLIMATE HUMAN CAPITAL PLC
104A Park Street, Mayfair, London, W1K 6NG, United Kingdom
Tel.: (44) 20 7318 1244
Web Site:
  http://www.climatecapital.com
Recruitment Services
N.A.I.C.S.: 541612

CLIMATE TECHNOLOGIES PTY LTD
26 Nylex Ave, Salisbury, 5108, SA, Australia
Tel.: (61) 883075100
Web Site:
  http://www.climatetechnologies.com
Sales Range: $50-74.9 Million
Emp.: 400
Refrigeration & Heating Equipment Mfr
N.A.I.C.S.: 333415
Ted Celi *(Mng Dir)*

CLIMATEROCK
25 Bedford Square, London, WC1B 3HH, United Kingdom
Tel.: (44) 2080507820   Ky
Web Site: https://www.climate-rock.com
Year Founded: 2021
CLRC—(NASDAQ)
Rev.: $1,092,273
Assets: $81,557,355
Liabilities: $84,887,322
Net Worth: ($3,329,967)
Earnings: ($675,874)

Emp.: 2
Fiscal Year-end: 12/31/22
Investment Services
N.A.I.C.S.: 523150
Per Regnarsson *(CEO)*

CLIME CAPITAL LIMITED
Level 12 20 Hunter Street, Sydney, 2000, NSW, Australia
Tel.: (61) 1300788568   AU
Web Site: http://clime.com.au
CAM—(ASX)
Rev.: $6,034,288
Assets: $106,881,883
Liabilities: $25,596,121
Net Worth: $81,285,762
Earnings: $2,889,600
Fiscal Year-end: 06/30/24
Investment Management Service
N.A.I.C.S.: 523999
Ronni Chalmers *(Board of Directors & Dir-Investment)*

Subsidiaries:

CBG Capital Limited   (1)
Level 7 1 Market Street, PO Box Q1286, Sydney, 2000, NSW, Australia
Tel.: (61) 2 8599 1160
Web Site: http://www.cbgcapital.com.au
Rev.: $2,866,740
Assets: $21,074,791
Liabilities: $770,344
Net Worth: $20,304,447
Earnings: $1,860,688
Fiscal Year-end: 06/30/2018
Investment Management Service
N.A.I.C.S.: 523940
Scott Maddock *(Portfolio Mgr)*

CLIME INVESTMENT MANAGEMENT LIMITED
L12 20 Hunter St, Sydney, 2000, NSW, Australia
Tel.: (61) 1300788568   AU
Web Site: https://www.clime.com.au
CIW—(ASX)
Rev.: $7,911,405
Assets: $18,471,319
Liabilities: $4,544,770
Net Worth: $13,926,548
Earnings: ($2,211,930)
Emp.: 7
Fiscal Year-end: 06/30/24
Holding Company; Investment Fund Management Services
N.A.I.C.S.: 551112
Neil Schafer *(Acting Co-CEO & Chm)*

Subsidiaries:

Clime Asset Management Pty. Ltd.   (1)
Level 7 1 Market Street, Sydney, 2000, NSW, Australia
Tel.: (61) 2 9252 8522
Web Site: http://www.clime.com.au
Sales Range: $25-49.9 Million
Emp.: 16
Investment Fund Management Services
N.A.I.C.S.: 523940
Rod Bristow *(Grp CEO)*

Optimise Media Group Limited   (1)
Exchange Street Buildings 35-37 Exchange Street, Norwich, NR2 1DP, United Kingdom
Tel.: (44) 1603697700
Web Site: https://optimisemedia.com
Emp.: 160
Mobile Advertising Services
N.A.I.C.S.: 541810

CLIMEON AB
Torshamnsgatan 44, 164 40, Stockholm, Sweden
Tel.: (46) 852800399
Web Site: https://www.climeon.com
Year Founded: 2011
CLIME.B—(OMX)
Rev.: $614,093
Assets: $42,088,273
Liabilities: $9,940,140

Net Worth: $32,148,133
Earnings: ($13,477,972)
Emp.: 40
Fiscal Year-end: 12/31/23
Renewable Energy Consulting Services
N.A.I.C.S.: 541690
Thomas Ostrom *(CEO)*

CLINICA DE MARLY SA
Calle 50 No 9-67, Bogota, Colombia
Tel.: (57) 13436600
Web Site: https://www.marly.com.co
CLIN.MARLY—(COLO)
Sales Range: Less than $1 Million
Health Care Srvices
N.A.I.C.S.: 621999
Luis Eduardo Cavelier Castro *(Gen Mgr)*

CLINICA LAS CONDES S.A.
Lo Fontecilla 441, PO Box 27014, Santiago, Chile
Tel.: (56) 2111002
Web Site: http://www.clc.cl
Year Founded: 1982
LAS.CONDES—(SGO)
Sales Range: $200-249.9 Million
Hospital Services
N.A.I.C.S.: 622110
Gonzalo Grebe Noguera *(CEO)*

CLINICAL COMPUTING PLC
IP City Centre 1 Bath Street, Ipswich, IP2 8SD, United Kingdom
Tel.: (44) 1473694760
Web Site: http://www.ccl.com
Year Founded: 1979
Sales Range: $1-9.9 Million
Emp.: 40
Clinical Information Management Software Developer
N.A.I.C.S.: 513210
Joseph G. Marlovits *(Sec & Dir-Fin)*

Subsidiaries:

Clinical Computing, Inc.   (1)
205 W 4th St Ste 810, Cincinnati, OH 45202
Tel.: (513) 651-3803
Web Site: http://www.ccl.com
Software Development & Support Services
N.A.I.C.S.: 541511
Barb Robinette *(Office Mgr)*

CLINICAL DESIGN TECHNOLOGIES LTD.
The Gallery Kingswharf The Quay, Exeter, EX2 4AN, United Kingdom
Tel.: (44) 1326352054
Medical Device Mfr
N.A.I.C.S.: 339112

CLINICAL GENOMICS PTY. LTD.
2 Eden Park Dr, 11 Julius Ave, North Ryde, 2113, NSW, Australia
Tel.: (61) 298875300
Web Site:
  http://www.clinicalgenomics.com
Cancer Diagnosis & Screening Products Mfr
N.A.I.C.S.: 339112
Lawrence LaPointe *(Co-Founder, Pres & Mng Dir)*

Subsidiaries:

Enterix Inc.   (1)
236 Fernwood Ave, Edison, NJ 08837
Tel.: (732) 346-1111
Web Site: http://www.insuretest.com
Biotechnology Products Mfr
N.A.I.C.S.: 541714

CLINICAL LASERTHERMIA SYSTEMS AB

Clinical Laserthermia Systems AB—(Continued)

Scheelevagen 2, 223 81, Lund, Sweden
Tel.: (46) 46152100
Web Site:
http://www.clinicallaser.com
CLS.B—(OMX)
Rev.: $162,366
Assets: $5,420,352
Liabilities: $3,719,778
Net Worth: $1,700,574
Earnings: ($7,073,315)
Emp.: 18
Fiscal Year-end: 12/31/20
Medical Equipment Mfr & Distr
N.A.I.C.S.: 339112
Lars-Erik Eriksson (CEO)

Subsidiaries:

Clinical Laserthermia Systems Americas Inc.   (1)
15707 Rockfield Blvd Ste 130, Irvine, CA 92618
Tel.: (949) 504-5440
Health Care Srvices
N.A.I.C.S.: 621999

CLINICAL TRIAL CONSULTANTS AB
Dag Hammarskjolds vag 10B, 752 37, Uppsala, Sweden
Tel.: (46) 186111306
Web Site: http://www.ctc-ab.se
Year Founded: 2011
Holding Company; Pharmaceutical, Clinical Research & Development Services
N.A.I.C.S.: 325412
Anders Millerhovf (CEO)

Subsidiaries:

Recipharm Uppsala AB   (1)
BjorKgatan, 753 23, Uppsala, Sweden
Tel.: (46) 18 16 40 00
Web Site: http://www.recipharm.com
Sales Range: $50-74.9 Million
Emp.: 240
Contract Pharmaceutical Research, Development & Manufacturing Services
N.A.I.C.S.: 325412
Carl Mikael Ericson (CEO)

CLINOMICS INC.
Suite 301-3 Bldg 110 Unist 50 Unist-Gil, Eonyang-Eup Ulju-Gun, Ulsan, Korea (South)
Tel.: (82) 7082866966
Web Site: https://www.clinomics.com
Year Founded: 2011
352770—(KRS)
Rev.: $17,704,778
Assets: $74,478,740
Liabilities: $33,676,829
Net Worth: $40,801,911
Earnings: ($7,849,797)
Emp.: 90
Fiscal Year-end: 12/31/22
Pharmaceutical Preparation Mfr
N.A.I.C.S.: 325412
Byung-Chul Kim (CEO & CEO-Genetics Expert)

CLINUVEL PHARMACEUTICALS LIMITED
Level 22 535 Bourke Street, Melbourne, 3000, VIC, Australia
Tel.: (61) 396604900   AU
Web Site: https://www.clinuvel.com
CLVLF—(OTCIQ)
Rev.: $50,355,763
Assets: $110,292,696
Liabilities: $14,090,613
Net Worth: $96,202,083
Earnings: $15,996,871
Emp.: 40
Fiscal Year-end: 06/30/22
Pharmaceuticals Mfr

N.A.I.C.S.: 325412
Philippe J. Wolgen (CEO & Mng Dir)

Subsidiaries:

Clinuvel (UK) Ltd.   (1)
Wesley House Bull Hill, Leatherhead, KT22 7AH, United Kingdom
Tel.: (44) 137 286 0765
Biotechnology Research Services
N.A.I.C.S.: 541714

Clinuvel AG   (1)
Neuhosstrasse 3D, 6340, Baar, Switzerland
Tel.: (41) 442537500
Sales Range: $25-49.9 Million
Emp.: 15
Pharmaceutical Preparation Mfr
N.A.I.C.S.: 325412

CLIO
27 Rue Du Hameau, 75015, Paris, France
Tel.: (33) 826101082
Web Site: http://www.clio.fr
Sales Range: $25-49.9 Million
Emp.: 51
Travel Agency
N.A.I.C.S.: 561510
Remy Boucharlat (Dir-CNRS Research)

CLIO COSMETICS CO LTD
66 Wangsimni-ro, Seongdong-gu, Seoul, Korea (South)
Tel.: (82) 800801510
Web Site:
https://www.cliocosmetic.com
Year Founded: 1997
237880—(KRS)
Rev.: $208,973,328
Assets: $187,060,172
Liabilities: $41,041,577
Net Worth: $146,018,595
Earnings: $7,768,844
Emp.: 327
Fiscal Year-end: 12/31/22
Cosmetic Product Mfr & Distr
N.A.I.C.S.: 325620
Hyun Ok Han (CEO)

CLIO INFOTECH LTD.
901/902 9th Floor Atlanta Centre Sonawala Lane Opp Udyog Bhavan, Goregaon East, Mumbai, 400 063, India
Tel.: (91) 2243211855
Web Site: http://www.clioinfotech.com
530839—(BOM)
Rev.: $27,142
Assets: $2,567,831
Liabilities: $1,031,541
Net Worth: $1,536,290
Earnings: ($60,092)
Emp.: 3
Fiscal Year-end: 03/31/21
Financial Support Services
N.A.I.C.S.: 523999
Sureshkumar Babulal Bafna (Chm & Mng Dir)

CLIP CORPORATION
Building 7F 1810 Uchiyama 3chome, Chikusa-ku, Nagoya, 464-0075, Aichi, Japan
Tel.: (81) 527325200
Web Site: https://www.clip-cor.co.jp
Year Founded: 1981
4705—(TKS)
Rev.: $20,067,960
Assets: $38,133,090
Liabilities: $4,765,810
Net Worth: $33,367,280
Earnings: $575,070
Emp.: 193
Fiscal Year-end: 03/31/24
Education Services
N.A.I.C.S.: 611710

CLIPPER LOGISTICS GROUP LTD.
Carlton Court Gelderd Road, Leeds, LS12 6LT, West Yorkshire, United Kingdom
Tel.: (44) 113 204 2050
Web Site:
http://www.clippergroup.co.uk
Year Founded: 1992
Sales Range: $250-299.9 Million
Emp.: 1,957
Logistic Services
N.A.I.C.S.: 541614
Steve Parkin (Chm)

Subsidiaries:

Clipper Logistics KG GmbH & Co.   (1)
Industriering Ost 93, 47906, Kempen, Germany
Tel.: (49) 21529105031
Web Site: http://www.clipperlogistics.de
Logistics Consulting Servies
N.A.I.C.S.: 541614

Northern Commercials (Mirfield) Ltd   (1)
Armytage Road, Brighouse, HD6 1PG, West Yorkshire, United Kingdom
Tel.: (44) 1484380111
Web Site: http://www.nor-com.co.uk
New & Used Automobile Dealer
N.A.I.C.S.: 441110
John Bullock (Dir-Mktg & Sls)

CLIPPER VENTURES PLC
Unit 1A Granary & Bakery, Royal Clarence Marina Weevil Lane, Gosport, PO12 1FX, United Kingdom
Tel.: (44) 2392526000   UK
Web Site: http://www.clipper-ventures.com
Sales Range: $10-24.9 Million
Emp.: 62
Boat & Yacht Race Organizer
N.A.I.C.S.: 711320
William Ward (CEO)

CLIQ DIGITAL AG
Grunstrasse 8, 40212, Dusseldorf, Germany
Tel.: (49) 2119350706
Web Site: https://www.cliqdigital.com
Year Founded: 2005
CLIQ—(DEU)
Rev.: $297,933,305
Assets: $145,802,935
Liabilities: $58,055,256
Net Worth: $87,747,680
Earnings: $31,246,493
Emp.: 139
Fiscal Year-end: 12/31/22
Mobile Entertainment & Game Development Services
N.A.I.C.S.: 513210
Ben Bos (Member-Mgmt Bd)

Subsidiaries:

Rheinkraft Production GmbH   (1)
Grunstrasse 8, 40212, Dusseldorf, Germany
Tel.: (49) 21195589893
Web Site: https://www.rheinkraft-production.de
Online Entertainment & Information Services
N.A.I.C.S.: 513210

CLIVE CHRISTIAN FURNITURE LIMITED
St Germaine St, Farnworth, Bolton, BL4 7 BG, United Kingdom
Tel.: (44) 1204702200   UK
Web Site:
http://www.clivechristian.clive.com
Year Founded: 1978
Emp.: 85
Luxury Wood Home Interior Products Designer, Mfr & Distr

N.A.I.C.S.: 337122
Guy Newton (Mng Dir)

CLIVE CHRISTIAN LIMITED
56 Haymarket, London, SW1 Y4RN, United Kingdom
Tel.: (44) 2078395345   UK
Web Site: http://www.clive.com
Year Founded: 1978
Sales Range: $25-49.9 Million
Emp.: 100
Holding Company; Perfume & Luxury Wood Home Interior Products Designer, Mfr & Distr
N.A.I.C.S.: 551112
Clive Christian (Founder & Chm)

Subsidiaries:

Clive Christian Perfume Limited   (1)
56 Haymarket, London, SW1Y 4RN, United Kingdom
Tel.: (44) 2078393434
Web Site: http://perfume.clive.com
Sales Range: $50-74.9 Million
Emp.: 7
Perfume Developer & Distr
N.A.I.C.S.: 424210

CLK HOLDING A.S.
Turan Gunes Blv Ilkbahar Mah 606 Sok No 24, Cankaya, 06550, Ankara, Turkiye
Tel.: (90) 312 491 64 00
Web Site: http://www.karkim.com
Year Founded: 2007
Holding Company
N.A.I.C.S.: 551112

CLOETTA AB
Landsvagen 50A, PO Box 2052, SE-174 02, Sundbyberg, Sweden
Tel.: (46) 852728800   SE
Web Site: https://www.cloetta.com
Year Founded: 1862
CLA.B—(OMX)
Rev.: $695,245,600
Assets: $1,130,094,560
Liabilities: $619,922,240
Net Worth: $510,172,320
Earnings: $34,304,480
Emp.: 2,653
Fiscal Year-end: 12/31/20
Chocolate Mfr
N.A.I.C.S.: 311351
Ewald Frenay (Pres-Middle)

Subsidiaries:

Candyking Holding AB   (1)
Englundavagen 7, PO Box 6036, SE-171 06, Solna, Sweden
Tel.: (46) 8 795 03 00
Web Site: http://www.candyking.com
Holding Company; Candy Whslr
N.A.I.C.S.: 551112
Frida Akerblom (CFO & VP-Bus Support)

Subsidiary (Non-US):

Candyking Danmark A/S   (2)
Kertemindevej 58-60, 8940, Randers, Denmark
Tel.: (45) 8 640 5499
Web Site: https://candyking.com
Candy Distr
N.A.I.C.S.: 424450

Candyking Finland Oy   (2)
Lemminkaisenkatu 32, PO Box 406, 20101, Turku, Finland
Tel.: (358) 10 303 41
Web Site: http://www.candyking.com
Candy Whlsr
N.A.I.C.S.: 424450

Candyking Norge AS   (2)
Engebrets vei 3, N-0275, Oslo, Norway
Tel.: (47) 69 35 58 88
Web Site: http://www.candyking.com
Candy Mfr
N.A.I.C.S.: 424450

Candyking Poland Sp. z o.o. (2)
Ul Bytomska 5, 01-612, Warsaw, Poland
Tel.: (48) 22 864 24 97
Web Site: http://www.candyking.pl
Candy Distr
N.A.I.C.S.: 424450

Subsidiary (Domestic):

Candyking Sweden AB (2)
Englundavagen 7, PO Box 6036, SE-171
06, Solna, Sweden
Tel.: (46) 8 795 03 00
Web Site: http://www.candyking.com
Candy Whlsr
N.A.I.C.S.: 424450

Subsidiary (Non-US):

Candyking UK Ltd. (2)
Fort Southwick James Callaghan Drive,
Fareham, PO17 6AR, Hants, United King-
dom
Tel.: (44) 2392 630 300
Web Site: http://www.candyking.com
Candy Whlsr
N.A.I.C.S.: 424450
Graham Richardson (Mng Dir)

Candymix Ireland Ltd. (2)
Unit 12 North Street Business Park,
Swords, Dublin, Ireland
Tel.: (353) 18700 920
Web Site: http://www.candyking.com
Candy Whlsr
N.A.I.C.S.: 424450

Cloetta Deutschland GmbH (1)
Neutorplatz 3, 46395, Bocholt, Germany
Tel.: (49) 2871272410
Chocolate Mfr
N.A.I.C.S.: 311352

Cloetta Holland B.V. (1)
Hoevestein 26, 4903 SC, Oosterhout, Neth-
erlands
Tel.: (31) 162 485 485
Web Site: http://www.cloetta.com
Emp.: 345
Confectionery Mfr
N.A.I.C.S.: 311352
Jacqueline Hoogerbrugge (Pres-Ops)

Subsidiary (Non-US):

Cloetta Danmark ApS (2)
Vallensbaekvej 18 D, 2605, Brondby, Den-
mark
Tel.: (45) 5 856 5555
Web Site: https://www.cloetta.dk
Emp.: 35
Confectionery Mfr & Distr
N.A.I.C.S.: 311352

Subsidiary (Domestic):

Malaco K/S (3)
Fabriksvej 6, 4200, Slagelse, Denmark
Tel.: (45) 58565555
Web Site: http://www.malacoleaf.com
Sales Range: $1-9.9 Million
Sugar Production
N.A.I.C.S.: 311313

Subsidiary (Non-US):

Cloetta Italia S.r.l. (2)
Via Milano 16, 26100, Cremona, Italy
Tel.: (39) 0372 4821
Web Site: http://cloetta.it
Emp.: 465
Confectionery Mfr & Distr
N.A.I.C.S.: 311352

Subsidiary (Domestic):

Sperlari, S.r.l. (3)
Via Milano 16, 26100, Cremona, Italy
Tel.: (39) 03724821
Web Site: http://www.sperlari.it
Confectionery Mfr
N.A.I.C.S.: 311340

Subsidiary (Non-US):

Cloetta Norge AS (2)
Fjordveien 3, 1363, Hovik, Norway
Tel.: (47) 6 781 8100
Web Site: https://www.cloetta.no
Emp.: 40
Confectionery Mfr & Distr

N.A.I.C.S.: 311352

RBV Leaf Belgium N.V. (2)
Everdongenlaan 25, 2300, Turnhout, Bel-
gium
Tel.: (32) 14405311
Sales Range: $25-49.9 Million
Emp.: 25
Confectionery
N.A.I.C.S.: 445292

Cloetta Suomi Oy (1)
Tel.: (358) 1030341
Chocolate Mfr
N.A.I.C.S.: 311352
Timo Lahermaa (Acct Mgr)

Cloetta Sverige AB (1)
Hjalmar Svenfelts vaeg, 590 69, Ljungsbro,
Ostergotland, Sweden
Tel.: (46) 13285000
Sales Range: $25-49.9 Million
Emp.: 200
Chocolate Mfr
N.A.I.C.S.: 311351
Thomas Wiesgickl (Mgr-Pur)

Cloetta UK Ltd. (1)
Fort Southwick James Callaghan Drive,
Fareham, PO17 6AR, Hampshire, United
Kingdom
Tel.: (44) 2392630300
Web Site: https://cloetta.co.uk
Confectionery Product Mfr & Distr
N.A.I.C.S.: 311352

CLOETTA NUTISAL AB
Andesitgatan 8, 254 68, Helsingborg,
Sweden
Tel.: (46) 42388388
Chocolate Mfr
N.A.I.C.S.: 311352

CLONTARF ENERGY PLC
162 Clontarf Road, Dublin, D03
F6Y0, Ireland
Tel.: (353) 18332833
Web Site:
　　https://www.clontarfenergy.com
CLON—(LSE)
Assets: $2,246,474
Liabilities: $1,858,549
Net Worth: $387,925
Earnings: ($1,107,652)
Fiscal Year-end: 12/31/23
Oil & Gas Exploration & Production
Services
N.A.I.C.S.: 211120
David Horgan (Mng Dir)

CLOOPEN GROUP HOLDING LIMITED
16/F Tower A Fairmont Tower 33
Guangshun North Main Street, Cha-
oyang District, Beijing, 100015, China
Tel.: (86) 1064775672　　　　Ky
Year Founded: 2014
RAASY—(OTCEM)
Rev.: $86,017,567
Assets: $335,166,886
Liabilities: $109,131,290
Net Worth: $226,035,596
Earnings: ($141,407,765)
Emp.: 1,397
Fiscal Year-end: 12/31/22
Holding Company
N.A.I.C.S.: 551112
Changxun Sun (Chm & CEO)

CLOSE BROTHERS GROUP PLC
10 Crown Place, London, EC2A 4FT,
United Kingdom
Tel.: (44) 2076553100
Web Site:
　　https://www.closebrothers.com
CBGL—(LSE)
Rev.: $1,462,082,909
Assets: $17,796,764,377
Liabilities: $15,468,023,228
Net Worth: $2,328,741,149

Earnings: $126,895,854
Emp.: 3,642
Fiscal Year-end: 07/31/24
Bank Holding Company; Merchant
Banking, Securities Brokerage &
Portfolio Management Services
N.A.I.C.S.: 551112
Martin Andrew (CEO-Asset Mgmt)

Subsidiaries:

Close Asset Management Holdings
Limited (1)
10 Exchange Square Primrose Street, Lon-
don, EC2A 2BY, United Kingdom
Tel.: (44) 2074264000
Property Management Services
N.A.I.C.S.: 531311

Subsidiary (Domestic):

Chartwell Group Limited (2)
17 Queen Street, Mayfair, London, W1J
5PH, United Kingdom
Tel.: (44) 207 409 0545
Web Site: https://www.chartwell-group.com
Sales Range: $10-24.9 Million
Emp.: 80
Corporate & Private Investment & Fund
Management Services
N.A.I.C.S.: 523940

Close Brewery Rentals Limited (1)
Unit 1 Kingfisher Park Headlands Business
Park, Ringwood, BH24 3NX, Hampshire,
United Kingdom
Tel.: (44) 1425485421
Web Site:
　　https://www.closebreweryrentals.co.uk
Breweries Container Rental Services
N.A.I.C.S.: 532490

Close Brothers Asset Finance
GmbH (1)
Grosse Bleiche 35-39, 55116, Mainz, Ger-
many
Tel.: (49) 61314909200
Web Site: http://www.closeassetfinance.de
Asset Finance Services
N.A.I.C.S.: 921130

Close Brothers Limited (1)
10 Crown Place, London, EC2A 4FT,
United Kingdom
Tel.: (44) 2083394949
Web Site:
　　https://www.closeassetfinance.co.uk
Equipment Leasing & Asset Financing Ser-
vices
N.A.I.C.S.: 532412

Close Brothers Vehicle Hire
Limited (1)
Lows Lane Stanton by Dale, Ilkeston, DE7
4QU, Derbyshire, United Kingdom
Tel.: (44) 8082585198
Web Site:
　　https://www.closebrothersvehiclehire.co.uk
Transportation Services
N.A.I.C.S.: 485999
Terry Ottey (Mng Dir)

Close Finance (CI) Limited (1)
Conway House Conway Street, Saint He-
lier, JE4 5SR, Jersey
Tel.: (44) 1534737341
Web Site: https://www.closefinanceci.com
Financial Investment Services
N.A.I.C.S.: 523999
Ruth Martin (Dir-Ops)

Close Premium Finance (1)
21st Floor Tolworth Tower Ewell Road, To-
worth, Surbiton, KT6 7EL, Surrey, United
Kingdom
Tel.: (44) 8702430026
Web Site: http://www.closepf.com
Sales Range: $200-249.9 Million
Emp.: 300
Premium Finance Products & Services
N.A.I.C.S.: 525990
John Willmott (COO)

Subsidiary (Non-US):

Close Premium Finance Ireland (2)
Building 1 Swift Square Santry Demesne,
Northwood, Dublin, 9, Ireland
Tel.: (353) 18622560

Web Site: https://www.closebrotherspf.ie
Premium Finance Products & Services
N.A.I.C.S.: 525990

Commercial Acceptances Limited (1)
8th Floor 101 Wigmore Street, London,
W1U 1QU, United Kingdom
Tel.: (44) 2038576350
Web Site: https://www.acceptances.co.uk
Short Team Loan Services
N.A.I.C.S.: 522291
Daniel Hertz (Mng Dir)

Corporate Asset Solutions
Limited (1)
Manor Farm Chilworth Old Village, South-
ampton, SO16 7JP, United Kingdom
Tel.: (44) 2382556934
Web Site: https://www.corporateasset.co.uk
Asset Management Services
N.A.I.C.S.: 523940

Winterflood Securities Limited (1)
The Atrium Building Cannon Bridge House
25 Dowgate Hill, London, EC4R 2GA,
United Kingdom
Tel.: (44) 2031000000
Emp.: 3,700
Securities Brokerage Services
N.A.I.C.S.: 523150

CLOSE THE LOOP LIMITED
43-47 Cleeland Road, Oakleigh
South, Melbourne, 3167, VIC, Austra-
lia
Tel.: (61) 1800242473　　　　AU
Web Site:
　　https://www.ctlgroup.com.au
Year Founded: 2001
CLG—(ASX)
Rev.: $88,631,414
Assets: $176,943,992
Liabilities: $96,054,639
Net Worth: $80,889,353
Earnings: $7,979,396
Fiscal Year-end: 06/30/23
Recycling Services
N.A.I.C.S.: 562111
Lawrence Jaffe (Chief Comml Officer)

Subsidiaries:

Crasti & Company Pty. Ltd. (1)
43-47 Cleeland Road, Oakleigh, 3167, VIC,
Australia
Tel.: (61) 294824822
Web Site: https://crasti.com.au
Sand & Landscaping Distr
N.A.I.C.S.: 423840

Foster International Packaging (Pty.)
Ltd. (1)
Unit 1 29 Bell Crescent Westlake Business
Park Westlake, Cape Town, 7945, South
Africa
Tel.: (27) 217011311
Web Site: https://fosterpackaging.com
Custom Packaging Services
N.A.I.C.S.: 561910

CLOUD AIR CO., LTD.
170 Sinwon-ro, Yeongtong-gu, Su-
won, Gyeonggi-do, Korea (South)
Tel.: (82) 312055300
Web Site: http://www.ctlinc.co.kr
Year Founded: 1993
036170—(KRS)
Rev.: $10,292,234
Assets: $86,922,785
Liabilities: $2,035,065
Net Worth: $84,887,720
Earnings: $3,204,572
Emp.: 46
Fiscal Year-end: 12/31/22
Printed Circuit Board Mfr
N.A.I.C.S.: 334412

CLOUD DX, INC.
100 - 72 Victoria Street South, Kitch-
ener, N2G 4Y9, ON, Canada
Tel.: (289) 488-1699
Web Site: https://www.clouddx.com
Year Founded: 2019

Cloud DX, Inc.—(Continued)

CDXFF—(OTCIQ)
Rev.: $1,368,183
Assets: $1,541,583
Liabilities: $14,990,244
Net Worth: ($13,448,661)
Earnings: ($7,812,137)
Emp.: 39
Fiscal Year-end: 12/31/23
Business Consulting Services
N.A.I.C.S.: 522299

CLOUD GLOBAL LTD.
Unit 7 No 1 Cargo Building Campsie
Drive Glasgow International Airport,
Paisley, PA3 2SG, United Kingdom
Tel.: (44) 141 447 0245
Web Site:
http://www.cloudglobal.co.uk
Year Founded: 2010
Aviation Services
N.A.I.C.S.: 336412

CLOUD INVESTMENT HOLD-INGS LIMITED
Unit B 7th Floor Connaught Harbour-front House, 35-36 Connaught Road
West, Sheung Wan, China (Hong
Kong)
Tel.: (852) 3104 8095   Ky
Web Site: http://www.cloud-grp.com
Year Founded: 1995
Sales Range: $1-9.9 Million
Holding Company
N.A.I.C.S.: 551112
Yu Keung Poon (Exec Dir)

Subsidiaries:

Q9 Technology Company Limited (1)
Suite 206 2/F Hewlett Centre 52-54 Hoi
Yuen Road Kwun Tong, Kowloon, China
(Hong Kong)
Tel.: (852) 25202226
Web Site: http://www.q9tech.com
Software Development Services
N.A.I.C.S.: 541511

CLOUD LIVE TECHNOLOGY GROUP CO., LTD.
Room 1006 Block C Dongxu Interna-
tional Center Building No 2 Yard No
2, Sihezhuang Road Fengtai District,
Beijing, 100070, China
Tel.: (86) 1083050986
Web Site: http://www.cltg.com.cn
Year Founded: 1999
002306—(SSE)
Rev.: $18,310,968
Assets: $27,758,484
Liabilities: $18,294,120
Net Worth: $9,464,364
Earnings: ($3,055,104)
Fiscal Year-end: 12/31/22
Restaurant Operators
N.A.I.C.S.: 722511
Chen Ji (Chm & Pres)

CLOUD MUSIC INC.
Room 1201 Block A No 353 Benjing
Avenue, Hangzhou International Expo
Center Qianjiang Century City Xi-
aoshan, Hangzhou, Zhejian,
China   Ky
Web Site: https://ir.music.163.com
Year Founded: 2013
9899—(HKG)
Rev.: $1,089,249,003
Assets: $1,607,575,183
Liabilities: $438,863,674
Net Worth: $1,168,711,509
Earnings: $101,653,467
Emp.: 1,359
Fiscal Year-end: 12/31/23
Music Streaming Services
N.A.I.C.S.: 518210
Li Yong (VP)

CLOUDBERRY CLEAN EN-ERGY ASA
Froyas gate 15, 0273, Oslo, Norway
Tel.: (47) 91302907
Web Site: https://www.cloudberry.no
Year Founded: 2017
CLOUD—(OSL)
Rev.: $56,345,834
Aoooto: $618,010,111
Liabilities: $191,575,836
Net Worth: $426,473,305
Earnings: $21,522,261
Emp.: 67
Fiscal Year-end: 12/31/23
Renewable Energy Services
N.A.I.C.S.: 221210
Anders J. Lenborg (CEO)

Subsidiaries:

Skogvind AS   (1)
Cloudberry Clean Energy Bergehus Froyas
Gate 15, 0273, Oslo, Norway
Tel.: (47) 92689347
Web Site: https://www.skogvind.no
Power Generation Services
N.A.I.C.S.: 562213

CLOUDBREAK DISCOVERY PLC
520 - 999 W Hastings St, Vancouver,
V6C 2W2, BC, Canada
Tel.: (604) 428-9480   UK
Web Site:
https://cloudbreakdiscovery.com
Year Founded: 2007
CDL—(LSE)
Rev.: $458,953
Assets: $4,599,497
Liabilities: $2,116,570
Net Worth: $2,482,927
Earnings: ($4,964,591)
Fiscal Year-end: 06/30/23
Mineral Mining Services
N.A.I.C.S.: 212390
Kyler Hardy (CEO)

CLOUDBUY PLC
5 Jupiter House Calleva Park, Alder-
maston, Reading, RG7 8NN, Berk-
shire, United Kingdom
Tel.: (44) 118 963 7000   UK
Web Site: http://www.cloudbuy.com
Year Founded: 1999
Rev.: $1,406,768
Assets: $1,676,105
Liabilities: $9,077,289
Net Worth: ($7,401,184)
Earnings: ($2,782,512)
Emp.: 39
Fiscal Year-end: 12/31/18
Software Development Services
N.A.I.C.S.: 513210

Subsidiaries:

cloudBuy India Private Ltd.   (1)
305 Level 3 Harnath Tower 117 PWD Road,
Jodhpur, Rajasthan, India
Tel.: (91) 2912980330
Software Publisher
N.A.I.C.S.: 513210

CLOUDCALL GROUP LIMITED
1 Colton Square, Leicester, LE1
1QH, United Kingdom
Tel.: (44) 2038544000   UK
Web Site: https://cloudcall.com
Year Founded: 2005
CALL—(AIM)
Rev.: $16,048,250
Assets: $21,919,032
Liabilities: $8,443,661
Net Worth: $13,475,371
Earnings: ($7,801,459)
Emp.: 171
Fiscal Year-end: 12/31/20
Computer Software Applications
N.A.I.C.S.: 513210

Simon William Cleaver (CEO)

Subsidiaries:

Cloudcall Limited   (1)
1 Colton Square, Leicester, LE1 1QH,
United Kingdom
Tel.: (44) 3303350000
Software Application Development Services
N.A.I.C.S.: 541511
Claire Smith (Head-QA)

Subsidiary (US):

Cloudcall, Inc.   (2)
320 Congress St, Boston, MA 02210
Tel.: (617) 982-1600
Computer Software Application Services
N.A.I.C.S.: 513210
Hope Nattell (Dir-Key Accts)

CLOUDCOCO GROUP PLC
Carrwood Park Selby Road, Leeds,
LS15 4LG, Cheshire, United Kingdom
Tel.: (44) 3334559885   UK
Web Site:
https://www.cloudcoco.co.uk
Year Founded: 1998
CLCO—(AIM)
Rev.: $11,007,036
Assets: $20,045,378
Liabilities: $13,019,177
Net Worth: $7,026,201
Earnings: ($2,889,228)
Emp.: 57
Fiscal Year-end: 09/30/21
Information Technology Services
N.A.I.C.S.: 541512
Mark Halpin (CEO)

Subsidiaries:

Accent Telecom UK Limited   (1)
Brooke House 4 The Lakes Bedford Road,
Northampton, NN4 7YD, United Kingdom
Tel.: (44) 870 950 1630
Web Site: http://www.accent-telecom.net
Telecommunication Servicesb
N.A.I.C.S.: 517112

Adept4 Managed IT Limited   (1)
7750 Daresbury Business Park Daresbury
Office Village, Warrington, WA4 4BS,
Cheshire, United Kingdom
Tel.: (44) 8082524444
Web Site: http://www.adept4.co.uk
Software Development Services
N.A.I.C.S.: 541512

CLOUDMINDS INC.
33rd Floor Unit B Tower 3 Wangjing
SOHO, Chaoyang District, Beijing,
100027, China
Tel.: (86) 1053856575   Ky
Year Founded: 2015
Rev.: $121,025,000
Assets: $97,032,000
Liabilities: $345,116,000
Net Worth: ($248,084,000)
Earnings: ($156,384,000)
Emp.: 680
Fiscal Year-end: 12/31/18
Holding Company
N.A.I.C.S.: 551112

CLOUDPAY
1 & 2 The Woodford Centre Lysander
Way Old Sarum, Salisbury, SP4 6BU,
Wilts, United Kingdom
Tel.: (44) 1722420700
Web Site: http://www.cloudpay.net
Sales Range: $25-49.9 Million
Emp.: 152
Payroll Management Software Solu-
tions
N.A.I.C.S.: 513210
Gareth Hughes (CTO)

CLOUDPOINT TECHNOLOGY BERHAD
Unit J-6-13 Block J Solaris Mont Kiara No 2 Jalan Solaris, Mont Kiara,

50480, Kuala Lumpur, Malaysia
Tel.: (60) 364113883
Web Site: https://www.cloudpoint-
technology.com
Year Founded: 2003
0277—(KLS)
Rev.: $23,975,185
Assets: $24,310,623
Liabilities: $8,852,634
Net Worth: $15,457,989
Earnings: $3,534,175
Emp.: 88
Fiscal Year-end: 12/31/23
Software Development Services
N.A.I.C.S.: 541511

Subsidiary (Non-US):

CLOUDR GROUP LIMITED
Rooms 501 5/F Building 12 No 998
Wenyi West Road, Haichuang Yuan
Wuchang Street Yuhang District,
Hangzhou, Zhejiang, China   Ky
Web Site: https://www.cloudr.cn
Year Founded: 2014
9955—(HKG)
Rev.: $510,984,714
Assets: $407,768,193
Liabilities: $163,347,225
Net Worth: $244,420,968
Earnings: ($45,323,438)
Emp.: 1,522
Fiscal Year-end: 12/31/23
Digital Marketing Services
N.A.I.C.S.: 541810
Ming Kuang (Founder)

CLOUDREPUBLIC AB
Karlavagen 64, Stockholm, 114 49,
Sweden
Tel.: (46) 86111190
Software Development Services
N.A.I.C.S.: 541511
Lars Bergkvist (Chm)

CLOUDTAG INC.
Floor 2 Willow House Cricket Square,
PO Box 709, Georgetown, KY1-1107,
Cayman Islands
Tel.: (345) 9494544
Web Site: http://www.cloudtag.com
Physiological Monitoring Technology
N.A.I.C.S.: 339112
Amit Ben-Haim (CEO)

CLOUDYN LTD.
22 Hamelacha St Bldg 3 2nd Fl,
48091, Rosh Ha'Ayin, Israel
Tel.: (972) 73 706 6967
Web Site: http://www.cloudyn.com
Year Founded: 2011
Optimization Engine Software Pub-
lisher
N.A.I.C.S.: 513210
Sharon Wagner (Co-Founder & CEO)

CLOVER BIOPHARMACEUTI-CALS, LTD.
49F Park Place 1598-1601 West
Nanjing Road, Jingan, Shanghai,
China   Ky
Web Site:
https://www.cloverbiopharma.com
Year Founded: 2007
2197—(HKG)
Rev.: $5,435,174
Assets: $290,960,623
Liabilities: $392,427,309
Net Worth: ($101,466,687)
Earnings: ($19,181,851)
Emp.: 387
Fiscal Year-end: 12/31/23
Biotechnology Research & Develop-
ment Services
N.A.I.C.S.: 541714
Joshua Liang (CEO)

CLOVER CORPORATION LIMITED

39 Pinnacle Road, PO Box 1111, Altona, 3025, VIC, Australia
Tel.: (61) 383475000
Web Site:
https://www.clovercorp.com.au
CLV—(ASX)
Rev.: $41,537,794
Assets: $56,351,495
Liabilities: $11,566,506
Net Worth: $44,784,989
Earnings: $1,011,619
Emp.: 60
Fiscal Year-end: 07/31/24
Natural Oils Sales
N.A.I.C.S.: 211130
Peter J. Davey *(CEO & Mng Dir)*

Subsidiaries:

Nu-Mega Ingredients Pty. Ltd. **(1)**
Tel.: (61) 38 369 2100
Web Site: http://www.nu-mega.com
Sales Range: $25-49.9 Million
Emp.: 30
Fatty Acids Mfr
N.A.I.C.S.: 325199

CLOVER HITECHNOLOGY CO., LTD.

57 Wolmyeong-ro 55beon-gil,
Heungdeok-gu, Cheongju, Chungbuk,
Korea (South)
Tel.: (82) 24533232
Web Site:
http://www.cloverhitech.com
043590—(KRS)
Rev.: $16,027,948
Assets: $27,941,489
Liabilities: $2,312,640
Net Worth: $25,628,849
Earnings: ($567,151)
Emp.: 42
Fiscal Year-end: 12/31/22
Transformer & Coil Mfr
N.A.I.C.S.: 334416

CLOVER INDUSTRIES LIMITED

200 Constantia Dr, Constantia Kloof,
1709, Roodepoort, South Africa
Tel.: (27) 11 471 1400   ZA
Web Site: http://www.clover.co.za
Year Founded: 2003
Sales Range: $650-699.9 Million
Food & Beverages Products Mfr
N.A.I.C.S.: 311999
Johann Vorster *(CEO)*

Subsidiaries:

Clover Dairy Namibia (Pty) Ltd. **(1)**
Main Road, Ongwediva, Windhoek, Namibia
Tel.: (264) 61260256
Fluid Product Mfr
N.A.I.C.S.: 311511

Clover Fonterra Ingredients (Pty)
Ltd. **(1)**
200 Constantia Drive, Constantia Kloof,
Roodepoort, 1709, South Africa
Tel.: (27) 114711400
Web Site: http://www.cloverfonterra.com
Cheese Powder Mfr
N.A.I.C.S.: 311513

Clover Swaziland (Pty) Ltd. **(1)**
Lot 511 Matsapha Ind Site King Mswati 3rd
Avenue, Matsapha, M200, Eswatini
Tel.: (268) 5184957
Fluid Product Mfr
N.A.I.C.S.: 311511

Clover Waters (Pty) Ltd. **(1)**
Plot 98 Doornkloof East, Irene, 0062, Gauteng, South Africa
Tel.: (27) 104170088
Fluid Product Mfr
N.A.I.C.S.: 311511

CLOVER PAKISTAN LTD.

Banglow No 23-B Lalazar Off MT
Khan Road, Karachi, Pakistan
Tel.: (92) 111256837
Web Site: https://www.clover.com.pk
Year Founded: 1986
CLOV—(PSX)
Rev.: $213,735
Assets: $440,626
Liabilities: $130,568
Net Worth: $310,058
Earnings: ($256,319)
Emp.: 4
Fiscal Year-end: 06/30/23
Food Products Mfr & Sales
N.A.I.C.S.: 311999
Muhammad Jamshed Azmat *(Chm)*

CLOVERDALE PAINT INC.

400 - 2630 Croydon Drive, Surrey,
V3Z 6T3, BC, Canada
Tel.: (604) 596-6261
Web Site:
https://www.cloverdalepaint.com
Year Founded: 1933
Paints Mfr & Distr
N.A.I.C.S.: 325510
Tim Vogel *(Chm & CEO)*

Subsidiaries:

Rodda Paint Co. **(1)**
6107 N Marine Dr, Portland, OR 97203
Tel.: (503) 521-4300
Web Site: http://www.roddapaint.com
Sales Range: $50-74.9 Million
Emp.: 300
Paints & Paint Additives
N.A.I.C.S.: 325510
Jeff Pellatz *(Controller)*

Subsidiary (Domestic):

Miller Paint Company, Inc. **(2)**
12812 NE Whitaker Way, Portland, OR
97230-1110
Tel.: (503) 255-0190
Web Site: http://www.millerpaint.com
Sales Range: $25-49.9 Million
Emp.: 200
Mfr of Paint & Allied Products
N.A.I.C.S.: 325510
Steve Dearborn *(Pres)*

CLP HOLDINGS LIMITED

8 Laguna Verde Avenue, Hung Hom,
Kowloon, China (Hong Kong)
Tel.: (852) 26788111   HK
Web Site: https://www.clpgroup.com
Year Founded: 1998
0002—(OTCIQ)
Rev.: $12,864,646,568
Assets: $30,164,223,549
Liabilities: $15,378,480,964
Net Worth: $14,785,742,584
Earnings: $190,039,235
Emp.: 8,318
Fiscal Year-end: 12/31/22
Holding Company; Electricity
Investor-Operator
N.A.I.C.S.: 551112
Michael David Kadoorie *(Chm)*

Subsidiaries:

Apraava Energy Private Limited **(1)**
7th Floor Fulcrum, Andheri East, Mumbai,
400 099, India
Tel.: (91) 2267588888
Web Site: https://www.apraava.com
Energy Infrastructure Services
N.A.I.C.S.: 221118

CLP Business Management (Beijing)
Company Limited **(1)**
Suite 1730 Building 1 China World Trade
Tower 1 Jianguomenwai Avenue, Beijing,
100004, China
Tel.: (86) 1065055608
Investment Services
N.A.I.C.S.: 523999

CLP Engineering Limited **(1)**
36F Asia Trade Centre 79 Lei Muk Road,

Kwai Chung, New Territories, China (Hong
Kong)
Tel.: (852) 26787900
Web Site: http://www.clpgroup.com
Sales Range: $25-49.9 Million
Emp.: 200
Electrical Engineering Services
N.A.I.C.S.: 541330

CLP Huanyu (Shandong) Biomass
Heat and Power Company
Limited **(1)**
Zhaihao Village Hubin Town, Boxing
County, Binzhou, Shandong, China
Tel.: (86) 5432169299
Biomass Mfr
N.A.I.C.S.: 325412

CLP India Private Limited **(1)**
7th Floor Fulcrum Sahar Road, Andheri
East, Mumbai, 400 099, India
Tel.: (91) 2267588888
Web Site: http://www.clpindia.in
Electronic Services
N.A.I.C.S.: 221118
Deepa Sebastian *(VP)*

CLP Power Hong Kong Limited **(1)**
188 Sai Yeung Choi Street South, Mongkok, Kowloon, China (Hong Kong) **(100%)**
Tel.: (852) 26782678
Web Site: https://www.clp.com.hk
Sales Range: $1-4.9 Billion
Emp.: 6,000
Electric Power Distr
N.A.I.C.S.: 221122
Betty So Siu Mai Yuen *(Vice Chm)*

CLP Power India Pvt. Ltd. **(1)**
7th Floor Fulcrum Sahar Road, Andheri
East, Mumbai, 400 099, Maharashtra, India
Tel.: (91) 2267588800
Web Site: http://www.clpindia.in
Sales Range: $75-99.9 Million
Emp.: 55
Power Generation Services
N.A.I.C.S.: 221112
Rajiv Ranjan Mishra *(Mng Dir)*

CLP Research Institute Limited **(1)**
8 Laguna Verde Avenue Hung Hom, Kowloon, China (Hong Kong)
Tel.: (852) 26788111
Integrated Electricity Supply Business &
Services
N.A.I.C.S.: 221122

CLPe Holdings Limited **(1)**
Unit 10 Level 10 Tower 1 Kowloon Commerce Centre 51 Kwai Cheong Road, Kwai
Chung, China (Hong Kong)
Tel.: (852) 26787900
Web Site: https://www.clpesolutions.com
Energy Infrastructure Services
N.A.I.C.S.: 221118

EnergyAustralia **(1)**
Level 33 385 Bourke Street, Melbourne,
3000, VIC, Australia **(100%)**
Tel.: (61) 386281000
Web Site:
http://www.energyaustralia.com.au
Sales Range: $500-549.9 Million
Emp.: 2,000
Gas & Electricity Distr
N.A.I.C.S.: 221210
Catherine Tanna *(Mng Dir)*

EnergyAustralia Yallourn Pty.
Ltd. **(1)**
Eastern Road, Yallourn, Latrobe, 3825, VIC,
Australia
Tel.: (61) 351282000
Electronic Services
N.A.I.C.S.: 221118
Paul Koopmans *(Mgr-Maintenance)*

Gujarat Paguthan Energy Corporation
Private Limited **(1)**
Plant Bharuch Palej Rd Village Paguthan,
Bharuch, 392 015, Gujarat, India **(100%)**
Tel.: (91) 2642671501
Web Site: http://www.clpindia.in
Sales Range: $50-74.9 Million
Emp.: 50
Combined Cycle Power Plant
N.A.I.C.S.: 221113

Hong Kong Nuclear Investment Company Limited **(1)**

8 Laguna Verde Avenue Hung Hom, Kowloon, China (Hong Kong)
Tel.: (852) 26788111
Web Site: https://www.hknuclear.com
Nuclear Power Generation Services
N.A.I.C.S.: 221113

CLPG PACKAGING INDUSTRIES SDN. BHD.

Plot 135 Jalan Perindustrian Bukit
Minyak 4 Kawasan Perindustrian,
Bukit Minyak, 14100, Bukit Mertajam,
Penang, Malaysia
Tel.: (60) 45010202   MY
Web Site: http://www.clpg.com.my
Year Founded: 2002
Plastic Corrugated Sheet Box & Partition Mfr
N.A.I.C.S.: 326130

Subsidiaries:

Corplast Packaging Industries Sdn.
Bhd. **(1)**
No 9 Jalan Sungai Chadong 8 Casin Industrial Park, Batu 5 Off Jalan Kapar, 42100,
Kelang, Selangor Darul Ehsan, Malaysia
Tel.: (60) 332918898
Web Site: http://www.corplast.com
Sales Range: $25-49.9 Million
Emp.: 36
Profile Plastic Sheets Mfr
N.A.I.C.S.: 326113
Tanchoon Hock *(Mgr-Production)*

CLPS INCORPORATION

10th Floor Millennium City III No 370
Kwun Tong Road, Kwun Tong, Kowloon, China (Hong Kong)
Tel.: (852) 37073600   Ky
Web Site: https://www.clpsglobal.com
Year Founded: 2005
CLPS—(NASDAQ)
Rev.: $150,356,539
Assets: $95,319,064
Liabilities: $29,810,263
Net Worth: $65,508,801
Earnings: $192,529
Emp.: 3,509
Fiscal Year-end: 06/30/23
Information Technology Service Provider
N.A.I.C.S.: 541511
Xiao Feng Yang *(Chm)*

CLS HOLDINGS PLC

16 Tinworth Street, London, SE11
5AL, United Kingdom
Tel.: (44) 2075827766   UK
Web Site:
https://www.clsholdings.com
CLI—(LSE)
Rev.: $189,809,256
Assets: $3,446,572,220
Liabilities: $1,639,854,216
Net Worth: $1,806,718,004
Earnings: $162,247,540
Emp.: 112
Fiscal Year-end: 12/31/21
Offices of Other Holding Companies
N.A.I.C.S.: 551112
David Fuller *(Sec & Head-HR)*

Subsidiaries:

Adlershofer Sarl **(1)**
Avenue de la Gare 65, 1611, Luxembourg,
Luxembourg
Tel.: (352) 26684881
Property Management Services
N.A.I.C.S.: 531311

Apex Tower Limited **(1)**
16 Tinworth Street, London, SE11 5AL,
United Kingdom
Tel.: (44) 2075827766
Real Estate Development Services
N.A.I.C.S.: 531390

Bulgarian Land Development
EAD **(1)**

CLS Holdings plc—(Continued)

47A Tsarigradsko Shose Blvd, 1124, Sofia, Bulgaria
Tel.: (359) 2 805 1910
Web Site: http://www.bld.bg
Sales Range: $25-49.9 Million
Commercial & Residential Real Estate Development & Construction Management Services
N.A.I.C.S.: 237210
Dimitar Safov (Gen Mgr)

CI Tower Investments Limited (1)
16 Tinworth Street, London, SE11 5AL, United Kingdom (100%)
Tel.: (44) 2075827766
Sales Range: $50-74.9 Million
Real Estate Investment Trust
N.A.I.C.S.: 525990

CLS Aberdeen Limited (1)
Unit 6 Spires Business Units Mugiemoss Road, Aberdeen, AB21 9NY, United Kingdom
Tel.: (44) 1224683111
Web Site: https://www.clsaberdeen.co.uk
Lighting Equipment Distr
N.A.I.C.S.: 423610

CLS Luxembourg Sarl (1)
33 Avenue de la Liberte, 1931, Luxembourg, Luxembourg
Tel.: (352) 27861217
Real Estate Services
N.A.I.C.S.: 531210

CLS Scotland Limited (1)
Unit 23 21 Easter Inch Court, West Lothian, Bathgate, EH48 2FJ, United Kingdom
Tel.: (44) 754 052 3779
Web Site: https://www.clsscotland.co.uk
Artificial Grass Installation Services
N.A.I.C.S.: 561730

CLSH Management Limited (1)
16 Tinworth Street, London, SE11 5AL, United Kingdom (100%)
Tel.: (44) 2075827766
Sales Range: $25-49.9 Million
Emp.: 50
Nonresidential Buildings Lessors
N.A.I.C.S.: 531120

Great West House Limited (1)
86 Bondway, London, SW6 5HG, United Kingdom (100%)
Tel.: (44) 2075827766
Sales Range: $25-49.9 Million
Emp.: 40
Real Estate Agents & Brokers Offices
N.A.I.C.S.: 531210

Grossglockner Sarl (1)
33 Avenue de la Liberte, 1931, Luxembourg, Luxembourg
Tel.: (352) 24527534
Property Management Services
N.A.I.C.S.: 531311

Hamersley International BV (1)
Burtmbester Van Reenensingel 101, Gouda, 2803PA, Netherlands (100%)
Tel.: (31) 182507775
Real Estate Investment Trust
N.A.I.C.S.: 525990
Per Sjoberg (Mng Dir)

Hermalux SARL (1)
33 Avenue de la Liberte, 1931, Luxembourg, Luxembourg
Tel.: (352) 26684020
Other Holding Companies Offices
N.A.I.C.S.: 551112

Kapellen Sarl (1)
33 Avenue de la Liberte, 1931, Luxembourg, Luxembourg
Tel.: (352) 26684756
Property Management Services
N.A.I.C.S.: 531311

Spring Gardens Limited (1)
1 Spring Gdns Tinworth Street, London, SE11 5EH, United Kingdom (100%)
Tel.: (44) 2075827766
Web Site: http://www.clsholdings.com
Sales Range: $50-74.9 Million
Emp.: 38
Real Estate Investment Trust

N.A.I.C.S.: 525990
Sten Mortstedt (Mng Dir)

Three Albert Embankment Limited (1)
16 Tinworth Street, London, SE11 5AL, United Kingdom (100%)
Tel.: (44) 2075827766
Sales Range: $25-49.9 Million
Emp.: 55
Other Real Estate Property Lessors
N.A.I.C.S.: 531190
Sten Mortstedt (Chm)

Vauxhall Cross Limited (1)
86 Bondway, London, SW8 1SF, United Kingdom (100%)
Tel.: (44) 2075827766
Web Site: http://www.clsholdings.com
Sales Range: $50-74.9 Million
Emp.: 55
Nonresidential Buildings Lessors
N.A.I.C.S.: 531120
Sten Mortstedt (Mng Dir)

CLUB DE HOCKEY CANADIEN, INC.
1275 rue Saint-Antoine Ouest, Montreal, H3C 5L2, QC, Canada
Tel.: (514) 932-2582　　　　Ca
Web Site: http://canadiens.nhl.com
Year Founded: 1909
Sales Range: $75-99.9 Million
Emp.: 150
Professional Hockey Franchise & Sports Arena Operator
N.A.I.C.S.: 711211
Rejean Houle (Pres-Canadiens Alumni Association)

Subsidiaries:

L'Arena des Canadiens, Inc. (1)
1909 avenue des Canadiens-de-Montreal, Montreal, H4B 5G0, QC, Canada
Tel.: (514) 932-2582
Web Site: http://www.centrebell.ca
Sports Arena & Entertainment Complex Operator
N.A.I.C.S.: 711310
Alain Gauthier (Exec VP & Gen Mgr)

Unit (Domestic):

evenko (2)
1275 Saint-Antoine Ouest, Montreal, H3C 5L2, QC, Canada
Tel.: (514) 790-2525
Web Site: http://www.evenko.ca
Music, Sports & Entertainment Promotion Services
N.A.I.C.S.: 711310
Jacques Aube (VP & Gen Mgr)

CLUB DE POLO Y EQUITACION SAN CRISTOBAL
Av San Josemaria Mons Escriva De Balaguer 5501, PO Box Correo 11, Vitacura, Santiago, Chile
Tel.: (56) 7156000　　　　CL
Web Site: http://www.clubdepolo.cl
Year Founded: 1947
POLO—(SGO)
Sales Range: Less than $1 Million
Sports Club
N.A.I.C.S.: 713910
Alejandro Banados Morande (Pres)

CLUB HIPICO DE SANTIAGO S.A.
Avda Blanco Encalada No 2540, PO Box 3674, Santiago, Chile
Tel.: (56) 6939600
Web Site: http://www.clubhipico.cl
Year Founded: 1869
HIPICO—(SGO)
Rev.: $15,629,008,260
Assets: $68,172,183,760
Liabilities: $20,047,417,060
Net Worth: $48,124,766,700
Earnings: ($1,416,229,920)
Fiscal Year-end: 12/31/19
Race Track & Veterinary Services

N.A.I.C.S.: 711212
Carlos Heller Solari (Pres)

CLUEY LIMITED
L2 / 117 Clarence St, Sydney, 2000, NSW, Australia
Tel.: (61) 1300182000　　　AU
Web Site: https://www.clueylearning.com.au
Year Founded: 2017
CLU—(ASX)
Rev.: $25,662,124
Assets: $17,045,706
Liabilities: $5,499,120
Net Worth: $11,546,587
Earnings: ($12,525,266)
Emp.: 155
Fiscal Year-end: 06/30/23
Educational Support Services
N.A.I.C.S.: 611710
Greg Fordred (Sec)

CLUJANA S.A.
1 Mai Square No 4-5, 400141, Cluj-Napoca, Romania
Tel.: (40) 264 437 157
Year Founded: 1911
CLUJ—(BUC)
Sales Range: $1-9.9 Million
Footwear Mfr
N.A.I.C.S.: 316210

CLUNE TECHNOLOGY GROUP
IDA Business & Technology Park Ring Road, Kilkenny, Ireland
Tel.: (353) 567783400
Web Site: https://www.clunetech.com
Year Founded: 1996
Emp.: 950
Financial, Tax & Travel Services
N.A.I.C.S.: 523999
Dave McGettrick (Mgr-Software Dev)

Subsidiaries:

Immedis, Ltd (1)
14 St Stephen's Green, Dublin, 2, Ireland
Tel.: (353) 14871537
Payroll & Employment Tax Services
N.A.I.C.S.: 523999
Ruairi Kelleher (CEO)

Subsidiary (US):

Expaticore Services LLC (2)
485C Route 1 S, Iselin, NJ 08830
Tel.: (212) 239-2625
Web Site: http://www.expaticore.com
Payroll Services
N.A.I.C.S.: 541214
David Leboff (Founder & Pres)

CLUNY CAPITAL CORP.
1 First Canadian Place 100 King St W Suite 6000, Toronto, M5X 1E2, ON, Canada
Tel.: (416) 482-3282　　　ON
Year Founded: 2011
TGSHF—(OTCIQ)
Rev.: $3,029,028
Assets: $1,077,259
Liabilities: $735,912
Net Worth: $341,347
Earnings: ($337,296)
Fiscal Year-end: 07/31/23
Investment Services
N.A.I.C.S.: 523999
Michael Frank (CEO & CFO)

CLUSTER TECHNOLOGY CO., LTD.
4-5-28 Shibukawacho, Higashiosaka, 577-0836, Osaka, Japan
Tel.: (81) 667262711
Web Site: https://www.cluster-tech.co.jp
Year Founded: 1996
4240—(TKS)
Rev.: $7,656,950

Assets: $12,938,870
Liabilities: $1,137,080
Net Worth: $11,801,790
Earnings: $183,400
Fiscal Year-end: 03/31/20
Metal Mould Mfr
N.A.I.C.S.: 333511
Yoshinori Adachi (Pres & CEO)

CLUTCH AUTO LIMITED
2E/14 First Floor Jhandewalan Extension, New Delhi, 110055, India
Tel.: (91) 1123683548
Web Site: http://www.clutchauto.com
Year Founded: 1971
Sales Range: $1-9.9 Million
Clutch Mfr & Exporter
N.A.I.C.S.: 336390
Vijay Krishan Metha (Chm & Mng Dir)

CLYDE & CO LLP
St Botolph Building 138 Houndsditch, London, EC3A 7AR, United Kingdom
Tel.: (44) 20 7876 5000　　　UK
Web Site: http://www.clydeco.com
Year Founded: 1933
Emp.: 3,800
Law firm
N.A.I.C.S.: 541110
Anthony Albertini (Partner)

Subsidiaries:

Clyde & Co US LLP (1)
Chrysler Bldg 405 Lexington Ave, New York, NY 10174
Tel.: (212) 710-3900
Web Site: http://www.clydeco.com
Law firm
N.A.I.C.S.: 541110
Eileen Sorabella (Partner)

CLYDE BLOWERS CAPITAL IM LLP
3 Redwood Crescent Peel Park, East Kilbride, G74 5PA, United Kingdom
Tel.: (44) 1355 575 000　　　UK
Web Site: http://www.clydeblowerscapital.com
Year Founded: 1999
Investment Holding Company
N.A.I.C.S.: 551112
Jim McColl (Founder, Chm & CEO)

Subsidiaries:

Clyde Blowers Ltd. (1)
One Redwood Crescent, Peel Park, East Kilbride, G74 5PA, United Kingdom
Tel.: (44) 1355575000
Web Site: http://www.clydeblowers.co.uk
Emp.: 35
Venture Capital & Private Equity Firm
N.A.I.C.S.: 523999
James Allan McColl (Chm & CEO)

Group (Non-US):

Clyde Bergemann Power Group (2)
Schillwiese 20, 46485, Wesel, Germany
Tel.: (49) 281815101
Web Site: http://www.cbpg.com
Sales Range: $100-124.9 Million
Emp.: 160
Holding Company; Power & Environmental Industry Cleaning, Air-Control & Ash Handling Equipment Developer & Mfr
N.A.I.C.S.: 551112
Franz Bartels (Pres & CEO)

Subsidiary (Non-US):

Clyde Bergemann Africa (Pty) Ltd (3)
11 Industrial Road, Kya Sands, Randburg, 2163, Gauteng, South Africa
Tel.: (27) 11 704 0580
Boiler Cleaning System & Air Pollution Control System Distr
N.A.I.C.S.: 423830

Clyde Bergemann Beekay India Private Limited (3)
C-7 Phase-II, Distt Gautambudh Nagar,

Noida, 201 305, Uttar Pradesh, India
Tel.: (91) 120 4073100
Web Site: http://www.clydebergemann.in
Emp.: 100
Dry Bottom Ash Handling System & Power
Boiler Distr
N.A.I.C.S.: 423830
Dilip Kumar Sinha *(Mng Dir)*

Clyde Bergemann Canada Ltd. (3)
19 Thorne St Ste 205, Cambridge, N1R
1S3, ON, Canada
Tel.: (866) 267-3068
Industrial Boiler Cleaning Equipment Mfr &
Distr
N.A.I.C.S.: 334513

**Clyde Bergemann Colombia
S.A.S.** (3)
Centro Ejecutivo Castilla Carrera 13 No
94A-25/45 Suite 401, Bogota, 110221, Co-
lombia
Tel.: (57) 1 622 4259
Dry Bottom Ash Handling System & Boiler
Cleaning System Dstr
N.A.I.C.S.: 423830

**Clyde Bergemann Controls Pvt.
Ltd** (3)
403 Imperial Heights Off O P Road, Akshar
Chowk, Vadodara, 390 020, India
Tel.: (91) 846 954 3021
Web Site: http://www.cbpg.com
Emp.: 5
Boiler Cleaning System & Air Pollution Con-
trol System Distr
N.A.I.C.S.: 423830
Sandeep Shah *(Mng Dir)*

Clyde Bergemann EP Tech S.r.l. (3)
Via Dei Principati 74, 84122, Salerno, Italy
Tel.: (39) 089 233292
Boiler Cleaning System & Air Pollution Con-
trol System Distr
N.A.I.C.S.: 423830
Luigi Scala *(Dir-Fin)*

Clyde Bergemann Eesti AS (3)
Mustamae Tee 5A, 10616, Tallinn,
Estonia (100%)
Tel.: (372) 6259565
Web Site: http://www.cdw.de
Sales Range: $25-49.9 Million
Emp.: 100
Industrial Boiler Cleaning Equipment Mfr &
Distr
N.A.I.C.S.: 334513

**Clyde Bergemann Energy & Environ-
mental Technology (Beijing) Co.,
Ltd.** (3)
Room 1208 Building 16 China Central
Place No 89 Jianguo Road, Chaoyang Dis-
trict, Beijing, 100025, China
Tel.: (86) 10 51650099
Dry Bottom Ash Handling System & Boiler
Cleaning System Dstr
N.A.I.C.S.: 423830

Clyde Bergemann Forest S.A. (3)
No 29 Jean Avenue Mermoz, Gosselies,
6041, Belgium (100%)
Tel.: (32) 71919410
Web Site: http://www.cbpg.com
Sales Range: $25-49.9 Million
Emp.: 15
Mfr of Power Equipment
N.A.I.C.S.: 335311
Jean-Michel Frech *(Gen Mgr)*

Subsidiary (Domestic):

Clyde Bergemann GmbH (3)
Schillwiese 20, Wesel, 46485,
Germany (100%)
Tel.: (49) 281815100
Web Site: http://www.clydebergemann.de
Sales Range: $25-49.9 Million
Emp.: 150
Industrial Boiler Cleaning Equipment Mfr &
Distr
N.A.I.C.S.: 334513
Volker Pantosky *(Dir-Fin)*

Subsidiary (Domestic):

**Clyde Bergemann DRYCON
GmbH** (4)
Schillwiese 20, 46485, Wesel, Germany
Tel.: (49) 2818150

Web Site: http://www.clydebergemann.de
Sales Range: $1-9.9 Million
Emp.: 40
Power & Industrial Boilers, Biomass Boilers
& Waste Incinerators Manufacturing Ser-
vices
N.A.I.C.S.: 332410
Kornelius Stuhlwaisenburg *(Gen Mgr)*

Subsidiary (Non-US):

**Clyde Bergemann Huatong Materials
Handling Co., Ltd.** (3)
No 602 Guoying Yihao Xizhimen Nanxiao
Street, Xicheng District, Beijing, 100035,
China
Tel.: (86) 10 58561956
Web Site: http://www.cbpg.com.ch
Dry Bottom Ash Handling System & Boiler
Cleaning System Dstr
N.A.I.C.S.: 423830
Ixao Wei Nong *(Mgr)*

Subsidiary (US):

Clyde Bergemann Inc. (3)
4015 Presidential Pkwy, Atlanta, GA
30340-3707 (100%)
Tel.: (770) 557-3600
Web Site: http://www.boilercleaning.org
Sales Range: $50-74.9 Million
Industrial Boiler Cleaning Equipment Mfr &
Distr
N.A.I.C.S.: 333998
Douglas Smith *(Mgr-Production & Logistics)*

Subsidiary (Domestic):

Anthony-Ross Company (4)
5600 SW Arctic Dr Ste 100, Beaverton, OR
97005-4101
Tel.: (503) 641-0545
Web Site: http://www.clydebergemann.com
Sales Range: $25-49.9 Million
Emp.: 100
Air System Solutions Mfr for Recovery Boil-
ers
N.A.I.C.S.: 333243

Subsidiary (Non-US):

Clyde Bergemann Limited (3)
47 Broad St Bridgeton, Glasgow, G40 2QR,
Scotland, United Kingdom (100%)
Tel.: (44) 1415505400
Web Site: http://www.clydebergemann.co.uk
Sales Range: $25-49.9 Million
Emp.: 60
Industrial Boiler Cleaning Equipment Mfr &
Distr
N.A.I.C.S.: 333310
Ian Carruthers *(Mgr-Sls)*

**Clyde Bergemann Materials Handling
Ltd** (3)
Lakeside Boulevard, Lakeside, Doncaster,
DN4 5PL, United Kingdom
Tel.: (44) 1302 552200
Ash Handling System & Air Pollution Con-
trol System Mfr
N.A.I.C.S.: 333248

**Clyde Bergemann Polska Sp. z
o.o.** (3)
Ul Murarska 27, 43-100, Tychy,
Poland (100%)
Tel.: (48) 322168412
Web Site:
http://www.clydebergemann.com.pl
Industrial Boiler Cleaning Equipment Mfr &
Distr
N.A.I.C.S.: 334513

Division (US):

**Clyde Bergemann Power Group
Americas Inc. - Air Pollution Control
Product Division** (3)
7380 Coca-Cola Dr Ste 126, Hanover, MD
21076
Tel.: (410) 368-7000
Emp.: 100
Air Pollution Control Product Mfr
N.A.I.C.S.: 333248

**Clyde Bergemann Power Group
Americas Inc. - Air-Gas Handling
Product Division** (3)
416 Lewiston Junction Rd, Auburn, ME
04211-2150

Tel.: (207) 784-1903
Air Gas Handling System & Product Mfr
N.A.I.C.S.: 333248

**Clyde Bergemann Power Group
Americas Inc. - Material Handling
Product Division** (3)
33 Sproul Rd, Malvern, PA 19355
Tel.: (610) 695-9700
Emp.: 100
Material Handling Product Mfr
N.A.I.C.S.: 333248
Denee Dambrosio *(Office Mgr)*

Subsidiary (Non-US):

**Clyde Bergemann Scandinavia
Oy** (3)
Juvantasku 3, 02920, Espoo, Finland
Tel.: (358) 9 8330 0600
Web Site: http://www.fi.cbpg.com
Emp.: 7
Material Handling Product & Spare Part
Distr
N.A.I.C.S.: 423830
Ralf Pettersson *(Mng Dir)*

**Clyde Bergemann TR Enerji Servis A.
S.** (3)
Omer Avni Mah Inonu Cad Gumussu Palas
No 18 TR-D 8, Beyoglu, Istanbul, Turkiye
Tel.: (90) 537 863 69 49
Boiler Cleaning System & Air Cooled Con-
denser Dist
N.A.I.C.S.: 423830
Metin Metin *(Mng Dir)*

Subsidiary (Domestic):

**Clyde Bergemann Termotec
GmbH** (3)
Emmelsumer Strasse 219, 46485, Wesel,
Germany
Tel.: (49) 281 815 34 0
Air Cooled Condenser & Heat Exchanger
Product Distr
N.A.I.C.S.: 423830

Subsidiary (Non-US):

Clyde Bergemann do Brasil Ltda. (3)
Av Iracy Berezoski Cayres 320, Distr Ind
Getulio Vargas II Mogi Guacu, Sao Paulo,
13849-104, Brazil
Tel.: (55) 19 3841 5086
Boiler Cleaning System & Air Pollution Con-
trol System Distr
N.A.I.C.S.: 423830

**Macawber Beekay Private
Limited** (3)
Beekay House C-450/451 Sector-10, Noida,
201 301, Uttar Pradesh, India
Tel.: (91) 120 4507700
Web Site: http://www.mbl.in
Emp.: 500
Material Handling Product Mfr
N.A.I.C.S.: 333248
Ajay Kumar Gupta *(Chm & Mng Dir)*

PT. Clyde Bergemann Indonesia (3)
Wisma Slipi 7th Floor Suite 708 Jl Let Jend
S Parman Kav 12, 11480, Jakarta, Indone-
sia
Tel.: (62) 21 532 8002
Materials Handling Product & Air Pollution
Control System Distr
N.A.I.C.S.: 423830
Antonius Christiawan *(Mgr-Sls)*

**Shanghai Clyde Bergemann Machin-
ery Company Ltd.** (3)
No 2200 Yangshupu Road, Shanghai,
200090, China (100%)
Tel.: (86) 2165396385
Web Site:
http://www.clydebergemann.com.cn
Sales Range: $25-49.9 Million
Emp.: 100
Industrial Boiler Cleaning Equipment Mfr &
Distr
N.A.I.C.S.: 333248
Franz Bartels *(Chm)*

Subsidiary (Domestic):

**David Brown Gear Systems
Limited** (2)
Park Road, Lockwood, Huddersfield, HD4
5DD, United Kingdom

Tel.: (44) 1484465500
Web Site: http://www.davidbrown.com
Sales Range: $100-124.9 Million
Emp.: 400
Industrial & Marine Gears, Machinery
Drives Systems & Pumps Mfr
N.A.I.C.S.: 333914

Subsidiary (Non-US):

**David Brown Gear Industries Austra-
lia Pty. Ltd.** (3)
13 to 19 Franklin Avenue Bulli, 2516, Syd-
ney, NSW, Australia
Tel.: (61) 242830300
Web Site: http://www.davidbrown.com
Sales Range: $25-49.9 Million
Emp.: 100
Speed Changer Driver & Gear Mfr
N.A.I.C.S.: 333612
William Stevens *(Gen Mgr)*

Subsidiary (Non-US):

Endat Oy (2)
Innopoli Tekniikantie 2, 02150, Espoo, Fin-
land
Tel.: (358) 4529 11111
Software Programming & Online Tool De-
velopment Services
N.A.I.C.S.: 541511

CLYDESDALE RESOURCES,
INC.
1008 409 Granville Street, Vancou-
ver, V6C 1T2, BC, Canada
Tel.: (780) 907-4980
CEO.H—(TSXV)
Rev.: $8,667
Assets: $179,004
Liabilities: $308,811
Net Worth: ($129,806)
Earnings: ($29,863)
Fiscal Year-end: 03/31/24
Copper Mining & Exploration Ser-
vices
N.A.I.C.S.: 212230

CLYDESTONE (GHANA) LIM-
ITED
14 Adebeto Crescent North Labone,
Accra, Ghana
Tel.: (233) 302772690
Web Site:
https://www.clydestone.com
Year Founded: 1989
CLYD—(GHA)
Rev.: $803,730
Assets: $1,090,542
Liabilities: $704,331
Net Worth: $386,211
Earnings: $57,111
Emp.: 420
Fiscal Year-end: 12/31/22
Information, Communication & Tech-
nology Solutions
N.A.I.C.S.: 541512
Paul Tse Jacquaye *(CEO)*

CM ENERGY TECH CO., LTD.
Unit 2706-2709 27/F One Harbour-
front, 18 Tak Fung Street Hunghom,
Kowloon, China (Hong Kong)
Tel.: (852) 28573667   Ky
Web Site:
http://www.cmicholding.com
0206—(HKG)
Rev.: $113,040,000
Assets: $278,674,000
Liabilities: $109,648,000
Net Worth: $169,026,000
Earnings: $25,890,000
Emp.: 442
Fiscal Year-end: 12/31/22
Drilling, Mechanical Handling, Solid
Control, Rig Power, Rig Drives, Ten-
sioning & Compensation Systems
Equipment Mfr
N.A.I.C.S.: 333120
Bing Hua Jiang *(Founder & Chm)*

CM Energy Tech Co. Ltd.—(Continued)

Subsidiaries:

**Alliance Offshore Drilling Pte
Limited**　　　　　　　　　　**(1)**
114 Lavender Street 01-66, Singapore,
338729, Singapore
Tel.: (65) 63865828
Industrial Design Services
N.A.I.C.S.: 541420
Paul Lim (Pres)

**Qingdao TSC Offshore Equipment
Co., Ltd**　　　　　　　　　　**(1)**
Wangjianyqu Liuting st, Chengyang District,
Qingdao, 266108, China
Tel.: (86) 53287718351
Sales Range: $50-74.9 Million
Emp.: 150
Offshore Equipment Mfr
N.A.I.C.S.: 333131

TSC Engineering Limited　　**(1)**
Unit 1-3 Marrtree Bus Park Ryefield Way,
Silsden, Keighley, BD20 0EF, Western York-
shire, United Kingdom
Tel.: (44) 1535656471
Sales Range: $25-49.9 Million
Emp.: 15
Offshore Equipment Mfr
N.A.I.C.S.: 333131

**TSC Manufacturing & Supply,
LLC**　　　　　　　　　　　　**(1)**
13788 West Rd Ste 100, Houston, TX
77041
Tel.: (832) 456-3900
Web Site: https://www.tscms.com
Sales Range: $10-24.9 Million
Fluid Pump Mfr & Whslr
N.A.I.C.S.: 333996

TSC Offshore (UK) Limited　**(1)**
ShipleyWharf Wharf St, Shipley, BD17
7DW, Western Yorkshire, United Kingdom
Tel.: (44) 1274531862
Web Site: http://www.tscoffshore.com
Sales Range: $50-74.9 Million
Emp.: 150
Offshore Equipment Mfr
N.A.I.C.S.: 333131

TSC Offshore China Ltd.　　**(1)**
Drilling Equipment Mfr
N.A.I.C.S.: 333132

TSC Offshore Corporation　　**(1)**
12550 NE, Houston, TX 77086-3201
Tel.: (713) 896-8800
Web Site: http://www.tscoffshore.com
Sales Range: $25-49.9 Million
Emp.: 75
Offshore Equipment Mfr
N.A.I.C.S.: 333131

TSC Offshore Limiteda　　　**(1)**
Drilling Equipment Mfr
N.A.I.C.S.: 333132

TSC Offshore Pte. Limited　**(1)**
2114 Lavender Street, Unit 01-66 CT Hub,
Singapore, 338729, Singapore
Tel.: (65) 67630328
Web Site: http://www.tscoffshore.com
Sales Range: $25-49.9 Million
Emp.: 10
Offshore Equipment Mfr
N.A.I.C.S.: 333131

CM TELECOM BV
Alpha House 100 Borough High
Street, SE1 1LB, London, United
Kingdom - England
Tel.: (44) 33765727000
Web Site: http://www.cm.com
Telecommunication Servicesb
N.A.I.C.S.: 517810
Jeroen van Glabbeek (CEO)

CM.COM N.V.
Konijnenberg 24, 4825 BD, Breda,
Netherlands
Tel.: (31) 765727000
Web Site: https://www.cm.com
Year Founded: 1999

CMCOM—(EUR)
Rev.: $293,888,950
Assets: $265,059,057
Liabilities: $236,044,817
Net Worth: $29,014,240
Earnings: ($31,702,175)
Emp.: 720
Fiscal Year-end: 12/31/23
Telecommunication Servicesb
N.A.I.C.S.: 517810
Jeroen van Glabbeek (Co-CEO &
Co-Founder)

Subsidiaries:

Appmiral B.V.B.A.　　　　　**(1)**
Stationsstraat 100, 2800, Mechelen, Bel-
gium
Tel.: (32) 499232872
Web Site: https://appmiral.com
Ticket Booking Services
N.A.I.C.S.: 561599

CM Telecom France S.A.S.　**(1)**
Rue La Fayette 34 Workspace n 302,
75009, Paris, France
Tel.: (33) 186262858
Communication & Payment Platform Ser-
vices
N.A.I.C.S.: 518210

**CM Telecom Singapore Private
Ltd.**　　　　　　　　　　　　**(1)**
Level 12 - 01 30 Raffles Place, Singapore,
048622, Singapore
Tel.: (65) 67979615
Information Technology Services
N.A.I.C.S.: 541511

CM Telecom South Africa Ltd.　**(1)**
16 Ebenezer Road The Foundry Green
Point, Cape Town, 8001, South Africa
Tel.: (27) 211802560
Information Technology Services
N.A.I.C.S.: 541511

CM.com Belgium N.V.　　　　**(1)**
Stationsstraat 100, 2800, Mechelen, Bel-
gium
Tel.: (32) 22556611
Information Technology Services
N.A.I.C.S.: 541511

CM.com Denmark AS　　　　**(1)**
Regus-Christians Brygge Christians Brygge
28, 1559, Copenhagen, Denmark
Tel.: (45) 31519312
Telecommunication Servicesb
N.A.I.C.S.: 561520

CM.com Germany GmbH　　**(1)**
Wiesenhuttenstrasse 11, 60329, Frankfurt
am Main, Germany
Tel.: (49) 32221096288
Information Technology Services
N.A.I.C.S.: 541511

CM.com Japan KK　　　　　**(1)**
6-28-9 Jingumae Tobu Building 6F,
Shibuya-ku, Tokyo, Japan
Tel.: (81) 368924177
Telecommunication Servicesb
N.A.I.C.S.: 561520

CX Company GmbH　　　　**(1)**
Rosenheimerstrasse 143c, 81671, Munich,
Germany
Tel.: (49) 32221096288
Communication & Payment Platform Ser-
vices
N.A.I.C.S.: 518210

Get-a-Ticket B.V.　　　　　**(1)**
Eendrachtlaan 102, 3526 LB, Utrecht, Neth-
erlands
Tel.: (31) 850020859
Web Site: https://getaticket.nl
Online Ticket Selling Services
N.A.I.C.S.: 561599

Your Ticket Provider B.V.　　**(1)**
Eendrachtlaan 102, 3526 LB, Utrecht, Neth-
erlands
Tel.: (31) 302040258
Web Site: https://www.yourticketprovider.nl
Online Ticket Selling Services
N.A.I.C.S.: 561599

CMA CGM S.A.

Boulevard Jacques Saade 4 quai
dArenc, 13235, Marseilles, Cedex 02,
France
Tel.: (33) 488919000
Web Site: http://www.cma-cgm.com
Year Founded: 1977
Rev.: $30,254,200,000
Assets: $32,730,900,000
Liabilities: $27,607,300,000
Net Worth: $5,133,600,000
Earnings: ($218,600,000)
Emp.: 87,932
Fiscal Year-end: 12/31/19
Holding Company for Shipping Activi-
ties
N.A.I.C.S.: 483111
Rodolphe Saade (CEO)

Subsidiaries:

ACOMAR　　　　　　　　　**(1)**
Aleea Blajel nr 9B, Bucharest, 031491, Ro-
mania
Tel.: (40) 723660987
Web Site: http://www.acomar.autogari.ro
Sea Freight Transportation Services
N.A.I.C.S.: 483111

ANL (CHINA) Limited　　　**(1)**
16FL Mingde International Plaza No 558
North Xizhang Road, Zhabei, Shanghai,
200071, China
Tel.: (86) 2166056633
Sea Freight Transportation Services
N.A.I.C.S.: 483111
Mel Lu (Asst Mgr-Sls)

ANL Container Line Pty Limited　**(1)**
Lvl 11 30 Convention Centre Place, South
Wharf, Melbourne, 3006, VIC,
Australia　　　　　　　　**(100%)**
Tel.: (61) 388425555
Web Site: http://www.anl.com.au
Cargo Shipping Distr
N.A.I.C.S.: 483111

Subsidiary (US):

US Lines　　　　　　　　　**(2)**
3601 S Harbor Blvd Ste 200, Santa Ana,
CA 92704
Tel.: (714) 751-3333
Web Site: http://www.uslines.com
Deep Sea Shipping Services
N.A.I.C.S.: 483111
Wendi Cain (Dir-Customer Svc)

ANL SINGAPORE　　　　　**(1)**
9 North Buona Vista Drive 03-02, The Me-
tropolis Tower 1, Singapore, 138588, Singa-
pore
Tel.: (65) 63233119
Sea Freight Transportation Services
N.A.I.C.S.: 483111
Victor Ang (Gen Mgr)

CEVA Logistics AG　　　　**(1)**
Grabenstrasse 25, 6340, Baar,
Switzerland　　　　　　　**(100%)**
Tel.: (41) 43 547 0061
Web Site: http://www.cevalogistics.com
Rev.: $7,356,000,000
Assets: $3,615,000,000
Liabilities: $3,370,000,000
Net Worth: $245,000,000
Earnings: ($242,000,000)
Emp.: 58,000
Fiscal Year-end: 12/31/2018
Freight Forwarding Services
N.A.I.C.S.: 488510
Mathieu Friedberg (CEO)

Subsidiary (Non-US):

CEVA Group plc　　　　　**(2)**
CEVA House Excelsior Road, Ashby de la
Zouch, LE65 1NU, Leics, United Kingdom
Tel.: (44) 3305877000
Web Site: http://www.cevalogistics.com
Sales Range: $5-14.9 Billion
Holding Company
N.A.I.C.S.: 551112

Subsidiary (Non-US):

CEVA Logistics B.V.　　　**(3)**
Siriusdreef 20, 2132 WT, Hoofddorp, Neth-
erlands
Tel.: (31) 237998000

Web Site: http://www.cevalogistics.com
Sales Range: $1-4.9 Billion
Emp.: 38,000
Supply Chain Management & Solutions
N.A.I.C.S.: 561499
Marvin O. Schlanger (Chm)

Subsidiary (Non-US):

CEVA Logistics Argentina　**(4)**
Ruta Provincial 36 500 1893, Buenos Aires,
Argentina
Tel.: (54) 2229492260
Web Site: http://www.cevalogistics.com
Supply Chain Management & Solutions
N.A.I.C.S.: 561499

CEVA Logistics Australia　　**(4)**
77 H Millers Road, Melbourne, Brooklyn,
3012, VIC, Australia
Tel.: (61) 399319900
Web Site: http://www.au.cevalogistics.com
Sales Range: $75-99.9 Million
Emp.: 305
Logistics
N.A.I.C.S.: 488510
Milton Tadeau Pimenta (Mng Dir-Australia &
New Zealand)

CEVA Logistics Austria GmbH　**(4)**
Wienersdorferstrasse 20-24 Obj Niederos-
terreich, 2514, Traiskirchen, Austria
Tel.: (43) 2236 8006
Web Site: http://www.cevalogistics.com
Supply Chain Management & Solutions
N.A.I.C.S.: 561499

CEVA Logistics Belgium　　**(4)**
Koningin Astridlaan 12, Willebroek, 2830,
Belgium
Tel.: (32) 38604500
Web Site: http://www.cevalogistics.com
Sales Range: $25-49.9 Million
Emp.: 80
Supply Chain Management & Solutions
N.A.I.C.S.: 561499

CEVA Logistics Czech Republic　**(4)**
Horelicka 335, Lodenice, 267 12, Czech
Republic
Tel.: (420) 311671660
Web Site: http://www.au.cevalogistics.com
Logistic Services
N.A.I.C.S.: 561499

CEVA Logistics France　　**(4)**
Aeroport International de Vatry Zac No 1
Rue Henri Guillaumet, BP 10394 Vatry,
51555, Longueil-Sainte-Marie, France
Tel.: (33) 3 26 26 6000
Web Site: http://www.au.cevalogistics.com
Sales Range: $25-49.9 Million
Emp.: 50
Logistic Services
N.A.I.C.S.: 488510

CEVA Logistics Germany　　**(4)**
Herriotstrasse 4, Rotseder Ring 5, Frank-
furt, 60528, Germany
Tel.: (49) 69867979
Web Site: http://www.de.cevalogistics.com
Sales Range: $25-49.9 Million
Emp.: 48
Logistic Services
N.A.I.C.S.: 488510
Diego Parra Mora (Dir-Bus Dev Contract
Logistics)

CEVA Logistics Greece　　**(4)**
Km 23 Old National Road, 19600, Mandra-
Attikis, Greece
Tel.: (30) 2105551361
Web Site: http://www.au.cevalogistics.com
Sales Range: $25-49.9 Million
Emp.: 31
Logistic Services
N.A.I.C.S.: 488510

CEVA Logistics Hungary　　**(4)**
Damjanich u. 14, 1041, Budapest, Hungary
Tel.: (36) 24555100
Sales Range: $25-49.9 Million
Emp.: 33
Logistic Services
N.A.I.C.S.: 488510
Benedek Kis (Head-Bus Dev-Europe)

CEVA Logistics Indonesia　　**(4)**
18th Floor Summitmas I Building, Jl Jend
Sudirman Kav 61 62, Jakarta, 12190, Indonesia

Tel.: (62) 2125201250
Web Site: http://www.cevalogistics.com
Sales Range: $25-49.9 Million
Emp.: 100
Logistic Services
N.A.I.C.S.: 488510

CEVA Logistics Italy (4)
Centro Direzionale Milanofiori, Strada 3 -
Palazzo B5, Assago, 20090, MI, Italy
Tel.: (39) 02892301
Logistic Services
N.A.I.C.S.: 488510
Gianclaudio Neri (Mng Dir)

CEVA Logistics Malaysia (4)
Lot 9A Jln Tiang U8/92 Section U8, Bukit
Jelutong, 40300, Shah Alam, Malaysia
Tel.: (60) 50368000
Web Site: http://www.cevalogistics.com
Sales Range: $50-74.9 Million
Emp.: 164
Logistic Services
N.A.I.C.S.: 488510

Subsidiary (US):

CEVA Logistics North America
Inc. (4)
10751 Deerwood Park Blvd Ste 200, Jack-
sonville, FL 32256
Tel.: (904) 928-1400
Web Site: http://www.cevalogistics.com
Sales Range: $50-74.9 Million
Emp.: 200
Supply Chain Management Services
N.A.I.C.S.: 561499

Division (Domestic):

CEVA Freight Management (5)
15350 Vickery Dr Ste 510, Houston, TX
77032
Tel.: (281) 618-3100
Web Site: http://www.cevalogistics.com
Freight Transportation, Logistics & Supply
Chain Management Services
N.A.I.C.S.: 488510

Subsidiary (Non-US):

CEVA Logistics Poland (4)
Ul Sw Michala 43, 61-119, Poznan, Poland
Tel.: (48) 61650368286
Web Site: http://www.cevalogistics.com
Sales Range: $100-124.9 Million
Emp.: 900
Supply Chain Management & Solutions
N.A.I.C.S.: 561499

Unit (Domestic):

CEVA Automotive Logistics
Poland (5)
Konwojowa 51, 43-346, Bielsko-Biala, Po-
land
Tel.: (48) 338135640
Web Site: http://www.cevalogistics.com
Logistic Services
N.A.I.C.S.: 488510

Subsidiary (Non-US):

CEVA Logistics Singapore (4)
No 15 Changi S St 2, Singapore, 486068,
Singapore
Tel.: (65) 72600
Web Site: http://www.cevalogistics.com
Sales Range: $200-249.9 Million
Emp.: 350
Logistic Services
N.A.I.C.S.: 488510

CEVA Logistics Spain (4)
Avenida Parc Logistic 25, Suvirats, 08040,
Barcelona, Spain
Tel.: (34) 933287502
Web Site: http://www.cevalogistics.com
Sales Range: $25-49.9 Million
Emp.: 60
Logistic Services
N.A.I.C.S.: 488510

CEVA Logistics Thailand (4)
1910 Electrolux Building New Petchburi
Road Bangkapi Huaykwang, Bangkok,
10310, Thailand
Tel.: (66) 27145000
Web Site: http://www.cevalogistics.com

Sales Range: $800-899.9 Million
Emp.: 3,149
Logistic Services
N.A.I.C.S.: 488510

CEVA Logistics Turkey (4)
Alemdaj Street Ceva Plz Umraniye, 34768,
Istanbul, Kavacik, Turkiye
Tel.: (90) 2164257000
Web Site: http://www.cevalogistics.com
Logistic Services
N.A.I.C.S.: 488510

CEVA Logistics United Kingdom (4)
Holly Lane, Atherstone, CV9 2RY, Warwick-
shire, United Kingdom
Tel.: (44) 844 800 4499
Sales Range: $1-4.9 Billion
Emp.: 7,500
Logistic Services
N.A.I.C.S.: 488510
Gary Haynes (Dir-Bus Dev)

Unit (Domestic):

CEVA Container Logistics (5)
Doranda Way Industrial Park Doranda Way,
West Bromwich, B71 4LE, West Midlands,
United Kingdom
Tel.: (44) 1215256060
Web Site: http://www.chep.com
Sales Range: $25-49.9 Million
Emp.: 70
Logistic Services
N.A.I.C.S.: 488510

Subsidiary (Non-US):

Stellar Value Chain Solutions Pvt.
Ltd. (2)
28 Dr E Borges Road Parel, Mumbai,
400012, India (96%)
Tel.: (91) 2232243223
Web Site: http://www.stellarvaluechain.com
Investment Services
N.A.I.C.S.: 523999
Anshuman Singh (Founder, Chm & Mng
Dir)

CMA CGM AND ANL HONG
KONG (1)
17/F Tower B Manulife Financial Ctr, Wai
Yip St, 223231, Hong Kong, China (Hong
Kong)
Tel.: (852) 31981688
Sea Freight Transportation Services
N.A.I.C.S.: 483111

CMA CGM AND ANL MALAYSIA
SDN BHD (1)
A-33A-11 Level 33A Menara UOA Bangsar
No 5 Jalan Bangsar Utama 1, 59000, Kuala
Lumpur, Malaysia
Tel.: (60) 22992888
Sea Freight Transportation Services
N.A.I.C.S.: 483111

CMA CGM ANTILLES GUYANE (1)
ZIP de la Pointe des grives, BP 574, Fort-
de-France, Martinique
Tel.: (596) 596553200
Sea Freight Transportation Services
N.A.I.C.S.: 483111

CMA CGM AUSTRALIA (1)
Level 10 30 Convention Centre Place, Mel-
bourne, 3006, VIC, Australia
Tel.: (61) 388425100
Sea Freight Transportation Services
N.A.I.C.S.: 483111

CMA CGM Algeria (1)
Quartier Des Affaires-Bab Ezzouar, 16024,
Algiers, Algeria
Tel.: (213) 2392 4267
Sea Freight Transportation Services
N.A.I.C.S.: 483111

CMA CGM America LLC (1)
5701 Lake Wright Dr, Norfolk, VA 23502
Tel.: (757) 961-2100
Emp.: 600
Sea Freight Transportation Services
N.A.I.C.S.: 483111
Ludovic Renou (Pres)

CMA CGM BELGIUM NV (1)
Klipperstraat 15, 2030, Antwerp, Belgium
Tel.: (32) 32023911
Sea Freight Transportation Services
N.A.I.C.S.: 483111

Eugene Vanfleteren (Mng Dir)

CMA CGM BOLIVIA (1)
Torre Duo Equipetrol Norte Cuarto Anillo
4200 Piso 3 Oficina 3A, Entre Victor Pinto
Y Jaime Roman, Santa Cruz, Bolivia
Tel.: (591) 33888077088
Sea Freight Transportation Services
N.A.I.C.S.: 483111
Bautista Ludy (Supvr-Import & Export)

CMA CGM CANADA (1)
740 notre-Dame Street West Suite 1330,
Montreal, H3C 3X6, QC, Canada
Tel.: (514) 908-7001
Sea Freight Transportation Services
N.A.I.C.S.: 483111

CMA CGM CENTRAL ASIA (1)
Al Farabi 75V/7 4th floor, 050059, Almaty,
Kazakhstan
Tel.: (7) 7272455310
Sea Freight Transportation Services
N.A.I.C.S.: 483111

CMA CGM CHILE SA (1)
Magdalena 140-Piso 17 OF 1700-El Golf,
Las Condes, Santiago, Chile
Tel.: (56) 224832000
Sea Freight Transportation Services
N.A.I.C.S.: 483111
Christian Martinic (CFO)

CMA CGM COLOMBIA S.A.S. (1)
Calle 93B No 17-25, Oficina 501-Edificio
Centro Internacional de Negocios, Bogota,
Colombia
Tel.: (57) 17458222
Sea Freight Transportation Services
N.A.I.C.S.: 483111

CMA CGM COSTA RICA (1)
50 Metros Al Oeste Del Restaurante Isla
Verde Carretera A Pavas, Lado Derecho
Color Azul Pavas, San Jose, Costa Rica
Tel.: (506) 22906410
Sea Freight Transportation Services
N.A.I.C.S.: 483111

CMA CGM CROATIA (1)
Zrtava Fasizma 2, 51000, Rijeka, Croatia
Tel.: (385) 51327595
Sea Freight Transportation Services
N.A.I.C.S.: 483111

CMA CGM DELMAS NIGERIA (1)
26 Creek Rd, Apapa, Lagos, Nigeria
Tel.: (234) 8039756631
Sea Freight Transportation Services
N.A.I.C.S.: 483111
Mike Ogbonna (Mgr-HR)

CMA CGM DEUTSCHLAND (1)
Kleiner Burstah 12, 20457, Hamburg, Ger-
many
Tel.: (49) 40235300
Sea Freight Transportation Services
N.A.I.C.S.: 483111
Ben Salam (Mgr-IT)

CMA CGM DOMINICANA (1)
Avenida Abraham Lincoln 504-Torre B&R-
9th Floor, Santo Domingo, Dominican Re-
public
Tel.: (809) 8097937020
Sea Freight Transportation Services
N.A.I.C.S.: 483111

CMA CGM Deniz Acenteligi A.S. (1)
Emaar Square Unalan Mahallesi Libadiye
Caddesi No 82/F Kat 9 and 10, Uskudar,
34700, Istanbul, Turkiye
Tel.: (90) 2168007000
Cargo Services
N.A.I.C.S.: 488510

CMA CGM Do Brasil Agencia Mar-
itima LTDA (1)
Avenida Paulista 283-12 andar- cj 121-Bela
Vista, 01311-000, Sao Paulo, Brazil
Tel.: (55) 1137080088
Sea Freight Transportation Services
N.A.I.C.S.: 483111
Sergio Lima (Dir-Ops)

CMA CGM ECUADOR (1)
Av Rodrigo Chavez S/N-Parque Empre-
sarial Colon Edificio Corporativo 2, Piso 5
Oficinas 501 Y 503, Guayaquil, Ecuador
Tel.: (593) 42136500
Sea Freight Transportation Services

N.A.I.C.S.: 483111
Javier Moreira Calderon (Gen Mgr)

CMA CGM ESTONIA LTD (1)
Tammsaare Business Centre-A H Tamm-
saare Str 47 Building A4 5th Floor, 11316,
Tallinn, Estonia
Tel.: (372) 6660540
Sea Freight Transportation Services
N.A.I.C.S.: 483111

CMA CGM FINLAND (1)
Televisiokatu 4, 00240, Helsinki, Finland
Tel.: (358) 96850188
Sea Freight Transportation Services
N.A.I.C.S.: 483111

CMA CGM GLOBAL INDIA (1)
India Bulls Financial Center-Tower 3-8th
Floor-Senapati Bapat Marg, Elphinstone,
400013, Mumbai, India
Tel.: (91) 2239888999
Sea Freight Transportation Services
N.A.I.C.S.: 483111

CMA CGM GREECE (1)
85 Akti Miaouli Street & 2 Flessa Street,
18538, Piraeus, Greece
Tel.: (30) 2104290011
Sea Freight Transportation Services
N.A.I.C.S.: 483111
Andreas Haimantas (Mgr-IT)

CMA CGM HOLLAND BV (1)
Achterdijk 51 55 Rhoon-Postbus 132-
Hoogvliet, 3190 AC, Rotterdam, Nether-
lands
Tel.: (31) 102998199
Sea Freight Transportation Services
N.A.I.C.S.: 483111
Peter-Jan Den Boer (Mgr-HR & Comm)

CMA CGM HUNGARY (1)
Vaci ut 135-139 Buiding C 6th Floor, 1138,
Budapest, Hungary
Tel.: (36) 18864350
Sea Freight Transportation Services
N.A.I.C.S.: 483111

CMA CGM IBERICA SAU (1)
Avda Ports D'Europa 100-4 Planta-Edifici
Service Center, 08040, Barcelona, Spain
Tel.: (34) 933196800
Sea Freight Transportation Services
N.A.I.C.S.: 483111
Amelie Humphreys (Mgr-Export Sls)

CMA CGM ITALY S.R.L. (1)
Via Silvio Pellico 1, 16128, Genoa, Italy
Tel.: (39) 01059671
Sea Freight Transportation Services
N.A.I.C.S.: 483111
Paolo Lo Bianco (Mng Dir)

CMA CGM JAMAICA LTD (1)
Shops 51 to 57 Kingston Mall-8 Ocean
Blvd-Kingston Cso, Kingston, Jamaica
Tel.: (876) 9225634
Sea Freight Transportation Services
N.A.I.C.S.: 483111
C. Leopold Nesbeth (Gen Mgr)

CMA CGM JAPAN (1)
15F Tennoz Yusen Bldg -2-2-20 Higashi,
Shinagawa, Tokyo, 140-0002, Japan
Tel.: (81) 357967904
Sea Freight Transportation Services
N.A.I.C.S.: 483111

CMA CGM KENYA (1)
Baywood Building 1st Floor Moi Avenue,
80100, Mombasa, Kenya
Tel.: (254) 709952300
Sea Freight Transportation Services
N.A.I.C.S.: 483111
Stephane Daou (Mng Dir)

CMA CGM MADAGASCAR (1)
3eme etage Immeuble Fitaratra, Ankoron-
drano, 101, Antananarivo, Madagascar
Tel.: (261) 20224990108
Sea Freight Transportation Services
N.A.I.C.S.: 483111

CMA CGM MAROC (1)
1 Avenue Pasteur-Tour Cma Cgm Coma-
nav, 20300, Casablanca, Morocco
Tel.: (212) 522444888
Sea Freight Transportation Services
N.A.I.C.S.: 483111
Omar Baroudi (Office Mgr)

CMA CGM S.A.—(Continued)

CMA CGM MEXICO (1)
Insurgentes 800-Piso 13-Col Del Valle, Del
Benito Juarez, 03100, Mexico, Mexico
Tel.: (52) 5553400940
Sea Freight Transportation Services
N.A.I.C.S.: 483111

CMA CGM MOZAMBIQUE (1)
Rua dos Desportistas N 833 4 andar-JAT
V-I Building, Maputo, Mozambique
Tel.: (258) 21301524
Sea Freight Transportation Services
N.A.I.C.S.: 483111
Laurent Demain (Gen Mgr)

CMA CGM NOUMEA (1)
30 Route de la baie des Dames, BP F5,
98848, Noumea, New Caledonia
Tel.: (687) 270193
Sea Freight Transportation Services
N.A.I.C.S.: 483111

CMA CGM PAKISTAN (PVT)
LTD (1)
5th Floor Bahria Complex IV Choudhry
Khaliq-uz-Zaman Road Gizri, 75600, Kara-
chi, Pakistan
Tel.: (92) 21111946873
Sea Freight Transportation Services
N.A.I.C.S.: 483111
Muhammad Owais Hingora (CFO & Sec)

CMA CGM PANAMA (1)
Federico Boyd Avenue & 49 Street Ph,
Bolsa De Valores De Panama, 2nd Floor
Bella Viata, Panama, Panama
Tel.: (507) 3064400
Sea Freight Transportation Services
N.A.I.C.S.: 483111
Jesus Florez (Supvr-Cargo & Ops)

CMA CGM PAPEETE (1)
2 Rue Wallis, BP 96, 98713, Papeete,
French Polynesia
Tel.: (689) 40545252
Sea Freight Transportation Services
N.A.I.C.S.: 483111

CMA CGM POLSKA LTD (1)
UL Polska 13A, 81-339, Gdynia, Poland
Tel.: (48) 586279700
Sea Freight Transportation Services
N.A.I.C.S.: 483111

CMA CGM PORTUGAL (1)
Rua Tierno Galvan Amoreiras Torre 3-16
Andar-B, 1070-274, Lisbon, Portugal
Tel.: (351) 213256220
Sea Freight Transportation Services
N.A.I.C.S.: 483111
Rui Gordino (Acct Mgr)

CMA CGM REUNION (1)
Boulevard des Mascareignes-ZAC Belve-
dere, CS51041, 97829, Le Port, Reunion
Tel.: (262) 262551010
Sea Freight Transportation Services
N.A.I.C.S.: 483111
Jerome Delhoume (Dir Gen)

CMA CGM ROMANIA (1)
Biharia Office Center Str Biharia Nr 26-
Sector 1, 011973, Bucharest, Romania
Tel.: (40) 213168251
Sea Freight Transportation Services
N.A.I.C.S.: 483111

CMA CGM SCANDINAVIA AS (1)
Vollsveien 13 C-Granfossen Naringspark,
Lysaker, 1366, Oslo, Norway
Tel.: (47) 66100300
Sea Freight Transportation Services
N.A.I.C.S.: 483111

CMA CGM SERBIA (1)
Bulevar Mihaila Pupina 10Z/116 1 Floor,
11070, Belgrade, Serbia
Tel.: (381) 113119161
Sea Freight Transportation Services
N.A.I.C.S.: 483111

CMA CGM SHIPPING AGENCIES
UKRAINE LTD (1)
10 Bunina St 5th Fl, 65026, Odessa,
Ukraine
Tel.: (380) 487777333
Sea Freight Transportation Services
N.A.I.C.S.: 483111
Anna Sapryko (Mgr-Sls)

CMA CGM SLOVENIA (1)
Vojkovo Nabrezje 30, 6000, Koper, Slove-
nia
Tel.: (386) 56625360
Sea Freight Transportation Services
N.A.I.C.S.: 483111
Bine Stancar (Gen Mgr)

CMA CGM ST LUCIA LTD (1)
Hibiscus Crescent - Sans Souci, Castries,
Saint Lucia
Tel.: (758) 7584517310
Sea Freight Transportation Services
N.A.I.C.S.: 483111
Cynthia Saint Omer (Mgr-Accounts)

CMA CGM ST MARTEEN (1)
8 Ground dove Road, Pointe Blanche,
Philipsburg, Saint Martin
Tel.: (721) 590690000000
Sea Freight Transportation Services
N.A.I.C.S.: 483111

CMA CGM SUDAN (1)
Office No 420 4th Fl Burj Libya Building
Nile Street, 1111, Khartoum, Sudan
Tel.: (249) 183246321
Sea Freight Transportation Services
N.A.I.C.S.: 483111

CMA CGM South Africa (Pty)
Ltd. (1)
57 Richefond Circle - Building A - Rid-
gevlew Office Park, Durban, 4319, South
Africa
Tel.: (27) 860262246
Cargo Services
N.A.I.C.S.: 488510

CMA CGM TRINIDAD LTD (1)
4th Floor Furness Building 90 Indepen-
dence Square, Port of Spain, Trinidad &
Tobago
Tel.: (868) 8686242546
Sea Freight Transportation Services
N.A.I.C.S.: 483111

CMA CGM TURKEY (1)
Guney Plaza Eski Buyukdere Cd No13
Maslak, 34398, Istanbul, Türkiye
Tel.: (90) 2123403000
Sea Freight Transportation Services
N.A.I.C.S.: 483111
Fadi Issa (Mng Dir)

CMA CGM UK Shipping Ltd (1)
12 Princes Parade, Liverpool, L3 1BG,
United Kingdom
Tel.: (44) 1512271771
Emp.: 270
Sea Freight Transportation Services
N.A.I.C.S.: 483111

CMA CGM VENEZUELA (1)
Av Bolivar Norte Torre Principal - Piso 11
Ph A, Valencia, Spain
Tel.: (34) 2415150250
Sea Freight Transportation Services
N.A.I.C.S.: 483111
Raul Rincon (Branch Mgr-Caracas & Mgr-
D&D)

Cheng Lie Navigation Co., Ltd. (1)
15F No 10 Sec 3 Minsheng East Road,
Zhongshan District, Taipei, 10480, Taiwan
Tel.: (886) 221832888
Web Site: http://www.cncline.com.tw
Sales Range: $50-74.9 Million
Emp.: 107
Intra-Asia Shipping Services
N.A.I.C.S.: 483111
Robert Sallons (Mng Dir)

Comanav (1)
7 bd de la Resistance, 20300, Casablanca,
Morocco
Tel.: (212) 22 30 30 12
Sales Range: $1-4.9 Billion
Emp.: 2,740
Cargo & Passengers Sea Transport Ser-
vices; Port Operations
N.A.I.C.S.: 483111

Compagnie Generale Maritime (1)
22 Quai De Galliene, Suresnes, 92158,
France (99%)
Tel.: (33) 146257000
Web Site: http://www.cma.com
Rev.: $1,033,000,000
Emp.: 290
Shipping

N.A.I.C.S.: 483111

Containerships-CMA CGM
GmbH (1)
Chilehaus A Fischertwiete 2, 20095, Ham-
burg, Germany
Tel.: (49) 40361580
Web Site:
    http://www.containershipsgroup.com
Maritime Transport Services
N.A.I.C.S.: 488390
Guillaume Lathelize (Co-Mng Dir)

Delmas (1)
1 Quai Colbert, BP 7007X, Le Havre,
76080, France
Tel.: (33) 232741000
Web Site: http://www.delmas.com
Sales Range: $200-249.9 Million
Emp.: 600
Deep Sea Cargo Shipping
N.A.I.C.S.: 483111
Mathieu Friedberg (Gen Mgr)

Subsidiary (Non-US):

Delmas (UK) Limited (2)
52 Charlotte Street, Birmingham, B3 1AR,
United Kingdom
Tel.: (44) 1212365046
Web Site: http://www.delmas.com
Maritime Shipping Services
N.A.I.C.S.: 483111

Kingston Freeport Terminal Ltd. (1)
Port Bustamante G P O, PO Box 214,
Kingston, Jamaica
Tel.: (876) 187692351415
Web Site: http://www.kftl-jm.com
Container Terminal Services
N.A.I.C.S.: 488310

LCL Logistix (India) Pvt. Ltd. (1)
Der Deutsche Parkz 3rd Floor, Adjacent to
Nahur Station Subhash Nagar Road
Bhandup W. Mumbai. 400 078.
India (60%)
Tel.: (91) 22 6640 9999
Web Site: http://www.lcllogistix.com
Emp.: 500
Transportation & Logistics Services
N.A.I.C.S.: 488510
Vibhu Prakash (CEO & Mng Dir)

Subsidiary (Non-US):

LCL Logistix Tanzania Ltd. (2)
2nd Floor Harbour View Towers Samora
Avenue, PO Box 6936, Dar es Salaam,
Tanzania
Tel.: (255) 2110851
Web Site: http://www.lcllogistix.com
Logistics Consulting Servies
N.A.I.C.S.: 541614

MacAndrews & Company
Limited (1)
75 King William Street 6th Floor, London,
EC4N 7BE, United Kingdom
Tel.: (44) 2072206100
Web Site: http://www.macandrews.com
Emp.: 500
Ocean Air & Land Transportation Distr
N.A.I.C.S.: 483111

Neptune Orient Lines Limited (1)
9 North Buona Vista Drive, #14-01 The Me-
tropolis Tower 1, Singapore, 138588,
Singapore (100%)
Tel.: (65) 62789000
Web Site: http://www.nol.com.sg
Sales Range: $5-14.9 Billion
Global Transportation, Logistics & Shipping
Services
N.A.I.C.S.: 488510
Lee Hwa Looi (Chief Compliance Officer,
Gen Counsel & Sec)

Subsidiary (Domestic):

APL Co. Pte. Ltd. (2)
9 North Buona Vista Drive #14-01 The Me-
tropolis Tower 1, Singapore, 138588,
Singapore (100%)
Tel.: (65) 6278 9000
Web Site: http://www.apl.com
Freight Shipping & Logistics Services
N.A.I.C.S.: 488510
Lars Kastrup (CEO)

Subsidiary (US):

APL (America) LLC (3)
3501 Jamboree Rd Ste 300, Newport
Beach, CA 92660
Tel.: (714) 885-8118
Freight Shipping & Cargo Handling Services
N.A.I.C.S.: 488510
Lars Kastrup (Pres)

Subsidiary (Domestic):

APL Maritime, Ltd. (4)
6110 Executive Blvd Ste 410, Rockville, MD
20852
Tel.: (301) 468-7511
Freight Shipping Services
N.A.I.C.S.: 483111

Subsidiary (Non-US):

APL Bangladesh Pvt. Ltd. (3)
4th Floor Finlay House, Agrabad Commer-
cial Area, Chittagong, 4100, Bangladesh
Tel.: (880) 31714063
Web Site: http://www.apllogistics.com
Freight Transportation Services
N.A.I.C.S.: 488510

Representative Office (Non-US):

APL Co. Pte. Ltd. - Europe
Office (3)
Eagle Court 9 Vine Street, Uxbridge, UB8
1QE, Mddx, United Kingdom
Tel.: (44) 1895202600
Freight Transportation Services
N.A.I.C.S.: 488510

APL Co. Pte. Ltd. - Middle East
Office (3)
4th Floor Rais Hassan Saadi Building
Mankhool Road Building, Bur Dubai District,
Dubai, United Arab Emirates
Tel.: (971) 4521 6000
Freight Transportation Services
N.A.I.C.S.: 488510

Subsidiary (Non-US):

APL Vietnam Limited (3)
17 Ba Huyen Thanh Quan Street, District 3,
Ho Chi Minh City, Vietnam
Tel.: (84) 8 3822 1199
Freight Transportation Services
N.A.I.C.S.: 488510

APL-NOL (M) Sdn. Bhd. (3)
Suite 18-03A Level 18 Menara MSC Cyber-
port, No 5 Jalan Bukit Meldrum, 80300, Jo-
hor Bahru, Johor, Malaysia
Tel.: (60) 7 291 3088
Freight Transportation Services
N.A.I.C.S.: 488510

Progeco (1)
4 Qusuai Garenc, 13002, Marseille, France
Tel.: (33) 495093760
Web Site: http://www.progeco.fr
Sales Range: $25-49.9 Million
Emp.: 30
Purchasing, Renting & Repairing of Mari-
time Shipping Containers
N.A.I.C.S.: 488390

CMBC CAPITAL HOLDINGS
LIMITED
45/F One Exchange Square 8 Con-
naught Place Central, Hong Kong,
China (Hong Kong)
Tel.: (852) 37288000   BM
Web Site: http://www.cmbccap.com
Year Founded: 1997
1141—(HKG)
Rev.: $102,252,578
Assets: $1,383,374,618
Liabilities: $1,179,456,473
Net Worth: $203,918,145
Earnings: ($55,666,118)
Emp.: 75
Fiscal Year-end: 12/31/22
Investment Holdings & Securities In-
vestment Services
N.A.I.C.S.: 523150
Jinze Li (Chm)

CMC CORPORATION

1-1-19 Heiwa, Naka-ku, Nagoya, 460-0021, Aichi, Japan
Tel.: (81) 523223351
Web Site: https://www.cmc.co.jp
Year Founded: 1962
2185—(TKS)
Rev.: $130,817,590
Assets: $175,449,140
Liabilities: $39,165,160
Net Worth: $136,283,980
Earnings: $12,492,580
Emp.: 862
Fiscal Year-end: 09/30/23
Printing Services
N.A.I.C.S.: 323111
Yukiyasu Sasa *(Pres & CEO)*

Subsidiaries:

CMC Solutions INC.   (1)
2-3-4 Nishiki Nagoya Nishiki Front Tower
7th floor, Naka-ku, Nagoya, 460-0003, Aichi, Japan
Tel.: (81) 522220880
Emp.: 109
Computer Software Consulting Services
N.A.I.C.S.: 541512

CMC Xmanicom Co., Ltd.   (1)
3-11-9 Ginza, Chuo-ku, Tokyo, 104-0061, Japan
Tel.: (81) 342139800
Web Site: https://www.cmc-xmanicom.co.jp
Digital Technology Services
N.A.I.C.S.: 541519

Cmc Asia Pacific Co., Ltd.   (1)
153/3 Goldenland Building Soi Mahardlekluang 1 Rajdamri Road, Lumpini, Bangkok, 10330, Thailand
Tel.: (66) 26521747
Document Preparation Services
N.A.I.C.S.: 561410

Gcmc Information Technology Co., Ltd.   (1)
Room B1 8th Floor Goldman Sachs Building No 109 Tiyu West Road, Tianhe District, Guangzhou, China
Tel.: (86) 208 981 1917
Web Site: https://www.cmc-china.cn
Document Preparation Services
N.A.I.C.S.: 561410

Kimura Information Technology Co., Ltd.   (1)
6-1 Oroshihonmachi, Saga, 849-0933, Japan
Tel.: (81) 95 231 3901
Web Site: https://www.k-idea.jp
Information Technology Services
N.A.I.C.S.: 541511

Main Co., Ltd.   (1)
2F Plex Building 3-12-17 Mita, Minato-ku, Tokyo, 108-0073, Japan
Tel.: (81) 354840541
Document Preparation Services
N.A.I.C.S.: 561410

Maruboshi Europe B.V.   (1)
Bright Offices Building A 3rd Floor La Guardiaweg 36-66, 1043 DJ, Amsterdam, Netherlands
Tel.: (31) 20 436 9191
Web Site: https://www.maruboshi.nl
Document Preparation Services
N.A.I.C.S.: 561410

Maruboshi Thailand Co., Ltd.   (1)
2 Jasmine City Bldg 20th Floor Unit 20A Soi Prasarnmitr Sukhumvit Road, Klongton Nua Wattana, Bangkok, 10110, Thailand
Tel.: (66) 22042245
Web Site: https://www.maruboshi.co.th
Emp.: 19
Document Preparation Services
N.A.I.C.S.: 561410
Takashi Okita *(Dir)*

CMC INVESTMENT JOINT STOCK COMPANY
Alley 83 Ngoc Hoi, Hoang Mai District, Hanoi, Vietnam
Tel.: (84) 438612718
Web Site: https://www.cmci.com.vn

CMC—(HNX)
Rev.: $4,930,400
Assets: $15,849,800
Liabilities: $9,850,100
Net Worth: $5,999,700
Earnings: ($175,200)
Fiscal Year-end: 12/31/22
Automobile Mfr
N.A.I.C.S.: 336110
Ngo Trong Vinh *(Chm-Mgmt Bd)*

CMC JOINT STOCK COMPANY
Lot B10 - B11 Thuy Van Industrial Park, Thuy Van, Viet Tri, Phu Tho, Vietnam
Tel.: (84) 2103991706
Web Site: https://www.cmctile.com.vn
Year Founded: 1960
CVT—(HNX)
Sales Range: Less than $1 Million
Construction Product Mfr
N.A.I.C.S.: 327120
Tran Duc Huy *(Chm & Deputy CEO)*

CMC MAGNETICS CORPORATION
15th Fl No 53 Ming Chuan W Road, Zhongshan Dist, Taipei, 10452, Taiwan
Tel.: (886) 225989890
Web Site: https://www.cmcnet.com.tw
2323—(TAI)
Rev.: $241,487,515
Assets: $833,723,439
Liabilities: $218,284,305
Net Worth: $615,439,134
Earnings: $57,530,885
Emp.: 577
Fiscal Year-end: 12/31/23
Optical Storage Media Developer
N.A.I.C.S.: 333248
Ming-Sen Wong *(Chm & Gen Mgr)*

Subsidiaries:

Hotan Corp.   (1)
751 N Canyons Pkwy, Livermore, CA 94551
Tel.: (925) 290-1000
Web Site: http://www.hotan.com
Optical Disk Distr
N.A.I.C.S.: 423690

Verbatim Corporation   (1)
1200 W T Harris Blvd, Charlotte, NC 28262
Tel.: (704) 547-6500
Web Site: http://www.verbatim.com
Emp.: 125
Mfr & Retailer of Data Recording & Storage & Technology
N.A.I.C.S.: 334610

Subsidiary (Non-US):

Verbatim (Hong Kong) Limited   (2)
Unit 1101-02 11/F Energy Plaza 92 Granville Road Tsim Sha Tsui East, Tsim Sha Tsui, Kowloon, China (Hong Kong)
Tel.: (852) 2814 1220
Emp.: 2
Storage Device Mfr & Distr
N.A.I.C.S.: 334112

Verbatim (Shenzhen) Int'l Trading Corp. Ltd.   (2)
Unit 2108 21/F Kingkey Binhe Time Tower No 9289 Binhe Road, Futian District, Shenzhen, 518040, China
Tel.: (86) 755 8826 4860
Web Site: http://www.verbatim.com.cn
Storage Device Mfr & Distr
N.A.I.C.S.: 334112

Subsidiary (Domestic):

Verbatim Americas, LLC   (2)
8210 University Executive Park Dr Ste 300, Charlotte, NC 28262
Tel.: (704) 547-6500
Web Site: http://www.verbatim.com
Emp.: 52
Storage Device Mfr & Distr
N.A.I.C.S.: 334112

Subsidiary (Non-US):

Verbatim Australia Pty Ltd   (2)
Unit 6 450 Princes Highway, Noble Park, 3174, VIC, Australia
Tel.: (61) 397908999
Web Site: https://www.verbatim.com.au
Sales Range: $25-49.9 Million
Emp.: 15
Storage Device Mfr & Distr
N.A.I.C.S.: 334112

Verbatim Espana S.A   (2)
Carretera Real 122-B 5 2a, 8960, Sant Just Desvern, Barcelona, Spain
Tel.: (34) 93 470 55 30
Web Site: http://www.verbatim.es
Emp.: 3
Storage Device Mfr & Distr
N.A.I.C.S.: 334112
Niels Johansen *(Gen Mgr)*

Verbatim GmbH   (2)
Dusseldorfer Str 13, 65760, Eschborn, Germany
Tel.: (49) 619690010
Web Site: https://www.verbatim-europe.com
Sales Range: $25-49.9 Million
Emp.: 5
Storage Device Mfr & Distr
N.A.I.C.S.: 334112

Verbatim Italia Spa a Socio unico   (2)
Via Roma 108, 20060, Cassina de' Pecchi, Milan, Italy
Tel.: (39) 029 530 1115
Web Site: http://www.verbatim-europe.co.uk
Storage Device Mfr & Distr
N.A.I.C.S.: 334112

Verbatim Limited   (2)
Prestige House 23-26 High Street, Egham, TW20 9DU, Surrey, United Kingdom
Tel.: (44) 1784 439 781
Web Site: http://www.verbatim-europe.co.uk
Sales Range: $25-49.9 Million
Emp.: 3
Storage Device Mfr & Distr
N.A.I.C.S.: 334112

Verbatim Marketing India Pvt. Ltd.   (2)
Soulstice 1st Floor Plot No 52 Sector-44, Gurgaon, 122003, Haryana, India
Tel.: (91) 981 119 4203
Web Site: http://www.verbatim.com.sg
Sales Range: $25-49.9 Million
Emp.: 2
Storage Device Mfr & Distr
N.A.I.C.S.: 334112

Verbatim Taiwan International Trading Corporate Ltd.   (2)
10F-1 No 40 Sec 2 Dunhua S Rd, Da-an District, Taipei, 10683, Taiwan
Tel.: (886) 2 2700 1086
Web Site: http://www.verbatim.com.sg
Sales Range: $25-49.9 Million
Emp.: 6
Storage Device Mfr & Distr
N.A.I.C.S.: 334112

CMC MARKETS UK PLC
133 Houndsditch, London, EC3A 7BX, United Kingdom
Tel.: (44) 2071708200   UK
Web Site:
    https://www.cmcmarkets.com
Year Founded: 1989
CMCX—(LSE)
Rev.: $403,755,127
Assets: $728,218,840
Liabilities: $263,767,013
Net Worth: $464,451,827
Earnings: $51,458,950
Emp.: 1,087
Fiscal Year-end: 03/31/23
Commodity Contracts Intermediation
N.A.I.C.S.: 523160
Peter Cruddas *(CEO)*

CMC METALS LTD.
Suite 1000 - 409 Granville St, Vancouver, V6C 1T2, BC, Canada
Tel.: (604) 602-0001

Web Site: https://www.cmcmetals.ca
CMB—(TSXV)
Assets: $797,495
Liabilities: $951,193
Net Worth: ($153,698)
Earnings: ($2,378,585)
Fiscal Year-end: 09/30/21
Mineral Exploration Services
N.A.I.C.S.: 213114

CMC TECHNOLOGIES ISRAEL LTD.
Eli Horovitz 19, Rehovot, Israel
Tel.: (972) 86637000
Web Site: http://www.cmcltd.co.il
Year Founded: 1999
Automation & Control Equipment Mfr
N.A.I.C.S.: 333248
Niv Bass *(Engr)*

Subsidiaries:

CMC Hi Tec Controlling Solutions Ltd.   (1)
horowitz 17 floor 1, 5225, Rehovot, Israel
Tel.: (972) 36316919
Web Site: http://www.cmcltd.co.il
Sales Range: $25-49.9 Million
Emp.: 8
Automated Electric Controls Mfr
N.A.I.C.S.: 334513
Rafi Bass *(Chief Mgr)*

CME GORUP BERHAD
Lot 19 Jalan Delima 1/1 Tmn Perindustrian Teknologi Tinggi Subang, 47500, Subang Jaya, Selangor Darul Ehsan, Malaysia
Tel.: (60) 356331188
Web Site: https://www.cme.com.my
CME—(KLS)
Rev.: $2,739,471
Assets: $25,079,153
Liabilities: $14,468,995
Net Worth: $10,610,159
Earnings: ($440,635)
Fiscal Year-end: 09/30/23
Fire Fighting Vehicles Mfr
N.A.I.C.S.: 336211
Azlan Omry Omar *(Exec Dir)*

CMG PHARMACEUTICAL CO., LTD.
B01 18-20 Cheongdam-dong, Gangnam-gu, Seoul, 135-949, Korea (South)
Tel.: (82) 318817661
Web Site: https://cmgpharma.net
Year Founded: 2001
058820—(KRS)
Rev.: $63,045,413
Assets: $163,570,708
Liabilities: $21,711,746
Net Worth: $141,858,962
Earnings: ($297,703)
Emp.: 248
Fiscal Year-end: 12/31/22
Pharmaceuticals Product Mfr
N.A.I.C.S.: 325412
Joohyung Lee *(CEO)*

CMG PTY. LTD.
19 Corporate Ave, Melbourne, 3178, Australia
Tel.: (61) 392374000
Web Site:
    http://www.cmggroup.com.au
Sales Range: $50-74.9 Million
Emp.: 300
Electric Motor Mfr & Distr
N.A.I.C.S.: 335312
Jack Gringlas *(Mng Dir)*

Subsidiaries:

CMG Electric Motors (Asia Pacific) Pte Ltd.   (1)
12 Tuas loop, Singapore, 637346, Singapore   (100%)

CMG Pty. Ltd.—(Continued)

Tel.: (65) 68633473
Web Site: http://www.cmggroup.com.sg
Sales Range: $25-49.9 Million
Emp.: 20
Motor & Generator Mfr
N.A.I.C.S.: 335312
Yapsay Jou *(Mng Dir)*

CMG Electric Motors (UK) Ltd. (1)
Unit A Stafford Park 2, Telford, TF3 3AR,
Shropshire, United Kingdom
Tel.: (44) 1952299606
Sales Range: $50-74.9 Million
Emp.: 8
Electrical Apparatus & Equipment Wiring
Supplies & Construction Material Whslr
N.A.I.C.S.: 423610

**CMG Electric Motors South Africa
(Pty) Ltd.** (1)
268 B Fleming Road Meadowdale, 1610,
Johannesburg, South Africa
Tel.: (27) 114531930
Web Site: http://www.cmggroup.co.za
Sales Range: $25-49.9 Million
Emp.: 50
Motor & Generator Mfr
N.A.I.C.S.: 335312

Regal Beloit Israel (1)
9 Bareket Street Zone 23, North Industrial
Park, 38900, Caesarea, Israel
Tel.: (972) 46270777
Sales Range: $25-49.9 Million
Emp.: 10
Motor & Generator Mfr
N.A.I.C.S.: 335312

Sankey Australia (1)
15 Gaine Rd, Dandenong, 3175, VIC,
Australia (100%)
Tel.: (61) 387875290
Web Site: http://www.sankey.com.au
Sales Range: $25-49.9 Million
Emp.: 45
Metal Products for Industry Designer & Mfr
N.A.I.C.S.: 332999
Neil Sellick *(Gen Mgr)*

**CMGE TECHNOLOGY GROUP
LIMITED**
13/F 8 Wyndham Street, Central,
China (Hong Kong)
Tel.: (852) 27006168 Ky
Year Founded: 2009
0302—(HKG)
Rev.: $381,030,437
Assets: $1,004,387,062
Liabilities: $205,246,688
Net Worth: $799,140,373
Earnings: ($30,449,952)
Emp.: 1,165
Fiscal Year-end: 12/31/22
Investment Management Service
N.A.I.C.S.: 523940
Jian Xiao *(Chm & CEO)*

CMIC HOLDINGS CO., LTD.
Hamamatsucho Bldg 1-1-1 Shibaura,
Minato-ku, Tokyo, 105-0023, Japan
Tel.: (81) 367798000 JP
Web Site: http://en.cmicgroup.com
Year Founded: 1985
2309—(TKS)
Rev.: $830,427,840
Assets: $882,738,560
Liabilities: $548,923,760
Net Worth: $333,814,800
Earnings: $19,582,640
Emp.: 7,878
Fiscal Year-end: 09/30/21
Holding Company; Support Services
for Pharmaceutical Development,
Manufacturing & Sales
N.A.I.C.S.: 551112
Kazuo Nakamura *(Chm & CEO)*

Subsidiaries:

BELL24-Cell Product, Inc. (1)
9-1-4 Nishi 4-Jo Minami, Obihiro, Hokkaido,
Japan

Tel.: (81) 155206411
Pharmaceutical Product & Medical Equip-
ment Mfr
N.A.I.C.S.: 339112

CMIC (Beijing) Co.Ltd. (1)
Unit 02 17th Floor East Twin Tower B-12
Jianguomenwai Avenue, Chaoyang District,
Beijing, 100022, China
Tel.: (86) 1065665220
Web Site: http://www.cmic.co.jp
Sales Range: $25-49.9 Million
Emp.: 20
Pharmaceutical Preparation Mfr
N.A.I.C.S.: 325412

CMIC Ashfield Co., Ltd. (1)
Hamamatsucho Building 1-1-1 Shibaura,
Minato-ku, Tokyo, 105-0023,
Japan (50.1%)
Tel.: (81) 367798141
Web Site: https://www.cmic-inizio.com
Emp.: 850
Pharmaceutical Industry Marketing Solu-
tions & Support Services
N.A.I.C.S.: 541613
Hiroshi Kizaki *(Pres & Operating Officer)*

**CMIC Asia-Pacific (Australia) Pty
Ltd** (1)
L16 71 Eagle St, Brisbane, 4000, QLD,
Australia
Tel.: (61) 227069947
Web Site: https://en.cmicgroup.com
Clinical Monitoring & Site Management Ser-
vices
N.A.I.C.S.: 621999

**CMIC Asia-Pacific (Hong Kong)
Limited** (1)
Unit C 4/F China Insurance Building 48
Cameron Road, Tsim Sha Tsui, Kowloon,
China (Hong Kong)
Tel.: (852) 95587593
Web Site: https://en.cmicgroup.com
Clinical Monitoring & Site Management Ser-
vices
N.A.I.C.S.: 621999

CMIC Asia-Pacific Pte. Ltd. (1)
6 Shenton Way 23-09 OUE Downtown 2,
Singapore, 068809, Singapore
Tel.: (65) 62222655
Web Site: https://www.cmicgroup.com
Support Services for Pharmaceutical Devel-
opment
N.A.I.C.S.: 325412

CMIC CMO Co., Ltd. (1)
1-588 Kanaya Higashi, Shimada, 428-0013,
Shizuoka, Japan
Tel.: (81) 547453191
Web Site: https://www.cmic-cmo.com
Sales Range: $150-199.9 Million
Emp.: 370
Pharmaceutical Product Mfr & Distr
N.A.I.C.S.: 325412

CMIC CMO Korea Co., Ltd. (1)
23 Oksan-ro 230beon-gil, Bucheon, 14521,
Gyeonggi-do, Korea (South)
Tel.: (82) 326785771
Web Site: https://www.cmic-cmo.co.kr
Emp.: 40
Pharmaceuticals Product Mfr
N.A.I.C.S.: 325412
Waedong Lee *(Pres)*

CMIC CMO Nishine Co., Ltd. (1)
154-13 Dai2-chiwari, Obuke, Hachimantai,
105-0023, Iwate Prefecture, Japan
Tel.: (81) 195765111
Emp.: 218
Pharmaceuticals Product Mfr
N.A.I.C.S.: 325412

CMIC CMO USA Corporation (1)
3 Cedar Brook Dr, Cranbury, NJ 08512
Tel.: (609) 395-9700
Pharmaceutical Research & Development
Services
N.A.I.C.S.: 541719
Hiro Sejima *(Pres)*

**CMIC Data Science Vietnam Com-
pany Limited** (1)
421 Tran Hung Dao Street, An Hai Tay
Ward Son Tra District, Da Nang, 550000,
Vietnam
Tel.: (84) 2363566444

Clinical Data Management Services
N.A.I.C.S.: 621999

**CMIC HealthCare Institute Co.,
Ltd.** (1)
Hamamatsucho Building 1 1-1 Shibaura,
Minato-ku, Tokyo, 105-0023, Japan
Tel.: (81) 367798160
Web Site: https://www.cmic-hci.com
Emp.: 900
Clinical Trial Facility Support Services
N.A.I.C.S.: 561210

CMIC Korea Co.Ltd. (1)
10F Gangnam N Tower 129 Teheran-ro,
Gangnam-gu, 06133, Seoul, 06133, Korea
(South)
Tel.: (82) 237083600
Web Site: http://www.cmic.co.kr
Pharmaceutical Preparation Mfr
N.A.I.C.S.: 325412

CMIC SS CMO Co. Ltd. (1)
2-37 Ariso, Izumi-shi, Toyama, 933-0251,
Japan
Tel.: (81) 766863501
Web Site: http://www.cmic.co.jp
Sales Range: $25-49.9 Million
Emp.: 50
Pharmaceutical Preparation Mfr
N.A.I.C.S.: 325412
Shinya Yamaguchi *(Pres)*

CMIC ShiftZero K.K. (1)
Web Site: http://www.shiftzerokk.com
Clinical CRO Services
N.A.I.C.S.: 541714

CMIC Solutions Co., Ltd. (1)
Hamamatsucho Building 17F 1-1-1,
Shibaura Minato-ku, Tokyo, 105-0023, Ja-
pan
Tel.: (81) 367798006
Web Site: http://www.cmic-career.co.jp
Temporary Staffing Services
N.A.I.C.S.: 561320
Yoshiyuki Hano *(Pres)*

CMIC, Inc. (1)
2860 Forbs Ave, Hoffman Estates, IL
60192-3702
Tel.: (847) 645-0407
Laboratory Bioanalytical Services
N.A.I.C.S.: 541380

CMIC-BS Co.Ltd. (1)
Hamamatsucho Building 17F 1-1-1
Shibaura, Minato - ku, Tokyo, 105-0023,
Japan
Tel.: (81) 367798006
Web Site: https://cmic-solutions.co.jp
Sales Range: $150-199.9 Million
Emp.: 700
All Other Business Support Services
N.A.I.C.S.: 561499

CMIC-CP Co. Ltd. (1)
Kongo Bldg 7-10-4 Nishi-Gotanda, 141-
0031, Tokyo, Shinagawa-ku, Japan
Tel.: (81) 357457085
Web Site: http://www.cmic.co.jp
Temporary Help Service
N.A.I.C.S.: 561320

CMIC-CRC Co. Ltd. (1)
2nd Floor Kongo Bldg 7-10-4 Nishi-
Gotanda, Shinagawa-ku, 141-0031, Tokyo,
Japan
Tel.: (81) 357456611
All Other Business Support Services
N.A.I.C.S.: 561499

**Haedong SS Pharmaceutical Co.
Ltd** (1)
157-3 Dodang-dong Wonmi-gu Puchon-city,
Seoul, Korea (South)
Tel.: (82) 326785771
Pharmaceutical Preparation Mfr
N.A.I.C.S.: 325412
Jong Chul Kim *(CEO)*

Healthclick Co., Ltd. (1)
7-10-4 Nishigotanda Kongo Building 1 2f,
Shinagawa-ku, Tokyo, 141-0031, Japan
Tel.: (81) 357456505
Web Site: http://www.healthclick.co.jp
Health Care Services
N.A.I.C.S.: 621999

MDS Co. Ltd. (1)
8F Nissei Kandasudacho Building 2-6-6

Kandasudacho, Chiyoda-ku, Tokyo, 101-
0041, Japan
Tel.: (81) 332560080
Emp.: 246
Power Distribution & Specialty Transformer
Mfr
N.A.I.C.S.: 335311
Satoshi Shitomi *(Pres & CEO)*

**CMISTONE VIET NAM JOINT
STOCK COMPANY**
No 27 Giai Phong Dong Tam, Hai Ba
Trung, Hanoi, Vietnam
Tel.: (84) 437875441
Web Site: http://www.cmistone.vn
Sales Range: $1-9.9 Million
Emp.: 60
Stone Quarry Services
N.A.I.C.S.: 212312
Trieu Van Nam *(Gen Dir)*

CMK CORPORATION
43/F Shinjuku I-LAND TOWER Bldg
6-5-1 Nishi-Shinjuku, Shinjuku-ku,
Tokyo, 163-1388, Japan
Tel.: (81) 353230231
Web Site: https://www.cmk-corp.com
Year Founded: 1961
6958—(TKS)
Rev.: $598,654,480
Assets: $869,915,660
Liabilities: $387,960,730
Net Worth: $481,954,930
Earnings: $25,481,550
Emp.: 1,155
Fiscal Year-end: 03/31/24
Circuit Board Mfr
N.A.I.C.S.: 334412
Isao Osawa *(Chm, Pres & CEO)*

Subsidiaries:

CMK America Corporation (1)
175 Handley Rd Ste 300, Tyrone, GA
30290
Tel.: (770) 632-7173
Sales Range: $50-74.9 Million
Emp.: 5
Circuit Board Distr
N.A.I.C.S.: 423690
Kazahiro Ouchi *(Pres)*

**CMK Corporation (Thailand) Co.,
Ltd.** (1)
1 Empire Tower 27th Floor Unit 2705 South
Sathorn Road Yannawa, Sathorn, Bangkok,
10120, Thailand
Tel.: (66) 26595713
Sales Range: $200-249.9 Million
Emp.: 1,000
Circuit Board Mfr
N.A.I.C.S.: 334412
Yasuhiro Miura *(Mng Dir)*

**CMK Corporation - G Station
Plant** (1)
236 Imai Shiba-machi, Isesaki, 372-0824,
Gunma, Japan
Tel.: (81) 270322063
Web Site: http://www.cmk-corp.com
Circuit Board Mfr
N.A.I.C.S.: 334412

**CMK Corporation - KIBAN Center
Plant** (1)
48-1 Toyatsuka-cho, Isesaki, 372-0825,
Gunma, Japan
Tel.: (81) 270328585
Sales Range: $400-449.9 Million
Emp.: 2,000
Flat Screen Televisions Mfr
N.A.I.C.S.: 334220

**CMK Corporation - Niigata Satellite
Plant** (1)
3-75-6 Higashi-ko, Seiro-machi
Kitakanbara-gun, Niigata, 957-0101, Japan
Tel.: (81) 252561311
Web Site: http://www.cmk-corp.com
Printed Circuit Board Mfr
N.A.I.C.S.: 334412

**CMK Corporation - Technical Center
Plant** (1)
1744-1 Naganuma-cho, Isesaki, 372-0855,

Gunma, Japan
Tel.: (81) 270324567
Web Site: http://www.cmk-corp.com
Industrial Technology Development Services
N.A.I.C.S.: 541715

CMK EUROPE N.V. (1)
Lammerdries 18 A, 2440, Geel, Belgium
Tel.: (32) 14259400
Web Site: http://www.cmk-corp.com
Sales Range: $25-49.9 Million
Emp.: 10
Printed Circuit Board Mfr
N.A.I.C.S.: 334412

CMK Electronics (Wuxi) Co., Ltd. (1)
65-A wuxi High-Tech Industrial Development
Zone, Wuxi National High & New Tech In-
dustrial Development Zone, Wuxi, 214028,
Jiangsu, China
Tel.: (86) 51085229255
Web Site: http://www.cmk-corp.com.cn
Printed Circuit Board Mfr
N.A.I.C.S.: 334412

CMK Finance Corporation (1)
Shinjuku I-Land Tower 43/F 6-5-1 Nishi-
Shinjuku, Shinjuku-Ku, Tokyo, 163-1388,
Japan
Tel.: (81) 353230231
Financial Support Services
N.A.I.C.S.: 523999

**CMK Kanbara Electronic
Corporation** (1)
1-2-5 Muramatsu-Kougyoudanchi, Gosen,
959-1739, Niigata, Japan
Tel.: (81) 250588737
Sales Range: $100-124.9 Million
Emp.: 297
Printed Circuit Board Mfr
N.A.I.C.S.: 334412
Kimura Makoto (Pres)

CMK Mechanics Corporation (1)
560 Shimoyoshida, Chichibu, 369-1503,
Saitama, Japan
Tel.: (81) 494771331
Web Site: http://www.cmk-mechanics.co.jp
Maintenance Machinery Equipment Mfr &
Sales
N.A.I.C.S.: 333248

CMK Multi Corporation (1)
3-75-6 Higashi-ko Seirou-machi,
Kitakanbara-gun, Niigata, 957-0101, Japan
Tel.: (81) 252561391
Web Site: http://www.cmk-corp.com
Rev.: $132,184,000
Emp.: 700
Printed Circuit Board Mfr
N.A.I.C.S.: 333248
Kazuo Inoue (Mgr-General Affairs Dept)

CMK Niigata Corporation (1)
3-75-6 Higashi-ko Seiro-machi,
Kitakanbara-gun, Niigata, 957-0101, Japan
Tel.: (81) 252561311
Web Site: http://www.cmk-corp.com
Printed Circuit Board Mfr
N.A.I.C.S.: 334412

CMK Products Corporation (1)
1-1-11 Tana Shioda, Chuo-ku, Sagamihara,
252-0245, Kanagawa, Japan
Tel.: (81) 427633188
Web Site: https://www.cmkp.co.jp
Sales Range: $100-124.9 Million
Emp.: 200
Printed Circuit Board Mfr
N.A.I.C.S.: 334412

CMKC (Dong Guan) Ltd. (1)
No 5 West Lane 1 Xiegang Square Middle
Road, Xiegang Town, Dongguan, Guang-
dong, China
Tel.: (86) 76987767751
Printed Wiring Board Mfr
N.A.I.C.S.: 334412

CMKC (Hong Kong) Ltd. (1)
Suites Nos 1201A 1215 12 F Exchange
Tower 33 Wang Chiu Rd, Kowloon Bay,
Kowloon, China (Hong Kong)
Tel.: (852) 27212252
Emp.: 120
Printed Circuit Board Mfr
N.A.I.C.S.: 334412

Yamanashi Sanko Co., Ltd. (1)
674 Shimojouminamiware Tatsuoka-cho,

Nirasaki, 407-0033, Yamanashi, Japan
Tel.: (81) 551228065
Web Site: http://www.cmk-corp.com
Sales Range: $50-74.9 Million
Emp.: 120
Electronic Printed Circuit Board Mfr
N.A.I.C.S.: 334412

CML GLOBAL CAPITAL LTD.
Suite 1200 833 4th Avenue South-
west, Calgary, T2P 3T5, AB, Canada
Tel.: (403) 216-3850　　　Ca
Year Founded: 1992
Sales Range: $10-24.9 Million
Emp.: 150
Investment Services
N.A.I.C.S.: 523999
Joy McDonald (Office Mgr)

Subsidiaries:

Aspen Property Management
Ltd. (1)
1300 112 4 Avenue SW, Calgary, T2P 0H3,
AB, Canada
Tel.: (403) 216-2660
Web Site: http://www.aspenproperties.ca
Sales Range: $25-49.9 Million
Industrial & Warehouse Properties Acquirer
& Developer
N.A.I.C.S.: 525990
R. Scott Hutcheson (Chm)

CML MICROSYSTEMS PLC
Oval Park, Langford, Maldon, CM9
6WG, Essex, United Kingdom
Tel.: (44) 1621875500　　　UK
Web Site:
　　https://www.cmlmicroplc.com
CML—(AIM)
Rev.: $28,894,276
Assets: $87,238,244
Liabilities: $22,759,449
Net Worth: $64,478,795
Earnings: $2,600,359
Fiscal Year-end: 03/31/24
Holding Company; Integrated Circuits
Mfr
N.A.I.C.S.: 551112
Nigel G. Clark (Co-Sec)

Subsidiaries:

CML Microcircuits (UK) Ltd. (1)
Oval Park, Langford, Maldon, CM9 6WG,
Essex, United Kingdom
Tel.: (44) 1621875500
Web Site: http://www.cmlmicro.com
Sales Range: $25-49.9 Million
Emp.: 80
Communication Integrated Circuits Mfr &
Distr
N.A.I.C.S.: 334413

Subsidiary (Non-US):

**CML Microcircuits (Singapore) Pte.
Ltd.** (2)
150 Kampong Ampat 05-03A KA Centre,
Singapore, 368324, Singapore
Tel.: (65) 62888129
Web Site: http://www.cmlmicro.com
Sales Range: $25-49.9 Million
Emp.: 5
Communication Integrated Circuits Mfr &
Supplier
N.A.I.C.S.: 334413
Dennis Ng Wee Han (Mng Dir-Sls)

Subsidiary (US):

CML Microcircuits (USA) Inc. (2)
486 N Patterson Ave Ste 301, Winston Sa-
lem, NC 27101
Tel.: (336) 744-5050
Web Site: http://www.cmlmicro.com
Sales Range: $25-49.9 Million
Emp.: 16
Communication Integrated Circuits Mfr &
Supplier
N.A.I.C.S.: 334413

Microwave Technology, Inc. (1)
4268 Solar Way, Fremont, CA 94538
Tel.: (510) 651-6700
Web Site: http://www.mwtinc.com

Amplifiers Mfr
N.A.I.C.S.: 334413
Nathan Zommer (Chm)

Radio Data Technology Ltd. (1)
Unit Bay 1 vitton Rd Industrial Estate E,
Witham, CM8 3UJ, Essex, United Kingdom
Tel.: (44) 1376501255
Web Site: http://www.radiodata.co.uk
Sales Range: $25-49.9 Million
Emp.: 15
Wireless Data Video & Telemetry Products
Mfr
N.A.I.C.S.: 334210

**CMM INFRAPROJECTS LIM-
ITED**
2/2 Old Palasiya F No 1 Khan Build-
ing, Old Palasiya, Indore, 452001,
India
Tel.: (91) 7312516386
CMMIPL—(NSE)
Rev.: $7,594,226
Assets: $17,993,428
Liabilities: $10,236,326
Net Worth: $7,757,102
Earnings: $27,519
Fiscal Year-end: 03/12/21
Construction Services
N.A.I.C.S.: 236210

CMO GROUP PLC
Burrington Business Park Burrington
Way, Plymouth, PL5 3LX, Devon,
United Kingdom
Tel.: (44) 1752692769　　　UK
Web Site: https://www.cmogroup.com
Year Founded: 2008
CMO—(AIM)
Rev.: $91,029,741
Assets: $49,100,518
Liabilities: $28,221,082
Net Worth: $20,879,436
Earnings: ($2,335,835)
Emp.: 6
Fiscal Year-end: 12/31/23
All Other Miscellaneous Retailers
N.A.I.C.S.: 459999

**CMO PUBLIC COMPANY LIM-
ITED**
4/18-19 Soi Nuanchan 56 Nuanchan
Buengkum, Bangkok, 10230, Thai-
land
Tel.: (66) 20883888
Web Site: https://www.cmo-
group.com
Year Founded: 1991
CMO—(THA)
Rev.: $37,277,424
Assets: $32,761,055
Liabilities: $22,376,693
Net Worth: $10,384,362
Earnings: ($4,569,327)
Emp.: 423
Fiscal Year-end: 12/31/23
Marketing Communication Services
N.A.I.C.S.: 561499
Nantiya Sowapast (CFO-Acting)

Subsidiaries:

Muse Corporation Company
Limited (1)
4/27 Soi Nuan Chan 56, Nuanchan Bueng
kum, Bangkok, 10230, Thailand
Tel.: (66) 962491495
Web Site: https://musecorporation.com
Live Streaming Services
N.A.I.C.S.: 518210

PM Center Co., Ltd. (1)
4/22 Soi Nuanchan 56, Nuanchan Bueng-
kum, Bangkok, 10230, Thailand
Tel.: (66) 20919888
Web Site: https://www.pmcenter.co.th
Light & Sound System Rental Services
N.A.I.C.S.: 532490

The Eyes Co., Ltd (1)
4/27 Soi Nuanchan 56, Nuanchan Buengkum, Bangkok, 10230, Thailand

Tel.: (66) 2 944 5683
Web Site: https://theeyes.co.th
Multimedia & Video Presentation Services
N.A.I.C.S.: 512131

CMOC GROUP LIMITED
North Yihe Huamei Shan Road, Lu-
anchuan, Luoyang, Henan, China
Tel.: (86) 37968658029
Web Site: https://en.cmoc.com
Year Founded: 1969
603993—(SHG)
Rev.: $17,309,821,864
Assets: $18,759,223,896
Liabilities: $11,507,050,760
Net Worth: $7,252,173,135
Earnings: $379,752,518
Emp.: 10,956
Fiscal Year-end: 12/31/20
Mineral Exploration Services
N.A.I.C.S.: 213115
Faben Li (Gen Mgr)

CMON LIMITED
201 Henderson Road 07/08 -01 Apex
Henderson, Singapore, 159545,
Singapore　　　　　　　Ky
Web Site: https://www.cmon.com
Year Founded: 2001
1792—(HKG)
Rev.: $45,337,007,000
Assets: $37,678,807,000
Liabilities: $19,063,382,000
Net Worth: $18,615,425,000
Earnings: $510,101,000
Emp.: 78
Fiscal Year-end: 12/31/22
Software Development Services
N.A.I.C.S.: 541511
Chern Ann Ng (Chm)

**CMP - CLASSIC AUTOMOTIVE
LTD**
1313 36 St NE, Calgary, T2A 6P9,
AB, Canada
Tel.: (403) 207-1000
Web Site: http://www.cmpauto.com
Sales Range: $150-199.9 Million
Emp.: 200
Automobile Sales & Servicing
N.A.I.C.S.: 441110
Bob Blevins (Dir-Svc)

**CMP ADVANCED MECHANI-
CAL SOLUTIONS LTD.**
1241 Cascades St, Chateauguay, J6J
4Z2, QC, Canada
Tel.: (450) 691-5510
Web Site:
　　http://www.cmpdifference.com
Year Founded: 1969
Rev.: $46,403,534
Emp.: 400
Metals Mfr
N.A.I.C.S.: 332431
Steve Zimmermann (Pres & CEO)

**CMP CAPITAL MANAGEMENT-
PARTNERS GMBH**
Kurfurstendamm 185, Berlin, 10707,
Germany
Tel.: (49) 303940690　　　De
Web Site: http://www.cm-p.de
Year Founded: 2000
Emp.: 17
Privater Equity Firm
N.A.I.C.S.: 523999
Kai Brandes (Mng Partner)

Subsidiaries:

Pressmetall Gunzenhausen GmbH &
Co. KG (1)
Alemannenstrasse 20, Gunzenhausen,
91710, Germany
Tel.: (49) 983150070
Web Site: http://www.pressmetall.de

CMP Capital Management-Partners
GmbH—(Continued)

Sales Range: $125-149.9 Million
Precision Product Mfr
N.A.I.C.S.: 332721
Simon Strauss *(Mgr-Sls)*

UKM Fahrzeugteile GmbH (1)
Salzstrasse 3, D 09629, Reinsberg, Germany
Tel.: (49) 35 242 65 61 115
Web Site: http://www.ukm-gruppe.com
Emp.: 300
Automotive Components Mfr
N.A.I.C.S.: 336390
Dieter Maier *(Mng Dir)*

CMP MINING INC.
Suite 2820 200 Granville Street, Vancouver, V6C 1S4, BC, Canada
Tel.: (778) 238-2333
Year Founded: 2018
CMP—(CNSX)
Rev.: $49
Assets: $124,958
Liabilities: $89,285
Net Worth: $35,673
Earnings: ($58,514)
Fiscal Year-end: 05/31/24
Mineral Exploration Services
N.A.I.C.S.: 212390
Rick Trotman *(CEO)*

CMR GMBH
Parkstrasse 49, Modling, Austria
Tel.: (43) 2236 86 59 48
Private Equity Company
N.A.I.C.S.: 523999

Subsidiaries:

Rofin-Sinar UK Ltd. (1)
Meadow Rd, Bridgehead Business Park,
Kingston upon Hull, HU13 0DG, United Kingdom
Tel.: (44) 1482650088
Web Site: http://www.rofin-uk.com
Sealed Carbon Dioxide Lasers Designer,
Developer & Mfr
N.A.I.C.S.: 334419
Jason LEe *(Dir-R&D)*

CMS CAMERON MCKENNA NABARRO OLSWANG LLP
Cannon Place 78 Cannon Street,
London, EC4N 6AF, United Kingdom
Tel.: (44) 20 73 67 3000
Web Site: http://www.cms.law
Year Founded: 1999
Law firm
N.A.I.C.S.: 541110
Penelope Warne *(Chm, Head-Energy & Sr Partner)*

Subsidiaries:

Nabarro LLP (1)
1 South Quay Victoria Quays, Sheffield, S2
5SY, United Kingdom
Tel.: (44) 114 279 4000
Law firm
N.A.I.C.S.: 541110

Olswang LLP (1)
Cannon Place 78 Cannon Street, London,
EC4N 6AF, United Kingdom
Tel.: (44) 20 7067 3000
Law firm
N.A.I.C.S.: 541110

CMS COMPUTERS LTD.
CMS Lake Road Center 70 Lake
Road, Kaycee Industries Compound,
Mumbai, 400 078, India
Tel.: (91) 2267489000
Web Site: http://www.cms.com
Sales Range: $100-124.9 Million
Emp.: 6,000
IT Consulting & Product Design Services & Solutions
N.A.I.C.S.: 541519
Rajiv Kaul *(Vice Chm & CEO)*

Subsidiaries:

CMS Computers Limited (1)
CMS Lake Rd Ctr 70 Lake Road Kaycee,
Industries Compound Bhandup, Mumbai,
400 078, India (100%)
Tel.: (91) 2267489000
Web Site: http://www.cms.co.in
Sales Range: $25-49.9 Million
Emp.: 200
Computer System Services
N.A.I.C.S.: 541512

CMS Traffic Systems Limited (1)
70 lake Road, Bhandup West, 400078,
Mumbai, India
Tel.: (91) 2230780222
All Other Support Activities for Transportation
N.A.I.C.S.: 488999

Kaycee Ind. Ltd. (1)
32 Ramjibhai Kamani Road, Ballard Estate,
Mumbai, 400 001, India (100%)
Tel.: (91) 2222613521
Web Site: http://www.kayceeindustries.com
Sales Range: $100-124.9 Million
Emp.: 300
Switchgear & Switchboard Apparate Mfr
N.A.I.C.S.: 335313
Santosh kumar Nair *(Gen Mgr)*

SYSTIME (1)
155 Millennium Business Park Mahape,
Navi, 400710, Mumbai, India (100%)
Tel.: (91) 2227783100
Web Site: http://www.systime.net
Sales Range: $25-49.9 Million
Emp.: 40
Business Solutions & Computer Related
Services
N.A.I.C.S.: 541519
Vishal Grover *(Pres & CEO)*

SYSTIME Computer Systems (I) (1)
Ltd.
SEEPZ Customs Wing, Andheri E, 400096,
Mumbai, India (100%)
Tel.: (91) 2228290051
Web Site: http://www.systime.net
Sales Range: $25-49.9 Million
Emp.: 80
Computer System Design Services
N.A.I.C.S.: 541512

CMS INFO SYSTEMS LIMITED
Lobby Level Grand Hyatt MumbaiOff
Western Express Highway, Santacruz
East, Mumbai, 400055, India
Tel.: (91) 2248897400   In
Web Site: https://www.cms.com
Year Founded: 2008
CMSINFO—(NSE)
Rev.: $231,334,812
Assets: $251,930,460
Liabilities: $64,596,967
Net Worth: $187,333,493
Earnings: $35,637,672
Emp.: 531
Fiscal Year-end: 03/31/23
Investment Management Service
N.A.I.C.S.: 523999

Subsidiaries:

Hemabh Technology Private (1)
Limited
Unit 1018 Rupa Solitaire Millennium Business Park, Mahape, Navi Mumbai, India
Tel.: (91) 2249857000
Web Site: https://hemabh.com
Security System Services
N.A.I.C.S.: 561621

CMST DEVELOPMENT CO., LTD.
27-28/F Block A Dingxing Building
Building 2 Yard 5, Fenghuangzui
Street Fengtai District, Beijing,
100073, China
Tel.: (86) 1052698788   CN
Web Site: https://www.cmstd.com.cn
Year Founded: 1996
600787—(SHG)
Rev.: $10,779,376,135

Assets: $3,365,350,120
Liabilities: $1,393,333,980
Net Worth: $1,972,016,140
Earnings: $89,923,532
Fiscal Year-end: 12/31/22
Logistic Services
N.A.I.C.S.: 541614
Fang Yongbin *(Chm)*

Subsidiaries:

CMST Guangzhou Company (1)
No 139 Dashadi West, Huangpu District,
Guangzhou, 510700, China
Tel.: (86) 20 82299020
Web Site: http://www.gzclogistics.com
Emp.: 60
Logistics Consulting Servies
N.A.I.C.S.: 541614
Pichao Huang *(Gen Mgr)*

Henry Bath & Son Limited (1)
12 Princes Parade, Liverpool, L3 1BG,
United Kingdom (51%)
Tel.: (44) 1512241800
Web Site: http://www.henrybath.com
Metal Wholesale Trade Broker
N.A.I.C.S.: 425120
Paul Wynne *(CFO)*

Subsidiary (Non-US):

Henry Bath B.V. (2)
Waalhaven Zuidzijde 21 Port Havens 2235,
3089 JH, Rotterdam, Netherlands
Tel.: (31) 102831000
Web Site: http://www.henrybath.com
Metal Wholesale Trade Broker
N.A.I.C.S.: 425120

Subsidiary (US):

Henry Bath LLC (2)
2400 Broening Hwy Ste 200, Baltimore, MD
21224
Tel.: (410) 633-7055
Web Site: http://www.henrybath.com
Metal Wholesale Trade Broker
N.A.I.C.S.: 425120

Subsidiary (Non-US):

Henry Bath Singapore Pte. Ltd. (2)
Warehouse SB8 Sembawang Wharves, 21
Deptford Road, Singapore, 759660, Singapore
Tel.: (65) 62662055
Web Site: http://www.henrybath.com
Sales Range: $25-49.9 Million
Emp.: 13
Metal Wholesale Trade Broker
N.A.I.C.S.: 425120
Sean Ginnane *(CEO)*

CMX GOLD & SILVER CORP.
148 - 555 Strathcona Blvd SW, PO
Box 74113, Calgary, T3H 3B6, AB,
Canada
Tel.: (403) 457-2697
Web Site:
https://www.cmxgoldandsilver.com
Assets: $525,971
Liabilities: $765,841
Net Worth: ($239,870)
Earnings: ($7,166)
Fiscal Year-end: 12/31/18
Gold & Silver Mining
N.A.I.C.S.: 212220
Jan M. Alston *(Pres & CEO)*

CN ASIA CORPORATION BHD.
Lot 7907 Batu 11 Jalan Balakong,
43300, Seri Kembangan, Selangor,
Malaysia
Tel.: (60) 389426888
Web Site: https://www.cnasia.com
Year Founded: 1994
CNASIA—(KLS)
Rev.: $4,137,928
Assets: $9,383,295
Liabilities: $2,620,303
Net Worth: $6,762,992
Earnings: $2,156,178)
Emp.: 52

Fiscal Year-end: 03/31/24
Industrial Equipment Mfr
N.A.I.C.S.: 811310
Lam Lee *(Mgr-Engineering & Head-Engineering)*

Subsidiaries:

Chip Ngai Engineering Works Sdn. (1)
Bhd.
Lot 7907 Batu 11 Jalan Balakong, 43300,
Seri Kembangan, Selangor, Malaysia
Tel.: (60) 389426888
Pressure Vessel Mfr
N.A.I.C.S.: 332420

CN ENERGY GROUP, INC.
Building 2-B Room 206 No 268
Shiniu Road, Liandu District, Lishui,
323010, Zhejiang, China
Tel.: (86) 57187555823   VG
Web Site: https://cneny.com
Year Founded: 2018
CNEY—(NASDAQ)
Rev.: $10,893,164
Assets: $24,222,051
Liabilities: $6,226,438
Net Worth: $17,995,613
Earnings: $1,667,812
Emp.: 167
Fiscal Year-end: 09/30/19
Holding Company
N.A.I.C.S.: 551112
Jinwu Huang *(CFO)*

CN INNOVATIONS HOLDINGS LIMITED
18/F Chung Nam Building 1 Lockhart
Road, Hong Kong, China (Hong
Kong)
Tel.: (852) 252 96111
Web Site: http://www.cn-
innovations.com
Emp.: 11,000
Holding Company; Innovative & Bio-
technology Research & Development
Products & Services
N.A.I.C.S.: 541714
Hot Hoi Chong *(Exec Dir)*

Subsidiaries:

CN Bio Innovations Limited (1)
BioPark Hertfordshire Broadwater Road,
Welwyn Garden City, Hertford, AL7 3AX,
Herts, United Kingdom
Tel.: (44) 1707 358 719
Web Site: http://www.cn-bio.com
Emp.: 7
Human Biomimetic Platforms for Testing &
Development of Therapeutics for Serious
Illnesses
N.A.I.C.S.: 541715
Maureen Coleman *(Chm)*

Subsidiary (Domestic):

CN Bio Innovations Limited (2)
Centre for Innovation & Enterprise Oxford
Univ Begbroke Science Pk, Begbroke Hill
Woodstock Rd, Begbroke, OX5 1PF, Ox-
fordshire, United Kingdom
Tel.: (44) 1865 309 600
Web Site: http://www.liverchip.com
Research, Development & Mfr of LiverChip
Products
N.A.I.C.S.: 325412
Emma Sceats *(COO)*

CN Innovations Co., Ltd. (1)
8F 2 No 15 Lane 360 Sec 1 Neihu Road,
Taipei, 114, Neihu, Taiwan
Tel.: (886) 27720 7700
Web Site: http://www.cn-innovations.com
Pharmaceutical Research & Development
In Vitro Models of Liver Infections & Serious
Diseases
N.A.I.C.S.: 541715
Patty Lin *(Exec Dir)*

CN Precision Casing (Shenzhen) Co., (1)
Ltd-Pinghu
No 93 Industrial Rd Fuchengao Industrial
Zone Pinghu Street, Longgang District,

518111, Shenzhen, Guangdong, China
Tel.: (86) 755 28320606
Mfr of Metal Receptacles
N.A.I.C.S.: 332312

**CN Precision Casing (Shenzhen)
Company Limited** (1)
Yayuan Rd Bantian Sub-district Longgang,
518129, Shenzhen, Guangdong, China
Tel.: (86) 755 28320606
Web Site: http://www.cn-innovations.com
Mfr of Machining Parts & Accessories
N.A.I.C.S.: 333517

CN Precision Casing Limited (1)
18/F Chung Nam Building 1 Lockhart Road,
Hong Kong, China (Hong Kong)
Tel.: (852) 25296111
Metal Coating Mfr & Distr
N.A.I.C.S.: 332812

**Green Mobility Innovations
Limited** (1)
PO Box 100, San Tin, Hong Kong, China
(Hong Kong)
Tel.: (852) 24436333
Web Site: https://www.gmi-hk.com
Electric Vehicle Mfr & Distr
N.A.I.C.S.: 336320

M-Solv Limited (1)
Oxonian Park Langford Locks, Kidlington,
Oxford, OX5 1FP, United Kingdom
Tel.: (44) 1865 844070
Web Site: http://www.m-solv.com
Laser Micromachining & Micro Deposition
Applications in Research, Design, Engineering & Manufacture
N.A.I.C.S.: 333248
Phil Rumsby *(CEO)*

Maxford Technology Limited (1)
18/F Chung Nam Building 1 Lockhart Road,
Hong Kong, China (Hong Kong)
Tel.: (852) 25296111
Metal Coating Mfr & Distr
N.A.I.C.S.: 332812

Maxford Technology, LLC (1)
2200 Calle De Luna, Santa Clara, CA
95054 (100%)
Tel.: (408) 855-8288
Web Site: http://www.maxfordtech.com
Mfr & Developer of Thin-Film Solar Medium
Solutions
N.A.I.C.S.: 326113
Stella Lau *(Mgr)*

TouchTurns LLC (1)
2225 Calle de Luna, Santa Clara, CA
95054
Tel.: (408) 645-2600
Web Site: http://www.touchturns.com
Design & Mfr of Prototype Touch Screen
Modules for Various Industries
N.A.I.C.S.: 541512
Shiou-Shiou Huang *(Dir-Customer Programs)*

Vitalink Industry (Shenzhen) Company Limited (1)
Yayuan Road Nan Keng Village Biantian
Sub-district, Longgang, Shenzhen, 518129,
Guangdong, China
Tel.: (86) 755 28320335
Mfr of In Vitro Products for Liver & Serious
Illnesses
N.A.I.C.S.: 325412

Vitalink Industry (Shenzhen) Company Limited-Pinghu (1)
Block 1-6 Fumin Industrial Park Second
Zone Pinghu Town Longgang, Shenzhen,
518111, Guangdong, China
Tel.: (86) 755 28321832
Mfr of Pharmaceutical Products for Liver
Illnesses
N.A.I.C.S.: 325412

Vitalink Korea Co., Ltd. (1)
Complex No 618 Hwang Deok 1-13
Youngdeok-dong IT Valley, Heungduk
Giheung-gu, Yongin, Gyeonggi, Korea
(South)
Tel.: (82) 3180655710
Metal Coating Mfr & Distr
N.A.I.C.S.: 332812

Vitalink Thin Film Technology (Suzhou) Co., Ltd. (1)

No 34 Dongjing Industrial Square No 9
Dongfu Rd Suzhou Industrial Park, Louweidong, Suzhou, 215123, Jiangsu, China
Tel.: (86) 512 62653313
Mfr of Thin Film Coating Technologies
N.A.I.C.S.: 332812

Vitalink Vietnam Co., Ltd. (1)
Land Lot XN-10, Van Trung Industrial Zone
Van Trung ward Viet Yen District, Viet Yen,
Bac Giang, Vietnam
Tel.: (84) 2046257888
Metal Coating Mfr & Distr
N.A.I.C.S.: 332812

**Winsky Industry Hong Kong
Limited** (1)
18/F Chung Nam Building 1 Lockhart Road,
Hong Kong, China (Hong Kong)
Tel.: (852) 25296111
Metal Coating Mfr & Distr
N.A.I.C.S.: 332812

**Zoltrix Material (Guangzhou)
Limited** (1)
No 58 Zhenxing Rd, Dagang Town,
Guangzhou, 511470, Guangdong, China
Tel.: (86) 020 84933433
Web Site: http://www.zoltrix-intl.com.hk
Mfr of Metal & Ceramic Parts by Metal Injection Molding
N.A.I.C.S.: 333511

iCreate Limited (1)
18/F Chung Nam Building 1 Lockhart Road,
Hong Kong, China (Hong Kong)
Tel.: (852) 34696000
Web Site: https://www.cni-icreate.com
Conductive Ink Mfr
N.A.I.C.S.: 325910

CN LOGISTICS INTERNATIONAL HOLDINGS LIMITED
13/F Park Sun Building 97-107 Wo Yi
Hop Road, Kwai Chung, New Territories, China (Hong Kong)
Tel.: (852) 27540638 Ky
Web Site:
https://www.cnlogistics.com.hk
Year Founded: 1991
2130—(HKG)
Emp.: 600
Holding Company
N.A.I.C.S.: 551112
Cheung Siu Ming Ringo *(Exec Dir)*

Subsidiaries:

CN Logistics (Japan) Limited (1)
8th Floor Nihonbashi-Kayabacho Place
1-7-9 Nihonbashi-Kakigaracho, Chuo-ku,
Tokyo, 103-0014, Japan
Tel.: (81) 358436246
Oil Transportation Services
N.A.I.C.S.: 481112

CN Logistics France S.A.S. (1)
383-385 Rue de la Belle Etoile, 95948,
Roissy-en-France, France
Tel.: (33) 158030233
Web Site: http://www.cnlogistics.fr
Oil Transportation Services
N.A.I.C.S.: 481112

CN Logistics Korea Co., Limited (1)
42 Gangnam-Daero 37-GIL, Seocho-gu,
Seoul, Korea (South)
Tel.: (82) 234870451
Oil Transportation Services
N.A.I.C.S.: 481112

CN Logistics S.R.L. (1)
Via Saronnino 3, 21040, Origgio, VA, Italy
Tel.: (39) 0287157260
Web Site: http://www.cnlogistics.it
Oil Transportation Services
N.A.I.C.S.: 481112

CN Logistics SA (1)
Corso San Gottardo NR 20, 6830, Chiasso,
Switzerland
Tel.: (41) 916018882
Oil Transportation Services
N.A.I.C.S.: 481112

**Guangzhou Jiahong International
Freight Forwarding Co., Ltd.** (1)
Rm1512 15F American Bank Plaza No 555

RenMinZhong Road, Guangzhou, 510145,
China
Tel.: (86) 2081301424
Oil Transportation Services
N.A.I.C.S.: 481112

CN NEGOCIOS, S.A.
Colima de Tibas de la Metalco 200
mts, Sur y 300 mts Este, San Jose,
Costa Rica
Tel.: (506) 2240 0960 CR
Web Site:
http://www.cnnegocios.com
Year Founded: 1998
Sales Range: $1-9.9 Million
Computers, Software & Telecommunications Products Distr
N.A.I.C.S.: 423430

CN RESOURCES INC.
255 Duncan Mill Road, North York,
M3B 3H9, ON, Canada
Tel.: (416) 510-2991 NV
Web Site: https://cn-resources-inc.business.site
Year Founded: 2010
CNRR—(OTCIQ)
Sales Range: Less than $1 Million
Mineral Exploration Services
N.A.I.C.S.: 212390
Oliver Xing *(Pres, CEO & CFO)*

CNA GROUP LTD.
28 Kaki Bukit Crescent Kaki Bukit
Techpark 1, Singapore, 416259, Singapore
Tel.: (65) 6511 0082
Web Site: http://www.cna.com.sg
Year Founded: 1990
Sales Range: $50-74.9 Million
Integrated System Solutions Services
N.A.I.C.S.: 811210
David Liang Eng Ong *(CEO-China)*

Subsidiaries:

CNA Engineering PVT Ltd (1)
Unit 7 CA Site No 1 JSS Campus 6th cross
Hal III Stage Kodihalli, Jeevan Bheemanagar, Bengaluru, 560008, Karnataka, India
Tel.: (91) 8025214096
Web Site: http://www.cnaindia.com
Sales Range: $25-49.9 Million
Emp.: 20
Automation Services
N.A.I.C.S.: 541330
Ramesh V. Murthy *(Gen Mgr)*

**CNA Integrated Technologies
(LLC)** (1)
Al Owais Bldg 2nd Fl No 206, PO Box
124276, BAI Karama, Dubai, United Arab
Emirates
Tel.: (971) 43343642
Sales Range: $25-49.9 Million
Emp.: 25
Plumbing Services
N.A.I.C.S.: 238220
Gumpalli Subba Rao *(CEO)*

CNA Technology Inc (1)
Rm 501 Don Pablo Bldg, 114 Amorsolo St,
Makati, 1204, Philippines
Tel.: (83) 28940850
Sales Range: $25-49.9 Million
Emp.: 30
Communication Management Services
N.A.I.C.S.: 541618

CNA-HTE Vietnam Co., Ltd. (1)
42 VSIP St 4 Vietnam Singapore Industrial
Park, Thuan An, Binh Duong, Vietnam
Tel.: (84) 6503743045
Web Site: http://www.cnavn.com
Building Automation System Installation &
Services
N.A.I.C.S.: 561790

GETC Asia Private Limited (1)
25 Woodlands Industrial Park E1, 5-5 Admiralty Industrial Park, Singapore, 757743,
Singapore
Tel.: (65) 63647577
Web Site: http://www.getcasia.com

Sales Range: $25-49.9 Million
Emp.: 6
Environmental Engineering Services
N.A.I.C.S.: 541330
Wing Sin Lui *(Gen Mgr)*

CNC HOLDINGS LIMITED
Suites 2708-2710 27/F Everbright
Centre, 108 Gloucester Road, Wanchai, China (Hong Kong)
Tel.: (852) 31042962 Ky
Web Site: http://www.cnctv.hk
Year Founded: 1989
8356—(HKG)
Rev.: $30,856,272
Assets: $22,560,021
Liabilities: $66,825,054
Net Worth: ($44,265,033)
Earnings: ($9,512,533)
Emp.: 240
Fiscal Year-end: 03/31/21
Investment Holding Company
N.A.I.C.S.: 523999
Kwok Cheung Kan *(Exec Dir)*

CNERGENZ BERHAD
No 34 36 38 & 40 Lorong IKS Bukit
Tengah Taman, 14000, Pulau Penang, Malaysia
Tel.: (60) 45088318
Web Site: https://www.cnergenz.com
Year Founded: 2004
CNERGEN—(KLS)
Rev.: $35,196,561
Assets: $43,462,778
Liabilities: $8,408,141
Net Worth: $35,054,637
Earnings: $3,096,430
Emp.: 64
Fiscal Year-end: 12/31/23
Electronic Products Mfr
N.A.I.C.S.: 334417
Yhin Choy Lye *(Co-Founder & Co-CEO)*

CNFC OVERSEAS FISHERY CO., LTD.
No 31 Minfeng Hutong Xidan,
Xicheng District, Beijing, 100032,
China
Tel.: (86) 1088067461
Web Site: http://www.cofc.com.cn
Year Founded: 1998
000798—(SSE)
Rev.: $83,779,488
Assets: $189,386,964
Liabilities: $54,868,320
Net Worth: $134,518,644
Earnings: $1,380,132
Fiscal Year-end: 12/31/22
Aquatic Product Distr
N.A.I.C.S.: 424460
Wenfeng Zong *(Chm)*

CNFINANCE HOLDINGS LIMITED
44/F Tower G No 16 Zhujiang Dong
Road, Tianhe District, Guangzhou,
510620, Guangdong, China
Tel.: (86) 62224206 Ky
Web Site: https://www.ir.cashchina.cn
Year Founded: 2014
CNF—(NYSE)
Rev.: $155,125,401
Assets: $2,218,774,948
Liabilities: $1,615,477,869
Net Worth: $603,297,079
Earnings: $20,737,190
Emp.: 930
Fiscal Year-end: 12/31/22
Holding Company
N.A.I.C.S.: 551112
Bin Zhai *(Chm & CEO)*

CNG TRAVEL GROUP PLC
Kilmurry, Kenmare, Co Kerry, Ireland
Tel.: (353) 64 40300

CNG Travel Group plc—(Continued)

Web Site: http://www.cngtravel.com
Year Founded: 1999
Sales Range: $25-49.9 Million
Emp.: 65
Corporate Travel Management Services
N.A.I.C.S.: 561599
Luke Mooney *(Chm)*

CNG VIETNAM JOINT STOCK COMPANY

No 475 Nguyen An Ninh Street Ward 9, Vung Tau, Ba Ria - Vung Tau, Vietnam
Tel.: (84) 2543574635
Year Founded: 2007
CNG—(HOSE)
Rev.: $128,214,730
Assets: $47,733,372
Liabilities: $22,904,810
Net Worth: $24,828,562
Earnings: $4,543,083
Emp.: 279
Fiscal Year-end: 12/31/23
Gas Distribution Services
N.A.I.C.S.: 221210
Nguyen Thi Hong Hai *(Chm)*

CNGR ADVANCED MATERIAL CO., LTD.

New Energy Industrial Park in Western China, Dalong Economic Development Zone Yuping County, Tongren, 554001, Guizhou, China
Tel.: (86) 8563238558
Web Site: https://www.cngrgf.com.cn
Year Founded: 2014
300919—(SSE)
Rev.: $4,260,261,096
Assets: $7,850,124,828
Liabilities: $4,493,545,524
Net Worth: $3,356,579,304
Earnings: $216,711,612
Fiscal Year-end: 12/31/22
Electrical Battery Mfr & Distr
N.A.I.C.S.: 335910
Weiming Deng *(Chm & Pres)*

CNH CO., LTD.

26F Dongbu Finance Center 432 Teheran-ro, Gangnam-gu, Seoul, Korea (South)
Tel.: (82) 232870700
Web Site: http://www.cnhcap.co.kr
Year Founded: 1989
023460—(KRS)
Rev.: $179,903,417
Assets: $414,561,791
Liabilities: $329,149,770
Net Worth: $85,412,022
Earnings: ($12,755,678)
Emp.: 11
Fiscal Year-end: 12/31/22
Holding Company
N.A.I.C.S.: 551112

CNH INDUSTRIAL N.V.

Cranes Farm Road, Basildon, SS14 3AD, Essex, United Kingdom
Tel.: (44) 2079251964   **NL**
Web Site: https://www.cnh.com
Year Founded: 2013
CNH—(NYSE)
Rev.: $24,687,000,000
Assets: $46,351,000,000
Liabilities: $38,171,000,000
Net Worth: $8,180,000,000
Earnings: $2,371,000,000
Emp.: 40,220
Fiscal Year-end: 12/31/23
Farm Machinery Mfr
N.A.I.C.S.: 551112
Suzanne Heywood *(Chm)*

Subsidiaries:

2 H Energy S.A.S.   **(1)**
Hautes Falaises Business Park, Saint-Leonard, 76400, Fecamp, France
Tel.: (33) 235106800
Web Site:
http://www.2henergy.fptindustrial.com
Generator Mfr
N.A.I.C.S.: 335312

Afin Broker de Asigurare - Reasigu-rare S.r.l.   **(1)**
11-15 Tipografilor, Bucharest, 13714, Romania
Tel.: (40) 213182862
Sales Range: $50-74.9 Million
Emp.: 5
Insurance Brokerage Services
N.A.I.C.S.: 524210

Afin Slovakia S.R.O.   **(1)**
D Bravsk Cesta 2, 841 04, Bratislava, Slovakia
Tel.: (421) 2 5941 8443
Automotive Distr
N.A.I.C.S.: 423110

AgDNA Technologies Pty Ltd.   **(1)**
Building 6 Suite 5 2404 Logan Rd, Eight Mile Plains, 4113, QLD, Australia
Tel.: (61) 730749503
Web Site: https://www.ag-dna.com
N.A.I.C.S.: 541618

Banco CNH Capital S.A.   **(1)**
Av Juscelino Kubitscheck de Oliveira 11 825 CIC, Curitiba, 81450-903, Brazil
Tel.: (55) 41 2107 7035
Web Site: http://www.bancocnh.com.br
Emp.: 20
Investment Management Service
N.A.I.C.S.: 523999

CNH America LLC   **(1)**
6900 Veterans Blvd, Burr Ridge, IL 60527-7111   **(83%)**
Tel.: (630) 887-2233
Agricultural, Construction & Mechanical Equipment Mfr
N.A.I.C.S.: 333120
Mark L. Mitchell *(Principal)*

Unit (Domestic):

CNH America - Benson   **(2)**
260 Hwy 12, Benson, MN 56215
Tel.: (320) 843-3333
Web Site: http://www.caseih.com
Sales Range: $125-149.9 Million
Emp.: 300
Dry & Liquid Fertilizer Application Mfr
N.A.I.C.S.: 333111

CNH America - Fargo   **(2)**
3401 7th Ave N, Fargo, ND 58102
Tel.: (701) 293-4400
Web Site: http://www.cnh.com
Rev.: $80,000,000
Emp.: 500
Tractor Mfr
N.A.I.C.S.: 333111

CNH America - Goodfield   **(2)**
600 E Peoria St, Goodfield, IL 61742
Tel.: (309) 965-2233
Web Site: http://www.cnh.com
Sales Range: $75-99.9 Million
Emp.: 350
Agricultural Soil Management Implements
N.A.I.C.S.: 115112

CNH America - New Holland   **(2)**
500 Diller Ave, New Holland, PA 17557
Tel.: (717) 355-1121
Web Site: http://www.cnh.com
Automotive Components Mfr
N.A.I.C.S.: 336110

CNH America - Racine   **(2)**
700 State St, Racine, WI 53404
Tel.: (262) 636-6011
Web Site: http://www.cnh.com
Sales Range: $50-74.9 Million
Emp.: 150
Construction Machinery & Equipment Mfr
N.A.I.C.S.: 333120

CNH America - Wichita   **(2)**
3301 South Hoover Rd, Wichita, KS 67215
Tel.: (316) 945-0111

Sales Range: $200-249.9 Million
Emp.: 600
Construction Equipment Mfr
N.A.I.C.S.: 333120
Peter Maitwe *(Engr-Mfg)*

Subsidiary (Non-US):

Case United Kingdom Limited   **(2)**
MTIB Building Unit 4 Triangle Business Park, Pentrebach, Merthyr Tydfil, CF48 4TQ, United Kingdom
Tel.: (44) 2921676213
Web Site: https://www.case-uk.co.uk
Financial Investment Services
N.A.I.C.S.: 523999

Subsidiary (Domestic):

Miller-St. Nazianz, Inc.   **(2)**
511 E Main St, Saint Nazianz, WI 54232-0127
Tel.: (920) 773-2121
Web Site: http://www.millerstn.com
Farm Equipment Mfr & Whslr
N.A.I.C.S.: 333111

Unit (Domestic):

New Holland Construction   **(2)**
245 E N Ave, Carol Stream, IL 60188
Tel.: (262) 636-6011
Web Site:
http://www.newhollandconstruction.com
Sales Range: $25-49.9 Million
Emp.: 40
Construction & Earth Moving Equipment Sales & Distr
N.A.I.C.S.: 423810
Giuseppe Fano *(Pres & CEO)*

CNH Belgium N.V.   **(1)**
Leon Claeysstraat 3a, 8210, Zedelgem, Belgium
Tel.: (32) 50253785
Web Site: https://www.cnhind-belgium.be
Agricultural Farm Machinery Mfr
N.A.I.C.S.: 333111

CNH Canada, Ltd.   **(1)**
1000 71 St E, Saskatoon, S7K 3S5, SK, Canada
Tel.: (306) 934-3500
Farm Equipment Mfr
N.A.I.C.S.: 333111

CNH Deutschland GmbH   **(1)**
Heinrich Fuchs Strasse 124, Heidelberg, 69126, Germany
Tel.: (49) 6221318500
Web Site: http://www.casece.com
Sales Range: $25-49.9 Million
Emp.: 12
Construction & Farm Equipment Mfr
N.A.I.C.S.: 333111

Subsidiary (Non-US):

CNH Baumaschinen GmbH   **(2)**
Tel.: (49) 3033990
Web Site: http://www.newholland.de
Construction Equipment Mfr
N.A.I.C.S.: 333120

Subsidiary (Non-US):

O & K - Hilfe GmbH   **(3)**
Tel.: (49) 3033990
Construction Machinery Mfr
N.A.I.C.S.: 333120

CNH Industrial Capital (India) Private Limited   **(1)**
4th Floor Rectangle No 1 Behind Marriot Hotel Commercial Complex D4, Saket, New Delhi, 110017, India
Tel.: (91) 1246659100
Financial Investment Services
N.A.I.C.S.: 523999

CNH Industrial Capital America LLC   **(1)**
PO Box 71264, Philadelphia, PA 19176-6264
N.A.I.C.S.: 524210

CNH Industrial Capital Australia Pty Limited   **(1)**
Locked Bag 3, Saint Marys, 1790, NSW, Australia
Tel.: (61) 1800807934

Web Site:
https://www.cnhindustrialcapital.com.au
Financial Investment Services
N.A.I.C.S.: 523999

CNH Industrial Capital Canada Ltd.   **(1)**
4475 North Service Road Suite 301, Burlington, L7L 4X7, ON, Canada
N.A.I.C.S.: 524210

CNH Industrial Capital LLC   **(1)**
Tel.: (262) 636-6011
Web Site:
https://www.cnhindustrialcapital.com
Rev.: $791,835,000
Assets: $13,179,479,000
Liabilities: $11,871,780,000
Net Worth: $1,307,699,000
Earnings: $219,122,000
Emp.: 380
Fiscal Year-end: 12/31/2022
Financial Products Management Services
N.A.I.C.S.: 522220
Douglas MacLeod *(CFO & Asst Treas)*

Subsidiary (Domestic):

ATI, Inc.   **(2)**
9220 Rumsey Rd Ste 100, Columbia, MD 21045
Tel.: (410) 992-3424
Web Site: https://www.atiinc.com
Facility Management Services
N.A.I.C.S.: 561210

CNH Industrial Capital Limited   **(1)**
Cranes Farm Road, Basildon, SS14 3AD, Essex, United Kingdom
Tel.: (44) 1268885400
Web Site:
https://www.cnhindustrialcapital.com
Financial Services
N.A.I.C.S.: 523999

CNH Industrial Italia s.p.a.   **(1)**
Lungo Stura Lazio 19, 10156, Turin, Italy
Tel.: (39) 0110072111
N.A.I.C.S.: 333111

CNH International S.A.   **(1)**
Riva Paradiso 14, 6902, Paradiso, Switzerland
Tel.: (41) 919853711
Web Site: http://www.cnh.com
Emp.: 10
Agricultural Machinery Distr
N.A.I.C.S.: 423820

Subsidiary (Domestic):

MBA AG   **(2)**
Zurichstrasse 50, 8303, Bassersdorf, Switzerland
Tel.: (41) 448386111
Web Site: https://vrp-machines.com
Construction Machinery Distr
N.A.I.C.S.: 423810

CNH Italia S.p.A   **(1)**
Viale Delle Nazioni 55, 41100, Modena, Italy
Tel.: (39) 059591111
Web Site: http://www.newholland.com
Tractors & Construction Machinery Mfr
N.A.I.C.S.: 333120

Subsidiary (Domestic):

CNH Services S.r.l.   **(2)**
Viale Delle Nazioni 55, Modena, 41122, Italy
Tel.: (39) 059 591 111
Agricultural & Construction Equipment Mfr
N.A.I.C.S.: 333111

CNH Latin America Ltda.   **(1)**
Avenida David Sarnoff 2 237 Cidade Industrial - Inconfidentes, 32210-900, Contagem, Minas Gerais, Brazil
Tel.: (55) 3121043225
Web Site: http://www.cnh.com
Construction Machinery Mfr
N.A.I.C.S.: 333120

CNH Portugal-Comercio de Tractores e Maquinas Agricolas Ltda   **(1)**
Rua Quinta Do Paizinho Nr 2 1, Alfragide, Amadora, 2790 237, Portugal
Tel.: (351) 214 24 59 40
Web Site: http://www.cnhindustrial.com

Sales Range: $25-49.9 Million
Emp.: 15
Farm Machinery & Equipment Distr
N.A.I.C.S.: 423820

CNH U.K. Limited (1)
Cranes Farm Road, Basildon, SS14 3AD,
United Kingdom
Tel.: (44) 1268533000
Emp.: 1,700
Farm Tractor & Engine Mfr
N.A.I.C.S.: 333111

Case Baumaschinen AG. (1)
Zurichstrasse 50, 8303, Bassersdorf, Switzerland
Tel.: (41) 448386111
Web Site: https://mba-maschinen.com
N.A.I.C.S.: 333120
Rene Vuagniaux (Co-Founder)

**Case Construction Machinery
(Shanghai) Co., Ltd** (1)
No 29 Workshop No 376 Debao Rd
Waigaoqiao Free Trade Zone, Shanghai,
200131, China (100%)
Tel.: (86) 2150481306
Construction Machinery Mfr
N.A.I.C.S.: 333120
Howard Dale (Mng Dir)

FPT Industrial S.p.A. (1)
Via Puglia 15, 10156, Turin, Italy
Tel.: (39) 080000378000
Web Site: https://www.fptindustrial.com
Automobile Mfr & Distr
N.A.I.C.S.: 336110

Subsidiary (Non-US):

FPT Industrial Argentina S.A. (2)
Carlos Maria Della Paolera 299 Piso 27,
Buenos Aires, 1001, Argentina
Tel.: (54) 1157765100
Automotive Distr
N.A.I.C.S.: 423110

FPT Motorenforschung AG (2)
Schlossgasse 2, 9320, Arbon,
Switzerland (100%)
Tel.: (41) 71 447 74 77
Web Site: http://www.fpt-
motorenforschung.ch
Emp.: 220
Automotive Engine Mfr
N.A.I.C.S.: 336390

Fiat Industrial Finance S.p.A. (1)
Via Nizza 250, Turin, 10126, Italy
Tel.: (39) 0110061111
Financial Management Services
N.A.I.C.S.: 523999

Subsidiary (US):

**Fiat Industrial Finance North America,
Inc.** (2)
7 Times Sq Tower Ste 4306, New York, NY
10036
Tel.: (212) 207-0910
Sales Range: $50-74.9 Million
Emp.: 6
Financial Management Services
N.A.I.C.S.: 523999

Fiat Industrial S.p.A. (1)
Via Nizza 250, 10126, Turin, Italy
Tel.: (39) 011 0061111
Web Site: http://www.fiatindustrial.com
Rev.: $34,710,993,450
Assets: $52,415,821,290
Liabilities: $44,713,036,550
Net Worth: $7,702,784,740
Earnings: $1,239,822,570
Emp.: 68,257
Fiscal Year-end: 12/31/2012
Holding Company; Agricultural & Construction Machinery Mfr
N.A.I.C.S.: 551112

Hemisphere GNSS (USA) Inc. (1)
8515 E Anderson Dr, Scottsdale, AZ 85255
Tel.: (480) 348-6380
Web Site: https://www.hemispheregnss.com
Emp.: 110
Positioning, Guidance & Machine Control
Products & Software Developer & Mfr
N.A.I.C.S.: 334511
Michael Whitehead (CTO)

Irisbus Iveco (1)

Parc Technologique de Lyon Bat B9 9 Allee
Irene Joliot Curie, Saint Priest, 69800,
Lyon, France
Tel.: (33) 472796500
Web Site: http://www.irisbus.com
Sales Range: $1-4.9 Billion
Emp.: 4,755
Bus & Coach Operating Services
N.A.I.C.S.: 485210

Plant (Domestic):

**Irisbus Iveco - ANNONAY
PLANT** (2)
Rue Ferdinand Janvier, BP 138, 7100, Annonay, France
Tel.: (33) 475326000
Automobile Mfr
N.A.I.C.S.: 336110

Plant (Non-US):

**Irisbus Iveco - VALLE UFITA
PLANT** (2)
Via Fondo Valle, 83040, Flumeri, Avellino,
Italy
Tel.: (39) 0825 4301
Web Site: http://www.irisbus.com
Bus & Coach Mfr
N.A.I.C.S.: 336110

**Iveco Arac Sanayi VE Ticaret
A.S.** (1)
Eyup Sultan Mahallesi Sekmen Caddesi No
12 Samandira, Sancaktepe, 34885, Istanbul, Turkiye
Tel.: (90) 2165611605
New Vehicle Dealer
N.A.I.C.S.: 441110

Iveco Austria GmbH (1)
Hetmanekgasse 14, 1231, Vienna, Austria
Tel.: (43) 1690110
New Vehicle Dealer
N.A.I.C.S.: 441110

Iveco Bayern GmbH (1)
Dieselstrasse 65, 90441, Nuremberg, Germany
Tel.: (49) 91196600
Web Site: https://www.iveco-bayern.de
New Vehicle Dealer
N.A.I.C.S.: 441110

Iveco Capital Services S.R.L. (1)
Str Caminului 54, Sat Manolache Ilfov,
Glina, Romania
Tel.: (40) 746166144
Financial Brokerage Services
N.A.I.C.S.: 523999

Iveco Danmark A/S (1)
Roholmsvej 19, 2620, Albertslund, Denmark
Tel.: (45) 44570500
New Vehicle Dealer
N.A.I.C.S.: 441110

Iveco Espana S.L. (1)
Avda de Aragon 402, 28022, Madrid, Spain
Tel.: (34) 913252273
New Vehicle Dealer
N.A.I.C.S.: 441110

Iveco Finland OY (1)
Kiilaniityntie 10, 02920, Espoo, Finland
Tel.: (358) 201557788
Web Site: https://www.iveco.com
New Vehicle Dealer
N.A.I.C.S.: 441110

Iveco Magirus AG (1)
Edisonstrasse 4, 85716, Unterschleissheim,
Germany
Tel.: (49) 89317710
New Vehicle Mfr & Dealer
N.A.I.C.S.: 336110

**Iveco Nord Nutzfahrzeuge
GmbH** (1)
Ausschlager Elbdeich 119, 20539, Hamburg, Germany
Tel.: (49) 40789610
New Vehicle Dealer
N.A.I.C.S.: 441110

**Iveco Nord-Ost Nutzfahrzeuge
GmbH** (1)
Nonnendammallee 25, 13599, Berlin, Germany
Tel.: (49) 30354860
Web Site: https://iveco-nord-ost.de

New Vehicle Dealer
N.A.I.C.S.: 441110

Iveco Norge A.S. (1)
Holmaveien 50, 1339, Voyenenga, Norway
Tel.: (47) 81559959
New Vehicle Dealer
N.A.I.C.S.: 441110
Hakan Jonsson (CEO)

Iveco Otomotiv Ticaret A.S. (1)
Eyup Sultan Mah Sekmen Cad No 12, Samandira Sancaktepe, 34885, Istanbul, Turkiye
Tel.: (90) 2163118953
Web Site: https://www.ivecooto.com.tr
New Vehicle Dealer
N.A.I.C.S.: 441110

Iveco Poland Sp. z o.o. (1)
Al Wyscigowa 6, 02-681, Warsaw, Poland
Tel.: (48) 225784300
New Vehicle Dealer
N.A.I.C.S.: 441110

Iveco Retail Limited (1)
Unit 4 Chancerygate way Hawley lane,
Farnborough, GU14 8FF, United Kingdom
Tel.: (44) 2034575445
Web Site: https://www.iveco-
dealership.co.uk
New Vehicle Mfr & Dealer
N.A.I.C.S.: 336110

Iveco S.p.A. (1)
Via Puglia 35, 10156, Turin, Italy (100%)
Tel.: (39) 0110072111
Web Site: https://www.iveco.com
Sales Range: $10-24.9 Million
Emp.: 31,000
Light, Medium & Heavy Commercial Vehicle
Mfr
N.A.I.C.S.: 336120

Subsidiary (Domestic):

ASTRA Veicoli Industriali S.p.A. (2)
Via Caorsana 79, 29122, Piacenza, PC,
Italy
Tel.: (39) 052354311
Web Site: https://www.astra-trucks.com
Industrial Vehicles & Dumpers Mfr & Sales
N.A.I.C.S.: 441227

Subsidiary (Non-US):

Altra S.p.A. (2)
Tel.: (39) 0108461270
Web Site: http://www.iveco.com
Truck & Bus Body Mfr
N.A.I.C.S.: 336211

Iveco Belgium NV SA (2)
A Gossetlaan 28a bus 3, 1702, Groot-Bijgaarden, Belgium
Tel.: (32) 24671211
Web Site: https://www.iveco.com
Commercial Vehicles Marketer & Sales
N.A.I.C.S.: 441227

Subsidiary (Domestic):

Iveco Defence Vehicles SpA (2)
Via Volta 6, 39100, Bolzano, BZ, Italy
Tel.: (39) 0471905111
Web Site:
http://www.ivecodefencevehicles.com
Military Vehicle Mfr
N.A.I.C.S.: 336992

Subsidiary (Non-US):

Iveco France S.A. (2)
6 Rue Nicolas Copernic, 78083, Trappes,
CEDEX, France
Tel.: (33) 130668394
Web Site: http://www.iveco.com
Commercial Vehicle Sales
N.A.I.C.S.: 423110

Subsidiary (Domestic):

**FPT - Powertrain Technologies
France S.A.** (3)
5 Rue Pierre Timbaud, 58600, Garchizy,
France
Tel.: (33) 386907100
Trucks Mfr
N.A.I.C.S.: 336212

Iveco Est Sas (3)
10 rue des Tuileries, 67460, Souffelweyer-

sheim, France (100%)
Tel.: (33) 388209620
Web Site: http://www.ivecoest.com
Emp.: 150
Automobile Dealers
N.A.I.C.S.: 441227
Francis Di Nallo (Mng Dir)

Iveco L.V.I. S.a.s. (3)
56 route de Grenoble, 69800, Saint Priest,
France
Tel.: (33) 472234747
Web Site: https://www.iveco-lvi.fr
New Vehicle Dealer
N.A.I.C.S.: 441110

Iveco Nord SAS (3)
2 Rue de Gamand, 59814, Lesquin, Cedex,
France
Tel.: (33) 320870460
New Vehicle Dealer
N.A.I.C.S.: 441110

Iveco Participations S.A.S. (3)
6 Rue Nicolas Copernic, 78190, Trappes,
France
Tel.: (33) 130668000
Motor Vehicle Truck Rental Services
N.A.I.C.S.: 532120

Subsidiary (Domestic):

Iveco Provence s.a.s. (4)
18 avenue de Rome ZI Les Estroublans,
CS 60175, 13785, Vitrolles, Cedex, France
Tel.: (33) 442775600
Web Site: https://www.iveco-provence.com
New Vehicle Dealer
N.A.I.C.S.: 441110

**Provence Distribution Services
S.a.r.l.** (4)
135 R Mayor de Montricher, 13854, Aix-en-Provence, France
Tel.: (33) 442549390
Motor Vehicle Truck Distr
N.A.I.C.S.: 423110

Subsidiary (Domestic):

Officine Brennero S.p.A. (2)
Via di Spini 13, 38121, Trento, Italy
Tel.: (39) 0461968300
Web Site: https://www.officinebrennero.it
New Vehicle Dealer
N.A.I.C.S.: 441110

**Iveco Sud-West Nutzfahrzeuge
GmbH** (1)
Flossworthstrasse 52-56, 68199, Mannheim, Germany
Tel.: (49) 62184430
Web Site: https://www.iveco-sued-west.de
New Vehicle Dealer
N.A.I.C.S.: 441110

Subsidiary (Non-US):

Iveco (Schweiz) AG (2)
Oberfeldstrasse 18, 8302, Kloten, Switzerland
Tel.: (41) 448044422
Web Site: https://kloten.iveco.ch
Automobile Mfr
N.A.I.C.S.: 336110

Iveco Czech Republic A.S. (2)
Dobrovskeho 74, 566 01, Vysoke Myto,
Czech Republic
Tel.: (420) 465451111
Sales Range: $25-49.9 Million
Emp.: 2,000
Buses & Coaches Mfr
N.A.I.C.S.: 336110

**Iveco International Trade Finance
S.A.** (2)
Riva Paradiso 14, Lugano, 6900, Switzerland
Tel.: (41) 919853711
Financial Management Services
N.A.I.C.S.: 523999

Iveco Ltd. (2)
Iveco House Station Rd, Watford, WD17
1SR, Herts, United Kingdom
Commercial Vehicles & Diesel Engines Mfr
N.A.I.C.S.: 333618

**Iveco Magirus Firefighting CAMIVA
S.A.S.** (2)

CNH Industrial N.V.—(Continued)

689 Avenue de Chambery, 73231, Saint-Alban-Leysse, France
Tel.: (33) 479756666
Web Site: http://www.camiva.com
Firefighting Vehicle Mfr
N.A.I.C.S.: 336120

Iveco Slovakia, s.r.o. (2)
Dubravska Cesta 2, PO Box 138, 841 04, Bratislava, Slovakia
Tel.: (421) 232609501
Web Site: https://www.iveco.com
Emp.: 12
Automobile Mfr & Distr
N.A.I.C.S.: 336110
Sergio Biancheri (Gen Mgr)

Iveco Trucks Australia Ltd (2)
Level 10 14 Mason Street, PO Box 117, Dandenong, 3175, VIC, Australia
Tel.: (61) 392382200
Web Site: http://www.iveco.com.au
Trucks Mfr
N.A.I.C.S.: 336120

Iveco Sweden A.B. (1)
Diabasgatan 1, 254 68, Helsingborg, Sweden
Tel.: (46) 42202070
New Vehicle Dealer
N.A.I.C.S.: 441110

Iveco Truck Centrum s.r.o. (1)
Prazska 330, 267 12, Lodenice, Czech Republic
Tel.: (420) 604298770
Motor Vehicle Dealers
N.A.I.C.S.: 441110

Iveco Truck Services S.R.L. (1)
Str Caminului nr 54, Sat Manolache, 077107, Glina, Ilfov, Romania
Tel.: (40) 374502350
Web Site: https://www.ivecotruckservices.ro
New Vehicle Dealer
N.A.I.C.S.: 441110

Iveco Ukraine LLC (1)
Leipzig 15A BC Merks 5th Floor, 01015, Kiev, Ukraine
Tel.: (380) 505205979
New Vehicle Dealer
N.A.I.C.S.: 441110

Iveco West Nutzfahrzeuge GmbH (1)
Vogelsanger Weg 55, 40470, Dusseldorf, Germany
Tel.: (49) 21190870
Web Site: https://www.iveco-west.de
New Vehicle Dealer
N.A.I.C.S.: 441110

Magirus Camiva S.a.s. (1)
686 Rue de Chantabord, 73026, Chambery, France
Tel.: (33) 479756666
Firefighting Vehicle Mfr
N.A.I.C.S.: 336120

Magirus Lohr GmbH (1)
Frikusweg 8, 8141, Premstaetten, Austria
Tel.: (43) 3135931220
Web Site: https://www.magirus-lohr.at
Firefighting Vehicle Mfr
N.A.I.C.S.: 336120

New Holland Fiat (India) Private Limited (1)
Plot No 09 Suite No - 301 Copia Corporate Suite, Jasola District Centre, New Delhi, 110025, India
Tel.: (91) 11 49024000
Web Site: http://www.newhollandindia.co.in
Emp.: 35
Agricultural Machinery Mfr
N.A.I.C.S.: 333111

Division (Domestic):

New Holland Fiat (India) Pvt. Ltd. - Parts Division (2)
Plot No 03 Udyog Kendra, Dist Gautam Budh Nagar, Noida, 201306, Uttar Pradesh, India
Tel.: (91) 1203056000
Sales Range: $400-449.9 Million
Emp.: 150
Agricultural & Construction Equipment Mfr

N.A.I.C.S.: 333120
Raunak Verma (Mng Dir)

New Holland Fiat (India) Pvt. Ltd. - Tractor Division (2)
Plot No 03 Udyog Kendra, Distt Gautam Budh Nagar, Noida, 201306, Uttar Pradesh, India
Tel.: (91) 1203056000
Sales Range: $400-449.9 Million
Emp.: 150
Agricultural & Construction Equipment Mfr
N.A.I.C.S.: 333120
Raunak Verma (Mng Dir)

OOO Afin Leasing Vostok LLC (1)
Leningradskaya Street 39 Building 6, 14100, Moscow, Russia
Tel.: (7) 495 504 04 45
Financial Lending Services
N.A.I.C.S.: 522220

OOO Iveco Russia (1)
St Leningradskaya 39 Bldg 6 10th Floor, 141400, Khimki, Moscow, Russia
Tel.: (7) 4955040442
Vehicle Mfr
N.A.I.C.S.: 336110

Potenza Technology Limited (1)
Unit A Charter Avenue Curriers Close, Industrial Estate, Coventry, CV4 8AW, West Midlands, United Kingdom
Tel.: (44) 2476083029
Web Site: https://www.ptech.co
Electric Vehicle Mfr
N.A.I.C.S.: 336320

Raven Applied Technologies, LLC (1)
205 E 6th St, Sioux Falls, SD 57104
Tel.: (605) 336-2750
Web Site: https://www.ravenind.com
Agriculture Product Distr
N.A.I.C.S.: 424910

Raven Europe, B.V. (1)
Nieuwe Steen 5, 1625 HV, Hoorn, Netherlands
Tel.: (31) 227549300
Farming Innovation Services
N.A.I.C.S.: 541715

Raven Industries, Inc. (2)
205 E 6th St, Sioux Falls, SD 57117-5107
Tel.: (605) 336-2750
Web Site: http://www.ravenind.com
Rev.: $348,359,000
Assets: $409,371,000
Liabilities: $78,016,000
Net Worth: $331,355,000
Earnings: $18,876,000
Emp.: 1,290
Fiscal Year-end: 01/31/2021
Extruded Plastic Sheeting Mfr
N.A.I.C.S.: 326199
Lon E. Stroschein (Exec Dir-Corp Dev)

Subsidiary (Domestic):

Colorado Lining International, Inc. (2)
1062 Singing Hills Rd, Parker, CO 80138
Tel.: (303) 841-2022
Web Site: http://www.coloradolining.com
Sales Range: $1-9.9 Million
Emp.: 63
Geomembrane Installation Services & Mfr
N.A.I.C.S.: 238990

Subsidiary (Non-US):

Navtronics BVBA (2)
Cipalstraat 3, 2440, Geel, Belgium
Tel.: (32) 14570642
Web Site: http://www.navtronics.be
Agricultural Machinery Mfr
N.A.I.C.S.: 333111

Raven Industries Australia Pty Ltd (2)
, Melbourne, 3000, VIC, Australia
Tel.: (61) 396717487
Web Site: http://www.ravenind.com
Precision Agriculture; Extruded Plastic Sheeting Mfr
N.A.I.C.S.: 326199

Raven Industries Canada, Inc. (2)
4 Industrial Drive West, Emerald Park, S4L 1C6, SK, Canada

Tel.: (605) 336-2750
N.A.I.C.S.: 333111

Division (Domestic):

Raven Industries, Inc. - Electronic Systems Division (2)
205 E 6th St, Sioux Falls, SD 57104 (100%)
Tel.: (605) 336 2750
Web Site: http://ravenind.com
Sales Range: $50-74.9 Million
Emp.: 147
Mfr & Assembler of Electronics
N.A.I.C.S.: 334412

Raven Industries, Inc. - Engineered Films Division (2)
821 W Algonquin St, Sioux Falls, SD 57104 (100%)
Tel.: (605) 335-0174
Web Site: https://www.viaflex.com
Sales Range: $25-49.9 Million
Emp.: 200
Plastic Film & Sheeting Mfr
N.A.I.C.S.: 326112
Wendy Kuhnert (Supvr-Customer Support)

Plant (Domestic):

Raven Industries, Inc. - Madison (3)
500 12th St SE, Madison, SD 57042
Tel.: (605) 335-0174
Web Site: http://ravenefd.com
Plastics Film & Sheeting Mfr
N.A.I.C.S.: 326112

Division (Domestic):

Raven Industries, Inc. - Flow Control Division (2)
205 E 6 St, Sioux Falls, SD 57104 (100%)
Tel.: (605) 336-2750
Web Site: http://www.ravenind.com
Sales Range: $150-199.9 Million
Emp.: 500
Flow Controls for Sprayers
N.A.I.C.S.: 334412

Subsidiary (Non-US):

Raven do Brasil Participacoes E Servicos Technicos Ltda (2)
Av Dr Roberto Moreira n 4500 Cond Clip Rua 1 n 328 Bairro Betel, Paulinia, 13148-150, Sao Paulo, Brazil
Tel.: (55) 1933055233
Electrical & Electronic Mfr
N.A.I.C.S.: 336320

SBG Innovatie BV (2)
Nieuwe Steen 5, 1625 HV, Hoorn, Netherlands
Tel.: (31) 227549300
Emp.: 30
Agricultural Machinery Mfr
N.A.I.C.S.: 333111

SAIC Fiat Powertrain Hongyan Co. Ltd. (1)
No 1 Huanghuan South Road, New North Zone, Chongqing, 401122, China
Tel.: (86) 2363212888
Web Site: http://www.sfhengine.com
Diesel Engine Mfr
N.A.I.C.S.: 333618

Sampierana S.p.A. (1)
Via Leonardo da Vinci 40, 47021, San Piero in Bagno, Italy
Tel.: (39) 0543904211
Web Site: https://www.sampierana.com
Earthmoving Machine & Spare Part Design Services
N.A.I.C.S.: 541420

Steyr Center Nord GmbH (1)
Kirchsee 1, Ruckersdorf, 2111, Harmannsdorf, Austria
Tel.: (43) 22646518
Agricultural Machinery Mfr
N.A.I.C.S.: 333111

TurkTraktor ve Ziraat Makineleri AS (1)
Gazi Mahallesi Anadolu Bulvari No 52 - 52A, Yenimahalle, Ankara, 06560, Turkiye (37.5%)
Tel.: (90) 3122333333
Web Site: http://www.turktraktor.com.tr

Tel.: (605) 336-2750
N.A.I.C.S.: 333111

Division (Domestic):

Sales Range: $400-449.9 Million
Agricultural Tractor Mfr & Distr
N.A.I.C.S.: 333111

UAB Iveco Capital Baltic (1)
Dunojaus g 20, LT-02104, Vilnius, Lithuania
Tel.: (370) 52758801
Vehicle Mfr
N.A.I.C.S.: 336110

Zona Franca Alari Sepauto S.A. (1)
Calle D 16-24 Pi Zona Franca, 08040, Barcelona, Spain
Tel.: (34) 932641360
Web Site: https://www.zfas.iveco.es
New Vehicle Dealer
N.A.I.C.S.: 441110
Jordi Sardina (Gen Mgr)

CNI RESEARCH LTD
A/120 Gokul Arcade Opp Garware House Sahar Road, Vile Parle E, Mumbai, 400 057, India
Tel.: (91) 2228383889
Web Site:
https://www.cniresearchltd.com
512018—(BOM)
Rev.: $1,072,535
Assets: $1,705,759
Liabilities: $6,211
Net Worth: $1,699,548
Earnings: $232,214
Emp.: 4
Fiscal Year-end: 03/31/22
Online Marketing Services
N.A.I.C.S.: 541613
Kishor P. Ostwal (Mng Dir)

CNIM CONSTRUCTIONS INDUSTRIELLES DE LA MEDITERRANEE SA
58 avenue de Wagram, 75017, Paris, France
Tel.: (33) 144311100 **FR**
Web Site: https://cnim-groupe.com
COM—(EUR)
Rev.: $768,142,234
Assets: $897,329,676
Liabilities: $1,061,794,522
Net Worth: ($164,464,846)
Earnings: ($160,798,258)
Emp.: 2,706
Fiscal Year-end: 12/31/20
Industrial Construction Services
N.A.I.C.S.: 237990
Christiane Dmitrieff (Vice Chm)

Subsidiaries:

Accord Lift Services Ltd. (1)
West Yoke Michaels Lane, Sevenoaks, TN15 7EP, United Kingdom (100%)
Tel.: (44) 1474879858
Web Site: http://www.accordlifts.co.uk
Sales Range: $25-49.9 Million
Emp.: 90
Engineeering Services
N.A.I.C.S.: 541330

Babcock Services, Inc. (1)
8113 W Quinault Ave Ste 201, Kennewick, WA 99336
Tel.: (509) 737-0812
Web Site: http://www.babcockservices.net
Equipment Finance Services
N.A.I.C.S.: 541620
K. E. Myers (Pres)

Babcock Wanson AG (1)
Oberebene Strasse - 63, 5620, Bremgarten, Switzerland (99.8%)
Tel.: (41) 566319580
Web Site: http://www.babcock-wanson.ch
Sales Range: $200-249.9 Million
Emp.: 680
Heavy & Civil Engineering Construction
N.A.I.C.S.: 237990

Babcock Wanson Holding SA (1)
106-110 Rue du Petit-Le-Roy, 94669, Chevilly-Larue, France (100%)
Tel.: (33) 149784400
Web Site: http://www.babcock-wanson.co

Sales Range: $1-4.9 Billion
Emp.: 3,500
Holding Company
N.A.I.C.S.: 551112

Subsidiary (Non-US):

Babcock Wanson Caldeiras Lda (2)
Rua Goncalves Zarco 1843 / 1867 Salas B
e J, 4450-685, Matosinhos, Portugal
Tel.: (351) 229 999 490
Web Site: http://www.babcock-wanson.pt
Motor & Generator Mfr
N.A.I.C.S.: 335312

Babcock Wanson Espana SA (2)
Carretera Bilbao Plentzia 31 Edificio Inbisa
- Planta 1a - Dpto 107, 48950, Erandio,
Vizcaya, Spain
Tel.: (34) 94 452 30 36
Web Site: http://www.babcock-wanson.es
Steam Boiler & Air Generator Mfr
N.A.I.C.S.: 333415

Babcock Wanson Italiana (2)
Via Roma 147, Cavenago di Brianza,
20873, Milan, Monza Brianza, Italy
Tel.: (39) 02 95 91 21
Web Site: http://www.babcock-wanson.it
Steam Boiler Mfr
N.A.I.C.S.: 333414

Babcock Wanson Maroc (1)
Bd Ali Yaata, Ain Sebaa, 20250, Casa-
blanca, Morocco (100%)
Tel.: (212) 522355618
Web Site: http://www.babcock-wanson.ma
Engineeering Services
N.A.I.C.S.: 541330

Babcock Wanson UK Ltd. (1)
7 Elstree Way, Borehamwood, WD6 1SA,
Hertfordshire, United Kingdom (25%)
Tel.: (44) 2089537111
Web Site: http://www.babcockwanson.co.uk
Sales Range: $25-49.9 Million
Emp.: 50
Mfr of Industrial Space & Process Heating
Equipment
N.A.I.C.S.: 333414
David Hatswell (Mng Dir)

Bertin Technologies SAS (1)
10 B Avenue Ampere, 78180, Montigny-le-
Bretonneux, France
Tel.: (33) 139 306 110
Web Site: http://www.bertin.fr
Healthcare & Electronic Software Develop-
ment Services
N.A.I.C.S.: 541511

Subsidiary (Domestic):

Bertin IT SAS (2)
10 Bis Avenue Ampere, 78180, Montigny-le-
Bretonneux, France
Tel.: (33) 1 3930 6000
Web Site: http://www.bertin-it.com
Automatic Speech Processing Services
N.A.I.C.S.: 621340

VERBALYS (2)
Courtaboeuf 3 Rue De La Terre De Feu,
Les Ulis, 91940, Essonne, France
Tel.: (33) 169298788
Business Management Consulting Services
N.A.I.C.S.: 541618

CNIM Babcock Central Europe
S.r.o. (1)
Grafick A 848-18, 15000, Prague, Czech
Republic (100%)
Tel.: (420) 257286880
Sales Range: $25-49.9 Million
Emp.: 10
Engineeering Services
N.A.I.C.S.: 541330

CNIM Babcock Polska Sp. Z.o.o (1)
ul Kosciuski 1c lok 504, 44-100, Gliwice,
Poland (100%)
Tel.: (48) 322306894
Web Site: http://www.babcock-wanson.pl
Sales Range: $25-49.9 Million
Emp.: 10
Communication & Energy Wire Mfr
N.A.I.C.S.: 335929

CNIM ECS LTD (1)
116-118 Chancery Lane, London, WC2A
1PP, United Kingdom

Tel.: (44) 20 7430 9362
Construction Engineering Services
N.A.I.C.S.: 541330
Alfredo Recchia (Mng Dir)

CNIM Environnement SA (1)
35 Rue De Bassano, 75008, Paris,
France (100%)
Tel.: (33) 144311100
Web Site: http://www.cnim.fr
Emp.: 40
Engineeering Services
N.A.I.C.S.: 541330

CNIM Hong Kong Limited (1)
B 120324 O Estate, Weaston Rd, Sha Tin,
China (Hong Kong) (99.99%)
Tel.: (852) 25703135
Sales Range: $50-74.9 Million
Emp.: 120
Plumbing Heating & Air-Conditioning Con-
tractors
N.A.I.C.S.: 238220

CNIM Insertion (1)
Route des Nourrices, 78850, Thiverval-
Grignon, Yvelines, France
Tel.: (33) 1 30 79 03 68
Sales Range: $10-24.9 Million
Emp.: 5
Waste Treatment & Disposal Services
N.A.I.C.S.: 562219
Marc-Henri Thimonier (Gen Mgr)

CNIM OUEST ARMOR (1)
Ld La Fontaine De Tremargat, Lantic,
22410, France
Tel.: (33) 296742527
Sales Range: $25-49.9 Million
Emp.: 5
Waste Treatment & Disposal Services
N.A.I.C.S.: 562219

CNIM Singapore Pte Ltd (1)
116 Lavender Street 03-08 Pek Chuan
Building, Singapore, 338730, Singapore
Tel.: (65) 62990212
Escalator Installation Services
N.A.I.C.S.: 238290

CNIM Transport Holding Srl (1)
35 Rue De Bassano, 75008, Paris,
France (100%)
Tel.: (33) 144311100
Web Site: http://www.cnim.com
Sales Range: $25-49.9 Million
Emp.: 60
Engineeering Services
N.A.I.C.S.: 541330

Subsidiary (Non-US):

CNIM Transport Equipment Co.,
Ltd (2)
Sane Road Cangjiang Industrial Park, Ga-
oming District, Foshan, 528500, Guang-
dong, China
Tel.: (86) 757 886 200 88
Web Site: http://www.cnim.com
Sales Range: $50-74.9 Million
Transportation Equipment Distr
N.A.I.C.S.: 423860

CNIM UK LTD (1)
116-118 Chancery Lane, London, WC2A
1PP, United Kingdom
Tel.: (44) 207 430 93 62
Waste Treatment & Disposal Services
N.A.I.C.S.: 562219

Curtis Canada Inc. (1)
1225 Rue Industrielle, J5R2E4, La Prairie,
QC, Canada (100%)
Tel.: (450) 619-2228
Web Site: http://www.curtisdoorsystems.com
Sales Range: $25-49.9 Million
Emp.: 100
Engineeering Services
N.A.I.C.S.: 541330

LAB GmbH (1)
Bludenzer Str 6, 70469, Stuttgart, Germany
Tel.: (49) 711 222 4935 0
Web Site: http://www.lab-stuttgart.cnan.com
Emp.: 15
Waste Treatment Plant Operating Services
N.A.I.C.S.: 562219

MES Environmental ltd. (1)
Crown Street, Wolverhampton, WV1 1QB,
United Kingdom (100%)

Tel.: (44) 1902352864
Web Site:
http://www.mesenvironmental.co.uk
Sales Range: $25-49.9 Million
Emp.: 30
Engineeering Services
N.A.I.C.S.: 541330

CNK INTERNATIONAL CO.,
LTD.
92 Gawonnonggong-gil Dain-myeon,
Uiseong-gun, Uiseong, 769971,
Gyeongbuk-do, Korea (South)
Tel.: (82) 54 861 9141
Web Site:
http://www.cnkinternational.co.kr
Precious Metal Distr
N.A.I.C.S.: 423940
Wu Taek Kim (CEO)

CNL CAPITAL E.K.E.S. AIFM
16 Massalias St, 10680, Athens,
Greece
Tel.: (30) 2107239300
Web Site: https://www.cnlcapital.eu
Year Founded: 2014
CNLCAP—(ATH)
Sales Range: Less than $1 Million
Financial Management Services
N.A.I.C.S.: 523320
Panagiotis Lekkas (Chm)

CNLIGHT CO., LTD.
Zone A Shishan Industrial Technology
Park, Nanhai District, Foshan,
528225, Guangdong Province, China
Tel.: (86) 757786695209
Web Site: https://www.cnlight.com
002076—(SSE)
Rev.: $21,923,460
Assets: $104,232,960
Liabilities: $66,709,656
Net Worth: $37,523,304
Earnings: $3,455,244
Emp.: 2,000
Fiscal Year-end: 12/31/22
Automobile Lamp Mfr
N.A.I.C.S.: 335139
Guo Sheng Chai (Chm)

Subsidiaries:

T C INTERNATIONAL TRADING
CO., LTD (1)
No 65 Charansanitwong Soi 40/1 Bang
Phlat, Bangkok, 10700, Thailand
Tel.: (66) 24383429
Web Site: http://www.cnlight-thai.com
Light Emitting Diode Distr
N.A.I.C.S.: 423610

CNMC GOLDMINE HOLDINGS
LIMITED
47 Scotts Road 03-03 Goldbell Tow-
ers, Singapore, 228233, Singapore
Tel.: (65) 62204621
Web Site: https://www.cnmc.com.hk
5TP—(CAT)
Rev.: $53,577,330
Assets: $59,743,013
Liabilities: $12,639,202
Net Worth: $47,103,811
Earnings: $5,073,564
Emp.: 382
Fiscal Year-end: 12/31/23
Gold Mining & Processing
N.A.I.C.S.: 212220
Xiang Xiong Lin (Founder & Chm)

Subsidiaries:

CMNM Mining Group Sdn. Bhd. (1)
Lot PT 6724 Kelewek Jalan Jeli, Tanah
Merah, 17500, Kelantan, Malaysia
Tel.: (60) 179797888
Gold Mining Services
N.A.I.C.S.: 212220

CNNC HUAYUAN TITANIUM
DIOXIDE CO., LTD.

68 Huacheng Avenue, Tianhe District,
Guangzhou, 004701, Guangdong,
China
Tel.: (86) 2088520851
Web Site: https://www.zhtb.com
Year Founded: 1989
002145—(SSE)
Rev.: $769,570,308
Assets: $1,639,918,332
Liabilities: $658,445,112
Net Worth: $981,473,220
Earnings: $90,302,472
Emp.: 2,400
Fiscal Year-end: 12/31/22
Titanium Dioxide Product Mfr
N.A.I.C.S.: 325180
Yuan Qiuli (Chm & Pres)

CNP ASSURANCES SA
4 Place Raoul Dautry, 75716, Paris,
Cedex 15, France
Tel.: (33) 142188888   FR
Web Site: https://www.cnp.fr
Year Founded: 1993
CNP—(EUR)
Rev.: $12,146,042,611
Assets: $481,767,524,077
Liabilities: $456,091,400,881
Net Worth: $25,676,123,196
Earnings: $2,256,209,295
Emp.: 6,023
Fiscal Year-end: 12/31/23
Personal Life & Investment Products
& Services
N.A.I.C.S.: 524298
Thomas Behar (CFO)

Subsidiaries:

Age d'Or Expansion SA (1)
12 rue du Ravelin, 10000, Troyes, France
Tel.: (33) 325829575
Web Site: http://www.agedorservices.com
Travel Services
N.A.I.C.S.: 561510

CNP Asfalistiki Ltd. (1)
17 Acropoleos Avenue, 2006, Strovolos,
Cyprus
Tel.: (357) 22887600
Web Site: http://www.cnpasfalistiki.com
Emp.: 146
Insurance Services
N.A.I.C.S.: 524210

CNP Assurances Compania de Se-
guros de Vida S.A (1)
Marcelo T de Alvear 1541, 1001, Buenos
Aires, Argentina
Tel.: (54) 8007777267
Web Site: http://www.cnp.com.ar
Sales Range: $50-74.9 Million
Emp.: 70
Personal insurance services
N.A.I.C.S.: 524298

CNP CYPRUS INSURANCE HOLD-
INGS LIMITED (1)
Acropoleos Avenue 17, 2006, Strovolos,
Cyprus
Tel.: (357) 22111213
Insurance Services
N.A.I.C.S.: 524210

CNP China (1)
2103 Full Link Plaza, 18 Chaoyangmenwai
Avenue, Beijing, 100020, China
Tel.: (86) 105882150
Web Site: http://www.cnp.fr
Insurance Services
N.A.I.C.S.: 524298

CNP EUROPE LIFE LTD (1)
Alexandra House The Sweepstakes, Balls-
bridge, Dublin, Ireland
Tel.: (353) 1 231 5080
Web Site: http://www.cnplife.ie
General Insurance Services
N.A.I.C.S.: 524210

CNP IAM (1)
4 Pl Raoul Dautry, Paris, 75716, France
Tel.: (33) 142189237
General Insurance Services
N.A.I.C.S.: 524210

CNP Assurances SA—(Continued)

CNP Italia SpA (1)
Via Dante 14, 20121, Milan, Italy
Tel.: (39) 0272601121
Web Site: http://www.cnp.it
Sales Range: $50-74.9 Million
Emp.: 15
Boat Insurance Services
N.A.I.C.S.: 524298

CNP Luxembourg SA (1)
1A Rue Pierre d'Aspelt, 1142, Luxembourg,
Luxembourg
Tel.: (352) 27956201
Web Site: http://www.cnpluxembourg.lu
Insurance Services
N.A.I.C.S.: 524210
Cedric Naut (Head-Acctg)

CNP VIDA (1)
Chandiano 10-2 Planta, Madrid, 28023,
Spain
Tel.: (34) 915243435
Web Site: http://www.cnpvida.es
General Insurance Services
N.A.I.C.S.: 524210

CNP Zois S.A (1)
Andreas Syggrou Avenue 162-166 Building
1, 176 71, Kallithea, Greece
Tel.: (30) 2103279420
Web Site: http://www.cnpzois.com
Insurance Services
N.A.I.C.S.: 524210
Xavier Antoine Vincent Larnaudie-Eiffel
(Chm)

Caixa Seguros (1)
SHN Quadra 01 Conjunto A Bloco E,
Brasilia, 70701-050, Brazil (51.75%)
Tel.: (55) 6121922995
Web Site: http://www.caixaseguros.com.br
Sales Range: $350-399.9 Million
Emp.: 740
Insurance Services
N.A.I.C.S.: 524298

Carres Blues (1)
Tour Maine Montparnasse 33 Ave Du
Maine, 4 place haoul dautri, 75015, Paris,
Cedex, France
Tel.: (33) 142188888
Web Site: http://www.carresbleus.fr
Sales Range: $50-74.9 Million
Emp.: 2,000
Health Insurance Services
N.A.I.C.S.: 524113
Marie Noelle (Sec)

Fongepar (1)
46 rue Jules Meline, 53098, Laval, Cedex
9, France
Tel.: (33) 9 69 39 69 70
Web Site: http://www.fongepar.fr
Insurance Services
N.A.I.C.S.: 524298

CNPLUS CO., LTD.
305 Sihwa Venture-ro, B-dong 3rd
floor, Siheung, Gyeonggi-do, Korea
(South)
Tel.: (82) 314340976
Web Site: https://www.icnplus.com
Year Founded: 2003
115530—(KRS)
Rev.: $33,013,719
Assets: $26,776,174
Liabilities: $17,872,694
Net Worth: $8,903,480
Earnings: $1,332,306
Emp.: 52
Fiscal Year-end: 12/31/22
High Precision Connector Mfr
N.A.I.C.S.: 334417

CNPV SOLAR POWER S.A.
Shengli Economic Development
Zone, Dongying, 257000, Shang-
dong, China
Tel.: (86) 546 7795555
Web Site: http://www.cnpv-
power.com
Year Founded: 2006
Sales Range: $250-299.9 Million
Emp.: 573

Ingots, Wafers, Cells & Solar Mod-
ules Mfr
N.A.I.C.S.: 335311
Bypina Veerraju Chaudary (COO)

Subsidiaries:

**CNPV Dongying Solar Power Com-
pany Limited,** (1)
West No 10 Road South No 0 Road Victory
Industrial Park, Dongying, 257000, Shan-
dong, China
Tel.: (86) 5467795555
Solar Power Equipment Mfr & Whslr
N.A.I.C.S.: 335999

**CNQC INTERNATIONAL HOLD-
INGS LTD.**
Room 601 6/F Exchange Tower No
33 Wang Chiu Road, Kowloon, China
(Hong Kong)
Tel.: (852) 31633980 Ky
Web Site: http://www.cnqc.com.hk
1240—(HKG)
Rev.: $1,054,695,555
Assets: $1,552,877,325
Liabilities: $1,148,925,323
Net Worth: $403,952,003
Earnings: ($65,412,600)
Emp.: 2,609
Fiscal Year-end: 12/31/22
Holding Company
N.A.I.C.S.: 551112
Michael Wing On Cheng (Chm)

Subsidiaries:

**BH-ZACD (Tuas Bay) Development
Pte. Ltd.** (1)
2 Bukit Merah Central, Singapore, 159835,
Singapore
Tel.: (65) 65001120
Web Site: http://www.zacdgroup.com
Property Development Services
N.A.I.C.S.: 531210

**Qingjian International (South Pacific)
Group Development Co., Pte.
Ltd.** (1)
47 Kallang Pudding Road 12-01 Crescent
Kallang, Singapore, 349318, Singapore
Tel.: (65) 67487117
Web Site: https://qingjian.com.sg
General Construction Services
N.A.I.C.S.: 236220

**Qingjian Realty (South Pacific) Group
Pte. Ltd.** (1)
60 Paya Lebar Road Paya Lebar Square
09-13, Singapore, 409051, Singapore
Tel.: (65) 64221621
Web Site: http://www.cnqc.com.sg
Property Development Services
N.A.I.C.S.: 531210

**Sunley M&E Engineering Pte.
Ltd.** (1)
47 Kallang Pudding Road 12-01 The Cres-
cent, Kallang, Singapore, 349318, Singa-
pore
Tel.: (65) 64221932
Web Site: https://sunley.com.sg
Building Construction Services
N.A.I.C.S.: 236220

Welltech Construction Pte. Ltd. (1)
61 Ubi Avenue 1 UB Point 05-16, Singa-
pore, 408941, Singapore
Tel.: (65) 62992858
General Construction Services
N.A.I.C.S.: 236220

CNS LINK CO., LTD.
1206 12F SK V1 Tower A 14 288
Beon-gil, Jungwon-gu, Seongnam,
Gyeonggi-do, Korea (South)
Tel.: (82) 7087866457
Web Site: https://www.cns-link.co.kr
Year Founded: 2000
Automotive Device Mfr & Distr
N.A.I.C.S.: 334290
Sang-Tae Ahn (CEO)

CNSHANGQUAN

E-COMMERCE CO., LTD.
68 Yuhuatai Software Avenue 5th
Floor, Nanjing, China
Tel.: (86) 25 83267999
Web Site:
http://www.cnshangquan.com
Integrated Marketing Platforms for
Businesses & Consumers
N.A.I.C.S.: 541519
Ingrid Ye Wang (CEO)

**CNSIG INNER MONGOLIA
CHEMICAL INDUSTRY CO.,
LTD.**
Alashan Economic Development
Zone, Wusitai Town, Alashan Zuoqi,
750336, China
Tel.: (86) 4838182718
Web Site: http://www.lantaicn.com
Year Founded: 1998
600328—(SHG)
Rev.: $2,550,017,724
Assets: $2,795,882,259
Liabilities: $1,098,466,237
Net Worth: $1,697,416,021
Earnings: $261,695,393
Emp.: 9,000
Fiscal Year-end: 12/31/22
Chemical Product Mfr & Distr
N.A.I.C.S.: 325180
Zhou Jie (Chm & Gen Mgr)

CNSX MARKETS INC.
100 King Street West Suite 7210,
Toronto, M5X 1E1, ON, Canada
Tel.: (416) 572-2000
Web Site: https://www.thecse.com
Sales Range: $25-49.9 Million
Emp.: 40
Stock Exchange Services
N.A.I.C.S.: 523210
Richard Carleton (CEO)

CNT GROUP LIMITED
Unit E 28/F CNT Tower 338 Hen-
nessy Road, Wanchai, China (Hong
Kong)
Tel.: (852) 25733288 BM
Web Site:
http://www.cntgroup.com.hk
0701—(HKG)
Rev.: $84,862,853
Assets: $293,442,143
Liabilities: $91,077,585
Net Worth: $202,364,558
Earnings: ($15,171,098)
Emp.: 608
Fiscal Year-end: 12/31/22
Holding Company; Industrial Paint
Manufacturing, Real Estate Invest-
ment & Metal Trading
N.A.I.C.S.: 551112
Chi Kwan Chong (Mng Dir)

Subsidiaries:

CPM Group Limited (1)
31st Floor CNT Tower 338 Hennessy Road,
Wanchai, China (Hong Kong)
Tel.: (852) 27920663
Web Site: https://www.cpmgroup.com.hk
Rev.: $81,988,748
Assets: $146,986,080
Liabilities: $80,565,593
Net Worth: $66,420,488
Earnings: ($12,555,053)
Emp.: 583
Fiscal Year-end: 12/31/2022
Holding Company; Industrial Paint Mfr
N.A.I.C.S.: 551112
Philip Ho Chuen Tsui (Mng Dir)

Subsidiary (Domestic):

**The China Paint Manufacturing Com-
pany (1932) Limited** (2)
31/ F Cnt Tower 338 Hennessy Road, Wanchai, China (Hong Kong)
Tel.: (852) 2 792 0663
Web Site: https://www.chinapaint.com

Sales Range: $25-49.9 Million
Emp.: 80
Paints Mfr
N.A.I.C.S.: 325510

Subsidiary (Non-US):

**The China Paint Mfg. Co., (Xinfeng)
Ltd.** (2)
101 Fourth Ave S No 903 Block D Pioneer
Home, Heping Dist, Shenyang, 110005, Lia-
oning, China
Tel.: (86) 2423502426
Industrial Paints Mfr
N.A.I.C.S.: 325510

**The China Paint Manufacturing
(Shenzhen) Co., Ltd.** (1)
Ya Bian Industrial Zone Huan Zhen Road,
Shajing Town Baoan District, Shenzhen,
Guangdong, China
Tel.: (86) 75533658888
Web Site: https://www.chinapaint.com
Paints Mfr
N.A.I.C.S.: 325510

CNT85 INC.
7F Shinan Building 512 Teheran-ro,
Gangnam-gu, Seoul, 13494,
Gyeonggi-do, Korea (South)
Tel.: (82) 234671900 KR
Web Site: https://www.cnt85.com
Year Founded: 1996
056730—(KRS)
Rev.: $825,169
Assets: $55,076,008
Liabilities: $34,297,714
Net Worth: $20,778,294
Earnings: ($6,561,259)
Emp.: 16
Fiscal Year-end: 12/31/20
Flaming Coals Whslr
N.A.I.C.S.: 423520

CNTEE TRANSELECTRICA SA
Str Olteni no 2-4 sector 3, 30786,
Bucharest, Romania
Tel.: (40) 374580453
Web Site:
https://www.transelectrica.ro
TEL—(BUC)
Rev.: $1,026,021,827
Assets: $1,824,301,622
Liabilities: $748,472,411
Net Worth: $1,075,829,210
Earnings: $45,988,355
Emp.: 1,980
Fiscal Year-end: 12/31/23
Electricity Transmission, System &
Market Operation
N.A.I.C.S.: 237130

Subsidiaries:

Formenerg S.A. (1)
Bulevardul Gheorghe Sincai nr 3 Sector 4,
Bucharest, Romania
Tel.: (40) 21 306 9900
Web Site: https://www.formenerg.ro
Professional Training Services
N.A.I.C.S.: 611430

Icemenerg SA (1)
Bd Energeticienilor 8, Sector 3, 032092,
Bucharest, Romania
Tel.: (40) 213465241
Web Site: http://www.icemenerg.ro
Sales Range: $75-99.9 Million
Emp.: 4
Eletric Power Generation Services
N.A.I.C.S.: 221111

Icemenerg Service SA (1)
B-dul Energeticienilor 8, Sector 3, 032092,
Bucharest, Romania
Tel.: (40) 213464786
Web Site: http://www.icemenerg-service.ro
Electricity Distribution Equipments & Control
Devices Mfr
N.A.I.C.S.: 334512

Smart SA (1)
Bucuresti B-dul Gen Gh Magheru nr 33,
Sector 1, 010325, Bucharest, Romania
Tel.: (40) 213054402

Web Site: http://www.smart-sa.ro
Electrical Engineering Services
N.A.I.C.S.: 541330

Teletrans SA (1)
16-18 Hristo Botev Boulevard, District 3,
030236, Bucharest, Romania
Tel.: (40) 213016014
Web Site: http://www.teletrans.ro
Sales Range: $50-74.9 Million
Emp.: 245
Telecommunication Servicesb
N.A.I.C.S.: 517810
Horia Hahaianu (Gen Mgr)

CNTUS CO.,LTD
21 Dosan-daero 50-gil, Gangnam-gu,
Seoul, 06056, Korea (South)
Tel.: (82) 25855915
Web Site: https://cntus.com
Year Founded: 2003
352700—(KRS)
Rev.: $108,595,287
Assets: $141,523,900
Liabilities: $13,887,160
Net Worth: $127,636,740
Earnings: $14,926,077
Emp.: 197
Fiscal Year-end: 12/31/22
Air Filter Mfr & Distr
N.A.I.C.S.: 333413

CO-OP ATLANTIC
123 Halifax St, PO Box 750, Monc-
ton, E1C 9R6, NB, Canada
Tel.: (506) 858-6000
Web Site: http://www.coopatlantic.ca
Year Founded: 1927
Sales Range: $250-299.9 Million
Emp.: 700
Groceries, Produce, General Mer-
chandise, Petroleum, Feed & Farm
Supplies Whslr
N.A.I.C.S.: 424910
Bryan Inglis (VP-Agriculture & Inde-
pendent Food)

Subsidiaries:

Avide Developments Inc. (1)
123 Halifax St, Moncton, E1C 8N5, NB,
Canada
Tel.: (506) 858-6000
Web Site: http://www.avide.com
Sales Range: $25-49.9 Million
Emp.: 20
Residential Development Services
N.A.I.C.S.: 236117

Country Ribbon Inc. (1)
902/907 East White Hills Road, PO Box
803, Saint John's, A1C 5L7, NL, Canada
Tel.: (709) 722-3751
Web Site: http://www.countryribbon.com
Frozen Chicken Whslr
N.A.I.C.S.: 424420
Don Styles (Plant Mgr)

Division (Domestic):

**Country Ribbon Inc. - Country Ribbon
Feed Division** (2)
1273 Topsail Road, PO Box 218, Mount
Pearl, A1N 2C2, NL, Canada
Tel.: (709) 368-3193
Frozen Chicken Whslr
N.A.I.C.S.: 424420

Maximum Alarm & Security Inc. (1)
33 Henri Dunant Street, Moncton, E1E 1E4,
NB, Canada
Tel.: (506) 858-6637
Web Site: http://www.maximumsecurity.ca
Business & Residential Security Systems
N.A.I.C.S.: 561621

CO-OPERATIVE GROUP LIM-
ITED
1 Angel Square, Manchester, M60
0AG, United Kingdom   UK
Web Site: http://www.coop.co.uk
Year Founded: 1844
Rev.: $12,895,781,240
Assets: $12,399,594,420

Liabilities: $8,504,972,040
Net Worth: $3,894,622,380
Earnings: ($197,967,120)
Emp.: 21,430
Fiscal Year-end: 01/05/19
Co-operative Business, Food Retail-
ing, Funerals & Travel Agencies
N.A.I.C.S.: 812210
Steve Murrells (CEO)

Subsidiaries:

Bridgford & Sons Limited (1)
23 Chorley Road, Manchester, M27 4AF,
United Kingdom
Tel.: (44) 161 793 1228
Funeral Services
N.A.I.C.S.: 812210

Brompton Homes Limited (1)
Unit 2 Brompton House The Cloisters, Co
Cork, Ballincollig, Ireland
Tel.: (353) 21 487 2567
Web Site: http://www.bromptonhomes.com
Home Development & Sale Services
N.A.I.C.S.: 236117

CIS Finance Ltd (1)
Cis Building, Manchester, M60 0AL, United
Kingdom
Tel.: (44) 161 832 8686
Financial Management Services
N.A.I.C.S.: 541611

Cannon St. (H.C.C.) Limited (1)
5 Manchester Chambers Cheapside, Old-
ham, OL1 1LF, United Kingdom
Tel.: (44) 1616337124
Emp.: 5
Health Care Srvices
N.A.I.C.S.: 621999
Stewart Preston (Gen Mgr)

**Co-operative Banking Group
Limited** (1)
New Century House, Manchester, M60
4ES, United Kingdom   (100%)
Tel.: (44) 8457212212
Web Site: http://www.co-
   operativebankinggroup.co.uk
Holding Company; Financial & Banking
Services
N.A.I.C.S.: 551112

Subsidiary (Domestic):

The Co-operative Bank p.l.c. (2)
1 Balloon St, PO Box 101, Manchester,
M60 4EP, United Kingdom   (100%)
Tel.: (44) 3457212212
Web Site: http://www.co-
   operativebank.co.uk
Commercial Banking Services
N.A.I.C.S.: 522110
Lesley McPherson (Dir-Comm)

Subsidiary (Domestic):

Platform Funding Limited (3)
PO Box 237, Plymouth, PL1 1WG, United
Kingdom
Tel.: (44) 1752236550
Web Site: http://www.platform.co.uk
Sales Range: $75-99.9 Million
Emp.: 200
Mortgage & Nonmortgage Loan Brokers
N.A.I.C.S.: 522310

Platform Home Loans Limited (3)
2 Harbour Exchange Square, London, E14
9FR, United Kingdom   (100%)
Tel.: (44) 2075124006
Web Site: http://www.platform.co.uk
Sales Range: $75-99.9 Million
Emp.: 200
Mortgage & Nonmortgage Loan Brokers
N.A.I.C.S.: 522310

smile (3)
Delf House, PO Box 600, Skelmersdale,
WN8 6GF, United Kingdom
Tel.: (44) 1614756108
Web Site: http://www.smile.co.uk
Internet Bank
N.A.I.C.S.: 523150

**Co-operative Funeralcare
Limited** (1)
12th Floor Oneangel Square, Hanover

Street, Manchester, M60 08D, United King-
dom
Tel.: (44) 800289120
Web Site: http://www.co-
   operativefuneralcare.co.uk
Sales Range: $25-49.9 Million
Emp.: 50
Funeral Services
N.A.I.C.S.: 812210

**Co-operative Group Food
Limited** (1)
1 Angel Square, Manchester, M60 0AG,
United Kingdom
Tel.: (44) 8000686727
Web Site: http://www.co-operativefood.co.uk
Sales Range: $800-899.9 Million
Emp.: 3,000
Community Food Retailer
N.A.I.C.S.: 445298
Rob Tindale (Mgr-Acq-North)

Co-operative Home Stores (1)
New Century House, Manchester, M60
4ES, United Kingdom
Tel.: (44) 1618341212
Web Site: http://www.co-operative.coop
Home Decorating Stores
N.A.I.C.S.: 449129

**Co-operative Legal Services
Limited** (1)
10 Warwick Lane, London, EC4M 7BP,
United Kingdom
Tel.: (44) 844 728 0435
Web Site: http://www.co-
   operativelegalservices.co.uk
Law firm
N.A.I.C.S.: 541110

Co-operatives e-Store Limited (1)
Sunwin House Chestergate, Merseyway,
Stockport, SK1 1NT, Cheshire, United King-
dom
Tel.: (44) 8457000100
Web Site:
   http://www.coopelectricalshop.co.uk
Electronic Goods
N.A.I.C.S.: 449210

Donald Wardle & Son Ltd (1)
Ratton Street, Stoke-on-Trent, ST1 2HH,
Staffordshire, United Kingdom
Tel.: (44) 1782 202 142
Pharmaceutical Products Distr
N.A.I.C.S.: 424210

Farmcare Limited (1)
One Angel Square Hanover St, Manchester,
M60 0AG, United Kingdom
Tel.: (44) 1618276117
Web Site: http://www.co-opfarmcare.com
Sales Range: $25-49.9 Million
Emp.: 8
Commercial Farming
N.A.I.C.S.: 111998
Richard Quinn (CEO)

**Funeral Services Northern Ireland
Limited** (1)
Bairds of Antrim 71 Church Street, Antrim,
BT41 4BE, United Kingdom
Tel.: (44) 28 9442 8230
Web Site: http://www.fsni.info
Funeral Services
N.A.I.C.S.: 812210

Green Cross Property Limited (1)
95 Musters Road, Nottingham, NG2 7PX,
Nottinghamshire, United Kingdom
Tel.: (44) 115 981 6604
Health Care Srvices
N.A.I.C.S.: 621999

**H Goodwin & Son (Newcastle)
Limited** (1)
Verona House, Newcastle, ST5 1LZ,
Staffordshire, United Kingdom
Tel.: (44) 178 261 6586
Funeral Services
N.A.I.C.S.: 812210

H H Birch & Son Limited (1)
Nab Wood Chapel of Rest Bingley Road
Nab Wood, Shipley, BD18 4BG, United
Kingdom
Tel.: (44) 1274 583467
Web Site:
   http://www.hhbirchfuneraldirectors.co.uk
Funeral Services

N.A.I.C.S.: 812210

McKenna Funerals Limited (1)
54 Meadow Street, Preston, PR1 1TR, Lan-
cashire, United Kingdom
Tel.: (44) 177 225 1694
Funeral Services
N.A.I.C.S.: 812210

Resomation Limited (1)
25 Honeywell Avenue, Glasgow, G33 6HS,
Scotland, United Kingdom
Tel.: (44) 1132057422
Web Site: http://resomation.com
Funeral Services
N.A.I.C.S.: 812210
Craig Sinclair (Dir-Engrg)

Shoefayre Limited (1)
Wigstone House, Kirkdale Road, Leicester,
LE18 4SU, S Wigston, United Kingdom
Tel.: (44) 01162785264
Fashion Footwear & Accessories
N.A.I.C.S.: 424340

**The Fairways Partnership
Limited** (1)
Roath Court Newport Road, Cardiff, CF24
1XP, United Kingdom
Tel.: (44) 2920 484 040
Funeral Services
N.A.I.C.S.: 812210

Travco Hotels Limited (1)
Travco House 92-94 Paul Street, London,
EC2A 4UX, United Kingdom
Tel.: (44) 20 7739 3333
Web Site: http://www.travco.co.uk
Emp.: 300
Hotel Reservation Services
N.A.I.C.S.: 561599

Voucher Travel Club Limited (1)
7 Main Street, Prestwick, KA9 1AA, United
Kingdom
Tel.: (44) 844 504 0849
Web Site:
   http://www.thevouchertravelclub.co.uk
Travel Tour Operating Services
N.A.I.C.S.: 561520

World Choice Limited (1)
2 Crown Square, Woking, GU21 6HR, Sur-
rey, United Kingdom
Tel.: (44) 1483545787
Web Site: http://www.worldchoice.co.uk
Travel Tour Operating Services
N.A.I.C.S.: 561520

CO-OPERATIVE INSURANCE
SOCIETY LIMITED
Miller St, Manchester, M60 0AL,
United Kingdom
Tel.: (44) 618328686
Web Site: http://www.cfs.co.uk
Sales Range: $750-799.9 Million
Insurance & Other Financial Services
N.A.I.C.S.: 524128
Mike Fairbairn (Dir-Risk)

CO-OPERATIVE PURCHASING
SERVICES LTD.
2nd Level Suite 2, PO Box 812, 420
Burwood Highway, Wantirna, 3152,
VIC, Australia
Tel.: (61) 0398012811
Web Site:
   http://www.purchasing.com.au
Sales Range: $25-49.9 Million
Emp.: 3
Co-operative Business Support Ser-
vices
N.A.I.C.S.: 541611
Max Fonovic (Mktg Mgr)

CO-PROSPERITY HOLDINGS
LIMITED
Wu Bao Industry-Area, Shishi,
362700, Fujian, China
Tel.: (86) 595 88922222   Ky
Web Site: http://www.co-
   prosperity.com
Sales Range: $50-74.9 Million
Emp.: 1,300

Co-Prosperity Holdings Limited—(Continued)

Textile Product Mfr & Whslr
N.A.I.C.S.: 313310
Siu Hung Sze (Chm)

Subsidiaries:

Shasing Shapheng Printing & Dyeing
Co., Ltd.　　　　　　　　　　(1)
Wu Bao Industry-Area, Shishi, 362700, Fu-
jian, China
Tel.: (86) 595 8892 2222
Textile Printing & Dyeing Services
N.A.I.C.S.: 313310

CO-TECH DEVELOPMENT CORP.
18F No 392 Ruiguang Rd Neihu Sci-
ence and Technology Park, Neihu
Dist, Taipei, 114, Taiwan
Tel.: (886) 266158899
Web Site: https://www.co-tech.com
8358—(TPE)
Rev.: $214,749,820
Assets: $239,664,329
Liabilities: $56,249,758
Net Worth: $183,414,571
Earnings: $19,264,356
Fiscal Year-end: 12/31/20
Copper Foil Mfr
N.A.I.C.S.: 331420
Frank Lee (Gen Mgr)

CO.DON AG
Warthestrasse 21, D-14513, Teltow,
D-14513, Germany
Tel.: (49) 332843460
Web Site: https://www.codon.de
CNWK—(DEU)
Rev.: $10,576,300
Assets: $28,404,921
Liabilities: $9,443,125
Net Worth: $18,961,796
Earnings: ($10,058,278)
Emp.: 131
Fiscal Year-end: 12/31/21
Therapeutics & Neurosurgical Market
Products Mfr
N.A.I.C.S.: 339112
Tilmann Bur (Member-Exec Bd)

CO.STAMP - SRL
Via Verdi 6, 23844, Sirone, LC, Italy
Tel.: (39) 031 875195
Holding Company
N.A.I.C.S.: 551112
Marco Corti (Owner & CEO)

Subsidiaries:

Costamp Group S.p.A.　　　　(1)
Via Verdi 6, 23844, Sirone, LC,
Italy　　　　　　　　　(90.99%)
Tel.: (39) 03 187 5195
Web Site: http://www.costampgroup.it
Rev.: $62,969,676
Assets: $120,602,035
Liabilities: $90,566,517
Net Worth: $30,035,519
Earnings: $952,433
Emp.: 274
Fiscal Year-end: 12/31/2020
Holding Company; Automotive Products Mfr
N.A.I.C.S.: 551112
Marco Corti (Chm & CEO)

CO2 CAPSOL AS
7th floor Thune Eureka Building
Drammensveien 126, 277, Oslo, Nor-
way
Tel.: (47) 41292013
Web Site:
　　https://www.capsoltechnologies.com
Year Founded: 2014
CAPSL—(OSL)
Rev.: $3,155,387
Assets: $13,460,861
Liabilities: $10,327,252
Net Worth: $3,133,609
Earnings: ($4,009,653)

Emp.: 20
Fiscal Year-end: 12/31/23
Biotechnology Research & Develop-
ment Services
N.A.I.C.S.: 541714
Cato Christiansen (CTO)

CO2 GRO INC.
40 King Stroot Woot Suito 5800, To-
ronto, M5H 3S1, ON, Canada
Tel.: (416) 315-7477　　　ON
Year Founded: 2010
BLONF—(OTCQB)
Rev.: $71,381
Assets: $1,040,593
Liabilities: $241,497
Net Worth: $799,096
Earnings: ($777,927)
Fiscal Year-end: 12/31/20
Agri-Industrial Reseach & Partner
N.A.I.C.S.: 541715
John Archibald (Pres & CEO)

CO2 SOLUTIONS, INC.
2300 rue Jean-Perrin Sainte-Foy,
Quebec, G2C 1T9, QC, Canada
Tel.: (418) 842-3456
Web Site: http://co2solutions.com
21O—(BER)
Waste Management Services
N.A.I.C.S.: 562998
Evan Price (CEO)

COACH A CO., LTD
2-1-30 Kudan-Minami, Chiyoda, To-
kyo, 102-0074, Japan
Tel.: (81) 3 32 37 80 50
Web Site: http://www.coacha.com
Year Founded: 2001
Professional & Management Develop-
ment Training
N.A.I.C.S.: 611430
Yoshiyuki Suzuki (Pres)

Subsidiaries:

Coach U, Inc.　　　　　　　(1)
2050 Beavercreek Rd Ste 101-399, Oregon
City, OR 97045
Tel.: (800) 482-6224
Web Site: http://www.coachu.com
Professional & Management Development
Training
N.A.I.C.S.: 611430
Jennifer Corbin (Pres & CEO)

COAL ASIA HOLDINGS INC.
3/F JTKC Centre 2155 Don Chino
Roces Ave, Makati, 1231, Philippines
Tel.: (63) 2 8138892
Web Site:
　　http://www.coalasiaholdings.com
Emp.: 60
Coal Mining
N.A.I.C.S.: 212115
Harald R. Tomintz (Chm)

COAL ENERGY S.A.
Antonovycha 64, Kiev, Ukraine
Tel.: (380) 442370274
Web Site:
　　https://www.coalenergy.com.ua
CLE—(WAR)
Sales Range: Less than $1 Million
Emp.: 6,387
Coal Mining & Production Services
N.A.I.C.S.: 212115
Oleksandr Ilchenko (CFO & Member-
Mgmt Bd)

COAL INDIA LIMITED
Coal Bhawan Premise No-04 MAR
Plot No-AF-III Action Area-1A, New-
town Rajarhat, Kolkata, 700156, West
Bengal, India
Tel.: (91) 3323245555　　　In
Web Site: https://www.coalindia.in

Year Founded: 1975
533278—(BOM)
Rev.: $17,550,071,484
Assets: $25,598,245,980
Liabilities: $18,566,758,896
Net Worth: $7,031,487,084
Earnings: $3,408,742,728
Emp.: 239,210
Fiscal Year-end: 03/31/23
Coal Production
N.A.I.C.S.: 324199
Chandan Kumar Dey (Dir-Fin)

Subsidiaries:

Bharat Coking Coal Limited　　(1)
Koyla Bhawan, Koyla Nagar, Dhanbad,
826005, Jharkhand, India　　(100%)
Tel.: (91) 326 2330203
Web Site: http://www.bccl.gov.in
Emp.: 100,000
Coal Mining Services
N.A.I.C.S.: 213113

Eastern Coalfields Limited　　(1)
10 Netaji Subhas Rd, Kolkata, 700001,
India　　　　　　　　(100%)
Tel.: (91) 3322488099
Web Site: http://www.mahanadicoal.nic.in
Sales Range: $350-399.9 Million
Emp.: 200
Coal Mining Services
N.A.I.C.S.: 213113
Chakravarty S. (Chm/Mng Dir-West Bengal)

Mahanadi Coalfields Limited　　(1)
Jagriti Vihar, PO Box UCE, Burla, Sambal-
pur, 768020, Orissa, India　　(100%)
Tel.: (91) 6632542461
Web Site: http://www.mahanadicoal.nic.in
Coal Mining Services
N.A.I.C.S.: 213113

Northern Coalfields Limited　　(1)
Singrauli District, Sidhi, 486889, Singrauli,
India　　　　　　　　(100%)
Tel.: (91) 7805266670
Web Site: http://www.ncl.nic.in
Sales Range: $750-799.9 Million
Emp.: 1,100
Coal Mining Services
N.A.I.C.S.: 213113
Prabhat Kumar Sinha (Chm & Mng Dir)

South Eastern Coalfields Limited　(1)
SECL Bhawan, Seepat Rd, Bilaspur,
495006, India　　　　　(100%)
Tel.: (91) 7752240582
Web Site: http://www.secl.nic.in
Sales Range: $1-4.9 Billion
Emp.: 86,000
Coal Mining Services
N.A.I.C.S.: 213113

Western Coalfields Limited　　(1)
Coal Estate Civil Lines, Nagpur, 440001,
Maharashtra, India　　　　(100%)
Tel.: (91) 7122511381
Web Site: http://www.esterncoal.in
Sales Range: $750-799.9 Million
Emp.: 2,000
Coal Mining Services
N.A.I.C.S.: 213113

COALA-LIFE GROUP AB
Regeringsgatan 29, PO Box 161 42,
103 23, Stockholm, Sweden
Tel.: (46) 841052000　　　SE
Web Site: http://www.rnb.se
COALA—(OMX)
Rev.: $2,329,286
Assets: $12,868,331
Liabilities: $8,067,168
Net Worth: $4,801,162
Earnings: ($17,326,082)
Emp.: 52
Fiscal Year-end: 12/31/22
Clothing Designer, Mfr & Distr
N.A.I.C.S.: 315250
Laszlo Kriss (Co-Chm)

Subsidiaries:

Brothers & Sisters Sverige AB　(1)
Ringvagen 115, 118 60, Stockholm, Sweden

Tel.: (46) 86424161
Clothing Retail Distr
N.A.I.C.S.: 458110
Anders Wiberg (Pres)

Departments & Stores Norway
AS　　　　　　　　　(1)
Nedre Slottsgate 8, 0157, Oslo, Norway
Tel.: (47) 22 00 40 15
Department Stores
N.A.I.C.S.: 455110

Jeanskompaniet AS　　　　(1)
Jernbaneg 1, D 3110, Tonsberg, Norway
Tel.: (47) 33318922
Jeans Clothing Distr
N.A.I.C.S.: 315210

COALSPUR MINES LIMITED
Level 1 28 Ord Street, West Perth,
6005, WA, Australia
Tel.: (61) 8 6555 2945　　　AU
Web Site: http://www.coalspur.com
Sales Range: Less than $1 Million
Emp.: 12
Coal Mining
N.A.I.C.S.: 212114
Dermot Lane (VP-Environmental)

Subsidiaries:

Coalspur Mines (Operations) Ltd.　(1)
Ste 880 550 11th Ave SW, Calgary, T2R
1M7, AB, Canada
Tel.: (403) 261-9997
Coal Mining Services
N.A.I.C.S.: 212115

COASIA HOLDINGS CO., LTD.
193 Namdongseo-ro, Namdong-gu,
Incheon, Korea (South)
Tel.: (82) 328132002
Web Site: https://www.coasia.com
Year Founded: 1987
045970—(KRS)
Rev.: $352,591,061
Assets: $314,796,859
Liabilities: $189,653,148
Net Worth: $125,143,711
Earnings: ($23,481,512)
Emp.: 229
Fiscal Year-end: 12/31/22
Holding Company
N.A.I.C.S.: 551112
Harrison Lee (Chm)

Subsidiaries:

C&CI Partners Co., Ltd.　　　(1)
19F 317 Teheran-ro, Gangnam-gu, Seoul,
Korea (South)
Tel.: (82) 221351694
Semiconductor Mfr
N.A.I.C.S.: 334413

COAsia Semi Korea Co., Ltd.　(1)
3F MK Tower 67 Jeongui-ro, Songpa-gu,
Seoul, Korea (South)
Tel.: (82) 269646284
Semiconductor Mfr
N.A.I.C.S.: 334413

CoAsia Corporation　　　　(1)
193 Namdongseo-ro, Namdong-gu, Jin-
cheon, Korea (South)
Tel.: (82) 269856099
Web Site: https://www.coasia.com
Semiconductor Product Mfr & Distr
N.A.I.C.S.: 334413

CoAsia Nexell Co., Ltd.　　　(1)
4F MK Tower 67 Jeongui-ro, Songpa-gu,
Seoul, 05835, Korea (South)
Tel.: (82) 7040990290
Web Site: https://www.coasianexell.com
Semiconductor Mfr
N.A.I.C.S.: 334413

Coasia Electronics Corp.　　(1)
13F No 3-2 Park St, Nangang District, Tai-
pei, 115, Taiwan
Tel.: (886) 226557699
Semiconductor Mfr
N.A.I.C.S.: 334413

COASIA MICROELECTRONICS CORP.

13F No 3-2 Park St, Nangang District, Taipei, Taiwan
Tel.: (886) 226557699
Web Site: https://www.coasia.com
Year Founded: 1997
8096—(TPE)
Rev.: $732,193,540
Assets: $202,078,823
Liabilities: $121,899,509
Net Worth: $80,179,314
Earnings: $37,895
Emp.: 127
Fiscal Year-end: 12/31/22
Electronic Component Mfr & Distr
N.A.I.C.S.: 334419
Hee-Jun Lee (Chm)

Subsidiaries:

CoAsia Electronics Corp. (Shanghai) Limited (1)
Room 903 9F Building B of Seazen Building No 3 Lane 388, Zhongjiang Road Putuo District, Shanghai, China
Tel.: (86) 2161231835
Electronic Components Mfr & Distr
N.A.I.C.S.: 334419

CoAsia Electronics Corp. (Shenzhen) Limited (1)
SZ 13A Zhongke Building Gaoxinnan 1st Road, Nanshan, Shenzhen, China
Tel.: (86) 75526743800
Electronic Components Mfr & Distr
N.A.I.C.S.: 334419

CoAsia Electronics Corp. (Singapore) Pte. Ltd. (1)
60 Paya Lebar Road 10-10 Paya Lebar Square, Singapore, 409051, Singapore
Tel.: (65) 69201392
Electronic Components Mfr & Distr
N.A.I.C.S.: 334419

CoAsia Korea Co., Ltd. (1)
A-38F 27 Dongtancheomdansaneop 1-ro, Hwaseong, Gyeonggi, Korea (South)
Tel.: (82) 269646253
Electric Equipment Mfr
N.A.I.C.S.: 334419

COASSETS LIMITED

6 Shenton Way 36-01 OUE Downtown 1, Singapore, 068809, Singapore
Tel.: (65) 6532 7008
Web Site: http://www.coassets.com
Rev.: $4,361,109
Assets: $21,642,189
Liabilities: $12,802,659
Net Worth: $8,839,530
Earnings: $1,358,272
Fiscal Year-end: 06/30/18
Web-Based Real Estate Services
N.A.I.C.S.: 531390
Goh Te-Win (Founder, CEO & Mng Dir)

COAST & COUNTRY HOUSING LTD.

14 Ennis Sq, Dormanstown, Redcar, TS10 5JR, Cleveland, United Kingdom
Tel.: (44) 1642771300
Web Site: http://www.cchousing-online.org.uk
Sales Range: $50-74.9 Million
Emp.: 600
Housing Services
N.A.I.C.S.: 624229
Paula Breen (Chm)

COAST DIGITAL, LTD.

6 Beacon End Courtyard London Rd, Stanway, Colchester, CO3 0NU, Essex, United Kingdom
Tel.: (44) 8454502086
Web Site:
http://www.coastdigital.co.uk

Year Founded: 2002
Sales Range: $10-24.9 Million
Emp.: 30
Advetising Agency
N.A.I.C.S.: 541810
James Frost (Chm)

COAST ENTERTAINMENT HOLDINGS LIMITED

Suite 601 83 Mount Street, North Sydney, 2060, NSW, Australia
Tel.: (61) 291684600   AU
Web Site:
http://www.ardentleisure.com
Year Founded: 2018
CEH—(ASX)
Rev.: $75,278,738
Assets: $176,708,614
Liabilities: $20,452,501
Net Worth: $156,256,114
Earnings: $1,706,331
Fiscal Year-end: 06/25/24
Holding Company; Theme Park & Entertainment Services
N.A.I.C.S.: 551112
Don Morris (Pres & CEO)

Subsidiaries:

Ardent Leisure Management Limited (1)
Level 16 61 Lavender Street, Milsons Point, 2061, NSW, Australia
Tel.: (61) 2 9409 3670
Web Site: http://www.ardentleisure.com
Entertainment Facilities Management Services
N.A.I.C.S.: 561110
Richard Johnson (CFO)

COAST INVESTMENT & DEVELOPMENT COMPANY K.S.C.C.

Coast Building Sharq Al Shuhada Street, PO Box 26755, Al Asima Governate Safat, 13128, Kuwait, 13128, Kuwait
Tel.: (965) 22230555
Web Site: https://www.coast.com.kw
Year Founded: 1975
COAST—(KUW)
Rev.: $9,581
Assets: $158,479,252
Liabilities: $4,663,565
Net Worth: $153,815,687
Earnings: ($33,369,973)
Emp.: 40
Fiscal Year-end: 12/31/20
Investment Services
N.A.I.C.S.: 523999
Fares Halal Madi (Sr VP-Compliance & Legal Affairs Grp)

Subsidiaries:

Coast Holding Corporation (1)
41 John St No 6, Babylon, NY 11702
Tel.: (631) 539-7441
Investment Management Service
N.A.I.C.S.: 541611

COAST SPAS MANUFACTURING INC

6315 202 Street, Langley, V2Y 1N7, BC, Canada
Tel.: (604) 514-8111
Web Site: https://www.coastspas.com
Year Founded: 1997
Rev.: $19,000,000
Emp.: 200
Hot Tubs & Spas Mfr
N.A.I.C.S.: 339999
Donald Elkington (Pres & CEO)

COAST TIRE & AUTO SERVICE, INC.

130 Somerset St Suite 150, Saint John, E2K 2X4, NB, Canada
Tel.: (506) 674-9620

Web Site: http://coasttire.com
Year Founded: 1984
Rev.: $44,519,850
Emp.: 300
Tire Supplier
N.A.I.C.S.: 441340
Ron Outerbridge (Pres & CEO)

COAST WHOLESALE APPLIANCES INC.

8488 Main Street, Vancouver, V5X 4W8, BC, Canada
Tel.: (604) 321-6644   Ca
Web Site:
http://www.coastwholesaleinc.com
Year Founded: 2010
Sales Range: $125-149.9 Million
Emp.: 274
Household Appliance Whslr
N.A.I.C.S.: 423620

COASTAL CARRIBEAN OIL & MINERALS LTD.

Clarendon House Church St, Hamilton, HM 11, Bermuda
Tel.: (441) 2951422
COCBF—(OTCIQ)
Sales Range: Less than $1 Million
Oil & Gas Exploration Services
N.A.I.C.S.: 213112

COASTAL CONTRACTS BHD.

Block G Lot 3B Bandar Leila WDT 259, 90009, Sandakan, Sabah, Malaysia
Tel.: (60) 89616263
Web Site:
https://www.coastalcontracts.com
COASTAL—(KLS)
Rev.: $70,610,703
Assets: $425,222,238
Liabilities: $55,118,085
Net Worth: $370,104,153
Earnings: $71,109,609
Emp.: 191
Fiscal Year-end: 12/31/23
Marine Services
N.A.I.C.S.: 541330
Dorothy Wei Kam Luk (Co-Sec)

COASTAL CORPORATION LIMITED

15-1-37/3 Jayaprada Apartments Nowroji Road, Maharanipeta, Visakhapatnam, 530002, Andhra Pradesh, India
Tel.: (91) 8912567118
Web Site:
https://www.coastalcorp.co.in
Year Founded: 1982
COASTCORP—(NSE)
Rev.: $68,848,280
Assets: $54,270,243
Liabilities: $26,346,193
Net Worth: $27,924,051
Earnings: $1,849,998
Emp.: 772
Fiscal Year-end: 03/31/22
Seafood Product Mfr & Whslr
N.A.I.C.S.: 311710
Thotolli Valsaraj (Mng Dir)

Subsidiaries:

Seacrest Seafoods Inc. (1)
7855 NW 12th St-Ste 221, Doral, FL 33126
Tel.: (305) 503-5306
Web Site: https://www.seacrestseafoods.us
Seafood Product Distr
N.A.I.C.S.: 424460

COASTAL FORD SALES LTD

5750 Lougheed Hwy, Burnaby, V5B 2Z9, BC, Canada
Tel.: (604) 294-6525
Web Site: http://www.coastalford.com
Year Founded: 1988
Rev.: $32,998,285

Emp.: 125
New & Used Car Dealers
N.A.I.C.S.: 441110
Donald Carson (Pres)

COASTAL GREENLAND LIMITED

Suite 1712-16 17th Floor China Merchants Tower Shun Tak Centre, 200 Connaught Road, Central, China (Hong Kong)
Tel.: (852) 2 877 9772
Web Site: http://www.coastal.com.cn
1124—(HKG)
Rev.: $869,454
Assets: $1,028,186,384
Liabilities: $573,365,370
Net Worth: $454,821,013
Earnings: ($139,490,193)
Emp.: 70
Fiscal Year-end: 03/31/22
Real Estate Investment & Property Management
N.A.I.C.S.: 237210
Ming Jiang (Chm & Mng Dir)

Subsidiaries:

Coastal Realty Development Co. Limited (1)
Rm 1708 17 Fl One Exchange Sq 8 Connaught Pl, Central, China (Hong Kong)
Tel.: (852) 28779772
Real Estate Property Development Services
N.A.I.C.S.: 531210
Ming Jiang (Chm & Mng Dir)

COASTAL ROADWAYS LIMITED

4 Black Burn Lane, Kolkata, 700 012, West Bengal, India
Tel.: (91) 3322376847
Web Site:
https://www.coastalroadways.com
Year Founded: 1968
520131—(BOM)
Rev.: $5,534,393
Assets: $2,253,601
Liabilities: $424,228
Net Worth: $1,829,373
Earnings: $169,943
Emp.: 50
Fiscal Year-end: 03/31/22
Transportation & Logistic Services
N.A.I.C.S.: 541614
Raja Saraogi (CFO)

COATS GROUP PLC

14 Aldermanbury Square 4th Floor, London, EC2V 7HS, United Kingdom
Tel.: (44) 2082105000   UK
Web Site: https://www.coats.com
Year Founded: 1755
COA—(LSE)
Rev.: $5,062,400,000
Assets: $2,809,400,000
Liabilities: $3,869,700,000
Net Worth: ($1,060,300,000)
Earnings: $142,200,000
Emp.: 15,000
Fiscal Year-end: 12/31/23
Investment Holding Company
N.A.I.C.S.: 551112
Simon Boddie (CFO)

Subsidiaries:

Coats (Turkiye) Iplik Sanayii AS (1)
Organize Sanayi Bolgesi Mavi Cadde No 2, Nilufer, 16220, Bursa, Turkiye
Tel.: (90) 2242431550
Apparel & Textile Product Mfr
N.A.I.C.S.: 314999

Coats Bangladesh Limited (1)
Novo Tower 270 Tejgaon Industrial Area, 1208, Dhaka, Bangladesh
Tel.: (880) 288709605
Sewing Thread Coat Mfr
N.A.I.C.S.: 315250

Coats Group plc—(Continued)

Md Al Kashem *(Dir-Mfg)*

Coats Bulgaria Eood (1)
7th Km Tzarigradsko Shousse, 1784, Sofia, Bulgaria
Tel.: (359) 29767741
Apparel & Textile Product Mfr
N.A.I.C.S.: 314999
Ivo Georgiev *(Gen Mgr & Comml Mgr)*

Coats Cadena Andina SA (1)
Av Santander 5E-87 Kennedy, Pereira, Colombia
Tel.: (57) 63398200
Web Site: http://www.coatscrafts.com
Apparel & Textile Product Mfr
N.A.I.C.S.: 314999

Coats Cadena Ltda. (1)
Marathon N 4046 Macul, Casilla 42, Macul, Santiago, Chile
Tel.: (56) 25954500
Apparel & Textile Product Mfr
N.A.I.C.S.: 314999

Coats Cadena S.A. (1)
Rufino T Dominguez 1864, 11400, Montevideo, Uruguay
Tel.: (598) 26139927
Apparel & Textile Product Mfr
N.A.I.C.S.: 314999

Coats Cadena SA (1)
De las Avellanas E2-74 Y EL Juncal, Quito, Ecuador
Tel.: (593) 2802020
Apparel & Textile Product Mfr
N.A.I.C.S.: 314999

Coats Cadena SA (1)
Av Nicolas Ayllon 2925, El Agustino, Lima, Peru
Tel.: (51) 16126200
Apparel & Textile Product Mfr
N.A.I.C.S.: 314999

Coats Cadena SA (1)
Av Romulo Gallegos con Calle Las Palmas Centro Gerencial Los Andes, Piso1 Oficina 1-I Boleita Norte, Caracas, Venezuela
Tel.: (58) 2122396233
Apparel & Textile Product Mfr
N.A.I.C.S.: 314999

Coats Eesti AS (1)
Ampri tee 9/4 Viimsi Vald, Lubja, 74010, Harjumaa, Estonia
Tel.: (372) 6306250
Apparel & Textile Product Mfr
N.A.I.C.S.: 314999

Coats Egypt For Manufacturing & Dyeing Sewing Thread SAE (1)
Industrial Area Zone B3 Plot 78, 10th of Ramadan City, Egypt
Tel.: (20) 122465660
Sewing Thread Coat Mfr
N.A.I.C.S.: 315250

Coats El Salvador, S.A. de C.V. (1)
Yona Franca Exportsalva Km 24 1/2 Carretera a Santa Ana Edif 18C, Lourdes Colon, La Libertad, El Salvador
Tel.: (503) 23384525
Apparel & Textile Product Mfr
N.A.I.C.S.: 314999

Coats Honduras, S.A. (1)
Zona Libre Inhdelva Edificio 13 800m Carretera a La Jutosa Cortes, Choloma, Honduras
Tel.: (504) 6170300
Apparel & Textile Product Mfr
N.A.I.C.S.: 314999
Wendy Velasquez *(Mgr-Bus)*

Coats Industrial Scandinavia AB (1)
Stationsvagen 2, PO Box 109, 516 22, Dalsjofors, Sweden
Tel.: (46) 33225300
Apparel & Textile Product Mfr
N.A.I.C.S.: 314999

Coats LLC (1)
53 Lenin Street, Oktyabrsky Luberetsky District, 140060, Moscow, Russia
Tel.: (7) 4955105184
Apparel & Textile Product Mfr
N.A.I.C.S.: 314999

Coats Maroc SA (1)
220 Bd Chefchaouni, Ain Sebaa, Casablanca, Morocco
Tel.: (212) 52266255051
Apparel & Textile Product Mfr
N.A.I.C.S.: 314999
Khadija Joua *(Mgr-Dyehouse)*

Coats Mexico S.A. de C.V. (1)
Periferico Sur 3325 Colonia San Jeronimo Lidice Delegacion Magdalena, Contreras Edificio Corum Piso 8, 10200, Mexico, Mexico
Tel.: (52) 5552271800
Apparel & Textile Product Mfr
N.A.I.C.S.: 314999
Fabio Moreno *(Dir-Mfg)*

Coats Opti Germany GmbH (1)
1 Suedwieke 180, 26817, Rhauderfehn, Germany
Tel.: (49) 49528040
Apparel & Textile Product Mfr
N.A.I.C.S.: 314999

Coats Patons (New Zealand) Ltd. (1)
3 Mana Place, Wiri, Auckland, 2104, New Zealand
Tel.: (64) 92620406
Apparel & Textile Product Mfr
N.A.I.C.S.: 314999

Coats Polska Sp. z o.o. (1)
ul Kaczencowa 16, 91-214, Lodz, Poland
Tel.: (48) 422540400390
Apparel & Textile Product Mfr
N.A.I.C.S.: 314999
Pawel Sterczewski *(Mgr-Quality)*

Coats Romania SRL (1)
Str Nicolae Balcescu Nr 71, Harghita, 535600, Odorheiu Secuiesc, Romania
Tel.: (40) 266207200
Apparel & Textile Product Mfr
N.A.I.C.S.: 314999
Katalin Sandor *(Mgr-Fin)*

Coats Shenzhen Limited (1)
Coats Industrial Park Fengtang Dadao, Tangwei Village Fuyong Town Baoan District, Shenzhen, 518103, China
Tel.: (86) 75527342288
Apparel & Textile Product Mfr
N.A.I.C.S.: 314999

Coats Stroppel AG (1)
Bruggerstrasse 21, 5400, Baden, Switzerland
Tel.: (41) 771609739
Apparel & Textile Product Mfr
N.A.I.C.S.: 314999

Coats Thread Exports (Private) Limited (1)
Level 8 No 479 HNB Towers TB Jayah Mw, Colombo, Sri Lanka
Tel.: (94) 115565500
Apparel & Textile Product Mfr
N.A.I.C.S.: 314999
Kishani Weerasinghe *(Mgr-Employee Rels)*

Coats Thread Germany GmbH (1)
Huefinger Strasse 28, 78199, Braunlingen, Germany
Tel.: (49) 7716090
Apparel & Textile Product Mfr
N.A.I.C.S.: 314999

Coats Threads (Thailand) Ltd. (1)
39/60 Moo 2 Tambol Bangkrachaw, Amphur Muang, 74000, Samutsakorn, Thailand
Tel.: (66) 34419100
Apparel & Textile Product Mfr
N.A.I.C.S.: 314999

Coats Ukraine Ltd. (1)
28A litera B Moskovskiy Prospekt, 04655, Kiev, Ukraine
Tel.: (380) 445864968
Apparel & Textile Product Mfr
N.A.I.C.S.: 314999

Coats de Nicaragua SA (1)
Esso Salvadorita 1/2 Cuadra Al Oeste Centro Perisferico Mod 8, Managua, Nicaragua
Tel.: (505) 8533439
Apparel & Textile Product Mfr
N.A.I.C.S.: 314999

Coats plc (1)
4 Longwalk Rd, Stockley Park, Uxbridge, UB11 1FE, United Kingdom
Tel.: (44) 845 603 0150
Web Site: http://www.coats.com
Holding Company; Sewing Thread, Yarn & Needlecraft Products Mfr & Distr
N.A.I.C.S.: 551112
Mike Clasper *(Chm)*

Subsidiary (Non-US):

Coats Australian Pty Ltd. (2)
2/56 Keys Road, Moorabbin, 3189, VIC, Australia
Tel.: (61) 39 555 3300
Web Site: https://www.coats.com
Thread
N.A.I.C.S.: 313110

Coats Cadena SA Argentina (2)
Parque Industrial La Cantabrica, Tres Arroyos 329 Haedo, 1706, Buenos Aires, Argentina
Tel.: (54) 1144896100
Web Site: http://www.coats.com
Thread Mills
N.A.I.C.S.: 313110

Coats Corrente Ltda-Fabrica Ipiranga (2)
Rua Do Manifesto 705, Ipiranga, 04209 000, Sao Paulo, Brazil
Tel.: (55) 11 4932 8000
Web Site: http://www.coatscorrente.com.br
Thread & Zipper Mfr
N.A.I.C.S.: 313110
Marco Camargo *(Pres)*

Coats Cucirini S.p.A. (2)
Via Milanese 20, Sesto San Giovanni, 2099, Milan, Italy
Tel.: (39) 026 410 9080
Web Site: http://www.coatscucirini.it
Thread & Knitting Yarns
N.A.I.C.S.: 313110

Coats Fabra SA (2)
MERIDIANA 350 13 PLANTA, Barcelona, 08027, Spain
Tel.: (34) 932908400
Web Site: http://www.coats.com
Rev.: $53,300,000
Emp.: 8
Industrial & Craft Thread
N.A.I.C.S.: 313110
Paul A. Forman *(Grp CEO)*

Coats GmbH (2)
Kaiserstrasse 1, 79341, Kenzingen, Germany
Tel.: (49) 7644802222
Web Site: http://www.makeitcoats.com
Craft & Leisure Products Mfr & Distr
N.A.I.C.S.: 313110

Unit (Non-US):

Coats Crafts UK (3)
Green Lane Mill, Holmfirth, HD9 2DX, W Yorkshire, United Kingdom
Tel.: (44) 1484681881
Web Site: http://www.makeitcoats.com
Sales Range: $25-49.9 Million
Emp.: 130
Craft & Leisure Products Distr
N.A.I.C.S.: 424310

Subsidiary (Non-US):

Coats Harlander Ges.m.b.H. (2)
Autokaderstrasse 31, 1210, Vienna, Austria
Tel.: (43) 1277160
Web Site: http://www.coatsharlander.at
Industrial & Craft Thread Products
N.A.I.C.S.: 313110

Coats Manila Bay, Inc. (2)
Lopez Jaena St, Bo Tanong Marikina City, Manila, 1803, Philippines
Tel.: (63) 29419590
Web Site: http://www.coats.com
Mfr of Thread
N.A.I.C.S.: 313110

Coats South Africa (Pty) Ltd. (2)
Kelly Rd hampshire No 14, PO Box 14, Hammarsdale, 3700, Kwa Zulu Natal, South Africa
Tel.: (27) 317362171
Web Site: http://www.coats.com
Industrial & Craft Thread

N.A.I.C.S.: 313110

Compania de Linha Coats & Clark, Lda. (2)
Apartado 444, Vila Nova de Gaia, 4431 968, Portugal
Tel.: (351) 223770700
Web Site: http://www.coatsclark.pt
Industrial & Craft Thread
N.A.I.C.S.: 313110

PT Coats Rejo Indonesia (2)
Jalan Raya Tajur No 24, 16720, Bogor, West Java, Indonesia
Tel.: (62) 3434240835
Emp.: 600
Thread, Yarn & Cloth
N.A.I.C.S.: 313110

Subsidiary (US):

Patrick Yarn Mill, Inc. (2)
501 York Rd, Kings Mountain, NC 28086-3360
Tel.: (704) 739-4119
Web Site: http://www.patrickyarns.com
Fiber, Yarn & Thread Mills
N.A.I.C.S.: 313110

Distribuidora Coats De Guatemala S.A. (1)
39 Av 3-47 zona 7 Colonia El Rodeo Ciudad, Guatemala, Guatemala
Tel.: (502) 2434007374
Apparel & Textile Product Mfr
N.A.I.C.S.: 314999

Gotex S.A. (1)
C/Ca N Alzina 79 Pol Ind Can Roqueta Sabadell, 08202, Barcelona, Spain
Tel.: (34) 937265622
Apparel & Textile Product Mfr
N.A.I.C.S.: 314999

J & P Coats Pakistan (Pvt) Limited (1)
112-113 Prime Office Lobby Park Towers Shahrah-e-Firdousi Clifton, Karachi, 75600, Pakistan
Tel.: (92) 21111115115
Apparel & Textile Product Mfr
N.A.I.C.S.: 314999
Mansoor Ali Zaidi *(Dir-Fin)*

Qingdao Coats Limited (1)
5 Longhai Road Qingdao Huanhai, Economic & Technological Development Zone Chengyang District, Qingdao, 266108, Shandong, China
Tel.: (86) 53281106232
Apparel & Textile Product Mfr
N.A.I.C.S.: 314999

Shanghai Coats Limited (1)
No 8 Building Export and Processing Garden, Songjiang Industrial Zone, Shanghai, 201613, China
Tel.: (86) 75527342789
Apparel & Textile Product Mfr
N.A.I.C.S.: 314999

Texon International Group Ltd. (1)
Skelton Industrial Estate, Saltburn-by-the-Sea, TS12 2LH, United Kingdom
Tel.: (44) 1287 650 551
Web Site: http://www.texon.com
Footwear Materials Design, Mfr & Distr
N.A.I.C.S.: 316210
Roksana Samborska-Skowron *(Mgr-NPD Grp)*

Subsidiary (Domestic):

Texon Management Ltd (2)
Skelton, Saltburn-by-the-Sea, TS12 2LH, United Kingdom
Tel.: (44) 1287 650 551
Footwear Materials Design, Mfr & Distr
N.A.I.C.S.: 424340
Gary Hollins *(Grp Dir-Ops)*

COBEPA S.A.
Rue de la Chancellerie 2 Box 1, 1000, Brussels, Belgium
Tel.: (32) 22133210
Web Site: https://www.cobepa.com
Year Founded: 1957
Rev: $1,169,749,983
Assets: $3,671,003,016

Liabilities: $102,151,493
Net Worth: $3,568,851,523
Earnings: $1,133,200,017
Fiscal Year-end: 12/31/21
Privater Equity Firm
N.A.I.C.S.: 523999
Jean-Marie Laurent Josi *(CEO)*

Subsidiaries:

BioAgilytix Labs, LLC   **(1)**
2300 Englert Dr, Durham, NC 27713
Tel.: (919) 381-6097
Web Site: http://www.bioagilytix.com
Sales Range: $10-24.9 Million
Emp.: 10
Assaying Services
N.A.I.C.S.: 541380
Linda Robbie *(COO)*

Subsidiary (Domestic):

Cambridge Biomedical Inc.   **(2)**
1320 Soldiers Field Road, Boston, MA
02135
Tel.: (617) 456-0700
Web Site: https://www.bioagilytix.com
Research & Development in Biotechnology
N.A.I.C.S.: 541714

Enoplastic SpA   **(1)**
Via Luigi Galvani 1, Bodio Lomnago, 21020,
Varese, Italy   **(57%)**
Tel.: (39) 0332 94 35 11
Web Site: http://www.enoplastic.com
Emp.: 400
Wine & Spirits Closures Mfr
N.A.I.C.S.: 332119
Michele Moglia *(CEO)*

Subsidiary (Non-US):

Sparflex SA   **(2)**
Za Dizy CS20300, 51209, Epernay, Cedex,
France
Tel.: (33) 326531111
Web Site: http://www.sparflex.com
Rev.: $34,500,000
Emp.: 180
Wines & Spirits Packaging Mfr
N.A.I.C.S.: 561910

Gerflor SA   **(1)**
50 cours de la Republique, 69627, Villeur-
banne, Cedex, France
Tel.: (33) 472651000
Web Site: http://www.gerflor.fr
Sales Range: $400-449.9 Million
Emp.: 30
Flooring Product Mfr
N.A.I.C.S.: 326199
Bertrand Chammas *(Chm & CEO)*

Subsidiary (US):

Connor Sport Court International,
Inc.   **(2)**
5445 W Harold Ghatty Dr, Salt Lake City,
UT 84116
Tel.: (800) 421-8112
Web Site: http://www.connorsportcourt.com
Sports Flooring Services
N.A.I.C.S.: 238330
Brandi Connolly *(Sr Dir-Mktg & Comm)*

Gerflor USA, Inc.   **(2)**
750 Veterans Pkwy, Bolingbrook, IL 60440
Tel.: (847) 394-3944
Web Site: https://www.gerflorusa.com
Floor, Wall Coverings & Accessories Mfr
N.A.I.C.S.: 238330
Benjamin Bachman *(CEO)*

Subsidiary (Domestic):

SnapLock Industries, Inc.   **(3)**
2330 W California Ave, Salt Lake City, UT
84104
Tel.: (801) 746-0143
Web Site: http://www.snaplock.com
Sales Range: $10-24.9 Million
Emp.: 40
Modular Flooring Products Mfr
N.A.I.C.S.: 238330
Jorgen Moller *(Mng Dir)*

Holding Socotec S.A.S.   **(1)**
Les Quadrants - 3 Avenue du Centre - Guyancourt CS 20732, 78182, Saint-Quentin-
en-Yvelines, Cedex, France

Tel.: (33) 1 30 12 80 00
Web Site: http://www.socotec.com
Holding Company; Building Inspection Ser-
vices
N.A.I.C.S.: 551112
Francis Caire *(Dir-HR)*

Division (US):

Forge Engineering, Inc.   **(2)**
2224 Trade Ctr Way, Naples, FL 34109
Tel.: (239) 514-4100
Web Site: http://www.forgeeng.com
Engineeering Services
N.A.I.C.S.: 541330
Matt H. Nolton *(CEO)*

Subsidiary (Domestic):

Socotec SA   **(2)**
3 avenue du Centre, 78280, Guyancourt,
France   **(63%)**
Tel.: (33) 1 30 12 80 00
Sales Range: $600-649.9 Million
Building Inspection Services
N.A.I.C.S.: 541350

Subsidiary (Non-US):

Certification International (UK)
Limited   **(3)**
Delta 100 Delta Business Park, Great West-
ern Way, Swindon, SN5 7XP, Wiltshire,
United Kingdom
Tel.: (44) 1793 492892
Web Site: http://www.cert-int.com
Emp.: 11
Assessment, Analysis & Certification of
Management Systems
N.A.I.C.S.: 561499
Emma Law *(Mng Dir)*

KHI Management International
Ltd.   **(3)**
Suite 308 3rd Floor 22 Park House, Park
Street, Croydon, CR0 1YE, Surrey, United
Kingdom
Tel.: (44) 208 688 2217
Web Site: http://www.kmil.co.uk
Emp.: 4
Consulting Services to Oil & Gas & Energy
Sectors
N.A.I.C.S.: 541690
J. J. Disetti *(Mng Dir)*

Subsidiary (US):

SOCOTEC, Inc.   **(3)**
360 Park Ave S 15th Fl, New York, NY
10010
Tel.: (212) 689-5389
Web Site: https://www.socotec.us
Sales Range: $10-24.9 Million
Emp.: 200
Engineeering Services
N.A.I.C.S.: 541330
Lori Boccadoro *(Principal)*

Subsidiary (Domestic):

Conversano Associates Inc.   **(4)**
70 Lafayette St Ste 3, New York, NY
10013-4000
Tel.: (212) 791-0818
Web Site:
    http://www.conversanoassociates.com
Landscape Architectural Services
N.A.I.C.S.: 541320
Lori Boccadoro *(Pres)*

Future Tech Consultants of New York,
Inc.   **(4)**
52 E 2nd St, Mineola, NY 11501
Tel.: (516) 355-0168
Web Site: http://www.ftcny.com
Sales Range: $1-9.9 Million
Emp.: 70
Building Inspection Services
N.A.I.C.S.: 541350
Michael Marchese *(Founder, Partner &
Exec VP)*

Synergen Consulting International
LLC   **(4)**
11750 Katy Fwy Ste 1000, Houston, TX
77079
Tel.: (800) 701-4248
Business Consulting, Nec, Nsk
N.A.I.C.S.: 541618
Bryan Byrd *(Pres)*

Veritas Advisory Group, Inc.   **(4)**
Thanksgiving Tower 1601 Elm St Ste 3600,
Dallas, TX 75201-7287
Tel.: (214) 720-1995
Web Site: http://www.veritasag.com
Emp.: 40
Child & Youth Services
N.A.I.C.S.: 624110
Rodney Sowards *(Pres)*

Subsidiary (Domestic):

Societe Internationale de Controle et
Approvisionnement SASU   **(3)**
143 Avenue Charles de Gaulle, 92200,
Neuilly, France
Tel.: (33) 1 49 03 73 80
Web Site: http://www.sica.fr
Emp.: 8
Third Party Inspection Services to Oil &
Gas Industry
N.A.I.C.S.: 541350
Jean-Jacques Munier *(Pres)*

COBRA BIOLOGICS HOLDING AB

Storjordenvagen 2, 864 31, Matfors,
Sweden
Tel.: (46) 607858600
Web Site: http://www.cobrabio.com
Sales Range: $10-24.9 Million
Emp.: 125
Recombinant Biological Product Mfr
N.A.I.C.S.: 325414
Thomas Eldered *(Chm)*

Subsidiaries:

Cobra Biologics Limited   **(1)**
Stephenson Building The Science Park,
Keele, ST5 5SP, Staffordshire, United King-
dom
Tel.: (44) 1782714181
Web Site: http://www.cobrabio.com
Microbial & Virus Production Facility Service
N.A.I.C.S.: 325412
Peter Coleman *(CEO)*

Plant (Non-US):

Cobra Biologics Ltd - Microbial Pro-
duction & Fill Finish Facility   **(2)**
Storjordenvagen 2, 864 31, Matfors, Swe-
den
Tel.: (46) 60 641 670
Biological Product Mfr
N.A.I.C.S.: 325414

COBRA RESOURCES PLC

9th Floor 107 Cheapside, London,
EC2V 6DN, United Kingdom
Tel.: (44) 893164938   UK
Web Site: https://cobraplc.com
Year Founded: 2018
COBR—(LSE)
Assets: $5,157,699
Liabilities: $288,959
Net Worth: $4,868,740
Earnings: ($642,689)
Fiscal Year-end: 12/31/22
Investment Management Service
N.A.I.C.S.: 523940
Craig Moulton *(Exec Dir)*

Subsidiaries:

Lady Alice Mines Pty Ltd.   **(1)**
Tel.: (61) 893164938
Investment Banking Services
N.A.I.C.S.: 523150

COBRA VENTURE CORPORA-TION

2489 Bellevue Avenue, West Vancou-
ver, V7V 1E1, BC, Canada
Tel.: (604) 922-2030
Web Site:
    https://www.cobraventure.com
Year Founded: 1999
CBVTF—(OTCIQ)
Rev.: $1,485,044
Assets: $2,702,178
Liabilities: $163,905

Net Worth: $2,538,273
Earnings: $292,033
Fiscal Year-end: 11/30/22
Oil & Gas Exploration Services
N.A.I.C.S.: 213112
Cyrus H. Driver *(CFO)*

COBRASMA S.A.

R Prof luis Eulalio de Bueno Vidigal
131, 6093085, Osasco, Sao Paulo,
Brazil
Tel.: (55) 1146238436
Web Site:
    http://www.cobrasma.com.br
Transportation Equipment Merchant
Whslr
N.A.I.C.S.: 423860
Luis Eulalio de Bueno Vidigal Filho
(Chm, Pres & CEO)

COBRE LIMITED

Level 10 Kyle House 27 Macquarie
Pl, Sydney, 2000, WA, Australia
Tel.: (61) 290488856   AU
Web Site: https://www.cobre.com.au
Year Founded: 2018
CBE—(ASX)
Rev.: $379,201
Assets: $20,538,967
Liabilities: $473,752
Net Worth: $20,065,214
Earnings: ($1,144,191)
Fiscal Year-end: 06/30/23
Mineral Exploration Services
N.A.I.C.S.: 212390
Martin Christopher Holland *(Chm)*

COBURG GROUP PLC

Unit 3 Harrington Way Warspite
Road, Woolwich, London, SE18 5NU,
United Kingdom
Tel.: (44) 2083170103   UK
Web Site: http://www.coburg-
group.com
Sales Range: $1-9.9 Million
Emp.: 33
Investment Holding Company
N.A.I.C.S.: 551112
Louisa E. Pino *(Sec)*

COBURN JAPAN CORPORA-TION

1-6-11 Minato, Chuo-ku, Tokyo, 104-
0043, Japan
Tel.: (81) 335535721
Web Site: http://www.coburn.co.jp
Year Founded: 1978
Sales Range: $25-49.9 Million
Emp.: 29
Holographic Films Mfr
N.A.I.C.S.: 326113
Toru Kojima *(Mng Dir)*

COBUS INDUSTRIES GMBH

Max Planck Ring 43, D-65205, Wies-
baden, Germany
Tel.: (49) 612295530
Web Site: http://www.cobus-
industries.de
Year Founded: 1978
Sales Range: $25-49.9 Million
Transportation Services
N.A.I.C.S.: 485113
Andreas Funk *(Sls Dir)*

COCA-COLA BOTTLERS JA-PAN HOLDINGS INC.

Tokyo Midtown Tower 9-7-1 Akasaka,
Minato-ku, Tokyo, 107-6211, Japan
Tel.: (81) 308509   JP
Web Site: https://en.ccbj-
holdings.com
Year Founded: 1960
2579—(FKA)
Rev.: $8,388,560,110
Assets: $8,733,911,480

Coca-Cola Bottlers Japan Holdings
Inc.—(Continued)

Liabilities: $4,089,389,010
Net Worth: $4,644,522,470
Earnings: ($531,419,840)
Emp.: 16,959
Fiscal Year-end: 12/31/19
Beverages Mfr
N.A.I.C.S.: 312111
Bjorn Ivar Ulgenes (CFO & VP)

Subsidiaries:

Coca-Cola Bottlers Japan Inc. (1)
Tokyo Midtown Tower 9-7-1, Akasaka
Minato-ku, Tokyo, 107-6211, Japan
Tel.: (81) 120308509
Web Site: https://en.ccbji.co.jp
Beverage Mfr & Distr
N.A.I.C.S.: 312111

Coca-Cola West Daisen Products
Co., Ltd. (1)
306-1 Kanayadani Hoki-cho, Saihaku-gun,
Tottori, 689-4213, Japan
Tel.: (81) 859399881
Soft Drinks Mfr
N.A.I.C.S.: 312111

Coca-Cola West Japan Customer
Service Co Ltd (1)
871 Taniyama, Koga, Fukuoka, Japan
Tel.: (81) 929446813
Web Site: http://www.ccwest.co.jp
Automatic Vending Machine Mfr
N.A.I.C.S.: 333310

Coca-Cola West Service Co.,
Ltd. (1)
7-9-66 Hakozaki, Higashi-Ku, Fukuoka,
812-0053, Japan
Tel.: (81) 926510843
Real Estate Manangement Services
N.A.I.C.S.: 531390

Coca-Cola West Vending Co.,
Ltd. (1)
7-9-66 Hakozaki, Higashi-Ku, Fukuoka,
812-0053, Japan
Tel.: (81) 926418554
Vending Machine Operators
N.A.I.C.S.: 445132

Kadiac Co., Ltd (1)
1 Senshukukominami, Sennan, Osaka, Ja-
pan
Tel.: (81) 724566248
Sales Range: $25-49.9 Million
Emp.: 25
Vending Machine Operators
N.A.I.C.S.: 333310

Kansai Beverage Service Company
Limited (1)
C-o Kinki Coca-Cola Bottling Co Ltd,
Settsu, Osaka, Japan
Tel.: (81) 663302250
Web Site: http://www.ccwest.co.jp
Sales Range: $150-199.9 Million
Emp.: 700
Business Service Centers
N.A.I.C.S.: 561439

Nippon Supplement Inc. (1)
Applause Tower 19-19 Chayamachi, Kita-
ku, Osaka, 530-0013, Japan
Tel.: (81) 663762220
Web Site: http://www.nippon-sapuri.com
Dietary Supplements Mfr
N.A.I.C.S.: 311999
Takeshi Masuda (Pres)

Shikoku Coca-Cola Bottling Co.,
Ltd. (1)
1378 Kasuga-cho, Takamatsu, 761-0197,
Kagawa, Japan (100%)
Tel.: (81) 878419191
Web Site: http://www.shikoku.ccbc.co.jp
Soft Drinks Mfr
N.A.I.C.S.: 312111
Hirohiro Hara (Pres & Dir)

Takamasamune Co Ltd (1)
12-12 Kozucho, Kurume, Fukuoka, 830-
0045, Japan
Tel.: (81) 942368811
Web Site: http://www.takamasamune.com

Wine & Distilled Alcoholic Beverage Mer-
chant Whlslr
N.A.I.C.S.: 424820
Tsukasa Sato (Pres)

West Japan Service Company
Limited (1)
7-9-66 Hakozaki, Higashi-Ku, Fukuoka,
Japan
Tel.: (81) 926510843
Insurance Agencies & Brokerages
N.A.I.C.S.: 524210

Wex Co., Ltd. (1)
1806-74 Miyanogi-cho, Inage-ku, Chiba,
263-0054, Japan
Tel.: (81) 432570857
Vending Machine Operators
N.A.I.C.S.: 445132

COCA-COLA EMBONOR S.A.
Av El Golf 40 piso 4, Las Condes,
Santiago, Chile
Tel.: (56) 22991400   CL
Web Site: https://www.embonor.cl
EMBONOR—(SGO)
Sales Range: $800-899.9 Million
Beverage Bottling Services
N.A.I.C.S.: 312111
Andres Vicuna Garcia-Huidobo (Chm
& Pres)

COCA-COLA EUROPACIFIC
PARTNERS PLC
Pemberton House Bakers Road, Ux-
bridge, UB8 1EZ, United Kingdom
Tel.: (44) 1895231313   UK
Web Site: https://www.ccep.com
Year Founded: 1904
CCEP—(NASDAQ)
Rev.: $19,751,780,704
Assets: $31,571,336,067
Liabilities: $22,963,522,556
Net Worth: $8,607,813,512
Earnings: $1,801,208,720
Emp.: 36,075
Fiscal Year-end: 12/31/23
Soft Drinks Mfr
N.A.I.C.S.: 551112
Damian Paul Gammell (CEO)

Subsidiaries:

CCEP Holdings Sverige AB (1)
Dryckesvagen 2C, 136 87, Haninge, Swe-
den
Tel.: (46) 850075000
N.A.I.C.S.: 312111

Coca-Cola Amatil Limited (1)
L13 40 Mount Street, North Sydney, 2060,
NSW, Australia (100%)
Tel.: (61) 292596222
Web Site: http://www.ccamatil.com
Holding Company; Carbonated & Non-
Carbonated Beverages Mfr & Distr
N.A.I.C.S.: 551112
Alison Watkins (Mng Dir-Grp)

Subsidiary (Domestic):

CCA Bayswater Pty Ltd (2)
Level 13 40 Mount Street, North Sydney,
2060, NSW, Australia
Tel.: (61) 397296788
Canned Fruits Jam & Vegetables Mfr
N.A.I.C.S.: 311411

Subsidiary (Non-US):

Coca-Cola Amatil (Fiji) Ltd (2)
Ratu Dovi Rd LBEst, Nasinu, Fiji
Tel.: (679) 3394333
Web Site: https://www.cocacolaep.com
Sales Range: $25-49.9 Million
Emp.: 290
Soft Drinks Mfr & Distr
N.A.I.C.S.: 312111
Roger Hare (Gen Mgr)

Coca-Cola Amatil (PNG) Ltd (2)
Erica St Lae, Lae, Morobe, Papua New
Guinea
Tel.: (675) 4721033
Web Site: http://www.ccamatilpng.com
Emp.: 200

Soft Drink Mfr & Distr
N.A.I.C.S.: 424490

Subsidiary (Domestic):

Coca-Cola Amatil Pty Ltd (2)
Level 13 40 Mount Street, North Sydney,
2060, NSW, Australia
Tel.: (61) 292596800
Sales Range: $1-4.9 Billion
Emp.: 2,000
Carbonated & Non-Carbonated Beverages
Mfr & Distr
N.A.I.C.S.: 312111

Subsidiary (Domestic):

Can Recycling (S.A.) Pty Ltd (3)
Level 13 40 Mount Street, Ottoway, North
Sydney, 2060, NSW, Australia
Tel.: (61) 883412511
Sales Range: $10-24.9 Million
Emp.: 12
Plastic Can Recycling Services
N.A.I.C.S.: 562920
Richard By (Mgr)

Crusta Fruit Juices Proprietary
Limited (3)
Level 13 40 Mount Street, North Sydney,
2060, NSW, Australia
Tel.: (61) 885410100
Sales Range: $10-24.9 Million
Emp.: 40
Fresh Juice Mfr
N.A.I.C.S.: 311411

Quenchy Crusta Sales Pty Ltd (3)
Level 13 40 Mount Street, Dry Creek, North
Sydney, 2060, NSW, Australia
Tel.: (61) 883590011
Soft Drink Distr
N.A.I.C.S.: 424490

Quirks Australia Pty Ltd (3)
198 Power St, Glendenning, 2761, NSW,
Australia
Tel.: (61) 288052500
Web Site: http://www.quirksaustralia.com.au
Commercial Refrigeration Rental & Installa-
tion Services
N.A.I.C.S.: 238220

Subsidiary (Domestic):

Feral Brewing Company Pty Ltd (2)
152 Haddrill Rd, PO Box 3265, Baskerville,
Perth, 6942, WA, Australia
Tel.: (61) 892962337
Web Site: https://www.feralbrewing.com.au
Brewery Product Whlsr
N.A.I.C.S.: 424810

Matila Nominees Pty Limited (2)
Level 13 40 Mount Street, North Sydney,
2060, NSW, Australia
Tel.: (61) 292596130
Soft Drinks Mfr
N.A.I.C.S.: 312111

Neverfail Bottled Water Co Pty
Limited (2)
Level 13 40 Mount Street, North Sydney,
2060, NSW, Australia
Tel.: (61) 294367000
Sales Range: $25-49.9 Million
Emp.: 200
Bottled Water Mfr & Distr
N.A.I.C.S.: 312112

Neverfail Springwater Co (Qld) Pty
Limited (2)
Level 13 40 Mount Street, North Sydney,
2060, NSW, Australia
Tel.: (61) 1300300204
Spring Water Distr
N.A.I.C.S.: 424490

Neverfail Springwater Limited (2)
Level 13 40 Mount Street, North Sydney,
2060, NSW, Australia
Tel.: (61) 133037
Sales Range: $50-74.9 Million
Emp.: 100
Spring & Bottled Water Distr
N.A.I.C.S.: 424490

Subsidiary (Non-US):

PT Coca-Cola Distribution
Indonesia (2)

South Quarter Tower C 22nd P Floor Jalan
R A Kartini Kav 8, Cilandak Barat Cilandak,
South Jakarta, 12430, Indonesia
Tel.: (62) 214603124
Soft Drink Distr
N.A.I.C.S.: 424490

Paradise Beverages (Fiji) Limited (2)
122-164 Foster Road Walu Bay, GPO Box
696, Suva, Fiji (89.6%)
Tel.: (679) 3315811
Web Site:
http://www.paradisebeverages.com.fj
Rev.: $47,864,688
Assets: $74,618,489
Liabilities: $11,749,133
Net Worth: $62,869,357
Earnings: $1,508,013
Emp.: 500
Fiscal Year-end: 12/31/2019
Beer, Ready-to-Drink Alcoholic Beverages &
Soft Drinks Mfr & Distr
N.A.I.C.S.: 312120
Joseph Rodan (Gen Mgr-Sls & Corp Affairs)

Vending Management Services
Ltd (2)
67a Norfolk Road, Masterton, New Zealand
Tel.: (64) 63770002
Web Site: http://www.vmsl.co.nz
Sales Range: $25-49.9 Million
Emp.: 25
Soft Drink Vending Machine Software De-
velopment Services
N.A.I.C.S.: 541511

Coca-Cola Erfrischungsgetranke
GmbH (1)
Stralauer Allee 4, 10245, Berlin, Germany
Tel.: (49) 30920401
Web Site: https://www.cocacolaep.com
Soft Drink Mfr, Bottler & Whlsr
N.A.I.C.S.: 312111
Frank Molthan (Chm)

Coca-Cola Europacific Partners (Fiji)
Pte. Limited (1)
Lot 1 Ratu Dovi Rd Laucala Beach Estate,
Nasinu, Fiji
Tel.: (679) 3394333
Emp.: 290
Soft Drinks Mfr & Distr
N.A.I.C.S.: 312111

Coca-Cola Europacific Partners Aus-
tralia Pty. Limited (1)
Level 13 40 Mount Street, North Sydney,
2060, NSW, Australia
Tel.: (61) 292596222
Web Site: https://www.cocacolaep.com
Drinking Product Distr
N.A.I.C.S.: 424490

Coca-Cola Europacific Partners Bel-
gium SRL/B.V. (1)
Bergensesteenweg 1424, 1070, Anderlecht,
Belgium
Tel.: (32) 78156156
Web Site: https://nl.coca-cola.be
Drinking Product Distr
N.A.I.C.S.: 424490

Coca-Cola Europacific Partners
Deutschland GmbH (1)
Stralauer Allee 4, 10245, Berlin, Germany
Tel.: (49) 30920401
Web Site: https://www.cocacolaep.com
Emp.: 6,500
Bottled Juice Mfr
N.A.I.C.S.: 311411

Coca-Cola Europacific Partners
France S.A.S. (1)
9 Chemin de Bretagne, 92784, Issy-les-
Moulineaux, Cedex, France
Tel.: (33) 158002600
Web Site: https://www.cocacolaep.com
Drinking Product Distr
N.A.I.C.S.: 424490

Coca-Cola Europacific Partners Great
Britain Limited (1)
Pemberton House Bakers Road, Uxbridge,
UB8 1EZ, Middx, United Kingdom
Tel.: (44) 1895231313
Emp.: 3,600
Soft Drinks Mfr & Distr
N.A.I.C.S.: 312111

Coca-Cola Europacific Partners Iberia, S.L.U. (1)

C/ Ribera de Loira 20-22, 28042, Madrid, Spain
Tel.: (34) 902246500
Emp.: 3,549
Soft Drinks Mfr & Distr
N.A.I.C.S.: 312111

Coca-Cola Europacific Partners Luxembourg sarl (1)
Rue des joncs 2, 1818, Howald, Luxembourg
Tel.: (352) 2485151
Soft Drinks Mfr & Distr
N.A.I.C.S.: 312111

Coca-Cola Europacific Partners Nederland B.V. (1)
Marten Meesweg 25J, 3068, Rotterdam, Netherlands
Tel.: (31) 102456900
Soft Drinks Mfr & Distr
N.A.I.C.S.: 312111

Coca-Cola Europacific Partners New Zealand Limited (1)
The Oasis -19 Carbine Road, Mount Wellington, Auckland, 1060, New Zealand
Tel.: (64) 800505123
N.A.I.C.S.: 312130

Coca-Cola Europacific Partners Norge AS (1)
Robsrudskogen 5, 1471, Lorenskog, Norway
Tel.: (47) 91508088
Web Site: https://www.coca-cola.no
Drinking Product Distr
N.A.I.C.S.: 424490

Coca-Cola Europacific Partners Papua New Guinea Limited (1)
PO Box 92 411, Lae, Lae Morobe, Papua New Guinea
Tel.: (675) 73731900
Web Site: https://www.cocacolaep.com
Drinking Product Distr
N.A.I.C.S.: 424490

Coca-Cola Europacific Partners Portugal Unipessoal LDA (1)
Quinta da Salmoura Cabanas, 2929-509, Azeitao, Portugal
Tel.: (351) 808200248
Emp.: 400
Soft Drinks Mfr & Distr
N.A.I.C.S.: 312111

Coca-Cola Europacific Partners Services Bulgaria EOOD (1)
2 Donka Ushlinova Str Garitage Park Office Building 4, 1766, Sofia, Bulgaria
Tel.: (359) 879636068
N.A.I.C.S.: 312111

Coca-Cola Europacific Partners Sverige AB (1)
Dryckesvagen 2C, 136 87, Haninge, Sweden
Tel.: (46) 850075000
Soft Drinks Mfr & Distr
N.A.I.C.S.: 312111

Coca-Cola European Partners France SAS (1)
9 chemin de Bretagne, 92784, Issy-les-Moulineaux, Cedex, France
Tel.: (33) 158002600
Soft Drink Product Mfr & Distr
N.A.I.C.S.: 312111

Coca-Cola European Partners Iberia, S.L.U. (1)
C/Ribera de Loira 20-22, 28042, Madrid, Spain
Tel.: (34) 900246500
Soft Drink Product Mfr & Distr
N.A.I.C.S.: 312111

Coca-Cola European Partners Island ehf. (1)
Stulahals 1, 110, Reykjavik, Iceland
Tel.: (354) 5252500
Web Site: https://www.cocacolaep.com
Emp.: 170
Soft Drinks, Beer & Other Beverages Distr
N.A.I.C.S.: 312111

Coca-Cola European Partners Nederland B.V. (1)

Marten Meesweg 25H, 3068 AV, Rotterdam, Netherlands
Tel.: (31) 102456900
Soft Drink Product Mfr

Coca-Cola European Partners Norge AS (1)
Robsrudskogen 5, 1471, Lorenskog, Norway
Tel.: (47) 91508088
Web Site: https://www.coca-cola.no
Soft Drink Product Mfr
N.A.I.C.S.: 312111

Coca-Cola European Partners Portugal Unipessoal, LDA (1)
Quinta da SalmouraCabanas, 2929-509, Azeitao, Portugal
Tel.: (351) 808200248
Web Site: https://www.cocacolaep.com
Soft Drink Product Mfr
N.A.I.C.S.: 312111

Coca-Cola European Partners US, LLC (1)
2500 Windy Ridge Pkwy, Atlanta, GA 30339
Tel.: (678) 260-3000
Web Site: http://www.cokecce.com
Rev.: $7,011,000,000
Assets: $7,611,000,000
Liabilities: $6,654,000,000
Net Worth: $957,000,000
Earnings: $596,000,000
Emp.: 11,500
Fiscal Year-end: 12/31/2015
Holding Company; Soft Drink Mfr, Bottler & Distr
N.A.I.C.S.: 551112
John Franklin Brock (CEO)

Subsidiary (Non-US):

Coca-Cola Enterprise SAS (2)
9 Chemin de Bretagne, 92130, Issy-les-Moulineaux, France (100%)
Tel.: (33) 158002600
Web Site: http://www.cokecce.fr
Soft Drink Mfr, Bottler & Distr
N.A.I.C.S.: 312111

Coca-Cola Enterprises Belgium SPRL (2)
Chaussee de Mons 1424, 1070, Brussels, Belgium (100%)
Tel.: (32) 25291511
Web Site: http://www.cocacolabelgium.be
Soft Drink Mfr, Bottler & Distr
N.A.I.C.S.: 312111

Coca-Cola Enterprises Great Britain Limited (2)
Pemberton House Bakers Road, Uxbridge, UB8 1EZ, Mddx, United Kingdom
Tel.: (44) 1895231313
Web Site: http://www.cokecce.co.uk
Holding Company; Soft Drink Mfr, Bottler & Distr
N.A.I.C.S.: 551112

Subsidiary (Domestic):

Coca-Cola Enterprises Limited (3)
Pemberton House Bakers Road, Uxbridge, UB8 1EZ, Middx, United Kingdom (100%)
Tel.: (44) 1895231313
Web Site: http://www.coco-cola.co.uk
Soft Drink Mfr, Bottler & Distr
N.A.I.C.S.: 312111

Subsidiary (Non-US):

Coca-Cola Enterprises Nederland B.V. (2)
Marten Meesweg 25 J, 3068 AV, Rotterdam, Netherlands (100%)
Tel.: (31) 102455400
Web Site: http://www.cocacolanederland.nl
Soft Drink Mfr, Bottler & Distr
N.A.I.C.S.: 312111

Coca-Cola Enterprises Norge AS (2)
Robskogen 5, PB 463, NO-1470, Lorenskog, Norway (100%)
Tel.: (47) 67924000
Web Site: http://www.coca-cola.no
Soft Drink Mfr, Bottler & Distr
N.A.I.C.S.: 312111
Per Hynne (Dir-Comm)

Coca-Cola Enterprises Sverige AB (2)
Dryckesvagen 2C, SE-13687, Haninge, Sweden
Tel.: (46) 20656070
Web Site: http://www.coca-cola.se
Soft Drink Mfr, Bottler & Distr
N.A.I.C.S.: 312111

Coca-Cola Iberian Partners, S.A.U. (1)
Torre de Cristal Piso Castellana 259 planta 9, 28046, Madrid, Spain
Tel.: (34) 902 246 500
Web Site: http://www.cocacolaiberianpartners.com
Soft Drink Mfr, Bottler & Distr
N.A.I.C.S.: 312111

Conversia IT, S.L.U. (1)
Av Mas Pins 150, Riudellots de la Selva, 17457, Girona, Spain
Tel.: (34) 902877192
Web Site: https://www.conversia.es
Emp.: 350
Software Services
N.A.I.C.S.: 541511

Kollex GmbH (1)
Kottbusser Damm 25-26, 10967, Berlin, Germany
Tel.: (49) 3025557426
Web Site: https://www.kollex.de
Information Technology Services
N.A.I.C.S.: 541519

COCA-COLA HBC AG
Turmstrasse 26, 6312, Steinhausen, Switzerland
Tel.: (41) 417260110 CH
Web Site: https://www.coca-colahellenic.com
CCH—(OTCIQ)
Rev.: $9,807,334,080
Assets: $10,508,147,340
Liabilities: $7,110,487,800
Net Worth: $3,397,659,540
Earnings: $443,112,720
Fiscal Year-end: 12/31/22
Holding Company; Soft Drink Bottler & Distr
N.A.I.C.S.: 551112
William W. Douglas III (Executives, Bd of Dirs)

Subsidiaries:

3E (Cyprus) Limited (1)
66 Kyriakos Matsis Avenue, Engomi, Nicosia, CY-2409, Cyprus (100%)
Tel.: (357) 22885000
Holding Company
N.A.I.C.S.: 551112
Lampou Lampos (CEO)

AS Coca-Cola HBC Eesti (1)
Mustamae Tee 16, 10617, Tallinn, Estonia
Tel.: (372) 6 503 100
Sales Range: $25-49.9 Million
Emp.: 110
Beverage Product Mfr
N.A.I.C.S.: 312111

CCB Management Services GmbH (1)
Am Euro Platz 2, 1120, Vienna, Austria
Tel.: (43) 1 81413 0
Web Site: http://www.cococolahelnic.com
Emp.: 950
Business Management Consulting Services
N.A.I.C.S.: 541618
Gary Brewster (Dir-Pkg)

CCHBC Armenia CJSC (1)
8/3 Tbilisi highway, Yerevan, 0052, Armenia
Tel.: (374) 1 138 3705
Web Site: https://am.coca-colahellenic.com
Soft Drinks Mfr
N.A.I.C.S.: 312111

CCHBC Bulgaria AD (1)
8 Racho Petkov Kazandjiata Str, Sofia, 1766, Bulgaria (99.4%)
Tel.: (359) 2 921 4600
Web Site: https://bg.coca-colahellenic.com
Sales Range: $10-24.9 Million
Soft Drinks Mfr
N.A.I.C.S.: 312111

Jurg Burkhalter (CEO)

Coca-Cola Beverages Austria GmbH (1)
Triesterstrasse 91, Vienna, 1100, Austria
Tel.: (43) 1 61060 230
Sales Range: $75-99.9 Million
Emp.: 500
Soft Drinks Mfr
N.A.I.C.S.: 312111
Thomas N. Benford (Exec VP-Florida)

Coca-Cola Beverages Ceska republika, s.r.o. (1)
Eeskobrodska 1329, Kyje, Prague, 198 21, Czech Republic
Tel.: (420) 28 3015111
Sales Range: $75-99.9 Million
Emp.: 30
Beverage Product Mfr
N.A.I.C.S.: 312111

Coca-Cola Beverages Slovenija d.o.o. (1)
Motnica 9, Trzin, 1236, Slovenia
Tel.: (386) 1 589 04 00
Web Site: http://www.coca-cola.si
Beverage Product Mfr
N.A.I.C.S.: 312120

Coca-Cola Beverages Ukraine Ltd. (1)
51st km of St Petersburg Highway Velyka Dymerka, Brovary District, Kiev, 07400, Ukraine
Tel.: (380) 44 490 0707
Web Site: https://ua.coca-colahelenic.com
Sales Range: $300-349.9 Million
Emp.: 2,300
Beverage Product Mfr
N.A.I.C.S.: 312111

Coca-Cola Bottlers Chisinau S.R.L. (1)
Chisinau Str Industriala 42, Chisinau, Moldova
Tel.: (373) 22 470 777
Beverage Mfr & Distr
N.A.I.C.S.: 312111

Coca-Cola HBC Austria GmbH (1)
Clemens-Holzmeister-Strasse 6, 1100, Vienna, Austria
Tel.: (43) 1610600
Web Site: https://at.coca-colahellenic.com
Beverage Mfr & Distr
N.A.I.C.S.: 312111

Coca-Cola HBC B-H d.o.o. (1)
Mostarsko raskrsce 1, Hadzici, Sarajevo, 71240, Bosnia & Herzegovina
Tel.: (387) 3 328 4100
Web Site: https://ba.coca-colahellenic.com
Emp.: 296
Beverage Product Mfr
N.A.I.C.S.: 312111

Coca-Cola HBC Cesko a Slovensko, s.r.o (1)
Ceskobrodska 1329, Kyje, 198 21, Prague, Czech Republic
Tel.: (420) 283015666
Web Site: https://cz.coca-colahellenic.com
Beverage Mfr & Distr
N.A.I.C.S.: 312111

Coca-Cola HBC Cyprus Ltd. (1)
66 Kyriakos Matsis Ave, Nicosia, Cyprus
Tel.: (357) 22885000
Web Site: https://cy.coca-colahellenic.com
Beverage Mfr & Distr
N.A.I.C.S.: 312111

Coca-Cola HBC Hrvatska d.o.o. (1)
Milana Sachsa 1, Zagreb, Croatia
Tel.: (385) 12480222
Web Site: https://hr.coca-colahellenic.com
Beverage Mfr & Distr
N.A.I.C.S.: 312111

Coca-Cola HBC Hungary Ltd. (1)
Nemedi ut 104, 2330, Dunaharaszti, Hungary
Tel.: (36) 2 450 01 00
Beverages Mfr
N.A.I.C.S.: 312111
Laszlo Kerekes (Dir-Sls)

Coca-Cola HBC Ireland Limited (1)
Huntstown Business Park Cappagh Road,

Coca-Cola HBC AG—(Continued)

Ballycoolin, Dublin, 11, Ireland
Tel.: (353) 1 880 7100
Web Site: http://ie.coca-colahellenic.com
Emp.: 750
Beverages Bottler & Supplier
N.A.I.C.S.: 312111

Coca-Cola HBC Italia S.r.l. (1)
Piazza Indro Montanelli 30 Sesto San Giovanni, 20099, Milan, Italy
Tel.: (39) 0227 0771
Web Site: https://it.coca-colahellenic.com
Emp.: 2,000
Beverage Mfr & Distr
N.A.I.C.S.: 312111

Coca-Cola HBC Kosovo L.L.C. (1)
Km 5 rr Prishtine-Shkup, 10000, Pristina, Kosovo
Tel.: (383) 38 540 690
Web Site: http://www.coca-colahellenickosovo.com
Sales Range: $300-349.9 Million
Emp.: 1,500
Soft Drink Distr
N.A.I.C.S.: 424490
Svetoslav Atanasov *(Exec Dir-Serbia & Montenegro)*

Coca-Cola HBC Northern Ireland Limited (1)
Knockmore Hill 12 Lissue Road, Lisburn, BT28 2SZ, United Kingdom
Tel.: (44) 2892 642000
Web Site: http://www.coca-colahellenicireland.com
Sales Range: $150-199.9 Million
Beverage Product Mfr
N.A.I.C.S.: 312111

Coca-Cola HBC Polska sp. z o.o. (1)
Zwirki i Wigury 16, 02-092, Warsaw, Poland
Tel.: (48) 22 519 51 00
Web Site: http://www.coca-cola.pl
Soft Drinks Mfr
N.A.I.C.S.: 312111

Coca-Cola HBC Romania Ltd. (1)
Global City Business Park Building 2 10 Bucuresti Nord Str, Ilfov, Voluntari, 077190, Romania
Tel.: (40) 21 202 1400
Web Site: https://ro.coca-colahellenic.com
Sales Range: $10-24.9 Million
Soft Drinks Mfr
N.A.I.C.S.: 312111
Dan Timotin *(Country Mgr-Sls)*

Coca-Cola HBC Slovenija d.o.o. (1)
Motnica 9, Trzin, 1236, Slovenia
Tel.: (386) 1 589 0400
Web Site: https://si.coca-colahellenic.com
Emp.: 92
Soft Drinks Mfr
N.A.I.C.S.: 312111

Coca-Cola HBC Switzerland Ltd (1)
Stationsstrasse 33, 8306, Bruttisellen, Switzerland
Tel.: (41) 44 835 9111
Web Site: https://ch.coca-colahellenic.com
Emp.: 700
Beverages Mfr & Distr
N.A.I.C.S.: 312111

Coca-Cola HBC ceska a Slovensko, s.r.o. (1)
KalinCiakova 33, Bratislava, Slovakia
Tel.: (421) 249494949
Web Site: https://www.coca-cola.sk
Beverages Mfr
N.A.I.C.S.: 312111

Coca-Cola HBC-Srbija d.o.o. (1)
14-16 Batajnicki Drum str, Zemun, 11080, Zemun, Serbia
Tel.: (381) 11 307 3100
Web Site: https://rs.coca-colahellenic.com
Beverage Product Mfr
N.A.I.C.S.: 312111

Coca-Cola Hellenic Bottling Company-Crna Gora d.o.o. (1)
Kuce Rakica bb, 81000, Podgorica, Montenegro
Tel.: (382) 11 3020 030
Beverages Mfr

N.A.I.C.S.: 312120

Coca-Cola Hellenic Procurement GmbH (1)
Am Euro Platz 2, Vienna, 1120, Austria
Tel.: (43) 1814130
Emp.: 950
Beverage Mfr & Whslr
N.A.I.C.S.: 312120
Zoltan Syposs *(Mgr-Quality)*

Finlandia Vodka Worldwide Ltd. (1)
Porkkalankatu 24, 180, Helsinki, Finland
Tel.: (358) 207200500
Web Site: http://www.finlandia.com
Sales Range: $75-99.9 Million
Emp.: 21
Alcoholic Beverages Mfr
N.A.I.C.S.: 424820

LLC Coca-Cola HBC Eurasia (1)
6 Italyanskaya, Orel, 302024, Russia
Tel.: (7) 4862 42 12 34
Beverage Product Mfr
N.A.I.C.S.: 312111

Lanitis Bros Ltd. (1)
66 Kyriakos Matsis Ave, Nicosia, 1515, Cyprus
Tel.: (357) 22885000
Web Site: http://www.cy.coca-colahellenic.com
Emp.: 293
Soft Drinks Mfr
N.A.I.C.S.: 327910
Andreas Pelekanos *(CFO)*

Lanitis Bros Public Ltd. (1)
66 Kyriakos Matsis Ave, PO Box 22000, Nicosia, 1515, Cyprus　　　　**(95.43%)**
Tel.: (357) 22885000
Web Site: http://www.cy.coca-colahellenic.com
Sales Range: $150-199.9 Million
Emp.: 560
Soft Drinks Mfr
N.A.I.C.S.: 312111

Nigerian Bottling Company Ltd. (1)
AG Leventis Building Iddo House, PO Box 1159, Iddo, Lagos, Nigeria
Tel.: (234) 1 270 6670
Web Site: https://ng.coca-colahellenic.com
Soft Drinks Mfr
N.A.I.C.S.: 312111
Ekuma Eze *(Dir-Pub Affairs & Comm)*

SIA Coca-Cola HBC Latvia (1)
Ulbrokas Street 40, Riga, 1039, Latvia
Tel.: (371) 6 710 9900
Web Site: https://poland-baltics.coca-colahellenic.com
Sales Range: $25-49.9 Million
Beverage Product Mfr
N.A.I.C.S.: 312120

Tsakiris S.A. (1)
Moulkia Area, PO Box 8485, 35200, Atalanti, Fthiotida, Greece
Tel.: (30) 2233032510
Web Site: http://www.tsakiris.gr
Sales Range: $25-49.9 Million
Emp.: 65
Potato Chips Mfr & Distr
N.A.I.C.S.: 311919
Aggelos Rorris *(Gen Mgr)*

UAB Coca-Cola HBC Lietuva (1)
Spaudos str 6-1, Vilnius, 05132, Lithuania
Tel.: (370) 37453057
Web Site: http://www.baltics.coca-colahellenic.com
Beverage Mfr & Distr
N.A.I.C.S.: 312111

Valser Services AG (1)
Stationsstrasse 33, 8306, Bruttisellen, Switzerland
Tel.: (41) 84 800 4400
Web Site: https://www.qwell.ch
Emp.: 150
Beverage Products Retailer
N.A.I.C.S.: 312111
Oliver Fritz *(CFO)*

COCA-COLA ICECEK A.S.

OSB Mahallesi Deniz Feneri Sk 4 Dudullu Umraniye, 34776, Istanbul, Turkiye

Tel.: (90) 2165284000
Web Site: https://www.cci.com.tr
Year Founded: 1964
CCOLA—(IST)
Rev.: $1,653,395,531
Assets: $1,813,621,504
Liabilities: $1,109,496,595
Net Worth: $704,124,909
Earnings: $143,345,060
Emp.: 9,224
Fiscal Year-end: 12/31/22
Soft Drink Bottler, Producer & Distr
N.A.I.C.S.: 312111
Meltem Metin *(Dir-Strategic Bus Dev)*

Subsidiaries:

(CC) Company for Beverage Industry/Ltd. (1)
Khabat Mousel Road, PO Box 29-0240, Erbil, Iraq
Tel.: (964) 66 255 9801
Soft Drink Mfr & Distr
N.A.I.C.S.: 312111
Sarmad Rasheed *(Mgr-Supply Chain)*

Al Waha for Soft Drinks, Juices, Mineral Water, Plastics, & Plastic Caps Production LLC (1)
Hilla Dewanya Road, Hillah, Iraq
Tel.: (964) 7507076978
Soft Drink Distr
N.A.I.C.S.: 424490

Azerbaijan Coca-Cola Bottlers Limited Liability Company (1)
Sulutepe qes Tagiyev kuc 1, AZ1000, Baku, Azerbaijan
Tel.: (994) 124091800
Soft Drink Distr
N.A.I.C.S.: 424490

Coca-Cola Bishkek Bottlers Closed Joint Stock Company (1)
69 Lushina str, 720027, Bishkek, Kyrgyzstan
Tel.: (996) 312357141
Soft Drink Mfr & Distr
N.A.I.C.S.: 312111
Nurzat Aidaralieva *(Supvr-HR)*

Coca-Cola Satis ve Dagitim A.S. (1)
Esenkent Mah Deniz Feneri Sk No 4, Umraniye, 34776, Istanbul, Turkiye
Tel.: (90) 2165284000
Web Site: https://www.ccsd.com.tr
Coca Cola Distr
N.A.I.C.S.: 424490

J.V. Coca-Cola Almaty Bottlers Limited Liability Partnership (1)
Gogol / Baizakov Str, 050026, Almaty, Kazakhstan
Tel.: (7) 727 250 76 79
Soft Drink Mfr & Distr
N.A.I.C.S.: 312111
Christina Afonina *(Mgr-Product Dev)*

The Coca-Cola Bottling Company of Jordan Limited (1)
PO Box 1004, Hanina, 17110, Madaba, Jordan
Tel.: (962) 53241172
Soft Drink Mfr & Distr
N.A.I.C.S.: 312111
Rokaya Ma'aitah *(Controller-Fin)*

Turkmenistan Coca-Cola Bottlers (1)
4/2 Hero of Turkmenistan Atamurat Niyazov Avenue, Ashgabat, 744000, Turkmenistan
Tel.: (993) 12434570
Soft Drink Mfr & Distr
N.A.I.C.S.: 312111
Cihat Kurt *(Gen Mgr)*

COCHEZ Y COMPANIA, S.A.

Eloy Alfaro No 15-33 Avenue Balboa Avenue, PO Box 0816-007696, Panama, Panama
Tel.: (507) 302 4444
Web Site: http://www.cochezycia.com
Year Founded: 1963
COCH—(PAN)
Sales Range: Less than $1 Million
Building Materials Whslr
N.A.I.C.S.: 444180

COCHIN MINERALS AND RUTILE LIMITED

VIII/224 Market Road, PB No 73, Aluva, 683101, Kerala, India
Tel.: (91) 4842626789
Web Site: https://www.cmrlindia.com
Year Founded: 1989
513353—(BOM)
Rev.: $32,674,387
Assets: $15,849,302
Liabilities: $4,195,328
Net Worth: $11,653,974
Earnings: $1,106,892
Emp.: 256
Fiscal Year-end: 03/31/21
Synthetic Rutile Mfr & Whslr
N.A.I.C.S.: 424690
Suresh Kumar P. *(Sec)*

COCHIN SHIPYARD LIMITED

Perumanoor, Kochi, 682015, India
Tel.: (91) 4842380181
Web Site: http://www.cochinshipyard.com
Year Founded: 1972
Sales Range: $300-349.9 Million
Emp.: 2,500
Ship Building & Repairing
N.A.I.C.S.: 336611
V. Kala *(Sec)*

COCHLEAR LIMITED

1 University Avenue Macquarie University, Sydney, 2109, NSW, Australia
Tel.: (61) 294286555　　　　　　**AU**
Web Site: https://www.cochlear.com
Year Founded: 1981
COH—(ASX)
Rev.: $1,492,788,455
Assets: $1,832,999,458
Liabilities: $604,033,117
Net Worth: $1,228,966,341
Earnings: $238,247,862
Emp.: 4,996
Fiscal Year-end: 06/30/24
Hearing Aid Mfr
N.A.I.C.S.: 339112
Richard Brook *(Pres-EMEA & Latin American Reg)*

Subsidiaries:

Cochlear (HK) Limited (1)
Units 1404-1406 Level 14 Leighton Centre 77 Leighton Road, Causeway Bay, China (Hong Kong)
Tel.: (852) 25305773
Web Site: https://www.cochlear.com
Hearing Aid Mfr
N.A.I.C.S.: 334510

Cochlear AG (1)
Peter Merian-Weg 4, 4052, Basel, Switzerland
Tel.: (41) 612058225
Web Site: https://www.cochlear.com
Sales Range: $25-49.9 Million
Emp.: 70
Hearing Aid Mfr
N.A.I.C.S.: 334510

Cochlear Americas Inc (1)
10350 Park Meadows Dr, Lone Tree, CO 80124
Tel.: (303) 790-9010
Web Site: https://www.cochlear.com
Sales Range: $100-124.9 Million
Emp.: 300
Hearing Device Mfr
N.A.I.C.S.: 334510

Cochlear Austria GmbH (1)
Millennium Tower 45 Stock Handelskai 94-96, 1200, Vienna, Austria
Tel.: (43) 13760026200
Medical Device Mfr
N.A.I.C.S.: 339112

Cochlear Benelux NV (1)
Schalienhoevedreef 20 i, 2800, Mechelen, Belgium
Tel.: (32) 15795511
Web Site: http://www.cochlear.com

Hearing Aid Mfr
N.A.I.C.S.: 334510

Cochlear Bone Anchored Solutions AB (1)
Konstruktionsvagen 14, 435 33, Molnlycke, Sweden
Tel.: (46) 317924400
Web Site: http://www.cochlear.com
Sales Range: $50-74.9 Million
Emp.: 220
Hearing Aid Mfr
N.A.I.C.S.: 334510
Antonny Manna *(Pres)*

Cochlear Canada Inc (1)
120 Adelaide St W Ste 2500, Toronto, M5H ITI, ON, Canada
Tel.: (416) 972-5082
Hearing Device Mfr
N.A.I.C.S.: 334510
Peter Billing *(VP)*

Cochlear Colombia SAS (1)
Avenida Carrera 9 n 115-06 Of 1201 Edificio Tierra Firme, Bogota, Colombia
Tel.: (57) 3153397169
Medical Device Mfr
N.A.I.C.S.: 339112

Cochlear Deutschland GmbH & Co. KG (1)
Mailander Strasse 4 a, 30539, Hannover, Germany
Tel.: (49) 511542770
Web Site: https://www.cochlear.de
Hearing Aid Mfr
N.A.I.C.S.: 334510

Cochlear Europe Finance GmbH (1)
Karl-Wiechert-Allee 76a, 30625, Hannover, Germany
Tel.: (49) 511542770
Web Site: http://www.cochlear.com
Sales Range: $50-74.9 Million
Emp.: 80
Financial Support Services
N.A.I.C.S.: 522291
Thomas Tott *(Gen Mgr)*

Cochlear Europe Limited (1)
6 Dashwood Lang Road Bourne Business Park, Addlestone, KT15 2HJ, Surrey, United Kingdom
Tel.: (44) 1932263640
Web Site: https://www.cochlear.com
Hearing Aid Mfr
N.A.I.C.S.: 334510
David Haston *(Dir)*

Cochlear France SAS (1)
135 Route de Saint-Simon, 31035, Toulouse, France
Tel.: (33) 805200016
Web Site: https://www.cochlear.fr
Sales Range: $25-49.9 Million
Emp.: 20
Hearing Aid Mfr
N.A.I.C.S.: 334510

Cochlear Italia SRL (1)
Via Larga 33, 40138, Bologna, Italy
Tel.: (39) 0516015311
Medical Device Mfr
N.A.I.C.S.: 339112

Cochlear Korea Limited (1)
2F Yongsan Centerville Asterium 25 Hangang-daero 30-gil, Yongsan-gu, Seoul, 04386, Korea (South)
Tel.: (82) 25334450
Web Site: https://www.cochlear.com
Emp.: 20
Hearing Device Mfr
N.A.I.C.S.: 334510

Cochlear Latinoamerica S.A. (1)
International Business Park Edificio 3835 Oficina 403, Panama, Panama
Tel.: (507) 8306220
Medical Device Mfr
N.A.I.C.S.: 339112

Cochlear Medical Device (Beijing) Co., Ltd. (1)
United 2208 Gemdale Tower B 91 Jianguo Road, Chaoyang District, Beijing, 100022, China
Tel.: (86) 1059097800
Medical Device Mfr

N.A.I.C.S.: 339112

Cochlear Medical Device Company India Private Limited (1)
Ground Floor Platina Building Plot No C59 G Block, Bandra Kurla Complex Bandra E, Mumbai, 400 051, India
Tel.: (91) 2067082935
Emp.: 2
Hearing Device Mfr
N.A.I.C.S.: 334510
Pisharody Vandana *(Country Mgr)*

Cochlear Mexico SA de CV (1)
Tamaulipas 150 Piso 9 Torre A Colonia Hipodromo Condesa, Delegacion Cuauhtemoc, 06170, Mexico, Mexico
Tel.: (52) 5552414500
Medical Device Mfr
N.A.I.C.S.: 339112

Cochlear Middle East FZ-LLC (1)
Dubai Health Care City, PO Box 380584, Dubai, United Arab Emirates
Tel.: (971) 48184400
Medical Device Mfr
N.A.I.C.S.: 339112

Cochlear Nordic AB (1)
Konstruktionsvagen 14, 435 33, Molnlycke, Sweden
Tel.: (46) 313351461
Web Site: https://www.cochlear.com
Hearing Aid Mfr
N.A.I.C.S.: 334510
Lotta Vedholm *(Gen Mgr)*

Cochlear Norway AS (1)
Brynsveien 13, 0667, Oslo, Norway
Tel.: (47) 22594700
Medical Device Mfr
N.A.I.C.S.: 339112

Cochlear Sweden Holdings AB (1)
Konstruktionsvagen 14, 435 33, Molnlycke, Sweden
Tel.: (46) 317924400
Web Site: http://www.cochlear.com
Emp.: 250
Hearing Aid Mfr
N.A.I.C.S.: 334510
Rom Mendel *(Pres)*

Cochlear Tibbi Cihazlar ve Saglik Hizmetleri Limited Sirketi (1)
Cubuklu Mah Bogazici Cad Bogazici Plaza No 6/1 Kavacik, Beykoz, Istanbul, 34805, Turkiye
Tel.: (90) 216 538 59 00
Web Site: http://www.cochlear.com.tr
Sales Range: $25-49.9 Million
Emp.: 20
Hearing Aid Mfr
N.A.I.C.S.: 334510

Cochlear Verwaltungs GmbH (1)
Mailander Strasse 4 a, 30539, Hannover, Germany
Tel.: (49) 511542770
Web Site: http://www.cochlear.com
Sales Range: $25-49.9 Million
Emp.: 15
Hearing Device Mfr
N.A.I.C.S.: 334510
Thomas Topp *(Gen Mgr)*

Nihon Cochlear Co Limited (1)
Ochanomizu-Motomachi Bldg 2-3-7 Hongo, Bunkyo-ku, Tokyo, 113-0033, Japan
Tel.: (81) 338170241
Web Site: http://www.cochlear.com
Hearing Aid Distr
N.A.I.C.S.: 423450

Sycle, LLC (1)
480 Green St, San Francisco, CA 94133
Web Site: http://www.web.sycle.net
Information Technology Services
N.A.I.C.S.: 541511
Jerry Schoffman *(Pres)*

COCOA PROCESSING COMPANY LIMITED
Heavy Industrial Area, Private Mail Bag, Tema, Ghana
Tel.: (233) 22212153
Web Site:
https://www.goldentreeghana.com
Year Founded: 1981

CPC—(GHA)
Rev.: $13,645,898
Assets: $152,506,410
Liabilities: $190,669,153
Net Worth: ($38,162,743)
Earnings: ($3,362,108)
Emp.: 430
Fiscal Year-end: 12/31/20
Cocoa Processor
N.A.I.C.S.: 311351
Nana Agyenim Boateng *(Mng Dir-Acting)*

COCOALAND HOLDINGS BERHAD
Lot 100 Jalan Industri 3/4 Rawang Integrated Industrial Park, 48000, Rawang, Selangor Darul Ehsan, Malaysia
Tel.: (60) 36 091 3131 MY
Web Site: http://www.cocoaland.com
COCOLND—(KLS)
Rev.: $52,049,123
Assets: $69,093,511
Liabilities: $8,871,561
Net Worth: $60,221,950
Earnings: $5,411,323
Emp.: 847
Fiscal Year-end: 12/31/21
Chocolate Mfr
N.A.I.C.S.: 311340
Mee Kiat Wong *(Co-Sec)*

COCOLONET CO., LTD.
15-1 Funato-Mae Kamata, Fukushima, 960-0102, Japan
Tel.: (81) 245736556
Web Site: https://www.cocolonet.jp
Year Founded: 1966
6060—(TKS)
Rev.: $66,331,350
Assets: $127,354,870
Liabilities: $70,693,950
Net Worth: $56,660,920
Earnings: $3,827,190
Emp.: 35
Fiscal Year-end: 03/31/24
Funeral & Wedding Services
N.A.I.C.S.: 812210
Kotaro Kanno *(Pres)*

COCONALA, INC.
20-1 Shibuya Infoss Tower 6F Sakuragaoka-cho, Shibuya-ku, Tokyo, 150-0031, Japan
Tel.: (81) 367127771
Web Site: https://www.coconala.co.jp
Year Founded: 2011
4176—(TKS)
Rev.: $40,977,360
Assets: $51,339,880
Liabilities: $27,790,960
Net Worth: $23,548,920
Earnings: $1,511,460
Fiscal Year-end: 08/31/24
Digital Marketing Services
N.A.I.C.S.: 541870
Akiyuki Minami *(Chm)*

COCOON HOLDINGS LIMITED
Room 14A Fortune House 61 Connaught, Road Central, Central, China (Hong Kong)
Tel.: (852) 25456883 Ky
Web Site: http://www.hugechina.com.hk
0428—(HKG)
Rev.: $580,380
Assets: $17,069,445
Liabilities: $1,986,068
Net Worth: $15,083,378
Earnings: ($6,130,073)
Emp.: 2
Fiscal Year-end: 12/31/22
Investment Services
N.A.I.C.S.: 523999
Carman Wing Yan Chan *(CEO)*

COCORPORT, INC.
Kanagawa Prefecture Sunako 2-5-11 Resona Kawasaki Building 4F, Kawasaki Ward, Kawasaki, 210-0006, Kanagawa, Japan
Tel.: (81) 442018474
Web Site: https://www.cocorport.co.jp
Year Founded: 2012
9346—(TKS)
Emp.: 714
Welfare Services
N.A.I.C.S.: 525120
Atsuya Sahara *(Pres)*

COCREATION GRASS CO., LTD.
Floor 18 Dadi Building No 56 Huaqiao Road, Nanjing, 210029, China
Tel.: (86) 2569811666
Web Site: https://www.ccgrass.com
Year Founded: 2004
605099—(SHG)
Rev.: $346,894,002
Assets: $397,394,155
Liabilities: $75,973,459
Net Worth: $321,420,696
Earnings: $62,763,082
Emp.: 4,000
Fiscal Year-end: 12/31/22
Artificial Turf Product Mfr
N.A.I.C.S.: 314110
Qiangxiang Wang *(Chm & Gen Mgr)*

Subsidiaries:

Altime Sport & Leisure GmbH (1)
Frankfurt Airport Center 1 Geb 234 HBK 52, 7th Floor A7-4 Hugo-Eckener-Ring, 60549, Frankfurt am Main, Germany
Tel.: (49) 6963199665
Artificial Grass Mfr
N.A.I.C.S.: 325220

CODA MINERALS LTD.
6 Altona Street, West Perth, 6005, WA, Australia
Tel.: (61) 862706331 AU
Web Site:
https://www.codaminerals.com
Year Founded: 2018
COD—(ASX)
Rev.: $69,873
Assets: $15,358,236
Liabilities: $560,027
Net Worth: $14,798,209
Earnings: ($5,061,397)
Emp.: 15
Fiscal Year-end: 06/30/23
Mineral Exploration Services
N.A.I.C.S.: 212390
Chris Stevens *(CEO)*

Subsidiaries:

Torrens Mining Ltd. (1)
Level 11 London House 216 St Georges Terrace, Perth, 6000, WA, Australia
Tel.: (61) 894810389
Web Site: https://www.torrensmining.com
Gold Mining & Exploration Services
N.A.I.C.S.: 213114

CODAN LIMITED
Technology Park 2 Second Avenue, Mawson Lakes, Salisbury, 5095, SA, Australia
Tel.: (61) 883050311 AU
Web Site: https://www.codan.com.au
Year Founded: 1959
CDA—(ASX)
Rev.: $367,560,762
Assets: $513,295,270
Liabilities: $214,863,113
Net Worth: $298,432,157
Earnings: $54,285,523
Fiscal Year-end: 06/30/24
Communication Equipment Mfr
N.A.I.C.S.: 334290

Codan Limited—(Continued)

David J. Simmons *(Chm)*

Subsidiaries:

Codan (UK) Ltd (1)
C4 Coxbridge Business Park Alton Rd,
Farnham, GU10 5EH, Surrey, United Kingdom
Tel.: (44) 1252717272
Web Site: http://www.codanradio.com
Emp.: 4
Communication Equipment Distr
N.A.I.C.S.: 423690
Mike Gathergood *(Mgr-Sls-Africa)*

Codan Ltd. - North America - LMR (1)
43 Erie Street, Victoria, V8V 1P8, BC,
Canada
Tel.: (250) 382-6139
Web Site: http://www.codanradio.com
Communication Equipment Distr
N.A.I.C.S.: 423690

Codan Radio Communications ME JLT (1)
305-306 Tower BB1 Mazaya Business Avenue Jumeirah Lake Towers, Dubai,
487067, United Arab Emirates
Tel.: (971) 44537201
Web Site: http://www.codanradio.com
Emp.: 6
Communication Equipment Distr
N.A.I.C.S.: 423690

Minelab Electronics Pty Ltd (1)
Technology Park 2 2nd Avenue Mawson
Lakes, Salisbury, 5095, SA, Australia
Tel.: (61) 882380888
Web Site: https://www.minelab.com
Emp.: 60
Metal Detecting Technologies
N.A.I.C.S.: 332999

Subsidiary (US):

Codan (US) Inc (2)
3501 W Sunflower Ave, Santa Ana, CA
92704
Tel.: (714) 545-2111
Web Site: https://www.codanusa.com
Communication Equipment Distr
N.A.I.C.S.: 423690

Minelab Americas Inc. (2)
123 Ambassador Dr Ste 123, Naperville, IL
60540
Tel.: (630) 401-8180
Web Site: https://www.minelab.com
Metal Detectors Sales, Service & Support
N.A.I.C.S.: 811210

Subsidiary (Non-US):

Minelab International Ltd (2)
Penrose One, Penrose Dock, Cork, T23
KW81, Ireland
Tel.: (353) 214232352
Web Site: https://www.minelab.com
Emp.: 22
Metal Detectors Sales, Service & Support
N.A.I.C.S.: 811210

Minelab de Mexico SA de CV (1)
Rio Mississippi 303 San Pedro Garza Garcia, 66220, Nuevo Leon, Mexico
Tel.: (52) 811 919 7623
Metal Detector Mfr & Distr
N.A.I.C.S.: 334519

Minetec Pty Ltd. (1)
Unit 2 29 Wellard Street, Bibra Lake, 6163,
WA, Australia
Tel.: (61) 8 9259 4955
Web Site: http://www.minetec.com.au
Sales Range: $25-49.9 Million
Emp.: 65
Designs & Manufactures Electronic Products & Associated Software for Communications Solutions for Mining Industry
N.A.I.C.S.: 334290

Zetron, Inc. (1)
12034 134th Ct Ne, Redmond, WA 98052-
2446
Tel.: (425) 820-6363
Web Site: http://www.zetron.com
Sales Range: $25-49.9 Million
Emp.: 290

Central Control Systems & Communications
Equipment Mfr
N.A.I.C.S.: 334220

Subsidiary (Non-US):

Zetron Australasia Pty Ltd., (2)
4/87 Webster Road, Stafford, 4053, QLD,
Australia
Tel.: (61) 738564888
Web Site: http://www.zetron.com
Sales Range: $25-49.9 Million
Emp.: 31
Communication Equipment Mfr
N.A.I.C.S.: 334290
Ranjan Bhagat *(VP & Gen Mgr)*

Zetron, Inc. (2)
27-29 Campbell Court Campbell Road
Bramley, Campbell Rd, Tadley, RG26 5EG,
Hampshire, United Kingdom
Tel.: (44) 1256880663
Web Site: https://www.zetron.com
Sales Range: $25-49.9 Million
Emp.: 16
Communication Equipment Mfr
N.A.I.C.S.: 334290
Brent Dippie *(Pres & CEO)*

CODENATURE CO., LTD.
1614 Daeryung Technotown 20th
Gasan Digital Street, Geumcheon-gu,
Seoul, Korea (South)
Tel.: 269492028   KR
Web Site: http://www.codenature.com
Year Founded: 1947
078940—(KRS)
Rev.: $3,445,172
Assets: $34,307,780
Liabilities: $15,832,480
Net Worth: $18,475,300
Earnings: ($8,766,596)
Emp.: 46
Fiscal Year-end: 12/31/22
Engineeering Services
N.A.I.C.S.: 541330
Sang Hoon Park *(CEO)*

CODERE S.A.
Avenida de Bruselas 26, 28108, Alcobendas, Madrid, Spain
Tel.: (34) 913542800
Web Site: http://www.codere.com
Year Founded: 1980
CDR—(MAD)
Sales Range: $1-4.9 Billion
Emp.: 18,314
Casinos, Bingo Halls & Horse Racetracks Operator
N.A.I.C.S.: 713210
Luis Arguello Alvarez *(Sec)*

Subsidiaries:

Codere Argentina S.A. (1)
Avda Libertador 1068 - 9 Piso, C1112ABN,
Buenos Aires, Argentina
Tel.: (54) 1148001000
Web Site: http://www.coderearg.com.ar
Gambling Services
N.A.I.C.S.: 713290

Codere Colombia S.A. (1)
Trasversal 95 bis A 25 D 41, Bogota, Colombia
Tel.: (57) 13264242
Gambling Services
N.A.I.C.S.: 713290

Codere Italia SPA (1)
Via Cornelia 498, 00166, Rome, Italy
Tel.: (39) 06 612551
Web Site: http://www.coderenetwork.it
Gambling Services
N.A.I.C.S.: 713290

Subsidiary (Domestic):

DP Service S.R.L. (2)
Via dell' Industria 13, Piove di Sacco, Italy
Tel.: (39) 0499704646
Liquid Crystal Display Mfr
N.A.I.C.S.: 334419

Codere Mexico, S.A. (1)
Av Industria Militar s/n Col Industria Militar

Del Miguel Hidalgo, 11600, Mexico, Mexico
Tel.: (52) 55 52017800
Gambling Services
N.A.I.C.S.: 713290

Codere Panama, S.A (1)
Torre Financial Center Torwer Bank Building
Calle 50 y Elvira Mendez, Piso 40,
Panama, Panama
Tel.: (507) 3774200
Gambling Services
N.A.I.C.S.: 713290

Codere Uruguay S.A. (1)
Jose M Guerra 3540 Hipodromo Nacional
de Maronas, 12000, Montevideo, Uruguay
Tel.: (598) 25117777
Web Site: http://www.carrasconobile.com.uy
Gambling Services
N.A.I.C.S.: 713290

Codere do Brasil Entretenimento Ltda (1)
Rua Helena 260 - conjuntos 82 e 84 Bairrio
Vila Olimpia, Sao Paulo, 04552-050, Brazil
Tel.: (55) 1137368400
Gambling Services
N.A.I.C.S.: 713290

INTERSARE S.A. (1)
Tv 95bis A 25d-41, Bogota, Colombia
Tel.: (57) 1770032000
Gambling Services
N.A.I.C.S.: 713290

CODES COMBINE CO., LTD.
42 Hancheon-ro 46-gil, Dongdaemun-
gu, Seoul, Korea (South)
Tel.: (82) 222391414
Web Site: http://www.codes-
combine.co.kr
Year Founded: 1995
047770—(KRS)
Rev.: $29,953,461
Assets: $64,475,103
Liabilities: $16,719,081
Net Worth: $47,756,021
Earnings: $5,826,191
Emp.: 56
Fiscal Year-end: 12/31/22
Women Apparel Mfr
N.A.I.C.S.: 315250

CODEX ACQUISITIONS PLC
9th Floor 107 Cheapside, London,
EC2V 6DN, United Kingdom   UK
Web Site: https://www.codexplc.com
Year Founded: 2021
CODX—(LSE)
Miscellaneous Financial Investment
Activities
N.A.I.C.S.: 523999

CODI-M CO., LTD.
9F 441 Teheran ro Gangnam, Seoul,
Korea (South)
Tel.: (82) 25549300
Web Site: http://codim.com
Year Founded: 1999
224060—(KRS)
Rev.: $15,425,795
Assets: $71,820,723
Liabilities: $42,698,782
Net Worth: $29,121,941
Earnings: ($18,021,742)
Emp.: 88
Fiscal Year-end: 12/31/22
Semiconductor & Related Device Mfr
N.A.I.C.S.: 334413

CODIBEL SA/NV
Rue Jules Bordet Zone C, 7180, Seneffe, Belgium
Tel.: (32) 6466 5092   BE
Web Site: http://www.codibel.be
Hair, Skin & Other Personal Care
Products Mfr
N.A.I.C.S.: 325620
Michel Knops *(Mng Dir)*

CODORNIU, S.A.

Edificio Alta 1-Av. Paisos Catalans
38, 08950, Esplugues de Llobregat,
Spain
Tel.: (34) 935051551
Web Site: http://www.codorniu.es
Year Founded: 1551
Wines & Champagne Producer
N.A.I.C.S.: 312130

COECLERICI S.P.A.
Piazza Generale Armando Diaz 7,
20123, Milan, Italy
Tel.: (39) 02624691   IT
Web Site: http://www.coeclerici.com
Year Founded: 1895
Rev.: $973,524,534
Assets: $362,841,359
Liabilities: $285,500,468
Net Worth: $77,340,891
Earnings: $7,945,407
Emp.: 1,266
Fiscal Year-end: 12/31/19
Raw Material Sourcing, Marketing &
Transporting Services
N.A.I.C.S.: 213113
Paolo Clerici *(Chm & CEO)*

Subsidiaries:

A. Billitz S.r.l. (1)
Via San Nicolo 15, 34121, Trieste, Porto
Franco, Italy   (100%)
Tel.: (39) 040313941
Web Site: http://www.billitztrieste.com
Sales Range: $50-74.9 Million
Emp.: 10
Trade Agent & Broker Services
N.A.I.C.S.: 425120

Adriafruit Italia S.r.l. (1)
Piazza Rossetti 2-8, 16129, Genoa,
Italy   (100%)
Tel.: (39) 01057672
Web Site: http://www.adriafruit.it
Sales Range: $50-74.9 Million
Emp.: 20
Organic Wholesale Foods
N.A.I.C.S.: 311999

Citco Curacao (1)
Kaya Flamboyan 9, PO Box 812, Willemstad, Curacao   (100%)
Tel.: (599) 97322555
Web Site: http://www.citco.com
Sales Range: $100-124.9 Million
Trust & Fiduciary Services
N.A.I.C.S.: 425120

Coeclerici Bulk Terminal Torres S.p.A. (1)
Via Martin Piaggio 17, 16122, Genoa,
Italy   (100%)
Tel.: (39) 0877285
Bulk Ship Carriers & Bare Boat Carriers
N.A.I.C.S.: 483111

Coeclerici Coal & Fuels S.p.A (1)
Via Manin 13, 20121, Milan, Italy   (100%)
Tel.: (39) 02624691
Sales Range: $50-74.9 Million
Emp.: 20
Bulk Ship Carriers & Bare Boat Carriers
N.A.I.C.S.: 488510

Coeclerici Coal & Fuels S.p.A. - Russia Branch (1)
4 Dobryninskij Pereulok 6/9, 119049, Moscow, Russia   (100%)
Tel.: (7) 0952376892
Web Site: http://www.coeclerici.com
Sales Range: $50-74.9 Million
Emp.: 16
Coal & Other Raw Materials Distr, Marketer
& Transporter
N.A.I.C.S.: 425120

Coeclerici Coal & Fuels SpA (1)
Piazza Generale Armando Diaz 7, 20123,
Milan, Italy   (100%)
Tel.: (39) 02624691
Web Site: http://www.coeclerici.com
Sales Range: $200-249.9 Million
Emp.: 300
Coal & Fuel Management Distr
N.A.I.C.S.: 425120

Coeclerici Coal Network, Inc. (1)

7697 Innovation Way Ste 100, Mason, OH
45040 **(70%)**
Tel.: (513) 701-0373
Web Site: http://www.coalnetwork.com
Coal Trading & Distribution Services
N.A.I.C.S.: 213113
Ramesh Malhotra *(Chm)*

Coeclerici Logistics S.p.A. **(1)**
Via Di Francia 28, 16149, Genoa,
Italy **(100%)**
Tel.: (39) 01060531
Web Site: http://www.coeclerici.com
Sales Range: $25-49.9 Million
Emp.: 20
Provider of Logistic & Transport Services of
Raw Materials
N.A.I.C.S.: 541614

Coeclerici Shipping S.p.A. **(1)**
Via De Francia 28, 16149, Genoa,
Italy **(100%)**
Tel.: (39) 01060531
Sales Range: $50-74.9 Million
Emp.: 15
Bulk Ship Carriers & Bare Boat Carriers
N.A.I.C.S.: 483111

Ing Ruggero Vio **(1)**
Via dell Avena 18, Marghera, 30175, Ven-
ice, Italy **(100%)**
Tel.: (39) 041931833
Web Site: http://www.vio.it
Sales Range: $25-49.9 Million
Emp.: 30
Handling Raw Materials & Transhipment,
Owners of Ships, Tugs, Coastal Barges &
Ocean Barges
N.A.I.C.S.: 483111
Ruggero Vio *(Comml Dir)*

Sidermar Di Navigazione S.p.A. **(1)**
Via XX Settembre 41, 16121, Genoa, Italy
Tel.: (39) 01056341
N.A.I.C.S.: 425120

Solas Shipping Agency S.r.l. **(1)**
Via Carlo Barabino no.16 S 5, 16129,
Genoa, Italy
Tel.: (39) 0108681207
Web Site: http://www.solas.it
Sales Range: $50-74.9 Million
Emp.: 10
Shipping Agency Services; Chartering &
Brokerage; Transports & Logistics
N.A.I.C.S.: 488510

Somocar Overseas N.V. **(1)**
De Ruyterkade 62, Willemstad,
Curacao **(100%)**
Tel.: (599) 9613077
Bulk Ship Carriers & Bare Boat Carriers
N.A.I.C.S.: 483111

COEGIN PHARMA AB

Medicon Village, 223 81, Lund, Swe-
den
Tel.: (46) 4561905066
Web Site: https://coeginpharma.com
COEGIN—(OMX)
Research & Development in Biotech-
nology
N.A.I.C.S.: 541714
Tore Duvold *(CEO)*

COELI AB

Sveavagen 24-26, 111 57, Stock-
holm, Sweden
Tel.: (46) 850622300
Web Site: http://www.coeli.se
Sales Range: $25-49.9 Million
Emp.: 100
Investment Services
N.A.I.C.S.: 523999
Mikael Smedeby *(Chm)*

COESIA S.P.A.

Via Battindarno 91, 40133, Bologna,
Italy
Tel.: (39) 0516474111 **IT**
Web Site: http://www.coesia.com
Rev.: $2,049,392,595
Assets: $2,955,641,432
Liabilities: $1,848,886,208
Net Worth: $1,106,755,224

Earnings: $189,760,480
Emp.: 7,555
Fiscal Year-end: 12/31/18
General Purpose Machinery Mfr
N.A.I.C.S.: 333998
Isabella Seragnoli *(Pres)*

Subsidiaries:

ACMA S.p.A. **(1)**
Via Colombo 1, 40131, Bologna, Italy
Tel.: (39) 051 634 9111
Web Site: http://www.acmavolpak.com
Emp.: 550
Packaging Machinery Mfr
N.A.I.C.S.: 333993

CIMA S.p.A. **(1)**
Via Fratelli Cairoli 8, 40055, Villanova di
Castenaso, Bologna, Italy
Tel.: (39) 0516032545
Web Site: http://www.cimaingranaggi.it
Automotive Gears Mfr
N.A.I.C.S.: 333612

Cerulean Ltd. **(1)**
Rockingham Drive Linford Wood East, Mil-
ton Keynes, MK14 6LY, United Kingdom
Tel.: (44) 1908233833
Web Site: http://www.cerulean.com
Tobacco Test Instrumentation Machinery Mfr
N.A.I.C.S.: 333248

Subsidiary (Non-US):

Cerulean Shanghai Company
Ltd. **(2)**
Unit 2011-2012 Commerce Spirit No 1258
Yu Yuan Road, Shanghai, 200050, China
Tel.: (86) 2161253288
Web Site: http://www.cerulean.com
Precision Test & Measuring Instrument Mfr
N.A.I.C.S.: 334515

Coesia Health & Beauty Inc. **(1)**
335 Chambers Brook Rd, Branchburg, NJ
08876
Tel.: (908) 707-8008
Packaging Machinery & Equipment Distr
N.A.I.C.S.: 423830

Coesia India Private Ltd. **(1)**
Plot No 49 50 of Gat No 343 Chakan-
Talegaon Road, 410 501, Pune, India
Tel.: (91) 2135 615900
Packaging Machinery & Equipment Distr
N.A.I.C.S.: 423830

FlexLink AB **(1)**
Byfogdegatan 11, Gothenburg, Sweden
Tel.: (46) 31 337 31 00
Web Site: http://www.flexlink.com
Conveyor System Mfr
N.A.I.C.S.: 333922
Klas Alander *(Mgr-Comm)*

Subsidiary (Non-US):

FlexLink Automation (Shanghai) Co.
Ltd. **(2)**
No 118 Plant No 3 Zhu Yuan Road, Pujiang
Town Minhang District, 201112, Shanghai,
China
Tel.: (86) 21 64118306
Conveyor System Distr
N.A.I.C.S.: 423830
Yee King Chew *(Mng Dir)*

FlexLink Automation Sdn Bhd **(2)**
No 13 Jalan Tiang U8/93 Seksyen U8 Bukit
Jelutong Industrial Park, 40150, Shah Alam,
Selangor, Malaysia
Tel.: (60) 3 7859 1891
Conveyor System Distr
N.A.I.C.S.: 423830
Tan Eng Chong *(Mng Dir)*

FlexLink Systems **(2)**
Kutojantie 7, 02630, Espoo, Finland
Tel.: (358) 40 6583030
Conveyor System Distr
N.A.I.C.S.: 423830
Lars Iven *(Area Mgr-Sls)*

FlexLink Systems **(2)**
Av Pacifico No 468 Oficina A Col El
Rosedal Del Coyoacan, 04330, Mexico,
Mexico
Tel.: (52) 55 5336 4545
Conveyor System Distr

N.A.I.C.S.: 423830
FlexLink Systems **(2)**
9 Eylul Mah Hava Egitim Yolu No 14/C,
Gaziemir, Izmir, Turkiye
Tel.: (90) 232 2518833
Conveyor System Distr
N.A.I.C.S.: 423830
Bahadir Coler *(Area Mgr-Sls)*

FlexLink Systems B.V. **(2)**
Diamantlaan 51, 2132WV, Hoofddorp, Neth-
erlands
Tel.: (31) 23 554 3100
Web Site: http://www.flexlink.com
Emp.: 10
Conveyor System Distr
N.A.I.C.S.: 423830
Hans Vos *(Gen Mgr)*

FlexLink Systems Canada, Inc. **(2)**
1-1549 Yorkton Court, Burlington, L7P 5B7,
ON, Canada
Tel.: (905) 639-6878
Conveyor System Distr
N.A.I.C.S.: 423830
Massimiliano Vicini *(Mng Dir)*

FlexLink Systems Espana, SL **(2)**
Llobregat 6 Nau 3 Pol Ind El Pla, Molins de
Rei, 08750, Barcelona, Spain
Tel.: (34) 93 680 4100
Conveyor System Distr
N.A.I.C.S.: 423830
Ramon Avalos *(Mng Dir)*

FlexLink Systems GmbH **(2)**
Schumannstrasse 155, 63069, Offenbach,
Germany
Tel.: (49) 69 83 832 0
Conveyor System Distr
N.A.I.C.S.: 423830
Olaf Witschass *(Mng Dir)*

FlexLink Systems India Pvt. Ltd. **(2)**
809 BPTP Park Centra Sector 30, Gurgaon,
122001, Haryana, India
Tel.: (91) 124 427 8844
Conveyor System Distr
N.A.I.C.S.: 423830

FlexLink Systems Kft. **(2)**
Rokolya utca 1-13, 1131, Budapest, Hun-
gary
Tel.: (36) 20 666 7008
Conveyor System Distr
N.A.I.C.S.: 423830
Gabor Halmos *(Mng Dir)*

FlexLink Systems Ltd **(2)**
2 Tanners Drive, Milton Keynes, MK14 5BN,
Blakelands, United Kingdom
Tel.: (44) 1908 327 200
Web Site: http://www.flexlink.com
Emp.: 25
Conveyor System Distr
N.A.I.C.S.: 423830
Steve Pinney *(Mng Dir)*

FlexLink Systems Ltda **(2)**
Condominio Thera Park Avenida 01 no 1
277, Bairro Fazenda Grande, 13213-086,
Jundiai, SP, Brazil
Tel.: (55) 11 4431 4000
Conveyor System Distr
N.A.I.C.S.: 423830
Daniel Goncalves *(Mng Dir)*

FlexLink Systems N.V. **(2)**
Ambachtenlaan 21/8 Industrieterrein Haas-
rode, 3001, Leuven, Belgium
Tel.: (32) 16 40 82 66
Web Site: http://www.flexlink.com
Conveyor System Distr
N.A.I.C.S.: 423830

FlexLink Systems Polska Sp. z
o.o. **(2)**
Ul Szkolna 30, 62-064, Plewiska, Poland
Tel.: (48) 61 654 7651
Conveyor System Distr
N.A.I.C.S.: 423830
Michal Kazmierczak *(Mng Dir)*

FlexLink Systems Pte Ltd **(2)**
1 Kaki Bukit View 04-01 Techview, Singa-
pore, 415941, Singapore
Tel.: (65) 6842 5855
Conveyor System Distr
N.A.I.C.S.: 423830

Sakari Kuikka *(Mng Dir-Asia Pacific South
East)*

FlexLink Systems Pty Ltd **(2)**
Unit 139/45 Gilby Rd, Mount Waverley,
3149, VIC, Australia
Tel.: (61) 3 9542 4400
Conveyor System Distr
N.A.I.C.S.: 423830
Peter Hutchings *(Mng Dir)*

FlexLink Systems S.P.A. **(2)**
Via Chivasso 15, 10098, Rivoli, Turin, Italy
Tel.: (39) 01 195 18 411
Conveyor System Distr
N.A.I.C.S.: 423830
Andrea Sambuy *(Mgr-Key Customer)*

FlexLink Systems SAS **(2)**
1 rue du Groupe Manoukian, Elancourt,
Elancourt, France
Tel.: (33) 1 30 68 53 50
Conveyor System Distr
N.A.I.C.S.: 423830
Jacky Lecomte *(Mgr-Sls)*

FlexLink Systems s.r.o. **(2)**
Budejovicka alej Antala Staska 2027/79,
140 00, Prague, Czech Republic
Tel.: (420) 234 703 303
Conveyor System Distr
N.A.I.C.S.: 423830
Petr Kukla *(Country Mgr-Sls)*

Subsidiary (US):

FlexLink Systems, Inc. **(2)**
6580 Snowdrift Rd, Allentown, PA 18106
Tel.: (610) 973-8200
Conveyor System Distr
N.A.I.C.S.: 423830
Dave Clark *(Dir-Area)*

Subsidiary (Non-US):

OOO FlexLink Systems **(2)**
Pulkovskoye Shosse 40/4, 196158, Saint
Petersburg, Russia
Tel.: (7) 8123180075
Web Site: http://www.flexline.com
Conveyor System Distr
N.A.I.C.S.: 423830

PT FlexLink Systems **(2)**
Jababeka Innovation Centre Jl Samsung 2
Block D2, Desa Mekarmukti Cikarang Ut-
ara, Bekasi, 17530, Jawa Barat, Indonesia
Tel.: (62) 21 2908 2769
Web Site: http://www.flexlink.com
Conveyor System Distr
N.A.I.C.S.: 423830
Roeland Blaak *(Mng Dir)*

GD S.p.A. **(1)**
Via Battindarno 921, 40133, Bologna, Italy
Tel.: (39) 0516474111
Web Site: http://www.gidi.it
Sales Range: $600-649.9 Million
Emp.: 2,250
Cigarette Rolling & Packaging Machinery
Mfr
N.A.I.C.S.: 333993

Subsidiary (Non-US):

G.D AUTOMATIC PACKAGING **(2)**
1st Derbenevsky pereulok 5 Business cen-
ter, Derbenevskaya Plaza Office 402,
115114, Moscow, Russia
Tel.: (7) 495 2215185
Web Site: http://www.coesia.com
Packaging Machinery Distr
N.A.I.C.S.: 423830

G.D AUTOMATISCHE VERPACK-
UNGSMASCHINEN GmbH **(2)**
Hans-Bockler Str 6-8, 40764, Langenfeld,
Germany
Tel.: (49) 217 3976 0
Packaging Machinery Distr
N.A.I.C.S.: 423830

G.D CHINA AUTOMATIC MACHIN-
ERY LTD. **(2)**
88 Container Port Road Tower 2 Ever Gain
Plaza Suite 2105-2107 21/F, Kwai Chung,
NT, China (Hong Kong)
Tel.: (852) 2511 0888
Packaging Machinery Distr
N.A.I.C.S.: 423830

Coesia S.p.A.—(Continued)

G.D China Limited (2)
Suite 2105-2107 21Fl Tower 2 Ever Gain Plaza, 88 Container Port Rd, Kwai Chung, NT, China (Hong Kong)
Tel.: (852) 25110888
Web Site: http://www.gidi.it
Sales Range: $25-49.9 Million
Emp.: 20
Cigarette Making & Packing Machinery Mfr
N.A.I.C.S.: 333993
Tom Chung (Mng Dir)

G.D Do Brasil (2)
Rua Dr Alfonso Vergueiro 1101, Sao Paulo, 02116-001, SP, Brazil
Tel.: (55) 1127952000
Web Site: http://www.coesia.com
Sales Range: $25-49.9 Million
Emp.: 200
Packaging Machinery Mfr
N.A.I.C.S.: 333993
Stefano Nanni (Pres)

G.D Germany (2)
Hans Bockler Strasse 6 8, Lagenfeld, 40764, Germany
Tel.: (49) 21739760
Web Site: http://www.gidi.it
Sales Range: $25-49.9 Million
Emp.: 80
N.A.I.C.S.: 332999
Rainhold Taesar (Mng Dir)

G.D Japan (2)
3-18-9 Tatsumi, Koto-ku, Tokyo, 135 0053, Japan
Tel.: (81) 335225360
Web Site: http://www.gidi.it
Sales Range: $25-49.9 Million
Emp.: 40
Cigarette Making & Packing Machinery Mfr
N.A.I.C.S.: 333993

G.D Russian Federation (2)
Panfilova street 19-1, Khimki, 141407, Moscow, Russia
Tel.: (7) 4957881000
Web Site: http://www.coesia.com
Cigarette Making & Packing Machinery Mfr
N.A.I.C.S.: 333993

G.D South East Asia (2)
1 Kaki Bukit View unit 04-01 Techview, 04 05 KA Center, Singapore, 415941, Singapore
Tel.: (65) 63831711
Sales Range: $25-49.9 Million
Emp.: 9
Cigarette Making & Packing Machinery Mfr
N.A.I.C.S.: 333993

G.D. INDIA PVT. LTD. (2)
Plot No 49 50 og Gat No 343 Chakan-Talegaon Road, Mahalunge Ingle Khed, Pune, 410501, Maharashtra, India
Tel.: (91) 2135615900
Packaging Machinery Distr
N.A.I.C.S.: 423830

GD Indonesia (2)
Jalan Kig Raya Barat G8 Kawasan Industri Gresik, 61121, Surabaya, East Java, Indonesia
Tel.: (62) 313985295
Cigarette Making & Packing Machinery Mfr
N.A.I.C.S.: 333993

Subsidiary (US):

GD USA, Inc. (2)
501 Southlake Blvd, Richmond, VA 23236-3042
Tel.: (804) 794-9777
Web Site:
http://www.gdpackagemachinery.com
Sales Range: $25-49.9 Million
Emp.: 190
Mfr of Packaging Machinery
N.A.I.C.S.: 811210

Division (Domestic):

ACMA GD (3)
501 Southlake Blvd, Richmond, VA 23236
Tel.: (804) 794-6688
Sales Range: $50-74.9 Million
Emp.: 150
Production & Packaging Machinery Mfr.
N.A.I.C.S.: 333993

Corniani ACMA GD (3)
501 Southlake Blvd, Richmond, VA 23236
Tel.: (804) 794-6688
Liquid Packaging Machinery Mfr
N.A.I.C.S.: 333993

Volpak Packaging Machines (3)
501 Southlake Blvd, Richmond, VA 23236
Tel.: (804) 794-6688
Packaging Machinery Mfr
N.A.I.C.S.: 333993

GDM SpA (1)
Via Circonvallazione Sud, Offanengo, 26010, Cremona, Italy
Tel.: (39) 0373530011
Web Site: http://www.gdm-spa.com
Emp.: 330
Packaging Machinery Mfr
N.A.I.C.S.: 333993
Marco Rosani (Mgr-R&D)

Hapa AG (1)
Chriesbaumstrasse 4, 8604, Volketswil, Switzerland
Tel.: (41) 433993200
Web Site: http://www.hapa.ch
Sales Range: $75-99.9 Million
Emp.: 220
Process & Packaging Solutions
N.A.I.C.S.: 333993
Mac Kenzie (Dir-Sls)

IPI s.r.l. (1)
Via Giuseppe Piermarini 19, San Sisto, 06132, Perugia, Italy
Tel.: (39) 075 528521
Web Site: http://www.ipi-srl.com
Packaging Machinery Mfr
N.A.I.C.S.: 333993

Laetus GmbH (1)
Sandwiesenstrasse 27, Alsbach-Hahnlein, 64665, Germany
Tel.: (49) 625750090
Web Site: http://www.laetus.com
Sales Range: $25-49.9 Million
Emp.: 90
Process & Packaging Solutions
N.A.I.C.S.: 333993
Christoph Staub (VP-Bus Dev & Startegy-Global)

Subsidiary (Non-US):

Laetus France Sarl. (2)
6 Avenue du Bois de l'Épine ZA du Bois de l'Epine, 91080, Courcouronnes, France
Tel.: (33) 169 874649
Packaging Machinery Distr
N.A.I.C.S.: 423830

Laetus Mexico S. de R.L. de C.V. (2)
Hector Gutierrez Av Insurgentes Sur No 1685 - int 804 Col Guadalupe In, Alvaro Obregon, 01020, Mexico, Mexico
Tel.: (52) 55 53364545
Packaging Machinery Distr
N.A.I.C.S.: 423830

Molins Tobacco Machinery Ltd. (1)
Regent Park Summerleys Rd, Princes Risborough, HP27 9LE, United Kingdom (100%)
Tel.: (44) 1844276600
Web Site: http://www.molins.com
Industrial Supplies Merchant Whslr
N.A.I.C.S.: 423840

Subsidiary (Non-US):

Molins sro (2)
Korandova 12, 301 00, Plzen, Czech Republic
Tel.: (420) 378 080 111
Web Site: http://www.molins.cz
Precision Test & Measuring Instrument Mfr
N.A.I.C.S.: 333310

Norden Machinery AB (1)
Sodra Vagen 30, 392 45, Kalmar, Sweden
Tel.: (46) 480 44 77 00
Web Site: http://www.nordenmachinery.com
Emp.: 250
Tube Filling Machine Distr
N.A.I.C.S.: 423830
Lars Hammarstedt (Mgr-Sls)

Subsidiary (Non-US):

Norden GmbH (2)

Friedrichstrasse 65, Kemnat, 73760, Ostfildern, Germany
Tel.: (49) 711 16725 0
Web Site: http://www.nordenpac.de
Tube Filling Machine Distr
N.A.I.C.S.: 423830
Guido Muller (Mng Dir)

R.A Jones Group Ltd (1)
2701 Crescent Springs Rd, Covington, KY 41017
Tel.: (859) 341-0400
Web Site: http://www.rajones.com
Packaging Machinery Mfr
N.A.I.C.S.: 333993

Subsidiary (Domestic):

R.A. Jones & Co. (2)
2701 Crescent Springs Rd, Covington, KY 41017
Tel.: (859) 341-0400
Web Site: http://www.rajones.com
Packaging Machinery Mfr
N.A.I.C.S.: 333993
Barry W. Shoulders (Pres & CEO)

R.A. Jones & Co. Inc. (2)
2701 Crescent Springs Rd, Covington, KY 41017-1504
Tel.: (859) 341-0400
Web Site: http://www.rajones.com
Packaging Machinery Mfr
N.A.I.C.S.: 333993

SACMO (1)
Zone Artisanale, 02760, Holnon, France
Tel.: (33) 3 23 09 30 60
Web Site: http://www.sacmo.com
Emp.: 90
Packaging Machinery Mfr
N.A.I.C.S.: 333993

Sirius Machinery AB (1)
c/o Kalix 4 avenue du Parana, ZA Courtaboeuf n4 Les Ulis, F-91978, Courtaboeuf, Cedex, France (100%)
Tel.: (33) 1 69 18 05 90
Web Site: http://www.siriusmachinery.com
Industrial Tube Filling Machinery Mfr
N.A.I.C.S.: 333248

Subsidiary (Domestic):

ADMV (2)
ZA Les Triboulieres, 38 460, Cremieu, France (100%)
Tel.: (33) 474904366
Web Site: http://www.admv.fr
Sales Range: $25-49.9 Million
Emp.: 20
Feeding & Automation Equipment Mfr
N.A.I.C.S.: 333248

Kalix (2)
4 Avenue du Parana, 91978, Les Ulis, Cedex, France (100%)
Tel.: (33) 33169180500
Web Site: http://www.kalix.fr
Sales Range: $25-49.9 Million
Emp.: 55
Packaging Machinery Mfr
N.A.I.C.S.: 333248

Volpak S.A (1)
Poligono Industrial Can Vinyalets, Santa Perpetua de Mogoda, Barcelona, 08130, Spain
Tel.: (34) 935446700
Web Site: http://www.volpak.com
Packaging Machinery Mfr
N.A.I.C.S.: 333993

Subsidiary (Domestic):

Laetus Iberica (2)
Poligono Industrial Can Vinyalets c/Can Vinyalets 4, Santa Perpetua de Mogoda, 08130, Barcelona, Spain
Tel.: (34) 93 5446072
Packaging Machinery Distr
N.A.I.C.S.: 423830

COEXPAN S.A.
Av de Madrid 72 Alcala de Henares, 28802, Madrid, Spain
Tel.: (34) 91 877 59 00
Web Site: http://www.coexpan.com
Year Founded: 1973
Plastic Mfr

N.A.I.C.S.: 326199
Raul Grana (Gen Mgr)

Subsidiaries:

COEXPAN Montonate S.r.l. (1)
Via Sandroni 40, Sumirago, I-21040, Varese, Italy
Tel.: (39) 0331989811
Web Site: http://www.coexpan.com
Plastics Product Mfr
N.A.I.C.S.: 326199
Attilia Menghini (Mng Dir)

Coexpan Brasil Embalagens Ltda (1)
Rod D Gabriel Paulino Bueno Couto 100, 13212-240, Jundiai, Brazil
Tel.: (55) 1145825029
Plastic Product Distr
N.A.I.C.S.: 423930
Cintia Damasio (Mgr-Indus)

Coexpan Deutschland GmbH (1)
Schwabenheimer Weg 105, 55543, Bad Kreuznach, Germany
Tel.: (49) 671886440
Plastic Product Distr
N.A.I.C.S.: 423930

Coexpan France SA (1)
4 Avenue de la Fontaine, BP 50065, 49071, Beaucouze, Cedex, France
Tel.: (33) 241368150
Plastic Product Distr
N.A.I.C.S.: 423930

Coexpan Mexico, S.A de C.V. (1)
Avda De las Fuentes N 78 Parque Industrial Finsa, El Marques, 76246, Queretaro, Mexico
Tel.: (52) 4421532200
Plastic Product Distr
N.A.I.C.S.: 423930

COFACE S.A.
1 Place Costes et Bellonte, CS 20003, 92276, Bois-Colombes, France
Tel.: (33) 149022929 FR
Web Site: https://www.coface.com
Year Founded: 1946
COFA—(EUR)
Rev.: $1,955,503,993
Assets: $9,120,022,664
Liabilities: $7,002,376,430
Net Worth: $2,117,646,234
Earnings: $305,533,132
Emp.: 3,704
Fiscal Year-end: 12/31/22
Credit Insurance & Credit Management Services
N.A.I.C.S.: 522299
Carole Lytton (Sec)

Subsidiaries:

Coface Egypt (1)
55 Mossaddak St Dokki, Cairo, Egypt
Tel.: (20) 233338000
Web Site: http://www.coface.com.eg
Sales Range: $50-74.9 Million
Emp.: 2
Commercial Banking Services
N.A.I.C.S.: 522110
Fady Henry (Gen Mgr)

Coface Holding AG (1)
Isaac-Fulda-Allee 1, 55124, Mainz, Germany
Tel.: (49) 61313230
Web Site: http://www.coface.de
Sales Range: $400-449.9 Million
Emp.: 700
Holding Company; Credit Insurance & Credit Management Services
N.A.I.C.S.: 551112

Subsidiary (Non-US):

Coface Austria Holding AG (2)
Stubenring 24, Vienna, 1010, Austria
Tel.: (43) 1515540
Web Site: http://www.coface.at
Sales Range: $75-99.9 Million
Emp.: 115
Holding Company; Credit Insurance & Credit Management Services

N.A.I.C.S.: 551112
K. R. Martina Dobringer *(Chm)*

Subsidiary (Domestic):

Coface Austria Bank AG (3)
Stubenring 24, 1010, Vienna, Austria
Tel.: (43) 1515540
Web Site: http://www.coface.at
Sales Range: $25-49.9 Million
Factoring Services
N.A.I.C.S.: 522390
Gabriele Duker *(Member-Mgmt Bd)*

Coface Austria Kreditversicherung AG (3)
Marxergasse 4c, 1030, Vienna, Austria
Tel.: (43) 1515540
Web Site: http://www.coface.at
Credit Insurance & Credit Management Services
N.A.I.C.S.: 522299
Andreas Henzl *(Dir-IT & Organisation)*

Subsidiary (Non-US):

Coface Central Europe Holding AG (2)
Stubenring 24, 1010, Vienna, Austria
Tel.: (43) 1515540
Web Site:
 http://www.cofacecentraleurope.com
Sales Range: $200-249.9 Million
Emp.: 640
Holding Company; Credit Insurance & Credit Management Services
N.A.I.C.S.: 522299
Karatina Komboksa *(Mng Dir)*

Branch (Non-US):

Coface Danmark (2)
Bulowsevej 3, 1870, Frederiksberg, Denmark
Tel.: (45) 33862500
Web Site: http://www.coface.dk
Sales Range: $10-24.9 Million
Emp.: 8
Credit Insurance & Credit Management Services
N.A.I.C.S.: 522299

Subsidiary (Domestic):

Coface Kreditversicherung AG (2)
Isaac-Fulda-Allee 1, Mainz, 55124, Germany
Tel.: (49) 61313230
Web Site: http://www.coface.de
Sales Range: $700-749.9 Million
Credit Insurance Services
N.A.I.C.S.: 524130
Stefan Brauel *(Member-Mgmt Bd)*

Coface Italia S.p.A. (1)
Via Giovanni Spadolini 4, I-20141, Milan, Italy
Tel.: (39) 0248335111
Web Site: http://www.coface.it
Sales Range: $200-249.9 Million
Emp.: 180
Holding Company; Credit Insurance & Credit Management Services
N.A.I.C.S.: 551112

Subsidiary (Domestic):

Coface Assicurazioni S.p.A. (2)
Via Giovanni Spadolini 4, Milan, 20141, Italy
Tel.: (39) 0248335111
Web Site: http://www.coface.it
Sales Range: $10-24.9 Million
Emp.: 100
Credit Insurance Services
N.A.I.C.S.: 524130

Coface North America Holding Company (1)
1350 Broadway Ste 2000, New York, NY 10018
Tel.: (212) 389-6500
Web Site: http://www.coface-usa.com
Sales Range: $100-124.9 Million
Emp.: 360
Holding Company; Credit Insurance & Credit Management Services
N.A.I.C.S.: 551112
Michael Ferrante *(Chm & CEO)*

Subsidiary (Domestic):

Coface North America, Inc. (2)
Windsor Corp Park Bldg 100 Ste 350 50 Millstone Rd, East Windsor, NJ 08520
Tel.: (609) 469-0400
Web Site: http://www.coface-usa.com
Credit Insurance & Credit Management Services
N.A.I.C.S.: 522299
Fredrik Murer *(CEO)*

Subsidiary (Domestic):

Coface Collections North America, Inc. (3)
2400 Veterans Blvd Ste 300, Kenner, LA 70062
Tel.: (504) 469-9545
Web Site: http://www.trustaltus.com
Sales Range: $10-24.9 Million
Emp.: 107
Commercial Debt Collection Services
N.A.I.C.S.: 561440
Thomas E. Brenan *(Pres)*

Coface Credit Management North America, Inc. (3)
50 Millstone Rd Windsor Corp Park Bldg 100 Ste 360, East Windsor, NJ 08520
Tel.: (609) 469-0400
Web Site: http://www.coface-usa.com
Credit Management Services
N.A.I.C.S.: 522299

Coface North America Insurance Company, Inc. (3)
50 Millstone Rd Windsor Corp Park Bldg 100 Ste 360, East Windsor, NJ 08520
Tel.: (609) 469-0400
Web Site: http://www.coface-usa.com
Corporate Credit & Political Risk Insurance Services
N.A.I.C.S.: 524130

Unit (Domestic):

Coface North America Political Risk (4)
1350 Broadway Ste 2000, New York, NY 10018
Tel.: (212) 389-6470
Web Site: http://www.coface-usa.com
Political Risk Insurance Services
N.A.I.C.S.: 525190

Coface Services (1)
1 rue de l'Union, 92843, Rueil-Malmaison, France
Tel.: (33) 147524360
Web Site: http://www.cofaceservices.fr
Sales Range: $900-999.9 Million
Emp.: 800
Business Intelligence & Receivables Management Services
N.A.I.C.S.: 522390
Philippe Brocca *(Dir-Receivables Recovery & Mgmt)*

Coface UK Holding Ltd. (1)
15 Appold St, London, EC2A 2DL, United Kingdom
Tel.: (44) 2073257500
Web Site: http://www.cofaceuk.com
Sales Range: $75-99.9 Million
Emp.: 180
Holding Company; Credit Management Services
N.A.I.C.S.: 551112
Xavier Denecker *(Mng Dir)*

Subsidiary (Domestic):

Coface Receivables Finance Limited (2)
Egale 1 80 St Albans Rd, Watford, WD17 1RP, Herts, United Kingdom
Tel.: (44) 1923478100
Web Site: http://www.coface.uk
Sales Range: $10-24.9 Million
Emp.: 100
Receivables Management Services
N.A.I.C.S.: 522390
Frederic Bourgeois *(Mng Dir)*

Coface UK Services Limited (2)
15 Appold Street, London, EC2A 2DL, United Kingdom
Tel.: (44) 2073257500
Web Site: http://www.cofaceuk.com

Sales Range: $10-24.9 Million
Emp.: 30
Credit Intermediation Services
N.A.I.C.S.: 522299
Trevor Byrne *(Mgr-Press)*

COFCO BIOTECHNOLOGY CO., LTD.
22F Building A ZT International Center Chaoyangmen South Avenue, Chao Yang District, Beijing, 100020, China
Tel.: (86) 1065047877   CN
Web Site: http://www.cofco.com
Year Founded: 1998
000930—(SSE)
Rev.: $2,796,494,220
Assets: $2,541,280,716
Liabilities: $784,666,116
Net Worth: $1,756,614,600
Earnings: $148,663,944
Emp.: 10,000
Fiscal Year-end: 12/31/22
Citric Acid, Amino Acid & Fuel Ethanol Mfr & Whslr
N.A.I.C.S.: 325199
Jiang Guojin *(Chm)*

Subsidiaries:

Anhui COFCO Biochemical & Galactic Lactic Acid Co., Ltd. (1)
Grain 1st Avenue, Bengbu, 233010, Anhui, China
Tel.: (86) 552 2081 288
Web Site: http://www.bglactic.com.cn
Emp.: 130
Lactic Acid Mfr & Whslr
N.A.I.C.S.: 325199

Subsidiary (Non-US):

B&G Japan Co., Ltd. (2)
15-19 Kami-osaki 2-chome, Shinagawa-ku, Tokyo, 141-0021, Japan
Tel.: (81) 3 6459 3646
Web Site: http://www.b-gjapan.com
Biochemical Distr
N.A.I.C.S.: 424910

COFCO CAPITAL HOLDINGS CO., LTD.
COFCO Fortune Building No 8 Chaoyangmen South Street, Chaoyang District, Beijing, 100020, China
Tel.: (86) 1085006688
Web Site: https://www.cofco-capital.com
Year Founded: 2007
002423—(SSE)
Rev.: $2,612,368,044
Assets: $16,468,765,560
Liabilities: $12,982,761,324
Net Worth: $3,486,004,236
Earnings: $83,817,396
Emp.: 4,200
Fiscal Year-end: 12/31/22
Steel Machinery Mfr
N.A.I.C.S.: 333310
Yanmin Sun *(Chm & Pres)*

COFCO JOYCOME FOODS LIMITED
COFCO Fortune Plaza No 8 Chao Yang Men South St, Chao Yang District, Beijing, 100020, China
Tel.: (86) 85228330666   Ky
Web Site: http://www.cofcomeat.com
Year Founded: 2014
1610—(HKG)
Rev.: $1,811,256,034
Assets: $2,582,569,267
Liabilities: $1,422,485,064
Net Worth: $1,160,084,203
Earnings: $50,113,534
Emp.: 9,980
Fiscal Year-end: 12/31/22
Meat Product Mfr & Distr
N.A.I.C.S.: 311611
Jianong Xu *(Mng Dir & Gen Mgr)*

COFCO LIMITED
COFCO Fortune Plaza No 8 Chao Yang Men South St, Chao Yang District, Beijing, 100020, China
Tel.: (86) 1085006688   CN
Web Site: http://www.cofco.com
Year Founded: 1952
Sales Range: $800-899.9 Million
Emp.: 12,000
Livestock & Poultry, Fruits, Vegetables, Canned Goods, Beverages, Confectionery & Condiments Import & Export Services
N.A.I.C.S.: 424520
Xiaohui Wu *(VP)*

Subsidiaries:

AON-COFCO Insurance Brokerage Co., Ltd. (1)
Rm 4105-4106 Jinmao Tower No 88 Century Av, Pudong New District, Shanghai, 200121, China
Tel.: (86) 21 38658000
Emp.: 200
Insurance Brokerage Services
N.A.I.C.S.: 524210
Crare Wu *(Mgr)*

AVIVA-COFCO Life Insurance Co., Ltd. (1)
19F Gateway Square Tower A No 18 North Section East 3rd Ring Rd, Chao Yang, Beijing, 100027, China
Tel.: (86) 10 84400888
Web Site: http://www.aviva-cofco.com.cn
Fire Insurance Services
N.A.I.C.S.: 524113
Winston Hou *(Mgr)*

COFCO (Hainan) Investment & Development Co., Ltd. (1)
Yalong Bay National Resort, Sanya, 572016, Hainan, China
Tel.: (86) 898 88568899
Web Site: http://www.cofco.com
Real Estate Manangement Services
N.A.I.C.S.: 531390

COFCO (Hong Kong) Co., Ltd. (1)
33 F Top Cofco Tower 262 Gloucester Road, Causeway Bay, China (Hong Kong)
Tel.: (852) 28330288
Real Estate Investment Services
N.A.I.C.S.: 531390

COFCO (Japan) Co., Ltd. (1)
8F 2-7-6 Nihonbashi-Kayabacho, Chuo-ku, Tokyo, 103-0025, Japan
Tel.: (81) 3 36687741
Food Products Distr
N.A.I.C.S.: 424690

COFCO (New York) Co., Ltd. (1)
Corporate Ctr 910 Sylvan Ave 1th Fl, Englewood Cliffs, NJ 07632
Tel.: (201) 568-6788
Oilseed Farming Services
N.A.I.C.S.: 111998

COFCO Argentina S.A. (1)
Carlos Pellegrini 1163 Piso 9, Buenos Aires, 1009, Argentina
Tel.: (54) 1141317100
Web Site: http://www.noblegrain.com.ar
Agriculture Product Distr
N.A.I.C.S.: 424590

COFCO Cereal Way Foods Co., Ltd. (1)
Rm 401 Tower B COFCO Plaza No 8 Jianguomennei Av, Beijing, 100005, China
Tel.: (86) 10 85001688
Food Products Mfr
N.A.I.C.S.: 311991

COFCO Commercial Property Investment Co., Ltd. (1)
Tower A COFCO Plaza, 8 Jianguomennei Street, Beijing, 100005, China
Tel.: (86) 1085006688
Commercial Real Estate Development & Management
N.A.I.C.S.: 531390

COFCO LeConte Foods (Shenzhen) Co., Ltd. (1)
No 1 Meixiu Rd Meilin Industrial Zone North

COFCO Limited—(Continued)

Ring Rd, Shenzhen, 518049, China
Tel.: (86) 755 83311056
Web Site: http://www.leconte.com.cn
Food Products Mfr
N.A.I.C.S.: 311991

COFCO Nutrition & Health Research Institute Co. Ltd. (1)
Fourth Road, South District Beiqijia Future Science and Technology City Changping, Beijing, 102209, China
Tel.: (86) 1056989818
Web Site: https://www.cofconhri.com
Health Research Institute Services
N.A.I.C.S.: 541715

COFCO Shenzhen Co., Ltd. (1)
F2 & F3 Xinglong Complex 9 Qingshui River Third Road, Hongling North Road, Luohu District, Shenzhen, 518024, China
Tel.: (86) 755 2231 6706
Web Site: http://www.cofcosz.com.cn
Food Logistics & Warehousing Services; Property Management
N.A.I.C.S.: 493190

COFCO Tunhe Sugar Co., Ltd. (1)
Floor 20 21 18 Block H China Merchants Bank Building No 2 Huanghe Road, Xinjiang, Urumqi, 830000, China
Tel.: (86) 9915571888
Web Site: https://www.cofcotunhe.com
Rev.: $3,711,997,088
Assets: $2,799,662,823
Liabilities: $1,281,707,276
Net Worth: $1,517,955,548
Earnings: $104,409,218
Fiscal Year-end: 12/31/2022
Food Processing & Sales of Tomato Sauce, Sugar, Fruit Jams & Other Agricultural By-Products
N.A.I.C.S.: 311999
Li Minghua (Chm)

China Agri-Industries Holdings Limited (1)
31st Floor COFCO Tower 262 Gloucester Road, Causeway Bay, China (Hong Kong)
Tel.: (852) 2833 0606
Web Site: http://www.chinaagri.com
Rev.: $13,895,374,048
Assets: $9,010,550,577
Liabilities: $4,771,762,403
Net Worth: $4,238,788,174
Earnings: $208,513,684
Emp.: 17,646
Fiscal Year-end: 12/31/2018
Holding Company; Agricultural Products Processing
N.A.I.C.S.: 551112
Muping Chang (VP-Commodity Risk Mgmt)

China Foods Limited (1)
33rd Floor COFCO Tower 262 Gloucester Road, Causeway Bay, China (Hong Kong)
Tel.: (852) 28330388
Web Site: https://www.chinafoodsltd.com
Rev.: $2,642,740,433
Assets: $2,315,032,516
Liabilities: $1,077,215,220
Net Worth: $1,237,817,296
Earnings: $146,049,424
Emp.: 19,076
Fiscal Year-end: 12/31/2020
Holding Company; Beverages, Wine, Confectionery & Consumer Edible Oil
N.A.I.C.S.: 551112
Peng Shen (Exec Dir)

Subsidiary (Non-US):

COFCO Food Marketing Services, Co., Ltd. (2)
Room 1321 Tower B COFCO Fortune plaza No 8, Chao Yang Men South St, Chao Yang, Beijing, 100020, China
Tel.: (86) 1085120501
Web Site: http://www.cofco.com
Kitchen Products & Brands Promotion
N.A.I.C.S.: 424990

COFCO Le Conte Food (Shenzhen) Co., Ltd. (2)
No 1 Meixiu Road Meilin Industrial Zone, Beihuan Road, Shenzhen, China (86%)
Tel.: (86) 755 8331 1056
Web Site: http://www.leconte.com.cn
Chocolate & Nonchocolate Confections Mfr

N.A.I.C.S.: 311351

COFCO Wines & Spirits Co. Ltd. (2)
11th Fl Tower A COFCO Plaza 8 Jianguomennei St, Dongcheng District, Beijing, 100005, China (100%)
Tel.: (86) 01085006688
Web Site: http://www.cofco.com
Wine & Liquor Production & Whslr
N.A.I.C.S.: 424820

Chongqing Xinfu Food Co., Ltd. (2)
Beigong Longqiao Town, Fuling District, Chongqing, 408000, China
Tel.: (86) 2372138000
Soybean Oil Mfr
N.A.I.C.S.: 311224

China National Native Produce & Animal By-Products Import & Export Corporation (1)
208 An Ding Men Wai Street, Beijing, 100011, China
Tel.: (86) 10 5123 6997
Web Site: http://www.tuhsu.com.cn
Diversified Trading Company
N.A.I.C.S.: 455219

Subsidiary (Domestic):

China Tea Co., Ltd. (2)
9th Fl 208 Andingmen Wai Street, Beijing, 100011, China
Tel.: (86) 1064204127
Web Site: http://www.chinatea.com.cn
Tea Cultivation, Production, Processing, Research & Sales
N.A.I.C.S.: 311920

Subsidiary (Domestic):

Fujian Tea Import & Export Co., Ltd. (3)
11 12 F Fortune Bldg 168 Hudong Rd, Fuzhou, 350003, Fujian, China
Tel.: (86) 59187853457
Web Site: http://www.fteast.com
Sales Range: $25-49.9 Million
Emp.: 80
Import & Export of Tea, Coffee & Other Miscellaneous Products
N.A.I.C.S.: 311920

Subsidiary (Domestic):

China Tuhsu Flavours & Fragrances Import & Export Corporation (2)
COFCO Fortune Plaza No.8 , Chao Yang Men South St, Beijing, 100020, China
Tel.: (86) 85018315
Web Site: http://www.ctff.com.cn
Processing, Domestic Marketing & Export of Natural Flavors, Synthetic Fragrances & Rosin & Turpentine Products
N.A.I.C.S.: 325180

Subsidiary (Non-US):

Lihai International Shipping Co., Ltd. (2)
10th Floor Top Glory Tower 262 Gloucester Road, Causeway Bay, China (Hong Kong)
Tel.: (852) 25289123
Web Site: http://www.lihai.com.hk
Sales Range: $25-49.9 Million
Emp.: 20
Maritime Cargo Shipping Services
N.A.I.C.S.: 488320
Pan Zhong Shan (Gen Mgr)

Chinatex Corporation Limited (1)
China Textile Center 19 Jianguomen Inner Street, Beijing, 100005, China
Tel.: (86) 1065281122
Web Site: https://www.chinatex.com
Apparels Mfr
N.A.I.C.S.: 315120
Fei Yuan (Pres & Chm)

Grandjoy Holdings Group Co., Ltd. (1)
27F Block A1 Wise R D Center No 8 LiuXian 1st Road XinAn Street, BaoAn District, Shenzhen, 518123, China
Tel.: (86) 1085017888
Web Site: http://www.grandjoy.com
Rev.: $5,092,939,757
Assets: $27,423,180,979
Liabilities: $21,040,947,164
Net Worth: $6,382,233,814

Earnings: ($202,895,810)
Emp.: 485
Fiscal Year-end: 12/31/2023
Residential Real Estate Development & Sales; Leasing & Management of Properties
N.A.I.C.S.: 531390
Zhou Zheng (Chm)

Subsidiary (Non-US):

Joy City Property Ltd. (2)
33/F COFCO Tower 262 Gloucester Road, Causeway Bay, China (Hong Kong) (64.18%)
Tel.: (852) 28330338
Web Site: https://www.joy-cityproperty.com
Rev.: $2,924,722,523
Assets: $19,656,490,277
Liabilities: $11,500,755,646
Net Worth: $8,155,734,631
Earnings: $154,521,151
Emp.: 3,794
Fiscal Year-end: 12/31/2022
Property Holding & Investment Services
N.A.I.C.S.: 551112
Zheng Zhou (Chm)

Snow-Lotus Cashmere Co., Ltd (1)
No 1 Zhong Rd Yinghai Industrial Park Yinghai Town, Daxing District, Beijing, 100076, China
Tel.: (86) 10 69274270
Fabric Product Mfr
N.A.I.C.S.: 314999

COFCO TECHNOLOGY & INDUSTRY CO., LTD.
No 186 Huihe Road, Wuxi, 214035, Jiangsu, China
Tel.: (86) 51085889571
Web Site: https://www.cofcoet.com
Year Founded: 1993
301058—(CHIN)
Rev.: $340,066,816
Assets: $591,977,548
Liabilities: $290,834,070
Net Worth: $301,143,478
Earnings: $30,660,253
Fiscal Year-end: 12/31/23
Engineeering Services
N.A.I.C.S.: 541330
Yufeng Duan (Sec)

COFFEE REPUBLIC TRADING LTD.
10 Rochester Row, Westminster, London, SW1P 1BS, United Kingdom
Tel.: (44) 2078285800
Web Site:
   http://www.coffeerepublic.co.uk
Year Founded: 1995
Sales Range: $10-24.9 Million
Emp.: 132
Holding Company; Coffee Shop Owner & Operator
N.A.I.C.S.: 551112
Teric Affara (CEO)

Subsidiaries:

Coffee Republic (UK) Limited (1)
109-123 Clifton St, London, EC2A 4LD, United Kingdom
Tel.: (44) 2070330600
Sales Range: $10-24.9 Million
Emp.: 6
Espresso & Coffee Bars Operating Services
N.A.I.C.S.: 722515

COFIDUR SA
79 Rue Saint-Melaine, 53000, Laval, France
Tel.: (33) 243674000
Web Site: https://www.cofidur-ems.com
ALCOF—(EUR)
Sales Range: $25-49.9 Million
Printed Circuit Mfr
N.A.I.C.S.: 334412
Henri Tranduc (Chm, CEO & CFO)

COFINA SGPS, S.A.
Rua Manuel Pinto de Azevedo 818, 4100-320, Porto, Portugal
Tel.: (351) 228346500
Web Site: https://www.cofina.pt
Year Founded: 1995
CFN—(EUR)
Rev.: $31,922,070
Assets: $147,288,449
Liabilities: $82,459,069
Net Worth: $64,829,381
Earnings: $11,279,190
Emp.: 686
Fiscal Year-end: 12/31/22
Newspaper Publishing Services
N.A.I.C.S.: 513110
Paulo Jorge dos Santos Fernandes (Chm)

Subsidiaries:

Cofina Media, SGPS, S.A. (1)
Rua Luciana Stegagno Picchio 3, Lisbon, 1549-023, Portugal
Tel.: (351) 21 318 5200
Online Media Publishing Services
N.A.I.C.S.: 513199
Paul Fernandes (CEO)

COFINIMMO S.A./N.V.
Avenue de Tervurenlaan 270, 1150, Brussels, Belgium
Tel.: (32) 23730000
Web Site:
   https://www.cofinimmo.com
COFB—(EUR)
Rev.: $342,932,225
Assets: $7,342,505,936
Liabilities: $3,385,036,693
Net Worth: $3,957,469,242
Earnings: $520,794,302
Emp.: 161
Fiscal Year-end: 12/31/22
Nonresidential Property Manager & Real Estate Investment Trust
N.A.I.C.S.: 525990
Jean-Edouard Carbonnelle (CEO)

COFINLUXE S.A.
6 Rue Anatole de la Forge, 75017, Paris, France
Tel.: (33) 155377172   FR
Web Site: http://www.cofinluxe.fr
Rev.: $20,200,000
Emp.: 44
Toilet Preparations
N.A.I.C.S.: 325620
Helene Hatte (Mgr-Fin)

COFIX GROUP LTD.
34 Weizman St, Kfar Saba, 4424712, Israel
Tel.: (972) 99733150
Web Site: https://cofix.co.il
Year Founded: 1992
CFX—(TAE)
Rev.: $85,934,796
Assets: $61,010,083
Liabilities: $55,951,650
Net Worth: $5,058,433
Earnings: ($3,724,548)
Emp.: 146
Fiscal Year-end: 12/31/23
Miscellaneous Financial Investment Activities
N.A.I.C.S.: 523999
Avi Katz (Co-Owner & Chm)

COFLE SPA
Via del Ghezzo 54, Trezzo sull Adda Lombardia, 20056, Milan, Italy
Tel.: (39) 029200201
Web Site: https://www.cofle.com
Year Founded: 1964
CFL—(ITA)
Rev.: $61,801,964
Assets: $66,757,046
Liabilities: $35,158,182

Net Worth: $31,598,864
Earnings: $2,823,373
Emp.: 571
Fiscal Year-end: 12/31/22
Pesticide & Other Agricultural Chemical Manufacturing
N.A.I.C.S.: 325320
Walter Barbieri *(Pres)*

Subsidiaries:

Cofle Do Brasil Ltda.   **(1)**
Av Prefeito Alberto Moura 200B, Minas Gerais, Sete Lagoas, 35702-383, Brazil
Tel.: (55) 3137724030
Motor Vehicle Parts Mfr & Distr
N.A.I.C.S.: 336390

Cofle TK Otomotiv AS   **(1)**
Gazi Bulvari Cad No 42, Tuzla, 34953, Istanbul, Turkiye
Tel.: (90) 2165931190
Motor Vehicle Parts Mfr & Distr
N.A.I.C.S.: 336390

Tabo Otomotiv AS   **(1)**
Kimyacilar Organize Sanayi Bolgesi Melek Aras Bulvari Organik, Cd No 23-25 Aydinli-Kosb Tuzla, 34953, Istanbul, Turkiye
Tel.: (90) 2165930550
Web Site: https://www.tabo.com.tr
Motor Vehicle Parts Mfr & Distr
N.A.I.C.S.: 336390

COFLUSA S.A.

Poligoni Industrial Inca s n, 07300, Inca, Spain
Tel.: (34) 971507000
Web Site: http://www.camper.com
Sales Range: $150-199.9 Million
Emp.: 600
Shoe Mfr, Retailer & Distr
N.A.I.C.S.: 316210

COFOE MEDICAL TECHNOLOGY CO., LTD.

816 Zhenhua Road, Yuhua, Changsha, 410000, Hunan, China
Tel.: (86) 73184150099
Web Site: https://www.cofoe.com
Year Founded: 2009
301087—(CHIN)
Rev.: $401,928,858
Assets: $879,463,617
Liabilities: $188,168,704
Net Worth: $691,294,913
Earnings: $35,814,056
Emp.: 4,000
Fiscal Year-end: 12/31/23
Medical Equipment Mfr & Distr
N.A.I.C.S.: 339112
Min Zhang *(Chm)*

Subsidiaries:

Jerry Medical Equipment (Shanghai) Co., Ltd.   **(1)**
Building 12 Lane 615 Fengdeng Road, Jiading District, Shanghai, China
Tel.: (86) 4009200318
Web Site: https://www.jerrymedical.com
Electric Wheelchair Mfr & Distr
N.A.I.C.S.: 339113

COFORGE LTD.

8 Balaji Estate Third Floor Guru Ravi Das Marg Kalkaji, New Delhi, 110019, India
Tel.: (91) 1141029297
Web Site: https://www.coforge.com
COFORGE—(NSE)
Rev.: $640,922,100
Assets: $479,579,100
Liabilities: $142,956,450
Net Worth: $336,622,650
Earnings: $63,609,000
Emp.: 11,094
Fiscal Year-end: 03/31/21
Custom Software Development, Enterprise Integration & Legacy Support
N.A.I.C.S.: 541511
Arvind Thakur *(Vice Chm & Mng Dir)*

Subsidiaries:

Coforge Airline Technologies GmbH   **(1)**
Lina-Ammon-Strasse 19b, 90741, Nuremberg, Germany
Tel.: (49) 91198870900
Information Technology Services
N.A.I.C.S.: 541511

Coforge DPA Ireland Limited   **(1)**
Behan House 10 Mount Street Lower, Dublin, Ireland
Tel.: (353) 12547000
Information Technology Services
N.A.I.C.S.: 541511

Coforge DPA Private Ltd.   **(1)**
Block B 6th Floor Q City SR No 109 110 111/12, Nanakramguda Village Serilingampally Mandal Ranga Reddy District, Hyderabad, 500032, India
Tel.: (91) 4044486666
Software Development Services
N.A.I.C.S.: 541511

Coforge GmbH   **(1)**
Bockenheimer Landstrasse 51-53, 60325, Frankfurt am Main, Germany
Tel.: (49) 694305330
Software Development Services
N.A.I.C.S.: 541511

Coforge Inc.   **(1)**
502 Carnegie Ctr Dr Ste 301, Princeton, NJ 08540
Tel.: (770) 290-6113
Software Development Services
N.A.I.C.S.: 541511

Coforge SmartServe Ltd.   **(1)**
223-224 Udyog Vihar Phase-1, Gurgaon, 122002, Haryana, India
Tel.: (91) 1244002702
Software Development Services
N.A.I.C.S.: 541511

Coforge U.K. Limited   **(1)**
2nd Floor 47 Mark Lane, London, EC3R 7QQ, United Kingdom
Tel.: (44) 2070020700
Information Technology Services
N.A.I.C.S.: 541511

Hole-in-the- Wall Education Limited   **(1)**
8 Balaji Estate Guru Ravi Das Marg Kalkaji, Kalkachi, New Delhi, 110 019, India
Tel.: (91) 9810288327
Web Site: http://www.hole-in-the-wall.com
Sales Range: $10-24.9 Million
Business & Secretarial Schools
N.A.I.C.S.: 611410

NIIT Airline Technologies GmbH   **(1)**
Lina-Ammon-Strasse 19b, 90741, Nuremberg, Germany
Tel.: (49) 91198870900
Web Site: http://www.airline.niit-tech.com
Information Technology Consulting Services
N.A.I.C.S.: 541512

NIIT Malaysia Sdn Bhd.   **(1)**
Suite G02 2310 Century Square Jalan Usahawan, 63000, Cyberjaya, Selangor, Malaysia   **(100%)**
Tel.: (60) 383135200
Web Site: http://www.niit.com.my
Sales Range: $25-49.9 Million
Custom Computer Programming Services
N.A.I.C.S.: 541511

NIIT Smart Serve Ltd   **(1)**
223-224 Udyog Vihar Phase - I, Gurgaon, 122002, Haryana, India
Tel.: (91) 124 4002702
Web Site: http://www.niitsmartserve.com
Business Process Outsourcing Services
N.A.I.C.S.: 561499

NIIT Technologies FZ LLC   **(1)**
Ground Fl Office No 4 Alshiba Building Out Source Zone, Near Academic City, Dubai, United Arab Emirates
Tel.: (971) 4 3692911
Sales Range: $25-49.9 Million
Emp.: 150
Software Training Services
N.A.I.C.S.: 611420
Pankaj Malik *(Sr VP & Head-Middle East)*

NIIT Technologies GmbH   **(1)**
Kandlgasse 18/4/9, 1070, Vienna, Austria
Tel.: (43) 17296262
Information Technology Consulting Services
N.A.I.C.S.: 541512

NIIT Technologies GmbH   **(1)**
Delitzscher Strass 9, Monheim, 40789, Germany
Tel.: (49) 21 7316 752 80
Information Technology Consulting Services
N.A.I.C.S.: 541512

Subsidiary (Non-US):

NIIT Technologies AG   **(2)**
Tribschenstrasse 9, Lucerne, 6005, Switzerland
Tel.: (41) 413604877
Web Site: http://www.niit-tech.ch
Sales Range: $25-49.9 Million
Emp.: 1
Information Technology Consulting Services
N.A.I.C.S.: 541511
Sujan Kotian *(Gen Mgr)*

NIIT Technologies Inc.   **(1)**
1050 Crown Pointe Pkwy Ste 300, Atlanta, GA 30338   **(100%)**
Tel.: (770) 551-9494
Sales Range: $25-49.9 Million
Emp.: 65
Custom Software Development, Enterprise Integration & Legacy Support
N.A.I.C.S.: 541511

NIIT Technologies Limited   **(1)**
2nd Floor 47 Mark Lane, London, EC3R 7QQ, United Kingdom
Tel.: (44) 2070020700
Web Site: http://www.advantagesuite.niit-tech.com
Software Platform & Cloud Services
N.A.I.C.S.: 518210

Subsidiary (Domestic):

Coforge Advantagego Limited   **(2)**
2nd Floor 47 Mark Lane, London, EC3R 7QQ, United Kingdom
Tel.: (44) 2076678600
Web Site: http://www.advantagego.com
Software Development Services
N.A.I.C.S.: 541511
Eugene Brien *(Head-Bus Dev)*

Subsidiary (Non-US):

Coforge BV   **(2)**
Regus WTC Zuidplein 36, 1077 XV, Amsterdam, Netherlands
Tel.: (31) 207997704
Software Development Services
N.A.I.C.S.: 541511

Coforge S.A.   **(2)**
2nd Floor Calle Mendez Alvaro 9, 28045, Madrid, Spain
Tel.: (34) 914008212
Software Development Services
N.A.I.C.S.: 541511

NIIT Technologies Pte Ltd   **(1)**
31 Kaki Bukit Road 3 05-08 Techlink, Singapore, 417818, Singapore
Tel.: (65) 68488300
Web Site: http://www.niit-tech.com
Sales Range: $10-24.9 Million
Emp.: 50
Software Training Services
N.A.I.C.S.: 611420

Subsidiary (Non-US):

Coforge Limited   **(2)**
1858/17 Interlink Tower 6th Floor Debaratna Road, Bangna TAI, Bangkok, 10260, Thailand
Tel.: (66) 2664303638
Software Development Services
N.A.I.C.S.: 541511

NIIT Technologies Pty Limited   **(1)**
Level 40 140 William Street, Melbourne, 3000, VIC, Australia
Tel.: (61) 396078264
Web Site: http://www.niit-tech.com
Sales Range: $10-24.9 Million
Emp.: 100
Software Training Services
N.A.I.C.S.: 611420

Whishworks IT Consulting Private Limited   **(1)**
Cyber Gateway C-Block 2nd Floor, Madhapur, Hyderabad, 500081, Telangana, India
Tel.: (91) 4042656565
Software Development Services
N.A.I.C.S.: 541511

COFRA HOLDING AG

Grafenauweg 10, PO Box 151, 6301, Zug, Switzerland
Tel.: (41) 417280000   **CH**
Web Site:
http://www.cofraholding.com
Year Founded: 2001
Investment Holding Company
N.A.I.C.S.: 551112
Sabine Leyre *(Head-HR Ops)*

Subsidiaries:

Bregal Freshstream LLP   **(1)**
Michelin House 81 Fulham Road, London, SW3 6RD, United Kingdom
Tel.: (44) 20 32829 8110
Web Site: http://www.freshstream.com
Privater Equity Firm
N.A.I.C.S.: 523999
Patrick Smulders *(Mng Partner)*

Bregal Investments LLP   **(1)**
81 Fulham Road 3rd Floor, London, SW3 6RD, United Kingdom
Tel.: (44) 207 408 1663
Web Site: http://www.bregal.com
Privater Equity Firm
N.A.I.C.S.: 523999
Edwin Niers *(CFO)*

Subsidiary (Domestic):

Bregal Capital LLP   **(2)**
Michelin House 81 Fulham Road, London, SW3 6RD, United Kingdom
Tel.: (44) 2075914200
Web Site: http://www.bregalcapital.com
Sales Range: $1-4.9 Billion
Privater Equity Firm
N.A.I.C.S.: 523999
Dwight Cupit *(CFO & Partner)*

Holding (Domestic):

Away Resorts Ltd.   **(3)**
IMEX Building 575-599 Maxted Road, Hemel Hempstead, HP2 7DX, Herts, United Kingdom
Tel.: (44) 1442221477
Web Site: http://www.awayresorts.co.uk
Home Management Services
N.A.I.C.S.: 721110
Carl Castledine *(CEO)*

QA Ltd.   **(3)**
Rath House 55 65 Uxbridge Road, Slough, SL1 1SG, Berks, United Kingdom   **(65%)**
Tel.: (44) 8450747839
Web Site: http://www.qa.com
Sales Range: $25-49.9 Million
Emp.: 200
Professional Training Programs & Services
N.A.I.C.S.: 611430
William Macpherson *(CEO)*

Holding (Non-US):

SHD AG   **(3)**
Rennweg 60, 56626, Andernach, Germany   **(67.6%)**
Tel.: (49) 2632 295 0
Web Site: http://www.shd.de
Sales Range: $50-74.9 Million
Emp.: 520
Information Technology Solutions
N.A.I.C.S.: 541519
Stefan Hahne *(Chm-Mgmt Bd)*

Subsidiary (Non-US):

ArtiCAD Ltd   **(4)**
3-5 Rickmansworth Road, Watford, WD18 0GX, Herts, United Kingdom
Tel.: (44) 1923 888101
Web Site: http://www.articad.com
Interior Design Software Developer
N.A.I.C.S.: 513210
Richard Turner *(CEO)*

COFRA Holding AG—(Continued)

Holding (Non-US):

proALPHA Software GmbH (3)
Auf dem Immel 8, 67685, Weilerbach, Germany
Tel.: (49) 6374 800 0
Web Site: http://www.proalpha.com
Sales Range: $50-74.9 Million
Emp.: 500
IT Consulting Services
N.A.I.C.S.: 541690
Friedrich Neumeyer (CEO)

Subsidiary (Non-US):

proALPHA France (4)
15a avenue de l'Europe, F-67300, Schiltigheim, France
Tel.: (33) 3 90 22 26 40
Web Site: http://www.proalpha.fr
Software Publisher
N.A.I.C.S.: 513210

Subsidiary (US):

proALPHA Software Corporation (4)
20 Trafalgar Sq Ste 403, Nashua, NH 03063
Tel.: (603) 881-3635
Software Publisher
N.A.I.C.S.: 513210

Co-Headquarters (US):

Bregal Investments, Inc. (2)
277 Park Ave, New York, NY 10172
Tel.: (212) 573-6235
Web Site: http://www.bregal.com
Private Equity Firm Services
N.A.I.C.S.: 523999
Quentin Van Doosselaere (Co-CEO)

Subsidiary (Domestic):

Bregal Partners, L.P. (3)
277 Park Ave 29th Fl, New York, NY 10172
Tel.: (212) 704-5350
Web Site: http://www.bregalpartners.com
Privater Equity Firm
N.A.I.C.S.: 523999
Robert Bergmann (Co-Founder & Mng Partner)

Holding (Domestic):

Advance Hydrocarbon Corporation (4)
PO Box 10275, College Station, TX 77842
Tel.: (979) 690-2226
Web Site: http://www.ahcus.com
Saltwater Disposal & Water-Hauling Services
N.A.I.C.S.: 213112

Blue Harvest Fisheries, LLC (4)
1152 Goodlette Rd N, Naples, FL 34102
Tel.: (239) 919-3475
Web Site: http://www.blueharvestfisheries.com
Shellfish Harvesting, Processing & Seafood
Marketing Services
N.A.I.C.S.: 114112
Keith Decker (Pres & CEO)

Subsidiary (Domestic):

Blue Harvest Foods, LLC (5)
1152 Goodlette Rd N, Naples, FL 34102
Tel.: (239) 919-3475
Seafood Distr
N.A.I.C.S.: 424460
Jeff Davis (Pres & CEO)

Division (Domestic):

Blue Harvest Foods, LLC - Fleet Division (6)
4 Washington St, Fairhaven, MA 02719
Tel.: (508) 997-7100
Sales Range: $1-9.9 Million
Shellfish Harvesting, Processing & Marketing
N.A.I.C.S.: 114112
Jorge Cordeiro (VP & Mgr-Fleet)

Blue Harvest Foods, LLC - Hygrade Division (6)
86 MacArthur Dr, New Bedford, MA 02740
Tel.: (508) 993-5700

Web Site: http://www.hygradeoceanproducts.com
Emp.: 100
Seafood Processor & Distr
N.A.I.C.S.: 424460
Douglas Barrows (VP-Scallop Div)

Co-Headquarters (US):

Bregal Sagemount (2)
277 Park Ave 29th Fl, New York, NY 10172
Tel.: (212) 704-5370
Web Site: http://www.sagemount.com
Privater Equity Firm
N.A.I.C.S.: 523999
Gene Yoon (Mng Partner)

Subsidiary (Domestic):

Lux Research, Inc. (3)
100 Franklin St 8th Fl, Boston, MA 02110
Tel.: (617) 502-5300
Web Site: http://www.luxresearchinc.com
Emerging Technologies Consulting Services
N.A.I.C.S.: 541690
Mike Coyne (Pres & CEO)

Subsidiary (Domestic):

Zik Energy Points Inc. (4)
100 N Washington St 1st Fl, Boston, MA 02108-5225
Tel.: (617) 957-7383
Web Site: http://www.energypoints.com
Technical Consulting Services
N.A.I.C.S.: 541690
Ory Zik (Founder & CEO)

C&A (China) Co., Ltd (1)
2299 Yanan Road West 3A88 Shanghai
Mart, Shanghai, 200336, China
Tel.: (86) 21 5253 4666
Web Site: http://www.canda.cn
Emp.: 300
Clothing Apparel Retailer
N.A.I.C.S.: 458110

C&A Belgie Comm. V. (1)
Jean Monnetlaan 1, 1804, Vilvoorde, Belgium
Tel.: (32) 2 257 69 60
Web Site: http://www.c-and-a.com
Clothing Apparel Retailer
N.A.I.C.S.: 458110

C&A Mexico S. de R.L. (1)
Av Camino al Iteso No 8350 Col El Mante, 45609, Tlaquepaque, Mexico
Tel.: (52) 33 38 84 66 10
Web Site: http://www.cyamexico.com
Clothing Apparel Retailer
N.A.I.C.S.: 458110

C&A Moda trgovina d.o.o. (1)
Oreskovica 6H/1, 10020, Zagreb, Croatia
Tel.: (385) 1 54 98 554
Clothing Apparel Retailer
N.A.I.C.S.: 458110

C&A Mode GmbH & Co. KG (1)
Bleichstrasse 20, 40211, Dusseldorf, Germany
Tel.: (49) 2111662747
Web Site: http://www.cunda.de
Operator of Family Clothing Stores
N.A.I.C.S.: 458110

Unit (Non-US):

C&A - Europe Head Office (2)
Senneberg, Jean Monnetlaan, 1804, Vilvoorde, Belgium
Tel.: (32) 22576333
Web Site: http://www.c-and-a.com
Rev.: $6,250,000,000
Emp.: 30,000
Operator of Family Clothing Stores
N.A.I.C.S.: 458110
Alain Caparros (CEO)

Subsidiary (Non-US):

C&A Mode AG (2)
Ohmstrasse 11, CP 5247, 8050, Zurich, Switzerland
Tel.: (41) 432883766
Web Site: http://www.c-e-a.ch
Sales Range: $250-299.9 Million
Emp.: 1,300
Family Clothing Stores Owner & Operator
N.A.I.C.S.: 458110

C&A Mode S.A. (1)
Oberneuhofstrasse 6, Baar, 1045, Zurich, Switzerland
Tel.: (41) 41 766 57 57
Web Site: http://www.c-and-a.com
Clothing Apparel Retailer
N.A.I.C.S.: 458110

C&A Polska Sp.z.o.o. (1)
Babka Tower Al Jana Pawla II 80, 00-175, Warsaw, Poland
Tel.: (48) 22 435 17 70
Web Site: http://www.c-and-a.com
Clothing Apparel Retailer
N.A.I.C.S.: 458110

COFRA Dusseldorf GmbH (1)
Carl-Theodor-Strasse 6, 40213, Dusseldorf, Germany
Tel.: (49) 211 3553348
Real Estate Management Services
N.A.I.C.S.: 531390

Redevco (Suisse) AG (1)
Bahnhofstrasse 73, Postfach 2076, 8021, Zurich, Switzerland
Tel.: (41) 44 213 15 50
Real Estate Management Services
N.A.I.C.S.: 531390

Redevco B.V. (1)
Zaterdagplein 1 Place du Samedi, 1000, Brussels, Belgium
Tel.: (32) 2 645 37 00
Web Site: http://www.redevco.com
Emp.: 50
Real Estate Management Services
N.A.I.C.S.: 531390
Zeen Jecky (Gen Mgr)

Redevco France S.A. (1)
14 rue Auber, 75009, Paris, France
Tel.: (33) 1 426 57200
Real Estate Management Services
N.A.I.C.S.: 531390

Redevco Netherlands (1)
Rembrandt Tower Amstelplein 1, 1096 HA, Amsterdam, Netherlands
Tel.: (31) 20 521 87 30
Real Estate Management Services
N.A.I.C.S.: 531390

Redevco Retail Espana S.L.U. (1)
Plaza Marques de Salamanca 3-4 2 planta, 28006, Madrid, Spain
Tel.: (34) 91 432 32 30
Real Estate Management Services
N.A.I.C.S.: 531390

Redevco Services Deutschland GmbH (1)
Bleichstrasse 14, 40211, Dusseldorf, Germany
Tel.: (49) 211 17 93 79 0
Real Estate Management Services
N.A.I.C.S.: 531390

Redevco UK (1)
1 James Street, London, W1U 1DR, United Kingdom
Tel.: (44) 20 7409 9777
Web Site: http://www.redevco.com
Real Estate Management Services
N.A.I.C.S.: 531390

COG FINANCIAL SERVICES LIMITED
Tel.: (61) 292999690
Web Site: https://www.cogfs.com.au
COG—(ASX)
Rev.: $333,186,902
Assets: $458,816,173
Liabilities: $322,842,274
Net Worth: $135,973,899
Earnings: $16,139,276
Fiscal Year-end: 06/30/24
Financial Services
N.A.I.C.S.: 523999

COGELEC SA
ZI de Maunit 370 rue de Maunit, 85290, Mortagne-sur-Sevre, France
Tel.: (33) 251650579
Web Site: http://www.cogelec.fr
Year Founded: 2000

ALLEC—(EUR)
Rev.: $72,855,724
Assets: $98,144,387
Liabilities: $89,413,843
Net Worth: $8,730,544
Earnings: $4,979,578
Emp.: 335
Fiscal Year-end: 12/31/23
Electronic Control System Distr
N.A.I.C.S.: 423690
Roger Leclerc (Chm & CEO)

Subsidiaries:

Intratone UK Ltd. (1)
Power Road Studios 114 Power Road, London, W4 5PY, United Kingdom
Tel.: (44) 2080379012
Web Site: https://www.intratone.uk.com
Electrical & Electronic Product Mfr
N.A.I.C.S.: 335999
Victor D'Allance (Country Mgr)

COGENINFRA SPA
Via Tetti dell'Oleo 17/25, Borgaro Torinese, Turin, 10071, Italy
Tel.: (39) 011 450 1466
Web Site: http://www.cogeninfra.it
Heating, Energy Efficiency & Utility Services
N.A.I.C.S.: 238220
Alexandra D'Herin (Project Engr)

Subsidiaries:

Elettra Investimenti SpA (1)
Via Duca Del Mare 19, 04100, Latina, Italy
Tel.: (39) 0773665876
Web Site: http://www.elettrainvestimenti.it
Eletric Power Generation Services
N.A.I.C.S.: 221122
Luca De Rita (CFO)

Subsidiary (Domestic):

Alea Heat & Power S.R.L. (2)
Via Duca del Mare 19, 04100, Latina, Italy
Tel.: (39) 0773665876
Web Site: http://www.aleahp.it
Thermal Energy Services
N.A.I.C.S.: 221118

Alea Mobilita' Urbana S.R.L. (2)
Via Duca del Mare 19, 04100, Latina, Italy
Tel.: (39) 07731510324
Web Site: http://www.aleamobilitaurbana.it
Car Sharing Services
N.A.I.C.S.: 532111

GEA S.r.l. (2)
Via G Ferrari 11, 00195, Rome, RM, Italy
Tel.: (39) 0637594511
Web Site: http://www.geaindustrialimentari.com
Engine Maintenance Services
N.A.I.C.S.: 811111

RedEn Srl (2)
Via Borgonuovo 27, 20121, Milan, Italy
Tel.: (39) 0236745650
Web Site: http://www.reden.energy
Thermal Energy Services
N.A.I.C.S.: 221118
Dario Piatti (Project Mgr & Engr-Plant Performance)

COGENT B2B LTD.
44 Tanners Drive, Milton Keynes, HP5 2SL, United Kingdom
Tel.: (44) 800 6899175
Web Site: http://www.cogentb2b.com
Business Consulting Services
N.A.I.C.S.: 541611
Kevin Dunstall (Mng Dir)

COGENT DEVELOPMENT GROUP LIMITED
Level 2 32 Martin Place, Sydney, 2000, NSW, Australia
Tel.: (61) 28 016 2819
Web Site: http://www.northernmining.com.au
NMI—(ASX)
Sales Range: $1-9.9 Million

Minerals Exploration
N.A.I.C.S.: 213115
Tony Ong *(Chm)*

COGENT ELLIOT
Heath Farm Hampton Ln, Meriden,
CV7 7LL, West Midlands, United
Kingdom
Tel.: (44) 121 627 5040   UK
Web Site: http://www.cogent.co.uk
Year Founded: 1936
Emp.: 150
N.A.I.C.S.: 541810
Bill Husselby *(Chm)*

COGIFRANCE SA
63 rue la Boetie, 75008, Paris,
France
Tel.: (33) 140172525
Web Site: http://www.cogifrance.fr
Real Estate Support Services
N.A.I.C.S.: 531390
Pierre Sasson *(Chm & CEO)*

COGIR MANAGEMENT COR-
PORATION
Place Portobello 7250 Boulevard
Taschereau Suite 200, Brossard, J4W
1M9, QC, Canada
Tel.: (450) 672-5090
Web Site: http://www.cogir.net
Year Founded: 1995
Emp.: 2,500
Real Estate Services
N.A.I.C.S.: 531390
Serge G. Duguay *(Founder)*

Subsidiaries:

COGIR Management Corporation -
Ontario Division   (1)
Whitby Mall 1615 Dundas Street East,
Whitby, L1N 2L1, ON, Canada
Tel.: (905) 434-2433
Real Estate Manangement Services
N.A.I.C.S.: 531390
Dan Acre *(Sr VP)*

COGITO MEDIA GROUP INC.
279 Sherbrooke West Suite 305,
Montreal, H2X 1Y2, QC, Canada
Tel.: (858) 531-5723   CO
Web Site:
    http://www.cogitomedias.com
Year Founded: 2007
Business Services
N.A.I.C.S.: 561499
Pierre Turgeon *(CEO)*

COGNA EDUCACAO S.A.
Av Paulista 901 2 Andar, Sao Paulo,
01311-100, Brazil
Tel.: (55) 1131337800   BR
Web Site: https://www.cogna.com.br
COGN3—(BRAZ)
Rev.: $1,014,428,000
Assets: $5,926,570,000
Liabilities: $3,383,525,000
Net Worth: $2,543,045,000
Earnings: ($1,117,747,000)
Emp.: 26,933
Fiscal Year-end: 12/31/20
Education Services
N.A.I.C.S.: 611710
Rodrigo Calvo Galindo *(Vice Chm &
CEO)*

Subsidiaries:

Anhanguera Educacional Participa-
coes S.A.   (1)
Al Maria Tereza 4266 - Sala 06, 13278181,
Valinhos, SP, Brazil
Tel.: (55) 19 3517 3799
Web Site: http://www.anhanguera.com
Sales Range: $1-4.9 Billion
Emp.: 18,300
Education Services
N.A.I.C.S.: 611710
Vitor Alaga Pini *(Dir-IR)*

SOMOS Educacao S.A.   (1)
Avenida das Nacoes Unidas 7221 1 Andar,
Setor B Pinheiros, Sao Paulo, 05425-902,
SP, Brazil
Tel.: (55) 113990 1443
Web Site:
    http://www.somoseducacao.com.br
Educational Materials Publisher
N.A.I.C.S.: 513130
Jose Carlos Reis de Magalhaes Neto
(Chm)

Subsidiary (Domestic):

Editora Atica S.A.   (2)
Av Otaviano Alves de Lima, Freguesia do
O, Sao Paulo, Brazil
Tel.: (55) 32 3215 7117
Web Site: http://www.atica.com.br
Book Publishers
N.A.I.C.S.: 513130

Maxiprint Grafica e Editora Ltda   (2)
Av portugal 155, Londrina, 86046-010, Bra-
zil
Tel.: (55) 43 3341 7546
Educational Support Services
N.A.I.C.S.: 611710

COGNAC FERRAND SASU
191 Avenue du General Leclerc,
78220, Viroflay, France
Tel.: (33) 1 3083 2244   FR
Web Site:
    http://www.cognacferrand.com
Cognac & Other Distilled Spirits Mfr &
Whslr
N.A.I.C.S.: 312140
Alexandre Gabriel *(Owner & CEO)*

Subsidiaries:

The West Indies Rum Distillery
Limited   (1)
Brighton Black Rock, Saint Michael,
BB12051, Barbados
Tel.: (246) 425 9301
Web Site: http://www.westindiesrum.com
Emp.: 62
Rum Distillery & Whslr
N.A.I.C.S.: 312140
Andrew Hassell *(Mng Dir)*

COGNETIVITY NEUROSCI-
ENCES LTD.
1980-1075 West Georgia Street, Van-
couver, V6E 3C9, BC, Canada
Tel.: (604) 688-9588
Web Site: http://www.cognetivity.com
CGNSF—(OTCQB)
Rev.: $35,489
Assets: $2,213,397
Liabilities: $9,949,785
Net Worth: ($7,736,388)
Earnings: ($5,815,325)
Emp.: 2,500
Fiscal Year-end: 01/31/23
Biotechnology Research & Develop-
ment Services
N.A.I.C.S.: 541714
Sina Habibi *(Co-Founder & CEO)*

COGNITA SCHOOLS LIMITED
5 & 7 Diamond Court Opal Drive
Eastlake Park Fox Milne, Milton
Keynes, MK15 0DU, United Kingdom
Tel.: (44) 1908 396 250
Web Site:
    http://www.cognitaschools.com
Year Founded: 2004
Sales Range: $250-299.9 Million
Emp.: 3,553
School Operator
N.A.I.C.S.: 611110
Dean Villa *(COO & Dir-Property)*

COGNITEC SYSTEMS GMBH
Grossenhainer Str 101 Tower B,
Dresden, 01127, Germany
Tel.: (49) 351862920
Web Site: http://www.cognitec.com
Year Founded: 2002

Sales Range: $10-24.9 Million
Emp.: 25
Developer of Facial Recognition Soft-
ware
N.A.I.C.S.: 513210
Alfredo Herrera *(CEO)*

Subsidiaries:

Cognitec Systems Pty Ltd   (1)
201 Sussex Street L20 Tower 2 Darling
Park, Sydney, 2000, NSW, Australia
Tel.: (61) 2 9006 1510
Software Distr
N.A.I.C.S.: 423430

COGNOR HOLDING S.A.
ul Zielona 26, 42-360, Poraj, Poland
Tel.: (48) 343160110
Web Site: https://cognorholding.eu
Year Founded: 1991
COG—(WAR)
Rev.: $3,004,221,217
Assets: $2,510,126,946
Liabilities: $1,139,986,754
Net Worth: $1,370,140,192
Earnings: $260,302,462
Fiscal Year-end: 12/31/23
Metal Service Centers & Other Metal
Merchant Wholesalers
N.A.I.C.S.: 423510
Przemyslaw Sztuczkowski *(Chm-
Mgmt Bd)*

COGNYTE SOFTWARE LTD.
33 Maskit, Herzliya Pituach, 4673333,
Israel
Tel.: (972) 99622300   IL
Web Site: https://www.cognyte.com
Year Founded: 2020
CGNT—(NASDAQ)
Rev.: $312,062,000
Assets: $443,078,000
Liabilities: $233,304,000
Net Worth: $209,774,000
Earnings: ($114,132,000)
Emp.: 1,652
Fiscal Year-end: 01/31/23
Software Development Services
N.A.I.C.S.: 541511
Amir Barel *(CTO)*

COGRA S.A.
Zone de Gardes, 48000, Mende,
France
Tel.: (33) 466653463
Web Site: https://www.cogra.fr
ALCOG—(EUR)
Wood Pellet Mfr
N.A.I.C.S.: 321999
Bernard C. Chapon *(CEO)*

COGSTATE LIMITED
Level 32 367 Collins Street, Mel-
bourne, 3000, VIC, Australia
Tel.: (61) 396641300   AU
Web Site: https://www.cogstate.com
Year Founded: 1999
CGS—(ASX)
Rev.: $43,427,773
Assets: $57,837,955
Liabilities: $16,916,148
Net Worth: $40,921,807
Earnings: $5,449,884
Emp.: 160
Fiscal Year-end: 06/30/24
Cognitive Testing Products Sales
N.A.I.C.S.: 424210
Paul Maruff *(Chief Innovation Officer)*

Subsidiaries:

Cogstate Healthcare LLC   (1)
195 Church St 4th Fl, New Haven, CT
06510
Tel.: (203) 773-5010
Healthcare Services
N.A.I.C.S.: 621999

COHEN PARTNERS CO. LTD.
2-2-15 Minami-Aoyama, Minato-ku,
Tokyo, Japan
Tel.: (81) 366748709
Year Founded: 2014
Management Consulting Services
N.A.I.C.S.: 541611

COHEN'S HOME FURNISH-
INGS LTD.
81 Kenmount Road, Saint John's,
A1B 4B7, NL, Canada
Tel.: (709) 739-6631
Web Site: https://www.cohens.ca
Year Founded: 1919
Furniture Retailer
N.A.I.C.S.: 449110
Brian Hann *(Dir-Sls)*

COHERIS SA
4 Rue du Port aux Vins, 92150,
Suresnes, France
Tel.: (33) 157326060   FR
Web Site: https://www.coheris.com
Year Founded: 1994
COH—(EUR)
Sales Range: $10-24.9 Million
Customer Relationship Management
& Business Intelligence Software
Publisher
N.A.I.C.S.: 513210
Thierry Engrand *(Chief Customer
Officer)*

Subsidiaries:

Coheris InfoCat Ltd.   (1)
Riverside House, 27-29 Vauxhall Grove,
London, SW8 1SY, United Kingdom
Tel.: (44) 2077357711
Web Site: http://www.infocat.co.uk
Business Intelligence Consultancy
N.A.I.C.S.: 561499

COHIBA MINERALS LIMITED
Level 21 459 Collins Street, Mel-
bourne, 3000, VIC, Australia
Tel.: (61) 386303321
Web Site:
    https://www.cohibaminerals.com.au
ALR—(ASX)
Rev.: $7,209
Assets: $7,100,464
Liabilities: $335,613
Net Worth: $6,764,851
Earnings: ($2,178,532)
Fiscal Year-end: 06/30/24
Gold & Other Metal Mining
N.A.I.C.S.: 212220
Justin Mouchacca *(Co-Sec)*

COHORT PLC
One Waterside Drive Arlington Busi-
ness Park, Theale, Reading, RG7
4SW, United Kingdom
Tel.: (44) 1189090390   UK
Web Site: https://www.cohortplc.com
CHRT—(AIM)
Rev.: $255,655,644
Assets: $318,733,275
Liabilities: $181,545,424
Net Worth: $137,187,851
Earnings: $19,300,720
Fiscal Year-end: 04/30/24
Information Management
N.A.I.C.S.: 541512
Simon Walther *(Dir-Finance & Co-
Sec)*

Subsidiaries:

Chess Dynamics Limited   (1)
Quadrant House North Heath Business
Park, Horsham, RH12 5QE, West Sussex,
United Kingdom
Tel.: (44) 140 324 9888
Web Site: https://www.chess-dynamics.com
Defence System Product Mfr
N.A.I.C.S.: 336992

Cohort plc—(Continued)

ELAC SONAR GmbH (1)
Neufeldtstrasse 10, 24118, Kiel, Germany
Tel.: (49) 4318830
Web Site: https://www.elac-sonar.de
Engine Equipment Mfr
N.A.I.C.S.: 333618
Bernd Szukay (Mng Dir)

MASS Consultants Limited (1)
Enterprise House Great North Road Little
Paxton, Saint Neots, PE19 6BN, Cam-
bridgeshire, United Kingdom
Tel.: (44) 1480222600
Web Site: http://www.mass.co.uk
Sales Range: $50-74.9 Million
Emp.: 90
Defence Security Consulting Services
N.A.I.C.S.: 928110
Chris Stanley (Mng Dir)

**Marlborough Communications
Limited** (1)
Dovenby Hall Balcombe Road, Horley, RH6
9UU, Surrey, United Kingdom (100%)
Tel.: (44) 1293 775071
Web Site:
http://www.marlboroughcomms.com
Sales Range: $25-49.9 Million
Emp.: 26
Communication Equipment Mfr
N.A.I.C.S.: 334290
Shane Knight (Mng Dir)

**Systems Consultants Services
Limited** (1)
Arlington House 1025 Arlington Bus Park,
Theale, Reading, RG7 4SA, West Berk-
shire, United Kingdom
Tel.: (44) 1189090200
Web Site: http://www.scs-ltd.co.uk
Sales Range: $25-49.9 Million
Emp.: 130
Defence & Security Consulting Services
N.A.I.C.S.: 541690

**Systems Engineering & Assessment
Ltd.** (1)
Beckington Castle 17 Castle Corner, Beck-
ington, Frome, BA11 6TA, Somerset, United
Kingdom
Tel.: (44) 137 385 2000
Web Site: https://www.sea.co.uk
Sales Range: $75-99.9 Million
Emp.: 260
Defence & Aerospace Engineering Solu-
tions
N.A.I.C.S.: 541330
Steven Hill (Mng Dir)

Vision4ce Limited (1)
Unit 4 Wokingham Commercial Centre
Molly Millars Lane, Wokingham, RG41 2RF,
Berkshire, United Kingdom
Tel.: (44) 118 979 7904
Web Site: https://www.vision4ce.com
Software Development Services
N.A.I.C.S.: 541511
Gordon Cain (Mng Dir)

COIL S.A./N.V.
Roosveld 5, 3400, Landen, Belgium
Tel.: (32) 11880188
Web Site: https://aloxide.com
Year Founded: 1972
ALCOI—(EUR)
Sales Range: $25-49.9 Million
Emp.: 111
Aluminium Products Mfr
N.A.I.C.S.: 331318
Tim Hutton (CEO)

Subsidiaries:

Coil SA/NV (1)
Roosveld 5, 3400, Landen, Flemish Bra-
bant, Belgium
Tel.: (32) 11880188
Web Site: http://www.coil.be
Sales Range: $25-49.9 Million
Emp.: 70
Metal Processing Services
N.A.I.C.S.: 332813
Tim Hutton (CEO)

Heywood Metal Finishers Ltd. (1)
Field Mills Red Dole Lane, Huddersfield,

HD2 1YG, West Yorkshire, United Kingdom
Tel.: (44) 1484533142
Sales Range: $25-49.9 Million
Emp.: 70
Aluminum Anodizing Services
N.A.I.C.S.: 331314
Peter Watts (Gen Mgr)

United Anodisers UK Limited (1)
Wallingford Rd, Uxbridge, UB8 2SR,
Middlesex, United Kingdom
Tel.: (44) 1895817700
Web Site: http://www.unitedanodisers.com
Emp.: 20
Aluminum Anodizing Services
N.A.I.C.S.: 331314
Peter Watts (Mng Dir)

COILLTE LTD.
Dublin Road, Newtown Mount Ken-
nedy, Wicklow, A63 DN25, County
Wicklow, Ireland
Tel.: (353) 1890367378
Web Site: http://www.coillte.ie
Year Founded: 1989
Sales Range: $200-249.9 Million
Emp.: 12,000
Forestry Wood Product & Forestry
Development Services
N.A.I.C.S.: 115310
Bernie Gray (Chm)

Subsidiaries:

Coillte North/Western Region (1)
Government Buildings Cranmore Rd, Sligo,
Ireland (100%)
Tel.: (353) 71 916 2663
Web Site: http://www.coillte.ie
Sales Range: $25-49.9 Million
Emp.: 110
Management Consulting Services
N.A.I.C.S.: 541618
David Gunning (CEO)

**Coillte Panel Products (UK)
Limited** (1)
Persimmon House Anchor Boulevard Cross-
ways Business Park, Dartford, DA2 6QH,
Kent, United Kingdom
Tel.: (44) 1322 424900
Web Site: http://www.dfosb.com
Business Support Services
N.A.I.C.S.: 561499
Malcolm Cowley (Mgr-Sls)

Medite Europe Ltd. (1)
Redmondstown, Clonmel, Co Tipperary,
Ireland (100%)
Tel.: (353) 526182300
Web Site: http://www.medite-europe.com
Sales Range: $75-99.9 Million
Emp.: 160
Holding Company
N.A.I.C.S.: 551112
Neill Foot (Mng Dir)

SmartPly Europe Limited (1)
Belview Slieverue, Waterford,
Ireland (100%)
Tel.: (353) 51851233
Web Site: http://www.smartply.com
Sales Range: $75-99.9 Million
Emp.: 250
Lumber Plywood Millwork & Wood Panel
Whslr
N.A.I.C.S.: 423310
Neil Foot (Mng Dir)

COIMA RES S.P.A
Piazza Gae Aulenti 12, 20154, Milan,
Italy
Tel.: (39) 02 655 0661
Web Site: http://www.coimares.com
Year Founded: 2016
7CO—(BER)
Rev.: $37,695,607
Assets: $991,838,725
Liabilities: $419,271,105
Net Worth: $572,567,620
Earnings: $35,805,284
Fiscal Year-end: 12/31/19
Real Estate Development Services
N.A.I.C.S.: 531390
Manfredi Catella (Founder & CEO)

COIMA RES SIIQ S.P.A.
Piazza Gae Aulenti 12, 20154, Milan,
Italy
Tel.: (39) 02632391
Web Site: http://www.coimares.com
Year Founded: 2016
CRES—(ITA)
Rev.: $50,662,444
Assets: $1,040,241,853
Liabilities: $392,195,456
Net Worth: $654,046,398
Earnings: $28,319,530
Emp.: 5
Fiscal Year-end: 12/31/21
Real Estate Investment Services
N.A.I.C.S.: 531190
Manfredi Catella (Founder & CEO)

**COINSHARES INTERNA-
TIONAL LIMITED**
2 Hill Street, Saint Helier, JE2 4UA,
Jersey
Tel.: (44) 1534513100
Web Site:
https://www.coinshares.com
Year Founded: 2008
CS—(OMX)
Rev.: $54,383,642
Assets: $3,448,892,992
Liabilities: $3,146,892,228
Net Worth: $302,000,764
Earnings: ($571,984,950)
Fiscal Year-end: 12/31/23
Investment Management Service
N.A.I.C.S.: 523999
Jean-Marie Mognetti (CEO)

Subsidiaries:

CoinShares (UK) Limited (1)
1st Floor 3 Lombard Street, London, EC3V
9AQ, United Kingdom
Tel.: (44) 1534513100
Asset Management Services
N.A.I.C.S.: 531390

CoinShares Capital, LLC (1)
437 Madison Ave 28th Fl, New York, NY
10022
Tel.: (646) 308-1518
Web Site: https://coinsharescapital.com
Financial Investment Services
N.A.I.C.S.: 523999

COINSILIUM GROUP LTD.
32 Threadneedle Street, London,
EC2R 8AY, United Kingdom
Tel.: (44) 2038894312
Web Site: https://www.coinsilium.com
Year Founded: 2015
CINGF—(OTCIQ)
Rev.: $15,582,896
Assets: $25,544,311
Liabilities: $5,167,199
Net Worth: $20,377,113
Earnings: $1,332,912
Emp.: 46
Fiscal Year-end: 12/31/20
Data Processing Services
N.A.I.C.S.: 518210
Eddy Travia (Co-Founder & CEO)

**COKA DUVANSKA INDUS-
TRIJA A.D.**
Proleterska Br 6, Coka, Serbia
Tel.: (381) 230471160
Web Site: https://www.dic-coka.co.rs
Year Founded: 1998
COKA—(BEL)
Rev.: $4,687,681
Assets: $4,526,922
Liabilities: $798,118
Net Worth: $3,728,804
Earnings: $571,908
Emp.: 37
Fiscal Year-end: 12/31/23
Tobacco Product Mfr
N.A.I.C.S.: 312230
Predrag Stojanovic (Gen Mgr)

COKAL LIMITED
Level 5 56 Pitt Street, Sydney, 2000,
NSW, Australia
Tel.: (61) 288233129 AU
Web Site: https://www.cokal.com.au
CKA—(ASX)
Rev.: $3,696,243
Assets: $44,970,023
Liabilities: $53,439,229
Net Worth: ($8,469,206)
Earnings: ($9,826,413)
Emp.: 173
Fiscal Year-end: 06/30/24
Coal Exploration Services
N.A.I.C.S.: 212115
James Coleman (CEO)

Subsidiaries:

PT Cokal (1)
The Belleza Office Tower 21 Floor Unit 3 &
5 Jl Letjend Soepeno Kav 34, Permata Hi-
jau Kebayoran Lama, Jakarta, 10210, Indo-
nesia
Tel.: (62) 2130027133
Coal Exploration Services
N.A.I.C.S.: 218113

COKE RESOURCES LIMITED
36 Outram Street, West Perth, 6005,
WA, Australia
Tel.: (61) 8 6336 6400 AU
Web Site:
http://www.cokeresources.com
Year Founded: 2011
Mineral Exploration Services
N.A.I.C.S.: 212290
Claude Strnadica (Exec Dir)

COKO-WERK GMBH & CO. KG
Porschestrasse 5, 32107, Bad Salzu-
flen, Germany
Tel.: (49) 522228990
Web Site: http://www.coko-werk.de
Year Founded: 1926
Rev.: $91,231,800
Emp.: 550
Vacuum Cleaner Mfr
N.A.I.C.S.: 335210
Klaus Wilhelm Dreskruger (Mng Dir)

Subsidiaries:

**Coko Werk Plastik Imalat Sanayi
Limited** (1)
Osb Gazi Osman Pasa Mah 23 Sok No11,
Cerkezkoy, Tekirdag, Turkiye
Tel.: (90) 2827352600
Emp.: 150
Plastic Product Distr
N.A.I.C.S.: 424610
Ayfer Demirci (Mgr-Quality)

Coko-Werk Polska Sp. z o.o. (1)
ul Dabrowskiego 225/243, 93-231, Lodz,
Poland
Tel.: (48) 422531100
Emp.: 250
Plastic Product Distr
N.A.I.C.S.: 424610

COKOLEND A.D.
Durada Brankovica 11, Paracin, Ser-
bia
Tel.: (381) 35569586 RS
Web Site: https://www.cokolend.rs
Year Founded: 1991
COKO—(BEL)
Rev.: $7,802,171
Assets: $9,581,105
Liabilities: $5,510,978
Net Worth: $4,070,128
Earnings: $564,476
Fiscal Year-end: 12/31/22
Chocolate Product Mfr
N.A.I.C.S.: 311351
Slobodan Obradovic (Mktg Mgr)

**COKYVINA JOINT STOCK
COMPANY**
178 Trieu Viet Vuong Street, Hai Ba

Trung District, Hanoi, Vietnam
Tel.: (84) 39781323
Web Site:
https://www.cokyvina.com.vn
CKV—(HNX)
Rev.: $81,034,400
Assets: $15,199,700
Liabilities: $7,283,300
Net Worth: $7,916,400
Earnings: $247,300
Fiscal Year-end: 12/31/23
Electronic & Broadcasting Equipment Mfr
N.A.I.C.S.: 334419

COL FINANCIAL GROUP, INC.
24/F East Tower Tektite Towers, Exchange Road Ortigas Center, Pasig, 1605, Philippines
Tel.: (63) 286515888
Web Site:
https://www.colfinancial.com
COL—(PHI)
Rev.: $22,595,907
Assets: $284,857,329
Liabilities: $246,819,545
Net Worth: $38,037,784
Earnings: $8,781,958
Emp.: 146
Fiscal Year-end: 12/31/20
Online Securities Brokerage Services
N.A.I.C.S.: 523150
Conrado F. Bate *(Pres & CEO)*

COL GROUP CO., LTD.
6th Floor Block E Yonghe Building No 28 Andingmen East Street, Dongcheng District, Beijing, 100007, China
Tel.: (86) 1051667567
Web Site: https://www.col.com
Year Founded: 2000
300364—(CHIN)
Rev.: $198,437,452
Assets: $258,589,571
Liabilities: $80,289,303
Net Worth: $178,300,268
Earnings: $12,597,187
Fiscal Year-end: 12/31/23
Digital Content Publishing Services
N.A.I.C.S.: 513199
Zhilei Tong *(Chm & Pres)*

COL PUBLIC COMPANY LIMITED
No 24 Soi On-Nut 66/1 Suangluang, Bangkok, 10250, Thailand
Tel.: (66) 20155555
Web Site: http://www.col.co.th
COL—(THA)
Rev.: $376,504,417
Assets: $325,851,985
Liabilities: $104,346,865
Net Worth: $221,505,121
Earnings: $25,762,916
Emp.: 3,573
Fiscal Year-end: 12/31/19
Office Products & Supplies
N.A.I.C.S.: 424120
Sahas Treetipbut *(Chm)*

Subsidiaries:

Hytexts Interactive Co., Ltd. **(1)**
No 3 Promphan Building 3rd Floor Room 7 Room No 701-702 Soilat Phrao 3, Lat Phrao Road Chom Phon Subdistrict Chatuchak District, Bangkok, 10900, Thailand
Tel.: (66) 20246690
Web Site: http://www.hytexts.com
Electronic Product Distr
N.A.I.C.S.: 513199

Officemate Omni Franchises Co., Ltd. **(1)**
919/555 South Tower Building Room No 4 5 6 9 14th Floor Silom Road, Silom Subdis-

trict Bang Rak District, Bangkok, 10500, Thailand
Tel.: (66) 659982988
Web Site: http://www.ofmplus.com
Office Equipment & Paper Distr
N.A.I.C.S.: 459410

COLAB CLOUD PLATFORMS LIMITED
125 2nd Floor, Shahpur Jat, New Delhi, 110049, Delhi, India
Tel.: (91) 8828865429
Web Site:
https://www.jsgleasinglimited.ltd
542866—(BOM)
Rev.: $180,097
Assets: $2,502,951
Liabilities: $116,106
Net Worth: $2,386,845
Earnings: $101,713
Emp.: 5
Fiscal Year-end: 03/31/23
Property Management Services
N.A.I.C.S.: 531311
Motibhai Jaksibhai Rabari *(CFO)*

COLABOR GROUP INC.
951 Rang du Canal Building A Local 103, Saint-Bruno-De-Montarville, Boucherville, J3V 0A6, QC, Canada
Tel.: (450) 449-4911
Web Site: https://www.colabor.com
Year Founded: 1962
GCL—(OTCIQ)
Rev.: $372,178,315
Assets: $179,481,630
Liabilities: $103,138,924
Net Worth: $76,342,705
Earnings: $6,134,640
Emp.: 636
Fiscal Year-end: 12/25/21
Food & Non-Food Products Distr
N.A.I.C.S.: 424490
Michel Delisle *(VP-IT)*

Subsidiaries:

Colabor LP **(1)**
1620 boulevard de Montarville, Boucherville, J4B 8P4, QC, Canada
Tel.: (450) 449-4911
Web Site: http://www.colabor.com
Sales Range: $50-74.9 Million
Emp.: 100
Food Marketing & Distribution
N.A.I.C.S.: 424490

Les Pecheries Norref Quebec Inc. **(1)**
4900 Rue Molson Rd, Montreal, H1Y 3J8, QC, Canada
Tel.: (514) 593-9999
Web Site: http://www.norref.com
Seafood Distr
N.A.I.C.S.: 424460

SKOR Wholesale Marketplace **(1)**
580 Industrial Road, London, N5V 1V1, ON, Canada
Tel.: (905) 669-3928
Web Site: http://skor.colabor.com
Sales Range: $125-149.9 Million
Emp.: 350
Food Service & Retail Products Marketer & Distr
N.A.I.C.S.: 424490

Subsidiary (Domestic):

SKOR Culinary Concepts Inc. **(2)**
1330 Crestlawn Dr, Mississauga, L4W 1P8, ON, Canada
Tel.: (905) 625-4447
Food Production for Caterers
N.A.I.C.S.: 722310
Sam Ruso *(Dir-Ops)*

COLAN TOTTE.CO., LTD.
Colantotte Bldg 2-10-26 Minamisenba, Chuo, Osaka, 542-0081, Japan
Tel.: (81) 662587350

Web Site:
https://www.colantotte.co.jp
Year Founded: 1997
7792—(TKS)
Healthcare Product Distr
N.A.I.C.S.: 456199

Subsidiaries:

Eurozone Brands Limited **(1)**
Fence House Fence Avenue, Macclesfield, SK10 1LT, United Kingdom
Tel.: (44) 1625347134
Web Site: https://www.eurozonebrands.com
Sporting Product Mfr & Distr
N.A.I.C.S.: 339920

COLAND HOLDINGS LIMITED
2F No 380 Fenglin Road, Xuhui District, Shanghai, China
Tel.: (86) 2154681666
Web Site:
http://www.colandpharma.com
4144—(TAI)
Rev.: $71,968,794
Assets: $143,497,191
Liabilities: $57,226,841
Net Worth: $86,270,350
Earnings: $2,678,221
Fiscal Year-end: 12/31/19
Pharmaceuticals Mfr
N.A.I.C.S.: 325412
William Robert Keller *(Chm)*

Subsidiaries:

Coland Pharmaceutical Co., Ltd. **(1)**
No 866 Halei Road Room 103 Zhang Jiang Hi-Tech Park, Shanghai, 201203, China
Tel.: (86) 86 21 5137 1880
Web Site: http://www.colandpharma.com
Pharmaceutical Products Mfr & Distr
N.A.I.C.S.: 325412
William Keller *(Chm)*

COLANDIS
Saint Elivet Route De Guingamp, 22300, Lannion, Cotes D Armor, France
Tel.: (33) 296467666
Sales Range: $10-24.9 Million
Emp.: 64
Grocery Stores
N.A.I.C.S.: 445110
Christian Coden *(Mgr-Mktg)*

COLBEAR ADVERTISING LIMITED
8 Durham Ln W Moor Pk, Doncaster, DN3 3FE, Yorkshire, United Kingdom
Tel.: (44) 1302836170
Web Site: http://www.colbear.co.uk
Year Founded: 1960
Sales Range: $10-24.9 Million
Emp.: 3
N.A.I.C.S.: 541810
Malcolm Colbear *(Chm)*

COLBUN S.A.
Av Apoquindo 4775 Piso 11 Las Condes, Santiago, Chile
Tel.: (56) 224604000
Web Site: https://www.colbun.cl
Year Founded: 1986
COLBUN—(SGO)
Rev.: $2,003,619,000
Assets: $6,660,723,000
Liabilities: $3,563,445,000
Net Worth: $3,097,278,000
Earnings: $403,830,000
Emp.: 1,200
Fiscal Year-end: 12/31/23
Electric Power Generation & Distribution Services
N.A.I.C.S.: 221112
Juan Eduardo Vasquez *(Mgr-Bus & Energy)*

COLEFAX GROUP PLC

19/23 Grosvenor Hill, London, W1K 3QD, United Kingdom
Tel.: (44) 2074932231 **UK**
Web Site:
https://www.colefaxgroupplc.com
Year Founded: 1957
CFX—(AIM)
Rev.: $135,269,140
Assets: $93,373,071
Liabilities: $53,294,728
Net Worth: $40,078,342
Earnings: $7,308,775
Fiscal Year-end: 04/30/24
Holding Company; Furnishing Fabrics & Wallpapers Designer & Distr
N.A.I.C.S.: 551112
David B. Green *(Chm & CEO)*

Subsidiaries:

Cowtan & Tout, Inc. **(1)**
148 39th St Spc B319, Brooklyn, NY 11232
Tel.: (212) 647-6900
Web Site: https://www.cowtan.com
Sales Range: $75-99.9 Million
Emp.: 140
Fabrics & Wallpaper
N.A.I.C.S.: 424310
Key Hall *(CEO)*

Jane Churchill Limited **(1)**
19-23 Grosvenor Hill, London, W1K 3QD, United Kingdom **(100%)**
Tel.: (44) 2088746484
Web Site: http://www.janechurchill.com
Sales Range: $25-49.9 Million
Emp.: 40
Home Furnishings Stores
N.A.I.C.S.: 449129
David B. Green *(Chm & CEO)*

Kingcome Sofas Limited **(1)**
24 Old Newton Road Heathfield, Bovey Tracey, Devon, TQ12 6RA, United Kingdom **(100%)**
Tel.: (44) 1626834800
Web Site: http://www.kingcomesofas.co.uk
Sales Range: $25-49.9 Million
Emp.: 50
Home Furnishings Stores
N.A.I.C.S.: 449129
F. Phipps *(Mng Dir)*

Sibyl Colefax & John Fowler Limited **(1)**
89 - 91 Pimlico Road, Belgravia, London, SW1W 8PH, United Kingdom **(100%)**
Tel.: (44) 2074932231
Web Site: http://www.sibylcolefax.com
Sales Range: $25-49.9 Million
Emp.: 35
Home Furnishings Stores
N.A.I.C.S.: 449129
Daniel Slowik *(Mgr-Antiques)*

Subsidiary (Non-US):

Colefax & Fowler GmbH **(2)**
Ottostrasse 13, 80333, Munich, Germany **(100%)**
Tel.: (49) 893399720
Web Site: http://www.colefax.com
Sales Range: $25-49.9 Million
Emp.: 3
Piece Goods Notions & Dry Goods Whslr
N.A.I.C.S.: 424310

COLEGIO BRITANICO SAINT MARGARET'S S.A.
Saint Margaret 150 Lomas de Montemar, PO Box 392 VINA, Concon, Chile
Tel.: (56) 32 245170
Web Site: http://www.stmargarets.cl
MARGARET'S—(SGO)
Sales Range: Less than $1 Million
Education Services
N.A.I.C.S.: 611710

COLEGIO INGLES CATOLICO DE LA SERENA S.A.
Avenida Estadio 1760, PO Box 205, La Serena, Chile
Tel.: (56) 512226044 **CL**

COLEGIO INGLES CATOLICO DE LA SER-
ENA S.A.—(Continued)

Web Site: https://www.cicls.cl
Year Founded: 1946
COLINSE—(SGO)
Sales Range: Less than $1 Million
Emp.: 104
Education Services
N.A.I.C.6.: 611710
Stuardo Erazo Robles (Pres)

COLEGIO LA MAISONNETTE S.A.
Av Luis Pasteur 6076, Vitacura, San-
tiago, Chile
Tel.: (56) 28162900
Web Site:
https://www.lamaisonnette.cl
MAISONNETT—(SGO)
Sales Range: Less than $1 Million
Emp.: 1
Education Services
N.A.I.C.S.: 611710
Carolina Liu Esperidion (CEO)

COLES GROUP LIMITED
800 Toorak Road, Hawthorn East,
Melbourne, 3123, VIC, Australia
Tel.: (61) 398295111   AU
Web Site:
https://www.colesgroup.com.au
COL—(ASX)
Holding Company; Alcoholic Bever-
age Distr
N.A.I.C.S.: 551112
Charlie Elias (CFO)

Subsidiaries:

Coles Retail Group Pty Ltd   (1)
800 Toorak Rd, Hawthorn East, Melbourne,
3123, VIC, Australia
Tel.: (61) 398293111
Web Site: http://www.colesgroup.com.au
Departmental Stores Operating Services
N.A.I.C.S.: 445110

Coles Supermarkets Australia Pty.
Ltd.   (1)
800 Toorak Road, Hawthorn East, Mel-
bourne, 3123, VIC, Australia
Tel.: (61) 3 9829 5111
Web Site: http://www.coles.com.au
Supermarket Operator
N.A.I.C.S.: 445110

Subsidiary (Domestic):

Coles Group Properties Pty Ltd   (2)
800 Toorak Rd, Tooronga, 3146, VIC, Aus-
tralia
Tel.: (61) 398293111
Web Site: http://www.coles.com.au
Store Real Estate Investor, Developer &
Property Manager
N.A.I.C.S.: 531390

Subsidiary (Domestic):

Coles Group Properties Holdings
Ltd   (3)
800 Toorak Rd, Hawthorn East, 3123, VIC,
Australia
Tel.: (61) 398293111
Store Properties Holding Company
N.A.I.C.S.: 551112

Subsidiary (Domestic):

Coles Online Pty Ltd   (2)
Ferntree Gully & Springvale Rds, Mulgrave,
3170, VIC, Australia
Tel.: (61) 395605645
Web Site: http://www.colesonline.com.au
Online Shopping Services
N.A.I.C.S.: 425120

Officeworks Ltd.   (1)
1123 Nepean Highway, Highett, 3190, VIC,
Australia
Tel.: (61) 395566700
Web Site: http://www.officeworks.com.au
Office Supplies
N.A.I.C.S.: 459410
Sarah Hunter (Mng Dir)

Subsidiary (Domestic):

Officeworks Businessdirect Pty
Ltd   (2)
236-262 East Boundary Road, Bentleigh,
3165, VIC, Australia
Tel.: (61) 1300 633 423
Web Site: http://www.officeworks.com.au
Stationery Store Operating Services
N.A.I.C.S.: 450410

e.colesgroup Pty Ltd   (1)
800 Toorak Rd, Hawthorn East, 3123, VIC,
Australia
Tel.: (61) 398295111
Web Site: http://www.coles.com.au
Supermarket Operating Services
N.A.I.C.S.: 445110

COLETTE
213 rue Saint-Honore, 75001, Paris,
France
Tel.: (33) 155353390
Web Site: http://www.colette.fr
Year Founded: 1997
Sales Range: $10-24.9 Million
Emp.: 70
Clothing Retailer
N.A.I.C.S.: 458110
Colette Roussaux (Chm & Mng Dir)

COLGATE-PALMOLIVE (PAKI-STAN) LTD
Lakson Square Building No 2 Sarwar
Shaheed Road, PO Box 112, Kara-
chi, 74200, Pakistan
Tel.: (92) 2138400000
Web Site:
https://www.colgate.com.pk
Year Founded: 1977
COLG—(PSX)
Rev.: $430,273,248
Assets: $170,689,170
Liabilities: $83,209,211
Net Worth: $87,479,959
Earnings: $37,449,996
Emp.: 1,217
Fiscal Year-end: 06/30/23
Healthcare & Personal Products Mfr
N.A.I.C.S.: 325611
Zulfiqar Ali Lakhani (CEO)

Subsidiaries:

Cyber Internet Services (Private)
Limited   (1)
V23G V6H Sir Ghulam Hussain Hidayatal-
lah Rd Civil Lines, Karachi, Sindh, Pakistan
Tel.: (92) 11 144 5566
Web Site: https://www.cyber.net.pk
Emp.: 700
Communication Network Services
N.A.I.C.S.: 517810
Saad Waqar (Project Mgr)

Ice Animations (Private) Limited   (1)
Lakson Square Building 3 Office 801-802
8th Floor Sarwar Shaheed Road, Karachi,
Pakistan
Tel.: (92) 213 840 0555
Web Site: https://www.iceanimations.com
Animation Services
N.A.I.C.S.: 512110

Lakson Investments Limited   (1)
Lakson Square Building 2 Sarwar Shaheed
Road, Karachi, 74200, Pakistan
Tel.: (92) 2111 152 5766
Web Site: https://www.li.com.pk
Investment Services
N.A.I.C.S.: 523999
Iqbal Ali (Chm)

Nayapay (Private) Limited   (1)
10th Floor Lakson Square Building 3 Sar-
war Shaheed Road, Karachi, Pakistan
Tel.: (92) 111222729
Web Site: http://www.nayapay.com
Digital Marketing Services
N.A.I.C.S.: 541613
Farrukh Amlani (COO)

COLIAN HOLDING S.A.
st Zdrojowa 1, Opatowek, 62-860,
Kalisz, Poland
Tel.: (48) 62 590 33 00
Web Site: http://www.colian.pl
Year Founded: 1918
Sales Range: $200-249.9 Million
Emp.: 353
Holding Company
N.A.I.O.O.: 551112

COLIBRI RESOURCE CORPO-RATION
Suite 700-105 Englehart Street,
Dieppe, E1A 8K2, NB, Canada
Tel.: (506) 383-4274   Ca
Web Site:
https://www.colibriresource.com
Year Founded: 2004
2CO1—(DEU)
Assets: $4,909,652
Liabilities: $1,798,479
Net Worth: $3,111,173
Earnings: ($592,576)
Fiscal Year-end: 12/31/23
Mineral Exploration Services
N.A.I.C.S.: 213114
Ronald J. Goguen (Pres & CEO)

COLIN MEAR ENGINEERING LTD
Combe St Nicholas Chard, Somerset,
TA20 3NL, United Kingdom
Tel.: (44) 1460269500
Web Site: http://www.cme-ltd.com
Sales Range: $10-24.9 Million
Emp.: 120
Machinery Equipment Mfr
N.A.I.C.S.: 333248
David Weatherill (Dir-Sls)

COLINA HOLDINGS BAHAMAS LIMITED
308 East Bay Street, PO Box
N-4728, Nassau, Bahamas
Tel.: (242) 3962100   BS
Web Site: http://www.colina.com
CHL—(BISX)
Rev.: $180,796,486
Assets: $859,103,545
Liabilities: $621,015,062
Net Worth: $238,088,483
Earnings: $17,764,726
Fiscal Year-end: 12/31/22
Holding Company; Insurance, Mort-
gage, Investment & Retirement Prod-
ucts & Services
N.A.I.C.S.: 551112
Emanuel M. Alexiou (Vice Chm)

Subsidiaries:

Colina Financial Advisors Ltd.   (1)
308 East Bay St 3rd Floor, PO Box CB-
12407, Nassau, New Providence, Bahamas
Tel.: (242) 5027010
Web Site: https://www.cfal.com
Financial Investment Services
N.A.I.C.S.: 523999
James H. Smith (Chm)

Colina General Insurance Agency &
Brokers Limited   (1)
Nassau Guardian Building Oakes Field,
Nassau, Bahamas
Tel.: (242) 322 5665
Web Site: http://www.colinageneral.com
General Insurance Services
N.A.I.C.S.: 524126

Colina General Insurance Agents &
Brokers Limited   (1)
Village Road, PO Box N-4728, Nassau,
Bahamas
Tel.: (242) 2426772050
Web Site: https://www.colina.com
General Insurance Agency Services
N.A.I.C.S.: 524210

Colina Insurance Limited   (1)
308 East Bay Street, PO Box N-4728, Nassau, Bahamas   (100%)

Tel.: (242) 3962100
Web Site: https://www.colina.com
Life & Health Insurance Products & Ser-
vices
N.A.I.C.S.: 524298
Emanuel M. Alexiou (Vice Chm)

Subsidiary (Non-US):

Colina Mortgage Corporation
Ltd.   (2)
Tel.: (242) 3964100
Emp.: 7
Mortgage Life Insurance Services
N.A.I.C.S.: 524126

Indigo Insurance (Cayman)
Limited   (1)
14 Harbour Walk, Grand Cayman, KY1-
1101, Cayman Islands
Tel.: (345) 7463446
Home & Car Insurance Services
N.A.I.C.S.: 524210

COLINZ LABORATORIES LIM-ITED
A/101 Pratik Estate Next to Fortis
Hospital Mulund Link Road, Mumbai,
400 078, India
Tel.: (91) 2225668002
Web Site: https://www.colinz.com
Year Founded: 1987
531210—(BOM)
Rev.: $866,779
Assets: $1,377,207
Liabilities: $381,941
Net Worth: $995,267
Earnings: $61,732
Emp.: 60
Fiscal Year-end: 03/31/21
Pharmaceutical Product Mfr & Whslr
N.A.I.C.S.: 325412
L. S. Mani (Compliance Officer &
Sec)

COLIPAYS
Zone Aeroportuaire de Gillot, 97438,
Sainte-Marie, Reunion
Tel.: (262) 262289999
Web Site: https://www.colipays.com
Year Founded: 1991
MLCLP—(EUR)
Sales Range: $1-9.9 Million
Flower Packaging & Delivery
N.A.I.C.S.: 459310
Frederic Faby (Chm & CEO)

COLLABOS CORPORATION
8-1 Sanbancho, Chiyoda-ku, Tokyo,
102-0075, Japan
Tel.: (81) 356233391
Web Site: https://www.collabos.com
Year Founded: 2001
3908—(TKS)
Sales Range: $10-24.9 Million
Emp.: 60
Call Center Software Solutions
N.A.I.C.S.: 513210
Takao Motegi (Pres)

COLLAS CRILL
Glategny Court, PO Box 140, Glat-
egny Esplanade, Saint Peter Port,
GY1 4EW, Guernsey
Tel.: (44) 1481 723191
Web Site: http://www.collascrill.com
Year Founded: 1948
Emp.: 115
Law firm
N.A.I.C.S.: 541110
Christopher Bound (Sr Partner)

Subsidiaries:

Charles Adams Ritchie &
Duckworth   (1)
Willow House Floor 2 Cricket Square, PO
Box 709, Georgetown, KY1-1107, Cayman
Islands
Tel.: (345) 949 4544
Web Site: http://www.card.com.ky

Emp.: 50
Law firm
N.A.I.C.S.: 541110
Alan G. de Saram *(Partner & Head-Corp, Comml & Investment Funds)*

COLLECTE LOCALISATION SATELLITES
11 rue Hermes, Parc Technologique du Canal, 31520, Ramonville-Saint-Agne, France
Tel.: (33) 5 6139 4700   FR
Web Site: http://www.cls.fr
Year Founded: 1986
Sales Range: $100-124.9 Million
Emp.: 750
Ocean Monitoring & Surveillance Support Services
N.A.I.C.S.: 541990
Christophe Vassal *(Pres)*

Subsidiaries:

ALTAMIRA Information SL   **(1)**
C Corsega 5e B 381-387, 08037, Barcelona, Spain
Tel.: (34) 931835750
Web Site: http://www.altamira-information.com
Satellite Telecommunication Services
N.A.I.C.S.: 517410

CLS America, Inc.   **(1)**
4390 Parliament Pl Ste Q, Lanham, MD 20706-4369
Tel.: (301) 925-4411
Web Site: http://www.clsamerica.com
Ocean Monitoring & Surveillance Support Services
N.A.I.C.S.: 541990

Collecte Localisation Satellites Peru S.A.C.   **(1)**
Jr Trinidad Moran 639, Lince, Lima, Peru
Tel.: (51) 14402717
Web Site: http://www.clsperu.pe
Satellite Telecommunication Services
N.A.I.C.S.: 517410

Horizon Marine, Inc.   **(1)**
15 Creek Rd, Marion, MA 02738
Tel.: (508) 748-1860
Web Site: http://www.horizonmarine.com
Marine Engineering Services
N.A.I.C.S.: 541330

Novacom Services SA   **(1)**
8-10 rue Hermes Parc Technologique du Canal, Ramonville-Saint-Agne, 31520, France
Tel.: (33) 561395000
Web Site: http://www.novacom-services.com
Satellite Telecommunication Services
N.A.I.C.S.: 517410

PROOCEANO   **(1)**
Av Rio Branco n 311-sala 1205, Centro, Rio de Janeiro, 20040-009, Brazil
Tel.: (55) 2125325666
Web Site: http://www.prooceano.com.br
Satellite Telecommunication Services
N.A.I.C.S.: 517410

PT CLS ARGOS INDONESIA   **(1)**
K-Link Tower Fl 25 Suite A Jl Gatot Subroto Kav 59 A, Jakarta, 12950, Indonesia
Tel.: (62) 2129026955
Satellite Telecommunication Services
N.A.I.C.S.: 517410

T.R.E. s.r.l.   **(1)**
Ripa di Porta Ticinese 79, 20143, Milan, Italy
Tel.: (39) 024343121
Web Site: http://www.treuropa.com
Satellite Telecommunication Services
N.A.I.C.S.: 517410

COLLECTION CONRAD C
9320 boul St-Laurent Suite 200, Montreal, H2N 1N7, QC, Canada
Tel.: (514) 385-9599
Web Site: http://www.conradc.com
Rev.: $10,433,394
Emp.: 120
Family Clothing Stores
N.A.I.C.S.: 458110

Conrad Cape *(Pres)*

COLLECTION HOUSE LIMITED
Tel.: (61) 732921000   AU
Web Site:
https://www.collectionhouse.com.au
Year Founded: 1992
CLH—(ASX)
Rev.: $57,714,794
Assets: $111,924,269
Liabilities: $81,421,479
Net Worth: $30,502,790
Earnings: ($24,510,418)
Emp.: 850
Fiscal Year-end: 06/30/21
Debt Collection Services
N.A.I.C.S.: 561440
Leigh Berkley *(Chm)*

Subsidiaries:

Collection House International BPO, Inc.   **(1)**
20th Floor Exxa Tower Bridgetowne C-5 Road Ugong Norte, Quezon City, Manila, 1110, Philippines
Tel.: (63) 73 292 1000
Business Support Services
N.A.I.C.S.: 561990

Collective Learning and Development Pty Ltd   **(1)**
Level 7 Green Square 515 St Paul's Terrace, Fortitude Valley, Brisbane, 4006, QLD, Australia
Tel.: (61) 300 367 370
Web Site: http://www.clad.net.au
Training Services
N.A.I.C.S.: 611430
Gary Lung *(Mgr-Learning & Dev)*

Jones King Lawyers Pty Ltd   **(1)**
Level 7 515 St Paul's Terrace, PO Box 2087, Fortitude Valley, 4006, QLD, Australia
Tel.: (61) 7 3225 0000
Web Site:
http://www.collectionhouse.com.au
Law firm
N.A.I.C.S.: 541110
Nathan Shaw *(Dir-Solicitor)*

Lion Finance Pty Ltd   **(1)**
L 3 484-488 Queen St, Brisbane, 4000, QLD, Australia
Tel.: (61) 1300 133 667
Financial Management Services
N.A.I.C.S.: 541611

Midstate CreditCollect Pty Ltd **(1)**
31 Grey Street, PO Box 1655, 3844, Traralgon, VIC, Australia
Tel.: (61) 1300 551 055
Web Site: http://www.creditcollect.com.au
Credit Management Service
N.A.I.C.S.: 561440
Jason Dowling *(Mgr-Bus)*

Receivables Management (NZ) Limited   **(1)**
PO Box 331049, Takapuna, Auckland, 0740, New Zealand
Tel.: (64) 3 288 0108
Web Site: https://www.rmlgroup.co.nz
Debt Collection Services
N.A.I.C.S.: 561440

Thinkme Finance Pty. Ltd.   **(1)**
Level 12 Skyring Terrace, Newstead, 4006, QLD, Australia
Tel.: (61) 732250006
Web Site: https://www.thinkme.com.au
Consumer & Personal Loans Services
N.A.I.C.S.: 522291

COLLECTIVE METALS INC.
Suite 409-22 Leader Lane, Toronto, M5E 0B2, ON, Canada
Tel.: (604) 968-4844   ON
Web Site:
https://www.collectivemetalsinc.com
Year Founded: 2018
COMT—(CNSX)
Assets: $3,041,396
Liabilities: $456,821
Net Worth: $2,584,575

Earnings: ($1,944,112)
Fiscal Year-end: 12/31/23
Mineral Mining Services
N.A.I.C.S.: 213115
Christopher Huggins *(CEO)*

COLLECTIVE MINING LTD.
82 Richmond St E 4th Floor, Toronto, M5C 1P1, ON, Canada
Tel.: (647) 931-7118
Web Site:
https://www.collectivemining.com
CNL—(NYSE)
Rev.: $424
Assets: $16,969,078
Liabilities: $4,246,762
Net Worth: $12,722,316
Earnings: ($19,133,658)
Emp.: 84
Fiscal Year-end: 12/31/23
Asset Management Services
N.A.I.C.S.: 523940
Paul Begin *(CFO)*

COLLECTOR AB
Lilla Bommens Torg 11, 411 04, Gothenburg, Sweden
Tel.: (46) 10 161 00 00
Web Site: http://www.collector.se
COLL—(OMX)
Rev.: $308,862,400
Assets: $4,636,232,160
Liabilities: $4,053,910,560
Net Worth: $582,321,600
Earnings: $35,525,280
Emp.: 301
Fiscal Year-end: 12/31/20
Banking & Financial Services
N.A.I.C.S.: 522110
Lena Apler *(Co-Chm)*

Subsidiaries:

Colligent Inkasso AB   **(1)**
Box 114 82, 404 30, Gothenburg, Sweden
Tel.: (46) 101610910
Web Site: http://www.colligent.se
Financial Services
N.A.I.C.S.: 541611

COLLEGE FORD LINCOLN LTD.
3975 - 1st Avenue South, Lethbridge, T1J 4P8, AB, Canada
Tel.: (403) 329-0333
Web Site:
http://www.collegefordlincoln.com
New & Used Car Dealers
N.A.I.C.S.: 441110
Ken Klassen *(Mgr-Parts)*

COLLEGE PARK MOTOR PRODUCTS LTD
4512 Railway Avenue, Vermilion, T9X 1E9, AB, Canada
Tel.: (780) 853-4646
Web Site:
http://www.collegeparkgm.com
Year Founded: 1997
Rev.: $11,476,733
Emp.: 25
New & Used Car Dealers
N.A.I.C.S.: 441110
Larry Alward *(Gen Mgr)*

COLLER CAPITAL LTD.
116 Park Street, London, W1K 6AF, United Kingdom
Tel.: (44) 2076318500
Web Site:
http://www.collercapital.com
Year Founded: 1990
Sales Range: $25-49.9 Million
Emp.: 50
Private Equity Secondaries Investment Services
N.A.I.C.S.: 523999
Jeremy Coller *(Founder, Chm & CIO)*

Subsidiaries:

Accentus Medical Plc   **(1)**
528 10 Unit 2 Rutherford Ave, Didcot, Harwell, OX11 0DF, Oxfordshire, United Kingdom
Tel.: (44) 1235434320
Web Site: http://www.accentus-medical.com
Sales Range: $25-49.9 Million
Emp.: 25
Developer of Medical Devices New Technology & Intellectual Property
N.A.I.C.S.: 334510
Philip Agg *(CEO)*

Coller Capital Limited   **(1)**
Level 19 Two International Finance Centre 8 Finance Street, Central, China (Hong Kong)
Tel.: (852) 2251 1594
Financial Management Services
N.A.I.C.S.: 523999
Peter Kim *(Partner-Investment)*

Coller Capital, Inc   **(1)**
950 3rd Ave, New York, NY 10022
Tel.: (212) 644-8500
Financial Management Services
N.A.I.C.S.: 523999
David M. Platter *(Head-Origination)*

Credit Agricole Private Equity S.A.   **(1)**
37-41 rue du Rocher, 75008, Paris, France
Tel.: (33) 143232121
Web Site: http://www.omnescapital.com
Privater Equity Firm
N.A.I.C.S.: 523999
Fabien Prevost *(CEO)*

Subsidiary (Domestic):

SLG Recycling   **(2)**
30 Avenue Charles Bedaux, 37000, Tours, France
Tel.: (33) 247376363
Web Site: http://www.slgrecycling.fr
Sales Range: $50-74.9 Million
Recycling Services
N.A.I.C.S.: 562119
Jean-Philippe Sepchat *(CEO)*

Joint Venture (Domestic):

Spherea Test & Services S.A.S. **(2)**
109 avenue Eisenhower, 31023, Toulouse, CEDEX 1, France
Tel.: (33) 5 34 55 40 00
Web Site: http://www.spherea.com
Sales Range: $100-124.9 Million
Emp.: 500
Electronic Equipment Repair & Maintenance Services in Aviation, Defense, Space, Energy & Transportation
N.A.I.C.S.: 811210
Patrick Freneuil *(CTO & VP-Product Lines)*

Subsidiary (Non-US):

Spherea Test & Services Ltd.   **(3)**
23-25 Cobham Road, Ferndown Industrial Estate, Wimborne, BH21 7PE, Dorset, United Kingdom
Tel.: (44) 1202 872800
Web Site: http://www.spherea.com
Sales Range: $25-49.9 Million
Emp.: 35
Test Engineering Services
N.A.I.C.S.: 541330
Dave Aspin *(Acct Mgr)*

Risksol Consulting Ltd.   **(1)**
Dallam Court Dallam Lane, Warrington, WA2 7LT, United Kingdom
Tel.: (44) 1925413984
Web Site: http://www.risksol.co.uk
Sales Range: $25-49.9 Million
Emp.: 22
Business & Management Consulting Services
N.A.I.C.S.: 541611

COLLETTE DINNIGAN PTY. LTD.
22-24 Hutchinson St Surry Hills, Sydney, 2010, NSW, Australia
Tel.: (61) 293610110
Web Site:
http://www.collettedinnigan.com.au

Collette Dinnigan Pty. Ltd.—(Continued)

Sales Range: $10-24.9 Million
Emp.: 100
Women's Clothing Designer
N.A.I.C.S.: 315120
Robyn Holt (CEO)

COLLIDER LIMITED
7 Morocco Street, London, SE1 3HB, United Kingdom
Tel.: (44) 203 019 3270　　　　　UK
Web Site:
　http://www.wearecollider.com
Year Founded: 2003
Emp.: 50
Advertising Services
N.A.I.C.S.: 541810
Anthony Jerges (CEO)

COLLIERS INTERNATIONAL GROUP INC.
1140 Bay Street Suite 4000, Toronto, M5S 2B4, ON, Canada
Tel.: (416) 960-9500　　　　　ON
Web Site: https://www.colliers.com
CIGI—(NASDAQ)
Rev.: $4,459,487,000
Assets: $5,098,177,000
Liabilities: $4,604,803,000
Net Worth: $493,374,000
Earnings: $46,253,000
Emp.: 18,450
Fiscal Year-end: 12/31/22
Holding Company; Residential & Commercial Real Estate Acquisition, Development & Brokerage Services
N.A.I.C.S.: 551112
Jay S. Hennick (Co-CEO & Chm-Global)

Subsidiaries:

Basalt Infrastructure Partners LLP　　　　　　　　　　　　　　(1)
4th Floor 25 Golden Square, London, W1F 9LU, United Kingdom　　　　(75%)
Tel.: (44) 2077663340
Web Site: https://www.basaltinfra.com
Infrastructure Asset Investment Advisory Services
N.A.I.C.S.: 523940
Rob Gregor (Mng Partner)

Subsidiary (US):

Basalt Infrastructure Partners LLC　　　　　　　　　　　　　　(2)
200 Park Ave S Ste 1501, New York, NY 10003
Tel.: (646) 661-3900
Web Site: https://www.basaltinfra.com
Infrastructure Equity Investment Services
N.A.I.C.S.: 523999

Subsidiary (Non-US):

Manx Telecom plc　　　　　　　　　(2)
Isle of Man Business Park Cooil Road, Braddan, IM99 1HX, Isle of Man
Tel.: (44) 1624624624
Web Site: http://www.manxtelecom.com
Sales Range: $100-124.9 Million
Telecommunications & Internet Services
N.A.I.C.S.: 517111
David Smith (Dir-Strategic Dev)

Holding (US):

Upper Peninsula Power Company　　　　　　　　　　　　(2)
PO Box 60055, Prescott, AZ 86304-6055
Tel.: (906) 449-2014
Web Site: http://www.uppco.com
Electric Power Supply Distr
N.A.I.C.S.: 221122
Nick Kates (CFO)

Holding (Domestic):

Wightlink Limited　　　　　　　　　(2)
Gunwharf Road, Portsmouth, PO1 2LA, Hants, United Kingdom
Tel.: (44) 333 999 7333
Web Site: http://www.wightlink.co.uk

Ferry Operator
N.A.I.C.S.: 483114
Keith Greenfield (CEO)

CB Richard Ellis of Virginia, Inc.　(1)
150 W Main St Ste 1100, Norfolk, VA 23510
Tel.: (757) 490-3300
Commercial Real Estate Brokerage Services
N.A.I.C.S.: 531210
Mike Harris (Controller)

Colliers Engineering & Design, Inc.　　　　　　　　　　　　　(1)
331 Newman Springs Rd Ste 203, Red Bank, NJ 07701-5699
Tel.: (732) 383-1950
Web Site: https://colliersengineering.com
Engineering & Consulting Services
N.A.I.C.S.: 541330
Richard M. Maser (Founder & Chm)

Subsidiary (Domestic):

Bolton Perez & Associates, Inc.　(2)
7205 NW 19th St Ste 201, Miami, FL 33126-1228
Tel.: (305) 392-3190
Web Site: http://www.bpamiami.com
Engineeering Services
N.A.I.C.S.: 541330
Joaquin Perez (Co-Founder & CEO)

Craig Testing Laboratories, Inc.　(2)
5439 Harding Hwy, Mays Landing, NJ 08330
Tel.: (609) 625-1700
Engineeering Services
N.A.I.C.S.: 541330

Branch (Domestic):

Maser Consulting　　　　　　　　　(2)
53 Frontage Rd Ste 110, Hampton, NJ 08827
Tel.: (908) 238-0900
Web Site: http://www.maserconsulting.com
Civil Engineering, Environmental, Geotechnical & Landscape Architecture
N.A.I.C.S.: 541320
Paul Sterbenz (Sr Principal, Div Dir & Mgr)

Maser Consulting　　　　　　　　　(2)
100 American Metro Blvd Ste 152, Hamilton, NJ 08619
Tel.: (609) 587-8200
Web Site: http://www.maserconsulting.com
Civil Engineering, GeoTech & Landscape Architecture
N.A.I.C.S.: 237990
S. Maurice Rached (Sr Principal & Dir-Traffic & Transportation)

Maser Consulting　　　　　　　　　(2)
553 Beckett Rd Bldg 4 Suite 408, Logan Township, NJ 08085
Tel.: (856) 467-3001
Web Site: http://www.maserconsulting.com
Environmental, Geotech & Landscape Architecture
N.A.I.C.S.: 541320

Maser Consulting　　　　　　　　　(2)
601 Route 73 N Suite 105, Marlton, NJ 08053
Tel.: (856) 797-0412
Web Site: http://www.maserconsulting.com
Civil Engineering, Environmental, Geotechnical & Landscape Architecture
N.A.I.C.S.: 237990

Maser Consulting　　　　　　　　　(2)
500 Scarborough Dr Ste 108, Egg Harbor Township, NJ 08234
Tel.: (609) 390-1927
Web Site: http://www.maserconsulting.com
Landscape Architecture & Civil Engineering
N.A.I.C.S.: 541320
Andrew Previti (Sr Principal & Dir-Div)

Maser Consulting　　　　　　　　　(2)
200 Vly Rd Ste 304, Mount Arlington, NJ 07856
Tel.: (973) 398-3110
Web Site: http://www.maserconsulting.com
Emp.: 41
Civil Engineering, Landscape Architecture & Geotechnical Services
N.A.I.C.S.: 237990

Maser Consulting　　　　　　　　　(2)

5660 W Cypress St Suite 5660F, Tampa, FL 33607
Tel.: (813) 207-1061
Web Site: http://www.maserconsulting.com
Civil Engineering, Geotechnical, Environmental & Landscape Architecture
N.A.I.C.S.: 237990

Maser Consulting　　　　　　　　　(2)
22375 Broderick Dr Ste 110, Sterling, VA 20166
Tel.: (703) 430-4330
Web Site: http://www.maserconsulting.com
Emp.: 20
Civil Engineering Services
N.A.I.C.S.: 237990

Maser Consulting　　　　　　　　　(2)
410 Eagleview Blvd Ste 104, Exton, PA 19341
Tel.: (610) 254-9140
Web Site: http://www.maserconsulting.com
Landscape Architecture & Civil Engineering Services
N.A.I.C.S.: 541320

Maser Consulting　　　　　　　　　(2)
190 Brodhead Rd Suite 210, Bethlehem, PA 18017
Tel.: (610) 868-4201
Web Site: http://www.maserconsulting.com
Civil Engineering, Landscape Architecture & Environmental Services
N.A.I.C.S.: 237990

Maser Consulting　　　　　　　　　(2)
11 Bradhurst Ave, Hawthorne, NY 10532
Tel.: (914) 347-7500
Web Site: http://www.maserconsulting.com
Architectural, Engineering & Transportation Services
N.A.I.C.S.: 541310

Maser Consulting　　　　　　　　　(2)
555 Hudson Vly Ave Ste 101, Windsor, NY 12553
Tel.: (845) 564-4495
Web Site: http://www.maserconsulting.com
Civil Engineering, Transportation, Geotechnical & Landscape Architecture Services
N.A.I.C.S.: 237990

Maser Consulting　　　　　　　　　(2)
777 Chestnut Ridge Rd Ste 202, Chestnut Ridge, NY 10977
Tel.: (845) 352-0411
Web Site: http://www.maserconsulting.com
Civil Engineering, Landscape Architecture & Geotechnical Services
N.A.I.C.S.: 237990

Maser Consulting　　　　　　　　　(2)
18 Computer Dr E, Albany, NY 12205
Tel.: (518) 459-3252
Web Site: http://www.maserconsulting.com
Civil Engineering, Geotechnical & Environmental Services
N.A.I.C.S.: 237990

Colliers International Holdings (USA), Inc.　　　　　　　　　　　　　(1)
601 Union St Ste 5300, Seattle, WA 98101
Tel.: (206) 223-0866
Emp.: 12,509
Holding Company; Commercial Real Estate Brokerage Services
N.A.I.C.S.: 551112
Jon Potvin (Mng Dir)

Subsidiary (Non-US):

Colliers International (Hong Kong) Ltd.　　　　　　　　　　　　　　(2)
Suite 5701 Central Plaza 18 Harbour Road, 18 Harbour Road, Wanchai, China (Hong Kong)
Tel.: (852) 28289888
Web Site: https://www.colliers.com
Sales Range: $50-74.9 Million
Emp.: 100
Commercial Real Estate Management & Brokerage Services
N.A.I.C.S.: 531210
Paul Baxter (COO-Asia)

Affiliate (Domestic):

Colliers International (Illinois)　　(2)
6250 N River Rd Ste 11-100, Rosemont, IL 60018
Tel.: (847) 698-8444

Commercial Real Estate Management & Brokerage Services
N.A.I.C.S.: 531210
Jim Carris (Exec Mng Dir)

Subsidiary (Non-US):

Colliers International (Singapore) Pte. Ltd.　　　　　　　　　　　　　(2)
1 Raffles Place 45-00 OUB Centre, Singapore, 048616, Singapore
Tel.: (65) 62232323
Sales Range: $75-99.9 Million
Emp.: 175
Commercial Real Estate Management & Brokerage Services
N.A.I.C.S.: 531210
Rimon Ambarchi (Exec Dir-Asia Indus Svcs)

Branch (Domestic):

Colliers International - Central California　　　　　　　　　　　　(2)
10000 Stockdale Hwy Ste 102, Bakersfield, CA 93311
Tel.: (661) 631-3800
Web Site: http://www.colliers.com
Sales Range: $25-49.9 Million
Emp.: 30
Real Estate Brokerage Services
N.A.I.C.S.: 531210
David A. Williams (Principal & Sr VP)

Colliers International - Columbus　(2)
8800 Lyra Dr Ste 650, Columbus, OH 43240
Tel.: (614) 436-9800
Web Site: http://www.colliers.com
Sales Range: $10-24.9 Million
Emp.: 45
Commercial Real Estate Brokerage Services
N.A.I.C.S.: 531210
Richard B. Schuen (CEO)

Colliers International - Hawaii　　(2)
Central Pacific Plz 220 S King St Ste 1800, Honolulu, HI 96813
Tel.: (808) 524-2666
Web Site: http://www.colliers.com
Sales Range: $25-49.9 Million
Emp.: 100
Property Management Services
N.A.I.C.S.: 531312
Sarah L. Morihara (Pres & Mng Dir)

Colliers International - New York　(2)
666 5th Ave, New York, NY 10103
Tel.: (212) 716-3500
Web Site: http://www.colliers.com
Rev.: $20,000,000
Emp.: 200
Real Estate Brokerage Services
N.A.I.C.S.: 531210
Michael T. Cohen (Pres-Tri-State Reg)

Colliers International - Philadelphia　　　　　　　　　　　　(2)
10 Penn Ctr 1801 Market St Ste 550, Philadelphia, PA 19103
Tel.: (215) 925-4600
Web Site: http://www.colliers.com
Real Estate Brokerage Services
N.A.I.C.S.: 531210
Rick Kingery (VP-Transaction Mgmt)

Affiliate (Domestic):

Colliers International - Richmond　(2)
2221 Edward Holland Dr Ste 600, Richmond, VA 23230
Tel.: (804) 320-5500
Real Estate Brokerage Services
N.A.I.C.S.: 531210
Michael G. Miller (Exec Mng Dir)

Branch (Domestic):

Colliers International - San Diego Region　　　　　　　　　　　　(2)
4350 La Jolla Village Dr Ste 500, San Diego, CA 92122
Tel.: (858) 455-1515
Web Site: http://www.colliers.com
Sales Range: $10-24.9 Million
Emp.: 75
Commercial Real Estate Management & Brokerage Services
N.A.I.C.S.: 531210
Jim Spain (Reg Mng Dir)

Colliers International - San Francisco **(2)**
101 2nd st 11th fl, San Francisco, CA 94105
Tel.: (415) 788-3100
Web Site: http://www.colliers.com
Sales Range: $50-74.9 Million
Emp.: 65
Commercial Real Estate Management & Brokerage Services
N.A.I.C.S.: 531210
Alan Collenette (Exec Mng Dir-Sacramento)

Subsidiary (Domestic):

Colliers International CT LLC **(2)**
1055 Washington Blvd, Stamford, CT 06901-2216
Tel.: (203) 324-0800
Sales Range: $1-9.9 Million
Emp.: 20
Real Estate Brokerage Services
N.A.I.C.S.: 531210
Robert C. Miller (Sr Mng Dir)

Subsidiary (Non-US):

Colliers International Holdings (Australia) Limited **(2)**
Level 30 Grosvenor Place 225 George Street, Sydney, 2000, NSW, Australia
Tel.: (61) 292570222
Web Site: https://www.colliers.com.au
Sales Range: $750-799.9 Million
Emp.: 1,400
Holding Company; Commercial Real Estate Management & Brokerage Services
N.A.I.C.S.: 551112

Subsidiary (Domestic):

Colliers International (NSW) Pty. Limited **(3)**
Level 30 Grosvenor Place 225 George Street, Sydney, 2000, NSW, Australia
Tel.: (61) 292570222
Sales Range: $150-199.9 Million
Emp.: 350
Commercial Real Estate Management & Brokerage Services
N.A.I.C.S.: 531210
John Kenny (CEO)

Colliers International (Victoria) Pty. Limited **(3)**
Level 30 Optus Centre 360 Elizabeth Street, 367 Collins St, Melbourne, 3000, VIC, Australia
Tel.: (61) 396298888
Emp.: 250
Commercial Real Estate Management & Brokerage Services
N.A.I.C.S.: 531210
John Marasco (CEO & Grp Mng Dir-Investment Sls)

Subsidiary (Non-US):

Colliers International Korea Ltd. **(2)**
9th FL Samhwa Tower Euljiro-5gil 16 Jung-gu, 10 Da-dong, Seoul, 100-180, Korea (South)
Tel.: (82) 267402000
Sales Range: $50-74.9 Million
Emp.: 15
Commercial Real Estate Management & Brokerage Services
N.A.I.C.S.: 531210
Sean Kim (Dir-Corp Svcs, Representation & Brokerage)

Subsidiary (Domestic):

Colliers International LI Inc. **(2)**
1981 Marcus Ave, Lake Success, NY 11042
Tel.: (516) 328-6500
Web Site: http://www.colliers.com
Sales Range: $1-9.9 Million
Emp.: 45
Real Estate Brokerage Services
N.A.I.C.S.: 531210
Herbert S. Agin (CEO)

Colliers International Management-Atlanta, LLC **(2)**
Promenade Ste 800 1230 Peachtree St NE, Atlanta, GA 30309
Tel.: (404) 888-9000
Web Site: http://www.colliers.com

Sales Range: $750-799.9 Million
Emp.: 150
Commercial Real Estate Brokerage & Property Management Services
N.A.I.C.S.: 531210
Scott Nelson (CEO-Occupier Svcs-Global)

Colliers International NJ LLC **(2)**
20 Waterview Blvd Ste 310, Parsippany, NJ 07054
Tel.: (973) 299-3000
Sales Range: $10-24.9 Million
Emp.: 30
Real Estate Brokerage Services
N.A.I.C.S.: 531210
Ward Greer (Sr Mng Dir)

Colliers International New England, LLC **(2)**
100 Federal St 13th Fl, Boston, MA 02110-1700
Tel.: (617) 330-8000
Emp.: 160
Commercial Real Estate Services
N.A.I.C.S.: 531210
Aaron Jodka (Natl Dir)

Affiliate (Domestic):

Colliers International Northeast Florida, Inc. **(2)**
76 S Laura St Ste 1500, Jacksonville, FL 32202
Tel.: (904) 358-1206
Emp.: 40
Commercial Real Estate Brokerage Services
N.A.I.C.S.: 531210
Christian Oldenburg (Mng Dir & Exec)

Subsidiary (Domestic):

Colliers International Real Estate Management Services (MI), Inc. **(2)**
2 Corporate Dr Ste 300, Southfield, MI 48076
Tel.: (248) 540-1000
Web Site: http://www.colliers.com
Sales Range: $50-74.9 Million
Emp.: 100
Real Estate Brokerage & Property Management
N.A.I.C.S.: 531210
Kyle Sischo (Mng Dir-West)

Colliers International Valuation & Advisory Services Inc. **(2)**
5796 Armada Dr Ste 210, Carlsbad, CA 92008
Tel.: (760) 444-8000
Web Site: http://www.pgpinc.com
Sales Range: $10-24.9 Million
Emp.: 25
Commercial & Industrial Real Estate Appraisals
N.A.I.C.S.: 531320

Subsidiary (Non-US):

Colliers Macaulay Nicolls Inc. **(2)**
200 Granville Street 19th Floor, Vancouver, V6C 2R6, BC, Canada
Tel.: (604) 681-4111
Web Site: http://www.colliers.com
Sales Range: $150-199.9 Million
Emp.: 400
Commercial Real Estate Broker
N.A.I.C.S.: 531210
Andrew Lord (Sr VP-Vancouver)

Subsidiary (Domestic):

CMN Calgary Inc. **(3)**
900 Royal Bank Building 335-8th Ave SW, Calgary, T2P 1C9, AB, Canada
Tel.: (403) 266-5544
Web Site: http://www.collierscanada.com
Sales Range: $50-74.9 Million
Emp.: 70
Commercial Real Estate Services
N.A.I.C.S.: 531210
Randy Fennessey (Exec VP)

Branch (Domestic):

Colliers International - Canada, Toronto Downtown Office **(3)**
1 Queen Street East Suite 2200, Toronto, M5C 2W5, ON, Canada
Tel.: (416) 777-2200

Sales Range: $75-99.9 Million
Emp.: 155
Commercial Real Estate Brokerage Services
N.A.I.C.S.: 531210
Brian Rosen (Pres)

Affiliate (Domestic):

Colliers Monroe Friedlander, Inc. **(2)**
1800 Central Pacific Plz 220 S King St, Honolulu, HI 96813
Tel.: (808) 524-2666
Web Site: http://www.colliers.com
Sales Range: $10-24.9 Million
Emp.: 100
Real Estate Brokerage & Property Management Services
N.A.I.C.S.: 531210

Colliers Paragon, LLC **(2)**
755 W Front St Ste 300, Boise, ID 83702
Tel.: (208) 345-9000
Web Site: http://www.colliers.com
Sales Range: $25-49.9 Million
Emp.: 50
Real Estate Brokerage Services
N.A.I.C.S.: 531210
George Iliff (Principal)

Subsidiary (Domestic):

Gehrki Commercial Real Estate, LLC **(2)**
835 Central Ave Ste 200, Hot Springs, AR 71901
Tel.: (501) 623-2200
Web Site: http://www.gehrki.com
Offices of Real Estate Agents & Brokers
N.A.I.C.S.: 531210
Brian Gehrki (Owner)

Manekin LLC **(2)**
5850 Waterloo Rd Ste 210, Columbia, MD 21045
Tel.: (410) 290-1400
Web Site: https://www.manekin.com
Sales Range: $75-99.9 Million
Emp.: 40
Real Estate Brokers & Agents
N.A.I.C.S.: 531210
Richard Alter (Pres & CEO)

Affiliate (Domestic):

Pacific Realty Commercial, LLC **(2)**
6464 Center St Ste 200, Omaha, NE 68106
Tel.: (402) 345-5866
Web Site: http://www.colliers.com
Sales Range: $10-24.9 Million
Emp.: 40
Commercial Real Estate Brokerage Services
N.A.I.C.S.: 531210
John D. Waldbaum (Vice Chm)

Subsidiary (Domestic):

Paracom LLC **(2)**
333 Bridge St NW Ste 1010, Grand Rapids, MI 49504
Tel.: (616) 774-3500
Sales Range: $10-24.9 Million
Emp.: 75
Real Estate Brokerage Services
N.A.I.C.S.: 531210
Steve Poole (VP)

Affiliate (Domestic):

Pittsburgh Commercial Real Estate, Inc. **(2)**
2 Gateway Ctr Ste 125 603 Stanwix St, Pittsburgh, PA 15222
Tel.: (412) 321-4200
Web Site: http://www.colliers.com
Sales Range: $25-49.9 Million
Emp.: 20
Commercial Real Estate Brokerage Services
N.A.I.C.S.: 531210
Gregg Broujos (Mng Dir & Principal)

West Shell Commercial, Inc. **(2)**
425 Walnut St Ste 1200, Cincinnati, OH 45202
Tel.: (513) 721-4200
Web Site: http://www.colliers.com
Sales Range: $10-24.9 Million
Emp.: 64

Commercial Real Estate Brokerage Services
N.A.I.C.S.: 531210
Shenan Murphy (CEO & Principal)

Subsidiary (Domestic):

Wilcoxon Construction, LLC **(2)**
15120A Southlawn Ln, Rockville, MD 20850
Tel.: (301) 340-6393
Web Site: http://www.wilcoxonconst.com
Emp.: 125
Swimming & Commercial Pool Contracting Services
N.A.I.C.S.: 238990
Jeff Tedder (Mgr-Repairs & Warranty)

Subsidiary (Domestic):

Paddock Swimming Pool Company **(3)**
15120-C Southlawn Ln, Rockville, MD 20850
Tel.: (301) 424-0790
Web Site: https://www.paddockpools.com
Swimming Pool Construction, Repair & Renovation Services
N.A.I.C.S.: 238990

Continental Real Estate Companies Commercial Properties Corp. **(1)**
2121 P De Leon Blvd 125, Coral Gables, FL 33134
Tel.: (305) 443-2121
Offices of Real Estate Agents & Brokers
N.A.I.C.S.: 531210

EnGlobe Corp. **(1)**
505 boul du Parc Technologique Bur 200, Quebec, G1P 4S9, QC, Canada
Tel.: (418) 781-0191
Web Site: https://www.englobecorp.com
Sales Range: $125-149.9 Million
Emp.: 346
Environmental Services & Waste Management
N.A.I.C.S.: 541620
Francois Santerre (VP-Ops-Soils & Materials Eng Quebec)

Subsidiary (Non-US):

Celtic Technologies Ltd. **(2)**
1210 Parkview Arlington Business Park, Theale, RG7 4TY, Reading, United Kingdom
Tel.: (44) 1189 167340
Web Site: http://www.celtic-ltd.com
Remediation Services
N.A.I.C.S.: 562910
Julia Roberts (Mng Dir-UK)

Subsidiary (Domestic):

GSI Environnement **(2)**
1501 Lionel-Boulet Blvd, Varennes, J3X 1P7, QC, Canada
Tel.: (450) 929-4949
Web Site: http://www.gsienv.ca
Sales Range: $25-49.9 Million
Emp.: 20
Environmental Management Services
N.A.I.C.S.: 541620

Tanknology Canada Inc. **(2)**
1800 Appleby Line Unit 4, Burlington, L7L 6A1, ON, Canada
Tel.: (905) 681-5542
Web Site: http://www.tanknology.ca
Sales Range: $25-49.9 Million
Emp.: 20
Construction of Building & Civil Engineering Work
N.A.I.C.S.: 237310

Harrison Street Real Estate Capital LLC **(1)**
444 W Lake St Ste 2100, Chicago, IL 60606 **(75%)**
Tel.: (312) 920-0500
Web Site: https://www.harrisonst.com
Real Estate Investment Firm
N.A.I.C.S.: 523999
Christopher Galvin (Co-Founder)

Subsidiary (Domestic):

Campus Crest Communities, Inc. **(2)**
2100 Rexford Rd Ste 414, Charlotte, NC 28211
Tel.: (704) 496-2500

Colliers International Group Inc.—(Continued)

Web Site: http://www.campuscrest.com
Sales Range: $100-124.9 Million
Emp.: 632
Real Estate Investment Services
N.A.I.C.S.: 531190

COLLINGWOOD RESOURCES CORP.
625 Howe Street Suite 420, Vancouver, V6C 2T6, BC, Canada
Tel.: (604) 697-0028
COLL.P—(TSXV)
Rev.: $12,709
Assets: $404,548
Liabilities: $31,862
Net Worth: $372,686
Earnings: ($47,678)
Fiscal Year-end: 03/31/24
Business Consulting Services
N.A.I.C.S.: 522299

COLLINS CO., LTD.
21F-8 No 95 Sec 1 Xintai 5th Rd,
Taipei, Taiwan
Tel.: (886) 227125311
Web Site: https://www.collins.com.tw
2906—(TAI)
Rev.: $261,652,268
Assets: $373,785,590
Liabilities: $160,844,266
Net Worth: $212,941,324
Earnings: $11,382,811
Emp.: 859
Fiscal Year-end: 12/31/23
Diversified Trading Services
N.A.I.C.S.: 561499
John Lee (Chm & Pres)

Subsidiaries:

Collins Fashion (Pvt) Ltd.   (1)
63 A Ward Place, Colombo, 00700, Sri
Lanka
Tel.: (94) 112686203
Garments Mfr
N.A.I.C.S.: 315120

Collins International Co., Ltd.   (1)
2100 Route 208, Fair Lawn, NJ 07410
Tel.: (201) 794-9200
Web Site:
    https://www.collinsinternational.com
Sales Range: $50-74.9 Million
Emp.: 7
Furniture Distr
N.A.I.C.S.: 423210

Colltex Garment Mfy Co. Ltd.   (1)
6th Floor Tung Hwa North Road, Taipei,
10508, Taiwan
Tel.: (886) 225460266
Sales Range: $25-49.9 Million
Emp.: 16
Knitwear & Sweaters Mfr
N.A.I.C.S.: 315120

Commend (H.K.) Ltd.   (1)
One Midtown 10th Floor Room 15 11 Hoi
Shing Rd, Tsuen Wan, China (Hong Kong)
Tel.: (852) 27459878
Emp.: 5
Casual Apparels Retailer
N.A.I.C.S.: 458110
Eric Wong (Mgr)

Quality Craft Ltd   (1)
Ste 301 17750 65 A Ave, Surrey, V3S 5N4,
BC, Canada
Tel.: (604) 575-5550
Web Site: http://www.qualitycraft.com
Emp.: 40
Home Hardware Products Distr
N.A.I.C.S.: 335220

COLLINS FOODS LIMITED
Level 3 KSD1 485 Kingsford Smith
Drive, Hamilton, 4007, QLD, Australia
Tel.: (61) 733520800
Web Site:
    https://www.collinsfoods.com
Year Founded: 1969

CKF—(ASX)
Rev.: $970,779,168
Assets: $924,708,880
Liabilities: $646,660,368
Net Worth: $278,048,512
Earnings: $36,276,325
Emp.: 20,000
Fiscal Year-end: 04/28/24
Fast Food Restaurant Operator
N.A.I.C.S.: 722513
Graham Maxwell (CEO & Mng Dir)

COLLINS INDUSTRIES, LTD.
3740-73 Avenue, Edmonton, T6B
2Z2, AB, Canada
Tel.: (780) 440-1414
Web Site: http://www.collins-industries-ltd.com
Year Founded: 1984
Rev.: $17,085,026
Emp.: 92
Steel Products Mfr
N.A.I.C.S.: 331221
Jason Collins (Pres)

COLLPLANT BIOTECHNOLO-GIES LTD.
4 Oppenheimer Street, PO Box 4132,
Rehovot, 7670104, Israel
Tel.: (972) 732325600
Web Site: https://www.collplant.com
Year Founded: 1981
CLGN—(NASDAQ)
Rev.: $10,959,000
Assets: $34,126,000
Liabilities: $5,786,000
Net Worth: $28,340,000
Earnings: ($7,019,000)
Emp.: 75
Fiscal Year-end: 12/31/23
Holding Company
N.A.I.C.S.: 551112
Roger James Pomerantz (Chm)

COLOMBO CITY HOLDINGS PLC
No 10 5th Floor Gothami Road, 08,
Colombo, Sri Lanka
Tel.: (94) 112691083
Year Founded: 1913
PHAR.N0000—(COL)
Rev.: $269,911
Assets: $7,111,277
Liabilities: $924,593
Net Worth: $6,186,685
Earnings: $263,402
Emp.: 4
Fiscal Year-end: 03/31/23
Pharmaceutical Product Retailer
N.A.I.C.S.: 456110
Weerasinghe A. G. (Chm)

COLOMBO DOCKYARD PLC
PO Box 906, Port of Colombo, 15,
Colombo, 15, Sri Lanka
Tel.: (94) 112429000   LK
Web Site: https://www.cdl.lk
Year Founded: 1974
DOCK.N0000—(COL)
Rev.: $90,848,264
Assets: $171,032,436
Liabilities: $143,992,224
Net Worth: $27,040,212
Earnings: $2,289,977
Emp.: 1,822
Fiscal Year-end: 12/31/22
Ship Building & Repairing Services
N.A.I.C.S.: 336611
Sarath De Costa (Vice Chm)

Subsidiaries:

Dockyard General Engineering Services (Pvt) Ltd.   (1)
223 Jayantha Mallimarachchi Mawatha, Colombo, 14, Sri Lanka
Tel.: (94) 11 252 7980
Web Site: https://www.dges.lk

Sales Range: $25-49.9 Million
Emp.: 54
Civil & Mechanical Engineering Services
N.A.I.C.S.: 237990
T. G. Weerasinghe (Gen Mgr)

Division (Domestic):

Dockyard General Engineering Services (Pvt) Ltd - Marine & Industrial
Hardware Division   (2)
2 Srimath Bandaranayaka Mawatha, Colombo, 12, Sri Lanka
Tel.: (94) 112424708
Marine & Industrial Hardware Mfr
N.A.I.C.S.: 332510

COLOMBO FORT INVEST-MENTS PLC
8-5/2 Leyden Bastian Road, 01, Colombo, 01, Sri Lanka
Tel.: (94) 112344485
Year Founded: 1983
CFI.N0000—(COL)
Rev.: $116,807
Assets: $5,962,198
Liabilities: $2,603
Net Worth: $5,959,595
Earnings: $277,224
Fiscal Year-end: 03/31/23
Bank & Financial Institution Services
N.A.I.C.S.: 522110
Rajaratnam A. (Chm)

COLOMBO LAND & DEVELOP-MENT CO.
3rd Floor Liberty Plaza 250 R A De
Mel Mawatha, 03, Colombo, 03, Sri
Lanka
Tel.: (94) 9425759357
Web Site: https://colomboland.com
Year Founded: 1981
CLND.N0000—(COL)
Rev.: $1,163,824
Assets: $42,679,897
Liabilities: $16,998,090
Net Worth: $25,681,807
Earnings: $991,002
Emp.: 35
Fiscal Year-end: 12/31/23
Real Estate Investment Management
Services
N.A.I.C.S.: 531390
Vasula Premawardhana (Co-CEO)

COLOMBO STOCK EX-CHANGE
04-01 West Block World Trade Center, Echelon Sq, Colombo, 1, Sri
Lanka
Tel.: (94) 0112446581
Web Site: http://www.cse.lk
Sales Range: $1-9.9 Million
Emp.: 100
Stock Exchange Services
N.A.I.C.S.: 523210
Surekha Sellahewa (CEO)

COLONIAL COAL INTERNA-TIONAL CORPORATION
Suite 200 595 Howe Street, Vancouver, V6C 2T5, BC, Canada
Tel.: (604) 568-4962   AB
Web Site: https://ccoal.ca
Year Founded: 2007
COX—(DEU)
Rev.: $148,531
Assets: $15,859,238
Liabilities: $90,578
Net Worth: $15,768,660
Earnings: ($4,075,353)
Fiscal Year-end: 07/31/24
Investment Services
N.A.I.C.S.: 523999
David Austin (Chm, Pres & CEO)

COLONIAL GARAGE AND DIS-TRIBUTORS LIMITED

59 Majors Path, Saint John's, A1A
4Z9, NL, Canada
Tel.: (709) 576-7278
Web Site:
    http://www.colonialautoparts.ca
Year Founded: 1926
Rev.: $14,393,160
Emp.: 110
Automotive Parts Supplier
N.A.I.C.S.: 441330
Douglas Squires (Pres)

COLONY FORD LINCOLN SALES
300 Queen Street E, Brampton, ON
L6V, ON, Canada
Tel.: (866) 980-4686
Web Site:
    http://www.colonyfordlincoln.com
New & Used Car Dealers
N.A.I.C.S.: 441110
Julie Ferreira (Mgr-Leasing)

COLONY TEXTILE MILLS LIM-ITED
Lower Ground Floor Ismail Aiwan-e-
Science Building 205 Ferozepur
Road, Lahore, 54600, Pakistan
Tel.: (92) 4235759231
Web Site:
    https://www.colonytextiles.com
Year Founded: 2005
CTM—(PSX)
Rev.: $75,983,509
Assets: $107,484,942
Liabilities: $67,958,481
Net Worth: $39,526,461
Earnings: $2,999,451
Emp.: 4,719
Fiscal Year-end: 06/30/23
Textile Products Mfr
N.A.I.C.S.: 313110
Fareed Mughis (CEO)

COLOPL INC.
Akasaka 9-7-2 Midtown East 6F,
Minato-ku, Tokyo, 107-0052, Japan
Tel.: (81) 367217770
Web Site: https://www.colopl.co.jp
Year Founded: 2008
3668—(TKS)
Rev.: $219,265,340
Assets: $579,217,550
Liabilities: $38,718,490
Net Worth: $540,499,060
Earnings: $13,421,370
Emp.: 1,277
Fiscal Year-end: 09/30/23
Game Applications
N.A.I.C.S.: 513210
Naruatsu Baba (Pres, CEO & COO)

COLOPLAST A/S
Holtedam 1-3, DK-3050, Humlebaek,
Denmark
Tel.: (45) 49111111   DK
Web Site: https://www.coloplast.com
Year Founded: 1954
COLOB—(CSE)
Rev.: $3,545,021,777
Assets: $6,968,355,255
Liabilities: $4,465,280,491
Net Worth: $2,503,074,764
Earnings: $692,075,068
Emp.: 15,913
Fiscal Year-end: 09/30/23
Healtcare Services
N.A.I.C.S.: 621399
Nicolai Buhl Andersen (Exec VP-Innovation)

Subsidiaries:

AMOENA GmbH & Co. KG   (1)
Kapellenweg 36, 83064, Raubling,
Germany   (85%)
Tel.: (49) 80358710
Web Site: https://www.amoena.com

Sales Range: $25-49.9 Million
Emp.: 120
N.A.I.C.S.: 621410
Ronny Lemmens *(Gen Mgr)*

Atos Medical ApS (1)
Holtedam 1-3, 3050, Humlebaek, Denmark
Tel.: (45) 70140435
Web Site: https://www.atosmedical.dk
Emp.: 1,200
Medical Device Mfr & Distr
N.A.I.C.S.: 339113

Atos Medical Austria GmbH (1)
Carl-Benz-Strasse 18, 3300, Amstetten, Austria
Tel.: (43) 747266595
Web Site: https://www.atosmedical.at
Medical Device Mfr & Distr
N.A.I.C.S.: 339113

Atos Medical B.V. (1)
Werner von Siemensstraat 11, 2712 PN, Zoetermeer, Netherlands
Tel.: (31) 795935000
Web Site: https://www.atosmedical.nl
Emp.: 1,200
Medical Device Mfr & Distr
N.A.I.C.S.: 339113

Atos Medical B.V.B.A. (1)
266 Rue Royale, BE-1210, Brussels, Belgium
Tel.: (32) 22185550
Medical Device Mfr & Distr
N.A.I.C.S.: 339113

Atos Medical Brasil Ltda. (1)
Rua Luis Correia de Melo 92, Vila Cruzeiro, Sao Paulo, 04726-220, Brazil
Tel.: (55) 1123052022
Web Site: https://www.atosmedical.com.br
Laryngectomy Care Device Mfr & Distr
N.A.I.C.S.: 334510

Atos Medical Canada Inc. (1)
20 Simona Drive Unit 5, Bolton, L7E 4K1, ON, Canada
Medical Device Mfr & Distr
N.A.I.C.S.: 339113

Atos Medical GmbH (1)
Mulheimer Strasse 3-7, 53840, Troisdorf, Germany
Tel.: (49) 8005353667
Web Site: https://www.atosmedical.de
Medical Device Mfr & Distr
N.A.I.C.S.: 339113

Atos Medical Inc. (1)
2801 S Moorland Rd, New Berlin, WI 53151-3743
Web Site: https://www.atosmedical.us
Emp.: 1,200
Medical Device Mfr & Distr
N.A.I.C.S.: 339113

Atos Medical Japan Inc. (1)
2F Shinkawa Sanko Building 1-3-17 Shinkawa, Chuo-ku, Tokyo, 104-0033, Japan
Tel.: (81) 345892830
Web Site: https://www.atosmedical.jp
Medical Equipment Mfr & Distr
N.A.I.C.S.: 334510

Atos Medical Ltd. (1)
12 Victoria Street, Lower Hutt, 5010, New Zealand
Tel.: (64) 45762100
Web Site: https://www.atosmedical.co.nz
Laryngectomy Care Device Mfr & Distr
N.A.I.C.S.: 334510

Atos Medical Poland Sp. z o.o. (1)
Al Jerozolimskie 162, 02-342, Warsaw, Poland
Tel.: (48) 222950016
Web Site: https://www.atosmedical.pl
Laryngectomy Care Device Mfr & Distr
N.A.I.C.S.: 334510

Atos Medical Pty. Ltd. (1)
31 / 6 - 8 Herbert Street, Saint Leonards, 2065, NSW, Australia
Tel.: (61) 1800286728
Web Site: https://www.atosmedical.com.au
Medical Device Mfr & Distr
N.A.I.C.S.: 339113

Atos Medical S.A.S. (1)

82 Rue des Meuniers, CS10015, Green Square Bat B, 92220, Bagneux, France
Tel.: (33) 149080100
Medical Equipment Mfr & Whslr
N.A.I.C.S.: 339112

Atos Medical S.L. (1)
Calle Consejo de Ciento 333 2a Planta, 08007, Barcelona, Spain
Tel.: (34) 900103014
Web Site: https://www.atosmedical.es
Laryngectomy Care Device Mfr & Distr
N.A.I.C.S.: 334510

Atos Medical S.R.L. (1)
Via San Crispino 46, 35129, Padova, Italy
Tel.: (39) 0498071429
Web Site: https://www.atosmedical.it
Emp.: 1,200
Medical Device Mfr & Distr
N.A.I.C.S.: 339113

Atos Medical UK Ltd. (1)
Cartwright House Tottle Road Riverside Business Park, Nottingham, NG2 1RT, United Kingdom
Tel.: (44) 1157841899
Web Site: https://www.atosmedical.co.uk
Laryngectomy Care Device Mfr & Distr
N.A.I.C.S.: 334510

Coloplast (1)
(100%)
Tel.: (45) 49111111
Web Site: http://www.coloplast.com
Sales Range: $150-199.9 Million
Emp.: 900
N.A.I.C.S.: 541720
Lars Arsmussen *(Mng Dir)*

Coloplast (China) Co. Ltd. (1)
No 202 Baocheng Road, Xiang Zhou District, Zhuhai, 519030, Guangdong, China   **(70%)**
Tel.: (86) 7568925800
Web Site: http://www.coloplast.cn
Sales Range: $25-49.9 Million
Emp.: 100
N.A.I.C.S.: 621410

Coloplast (China) Medical Devices Ltd. (1)
Room 1001-1007 Building 22 5A Shuguang Xili, Chaoyang District, Beijing, 100028, China
Tel.: (86) 1059201888
Health Care Product Mfr & Distr
N.A.I.C.S.: 339112

Coloplast (Hong Kong) Ltd. (1)
788 Cheung Sha Wan Road Lai Chi Kok Room 2606-07 26th Floor, Luo Shi Commercial Plaza, Kowloon, China (Hong Kong)
Tel.: (852) 36287488
Surgical Instrument Mfr
N.A.I.C.S.: 339112

Coloplast (India) Private Limited (1)
Unit No 0-108 Plot No 4 Salcon Aurum, District Centre Jasola, New Delhi, 110025, India
Tel.: (91) 1140800400
Sales Range: $25-49.9 Million
Emp.: 45
Surgical Instrument Mfr
N.A.I.C.S.: 339112

Coloplast AB (1)
Kungsparksvagen 2, 43439, Kungsbacka, Sweden   **(100%)**
Tel.: (46) 30033256
Web Site: https://www.coloplast.se
Sales Range: $10-24.9 Million
Emp.: 30
N.A.I.C.S.: 621410

Coloplast AG (1)
Euro Business Center Blegistrasse 1, 6343, Rotkreuz, Switzerland   **(100%)**
Tel.: (41) 7997979
Sales Range: $10-24.9 Million
Emp.: 12
N.A.I.C.S.: 621410

Coloplast B.V. (1)
(100%)
Tel.: (31) 334544444
Web Site: https://www.coloplast.nl
Sales Range: $10-24.9 Million
Emp.: 70
Healthcare Products & Services

N.A.I.C.S.: 621999

Coloplast Beteiligungs GmbH (1)
Kuehnstrasse 75, 22045, Hamburg, 22045, Germany   **(100%)**
Tel.: (49) 406698070
Web Site: http://www.coloplast.de
Sales Range: $25-49.9 Million
Emp.: 200
N.A.I.C.S.: 621410
Michael Zwiek *(Pres)*

Coloplast Business Centre Sp. z o.o. (1)
Piastow Office Center Budynek B Al Piastow 30, 71-064, Szczecin, Poland
Tel.: (48) 918817500
Web Site: https://www.cpbc.pl
Emp.: 10,000
Information Technology Services
N.A.I.C.S.: 541512

Coloplast Canada Corporation (1)
2401 Bristol Circle Suite 205A, Oakville, L6H 5S9, ON, Canada   **(100%)**
Tel.: (905) 820-7588
Web Site: https://www.coloplast.ca
Sales Range: $10-24.9 Million
Emp.: 50
N.A.I.C.S.: 621410

Coloplast Corp. (1)
1601 W River Rd N, Minneapolis, MN 55411
Tel.: (612) 337-7800
Web Site: https://www.coloplast.us
Developer & Mfr of Healthcare Products & Services
N.A.I.C.S.: 339112

Coloplast Croatia (1)
Utinjska 40, 10020, Zagreb, Croatia
Tel.: (385) 14550101
Web Site: https://www.coloplast.hr
Sales Range: $25-49.9 Million
Emp.: 11
Surgical Instrument Mfr
N.A.I.C.S.: 339112

Coloplast Czech Republic (1)
Radlicka 740/113 B, 158 00, Prague, Czech Republic
Tel.: (420) 244470212
Sales Range: $25-49.9 Million
Emp.: 14
Surgical Instrument Mfr
N.A.I.C.S.: 339112

Coloplast Distribution Center (1)
475 Riverside Pkwy, Lithia Springs, GA 30122
Tel.: (770) 281-8400
Medical Instrument Distr
N.A.I.C.S.: 423450

Coloplast GmbH (1)
Thomas-Klestil -10th place, Schwechat, 1030, Vienna, Austria   **(100%)**
Tel.: (43) 170757510
Sales Range: $10-24.9 Million
Emp.: 20
N.A.I.C.S.: 621410

Coloplast GmbH (1)
At Neumarkt 42, 22041, Hamburg, Germany   **(100%)**
Tel.: (49) 4066980777
Web Site: https://www.coloplast.de
Emp.: 550
N.A.I.C.S.: 621410

Coloplast Greece (1)
Gionas 1A, Attiki, 14451, Metamorfosis, Greece
Tel.: (30) 2102020232
Medical Instrument Mfr
N.A.I.C.S.: 339112

Coloplast Hungary Kft. (1)
(100%)
Tel.: (36) 34520500
Web Site: https://www.coloplast.hu
Sales Range: $125-149.9 Million
Emp.: 900
N.A.I.C.S.: 621410

Coloplast Ii Portugal, Unipessoal Lda. (1)
Rua Tierno Galvan 10 Torre 3 - Piso 13 Torres das Amoreiras, 1070-274, Lisbon, Portugal

Tel.: (351) 214985400
Web Site: https://www.coloplast.pt
Medical Device Mfr & Distr
N.A.I.C.S.: 339113

Coloplast Israel (1)
5 Malakah St Beit Haogan, Foleg Business Park, Netanya, 4250540, Israel
Tel.: (972) 97667030
Emp.: 15
Medical Equipment Distr
N.A.I.C.S.: 423450

Coloplast K.K. (1)
Italian Cultural Institute Building 11F 2-1-30 Kudanminami, Chiyoda Ku, Tokyo, 102-0074, Japan
Tel.: (81) 120664469
Web Site: https://www.coloplast.co.jp
Sales Range: $25-49.9 Million
Emp.: 90
N.A.I.C.S.: 621410

Coloplast Korea Limited (1)
9th floor Changgang Building 86 Mapodaero 22 Dohwa-dong, Mapo-gu, Seoul, 04168, Korea (South)
Tel.: (82) 15887866
Web Site: https://www.coloplast.co.kr
Medical Instrument Mfr
N.A.I.C.S.: 339112

Coloplast Manufacturing Us, LLC (1)
1940 Commerce Dr, North Mankato, MN 56002
Medical Device Mfr & Distr
N.A.I.C.S.: 339113

Coloplast N.V. (1)
Guido Gezellestraat 121, Beersel, 1654, Huizingen, Belgium   **(100%)**
Tel.: (32) 2 334 3535
Web Site: https://www.coloplast.be
Sales Range: $10-24.9 Million
Emp.: 35
N.A.I.C.S.: 621410

Coloplast Norge AS (1)
Ryenstubben 10, 0679, Oslo, Norway   **(100%)**
Tel.: (47) 22575000
Web Site: https://www.coloplast.no
Sales Range: $25-49.9 Million
Emp.: 30
N.A.I.C.S.: 621410

Coloplast OOO (1)
Leningradsky prospect 72 building 2, 125315, Moscow, Russia
Tel.: (7) 4959375390
Web Site: http://www.coloplast.ru
Sales Range: $25-49.9 Million
Emp.: 2
Surgical Appliance Mfr
N.A.I.C.S.: 339113

Coloplast OY (1)
Ayritie 12 B, 01510, Vantaa, Finland
Tel.: (358) 98946750
Sales Range: $25-49.9 Million
Emp.: 16
Medical Device Mfr
N.A.I.C.S.: 339112

Coloplast Portugal Lda. (1)
Praca Nuno Rodrigues dos Santos 7 rooms 19/20, 1600-171, Lisbon, Portugal
Tel.: (351) 214985400
Web Site: https://www.coloplast.pt
Sales Range: $25-49.9 Million
Emp.: 6
Medical Device Mfr
N.A.I.C.S.: 339112

Coloplast Productos Medicos S.A. (1)
(100%)
Tel.: (34) 900210494
Web Site: https://www.coloplast.es
Sales Range: $10-24.9 Million
Emp.: 40
N.A.I.C.S.: 621410

Coloplast Pty. Ltd. (1)
Level 4 1 Acacia Place, Ferntree Business Park, Notting Hill, 3168, VIC, Australia   **(100%)**
Tel.: (61) 395411111
Web Site: https://www.coloplast.com.au
Sales Range: $10-24.9 Million
Emp.: 40
N.A.I.C.S.: 621410

Coloplast A/S—(Continued)

Coloplast S.p.A. (1)
Via dei Trattati Comunitari Europei 1957-
2007 9 / F, 40127, Bologna, Italy **(100%)**
Tel.: (39) 0514138000
Web Site: https://www.coloplast.it
Sales Range: $25-49.9 Million
Emp.: 120
N.A.I.C.S.: 621410

Coloplast Shared Services Sp.
z.o.o (1)
Ul Piast 30, Szczecin, 71064, West Po-
meranian, Poland
Tel.: (48) 91 881 75 00
Financial Investment Services
N.A.I.C.S.: 523999

Coloplast Slovakia (1)
Obchodne Zastupitelstvo Dolna 62, Banska
Bystrica, 97401, Slovakia
Tel.: (421) 484153761
Surgical Instrument Mfr
N.A.I.C.S.: 339112

Coloplast Slovenia (1)
Zelezna Cesta 16, 1000, Ljubljana, Slove-
nia
Tel.: (386) 12807530
Web Site: https://www.coloplast.si
Emp.: 3
Medical Device Mfr
N.A.I.C.S.: 339112
Albert Karner (Gen Mgr)

Coloplast Sp.z.o.o. (1)
Ul Inflancka 4, 00189, Warsaw,
Poland **(100%)**
Tel.: (48) 45 911 1111
Web Site: https://www.coloplast.pl
Sales Range: $10-24.9 Million
Emp.: 34
N.A.I.C.S.: 621410

Coloplast Spain (1)
Condesa del Venadito 5 4 Planta, 28027,
Madrid, Spain
Tel.: (34) 913141802
Web Site: http://www.coloplast.es
Sales Range: $50-74.9 Million
Emp.: 120
Medical Device Mfr
N.A.I.C.S.: 339112

Coloplast Taiwan Co., Ltd. (1)
Room 604 6th Floor No 129 Section 3 Min-
sheng East Road, Songshan District Univer-
sal Commercial Building, Taipei, Taiwan
Tel.: (886) 227212727
Web Site: https://www.coloplast.tw
Wound & Skin Care Services
N.A.I.C.S.: 621999

Coloplast Turkiye Medikal Gerecler
San. Ve Tic. A.S. (1)
Bayar Caddesi Gulbahar Sokak Perdemsac
Plaza 2 No 19, Kozyatagi, Istanbul, Turkiye
Tel.: (90) 2166658000
Web Site: https://www.coloplast.com.tr
Wound & Skin Care Services
N.A.I.C.S.: 621999

Coloplast UK Ltd. (1)
Nene Hall Peterborough Business Park,
Orton, Peterborough, PE2 6FX, Cambs,
United Kingdom **(100%)**
Tel.: (44) 1733392000
Web Site: https://www.coloplast.co.uk
Sales Range: $25-49.9 Million
Emp.: 180
N.A.I.C.S.: 621410

Coloplast Ukraine A/S (1)
Gertzena Str 17-25 Office 20, 04050, Kiev,
4050, Ukraine
Tel.: (380) 445072512
Sales Range: $25-49.9 Million
Emp.: 1
Medical Equipment Mfr
N.A.I.C.S.: 334510
Nataly Plyska (Gen Mgr)

Coloplast de Argentina S.A. (1)
S A Bouchard 547 Piso 8, Buenos Aires,
C1106ABG, Argentina **(100%)**
Tel.: (54) 1139855900
Web Site: https://www.coloplast.com.ar
Sales Range: $10-24.9 Million
Emp.: 40
N.A.I.C.S.: 621410

Sandigo Caratini (Pres)

Coloplast de Costa Rica S.A. (1)
Zona Franca Metropolitana Barreakde
Heredia, 1023006, Heredia, Costa
Rica **(100%)**
Tel.: (506) 2933034
Sales Range: $1-9.9 Million
Emp.: 240
N.A.I.C.S.: 621410

Coloplast do Brasil Ltda. (1)
Avenida Nove de Julho 5229 - Jardim Pau-
lista, Sao Paulo, 01407-907, Brazil **(100%)**
Tel.: (55) 8002858687
Web Site: https://www.coloplast.com.br
Sales Range: $25-49.9 Million
Emp.: 6
N.A.I.C.S.: 621410

Comfort Medical, LLC (1)
4240 NW 120th Ave, Coral Springs, FL
33065
Web Site: https://www.comfortmedical.com
Medical Product Distr
N.A.I.C.S.: 423450

Laboratoires Coloplast (1)
Les Jardins du Golf 6 rue de Rome, 93561,
Rosny-sous-Bois, France
Tel.: (33) 15 663 1700
Web Site: https://www.coloplast.fr
Developer of Custom Medical Care Prod-
ucts & Services
N.A.I.C.S.: 621511

Lilial S.A.S. (1)
1 Rue Francis Inizan, CS 70054, 49800,
Trelaze, Cedex, France
Tel.: (33) 805040062
Web Site: https://www.lilial.fr
Medical Equipment Distr
N.A.I.C.S.: 423450

Rocky Mountain Medical, LLC (1)
616 Arrawanna St, Colorado Springs, CO
80909
Tel.: (719) 337-6132
Web Site:
    https://www.rockymountainmedical.org
Medical Marijuana Distr
N.A.I.C.S.: 424990

COLORADO PEINTURES

Road Mly Thami Km 15 Rural Com-
mune Oulad Azouz Dar Bouaaza,
Casablanca, Nouacer, Morocco
Tel.: (212) 522352335
Web Site: https://www.colorado.ma
Year Founded: 1957
COL—(CAS)
Sales Range: Less than $1 Million
Paint Retailer
N.A.I.C.S.: 444120
Berrada Soleiman (Chm)

COLORAY INTERNATIONAL
INVESTMENT CO., LTD.

Suite 3201 Jardine house 1 Con-
naught Place, Central, China (Hong
Kong)
Tel.: (852) 220888526
Web Site: https://www.coloray.co.kr
Year Founded: 2013
900310—(KRS)
Rev.: $292,514
Assets: $1,237,233
Liabilities: $114,349
Net Worth: $1,122,884
Earnings: $125,710
Emp.: 111
Fiscal Year-end: 12/31/21
Cosmetic Product Mfr & Distr
N.A.I.C.S.: 325620

COLORCHIPS NEWS MEDIA
LTD.

House No 8-3-833/85 & 85A Plot No
85 Phase 1 Kamalapuri Colony,
Hyderabad, 500073, Telangana, India
Tel.: (91) 4031923239
Web Site:
    https://www.colorchipsindia.com
Year Founded: 1985

540023—(BOM)
Rev.: $767,463
Assets: $4,324,424
Liabilities: $172,694
Net Worth: $4,151,730
Earnings: $48,982
Emp.: 14
Fiscal Year-end: 03/31/22
Animated Cartoon Production Ser-
vices
N.A.I.C.S.: 512110
Ramabhotla Srinivasa Sudhish (Chm
& Mng Dir)

COLORLAND ANIMATION LTD.

1802 Shatin Galleria Shan Meid St
18224 Fotan Shat, Hong Kong, China
(Hong Kong)
Tel.: (852) 23669013
Web Site: http://www.colorland-
animation.com
Year Founded: 1991
Sales Range: $25-49.9 Million
Emp.: 194
Motion Picture & Video Animation
Services
N.A.I.C.S.: 512199
Louis Sek (CEO)

COLORLIGHT CLOUD TECH
LTD.

37F-39F Building 8 Area A Shenzhen
International Innovation Valley, Nan-
shan District, Shenzhen, 518055,
China
Tel.: (86) 4008770775
Web Site:
    https://en.colorlightinside.com
Year Founded: 2012
301391—(CHIN)
Rev.: $141,221,381
Assets: $396,664,336
Liabilities: $86,412,314
Net Worth: $310,252,021
Earnings: $28,064,535
Emp.: 1,000
Fiscal Year-end: 12/31/23
LCD Products Mfr
N.A.I.C.S.: 334413

Subsidiaries:

Colorlight Cloud B.V. (1)
Kanaaldijk-Noord 109D, 5642 JA, Eind-
hoven, Netherlands
Tel.: (31) 408517523
LED System Services
N.A.I.C.S.: 339930

Colorlight US, Inc. (1)
3406 W Burbank Blvd, Burbank, CA 91505
Tel.: (949) 536-5586
Light Emitting Diode Control System Ser-
vices
N.A.I.C.S.: 926150

COLORPAK INDONESIA TBK

No 7 Pasir Jaya Jatiuwung, JI Industri
II Blok F, Tangerang, 15135, Banten,
Indonesia
Tel.: (62) 215901962
Web Site: https://www.colorpak.co.id
Year Founded: 1988
CLPI—(INDO)
Rev.: $52,361,567
Assets: $50,426,057
Liabilities: $14,337,147
Net Worth: $36,088,910
Earnings: $3,422,881
Emp.: 108
Fiscal Year-end: 12/31/23
Printing Ink Mfr
N.A.I.C.S.: 325910
Santoso Jiemy (Chm)

COLORSTARS GROUP

10F No 566 Jung Jeng Road, Sindian
District, New Taipei City, 231, Taiwan
Tel.: (886) 2 8667 6600   NV

Web Site: http://www.colorstars.com
Year Founded: 2005
Rev.: $3,291
Assets: $63,615
Liabilities: $295,508
Net Worth: ($231,893)
Earnings: ($334,986)
Emp.: 2
Fiocal Year ond: 12/31/18
LED Lighting Products Developer &
Mfr
N.A.I.C.S.: 335139

COLOUR LIFE SERVICES
GROUP CO., LTD.

12th Floor Colour Life Building Mei-
long Road Liuxian Avenue, Bao an
District, Shenzhen, China
Tel.: (86) 75523041818
Web Site: http://www.colourlife.hk
1778—(HKG)
Rev.: $551,012,105
Assets: $1,577,517,113
Liabilities: $879,734,118
Net Worth: $697,782,995
Earnings: $83,048,247
Emp.: 14,459
Fiscal Year-end: 12/31/20
Real Estate Manangement Services
N.A.I.C.S.: 531311
Jun Pan (Chm)

Subsidiaries:

Steadlink Asset Management Pte
Ltd. (1)
1557 Keppel Rd 02-26 Inchape Marketing
Bldg, Singapore, 89066, Singapore
Tel.: (65) 68849113
Web Site: http://www.steadlink.com
Residential Property Management Services
N.A.I.C.S.: 531311
Michael Tan (Mng Dir)

COLOURED TIES CAPITAL
INC.

Suite 915 - 700 West Pender Street,
Vancouver, V6C 1G8, BC, Canada
Tel.: (604) 805-4602
Web Site:
    https://www.colouredtiescapital.com
TIE—(TSXV)
Rev.: $723,609
Assets: $16,893,337
Liabilities: $291,790
Net Worth: $16,601,546
Earnings: ($408,350)
Emp.: 6
Fiscal Year-end: 09/30/22
Oil & Gas Exploration Services
N.A.I.C.S.: 213112
Kulwant Malhi (CEO & CFO-Acting)

Subsidiaries:

Americas Potash Peru S.A. (1)
Av Carlos Villaran N 860, La Victoria, Lima,
Peru
Tel.: (51) 73322742
Potash Mining Services
N.A.I.C.S.: 212390

GrowMax Agri Corp. (1)
3911 Trasimene Cres SW, Calgary, T3E
7J6, AB, Canada
Tel.: (403) 685-1888
Web Site: http://www.growmaxagricorp.com
Sales Range: $50-74.9 Million
Emp.: 1
Potash Fertilizer Mfr
N.A.I.C.S.: 212390
Barclay W. Hambrook (Co-Chm & CEO)

COLOWIDE CO., LTD.

Landmark Tower 12F 2-2-1 Minatomi-
rai, Nishi-ku, Yokohama, 220-8112,
Kanagawa, Japan
Tel.: (81) 452745970
Web Site: http://www.colowide.co.jp
Year Founded: 1963
Sales Range: $450-499.9 Million

Emp.: 2,709
Restaurant Services
N.A.I.C.S.: 722511

Subsidiaries:

COLOWIDE MD Co., Ltd. **(1)**
Landmark Tower 13F 2-2-1 Minatomirai,
Nishi-ku, Yokohama, 220-8112, Kanagawa-
ken, Japan
Tel.: (81) 274 5970
Web Site: http://www.colowide.co.jp
Restaurant Management Services
N.A.I.C.S.: 722511
Yutaka Yomoda (CEO)

Subsidiary (Non-US):

COLOWIDE ASIA CO., LTD. **(2)**
Shop A 17F Lee Theater Plaza 99 Percival
Street, Causeway Bay, Hong Kong, China
(Hong Kong)
Tel.: (852) 23695398
Restaurant Management Services
N.A.I.C.S.: 722511

COLOWIDE VIETNAM., JSC. **(2)**
35 Quang Trung g Phuong Tran Hung Dao,
Quan Hoan Kiem Thanh Pho, Hanoi, Viet-
nam
Tel.: (84) 2745984
Restaurant Management Services
N.A.I.C.S.: 722511

REINS INTERNATIONAL (SINGA-
PORE) PTE. LTD. **(1)**
11 Tanjong Katong Road One KM 01-16,
Singapore, 437157, Singapore
Tel.: (65) 63624001
Web Site: http://www.gyu-kaku.com.sg
Restaurant Management Services
N.A.I.C.S.: 722511

COLRUYT GROUP N.V.
Edingensesteenweg 196, 1500, Halle,
Belgium
Tel.: (32) 23635545
Web Site:
https://www.colruytgroup.com
COLR—(EUR)
Rev.: $12,197,282,968
Assets: $6,381,075,272
Liabilities: $3,277,067,144
Net Worth: $3,104,008,128
Earnings: $510,947,840
Emp.: 31,189
Fiscal Year-end: 03/31/21
Frozen Food Product Distr
N.A.I.C.S.: 424420
Stefan Goethaert (CEO)

Subsidiaries:

Alvocol N.V. **(1)**
Wilgenveld 196, Halle, 1500, Vlaams Bra-
bant, Belgium
Tel.: (32) 23601040
Logistics Consulting Servies
N.A.I.C.S.: 541614

BODEGAS BVBA **(1)**
Rijksweg 10 A, 2880, Bornem, Belgium
Tel.: (32) 3 899 38 55
Web Site: http://www.bodegas.be
Beverages Mfr
N.A.I.C.S.: 312130
Marc de Parade (Gen Mgr)

Banden Deproost BV **(1)**
Zinkstraat 6, 1500, Halle, Belgium
Tel.: (32) 23603434
Tire Distr
N.A.I.C.S.: 441340

Bio-Planet N.V. **(1)**
V Desmesmaekerstraat 167, 1500, Halle,
Belgium
Tel.: (32) 23635010
Web Site: https://www.bioplanet.be
Sales Range: $50-74.9 Million
Emp.: 163
Supermarket Operator
N.A.I.C.S.: 445110

Buurtwinkels OKay NV **(1)**
Victor Demesmaekerstraat 167, 1500,
Halle, Belgium
Tel.: (32) 23616774

Grocery Product Distr
N.A.I.C.S.: 445110

Codi-France S.A.S. **(1)**
4 Rue des Entrepots, 39700, Rochefort-sur-
Nenon, France
Tel.: (33) 384707400
Web Site: https://www.codifrance.fr
Supermarket Operator
N.A.I.C.S.: 445110

Colruyt IT Consultancy India Private
Limited **(1)**
Building No 21 Mind Space Raheja IT Park,
Hitec City Madhapur, Hyderabad, 500081,
Telangana, India
Tel.: (91) 4030438000
Emp.: 450
Information Technology Services
N.A.I.C.S.: 541519

Colruyt Luxembourg S.A. **(1)**
Boulevard FW Raiffeisen 5, 2411, Luxem-
bourg, Luxembourg
Tel.: (352) 26 32 27 29
Web Site: http://www.colruyt.lu
Supermarket Operator
N.A.I.C.S.: 445110

Colruyt Retail France SAS **(1)**
4 rue des entrepots, 39700, Rochefort-sur-
Nenon, France
Tel.: (33) 384707400
Grocery Product Distr
N.A.I.C.S.: 424490

DATS24 N.V. **(1)**
Edingensesteenweg 196, 1500, Halle, Bel-
gium
Tel.: (32) 23635152
Web Site: https://customer.dats24.be
Petroleum Bulk Station Operator
N.A.I.C.S.: 424710

Daltix NV **(1)**
Ottergemsesteenweg-Zuid 808 B160, 9000,
Gent, Belgium
Tel.: (32) 32461233
Information Technology Services
N.A.I.C.S.: 541519
Jonas Deprez (CEO)

Daltix Unipessoal Lda. **(1)**
Av Antonio Augusto Aguiar 130, 1050-020,
Lisbon, Portugal
Tel.: (351) 215842747
N.A.I.C.S.: 449210

Dimaco UK Limited **(1)**
Unit D Firs Farm West End, Stagsden,
Kempston, MK43 8TW, Bedford, United
Kingdom
Tel.: (44) 1234851515
Web Site: https://www.dimaco.co.uk
Emp.: 9
Food Inspection Services
N.A.I.C.S.: 561499

DreamBaby N.V. **(1)**
Edingensesteenweg 75, 1500, Halle, Bel-
gium
Tel.: (32) 2 361 39 15
Web Site: http://www.dreambaby.be
Baby Products Retailer
N.A.I.C.S.: 459120

DreamLand N.V. **(1)**
Bergensesteenweg 83, 1500, Halle, Bel-
gium
Tel.: (32) 23800285
Web Site: http://www.dreamland.be
Supermarket Operator
N.A.I.C.S.: 445110

E-Logistics N.V. **(1)**
Leuvensesteenweg 375, 1930, Zaventem,
Belgium
Tel.: (32) 2 720 85 27
Logistics Management Services
N.A.I.C.S.: 541614

Foodinvest N.V. **(1)**
Rijksweg 6, 2880, Bornem, Belgium
Tel.: (32) 3 633 23 30
Web Site: http://www.foodinvest.com
Food Product Retailer
N.A.I.C.S.: 445110

Foodlines B.V.B.A. **(1)**
Rijksweg 6, Bornem, 2880, Belgium
Tel.: (32) 3 637 53 57

Supermarket Operator & Catering Services
N.A.I.C.S.: 445110

Immoco S.A.S. **(1)**
1 Faubourg de Belfort, 68700, Cernay,
France
Tel.: (33) 8 99 18 06 82
Supermarket Operator
N.A.I.C.S.: 445110

Pro a Pro Distribution **(1)**
Impasse de Grece ZI Albasud, 82006, Mon-
tauban, France
Tel.: (33) 563213200
Web Site: https://www.proapro.fr
Emp.: 1,825
Food Products Distr
N.A.I.C.S.: 424490
Corinne Lourties (Mgr-Quality)

Subsidiary (Domestic):

Codifrais S.A.S. **(2)**
ZAC Paris Oise, Longueil-Sainte-Marie,
60126, France
Tel.: (33) 3 44 38 60 00
Web Site: http://www.codifrais.com
Dairy Product Whslr
N.A.I.C.S.: 424430

Puur NV **(1)**
Lummense Pebble 51, 3500, Hasselt, Bel-
gium
Tel.: (32) 11283333
Web Site: https://puuroffice.be
Furniture & Home Furnishing Mfr
N.A.I.C.S.: 337121

Retail Partners Colruyt Group
NV **(1)**
De Regenboog 8, 2800, Mechelen, Belgium
Tel.: (32) 25831111
Web Site:
https://www.retailpartnerscolruytgroup.be
N.A.I.C.S.: 423620

S.A.S Colruyt Distribution France **(1)**
4 Rue des Entrepots, 39700, Rochefort-sur-
Nenon, France
Tel.: (33) 3 84 70 74 00
Web Site: http://www.colruyt.fr
Sales Range: $400-449.9 Million
Emp.: 2,000
Supermarket Operator
N.A.I.C.S.: 445110

SPAR retail NV **(1)**
Industrielaan 23, Ternat, 1740, Belgium
Tel.: (32) 2 583 11 11
Web Site: http://www.sparretail.be
Sales Range: $100-124.9 Million
Emp.: 255
Food Product Retailer & Distr
N.A.I.C.S.: 445110
Dirk Depoorter (Gen Mgr)

Smart Technics NV **(1)**
Craenendonck 15, 3000, Leuven, Belgium
Tel.: (32) 472135627
Web Site: https://smarttechnics.be
Information Technology Services
N.A.I.C.S.: 541519

Solucious S.A. **(1)**
Edingensesteenweg 196, 1500, Halle, Bel-
gium
Tel.: (32) 23338888
Web Site: https://www.solucious.be
Sales Range: $150-199.9 Million
Emp.: 399
Food & Non-Food Products Whslr
N.A.I.C.S.: 424490

Symeta Hybrid NV **(1)**
Interleuvenlaan 30, 3001, Leuven, Belgium
Tel.: (32) 16841050
Web Site: https://symeta-hybrid.com
Information Technology Services
N.A.I.C.S.: 541519

Symeta N.V. **(1)**
Beertsestraat 273, 1500, Halle, Belgium
Tel.: (32) 2 360 01 90
Web Site: http://www.symeta.com
Sales Range: $50-74.9 Million
Emp.: 125
Printing Services
N.A.I.C.S.: 323111
Jo Van De Weghe (Mgr-Sls & Mktg)

COLSON CAPITAL CORP.

520 3rd Street SW Suite 1900, Cal-
gary, T2P 0R3, AB, Canada
Tel.: (403) 471-4039
Year Founded: 2014
Assets: $324,125
Liabilities: $9,122
Net Worth: $315,003
Earnings: ($29,508)
Business Consulting Services
N.A.I.C.S.: 522299
Ken Yoon (CEO)

COLT CZ GROUP SE
namesti Republiky 2090/3a, Prague
1, 110 00, Prague, Czech Republic
Tel.: (420) 222814617
Web Site:
https://www.coltczgroup.com
Year Founded: 2013
CZGZF—(OTCIQ)
Rev.: $664,283,943
Assets: $1,161,579,739
Liabilities: $746,844,612
Net Worth: $414,735,127
Earnings: $91,334,374
Emp.: 2,111
Fiscal Year-end: 12/31/23
Holding Company
N.A.I.C.S.: 551112
Dennis Veilleux (Mng Dir)

Subsidiaries:

Ceska zbrojovka a.s. **(1)**
Svatopluka Cecha 1283, 688 01, Uhersky
Brod, Czech Republic
Tel.: (420) 572655230
Web Site: https://www.czub.cz
Emp.: 1,390
Automobile Parts Mfr & Distr
N.A.I.C.S.: 336413

COLT RESOURCES INC.
500 Place D'Armes Suite 1800, Mon-
treal, H2Y 2W2, QC, Canada
Tel.: (438) 259-3315   BC
Web Site:
http://www.coltresources.com
Year Founded: 2000
Sales Range: Less than $1 Million
Gold, Uranium & Other Metal-Based
Mineral Mining
N.A.I.C.S.: 212220
Randy A. Foutch (Founder)

COLTENE HOLDING AG
Feldwiesenstrasse 20, 9450, Altstat-
ten, Switzerland
Tel.: (41) 717575380   CH
Web Site: https://www.coltene.com
CLTN—(SWX)
Rev.: $316,233,188
Assets: $211,475,183
Liabilities: $89,849,037
Net Worth: $121,626,146
Earnings: $35,908,359
Emp.: 1,242
Fiscal Year-end: 12/31/21
Holding Company; Dental Products &
Devices Mfr & Distr
N.A.I.C.S.: 551112
Martin Schaufelberger (CEO)

Subsidiaries:

Coltene/Whaledent AG **(1)**
Feldwiesenstrasse 20, 9450, Altstatten,
Switzerland
Tel.: (41) 717575300
Web Site: http://www.coltene.com
Sales Range: $25-49.9 Million
Emp.: 120
Dental Equipment Mfr
N.A.I.C.S.: 339114
Martin Schaufelberger (CEO)

Coltene/Whaledent GmbH + Co.
KG **(1)**
Raiffeisenstrasse 30, PO Box 1150, 89122,
Langenau, Germany
Tel.: (49) 73458050

COLTENE Holding AG—(Continued)

Web Site: http://www.ap.coltene.com
Sales Range: $25-49.9 Million
Emp.: 100
Dental Equipment Mfr
N.A.I.C.S.: 339114

Subsidiary (Domestic):

B I P Boatmungsprodukte Gmbl I　(2)
Talstrasse 16, Neunkirchen-Seelscheid,
53819, Wurzburg, Germany
Tel.: (49) 224792160
Web Site: http://www.b-und-p.com
Medical Dental & Hospital Equipment &
Supplies Whslr
N.A.I.C.S.: 423450

Coltene/Whaledent Inc.　(1)
235 Ascot Pkwy, Cuyahoga Falls, OH
44223-3701
Tel.: (330) 916-8800
Sales Range: $100-124.9 Million
Emp.: 300
Dental Product & Device Mfr
N.A.I.C.S.: 339114

Subsidiary (Domestic):

Diatech Inc.　(2)
PO Box 22648, Charleston, SC 29413
Tel.: (843) 849-3700
Web Site: http://www.diatechusa.com
Emp.: 5
Dental Instruments & Supplies Mfr & Whslr
N.A.I.C.S.: 339114
Alicia Oliver (Pres)

Endodent Inc　(2)
851 Meridian St, Duarte, CA 91010-3588
Tel.: (626) 359-5715
Dental Equipment Distr
N.A.I.C.S.: 423450

Coltene/Whaledent Ltd　(1)
The President Ste A Kendal House, Bur-
gess Hill, RH15 9NF, West Sussex, United
Kingdom
Tel.: (44) 1444235486
Web Site: http://www.coltene.com
Sales Range: $25-49.9 Million
Emp.: 20
Dental Equipment Mfr
N.A.I.C.S.: 339114

Coltene/Whaledent Private
Limited　(1)
106/107 Hallmark Vasant Oscar LBS Marg,
Mulund West, Mumbai, 400080, Maharash-
tra, India
Tel.: (91) 2225923626
Dental Supplies Distr
N.A.I.C.S.: 423450

Coltene/Whaledent S.a.r.l.　(1)
75 Bld Alexandre Oyon, 72058, Le Mans,
France
Tel.: (33) 243393030
Web Site: http://www.coltene.com
Sales Range: $25-49.9 Million
Emp.: 16
Dental Equipment Mfr
N.A.I.C.S.: 339114

Dentalia Kft　(1)
Akacfa Utca 86, 2060, Bicske, Fejer, Hun-
gary
Tel.: (36) 22261159
Dental Equipment Mfr
N.A.I.C.S.: 339114

**COLTERRA CAPITAL CORPO-
RATION**
4999 St Catherine Street West Suite
300, Montreal, H3Z 1T3, QC, Canada
Tel.: (514) 487-1515
Web Site:
　http://www.colterracapital.com
Real Estate Investment Services
N.A.I.C.S.: 523999
Robert Berger (Principal)

**COLUMBIA DBL (PTY) LIM-
ITED**
Waggie Rd, PO Box 287, Blackheath,
Cape Town, 7581, Western Cape,
South Africa

Tel.: (27) 219051665
Sales Range: $25-49.9 Million
Emp.: 200
Masonry Bricks & Blocks Mfr
N.A.I.C.S.: 327331

**COLUMBIA MANUFACTURING
CO LTD.**
4575 Tillicum Street, Burnaby, V5J
3J9, BC, Canada
Tel.: (604) 437-3377
Web Site:
　https://www.columbiaskylights.com
Year Founded: 1955
Sales Range: $10-24.9 Million
Emp.: 100
Flat Glass Mfr
N.A.I.C.S.: 327211
Mike Williams (Pres)

Subsidiaries:

Columbia Glazing Systems Inc.　(1)
1538 Kebet Way, Port Coquitlam, V3C
5M5, BC, Canada
Tel.: (604) 421-6591
Web Site: http://www.columbiaglazing.com
Glass Mfr
N.A.I.C.S.: 327110
Akbar Virani (VP & Gen Mgr)

**COLUMBIA PETRO CHEM PVT.
LTD.**
Triveni 32nd Road Bandra West,
Mumbai, 400050, Maharashtra, India
Tel.: (91) 2266002313
Web Site:
　https://www.columbiapetro.com
White Oils, Transformer Oils & All
Kinds of Petroleum Jellies Mfr
N.A.I.C.S.: 325412
Kuldeep Halwasiya (Co-Founder)

Subsidiaries:

Cupid Ltd.　(1)
A-68 MIDC Malegaon, Sinnar, Nashik,　(67.84%)
422113, India
Tel.: (91) 2551230280
Web Site: https://www.cupidlimited.com
Rev.: $22,399,227
Assets: $25,775,336
Liabilities: $2,962,992
Net Worth: $22,812,344
Earnings: $4,311,066
Emp.: 100
Fiscal Year-end: 03/31/2023
Personal Care Product Mfr
N.A.I.C.S.: 456199
Omprakash Chhangamal Garg (Chm & Mng
Dir)

COLUMBUS A/S
Lautrupvang 6, DK- 2750, Ballerup,
Denmark
Tel.: (45) 70205000　　　　　DK
Web Site:
　https://www.columbusglobal.com
Year Founded: 1989
COLUM—(CSE)
Rev.: $201,043,828
Assets: $171,310,935
Liabilities: $69,097,828
Net Worth: $102,213,106
Earnings: ($1,636,932)
Emp.: 1,550
Fiscal Year-end: 12/31/22
Software Development & Services
N.A.I.C.S.: 513210
Hans-Henrik Thrane (CFO)

Subsidiaries:

Client Strategy Group, LLC　(1)
8555 Sweet Valley Dr Ste Q, Valley View,
OH 44125　(100%)
Tel.: (216) 524-2574
Web Site: http://www.csgax.com
Sales Range: $1-9.9 Million
Emp.: 19
Information Technology Advisory Services
N.A.I.C.S.: 541618
Joel s. Pietrantozzi (Exec VP)

Columbus Deutschland GmbH　(1)
Kaistrasse 5, 40221, Dusseldorf, Germany
Tel.: (49) 21116781253
Web Site: https://www.columbusglobal.com
Information Technology Services
N.A.I.C.S.: 541511

Columbus Eesti AS　(1)
Siduri 3, 11313, Tallinn, Estonia
Tel.: (372) 606 2600
Web Site: https://www.columbusglobal.com
Information Technology Services
N.A.I.C.S.: 541511

Columbus Global (UK) Ltd.　(1)
Lugano House Lake View Business Park
Lake View Drive, Annesley, Nottingham,
NG15 0ED, United Kingdom
Tel.: (44) 1159902200
Web Site: https://www.columbusglobal.com
Information Technology Services
N.A.I.C.S.: 541511

Columbus M3 Danmark ApS　(1)
Lautrupvang 6, 2750, Ballerup, Denmark
Tel.: (45) 7 020 5000
Information Technology Services
N.A.I.C.S.: 541511

Columbus Norway AS　(1)
Dronning Eufemias gate 16, 0191, Oslo,
Norway
Tel.: (47) 23058500
Web Site: https://www.columbusglobal.com
Emp.: 50
Software Development Services
N.A.I.C.S.: 541511

Columbus Sweden AB　(1)
Drottninggatan 71D, 111 36, Stockholm,
Sweden
Tel.: (46) 854527550
Web Site: https://www.columbusglobal.com
Information Technology Services
N.A.I.C.S.: 541511

InterDyn BMI　(1)
2277 W Hwy 36 Ste 300, Saint Paul, MN
55113
Tel.: (651) 639-0575
Web Site: http://www.interdynbmi.com
Emp.: 50
Information Technology Software Integration
& Consulting Services
N.A.I.C.S.: 541519
John Hendrickson (CEO)

Sherwood Manufacturing Co.,
Inc.　(1)
1717 E Morten Ave Ste 270, Phoenix, AZ
85020
Tel.: (602) 943-9696
Web Site: http://www.sherwood.com
Sales Range: $1-9.9 Million
Emp.: 10
Software Publisher
N.A.I.C.S.: 513210
Ed Bonaski (Dir-Sls)

Tridea Partners, LLC.　(1)
380 Stevens Ave Ste 305, Solana Beach,
CA 92075
Tel.: (858) 755-3700
Web Site: http://www.trideapartners.com
Sales Range: $1-9.9 Million
Emp.: 24
Information Technology Consulting Services
N.A.I.C.S.: 541512
Matthew Boese (Co-Founder & Partner-
Consulting Svcs)

UAB Columbus Lietuva　(1)
Savanoriu PR 321C, 50120, Kaunas, Lithu-
ania
Tel.: (370) 3 775 0565
Web Site: https://www.columbusglobal.com
Information Technology Services
N.A.I.C.S.: 541511

COLUMBUS ENERGY LIMITED
Suite 701 595 Howe Street, Vancou-
ver, V6C 2T5, BC, Canada
Tel.: (604) 684-7619　　　　　BC
Web Site:
　http://www.columbusenergy.ca
CEL—(TSXV)
Assets: $2,438
Liabilities: $260,442

Net Worth: ($258,004)
Earnings: ($64,839)
Emp.: 3
Fiscal Year-end: 12/31/20
Oil & Gas Exploration Services
N.A.I.C.S.: 211120
Glen MacDonald (CEO & CFO)

COLUMBUS ENERGY SA
Ul Jasnogorska 9, 31-358, Krakow,
Poland
Tel.: (48) 123073090
Web Site:
　https://www.columbusenergy.pl
Year Founded: 2010
CLC—(WAR)
Rev.: $118,155,742
Assets: $163,765,243
Liabilities: $173,443,597
Net Worth: ($9,678,354)
Earnings: ($16,558,689)
Fiscal Year-end: 12/31/23
Renewable Energy Services
N.A.I.C.S.: 221210
David Zielinski (CEO)

COLY, INC.
4-2-6 Akasaka, Minato-Ku, Tokyo,
107-0052, Japan
Tel.: (81) 335050333
Web Site: https://www.colyinc.com
Year Founded: 2014
4175—(TKS)
Application Development Services
N.A.I.C.S.: 541511
Mizuki Nakajima (Founder, Chm &
Pres)

COM2US CORPORATION
12F BYC Highcity A Bldg 131 Gasan
Digital 1-ro, Geumcheon-gu, Seoul,
Korea (South)
Tel.: (82) 262926000
Web Site: http://www.com2us.com
Year Founded: 1998
078340—(KRS)
Rev.: $550,043,919
Assets: $1,463,710,864
Liabilities: $441,801,417
Net Worth: $1,021,909,446
Earnings: ($7,152,059)
Emp.: 1,411
Fiscal Year-end: 12/31/22
Mobile Game Developing Services
N.A.I.C.S.: 513210
Byeong Jun Song (CEO)

COM2US HOLDINGS
4F A-dong 131 Gasan Digital 1-ro,
Geumcheon-gu, Seoul, Korea (South)
Tel.: (82) 28765252
Web Site: http://www.gamevil.com
Year Founded: 2000
063080—(KRS)
Rev.: $89,148,651
Assets: $451,852,607
Liabilities: $228,560,728
Net Worth: $223,291,879
Earnings: ($42,144,694)
Emp.: 218
Fiscal Year-end: 12/31/22
Mobile Video Game Developer
N.A.I.C.S.: 513210

Subsidiaries:

GAMEVIL USA, Inc.　(1)
999 N Sepulveda Blvd Ste 150, El Se-
gundo, CA 90245
Tel.: (310) 320-3400
Mobile Game Publishing Services
N.A.I.C.S.: 513210

**COM7 PUBLIC COMPANY LIM-
ITED**
549/1 Sanphawut Rd, Bangna Tai
Bangna, Bangkok, 10260, Thailand
Tel.: (66) 20177777

Web Site:
  https://www.comseven.com
Year Founded: 2004
COM7—(THA)
Rev.: $2,032,977,586
Assets: $670,722,055
Liabilities: $431,709,533
Net Worth: $239,012,521
Earnings: $85,656,188
Emp.: 4,506
Fiscal Year-end: 12/31/23
Electronic Products Import & Sale
N.A.I.C.S.: 449210
Siripong Sombutsiri *(Chm)*

COMAL S.P.A.
Industrial Area 2 Pini SS Aurelia km
113, Montalto di Castro, 01014, Viterbo, VT, Italy
Tel.: (39) 0766879718
Web Site:
  https://www.comalgroup.com
Year Founded: 2001
CML—(EUR)
Construction Engineering Services
N.A.I.C.S.: 541330
Alfredo Balletti *(CEO)*

COMALEX SA
Str Libertatii 211 Bl L8-l9, Alexandria,
Teleorman, Romania
Tel.: (40) 247317623
COKG—(BUC)
Rev.: $149,918
Assets: $340,804
Liabilities: $109,742
Net Worth: $231,062
Earnings: $1,851
Emp.: 3
Fiscal Year-end: 12/31/23
Real Estate Prorperty Leasing Services
N.A.I.C.S.: 531190

COMALIMENT SA
Strada Horea Nr1 Apt 5, Caras-Severin, Resita, Romania
Tel.: (40) 255212515
OMAL—(BUC)
Rev.: $250,430
Assets: $534,481
Liabilities: $60,244
Net Worth: $474,238
Earnings: $26,736
Emp.: 4
Fiscal Year-end: 12/31/23
Grocery Store Operator
N.A.I.C.S.: 445110

COMANCHE INTERNATIONAL PCL
161 Soi Sukhumvit 55 Thong Lor
Klongtan Nua, Wattana, Bangkok,
10110, Thailand
Tel.: (66) 26933569
Web Site:
  https://investor.comanchepcl.com
COMAN—(THA)
Rev.: $8,848,684
Assets: $12,141,283
Liabilities: $1,950,566
Net Worth: $10,190,716
Earnings: $79,470
Emp.: 40
Fiscal Year-end: 12/31/23
Information Technology Services
N.A.I.C.S.: 541519
Wasawat Prasertsin *(CEO)*

Subsidiaries:

Comanche International Malaysia
Sdn. Bhd.   **(1)**
Suite 8-1 and 8-2 Level 8 Menara CIMB No
1 Jalan Stesen Sentral 2, 50470, Kuala
Lumpur, Malaysia
Tel.: (60) 322988469

Web Site:
  http://www.comanchesoftware.com
Information Technology Services
N.A.I.C.S.: 541511

Comanche International Vietnam Co.,
Ltd.   **(1)**
157-159 Nguyen Dinh Chieu, Ward 6 District 3, Ho Chi Minh City, Vietnam
Tel.: (84) 839300755
Information Technology Services
N.A.I.C.S.: 541511

COMANY INC.
1-93 Kougyou-Danchi, Komatsu-shi,
Ishikawa, 923-8502, Japan
Tel.: (81) 761211144
Web Site: http://www.comany.co.jp
7945—(TKS)
Rev.: $313,235,120
Assets: $362,080,400
Liabilities: $129,189,280
Net Worth: $232,891,120
Earnings: $10,357,600
Emp.: 1,378
Fiscal Year-end: 03/31/22
Partitions & Paneling Systems Mfr
N.A.I.C.S.: 337215
Kenta Tsukamoto *(Pres)*

Subsidiaries:

Comany Inc. - Market Development
Division   **(1)**
14F East Wing Chiyoda First Building 3-8-1
Nishikanda Chiyoda, Tokyo, Japan
Tel.: (81) 362611091
Metal Product Distr
N.A.I.C.S.: 423510

COMARCH S.A.
Al Jana Pawla II 39a, 31-864, Krakow, Poland
Tel.: (48) 126461000
Web Site: https://www.comarch.com
Year Founded: 1993
CMR—(WAR)
Rev.: $377,855,384
Assets: $484,393,441
Liabilities: $229,210,811
Net Worth: $255,182,630
Earnings: $27,737,517
Emp.: 6,348
Fiscal Year-end: 12/31/19
Information Technology Solutions &
Services
N.A.I.C.S.: 513210
Marcin Warwas *(Vice Chm-Mgmt Bd & Dir-Svcs Div)*

Subsidiaries:

CA Consulting SA   **(1)**
street Pulawska 525, 02-844, Warsaw,
Masovian, Poland
Tel.: (48) 221605700
Web Site: https://caconsulting.pl
Computer Software Consulting Services
N.A.I.C.S.: 541511

Comarch AG   **(1)**
Chemnitzer Str 59b, 01187, Dresden, Germany
Tel.: (49) 35132013200
Web Site: http://www.comarch.de
Sales Range: $25-49.9 Million
Information Technology Consulting Services
N.A.I.C.S.: 541611

Comarch Chile SpA   **(1)**
Calle Bucarest 150 oficina 402, Providencia
Region Metropolitana, Santiago, Chile
Tel.: (56) 222477570
Software Development & Publishing Services
N.A.I.C.S.: 513210

Comarch LLC   **(1)**
18/7 Kutuzova Str, 01133, Kiev, Ukraine
Tel.: (380) 444922842
Software Development & Publishing Services
N.A.I.C.S.: 513210

Comarch Luxembourg S.a r.l.   **(1)**

Rue de Merl 63-65, L-2146, Luxembourg,
Luxembourg
Tel.: (352) 22723697
Software Development & Publishing Services
N.A.I.C.S.: 541511

Comarch Malaysia SDN. BHD.   **(1)**
B-3A-06 Block B West PJ8 Service Suites
No 23 Jalan Barat Seksyen 8, Petaling
Jaya, 46050, Malaysia
Tel.: (60) 376117040
Software Development & Publishing Services
N.A.I.C.S.: 513210

Comarch Middle East FZ-LLC   **(1)**
Dubai Internet City Building 17 Room 158,
PO Box 500824, Dubai, United Arab Emirates
Tel.: (971) 44477417
Software Development & Publishing Services
N.A.I.C.S.: 513210

Comarch OOO   **(1)**
Kazachiy Pereulok 5/2 bld 1 floor/room 2/2,
119017, Moscow, Russia
Tel.: (7) 4951341429
Web Site: http://www.comarch.com
Software Development & Consulting Services
N.A.I.C.S.: 541511

Comarch Panama Inc.   **(1)**
Via Ricardo J Alfaro Building P H Century
Tower 7th Floor Office 721, Panama,
Panama
Tel.: (507) 2632569
Software Development & Publishing Services
N.A.I.C.S.: 513210

Comarch R&D S.A.R.L.   **(1)**
82 Allee Galilee, 38330, Montbonnot-Saint-Martin, France
Tel.: (33) 457582300
Web Site: https://www.comarch.com
Software Development & Consulting Services
N.A.I.C.S.: 541511

Comarch Schilling GmbH   **(1)**
Anne-Conway-Strasse 2, 28359, Bremen,
Germany
Tel.: (49) 421201400
Sales Range: $25-49.9 Million
Emp.: 30
Software Development & Consulting Services
N.A.I.C.S.: 541511
Jens Goedel *(Mgr)*

Comarch Sistemas LTDA   **(1)**
Av Roque Petroni Junior 1089 10 andar,
04707-900, Sao Paulo, Brazil
Tel.: (55) 1139950400
Software Development & Publishing Services
N.A.I.C.S.: 513210

Comarch Software S.A.R.L.   **(1)**
12 Place Saint Hubert, 59000, Lille, France
Tel.: (33) 359560684
Web Site: http://www.comarch.fr
Sales Range: $25-49.9 Million
Software Development & Consulting Services
N.A.I.C.S.: 541511

Comarch Software und Beratung   **(1)**
Fasanenstrasse 4, 10623, Berlin, Germany
Tel.: (49) 307679670
Web Site: http://www.comarch.com
Software Development & Consulting Services
N.A.I.C.S.: 541511

Comarch Solutions GmbH   **(1)**
Messerschmitt Str 4, Munich, 80992, Bayern, Germany
Tel.: (49) 89143290
Web Site: http://www.comarch.com
Sales Range: $25-49.9 Million
Emp.: 50
Software Development & Consulting Services
N.A.I.C.S.: 541511

Comarch Solutions GmbH   **(1)**
Nussdorfer Lande 23, 1190, Vienna, Austria

Tel.: (43) 1910660
Web Site: http://www.comarch.com
Sales Range: $25-49.9 Million
Software Development & Consulting Services
N.A.I.C.S.: 541511

Comarch Swiss AG   **(1)**
Bahnhofstr 21b, 9471, Buchs, St. Gallen,
Switzerland
Tel.: (41) 817555500
Sales Range: $25-49.9 Million
Emp.: 25
Software Development & Consulting Services
N.A.I.C.S.: 541511

Comarch Technologies Oy   **(1)**
Technopolis Business Park Innopoli II
Tekniikantie 14, 02150, Espoo, Finland
Tel.: (358) 486215199
Software Development & Publishing Services
N.A.I.C.S.: 513210

Comarch UK Ltd.   **(1)**
Terminal House 52 Grosvenor Gardens,
London, SW1W 0AU, United Kingdom
Tel.: (44) 2074678700
Software Development & Publishing Services
N.A.I.C.S.: 513210
Oskar Wierchowicz *(Mng Dir)*

Subsidiary (Non-US):

Comarch Japan KK   **(2)**
Level 28 Shinagawa Intercity Tower A
2-15-1 Konan, Minato-ku, Tokyo, 108-6028,
Japan
Tel.: (81) 367176080
Software Development & Publishing Services
N.A.I.C.S.: 513210

Comarch Vietnam Co. Ltd.   **(1)**
No 128 Nguyen Phi Khanh Street Tan Dinh
Ward District 1, Ho Chi Minh City, Vietnam
Tel.: (84) 838206218
Software Development & Consulting Services
N.A.I.C.S.: 541511

Geopolis sp. z o.o.   **(1)**
ul Wloclawska 167, 87-100, Torun, Poland
Tel.: (48) 544139999
Software Development & Publishing Services
N.A.I.C.S.: 513210

iComarch24 SA   **(1)**
Al Jana Pawla II 39a, 31-864, Krakow, Poland
Tel.: (48) 126848880
Data Protection & Security Services
N.A.I.C.S.: 541513

iReward24 SA   **(1)**
Aleja Jana Pawla II 39A, 31-864, Krakow,
Lesser Poland, Poland
Tel.: (48) 126877000
Software Development & Consulting Services
N.A.I.C.S.: 541512

COMAT AUTO SA
90 Timisoara Blvd Sector 6, Bucharest, 061334, Romania
Tel.: (40) 214440223
Web Site: http://www.comat-auto.ro
Sales Range: $1-9.9 Million
Emp.: 68
Motor Vehicle Parts & Accessories
Distr
N.A.I.C.S.: 423120
Eugen Stanculescu *(Pres)*

COMAT CARAS SEVERIN SA
Str Moniom 113, Caras-Severin,
Resita, Romania
Tel.: (40) 255231317
OMSE—(BUC)
Rev.: $37,263
Assets: $509,916
Liabilities: $113,601
Net Worth: $396,315
Earnings: ($23,839)

Comat Caras Severin SA—(Continued)

Emp.: 1
Fiscal Year-end: 12/31/23
Metal Ores Whslr
N.A.I.C.S.: 423520
Dorel Ienovan (Pres)

COMAT TECHNOLOGIES (P) LTD.

No 333 Nova Miller Thimmaiah Road,
Vasanth Nagar, Bengaluru, 560052,
India
Tel.: (91) 8022343000
Web Site: http://www.comat.com
Year Founded: 1995
Sales Range: $1-9.9 Million
Business Consulting, Technology Integration, Back Office & Field Services to the Government, Public & Private Sectors
N.A.I.C.S.: 541611
Shashi K. Patil (COO)

Subsidiaries:

Comat Europe   (1)
Eerste Helmersstraat 267 H, 1054 DZ, Amsterdam, Netherlands
Tel.: (31) 20 4123881
Business Consultants
N.A.I.C.S.: 541611

Comat Technologies, Inc.   (1)
14716 Maine Cove Terr Ste B, North Potomac, MD 20878
Tel.: (240) 498-5453
Business Consultants
N.A.I.C.S.: 541611

COMBA TELECOM SYSTEMS HOLDINGS LIMITED

611 East Wing No 8 Science Park
West Avenue Hong Kong Science
Park, Tai Po, Hong Kong, China
(Hong Kong)
Tel.: (852) 26366861
Web Site: http://www.comba-telecom.com
2342—(HKG)
Rev.: $811,496,318
Assets: $1,348,422,405
Liabilities: $842,919,840
Net Worth: $505,502,565
Earnings: $18,295,740
Emp.: 5,300
Fiscal Year-end: 12/31/22
Holding Company; Wireless Telecommunications Infrastructure & Services
N.A.I.C.S.: 551112
Tung Ling Fok (Chm)

Subsidiaries:

Comba Telecom Co. Ltd.   (1)
No 240/32 240/34 Ayothaya Tower 18th Fl
Ratchadapisek Rd, Huaykwang, Bangkok,
10320, Thailand   (100%)
Tel.: (66) 2 274 1618
Web Site: https://www.comba-telecom.com
Sales Range: $25-49.9 Million
Emp.: 4
Cellular & Other Wireless Telecommunications
N.A.I.C.S.: 517112

Comba Telecom Inc.   (1)
568 Gibraltar Dr, Milpitas, CA 95035
Tel.: (408) 526-0180
Emp.: 18
Wireless Systems Mfr
N.A.I.C.S.: 334515
Thuy Nguyen (Office Mgr)

Comba Telecom India Private
Limited   (1)
E 172 Greater Kailash Part I, New Delhi,
110048, India
Tel.: (91) 11 4173 9997
Web Site: http://www.comba-telecom.com
Telecommunications Equipment Mfr
N.A.I.C.S.: 334220

Comba Telecom Ltda   (1)

Av Doutor Chucri Zaidan n 1550 - Capital
Corporate Building 29th floor, Vila Cordeiro,
Sao Paulo, 04583-110, Brazil
Tel.: (55) 1135094800
Web Site: https://www.comba-telecom.com.br
Sales Range: $25-49.9 Million
Emp.: 4
Telecommunications Equipment Mfr
N.A.I.C.S.: 004210

Comba Telecom Systems (Singapore)
Pte. Ltd.   (1)
44 Kallang Place Four Star Building 04-05/06/07/08, Singapore, 339172,
Singapore   (100%)
Tel.: (65) 6 345 4908
Web Site: https://www.comba-telecom.com
Sales Range: $75-99.9 Million
Emp.: 50
Other Electronic Parts & Equipment Whslr
N.A.I.C.S.: 423690

Comba Telecom Systems
Limited   (1)
Unit 611 Building 8W Hong Kong Science
Park, Pak Shek Kok, Hong Kong, China
(Hong Kong)
Tel.: (852) 26366861
Web Site: http://www.comba-telecom.com
Sales Range: $25-49.9 Million
Emp.: 60
Wireless Telecommunication Services
N.A.I.C.S.: 517121

Comba Telecom Technology
(Guangzhou) Limited   (1)
No 10 Shenzhou Road Science City, Luogang District, Guangzhou, Guangdong,
China   (100%)
Tel.: (86) 2028390000
Web Site: https://www.comba.com.cn
Other Communications Equipment Mfr
N.A.I.C.S.: 334290

Comban Telecom Systems AB   (1)
Gardsfogdevagen 12 -14, Bromma, 168 67,
Stockholm, Sweden   (100%)
Tel.: (46) 704229585
Other Electronic Parts & Equipment Whslr
N.A.I.C.S.: 423690

P.T. Comba Telecom Network
Indonesia   (1)
Menara Kuningan 8th Floor Unit 8L JI HR
Rasuna Said Kav 5 Block X-7, Jakarta,
12940, Indonesia
Tel.: (62) 212526203
Web Site: https://www.comba.id
Wireless Telecommunication Services
N.A.I.C.S.: 541618

WaveLab Inc.   (1)
12007 Sunrise Valley Dr Ste 450, Reston,
VA 20191-3489   (100%)
Tel.: (703) 860-3522
Web Site: https://www.wave-lab.com
Sales Range: $25-49.9 Million
Emp.: 100
Other Computer Peripheral Equipment Mfr
N.A.I.C.S.: 334118

COMBAT DRUGS LIMITED

4th Floor Plot No 94 Sagar Society
Rd No 2, Banjara Hills, Hyderabad,
500034, Telangana, India
Tel.: (91) 4048536100   In
Web Site: https://www.combatdrugs.in
Year Founded: 1986
Pharmaceuticals Product Mfr
N.A.I.C.S.: 325412
Suchit Mohan Lal (Mng Dir)

COMBELL NV

Skaldenstraat 121, 9042, Gent, Belgium
Tel.: (32) 92187979
Web Site: http://www.combell.com
Hosting Services
N.A.I.C.S.: 518210
Romy Vandevelde (Coord-Mktg)

Subsidiaries:

TransIP Group BV   (1)

Schipholweg 9B, 2316 XB, Leiden, Netherlands
Tel.: (31) 715241919
Web Site: http://www.transip.eu
Managed Internet Services
N.A.I.C.S.: 518210
Jeroen Hupscher (CEO)

Subsidiary (Domestic):

IT-Ernity Internet Services BV   (2)
Stadionpiein 23, 8025 CP, Zwolle, Netherlands
Tel.: (31) 88 00 74 999
Web Site: http://www.it-ernity.nl
Managed Internet Services
N.A.I.C.S.: 518210

COMBEST HOLDINGS LIMITED

Flat M-N 24/F Houston Industrial
Building 32-40 Wang Lung Street,
Tsuen Wan, New Territories, China
(Hong Kong)
Tel.: (852) 22308917   Ky
Web Site:
    http://www.combestholdings.com
Year Founded: 2001
Sales Range: $1-9.9 Million
Emp.: 10
Holding Company
N.A.I.C.S.: 551112
Wong Hung Yuen Yee (Chief Investment Officer)

COMBI CORPORATION

2-6-7 Motoasakusa, Taito-ku, Tokyo,
111-0041, Japan
Tel.: (81) 487971000
Web Site: http://www.combi.co.jp
Year Founded: 1957
Sales Range: $250-299.9 Million
Emp.: 345
Children Product Toy Game Exercise
Machine Home Health Apparate &
Medical Device Mfr
N.A.I.C.S.: 339930

Subsidiaries:

Combi (Shanghai) Co., Ltd.   (1)
Huaihai Financial Mansion 23F No 200
Huaihai Zhong Road, Shanghai, 200021,
China
Tel.: (86) 2163852688
Web Site: http://www.combi.com.cn
Sales Range: $75-99.9 Million
Emp.: 200
Baby Products Sales & Marketing
N.A.I.C.S.: 423920

Combi Asia Limited   (1)
Room 1003 10th Floor HK Pacific Center,
Kowloon, China (Hong Kong)   (100%)
Tel.: (852) 23662899
Web Site: http://www.combi.com.hk
Sales Range: $50-74.9 Million
Emp.: 60
Baby Products Whslr
N.A.I.C.S.: 423990
Season Ip (Mgr-Mktg)

Subsidiary (Non-US):

Combi (Taiwan) Co., Ltd.   (2)
6F 6 Lane 360 Nei Hu Road Sec 1, Taipei,
11493, Taiwan
Tel.: (886) 226578822
Web Site: http://www.combi.com.tw
Baby Products Sales & Marketing
N.A.I.C.S.: 423920

Combi Korea Co., Ltd.   (2)
1805 Tower 2 No 3, Seongsu-gu, Seoul,
Korea (South)
Tel.: (82) 24990872
Web Site: http://www.combi.co.kr
Sales Range: $25-49.9 Million
Emp.: 20
Baby Products Retailer
N.A.I.C.S.: 458110

Ningbo Combi Baby Goods Co.,
Ltd   (2)
No 200 Huaihai Zhong Rd Shanghai Huai-

hai Financial Bldg 23Fl, Shanghai,
China   (100%)
Tel.: (86) 21 6385 2688
Web Site: http://www.combi.co.jp
Baby Products Mfr
N.A.I.C.S.: 339930

Combi Next Corporation   (1)
2-6-7 Moto-Asakusa, Taito-ku, Tokyo, 111-0041, Japan   (100%)
Tel.: (81) 3 5828 8074
Web Site: http://combimini.jp
Emp.: 76
Development, Production & Sales of Baby
Wear & Baby Bedding
N.A.I.C.S.: 315250
Junichiro Ishikawa (Pres)

Combi USA, Inc.   (1)
1962 Hwy 160 W Ste 100, Fort Mill, SC
29708-8027   (100%)
Tel.: (803) 548-6633
Web Site: http://www.combi-intl.com
Mfr & Marketer of Baby Products
N.A.I.C.S.: 423990

CombiWith Corporation   (1)
2-6-7 Motoasakusa, Taito-ku, Tokyo, 111-0041, Japan   (100%)
Tel.: (81) 358287631
Web Site: http://www.combiwith.co.jp
Sales Range: $150-199.9 Million
Sporting & Recreational Goods & Supplies
Whslr
N.A.I.C.S.: 423910
Ichiro Suzuki (Pres)

COMBIGENE AB

Agavagen 52A, 181 55, Lidingo,
Sweden
Web Site:
    https://www.combigene.com
Year Founded: 1990
COMBI—(OMX)
Rev.: $656,384
Assets: $11,296,789
Liabilities: $389,234
Net Worth: $10,907,556
Earnings: ($3,340,489)
Emp.: 8
Fiscal Year-end: 12/31/23
Biotechnology Research & Development Services
N.A.I.C.S.: 541714
Jan Nilsson (CEO)

COMBIMILL OU

Olustvere tee 5A, Koidama, 71504,
Estonia
Tel.: (372) 4342080   EE
Web Site: http://www.combimill.ee
Year Founded: 2012
Emp.: 65
Pine Sawn Timber Production
N.A.I.C.S.: 321113
Virko Lepmets (Owner)

Subsidiaries:

Combimill Reopalu OU   (1)
Turi Vald, Reopalu, 72811, Jarvamaa, Estonia
Tel.: (372) 3838150
Web Site: http://www.combimill.ee
Sales Range: $10-24.9 Million
Emp.: 50
Renewable Wood for Building & Construction Distr
N.A.I.C.S.: 423310
Marek Moorits (Member-Mgmt Bd)

COMBINE WILL INTERNATIONAL HOLDINGS LIMITED

Room 901-3 Block 4 Tai Ping Industrial Centre, 51A Ting Kok Road, Tai
Po, NT, China (Hong Kong)
Tel.: (852) 26651678   Ky
Web Site:
    https://www.combinewill.com
N0Z—(SES)
Rev.: $171,022,380
Assets: $196,678,568
Liabilities: $104,859,825

Net Worth: $91,818,743
Earnings: $5,451,518
Emp.: 7,700
Fiscal Year-end: 12/31/22
Holding Company; Plastic & Die-Cast Products Mfr
N.A.I.C.S.: 551112
Dominic Jo Tak Tam *(Chm & CEO)*

Subsidiaries:

Altrust Precision Tooling (Dongguan)
Co., Ltd.   (1)
Xin Cheng Ind District Hengli Town, Dong-guan, Guangdong, China
Tel.: (86) 76983732298
Web Site: http://www.altrust.com.cn
Tool Mfr
N.A.I.C.S.: 333517

Unifaith Machine Tools Company
Limited   (1)
9B Block 3 Tai Ping Ind Centre 53 Ting Kok Road, Tai Po, New Territories, China (Hong Kong)
Tel.: (852) 26510399
Web Site: http://www.unifaithco.com
Rev.: $8,940,197
Emp.: 10,000
Industrial Machinery Distr
N.A.I.C.S.: 423830

COMBINED GROUP CONTRACTING COMPANY KSCC
Block No 2 Plot No 284 Al Ardiya Industrial, Kuwait, Kuwait
Tel.: (965) 22254545
Web Site: https://www.cgc-kw.com
Year Founded: 1965
CGC—(KUW)
Rev.: $579,497,313
Assets: $767,769,946
Liabilities: $637,646,700
Net Worth: $130,123,246
Earnings: ($27,464,520)
Emp.: 8,328
Fiscal Year-end: 12/31/20
Mechanical, Sanitary & Building Construction Contractor
N.A.I.C.S.: 238190
Abdul Rahman Mousa Al Marouf
(Chm)

Subsidiaries:

Al Marouf and Al Barjas Combined
for General Trading and Contracting
Company - Abdul Rahman Mousaa Al
Marouf and Partner's - W.L.L.   (1)
Block No 2 Plot No 284 Al Ardiya Industrial, Kuwait, Kuwait
Tel.: (965) 22254545
Housing & Building Construction Services
N.A.I.C.S.: 541330

Combined General for General Trad-
ing & Contracting Co. W.L.L.   (1)
Block No 2 Plot No 284, Al Ardiya Industrial, Kuwait, Kuwait
Tel.: (965) 22050333
Oil & Gas Services
N.A.I.C.S.: 213112

Combined Group Contracting Co.
W.L.L.   (1)
South Ghubra-Way 3709-Villa No 1119, Muscat, Oman
Tel.: (968) 24235111
Building Construction & Asphalt Services
N.A.I.C.S.: 238990

Combined Group Contracting Global
Co. W.L.L.   (1)
North Ghubra Block No 1/130-Street 238-Building No 1/1/96-Flat 32, Muscat, Oman
Tel.: (968) 24491400
Building Construction & Asphalt Services
N.A.I.C.S.: 238990

Combined Group Factories Company
W.L.L.   (1)
Building no-59 Street 850 Zone 23, PO Box 23256, Doha, Qatar
Tel.: (974) 44520520
Road Construction Services

N.A.I.C.S.: 237310

Combined Group Rocks Company-
K.S.C.   (1)
Area No 5 Plot No 85 Unit 11 Floor 6 Al EqailaAl Bairaq Mall, Safat, Kuwait, Kuwait
Tel.: (965) 23824191
Real Estate Services
N.A.I.C.S.: 531390

Combined Group Trading & Contract-
ing Co. W.L.L.   (1)
Building no-59 Street 850 Zone 23, PO Box 23256, Doha, Qatar
Tel.: (974) 44520520
Road Construction Services
N.A.I.C.S.: 237310

Combined Group Trading and Con-
tracting Global - L.L.C.   (1)
Flat No 1119/b Building No 1119 Bousher Muscatgovernorate, Al-Ghubrá, Oman
Tel.: (968) 24491400
Housing & Building Construction Services
N.A.I.C.S.: 541330

Combined International Real Estate
Company- K.S.C.   (1)
Block No 2 Plot No 284, Al Ardiya Industrial Safat, Kuwait, Kuwait
Tel.: (965) 22254545
Real Estate Services
N.A.I.C.S.: 531390

Syrian Combined Group Contracting
Co. W.L.L.   (1)
Al-Shalan Opposite Fast Meal Chickens-Samadi and Attar Building-T 1, Damascus, Syria
Tel.: (963) 114445001
Road Construction Services
N.A.I.C.S.: 237310

COMBINED MOTOR HOLDINGS LIMITED
1 Wilton Crescent Umhlanga Ridge, Durban, 4319, South Africa
Tel.: (27) 315804200   ZA
Web Site: https://www.cmh.co.za
CMH—(JSE)
Rev.: $699,242,655
Assets: $282,399,389
Liabilities: $207,913,358
Net Worth: $74,486,031
Earnings: $22,246,039
Emp.: 2,555
Fiscal Year-end: 02/29/24
Holding Company; New Car Dealerships
N.A.I.C.S.: 551112
Stuart K. Jackson *(Dir-Fin)*

Subsidiaries:

Bonerts (Pty) Ltd   (1)
7-14 Barney Rd, Benrose, Johannesburg, 2094, Gauteng, South Africa
Tel.: (27) 115384600
Web Site: http://www.bonerts.co.za
Sales Range: $50-74.9 Million
Used Automotives & Parts Retailer
N.A.I.C.S.: 423110
Hein Pretorius *(Mgr-Parts)*

CMH Car Hire (Pty) Ltd   (1)
109 Monty Naicker Street, Durban, 4001, Kwazulu-Natal, South Africa
Tel.: (27) 112309999
Web Site: http://www.firstcarrental.co.za
Sales Range: $150-199.9 Million
Emp.: 468
Car Rental Services
N.A.I.C.S.: 532111

Cmh Autogas Products (Pty) Ltd   (1)
1 Wilton Crescent, Umhlanga Ridge, Durban, 4319, Kwazulu-Natal, South Africa
Tel.: (27) 315804200
Web Site: http://www.cmh.co.za
Sales Range: $25-49.9 Million
Emp.: 6
Automotive Gas Conversion Services
N.A.I.C.S.: 811111

COMBINEDX AB

Tynasgatan 10, 652 16, Karlstad, Sweden
Tel.: (46) 544002510
Web Site:
    https://www.combinedx.com
Year Founded: 1993
CX—(OMX)
Rev.: $76,012,073
Assets: $62,868,546
Liabilities: $25,552,445
Net Worth: $37,316,100
Earnings: $7,038,339
Emp.: 595
Fiscal Year-end: 12/31/23
Information Technology Services
N.A.I.C.S.: 541512
Jorgen Qwist *(Pres)*

COMBOIOS DE PORTUGAL
Calcada do Duque 20, 1294-109, Lisbon, Portugal
Tel.: (351) 707210220
Web Site: http://www.cp.pt
Railroad Operator
N.A.I.C.S.: 482111

COMCATER PTY. LTD.
156 Swann Dr Derrimut, Melbourne, 3030, VIC, Australia
Tel.: (61) 3 8369 4600   AU
Web Site:
    http://www.comcater.com.au
Year Founded: 1979
Sales Range: $25-49.9 Million
Emp.: 160
Food Service Equipment Supplier
N.A.I.C.S.: 423490
Michael Wood *(CEO)*

COMCEREAL SA BACAU
Calea Moldovei 94, Bacau, Romania
Tel.: (40) 234524453   RO
CMBC—(BUC)
Sales Range: $1-9.9 Million
Emp.: 58
Grain Storage Services & Whslr
N.A.I.C.S.: 424510
Costel Donici *(Pres & Gen Mgr)*

COMCEREAL SA BOTOSANI
Calea Nationala No 41, Botosani, Romania
Tel.: (40) 231512781   RO
Web Site: https://www.comcerealbt.ro
CBOT—(BUC)
Rev.: $29,558,241
Assets: $10,908,337
Liabilities: $7,072,359
Net Worth: $3,835,978
Earnings: ($891,136)
Emp.: 171
Fiscal Year-end: 12/31/20
Grain Storage Services & Whslr
N.A.I.C.S.: 424510
Marian Andreev *(Pres)*

COMCEREAL SA BUCURESTI
Str Brezoianu Nr 12 Etaj 1 Ap 5 Cam 1 Sector 5, Bucharest, Romania
Tel.: (40) 213135467   RO
Web Site:
    https://www.comcerealbucuresti.ro
Year Founded: 1996
CMIL—(BUC)
Grain & Animal Feed Storage Services & Whslr
N.A.I.C.S.: 424510
Florica Nucuta *(Pres)*

COMCEREAL SA SLOBOZIA
Str Matei Basarab no 137, Slobozia, Ialomita, Romania
Tel.: (40) 243236941   RO
Web Site:
    https://www.comcerealslobozia.ro

COCB—(BUC)
Rev.: $38,086
Assets: $2,167,910
Liabilities: $569,279
Net Worth: $1,598,630
Earnings: ($38,086)
Emp.: 2
Fiscal Year-end: 12/31/20
Grain Storage Services & Whslr
N.A.I.C.S.: 424510
Marian Balan *(Pres, Gen Dir & Gen Mgr)*

COMCEREAL SA TULCEA
73 Isaccei street 3rd floor, Tulcea, Romania
Tel.: (40) 240534061   RO
Web Site:
    https://www.comcerealtulcea.ro
Year Founded: 1995
CTUL—(BUC)
Rev.: $13,915,034
Assets: $12,226,930
Liabilities: $4,246,697
Net Worth: $7,980,233
Earnings: $51,877
Emp.: 47
Fiscal Year-end: 12/31/20
Grain Storage Services & Whslr
N.A.I.C.S.: 424510
Emilian-Mihai Niculescu *(Gen Mgr)*

COMCM S.A.
Bd Aurel Vlaicu Nr 144, Constanta, Romania
Tel.: (40) 241617308
Web Site: https://www.comcm.ro
CMCM—(BUC)
Rev.: $274,165
Assets: $41,454,035
Liabilities: $25,519,094
Net Worth: $15,934,941
Earnings: ($889,257)
Fiscal Year-end: 12/31/22
Warehouse Rental Services
N.A.I.C.S.: 531130

Subsidiaries:

Scut SA   (1)
Bld A Vlaicu Nr 144, Constanta, Romania
Tel.: (40) 241 622016
Sales Range: $400-449.9 Million
Emp.: 12
Building Construction Services
N.A.I.C.S.: 236220
Constantin Fratila *(Pres & Gen Mgr)*

COMDAT DATASYSTEMS AG
Wagistrasse 23, 8952, Schlieren, Switzerland
Tel.: (41) 447382424
Web Site: http://www.comdat.ch
Year Founded: 1988
Sales Range: $10-24.9 Million
Information & Communications Technology Services
N.A.I.C.S.: 541519
Sergio Kaufmann *(Mng Dir)*

Subsidiaries:

ServiceOne AG   (1)
Hertistrasse 26, Wallisellen, 8304, Bulach, Switzerland
Tel.: (41) 44 877 73 73
Information Technology Solutions & Services Specializing in Imaging, Printing & Multimedia; Supplier of Photocopying Machines & Other Imaging Products
N.A.I.C.S.: 541512
Andreas Spahni *(Gen mgr)*

COME AND STAY S.A.
22 bis rue des Volontaires, 75015, Paris, France
Tel.: (33) 142849696
Year Founded: 2000
Sales Range: $25-49.9 Million
Emp.: 144

Come and Stay S.A.—(Continued)

Email & Mobile Advertising Services
N.A.I.C.S.: 541890
Carole Walter (Chm, CEO & Dir Gen)

Subsidiaries:

Come&Stay DKH A/S   (1)
Lindedej, 655220, Odense, Denmark
Tel.: (45) 70260006
Sales Range: $25-49.9 Million
Emp.: 10
Mobile Phone Advertising Services
N.A.I.C.S.: 541810

Come&Stay Spain SL   (1)
Zurdano 45 1Fl, 28010, Madrid, Spain
Tel.: (34) 915343972
Sales Range: $25-49.9 Million
Emp.: 6
Mobile Phone Advertising Services
N.A.I.C.S.: 541810

**COME SURE GROUP (HOLD-
INGS) LIMITED**
Units 8-10 8th Floor Cornell Centre
50 Wing Tai Road, Chai Wan, China
(Hong Kong)
Tel.: (852) 2 889 0310
Web Site: http://www.comesure.com
0794—(HKG)
Rev.: $151,844,414
Assets: $167,579,071
Liabilities: $85,231,145
Net Worth: $82,347,926
Earnings: ($5,143,980)
Emp.: 1,174
Fiscal Year-end: 03/31/22
Paper Packaging Industry
N.A.I.C.S.: 322130
Wa Pan Chong (Pres & CEO)

Subsidiaries:

Wise Luck International (HK)
Limited   (1)
RM 1505 South China Ind Building No 1
Chun Pin Street, Kwai Chung, New Territo-
ries, China (Hong Kong)
Tel.: (852) 24800681
Web Site: http://www.leathergoods.com.cn
Emp.: 500
Leather Goods Mfr
N.A.I.C.S.: 316990

COME TO AGREEMENT LTD.
376 Highway 7 East Suite 218, Rich-
mond Hill, L4B 0C7, ON, Canada
Web Site:
    https://cometoagreement.com
Year Founded: 1999
Software Development Services
N.A.I.C.S.: 541511

**COME TRUE BIOMEDICAL,
INC.**
10-6/F No 17 Cheng-te Road Ta-
tung, Taipei, Taiwan
Tel.: (886) 277230555
6236—(TPE)
Rev.: $1,002,314
Assets: $7,155,708
Liabilities: $636,932
Net Worth: $6,518,776
Earnings: ($740,643)
Fiscal Year-end: 12/31/22
Integrated Circuit Mfr & Distr
N.A.I.C.S.: 334413
Heng-Tsun Kuo (Chm & Pres)

**COMEAUS SEA FOODS LIM-
ITED**
60 Saulnierville Rd, PO Box 39,
Saulnierville, B0W 2Z0, NS, Canada
Tel.: (902) 769-2101
Web Site:
    http://www.comeausea.com
Year Founded: 1946
Rev.: $52,000,000
Emp.: 278

Sea Food Products
N.A.I.C.S.: 311710
Bernardin J. Comeau (Co-Founder)

COMEFLY OUTDOOR CO LTD
Building 1 No 895 Shiji Avenue, Qu-
zhou, 324000, Zhejiang, China
Tel.: (86) 57427718107
603908—(SHG)
Rev.: $201,590,644
Assets: $188,295,761
Liabilities: $113,315,450
Net Worth: $74,980,311
Earnings: $19,743,455
Fiscal Year-end: 12/31/22
Outdoor Apparel Mfr & Distr
N.A.I.C.S.: 315250

COMELF SA
Str Industriei nr 4, 420063, Bistrita,
Romania
Tel.: (40) 263234462
Web Site: https://www.comelf.ro
CMF—(BUC)
Rev.: $40,000,130
Assets: $35,979,770
Liabilities: $18,370,912
Net Worth: $17,608,858
Earnings: $2,008,315
Emp.: 633
Fiscal Year-end: 12/31/23
Mining Machinery & Equipment Mfr
N.A.I.C.S.: 332410
Save Constantin (Chm & Pres)

COMER INDUSTRIES S.P.A.
Via Magellano 27, 42046, Reggiolo,
Italy
Tel.: (39) 0522974111   IT
Web Site:
    http://www.comerindustries.com
Year Founded: 1970
Rev.: $131,415,604
Emp.: 1,200
Mfr, Designs & Markets Engineering
Systems & Mechatronic Solutions for
Power Transmission
N.A.I.C.S.: 541330
Fabio Storchi (Chm)

Subsidiaries:

Comer (Shanghai) Trading Company
Ltd   (1)
Room 2001 No 398 Sun Young Center, Ji-
angsu Road Changhing Distric, 200050,
Shanghai, China
Tel.: (86) 2162112718
Web Site:
    http://www.comerindustries.com.cn
Engineeering Services
N.A.I.C.S.: 541330

Comer GmbH   (1)
Im Heetwinkel 19, 46514, Schermbeck,
Germany
Tel.: (49) 2853912670
Engineeering Services
N.A.I.C.S.: 541330

Comer Inc.   (1)
12730 Virkler Dr, Charlotte, NC
28273-3885   (100%)
Tel.: (704) 588-8400
Web Site: http://www.comerinc.com
Sales Range: $75-99.9 Million
Emp.: 38
Garden Machinery Equipment Mfr
N.A.I.C.S.: 423820

Comer Industries (Shaoxing) Com-
pany Ltd.   (1)
Chang Zhuang Lou, Hua She, 312033,
Shaoxing, Zhejiang, China
Tel.: (86) 57584084080
Agricultural Equipment Mfr
N.A.I.C.S.: 333111

Comer Industries GmbH   (1)
Albert Einstein Strasse 1, 70806, Kornwes-
theim, Germany   (100%)
Tel.: (49) 7154801100

Sales Range: $25-49.9 Million
Emp.: 5
Engineeering Services
N.A.I.C.S.: 541330

Comer Industries Inc   (1)
12730 Virkler Dr, Charlotte, NC 28273-3882
Tel.: (704) 588-8400
Web Site: http://www.comerinc.com
Sales Range: $25-49.9 Million
Emp.: 42
Heavy & Civil Engineering Construction
N.A.I.C.S.: 237990
Fabio Storchi (Owner)

Comer Industries S.p.A. - Cavriago
Unit   (1)
Via Prati Vecchi 37, 42025, Cavriago, Italy
Tel.: (39) 0522943838
Emp.: 270
Industrial Machinery & Tool Mfr
N.A.I.C.S.: 333517

Comer Industries S.p.A. - Mantova
Unit   (1)
Via Guido Rossa 10, Pegognaga, 46020,
Mantua, Italy
Tel.: (39) 0522974432
Industrial Machinery & Tool Mfr
N.A.I.C.S.: 333517

Comer Industries S.p.A. - Matera
Unit   (1)
1 traversa Enzo Ferrari Area Industriale La
Martella, 75100, Matera, Italy
Tel.: (39) 0835302111
Industrial Machinery & Tool Mfr
N.A.I.C.S.: 333517

Comer Industries Sarl   (1)
Parc de l'Esplanade, 28 Rue Paul Henri
Spaak, 77462, Paris, Saint Thibault des V,
France   (100%)
Tel.: (33) 160310371
Web Site: http://www.comerindustries.com
Sales Range: $50-74.9 Million
Emp.: 10
Farm & Garden Machinery & Equipment
Whslr
N.A.I.C.S.: 423820

Comer Industries U.K. Ltd   (1)
Units 2-3 Heath Road, Merry Lees Industrial
Estate D, Leicester, LE9 9FE, United King-
dom
Tel.: (44) 1530231504
Web Site: http://www.comeindustriesr.com
Sales Range: $50-74.9 Million
Emp.: 9
Farm & Garden Machinery & Equipment
Whslr
N.A.I.C.S.: 423820

Comer Industries do Brasil Ltda.   (1)
Rua Palmyro d'Andrea 22 - Cep 13 Jardim
Porto Real II, 13485-404, Limeira, Brazil
Tel.: (55) 1934429627
Engineeering Services
N.A.I.C.S.: 541330

COMERCIAL GASSO SA
Poligon Industrial Can Calderon
C/Murcia 35 Nave C, 8030, Sant Boi
de Llobregat, Barcelona, Spain
Tel.: (34) 936529800
Web Site: http://www.gasso.com
Sales Range: $25-49.9 Million
Emp.: 60
Mfr & Distr of Hose, Hose Fittings &
Hose Assemblies
N.A.I.C.S.: 326220
Jordi Gasso (CEO)

Subsidiaries:

GASSO PORTUGAL Lda   (1)
Praceta Emidio Santana Zona Industrial
Casal Do Marco Lote 13 B, Aldeia de Paio
Pires, 2840588, Portugal
Tel.: (351) 21 2267850
Web Site: http://www.gasso.com
Sales Range: $50-74.9 Million
Emp.: 5
Rubber Hose Distr
N.A.I.C.S.: 423840
Paulo Santos (Mgr)

COMET HOLDING AG

Herrengasse 10, PO Box 141, 3175,
Flamatt, Switzerland
Tel.: (41) 317449000
Web Site: https://comet.tech
COTN—(SWX)
Rev.: $650,105,322
Assets: $617,296,009
Liabilities: $249,743,902
Net Worth: $367,552,106
Earnings: $86,595,344
Emp.: 1,382
Fiscal Year-end: 12/31/22
Holding Company; Non-Destructive
Testing, Security & Semiconductor
Industry Equipment Systems & Com-
ponents Mfr
N.A.I.C.S.: 551111
Rolf Huber (Vice Chm)

Subsidiaries:

COMET AG   (1)
Herrengasse 10, 3175, Flamatt, Switzerland
Tel.: (41) 317449000
Web Site: http://www.comet.ch
Solar Cells Mfr & Distr
N.A.I.C.S.: 334413

COMET Electronics Co. Ltd.   (1)
1201 Guiqiao Road Building 10 1st Floor,
Jin Qiao Export Processing Zone Pudong,
Shanghai, 201206, China
Tel.: (86) 21 6879 9000
Web Site: http://www.comet-group.com
X-ray Equipment Mfr
N.A.I.C.S.: 334510

COMET Mechanical Equipment
(Shanghai) Co. Ltd   (1)
1201 Guiqiao Road Building 10 1st Floor,
Jin Qiao Export Processing Zone Pudong,
Shanghai, 201206, China
Tel.: (86) 2168799000
Web Site: http://www.comet-group.com
Vacuum Capacitor Mfr
N.A.I.C.S.: 334416

COMET Technologies USA, Inc.   (1)
100 Trap Falls Rd Ext, Shelton, CT 06484
Tel.: (203) 447-3165
Web Site: http://www.comet-group.com
X-Ray Component Distr
N.A.I.C.S.: 423690

Unit (Domestic):

COMET Technologies USA, Inc. -
Plasma Control Technologies   (2)
2360 Bering Dr, San Jose, CA 95131
Tel.: (408) 325-8770
Web Site: http://www.comet-pct.com
Sales Range: $25-49.9 Million
Emp.: 49
Vacuum Capacitor Mfr
N.A.I.C.S.: 334416

COMET Technologies USA, Inc. -
X-Ray Systems   (2)
5675 Hudson Industrial Parkway, Hudson,
OH 44336
Tel.: (330) 798-4800
Web Site: http://www.comet-group.com
Sales Range: $50-74.9 Million
Emp.: 8
X-Ray Equipment Distr
N.A.I.C.S.: 423450

Comet Solutions Taiwan Ltd.   (1)
1F No 120 Guangming Rd, Qionglin Town-
ship, Hsinchu, 307001, Taiwan
Tel.: (886) 35922398
Emp.: 10
Electrical & Electronic Mfr
N.A.I.C.S.: 336320

Comet Technologies Korea Co.
Ltd.   (1)
Suwon Venture Plaza Bldg Room 402 48
Samsung-ro 168 beon-gil, Yeongtong-gu,
Suwon, 16676, Gyeonggi, Korea (South)
Tel.: (82) 7043371282
Electric Equipment Mfr
N.A.I.C.S.: 334419

Object Research Systems (ORS)
Inc.   (1)
460 Saint-Catherine St W Suite 600, Montreal, H3B 1A7, QC, Canada

Tel.: (514) 843-3861
Web Site: https://www.theobjects.com
Research & Development Services
N.A.I.C.S.: 541714

YXLON International GmbH (1)
Essener Bogen 15, 22419, Hamburg, Germany
Tel.: (49) 40527290
Web Site: http://www.yxlon.com
X-Ray Inspection Equipment Mfr
N.A.I.C.S.: 334517
Keith Bryant (Dir-Electronics Sls-Global)

Subsidiary (Non-US):

YXLON International A/S (2)
Helgeshoj Alle 38, Taastrup, 2630, Denmark
Tel.: (45) 72407700
Web Site: http://www.cph.yxlon.com
Sales Range: $10-24.9 Million
Emp.: 35
X-Ray Testing & Diagnostic Services
N.A.I.C.S.: 541380
Hans Rysgaart (Gen Mgr)

Subsidiary (Domestic):

YXLON International CT Development GmbH (2)
Am Walzwerk 41, Hattingen, D 45527, Germany
Tel.: (49) 2324 5629 0
Web Site: http://www.yxlon.com
Emp.: 6
X-Ray Inspection & Diagnostic Services
N.A.I.C.S.: 541380

YXLON International Feinfocus GmbH (2)
Im Bahlbrink 11-13, 30827, Garbsen, Germany
Tel.: (49) 513170980
Web Site: http://www.yxlon.com
Sales Range: $10-24.9 Million
Emp.: 50
X-Ray Inspection & Diagnostic Services
N.A.I.C.S.: 541380

Subsidiary (US):

YXLON International Inc. (2)
5675 Hudson Industrial Pkwy, Hudson, OH 44236
Tel.: (330) 798-4800
Web Site: http://www.yxlon.com
Sales Range: $25-49.9 Million
Emp.: 25
X-Ray Testing Systems & Services
N.A.I.C.S.: 541380

Subsidiary (Non-US):

YXLON International K.K. (2)
New Stage Yokohama Bldg 1st Floor 1-1-32 Shinurashima-cho, Kanagawa-ku, Yokohama, 221-0031, Japan
Tel.: (81) 454501730
Web Site: http://www.yxlon.co.jp
Sales Range: $25-49.9 Million
Emp.: 20
X-Ray Inspection & Diagnostic Services
N.A.I.C.S.: 541380

Yxlon (Beijing) X-Ray Equipment Trading Co. Ltd. (1)
C07 First Floor Building 2 Zhongke Industrial Park 103, Beiqing Road Haidian District, Beijing, 100004, China
Tel.: (86) 1088579581
Electrical & Electronic Mfr
N.A.I.C.S.: 336320

COMET INDUSTRIES LTD.
Suite 1710 1177 West Hastings Street, Vancouver, V6E 2L3, BC, Canada
Tel.: (604) 640-6357   Ca
Web Site: https://www.cometindustries.ca
Year Founded: 1972
CMU—(TSXV)
Rev.: $332,194
Assets: $2,074,348
Liabilities: $711,653
Net Worth: $1,362,695
Earnings: $281,773
Fiscal Year-end: 01/31/22

Metal Mining Services
N.A.I.C.S.: 212290
Richard J. Angus (CFO)

COMET RESOURCES LIMITED
Suite 9 330 Churchill Avenue, Subiaco, 6008, WA, Australia
Tel.: (61) 864891600
Web Site: http://www.cometres.com.au
CRL—(ASX)
Assets: $4,260,182
Liabilities: $670,491
Net Worth: $3,589,691
Earnings: $316,185
Emp.: 3
Fiscal Year-end: 06/30/22
Zinc & Lead Exploration & Mining Services
N.A.I.C.S.: 212230
Sonu Cheema (Sec)

COMET RIDGE LIMITED
Level 3 410 Queen Street, Brisbane, 4000, QLD, Australia
Tel.: (61) 732213661
Web Site: https://www.cometridge.com.au
COI—(ASX)
Rev.: $130,876
Assets: $80,329,861
Liabilities: $31,915,064
Net Worth: $48,414,797
Earnings: ($4,784,322)
Fiscal Year-end: 06/30/24
Oil, Gas & Coal Exploration & Mining Services
N.A.I.C.S.: 211120
Tor McCaul (Mng Dir)

Subsidiaries:

Chartwell Energy Limited (1)
Level 3 283 Elizabeth Street, Brisbane, 4000, QLD, Australia
Tel.: (61) 732213661
Web Site: http://www.cometridge.com.au
Sales Range: $50-74.9 Million
Emp.: 10
Coal Seam Gas Exploration Services
N.A.I.C.S.: 213112

Comet Ridge USA, Inc. (1)
600 17th St Ste 800-S, Denver, CO 80202   (100%)
Tel.: (303) 226-1300
Web Site: http://www.cometridgeresources.com
Sales Range: $50-74.9 Million
Emp.: 20
Oil & Gas Exploration
N.A.I.C.S.: 213111
Andy Lydyard (CEO)

Joint Venture (Domestic):

Comet Ridge Resources, LLC (2)
600 17th St Ste 800-S, Denver, CO 80202
Tel.: (303) 226-1300
Web Site: http://www.cometridgeresources.com
Oil & Gas Exploration
N.A.I.C.S.: 213111

COMET SA
Str Barsei Nr 2 Depozit 27 Complex Industrial/Comercial, Ilfov, Voluntari, Romania
Tel.: (40) 21 310 29 10
Sales Range: Less than $1 Million
Emp.: 7
Freight Transportation Services
N.A.I.C.S.: 484220
Reyad A. Tuama (Pres)

COMET UMETNI BRUSI IN NEKOVINE, D.D.
Tovarniska 5, 3214, Zrece, Slovenia
Tel.: (386) 386375750
Web Site: http://www.comet.si
Year Founded: 1958

Sales Range: $50-74.9 Million
Emp.: 750
Grinding Tools Mfr
N.A.I.C.S.: 327910
Ales Mikeln (Gen Mgr)

Subsidiaries:

Cobra GmbH (1)
St Michael ob Bleiburg 47, 9143, Saint Michael, Austria
Tel.: (43) 423535500
Web Site: http://www.cobra-austria.at
Rev.: $13,222,000
Emp.: 9
Abrasive Products Mfr & Whslr
N.A.I.C.S.: 327910

Ecopack, d.o.o. (1)
Tovarniska Cesta 5, 3214, Zrece, Slovenia
Tel.: (386) 37575494
Web Site: http://www.ecopack.si
Sales Range: $25-49.9 Million
Emp.: 10
Gasket Packing & Sealing Device Mfr
N.A.I.C.S.: 339991

Toroflex GmbH (1)
Esbachgraben 17, Bindlach, 95463, Germany
Tel.: (49) 920865810
Web Site: http://www.toroflex.de
Sales Range: $25-49.9 Million
Emp.: 15
Abrasive Products Mfr & Whslr
N.A.I.C.S.: 327910
Tita Klea (Mng Dir)

COMFORIA RESIDENTIAL REIT, INC.
21-1 Dogenzaka 1-chome, Shibuya-ku, Tokyo, Japan
Tel.: (81) 364553388
Web Site: https://www.comforia-reit.co.jp
Year Founded: 2010
3282—(TKS)
Rev.: $82,786,760
Assets: $2,466,133,950
Liabilities: $1,290,503,270
Net Worth: $1,175,630,680
Earnings: $32,305,910
Fiscal Year-end: 07/31/20
Real Estate Investment Services
N.A.I.C.S.: 531210
Takashi Sakamoto (Exec Dir)

COMFORT COMMOTRADE LIMITED
A-301 Hetal Arch Above Union Bank of India SV Road, Malad West, Mumbai, 400064, India
Tel.: (91) 2268948500
Web Site: http://www.comfortcommotrade.com
Year Founded: 1994
534691—(BOM)
Rev.: $20,732,303
Assets: $6,875,300
Liabilities: $2,558,829
Net Worth: $4,316,471
Earnings: $216,230
Emp.: 12
Fiscal Year-end: 03/31/22
Commodity Brokerage Services
N.A.I.C.S.: 523160
Rajeev Kumar Pathak (CFO)

Subsidiaries:

Comfort Securities Limited (1)
A-301 Hetal Arch S V Road Opp Natraj Marke, Malad West, Mumbai, 400064, Maharashtra, India
Tel.: (91) 2228825509
Web Site: https://www.comfortsecurities.co.in
Financial Investment Services
N.A.I.C.S.: 523999
Anil Agrawal (Founder)

COMFORT FINCAP LIMITED
A-301 Hetal Arch S V Road Opp Na-

traj Market, Malad West, Mumbai, 400064, India
Tel.: (91) 2268948500   In
Web Site: https://www.comfortfincap.com
Year Founded: 1982
535267—(BOM)
Rev.: $1,520,314
Assets: $10,037,323
Liabilities: $4,471,466
Net Worth: $5,565,857
Earnings: $570,567
Emp.: 9
Fiscal Year-end: 03/31/21
Non Banking Financial Services
N.A.I.C.S.: 523999
Bharat N. Shiroya (CEO)

COMFORT GLOVES BERHAD
Lot 821 Jalan Matang, 34750, Perak, Malaysia
Tel.: (60) 58472777   MY
Web Site: https://www.comfort-rubber.com.my
COMFORT—(KLS)
Rev.: $344,187,206
Assets: $291,945,881
Liabilities: $60,546,642
Net Worth: $231,399,239
Earnings: $104,325,977
Fiscal Year-end: 12/31/21
Investment Holding Services
N.A.I.C.S.: 551112
Joo Yong Lau (Exec Dir)

Subsidiaries:

Comfort Rubber Gloves Industries Sdn. Bhd. (1)
Lot 821 Jalan Matang, Matang, 34750, Perak, Malaysia
Tel.: (60) 58472777
Web Site: https://www.comfort-rubber.com.my
Natural Rubber Product Mfr
N.A.I.C.S.: 326299
Chan Seng Fatt (Chm)

Subsidiary (Domestic):

Gallant Quality Sdn. Bhd. (2)
Lot 1874 Jalan Kampung Dew Simpang Halt, 34700, Taiping, Perak, Malaysia
Tel.: (60) 58494931
Web Site: http://www.gallant-quality.com.my
Glove Mfr
N.A.I.C.S.: 315990

COMFORT INTECH LIMITED
106 Avkar Algani Nagar Kalaria, Daman, 396 210, India
Tel.: (91) 2268948500
Web Site: https://www.comfortintech.com
Year Founded: 1994
531216—(BOM)
Rev.: $18,088,502
Assets: $19,938,678
Liabilities: $4,210,861
Net Worth: $15,727,817
Earnings: $1,060,905
Emp.: 9
Fiscal Year-end: 03/31/22
Financial Services
N.A.I.C.S.: 522291
Ankur Agrawal (Exec Dir)

COMFORT-SERVICE PJSC
15 Sim'i Hohlovih str, Kiev, Ukraine
Tel.: (380) 44 590 29 27
Web Site: http://www.comfort-service.com
Air-Conditioning, Room Heating & Ventilation System Mfr
N.A.I.C.S.: 333415

COMFORTDELGRO CORPORATION LIMITED
205 Braddell Road, Singapore, 579701, Singapore

ComfortDelGro Corporation Limited—(Continued)

Tel.: (65) 63838833
Web Site:
https://www.comfortdelgro.com
Year Founded: 1971
CDGLY—(OTCIQ)
Rev.: $2,801,630,233
Assets: $3,483,364,209
Liabilities: $1,260,763,246
Net Worth: $2,222,600,963
Earnings: $161,911,819
Emp.: 22,972
Fiscal Year-end: 12/31/22
Public Passenger Transport Services
N.A.I.C.S.: 485999
Tammy I-Lin Tan (Chief Corp Comm
Officer)

Subsidiaries:

Beijing Jin Jian Taxi Services Co.,
Ltd. **(1)**
Beijing Jian Jian Office Building Shifu Road
A2, Shi Jing Shan District, Beijing, 100042,
China
Tel.: (86) 1088951608
Transit Services
N.A.I.C.S.: 485999
Emily Wu (Gen Mgr)

Buslink Alice Springs Pty. Ltd. **(1)**
7 Kidman Street, Alice Springs, 0870, NT,
Australia
Tel.: (61) 889525611
Logistic Services
N.A.I.C.S.: 541614

Buslink Broken Hill Pty. Ltd. **(1)**
563-565 Chapple Lane, Broken Hill, 2880,
NSW, Australia
Tel.: (61) 880873311
Logistic Services
N.A.I.C.S.: 541614

Buslink Gladstone Pty. Ltd. **(1)**
9 Lyons Street, Gladstone, 4680, QLD, Aus-
tralia
Tel.: (61) 749721670
Logistic Services
N.A.I.C.S.: 541614

Buslink NT Pty. Ltd. **(1)**
113 Pruen Road, PO Box 1426, Berrimah,
0828, NT, Australia
Tel.: (61) 889442444
Logistic Services
N.A.I.C.S.: 541614

Buslink Sunraysia Pty. Ltd. **(1)**
10 Bathurst Court, Mildura, 3500, VIC, Aus-
tralia
Tel.: (61) 350230274
Logistic Services
N.A.I.C.S.: 541614

Buslink Sunshine Coast Pty. Ltd. **(1)**
11 Page Street, Kunda Park, 4556, QLD,
Australia
Tel.: (61) 754766622
Logistic Services
N.A.I.C.S.: 541614
Bertram Birk (Gen Mgr)

CDC Oakleigh Pty. Ltd. **(1)**
1340-1344 North Rd South, Oakleigh, 3167,
VIC, Australia
Tel.: (61) 385456000
Logistic Services
N.A.I.C.S.: 541614

CDC Sunshine Pty. Ltd. **(1)**
14 Carrington Dr, Sunshine, 3020, VIC,
Australia
Tel.: (61) 393900111
Logistic Services
N.A.I.C.S.: 541614
Shaun Lawson (Mgr-Delivery Svc)

CDC Tullamarine Pty. Ltd. **(1)**
1-13 Louis Street, Airport West, Tullama-
rine, 3042, VIC, Australia
Tel.: (61) 393386466
Logistic Services
N.A.I.C.S.: 541614

CDC Victoria Pty. Ltd. **(1)**
28 Prosperity Street, Truganina, 3029, VIC,
Australia

Tel.: (61) 399779999
Web Site: https://www.cdcvictoria.com.au
Emp.: 1,000
Transit Services
N.A.I.C.S.: 485999
Marcelle Davis (Gen Mgr-People, Culture &
Ops)

Subsidiary (Domestic):

CDC Ballarat Pty. Ltd. **(2)**
804 Norman St, Ballarat, 3350, VIC, Austra-
lia
Tel.: (61) 353317777
Logistic Services
N.A.I.C.S.: 541614

CDC Geelong Pty. Ltd. **(2)**
65 Edols St, North Geelong, 3215, VIC,
Australia
Tel.: (61) 352405000
Logistic Services
N.A.I.C.S.: 541614

CDC Wyndham Pty. Ltd. **(1)**
28 Prosperity Street, Truganina, 3029, VIC,
Australia
Tel.: (61) 399779900
Logistic Services
N.A.I.C.S.: 541614

Chengdu ComfortDelGro Qingyang
Driving School Co., Ltd. **(1)**
Wen Jia Hong Nian Zi, Qing Yang Zone,
Chengdu, 610091, Sichuan, China
Tel.: (86) 2887070700
Transit Services
N.A.I.C.S.: 485999
Dennis Lim (CEO)

Chengdu ComfortDelGro Taxi Co.,
Ltd. **(1)**
801-1802 18/F Building 3 West International
Jewelry Center No 52, Shuxi Road Jinniu
District, Chengdu, 610037, Sichuan, China
Tel.: (86) 2884715206
Transit Services
N.A.I.C.S.: 485999

CityCab (Shenyang) Co., Ltd. **(1)**
No 52 Wen Hua East Road, Shenhe Dis-
trict, Shenyang, 110015, Liaoning, China
Tel.: (86) 2424207819
Transit Services
N.A.I.C.S.: 485999
Marc Tay (CEO)

CityCab Pte. Ltd. **(1)**
600 Sin Ming Avenue, Singapore, 575733,
Singapore
Tel.: (65) 65551188
Web Site: http://www.cdgtaxi.com.sg
Transit Services
N.A.I.C.S.: 485999

CityFleet Networks Limited **(1)**
7 Woodfield Road, London, W9 2BA, United
Kingdom
Tel.: (44) 22074321630
Web Site: http://www.cityfleetnetworks.com
Transit Services
N.A.I.C.S.: 485999
Steven Bearman (Mgr-Data Analytics)

Subsidiary (Domestic):

Addison Lee Limited **(2)**
35-37 William Road, London, NW1 3ER,
United Kingdom
Tel.: (44) 2073878888
Web Site: http://www.addisonlee.com
Transportation Services
N.A.I.C.S.: 485999

Computer Cab (Aberdeen)
Limited **(2)**
Burnside Drive, Aberdeen, AB21 0HW,
United Kingdom
Tel.: (44) 1224353535
Web Site: http://www.comcab-
aberdeen.co.uk
Logistic Services
N.A.I.C.S.: 541614
Scott Milne Douglas (Gen Mgr)

Computer Cab (Liverpool)
Limited **(2)**
Abbey House 5-7 Falkland Street, Liver-
pool, L3 8HB, United Kingdom
Tel.: (44) 1512982222
Web Site: http://www.comcab-liverpool.co.uk

Logistic Services
N.A.I.C.S.: 541614

Computer Cab plc **(2)**
Advantage House Unit 7-8, Mitre Bridge
Industrial Park Mitre Way, London, W10
6AU, United Kingdom
Tel.: (44) 2079080271
Transit Services
N.A.I.C.S.: 485000
Rudy Tan Lai (CEO)

Flightlink International Limited **(2)**
104 Cannon Workshops Cannon Drive,
London, E14 4AS, United Kingdom
Tel.: (44) 2075374777
Transit Services
N.A.I.C.S.: 485999

Westbus Coach Services Limited **(2)**
12 Rigby Lane, Hayes, London, UB3 1ET,
Middlesex, United Kingdom
Tel.: (44) 2087564099
Web Site: https://www.westbus.co.uk
Transit Services
N.A.I.C.S.: 485999
Tim Miles (Gen Mgr)

CityLimo Leasing (M) Sdn. Bhd. **(1)**
No 10 SS13/6, Subang Jaya Industrial Es-
tate, 47500, Subang Jaya, Selangor, Malay-
sia
Tel.: (60) 356381818
Web Site: https://www.citylimo.com.my
Car & Vehicle Leasing Services
N.A.I.C.S.: 532112

Comfort Transportation Pte Ltd **(1)**
383 Sin Ming Drive, Singapore, 575717,
Singapore
Transit Services
N.A.I.C.S.: 485999

ComfortDelGro Bus Pte Ltd **(1)**
205 Braddell Road, Singapore, 579701,
Singapore
Web Site: https://www.comfortdelgro.com
Transit Services
N.A.I.C.S.: 485999

ComfortDelGro Cabcharge Pty.
Ltd. **(1)**
29 Foundry Road, Seven Hills, 2147, NSW,
Australia **(100%)**
Tel.: (61) 298900000
Web Site: http://www.cdcbus.com.au
Sales Range: $50-74.9 Million
Emp.: 120
Passenger Bus Service Operator; Joint
Venture of ComfortDelGro Corporation Lim-
ited (51%) & Cabcharge Australia Limited
(49%)
N.A.I.C.S.: 485113

ComfortDelGro Corporation Australia
Pty. Ltd. **(1)**
28 Prosperity Street, Truganina, 3029, VIC,
Australia
Tel.: (61) 399779999
Emp.: 4,800
Transit Services
N.A.I.C.S.: 485999
Nicholas Yap (CEO)

Subsidiary (Domestic):

A2B Australia Limited **(2)**
Cabcharge House 152-162 Riley Street,
Sydney, 2010, NSW, Australia **(100%)**
Tel.: (61) 293329248
Web Site: http://www.a2baustralia.com
Rev.: $96,645,674
Assets: $136,437,752
Liabilities: $70,438,145
Net Worth: $65,999,607
Earnings: ($21,313,873)
Fiscal Year-end: 06/30/2022
Electronic Taxi Fare Payment Systems De-
veloper & Mfr
N.A.I.C.S.: 488999

Subsidiary (Domestic):

13cabs Innovations Pty. Ltd. **(3)**
9-13 ORiordan Street, Alexandria, 2015,
NSW, Australia
Tel.: (61) 290202000
Passenger Taxi Services
N.A.I.C.S.: 485310

Black Cabs Combined Pty Ltd **(3)**

37-41 Oxford Street, Oakleigh, 3166, VIC,
Australia
Tel.: (61) 392773700
Web Site: http://www.13cabs.com.au
Sales Range: $50-74.9 Million
Emp.: 200
Taxi Service
N.A.I.C.S.: 485310

Cabcharge Payments Pty. Ltd. **(3)**
9-13 O Riordan Street, Alexandria, 2015,
NSW, Australia
Tel.: (61) 293329222
Web Site: https://www.cabcharge.com.au
Taxicab Card Advertising Services
N.A.I.C.S.: 541850

Combined Communications Network
Pty Ltd **(3)**
9-13 O Riordan Street, Alexandria, 2015,
NSW, Australia **(100%)**
Tel.: (61) 290202244
Web Site: http://www.ccnetwork.com.au
Sales Range: $50-74.9 Million
Emp.: 200
Taxi Service
N.A.I.C.S.: 485310

EFT Solutions Pty Ltd **(3)**
1/9 Apollo Street, Warriewood, Sydney,
2102, NSW, Australia
Tel.: (61) 290202180
Web Site: http://www.eftsolutions.com.au
Software Development Consulting Services
N.A.I.C.S.: 541512

Kingscliff Tweed Coast Taxis Pty.
Ltd. **(3)**
5/44-46 Ourimbah Road, Tweed Heads,
2485, NSW, Australia
Tel.: (61) 477666991
Web Site: https://www.kingsclifftaxis.com.au
Passenger Taxi Services
N.A.I.C.S.: 485310

Subsidiary (US):

Mobile Technologies International
LLC **(3)**
12150 E Briarwood Ave Ste 110, Centen-
nial, CO 80112
Tel.: (303) 882-0893
Electronic Taxi Fare Payment Systems De-
veloper & Mfr
N.A.I.C.S.: 541714

Subsidiary (Domestic):

Mobile Technologies International Pty.
Ltd. **(3)**
Level 3 18-20 Compark Circuit, Mulgrave,
3170, VIC, Australia
Tel.: (61) 385264800
Taxicab Dispatch Services
N.A.I.C.S.: 485310

Newcastle Taxis Ltd **(3)**
5/8 Channel Road, Mayfield West,
Newcastle, 2304, NSW, Australia
Tel.: (61) 249405955
Web Site: http://www.newcastletaxis.com.au
Sales Range: $25-49.9 Million
Emp.: 30
Taxi Service
N.A.I.C.S.: 485310

Taxi Combined Services Pty Ltd **(3)**
9-13 O Riordan St, Alexandria, 2015, NSW,
Australia **(100%)**
Tel.: (61) 290202244
Web Site: http://www.taxicombined.com.au
Sales Range: $50-74.9 Million
Emp.: 200
Taxi Service
N.A.I.C.S.: 485310
Frederick Lukabyo (CEO)

Tweed Heads Coolangatta Taxi Ser-
vice Pty. Ltd. **(3)**
5/44-46 Ourimbah Road, Tweed Heads,
2485, NSW, Australia
Tel.: (61) 755363371
Web Site: https://tweedtaxis.com.au
Passenger Taxi Services
N.A.I.C.S.: 485310

Yellow Cabs of Sydney Pty. Ltd. **(3)**
9-13 O Riordan Street, Alexandria, 2015,
Australia **(100%)**
Tel.: (61) 290202244

Web Site: http://www.yellowcabs.com
Sales Range: $50-74.9 Million
Emp.: 200
Taxi Service
N.A.I.C.S.: 485310
Frederick Lukabyo *(CEO)*

ComfortDelGro Driving Centre Pte.
Ltd. (1)
205 Ubi Ave 4, Singapore, 408805, Singapore
Tel.: (65) 68418900
Web Site: https://www.cdc.com.sg
Commercial Services
N.A.I.C.S.: 561499

ComfortDelGro Engineering Pte
Ltd (1)
205 Braddell Road, Singapore, 579701,
Singapore
Tel.: (65) 6 383 6280
Web Site: https://www.cdge.com.sg
Transit Services
N.A.I.C.S.: 485999
May Yin *(Asst Mgr)*

ComfortDelGro Insurance Brokers
Pte. Ltd. (1)
205 Braddell Road, Singapore, 579701,
Singapore
Tel.: (65) 63838833
Transit Services
N.A.I.C.S.: 485999
Chua Beng Peng *(CEO)*

ComfortDelGro Irish Citylink
Limited (1)
Irish Citylink 17 Forster St, Galway, Ireland
Tel.: (353) 91564164
Web Site: https://www.citylink.ie
Emp.: 500
Transit Services
N.A.I.C.S.: 485999
Colette Lally *(Gen Mgr)*

ComfortDelGro Rent-A-Car
(Chengdu) Co., Ltd. (1)
No 77 Chuan Jian Road, Jinniu District,
Shenyang, 610081, Sichuan, China
Tel.: (86) 2884718859
Transit Services
N.A.I.C.S.: 485999

ComfortDelGro Rent-A-Car Pte.
Ltd. (1)
205 Braddell Road, Singapore, 579701,
Singapore
Tel.: (65) 68820888
Web Site: https://www.cdgrentacar.com.sg
Car & Vehicle Leasing Services
N.A.I.C.S.: 532112
Christie Ho *(Sr Mgr-Sls)*

Forest Coach Lines Pty. Limited (1)
335 Mona Vale Rd, Terrey Hills, 2084,
NSW, Australia
Tel.: (61) 294502277
Web Site:
   http://www.forestcoachlines.com.au
Emp.: 250
Transit Services
N.A.I.C.S.: 485999

Guangzhou Xin Tian Wei Transporta-
tion Development Co., Ltd. (1)
No 633 Yanling Road, Guangzhou, 510650,
Guangdong, China
Tel.: (86) 2089285680
Web Site: https://www.tianhebus.com
Transit Services
N.A.I.C.S.: 485999

JIC Inspection Services Pte. Ltd. (1)
53 Pioneer Road, Singapore, 628505, Singapore
Tel.: (65) 68639639
Transit Services
N.A.I.C.S.: 485999
Sim Wing Yew *(CEO)*

Jilin ComfortDelGro Taxi Co.,
Ltd. (1)
West side of Chengnan Street, High-tech
Industrial Development Zone, Jilin, Jilin,
China
Tel.: (86) 43264565609
Transit Services
N.A.I.C.S.: 485999
Ni Xi Peng *(Gen Mgr)*

Metroline Limited (1)
ComfortDelGro House 3rd Floor 329 Edgware Road, Cricklewood, London, NW2
6JP, United Kingdom
Tel.: (44) 3432221234
Web Site: https://www.metroline.co.uk
Transit Services
N.A.I.C.S.: 485999
Sean O'Shea *(CEO)*

Moove Media Pte. Ltd. (1)
600 Sin Ming Ave CityCab Building Level 2,
Singapore, 575733, Singapore
Tel.: (65) 63837035
Web Site: https://www.moovemedia.com.sg
Transit Services
N.A.I.C.S.: 485999
Chng Peng Yam *(Mgr-Ops)*

Subsidiary (Non-US):

Moove Media Australia Pty. Ltd. (2)
15 Belvoir Street, Surry Hills, 2010, NSW,
Australia
Tel.: (61) 296901144
Web Site: https://www.moovemedia.com.au
Advertising Services
N.A.I.C.S.: 541810
Mark Wooldridge *(Gen Mgr)*

Nanjing ComfortDelGro Dajian Taxi
Co., Ltd. (1)
38 Kazimen Street, Yu Hua Tai District,
Nanjing, 210012, Jiangsu, China
Tel.: (86) 2558721710
Transit Services
N.A.I.C.S.: 485999

Nanjing ComfortDelGro Xixia Driver
Training Co., Ltd. (1)
33 Jingtian Road, Xigang Sub-district Qixia
District, Nanjing, 210033, Jiangsu, China
Tel.: (86) 2585711368
Transit Services
N.A.I.C.S.: 485999

Nanning Comfort Transportation Co.,
Ltd. (1)
Room 202 2nd Floor Block A Building 15
No 68 Ke Yuan Avenue, Nanning, 530007,
Guangxi, China
Tel.: (86) 7715816783
Transit Services
N.A.I.C.S.: 485999

National Patient Transport Pty.
Ltd. (1)
3/158-168 Browns Road, Noble Park North,
Melbourne, 3174, VIC, Australia
Tel.: (61) 385884888
Web Site: https://www.nptgroup.com.au
Transit Services
N.A.I.C.S.: 485999
Jeffrey Wilson *(CEO)*

Subsidiary (Domestic):

Platinum Healthcare Pty. Ltd. (2)
Level 1 Suite 1 22 Hardy Street, South
Perth, 6151, WA, Australia
Tel.: (61) 894704075
Web Site:
   http://www.platinumhealthcare.com.au
Health Care Srvices
N.A.I.C.S.: 621999

Western Sydney Repair Centre Pty
Ltd (2)
93 Lee Holm Rd, Saint Marys, 2760, NSW,
Australia
Tel.: (61) 1300977200
Web Site: http://www.ws-rc.com.au
Automotive Services
N.A.I.C.S.: 811111

New Adventure Travel Limited (1)
Coaster Place, Cardiff, CF10 4XZ, United
Kingdom
Tel.: (44) 2920442040
Web Site:
   https://www.adventuretravel.cymru
Transit Services
N.A.I.C.S.: 485999

Qcity Transit Pty. Ltd. (1)
11 Bass Street, Queanbeyan, 2620, NSW,
Australia
Tel.: (61) 262993722
Web Site: https://www.qcitytransit.com.au
Emp.: 220

Transit Services
N.A.I.C.S.: 485999
Stephen Bushby *(Mgr-Depot)*

SBS Transit DTL Pte. Ltd. (1)
205 Braddell Road, Singapore, 579701,
Singapore
Tel.: (65) 62848866
Transit Services
N.A.I.C.S.: 485999

SBS Transit Ltd. (1)
205 Braddell Road, Singapore, 579701,
Singapore
Tel.: (65) 62848866
Web Site: https://www.sbstransit.com.sg
Sales Range: $300-349.9 Million
Emp.: 7,136
Bus Transportation Services
N.A.I.C.S.: 485113
Kum Ee Chew *(VP-Fin)*

Scottish Citylink Coaches
Limited (1)
Buchanan Bus Station Killermont Street,
Glasgow, G2 3NW, United
Kingdom (65%)
Tel.: (44) 141 352 4444
Web Site: https://www.citylink.co.uk
Logistic Services
N.A.I.C.S.: 541614

Shanghai City Qi Ai Taxi Services
Co., Ltd. (1)
10F No 285 Lu Jia Bang Road, Shanghai,
200011, China
Tel.: (86) 2163135248
Transit Services
N.A.I.C.S.: 485999

Shenyang ComfortDelGro Taxi Co.,
Ltd. (1)
No 52 Wen Hua East Road, Shenhe District, Shenyang, 110015, Liaoning, China
Tel.: (86) 2424207819
Transit Services
N.A.I.C.S.: 485999

Suzhou Comfort Taxi Co., Ltd. (1)
Room A506 No 199 Dong Xing Road, Industrial Park, Suzhou, 215000, China
Tel.: (86) 51267620203
Transit Services
N.A.I.C.S.: 485999
Laurence Lee *(CEO)*

Swan Taxis Pty. Ltd. (1)
7 Harvey St, PO Box 4058, Victoria Park,
6100, WA, Australia
Tel.: (61) 894222222
Web Site: https://www.swantaxis.com.au
Transit Services
N.A.I.C.S.: 485999

Subsidiary (Domestic):

ComfortDelGro Swan Pty. Ltd. (2)
24 Rudloc Road, Morley, 6062, WA, Australia
Tel.: (61) 893753331
Transit Services
N.A.I.C.S.: 485999
Carey John Marshall *(CEO)*

VICOM Ltd. (1)
385 Sin Ming Drive, Singapore, 575718,
Singapore
Tel.: (65) 64584555
Web Site: https://www.vicom.com.sg
Rev.: $84,755,737
Assets: $148,732,106
Liabilities: $48,526,093
Net Worth: $100,206,014
Earnings: $21,217,905
Emp.: 940
Fiscal Year-end: 12/31/2023
Technical Testing & Inspection Services
N.A.I.C.S.: 541380
Chun Wah Yip *(VP-Ops Support)*

Subsidiary (Non-US):

Blue Mountains Transit Pty. Ltd. (2)
25 Great Western Highway, Valley Heights,
Sydney, 2777, NSW, Australia
Tel.: (61) 247511077
Transit Services
N.A.I.C.S.: 485999

Hillsbus Co Pty. Ltd. (2)

29 Foundry Road, Seven Hills, 2147, NSW,
Australia
Tel.: (61) 298900000
Web Site: https://cdcbus.com.au
Transit Services
N.A.I.C.S.: 485999
Wayne Jeff *(CEO)*

Subsidiary (Domestic):

Setsco Services Pte. Ltd. (2)
531 Bukit Batok Street 23, Singapore,
659547, Singapore
Tel.: (65) 65667777
Web Site: https://www.setsco.com
Consultancy Services
N.A.I.C.S.: 541618
Lay Kuan Koh *(Mgr)*

Subsidiary (Domestic):

Setsco Consultancy International Pte.
Ltd. (3)
18 Teban Gardens Crescent, Singapore,
608925, Singapore
Tel.: (65) 65667777
Transit Services
N.A.I.C.S.: 485999

Subsidiary (Non-US):

Setsco Services (M) Sdn. Bhd. (3)
31 Jalan Industri Mas 12 Taman Mas,
47100, Puchong, Selangor, Malaysia
Tel.: (60) 380526822
Transit Services
N.A.I.C.S.: 485999
Chia Wing Too *(Gen Mgr)*

Vietnam Taxi Co., Ltd. (1)
Lot IV - 15B Road 4 - Tan Binh IP, Tay
Thanh Ward Tan Phu District, Ho Chi Minh
City, Vietnam
Tel.: (84) 2838155152
Web Site: http://www.vinataxi.vn
Transit Services
N.A.I.C.S.: 485999

COMINCA SA
Str Octavian Goga 4, Bihor, Oradea,
Romania
Tel.: (40) 259 435900
Sales Range: Less than $1 Million
Emp.: 3
Meat Processing & Preservation Services
N.A.I.C.S.: 311612

COMINCO S.A.
Magheru Boulevard no 31 1 Sector,
Bucharest, Romania
Tel.: (40) 213672853
Web Site: http://www.cominco.ro
Sales Range: $25-49.9 Million
Emp.: 336
General Contracting Services
N.A.I.C.S.: 236116
Gheorghe Gemanar *(Chm)*

COMINIX CO., LTD.
JRE-Sakaisuji-Hommachi Bldg 1-8-14
Minamihommachi, Chuo-ku, Osaka,
541-0054, Japan
Tel.: (81) 676638208
Web Site: https://www.cominix.jp
Year Founded: 1950
3173—(TKS)
Rev.: $189,336,840
Assets: $121,994,160
Liabilities: $70,158,540
Net Worth: $51,835,620
Earnings: $3,562,790
Emp.: 472
Fiscal Year-end: 03/31/24
Industrial Machinery & Equipment
Distr
N.A.I.C.S.: 423830
Shigemasa Yanagawa *(Chm, Pres &*
CEO)

Subsidiaries:

COMINIX (PHILIPPINES), INC. (1)
2nd Fl LTI Administration Building 1 North

Cominix Co., Ltd.—(Continued)

Main Avenue, Laguna Technopark, Binan, 4024, Laguna, Philippines
Tel.: (63) 495440240
Electronic Device Whslr
N.A.I.C.S.: 423610

COMINIX MEXICO S.A. de C.V.   (1)
Av Murano No 151 Local 2 Col Las Eras 2a seccion, 36640, Irapuato, Guanajuato, Mexico
Tel.: (52) 14626247732
Industrial Equipment Whsr
N.A.I.C.S.: 423840

COMINIX VIETNAM CO., LTD   (1)
1201 12F Hanoi Tung Shing Square 2 Ngo Quyen, Hoan Kiem District, 10000, Hanoi, Vietnam
Tel.: (84) 2439387758
Web Site: http://www.cvc.com.vn
Electronic Device Whslr
N.A.I.C.S.: 423610

Cominix India Private Limited   (1)
Ground Floor Lavelle Mansion 1/2 Convent Building Lavelle Road, Bengaluru, 560 001, India
Tel.: (91) 804 128 1222
Cutting Tool Mfr
N.A.I.C.S.: 333515

Cominix Trading Philippines, Inc.   (1)
Relta Bldg 201 Rodeo Drive Laguna Bel - Air 2 Don Jose, Santa Rosa, 4026, Laguna, Philippines
Tel.: (63) 49 508 0656
Cutting Tool Mfr
N.A.I.C.S.: 333515

Cominix U.S.A., Inc.   (1)
5887 Glenridge Dr Ste 280, Atlanta, GA 30328
Tel.: (470) 545-9178
Web Site: https://cominix-usa.localinfo.jp
Motor Vehicles Mfr
N.A.I.C.S.: 336110

PT.COMINIX INDONESIA   (1)
Jl Inti 1 Blok C1 No 07, Gedung Cikarang Technopark Bekasi International Industrial Estate, Bekasi, 17550, Jawa Barat, Indonesia
Tel.: (62) 2189903060
Electronic Device Whslr
N.A.I.C.S.: 423610

Sakusaku Co., Ltd.   (1)
5th floor Toyo Building 1-8-5 Ebisu, Shibuya-ku, Tokyo, 150-0013, Japan
Tel.: (81) 35 423 7939
Web Site: https://www.saku-saku.co.jp
Information Technology Services
N.A.I.C.S.: 541511

Toshinshokai Co., Ltd.   (1)
3-22-2 Minamimagome, Ota-ku, Tokyo, 143-0025, Japan
Tel.: (81) 33 777 1045
Web Site: https://www.toshin-shokai.co.jp
Interior Good Whslr
N.A.I.C.S.: 423220

ZHONGBAN TRADING (SHANGHAI) CO., LTD.   (1)
Room 302 Bingu Building No 369 Weining Road, Shanghai, 200336, China
Tel.: (86) 2161136251
Web Site: http://www.cominix.com.cn
Industrial Equipment Whsr
N.A.I.C.S.: 423840

Zhongban Trade Shanghai Co., Ltd.   (1)
Room 1601 Haiyi Business Building No 310 Tianshan Road, Shanghai, 200336, China
Tel.: (86) 216 113 6251
Cutting Tool Mfr
N.A.I.C.S.: 333515

COMINTEL CORPORATION BERHAD
No 1 & 3 Jalan Jalil Jaya 3 Jalil Link Bukit Jalil, 57000, Kuala Lumpur, Selangor Darul Ehsan, Malaysia
Tel.: (60) 389987666
Web Site:
    https://www.comcorp.com.my

Year Founded: 2003
BNASTRA—(KLS)
Rev.: $39,929,312
Assets: $29,128,466
Liabilities: $20,146,878
Net Worth: $8,981,587
Earnings: $3,496,931
Emp.: 83
Fiscal Year ond: 01/31/23
Communication & System Integration Services
N.A.I.C.S.: 238210
Keng Hok Leng (Mng Dir)

COMINTELLI AB
Kista Science Tower, 164 51, Stockholm, Sweden
Tel.: (46) 86637600
Web Site: https://comintelli.com
Year Founded: 1999
Software Development Services
N.A.I.C.S.: 541511
Jesper Martell (CEO)

COMISION FEDERAL DE ELECTRICIDAD
Reforma 164 Col Juarez, 06598, Mexico, DF, Mexico
Tel.: (52) 1 800 800 8765
Web Site: http://www.cfe.gob.mx
Year Founded: 1937
Sales Range: $15-24.9 Billion
Emp.: 77,000
Electric Power Distr
N.A.I.C.S.: 221122
Francisco J. Santoyo Vargas (Dir-Fin)

COMITAL S.P.A.
Strada Brandizzo 130, 10088, Volpiano, Turin, Italy
Tel.: (39) 011 982 2111
Web Site: http://www.comital.com
Year Founded: 1935
Sales Range: $500-549.9 Million
Emp.: 1,750
Reclaimed Aluminum & Rubber Products
N.A.I.C.S.: 326299
Corrado Ariaudo (Chm & Mng Dir)

Subsidiaries:

Comital Alluminio Volpiano   (1)
Strada Brandizzo 130, 10088, Volpiano, Turin, Italy
Tel.: (39) 011 982 2111
Web Site: http://www.comitalalluminio.it
Rolled Aluminum
N.A.I.C.S.: 322220

Comital Cofresco S.p.A.   (1)
Strada Brandizzo 130, Volpiano, 10088, Turin, Italy
Tel.: (39) 0119822111
Flexible Food Wrap
N.A.I.C.S.: 322220

Comital Skultuna AB   (1)
Ostra Verken, Box 43, 726 20, Skultuna, Sweden
Tel.: (46) 21 540 4100
Web Site: http://www.comital.se
Emp.: 65
Aluminum Foil Mfr
N.A.I.C.S.: 331315

COMJOYFUL INTERNATIONAL COMPANY
Rroom 208 Unit 2 Bldg 4 Futai Community, North New District, Beijing, 100600, Guizhou, China
Tel.: (86) 13823320440
KJFI—(OTCIQ)
Mineral Exploration Services
N.A.I.C.S.: 213115
Alexander Shiu Yin Mak (Pres & CEO)

COMLAND COMMERCIAL LIMITED

Lunar House Mercury Park, High Wycombe, HP10 0HH, United Kingdom
Tel.: (44) 1628535777   UK
Web Site: http://www.comland.co.uk
Sales Range: $25-49.9 Million
Emp.: 14
Commercial Property Development Services
N.A.I.C.S.: 531300
Stuart Crossley (Chm & CEO)

COMMAND POLYMERS LIMITED
Mouza Malancha J L No87 P O Narayanpur P S Bhangar, District 24 Parganas South, Kolkata, 743502, West Bengal, India
Tel.: (91) 6289509962
Web Site:
    https://www.commandpolymers.com
Year Founded: 1998
543843—(BOM)
Polymer Product Mfr & Distr
N.A.I.C.S.: 325211
Sikha Banka (Sec)

COMMANDER RESOURCES LTD.
11th Floor 1111 Melville Street, Vancouver, V6E 3V6, BC, Canada
Tel.: (604) 685-5254   BC
Web Site:
    https://www.commander.com
Year Founded: 1987
CMD—(TSXV)
Rev.: $40,931
Assets: $580,550
Liabilities: $353,270
Net Worth: $227,279
Earnings: ($478,722)
Fiscal Year-end: 12/31/23
Gold & Base Metal Mining Services
N.A.I.C.S.: 212220
Janice Davies (Sec)

COMMAX CO., LTD.
Doonchondaero 494, Jungwongu, Seongnam, 13229, Gyeonggido, Korea (South)
Tel.: (82) 317318791
Web Site: https://www.commax.com
Year Founded: 1976
036690—(KRS)
Rev.: $119,650,952
Assets: $73,179,059
Liabilities: $35,845,729
Net Worth: $37,333,330
Earnings: ($4,099,192)
Emp.: 198
Fiscal Year-end: 12/31/22
Automatic Home Control Appliance Mfr
N.A.I.C.S.: 334512
Paolo Byun (CEO)

Subsidiaries:

Tianjin Central Electronic Corporation   (1)
NO 2 Chen Hong Ro Wuqing Development Area, Tianjin, China
Tel.: (86) 2137392206
Emp.: 200
Electronic Components Mfr
N.A.I.C.S.: 334419

COMMCENTER S.A.
Avda del Ferrocarril 74, 15008, A Coruna, Spain
Tel.: (34) 902222255
Web Site:
    https://www.commcenter.es
Year Founded: 2009
CMM—(MAD)
Sales Range: $10-24.9 Million
Emp.: 100
Telecommunication Servicesb
N.A.I.C.S.: 517111

Jose Luis Otero Barros (Pres)

COMMERCE ONE HOLDINGS, INC.
4-2-1 Kudankita, Chiyoda-ku, Tokyo, 102-0073, Japan
Tel.: (81) 362616677
Web Site: https://www.cm-one.jp
Year Founded: 2006
4496—(TKS)
Rev.: $23,511,770
Assets: $25,660,020
Liabilities: $6,861,180
Net Worth: $18,798,840
Earnings: $2,736,540
Emp.: 176
Fiscal Year-end: 03/31/24
Holding Company
N.A.I.C.S.: 551112
Kiwamu Shimizu (Dir)

COMMERCE RESOURCES CORP.
Suite 1450 - 789 West Pender Street, Vancouver, V6C 1H2, BC, Canada
Tel.: (604) 484-2700
Web Site:
    https://www.commerceresources.com
Year Founded: 1999
CMRZF—(OTCQX)
Rev.: $14,621
Assets: $57,253,660
Liabilities: $1,249,119
Net Worth: $56,004,541
Earnings: ($566,027)
Emp.: 2
Fiscal Year-end: 10/31/22
Mineral Exploration Services
N.A.I.C.S.: 213114
David Hodge (CEO)

COMMERCIAL BANK INTERNATIONAL P.S.C.
Jumeirah Street Jumeirah 1, PO Box 4449, Dubai Festival City, Dubai, United Arab Emirates
Tel.: (971) 45039000
Web Site: https://www.cbiuae.com
Year Founded: 1991
CBI—(ABU)
Rev.: $290,557,617
Assets: $5,166,021,364
Liabilities: $4,383,800,976
Net Worth: $782,220,388
Earnings: $46,460,739
Emp.: 453
Fiscal Year-end: 12/31/23
Commercial Banking Services
N.A.I.C.S.: 522110
Mohammad Sultan Al Qadi (Co-Chm)

COMMERCIAL BANK OF AFRICA LIMITED
Mara & Ragati Roads, Upperhill, Nairobi, Kenya
Tel.: (254) 20 288 4000   KE
Web Site: http://www.cbagroup.com
Sales Range: $250-299.9 Million
Commericial Banking
N.A.I.C.S.: 522110
Desterio A. Oyatsi (Chm)

COMMERCIAL BANK OF CEYLON PLC
Commercial House No 21 Sir Razik Fareed Mawatha, PO Box 856, 1, Colombo, 1, Sri Lanka
Tel.: (94) 112486000   LK
Web Site: https://www.combank.lk
COMB.N0000—(COL)
Rev.: $933,347,572
Assets: $8,320,475,031
Liabilities: $7,611,535,335
Net Worth: $708,939,696
Earnings: $544,839,759
Emp.: 5,060

Fiscal Year-end: 12/31/22
Banking Services
N.A.I.C.S.: 522110
Naveen Sooriyaarachchi *(Deputy Gen Mgr-Corp Banking)*

Subsidiaries:

CBC Finance Limited **(1)**
187 Katugastota Rd, Kandy, 20000, Sri Lanka
Tel.: (94) 81 220 0272
Web Site: https://www.cbcfinance.lk
Banking Services
N.A.I.C.S.: 522110
Dharmasena Dheerasinghe *(Chm)*

CBC Myanmar Microfinance Company Limited **(1)**
No 15 Street, Ward 4 Lewe Township Nay Pyi Taw, Pyinmana, Myanmar
Tel.: (95) 6730566
Web Site: http://www.cbcmy.com
Banking Services
N.A.I.C.S.: 522110
Dharma Dheerasinghe *(Chm)*

CBC Tech Solutions Limited **(1)**
No 285 3rd Floor Galle Road, Colombo, 03, Sri Lanka
Tel.: (94) 11 257 4417
Web Site: https://www.cbctechsol.com
Banking Services
N.A.I.C.S.: 522110
Keerthi Mediwake *(CEO)*

Commercial Bank of Maldives Private Limited **(1)**
H Filigasdhoshuge Ameeru Ahmed Magu, Male, 20066, Maldives
Tel.: (960) 333 2668
Web Site: https://www.cbmmv.com
Banking Services
N.A.I.C.S.: 522110
Ahmed Nazeer *(Chm)*

Commercial Development Company Ltd. **(1)**
No 98 York street, Colombo, 1, Sri Lanka **(94.55%)**
Tel.: (94) 11 2328 193
Web Site: http://www.combank.net
Property Development Services
N.A.I.C.S.: 531390

Commercial Insurance Brokers (Pvt) Limited **(1)**
347 Dr Colvin R De Silva Mawatha Union Place, Colombo, Sri Lanka
Tel.: (94) 117600600
Web Site: http://www.cib.lk
Insurance Services
N.A.I.C.S.: 524210

ONEzero Company Ltd. **(1)**
3rd Floor Commercial Bank Building Backup Center 2085 Galle Road, Colombo, Sri Lanka **(100%)**
Tel.: (94) 112445010
IT Services
N.A.I.C.S.: 541519

COMMERCIAL BANK OF DUBAI PSC
Al Ittihad Street, PO Box 2668, Dubai, United Arab Emirates
Tel.: (971) 600575556   **AE**
Web Site: https://www.cbd.ae
Year Founded: 1969
CBD—(DFM)
Rev.: $1,606,321,067
Assets: $35,110,395,050
Liabilities: $30,814,709,675
Net Worth: $4,295,685,375
Earnings: $721,347,965
Emp.: 1,200
Fiscal Year-end: 12/31/23
Banking Services
N.A.I.C.S.: 522110
Abdul Rahim Al Nimer *(Gen Mgr-Corp Banking)*

Subsidiaries:

CBD Financial Services LLC **(1)**
PO Box 2668, Dubai, United Arab Emirates

Tel.: (971) 43055889
Web Site: http://www.cbdfs.ae
Financial Investment & Brokerage Services
N.A.I.C.S.: 523999

COMMERCIAL BANK OF KUWAIT S.A.K.
Mubarak Al Kabeer Street, PO Box 2861, Safat, 13029, Kuwait, 13029, Kuwait
Tel.: (965) 22990000   **KW**
Web Site: https://www.cbk.com
Year Founded: 1960
CBK—(KUW)
Rev.: $548,769,963
Assets: $16,032,091,671
Liabilities: $13,621,577,303
Net Worth: $2,410,514,368
Earnings: $197,390
Emp.: 690
Fiscal Year-end: 12/31/19
Banking Services
N.A.I.C.S.: 522110
Nouf Salem Al-Ali Al-Sabah *(Gen Mgr-Corp Comm Div)*

Subsidiaries:

Al-Tijari Financial Brokerage Company K.S.C. **(1)**
Mubarak Al Kabeer Street, Commercial District II Block 5 Office 106-105-104-103 Sharq, Kuwait, Kuwait
Tel.: (965) 1837777
Web Site: https://www.tijarifb.com
Financial Brokerage Services
N.A.I.C.S.: 523999

COMMERCIAL FACILITIES COMPANY S.A.K.C.
Abdullah Al-Ahmed Street Sharq, PO Box 24284, Tashelat Bilding Commercial Facilities Company Building Safat, Kuwait, 13103, Kuwait
Tel.: (965) 1833232
Web Site: http://www.cfc-kw.com
Year Founded: 1977
FACIL—(KUW)
Rev.: $59,295,896
Assets: $1,040,158,710
Liabilities: $500,659,489
Net Worth: $539,499,222
Earnings: $43,392,858
Emp.: 192
Fiscal Year-end: 12/31/19
Installment Credit & Loan Services
N.A.I.C.S.: 522310
Abdallah Saud Abdulaziz Al-Humaidhi *(Vice Chm & CEO)*

COMMERCIAL INTERNATIONAL BANK (EGYPT) S.A.E.
Nile Tower Building 21/23 Charles de Gaulle, PO Box 2430, Cairo, Giza, Egypt
Tel.: (20) 237472000   **EG**
Web Site: https://www.cibeg.com
Year Founded: 1975
CMGJY—(OTCIQ)
Rev.: $2,193,867,683
Assets: $17,606,597,080
Liabilities: $15,695,047,704
Net Worth: $1,911,549,376
Earnings: $625,690,458
Emp.: 7,917
Fiscal Year-end: 12/31/23
Commercial Banking Services
N.A.I.C.S.: 522110
Hisham Ezz Al-Arab *(Chm & Mng Dir)*

COMMERCIAL LIGHTING PRODUCTS LTD.
1535 Cliveden Ave, Delta, V3M 6P7, BC, Canada
Tel.: (604) 540-4999
Web Site: https://www.comlight.com
Rev.: $13,041,743
Emp.: 80

Electrical Products Distr
N.A.I.C.S.: 423610
Dan Robinson *(Mgr-Edmonton)*

COMMERCIAL SPRING AND TOOL COMPANY LIMITED
160 Watline Avenue, Mississauga, L4Z 1R1, ON, Canada
Tel.: (905) 568-3899
Web Site: https://www.commercialspring.com
Year Founded: 1973
Rev.: $51,007,704
Emp.: 450
Spring & Wire Mfr
N.A.I.C.S.: 332613
Frank Martinitz *(Founder)*

COMMERCIAL SYN BAGS LIMITED
Commercial House 3-4 Jaora Compound M Y H Road, Indore, 452 001, Madhya Pradesh, India
Tel.: (91) 7312704007
Web Site: https://www.comsyn.com
Year Founded: 1986
539986—(BOM)
Rev.: $29,355,485
Assets: $26,850,369
Liabilities: $16,108,092
Net Worth: $10,742,277
Earnings: $1,635,666
Emp.: 2,487
Fiscal Year-end: 03/31/21
Flexible Container Product Mfr & Distr
N.A.I.C.S.: 314910
Anil Choudhary *(Chm & Mng Dir)*

COMMERZBANK AG
Kaiserplatz, 60311, Frankfurt am Main, Germany
Tel.: (49) 6913620   **De**
Web Site: https://www.commerzbank.de
Year Founded: 1870
CBK100—(OTCIQ)
Assets: $570,886,411,384
Liabilities: $535,570,151,306
Net Worth: $35,316,260,078
Earnings: $2,455,017,110
Emp.: 38,565
Fiscal Year-end: 12/31/23
Bank Holding Company; Corporate Banking Services
N.A.I.C.S.: 551111
Jorg Oliveri del Castillo-Schulz *(COO)*

Subsidiaries:

Bankowy Dom Hipoteczny Sp. z. o.o. **(1)**
M st Warszawa Armii Ludowej 26, 00-609, Warsaw, Poland
Tel.: (48) 22 579 75 12
Real Estate Manangement Services
N.A.I.C.S.: 531390

CB Euregio GmbH **(1)**
Kaiserstr 16, 60311, Frankfurt am Main, Germany
Tel.: (49) 6913620
Real Estate Manangement Services
N.A.I.C.S.: 531390

CBG Commerz **(1)**
Kaiserstrasse 16, 60311, Frankfurt am Main, Germany **(100%)**
Tel.: (49) 6913629224
Web Site: http://www.firmenkunden.commerzbank.de
Sales Range: $1-9.9 Million
Private Equity & Venture Capital Management
N.A.I.C.S.: 523910
Klaus Sachse *(Mng Dir)*

Subsidiary (Domestic):

CBG Commerz Beteiligungsgesellschaft Holding mbH **(2)**

Kaiserstrasse 16, PO Box 2, 60311, Frankfurt am Main, Germany **(100%)**
Tel.: (49) 6913629224
Web Site: https://www.firmenkunden.commerzbank.de
Sales Range: $50-74.9 Million
Emp.: 13
Private Equity & Venture Capital
N.A.I.C.S.: 523910

CBG Commerz Beteiligungskapital GmbH & Co. KG **(1)**
Kaiserstrasse 16, 60311, Frankfurt am Main, Germany
Tel.: (49) 6913629224
Web Site: https://www.firmenkunden.commerzbank.de
Finance Investment Services
N.A.I.C.S.: 523999

CG Real Estate Luxemburg S.a.r.l. **(1)**
25 Rue Edward Steichen, 2540, Luxembourg, Luxembourg
Tel.: (352) 47 79 11 25 02
Real Estate Development Services
N.A.I.C.S.: 531390

CGG Canada Grundbesitz GmbH **(1)**
Klopstockstr 5, 65187, Wiesbaden, Germany
Tel.: (49) 61171050
Financial Management Services
N.A.I.C.S.: 523999

CGI mbH **(1)**
Kraussbarger Reng 56, 65205, Wiesbaden, Germany **(75%)**
Tel.: (49) 6117105285
Web Site: http://www.hausinvest.de
Sales Range: $100-124.9 Million
Emp.: 250
Corporate Banking Services
N.A.I.C.S.: 522299

CRI Zweite Beteiligungsgesellschaft mbH **(1)**
Friedrichstr 25, 65185, Wiesbaden, Germany
Tel.: (49) 61171050
Emp.: 500
Real Estate Manangement Services
N.A.I.C.S.: 531390
Andreas Muschter *(CEO)*

CSA COMMERZ SOUTH AFRICA (PROPRIETARY) LIMITED **(1)**
Le Val-North Block Ground Floor 45 Jan Smuts Avenue, Johannesburg, 2193, South Africa
Tel.: (27) 11 486 0565
Sales Range: $50-74.9 Million
Emp.: 4
Commercial Banking Services
N.A.I.C.S.: 522110

CSK Sp. z o.o. **(1)**
ul Piotrkowska 173, Lodz, 90-447, Poland
Tel.: (48) 22 768 79 01
Web Site: http://www.csk-jachranka.pl
Facilities Management Services
N.A.I.C.S.: 561210

Collegium Glashutten Zentrum fur Kommunikation GmbH **(1)**
Wustemser Strasse 1, Oberems, 61479, Glashutten, Germany **(100%)**
Tel.: (49) 6082200
Web Site: https://www.collegium-glashuetten.de
Sales Range: $50-74.9 Million
N.A.I.C.S.: 522299

ComTS Finance GmbH **(1)**
Kaiserslauterer Str 75, 06128, Halle, Germany
Tel.: (49) 69935335725
Web Site: https://www.comts.de
Commercial Banking Services
N.A.I.C.S.: 522110

ComTS GmbH **(1)**
Juri-Gagarin-Ring 86, 99084, Erfurt, Germany
Tel.: (49) 69935338700
Web Site: https://www.comts.de
Commercial Banking Services
N.A.I.C.S.: 522110

Commerzbank AG—(Continued)

ComTS Logistics GmbH (1)
Lorenzweg 42, 39124, Magdeburg, Germany
Tel.: (49) 69935340203
Commercial Banking Services
N.A.I.C.S.: 522110

ComTS Mitte GmbH (1)
Juri-Gagarin-Ring 86, 99084, Erfurt, Germany
Tel.: (49) 3612 417 1300
Web Site: https://www.comtsmitte.de
Commercial Banking Services
N.A.I.C.S.: 522110

ComTS Nord GmbH (1)
Lorenzweg 42, 39124, Magdeburg, Germany
Tel.: (49) 39174488120
Commercial Banking Services
N.A.I.C.S.: 522110

ComTS Ost GmbH (1)
Kaiserslauterer Str 75, 06128, Halle, Germany
Tel.: (49) 34513197119
Commercial Banking Services
N.A.I.C.S.: 522110

ComTS Rhein-Ruhr GmbH (1)
Friedrich-Wilhelm-Str 12-14, 47051, Duisburg, Germany
Tel.: (49) 20375962050
Commercial Banking Services
N.A.I.C.S.: 522110

ComTS West GmbH (1)
Unionstr 3, 59067, Hamm, Germany
Tel.: (49) 23819725319
Commercial Banking Services
N.A.I.C.S.: 522110

Commerz (East Asia) Ltd. (1)
29/F Two International Finance Ctr 8 Finance St Ctr, Hong Kong, China (Hong Kong) (100%)
Tel.: (852) 28429609
Web Site: https://www.commerzbank.com
Sales Range: $50-74.9 Million
Emp.: 80
Banking Services
N.A.I.C.S.: 522299

Commerz (Nederland) N.V. (1)
Strawinskylaan 2501, 1077 ZZ, Amsterdam, Netherlands
Tel.: (31) 205574911
Web Site: http://www.commerzbank.nl
Investment Banking Services
N.A.I.C.S.: 523150
Dirk Dreiskamper (Country Mgr)

Commerz Building and Management GmbH (1)
Lindenallee 17-23, 45127, Essen, Germany
Tel.: (49) 2018219700
Web Site: https://www.commerzbuilding.de
Residential Property Management Services
N.A.I.C.S.: 531311

Commerz Business Consulting GmbH (1)
Lateral Towers Frankfurt Neue Borsenstrasse 1, 60487, Frankfurt am Main, Germany
Tel.: (49) 69935310069
Web Site: https://www.commerz-business-consulting.de
Business Management Consulting Services
N.A.I.C.S.: 541618

Commerz Finanz-Management GmbH (1)
KaiserStrasse 16, Frankfurt am Main, 60261, Germany (100%)
Tel.: (49) 6913620
Web Site: http://www.commerzbank.com
Sales Range: $350-399.9 Million
Emp.: 1,000
Personal Asset Planning Services
N.A.I.C.S.: 523940
Martin Blessing (Pres)

Commerz Global Service Solutions Sdn. Bhd. (1)
Level 13 Tower 3 Avenue 7 Bangsar South City No 8 Jalan Kerinchi, 59200, Kuala Lumpur, Malaysia

Tel.: (60) 327269700
Web Site: https://www.commerz-gss.com
Information Technology & Software Development Services
N.A.I.C.S.: 541512

Commerz Grundbesitz Gestao de Centros Commerciais, Sociedade Unipessoal, Lda. (1)
R Carmo 2, Lisbon, 1200-094, Portugal
Tel.: (351) 213210600
Sales Range: $50-74.9 Million
Emp.: 4
Financial Management Services
N.A.I.C.S.: 523999

Commerz Grundbesitz Investmentgesellschaft mbH (1)
Friedrich Str 25, D 65183, Wiesbaden, Germany (75%)
Tel.: (49) 611710501
Web Site: http://www.hausinvest.com
Sales Range: $100-124.9 Million
Emp.: 200
Investment Services
N.A.I.C.S.: 523940

Commerz Markets LLC (1)
225 Liberty St, New York, NY 10281-1050
Tel.: (212) 266-7200
Web Site: https://www.commerzmarkets.com
Securities Brokerage Services
N.A.I.C.S.: 523150
John Geremia (Mgr)

Commerz Real AG (1)
Friedrichstrasse 25, 65185, Wiesbaden, Germany (100%)
Tel.: (49) 61171050
Web Site: https://www.commerzreal.com
Sales Range: $200-249.9 Million
Lessor in Real Estate Leasing Contracts
N.A.I.C.S.: 531110
Henning Koch (Chm)

Subsidiary (Domestic):

Commerz Real Asset Structuring GmbH (2)
Mercedesstrasse 6, 40470, Dusseldorf, Germany
Tel.: (49) 211 7708 0
Web Site: http://www.commerzreal.com
Asset Management Services
N.A.I.C.S.: 523940

Commerz Real Baucontract GmbH (2)
Mercedesstrasse 6, 40470, Dusseldorf, Germany
Tel.: (49) 211 77080
Real Estate Management Services
N.A.I.C.S.: 531390

Commerz Real Baumanagement GmbH (2)
Tolzer Str 2, 82031, Grunwald, Germany
Tel.: (49) 8915709800
Construction Management Services
N.A.I.C.S.: 237990

Commerz Real Finanzierungsleasing GmbH (2)
Mercedesstr 6, 40470, Dusseldorf, Germany
Tel.: (49) 211 77080
Web Site: http://www.commerzreal.com
Real Estate Management Services
N.A.I.C.S.: 531390

Commerz Real Fonds Beteiligungsgesellschaft mbH (2)
Mercedesstrasse 6, 40470, Dusseldorf, Germany
Tel.: (49) 21177082200
Web Site: https://cfb.commerzreal.com
Fund Management Services
N.A.I.C.S.: 525990

Commerz Real Investmentgesellschaft mbH (2)
Friedrichstrasse 25, 65185, Wiesbaden, Germany
Tel.: (49) 61171050
Web Site: https://cri.commerzreal.com
Sales Range: $150-199.9 Million
Real Estate Investment Services
N.A.I.C.S.: 531390

Commerz Real Mobilienleasing GmbH (2)
Mercedesstrasse 6, 40470, Dusseldorf, Germany
Tel.: (49) 21177082222
Web Site: https://mobilienleasing.commerzreal.com
Industrial Machinery Leasing Services
N.A.I.C.S.: 532490

Subsidiary (Domestic):

Commerz Real Direkt GmbH i.L. (3)
Mercedesstr 6, 40470, Dusseldorf, Germany
Tel.: (49) 69 239121
Real Estate Manangement Services
N.A.I.C.S.: 531390

Commerz Real IT-Leasing GmbH (3)
Mercedesstrasse 6, 40470, Dusseldorf, Germany
Tel.: (49) 211 77082389
Web Site: http://www.commerzreal.com
Financial Management Services
N.A.I.C.S.: 523999
Michael Buecker (Gen Mgr)

Commerz Real Mietkauf GmbH (3)
Mercedesstrasse 6, 40470, Dusseldorf, Germany
Tel.: (49) 211 77080
Real Estate Manangement Services
N.A.I.C.S.: 531390

Subsidiary (Domestic):

Commerz Real Partner Sud GmbH (2)
Mercedesstr 6, 40470, Dusseldorf, Germany
Tel.: (49) 211 77080
Real Estate Management Services
N.A.I.C.S.: 531390

Commerz Real Projektconsult GmbH (2)
Mercedesstr 6, 40470, Dusseldorf, Nordrhein-Westfalen, Germany
Tel.: (49) 0211 77080
Web Site: http://www.commerzreal.com
Sales Range: $150-199.9 Million
Emp.: 300
Real Estate Management Services
N.A.I.C.S.: 531390
Markus Esser (Mgr-Presentation)

Commerz Real Vertrieb GmbH (2)
Mercedesstr 6, 40470, Dusseldorf, Nordrhein-Westfalen, Germany
Tel.: (49) 211 77082131
Web Site: http://www.commerzreal.com
Real Estate Development Services
N.A.I.C.S.: 531390

Commerz Real Verwaltung und Treuhand GmbH (2)
Mercedesstr 6, 40470, Dusseldorf, Germany
Tel.: (49) 21177080
Real Estate Manangement Services
N.A.I.C.S.: 531390

Commerz Real Autoservice GmbH i.L. (1)
Ludwig-Erhard-Allee 9, 40227, Dusseldorf, Germany
Tel.: (49) 211 77080
Automobile Leasing Services
N.A.I.C.S.: 532112

Commerz Real Digitale Vertriebs- und Service GmbH (1)
Friedrichstrasse 25, 65185, Wiesbaden, Germany
Tel.: (49) 61171050
Commercial Banking Services
N.A.I.C.S.: 522110

Commerz Real France & South EURL (1)
21 Rue Balzac, 75008, Paris, France
Tel.: (33) 156883788
Commercial Banking Services
N.A.I.C.S.: 522110
Maeva Montusclat (Office Mgr)

Commerz Real Fund Management S.a r.l. (1)

25 Rue Edward Steichen, 2540, Luxembourg, Luxembourg
Tel.: (352) 4779112502
Commercial Banking Services
N.A.I.C.S.: 522110

Commerz Real Kapitalverwaltungsgesellschaft mbH (1)
Mercedesstrasse 6, 40470, Dusseldorf, Germany
Tel.: (49) 21177080
Web Site: https://crkvg.commerzreal.com
Commercial Banking Services
N.A.I.C.S.: 522110

Commerz Real North Ltd. (1)
30 Gresham Street, London, EC2V 7PG, United Kingdom
Tel.: (44) 2074753502
Commercial Banking Services
N.A.I.C.S.: 522110
Thomas Longerich (Mng Dir)

Commerz Real West BV (1)
Handelsweg 53, 1181 ZA, Amstelveen, Netherlands
Tel.: (31) 203011930
Commercial Banking Services
N.A.I.C.S.: 522110

Commerz Real Western Europe GmbH (1)
Friedrichstr 25, 65185, Wiesbaden, Germany
Tel.: (49) 611 7105 0
Real Estate Manangement Services
N.A.I.C.S.: 531390

Commerz Securities Hong Kong Limited (1)
15th Floor Lee Garden One, 33 Hysan Avenue, Causeway Bay, China (Hong Kong)
Tel.: (852) 39 88 09 88
Security Brokerage Services
N.A.I.C.S.: 523150
Volkhardt Kruse (Gen Mgr)

Commerz Services Holding GmbH (1)
Group Delivery Center Neue Borsenstrasse 1, 60487, Frankfurt, Germany
Tel.: (49) 6913654093
Commercial Banking Services
N.A.I.C.S.: 522110

Commerz Systems GmbH (1)
Helfmann-Park 5, 65760, Eschborn, Germany
Tel.: (49) 69136 43100
Web Site: http://www.commerzsystems.com
Information Technology Consulting Services
N.A.I.C.S.: 541512

Commerz Transaction Services Mitte GmbH (1)
Juri-Gagarin-Ring 86, 99084, Erfurt, Germany
Tel.: (49) 361 67870
Financial Transaction Processing Services
N.A.I.C.S.: 522320

Commerz Transaction Services Nord GmbH (1)
Lorenzweg 42, Magdeburg, 39124, Germany
Tel.: (49) 391 74488100
Web Site: http://www.comts.de
Sales Range: $200-249.9 Million
Emp.: 350
Financial Transaction Processing Services
N.A.I.C.S.: 522320
Marcus Recksiek (Gen Mgr)

Commerz Transaction Services West GmbH (1)
Unionstr 3, Hamm, 59067, Germany
Tel.: (49) 691 3620
Web Site: http://www.commerzbank.de
Financial Transaction Processing Services
N.A.I.C.S.: 522320
Martin Artin (Gen Mgr)

CommerzFactoring GmbH (1)
Grosse Bleiche 35- 39, D-55116, Mainz, Germany
Tel.: (49) 6131202460
Web Site: https://www.commerzfactoring.de
Financial Management Services
N.A.I.C.S.: 523999
Philipp Schiemann (Mng Dir)

CommerzLeasing und Immobilien GmbH (1)
Mercedesstrasse 6, 40470, Dusseldorf,
Germany (100%)
Tel.: (49) 21177080
Web Site: http://www.commerzreal.com
Sales Range: $700-749.9 Million
Leasing & Real Estate Financing
N.A.I.C.S.: 522299

Subsidiary (Domestic):

**ALTINUM GVG mbH & Co.
Sonnenhof** (2)
Sonninstrasse 24-28, 20097, Hamburg,
Germany (100%)
Corporate Banking Services
N.A.I.C.S.: 522299

Subsidiary (Non-US):

BRE Leasing Sp. z o.o. (2)
Ul Ks I Skorupki 5, Warsaw, 00 963,
Poland (51%)
Tel.: (48) 223201800
Web Site: http://www.bre-leasing.com.pl
Sales Range: $100-124.9 Million
Emp.: 160
N.A.I.C.S.: 522299

Subsidiary (Domestic):

BREL-COM Sp. z o. o. (3)
ul Ks I Skorupki 5, 00-963, Warsaw, Poland
Tel.: (48) 22 320 1800
Financial Investment Services
N.A.I.C.S.: 523999

Subsidiary (Domestic):

**CFB Commerz Fonds Beteiligungs
GmbH** (2)
Mercedesstrasse 6, 40470, Dusseldorf,
Germany (100%)
Tel.: (49) 2117708200
Web Site: http://www.cfb.commerzreal.com
Sales Range: $150-199.9 Million
Closed-End Funds for German Equity Market; Leasing Fund Service
N.A.I.C.S.: 525990

CommerzLeasing GmbH (2)
Ludwig-Landmann-Str 349, 60487, Frankfurt am Main, Germany
Tel.: (49) 6997992901
Investment Management Service
N.A.I.C.S.: 523940

**FABA Vermietungsgesellschaft
mbH** (2)
Kaiserplatz, Frankfurt am Main, 60311,
Germany (95%)
Tel.: (49) 6913620
Banking Services
N.A.I.C.S.: 522299

CommerzTrust GmbH (1)
Mainzer Landstrasse 153, 60327, Frankfurt
am Main, Germany
Tel.: (49) 6913654233
Web Site: https://www.commerztrust.de
Sales Range: $50-74.9 Million
Emp.: 9
Pension Fund Management Services
N.A.I.C.S.: 525110

Commerzbank (Budapest) RT (1)
Szechenyi Rakpart 8, 1054, Budapest,
Hungary (100%)
Tel.: (36) 013748100
Web Site: http://www.commerzbank.hu
Sales Range: $100-124.9 Million
Emp.: 160
Corporate Banking Services
N.A.I.C.S.: 522299

Commerzbank (Eurasija) SAO (1)
(100%)
Tel.: (7) 4957974800
Web Site: https://www.commerzbank.ru
Sales Range: $50-74.9 Million
Emp.: 100
Corporate Banking Services
N.A.I.C.S.: 522299
Gernot Kleckner (Gen Mgr)

Commerzbank (Nederland) N.V. (1)
Strawinskylaan 2501, PO Box 75444, NL
1077 ZZ, Amsterdam, Netherlands (100%)
Tel.: (31) 205574911

Web Site: http://www.commerzbank.com
Sales Range: $10-24.9 Million
Emp.: 40
Corporate Banking Services
N.A.I.C.S.: 522299
Dirk Dreiskaemper (Gen Mgr)

**Commerzbank AG - New York
Branch** (1)
225 Liberty St, New York, NY
10281-1050 (100%)
Tel.: (212) 266-7200
Web Site: http://www.commerzbank.com
Sales Range: $200-249.9 Million
Emp.: 300
Banking
N.A.I.C.S.: 523150
Martin Preissler (Mng Dir-Client Relationship Mgmt)

Commerzbank Auslandsbanken Holding AG (1)
Kaiserstrasse 16, 60311, Frankfurt am
Main, Germany
Tel.: (49) 69 13620
Investment Management Service
N.A.I.C.S.: 523940

Commerzbank Auslandsbanken Holding Nova GmbH (1)
Kaiserstr 16, Frankfurt, 60311, Hessen,
Germany
Tel.: (49) 6913620
Investment Management Service
N.A.I.C.S.: 523940

Commerzbank Belgium S.A.N.V. (1)
29 Boulevard Louis Schmidt, 1040, Brussels, Belgium (100%)
Tel.: (32) 27431811
Web Site: http://www.commerzbank.be
Sales Range: $50-74.9 Million
International Banking Services
N.A.I.C.S.: 522299

**Commerzbank Brasil S.A. - Banco
Multiplo** (1)
Avenida Dr Chucri Zaidan Morumbi
Corporate-Diamond Tower 11th floor, Sao
Paulo, 04711-130, Brazil
Tel.: (55) 114 766 1600
Web Site: https://www.commerzbank.com.br
Commercial Banking Services
N.A.I.C.S.: 522110
Joachim Spengler (COO)

**Commerzbank Capital Investment
Company Limited** (1)
30 Gresham Street, London, EC2V 3PG,
United Kingdom
Tel.: (44) 2076238000
Web Site: http://www.commerzbank.com
Investment Management Service
N.A.I.C.S.: 523940

**Commerzbank Capital Markets
Corporation** (1)
2 World Financial Ctr 31st Fl, New York, NY
10281-1050 (100%)
Tel.: (212) 703-4000
Web Site: http://www.commerzbank.us
Sales Range: $200-249.9 Million
Emp.: 270
Financial Services
N.A.I.C.S.: 522299
C. Warren Carter (Mng Dir)

Commerzbank Duisburg (1)
Koenigstrasse 15-19, 47051, Duisburg,
Germany
Tel.: (49) 203 2823 0
Web Site: http://www.commerzbank.de
Commercial Banking Services
N.A.I.C.S.: 522110

**Commerzbank Finance & Covered
Bond S.A.** (1)
25 rue Edward Steichen, L-2540, Luxembourg, Luxembourg
Tel.: (352) 4779111
Web Site: https://www.commerzbank-fcb.com
Commercial Banking Services
N.A.I.C.S.: 522110

Commerzbank Finance BV (1)
Strawinskylaan 2501, 1077 ZZ, Amsterdam,
Netherlands
Tel.: (31) 205574911
Financial Management Services

N.A.I.C.S.: 523999

Commerzbank Futures LLC (1)
2 World Financial Ctr, New York, NY
10281-1008 (100%)
Tel.: (312) 360-1175
Sales Range: $50-74.9 Million
Emp.: 22
Financial & Banking Services
N.A.I.C.S.: 523160

**Commerzbank Holdings France
SAS** (1)
86 Boulevard Haussmann, 75008, Paris,
France
Tel.: (33) 144941700
Investment Management Service
N.A.I.C.S.: 523999

**Commerzbank Immobilien- und Vermogensverwaltungsgesellschaft
mbH** (1)
Kaiserstr 16, 60311, Frankfurt, Germany
Tel.: (49) 6913620
Web Site: https://www.commerzbankag.com
Emp.: 2,000
Commercial Banking Services
N.A.I.C.S.: 522110
Martin Blessing (CEO)

Commerzbank Inlandsbanken Holding GmbH (1)
Tel.: (49) 69271190
Investment Management Service
N.A.I.C.S.: 523940

Subsidiary (Domestic):

Comdirect Bank AG (2)
Pascalkehre 15, 25451, Quickborn,
Germany (100%)
Tel.: (49) 41067040
Web Site: http://www.comdirect.de
Sales Range: $10-24.9 Million
Full Banking Services
N.A.I.C.S.: 522299

**Commerzbank Investments (UK)
Limited** (1)
30 Gresham Street, London, EC2V 7PG,
United Kingdom
Tel.: (44) 2076238000
Emp.: 800
Investment Management Service
N.A.I.C.S.: 523940
Jochen Muller (Mng Dir & Country Mgr-Corp Client Bus)

Commerzbank Leasing Limited (1)
30 Gresham Street, London, EC2V 7PG,
United Kingdom
Tel.: (44) 2076238000
Financial Lending Services
N.A.I.C.S.: 522220

**Commerzbank Online Ventures
Limited** (1)
30 Gresham Street, London, EC2V 7PG,
United Kingdom
Tel.: (44) 20 7623 7000
Venture Capital Management Services
N.A.I.C.S.: 523910

**Commerzbank Property Management
& Services Limited** (1)
30 Gresham Street, London, EC2V 3PG,
United Kingdom
Tel.: (44) 20 7623 8000
Real Estate Management Services
N.A.I.C.S.: 531390

**Commerzbank Representative Office
Nigeria Limited** (1)
The Adunola House 5th Floor Wing A Banana Island Ikoyi, Lagos, Nigeria
Tel.: (234) 8074728082
Financial Investment Services
N.A.I.C.S.: 523940

**Commerzbank Representative Office
Panama, S.A.** (1)
Ph Torre de las Americas Torre C Piso 27
Oficina 2701 Punta Pacifica, Panama,
Panama
Tel.: (507) 3403101
Financial Investment Services
N.A.I.C.S.: 523999

**Commerzbank Sao Paulo Servicos
Ltda.** (1)

R Pedroso Alvarenga 1208 an16, Sao
Paulo, 04531-004, Brazil
Tel.: (55) 11 30799790
Financial Investment Services
N.A.I.C.S.: 523940

Commerzbank Securities Ltd. (1)
30 Gresham Street, London, EC2V 7PG,
United Kingdom
Tel.: (44) 2076238000
Security Brokerage Services
N.A.I.C.S.: 523150

**Commerzbank Securities Nominees
Limited** (1)
30 Gresham Street, London, WC2H 7WG,
United Kingdom
Tel.: (44) 20 7623 8000
Security Brokerage Services
N.A.I.C.S.: 523150

Commerzbank U.S. Finance, Inc. (1)
55 Broad St, New York, NY 10004-2501
Tel.: (212) 244-1500
Financial Management Services
N.A.I.C.S.: 523999

Deutsche Schiffsbank AG (1)
Domshof 17, D 28195, Bremen,
Germany (100%)
Tel.: (49) 42136090
Web Site: http://www.schiffsbank.com
Sales Range: $100-124.9 Million
Emp.: 168
Cargo Ship Financing & Mortgage Loan
Services
N.A.I.C.S.: 522220

Direktservice Commerz GmbH (1)
Am Silberpalais 1, 47057, Duisburg, Germany
Tel.: (49) 20330470
Web Site:
https://www.commerzdirektservice.de
Financial & Insurance Products Advisory &
Support Service; Technical Assistance; Direct Sales; Consulting Services
N.A.I.C.S.: 525990
Stefan Homp (Mng Dir)

Dresdner Bank AG (1)
Jurgen Ponto Platz 1, 60301, Frankfurt am
Main, Germany
Tel.: (49) 692630
Web Site: http://www.dresdner-bank.com
Sales Range: $800-899.9 Million
Emp.: 21,341
Banking Services
N.A.I.C.S.: 522110
Stephan Engels (CFO)

Subsidiary (Non-US):

**Commerzbank Holdings (UK)
Limited** (2)
30 Gresham Street, London, EC2V 7PG,
United Kingdom
Tel.: (44) 2076537000
Sales Range: $1-4.9 Billion
Emp.: 6,000
International Banking, Securities Trading &
Venture Capital Services
N.A.I.C.S.: 525990
Herbert Walter (Chm)

Subsidiary (Non-US):

Dresdner Kleinwort (3)
Plac Trzech Krzyzy 18, 00-499, Warsaw,
Poland
Tel.: (48) 225253000
Web Site: http://www.Dresdner-bank.pl
Sales Range: $50-74.9 Million
Emp.: 35
Investment Bank
N.A.I.C.S.: 523150

**Dresdner Kleinwort Deutschland
GmbH** (3)
Theodor Heuss Allee 44 46, 60486, Frankfurt, Germany
Tel.: (49) 697130
Web Site: http://www.dresdnerkleinwort.de
Investment Banking
N.A.I.C.S.: 523150

Dresdner Kleinwort France SA (3)
5 Blvd De La Madeleine, 75001, Paris,
France
Tel.: (33) 170368500

Commerzbank AG—(Continued)

Web Site: http://www.bkid.com
Sales Range: $50-74.9 Million
Emp.: 40
Investment Banking
N.A.I.C.S.: 523150
Pavid Manson (Mng Dir)

Dresdner Kleinwort Limited (3)
21/F Cheung Kong Ctr, 2 Queens Rd, Central, China (Hong Kong)
Tel.: (852) 4724888
Sales Range: $50-74.9 Million
Emp.: 20
Investment Banking
N.A.I.C.S.: 523150

Dresdner Kleinwort Shanghai (3)
39th Floor Jin Mao Tower, 88 Century Boulevard, Shanghai, 200120, China
Tel.: (86) 21 3866 5588
Investment Banking Services
N.A.I.C.S.: 523150

Subsidiary (Non-US):

Dresdner Bank Mexico S.A. (2)
Bosque De Alisos No 47 A 4th Fl, Col
Bosques De Las Lomas, 05120, Mexico,
DF, Mexico
Tel.: (52) 5552583000
Web Site: http://www.dbla.com
Sales Range: $50-74.9 Million
Emp.: 21
Investment Bank
N.A.I.C.S.: 523150

Dresdner Bank ZAO (2)
23 Malaya Morskaya Ul, 190000, Saint Petersburg, Russia
Tel.: (7) 8121185151
Web Site: http://www.dresdner-bank.ru
Sales Range: Less than $1 Million
Emp.: 150
Banking Services
N.A.I.C.S.: 522320

Subsidiary (Domestic):

KGAL GmbH & Co. KG (2)
Tolzer Strasse 15, 82031, Grunwald, Germany
Tel.: (49) 8 964 1430
Web Site: https://www.kgal.de
Emp.: 338
Debt Financing
N.A.I.C.S.: 522299
Gert Waltenbauer (CEO, Mng Dir & Member-Mgmt Bd)

Affiliate (Domestic):

AL Ships GmbH (3)
Toelzer Strasse 15, 82031, Grunwald, Germany
Tel.: (49) 8964143424
Web Site: http://www.kgal.de
Sales Range: $25-49.9 Million
Emp.: 10
Ship Management Services
N.A.I.C.S.: 488390
Jochen Korber (Mng Dir)

Subsidiary (Domestic):

AL.systems GmbH (3)
Toelzer Strasse 15, 82031, Grunwald, Germany
Tel.: (49) 896283410
Web Site: http://www.kgal.de
Emp.: 350
IT Support & Services
N.A.I.C.S.: 541618

Subsidiary (Non-US):

EUROASSET Italia S.r.l. (3)
Piazza Velasca 4, 20122, Milan, Italy
Tel.: (39) 028696101
Web Site: http://www.kgal-gruppe.de
Real Estate Investment
N.A.I.C.S.: 531390

Joint Venture (Domestic):

**GOAL German Operating Aircraft
Leasing GmbH** (3)
Toelzer Strasse 15, 82031, Grunwald,
Germany (60%)
Tel.: (49) 8 964 1430

Web Site: https://www.goal-leasing.com
Aircraft Leasing Services
N.A.I.C.S.: 532411
Christian Schloemann (Mng Dir & Head-Fin)

Subsidiary (Non-US):

**KGAL Asset Management Osterreich
GmbH** (3)
Dresdner Strasse 16, 1200, Vienna, Austria
Tel.: (43) 13 344 8290
Web Site: https://www.kgal.at
Real Estate Investment Services
N.A.I.C.S.: 531390
Thomas Krischke (Mng Dir)

Joint Venture (Domestic):

Lufthansa Leasing GmbH (3)
Tolzer Strasse 15, 82031, Grunwald,
Germany (51%)
Tel.: (49) 8964143203
Aircraft Leasing Services
N.A.I.C.S.: 532411
Jochen Horger (Mng Dir)

Subsidiary (Domestic):

**Reuschel & Co.
Kommanditgesellschaft** (2)
Maximiliansplatz 13, 80285, Munich, Germany
Tel.: (49) 8923950
Web Site: http://www.donner-reuschel.de
Sales Range: $150-199.9 Million
Emp.: 500
Banking Services
N.A.I.C.S.: 522110

Elco Leasing Limited (1)
30 Gresham Street, London, EC2V 7PG,
United Kingdom
Tel.: (44) 2076537000
Financial Lending Services
N.A.I.C.S.: 522220

**Erste Europaische Pfandbrief- und
Kommunalkreditbank
Aktiengesellschaft** (1)
25 Rue Edward Stiechen, Postfach 2133,
1021, Luxembourg, Luxembourg
Tel.: (352) 26 3481
Web Site: http://wwweepk.lu
Emp.: 450
Financial Investment Services
N.A.I.C.S.: 523940
Gerard-Jan Bais (Mng Dir)

Espacio Leon Propco S.L.U. (1)
Calle Pinar 7 - Piso 5 IZ, Madrid, 28006,
Spain
Tel.: (34) 987237929
Emp.: 6
Real Estate Development Services
N.A.I.C.S.: 531390
Alfonso Colimo (Gen Mgr)

EuREAM GmbH (1)
Friedrichstr 25, 65183, Wiesbaden, Germany
Tel.: (49) 61171050
Sales Range: $200-249.9 Million
Emp.: 300
Financial Management Services
N.A.I.C.S.: 523999

Subsidiary (Non-US):

**Eurohypo Europaische Hypotheken-
bank S.A.** (2)
Airport Ctr 5 Rue Heienhaff, L-1736, Senningerberg, Luxembourg
Tel.: (352) 26345511
Web Site:
http://www.hypothekenbankfranfurt.lu
Sales Range: $25-49.9 Million
Emp.: 34
Mortgage Banking Services
N.A.I.C.S.: 522310

FM LeasingPartner GmbH (1)
Gewerbepark 33 - 35, 49143, Bissendorf,
Germany
Tel.: (49) 5402 920 2100
Web Site: https://www.fm-leasingpartner.de
Financial Management Services
N.A.I.C.S.: 523999
Wolfgang Muller (Mng Dir)

**GRANADA Investment GmbH
i.L.** (1)
Mercedesstr 6, 40470, Dusseldorf, Germany
Tel.: (49) 21177080
Financial Management Services
N.A.I.C.S.: 523999

**GVG Gesellschaft zur Verwertung
von Grundbesitz mit beschrankter
Haftung** (1)
Helfmann-Park 5, 65760, Eschborn, Germany
Tel.: (49) 6925480
Real Estate Development Services
N.A.I.C.S.: 531390

Branch (Non-US):

**Eurohypo Europaische Hypotheken-
bank S.A. Dublin Branch** (2)
Commerzbank House, Guild St, Dublin 1,
Ireland
Tel.: (353) 16491618
Web Site: http://www.eurohypo.lu
N.A.I.C.S.: 522299

**Gesellschaft fur Kreditsicherung
mbH** (1)
Burgstr 28, 10178, Berlin, Germany
Tel.: (49) 3016632301
Web Site: https://www.pdp.de
Credit Protection Services
N.A.I.C.S.: 812990
Dirk Stein (CEO)

**Grundbesitzgesellschaft Berlin
mbH** (1)
Helfmann-Park 5, 65760, Eschborn, Germany
Tel.: (49) 6925480
Real Estate Management Services
N.A.I.C.S.: 531390

H 47 GmbH & Co. KG (1)
Mercedesstr 6, 40470, Dusseldorf, Germany
Tel.: (49) 2177080
Real Estate Agency Services
N.A.I.C.S.: 531210

**H 47 Verwaltungsgesellschaft
mbH** (1)
Mercedesstr 6, 40470, Dusseldorf, Germany
Tel.: (49) 211 77080
Financial Investment Services
N.A.I.C.S.: 523940

**HVI Handels- und Verwertungsgesell-
schaft fur Immobilien mbH** (1)
Mercedesstr 6, Dusseldorf, 40470, Germany
Tel.: (49) 21177080
Emp.: 1,000
Real Estate Management Services
N.A.I.C.S.: 531390

**IWP International West Pictures
GmbH & Co. Erste Produktions
KG** (1)
Stadtwaldgurtel 13, Cologne, 50935, Germany
Tel.: (49) 22194997166
Emp.: 2
Business Management Consulting Services
N.A.I.C.S.: 541618
Arnd Ludwig (Gen Mgr)

**Immobilien-Vermietungsgesellschaft
Reeder & Co. Objekt Airport Burocen-
ter Dresden KG** (1)
Mercedesstr 6, 40470, Dusseldorf, Germany
Tel.: (49) 21177080
Real Estate Brokerage Services
N.A.I.C.S.: 531210

**Immobilienverwaltungs- und Ver-
triebsgesellschaft Villen am Glienicker
Horn mbH** (1)
Potsdamer Str 125, 10783, Berlin, Germany
Tel.: (49) 3026532633
Real Estate Management Services
N.A.I.C.S.: 531390

**Immobilienverwaltungsgesellschaft
Grammophon Buropark mbH** (1)
Potsdamer Str 125, Berlin, 10783, Germany

Tel.: (49) 30 26532633
Real Estate Manangement Services
N.A.I.C.S.: 531390

**Immobilienverwaltungsgesellschaft
Schlachthof Offenbach mbH** (1)
Helfmann-Park 5, 65760, Eschborn, Germany
Tel.: (49) 69 298980
Property Management Services
N.A.I.C.S.: 523940

KENSTONE GmbH (1)
Helfmann-Park 5, 65760, Eschborn, Germany
Tel.: (49) 69935345330
Web Site: https://www.kenstone.de
Emp.: 80
Real Estate Manangement Services
N.A.I.C.S.: 531390
Martinus Kurth (Mng Dir & Member-Exec
Bd)

**KTC Kommunikations- und Trainings-
Center Konigstein GmbH** (1)
Olmuhlweg 65, 61462, Konigstein, Germany
Tel.: (49) 6 174 2950
Web Site: http://www.ktc-koenigstein.com
Sales Range: $25-49.9 Million
Home Management Services
N.A.I.C.S.: 721110
Andrers Noldmann (Mng Dir)

LOFRA GmbH & Co.KG (1)
80 Frankfurt Department, 60261, Frankfurt
am Main, Germany
Tel.: (49) 69 13620
Real Estate Development Services
N.A.I.C.S.: 531390

**LOFRA Verwaltungs-Gesellschaft
mbH** (1)
Jurgen-Ponto-Platz, 60329, Frankfurt am
Main, Germany
Tel.: (49) 21177080
Financial Investment Services
N.A.I.C.S.: 523940

**LSF Loan Solutions Frankfurt
GmbH** (1)
Helfmann-Park 5, 65760, Eschborn,
Germany (100%)
Tel.: (49) 6913620
Web Site:
https://www.loansolutionsfrankfurt.com
Mortgage Lending Services
N.A.I.C.S.: 522292
Dirk W. Schuh (Member-Exec Bd)

Subsidiary (Domestic):

**Forum Immobiliengesellschaft
mbH** (2)
Rosental 102, 53111, Bonn, Germany
Tel.: (49) 228 449 0133
Web Site: https://www.forum-immo.de
Real Estate Development Services
N.A.I.C.S.: 531390
Thomas Fellmy (Mng Dir)

**G-G-B Gebaude- und Grundbesitz
GmbH** (2)
Helfmann-Park 5, 65760, Eschborn, Germany
Tel.: (49) 6925480
Real Estate Development Services
N.A.I.C.S.: 531390

**Nordboden Immobilien- und Han-
delsgesellschaft mbH** (2)
Helfmann-Park 5, 65760, Eschborn, Germany
Tel.: (49) 69 254827265
Real Estate Management Services
N.A.I.C.S.: 531390

**TARA Immobiliengesellschaft
mbH** (2)
Helfmann-Park 5, 65760, Eschborn, Germany
Tel.: (49) 69 25480
Real Estate Development Services
N.A.I.C.S.: 531390

TARA Immobilienprojekte GmbH (2)
Helfmann-Park 5, 65760, Eschborn, Hessen, Germany
Tel.: (49) 69 25480
Real Estate Development Services

N.A.I.C.S.: 531390

TARA Property Management GmbH (2)
Helfmann-Park 5, 65760, Eschborn, Germany
Tel.: (49) 6925480
Real Estate Development Services
N.A.I.C.S.: 531390

Unica Immobiliengesellschaft mbH (2)
Helfmann-Park 5, 65760, Eschborn, Germany
Tel.: (49) 69 254821935
Real Estate Management Services
N.A.I.C.S.: 531390

WESTBODEN-Bau- und Verwaltungsgesellschaft mbH (2)
Helfmann-Park 5, 65760, Eschborn, Germany
Tel.: (49) 69 23820
Real Estate Development Services
N.A.I.C.S.: 531390

gr Grundstucks GmbH Objekt Corvus & Co. (2)
Eschborner Landstr 42, 60489, Frankfurt, Germany
Tel.: (49) 6974749690
Real Estate Development Services
N.A.I.C.S.: 531390

Main Incubator GmbH (1)
Eschersheimer Landstrasse 6, 60322, Frankfurt am Main, Germany
Tel.: (49) 6971913870
Web Site: https://neosfer.de
Commercial Banking Services
N.A.I.C.S.: 522110
Julian Burklein (Mgr-Investment)

Morris (S.P.) Holdings Limited (1)
30 Gresham Street, London, EC2V 7PG, United Kingdom
Tel.: (44) 2076238000
Investment Management Service
N.A.I.C.S.: 523940

Neosfer GmbH (1)
Eschersheimer Landstrasse 6, 60322, Frankfurt am Main, Germany
Tel.: (49) 6971913870
Web Site: https://neosfer.de
Emp.: 35
Financial Services
N.A.I.C.S.: 541611

Neugelb Studios GmbH (1)
Zeughofstrasse 20, 10997, Berlin, Germany
Tel.: (49) 6926958654
Web Site: https://neugelb.com
Commercial Studio Services
N.A.I.C.S.: 541430
Morvarid Ahmadi (Mgr-Ops)

Openspace GmbH (1)
Kleiststrasse 23, 10787, Berlin, Germany
Tel.: (49) 15173032565
Business Support Services
N.A.I.C.S.: 561499
Andre Armbrust (Mgr-Fin & Ops)

Pisces Nominees Limited (1)
30 Gresham Street, London, EC2V 7PG, United Kingdom
Tel.: (44) 2076238000
Financial Investment Services
N.A.I.C.S.: 523999

Public Joint Stock Company "Bank Forum" (1)
17/52 Bohdana Khmelnytskoho St, Kiev, 01030, Ukraine
Tel.: (380) 44581 04 34
Web Site: http://www.forum.ua
Sales Range: $350-399.9 Million
Emp.: 700
Financial Management Services
N.A.I.C.S.: 523999

RAVENNA Krakow Sp. z.o.o. (1)
Ks Skorupki 5, Warsaw, Poland
Tel.: (48) 223201805
Financial Management Services
N.A.I.C.S.: 523999

SOLTRX Transaction Services GmbH (1)

Wiesenstrasse 70 b 5, 40549, Dusseldorf, Germany
Tel.: (49) 211506550
Web Site: https://www.s-t-services.com
Financial Transaction Processing Services
N.A.I.C.S.: 522320

Sterling Energy LLC (1)
1225 17th St Ste 2520, Denver, CO 80202
Tel.: (720) 881-7100
Eletric Power Generation Services
N.A.I.C.S.: 221118

Wijkertunnel Beheer III B.V. (1)
Strawinskylaan 2501, 1077ZZ, Amsterdam, Netherlands
Tel.: (31) 205574660
Financial Investment Services
N.A.I.C.S.: 523940

Yellowfin Asset Management GmbH (1)
Commerzbank Junghofstr 13 -15, 60311, Frankfurt am Main, Germany
Tel.: (49) 6913626824
Web Site: https://www.yellowfin-am.de
Asset Management Services
N.A.I.C.S.: 531390

mBank Hipoteczny S.A. (1)
Ul Prosta 18, 00-850, Warsaw, Poland
Tel.: (48) 662169775
Web Site: https://www.mhipoteczny.pl
Commercial Banking Services
N.A.I.C.S.: 522110
Piotr Cyburt (Chm)

mBank S.A. (1)
18 Prosta Street, 00-850, Poland (69.6%)
Tel.: (48) 228290000
Web Site: https://www.mbank.pl
Rev.: $3,766,962,643
Assets: $57,667,813,877
Liabilities: $54,177,665,004
Net Worth: $3,490,148,873
Earnings: $6,112,297
Emp.: 7,319
Fiscal Year-end: 12/31/2023
Corporate Banking Services
N.A.I.C.S.: 522110
Cezary Stypulkowski (Chm-Mgmt Bd & CEO)

Subsidiary (Domestic):

BRE Faktoring S.A. (2)
Ul Krolewska 14, 00-065, Warsaw, Poland
Tel.: (48) 22 829 14 60
Web Site: http://www.brefaktoring.pl
Sales Range: $50-74.9 Million
Emp.: 55
Factoring Services
N.A.I.C.S.: 522299
Pawla Pryla (VP)

BRE Holding Sp. z o.o. (2)
Senatorska 18/3, Warsaw, Poland
Tel.: (48) 228291206
Investment Management Service
N.A.I.C.S.: 523940

BRE Property Partner Sp. z o.o. (2)
ul Krolewska 14, 00-065, Warsaw, Poland
Tel.: (48) 225267402
Web Site: https://www.brepp.pl
Real Estate Development Services
N.A.I.C.S.: 531390

BRE Wealth Management S.A. (2)
ul Krolewska 14, 00-065, Warsaw, Poland
Tel.: (48) 426376660
Web Site: http://www.mbank.pl
Asset Management Services
N.A.I.C.S.: 523940
Malgorzata Janczewska (Pres)

BRE.locum S.A. (2)
ul Piotrkowska 173, 90-447, Lodz, Poland
Tel.: (48) 42 230 10 57
Real Estate Development Services
N.A.I.C.S.: 531390

Dom Inwestycyjny BRE Banku SA (2)
ul Wspolna 47/49, 00-684, Warsaw, Poland
Tel.: (48) 226974700
Web Site: http://www.dibre.pl
Securities Brokerage Services
N.A.I.C.S.: 523210
Jaroslaw Kowalczuk (Pres)

Garbary Sp. z o.o. (2)
Ul Garbary 101/111, 61-757, Poznan, Poland
Tel.: (48) 61 8513750
Web Site: http://www.garbary.pl
Real Estate Development Services
N.A.I.C.S.: 531390

mCorporate Finance S.A. (2)
ul Senatorska 18, 00-082, Warsaw, Poland
Tel.: (48) 22 33 22 000
Web Site: http://www.mcf.pl
Sales Range: $25-49.9 Million
Emp.: 30
Investment Banking Services
N.A.I.C.S.: 523150
Michal Iwanicki (CEO)

mFinance France S.A. (1)
23 Rue De La Paix 3 Place De I Opera, 75002, Paris, France
Tel.: (33) 144941891
Commercial Banking Services
N.A.I.C.S.: 522110
Oliver Leo Koepke (Pres)

COMMEX TECHNOLOGY LTD.
B-40 Unit No-42 4th Floor Vasudev Chambers Opp Wilson Pen company Old, Nagardas Road Andheri East, Mumbai, 400069, India
Tel.: (91) 2226212117
Web Site:
　http://www.commextechnology.com
Rev.: $1,043
Assets: $1,098,163
Liabilities: $1,292,585
Net Worth: ($194,422)
Earnings: ($8,299,362)
Fiscal Year-end: 03/31/18
Software Products & Solutions
N.A.I.C.S.: 541511
Ajay Raut (CFO)

COMMITTED CARGO CARE LIMITED
A-406 Road No 4 Street No 8, Mahipalpur, New Delhi, 110037, India
Tel.: (91) 1146151111
Web Site:
　https://www.committedgroup.com
Year Founded: 1998
COMMITTED—(NSE)
Rev.: $14,838,237
Assets: $4,866,338
Liabilities: $1,369,972
Net Worth: $3,496,365
Earnings: $646,202
Fiscal Year-end: 03/31/23
Freight Shipping Services
N.A.I.C.S.: 488510

COMMIXT S.A.
Str Mihai Eminescu Nr 88 Camera 1, Ilfov, Buftea, Romania
Tel.: (40) 213515596
CMBU—(BUC)
Rev.: $47,605
Assets: $100,309
Liabilities: $115,894
Net Worth: ($15,585)
Earnings: ($114,373)
Emp.: 2
Fiscal Year-end: 12/31/22
Wood Products Mfr
N.A.I.C.S.: 333243
Paula Balan (Pres & Gen Mgr)

COMMONWEALTH BANK OF AUSTRALIA
South 11 Harbour Street, Level 1 Commonwealth Bank Place, Sydney, 2000, NSW, Australia
Tel.: (61) 293782000　　　AU
Web Site:
　https://www.commbank.com.au
Year Founded: 1911
CBAUF—(OTCIQ)
Rev.: $40,761,217,782
Assets: $837,390,488,023

Liabilities: $788,587,069,420
Net Worth: $48,803,418,604
Earnings: $6,330,795,914
Emp.: 32,259
Fiscal Year-end: 06/30/24
Financial Investment Services
N.A.I.C.S.: 523999
Alan Docherty (CFO)

Subsidiaries:

ASB Bank Limited (1)
ASB North Wharf 12 Jellicoe Street, PO Box 35, Shortland St, Auckland, 1140, New Zealand (100%)
Tel.: (64) 93778930
Web Site: https://www.asb.co.nz
Sales Range: $200-249.9 Million
Emp.: 500
International Banking
N.A.I.C.S.: 522299
Jonathan Peter Hartley (Deputy Chm)

Subsidiary (Domestic):

ASB Group Investments Limited (2)
12 Jellicoe St Auckland Central, Auckland, 1010, New Zealand
Tel.: (64) 93778930
Web Site: http://www.asb.co.nz
Emp.: 500
Investment Management Service
N.A.I.C.S.: 523999
Barbara Chapman (CEO)

ASB Securities Limited (2)
135 Albert Street, PO Box 35, Shortland Street, Auckland, 1140, New Zealand
Tel.: (64) 9 369 4602
Web Site: http://www.asb.co.nz
Sales Range: $25-49.9 Million
Emp.: 50
Online Securities Trading Service
N.A.I.C.S.: 518210

Bank of Western Australia Ltd. (1)
PO Box E237, Level 20 BankW Tower, Perth, 6841, WA, Australia
Tel.: (61) 894492840
Web Site: https://www.bankwest.com.au
Banking Services
N.A.I.C.S.: 522110

CBFC Limited (1)
Level 7 48 Martin Place, Sydney, 2000, NSW, Australia
Tel.: (61) 293783876
Web Site: http://www.cba.com
Financial Services
N.A.I.C.S.: 522299

CTB Australia Limited (1)
13F 1 Exchange square No 8 Connaught Place, Central, China (Hong Kong)
Tel.: (852) 28447500
Financial Management Services
N.A.I.C.S.: 523999

Colonial Holding Company Limited (1)
Ground Floor Tower 1 201 Sussex Street, Sydney, 2000, NSW, Australia
Tel.: (61) 291187220
Investment Management Service
N.A.I.C.S.: 523999

Subsidiary (Domestic):

Avanteos Investments Limited (2)
Camberwell Shopping 105 Camberwell Rd, Hawthorn East, 3123, VIC, Australia
Tel.: (61) 398055111
Web Site:
　http://www3.colonialfirststate.com.au
Investment Management Service
N.A.I.C.S.: 523999
Linda Elkins (Exec Gen Mgr & Exec Dir)

Colonial First State Group Limited (2)
Level 29 52 Martin Place, Sydney, 2000, NSW, Australia (100%)
Tel.: (61) 292733000
Web Site:
　http://www3.colonialfirststate.com.au
Holding Company; Financial & Real Estate Asset Management Services
N.A.I.C.S.: 551112

Commonwealth Bank of Australia—(Continued)

Bryce Quirk *(Gen Mgr-Advice Relation-ships)*

Joint Venture (Non-US):

Anglian Water Group Limited (3)
Lancaster House Lancaster Way Ermine Business Park, Huntingdon, PE29 6XU, Cambs, United Kingdom (32.3%)
Tel.: (44) 1480323000
Web Site: https://www.awg.com
Sales Range: $1-4.9 Billion
Emp.: 5,967
Holding Company; Water Supply, Sewerage & Property Development Services
N.A.I.C.S.: 551112
Stephen Billingham *(Chm)*

Subsidiary (Domestic):

AWG Property Limited (4)
47 Melville Street, Edinburgh, EH4 7HL, United Kingdom
Tel.: (44) 01313431000
Web Site: http://www.awgproperty.co.uk
Sales Range: $50-74.9 Million
Emp.: 30
Commercial & Residential Property Investment & Development
N.A.I.C.S.: 531390
Tony Donnelly *(Chm)*

Anglian Water Services Limited (4)
Lancaster House Lancaster Way Ermine Business Park, Huntingdon, PE29 6XU, Cambridgeshire, United Kingdom
Tel.: (44) 3457919155
Web Site: https://www.anglianwater.co.uk
Rev.: $1,719,141,394
Assets: $14,320,002,386
Liabilities: $12,272,438,616
Net Worth: $2,047,563,770
Earnings: ($41,623,856)
Emp.: 4,764
Fiscal Year-end: 03/31/2019
Water Supply Distribution & Sewerage Services
N.A.I.C.S.: 221310
Peter Simpson *(CEO & Member-Mgmt Bd)*

Subsidiary (Domestic):

Colonial First State Property Limited (3)
Level 5 Tower 3 300 Barangaroo Avenue, Sydney, 2000, NSW, Australia (100%)
Tel.: (61) 290105200
Web Site: https://www.firstsentierinvestors.com
Property Acquisition, Development & Management Services
N.A.I.C.S.: 531390

Commonwealth Managed Investments Limited (3)
Darling Park Tower 1 201 Sussex Street, Sydney, 2000, NSW, Australia
Tel.: (61) 2 9303 3500
Investment Funds Trustee
N.A.I.C.S.: 523991

Holding (Non-US):

Coriance SAS (3)
Immeuble Horizon 1 10 Allee Bienvenue, 93885, Noisy-le-Grand, France
Tel.: (33) 149147979
Web Site: https://www.groupe-coriance.fr
Industrial Heating & Cooling Network Operating Services
N.A.I.C.S.: 238220

Ferngas Netzgesellschaft mbH (3)
Reichswaldstrasse 52, 90571, Schwaig, Germany
Tel.: (49) 91199007960
Web Site: https://www.ferngas.de
Natural Gas Distribution Services
N.A.I.C.S.: 221210
Dieter Bochmann *(Mng Dir)*

Subsidiary (Domestic):

Financial Wisdom Limited (2)
Ground L Tower 1 201 Sussex St, Sydney, 2000, NSW, Australia
Tel.: (61) 1800024864
Web Site:
http://www.financialwisdom.com.au

Financial Advisory Services
N.A.I.C.S.: 523940

CommBank Europe Limited (1)
Level 3 Strand Towers 36 The Strand, Sliema, SLM07, Malta
Tel.: (356) 6 21 320812
Web Site: http://www.commbank.com.au
Commercial Banking Services
N.A.I.C.S.: 522110

CommBank Management Consulting (Asia) Co Limited (1)
Rm 1501-1505 15/F Chater Hse 8 Connaught Rd C, Central District, Hong Kong, China (Hong Kong)
Tel.: (852) 36678900
Sales Range: $50-74.9 Million
Emp.: 100
Insurance Management Services
N.A.I.C.S.: 524298

Commonwealth Bank of Australia - Beijing (1)
Level 46 China World Tower A No 1 Jianguomenwai Ave, Beijing China World Trade Ctr, Beijing, 100004, China
Tel.: (86) 1056803000
Web Site: http://www.commbank.au
Sales Range: $75-99.9 Million
Emp.: 5
N.A.I.C.S.: 522299

Commonwealth Bank of Australia - Grand Cayman (1)
PO Box 501, CBA Grand Cayman, Georgetown, Grand Cayman, Cayman Islands
N.A.I.C.S.: 522299

Commonwealth Bank of Australia - Hong Kong (1)
Suite 1401 One Exchange Square 8 Connaught Place, Central, China (Hong Kong)
Tel.: (852) 28447500
Web Site: http://www.commbank.com.au
Sales Range: $50-74.9 Million
Emp.: 45
International Bankers
N.A.I.C.S.: 522299

Commonwealth Bank of Australia - Japan (1)
8F Toranomon Waiko Building 5-12-1, Toranomon Minato-ku, Tokyo, 105-0001, Japan
Tel.: (81) 354007280
Web Site: http://www.commbank.co.jp
Sales Range: $50-74.9 Million
Emp.: 18
International Bankers
N.A.I.C.S.: 522299
Martin Spann *(Country Mgr)*

Commonwealth Bank of Australia - Shanghai (1)
Level 43-031 Hang Seng Bank Tower 1000 Lujiazui Ring Road, Pudong, Shanghai, China
Tel.: (86) 2161238900
Web Site: http://www.commbank.com.au
Sales Range: $75-99.9 Million
Emp.: 3
Commericial Banking
N.A.I.C.S.: 522299

Commonwealth Bank of Australia - U.S.A. (1)
Level 30 599 Lexington Ave, New York, NY 10022-7664
Tel.: (212) 848-9200
Web Site: http://www.commbank.com.au
Sales Range: $50-74.9 Million
Emp.: 48
International Banking
N.A.I.C.S.: 522110

Commonwealth Bank of Australia - UK (1)
60 Ludgate Hill, London, EC4M 7AW, United Kingdom
Tel.: (44) 61132221
Web Site: http://www.combank.com.au
Sales Range: $50-74.9 Million
Emp.: 100
International Bankers
N.A.I.C.S.: 522299
Paul Orchard *(Gen Mgr)*

Commonwealth Securities Limited (1)

Locked Bag 22, Australia Square, Sydney, 1215, NSW, Australia
Tel.: (61) 291151417
Web Site: http://www.comsec.com.au
Security Brokerage Services
N.A.I.C.S.: 523150

JDV Limited (1)
L7 141 St Georges Tce, Perth, WA, Australia (100%)
Tel.: (61) 892660222
Web Site: http://www.jdv.com.au
Securities Brokerage
N.A.I.C.S.: 523150

Securitisation Advisory Services Pty Limited (1)
201 Sussex St, Sydney, 2000, NSW, Australia
Tel.: (61) 299534834
Investment Advisory Services
N.A.I.C.S.: 523940
Robyn Taylor *(Sec)*

COMMONWEALTH PLYWOOD CO. LTD.
15 Labelle Blvd, PO Box 90, Sainte-Therese, J7E 4H9, QC, Canada
Tel.: (450) 435-6541
Web Site:
http://www.commonwealth.info
Year Founded: 1940
Sales Range: $550-599.9 Million
Emp.: 1,000
Wood Product Mfr & Distr
N.A.I.C.S.: 321113
W. T. Caine *(Pres)*

Subsidiaries:

Commonwealth Plywood Co. Ltd. - Seasons Flooring Division (1)
805 boulevard Cristini, Lachute, J8H 4N6, QC, Canada
Tel.: (450) 562-3515
Web Site: http://www.seasonsflooring.com
Wood Product Distr
N.A.I.C.S.: 423310
Colin Lindsay *(VP)*

COMMS GROUP LTD
Level 3 45 Clarence St, Sydney, 2000, NSW, Australia
Tel.: (61) 1300722320   AU
Web Site:
https://www.nexttelecom.com.au
Year Founded: 2008
CCG—(ASX)
Rev.: $37,033,071
Assets: $37,693,067
Liabilities: $16,476,205
Net Worth: $21,216,863
Earnings: ($68,841)
Emp.: 65
Fiscal Year-end: 06/30/24
Information Technology Services
N.A.I.C.S.: 541511
Peter McGrath *(CEO & Mng Dir)*

Subsidiaries:

Binary Networks Pty. Ltd. (1)
Suite 14 202 Ferntree Gully Road, Notting Hill, 3168, VIC, Australia
Tel.: (61) 390208400
Web Site:
https://www.binarynetworks.com.au
Business Communication & Network Services
N.A.I.C.S.: 561499

Next Telecom Pty. Ltd. (1)
Level 3 45 Clarence St, Sydney, 2000, NSW, Australia
Tel.: (61) 1300006398
Web Site: https://nexttelecom.com.au
Emp.: 120
Cloud Communications Services
N.A.I.C.S.: 517810

OnPlatinum ICT Pty. Ltd. (1)
Suite 1201 Level 12 The Rocket 203 Robina Town Centre Drive, Robina, 4226, QLD, Australia
Tel.: (61) 756767215

Web Site: https://onplatinum.com.au
Information & Communications Technology Services
N.A.I.C.S.: 518210

Tango Technology Pty. Ltd. (1)
Level 10 Suite 10 01 60 Pitt Street, Sydney, 2000, NSW, Australia
Tel.: (61) 280010250
Web Site:
https://www.tangotechnology.com.au
Information Technology Services
N.A.I.C.S.: 541511

COMMSEED CORP
7F Shin-Ochanomizu Urban Trinity Building 2-3 Kanda Surugadai, Chiyoda, Tokyo, 101-0062, Japan
Tel.: (81) 352893111
Web Site: https://www.commseed.net
Year Founded: 1991
37390—(NGO)
Sales Range: Less than $1 Million
Software Development Services
N.A.I.C.S.: 541511
Kenji Tsukahara *(Chm, Pres & CEO)*

COMMUNICATION AND SYSTEM SOLUTION PUBLIC COMPANY LIMITED
329 Moo 3 Banmai, Pakkred, Nonthaburi, 11120, Thailand
Tel.: (66) 20181111
Web Site: https://www.cssthai.com
Year Founded: 1994
CSS—(THA)
Rev.: $1,138,280,589
Assets: $91,504,764
Liabilities: $39,401,096
Net Worth: $52,103,668
Earnings: $236,961
Emp.: 285
Fiscal Year-end: 12/31/23
Electrical Cable, Wire & Engineering Products Distribution & Installation
N.A.I.C.S.: 423610
Sompong Kangsawiwat *(Chm, Pres & CEO)*

Subsidiaries:

Neonworx Communications (Thailand) Co., Ltd. (1)
10 Soi Nakniwas 47 Nakniwas Road, Ladprao, Bangkok, 10230, Thailand
Tel.: (66) 25396693
Web Site: https://www.neonworx.co.th
Wireless Communication Infrastructure Services
N.A.I.C.S.: 517112
Wuttichai Kulsirichaiwat *(Project Mgr)*

COMMUNICATION WEAVER CO., LTD.
Coweaver B/D 45 Magokjungang 8-ro 7-gil, Gangseo-gu, Seoul, 07792, Korea (South)
Tel.: (82) 231403300   KR
Web Site: https://www.coweaver.co.kr
Year Founded: 2000
056360—(KRS)
Rev.: $68,752,464
Assets: $129,541,982
Liabilities: $28,527,357
Net Worth: $101,014,625
Earnings: $3,446,214
Emp.: 171
Fiscal Year-end: 12/31/22
Optical Transmission Equipment Mfr
N.A.I.C.S.: 334210
Ki-Hyuk Sung *(CEO)*

COMMUNICATIONS FIJI LTD.
231 Waimanu Road, Private Mail Bag, Suva, Fiji
Tel.: (679) 331 4766   FJ
Web Site: http://www.cfl.com.fj
Year Founded: 1985

CFL—(SPSE)
Rev.: $5,006,099
Assets: $8,551,121
Liabilities: $1,445,685
Net Worth: $7,105,436
Earnings: $400,186
Emp.: 190
Fiscal Year-end: 12/31/20
Telecommunication Servicesb
N.A.I.C.S.: 517810
William Parkinson *(Founder & Chm)*

COMMUNICATIONS INVEST-MENT PARTNERS LIMITED
Suite 600, 570 Queen Street, Fredericton, E3B 6Z6, NB, Canada
Web Site: http://www.ciplimited.com
Investment Activities
N.A.I.C.S.: 523999
Hans Lipman *(Pres)*

COMMUNICORP GROUP LTD.
5th Floor Marconi House Digges Lane, Dublin, D02 TD60, Ireland
Tel.: (353) 16111111   IE
Web Site:
   http://www.communicorpmedia.com
Year Founded: 1989
Sales Range: $50-74.9 Million
Emp.: 1,200
Radio Stations Owner & Operator
N.A.I.C.S.: 516110
Denis O'Brien *(Founder & Owner)*

Subsidiaries:

Oy Metroradio Finland AB   **(1)**
Pursimiehenkatu 29-31 C, 00150, Helsinki, Finland   **(100%)**
Tel.: (358) 207768360
Web Site: http://www.metroradio.fi
Sales Range: $25-49.9 Million
Emp.: 30
Radio Stations Owner & Operator
N.A.I.C.S.: 516110

COMMUNITY INVESTMENT HOLDINGS (PTY) LTD.
180 Garstfontein Road Ashlea Gardens Office Park Building 5, Menlyn, Pretoria, 0081, South Africa
Tel.: (27) 123469065   ZA
Web Site: http://www.ciholdings.co.za
Year Founded: 1995
Investment Holding Company Services
N.A.I.C.S.: 551112
Joe Madungandaba *(Co-Founder & CEO)*

Subsidiaries:

Malesela Taihan Electric Cable (Pty) Ltd.   **(1)**
273 General Hertzog Rd, Peacehaven, Vereeniging, 1939, Gauteng, South Africa   **(51%)**
Tel.: (27) 164508200
Web Site: https://www.m-tec.co.za
Non-Ferrou Cable Mfr
N.A.I.C.S.: 335929

COMMUTER TRANSPORT ENGINEERING (PTY) LTD.
23 Belvedere Avenue, Oranjezicht, Cape Town, South Africa
Tel.: (27) 21 461 2695   ZA
Web Site: http://www.ctegroup.co.za
Year Founded: 1999
Rail Car Refurbishment & Manufacture
N.A.I.C.S.: 336510
Patricia Norris *(CEO)*

COMMVESCO LEVINSON VINER GROUP INC
485 Bank St, Ottawa, K2P 1Z2, ON, Canada
Tel.: (613) 728-2000

Web Site: http://www.clvgroup.com
Rev.: $18,107,735
Emp.: 200
Real Estate Agents & Brokers
N.A.I.C.S.: 524210
Mike McGahan *(Pres)*

COMO CO., LTD.
505-1 Shimonotsubo Muranaka, Komaki, 485-0082, Aichi, Japan
Tel.: (81) 568737050
Web Site: https://www.comoshop.jp
Year Founded: 1947
2224—(TKS)
Rev.: $48,312,490
Assets: $35,125,540
Liabilities: $21,773,340
Net Worth: $13,352,200
Earnings: $277,620
Emp.: 163
Fiscal Year-end: 03/31/24
Bread Mfr & Distr
N.A.I.C.S.: 311999
Katsumi Kinoshita *(Pres)*

COMO DIFFUSION INC.
255 Boul Decarie, Saint Laurent, H4N 2L7, QC, Canada
Tel.: (514) 286-2666
Web Site: http://www.freddavid.com
Rev.: $73,764,000
Emp.: 75
Apparels Mfr
N.A.I.C.S.: 315990
Helaine Peters *(Pres)*

COMO ENGINEERS PTY. LTD.
130 Stirling Highway North Fremantle, Mosman Park, Perth, 6159, WA, Australia
Tel.: (61) 8 9432 0100   AU
Web Site:
   http://www.comoeng.com.au
Year Founded: 1986
Sales Range: $10-24.9 Million
Emp.: 40
Mining Engineering Services
N.A.I.C.S.: 541330
Richard Ladyman *(Chm)*

COMO HOTELS & RESORTS (ASIA) PTE. LTD.
COMO House 6B Orange Grove Road, Singapore, 258332, Singapore
Tel.: (65) 6304 1488
Web Site:
   http://www.comohotels.com
Hotels & Resorts Owner & Operator
Kevin J. Abramowicz *(VP-Ops)*

Subsidiaries:

COMO Hotels & Resorts Ltd.   **(1)**
17 Old Park Lane, London, W1K 1QT, United Kingdom
Tel.: (44) 20 7447 1049
Hotels & Resorts Owner & Operator
N.A.I.C.S.: 721110
Chris Orlikowski *(Mgr-PR & Mktg)*

COMO Hotels & Resorts USA   **(1)**
111 8th Ave 9th Fl, New York, NY 10011
Tel.: (212) 462-7370
Hotels & Resorts Owner & Operator
N.A.I.C.S.: 721110
Sharon Lee Thony *(Dir-PR & Mktg)*

COMOX VALLEY DODGE CHRYSLER JEEP RAM LTD.
4847 Island Hwy North, Courtenay, V9N 5Y8, BC, Canada
Tel.: (250) 338-5451
Web Site:
   http://www.comoxvalleydodge.com
Sales Range: $10-24.9 Million
New & Used Car Dealers
N.A.I.C.S.: 441110
Mike Marchi *(Principal)*

COMP S.A.
Jutrzenki 116, 02-230, Warsaw, Poland
Tel.: (48) 225703800
Web Site: https://www.comp.com.pl
Year Founded: 1990
CMP—(WAR)
Rev.: $253,430,640
Assets: $233,357,977
Liabilities: $116,922,002
Net Worth: $116,435,975
Earnings: ($12,926,575)
Fiscal Year-end: 12/31/23
Information Technology Security Services
N.A.I.C.S.: 561621
Grzegorz Nalezyty *(Chm-Supervisory Bd)*

COMPA S.A.
H Coanda 8, 550234, Sibiu, Romania
Tel.: (40) 269230888
Web Site: https://www.compa.ro
Year Founded: 1970
CMP—(BUC)
Rev.: $171,055,345
Assets: $165,513,125
Liabilities: $56,599,426
Net Worth: $108,913,700
Earnings: $119,057
Emp.: 1,792
Fiscal Year-end: 12/31/23
Motor Vehicle Parts & Accessories Mfr
N.A.I.C.S.: 336340
Ioan Deac *(Chm, CEO & Member-Exec Bd)*

Subsidiaries:

Trans C.A.S. S.R.L.   **(1)**
Str Henri Coanda Nr 12, Sibiu, Romania
Tel.: (40) 269238230
Motor Vehicle Air-Conditioning Mfr
N.A.I.C.S.: 333415

COMPACT METAL INDUSTRIES LTD.
120 Pioneer Road 01-02, Singapore, 639597, Singapore
Tel.: (65) 6863 3268   SG
Web Site:
   http://www.compact.com.sg
Year Founded: 1973
Sales Range: $10-24.9 Million
Emp.: 1,192
Aluminum Windows & Doors & Extruded Aluminum Mfr
N.A.I.C.S.: 332321

Subsidiaries:

Aluform Marketing Pte Ltd.   **(1)**
120 Pioneer Road #01-02, Singapore, 639597, Singapore
Tel.: (65) 68979780
Web Site: http://www.aluform.com.sg
Sales Range: $25-49.9 Million
Emp.: 35
Building Architectural Products Supply & Installation
N.A.I.C.S.: 238390
Chng Gim Huag *(Pres)*

Compact Metal Industries Sdn Bhd   **(1)**
77 Jalan Riang 21, Taman Gembira Johore Baru, Johor, 81200, Malaysia
Tel.: (60) 73348370
Aluminum Window & Door Mfr
N.A.I.C.S.: 332321

Subsidiary (Non-US):

INTEGRATE PTE LTD   **(2)**
120 Pioneer Road 01-02, Singapore, 639597, Singapore
Tel.: (65) 6897 9780
Web Site: http://www.integrate.com.sg
Emp.: 10
Steel Mfrs
N.A.I.C.S.: 331110

Garry Ang *(Gen Mgr)*

FacadeMaster Pte Ltd.   **(1)**
20 Pioneer Road #04-01, 639597, Singapore, Singapore
Tel.: (65) 68631836
Building Facade Contracting Services
N.A.I.C.S.: 332311

Integrate Marketing Pte Ltd.   **(1)**
120 Pioneer Rd 01-02, Singapore, 639597, Singapore
Tel.: (65) 68979780
Web Site: http://www.integrate.com.sg
Sales Range: $25-49.9 Million
Emp.: 25
Building Components & Accessories Mfr & Distr
N.A.I.C.S.: 444180
Gary Ang *(Gen Mgr)*

PT Cakra Compact Aluminium Industries   **(1)**
Jl Raya Medan Tg Morawa Km 11, PO Box 2345, North Sumatera, Medan, Indonesia
Tel.: (62) 617940246
Web Site: http://www.cakracompact.com
Aluminum Window & Door Mfr
N.A.I.C.S.: 332321
Albert Quek *(Gen Mgr)*

Selaco Aluminium Berhad   **(1)**
Lot 280 Jalan Timah Pasir Gudang Ind Estate, Gudang Johore, Johor, 81700, Malaysia
Tel.: (60) 72514062
Web Site: http://www.selaco.com.my
Sales Range: $100-124.9 Million
Emp.: 300
Aluminum Window & Door Mfr
N.A.I.C.S.: 332321
Poh Thun Ching *(Gen Mgr)*

COMPAGNIA DEI CARAIBI S.P.A.
Via Ribes 3, Colleretto Giacosa, 10100, Turin, TO, Italy
Tel.: (39) 0125791104
Web Site:
   https://www.compagniadeicaraibi.com
Year Founded: 1995
TIME—(EUR)
Rev.: $68,959,315
Assets: $46,194,891
Liabilities: $23,669,497
Net Worth: $22,525,395
Earnings: $2,495,655
Emp.: 73
Fiscal Year-end: 12/31/22
Alcoholic Beverage Distr
N.A.I.C.S.: 424820
Edelberto Baracco *(Pres)*

COMPAGNIA FINANZIARIA DE BENEDETTI S.P.A.
Via Ciovassino 1, 20121, Milan, Italy
Tel.: (39) 02722701
Web Site: http://www.cofide.it
Year Founded: 1976
Sales Range: $1-4.9 Billion
Holding Company; Publishing, Food Machinery Manufacturing, Automotive Components, Tobacco Machinery, Specialty Foods, Real Estate & Financial Services
N.A.I.C.S.: 551112
Rodolfo De Benedetti *(Chm)*

Subsidiaries:

CIR S.p.A.   **(1)**
Via Ciovassino 1, 20121, Milan, Italy
Tel.: (39) 02722701
Web Site: https://www.cirgroup.it
Rev.: $2,253,545,274
Assets: $4,259,451,571
Liabilities: $3,046,171,535
Net Worth: $1,213,280,037
Earnings: $20,036,279
Emp.: 17,668
Fiscal Year-end: 12/31/2020
Holding Company; Publishing, Media, Automotive Components, Specialty Food, Real Estate, Utilities & Food Machinery

Compagnia Finanziaria de Benedetti
S.p.A.—(Continued)
N.A.I.C.S.: 551112
Rodolfo De Benedetti (Chm)

Subsidiary (Domestic):

Sogefi S.p.A. **(2)**
Via Flavio Gioia 8, Milan, Italy **(52.43%)**
Tel.: (39) 02467601
Web Site: http://www.sugefigroup.com
Sales Range: $1-4.9 Billion
Emp.: 6,100
Automotive Filters Mfr
N.A.I.C.S.: 336390
Rodolfo De Benedetti (Chm)

Subsidiary (Non-US):

Filtrauto S.A. **(3)**
7 Ave Du 8 Mai 1945, 78286, Guyancourt,
Cedex, France
Tel.: (33) 16 137 4300
Web Site: http://www.filtrauto.com
Sales Range: $350-399.9 Million
Emp.: 1,050
Mfr of Automotive Filters
N.A.I.C.S.: 336110

Division (Non-US):

Filtrauto Do Brasil Ltda. **(4)**
Avenue Piraporanha No 251, Sao Bernardo
do Campo, 019891000, MG, Brazil
Tel.: (55) 01143142400
Industrial Filter Mfr
N.A.I.C.S.: 336390

Filtrauto Slovenija **(4)**
Obrat Jesenice, C Franceta Mesarna 15,
4270, Jesenice, Slovenia
Web Site: http://www.filtrauto.com
Industrial Filter Mfr
N.A.I.C.S.: 336390

Subsidiary (Non-US):

Sogefi Filtration Argentina S.A. **(3)**
Aguilar 3003, Remedios de Escalada, Bue-
nos Aires, Argentina
Tel.: (54) 114 220 4600
Web Site: http://www.sogefi.com.ar
Industrial Filter Mfr
N.A.I.C.S.: 336390

Sogefi Filtration D.O.O. **(3)**
Ladja 11, 1215, Medvode, Slovenia
Tel.: (386) 61 362 9013
Web Site: http://www.sogeci.com
Sales Range: $50-74.9 Million
Emp.: 159
Industrial Filter Mfr
N.A.I.C.S.: 333998

Sogefi Industria de Autopecas
Ltda. **(3)**
Av Piraporinha 251, San Bernardo do
Campo, 09891-000, Sao Paulo, Brazil
Tel.: (55) 117592400
Web Site: http://www.sogefi.com.br
Mfr & Sales of Filters
N.A.I.C.S.: 333310

Charleston Holding HmbH **(1)**
Hiebelerstrasse 29, 87629, Fussen, Ger-
many
Tel.: (49) 8362505820
Web Site: http://www.charleston.de
Healtcare Services
N.A.I.C.S.: 621999

KOS Spa **(1)**
Via Durini 9, 20121, Milan, Italy
Tel.: (39) 026713291
Web Site: http://www.kosgroup.com
Healtcare Services
N.A.I.C.S.: 621999

Saire S.R.L **(1)**
9 Via Giotto, 39100, Bolzano, Italy
Tel.: (39) 0471250006
Non Flammable Materials Mfr
N.A.I.C.S.: 922160

COMPAGNIA IMMOBILIARE AZIONARIA S.P.A.

Via G Borgazzi 2, 20122, Milan,
20122, MI, Italy
Tel.: (39) 0258219883

Web Site: https://www.c-i-a.it
Year Founded: 2002
CIA—(ITA)
Sales Range: $10-24.9 Million
Emp.: 3
Real Estate Manangement Services
N.A.I.C.S.: 531390
Angelo Riccardi (Chm)

COMPAGNIE AERIENNE IN-TER REGIONALE EXPRESS SA

Aeroport de Rochambeau, 97351,
Matoury, French Guiana
Tel.: (594) 293630
Web Site: http://www.airguyane.com
Sales Range: $25-49.9 Million
Airline Operator
N.A.I.C.S.: 481111

COMPAGNIE AGRICOLE DE LA CRAU SA

34 route d Ecully, BP 94, 69570, Dar-
dilly, France
Tel.: (33) 472522200
Web Site: http://www.compagnie-
agricole-de-la-crau.fr
Agriculture Product Distr
N.A.I.C.S.: 484220
Claude Gros (Chm & CEO)

COMPAGNIE CHAMPENOISE PH-CHPIPER HEIDSIECK SAS

12 allee du Vignoble, 51100, Reims,
France
Tel.: (33) 33 26 84 43 00
Web Site: http://www.piper-
heidsieck.com
Wine & Champagne Mfr
N.A.I.C.S.: 424820

Subsidiaries:

Folio Wine Company, LLC **(1)**
550 Gateway Dr Ste 220, Napa, CA
94558 **(60%)**
Tel.: (707) 256-2700
Web Site: http://www.foliowine.com
Beer, Wine & Liquor Stores
N.A.I.C.S.: 445320
Michael Mondavi (Co-Founder & Chm)

COMPAGNIE COLONIALE

717 rue de la Gare, Dissay, 86130,
Saint-Georges-les-Baillargeaux,
France
Tel.: (33) 5 49 62 82 10
Web Site: http://www.compagnie-
coloniale.com
Sales Range: $1-9.9 Million
Emp.: 15
Tea Mfr & Distr
N.A.I.C.S.: 311920
Vincent Balay (Pres)

COMPAGNIE D'APPAREILS ELECTRIQUES PEERLESS LIMITEE

9145 Rue Boivin, Montreal, H8R 2E5,
QC, Canada
Tel.: (514) 595-1671
Web Site: http://www.peerless-
electric.com
Commercial & Industry Light Mfr
N.A.I.C.S.: 335132
Barry Fagen (Pres)

COMPAGNIE DE L'OCCIDENT POUR LA FINANCE ET L'INDUSTRIE S.A.

2 rue de l'Eau, 1449, Luxembourg,
Luxembourg
Tel.: (352) 299 230
Web Site: http://www.cofi.lu
Year Founded: 1971
Bank Holding Company
N.A.I.C.S.: 551111

Massimo Trabaldo Togna (Vice Chm)

Subsidiaries:

PKB Privatbank SA **(1)**
Via S Balestra 1, Lugano, 6900, Switzer-
land
Tel.: (41) 91 913 3535
Web Site: http://www.pkb.ch
Emp.: 200
Private Banking
N.A.I.C.S.: 523150
Henry Peter (Chm)

COMPAGNIE DE SAINT-GOBAIN SA

Tour Saint-Gobain - 12 place de
L'Iris, La Defense, 92096, Paris, Ce-
dex, France
Tel.: (33) 188540000
Web Site: https://www.saint-
gobain.com
Year Founded: 1665
CODGF—(OTCIQ)
Rev.: $52,924,163,822
Assets: $63,250,910,705
Liabilities: $37,025,057,959
Net Worth: $26,225,852,747
Earnings: $3,042,278,398
Emp.: 159,145
Fiscal Year-end: 12/31/23
Glass, Plastics, Ceramics & Other
Construction Materials Mfr & Distr
N.A.I.C.S.: 551112
Laurence Pernot (VP-Comm)

Subsidiaries:

Agence Haguenau Point P **(1)**
99 Rte De Bitche, PO Box 10175, 67506,
Haguenau, Cedex, France **(61.41%)**
Tel.: (33) 3 88 90 66 20
Hardware Retailer
N.A.I.C.S.: 444140

Alp'Verre **(1)**
8 Rue Des Terrasses, BP 48 74962, Cran-
Gevrier, Cedex, France **(100%)**
Tel.: (33) 450572200
Sales Range: $25-49.9 Million
Emp.: 70
Glass Mfr
N.A.I.C.S.: 327211

Ashworth **(1)**
Hither Airsworth Rd, Radcliffe, M26 4AF,
United Kingdom **(100%)**
Tel.: (44) 1617233468
Web Site: http://www.ashworth.eu.com
Sales Range: $25-49.9 Million
Emp.: 100
Pipe & Tube Systems
N.A.I.C.S.: 326122
Bill Willocks (Mng Dir)

Atlantique Menuiseries Fermetures
(A.M.F.) **(1)**
Route Du Poire, 85190, Aizenay,
France **(46.08%)**
Tel.: (33) 251455145
Web Site: http://www.saint-gobain.com
Flat Glass Mfr
N.A.I.C.S.: 327211

Auvergne Isolation **(1)**
Montmurat, 15600, Maurs, France **(100%)**
Tel.: (33) 471491900
Web Site: http://www.glasssolutions.fr
Industrial Glass Products Mfr
N.A.I.C.S.: 327211

BPB GYPSUM BV **(1)**
20 Parallelweg, 4878AH, Etten-Leur, Neth-
erlands
Tel.: (31) 76 5080000
Web Site: http://www.saint-gobain.fr
Gypsum Product Mfr
N.A.I.C.S.: 327420

BPB Placo S.A. **(1)**
34 Ave Franklin Roosevelt, 92282,
Suresnes, France
Tel.: (33) 146254625
Sales Range: $900-999.9 Million
Emp.: 1,887
Gypsum Products
N.A.I.C.S.: 327420

Barbe **(1)**
Roch Glas, 29200, Brest, France **(79.17%)**
Tel.: (33) 298032982
Web Site: http://www.pointp.fr
Sales Range: $25-49.9 Million
Emp.: 50
Hardware Retailer
N.A.I.C.S.: 444140

Beijing SEPR Refracories Co.,
Ltd. **(1)**
No 10 Nan Xin Road Nan Kou County,
Changping District, Beijing, 102202, China
Tel.: (86) 10 89791418
Web Site: http://www.saint-gobain.com.cn
Electro Fuse Product Mfr
N.A.I.C.S.: 335931

Beton Manufacture de Vitre **(1)**
3 Rue de Plague, 35500, Vitre, France
Tel.: (33) 223551320
Concrete Mfr
N.A.I.C.S.: 327320

Bourgeois **(1)**
3 rue de Langeais ZIL, BP 146, 49301,
Cholet, Cedex, France **(79%)**
Tel.: (33) 241461877
Hardware Retailer
N.A.I.C.S.: 444140

Brasilit SA **(1)**
Avenida Santa Marina 482 1 Andar, 05036
903, Sao Paulo, Agua Branca,
Brazil **(92.5%)**
Tel.: (55) 11 2246 7000
Web Site: http://www.brasilit.com.br
Sales Range: $200-249.9 Million
Emp.: 600
Mfr of Fibre-Cement Sheets & Mouldings
N.A.I.C.S.: 324122

Building Products of Canada
Corp. **(1)**
9510 Street Patrick Street, La Salle, H8R
1R9, QC, Canada
Tel.: (514) 364-0161
Web Site: http://www.bpcan.com
Sales Range: $25-49.9 Million
Ceiling, Structural & Acoustical Panel Mfr;
Shingle Mfr
N.A.I.C.S.: 324122

Cedeo **(1)**
Rue Berthe Warret, 62000, Arras,
France **(61.64%)**
Tel.: (33) 321505252
Hardware Retailer
N.A.I.C.S.: 444140

Central Saint-Gobain Co., Ltd. **(1)**
Kowa Hitotsubashi Building 2F 3-7-1,
Kanda Nishiki-cho Chiyoda-ku, Tokyo, 101-
0054, Japan **(35%)**
Tel.: (81) 332597694
Sales Range: $25-49.9 Million
Emp.: 40
Automotive Glass Sales
N.A.I.C.S.: 811212
Koshinori Nakayama (Pres)

Centre Est Vitrage **(1)**
27 Rue Paul Sabatier Prolongee Industrial
Zone Confreries, 71530, Crissey, France
Tel.: (33) 385464612
Sales Range: $50-74.9 Million
Emp.: 110
Glass Products Mfr
N.A.I.C.S.: 327211
Christophe Lognone (Gen Mgr)

Ceramidi **(1)**
Le Bugarel-Bruniquel, 82800, Negrepelisse,
France **(61.41%)**
Flat Glass Mfr
N.A.I.C.S.: 327211

Chryso SAS **(1)**
7 Rue de l'Europe Zone Industrielle, Ser-
maises du Loiret, 45300, France
Tel.: (33) 2 38 34 58 00
Web Site: http://www.chryso.fr
Admixtures for Cement, Concrete & Gyp-
sum Designer, Mfr & Distr
N.A.I.C.S.: 325998
Eric Lebre (Sls Dir)

Subsidiary (Non-US):

Chryso UK Ltd. **(2)**
9 Brunel Close Drayton Fields Industrial

Estate, Daventry, NN11 8RB, Northants, United Kingdom
Tel.: (44) 1327707976
Web Site: http://www.chryso.com
Admixtures for Concrete, Cement & Gypsum Designer, Mfr & Distr
N.A.I.C.S.: 325998
Iain Bonfield *(Mgr-Cement)*

Subsidiary (US):

Chryso, Inc.   (2)
1611 State Hwy 276, Rockwall, TX 75032
Tel.: (812) 256-4220
Web Site: http://us.chryso.com
Admixtures for Concrete, Cement & Gypsum Designer, Mfr & Distr
N.A.I.C.S.: 325998
Lew Cook *(Pres)*

Companhia Brasileira de Cristal   (1)
Rua Jose Mattar, 201 Jardim Sao Dimas, Sao Jose dos Campos, 12245-450, SP, Brazil   **(38.13%)**
Flat Glass Mfr
N.A.I.C.S.: 327211

Comptoir General des Glaces et Produits Verriers   (1)
8 Route Des Champs Fourgons, 92233, Gennevilliers, France   **(100%)**
Tel.: (33) 146139400
Sales Range: $50-74.9 Million
Emp.: 30
Distr of Glass Products
N.A.I.C.S.: 423390

Consumers Sklo Zorya   (1)
1 Promyslova St, Zorya Village, Rivne, 35314, Ukraine
Tel.: (380) 362692104
Web Site: http://www.ua.verallia.com
Rev.: $57,876,882
Emp.: 542
Glass Container Mfr
N.A.I.C.S.: 327213

Coramine S.A.S.   (1)
ZI 2 Avenue Etienne Audibert, BP 90034, 60302, Senlis, Cedex, France
Tel.: (33) 344531098
Web Site: http://www.coramine.fr
Sales Range: $25-49.9 Million
Emp.: 60
Gypsum Product Mfr
N.A.I.C.S.: 327420
Maxime Berrios *(Gen Mgr)*

Courbu Vitrages   (1)
ZI Du Phare, 33700, Merignac, France   **(100%)**
Tel.: (33) 557923131
Web Site: http://www.saint-gobain-glass.com
Sales Range: $25-49.9 Million
Emp.: 70
Mfr of Glass Products
N.A.I.C.S.: 327211

Decoupage et Mecanique de l'Ouest   (1)
68 Rue Denis Papin, 49500, Segre, Cedex, France   **(100%)**
Tel.: (33) 241921203
Web Site: http://www.d-m-o.fr
Sales Range: $25-49.9 Million
Emp.: 6
Flat Glass
N.A.I.C.S.: 327211

Deutsche Terranova Industrie   (1)
Metternicher Strasse 17, D-53919, Weilerswist, Germany   **(79.09%)**
Tel.: (49) 22546050
Flat Glass Mfr
N.A.I.C.S.: 327211

Dispano   (1)
8 Blvd Ferdinand De Lesseps, 76000, Rouen, France   **(79.21%)**
Tel.: (33) 235983838
Web Site: http://www.dispano.com
Sales Range: $25-49.9 Million
Emp.: 30
N.A.I.C.S.: 327211

Distribution Sanitaire Chauffage SAS   (1)
2 Avenue des Charmes - ZAC du Parc Alata, Verneuil en Halatte, 60550, France

Tel.: (33) 3 44 55 82 00
Web Site: http://www.cedeo.fr
Sanitary Ware Mfr
N.A.I.C.S.: 332999

Doganer Alci Madencilik Enerji Ithalat Ihracat Pazarlama Ticaret Ve Sanayi A.S.   (1)
Cetin Emec Bulvari 1042 Cadde 1296 Sokak No 7, Ovecler, Ankara, 1296, Turkiye
Tel.: (90) 312478 26 01
Web Site: http://www.doganeralci.com.tr
Plaster Board Mfr
N.A.I.C.S.: 327420

Eckelt Glas GmbH   (1)
Resthofstrasse 18, Steyr, 4400, Austria
Tel.: (43) 72528940
Web Site: http://www.eckelt.at
Sales Range: $125-149.9 Million
Emp.: 300
Flat Glass Mfr
N.A.I.C.S.: 327211

Eurocoustic   (1)
7 Pl De Saverne, 92400, Courbevoie, France   **(98.31%)**
Tel.: (33) 156370240
Web Site: http://www.eurocoustic.com
Sales Range: $50-74.9 Million
Emp.: 160
Provider of Thermal & Acoustic Insulation Services
N.A.I.C.S.: 327993
Jean-Francois Lelievre *(Gen Mgr)*

Expobois   (1)
Les Perrasses, 74230, Thones, France   **(79.19%)**
Flat Glass Mfr
N.A.I.C.S.: 327211

Faba Autoglas Technik GmbH   (1)
Blomberger Weg 6, 13437, Berlin, Germany   **(99.79%)**
Tel.: (49) 304147390
Web Site: http://www.faba-autoglas.com
Sales Range: $25-49.9 Million
Emp.: 30
Flat Glass Mfr
N.A.I.C.S.: 327211
Raphael Kueff *(Gen Mgr)*

Fabresines   (1)
11-17, rue Constantin-Pecqueur, 95157, Taverny, Cedex, France   **(79.05%)**
Tel.: (33) 1 34 18 08 78
Paints Mfr
N.A.I.C.S.: 325510

FiberGlass Colombia S.A.   (1)
Calle 3ra No 3 - 49 Este, Mosquera, Colombia
Tel.: (57) 18933030
Web Site: http://www.fiberglasscolombia.com
Glass Products Mfr
N.A.I.C.S.: 327215

Fibras Fivenglass SA   (1)
Soco Industrial Zone North Facing Street Polifilm, Altimira, Venezuela
Tel.: (58) 2443220409
Web Site: http://www.fivenglass.com.ve
Sales Range: $25-49.9 Million
Emp.: 11
Glass Product Distr
N.A.I.C.S.: 423330

Flachglas Torgau GmbH   (1)
Solar Strasse 1, 04860, Torgau, Germany
Tel.: (49) 34217510
Web Site: http://www.saint-gobain.com
Mfr of Glass Products
N.A.I.C.S.: 327211

Galvano Groothandel BV   (1)
Dillenburgstraat 12, 5652 AP, Eindhoven, Netherlands
Tel.: (31) 40214 14 14
Web Site: http://www.galvano.nl
Sales Range: $50-74.9 Million
Emp.: 85
Sanitaryware Distr
N.A.I.C.S.: 423720
Erik van Stiphout *(Sr Product Mgr)*

Giraud   (1)
Route De Roanne, 69240, Pont-Trambouze, France   **(59.18%)**
Tel.: (33) 4 74 64 54 44

Web Site: http://www.saint-gobain.com
Frames Mfr
N.A.I.C.S.: 332321

Glaceries de Saint-Roch Germania   (1)
Viktoriaallee 3 5, 52066, Aachen, Germany   **(99.49%)**
Tel.: (49) 2415160
Web Site: http://www.saint-gobain-glass.com
Sales Range: $125-149.9 Million
Emp.: 300
Mfr of Glass Products
N.A.I.C.S.: 327211

Glaceries de Saint-Roch SA   (1)
World Trade Center Tour 1Bld E, Jacqmain 162, Bte 48., 1210, Brussels, Belgium   **(99.54%)**
Sales Range: $200-249.9 Million
Emp.: 750
Mfr & Transformer of Flat Glass
N.A.I.C.S.: 327211

Subsidiary (Non-US):

Glasfabriek Sas van Gent B.V.   (2)
Westkade 20, PO Box 4, 4550 AA, Sasvan-Gent, Netherlands   **(100%)**
Tel.: (31) 115458000
Web Site:
   http://www.saint-gobain-glass.com
Rev.: $25,497,000
Emp.: 120
Fabricator of Reflective Glass; Tempered Glass; Enameled Glass; Insulating Glass
N.A.I.C.S.: 327211

Glas Ziegler GesmbH   (1)
Liesinger Flurgasse 10, 1230, Vienna, Austria
Tel.: (43) 1869 26 460
Web Site: http://www.austria.sggs.com
Flat Glass Mfr
N.A.I.C.S.: 327211

Glashuset i Sverige AB   (1)
Annkristin Backstrom, Glashuset Burs, Burs Anges 231, 623 49, Gotland, Sweden   **(99.5%)**
Tel.: (46) 498483077
Web Site: http://www.glashuset.se
Sales Range: $25-49.9 Million
Emp.: 10
Mfr of Glass Products
N.A.I.C.S.: 327211

Gobba Vitrage   (1)
21 Ave Marcellin Berthelot, PO Box 7, 38200, Vienne, France   **(100%)**
Tel.: (33) 474537553
Web Site: http://www.saint-gobain-glass.com
Sales Range: $25-49.9 Million
Emp.: 90
Flat Glass Mfr
N.A.I.C.S.: 327211

International Saint-Gobain   (1)
10 rue Saint-Pierre, CH-1700, Fribourg, Switzerland   **(100%)**
Tel.: (41) 19 61 37 22 15 22
Holding Company
N.A.I.C.S.: 551112

Jiangsu Donghai Saint-Gobain Co. Ltd.   (1)
105 West Heping Road, Donghai, 222 300, Jiangsu, China   **(69.44%)**
Flat Glass
N.A.I.C.S.: 327211

K par K   (1)
66 Blvd Felix Faure, 93300, Aubervilliers, France   **(59.15%)**
Tel.: (33) 148344022
Web Site: http://www.kpark.fr
Sales Range: $25-49.9 Million
Emp.: 48
Windows Retailer
N.A.I.C.S.: 423220

KAIMANN GmbH   (1)
Hansastrasse 2-5, 33161, Paderborn, Germany
Tel.: (49) 525798500
Web Site: http://www.kaimann.com
Rev.: $82,614,620
Emp.: 228

Elastomeric & Polyethylene Insulation System Mfr
N.A.I.C.S.: 325212
Wilhelm Kaimann *(Founder)*

Subsidiary (Non-US):

Kaimann B.V.   (2)
Patronaatstraat 82, 6466 HR, Kerkrade, Holland, Netherlands
Tel.: (31) 628885336
Web Site: http://www.kaimann.com
Elastomeric Insulation Product Distr
N.A.I.C.S.: 424690
Henry Hanssen *(Mgr-Sls)*

Kaimann France SAS   (2)
ZI Intercommuncale Rue Henri Seiller, CS 60004, 68501, Guebwiller, Cedex, France
Tel.: (33) 389506920
Web Site: http://www.kaimann.com
Elastomeric Insulation Product Distr
N.A.I.C.S.: 424690

Kaimann Iberia s.l.   (2)
C / Torres Jonama 64, Palafrugell, 17200, Girona, Spain
Tel.: (34) 972904100
Web Site: http://www.kaimann.com
Elastomeric Insulation Product Distr
N.A.I.C.S.: 424690
Marti Niell *(Bus Mgr-Spain & Portugal)*

Kaimann Italia s.r.l   (2)
Dell Industria Sud 12 Loc Cason I, Rivoli Veronese, 37010, Verona, Italy
Tel.: (39) 0456261222
Web Site: http://www.kaimann.com
Elastomeric Insulation Product Distr
N.A.I.C.S.: 424690

Kaimann UK Ltd   (2)
House Business Centre Brideok Street, Oldham, OL4 2 HB, United Kingdom
Tel.: (44) 1616273289
Web Site: http://www.kaimann.com
Elastomeric Insulation Product Distr
N.A.I.C.S.: 424690
Stuart Allely *(Mgr-Technical)*

KBS AG   (1)
Industriestrasse 16, Veltheim, 5106, Switzerland
Tel.: (41) 56 463 68 68
Web Site: http://www.kbs-ag.ch
Emp.: 30
Construction Materials Distr
N.A.I.C.S.: 423390
Bernhard Lanzendorfer *(Mng Dir)*

Kaycan Ltd.   (1)
3075 Trans-Canada Hwy, Pointe-Claire, H9R 1B4, QC, Canada
Tel.: (514) 694-5855
Web Site: http://www.kaycan.com
Sales Range: $50-74.9 Million
Emp.: 160
Vinyl Siding, Particle Board & Laminate Flooring Mfr
N.A.I.C.S.: 423330
Lionel Dubrofsky *(Pres)*

Subsidiary (US):

KP Building Products Ltd.   (2)
820 Highway 7 N, Holly Springs, MS 38635-1347
Web Site: https://kpvinylsiding.com
Building Materials Whslr
N.A.I.C.S.: 444180

Subsidiary (Domestic):

Uniboard Canada Inc.   (2)
2540 Boulevard Daniel Johnson Suite 500, Laval, H7T 2S3, QC, Canada
Tel.: (450) 682-5240
Web Site: http://www.uniboard.com
Melamine Panels, Medium Density Fiberboard & Particleboard Mfr
N.A.I.C.S.: 321219

Subsidiary (Domestic):

MDF La Baie Inc.   (3)
5373 Chemin Street Anicet, CP 1053, La Baie, G7B 3P2, QC, Canada
Tel.: (418) 677-2000
Sales Range: $50-74.9 Million
Emp.: 125
Producer of Medium Density Fiberboard

Compagnie de Saint-Gobain SA—(Continued)

N.A.I.C.S.: 321219

Division (Domestic):

Uniboard Canada, Inc.-LDI Division
904 Rte 309, Lac-des-Iles, J0W 1J0, QC, Canada
Tel.: (819) 597-2521
Web Site: http://www.uniboard.com
Sales Range: $25-49.9 Million
Emp.: 85
Mfr of Laminated Boards
N.A.I.C.S.: 321219

Division (US):

Uniboard Fostoria Inc. **(3)**
1600 N Main St, Fostoria, OH 44830-1941
Tel.: (419) 435-6674
Web Site: http://www.uniboard.com
Sales Range: $25-49.9 Million
Emp.: 30
Mfr of Particle Board
N.A.I.C.S.: 321219

Division (Domestic):

Uniboard Mont Laurier Inc. **(3)**
845 Rue J B Reid, Mont Laurier, J9L 3W3, QC, Canada
Tel.: (819) 623-7133
Web Site: http://www.uniboard.com
Sales Range: $50-74.9 Million
Emp.: 130
Melanine Particle Board Producers
N.A.I.C.S.: 321219

Uniboard New Liskeard, Inc. **(3)**
Hwy 11B, PO Box 1840, New Liskeard, P0J 1P0, ON, Canada
Tel.: (705) 647-6775
Web Site: http://www.uniboard.com
Sales Range: $25-49.9 Million
Emp.: 80
Produce Melanine Particle Board
N.A.I.C.S.: 321219

Uniboard Sayabec, Inc. **(3)**
152 Rte Pouliot, Sayabec, G0J 3K0, QC, Canada
Tel.: (418) 536-5465
Web Site: http://www.uniboard.com
Melanine Particle Board Mfr
N.A.I.C.S.: 321219
Alexandre Bedard *(Dir-HR)*

Subsidiary (Domestic):

Uniboard Surface Inc. **(3)**
5555 Ernest Cormier St, Laval, H7C 2S9, QC, Canada
Tel.: (514) 335-2003
Sales Range: $50-74.9 Million
Mfr of Laminated Flooring
N.A.I.C.S.: 321219

Division (Domestic):

Uniboard Unires, Inc. **(3)**
970 Echo St, PO Box 2700, Val d'Or, J9P 6L1, QC, Canada
Tel.: (819) 825-6550
Web Site: http://www.uniboard.com
Sales Range: $50-74.9 Million
Emp.: 30
Mfr of Resins & Formaldehyde
N.A.I.C.S.: 321999

Uniboard Val d'Or, Inc. **(3)**
2700 Boul Jean-Jacques Cossette, Val d'Or, J9P 5G6, QC, Canada
Tel.: (819) 825-6550
Web Site: http://www.uniboard.com
Sales Range: $50-74.9 Million
Emp.: 240
Mfr of Resins & Formaldehyde
N.A.I.C.S.: 321219
Sylvain Cote *(Mng Dir)*

Keraglass SNC **(1)**
Rue du Saint Laurent, 77167, Bagneaux-sur-Loing, France
Tel.: (33) 164764700
Web Site: http://www.eurokera.com
Sales Range: $50-74.9 Million
Emp.: 200
Flat Glass Mfr
N.A.I.C.S.: 327211

Gilles Grandpierre *(Gen Mgr)*

LIN YI SAINT-GOBAIN REFRACTORY CO., LTD **(1)**
Fuzhuang, Luozhuang District, Linyi, China
Tel.: (86) 539 850 8889
Gypsum Product Mfr
N.A.I.C.S.: 327420

LVI-DAHL OY **(1)**
Robert Huberin tie 5, 01510, Vantaa, Finland
Tel.: (358) 20 759 4200
Web Site: http://www.lvi-dahl.fi
Industrial Steel Pipe Distr
N.A.I.C.S.: 423510
Timo Kahila *(CFO)*

La Basquaise de CD **(1)**
Rue de l'Industrie, ZI des Pontois, 64600, Anglet, France **(79.23%)**
Flat Glass Mfr
N.A.I.C.S.: 327211

La Savoisienne de CD **(1)**
84 BP 732, 74015, Annecy, Cedex, France **(79.23%)**
Flat Glass Mfr
N.A.I.C.S.: 327211

La Venecia Iberiaglass S.L. **(1)**
Cima Do Alle-Filueira, 36500, Lalin, Spain
Tel.: (34) 986 78 72 51
Flat Glass Mfr
N.A.I.C.S.: 327211

La Veneciana Centro S.A. **(1)**
Principal Uerdara 32 Fl 8, Paseo de la Castellana 77, 28046, Madrid, Spain **(73.1%)**
Tel.: (34) 913972000
Web Site: http://www.saint-gobain-glass.com
Rev.: $97,447,100
Emp.: 849
Distr, Processor & Installer of Glass Products & Mirrors
N.A.I.C.S.: 327211
Antonio Garabe *(Mng Dir)*

Lagrange Production **(1)**
Route de Montauban 2, 31340, La Magdeleine-sur-Tarn, France **(59.17%)**
Tel.: (33) 561378880
Web Site: http://www.lapeyre.fr
Sales Range: $50-74.9 Million
Emp.: 200
Flat Glass Mfr
N.A.I.C.S.: 327211

Lapeyre Services (LGS) **(1)**
2 Rue Andre Karman, PO Box 149, 93304, Aubervilliers, France **(59.04%)**
Tel.: (33) 148117400
Web Site: http://www.lapeyre.com
Sales Range: $100-124.9 Million
Emp.: 400
Data Processing
N.A.I.C.S.: 518210

Les Menuiseries Francaises **(1)**
Route De Roanne, 69240, Lyon, France
Tel.: (33) 474645444
Web Site: http://www.menuiseries-francaises.fr
Rev.: $24,700,000
Emp.: 25
Wood Housing Materials Mfr
N.A.I.C.S.: 423310

Les Zelles **(1)**
ZI Les Ecorces, BP 7, 88250, La Bresse, France **(59.18%)**
Tel.: (33) 329255311
Web Site: http://www.leszelles.fr
Mfr of PVC & Aluminium Windows
N.A.I.C.S.: 332321

MAG Isover K.K. **(1)**
3-7 Kojimachi, Chiyoda-ku, Tokyo, 102-0083, Japan
Tel.: (81) 3 3288 6300
Web Site: http://www.mag.co.jp
Fiber Glass Insulation Product Mfr & Distr
N.A.I.C.S.: 327993

MS Brico **(1)**
44 Rue De Rohrwiller, 67240, Bischwiller, France **(78.95%)**
Tel.: (33) 388062857
Hardware Retailer
N.A.I.C.S.: 444140

Mabetoc **(1)**
87, rue de Paris, 76800, Saint Etienne-du-Rouvray, France **(30.82%)**
Flat Glass Mfr
N.A.I.C.S.: 327211

Menuiserie du Centre **(1)**
Ave Martial Lapeyre, 15210, Ydes, France **(59.18%)**
Tel.: (33) 471670000
Sales Range: $100-124.9 Million
Emp.: 300
Furniture Mfr
N.A.I.C.S.: 332510

Metz Woippy Cedeo **(1)**
34-36 Route de Thionville, BP 86270, 57062, Metz, Cedex 2, France **(61.64%)**
Tel.: (33) 387310266
Web Site: http://www.cedeo.fr
Plumbing Supplies Retailer
N.A.I.C.S.: 444180

Miroiterie du Rhin **(1)**
Rue De Industrie, PO Box 24, 68126, Bennwihr Gare, France **(100%)**
Tel.: (33) 389208888
Web Site: http://www.saint-gobain-glass.com
Sales Range: $25-49.9 Million
Emp.: 100
Mfr of Glass Products
N.A.I.C.S.: 327211

Miroiteries de L'Ouest Atlantique **(1)**
Zone Des Rochettes, BP 56, 44550, Montoir-de-Bretagne, France **(99.98%)**
Tel.: (33) 240002323
Glass Products Mfr
N.A.I.C.S.: 327211
Courvoisies Dear *(Gen Mgr)*

Miroiteries de l'Ouest Semiver Climaver **(1)**
Rue D'Alembert, BP 510, 22005, Saint-Brieuc, France **(99.97%)**
Tel.: (33) 296682268
Web Site: http://www.saint-gobain-glass.com
Industrial Products Mfr
N.A.I.C.S.: 334513

Modenfix Italia SRL **(1)**
Via Fosse Ardeatine 2, I-41042, Fiorano-Modenese, Italy **(73.34%)**
Tel.: (39) 059556115
N.A.I.C.S.: 327211

Natec **(1)**
Le Closeau rue de Brie, BP 84 77170, Servon, France **(79.98%)**
Flat Glass Mfr
N.A.I.C.S.: 327211

Optimera A/S **(1)**
Ostre Aker Vei 260, 0976, Oslo, Norway
Tel.: (47) 22168800
Web Site: http://www.optimera.no
Building Materials Distr
N.A.I.C.S.: 423320
Asbjorn Vennebo *(CEO)*

PAM Colombia SA **(1)**
KM 3 5 Autopista Medellin Costado Sur Terminal Terrestre De Carga, Etapa 1 Modulo 3 Bodega 9, 140165, Cota, Colombia
Tel.: (57) 317 657 47 23
Web Site: http://www.pamcol.com
Iron Pipe Mfr
N.A.I.C.S.: 331210

POINT P DEVELOPPEMENT **(1)**
Le Mozart 13/15 rue Germaine Tailleferre, 75019, Paris, France
Tel.: (33) 140033300
Web Site: http://www.saint-gobain.com
Building Materials Distr
N.A.I.C.S.: 423330

PT Prima Rezeki Pertiwi **(1)**
Jl Jend Sudirman Kav 60 Menara Sudirman Lt 11, Jakarta, 12190, Indonesia
Tel.: (62) 21 52921135
Gypsum Product Mfr
N.A.I.C.S.: 327420

PT Saint-Gobain Winter Diamas **(1)**
Jl Raya Bekasi Km 27 Pondok Ungu, Bekasi, 17124, Indonesia
Tel.: (62) 21 88986262

Web Site: http://www.sgabrasives-indonesia.com
Abrasive Product Mfr
N.A.I.C.S.: 327910

PT. Saint-Gobain Abrasives Indonesia **(1)**
Jl Rungkut Industri IV/17 A-B, Surabaya, 60292, Indonesia
Tel.: (62) 31 8474050
Web Site: http://www.sgabrasives-indonesia.com
Abrasive Product Mfr
N.A.I.C.S.: 327910

Participations des Ardennes **(1)**
21-23, rue des Ardennes, 75019, Paris, France **(79.23%)**
Flat Glass Mfr
N.A.I.C.S.: 327211

Partidis S.A.S. **(1)**
Les Miroirs 18 avenue d'Alsace, 92400, Courbevoie, France
Tel.: (33) 1 47 62 53 00
Web Site: http://www.saint-gobain.fr
Building Materials Distr
N.A.I.C.S.: 444180

Subsidiary (Domestic):

La Plateforme du Batiment **(2)**
7 Rue Benjamin Constant, 75927, Paris, France
Tel.: (33) 1 42 03 85 00
Web Site: http://www.laplateforme.com
Building Materials Distr
N.A.I.C.S.: 444180

Pastural **(1)**
Allee de Cumieres, 51200, Epernay, France **(59.17%)**
Tel.: (33) 326511551
Web Site: http://www.pastural.fr
Sales Range: $125-149.9 Million
Emp.: 300
Wood Products
N.A.I.C.S.: 321911

Point P **(1)**
3 Rue Christian De Wett, Villeurbanne, 69628, Cedex, France **(61.61%)**
Tel.: (33) 472134499
Web Site: http://www.pointp.fr
Tile, Wood, Panels, Flooring & Structural Woodwork Mfr
N.A.I.C.S.: 337126

Point P **(1)**
17, route de Bellevue, 16710, Saint Yrieix, France **(79.21%)**
Tel.: (33) 555621084
Hardware Retailer
N.A.I.C.S.: 444140

Point P **(1)**
12 Rue Curie Nord, 6800, Colmars, France **(78.96%)**
Tel.: (33) 389201605
Web Site: http://www.pointp.fr
Sales Range: $25-49.9 Million
Emp.: 30
Hardware Retailer
N.A.I.C.S.: 444140
David Stull *(Gen Mgr)*

Point P SA **(1)**
13-15 rue Germaine Tailleferre, Paris, 75019, France **(79.23%)**
Tel.: (33) 140033300
Web Site: http://www.groupe-pointp.fr
Sales Range: $25-49.9 Million
Emp.: 20
Construction Materials Distr
N.A.I.C.S.: 444180
Marieange Evrard *(Supvr-Logistics)*

Subsidiary (Domestic):

Brossette SAS **(2)**
23 rue Crepet, 69007, Lyon, France
Tel.: (33) 472720505
Web Site: http://www.brossette.fr
Plumbing & Heating Supplies Distr
N.A.I.C.S.: 423720

Subsidiary (Non-US):

SG DISTRIBUZIONE SRL **(2)**
6 Via Ettore Romagnoli, 20146, Corsico, Italy

Tel.: (39) 02 89 30 16 14
Sales Range: $25-49.9 Million
Construction Materials Distr
N.A.I.C.S.: 423390

Point P Trouillard **(1)**
Zone Ouest De Malleve 4 Blvd Jean Moulin, 44006, Nantes, France **(79.21%)**
Tel.: (33) 240384242
Web Site: http://www.pointp.fr
Hardware Retailer
N.A.I.C.S.: 444140
Juy Piltric *(Pres)*

Pritex Limited **(1)**
Wellington, Somerset, TA21 8NN, United Kingdom
Tel.: (44) 1823664271
Web Site: http://www.pritex.co.uk
Emp.: 240
Automotive Acoustic Insulation Products Mfr
N.A.I.C.S.: 336390
Gareth Jones *(Mng Dir)*

Productora de Abrasivos Ltda. **(1)**
Km 20 Carretera Occidente Via Madrid, Cundinamarca, Colombia
Tel.: (57) 1893 3993
Abrasive Product Mfr
N.A.I.C.S.: 327910

Productora de Abrasivos Pabsa Ltda **(1)**
Carrera 18 No 86-A-14, Bogota, Colombia **(99.9%)**
Tel.: (57) 1 82 76 266
Abrasive Product Mfr
N.A.I.C.S.: 327910

Quincaillerie Lorraine **(1)**
13 Rue Gabriel Faure, 54140, Jarville, France **(61.54%)**
Tel.: (33) 383562600
N.A.I.C.S.: 327211

Rayen Cura, S.A.I.C. **(1)**
Carril Nacional n 6 070 5525 Rodeo de la Cruz, Guaymallen, Mendoza, Argentina
Tel.: (54) 2614130200
Web Site: http://ar.verallia.com
Glass Bottle Mfr
N.A.I.C.S.: 327213

Rencol Tolerance Rings Ltd. **(1)**
Unit 16 Concorde Rd Patchway, Bristol, BS34 5TB, United Kingdom
Tel.: (44) 1179381700
Automotive Fastener Mfr
N.A.I.C.S.: 336390

S-G API BV **(1)**
Newtonweg 1, 3846 BJ, Harderwijk, Netherlands
Tel.: (31) 341 474 600
Web Site: http://www.api.nl
Ceiling Product Mfr
N.A.I.C.S.: 335132

S.G. Materiaux de Construction **(1)**
Les Miroirs 18 avenue d'Alsace, F-92400, Courbevoie, Cedex, France
Tel.: (33) 147623000
Web Site: http://www.saint-gobain.com
Sales Range: $200-249.9 Million
Emp.: 1,000
Construction Product Mfr
N.A.I.C.S.: 327120

Subsidiary (Non-US):

BPB Gyproc **(2)**
ul Elektrozavodskaya 27/8, Moscow, 107023, Russia
Tel.: (7) 495 775 1510
Web Site: http://www.gyproc.ru
Gypsum Product Mfr & Training Center
N.A.I.C.S.: 327420

BPB Gypsum (Pty) Ltd. **(2)**
PO Box 700, 1400, Germiston, South Africa
Tel.: (27) 3455300
Web Site: http://www.bpbsi.com
Sales Range: $125-149.9 Million
Emp.: 376
Gypsum Product Mfr
N.A.I.C.S.: 327420

BPB Gypsum Uretim ve Ticaret Ltd. Sti (Trading)
Koroglu Caddesi Ugur Mumcu Nun, Gazios-

manpasa Sokagi 1 4, Ankara, 06700, Turkiye
Tel.: (90) 3124481617
Web Site: http://www.rigips.com
Sales Range: $25-49.9 Million
Emp.: 100
Gypsum Product Mfr
N.A.I.C.S.: 327420

BPB Iberplaco SA **(2)**
Montaner 267 Principal 2 A, 08021, Barcelona, Spain
Tel.: (34) 934141987
Web Site: http://www.placosa.es
Gypsum Product Mfr
N.A.I.C.S.: 327420

BPB Italia SpA **(2)**
Via Matteotti 62, Cinisello, 20092, Milan, Balsamo, Italy
Tel.: (39) 02611151
Web Site: http://www.bpbitalia.it
Gypsum Product Mfr
N.A.I.C.S.: 327420

BPB Limitada **(2)**
Av Das FPLM No 1839, Maputo, Mozambique
Tel.: (258) 21461388
Web Site: http://www.saintgobain.com
Sales Range: $25-49.9 Million
Emp.: 30
Gypsum Product Mfr
N.A.I.C.S.: 327420

BPB Netherlands B.V. **(2)**
Stuartweg 1B, 4131 MH, Vianen, Netherlands
Tel.: (31) 347325100
Web Site: http://www.gyproc.nl
Sales Range: $25-49.9 Million
Emp.: 50
Plasterboard & Gypsum Products Whslr
N.A.I.C.S.: 423390
Quirign Rini *(Gen Mgr)*

BPB Plc **(2)**
Aldwych House, 81 Aldwych, London, WC2B 4HQ, United Kingdom
Tel.: (44) 147625200
Web Site: http://www.bpb.com
Holding Company
N.A.I.C.S.: 551112

British Gypsum Ltd. **(2)**
East Leake, Loughborough, LE12 6HX, Leics, United Kingdom
Tel.: (44) 1159451000
Web Site: http://www.british-gypsum.com
Sales Range: $350-399.9 Million
Building & Industrial Plasters, Plasterboard, Partitioning, Ceiling & Lining Systems, Thermal, Fire & Sound Insulation Products, Floor Screed, Tools & Accessories Mfr
N.A.I.C.S.: 327420
Jan Rideout *(Dir-Tech & Innovation)*

Affiliate (Domestic):

British Gypsum-Isover Ltd. **(3)**
Whitehouse Industrial Estate Norwich Rd, Runcorn, WA7 3DP, Cheshire, United Kingdom
Tel.: (44) 928719197
Sales Range: $50-74.9 Million
Emp.: 150
Insulation Product Mfr
N.A.I.C.S.: 327993

Subsidiary (Non-US):

CIA Industrial El Volcan SA **(2)**
Agustinas 1357 Piso 10, Santiago, Chile
Tel.: (56) 24830500
Web Site: http://www.volcan.cl
Sales Range: $450-499.9 Million
Gypsum Product Mfr
N.A.I.C.S.: 327420

Donn Products (Pty) Ltd. **(2)**
PO Box 700, 1400, Germiston, South Africa
Tel.: (27) 113455300
Web Site: http://www.saint-gobain.co.za
Sales Range: $25-49.9 Million
Emp.: 86
Gypsum Product Mfr
N.A.I.C.S.: 327420
Criig Rinkin *(Dir-Fin)*

Donn South Africa (Pty) Ltd. **(2)**
77 Ostend Road Extn 7 Germiston S, PO

Box 700, Randfontein, 1401, Gauteng, South Africa
Tel.: (27) 113455300
Sales Range: $50-74.9 Million
Emp.: 150
Gypsum Product Mfr
N.A.I.C.S.: 327420
Patricia Gumede *(Dir-HR)*

Fulmar Insurance Company Ltd. **(2)**
La Mielle La Rte De La Margion, Richmond, Saint Peter Port, GY7 9XH, Guernsey
Tel.: (44) 1481267618
Sales Range: $50-74.9 Million
Emp.: 1
Insurance Services
N.A.I.C.S.: 524298

Gypco Shanghai **(2)**
968 Wang Qiao Road Wang Qiao Industrial Zone, Pudong, Shanghai, 201201, China
Tel.: (86) 5838 5838
Gypsum Product Mfr
N.A.I.C.S.: 327420

Gyproc A/S **(2)**
Hareskovvej 12, 4400, Kalundborg, Denmark
Tel.: (45) 59570330
Web Site: http://www.gyproc.com
Sales Range: $25-49.9 Million
Emp.: 100
Plasterboard & Gypsum Plasters
N.A.I.C.S.: 423390

Gyproc AB **(2)**
Karlmarlde Den, PO Box 153, Balsta, 746 37, Sweden
Tel.: (46) 171415400
Web Site: http://www.gyproc.se
Sales Range: $25-49.9 Million
Emp.: 100
Plaster Board Mfr
N.A.I.C.S.: 327420
Mats Lindstrom *(Mgr-Fin)*

Gyproc AS **(2)**
Habornveien 59, 1630, Fredrikstad, Norway
Tel.: (47) 69357500
Web Site: http://www.gyproc.no
Sales Range: $25-49.9 Million
Emp.: 65
Plasterboard & Gypsum Plasters
N.A.I.C.S.: 423390

Gypsum Industries (Ireland) Limited **(2)**
Unit 14 Park West Industrial Park, Dublin, Ireland
Tel.: (353) 1 6298400
Web Site: http://www.gyproc.ie
Sales Range: $25-49.9 Million
Emp.: 40
Gypsum Product Mfr
N.A.I.C.S.: 327420
Mark O'Reilly *(Reg Mgr-Sls)*

Gypsum Industries (Pvt) Ltd. **(2)**
2 Delport Road Msasa, Amby, Harare, Zimbabwe
Tel.: (263) 4496392
Gypsum Product Mfr
N.A.I.C.S.: 327420

Gypsum Industries (UK) Ltd. **(2)**
East Leake, Loughborough, LE12 6HX, Leicestershire, United Kingdom
Tel.: (44) 1159451000
Web Site: http://www.british-gypsum.com
Sales Range: $200-249.9 Million
Emp.: 1,000
Gypsum Product Mfr
N.A.I.C.S.: 327420
Mike Chaldecott *(Mng Dir)*

LM Materiaux SA **(2)**
150 Chaussee De Namur, 1300, Wavre, Belgium
Tel.: (32) 482911
Web Site: http://www.lmmateriaux.be
Sales Range: $10-24.9 Million
Emp.: 40
Gypsum Product Mfr
N.A.I.C.S.: 327420

Moy-Isover Ltd. **(2)**
Ardfinnan Clonmel, Tipperary, 14, Ireland
Tel.: (353) 5266100
Web Site: http://www.moyisover.ie
Sales Range: $25-49.9 Million
Emp.: 80
Insulation Material Mfr & Distr

N.A.I.C.S.: 327993
Padraig Barry *(Mng Dir)*

Placo Argentina S.A. **(2)**
556 Lavalle Piso 3e, Buenos Aires, Argentina
Tel.: (54) 11 51 734100
Web Site: http://www.saint-gobain.com
Gypsum Product Mfr
N.A.I.C.S.: 327420

Placo do Brasil Ltda. **(2)**
Av Valentina Mello Freire Borenstein 333 Bairro Jardim Sao Francisco, Mogi Das Cruzes, CEP 08735 270, Sao Paulo, SP, Brazil
Tel.: (55) 11 3186 8900
Web Site: http://www.placo.com.br
Sales Range: $25-49.9 Million
Emp.: 60
Gypsum Product Mfr
N.A.I.C.S.: 327420

Rigips AG **(2)**
Gewerbepark, Postfach 5506, 5506, Magenwil, Switzerland
Tel.: (41) 628874444
Web Site: http://www.rigips.ch
Sales Range: $50-74.9 Million
Emp.: 150
Plasterboard & Gypsum Plasters
N.A.I.C.S.: 423390
Thomas Breu *(CEO)*

Rigips Austria GmbH **(2)**
Unterkainisch 24, A 8990, Bad Aussee, Austria
Tel.: (43) 36225050
Web Site: http://www.rigips.com
Sales Range: $25-49.9 Million
Emp.: 90
Gypsum Product Mfr
N.A.I.C.S.: 327420
Gunter Kowald *(Mgr-Logistics)*

Rigips Bosnia **(2)**
Kolodvorska 12, 71 000, Sarajevo, Bosnia & Herzegovina
Tel.: (387) 33660380
Web Site: http://www.rigips.com
Plasterboard & Gypsum Plasters
N.A.I.C.S.: 423390

Rigips Bulgaria E.O.O.D. **(2)**
Buiness Park Sofia, Building 12B Office 307, 1766, Sofia, Bulgaria
Tel.: (359) 29769500
Web Site: http://www.rigips.com
Plasterboard & Gypsum Plasters
N.A.I.C.S.: 423390
Mirena Georgieva *(Head Accountant)*

Rigips Croatia **(2)**
Predstavnistvo u RH Hondlova 2, Zagreb, 10000, Croatia
Tel.: (385) 12335570
Web Site: http://www.rigips.com
Sales Range: $50-74.9 Million
Emp.: 4
Plasterboard & Gypsum Plasters
N.A.I.C.S.: 423390
Hrvoje Miocic *(Country Mgr)*

Rigips Hungaria Gipszkarton Kft **(2)**
Zador U 4, 1181, Budapest, Hungary
Tel.: (36) 12960500
Web Site: http://www.rigips.hu
Sales Range: $25-49.9 Million
Emp.: 51
Gypsum Product Mfr
N.A.I.C.S.: 327420

Rigips Polska-Stawiany Sp. z o.o. **(2)**
Szarbkow 73, PL 02 677, Pinczow, Poland
Tel.: (48) 224571457
Web Site: http://www.rigips.com
Sales Range: $25-49.9 Million
Emp.: 200
Gypsum Product Mfr
N.A.I.C.S.: 327420

Rigips Slovakia sro **(2)**
Wlaisk 44, 91701, Trnava, Slovakia
Tel.: (421) 335514376
Web Site: http://www.rigips.sk
Sales Range: $25-49.9 Million
Emp.: 80
Gypsum Product Mfr
N.A.I.C.S.: 327420

Compagnie de Saint-Gobain SA—(Continued)

Rigips Slovenia (2)
Ulica Bratov Babnik 12, 1000, Ljubljana, Slovenia
Tel.: (386) 1500 18 10
Web Site: http://www.rigips.com
Sales Range: $25-49.9 Million
Gypsum Product Mfr
N.A.I.C.S.: 327420
Joze Polajner (Exec Dir)

Rigips Verwaltungs GmbH (2)
PO Box 110948, 40509, Dusseldorf, Germany
Tel.: (49) 21155030
Web Site: http://www.rigips.de
Sales Range: $25-49.9 Million
Emp.: 18
Gypsum Products
N.A.I.C.S.: 327420

Subsidiary (Domestic):

SOVAC Grosshandel und Vertretungen in Industrieprodukten GmbH (3)
Feldhauser Str 261, 45896, Gelsenkirchen, Germany
Tel.: (49) 209 3603996
Packaging Material Distr
N.A.I.C.S.: 423840

Saint-Gobain Rigips GmbH (3)
Schanzenstrasse 84, 40549, Dusseldorf, Germany
Tel.: (49) 21155030
Web Site: https://www.rigips.de
Sales Range: $25-49.9 Million
Gypsum Product Mfr
N.A.I.C.S.: 327420

Holding (Domestic):

Perlit Thermoputz Ersen GmbH (4)
Grimelsheimer Strasse 43, D 34396, Liebenau, Germany
Tel.: (49) 5676237
Sales Range: $75-99.9 Million
Emp.: 5
Building Materials Mfr
N.A.I.C.S.: 326199
Martin Pilger (Mng Dir)

Subsidiary (Non-US):

SIA Gyproc (2)
Daugavgrivas 93, LV-1007, Riga, Latvia
Tel.: (371) 7472999
Gypsum Product Mfr
N.A.I.C.S.: 327420

Saint-Gobain Construction Product Russia Insulation (2)
Smychka street 60, 140301, Moscow, Russia
Tel.: (7) 495 775 15 12
Construction Materials Distr
N.A.I.C.S.: 423390

Saint-Gobain Construction Products (Malaysia) Sdn Bhd (2)
No 1 Jalan Sultan Mohamad 4 Kawasan Perindustrian Bandar, Sultan Suleiman, 42000, Port Klang, Selangor, Malaysia
Tel.: (60) 331695588
Web Site: http://www.bpbmalaysia.com
Plasterboard & Gypsum Plasters
N.A.I.C.S.: 423390

Saint-Gobain Construction Products Belgium NV (2)
Sint-Jansweg 9 Haven 1602, 9130, Kallo, Belgium
Tel.: (32) 33602211
Web Site: https://www.gyproc.be
Emp.: 250
Plasterboard & Gypsum Plasters
N.A.I.C.S.: 423390
Rini Quinto (Gen Mgr)

Saint-Gobain Construction Products Belgium NV (2)
Sint Jansweg 9 Haven 1602, 9130, Kallo, Belgium
Tel.: (32) 3 360 22 11
Web Site: http://www.gyproc.be
Construction Materials Whslr
N.A.I.C.S.: 423390

Subsidiary (Domestic):

Saint-Gobain Gyproc Belgium NV (3)

Sint-Jansweg 9 Haven 1602, 9130, Kallo, Belgium
Tel.: (32) 3 3602211
Web Site: http://www.gyproc.be
Emp.: 250
Construction Materials Distr
N.A.I.C.S.: 423390
Rini Quiregn (Gen Mgr)

Subsidiary (Non-US):

Saint-Gobain Construction Products CZ A.S. (2)
Radiova 3, 102 00, Prague, 10, Czech Republic
Tel.: (420) 226292223
Web Site: https://www.cz.weber
Construction Material Mfr & Distr
N.A.I.C.S.: 327120
Martin Soucek (Gen Mgr)

Saint-Gobain Construction Products CZ a.s. (2)
Pocernicka 272/96, 108 03, Prague, 10, Czech Republic
Tel.: (420) 296 411 777
Web Site: http://www.rigips.cz
Gypsum Product Mfr
N.A.I.C.S.: 327420
Nikola Hoffmann (Dir)

Saint-Gobain Construction Products Finland (2)
Stromberginkuja 2, Helsinki, 380, Finland
Tel.: (358) 10 44 22 00
Sales Range: $25-49.9 Million
Emp.: 400
Construction Materials Distr
N.A.I.C.S.: 423330
Olli Nikula (Mgr)

Saint-Gobain Construction Products Hungary Kft. (2)
46 Becsi ut 07/5 hrsz, 2085, Pilisvorosvar, Hungary
Tel.: (36) 26 36 77 00
Web Site: http://www.weber-terranova.hu
Construction Materials Distr
N.A.I.C.S.: 423390

Saint-Gobain Construction Products Nederland BV (2)
Parallelweg 20, Etten-Leur, 4878 AH, Netherlands
Tel.: (31) 765080000
Web Site: http://www.saint-gobain.com
Sales Range: $125-149.9 Million
Emp.: 350
Construction Materials Distr
N.A.I.C.S.: 423390
Frank Poel (Gen Mgr)

Saint-Gobain Construction Products Romania SRL (2)
Str December 22 1989 No 23, 401113, Turda, Romania
Tel.: (40) 264312044
Web Site: https://www.ro.weber
Emp.: 100
Gypsum Based Building Product Mfr
N.A.I.C.S.: 327420
Mircea Popescu (Gen Mgr)

Saint-Gobain Construction Products Slovakia s.r.o. (2)
Stara Vajnorska 139, 831 04, Bratislava, Slovakia
Tel.: (421) 2 4445 3022
Adhesive & Paint Product Mfr
N.A.I.C.S.: 325520

Saint-Gobain Construction Products South Africa Ltd. (2)
77 Ostend Road Delville East Rand, Germiston, 1401, Gauteng, South Africa
Tel.: (27) 113455300
Web Site: http://www.saint-gobain.co.za
Construction Material Mfr & Distr
N.A.I.C.S.: 327420

Saint-Gobain Construction Products Ukraine (2)
13 Maryny Raskovoi St, 02660, Kiev, Ukraine
Tel.: (380) 44 498 70 55
Web Site: http://www.isober.ua
Plaster Mfr & Distr
N.A.I.C.S.: 327420

Saint-Gobain Construction Products Vietnam Limited (2)
Lot C23B Hiep Phuoc IP, Nha Be Dist, Ho Chi Minh City, Vietnam
Tel.: (84) 8 3781 8461
Web Site: http://www.gyproc.vn
Gypsum Product Mfr
N.A.I.C.S.: 327420

Saint-Gobain Hellas ABEE (2)
5 Kleisouras, Metamorfosi, 14452, Athens, Greece
Tel.: (30) 2102831804
Web Site: http://www.rigips.com
Sales Range: $25-49.9 Million
Emp.: 28
Gypsum Product Mfr
N.A.I.C.S.: 327420
Tatas George (Gen Mgr)

Saint-Gobain Isover G+H AG (2)
Burgermeister Grunzweig Strasse 1, D 67059, Ludwigshafen, Germany (99.87%)
Tel.: (49) 6215010
Web Site: http://www.isover.de
Sales Range: $400-449.9 Million
Thermal, Acoustic, Refrigeration & Fire-Protection Insulating Materials Distr & Mfr
N.A.I.C.S.: 321999

Subsidiary (Non-US):

Saint Gobain Isover Benelux (3)
Pleinlaan 5, 1050, Brussels, Belgium (99%)
Tel.: (32) 26458821
Web Site: http://www.isover.be
Sales Range: $25-49.9 Million
Emp.: 20
Insulation Product Mfr
N.A.I.C.S.: 327993

Saint Gobain Isover Italia S.p.A. (3)
Via Ettore Romagnoli 6, 20146, Milan, Italy (91.35%)
Tel.: (39) 0000242431
Web Site: http://www.isover.it
Sales Range: $50-74.9 Million
Emp.: 200
Building & Industrial Glass Wool & Mineral Fibre Insulation Mfr & Distr
N.A.I.C.S.: 327993

Saint-Gobain Isover (3)
Parallelweg 20, 4878 AH, Etten-Leur, Netherlands (98.75%)
Tel.: (31) 765080000
Web Site: http://www.isover.nl
Sales Range: $125-149.9 Million
Emp.: 400
Insulation Product Mfr
N.A.I.C.S.: 326140

Saint-Gobain Isover A/S (3)
Ostermarksvej 4, 6580, Vamdrup, Denmark (98.75%)
Tel.: (45) 72171717
Web Site: http://www.isover.dk
Sales Range: $50-74.9 Million
Emp.: 200
Insulation Materials & Systems Mfr
N.A.I.C.S.: 327993
Mogens Nielsen (Mng Dir)

Saint-Gobain Isover AB (3)
Storgatan 29, 26782, Billesholm, Sweden (99.66%)
Tel.: (46) 4284000
Web Site: http://www.isover.se
Sales Range: $125-149.9 Million
Emp.: 380
Insulating Materials Distr & Mfr
N.A.I.C.S.: 327993

Saint-Gobain Isover Argentina S.A. (3)
Calle Bouchard y Enz, Llavallol, Buenos Aires, B 1836 AWB, Argentina (76.26%)
Tel.: (54) 1142395200
Web Site: http://www.isover-argentina.com.ar
Sales Range: $50-74.9 Million
Emp.: 130
Glass Wool Products Mfr
N.A.I.C.S.: 327211
Yanina Balboa (Head-HR)

Saint-Gobain Isover Austria AG (3)
Prager Str 77, 2000, Stockerau, Austria (98.43%)

Tel.: (43) 22666060
Web Site: http://www.isover.at
Sales Range: $50-74.9 Million
Emp.: 180
Fiber Glass Products Mfr
N.A.I.C.S.: 327993
Daniel Dominei (CEO)

Saint-Gobain Isover S.A. (3)
Rte de Payerne 1, PO Box 145, CH-1522, Lucens, Switzerland (96.53%)
Tel.: (41) 219060111
Web Site: https://www.isover.ch
Sales Range: $50-74.9 Million
Emp.: 230
Insulating Materials & Fiber-Reinforcements Distr & Mfr
N.A.I.C.S.: 321999

Saint-Gobain Isover SA (3)
Route de Payerne 1, 1522, Lucens, Switzerland
Tel.: (41) 21 906 01 11
Web Site: http://www.isover.ch
Mineral Wool Mfr
N.A.I.C.S.: 327993
Daniel Schild (Mktg Dir)

Subsidiary (Non-US):

Plafometal SAS (4)
Route de Phades, 08800, Montherme, France
Tel.: (33) 324595400
Web Site: http://www.plafometal.com
Sales Range: $25-49.9 Million
Emp.: 80
Metal Products Mfr
N.A.I.C.S.: 332999

Subsidiary (Non-US):

Saint-Gobain Rakennustuotteet Oy (3)
Kerkkolankatu 37 39, 05801, Hyvinkaa, Finland (100%)
Tel.: (358) 1400684898
Web Site: http://www.isover.fi
Sales Range: $50-74.9 Million
Emp.: 200
Glass Products Mfr
N.A.I.C.S.: 327211

Subsidiary (Domestic):

Superglass Dammstoffe GmbH (3)
Industriestrasse 12, Darmstadt, 64297, Germany
Tel.: (49) 6151153680
Web Site: http://www.superglass.de
Sales Range: $25-49.9 Million
Emp.: 20
Insulation Material Distr
N.A.I.C.S.: 423330
Danijel Lucic (Mng Dir)

Subsidiary (Domestic):

Saint-Gobain Weber (2)
Rue de Brie, 77170, Servon, France
Tel.: (33) 1 6062 1300
Web Site: http://www.e-weber.com
Sales Range: $75-99.9 Million
Emp.: 200
Holding Company; Construction Mortar, Insulation & Other Building Materials Mfr & Distr
N.A.I.C.S.: 551112

Subsidiary (Non-US):

Saint Gobain Weber Terranova, spol. s.r.o. (3)
Stara Vajnorska 139, 831 04, Bratislava, Slovakia (79%)
Tel.: (421) 244453022
Web Site: http://www.weber-terranova.sk
Sales Range: $25-49.9 Million
Emp.: 100
Construction Materials Mfr
N.A.I.C.S.: 423390

Saint-Gobain Byggevarer AS (3)
Sandstuveien 68, 0680, Oslo, Norway
Tel.: (47) 4455
Web Site: https://www.weber-norge.no
Sales Range: $125-149.9 Million
Pre-mixed Mortar & Clay Products Mfr & Distr
N.A.I.C.S.: 327120

Kristin Roed Eriksen *(Mng Dir)*

Saint-Gobain Byggprodukter AB **(3)**
Gardsvagen 18, 169 70, Solna, Sweden
Tel.: (46) 86256100
Web Site: http://www.weber.se
Sales Range: $25-49.9 Million
Emp.: 70
Pre-mixed Mortar & Clay Products Mfr & Distr
N.A.I.C.S.: 327120
Lars-Erik Edgarsson *(Mng Dir)*

Saint-Gobain Weber A/S **(3)**
Randersvej 75, Randers, 8940, Denmark
Tel.: (45) 70101025
Web Site: http://www.weber.dk
Sales Range: $25-49.9 Million
Emp.: 100
Pre-mixed Mortar & Clay Products Mfr & Distr
N.A.I.C.S.: 327120
Torben Dyrberg *(Mng Dir)*

Saint-Gobain Weber AG **(3)**
Tafernstrasse 11b, Dattwil, CH-5405, Baden, Switzerland
Tel.: (41) 564842424
Web Site: https://www.ch.weber
Sales Range: $25-49.9 Million
Emp.: 100
Pre-mixed Mortar & Clay Products Mfr & Distr
N.A.I.C.S.: 327120

Saint-Gobain Weber Beamix B.V. **(3)**
Hastelweg 161, 5652 CJ, Eindhoven, Netherlands
Tel.: (31) 40 259 7911
Web Site: http://www.weber-beamix.nl
Sales Range: $50-74.9 Million
Emp.: 130
Pre-mixed Mortar & Clay Products Mfr & Distr
N.A.I.C.S.: 327120
Bas Huysmans *(Mng Dir)*

Saint-Gobain Weber Belgium NV/SA **(3)**
Oostvaarrtdijk 10, 1850, Grimbergen, Belgium
Tel.: (32) 2254 7854
Web Site: http://www.weber-belgium.be
Sales Range: $25-49.9 Million
Emp.: 50
Pre-mixed Mortar & Clay Products Mfr & Distr
N.A.I.C.S.: 327120
Pascal Remy *(CEO)*

Saint-Gobain Weber Cemarksa SA **(3)**
Ctra C-17 Km 2, Montcada, Barcelona, 8110, Montcada I Reixac, Spain
Tel.: (34) 935 72 65 00
Web Site: http://www.weber.es
Concrete Products Mfr
N.A.I.C.S.: 327390

Saint-Gobain Weber Co., Ltd. **(3)**
14th Fl Gypsum Metropolitan Bldg 539/3 Sri-Ayutthaya Rd, Phayathai Ratchathewi, Bangkok, 10400, Thailand
Tel.: (66) 2 245 8777
Web Site: http://www.weberthai.com
Emp.: 150
Concrete Products Mfr
N.A.I.C.S.: 327390
Pimjai Utadej *(Mng Dir)*

Subsidiary (Domestic):

Saint-Gobain Weber France **(3)**
Rue de Brie, 77170, Servon, France
Tel.: (33) 1 6062 1300
Web Site: http://www.weber.fr
Construction Mortar, Insulation & Other Building Materials Mfr & Distr
N.A.I.C.S.: 327120

Subsidiary (Domestic):

Optiroc SA **(4)**
1431 Chemin du Mas de Sorbier, ZI de Grezan, 30034, Nimes, Cedex 1, France
Tel.: (33) 466280020
Web Site: http://www.optiroc.fr
Sales Range: $25-49.9 Million
Emp.: 25
Pre-mix Mortar & Clay Products Mfr

N.A.I.C.S.: 327390

Subsidiary (Non-US):

Saint-Gobain Weber GmbH **(3)**
Schanzenstrasse 84, D-40549, Dusseldorf, Germany
Tel.: (49) 211913690
Web Site: https://www.de.weber
Insulation, Flooring & Tiling Systems Mfr
N.A.I.C.S.: 327120

Saint-Gobain Weber Limited **(3)**
Enterprise Way Maulden Road, Flitwick, MK45 5BY, Beds, United Kingdom
Tel.: (44) 870 333 0070
Web Site: http://www.netweber.co.uk
Sales Range: $50-74.9 Million
Emp.: 200
Industrial Mortar Mfr
N.A.I.C.S.: 332992
Allan Hodge *(Dir-Comml)*

Saint-Gobain Weber Lujian Building Materials (Shanghai) Co., Ltd. **(3)**
Rm 1816-1818 Ocean Tower 550 Yan, 200001, Shanghai, China
Tel.: (86) 21 63618869
Web Site: http://www.weber-china.cn
Sales Range: $25-49.9 Million
Emp.: 100
Industrial Mortar Mfr
N.A.I.C.S.: 327120

Subsidiary (Domestic):

Saint-Gobain Weber Netservices **(3)**
Le Closeau Rue de Brie, 77170, Servon, France
Tel.: (33) 1 6062 1300
Information Technology Services
N.A.I.C.S.: 541513

Subsidiary (Non-US):

Saint-Gobain Weber Oy Ab **(3)**
Stromberginkuja 2, PL 70, FIN 00381, Helsinki, Finland
Tel.: (358) 10442200
Web Site: http://www.e-weber.fi
Pre-mixed Mortar & Clay Products Mfr & Distr
N.A.I.C.S.: 327120
Olli Nikula *(Mng Dir)*

Saint-Gobain Weber Portugal S.A. **(3)**
Zona Industrial de Taboeira Apartado 3016, Esgueira, 3800-055, Aveiro, Portugal
Tel.: (351) 234 30 11 30
Web Site: http://www.weber.com.pt
Concrete Products Mfr
N.A.I.C.S.: 327390

Saint-Gobain Weber South Africa (Pty) Ltd. **(3)**
77 Ostend Road, Germiston, South Africa
Tel.: (27) 11 345 5300
Web Site: http://www.weber-tylon.co.za
Industrial Mortar Mfr
N.A.I.C.S.: 327120

Plant (Domestic):

Saint-Gobain Weber South Africa (Pty) Ltd. - Alrode Factory **(4)**
Corner Potgieter & Bosworth St, Alberton, 1451, Gauteng, South Africa
Tel.: (27) 116178500
Tile Adhesives Mfr
N.A.I.C.S.: 325520

Saint-Gobain Weber South Africa (Pty) Ltd. - Cape Town Factory **(4)**
10 Grenville Avenue Epping 1, Cape Town, 7475, South Africa
Tel.: (27) 215303800
Web Site: http://www.weber-tylon.co.za
Sales Range: $25-49.9 Million
Emp.: 30
Clay Refractory Mortar Mfr
N.A.I.C.S.: 327120
Gary Mathews *(Plant Mgr)*

Saint-Gobain Weber South Africa (Pty) Ltd. - Kwazulu Natal Factory **(4)**
107 Eskom Road New Germany, Durban, 3601, South Africa
Tel.: (27) 31 705 4569

Web Site: http://www.weber-tylon.co.za
Sales Range: $25-49.9 Million
Emp.: 26
Industrial Mortar Mfr
N.A.I.C.S.: 327120
Bongani Khoza *(Gen Mgr)*

Saint-Gobain Weber South Africa (Pty) Ltd. - Port Elizabeth Factory **(4)**
1 Buick Street Markman, 6061, Port Elizabeth, South Africa
Tel.: (27) 41 461 1508
Web Site: http://www.weber-tylon.co.za
Industrial Mortar Mfr
N.A.I.C.S.: 327120

Subsidiary (Non-US):

Saint-Gobain Weber Stahel-Keller AG **(3)**
Technoramastrasse 9, CH-8404, Winterthur, Switzerland **(79.09%)**
Web Site: http://www.weber-stahel-keller.ch
Flat Glass Mfr
N.A.I.C.S.: 327211

Saint-Gobain Weber Yapi Kimyasallari San. ve Tic. A.S **(3)**
Ansizca Koyu Ansizca Ic Kisim Sanayi Sokak No 284, Kemalpasa, 35171, Izmir, Turkiye
Tel.: (90) 232 397 07 00
Web Site: http://www.weber.com.tr
Sales Range: $50-74.9 Million
Emp.: 150
Construction Mortar Mfr
N.A.I.C.S.: 327120

Saint-Gobain statybos gaminiai UAB **(3)**
Menulio 7, 04326, Vilnius, Lithuania
Tel.: (370) 52301618
Web Site: http://www.weber.lt
Sales Range: $25-49.9 Million
Emp.: 25
Pre-mixed Mortar & Clay Products Mfr & Distr
N.A.I.C.S.: 327120
Mart Arro *(Reg Dir-Balkans)*

Subsidiary (Non-US):

Thai Gypsum Products Pcl. **(2)**
Gypsum Metropolitan Tower 539 2 Si Ayutthaya Road, Ratchathewi, Bangkok, 10400, Thailand
Tel.: (66) 26408600
Web Site: http://www.gyproc.co.th
Gypsum Product Mfr
N.A.I.C.S.: 327420

SAE Asti **(1)**
13, avenue de la Republique, 92400, Courbevoie, France **(100%)**
Flat Glass Mfr
N.A.I.C.S.: 327211

SAINT GOBAIN AMERICA S.A. DE C.V. **(1)**
AV Horacio 1855-502 Los Morales, Tijuana, Mexico
Tel.: (52) 6646254168
Sales Range: $125-149.9 Million
Emp.: 282
Abrasive Product Mfr
N.A.I.C.S.: 327910

SAINT GOBAIN GLASS OPERADORA S.A. DE C.V. **(1)**
Av Nicolas Bravo No 5 Parque Industrial Cuautla, Ayala, Morelos, Mexico
Tel.: (52) 735 35 4 81 00
Flat Glass Mfr
N.A.I.C.S.: 327211

SAINT GOBAIN GYPSUM OPERADORA SA DE CV **(1)**
Av Nicolas Bravo 5, 62715, Cuautla, Morelos, Mexico
Tel.: (52) 444 824 08 88
Sales Range: $25-49.9 Million
Emp.: 100
Gypsum Product Mfr
N.A.I.C.S.: 327420

SAINT GOBAIN PERU SA **(1)**
Av los Faisanes Nro 157 La Campina, Chorrillos, Lima, Peru
Tel.: (51) 12524034

Web Site: http://www.saint-gobain.com.pe
Flat Glass Mfr
N.A.I.C.S.: 327211

SAINT-GOBAIN ACHATS **(1)**
Les Miroirs 18 avenue d'Alsace, 92400, Courbevoie, France
Tel.: (33) 1 47 62 48 00
Sales Range: $200-249.9 Million
Emp.: 1,000
Glass Products Mfr
N.A.I.C.S.: 327215

SAINT-GOBAIN ADFORS CZ FABRICS S.R.O. **(1)**
Sokolovska 106, 570 21, Litomysl, Czech Republic
Tel.: (420) 461 651 111
Web Site: http://www.sg-adfors.com
Emp.: 1,000
Textile Fabric Product Mfr
N.A.I.C.S.: 314999
Milos Pavlis *(Gen Mgr)*

SAINT-GOBAIN ADFORS CZ GLASS MAT S.R.O. **(1)**
Sokolovska 106, 570 21, Litomysl, Czech Republic
Tel.: (420) 461 651 111
Web Site: http://www.vertex.cz
Glass Products Mfr
N.A.I.C.S.: 327215

SAINT-GOBAIN ASSESSORIA e ADMINISTRACAO LTDA. **(1)**
Avenida Santa Marina 482, Agua Branca, 05036-903, Sao Paulo, Brazil
Tel.: (55) 11 2246 7600
Float Glass Products Mfr
N.A.I.C.S.: 327211

SAINT-GOBAIN AUTOVER OSTERREICH GMBH **(1)**
Brown-Boveri-Strasse 8 B17 Bauteil 2, 2351, Wiener Neudorf, Austria
Tel.: (43) 2236 90 320
Web Site: http://www.autover.at
Automotive Glass Product Distr
N.A.I.C.S.: 423120

SAINT-GOBAIN CANALIZACION CHILE SA **(1)**
Antillanca Norte 600 Parque Industrial Vespucio - Lo Echevers, Pudahuel, Santiago, Chile
Tel.: (56) 2444 1300
Abrasive Product Mfr
N.A.I.C.S.: 327910

SAINT-GOBAIN CONCEPTIONS VERRIERES **(1)**
Les Miroirs 18 avenue d'Alsace, 92400, Courbevoie, France
Tel.: (33) 1 47 62 48 00
Glass Products Mfr
N.A.I.C.S.: 327215

SAINT-GOBAIN CONSULTING INFORMATION AND ORGANIZATION **(1)**
Les Miroirs 18 Avenue D'alsace, 92400, Courbevoie, France
Tel.: (33) 147623700
Web Site: http://wwwsaint-gobain.com
Business Management Consulting Services
N.A.I.C.S.: 541611

SAINT-GOBAIN DE COLOMBIA SA **(1)**
Carrera 7 North 26-20 Piso 20, 76164, Bogota, Colombia
Tel.: (57) 1 255 7756
Flat Glass Mfr
N.A.I.C.S.: 327211

SAINT-GOBAIN DEVELOPPEMENT MAROC **(1)**
2 Allee Des Figuiers Ain Sebaa, 20250, Casablanca, Morocco
Tel.: (212) 522 665 731
Flat Glass Mfr
N.A.I.C.S.: 327211

SAINT-GOBAIN DEVISA S.A. **(1)**
Paseo Castellana 77, 28046, Madrid, Spain
Tel.: (34) 913 97 20 71
Flat Glass Mfr
N.A.I.C.S.: 327211

SAINT-GOBAIN DIAMANT-WERKZEUGE GMBH & CO. KG **(1)**

Compagnie de Saint-Gobain SA—(Continued)

Schutzenwall 13-17, Norderstedt, 22844, Germany
Tel.: (49) 4052580
Abrasive Product Mfr
N.A.I.C.S.: 327910
Dirk Borgmann (Gen Mgr)

SAINT-GOBAIN FACILITAS PORTU-GAL, SOCIEDADE UNIPESS (1)
Estrada Nacional 10 Lugar de Dom Pedro, Santa Iria de Azoia, 2690, Portugal
Tel.: (351) 219534622
Glass Products Mfr
N.A.I.C.S.: 327215

SAINT-GOBAIN FORMULA GMBH (1)
Kutzhutte, 37445, Walkenried, Germany
Tel.: (49) 5525 203 0
Web Site:
http://www.saintgobainformula.com
Emp.: 115
Gypsum Product Mfr
N.A.I.C.S.: 327420
Falk Wasner (Mgr-Sls-Austria & Switzerland Area)

SAINT-GOBAIN GLASS ESTONIA SE (1)
Kirde 2, 61506, Elva, Estonia
Tel.: (372) 7303300
Web Site: http://www.sekurit.ee
Sales Range: $50-74.9 Million
Emp.: 230
Glass Products Mfr
N.A.I.C.S.: 327215

SAINT-GOBAIN GLASS HELLAS (1)
Av Kalamakiou 37, Alimos, Athens, 17455, Greece
Tel.: (30) 210 9854407
Web Site: http://www.saint-gobain-glass.com
Emp.: 2
Glass Products Mfr
N.A.I.C.S.: 327215
Galia Tsatos (Gen Mgr)

SAINT-GOBAIN GLASS SOLUTIONS CZ, s.r.o. (1)
Sklenarska 7, Horni Herspice, 619 00, Brno, Czech Republic
Tel.: (420) 543 426 111
Web Site: http://www.sggscz.com
Insulating Glass Mfr
N.A.I.C.S.: 327215

SAINT-GOBAIN GLASS SOLUTIONS MENUISIERS INDUSTRIEL (1)
Z I de St-Pierre des Echaubrognes, Mauleon, 79700, France
Tel.: (33) 5 49 82 15 15
Flat Glass Mfr
N.A.I.C.S.: 327211

SAINT-GOBAIN GLASS SOLUTIONS PARIS - NORMANDIE (1)
Zi Caen Ouest, BP 21, 14650, Carpiquet, France
Tel.: (33) 2 31 71 14 14
Flat Glass Mfr & Whslr
N.A.I.C.S.: 327211

SAINT-GOBAIN GLASS SOLUTIONS SUD-OUEST (1)
ZI Du Phare 3 Rue Gay Lussac, Merignac, 33700, France
Tel.: (33) 5 57 92 31 31
Web Site: http://www.glasssolutions.com
Emp.: 420
Flat Glass Mfr
N.A.I.C.S.: 327211

SAINT-GOBAIN GLASSOLUTIONS NITRASKLO, s.r.o. (1)
Levicka 3, 950 15, Nitra, Slovakia
Tel.: (421) 37655 66 21
Emp.: 150
Flat Glass Mfr
N.A.I.C.S.: 327211
Kaluza Kova (Mgr-Fin)

SAINT-GOBAIN GRADBENI IZDELKI d.o.o. (1)
Ljubljanska cesta 68, 1290, Grosuplje, Slovenia

Tel.: (386) 17818010
Adhesive & Ceramic Product Mfr
N.A.I.C.S.: 325520

SAINT-GOBAIN GRADEVINSKI PROIZVODI HRVATSKA D.O.O. (1)
Hondlova 2/9 1 kat, Zagreb, 10 000, Croatia
Tel.: (385) 1 3010 202
Web Site: http://www.isover.hr
Sales Range: $250-299.9 Million
Emp.: 12
Adhesive Product Distr
N.A.I.C.S.: 424690
Mirsad Begovic (Gen Mgr)

SAINT-GOBAIN GUSS-ROHRVERTIEB OSTERREICH GMBH (1)
Archenweg 52, Innsbruck, 6020, Austria
Tel.: (43) 5123417170
Web Site: http://www.saint-gobain.de
Emp.: 4
Steel Pole Mfr
N.A.I.C.S.: 331210
Albert Moelter (Gen Mgr)

SAINT-GOBAIN HPM RUS. OOO (1)
19th floor 8 Preobrazhenskaya sq, 107061, Moscow, Russia
Tel.: (7) 4952288110
Web Site: http://www.sgabrasives.ru
Sales Range: $25-49.9 Million
Emp.: 30
Abrasive Product Mfr
N.A.I.C.S.: 327910
German Kuznetsov (Reg Mgr-Sls)

SAINT-GOBAIN IDAPLAC, S.L. (1)
C/ Albert Einstein 25 Pol Ind, 08940, Cornella de Llobregat, Barcelona, Spain
Tel.: (34) 902250606
Web Site: https://www.distriplac.com
Sales Range: $25-49.9 Million
Emp.: 45
Insulation Roofing Material Distr
N.A.I.C.S.: 423330
Isabell Pla Gonzalez (Dir-HR)

SAINT-GOBAIN INDUSTRIAL CE-RAMICS PTY LTD (1)
326 Settlement Road, Thomastown, Melbourne, 3074, VIC, Australia
Tel.: (61) 394630050
Web Site: http://www.hexoloy.com
Sales Range: $25-49.9 Million
Emp.: 10
Ceramic Products Mfr
N.A.I.C.S.: 327120

SAINT-GOBAIN INTERSERVICES S.A. (1)
Les Miroirs 18 avenue d'Alsace, Courbevoie, 92400, France
Tel.: (33) 1 47 62 48 00
Web Site: http://www.saint-gobain.com
Glass Products Mfr
N.A.I.C.S.: 327215

SAINT-GOBAIN LIMITED (1)
Saint-Gobain House Binley Business Park, Coventry, CV3 2TT, United Kingdom
Tel.: (44) 2476 56 0700
Web Site: http://www.saint-gobain.co.uk
Emp.: 500
Construction Materials Distr
N.A.I.C.S.: 423330
Sam Armstead (Acct Mgr-Natl)

SAINT-GOBAIN MALAYSIA SDN BHD. (1)
No. 1 Jalan Sultan Mohamad 4 Kawasan Perindustrian Bandar Suleiman, 42000, Port Klang, Selangor, Malaysia
Tel.: (60) 33169 5588
Web Site: http://www.bpbmalaysia.com
Gypsum Board Mfr
N.A.I.C.S.: 327420

SAINT-GOBAIN PARTICIPACOES LTDA (1)
Av Santa Marina 482 - 4 andar, Agua Branca, 05036-903, Sao Paulo, Brazil
Tel.: (55) 11 22467600
Glass Products Mfr
N.A.I.C.S.: 327215

SAINT-GOBAIN PIPE SYSTEMS BV (1)

Markerkant 10-17, Almere, 1316 AB, Netherlands
Tel.: (31) 365333344
Web Site: http://www.sgps.nl
Sales Range: $25-49.9 Million
Emp.: 15
Iron Pipe Mfr
N.A.I.C.S.: 331210
Esther Lindeman (Mgr-Mktg)

SAINT-GOBAIN PLACO SAS (1)
34 Avenue Franklin-Rooseveit, Suresnes, 92282, France
Tel.: (33) 1 46 25 46 25
Web Site: http://www.placo.fr
Plaster Board Mfr
N.A.I.C.S.: 327420

SAINT-GOBAIN POLSKA SP. Z O.O. (1)
Al Jerozolimskie 204, 02-486, Warsaw, Poland
Tel.: (48) 225788540
Web Site: http://www.sgdb.pl
Sales Range: $25-49.9 Million
Emp.: 30
Glass Products Mfr
N.A.I.C.S.: 327215

SAINT-GOBAIN PRODUITS POUR LA CONSTRUCTION SAS (1)
Les Miroirs 18 avenue d'Alsace, 92400, Courbevoie, France
Tel.: (33) 1 47 62 34 00
Web Site: http://www.saint-gobain.fr
Construction Material Mfr & Distr
N.A.I.C.S.: 327120

SAINT-GOBAIN SERVICES AUS-TRIA GMBH (1)
Unterkainisch 24, Bad Aussee, 8990, Austria
Tel.: (43) 3622 505 0
Flat Glass Mfr
N.A.I.C.S.: 327211

SAINT-GOBAIN SERVICES RH FRANCE (1)
Rue de l Ambassadeur, 78700, Conflans-Sainte-Honorine, France
Tel.: (33) 134904000
Human Resource Consulting Services
N.A.I.C.S.: 541612

SAINT-GOBAIN SOLAR GARD AUS-TRALIA PTY LTD. (1)
1/6 Stanton Rd, Seven Hills, 2147, NSW, Australia
Tel.: (61) 2 9838 8888
Web Site: http://www.solargard.com.au
Safety Window Film Mfr & Distr
N.A.I.C.S.: 326113

SAINT-GOBAIN SOLAR GARD NV (1)
Karreweg 18, Zulte, 9870, Belgium
Tel.: (32) 9240 95 69
Web Site: http://www.solargard.be
Sales Range: $25-49.9 Million
Emp.: 25
Safety Window Film Mfr & Distr
N.A.I.C.S.: 326113
Peter Staelens (Reg Mgr)

SAINT-GOBAIN SOLAR GARD UK, LTD (1)
Unit 13 Ball Mill Top Business Park, Grimley, Worcester, WR2 6LS, Worcestershire, United Kingdom
Tel.: (44) 1905 640400
Web Site: http://www.solargard.co.uk
Safety Window Film Mfr & Distr
N.A.I.C.S.: 326113
Ian Penfold (Mgr-Sls)

SAINT-GOBAIN SOLAR SYSTEMS S.A. (1)
18 Avenue d'Alsace, Courbevoie, 92400, France
Tel.: (33) 147623400
Photovoltaic Product Mfr
N.A.I.C.S.: 334413

SEPR India Limited (1)
Kanjikode West, PB No 1, 678 623, Palakkad, Kerala, India
Tel.: (91) 4913080333
Web Site: http://www.saint-gobain.co.in
Sales Range: $125-149.9 Million
Emp.: 500
Refractory Material Mfr

N.A.I.C.S.: 327120
V. Venkatesh (Head-Mfg)

SEPR Keramik GmbH & CO KG (1)
Concordiaplatz 3, Cologne, 51143, Germany
Tel.: (49) 2203 956 479
Web Site: http://www.saint-gobain.de
Sales Range: $50-74.9 Million
Emp.: 4
Refractory Material Distr
N.A.I.C.S.: 423840
Axel Hesse (Mgr)

Subsidiary (Domestic):

Saint-Gobain Ceramic Materials GmbH (2)
Concordiaplatz 3, 51143, Cologne, Germany
Tel.: (49) 2203 956 401
Web Site: http://www.sic.saint-gobain.com
Silicon Carbide Powder Mfr
N.A.I.C.S.: 325180

Saint-Gobain IndustrieKeramik Roedental GmbH (2)
Oeslauer St No 35, Postfach 1144, Rodental, 96472, Germany
Tel.: (49) 9563 724 0
Refractory Product Mfr & Distr
N.A.I.C.S.: 327120
Hans Ulrich Dorst (Engr-Sls)

Saint-Gobain Performance Plastics Isofluor GmbH (2)
Borsigstrasse 13 - 15, 41469, Neuss, Germany
Tel.: (49) 2137917890
Web Site: http://www.isofluor.de
Plastic Tubing Mfr
N.A.I.C.S.: 326199
Petra Krause (Mgr-Customer Svc)

SEPR Refractories India Ltd (1)
Kanjikode West, PB No 1, Palakkad, 678623, Kerala, India
Tel.: (91) 3080333
Web Site: http://www.saint-gobain.co.in
Glass Products Mfr
N.A.I.C.S.: 327215

Division (Domestic):

Saint-Gobain Weber (India) Ltd (2)
Level 5 Leela Business Park Andheri-Kurla Road, Andheri East, Mumbai, 400059, India
Tel.: (91) 2240212121
Web Site: http://www.weber.co.in
Emp.: 20
Adhesive Product Mfr
N.A.I.C.S.: 325520
Raju Dayani (Mng Dir)

SFIC (1)
2 Route Du Bassin 5, 92230, Gennevilliers, France (100%)
Tel.: (33) 140033426
Sales Range: $100-124.9 Million
Emp.: 500
Hardware Retailer
N.A.I.C.S.: 444140

SGGS Belgium SA (1)
Boulevard Industriel 129, 1070, Brussels, Belgium
Tel.: (32) 2 556 37 10
Web Site: http://www.glassolutions.be
Sales Range: $25-49.9 Million
Emp.: 53
Flat Glass Mfr
N.A.I.C.S.: 327211
Annie Coppins (Gen Mgr)

SGGS GLASINDUSTRIE BOERMANS (1)
Schampbergstraat 34, 3511, Hasselt, Belgium
Tel.: (32) 11858585
Sales Range: $25-49.9 Million
Emp.: 100
Flat Glass Mfr
N.A.I.C.S.: 327211
Koen Driesmans (Mng Dir)

SHANGHAI SEPR ZIRCONIUM PRODUCTS CO., LTD (1)
1441 Beidi Road, Minghang, Shanghai, 201106, China
Tel.: (86) 21 5218 9065

Zirconia Powder & Zirconium Chemical Mfr
N.A.I.C.S.: 325998

SOLAR GARD NORDIC AB **(1)**
Stockholmsvagen 21, Rimbo, 762 21, Norr-
talje, Sweden
Tel.: (46) 175748 80
Web Site: http://www.solargard.se
Emp.: 4
Safety Window Film Mfr & Distr
N.A.I.C.S.: 326113
Niklas Falck (Mgr-Market)

**Saint Gobain Autover France
S.A.** **(1)**
Zac De Mariage 41 Rue De Bruyeres,
69330, Pusignan, France **(99.69%)**
Tel.: (33) 557195800
Web Site: http://www.autover.fr
Glass Products Mfr
N.A.I.C.S.: 524126

**Saint Gobain Autover France
S.A.S.** **(1)**
ZI De La Bihardais, PO Box 73, 35175,
Bruz, France **(80%)**
Tel.: (33) 299058545
Web Site: http://www.autover.fr
Sales Range: $25-49.9 Million
Emp.: 18
Mfr of Glass Products
N.A.I.C.S.: 327211

Saint Gobain Ecophon AB **(1)**
Yttervagen, PO Box 500, Hyllinge, 26503,
Sweden **(99.66%)**
Tel.: (46) 42179900
Web Site: http://www.ecophon.com
Sales Range: $100-124.9 Million
Emp.: 350
Mfr of Acoustic Ceilings & Wall Absorber
Systems .
N.A.I.C.S.: 238310
Francois Michel (Pres)

Subsidiary (Non-US):

Decoustics Limited **(2)**
61 Royal Group Crescent, Woodbridge,
L4H 1X9, ON, Canada **(100%)**
Tel.: (905) 652-5200
Web Site: http://www.decoustics.com
Sales Range: $25-49.9 Million
Emp.: 100
Acoustic Paneling
N.A.I.C.S.: 238310
Eric Marceau (Gen Mgr)

Saint Gobain SA **(1)**
Paseo de La Castellana N 77, Edificio Ed-
erra Planta 10, 28046, Madrid,
Spain **(100%)**
Tel.: (34) 913972669
Web Site: http://www.saintgobainglass.com
Sales Range: $25-49.9 Million
Emp.: 30
Mfr of Cast Iron Pipes & Fittings
N.A.I.C.S.: 331511

**Saint-Gobain ADFORS Deutschland
GmbH** **(1)**
Rossauweg 14, 93333, Neustadt an der
Donau, Germany
Tel.: (49) 94452030
Web Site: https://www.adfors-neustadt.de
Fiberglass, Wallboards Finishing & Cover-
ing, Industrial Fabrics, Lighting Fabrics,
Geotextile & Other Construction Products
Mfr
N.A.I.C.S.: 424950

Saint-Gobain Abrasifs **(1)**
ZI 8 Rue De La Taye, BP 45, 28110, Luce,
Cedex, France **(99.9%)**
Tel.: (33) 237916400
Abrasive Product Mfr
N.A.I.C.S.: 327910

Subsidiary (Domestic):

Saint Gobain Abrasives **(2)**
Zides Vegnes 43 Rue Saint Andre, 93012,
Bobigny, France **(99.9%)**
Tel.: (33) 148432728
Sales Range: $25-49.9 Million
Emp.: 45
Mfg Abrasive Products
N.A.I.C.S.: 327910

**Saint-Gobain Abrasives Nederland
B.V.** **(1)**

Prins Bernhardplein 200, Amsterdam, Neth-
erlands
Tel.: (31) 20 521 4777
Abrasive Product Mfr
N.A.I.C.S.: 327910

**Saint-Gobain Abrasivos Argentina
SA** **(1)**
Franklin 787, Buenos Aires, C1405 DEG,
Argentina
Tel.: (54) 11 5901 3622
Abrasive Product Mfr
N.A.I.C.S.: 327910

**Saint-Gobain Abrasivos Brasil
Ltda** **(1)**
Av Santa Marina 482 - 4 andar, Sao Paulo,
Brazil
Tel.: (55) 11 64 645206
Web Site: http://www.sgabrasivos.com.br
Abrasive Product Mfr
N.A.I.C.S.: 327910

**Saint-Gobain Adfors Austria
GmbH** **(1)**
Industriestrasse 11, Hornstein, 7053, Austria
Tel.: (43) 2689 2234 0
Web Site: http://www.saint-gobain.fr
Sales Range: $25-49.9 Million
Emp.: 74
Glass Products Mfr
N.A.I.C.S.: 327215
Milos Pavlis (Gen Mgr)

Saint-Gobain Adfors CZ S.R.O. **(1)**
Sokolovska 106, 570 21, Litomysl, Czech
Republic
Tel.: (420) 461651111
Web Site: https://www.silnydikylidem.cz
Fiber Glass Products Mfr
N.A.I.C.S.: 327215

Saint-Gobain Adfors Italia S.p.A. **(1)**
Via Piave 29, 17047, Vado Ligure, Savona,
Italy
Tel.: (39) 019 2160013
Web Site: http://www.saint-gobain.it
Glass Veil Mfr
N.A.I.C.S.: 327215

**Saint-Gobain Advanced Ceramics
(Shanghai) Co. Ltd** **(1)**
No 12 Lane 3679 Jin Du Road Xin Zhuang
Industrial Zone, Shanghai, 201108, China
Tel.: (86) 21 64899993
Web Site: http://www.saint-gobain.com.cn
Sales Range: $50-74.9 Million
Emp.: 150
Ceramic Filter & Refractory Material Mfr
N.A.I.C.S.: 327120

Saint-Gobain Autover **(1)**
Chaussee Romaine 60, Bastogne, 6600,
Belgium
Tel.: (32) 61 210 940
Web Site: http://www.autover.com
Sales Range: $25-49.9 Million
Emp.: 130
Automotive Glass Product Mfr
N.A.I.C.S.: 327215
Rals Pennartz (Mgr)

**Saint-Gobain Autover Direktglas
AB** **(1)**
Fagelviksvagen 15, Norsborg, 145 53, Swe-
den
Tel.: (46) 8449 57 00
Web Site: http://www.autover.se
Sales Range: $25-49.9 Million
Emp.: 35
Automotive Glass Product Mfr
N.A.I.C.S.: 327215
Thomas Bennet (CEO)

Saint-Gobain Autover France **(1)**
ZAC de Mariage 41 Rue Des Bruyeres,
69330, Pusignan, France **(100%)**
Tel.: (33) 820228228
Web Site: http://www.autover.fr
Glass Products Mfr
N.A.I.C.S.: 327211

Saint-Gobain Autover Hellas S.A. **(1)**
Pontou B KTEO Area, Kalochori, 570 09,
Greece
Tel.: (30) 2310 798770
Web Site: http://www.autover.gr
Automotive Glass Product Mfr
N.A.I.C.S.: 327215

**Saint-Gobain Building Distribution
(Ireland) Ltd.** **(1)**
648 Springfield Road, Belfast, BT12 7EH,
United Kingdom
Tel.: (44) 28 9024 3661
Sales Range: $75-99.9 Million
Emp.: 250
Timber Products Distr
N.A.I.C.S.: 423990

Saint-Gobain Canalizacao S.A. **(1)**
Via Dr Sergio Braga 452, 27330-050, Barra
Mansa, Brazil **(81%)**
Tel.: (55) 2440091301
Web Site: https://www.sgpam.com.br
Sales Range: $200-249.9 Million
Emp.: 800
Mfr of Ductile Iron Pipes & Fittings; Hydrau-
lic Valves
N.A.I.C.S.: 332919

**Saint-Gobain Ceramic Materials
(Zhengzhou) Co., Ltd.** **(1)**
DengFeng YangCheng Industrial District,
Zhengzhou, 452477, Henan, China
Tel.: (86) 371 6295 7952
Web Site: http://www.saint-gobain-
zz.com.cn
Ceramic Products Mfr
N.A.I.C.S.: 327212

**Saint-Gobain Ceramics & Plastics
Plc** **(1)**
Mill Lane Rainford, Saint Helens, WA11
8LP, United Kingdom
Tel.: (44) 1744 882941
Ceramic & Plastic Product Mfr
N.A.I.C.S.: 327212
Paul Murai (Plant Mgr)

Saint-Gobain Condotte S.p.A. **(1)**
Via Allegro 1, I 16016, Cogoleto,
Italy **(100%)**
Tel.: (39) 01091711
Web Site: http://www.tubighisa.it
Glass Products Mfr
N.A.I.C.S.: 327211

Saint-Gobain Corporation **(1)**
750 E Swedesford Rd, Valley Forge, PA
19482-0101
Tel.: (610) 341-7000
Web Site: http://www.saint-gobain-
corporation.com
Sales Range: $250-299.9 Million
Emp.: 600
Holding Company
N.A.I.C.S.: 551112
Thomas Kinisky (Chief Innovation Officer &
Chm-North America)

Subsidiary (Non-US):

**CERTAINTEED GYPSUM NORTH
AMERICAN SERVICES, INC.** **(2)**
2424 Lakeshore Road West, Mississauga,
L5J 1K4, ON, Canada
Tel.: (905) 823-9881
Gypsum Product Mfr
N.A.I.C.S.: 327420

Subsidiary (Domestic):

Carborundum Ventures Inc. **(2)**
23 Acheson Dr, Niagara Falls, NY
14303-1555 **(100%)**
Tel.: (716) 278-6299
Flat Glass Mfr
N.A.I.C.S.: 813930

CertainTeed Corporation **(2)**
20 Moores Road, Malvern, PA
19355 **(100%)**
Web Site: http://www.certainteed.com
Glass Container Mfr
N.A.I.C.S.: 327213
Mark Rayfield (CEO)

Subsidiary (Domestic):

**CERTAINTEED GYPSUM AND CEIL-
ING MANUFACTURING, INC.** **(2)**
4300 W Cypress St Ste 500, Tampa, FL
33607
Tel.: (813) 286-3900
Web Site: http://www.saint-gobain.fr
Gypsum Product Mfr
N.A.I.C.S.: 327420

CERTAINTEED GYPSUM, INC. **(3)**

4300 500 W Cypress St, Tampa, FL 33607
Tel.: (813) 286-3900
Web Site: http://www.saint-gobain.fr
Gypsum Product Mfr
N.A.I.C.S.: 327420
Missy Merfeld (Reg Mgr-Sls)

CTKC Corporation **(3)**
c/o Deleware Management Co. 750 E.
Swedesford Rd., Valley Forge, PA
19482 **(100%)**
Tel.: (302) 574-8914
Flat Glass
N.A.I.C.S.: 327211

Branch (Domestic):

CertainTeed **(3)**
1077 Pleasant St, Norwood, MA
02062-4609 **(100%)**
Tel.: (781) 551-0656
Web Site: http://www.certainteed.com
Sales Range: $75-99.9 Million
Emp.: 160
Mfr of Building Materials & Machinery
N.A.I.C.S.: 324122
Dennis Kennedy (Controller)

Unit (Domestic):

CertainTeed Ceilings **(3)**
750 E Swedesford Rd, Valley Forge, PA
19482 **(100%)**
Tel.: (610) 341-7000
Web Site: http://www.certainteed.com
Sales Range: $1-9.9 Million
Emp.: 12
Acoustic Ceiling Products
N.A.I.C.S.: 238310
Anna Maria Hessler (Controller)

Subsidiary (Domestic):

**CertainTeed Corporation
Foundation** **(3)**
750 E Swedesford Rd, Valley Forge, PA
19482 **(100%)**
Tel.: (610) 341-7000
Web Site: http://www.certainteed.com
Sales Range: $125-149.9 Million
Emp.: 500
Mfr of Flat Glass Products
N.A.I.C.S.: 327213

Unit (Domestic):

**CertainTeed Corporation Technical
Center** **(3)**
1400 Union Meeting Rd, Blue Bell, PA
19422 **(100%)**
Tel.: (610) 341-7000
Web Site: http://www.certainteed.com
Sales Range: $250-299.9 Million
Emp.: 600
Flat Glass, Glass Containers, Insulation,
Reinforcements, Building Materials, Abra-
sives, Industrial Ceramics & Pipes Mfr
N.A.I.C.S.: 327213

Subsidiary (Domestic):

CertainTeed Foreign Sales Corp. **(3)**
PO Box 860, Valley Forge, PA
19482-0860 **(100%)**
Tel.: (610) 341-7000
Web Site: http://www.certainteed.com
Sales Range: $250-299.9 Million
Emp.: 600
Sales Services
N.A.I.C.S.: 327213

**CertainTeed GYPSUM MANUFAC-
TURING, INC** **(3)**
4300 500 W Cypress St, Tampa, FL 33607
Tel.: (813) 286-3900
Gypsum Product Mfr
N.A.I.C.S.: 327420
Peter Mayer (VP-Innovation & Tech)

**CertainTeed GYPSUM WEST
VRGINIA, INC.** **(3)**
4300 500 W Cypress St, Tampa, FL 33607
Tel.: (813) 286-3900
Gypsum Product Mfr
N.A.I.C.S.: 327420

Unit (Domestic):

CertainTeed Machine Works **(3)**
101 Hatfield Rd, Winter Haven, FL 33880
Tel.: (800) 237-7841

Compagnie de Saint-Gobain SA—(Continued)

Web Site:
http://www.certainteedmachineworks.com
Blowing & Fireproofing Machines, Spray
Foam Equipment, Vacuums & Accessories
Mfr & Equipment Installation & Maintenance
Services
N.A.I.C.S.: 333413

Subsidiary (Domestic):

**Continental Building Products,
Inc.** (3)
12950 Worldgate Dr Ste 700, Herndon, VA
20170
Tel.: (703) 480-3800
Web Site: http://www.certainteed.com
Gypsum Wallboard & Finishing Products
Mfr
N.A.I.C.S.: 327420
Chris Hagen (Gen Mgr)

Finish Line Products, Inc. (3)
747 Tucker Rd, Winder, GA 30680-8370
Tel.: (770) 307-1503
Web Site: http://www.finishline-products.com
Construction Machinery Mfr
N.A.I.C.S.: 333120

SimTek Fence, Inc. (3)
1330 W 400 N, Orem, UT 84057
Tel.: (801) 655-5236
Industrial Fence Products Mfr
N.A.I.C.S.: 326199

Subsidiary (Non-US):

**CertainTeed Gypsum Canada,
Inc.** (2)
3304 58th Avenue S E, Calgary, T2C 0B3,
AB, Canada
Tel.: (403) 279-2112
Web Site: http://www.saint-gobain-
northamerica.com
Gypsum Product Mfr
N.A.I.C.S.: 327420
Sidney Anderson (Gen Mgr)

CertainTeed Insulation (2)
3985 Belgreen Drive, Ottawa, K1G 3N2,
ON, Canada
Tel.: (613) 736-1215
Web Site: http://www.saint-gobain-
northamerica.com
Emp.: 150
Glass Products Mfr
N.A.I.C.S.: 327215
Gerald Amannt (Plant Mgr)

Subsidiary (Domestic):

Corhart Refractories Corp. (2)
10300 Ormsby Park Pl Ste 450 , Louisville,
KY 40223-6185
Tel.: (502) 423-6324
Sales Range: $100-124.9 Million
Emp.: 450
Fire Brick Mfr
N.A.I.C.S.: 327120

Joint Venture (Domestic):

Eurokera North America, Inc. (2)
140 Chase Blvd, Fountain Inn, SC 29644-
8082
Tel.: (864) 963-8082
Web Site: http://pyro.eurokera.com
Sales Range: $25-49.9 Million
Emp.: 50
Flat Glass Mfr
N.A.I.C.S.: 327211

Subsidiary (Domestic):

GCP Applied Technologies Inc. (2)
62 Whittemore Ave, Cambridge, MA 02140-
1623
Tel.: (617) 876-1400
Web Site: http://www.gcpat.com
Rev.: $970,100,000
Assets: $1,446,600,000
Liabilities: $774,700,000
Net Worth: $671,900,000
Earnings: $21,200,000
Emp.: 1,800
Fiscal Year-end: 12/31/2021
Chemical Products Mfr
N.A.I.C.S.: 325998
Michael W. Valente (Gen Counsel, Sec &
VP)

HCS Corporation (2)
22626 85th Pl S, Kent, WA 98031-2469
Tel.: (253) 854-4945
Web Site: http://www.hotcell.com
Rev.: $3,800,000
Emp.: 11
Radiation Shielding Windows Mfr
N.A.I.C.S.: 327215
Jean Philippe Lacharmme (Pres & CEO)

International Cellulose Corp. (2)
12315 Robin Blvd, Houston, TX 77045
Tel.: (713) 433-6701
Web Site: https://www.spray-on.com
Paper Mills
N.A.I.C.S.: 322120
Juan Llinas (Coord-Inventory)

Meyer Laminates, Inc. (2)
1264 La Quinta Dr 41, Orlando, FL 32809
Tel.: (407) 857-6353
Rev.: $55,000,000
Emp.: 64
Lumber Plywood & Millwork
N.A.I.C.S.: 423310

Subsidiary (Non-US):

**Pyramid Specialities Products
Ltd.** (2)
17 Chemin De l Aviation, Pointe-Claire,
H9R 4Z2, QC, Canada (100%)
Tel.: (514) 694-6788
Sales Range: $25-49.9 Million
Emp.: 30
Glass Mfr
N.A.I.C.S.: 327215

Subsidiary (Domestic):

SAGE Electrochromics, Inc. (2)
2 Sage Way, Faribault, MN 55021 (100%)
Tel.: (507) 331-4848
Web Site: http://www.sageglass.com
Sales Range: $10-24.9 Million
Electronically Tintable Window Glass Mfr
N.A.I.C.S.: 327211
John Van Dine (Founder)

**SAINT-GOBAIN ADVANCED CE-
RAMICS CORPORATION** (2)
168 Creekside Dr, Amherst, NY 14303
Tel.: (716) 691-2051
Web Site: http://www.bn.saint-gobain.com
Sales Range: $25-49.9 Million
Emp.: 75
Chemical Products Mfr
N.A.I.C.S.: 325998
Scott Kuppinger (Bus Mgr)

**SAINT-GOBAIN GLASS EXPROVER
NORTH AMERICA CORP.** (2)
15825 N 71st St Ste 205, Scottsdale, AZ
85254
Tel.: (480) 607-9400
Web Site: http://www.exprover.saint-gobain-
glass.com
Flat Glass Mfr & Exporter
N.A.I.C.S.: 327211

Subsidiary (Non-US):

**SAINT-GOBAIN SOLAR GARD
CANADA, INC** (2)
760 Pacific Road Unit 1, Oakville, L6L 6M5,
ON, Canada
Tel.: (800) 595-8468
Sales Range: $25-49.9 Million
Emp.: 4
Window Film Distr
N.A.I.C.S.: 423330
Frank MacKay (Gen Mgr)

Subsidiary (Domestic):

**SAINT-GOBAIN SOLAR GARD,
LLC** (2)
4540 Viewridge Ave, San Diego, CA 92123
Tel.: (877) 273-4364
Web Site: http://www.solargard.com
Window Film Mfr & Distr
N.A.I.C.S.: 326113

Subsidiary (Non-US):

**SG Ceramics Materials Canada
Inc.** (2)
8001 Daly St, Niagara Falls, L2G 6S2, ON,
Canada
Tel.: (905) 295-4311

Sales Range: $25-49.9 Million
Emp.: 36
Abrasive Product Mfr
N.A.I.C.S.: 327910

Subsidiary (Domestic):

Saint Gobain (2)
5300 Gerber Rd, Fort Smith, AR
72904 (100%)
Tel.: (479) 782-2001
Web Site: http://www.nortonproppants.com
Sales Range: $50-74.9 Million
Emp.: 150
Industrial Ceramic Products Mfr
N.A.I.C.S.: 327910
Jack Larry (Gen Mgr)

Saint Gobain BTI (2)
43 Bibber Pkwy, Brunswick, ME 04011-
7357
Tel.: (207) 729-7792
Web Site: http://www.sgtf.com
Sales Range: $10-24.9 Million
Emp.: 139
Mfr of Reinforcement Fabrics for Composite
Materials Used in Boats, Skis, Automotive
Parts & Industrial Tanks & Pipes
N.A.I.C.S.: 313210

Saint-Gobain (2)
1 New Bond St, Worcester, MA 01606
Tel.: (508) 795-5000
Web Site: http://www.nortonabrasives.com
Sales Range: $500-549.9 Million
Emp.: 1,200
Mfr of Abrasives Products
N.A.I.C.S.: 551112
Jean-Francois Phelizon (Sr VP)

**Saint-Gobain ADFORS America,
Inc.** (2)
1795 Baseline Rd, Grand Island, NY 14072-
2010
Tel.: (716) 775-3900
Web Site: https://www.adfors.com
Reinforcement Fabrics Mfr
N.A.I.C.S.: 313230
Mike Heburn (Dir-Ops)

Subsidiary (Domestic):

New York Wire Company (3)
500 E Middle St, Hanover, PA 17331-2027
Tel.: (717) 637-3795
Web Site: http://www.newyorkwireind.com
Sales Range: $100-124.9 Million
Emp.: 500
Screening, Industrial Mesh & Drawn Wire
Products
N.A.I.C.S.: 332618
Jeffrey B. Roscoe (Dir-Sls)

Branch (Domestic):

Braeburn Alloy Steel (4)
101 Braeburn Rd, Lower Burrell, PA 15068-
2259
Tel.: (724) 224-6900
Web Site: http://www.braeburnsteel.com
Sales Range: $10-24.9 Million
Emp.: 70
Mfr of Alloy Tool Steel
N.A.I.C.S.: 331110

New York Wire Company (3)
1497 Industrial Rd, Walterboro, SC 29488
Tel.: (843) 538-8041
Sales Range: $75-99.9 Million
Emp.: 300
Fiberglass Products
N.A.I.C.S.: 326199

Subsidiary (Domestic):

Saint-Gobain Abrasives, Inc (2)
1 New Bond St, Worcester, MA 01606-0008
Tel.: (254) 918-2313
Web Site: http://www.sgabrasives.com
Emp.: 1,000
Abrasive Materials Mfr
N.A.I.C.S.: 327910
John Crowe (Pres)

Subsidiary (Domestic):

ABC Superabrasives (3)
1401 E Lackawanna St, Olyphant, PA
18447
Tel.: (570) 383-3261

Web Site:
http://www.abcsuperabrasives.com
Sales Range: $25-49.9 Million
Emp.: 32
Diamond Powder
N.A.I.C.S.: 327910
Brian Schaffer (Mgr)

Norton Company (3)
1 New Bond St, Worcester, MA
01606 (100%)
Tel.: (508) 795-5000
Web Site: http://www.nortonabrasives.com
Sales Range: $250-299.9 Million
Emp.: 1,000
Holding Company
N.A.I.C.S.: 551112
Dean Arvidson (Dir-Technical Mktg)

Subsidiary (Domestic):

Norton Abrasive Exports (4)
1 New Bond St, Worcester, MA
01606 (100%)
Tel.: (508) 795-5000
Web Site: http://www.sgabrasives.com
Sales Range: $400-449.9 Million
Emp.: 1,000
Mfr of Automotive & Industrial Welding
Products
N.A.I.C.S.: 551112
Mark Rayfield (VP)

**Saint-Gobain Industrial Ceramics
Inc.** (4)
1 New Bond St, Worcester, MA
01606 (100%)
Tel.: (508) 795-5000
Web Site: http://www.refractories.saint-
gobain.com
Sales Range: $400-449.9 Million
Emp.: 1,000
Flat Glass Mfr
N.A.I.C.S.: 327910

Saint-Gobain NorPro (4)
3840 Fishcreek Rd, Stow, OH
44224-4305 (100%)
Tel.: (330) 673-5860
Web Site: http://www.norpro.saint-
gobain.com
Sales Range: $25-49.9 Million
Emp.: 70
Mfr & Designer of Packings & Trays
N.A.I.C.S.: 333132
Paul Szymborski (Dir-Sls & Mktg)

**Saint-Gobain Performance Plastics
Corp.** (4)
31500 Solon Rd, Solon, OH 44139 (100%)
Web Site: http://www.plastics.saint-
gobain.com
Engineered Plastic Products & High Perfor-
mance Polymer Products Mfr
N.A.I.C.S.: 326199

Subsidiary (Non-US):

**Al Rushaid Eastman Arabia
Limited** (5)
Dhahran Airport, PO Box 539, Dhahran,
31932, Saudi Arabia (37.5%)
Tel.: (966) 38980028
Mfr of Glass Products
N.A.I.C.S.: 327211

Bicron Products PPL (5)
SB Billimoria Co 70/3 Miller Road, Benga-
luru, 560 052, India (100%)
Web Site: http://www.bicron.com
Crystals & Detectors Mfr
N.A.I.C.S.: 327215

EFESIS Schleiftechnik GmbH (5)
Dr Georg Schafer Strasse 1, D 97447,
Gerolzhofen, Germany (100%)
Tel.: (49) 93826020
Web Site: http://www.efesis.de
Sales Range: $125-149.9 Million
Emp.: 160
Mfr of Glass Products
N.A.I.C.S.: 327211
Ripp Stein (Mgr)

Grindwell Norton Ltd. (5)
Leela Business Park 5th Level, Andheri
Kurla Road Andheri E, Mumbai, 400059,
India (51%)
Tel.: (91) 2240212121

Sales Range: $75-99.9 Million
Emp.: 75
Mfr & Sales of Abrasive Products
N.A.I.C.S.: 327910
Krishna Prasad *(Gen Mgr)*

Subsidiary (Domestic):

Hycomp, LLC (5)
17960 Englewood Dr, Cleveland, OH 44130
Tel.: (440) 234-2002
Web Site: http://www.hycompinc.com
All Other Plastics Product Mfr
N.A.I.C.S.: 326199
Robert Scoular *(Pres & CEO)*

Subsidiary (Non-US):

Norton Insurance Limited (5)
30 Cedar Avenue, Hamilton, 5,
Bermuda (100%)
Captive Insurance Company
N.A.I.C.S.: 524298

Norton Pampus GmbH (5)
Am Nordkanal 37, D-47877, Willich,
Germany (100%)
Tel.: (49) 215460310
Fluoropolymers
N.A.I.C.S.: 325211

**SAINT-GOBAIN ABRASIVES
A/S** (5)
Korskildeeng 5, 2670, Greve, Denmark
Tel.: (45) 467 552 44
Web Site: http://www.s-ga.dk
Emp.: 10
Abrasive Product Mfr
N.A.I.C.S.: 327910

**SAINT-GOBAIN ABRASIVOS CO-
LOMBIA LTDA** (5)
Km 20 Carretera Occidente, Mosquera,
Colombia
Tel.: (57) 1 8933993
Abrasive Product Mfr
N.A.I.C.S.: 327910

**SAINT-GOBAIN ABRASIVOS
LIMITADA** (5)
Av Vitacura 9990 - of 302 - Vitacura, San-
tiago, Chile
Tel.: (56) 2 342 3851
Abrasive Product Mfr
N.A.I.C.S.: 327910

**SAINT-GOBAIN ABRASIVOS, S.A.
DE C.V.** (5)
Carretera Matamoros Brecha E-99 Parque
Industrial Reynosa, 88780, Reynosa,
Tamps, Mexico
Tel.: (52) 899131 07 40
Web Site: http://www.saint-gobain-
northamerica.com
Abrasive Product Mfr
N.A.I.C.S.: 327910

Saint Gobain Abrasives Pty. Ltd. (5)
4 Colbert Rd, Campbellfield, 3061,
Australia (99.97%)
Tel.: (61) 393586100
Web Site: http://www.saintgobain.com.au
Sales Range: $75-99.9 Million
Emp.: 100
Abrasive Products, Industrial Ceramics,
Chemical Process Products, Sealants,
Safety Products, Construction Products &
Pressure Sensitive Tapes Mfr
N.A.I.C.S.: 327910
Taeke Meerveld *(Mng Dir)*

Subsidiary (Domestic):

**Saint Gobain Performance Plastics
Corporation** (5)
1199 S Chillicothe Rd, Aurora, OH 44202
Tel.: (216) 245-0529
Web Site: http://www.plastics.saint-
gobain.com
Sales Range: $75-99.9 Million
Emp.: 60
Aircraft Body & Wing Assemblies & Parts
N.A.I.C.S.: 336413

Subsidiary (Non-US):

Saint-Gobain Abrasifs SA (5)
Rue De I Ambassadeur, PO Box 8, 78702,
Conflans-Sainte-Honorine,
France (99.91%)

Tel.: (33) 134904000
Web Site: http://www.norton-abrasifs.com
Sales Range: $250-299.9 Million
Emp.: 500
Mfr & Retailer of Abrasive Products, Seal-
ants, Construction Products, Industrial Ce-
ramics
N.A.I.C.S.: 327910
Thomas Petuaud-Letang *(Mng Dir)*

**Saint-Gobain Abrasives (Pty.)
Ltd.** (5)
Unit 2 Monteer Road, Isando, 1600, South
Africa (99.91%)
Tel.: (27) 119612000
Web Site: http://www.saint-gobain.com
Abrasive Product Mfr
N.A.I.C.S.: 327910

**Saint-Gobain Abrasives (Suzhou)
Co., Ltd.** (5)
No 45 Ting Lan Road Suzhou Industrial
Park, 215123, Suzhou, Jiangsu, China
Tel.: (86) 51262898050
Sales Range: $125-149.9 Million
Emp.: 150
Abrasive Product Mfr
N.A.I.C.S.: 327910
Franck Guo *(Gen Mgr)*

Saint-Gobain Abrasives AB (5)
PO Box 305, 177 25, Jarfalla,
Sweden (99%)
Tel.: (46) 858088100
Web Site: http://www.saint-gobain.se
Sales Range: $10-24.9 Million
Emp.: 27
Mfr of Abrasive Products, Industrial Ceram-
ics & Construction Products
N.A.I.C.S.: 327910

Saint-Gobain Abrasives BV (5)
Groenloseweg 28, 7151 HW, Eibergen,
Netherlands (99%)
Tel.: (31) 545471766
Sales Range: $75-99.9 Million
Emp.: 20
Mfr of Abrasive Products
N.A.I.C.S.: 327910

**Saint-Gobain Abrasives Canada
Inc** (5)
3 Beach Road, PO Box 3008, Hamilton,
L8L 7Y5, ON, Canada (100%)
Tel.: (905) 547-2551
Web Site: http://www.sga.com
Sales Range: $50-74.9 Million
Emp.: 50
Mfr of Grinding Wheels
N.A.I.C.S.: 327910

Saint-Gobain Abrasives Gmbh (5)
Birkenstrasse 45-49, Wesseling, 50389,
Germany
Tel.: (49) 22367031
Web Site: http://www.saint-gobain-
abrasives.com
Abrasive Product Mfr
N.A.I.C.S.: 327910
Pierra Roeder *(Dir-Fin)*

Saint-Gobain Abrasives Limited (5)
Doxey Rd, Stafford, ST16 1EA, Stafford-
shire, United Kingdom (100%)
Tel.: (44) 1785223281
Web Site: http://www.saint-gobain.co.uk
Abrasive Product Mfr
N.A.I.C.S.: 327910
Budhi Chilkoti *(Mng Dir)*

Saint-Gobain Abrasives Ltd (5)
70 Wharf Rd Te Atatu Peninsula, PO Box
45005, Auckland, 0610, New
Zealand (100%)
Tel.: (64) 98347119
Web Site: http://www.saintgobain.com
Sales Range: $50-74.9 Million
Emp.: 40
Mfr & Retailer of Pressure Sensitive Tapes,
Abrasive Products, Construction Products
N.A.I.C.S.: 327910
Kavin Dennis *(Mgr-Warehouse)*

Saint-Gobain Abrasives Malaysia (5)
Ste 210 1st Fl Block A Kelana Ctr Point No
3, Jalan SS7/19 Kalana Jaya, 47301, Petal-
ing Jaya, Malaysia (100%)
Tel.: (60) 356389550
Web Site: http://www.sg-abrasives.com

Sales Range: $75-99.9 Million
Emp.: 10
Mfr of Abrasive Products
N.A.I.C.S.: 327910
David Yan *(Mgr-Sls)*

Saint-Gobain Abrasives S.A. (5)
Bd J F Kennedy 190, 4930, Bascharage,
Luxembourg (99.9%)
Tel.: (352) 504011
Web Site: http://www.construction.norton.eu
Sales Range: $125-149.9 Million
Emp.: 114
Mfr & Sale of Construction & Abrasive Prod-
ucts
N.A.I.C.S.: 327910

Saint-Gobain Abrasives S.R.O. (5)
Vinohradska 184, 130 52, Prague, Czech
Republic
Tel.: (420) 267 132 029
Web Site: http://www.sgabrasives.cz
Sales Range: $50-74.9 Million
Emp.: 29
Abrasive Product Mfr
N.A.I.C.S.: 327910

Saint-Gobain Abrasives SA/NV (5)
Industrielaan 129, Brussels, 1070,
Belgium (99.91%)
Tel.: (32) 22672100
Web Site: http://www.saint-gobain.com
Sales Range: $75-99.9 Million
Emp.: 15
Abrasive Materials Mfr
N.A.I.C.S.: 327910
Frans Van Roy *(Gen Mgr)*

**Saint-Gobain Abrasives Thailand
Ltd.** (5)
539/2 Gypsum Metropolitan Tower 13th
Floor Sri Ayudhya Road, Phayathai
Ratchathewi, Bangkok, 10400, Thailand
Tel.: (66) 26405440
Web Site: http://www.abrasivesthailand.com
Sales Range: $125-149.9 Million
Emp.: 130
Abrasive Product Mfr
N.A.I.C.S.: 327910

Saint-Gobain Abrasivi S.p.A (5)
Via Per Cesano Boscone 4, I-20094, Milan,
Italy (99.91%)
Tel.: (39) 0244851
Abrasive Products, Industrial Ceramics &
Construction Products Mfr
N.A.I.C.S.: 327910

Saint-Gobain Abrasivi S.p.A. (5)
Via per Cesano Boscone 4, Corsico, MI,
Italy (99%)
Tel.: (39) 02 44 85 293
Web Site: http://www.grinding.it
Sales Range: $50-74.9 Million
Emp.: 32
Abrasive Textiles & Related Products Mfr
N.A.I.C.S.: 327910

Saint-Gobain Abrasivos CA (5)
Av Alberto Ravell Galpon Saint Gobain Ur-
banizacion, Los Teques, Venezuela
Tel.: (58) 212 210 48 00
Web Site: http://www.saint-gobain.com.mx
Abrasive Product Mfr
N.A.I.C.S.: 327910

Saint-Gobain Abrasivos Lda (5)
122 Zona Industrial De Maia I Sector VIII
Apartado 6550, Gemunde, Maia, 4476-908,
Portugal
Tel.: (351) 229 437 940
Web Site: http://www.sgabrasivos.com.br
Abrasive Product Mfr
N.A.I.C.S.: 327910

Saint-Gobain Abrasivos SA (5)
Carretera De Guipuzcoa Km 7 5 162 Ber-
rioplano, E 31195, Correos, Pamplona,
Spain (100%)
Tel.: (34) 948306000
Web Site: http://www.norton.co.es
Sales Range: $125-149.9 Million
Emp.: 130
Abrasive & Construction Products Mfr
N.A.I.C.S.: 327910
Tedro Busto *(Gen Mgr)*

**Saint-Gobain Ceramic Materials
AS** (5)
Mordhaim, PO Box 113, N 4790, Lillesand,
Norway (100%)

Tel.: (47) 37260000
Web Site: http://www.sic.saint-gobain.com
Sales Range: $250-299.9 Million
Mfr of Abrasive Grain
N.A.I.C.S.: 327910

**Saint-Gobain Ceramic Materials
Canada Inc.** (5)
8001 Daly St, Niagara Falls, L2G 6S2, ON,
Canada (100%)
Tel.: (905) 295-4311
Web Site: http://www.saint-gobain-
northamerica.com
Sales Range: $100-124.9 Million
Emp.: 40
Mfr of Industrial Ceramics
N.A.I.C.S.: 212323

**Saint-Gobain Ceramic Materials Weil-
erswist GmbH** (5)
Metternicher Strasse 3, D 53919, Weiler-
swist, Germany (100%)
Tel.: (49) 225496070
Web Site: http://www.saintgobain.com
Sales Range: $50-74.9 Million
Emp.: 10
Mfr of Textiles & Related Products
N.A.I.C.S.: 313210

**Saint-Gobain Ceramicas Industriales
S.A.** (5)
Poligono Industrial Aquiberia, Castellbisbal,
8755, Barcelona, Spain (100%)
Tel.: (34) 936828140
Web Site: http://www.saintgobain.com
Sales Range: $75-99.9 Million
Emp.: 75
Glass & Plastic Products Mfr
N.A.I.C.S.: 327211

**Saint-Gobain Industrial Ceramics
Ltd.** (5)
Mill Ln Rainford Merseyside, Saint Helens,
WA11 8LP, United Kingdom (100%)
Tel.: (44) 01744882941
Web Site: http://www.refractories.saint-
gobain.com
Sales Range: $50-74.9 Million
Emp.: 50
Specialised Refractory Materials Mfr
N.A.I.C.S.: 327120

Saint-Gobain K.K. (5)
Saint Gobain bldg 7 Koji-machi 3-chome,
Chiyoda-ku, Tokyo, 102 0083,
Japan (100%)
Tel.: (81) 332630281
Web Site: http://www.saint-gobain.com.jp
Sales Range: $75-99.9 Million
Emp.: 50
Provider of Management & Marketing Ser-
vices & Sale of Chemical Process Products
N.A.I.C.S.: 424690

**Saint-Gobain Performance Plastics
Chaineux SA** (5)
Ave Du Parc 18, Chaineux, 4650,
Belgium (100%)
Tel.: (32) 87322011
Web Site: http://www.saint-goabin.com
Sales Range: $75-99.9 Million
Emp.: 70
Ceramics & Plastics Mfr
N.A.I.C.S.: 326199
Tim De Greift *(Mng Dir)*

Subsidiary (Domestic):

**Saint-Gobain Performance Plastics
Corp.** (5)
1 Sealants Pk, Granville, NY
12832-1652 (100%)
Tel.: (518) 642-2200
Web Site: http://www.fff.saint-gobain.com
Sales Range: $100-124.9 Million
Emp.: 100
Mfr of Industrial Tapes Foams Films &
Laminates Health Care Products
N.A.I.C.S.: 326199
Phil Guy *(Gen Mgr)*

**Saint-Gobain Performance Plastics
Corporation** (5)
701 Daniel Webster Hwy, Merrimack, NH
03054-2713 (100%)
Tel.: (603) 424-9000
Web Site: http://www.saint-gobain.com
Sales Range: $100-124.9 Million
Emp.: 260
High Performance Engineered Products &
Materials Systems Mfr

Compagnie de Saint-Gobain SA—(Continued)

N.A.I.C.S.: 313320

Holding (Non-US):

Chemfab Japan, Ltd. (6)
3-20-1 Miyoshi-cho,, Fuchu, Tokyo, 183-0045, Japan
Tel.: (81) 42 358 5530
Industrial Plastics Mfr
N.A.I.C.S.: 333511

Saint-Gobain Performance Plastics Brasil (6)
Rodovia Regis Bittencourt, PO Box 3, 06850-970, Sao Paulo, Brazil (100%)
Tel.: (55) 1141471499
Web Site:
http://www.ceramicmaterials.saint-gobain.com
Emp.: 30
Plastic Mfr
N.A.I.C.S.: 326140

Saint-Gobain Performance Plastics Cologne GmbH (6)
Am Nordkanal 37, 47877, Willich, Germany (100%)
Tel.: (49) 2154 60190
Web Site: http://www.fff.saint-gobain.com
Sales Range: $10-24.9 Million
Emp.: 30
Performance Plastics Mfr
N.A.I.C.S.: 325211

Saint-Gobain Performance Plastics Ireland Ltd (6)
Cooraclare Rd, Kilrush, County Clare, Ireland (100%)
Tel.: (353) 659080170
Web Site: http://www.chemfab.com
Emp.: 80
Mfr of Coated Fabrics
N.A.I.C.S.: 313320

Tygaflor Ltd. (6)
Bay 3 Transpennine Estate, Rochdale, OL11 2PX, Lancs, United Kingdom (100%)
Tel.: (44) 1706746900
Web Site: http://www.fffeurope.saint-gobain.com
Emp.: 30
PTFE Coated Fabrics, Conveyor Belts & Films Mfr
N.A.I.C.S.: 313220
Peter Appleton (Gen Mgr)

Subsidiary (Non-US):

Saint-Gobain Performance Plastics Pampus GmbH (5)
Am Nordkanal 37, Willich, 47877, Germany (100%)
Tel.: (49) 2154600
Web Site: http://www.saint-gobain.com
Sales Range: $250-299.9 Million
Emp.: 370
Mfr of Engineered Plastic Products & Materials, High Performance Polymer Products
N.A.I.C.S.: 326199

Saint-Gobain Performance Plastics Shanghai (5)
1468 Kun Yang Road Minhong Development Zone, Shanghai, 200245, China (100%)
Tel.: (86) 2154721568
Web Site: http://www.saintgobain.com
Sales Range: $75-99.9 Million
Emp.: 100
Mfr of Plastic Products
N.A.I.C.S.: 326199
Lucia Sun (Mng Dir)

Societe Europeenne des Produits Refractaires (5)
Les Miroirs La Defense, 92096, Paris, Cedex, France (100%)
Tel.: (33) 0147623700
Sales Range: $450-499.9 Million
Mfr of Electrofused Refractory Products
N.A.I.C.S.: 327120

Subsidiary (Non-US):

SEPR Italia S.p.A. (6)
Via del Teroldego 1, I-38016, Mezzocorona, Trento, Italy (100%)
Tel.: (39) 0461616666

Web Site: http://www.saint-gobain-glass.com
Sales Range: $50-74.9 Million
Emp.: 1,000
Mfr of Electrofused Refractory Products
N.A.I.C.S.: 327120
Sargeo Mazzolane (Gen Mgr)

Subsidiary (Domestic):

Saint-Gobain Centre de Recherche et d'Etudes Europeennes (6)
550 Avenue Alphonse Jauffret, 84306, Cavaillon, France
Tel.: (33) 4 32 50 09 00
Laboratory Testing Services
N.A.I.C.S.: 541380
Chloe Bigenwald (Mgr-HR)

Saint-Gobain Cristaux (6)
104 Rue De Larchant, PO Box 521, 77140, Nemours, France (100%)
Tel.: (33) 164451010
Web Site: http://www.test-cdph.saint-gobain.com
Sales Range: $10-24.9 Million
Emp.: 100
Mfr of Pure Fused Silica Tubing for the Lamp Industry; Silica Wool, Felts & Yarns
N.A.I.C.S.: 331491
Corrine Gathy (Product Mgr)

Saint-Gobain Materiaux Ceramiques SA (6)
Les Miroirs 18 avenue d'Alsace, 92400, Courbevoie, France
Tel.: (33) 147623700
Web Site: http://www.saint-gobain.fr
Ceramic Wall Mfr
N.A.I.C.S.: 327120

Subsidiary (Domestic):

Saint-Gobain Coating Solutions (7)
50 Rue du Mourelet, BP 90966, 84000, Avignon, France
Tel.: (33) 4 9085 8500
Web Site: http://www.coatingsolutions.saint-gobain.com
Emp.: 30
Abrasive Product Mfr
N.A.I.C.S.: 327910
Thomas Wery (Product Mgr-Mktg-Export Sls)

Subsidiary (Domestic):

Savoie Refractaires (6)
10 Rue Del Industrie, Venissieux, France (99.99%)
Tel.: (33) 478781300
Web Site: http://www.sepr.fr
Emp.: 33
Mfr of Special Refractories
N.A.I.C.S.: 327120

Valoref SA (6)
Cruise Zone Industrielle, Bollene, 84500, France
Tel.: (33) 4 90 40 5000
Web Site: http://www.valoref.com
Emp.: 20
Waste Management Services
N.A.I.C.S.: 562998
Bruno Dorier (Gen Mgr)

Subsidiary (Domestic):

Warren Diamond Powder Company, Inc. (4)
1401 E Lackawanna St Mid Valley Industrial Park, Olyphant, PA 18447-2152
Tel.: (570) 383-3261
Web Site: http://www.warrendiamond.com
Sales Range: $1-9.9 Million
Emp.: 50
Diamond Wheels & Diamond Electroplated Products Mfr
N.A.I.C.S.: 327910

Subsidiary (Domestic):

Saint-Gobain Abrasives, Inc. - Chicago (3)
200 E Fullerton, Carol Stream, IL 60188 (100%)
Tel.: (630) 868-8060
Web Site: http://www.saint-gobain-northamerica.com

Sales Range: $50-74.9 Million
Emp.: 125
Diamond Cutting Tools For Turning Boring Burnishing
N.A.I.C.S.: 332216

Saint-Gobain Abrasives, Inc. - Philadelphia (3)
200 Commerce Dr, Montgomeryville, PA 18936-9640
Tel.: (215) 855-4300
Sales Range: $1-9.9 Million
Emp.: 55
Abrasive Materials Mfr
N.A.I.C.S.: 327910

Subsidiary (Non-US):

Saint-Gobain Adfors Canada Ltd (2)
201 Hugel Ave, Midland, L4R 4G1, ON, Canada
Tel.: (705) 526-7867
Fiber Glass Products Mfr
N.A.I.C.S.: 326199

Subsidiary (Domestic):

Saint-Gobain Autover Inc (2)
3351 SW Blvd, Grove City, OH 43123
Tel.: (614) 801-2290
Web Site: http://www.autover.us
Automotive Glass Product Mfr
N.A.I.C.S.: 327215
Christian Persson (Gen Mgr)

Saint-Gobain Ceramics & Plastics (2)
10300 Ormsby Park Pl Ste 450, Louisville, KY 40223-6185
Tel.: (502) 423-6324
Web Site: http://www.refractories.saint-gobain.com
Sales Range: $125-149.9 Million
Emp.: 450
Industrial Inorganic Chemicals
N.A.I.C.S.: 325180

Subsidiary (Domestic):

Phoenix Coating Resources, Inc. (3)
2377 State Road 37 S, Mulberry, FL 33860
Tel.: (863) 425-1430
Sales Range: $50-74.9 Million
Emp.: 25
Ceramic Ingots Mfr
N.A.I.C.S.: 336413
John Wehrung (Pres)

Saint-Gobain Ceramics (3)
23 Acheson Dr, Niagara Falls, NY 14303-1555 (100%)
Tel.: (716) 278-6233
Web Site: http://www.hexoloy.com
Sales Range: $50-74.9 Million
Emp.: 200
High Temperature Ceramic Fiber Insulation & Refractory Products, Polyester Resins & Resin Components Producer
N.A.I.C.S.: 327120
Steve Elliott (Mgr-Worldwide Armor)

Z-Tech LLC (3)
8 Dow Rd, Bow, NH 03304
Tel.: (603) 228-1305
Web Site: http://www.z-techzirconia.com
Sales Range: $1-9.9 Million
Emp.: 20
Zirconia Powder Mfr
N.A.I.C.S.: 325180
Larry Sohl (Mgr-Ops)

Subsidiary (Domestic):

Saint-Gobain Ceramics Structural Ceramics Inc (2)
23 Acheson Dr, Niagara Falls, NY 14303
Tel.: (716) 278-6233
Web Site: http://www.hexoloy.com
Emp.: 150
Ceramic Materials Mfr
N.A.I.C.S.: 327120
Chris Reilly (Plant Mgr)

Subsidiary (Non-US):

Saint-Gobain Ceramics SC (3)
3-7 Kojimachi, Chiyoda-ku, Tokyo, 102-0083, Japan
Tel.: (81) 332630289
Web Site: http://www.hexoloy.com
Glass Ceramic Mfr

N.A.I.C.S.: 327212

Subsidiary (Domestic):

Saint-Gobain Desjonqueres Manufacturing, Inc (2)
9141 Technology Dr, Covington, GA 30014 (99.99%)
Tel.: (770) 786-1952
Flat Glass Mfr
N.A.I.C.S.: 327213

Saint-Gobain Sekurit USA (2)
5700 18 MILE RD, Sterling Heights, MI 48314
Tel.: (586) 532-9500
Web Site: http://www.saint-gobain-sekurit.com
Sales Range: $25-49.9 Million
Emp.: 8
Windshield Mfr
N.A.I.C.S.: 327211
Rodrigo Bedoya (Gen Mgr)

Saint-Gobain Winter Inc (2)
100 Wilhelm Winter St, Travelers Rest, SC 29690-2226 (100%)
Tel.: (864) 834-4145
Web Site: http://www.saintgobain.com
Sales Range: $25-49.9 Million
Emp.: 80
Abrasive Product Mfr
N.A.I.C.S.: 327910

Vetrotech Saint-Gobain North America Inc. (2)
2108 B St NW Ste 110, Auburn, WA 98001-1624 (100%)
Tel.: (253) 333-0660
Web Site: http://www.vetrotechusa.com
Sales Range: $25-49.9 Million
Emp.: 5
Fire Rated Glass Products Mfr
N.A.I.C.S.: 327211
Christian Miller (Gen Mgr)

Saint-Gobain Crystals NV (1)
Nieuwe weg 109, 3765 GC, Soest, Netherlands
Tel.: (31) 35 602 97 00
Web Site: http://www.saint-gobain.de
Crystal Product Mfr
N.A.I.C.S.: 327215

Saint-Gobain Deutsche Glas GmbH (1)
Viktoria Allee 3 5, D 52066, Aachen, Germany (99.79%)
Tel.: (49) 2415160
Web Site: http://www.saint-gobain-glass.de
Rev.: $385,112,992
Emp.: 200
Holding Company; Distributor of Flat Glass for the Building Industry
N.A.I.C.S.: 551112

Saint-Gobain Distribucion Construccion, S.L (1)
C/ Verneda del Congost s/n-Pol Ind El Pedregar, 08160, Montmelo, Spain
Tel.: (34) 935723600
Building Materials Distr
N.A.I.C.S.: 444180

Saint-Gobain Distribution Batiment (1)
Les Miroirs 18 Ave Dalsace, Courbevoie, 92096, France (100%)
Tel.: (33) 3147624840
Web Site: http://www.saint-gobain.com
Sales Range: $50-74.9 Million
Emp.: 60
Construction Materials Distr
N.A.I.C.S.: 212321

Subsidiary (Non-US):

Dahl International AB (2)
Karlsbodavagen 2, PO Box 11076, 16811, Bromma, Sweden (100%)
Tel.: (46) 87642200
Web Site: http://www.dahlinternational.com
Sales Range: $50-74.9 Million
Emp.: 10
Wholesale Suppliers of Tubes, Pipes, Fittings, Non-ferrous Metals, Heating, Sanitary & Hospital Equipment, Industrial Supplies & Contractor's Tools
N.A.I.C.S.: 423690

Subsidiary (Non-US):

Brodrene Dahl A/S **(3)**
Park Alle 370, 2605, Brondby,
Denmark **(100%)**
Tel.: (45) 48784000
Web Site: https://www.bd.dk
Sales Range: $50-74.9 Million
Metal Product Whslr
N.A.I.C.S.: 423510
Lars Fournais *(Pres)*

Brodrene Dahl A/S **(3)**
Grenseveien 5, Oslo, 6146,
Norway **(100%)**
Tel.: (47) 22725500
Web Site: http://www.dahl.no
Heating, Ventilation & Sanitation Supplier
N.A.I.C.S.: 238220
Torbjorn L. Vik *(Dir-Mktg)*

Subsidiary (Domestic):

Dahl Sverige **(3)**
Ulcsattragagen 1, Jarfalla, 17722, Sweden
Tel.: (46) 858359500
Web Site: https://www.dahl.se
Food Distr & Whslr
N.A.I.C.S.: 424490
Goran Dahlin *(Dir-Mktg)*

Subsidiary (Non-US):

Gibbs and Dandy PLC **(2)**
226 Dallow Road, Luton, LU 1JG, United
Kingdom
Tel.: (44) 1582798798
Web Site: http://www.gibbsanddandy.com
Emp.: 345
Building Supply Store Operator
N.A.I.C.S.: 444110
Luis Garcia Angeles *(Mgr-Org Dev)*

Jewson Ltd. **(2)**
Merchant House Binley Business Park Bin-
ley, Coventry, CV3 2TT, Westmidland,
United Kingdom **(100%)**
Tel.: (44) 2476438400
Web Site: http://www.jewson.co.uk
Timber & Building Material Merchants
N.A.I.C.S.: 444180
Thierry Dufour *(Mng Dir)*

PDM Ltd. **(2)**
Old Milltown Kill, Kildare, Ireland **(100%)**
Tel.: (353) 45877165
Web Site: http://www.pdm.ie
Sales Range: $25-49.9 Million
Emp.: 30
Mfr of Fencing & Fabricator of Transmission
Poles
N.A.I.C.S.: 321999
Brendan Giddonn *(Mng Dir)*

Subsidiary (Domestic):

Placoplatre SA **(2)**
12 Place de Ilris, 92400, Courbevoie,
France
Tel.: (33) 188540000
Web Site: https://www.placo.fr
Sales Range: $550-599.9 Million
Construction Materials Mfr
N.A.I.C.S.: 444110

Subsidiary (Non-US):

Raab Karcher Baustoffe GmbH **(2)**
Hanauer Landstrasse 150, 60314, Frankfurt
am Main, Germany
Tel.: (49) 694050502
Web Site: http://www.raabkarcher.de
Building Materials, Tiles, Sanitary Fittings &
Heating
N.A.I.C.S.: 444110
Dieter Babiel *(Dir-Personnel)*

Subsidiary (Non-US):

Raab Karcher Bouwstoffen **(3)**
Kanaalstraat 295, 7547, Enschede, Neth-
lands
Tel.: (31) 534800150
Web Site: http://www.raabkarcher.nl
Sales Range: $25-49.9 Million
Emp.: 8
Distr of Construction Materials
N.A.I.C.S.: 444180

Raab Karcher Bouwstoffen B.V. **(3)**

Huifakkerstraat 20, 4815 PN, Breda, Neth-
erlands
Tel.: (31) 765731400
Web Site: http://www.raabkarcher.nl
Sales Range: $250-299.9 Million
Emp.: 7
Tiles Mfr
N.A.I.C.S.: 327120
Rom Danver Looeg *(Gen Mgr)*

Raab Karcher France S.A. **(3)**
10, Quai Paul Doumer, 92411, Courbevoie,
Cedex, France
Tel.: (33) 1 47 68 45 65
Coal Preparation & Distribution Services
N.A.I.C.S.: 324199

Subsidiary (Domestic):

Raab Karcher Hamm **(3)**
Hafenstrasse 142, 59067, Hamm, Germany
Tel.: (49) 2381940800
Web Site: http://www.raabkarcher.de
Sales Range: $25-49.9 Million
Emp.: 20
Tiles Mfr
N.A.I.C.S.: 327120
Jasinto Arcos *(Gen Mgr)*

Subsidiary (Non-US):

Raab Karcher Nederland B.V. **(3)**
Kamerlingh Onnesweg 10 A, 3316 GL, Dor-
drecht, Netherlands
Tel.: (31) 786521600
Web Site: http://www.raabkarcher.nl
Sales Range: $25-49.9 Million
Emp.: 10
Adhesive Tapes
N.A.I.C.S.: 325520
Neck Hareng *(Mng Dir)*

Subsidiary (Domestic):

**Raab Karcher Sanitar Heizung
Fliesen GmbH** **(3)**
Muenchener Str. 101, 85737, Ismaning,
Germany
Heating System Mfr
N.A.I.C.S.: 333414

**Saint-Gobain Distribution Denmark
A/S** **(1)**
Park Alle 370, Brondby, 2605, Denmark
Tel.: (45) 48784000
Web Site: http://www.saint-gobain.de
Rev.: $792,834,000
Emp.: 1,500
Construction Materials Distr
N.A.I.C.S.: 423330
Sus Nielsen *(Mgr)*

**Saint-Gobain Distribution Nordic
AB** **(1)**
Box 67, 177 22, Jarfalla, Sweden
Tel.: (46) 8 764 22 00
Building Materials Distr
N.A.I.C.S.: 423330

**Saint-Gobain Distribution The Nether-
lands BV** **(1)**
Atlasstraat 1, 5047 RG, Tilburg, Nether-
lands
Tel.: (31) 134580000
Sales Range: $50-74.9 Million
Emp.: 60
Construction Materials Distr
N.A.I.C.S.: 423390

Saint-Gobain Ecophon A/S **(1)**
Hammerholmen 18E, 2650, Hvidovre, Den-
mark
Tel.: (45) 36770909
Web Site: https://www.ecophon.com
Emp.: 1,100
Acoustic Product Mfr
N.A.I.C.S.: 332323
Max Falck *(Gen Mgr)*

Saint-Gobain Ecophon BV **(1)**
Parallelweg 17, 4878 AH, Etten-Leur, Neth-
erlands
Tel.: (31) 76 502 00 00
Web Site: http://www.ecophon.nl
Acoustic Product Mfr
N.A.I.C.S.: 327120
Menno van der Kooij *(Mgr-Customer Svc)*

Saint-Gobain Ecophon CZ s.r.o. **(1)**
Smrckova 2485/4, 180 00, Prague, 8,
Czech Republic

Tel.: (420) 220406580
Web Site: http://www.ecophon.cz
Sales Range: $25-49.9 Million
Emp.: 7
Acoustics & Lighting Products Mfr
N.A.I.C.S.: 335132
Daniel Benes *(Sr Mgr-Sls-Eastern Bohemia
& Prague)*

Saint-Gobain Ecophon Ltd **(1)**
Old Brick Kiln Monk Sherborne, Tadley,
RG26 5PP, United Kingdom
Tel.: (44) 1256 850977
Web Site: http://www.ecophon.com
Sales Range: $25-49.9 Million
Emp.: 50
Acoustic Wall Panel Mfr
N.A.I.C.S.: 332323
Joanne Hilton *(Mgr-Comml)*

**Saint-Gobain Ecophon Production
A/S** **(1)**
Hammerholmen 18E, 2650, Hvidovre, Den-
mark
Tel.: (45) 36 77 09 09
Web Site: http://www.ecophon.dk
Sales Range: $25-49.9 Million
Emp.: 20
Acoustic Product Mfr
N.A.I.C.S.: 332323

Saint-Gobain Emballage **(1)**
Les Miroirs - 18 avenue d'Alsace - 92400,
18 avenue d'Alsace, 92096, Courbevoie,
92096, France
Tel.: (33) 147623800
Web Site: http://www.saint-gobain-
emballage.fr
Sales Range: $450-499.9 Million
Emp.: 1,862
Mfr of Glass Containers, Bottles & Industrial
Jars
N.A.I.C.S.: 327212

Subsidiary (Domestic):

Saga Decor S.A.S. **(2)**
328 Rue Pasteur, 60700, Pont-Saint-
Maxence, France
Tel.: (33) 3 44 317 777
Web Site: http://www.saga-decor.com
Sales Range: $50-74.9 Million
Emp.: 130
Glass Container Mfr
N.A.I.C.S.: 327213

Subsidiary (Domestic):

VG Emballage SAS **(3)**
6062 Rue Hauteville, 75463, Paris, Cedex
10, France **(99.98%)**
Tel.: (33) 149291313
Web Site: http://www.vg-emballage.com
Glass, Plastic Containers & Fittings Distr
N.A.I.C.S.: 423840

Verreries de l'Orne SAS **(3)**
Route De Joue Du Plain, 61150, Ecouche,
France **(99.98%)**
Tel.: (33) 233122810
Sales Range: $50-74.9 Million
Decoration of Glass Containers
N.A.I.C.S.: 327215

Subsidiary (Domestic):

Saint-Gobain Desjonqueres **(2)**
Les Miroirs 18 Ave Dalsace, 92400,
Courbevoie, France **(99.99%)**
Tel.: (33) 147623330
Web Site: http://www.saint-gobain-
desjonqueres.fr
Sales Range: $400-449.9 Million
Mfr of Small Glass Bottles for Perfume &
Pharmaceutical Industry
N.A.I.C.S.: 327212

VOA Verrerie d'Albi SA **(2)**
Rue Francois Arago, 81011, Albi, France
Tel.: (33) 5 63 78 10 36
Web Site: http://www.voa.fr
Sales Range: $100-124.9 Million
Emp.: 300
Glass Container Mfr
N.A.I.C.S.: 327213
Fabian Marion *(Mng Dir)*

Saint-Gobain Envases SA **(1)**
Km 1 5 caminoRosario a Quinto de Tel-
coco, Rengo, Chile
Tel.: (56) 7 295 9100

Wine Bottle Mfr
N.A.I.C.S.: 327213

**Saint-Gobain Euroveder Italia
SpA** **(1)**
Via Maestri del Lavoro 12/14, 12020, Cer-
vasca, Italy
Tel.: (39) 0171 6851
Glass Products Mfr
N.A.I.C.S.: 327215

**Saint-Gobain Euroveder Operadora
S.A. de C.V.** **(1)**
Nicolas Bravo No 5 Parque Industrial
Cuautla, 62715, Mexico, Mexico
Tel.: (52) 5552791600
Web Site: http://www.saintgobain.com
Sales Range: $1-4.9 Billion
Emp.: 3,000
Construction Materials Distr
N.A.I.C.S.: 423390
Dominique Sam *(Gen Mgr)*

**Saint-Gobain Foundry (Ma'anshan)
Co., Ltd.** **(1)**
Huangong Road Cihu, Ma'anshan, 243052,
Anhui, China
Tel.: (86) 5553507801
Iron Pipe Mfr
N.A.I.C.S.: 331210

Saint-Gobain Foundry Co. Ltd. **(1)**
No 1 Huagong Road Cihu Industrial Zone,
Ma'anshan, 243052, Anhui, China
Tel.: (86) 5553507801
Iron Foundry Services
N.A.I.C.S.: 331511

Saint-Gobain Glass Benelux SA **(1)**
Rue des Glaces Nationales 169, 5060,
Sambreville, Belgium
Tel.: (32) 71261211
Web Site: http://www.befr.saint-gobain-
glass.com
Flat Glass Mfr
N.A.I.C.S.: 327211

Saint-Gobain Glass Finland Oy **(1)**
Koskelontie 21, 02920, Espoo, Finland
Tel.: (358) 9854 5030
Web Site: http://www.autover.fi
Automotive Glass Product Mfr
N.A.I.C.S.: 327215

Saint-Gobain Glass France SA **(1)**
Les Miroirs 18 Avenue D'alsace, 92400,
Courbevoie, France
Tel.: (33) 147623400
Web Site: http://wwwsaint-gobain.fr
Glass Products Mfr
N.A.I.C.S.: 327215

Subsidiary (Domestic):

**Saint-Gobain Glass Logistics
S.A.S** **(2)**
1 bis rue de Pise, BP 20074, 60777,
Thourotte, France
Tel.: (33) 344 906 161
Web Site: http://www.sggl.eu
Sales Range: $10-24.9 Million
Emp.: 40
Glass Transportation Services
N.A.I.C.S.: 541614
Mouhssine Azziz *(Mgr-IT)*

Saint-Gobain Sovis SAS **(2)**
1DIS Ave Gu General Ge Gaulle, BP 202,
02407, Chateau-Thierry, France
Tel.: (33) 323838300
Web Site: http://www.sovis.com
Glass Products Mfr
N.A.I.C.S.: 327215
Omar El Karzazi *(Mng Dir)*

Saint-Gobain Sully S.A.S. **(2)**
16 Route d'Isdes, 45600, Sully-sur-Loire,
France
Tel.: (33) 2 38 37 30 00
Web Site: http://www.saint-gobain-sully.com
Sales Range: $100-124.9 Million
Emp.: 500
Automotive Glass Product Mfr
N.A.I.C.S.: 327215

Samin S.A. **(2)**
18 Avenue Malvesin, 92403, Courbevoie,
France
Tel.: (33) 146919846
Web Site: http://www.samin.fr

Compagnie de Saint-Gobain SA—(Continued)

Mineral Mining Services
N.A.I.C.S.: 212390

Saint-Gobain Glass India Ltd. (1)
A-1 SIPCOT Industrial Park Sriperumbudur,
602105, Kanchipuram, Tamil Nadu, India
Tel.: (91) 4427162832
Web Site: http://www.saint-gobain.co.in
Flat Glass Mfr
N.A.I.C.S.: 327211

**Saint-Gobain Glass Italia Logistica
Servizi S.r.l.** (1)
Via Ponte A Piglieri 2, 1 56121, Pisa,
Italy (100%)
Tel.: (39) 050516446
Web Site: http://it.saint-gobain-glass.com
Sales Range: $200-249.9 Million
Emp.: 600
Mfr of Fabricated Glass Products for the
Automotive & Building Industry
N.A.I.C.S.: 327211

Subsidiary (Non-US):

Emmaboda Glas AB (2)
PO Box 153, 36122, Emmaboda,
Sweden (99.64%)
Tel.: (46) 47118800
Web Site: http://www.emmabodaglas.se
Sales Range: $25-49.9 Million
Emp.: 200
Fabrication of Insulating & Tempered Glass
for the Building Industry
N.A.I.C.S.: 327213
Jari Johansson (Gen Mgr)

Scanglas A/S (2)
Vandvaeksvej 20, Kjellerup, 8620,
Denmark (100%)
Tel.: (45) 70332700
Web Site: http://www.scanglas.dk
Sales Range: $100-124.9 Million
Emp.: 450
Mfr of Insulation & Tempered Glass
N.A.I.C.S.: 327215
Peter Moller (Mng Dir)

Saint-Gobain Glass Italia SpA (1)
Via Ponte a Piglieri 2, Pisa, Italy
Tel.: (39) 050 516111
Web Site: http://www.saint-gobain.it
Emp.: 100
Glass Products Mfr
N.A.I.C.S.: 327215
Marco Ravasi (Gen Mgr)

**Saint-Gobain Glass Mexico, S.A. de
C.V** (1)
Av Nicolas Bravo 5 Parque Industrial
Cuautla, Municipio De Ayala, Morelos,
62741, Mexico
Tel.: (52) 7353548100
Web Site: http://www.saint-gobain-
glass.com.mx
Sales Range: $125-149.9 Million
Emp.: 350
Mfr of Glass Products
N.A.I.C.S.: 327211

Saint-Gobain Glass Nordic A/S (1)
Dampfrgevej 26, DK 2100, Copenhagen,
Denmark (99.64%)
Tel.: (45) 35256400
Web Site: http://www.saint-gobain-glass.dk
Flat Glass Mfr
N.A.I.C.S.: 327211

Saint-Gobain Glass Polska (1)
Ul Szklanych Domow 1, PL 425320, Dab-
rowa Gornicza, Poland (99.87%)
Tel.: (48) 322954000
Web Site: http://www.saint-gobain-
glass.com
Sales Range: $125-149.9 Million
Emp.: 280
Mfr of Glass Products
N.A.I.C.S.: 327211

Subsidiary (Domestic):

**Saint-Gobain Euroveder Polska Sp. z
o.o.** (2)
ul Szklarska 27, 68-205, Zary, Poland
Tel.: (48) 68363 38 10
Sales Range: $25-49.9 Million
Emp.: 100
Gypsum Product Mfr

N.A.I.C.S.: 327420

**Saint-Gobain Glass Portugal Vidro
Plano SA** (1)
EN 10 - Apartado 1713, 2691-652, Santa
Iria de Azoia, Portugal
Tel.: (351) 21 953 4600
Flat Glass Mfr
N.A.I.C.S.: 327211

Subsidiary (Domestic):

**Covipor-CIA Vidreira do Norte
Ltda.** (2)
Apartado 59 Santa Christina do Couto,
4784-909, Santo Tirso, Portugal
Tel.: (351) 252 80 82 00
Web Site: http://www.saint-gobain.fr
Sales Range: $25-49.9 Million
Emp.: 50
Flat Glass Mfr
N.A.I.C.S.: 327211
Manuel Fernandes (Mng Dir)

**Saint-Gobain Glass Romania
SRL** (1)
Business unit ABRAZIVI 61 Str Varianta
Nord, Calarasi, 910053, Bucharest, Roma-
nia
Tel.: (40) 261839709
Sales Range: $50-74.9 Million
Emp.: 250
Glass Products Mfr
N.A.I.C.S.: 327215

**Saint-Gobain Glass Solution
BURNIAT** (1)
Industrielaan 129, Brussels, 1070, Belgium
Tel.: (32) 25211071
Emp.: 40
Flat Glass Mfr
N.A.I.C.S.: 327211

**Saint-Gobain Glass Solution FRAN-
KENGLAS NV** (1)
Middenweg 11, Hamont, 3930, Belgium
Tel.: (32) 11810820
Web Site: http://www.belgique.sggs.com
Sales Range: $25-49.9 Million
Emp.: 40
Flat Glass Mfr
N.A.I.C.S.: 327211
Rony Gielen (Mgr-Sls)

**Saint-Gobain Glass Solution Glorious
NV** (1)
Kortrijksestraat 174, Kuurne, 8520, Belgium
Tel.: (32) 56 365 365
Web Site: http://www.glorieux.be
Sales Range: $25-49.9 Million
Emp.: 100
Flat Glass Mfr
N.A.I.C.S.: 327211
Luc Barbier (Gen Mgr)

**Saint-Gobain Glass Solution
MIROVER NV** (1)
Wervikstraat 225, 8930, Menen, Belgium
Tel.: (32) 56521080
Emp.: 20
Flat Glass Mfr
N.A.I.C.S.: 327211
Bengamen Tuck (Gen Mgr)

**Saint-Gobain Glass Solution Sas
Glas** (1)
Westkade 20, 4551 BV, Sas-van-Gent,
Netherlands
Tel.: (31) 115 458000
Web Site: http://www.sasglas.nl
Sales Range: $25-49.9 Million
Emp.: 99
Glass Products Mfr
N.A.I.C.S.: 327215

**Saint-Gobain Glass Solution
WAGENER-JOWACO EUPEN** (1)
rue de Herbesthal 303, 4700, Eupen, Bel-
gium
Tel.: (32) 87321111
Sales Range: $25-49.9 Million
Emp.: 17
Flat Glass Mfr
N.A.I.C.S.: 327211

Saint-Gobain Glass UK Ltd (1)
Weeland Road Eggborough, Goole, DN14
0FD, East Yorkshire, United Kingdom
Tel.: (44) 1977 666100

Web Site: http://uk.saint-gobain-glass.com
Sales Range: $50-74.9 Million
Emp.: 200
Glass Products Mfr
N.A.I.C.S.: 327215
Steve Severs (Mng Dir)

Subsidiary (Domestic):

Saint-Gobain Glasssolutions (2)
Binley 1 Herald Way, Coventry, CV3 2ZJ,
West Midland, United Kingdom
Tel.: (44) 2476547400
Web Site: http://uk.saint-gobain-glass.com
Rev.: $119,792,000
Emp.: 200
Glass Products Mfr
N.A.I.C.S.: 327211
Simon Carin (Mng Dir)

**Saint-Gobain Gussrohr GmbH & Co.
KG** (1)
Saarbrucker Strasse 51, 66130, Saar-
brucken, Germany (100%)
Tel.: (49) 68187011
Web Site: http://www.saint-gobain-
gussrohr.de
Sales Range: $100-124.9 Million
Emp.: 400
Mfr of Cast Iron Pipe, Joints, Machine &
Rough Castings for Transportation Vehicles
N.A.I.C.S.: 331511
Laurent Huwdlonjeau (Mng Dir)

Saint-Gobain Gyproc India Ltd (1)
5th Level Leela Business Park Andheri
Kurla Road, Andheri East, Mumbai, 400
059, India
Tel.: (91) 22 40212121
Web Site: http://www.saint-gobaingyproc.in
Sales Range: $25-49.9 Million
Emp.: 90
Gypsum Product Mfr
N.A.I.C.S.: 327420
Mriganka Sinha (Mgr-Mktg)

Plant (Domestic):

**Saint-Gobain Gyproc India Ltd - Ben-
galuru Plant** (2)
Plot No 10-17 KIADB Industrial area Harao-
halli V & P Kanakapura TQ, Ramanagaram,
Bengaluru, 562 112, Karnataka, India
Tel.: (91) 8027563370
Gypsum Product Mfr
N.A.I.C.S.: 327420

**Saint-Gobain Gyproc Nederland
BV** (1)
Stuartweg 1B, Vianen, 4131 NH, Nether-
lands
Tel.: (31) 347325 100
Web Site: http://www.gyproc.nl
Sales Range: $25-49.9 Million
Emp.: 80
Architectural Facade Mfr
N.A.I.C.S.: 332323
Peter Janmaat (Gen Dir)

**Saint-Gobain Gyproc South Africa
(Pty) Ltd** (1)
77 Ostend Road, Germiston, 1400, South
Africa
Tel.: (27) 11 345 5300
Web Site: http://www.gyproc.co.za
Emp.: 100
Building Materials Mfr
N.A.I.C.S.: 327120
Frank Clark (Plant Mgr)

**Saint-Gobain Gypsum (Changzhou)
Co., Ltd.** (1)
No 25 Tongjiang North Road Chunjiang
Town, Xinbei District, 213022, Changzhou,
China
Tel.: (86) 51988020300
Sales Range: $25-49.9 Million
Emp.: 100
Gypsum Product Mfr
N.A.I.C.S.: 327420

**Saint-Gobain Gypsum China
(Shanghai)** (1)
No 968 Wangqiao Road, Pudong New
Area, Shanghai, China
Tel.: (86) 2158385838
Gypsum Product Mfr
N.A.I.C.S.: 327420

**Saint-Gobain Gypsum Materials
Shanghai** (1)

Wang Kiu Rd 968 Jinqiao Development
Zone, Pudong New Area, Shanghai,
201201, China
Tel.: (86) 21 58385838
Sales Range: $50-74.9 Million
Emp.: 200
Gypsum Product Mfr
N.A.I.C.S.: 327420

Saint-Gobain Gypsum SA de CV (1)
Av Industria No 4950, San Luis Potosi,
78395, Mexico
Tel.: (52) 444824 0888
Gypsum Product Mfr
N.A.I.C.S.: 327420

**Saint-Gobain HPM Polska sp
zoo** (1)
ul Norton 1, 62-600, Kolo, Poland
Tel.: (48) 632617100
Web Site: http://www.saint-
gobain.abrasives.pl
Sales Range: $450-499.9 Million
Emp.: 2,000
Abrasive Product Mfr
N.A.I.C.S.: 327910

**Saint-Gobain Hanglas Japan
K.K.** (1)
3-7 Kojimachi, Chiyoda-ku, Tokyo, 102-
0083, Japan
Tel.: (81) 352750889
Web Site: http://www.saint-gobain.co.jp
Sales Range: $25-49.9 Million
Emp.: 12
Glass Products Mfr
N.A.I.C.S.: 327215
Philippe Schwindenhammer (Pres)

**Saint-Gobain Hornstein Glastextil
GmbH** (1)
Industriestr II/7, 7053, Hornstein, Austria
Tel.: (43) 2689 2234
Web Site: http://www.atforce.com
Sales Range: $25-49.9 Million
Emp.: 70
Fiber Glass Products Mfr
N.A.I.C.S.: 327215
Milos Pavlis (Mgr)

**Saint-Gobain Isover (Gu'an) Glass
Wool Co., Ltd.** (1)
NO 5 Yong Kang Road Guan Town, 65500,
Langfang, China
Tel.: (86) 316 616 3540
Gypsum Product Mfr
N.A.I.C.S.: 327420

Saint-Gobain Isover Espana (1)
Edificio Ederra Centro Azca, PO Box 77,
28046, Madrid, Spain (73.13%)
Tel.: (34) 913972000
Web Site: http://www.isover.net
Mfr of Glass Products
N.A.I.C.S.: 327211

**Saint-Gobain Materiaux Ceramiques
Benelux SA** (1)
Route de Villers 19, Hody, 4162, Anthisnes,
Belgium
Tel.: (32) 4 383 98 34
Abrasive Product Mfr
N.A.I.C.S.: 327910

**Saint-Gobain Mexico S.A. de
C.V.** (1)
Av Nicolas Bravo 5 Villarreal Lomas de
Cuautla, 62741, Cuautla, Morelos, Mexico
Tel.: (52) 7353548100
Web Site: http://www.saint-gobain-
glass.com.mx
Sales Range: $125-149.9 Million
Emp.: 400
Glass Products Mfr
N.A.I.C.S.: 327215
Jose Villela (Pres)

Saint-Gobain Mondego S.A. (1)
Apto 2030 Fontela, 3081 901, Figueira da
Foz, Portugal (75.76%)
Tel.: (351) 233403100
Web Site: http://www.sgmondego.com
Sales Range: $50-74.9 Million
Emp.: 250
Mfr of Glass Products
N.A.I.C.S.: 327211
Paulo Pinto (Gen Mgr)

**Saint-Gobain Nederland Beheer
BV** (1)

Huifakkerstraat 18, Breda, 4815 PN, Netherlands
Tel.: (31) 76 548 1500
Web Site: http://www.saint-gobain.com
Glass Products Mfr
N.A.I.C.S.: 327211

Saint-Gobain NorPro GmbH (1)
Am Bahnhof, Steinefrenz, 56414, Germany
Tel.: (49) 64359657 0
Web Site: http://www.norpro.saint-gobain.com
Emp.: 28
Plastics Product Mfr
N.A.I.C.S.: 326199
Frlk Ast (Mgr)

Saint-Gobain Oberland AG (1)
Oberlandstrasse, PO Box 1160, 88410, Bad Wurzach, Germany (96.67%)
Tel.: (49) 7564180
Web Site: http://www.saint-gobain-oberland.de
Sales Range: $125-149.9 Million
Emp.: 500
Mfr of Glass Products
N.A.I.C.S.: 327213
S. Jaenecke (CEO & Mng Dir)

Subsidiary (Domestic):

GPS Glas Produktions Service GmbH (2)
Ruhrglasstrasse 50, 45329, Essen, Germany
Tel.: (49) 201 36 00 771
Web Site: http://www.gps-essen.de
Sales Range: $25-49.9 Million
Emp.: 80
Glass Making Machinery Mfr
N.A.I.C.S.: 333248

Saint-Gobain Orsil s.r.o. (1)
Cermakova # 7 Block 2, CZ 120 00, Prague, Czech Republic (100%)
Tel.: (420) 221429600
Web Site: http://www.isover.cz
Sales Range: $25-49.9 Million
Emp.: 30
Insulation Product Mfr
N.A.I.C.S.: 327993

Saint-Gobain PAM Cz S.R.O (1)
Tovarni 388, 267 01, Kraluv Dvur, Czech Republic
Tel.: (420) 311 712 611
Web Site: http://www.saint-gobain-pam.cz
Cast Iron Product Mfr
N.A.I.C.S.: 331210

Saint-Gobain PAM Deutschland GmbH (1)
Saarbrucker Strasse 51, 66130, Saarbrucken, Germany
Tel.: (49) 68187010
Web Site: https://www.pamline.de
Iron Pipe Distr
N.A.I.C.S.: 423510
Burkhard Schmolck (Gen Mgr)

Subsidiary (Domestic):

Saint-Gobain HES Gmbh (2)
Saarbrucker Str 51, 66130, Saarbrucken, Germany
Tel.: (49) 220397840
Web Site: http://www.saint-gobain-hes.de
Iron Pipe Distr
Frlk Ast (Mgr)
N.A.I.C.S.: 423510

Saint-Gobain PAM Italia SpA (1)
Via Romagnoli 6, 20146, Milan, Italy
Tel.: (39) 02 42 43 281
Web Site: http://www.pamline.it
Iron Pipe Mfr
N.A.I.C.S.: 331210

Saint-Gobain PAM Portugal SA (1)
Est Nac 10 - Lugar de D Pedro - Apartado 1708, 2691-901, Santa Iria de Azoia, Portugal
Tel.: (351) 218 925 000
Web Site: http://www.saint-gobain-pam.pt
Sales Range: $25-49.9 Million
Emp.: 15
Steel Pole Mfr
N.A.I.C.S.: 331210
Sandra Sa (Dir-Fin)

Saint-Gobain PAM UK (1)
Lows Lane, Stanton-by-Dale, Ilkeston, DE7

4QU, Derbyshire, United Kingdom (100%)
Tel.: (44) 1159305000
Web Site: http://www.saint-gobain-pam.co.uk
Sales Range: $400-449.9 Million
Emp.: 1,400
Mfr Ductile Iron Pipes for Water Supply Systems & Sewerage
N.A.I.C.S.: 331511
Paul Minchin (Mng Dir)

Saint-Gobain PAM UK (1)
Sinclair Works Station Rd Ketley, Telford, TF1 5AD, Shropshire, United Kingdom (99%)
Tel.: (44) 1952262500
Web Site: http://www.saint-gobain-pam.co.uk
Sales Range: $150-199.9 Million
Emp.: 140
Pipes Mfr
N.A.I.C.S.: 332996
Andy Burnhan (Dir-Site)

Saint-Gobain PAM UK (1)
Holwell Works Asfordby Hill, Melton Mowbray, LE14 3RE, Leicestershire, United Kingdom (100%)
Tel.: (44) 1664812812
Web Site: http://www.saint-gobain-pam.co.uk
Sales Range: $200-249.9 Million
Emp.: 150
Flat Glass Mfr
N.A.I.C.S.: 327211
Paul Minchin (Mng Dir)

Saint-Gobain PPC Italia SpA (1)
Via E Romagnoli 6, 20146, Milan, Italy
Tel.: (39) 02611151
Web Site: http://www.gyproc.it
Gypsum Product Mfr
N.A.I.C.S.: 327420

Saint-Gobain PPL Korea Co Ltd. (1)
13f Dongsin Bldg 141-28 Samseung1-dong, Gangnam-gu, Seoul, 135-090, Korea (South)
Tel.: (82) 2 3706 9334
Web Site: http://www.sgppl.co.kr
Sales Range: $25-49.9 Million
Emp.: 30
Chemical Products Mfr
N.A.I.C.S.: 325998

Saint-Gobain Pam S.A. (1)
91 Ave De La Liberation, Nancy, 54076, France (100%)
Tel.: (33) 383952000
Web Site: http://www.pont-a-mousson.com
Sales Range: $400-449.9 Million
Emp.: 2,000
Mfr of Ductile Iron Pipes & Hydraulic Parts for Water Supply Systems, Irrigation, Sewerage & Drainage; Ductile Iron for Building
N.A.I.C.S.: 331210

Subsidiary (Domestic):

Saint-Gobain Seva (2)
43 Rue Du Pont De Fer, PO Box 176, Chalon-sur-Saone, 71100, France (100%)
Tel.: (33) 385472500
Web Site: http://www.saint-gobain-seva.com
Sales Range: $75-99.9 Million
Emp.: 360
Mfr of Equipment for all Industries, Injection Moulds, Fibre Plates, Glass Moulds
N.A.I.C.S.: 333310
Francois Jacquement (CEO)

Saint-Gobain Performance Plastics Corby Ltd. (1)
13 Earlstrees Rod, Corby, NN17 4NP, United Kingdom
Tel.: (44) 15 3627 6000
Sales Range: $25-49.9 Million
Emp.: 18
Adhesive Mfr & Distr
N.A.I.C.S.: 325520
Ian Beresford (Product Mgr)

Saint-Gobain Performance Plastics Espana S.A. (1)
Poligono El Sequero 45-46, Agoncillo, 26150, La Rioja, Spain
Tel.: (34) 94 14 86 035
Sales Range: $25-49.9 Million
Emp.: 41
Plastics Product Mfr

N.A.I.C.S.: 326199
Ribera Aldama (Controller)

Saint-Gobain Performance Plastics Europe, S.A. (1)
La Mothe-Aux-Aulnaies, 89120, Charny, France
Tel.: (33) 3 86 63 78 78
Sales Range: $50-74.9 Million
Emp.: 160
Plastics Product Mfr
N.A.I.C.S.: 326199

Subsidiary (Domestic):

Saint-Gobain Adfors France (2)
517 Avenue de la Boisse, 73025, Chambery, France
Tel.: (33) 4 79 68 32 18
Textile Fabric Product Mfr
N.A.I.C.S.: 313310

Saint-Gobain Materiaux Innovants (2)
Les Miroirs 18 avenue d'Alsace, 92400, Courbevoie, France
Tel.: (33) 1 47 62 30 00
Web Site: http://www.saint-gobain-materiaux-innovants.com
Architectural Components Mfr
N.A.I.C.S.: 332323

Saint-Gobain Performance Plastics Kontich NV (1)
Heiveldekens 22, 2550, Kontich, Belgium
Tel.: (32) 34 58 28 28
Polymer Component Mfr
N.A.I.C.S.: 325212

Saint-Gobain Performance Plastics Rencol Limited (1)
Unit 16 Concorde Road Patchway, Bristol, BS34 5TB, United Kingdom
Tel.: (44) 117 9381 700
Web Site: http://www.rencol.co.uk
Emp.: 100
Precision Spring Component Mfr & Distr
N.A.I.C.S.: 332613

Saint-Gobain Performance Plastics Sipro GmbH (1)
Zabernerstrasse 25, 65203, Wiesbaden, Germany
Tel.: (49) 611928130
Web Site: http://www.sipro.de
Sales Range: $25-49.9 Million
Emp.: 15
Plastics Product Mfr
N.A.I.C.S.: 326199

Saint-Gobain Performance Plastics Verneret (1)
La Mothe Aux Aulnaies, 89120, Charny, France (100%)
Tel.: (33) 386637878
Sales Range: $50-74.9 Million
Emp.: 160
Silicone & Polymer Extruded Products Mfr
N.A.I.C.S.: 325211

Saint-Gobain Pipe Systems Belgium SA/NV (1)
Raatshovenstraat 2, 3400, Landen, Belgium
Tel.: (32) 11880100
Web Site: http://www.sgps.be
Sales Range: $25-49.9 Million
Emp.: 30
Iron Pipe Mfr
N.A.I.C.S.: 331210
Raphael Roquet (Gen Mgr)

Saint-Gobain Pipe Systems Oy (1)
Merstolantie 16, Harjavalta, 29200, Finland
Tel.: (358) 207 424600
Web Site: http://www.sgps.fi
Steel Pole Mfr
N.A.I.C.S.: 331210
Matti Andersin (Mng Dir)

Saint-Gobain Pipeline Hong Kong Ltd. (1)
15/F Hermes Commercial Centre 4-4A Hillwood Road, Kowloon, China (Hong Kong)
Tel.: (852) 2735 7825
Web Site: http://www.saint-gobain.com.cn
Iron Pipe Mfr
N.A.I.C.S.: 331210
Eddy Yeung (Mgr-Tech)

Saint-Gobain Pipelines Co. Ltd. (1)

Huangong Road Cihu, Ma'anshan, 243052, Anhui, China
Tel.: (86) 5553508041
Web Site: http://www.saint-gobain.com.cn
Rev.: $199,529,890
Emp.: 954
Steel Pole Mfr
N.A.I.C.S.: 331210
Mina Yang (Mgr)

Saint-Gobain Pipelines South Africa (Pty) Limited (1)
200 Watt Road Pretoria West, PO Box 631, Pretoria, 0001, South Africa
Tel.: (27) 12 380 4600
Web Site: http://www.saint-gobain-pipelines.co.za
Sales Range: $200-249.9 Million
Emp.: 580
Iron Pipe Mfr
N.A.I.C.S.: 331210
Paul Martin (Mgr-Mktg)

Saint-Gobain Produits Industriels (1)
Commune De Condren, 2700, Tergnier, France (100%)
Tel.: (33) 323578181
Web Site: http://www.saint-gobain-glass.com
Mfr of Glass Products
N.A.I.C.S.: 327211

Saint-Gobain Proppants (Guanghan) Co., Ltd. (1)
Anle Village Nan Xing Town, Guanghan, 618305, China
Tel.: (86) 83 8550 3612
Glass Products Mfr
N.A.I.C.S.: 327211

Saint-Gobain Quartz (Jinzhou) Company Ltd. (1)
N 94A Jiefang West Road, Jinzhou, 121003, Liaoning, China
Tel.: (86) 4165172901
Web Site: http://www.quartz.saint-gobain.com
Construction Materials Distr
N.A.I.C.S.: 423390

Saint-Gobain Quartz S.A.S. (1)
BP 102, Nemours, 77793, France
Tel.: (33) 1 64 45 45 00
Web Site: http://www.quartz.saint-gobain.com
Quartz Product Mfr
N.A.I.C.S.: 334419

Saint-Gobain Rigips Alci Sanayi ve Ticaret Anonim A.S (1)
Ilkbahar Mahallesi 606 Sokak No 8, Cankaya, 06550, Ankara, Turkiye
Tel.: (90) 312 463 63 63
Web Site: http://www.rigips.com.tr
Gypsum Product Mfr
N.A.I.C.S.: 327420

Saint-Gobain Schleifmittel GmbH (1)
Birkenstrasse 45-49, 50389, Wesseling, Germany
Tel.: (49) 2236 89960
Abrasive Product Mfr
N.A.I.C.S.: 327910

Saint-Gobain Solar S.r.l. (1)
Via Ettore Romagnoli n 6, 20146, Milan, Italy
Tel.: (39) 02 4243798
Web Site: http://www.saint-gobain-solar.com
Photovoltaic Product Mfr
N.A.I.C.S.: 334413

Saint-Gobain Solar Systems SA (1)
Ecostart 2 rue du Commerce, 3895, Foetz, Luxembourg
Tel.: (352) 80 70 96 20
Sales Range: $25-49.9 Million
Emp.: 40
Photovoltaic Product Mfr
N.A.I.C.S.: 334413

Saint-Gobain South Africa Pty. Ltd. (1)
Private /peg Xcity 30, PO Box 30, Springs, 1560, South Africa
Tel.: (27) 113608200
Web Site: http://wwwisoder.co.za
Sales Range: $150-199.9 Million
Emp.: 260

Compagnie de Saint-Gobain SA—(Continued)

Mfr, Sales & Marketing of Composites, Raw Materials & Insulation Products for Industrial & Building Applications.
N.A.I.C.S.: 327993
Johan G Oosthuizen *(Gen Mgr-Building Insulation)*

Saint-Gobain Stradal **(1)**
47 Avenue des Genottes, 95800, Cergy, Pontoise, France **(60%)**
Tel.: (33) 1 34 25 5555
Web Site: http://www.stradal.fr
Sales Range: $25-49.9 Million
Emp.: 60
Mfr of Construction Materials
N.A.I.C.S.: 333120

Saint-Gobain TM K.K. **(1)**
3-7 Kojimachi, Chiyoda-ku, Tokyo, 102-0083, Japan
Tel.: (81) 332631430
Web Site: http://www.saint-gobain-tm.com
Sales Range: $25-49.9 Million
Emp.: 12
Ceramic Materials Mfr
N.A.I.C.S.: 327120
Kozaki Chiba *(Plant Mgr)*

Saint-Gobain Transformados S.A. **(1)**
C/ Los Corrales Parcelas C5 y C6 Poligono Industrial La Ballestera, Alovera, 19208, Spain
Tel.: (34) 949 20 98 93
Web Site: http://www.sgtransformados.com
Emp.: 50
Steel Structure Installation Services
N.A.I.C.S.: 237990
Mario Baequero *(Dir)*

Saint-Gobain Vetrerie SPA **(1)**
Via Del Lavoro 1, Lonigo, 36045, SV, Italy **(92.51%)**
Tel.: (39) 0444725700
Web Site: http://www.verallia.it
Sales Range: $450-499.9 Million
Emp.: 1,126
Mfr of Jars & Water Bottles
N.A.I.C.S.: 327213

Saint-Gobain Vetrotex (Thailand) Ltd. **(1)**
79 24 Moo 2 Srinakharin Rd, Nongbon, Bangkok, 10260, Thailand **(100%)**
Tel.: (66) 236602408
Web Site: http://www.saint-gobain-vetrotex.co.th
Sales Range: $25-49.9 Million
Emp.: 100
Mfr of Glass-Fiber-Reinforced Precast Concrete
N.A.I.C.S.: 327211

Saint-Gobain Vetrotex Deutschland GmbH **(1)**
Viktoriaallee 3 - 5, D-52066, Aachen, Germany **(100%)**
Tel.: (49) 2415160
Web Site: http://www.vetrotextextiles.com
Sales Range: $25-49.9 Million
Emp.: 250
Mfr of Textiles & Yarns
N.A.I.C.S.: 313210

Saint-Gobain Vicasa SA **(1)**
Paseo de la Castellana 77, 28046, Madrid, Spain **(73.06%)**
Tel.: (34) 913972336
Web Site: http://www.vicasa.es
Sales Range: $25-49.9 Million
Emp.: 100
Mfr of Glass & Bottle Products
N.A.I.C.S.: 327211

Saint-Gobain Vidros S.A. **(1)**
Avenida Santa Marina 482 2nd Fl, 05036-903, Sao Paulo, SP, Brazil **(100%)**
Tel.: (55) 1138747988
Web Site: http://www.saint-gobain-vidros.com.br
Sales Range: $450-499.9 Million
Emp.: 2,000
Mfr of Baking & Glass Products
N.A.I.C.S.: 327211

Saint-Gobain Vitrage **(1)**
Les Miroirs 18 Ave D Alsace, F 92400, Courbevoie, France **(100%)**

Tel.: (33) 147623030
Web Site: http://www.saint-gobain-vitrage.com
Sales Range: $200-249.9 Million
Emp.: 1,000
Flat Glass Mfr
N.A.I.C.S.: 327211

Subsidiary (Domestic):

Eurofloat SAS **(2)**
Zone Industrielle Et Portuaire, 38150, Salaise-sur-Sanne, France **(100%)**
Tel.: (33) 474293075
Sales Range: $50-74.9 Million
Emp.: 194
Glass Products Mfr
N.A.I.C.S.: 327211
Emmanuel Abt *(Gen Mgr)*

Le Vitrage du Midi **(2)**
ZI Sud, BP 68, 30301, Beaucaire, Cedex, France **(99.98%)**
Tel.: (33) 466598080
Web Site: http://www.saint-gobain-glass.com
Sales Range: $25-49.9 Million
Emp.: 90
Tempered, Laminated & Double Glazed Glass Mfr
N.A.I.C.S.: 327212

Miroiteries de l'Ouest Armorique **(2)**
ZI Kerpont 570 Rue Daniel Trudaine, 56850, Caudan, France **(99.93%)**
Tel.: (33) 297765233
Sales Range: $25-49.9 Million
Emp.: 80
Holding Company; Glass Distr
N.A.I.C.S.: 423390

Saint-Gobain Sekurit France **(2)**
Rue Du Marechal Joffre, 60150, Thourotte, France **(100%)**
Tel.: (33) 344923700
Sales Range: $400-449.9 Million
Glass Products Mfr
N.A.I.C.S.: 327211
Lecomte Annesothie *(Sec)*

Subsidiary (Non-US):

Saint-Gobain Sekurit (Shanghai) Co., Ltd. **(3)**
No 45 Wen Jing Road Minhang Development Zone, Shanghai, 200245, China
Tel.: (86) 21 64626550
Automotive Glass Mfr
N.A.I.C.S.: 327215

Saint-Gobain Sekurit Benelux S.A. **(3)**
Rue Des Glaces Nationales 169, B 5060, Sambreville, Belgium **(99.79%)**
Tel.: (32) 712161586
Web Site: http://www.saint-gobain-sekurit.com
Sales Range: $125-149.9 Million
Emp.: 450
Mfr & Sale of Glass Products
N.A.I.C.S.: 327211

Subsidiary (Domestic):

Saint-Gobain Autover Distribution SA **(4)**
Chaussee Romaine 60, Bastogne, 6600, Belgium
Tel.: (32) 61 210 940
Web Site: http://www.saint-gobain.com
Emp.: 113
Automotive Glass Product Distr
N.A.I.C.S.: 423120
Ralf Pennartz *(Office Mgr)*

Subsidiary (Non-US):

Saint-Gobain Sekurit CR Spol S.R.O. **(3)**
Masarykova 1404, 268 01, Horovice, Czech Republic
Tel.: (420) 311 541 111
Web Site: http://www.saint-gobain-sekurit.cz
Sales Range: $100-124.9 Million
Emp.: 500
Automotive Glass Product Mfr
N.A.I.C.S.: 336390
Martina Hasmanova *(Gen Dir & Mgr)*

Saint-Gobain Sekurit Deutschland Beteiligungen GmbH **(3)**

Viktoriaallee 3-5, Aachen, 52066, Germany
Tel.: (49) 2419470
Flat Glass Mfr
N.A.I.C.S.: 327211

Subsidiary (Domestic):

Saint-Gobain Autover Deutschland GmbH **(4)**
Boschstr 61-65, 50171, Kerpen, Germany
Tel.: (49) 22736084900
Web Site: https://www.sekurit-service.com
Sales Range: $25-49.9 Million
Emp.: 67
Automotive Glass Product Mfr
N.A.I.C.S.: 336390
Bernd Kummerle *(Mng Dir)*

Subsidiary (Domestic):

Freudenberger Autoglas GmbH **(5)**
Karl-Weinmair-Strasse 5, 80807, Munich, Germany
Tel.: (49) 893582740
Web Site: https://www.freudenberger-autoglas.de
Automotive Glass Mfr
N.A.I.C.S.: 327215

Subsidiary (Non-US):

Saint-Gobain Sekurit India Limited **(3)**
Plot No 616 and 617 Village Kuruli Pune-Nashik Road, Chakan, Pune, 410 510, Maharashtra, India
Tel.: (91) 2135676400
Web Site: https://www.sekuritindia.com
Rev.: $23,235,334
Assets: $24,827,348
Liabilities: $3,143,577
Net Worth: $21,683,772
Earnings: $3,461,651
Emp.: 93
Fiscal Year-end: 03/31/2023
Automotive Glass Distr
N.A.I.C.S.: 423120
Padmanabha Shetty *(Chm)*

Saint-Gobain Sekurit Maroc **(3)**
Zone Franche d'Exportation de Kenitra, 14000, Kenitra, Morocco
Tel.: (212) 522 665 731
Web Site: http://www.saint-gobin.com
Emp.: 170
Flat Glass Mfr
N.A.I.C.S.: 327211
Philippe Mesureur *(Gen Mgr)*

Saint-Gobain Sekurit Mexico, S.A. de C.V. **(3)**
Avenida Nicolas Bravo 8 Parque Industrial Cuautla Municipio de Ayala, 62715, Morelos, Mexico **(59.83%)**
Tel.: (52) 7353548000
Web Site: http://www.saint-gobain-sekurit.com
Sales Range: $200-249.9 Million
Emp.: 800
Automotive Glazing Mfr
N.A.I.C.S.: 327211

Saint-Gobain Sekurit Portugal Vidro Automovel SA **(3)**
Estrada Nacional 10 Apartado 1731, Santa Iria de Azoia, 2691901, Portugal
Tel.: (351) 219 429 600
Web Site: http://www.saint-gobain-sekurit.com
Sales Range: $25-49.9 Million
Emp.: 100
Automotive Glass Product Mfr
N.A.I.C.S.: 327215
Rui Padrao *(Gen Mgr)*

Subsidiary (Domestic):

Saint-Gobain Autover Portugal S.A. **(4)**
Rua 25 de Abril 460, 4405-445, Serzedo, Portugal
Tel.: (351) 227536140
Web Site: http://www.autover.pt
Automotive Glass Product Distr.
N.A.I.C.S.: 423120

Subsidiary (Non-US):

Saint-Gobain Sekurit Thailand Co., Ltd. **(3)**

64/8 Moo 4 Tumbol Pluakdeng Amphur Pluakdeng, Rayong, 21140, Thailand
Tel.: (66) 38954477
Web Site: http://www.saint-gobain.co.th
Automotive Glass Product Mfr
N.A.I.C.S.: 327215

Saint-Gobain Sekurit de Colombia S.A. **(3)**
Carrera 7 N 20-20 Piso 20, Bogota, 76104, Colombia
Tel.: (57) 1 255 7756
Glass Products Mfr
N.A.I.C.S.: 327215

Subsidiary (Domestic):

Societe Industrielle des Vitrages d'Aquitaine **(2)**
Zone Industrielle, PO Box 50, 33230, Coutras, France **(100%)**
Tel.: (33) 557498100
Web Site: http://www.saint-gobain-glass.com
Sales Range: $50-74.9 Million
Emp.: 150
Mfr of Tempered & Laminated Glass & Double Glazing Products
N.A.I.C.S.: 327215
Geanluc Camus *(Mng Dir)*

Saint-Gobain Wanner SA **(1)**
Resina 16, Villaverde, 28021, Madrid, Spain **(73.13%)**
Tel.: (34) 917233410
Emp.: 200
Mfr of Industrial & Insulation Products
N.A.I.C.S.: 327993

Sanitaire Comtois **(1)**
6, avenue Gaulard, 75019, Paris, France **(61.4%)**
Flat Glass Mfr
N.A.I.C.S.: 327211

Sanitas Troesch AG **(1)**
Hardturmstrasse 101, 8031, Zurich, Switzerland
Tel.: (41) 444461010
Web Site: https://www.sanitastroesch.ch
Sales Range: $50-74.9 Million
Emp.: 120
Sanitary Ware Mfr
N.A.I.C.S.: 332999
Michael Schumacher *(CEO)*

Scandi-Glass A/S **(1)**
Ashaugveien 62, N 3107, Sem, Norway **(99.64%)**
Tel.: (47) 33300400
Web Site: http://www.scandi-glass.no
Sales Range: $25-49.9 Million
Emp.: 32
Mfr of Glass Products
N.A.I.C.S.: 327211

Scanpac AB **(1)**
Kemivagen 7, Glanshammar, 705 97, Orebro, Sweden
Tel.: (46) 19463400
Web Site: http://www.dalapro.se
Emp.: 30
Concrete Ready Mix Mfr
N.A.I.C.S.: 327320
Patrick Bjorkegren *(CEO)*

Schafer GmbH **(1)**
Alfred-Weckesser-Strasse 6, 76669, Bad Schonborn, Germany
Tel.: (49) 7253 94210
Roofing Product Distr
N.A.I.C.S.: 423330

Sekurit Saint-Gobain Deutschland GmbH & Co. KG **(1)**
Viktoria Allee 3-5, D 52066, Aachen, Germany **(100%)**
Tel.: (49) 02419470
Web Site: http://www.saint-gobain-glass.com
Rev.: $239,403,120
Emp.: 250
Mfr of Glass Products
N.A.I.C.S.: 327211

Sekurit Saint-Gobain Italia S.R.L. **(1)**
Via Saluzzo 95, I 12038, Savigliano, Cuneo, Italy **(99.15%)**
Tel.: (39) 0172727111
Web Site: http://www.saintgobain.com

Mfr of Glass Products
N.A.I.C.S.: 327211

Subsidiary (Domestic):

S.G. Autover Italia S.R.L. (2)
Via Ettore Romagnoli 6, 20146, Milan, Italy
Tel.: (39) 02 900 788 1
Web Site: http://www.autover.it
Flat Glass Mfr
N.A.I.C.S.: 327211

Sicurglass Sud SRL (2)
Via Riosecco localita Canfora, Fisciano,
84084, Salerno, Italy
Tel.: (39) 0898 283411
Glass Products Mfr
N.A.I.C.S.: 327215

**Sekurit Saint-Gobain Scandinavia
AB** (1)
Bruksgatan 18, PO Box 84, Eslov, 24138,
Gusdh, Sweden (99%)
Tel.: (46) 41366800
Web Site: http://www.smartarutor.se
Sales Range: $25-49.9 Million
Emp.: 45
Glass Products Mfr & Distr
N.A.I.C.S.: 327211

**Sekurit Saint-Gobain Torgau
GmbH** (1)
Solarstr 5, D 04860, Torgau, Torgua,
Germany (99.77%)
Tel.: (49) 34217530
Web Site:
   http://www.saint-gobain-saturet.com
Rev.: $175,424,700
Emp.: 100
Mfr of Glass Products
N.A.I.C.S.: 327211
Juergen Koeppe (Plant Mgr)

Servilog (1)
Routede Cholet, BP 389, 85304, Challans,
France (46.02%)
Flat Glass Mfr
N.A.I.C.S.: 327211

**Societe Atlantique de
Prefabrication** (1)
Chemin des Anglais, BP 101 44470, Car-
quefou, France (79.21%)
N.A.I.C.S.: 327211

Societe Verriere Francaise (1)
Centre De Commerce De Gross, PO Box
424, 59814, Lesquin, France (100%)
Tel.: (33) 320870340
Web Site:
   http://www.saint-gobain-glass.com
Rev.: $4,041,473
Emp.: 175
Distr of Glass Products & Automatic Doors
N.A.I.C.S.: 423390

Societe Verriere d'Encapsulation (1)
Rue Del Europe, 60400, Noyon,
France (100%)
Tel.: (33) 344098800
Sales Range: $50-74.9 Million
Emp.: 200
Flat Glass Mfr
N.A.I.C.S.: 327211

Societe Verriere de l'Atlantique (1)
178 Boulevard Andre Bahonneau, BP 48,
49800, Trelaze, France (99.99%)
Tel.: (33) 241376520
Web Site: http://www.saint-gobain-
glass.com
Sales Range: $25-49.9 Million
Emp.: 70
Tempered Glass & Double Glazing
N.A.I.C.S.: 327212
Olivier Lallemant (Mng Dir)

**Societe de Commercialisation de
Fournitures pour l'Industrie et la
Construction** (1)
13-15 Rue Germaine Tailleferre, 75019,
Paris, Cedex 19, France (99.91%)
Tel.: (33) 00140033411
Sales Range: $25-49.9 Million
Emp.: 50
Mfr of Fabric Products
N.A.I.C.S.: 332999

**Societe des Tuyaux Armes de la
Charente** (1)

Les Maisons Rouges, 16460, Chenon,
France (39.61%)
Tel.: (33) 545225584
Concrete Products Mfr
N.A.I.C.S.: 327332

Soprover (1)
LID 1 Ere Ave, PO Box 64, 5 Eme Rue,
6510, Carros, France (100%)
Tel.: (00) 400201102
Web Site: http://www.soprover.com
Sales Range: $25-49.9 Million
Emp.: 35
Distr of Glass Products
N.A.I.C.S.: 423390

Sovedys (1)
523 Rue Emile Zola, BP 67, 73491, La Ra-
voire, Cedex, France (100%)
Tel.: (33) 4 79 72 99 60
Web Site: http://www.saint-gobain.com
Sales Range: $50-74.9 Million
Emp.: 80
Flat Glass Products & Automatic Doors
Distr
N.A.I.C.S.: 327211

Spafi (1)
Les Miroirs 18 Ave d'Alsace, 92400,
Courbevoie, France (100%)
Tel.: (33) 147623000
Sales Range: $250-299.9 Million
Emp.: 1,000
Holding Company
N.A.I.C.S.: 551112

Stradal Environnement (1)
47 Ave des Genottes, 95800, Cergy, Pon-
toise, France (61.64%)
Tel.: (33) 1 34 255555
Web Site: http://www.stradal.fr
Sales Range: $250-299.9 Million
Emp.: 1,200
Mfr of Industrial Materials
N.A.I.C.S.: 333511

TBF Malaisie (1)
N-2 Jalan Teknologi 8 Plo 26, Mengkibol
Industrial Area, PO Box 135, 86000, Kelu-
ang, Malaysia (44.07%)
Mfr of Glass Products
N.A.I.C.S.: 327211

Thuon SA (1)
53 Ave Gaston Cabannes, 33270, Floirac,
France (79.21%)
Tel.: (33) 557809809
Web Site: http://www.thuon.fr
Sales Range: $25-49.9 Million
Emp.: 55
Hardware Retailer
N.A.I.C.S.: 444140

Tuyaux et Agglomeres Vendeens (1)
ZI LA Folie 5 rue Bollee La Chaise Vicomte,
85310, Saint Florent-des-Bois,
France (38.82%)
Concrete Mfr
N.A.I.C.S.: 327332

Unicorn Precidia SA (1)
rue de la Vallee, 14100, Lisieux,
France (99%)
Flat Glass Mfr
N.A.I.C.S.: 327211

United Paints & Chemicals S.A.E (1)
17 Bahgat Ali Street, Zamalek, Cairo, 2,
Egypt
Tel.: (20) 227368283
Web Site: http://www.uhcegypt.com
Emp.: 185
Tile & Terrazzo Contractors
N.A.I.C.S.: 238340
Ali Moussa (Pres)

**VETROTECH SAINT-GOBAIN BEN-
ELUX NV** (1)
Hulsenweg 21, Nederweert, 6031SP, Neth-
erlands
Tel.: (31) 495 57 44 35
Web Site: http://www.vetrotech.com
Sales Range: $25-49.9 Million
Emp.: 20
Fire Resistant Glass Product Mfr
N.A.I.C.S.: 327215
Arnold Sirag (Gen Mgr)

**VETROTECH SAINT-GOBAIN
FRANCE** (1)

21 Square Saint-Charles, Paris, 75012,
France
Tel.: (33) 1 534 66 789
Web Site: http://www.vetrotech.com
Sales Range: $25-49.9 Million
Emp.: 11
Fire Resistant Glass Product Mfr
N.A.I.C.S.: 327215
Jerome Bastien (Gen Dir)

**VETROTECH Saint-Gobain Poland
Sp. z o.o.** (1)
ul Pilsudskiego 18, Namyslow, 46100, Po-
land
Tel.: (48) 77 410 5420
Web Site: http://www.vetrotech.com
Sales Range: $50-74.9 Million
Emp.: 6
Fire Resistant Glass Distr
N.A.I.C.S.: 423390

Van Keulen BV (1)
TT Vasumweg 151, Amsterdam, 1033 SG,
Netherlands
Tel.: (31) 20 4604300
Web Site: http://www.van-keulen.nl
Sales Range: $50-74.9 Million
Emp.: 60
Building Materials Distr
N.A.I.C.S.: 423330
Jan Visser (Mgr-Pur)

Vemac Srl (1)
Via Prati 67, 65124, Pescara, Italy
Tel.: (39) 08541691
Web Site: http://www.vemac.it
Sales Range: $75-99.9 Million
Emp.: 107
Building Materials Distr
N.A.I.C.S.: 423320
Carlo Giansante (Gen Mgr)

Verrerie Aurys (1)
ZI Pommenauque Rue Gravier, PO Box
170, 50500, Carentan, France (100%)
Tel.: (33) 233716500
Web Site: http://www.saint-gobain-
glass.com
Sales Range: $50-74.9 Million
Emp.: 250
Flat Glass Mfr
N.A.I.C.S.: 327211
Stephane Reyniers (Gen Mgr)

Verrerie de Saint-Just (1)
ZI La Verreie, 42176, Saint Just-Saint Ram-
bert, Cedex, France (100%)
Tel.: (33) 477362121
Web Site: http://www.saint-just.com
Sales Range: $25-49.9 Million
Emp.: 49
Mfr of Glass Products
N.A.I.C.S.: 327211

Vertec (1)
Les Miroirs, 18, avenue d'Alsace, 92400,
Courbevoie, France (100%)
Holding Company
N.A.I.C.S.: 551112

**Vetrotech Saint-Gobain Atlantique
SarL** (1)
21 Sq Saint Charles, 75012, Paris,
France (100%)
Tel.: (33) 53466789
Web Site: http://www.vetrotex.com
Sales Range: $25-49.9 Million
Emp.: 12
Mfr of Fiber Glass Reinforcements
N.A.I.C.S.: 327211

**Vetrotech Saint-Gobain Central &
Eastern Europe AG** (1)
Siegfried-Marcus-Strasse 1, 4400, Steyr,
Austria
Tel.: (43) 7252 90 90 90
Web Site: http://www.vetrotech.com
Fire Resistant Glass Product Mfr
N.A.I.C.S.: 327215

**Vetrotech Saint-Gobain International
AG** (1)
Bernstrasse 43, 3175, Flamatt, Switzerland
Tel.: (41) 31 336 81 81
Web Site: http://www.vetrotech.com
Sales Range: $25-49.9 Million
Emp.: 80
Fire Resistant Glass Product Mfr
N.A.I.C.S.: 327215
Rrito Comitta (Mng Dir)

Vetrotech Saint-Gobain UK Ltd (1)
Glenewes House Gtwy Dr, Leeds, LS19
7XY, Westyorkshire, United
Kingdom (100%)
Tel.: (44) 1132391500
Web Site: http://www.vetrotech.com
Sales Range: $25-49.9 Million
Emp.: 50
Mfr of Glass Products
N.A.I.C.S.: 327211

Vetrotex Italia S.p.A. (1)
Via E Romagnoli 6, I 20146, Milan,
Italy (100%)
Tel.: (39) 0000242431
Sales Range: $200-249.9 Million
Emp.: 600
Fiber Reinforcement Materials
N.A.I.C.S.: 327215

W.A.W. Spol S.R.O. (1)
Mlynske luhy 17, 821 05, Bratislava, Slova-
kia
Tel.: (421) 248209801
Sanitaryware Distr
N.A.I.C.S.: 423720

**ZAO "Saint-Gobain
Kavminsteklo"** (1)
Zavodskaya Str 1, 357217, Mineralnye
Vody, Russia
Tel.: (7) 87922 7 75 25
Web Site: http://www.sgpackaging.ru
Glass Bottle Mfr
N.A.I.C.S.: 327213

Zao Zavod Minplita (1)
Sosnovskiy r-n d Talovka, 456538, Chely-
abinsk, Russia
Tel.: (7) 351 247 17 01
Glass Products Mfr
N.A.I.C.S.: 327215

COMPAGNIE DES ALPES S.A.

50/52 Boulevard Haussmann, 75009,
Paris, France
Tel.: (33) 146848800   FR
Web Site:
   https://www.compagniedesalpes.com
Year Founded: 1989
CDA—(EUR)
Rev.: $756,159,815
Assets: $2,443,915,105
Liabilities: $1,473,690,253
Net Worth: $970,224,851
Earnings: ($135,614,891)
Emp.: 4,315
Fiscal Year-end: 09/30/20
Tourist Destination Operator
N.A.I.C.S.: 713990
Dominique Marcel (Chm & CEO)

Subsidiaries:

**Aquarium Geant De Saint Malo
SAS** (1)
Avenue du General Patton, 35400, Saint-
Malo, France
Tel.: (33) 299211900
Web Site: https://www.aquarium-st-
malo.com
Sales Range: $50-74.9 Million
Emp.: 20
Aquarium Management Services
N.A.I.C.S.: 712130

Belpark BV (1)
Meenseweg 497, 8902, Ieper, West Flan-
ders, Belgium
Tel.: (32) 57468686
Web Site: https://www.bellewaerde.be
Sales Range: $50-74.9 Million
Emp.: 100
Recreational Services
N.A.I.C.S.: 713110

CDA Financement SNC (1)
52 Boulevard Haussmann, 75009, Paris,
France
Tel.: (33) 146848800
Financial Support Services
N.A.I.C.S.: 541611

CDA-DS SAS (1)
89 Rue Escudier, 92100, Boulogne-
Billancourt, 92100, Hauts De Seine, France
Tel.: (33) 146848800

Compagnie des Alpes S.A.—(Continued)

Web Site: http://www.compagniedesalpes.fr
Sales Range: $75-99.9 Million
Emp.: 200
Recreational Services
N.A.I.C.S.: 713110
Aumont Bruno *(Gen Mgr)*

ECOBIOGESTION SAS (1)
Le Bioscope, 68190, Ungersheim, France
Tel.: (33) 389624300
Web Site: http://www.lebioscope.com
Recreational Services
N.A.I.C.S.: 713110

Familypark GmbH Inc. (1)
Marchenparkweg 1, Sankt Margarethen im Burgenland, 7062, Eisenstadt, Austria
Tel.: (43) 268560707
Web Site: https://www.familypark.at
Entertainment Park Operator
N.A.I.C.S.: 713110
Filip de Witte *(CEO)*

France Miniature SAS (1)
Boulevard Andre Malraux, 78990, Elancourt, France
Tel.: (33) 130161630
Web Site: https://www.franceminiature.fr
Sales Range: $50-74.9 Million
Emp.: 11
Recreational Services
N.A.I.C.S.: 713110

Grevin & Cie (1)
BP 8, 60128, Plailly, France
Tel.: (33) 344628787
Amusement Park Operator
N.A.I.C.S.: 713990
Guy Vassel *(VP-Corp Comm)*

Subsidiary (Non-US):

Grevin Deutschland GmbH (2)
Aurorastrasse 50, Sauerland, 59909, Bestwig, Germany
Tel.: (49) 2905810
Web Site: https://fortfun.de
Sales Range: $25-49.9 Million
Emp.: 40
Recreational Services
N.A.I.C.S.: 713110
Andreas Sievering *(Mng Dir)*

Hellendoorn Avonturen Park BV (2)
Avonturenpark Hellendoorn Luttenbergerweg 22, 7447 PB, Hellendoorn, Netherlands
Tel.: (31) 548659159
Web Site: https://www.avonturenpark.nl
Sales Range: $150-199.9 Million
Emp.: 400
Recreational Services
N.A.I.C.S.: 713110

Grevin & Cie Touraine SAS (1)
les Hauts Boeufs, 37400, Lussault-sur-Loire, Indre-et-Loire, France
Tel.: (33) 2 47 23 44 44
Recreational Services
N.A.I.C.S.: 713110

Meribel Alpina SAS (1)
Meribel Les Allues, 73550, Tours-en-Savoie, France
Tel.: (33) 479086532
Web Site: http://www.skipass-meribel.com
Travel & Tourism Services
N.A.I.C.S.: 561510
Phillippa Goodfellow *(Mgr-Corp Bus)*

Subsidiary (Domestic):

Grand Massif Domaines Skiables SA (2)
Telepherique de Flaine-Les Grandes Platieres-Flaine, FK4300, Hautevelle, France
Tel.: (33) 450904000
Web Site: https://www.grand-massif.com
Ski Resort Operator
N.A.I.C.S.: 713920
Frederic Marion *(CEO)*

Musee Grevin SA (1)
10 Boulevard Montmartre, 75009, Paris, France   **(95.88%)**
Tel.: (33) 147708505
Web Site: http://www.grevin-paris.com
Wax Museum Operator
N.A.I.C.S.: 712110

Yves Delhommeau *(Mng Dir-Acting & Dir-Publ)*

Parc Asterix SAS (1)
Parc Asterix, BP 8, 60128, Plailly, France
Tel.: (33) 986868687
Web Site: https://www.parcasterix.fr
Recreational Services
N.A.I.C.S.: 713110

Pleasurewood HIlls Ltd (1)
Leisure Way, Lowestoft, NR32 4TZ, Suffolk, United Kingdom
Tel.: (44) 1502586000
Web Site: https://www.pleasurewoodhills.com
Recreational Services
N.A.I.C.S.: 713110

SCV DOMAINE SKIABLE SA (1)
Place du Telepherique Le Serre d'Aigle, Chantemerle Saint-Chaffrey, 05330, Les Hautes-Rivieres, France
Tel.: (33) 492255500
Web Site: https://www.tousengages-serrechevalier.com
Travel & Tourism Services
N.A.I.C.S.: 561510

SEVABEL SAS (1)
Gare de la telecabine du Mont de la Chambre Les Menuires, BP 2, Les Belleville, 73440, Saint-Martin-de-Belleville, France
Tel.: (33) 479006275
Web Site: https://www.skipass-lesmenuires.com
Travel & Tourism Services
N.A.I.C.S.: 561510
M. Didier Bobillier *(Gen Mgr)*

STVI SAS (1)
Gare Centrale, Val-d'Isere, 73150, Isere, France
Tel.: (33) 479060035
Web Site: http://www.valdisere.ski
Travel & Tourism Services
N.A.I.C.S.: 561510
Simonin Olivier *(Gen Mgr & Dir-Publication)*

Safari Africain de Port Saint Pere SA (1)
La Chevallerie, 44710, Port-Saint-Pere, Loire-Atlantique, France
Tel.: (33) 240048282
Recreational Services
N.A.I.C.S.: 713110

SwissAlp SA (1)
Chemin Frank Thomas 36, 1208, Geneva, Switzerland
Tel.: (41) 227040670
Investment & Real Estate Management Services
N.A.I.C.S.: 523999

WALIBI HOLLAND BV (1)
Spijkweg 30, 8256 RJ, Biddinghuizen, Netherlands
Tel.: (31) 321329999
Web Site: https://www.walibi.nl
Entertainment Park Operator
N.A.I.C.S.: 713110
Egbert de Jong *(Ops Mgr)*

COMPAGNIE DES LEVURES LESAFFRE SA

137 rue Gabriel Peri, Marcq-en-Baroeul, 59 700, France
Tel.: (33) 320816100
Web Site: http://www.lesaffre.com
Year Founded: 1853
Sales Range: $1-4.9 Billion
Emp.: 7,200
Yeast Production
N.A.I.C.S.: 311213
Lucien Lesaffre *(Chm & CEO)*

Subsidiaries:

ASMUSSEN GmbH (1)
Franz-Hellner-Str 61, 41751, Viersen, Germany
Tel.: (49) 21621025116
Web Site: http://www.asmussen-gmbh.de
Yeast Distr
N.A.I.C.S.: 424490

Agrauxine S.A. (1)

2 Rue Henri Becquerel, 49070, Beaucouze, France
Tel.: (33) 2 41 77 39 91
Web Site: http://www.agrauxine.com
Agricultural Chemical Mfr
N.A.I.C.S.: 325320

Plant (Domestic):

Agrauxine S.A. - Loches Factory (2)
18 route de Mauvieres ZI de Tivoli, 37600, Loches, France
Tel.: (33) 2 47 59 00 45
Agricultural Chemical Mfr
N.A.I.C.S.: 325320

Agrauxine S.A. - Plomelin Factory (2)
Route des Chateaux, 29700, Plomelin, France
Tel.: (33) 9 62 17 87 84
Agricultural Chemical Mfr
N.A.I.C.S.: 325320

Algist Bruggeman S.A. (1)
Langerbruggekaai 37, 9000, Gent, Belgium
Tel.: (32) 9 257 08 08
Web Site: http://www.algistbruggeman.be
Yeast Mfr
N.A.I.C.S.: 311999

Bio Springer S.A. (1)
103 rue Jean Jaures, 94704, Maisons-Alfort, France
Tel.: (33) 1 49 77 18 45
Web Site: http://www.biospringer.com
Yeast Mfr
N.A.I.C.S.: 311999

Subsidiary (Non-US):

Bio Springer Asia (2)
299 Longcao road, Xuhui District, Shanghai, China
Tel.: (86) 21 61281521
Web Site: http://www.biospringer.com.cn
Yeast Mfr
N.A.I.C.S.: 311999
Michael Xu *(Dir-Mktg)*

Bio Springer Pacific (2)
37 Day St North, Silverwater, Sydney, 2128, NSW, Australia
Tel.: (61) 2 8748 8200
Yeast Mfr
N.A.I.C.S.: 311999

Plant (Domestic):

Bio Springer S.A. - Yeast extracts Factory (2)
6 rue de Saint-Nazaire-Zone Portuaire Sud, 67100, Strasbourg, France
Tel.: (33) 3 88 40 53 53
Yeast Mfr
N.A.I.C.S.: 311999

Subsidiary (Non-US):

Bio Springer South America (2)
Rua Francisco Juliatto 2075, 13278-804, Valinhos, Brazil
Tel.: (55) 19 3881 8471
Yeast Mfr
N.A.I.C.S.: 311999
Alexandre Carvalho *(Mgr-QEHS)*

Biospringer Guangxi YiPinXian Co. LTD (2)
2500 Tianranqiao Road, Laibin, Guangxi, China
Tel.: (86) 772 4066017
Yeast Mfr
N.A.I.C.S.: 311999

Compania Internacional de Productos Universales Alimenticios Ltda (1)
La Union San Diego Del Liceo Mario Quiros Sasso, 800 oeste y 75 sur Frente Proval Seguridad, Cartago, Costa Rica
Tel.: (506) 2279 5863
Web Site: http://www.redstar.co.cr
Food Products Distr
N.A.I.C.S.: 424490

DCL Yeast Limited (1)
Alloa Business Centre Alloa Business Park, Whins Road, Alloa, FK10 3SA, Clackmannanshire, United Kingdom
Tel.: (44) 20 8643 1818
Web Site: http://www.dclyeast.co.uk

Yeast Mfr
N.A.I.C.S.: 311999

Dosu Maya Mayacilik AS (1)
E-5 Highway Evrensekiz Intersection, Luleburgaz, Turkiye
Tel.: (90) 288 4439826
Web Site: http://www.dosumaya.com.tr
Food Products Distr
N.A.I.C.S.: 424490

FALA GmbH (1)
Dr Georg-Schaeffler-Str 1, 77815, Buhl, Germany
Tel.: (49) 7223 28166 0
Web Site: http://www.fala-hefe.de
Emp.: 30
Food Products Distr
N.A.I.C.S.: 424490

GBI Argentina (1)
Finca El Progreso Ruta provincial 21 Km 11, Cerrillos, Salta, Argentina
Tel.: (54) 38 74 71 71 64
Food Products Distr
N.A.I.C.S.: 424490

KVASAC d.o.o. (1)
Prudnicka 98, 10291, Prigorje Brdovecko, Croatia
Tel.: (385) 1 3349 900
Web Site: http://www.kvasac.hr
Yeast Mfr
N.A.I.C.S.: 311999
Miroslav Botic *(Mgr-Mktg & Sls)*

Klipfel Hefe AG (1)
Im Kunzental 6, 4310, Rheinfelden, Switzerland
Tel.: (41) 61 836 88 88
Web Site: http://www.klipfel.ch
Yeast Mfr
N.A.I.C.S.: 311999

LESAFFRE INGREDIENTS SERVICES SA (1)
67 rue de la Gare, 50510, Cerences, France
Tel.: (33) 2 33 91 40 00
Web Site: http://www.lesaffre-ingredients-services.com
Food Products Distr
N.A.I.C.S.: 424490
Francois Cachot *(Dir-Sls & Gen Mgr)*

Subsidiary (Non-US):

Lesaffre Ingredients Services Polska Sp. z o.o. (2)
Ul Szczytnicka 27, 59-220, Legnica, Poland
Tel.: (48) 76 862 74 12
Food Products Distr
N.A.I.C.S.: 424490

LFA Celtic Limited (1)
Atlantic Avenue Westpark Business Campus, Shannon, Co Clare, Ireland
Tel.: (353) 61 708 099
Web Site: http://www.yeastsolutions.co.uk
Animal Feed Mfr
N.A.I.C.S.: 311119

Lesaffre (Far East) Ltd. (1)
Units 2601-03 26th CEO Tower 77 Wing Hong Street, Cheung Sha Wan, Kowloon, China (Hong Kong)
Tel.: (852) 2508 1218
Web Site: http://www.lesaffre.com.hk
Food Products Distr
N.A.I.C.S.: 424490

Lesaffre (Mingguang) Co., Ltd. (1)
23 Chi He Da Dao, Mingguang, 239400, Anhui, China
Tel.: (86) 550 809 9268
Yeast Mfr
N.A.I.C.S.: 311999

Lesaffre Argentina S.A. (1)
Jose Antonio Cabrera 4338, C1414BGD, Buenos Aires, Argentina
Tel.: (54) 11 4833 8000
Web Site: http://www.lesaffre.com.ar
Yeast Mfr
N.A.I.C.S.: 311999

Lesaffre Australia Pacific Pty Ltd (1)
8-10 Berends Drive, PO Box 4186, Dandenong South, 3164, VIC, Australia
Tel.: (61) 3 9706 5334

Web Site:
http://www.lesaffreaustraliapacific.com.au
Emp.: 40
Yeast Mfr
N.A.I.C.S.: 311999
Russell Cotterell *(Mgr-Natl Pur & Logistics)*

Lesaffre Austria AG (1)
IZ NO-Sud Strasse 7 Objekt 58B, 2355,
Wiener Neudorf, Austria
Tel.: (43) 2236 677 988 0
Web Site: http://www.lesaffre.at
Yeast Mfr
N.A.I.C.S.: 311999

Lesaffre Bulgaria EOOD (1)
Europe Trade Center - 7 Bd Iskarsko
chaussee Building 6 office 1, Sofia, 1528,
Bulgaria
Tel.: (359) 2 873 14 39
Web Site: http://www.lesaffre.bg
Yeast Distr
N.A.I.C.S.: 424490
Nanko Kolev *(Mgr-Sls)*

Lesaffre Cesko, a.s. (1)
Hodolanska 1296/34, 779 00, Olomouc,
Czech Republic
Tel.: (420) 58 74 19 321
Web Site: http://www.lesaffre.cz
Yeast Distr
N.A.I.C.S.: 424490
Igor Nosek *(Dir-Fin)*

Lesaffre Chile S.A. (1)
Las Esteras Norte 2751, Quilicura, San-
tiago, Chile (100%)
Tel.: (56) 226408500
Web Site: http://www.lesaffre.cl
Sales Range: $25-49.9 Million
Emp.: 200
Bakery Product Whslr
N.A.I.C.S.: 424490

Lesaffre Colombia Ltda (1)
Avenida 6 n 13n - 50 Oficina 1209 Boule-
vard de la Sexta, Valle, Cali, Colombia
Tel.: (57) 2 4852861
Web Site: http://www.lesaffre.com.co
Yeast Mfr
N.A.I.C.S.: 311999

Lesaffre Iberica S.A. (1)
Avenida Santander n 138, 47011, Vall-
adolid, Spain
Tel.: (34) 983 23 29 07
Web Site: http://www.lesaffre.es
Yeast Mfr
N.A.I.C.S.: 311999
Jesus Pedro Morchon Gonzalez *(Mgr-Pkg)*

Lesaffre International Corp. (1)
7475 W Main St, Milwaukee, WI 53214
Tel.: (414) 615-4120
Web Site: http://www.lesaffre.com
Rev.: $139,800,000
Emp.: 100
Holding Company; Yeast Production
N.A.I.C.S.: 551112

Subsidiary (Domestic):

Lesaffre Yeast Corp. (2)
7475 W Main St, Milwaukee, WI 53214
Tel.: (414) 615-4120
Web Site: http://www.lesaffreyeastcorp.com
Rev.: $37,100,000
Emp.: 50
Groceries & Related Products, Nec
N.A.I.C.S.: 424490
Mark Miller *(Mgr-Baking Center)*

Lesaffre Italia S.p.A. (1)
Piazzale Zuccherificio - S Quirico 2, Sissa
Trecasali, 43018, Parma, Italy
Tel.: (39) 0521 87 80 11
Web Site: http://www.lesaffreitalia.com
Yeast Mfr
N.A.I.C.S.: 311999

**Lesaffre Magyarorszag Elesztogyarto
es Kereskedelmi Kft.** (1)
Gyar u 5-9, 1222, Budapest, Hungary
Tel.: (36) 6 1 226 6311
Web Site: http://www.lesaffre.hu
Yeast Mfr
N.A.I.C.S.: 311999

**Lesaffre Management (Shanghai)
Co., Ltd** (1)
Building 2A 1/F TianHua Information Tech-

nology Service Park, Xuhui District, Shang-
hai, 200235, China
Tel.: (86) 21 61152788
Web Site: http://www.lesaffre.com.cn
Yeast Mfr
N.A.I.C.S.: 311999
Bernard Kam *(Dir-Mktg)*

Lesaffre Maroc (1)
Rue Ibn El Banaa Q I Sidi Brahim, BP
2127, 30000, Fes, Morocco
Tel.: (212) 535 73 75 30
Food Products Distr
N.A.I.C.S.: 424490

Lesaffre Nordic AB (1)
Taljegardsgatan 11C, 431 53, Molndal,
Sweden
Tel.: (46) 31 301 50 20
Web Site: http://www.lesaffre.se
Food Products Distr
N.A.I.C.S.: 424490

Lesaffre Peru S.A.C. (1)
Av Guardia Peruana N 1483 Urbanizacion
La Campina, Chorrillos, Peru
Tel.: (51) 1 467 2300
Web Site: http://www.lesaffre.com.pe
Yeast Mfr
N.A.I.C.S.: 311999

Lesaffre Polska S.A. (1)
ul Dworcowa 36, 46-250, Wolczyn, Poland
Tel.: (48) 77 418 82 80
Web Site: http://www.lesaffre.pl
Yeast Mfr
N.A.I.C.S.: 311999

Lesaffre RS d.o.o. (1)
Milutina Milankovica 11b, 11070, Novi Beo-
grad, Serbia
Tel.: (381) 11 655 6 550
Food Products Distr
N.A.I.C.S.: 424490
Ivan Spasojevic *(Mgr-Supply Chain)*

Lesaffre Romania S.R.L. (1)
Str Drumul Garii Otopeni nr 66-68 oras,
Otopeni, Ilfov, Romania
Tel.: (40) 21 351 20 31
Yeast Mfr
N.A.I.C.S.: 311999

Lesaffre Slovensko, a.s. (1)
Piestanska ulica 3, 917 01, Trnava, Slova-
kia
Tel.: (421) 55 72 62 6
Web Site: http://www.lesaffre.sk
Food Products Distr
N.A.I.C.S.: 424490

Lesaffre Ukraine LLC (1)
9 Boryspilska str Building 91 floor 4, 2099,
Kiev, Ukraine
Tel.: (380) 443 69 51 35
Web Site: http://www.lesaffre.ua
Emp.: 60
Food Products Distr
N.A.I.C.S.: 424490
Natalia Karlenko *(Head-Mktg Dept)*

Lesaffre Uruguay S.A. (1)
Elias Regules 4863, 12900, Montevideo,
Uruguay
Tel.: (598) 23573736
Web Site: http://www.lesaffre.com.uy
Food Products Distr
N.A.I.C.S.: 424490

**Levaduras Y Avios Azteca, S.A. De
C.V.** (1)
Calle 4 No 184 Col Granjas San Antonio
Delegacion Iztapalapa, 09070, Mexico,
Mexico
Tel.: (52) 55 3687 9900
Food Products Distr
N.A.I.C.S.: 424490

NattoPharma ASA (1)
Lilleakerveien 2B, 0283, Oslo,
Norway (100%)
Tel.: (47) 40 00 90 08
Web Site: http://www.nattopharma.com
Pharmaceuticals Mfr
N.A.I.C.S.: 325412
Hogne Vik *(Chief Medical Officer)*

Subsidiary (US):

NattoPharma USA, Inc. (2)
95 Newfield Ave Ste C, Edison, NJ 08837

Tel.: (609) 454-2992
Oil & Gas Services
N.A.I.C.S.: 325412

Omniabios S.R.L. (1)
Via Industriale 34, Bagnolo Mella, 25021,
Brescia, Italy
Tel.: (39) 030 6820420
Food Products Distr
N.A.I.C.S.: 424490

Ozmaya Sanayi A.S. (1)
Turlubas Mahallesi Dr Devlet Bahceli Bul-
vari No 2 PK50, Ceyhan, 01960, Adana,
Turkiye
Tel.: (90) 322 613 79 20
Web Site: http://www.ozmaya.com.tr
Yeast Mfr
N.A.I.C.S.: 311999

Subsidiary (Non-US):

Iran Mayeh Company (2)
Opposite of Motojon Dorman diesel Road,
Tabriz, Iran
Tel.: (98) 411 4459761
Web Site: http://www.iranmayeh.com
Yeast Mfr
N.A.I.C.S.: 311999
Asaf Metin Ekici *(Gen Mgr)*

Unit (Domestic):

**Iran Mayeh Company - Southeast
Unit** (3)
No 273 Shahid Dastgerdi Ave West Zafar,
St Afrigha Boulevard, Tehran, Iran
Tel.: (98) 21 88870238
Yeast Mfr
N.A.I.C.S.: 311999

Plant (Domestic):

**Ozmaya Sanayi A.S. - Yeast & Ingre-
dient Factory** (2)
Tasova Yolu Uzeri 6 km, Amasya, Turkiye
Tel.: (90) 358 231 15 00
Yeast Mfr
N.A.I.C.S.: 311999

PJSC Nadezhda (1)
10 st 27th Partzyizd, 50102, Krivoy Rog,
Ukraine
Tel.: (380) 564 93 66 30
Food Products Distr
N.A.I.C.S.: 424490

PT Saf Indonesia (1)
Komplek Rukan Puri Mutiara Blok BG No
05-06 Jalan Griya Utama, Sunter Agung,
Jakarta, 14350, Indonesia
Tel.: (62) 21 29569527
Yeast Mfr
N.A.I.C.S.: 311999
Gregorius Sukamulyo *(Gen Mgr)*

Plant (Domestic):

**PT Saf Indonesia - Sidoarjo
Factory** (2)
Komplek Pergudangan Sinar Gedangan
Blok A-15 Jalan Raya, Wedi Betro Gedan-
gan, Sidoarjo, 61254, Indonesia
Tel.: (62) 31 8012065
Yeast Mfr
N.A.I.C.S.: 311999

SAF IVOIRE Sarl (1)
Rue des Alizes - G99 Zone 4 C 18, BP
1206, Abidjan, Cote d'Ivoire
Tel.: (225) 21 75 70 45
Food Products Distr
N.A.I.C.S.: 424490

Saf Djazair, spa (1)
Hai Ben Amar, BP 66C, Hamadi, 35015,
Boumerdes, Algeria
Tel.: (213) 21 81 96 58
Food Products Distr
N.A.I.C.S.: 424490

Saf Neva OOO (1)
7 Maril Rubtsovoy str, 141410, Khimki, Rus-
sia
Tel.: (7) 4986995376
Web Site: http://www.lesaffre.ru
Yeast Mfr
N.A.I.C.S.: 311999

Plant (Domestic):

**Saf Neva OOO - Bread Making Im-
provers Factory** (2)

13 Beloostrovskaya str, 197342, Saint Pe-
tersburg, Russia
Tel.: (7) 8126678570
Yeast Mfr
N.A.I.C.S.: 311999

**Saf Neva OOO - Kurgan Yeast
Factory** (2)
122 Kuibysheva str, 640006, Kurgan, Rus-
sia
Tel.: (7) 3522 600 127
Web Site: http://www.lesaffre.ru
Yeast Mfr
N.A.I.C.S.: 311999
Timothe Dupon *(Gen Mgr)*

**Saf Neva OOO - Ouzlovaya Yeast
Factory** (2)
2 Druzhby Str, Toulskaya region, 301605,
Uzlovaya, Russia
Tel.: (7) 48731 53 180
Yeast Mfr
N.A.I.C.S.: 311999

Saf do Brasil Ltda (1)
Rua Guatemala 416 - Penha Circular,
21020-170, Rio de Janeiro, Brazil
Tel.: (55) 21 2109 5700
Food Products Distr
N.A.I.C.S.: 424490

Safisis (1)
Zone artisanale Rue Mancamp, 40140,
Soustons, France
Tel.: (33) 5 58 41 34 01
Web Site: http://www.safisis.com
Emp.: 60
Chemical Products Mfr
N.A.I.C.S.: 325199
Bernard Azais *(CEO)*

Safmex SA de CV (1)
Km 57 5 Carretera Mexico Toluca, Parque
Industrial, Toluca, 50200, Mexico
Tel.: (52) 7224624200
Web Site: http://www.safmex.com.mx
Sales Range: $100-124.9 Million
Emp.: 300
Yeast Production
N.A.I.C.S.: 311213

Subsidiary (Domestic):

Panadis, S.A. de C.V. (2)
Av Dr Gustavo Baz No 109 Int D Col San
Pedro Barrientos, 54010, Tlalnepantla,
Mexico
Tel.: (52) 55 16 65 22 43
Web Site: http://www.panadis.com.mx
Food Products Distr
N.A.I.C.S.: 424490

Sil Fala SARL (1)
8 rue de Saint-Nazaire, BP 62 028, 67026,
Strasbourg, Cedex, France
Tel.: (33) 3 88 40 54 54
Yeast Mfr
N.A.I.C.S.: 311999
Vincent Dzedzej *(Mgr)*

Voronezhskie Drojji LLC (1)
106 Dimitrova street, 394028, Voronezh,
Russia
Tel.: (7) 473 267 97 00
Web Site: http://www.drojji.ru
Food Products Mfr
N.A.I.C.S.: 311999

Zymes Lesaffre S.A. (1)
Attiki Odos Arees Velanidies, 19300, Aspro-
pyrgos, Greece
Tel.: (30) 210 48 35 386
Web Site: http://www.zymes.gr
Food Products Distr
N.A.I.C.S.: 424490

COMPAGNIE DES TRAMWAYS DE ROUEN SA
Tour Bollore 31-32 quai de Dion Bou-
ton, 92811, Puteaux, Cedex, France
Tel.: (33) 146964433
Web Site: https://www.tramways-de-
rouen.com
MLTRA—(EUR)
Sales Range: Less than $1 Million
Holding Company
N.A.I.C.S.: 551112
Thibaut de Rivoire *(CEO)*

Compagnie du Bois Sauvage SA—(Continued)

COMPAGNIE DU BOIS SAUVAGE SA
Rue du Bois Sauvage 17, 1000, Brussels, Belgium
Tel.: (32) 22275450
Web Site: https://www.bois-sauvage.be
Rev.: $254,557,327
Assets: $690,268,115
Liabilities: $147,037,636
Net Worth: $543,230,479
Earnings: ($14,622,211)
Fiscal Year-end: 12/31/18
Holding Company; Real Estate, Industrial & Financial Management Services
N.A.I.C.S.: 551112
Valerie Paquot *(Bd of Dirs & Chm)*

Subsidiaries:

Corne Port-Royal Chocolatier S.A. **(1)**
Avenue Vesale 12, 1300, Wavre, Belgium
Tel.: (32) 25682360
Web Site: http://www.corneportroyal.com
Chocolate Mfr
N.A.I.C.S.: 311351
Els De Vos *(Dir-Mktg)*

Subsidiary (Domestic):

Artista Chocolates SA **(2)**
Avenue Mercator 10, 1300, Wavre, Belgium
Tel.: (32) 10241366
Web Site: http://www.artistachoc.be
Chocolate Mfr
N.A.I.C.S.: 311351

Neuhaus NV **(1)**
PO Box 2, Vlezenbeek, 1602, Brussels, Belgium
Tel.: (32) 25682211
Web Site:
   http://www.neuhauschocolates.com
Chocolate Mfr
N.A.I.C.S.: 311351

COMPAGNIE DU CAMBODGE SA
31-32 Quai de Dion Bouton, 92811, Puteaux, Cedex, France
Tel.: (33) 146964433
Web Site: https://www.compagnie-du-cambodge.com
CBDG—(EUR)
Sales Range: $50-74.9 Million
Transportation & Logistics Services
N.A.I.C.S.: 488510
Cyrille Bollore *(Chm-Mgmt Bd)*

COMPAGNIE DU MONT BLANC - SA
35 place de la Mer de Glace, 74400, Chamonix-Mont-Blanc, France
Tel.: (33) 450532275
Web Site:
   https://www.compagniedumont.fr
Year Founded: 2000
MLCMB—(EUR)
Sales Range: $100-124.9 Million
Emp.: 455
Ski Lift & Tow Operator
N.A.I.C.S.: 713920
Mathieu Dechavanne *(Pres & Mng Dir)*

COMPAGNIE FINANCIERE DE NEUFCOUR S.A.
rue Churchill 26 Romsee Fleron, 4624, Liege, Belgium
Tel.: (32) 43586944
Web Site: http://www.neufcour.com
NEU—(EUR)
Sales Range: $1-9.9 Million
Real Estate Manangement Services
N.A.I.C.S.: 531210
Jacques Janssen *(Chm & CEO)*

COMPAGNIE FINANCIERE ET DE PARTICIPATIONS ROULLIER SA
27 Franklin Roosevelt Avenue, 35400, Saint-Malo, France
Tel.: (33) 299206520
Web Site: http://www.roullier.com
Year Founded: 1959
Sales Range: $1-4.9 Billion
Emp.: 8,000
Fertilizers, Agrochemicals & Food Products Mfr
N.A.I.C.S.: 325311
Daniel Roullier *(Chm-Supervisory Bd)*

Subsidiaries:

Agriplas Company **(1)**
55 Boulevard Jules Verger, BP 10180, Dinard, 35803, Saint-Malo, Cedex, France
Tel.: (33) 299165100
Web Site: http://www.agriplas.com
Plastic Packaging Item Mfr
N.A.I.C.S.: 326112

Comercializadora Timac Agro Chile Limitada **(1)**
Napoleon 3565 Ap 202, Las Condes, Santiago, Chile
Tel.: (56) 226567527
Agricultural Chemical Product Mfr
N.A.I.C.S.: 325320
Mariana Lira Lukacs *(Reg Sls Mgr)*

Ker Cadelac SA **(1)**
Rue du Bourgeon, BP 40 217, 22602, Loudeac, France
Tel.: (33) 296661717
Web Site: http://www.kercadelac.fr
Food Products Mfr
N.A.I.C.S.: 311999

SQM - Vitas Brasil Ltda. **(1)**
Via Candeias Km 01 Sem Numero Lote 4 Bairro Cia Norte, Caixa Postal 138, Candeias, 43805-190, Bahia, Brazil
Tel.: (55) 7136023056
Agricultural Chemical Product Mfr.
N.A.I.C.S.: 325320
Marcio Wasem *(CFO)*

Sqm Vitas Peru S.A.C. **(1)**
Avenida Circunvalacion del Club Golf Los Incas N 154 Oficina 1401, Santiago de Surco, Lima, Peru
Tel.: (51) 16112121
Web Site: http://www.sqm-vitas.com
Agricultural Chemical Product Mfr.
N.A.I.C.S.: 325320

Timab Magnesium SAS **(1)**
57 Bd Jules Verger, Dinard, 35800, Saint-Malo, France
Tel.: (33) 223152491
Web Site: http://www.timabmagnesium.com
Agricultural Chemical Product Mfr
N.A.I.C.S.: 325320
Maxime Martinaud *(Sls Mgr)*

Timac Agro Algerie, Sarl **(1)**
Zone Industrielle de Baba Ali, Birtouta, Algiers, 16045, Algeria
Tel.: (213) 23570196
Agricultural Chemical Product Mfr
N.A.I.C.S.: 325320
B. Hakim *(Natl Sls Mgr)*

Timac Agro Argentina S.A. **(1)**
Rodriguez de Busto 4086 Piso 2 Oficina 204 Alto Verde, X5009DYJ, Cordoba, Spain
Tel.: (34) 3514421600
Agricultural Chemical Product Mfr
N.A.I.C.S.: 325320

Timac Agro Avrasya Ziraat San.ve Tic. A.S. **(1)**
Cubuklu Mh O Veli Kanik Cd Yavuz Sk Yavuz Mutlu Plaza No 1 K 3 Kavacik, Beykoz, Istanbul, Turkiye
Tel.: (90) 2163311031
Web Site: http://www.tr.timacagro.com
Agriculture Product Distr
N.A.I.C.S.: 424590
Ali Becerik *(Mgr-Bus Unit)*

Timac Agro International SAS **(1)**
27 av Franklin Roosevelt, BP 70158, 35408, Saint-Malo, France

Tel.: (33) 299206520
Web Site: http://www.timacagro.com
Phosphatic Fertilizer Mfr & Distr
N.A.I.C.S.: 325312

Subsidiary (Non-US):

Timac Agro Polska Sp.Z.O.O. **(2)**
Ul Batorowska 15, 62-081, Wysogotowo, Poland
Tel.: (48) 695554444
Agriculture Granulated & Liquid Fertilizer Mfr
N.A.I.C.S.: 325320

Timac Agro LT, UAB **(1)**
Svitrigailos g 11M, LT-03228, Vilnius, Lithuania
Tel.: (370) 62099121
Web Site: http://www.timacagro.lt
Agriculture Product Distr
N.A.I.C.S.: 424590
Arunas Jusas *(Country Mgr)*

Timac Agro Latvia Sia **(1)**
Atmodas iela 19, Jelgava, LV-3007, Latvia
Tel.: (371) 20281028
Web Site: http://www.lv.timacagro.com
Agriculture Product Distr
N.A.I.C.S.: 424590
Lauris Petersons *(Country Mgr)*

Timac Agro Maroc SA **(1)**
Oasis Dar-el-Beida, Casablanca, Morocco
Tel.: (212) 522255728
Agricultural Chemical Product Mfr
N.A.I.C.S.: 325320

Timac Agro Nederland B.V. **(1)**
Postbus 4365, 3006 AJ, Rotterdam, Netherlands
Tel.: (31) 102045553
Web Site: http://www.timac-agro.nl
Agriculture Product Distr
N.A.I.C.S.: 424590

Timac Agro Paraguay S.A. **(1)**
Avda Parana-Centro Comercial Country Club Alto Parana Alto Parana, Hernandarias, Paraguay
Tel.: (595) 983810700
Agricultural Chemical Product Mfr
N.A.I.C.S.: 325320

Timac Agro Romania Srl. **(1)**
Bulevardul Dimitrie Pompeiu 10A, Bucharest, 077190, Romania
Tel.: (40) 213132685
Agricultural Chemical Product Mfr.
N.A.I.C.S.: 325320

Timac Agro Slovakia, S.r.o. **(1)**
Oravska 1543/13, 903 01, Senec, Slovakia
Tel.: (421) 245923568
Web Site: http://www.sk.timacagro.com
Agriculture Product Distr
N.A.I.C.S.: 424590
Sebastian Stankovsky *(Reg Mgr)*

Timac Agro Sverige AB **(1)**
Sundsvagen 14, Alnarp, 230 53, Lomma, Sweden
Tel.: (46) 3780241
Web Site: http://www.se.timacagro.com
Agricultural Chemical Product Mfr
N.A.I.C.S.: 325320

Timac Agro UK Ltd. **(1)**
Daniel Hall Building Rothamsted West Common, Harpenden, AL5 2JQ, United Kingdom
Tel.: (44) 1582958444
Agricultural Chemical Product Mfr
N.A.I.C.S.: 325320
Ed Tame *(Country Mgr)*

Timac Agro USA Inc. **(1)**
153 Angstadt Ln, Reading, PA 19607
Tel.: (610) 375-7272
Emp.: 200
Agricultural Chemical Product Mfr
N.A.I.C.S.: 325320
Pete Gaidis *(CFO)*

Timac Agro Ukraine LLC **(1)**
5 Dovnar-Zapolskogo str, Kiev, 04116, Ukraine
Tel.: (380) 444862191
Agricultural Chemical Product Mfr
N.A.I.C.S.: 325320
Yevgen Dontsov *(Country Mgr)*

Timac Agro Uruguay S.A. **(1)**
Juanico, Canelones, Uruguay
Tel.: (598) 43359595
Agricultural Chemical Product Mfr
N.A.I.C.S.: 325320

VITAS Portugal, Lda. **(1)**
Rua Hermano Neves 18 Piso 4-Office 10, 1600-477, Lisbon, Portugal
Tel.: (351) 217502050
Web Site: http://www.vitas.pt
Chemical Products Mfr
N.A.I.C.S.: 325998
Teresa Caldeira *(CFO)*

Van Mannekus & Co. B.V. **(1)**
Nieuwe Waterwegstraat 45, NL 3115 HE, Schiedam, Netherlands **(50%)**
Tel.: (31) 10 40 91 500
Web Site: http://www.mannekus.com
Sales Range: $25-49.9 Million
Emp.: 35
Magnesium Oxide Processor & Trader
N.A.I.C.S.: 325998
Timothee Le Moulec *(Dir-Sls)*

Subsidiary (Domestic):

Van Mannekus Universal V.O.F. **(2)**
Oudlandsedijk 8, Oudenbosch, NL 4731 TB, Netherlands
Tel.: (31) 165312740
Web Site: http://www.mannekus.com
Sales Range: $25-49.9 Million
Emp.: 8
Magnesium Oxide Processor & Distr
N.A.I.C.S.: 325998
Alexander Dietz *(Mgr-Fin)*

WEISS France SAS **(1)**
95 rue Derobert, 73400, Ugine, France
Tel.: (33) 479890707
Web Site: http://www.weissboiler.com
Emp.: 45
Biomass Boiler Mfr
N.A.I.C.S.: 332410
Frederic Autret *(CEO)*

William Houde Ltd. **(1)**
8 3e rang Ouest, Saint Simon, J0H 1Y0, QC, Canada
Web Site: http://www.williamhoude.com
Agriculture Product Distr
N.A.I.C.S.: 424590
Mathieu Belanger *(CFO)*

COMPAGNIE FINANCIERE RICHEMONT S.A.
50 chemin de la Chenaie, Bellevue, 1293, Geneva, Switzerland
Tel.: (41) 227213500   **CH**
Web Site: https://www.richemont.com
Year Founded: 1988
CFR—(SWX)
Rev.: $22,249,082,627
Assets: $46,061,946,819
Liabilities: $23,792,359,119
Net Worth: $22,269,587,700
Earnings: $2,541,549,747
Emp.: 37,117
Fiscal Year-end: 03/31/24
Holding Company; Jewelry, Watches, Writing Instruments & Other Luxury Goods Whslr & Retailer
N.A.I.C.S.: 551112
Johann P. Rupert *(Chm)*

Subsidiaries:

Alfred Dunhill Limited **(1)**
5-7 Mandeville Pl, London, W1U 3AY, United Kingdom
Tel.: (44) 2078388000
Web Site: http://www.dunhill.com
Sales Range: $50-74.9 Million
Emp.: 150
Luxury Watches Mfr
N.A.I.C.S.: 334519
Laurent Malecaze *(CEO)*

Baume & Mercier S.A. **(1)**
50 Chemin de la Chenaie, Bellevue, Geneva, 1293, Switzerland
Tel.: (41) 229995151
Web Site: http://www.baume-et-mercier.com
Emp.: 70
Watch & Clocks

N.A.I.C.S.: 334519
Alain Zimmernann *(CEO)*

Subsidiary (US):

Baume & Mercier, Inc. **(2)**
645 5th Ave Fl 6, New York, NY 10022-5346
Tel.: (212) 593-0444
Sales Range: $50-74.9 Million
Watch Whslr
N.A.I.C.S.: 423940

Buccellati Holding Italia S.p.A. **(1)**
Via Ludovico Mancini 1, Milan,
Italy **(100%)**
Tel.: (39) 02 545 66 33
Web Site: http://www.buccellati.com
Jewelry Mfr & Distr
N.A.I.C.S.: 339910
Mario Buccellati *(Founder)*

Cartier International SA Geneve **(1)**
8 Blvd James-Fazy, Geneva, 1201, Switzerland
Tel.: (41) 227212400
Web Site: http://www.cartier.com
Sales Range: $25-49.9 Million
Emp.: 100
Luxury Watches Mfr
N.A.I.C.S.: 334519

Cartier SA **(1)**
Blvd James Fazy 8, Geneva, 1201, Switzerland
Tel.: (41) 227212400
Luxury Watches & Jewelry Mfr
N.A.I.C.S.: 334519

Chloe SAS **(1)**
5 avenue Percier, 75008, Paris, France
Tel.: (33) 144943333
Web Site: http://www.chloe.com
Clothe Product Distr
N.A.I.C.S.: 424350

International Watch Co. Ag **(1)**
Baumgartenstr 15, Schaffhausen, 8201,
Switzerland
Tel.: (41) 526356565
Web Site: http://www.iwc.com
Sales Range: $200-249.9 Million
Emp.: 750
Watch & Clock Mfr
N.A.I.C.S.: 334519
George Kern *(CEO)*

James Purdey & Sons Limited **(1)**
Audley House 57 - 58 South Audley Street,
London, W1K 2ED, United Kingdom
Tel.: (44) 2074991801
Web Site: https://www.purdey.com
Emp.: 60
Gun & Rifles Mfr
N.A.I.C.S.: 332994
James Horne *(Chm)*

Manufacture Jaeger-LeCoultre
SA **(1)**
Rue de la Golisse 8, Le Sentier, 1347,
Vaud, Switzerland
Tel.: (41) 218450202
Web Site: http://www.jaeger-lecoultre.com
Luxury Watches Mfr
N.A.I.C.S.: 334519

Manufacture Roger Dubuis SA **(1)**
2 rue Andre De Garrini, 1217, Meyrin,
Switzerland **(100%)**
Tel.: (41) 227832828
Web Site: http://www.rogerdubuis.com
Sales Range: $100-124.9 Million
Emp.: 200
Luxury Watches Mfr
N.A.I.C.S.: 334519
Jean-Marc Pontroue *(CEO)*

Minerva S.A. **(1)**
Avenida Antonio Manco Bernardes s/n Barretos, Sao Paulo, 14781-545, Brazil
Tel.: (55) 1733213355
Web Site: https://www.minervafoods.com
Rev.: $5,541,805,034
Assets: $5,892,664,384
Liabilities: $5,756,744,755
Net Worth: $135,919,629
Earnings: $81,511,180
Fiscal Year-end: 12/31/2023
Food Product Mfr & Distr
N.A.I.C.S.: 311615
Fernando Galletti de Queiroz *(CEO)*

Subsidiary (Non-US):

JBS Argentina S.A. **(2)**
Thomas Edison 2659 3 andar, Martinez,
Buenos Aires, Argentina
Tel.: (54) 11 4006 8800
Web Site: http://www.swift.com.ar
Meat Processing & Products Mfr
N.A.I.C.S.: 311612

Montblanc Deutschland GmbH **(1)**
Hellgrundweg 98, 22525, Hamburg, Germany
Tel.: (49) 40840010
N.A.I.C.S.: 334519

Montblanc International BV **(1)**
Herengracht 436, 1017 BZ, Amsterdam,
North Holland, Netherlands
Tel.: (31) 203428677
Web Site: http://www.montblanc.com
Sales Range: $25-49.9 Million
Emp.: 20
High Quality Writing Instruments Mfr
N.A.I.C.S.: 339940
Nicolas Baretzki *(CEO)*

Montblanc Italia Srl **(1)**
Via Benigno Crespi 26, 20159, Milan, Italy
Tel.: (39) 0800397182
N.A.I.C.S.: 334519

Montblanc-Simplo GmbH **(1)**
Web Site: http://www.montblanc.com
Sales Range: $450-499.9 Million
Emp.: 1,100
Luxury Watches & Writing Instruments Mfr
N.A.I.C.S.: 334519

Subsidiary (Non-US):

Montblanc Suisse SA **(2)**
1 Chemin de la Papeterie, 1290, Versoix,
Geneve, Switzerland
Tel.: (41) 22 775 38 00
Web Site: http://www.montblanc.com
Luxury Watches Mfr
N.A.I.C.S.: 334519

Peter Millar Inc. **(1)**
4361-105 Lassiter at N Hills Ave, Raleigh,
NC 27609
Tel.: (919) 571-2727
Web Site: http://www.petermillar.com
Fabric Clothing Retailer
N.A.I.C.S.: 458110

Piaget S.A. **(1)**
37 chemin du champ des filles, La Cote aux
Fees, Plan-les-Ouates, 1228, Switzerland
Tel.: (41) 228844844
Web Site: http://www.piaget.com
Sales Range: $100-124.9 Million
Emp.: 400
Luxury Watches Mfr
N.A.I.C.S.: 334519
Chabi Nouri *(CEO)*

RLG do Brasil Varejo Ltda. **(1)**
Av Brigadeiro Faria Lima 2 232, Sao Paulo,
01451-000, Brazil
Tel.: (55) 1143802120
N.A.I.C.S.: 423940

Richemont Asia Pacific Limited **(1)**
6 F Jardine House, 1 Connaught Pl, Central, China (Hong Kong)
Tel.: (852) 25327200
Web Site: http://www.richemont.com
Sales Range: $100-124.9 Million
Emp.: 500
Luxury Watches Mfr
N.A.I.C.S.: 334519

Richemont Australia Pty Limited **(1)**
Level 8 74 Castlereagh Street, Sydney,
2000, NSW, Australia
Tel.: (61) 800130000
N.A.I.C.S.: 423940

Richemont Holdings (UK)
Limited **(1)**
15 Hill St, London, W1J 5QT, United Kingdom
Tel.: (44) 2074992539
Web Site: http://www.richemont.com
Sales Range: $25-49.9 Million
Emp.: 50
Luxury Watches Mfr
N.A.I.C.S.: 334519

Richemont Iberia SL **(1)**
Paseo de la castellana 141, Madrid, 28046,
Spain
Tel.: (34) 91 4548972
Web Site: http://www.richemont.com
Sales Range: $50-74.9 Million
Emp.: 180
Luxury Watches Mfr
N.A.I.C.S.: 334519
Phlilppe Guillaumet *(CEO)*

Richemont International SA **(1)**
50 Chemin De La Chenaie, Bellevue, 1293,
Geneva, Switzerland
Tel.: (41) 227213000
N.A.I.C.S.: 423940

Richemont Northern Europe
GmbH **(1)**
Landsberger Str 302 306, Munich, 80687,
Germany
Tel.: (49) 89559840
Web Site: http://www.richemont.com
Sales Range: $50-74.9 Million
Emp.: 120
Luxury Watches Mfr
N.A.I.C.S.: 334519
Robert Hell *(Mng Dir)*

Richemont Suisse SA **(1)**
50 Chemin de la Chenaie, Bellevue, 1293,
Geneva, Switzerland
Tel.: (41) 223675330
Luxury Watches Mfr
N.A.I.C.S.: 334519

Richemont de Mexico SA de CV **(1)**
Perif Blvd Manuel Avila Camacho 138 Lomas De Chapultepec, Miguel Hidalgo,
11560, Mexico, Mexico
Tel.: (52) 8003104810
Web Site: https://www.montblanc.com.mx
N.A.I.C.S.: 334519

Societe Cartier SAS **(1)**
13 Rue De La Paix, 75002, Paris, France
Tel.: (33) 142184383
N.A.I.C.S.: 423940

Vacheron And Constantin S.A. **(1)**
Chemin du Tourbillon 10, Plan-les-Ouates,
1228, Switzerland
Tel.: (41) 229302005
Web Site: http://www.vacheron-constantin.com
Sales Range: $25-49.9 Million
Emp.: 500
Luxury Watches Mfr
N.A.I.C.S.: 334519
Gulien Marchemoir *(Mng Dir)*

Van Cleef & Arpels SA **(1)**
Route des Biches 8, Villars-sur-Glane,
1752, Fribourg, Switzerland
Tel.: (41) 264079511
Web Site: http://www.vancleef-arpels.com
Sales Range: $25-49.9 Million
Emp.: 60
Luxury Watches Mfr
N.A.I.C.S.: 334519
Jorg Schaufelberger *(Dir-Finance)*

Watchfinder.co.uk Limited **(1)**
15 Hill Street, London, W1J 5QT, United
Kingdom
Tel.: (44) 1622806245
Web Site: http://www.watchfinder.co.uk
Watch Mfr & Distr
N.A.I.C.S.: 334519

YOOX NET-A-PORTER Group
S.p.A. **(1)**
Via Morimondo 17, 20143, Milan, Italy
Tel.: (39) 0283112811
Web Site: https://www.ynap.com
Online Fashion Retailer
N.A.I.C.S.: 458110
Silvia Scagnelli *(Dir-Corp Dev, IR & Fin Comm)*

Subsidiary (Non-US):

The Net-a-Porter Group Ltd. **(2)**
1 The Village Offices Westfield Ariel Way,
London, W12 7GF, United Kingdom
Tel.: (44) 2034714510
Web Site: http://www.net-a-porter.com
Online & Mail Order Fashion Retailer
N.A.I.C.S.: 455110
Alison Loehnis *(Pres-Luxury-Div)*

Yoox Asia Limited **(1)**
9/F Goodman Interlink 39 Tsing Yi Road
Tsing Yi, Hong Kong, China (Hong Kong)
Tel.: (852) 27300273
N.A.I.C.S.: 424350

COMPAGNIE GENERAL BEARING SERVICE, INC.
490 Kent Street, Ottawa, K2P 2B7,
ON, Canada
Tel.: (613) 238-8100
Rev.: $30,434,597
Emp.: 100
Industrial Supplies Whslr
N.A.I.C.S.: 423840
Pierre Bouchard *(Pres)*

COMPAGNIE GENERALE DES ETABLISSEMENTS MICHELIN SCA
23 Place des Carmes Dechaux,
63000, Clermont-Ferrand, Cedex 9,
France
Tel.: (33) 473322000   FR
Web Site: https://www.michelin.com
Year Founded: 1863
ML—(EUR)
Rev.: $30,854,737,751
Assets: $38,145,909,778
Liabilities: $19,674,077,272
Net Worth: $18,471,832,506
Earnings: $2,168,141,593
Emp.: 124,918
Fiscal Year-end: 12/31/22
Automobile Parts Mfr
N.A.I.C.S.: 551112
Barbara Dalibard *(Chm-Supervisory Bd)*

Subsidiaries:

ATS Euromaster Limited **(1)**
Vantage Point 20 Upper Portland Street,
Aston, Birmingham, B6 5TW, United Kingdom
Tel.: (44) 370 066 3621
Web Site: https://www.atseuromaster.co.uk
Tire & Car Maintenance Services
N.A.I.C.S.: 811198
Grahame Wright *(Grp Dir-Mktg)*

Advantico GmbH **(1)**
Harrlachweg 3 Eastsite III Office Unit 3 3,
68163, Mannheim, Germany
Tel.: (49) 62143734397
Web Site: https://advantico.de
N.A.I.C.S.: 336320
Jochen Gehrke *(Mng Dir)*

Bearcat Tyres Pty Ltd **(1)**
2/10 Amax Ave, Girraween, 2145, NSW,
Australia
Tel.: (61) 296888888
Web Site: https://www.bearcat.com.au
N.A.I.C.S.: 326211

Blackcircles.com Limited **(1)**
1 Tanfield, Edinburgh, EH3 5DA, United
Kingdom
Tel.: (44) 172 172 5050
Web Site: https://www.blackcircles.com
Motor Vehicle Tool & Equipment Distr
N.A.I.C.S.: 423120

Camso Cis LLC **(1)**
5 Gostinichnaya Street, Moscow, 127106,
Russia
Tel.: (7) 4957887251
Construction Equipment Mfr
N.A.I.C.S.: 333120

Camso Deutschland GmbH **(1)**
Kopenhagener Strasse 1, Duisburg, 47229,
Germany
Tel.: (49) 206590670
Automotive Tires Distr
N.A.I.C.S.: 423130

Camso Distribucion Mexico, S.A. de
C.V. **(1)**
Carr Tlalnepantla-Cuautitlan 1100A, Tultitlan, Mexico, 54915, Mexico
Tel.: (52) 15558842245
Construction Equipment Mfr
N.A.I.C.S.: 333120

Compagnie Generale des Etablissements Michelin
SCA—(Continued)

Camso Distribution Canada Inc. (1)
5485 Tomken Rd, Mississauga, L4W 3Y3,
ON, Canada
Construction Equipment Mfr
N.A.I.C.S.: 333120

Camso France SAS (1)
4 rue du 19 mars 1962, Le Malesherbois,
Paris, 45330, France
Tel.: (33) 238327229
Construction Handling Equipment & Machinery Mfr
N.A.I.C.S.: 333120

Camso Holding Brasil Ltda (1)
Rua 24 de Maio 237, Santo Andre, 09110-150, Sao Paulo, Brazil
Tel.: (55) 1144276656
Construction Equipment Mfr
N.A.I.C.S.: 333120

Camso Inc. (1)
Rifki Tongsir Caddesi No 85, Istanbul,
34854, Türkiye
Tel.: (90) 2164891500
Construction Equipment Mfr
N.A.I.C.S.: 333120

Camso Industrielle Hungary Kft. (1)
Ipartelep HRSZ 0362/23, Kulcs, 2458,
Bicske, Hungary
Tel.: (36) 25251456
Construction Handling Equipment & Machinery Mfr
N.A.I.C.S.: 333120

Camso International S.a.r.l. (1)
65 Avenue de la Gare, Luxembourg, 1611,
Luxembourg
Tel.: (352) 261999
Construction Handling Equipment & Machinery Mfr
N.A.I.C.S.: 333120
Antonin Konopka (Mgr-Bus Dev)

Camso Italy S.p.A. (1)
Strada Statale Vigevanese Q re Ind le Mirabelle, Ozzero, 20080, Milan, Italy
Tel.: (39) 0294608758
Construction Handling Equipment & Machinery Mfr
N.A.I.C.S.: 333120

Camso Japan Co., Ltd. (1)
Nisso Bldg 16 Shin-Yokohama 3-8-8,
Kohoku-ku, Yokohama, 222-0033, Japan
Tel.: (81) 454711273
Construction Equipment Mfr
N.A.I.C.S.: 333120

**Camso Lastik Ticaret Limited
Sirketi** (1)
Rifki Tongsir Cad no 64, Istanbul, 34841,
Turkiye
Tel.: (90) 2164891500
Construction Machinery Mfr
N.A.I.C.S.: 333120

Camso Nederland B.V. (1)
Veldwade 10, 3439 LE, Nieuwegein, Netherlands
Tel.: (31) 30 280 2040
Web Site: https://www.camso.nl
Automotive Tire Retailer
N.A.I.C.S.: 423130
Cas Van Piekeren (Reg Sls Mgr)

Camso New Zealand Limited (1)
36A Sir William Ave, East Tamaki, 2013,
Auckland, New Zealand
Tel.: (64) 92539097
Construction Equipment Mfr
N.A.I.C.S.: 333120

Camso Polska S.A. (1)
ul Trakt Brzeski 35, Warsaw, 05-077, Poland
Tel.: (48) 227831787
Construction Handling Equipment & Machinery Mfr
N.A.I.C.S.: 333120
Lukasz Roslon (Reg Sls Mgr)

Camso Schweiz AG (1)
Ebnatstrasse 150 A, Schaffhausen, 8200,
Switzerland
Tel.: (41) 525602727
Construction Machinery Mfr

N.A.I.C.S.: 333120

Camso Spain, S.L. (1)
Poligono Industrial Valdeconsejo, Cuarte de
Huerva, 50410, Spain
Tel.: (34) 976505119
Construction Handling Equipment & Machinery Mfr
N.A.I.C.S.: 333120

Camso Taeryuk Ltd. (1)
118-209 41 Yutongdanji1-ro, Gangseo-gu,
Busan, 46721, Korea (South)
Tel.: (82) 1028788472
Construction Equipment Mfr
N.A.I.C.S.: 333120

Camso UK Limited (1)
Unit 35A Vale Business Park, Cowbridge,
South Wales, CF71 7PF, Glamorgan,
United Kingdom
Tel.: (44) 1446774914
Construction Machinery Mfr
N.A.I.C.S.: 333120

Camso Vietnam Co., Ltd. (1)
02 Ngo Duc Ke Street Me Linh Point Tower
7th Floor, Ho Chi Minh City, 70000, Vietnam
Tel.: (84) 835202824
Construction Equipment Mfr
N.A.I.C.S.: 333120
Dung Nguyen (Production Mgr)

**Compagnie Financiere Michelin
SCmA** (1)
Route Louis-Braille 10-12, 1763, Granges-Paccot, Switzerland
Tel.: (41) 264674444
Investment & Financial Management Services
N.A.I.C.S.: 523999

**Dunlop Conveyor Belting Ghana
Limited** (1)
MBC Yard Off Sansu Mine Road, Obuasi,
Ghana
Tel.: (233) 540132390
Web Site: https://dunlopservice.com.gh
N.A.I.C.S.: 332999

**Dunlop Conveyor Belting Polska
sp.zo.o** (1)
Ul Uniwersytecka 13, 40-007, Katowice,
Poland
Tel.: (48) 327847862
Web Site: https://dunlopssc.com
N.A.I.C.S.: 541614

Dunlop Service B.V. (1)
Heemst 2, Klazienaveen, 7892 AL, Emmen,
Netherlands
Tel.: (31) 591314171
Industrial Conveyor Belt Material Mfr
N.A.I.C.S.: 333922

Euromaster (Suisse) S.A. (1)
Industriestrasse 30, 3186, Dudingen, Switzerland
Tel.: (41) 264932988
Automotive Tire Mfr
N.A.I.C.S.: 326211

Euromaster AB (1)
Stormhallsv 6, Box 1134, 432 15, Varberg,
Sweden
Tel.: (46) 34082900
Web Site: http://www.euromaster.com
Emp.: 50
Automotive Tires Distr
N.A.I.C.S.: 423130
Yvan Guerassimoff (CEO)

**Euromaster Automocion y Servicios,
S.A.** (1)
Calle Albarracin 34, 28037, Madrid, Spain
Tel.: (34) 913791200
Web Site: http://www.euromaster.com
Emp.: 200
Tire Retreading Services
N.A.I.C.S.: 326111
Faulsto Casetta (Gen Mgr)

Euromaster Bandenservice B.V. (1)
Tel.: (31) 57 067 9790
Web Site: https://www.euromaster.nl
Tire Mfr & Distr
N.A.I.C.S.: 326211

**Euromaster Ceska Republika
s.r.o.** (1)

Lomnickeho 1705/5, 140 00, Prague, Czech
Republic
Tel.: (420) 241406366
Web Site: https://www.euromaster.cz
Tire & Car Maintenance Services
N.A.I.C.S.: 811198
Tomas Marek (Mgr-Technical IT/IS)

Euromaster Danmark A/S (1)
Kroyer Kielbergs Vej 3 1 th, 8660, Skanderborg, Denmark
Tel.: (45) 87282828
Web Site: https://www.euromaster.dk
Automotive Tires Distr
N.A.I.C.S.: 423130
Ovei Chler (Gen Mgr)

Euromaster France S.N.C (1)
Immeuble Sun 180 Avenue de l'Europe,
38330, Montbonnot-Saint-Martin, France
Tel.: (33) 4 76 61 28 00
Web Site: http://www.euromaster.fr
Tire & Automotive Maintenance Services
N.A.I.C.S.: 811198

Euromaster GmbH (1)
Theodor-Heuss-Anlage 12, 68165, Mannheim, Germany
Tel.: (49) 621717800
Web Site: https://www.euromaster.de
Sales Range: $25-49.9 Million
Emp.: 140
Automotive Wheel Maintenance Services
N.A.I.C.S.: 811121
Matthias Schubert (Gen Mgr)

Euromaster Italia S.r.l. (1)
Centro Direzionale Bodio 3 Viale Luigi Bodio 37, 20158, Milan, MI, Italy
Tel.: (39) 020 066 4500
Web Site: https://www.euromaster-pneumatici.it
Tire & Car Maintenance Services
N.A.I.C.S.: 811198
Maurizio Bramezza (Mktg Dir)

**Euromaster Lastik Ve Servis Limited
Sirketi** (1)
Levent Mah Meltem Sk Is Kuleleri Kule 3
Apt No 14/15 4, Levent Besiktas, 34430,
Istanbul, Turkiye
Tel.: (90) 212 357 0600
Web Site: https://www.euromaster.com.tr
Vehicle Maintenance Services
N.A.I.C.S.: 811198

Euromaster Polska sp. z.o.o. (1)
Domaniewska 45, 02-672, Warsaw, Poland
Tel.: (48) 223956290
Web Site: https://www.euromaster.pl
N.A.I.C.S.: 811198

Euromaster Reifenservice GmbH (1)
Triester Strasse 336, 1230, Vienna, Austria
Tel.: (43) 16 994 5370
Web Site: https://www.euromaster.at
Automotive Tire & Car Services
N.A.I.C.S.: 811198
Christian Ganss (Acct Mgr)

**Euromaster Tyre & Services Romania
S.A.** (1)
Soseaua Bucuresti Nord nr 10 Global City
Business Park Building O11, Floor 4 Room
1 Ilfov, Voluntari, Romania
Tel.: (40) 311303701
Web Site: http://www.euromaster.ro
Tire & Car Maintenance Services
N.A.I.C.S.: 811198
Maxim Jelena (CFO)

Eurowheel BVBA (1)
Moerbroek 27 IZ Klein Gent, Herenthout,
2270, Antwerp, Belgium
Tel.: (32) 1 422 0770
Web Site: https://www.eurowheel.be
Industrial Lift Truck Wheel Mfr
N.A.I.C.S.: 336390

Fenner Dunlop Chile SpA (1)
Ruta 26 Kilometro 15 S/N Sector Salar Del
Carmen Edificio B Modulo 7, Antofagasta,
Chile
Tel.: (56) 552492314
N.A.I.C.S.: 213113
Pablo Maass (Acct Mgr)

Fenner Dunlop Italia S.r.l. (1)
Via Don Primo Mazzolari, 24054, Calcio,
BG, Italy
Tel.: (39) 0363906266

N.A.I.C.S.: 333922

Fenner Dunlop Maroc SARL (1)
6 sis Parc Tawfic Route Secondaire de 111
de Zenata-Ain Sebaa, Casablanca, Morocco
Tel.: (212) 66 131 2421
Web Site: https://www.dunlopservice.ma
Construction Machinery Mfr
N.A.I.C.S.: 333120

Fenner Dunlop S.L. (1)
Poligon Ind Magarola Carrer de les tres rieres nave 1 y 2, Esparreguera, 08292, Barcelona, Spain
Tel.: (34) 937704597
Industrial Conveyor Belt Material Mfr
N.A.I.C.S.: 333922

Fenner Dunlop SARL (1)
ZAC de la Clef Saint Pierre 8 Rue Blaise
Pascal, 78990, Elancourt, France
Tel.: (33) 130555419
Industrial Conveyor Belt Material Mfr
N.A.I.C.S.: 333922

**Hallite Sealing Solutions India Private
Limited** (1)
Peenya Industrial Area, Bengaluru, 560
058, India
Tel.: (91) 802372600001
Industrial Equipment Retailer
N.A.I.C.S.: 423130
Selvaraj Manjunath (Fin Mgr)

Hallite Seals Americas, LLC (1)
50777 Varsity Ct, Wixom, MI 48393
Tel.: (248) 668-5200
N.A.I.C.S.: 333995

**Hallite Seals Australia Pty
Limited** (1)
Unit 1 9 Bushells Place, Wetherill Park,
2164, NSW, Australia
Tel.: (61) 288861665
Industrial Machinery Mfr & Distr
N.A.I.C.S.: 333248

**Hallite Shanghai Company
Limited** (1)
785 Xing Rong Road, Jiading Industrial
Park Jiading District, Shanghai, 201807,
China
Tel.: (86) 2133517272
Industrial Machinery Mfr & Distr
N.A.I.C.S.: 333248
Vincent Chong (Mng Dir)

ITC International Tire NV (1)
Guddegemstraat 45, 2160, Wommelgem,
Belgium
Tel.: (32) 33531112
Web Site: https://www.itc-tires.be
N.A.I.C.S.: 326211

Ihle Anvelope SRL (1)
B-dul Fratii Golesti Nr 13 Cam 1 Et 2, 110
174, Pitesti, Romania
Tel.: (40) 213021700
Automotive Tires Distr
N.A.I.C.S.: 423130

Ihle Czech, s.r.o. (1)
Radynska 573/4, 326 00, Plzen, Czech
Republic
Tel.: (420) 84 495 6515
Web Site: https://www.ihlenet.de
Automotive Tires Distr
N.A.I.C.S.: 423130

Ihle Magyarorszag Kft. (1)
Erdelyi U 4, 2900, Komarom, Hungary
Tel.: (36) 15775287
N.A.I.C.S.: 562920
Peter Szabo (Mng Dir)

Ihle Slovakia s.r.o. (1)
Dubravska cesta 2, 841 04, Bratislava, Slovakia
Tel.: (421) 850123124
Tire & Complete Wheel Whslr
N.A.I.C.S.: 423130

Ihle Tires GmbH (1)
Heinkelstr 13, 76461, Muggensturm, Germany
Tel.: (49) 72229823996
Web Site: https://www.ihlenet.de
N.A.I.C.S.: 562920
Juliette Ribbert (Mng Dir)

Ihle pnevmatike, d.o.o. **(1)**
Ulica Vita Kraigherja 5, 2000, Maribor, Slovenia
Tel.: (386) 38615830969
Tire & Complete Wheel Whslr
N.A.I.C.S.: 423130

Industrial International Tire Company
NV **(1)**
Guddegemstraat 45, Wommelgem, 2160, Antwerp, Belgium
Tel.: (32) 33531112
Web Site: http://www.itc-tires.be
Motor Vehicle Parts Whslr
N.A.I.C.S.: 423120
Gregory Mespreuve *(CEO)*

Industrial Levorin S.A. **(1)**
Av Monteiro Lobato 2641, Guarulhos, 07190-901, Sao Paulo, Brazil
Tel.: (55) 8000070731
Web Site: https://levorin.com.br
Tire Product Mfr
N.A.I.C.S.: 326212
Jederson Faria *(Mgr-Maintenance)*

Klinge Holdings Pty Ltd **(1)**
Suite 1A 1st Floor 201 Leichhardt Street, Spring Hill, Brisbane, 4000, QLD, Australia
Tel.: (61) 73 839 3077
Web Site: https://www.klinge.com.au
Tire Product Mfr
N.A.I.C.S.: 326212

Laurent Reifen GmbH **(1)**
Sachsenhausener Str 29a, 16515, Oranienburg, Germany
Tel.: (49) 330183450
Tire Retreading Services
N.A.I.C.S.: 326211

Manufacture Francaise des Pneumatiques Michelin **(1)**
Place des Carmes Dechaux, 63040, Clermont-Ferrand, Cedex, France **(100%)**
Tel.: (33) 47 332 2000
Web Site: https://www.michelin.fr
Sales Range: $25-49.9 Million
Emp.: 33
Tires & Tubes Mfr
N.A.I.C.S.: 326211

Subsidiary (Domestic):

Kleber Pneumatiques SA **(2)**
Place des Carmes Dechaux, 63040, Clermont, Ferrand, France **(98.3%)**
Tel.: (33) 4 73 32 2000
Web Site: http://www.kleber.fr
Mfr of Tires & Rubber Products
N.A.I.C.S.: 326211

Subsidiary (Non-US):

Kleber Reifen GmbH **(3)**
Michelinstrasse 4, 76185, Karlsruhe, Germany **(100%)**
Tel.: (49) 7215300
Web Site: http://www.kleber-reifen.de
Sales Range: $450-499.9 Million
Tires & Tubes Mfr
N.A.I.C.S.: 326211

Masternaut GmbH **(1)**
Ohmstrasse 3, 80802, Munich, Germany
Tel.: (49) 8926207256
Information Technology Services
N.A.I.C.S.: 541511

Masternaut Limited **(1)**
Priory Park Great North Road, Aberford, Leeds, LS25 3DF, United Kingdom
Tel.: (44) 113 281 4000
Web Site: https://www.masternaut.com
Sales Range: $25-49.9 Million
Emp.: 150
Vehicle Tracking Software & Services
N.A.I.C.S.: 513210
Dhruv S. Parekh *(CEO)*

Subsidiary (Non-US):

Masternaut AB **(2)**
Wallingatan 34, Askim, 111 24, Stockholm, Sweden
Tel.: (46) 31 748 5950
Web Site: https://www.masternaut.com
Sales Range: $10-24.9 Million
Emp.: 10
Vehicle Tracking Services
N.A.I.C.S.: 334419

Masternaut Deutschland GmbH **(2)**
Keltenring 13, D-82041, Munich, Oberhaching, Germany
Tel.: (49) 896283310
Vehicle Tracking Services
N.A.I.C.S.: 334419
Nigel Ciesse *(Office Mgr)*

Masternaut International S.A.S. **(2)**
4 Rue Charles Cros, 24700, Louviers, France
Tel.: (33) 232253700
Web Site: http://www.masteraut.com
Sales Range: $25-49.9 Million
Emp.: 200
Vehicle Tracking Software & Services
N.A.I.C.S.: 513210
Marc Trollet *(Mng Dir)*

Subsidiary (Domestic):

Three X Communication Limited **(2)**
11 Stable Courtyard Broughton Hall, Skipton, BD23 3AE, North Yorkshire, United Kingdom
Tel.: (44) 8444150150
Web Site: http://www.threex.co.uk
Sales Range: $25-49.9 Million
Emp.: 10
Mobile Software Solutions
N.A.I.C.S.: 541511
Andrew Tillman *(CEO)*

Michelin AIM FZCO **(1)**
DAFZA - 8WA 2nd Floor, PO Box 54842, Dubai, United Arab Emirates
Tel.: (971) 8000120209
Web Site: https://middle-east.michelin.com
N.A.I.C.S.: 326211

Michelin Air Services **(1)**
23 Place Des Carmes Dechaux, 63040, Clermont-Ferrand, France
Tel.: (33) 473322000
Tire Mfr & Distr
N.A.I.C.S.: 326211

Michelin Algerie SPA **(1)**
Route De Birkhadem Bachdjerrah, 16040, Algiers, Algeria
Tel.: (213) 21268197
Tiles Mfr
N.A.I.C.S.: 326211

Michelin America do Sul **(1)**
Avenida das Americas 700 Bloco 4, Barra da Tijuca, Rio de Janeiro, CEP 22640-100, RJ, Brazil **(100%)**
Tel.: (55) 2124294646
Web Site: http://www.michelin.com.br
Sales Range: $1-4.9 Billion
Emp.: 6,000
Marketing of Tires
N.A.I.C.S.: 441340

Michelin Argentina Sociedad Anonima, Industrial, Comercial y Financiera **(1)**
Calle Lascano, 5130, Buenos Aires, Argentina
Tel.: (54) 1146303030
Automotive Tire Mfr
N.A.I.C.S.: 326211

Michelin Asia-Pacific Pte Ltd **(1)**
77 Robinson Rd 34-01 & 35-01 Robinson 77, Singapore, 068896, Singapore
Tel.: (65) 64389400
Automotive Tire Mfr & Distr
N.A.I.C.S.: 326211

Subsidiary (Non-US):

Michelin Asia (Hong Kong) Limited **(2)**
3406 34/F West Tower Shun Tak Centre 168-200 Connaught Road Central, Sheung Wan, Hong Kong, China (Hong Kong)
Tel.: (852) 28817287
Web Site: http://www.michelin.com.hk
Automotive Tires Distr
N.A.I.C.S.: 423130

Subsidiary (Domestic):

Michelin Asia (Singapore) Co. Pte. Ltd. **(2)**
78 Shenton Way 23-01 and 24-02, Singapore, 079120, Singapore
Tel.: (65) 6 438 9500

Web Site: https://www.michelin.com.sg
Automotive Tires Distr
N.A.I.C.S.: 423130

Subsidiary (Non-US):

Michelin Chun Shin Ltd. **(2)**
5F-1 No 190 Sec 3 Datong Rd, Xizhi Dist, Taipei, 22103, Taiwan
Tel.: (886) 286471111
Web Site: http://www.michelin.com.tw
Emp.: 50
Automotive Tire Mfr
N.A.I.C.S.: 326211
Jay Mao *(CEO)*

Michelin Korea Company Limited **(2)**
15th Fl 157-1 Samsung Dong Kangnam, Seoul, Korea (South) **(100%)**
Tel.: (82) 262405590
Web Site: http://www.michelin.co.kr
Sales Range: $25-49.9 Million
Emp.: 45
Distr of Tires
N.A.I.C.S.: 441340

Michelin Thai Holding Co., Ltd. **(2)**
252 Paholyothin Rd, Phaya Thai, Bangkok, 10400, Thailand
Tel.: (66) 26193000
Investment Management Service
N.A.I.C.S.: 523999

Holding (Domestic):

Michelin Siam Group Co., Ltd. **(3)**
252 Phaholyothin Road Samsaen Nai, Payathai, Bangkok, 10400, Thailand **(90%)**
Tel.: (66) 2 619 3000
Web Site: http://www.michelin.co.th
Sales Range: $1-4.9 Billion
Emp.: 6,300
Holding Company; Automotive Tires Mfr
N.A.I.C.S.: 551112

Subsidiary (Domestic):

Michelin Siam Co., Ltd. **(4)**
19th Floor The 9th Tower Grand Rama9 Building A 33/4 Rama9 Road, Huay Kwang, Bangkok, 10310, Thailand
Tel.: (66) 2 700 3993
Web Site: https://en.michelin.co.th
Sales Range: $1-4.9 Billion
Automotive Tire Mfr
N.A.I.C.S.: 326211

Plant (Domestic):

Michelin Siam Co., Ltd. - Nongkhae Plant **(5)**
Siam Cement Industrial Estate 57 Moo, 6 Nongkhakradee Road, Nongkhae, 18140, Sarburi, Thailand
Tel.: (66) 36373276 89
Web Site: http://www.michelin.co.th
Sales Range: $200-249.9 Million
Emp.: 900
Heavy Truck Tires & Bus Tires Mfr
N.A.I.C.S.: 326211

Michelin Siam Co., Ltd. - Si Racha Plant **(5)**
87/11 Moo 2 Sukhumvit Road, Laemchabang Industrial Estate, Tung Sukhla, Si Racha, 20230, Chon Buri, Thailand
Tel.: (66) 384905349
Web Site: http://www.michelin.co.th
Sales Range: $650-699.9 Million
Emp.: 1,200
Automotive Tire Mfr
N.A.I.C.S.: 326211

Subsidiary (Non-US):

Michelin Vietnam Company Limited **(2)**
8th Floor VFC Tower 29 Ton Duc Thang Street, District 1, Ho Chi Minh City, Vietnam
Tel.: (84) 8 3911 8115
Automotive Tire Mfr & Distr
N.A.I.C.S.: 326211

Nihon Michelin Tire Co., Ltd. **(2)**
Fujimi Bldg 6-1 Fujimi 1-chome, Chiyoda-ku, Tokyo, 102-8176, Japan
Tel.: (81) 352102732
Automotive Tire Mfr & Distr
N.A.I.C.S.: 326211

Shanghai Michelin Warrior Tire Co., Ltd. **(2)**
No 2915 Jianchuan Rd, Minhang Dist, Shanghai, 201111, China
Tel.: (86) 2134054888
Automotive Tire Mfr & Distr
N.A.I.C.S.: 326211

Subsidiary (Domestic):

Societe des Matieres Premieres Tropicales Pte. Ltd. **(2)**
78 Shenton Way 23-02, Singapore, 079120, Singapore
Tel.: (65) 64389500
Emp.: 50
Automotive Tire Mfr
N.A.I.C.S.: 326211

Michelin Australia Pty Ltd **(1)**
51-57 Fennell Street, Port Melbourne, 3207, VIC, Australia
Tel.: (61) 130 072 7878
Web Site: https://www.michelin.com.au
Automobile Parts Mfr
N.A.I.C.S.: 336390
Shane Badley *(Mgr-HR)*

Michelin Belux S.A. **(1)**
Brusselsesteenweg 494, Asse, 1731, Belgium
Tel.: (32) 22744211
Emp.: 150
Automotive Tires Distr
N.A.I.C.S.: 423130

Michelin Chile Ltda. **(1)**
Luis Carrera 1131, Comuna, Vitacura, Chile
Tel.: (56) 80 022 1200
Web Site: https://www.michelin.cl
Sales Range: $25-49.9 Million
Emp.: 80
Automotive Tire Mfr
N.A.I.C.S.: 326211

Michelin Corporation **(1)**
1 Pkwy S, Greenville, SC 29615-5022
Tel.: (864) 458-5000
Web Site: http://www.michelin-us.com
Rev.: $200,000,000
Emp.: 1,500
Sales of Automobile Tires Pneumatic
N.A.I.C.S.: 326211

Subsidiary (Domestic):

Michelin North America, Inc. **(2)**
1 Pkwy S, Greenville, SC 29615
Tel.: (864) 458-5000
Web Site: https://michelinmedia.com
Sales Range: $1-4.9 Billion
Emp.: 22,300
Tiles Mfr
N.A.I.C.S.: 326211
Kaz Holley *(Dir-BFGoodrich, Uniroyal, Private & Assoc Brands)*

Subsidiary (Domestic):

American Synthetic Rubber Company **(3)**
4500 Camp Ground Rd, Louisville, KY 40216-4675
Tel.: (502) 449-8300
Web Site: http://www.americansyntheticrubberco.com
Sales Range: $25-49.9 Million
Emp.: 360
Production of Synthetic Rubber & Liquid Polymers
N.A.I.C.S.: 325212
Guillaume Coiraton *(Ops Mgr)*

Lehigh Technologies Inc. **(3)**
120 Royal Woods Ct SW, Tucker, GA 30084-0084
Tel.: (678) 495-2200
Web Site: http://www.lehightechnologies.com
Specialty Chemicals Company; Micronized Rubber Powder Products
N.A.I.C.S.: 325998
Kedar Murthy *(VP-Tire Materials)*

Michelin Aircraft Tire Corporation **(3)**
1 Pkwy S, Greenville, SC 29615 **(100%)**
Tel.: (864) 458-5000
Web Site: http://www.airmichelin.com
Sales Range: $50-74.9 Million
Emp.: 150
Aircraft Tires Mfr

Compagnie Generale des Etablissements Michelin SCA—(Continued)

N.A.I.C.S.: 326211
Brian Bergman (Engr-Matl Res)

Michelin Americas Research & Development (3)
515 Michelin Rd, Greenville, SC 29605
Tel.: (864) 422-4000
Web Site: http://www.michelin-us.com
Sales Range: $150-199.9 Million
Emp.: 900
Commercial Physical Research
N.A.I.C.S.: 541715
Nicolas Prigent (Dir-Mktg)

Subsidiary (Non-US):

Michelin North America (Canada) Inc. (3)
2500 Daniel-Johnson Suite 500, Laval, H7L
3K8, QC, Canada (100%)
Tel.: (450) 978-4700
Web Site: https://www.michelin.ca
Sales Range: $25-49.9 Million
Emp.: 150
Commercial Tire Distr
N.A.I.C.S.: 441340
Jean Moreau (VP-Personnel)

Subsidiary (Domestic):

Oliver Rubber Company (3)
408 Telephone Ave, Asheboro, NC 27205
Tel.: (336) 629-1436
Web Site: http://www.oliverrubber.com
Sales Range: $100-124.9 Million
Emp.: 285
Retread Rubber, Bonding Gum & Equipment Mfr
N.A.I.C.S.: 326291
Michael James (Mgr-Methods)

Streetwise Maps, Inc. (3)
4376 Independence Ct, Sarasota, FL 34234
Tel.: (941) 358-1956
Web Site: http://www.streetwisemaps.com
Sales Range: $1-9.9 Million
Emp.: 12
Travel Literature Publisher
N.A.I.C.S.: 513120
Michael Brown (Pres)

TCI Tire Centers, LLC (3)
310 Inglesby Pkwy, Duncan, SC 29334
Tel.: (864) 329-2700
Web Site: http://www.tirecenters.com
Sales Range: $600-649.9 Million
Emp.: 2,400
Automotive Tire Whslr
N.A.I.C.S.: 423130
Cara Cornelius (Sr Dir-Supply Chain & Logistics)

Subsidiary (Domestic):

TCI Tire Centers (4)
4771 Hollins Ferry Rd, Baltimore, MD
21227
Tel.: (410) 247-4464
Web Site: http://www.tirecenters.com
Sales Range: $25-49.9 Million
Emp.: 25
Automotive Tire Whslr
N.A.I.C.S.: 423130

Subsidiary (Non-US):

Uniroyal Goodrich Canada, Inc. (3)
131 Goodrich Dr, Kitchener, N2G 4S5, ON,
Canada (100%)
Tel.: (519) 894-7800
Web Site: http://www.michelin.ca
Sales Range: $25-49.9 Million
Emp.: 15
Mfr of Tires
N.A.I.C.S.: 326211

Subsidiary (Domestic):

Uniroyal Goodrich Intellectual (3)
1 Pkwy S, Greenville, SC 29615-5022
Tel.: (864) 458-5000
Web Site: http://www.michelin-us.com
Mfr & Sales of Auotmobile Tires
N.A.I.C.S.: 326211
James M. Micali (CEO)

Michelin Espana Portugal, S.A. (1)
Avda de Los Encuartes 19, 28760, Tres

Cantos, Spain
Tel.: (34) 914105000
Automotive Tire Mfr & Distr
N.A.I.C.S.: 326211

Michelin Finance (Pays-Bas) B.V. (1)
Huub van Doorneweg 2, 5151 DT, Drunen,
Netherlands
Tel.: (31) 416384142
Financial Management Services
N.A.I.C.S.: 523999
John Corsen (Gen Mgr)

Michelin Finanz Gesellschaft fur Beteiligungen AG & Co. OHG (1)
Michelinstrasse 4, 76185, Karlsruhe, Germany
Tel.: (49) 7215300
Automotive Tire Mfr
N.A.I.C.S.: 326211

Michelin Hungaria Tyre Manufacture Ltd. (1)
Kerepesi Ut 17, 1087, Budapest, Hungary
Tel.: (36) 42 502 600
Web Site: http://www.michelin.com
Emp.: 441
Automotive Tire Mfr
N.A.I.C.S.: 326211

Michelin India Private Limited (1)
Shyamala Towers 3rd Floor 136 Arcot
Road, Saligramam, Chennai, 600093, India
Tel.: (91) 4467916302
Web Site: https://www.michelin.in
N.A.I.C.S.: 326211

Michelin India TamilNadu Tyres Private Limited (1)
9th Floor Shyamala Towers No 136 Arcot
Road Saligramam, Saligramam, Chennai,
600 093, India
Tel.: (91) 44 3993 6000
Sales Range: $200-249.9 Million
Emp.: 100
Automotive Tire Mfr
N.A.I.C.S.: 326211
Nicolas Beaumont (Mng Dir)

Michelin India Tyres Private Limited (1)
7th Fl The Pinnacle Business Tower Shooting Range Rd Surajkund, Faridabad,
121001, India
Tel.: (91) 1293097777
Web Site: http://www.michelin.in
Sales Range: $150-199.9 Million
Emp.: 300
Automotive Tire Mfr & Distr
N.A.I.C.S.: 326211

Michelin Lastikleri Ticaret A.S. (1)
Buyukdere Cad Tekfen Tower No 209,
34394, Istanbul, Turkiye
Tel.: (90) 2123175200
Automotive Tire Mfr
N.A.I.C.S.: 326211

Michelin Malaysia Sdn. Bhd. (1)
901 & 904 Level 9 Uptown 2 No 2 Jalan
SS21/37, Damansara Uptown, 47400, Petaling Jaya, Malaysia
Tel.: (60) 37 680 3888
Web Site: https://www.michelin.com.my
Auto Parts Mfr
N.A.I.C.S.: 336390
Boon Keat Kuang (Sr Acct Mgr)

Michelin Nederland N.V. (1)
Europalaan 30, 5232 BC, 's-
Hertogenbosch, Netherlands
Tel.: (31) 732061200
Web Site: https://www.michelin.nl
N.A.I.C.S.: 326211

Michelin Nordic AB (1)
Arstaangsvagen 11, PO Box 47175, Stockholm, 100 74, Sweden
Tel.: (46) 87090700
Emp.: 120
Automotive Tires Distr
N.A.I.C.S.: 423130
Vincent Pinot (Mng Dir)

Michelin Polska S.A. (1)
ul Leonharda 9, 10-454, Olsztyn, Poland
Tel.: (48) 895323315
Web Site: https://www.michelin.pl
Emp.: 4,500

Tiles Mfr
N.A.I.C.S.: 326211
John Young (Gen Mgr)

Michelin Recherche et Technique S.A. (1)
Route Louis-Braille 10, Granges-Paccot,
1763, Switzerland
Tel.: (41) 264674444
Automotive Tire Mfr
N.A.I.C.S.: 326211

Michelin Reifenwerke KGaA (1)
Michelinstrasse 4, 76185, Karlsruhe,
Germany (100%)
Tel.: (49) 7215300
Web Site: https://www.michelin.de
Sales Range: $450-499.9 Million
Emp.: 1,400
Mfr of Tires
N.A.I.C.S.: 326211

Michelin Romania S.A. (1)
Soseaua Bucuresti-Nord nr 10 Building O1
floor 3, Global City Business Park Voluntari
Ilfov County, 077190, Bucharest, Romania
Tel.: (40) 800896551
Web Site: https://www.michelin.ro
Sales Range: $75-99.9 Million
Emp.: 150
Automotive Tire Mfr & Distr
N.A.I.C.S.: 326211
Eric Faidy (Gen Mgr)

Michelin Suisse S.A. (1)
Route Jo Siffert 36, 1762, Givisiez, Switzerland
Tel.: (41) 80022111180
Web Site: https://www.michelin.ch
N.A.I.C.S.: 326211

Michelin Tyre Company South Africa (Proprietary) Limited (1)
Clearwater Buisness park Atlas Rd Bokburger, Bedfordview, 1655, South Africa
Tel.: (27) 115790300
Web Site: http://www.michelin.co.za
Sales Range: $50-74.9 Million
Emp.: 100
Automotive Tire Mfr & Distr
N.A.I.C.S.: 326211
Guillermo Antunez (Gen Mgr)

Michelin Tyre P.L.C. (1)
Campbell Rd, Stoke-on-Trent, ST4 4EY,
United Kingdom (100%)
Tel.: (44) 1782402000
Web Site: http://www.michelin.co.uk
Mfr of Tires
N.A.I.C.S.: 326211
Mike Lawton (Head-Comm-North Europe)

Subsidiary (Domestic):

Associated Tyre Specialists Limited (2)
Brixton Hill, London, SW2 1SD, United
Kingdom
Tel.: (44) 2086716800
Automotive Tire Mfr & Distr
N.A.I.C.S.: 326211

Fenner Group Holdings Limited (2)
Hesslewood Country Office Park Ferriby
Road, Hessle, HU13 0PW, East Yorkshire,
United Kingdom
Tel.: (44) 1482626500
Web Site: https://www.fenner.com
Holding Company; Reinforced Polymer
Technologies Developer, Mfr & Whslr
N.A.I.C.S.: 551112

Subsidiary (US):

American Industrial Plastic, LLC (3)
724 Fentress Blvd, Daytona Beach, FL
32114
Tel.: (386) 274-5335
Web Site: https://www.aipprecision.com
Precision-Machined Plastic Products Mfr
N.A.I.C.S.: 326199
John MacDonald (Pres)

Charter Medical, Ltd. (3)
3948-A Westpoint Blvd, Winston Salem, NC
27103
Tel.: (866) 458-3116
Web Site: https://chartermedical.com
Bioprocess Containers & Medical Devices
Whslr

N.A.I.C.S.: 423450

Subsidiary (Domestic):

Fenner Dunlop Limited (3)
Hesslewood Country Office Park, Ferriby
Road, Hessle, HU13 0PW, E Yorkshire,
United Kingdom
Tel.: (44) 1482 626 531
Web Site: http://www.fennerdunlop.com
Conveyor Belting System Mfr & Distr
N.A.I.C.S.: 333922

Subsidiary (Non-US):

Fenner Conveyor Belting (South Africa) (Pty) Limited (4)
21 Diesel Road, Isando, 1600, South Africa
Tel.: (27) 119741902
Web Site: https://www.fennersouthafrica.com
Conveyor Belts Mfr
N.A.I.C.S.: 333922

Fenner Conveyor Belting Private Limited (4)
Dindigul Road, Nagari, Madurai, 625 221,
India
Tel.: (91) 4522464201
Web Site: https://fennerconveyorbelting.com
Conveyor Belts Mfr
N.A.I.C.S.: 333922

Subsidiary (US):

Fenner Dunlop Americas, LLC (4)
200 Corporate Ctr Dr Ste 220, Coraopolis,
PA 15108
Tel.: (412) 249-0700
Web Site:
 http://www.fennerdunlopamericas.com
Holding Company; Conveyor Belting & Systems Mfr, Distr & Support Services
N.A.I.C.S.: 551112

Subsidiary (Domestic):

Fenner Dunlop Conveyor Systems & Services, LLC (5)
Omega Corp Ctr 1000 Omega Dr Ste 1400,
Pittsburgh, PA 15205
Tel.: (412) 249-0700
Conveyor Belting & Systems Mfr & Distr
N.A.I.C.S.: 333922

Subsidiary (Domestic):

Fenner Dunlop (Atlanta), Inc. (6)
325 Gateway Dr, Lavonia, GA 30553
Tel.: (706) 356-4844
Web Site:
 http://www.fennerdunlopamericas.com
Conveyor Belting System Mfr & Distr
N.A.I.C.S.: 333922

Subsidiary (Non-US):

Fenner Dunlop (Bracebridge) Inc. (6)
700 Ecclestone Drive, PO Box 2230, Bracebridge, P1L 1W1, ON, Canada
Tel.: (705) 645-4431
Conveyor Belting Mfr
N.A.I.C.S.: 333922

Subsidiary (Domestic):

Fenner Dunlop (Port Clinton), Inc. (6)
5225 W Lakeshore Dr Bldg 320, Port Clinton, OH 43452
Tel.: (419) 635-2191
Web Site: https://fennerdunlopamericas.com
Mfr of Rubber Conveyor Belting
N.A.I.C.S.: 333922

Fenner Dunlop (Toledo), LLC (6)
146 S Westwood St, Toledo, OH 43607
Tel.: (419) 534-5300
Mfr of Conveyor Belts
N.A.I.C.S.: 333922

Fenner Dunlop Conveyor Services, LLC (6)
3312 Garman Rd, Gillette, WY 82716-1535
Tel.: (307) 682-2529
Conveyor Belt Repair Services
N.A.I.C.S.: 811310

Subsidiary (Non-US):

Fenner Dunlop Australia Pty. Ltd. (4)

268-280 Geelong Road, West Footscray, 3012, VIC, Australia
Tel.: (61) 396804500
Web Site: https://www.fenner.com.au
Conveyor Belting Mfr
N.A.I.C.S.: 333922

Subsidiary (Domestic):

Fenner Dunlop Whyalla Ptd. Ltd   (5)
Shiell Street, Whyalla, 5600, SA, Australia   **(100%)**
Tel.: (61) 886444100
Conveyor Belt Products Distr
N.A.I.C.S.: 423830

rEscan International Pty. Limited   (5)
1/14 Accolade Street, Morisset, 2264, NSW, Australia   **(100%)**
Tel.: (61) 249732399
Conveyor Belt Distr & Diagnostic Services
N.A.I.C.S.: 423830

Subsidiary (Non-US):

Fenner Dunlop BV   (4)
Oliemolenstraat 2,, 9203 ZP, Drachten, Netherlands
Tel.: (31) 512585555
Conveyor Belts Mfr
N.A.I.C.S.: 333922

Subsidiary (US):

Fenner, Inc.   (3)
187 W Airport Rd, Lititz, PA 17543 **(100%)**
Tel.: (717) 665-2421
Web Site: https://www.fennerdrives.com
Mfr of Industrial Belting, Power Transmission & Motion Control Components
N.A.I.C.S.: 314999

Subsidiary (Domestic):

Hallite Seals International Ltd   (3)
130 Oldfield Road, Hampton, TW12 2HT, Middlesex, United Kingdom
Tel.: (44) 2089412244
Web Site: https://hallite.com
Sealing Technologies Mfr & Distr
N.A.I.C.S.: 339991

Subsidiary (US):

CDI Energy Products, Inc.   (4)
8103 Rankin Rd, Humble, TX 77396   **(100%)**
Tel.: (281) 446-6662
Web Site: http://www.cdiproducts.com
Plastic Sealing Product Mfr
N.A.I.C.S.: 339991

Division (Domestic):

EGC Critical Components   (5)
8103 Rankin Rd, Humble, TX 77396
Tel.: (281) 774-6100
Web Site: http://www.egccomponents.com
Plastic Sealing Product Mfr
N.A.I.C.S.: 339991

Subsidiary (Domestic):

Hallite Seals International Ltd   (4)
130 Oldfield Road, Hampton, TW12 2HT, Middlesex, United Kingdom
Tel.: (44) 2089412244
Web Site: https://www.hallite.com
Hydraulic & Pneumatic Seal Mfr
N.A.I.C.S.: 339991

Subsidiary (Non-US):

Dichtelemente Hallite GmbH   (5)
Billwerder Ring 17, 21035, Hamburg, Germany
Tel.: (49) 407347480
Web Site: https://hallite.com
Hydraulic & Pneumatic Seal Mfr
N.A.I.C.S.: 332912

Hallite (France) Limited   (5)
Z A Les Petits Carreaux 1 Av Des Lys, 94385, Bonneuil-sur-Marne, France
Tel.: (33) 143778550
Web Site: http://www.hallite.fr
Hydraulic & Pneumatic Seal Mfr
N.A.I.C.S.: 339991

Hallite Italia Srl   (5)
Via Francia 21, Localita Guasticce, 57017, Colle Salvetti, Livorno, Italy

Tel.: (39) 0586428287
Web Site: https://hallite.com
Hydraulic Seals Mfr
N.A.I.C.S.: 339991

Hallite Seals (Canada) Limited   (5)
5630 Kennedy Road, Mississauga, L4Z 2A9, ON, Canada
Tel.: (905) 361-2350
Web Site: https://hallite.com
Hydraulic Seals Mfr
N.A.I.C.S.: 339991

Subsidiary (Domestic):

James Dawson & Son Ltd.   (3)
Tritton Rd, Lincoln, LN6 7AF, United Kingdom
Tel.: (44) 1522781800
Web Site: https://www.james-dawson.com
Rubber Hose Mfr
N.A.I.C.S.: 326220
Amit Kaul *(Mgr-Sls-India)*

Subsidiary (US):

National Bearings Co.   (3)
311 W Stiegel St, Manheim, PA 17545
Tel.: (800) 243-3374
Web Site: http://www.nationalbearings.com
Ball & Roller Bearing Mfr
N.A.I.C.S.: 332991

Michelin Tyre Services Company Ltd.   (1)
Plot 2A Ijora Causeway, PO Box 2842, Ijora, Lagos, Nigeria
Tel.: (234) 8034144341
N.A.I.C.S.: 326211

Michelin Ukraine LLC   (1)
19 G Skovorody St Podil Plaza BC 7 Fl, Kiev, 4070, Ukraine
Tel.: (380) 444903462
Automotive Tire Mfr
N.A.I.C.S.: 326211

NexTraq LLC   (1)
303 Perimeter Ctr N Ste 800, Atlanta, GA 30346
Web Site: https://www.nextraq.com
N.A.I.C.S.: 326211

PT Michelin Indonesia   (1)
Pondok Indah Office Tower 2 Lt 12 Jl Sultan Iskandar Muda Kav V-TA, Pondok Indah Kav V-TA, Jakarta Selatan, 12310, Indonesia
Tel.: (62) 212 935 3600
Web Site: https://www.michelin.co.id
Auto Parts Mfr
N.A.I.C.S.: 336390
Fritz Mueller *(Comml Dir)*

PT Multistrada Arah Sarana Tbk. (1)
Jl Raya Lemahabang km 58 3 Desa Karangsari Timur Bekasi, Jawa Barat, Cikarang, 17550, Indonesia   **(88%)**
Tel.: (62) 2189140333
Web Site: https://www.multistrada.co.id
Rev.: $488,891,053
Assets: $523,557,484
Liabilities: $142,556,456
Net Worth: $381,001,028
Earnings: $75,341,548
Emp.: 2,953
Fiscal Year-end: 12/31/2023
Tiles Mfr
N.A.I.C.S.: 336390
Steven Gommert Vette *(Chm)*

PTG Reifendruckregelsysteme GmbH   (1)
Habichtweg 9, 41468, Neuss, Germany
Tel.: (49) 213 152 3760
Web Site: https://www.ptg.info
Automotive Tires Distr
N.A.I.C.S.: 423130
Cyrille Beau *(Exec Dir)*

Pneu Laurent S.N.C   (1)
Route de Sauvigny-le-bois, PO Box 127, 89204, Avallon, France
Tel.: (33) 386314300
Web Site: http://www.pneulaurent.fr
Tire Retreading Services
N.A.I.C.S.: 326212

Pneumatiques Kleber S.A   (1)
Zoning Industriel Croix de Metz, Toul, 54200, France

Tel.: (33) 3 83 63 30 00
Automotive Tire Mfr
N.A.I.C.S.: 326211

S.O.D.G.   (1)
Blvd Louis Chartoire, 63100, Clermont-Ferrand, France
Tel.: (33) 473235713
Automotive Tire Mfr
N.A.I.C.S.: 326211

SanaVita Medical, LLC   (1)
551 E Church Ave, Telford, PA 18969
Tel.: (267) 517-3220
Web Site: https://sanavitamedical.com
Medical Device Mfr
N.A.I.C.S.: 339112
Charlene Grilletto *(Dir-Quality & Regulatory)*

Sascar Tecnologia e Seguranga Automotiva S.A.   (1)
Alameda Araguaia 2 104 11 Andar Torre 1 Tambore, Barueri, 06455-000, SP, Brazil
Tel.: (55) 40026004
N.A.I.C.S.: 326211

Servicios y Asistencia OK24, S.L.   (1)
C/ Albarracin 34 3, 28037, Madrid, Spain
Tel.: (34) 90 223 0393
Web Site: https://www.ok24horas.com
Motor Vehicle Maintenance & Repair Services
N.A.I.C.S.: 811198

Seva Engenharia Eletronica S.A. (1)
Jose Maria Lacerda 1 900 Cidade Industrial, Contagem, 32210120, MG, Brazil
Tel.: (55) 3132111000
Web Site: https://renanrios.site44.com
N.A.I.C.S.: 326211

Societe Moderne du Pneumatique Camerounais   (1)
Bonambappe - Zi, BP1039, Bonaberi, Douala, Cameroon
Tel.: (237) 699907323
N.A.I.C.S.: 326211

Suomen Euromaster Oy   (1)
Nuolihaukantie 5, 28220, Pori, Finland
Tel.: (358) 26340600
Automotive Tires Distr
N.A.I.C.S.: 423130

Tablet, Inc.   (1)
6 West 18th St 5th Fl, New York, NY 10011
Web Site: http://www.tablethotels.com
Travel Arrangement & Reservation Services
N.A.I.C.S.: 561599

The Secant Group, LLC   (1)
551 E Church Ave, Telford, PA 18969
Web Site: https://secant.com
Medical Device Mfr
N.A.I.C.S.: 339112
Jeff H. Robertson *(Pres)*

The Wine Advocate, Inc.   (1)
855 Bordeaux Way Ste 200, Napa, CA 94558
Tel.: (707) 255-5337
Web Site: https://www.robertparker.com
Emp.: 100
Wine Magazine Publisher
N.A.I.C.S.: 513102

Tigar Tyres d.o.o.   (1)
213 Nikole Pasica Str, 18300, Pirot, Serbia
Tel.: (381) 10 313 130
Web Site: http://www.michelin.com
Emp.: 2,188
Tire Mfr & Distr
N.A.I.C.S.: 326211

Tire Centers West, LLC   (1)
310 Inglesby Pkwy, Duncan, SC 29334-0218
Tel.: (864) 329-2700
Web Site: https://www.tirecenters.com
N.A.I.C.S.: 326211

Tirecorp GmbH   (1)
Heinkelstrasse 13, 76461, Muggensturm, Germany
Tel.: (49) 800 215 6017
Web Site: https://www.tirecorp.net
Automotive Tires Distr
N.A.I.C.S.: 423130

Transityre B.V.   (1)

Eikdonk 5, PO Box 6578, 4802 HN, Breda, Netherlands
Tel.: (31) 765792300
N.A.I.C.S.: 326211

ViaMichelin North America LLC (1)
PO Box 19001, Greenville, SC 29602-9001
Web Site: http://www.michelinman.com
Tire Product Mfr
N.A.I.C.S.: 326212

COMPAGNIE HET ZOUTE NV

Prins Filiplaan 53, 8300, Knokke-Heist, Belgium
Tel.: (32) 50621111
Web Site:
http://www.compagniezoute.be
Real Estate Investment Services
N.A.I.C.S.: 531210
Philippe De Meestere *(CEO)*

Subsidiaries:

Compagnie Immobiliere D'Hardelot SAS   (1)
27 rue des Anglais, Hardelot Plage, 62152, Neufchatel-Hardelot, France
Tel.: (33) 321108900
Web Site: http://www.hardelot.fr
Real Estate Development Services
N.A.I.C.S.: 531210

Royal Zoute Golf Club SA   (1)
Sparrendreef 1A, 8300, Knokke-Heist, Belgium
Tel.: (32) 50601227
Web Site: http://www.rzgc.be
Restaurant Operators
N.A.I.C.S.: 722511

COMPAGNIE LEBON SA

24 Rue Murillo, 75008, Paris, France
Tel.: (33) 144299800
Web Site:
https://www.compagnielebon.fr
Year Founded: 1847
LBON—(EUR)
Sales Range: $100-124.9 Million
Holding Company
N.A.I.C.S.: 551112
Henri de Pracomtal *(Chm)*

Subsidiaries:

Esprit de France SAS   (1)
24 rue Murillo, 75008, Paris, France
Tel.: (33) 14 429 9845
Web Site: https://www.esprit-de-france.com
Hotel Services
N.A.I.C.S.: 721110
Camille Binz *(Dir-Publications)*

Paluel-Marmont Capital SA   (1)
24 rue Murillo, 75008, Paris, France
Tel.: (33) 14 429 9823
Web Site: https://www.paluel-marmont-capital.fr
Private Equity Firm Services
N.A.I.C.S.: 523940

Subsidiary (Domestic):

Securinfor SA   (2)
38 Place de la Seine, 94533, Rungis, France   **(52%)**
Tel.: (33) 141735600
Web Site: http://www.securinfor.fr
Information Technology Services
N.A.I.C.S.: 541513
Pierre-Yves Chain *(Dir-Dev)*

COMPAGNIE MARITIME BELGE S.A.

De Gerlachekaai 20, BE 2000, Antwerp, Belgium
Tel.: (32) 32475911
Web Site: http://www.cmb.be
Year Founded: 1895
Sales Range: $50-74.9 Million
Cargo Transportation Services
N.A.I.C.S.: 483111
Marc Saverys *(Chm, CEO & Mng Dir)*

Subsidiaries:

Bocimar Belgium NV   (1)

Compagnie Maritime Belge S.A.—(Continued)

De Gerlachekaai 20, Antwerp, 2000, Belgium
Tel.: (32) 32475111
Web Site: http://www.cmb.be
Sales Range: $25-49.9 Million
Emp.: 40
Container Shipping ervices
N.A.I.C.S.: 488390
Marc Saverys (Gen Mgr)

Bocimar Hong Kong Limited   (1)
Room 3206 32nd Floor Lippo Centre Tower Two 89 Queensway, Admiralty, Central, China (Hong Kong)
Tel.: (852) 2861 3880
Marine Transportation Services
N.A.I.C.S.: 488390

Bocimar International N.V.   (1)
De Gerlachekaai 20, Antwerp, 2000, Belgium   **(100%)**
Tel.: (32) 32475911
Web Site: http://www.cmb.be
Sales Range: $350-399.9 Million
Emp.: 30
Deep Sea Freight Transportation Services
N.A.I.C.S.: 483111
Benoit Timmermans (Chief Comml Officer)

Bocimar NV   (1)
De Gerlachekaai 20, 2000, Antwerp, Belgium
Tel.: (32) 32475111
Sales Range: $25-49.9 Million
Emp.: 30
Marine Cargo Handling Services
N.A.I.C.S.: 488320

CMB Japan Limited   (1)
Room 401 Authentic Hanzomon 2 Kojimachi 2 Chome, Chiyoda-ku, Tokyo, 102-0083, Japan
Tel.: (81) 332649861
Marine Cargo Handling Services
N.A.I.C.S.: 488320

CMB NV   (1)
De Gerlachekaai 20, Antwerp, 2000, Belgium
Tel.: (32) 32475911
Sales Range: $50-74.9 Million
Emp.: 200
Marine Cargo Handling Services
N.A.I.C.S.: 488320

CMB Services SA   (1)
20 Rue de Hollerich, 1740, Luxembourg, Luxembourg
Tel.: (352) 4828501
Sales Range: $25-49.9 Million
Emp.: 1
Water Transportation Services
N.A.I.C.S.: 488390

Hessenatie Logistics NV   (1)
Schalienstraat 3, 2000, Antwerp, Belgium   **(100%)**
Tel.: (32) 32165900
Sales Range: $25-49.9 Million
Emp.: 25
Logistic Services
N.A.I.C.S.: 541614

Portline-Transportes Maritimos Internacionais SA   (1)
Avenida Infante D Henrique N 332-3rd Floor, 1849-025, Lisbon, Portugal
Tel.: (351) 218391800
Web Site: http://www.portline.pt
Cargo Handling Services
N.A.I.C.S.: 488320

Sakura International KK   (1)
7-26-3 Kameido, Koto-Ku, Tokyo, 136-0071, Japan
Tel.: (81) 356273308
Cargo Handling Services
N.A.I.C.S.: 488320

COMPAGNIE MERCOSUR GRECEMAR SA
6 Place de la Madeleine, FR-75008, Paris, France
Tel.: (33) 648507571
Web Site:
    https://www.cmgcleantech.com
MLCMG—(EUR)

Sales Range: Less than $1 Million
Holding Company
N.A.I.C.S.: 551112
John Darling (Principal)

COMPAGNIE MONEGASQUE DE BANQUE
23 avenue de la Costa, 98000, Monaco, Monaco
Tel.: (377) 93157777
Web Site: http://www.cmb.mc
Year Founded: 1976
Rev.: $105,154,854
Assets: $4,844,437,090
Liabilities: $3,771,882,216
Net Worth: $1,072,554,874
Earnings: $13,807,874
Emp.: 224
Fiscal Year-end: 12/31/18
Banking Services
N.A.I.C.S.: 522110
Etienne Franzi (Chm)

Subsidiaries:

CMB Wealth Management Ltd   (1)
33 Grosvenor Place, London, SW1X 7HY, United Kingdom
Tel.: (44) 2030369595
Financial Advisory Services
N.A.I.C.S.: 522292

COMPAL BROADBAND NETWORKS, INC.
Floor 1 No 1 Taiyuan 1st Street, Hsinchu County, Zhubei, 30288, Taiwan
Tel.: (886) 35600066
Web Site: https://www.icbn.com.tw
Year Founded: 2009
6674—(TAI)
Rev.: $38,067,103
Assets: $54,649,332
Liabilities: $17,020,275
Net Worth: $37,629,058
Earnings: ($10,664,475)
Emp.: 1,000
Fiscal Year-end: 12/31/23
Transaction Device Mfr & Distr
N.A.I.C.S.: 334118
Tsung-Pin Weng (Chm)

COMPAL ELECTRONICS, INC.
No 581 581-1 Ruiguang Rd, Neihu District, Taipei, 11492, Taiwan
Tel.: (886) 287978588   TW
Web Site: https://www.compal.com
Year Founded: 1984
COMEL—(LUX)
Rev.: $29,600,562,799
Assets: $13,656,347,872
Liabilities: $9,504,990,808
Net Worth: $4,151,357,065
Earnings: $285,485,352
Emp.: 72,257
Fiscal Year-end: 12/31/23
Computer Realted Product Mfr
N.A.I.C.S.: 334111
Rock Sheng-Hsiun Hsu (Chm & Pres)

Subsidiaries:

Aco Smartcare Co., Ltd.   (1)
1F No 8-1 Nandong Rd, Pingzhen Dist, Taoyuan, 324, Taiwan
Tel.: (886) 35820446
Web Site: https://acohealthcare.com
N.A.I.C.S.: 541990

Arcadyan Technology Corporation   (1)
No 8 Sec 2 Guangfu Rd, Hsin-chu, 30071, Taiwan   **(50%)**
Tel.: (886) 35727000
Web Site: https://www.arcadyan.com.tw
Rev.: $1,672,982,114
Assets: $1,260,625,185
Liabilities: $773,360,512
Net Worth: $487,264,673
Earnings: $78,145,326
Emp.: 5,356
Fiscal Year-end: 12/31/2023

Wireless Networking Equipment Mfr
N.A.I.C.S.: 334220
Mike Lu (Exec VP)

Bizcom Electronics, Inc.   (1)
1171 Montague Expy, Milpitas, CA 95035
Tel.: (408) 262-7877
Web Site: https://www.bizcom-us.com
Sales Range: $75-99.9 Million
Emp.: 320
Computer Peripheral Distr
N.A.I.C.S.: 423430

Compal Mexico   (1)
Avenida Rio Bravo 1230, Zaragoza, 32700, Chihuahua, Mexico
Tel.: (52) 6566820340
Sales Range: $450-499.9 Million
Emp.: 1,959
LCD TV Mfr
N.A.I.C.S.: 334419

Subsidiary (US):

Amexcom Electronics, Inc.   (2)
9555 Plaza Cir Ste B, El Paso, TX 79927-2005   **(100%)**
Tel.: (915) 858-7533
Sales Range: $25-49.9 Million
Emp.: 5
TV Components Mfr
N.A.I.C.S.: 334310

Poindus Systems UK Limited   (1)
3 Devonshire Business Park, Hampshire, Basingstoke, RG21 6XN, United Kingdom
Tel.: (44) 1256331336
Web Site: https://www.poindus.com
Electronics Component Mfr & Distr
N.A.I.C.S.: 334419

Sceptre Industries, Inc.   (1)
16800 Gale Ave, City of Industry, CA 91745
Tel.: (626) 369-3698
Web Site: https://www.sceptre.com
Sales Range: $25-49.9 Million
Emp.: 70
Computer Equipment Mfr
N.A.I.C.S.: 334118

COMPANHIA BRASILEIRA DE DISTRIBUICAO
Av Brigadeiro Luis Antonio 3172, Jardim Paulista, Sao Paulo, CEP 01402-901, SP, Brazil
Tel.: (55) 1138860421   BR
Web Site: https://www.gpari.com.br
Year Founded: 1981
CBD—(NYSE)
Rev.: $3,441,125,380
Assets: $3,941,652,708
Liabilities: $3,097,549,121
Net Worth: $844,103,587
Earnings: ($381,473,328)
Emp.: 39,990
Fiscal Year-end: 12/31/23
Supermarket & Hypermarket Owner & Operator
N.A.I.C.S.: 445110
Jean-Charles Henri Naouri (Chm)

Subsidiaries:

Auto Posto Imperio Ltda.   (1)
Rua Joaquim Carlos 1380, 03019-000, Sao Paulo, Brazil
Tel.: (55) 11 22917166
Supermarket Operator
N.A.I.C.S.: 445110

Casa Bahia Contact Center Ltda   (1)
Rua da Graca 873, Sao Paulo, Brazil
Tel.: (55) 1142256000
Business Consulting Services
N.A.I.C.S.: 541611

Devoto Hermanos S.A.   (1)
Jaime Zudanez N 2627, Montevideo, Uruguay
Tel.: (598) 26018050
Web Site: https://www.devoto.com.uy
Grocery Product Distr
N.A.I.C.S.: 445110

Leji Intermediacao S.A.   (1)
Avenida Brigadeiro Luiz Antonio N 3 142, Bairro Jardim Paulista, Sao Paulo, 01402-000, Brazil

Tel.: (55) 8008789887
Web Site: https://www.jamesdelivery.com.br
N.A.I.C.S.: 624210

Logistica Transporte Y Servicios Asociados S.A.S.   (1)
Calle 43 Sur 48 - 127 Antioquia, Envigado, Colombia
Tel.: (57) 46049650
Web Site: https://www.ltsa.com.co
N.A.I.C.S.: 541614

Place2B Servicos Imobiliarios Ltda.   (1)
Av Brig Luis Antonio 3176 - 3 Andar, Sao Paulo, 01402-000, Brazil
Tel.: (55) 1141715807
Web Site: https://place2b.com
N.A.I.C.S.: 531210

Via Varejo S.A.   (1)
R Joao Pessoa 83, 09520-010, Sao Caetano do Sul, SP, Brazil
Tel.: (55) 1142258668
Web Site: http://www.viavarejo.com.br
Rev.: $5,156,682,797
Assets: $5,719,597,281
Liabilities: $5,102,161,070
Net Worth: $617,436,211
Earnings: ($469,244,370)
Emp.: 37,958
Fiscal Year-end: 12/31/2023
Electronic Retail Store Operator
N.A.I.C.S.: 449210
Arnaud Daniel Charles Walter Joachim Strasser (Vice Chm)

COMPANHIA CACIQUE DE CAFE SOLUVEL
R Horacio Sabino Coimbra 100, 86072900, Londrina, PR, Brazil
Tel.: (55) 43 4009 6186
Web Site: http://www.cafepele.com.br
Year Founded: 1959
Sales Range: $300-349.9 Million
Emp.: 1,322
Coffee Mfr & Whslr
N.A.I.C.S.: 311920
Paulo Roberto Ferro (Dir-IR)

COMPANHIA CELG DE PARTICIPACOES - CELGPAR
Rua 88-A Quadra F-37 Lote 13 n 116, Setor Sul, Goiania, 74805-080, GO, Brazil
Tel.: (55) 34145910   BR
Web Site:
    http://www.celgpar.celggt.com
Year Founded: 2006
GPAR3—(BRAZ)
Sales Range: Less than $1 Million
Investment Management Service
N.A.I.C.S.: 523940
Marcos Roberto Silva (Dir-Investor Relations)

COMPANHIA DE FERRO LIGAS DA BAHIA - FERBASA
290 Ewerton Visco St Ed Boulevard Side Empresarial Caminho das Arvores, 25 floor, Salvador, 41820-022, Bahia, Brazil
Tel.: (55) 7134043065   BR
Web Site: https://www.ferbasa.com.br
Year Founded: 1961
FESA4—(BRAZ)
Rev.: $316,790,989
Assets: $679,964,606
Liabilities: $224,869,734
Net Worth: $455,094,871
Earnings: $54,758,754
Emp.: 2,800
Fiscal Year-end: 12/31/19
Ferrochrome Alloy Mfr
N.A.I.C.S.: 331110
Silvano de Souza Andrade (CEO)

Subsidiaries:

Companhia de Ferro Ligas da Bahia - Ferbasa - The Pojuca Factory   (1)

Estrada de Santiago, Ipojuca, 48120-000, Brazil
Tel.: (55) 7136458700
Web Site: http://www.ferbasa.com.br
Steel Products Mfr
N.A.I.C.S.: 331110

COMPANHIA DE FIACAO E TECIDOS CEDRO E CACHOEIRA
Tel.: (55) 3132355000   BR
Web Site: https://cedro.com.br
Year Founded: 1872
Rev.: $130,217,462
Assets: $140,817,550
Liabilities: $103,372,056
Net Worth: $37,445,494
Earnings: ($2,669,391)
Fiscal Year-end: 12/31/19
Textile Products Mfr
N.A.I.C.S.: 313210

COMPANHIA DE PARTICIPA-COES ALIANCA DA BAHIA
Rua Pinto Martins n 11 - Comercio, Salvador, 40015-020, Bahia, Brazil
Tel.: (55) 7136161013
Web Site:
    http://www.aliancaparticipacoes.com
Year Founded: 1997
PEAB4—(BRAZ)
Rev.: $8,859,155
Assets: $157,403,868
Liabilities: $34,777,533
Net Worth: $122,626,335
Earnings: $2,169,250
Emp.: 35
Fiscal Year-end: 12/31/23
Investment Management Service
N.A.I.C.S.: 523940
Antonio Tavares Da Camara *(Dir-IR)*

COMPANHIA DE SANEA-MENTO BASICO DO ESTADO DE SAO PAULO - SABESP
Rua Costa Carvalho 300, 05429-900, Sao Paulo, Brazil
Tel.: (55) 1133888000   BR
Web Site: http://www.sabesp.com.br
SBS—(NYSE)
Rev.: $5,099,622,295
Assets: $12,258,641,340
Liabilities: $6,304,433,343
Net Worth: $5,954,207,997
Earnings: $702,668,461
Emp.: 11,170
Fiscal Year-end: 12/31/23
Public Water & Sewage Systems Operator
N.A.I.C.S.: 221310
Alceu Segamarchi *(Officer-Tech, Enterprises & Environment)*

COMPANHIA DE SANEA-MENTO DE MINAS GERAIS COPASA MG
Rua Mar de Espanha 525, Belo Horizonte, 30330900, MG, Brazil
Tel.: (55) 32501386
Web Site: https://www.copasa.com.br
Year Founded: 1963
CSMG3—(BRAZ)
Rev.: $1,323,605,013
Assets: $2,536,576,504
Liabilities: $1,182,681,365
Net Worth: $1,353,895,139
Earnings: $246,571,560
Emp.: 9,542
Fiscal Year-end: 12/31/23
Sewage Treatment Services
N.A.I.C.S.: 221320
Andre Macedo Faco *(Chm)*

COMPANHIA DE SANEA-MENTO DO PARANA SANEPAR
Rua Engenheiros Reboucas 1376, 80215-900, Curitiba, Parana, Brazil
Tel.: (55) 4133303000   BR
Web Site: http://site.sanepar.com.br
SAPR11—(BRAZ)
Rev.: $1,124,887,977
Assets: $3,361,381,545
Liabilities: $1,619,510,691
Net Worth: $1,741,870,053
Earnings: $268,740,809
Emp.: 6,121
Fiscal Year-end: 12/31/23
Water Supply & Treatment Services
N.A.I.C.S.: 221310

COMPANHIA DE SEGUROS ALIANCA DA BAHIA
Rua Pinto Martins 11 Ed Comendador Pedreira - Comercio, Salvador, 40015-020, BA, Brazil
Tel.: (55) 71 3616 1055
Web Site: http://www.alba.com.br
Year Founded: 1870
CSAB3—(BRAZ)
Sales Range: $10-24.9 Million
Emp.: 133
Insurance Management Services
N.A.I.C.S.: 524298
Antonio Tavares Da Camara *(Dir-IR)*

COMPANHIA ENERGETICA DE BRASILIA - CEB
SGAN Quadra 601 Bloco H Salas 2010 a 2023, Asa Norte, Brasilia, 70830-010, DF, Brazil
Tel.: (55) 37741001   BR
Web Site: http://www.ceb.com.br
Year Founded: 1968
CEBR5—(BRAZ)
Rev.: $72,657,599
Assets: $291,779,082
Liabilities: $30,256,569
Net Worth: $261,522,513
Earnings: $51,140,649
Fiscal Year-end: 12/31/23
Investment Management Service
N.A.I.C.S.: 523940
Bras Kleyber Borges Teodoro *(Dir-Investor Relations)*

COMPANHIA ENERGETICA DE MINAS GERAIS - CEMIG
Avenida Barbacena 1200, Belo Horizonte, 30190-131, MG, Brazil
Tel.: (55) 8007283838
Web Site: https://www.cemig.com.br
Year Founded: 1952
CIG—(NYSE)
Rev.: $7,348,688,802
Assets: $10,968,192,242
Liabilities: $6,051,251,371
Net Worth: $4,916,940,871
Earnings: $1,150,064,812
Emp.: 4,917
Fiscal Year-end: 12/31/23
Electricity Generation, Transmission & Distribution Services
N.A.I.C.S.: 926130
Dimas Costa *(Chief Comml Officer, Chief Trading Officer & Member-Exec Bd)*

Subsidiaries:

Cemig Distribuicao S.A.   (1)
Av Barbacena 1 200 - 5 Andar - Ala B1, Bairro Santo Agostinho, Belo Horizonte, 30190-131, Minas Gerais, Brazil
Tel.: (55) 3135065028
Electric Power Distribution Services
N.A.I.C.S.: 221122

Cemig Geracao e Transmissao S.A.   (1)
Avenida Barbacena n 1 200 12 Andar Ala B1 Bairro Santo Agostinho, Belo Horizonte, 30190-131, Minas Gerais, Brazil
Tel.: (55) 3135065024

Electric Power Generation & Distribution Services
N.A.I.C.S.: 221118
Luiz Fernando Rolla *(CFO)*

Cemig Telecomunicacoes S.A.   (1)
Rua dos Inconfidentes 1051 - Terreo e 1a sobreloja, Funcionarios, 30140-120, Belo Horizonte, Minas Gerais, Brazil
Tel.: (55) 31 3307 6300
Web Site: http://www.infovias.com.br
Telecommunication Servicesb
N.A.I.C.S.: 517810

Cemig Trading S.A.   (1)
Av Barbacena 1200 Ala 5 A1 Parte 1 Sto Agostinho, Belo Horizonte, 30190-131, Minas Gerais, Brazil
Tel.: (55) 3132993711
Electric Power Distribution Services
N.A.I.C.S.: 221122

Central Termeletrica de Cogeracao S.A.   (1)
Av Barbacena 1 200, Belo Horizonte, 30123-970, Minas Gerais, Brazil
Tel.: (55) 3132502015
Electric Power Distribution Services
N.A.I.C.S.: 221122

Efficientia S.A.   (1)
Rua Aimores 3000 12 Andar - Barro Preto, Ed Minerva, 30140-073, Belo Horizonte, Minas Gerais, Brazil
Tel.: (55) 31 3273 8133
Web Site: http://www.efficientia.com.br
Electric Power Mfr & Distr
N.A.I.C.S.: 221111

Empresa de Servicos e Comercializacao de Energia Eletrica S.A.   (1)
Rua dos Aimores 3000 - Barro Preto, Belo Horizonte, 30140-073, Minas Gerais, Brazil
Tel.: (55) 31 3506 3838
Eletric Power Generation Services
N.A.I.C.S.: 221118

Horizontes Energia S.A.   (1)
Praia do Flamengo 66 1509B, Flamengo, Rio de Janeiro, Brazil
Tel.: (55) 21 2225 2209
Web Site:
    http://www.horizonteenergia.com.br
Eletric Power Generation Services
N.A.I.C.S.: 221118

Rio Minas Energia Participacoes S.A.   (1)
Av Rio Branco 123, Marechal Falorinno 168 20080-0, Rio de Janeiro, 20040-005, Brazil
Tel.: (55) 2122112980
Web Site: http://www.light.com.br
Sales Range: $1-4.9 Billion
Emp.: 4,000
Holding Company
N.A.I.C.S.: 551112

Subsidiary (Domestic):

Light Servicos de Eletricidade S.A.   (2)
Avenida Marechal Floriano 168, Rio de Janeiro, 20080 002, Brazil
Tel.: (55) 2122112794
Web Site: http://www.light.com.br
Sales Range: $1-4.9 Billion
Electric Power Generalization, Transmission & Distribution
N.A.I.C.S.: 335311
Selma Oliveira *(Mgr-HR)*

COMPANHIA HABITASUL DE PARTICIPACOES
Av Carlos Gomes 400 5th floor, Boa vista, Porto Alegre, 90480900, RS, Brazil
Tel.: (55) 5132203535
Web Site:
    https://www.habitasul.com.br
Year Founded: 1967
HBTS5—(BRAZ)
Rev.: $56,753,006
Assets: $284,569,092
Liabilities: $162,331,559
Net Worth: $122,237,533
Earnings: $50,247,045
Fiscal Year-end: 12/31/23

Real Estate Development Services
N.A.I.C.S.: 531390
Pericles de Freitas Druck *(Chm, CEO & Member-Exec Bd)*

COMPANHIA INDUSTRIAL CATAGUASES
Praca Jose Inacio Peixoto 28, Caixa Postal 29, Cataguases, 36772-900, MG, Brazil
Tel.: (55) 3234222211   BR
Web Site:
    http://www.cataguases.com.br
Year Founded: 1936
CATA4—(BRAZ)
Rev.: $62,271,818
Assets: $77,039,670
Liabilities: $39,610,716
Net Worth: $37,428,954
Earnings: $4,144,874
Fiscal Year-end: 12/31/23
Textile Product Mfr & Whslr
N.A.I.C.S.: 313310
Tiago Inacio Peixoto *(CEO & Comml Dir)*

COMPANHIA MELHORAMEN-TOS DE SAO PAULO
Rua Tito 479 - Vila Romana Lapa, 05051-000, Sao Paulo, 05051-000, Brazil
Tel.: (55) 1138740600
Web Site:
    http://www.melhoramentos.com.br
Year Founded: 1890
MSPA4—(BRAZ)
Rev.: $31,511,592
Assets: $253,244,662
Liabilities: $103,342,984
Net Worth: $149,901,678
Earnings: $1,408,269
Fiscal Year-end: 12/31/23
Investment Management Service
N.A.I.C.S.: 523940
Sergio Sesiki *(Dir-IR)*

COMPANHIA PARANAENSE DE ENERGIA
Rua Coronel Dulcidio 800, 80420-170, Curitiba, Parana, Brazil
Tel.: (55) 4133314011   BR
Web Site: http://www.copel.com
Year Founded: 1954
ELP—(NYSE)
Rev.: $4,215,604,362
Assets: $9,555,536,325
Liabilities: $5,493,058,319
Net Worth: $4,062,478,006
Earnings: $220,956,962
Emp.: 6,029
Fiscal Year-end: 12/31/22
Electric Power Generator, Transporter & Distr; Communications & Telecommunications Services
N.A.I.C.S.: 221122
Adriano Rudek de Moura *(CFO, Chief IR Officer & Member-Exec Bd)*

Subsidiaries:

Bela Vista Geracao De Energia S.A.   (1)
Rua Coronel Dulcidio 800, Curitiba, CEP 80420-170, Brazil
Tel.: (55) 80006445445
Web Site: https://pchbelavista.com.br
Hydroelectric Power Mfr
N.A.I.C.S.: 335311

CEOLPAR - CENTRAIS EOLICAS DO PARANA LTDA.   (1)
Br 280 Km 26 S/n, Palmas, Parana, Brazil
Tel.: (55) 46 32626452
Electric Power Distribution Services
N.A.I.C.S.: 221122

COMPAGAS - CIA. PARANAENSE DE GAS   (1)

Companhia Paranaense de Energia—(Continued)

Pasteur 463, Curitiba, 80250-080, Parana, Brazil
Tel.: (55) 4133121900
Web Site: http://www.compagas.com.br
Sales Range: $125-149.9 Million
Emp.: 130
Natural Gas Distr
N.A.I.C.S.: 221210

Copel Companhia Energia S/A　　**(1)**
Rua Coronel Dulcidio 800, Curitiba, 80420-170, Brazil
Tel.: (55) 4133223535
Web Site: http://www.copel.com
Sales Range: $50-74.9 Million
Emp.: 100
Holding Company
N.A.I.C.S.: 551112

Copel Distribuicao SA　　**(1)**
Rua Jose Izidoro Biazetto 158 - bloco C, Curitiba, 81200-240, Parana, Brazil
Tel.: (55) 4133314141
Electric Power Distribution
N.A.I.C.S.: 221122

Costa Oeste Transmissora De Energia S.A.　　**(1)**
Rua Jose Izidoro Biazetto 158 Bloca A, Curitiba, 81200-240, PR, Brazil
Tel.: (55) 4133314065
Web Site: https://costaoesteenergia.com.br
Electric Power Transmission Services
N.A.I.C.S.: 221122

ELEJOR - CENTRAIS ELETRICAS DO RIO JORDAO S.A.　　**(1)**
Tel.: (55) 4132620106
Web Site: http://www.elejor.com.br
Sales Range: $75-99.9 Million
Emp.: 10
Eletric Power Generation Services
N.A.I.C.S.: 221118

Marumbi Transmissora De Energia S.A.　　**(1)**
Jose Izidoro Biazetto, Mossungue, Curitiba, 81200-240, Brazil
Tel.: (55) 4133314065
Web Site: https://marumbienergia.com.br
Electric Power Distr
N.A.I.C.S.: 423610

Mata De Santa Genebra Transmissao S.A.　　**(1)**
Avenida Jundiai 1184 - 5th floor Anhangabau, Jundiai, Sao Paulo, 13208053, Brazil
Tel.: (55) 8003004468
Web Site: https://www.msgtrans.com.br
Electric Power Distr
N.A.I.C.S.: 423610

Santa Maria Energias Renovaveis S.A.　　**(1)**
Av Angelo Giuberti n 385, Esplanada, Colatina, 29702-712, Brazil
Tel.: (55) 27996562940
Web Site: https://portal.elfsm.com.br
Eletric Power Generation Services
N.A.I.C.S.: 221118

UEGA - USINA ELETRICA A GAS DE ARAUCARIA LTDA,　　**(1)**
Rua Visconde do Rio Branco 1341 9 Andar, Curitiba, Parana, Brazil
Web Site: http://www.uega.com.br
Sales Range: $75-99.9 Million
Emp.: 13
Eletric Power Generation Services
N.A.I.C.S.: 221118

Ueg Araucaria S.A.　　**(1)**
Rua Jose Izidoro Biazetto 158 Bloco C, Bairro Mossungue, Curitiba, 81200-240, Brazil　　**(81.2%)**
Tel.: (55) 4132415100
Web Site: https://www.uega.com.br
Generation & Thermoelectric Power Services
N.A.I.C.S.: 561790

Uirapuru Transmissora de Energia, Ltda　　**(1)**
Av Deputado Antonio Edu Vieira 999 Terreo Bairro Pantanal, Florianopolis, 88040-901, Santa Catarina, Brazil　　**(75%)**
Tel.: (55) 48 3231 7282

Web Site: http://www.uirapuruenergia.com.br
Power Transmission Line Construction Services
N.A.I.C.S.: 237130

COMPANHIA SIDERURGICA NACIONAL

Av Brigadeiro Faria Lima 3400 - 20th Floor, 04538-132, Sao Paulo, SP, Brazil
Tel.: (55) 1130497100　　**BR**
Web Site: http://www.csn.com.br
Year Founded: 1941
SID—(NYSE)
Rev.: $8,528,617,570
Assets: $16,409,375,518
Liabilities: $12,215,241,059
Net Worth: $4,194,134,459
Earnings: $416,739,941
Fiscal Year-end: 12/31/22
Steel & Tin Mfr
N.A.I.C.S.: 331110
Marcelo Cunha Ribeiro *(CFO & Chief IR Officer)*

Subsidiaries:

CSN Cimentos　　**(1)**
Ave Brigadeiro Faria Lima 3400, 20 deg andar Itaim Bibi, Sao Paulo, 04538-132, Sao Paulo, Brazil
Tel.: (55) 1130497100
Web Site: http://www.csn.com.br
Sales Range: $1-4.9 Billion
Emp.: 7,000
Steel Products Mfr
N.A.I.C.S.: 331221

CSN Parana　　**(1)**
Rodovia PR 423 5500, Estacao, Araucaria, 83705 000, Parana, Brazil
Tel.: (55) 4136418015
Web Site: http://www.csn.com.br
Sales Range: $25-49.9 Million
Emp.: 26
Galvanized Steel Products Mfr
N.A.I.C.S.: 332111

CSN Porto Real　　**(1)**
Ave Renato Monteiro 7777, Porto Real, 27570 000, RJ, Brazil
Tel.: (55) 2433582900
Sales Range: $100-124.9 Million
Emp.: 400
Galvanized Automotive Products Mfr
N.A.I.C.S.: 441330

Inal Nordeste S.A.　　**(1)**
Rua do Aluminio s/n Lotes de 01 a 06 - Quadra II, Polo de Apoio, Camacari, 42 800 970, Bahia, Brazil
Tel.: (55) 7121042104
Steel Products Service Centre
N.A.I.C.S.: 331110

LafargeHolcim (Brasil) S.A.　　**(1)**
Av Almirante Barroso, 52-15 Andar Centro, CEP 20031-000, Rio de Janeiro, Brazil
Tel.: (55) 21 3804 3100
Web Site: http://www.lafargeholcim.com.br
Cement Mfr
N.A.I.C.S.: 327310
Andre Martin *(Pres)*

Plant (Domestic):

LafargeHolcim (Brasil) S.A. - Barroso Plant　　**(2)**
R Tiradentes S/N, Rosario, 36212-000, Barroso, Brazil
Tel.: (55) 32 3359 3200
Web Site: http://www.lafargeholcim.com.br
Cement Mfr
N.A.I.C.S.: 327310

LafargeHolcim (Brasil) S.A. - Cantagalo Plant　　**(2)**
Rodovia 166 Km 8, Fazenda Saudade, 28520-000, Cantagalo, Brazil
Tel.: (55) 22 2555 0433
Web Site: http://www.lafargeholcim.com.br
Cement Mfr; Construction Material Whslr
N.A.I.C.S.: 327310

Lusosider Projectos Siderurgicos S.A.　　**(1)**
Paio Pires, 2840-075, Seixal, Setubal, Portugal
Tel.: (351) 212278300
Web Site: http://www.lusosider.pt
Sales Range: $100-124.9 Million
Emp.: 300
Metallurgy Machines Mfr & Distr
N.A.I.C.S.: 333248

Metalgrafica Iguacu S.A.　　**(1)**
R Minas Gerais 1231, 84070-040, Ponta Grossa, PR, Brazil
Tel.: (55) 4232192822
Metal Can Mfr & Whslr
N.A.I.C.S.: 332431

Sepetiba Tecon S.A.　　**(1)**
Estrada da Ilha da Madeira s ñ parte Porto de Itaguai, Ilha da Madeira, Itaguai, 23826 600, Rio de Janeiro, Brazil
Tel.: (55) 2126889366
Web Site: http://www.sepetibatecon.com.br
Logistic Services
N.A.I.C.S.: 541614

Stahlwerk Thuringen GmbH　　**(1)**
Kronacher Strasse 6, Unterwellenborn, 07333, Germany
Tel.: (49) 36714450
Web Site: http://www.stahlwerk-thueringen.de
Sales Range: $500-549.9 Million
Emp.: 700
Steel Products Mfr
N.A.I.C.S.: 331221

Terminal de Carvao　　**(1)**
Estrada da Ilha da Madeira s/n deg, Parte, Porto de Itaguai, Ilha da Madeira, Itaguai, Rio de Janeiro, Brazil
Tel.: (55) 21 26871787
Logistic Services
N.A.I.C.S.: 541614

COMPANIA AGROPECUARIA COPEVAL S.A.

Av Manuel Rodriguez 1099, PO Box 301, San Fernando, Chile
Tel.: (56) 722720000
Web Site: https://www.copeval.cl
Year Founded: 1956
COPEVAL—(SGO)
Sales Range: Less than $1 Million
Fertilizer Mfr
N.A.I.C.S.: 325314

COMPANIA ANONIMA NACIONAL TELEFONOS DE VENEZUELA

Avenida Libertador Centro Nacional De Telecom, Apartado Postal 1226, Edificio NEA Piso 1, Caracas, 1010, Venezuela
Tel.: (58) 2125006800
Web Site: http://www.cantv.com.ve
Year Founded: 1930
TDV.D—(BVC)
Sales Range: $1-9.9 Million
Emp.: 8,623
Provider of Telecommunications Services
N.A.I.C.S.: 517111
Carlos Figueira *(Mng Dir)*

Subsidiaries:

Cantv.net　　**(1)**
2da Av con 3era Transversal Los Cortijos de Lourdes, Edif Cantv Los Cortijos, Caracas, 1060, Venezuela
Tel.: (58) 2 9013850
Wireless Communication Services
N.A.I.C.S.: 517112

Caveguias　　**(1)**
2da Av con 3era Transversal Los Cortijos de Lourdes, Caracas, Venezuela
Tel.: (58) 5960110
Telephone Directory Services
N.A.I.C.S.: 513140

Movilnet　　**(1)**
Calle Londres con New York - Edif Movilnet

- Las Mercedes, Caracas, Venezuela
Tel.: (58) 212 9092443
Web Site: http://www.movilnet.com.ve
Wireless Communication Services
N.A.I.C.S.: 517112

COMPANIA CHILENA DE FOSFOROS S.A.

Los Conquistadores 1700 Piso 15, Providencia, Santiago, Chile
Tel.: (56) 227076200
Web Site: https://www.fosforos.cl
Year Founded: 1913
FOSFOROS—(SGO)
Sales Range: Less than $1 Million
Splint Mfr
N.A.I.C.S.: 339113

COMPANIA DE MINAS BUENAVENTURA SAA

Las Begonias 415 Piso 19, San Isidro, 15046, Lima, Peru
Tel.: (51) 14192500　　**Pe**
Web Site:
　https://www.buenaventura.com
Year Founded: 1953
BVN—(NYSE)
Rev.: $824,802,000
Assets: $4,503,227,000
Liabilities: $1,340,286,000
Net Worth: $3,162,941,000
Earnings: $602,935,000
Emp.: 2,687
Fiscal Year-end: 12/31/22
Ore Mining & Exploration Services
N.A.I.C.S.: 212290
Roque Eduardo Benavides Ganoza *(Chm)*

Subsidiaries:

Consorcio Energetico de Huancavelica S.A.　　**(1)**
Calle Las Begonias 415 - piso 19 San Isidro, Lima, Peru
Tel.: (51) 14717278
Sales Range: $125-149.9 Million
Emp.: 200
Electric Power Distr
N.A.I.C.S.: 221122

Contacto Corredores de Seguros S.A.　　**(1)**
Del Pinar 180, Chacarilla Santiago de Surco, Lima, Peru
Tel.: (51) 6166565
Web Site: https://www.contacto.com.pe
Sales Range: $50-74.9 Million
Emp.: 16
All Other Nonmetallic Mineral Mining
N.A.I.C.S.: 212390

Inversiones Colquijirca S.A.　　**(1)**
Av Javier Prado Oeste 2173, Lima, 27, Peru
Tel.: (51) 16113900
Investment Management Service
N.A.I.C.S.: 523999

Minera Julcani S.A.de C.V.　　**(1)**
Calle Alce Blanco 8 El Venado, Hidalgo, Mexico, Mexico
Tel.: (52) 7711386142
Sales Range: $50-74.9 Million
Emp.: 5
Mineral Mining Services
N.A.I.C.S.: 212390
Mario Calderon *(Gen Mgr)*

Minera La Zanja S.R.L.　　**(1)**
Carlos Villaran 790 Santa Catalina, La Victoria, Lima, Peru
Tel.: (51) 14192500
Gold Ore Mining
N.A.I.C.S.: 212220

Sociedad Minera El Brocal S.A.A.　　**(1)**
Web Site: http://www.elbrocal.com.pe
Sales Range: $50-74.9 Million
Emp.: 50
Lead Ore & Zinc Ore Mining
N.A.I.C.S.: 212230

COMPANIA DE NAVIGATIE FLUVIALA ROMANA NAVROM S.A. GALATI

Str Portului nr 34, 800025, Galati, Romania
Tel.: (40) 236 461022
Web Site: http://www.navrom.ro
Year Founded: 1890
Inland Freight Water Transport Services
N.A.I.C.S.: 483211
Catalin Eduard Tiganus *(Gen Dir)*

Subsidiaries:

Navrom Bac S.R.L.   **(1)**
Punct de Trecere Bac - Faleza, Dunarii, Galati, 800382, Romania
Tel.: (40) 236 496627
Web Site: http://www.navrombac.com
Emp.: 70
Marine Transportation Services
N.A.I.C.S.: 483211
Marilena Vaslache *(Gen Mgr)*

Navrom Centru de Afaceri S.R.L. **(1)**
Str Portului 23 Hotel Mercur et 2, Galati, Romania
Tel.: (40) 236 411048
Marine Transportation Services
N.A.I.C.S.: 483211

Navrom Delta S.A.   **(1)**
Str Portului 26, Tulcea, Romania
Tel.: (40) 240 511553
Web Site: http://www.navromdelta.ro
Marine Transportation Services
N.A.I.C.S.: 483211

Navrom Shipyard S.R.L.   **(1)**
Str Portului 54, Galati, Romania
Tel.: (40) 236 460990
Marine Transportation Services
N.A.I.C.S.: 483211

COMPANIA DE SEGUROS DE VIDA CAMARA SA

Av La Encalada No 1388 Office 701 Polo Hunt I Building, Santiago de Surco, Lima, Peru
Tel.: (51) 6042000
Insurance Services
N.A.I.C.S.: 524210

COMPANIA DE SEGUROS DE VIDA CRUZ DEL SUR S.A

El Golf 150, Las Condes, Santiago, Chile
Tel.: (56) 2 461 8000
Web Site: http://www.cruzdelsur.cl
Year Founded: 1992
Sales Range: $200-249.9 Million
Emp.: 1,000
Insurance & Financial Services
N.A.I.C.S.: 524298
Andres Lehuede *(VP-Corp)*

Subsidiaries:

Principal Creditos Hipotecarios,
S.A.   **(1)**
Avenida Apoquindo 3600 Piso 10 Las Condes, Santiago, Chile   **(100%)**
Tel.: (56) 2 2810 7000
Web Site: http://www.principal.cl
Sales Range: $1-9.9 Million
Emp.: 38
Mortgage Loans & Investments Services
N.A.I.C.S.: 522310

COMPANIA ELECTRO META-LURGICA S.A.

Av Andres Bello 2233 piso 11 y 12, Providencia, Santiago, Chile
Tel.: (56) 223614020
Web Site: https://www.me-elecmetal.com
Year Founded: 1917
ELECMETAL—(SGO)
Rev.: $1,329,655,287
Assets: $1,743,154,048
Liabilities: $958,395,978

Net Worth: $784,758,070
Earnings: $50,125,102
Emp.: 1,218
Fiscal Year-end: 12/31/23
Steel Products Mfr
N.A.I.C.S.: 331513

Subsidiaries:

Hendaya S.A.   **(1)**
Av Americo Vespucio Oriente 1353, Puda-huel, Santiago, Chile
Tel.: (56) 225982200
Web Site: http://www.hendayasac.cl
Healthy Food Services
N.A.I.C.S.: 456191

ME Elecmetal Comercial Peru
S.A.C.   **(1)**
Av La Encalada 1257 of 503 Centro Empresarial La Encalada, Santiago de Surco, Lima, Peru
Tel.: (51) 16768716
Industrial Machinery Distr
N.A.I.C.S.: 423830

Vina Carmen S.A.   **(1)**
Apoquindo 3669 Of 701, Las Condes, Santiago, Chile
Tel.: (56) 223622000
Web Site: http://www.carmen.com
Wine Mfr
N.A.I.C.S.: 312130

COMPANIA ESPANOLA DE VIVIENDAS EN ALQUILER S.A.

Avda Meridiana 350 5th floor, 8027, Barcelona, Spain
Tel.: (34) 932744884
Web Site: https://www.cevasa.com
Year Founded: 1968
CEV—(MAD)
Sales Range: Less than $1 Million
Real Estate Development Services
N.A.I.C.S.: 531390

COMPANIA INDUSTRIAL DE TABACOS MONTE PAZ S.A.

San Ramon 716, CP 11800, Montevideo, Uruguay
Tel.: (598) 22008821   **UY**
Web Site:
    http://www.montepaz.com.uy
Year Founded: 1881
Sales Range: $25-49.9 Million
Emp.: 450
Cigarettes & Tobacco Products Mfr
N.A.I.C.S.: 312230
Luis Bensusan *(Dir-Mktg)*

COMPANIA INDUSTRIAL EL VOLCAN SA

Agustinas 1357 Piso10, Santiago, Chile
Tel.: (56) 4830500
VOLCAN—(SGO)
Sales Range: Less than $1 Million
Industrial Raw Material Mfr
N.A.I.C.S.: 333248
Bernardo Matte Larrain *(Chm)*

COMPANIA LEVANTINA DE EDIFICACION Y OBRAS PUBLICAS SA

C/Santa Cruz de la Zarza 3, 46021, Valencia, Spain
Tel.: (34) 963 393090   **ES**
Web Site: http://www.cleop.es
Year Founded: 1946
Sales Range: $200-249.9 Million
Heavy Construction & Public Works Management
N.A.I.C.S.: 236220
Carlos Turro Homedes *(Chm)*

COMPANIA LOGISTICA DE HIDROCARBUROS CLH, S.A.

C/ Titan 13, 28045, Madrid, Spain
Tel.: (34) 91 7746000   **ES**

Web Site: http://www.clh.es
Year Founded: 1927
Rev.: $746,087,687
Assets: $2,514,456,374
Liabilities: $2,209,171,339
Net Worth: $305,285,035
Earnings: $266,840,241
Emp.: 1,737
Fiscal Year-end: 12/31/18
Logistics Services; Hydrocarbons, Chemical Products, Derivatives & Residues Storage, Transport & Distribution
N.A.I.C.S.: 541614
Jose Luis Lopez de Silanes Busto *(Chm)*

Subsidiaries:

CLH Aviacion, S.A   **(1)**
Calle Titan 13, Madrid, 28045, Spain
Tel.: (34) 917746188
Warehousing & Freight Forwarding Services
N.A.I.C.S.: 493110

COMPANIA MINERA ANTAMINA S.A.

Av Avenue El Derby 055 Building, Cronos Torre 1 Piso 8 Surco, Lima, Peru
Tel.: (51) 12173000
Web Site: http://www.antamina.com
Sales Range: $450-499.9 Million
Emp.: 1,500
Copper Ore Mining Services
N.A.I.C.S.: 212230
Enrique Alania Vera *(Mgr-Logistics)*

COMPANIA NACIONAL DE TELEFONOS TELEFONICA DEL SUR S.A.

San Carlos Nro 107, PO Box 288-V, Valdivia, Chile
Tel.: (56) 223000
Web Site:
    http://www.telefonicadelsur.cl
Telecommunication Servicesb
N.A.I.C.S.: 517810
Juan Carlos Valenzuela Herrera *(CEO)*

COMPANIA NATIONALA POSTA ROMANA S.A.

Blvd Dacia 140 Sector 2, 020065, Bucharest, Romania
Tel.: (40) 219393
Web Site: http://www.posta-romana.ro
Postal Service
N.A.I.C.S.: 491110
Dan Mihai Toader *(Chm & CEO)*

COMPANIA SUDAMERICANA DE VAPORES, S.A.

Apoquindo 2827 14th floor, PO Box 49-V, Las Condes, 7550268, Santiago, Chile
Tel.: (56) 225886000
Web Site: https://csav.com
Year Founded: 1872
VAPORES—(SGO)
Sales Range: $1-4.9 Billion
Emp.: 4,211
Freight Shipping Services
N.A.I.C.S.: 488510
Francisco Perez Mackenna *(Chm)*

Subsidiaries:

CSAV Inversiones Navieras S.A. **(1)**
Plaza Sotomayor 50 Valparaiso, Valparaiso, Chile
Tel.: (56) 32 2203000
Web Site: http://www.csav.cl
Sales Range: $125-149.9 Million
Emp.: 400
Navigational Shipping Services
N.A.I.C.S.: 488330
Arturo Racke *(Reg Mgr)*

SOCIEDAD MATRIZ SAAM S.A.   **(1)**
Avenida Apoquindo 4800 Torre II piso 18th, Las Condes, Santiago, Chile
Tel.: (56) 227318240
Web Site: http://www.saam.com
Rev.: $529,793,000
Assets: $1,617,989,000
Liabilities: $789,241,000
Net Worth: $828,748,000
Earnings: $67,780,000
Emp.: 8,161
Fiscal Year-end: 12/31/2019
Port Operator
N.A.I.C.S.: 488310
Macario R. Valdes *(CEO)*

Sudamericana, Agencias Aereas y
Maritimas S.A.   **(1)**
Blanco 895 Valparaiso, Valparaiso, 2370554, Chile
Tel.: (56) 600 600 72 26
Web Site: http://www.saam.cl
Sales Range: $550-599.9 Million
Emp.: 200
Navigational Shipping & Transportation Services
N.A.I.C.S.: 488330
O. Alejandro Garcia Huidobro *(Mng Dir)*

Subsidiary (Non-US):

Tollo Shipping Co. S.A.   **(2)**
Roberto Motta Ave Capital Plaza Building 15th Fl Costa Valeste, Panama, Panama
Tel.: (507) 2636066
Deep Sea Transportation Services
N.A.I.C.S.: 483111

COMPANIA VINICOLA DEL NORTE DE ESPANA, S.A.

Barrio de la Estacion S/N, 26200, Haro, La Rioja, Spain
Tel.: (34) 941 304 800
Web Site: http://www.cvne.com
Year Founded: 1879
Sales Range: $10-24.9 Million
Wine Mfr & Whslr
N.A.I.C.S.: 312130
Victor Juan de Urrutia Vallejo *(Chm)*

COMPANIAS CIC SA

Avda Esquina Blanca 960, 810, Santiago, 810, Chile
Tel.: (56) 25304000
CIC—(SGO)
Sales Range: Less than $1 Million
Furniture Product Mfr & Distr
N.A.I.C.S.: 337121

COMPANY K PARTNERS LIMITED

14F 620 Teheran-Ro, Gangnam-Gu, Seoul, 06174, Korea (South)
Tel.: (82) 25688470
Web Site: https://www.kpartners.co.kr
Year Founded: 2006
307930—(KRS)
Emp.: 14
Venture Capital Services
N.A.I.C.S.: 523910
Koo Lee *(Officer-Investments)*

COMPANY MARGIN PURPOSE LTD.

Zhabotinski 7, Ramat Gan, 5252007, Israel
Tel.: (972) 3 613 8484
Web Site: http://www.aviv.co.il
Year Founded: 1989
Software Development Services
N.A.I.C.S.: 541511

COMPARTAMOS FINANCIERA

Avenida Alfredo Benavides, Miraflores, Lima, 15047, Peru
Tel.: (51) 6194160
COMPFC1—(LIM)
Rev.: $338,236,850
Assets: $1,361,552,370
Liabilities: $1,129,158,502
Net Worth: $232,393,868

Compartamos Financiera—(Continued)

Earnings: $31,453,863
Fiscal Year-end: 12/31/23
Financial Services
N.A.I.C.S.: 522320

COMPASS GOLD CORPORATION

Suite 800 365 Bay Street, Toronto,
M5H 2V1, ON, Canada
Tel.: (416) 596-0996　　　　　　　**BC**
Web Site:
　　https://www.compassgoldcorp.com
Year Founded: 1988
COGDF—(OTCIQ)
Assets: $16,880,459
Liabilities: $841,817
Net Worth: $16,038,642
Earnings: ($516,746)
Fiscal Year-end: 12/31/23
Mineral Exploration Services
N.A.I.C.S.: 213114
Greg Taylor (Dir-IR & Corp Comm)

COMPASS GROUP PLC

Compass House Guildford Street,
Chertsey, KT16 9BQ, Surrey, United
Kingdom
Tel.: (44) 1932573000　　　　　　　**UK**
Web Site: https://www.compass-
　　group.com
Year Founded: 1987
CMPGF—(OTCIQ)
Rev.: $39,166,877,051
Assets: $22,216,611,967
Liabilities: $15,701,842,969
Net Worth: $6,514,768,998
Earnings: $1,663,721,283
Emp.: 550,000
Fiscal Year-end: 09/30/23
Food Products Distr
N.A.I.C.S.: 551112
Alison Yapp (Gen Counsel & Sec)

Subsidiaries:

14Forty Limited　　　　　　　　　　**(1)**
Parklands Court 24 Parklands, Rednal, Birmingham, B45 9PZ, United Kingdom
Tel.: (44) 1214575700
Web Site: https://14forty.co.uk
N.A.I.C.S.: 561210

28 Villages Pty Ltd.　　　　　　　　**(1)**
43 Outram St, West Perth, 6005, WA, Australia
Tel.: (61) 861869470
Web Site: https://28villages.com.au
N.A.I.C.S.: 722320

7000 Set Meal SAS　　　　　　　　**(1)**
28 rue des Granges Galand, 37 550, Saint-Avertin, France
Tel.: (33) 247481030
Web Site: http://www.7000info.com
Catering Services
N.A.I.C.S.: 722320

**Bottle Lab Technologies Private
Limited**　　　　　　　　　　　　　　　**(1)**
SmartQ Opp BDA Head Office 1st Floor
Future Group Sankey Rd, VK Kalyani Commercial Complex, Bengaluru, 560051, Karnataka, India
Tel.: (91) 8043758844
Web Site: https://www.thesmartq.com
Emp.: 300
Food Service
N.A.I.C.S.: 722511

C&B Holdings, LLC　　　　　　　　**(1)**
4862 E Baseline Rd Ste 103, Mesa, AZ 85206
Tel.: (480) 588-2305
Web Site: http://www.getourhousedeals.com
Property Rental Services
N.A.I.C.S.: 531110

Caf-Caf Inc.　　　　　　　　　　　　**(1)**
5-B Rue Montgolfier, Boucherville, J4B8C4, QC, Canada
Web Site: https://cafcaf.com
N.A.I.C.S.: 424490

Canteen of Canada Limited　　　　**(1)**
1 Prologis Boulevard Suite 400, Mississauga, L5W 0G2, ON, Canada
Web Site: https://www.canteencanada.com
N.A.I.C.S.: 424490

Chef's Hall, Inc.　　　　　　　　　　**(1)**
111 Richmond St W, Toronto, M5H 2G4, ON, Canada
Tel.: (416) 300-9081
Web Site: https://www.chefshall.com
Restaurant Services
N.A.I.C.S.: 722511

**Compass Catering Services, Ireland
Limited**
3rd Floor 43a Yeats Way Parkwest Business Park, Dublin, D12 P5V6, Ireland
Tel.: (353) 16296100
Web Site: http://www.compass-group.ie
Emp.: 2,300
Food & Beverage Services
N.A.I.C.S.: 722511
Chris Chidley (Mng Dir)

**Compass Catering Y Servicios Chile
Limitada**　　　　　　　　　　　　　　　**(1)**
Av Las Condes 11 774 7th Floor, Vitacura, Santiago, Chile
Tel.: (56) 225910600
Web Site: http://www.compass-group.cl
Food Service
N.A.I.C.S.: 722310

**Compass Group (Australia) Pty
Ltd**　　　　　　　　　　　　　　　　　**(1)**
35-51 Mitchell Street, McMahons Point, 2060, NSW, Australia
Tel.: (61) 297974900
Emp.: 13,000
Restaurant & Catering Services
N.A.I.C.S.: 722320
Lara Peake (Gen Counsel & Sec)

Compass Group (Schweiz) AG　　　**(1)**
Oberfeldstrasse 14, 8302, Kloten, Switzerland
Tel.: (41) 435571111
Web Site: https://welcome.compass-group.ch
Emp.: 80
Restaurant Operating Services
N.A.I.C.S.: 722511
Ursi Zweifel (Head-Mktg & Comm)

Subsidiary (Domestic):

Restorama AG　　　　　　　　　　　**(2)**
Oberfeldstrasse 14, Kloten, 8302, Switzerland
Tel.: (41) 435571111
Emp.: 100
Professional Catering Services
N.A.I.C.S.: 722320
Hunts Poesch (Gen Mgr)

Compass Group AB　　　　　　　　**(1)**
Evenemangsgatan 2C floor 7, Box 1183, 171 23, Solna, Sweden
Tel.: (46) 858008200
Web Site: http://www.compass-group.se
Emp.: 2,700
Food & Beverage Services
N.A.I.C.S.: 722511
Tess Humble Dillner (Dir-Ops Excellence)

Compass Group Belgilux S.A.　　　**(1)**
Tel.: (32) 22432211
Web Site: http://www.compass-group.be
Emp.: 2,000
Food Service
N.A.I.C.S.: 722310
Annelies Samyn (Mgr-Contract)

**Compass Group Czech Republic
s.r.o.**　　　　　　　　　　　　　　　　**(1)**
Jankovcova 1603/47a, Holesovice, 170 00, Prague, Czech Republic
Tel.: (420) 220302111
Web Site: http://www.compass-group.cz
Catering Services
N.A.I.C.S.: 722320

Compass Group Danmark A/S　　　**(1)**
Rued Langgaards Vej 8 1st floor, 2300, Copenhagen, Denmark
Tel.: (45) 72228888
Web Site: https://www.compass-group.dk
Catering Services
N.A.I.C.S.: 722320

Anja Faergemann Jensen (Mgr-Mktg &
Comm)

**Compass Group Deutschland
GmbH**　　　　　　　　　　　　　　　　**(1)**
Helfmann-Park 2, 65760, Eschborn, Germany
Tel.: (49) 6196478500
Sales Range: $25-49.9 Million
Emp.: 200
Restaurant & Catering Services
N.A.I.C.S.: 722320

Subsidiary (Domestic):

Medirest GmbH & Co OHG　　　　**(2)**
Helfmann-Park 2, 65760, Eschborn, Germany
Tel.: (49) 6196478500
Food Catering Services
N.A.I.C.S.: 722320

Compass Group FS Finland Oy　　**(1)**
Mannerheimintie 117, Box 131, 00280, Helsinki, Finland
Tel.: (358) 107296000
Web Site: https://www.compass-group.fi
Food Service
N.A.I.C.S.: 722310
Maarit Parikka (Acct Dir)

Compass Group FS Norway A/S　　**(1)**
Drengsrudbekken 12, 1383, Asker, Norway
Tel.: (47) 66776280
Web Site: https://www.compass-group.no
Emp.: 2,300
Food & Beverage Services
N.A.I.C.S.: 722511
Robbie Robertson (Mng Dir)

Compass Group France SAS　　　**(1)**
89 91 Rue Du Faubourg Saint Honore, F 75008, Paris, France　　　　　**(100%)**
Tel.: (33) 155272300
Sales Range: $10-24.9 Million
Emp.: 40
Catering & Hospitality Services
N.A.I.C.S.: 722320

Subsidiary (Domestic):

**Compass Group France Holdings
SAS**　　　　　　　　　　　　　　　　**(2)**
123 Avenue de la Republique, 92320, Chatillon, France
Tel.: (33) 176610000
Investment Management Service
N.A.I.C.S.: 523999

Compass Group Holdings PLC　　　**(1)**
Compass House Guildford Street, Chertsey, KT16 9BQ, Surrey, United Kingdom
Tel.: (44) 1932573000
Web Site: https://www.compass-group.com
Sales Range: $50-74.9 Million
Emp.: 250
Holding Company
N.A.I.C.S.: 551112

Compass Group Hong Kong Ltd.　　**(1)**
Room 805 8/F New Kowloon Plaza 38 Tai Kok Tsui Road, Kowloon, China (Hong Kong)
Tel.: (852) 25186888
Web Site: https://www.compass-hk.com
Emp.: 1,100
Pantry Services
N.A.I.C.S.: 624210

Compass Group International BV　　**(1)**
Haaksbergweg 70 Floor 11, 1101 DZ, Amsterdam, Netherlands
Tel.: (31) 205643700
Web Site: https://www.compass-group.nl
Holding Company
N.A.I.C.S.: 551112

Compass Group Italia S.p.A　　　　**(1)**
Via Angelo Scarsellini N 14, 20161, Milan, Italy
Tel.: (39) 02480531
Emp.: 3,437
Catering Services
N.A.I.C.S.: 722320

Compass Group Nederland BV　　　**(1)**
Laarderhoogtweg 11, 1101 DZ, Amsterdam, Netherlands
Tel.: (31) 20 564 3700
Web Site: https://www.compass-group.nl
Catering, Hospitality & Support Services

N.A.I.C.S.: 722320

Subsidiary (Domestic):

**Compass Group Nederland Holding
BV**　　　　　　　　　　　　　　　　　**(2)**
Laarderhoogtweg 11, 1101 DZ, Amsterdam, Netherlands
Tel.: (31) 205643770
Web Site: http://www.compass-group.nl
Holding Company; Catering, Hospitality & Support Services
N.A.I.C.S.: 551112

**Compass Group New Zealand
Limited**　　　　　　　　　　　　　　　**(1)**
The Textile Centre Level 3 1 Kenwyn St, Ellerslie, Parnell, 1052, New Zealand
Tel.: (64) 95251093
Web Site: https://www.compass-group.co.nz
Catering Services
N.A.I.C.S.: 722320

Compass Group North America　　　**(1)**
2400 Yorkmont Rd, Charlotte, NC
28217-4511　　　　　　　　　　**(100%)**
Tel.: (704) 328-4000
Sales Range: $5-14.9 Billion
Emp.: 1,200
Regional Managing Office; Vending & Food Service Contractors
N.A.I.C.S.: 551114
Gary Green (CEO)

Subsidiary (Domestic):

**Chartwells Higher Education Dining
Services**　　　　　　　　　　　　　　**(2)**
2 International Dr, Rye Brook, NY 10573
Tel.: (855) 942-8437
Web Site: http://chartwellshighered.com
Food Service Management & Hospitality Services
N.A.I.C.S.: 722320
Lisa McEuen (CEO)

Subsidiary (Domestic):

Fresh Ideas Management, LLC　　　**(3)**
2000 E Broadway Ste 166, Columbia, MO 65201
Tel.: (573) 445-4321
Web Site: https://www.freshideasfood.com
Sales Range: $1-9.9 Million
Emp.: 130
Eating Place
N.A.I.C.S.: 722320
John Orscheln (Principal)

Subsidiary (Non-US):

Compass Group Canada Ltd.　　　　**(2)**
1 Prologis Blvd Suite 400, Mississauga, L5W 0G2, ON, Canada　　　　**(100%)**
Tel.: (519) 679-2661
Sales Range: $25-49.9 Million
Emp.: 130
Business Institutional Contract Caterer
N.A.I.C.S.: 722320
Anika Malik (VP-Comm)

Subsidiary (Domestic):

Compass Group USA, Inc.　　　　　**(2)**
2400 Yorkmont Rd, Charlotte, NC 28217-4511
Tel.: (704) 329-4000
Sales Range: $650-699.9 Million
Emp.: 1,000
Holding Company; Vending & Food Services
N.A.I.C.S.: 551112

Unit (Domestic):

Bateman Senior Meals　　　　　　　**(3)**
3110 W Pinhook Rd Ste 201, Lafayette, LA 70508
Tel.: (337) 593-0433
Sales Range: $10-24.9 Million
Emp.: 3
Food Service
N.A.I.C.S.: 624120

Subsidiary (Domestic):

Bon Appetit Management Co　　　　**(3)**
201 Redwood Shores Pkwy Ste 100, Redwood Shores, CA 94065
Tel.: (650) 798-8000
Web Site: https://www.bamco.com

Restaurant Operating Services
N.A.I.C.S.: 722511
Fedele Bauccio *(Co-Founder & CEO)*

Unit (Domestic):

Chartwells USA **(3)**
2400 Yorkmont Rd, Charlotte, NC 28217-4511
Tel.: (704) 329-4000
Sales Range: $650-699.9 Million
Emp.: 1,000
Food Service Contractors
N.A.I.C.S.: 722310

Division (Domestic):

Compass Group USA, Inc. - Canteen Division **(3)**
2400 Yorkmont Rd, Charlotte, NC 28217
Tel.: (704) 329-4000
Web Site: http://www.canteen.com
Sales Range: $200-249.9 Million
Emp.: 1,000
Vending Machine Operators
N.A.I.C.S.: 445132
Peter Fetherson *(CEO)*

Subsidiary (Domestic):

CulinArt, Inc. **(4)**
175 Sunnyside Blvd, Plainview, NY 11803-6769
Tel.: (516) 437-2700
Web Site: https://www.culinartgroup.com
Corporate Dining Services
N.A.I.C.S.: 722310
Joseph Sargis *(VP-Fin)*

Subsidiary (Domestic):

Crothall Services Group, Inc. **(3)**
1500 Liberty Rdg Dr Ste 210, Wayne, PA 19087
Tel.: (610) 249-0420
Web Site: http://www.crothall.com
Sales Range: $25-49.9 Million
Emp.: 60
Building Maintenance Contracting Service
N.A.I.C.S.: 561720

Subsidiary (Non-US):

SSC Service Solutions **(4)**
Tel.: (865) 546-8880
Web Site: http://www.sscserv.com
Janitorial Service, Contract Basis
N.A.I.C.S.: 561720
Shannon Thornton *(VP)*

Subsidiary (Domestic):

Eurest Services, Inc. **(3)**
2400 Yorkmont Rd, Charlotte, NC 28217
Tel.: (704) 328-4000
Janitorial & Facility Support Services
N.A.I.C.S.: 561210
Tony McDonald *(CEO)*

Subsidiary (Non-US):

Eurest Colectividades SA **(4)**
Calle Pinar de San Jose 98 1a, 28054, Madrid, Aravaca, Spain **(69.54%)**
Tel.: (34) 915425339
Web Site: https://iara.eurest.es
Catering & Hospitality Services
N.A.I.C.S.: 722320

Eurest Deutschland GmbH **(4)**
Helfmann-Park 2, 65760, Eschborn, Germany **(69.52%)**
Tel.: (49) 6196478500
Sales Range: $150-199.9 Million
Emp.: 1,500
Catering & Hospitality Services
N.A.I.C.S.: 722320

Eurest Nederland BV **(4)**
Paasheuvelweg 4, Postbus 22875, 1100 DJ, Amsterdam, Netherlands **(64.32%)**
Catering & Hospitality Services
N.A.I.C.S.: 722320

Eurest Services GmbH **(4)**
Helfmann-Park 2, 65760, Eschborn, Germany
Tel.: (49) 6196478790
Web Site: http://www.eurest-services.de
Restaurant Operating Services
N.A.I.C.S.: 722511

Unit (Domestic):

FLIK International **(3)**
2 International Dr, Rye Brook, NY 10573
Tel.: (914) 935-5300
Web Site: https://www.flik-usa.com
Sales Range: $25-49.9 Million
Emp.: 125
Food Service Contractors
N.A.I.C.S.: 722310

Subsidiary (Domestic):

Foodbuy LLC **(3)**
1105 Lakewood Pkwy Ste 400, Alpharetta, GA 30009
Tel.: (678) 256-8000
Web Site: https://www.foodbuy.com
Food Catering Services
N.A.I.C.S.: 722320

Levy Restaurants, Inc. **(3)**
980 N Michigan Ave, Chicago, IL 60611-4501
Tel.: (312) 664-8200
Sales Range: $25-49.9 Million
Emp.: 170
Restaurant & Sports Arena Dining Services
N.A.I.C.S.: 722511
Alison Weber *(Chief Creative Officer)*

Branch (Domestic):

Levy Restaurants **(4)**
980 N Michigan Ave, Chicago, IL 60611-4501
Tel.: (312) 664-8200
Web Site: https://www.levyrestaurants.com
Sales Range: $10-24.9 Million
Food Service Operations
N.A.I.C.S.: 722410
Larry Levy *(Founder & Chm)*

Subsidiary (Domestic):

Prom Management Group, Inc. **(4)**
484 Inwood Ave N, Saint Paul, MN 55128
Tel.: (651) 501-8191
Sales Range: $1-9.9 Million
Caterers
N.A.I.C.S.: 722320

Subsidiary (Domestic):

Morrison Management Specialists, Inc. **(3)**
400 Northridge Rd Ste 600, Atlanta, GA 30030
Tel.: (404) 845-3330
Web Site: https://www.morrisonhealthcare.com
Food, Nutrition & Dining Services to the Health Care & Senior Living Industries
N.A.I.C.S.: 621999
Gene Dolloff *(Pres-Morrison Sr Dining)*

Restaurant Associates Corporation **(3)**
132 W 31st St Ste 601, New York, NY 10001
Tel.: (212) 613-5500
Sales Range: $450-499.9 Million
Emp.: 50
Restaurant Management Services
N.A.I.C.S.: 722511
Michael Gallagher *(Pres-Managed Svcs)*

Compass Group Poland Sp. Z o.o. **(1)**
ul Jana Olbrachta 94, 01-102, Warsaw, Poland
Tel.: (48) 224634400
Web Site: https://www.compass-group.pl
Catering Services
N.A.I.C.S.: 722320
Justyna Pawlik *(Specialist-HR & Payroll)*

Compass Group Procurement Ltd **(1)**
Compass House Guildford Street, Chertsey, KT16 9BQ, United Kingdom
Tel.: (44) 1932573000
Web Site: https://www.compass-group.com
Sales Range: $25-49.9 Million
Emp.: 500
Restaurant Operating Services
N.A.I.C.S.: 722511

Compass Group Rus OOO **(1)**
20 Kulakova Str Building 1, 123592, Mos-

cow, Russia
Tel.: (7) 4959884606
Web Site: http://www.compass-group.ru
Food & Beverage Services
N.A.I.C.S.: 722511
Nicos Antoniades *(CEO & Mng Dir)*

Compass Group Services Colombia S.A. **(1)**
Calle 98 11b - 29 PBX, Bogota, Colombia
Tel.: (57) 15140088
Web Site: https://www.compass-group.com.co
Food Service
N.A.I.C.S.: 722310

Compass Group Slovakia s. r. o. **(1)**
Karadzicova 2, 811 09, Bratislava, Slovakia
Tel.: (421) 250203681
Web Site: http://www.compass-group.sk
Catering Services
N.A.I.C.S.: 722320

Compass Group Southern Africa (Pty) Ltd **(1)**
22 Milkyway Ave Frankenwald, Sandton, 2090, South Africa
Tel.: (27) 112092400
Web Site: https://www.empactgroup.co.za
Sales Range: $800-899.9 Million
Emp.: 620
Restaurant Operating Services
N.A.I.C.S.: 722511
Clive Cowley *(Reg Mgr)*

Compass Group Sweden AB **(1)**
Tel.: (46) 858008200
Web Site: http://www.compass-group.se
Food Service
N.A.I.C.S.: 722310
Robbie Robertson *(COO)*

Compass Group, UK & Ireland Limited **(1)**
Parklands Court 24 Parklands, Birmingham Great Park Rubery, Birmingham, B45 9PZ, United Kingdom **(100%)**
Tel.: (44) 1214575000
Web Site: https://www.compass-group.co.uk
Sales Range: $25-49.9 Million
Emp.: 120
Catering, Hospitality & Support Services
N.A.I.C.S.: 722320
Dennis Hogan *(Mng Dir)*

Compass India Support Services Private Limited **(1)**
401 4th Floor Tower-A Spaze I-Tech Park Sohna Road Sector-49, Gurgaon, 122018, Haryana, India
Tel.: (91) 1244975400
Web Site: http://www.compass-group.co.in
Food Service
N.A.I.C.S.: 722310

Core Works, LLC **(1)**
23445 Clay Rd, Katy, TX 77449
Tel.: (281) 968-9700
Web Site: http://www.coreworks-usa.com
Aluminium Heat Exchanger Mfr
N.A.I.C.S.: 332410

Cosmopolitan Catering, LLC **(1)**
1288 Reamwood Ave, Sunnyvale, CA 94089
Tel.: (408) 732-1400
Web Site: https://www.cosmocaters.com
Catering Services
N.A.I.C.S.: 722320
Jacob Caputo *(Owner-Kitchen Ops)*

Crothall Healthcare Inc. **(1)**
1500 Liberty Ridge Dr Ste 210, Wayne, PA 19087
Tel.: (610) 520-8100
Web Site: https://www.crothall.com
Healtcare Services
N.A.I.C.S.: 621610

CulinArt Group, Inc. **(1)**
6 International Dr 1st Fl Ste 130, Rye Brook, NY 10573
Tel.: (484) 870-6708
Web Site: http://culinartgroup.com
N.A.I.C.S.: 722320
Peter Witkowski *(Pres)*

Culinaire Des Pays de L'Adour SAS **(1)**
Culinary Country of Adour Artisanal Zone, 40 500, Bas-Mauco, France

Tel.: (33) 558053660
Web Site: https://www.restauration-collective-laculinaire.fr
Emp.: 29
Food Service
N.A.I.C.S.: 722310

Dine Contract Catering Limited **(1)**
First Floor EngineRooms Birchwood Park, Warrington, WA3 6YN, United Kingdom
Tel.: (44) 1925282330
Web Site: https://www.dine-contract-catering.com
Catering Services
N.A.I.C.S.: 722320

Dynamic Vending, Inc. **(1)**
5433 Eagle Industrial Ct, Hazelwood, MO 63042
Tel.: (314) 895-1685
Web Site: https://www.dynamicvending.com
Vending Machine Mfr & Distr
N.A.I.C.S.: 333310

ESS Mobile Offshore Units A/S **(1)**
Forusparken 2, 4031, Stavanger, Norway
Tel.: (47) 51898800
Food & Beverage Services
N.A.I.C.S.: 722511

East Coast Catering (NS) Limited **(1)**
10 Morris Drive Unit 35, Dartmouth, B3B 1K8, NS, Canada
Tel.: (902) 466-0150
Catering Services
N.A.I.C.S.: 722320
Michael Rose *(Ops Mgr)*

East Coast Catering Limited **(1)**
30 Queen's Road, Saint John's, A1C 2A5, NL, Canada
Tel.: (709) 576-1741
Web Site: https://www.eccltd.ca
Catering Services
N.A.I.C.S.: 722320
Mike Deley *(CEO)*

Eishoku-Medix, Inc. **(1)**
4-1-1 Hakata Ekimae Nihon Seimei Hakata Ekimae No 2 Building 5th Floor, Hakata-ku, Fukuoka, Japan
Tel.: (81) 924378714
Web Site: http://eishoku-mdx.compassgroup-japan.jp
Food Contracting Services
N.A.I.C.S.: 722310

Equinoxe Solutions Limited **(1)**
Ongar Business Centre The Gables Fyfield Road, Essex, CM5 0GA, United Kingdom
Tel.: (44) 1277364655
N.A.I.C.S.: 541614

Eurest (Portugal) - Sociedade Europeia de Restaurantes, Lda. **(1)**
Prime Building Av da Quinta Grande n 53 - 6, 2610-156, Amadora, Portugal
Tel.: (351) 217913600
Web Site: https://www.eurest.pt
Food & Beverage Services
N.A.I.C.S.: 722511

Eurest Bremen GmbH **(1)**
Theodor-Heuss-Allee 20 SWB, 28215, Bremen, Germany
Tel.: (49) 4213593284
Food Service
N.A.I.C.S.: 722310

Eurest Etteremuzemelteto Korlatolt Felelossegu Tarsasag **(1)**
Science Park Office Building Irinyi Jozsef utca 4-20, 1117, Budapest, Hungary
Tel.: (36) 13710810
Web Site: http://www.eurest.hu
Catering Services
N.A.I.C.S.: 722320

Eurest Luxembourg S.A. **(1)**
1-5 rue de l'Innovation, 1896, Kockelscheuer, Luxembourg
Tel.: (352) 2637311
Web Site: https://www.eurest.lu
Catering Services
N.A.I.C.S.: 722320

Eurest Proper Meals de Mexico S.A. de C.V. **(1)**
Jaime Balmes 11 Torre D Floor 1 Miguel Hidalgo Delegation, Polanco I Secc Colonia

Compass Group PLC—(Continued)

Polanco, 11510, Mexico, Mexico
Tel.: (52) 15591383600
Web Site: http://www.eurest.com.mx
Food Contracting Services
N.A.I.C.S.: 722310

Eurest ROM SRL (1)
Calea Serban Voda nr 133 Cladirea B etaj
I sector 4, District 4, Bucharest, Romania
Tel.: (40) 212107882
Web Site: http://www.compass-group.ro
Catering Services
N.A.I.C.S.: 722320

Eurest Restaurationsbetriebsgesellschaft m.b.H (1)
IZD Tower Wagramer Strasse 19/4, 1220,
Vienna, Austria
Tel.: (43) 171246210
Web Site: https://www.eurest.at
Food Service
N.A.I.C.S.: 722310
Georg Hirsch-Stronstorff (Mng Dir)

Eurest Services B.V. (1)
Laarderhoogtweg 11, 1100 DJ, Amsterdam,
Netherlands
Tel.: (31) 205643700
Web Site: http://www.eurestservices.nl
Facility Services
N.A.I.C.S.: 561210
Jan Kraaijvanger (Mgr-Subcontracting)

Eurest UK Limited (1)
Parklands Court 24 Parklands, Rednal, Birmingham, B45 9PZ, United Kingdom
Tel.: (44) 1214575700
Web Site: https//eurest.co.uk
N.A.I.C.S.: 722310
Jason Trotman (Head-Culinary Ops)

Euroserve Guvenlik A.S. (1)
Libadiye Caddesi Emaar Plaza No 82F/73
K 23-24, Unalan Mahallesi, Istanbul, Turkiye
Tel.: (90) 2165789700
Web Site:
https://www.euroserveguvenlik.com.tr
Security Guard Services
N.A.I.C.S.: 561612

Famous Flavours B.V. (1)
Luzernestraat 57, 2153 GM, Nieuw-Vennep,
Netherlands
Tel.: (31) 204160020
Web Site: http://www.famousflavours.nl
Catering Services
N.A.I.C.S.: 722320

Fazer Food Services Oy (1)
Laulukuja 6, 420, Helsinki, Finland
Tel.: (358) 20 7296000
Web Site: http://www.fazer.com
Food Mfr
N.A.I.C.S.: 311999
Jaana Korhola (Mng Dir)

Subsidiary (Non-US):

Fazer Food Services A/S (2)
Tel.: (45) 63113310
Web Site: http://www.fazer.dk
Food Mfr
N.A.I.C.S.: 311999
Ulrik Greve (Mgr-Fin)

Fazer Food Services AB (2)
Tel.: (46) 84707200
Web Site: http://www.fazer.se
Food Mfr
N.A.I.C.S.: 311999
Joakim Nilsson (Mng Dir)

Fazer Food Services AS (2)
Tel.: (47) 23897900
Web Site: http://www.fazer.no
Food Mfr
N.A.I.C.S.: 311999
Silje Vegsund (Mgr-Ops)

Feedr Limited (1)
52 Tabernacle Street, London, EC2A 4NJ,
United Kingdom
Tel.: (44) 2038902200
Web Site: https://feedr.co
N.A.I.C.S.: 722310

Flinckheuvel BV (1)
Sint-Jobsteenweg 25, s Gravenwezel, 2970,
Antwerp, Belgium

Tel.: (32) 38778810
Web Site: https://flinckheuvel.be
N.A.I.C.S.: 722310

Food affairs GmbH (1)
Helfmann-Park 2, 65760, Eschborn, Germany
Tel.: (49) 61964785660
Web Site: http://www.food-affairs.de
Restaurant Services
N.A.I.C.S.: 722511
Teresa Singh (Bus Mgr)

Foodbuy Pty Ltd (1)
35-51 Mitchell Street, McMahons Point,
2060, NSW, Australia
Tel.: (61) 297974900
Web Site: http://www.foodbuy.com.au
Procurement Services
N.A.I.C.S.: 541990
Andrew Brightmore (Exec Dir)

Fresh & Ready Foods LLC (1)
251 Little Falls Dr, Wilmington, DE 19808
Web Site: https://freshandreadyfoods.com
N.A.I.C.S.: 311991

Gourmet Dining, LLC (1)
285 Madison Ave, Madison, NJ 07940
Tel.: (973) 443-8659
Web Site: http://www.gourmetdining.co
Emp.: 2,500
Food Management Services
N.A.I.C.S.: 722511

Innoclean S.A. (1)
Tel.: (352) 263735
Web Site: http://www.innoclean.lu
Cleaning Service
N.A.I.C.S.: 561720

J&M Catering Services NV (1)
Boomsesteenweg 28, 2627, Schelle, Belgium
Tel.: (32) 38778810
Web Site: https://www.jmcatering.be
N.A.I.C.S.: 722310

Kanne Cafe GmbH (1)
Helfmann-Park 2, 65760, Eschborn, Germany
Tel.: (49) 6196478500
Web Site: https://www.kanne-cafe.de
N.A.I.C.S.: 722310
Daniela Kautz (Mng Dir)

Kasteel Van Brasschaat NV (1)
Gemeentepark 5, 2930, Brasschaat, Belgium
Tel.: (32) 38778810
Web Site: https://kasteelvanbrasschaat.be
N.A.I.C.S.: 721110

Keith Prowse Limited (1)
Webb Ellis House Rugby Road, Twickenham, TW1 1DS, United Kingdom
Tel.: (44) 2088437699
Web Site: https://www.keithprowse.co.uk
N.A.I.C.S.: 561599
Jeff Banks (Head-Strategic Sls)

Leonardi GmbH & Co. KG (1)
Konrad-Zuse-Platz 2, 81829, Munich, Germany
Tel.: (49) 89143417510
Web Site: http://www.leonardi-kg.de
Food Service
N.A.I.C.S.: 722310

Leonardi HPM GmbH (1)
Konrad-Zuse-Platz 2, 81829, Munich, Germany
Tel.: (49) 89143417510
Web Site: http://www.leonardi-kg.de
Food Service
N.A.I.C.S.: 722310

Leonardi SVM GmbH (1)
Konrad-Zuse-Platz 2, 81829, Munich, Germany
Tel.: (49) 89143417510
Web Site: http://www.leonardi-svm.de
Food Service
N.A.I.C.S.: 722310

Levy Restaurants France SAS (1)
123 avenue de la Republique, 92360, Chatillon, France
Tel.: (33) 158701758
Web Site: https://www.levyrestaurants.fr
Restaurant Services

N.A.I.C.S.: 722511

Mazzone Hospitality, LLC (1)
743 Pierce Rd, Clifton Park, NY 12065
Tel.: (518) 690-0293
Web Site:
https://www.mazzonehospitality.com
Emp.: 1,100
Catering Services
N.A.I.C.S.: 722320
Angelo Mazzone (Founder)

Nextonline Limited (1)
Plot 9 Road 113/A, Gulshan, Dhaka, 1360,
Bangladesh
Tel.: (880) 9614000121
Web Site: https://www.nextonline.com
N.A.I.C.S.: 541511

Occitanie Restauration SAS (1)
Lieu dit La Prade Route de Castres, 81580,
Soual, France
Tel.: (33) 563754031
Web Site: http://www.occitanie-restauration.fr
Food Service
N.A.I.C.S.: 722310

Oceane de Restauration SAS (1)
Atlanparc building M-Zone de Kerluheme-3
rue Camille Claudel, 56890, Plescop,
France
Tel.: (33) 297445450
Web Site: http://www.oceane-de-restauration.fr
Food Service
N.A.I.C.S.: 722310

PLURAL servicepool GmbH (1)
Sankt-Florian-Weg 1, 30880, Laatzen, Germany
Tel.: (49) 51176340
Web Site: http://www.plural.de
Hygiene Management Services
N.A.I.C.S.: 561720

Puy Du Fou Restauration SAS (1)
Puy du Fou, CS 70 025, 85590, Les
Epesses, France
Tel.: (33) 820091010
Web Site: https://www.puydufou.com
Hotel Services
N.A.I.C.S.: 722511

Rank + Rally, LLC (1)
980 N Michigan Ave, Chicago, IL 60611
Web Site: http://www.rankandrally.com
Sporting Goods Retailer
N.A.I.C.S.: 459110

**Restaurant Associates (Australia)
PTY Ltd** (1)
35-51 Mitchell Street, McMahons Point,
2060, NSW, Australia
Tel.: (61) 297974900
Web Site:
https://www.restaurantassociates.com.au
Restaurant Services
N.A.I.C.S.: 722511

**Royal Business Restaurants
GmbH** (1)
Katharinenstr 7, 83043, Bad Aibling, Germany
Tel.: (49) 80619381899
Web Site: http://www.royal-restaurants.com
Emp.: 120
Restaurant Services
N.A.I.C.S.: 722511
Thomas Grieser (Mng Dir)

Scolarest - zarizeni skolniho stravovani spol. s.r.o (1)
Jankovcova 1603/47a, 170 00, Prague,
Czech Republic
Tel.: (420) 731438529
Web Site: http://www.scolarest.cz
Catering Services
N.A.I.C.S.: 722320
Adela Dolezalova (Mktg Mgr)

**Seiyo Food-Compass Group,
Inc.** (1)
Hamarikyu Kensetsu Plaza Bldg 4F/5F
5-5-12 Tsukiji, Chuo-ku, Tokyo, 104-0045,
Japan
Tel.: (81) 335440351
Sales Range: $1-4.9 Billion
Emp.: 1,630
Food Service, Catering & Hospitality Services

N.A.I.C.S.: 722310

Servicios Renovados de Alimentacion, S.A.U. (1)
Calle Castilla 8-10 bajos, 50009, Zaragoza,
Spain
Tel.: (34) 902102037
Web Site: https://www.seral-service.com
Emp.: 1,450
Catering Services
N.A.I.C.S.: 722320

Shing Hin Catering Group Ltd. (1)
Room 805 8/F New Kowloon Plaza 38 Tai
Kok Tsui Road, Kowloon, China (Hong
Kong)
Tel.: (852) 25186888
Web Site: http://www.shinghin.com
Catering Services
N.A.I.C.S.: 722320

**Sofra Yemek Uretim Ve Hizmet
A.S.** (1)
Unalan Mahallesi Libadiye Caddesi Emaar
Plaza No 82F K 23-24, Uskudar, Istanbul,
Turkiye
Tel.: (90) 2165789700
Web Site: https://www.sofragrup.com
Catering Services
N.A.I.C.S.: 722320

Sopregim SAS (1)
Smart-Up Building - Hall A 123 avenue de
la Republique, 92320, Chatillon, France
Tel.: (33) 176610521
Web Site: https://www.sopregim.fr
Restaurant Services
N.A.I.C.S.: 722511

SpenDifference LLC (1)
2000 Clay St 3rd Fl, Denver, CO 80211
Tel.: (303) 531-2680
Web Site: http://www.spendifference.com
Logistics & Supply Chain Services
N.A.I.C.S.: 541614
Maryanne Rose (Pres & CEO)

Statewide Services, Inc. (1)
72120 Magnesia Falls Dr, Rancho Mirage,
CA 92270
Tel.: (760) 699-5434
Web Site: http://www.statewideinc.net
Construction Contracting Services
N.A.I.C.S.: 236220
Oscar Lua (Partner & Project Mgr)

Sud Est Traiteur SAS (1)
9 rue des Vergers, Mudaison, 34130, Le
Cres, France
Tel.: (33) 467871600
Web Site: https://www.sud-est-traiteur.fr
Food Service
N.A.I.C.S.: 722310

**Touchpoint Support Services,
LLC** (1)
400 Northridge Rd, Sandy Springs, GA
30350
Web Site: https://www.iamtouchpoint.com
Emp.: 11,000
Food & Beverage Services
N.A.I.C.S.: 722511
Scott MacLellan (CEO)

Victor Kramer Co., Inc. (1)
305 6th Ave, Seaside Heights, NJ 08751
Tel.: (201) 628-5219
Web Site: http://www.victorkramer.com
Hospital Laundry Processing
N.A.I.C.S.: 812332
Steve Miller (VP & Gen Mgr)

Xandrion B.V. (1)
Stationsweg 95, 6711 PM, Ede, Netherlands
Tel.: (31) 318421655
Web Site: http://www.xandrion.nl
Framework Contract Services
N.A.I.C.S.: 561990

Xandrion Belgie BVBA (1)
Hermeslaan 1H, 1831, Diegem, Belgium
Tel.: (32) 22432323
Web Site: https://www.xandrion.be
Food Service
N.A.I.C.S.: 722310

COMPASS PATHWAYS PLC
3rd Floor 1 Ashley Road, Altrincham,
WA14 2DT, Cheshire, United Kingdom

Tel.: (44) 8000325911 UK
Web Site:
https://www.compasspathways.com
Year Founded: 2020
CMPS—(NASDAQ)
Rev.: $19,306,000
Assets: $197,294,000
Liabilities: $16,014,000
Net Worth: $181,280,000
Earnings: ($91,505,000)
Emp.: 181
Fiscal Year-end: 12/31/22
Holding Company
N.A.I.C.S.: 551112
George Goldsmith *(Co-Founder)*

COMPAX SOFTWARE DEVEL-OPMENT GMBH
Hebbelplatz 5/Top 3, 1100, Vienna,
Austria
Tel.: (43) 69916805180
Web Site: https://compaxdigital.com
Year Founded: 1994
Emp.: 650
IT Services
N.A.I.C.S.: 513210

COMPEQ MANUFACTURING CO., LTD.
No.91 Ln 814 Daxin Rd Shin-juang
Vil, Luzhu Dist, Taoyuan, 338114,
Taiwan
Tel.: (886) 33231111
Web Site:
https://www.compeq.com.tw
Year Founded: 1973
2313—(TAI)
Rev.: $2,193,622,109
Assets: $2,587,038,000
Liabilities: $1,303,393,423
Net Worth: $1,283,644,577
Earnings: $136,314,950
Emp.: 15,709
Fiscal Year-end: 12/31/23
Printed Circuit Board Mfr
N.A.I.C.S.: 334412
P. K. Chiang *(Chm & Pres)*

Subsidiaries:

COMPEQ Manufacturing(Suzhou)
Co., Ltd.   (1)
Block 20TH Suchun Industrial Square No
428 Xinglong Street, Suzhou Industrial
Park, Suzhou, 215021, Jiangsu, China
Tel.: (86) 51262836001
Printed Circuit Board Distr
N.A.I.C.S.: 334412

COMPEQ Technology (Huizhou) Co.,
Ltd.   (1)
No 168 Huguang Road, Huzhen Town Bo-
luo County, Huizhou, 516139, Guangdong,
China
Tel.: (86) 7526301111
Printed Circuit Board Distr
N.A.I.C.S.: 423690

Compeq Manufacturing Co., Ltd. -
Luchu Plant   (1)
No 91 Lane 814 Ta-Hsin Road Shin Ch-
uang Village, Lu Chu Hsiang, Taoyuan,
Taiwan
Tel.: (886) 33231111
Sales Range: $800-899.9 Million
Printed Circuit Board Mfr
N.A.I.C.S.: 334412
Charles Wu *(Chm)*

Compeq Manufacturing(Huizhou) Co.,
Ltd.   (1)
No 168 Huguang Rd, Huzhen Town Boluo
County, Huizhou, 516139, Guandong,
China
Tel.: (86) 7526301111
Web Site: http://www.compeq.com.tw
Sales Range: $800-899.9 Million
Printed Circuit Board Mfr
N.A.I.C.S.: 334412

Initial Technology Pte Ltd   (1)
Blk 750A Chai Chee Road 07-13 Viva Busi-

ness Park, Singapore, 469001, Chai Chee,
Singapore
Tel.: (65) 6 338 7933
Web Site: http://www.compeq.com.tw
Sales Range: $25-49.9 Million
Emp.: 3
Printed Circuit Boards Mfr & Distr
N.A.I.C.S.: 334412

COMPERIA.PL SA
Ul Konstruktorska 13, 02-673, War-
saw, Poland
Tel.: (48) 226429119
Web Site: https://www.comperia.pl
CPL—(WAR)
Rev.: $11,248,476
Assets: $6,215,701
Liabilities: $1,830,030
Net Worth: $4,385,671
Earnings: ($146,596)
Fiscal Year-end: 12/31/23
Online Financial Services
N.A.I.C.S.: 522210
Szymon Stanislaw Fiecek *(Chm &
Member-Mgmt Bd)*

COMPETENT AUTOMOBILES CO. LTD.
Competent House F-14 Connaught
Place, New Delhi, 110 001, India
Tel.: (91) 1126812682
Web Site: https://www.competent-
maruti.com
Year Founded: 1985
531041—(BOM)
Rev.: $170,712,497
Assets: $69,469,355
Liabilities: $30,468,274
Net Worth: $39,001,080
Earnings: $2,655,648
Emp.: 1,787
Fiscal Year-end: 03/31/22
Automobile Sales & Services
N.A.I.C.S.: 811198
Raj Chopra *(Chm & Mng Dir)*

COMPETITION CHEVROLET LTD.
40 Boulder Blvd, Stony Plain, T7Z
1V7, AB, Canada
Tel.: (780) 963-6121
Web Site:
http://www.competitionchevrolet.com
Rev.: $55,000,000
Emp.: 60
New & Used Car Dealers
N.A.I.C.S.: 441110
Julius Prodorutti *(Gen Mgr-Sls)*

COMPETITION TOYOTA LTD.
1515 Rob Panzer Drive, London,
N5X 0M7, ON, Canada
Tel.: (519) 451-3880
Web Site:
https://www.northlondontoyota.com
Year Founded: 1964
Rev.: $14,172,027
Emp.: 31
New & Used Car Dealers
N.A.I.C.S.: 441110
Kevin Laurie *(Principal)*

COMPETITIVE FOODS AUS-TRALIA PTY. LTD.
L1 355 Scarborough Beach Rd, Os-
borne Park, 6017, Western Australia,
Australia
Tel.: (61) 892429400
Sales Range: $450-499.9 Million
Emp.: 13,063
Franchise Restaurant Operator
N.A.I.C.S.: 722513
John Cowin *(Owner)*

COMPLEX COMET SA
Bulevardul Timisoara nr 84 sector 6,
Bucharest, Romania

Tel.: (40) 214441866
Web Site:
https://www.complexcomet.ro
COET—(BUC)
Rev.: $182,097
Assets: $2,369,462
Liabilities: $58,145
Net Worth: $2,311,317
Earnings: ($2,367)
Emp.: 3
Fiscal Year-end: 12/31/23
Real Estate Prorperty Leasing Ser-
vices
N.A.I.C.S.: 531190

COMPLUS TECHNOLOGIES SE
Unter den Platanen 24, 14774, Bran-
denburg, Germany
Tel.: (49) 3381804360
Web Site: http://www.complus-
technologies.de
Information Technology Services
N.A.I.C.S.: 519290
Uwe Maiberg *(Chm-Mgmt Bd)*

COMPODIUM INTERNATIONAL AB
Vastra Varvsgatan 31, 972 36, Lulea,
Sweden
Tel.: (46) 92077441
Web Site:
https://www.compodium.com
Year Founded: 1997
8OB0—(DEU)
Rev.: $2,671,392
Assets: $4,763,039
Liabilities: $1,346,120
Net Worth: $3,416,920
Earnings: ($2,054,917)
Emp.: 16
Fiscal Year-end: 12/31/23
Electronic Equipment Distr
N.A.I.C.S.: 423690
Johan Bengtsson *(Chief Comml
Officer)*

COMPONENTA CORPORATION
Teknobulevardi 7, FI-01530, Vantaa,
Finland
Tel.: (358) 1040300 FI
Web Site:
https://www.componenta.com
CTH1V—(HEL)
Rev.: $56,776,902
Assets: $60,584,426
Liabilities: $42,778,652
Net Worth: $17,805,774
Earnings: $16,349,956
Emp.: 602
Fiscal Year-end: 12/31/19
Industrial & Automotive Components
Mfr & Distr
N.A.I.C.S.: 336350
Harri Suutari *(Chm)*

Subsidiaries:

Componenta A.S.   (1)
Cad no 14, Manisa, 45000, Turkiye
Tel.: (90) 2362338057
Web Site: http://www.componenta.com
Emp.: 800
Lathes & Drilling Machines Mfr
N.A.I.C.S.: 333517

Componenta Albin AB   (1)
Hantverkargatan 3, PO Box 115, SE 681
23, Kristinehamn, Sweden
Tel.: (46) 550410500
Web Site: http://www.componenta.com
Sales Range: $50-74.9 Million
Emp.: 110
Industrial Component Mfr
N.A.I.C.S.: 333310

Componenta Castings Oy   (1)
Bremerintie 6, 03600, Karkkila, Finland
Tel.: (358) 505268380
Metal Component Mfr

N.A.I.C.S.: 333519

Componenta Finland Oy   (1)
Bremerintie 6, 03600, Karkkila, Finland
Tel.: (358) 1040300
Web Site: http://www.componenta.com
Sales Range: $100-124.9 Million
Emp.: 265
Cast Iron Components Mfr
N.A.I.C.S.: 331110

Componenta Frammestad AB   (1)
Frammestadvagen 29, 465 97, Nossebro,
Sweden
Tel.: (46) 104507500
Web Site: http://www.componenta.com
Sales Range: $75-99.9 Million
Emp.: 125
Cast Components Distr
N.A.I.C.S.: 423510

Componenta France S.A.S.   (1)
16 Rue Ampere, 95300, Pontoise, Val-
d'Oise, France
Tel.: (33) 134246750
Web Site: http://www.componenta.com
Sales Range: $25-49.9 Million
Emp.: 3
Iron Casting Mfr
N.A.I.C.S.: 331511

Componenta Italy S.r.l.   (1)
Corso Unione Sovietica 612/21, Turin,
10135, Italy
Tel.: (39) 0110864811
Web Site: http://www.componenta.com
Sales Range: $50-74.9 Million
Emp.: 4
Cast Components Distr
N.A.I.C.S.: 423510

Componenta Manufacturing Oy   (1)
Onkapannu 4, FI-40700, Jyvaskyla, Finland
Tel.: (358) 505778089
Metal Components Mfr & Distr
N.A.I.C.S.: 332510

Componenta Netherlands B.V.   (1)
Copernicusstraat 9, 6003 DE, Weert, Lim-
burg, Netherlands
Tel.: (31) 495513800
Sales Range: $75-99.9 Million
Emp.: 250
Cast Components Distr
N.A.I.C.S.: 423510
Theo Hendrikx *(Mgr-HR)*

Componenta USA, LLC   (1)
407 Northpark Blvd, Huxley, IA 50124
Tel.: (515) 597-4201
Web Site: http://www.componenta.com
Printed Circuit Board Components Distr
N.A.I.C.S.: 334417

Componenta Wirsbo AB   (1)
PO Box 102, 730 61, Virsbo, Sweden
Tel.: (46) 22339500
Web Site: http://www.componentawirsbo.se
Sales Range: $50-74.9 Million
Emp.: 210
Axles & Transmission Components Mfr
N.A.I.C.S.: 336390
Goran Jansson *(Dir-Bus Unit)*

Karkkilan Laakarikeskus Oy   (1)
Valurinkatu 2 A 1, Karkkila, 3600, Finland
Tel.: (358) 104032633
Web Site:
http://www.karkkilanlaakarikeskus.fi
Sales Range: $10-24.9 Million
Emp.: 8
General Medical Services
N.A.I.C.S.: 622110
Jussi Piironen *(Mgr)*

Vanhan Ruukin Kiinteistopalvelu
Oy   (1)
Panuntie No 4, PO Box 00610, Helsinki,
3600, Finland
Tel.: (358) 10 40300
Web Site: http://www.componenta.com
Sales Range: $50-74.9 Million
Emp.: 20
Real Estate Manangement Services
N.A.I.C.S.: 531390

COMPONENTE AUTO S.A.
Maximilian Popovici str no 59, To-
poloveni, 115500, Arges, Romania
Tel.: (40) 248 607 120

Componente Auto S.A.—(Continued)

Web Site: http://www.catgroup.ro
Sales Range: $10-24.9 Million
Emp.: 348
Automobile Parts Mfr
N.A.I.C.S.: 336390

COMPOSITE ALLIANCE GROUP INC.

Bankers Hall West Tower Suite 1000,
888 3rd Street Southwest, Calgary,
T2P 5C5, AB, Canada
Tel.: (403) 870-7383   **AB**
Year Founded: 2008
CAG—(TSXV)
Rev.: $10,839,379
Assets: $10,287,097
Liabilities: $12,947,549
Net Worth: ($2,660,452)
Earnings: ($613,612)
Emp.: 2
Fiscal Year-end: 12/31/23
Investment Services
N.A.I.C.S.: 523999
James G. Louie (Pres & CEO)

COMPOSITE LIMITED

Eastleigh House Upper Market
Street, Eastleigh, SO50 9RD, Hamp-
shire, United Kingdom
Tel.: (44) 2380645700
Web Site:
      http://www.compositeltd.co.uk
Year Founded: 1989
Rev.: $26,863,705
Emp.: 55
Construction Services
N.A.I.C.S.: 236220
Roy Nield-Dumper (Mng Dir)

COMPPIL SA

Str Muncii Nr 2, Piatra Neamt, Roma-
nia
Tel.: (40) 233 210 597
Web Site: http://www.comppil.ro
Year Founded: 1997
Sales Range: $1-9.9 Million
Emp.: 5
Hide, Skins & Leather Whslr
N.A.I.C.S.: 424990

COMPREHENSIVE HEALTH-CARE SYSTEMS INC.

2440 Kensington Road NW, Calgary,
T2N3S1, AB, Canada
Tel.: (403) 613-7310
CHS—(TSXV)
Rev.: $3,835,660
Assets: $966,880
Liabilities: $23,871,472
Net Worth: ($22,904,592)
Earnings: ($3,581,988)
Fiscal Year-end: 12/31/23
Business Consulting Services
N.A.I.C.S.: 522299
Hassan Mohaideen (Chm, Pres &
CEO)

COMPREHENSIVE LAND DE-VELOPMENT & INVESTMENT PLC

Mekka Street Al Mutakamelah Build-
ing No 146 First Floor No 106, PO
Box 739, Kilo Circle, Amman, 11118,
Jordan
Tel.: (962) 65540541
ATTA—(AMM)
Rev.: $64,253
Assets: $13,551,777
Liabilities: $599,027
Net Worth: $12,952,750
Earnings: ($379,391)
Emp.: 3
Fiscal Year-end: 12/31/20
Land Acquisition Services
N.A.I.C.S.: 237210

COMPREHENSIVE LEASING CO.

207 Zahran Street, PO Box 739, Am-
man, 11118, Jordan
Tel.: (962) 65822110
Web Site: https://www.c-leasing.com
Year Founded: 2004
LEAS—(AMM)
Rev.: $19,453,216
Assets: $127,447,880
Liabilities: $99,607,381
Net Worth: $27,840,499
Earnings: $5,632,973
Emp.: 80
Fiscal Year-end: 12/31/20
Industrial Machinery & Equipment
Leasing Services
N.A.I.C.S.: 532440
Eliya Jad Wakileh (Gen Mgr)

COMPREHENSIVE MULTIPLE PROJECTS COMPANY PLC

King Abdullah Second industrial city,
PO Box 141220, Amman, 11814,
Jordan
Tel.: (962) 64023540
Year Founded: 1994
INOH—(AMM)
Sales Range: $1-9.9 Million
Emp.: 100
Storage Battery Mfr
N.A.I.C.S.: 335910
Manule Azzam (Gen Mgr)

COMPREMUM S.A.

ul Bulgarska 69/73, 60-320, Poznan,
Poland
Tel.: (48) 538550394
Web Site: https://compremum.pl
Year Founded: 1973
CPR—(WAR)
Rev.: $81,245,427
Assets: $136,469,512
Liabilities: $71,579,014
Net Worth: $64,890,498
Earnings: $5,715,193
Fiscal Year-end: 12/31/23
Construction & Engineering Services
N.A.I.C.S.: 236220
Michal Ulatowski (Vice Chm-Mgmt
Bd)

COMPRENDIUM STRUC-TURED FINANCING GMBH

Feringastrasse 10B, Unterfohring,
D-85774, Munich, Germany
Tel.: (49) 89960740   **De**
Web Site:
      http://www.comprendium.com
Sales Range: $25-49.9 Million
Emp.: 100
Office Equipment Sales Financing &
Leasing Services
N.A.I.C.S.: 532420
John W. Boo (CEO & Member-Mgmt
Bd)

COMPRESSOR SAZI TABRIZ CO.

Valiasr Ave Mirdamad Corner Eskan
Bldg Tower B, Tehran, Iran
Tel.: (98) 21 8798755
Web Site: http://www.cst-ir.com
Year Founded: 1987
Emp.: 215
Air Compressor Mfr
N.A.I.C.S.: 333912

COMPTA - EQUIPAMENTOS E SERVICOS DE INFORMATICA, S.A.

11 Miraflores Alameda Fernao Lopes
12, 1495-190, Alges, Portugal
Tel.: (351) 214 134 200
Web Site: http://www.compta.pt

Year Founded: 1972
Rev.: $26,773,836
Earnings: ($1,903,267)
Emp.: 240
Fiscal Year-end: 12/31/18
Information Technology Services
N.A.I.C.S.: 541512
Armindo Lourenco Monteiro (Chm)

COMPTOIR GROUP PLC

Unit 2 Plantain Place Crosby Row,
London, SE1 1YN, United Kingdom
Tel.: (44) 2074861111   **UK**
Web Site:
      https://www.comptoirlibanais.com
Year Founded: 2000
COM—(AIM)
Rev.: $42,152,516
Assets: $43,537,973
Liabilities: $37,083,686
Net Worth: $6,454,287
Earnings: $798,752
Emp.: 597
Fiscal Year-end: 01/01/23
Restaurant Operators
N.A.I.C.S.: 722511

COMPU B LTD.

23 Erica Road Stacey Bushes, MIlton
Keynes, MK12 6HS, United Kingdom
Tel.: (44) 2033552345
Web Site: http://www.compub.com
Technological Products Mfr
N.A.I.C.S.: 334118
Ed Clarkin (Chief Comml Officer)

Subsidiaries:

Stormfront Retail Limited   **(1)**
Unit 1B Newton Centre Matford Business
Park, Exeter, EX2 8GN, United Kingdom
Tel.: (44) 3330044111
Web Site: http://www.stormfront.co.uk
Sales Range: $25-49.9 Million
Emp.: 105
Electronic Store Operator
N.A.I.C.S.: 449210

COMPU-QUOTE INC.

3600 Rhodes Drive, Windsor, N8W
5A4, ON, Canada
Tel.: (519) 974-7283
Web Site: http://www.compu-
      quote.com
Year Founded: 1983
Rev.: $10,588,370
Emp.: 175
Computer Programming Services
N.A.I.C.S.: 541511
James Nickelo (Sr VP)

COMPUAGE INFOCOM LTD.

D601 Lotus Corporate Park, Western
Express Highway Goregaon East,
Mumbai, 400 063, India
Tel.: (91) 2267114444
Web Site:
      https://www.compuageindia.com
Year Founded: 1987
532456—(BOM)
Rev.: $576,569,366
Assets: $161,141,089
Liabilities: $127,326,599
Net Worth: $33,814,490
Earnings: $3,651,170
Emp.: 704
Fiscal Year-end: 03/31/22
Computer Peripheral Distr
N.A.I.C.S.: 541519
Atul H. Mehta (Chm & Mng Dir)

Subsidiaries:

Compuage Infocom (S) Pte. Ltd.   **(1)**
69 Ubi Crescent 03 - 04 CES Building, Sin-
gapore, 408561, Singapore
Tel.: (65) 68444356
Web Site: http://www.compuageindia.com
Emp.: 11
Computer Hardware Distr

N.A.I.C.S.: 423710
Atul Mehta (CEO & Mng Dir)

Lancor Projects Limited   **(1)**
No 78 Vbc Jewellery Building 2nd Floor G
N Chetty Road, Theagaraya Nagar, Chen-
nai, 600 017, India
Tel.: (91) 44 28344708
Property Development Services
N.A.I.C.S.: 531190

COMPUCASE ENTERPRISE CO., LTD.

No 225 Lane 54 Sec 2 An-Ho Rd,
Tainan City, Taiwan
Tel.: (886) 63560606
Web Site: https://www.hec-
      group.com.tw
Year Founded: 1979
3032—(TAI)
Rev.: $266,023,503
Assets: $270,993,384
Liabilities: $133,412,337
Net Worth: $137,581,047
Earnings: $24,445,076
Fiscal Year-end: 12/31/23
Computer Peripherals Mfr
N.A.I.C.S.: 334118

Subsidiaries:

Compucase Europe GmbH   **(1)**
Im Huelsenfeld 9, 40721, Hilden, Germany
Tel.: (49) 21 039 8810
Web Site: https://www.hec-group.com.tw
Computer Peripheral Equipment Mfr
N.A.I.C.S.: 334118

Compucase Japan Co., Ltd.   **(1)**
Shin - Yokohama Union Building ANNEX 1F
3-24-5 Shin-Yokohama, Kohoku-ku, Yoko-
hama, 222-0033, Kanagawa, Japan
Tel.: (81) 454705948
Web Site: https://www.hec-group.jp
Computer Peripherals Mfr
N.A.I.C.S.: 334118

Compucase UK. Ltd.   **(1)**
15 Alston Drive Bradwell, Abbey, Milton
Keynes, MK13 9HA, Buckinghamshire,
United Kingdom
Tel.: (44) 1908 317 666
Web Site: http://www.compucase-hec.co.uk
Sales Range: $25-49.9 Million
Emp.: 2
Computer Hardware Accessories Mfr
N.A.I.C.S.: 334118

HEC Korea Co.,Ltd.   **(1)**
506 Unitechvil Ilsan-ku, Koyang, 411-842,
Gyeonggi-do, Korea (South)
Tel.: (82) 31 909 7080
Web Site: http://www.heckorea.co.kr
Computer Peripherals Mfr
N.A.I.C.S.: 334118

COMPUCOM SOFTWARE LTD

IT 14-15 EPIP Sitapura, Jaipur,
302022, Rajasthan, India
Tel.: (91) 1412770131
Web Site:
      https://www.compucom.co.in
COMPUSOFT—(NSE)
Rev.: $7,060,831
Assets: $22,578,151
Liabilities: $3,405,620
Net Worth: $19,172,531
Earnings: $1,736,266
Emp.: 998
Fiscal Year-end: 03/31/22
Software Develoment
N.A.I.C.S.: 541511
Surendra Kumar Surana (Mng Dir)

COMPUCON S.A.

9th km of Thessaloniki Thermi, PO
Box 60445, 57001, Thessaloniki,
Greece
Tel.: (30) 2310 490300
Web Site: http://www.compucon.gr
Year Founded: 1993
Emp.: 27

Embroidery Software Development
Services
N.A.I.C.S.: 541511
Vasilis Thomaidis *(Pres & CEO)*

Subsidiaries:

COMPUCON JAPAN Co. Ltd   (1)
1-52-4 Akabane Kita-Ku, Tokyo, 115-0045,
Japan
Tel.: (81) 3 5249 8680
Web Site: http://www.compucon.jp
Software Distribution Services
N.A.I.C.S.: 423430

COMPUCON USA L.L.C.   (1)
1011 Lemons Rd, Stokesdale, NC 27357
Tel.: (336) 294-0604
Web Site: http://www.compuconusa.com
Software Distribution Services
N.A.I.C.S.: 423430

COMPUGATES HOLDINGS BERHAD

No 3 Jalan PJU 1 41 Dataran Prima,
47301, Petaling Jaya, Selangor, Ma-
laysia
Tel.: (60) 378808133   MY
Web Site:
    https://www.compugates.com
Year Founded: 1997
COMPUGT—(KLS)
Rev.: $1,249,668
Assets: $39,690,000
Liabilities: $7,557,430
Net Worth: $32,132,570
Earnings: ($1,759,288)
Emp.: 200
Fiscal Year-end: 12/31/22
Holding Company; Cellular Phones &
Accessories Distr
N.A.I.C.S.: 551112
Thoo Chan See *(Exec Dir)*

COMPUGEN INC.

100 Via Renzo Drive, Richmond Hill,
L4S 0B8, ON, Canada
Tel.: (905) 707-2000
Web Site: http://www.compugen.com
Year Founded: 1981
Sales Range: $75-99.9 Million
Emp.: 1,500
IT Solutions & Services
N.A.I.C.S.: 541511
Karen Atkinson *(VP)*

Subsidiaries:

Compugen Finance Inc.   (1)
25 Leek Cres, Richmond Hill, L4B 4B3, ON,
Canada
Tel.: (905) 695-8237
Computer Hardware & Software Leasing
Services
N.A.I.C.S.: 532420

COMPUGEN LTD.

Azrieli Center 26 Harokmim Street
Building D, Holon, 5885849, Israel
Tel.: (972) 37658585   II
Web Site: https://www.cgen.com
Year Founded: 1993
CGEN—(NASDAQ)
Rev.: $7,500,000
Assets: $94,176,000
Liabilities: $16,496,000
Net Worth: $77,680,000
Earnings: ($33,694,000)
Emp.: 69
Fiscal Year-end: 12/31/22
Biotechnology Therapeutic & Diag-
nostic Products Discovery & Devel-
oper
N.A.I.C.S.: 325414
Anat Cohen-Dayag *(Pres & CEO)*

Subsidiaries:

Compugen USA, Inc.   (1)
560 S Winchester Blvd Ste 500, San Jose,
CA 95128   (100%)
Tel.: (408) 236-7336

Web Site: http://www.cgen.com
Biotechnology Therapeutic & Diagnostic
Products Discovery & Developer
N.A.I.C.S.: 325414

Evogene Ltd.   (1)
13 Gad Feinstein Street Park Rehovot, PO
Box 4173, Ness Ziona, 7414002, Israel
Tel.: (972) 89311900
Web Site: http://www.evogene.com
Rev.: $1,675,000
Assets: $56,126,000
Liabilities: $21,336,000
Net Worth: $34,790,000
Earnings: ($29,844,000)
Emp.: 133
Fiscal Year-end: 12/31/2022
Crop Genetic Services
N.A.I.C.S.: 115112
Martin S. Gerstel *(Chm)*

Keddem Bioscience Ltd.   (1)
11 Ha'amal Street, Southern Industrial
Zone, Ashkelon, 78785, Israel   (100%)
Tel.: (972) 86711859
Small Molecule Drug Discovery
N.A.I.C.S.: 541715

COMPUGROUP MEDICAL SE & CO. KGAA

Maria Trost 21, 56070, Koblenz, Ger-
many
Tel.: (49) 26180000   De
Web Site: https://www.cgm.com
Year Founded: 1984
COP—(DUS)
Rev.: $1,028,354,994
Assets: $1,923,143,801
Liabilities: $1,138,375,820
Net Worth: $784,767,981
Earnings: $90,177,381
Emp.: 7,814
Fiscal Year-end: 12/31/20
Holding Company; Healthcare Indus-
try Software Publisher
N.A.I.C.S.: 551112
Klaus Esser *(Vice Chm)*

Subsidiaries:

4K S.R.L.   (1)
Via Privata Sartirana 3, 20144, Milan, Italy
Tel.: (39) 0287176193
Web Site: https://www.4ksrl.it
Pharmaceutical Delivery Services
N.A.I.C.S.: 811210

ADVANCE AB   (1)
Datavagen 29, PO Box 9249, Gothenburg,
40095, Sweden
Tel.: (46) 317601800
Web Site: http://www.advance.se
Sales Range: $10-24.9 Million
Emp.: 60
Online Health Care Services
N.A.I.C.S.: 621491

AESCU DATA Gesellschaft fur Daten-
verarbeitung mbH   (1)
Pachergasse 17, 4400, Steyr, Austria
Tel.: (43) 494171696201
Web Site: http://www.aescudata.de
Sales Range: $25-49.9 Million
Emp.: 22
Software Development Services
N.A.I.C.S.: 541511
Karl Pranzl *(Mng Dir)*

ALBIS Arzteservice Product GmbH &
Co KG   (1)
Maria Trost 23, Koblenz, 56070, Germany
Tel.: (49) 26180001600
Web Site: http://www.albis.de
Sales Range: $25-49.9 Million
Emp.: 60
Software Development Services
N.A.I.C.S.: 541511
Volker Scheuble *(Mng Dir)*

Aescudata GmbH   (1)
Bahnhofstrasse 37, 21423, Winsen, Ger-
many
Tel.: (49) 4171696100
Web Site: http://www.aescudata.de
Sales Range: $25-49.9 Million
Emp.: 45
Software Development Services

N.A.I.C.S.: 541511
Karl Pranzl *(Mng Dir)*

Ascon Hosting Facilities B.V.   (1)
Nobelweg 32, 6101, Echt, Netherlands
Tel.: (31) 9003876633
Web Site: http://www.euroned.eu
Healthcare Industry Software Publisher
N.A.I.C.S.: 513210

Ascon Software B.V.   (1)
Nobelweg 32, 6101, Echt, Netherlands
Tel.: (31) 9003876633
Web Site: http://www.euroned.eu
Healthcare Industry Software Publisher
N.A.I.C.S.: 513210

CGM Bilgi Sistemleri A.S.   (1)
Teknopark B2 Blok Kat 1 Esenler, Yildiz
Teknik Universitesi Davutpasa Kampusu,
34220, Istanbul, Turkiye
Tel.: (90) 212 3060000
Web Site: http://www.cgmturkiye.com
Healthcare Software Publisher
N.A.I.C.S.: 513210

CGM Lab Belgium SA   (1)
Rue Pres Champs 25b Barchon, 4671,
Liege, Belgium
Tel.: (32) 43879393
Healthcare Field Software Publisher
N.A.I.C.S.: 513210

CGM Lab Deutschland GmbH   (1)
Schlaraffiastr 1, 44867, Bochum, Germany
Tel.: (49) 26154001000
Healthcare Field Software Publisher
N.A.I.C.S.: 513210

CGM Lab France SAS   (1)
55 Avenue des Champs Pierreux, 92012,
Nanterre, Cedex, France
Tel.: (33) 142748670
Healthcare Field Software Publisher
N.A.I.C.S.: 513210

CGM South Africa (Pty) Ltd.   (1)
1 Proton Street Techno Park, PO Box 6089,
7612, Stellenbosch, South Africa
Tel.: (27) 21 8866160
Web Site: http://www.cgm.com
Emp.: 2
Healthcare Industry Software Publisher
N.A.I.C.S.: 513210
Mervyn Cookson *(Mng Dir)*

CoSi Medical IT GmbH   (1)
In the Kappeleswiesen 7, 72488, Sigmarin-
gen, Germany
Tel.: (49) 26154005100
Web Site: http://www.cosinet.de
Telematic Infrastructure Services
N.A.I.C.S.: 517810

CompuDENT Praxiscomputer GmbH
& Co. KG   (1)
Maria Trost 25, Koblenz, 56070, Germany
Tel.: (49) 26180001900
Web Site: http://www.compudent.de
Sales Range: $25-49.9 Million
Emp.: 100
Online Dental Information Provider
N.A.I.C.S.: 541715

Subsidiary (Domestic):

Intermedix Deutschland GmbH   (2)
Maria Trost 21, 56070, Koblenz, Germany
Tel.: (49) 8989744500
Web Site: http://www.intermedix.de
Sales Range: $10-24.9 Million
Emp.: 27
Medical Information Services
N.A.I.C.S.: 621491
Christine Hackler-Anlauf *(Sr Project Mgr-
Healthcare Solutions)*

CompuGroup Medical Belgium
bvba   (1)
Brusselsesteenweg 283/10, 9230, Wetteren,
Belgium
Tel.: (32) 93217270
Web Site: http://www.cgm.com
Medical Industry Software Publisher
N.A.I.C.S.: 513210
Norbert Fishl *(Gen Mgr)*

Subsidiary (Domestic):

Barista Software BVBA   (2)
Kempische Steenweg 297 bus 6, 3500,

Hasselt, Belgium
Tel.: (32) 89680801
Web Site: https://www.daktari.be
Healthcare Field Software Publisher
N.A.I.C.S.: 513210

Compufit BVBA   (2)
Slijkensesteenweg 3, 8400, Oostende, Bel-
gium
Tel.: (32) 59270570
Healthcare Field Software Publisher
N.A.I.C.S.: 513210

CompuGroup Medical CEE
GmbH   (1)
Rinnbockstrasse 3, 1030, Vienna, Austria
Tel.: (43) 171516230
Web Site:
    http://www.report.compugroup.com
Sales Range: $25-49.9 Million
Emp.: 250
Software Development Services
N.A.I.C.S.: 541511
Willibald Salomon *(Mng Dir)*

Subsidiary (Domestic):

Intermedix Osterreich GmbH   (2)
Ricoweg 22, 2351, Wiener Neudorf, Austria
Tel.: (43) 22368000800
Web Site: http://www.intermedix.at
Sales Range: $25-49.9 Million
Emp.: 2
Healthcare Software Services
N.A.I.C.S.: 541511

Systema HIS Human Information
Systems Gesellschaft mbH   (2)
Pachergasse 4, 4400, Steyr, Austria
Tel.: (43) 72525870
Web Site: http://www.systema.info
Sales Range: $25-49.9 Million
Software Development Services
N.A.I.C.S.: 541511
Willibald Salomon *(Gen Mgr)*

CompuGroup Medical CEE
GmbH   (1)
Rinnbockstrasse 3, 1030, Vienna, Austria
Tel.: (43) 171516230
Healthcare Field Software Publishing Ser-
vices
N.A.I.C.S.: 513210

Subsidiary (Domestic):

CGM Arztsysteme Osterreich
GmbH   (2)
Ricoweg 22, 2351, Wiener Neudorf, Austria
Tel.: (43) 50818100
Healthcare Field Software Publisher
N.A.I.C.S.: 513210
Martin Schauperl *(Gen Mgr)*

CGM Clinical Osterreich GmbH (2)
Pachergasse 4, 4400, Steyr, Austria
Tel.: (43) 72525870
Healthcare Field Software Publisher
N.A.I.C.S.: 513210
Felix Frick *(Sr Mgr-Dev)*

CompuGroup Medical Ceska repub-
lika s.r.o.   (1)
Budova C Office Park Nove Butovice Bu-
charova 2657/12, 158 00, Prague, 5, Czech
Republic
Tel.: (420) 246007900
Web Site: http://www.cgm.com
Healthcare Industry Software Publisher
N.A.I.C.S.: 513210

CompuGroup Medical Denmark
A/S   (1)
Olof Palmes Alle 44, 8200, Aarhus, Den-
mark
Tel.: (45) 70301340
Web Site: https://www.cgm.com
Healthcare Industry Software Publisher
N.A.I.C.S.: 513210

CompuGroup Medical Dentalsysteme
GmbH   (1)
Maria Trost 25, 56070, Koblenz, Germany
Tel.: (49) 26180001900
Web Site: http://www.cgm-dentalsysteme.de
Sales Range: $350-399.9 Million
Emp.: 1,000
Software Development Services
N.A.I.C.S.: 541511

CompuGroup Medical SE & Co. KGaA—(Continued)

CompuGroup Medical Deutschland AG (1)
Maria Trost 21, 56070, Koblenz, Germany
Tel.: (49) 26180001521
Web Site: http://www.cgm.com
Emp.: 1,200
Medical Software Publisher
N.A.I.C.S.: 513210

Subsidiary (Domestic):

CGM Clinical Deutschland GmbH (2)
Maria Trost 25, 56070, Koblenz, Germany
Tel.: (49) 26180001780
Web Site: https://www.cgm.com
Emp.: 150
Health Care Srvices
N.A.I.C.S.: 621491
Thomas Simon (Member-Mgmt Bd)

CGM Medistar Systemhaus GmbH (2)
Maria Trost 23, 56070, Koblenz, Germany
Tel.: (49) 261 1349 2000
Web Site: http://www.k-line.de
Medical Practice Support Products & Services
N.A.I.C.S.: 561499
Tobias Klein (Member-Mgmt Bd)

Subsidiary (Domestic):

K-Line Praxislosungen GmbH (3)
Maria-Merian-Strasse 9, 24145, Kiel, Germany
Tel.: (49) 4317103105
Web Site: http://www.k-line.de
Medical Management Consulting Services
N.A.I.C.S.: 541611

Subsidiary (Domestic):

Gotthardt Informationssysteme GmbH (4)
Maria Trost 1, 56070, Koblenz, Germany
Tel.: (49) 261988756
Web Site: http://www.gotthardt.de
Digital Communication Services
N.A.I.C.S.: 517810
Jurgen Richter (Head-Sls Dept)

Subsidiary (Domestic):

CGM Mobile Software GmbH (2)
Dessauer Strasse 28/29, 10963, Koblenz, Germany
Tel.: (49) 26180000
Healthcare Field Software Publisher
N.A.I.C.S.: 513210

Subsidiary (Non-US):

CompuGroup Medical Bilgi Sistemleri A.S. (2)
Teknopark B2 Blok Kat 1 Esenler Kampusu Yildiz Teknik Universitesi, Davutpasa, 34220, Istanbul, Turkiye
Tel.: (90) 2123060000
Software Development Services
N.A.I.C.S.: 513210

Subsidiary (Domestic):

CompuGroup Medical Deutschland AG Geschaftsbereich HIS (2)
Schlaraffiastr 1, Bochum, 44867, Germany
Tel.: (49) 2324 920 90
Web Site: http://www.cgm.com
Health Care Srvices
N.A.I.C.S.: 621491
Michael Franz (VP-Bus Dev)

Turbomed Vertriebs- und Service GmbH (2)
Maria Trost 21, 56070, Koblenz, Germany
Tel.: (49) 26113492000
Web Site: http://www.cgm-systemhaus.org
Healthcare Field Software Publisher
N.A.I.C.S.: 513210

CompuGroup Medical France SAS (2)
55 Avenue des Champs Pierreux, 92012, Nanterre, Cedex, France
Tel.: (33) 147162700
Healthcare Field Software Publisher
N.A.I.C.S.: 513210

CompuGroup Medical Hellas S.A. (1)
Soumela St 23 Kalamaria, 55 132, Thessaloniki, Greece
Tel.: (30) 2310 432 885
Web Site: http://www.compugroup.com
Sales Range: $25-49.9 Million
Emp.: 3
Medical Software Development Services
N.A.I.C.S.: 541511

CompuGroup Medical Inc. (1)
3838 N Central Ave Ste 1600, Phoenix, AZ 85012
Tel.: (602) 258-3530
Web Site: http://www.cgm.com
Emp.: 50
Medical Software Publisher
N.A.I.C.S.: 513210
Werner Rodorff (CTO)

Subsidiary (Domestic):

Schuyler House Inc. (2)
26027 Huntington Ln Ste F, Valencia, CA 91355
Tel.: (661) 257-8094
Web Site: http://schuylerhouse.com
Sales Range: $1-9.9 Million
Emp.: 18
Professional Equipment & Supplies Merchant Whslr
N.A.I.C.S.: 423490
Janet Chennault (VP)

CompuGroup Medical Italia Holding S.r.l. (1)
Foro Buonaparte 70, 20121, Milan, Italy
Tel.: (39) 0284269401
Healthcare Field Software Publishing Services
N.A.I.C.S.: 513210

Subsidiary (Domestic):

Farma3tec S.r.l. (2)
Foro Buonaparte 70, 20121, Milan, Italy
Tel.: (39) 059704911
Healthcare Field Software Publishing Services
N.A.I.C.S.: 513210

Subsidiary (Domestic):

Mondofarma S.r.l. (3)
Via della Fontina 2, Chiusi, 53043, Siena, Italy
Tel.: (39) 057823311
Healthcare Field Software Publisher
N.A.I.C.S.: 513210

Subsidiary (Domestic):

Qualita in Farmacia S.r.l. (2)
Corso Vercelli 120 c/d, 28100, Novara, Italy
Tel.: (39) 0321481500
Healthcare Field Software Publisher
N.A.I.C.S.: 513210

Studiofarma S.r.l. (2)
Foro Buonaparte 70, 20121, Milan, Italy
Tel.: (39) 0303558211
Healthcare Field Software Publisher
N.A.I.C.S.: 513210

Vega Informatica e Farmacia Srl (2)
Via Vigentina angolo Via Leopoldo Pollak, 27100, Pavia, Italy
Tel.: (39) 0382560028
Healthcare Field Software Publisher
N.A.I.C.S.: 513210

CompuGroup Medical Italia S.p.A. (1)
Via A Olivetti 10, 70056, Molfetta, 70056, BA, Italy
Tel.: (39) 0803383111
Web Site: http://www.cgm.com
Healthcare Industry Software Publisher
N.A.I.C.S.: 513210
Emanuele Mugnani (Sr VP-Southern European Reg)

Subsidiary (Domestic):

CGM XDENT Software S.r.l. (2)
Piazza Cairoli 1, 97100, Ragusa, Italy
Tel.: (39) 0932681600
Healthcare Field Software Publisher
N.A.I.C.S.: 513210

Fablab S.r.l. (2)
Foro Buonaparte 70, 20121, Milan, Italy
Tel.: (39) 0284269400
Web Site: https://www.fab-lab.it
Digital Communication Services
N.A.I.C.S.: 517810
Piero Conte (Gen Mgr)

CompuGroup Medical Lab AB (1)
Cirkolgatan 14, 781 72, Borlange, Sweden
Tel.: (46) 243217600
Web Site: http://www.cgm.com
Sales Range: $10-24.9 Million
Emp.: 50
Analytical Laboratory Information Development Services
N.A.I.C.S.: 621511

CompuGroup Medical Malaysia Sdn Bhd (1)
Unit L3-E-3A Level 3 Enterprise 4 Technology Park Malaysia, Lebuhraya Puchong-Sg, 57000, Kuala Lumpur, Malaysia
Tel.: (60) 899 66 700
Web Site: http://www.cgm.com
Healthcare Industry Software Publisher
N.A.I.C.S.: 513210

CompuGroup Medical Managementgesellschaft mbH (1)
Schlaraffiastr 1, 44867, Bochum, Germany
Tel.: (49) 2327944685
Web Site: http://www.cgm.de
Business Support Services
N.A.I.C.S.: 561499

CompuGroup Medical Norway AS (1)
Lysaker Torg 15 5 etg, PO Box 163, 1366, Lysaker, Norway
Tel.: (47) 21936300
Web Site: https://www.cgm.com
Sales Range: $10-24.9 Million
Emp.: 50
Health Care & Software Services
N.A.I.C.S.: 541511
Tomas Teoerring (Head-Team Support)

CompuGroup Medical Polska sp. z o.o. (1)
Ul Do Dysa 9, 20-149, Lublin, Poland
Tel.: (48) 814442015
Web Site: https://www.cgm.com
Healthcare Industry Software Publisher
N.A.I.C.S.: 513210

CompuGroup Medical Schweiz AG (1)
Gartenstrasse 9, 3007, Bern, Switzerland
Tel.: (41) 319242121
Web Site: https://www.cgm.com
Healthcare Industry Software Publisher
N.A.I.C.S.: 513210

CompuGroup Medical Slovensko s.r.o. (1)
Galvaniho 7/D, 82104, Bratislava, Slovakia
Tel.: (421) 253418075
Web Site: https://www.cgm.com
Emp.: 2
Healthcare Industry Software Publisher
N.A.I.C.S.: 513210

CompuGroup Medical Software GmbH (1)
Maria Trost 21, 56070, Koblenz, Germany
Tel.: (49) 26180000
Web Site: http://www.cgm.com
Software Development Services
N.A.I.C.S.: 541511

Subsidiary (Non-US):

CGM Software RO SRL (2)
Bld Chimiei 2Bis, 700291, Iasi, Romania
Tel.: (40) 785344863
Healthcare Field Software Publisher
N.A.I.C.S.: 513210

Subsidiary (Domestic):

La-Well Systems GmbH (2)
Hartwig-Mildenberg-Str 5-9, 32257, Bunde, Germany
Tel.: (49) 52231893500
Web Site: https://elvi.de
Healthcare Field Software Publisher
N.A.I.C.S.: 513210

CompuGroup Medical Solutions SAS (1)
40 av Theroigne de Mericourt CS 59975, 34967, Montpellier, Cedex 2, France
Tel.: (33) 8 2036 3605
Web Site: http://www.cgm.com
Healthcare Industry Software Publisher
N.A.I.C.S.: 513210

CompuGroup Medical South Africa (Pty) Ltd. (1)
Block 0 Upper Ground Floor 1 Warehouse Building 4 Waterford Place, Century City, Cape Town, 7441, South Africa
Tel.: (27) 861633334
Web Site: https://www.cgm.com
Sales Range: $10-24.9 Million
Emp.: 11
Health Care Srvices
N.A.I.C.S.: 621491
Mervyn Cookson (Mng Dir)

Subsidiary (Domestic):

Intermedix SA (Pty) Ltd. (2)
Aurecon Building 4th Floor 1 Century City Drive Century City, Cape Town, 7446, South Africa
Tel.: (27) 210451556
Web Site: http://www.intermedix.co.za
Marketing Communication Services
N.A.I.C.S.: 541613

CompuGroup Medical Sweden AB (1)
Rattarvagen 3, 169 68, Solna, Sweden
Tel.: (46) 84115550
Web Site: https://www.cgm.com
Health Care Srvices
N.A.I.C.S.: 621491

CompuGroup Medical Sweden AB (1)
Olof Palmes gata 23 plan 4 2 tr, 111 22, Stockholm, Sweden
Tel.: (46) 84115550
Web Site: http://www.cgm.com
Sales Range: $10-24.9 Million
Emp.: 20
Health Care Srvices
N.A.I.C.S.: 621491

CompuGroup Medical Sweden AB (1)
Lilla Bommen 4a, 411 04, Gothenburg, Sweden
Tel.: (46) 300568000
Web Site: http://www.cgm.com
Healthcare Industry Software Publisher
N.A.I.C.S.: 513210

Subsidiary (Domestic):

Lorensbergs Communication AB (2)
Lilla Bommen 4A, 411 04, Gothenburg, Sweden
Tel.: (46) 317206300
Web Site: http://www.cgm.com
Healthcare Industry Software Publisher
N.A.I.C.S.: 513210
Sabine Anspach (VP)

CompuGroup Osterreich GmbH (1)
Geranienstrasse 1, 4481, Asten, Austria
Tel.: (43) 50818100
Web Site: http://www.compugroup.at
Emp.: 42
Healthcare Industry Software Publisher
N.A.I.C.S.: 513210
Gerhard Stimac (Gen Mgr)

CompuGroup Services GmbH (1)
Maria Trost 21, 56070, Koblenz, Germany
Tel.: (49) 26180001150
Software Development Services
N.A.I.C.S.: 541511
Andreas Koll (Gen Mgr)

Effepieffe S.r.l. (1)
Via Mazzini 13, 20812, Limbiate, MB, Italy
Tel.: (39) 02 0061 9826
Web Site: http://www.effepieffe.it
Healthcare Industry Software Publisher
N.A.I.C.S.: 513210

HABA Computer Aktiengesellschaft (1)
Rutersbarg 46, 22529, Hamburg, Germany
Tel.: (49) 405542240
Web Site: https://www.haba-ag.de
Software Publisher
N.A.I.C.S.: 513210

HCS - Health Communication Service GmbH (1)
Ricoweg 22, 2351, Wiener Neudorf, Austria
Tel.: (43) 22368000600
Web Site: http://www.hcs.at
Emp.: 15
Healthcare Industry Software Publisher
N.A.I.C.S.: 513210
Gerhard Stimac (Mng Dir)

INMEDEA GmbH (1)
Gerhard Kindler St 6, 72770, Reutlingen, Germany
Tel.: (49) 7121127060
Web Site: http://www.inmedea.com
Sales Range: $25-49.9 Million
Emp.: 6
Medical Software Development Services
N.A.I.C.S.: 541511

INNOMED Gesellschaft fur medizinische Softwareanwendungen GmbH (1)
Ricoweg 22, 2351, Wiener Neudorf, Austria
Tel.: (43) 22368000
Web Site: http://www.innomed.at
Healthcare Industry Software Publisher
N.A.I.C.S.: 513210

INSIGHT Health GmbH (1)
Auf der Lind 10 a/3, 65529, Waldems-Esch, Germany
Tel.: (49) 61269550
Web Site: https://www.insight-health.de
Information Services
N.A.I.C.S.: 518210

Imagine Editions SAS (1)
11 Boulevard Marsan de Montbrun, Soulac-sur-Mer, 33780, Gironde, France
Tel.: (33) 564101101
Healthcare Field Software Publisher
N.A.I.C.S.: 513210

Intermedix Ceska republika s.r.o. (1)
Jeremiasova 1422/7, 155 00, Prague, Czech Republic
Tel.: (420) 246 007 900
Web Site: http://www.intermedix.cz
Emp.: 2
Healthcare Industry Software Publisher
N.A.I.C.S.: 513210

Intermedix France S.a.r.l. (1)
Le Capitole 55 Avenue des Champs-Pierreux, 92000, Nanterre, France
Tel.: (33) 147162723
Web Site: https://www.intermedix.fr
Sales Range: $25-49.9 Million
Emp.: 7
Software Development & Communications Services
N.A.I.C.S.: 541511

KMS Vertrieb und Services GmbH (1)
Inselkammerstrasse 1, 82008, Unterhaching, Germany
Tel.: (49) 896655090
Web Site: https://www.kms.ag
Emp.: 120
Software Development Services
N.A.I.C.S.: 541511

KoCo Connector GmbH (1)
Dessauer Strasse 28/29, 10963, Berlin, Germany
Tel.: (49) 302464900
Web Site: https://www.kococonnector.com
Telematic Infrastructure Services
N.A.I.C.S.: 517810

Lauer-Fischer GmbH (1)
Dr Mack Strasse 95, 90762, Furth, Germany
Tel.: (49) 91174320
Web Site: http://www.cgm.com
Medical Software Developer
N.A.I.C.S.: 513210

Subsidiary (Domestic):

IS Informatik Systeme Gesellschaft fur Informationstechnik mbH (2)
Maria Trost 25, 56070, Koblenz, Germany
Tel.: (49) 91174320
Web Site: https://www.isgmbhkl.com
Pharmaceutical Software Services
N.A.I.C.S.: 513210

Le Reseau Sante Sociale SAS (1)
212 Ave Paul Doumer, 92508, Rueil-Malmaison, France
Tel.: (33) 147162700
Web Site: http://www.lereseausantesocial.fr
Sales Range: $50-74.9 Million
Emp.: 41
Online Medical Services
N.A.I.C.S.: 524114

MEDISTAR Praxiscomputer GmbH (1)
Karl Wiechert Allee 64, 30625, Hannover, Germany
Tel.: (49) 511540500
Web Site: http://www.cgm.com
Sales Range: $25-49.9 Million
Emp.: 104
Software Development Services
N.A.I.C.S.: 541511

MedXpert Healthcare Ssolutions GmbH (1)
Innsbrucker Strabe 83, A 6060, Hall in Tirol, Tyrol, Austria
Tel.: (43) 5223 20 45 90
Sales Range: $10-24.9 Million
Emp.: 12
Health Care Srvices
N.A.I.C.S.: 621491

Medical Net SAS (1)
59A Avenue de Toulouse, 34070, Montpellier, France
Tel.: (33) 467271402
Web Site: http://www.medicalnet.fr
Online Medical Services
N.A.I.C.S.: 621491
Gulean Gomez (Mgr)

Medigest Consultores S.L. (1)
Calle de Raimundo Fernandez Villaverde 28 Escalera 2 Planta 1, 28003, Madrid, Spain
Tel.: (34) 915569716
Web Site: https://www.medigest.com
Healthcare Industry Software Publisher
N.A.I.C.S.: 513210

Subsidiary (Domestic):

Farmages Software S.L. (2)
Santisimo 24, Bolanos, 13260, Ciudad Real, Spain
Tel.: (34) 926884010
Web Site: http://www.farmages.com
Software Development Services
N.A.I.C.S.: 513210

OWL Computer SL (2)
Calle Orense n 6 Floor 1 Office 2, Madrid, Spain
Tel.: (34) 914747227
Software Development Services
N.A.I.C.S.: 513210

PROMED A.S. (1)
Profilo Plz B Blok Zemin Kat Cemal Sahir, Sokak No 26-28, 34394, Istanbul, Turkiye
Tel.: (90) 2123120000
Web Site: http://www.promedtibbi.com
Sales Range: $100-124.9 Million
Emp.: 200
Third Party Administration Services
N.A.I.C.S.: 524292

Profdoc ASA (1)
Torg 15 4 etasje, Lysaker, Norway
Tel.: (47) 21936370
Web Site: http://www.profdoc.no
Sales Range: $25-49.9 Million
Emp.: 5
Healthcare & Software Development Services
N.A.I.C.S.: 541511

Subsidiary (Non-US):

Profdoc Sdn Bhd (2)
Unit L3-I-2 Level 3 Enterprise 4 Tech Park Malaysia, Lebuhraya Puchong-Sg Bes, 57000, Kuala Lumpur, Malaysia
Tel.: (60) 389966700
Web Site: http://www.profdoc.com.my
Sales Range: $10-24.9 Million
Health Care & Information Technology Services
N.A.I.C.S.: 621491

Qualizorg B.V. (1)

Keulenstraat 1, 7418 ET, Deventer, Netherlands
Tel.: (31) 570820219
Web Site: https://qualizorg.nl
Healthcare Field Software Publisher
N.A.I.C.S.: 513210

Telemed Online Service fur Heilberufe GmbH (1)
Maria Trost 21, 56070, Koblenz, Germany
Tel.: (49) 1805040008
Web Site: http://www.telemed.de
Sales Range: $10-24.9 Million
Emp.: 18
Online Health Care Services
N.A.I.C.S.: 621491

Tepe International Health Information Systems A.S. (1)
Office No 307 Al Khozama Ctr, PO Box 53215, 11583, Riyadh, Saudi Arabia
Tel.: (966) 1 219 1160
Sales Range: $10-24.9 Million
Emp.: 15
Medical Information Services
N.A.I.C.S.: 621491

Tipdata Medical Software (1)
Plz B Block No 26-28, Ground Fl Profilo, 34394, Istanbul, Turkiye
Tel.: (90) 2123060080
Web Site: http://www.tipdata.com.tr
Sales Range: $25-49.9 Million
Emp.: 10
Medical Software Development Services
N.A.I.C.S.: 541511
Fatna Zakaryan (Gen Mgr)

TurboMed EDV GmbH (1)
Maria Trost 23, Molfsee, 56070, Germany
Tel.: (49) 26180002350
Web Site: http://www.cgm.com
Medical Data Services
N.A.I.C.S.: 513140

eMDs, Inc. (1)
10901 Stonelake Blvd Ste 200, Austin, TX 78759
Tel.: (512) 257-5200
Web Site: http://emds.com
Software Publisher
N.A.I.C.S.: 513210
Derek Pickell (CEO)

Subsidiary (Domestic):

Aprima Medical Software, Inc. (2)
1010 E Arapaho Rd Ste 100, Richardson, TX 75081
Tel.: (844) 427-7462
Web Site: http://www.aprima.com
Software & Technology Development Services for Healthcare Industry
N.A.I.C.S.: 513210
Jeffrey S. Hyman (Chief Medical Officer)

ifap Service-Institut fur Arzte und Apotheker GmbH (1)
Bunsenstrasse 7, 82152, Martinsried, Germany
Tel.: (49) 89897440
Web Site: https://www.ifap.de
Emp.: 60
Medical Information Data Bank Operator
N.A.I.C.S.: 513140
Mathias Schindl (Gen Mgr)

n-design Gesellschaft fur Systematische Gestaltungen mbH (1)
Alpenerstr 16, 50825, Cologne, Germany
Tel.: (49) 2212228960
Web Site: http://www.n-design.de
Software Development Services
N.A.I.C.S.: 541511

COMPULAB LTD.
17 HaYetsira Street Moradot HaCarmel Industrial Park, PO Box 687, Yoqne'am Illit, 2069208, Israel
Tel.: (972) 4 8290100   **Il**
Web Site: http://www.compulab.com
Year Founded: 1992
Sales Range: $10-24.9 Million
Emp.: 78
Software Development Services
N.A.I.C.S.: 541511
Gideon Yampolsky (Chm & CEO)

COMPUMEDICS LIMITED
30-40 Flockhart Street, Abbotsford, 3067, VIC, Australia
Tel.: (61) 384207300   **AU**
Web Site:
    https://www.compumedics.com.au
Year Founded: 1987
CMP—(ASX)
Rev.. $33,199,118
Assets: $26,948,451
Liabilities: $14,788,996
Net Worth: $12,159,455
Earnings: ($225,694)
Emp.: 155
Fiscal Year-end: 06/30/24
Medical Diagnostic Equipment Mfr
N.A.I.C.S.: 334510
Warwick Freeman (CTO)

Subsidiaries:

Compumedics Europe GmbH (1)
Petriplatz 5, 09599, Freiberg, Germany
Tel.: (49) 3731 259 6554
Medical Device Mfr & Distr
N.A.I.C.S.: 334510

Compumedics France SAS (1)
2 Rue Henry Bergson, 67000, Strasbourg, France
Tel.: (33) 98 106 2869
Medical Device Mfr & Distr
N.A.I.C.S.: 334510

Compumedics Germany GmbH (1)
Josef-Schuettler-Strasse 2, 78224, Singen, Germany
Tel.: (49) 7731797690
Web Site: http://www.dwl.de
Sales Range: $25-49.9 Million
Emp.: 25
Doppler Systems & Accessories Mfr
N.A.I.C.S.: 334510
Christoph Witte (Mng Dir-DWL)

Compumedics USA, Inc. (1)
5015 W WT Harris Blvd Ste E, Charlotte, NC 28269
Tel.: (704) 749-3200
Web Site: http://www.compumedicsusa.com
Sales Range: $25-49.9 Million
Emp.: 30
Neurodiagnostic Laboratory Products Whslr
N.A.I.C.S.: 424210

Division (Domestic):

Compumedics Limited - Compumedics Sleep Division (2)
5015 W WT Harris Blvd Ste E, Charlotte, NC 28269-1582
Tel.: (704) 749-3200
Web Site: http://www.compumedicsusa.com
Diagnostic Equipment Mfr
N.A.I.C.S.: 334510
David Burton (CEO)

Compumedics Limited - Neuroscan Division (2)
5015 W WT Harris Blvd Ste E, Charlotte, NC 28269-1582
Tel.: (704) 749-3200
Web Site: http://www.neuroscan.com
Sales Range: $25-49.9 Million
Emp.: 15
Diagnostic Equipment Mfr
N.A.I.C.S.: 334510
Curtis W. Ponton (VP)

DWL USA Inc. (1)
4062 Flying C 37, Cameron Park, CA 95682
Tel.: (760) 753-7319
Web Site: https://www.dwl.de
Medical Device Mfr & Distr
N.A.I.C.S.: 334510
Dan Henry (Reg Sls Mgr)

COMPUTACENTER PLC
Hatfield Business Park Hatfield Avenue, Hatfield, AL10 9TW, Hertfordshire, United Kingdom
Tel.: (44) 1707631000   **UK**
Web Site:
https://www.computacenter.com

Computacenter plc—(Continued)

CCC—(LSE)
Rev.: $7,793,717,250
Assets: $3,951,000,900
Liabilities: $2,900,676,900
Net Worth: $1,050,324,000
Earnings: $221,868,900
Emp.: 16,000
Fiscal Year-end: 12/31/22
Holding Company; Information Technology Management & Outsourcing Services
N.A.I.C.S.: 551112
Mike Norris (CEO)

Subsidiaries:

Amazon Energy Limited (1)
2nd Floor Berkeley Square House Mayfair, London, W1J 6BD, United Kingdom
Tel.: (44) 2039846286
Web Site: http://www.amazon-energy.com
Engineering Procurement & Construction Services
N.A.I.C.S.: 541330

Business IT Source, Inc. (1)
850 Asbury Dr, Buffalo Grove, IL 60089
Tel.: (847) 793-0600
Web Site: http://www.bitsinc.com
Information Technology Consulting Services
N.A.I.C.S.: 541512
Bob Frauenheim (CEO)

Compufix Limited (1)
141 Parkwood Rd, Southbourne, Bournemouth, BH5 2BT, United Kingdom
Tel.: (44) 7803229051
Web Site: http://www.compufix.co.uk
IT Infrastructure Services
N.A.I.C.S.: 518210

Computacenter (U.S.) Inc. (1)
462 7th Ave 17th Fl, New York, NY 10018
Tel.: (714) 861-2200
IT Infrastructure Services
N.A.I.C.S.: 518210
Justin Griffin (Sr VP-Sls)

Computacenter (UK) Ltd. (1)
Hatfield Business Park Hatfield Avenue, Hatfield, AL10 9TW, Hertfordshire, United Kingdom (100%)
Tel.: (44) 1707631000
Web Site: http://www.computacenter.com
Information Technology Management & Outsourcing Services
N.A.I.C.S.: 541512

Subsidiary (Domestic):

RD Trading Limited (2)
Tekhnicon Springwood, Braintree, CM7 2YN, Essex, United Kingdom (100%)
Tel.: (44) 1376336400
Emp.: 300
IT Asset Management Services
N.A.I.C.S.: 523940

Computacenter AG (1)
Riedstrasse 14, 8953, Dietikon, Switzerland
Tel.: (41) 433224080
IT Infrastructure Services
N.A.I.C.S.: 518210

Computacenter BV (1)
Gondel 1, 1186 MJ, Amstelveen, Netherlands
Tel.: (31) 884358000
IT Infrastructure Services
N.A.I.C.S.: 518210

Computacenter France S.A. (1)
229 rue de la Belle Etoile, BP 52387, ZI Paris Nord II, 95943, Roissy-en-France, Cedex, France
Tel.: (33) 148174100
Web Site: https://www.computacenter.com
Sales Range: $150-199.9 Million
Emp.: 600
IT Infrastructure Services
N.A.I.C.S.: 541512

Computacenter GmbH (1)
Stachegasse 13, 1120, Vienna, Austria
Tel.: (43) 1801910
IT Infrastructure Services
N.A.I.C.S.: 541512

Computacenter Holding GmbH (1)
Werner-Eckert-Str 16-18, 81829, Munich, Germany
Tel.: (49) 89457120
Web Site: http://www.computacenter.com
Sales Range: $75-99.9 Million
Emp.: 500
IT Infrastructure Services
N.A.I.C.S.: 541512

Computacenter Mexico S.A. de C.V. (1)
Av Paseo de la Reforma No 412 - 5 Col Juarez Delegacion, Cuauhtemoc, 06600, Mexico, Mexico
Tel.: (52) 5568440700
IT Infrastructure Services
N.A.I.C.S.: 518210

Computacenter NV/SA (1)
Ikaroslaan 31, 1930, Zaventem, Belgium
Tel.: (32) 27049411
Web Site: http://www.eshop.computacenter.com
Sales Range: $25-49.9 Million
Emp.: 60
IT Infrastructure Services
N.A.I.C.S.: 541512
Tom Struye (Mgr-Sls)

Computacenter PSF SA (1)
1115 Parc d Activite, Capellen, 8308, Luxembourg
Tel.: (352) 262911
Web Site: http://www.computacenter.com
Sales Range: $25-49.9 Million
Emp.: 50
IT Infrastructure Services
N.A.I.C.S.: 541512

Computacenter Services & Solutions (Pty) Limited (1)
Building Parc du Cap Mispel Road, Bellville, 7535, Cape Town, South Africa
Tel.: (27) 219574900
IT Infrastructure Services
N.A.I.C.S.: 518210

Computacenter Services (Iberia) SLU (1)
Carrer Sancho De Avila 52 - 58, 08018, Barcelona, Spain
Tel.: (34) 936207000
Web Site: http://www.computacenter.com
International Call Centre Services
N.A.I.C.S.: 561422

Computacenter Services (Malaysia) Sdn Bhd (1)
Level 9 - Tower 1 Puchong Financial Corporate Centre Jalan Puteri 1/2, Bandar Puteri, 47100, Puchong, Selangor, Malaysia
Tel.: (60) 377249626
IT Infrastructure Services
N.A.I.C.S.: 518210
Jerry Tan (Project Mgr)

Computacenter Services Kft (1)
Haller Gardens Building D 1st Floor Soroksari ut 30-34, Budapest, 1095, Hungary
Tel.: (36) 17777488
IT Infrastructure Services
N.A.I.C.S.: 518210

FusionStorm, Inc. (1)
2 Bryant St Ste 150, San Francisco, CA 94105
Tel.: (415) 623-2626
Web Site: http://www.fusionstorm.com
Sales Range: $400-449.9 Million
Emp.: 200
Custom Computer Programming & IT Services
N.A.I.C.S.: 541511
John G. Varel (Founder & Chm)

Misco Solutions B.V. (1)
Gondel 1, 1186 MJ, Amstelveen, Netherlands
Tel.: (31) 884358222
Web Site: http://www.miscosolutions.nl
Information Technology Services
N.A.I.C.S.: 519290

Subsidiary (Non-US):

Misco Italy Computer Supplies S.p.A. (2)
Il Girasole U D V 201, Lacchiarella, 20084, MI, Italy

Tel.: (39) 02900151
Web Site: http://www.misco.it
Rev.: $35,024,400
Emp.: 130
Catalog & Mail-Order Houses
N.A.I.C.S.: 449210
Roberto Cesate (Mgr-Center)

TeamUltra Limited (1)
Pinkneys Drive, Maidenhead, SL6 5DS, Berkshire, United Kingdom
Tel.: (44) 1628638001
Web Site: http://www.teamultra.net
IT Infrastructure Services
N.A.I.C.S.: 518210
Mike Beale (Mng Dir)

COMPUTER & TECHNOLOGIES HOLDINGS LIMITED
18th Floor of Viva Place No 36 Heung Yip Road Wong Chuk Hang H K, 100 Cyberport Road, Hong Kong, China (Hong Kong)
Tel.: (852) 25038000
Web Site: https://www.ctil.com
Year Founded: 1991
0046—(HKG)
Rev.: $34,261,673
Assets: $86,507,475
Liabilities: $19,813,373
Net Worth: $66,694,103
Earnings: $5,988,038
Emp.: 361
Fiscal Year-end: 12/31/22
Information Technology Services
N.A.I.C.S.: 541512
Cheung Shing Ng (Founder & Chm)

Subsidiaries:

Computer & Technologies (Shanghai) Co., Ltd (1)
1-2/F Building 10 99 Tian Zhou Road, Caohejing High-Tech Park, Shanghai, 200233, China
Tel.: (86) 2164952200
Computer System Network Integration Services
N.A.I.C.S.: 541512

Computer & Technologies Integration Limited (1)
Room 2218 22/F Shartex Plaza, 88 Zun Yi Road South, Shanghai, 200336, China
Tel.: (86) 2162197131
Web Site: http://www.ctil.com
Information Technology & Networks with Related Design, Implementation & Support Services
N.A.I.C.S.: 541512

Computer & Technologies Solutions Limited (1)
Level 10 Cyberport 2, 100 Cyberport Road, Hong Kong, China (Hong Kong)
Tel.: (852) 25038222
Web Site: http://www.ctil.com
Sales Range: $50-74.9 Million
Emp.: 180
Applicaton Software Development Services & Internet Solutions with Related Consulting, Implementation & Outsourcing Services
N.A.I.C.S.: 541511

Computer And Technologies International Limited (1)
Level 10 Cyberport 2 100 Cyberport Road, Hong Kong, China (Hong Kong)
Tel.: (852) 25038000
Web Site: https://www.ctil.com
Computer System Network Integration Services
N.A.I.C.S.: 541512

Global e-Business Services Limited (1)
Level 10 Cyberport 2 100 Cyberport Road, Hong Kong, China (Hong Kong)
Tel.: (852) 8 123 8122
Web Site: https://www.ge-ts.com.hk
Sales Range: $25-49.9 Million
Emp.: 100
Internet & Related Business Process Outsourcing Services
N.A.I.C.S.: 541511

Global e-Trading Services Limited (1)
Level 10 Cyberport 2 100 Cyberport Road, Hong Kong, China (Hong Kong)
Tel.: (852) 81238122
Web Site: https://www.ge-ts.com.hk
Online Trading Services
N.A.I.C.S.: 425120

IPL Research Limited (1)
Level 10 Cyberport 2 100 Cyberport Road, Hong Kong, China (Hong Kong)
Tel.: (852) 28034026
Web Site: https://www.iplresearch.com
Sales Range: $25-49.9 Million
Emp.: 17
Human Resource Management & Related Application Software
N.A.I.C.S.: 541618

Maxfair Technologies Holdings Ltd. (1)
1F Efficiency House 35 Tai Yau Street, San Po Kong, Kowloon, China (Hong Kong)
Tel.: (852) 21041828
Web Site: http://www.maxfair.com
Sales Range: $25-49.9 Million
Emp.: 10
Digital Audio/Video Related Systems & Software Distr
N.A.I.C.S.: 449210

Sanyo Extended System Services Limited (1)
Rm 1605 Shun Tak Centre West Tower 168-200 Connaught Road Central, Sheung Wan, China (Hong Kong)
Tel.: (852) 28809119
Web Site: http://www.enwtravel.com
Software Retail & Services
N.A.I.C.S.: 513210
Billy Lam (Gen Mgr)

Shanghai Shangluo Software Co., Ltd (1)
1-2/F Building 10 99 Tian Zhou Road Caohejing High-Tech Park, Shanghai, 200233, China
Tel.: (86) 2164952200
Web Site: http://www.iplresearch.com.cn
Human Resource Software Development Services
N.A.I.C.S.: 541511

Y&A Professional Services Limited (1)
29 F Prosperity Millennia Plaza 663 Kings Road, North Point, China (Hong Kong)
Tel.: (852) 2139 2121
Web Site: http://www.ctil.com
Sales Range: $25-49.9 Million
Emp.: 50
Information Technology Consulting Services
N.A.I.C.S.: 541618

COMPUTER AGE MANAGEMENT SERVICES LIMITED
No 158 Rayala Towers Tower - I 3rd Floor Anna Salai, Chennai, 600002, India
Tel.: (91) 4428432650
Web Site: https://www.camsonline.com
Year Founded: 1988
543232—(BOM)
Rev.: $100,362,239
Assets: $114,923,513
Liabilities: $44,507,026
Net Worth: $70,416,487
Earnings: $28,022,262
Emp.: 3,894
Fiscal Year-end: 03/31/21
Financial Transaction Processing Services
N.A.I.C.S.: 522320
Anish Sawlani (Head-Acct Mgmt)

Subsidiaries:

CAMS Financial Information Services Private Limited (1)
5th Floor Rayala Towers - I 158 Anna Salai, Chennai, 600 002, India
Tel.: (91) 9993009855
Web Site: https://www.camsfinserv.com
Financial Institution Services

N.A.I.C.S.: 921130

CAMS Insurance Repository Services Limited (1)
No 178/10 Kodambakkam High Road Ground Floor Opp Hotel Palmgrove, Nungambakkam, Chennai, 600 034, India
Tel.: (91) 4428317219
Web Site: https://www.camsrepository.com
Insurance Repository Services
N.A.I.C.S.: 524298
R. Seshadri (Head-Operations)

Sterling Software Private Limited (1)
New No 10 Old No 178 M G R Salai 3rd Floor, Nungambakkam, Chennai, 600034, India
Tel.: (91) 4442002000
Web Site: https://sterlingsoftware.global
Information Technology Services
N.A.I.C.S.: 541511
Selena D. (CTO)

Think Analytics India Private Limited (1)
B 2078 Oberoi Garden Estate, Chandivali, 400072, Maharashtra, India
Tel.: (91) 8779798844
Web Site: https://think360.ai
Emp.: 120
Information Technology Services
N.A.I.C.S.: 541512

Think360 AI, Inc. (1)
B 2078 Oberoi Garden Estate Chandivali, Andheri East, Mumbai, 400072, India
Tel.: (91) 8779798844
Web Site: https://think360.ai
Emp.: 120
Information Technology Services
N.A.I.C.S.: 541519

COMPUTER BOULEVARD INC.
Unit B 1250 St James Street, Winnipeg, R3H 0L1, MB, Canada
Tel.: (204) 772-1088
Web Site: http://www.cbit.ca
Year Founded: 2001
Rev.: $12,814,223
Emp.: 50
Computers Parts Supplies
N.A.I.C.S.: 449210
George Yung (Owner)

COMPUTER DIRECT GROUP LTD.
HA'AMAL 1, P'ARK AFEK, Rosh Ha'Ayin, Israel
Tel.: (972) 39767536
Year Founded: 1991
CMDR—(TAE)
Rev.: $1,021,557,658
Assets: $622,160,510
Liabilities: $406,388,445
Net Worth: $215,772,065
Earnings: $52,846,525
Fiscal Year-end: 12/31/23
Computer System Design Services
N.A.I.C.S.: 541512
Nitzan Sapir (Chm)

COMPUTER ENGINEERING & CONSULTING LTD.
JR Ebisu Bldg 5-5 Ebisu Minami 1-chome, Shibuya-ku, Tokyo, 150-0022, Japan
Tel.: (81) 357892441
Web Site: https://www.cec-ltd.co.jp
9692—(TKS)
Rev.: $376,649,160
Assets: $364,362,190
Liabilities: $75,182,360
Net Worth: $289,179,830
Earnings: $32,195,690
Emp.: 2,330
Fiscal Year-end: 01/31/24
Software Development Services
N.A.I.C.S.: 541511
Hirosato Iwasaki (Chm)

Subsidiaries:

Computer Engineering & Consulting (Shanghai), Ltd. (1)
A unit 10/ F Global Harbor Tower B 1188 KaiXuan N Rd, Putuo District, Shanghai, 200063, China
Tel.: (86) 2161076360
Web Site: https://www.cec-ltd.cn
Sales Range: $25-49.9 Million
Software Development Services
N.A.I.C.S.: 541511

ESECTOR, Ltd. (1)
JR Ebisu Building 8F 1-5-5 Ebisu Minami, Shibuya-ku, Tokyo, 150-0022, Japan
Tel.: (81) 357892443
Web Site: https://www.esector.co.jp
Software Development Services
N.A.I.C.S.: 541511

Foresight System Co., Ltd. (1)
Miiwa Kyushu General Building 1-4-6 Nagahama, Chuo-ku, Fukuoka, 810-0072, Japan
Tel.: (81) 927523580
Web Site: https://www.foresight.co.jp
Sales Range: $75-99.9 Million
Emp.: 477
Software Development Services
N.A.I.C.S.: 541511

Nishitele Information & Science Co., Ltd (1)
1-12-17 Hakataeki-higashi, Hakata-ku, Fukuoka, 812-0013, Japan
Tel.: (81) 92 482 7907
Web Site: http://www.nishitele.co.jp
Software Development Services
N.A.I.C.S.: 541511

Oita Computer Engineering & Consulting, Ltd. (1)
21-1 Kumano, Kitsuki, 873-0008, Oita, Japan
Tel.: (81) 978641111
Web Site: https://www.oita-cec.co.jp
Sales Range: $25-49.9 Million
Emp.: 70
Software Development & Consulting Services
N.A.I.C.S.: 541512

COMPUTER FORMS (MALAYSIA) BERHAD
Lot 2 Jalan Usahawan 5 PKNS Setapak Industrial Area, Off Jalan Genting Kelang, 53300, Kuala Lumpur, Malaysia
Tel.: (60) 340233611   **MY**
Web Site: https://www.cfm.com.my
Year Founded: 1972
CFM—(KLS)
Rev.: $8,783,982
Assets: $29,076,469
Liabilities: $2,595,547
Net Worth: $26,480,922
Earnings: ($2,568,539)
Fiscal Year-end: 09/30/23
Computer Forms Mfr
N.A.I.C.S.: 323111
Muhayuddin Musa (CEO & Mng Dir)

Subsidiaries:

CFM Printing & Stationery Sdn. Bhd (1)
Lot 2 Block A Jalan Usahawan 5 Off Jalan Genting Kelang, PKNS Setapak Industrial Area, 53300, Kuala Lumpur, Malaysia
Tel.: (60) 340210888
Web Site: http://www.cfm.com.my
Emp.: 150
Commercial Offset Printing Services
N.A.I.C.S.: 323111

CFM Toppan Forms (Malaysia) Sdn. Bhd. (1)
Lot 2 Block B Jalan Usahawan 5 Off Jalan Genting Kelang, PKNS Setapak Industrial Area, 53300, Kuala Lumpur, Malaysia
Tel.: (60) 340237628
Web Site: http://www.cfmtf.com.my
Outsource Data Printing & Direct Mailer Services; Owned by Computer Forms (Malaysia) Berhad, by Toppan Forms (Singapore) Pte. Ltd. & by Cardsys Sdn. Bhd.
N.A.I.C.S.: 323111

Contipak Noron Sdn. Bhd. (1)
Tel.: (60) 340238218
Flexible Packaging Materials Mfr

N.A.I.C.S.: 322220
Hong Camliang (Mgr-Mktg)

COMPUTER GRAPHICS INTERNATIONAL INC.
Room 01B 02/F Podium Building Guodu Golf Garden North of Xinsha Road, Futian District, Shenzhen, 518048, China
Tel.: (86) 755 2221 1114   **NV**
Year Founded: 2003
Sales Range: $1-9.9 Million
Emp.: 104
3D Digital Video Services
N.A.I.C.S.: 512110

COMPUTER INSTITUTE OF JAPAN LTD.   JP
Web Site: http://www.cij.co.jp
Year Founded: 1976
4826—(TKS)
Rev.: $160,059,260
Assets: $115,051,340
Liabilities: $24,805,360
Net Worth: $90,245,980
Earnings: $5,896,560
Emp.: 1,620
Fiscal Year-end: 06/30/24
Computer Software & Systems Developer & Mfr
N.A.I.C.S.: 541512
Masami Takamisawa (Mng Exec Officer)

Subsidiaries:

Business Soft Service Co., Ltd. (1)
18-14 Shinmachi Chiba Shinmachi Building 5F, Chuo-ku, Chiba, 260-0028, Japan
Tel.: (81) 433063170
Web Site: http://www.we-bss.com
Emp.: 56
Software Development Services
N.A.I.C.S.: 541511
Sumio Izumi (Pres)

CIJ Manage System, Inc. (1)
Yokohama NT Bldg, 1 2 24 Hiranuma Nishi Ku, Yokohama, 220 0023, Japan **(100%)**
Tel.: (81) 453240111
Web Site: http://www.cij.com
Sales Range: $25-49.9 Million
Emp.: 10
Computer Research
N.A.I.C.S.: 541512

CIJ NExt Co., Ltd. (1)
Gate City Ohsaki West Tower 22F 1-11-1 Osaki, Shinagawa-ku, Tokyo, 141-0032, Japan **(100%)**
Tel.: (81) 357407451
Web Site: http://www.cij-next.co.jp
Sales Range: Less than $1 Million
Emp.: 523
Business Systems Development & Design of Semiconductors, Temporary Personnel Placements & Sales of Packaged Software Products
N.A.I.C.S.: 561499
Mitsuo Sato (Pres)

CIJ Solutions, Ltd. (1)
Bunshodo Building 5-1-1 Ueno, Taito-ku, Tokyo, 110-0005, Japan
Tel.: (81) 358163100
Web Site: http://www.csol.jp
Sales Range: $25-49.9 Million
Emp.: 19
Enterprise Management Software Development Services
N.A.I.C.S.: 541511

Subsidiary (Domestic):

CIJ Wave Ltd. (2)
3-8-10 Gudotaguro, Shimanto, 787-0019, Kochi, Japan
Tel.: (81) 88 037 5240
Web Site: https://www.cijwave.co.jp
Senior Citizen Nursing Homes Operation Services
N.A.I.C.S.: 623312

Custanet Co., Ltd. (1)
8F Hakata 1091 Building 1-2-2 Hakataeki

Minami, Hakata-Ku, Fukuoka, 812-0016, Japan
Tel.: (81) 92 481 9560
Web Site: https://www.custa-net.co.jp
Emp.: 83
Enterprise Management Software Development Services
N.A.I.C.S.: 541511

I-Bridge Systems Philippines Inc. (1)
1802-1803 Hanston Square Bldg No 17 San Miguel Ave Ortigas Center, Pasig, 1605, Philippines
Tel.: (63) 284770223
Web Site: https://www.i-bridge.com.ph
Information Technology Services
N.A.I.C.S.: 541511

Kanazawa Software Co., Ltd. (1)
36-1 Nakanosato-Machiri Shiroyama, Kanazawa, 920 2147, Ishikawa, Japan
Tel.: (81) 76 273 5011
Business Management Software Development Services
N.A.I.C.S.: 541511

Kochi Software Center Ltd. (1)
105-25 Hongucho, Kochi, 780-0945, Japan
Tel.: (81) 88 850 9222
Web Site: https://www.k-sc.co.jp
Emp.: 4
Information Technology Training & Education Services
N.A.I.C.S.: 611420

Shanghai Technodia System Integration Co., Ltd. (1)
Shanghai Jinling Business Plaza 3F Building A 801 Yishan Road, Shanghai, 200233, China **(100%)**
Tel.: (86) 2154260606
Web Site: http://www.technodia.com.cn
Computer System Design Services
N.A.I.C.S.: 541512
Xiao Jiongsen (Chm)

COMPUTER MANAGEMENT CO., LTD.
Bay Area Oak Prio Tower 3F 6F Benten 1-2-30, Minato-ku, Osaka, 552-0007, Japan
Tel.: (81) 643957730
Web Site: https://www.cmknet.co.jp
Year Founded: 1981
4491—(TKS)
Rev.: $47,552,340
Assets: $31,384,280
Liabilities: $10,252,110
Net Worth: $21,132,170
Earnings: $2,161,470
Emp.: 694
Fiscal Year-end: 03/31/24
Information Technology Services
N.A.I.C.S.: 541512
Katsuaki Takenaka (Pres)

COMPUTER MIND CO., LTD.
5F Omiya Miyazakidai Building 2-10-9 Miyazaki, Miyamae-ku, Kawasaki, 216-0033, Japan
Tel.: (81) 448569922
Web Site: https://www.cmind.co.jp
Year Founded: 1978
2452—(TKS)
Rev.: $2,807,200
Assets: $2,400,640
Liabilities: $1,316,480
Net Worth: $1,084,160
Earnings: $106,480
Fiscal Year-end: 03/31/22
Information Technology Services
N.A.I.C.S.: 541512
Kenichi Matsuzawa (Sr Mng Dir, Exec Officer & Dir)

COMPUTER MODELLING GROUP LTD.
3710 33 Street NW, Calgary, T2L 2M1, AB, Canada
Tel.: (403) 531-1300   **AB**
Web Site: https://www.cmgl.ca
Year Founded: 1978

Computer Modelling Group Ltd.—(Continued)

CMG—(TSX)
Rev.: $51,788,501
Assets: $97,900,777
Liabilities: $61,354,220
Net Worth: $36,546,557
Earnings: $14,397,863
Emp.: 184
Fiscal Year-end: 03/31/22
Oil & Gas Reservoir Modelling &
Simulation Software; Oil Recovery
Processes, Reservoir Engineering,
Consulting, Training & Technical Sup-
port
N.A.I.C.S.: 213112
Kathy L. Krug *(Sec)*

Subsidiaries:

Bluware, Inc.   (1)
16285 Park 10 Pl Ste 300, Houston, TX
77084
Tel.: (713) 335-1500
Web Site: http://www.bluware.com
Sales Range: $10-24.9 Million
Emp.: 80
Custom Computer Programming Services
N.A.I.C.S.: 541511
Richard Jones *(Pres)*

CMG (Europe) Limited   (1)
Suite 4 Isis Building Howbery Park, Walling-
ford, OX10 8BA, United Kingdom
Tel.: (44) 1491821114
Computer Simulation Services
N.A.I.C.S.: 541511

CMG Middle East FZ LLC   (1)
Building 12 Office 320, PO Box 500 446,
Dubai Internet City, Dubai, United Arab
Emirates
Tel.: (971) 44345190
Computer Simulation Services
N.A.I.C.S.: 541511
Dale Riley *(Reg Mgr)*

Computer Modelling Group Inc.   (1)
450 Gears Rd Ste 600, Houston, TX 77067
Tel.: (281) 872-8500
Computer Simulation Services
N.A.I.C.S.: 541511

COMPUTER POINT LIMITED
1/1B Upper Wood Street, Kolkata,
700017, West Bengal, India
Tel.: (91) 3322814418
Web Site:
   http://www.computerpoint.co.in
Year Founded: 1984
Rev.: $816,776
Assets: $5,789,643
Liabilities: $596,757
Net Worth: $5,192,885
Earnings: $949
Emp.: 15
Fiscal Year-end: 03/31/18
Information Technology Consulting
Services
N.A.I.C.S.: 541512
A. Jain *(Exec Dir)*

**COMPUTER STATIONERY IN-
DUSTRY S.A.O.G.**
No 7 Rusayl Industrial Estate, PO
Box 13, 124, Rusayl, Oman
Tel.: (968) 24446160
Web Site: https://www.csiops.com
Year Founded: 1985
CSII—(MUS)
Rev.: $3,228,633
Assets: $7,118,316
Liabilities: $2,500,694
Net Worth: $4,617,622
Earnings: ($777,238)
Emp.: 78
Fiscal Year-end: 12/31/21
Computer Sales & Services
N.A.I.C.S.: 423430

**COMPUTERS & CONTROLS
LTD.**

80-82 Edward Street, Port of Spain,
Trinidad & Tobago
Tel.: (868) 2012388
Web Site:
   http://www.computerscontrols.com
Sales Range: $125-149.9 Million
Emp.: 50
Newspaper Publishers
N.A.I.C.S.: 334118
Sharon Sabga *(Gen Mgr)*

COMPUTERSHARE LIMITED
Yarra Falls 452 Johnston Street, Ab-
botsford, 3067, VIC, Australia
Tel.: (61) 394155000   AU
Web Site:
   https://www.computershare.com
Year Founded: 1978
CPU—(ASX)
Rev.: $2,972,811,000
Assets: $5,118,619,000
Liabilities: $3,170,016,000
Net Worth: $1,948,603,000
Earnings: $493,170,000
Emp.: 12,000
Fiscal Year-end: 06/30/24
Securities Registration & Transfer
Services
N.A.I.C.S.: 561499
Dominic Matthew Horsley *(Sec)*

Subsidiaries:

CIS Company Secretaries (Pty)
Ltd   (1)
70 Marshall Street, Johannesburg, 2001,
South Africa
Tel.: (27) 861100933
Financial Investment Services
N.A.I.C.S.: 523999

CMC Funding, Inc.   (1)
PO Box 636005, Littleton, CO 80163-6005
Tel.: (720) 241-7537
Web Site:
   https://www.cmc.servicingloans.com
Financial Services
N.A.I.C.S.: 522390

Capital Markets Cooperative,
LLC   (1)
8800 Baymeadows Way W Ste 300, Jack-
sonville, FL 32256
Tel.: (904) 543-0052
Web Site: https://www.capmkts.org
Financial Services
N.A.I.C.S.: 522390
Tom Millon *(CEO)*

Computershare Communication Ser-
vices GmbH   (1)
Hansastr 15b, 80686, Munich, Germany
Tel.: (49) 8930903691
Financial Investment Services
N.A.I.C.S.: 523999

Computershare Corporate Trust   (1)
9062 Old Annapolis Rd MAC R1204-010,
Columbia, MD 21045   (100%)
Tel.: (443) 367-3940
Rev.: $440,000
Emp.: 2,000
Trust Services
N.A.I.C.S.: 523991

Computershare Italy S.r.l.   (1)
Via Lorenzo Mascheroni 19, 20145, Milan,
Italy
Tel.: (39) 0246776811
Financial Investment Services
N.A.I.C.S.: 523999

Computershare Netherlands B.V.   (1)
Blaak 34, 3011 TA, Rotterdam, Netherlands
Tel.: (31) 102298488
Financial Investment Services
N.A.I.C.S.: 523999

Computershare Schweiz AG   (1)
Baslerstrasse 90, 4600, Olten,
Switzerland   (100%)
Tel.: (41) 622057700
Web Site: http://www.computershare.com
Securities Registration & Transfer Services
N.A.I.C.S.: 561499

Steffen Herfurth *(Grp Reg Dir-Continental
Europe)*

Computershare South Africa (Pty)
Ltd   (1)
Rosebank Towers 15 Biermann Avenue,
Rosebank, Gauteng, South Africa
Tel.: (27) 113705000
Financial Investment Services
N.A.I.C.S.: 523999

Georgeson LLC   (1)
1290 Ave of the Americas 9th Fl, New York,
NY 10104
Tel.: (212) 440-9800
Web Site: https://www.georgeson.com
Financial Investment Services
N.A.I.C.S.: 523999
William Jackson *(Pres & CEO)*

Georgeson S.L.   (1)
Edificio Iberia Mart I c/Pedro Teixeira 8-pl 8,
28020, Madrid, Spain
Tel.: (34) 917010948
Financial Investment Services
N.A.I.C.S.: 523999
Carlos Saez Gallego *(Head-Country)*

Georgeson S.r.l.   (1)
Via Emilia 88, 00187, Rome, Italy
Tel.: (39) 0642171201
Financial Investment Services
N.A.I.C.S.: 523999
Lorenzo Casale *(Head-Market)*

Georgeson Shareholder Communica-
tions Australia Pty. Ltd.   (1)
Level 3 60 Carrington Street, Sydney, 2001,
NSW, Australia
Tel.: (61) 282165700
Financial Services
N.A.I.C.S.: 523999
Laks Meyyappan *(CEO)*

Georgeson Shareholder SAS   (1)
10 place Vendome, 75001, Paris, France
Tel.: (33) 142603654
Financial Investment Services
N.A.I.C.S.: 523999
Matthieu Simon Blavier *(Head-Market)*

Gilardi & Co., LLC   (1)
1 McInnis Pkwy Ste 250, San Rafael, CA
94903
Tel.: (415) 458-3000
Web Site: https://www.gilardi.com
Sales Range: $25-49.9 Million
Emp.: 80
Administrative Management & General
Management Consulting Service
N.A.I.C.S.: 541611
Peter L. Crudo *(Exec VP-Class Action
Svcs)*

Homeloan Management Limited   (1)
Gateway House Gargrave Road, Skipton,
BD23 2HL, N Yorkshire, United Kingdom
Tel.: (44) 1756776729
Web Site: http://www.hml.co.uk
Emp.: 1,200
Mortgage & Nonmortgage Loan Brokers
N.A.I.C.S.: 522310
Swen Nicolaus *(Head-Portfolio Trading &
Security Svcs)*

LenderLive Network, LLC   (1)
710 S Ash St Ste 200, Glendale, CO 80246
Web Site: http://www.lenderlive.com
Mortgage Services
N.A.I.C.S.: 523999
Rick Seehausen *(Founder)*

RicePoint Administration Inc.   (1)
1480 Richmond St 204, London, N6G 0J4,
ON, Canada
Tel.: (519) 601-7423
Web Site: https://www.ricepoint.com
Financial Administration Services
N.A.I.C.S.: 523999
Michael Mooney *(Sr VP-Bus Dev)*

Rosolite Mortgages Limited   (1)
PO Box 121, Skipton, BD23 9FL, United
Kingdom
Tel.: (44) 3707020066
Web Site:
   https://www.rosolitemortgages.co.uk
Mortgage Services
N.A.I.C.S.: 522310

Servizio Titoli S.p.A.   (1)

Via Lorenzo Mascheroni, 20145, Milan, Italy
Tel.: (39) 0246776811
Web Site: http://www.serviziotitoli.it
Sales Range: $10-24.9 Million
Emp.: 50
Corporate Finance Advisory Services
N.A.I.C.S.: 541618
Luca Matteo Lombardo *(Mng Dir)*

Siberite Mortgages Limited   (1)
PO Box 122, Skipton, BD23 9FP, United
Kingdom
Tel.: (44) 3707020076
Web Site:
   https://www.siberitemortgages.co.uk
Mortgage Services
N.A.I.C.S.: 522310

Specialized Loan Servicing LLC   (1)
6200 S Quebec St, Greenwood Village, CO
80111
Web Site: https://www.sls.net
Mortgage Loan Services
N.A.I.C.S.: 522310

COMPUTIME GROUP LIMITED
6/F Building 20E Phase 3 Hong Kong
Science Park, 20 Science Park East
Avenue Shatin, Hong Kong, New Ter-
ritories, China (Hong Kong)
Tel.: (852) 2 260 0300
Web Site: http://www.computime.com
0320—(HKG)
Rev.: $539,759,502
Assets: $361,139,357
Liabilities: $181,871,602
Net Worth: $179,267,754
Earnings: $10,798,206
Emp.: 4,900
Fiscal Year-end: 03/31/22
Tools & Instruments
N.A.I.C.S.: 334513
Ho Auyang *(Founder & Chm)*

Subsidiaries:

Asia Electronics HK Technologies
Limited   (1)
9/F Tower One Lippo Centre 89 Queens-
way, Wanchai, China (Hong Kong)
Tel.: (852) 22600300
Web Site: http://www.asiaelectronics.com.hk
Electronic Control Products Distr
N.A.I.C.S.: 423610

Computime Limited   (1)
Tel.: (852) 22600300
Web Site: http://www.computime.com
Emp.: 100
Electronic Control Products Mfr & Distri
N.A.I.C.S.: 334514

Salus Controls GmbH   (1)
Dieselstrasse 34, Muhlheim am Main,
63165, Muhlheim, Germany
Tel.: (49) 6108825850
Web Site: https://saluscontrols.com
Sales Range: $50-74.9 Million
Emp.: 10
Electronic Control Products Distr
N.A.I.C.S.: 423610

Salus Controls Plc   (1)
Units 8-10 Northfield Business Park Forge
Way, Parkgate, Rotherham, S60 1SD,
South Yorkshire, United Kingdom
Tel.: (44) 1226323961
Web Site: http://salus-controls.com
Sales Range: $25-49.9 Million
Emp.: 35
Electronic Control Products Distr
N.A.I.C.S.: 423610
Robert Fenton *(Reg Mgr-NE & NW)*

Salus Controls Romania s.r.l.   (1)
Strada Traian Vuia Nr 126, Cluj-Napoca,
400396, Romania
Tel.: (40) 364435696
Web Site: http://www.salus-controls.com
Electronic Control Technology Services
N.A.I.C.S.: 238210
Florin Huci *(Reg Sls Mgr)*

Salus Nordic A/S   (1)
Ronhojvej 12, 8300, Odder, Denmark
Tel.: (45) 53534499
Web Site: http://www.salus-controls.com
Electronic Control Technology Services

N.A.I.C.S.: 238210

Salus North America, Inc. (1)
850 Main St, Redwood City, CA 94063
Tel.: (650) 360-1725
Web Site: http://www.salusinc
Hydronic Product Mfr
N.A.I.C.S.: 333414

COMPUTRONICS HOLDINGS LIMITED
Unit 1 103 Lewis Road, Knoxfield, 3180, VIC, Australia
Tel.: (61) 398012566
Web Site: http://computronics.co
Year Founded: 1976
Sales Range: $5-14.9 Billion
Emp.: 65
Microcomputer-Based Products Developer & Mfr
N.A.I.C.S.: 334118
Murray Smith *(Sec)*

COMPUVISION SYSTEMS INC.
310 Circle Drive, Saint Albert, T8N 7L5, AB, Canada
Tel.: (780) 415-5093
Web Site: http://www.compuvision.biz
Year Founded: 1992
Rev.: $15,751,883
Emp.: 104
Computer Related Works & IT Services
N.A.I.C.S.: 541519

COMRADE APPLIANCES LIMITED
39 I Level Deewan Centre Swami Vivekananda Rd Jogeshwari West, Mumbai, 400102, Maharashtra, India
Tel.: (91) 1800226695
Web Site: https://www.comrade.net.in
Year Founded: 2017
543921—(BOM)
Rev.: $3,601,963
Assets: $3,212,794
Liabilities: $2,441,915
Net Worth: $770,879
Earnings: $19,902
Fiscal Year-end: 03/31/22
Household Appliance Mfr & Distr
N.A.I.C.S.: 334512
Khursheed Alam *(Mng Dir)*

COMREP SA
No 32nd Gh Grigore Cantacuzino Street, Prahova, Ploiesti, Romania
Tel.: (40) 244513145
Web Site: https://www.comrepsa.ro
COTN—(BUC)
Rev.: $5,384,245
Assets: $4,076,439
Liabilities: $1,900,450
Net Worth: $2,175,989
Earnings: $8,978
Emp.: 131
Fiscal Year-end: 12/31/23
Oil & Natural Gas Extraction Services
N.A.I.C.S.: 213112

COMRIT INVESTMENTS 1 LP
9 Ahad Ha'am Street, Tel Aviv, 6129101, Israel
Tel.: (972) 35199936
Real Estate Services
N.A.I.C.S.: 531390

COMSA EMTE S.L.
Edificio Numancia 1, 08014, Barcelona, Spain
Tel.: (34) 933662100
Web Site:
  http://www.comsaemte.com
Sales Range: $1-4.9 Billion
Emp.: 9,095
Engineering & Construction Services
N.A.I.C.S.: 237990
Jorge Miarnau Montserrat *(Chm)*

Subsidiaries:

COMSA Brazil Ltda. (1)
Edificio Paulista Seguros Rua Geraldo Flausino Gomes 78 CJ 43 e 44, 04575-060, Sao Paulo, Broklin, Brazil
Tel.: (55) 11 2594 7951
Web Site: http://www.comsa.com
Emp.: 15
Engineering Services
N.A.I.C.S.: 541330
Joaquim Paladio *(Area Mgr-Engrg Div)*

COMSA EMTE CHINA (1)
Room 117 Golden Land Building N 32 Liang Ma Qiao Road, Chaoyang, 100010, Beijing, China
Tel.: (86) 10 8451 3356
Engineering Services
N.A.I.C.S.: 541330
Jordi Faine *(Country Mgr)*

COMSA EMTE PERU S.A.C. (1)
Av Jorge Chavez 263 Oficinas 201, Miraflores, Lima, Peru
Tel.: (51) 1 253 60 01
Engineering Services
N.A.I.C.S.: 541330

COMSA EMTE-Ecuador (1)
Av La Coruna E25-58 y Av 12 de Octubre Edificio Altana Plaza, Piso 3 Oficina 307, Quito, Ecuador
Tel.: (593) 2 3230 363
Engineering Services
N.A.I.C.S.: 541330

Comsa Altyapi Ltd.Sti (1)
Mustafa Kemal Mah Eskisehir Devlet Yolu 9 km Tepe Prime no 266, C Block Daire 52, 06800, Cankaya, Ankara, Turkiye
Tel.: (90) 312 988 1101
Engineering Services
N.A.I.C.S.: 541330

Comsa Emte France (1)
30 bis Ancienne Route Imperiale, 31120, Toulouse, Portet Sur Garonne, France
Tel.: (33) 534 619 890
Engineering Services
N.A.I.C.S.: 541330
Angel Rocamora Puigpinos *(CFO & Dir-Fin & Admin)*

Comsa Emte SAS (1)
Carrera 11A numero 93 A-62 Oficina 304, Bogota, Colombia
Tel.: (57) 1 236 5532
Engineering Services
N.A.I.C.S.: 541330

Comsa Emte USA, Inc. (1)
315 Montgomery St 9th Fl, San Francisco, CA 94104
Tel.: (415) 829-4260
Engineering Services
N.A.I.C.S.: 541330
Daniel Jauregui Alonso *(Area Mgr)*

Comsa Emte, S.A. de C.V. (1)
Av Insurgentes Sur 664 Piso 9, Mexico, 03100, Mexico
Tel.: (52) 55 4973 8000
Engineering Services
N.A.I.C.S.: 541330
Alfredo Fernandez *(Area Mgr)*

Comsa Suisse SA (1)
Via Ceresio 24, Pregassona, 6963, Lugano, Switzerland
Tel.: (41) 91 921 29 80
Engineering Services
N.A.I.C.S.: 541330
Josep Martra *(Dir-Agency & Project Mgr)*

Comsa de Argentina Sa (1)
Avda Santa Fe 1845 piso 4 Oficina B, 1123, Buenos Aires, Argentina
Tel.: (54) 114 816 25 22
Engineering Services
N.A.I.C.S.: 541330

E.m.t.e. s.a.r.l (1)
33 Av Hassan Seghir 4eme etage N 4/4, Casablanca, Morocco
Tel.: (212) 5 22 31 14 13
Engineering Services
N.A.I.C.S.: 541330

EMTE Cleanroom S.A. (1)
Gran Via de les Corts Catalanes 184 5 3,
08038, Barcelona, Spain
Tel.: (34) 932988980
Sales Range: $25-49.9 Million
Emp.: 49
Clean Room Engineering & Construction Services
N.A.I.C.S.: 541330

EMTE INSTALACIONES (1)
Avda Baix Llobregat 10 08950 Esplugues de Llobregat, Barcelona, Spain
Tel.: (34) 934809292
Web Site: http://www.grupoemte.com
Sales Range: $25-49.9 Million
Emp.: 100
Engineering Services
N.A.I.C.S.: 541330

EMTE ME ZONA FRANCA S.A. (1)
Ruta 101 km 23 500 Parque de las Ciencias Edificio Office 101, PO Box 007, 14 000, Canelones, Uruguay
Tel.: (598) 2 682 9725
Engineering Services
N.A.I.C.S.: 541330

Emte Andora, S.a. (1)
c/L'Anglada Casa Font, 300, Ordino, Andorra
Tel.: (376) 73 77 27
Engineering Services
N.A.I.C.S.: 541330

Emte, Lda (1)
Av Dom Joao II 1 06 2 2 C Edificio Atlantis 2 piso Esc 2 1, 1990-095, Lisbon, Portugal
Tel.: (351) 214 107 121
Engineering Services
N.A.I.C.S.: 541330

COMSTOCK METALS LTD.
310 - 850 West Hastings Street, Vancouver, V6C 1E1, BC, Canada
Tel.: (604) 639-4533   BC
Web Site: http://www.comstock-metals.com
Year Founded: 2007
CMMMF—(OTCEM)
Rev.: $874
Assets: $579,403
Liabilities: $363,526
Net Worth: $215,877
Earnings: ($924,254)
Fiscal Year-end: 09/30/23
Metal Mining
N.A.I.C.S.: 212290
Darren Charles Urquhart *(CFO & CFO)*

COMSYS HOLDINGS CORPORATION
17-1 Higashigotanda 2-chome, Shinagawa-ku, Tokyo, 141-8647, Japan
Tel.: (81) 334487000
Web Site: https://www.comsys-hd.co.jp
Year Founded: 2003
1721—(TKS)
Rev.: $3,775,539,460
Assets: $3,401,816,670
Liabilities: $968,973,120
Net Worth: $2,432,843,550
Earnings: $181,464,330
Emp.: 17,405
Fiscal Year-end: 03/31/24
Holding Company; Telecommunications Networks Construction, Information Technology Support & Social Systems Management Services
N.A.I.C.S.: 551112
Takashi Kagaya *(Chm & Pres)*

Subsidiaries:

COMSYS JOHO System Corporation (1)
3-23-14 Takanawa, Minato-ku, Tokyo, 108-8610, Japan
Tel.: (81) 334488100
Web Site: https://www.comjo.co.jp
Emp.: 627
Information Technology Services

N.A.I.C.S.: 541519

Comsys Shared Services Corporation (1)
Tel.: (81) 334487141
Web Site: http://www.comsys-ss.co.jp
Sales Range: $25-49.9 Million
Emp.: 150
Business Development & Shared Services
N.A.I.C.S.: 541720

Hokuriku Denwa Kouji Co., Ltd. (1)
ten chome address 1 153, Yonaizumi cho, Kanazawa, 921 8044, Ishikawa, Japan
Tel.: (81) 76 2216116
Web Site: http://www.hokuwa.co.jp
Rev.: $105,823,926
Assets: $85,858,857
Liabilities: $37,482,769
Net Worth: $48,376,087
Earnings: $777,411
Emp.: 458
Fiscal Year-end: 03/31/2019
Construction Engineering Services
N.A.I.C.S.: 541330
Yasuo Mori *(Pres)*

Subsidiary (Domestic):

Toyama Telephone Construction Corporation (2)
1262 Yokataaraya, Toyama, 930-2243, Japan
Tel.: (81) 764355560
Web Site: https://www.toyama-denwa.co.jp
Emp.: 84
Engineering Services
N.A.I.C.S.: 541330
Asahi Daxiong *(Representative Dir)*

NDS Co., Ltd. (1)
2-15-18 Chiyoda, Naka-ku, Nagoya, 460-0012, Aichi, Japan
Tel.: (81) 52 263 5011
Web Site: http://www.nds-g.co.jp
Earnings: $253,843,080
Emp.: 2,787
Fiscal Year-end: 03/31/2019
Communications Infrastructure, Housing & Real Estate, Mobile & IT Related Services
N.A.I.C.S.: 523999
Toshiaki Hirata *(Mng Exec Officer)*

Subsidiary (Domestic):

Aichi NDS Co., Ltd. (2)
8-61 Shoho-cho, Minato-ku, Nagoya, 455-0074, Japan
Tel.: (81) 523845611
Communications Infrastructure Services
N.A.I.C.S.: 517810

Dainichi Tsushin Co., Ltd. (2)
9-23 Senzoku-cho, Toyota, Achi, Japan
Tel.: (81) 565331131
Web Site: http://www.dainichi-com.co.jp
Electrical Contractors & Optic Cables Mfr
N.A.I.C.S.: 238210

Hamamatsu NDS Co., Ltd. (2)
34 Marutuka cho, Higashi-ku Shizuoka, Hamamatsu, 435-0046, Japan
Tel.: (81) 534626191
Web Site: http://www.hama-n.co.jp
Electrical Contractor
N.A.I.C.S.: 238210

Mitsuboshi Techno Co., Ltd. (2)
26-22 Kyoto-machi, Kanazawa, 920-0848, Ishikawa, Japan
Tel.: (81) 762527201
Web Site: http://www.mituboshi.co.jp
Electrical Contractor
N.A.I.C.S.: 238210
Kimihiro Kamei *(Pres)*

NDS INFORMATION SYSTEM CO., LTD (2)
8th floor ONEST Nagoya Nishiki Square 1-8-6 Nishiki, Naka-Ku, Nagoya, 460-0003, Aichi, Japan
Tel.: (81) 522235255
Web Site: https://www.nds-infos.co.jp
Emp.: 255
Software Development Services
N.A.I.C.S.: 541511

NDS Lease Co., Ltd. (2)
5-48 Heiwagaoka, Meito-ku, Nagoya, 465-0097, Japan
Tel.: (81) 527732211

COMSYS Holdings Corporation—(Continued)

Web Site: https://www.nds-g.co.jp
Emp.: 28
Passenger Car Rental
N.A.I.C.S.: 532111

NDS Solution Co., Ltd. (2)
Kawamoto Building 3F 4-11-39 Osu, Aichi
Naka-Ku, Nagoya, 460 0011, Japan
Tel.: (81) 522492112
Web Site: http://www.nsol.co.jp
Consumer Electronics Repair & Mainte-
nance Services
N.A.I.C.S.: 811210
Tomohiro Suzuki (Pres)

NDS.TS Co., Ltd. (2)
2-3-4 Shin-Yokohama, Kohoku-ku, 222-
0033, Yokohama, 222-0033, Kanagawa,
Japan
Tel.: (81) 456206353
Web Site: https://www.nds-g.co.jp
Embedded Development Software Services
N.A.I.C.S.: 513210

Santsu Kensetsu Koji Co., Ltd. (2)
644 6 Onoe cho, Matsusaka, 515-2109,
Mie, Japan
Tel.: (81) 598 56 9006
Web Site: http://www.nds-g.co.jp
Electrical Contractor
N.A.I.C.S.: 238210

Shizuoka NDS Co., Ltd. (2)
3-25-25 Kawai, Aoi-Ku, Shizuoka, 420-
0923, Japan
Tel.: (81) 542650025
Web Site: https://www.shizuoka-nds.co.jp
Emp.: 129
Electrical Contractor
N.A.I.C.S.: 238210
Osamu Nakano (Pres)

Toho Koji Co., Ltd. (2)
2324 Makigaya, Aoi-Ku, 421-1221, Shi-
zuoka, Japan
Tel.: (81) 54 276 1177
Web Site: http://www.nds-g.co.jp
Electrical Contractor
N.A.I.C.S.: 238210
Masafumi Nishimura (Pres)

Tomei Tsushin Kogyo Co., Ltd. (2)
100-3 Amaikekoda-cho, Inazawa, 492-8274,
Aichi, Japan
Tel.: (81) 587 23 3535
Web Site: http://www.tomei.co.jp
Telecommunications Equipment Mfr
N.A.I.C.S.: 334290
Yoshiaki Hatano (Pres & CEO)

Nippon COMSYS Corporation (1)
2-17-1 Higashi-gohanda Shinagawa-Ku,
Tokyo, 141-8647, Japan
Tel.: (81) 334487030
Web Site: http://www.comsys.co.jp
Sales Range: $450-499.9 Million
Emp.: 1,138
Telecommunications & Electrical Engineer-
ing Services
N.A.I.C.S.: 517810

Subsidiary (Domestic):

COMSYS Engineering Co., Ltd. (2)
Shinagawa Konan Building 5F 5-4-30 Ko-
nan, Minato-ku, Tokyo, Japan
Tel.: (81) 368103890
Web Site: http://www.comsys-eng.co.jp
Emp.: 678
Engineeering Services
N.A.I.C.S.: 541330

COMSYS Net Corporation (2)
8F Jinno Shoji Building 1-25-13 Higashig-
otanda, Shinagawa-ku, Tokyo, 141-0022,
Japan
Tel.: (81) 334480921
Web Site: https://www.comsysnet.co.jp
Emp.: 230
Communication Equipment Installation Ser-
vices
N.A.I.C.S.: 334290

**COMSYS Tohoku Techno Co.,
Ltd.** (2)
Comsys Sendai Building 5F 8-36 Shimizu-
koji, Wakabayashi-Ku, Sendai, 984-0075,
Japan
Tel.: (81) 227231742

Web Site: http://www.comsys-tt.co.jp
Emp.: 152
Software Development Services
N.A.I.C.S.: 541511

COMSYS Tsusan Co., Ltd. (2)
3-21-12 Shirokane, Minato-Ku, Tokyo, 108-
0072, Japan **(100%)**
Tel.: (81) 334487278
Web Site: http://www.tusan.co.jp
Sales Range: $50-74.9 Million
Emp.: 70
Telecommunications Equipment Leasing
Services
N.A.I.C.S.: 532490
Kazuya Oiwa (Pres)

**Tokushima Tsushinkensetsu Co.,
Ltd.** (2)
3-2-33 Shinhamacho, Tokushima, 770-8006,
Japan
Tel.: (81) 886621060
Construction Engineering Services
N.A.I.C.S.: 237990

Tsushin Densetsu Co., Ltd. (2)
4F Shinbashi Annex 5-35-10 Shinbashi,
Minato-ku, Tokyo, 105-0004, Japan
Tel.: (81) 334345101
Web Site: https://www.tsuden.co.jp
Engineeering Services
N.A.I.C.S.: 541330

**SANWA COMSYS Engineering
Corporation** (1)
Oval Court Osaki Mark West 2-17-1 Hi-
gashigotanda, Shinagawa-ku, Tokyo, 141-
0022, Japan
Tel.: (81) 363653111
Web Site: https://www.sancom-eng.co.jp
Sales Range: $150-199.9 Million
Emp.: 1,774
Telecommunication Engineering Services
N.A.I.C.S.: 541330

Subsidiary (Domestic):

SANWA Denshi Inc. (2)
2-1-6 Sarugakucho Chiyoda-ku, Tokyo, 101-
0064, Japan
Tel.: (81) 332913131
Web Site: http://www.sanwadenshi.com
Sales Range: $75-99.9 Million
Emp.: 450
Telecommunications & Electrical Engineer-
ing Services
N.A.I.C.S.: 541330

**SUNCOM Technology
Corporation** (2)
4-16-25 Nakajujo, Kita-ku, Tokyo, 114-0032,
Japan
Tel.: (81) 359247051
Web Site: https://www.s-ton.com
Sales Range: $25-49.9 Million
Emp.: 175
Engineeering Services
N.A.I.C.S.: 541330

Subsidiary (Non-US):

Sannect Co., Ltd. (2)
Web Site: http://www.sannect.jp
Sales Range: $25-49.9 Million
Emp.: 45
General Construction & Infrastructure Ser-
vices
N.A.I.C.S.: 236220

Sysken Corporation (1)
14-45 Hagiwaramachi, Chuo-ku, Kuma-
moto, 860-0832, Japan
Tel.: (81) 96 2851111
Web Site: http://www.sysken.co.jp
Emp.: 584
Communication Facility Construction Ser-
vices, Transport & Tourism Permission
N.A.I.C.S.: 236220
Hidenori Fukumoto (Pres & CEO)

TOSYS Niigata Co., Ltd. (1)
2-4-5 Matoba Ryutsu, Nishi-Ku, Niigata,
950-2032, Japan **(89.2%)**
Tel.: (81) 252111600
Web Site: https://www.ts-niigata.co.jp
Telecommunication Servicesb
N.A.I.C.S.: 517112

TSUKEN Corporation (1)
15-1-23 Kita 4 West, Chuo-ku, Sapporo,

060-0004, Japan
Web Site: http://www.tsuken.co.jp
Emp.: 2,126
Telecommunication Equipment Maintenance
Services
N.A.I.C.S.: 811210

COMTEC INC.
Seavans N building 10F 1-2-1
Shibaura, Minato-ku, Tokyo, 105-
6791, Japan
Tel.: (81) 3 5419 5551   JP
Web Site: http://www.ct-net.co.jp
Year Founded: 1976
Sales Range: $100-124.9 Million
Emp.: 997
Information Technology Support Ser-
vices
N.A.I.C.S.: 541519
Yoshinori Ikura (Chm)

**COMTEC SOLAR SYSTEMS
GROUP LIMITED**
16 Yuan Di Road Nanhui Industrial
Zone, Shanghai, 201314, China
Tel.: (86) 2168043010   Ky
Web Site:
http://www.comtecsolar.com
0712—(HKG)
Rev.: $5,214,456
Assets: $42,533,618
Liabilities: $65,580,700
Net Worth: ($23,047,081)
Earnings: ($7,116,736)
Emp.: 43
Fiscal Year-end: 12/31/22
Investment Services
N.A.I.C.S.: 523999
John Yi Zhang (Chm)

Subsidiaries:

**Comtec Solar (Jiangsu) Co.,
Limited** (1)
12 East Sea Highway, HaiAn County, Nan-
tong, 226600, Jiangsu, China
Tel.: (86) 51388971308
Solar Grade Product Mfr
N.A.I.C.S.: 334413

**Comtec Solar International (M) Sdn.
Bhd.** (1)
Lot 3211 Block 12 Jalan Usaha Jaya Sama-
jaya Free Industrial Zone, Muara Tebas
Land District, 93350, Kuching, Sarawak,
Malaysia
Tel.: (60) 82262000
Solar Grade Product Mfr
N.A.I.C.S.: 334413

**Shanghai Comtec Solar Technology
Co., Ltd.** (1)
No 16 Yuandi Rd Nanhui Industrial Zone,
Shanghai, China
Tel.: (86) 2168043010
Solar Ingot & Wafer Mfr
N.A.I.C.S.: 334413

COMTEC SYSTEMS CO., LTD.
Comtec Building 343 Gamasan-ro,
Yeongdeungpo-gu, Seoul, Korea
(South)
Tel.: (82) 232890114
Web Site: https://www.comtec.co.kr
Year Founded: 1983
031820—(KRS)
Rev.: $544,452,819
Assets: $428,300,034
Liabilities: $274,991,181
Net Worth: $153,308,853
Earnings: $25,718,967
Emp.: 532
Fiscal Year-end: 12/31/22
Information Technology Services
N.A.I.C.S.: 541512
Kwon Chang-Wan (Exec Officer)

COMTRADE GROUP B.V.
Savski nasip 7, 11070, Belgrade,
Serbia
Tel.: (381) 11 2015 600   NL

Web Site: http://www.comtrade.com
Emp.: 1,500
Holding Company; Information Tech-
nology Solutions & Software Engi-
neering Services
N.A.I.C.S.: 551112
Veselin Jevrosimovic (Chm)

Subsidiaries:

ComTrade GmbH (1)
Hirschstettner Strasse 19-21/Z/109, A-1220,
Vienna, Austria
Tel.: (43) 19949650
Web Site: http://www.hermes-softlab.de
Software Engineering Services
N.A.I.C.S.: 334610

**ComTrade Software Solutions
GmbH** (1)
Stefan-George-Ring 29, 81929, Munich,
Germany
Tel.: (49) 89309040222
Web Site: http://www.hermes-softlab.de
Sales Range: $25-49.9 Million
Emp.: 3
Information Retrieval Services
N.A.I.C.S.: 541511
Michael Zitmann (Mng Dir)

**ComTrade Software Solutions
Limited** (1)
23 Priory Hall Stillorgan Road, Dublin,
8a94aek18, Ireland
Tel.: (353) 16614030
Web Site: http://www.comtrade.com
Sales Range: $25-49.9 Million
Emp.: 20
Software Engineering Services
N.A.I.C.S.: 334610
Brendan Garland (Controller-Fin)

ComTrade USA West, Inc. (1)
625 Ellis St Ste 201 B, Mountain View, CA
94043
Tel.: (650) 968-2562
Web Site: http://www.comtrade.com
Software Engineering Services
N.A.I.C.S.: 334610

ComTrade d.o.o. (1)
Litijska 51, 1000, Ljubljana, Slovenia
Tel.: (386) 15865200
Web Site: http://www.comtrade.com
Software Engineering & Consulting Services
N.A.I.C.S.: 541512
Viki Prasnitar (Dir-Fin)

Comtrade Inc. (1)
275 Grove St Ste 2-400, Newton, MA
02466
Tel.: (617) 663-4871
Software Development Services
N.A.I.C.S.: 541511

COMTRONIC COMPUTER INC.
30 Kinnear Court Unit 1, Richmond
Hill, L4B 1K8, ON, Canada
Tel.: (905) 881-3606
Web Site: http://www.comtronic.ca
Year Founded: 1987
Sales Range: $25-49.9 Million
Computer System Distr
N.A.I.C.S.: 423430
Jimmy Yong (Mgr)

COMTURE CORPORATION
Gatecity Osaki East Tower 1-11-2
Osaki, Shinagawa-ku, Tokyo, 141-
0032, Japan
Tel.: (81) 357459700
Web Site: https://www.comture.com
3844—(TKS)
Rev.: $225,962,850
Assets: $154,951,620
Liabilities: $43,870,570
Net Worth: $111,081,050
Earnings: $20,722,350
Emp.: 1,912
Fiscal Year-end: 03/31/24
Computer System Design Services
N.A.I.C.S.: 541512
Koichi Mukai (Chm & CEO)

Subsidiaries:

Comture Network Corporation **(1)**
Ariake Central Tower 9F 3-7-18 Ariake,
Koto-ku, Tokyo, 135-0063, Japan
Tel.: (81) 357459706
Web Site: https://www.comture-net.com
Emp.: 410
IT Infrastructure Construction Services
N.A.I.C.S.: 236220

Takt Systems, Inc. **(1)**
Higashi-Gotanda Square 4F 2-10-2 Higashi-
Gotanda, Shinagawa-ku, Tokyo, 141-0022,
Japan
Tel.: (81) 334453100
Web Site: https://www.takt.co.jp
Emp.: 116
Software Development Services
N.A.I.C.S.: 541511

COMUTO SA
84 avenue de la Republique, Paris,
75011, France
Tel.: (33) 6 61 83 16 69
Web Site: http://www.blablacar.com
Year Founded: 2006
Emp.: 150
Ride-Sharing Technology Developer
N.A.I.C.S.: 513210
Francis Nappez (Co-Founder & CTO)

COMVEX S.A.
Port Precincts Berth 80-84, 900900,
Constanta, Romania
Tel.: (40) 241639016
Web Site: https://www.comvex.ro
Year Founded: 1991
CMVX—(BUC)
Rev.: $98,819,202
Assets: $133,570,392
Liabilities: $42,294,692
Net Worth: $91,275,700
Earnings: $40,845,281
Emp.: 416
Fiscal Year-end: 12/31/23
Bulk Raw Material Handling
N.A.I.C.S.: 488320
Viorel Panait (Chm)

COMVITA LIMITED
23 Wilson Road South, Paengaroa,
Te Puke, 3189, New Zealand
Tel.: (64) 75331426   NZ
Web Site: https://www.comvita.co.nz
Year Founded: 1974
CVT—(NZX)
Rev.: $140,068,780
Assets: $214,572,967
Liabilities: $71,438,995
Net Worth: $143,133,971
Earnings: $6,616,029
Emp.: 504
Fiscal Year-end: 06/30/23
Health & Beauty Product Whslr
N.A.I.C.S.: 456120
Neil John Craig (Chm)

COMWAVE NETWORKS, INC.
61 Wildcat Road, Toronto, M3J 2P5,
ON, Canada
Tel.: (662) 85779
Web Site: http://www.comwave.net
Telecommunication Servicesb
N.A.I.C.S.: 517112
Yuval Barzakay (Pres)

Subsidiaries:

Radiant Communications Corp. **(1)**
1600 1050 W Pender St, Vancouver, V6E
4T3, BC, Canada
Tel.: (604) 257-0500
Web Site: http://www.radiant.net
Sales Range: $25-49.9 Million
Emp.: 83
Internet & Other Communication Services
N.A.I.C.S.: 517810
Jason Leeson (CTO & Exec VP)

**CON-PRO INDUSTRIES
CANADA LTD.**
765 Marion Street, Winnipeg, R2J
0K6, MB, Canada
Tel.: (204) 233-3717
Web Site: https://www.conpro.mb.ca
Year Founded: 1969
Rev.: $14,345,917
Emp.: 40
Building Contractors
N.A.I.C.S.: 238290

CONAFI PRESTITO S.P.A.
Via Aldo Barbaro 15, 10143, Turin,
Italy
Tel.: (39) 0117710320
Web Site: https://www.conafi.it
CNP—(ITA)
Sales Range: $10-24.9 Million
Emp.: 146
Personal Financial Services
N.A.I.C.S.: 525990
Nunzio Chiolo (Chm & Mng Dir)

CONAIR GROUP INC.
1510 Tower Street, Abbotsford, BC,
Canada
Tel.: (604) 855-1171
Web Site: http://www.conair.ca
Rev.: $15,670,987
Emp.: 165
Aerial Fire Control Products & Ser-
vices
N.A.I.C.S.: 115310
Barry Marsden (Chm)

CONALVIAS S.A.
Avenida 7 Nte 23 N-64, Cali, Colom-
bia
Tel.: (57) 2 4411700
Web Site: http://www.conalvias.com
Year Founded: 1980
Sales Range: $250-299.9 Million
Emp.: 500
Highway & Street Construction Ser-
vices
N.A.I.C.S.: 237310
Andres Jaramillo Lopez (CEO)

Subsidiaries:

Conalvias Servicios S.A.S. **(1)**
Cl 94 A 11 A - 50 Of 102, Bogota, Colombia
Tel.: (57) 16219342
Civil Engineering Services
N.A.I.C.S.: 541330

Conalvias USA, LLC. **(1)**
1001 Cypress Creek Rd Ste 200, Fort Lau-
derdale, FL 33309
Tel.: (954) 771-1095
Web Site: http://www.conalviasusa.com
Emp.: 60
Civil Engineering Services
N.A.I.C.S.: 541330
Nyree Quintero (VP)

CONART ENGINEERS LIMITED
17 Jay Bharat Society Nr Solanki Pal-
ace 3rd Road, Khar West, Mumbai,
400 052, Maharashtra, India
Tel.: (91) 9099982661
Web Site:
   https://www.conartengineers.com
Year Founded: 1973
522231—(BOM)
Rev.: $3,094,815
Assets: $3,496,598
Liabilities: $580,482
Net Worth: $2,916,116
Earnings: $141,300
Emp.: 21
Fiscal Year-end: 03/31/21
Residential Building Construction
Services
N.A.I.C.S.: 236220
Jitendra Shankerlal Sura (Chm &
Mng Dir)

CONATEL, S.A.
Ejido 1690, Montevideo, 11200, Uru-
guay
Tel.: (598) 2902 0314
Web Site: http://www.conatel.com.uy
Year Founded: 1936
Sales Range: $75-99.9 Million
Emp.: 200
Computer & IT Consulting Services
N.A.I.C.S.: 541690
Juan Carlos Duarte Dure (Pres)

CONBUZZ CO., LTD.
563 Baegok-daero Idong-myeon,
Cheoin-gu, Yongin, Gyeonggi-do, Ko-
rea (South)
Tel.: (82) 7048584652
Web Site: http://www.conbuzz.co.kr
Year Founded: 2009
109070—(KRS)
Rev.: $22,067,538
Assets: $25,273,672
Liabilities: $13,927,275
Net Worth: $11,346,396
Earnings: ($7,595,465)
Emp.: 43
Fiscal Year-end: 12/31/22
Paper Products Mfr
N.A.I.C.S.: 322299
Jong Yun Gwak (CEO)

**CONCARDIS PAYMENT
GROUP GMBH**
Helfmann-Park 7, Eschborn, Frankfurt
am Main, 65760, Germany
Tel.: (49) 69 7922 0
Web Site: http://www.concardis.com
Full-service Payment Provider
N.A.I.C.S.: 522320
Robert Hoffmann (CEO)

Subsidiaries:

Concardis GmbH **(1)**
Helfmann-Park 7, Eschborn, 65760, Frank-
furt am Main, Germany
Tel.: (49) 69 7922 0
Web Site: http://www.concardis.com
Financial & Business Services
N.A.I.C.S.: 522320
Mark Freese (CFO)

CONCAS SA
Str Transilvaniei nr 163, 120171, Bu-
zau, 120171, Romania
Tel.: (40) 372704840
Web Site: https://www.concas.ro
CONK—(BUC)
Rev.: $16,900,973
Assets: $15,269,679
Liabilities: $6,760,203
Net Worth: $8,509,476
Earnings: $639,781
Emp.: 229
Fiscal Year-end: 12/31/23
Building Construction Services
N.A.I.C.S.: 236116

CONCEJO AB
Vastra Finnbodavagen 2-4, PO Box
5028, SE-131 05, Nacka, Sweden
Tel.: (46) 856305300
Web Site: https://concejo.se
Year Founded: 1994
CNCJO.B—(OMX)
Sales Range: $25-49.9 Million
Safety, Environment & Navigation
Products & Systems Mfr
N.A.I.C.S.: 922160
Lars Hakansson (CFO)

**CONCENTRA CONSULTING
LIMITED**
Thames House 18 Park Street, Lon-
don, SE1 9EQ, United Kingdom
Tel.: (44) 20 7099 6910
Web Site: http://www.concentra.co.uk
Year Founded: 2005

Sales Range: $10-24.9 Million
Emp.: 80
Technology Consulting Services
N.A.I.C.S.: 541690
Rupert Morrison (Mng Dir)

CONCENTRA NV
Herkenrodesingel 16, 3500, Hasselt,
Belgium
Tel.: (32) 11 878 111   BE
Web Site: http://www.concentra.be
Emp.: 250
Holding Company
N.A.I.C.S.: 551112
Marc Vangeel (CEO)

Subsidiaries:

LMG Netherlands II B.V. **(1)**
Mercator 3, 6135 KW, Sittard, Netherlands
Tel.: (31) 46 411 6000
Web Site: http://www.bereiklimburg.nl
Newspaper Publishers
N.A.I.C.S.: 513110
Roger Scholtes (Comml Dir)

**CONCENTRATED LEADERS
FUND LIMITED**
Level 12 37 Bligh Street Sydney,
Sydney, 2000, NSW, Australia
Tel.: (61) 2 9357 0788
Web Site: http://www.clfund.com.au
Year Founded: 1987
Sales Range: $1-9.9 Million
Investment Services
N.A.I.C.S.: 523940
Brian Sherman (Chm)

CONCENTRIC AB
102 42 Stockholm, Box 5058, Linkop-
ing, Sweden
Tel.: (46) 13250360   SE
Web Site:
   https://www.concentricab.com
COIC—(OMX)
Rev.: $183,364,160
Assets: $249,897,760
Liabilities: $119,638,400
Net Worth: $130,259,360
Earnings: $25,026,400
Emp.: 747
Fiscal Year-end: 12/31/20
Hydraulics & Diesel Engine Pump Mfr
N.A.I.C.S.: 333996
Kenth Eriksson (Chm)

Subsidiaries:

Concentric Birmingham Ltd. **(1)**
Gravelly Park Tyburn Road, Birmingham,
B24 8HW, United Kingdom
Tel.: (44) 1213272081
Web Site: http://www.concentric.co.uk
Hydraulics & Diesel Engine Pump Mfr
N.A.I.C.S.: 333996

Concentric Hof GmbH **(1)**
Hofer Str 19, Postfach 15 07, 95030, Hof,
Germany
Tel.: (49) 92818950
Sales Range: $50-74.9 Million
Emp.: 170
Hydraulics & Diesel Engine Pump Mfr
N.A.I.C.S.: 333996

Concentric Innovations AB **(1)**
Isafjordsgatan 39b, Kista, Stockholm, 164
40, Sweden
Tel.: (46) 43332400
Hydraulic Pumps Mfr
N.A.I.C.S.: 333996

Concentric Itasca Inc. **(1)**
800 Hollywood Ave, Itasca, IL 60143-1353
Tel.: (630) 773-3355
Sales Range: $25-49.9 Million
Emp.: 100
Hydraulics & Diesel Engine Pump Mfr
N.A.I.C.S.: 333996

Concentric Korea LLC **(1)**
Hyundai World Tower RM1211 907, Mok-
dong Yangcheon-gu, Seoul, 158-735, Korea
(South)

Concentric AB—(Continued)

Tel.: (82) 226777960
Pumps Mfr
N.A.I.C.S.: 333996

Concentric Pumps (Suzhou) Co. Ltd. (1)
47 Dongjing Industrial Park 9 Dong Fu Lu SIP, Suzhou, Jiangsu, China
Tel.: (86) 51287175115
Hydraulics & Diesel Engine Pump Mfr
N.A.I.C.S.: 333996

Concentric Pumps Pune Pvt. Ltd. (1)
Gat No 26/1 27 & 28 Part Near Sanghar Warehousing Off Pune-Nagar Road, Vill Lonikand Taluka Haveli, Pune, 412 216, India
Tel.: (91) 2066142300
Hydraulics & Diesel Engine Pump Mfr
N.A.I.C.S.: 333996

Concentric Rockford Inc. (1)
2222 15th St, Rockford, IL 61104-7313
Tel.: (815) 398-4400
Sales Range: $100-124.9 Million
Emp.: 275
Hydraulics & Diesel Engine Pump Mfr
N.A.I.C.S.: 333996

Concentric Srl (1)
Via Ripamonti 129, 20141, Milan, Italy
Tel.: (39) 0256805501
Hydraulic Pumps Mfr
N.A.I.C.S.: 333996

Engineered Machined Products Inc. (1)
3111 N 28th St, Escanaba, MI 49829
Tel.: (906) 789-7497
Web Site: http://www.emp-corp.com
Sales Range: $25-49.9 Million
Emp.: 460
Supplier of Motor Vehicle Parts & Accessories
N.A.I.C.S.: 333611
Brandon Larche *(Pres & COO)*

GKN Sinter Metals de Argentina S.A. (1)
Piedras 383 3er Piso, 1070, Buenos Aires, Argentina
Tel.: (54) 1143311219
Sales Range: $10-24.9 Million
Emp.: 166
Engine Pump Mfr
N.A.I.C.S.: 333914

LICOS Trucktec GmbH (1)
Bergheimer Str 1, 88677, Markdorf, Germany
Tel.: (49) 754495460
Web Site: http://www.licostrucktec.com
Sales Range: $10-24.9 Million
Emp.: 55
Electromagnetic Water Pump Clutch Mfr
N.A.I.C.S.: 335314

CONCEPCION INDUSTRIAL CORPORATION
308 Sen Gil Puyat Avenue, Makati, 1209, Metro Manila, Philippines
Tel.: (63) 2 7721819
Web Site: http://www.cic.ph
Year Founded: 1962
Air Conditioning Product Distr
N.A.I.C.S.: 423730
Raul Joseph A. Concepcion *(Chm, Pres & CEO)*

Subsidiaries:

Concepcion Carrier Air Conditioning Corporation (1)
Km 20 East Service Road South Superhighway, Alabang, Muntinlupa, Philippines
Tel.: (63) 28635555
Web Site: http://www.carrier.com.ph
Air Conditioning System Mfr
N.A.I.C.S.: 333415
Raul Joseph *(Mng Dir)*

Concepcion Durables Inc. (1)
308 Jose Concepcion Building Sen Gil Puyat Avenue, Makati, 1209, Philippines
Tel.: (63) 495430132

Electric Appliances Mfr
N.A.I.C.S.: 335220

CONCERN BELNEFTEKHIM
73 Dzerzhinsky Ave, 220116, Minsk, Belarus
Tel.: (375) 172690207
Web Site: http://www.belneftekhim.by
Year Founded: 1997
Sales Range: $1-4.9 Billion
Emp.: 120,000
Petrochemical & Chemical Product Mfr
N.A.I.C.S.: 324110
Valery Kazakeeich *(Pres)*

Subsidiaries:

Belorusneft Republican Unitary Enterprise (1)
ul Rogachevskaya 9, 246003, Gomel, Belarus
Tel.: (375) 232579263
Web Site: http://www.beloil.by
Oil Exploration & Production
N.A.I.C.S.: 211120

Borisov Plastic Products Plant Open Joint-Stock Company (1)
Ul Daumana 97, Borisov, 222120, Minsk, Belarus
Tel.: (375) 177734356
Plastics Product Mfr
N.A.I.C.S.: 326199

Grodno Azot JSC (1)
Slavinskogo Street 4, 230026, Grodno, Belarus
Tel.: (375) 1522741980
Web Site: http://www.grodno-khim.by
Composites & Other Chemicals Mfr
N.A.I.C.S.: 325998

CONCERN GALNAFTOGAS PJSC
1 Plastova Str, 79056, L'viv, Ukraine
Tel.: (380) 32 298 96 01
Web Site: http://www.galnaftogas.com
GLNG—(UKR)
Sales Range: Less than $1 Million
Petroleum Product Whslr
N.A.I.C.S.: 424720
Nazar Kupybida *(CEO)*

CONCERN GENERAL INVEST LLC
73/1 Sadovnicheskaya St Floor 2 Office 12, 115035, Moscow, Russia
Tel.: (7) 4957270077
Web Site: http://www.generalinvest.ru
Year Founded: 2009
Sales Range: Less than $1 Million
Investment Banking Services
N.A.I.C.S.: 523150
Vincenzo Trani *(Founder, Chm & Pres)*

CONCERN WORLDWIDE
52-55 Lower Camden Street, Dublin, D02 H425, Ireland
Tel.: (353) 14177700
Web Site: http://www.concern.net
Sales Range: $125-149.9 Million
Emp.: 3,900
Emergency & Development Services in Developing Countries
N.A.I.C.S.: 541990
Dominic MacSorley *(CEO)*

Subsidiaries:

Concern Worldwide Limited (1)
13 14 Calico House Clove Hitch Quay, London, SW11 3TN, United Kingdom
Tel.: (44) 20 7801 1850
Web Site: http://www.concern.net
Emp.: 40
Grantmaking Services
N.A.I.C.S.: 813211
Sarah Mollo *(Head-Comm)*

CONCESSIONARIA AUTO RAPOSO TAVARES S.A.
Av Getulio Vargas 20-59, Bauru, 17017-383, SP, Brazil
Tel.: (55) 1431042300
Web Site:
http://www.cart.invepar.com.br
Emp.: 100
Highway Construction Services
N.A.I.C.S.: 237310
Eduardo Marques De Almeida Dantas *(CEO)*

CONCESSIONARIA ECOVIAS DOS IMIGRANTES S.A.
Rua Gomes De Carvalho 1510.3 Andar, Sao Paulo, 04547-005, Brazil
Tel.: (55) 1143588100
Web Site: http://www.ecovias.com.br
Emp.: 100
Highway Construction Services
N.A.I.C.S.: 237310
Ronald Dennis Marangon *(Dir-IR)*

CONCESSIONARIA RODOVIAS DO TIETE S.A.
Rod Comendador Mario Dedini Km 108-Mais 60, 13320-970, Salto, SP, Brazil
Tel.: (55) 1146027900
Web Site:
http://www.rodoviasdotiete.com.br
Emp.: 100
Highway Construction Services
N.A.I.C.S.: 237310
Emerson Luiz Bittar *(CEO)*

CONCESSIONARIA ROTA DAS BANDEIRAS S.A.
Rodovia D Pedro Sp-065 Km 110 400 Pista Sul S/N, Sitio da Moenda, Itatiba, 13252-800, SP, Brazil
Tel.: (55) 1148948501
Web Site:
http://www.rotadasbandeiras.com.br
Emp.: 100
Highway Construction Services
N.A.I.C.S.: 237310
Douglas Longhi *(CEO)*

CONCH ANHUI ENERGY SAVING AND ENVIRONMENT PROTECTION NEW MATERIAL CO LTD
Gangwang Road No 38 of economic and technological development zone, Wuhu, 241000, Anhui, China
Tel.: (86) 5538396866
Web Site: https://pvc.conch.cn
Year Founded: 1995
000619—(SSE)
Rev.: $770,514,428
Assets: $714,896,667
Liabilities: $354,602,706
Net Worth: $360,293,961
Earnings: ($12,945,077)
Fiscal Year-end: 12/31/22
Plastic Materials Mfr
N.A.I.C.S.: 326199

CONCHA PLC
44 Albemarle Street, London, W1S 4JJ, United Kingdom
Tel.: (44) 77 6777 5888
Web Site: http://www.concha-plc.com
Rev.: $10,793
Assets: $1,856,389
Liabilities: $122,770
Net Worth: $1,733,619
Earnings: ($6,640,369)
Emp.: 4
Fiscal Year-end: 06/30/17
Investment Evaluation
N.A.I.C.S.: 523940
Russell J. Backhouse *(Fin Dir)*

Subsidiaries:

Hot Tuna Australia Pty Ltd. (1)
Level 7 28 Foveaux Street, Surry Hills, 2010, NSW, Australia
Tel.: (61) 292804411
Web Site: http://www.hot-tuna.com.au
Surf Apparel Mfr & Marketer
N.A.I.C.S.: 424350

CONCIVIA SA
Tel.: (40) 239616281
Web Site: https://www.concivia.ro
COKJ—(BUC)
Rev.: $38,869,466
Assets: $39,810,115
Liabilities: $21,584,670
Net Worth: $18,225,445
Earnings: $6,070,674
Emp.: 324
Fiscal Year-end: 12/31/23
Building Construction Services
N.A.I.C.S.: 236116

CONCORD BIOTECH LIMITED
16th Floor B-Wing Mondeal Heights Iscon Cross Road SG Highway, Ahmedabad, 380015, Gujarat, India
Tel.: (91) 7968138700
Web Site:
https://www.concordbiotech.com
Year Founded: 2000
543960—(BOM)
Rev.: $107,683,473
Assets: $183,575,216
Liabilities: $26,987,192
Net Worth: $156,588,024
Earnings: $28,860,920
Emp.: 1,234
Fiscal Year-end: 03/31/23
Biotechnology Research & Development Services
N.A.I.C.S.: 541714

CONCORD BLUE ENGINEERING GMBH
Konigsallee 6-8, 40212, Dusseldorf, Germany
Tel.: (49) 211 320364
Web Site:
http://www.concordblueenergy.com
Year Founded: 1998
Sales Range: $10-24.9 Million
Emp.: 100
Waste To Energy Services
N.A.I.C.S.: 562998
Christopher Thannhaeuser *(Founder & Chm)*

Subsidiaries:

Blue Tower GmbH (1)
Konrad Adenauer Strasse 9-13, 45699, Herten, Germany
Tel.: (49) 2366305268
Web Site: http://www.blue-tower.de
Eletric Power Generation Services
N.A.I.C.S.: 221112

Concord Blue Technology Ltd. (1)
101 Dheeraj Arma 1st Floor Anant Kanekar Marg, Bandra E, Mumbai, 400051, India
Tel.: (91) 22 67049000
Waste Disposal & Recycling Services
N.A.I.C.S.: 562998
Jeevan Prakash Nain *(Assoc Gen-Mgr)*

Concord Blue USA, Inc. (1)
12424 Wilshire Blvd Ste 660, Los Angeles, CA 90025
Tel.: (310) 979-2900
Waste Disposal & Recycling Services
N.A.I.C.S.: 562998
Wesley Bilson *(Pres & CEO)*

CONCORD CONCRETE PUMPS INC.
1608 Broadway St, Port Coquitlam, V3C 2M8, BC, Canada
Tel.: (604) 468-7867

Web Site:
http://www.concordpumps.ca
Year Founded: 1998
Rev.: $14,085,082
Emp.: 50
Trucks & Parts Mfr
N.A.I.C.S.: 333924
Izidro Flores *(Owner & Pres)*

CONCORD CONTROL SYS-TEMS LIMITED

G-36 UPSIDC Industrial Area Deva
Road, Chinhut, Lucknow, 226019,
Uttar Pradesh, India
Tel.: (91) 7800008700
Web Site:
https://www.concordgroup.in
Year Founded: 2011
543619—(BOM)
Rev.: $5,949,032
Assets: $3,569,139
Liabilities: $1,022,948
Net Worth: $2,546,190
Earnings: $653,354
Emp.: 93
Fiscal Year-end: 03/31/23
Electronic Components Mfr
N.A.I.C.S.: 334419

CONCORD DRUGS LIMITED

Survey No 249, Brahmanapally V
Hayathnagar M R R District, Hydera-
bad, 501511, Telangana, India
Tel.: (91) 9052779505
Web Site:
https://www.concorddrugs.in
Year Founded: 1995
538965—(BOM)
Rev.: $7,023,143
Assets: $6,808,989
Liabilities: $3,155,402
Net Worth: $3,653,586
Earnings: $447,952
Fiscal Year-end: 03/31/21
Pharmaceuticals Mfr
N.A.I.C.S.: 325412
Nagi Reddy *(Mng Dir)*

CONCORD INTERNATIONAL SECURITIES CO., LTD.

10 3 Section Ximen Rd, Tainan City,
70444, Taiwan
Tel.: (886) 62219777
Web Site: http://www.wintan.com.tw
5864—(TPE)
Rev.: $1,292,687
Assets: $173,016,321
Liabilities: $38,813,245
Net Worth: $134,203,077
Earnings: ($70,243,880)
Fiscal Year-end: 12/31/22
Securities Brokerage Services
N.A.I.C.S.: 523150
Wen-Pin Li *(Chm)*

CONCORD INVESTMENTBANK AG

Grosse Gallusstrasse 9, D 60311,
Frankfurt, Germany
Tel.: (49) 6950951270   De
Year Founded: 1998
Sales Range: $25-49.9 Million
Emp.: 76
Investment Banking & Securities Bro-
kerage Services
N.A.I.C.S.: 523150
Mathias Schmid *(Partner)*

Subsidiaries:

Concord Financial Intermediary
GmbH   (1)
Grosse Gallusstrasse 1-7, 60311, Frankfurt,
Germany
Tel.: (49) 6950951600
Web Site: http://www.concord-ag.de
Securities Brokerage Services
N.A.I.C.S.: 523150

CONCORD MEDICAL SER-VICES HOLDINGS LIMITED

26A1-26A5 Hanwei Building No 7
Guanghua Road, East District, Bei-
jing, 100013, China
Tel.: (86) 1059036688   Ky
Web Site:
https://www.concordmedical.com
CCM—(NYSE)
Rev.: $74,407,676
Assets: $838,217,628
Liabilities: $596,333,075
Net Worth: $241,884,554
Earnings: ($73,524,175)
Emp.: 727
Fiscal Year-end: 12/31/23
Radiotherapy & Diagnostic Imaging
Centers
N.A.I.C.S.: 621512
Jianyu Yang *(Chm & CEO)*

Subsidiaries:

Concord Healthcare Singapore Pte.
Ltd.   (1)
19 Adam Road, 289891, Singapore, Singa-
pore
Tel.: (65) 69333733
Web Site: http://www.concordhospital.sg
Cancer Treatment Medical Facility
N.A.I.C.S.: 622310
Kong Yaw Yap *(Chm)*

CONCORD NEW ENERGY GROUP LIMITED

Suite 3901 39/F Far East Finance
Centre 16 Harcourt Road, Admiralty,
Hong Kong, China (Hong Kong)
Tel.: (852) 37661066
Web Site:
http://www.cwpgroup.com.hk
0182—(HKG)
Rev.: $376,183,267
Assets: $3,815,021,246
Liabilities: $2,678,498,410
Net Worth: $1,136,522,837
Earnings: $129,977,968
Emp.: 2,574
Fiscal Year-end: 12/31/22
Investment Holding Company
N.A.I.C.S.: 523940
Jianhong Liu *(Vice Chm)*

CONCORD PROJECTS LTD.

200 - 1277 Henderson Highway, Win-
nipeg, R2G 1M3, MB, Canada
Tel.: (204) 339-1651
Web Site:
https://www.concordprojects.com
Year Founded: 1978
Sales Range: $10-24.9 Million
General Contractor & Construction
Management
N.A.I.C.S.: 541330
Bryan Rychliski *(Sr VP)*

CONCORD SECURITY CORP.

925-4710 Kingsway Metrotower I,
Burnaby, V5H 4M2, BC, Canada
Tel.: (604) 689-4005
Web Site:
http://www.concordsecurity.com
Year Founded: 1983
Sales Range: $10-24.9 Million
Security Services
N.A.I.C.S.: 561612
John Henry *(Pres & CEO)*

CONCORDIA FINANCIAL GROUP, LTD.

7-1 Nihonbashi 2-chome 34th floor,
Chuo-ku Tokyo Nihombashi Tower,
Tokyo, 103-6034, Japan
Tel.: (81) 352008201   JP
Web Site: https://www.concordia-fg.jp
Year Founded: 2016
7186—(TKS)
Rev.: $2,368,382,830

Assets: $161,163,116,320
Liabilities: $152,670,806,450
Net Worth: $8,492,309,870
Earnings: $79,320
Emp.: 5,434
Fiscal Year-end: 03/31/24
Bank Holding Company
N.A.I.C.S.: 551111
Yasuyoshi Oya *(Pres)*

Subsidiaries:

The Bank of Yokohama, Ltd.   (1)
1-1 Minatomirai 3-chome, Nishi-ku, Yoko-
hama, 220-8611, Kanagawa, Japan
Tel.: (81) 452251111
Web Site: http://www.boy.co.jp
Sales Range: $1-4.9 Billion
Emp.: 4,622
Commercial & Investment Banking
N.A.I.C.S.: 522110
Yasuyoshi Oya *(Pres)*

Subsidiary (Non-US):

Hamagin Finance Co., Ltd.   (2)
Leasing & Factoring Services
N.A.I.C.S.: 525990

Subsidiary (Domestic):

Hamagin Research Institute Ltd   (2)
3-1-1 Minatomirai 4th Floor, Bank of Yoko-
hama head office building Nishi-ku, Yoko-
hama, 220-8616, Kanagawa, Japan
Tel.: (81) 452252371
Web Site: http://www.yokohama-ri.co.jp
Sales Range: $25-49.9 Million
Emp.: 88
Business Management Consulting Services
N.A.I.C.S.: 541611
Yoshio Ota *(Mng Dir)*

Hamagin Tokai Tokyo Securities Co.,
Ltd.   (2)
3-1-1 Minato Mirai, Nishi-ku, Yokohama,
220-0012, Kanagawa, Japan
Tel.: (81) 452251133
Web Site: https://www.hamagintt.co.jp
Sales Range: $100-124.9 Million
Emp.: 284
Securities Brokerage Services
N.A.I.C.S.: 523150

Yokohama Capital Co., Ltd.   (2)
Blue Avenue 12F 4-4-2 Minatomirai, Nishi
ku, Yokohama, 220-0012, Kanagawa, Ja-
pan
Tel.: (81) 452252331
Investments & Financing Services
N.A.I.C.S.: 523940

The Higashi-Nippon Bank, Ltd.   (1)
11-2 Nihonbashi 3-Chome, Chuo-ku, Tokyo,
103-8238, Japan
Tel.: (81) 332736221
Web Site: http://www.higashi-
nipponbank.co.jp
Emp.: 1,403
Commericial Banking
N.A.I.C.S.: 522110
Tomoo Ookanda *(Pres)*

CONCRAFT HOLDING CO., LTD.

2F No 35 chengtian Road Tucheng
Dist, Tucheng Dist, New Taipei City,
23674, Taiwan
Tel.: (886) 222689986   TW
Web Site:
https://www.concraft.com.tw
Year Founded: 1991
4943—(TAI)
Rev.: $55,064,389
Assets: $90,802,083
Liabilities: $85,605,903
Net Worth: $5,196,180
Earnings: ($8,095,915)
Emp.: 3,000
Fiscal Year-end: 12/31/23
Electronic Connector Mfr & Distr
N.A.I.C.S.: 334417

Subsidiaries:

Concraft Precision Electronic (Baoying) Co., Ltd.   (1)

No 108 Suzhong-North Rd, Baoying
County, Yangzhou, 225800, Jiangsu, China
Tel.: (86) 51488278878
Connector Mfr
N.A.I.C.S.: 334417

Concraft Precision Industrial Co.,
Ltd.   (1)
7F No 32 Zhongcheng Rd Tucheng Dist,
New Taipei City, 236, Taiwan
Tel.: (886) 222689986
Connector Mfr
N.A.I.C.S.: 334417

Kunshan Dragonstate Electronic
Technology Co., Ltd.   (1)
No 688 Huangpujiangbei Rd, Zhoushi Town,
Kunshan, 215313, Jiangsu, China
Tel.: (86) 15850308879
Emp.: 1,000
Connector Mfr
N.A.I.C.S.: 334417

CONCRETE AGGREGATES CORPORATION

7th Floor West Wing Estancia Offices
Capitol Commons Meralco Avenue,
Pasig, Philippines
Tel.: (63) 26311231
Web Site: https://www.cac.com.ph
CA—(PHI)
Rev.: $802,601
Assets: $7,003,961
Liabilities: $786,509
Net Worth: $6,217,452
Earnings: $437,818
Emp.: 2
Fiscal Year-end: 12/31/21
Concrete Mfr
N.A.I.C.S.: 238110
Ronilo B. Quiat *(Head-Special Proj-
ects)*

CONCRETE ENGINEERING PRODUCTS BERHAD

22nd Floor Menara Promet KHJalan
Sultan Ismail, 50250, Kuala Lumpur,
Malaysia
Tel.: (60) 321441066
Web Site: https://www.cepco.com.my
CEPCO—(KLS)
Rev.: $20,909,167
Assets: $34,519,575
Liabilities: $19,291,753
Net Worth: $15,227,822
Earnings: ($4,168,180)
Fiscal Year-end: 08/31/21
Concrete Piles & Poles Mfr & Distr
N.A.I.C.S.: 238120
Norakhmar Baharom *(Sec)*

Subsidiaries:

Concrete Engineering Products Ber-
had - Batang Kali Factory   (1)
Lot A3 Kawasan Perindustrian MIEL,
44300, Batang Kali, Selangor Darul Ehsan,
Malaysia
Tel.: (60) 360914201
Concrete Products Mfr
N.A.I.C.S.: 327390

Concrete Engineering Products Ber-
had - Nilai Factory   (1)
Lot 7106 Kaw Perindustrian Nilai, 71800,
Nilai, Negeri Sembilan, Malaysia
Tel.: (60) 67992841
Concrete Products Mfr
N.A.I.C.S.: 327390

Concrete Engineering Products Ber-
had - Pasir Gudang Factory   (1)
PLO 337 Jalan Suasa Pasir Gudang Indus-
trial Estate, 81700, Pasir Gudang, Johor,
Malaysia
Tel.: (60) 72511048
Web Site: http://www.cepco.com.my
Emp.: 200
Concrete Products Mfr
N.A.I.C.S.: 327390

Concrete Engineering Products Berhad - Rawang Factory   (1)
PT 643 Batu 20 Jalan Ipoh, 48000, Raw-

CONCRETE ENGINEERING PRODUCTS BERHAD

Concrete Engineering Products Berhad—(Continued)

ang, Selangor, Malaysia
Tel.: (60) 360914201
Concrete Products Mfr
N.A.I.C.S.: 327390

Concrete Engineering Products Berhad - Sungai Petani Factory **(1)**
Lot 63 Bakar Arang Industrial Estate, 08000, Sungai Petani, Kedah, Malaysia
Tel.: (60) 44210891
Concrete Products Mfr
N.A.I.C.S.: 327390

CONCRETE INFRA & MEDIA LIMITED
10 Phears Lane 2nd Floor P.S. Bowbazar, Kolkata, 700012, West Bengal, India
Tel.: (91) 3340084389
Web Site:
http://www.concretecredit.in
539266—(BOM)
Rev.: $18
Assets: $1,083,314
Liabilities: $10,592
Net Worth: $1,072,722
Earnings: ($10,286)
Emp.: 6
Fiscal Year-end: 03/31/20
Financial Investment Services
N.A.I.C.S.: 523999
Rajeev Kumar Verma *(Exec Dir)*

CONCRETE VALLEY GROUP BV
Lelyweg 23, 4612 PS, Bergen-op-Zoom, Noord-Brabant, Netherlands
Tel.: (31) 164 274 250
Web Site:
http://www.concretevalley.nl
Year Founded: 2012
Glass, Ceramics & Concrete Products Mfr
N.A.I.C.S.: 327390

Subsidiaries:

Waco BV **(1)**
Lelyweg 23, 4612 PS, Bergen-op-Zoom, Netherlands
Tel.: (31) 164274200
Web Site: http://www.waco.nl
Precast Concrete Products Developer & Mfr
N.A.I.C.S.: 327390
Ron van Boven *(Sls Mgr)*

CONCURRENT TECHNOLOGIES PLC
4 Gilberd Court Newcomen Way, Colchester, CO4 9WN, Essex, United Kingdom
Tel.: (44) 120675262 **UK**
Web Site: https://www.gocct.com
Year Founded: 1985
CNC—(LSE)
Rev.: $40,300,848
Assets: $60,885,550
Liabilities: $16,281,567
Net Worth: $44,603,982
Earnings: $4,930,791
Emp.: 142
Fiscal Year-end: 12/31/23
Embedded Computer Product Mfr & Distr
N.A.I.C.S.: 334418
David Evans-Hughes *(Dir-Engrg)*

Subsidiaries:

Concurrent Technologies Inc. **(1)**
400 W Cummings Park Ste 1300, Woburn, MA 01801
Tel.: (781) 933-5900
Peripheral Equipment Mfr & Distr
N.A.I.C.S.: 334118

CONDADO PROPERTIES, INC.
Edif Pacific Village Ave Chiriqui Punta

Punta Pacifica, PO Box 0831-01715, Panama, Panama
Tel.: (507) 209 3600
Year Founded: 2012
CONP—(PAN)
Sales Range: Less than $1 Million
Real Estate Development Services
N.A.I.C.S.: 531390

CONDECO LTD.
8th Floor Exchange Tower 2 Harbour Exchange Square, London, E14 9GE, United Kingdom
Tel.: (44) 2070012083
Web Site:
http://www.condecosoftware.com
Business Technology Services
N.A.I.C.S.: 561499
Lynda Lowe *(CMO)*

Subsidiaries:

Interactive Ideas, LLC **(1)**
325 Duffy Ave Ste N, Hicksville, NY 11801
Tel.: (516) 935-0877
Web Site: http://www.myvrm.com
Scheduling Software Providers
N.A.I.C.S.: 513210
Larry Roher *(CEO)*

CONDEPOLS, S.A.
Avenida Iberoamerica 35, Alcala la Real, 23680, Jaen, Spain
Tel.: (34) 953102100 **ES**
Web Site: http://www.condepols.es
Year Founded: 1965
Petroleum & Petrochemical Products Mfr
N.A.I.C.S.: 324199
Jose Manuel Muriel *(Pres)*

CONDMAG S.A.
52 Avram Iancu St, 500075, Brasov, Romania
Tel.: (40) 268414954 **RO**
Web Site: http://www.condmag.ro
Sales Range: $25-49.9 Million
Emp.: 783
Pipeline Construction Services
N.A.I.C.S.: 237120
Alexandru Liviu Tatar *(Member-Mgmt Bd)*

CONDOR GOLD PLC
7/8 Innovation Place Douglas Drive, Godalming, GU7 1JX, Surrey, United Kingdom
Tel.: (44) 2074932784
Web Site:
https://www.condorgold.com
COG—(TSX)
Assets: $55,768,350
Liabilities: $493,845
Net Worth: $55,274,505
Earnings: ($3,047,385)
Fiscal Year-end: 12/31/22
Nonferrous Metal (except Aluminum) Smelting & Refining
N.A.I.C.S.: 331410
Mark L. Child *(Chm & CEO)*

Subsidiaries:

Condor S.A. **(1)**
Del Gimnasio Hercules 1 Cuadra al Sur 2 Cuadras arriba, Apartamento Isolsa No 2, Managua, 14002, Nicaragua
Tel.: (505) 22701930
Mineral & Ore Product Distr
N.A.I.C.S.: 423520

CONDOR PETROLEUM INC.
Tel.: (403) 201-9694 **AB**
CPI—(TSX)
Rev.: $3,955,526
Assets: $34,806,941
Liabilities: $17,395,436
Net Worth: $17,411,506
Earnings: ($7,728,924)

Emp.: 78
Fiscal Year-end: 12/31/19
Oil & Gas Exploration Services
N.A.I.C.S.: 211120
Dennis Balderston *(Chm)*

Subsidiaries:

Falcon Oil & Gas Ltd. **(1)**
90 Shevchenko Str BC Karatal 9th Floor Office 91, Almaty, 050022, Kazakhstan
Tel.: (7) 7273137642
Oil & Gas Exploration Services
N.A.I.C.S.: 211120

Marsa Turkey B.V. **(1)**
Kizilirmak Mah 1450 Sokak No 1, Ankara Ticaret Merkezi B-Blok Kat 11 Daire 57 Cankaya, 06530, Ankara, Türkiye
Tel.: (90) 3124661322
Web Site: http://www.marsaturkeybvtab.com
Oil & Gas Exploration Services
N.A.I.C.S.: 211120

CONDOR RESOURCES INC.
Suite 615 800 W Pender Street, Vancouver, V6C 2V6, BC, Canada
Tel.: (604) 642-5707
Web Site:
https://www.condorresources.com
Year Founded: 2004
CNRIF—(OTCIQ)
Rev.: $33,634
Assets: $7,929,362
Liabilities: $99,280
Net Worth: $7,830,082
Earnings: $923,877
Fiscal Year-end: 02/29/24
Mineral Exploration Services
N.A.I.C.S.: 213114
Graham H. Scott *(Sec)*

Subsidiaries:

Condor Exploration Peru S.A.C. **(1)**
Av Javier Prado Este No 1184 Int 302 Urb Corpac, San Isidro, Lima, Peru
Tel.: (51) 1 2266267
Web Site: http://www.condorresources.com
Emp.: 7
Mineral Mining Services
N.A.I.C.S.: 212390
Ever Marquerz *(VP)*

CONDOR TCM SA
Bd Carol I Nr 15-17, Sinaia, Prahova, Romania
Tel.: (40) 244 313 998
Sales Range: Less than $1 Million
Emp.: 7
Building Construction Services
N.A.I.C.S.: 236116

CONDOR TECHNOLOGIES NV
Zuiderlaan 1-3 bus 8, 9000, Gent, Belgium
Tel.: (32) 92415880
Web Site:
https://www.condorflash.com
Year Founded: 2010
MLMFI—(EUR)
Sales Range: Less than $1 Million
Dental Equipment Merchant Whslr
N.A.I.C.S.: 423450
Guy De Vreese *(Mng Dir)*

CONDORUM SK, S.R.O.
Stromova 16, Bratislava, 83302, Slovakia
Tel.: (421) 2 59 307 310
Sales Range: $150-199.9 Million
Supermarket Operator
N.A.I.C.S.: 445110
Michal Holik *(Chm)*

CONDUCTORES Y CABLES DEL PERU S.A.C.
Av Los Frutales 334, Ate-Vitarte, Lima, 15023, Peru
Tel.: (51) 1713 6000
Web Site: http://www.ceper.com.pe

Sales Range: $25-49.9 Million
Emp.: 150
Cable Mfr
N.A.I.C.S.: 335929
Fernando Barron *(CEO)*

CONDUIT CAPITAL LIMITED
67 Carlisle Street Paarden Eiland, Bryanston, Cape Town, 7405, South Africa
Tel.: (27) 105000827
Web Site:
https://www.conduitcapital.co.za
Year Founded: 1998
CND—(JSE)
Rev.: $132,997,055
Assets: $96,125,426
Liabilities: $94,948,254
Net Worth: $1,177,172
Earnings: ($9,945,341)
Emp.: 8
Fiscal Year-end: 06/30/21
Investment Holding Company
N.A.I.C.S.: 523150
Lourens Erasmus Louw *(CFO, Fin Dir & Sec)*

Subsidiaries:

Constantia Insurance Company Limited **(1)**
Nicol Main Office Park 2 Bruton Road, Bryanston, Johannesburg, 2191, South Africa
Tel.: (27) 11 686 4200
Web Site: https://www.constantiagroup.co.za
Financial Insurance Services
N.A.I.C.S.: 524298
Peter Goeffrey Todd *(CEO)*

Constantia Life Limited **(1)**
10 Dorp Street, Cape Town, 8000, Western Cape, South Africa
Tel.: (27) 214248040
Web Site: http://www.constantiagroup.co.za
Sales Range: $50-74.9 Million
Fire Insurance Services
N.A.I.C.S.: 524210
David Harpur *(Chm)*

Goodall and Bourne Properties (Proprietary) Limited **(1)**
10 Dorp St, Cape Town, 8000, South Africa
Tel.: (27) 214248040
Property Management Services
N.A.I.C.S.: 531312

On Line Lottery Services (Proprietary) Limited **(1)**
PO Box 97, Melrose Arch, Johannesburg, 2076, Gauteng, South Africa
Tel.: (27) 116864200
Web Site: http://www.loottofun.co.za
Online Lottery Services
N.A.I.C.S.: 713290

CONDUIT HOLDINGS LIMITED
Ideation House 94 Pitts Bay Road, Pembroke, HM08, Bermuda
Tel.: (441) 4412761000 **BM**
Web Site:
https://www.conduitreinsurance.com
Year Founded: 2020
CRE—(LSE)
Rev.: $429,500,000
Assets: $1,568,400,000
Liabilities: $754,000,000
Net Worth: $814,400,000
Earnings: ($89,700,000)
Emp.: 47
Fiscal Year-end: 12/31/22
Holding Company
N.A.I.C.S.: 551112
Elaine Whelan *(CFO)*

CONDUITY CAPITAL PLC
Finsgate 5-7 Cranwood Street, London, EC1V 9EE, United Kingdom
Tel.: (44) 207 653 9850 **UK**
Web Site: http://www.conduitycapital.co.uk
Year Founded: 2005
CCAP—(LSE)

Sales Range: Less than $1 Million
Crystal & Precious Stone Distr
N.A.I.C.S.: 423940
Song Hua Phang *(CEO)*

CONDURIL, ENGENHARIA S.A.
Av Eng Duarte Pacheco 1835 Ermes-inde, 4445-416, Porto, 4445-416, Portugal
Tel.: (351) 229773920
Web Site: https://www.conduril.pt
Year Founded: 1959
CDU—(EUR)
Rev.: $202,483,004
Assets: $399,460,625
Liabilities: $202,110,098
Net Worth: $197,350,527
Earnings: $2,497,266
Emp.: 2,522
Fiscal Year-end: 12/31/23
Civil Engineering Services
N.A.I.C.S.: 541330
Antonio Luis Amorim Martins *(Chm)*

Subsidiaries:

ENOP - Engenharia e Obras Publi-cas, Lda. **(1)**
Estrada Nacional N 4 Tchumene 2 - Parcela N 3380/12, Matola, Mozambique
Tel.: (258) 21483120
Construction Services
N.A.I.C.S.: 237310

Metis Engenharia, Lda. **(1)**
Parque Industrial Viana Bairro Kapalanga, Viana, Angola
Tel.: (244) 939212517
Construction Services
N.A.I.C.S.: 237310

CONE AUTOMOBILES
8 Bd Du President Wilson, Dole, 39100, Dijon, France
Tel.: (33) 384826701
Rev.: $23,600,000
Emp.: 54
New & Used Car Dealers
N.A.I.C.S.: 441110
Vincent Deffeuille *(Pres)*

CONECT BUSINESS PARK SA
Bdul Dimitrie Pompei 10A, Bucharest, Romania
Tel.: (40) 213172828
Web Site:
https://www.conectbusinesspark.ro
COEC—(BUC)
Rev.: $4,129,768
Assets: $31,521,981
Liabilities: $13,819,304
Net Worth: $17,702,677
Earnings: $94,046
Emp.: 18
Fiscal Year-end: 12/31/23
Power Distribution Apparatus Mfr
N.A.I.C.S.: 335999

CONESTOGA COLD STORAGE
299 Trillium Drive, Kitchener, N2E 1W9, ON, Canada
Tel.: (519) 748-5415
Web Site:
http://www.coldstorage.com
Year Founded: 1974
Sales Range: $10-24.9 Million
Cold Storage Warehouses
N.A.I.C.S.: 493120
Larry Laurin *(Founder)*

CONEX PRAHOVA SA
Soseaua Giurgiului nr 45 parter cam 21 sector 4, Bucharest, Romania
Tel.: (40) 744533315
COLK—(BUC)
Rev.: $3,851
Assets: $1,149,829
Liabilities: $452,709
Net Worth: $697,121

Earnings: ($51,538)
Emp.: 3
Fiscal Year-end: 12/31/22
Construction Engineering Services
N.A.I.C.S.: 541330

CONFECCOES PORTO GRANDE, LDA
Cha de Cricket, CP 587, Mindelo, Sao Vicente, Cape Verde
Tel.: (238) 303020
Web Site: http://www.portogrande.net
Year Founded: 1994
Sales Range: $25-49.9 Million
Emp.: 140
Shirt Mfr
N.A.I.C.S.: 315250

CONFECTII VASLUI S.A.
Strada Maresal Constantin Prezan Nr 11, 730091, Vaslui, Romania
Tel.: (40) 235311840
Web Site:
http://www.confectiivaslui.com
Year Founded: 1965
Outerwear Products Mfr
N.A.I.C.S.: 315120
Ioan Ciprian Jude *(Pres)*

CONFEDERATION NATIONALE DU CREDIT MUTUEL
88-90 rue Cardinet, 75847, Paris, Cedex 17, France
Tel.: (33) 1 53 01 87 94
Web Site:
http://www.creditmutuel.com
Year Founded: 1958
Rev.: $19,089,133,560
Liabilities: $975,639,949,760
Net Worth: $66,855,642,000
Earnings: $4,227,471,500
Emp.: 82,794
Fiscal Year-end: 12/31/19
Banking Cooperative Organization
N.A.I.C.S.: 813910
Nicolas Thery *(Chm)*

Subsidiaries:

Banque Regionale De L'Ain **(1)**
14 Pl Des Terreaux, Belley, 01300, France **(100%)**
Tel.: (33) 479812327
Sales Range: $50-74.9 Million
Emp.: 10
Banking & Finance
N.A.I.C.S.: 523940

Banque Scalbert Dupont **(1)**
33 Ave Le Corbusier, BP 322, F 59020, Lille, Cedex, France **(100%)**
Tel.: (33) 320126464
Web Site: http://www.cic.fr
Sales Range: $700-749.9 Million
Emp.: 2,200
Banking & Finance
N.A.I.C.S.: 523940
Stelli Premaor *(Pres)*

Banque Transatlantique **(1)**
26 avenue Franklin D Roosevelt, 75008, Paris, France **(73.38%)**
Tel.: (33) 156887777
Web Site:
http://www.banquetransatlantique.com
Sales Range: $1-4.9 Billion
Commericial Banking
N.A.I.C.S.: 522110
Bruno Julien-Laferriere *(Chm)*

Bonnasse Lyonnaise de Banque **(1)**
448 Ave Du Prado, 13008, Marseilles, France **(100%)**
Tel.: (33) 491236767
Web Site: http://www.blb.cic.fr
Sales Range: $50-74.9 Million
Emp.: 100
Banking & Finance
N.A.I.C.S.: 523940

CIC Iberbanco **(1)**
6 avenue de Provence, 75009, Paris, Cedex, France

Tel.: (33) 145969696
Web Site: http://www.cic-iberbanco.com
Commercial Banking & Financial Services
N.A.I.C.S.: 522110

Credit Industriel d'Alsace et de Lorraine **(1)**
31 Rue Jean Wenger Valentin, BP 477, 67958, Strasbourg, Cedex 9, France **(100%)**
Tel.: (33) 388377123
Web Site: http://www.banquecial.fr
Sales Range: $350-399.9 Million
Emp.: 600
Banking & Finance
N.A.I.C.S.: 523940

Credit Industriel de Normandie **(1)**
2 bis rue Duguay Trouin, 76041, Rouen, Cedex, France **(100%)**
Tel.: (33) 2 35 08 6400
Web Site: http://www.cic.fr
Sales Range: $75-99.9 Million
Emp.: 78
Banking & Finance
N.A.I.C.S.: 523940

Credit Industriel et Commercial SA **(1)**
6 avenue de Provence, 75009, Paris, France
Tel.: (33) 145969696
Web Site: http://www.cic.fr
Rev.: $2,060,319,200
Assets: $144,998,557,280
Liabilities: $134,242,972,340
Net Worth: $10,755,584,940
Earnings: $1,021,774,580
Emp.: 3,433
Fiscal Year-end: 12/31/2017
Banking, Asset Management, Leasing, Securities & Insurance Services
N.A.I.C.S.: 522110
Nicolas Thery *(Chm)*

Credit Mutuel Arkea S.A. **(1)**
1 rue Louis Lichou, 29480, Paris, France
Tel.: (33) 2 98 00 22 22
Web Site: http://www.arkea.com
Emp.: 8,700
Bank Holding Company
N.A.I.C.S.: 551111
Ronan Le Moal *(CEO)*

Credit Mutuel Nord Europe Belgium NV **(1)**
Avenue des Arts 6-9, 1210, Brussels, Belgium
Tel.: (32) 2 289 82 00
Web Site: http://www.creditmutuel.fr
Banking Services
N.A.I.C.S.: 522110

Subsidiary (Domestic):

Beobank NV/SA **(2)**
General Jacqueslaan 263G, 1050, Brussels, Belgium **(100%)**
Tel.: (32) 26265050
Web Site: http://www.beobank.be
Sales Range: $50-74.9 Million
Commercial Banking Services
N.A.I.C.S.: 522110

Keytrade Bank S.A. **(2)**
Boulevard du Souverain 100, 1170, Brussels, Belgium
Tel.: (32) 2 679 90 00
Web Site: http://www.keytradebank.be
Banking Services
N.A.I.C.S.: 522110
Thierry Ternier *(CEO)*

Socapi **(1)**
42 Rue De Mathurins, 75008, Paris, France **(100%)**
Tel.: (33) 144715200
Web Site: http://www.socapi.com
Sales Range: $50-74.9 Million
Emp.: 100
Insurance
N.A.I.C.S.: 524113

TARGOBANK AG & Co. KGaA **(1)**
Kasernenstrasse 10, 40213, Dusseldorf, Germany
Tel.: (49) 21189840
Web Site: http://www.targobank.de
Commercial Banking & Financial Services
N.A.I.C.S.: 522110

Berthold Rusing *(Member-Mgmt Bd-Corp Customers)*

Subsidiary (Domestic):

TARGO Commercial Finance AG **(2)**
Heinrich-von-Brentano-Strasse 2, 55130, Mainz, Germany
Tel.: (49) 6131 4647 0
Web Site: http://www.targocf.de
Emp.: 500
Sales Financing & Lending Services
N.A.I.C.S.: 522220
Joachim Secker *(Chm-Mgmt Bd & CEO)*

Subsidiary (Domestic):

TARGO Leasing GmbH **(3)**
Fritz-Vomfelde-Sgtrasse 2-4, 40547, Dusseldorf, Germany
Tel.: (49) 211 5350 0
Commercial Sales Financing & Leasing Services
N.A.I.C.S.: 522220
Markus Haring *(Mng Dir)*

CONFERIZE A/S
Soelvgade 38E, Copenhagen, 1307, Denmark
Tel.: (45) 31211726
CONFRZ—(NASDAQ)
Emp.: 3
Software Development Services
N.A.I.C.S.: 541511
Soren Dalsgaard Hansen *(CFO)*

CONFIDENCE CEMENT PLC
Unique Trade Center Level-7 8 Panthopath karwan Bazar, Dhaka, 1215, Bangladesh
Tel.: (880) 2333311471
Web Site:
https://confidencecement.com.bd
Year Founded: 1994
CONFIDCEM—(CHT)
Rev.: $53,584,041
Assets: $134,030,681
Liabilities: $66,642,030
Net Worth: $67,388,651
Earnings: $14,392,573
Emp.: 780
Fiscal Year-end: 06/30/21
Cement Mfr
N.A.I.C.S.: 327310
Rezaul Karim *(Chm)*

CONFIDENCE FINANCE AND TRADING LIMITED
9 Botawala Building 3rd Floor 11/13 Horniman Circle, Fort, Mumbai, 400 001, India
Tel.: (91) 2222662150
Web Site: https://www.ctcl.co.in
504340—(BOM)
Rev.: $92,387
Assets: $3,298,535
Liabilities: $344,013
Net Worth: $2,954,523
Earnings: ($395)
Emp.: 8
Fiscal Year-end: 03/31/21
Commodity Trading Services
N.A.I.C.S.: 523160
Amruth Joachim Coutinho *(Mng Dir)*

CONFIDENCE FUTURISTIC ENERGETECH LIMITED
D-9 Jangpura Extension, New Delhi, 110014, Delhi, India
Tel.: (91) 1165392244
Web Site:
https://www.globeindustrials.com
Year Founded: 1985
539991—(BOM)
Rev.: $192,451
Assets: $4,217,236
Liabilities: $3,033,999
Net Worth: $1,183,237
Earnings: $1,242
Emp.: 3

Confidence Futuristic Energetech
Limited—(Continued)

Fiscal Year-end: 03/31/21
Finance Management Services
N.A.I.C.S.: 541219

CONFIDENCE INTELLIGENCE HOLDINGS LIMITED

Building 7 New Development Zone
Fuyong Street, Baishixia East Baoan,
Shenzhen, China
Tel.: (86) 75527308407   Ky
Web Site: http://www.szxinken.com
Year Founded: 2000
1967—(HKG)
Rev.: $36,960,019
Assets: $57,763,368
Liabilities: $14,762,920
Net Worth: $43,000,448
Earnings: ($993,611)
Emp.: 754
Fiscal Year-end: 12/31/22
Holding Company
N.A.I.C.S.: 551112
Hao Li (Chm & CEO)

CONFIDENCE PETROLEUM INDIA LTD

34 Confidence Tower Central Bazaar
Road Ramdaspeth, Near Mahalaxmi
Hotel Andheri East, Nagpur, 440010,
Maharshtra, India
Tel.: (91) 8956276739
Web Site:
   https://www.confidencegroup.co
CONFIPET—(NSE)
Rev.: $118,199,145
Assets: $107,684,522
Liabilities: $32,027,910
Net Worth: $75,656,613
Earnings: $6,753,324
Fiscal Year-end: 03/31/21
Oil Marketer & Distr
N.A.I.C.S.: 324191
Nitin Punamchand Khara (Chm, CEO & Mng Dir)

CONFIGURA SVERIGE AB

Storgatan 13, Box 13, SE-58102,
Linkoping, Sweden
Tel.: (46) 13377800
Web Site: http://www.configura.com
Rev.: $27,841,809
Assets: $36,459,436
Liabilities: $9,850,269
Net Worth: $26,609,167
Earnings: ($83,747)
Emp.: 236
Fiscal Year-end: 12/31/20
Computer Software Developer
N.A.I.C.S.: 541512
Tommy Johansson (Chm)

Subsidiaries:

Projectmatrix Corp.   (1)
11240 Cornell Park Dr Ste 102, Cincinnati,
OH 45242
Tel.: (513) 554-1665
Web Site: http://projectmatrix.com
Sales Range: $1-9.9 Million
Emp.: 17
Management Consulting Services
N.A.I.C.S.: 541611
Mark Herrin (Pres)

CONFINVEST F.L. S.P.A.

Via Della Posta 8-Piazza Affari,
20123, Milan, Italy
Tel.: (39) 0286455047
Web Site: https://www.confinvest.it
CFV—(ITA)
Sales Range: Less than $1 Million
Financial Investment Services
N.A.I.C.S.: 523940
Giacomo Andreoli (CEO)

CONFIPETROL S.A.

Carrera 15 No 98-06 Oficina 401,
Bogota, Colombia
Tel.: (57) 5082008
Web Site: http://www.confipetrol.com
Sales Range: $75-99.9 Million
Emp.: 1,500
Oil & Gas Industry Maintenance Ser-
vices
N.A.I.C.S.: 213112
Oscar Jeovanny Fernandez (CEO)

CONFLOW LIMITED

President Park, President Way, Shef-
field, S47 UR, United Kingdom
Tel.: (44) 1142240000
Web Site: http://www.conflow.com
Year Founded: 2014
Mining Industry Machinery Mfr
N.A.I.C.S.: 333131

Subsidiaries:

Conflow Inc.   (1)
270 Meadowlands Blvd, Washington, PA
15301-8903   (100%)
Tel.: (724) 746-0200
Web Site: http://www.conflow.com
Mining Industry Machinery Mfr & Distr
N.A.I.C.S.: 423810

CONFORCE INTERNATIONAL, INC.

51A Caldari Road 2nd Floor, Con-
cord, L4K 4G3, ON, Canada
Tel.: (416) 234-0266   DE
CFRI—(OTCIQ)
Flooring for Container Shipping &
Highway Trailer Businesses
N.A.I.C.S.: 321918

Subsidiaries:

Conforce 1 Container Terminals
Inc.   (1)
584 Hazelhurst Dr, Mississauga, L5J 4T8,
ON, Canada
Tel.: (905) 855-2171
Web Site:
   http://www.conforce1.buildingmy.com
Emp.: 5
Containers Handling & Storage Services
N.A.I.C.S.: 488320
Marino Kulas (Pres)

CONG TY CO PHAN LOGIS-TICS VINALINK

226/2 Le Van Sy Ward 1, Ho Chi
Minh City, Vietnam
Tel.: (84) 2839919259
Web Site:
   https://www.vinalinklogistics.com
Year Founded: 1999
VNL—(HOSE)
Rev.: $30,041,145
Assets: $16,088,600
Liabilities: $4,977,207
Net Worth: $11,111,393
Earnings: $1,537,337
Emp.: 310
Fiscal Year-end: 12/31/23
Freight Transportation Services
N.A.I.C.S.: 483111
Thi Duy Thao Hoang (Deputy Dir-HR-Office Mgmt Div)

Subsidiaries:

Vinalink Logistics (Cambodia) Co.,
Ltd.   (1)
Regency Complex C Ground Floor Unit 10-
11C 168 Samdach Monireth Blvd, St 217
Sangkat Tomnubteuk, Phnom Penh, Cam-
bodia
Tel.: (855) 23967979
Logistic Services
N.A.I.C.S.: 541614

CONGA FOODS PTY. LTD.

70 Bell St, Preston, 3072, VIC, Australia
Tel.: (61) 394879500

Web Site:
   http://www.congafoods.com.au
Year Founded: 1949
Grocery Distr
N.A.I.C.S.: 445110
Miki Stefanovic (Gen Mgr-Supply Chain)

CONGATEC AG

Auwiesenstrasse 5, 94469, Deggen-
dorf, Germany
Tel.: (49) 991 2700 0
Web Site: http://www.congatec.com
Year Founded: 2004
Sales Range: $75-99.9 Million
Emp.: 260
Computer Parts Distr
N.A.I.C.S.: 423430
Jason L. Carlson (CEO)

Subsidiaries:

congatec Asia Ltd.   (1)
14F-2 No 270 Sec 4 Zhongxiao E Rd,
00106, Taipei, Taiwan
Tel.: (886) 227754645
Computer Peripheral Equipment Distr
N.A.I.C.S.: 423430
Mike Chao (Gen Mgr)

congatec Australia Pty Ltd.   (1)
Unit 2 62 59 Township Drive, Burleigh
Heads, 4219, QLD, Australia
Tel.: (61) 55200841
Computer Peripheral Equipment Distr
N.A.I.C.S.: 423430
Joakim Lund (Chief Comml Officer)

congatec China Technology Ltd.   (1)
Sunyoung Center 901 Building B No 28 Xu-
anhua Road, Changning, Shanghai,
200050, China
Tel.: (86) 2160255862
Computer Peripheral Equipment Distr
N.A.I.C.S.: 423430

congatec Japan K.K.   (1)
Shiodome building 301 Hamamatsucho
1-2-7, Minato-ku, Tokyo, 105-0013, Japan
Tel.: (81) 64359250
Computer Peripheral Equipment Distr
N.A.I.C.S.: 423430

congatec sro   (1)
Zahradnicka 6, 603 00, Brno, Czech Re-
public
Tel.: (420) 777310891
Computer Peripheral Equipment Distr
N.A.I.C.S.: 423430

congatec, Inc.   (1)
6262 Ferris Sq, San Diego, CA 92121
Tel.: (858) 457-2600
Computer Peripheral Equipment Distr
N.A.I.C.S.: 423430
Franz Fischer (Dir-Technical Solution Cen-
ter)

CONGEBEC CAPITAL LTEE.

810 Avenue Godin, Quebec, G1M
2X9, QC, Canada
Tel.: (418) 683-3491   Ca
Web Site: http://www.congebec.com
Year Founded: 1974
Sales Range: $100-124.9 Million
Emp.: 400
Cold Storage & Logistics Services
N.A.I.C.S.: 493120
Nicholas P. Pedneault (Pres)

Subsidiaries:

Westco MultiTemp Distribution Cen-
tres Inc.   (1)
1555 Chevrier Blvd, Winnipeg, R3T 1Y7,
MB, Canada
Tel.: (204) 475-5570
Multi-Temperature Warehousing & Logistics
Services
N.A.I.C.S.: 493110

CONICO LIMITED

Level 15 197 St Georges Terrace,
Perth, 6000, WA, Australia
Tel.: (61) 892825889

Web Site: https://www.conico.com.au
CNJ—(ASX)
Rev.: $23,196
Assets: $2,319,005
Liabilities: $170,098
Net Worth: $2,148,907
Earnings: ($23,422,115)
Emp.: 40
Fiscal Year-end: 06/30/24
Cobalt, Nickel & Manganese Oxide
Exploration
N.A.I.C.S.: 212290
Gregory Howard Solomon (Chm)

CONIFEX TIMBER INC.

980-700 West Georgia Street, PO
Box 10070, Vancouver, V7Y 1B6,
BC, Canada
Tel.: (604) 216-2949
Web Site: https://www.conifex.com
Year Founded: 2007
CFF—(TSX)
Rev.: $120,451,760
Assets: $353,147,087
Liabilities: $257,788,159
Net Worth: $95,358,929
Earnings: ($153,223,470)
Emp.: 620
Fiscal Year-end: 12/31/19
Structural Grade SPF Dimension
Lumber Mfr
N.A.I.C.S.: 321999
Kenneth A. Shields (Chm, Pres & CEO)

Subsidiaries:

Suwannee Lumber Company
LLC   (1)
40 SW 10th St, Cross City, FL 32628
Tel.: (352) 498-3363
Web Site: http://www.suwanneelumber.com
Sales Range: $10-24.9 Million
Lumber, Plywood, Millwork & Wood Panel
Merchant Whslr
N.A.I.C.S.: 423310
Frank Faircloth (Chm)

CONLOC S.A.

Str Tudor Vladimirescu Nr 23, Judet
Buzau, Ramnicu Sarat, Romania
Tel.: (40) 238 561 763   RO
Web Site: http://www.conloc-sa.ro
Sales Range: $1-9.9 Million
Emp.: 37
Residential & Non-Residential Build-
ing Construction Services
N.A.I.C.S.: 236116

CONNACHER OIL & GAS LIM-ITED

Suite 1040 640 5th Avenue SW, Cal-
gary, T2P 3G4, AB, Canada
Tel.: (403) 538-6201   Ca
Web Site:
   http://www.connacheroil.com
Year Founded: 1997
Sales Range: $150-199.9 Million
Emp.: 168
Oil & Gas Services
N.A.I.C.S.: 211120
Merle D. Johnson (CEO)

Subsidiaries:

Great Divide Pipeline Limited   (1)
900 332-6 Ave SW, Calgary, T2P 0B2, AB,
Canada
Tel.: (403) 538-6201
Oil & Gas Exploration Services
N.A.I.C.S.: 211120

CONNECT BIOPHARMA HOLD-INGS LIMITED

East R&D Building 3rd floor 6 Beijing
West Road, East R&D Building, Ta-
icang, 215400, Jiangsu, China
Tel.: (86) 51253577866   Ky

Web Site:
https://www.connectbiopharm.com
Year Founded: 2012
CNTB—(NASDAQ)
Rev.: $1,580,000
Assets: $125,892,000
Liabilities: $24,849,000
Net Worth: $101,043,000
Earnings: ($59,503,000)
Emp.: 81
Fiscal Year-end: 12/31/23
Biotechnology Research & Development Services
N.A.I.C.S.: 541714
Zheng Wei (Co-Founder & CEO)

CONNECT LOGISTICS SERVICES INC
50 Corriveau Avenue, Saint Albert, T8N 3T5, AB, Canada
Tel.: (780) 458-4492
Web Site: http://www.connect-logistics.com
Rev.: $22,070,400
Emp.: 230
Liquor Whslr
N.A.I.C.S.: 424820
Bruce Anderson (Gen Mgr-Ops)

CONNECTED MINERALS LIMITED
Level 24 44 St Georges Terrace, Perth, 6000, WA, Australia
Tel.: (61) 862115099   AU
Web Site:
https://connectedminerals.com.au
CML—(ASX)
Rev.: $916,867
Assets: $1,565,704
Liabilities: $2,599,980
Net Worth: ($1,034,276)
Earnings: ($4,361,722)
Fiscal Year-end: 06/30/21
Investment Services
N.A.I.C.S.: 523999
Simon Whybrow (Sec)

CONNECTENS B.V.
Kabelstraat 13, 7483 PR, Haaksbergen, Netherlands
Tel.: (31) 535730303
Web Site: https://connectens.nl
Information Technology Services
N.A.I.C.S.: 541512

CONNEX TELECOMMUNICATIONS INC.
44 East Beaver Creek Suite 16, Richmond Hill, L4B 1G8, ON, Canada
Tel.: (905) 944-6500
Web Site:
http://www.connexservice.ca
Sales Range: $100-124.9 Million
Emp.: 456
Wireless Communication Network System Services
N.A.I.C.S.: 334220

CONNEXION MOBILITY LTD
Level 3 162 Collins Street, Melbourne, 3000, VIC, Australia
Tel.: (61) 395292655   AU
Web Site:
https://connexionmobility.com
CXZ—(ASX)
Rev.: $6,571,408
Assets: $5,374,934
Liabilities: $1,181,325
Net Worth: $4,193,609
Earnings: $1,256,762
Fiscal Year-end: 06/30/24
Software Applications
N.A.I.C.S.: 513210
Peter Torre (Sec)

CONNOR, CLARK & LUNN FI-

NANCIAL GROUP
1400 130 Ling Street West, PO Box 240, Toronto, M5X 1C8, ON, Canada
Tel.: (416) 862-2020
Web Site: http://www.cclgroup.com
Privater Equity Firm
Michael Guichon (Mng Dir)

Subsidiaries:

Banyan Capital Partners   (1)
1400-130 King Steet West, PO Box 240, Toronto, M5X 1C8, ON, Canada
Tel.: (416) 216-7076
Web Site:
https://banyancapitalpartners.ccl.com
Privater Equity Firm
N.A.I.C.S.: 523999
Jeff Wigle (Mng Dir)

Subsidiary (Domestic):

Oakcreek Golf & Turf LP   (2)
3816 64th Avenue, Calgary, T2C 2B4, AB, Canada
Tel.: (403) 279-2907
Golf Transportation Services
N.A.I.C.S.: 488999
Barrie Carpenter (Pres)

Subsidiary (US):

Simpson Norton Corporation   (3)
4144 S Bullard Ave, Goodyear, AZ 85338
Tel.: (623) 932-5116
Web Site: http://www.simpsonnorton.com
Lawn & Garden Machinery & Equipment
N.A.I.C.S.: 423820
Joe Goodwin (Sls Mgr)

Connor, Clark & Lunn
Infrastructure   (1)
1400 130 King Street West, PO Box 240, Toronto, M5X 1C8, ON, Canada
Tel.: (416) 862-2020
Web Site:
https://cclinfrastructure.cclgroup.com
Asset Management Company
N.A.I.C.S.: 523999
David Chatburn (Mng Dir)

Joint Venture (Domestic):

Regional Power, Inc.   (2)
6755 Mississauga Rd Ste 308, Mississauga, L5N7Y2, ON, Canada
Tel.: (416) 593-4717
Web Site: http://www.regionalpower.com
Developer, Manager & Operator of Hydroelectric Facilities
N.A.I.C.S.: 221111
James Carter (VP-Dev & Ops)

CONOIL PLC.
38/39 Marina, Lagos, Nigeria
Tel.: (234) 170370025
Web Site: https://www.conoilplc.com
Year Founded: 1927
CONOIL—(NIGE)
Rev.: $97,278,494
Assets: $48,785,881
Liabilities: $30,271,892
Net Worth: $18,513,989
Earnings: $3,669,699
Emp.: 163
Fiscal Year-end: 12/31/22
Petroleum Product Distr
N.A.I.C.S.: 424720
Abimbola Michael-Adenuga (Exec Dir)

CONPOREC INC.
3125 Joseph-Simard, Sorel-Tracy, J3P 5N3, QC, Canada
Tel.: (450) 746-9996   BC
Web Site: http://www.conporec.com
Year Founded: 1987
Sales Range: Less than $1 Million
Emp.: 5
Waste Treatment & Disposal Services
N.A.I.C.S.: 562219
Jean Shoiry (Pres)

Subsidiaries:

Conporec S.A.S.   (1)
52 Rue de Emerainville, 77183, Croissy-Beaubourg, France
Tel.: (33) 164078614
Waste Management Services
N.A.I.C.S.: 221320

CONQUEST RESOURCES LIMITED
55 University Avenue Suite 1805, Toronto, M5J 2H7, ON, Canada
Tel.: (647) 728-4126
Web Site:
https://www.conquestresources.com
Year Founded: 1945
CQR—(OTCIQ)
Assets: $4,196,341
Liabilities: $485,520
Net Worth: $3,710,821
Earnings: ($3,673,933)
Fiscal Year-end: 12/31/20
Mineral Exploration Services
N.A.I.C.S.: 213114
John F. Kearney (Chm)

Subsidiaries:

African Gold B.V.   (1)
Prinsengracht 701, Amsterdam, 1017 JV, Netherlands
Tel.: (31) 206163141
Gold Mining Services
N.A.I.C.S.: 212220
Terence McKillen (Mgr)

CONRAD ASIA ENERGY LTD.
84 Amoy Street 03-01, Singapore, 069903, Singapore
Tel.: (65) 65179700   SG
Web Site: https://conradasia.com
Year Founded: 2010
CRD—(ASX)
Rev.: $179,537
Assets: $36,006,159
Liabilities: $5,040,877
Net Worth: $30,965,282
Earnings: ($9,728,665)
Fiscal Year-end: 12/31/23
Natural Gas Exploration Service
N.A.I.C.S.: 211130
David Johnson (COO)

CONRAN HOLDINGS LIMITED
22 Shad Thames, London, SE1 2YU, United Kingdom
Tel.: (44) 2074038899   UK
Web Site: http://www.conran.com
Year Founded: 1993
Sales Range: $25-49.9 Million
Emp.: 100
Holding Company
N.A.I.C.S.: 551112

Subsidiaries:

Conran & Partners Ltd.   (1)
22 Shad Thames, London, SE1 2YU, United Kingdom
Tel.: (44) 20 7403 8899
Web Site:
http://www.conranandpartners.com
Sales Range: $25-49.9 Million
Emp.: 18
Brand, Product, Interior & Architectural Design Services
N.A.I.C.S.: 541490
Tim Bowder-Ridger (CEO & Sr Partner)

Conran Contracts Limited   (1)
22 Shad Thames, London, SE1 2YU, United Kingdom
Tel.: (44) 20 7403 8899
Web Site:
http://www.conranshopcontracts.co.uk
Furniture Distr
N.A.I.C.S.: 423210
Terence Conran (Chm)

The Conran Shop Ltd.   (1)
3 Flatten Way High Street, Syston, LE7 1GU, United Kingdom

Tel.: (44) 844 848 4000
Web Site: http://www.conranshop.co.uk
Home Furnishings Retailer
N.A.I.C.S.: 449129
Jessica Rembert (Mgr-Mktg)

CONROS CORPORATION
125 Bermondsey Rd, Toronto, ON, Canada
Tel.: (416) 757-6700
Web Site: http://www.conros.com
Year Founded: 1970
Rev.: $20,900,000
Emp.: 475
Adhesive Mfr
N.A.I.C.S.: 325520
Clarence J. Chandran (Pres)

CONROY GOLD & NATURAL RESOURCES PLC
3300 Lake Drive, Citywest Business Campus, Dublin, D24 TD21, Ireland
Tel.: (353) 14796180   IE
Web Site:
https://www.conroyresources.com
Year Founded: 1995
CGNR—(AIM)
Assets: $29,830,510
Liabilities: $4,216,365
Net Worth: $25,614,145
Earnings: ($392,220)
Fiscal Year-end: 05/31/23
Gold Mining & Exploration Services
N.A.I.C.S.: 212220
Maureen T. A. Jones (Mng Dir & Sec)

CONSEC CORPORATION
4-6-8 Shoko Center, Nishi-ku, Hiroshima, 733-0833, Japan
Tel.: (81) 822775451
Web Site: https://www.consec.co.jp
Year Founded: 1967
9895—(TKS)
Rev.: $97,584,080
Assets: $113,798,080
Liabilities: $38,797,440
Net Worth: $75,000,640
Earnings: $580,800
Fiscal Year-end: 03/31/22
Industrial Machinery Mfr
N.A.I.C.S.: 333248
Hidetaka Sasaki (Chm)

Subsidiaries:

CONSEC CORPORATION - Hiroshima Plant   (1)
552-1 Umenokida Kamikofukawa, Itsukaiti-Cho Saeki-Ku, Hiroshima, 7315104, Japan
Tel.: (81) 829271877
Drilling Equipment Mfr
N.A.I.C.S.: 333131

CONSECUTIVE INVESTMENT & TRADING COMPANY LTD.
23 Ganesh Chandra Avenue 3rd Floor, Kolkata, 700 013, West Bengal, India
Tel.: (91) 3322115493
Web Site:
https://www.consecutive.com
Year Founded: 1982
539091—(BOM)
Rev.: $24,335
Assets: $652,095
Liabilities: $619
Net Worth: $651,476
Earnings: $13,372
Fiscal Year-end: 03/31/21
Financial Investment Services
N.A.I.C.S.: 523999
Nabin Kumar Samanta (Compliance Officer & Sec)

CONSELLGRUPPE
Schwedlerstrasse 6, 60314, Frankfurt am Main, Germany
Tel.: (49) 69 42 72 85 600

Consellgruppe—(Continued)

Web Site: http://www.consell.de
Year Founded: 1979
Rev.: $39,000,000
Emp.: 30
N.A.I.C.S.: 541810
Peter Ringer *(Dir-Creative)*

CONSENSUS ASSET MAN-AGEMENT AB

Betagatan 2, 431 49, Molndal, Sweden
Tel.: (46) 317455000
Web Site:
https://www.consensusam.se
5XI—(DEU)
Financial Management Services
N.A.I.C.S.: 522320
Patrik Soko *(CEO)*

CONSERVATIVE PARTY

4 Matthew Parker Street, London,
SW1H 9HQ, United Kingdom
Tel.: (44) 2072229000
Web Site:
https://www.conservatives.com
Year Founded: 1870
Political Organization Services
N.A.I.C.S.: 813940

CONSERVES ET SALAISONS VANELLI

131 Avenue Jalday, 64500, Saint-Jean-de-Luz, France
Tel.: (33) 559511770
Web Site: http://www.vanelli.com
Sales Range: $10-24.9 Million
Emp.: 62
Fish & Seafoods
N.A.I.C.S.: 424460
Jean-Marc Lecompte *(Mgr-Fin)*

CONSILIUM SGR P.A.

Via Quintino Sella 4, 20121, Milan,
Italy
Tel.: (39) 02 7260 191
Web Site:
http://www.consiliumsgr.com
Privater Equity Firm
N.A.I.C.S.: 523999
Stefano Iamoni *(Founding Partner)*

Subsidiaries:

Gelit Srl **(1)**
Via Ninfina km 2700, Doganella di Ninfa,
04013, Latina, Italy
Tel.: (39) 06 961051
Web Site: http://gelit.it
Frozen Food Products & Snacks Mfr & Marketer
N.A.I.C.S.: 311412
Giulio Panella *(Sls Mgr)*

CONSILIUM SGR SPA

Via Quintino Sella 4, 20121, Milan,
Italy
Tel.: (39) 027260191
Web Site: http://www.consiliumsgr.it
Privater Equity Firm
N.A.I.C.S.: 523999
Antonio Glorioso *(CEO)*

CONSOLE LABS S.A.

Leborska 3B, 80-386, Gdansk, Poland
Tel.: (48) 601773344
Web Site: https://www.console-labs.com
Year Founded: 2018
CLA—(WAR)
Emp.: 20
Software Development Services
N.A.I.C.S.: 541511
Marcin Wesolowski *(Chm & Pres)*

CONSOLIDATED BAKERIES

(JAMAICA) LTD.

2F Valentine Drive, Kingston, 19,
Jamaica
Tel.: (876) 92411513
Web Site: https://www.purity.com.jm
Year Founded: 1957
PURITY—(JAM)
Rev.: $9,830,451
Assets: $7,314,308
Liabilities: $2,709,156
Net Worth: $4,605,242
Earnings: $84,170
Fiscal Year-end: 12/31/23
Bakery & Cake Product Mfr
N.A.I.C.S.: 311811
Anthony V. Chang *(Chm, CEO & Mng Dir)*

CONSOLIDATED CONSTRUC-TION CONSORTIUM LTD

8/33 Padmavathiyar Road Jeypore
Colony, Gopalapuram, Chennai,
600086, India
Tel.: (91) 4423454500
Web Site: https://www.ccclindia.com
CCCL—(BOM)
Rev.: $18,589,512
Assets: $167,618,492
Liabilities: $240,443,235
Net Worth: ($72,824,743)
Earnings: ($19,225,233)
Emp.: 280
Fiscal Year-end: 03/31/22
Construction Engineering Services
N.A.I.C.S.: 541330
Vakati Govinda Reddy Janarthanam
(Dir-Ops)

Subsidiaries:

CCCL Infrastructure Ltd. **(1)**
No 1 Third St Luz Ave Behind Nageswara
Rao Pk Mylapore, Chennai, 600004, Tamil
Nadu, India
Tel.: (91) 4423454800
Sales Range: $25-49.9 Million
Emp.: 20
Construction Management Services
N.A.I.C.S.: 236220

Cccl Pearl City Food Port Sez
Limited **(1)**
No 1 Third Street Luz Avenue Behind Nageswara Rao Park, Mylapore, Chennai,
600004, India
Tel.: (91) 442 345 4800
Web Site: https://www.pearlcityfoodport.com
Food Raw Material Mfr
N.A.I.C.S.: 311999

CONSOLIDATED CONTRAC-TORS INTERNATIONAL COM-PANY S.A.L.

62B Kifissias Avenue-Amaroussion,
PO Box 61092, Athens, 15125,
Greece
Tel.: (30) 2106182000 GR
Web Site: http://www.ccc.net
Year Founded: 1952
Sales Range: $1-4.9 Billion
Emp.: 600
Construction & Engineering Services
N.A.I.C.S.: 541330
Tawfic S. Khoury *(Deputy Chm)*

Subsidiaries:

Consolidated Contractors Company
(Kuwait) W.L.L. **(1)**
E Ahmadi Block 33, PO Box 509, Kuwait,
13006, Kuwait
Tel.: (965) 3980390
Web Site: http://www.ccc.gr
Contracting Services
N.A.I.C.S.: 236220

Consolidated Contractors Company
Ltd. **(1)**
Jabal Amman Sinan Bin Khafaji Street,
Near Zahran Post Office, PO Box 830392,
Amman, 11183, Jordan
Tel.: (962) 64568403

Web Site: http://www.ccc.gr
Contracting Services
N.A.I.C.S.: 236220

Consolidated Contractors Interna-
tional (UK) Ltd. **(1)**
11A West Halkin Str, Belgravia, London,
SW1X 8JL, United Kingdom
Tel.: (44) 2072595900
Sales Range: $25-49.9 Million
Emp.: 30
Contracting Services
N.A.I.C.S.: 236220
Andoine Mattar *(Mng Dir)*

CONSOLIDATED FASTFRATE INC.

9701 Hwy 50, Woodbridge, Vaughan,
L4H 2G4, ON, Canada
Tel.: (905) 893-2600
Web Site: http://www.fastfrate.com
Sales Range: $125-149.9 Million
Emp.: 1,310
Freight Forwarding Services
N.A.I.C.S.: 484110
Manny Calandrino *(Pres & COO)*

CONSOLIDATED FASTFRATE INC.

9701 Highway 50, Woodbridge, L4H
2G4, ON, Canada
Tel.: (905) 893-3200
Web Site: http://www.fastfrate.com
Transportation, Warehousing & Distri-
bution Services
N.A.I.C.S.: 532411
Manny Calandrino *(Pres & CEO)*

Subsidiaries:

Asl Distribution Services Limited **(1)**
2160 Buckingham Road, Oakville, L6H
6M7, ON, Canada
Tel.: (905) 829-5141
Web Site: http://www.asldistribution.com
Transportation & Warehouse Services
N.A.I.C.S.: 488999
Cole Dolny *(Pres)*

CONSOLIDATED FINVEST & HOLDINGS LIMITED

Plot No-12 Sector B-1 Local Shop-
ping Complex Vasant Kunj, New
Delhi, 110 070, India
Tel.: (91) 1126139256
Web Site:
https://www.consofinvest.com
CONSOFINVT—(NSE)
Rev.: $1,334,136
Assets: $183,048,661
Liabilities: $2,086,830
Net Worth: $180,961,831
Earnings: ($23,757,782)
Emp.: 2
Fiscal Year-end: 03/31/19
Holding Company
N.A.I.C.S.: 551112
Sanjiv Kumar Agarwal *(Mng Dir)*

Subsidiaries:

Jindal Photo Investments Limited **(1)**
11/5B Basement 01 Opposite Telephone
Exchange Pusa Road, New Delhi, 110 005,
India
Tel.: (91) 1125767000
Web Site: https://www.jindalpil.com
Financial Investment Services
N.A.I.C.S.: 523999

CONSOLIDATED FIRSTFUND CAPITAL CORPORATION

837 W Hastings Street Ste 304, Van-
couver, V6C 3N6, BC, Canada
Tel.: (604) 683-6611
FFP—(TSXV)
Rev.: $270,404
Assets: $555,586
Liabilities: $119,972
Net Worth: $435,614
Earnings: $5,712

Fiscal Year-end: 12/31/23
Asset Management Services
N.A.I.C.S.: 523940

CONSOLIDATED FISHERIES LTD.

Waverley House, PO Box 383, Stan-
ley, Falkland Islands
Tel.: (500) 22277
Web Site:
http://www.consolidatedfisheries.com
Year Founded: 1994
Sales Range: $25-49.9 Million
Emp.: 60
Fishing Services; Vessel Owner &
Operator
N.A.I.C.S.: 114119

CONSOLIDATED GENERAL MINERALS PLC

Bahnhofstrasse 23, Zug, 6300, Swit-
zerland
Tel.: (41) 417109055
Web Site: http://www.cgmplc.com
Sales Range: Less than $1 Million
Emp.: 1
Mineral Processing Services
N.A.I.C.S.: 213115
Jean-Pierre Conrad *(Sec)*

CONSOLIDATED HALLMARK INSURANCE PLC.

266 Ikorodu Road, Obanikoro, Lagos,
Nigeria
Tel.: (234) 12912543
Web Site: http://www.chiplc.com
CHIPLC—(NIGE)
Rev.: $27,406,014
Assets: $40,909,574
Liabilities: $17,388,818
Net Worth: $23,520,755
Earnings: $2,063,565
Emp.: 207
Fiscal Year-end: 12/31/21
Insurance Services
N.A.I.C.S.: 524298
Eddie A. Efekoha *(Mng Dir)*

Subsidiaries:

CHI Microinsurance Limited **(1)**
5A Sawyer Crescent Anthony, Lagos, Nige-
ria
Tel.: (234) 8090557508
Web Site: http://www.chimicroinsure.com
Insurance Agency Services
N.A.I.C.S.: 524298
Karieren Pius *(CEO)*

Grand Treasurers Limited **(1)**
Plot 33D Bishop Aboyade Cole Street Victo-
ria Island, Lagos, Nigeria
Tel.: (234) 9045590800
Web Site: http://www.gtl.ng
Financial Services
N.A.I.C.S.: 523940
Eddie Efekoha *(Chm)*

CONSOLIDATED HCI HOLD-INGS CORP.

Suite 2100 40 King Street West, To-
ronto, M5H 3C2, ON, Canada
Tel.: (905) 851-7741
Year Founded: 1986
ATMO—(CNSX)
Rev.: $782
Assets: $244,071
Liabilities: $326,993
Net Worth: ($82,922)
Earnings: ($218,256)
Emp.: 6
Fiscal Year-end: 09/30/20
Real Estate Development Services
N.A.I.C.S.: 531390
Bradley Morris *(CEO)*

CONSOLIDATED INFRA-STRUCTURE GROUP LIMITED

First Floor 30 Melrose Boulevard,

Melrose Arch, Johannesburg, 2196, South Africa
Tel.: (27) 11 280 4040   ZA
Web Site: http://www.ciglimited.co.za
Rev.: $67,949,257
Assets: $285,359,754
Liabilities: $65,260,494
Net Worth: $220,099,260
Earnings: ($20,207,397)
Emp.: 1,932
Fiscal Year-end: 08/31/19
Building Materials Whslr
N.A.I.C.S.: 423320
Raoul Gamsu *(CEO)*

Subsidiaries:

CIGenCo SA Proprietary Limited   (1)
5th Floor Raffles Tower 19 Cybercity, Ebene, Mauritius
Tel.: (230) 403 5555
Mining Infrastructure Services
N.A.I.C.S.: 213113

Conlog (Pty) Ltd   (1)
270 Felix Dlamini Road Overport, Durban, 4001, KwaZulu-Natal, South Africa
Tel.: (27) 31 268 1227
Web Site: http://www.conlog.co.za
Electricity Utility Services
N.A.I.C.S.: 221122
Pretty Ntombela *(Mgr-Prod Pur)*

Consolidated Power Maintenance (Pty) Limited   (1)
37 Richards Drive Halfway House, Midrand, 1685, Gauteng, South Africa
Tel.: (27) 118054281
Web Site: http://www.conco.co.za
Eletric Power Generation Services
N.A.I.C.S.: 221118
Andreas Richelmann *(Mng Dir)*

Consolidated Power Projects (Pty) Limited   (1)
37 Richards Drive Halfway House, Midrand, 1685, South Africa
Tel.: (27) 11 805 4281
Web Site: http://www.conco.co.za
Emp.: 500
Electric Power Distr
N.A.I.C.S.: 221122
Johnny Dladla *(CEO)*

Drift Supersand (Proprietary) Limited   (1)
Plot 121 Abraham Van Wyk Road, Roodepoort, 1724, Gauteng, South Africa
Tel.: (27) 116621207
Construction Materials Distr
N.A.I.C.S.: 423390
Jannie Hooman *(Gen Mgr)*

West End Claybrick (Proprietary) Limited   (1)
Plot 70 Zuurbekom On N12 Highway Between Westonaria & Lenasia, Old Potchefstroom Road - N12 Moroka Bypass, Westonaria, South Africa
Tel.: (27) 8619378363
Web Site:
   http://www.westendclaybrick.co.za
Clay Bricks Mfr & Distr
N.A.I.C.S.: 423320

CONSOLIDATED OPERATIONS GROUP LIMITED

Level 1 72 Archer Street, Chatswood, 2067, NSW, Australia
Tel.: (61) 292999690
Web Site:
   http://www.coglimited.com.au
Investment Management Service
N.A.I.C.S.: 523940
David Franks *(Sec)*

Subsidiaries:

Consolidated Finance Group Pty Limited   (1)
Level 1 74 Doncaster Road, Balwyn, 3104, VIC, Australia   **(100%)**
Tel.: (61) 420 949 233
Web Site: http://cfgroup.com.au
Finance Brokerage Services
N.A.I.C.S.: 522310

Platform Consolidated Group Pty Limited   (1)
Level 7 77 Berry Street, North Sydney, 2060, NSW, Australia
Tel.: (61) 1300 88 77 54
Web Site:
   http://www.platformconsolidated.com.au
Finance Brokerage Services
N.A.I.C.S.: 522310

Subsidiary (Domestic):

Fleet Network Pty Limited   (2)
1/28 Hasler Rd, Osborne Park, 6017, WA, Australia
Tel.: (61) 1300738601
Web Site: http://www.fleetnetwork.com.au
Vehicle Leasing Services
N.A.I.C.S.: 522220
Greg Peters *(Gen Mgr)*

Mildura Finance Pty Limited   (2)
158-164 Langtree Avenue, Mildura, 3500, VIC, Australia
Tel.: (61) 350510400
Web Site: http://mildurafinance.com.au
Finance Brokerage Services
N.A.I.C.S.: 522310
Andrew Black *(Mgr-Bus Dev)*

National Direct Finance (Australia) Pty Limited   (2)
1 Elgin Street, Hawthorn, 3122, VIC, Australia
Tel.: (61) 383178586
Web Site:
   http://nationaldirectfinance.com.au
Finance Brokerage Services
N.A.I.C.S.: 522310
David Zuegn *(Sr Mgr-Lending-VIC)*

The Mardent Group Pty Limited   (2)
80 Ipswich Road, Woolloongabba, 4102, QLD, Australia
Tel.: (61) 404847857
Web Site: http://themardentgroup.com
Finance Brokerage Services
N.A.I.C.S.: 522310

CONSOLIDATED PRESS HOLDINGS LIMITED

Level 3 54 Park Street, Sydney, 2000, NSW, Australia
Tel.: (61) 292828000   AU
Sales Range: $200-249.9 Million
Investment Holding Company
N.A.I.C.S.: 551112
James Douglas Packer *(Chm & CEO)*

CONSOLIDATED TIN MINES LIMITED

395 Lake Street, Cairns, 4870, QLD, Australia
Tel.: (61) 740323319
Web Site: http://www.csdtin.com.au
Year Founded: 2007
Rev.: $1,754,121
Assets: $9,926,182
Liabilities: $2,093,387
Net Worth: $7,832,795
Earnings: ($1,111,291)
Emp.: 17
Fiscal Year-end: 06/30/15
Tin Mining Services
N.A.I.C.S.: 212290
Ralph De Lacey *(Founder & Exec Mng Dir)*

CONSOLIDATED WATER CO. LTD.

Regatta Office Park Windward Three 4th Fl West Bay Road, PO Box 1114, Georgetown, KY1-1102, Grand Cayman, Cayman Islands
Tel.: (345) 9454277   Ky
Web Site: https://www.cwco.com
Year Founded: 1973
CWCO—(NASDAQ)
Rev.: $94,104,972
Assets: $193,006,849
Liabilities: $25,242,660
Net Worth: $167,764,189

Earnings: $5,856,294
Emp.: 223
Fiscal Year-end: 12/31/22
Seawater Desalination Plants & Water Distribution Systems Developer & Operator
N.A.I.C.S.: 221310
Frederick W. McTaggart *(Pres & CEO)*

Subsidiaries:

Aerex Industries, Inc.   (1)
3504 Industrial 27th St, Fort Pierce, FL 34946   **(100%)**
Tel.: (772) 448-5800
Web Site: http://www.aerexglobal.com
Sales Range: $1-9.9 Million
Emp.: 150
Customized Membrane Systems & Vessel Products Solutions & Treatments for Water & Wastewater, Purification & Recovery Processes
N.A.I.C.S.: 332312

Cayman Water Company Limited   (1)
Windward 3 4th Floor West Bay Road, Georgetown, KY1-1102, Grand Cayman, Cayman Islands
Tel.: (345) 9454277
Web Site: https://caymanwater.com
Sales Range: $75-99.9 Million
Emp.: 70
Water Supply Services
N.A.I.C.S.: 221310
Frederick W. McTaggart *(Pres & CEO)*

Consolidated Water (Bahamas) Limited   (1)
Soldier Road - West, PO Box CR, 54030, Nassau, Bahamas
Tel.: (242) 2424612000
Water Purification Equipment Whslr
N.A.I.C.S.: 423720
Bryan Russell *(Gen Mgr)*

DesalCo (Barbados) Ltd   (1)
Golf Club Road, Sandy Lane, Saint James, Barbados
Tel.: (246) 432 1153
Water Supply Services
N.A.I.C.S.: 221310

DesalCo Limited   (1)
Regatta Office Park Windward 3, PO Box 1114, West Bay Road, Georgetown, KY1-1102, Grand Cayman, Cayman Islands
Tel.: (345) 9462247
Web Site: http://www.cwco.com
Sales Range: $50-74.9 Million
Emp.: 70
Water Supply Services
N.A.I.C.S.: 221310

Ocean Conversion (BVI) Ltd.   (1)
PO Box 122, Road Town, Tortola, VG1110, Virgin Islands (British)
Tel.: (284) 2844951266
Water Purification Equipment Whslr
N.A.I.C.S.: 423720
Darwn Peters *(Office Mgr)*

Ocean Conversion (Cayman) Limited   (1)
Regatta Office Pk Windward 3 4th Fl W Bay Rd, PO Box 1114, Grand Cayman, KY1-1102, Cayman Islands
Tel.: (345) 3459454277
Waste Treatment Services
N.A.I.C.S.: 221310

PERC Water Corporation   (1)
959 S Coast Dr Ste 315, Costa Mesa, CA 92626   **(100%)**
Tel.: (714) 352-7750
Web Site: http://www.percwater.com
Water Recycling Services
N.A.I.C.S.: 924110
Robert J. Nespeca *(VP-Asset Mgmt)*

Subsidiary (Domestic):

Ramey Environmental Compliance Inc.   (2)
5959 Iris Pkwy, Frederick, CO 80504
Tel.: (303) 833-5535
Web Site: http://www.recinc.net
Scientific & Technical Consulting Services
N.A.I.C.S.: 541690

Jeff Rabas *(VP-Ops)*

PT Consolidated Water Bali   (1)
Jl Desa Sawangan No 06 Sawangan-Nusa Dua, Badung, Bali, 80363, Indonesia
Tel.: (62) 3618498886
Web Site: https://www.cwbali.co.id
Water Purification Equipment Whslr
N.A.I.C.S.: 423720

Waterfield Company Limited   (1)
Corner of Windsor Field Road J F Kennedy Drive, Nassau, CR-54030, Bahamas
Tel.: (242) 3773451
Water Supply Services
N.A.I.C.S.: 221310

CONSORCIO ALFA DE ADMINISTRACAO S.A.

Al Santos 466 - 2 Floor, 1418000, Sao Paulo, Brazil
Tel.: (55) 11 3175 5493
Year Founded: 1952
BRGE11—(BRAZ)
Investment Management Service
N.A.I.C.S.: 523940
Marco Aurelio Neto Arnes *(Dir-IR)*

CONSORCIO ARA, S.A.B. DE C.V.

Park Plaza Torre II Av Javier Barros Sierra 540 Piso 1 Oficina 101, Cuajimalpa, 01210, Mexico, Mexico
Tel.: (52) 5552463100   MX
Web Site:
   https://www.consorcioara.com.mx
Year Founded: 1977
ARA—(MEX)
Rev.: $397,673,672
Assets: $1,346,720,417
Liabilities: $470,278,203
Net Worth: $876,442,213
Earnings: $39,094,806
Emp.: 3,598
Fiscal Year-end: 12/31/23
Construction & Property Development Services
N.A.I.C.S.: 236117
German Ahumada Alduncin *(Vice Chm)*

Subsidiaries:

Promotora y Desarrolladora de Centros Comerciales, S. A. de C. V.   (1)
Paseo De Los Tamarindos No 90 Torre I Piso 24, Mexico, 06700, Mexico
Tel.: (52) 5555968864
Residential Building Construction Services
N.A.I.C.S.: 236115

CONSORCIO ARISTOS, S.A.B. DE C.V.

Av Revolucion N 528, Col San Pedro de los Pinos, Mexico, Mexico
Tel.: (52) 5555748077
Web Site:
   https://www.consorcioaristos.org
Year Founded: 1955
ARISTOS—(MEX)
Rev.: $238,923
Assets: $375,501
Liabilities: $90,502
Net Worth: $284,999
Earnings: $8,661
Emp.: 2,515
Fiscal Year-end: 12/31/23
Industrial Structure Construction Services
N.A.I.C.S.: 236210
Sergio de la Fuente Mendoza *(CEO)*

CONSORCIO CEMENTERO DEL SUR SA

Republica de Panama 2461, Santa Catalina La Victoria, Lima, Peru
Tel.: (51) 1 470 7170
Private Investment Firm
N.A.I.C.S.: 523999

Consorcio Cementero del Sur SA—(Continued)

Subsidiaries:

Cementos Otorongo, S.A.C.   **(1)**
Calle Los Gavilanes No 159 San Isidro,
Lima, 2727, Peru
Tel.: (51) 12411275
Cement & Concrete Product Mfr
N.A.I.C.S.: 327320

Yura Chile SA   **(1)**
Barros Arana 3098, 1031521, Arica, Chile
Tel.: (56) 983912013
Web Site: http://www.yura.cl
Cement Mfr
N.A.I.C.S.: 327310

**CONSORCIO HOGAR, S.A.B.
DE C.V.**
Av Santa Fe No 485 Piso 3, Cruz
Manca, 5349, Mexico, Mexico
Tel.: (52) 91779090
Web Site: http://www.hogar.com.mx
Residential Building Construction
Services
N.A.I.C.S.: 236115
Paul Davis Carstens *(Mng Dir)*

CONSORT NT SA
58 boulevard Gouvion-Saint-Cyr,
75017, Paris, France
Tel.: (33) 140880505
Web Site: http://www.consort-
group.com
MLCNT—(EUR)
Sales Range: $150-199.9 Million
Building Architectural Design Services
N.A.I.C.S.: 541310
Nathalie Chove Legre *(VP-Comm)*

**CONSTANCE HOTELS SER-
VICES LIMITED**
5thFloor Labama House 35 Sir Wil-
liam Newton Street, Port Louis, Mau-
ritius
Tel.: (230) 2124173
Web Site:
  http://www.constancehotels.com
CHSL—(MAU)
Rev.: $129,179,407
Assets: $385,088,663
Liabilities: $253,541,891
Net Worth: $131,546,772
Earnings: $7,240,544
Emp.: 3,126
Fiscal Year-end: 12/31/23
Home Management Services
N.A.I.C.S.: 721110
George J. Dumbell *(Chm)*

**CONSTANCE LA GAIETE CO.
LTD.**
3rd Floor Labama House35 Sir Wil-
liam Newton Street, Port Louis, Mau-
ritius
Tel.: (230) 460600   MU
Web Site: https://www.clgmu.com
CSE—(MAU)
Rev.: $16,496,218
Assets: $33,624,635
Liabilities: $11,917,778
Net Worth: $21,706,857
Earnings: $11,962,281
Fiscal Year-end: 12/31/23
Sugar Milling Services
N.A.I.C.S.: 311314
Clement D. Rey *(CEO & Exec Dir)*

**CONSTANTINOU BROS DE-
VELOPERS PLC**
Posidonos 77, Paphos, Cyprus
Tel.: (357) 26813060
Building Construction Services
N.A.I.C.S.: 236220

**CONSTANTINOU BROS HO-
TELS LTD**

Theas Afroditis Ave, 8101, Paphos,
Cyprus
Tel.: (357) 26964500
Web Site: https://www.cbh-
cyprus.com
Year Founded: 1979
CBH—(CYP)
Sales Range: Less than $1 Million
Home Management Services
N.A.I.C.S.: 721110
Andreas Constantinou *(Exec VP)*

**CONSTANTINOU BROS PROP-
ERTIES PLC**
77 Poseidonos Street, PO Box
60182, Kato Pafos, 8101, Paphos,
Cyprus
Tel.: (357) 26933979
Web Site:
  http://www.constantinoubros.com
Year Founded: 1979
Building Construction Services
N.A.I.C.S.: 236220
Andreas Constantinou *(Co-Founder)*

**CONSTELLATION RE-
SOURCES LIMITED**
Level 9 28 The Esplanade, Perth,
6000, WA, Australia
Tel.: (61) 893226322   AU
Web Site:
  https://www.constellation.com.au
CR1—(ASX)
Rev.: $55,196
Assets: $1,790,412
Liabilities: $67,632
Net Worth: $1,722,780
Earnings: ($1,263,968)
Fiscal Year-end: 06/30/24
Mineral Exploration & Development
Services
N.A.I.C.S.: 212220
Peter Woodman *(Mng Dir)*

**CONSTELLATION SOFTWARE
INC.**
Ste 1200 - 20 Adelaide Street East,
Toronto, M5C 2T6, ON, Canada
Tel.: (416) 861-2279   ON
Web Site:
  https://www.csisoftware.com
Year Founded: 1995
W9C—(MUN)
Rev.: $8,407,000,000
Assets: $10,899,000,000
Liabilities: $8,938,000,000
Net Worth: $1,961,000,000
Earnings: $565,000,000
Emp.: 50,000
Fiscal Year-end: 12/31/23
Software Developer
N.A.I.C.S.: 513210
Mark Leonard *(Chm & Pres)*

Subsidiaries:

Charter Software, Inc.   **(1)**
5951 S Middlefield Rd Ste 200, Littleton,
CO 80123
Tel.: (303) 932-6875
Web Site: http://www.chartersoftware.com
Custom Computer Programming Services
N.A.I.C.S.: 541511

Constellation Homebuilder Systems
Inc.   **(1)**
75 Frontenac Drive West Wing, Markham,
L3R 6H2, ON, Canada   **(100%)**
Tel.: (905) 943-6140
Web Site: http://www.constellationhb.com
Sales Range: $25-49.9 Million
Emp.: 100
Software for Homebuilders
N.A.I.C.S.: 334610

Subsidiary (US):

G1440 Inc.   **(2)**
11350 McCormick Rd Plz III Ste 200, Hunt
Valley, MD 21031

Tel.: (410) 843-3800
Web Site: https://www.g1440.com
Sales Range: $25-49.9 Million
Information Technology Consulting & Staff-
ing Services
N.A.I.C.S.: 519290

Integrated Dealer Systems, Inc.   **(2)**
12339 Wake Union Church Rd Ste 107,
Wake Forest, NC 27587   **(100%)**
Tel.: (919) 790-5442
Web Site: https://www.ids-astra.com
Sales Range: $25-49.9 Million
Emp.: 7
Software Solutions for the RV, Marine &
Automotive Industries
N.A.I.C.S.: 541511
Mark Jakobsen *(Dir-Client Svcs)*

Majiq Inc.   **(2)**
8343 154th Ave NE Ste 200, Redmond, WA
98052
Tel.: (425) 881-7100
Web Site: https://www.majiq.com
Sales Range: $25-49.9 Million
Paper Industry Software Development Ser-
vices
N.A.I.C.S.: 327910
David Pawelke *(VP-Sls)*

Market Leader, Inc.   **(2)**
3633 136th Pl SE Ste 300, Bellevue, WA
98006
Web Site: https://www.marketleader.com
Holding Company; Online Real Estate Marketing Software Developer & Services
N.A.I.C.S.: 551112

Monolith Corporation   **(2)**
12339 Wake Union Church Rd Ste 107,
Wake Forest, NC 27587-4512
Tel.: (919) 878-1900
Web Site: https://www.monolith.com
Sales Range: $50-74.9 Million
Emp.: 6
Information Technology Solutions
N.A.I.C.S.: 541519

POMS Corp.   **(2)**
196 Van Buren St Ste 200, Herndon, VA
20171-4633
Tel.: (703) 574-9900
Web Site: https://www.poms.com
Sales Range: $10-24.9 Million
Emp.: 50
Computer Related Consulting Services
N.A.I.C.S.: 541511

Quantitative Medical Systems,
Inc.   **(2)**
6001 Shellmound St, Emeryville, CA 94608
Tel.: (510) 654-9200
Web Site: http://www.qms-us.com
Sales Range: $1-9.9 Million
Emp.: 20
Custom Computer Programming Services
N.A.I.C.S.: 541511
Paul Benson *(Gen Mgr)*

Crealogix Holding AG   **(1)**
Maneggstrasse 17, 8041, Zurich, Switzer-
land
Tel.: (41) 4584048000
Web Site: https://www.crealogix.com
Rev.: $90,239,468
Assets: $86,768,293
Liabilities: $61,883,592
Net Worth: $24,884,701
Earnings: $32,151
Emp.: 383
Fiscal Year-end: 06/30/2023
IT & Software Consulting Services
N.A.I.C.S.: 541511
Richard Dratva *(Vice Chm & Chief Strategy
Officer)*

Subsidiary (Domestic):

C-Channel AG   **(2)**
Bosch 838, 6331, Hunenberg, Switzerland
Tel.: (41) 417845555
Web Site: http://www.c-channel.ch
Sales Range: $25-49.9 Million
Emp.: 25
Internet Banking Services
N.A.I.C.S.: 517810

Subsidiary (Non-US):

Crealogix (Deutschland) AG   **(2)**

Breitscheidstrasse 10, 70174, Stuttgart,
Germany
Tel.: (49) 71 161 4160
Web Site: http://banking.crealogix.com
Internet Banking Services
N.A.I.C.S.: 517810

Subsidiary (Domestic):

Crealogix AG   **(2)**
Maneggstrasse 17, 8041, Zurich, Switzer-
land
Tel.: (41) 58 404 8000
Web Site: https://crealogix.com
IT Solutions
N.A.I.C.S.: 517810
Thomas Avedik *(Gen Mgr)*

Subsidiary (Non-US):

Crealogix BaaS GmbH & Co. KG   **(2)**
Am Hofbraeuhaus 1, 96450, Coburg, Ger-
many
Tel.: (49) 95 615 5430
Digital Banking Services
N.A.I.C.S.: 522110

Crealogix MBA Ltd.   **(2)**
21-22 Staple Gardens, Winchester, SO23
8SR, United Kingdom
Tel.: (44) 196 284 1494
Digital Banking Services
N.A.I.C.S.: 522110

Crealogix Pte. Ltd.   **(2)**
5 Shenton Way Level 10-01 UIC Building,
Singapore, 068808, Singapore
Tel.: (65) 6 932 2804
Digital Banking Services
N.A.I.C.S.: 522110

Innofis Esgm S.L.   **(2)**
Balmes 150, 08008, Barcelona, Spain
Tel.: (34) 936671855
Web Site: https://retail.innofis.com
Digital Banking Solutions & Software Ser-
vices
N.A.I.C.S.: 522110

Saudi Crealogix Single-Partner
LLC   **(2)**
Al Tawuniya Tower South Tower Level 16
King Fahad Road, Riyadh, Saudi Arabia
Tel.: (966) 55 197 7775
Digital Banking Services
N.A.I.C.S.: 522110

Subsidiary (Domestic):

Swiss Learning Hub AG   **(2)**
Maneggstrasse 17, 8041, Zurich, Switzer-
land
Tel.: (41) 58 404 8870
Web Site:
  https://www.swisslearninghub.com
Educational Support Services
N.A.I.C.S.: 611710
Urs Widmer *(CEO)*

Emphasys Computer Solutions,
Inc.   **(2)**
3890 Charlevoix Ave Ste 370, Petoskey, MI
49770
Tel.: (231) 347-8787
Web Site: http://www.emphasys-
software.com
Business Management Software Develop-
ment Services
N.A.I.C.S.: 541511

Subsidiary (Domestic):

Emphasys Software Inc.   **(2)**
333 N Canyons Pkwy Ste 211, Livermore,
CA 94551   **(100%)**
Tel.: (925) 243-9393
Web Site: http://www.emphasys-
software.com
Software Reproducing
N.A.I.C.S.: 334610

SymPro, Inc.   **(2)**
2200 Powell St Ste 1170, Emeryville, CA
94608
Tel.: (510) 655-0900
Web Site: http://www.sympro.com
Treasury Management Software Solutions
N.A.I.C.S.: 513210
Mike Eyme *(Pres)*

FOG Software Group   **(1)**

10275 W Higgins Rd Ste 250, Rosemont, IL 60018
Tel.: (847) 572-4450
Software Management & Acquisition Services
N.A.I.C.S.: 513210
Andy Hodge *(Mgr-Portfolio)*

Subsidiary (Domestic):

Vortx Inc. **(2)**
700 Mistletoe Rd Ste 206, Ashland, OR 97520-1405
Tel.: (541) 201-9965
Web Site: https://www.vortx.com
Custom Computer Programming Services
N.A.I.C.S.: 541511
Dana Greaves *(Founder & CEO)*

Friedman Corporation **(1)**
10275 W Higgins Rd Ste 250, Rosemont, IL 60018
Tel.: (847) 948-7180
Web Site: https://www.friedmancorp.com
Sales Range: $25-49.9 Million
Software Development Services
N.A.I.C.S.: 541511
Mark Thompson *(Pres)*

Subsidiary (Domestic):

ASA Automotive Systems, LLC **(2)**
136 Harvey Rd Ste B 110, Londonderry, NH 03053
Tel.: (603) 889-8700
Web Site: http://www.asaauto.com
Tiles Mfr
N.A.I.C.S.: 326211
Marc Belanski *(Pres-Grp)*

Subsidiary (Non-US):

Albat+Wirsam Software GmbH **(2)**
Konrad-adenauer-strasse 15, 35440, Linden, Germany
Tel.: (49) 6403 9700
Web Site: http://www.a-w.com
Sales Range: $25-49.9 Million
Emp.: 190
Software Development Services
N.A.I.C.S.: 541511

Subsidiary (Domestic):

CORESense Inc. **(2)**
125 High Rock Ave, Saratoga Springs, NY 12866
Tel.: (518) 306-3043
Web Site: https://www.coresense.com
Ecommerce & Retail Management Software Solutions
N.A.I.C.S.: 513210

Subsidiary (Non-US):

NedSense NedGraphics B.V. **(2)**
Laanakkerweg 2b, 4131 PA, Vianen, Netherlands
Tel.: (31) 347760012
Web Site: http://www.nedgraphics.com
Fashion & Textile Industry Computer Aided Design Solutions
N.A.I.C.S.: 513210

Subsidiary (Non-US):

NedGraphics BvBa **(3)**
Gentseweg 242A, 8792, Desselgem, Belgium
Tel.: (32) 56782800
Web Site: http://www.nedgraphics.com
Fashion & Textile Industry Computer Aided Design & Manufacturing Software Distr
N.A.I.C.S.: 423430

NedGraphics SAS **(3)**
B Asap-Consiel 12 Rue Lafayette, 75009, Paris, France
Tel.: (33) 153262626
Web Site: http://www.nedgraphics.com
Fashion & Textile Industry Computer Aided Design & Manufacturing Software Distr
N.A.I.C.S.: 423430

NedGraphics Srl **(3)**
Via Trento 7, 22074, Lomazzo, CO, Italy
Tel.: (39) 0296778118
Web Site: http://www.nedgraphics.com
Fashion & Textile Industry Computer Aided Design & Manufacturing Software Distr
N.A.I.C.S.: 423430

Subsidiary (US):

NedGraphics, Inc. **(3)**
20 W 37th St 4th Fl, New York, NY 10018
Tel.: (212) 921-2727
Web Site: http://www.nedgraphics.com
Fashion & Textile Industry Computer Aided Design & Manufacturing Software Developer, Publisher & Distr
N.A.I.C.S.: 513210

Subsidiary (Domestic):

NedGraphics of Tennessee, Inc. **(4)**
10130 Mallard Creek Rd Ste 300, Charlotte, NC 28262-6001
Tel.: (704) 357-3580
Web Site: http://www.nedgraphics.com
Fashion & Textile Industry Computer Aided Design & Manufacturing Software Distr
N.A.I.C.S.: 423430

Subsidiary (Non-US):

SC NedSense Srl. **(3)**
Str Badea Cartan 15 Sector 2, Bucharest, Romania
Tel.: (40) 212122417
Web Site: http://www.nedgraphics.com
Fashion & Textile Industry Software Distr
N.A.I.C.S.: 423430

Subsidiary (Domestic):

Varsity Logistics, Inc. **(2)**
1111 Bayhill Dr Ste 210, San Bruno, CA 94066
Tel.: (650) 392-7979
Web Site: http://www.varsitylogistics.com
Shipping Software Development Services
N.A.I.C.S.: 541511

Viewlocity Technologies U.S. LLC **(2)**
5339 Alpha Rd Ste 170, Dallas, TX 75240
Tel.: (972) 715-0300
Web Site: https://www.viewlocity.com
Supply Chain Software Developer & Publisher
N.A.I.C.S.: 513210

XDATA Solutions Inc. **(2)**
129 Dixie Way S Ste A, South Bend, IN 46637
Tel.: (574) 968-8115
Web Site: http://www.xdata.com
Enterprise Resource Planning Software Developer
N.A.I.C.S.: 513210

Jonas Software Ltd. **(1)**
45 Vogell Road Suite 500, Richmond Hill, L4B 3P6, ON, Canada **(100%)**
Tel.: (905) 886-0544
Web Site: http://www.jonassoftware.com
Sales Range: $50-74.9 Million
Emp.: 170
Software Reproducing Services
N.A.I.C.S.: 334610
Barry Symons *(CEO)*

Subsidiary (US):

Computrition, Inc. **(2)**
8521 Fallbrook Ave Ste 100, West Hills, CA 91304
Web Site: https://www.computrition.com
Healthcare Software Development Services
N.A.I.C.S.: 541511
Dominic Mittelholzer *(VP-Sls)*

Efficient Workflow Solutions LLC **(2)**
454 Main St, Grand Junction, CO 81501
Tel.: (970) 256-1616
Web Site: http://www.moverssuite.com
Sales Range: $25-49.9 Million
Emp.: 17
Software Publisher
N.A.I.C.S.: 513210

Innovative Computer Solutions, Inc. **(2)**
2430 Hwy 34 Ste A22, Manasquan, NJ 08736
Tel.: (732) 223-0909
Web Site: http://www.winepos.com
Point of Sale & Inventory Systems Developer
N.A.I.C.S.: 513210
Jim McMillan *(Gen Mgr)*

Subsidiary (Non-US):

Jonas Computing (UK) Ltd. **(2)**
Avenue House 17 East End Road, Finchley, London, N3 3QE, United Kingdom
Tel.: (44) 208 343 1119
Software Developer
N.A.I.C.S.: 513210

Subsidiary (Domestic):

AMI Education Solutions Ltd **(3)**
Hithercroft Road Industrial Estate, Wallingford, OX10 9BT, OXON, United Kingdom
Tel.: (44) 8456 717 101
Web Site: http://www.amieducation.com
Sales Range: $10-24.9 Million
Educational Support Services
N.A.I.C.S.: 611710

Subsidiary (US):

Shortcuts Software, Inc. **(2)**
7711 Centre Ave Ste 650, Huntington Beach, CA 92647
Tel.: (562) 491-1600
Web Site: https://www.shortcuts.net
Sales Range: $1-9.9 Million
Emp.: 30
Software Solutions for Salon & Spa Markets
N.A.I.C.S.: 513210
Richard Wildey *(Gen Mgr)*

Springer-Miller Systems **(2)**
782 Mountain Rd, Stowe, VT 05672
Tel.: (802) 253-7377
Web Site: https://www.springermiller.com
Software Publisher
N.A.I.C.S.: 513210
Penka Sevova *(Gen Mgr-SpaSoft)*

Branch (Non-US):

Springer-Miller International, LLC **(3)**
708 Block B Menara Amcorp 18 Jalan Persiaran Barat, 46050, Petaling Jaya, Selangor, Malaysia
Tel.: (60) 379569912
Web Site: http://www.springermiller.com
Software Publisher
N.A.I.C.S.: 513210
Daphne Wong *(Gen Mgr)*

Branch (Domestic):

Springer-Miller Systems - Nevada **(3)**
2485 Village View Dr, Henderson, NV 89074
Tel.: (702) 896-8200
Web Site: https://www.springermiller.com
Emp.: 20
Software Publisher
N.A.I.C.S.: 513210
Pat Barfield *(Reg Sls Mgr)*

Lumine Group Inc. **(1)**
5060 Spectrum Way Suite 100, Mississauga, L4W 5N5, ON, Canada
Tel.: (647) 469-8295
Web Site: https://www.luminegroup.com
Emp.: 53
Software Devolepment
N.A.I.C.S.: 513210
David Nyland *(CEO)*

Subsidiary (US):

WideOrbit Inc. **(2)**
1160 Battery St Ste 300, San Francisco, CA 94111
Tel.: (415) 675-6700
Web Site: http://www.wideorbit.com
Business Management Software Publisher
N.A.I.C.S.: 513210
Eric R. Mathewson *(Founder & CEO)*

Multi-Systems Inc. **(1)**
7600 N 15th St Suite 250, Phoenix, AZ 85020 **(100%)**
Tel.: (602) 870-4200
Web Site: http://www.msisolutions.com
Cloud Services Technology & Solutions for the Hospitality Industries
N.A.I.C.S.: 513210

N. Harris Computer Corporation **(1)**
1 Antares Drive Suite 400, Ottawa, K2E 8C4, ON, Canada **(100%)**
Tel.: (613) 226-5511
Web Site: https://www.harriscomputer.com

Computer Systems Mfr
N.A.I.C.S.: 541512
Jeff Bender *(CEO)*

Subsidiary (Domestic):

ACCEO Solutions, Inc. **(2)**
75 Queen Street Suite 5100, Montreal, H3C 2N6, QC, Canada
Tel.: (514) 288-7161
Web Site: https://www.acceo.com
Business Information Technology Services
N.A.I.C.S.: 541512
Erick Lamarche *(Exec VP-Retail Solutions)*

Subsidiary (Domestic):

ACCEO Solutions, Inc. - Quebec **(3)**
1291 Jules Verne Avenue Suite 300, L'Ancienne-Lorette, G2E 6L6, QC, Canada
Tel.: (418) 877-0088
Business Information Technology Services
N.A.I.C.S.: 423430

ProfitMaster Canada Inc. **(3)**
1000 Lorimer Blvd 2, Winnipeg, R3P 1C8, MB, Canada
Tel.: (204) 889-5320
Business Management Software Development Services
N.A.I.C.S.: 513210

Subsidiary (Domestic):

Advanced Utility Systems Corporation **(2)**
2235 Sheppard Avenue East Suite 1400, Toronto, M2J 5B5, ON, Canada **(100%)**
Tel.: (416) 496-0149
Web Site: http://www.advancedutility.com
Customer Information & Billing Solutions Software
N.A.I.C.S.: 334610

Subsidiary (US):

Amazing Charts LLC **(2)**
1600 Division Rd Ste 2000, West Warwick, RI 02893
Tel.: (613) 226-5511
Web Site: https://amazingcharts.com
Electronic Health Record Software & Services
N.A.I.C.S.: 513210

Subsidiary (Domestic):

CareTracker, Inc. **(3)**
1600 Div Rd Ste 2000, West Warwick, RI 02893
Tel.: (866) 382-5932
Healtcare Services
N.A.I.C.S.: 621610
Russ Keene *(Exec VP)*

Subsidiary (Domestic):

Pulse Systems, Inc. **(4)**
3020 N Cypress Dr Ste 200, Wichita, KS 67226
Tel.: (316) 636-5900
Web Site: https://www.pulseinc.com
Sales Range: $10-24.9 Million
Emp.: 115
Electronic Health Record, Practice Management & Revenue Cycle Management Solutions
N.A.I.C.S.: 513210

Subsidiary (US):

Asolva, Inc. **(2)**
80 S Lk Ave, Pasadena, CA 91101
Web Site: http://www.asolva.com
Custom Computer Programming Services
N.A.I.C.S.: 541511
Chun Wong *(Founder & CEO)*

Bizmatics Inc. **(2)**
20863 Stevens Creek Blvd, Cupertino, CA 95014
Tel.: (408) 873-3030
Web Site: http://www.bizmaticsinc.com
Rev.: $3,060,000
Emp.: 20
Data Processing, Hosting & Related Services
N.A.I.C.S.: 518210
Vinay Dheshpande *(CEO)*

Constellation Software Inc.—(Continued)

Capital Computer Associates, Inc. (2)
1 Cerone Commercial Dr, Albany, NY 12205
Tel.: (518) 435-0500
Web Site: http://www.cap-comp.com
Sales Range: $1-9.9 Million
Emp.: 10
Custom Computer Programming Services
N.A.I.C.S.: 541511

Subsidiary (Domestic):

Cogsdale Corporation (2)
18 Great George Street, Charlottetown, C1A 4J6, PE, Canada
Tel.: (902) 892-3101
Web Site: http://www.cogsdale.com
Service-Oriented Business Solutions for Local Governments & Utilities
N.A.I.C.S.: 513210

Subsidiary (US):

Computer Software Innovations, Inc. (2)
900 E Main St Ste T, Easley, SC 29640
Tel.: (864) 855-3900
Computer Software Solutions
N.A.I.C.S.: 541511

Subsidiary (Domestic):

Copernic Inc. (2)
400 Jean-Lesage Blvd, Quebec, G1K 8W1, QC, Canada
Tel.: (418) 527-0528
Web Site: http://www.copernic.com
Sales Range: $1-9.9 Million
Emp.: 25
Internet Marketing & Information Retrieval Services
N.A.I.C.S.: 517810

Subsidiary (Domestic):

LTRIM Technologies (3)
140440 Armand Frappier Blvd, Laval, H7V 4B4, QC, Canada (100%)
Tel.: (450) 681-3171
Web Site: http://www.ltrim.com
Semiconductor Mfr
N.A.I.C.S.: 334413

Subsidiary (US):

Core Technology Corp. (2)
5859 W Saginaw Hwy Ste 217, Lansing, MI 48917
Tel.: (517) 627-1521
Web Site: https://www.coretechcorp.com
Sales Range: $1-9.9 Million
Software Publisher
N.A.I.C.S.: 513210
David Hadsall (Pres)

Subsidiary (Domestic):

Eagle Advantage Solutions, Inc. (2)
133 Parkwood Cir, Carrollton, GA 30117-8756
Tel.: (770) 834-5283
Web Site: https://www.eagleadvantage.com
Public Safety Software Developer
N.A.I.C.S.: 513210
Cathy Guillebeau (Pres)

Escholar, LLC (2)
222 Bloomingdale Rd, White Plains, NY 10605
Tel.: (914) 989-2900
Web Site: http://www.escholar.com
Sales Range: $1-9.9 Million
Emp.: 11
Magnetic & Optical Recording Media Mfr
N.A.I.C.S.: 334610
Shawn Bay (Founder & CEO)

IMD Soft (2)
300 1st Ave, Needham Heights, MA 02494
Tel.: (781) 449-5567
Web Site: http://www.imd-soft.com
Rev.: $1,256,000
Emp.: 8
Custom Computer Programming Services
N.A.I.C.S.: 541511
Eran David (CTO)

Iatric Systems, Inc. (2)
100 Quannapowitt Pkwy Unit 405, Wakefield, MA 01880

Tel.: (978) 805-4100
Web Site: http://www.iatric.com
Healthcare Software Developer
N.A.I.C.S.: 541511
Frank J. Fortner (Pres & COO)

Ingenious Med, Inc. (2)
400 Galleria Pkwy SE Ste 1600, Atlanta, GA 30339
Tel.: (404) 815-0862
Web Site: https://www.ingeniousmed.com
Healthcare Software Development Services
N.A.I.C.S.: 541511
Steven T. Liu (Founder & Chief Medical Officer)

Subsidiary (Domestic):

MS Govern (2)
1 Antares Drive Suite 400, Ottawa, K2E 8C4, ON, Canada (100%)
Tel.: (613) 226-5511
Web Site: http://www.msgovern.com
Software Solutions for Government & Public Safety Organizations
N.A.I.C.S.: 334610
Fabrice Olivier (VP-R&D)

Subsidiary (US):

Innoprise Software, Inc. (3)
520 Zang St Ste 200, Broomfield, CO 80021
Tel.: (303) 226-0050
Web Site: http://www.msgovern.com
Sales Range: $25-49.9 Million
Emp.: 25
Software Developer
N.A.I.C.S.: 513210

Subsidiary (US):

Mid America Computer Corp. (2)
111 Admiral Dr, Blair, NE 68008
Tel.: (402) 426-6222
Web Site: http://www.maccnet.com
Rev.: $16,425,191
Emp.: 200
Data Processing Services
N.A.I.C.S.: 518210
Bob Sims (COO & Exec VP)

Subsidiary (Domestic):

Carrier Management Systems, Inc. (3)
1242 N 4th, Abilene, TX 79601
Tel.: (325) 677-5900
Web Site: https://nams.net
Sales Range: $1-9.9 Million
Emp.: 15
Prepackaged Software
N.A.I.C.S.: 513210
Paul Bilberry (Pres)

Subsidiary (US):

Pacific Medical Management Services, Inc (2)
371 Van Ness Way Ste 210, Torrance, CA 90501-6297
Tel.: (503) 695-5200
Management Consulting Services
N.A.I.C.S.: 541618
Maria C. Hack (Pres)

Picis Clinical Solutions, Inc. (2)
100 Quannapowitt Pkwy Ste 405, Wakefield, MA 01880-1321
Tel.: (781) 557-3000
Web Site: http://www.picis.com
Emp.: 500
Healthcare Information Systems
N.A.I.C.S.: 541512
Marc Lloses Padilla (VP-R&D)

Subsidiary (Non-US):

Picis Clinical Solutions S.A. (3)
Carrer del Cister 2, 08022, Barcelona, Spain
Tel.: (34) 93 547 8303
Web Site: http://www.picis.com
Healthcare Information Systems
N.A.I.C.S.: 541512

Subsidiary (Domestic):

Picis Clinical Solutions, Ltd. (3)
100 Quannapowitt Parkway Ste 405, Wakefield, MA 01880

Tel.: (781) 557-3000
Web Site: http://www.picis.com
Healthcare Information Systems
N.A.I.C.S.: 541512

Subsidiary (US):

Questline, Inc. (2)
2025 Riverside Dr, Upper Arlington, OH 43221
Web Site: http://www.questline.com
Sales Range: $1-9.9 Million
Emp.: 24
Online Service Providers
N.A.I.C.S.: 561499
Dave Reim (Pres & CEO)

Solutions, Inc. (2)
2311 W 18th St, Spencer, IA 51301-2631
Tel.: (712) 262-4520
Web Site: https://www.gmdsolutions.com
Sales Range: $1-9.9 Million
Emp.: 24
Government Software Developer
N.A.I.C.S.: 513210
Alaire Nielsen (CFO, VP & Office Mgr)

Subsidiary (Domestic):

Syscon Justice Systems, Inc. (2)
3600 Lysander Lane Suite 300, Richmond, V7B 1C3, BC, Canada
Tel.: (604) 606-7650
Web Site: http://www.syscon.net
Prison Management Software Publisher & Consulting Services
N.A.I.C.S.: 513210
Kerry Lynn (Exec VP)

Subsidiary (US):

digiChart Inc. (2)
100 Winners Cir N Ste 450, Brentwood, TN 37027
Web Site: http://www.digichart.com
Software Provider to Medical Practices
N.A.I.C.S.: 513210

Subsidiary (Non-US):

i2 Ltd. (2)
The Visual Space Capital Park Fulbourn, Cambridge, CB21 5XH, United Kingdom
Tel.: (44) 1223728600
Sales Range: $25-49.9 Million
Emp.: 170
Developer of Visual Investigative Analysis Software
N.A.I.C.S.: 513210

Subsidiary (US):

Rosoka Software, Inc. (3)
950 Herndon Pkwy Ste 280, Herndon, VA 20170-5537
Tel.: (703) 391-0381
Web Site: http://www.rosoka.com
Computer System Design Services
N.A.I.C.S.: 541512
Gregory Roberts (CEO)

i2 Inc. (3)
1430 Spring Hill Rd Ste 600, McLean, VA 22102
Tel.: (703) 921-0195
Web Site: http://www.i2inc.com
Sales Range: $75-99.9 Million
Developer of Visual Investigative Analysis Software
N.A.I.C.S.: 513210

Perseus Operating Group (1)
75 Frontenac Drive West Wing, Markham, L3R 6H2, ON, Canada
Web Site: https://www.csiperseus.com
Software Publisher
N.A.I.C.S.: 513210
Mark Leonard (Pres)

Subsidiary (US):

Mortgage Builder Software, Inc. (2)
2 Towne Sq Ste 150, Southfield, MI 48076
Tel.: (947) 985-9371
Web Site: https://www.mortgagebuilder.com
Emp.: 80
Mortgage Software Developer
N.A.I.C.S.: 541511
Stephen Ryczek (Pres & Gen Mgr)

Subsidiary (Domestic):

GCC Servicing Systems, Inc. (3)
24370 Northwestern Hwy, Southfield, MI 48075
Tel.: (248) 352-1560
Data Processing, Hosting & Related Services
N.A.I.C.S.: 518210

Subsidiary (US):

Optimal Blue (2)
5340 Legacy Dr Bldg 2 2nd Fl, Plano, TX 75024
Tel.: (972) 781-0200
Web Site: http://www2.optimalblue.com
Emp.: 500
Software Developer & Publisher
N.A.I.C.S.: 518210
Sue Baker (VP-Product & Client Svcs)

Subsidiary (Domestic):

Comergence Compliance Monitoring, LLC (3)
25910 Acero Ste 260, Mission Viejo, CA 92691
Tel.: (972) 781-0200
Web Site:
  http://www.comergencecompliance.com
Financial Services
N.A.I.C.S.: 523999
Scott Happ (CEO)

QuadraMed Corporation (1)
12110 Sunset Hills Rd Ste 600, Reston, VA 20190
Tel.: (703) 709-2300
Web Site: http://www.quadramed.com
Sales Range: $150-199.9 Million
Emp.: 650
Software, Web-Enabled Solutions & Professional Consulting Services to Hospitals & Healthcare Providers for Information Management
N.A.I.C.S.: 541511

Tecplot, Inc. (1)
3535 Factoria Blvd SE Ste 550, Bellevue, WA 98006
Tel.: (425) 653-1200
Web Site: https://www.tecplot.com
Software Development Services
N.A.I.C.S.: 541511
Alan Klug (Pres)

Topicus.com Inc. (1)
Singel 25 7411 HW, Deventer, Netherlands
Tel.: (31) 570662662
Web Site: http://www.topicus.com
Rev.: $1,241,829,120
Assets: $1,584,233,359
Liabilities: $930,206,425
Net Worth: $654,026,935
Earnings: $127,416,933
Emp.: 8,000
Fiscal Year-end: 12/31/2023
Software Development Services
N.A.I.C.S.: 541511
Robin Van Poelje (Chm & CEO)

Subsidiary (Domestic):

Total Specific Solutions (TSS) B.V. (2)
Ringwade 61 F, Nieuwegein, Netherlands
Tel.: (31) 88 660 33 33
Web Site:
  https://www.totalspecificsolutions.com
Software Development Services
N.A.I.C.S.: 513210

Subsidiary (Non-US):

Sygnity S.A. (3)
ul Postepu 17B, 02-676, Warsaw, Poland (72.68%)
Tel.: (48) 222908800
Web Site: https://www.sygnity.pl
Rev.: $73,982,723
Assets: $82,875,508
Liabilities: $26,834,604
Net Worth: $56,040,904
Earnings: $12,688,516
Emp.: 628
Fiscal Year-end: 12/31/2023
IT Solutions & Services
N.A.I.C.S.: 541512

Inga Jedrzejewska *(CFO & Member-Mgmt Bd)*

Vela Software International Inc. **(1)**
360 Adelaide Street West Suite 500, Toronto, M5V 1R7, ON, Canada
Tel.: (416) 861-2279
Web Site:
    https://www.velasoftwaregroup.com
Software Development Services
N.A.I.C.S.: 541511
Damian Mckay *(CEO)*

Division (Domestic):

Aquila Software **(2)**
26 Soho Street Suite 400, Toronto, M5T 1Z7, ON, Canada
Tel.: (416) 861-2279
Web Site: https://www.aquilasw.com
Software Development Services
N.A.I.C.S.: 513210
Daniel Lee *(CEO)*

Subsidiary (US):

Cibar, Inc. **(3)**
4575 Hilton Pkwy Ste 201, Colorado Springs, CO 80907
Tel.: (719) 260-6700
Web Site: http://www.cibar.com
Sales Range: $1-9.9 Million
Emp.: 16
Custom Computer Programming Services, Nsk
N.A.I.C.S.: 541511
Loren Shannon *(CEO)*

Volaris Group Inc. **(1)**
5060 Spectrum Way Suite 100, Mississauga, L4W 5N5, ON, Canada
Tel.: (647) 951-9345
Web Site: https://www.volarisgroup.com
Holding Company; Specialized Business Software Publisher
N.A.I.C.S.: 551112
Mark Miller *(CEO)*

Subsidiary (Non-US):

AdaptIT Holdings Limited **(2)**
152 14th Road Midrand, Midrand, 2196, Gauteng, South Africa **(63.87%)**
Tel.: (27) 104940000
Web Site: http://www.adaptit.co.za
Rev.: $102,280,407
Assets: $115,180,547
Liabilities: $66,887,589
Net Worth: $48,292,958
Earnings: $5,430,854
Emp.: 1,088
Fiscal Year-end: 06/30/2019
Software Solutions Services
N.A.I.C.S.: 513210
Tiffany Dunsdon *(CEO)*

Subsidiary (Non-US):

Adapt IT Australasia (Pty) Ltd **(3)**
Level 12 360 Collins Street, Melbourne, 3000, VIC, Australia
Tel.: (61) 399464222
Information Technology Services
N.A.I.C.S.: 541511

Adapt IT Botswana (Pty) Ltd **(3)**
Fairscape Precinct Plot 70667, Fairgrounds Office Park Building 2 Floor 5, Gaborone, Botswana
Tel.: (267) 3167456
Information Technology Services
N.A.I.C.S.: 541511

Adapt IT International Limited **(3)**
Building 10 Uniciti Business Park Riviere Noire Road, Bambous, 90203, Mauritius
Tel.: (230) 4529349
Information Technology Services
N.A.I.C.S.: 541511

Adapt IT Nigeria Limited **(3)**
10 Akiongun Street New Market Oniru Victoria Island, Lagos, Nigeria
Tel.: (234) 14545042
Information Technology Services
N.A.I.C.S.: 541511

Adapt IT Solutions Limited **(3)**
Baobab Suite 2nd Floor Riverside Green Suite Riverside Drive, Nairobi, Kenya
Tel.: (254) 715361020

Information Technology Services
N.A.I.C.S.: 541511

Adapt IT Solutions Pte Limited **(3)**
1 Neil Road 02-01, Singapore, 088804, Singapore
Tel.: (65) 66929044
Information Technology Services
N.A.I.C.S.: 541511

Subsidiary (Domestic):

Micros South Africa (Pty) Ltd **(3)**
152 14th Road, Noordwyk, Midrand, 1687, South Africa
Tel.: (27) 117455333
Web Site: https://www.micros.co.za
Information Technology Services
N.A.I.C.S.: 541511
Reginald Sibeko *(Mng Dir)*

Subsidiary (US):

AssetWorks, Inc. **(2)**
998 Old Eagle School Rd Ste 1215, Wayne, PA 19087
Tel.: (610) 687-9202
Web Site: https://www.assetworks.com
Enterprise Asset Management Software & Solutions
N.A.I.C.S.: 513210
Michael Borello *(VP-Property Risk & Asset Mgmt-Div)*

Subsidiary (Domestic):

SoftChalk LLC **(3)**
22 S Auburn Ave, Richmond, VA 23221-2910
Web Site: http://www.softchalk.com
Software Publisher
N.A.I.C.S.: 513210
Corey Davis *(Exec Dir-OC Global)*

Subsidiary (Domestic):

Bravura Security, Inc. **(2)**
1401-1st Street S E Suite 500, Calgary, T2G 2J3, AB, Canada
Tel.: (403) 233-0740
Web Site: https://www.bravurasecurity.com
Sales Range: $25-49.9 Million
Emp.: 140
Access Management Software Development Services
N.A.I.C.S.: 541511
Gideon Shoham *(Co-Founder)*

Subsidiary (US):

Constellation Justice Systems Inc. **(2)**
141 Sullys Trl Ste 3, Pittsford, NY 14534
Tel.: (585) 218-0420
Software Reproducing
N.A.I.C.S.: 334610

Courtview Justice Solutions Inc. **(2)**
5399 Lauby Rd, North Canton, OH 44720
Tel.: (330) 470-4280
Web Site: http://www.courtview.com
Software Development Services
N.A.I.C.S.: 541511

Datapro, Inc. **(2)**
770 Ponce De Leon Blvd, Coral Gables, FL 33134
Tel.: (305) 374-0606
Web Site: http://datapromiami.com
Rev.: $10,000,000
Emp.: 54
Computer System Design Services
N.A.I.C.S.: 541512
Ricardo R. Montero *(Founder)*

EnvisionWare, Inc. **(2)**
1 Sugarloaf Ctr 1960 Satellite Blvd Ste 4100, Duluth, GA 30097-4127
Tel.: (678) 382-6500
Web Site: https://www.envisionware.com
Custom Computer Programming Services
N.A.I.C.S.: 541511
Michael Monk *(Co-Founder & CEO)*

Subsidiary (Non-US):

Flash Networks Ltd. **(2)**
7 Sapir Road, PO Box 2070, Herzliyya, 4685211, Israel
Tel.: (972) 9 958 0666
Web Site: http://www.flashnetworks.com

Mobile Internet Services
N.A.I.C.S.: 513199
Ofer Gottfried *(CTO)*

Subsidiary (US):

Flash Networks Inc. **(3)**
505 Thornall St Ste 205, Edison, NJ 08837
Tel.: (732) 205-9401
Mobile Internet Services
N.A.I.C.S.: 517121

Subsidiary (Non-US):

Flash Networks Singapore Pte Ltd **(3)**
71 Bukit Batok Crescent 80-90 Prestige Centre, Singapore, 658071, Singapore
Tel.: (65) 63162265
Mobile Internet Services
N.A.I.C.S.: 517121

Subsidiary (Domestic):

Incognito Software Systems Inc. **(2)**
375 Water Street Suite 500, Vancouver, V6B 5C6, BC, Canada
Tel.: (604) 688-4332
Web Site: https://www.incognito.com
Internet-Related Software Services
N.A.I.C.S.: 561499
Pete Koat *(COO)*

Subsidiary (US):

MedAptus, Inc. **(2)**
4917 Waters Edge Dr Ste 135, Raleigh, NC 27606
Tel.: (617) 896-4000
Web Site: https://www.medaptus.com
Sales Range: $1-9.9 Million
Software Publisher
N.A.I.C.S.: 513210
Ryan Secan *(Chief Medical Officer)*

RAF Technology Inc. **(2)**
15400 NE 90th St Ste 300, Redmond, WA 98052
Tel.: (425) 867-0700
Web Site: http://www.raf.com
Rev.: $6,000,000
Emp.: 30
Custom Computer Programming Services
N.A.I.C.S.: 541511
Bryan Turner *(CTO)*

Subsidiary (Non-US):

Sicap Schweiz AG **(2)**
Oberdorfstrasse 2, 6340, Baar, Switzerland
Tel.: (41) 58 822 90 00
Web Site: http://www.sicap.com
Telecommunication Networking Services
N.A.I.C.S.: 517810
Richard Choi *(CEO)*

Subsidiary (Domestic):

Trapeze Software Inc. **(2)**
5800 Explorer Drive 5th Floor, Mississauga, L4W 5K9, ON, Canada
Tel.: (905) 629-8727
Web Site: http://www.trapezesoftware.com
Software Development Services
N.A.I.C.S.: 541511

Subsidiary (US):

Cultura Technologies Inc. **(3)**
3820 Mansell Rd Ste 375, Alpharetta, GA 30022
Tel.: (678) 249-3200
Web Site: https://www.culturatech.com
Agricultural Software Development Services
N.A.I.C.S.: 541511
Rich Reynertson *(COO & Mng Dir-Grain & Oilseed)*

Subsidiary (Domestic):

Red River Software **(4)**
4150 19th Ave S Unit 202, Fargo, ND 58103
Tel.: (701) 281-0781
Web Site: http://www.redriversoftware.com
Software Publisher
N.A.I.C.S.: 513210

Subsidiary (Domestic):

Modaxo Inc. **(3)**
5060 Spectrum Way Suite 100, Missis-

sauga, L4W 5N5, ON, Canada
Tel.: (416) 473-6302
Web Site: https://www.modaxo.com
Emp.: 100
Software Development Services
N.A.I.C.S.: 513210
Bill Delaney *(CEO)*

Subsidiary (US):

Transloc Inc. **(4)**
4505 Emperor Blvd Ste 120, Durham, NC 27703
Web Site: http://www.transloc.com
Transportation Technology Services
N.A.I.C.S.: 541511
Brett Wheatley *(CEO)*

TripSpark Technologies **(4)**
5265 Rockwell Dr NE, Cedar Rapids, IA 52402
Tel.: (877) 448-7273
Web Site: https://www.tripspark.com
Integrated Software & Hardware Solutions
N.A.I.C.S.: 513210

Subsidiary (Domestic):

Routematch Software, Inc. **(5)**
1230 Peachtree St NE Ste 2800, Atlanta, GA 30309-3458
Tel.: (404) 876-5160
Web Site: http://www.routematch.com
Software Publisher
N.A.I.C.S.: 513210

Subsidiary (Non-US):

Trapeze Group (UK) Limited **(3)**
A1 South Methuen Park, Chippenham, SN14 0GT, Wiltshire, United Kingdom
Tel.: (44) 8082811039
Web Site: http://www.trapezegroup.co.uk
Sales Range: $25-49.9 Million
Transportation Software Development Services
N.A.I.C.S.: 541511

Trapeze Group Deutschland GmbH **(3)**
Schmalbachstrasse 16, 38112, Braunschweig, Germany
Tel.: (49) 531701040
Web Site: http://www.trapezegroup.de
Transportation Software Development Services
N.A.I.C.S.: 541511

Trapeze Group Europe A/S **(3)**
Sommervej 31 D 4, 8210, Aarhus, Denmark
Tel.: (45) 87441600
Web Site: https://www.trapezegroup.dk
Software Development Services
N.A.I.C.S.: 541511
Jesper Ulsted *(CEO)*

Trapeze ITS Germany GmbH **(3)**
Nonnendammallee 101, 13629, Berlin, Germany
Tel.: (49) 30 386 20772
Web Site: http://www.trapezeits.de
Sales Range: $25-49.9 Million
Emp.: 6
Transportation Software Development Services
N.A.I.C.S.: 541511

Trapeze ITS Switzerland GmbH **(3)**
Industrieplatz 3, Neuhausen, 8212, Switzerland
Tel.: (41) 589111111
Sales Range: $25-49.9 Million
Emp.: 23
Transportation Software Development Services
N.A.I.C.S.: 541511
Hans-Peter Schaer *(CEO)*

Trapeze Poland sp. z o.o. **(3)**
ul Muchoborska 18, 54-424, Wroclaw, Poland
Tel.: (48) 71 7985 820
Sales Range: $25-49.9 Million
Emp.: 6
Software Development Services
N.A.I.C.S.: 541511
Wojciech Palczynski *(Mng Dir)*

Subsidiary (US):

Trapeze Software Group, Inc. **(3)**

Constellation Software Inc.—(Continued)

8360 E Via de Ventura Ste L 200, Scottsdale, AZ 85258
Tel.: (480) 627-8400
Web Site: http://www.trapezegroup.com
Emp.: 10
Software Development Services
N.A.I.C.S.: 541511

Subsidiary (US):

Tribute Inc. (2)
141 Broad Blvd Ste 206, Cuyahoga Falls, OH 44221
Tel.: (330) 656-3006
Web Site: https://www.tribute.com
Sales Range: $1-9.9 Million
Software Publisher
N.A.I.C.S.: 513210
Tim Reynolds (CEO)

Wennsoft Inc. (2)
1970 S Calhoun Rd, New Berlin, WI 53151-2214
Tel.: (262) 821-4100
Web Site: http://www.wennsoft.com
Sales Range: $10-24.9 Million
Emp.: 120
Computer Software Development
N.A.I.C.S.: 541511
Tim Conroy (Exec VP-Pro Svcs)

Wynne Systems, Inc. (2)
2601 Main St Ste 270, Irvine, CA 92614
Tel.: (949) 224-6300
Web Site: https://www.wynnesystems.com
Rental Management Software Publisher
N.A.I.C.S.: 513210
Tran Ly (Gen Mgr)

CONSTELLATION TECHNOLOGIES LIMITED

Level 7 420 Collins Street, Melbourne, 3000, VIC, Australia
Tel.: (61) 467559037   AU
Web Site: https://www.ccp-technologies.com
Year Founded: 1982
CT1—(ASX)
Rev.: $898,819
Assets: $851,661
Liabilities: $269,251
Net Worth: $582,411
Earnings: ($81,241)
Fiscal Year-end: 06/30/24
Software Publisher
N.A.I.C.S.: 513210
Phillip Hains (Co-Sec)

CONSTELLIUM SE

Washington Plaza 40-44 rue, Washington, 75008, Paris, France
Tel.: (33) 73014620   NL
Web Site:
  https://www.constellium.com
CSTM—(NYSE)
Rev.: $7,812,432,549
Assets: $5,030,218,001
Liabilities: $4,097,776,818
Net Worth: $932,441,183
Earnings: $139,218,649
Emp.: 12,000
Fiscal Year-end: 12/31/23
Holding Company; Rolled & Extruded Aluminum Products
N.A.I.C.S.: 551112
Peter Basten (Pres-Pkg & Automotive Rolled Products Bus Unit)

Subsidiaries:

Constellium (1)
40-44 rue Washington, F-75008, Paris, France (51%)
Tel.: (33) 1 7301 4600
Web Site: http://www.constellium.com
Aluminium Products Mfr
N.A.I.C.S.: 332999

Subsidiary (US):

Constellium Automotive USA, LLC (2)
46555 Magellan Dr, Novi, MI 48377

Tel.: (248) 668-3200
Web Site: http://www.constellium.com
Sales Range: $25-49.9 Million
Emp.: 50
Aluminum Automotive Products Mfr
N.A.I.C.S.: 332999

Subsidiary (Domestic):

Constellium Aviatube SAS (2)
15 rue de Grande-Bretagne, Zone Industrielle, Carquefou, 44470, France
Tel.: (33) 240184700
Web Site: http://www.constellium.com
Sales Range: $100-124.9 Million
Emp.: 500
Aluminum Tube Mfr
N.A.I.C.S.: 331318

Subsidiary (Non-US):

Constellium Extrusions Decin s.r.o. (2)
Ustecka 37, 405 02, Decin, Czech Republic
Tel.: (420) 412508111
Sales Range: $125-149.9 Million
Emp.: 600
Extruded, Cast, Pressed & Drawn Aluminum Products Mfr
N.A.I.C.S.: 331318
Josef Kreuter (Production Mgr & Mgr-Technical)

Constellium Extrusions Landau GmbH (2)
Landkommissarstrasse 16, Industriegebiet Ost, 76829, Landau in der Pfalz, Germany
Tel.: (49) 63419570
Sales Range: $100-124.9 Million
Emp.: 460
Aluminum Extruded Product Mfr
N.A.I.C.S.: 331318
Peter Pasten (Mng Dir)

Subsidiary (Domestic):

Constellium Sabart SAS (2)
Usine de Sabart 9400, Tarascon, France
Tel.: (33) 561024000
Aluminum Component Mfr
N.A.I.C.S.: 331318

Subsidiary (Non-US):

Constellium Switzerland AG (2)
Max Hoegger-Strasse 6, PO Box 1907, 8048, Zurich, Switzerland
Tel.: (41) 444386600
Web Site: http://www.constellium.com
Emp.: 75
Transportation Industry Engineered Aluminum Components Mfr
N.A.I.C.S.: 332999

Subsidiary (Domestic):

Constellium Ussel SAS (2)
Zone Industrielle La Petite Borde, PO Box 48, 19202, Ussel, Cedex, France
Tel.: (33) 5 5546 5546
Web Site: http://www.constellium.com
Sales Range: $50-74.9 Million
Emp.: 250
Aluminum Aerospace Castings
N.A.I.C.S.: 331523
Laurent Micoulet (Mng Dir)

Subsidiary (Non-US):

Constellium Valais SA (2)
Rue des Laminoirs, CH-3960, Sierre, Switzerland
Tel.: (41) 27 457 5111
Web Site: http://www.constellium.com
Extruded & Engineered Aluminum Component Mfr
N.A.I.C.S.: 332999

CONSTI OYJ

Valimotie 16, 380, Helsinki, Finland
Tel.: (358) 102886000
Web Site: https://www.consti.fi
CONSTI—(HEL)
Rev.: $329,394,561
Assets: $133,060,652
Liabilities: $93,986,618
Net Worth: $39,074,034
Earnings: $9,163,609
Emp.: 975

Fiscal Year-end: 12/31/22
Building Maintenance Services
N.A.I.C.S.: 561790
Esa Korkeel (CEO)

CONSTREXIM NO. 8 INVESTMENT & CONSTRUCTION JSC

Constrexim Building 8 Km 8 Nguyen Trai Street Thanh Xuan Bac Ward, Thanh Xuan District, Hanoi, Vietnam
Tel.: (84) 435543197
Web Site:
  https://www.constrexim8.com.vn
CX8—(HNX)
Rev.: $9,257,200
Assets: $11,138,000
Liabilities: $8,332,600
Net Worth: $2,805,400
Earnings: $47,000
Fiscal Year-end: 12/31/22
Building Construction Services
N.A.I.C.S.: 236116
Vu Duc Tien (Chm)

CONSTRONICS INFRA LIMITED

No 3/2 Third Floor Narasimmapuram Sai Baba Colony, Mylapore, Chennai, 600004, Tamil Nadu, India
Tel.: (91) 4448589999
Web Site:
  https://constronicsinfra.com
523844—(BOM)
Rev.: $101,780
Assets: $124,935
Liabilities: $95,124
Net Worth: $29,811
Earnings: $6,791
Emp.: 9
Fiscal Year-end: 03/31/23
Orthopedic Implants & Instruments Mfr
N.A.I.C.S.: 339113
Sundararaghavan R. (Mng Dir)

CONSTRUCCIONES Y AUXILIAR DE FERROCARRILES S.A.

Jose Miguel Iturrioz 26 Beasain, 20200, Guipuzcoa, Spain
Tel.: (34) 943880100   ES
Web Site: https://www.caf.net
Year Founded: 1917
CAF—(MAD)
Rev.: $2,909,009,928
Assets: $4,840,959,924
Liabilities: $4,006,253,236
Net Worth: $834,706,689
Earnings: ($69,327,173)
Emp.: 13,179
Fiscal Year-end: 12/31/19
Railway Equipment & Components Mfr & Distr
N.A.I.C.S.: 336510
Andres Arizkorreta Garcia (Chm & CEO)

Subsidiaries:

Actren Mantenimiento Ferroviario, S.A. (1)
Complejo Ferroviario Fuencarral C/ Antonio Cabezon s/n, 28034, Madrid, Spain
Tel.: (34) 915010396
Web Site: http://www.actren.es
Train Maintenance Services
N.A.I.C.S.: 488210

CAF Argelia EURL (1)
Residence Petit Hydra Entree E107 Paradou, Hydra, Algeria
Tel.: (213) 21600807
Railway Vehicle Mfr
N.A.I.C.S.: 336510

CAF Brasil Industria e Comercio, S.A. (1)
Rua Tabapua n 81 - 10 andar, Itaim Bibi, Sao Paulo, 04533-010, Brazil
Tel.: (55) 1130740600
Railway Vehicle Mfr

N.A.I.C.S.: 336510

CAF Chile, S.A. (1)
Avenida de los Conquistadores 1700 27th fl, Comuna de Providencia, 06252, Santiago, Chile
Tel.: (56) 24737200
Railway Equipment Mfr
N.A.I.C.S.: 336350

CAF Deutschland GmbH (1)
Seidlstrasse 26, 80335, Munich, Germany
Tel.: (49) 89544790100
Railway Vehicle Mfr
N.A.I.C.S.: 336510

CAF Francia, S.A.S. (1)
9 to 11 Rue Benoit Malon, Suresnes, Cedex, France
Tel.: (33) 145064400
Web Site: http://www.caf.fr
Sales Range: $25-49.9 Million
Emp.: 10
Railway Equipments Mfr
N.A.I.C.S.: 488210

CAF Hungary Kft. (1)
Vaci ut 22-24 7 emelet, 1132, Budapest, Hungary
Tel.: (36) 18089444
Railway Vehicle Mfr,
N.A.I.C.S.: 336510

CAF India Private Limited (1)
Pullman/Novotel Commercial Tower 6th Floor Asset No 2, Hospitality District Near IGI Airport, New Delhi, 110037, India
Tel.: (91) 1140250000
Railway Vehicle Mfr
N.A.I.C.S.: 336510

CAF Israel Rails Ltd. (1)
Sapir Tower Tuval 40 36 Floor, Ramat Gan, Israel
Tel.: (972) 3720002
Railway Vehicle Mfr
N.A.I.C.S.: 336510

CAF Italia, S.R.L. (1)
Via Santa Croce in Gerusalemme 96, 00185, Rome, Italy
Tel.: (39) 0677073142
Web Site: http://www.cafitalia.eu
Train Maintenance Services
N.A.I.C.S.: 488210

CAF Mexico, S.A. de C.V. (1)
Oriente 1 piso Col Buenavista Delegacion Cuauhtemoc, Cruz Atoyac, Mexico, 6350, Mexico
Tel.: (52) 5556887543
Web Site: http://www.caf.es
Sales Range: $25-49.9 Million
Emp.: 80
Railway Equipments Mfr
N.A.I.C.S.: 488210

CAF Power & Automation, S.L.U. (1)
Parque Tecnologico de San Sebastian Pso Mikeletegi 58 - 2, 20009, San Sebastian, Spain
Tel.: (34) 943309251
Web Site: http://www.cafpower.com
Electric Traction Equipment Mfr
N.A.I.C.S.: 335312

CAF Rail Australia Pty Ltd (1)
Level 20 Suite 2002 321 Kent St, Sydney, 2000, NSW, Australia
Tel.: (61) 280845119
Railway Vehicle Mfr
N.A.I.C.S.: 336510

CAF Rail UK Limited (1)
The TechnoCentre Puma Way, Coventry, CV1 2TT, United Kingdom
Tel.: (44) 2476158195
Railway Vehicle Mfr
N.A.I.C.S.: 336510

CAF Signalling, S.L.U. (1)
C/ Juan Fermin Gilisagasti 4 2 a Planta, 20018, San Sebastian, Gipuzkoa, Spain
Tel.: (34) 943805575
Web Site: http://www.cafsignalling.com
Railway Signaling System Mfr & Distr
N.A.I.C.S.: 334290

CAF Turnkey & Engineering, S.L.U. (1)
Laida Bidea Edificio 205 2 a Planta, Parque

cientifico y Tecnologico de Bizkaia, 48170, Zamudio, Bizkaia, Spain
Tel.: (34) 946819550
Web Site: http://www.cafte.com
Emp.: 250
Construction & Engineering Services
N.A.I.C.S.: 541330

CAF USA, Inc. (1)
1401 K St NW Ste 1003, Washington, DC 20005
Tel.: (202) 898-4848
Web Site: https://www.cafusa.com
Railway Industries
N.A.I.C.S.: 488210
Virginaa Verdeja (VP)

Centro de Ensayos y Analisis Cetest, S.L. (1)
Lazkaibar s/n, 20200, Beasain, Spain
Tel.: (34) 943028690
Web Site: http://www.cetestgroup.com
Railway Testing Services
N.A.I.C.S.: 488210

Construcciones y Auxiliar de Ferro-carriles Argentina, S.A. (1)
Chacabuco 380 1er Piso, C1069AAH, Buenos Aires, Argentina
Tel.: (54) 1143434500
Train Maintenance Services
N.A.I.C.S.: 488210

Euromaint Gruppen AB (1)
Svetsarvagen 10, 171 41, Solna, Sweden
Tel.: (46) 8 515 15 000
Web Site: http://www.euromaint.com
Holding Company; Locomotive Repair & Maintenance Services
N.A.I.C.S.: 551112

Subsidiary (Domestic):

EuroMaint AB (2)
Vretenvagen 11, 171 41, Solna, Sweden
Tel.: (46) 8 515 15 000
Web Site: http://www.euromaint.se
Sales Range: $550-599.9 Million
Emp.: 1,100
Maintenance Services
N.A.I.C.S.: 488210

Subsidiary (Domestic):

EuroMaint Rail AB (3)
Vretenvagen 11, 171 41, Solna, Sweden
Tel.: (46) 851515000
Web Site: http://www.euromaint.com
Railway Technical Maintenance Services
N.A.I.C.S.: 488210
Matts Lindqvist (Bus Unit Mgr)

Geminys S.L. (1)
Parque Tecnologico de Miramon po Mikeletegi 55 1, 20009, Guipuzcoa, San Sebastian, Spain
Tel.: (34) 943 309 102
Web Site: http://www.geminys.com
Sales Range: $25-49.9 Million
Emp.: 50
Engineering & Construction Services
N.A.I.C.S.: 541330
Isabel Azanza (CEO)

Inversiones en Concesiones Ferroviarias, S.A. (1)
Jose Miguel Iturrioz, 26 Beasain, Guipuzcoa, 20200, Spain
Tel.: (34) 914352500
Web Site: http://www.cas.com
Sales Range: $100-124.9 Million
Emp.: 2,000
Railway Investment Services
N.A.I.C.S.: 523999
Andres Arizcorreta (CEO)

Lander Simulation & Training Solutions, S.A. (1)
Portuetxe 23A Local B3, 20018, San Sebastian, Gipuzkoa, Spain
Tel.: (34) 943217491
Web Site: http://www.landersimulation.com
Simulation & Training Services
N.A.I.C.S.: 611430

Rail Line Components, S.L.U. (1)
P I Apatta Erreka Uzturre Kalea 1 Local 101, 20400, Ibarra, Spain
Tel.: (34) 943028646
Web Site: http://www.rlcomponents.net

Railway Vehicle Parts & Component Distr
N.A.I.C.S.: 423860

Sermanfer, S.A.U. (1)
Servicios Centrales c/ Industrias n 4 Planta 2 Oficina 7, 28923, Alcorcon, Madrid, Spain
Tel.: (34) 916138054
Web Site: http://www.sermanfer.net
Railway Maintenance Services
N.A.I.C.S.: 488210

Solaris Austria GmbH (1)
Robinigstrasse 13, 5020, Salzburg, Austria
Tel.: (43) 662871928
Web Site: http://www.solarisbus
Bus & Trolleybus Mfr
N.A.I.C.S.: 336510

Solaris Bus & Coach Latvia Ltd. (1)
Gulbju iela 35, Riga, LV-1076, Latvia
Tel.: (371) 67815424
Bus & Trolleybus Mfr
N.A.I.C.S.: 336510

Solaris Bus & Coach Romania S.R.L. (1)
Str Corabia nr 53 B sector 2, Bucharest, Romania
Tel.: (40) 213611956
Web Site: http://www.solarisbus.com
Bus & Trolleybus Mfr
N.A.I.C.S.: 336510

Solaris Bus & Coach, Sp. z o.o. (1)
ul Obornicka 46, Bolechowo-Osiedle Owinska, 62-005, Poznan, Poland
Tel.: (48) 616672333
Web Site: http://www.solarisbus.com
Bus & Trolleybus Mfr
N.A.I.C.S.: 336510
Javier Calleja (CEO)

Solaris Bus Iberica, S.L.U. (1)
Avenida de Castilla 1 Pol Industrial Las Fronteras, 28830, San Fernando de Henares, Madrid, Spain
Tel.: (34) 912279199
Bus & Trolleybus Mfr
N.A.I.C.S.: 336510

Solaris Czech spol. S.R.O. (1)
Radvanicka 802/13, Michalkovice, 715 00, Ostrava, Czech Republic
Tel.: (420) 596232111
Web Site: http://www.solarisbus.com
Bus & Trolleybus Mfr
N.A.I.C.S.: 336510

Solaris France S.A.R.L. (1)
10 rue Charles Picard ZI Les Jonquieres, 57365, Ennery, France
Tel.: (33) 387734946
Web Site: http://www.solarisbus.com
Bus & Trolleybus Mfr
N.A.I.C.S.: 336510

Solaris Italia S.R.L. (1)
Via di Settebagni 390, 00139, Rome, Italy
Tel.: (39) 0688816435
Web Site: http://www.solarisbus.com
Bus & Trolleybus Mfr
N.A.I.C.S.: 336510

Solaris Norge AS (1)
Stromsveien 179, 0664, Oslo, Norway
Tel.: (47) 66991700
Web Site: http://www.solarisbus.com
Bus & Trolleybus Mfr
N.A.I.C.S.: 336510

Solaris Sverige AB (1)
Sadelgatan 8, 213 77, Malmo, Sweden
Tel.: (46) 40214200
Web Site: https://www.solarisbus.com
Bus & Trolleybus Mfr
N.A.I.C.S.: 336510

Tradinsa Industrial, S.L. (1)
Urbanizacion Zona 2 l'Estacio 29, Puigverd, 25153, Lleida, Cataluna, Spain
Tel.: (34) 973770713
Web Site: http://www.tradinsa.com
Railway Maintenance Services
N.A.I.C.S.: 488210

Trainelec, S.L. (1)
Polygon Katategi, Plot 3a Pavilion no 1, 20271, Guipuzcoa, Spain
Tel.: (34) 943690870
Web Site: http://www.trainelec.com
Railway Trains Equipment Mfr

N.A.I.C.S.: 488210

Trenes de Navarra, S.A.U. (1)
Poligono Industrial Parcela P1, 31590, Castejon, Navarra, Spain
Tel.: (34) 948814596
Web Site: http://www.trenasa.net
Railway Equipment Mfr & Distr
N.A.I.C.S.: 336510

CONSTRUCTII BIHOR SA
Str Berzei Nr 4, Bihor, Oradea, Romania
Tel.: (40) 259417512
Web Site:
    http://www.constructiibihor.ro
COBJ—(BUC)
Rev.: $20,560,044
Assets: $21,911,038
Liabilities: $13,872,941
Net Worth: $8,038,097
Earnings: $521,820
Emp.: 182
Fiscal Year-end: 12/31/20
Building Construction Services
N.A.I.C.S.: 236116

CONSTRUCTII COMPLEXE SA
B-Dul 1 Decembrie 1918 Nr 1Bis, Buzau, Romania
Tel.: (40) 238416720
Web Site: https://www.scccbuzau.ro
CPLB—(BUC)
Rev.: $611,651
Assets: $1,640,517
Liabilities: $315,929
Net Worth: $1,324,588
Earnings: ($327,929)
Emp.: 33
Fiscal Year-end: 12/31/23
Highway Construction Services
N.A.I.C.S.: 237990

CONSTRUCTII FEROVIARE CRAIOVA SA
Str Aleea I Bariera Valcii nr 28, CP 200100, Craiova, Dolj, Romania
Tel.: (40) 251414073
Web Site:
    http://constructii.feroviare.com
CFED—(BUC)
Rev.: $295,197
Assets: $659,768
Liabilities: $379,549
Net Worth: $280,220
Earnings: $3,990
Emp.: 2
Fiscal Year-end: 12/31/23
Road Construction
N.A.I.C.S.: 237310

CONSTRUCTII FEROVIARE SA
Str Egalitatii Nr 2, 800029, Galati, Romania
Tel.: (40) 745345290
Web Site: https://www.sccfgalati.ro
Year Founded: 1966
CORO—(BUC)
Rev.: $1,219,970
Assets: $2,101,988
Liabilities: $200,208
Net Worth: $1,901,781
Earnings: $13,725
Emp.: 35
Fiscal Year-end: 12/31/23
Highway Construction Services
N.A.I.C.S.: 237990
Tudoriu Constantin-Sorin (Pres)

CONSTRUCTII HIDROTEHNICE SA
str Toma Cozma nr 13, 700554, Iasi, Romania
Tel.: (40) 372733339
Web Site: https://www.conhidro.ro
CHIA—(BUC)
Rev.: $2,292,052
Assets: $9,433,580

Liabilities: $1,603,433
Net Worth: $7,830,147
Earnings: $16,305
Emp.: 58
Fiscal Year-end: 12/31/22
Dam Construction Services
N.A.I.C.S.: 237990
Careja Ioan (Deputy Gen Dir)

CONSTRUCTION & MATERI-ALS TRADING JOINT STOCK COMPANY
Floor 6 9-19 Ho Tung Mau Street District 1, Ho Chi Minh City, Vietnam
Tel.: (84) 8 3829 5488
Web Site: http://www.cnt.com.vn
Year Founded: 1981
Sales Range: $125-149.9 Million
Civil Engineering Services
N.A.I.C.S.: 237990

CONSTRUCTION ALBERT JEAN LTD.
4045 Parthenais Street, Montreal, H2K 3T8, QC, Canada
Tel.: (514) 522-2121
Web Site: http://www.albertjean.com
Sales Range: $10-24.9 Million
Emp.: 75
Building Construction Company
N.A.I.C.S.: 236220
Pierre Albert (Pres & COO)

CONSTRUCTION DISTRIBU-TION & SUPPLY COMPANY INC
4630 Dufferin Street Unit 8A, North York, M3H 5S4, ON, Canada
Tel.: (416) 665-8006
Web Site: http://www.cdsco.net
Year Founded: 1968
Rev.: $21,736,238
Emp.: 100
Building Construction
N.A.I.C.S.: 423390
Stan Lazar (VP)

CONSTRUCTION ENGINEER-ING GROUP CO., LTD.
Business Centre A-1 Shuidian Plaza Blck 1 No 312 Prt Ave, N 1 Wst of Gnsn Av Xintang Town Zengcheng City, Guangzhou, 511340, Guangdong, China
Tel.: (86) 2061776998
Web Site: http://www.gdsdej.com
002060—(SSE)
Rev.: $2,373,304,752
Assets: $5,669,561,196
Liabilities: $5,087,806,776
Net Worth: $581,754,420
Earnings: $54,886,572
Fiscal Year-end: 12/31/22
Construction Engineering Services
N.A.I.C.S.: 541330
Yanhui Xie (Chm)

CONSTRUCTION JOINT STOCK COMPANY 47
08th BienCuong st, Quy Nhon, BinhDinh, Vietnam
Tel.: (84) 2563522166
Web Site: https://www.xaydung47.vn
Year Founded: 1975
C47—(HOSE)
Rev.: $40,625,837
Assets: $74,488,529
Liabilities: $56,469,626
Net Worth: $18,018,902
Earnings: $607,700
Fiscal Year-end: 12/31/23
Civil Engineering Services
N.A.I.C.S.: 237990
Nguyen Luong Am (Chm & Gen Dir)

CONSTRUCTION JOINT

CONSTRUCTION JOINT—(CONTINUED)

STOCK COMPANY NO 5
137 Le Quang Dinh P 14, Q Binh
Thanh, Ho Chi Minh City, Vietnam
Tel.: (84) 862583425
Web Site: https://www.sc5.vn
SC5—(HOSE)
Rev.: $107,437,858
Assets: $104,647,794
Liabilities: $90,014,254
Net Worth: $14,633,540
Earnings: $1,500,010
Fiscal Year-end: 12/31/23
Building Construction Services
N.A.I.C.S.: 236220

CONSTRUCTION LONGER INC.
175 rue Leger, Sherbrooke, J1L 1M2,
QC, Canada
Tel.: (819) 564-0115
Web Site:
    http://www.constructionlonger.com
Year Founded: 1979
Sales Range: $25-49.9 Million
Building Contractors
N.A.I.C.S.: 238390
Luc Auclair (Chm & Pres)

CONSTRUCTION MATERIALS INDUSTRIES & CONTRACTING CO. SAOG
PO Box 36, 327, Sohar, Oman
Tel.: (968) 26752247
Web Site: https://www.cmioman.com
Year Founded: 1977
CMII—(MUS)
Rev.: $6,379,402
Assets: $20,256,365
Liabilities: $3,434,988
Net Worth: $16,821,377
Earnings: ($378,496)
Fiscal Year-end: 12/31/23
Lime Stone Product Mfr & Whslr
N.A.I.C.S.: 212311
Hussam Hisham Bostami (Vice Chm)

CONSTRUCTION SOCAM LTEE
3300 ave Francis Hughes, Laval, H7L
5A7, QC, Canada
Tel.: (450) 662-9000
Web Site: http://www.socam.ca
Year Founded: 1985
Rev.: $11,563,678
Emp.: 40
Construction Management
N.A.I.C.S.: 236220
Francois Chevrier (Pres)

CONSTRUCTIONS DE LA COTE D'EMERAUDE
2 Zone Industrielle rue du Petit Pre,
BP 26318, 22106, Rennes, Cedex,
France
Tel.: (33) 296395091
Web Site: http://www.cce-
    constructions.com
Rev.: $20,700,000
Emp.: 76
Nonresidential Construction
N.A.I.C.S.: 236220
Claude Andriex (Mgr-Pur)

CONSTRUCTIONS METAL-LIQUES D'OBERNAI
2 rue des Bonnes Gens, 67210,
Obernai, France
Tel.: (33) 388494750   FR
Web Site: http://www.cmo-obernai.fr
Year Founded: 1992
Sales Range: $10-24.9 Million
Emp.: 100
Fabricated Structural Metal
N.A.I.C.S.: 332312

Francois Jehle (Dir Gen)

CONSTRUCTORA CONCON-CRETO SA
Carrera 43A No 18 Sur-135 4to piso
Sao Paulo Plaza, Medellin, Colombia
Tel.: (57) 6044025700
Web Site:
    https://www.conconcreto.com
Year Founded: 1961
CONCONCRETO—(COLO)
Rev.: $315,412,115
Assets: $749,927,902
Liabilities: $389,441,391
Net Worth: $360,486,511
Earnings: $227,115
Fiscal Year-end: 12/31/23
Engineering & Construction Services
N.A.I.C.S.: 541330
Juan Luis Aristizabal Velez (CEO)

CONSTRUTORA ADOLPHO LINDENBERG S.A.
Rua Joaquim Floriano 466 BL Calle 2
Anda, Sao Paulo, 04534-002, Brazil
Tel.: (55) 1130412700
Web Site:
    https://www.lindenberg.com.br
CALI3—(BRAZ)
Rev.: $17,109,454
Assets: $39,024,328
Liabilities: $33,477,413
Net Worth: $5,546,915
Earnings: $1,730,037
Fiscal Year-end: 12/31/23
Commercial Property Development
Services
N.A.I.C.S.: 531210
Sergio Garrido Cincura (CTO)

CONSTRUTORA BETER S.A.
Av Heitor Antonio Eiras Garcia 3270,
5564100, Sao Paulo, Brazil
Tel.: (55) 11 3301 4400
Web Site: http://www.beter.com.br
Civil Engineering Construction Ser-
vices
N.A.I.C.S.: 236220
Alberto Jose Aulicino Neto (Dir-IR)

CONSTRUTORA TENDA S.A.
Rua Boa Vista 280, Sao Paulo,
01012-001, Brazil
Tel.: (55) 1131119909
Web Site: http://www.tenda.com
TEND3—(BRAZ)
Rev.: $518,955,135
Assets: $812,489,029
Liabilities: $657,962,479
Net Worth: $154,526,551
Earnings: ($18,324,663)
Fiscal Year-end: 12/31/23
Building Construction Services
N.A.I.C.S.: 236116
Claudio Jose Carvalho de Andrade
(Chm)

CONSULTANTS F.DRAPEAU INC.
1915 de l'industrie boulevard, Saint-
Mathieu-de-Beloeil, J3G 4S5, QC,
Canada
Tel.: (450) 467-2642
Web Site: http://www.fdrapeau.com
Rev.: $13,092,890
Emp.: 30
Commercial & Industrial Machines
Repair Services
N.A.I.C.S.: 811310
Francois M. Drapeau (Founder)

CONSULTATIO SA
Leandro N Alem 815 Piso 12,
C1001AAD, Buenos Aires, Argentina
Tel.: (54) 1143188000   Ar

Web Site:
    https://www.consultatio.com.ar
Sales Range: $25-49.9 Million
Emp.: 120
Real Estate Services
N.A.I.C.S.: 531390
Eduardo F. Costantini (Chm & CEO)

CONSUMERS CHOICE HOME IMPROVEMENTS CORP
445 Finchdene Square, Scarborough,
M1X 1B7, ON, Canada
Tel.: (416) 335-8353
Web Site:
    http://www.consumerschoice.ca
Year Founded: 1990
Rev.: $16,300,000
Emp.: 125
Doors & Windows Installation Service
N.A.I.C.S.: 321911
Sab Cipro (Mgr-Installation)

CONSUN PHARMACEUTICAL GROUP LIMITED
71 Dongpeng Avenue East District,
Guangzhou Economic and Techno-
logical Development Zone,
Guangzhou, Guangdong, China
Tel.: (86) 2082264529
Web Site:
    http://www.chinaconsun.com
1681—(HKG)
Rev.: $328,486,860
Assets: $686,890,152
Liabilities: $204,053,850
Net Worth: $482,836,302
Earnings: $95,991,059
Emp.: 3,009
Fiscal Year-end: 12/31/22
Pharmaceuticals Mfr
N.A.I.C.S.: 325412
Yubao An (Chm)

CONSUS ASSET MANAGE-MENT CO., LTD.
31 Gukjegeumyung-ro 8-gil
Yeongdeungpo-gu, Seoul, Korea
(South)
Tel.: (82) 2 2077 5000   KR
Web Site: http://www.consus.co.kr
Year Founded: 2004
Investment Asset Management Ser-
vices
N.A.I.C.S.: 523940
Young-Jae Kim (Chm & Co-CEO)

CONSUS REAL ESTATE AG
Kurfurstendamm 188-189, 10707,
Berlin, Germany
Tel.: (49) 30 965 357 90 260   De
Web Site: http://www.consus.ag
Year Founded: 1983
CC1—(DEU)
Rev.: $751,554,844
Assets: $5,325,287,056
Liabilities: $4,133,314,791
Net Worth: $1,191,972,265
Earnings: ($5,638,495)
Emp.: 975
Fiscal Year-end: 12/31/19
Real Estate Manangement Services
N.A.I.C.S.: 531210
Andreas Steyer (CEO & Chm-Mgmt
Bd)

Subsidiaries:

CG TEC Service GmbH   (1)
Haferkornstr 7, 04129, Leipzig, Germany
Tel.: (49) 3419621089632
Web Site: http://www.cgtec-tga.de
Building Material Mfr & Distr
N.A.I.C.S.: 327120

City-Hausverwaltung GmbH   (1)
Haferkornstrasse 7, 04129, Leipzig, Ger-
many
Tel.: (49) 3412155190
Web Site: http://www.city-hausverwaltung.de

Real Estate Development Services
N.A.I.C.S.: 531390

Consus Deutschland GmbH   (1)
Giesseralle 19, 47877, Willich, Germany
Tel.: (49) 21544868666
Web Site: http://www.consus-
    deutschland.de
Real Estate Development Services
N.A.I.C.S.: 531300

SSN Cube GmbH   (1)
Oscar-Walcker-Strasse 26, 71636, Ludwigs-
burg, Germany
Tel.: (49) 71138060797
Web Site: http://www.ssn-cube-gmbh.de
Building Construction & Civil Engineering
Services
N.A.I.C.S.: 541330

SSN Gebaudetechnik GmbH   (1)
Borsigstrasse 9, 38446, Wolfsburg, Ger-
many
Tel.: (49) 53614647100
Web Site: http://www.ssn-gbt.de
Construction Services
N.A.I.C.S.: 236220

CONTACT ENERGY LIMITED
Harbour City Tower 29 Brandon
Street, Wellington, 6011, New Zea-
land
Tel.: (64) 44994001   NZ
Web Site:
    https://www.contactenergy.co.nz
Year Founded: 1996
CEN—(ASX)
Rev.: $1,266,746,411
Assets: $3,473,684,211
Liabilities: $1,796,650,718
Net Worth: $1,677,033,493
Earnings: $75,956,938
Emp.: 1,242
Fiscal Year-end: 06/30/23
Gas & Electricity Services
N.A.I.C.S.: 213112
James Kilty (Chief Generation & Dev
Officer)

Subsidiaries:

Empower Limited   (1)
Level 1 Harbour City Tower 29 Brandon St,
Wellington, 6011, New Zealand   (100%)
Tel.: (64) 44994001
Web Site: http://www.empower.co.nz
Sales Range: $75-99.9 Million
Emp.: 65
Electricity Retailer
N.A.I.C.S.: 221122
Dennis Barnes (CEO)

CONTACTLAB
81 Oxford Street, London, W1D 2EU,
United Kingdom
Tel.: (44) 207 903 5295
Web Site: http://www.contactlab.com
Emp.: 130
Digital Marketing Solutions
N.A.I.C.S.: 513210
Massimo Fubini (Founder & CEO)

CONTAGIOUS GAMING INC.
59B Grafton Street, Charlottetown,
C1A 1K8, PE, Canada
Tel.: (647) 984-1244   BC
Web Site:
    https://www.contagiousgaming.com
Year Founded: 1993
KSMRF—(OTCIQ)
Assets: $27,325
Liabilities: $1,694,592
Net Worth: ($1,667,267)
Earnings: ($351,411)
Fiscal Year-end: 03/31/23
Gaming Software Developer
N.A.I.C.S.: 513210
Peter Glancy (CEO)

CONTAINE TECHNOLOGIES LTD.
313142 341P 342 Gokul Nagar, Mar-

riguda Mallapur Secunderabad, Hyderabad, 500076, Telangana, India
Tel.: (91) 9100777440
Web Site: https://www.containe.in
Year Founded: 2008
543606—(BOM)
Software Development Services
N.A.I.C.S.: 541511

CONTAINER CORPORATION OF INDIA LTD.
CONCOR Bhawan C-3 Mathura Road Opposite Apollo Hospital, New Delhi, 110076, India
Tel.: (91) 1141673093
Web Site:
   https://www.concorindia.co.in
Year Founded: 1988
531344—(NSE)
Rev.: $914,207,385
Assets: $1,693,985,475
Liabilities: $1,404,733,785
Net Worth: $289,251,690
Earnings: $68,333,265
Emp.: 1,400
Fiscal Year-end: 03/31/21
Logistics Support Services
N.A.I.C.S.: 541614
Harish Chandra *(Exec Dir-F&CS)*

Subsidiaries:

CONCOR Air Ltd.   (1)
2nd Floor Import Heavy Cargo Building Air Cargo Complex Sahar Andheri, Mumbai, 400 099, India
Tel.: (91) 2266859840
Logistics Consulting Servies
N.A.I.C.S.: 541614

Fresh & Healthy Enterprises Ltd. (1)
FHEL CA Store HSIIDC Industrial Estate Rai, Sonipat, 131 029, Haryana, India
Tel.: (91) 309996029370
Web Site: http://www.fhel.co.in
Logistics Consulting Servies
N.A.I.C.S.: 541614
Mohan Lal Arora *(CEO)*

CONTAINERWAY INTERNATIONAL LIMITED
B-402 Rishi apprtments Alaknanda Kalkaji, New Delhi, 110 019, India
Tel.: (91) 1204546106   In
Web Site:
   https://www.containerway.in
Year Founded: 1985
540597—(BOM)
Assets: $390,082
Liabilities: $504,044
Net Worth: ($113,962)
Earnings: ($13,018)
Emp.: 1
Fiscal Year-end: 03/31/23
Logistics Management Services
N.A.I.C.S.: 541614
Supriya Chhikara *(Exec Dir)*

CONTAKT WORLD TECHNOLOGIES CORP.
409 Granville Street Suite 1000, Vancouver, V6C 1T2, BC, Canada
Tel.: (760) 449-2509
Web Site:
   https://infinitystoneventures.com
GEMS—(CNSX)
Rev.: $588,558
Assets: $1,806,386
Liabilities: $7,842,511
Net Worth: ($6,036,125)
Earnings: ($3,174,607)
Emp.: 1
Fiscal Year-end: 08/31/22
Analytics Software Services
N.A.I.C.S.: 541511

CONTANGO GROUP PTY. LTD.
Level 27 35 Collins Street, Melbourne, 3000, VIC, Australia

Tel.: (61) 3 9222 2333   AU
Web Site:
   http://www.contango.com.au
Sales Range: $25-49.9 Million
Emp.: 15
Holding Company; Asset Management Services
N.A.I.C.S.: 551112
Paul Shannon *(CFO)*

Subsidiaries:

NAOS Small Cap Opportunities Company Limited   (1)
Level 34 MLC Centre 19 Martin Place, Sydney, 3000, NSW, Australia
Tel.: (61) 290021576
Web Site: http://www.naos.com.au
Assets: $74,500,534
Liabilities: $21,643,296
Net Worth: $52,857,238
Earnings: ($16,213,942)
Emp.: 10
Fiscal Year-end: 06/30/2024
Equity Investment Firm
N.A.I.C.S.: 523999
Trevor Carroll *(Chm)*

CONTANGO HOLDINGS PLC
1 Charterhouse Mews, London, EC1M 6BB, United Kingdom
Tel.: (44) 2034635000   UK
Web Site: https://www.contango-
   holdings-plc.co.uk
Year Founded: 2016
CGO—(LSE)
Assets: $20,490,561
Liabilities: $2,904,174
Net Worth: $17,586,387
Earnings: ($7,595,532)
Fiscal Year-end: 05/31/23
Investment Management Service
N.A.I.C.S.: 523940
Carl Esprey *(Exec Dir)*

CONTEL CORPORATION LIMITED
13th Fl Dawning Bldg 12 Keji Nan Road, Nanshan District, Shenzhen, China
Tel.: (86) 75533300988
Web Site:
   http://www.conteldigital.com
Sales Range: $50-74.9 Million
Emp.: 4,500
Digital Electronic Products Mfr
N.A.I.C.S.: 334419
Choi Fan Toon *(Sec)*

CONTEMPORARY AMPEREX TECHNOLOGY CO., LTD.
No 2 Xingang Road, Zhangwan Town Jiaocheng District, Ningde, 352100, Fujian, China
Tel.: (86) 5932583668
Web Site: https://www.catl.com
Year Founded: 2011
300750—(SSE)
Rev.: $46,134,596,196
Assets: $84,373,709,940
Liabilities: $59,535,663,876
Net Worth: $24,838,046,064
Earnings: $4,314,374,064
Emp.: 118,914
Fiscal Year-end: 12/31/22
Battery Mfr
N.A.I.C.S.: 335910
Jia Zhou *(Vice Chm)*

Subsidiaries:

Beijing Li Contemporary Amperex Technology Limited   (1)
Zhonghai Square Jianwai Street, Chaoyang District, Beijing, 100000, China
Tel.: (86) 10597726518014
Automotive Battery Mfr
N.A.I.C.S.: 335311

Contemporary Amperex Technology GmbH   (1)
Bayerstr 83-85a, 80335, Munich, Germany
Tel.: (49) 362866360
Automotive Battery Mfr
N.A.I.C.S.: 335311

Contemporary Amperex Technology Japan KK   (1)
11F Landmark Tower Minatomirai 2-2-1, Nishi-ku, Yokohama, 220-8111, Kanagawa, Japan
Tel.: (81) 452649138
N.A.I.C.S.: 335910

Contemporary Amperex Technology Thuringia GmbH   (1)
Robert-Bosch-Strasse 1, 99310, Arnstadt, Germany
Tel.: (49) 362866360
Automotive Battery Mfr
N.A.I.C.S.: 335311

Contemporary Amperex Technology USA Inc.   (1)
No 2114 Austin Ave, Rochester Hills, MI 48309
Tel.: (248) 289-6200
Automotive Battery Mfr
N.A.I.C.S.: 335311
Greg Denomy *(Sr Mgr-Engrg)*

Guangdong Ruiqing Contemporary Amperex Technology Limited   (1)
No 1 Shidai Road, High-Tech Development Zone, Zhaoqing, 526000, Guangdong, China
Tel.: (86) 7586626509
N.A.I.C.S.: 335910

Jiangsu Contemporary Amperex Technology Limited   (1)
No 1000 Chengbei Road, Liyang, 213300, Jiangsu, China
Tel.: (86) 51968260023
N.A.I.C.S.: 335910

Qinghai Contemporary Amperex Technology Limited   (1)
No 182 Chuangye Road Nanchuan Industry Park, Xining, 810000, Qinghai, China
Tel.: (86) 9717461888
N.A.I.C.S.: 335910

Ruiting Contemporary Amperex Technology (Shanghai) Limited   (1)
Building 3 Building 4 Building 5 No 168 Xinsiping Road, Pilot Free Trade Zone Lin-Gang Special Area, Shanghai, 201306, China
Tel.: (86) 2161189968
N.A.I.C.S.: 335910

Sichuan Contemporary Amperex Technology Limited   (1)
No 1 Industry Avenue, Lingang Economic Development Zone, Yibin, 644000, Sichuan, China
Tel.: (86) 8318258888
N.A.I.C.S.: 335910

CONTEMPRO FOR HOUSING PROJECTS PLC
AL-Swaifia-AL-Amad Complex, PO Box 831223, Amman, 11183, Jordan
Tel.: (962) 65859510
Year Founded: 2002
COHO—(AMM)
Rev.: $1,313,355
Assets: $9,770,991
Liabilities: $411,889
Net Worth: $9,359,102
Earnings: ($85,041)
Emp.: 11
Fiscal Year-end: 12/31/20
Real Estate Investment Services
N.A.I.C.S.: 531390

CONTENT MANAGEMENT CONSULTING APS
Ravnsborggade 8b 5 sal, 2200, Copenhagen, Denmark
Tel.: (45) 71 99 88 80
Web Site: http://www.cm-consult.com
Year Founded: 2003

IT Services
N.A.I.C.S.: 541512
Christian Storm Rasmussen *(Mgr-SIs)*

CONTENT SQUARE SAS
5 boulevard de la Madeleine, 75001, Paris, France
Tel.: (33) 183758800
Web Site: http://contentsquare.com
Software Publisher
N.A.I.C.S.: 513210
Benoit Fouilland *(CFO)*

Subsidiaries:

ClickTale Ltd.   (1)
2 JabotinskySt, 5250501, Ramat Gan, Israel
Tel.: (972) 36138152
Web Site: http://www.clicktale.com
Sales Range: $10-24.9 Million
Computer Related Customer Experience Analytics
N.A.I.C.S.: 513210
Tal Schwartz *(Co-Founder & Chm)*

CONTENT VENTURES LIMITED
Sheperds Central Sheperd's Bush, Charecroft Way, London, W14 0EH, United Kingdom
Tel.: (44) 2074719393
Sales Range: $10-24.9 Million
Emp.: 50
Media Holding Company; Television Broadcasting, Program Distribution & Music Publishing Services
N.A.I.C.S.: 551112
Martin Johnston *(Dir-Fin)*

Subsidiaries:

Apace Music Limited   (1)
Unit LG3 Shepherds Bldg, Charecroft Way, London, W14 0EH, United Kingdom
Tel.: (44) 207 4719270
Web Site: http://www.apacemusic.co.uk
Music Publishing Services
N.A.I.C.S.: 512230

Pro-Active Projects Limited   (1)
Unit 10 Warren Bus Park, Knockdown, Tetbury, GL8 8QY, Gloucestershire, United Kingdom
Tel.: (44) 1454232212
Web Site: http://www.proactivetv.com
Television Production Services
N.A.I.C.S.: 334220

Steadfast International Limited   (1)
Shepherds Central Sheperd's Bush, Charecroft Way, London, W14 0EH, United Kingdom
Tel.: (44) 20 7471 9393
Television Program Distr
N.A.I.C.S.: 517111

Steadfast Television Limited   (1)
Shepherds Central, Charecroft Way, London, W14 0EH, United Kingdom
Tel.: (44) 2074719250
Television Program Distr
N.A.I.C.S.: 517111

CONTENTREEJOONGANG CORP.
156 Dosandaero, Gangnam-gu, Seoul, 135-812, Korea (South)
Tel.: (82) 230150555
Web Site:
   https://www.contreej.com
Year Founded: 1987
036420—(KRS)
Rev.: $653,523,000
Assets: $1,985,098,753
Liabilities: $1,454,559,391
Net Worth: $530,539,362
Earnings: ($61,093,562)
Emp.: 136
Fiscal Year-end: 12/31/22
Investment Management Service
N.A.I.C.S.: 523999

ContentreeJoongAng corp.—(Continued)

Nam Jung-Kwun (*Co-CEO & Exec Dir*)

CONTEXTA AG
Wasserwerkgasse 17/19, Bern, 3000, Switzerland
Tel.: (41) 31 310 88 88 **CH**
Web Site: http://www.contexta.ch
Year Founded: 1968
Sales Range: $10-24.9 Million
Emp.: 58
Advetising Agency
N.A.I.C.S.: 541810
Nadine Borter (*Owner & CEO*)

CONTEXTVISION AB
Kungsgatan 50, Stockholm, 111 35, Sweden
Tel.: (46) 87503550
CONTXO—(OMX)
Rev.: $11,540,270
Assets: $9,154,327
Liabilities: $2,923,094
Net Worth: $6,231,232
Earnings: $2,696,620
Emp.: 35
Fiscal Year-end: 12/31/22
Software Development Services
N.A.I.C.S.: 541511
Fredrik Palm (*CEO*)

Subsidiaries:

Inify Laboratories AB **(1)**
Scheeles Vag 3, 171 65, Solna, Sweden
Tel.: (46) 8267330
Web Site: https://www.inify.com
Laboratory Services
N.A.I.C.S.: 541380

CONTIKI TOURS INTERNATIONAL LIMITED
c/o Consolidated Services Limited, PO Box 2257, Hamilton, Bermuda
Tel.: (441) 2958313
Holding Company; Tour Operators & Travel Agencies
N.A.I.C.S.: 551112

Subsidiaries:

Contiki Holidays (Australia) Pty Ltd **(1)**
Travel House 35 Grafton Street, Bondi Junction, Sydney, 2022, NSW, Australia
Tel.: (61) 295112200
Web Site: http://www.contiki.com
Sales Range: $25-49.9 Million
Emp.: 100
Travel Agency
N.A.I.C.S.: 561510

CONTIL INDIA LIMITED
811 Siddharth Complex R C Dutt Road Alkapuri, Baroda, 390 007, Gujarat, India
Tel.: (91) 2652342680
Web Site:
https://www.contilgroup.com
Year Founded: 1994
531067—(BOM)
Rev.: $2,005,807
Assets: $1,016,457
Liabilities: $185,398
Net Worth: $831,059
Earnings: $86,558
Emp.: 7
Fiscal Year-end: 03/31/21
Investment Management Service
N.A.I.C.S.: 523940
Krishna H. Contractor (*Chm & Mng Dir*)

CONTINENTAL AKTIENGESELLSCHAFT
Vahrenwalder Strasse 9, D-30165, Hannover, Germany
Tel.: (49) 51193801 **De**

Web Site:
https://www.continental.com
Year Founded: 1871
CON—(MUN)
Rev.: $45,722,847,335
Assets: $41,674,183,336
Liabilities: $26,577,767,603
Net Worth: $15,096,415,733
Earnings: $1,276,515,268
Emp.: 202,763
Fiscal Year-end: 12/31/23
Automotive Braking & Suspension Systems, Electronic Motors & Components, Passenger & Commercial Vehicle Tires, Belts & Hoses Mfr
N.A.I.C.S.: 336390
Helmut Matschi (*Member-Exec Bd*)

Subsidiaries:

ContiTech AG **(1)**
Vahrenwalder Str 9, 30165, Hannover, Germany
Tel.: (49) 51193802
Web Site: http://www.continental-industry.com
Emp.: 27,249
Rubber & Plastic Products Mfr
N.A.I.C.S.: 326220

Affiliate (Domestic):

Benecke-Kaliko AG **(2)**
Benecke-kaiko 40, Hannover, 30419, Germany **(100%)**
Tel.: (49) 51163020
Web Site: http://www.benecke-kaliko.de
Sales Range: $300-349.9 Million
Emp.: 1,000
Producer of Tires & Rubber & Plastic Industrial Articles, Mechanical, Electronic Brake Systems
N.A.I.C.S.: 314994

Subsidiary (Domestic):

Konrad Hornschuch AG **(3)**
Salinenstrasse 1, 74679, Weissbach, Germany
Tel.: (49) 7947810
Web Site: http://www.skai.com
Films, Foils & Artificial Leather Designer & Mfr
N.A.I.C.S.: 326113
Roger H. Liebel (*Chm-Exec Bd*)

Subsidiary (Non-US):

Hornschuch France SARL **(4)**
2 rue Vincent Van Gogh, 93360, Neuilly-Plaisance, France
Tel.: (33) 143 099000
Web Site: http://www.hornschuch.fr
Films, Foils & Artificial Leather Designer & Mfr
N.A.I.C.S.: 326113

Hornschuch Italia S.r.l. **(4)**
Via della Moia 1, Arese, 20020, Milan, Italy
Tel.: (39) 02 9345481
Web Site: http://www.hornschuch.it
Films, Foils & Artificial Leather Designer & Mfr
N.A.I.C.S.: 326113

Hornschuch UK Ltd. **(4)**
Palmerston House 814 Brighton Road, Purley, London, CR8 2BR, Surrey, United Kingdom
Tel.: (44) 7984303636
Web Site: http://www.hornschuch.com
Films, Foils & Artificial Leather Designer & Mfr
N.A.I.C.S.: 326113

Subsidiary (US):

O'Sullivan Films, Inc. **(4)**
1944 Vly Ave, Winchester, VA 22601
Tel.: (540) 667-6666
Web Site: http://www.osul.com
Film & Artificial Leather Solutions Mfr
N.A.I.C.S.: 326113
Scott Krueger (*CEO*)

Subsidiary (Non-US):

OOO Hornschuch RUS **(4)**
House 9 Industrial Passage Village of

Besedy, Leninsky District, 142715, Moscow, Russia
Tel.: (7) 4951362676
Web Site: http://www.hornschuch.ru
Films, Foils & Artificial Leather Designer & Mfr
N.A.I.C.S.: 326113
Dmitriy Khan (*Country Mgr-Sls*)

Unit (Domestic):

ContiTech Antriebssysteme GmbH **(2)**
Phillipsborn strasse 1, 30165, Hannover, Germany
Tel.: (49) 05119385306
Web Site: http://www.contitech.de
Sales Range: $550-599.9 Million
Emp.: 2,744
Mfr of Automotive Drive Belts
N.A.I.C.S.: 326220

Subsidiary (Non-US):

ContiTech Power Transmission System (Shanghai) Co., Ltd. **(3)**
22F Tian An Center 338 Nanjing Road West, Shanghai, 200003, China
Tel.: (86) 21 6141 8325
Automotive Power Transmission Equipment Distr
N.A.I.C.S.: 423120

ContiTech Roulunds Rubber A/S **(3)**
Orstedsgade 19 st, 5000 C, Odense, Denmark
Tel.: (45) 63133400
Web Site: http://www.roulundsrubber.com
Sales Range: $75-99.9 Million
Emp.: 4
Mfr of Rubber Belts
N.A.I.C.S.: 326220

Subsidiary (Non-US):

ContiTech Belgium BVBA **(2)**
Uitbreidingstraat 42-46, 2600, Berchem, Belgium
Tel.: (32) 3 20674 20
Web Site: http://www.contitech-benelux.com
Rubber & Plastic Products Mfr
N.A.I.C.S.: 326299
Tobias Mahrenholz (*Mng Dir*)

ContiTech Continental Suisse S.A. **(2)**
Lerzenstrasse 19, 8953, Dietikon, Switzerland
Tel.: (41) 433432010
Web Site: http://www.contitech.ch
Emp.: 2
Automotive Belt, Spring & Hose Mfr
N.A.I.C.S.: 336390

ContiTech Fluid Monterrey Servicios, S.A. de C.V. **(2)**
Carretera Nacional Monterrey, Cd Victoria Km 205+850, Montemorelos, 67500, NL, Mexico **(100%)**
Tel.: (52) 8262630000
Sales Range: $125-149.9 Million
Emp.: 250
Automotive Air Conditioning Component Mfr
N.A.I.C.S.: 336390

ContiTech France SNC **(2)**
3 Rue Fulgence Bienvenue, 92631, Gennevilliers, France
Tel.: (33) 141479292
Web Site: http://www.contitech.fr
Emp.: 20
Rubber & Plastic Products Mfr
N.A.I.C.S.: 326299
Als Homeyer (*Gen Mgr*)

ContiTech Japan Co. Ltd. **(2)**
Technowave 100 Bldg 15 F 1-25 Shin Urashima-cho 1-chome, Kanagawa-ku, 221-0031, Yokohama, Japan
Tel.: (81) 45444 3659
Web Site: http://www.contitech.jp
Sales Range: $25-49.9 Million
Emp.: 11
Rubber & Plastic Products Distr
N.A.I.C.S.: 424990

ContiTech Kautschuk- und Kunststoff-Vertriebsgesellschaft **(2)**
Gewerbestr 14, Postfach 115, 2351, Wiener Neudorf, Austria

Tel.: (43) 2236 49 101
Sales Range: $25-49.9 Million
Emp.: 16
Offset Printing Blanket Distr
N.A.I.C.S.: 423840
Herr Stefan Fuhrmann (*Mng Dir*)

Subsidiary (US):

ContiTech North America, Inc. **(2)**
136 Summit Ave, Montvale, NJ 07645
Tel.: (201) 930-0600
Web Site: http://www.contitech-usa.com
Sales Range: $25-49.9 Million
Emp.: 35
Automotive Hose, Belt & Spring Mfr
N.A.I.C.S.: 336390

Subsidiary (Domestic):

ContiTech Beattie Corp. **(3)**
11535 Brittmoore Park Dr, Houston, TX 77041
Tel.: (832) 327-0141
Web Site: http://www.contitechbeattie.com
Rubber Hose Mfr
N.A.I.C.S.: 326220

Veyance Technologies, Inc. **(3)**
703 S Cleveland-Massillon Rd, Fairlawn, OH 44333-3023
Tel.: (330) 664-7000
Web Site: http://www.veyance.com
Engineered Rubber Product Mfr
N.A.I.C.S.: 326291

Subsidiary (Non-US):

Veyance Technologies Europe, d.o.o. **(4)**
Skofjeloska cesta 6, 4000, Kranj, Slovenia
Tel.: (386) 42078000
Web Site: http://www.veyance.eu
Tires & Inner Tubes Mfr
N.A.I.C.S.: 326211

Subsidiary (Non-US):

ContiTech Print Service (S) Pte. Ltd. **(2)**
1 Ubi View 03-17 Focus One, Singapore, 408555, Singapore
Tel.: (65) 65097603
Sales Range: $25-49.9 Million
Emp.: 10
Offset Printing Blanket Distr
N.A.I.C.S.: 423840

ContiTech Printing Blanket Shanghai Ltd. **(2)**
No 16 Factory Zone A No 6999 Chuansha Road Chuansha Economic Park, Pudong New District, 201202, Shanghai, China
Tel.: (86) 21 5868 1050
Sales Range: $25-49.9 Million
Emp.: 5
Offset Printing Blanket Distr
N.A.I.C.S.: 423840

ContiTech Scandinavia AB **(2)**
Finlandsgatan 18, 164 74, Kista, Sweden
Tel.: (46) 84441330
Web Site: http://www.contitech.se
Automobile Parts Mfr
N.A.I.C.S.: 336390

Subsidiary (Domestic):

ContiTech Techno-Chemie GmbH **(2)**
Dieselstrasse 4, 61184, Karben, Germany
Tel.: (49) 60399900
Web Site: http://www.contitech.de
Rubber & Plastic Products Mfr
N.A.I.C.S.: 326299

Subsidiary (Non-US):

ContiTech Anoflex S.A.S. **(3)**
2-12 Avenue Barthelemy Thimonnier, 69300, Caluire-et-Cuire, France
Tel.: (33) 478987070
Web Site: http://www.contitech.fr
Rubber & Plastic Hoses Mfr
N.A.I.C.S.: 326220

ContiTech Fluid Automotive Hungaria Kft. **(3)**
Rakosi Ut 3, Mako, 6900, Hungary
Tel.: (36) 62511766
Web Site: http://www.contitech.hu

Rubber & Plastic Fluid Hoses Mfr
N.A.I.C.S.: 326220
Levente Szurszabo *(Mng Dir)*

ContiTech Fluid Automotive Romania SRL (3)
Str Mihai Viteazu Nr 125, Carei, 445100, Romania
Tel.: (40) 261806110
Sales Range: $350-399.9 Million
Emp.: 1,700
Fluid Hoses Mfr
N.A.I.C.S.: 332912

ContiTech Fluid Korea Ltd. (3)
Palbok-dong 1-333 Jeon Buk, Jeonju, 54844, Korea (South)
Tel.: (82) 632143740
Web Site: http://www.contitech-korea.com
Emp.: 25
Automobile Hose Mfr
N.A.I.C.S.: 336330
Hendrik Steffen *(Mng Dir-Fluid Tech)*

ContiTech Fluid Shanghai Co., Ltd. (3)
No 588 XinRun Road XinQiao Town, Songjiang, 201612, Shanghai, China
Tel.: (86) 2167629375
Power Steering Hose Line Mfr
N.A.I.C.S.: 336390

Subsidiary (Domestic):

ContiTech Kuhner GmbH & Cie. KG (3)
Talstrasse 1-6, 71570, Oppenweiler, Germany
Tel.: (49) 7191 4810
Sales Range: $125-149.9 Million
Emp.: 40
Rubber & Plastic Products Mfr
N.A.I.C.S.: 326299
Florian Sauth *(Gen Mgr)*

ContiTech MGW GmbH (3)
Seehafenstr 16, 21079, Hamburg, Germany
Tel.: (49) 40 7667 01
Web Site: http://www.ac-hoses.de
Plastic & Rubber Hoses Mfr
N.A.I.C.S.: 326220
Joachim Geimer *(Chm & Mng Dir)*

Subsidiary (Non-US):

ContiTech Romania S.R.L. (3)
Str Otto Rudolf nr 4, 300522, Timisoara, Romania
Tel.: (40) 256301527
Web Site: http://www.contitech.ro
Sales Range: $350-399.9 Million
Emp.: 1,700
Automobile Parts Mfr
N.A.I.C.S.: 336390

ContiTech Rubber Industrial Kft. (3)
Budapesti Ut 10, Szeged, 6728, Hungary
Tel.: (36) 62 566 700
Web Site: http://www.contitech.hu
Textile Conveyor Belt & Industrial Hoses Mfr
N.A.I.C.S.: 333248
Regina Gensigora *(Mng Dir)*

Subsidiary (Non-US):

Kolubara Univerzal d.o.o. (4)
Kosmajska Ulica bb, Veliki Crljeni, Belgrade, 11563, Serbia
Tel.: (381) 11 8120 759
Web Site: http://www.kolubarauniverzal.com
Sales Range: $25-49.9 Million
Emp.: 190
Rubber Products Mfr
N.A.I.C.S.: 326299

Subsidiary (Domestic):

ContiTech Schlauch GmbH (3)
Continentalstr 3-5, 34497, Korbach, Germany
Tel.: (49) 5631580
Rubber & Plastic Hoses Mfr
N.A.I.C.S.: 326220
Ulrich Spitzer *(Gen Mgr)*

Subsidiary (US):

ContiTech Thermopol LLC (3)
9 Interstate Dr, Somersworth, NH 03878-1210
Tel.: (603) 692-6300

Silicone Rubber Hose Mfr
N.A.I.C.S.: 326220
John Stokes *(Mgr-Pur)*

Subsidiary (Non-US):

Continental do Brasil Produtos Automotivos Ltda. (3)
Av Continental 2777 Distrito Industrial Cyro Martins, 84043-735, Ponta Grossa, Parana, Brazil
Tel.: (55) 4233112300
Web Site: http://www.conti.com.br
Automotive Tyre Mfr & Distr
N.A.I.C.S.: 326211
Renato Sarzano *(Gen Mgr)*

Subsidiary (Domestic):

ContiTech Transportbandsysteme GmbH (2)
Breslauer Strasse 14, 37154, Northeim, Germany
Tel.: (49) 5551 702 207
Steel Cable & Conveyor Belt Installation Services & Mfr
N.A.I.C.S.: 333922

Subsidiary (Non-US):

ContiTech Conveyor Belt Group (3)
No 1 No 1333 Xin Da Road Qingpu Town, Qingpu District, Shanghai, 201700, China
Tel.: (86) 21 6921 4910
Conveyor Belts Mfr
N.A.I.C.S.: 333922

Branch (Domestic):

ContiTech Transportbandsysteme GmbH (3)
Clausthalstrasse 2, Moers, 47441, Germany
Tel.: (49) 28411440
Web Site: http://www.contitech.de
Sales Range: $25-49.9 Million
Emp.: 95
Mfr of Components for Industrial Conveying Equipment & Engineered Products
N.A.I.C.S.: 333922

Subsidiary (Non-US):

ContiTech United Kingdom Ltd. (2)
Unit 2 Castle Mound Way Central Park, Rugby, CV23 0WB, Warwickshire, United Kingdom
Tel.: (44) 1788571482
Web Site: http://www.contitech.co.uk
Emp.: 1
Rubber & Plastic Products Mfr
N.A.I.C.S.: 326299

Unit (Domestic):

ContiTech Vibration Control GmbH (2)
Jadekamp 30, Postfach 21 04 69, 30419, Hannover, Germany
Tel.: (49) 51197666213
Web Site: http://www.continental-industry.com
Sales Range: $250-299.9 Million
Emp.: 1,599
Mfr of Engine & Chassis Mounts, Dampers & Sealing Systems
N.A.I.C.S.: 336330

Subsidiary (Non-US):

Continental Industrias del Caucho S.A. (2)
Cityparc Ronda De Dalt Ctra de Hospitalet 147, E 08940, Barcelona, Cornella, Spain (100%)
Tel.: (34) 93 480 0400
Web Site: http://www.contitech.de
Sales Range: $25-49.9 Million
Emp.: 8
Producer of Tires, Rubber & Plastic Industrial Articles, Mechanical & Electronic Brake Systems
N.A.I.C.S.: 314994

Continental Tyre and Rubber Singapore Pte. Ltd. (2)
80 Boon Keng Road Continental Building, Singapore, 339780, Singapore
Tel.: (65) 65800000
Web Site: http://www.contitech.sg

Sales Range: $25-49.9 Million
Emp.: 7
Rubber Product Distr
N.A.I.C.S.: 424990

Contitech Hycop AB (2)
Finlandsgatan 18, Box 38, 164 93, Kista, Sweden (100%)
Tel.: (46) 84441330
Web Site: http://www.contitech.se
Sales Range: Less than $1 Million
Emp.: 89
Producer of Tires & Rubber & Plastic Industrial Articles, Mechanical, Electronic Brake Systems
N.A.I.C.S.: 314994

Dunlop Oil & Marine Ltd. (2)
Moody Lane Pyewipe, Grimsby, DN31 2SY, United Kingdom
Tel.: (44) 1472 359281
Web Site: http://www.dunlop-oil-marine.co.uk
Sales Range: $50-74.9 Million
Emp.: 180
Oil & Gas Hoses Mfr & Distr
N.A.I.C.S.: 326220

Affiliate (Non-US):

IMAS A.E. (2)
Industrial Zone, PO Box 1050, Volos, 38500, Greece (94%)
Tel.: (30) 2421096500
Web Site: http://www.contitech.de
Sales Range: $50-74.9 Million
Emp.: 250
Industrial Rubber Goods & Elastometer Technology
N.A.I.C.S.: 326291

Subsidiary (Domestic):

Phoenix Compounding Technology GmbH (2)
Hannoversche Strasse 88, 21079, Hamburg, Germany
Tel.: (49) 40766701
Web Site: http://www.phoenix-compounding.eu
Rubber Products Mfr
N.A.I.C.S.: 326299
Peter Scholtissek *(Mng Dir)*

ContiTech AGES S.P.A. (1)
Via Trinita 80, 10026, Santena, Italy (100%)
Tel.: (39) 01194201
Web Site: http://www.contitech.de
Sales Range: $350-399.9 Million
Emp.: 1,063
Producer of Tires & Rubber & Plastic Industrial Articles, Mechanical, Electronic Brake Systems
N.A.I.C.S.: 314994

Continental Automotive (Thailand) Co. Ltd (1)
444 Olympia Thai Tower 4F Ratchadapisek Road Samsennok, Huay Kwang, Bangkok, 10310, Thailand
Tel.: (66) 2 512 5658
Sales Range: $150-199.9 Million
Emp.: 49
Automobile Parts Distr
N.A.I.C.S.: 423120

Continental Automotive Austria GmbH (1)
Dresdner Strasse 91, 1200, Vienna, Austria
Tel.: (43) 1 33144 0
Sales Range: $50-74.9 Million
Emp.: 20
Automobile Parts Mfr
N.A.I.C.S.: 336390
Alem Helias *(Gen Mgr)*

Continental Automotive Canada, Inc. (1)
700 Park Avenue East, Chatham, N7M 5M7, ON, Canada
Tel.: (519) 352-6700
Automobile Parts Mfr
N.A.I.C.S.: 336390

Continental Automotive Components (India) Private Ltd. (1)
53B Bommasandra Industrial Area Phase 1, Bengaluru, 560 099, India
Tel.: (91) 80 6611 5645

Automotive Parts Mfr & Distr
N.A.I.C.S.: 336390
Debjani Roy *(Gen Mgr)*

Continental Automotive Electronics LLC. (1)
249 Geumho-ri Buyong-myeon, Cheongwon, 363-942, Chungcheongbuk-do, Korea (South)
Tel.: (82) 432706114
Web Site: http://www.continental-corporation.co.kr
Automotive Electronic Component Mfr
N.A.I.C.S.: 336320

Continental Automotive France SAS (1)
1 Avenue Paul Ourliac, 31100, Toulouse, France
Tel.: (33) 561198888
Automotive Electronic Parts Mfr
N.A.I.C.S.: 336320

Continental Automotive Japan KK (1)
Technowave 100 Bldg 15F, Kanagawa-ku, 221-0031, Yokohama, Japan
Tel.: (81) 454444131
Web Site: http://www.vdo.com
Automobile Parts Mfr
N.A.I.C.S.: 336390

Continental Automotive S.A. de C.V (1)
Poniente Km 4 2, 66350, Santa Catarina, Nuevo Leon, Mexico
Tel.: (52) 818 124 4001
Automotive Accessories Mfr
N.A.I.C.S.: 336390

Continental Automotive Spain S.A. (1)
C/ Sepulveda 11, Madrid, 28108, Alcobendas, Spain
Tel.: (34) 916572121
Web Site: http://www.vdo.es
Automobile Parts Mfr
N.A.I.C.S.: 336390

Continental Automotive Systems (Shanghai) Co., Ltd (1)
Continental Automotive Tech Center Jiading 100 Huirong Road, Jiading Industrial Zone, 201807, Shanghai, China
Tel.: (86) 21 3916 5000
Automotive Electronic Parts Mfr
N.A.I.C.S.: 336320

Continental Automotive Systems Czech Republic s.r.o. (1)
Kopanska u 1713, 744 01, Frenstat pod Radhostem, Czech Republic
Tel.: (420) 556881111
Web Site: http://www.continental-corporation.com
Automotive Electronic Parts Mfr
N.A.I.C.S.: 336320

Continental Automotive Systems Management Co., Ltd (1)
Nanjing West Road 338 Tian An Center Building 23F, 200003, Shanghai, China
Tel.: (86) 21 6141 8282
Automobile Parts Mfr
N.A.I.C.S.: 336390

Continental Automotive Systems US, Inc. (1)
1 Continental Dr, Auburn Hills, MI 48326
Tel.: (248) 209-4000
Web Site: http://www.continental-corpaoration.com
Sales Range: $1-4,9 Billion
Emp.: 6,000
Automotive Brake System & Chassis Component Developer & Mfr
N.A.I.C.S.: 336390
Samir Salman *(CEO)*

Plant (Domestic):

Continental Automotive Systems US, Inc. (2)
1 Continental Blvd, Auburn Hills, MI 48326
Tel.: (248) 209-4000
Web Site: http://usa.vdo.com
Sales Range: $350-399.9 Million
Emp.: 1,500

Continental Aktiengesellschaft—(Continued)

Automotive Electronics & Safety Equipment
Developer & Mfr
N.A.I.C.S.: 336390

Continental Automotive Systems US,
Inc. (2)
100 Electronics Blvd SW, Huntsville, AL
35824
Tel.: (256) 464-2000
Web Site: http://www.conti-online.com
Sales Range: $350-399.9 Million
Emp.: 2,300
Automotive Brake System & Chassis Com-
ponent Mfr
N.A.I.C.S.: 336390

Continental Automotive Systems US,
Inc. (2)
15001 Commerce Dr N, Dearborn, MI
48120
Tel.: (313) 583-5980
Web Site: http://www.continental-
corporation.com
Sales Range: $25-49.9 Million
Emp.: 70
Automotive Brake System & Chassis Com-
ponent Mfr
N.A.I.C.S.: 336390

Continental Automotive Systems,
Inc (1)
16 Ring Road LISP2-SEZ, 4027, Calamba,
Laguna, Philippines
Tel.: (63) 49 545 1463
Automotive Electronic Parts Mfr
N.A.I.C.S.: 336320

Continental Automotive Trading
S.r.l. (1)
Via Matteotti 62, 20026, Novate Milanese,
Milan, Italy
Tel.: (39) 02356801
Sales Range: $25-49.9 Million
Emp.: 30
Automobile Parts Distr
N.A.I.C.S.: 423120
Nicola Comes (Gen Mgr)

Continental Benelux S.A. (1)
Avenue du Parc Industriel 1E Av 36, 4040,
Herstal, Liege, Belgium (100%)
Tel.: (32) 42485700
Web Site: http://www.conteonline.com
Sales Range: $25-49.9 Million
Emp.: 20
Motor Vehicle Parts Mfr
N.A.I.C.S.: 336390

Continental Chassis & Safety
Division (1)
Geurickstrasse 7, Frankfurt am Main,
60488, Germany
Tel.: (49) 6976031
Web Site: http://www.
Sales Range: $5-14.9 Billion
Emp.: 27,809
Automotive Brake & Chassis Component
Developer & Mfr
N.A.I.C.S.: 336340
Ralf H. Cramer (Mng Dir)

Subsidiary (Domestic):

Conti Temic Microelectonics
GmbH (2)
Sieboldstrasse 19, 90411, Nuremberg,
Germany (100%)
Tel.: (49) 91195260
Web Site: http://www.contenital-
corporation.com
Sales Range: $350-399.9 Million
Emp.: 2,300
Automotive Electronic Component Mfr
N.A.I.C.S.: 336390
Barbel Moesker-Weishaeupl (Mng Dir)

Continental Automotive GmbH (2)
Siemensstrasse 12, Regensburg, 93055,
Germany
Tel.: (49) 94179002
Automotive Safety, Powertrain & Interior
Component Developer & Mfr.
N.A.I.C.S.: 336390

Continental Automotive GmbH (2)
Sodener Str 9, 65824, Schwalbach, Ger-
many
Tel.: (49) 6196870

Web Site: http://www.continental-
corporation.com
Sales Range: $350-399.9 Million
Emp.: 1,300
Automotive Brake & Safety Component Mfr
N.A.I.C.S.: 336390

Continental Safety Engineering Inter-
national GmbH (2)
Carl Zeiss Strasse 9, Alzenau, 63755, Ger-
many
Tel.: (49) 60239420
Web Site: http://www.continental-
corporation.com
Sales Range: $25-49.9 Million
Emp.: 125
Automotive Safety Component & Restraint
System Mfr
N.A.I.C.S.: 336390

Continental Commercial Vehicle Tires
Division (1)
Vahrenwalder Strasse 9, 30165, Hannover,
Germany
Tel.: (49) 51193801
Web Site: http://www.continental.de
Sales Range: $1-4.9 Billion
Emp.: 8,000
Commercial Vehicle Tire Mfr
N.A.I.C.S.: 326211

Subsidiary (Non-US):

Barum Continental spol. s.r.o. (2)
Objizdna 1628, 765 02, Otrokovice, Czech
Republic (70%)
Tel.: (420) 577511111
Web Site: http://www.barum.cz
Sales Range: $800-899.9 Million
Emp.: 4,300
Mfr of Tires
N.A.I.C.S.: 326211

Continental Matador s.r.o. (2)
Terezie Vansovej 1054, 020 01, Puchov,
Slovakia
Tel.: (421) 424611111
Web Site: http://www.matador-belts.com
Sales Range: $200-249.9 Million
Emp.: 1,000
Commercial Vehicle Tire Mfr
N.A.I.C.S.: 326211

Continental General Tire Inc. (1)
6110 Cantay Rd, Mississauga, L5R 3W5,
ON, Canada (100%)
Tel.: (905) 856-4363
Web Site: http://www.continentaltire.com
Sales Range: $200-249.9 Million
Emp.: 25
Mfr & Distributor of Tires
N.A.I.C.S.: 326211

Continental Interior Division (1)
Siemensstrasse 12, 93055, Regensburg,
Germany
Tel.: (49) 9417900
Sales Range: $5-14.9 Billion
Emp.: 33,000
Automobile Gauge, Display & Interior Com-
ponent Mfr
N.A.I.C.S.: 336360
Helmut Matschi (Mng Dir)

Subsidiary (Non-US):

Continental Automotive Components
Malaysia Sdn. Bhd. (2)
2455 MK 1 Tingkat Perusahaan 2 A Prai
Industrial Estate, 13600, Penang, Malaysia
Tel.: (60) 43819100
Web Site: http://www.continental-
corporation.com
Sales Range: $200-249.9 Million
Emp.: 1,000
Automotive Electronic Components Devel-
oper & Mfr
N.A.I.C.S.: 336390

Plant (Non-US):

Continental Automotive Czech Re-
public s.r.o. (2)
Prumyslova 1851, 250 01, Brandys nad
Labem, Czech Republic
Tel.: (420) 326931500
Web Site: http://www.conti-online.com
Sales Range: $350-399.9 Million
Emp.: 1,700
Automotive Components Mfr

N.A.I.C.S.: 336390
Klaus Evers (Head-Production)

Plant (Domestic):

Continental Automotive GmbH (2)
Heinrich Hertz Strasse 45, Villingen-
Schwenningen, 78052, Germany
Tel.: (49) 7721670
Web Site: http://www.continental-
cooperation.com
Sales Range: $400-449.9 Million
Emp.: 1,300
Commercial Vehicle Information System
Developer & Mfr
N.A.I.C.S.: 336390

Subsidiary (Non-US):

Continental Automotive Pte. Ltd. (2)
Block 28 Ayer Rajah Crescent 08 05 08,
Singapore, 139959, Singapore
Tel.: (65) 67799714
Web Site: http://www.continental-
corporation.com
Sales Range: $100-124.9 Million
Emp.: 400
Automotive Multimedia & Navagation Sys-
tem Developer & Mfr
N.A.I.C.S.: 336390

Plant (Non-US):

Continental Automotive Spain,
S.A. (2)
Calle Sepulveda 11, 28108, Alcobendas,
Madrid, Spain
Tel.: (34) 916572121
Web Site: http://www.vdo.com
Sales Range: $25-49.9 Million
Emp.: 79
Commercial Vehicle Information System
Developer & Mfr
N.A.I.C.S.: 336390

Subsidiary (Non-US):

Continental Automotive Switzerland
AG (2)
Industriestrasse 18, 9464, Ruthi, Switzer-
land
Tel.: (41) 717679111
Web Site: http://www.continental-
corporation.com
Sales Range: $25-49.9 Million
Emp.: 160
Automotive Electronic Component Devel-
oper & Mfr
N.A.I.C.S.: 336390
Hans Pauer (CEO)

Continental Automotive Trading Ned-
erland B.V. (2)
Het Schakelplein 22, 5651 GR, Eindhoven,
Netherlands
Tel.: (31) 403023500
Web Site: http://www.continental-
corporation.com
Sales Range: $25-49.9 Million
Emp.: 20
Commercial Vehicle Information System
Developer & Mfr
N.A.I.C.S.: 336390

Continental Automotive Trading UK
Ltd. (2)
36 Gravelly Industrial Park, Birmingham,
B24 8TA, United Kingdom
Tel.: (44) 1213261234
Web Site: http://www.vdo.com.uk
Sales Range: $25-49.9 Million
Emp.: 190
Commercial Vehicle Information System
Developer & Mfr
N.A.I.C.S.: 336390

Plant (Non-US):

Continental Brasil Industria Automo-
tiva Ltda. (2)
Av Sen Adolf Schindling 131, Guarulhos,
07042-020, SP, Brazil
Tel.: (55) 1124233400
Web Site: http://www.vdo.com.br
Sales Range: $400-449.9 Million
Emp.: 1,100
Automotive Electronic Mfr
N.A.I.C.S.: 336390

Continental Brasil Industria Automo-
tiva Ltda. (2)
Rua Marechal Rongon 1768, Salto, 011,
SP, Brazil
Tel.: (55) 1140288150
Web Site: http://www.continental-
corporation.com.br
Sales Range: $75-99.9 Million
Emp.: 500
Automotive Interior Component Developer &
Mfr
N.A.I.C.S.: 336390

Subsidiary (Non-US):

Continental Pty Ltd (2)
2 Scholar Drive, Bundoora, Melbourne,
3083, VIC, Australia
Tel.: (61) 394681151
Web Site: http://www.continental-
corporation.com
Sales Range: $75-99.9 Million
Emp.: 300
Automobile Instrumentation Equipment De-
veloper & Mfr
N.A.I.C.S.: 336390

Plant (Domestic):

Continental Pty. Ltd. - Melbourne
Plant (3)
67 93 National Boulevard, Melbourne,
3061, VIC, Australia
Tel.: (61) 383594300
Sales Range: $100-124.9 Million
Emp.: 300
Automotive Instrumentation Equipment Mfr
N.A.I.C.S.: 336390

Subsidiary (Non-US):

Continental Trading GmbH (2)
Flachgasse 54 58, Vienna, 1150, Austria
Tel.: (43) 1981270
Sales Range: $25-49.9 Million
Emp.: 20
Commercial Vehicle Information System
Developer & Mfr
N.A.I.C.S.: 336390

Continental VDO Automotive,
S.A. (2)
Carretera Ullastrell S H, 8191, Barcelona,
Spain
Tel.: (34) 935862880
Web Site: http://www.vdo.es
Sales Range: $100-124.9 Million
Emp.: 500
Automotive Electronic Component Mfr
N.A.I.C.S.: 336390

Continental Italia S.p.A. (1)
Via G Winckelmann 1, 20146, Milan,
Italy (100%)
Tel.: (39) 02424101
Web Site: http://www.contionline.com
Sales Range: $25-49.9 Million
Emp.: 115
Producer of Tires & Rubber & Plastic Indus-
trial Articles, Mechanical, Electronic Brake
Systems
N.A.I.C.S.: 314994

Continental Mabor (1)
Rua Adelino Leitao 330, Lousado, Vila
Nova de Famalicao, 4760-606, Lousado,
Portugal (100%)
Tel.: (351) 252499200
Web Site: http://www.conti.online.com
Sales Range: $450-499.9 Million
Emp.: 3,000
Mfr of Tires
N.A.I.C.S.: 326211
Peter Carreira (Pres)

Continental Mechanical Components
Germany GmbH (1)
Schorndorfer Strasse 91, 93426, Roding,
Germany
Tel.: (49) 9461914407
Web Site: http://www.continental.com
Automotive Electronic Parts Mfr
N.A.I.C.S.: 336320

Continental Passenger & Light Truck
Tires Division (1)
Vahrenwalder Strasse 9, Hannover, 30165,
Germany
Tel.: (49) 51193801
Web Site: http://www.conti-online.com

Sales Range: $1-4.9 Billion
Emp.: 25,000
Passenger Vehicle & Light Truck Tire Developer & Mfr
N.A.I.C.S.: 326211

Subsidiary (Non-US):

Continental Tyre Group Ltd. **(2)**
Continental House 191 High St, West Drayton, UB7 7XW, Middlesex, United
Kingdom **(100%)**
Tel.: (44) 1895425900
Web Site: http://www.conti-online.com
Sales Range: $50-74.9 Million
Emp.: 150
Passenger Vehicle Tire Mfr
N.A.I.C.S.: 326211
Mat Wilkinson *(Comml Dir)*

Semperit Reifen GesmbH **(2)**
Wienersdorfer Str 20 24, A 2514,
Traiskirchen, Austria **(100%)**
Tel.: (43) 22525012660
Web Site: http://www.semperit.com
Sales Range: $100-124.9 Million
Emp.: 300
Mfr of Tires
N.A.I.C.S.: 326211

Continental Properties Mexico SA de CV **(1)**
Camino a la Tijera No 3, 45640, Guadalajara, Mexico
Tel.: (52) 33 381 820 03
Web Site: http://www.continental.com
Emp.: 450
Real Estate Development Services
N.A.I.C.S.: 531390

Continental Sime Tyre Sdn Bhd **(1)**
4 Jalan Tandang, 46050, Petaling Jaya, Selangor Darul Ehsan, Malaysia
Tel.: (60) 377878888
Web Site: http://www.conti-online.com
Sales Range: $450-499.9 Million
Emp.: 1,500
Tire Mfr; Joint Venture of Continental AG & Sime Darby Berhad
N.A.I.C.S.: 326211

Division (Domestic):

Continental Sime Tyre Marketing Sdn. Bhd. **(2)**
4 Jalan Tandang, PO Box 66, 46050, Petaling Jaya, Selangor, Malaysia
Tel.: (60) 377818833
Web Site: http://www.conti-sime.com
Sales Range: $75-99.9 Million
Emp.: 1,400
Aircraft Tires Mfr
N.A.I.C.S.: 326211
Henry Benoit *(CEO)*

Continental Suisse S A **(1)**
Lerzenstrasse 19A, Postfach 840, 8953,
Dietikon, Zurich, Switzerland **(100%)**
Tel.: (41) 447455600
Web Site: http://www.contionline.de
Sales Range: $25-49.9 Million
Emp.: 100
Producer of Tires & Rubber & Plastic Industrial Articles, Mechanical, Electronic Brake Systems
N.A.I.C.S.: 314994

Continental Temic Electronics Philippines Inc. **(1)**
16 Ring Road LISP2-SEZ, 4027, Calamba, Laguna, Philippines
Tel.: (63) 27867001
Web Site: http://www.continental-corporation.com
Emp.: 80
Automotive Electronic Brake System & Sensor Cluster Mfr
N.A.I.C.S.: 336340

Continental Teves AG & Co. oHG **(1)**
Guerickestrasse 7, Frankfurt am Main, 60488, Germany
Tel.: (49) 69 76031
Automotive Braking System & Component Distr
N.A.I.C.S.: 423120

Continental Teves Hungary Kft. **(1)**
Hazgyari Ut 6-8, Veszprem, 8200, Hungary

Tel.: (36) 88 540100
Web Site: http://www.continental.com
Automobile Parts Distr
N.A.I.C.S.: 423120
Peter Vajda *(Mgr-Pur)*

Continental Teves Inc. **(1)**
13456 Lovers Ln, Culpeper, VA 22701
Tel.: (540) 825-4100
Web Site: http://www.vdo.com
Automotive Braking Component Mfr
N.A.I.C.S.: 336340

Continental Teves Portugal Sistemas de Travagem LDA **(1)**
Estrada National 252 KM 11, 2950-402,
Palmela, Portugal
Tel.: (351) 21 238 7500
Automotive Braking System Mfr & Distr
N.A.I.C.S.: 336340

Continental Teves UK Ltd. **(1)**
Waun-y-Pound, Ebbw Vale, NP3 6PL,
United Kingdom
Tel.: (44) 1495 350350
Sales Range: $50-74.9 Million
Emp.: 140
Motor Vehicle Brake System Mfr
N.A.I.C.S.: 336340
Mark Langshaw *(Gen Mgr)*

Continental Tire the Americas, LLC **(1)**
1830 MacMillan Park Dr, Fort Mill, SC
29707 **(100%)**
Tel.: (704) 588-5895
Web Site: http://www.continentaltire.com
Passenger Vehicle Tire Mfr
N.A.I.C.S.: 326211
Daryl Hollnagel *(VP-HR Legal)*

Plant (Domestic):

Continental Tire North America **(2)**
11525 N Hwy 42, Mount Vernon, IL
62864-0022 **(100%)**
Tel.: (618) 242-7100
Web Site: http://www.continentaltire.com
Sales Range: $400-449.9 Million
Commercial Vehicle Tire Developer & Mfr
N.A.I.C.S.: 326211
Hank Eisenga *(VP-Mfg)*

Subsidiary (Domestic):

Hill Tire Company **(2)**
100 Hill Industrial Blvd, Forest Park, GA
30297
Tel.: (404) 361-6337
Web Site: http://www.hilltireco.com
Automotive Tire Retreading Services
N.A.I.C.S.: 326212
David Hill *(Mgr)*

Continental Trading France SAS **(1)**
1 Rue de Clairefontaine, 78512, Rambouillet, France
Tel.: (33) 1 34 57 40 36
Motor Vehicle Electronic Parts Distr
N.A.I.C.S.: 423690

Continental Trading UK Ltd. **(1)**
36 Gravelly Industrial Park, Birmingham,
B24 8TA, United Kingdom
Tel.: (44) 800 215 315
Sales Range: $50-74.9 Million
Emp.: 10
Automobile Parts Distr
N.A.I.C.S.: 423120
Paul Jennings *(Reg Head-Sls)*

Elektrobit Automotive GmbH **(1)**
Am Wolfsmantel 46, 91058, Erlangen,
Germany **(100%)**
Tel.: (49) 913177010
Web Site:
http://www.automotive.elektrobit.com
Emp.: 3,500
Automotive Embedded Software Developer & Component Integration Services
N.A.I.C.S.: 541511

Subsidiary (Non-US):

Elektrobit Austria GmbH **(2)**
Kaiserstr 45 / Stiege 2, 1070, Vienna, Austria
Tel.: (43) 1599830
Web Site: http://www.elektrobit.com
Automotive Embedded Software Developer & Component Integration Services

N.A.I.C.S.: 541511

Subsidiary (US):

Elektrobit Automotive Americas Inc. **(2)**
22745 29th Dr SE Ste 200, Bothell, WA
98021
Tel.: (425) 686-3100
Web Site: http://www.elektrobit.com
Automotive Embedded Software Developer & Component Integration Services
N.A.I.C.S.: 541511

Subsidiary (Non-US):

Elektrobit Automotive Software (Shanghai) Co., Ltd. **(2)**
2205 Wentong Building 739 Kunming Road,
Yangpu District, Shanghai, 200082, China
Tel.: (86) 2150431951
Web Site: http://www.elektrobit.com
Software Developer
N.A.I.C.S.: 513210

Elektrobit France SAS **(2)**
8 Avenue Eiffel 2 Etage, 78420, Carrieres-sur-Seine, France
Tel.: (33) 134802900
Web Site: http://www.elektrobit.com
Automotive Embedded Software Developer & Component Integration Services
N.A.I.C.S.: 541511

Elektrobit Nippon K.K. **(2)**
Osaki New City No 1 Building 1-6-1 Osaki,
Shinagawa-ku, Tokyo, 141-0032, Japan
Tel.: (81) 364217140
Web Site: http://www.elektrobit.com
Electronic Components Mfr
N.A.I.C.S.: 334419

General Tyre East Africa Ltd. **(1)**
Chemi Industrial Area, PO Box 554, NIL,
Arusha, Tanzania **(15%)**
Tel.: (255) 272503341
Sales Range: $125-149.9 Million
Emp.: 400
Mfr & Sales of Tires
N.A.I.C.S.: 326211

OOO Continental Automotive RUS **(1)**
Zolotorozhsky Val 34 Build 6, Moscow,
111033, Russia
Tel.: (7) 495 646 76 88
Web Site:
http://www.continentalcorporation.com
Automobile Parts Distr
N.A.I.C.S.: 423120

Otomotiv Lastikleri Tevzi AS **(1)**
Kucukbakkalkoy Mah Kayisdagi Cad Allianz Tower No 1/26, Atasehir, 34750, Istanbul,
Turkiye **(89.66%)**
Tel.: (90) 2165870000
Sales Range: $75-99.9 Million
Emp.: 35
Automotive Tires Distr
N.A.I.C.S.: 423130
Serkan Erat *(Mgr-Sls)*

SC Continental Automotive Romania S.R.L. **(1)**
Strada Siemens Nr 1, 300704, Timisoara,
Romania
Tel.: (40) 256 25 35 02
Web Site: http://www.continental-automotive.com
Emp.: 5,000
Automotive Software Development Services
N.A.I.C.S.: 541511
Elena-Daria Tanasa *(Coord-PR)*

Zonar Systems, LLC **(1)**
18200 Cascade Ave S, Seattle, WA 98188
Tel.: (206) 878-2459
Web Site: http://www.zonarsystems.com
Electronic Inspection, Tracking & Operations Solutions
N.A.I.C.S.: 334419
H. Kevin Mest *(Sr VP-Passenger Svcs)*

e.solutions GmbH **(1)**
Frauenweiherstrasse 17, 91058, Erlangen,
Germany
Tel.: (49) 84583332100
Web Site: http://www.esolutions.de
Emp.: 500
Automotive Infotainment Mfr

N.A.I.C.S.: 336110

CONTINENTAL CHEMICALS LIMITED
A-7 Sector 7, Noida, 201 301, Uttar
Pradesh, India
Tel.: (91) 1202423316
Web Site:
https://www.continentalchemical.com
Year Founded: 1984
506935—(BOM)
Rev.: $132,133
Assets: $663,141
Liabilities: $152,203
Net Worth: $510,938
Earnings: $19,574
Emp.: 3
Fiscal Year-end: 03/31/21
Chemical Products Mfr
N.A.I.C.S.: 325998
Pradeep Kumar Chopra *(Chm)*

CONTINENTAL CONTROLS LIMITED
B-10 Tirupati Udyog Nagar Sativli
Road, Waliv Vasai East, 401206,
Thane, 401206, Maharashtra, India
Tel.: (91) 8669990611
Web Site:
https://www.newkrishna.com
531460—(BOM)
Rev.: $836,851
Assets: $1,545,260
Liabilities: $936,537
Net Worth: $608,723
Earnings: $124,830
Fiscal Year-end: 03/31/21
Electrical Component Mfr
N.A.I.C.S.: 335999
Navin G. Thakkar *(Chm & Mng Dir)*

CONTINENTAL DEVICE INDIA PRIVATE LIMITED
C-120 Naraina Industrial Area I, New
Delhi, 110028, India
Tel.: (91) 11 4141 1112 In
Web Site: http://www.cdil.com
Semiconductor Devices Mfr
N.A.I.C.S.: 334413

CONTINENTAL ENERGY CORPORATION
1500-1055 West Georgia Street, Vancouver, V6E 4N7, BC, Canada
Tel.: (604) 687-5700 BC
Web Site:
http://www.continentalenergy.com
CPPXF—(OTCBB)
Assets: $92,306
Liabilities: $793,966
Net Worth: ($701,660)
Earnings: ($355,119)
Emp.: 5
Fiscal Year-end: 06/30/20
Oil & Gas Exploration Services
N.A.I.C.S.: 211120
Richard L. McAdoo *(Chm & CEO)*

CONTINENTAL FILM D.O.O.
Zavrtnica 17 Hrvatska, 10000, Zagreb, Croatia
Tel.: (385) 16194660
Web Site: http://www.continental-film.hr
Sales Range: $1-9.9 Million
Emp.: 40
Motion Picture Distr
N.A.I.C.S.: 512120
Enver Hadziabdic *(Pres)*

CONTINENTAL HOLDINGS CORP.
23F 95 Dun Hua South Road Sec 2,
Taipei, 10682, Taiwan
Tel.: (886) 237012000

Continental Holdings Corp.—(Continued)

Web Site: https://www.continental-holdings.com
Year Founded: 2010
3703—(TAI)
Rev.: $1,000,910,522
Assets: $2,564,199,910
Liabilities: $1,557,767,363
Net Worth: $1,006,432,546
Earnings: $43,506,817
Emp.: 2,575
Fiscal Year-end: 12/31/23
Holding Company; Construction & Engineering Services
N.A.I.C.S.: 551112
Nita Ing *(Chm)*

Subsidiaries:

Blue Whale Water Technologies
Corporation　　　　　　　　**(1)**
No 100 Baoya Road, Fengshan Dist, Kaohsiung, 830, Taiwan
Tel.: (886) 77538850
Web Site: http://www.bluewhale-watertech.com
Wastewater Reclamation Services
N.A.I.C.S.: 221320

Continental Consulting Limited
Company　　　　　　　　　**(1)**
23F No 95 Section 2 Dunhua S Road Sec 2, Taipei, 106, Taiwan
Tel.: (886) 237015858
Management Consulting Services
N.A.I.C.S.: 541611

Continental Engineering
Corporation　　　　　　　　**(1)**
No 95 Dunhua S Rd Sec 2, Taipei, 106, Taiwan
Tel.: (886) 237011000
Web Site: http://www.continental-engineering.com
Sales Range: $150-199.9 Million
Emp.: 791
Heavy Engineering Construction Services
N.A.I.C.S.: 541330
Nita Ing *(Chm)*

Subsidiary (US):

American Bridge Holding
Company　　　　　　　　　**(2)**
1000 American Bridge Way, Coraopolis, PA 15108-1266
Tel.: (412) 631-1000
Web Site: https://www.americanbridge.net
Sales Range: $125-149.9 Million
Emp.: 300
Holding Company
N.A.I.C.S.: 551112

Subsidiary (Domestic):

American Bridge Company　　**(3)**
1000 American Bridge Way, Coraopolis, PA 15108
Tel.: (412) 631-1000
Web Site: https://www.americanbridge.net
Engineering Services; Manufacture, Erection & Rehabilitation of Bridges & Other Structures; Underwater & Heavy Concrete Construction
N.A.I.C.S.: 238120
Kwadwo Osei-Akoto *(VP-Special Projects-New York)*

Subsidiary (Domestic):

American Bridge Manufacturing
Company　　　　　　　　　**(4)**
1000 American Bridge Way, Coraopolis, PA 15108
Tel.: (412) 631-1000
Web Site: https://www.americanbridge.net
Bridge Manufacturing
N.A.I.C.S.: 237310

Subsidiary (Domestic):

CEC Commercial Development
Corporation　　　　　　　　**(2)**
No 218 Legun 3rd Road, Taipei, 104, Taiwan
Tel.: (886) 28 502 0208

Web Site: http://www.continental-holdings.com
Sales Range: $50-74.9 Million
Emp.: 7
Commercial Complex Development & Management Services
N.A.I.C.S.: 531311

Subsidiary (Non-US):

CEC International Corporation (India)
Private Limited　　　　　　**(2)**
Flat No 211 Pocket A/3 Sector -7, Rohini, New Delhi, 110 085, India
Tel.: (91) 124 458 8888
Web Site: https://www.cici.co.in
Sales Range: $50-74.9 Million
Emp.: 110
Commercial Building Construction Services
N.A.I.C.S.: 236220
Rajiv Kumar *(Sec & Asst VP-Legal)*

CEC International Malaysia Sdn.
Bhd.　　　　　　　　　　　**(2)**
Wisma MABA 7th FL No 6 Jalan Hang Jebat, 50150, Kuala Lumpur, Malaysia
Tel.: (60) 320705007
Construction & Engineering Services
N.A.I.C.S.: 541330

Subsidiary (Domestic):

Hsin Dar Environment
Corporation　　　　　　　　**(2)**
19F 95 Tun Hua South Road Section 2, Taipei, 10682, Taiwan
Tel.: (886) 237016212
Sales Range: $25-49.9 Million
Emp.: 26
Commercial Building Construction Services
N.A.I.C.S.: 236220
Jerry Chou *(Pres)*

North Shore Corp.　　　　　**(2)**
13F No 95 Dunhua S Rd Sec 2, Da-an District, Taipei, 106, Taiwan
Tel.: (886) 237016271
Web Site: http://www.northshore.com.tw
Emp.: 14
Commercial Building Construction Services
N.A.I.C.S.: 236220
Jerry Chou *(Pres)*

HDEC Construction Corporation　**(1)**
No 95 Dunhua S Rd Sec 2, Daan District, Taipei, 106, Taiwan
Tel.: (886) 237015000
Underground Pipeline Construction Services
N.A.I.C.S.: 237110

CONTINENTAL HOLDINGS LIMITED

Flats M and N 1/F Kaiser Estate Phase 3 11 Hok Yuen Street, Hunghom, Kowloon, China (Hong Kong)
Tel.: (852) 23638882　　　　　HK
Web Site:
　http://www.continental.com.hk
0513—(HKG)
Rev.: $77,894,375
Assets: $498,510,796
Liabilities: $182,978,509
Net Worth: $315,532,287
Earnings: $4,960,829
Emp.: 532
Fiscal Year-end: 06/30/22
Investment Management Service
N.A.I.C.S.: 523999
Charles Sing chuk Chan *(Exec Dir)*

Subsidiaries:

C.J. (UK) Limited　　　　　　**(1)**
3rd Floor Lumiere House Elstree Way, Borehamwood, WD6 1JH, Hertfordshire, United Kingdom
Tel.: (44) 208 207 4760
Jewellery Product Mfr & Distr
N.A.I.C.S.: 339910

CJ USA LLC　　　　　　　　**(1)**
2100 Felver Ct, Rahway, NJ 07065
Tel.: (732) 827-5000
Jewellery Product Mfr & Distr
N.A.I.C.S.: 339910

Continental Jewellery (Jiangmen)
Co., Ltd.　　　　　　　　　**(1)**
62 Huandao Donglu Chaolian, Pengjiang District, Jiangmen, China
Tel.: (86) 7503723338
Jewelry Mfr
N.A.I.C.S.: 339910

Continental Jewellery (UK) Ltd.　**(1)**
Sovereign Court 7-9 Graham Street, Hockley, Birmingham, B1 3JR, United Kingdom
Tel.: (44) 1212363638
Emp.: 50
Jewellery Distr
N.A.I.C.S.: 423940
Laurence Blunt *(Gen Mgr)*

Continental Jewelry (U.S.A.) Inc.　**(1)**
115 W 30th St Ste 300, New York, NY 10001
Tel.: (212) 695-3303
Investment Management Service
N.A.I.C.S.: 523999

Novell Enterprises, Inc.　　　**(1)**
2100 Felver Ct, Rahway, NJ 07065　　　　　　　　　　**(85%)**
Tel.: (732) 428-8300
Web Site:
　http://www.novelldesignstudio.com
Jewelry Mfr
N.A.I.C.S.: 339910

Top Label International Limited　**(1)**
Unit M 1/F Kaiser Estate Phase 3 11 Hok Yuen Street, Hunghom, Kowloon, China (Hong Kong)
Tel.: (852) 2 363 8882
Web Site: https://toplabelintl.com
Food & Beverage Distr
N.A.I.C.S.: 424490

CONTINENTAL INSURANCE LIMITED

Advanced Noorani Tower 13 th Floor, 1 Mohakhali C/A, Dhaka, 1212, Bangladesh
Tel.: (880) 258817491
Web Site: https://www.cilbd.com
Year Founded: 1999
CONTININS—(CHT)
Rev.: $1,373,942
Assets: $13,821,423
Liabilities: $5,343,615
Net Worth: $8,477,808
Earnings: $997,937
Emp.: 330
Fiscal Year-end: 12/31/23
General Insurance Services
N.A.I.C.S.: 524210
Imtiaz Musa *(Vice Chm)*

CONTINENTAL MUSHROOM CORP.

2545 9th Line Rd, Metcalfe, K0A 2P0, ON, Canada
Tel.: (613) 821-1411
Web Site:
　http://www.continentalmushroom.ca
Year Founded: 1972
Rev.: $13,008,323
Emp.: 260
Mushroom Producer & Supplier
N.A.I.C.S.: 111411
Lyle Whitham *(Gen Mgr)*

CONTINENTAL PETROLEUMS LIMITED

A-2 Opp Udyog Bhawan Tilak Marg C-Scheme, Jaipur, 302 005, India
Tel.: (91) 9414111971
Web Site: https://www.conpetco.com
Year Founded: 1986
523232—(BOM)
Rev.: $16,601,294
Assets: $5,229,725
Liabilities: $2,851,553
Net Worth: $2,378,171
Earnings: $555,883
Emp.: 50
Fiscal Year-end: 03/31/22
Lubricating Oil & Grease Mfr

N.A.I.C.S.: 324191
Madan Lal Khandelwal *(Chm & Mng Dir)*

CONTINENTAL SECURITIES LIMITED

Flat No 301 Metro Plaza Parivahan Marg, Jaipur, 302 001, Rajasthan, India
Tel.: (91) 1412943037
Web Site:
　https://www.continentalsecurity.com
Year Founded: 1990
538868—(BOM)
Rev.: $111,582
Assets: $884,652
Liabilities: $26,850
Net Worth: $857,802
Earnings: $35,831
Emp.: 2
Fiscal Year-end: 03/31/21
Consumer Lending Services
N.A.I.C.S.: 522291
Madan Lal Khandelwal *(Chm)*

CONTINENTALE SEEDS & CHEMICALS LIMITED

Fourth Floor C-67 Dda Sheds Pocket A Okhla Phase I, Okhla Industrial Area, New Delhi, 110020, India
Tel.: (91) 1140582674
Web Site:
　https://www.continentalseeds.co.in
Year Founded: 1983
CONTI—(NSE)
Rev.: $13,063,619
Assets: $4,562,585
Liabilities: $2,920,165
Net Worth: $1,642,420
Earnings: $51,178
Emp.: 34
Fiscal Year-end: 03/12/21
Seed Mfr
N.A.I.C.S.: 111191
Praveen Rastogi *(Mng Dir)*

CONTINENTALE HOLDING AG

Ruhrallee 92, 44139, Dortmund, Germany
Tel.: (49) 2319190
Web Site: http://www.continentale.de
Year Founded: 1926
Sales Range: $1-4.9 Billion
Emp.: 3,000
Holding Company; Insurance Services
N.A.I.C.S.: 551112
Rolf Bauer *(CEO)*

Subsidiaries:

Mannheimer AG Holding　　　**(1)**
Augustaanlage 66, D 68165, Mannheim, Germany　　　　　　　　**(100%)**
Tel.: (49) 18022024
Web Site: http://www.mannheimer.de
Property, Casualty & Re-Insurance Carrier
N.A.I.C.S.: 524126

Subsidiary (Domestic):

Mannheimer Krankenversicherung
AG　　　　　　　　　　　　**(2)**
Augustaanlage 66, 68165, Mannheim, Germany
Tel.: (49) 18022024
Web Site: http://www.mannheimer.de
Sales Range: $50-74.9 Million
Emp.: 25
Health Insurance Carrier
N.A.I.C.S.: 524114

Mannheimer Versicherung AG　**(2)**
Augustaanlage 66, D 68165, Mannheim, Germany
Tel.: (49) 18022024
Web Site: http://www.mannheimer.de
Sales Range: $150-199.9 Million
Emp.: 350
Property & Casualty Insurance Carrier
N.A.I.C.S.: 524126

CONTOUR SHOWERS LIMITED
Siddom Street, Winsford, CW7 2BA, Cheshire, United Kingdom
Tel.: (44) 1606592586
Web Site: http://www.contour-showers.co.uk
Year Founded: 1959
Rev.: $16,934,636
Emp.: 66
Shower Mfr
N.A.I.C.S.: 332913
William Hogg *(Mng Dir)*

CONTOURGLOBAL LIMITED
55 Baker St 5th Fl, London, W1U8EW, United Kingdom
Tel.: (44) 2036269030   UK
Web Site:
https://www.contourglobal.com
GLO—(LSE)
Rev.: $1,410,700,000
Assets: $6,370,800,000
Liabilities: $6,033,100,000
Net Worth: $337,700,000
Earnings: $28,600,000
Emp.: 1,435
Fiscal Year-end: 12/31/20
Holding Company
N.A.I.C.S.: 551112
Joseph C. Brandt *(Co-Founder, Pres & CEO)*

Subsidiaries:

Chapada do Piaui II Holding S.A. **(1)**
Rua Leopoldo Couto de Magalhaes Junior 758 - conjunto 31 parte kk, Itaim bibi, Sao Paulo, 04542-000, SP, Brazil
Tel.: (55) 1131477100
Power Generation Services
N.A.I.C.S.: 221118

Contour Global Do Brasil Participacoes Ltda **(1)**
Rua Leopoldo Couto de Magalhaes Jrl 758 Cj 31 Itaim Bibi, Sao Paulo, 04542-000, Brazil
Tel.: (55) 11 3147 7100
Power Generation & Distribution Services
N.A.I.C.S.: 221118
Alessandra Marinheiro *(CEO & Exec VP)*

Subsidiary (Domestic):

Afluente Geracao de Energia Eletrica SA **(2)**
Praia Do Flamengo 78 - 10 Floor, 22210030, Rio de Janeiro, Brazil **(79%)**
Tel.: (55) 21 3235 9824
Rev.: $8,675,314
Assets: $53,106,810
Liabilities: $2,690,367
Net Worth: $50,416,443
Earnings: $5,824,751
Fiscal Year-end: 12/31/2018
Eletric Power Generation Services
N.A.I.C.S.: 221118

Contour Global LLC **(1)**
350 Madison Ave 21st Fl, New York, NY 10017
Tel.: (646) 386-9900
Web Site: http://www.contourglobal.com
Sales Range: $1-9.9 Million
Emp.: 1,500
Holding Company; Electric Power & Heating Plant Developer & Operator
N.A.I.C.S.: 551112
Joseph C. Brandt *(Pres & CEO)*

Subsidiary (Domestic):

Contour Global Management, Inc. **(2)**
650 5th Ave, New York, NY 10019
Tel.: (646) 386-9900
Web Site: http://www.contourglobal.com
Electric Power & Heating Plant Operator
N.A.I.C.S.: 221118

ContourGlobal Hydro Cascade CJSC **(1)**
2/2 Melik-Adamyan str, Yerevan, 0010, Armenia
Tel.: (374) 11520017
Power Generation Services

N.A.I.C.S.: 221118
ContourGlobal Management Sofia EOOD **(1)**
48 Sitnyakovo Blvd Floor 9 l, Sofia, 1505, Bulgaria
Tel.: (359) 28102323
Power Generation Services
N.A.I.C.S.: 221118

ContourGlobal Maritsa East 3 AD **(1)**
Mednikarovo, Stara Zagora, 6294, Bulgaria
Tel.: (359) 42663251
Power Generation Services
N.A.I.C.S.: 221118

Galheiros Geracao de Energia Eletrica S.A. **(1)**
Estrada Sao Domingos s/n Km 8 2 Zona Rural, Sao Domingos, Sao Paulo, 73860-000, GO, Brazil
Tel.: (55) 6234259604
Power Generation Services
N.A.I.C.S.: 221118

Rio Pch I S.A. **(1)**
Rod RJ 230 KM 53 Zona Rural, Bom Jesus do Itabapoana, Rio de Janeiro, 28360-000, RJ, Brazil
Tel.: (55) 2238339701
Power Generation Services
N.A.I.C.S.: 221118

Termosolar Alvarado, S.L. **(1)**
Carretera Corte de Peleas Km 14 BA-022 Alvarado, 06170, Badajoz, Spain
Tel.: (34) 924940434
Renewable Energy Generation Services
N.A.I.C.S.: 221118

Termosolar Majadas, S.L. **(1)**
Camino Puente Bazagona, Majadas de Tietar, 10529, Caceres, Spain
Tel.: (34) 927870043
Power Generation Services
N.A.I.C.S.: 221118

Termosolar Palma Saetilla, S.L. **(1)**
Carretera Canada del Rosal Km 9, Palma del Rio, 14700, Cordoba, Spain
Tel.: (34) 957851020
Power Generation Services
N.A.I.C.S.: 221118

CONTRACT CHEMICALS LTD.
Penrhyn Rd Knowsley Business Park, Prescot, L34 9HY, Merseyside, United Kingdom
Tel.: (44) 1515488840   UK
Web Site: http://www.contract-chemicals.com
Year Founded: 1977
Sales Range: $25-49.9 Million
Emp.: 100
Fine & Specialty Chemicals Mfr
N.A.I.C.S.: 325998
Mike Holding *(Mng Dir)*

CONTRACTING & MARINE SERVICES CO. (S.A.K.)
Al Murqab -Trade district 9 - junction of Mubarak Al-Kabeer Street, and Al Shuhada Street-Chamber of Commerce and Industry of Kuwait Build, 13089, Kuwait, Kuwait
Tel.: (965) 22410274
Web Site: http://www.cms-kw.com
Year Founded: 1973
Sales Range: $250-299.9 Million
Marine Construction Services
N.A.I.C.S.: 237990
Hisham Sulaiman Mohammad Al-Otaibi *(CEO)*

CONTRAF-NICOTEX-TOBACCO GMBH
Herbststrasse 8, Heilbronn, 74072, Germany
Tel.: (49) 7131898550
Web Site: http://www.cntleaf.com
Year Founded: 1982
Rev.: $21,155,200
Emp.: 17

Pharmaceutical Ingredient Mfr
N.A.I.C.S.: 325998
Sascha Siemann *(Mng Dir)*

CONTRAST LIGHTING M.L. INC.
1009 rue du Parc Industriel, Saint-Jean-Chrysostome-De-Levi, G6Z 1C5, QC, Canada
Tel.: (418) 839-4624
Web Site:
http://www.contrastlighting.com
Year Founded: 1989
Rev.: $10,100,000
Emp.: 85
Lighting Product Mfr
N.A.I.C.S.: 335131
Benoit Dupuy *(Gen Mgr)*

CONTREL TECHNOLOGY CO., LTD.
No 9 Nanke 6th Rd, Tainan Science-Based Industrial Park, Taipei, 744, Taiwan
Tel.: (886) 65051188
Web Site: https://www.contrel.com.tw
Year Founded: 1998
8064—(TPE)
Rev.: $122,582,278
Assets: $217,262,640
Liabilities: $114,840,134
Net Worth: $102,422,506
Earnings: $11,813,276
Fiscal Year-end: 12/31/22
Testing Equipment Mfr
N.A.I.C.S.: 334519
Yen Jui-Hsiung *(Chm)*

Subsidiaries:

Ever Lumin Incorporation **(1)**
No 9 Nan-Ke 6th Rd Tainan Science-Based Industrial Park, Tainan City, 744094, Taiwan
Tel.: (886) 65051188
Electronic Equipment Mfr & Distr
N.A.I.C.S.: 335314

F.S.E Corporation **(1)**
3F No 57 Wuquan Rd, Wugu Dist, New Taipei City, 24886, Taiwan
Tel.: (886) 222902333
Web Site: https://www.fsefulin.com
Optoelectronic Equipment Mfr & Distr
N.A.I.C.S.: 334413

iAmech Technology Inc. **(1)**
3F/5F No 2-1 Wuquan Rd, Wugu Dist, New Taipei City, 24886, Taiwan
Tel.: (886) 222990118
Web Site: https://www.iamech.com.tw
Automated Storage & Retrieval System Mfr
N.A.I.C.S.: 333922

CONTROL & APPLICATIONS GROUP
15th Floor Al Masraf Building Sheikh Hamdan Street, PO Box 3687, Abu Dhabi, United Arab Emirates
Tel.: (971) 26767965
Web Site: http://www.cagroup.ae
Year Founded: 1977
Engineering Solutions
N.A.I.C.S.: 541330
Rashed Bin Jabr Al Suwaidi *(Chm)*

CONTROL BIONICS LIMITED
Level 4 11-13 Pearson Street, Cremorne, 3121, VIC, Australia
Tel.: (61) 398973576   AU
Web Site:
https://www.controlbionics.com
Year Founded: 2005
CBL—(ASX)
Rev.: $3,986,511
Assets: $5,670,096
Liabilities: $1,009,698
Net Worth: $4,660,398
Earnings: ($3,671,605)
Fiscal Year-end: 06/30/23
Health Care Srvices

N.A.I.C.S.: 621610
Brett Crowley *(Sec)*

CONTROL PRINT LTD.
C-106 Hind Saurashtra Industrial Estate Andheri-Kurla Road Marol Naka, Andheri East, Mumbai, 400059, India
Tel.: (91) 2228599065
Web Site:
https://www.controlprint.com
Year Founded: 1991
522295—(BOM)
Rev.: $27,874,215
Assets: $39,594,487
Liabilities: $7,831,087
Net Worth: $31,763,400
Earnings: $3,965,557
Emp.: 749
Fiscal Year-end: 03/31/21
Automobile Mfr
N.A.I.C.S.: 336110
Basant S. Kabra *(Chm & Co-Mng Dir)*

Subsidiaries:

Control Print Limited **(1)**
No 243/1 Makola Road, Kiribathgoda, Colombo, Sri Lanka
Tel.: (94) 112670961
Molding Equipment Mfr
N.A.I.C.S.: 333248

Liberty Chemicals Private Limited **(1)**
203 Thakker Height Subhash Nagar Village Road Opp CEAT Tyres, Near Nahur Station Bhandup W, Mumbai, 400078, India
Tel.: (91) 2221671071
Web Site: http://www.libertychemical.com
Polymer Additives Mfr
N.A.I.C.S.: 325211

CONTROL RISKS GROUP HOLDINGS LTD.
Cottons Centre Cottons Lane, London, SE1 2QG, United Kingdom
Tel.: (44) 20 7970 2100   UK
Web Site:
http://www.controlrisks.com
Year Founded: 1975
Sales Range: $300-349.9 Million
Emp.: 1,983
Holding Company; Risk Management Consulting Services
N.A.I.C.S.: 551112
Richard Fenning *(CEO)*

Subsidiaries:

Control Risks East Africa **(1)**
4th floor Hanover Building 14 Riverside, Nairobi, Kenya
Tel.: (254) 205130900
Management Consulting Services
N.A.I.C.S.: 541611

CONTROLADORA MABE S.A. DE C.V.
3 Colonia Barrientos Zona Industria, Mexico, 54110, Mexico
Tel.: (52) 55 9178 8200
Web Site: http://www.mabe.cc
Sales Range: $1-4.9 Billion
Emp.: 23,000
Household Appliances Mfr
N.A.I.C.S.: 335220
Luis Berrondo Avalos *(Chm, Pres & CEO)*

Subsidiaries:

Atlas Electrica, S.A. **(1)**
Carretera a Heredia Km 12, Heredia, Costa Rica
Tel.: (506) 22772000
Web Site: http://www.atlas.co.cr
Sales Range: $100-124.9 Million
Emp.: 1,300
Home Electronics & Appliances Mfr
N.A.I.C.S.: 335210
Alonso Lizano Salazar *(Mgr-Products)*

Controladora Mabe S.A. de C.V.—(Continued)

CONTROLADORA VUELA COMPANIA DE AVIACION, S.A.B. DE C.V.

Av Antonio Dovali Jaime No 70 13th Floor Tower B, Colonia Zedec Santa Fe, Mexico, 01210, Mexico
Tel.: (52) 5552616400　　**MX**
Web Site: http://www.volaris.com
Year Founded: 2005
VLRS—(NYSE)
Rev.: $2,847,190,000
Assets: $4,467,653,000
Liabilities: $4,232,916,000
Net Worth: $234,737,000
Earnings: ($80,224,000)
Emp.: 7,364
Fiscal Year-end: 12/31/22
Air Transportation
N.A.I.C.S.: 481111
Brian Hanna Franke *(Chm)*

Subsidiaries:

Servicios Administrativos Volaris, S.A. de C.V　　　　　**(1)**
Av Antonio Dovali Jaime No 70 13th Floor Tower B Colonia Zedec, Santa Fe, Mexico, 01210, Mexico
Tel.: (52) 5552616400
Payroll Processing Services
N.A.I.C.S.: 541214

CONTROLCIRCLE LTD.

Chatfield Court 56 Chatfield Road, London, SW11 3UL, United Kingdom
Tel.: (44) 8454591111
Web Site:
　http://www.controlcircle.com
Year Founded: 2001
Sales Range: $10-24.9 Million
Emp.: 500
IT Services
N.A.I.C.S.: 541512
Lee Carr *(Head-Server Tech)*

CONVANO, INC.

Sakuragaoka-cho 22-14 NES Building S B3F, Shibuya, Tokyo, 150-0031, Kariya, Japan
Tel.: (81) 337701190
Web Site: https://convano.com
Year Founded: 2007
6574—(TKS)
Rev.: $17,113,290
Assets: $19,843,220
Liabilities: $8,976,380
Net Worth: $10,866,840
Earnings: ($1,315,390)
Emp.: 424
Fiscal Year-end: 03/31/24
Consumer Electronics Repair & Maintenance Services
N.A.I.C.S.: 811210
Shigehito Tsuboi *(Chm, Pres, CEO, CFO & Sec)*

CONVATEC GROUP PLC

3 Forbury Place, 23 Forbury Road, Reading, RG1 3JH, United Kingdom
Tel.: (44) 1189528100
Web Site:
　http://www.convatecgroup.com
CTEC—(LSE)
Rev.: $2,072,500,000
Assets: $3,592,000,000
Liabilities: $1,982,300,000
Net Worth: $1,609,700,000
Earnings: $62,900,000
Fiscal Year-end: 12/31/22
Medicinal Product Mfr
N.A.I.C.S.: 339112
Frank Schulkes *(CFO)*

Subsidiaries:

ConvaTec (Australia) Pty Limited　**(1)**
Level 1 5 Nexus Court Nexus Corporate

Park, Mulgrave, 3170, VIC, Australia
Tel.: (61) 1800339412
Web Site: https://www.convatec.co.nz
Medical Device Mfr & Distr
N.A.I.C.S.: 339112
Paul Moraviec *(Co-CEO)*

ConvaTec (Singapore) Pte Limited　　　　　**(1)**
456 Alexandra Road Fragrance Empire Building 18-02, Singapore, 119962, Singapore
Tel.: (65) 62459838
Web Site: https://www.convatec.com.sg
Medical Device Mfr & Distr
N.A.I.C.S.: 339112

ConvaTec (Sweden) AB　　**(1)**
Gustav III s Boulevard 42 plan 9, PO Box 15 138, 169 73, Solna, Sweden
Tel.: (46) 20212222
Web Site: https://www.convatec.se
Medical Device Mfr & Distr
N.A.I.C.S.: 339112

ConvaTec (Thailand) Co. Limited　**(1)**
Unit No 5 9th Floor M Thai Tower 87 Wireless Road, Lumpini Patumwan, Bangkok, 10330, Thailand
Tel.: (66) 26147000
Medical Device Mfr & Distr
N.A.I.C.S.: 339112

ConvaTec Argentina SRL　　**(1)**
Cerrito 1070 - Piso 3 - Departamento 71, 1010, Buenos Aires, Argentina
Tel.: (54) 2320351010
Web Site: https://www.convatec.com.ar
Medical Device Mfr & Distr
N.A.I.C.S.: 339112

ConvaTec Belgium BVBA　　**(1)**
Parc De l'Alliance Boulevard de France 9, 1420, Braine-l'Alleud, Belgium
Tel.: (32) 36666583
Web Site: https://www.convatec.be
Medical Device Mfr & Distr
N.A.I.C.S.: 339112

ConvaTec Canada Limited　　**(1)**
1425 Trans-Canada Highway Suite 100, Dorval, H9P 2V3, QC, Canada
Tel.: (336) 297-3087
Web Site: https://www.convatec.ca
Medical Device Mfr & Distr
N.A.I.C.S.: 339112

ConvaTec Ceska Republika s.r.o.　**(1)**
Olivova 4/2096, 110 00, Prague, Czech Republic
Tel.: (420) 225109111
Web Site: https://www.convatec.cz
Medical Device Mfr & Distr
N.A.I.C.S.: 339112

ConvaTec China Limited　　**(1)**
Room 1105-1106 Building 1 Jingyao Business Plaza No 133 Yaolong Road, Pudong New District, Shanghai, 200124, China
Tel.: (86) 2180308991
Web Site: https://www.convatec.com
Medical Device Mfr & Distr
N.A.I.C.S.: 339112

ConvaTec Denmark A/S　　**(1)**
Ostmarken 3A, 2860, Soborg, Denmark
Tel.: (45) 48167474
Web Site: https://www.convatec.dk
Medical Device Mfr & Distr
N.A.I.C.S.: 339112

ConvaTec Dominican Republic Inc.　　　　　**(1)**
Highway 30 de mayo Km 13 5, Santo Domingo, Dominican Republic
Tel.: (809) 2892222
Medical Device Mfr & Distr
N.A.I.C.S.: 339112

ConvaTec Hellas Medical Products S.A.　　　　　**(1)**
Mesogeion St 392A, Agia Paraskevi Attica, 15341, Athens, Greece
Tel.: (30) 2106564740
Web Site: https://www.convatec.gr
Medical Device Mfr & Distr
N.A.I.C.S.: 339112

ConvaTec Hong Kong Limited　**(1)**
Unit 1901 19/F Yue Xiu Building 160-174 Lockhart Rd, Wanchai, China (Hong Kong)

Tel.: (852) 25169182
Web Site: https://www.convatec.com.hk
Medical Device Mfr & Distr
N.A.I.C.S.: 339112

ConvaTec India Private Limited　**(1)**
Unit No 206 Second Floor Tower-B DIGITAL GREENS Sector-61, Golf Course Extension Road, Gurgaon, 122102, Haryana, India
Tel.: (91) 8002674989
Web Site: https://www.convatec.co.in
Medical Device Mfr & Distr
N.A.I.C.S.: 339112

ConvaTec Italia S.r.l.　　**(1)**
Via della Sierra Nevada 60, 00144, Rome, Italy
Tel.: (39) 03489412247
Web Site: https://www.convatec.com
Medical Device Mfr & Distr
N.A.I.C.S.: 339112

ConvaTec Japan KK　　**(1)**
1-1-7 Glass City Koraku, Bunkyo-ku, Tokyo, 112-0004, Japan
Tel.: (81) 120532384
Web Site: https://www.convatec.com
Medical Device Mfr & Distr
N.A.I.C.S.: 339112
Yoshihko Ohashi *(VP & Gen Mgr)*

ConvaTec Korea, Ltd.　　**(1)**
66 Yeongdong-daero 112-gil American Standard Bathhouse Building, 4th Floor Gangnam-gu, Seoul, Korea (South)
Tel.: (82) 8034536333
Web Site: https://www.convatec.co.kr
Medical Device Mfr & Distr
N.A.I.C.S.: 339112

ConvaTec Limited　　**(1)**
Unit 20 First Avenue, Deeside Industrial Park, Deeside, CH52NU, Flintshire, United Kingdom
Tel.: (44) 1244284882
Web Site: https://www.convatec.co.uk
Medical Device Mfr & Distr
N.A.I.C.S.: 339112

ConvaTec Malaysia Sdn Bhd　**(1)**
Suite 28-1 Level 28 Vertical Corporate Tower B Avenue 10 The Vertical, Bangsar South City No 8 Jalan Kerinchi, 59200, Kuala Lumpur, Selangor, Malaysia
Tel.: (60) 122870856
Web Site: https://www.convatec.com.my
Medical Device Mfr & Distr
N.A.I.C.S.: 339112

ConvaTec Middle East & Africa LLC　　　　　**(1)**
22 Kamal El Din Hussein St 3rd Floor, Heliopolis Sheraton, 11977, Cairo, Egypt
Tel.: (20) 224191142
Medical Device Mfr & Distr
N.A.I.C.S.: 339112

ConvaTec Nederland B.V.　　**(1)**
Houttuinlaan 5F, 3447 GM, Woerden, Netherlands
Tel.: (31) 348436941
Medical Device Mfr & Distr
N.A.I.C.S.: 339112

ConvaTec Norway AS　　**(1)**
Nils Hansens vei 8, 0667, Oslo, Norway
Tel.: (47) 21096790
Web Site: https://www.convatec.no
Medical Device Mfr & Distr
N.A.I.C.S.: 339112

ConvaTec Peru S.A.C.　　**(1)**
Calle Monte Rosa 255 Int 301 Urb, Chacarilla Santiago de Surco, Lima, Peru
Tel.: (51) 946305159
Web Site: https://www.convatec.com.pe
Medical Device Mfr & Distr
N.A.I.C.S.: 339112

ConvaTec Polska Sp. z o.o.　**(1)**
Rondo Daszynskiego 1, 00-843, Warsaw, Poland
Tel.: (48) 225796650
Web Site: https://www.convatec.com
Medical Device Mfr & Distr
N.A.I.C.S.: 339112

ConvaTec Saglik Urunleri Limited Sirketi　　　　　**(1)**
Ayazaga Mah Mimar Sinan Sok A Blok No

21A Inner Door No 9, Sariyer, 34396, Istanbul, Turkiye
Tel.: (90) 2164165200
Web Site: https://www.convatec.com.tr
Medical Device Mfr & Distr
N.A.I.C.S.: 339112

ConvaTec South Africa (Pty) Limited　　　　　**(1)**
Office 1 4 First floor 16 Baker Street, Rosebank, Johannesburg, 2196, South Africa
Tel.: (27) 108803833
Medical Device Mfr & Distr
N.A.I.C.S.: 339112

ConvaTec Technologies Inc.　**(1)**
3993 Howard Hughes Pkwy Ste 250, Las Vegas, NV 89169-6754
Medical Device Mfr & Distr
N.A.I.C.S.: 339112

EuroTec B.V.　　　　**(1)**
Schotsbossenstraat 8, 4705 AG, Roosendaal, Netherlands
Tel.: (31) 165551226
Web Site: https://www.eurotec.eu
Medical Device Mfr & Distr
N.A.I.C.S.: 339112
Peter Kempen *(Gen Mgr)*

EuroTec GmbH　　　　**(1)**
Unter dem Hofe 5, 58099, Hagen, Germany
Tel.: (49) 233162450
Web Site: https://www.eurotec.team
Emp.: 215
Medical Device Mfr & Distr
N.A.I.C.S.: 339112

J & R Medical, LLC　　　**(1)**
4635 SWT Fwy Ste 800, Houston, TX 77027-7105
Web Site: https://www.jandrmedical.com
Professional Equipment & Supplies Merchant Whslr
N.A.I.C.S.: 423490

Laboratoires ConvaTec SAS　**(1)**
Sigma building 90 Boulevard National, 92250, La Garenne-Colombes, France
Tel.: (33) 156471800
Web Site: https://www.convatec.fr
Medical Device Mfr & Distr
N.A.I.C.S.: 339112
Timothy P. Moran *(Co-Pres)*

Papyro-Tex A/S　　　　**(1)**
ConvaTec Harlev Skinderskovvej 32-36, 2730, Herlev, Denmark
Tel.: (45) 44944000
Medical Device Mfr & Distr
N.A.I.C.S.: 339112

South Shore Medical Supply, Inc.　　　　　**(1)**
58 Norfolk Ave Unit 2, South Easton, MA 02375-1907
Tel.: (508) 230-7272
Medical Device Mfr & Distr
N.A.I.C.S.: 339112

Wilmington Medical Supply, Inc.　**(1)**
1206 N 23rd St, Wilmington, NC 28405
Web Site: https://www.wmsuro.com
Medical Device Mfr & Distr
N.A.I.C.S.: 339112

ZAO ConvaTec　　　　**(1)**
Kosmodamianskaya Nab 52 Building 1 9th Floor, 115054, Moscow, 115054, Russia
Tel.: (7) 4956637030
Web Site: https://www.convatec-russia.ru
Medical Device Mfr & Distr
N.A.I.C.S.: 339112

CONVENI B.V.

Willige Laagt 2, 5757 PZ, Liessel, Netherlands
Tel.: (31) 493 348 700
Web Site: http://www.conveni.nl
Sales Range: $25-49.9 Million
Emp.: 150
Prepared Food Mfr
N.A.I.C.S.: 311991

CONVENIENCE FOODS LANKA PLC

133 7th LaneOff Borupana Road, Kandawala, Ratmalana, Sri Lanka

Tel.: (94) 115003000
Web Site:
https://www.muncheelk.com
Year Founded: 1991
SOY.N0000—(COL)
Rev.: $26,768,087
Assets: $16,173,297
Liabilities: $8,049,966
Net Worth: $8,123,331
Earnings: $1,732,651
Emp.: 355
Fiscal Year-end: 03/31/23
Food Products Mfr
N.A.I.C.S.: 311999

CONVENIENCE RETAIL ASIA LIMITED

15th Floor LiFung Centre 2 On Ping Street Siu Lek Yuen Shatin, Hong Kong, NT, China (Hong Kong)
Tel.: (852) 29916300
Web Site: http://www.cr-asia.com
831—(HKG)
Rev.: $153,705,595
Assets: $173,370,531
Liabilities: $98,709,942
Net Worth: $74,660,589
Earnings: $405,054,725
Emp.: 2,700
Fiscal Year-end: 12/31/20
Convenience Store Operator
N.A.I.C.S.: 445131
Richard Lap Bun Yeung (CEO)

Subsidiaries:

Saint Honore Cake Shop Limited **(1)**
14/F LiFung Centre 2 On Ping Street, Siu Lek Yuen, Sha Tin, New Territories, China (Hong Kong)
Tel.: (852) 29916677
Web Site: http://www.sthonore.com
Emp.: 2,400
Bakery Product Mfr & Distr
N.A.I.C.S.: 311812
Avis Wong (Asst Mgr-Mktg)

Saint Honore Holdings Co. Ltd **(1)**
5F Express Industrial Building, 43 Heung Yip Road, Hong Kong, China (Hong Kong)
Tel.: (852) 28730832
Web Site: http://www.sthonore.com
Sales Range: $75-99.9 Million
Emp.: 1,950
Bakery
N.A.I.C.S.: 311811

CONVENTIVE TECHNOLOGIES LTD.

4F No 419 Jhonghe Rd, Yonghe Dist, New Taipei City, 234, Taiwan
Tel.: (886) 286601023
Web Site: http://www.coventive.com
Year Founded: 2000
CVTTF—(OTCIQ)
Sales Range: Less than $1 Million
Computer Peripheral Distr
N.A.I.C.S.: 423430

CONVERGE TECHNOLOGY SOLUTIONS CORP.

161 Bay St Suite 2325, Toronto, M5J 2S1, ON, Canada
Tel.: (416) 360-1495   Ca
Web Site:
https://www.convergetp.com
Year Founded: 2016
CTSDF—(OTCQX)
Rev.: $1,195,199,457
Assets: $1,070,813,808
Liabilities: $563,248,641
Net Worth: $507,565,168
Earnings: $12,802,794
Fiscal Year-end: 12/31/21
Information Technology Solutions Services
N.A.I.C.S.: 518210
Shaun Maine (CEO)

Subsidiaries:

CarpeDatum LLC **(1)**
3131 S Vaughn Way, Aurora, CO 94706-1129
Tel.: (303) 627-8000
Web Site: http://www.carpedatuminc.com
Business Intelligence & Performance Management Consulting Services
N.A.I.C.S.: 541611
Steven Garno (Partner)

Creative Breakthroughs, Inc. **(1)**
1260 Woodward Heights, Ferndale, MI 48220
Tel.: (248) 519-4000
Web Site: http://www.cbihome.com
Sales Range: $10-24.9 Million
Emp.: 95
Custom Data Reliability & IT Advisory Solutions
N.A.I.C.S.: 518210
Steve Barone (CEO & Pres)

Datatrend Technologies, Inc. **(1)**
121 Cheshire Ln Ste 700, Minnetonka, MN 55305
Tel.: (952) 931-1203
Web Site: http://www.datatrend.com
Computer System Design Services
N.A.I.C.S.: 541512

Essex Technology Group, Inc. **(1)**
201 W Passaic St, Rochelle Park, NJ 07662
Tel.: (201) 712-1999
Web Site: http://www.essextec.com
Wall Street-based Cloud, Cognitive & Cybersecurity Solutions Provider
N.A.I.C.S.: 541511
Dennis Burke (Co-Founder & Chm)

Lighthouse Computer Services, Inc. **(1)**
6 Blackstone Vly Pl Ste 205, Lincoln, RI 02865
Tel.: (401) 334-0799
Web Site: http://www.lighthousecs.com
Computer System Design Services
N.A.I.C.S.: 541512

Nordisk Systems Inc. **(1)**
6400 SE Lk Ste 450, Portland, OR 97222
Tel.: (503) 353-7555
Web Site: http://www.nordisksystems.com
Computer & Computer Peripheral Equipment & Software Merchant Whslr
N.A.I.C.S.: 423430
Deney Dentel (Pres & CEO)

PC Specialists, Inc. **(1)**
10240 Flanders Court, San Diego, CA 92121
Tel.: (858) 566-1900
Web Site: http://www.tig.com
Sales Range: $25-49.9 Million
Emp.: 300
System Integration Services
N.A.I.C.S.: 541512
Bruce Geier (Pres & CEO)

Subsidiary (Domestic):

Obsidian Technologies, Inc. **(2)**
1599 Oak St, Eugene, OR 97401
Tel.: (541) 242-1000
Web Site:
http://www.obsidiantechnologies.com
Sales Range: $1-9.9 Million
Internet Communications Systems Services
N.A.I.C.S.: 541990
David Markey (Pres)

Paragon Development Systems, Inc. **(1)**
13400 Bishops Ln Ste 190, Brookfield, WI 53005
Tel.: (262) 569-5300
Web Site: http://www.pdsit.net
Identity & Access Management, Cloud Computing & Other Computer Related Services
N.A.I.C.S.: 518210
Asif Naseem (Pres & CEO)

Subsidiary (Domestic):

Works Computing LLC **(2)**
1801 American Blvd E Ste 12, Bloomington, MN 55425

Tel.: (952) 746-1580
Information Technology Solutions
N.A.I.C.S.: 518210

Software Information Systems LLC **(1)**
165 Barr St, Lexington, KY 40507
Tel.: (859) 977-4747
Web Site: http://www.thinksis.com
Computer & Computer Peripheral Equipment & Software Merchant Whslr
N.A.I.C.S.: 423430
Steve Sigg (Pres & CEO)

VSS, LLC **(1)**
382 Galleria Pkwy Ste 400, Madison, MS 39110
Tel.: (601) 853-8550
Web Site: http://www.vss-inc.com
Sales Range: $75-99.9 Million
Emp.: 85
Computers & Software Solutions
N.A.I.C.S.: 541511
Robert L. Jernoske Jr. (CEO)

CONVERGENCE PARTNERS (PTY) LIMITED

3rd Floor 30 Jellicoe Avenue, Rosebank, 2196, South Africa
Tel.: (27) 115505320
Web Site:
https://www.convergence.com
Year Founded: 2006
Privater Equity Firm
N.A.I.C.S.: 523940
Andile NgCaba (Chm & Founding Partner)

CONVERGENT FINANCE LLP

B-1605, One BKC, Bandra-Kurla Complex, Bandra East,, Mumbai, 400051, India
Tel.: (91) 2240403300
Web Site:
https://convergentfinance.com
Year Founded: 2018
Emp.: 100
Financial Services
N.A.I.C.S.: 523999
Harsha Raghavan (Mng Partner)

CONVERGENZE S.P.A.

Via Seliano 2 Capaccio Paestum, 84047, Salerno, Italy
Tel.: (39) 08281962102
Web Site: https://www.convergenze.it
Year Founded: 2005
CVG—(EUR)
Telecommunication Servicesb
N.A.I.C.S.: 517810
Grazia Pingaro (Vice Chm)

CONVERSION CAPITAL PARTNERS LTD.

Craven House 16 Northumberland Avenue, London, WC2N 5AP, United Kingdom
Tel.: (44) 20 7808 4758   UK
Year Founded: 2003
Private Investment Firm
N.A.I.C.S.: 523999
William Ty Comfort III (Principal)

Subsidiaries:

Vendome Group, LLC **(1)**
6 E 32nd St 8th Fl, New York, NY 10016-5422
Tel.: (212) 812-8420
Web Site: http://www.vendomegrp.com
Sales Range: $25-49.9 Million
Emp.: 33
Periodical Publishers
N.A.I.C.S.: 513120
Donna Paglia (Dir-Special Projects & Directories)

CONVERTIDORA INDUSTRIAL S.A.B. DE C.V

Rio de la Loza N 2073 Col Atlas, 44800, Guadalajara, Jalisco, Mexico

Tel.: (52) 3336686901
Web Site: http://www.conver.com.mx
Year Founded: 1979
CONVER—(MEX)
Rev.: $87,970,606
Assets: $115,667,933
Liabilities: $66,823,008
Net Worth: $48,844,925
Earnings: ($1,368,843)
Emp.: 1,240
Fiscal Year-end: 12/31/23
Plastic Packaging Products Mfr
N.A.I.C.S.: 326112
Alejandro De La Garza Hesles (Chm & CEO)

CONVERTO AS

Keiser Wilhelms Gate 24/26, 6003, Alesund, Norway
Tel.: (47) 90010617
Web Site: http://www.converto.no
Year Founded: 2009
Investment Management & Advisory Services
N.A.I.C.S.: 523940
Frank Ove Reite (Chm)

CONVINI SVERIGE AB

Industrivagen 7, 171 48, Solna, Sweden
Tel.: (46) 200 333 535   SE
Web Site: http://www.convini.se
Year Founded: 1995
Food & Beverage Supplier
N.A.I.C.S.: 722310
Mats Palmquist (CEO)

Subsidiaries:

Kaffeknappen AB **(1)**
Gavlegatan 12 A, Stockholm, 113 30, Sweden
Tel.: (46) 8 34 55 55
Web Site: http://www.convini.se
Coffee Bean & Coffee Machine Whslr
N.A.I.C.S.: 424490
Boban Knezevic (Mng Dir)

CONVIVIALITY PLC

Weston Road, Crewe, CW1 6BP, United Kingdom
Tel.: (44) 1270 614710   UK
Web Site:
http://www.conviviality.co.uk
Food & Drink Retailers & Wholesalers
N.A.I.C.S.: 445298

CONVUM LTD.

2-6-18 Shimomaruko, Ohta-ku, Tokyo, 146-0092, Japan
Tel.: (81) 337591491
Web Site: https://www.convum.co.jp
Year Founded: 1951
6265—(TKS)
Rev.: $13,641,160
Assets: $43,249,000
Liabilities: $2,226,260
Net Worth: $41,022,740
Earnings: $1,680,330
Emp.: 142
Fiscal Year-end: 12/31/23
Vacuum Equipment Mfr
N.A.I.C.S.: 333912

Subsidiaries:

CONVUM USA, INC. **(1)**
13105 Ramona Blvd ste I, Irwindale, CA 91706
Tel.: (626) 581-0297
Pneumatic Equipment Distr
N.A.I.C.S.: 423830
Maribel Herrera (Mgr-Sls)

Convum (Thailand) Co., Ltd. **(1)**
No 1 Md Tower 11Fl Zone B Soi Bangna-Trad 25 Bangna, Bangkok, 10260, Thailand
Tel.: (66) 27695851
Pneumatic Equipment Distr
N.A.I.C.S.: 423830

Convum Ltd.—(Continued)

Convum Korea Co., Ltd. (1)
1204 KCC Welltz Valley 205 Gasan Digital
1Ro Gasandong Geumchoen-Gu, Seoul,
Korea (South)
Tel.: (82) 261118007
Pneumatic Equipment Distr
N.A.I.C.S.: 423830

Das Services, Inc. (1)
435 W Alondra Blvd, Gardena, CA 90248
Tel.: (949) 582-3908
Web Site: https://www.dasservicesinc.com
Industrial Machinery Equipment Distr
N.A.I.C.S.: 423830

Delta Equipment S.A. (1)
15/19 Rue Fernand Drouilly, 92250, La
Garenne-Colombes, France
Tel.: (33) 14 242 1144
Web Site: https://www.delta-equipement.fr
Emp.: 24
Automation Machinery Equipment Mfr
N.A.I.C.S.: 333248

Fluidpoint, A.S. (1)
Trebohosticka 2283/2, 100 00, Prague,
Czech Republic
Tel.: (420) 272 123 2237
Web Site: https://www.fluidpoint.cz
Pneumatic Automation & Robotics Mfr
N.A.I.C.S.: 333998

**MYOTOKU TECHNOLOGIES
INC.** (1)
No 15 Ln 5 Minquan St Shulin Dist, New
Taipei City, Taiwan
Tel.: (886) 226686929
Pneumatic Equipment Distr
N.A.I.C.S.: 423830

**Myotoku Convum China Co.,
Ltd.** (1)
4/FC 16 Building No 129 North Fute Road,
Pilot free trade zone, Shanghai, 200131,
China
Tel.: (86) 215 271 2075
Web Site: https://www.convum.co.jp
Pneumatic Equipment Distr
N.A.I.C.S.: 423830

Myotoku Ltd. - Iwate Plant (1)
Esashi Core Industrial Park 10-5 Matsuna-
gane Iwayadou Esashi-Ku, Oshu, Iwate,
Japan
Tel.: (81) 197350480
Pneumatic Equipment Mfr
N.A.I.C.S.: 333922

**Pneumec Kontrolls Private
Limited** (1)
139/4 1st Floor 1st Main 1st Block Dr Raj-
kumar Road, Rajajinagar, Bengaluru,
560010, India
Tel.: (91) 984 512 2462
Web Site: https://www.pneumec.in
Industrial Machinery Equipment Distr
N.A.I.C.S.: 423830

**Pumas Automation & Robotics Pte.
Ltd.** (1)
209 Henderson Road 03-07, Henderson
Industrial Park, Singapore, 159551, Singa-
pore
Tel.: (65) 6 278 3289
Web Site: https://pumasautomation.com
Electronic Parts & Equipment Distr
N.A.I.C.S.: 423690

**Schlumpf Industrieprodukte
GmbH** (1)
Sennweidstrasse 41, 6312, Steinhausen,
Switzerland
Tel.: (41) 41 619 8887
Web Site: https://www.schlumpf-industrie.ch
Professional & Commercial Equipment
Whslr
N.A.I.C.S.: 423490

Westec Automation Ltd. (1)
165A Hepburn Road, Glendene, Auckland,
New Zealand
Tel.: (64) 9 838 4972
Web Site: https://www.westec.co.nz
Pneumatic Component Distr
N.A.I.C.S.: 423830

CONWAY MARSH GARRETT

TECHNOLOGIES LIMITED
Unit I1 Thompson Drive Base Busi-
ness Park, Rendlesham, Woodbridge,
IP12 2TZ, Suffolk, United Kingdom
Tel.: (44) 1394 445 100   **UK**
Web Site:
http://www.cmgtechnologies.co.uk
Sales Range: $25-49.9 Million
Emp.: 30
Metal, Ceramic & Plastic Injected
Moulding Mfr
N.A.I.C.S.: 331523
Rachel Conway *(Mgr-Sls & Mktg)*

COOCON CORP.
19F KnK Digital Tower 220 Yeongsin-
ro, Yeongdeungpo-Gu, Seoul, Korea
(South)
Tel.: (82) 237799199
Web Site: https://www.coocon.net
Year Founded: 2006
294570—(KRS)
Emp.: 172
Information Provision Services
N.A.I.C.S.: 519290
Jong-Hyun Kim *(CEO)*

**COOGEE CHEMICALS PTY
LTD.**
Corner Patterson & Kwinana Beach
Roads, PO Box 5051, Rockinghim
Beach, Kwinana, 6167, WA, Australia
Tel.: (61) 894398200   **AU**
Web Site: http://www.coogee.com.au
Year Founded: 1971
Sales Range: $50-74.9 Million
Emp.: 350
Industrial, Agricultural & Mineral Pro-
cessing Chemical Mfr
N.A.I.C.S.: 325998
William Gordon Martin *(Exec Dir)*

Subsidiaries:

Coogee Chemicals (Mt Isa) Pty
Ltd   (1)
911 North Ridge Rd, Mount Isa, 4825, QLD,
Australia
Tel.: (61) 747439863
Chemical Products Mfr
N.A.I.C.S.: 325199

Coogee Chemicals Pty Ltd. - Metha-
nol Facility   (1)
171 Fitzgerald Rd, Laverton, 3026, VIC,
Australia
Tel.: (61) 393602000
Chemical Products Mfr
N.A.I.C.S.: 325199

Pride Chem Industries Sdn Bhd   (1)
Plo 232 Jalan Keluli 1, Pasir Gudang Indus-
trial Estate, Pasir Gudang, 81700, Johor
Bahru, Malaysia
Tel.: (60) 72526755
Sales Range: $50-74.9 Million
Emp.: 7
Chemical & Fertilizer Mineral Mining
N.A.I.C.S.: 212390
Lim Kaming *(Gen Mgr)*

COOKBIZ CO., LTD.
8F LUCID SQUARE UMEDA 2-7-18
Shibata, Kita-ku, Osaka, 530-0012,
Japan
Tel.: (81) 663749915
Web Site: https://corp.cookbiz.co.jp
6558—(TKS)
Rev.: $18,894,850
Assets: $24,396,690
Liabilities: $13,577,350
Net Worth: $10,819,340
Earnings: $1,893,030
Emp.: 133
Fiscal Year-end: 11/30/23
Human Resource Consulting Ser-
vices
N.A.I.C.S.: 541612
Kenji Yabuno *(Pres & CEO)*

COOKE, INC.
40 Wellington Row, Saint John, E2L
3H3, NB, Canada
Tel.: (506) 694-4928
Web Site:
http://www.cookeseafood.com
Year Founded: 1985
Holding Company
N.A.I.C.S.: 551112
Glenn Cooke *(CEO)*

Subsidiaries:

Cooke Aquaculture Inc.   (1)
874 Main St, Blacks Harbour, E5H 1E6,
NB, Canada   **(100%)**
Tel.: (506) 456-6600
Web Site: http://www.cookeaqua.com
Sales Range: $25-49.9 Million
Emp.: 1,700
Salmon Farming, Processing & Sales
N.A.I.C.S.: 112511
Glenn Cooke *(CEO)*

Subsidiary (US):

Icicle Seafoods, Inc.   (2)
4019 21st Ave W, Seattle, WA
98199-1251   **(100%)**
Tel.: (206) 282-0988
Web Site: http://www.icicleseafoods.com
Seafood Harvesting & Processing Services
N.A.I.C.S.: 311710
Julianne Curry *(Mgr-Pub Affairs-Petersburg)*

Subsidiary (Domestic):

Kelly Cove Salmon Ltd.   (2)
61 Wallace Cove Rd, Blacks Harbour, E5H
1E6, NB, Canada
Tel.: (506) 456-6600
Web Site: http://www.cookeaqua.com
Sales Range: $1-9.9 Million
Emp.: 60
Salmon Farming
N.A.I.C.S.: 112511

Shoreland Transport Inc.   (2)
35 Magaguadavic Dr, Saint George, E5C
3H8, NB, Canada
Tel.: (506) 755-1460
Web Site: https://shorelandtransport.com
Freight Transportation Services
N.A.I.C.S.: 483111

True North Salmon Co. Ltd.   (2)
874 Main Street, Blacks Harbour, E5H 1E6,
NB, Canada
Tel.: (506) 456-6600
Web Site: https://www.truenorthseafood.com
Sales Range: $50-74.9 Million
Emp.: 55
Salmon Harvesting, Processing & Marketing
N.A.I.C.S.: 424460

Omega Protein Corporation   (1)
610 Menhaden Rd, Reedville, VA 22539
Tel.: (804) 453-6262
Web Site: http://www.omegaprotein.com
Omega-3 Fish Oil & Fish Meal Products
Processor, Marketer & Distr
N.A.I.C.S.: 311710

Subsidiary (Non-US):

Bioriginal Europe/Asia B.V.   (2)
Bosland 40, 3258 AC, Den Bommel, Neth-
erlands
Tel.: (31) 187618020
Web Site: http://www.bioriginal.nl
Biological Product Mfr
N.A.I.C.S.: 325414

Bioriginal Food & Science
Corporation   (2)
102 Melville Street, Saskatoon, S7J 0R1,
SK, Canada
Tel.: (306) 975-1166
Web Site: http://www.bioriginal.com
Health Food Products Mfr
N.A.I.C.S.: 456191
Joe Vidal *(Pres)*

Subsidiary (Domestic):

InCon Processing Systems, Inc.   (2)
PO Box 268, Saint Charles, IL 60174
Tel.: (630) 549-0394
Web Site: http://www.ips-gigk.com
Distillation Chemical Mfr

N.A.I.C.S.: 325199
Ralph Scully *(VP-Sls)*

Omega Shipyard, Inc. (2)
5659 Elder Ferry Rd, Moss Point, MS
39563
Tel.: (228) 475-9052
Drydock & Shipping Services
N.A.I.C.S.: 488320

COOKPAD INC.
4-20-3 Ebisu, Shibuya-ku, Tokyo,
150-6012, Japan
Tel.: (81) 2123362301
Web Site: http://info.cookpad.com
Year Founded: 1997
2193—(TKS)
Rev.: $53,933,630
Assets: $103,492,730
Liabilities: $6,168,300
Net Worth: $97,324,430
Earnings: ($15,803,610)
Emp.: 50
Fiscal Year-end: 12/31/23
Online Cooking Recipe Website Op-
erator
N.A.I.C.S.: 513140

**COOKS COFFEE COMPANY
LIMITED**
VCFO Level 1 96 St Georges Bay
Road Parnell, Grafton, Auckland,
1052, New Zealand
Tel.: (64) 93040567
Web Site:
https://www.cooksglobalfoods.com
Year Founded: 2008
OCC—(NZX)
Rev.: $5,300,468
Assets: $26,441,225
Liabilities: $24,717,063
Net Worth: $1,724,162
Earnings: ($314,922)
Emp.: 26
Fiscal Year-end: 03/31/22
Food Products Mfr
N.A.I.C.S.: 311999
Richard Chew *(CFO)*

Subsidiaries:

Esquires Coffee Houses Ireland
Limited   (1)
Vision House 16 Briarhill Business Park,
Ballybrit Co Galway, Galway, Ireland
Tel.: (353) 91452187
Web Site: http://www.esquirescoffee.ie
Coffee Product Mfr
N.A.I.C.S.: 311920

Esquires Coffee UK Limited   (1)
Suite 509 1 Putney Bridge Approach, Lon-
don, SW6 3BQ, United Kingdom
Tel.: (44) 2072515166
Web Site: http://www.esquirescoffee.co.uk
Coffee Product Mfr
N.A.I.C.S.: 311920

**COOKSVILLE DODGE CHRYS-
LER INC.**
290 Dundas Street East, Missis-
sauga, L5A 1W9, ON, Canada
Tel.: (905) 279-3031
Web Site:
http://www.cooksvillechrysler.com
New & Used Car Dealers
N.A.I.C.S.: 441110
Michael Buchanan *(Gen Mgr)*

**COOL CAPS INDUSTRIES LIM-
ITED**
23 Sarat Bose Road Suite 1C An-
napurna apartment, Kolkata, 700020,
India
Tel.: (91) 9831772104
Web Site:
https://www.coolcapsindustries.in
Year Founded: 1994
COOLCAPS—(NSE)
Rev.: $21,943,505

Assets: $16,283,952
Liabilities: $11,966,729
Net Worth: $4,317,223
Earnings: $684,563
Emp.: 73
Fiscal Year-end: 03/31/23
Packaging Material Distr
N.A.I.C.S.: 423840

COOL CHIPS PLC

Suite 3G Eurolife Building 1 Corral
Road, Gibraltar, Gibraltar
Tel.: (350) 442075043593
Web Site: https://www.coolchips.com
Year Founded: 1997
COLCF—(OTCEM)
Sales Range: Less than $1 Million
Real Estate Manangement Services
N.A.I.C.S.: 531110
Rodney T. Cox (Chm, CEO & CFO)

COOL COMPANY LTD.

2nd Floor SE Pearman Building 9
Par-la-Ville Road, Hamilton, HM11,
Bermuda
Tel.: (441) 295 4705
Web Site: https://www.coolcoltd.com
Year Founded: 2009
COOL—(OSL)
Natural Gas Distribution Services
N.A.I.C.S.: 221210
John P. Boots (CFO)

COOL LINK (HOLDINGS) LIM-ITED

33 Chin Bee Crescent, Singapore,
619901, Singapore
Tel.: (65) 63166659   Ky
Web Site:
    https://www.coollink.com.sg
Year Founded: 2001
8491—(HKG)
Rev.: $23,301,522
Assets: $24,214,194
Liabilities: $13,793,077
Net Worth: $10,421,116
Earnings: ($811,179)
Emp.: 63
Fiscal Year-end: 12/31/23
Food Products Distr
N.A.I.C.S.: 424420
Seow Gee Tan (Co-Founder, Chm,
Mng Dir & Compliance Officer)

Subsidiaries:

Cool Link & Marketing Pte. Ltd. **(1)**
33 Chin Bee Crescent, Singapore, 619901,
Singapore
Tel.: (65) 63166659
Packaged Frozen Food Distr
N.A.I.C.S.: 424420

COOLABAH METALS LIMITED

Level 8 London House 216 St
George's Terrace, Perth, 6000, WA,
Australia
Tel.: (61) 894810389   AU
Web Site:
    https://www.coolabahmetals.com.au
Year Founded: 2021
CBH—(ASX)
Rev.: $33,214
Assets: $3,595,826
Liabilities: $189,012
Net Worth: $3,406,814
Earnings: ($1,707,121)
Fiscal Year-end: 06/30/23
Metal Exploration Services
N.A.I.C.S.: 213114
Cameron Provost (Mng Dir)

COOLGIANTS AG

Julius-Bamberger-Str 1, 28279,
Bremen, Germany
Tel.: (49) 4218392110
Web Site: http://www.coolgiants.de
Household Appliance Distr

N.A.I.C.S.: 423720
Kersten Hoppe (Co-CEO)

COOLPAD GROUP LIMITED

No 2 Flat Coolpad Cyber Park
Mengxi Blvd, Northern Part of Sci-
ence & Technology Park Nanshan
District, Shenzhen, 518057, China
Tel.: (86) 75583301199   Ky
Web Site: http://www.coolpad.com.hk
Year Founded: 1993
Sales Range: $1-4.9 Billion
Emp.: 5,634
Holding Company; Wireless Telecom-
munications Solutions & Equipment
Whslr
N.A.I.C.S.: 551112
Wenyan Pan (CIO)

Subsidiaries:

Coolpad Technologies Inc. **(1)**
6256 Greenwich Dr 550, San Diego, CA
92122
Tel.: (858) 677-0888
Mobile Accessory Distr
N.A.I.C.S.: 423620

Digital Tech Inc. **(1)**
300-6660 Kennedy Rd, Mississauga, L5T
2M9, ON, Canada
Tel.: (905) 766-4080
Mobile Accessory Distr
N.A.I.C.S.: 423620

Dongguan Yulong Telecommunication
Tech Co., Ltd. **(1)**
Area C Northern Industrial City Songshan
Lake Science And Tech, Dongguan,
518057, Guangdong, China
Tel.: (86) 76988980888
Mobile Accessory Distr
N.A.I.C.S.: 423620

COOLPOINT INNONISM HOLD-ING LIMITED

Unit 315A 3/F Building 5W Phase,
One Hong Kong Science Park Pak
Shek Kok, Hong Kong, China (Hong
Kong)
Tel.: (852) 21997866   Ky
Web Site: http://www.dcb.com.hk
Year Founded: 2008
8040—(HKG)
Rev.: $29,004,378
Assets: $16,144,427
Liabilities: $4,797,540
Net Worth: $11,346,887
Earnings: $329,931
Emp.: 65
Fiscal Year-end: 03/31/21
Residential Remodeling Services
N.A.I.C.S.: 236118
Dennis Tsang Fu Cheng (Co-
Founder, Chm & CEO)

COOMEVA ENTIDAD PROMO-TORA DE SALUD SA

Cr, 169399, Cali, Colombia
Tel.: (57) 22184706
COOMEVAEPS—(COLO)
Sales Range: Less than $1 Million
Health Care Srvices
N.A.I.C.S.: 621511

COOP NORGE SA

Ostre Aker vei 264, 0977, Oslo, Nor-
way
Tel.: (47) 22 89 95 95
Web Site: http://www.coop.no
Emp.: 2,600
Grocery Store Operator
N.A.I.C.S.: 445110
Ola H. Strand (CEO)

Subsidiaries:

Coop Norge Grorud Eiendom AS **(1)**
Akeroveien 264, Oslo, 0977, Norway
Tel.: (47) 22899595
Web Site: http://www.coop.no

Emp.: 900
All Other General Merchandise Stores
N.A.I.C.S.: 455219

Coop Norge Industri AS **(1)**
Ostre Aker Vei 264, Oslo, 977, Norway
Tel.: (47) 22899500
Web Site: http://www.coop.no
Sales Range: $250-299.9 Million
Emp.: 800
Dairy Products, except Dried or Canned
Whslr
N.A.I.C.S.: 424430
Svein Fanebust (Pres)

Coop Norge Kaffe AS **(1)**
Filipstadveien 15, 0250, Oslo,
Norway   **(100%)**
Tel.: (47) 22899999
Web Site: http://www.coop.no
Sales Range: $25-49.9 Million
Emp.: 100
Roasted Nuts & Peanut Butter Mfr
N.A.I.C.S.: 311911

Coop Trading A/S **(1)**
Helgeshoj Alle 57, Hoje Taastrup, 2620,
Denmark
Tel.: (45) 8853 0000
Web Site: http://www.cooptrading.com
Internordic Procurement of Branded Prod-
ucts
N.A.I.C.S.: 455219
Rene Sandberg (Mgr-Strategy & Coordina-
tion)

Goman Bakeriet AS **(1)**
Lorenveien 55, 0580, Oslo,
Norway   **(100%)**
Tel.: (47) 22078650
Web Site: http://www.coop.no
Commercial Bakeries
N.A.I.C.S.: 311812

Norsk Butikkdrift AS **(1)**
Nydalsveien 24, 0484, Oslo, Norway
Tel.: (47) 22899595
Retail Stores Operator
N.A.I.C.S.: 424410

COOP SUPERMARKTEN B.V..

Kerkbuurt 38a, 1551 AE, Westzaan,
Netherlands
Tel.: (31) 75 628 2992
Year Founded: 1891
Supermarkets & Other Grocery
Stores
N.A.I.C.S.: 445110

COOP-GRUPPE GENOSSEN-SCHAFT

Thiersteinerallee 12, Postfach 2550,
4002, Basel, Switzerland
Tel.: (41) 848 888 444   CH
Web Site: http://www.coop.ch
Year Founded: 1890
Rev.: $30,514,878,080
Assets: $21,064,770,560
Liabilities: $10,494,284,160
Net Worth: $10,570,486,400
Earnings: $655,957,120
Emp.: 90,307
Fiscal Year-end: 12/31/19
Holding Company; Retail Store Op-
erator
N.A.I.C.S.: 551112
Irene Kaufmann-Brandli (Vice Chm)

Subsidiaries:

Argo AG **(1)**
Baumlimattstrasse, CH 4313, Mohlin,
Switzerland   **(100%)**
Tel.: (41) 618559900
Web Site: http://www.argo-ag.ch
Sales Range: $25-49.9 Million
Emp.: 50
Hosiery
N.A.I.C.S.: 315120

Bell Food Group AG **(1)**
Elsasserstrasse 174, 4056, Basel,
Switzerland   **(66.29%)**
Tel.: (41) 583262000
Web Site: https://www.bellfoodgroup.com
Rev.: $5,023,033,266

Assets: $3,642,483,584
Liabilities: $1,965,394,457
Net Worth: $1,677,089,127
Earnings: $144,208,301
Emp.: 12,337
Fiscal Year-end: 12/31/2023
Holding Company; Meat, Poultry, Seafood &
Charcuterie Production & Sales; Perishable
Fresh Foods & Non-perishable Food Prod-
ucts Mfr & Sales
N.A.I.C.S.: 551112
Hansueli Loosli (Chm)

Subsidiary (Non-US):

Abraham GmbH **(2)**
Brookdamm 21, 21217, Seevetal, Germany
Tel.: (49) 40 7680050
Web Site: http://www.abraham.de
Meat Products Processing & Sales
N.A.I.C.S.: 424470
Christian Schroder (CEO & Head-Distr &
Mktg)

Bell Benelux N.V. **(2)**
Z 3 Doornveld 70, Asse, 1731, Vlaams Bra-
bant, Belgium
Tel.: (32) 24816666
Emp.: 30
Food Products Distr
N.A.I.C.S.: 424460
Steven Van Pares (Mgr-Sls)

Bell Deutschland Holding GmbH **(2)**
Brookdamm 21, Seevetal, 21217, Nieder-
sachsen, Germany
Tel.: (49) 407680050
Web Site: http://www.bellfoodgroup.com
Holding Company
N.A.I.C.S.: 551112

Bell Nederland B.V. **(2)**
De Molen 4, Houten, Utrecht, 3994 DB,
Netherlands
Tel.: (31) 306346090
Veal Product Mfr
N.A.I.C.S.: 311615

Bell Polska Sp. z o.o **(2)**
Ul Mokra 11, 32-005, Niepolomice, Poland
Tel.: (48) 122810030
Web Site: http://www.bellpolska.com.pl
Meat Processing Services
N.A.I.C.S.: 311612

Subsidiary (Domestic):

Bell Schweiz AG **(2)**
Elsasserstrasse 174, Basel, 4056,
Switzerland   **(60%)**
Tel.: (41) 613262626
Web Site: http://www.bell.ch
Sales Range: $800-899.9 Million
Emp.: 1,000
Meat Processing & Marketing
N.A.I.C.S.: 311611

Frigo St. Johann AG **(2)**
Neudorfstrasse 90, 4056, Basel, Switzer-
land
Tel.: (41) 61 327 1133
Web Site: http://www.frigo-ag.ch
Meat Products Processing & Sales
N.A.I.C.S.: 424470

Huegli Holding AG **(2)**
Bleichestrasse 31, 9323, Steinach,
Switzerland   **(50.2%)**
Tel.: (41) 714472211
Web Site: http://www.huegli.com
Sales Range: $350-399.9 Million
Emp.: 1,506
Food & Food Products Mfr & Distr
N.A.I.C.S.: 424420
Andreas Seibold (CFO)

Subsidiary (Non-US):

Ali-Big Industria Alimentare s.r.l. **(3)**
Via per Airuno 25/A, 23883, Brivio, Italy
Tel.: (39) 0399162800
Web Site: http://www.ali-big.it
Preserved Foods Mfr
N.A.I.C.S.: 311999

Erntesegen Naturkost GmbH **(3)**
Schutzenstrasse 24, 78315, Radolfzell,
Germany
Tel.: (49) 7732807 1
Web Site: http://www.erntesegen.de
Edible Organic Salts Retailer

Coop-Gruppe Genossenschaft—(Continued)

N.A.I.C.S.: 424490

Heirler Cenovis GmbH (3)
Schutzenstrasse 24, 78315, Radolfzell,
Germany
Tel.: (49) 77328071
Web Site: http://www.heirler-cenovis.de
Convenience Foods Mfr & Distr
N.A.I.C.S.: 311412

Huegli UK Ltd. (3)
Oxleasow Road East Moons Moat, Red-
ditch, B98 0RE, Worcs, United Kingdom
Tel.: (44) 1527514777
Convenience Food Mfr & Distr
N.A.I.C.S.: 311412
Richard Bailey (Dir-Comml)

Hugli Food Elelmiszeripari Kft. (3)
Vaci ut 152-156, 1138, Budapest, Hungary
Tel.: (36) 614500033
Web Site: http://www.huegli.hu
Convenience Food Mfr & Distr
N.A.I.C.S.: 311999

Hugli Food Polska sp.z o.o. (3)
Zwirki 17, 90539, Lodz, Poland
Tel.: (48) 4266110081
Web Site: http://www.huegli.com
Convenience Foods Mfr & Retailer
N.A.I.C.S.: 311999

Hugli Food Slovakia s.r.o. (3)
Nam Slov Uceneho Tovarisstva 1552 6,
91701, Trnava, Slovakia
Tel.: (421) 335586357
Convenience Foods Mfr & Retailer
N.A.I.C.S.: 311999

**Hugli Nahrmittel -Erzeugung
Ges.m.b.H** (3)
Schafferhofstrasse 14, 6971, Hard, Austria
Tel.: (43) 5574694 133
Web Site: http://www.hueglifoodservice.com
Convenience Food Retailer
N.A.I.C.S.: 445131
Thomas Kofler (Mgr)

Hugli Nahrungsmittel GmbH (3)
Guttinger Strasse 23, 78315, Radolfzell,
Germany
Tel.: (49) 77328070
Web Site: http://www.huegli.de
Convenience Foods Mfr
N.A.I.C.S.: 311412
Wolfgang Zeh (Dir-Sls)

Inter - Planing GmbH (3)
Kirchsteigstr 10, 86476, Neuburg an der
Kammel, Germany
Tel.: (49) 828399880
Web Site: http://www.inter-planing.de
Convenience Food Retailer
N.A.I.C.S.: 445131

Natur Compagnie GmbH (3)
Schutzenstrasse 24, 78315, Radolfzell,
Baden-Wurttemberg, Germany
Tel.: (49) 77328073
Web Site: http://www.natur-compagnie.de
Organic Food Whslr
N.A.I.C.S.: 424990

Subsidiary (Non-US):

**ZIMBO Fleisch- und Wurstwaren
GmbH & Co. KG** (2)
Wasserstrasse 223, 44799, Bochum, Ger-
many
Tel.: (49) 234 9553 7000
Web Site: http://www.zimbo.de
Meat Products Processing & Sales
N.A.I.C.S.: 424470

Chocolats Halba (1)
Alte Winterthurstrasse 1, PO Box 8340,
Wallisellen, 8304, Switzerland (100%)
Tel.: (41) 448771010
Web Site: http://www.chocolatshalba.ch
Sales Range: $25-49.9 Million
Emp.: 250
Chocolate Product Mfr
N.A.I.C.S.: 311352
Anton von Weissenfluh (Gen Mgr)

Coop Hostellerie AG (1)
Thiersteinerallee 12, Basel, 2550,
Switzerland (100%)
Tel.: (41) 613366666

N.A.I.C.S.: 455110
Hansueli Loosli (CEO)

Coop Immobilien AG (1)
Kasparstrasse 7, 3027, Bern, Switzerland
Tel.: (41) 31 998 64 00
Emp.: 30
Real Estate Manangement Services
N.A.I.C.S.: 531390
Jean-Marc Chapuis (Gen Mgr)

Coop Mineraloel AG (1)
Hegenheimermattweg 65, Allschwil, 4123,
Switzerland (51%)
Tel.: (41) 614854141
Web Site: http://www.coop-pronto.ch
Sales Range: $25-49.9 Million
Emp.: 79
Service Station Chain
N.A.I.C.S.: 517810
Roger Oser (Mng Dir)

**Coop Schweiz - CWK-SCS
Division** (1)
St Gallerstrasse 180, Postfach 53, 8404,
Winterthur, Switzerland
Tel.: (41) 522344400
Web Site: http://www.steinfels-swiss.ch
Cosmetics Products Mfr
N.A.I.C.S.: 325620

**Coop Schweiz - Interdiscount
Division** (1)
Bernstrasse 90, 3303, Jegenstorf, Switzer-
land
Tel.: (41) 31 764 44 44
Online Apparel Retailer
N.A.I.C.S.: 424490

**Coop Schweiz - Swissmill
Division** (1)
Sihlquai 306, Postfach, 8037, Zurich, Swit-
zerland
Tel.: (41) 44 447 25 25
Web Site: http://www.swissmill.ch
Food Products Mfr
N.A.I.C.S.: 311999

Coop-ITS-Travel AG (1)
Grabenwisstrasse 1, 8604, Volketswil, Swit-
zerland
Tel.: (41) 44 908 28 28
Web Site: http://www.itscoop.ch
Emp.: 20
Travel Tour Operator
N.A.I.C.S.: 561510
Andreas Restle (Mng Dir)

Dipl. Ing. Fust AG (1)
Buchental 4, Oberburen-Uzwil, 9245, Swit-
zerland
Tel.: (41) 719555050
Web Site: http://www.fust.ch
Sales Range: $25-49.9 Million
Emp.: 50
Domestic Appliance Retailer
N.A.I.C.S.: 335220
Thomas Cecar (Mng Dir)

Subsidiary (Domestic):

Service 7000 AG (2)
Molliserstrasse 41, Wiggis Park, CH 8754,
Netstal, Glarus, Switzerland
Tel.: (41) 556453700
Web Site: http://www.service7000.ch
Sales Range: $25-49.9 Million
Emp.: 100
Repair Services
N.A.I.C.S.: 811412
Martin Reithebuch (Mgr)

Eurogroup Deutschland GmbH (1)
Katzbergstr 1a, Langenfeld, 40764, Ger-
many
Tel.: (49) 2173392500
Fruit & Vegetable Whslr
N.A.I.C.S.: 424480

Eurogroup SA (1)
17 Ypsilantou Str, Magoula, 19018, Greece
Tel.: (30) 210 55 19 800
Web Site: http://www.eurogroup.gr
Logistics Consulting Servies
N.A.I.C.S.: 541614

Gastro Star AG (1)
Huttenwiesenstrasse 4, 8108, Dallikon,
Switzerland
Tel.: (41) 44 847 55 55
Web Site: http://www.gastrostar.ch

Emp.: 100
Fruit & Vegetable Whslr
N.A.I.C.S.: 424480
Ueli Foster (Gen Mgr)

Hilcona Convenience AG (1)
Ruppenswilerstrasse 5, Schafisheim, 5503,
Switzerland
Tel.: (41) 41 989 87 00
Convenience Retailer
N.A.I.C.S.: 445131

Hilcona Fresh Express (1)
Industriestrasse 5, 5242, Lupfig, Switzer-
land
Tel.: (41) 588953000
Web Site: http://www.hilcona.com
Packaged Frozen Food Distr
N.A.I.C.S.: 424420

Import Parfumerien AG (1)
Rudolf Diesel Strasse 25, Postfach 336,
8404, Winterthur, Switzerland (100%)
Tel.: (41) 522343322
Web Site: http://www.impo.ch
Sales Range: $25-49.9 Million
Emp.: 40
Department Store Retailer
N.A.I.C.S.: 455110

Maison de Savoie SAS (1)
108, route des Iles, PO Box 51, 73210,
Aime, Cedex, France
Tel.: (33) 479 094100
Meat Product Whslr
N.A.I.C.S.: 424470

Nutrex AG (1)
Juraweg 5, CH 3292, Busswil,
Switzerland (100%)
Tel.: (41) 323842141
Web Site: http://www.nutrex.ch
Rev.: $20,026,100
Emp.: 15
Vinegar Production & Pickled Products
N.A.I.C.S.: 311423
Gerhard Marty (CEO)

**OHG REWE-Foodservice GmbH &
Co.** (1)
Wilhelm Theodor Romheld Str 18, Mainz,
55130, Germany
Tel.: (49) 613150 20
Web Site: http://www.rewe-foodservice.de
Food Products Mfr
N.A.I.C.S.: 311991

Panofina AG (1)
Alte Winterthurer strasse 1, CH 8304, Walli-
sellen, Switzerland (100%)
Tel.: (41) 18771111
Web Site: http://www.halba.ch
Sales Range: $50-74.9 Million
Emp.: 290
Bakery & Confectionery Products
N.A.I.C.S.: 311812

Pasta Gala SA (1)
Rue du Dr-Yersin 10, CH-1110, Morges,
Switzerland (100%)
Tel.: (41) 218011332
Sales Range: $25-49.9 Million
Emp.: 51
Mfr & Sales of Pasta
N.A.I.C.S.: 311824

Pearlwater Mineralquellen AG (1)
Unners Z'Matt, Termen, 3912, Switzerland
Tel.: (41) 27 928 68 00
Emp.: 41
Bottled Water Distr
N.A.I.C.S.: 424490
Daniel Walker (Mng Dir)

RailCare AG (1)
Altgraben 23, 4624, Harkingen, Switzerland
Tel.: (41) 62 389 00 90
Web Site: http://www.railcare.ch
Emp.: 300
Railway Transport Services
N.A.I.C.S.: 488999
Philipp Wejnuller (Gen Mgr)

Saloir de Virieu SAS (1)
500 en Mussignin, 01510, Virieu-le-Grand,
France
Tel.: (33) 479 878064
Meat Processing Services
N.A.I.C.S.: 311612

Sanchez Alcaraz S.L.U. (1)

C/ Encinar 211-212, 45950, Casarrubios del
Monte, Toledo, Spain
Tel.: (34) 918609195
Web Site: http://www.sanchezalcaraz.com
Emp.: 50
Meat Product Whslr
N.A.I.C.S.: 424470

Schwarz Viva AG (1)
Schurmattstrasse 4, 6234, Villigon, Switzer-
land
Tel.: (41) 56 297 81 81
Fruit & Vegetable Whslr
N.A.I.C.S.: 424480

Steinfels Cleaning Systems (1)
St Galler Strasse 180, 8411, Winterthur,
Switzerland (100%)
Tel.: (41) 522344400
Web Site: http://www.scs-ag.ch
Rev.: $5,224,200
Emp.: 75
N.A.I.C.S.: 455110
Rodney L Cox (Gen Mgr)

TopTip (R. Muller AG) (1)
Kollikerstrasse 80, CH-5036, Oberentfelden,
Switzerland (100%)
Tel.: (41) 627371111
Web Site: http://www.toptip.ch
Rev.: $100,130,500
Emp.: 700
N.A.I.C.S.: 455110
Oliver Roth (Gen Mgr)

**Transgourmet Immobilien GmbH &
Co. KG** (1)
Emil Riedl Weg 6, Pullach, 82049, Bayern,
Germany
Tel.: (49) 895 1200
Food Mfr
N.A.I.C.S.: 311991

Transgourmet Schweiz AG (1)
Lochackerweg 5, 3302, Moosseedorf, Swit-
zerland
Tel.: (41) 31 858 48 48
Web Site: http://www.transgourmet.ch
Food Products Mfr
N.A.I.C.S.: 311991

Transgourmet Seafood (1)
An der Packhalle IX Nr 11, 27572, Bremer-
haven, Germany
Tel.: (49) 471 142910
Web Site: http://www.tg-seafood.de
Seafood Mfr
N.A.I.C.S.: 311999

Val de Lyon SAS (1)
302 chaussee Beauvoir, 69590, Saint-
Symphorien-sur-Coise, France
Tel.: (33) 478 443013
Web Site: http://www.mossieurpolette.fr
Emp.: 4,000
Meat Processing Services
N.A.I.C.S.: 311612
Stefano Bianchi (Mng Dir)

**WINE AG VALENTIN & VON
SALIS** (1)
Via da la Staziun 43, 7504, Pontresina,
Switzerland
Tel.: (41) 81 838 84 84
Web Site: http://www.valentin-wine.ch
Wine Mfr
N.A.I.C.S.: 312130

ZIMBO Czechia s.r.o. (1)
Na Zatorach 8, Holesovice, 170 00, Prague,
Czech Republic
Tel.: (420) 266 712 048
Meat Product Whslr
N.A.I.C.S.: 424470

ZIMBO Husipari Termelo Kft. (1)
Ipari Park 5, Perbal, Hungary
Tel.: (36) 26570500
Web Site: http://www.zimbo.hu
Meat Processing Services
N.A.I.C.S.: 311612

**COOPER COATED COIL MAN-
AGEMENT LIMITED**
Rectory Court Old Rectory Lane,
Alvechurch, Birmingham, B48 7SX,
United Kingdom
Tel.: (44) 121 285 1560   UK
Web Site:
http://www.arcspecialist.co.uk

Year Founded: 2013
Holding Company; Specialty Products Mfr
N.A.I.C.S.: 551112
Andrew Richardson *(CEO)*

Subsidiaries:

Cooper Coated Coil Ltd. **(1)**
38 & 39 Planetary Industrial Estate, Wolverhampton, WV13 3XB, United Kingdom
Tel.: (44) 1902 867 900
Web Site: http://www.coopercoated.co.uk
Pre-Coated Metal Consumer Products Designer, Mfr & Whslr
N.A.I.C.S.: 332999
Kevin Tranter *(Mng Dir)*

Toolspec Manufacturing Company Ltd. **(1)**
Unit E Sedgwick Road, Luton, LU4 9DT, Beds, United Kingdom
Tel.: (44) 1582 572 626
Web Site: http://www.toolspec.co.uk
Sales Range: $1-9.9 Million
Emp.: 60
Specialized Tubular & Sectionional Metal Products & Tools Mfr & Whslr
N.A.I.C.S.: 332999
Mark Blythe *(Mng Dir)*

Tube Bend Form International Limited **(1)**
Unit 7 Bloxwich Lane, Bloxwich Lane Industrial Estate, Walsall, WS2 8TF, United Kingdom
Tel.: (44) 1922 725 505
Web Site: http://www.tbfinternational.co.uk
Custom Metal Tube Bending & Laser Cutting Services
N.A.I.C.S.: 332999

COOPER ENERGY LIMITED
Level 8 70 Franklin St, Adelaide, 5000, SA, Australia
Tel.: (61) 881004900
Web Site:
http://www.cooperenergy.com.au
COE—(ASX)
Rev.: $146,265,357
Assets: $816,764,153
Liabilities: $537,887,284
Net Worth: $278,876,869
Earnings: ($76,194,578)
Emp.: 128
Fiscal Year-end: 06/30/24
Oil & Gas Exploration & Well Drilling
N.A.I.C.S.: 211120
David P. Maxwell *(Mng Dir)*

COOPER METALS LIMITED
Level 11 216 St Georges Terrace, Perth, 6000, WA, Australia
Tel.: (61) 410504272   AU
Web Site:
https://www.coopermetals.com.au
Year Founded: 2021
CPM—(ASX)
Rev.: $3,286
Assets: $4,717,472
Liabilities: $144,745
Net Worth: $4,572,727
Earnings: ($662,229)
Fiscal Year-end: 06/30/23
Metal Exploration Services
N.A.I.C.S.: 213114
Michael Frayne *(Chm)*

COOPERATIEVE CENTRALE RAIFFEISEN-BOERENLEENBANK B.A.
Croeselaan 18, 3521 CB, Utrecht, Netherlands   NI
Year Founded: 1898
Rev.: $8,483,000,000
Assets: $590,598,000,000
Liabilities: $549,251,000,000
Net Worth: $41,347,000,000
Earnings: $2,203,000,000
Fiscal Year-end: 12/31/19

Bank Holding Company; Banking & Financial Management Services
N.A.I.C.S.: 551111
Bas Brouwers *(CFO)*

Subsidiaries:

Banco Rabobank International Brasil S.A. **(1)**
Av Nacoes Unidas 12995 8 andar 7th Floor, 04578-000, Sao Paulo, SP, Brazil
Tel.: (55) 1155037000
Web Site: http://www.rabobank.com.br
Sales Range: $100-124.9 Million
Emp.: 250
Commericial Banking
N.A.I.C.S.: 522110
Erik Peek Y. Van Eyken *(Pres)*

De Lage Landen International BV **(1)**
Vestdijk 5, Eindhoven, 5611 CA, Netherlands **(100%)**
Tel.: (31) 402339911
Web Site: http://www.dllgroup.com
Sales Range: $1-4.9 Billion
Holding Company; Asset Based Financing Services
N.A.I.C.S.: 551112
Bill Stephenson *(Chm-Exec Bd & CEO)*

Subsidiary (Domestic):

Athlon Holding N.V. **(2)**
Boeing Ave 280 119cz, Amersfoort, Netherlands
Tel.: (31) 235675700
Web Site: http://www.athloncarlease.com
Sales Range: $900-999.9 Million
Emp.: 600
Car Leasing & Car Body Repair Services
N.A.I.C.S.: 811111
Jan E. Demper *(Sec)*

Subsidiary (Non-US):

De Lage Landen Chile S.A. **(2)**
Avenida del Valle 750 Oficina 501 Huechuraba, 8580659, Santiago, Chile
Tel.: (56) 2 2935 3900
Emp.: 25
Financial Management Services
N.A.I.C.S.: 523999
Eduardo Wanderer *(Country Mgr)*

De Lage Landen Co., Ltd. **(2)**
8th Floor Trade Center Trade Tower 159-1 Samsung 1-dong, Gangnam-gu, Seoul, 135-729, Korea (South)
Tel.: (82) 2 564 1928
Financial Management Services
N.A.I.C.S.: 523999
Hyun Chul Park *(Country Mgr)*

De Lage Landen Faktoring A.S. **(2)**
Kustepe Mah Mecidiyekoy Yolu Caddesi No 12 Trump Towers Ofis Kulesi, 34387, Istanbul, Turkiye
Tel.: (90) 212 370 9801
Emp.: 20
Financial Management Services
N.A.I.C.S.: 523999
Oguz Caneri *(Gen Mgr)*

De Lage Landen Financial Services Canada Inc. **(2)**
3450 Superior Court Unit 1, Oakville, L6L 0C4, ON, Canada
Tel.: (905) 901-6300
Financial Management Services
N.A.I.C.S.: 523999
Stewart Grant *(VP-Sls & Mktg)*

De Lage Landen K.K. **(2)**
Ark Mori Building 12th Floor 1-12-32 Akasaka, Minato-ku, Tokyo, 107-6012, Japan
Tel.: (81) 3 4360 8270
Financial Management Services
N.A.I.C.S.: 523999

De Lage Landen Leasing GmbH **(2)**
Hansaallee 249, 40549, Dusseldorf, Germany **(100%)**
Tel.: (49) 21152680
Web Site: http://www.delagelanden.com
Sales Range: $100-124.9 Million
Emp.: 150
Leasing, Business & Consumer Finance Solutions
N.A.I.C.S.: 525990

De Lage Landen Leasing Ltd. **(2)**
Building 7 Croxley Green Business Park, PO Box 430, Hatters Lane, Watford, WD18 8EZ, Hertfordshire, United Kingdom **(100%)**
Tel.: (44) 1923810083
Web Site: http://www.delagelanden.com
Sales Range: $75-99.9 Million
Emp.: 100
Leasing, Business & Consumer Finance Solutions
N.A.I.C.S.: 525990

De Lage Landen Leasing Ltd. **(2)**
1 George's Dock House IFSC, Dublin, 1, Ireland **(100%)**
Tel.: (353) 14814100
Web Site: http://www.delagelanden.com
Sales Range: $75-99.9 Million
Emp.: 45
Leasing, Business & Consumer Finance Solutions
N.A.I.C.S.: 525990
David Ritchie *(Mng Dir)*

De Lage Landen Leasing N.V. **(2)**
Blarenberglaan 3C, 2800, Machelen, Belgium **(100%)**
Tel.: (32) 15369411
Web Site: http://www.delagelanden.com
Sales Range: $50-74.9 Million
Emp.: 40
Leasing, Business & Consumer Finance Solutions
N.A.I.C.S.: 525990

De Lage Landen Leasing S.p.A. **(2)**
Viale Monte Grappa 4, 20124, Milan, Italy
Tel.: (39) 02636941
Web Site: http://www.delagelanden.com
Sales Range: $75-99.9 Million
Emp.: 80
Leasing, Business & Consumer Finance Solutions
N.A.I.C.S.: 525990

De Lage Landen Pte. Limited **(2)**
38 Beach Road 26-11 South Beach Tower, Singapore, 068896, Singapore
Tel.: (65) 6645 4588
Financial Management Services
N.A.I.C.S.: 523999
Juan Long *(Head-Fin-Asia)*

Obvion N.V. **(1)**
Burgemeester De Hesselleplein 31, Postbus 3005, 6411 CH, Heerlen, Netherlands
Tel.: (31) 88 147 04 44
Web Site: http://www.obvion.nl
Emp.: 500
Mortgage Brokerage Services
N.A.I.C.S.: 522310
Natasja Theunissen *(Mgr-Funding & Risk)*

PT. Bank Rabobank International Indonesia **(1)**
Plaza 89 Lantai 9 Jl HR Rasuna Said, Kav X-7 No 6, Jakarta, 12940, Indonesia **(56.94%)**
Tel.: (62) 21 252 0876
Web Site: http://www.rabobank.co.id
Sales Range: $50-74.9 Million
Emp.: 50
Commercial Banking Services
N.A.I.C.S.: 522110
Joseph F. P. Luhukay *(Chm)*

Rabo AgriFinance, Inc. **(1)**
1 CityPlace Dr Ste 200, Saint Louis, MO 63141
Tel.: (314) 687-4000
Web Site: http://www.raboag.com
Sales Range: $50-74.9 Million
Emp.: 100
Agricultural Real Estate Lending & Financing Services
N.A.I.C.S.: 522291
Scott Cline *(Sr Mgr-Relationship-Vendor Fin-Bettendorf)*

Subsidiary (Domestic):

Rabo AgriInsurance Services, Inc. **(2)**
6919 Chancellor Dr, Cedar Falls, IA 50613
Tel.: (319) 277-4444
Web Site: http://www.rabobankamerica.com
Sales Range: $50-74.9 Million
Emp.: 100
Agricultural Insurance & Lending Services

N.A.I.C.S.: 524210
Tad Mozena *(VP-Insurance)*

Rabo Capital Services, Inc. **(1)**
245 Park Ave, New York, NY 10167
Tel.: (212) 916-7800
Web Site: http://www.rabobankamerica.com
Sales Range: $125-149.9 Million
Emp.: 200
Corporate Banking, Financial Market & Merger Advisory Services
N.A.I.C.S.: 523150

Rabo India Finance Pvt Ltd **(1)**
Forbes Building 2nd Floor, Mumbai, 400 001, India
Tel.: (91) 2222034567
Web Site: http://www.rabobank.com
Sales Range: $50-74.9 Million
Emp.: 70
Commericial Banking
N.A.I.C.S.: 522110

Rabo Vastgoedgroep Holding N.V. **(1)**
Westerdorpsstraat 66, Hoevelaken, 3871AZ, Netherlands
Tel.: (31) 332539111
Web Site:
http://www.raborealestategroup.com
Rev.: $1,777
Assets: $23,221
Liabilities: $22,013
Net Worth: $1,208
Earnings: ($216)
Emp.: 1,809
Fiscal Year-end: 12/31/2014
Holding Company; Real Estate Development, Finance & Asset Management Services
N.A.I.C.S.: 551112
Jos H. P. M. van Lange *(Chm)*

Subsidiary (Domestic):

Bouwfonds Property Development B.V. **(2)**
IJsbaanpad 1, 1076 CV, Amsterdam, Netherlands **(100%)**
Tel.: (31) 20 304 9999
Web Site: http://www.bpdeurope.com
Emp.: 1,100
Residential Real Estate Development
N.A.I.C.S.: 237210

FGH Bank N.V. **(2)**
Leidseveer 50, NL-3511 SB, Utrecht, Netherlands **(100%)**
Tel.: (31) 302323911
Sales Range: $100-124.9 Million
Emp.: 250
Real Estate Banking Services
N.A.I.C.S.: 522292

Fondsenbeheer Nederland B.V. **(2)**
Utrechtsweg 12, 3811 NB, Amersfoort, Netherlands **(100%)**
Tel.: (31) 332539428
Web Site: http://www.fondsenbeheer.nl
Sales Range: $50-74.9 Million
Emp.: 90
Investment Fund & Trust Management
N.A.I.C.S.: 523991

MAB Development Group B.V. **(2)**
PO Box 1, Hague, 3800AA, Netherlands **(100%)**
Tel.: (31) 703068400
Web Site: http://www.mab.com
Sales Range: $50-74.9 Million
Emp.: 40
Holding Company; Commercial Real Estate Development & Construction Services
N.A.I.C.S.: 551112
J.G.F. Eijkemans *(Mng Dir-Intl)*

Subsidiary (Domestic):

MAB Development Nederland B.V. **(3)**
Wijnhaven 60, Hague, 2500 CK, Netherlands **(100%)**
Tel.: (31) 703068400
Web Site: http://www.mab.com
Sales Range: $50-74.9 Million
Emp.: 40
Commercial Real Estate Development & Construction Services
N.A.I.C.S.: 237210
Cees B. van Boven *(Mng Dir)*

Cooperatieve Centrale Raiffeisen-Boerenleenbank
B.A.—(Continued)

Subsidiary (Domestic):

Rabo Private Equity (2)
Croeselaan 28, 3521 Cb, Utrecht, Netherlands
Tel.: (31) 30 712 36 27
Web Site: http://raboprivateequity.com
Investment Services
N.A.I.C.S.: 523999
Robert Bar (Assoc Dir)

Subsidiary (Domestic):

Redwave BV (3)
Handelskade 6, Beverwijk, 1948 NA, Netherlands
Tel.: (31) 251262400
Web Site: http://www.redwave.nl
Employment Services
N.A.I.C.S.: 561311

**Rabobank Australia & New Zealand
Group** (1)
Level 16 Darling Park Tower 3, 201 Sussex
St, Sydney, 2000, NSW, Australia
Tel.: (61) 281154000
Web Site: http://www.rabobank.com.au
Sales Range: $250-299.9 Million
Emp.: 700
Regional Managing Office
N.A.I.C.S.: 551114
Peter Knoblanche (Mng Dir)

Subsidiary (Domestic):

Rabo Australia Limited (2)
Level 16 Darling Park Tower 3, 201 Sussex
Street, Sydney, 2000, NSW, Australia
Tel.: (61) 281154000
Web Site: http://www.rabobank.com.au
Sales Range: $400-449.9 Million
Emp.: 500
Corporate Banking, Financial Market &
Merger Advisory Services
N.A.I.C.S.: 523150
William P. Gurry (Chm)

Rabobank Australia Limited (2)
Level 16 Darling Park Tower 3 Sussak St
201, 201 Sussex Street, Sydney, 2000,
NSW, Australia
Tel.: (61) 292344200
Web Site: http://www.rabobank.com.au
Sales Range: $300-349.9 Million
Emp.: 700
Commericial Banking
N.A.I.C.S.: 522110
Ruurd Weulen Kranenberg (CFO & Chief
Risk Officer)

Subsidiary (Non-US):

Rabobank New Zealand Limited (2)
Level 23 157 Lambton Quay, Wellington,
6011, New Zealand
Tel.: (64) 48192700
Web Site: http://www.rabobank.co.nz
Sales Range: $50-74.9 Million
Emp.: 100
Commercial Banking Services
N.A.I.C.S.: 522110
Ruurd Weulen Kranenberg (Deputy CEO,
CFO & Chief Risk Officer)

Rabobank Chile S.A. (1)
Av Del Valle 714 Huechuraba, Santiago,
8580659, Chile
Tel.: (56) 2 449 8000
Web Site: http://www.rabobank.cl
Emp.: 300
Commercial Banking Services
N.A.I.C.S.: 522110
Brenda de Swart (Mgr-Desk-Intl)

Rabobank Curacao NV (1)
Kayamensing Jombi 14, Zeelandia Office
Park, Willemstad, 3876, Curacao
Tel.: (599) 94652011
Web Site: http://www.rabobank.nl
Sales Range: $50-74.9 Million
Emp.: 15
Banking & Financial Services
N.A.I.C.S.: 522210

Rabobank France (1)
69 Blvd Haussmann, 75008, Paris,
France (100%)
Tel.: (33) 144718200

Web Site: http://www.rabobank.com
Sales Range: $50-74.9 Million
Emp.: 20
Banking & Financial Services
N.A.I.C.S.: 522210

Rabobank Ireland plc (1)
Tharlemont Place, Dublin, 2, Ireland
Tel.: (353) 16076100
Web Site: http://www.rabobank.ie
Sales Range: $50-74.9 Million
Emp.: 80
Commericial Banking
N.A.I.C.S.: 522110
Barry Henry (Head-Loan Products Grp)

Rabobank Singapore (1)
77 Robinson Rd 08-00, Singapore, 68896,
Singapore (100%)
Tel.: (65) 363363
Web Site: http://www.rabobank.com.sg
Sales Range: $100-124.9 Million
Emp.: 180
Banking & Financial Services
N.A.I.C.S.: 522210

Schretlen & Co N.V. (1)
Apollogebouw - Apollolaan 153, Postbus
1869, 1077 AS, Amsterdam, Netherlands
Tel.: (31) 20 777 88 00
Web Site: http://www.schretlen.com
Commercial Banking Services
N.A.I.C.S.: 522110
Patrick Levering (Mgr-Internal Control)

Vista Hypotheken B.V. (1)
PO Box 85353, 3508 AJ, Utrecht, Netherlands
Tel.: (31) 658942787
Web Site: https://www.vistahypotheken.nl
Mortgage Loan Services
N.A.I.C.S.: 522310
Stan Pijnenburg (Chief Financial & Risk Officer)

COOPERATIVA A.D.
Bulevar Vojvode Misica 37-39 III
sprat, 11000, Belgrade, Serbia
Tel.: (381) 11 3692 513
Web Site: http://www.coop.rs
Year Founded: 1951
COOP—(BEL)
Sales Range: Less than $1 Million
Emp.: 3
Fruit & Vegetable Processing Services
N.A.I.C.S.: 311411
Jasmina Jevtic (Exec Dir)

**COOPERATIVE CENTRAL
BANK LTD.**
8 Gregorios Afxentiou Street, PO Box
24537, 1096, Nicosia, Cyprus
Tel.: (357) 22743000
Web Site:
http://www.coopbank.com.cy
Sales Range: $50-74.9 Million
Emp.: 220
Banking Services
N.A.I.C.S.: 522110
Demetris Stavrou (CEO & Bd Mem)

**COOPERATIVE FORESTIERE
BOURGOGNE LIMOUSIN
(CFBL)**
Parc de l'Empereur, BP 85, 19203,
Ussel, Cedex, France
Tel.: (33) 5 55 46 35 00
Web Site: http://www.cfbl.fr
Sales Range: $25-49.9 Million
Emp.: 66
Forestry Services
N.A.I.C.S.: 115310
Lionel Say (Gen Mgr)

COOPERS BREWERY LIMITED
461 South Road Regency Park, Adelaide, 5010, SA, Australia
Tel.: (61) 884401800   AU
Web Site: http://www.coopers.com.au
Year Founded: 1862
Sales Range: $50-74.9 Million

Emp.: 125
Malt Beverages Brewer
N.A.I.C.S.: 312120
Glenn Cooper (Chm)

Subsidiaries:

Catalina Products, LLC (1)
5620 N Kolb Rd Ste 205, Tucson, AZ
85750
Tel.: (520) 529-0839
Web Site: http://www.mrbeer.com
Sales Range: $25-49.9 Million
Emp.: 20
Home Brewery Systems & Supplies
N.A.I.C.S.: 312120
Rick Zich (CFO)

Premium Beverages Limited (1)
2/11 Sabre Drive, Port Melbourne, 3207,
VIC, Australia
Tel.: (61) 3 9245 1900
Web Site:
http://www.premiumbeverages.com.au
Beer Whslr
N.A.I.C.S.: 424810
Andrew Cooper (Acct Mgr-Natl)

COOPERS PARK CORPORATION
900-1095 West Pender St, Vancouver, V6E 2M6, BC, Canada
Tel.: (604) 662-8383
Web Site:
https://www.cooperspark.com
Sales Range: Less than $1 Million
Construction Services
N.A.I.C.S.: 236220

Subsidiaries:

Coopers Park Investment Holdings
Limited (1)
1095 Pender St W Ste 900, Vancouver,
V6E 2M6, BC, Canada
Tel.: (604) 662-8383
Investment Management Service
N.A.I.C.S.: 523999

COOTEK (CAYMAN) INC.
9-11F No 16 Lane 399 Xinlong Road,
Minhang District, Shanghai, 201101,
China
Tel.: (86) 2164856352   Ky
Web Site: http://ir.cootek.com
Year Founded: 2012
CTKYY—(OTCIQ)
Rev.: $83,926,614
Assets: $21,385,287
Liabilities: $20,254,451
Net Worth: $1,130,836
Earnings: $515,014
Emp.: 181
Fiscal Year-end: 12/31/22
Mobile Application Development Services
N.A.I.C.S.: 541511
Karl Kan Zhang (Co-Founder, Chm &
CTO)

COPA CORPORATION, INC.
Ebisu Park Hills 6th floor 2-23-7
Ebisu Minami, Shibuya-ku, Tokyo,
150-0022, Japan
Tel.: (81) 357244302
Web Site: https://www.copa.co.jp
Year Founded: 1998
7689—(TKS)
Television Product Distr
N.A.I.C.S.: 423620
Taisuke Yoshimura (Founder & Pres)

COPA HOLDINGS, S.A.
Avenida Principal y Avenida de la
Rotonda Costa del Este, Complejo
Business Park Torre Norte Parque
Lefevre, Panama, Panama
Tel.: (507) 30427774   Pa
Web Site: https://copa.gcs-web.com
CPA—(NYSE)
Rev.: $2,965,033,000

Assets: $4,690,362,000
Liabilities: $3,198,252,000
Net Worth: $1,492,110,000
Earnings: $348,054,000
Emp.: 7,265
Fiscal Year-end: 12/31/22
International Airline Passenger &
Cargo Services
N.A.I.C.S.: 481111
Pedro Heilbron (CEO)

Subsidiaries:

AeroRepublica, S.A. (1)
Street 40A 13 13 1st Floor, Bogota,
Colombia (99.8%)
Tel.: (57) 13209090
Web Site: http://www.aerorepublica.com
Other Support Activities for Air Transportation
N.A.I.C.S.: 488190

Compania Panamena de Aviacion,
S.A. (1)
Boulevard Costa del Este, Avenida Principal, Panama, Panama (99.8%)
Tel.: (507) 3033348
Web Site: http://www.copaair.com
Other Support Activities for Air Transportation
N.A.I.C.S.: 488190

COPAM-COMPANHIA PORTUGUESA DE AMIDOS SA
Rua Deputado Pedro Botelho Neves,
Sao Joao da Talha, 2695-722, Loures, Portugal
Tel.: (351) 219947500   PT
Web Site: https://copam.pt
Year Founded: 1937
CPA—(EUR)
Starch & Glucose Syrup Product Mfr
N.A.I.C.S.: 311221

COPAP INC.
755 boul St Jean Suite 305, Pointe-
Claire, H9R 5M9, QC, Canada
Tel.: (514) 693-9150
Web Site: http://www.copap.com
Year Founded: 1990
Rev.: $104,300,000
Emp.: 14
Pulp & Paper Products Distr
N.A.I.C.S.: 322110
Denys Lamarre (VP-Legal Affairs)

Subsidiaries:

Copap Europe SAS (1)
345 rue d'Estienne d'Orves Immeuble le
Simpar, 92700, Colombes, France
Tel.: (33) 179620262
Paper Product Distr
N.A.I.C.S.: 423390
Olivier Wackernie (Mgr-Sls)

CopapAmericas LLC (1)
755 Alamanda St, Boca Raton, FL 33486
Tel.: (561) 347-8415
Paper Product Distr
N.A.I.C.S.: 423390

**COPARTNER TECHNOLOGY
CORPORATION**
4F No 16 Jian 8th Rd, Zhonghe Dist,
New Taipei City, 23511, Taiwan
Tel.: (886) 82265658
Web Site:
https://www.copartner.com.tw
Year Founded: 1987
3550—(TAI)
Rev.: $119,120,307
Assets: $138,535,689
Liabilities: $89,779,453
Net Worth: $48,756,236
Earnings: ($11,858,039)
Fiscal Year-end: 12/31/23
Cable & Wire Mfr & Distr
N.A.I.C.S.: 335921
Carol Cheng (Fin Dir)

Subsidiaries:

Cablex Metal Material (AnFu) Co., Ltd. **(1)**
Advanced Equipment Manufacturing Industrial Park, High-tech Industrial Park Anfu County, Jian, Jiangxi, China
Tel.: (86) 7967628866
Cable Wire Mfr & Distr
N.A.I.C.S.: 335921

Cablex Wire & Cable (KunShan) Mfg. Limited **(1)**
No 168 Bin jiang South Road, Zhangpu Town, Kunshan, Jiangsu, China
Tel.: (86) 51257952539
Cable & Wire Product Mfr
N.A.I.C.S.: 332618

Cablex Wire (ShenZhen) Mfg Co., Ltd. **(1)**
Level 3 No 52-9 Fengtang Avenue, Rentian Village Fuhai Street Bao'an District, Shenzhen, Guangdong, China
Tel.: (86) 7552 731 2988
Cable & Wire Product Mfr
N.A.I.C.S.: 332618

Copartner Technology (ShenZhen) Co., Ltd. **(1)**
No 52-7 52-9 Fengtang Road, Rentian Village Fuhai Town Baoan District, Shenzhen, Guangdong, China
Tel.: (86) 75527312988
Cable & Wire Product Mfr
N.A.I.C.S.: 332618

Copartner Wire & Cable (ShenZhen) Co Ltd **(1)**
No 68 Xintang Road XianTian Village FuYong Town Baoan, Shenzhen, Guangdong, China
Tel.: (86) 75527312988
Insulated Wire & Cable Mfr
N.A.I.C.S.: 331318

Huisheng Plastics (Shen Zhen) Co Ltd **(1)**
No 2 Ninety-nine Industrial Area, Minzhu Village Shajing Town Baoan District, Shenzhen, Guangdong, China
Tel.: (86) 7553 386 7988
Web Site: http://en.copartner.com.tw
Cable & Wire Mfr
N.A.I.C.S.: 331318

Jia Xin New Materials (AnFu) Co., Ltd. **(1)**
Mechatronics Avenue High tech Industrial Park, Anfu County, Jian, Jiangxi, China
Tel.: (86) 7967628668
Cable Wire Mfr & Distr
N.A.I.C.S.: 335921

Jia Xin Plastic (ShenZhen) Co., Ltd. **(1)**
3th Industrial Zone, Bitou Village Songgang Town Baoan District, Shenzhen, Guangdong, China
Tel.: (86) 75527130251
Cable & Wire Product Mfr
N.A.I.C.S.: 332618

Shen Zhen Copartner Communication Co Ltd **(1)**
No 8-9 Dayangtian Industrial Area, Wanfeng Village Shajing Town Baoan District, Shenzhen, Guangdong, China
Tel.: (86) 7556 186 0608
Web Site: http://www.copartner.com.tw
Insulated Wire & Cable Mfr
N.A.I.C.S.: 331318

Shin Ya Wire & Cable (ShenZhen) Co., Ltd. **(1)**
No 52-5 Fengtang Avenue, Xintian Village Fuyong Town Baoan District, Shenzhen, Guangdong, China
Tel.: (86) 75529851157
Cable & Wire Product Mfr
N.A.I.C.S.: 332618

United Electric Wire (KunShan) Co., Ltd. **(1)**
168 Binjiang South Road, Zhangpu Town Kunshan City, Suzhou, Jiangsu, China
Tel.: (86) 51257954165
Web Site: https://en.kscopartner.cn
Automobile Equipment Mfr

N.A.I.C.S.: 336320

Wanfu Plastic (ShenZhen) Co., Ltd. **(1)**
South Side of the First Floor No 9 Jiujiu Industrial Road, West Industrial Park Shatou Community Shajing Street Bao'an District, Shenzhen, Guangdong, China
Tel.: (86) 7552 726 9839
Cable & Wire Product Mfr
N.A.I.C.S.: 332618

Wujiang Wanfeng Plastic Cement Co., Ltd. **(1)**
No 44 Tongxin East Road, Wan jiang District Songling Town Wujiang District, Suzhou, Jiangsu, China
Tel.: (86) 51263397869
Cable & Wire Product Mfr
N.A.I.C.S.: 332618

Yanfu Copartner Technology (ShenZhen) Co., Ltd **(1)**
No 68 Xintang Road XianTian Village, FuYong Town BaoAn, Shenzhen, Guangdong, China
Tel.: (86) 755 27312988
Web Site: http://www.copartner.com.tw
Cable & Wire Mfr
N.A.I.C.S.: 331318

COPAUR MINERALS INC.
888-700 W Georgia Street, Vancouver, V7Y 1G5, BC, Canada
Tel.: (604) 317-3090 Ca
Web Site: https://copaur.com
Year Founded: 1985
RFC4—(DEU)
Rev.: $5,264
Assets: $28,933,849
Liabilities: $338,833
Net Worth: $28,595,016
Earnings: ($1,006,737)
Fiscal Year-end: 06/30/24
Mineral Exploration Services
N.A.I.C.S.: 213114
Kristopher J. Raffle (VP-Exploration)

Subsidiaries:

New Placer Dome Gold Corp. **(1)**
605-815 Hornby Street, Vancouver, V6Z 2E6, BC, Canada
Tel.: (604) 620-8406
Web Site: http://www.newplacerdome.com
Assets: $12,096,443
Liabilities: $81,085
Net Worth: $12,015,358
Earnings: ($2,990,069)
Fiscal Year-end: 06/30/2020
Gold Mining Services
N.A.I.C.S.: 212220

COPEL TELECOMUNICACOES S.A.
Rua Jose Izidoro Biazetto 158 - Bloco A - Mossungue, Curitiba, 81200-240, Parana, Brazil
Tel.: (55) 41 3310 5050
Sales Range: $100-124.9 Million
Emp.: 500
Telecommunication Servicesb
N.A.I.C.S.: 517810
Lindolfo Zimmer (CEO)

COPENHAGEN CAPITAL A/S
Niels Hemmingsens Gade 4, 1153, Copenhagen, Denmark
Tel.: (45) 70271060
Web Site: https://www.copenhagencapital.dk
Year Founded: 2008
CPHCAP.ST—(CSE)
Rev.: $6,990,449
Assets: $159,031,613
Liabilities: $89,660,176
Net Worth: $69,371,437
Earnings: ($11,371,881)
Emp.: 7
Fiscal Year-end: 12/31/23
Investment Services
N.A.I.C.S.: 523150

Lisbeth Bak (CEO)

COPENHAGEN MALMO PORT
Containervej 9, PO Box 900, Copenhagen, 2150, Denmark
Tel.: (45) 35461111 DK
Web Site: http://www.cmport.com
Sales Range: $100-124.9 Million
Emp.: 450
Cargo Transportation Administration
N.A.I.C.S.: 926120
Barbara Scheel Agersnap (CEO)

Subsidiaries:

Copenhagen Malmo Port **(1)**
Terminalgatan 18, PO Box 566, Malmo, 20125, Sweden **(100%)**
Tel.: (46) 406804100
Web Site: http://www.cmport.com
Sales Range: $1-9.9 Million
Emp.: 400
Shipping Terminal
N.A.I.C.S.: 488320
Jopam Roestim (Mng Dir)

COPERNICO SIM SPA
Via Cavour 20, 33100, Udine, Italy
Tel.: (39) 0432229835
Web Site: https://www.copernicosim.it
COP—(ITA)
Sales Range: Less than $1 Million
Investment Advisory Services
N.A.I.C.S.: 523940
Saverio Scelzo (Chm & CEO)

COPERSUCAR S.A.
Avenida Paulista 287, 01311-000, Sao Paulo, SP, Brazil
Tel.: (55) 1126188166 BR
Web Site:
http://www.copersucar.com.br
Year Founded: 2008
Sales Range: $1-4.9 Billion
Emp.: 7,851
Sugar & Ethanol Production
N.A.I.C.S.: 311314
Luis Roberto Pogetti (Chm)

Subsidiaries:

Copersucar North America LLC **(1)**
6100 Tower Cir Ste 500, Franklin, TN 37067
Tel.: (615) 778-2898
Emp.: 92
Logistics Consulting Servies
N.A.I.C.S.: 541614
Josh Bailey (CEO)

COPILOT CAPITAL LIMITED
21 Golden Square, Soho, London, W1F 9JN, United Kingdom
Tel.: (44) 3332424008
Web Site: https://www.copilotcptl.com
Emp.: 100
Investment Services
N.A.I.C.S.: 523999

COPITRAK INC.
8390 Mayrand Street, Montreal, H4P 2C9, QC, Canada
Tel.: (514) 737-7747
Year Founded: 1976
Sales Range: $10-24.9 Million
Emp.: 25
Expense Management Hardware Developer & Software Designer
N.A.I.C.S.: 513210
Mark Levine (Pres & CEO)

COPLAND ROAD CAPITAL CORPORATION
217 Queen St W 401, Toronto, M5V 0R2, ON, Canada
Tel.: (647) 242-4258
Web Site: https://copland-road.com
Year Founded: 2002
CRCC—(CNSX)
Rev.: $51,425

Assets: $719,373
Liabilities: $110,155
Net Worth: $609,218
Earnings: ($331,399)
Emp.: 54
Fiscal Year-end: 12/31/22
Real Estate Manangement Services
N.A.I.C.S.: 531390
Bruce Langstaff (Chm)

COPLUS INC.
No 50 Keji 2nd Rd, Annan Dist, Tainan City, 709031, Taiwan
Tel.: (886) 63840179
Web Site: https://www.coplus.com.tw
Year Founded: 1964
2254—(TAI)
Automatic Equipment Mfr & Distr
N.A.I.C.S.: 334512

COPOL INTERNATIONAL LTD.
69 Hartigan Drive, PO Box 70, North Sydney, B2A 3M4, NS, Canada
Tel.: (902) 794-9685
Web Site:
https://www.copolinternational.com
Year Founded: 1992
Rev.: $10,899,234
Emp.: 55
Film Products Mfr
N.A.I.C.S.: 326113
Denis Lanoe (VP-Ops)

COPPER CORE LTD.
275 Carrier Drive, Toronto, M9W 5Y8, ON, Canada
Tel.: (416) 675-1177
Web Site: http://www.coppercore.com
Sales Range: $10-24.9 Million
Emp.: 80
Automotive Radiators, Oil Coolers & Air Coolers Mfr
N.A.I.C.S.: 336390
Dan Pawlick (Pres & CEO)

COPPER FOX METALS INC.
Suite 650 340 - 12th Avenue SW, Calgary, T2R 1L5, AB, Canada
Tel.: (403) 264-2820
Web Site:
https://www.copperfoxmetals.com
CPFXF—(OTCQX)
Rev.: $3,692
Assets: $63,367,492
Liabilities: $1,470,517
Net Worth: $61,896,976
Earnings: ($1,009,897)
Emp.: 4
Fiscal Year-end: 10/31/22
Copper Exploration & Development Services
N.A.I.C.S.: 212230
Elmer B. Stewart (Chm, Pres & CEO)

COPPER LAKE RESOURCES LTD.
1 King Street Suite 4800, Toronto, M5H 1A1, ON, Canada
Tel.: (416) 561-3626
Web Site:
https://www.copperresources.com
Year Founded: 1984
WTCZF—(OTCIQ)
Assets: $2,620,509
Liabilities: $191,451
Net Worth: $2,429,058
Earnings: ($2,275,858)
Fiscal Year-end: 10/31/22
Metal Mining Exploration Service
N.A.I.C.S.: 212290
Terrence L. MacDonald (CEO)

COPPER NORTH MINING CORP.
1120 - 1095 W Pender St, Vancouver, V6E 2M6, BC, Canada

Copper North Mining Corp.—(Continued)

Tel.: (604) 398-3210 BC
Web Site:
http://www.coppernorthmining.com
Year Founded: 2011
COL—(TSXV)
Rev.: $276
Assets: $13,215,618
Liabilities: $1,325,976
Net Worth: $11,889,641
Earnings: ($247,605)
Fiscal Year-end: 12/31/19
Copper Mining
N.A.I.C.S.: 212230
John Cumming (Pres & CEO)

COPPER SEARCH LIMITED
21 Sydenham Road, PO Box 3429,
Norwood, 5067, SA, Australia
Tel.: (61) 871009051 AU
Web Site:
https://www.coppersearch.com.au
Year Founded: 2021
CUS—(ASX)
Rev.: $389,474
Assets: $4,353,309
Liabilities: $462,700
Net Worth: $3,890,609
Earnings: ($2,306,017)
Emp.: 1
Fiscal Year-end: 06/30/23
Mineral Exploration Services
N.A.I.C.S.: 212390

COPPER STANDARD RE-SOURCES INC.
Suite 3200 733 Seymour Street, Van-
couver, V6B 0S6, BC, Canada
Tel.: (604) 628-1110
Web Site: https://pucaragold.com
CSR—(CNSX)
Investment Services
N.A.I.C.S.: 523999
Matt Fargey (CEO)

COPPER STRIKE LIMITED
Level 20 140 St Georges Terrace,
Perth, 6000, WA, Australia
Tel.: (61) 892003429 AU
Web Site:
https://www.copperstrike.com.au
Year Founded: 2004
CSE—(ASX)
Assets: $11,200,378
Liabilities: $958,034
Net Worth: $10,242,344
Earnings: ($1,117,428)
Emp.: 2
Fiscal Year-end: 06/30/22
Mineral Exploration Services
N.A.I.C.S.: 213115
Stefan Ross (Co-Sec)

COPPERCORP RESOURCES INC.
800 Pender St W Suite 550, Vancou-
ver, V6C 2V6, BC, Canada
Tel.: (604) 970-8032 BC
Web Site:
https://www.coppercorpinc.com
Year Founded: 2020
CPCPF—(OTCQB)
Rev.: $126,717
Assets: $5,952,329
Liabilities: $261,077
Net Worth: $5,691,252
Earnings: ($3,138,762)
Fiscal Year-end: 12/31/22
Mineral Mining Services
N.A.I.C.S.: 213115
Rob Scott (CFO)

COPPERHEAD RESOURCES INC.
607-1750 Davie Street, Vancouver,
V6G 1W3, BC, Canada
Tel.: (647) 368-7789 BC
Web Site:
https://copperheadresourcesinc.com
Year Founded: 2022
CUH—(CNSX)
Rev.: $8,747
Assets: $250,233
Liabilities: $50,711
Net Worth: $199,522
Earnings: ($251,082)
Fiscal Year-end: 12/31/23
Mineral Mining Services
N.A.I.C.S.: 449210
Matthew Larsen (VP-Corporate De-
velopment)

COPPERMOLY LIMITED
Unit 2 42 Morrow Street, Taringa,
4068, QLD, Australia
Tel.: (61) 732177544
Web Site:
https://www.coppermoly.com.au
COY—(ASX)
Rev.: $21,818
Assets: $2,252,271
Liabilities: $91,727
Net Worth: $2,160,544
Earnings: ($668,506)
Fiscal Year-end: 06/30/24
Copper & Gold Mining & Exploration
Services
N.A.I.C.S.: 212230
Wanfu Huang (Mng Dir)

Subsidiaries:

Copper Quest PNG Ltd (1)
Unit 2 42 Morrow Street, Taringa, Brisbane,
4001, QLD, Australia
Tel.: (61) 732177544
Web Site: http://www.coppermoly.com.au
Sales Range: $50-74.9 Million
Emp.: 3
Copper Exploration Services
N.A.I.C.S.: 212230

COPPERSTONE RESOURCES AB
Fasadvagen 43, 981 41, Kiruna,
Sweden
Tel.: (46) 58088890 SE
Web Site: http://www.copperstone.se
Year Founded: 2006
COPP.B—(OMX)
Rev.: $5,035,068
Assets: $42,462,232
Liabilities: $6,228,644
Net Worth: $36,233,588
Earnings: $843,451
Emp.: 12
Fiscal Year-end: 12/31/20
Metal Exploration & Mining Services
N.A.I.C.S.: 212290
Michael Mattson (CEO)

Subsidiaries:

Argo AB (1)
Kungsgatan 62, Uppsala, 753 18, Uppland,
Sweden
Tel.: (46) 58088890
Sales Range: $50-74.9 Million
Emp.: 2
Mining Machinery Equipments Whslr
N.A.I.C.S.: 423810

Avalon Minerals Viscaria AB (1)
Hogstromsgatan 16, 931 33, Skelleftea,
Vasterbotten, Sweden (100%)
Tel.: (46) 98010910
Metal Ore Mining Services
N.A.I.C.S.: 212290

Kopparberg Mining Exploration
AB (1)
Kungsgatan 62, 753 18, Uppsala,
Sweden (100%)
Tel.: (46) 18560000
Sales Range: $25-49.9 Million
Minerals Exploration & Mining
N.A.I.C.S.: 212230

COPPERWIRED PUBLIC COM-PANY LIMITED
159/6 Sermmit Tower Floor 2nd
Room 201-202 Sukhumvit 21, Asoke
Klongtoeynuea Wattana, Bangkok,
10110, Thailand
Tel.: (66) 266529503 TH
Year Founded: 2000
CPW—(THA)
Rev.: $218,578,554
Assets: $59,529,888
Liabilities: $34,525,274
Net Worth: $25,004,614
Earnings: $3,773,182
Emp.: 708
Fiscal Year-end: 12/31/23
Mobile Phone Retailer
N.A.I.C.S.: 449210
Paramate Rienjaroensuk (CEO)

COPRO HOLDINGS CO., LTD.
3-28-12 Meieki, Nakamura-Ku, Na-
goya, 450-6427, Japan
Tel.: (81) 525892939
Web Site: https://www.copro-h.co.jp
7059—(TKS)
Rev.: $159,221,620
Assets: $80,281,702
Liabilities: $26,655,744
Net Worth: $53,625,958
Earnings: $9,669,380
Emp.: 4,189
Fiscal Year-end: 03/31/24
Holding Company Services
N.A.I.C.S.: 551112
Kosuke Kiyokawa (CEO)

Subsidiaries:

ATMOS Co., Ltd. (1)
1304 13F Nagoya Mitsui New Bldg 1-24-20,
Meiekiminami Nakamura-ku, Nagoya, 450-
0003, Japan
Tel.: (81) 524859366
Web Site: https://www.atmos-n.co.jp
Human Resouce Services
N.A.I.C.S.: 541612

Copro Vietnam Co., Ltd. (1)
Level 1 6 Daeha Businee Center Building
360 Kim Ma, Ngoc Khanh Ward Ba Dinh
Dist, Hanoi, Vietnam
Tel.: (84) 339598705
Web Site: https://www.copro-vn.com
Construction Services
N.A.I.C.S.: 236220

Value Ark Consulting Co., Ltd. (1)
Sapia Tower 18F 1-7-12 Marunouchi,
Chiyoda-ku, Tokyo, 100-0005, Japan
Tel.: (81) 363161172
Web Site: https://www.value-ark.com
Emp.: 32
Human Resouce Services
N.A.I.C.S.: 541612

COPUS KOREA CO., LTD.
8F DMC Iaan Sangam 2 nd Complex
361 World Cup Buk-ro, Mapo-gu,
Seoul, 03908, Korea (South)
Tel.: (82) 25681317
Web Site: https://www.copus.co.kr
Year Founded: 2005
322780—(KRS)
Rev.: $22,449,103
Assets: $107,609,410
Liabilities: $71,094,608
Net Worth: $36,514,802
Earnings: $1,098,300
Emp.: 19
Fiscal Year-end: 12/31/22
Digital Marketing Services
N.A.I.C.S.: 541870
Sun-Mi Heo (Mgr-Team)

COQUITLAM CHRYSLER DODGE JEEP LTD.
2960 Christmas Way, Coquitlam,
V3C4E6, BC, Canada
Tel.: (604) 469-5600

Web Site:
http://www.coquitlamchrysler.com
Year Founded: 1975
Rev.: $42,831,828
Emp.: 85
New & Used Car Dealers
N.A.I.C.S.: 441110
Jeff Kornatowsky (Gen Mgr)

CORAL INDIA FINANCE & HOUSING LIMITED
Dalamal House 4th Floor Jamnalal
Bajaj Marg, Nariman Point, Mumbai,
400 021, India
Tel.: (91) 2222853910
Web Site:
https://www.coralhousing.in
CORALFINAC—(NSE)
Rev.: $3,730,245
Assets: $20,831,197
Liabilities: $1,447,173
Net Worth: $19,384,024
Earnings: $2,371,142
Emp.: 5
Fiscal Year-end: 03/31/22
Housing Loan & Financial Services
N.A.I.C.S.: 522310
Navin B. Doshi (Mng Dir)

CORAL LABORATORIES LTD.
3-B Patanwala Industrial Estate LBS
Marg, Ghatkopar West, Mumbai,
400086, India
Tel.: (91) 2225008208
Web Site: https://www.corallab.com
524506—(BOM)
Rev.: $10,192,854
Assets: $20,903,471
Liabilities: $2,343,660
Net Worth: $18,559,811
Earnings: $772,783
Emp.: 109
Fiscal Year-end: 03/31/23
Medical Laboratory Services
N.A.I.C.S.: 621511
Nirali Mehta (Officer-Compliance &
Sec)

CORAL NEWSPRINTS LTD.
A-138 1st Floor Vikas Marg, Shakar-
pur, Delhi, 110 092, India
Tel.: (91) 1122010998
Web Site:
https://www.coralnewsprintsltd.com
Year Founded: 1992
530755—(BOM)
Rev.: $786,751
Assets: $668,299
Liabilities: $1,595,864
Net Worth: ($927,565)
Earnings: ($253,553)
Fiscal Year-end: 03/31/21
Paper & Craft Paper Mfr
N.A.I.C.S.: 322120
Pushpendra Singh Chauhan (CEO)

CORAL PRODUCTS PLC
Southmoor Road Roundthorn Indus-
trial Estate, Wythenshawe, Man-
chester, M23 9DS, Merseyside,
United Kingdom
Tel.: (44) 1942272882 UK
Web Site: https://coralproducts.com
Year Founded: 1989
CRU—(AIM)
Rev.: $31,386,672
Assets: $32,148,084
Liabilities: $15,761,228
Net Worth: $16,386,855
Earnings: $106,598
Emp.: 171
Fiscal Year-end: 04/30/19
Video & DVD Packaging Mfr
N.A.I.C.S.: 322220
Sharon Adele Gramauskas (Sec &
Dir-Fin)

Subsidiaries:

Coral Products (Mouldings) Limited (1)
North Florida Road, Haydock Industrial Estate, Haydock, WA11 9TP, Merseyside, United Kingdom
Tel.: (44) 1942272882
Web Site: http://www.coralmouldingsltd.com
Molded Plastic Product Mfr & Distr
N.A.I.C.S.: 326199

Customised Packaging Limited (1)
Denton Business Park Units 2-4 Windmill Lane, Denton, Manchester, M34 3SP, United Kingdom
Tel.: (44) 1613208318
Web Site:
https://customisedpackaging.co.uk
Plastics Product Mfr & Distr
N.A.I.C.S.: 326199

Global One-Pak Limited (1)
Hyde Park House Cartwright Street, Newton, Hyde, SK14 4EH, Cheshire, United Kingdom
Tel.: (44) 1613671212
Web Site: http://www.gop.co.uk
Lotion Pump Distr
N.A.I.C.S.: 423830

Interpack Limited (1)
North Florida Road, Haydock Industrial Estate, Haydock, WA11 9TP, Merseyside, United Kingdom
Tel.: (44) 1942726986
Web Site: http://www.interpackltd.co.uk
Plastic Bucket Mfr & Distr
N.A.I.C.S.: 326199

Tatra Rotalac Limited (1)
Southmoor Road, Wythenshawe, Manchester, M23 9DS, United Kingdom
Tel.: (44) 1619469460
Web Site: http://www.tatra-rotalac.com
Plastics Product Mfr
N.A.I.C.S.: 326199

CORALISLE GROUP LTD.
Jardine House 33-35 Reid Street, PO Box HM 1559, Hamilton, HM FX, Bermuda
Tel.: (441) 2943700
Web Site:
http://bermuda.cgcoralisle.com
Property & Casualty Insurance Services
N.A.I.C.S.: 524126
S. Naz Farrow (CEO & Exec Dir)

CORAZA INTEGRATED TECHNOLOGY BERHAD
2777 Lorong Industri 5 Kawasan Industri Bukit Panchor, 14300, Nibong Tebal, Pulau Pinang, Malaysia
Tel.: (60) 45958888   MY
Web Site:
https://www.corazaintech.com
Year Founded: 2001
CORAZA—(KLS)
Rev.: $30,338,142
Assets: $29,732,333
Liabilities: $10,903,464
Net Worth: $18,828,869
Earnings: $3,114,155
Fiscal Year-end: 12/31/22
Sheet Metal Work Mfg
N.A.I.C.S.: 332322
Fook San Ng (Chm)

Subsidiaries:

Coraza Systems Malaysia Sdn. Bhd. (1)
Lot 2777 Lorong Industri 5 Kawasan Industri Bukit Panchor, Seberang Perai Selatan, 14300, Nibong Tebal, Penang, Malaysia
Tel.: (60) 45958888
Precision Machined Components Mfr & Distr
N.A.I.C.S.: 332613

CORAZON MINING LIMITED

Level 3 33 Ord St, West Perth, 6005, WA, Australia
Tel.: (61) 861666361
Web Site:
https://www.corazon.com.au
CZN—(ASX)
Rev.: $7,902
Assets: $14,306,397
Liabilities: $563,545
Net Worth: $13,742,852
Earnings: ($1,202,717)
Emp.: 2
Fiscal Year-end: 06/30/22
Exploration Services
N.A.I.C.S.: 213114
Brett Sidney Smith (Mng Dir)

CORBIN COMMUNICATIONS LIMITED
9 Long Circular Road, PO Box 1032, Port of Spain, Trinidad & Tobago
Tel.: (868) 6221409
Web Site:
http://www.corbintrinidad.com
Year Founded: 1952
Advetising Agency
N.A.I.C.S.: 541810
Ronald G. Murray (Chm & CEO)

Subsidiaries:

Corbin Communications Limited (1)
Welchers Great House, Welchers, Saint Michael, Barbados
Tel.: (246) 436 6814
Emp.: 20
Advertising Agencies
N.A.I.C.S.: 541810
Jennifer St. Hill (Media Dir)

CORBION N.V.
Piet Heinkade 127, 1019 GM, Amsterdam, Netherlands
Tel.: (31) 205906911   NI
Web Site: https://www.corbion.com
Year Founded: 1903
CSNVF—(OTCIQ)
Rev.: $1,211,658,760
Assets: $1,319,743,880
Liabilities: $685,972,040
Net Worth: $633,771,840
Earnings: $89,784,344
Emp.: 2,267
Fiscal Year-end: 12/31/20
Food Ingredient & Biomaterials Mfr
N.A.I.C.S.: 311999
Rudolph Harold Peter Markham (Vice Chm-Supervisory Bd)

Subsidiaries:

Caravan Ingredients (1)
550 S 18th St, Kansas City, KS 66105-1104
Tel.: (816) 561-9050
Web Site:
http://www.caravaningredients.com
Sales Range: $25-49.9 Million
Emp.: 100
Mfr of Bakery Ingredients & Related Products
N.A.I.C.S.: 311999
Bill McGowan (Pres & CEO)

Corbion - PURAC Division (1)
Arkelsedijk 46, 4200 AA, Gorinchem, Netherlands
Tel.: (31) 18 369 5695
Web Site: http://www.purac.com
Rev.: $143,226,000
Emp.: 400
Naturally Fermented Lactic Acid & Derivatives
N.A.I.C.S.: 325411

Subsidiary (Non-US):

PURAC Asia Pacific Pte. Ltd. (2)
3 International Business Park 06-19 Nordic European Centre, Singapore, 609927, Singapore
Tel.: (65) 63491350
Sales Range: $25-49.9 Million
Emp.: 20

Marketing Company for Lactic Acid & Additives
N.A.I.C.S.: 424690

Subsidiary (Domestic):

PURAC Biochem BV (2)
Arkelsedijk 46, 4206 AC, Gorinchem, Netherlands (100%)
Tel.: (31) 183695695
Web Site: https://www.purac.com
Sales Range: $75-99.9 Million
N.A.I.C.S.: 311313

Subsidiary (Non-US):

PURAC Bioquimica S.A. (2)
Gran Vial 19-25, 08160, Montmelo, Barcelona, Spain (100%)
Tel.: (34) 935686300
Sales Range: $50-74.9 Million
Emp.: 120
Mfr of Lactic Acid & Derivatives
N.A.I.C.S.: 325411
Xaeief Cafas (Dir-Comml)

PURAC Japan K.K. (2)
Gluck Daikanyama 4F 2 11 12 Ebisu Nishi, Shibuya Ku, Tokyo, 150 0021, Japan (100%)
Tel.: (81) 357286700
Web Site: http://www.corbion.com
Sales Range: $25-49.9 Million
Emp.: 14
Lactic Acid
N.A.I.C.S.: 325199

PURAC Sinteses (2)
Ave Rui Barbosa 521, Sao Paulo, 28013-000, Brazil (100%)
Tel.: (55) 2227377200
Web Site: http://www.purac.com
Sales Range: $50-74.9 Million
Emp.: 200
Naturally Fermented Lactic Acid & Derivatives
N.A.I.C.S.: 325411

Purac China (2)
Unit 16-18 28F T2 Lane 166 Minhong Road, Minhang District, Shanghai, 201100, China
Tel.: (86) 216 406 6773
Web Site: http://www.purac.com
Bakery Product Distr
N.A.I.C.S.: 424420

Purac Deutschland Gmbh (2)
Mainzer Str 160, 55411, Bingen, Germany
Tel.: (49) 672118174
Sales Range: $25-49.9 Million
Emp.: 10
Specialty Chemicals Distr
N.A.I.C.S.: 424690

Purac India Private Limited (2)
Awfis 12B/5 B wing Thane Belapur Road Gavate wadi, Empire Tower Reliable Tech Park MIDC Airoli, Navi Mumbai, 400708, Maharashtra, India
Tel.: (91) 224 923 4938
Web Site: http://www.purac.com
Bakery Product Distr
N.A.I.C.S.: 424420

Purac Korea (2)
402 Suin Bldg Jamwon-dong 18 Naruteo-ro 12-gil, Seocho-gu, Seoul, 06527, Korea (South)
Tel.: (82) 2 532 9623
Web Site: http://www.purac.com
Bakery Food Products Distr
N.A.I.C.S.: 424420

Purac Mexico S de RL de CV (2)
Av Insurgentes Sur 1787 Piso 8, Col Guadalupe Inn Delegacion Alvaro Obregon, CP 01020, Mexico, Mexico
Tel.: (52) 5590004844
Sales Range: $25-49.9 Million
Emp.: 13
Bakery Food Products Distr
N.A.I.C.S.: 424420

Purac Polska Sp. z o.o. (2)
Dzildowska 11, 1184, Warsaw, Poland
Tel.: (48) 224047772
Emp.: 3
Food Products & Beverage Mfr
N.A.I.C.S.: 311999
Beata Popielarz (Gen Mgr)

Purac Thailand Ltd (2)
3 Moo 2 - Asia Industrial Estate, T Banchang A Banchang, Rayong, 21130, Thailand
Tel.: (66) 38 698 800
Sales Range: $25-49.9 Million
Emp.: 25
Bakery Food Products Mfr
N.A.I.C.S.: 311813

Corbion Group Netherlands B.V. (1)
Neanoord 13, 1112XE, Diemen, Netherlands (100%)
Tel.: (31) 5906911
Sales Range: $25-49.9 Million
Emp.: 250
N.A.I.C.S.: 311313

CORBOX CORPORATION
Purok Gemelina, Tayud Lilo-an, Cebu, 6002, Philippines
Tel.: (63) 324249181
Web Site: http://www.corboxcorp.com
Packaging & Containers Company
N.A.I.C.S.: 322211
Ernie Frio (Plant Mgr)

CORCEL PLC
WeWork 71-91 Aldwych House, London, WC2B 4HN, United Kingdom
Tel.: (44) 2077479960
Web Site: http://www.regency-mines.com
CRCL—(AIM)
Rev.: $31,228
Assets: $6,613,454
Liabilities: $2,371,937
Net Worth: $4,241,517
Earnings: ($2,889,228)
Emp.: 5
Fiscal Year-end: 06/30/22
Mineral Exploration Services
N.A.I.C.S.: 212230
Stephen F. Ronaldson (Sec)

Subsidiaries:

Atlas Petroleum Exploration Worldwide, Ltd. (1)
18000 Groeschke Rd Ste A1, Houston, TX 77084 (90%)
Tel.: (713) 554-8900
Web Site: http://www.apxww.com
Sales Range: $1-9.9 Million
Emp.: 40
Drilling Oil & Gas Wells
N.A.I.C.S.: 213111
Jeniffer Flores (Sec)

CORDANT GROUP PLC
Chevron House 346 Long Lane, Hillingdon, UB10 9PF, Middlesex, United Kingdom
Tel.: (44) 1895 201 800   UK
Web Site:
http://www.cordantgroup.com
Year Founded: 1957
Sales Range: $750-799.9 Million
Emp.: 30,000
Recruitment & Integrated Facility Services
N.A.I.C.S.: 561210
Guy Pakenham (Mng Dir)

Subsidiaries:

Staffgroup Ltd. (1)
Chevron House 346 Long Lane Hillingdon, Uxbridge, UB10 9PF, Middlesex, United Kingdom
Tel.: (44) 207 803 0606
Web Site: http://www.staffgroup.com
Emp.: 73
Employee Recruitment Services
N.A.I.C.S.: 541612
Saman Tabrizi (Mng Dir-Germany)

Subsidiary (Non-US):

Earthstaff GmbH (2)
Neuer Wall 63, 20354, Hamburg, Germany
Tel.: (49) 40808093240
Web Site: http://www.earthstaff.com
Recruitment Services

Cordant Group PLC—(Continued)
N.A.I.C.S.: 541612

Eurostaff Finance GmbH (2)
Freidrichstrasse 200, Berlin, 10117, Germany
Tel.: (49) 303001406
Recruitment Services
N.A.I.C.S.: 541612

Eurostaff Group GmbH (2)
Graben 5, 6300, Zug, Switzerland
Tel.: (41) 417298842
Web Site: http://www.eurostaffgroup.com
Recruitment Services
N.A.I.C.S.: 541612
William Brewer (Head-Fin & Recruitment)

UKFM Group Ltd (1)
100E Cumbernauld Road, Glasgow, G69 9AB, United Kingdom
Tel.: (44) 8702416697
Web Site: http://www.ukfmgroup.com
Air Conditioning System Installation Services
N.A.I.C.S.: 238220
Lesley Carruthers (Mgr-Admin)

CORDEL GROUP PLC
10 John Street, London, WC1N 2EB, United Kingdom UK
Web Site: https://www.cordel.ai
Year Founded: 2013
CRDL—(AIM)
Rev.: $4,361,649
Assets: $6,088,618
Liabilities: $1,293,016
Net Worth: $4,795,602
Earnings: ($755,049)
Emp.: 27
Fiscal Year-end: 06/30/23
Software Development Services
N.A.I.C.S.: 541511

CORDET CAPITAL PARTNERS LLP
2 St James's Market, London, SW1Y 4AH, United Kingdom
Tel.: (44) 2071005502
Web Site: http://www.cordet.com
Year Founded: 2013
Financial Services
N.A.I.C.S.: 523999
Magnus Lindquist (Co-Mng Partner)

Subsidiaries:

FLABEG Holding GmbH (1)
Waldaustrasse 13, 90441, Nuremberg, Germany
Tel.: (49) 911964560
Web Site: http://www.flabeg.com
Holding Company
N.A.I.C.S.: 551112
Andreas Katzer (CEO)

Subsidiary (Domestic):

Flabeg Deutschland GmbH (2)
Waldaustrasse 13, 90441, Nuremberg, Germany
Tel.: (49) 911964560
Web Site: http://www.flabeg.com
Mirror & Technical Glass Component Mfr
N.A.I.C.S.: 327211
Andreas Katzer (CEO & Mng Dir)

Subsidiary (US):

FLABEG Technical Glass Corp. (3)
451 Church St, Naugatuck, CT 06770
Tel.: (203) 729-5227
Sales Range: $50-74.9 Million
Flat Glass, Mirror & Technical Glass Component Mfr
N.A.I.C.S.: 327211

CORDIANT DIGITAL INFRA-STRUCTURE LIMITED
East Wing Trafalgar Court Les Banques, PO Box 656, Saint Peter Port, GY1 3PP, Guernsey
Tel.: (44) 1481742742 GG

Web Site:
https://www.cordiantdigitaltrust.com
Year Founded: 2021
CORD—(LSE)
Rev.: $126,054,027
Assets: $1,367,458,977
Liabilities: $205,302,954
Net Worth: $1,162,156,023
Earnings: $101,356,981
Fiscal Year-end: 03/31/24
Investment Management Service
N.A.I.C.S.: 523999
Benn Mikula (Partner)

Subsidiaries:

Norkring Belgie N.V. (1)
Houtvesterdreef 1, 2900, Schoten, Belgium
Tel.: (32) 220000
Web Site: https://www.norkring.be
Television & Radio Broadcasting Services
N.A.I.C.S.: 516110

CORDINA CHICKEN FARMS PTY. LTD.
55 Mandoon Road, Girraween, 2145, NSW, Australia
Tel.: (61) 299121700
Web Site: http://www.cordina.com.au
Year Founded: 1948
Meat Product Distr
N.A.I.C.S.: 424470
Louise Cordina (CEO)

CORDLIFE GROUP LIMITED
1 Yishun Industrial Street 1 06-01/09 A Posh BizHub, Singapore, 768160, Singapore
Tel.: (65) 62380808
Web Site: https://www.cordlife.com
Year Founded: 2001
CLIFF—(OTCIQ)
Rev.: $40,871,434
Assets: $168,947,758
Liabilities: $69,408,670
Net Worth: $99,539,089
Earnings: $3,620,600
Fiscal Year-end: 12/31/22
Stem Cell Banking Services
N.A.I.C.S.: 621511
Choon Hou Ho (Chm-Acting)

Subsidiaries:

Cordlife (Hong Kong) Limited (1)
Unit G15 G/F Biotech Centre 2 No 11 Science Park West Avenue, Hong Kong Science Park, Sha Tin, New Territories, China (Hong Kong)
Tel.: (852) 39802888
Web Site: https://www.cordlife.com.hk
Blood Banking Services
N.A.I.C.S.: 621991
Jennifer Teo (Deputy Dir-Medical)

Cordlife Medical Phils., Inc. (1)
Unit 104 Building H UP-AyalaLand Technohub Commonwealth Avenue Bgy, UP Campus Diliman, Quezon City, 1101, Philippines
Tel.: (63) 284701735
Web Site: https://www.cordlife.ph
Blood Banking Services
N.A.I.C.S.: 621991
Lorna Calingasan (Mktg Mgr)

Cordlife Sciences (India) Pvt. Ltd. (1)
Unit No 1102 11th Floor Acropolis Mall 1858/1 Rajdanga Main Rd, Kasba, Kolkata, 700107, West Bengal, India
Tel.: (91) 9830166200
Web Site: https://www.cordlifeindia.com
Blood Banking Services
N.A.I.C.S.: 621991
Shilpi Chowdhury (Mktg Mgr)

Healthbaby Biotech (Macau) Co., Limited (1)
Avenida do Infante D Henrique No 43-53A Block 21-F, Macau, China (Macau)
Tel.: (853) 28786717
Blood Banking Services
N.A.I.C.S.: 621991

PT. Cordlife Persada (1)
Jalan Bungur Besar Raya No 23, Gunung Sahari Selatan Kemayoran, Jakarta Pusat, 10610, Indonesia
Tel.: (62) 2180864674
Web Site: https://www.cordlife.co.id
Blood Banking Services
N.A.I.C.S.: 621991
Lim Heru Harliman (Head-Mktg & Bus Intelligence)

Stemlife Berhad (1)
B-8-15 Megan Avenue II 12 Jalan Yap Kwan Seng, 50450, Kuala Lumpur, Malaysia
Tel.: (60) 321638800
Web Site: https://www.stemlife.com
Blood Banking Services
N.A.I.C.S.: 621991
Kamalan Asokan (Mgr-Facility & Fulfilment)

CORDOBA MINERALS CORP.
Suite 606 - 999 Canada Place, Vancouver, V6C 3E1, BC, Canada
Tel.: (604) 689-8765 BC
Web Site:
https://www.cordobaminerals.com
Year Founded: 2009
CDBMF—(OTCQB)
Assets: $8,374,738
Liabilities: $950,573
Net Worth: $7,424,164
Earnings: ($21,706,267)
Fiscal Year-end: 12/31/20
Gold Mining Services
N.A.I.C.S.: 212220
Sarah Armstrong-Montoya (Pres & CEO)

CORDOVACANN CORP.
217 Queen Street West Suite 401, Toronto, M5V 0R2, ON, Canada
Tel.: (917) 843-2169 Ca
Web Site: https://cordovacann.com
Year Founded: 1997
CDVA—(CNSX)
Rev.: $10,086,407
Assets: $6,984,083
Liabilities: $8,882,629
Net Worth: ($1,898,546)
Earnings: ($932,130)
Fiscal Year-end: 06/30/24
Cannabis-Derived Mfr
N.A.I.C.S.: 325412
Ashish Kapoor (CFO & Sec)

CORDS CABLE INDUSTRIES LTD.
94 1st Floor Old Ishwar Nagar Okhla Industrial Area, Near Shambhu Dayal Bagh Phase-III, New Delhi, 110020, India
Tel.: (91) 1140551200
Web Site:
https://www.cordscable.com
CORDSCABLE—(NSE)
Rev.: $44,327,829
Assets: $40,106,990
Liabilities: $20,216,114
Net Worth: $19,890,876
Earnings: $594,498
Emp.: 212
Fiscal Year-end: 03/31/21
Cable Mfr
N.A.I.C.S.: 335921
Sanjeev Kumar (Exec Dir)

CORDSTRAP NETHERLANDS B.V.
Nobelstraat 1, 5807 GA, Oostrum, Netherlands
Tel.: (31) 478 519 000
Web Site: http://www.cordstrap.com
Sales Range: $100-124.9 Million
Emp.: 400
Cargo Securing System Mfr
N.A.I.C.S.: 326199

Subsidiaries:

Cordstrap (Middle East) Ltd. (1)
PO Box 61287, Jebel Ali, Dubai, United Arab Emirates
Tel.: (971) 4 8807877
Web Site: http://www.cordstrap.com
Marine Cargo Handling Services
N.A.I.C.S.: 488320
Ramanan Eranath Vengall (Mgr-Sis)

Cordstrap (Thailand) Co., Ltd. (1)
Harbor Mall Building 6th Floor Room 6A01 4/222 Moo 10 Sukhumvit Road, Thungsukla, Si Racha, 20230, Chonburi, Thailand
Tel.: (66) 38 110 901
Marine Cargo Handling Services
N.A.I.C.S.: 488320
Kitipong Chaisri (Country Mgr)

Cordstrap Canada (1)
Suite 404-499 Canada Place, Vancouver, V6C 3EZ, BC, Canada
Tel.: (604) 218-5795
Plastics Product Mfr
N.A.I.C.S.: 326199

Cordstrap Deutschland GmbH (1)
Tackweg 41, 47918, Tonisvorst, Germany
Tel.: (49) 2151 78880
Web Site: http://www.cordstrap.com
Emp.: 2
Cargo Securing System Mfr
N.A.I.C.S.: 326199

Cordstrap Espana s.l.u. (1)
Avenida Francesc Macia 60 13 fl Door 3, 8207, Sabadell, Spain
Tel.: (34) 90 2565 071
Web Site: http://www.cordstrap.net
Emp.: 12
Cargo Securing System Mfr
N.A.I.C.S.: 326199
Jose Garcia (Mgr-Comml)

Cordstrap France Sarl (1)
5 7 Ave du General de Gaulle, 60300, Senlis, France
Tel.: (33) 3 44258181
Web Site: http://www.cordstrap.com
Emp.: 7
Cargo Securing System Mfr
N.A.I.C.S.: 326199
Gregory Sauquembergue (Gen Mgr)

Cordstrap India Private Limited (1)
Suite 47 Vatika Business Centre Level 5 Tech Park 1 Airport Road Y, Yerwada, Pune, 411006, India
Tel.: (91) 20 4011 1420
Web Site: http://www.cordstrap.com
Emp.: 10
Cargo Securing System Mfr
N.A.I.C.S.: 326199
Jon Blower (Mng Dir)

Cordstrap Ireland Limited (1)
41 Percy Place, Dublin, 4, Ireland
Tel.: (353) 1 4977660
Web Site: http://www.cordstrap.net
Emp.: 25
Cargo Securing System Mfr
N.A.I.C.S.: 326199
Henk Van Zijl (Country Mgr)

Cordstrap Italia S.r.l. (1)
Via Papa Giovanni Paolo1 No 422, 21040, Uboldo, Italy
Tel.: (39) 02 96783625
Web Site: http://www.cordstrap.com
Emp.: 20
Cargo Securing System Mfr
N.A.I.C.S.: 326199
Dario Tofani (Mng Dir)

Cordstrap Load Securing Systems (Wuxi) Co., Ltd (1)
No 168 Yuan Road Shuofang Industrial Park, Wuxi, China
Tel.: (86) 510 853 11 666
Web Site: http://www.cordstrap.com
Cargo Securing System Mfr
N.A.I.C.S.: 326199

Cordstrap Malaysia Sdn Bhd (1)
No 28 Jalan Kasuarina 12 Bandar Ambang Botanic, 41200, Kelang, Malaysia
Tel.: (60) 3 3325 1616
Cargo Securing System Mfr

Subsidiaries:

N.A.I.C.S.: 326199
Stefan Becker *(Mgr-Comml)*

Cordstrap Mexico, S.A. de C.V. (1)
Av Manuel Gomez Morin No 3881 Oficina 2
Colonia Centro Sur, 76090, Queretaro,
Mexico
Tel.: (52) 442 229 1561
Web Site: http://www.cordstrap.net
Emp.: 1
Cargo Securing System Mfr
N.A.I.C.S.: 326199
Barry van Soest *(Mgr-Comml)*

Cordstrap Polska SP. Z O.O. (1)
ul Pasjonatow 15, Zakrzewo, 62-070, Dop-
iewo, Poland
Tel.: (48) 61 652 51 52
Web Site: http://www.cordstrap.com
Emp.: 15
Cargo Securing System Mfr
N.A.I.C.S.: 326199
Filip Czerwinski *(Gen Mgr)*

Cordstrap SA (Pty) Ltd (1)
Highway way Ub=nit 10b minuach rd eden-
berg jpjphnene, Cape Town, 8508, South
Africa
Tel.: (27) 21 704 0090
Web Site: http://www.cordstrap.com
Emp.: 9
Cargo Securing System Mfr
N.A.I.C.S.: 326199
Barry Hugo *(Mgr-Comml)*

Cordstrap UK Ltd. (1)
Paddock Road West Pimbo, Skelmersdale,
WN8 9PL, Lancashire, United Kingdom
Tel.: (44) 1695 554700
Web Site: http://www.cordstrap.com
Emp.: 20
Cargo Securing System Mfr
N.A.I.C.S.: 326199
Alan Green *(Country Mgr)*

Cordstrap USA, Inc. (1)
2000 S Sylvania Ave Ste 101, Sturtevant,
WI 53177-2102
Tel.: (262) 898-6670
Web Site: http://www.cordstrap.net
Sales Range: $25-49.9 Million
Emp.: 49
Cargo Securing System Mfr
N.A.I.C.S.: 326199
Tom Keefe *(VP-Sls)*

Cordstrap, s.r.o. (1)
Jakubska 2, Prague, 11000, Czech Repub-
lic
Tel.: (420) 776 772 171
Cargo Securing System Mfr
N.A.I.C.S.: 326199

SIA Cordstrap Baltic (1)
7a Ganibu dambis, Riga, 1045, Latvia
Tel.: (371) 67 320087
Marine Cargo Handling Services
N.A.I.C.S.: 488320
Salvis Krumins *(Mgr-Comml)*

CORE ASSETS CORP.
1450 - 789 West Pender Street, Van-
couver, V6C 1H2, BC, Canada
Tel.: (604) 681-1568
Web Site:
    https://www.coreassetscorp.com
CC—(OTCIQ)
Rev.: $1,384
Assets: $2,378,960
Liabilities: $81,218
Net Worth: $2,297,742
Earnings: ($837,334)
Fiscal Year-end: 09/30/21
Mineral Exploration & Mining Ser-
vices
N.A.I.C.S.: 213115
Jody Bellefleur *(CFO)*

**CORE CANADIAN DIVIDEND
TRUST**
121 King Street West Suite 2600, P
O Box 113, Toronto, M5H 3T9, ON,
Canada
Tel.: (416) 681-3966
Web Site:
    http://www.strathbridge.com

Year Founded: 2006
CDD.UN—(TSX)
Rev.: $446,464
Assets: $2,407,785
Liabilities: $767,541
Net Worth: $1,640,244
Earnings: $260,181
Fiscal Year-end: 12/31/19
Financial Investment Services
N.A.I.C.S.: 523999
John P. Mulvihill *(Chm & CEO)*

**CORE COMMUNICATION SER-
VICES LTD.**
Elizabeth House 11 York Road, Lon-
don, SE1 7NX, United Kingdom
Tel.: (44) 8081300808
Web Site: http://www.coretel.co.uk
Year Founded: 2005
Sales Range: $25-49.9 Million
Emp.: 15
International Mobile Telecommunica-
tions Services
N.A.I.C.S.: 517112
Tony Greaves *(Founder)*

CORE CORPORATION
1-22-3 Sangenjaya Setagaya-ku, To-
kyo, 154-8552, Japan
Tel.: (81) 337955111
Web Site: http://www.core.co.jp
Year Founded: 1969
2359—(TKS)
Rev.: $158,626,780
Assets: $157,906,290
Liabilities: $45,516,460
Net Worth: $112,389,830
Earnings: $15,004,700
Emp.: 1,527
Fiscal Year-end: 03/31/24
IT Services
N.A.I.C.S.: 541519
Ryohei Tanemura *(Chm & CEO)*

Subsidiaries:

Accord System Co., Ltd. (1)
2-11-26 Sangenjaya Core No 2 Building,
Setagaya-ku, Tokyo, 154-0024,
Japan (100%)
Tel.: (81) 3 5433 6640
Web Site: http://www.core.co.jp
Computer System Design Services
N.A.I.C.S.: 541512
Yuichi Taguchi *(Pres & Dir)*

Active Brains & Trust Co., Ltd. (1)
4-8-10 Ebisu, Shibuya-ku, Tokyo, 150-0013,
Japan
Tel.: (81) 364502143
Web Site: https://www.active-brains-trust.jp
Custom Computer Programming Services
N.A.I.C.S.: 541511

Answer and Consulting Co., Ltd (1)
Suzawa Building 4-7-10 Honmachi Nihon-
bashi, Chuo-ku, Tokyo, 103-0023, Japan
Tel.: (81) 3 3242 2671
Web Site: http://www.core.co.jp
Custom Computer Programming Services
N.A.I.C.S.: 541511

Beijing CORE Software Co., Ltd. (1)
24B Block A Linda Building No 8
Dongtucheng Road, Chaoyang District, Bei-
jing, 100013, China
Tel.: (86) 1084511277
Web Site: http://www.coresoft.com.cn
Sales Range: $25-49.9 Million
Emp.: 50
Software Publisher
N.A.I.C.S.: 513210

CORE Industries Co., Ltd (1)
1-22-3 Sangenjaya, Tokyo Core Building
Setagaya-ku, Tokyo, 154-8552, Japan
Tel.: (81) 337955111
Web Site: http://www.core.co.jp
Computer & Computer Peripheral Equip-
ment & Software Whslr
N.A.I.C.S.: 423430

CORENet International Co., Ltd. (1)
11-1 Minami-Kurokawa, Asao-ku, Kawasaki,

215-0034, Kanagawa, Japan
Tel.: (81) 44 988 7711
Information Technology Consulting Services
N.A.I.C.S.: 541512

DISEC Co., Ltd (1)
1-21-35 Kusatsu Shinmachi Nishiku MIXIS
Building 2F, Hiroshima, 733-0834, Japan
Tel.: (81) 822788777
Web Site: https://www.disec.co.jp
Sales Range: $25-49.9 Million
Emp.: 50
Custom Computer Programming Services
N.A.I.C.S.: 541511
Hiromitsu Yokota *(Pres)*

GIGA Co., Ltd (1)
9F Core Building 2 2-11-26, Sangenjaya
Setagaya-ku, Tokyo, 154-0024, Japan
Tel.: (81) 354336601
Web Site: https://www.giga.core.co.jp
Emp.: 159
Custom Computer Programming Services
N.A.I.C.S.: 541511

**Institute of Bio-Medical and Welfare
Engineering Co., Ltd** (1)
1-1-36 Higashikokushi, Ube, 755-0068,
Yamaguchi, Japan
Tel.: (81) 836371281
Web Site: https://www.ibmw.co.jp
Surgical & Medical Instruments Mfr
N.A.I.C.S.: 339112

**KN Information Systems
Corporation** (1)
2-6-31 Hikari-cho, Higashi-ku, Hiroshima,
732-0052, Japan
Tel.: (81) 822611256
Web Site: https://www.knc.co.jp
Sales Range: $25-49.9 Million
Emp.: 46
All Other Information Services
N.A.I.C.S.: 519290

**Koga-city Information Center Co.,
Ltd.** (1)
2-3-50 Chuo-cho, Koga, 306-0033, Ibaraki,
Japan
Tel.: (81) 280 22 0701
Information Technology Consulting Services
N.A.I.C.S.: 541512

Lambda System Inc. (1)
2-11-26 Sangenjaya Core No 2 Building,
Setagaya-ku, Tokyo, 154-0024,
Japan (100%)
Tel.: (81) 357873366
Web Site: https://www.lambda.co.jp
Emp.: 88
Computer Software & Hardware Mfr & Distr
N.A.I.C.S.: 334118
Mizuoka Takashi *(Auditor)*

PRONET Co., Ltd (1)
11-1 Minamikurokawa, Asao-ku, Kawasaki,
215-0034, Kanagawa, Japan
Tel.: (81) 449810890
Web Site: http://www.core-pronet.co.jp
Wood Container & Pallet Mfr
N.A.I.C.S.: 321920

Resona Inc. (1)
675 Nirazukamachi, Isesaki, 372-0813,
Gunma, Japan
Tel.: (81) 27 030 1278
Information Technology Services
N.A.I.C.S.: 541519

Shanghai CORE Co., Ltd (1)
Room 11501 SPSP Building 498 498 Guo-
ShouJing Rd, Pudong New Area, 201203,
Shanghai, China
Tel.: (86) 2150802815
Custom Computer Programming Services
N.A.I.C.S.: 541511

System Creative Co., Ltd (1)
8272-2 Minamiyokoichicho, Miyakonojo,
885-0092, Miyazaki, Japan
Tel.: (81) 986222937
Web Site: https://sc.poi.ne.jp
Emp.: 20
Custom Computer Programming Services
N.A.I.C.S.: 541511

**Tohoku Information Center Co.,
Ltd.** (1)
6162-10 Tookamachi, Shinjo, 996-0091,
Yamagata, Japan

Tel.: (81) 233 29 2411
Information Technology Consulting Services
N.A.I.C.S.: 541512

**CORE ECONOMY INVEST-
MENT GROUP LIMITED**
Suites 04 05 19/F Harbour Centre 25
Harbour Road, Wanchai, China
(Hong Kong)
Tel.: (852) 28517622
Web Site: http://www.ceig.hk
0339—(HKG)
Rev.: $22,050
Assets: $1,788,323
Liabilities: $812,860
Net Worth: $975,462
Earnings: ($1,504,243)
Emp.: 12
Fiscal Year-end: 12/31/22
Securities
N.A.I.C.S.: 525990
Daming Wang *(Exec Dir)*

**CORE EDUCATION AND
TECHNOLOGIES LTD.**
Lotus Business Park 10th floor Plot
No C-21 Dalia Industrial Estate, Off
Link Road Andheri W, Navi Mumbai,
400 053, India
Tel.: (91) 22 33066 800
Web Site: http://www.core-
edutech.com
Year Founded: 2003
Sales Range: $200-249.9 Million
Emp.: 106
Educational Software Development
Services
N.A.I.C.S.: 541511
Sanjeev Mansotra *(Chm & CEO)*

Subsidiaries:

**CORE Careers & Skill Developments
Limited** (1)
Harborside Financial Ctr Plz 10 Ste 208 3
2nd St, Jersey City, NJ 07311
Tel.: (888) 778-7737
Sales Range: $10-24.9 Million
Emp.: 50
Educational Support Services
N.A.I.C.S.: 611710

**CORE Education & Consulting Solu-
tions (UK) Ltd.** (1)
Brough Business Centre Skillings Lane,
Brough, HU15 1EN, United Kingdom
Tel.: (44) 1482 601100
Web Site: http://www.coreeducation.co.uk
Educational Software Publishing & Consult-
ing Services
N.A.I.C.S.: 611710

Subsidiary (Domestic):

ITN Mark (UK) (2)
1 Fetter Lane, London, EC4A 1BR, United
Kingdom
Tel.: (44) 20 8326 1100
Web Site: http://www.itnmark.com
Teacher Recruitment Services
N.A.I.C.S.: 561311
Tania Jordan *(Mgr-Programme)*

**CORE Education & Consulting Solu-
tions FZ-LLC** (1)
Vision Twr 21st Fl 2102, Dubai, United Arab
Emirates
Tel.: (971) 4 4508801
Web Site: http://www.coreedutech.com
Educational Consulting Services
N.A.I.C.S.: 611710

**CORE Education & Consulting Solu-
tions, Inc.** (1)
3 Ravinia Dr, Atlanta, GA 30346
Tel.: (678) 578-7711
Web Site: http://www.coreecs.com
Sales Range: $10-24.9 Million
Emp.: 60
Educational Consulting Services
N.A.I.C.S.: 611710
Shekhar Iyer *(Pres)*

Core Education and Technologies Ltd.—(Continued)

CORE Projects & Technologies FZC (1)
Dubai Knowledge Village, Dubai, United Arab Emirates
Tel.: (971) 44508801
Web Site: http://www.core-edutech.com
Sales Range: $25-49.9 Million
Emp.: 20
Software Development Services
N.A.I.C.S.: 541511
Atul Tuli (Pres)

CORE Projects and Technologies Ltd. (1)
10th Floor Plot No C-21 Lotus Business Park Dalia Industrial Estate, Off Link Road Andheri, Mumbai, 400 053, Maharashtra, India
Tel.: (91) 2233066800
Sales Range: $25-49.9 Million
Emp.: 70
Information Technology Consulting Services
N.A.I.C.S.: 541512

CORE EQUITY HOLDINGS SA
Avenue Louise 326, 1050, Brussels, Belgium
Tel.: (32) 2893 01 00
Web Site:
   http://www.coreequityholdings.com
Privater Equity Firm
N.A.I.C.S.: 523999
Pierre Heinrich (Partner)

Subsidiaries:

Provalliance, SAS (1)
133 Rue Du Faubourg Saint Honore, Paris, 75008, France (54%)
Tel.: (33) 153355335
Web Site: http://www.provalliance.fr
Hair Salon Operator
N.A.I.C.S.: 812112
Marc Aublet (CEO)

CORE LABORATORIES N.V.
Van Heuven Goedhartlaan 7 B, 1181 LE, Amstelveen, Netherlands
Tel.: (31) 204203191   NI
Web Site: http://www.corelab.com
Year Founded: 1936
CLB—(NYSE)
Rev.: $489,735,000
Assets: $578,354,000
Liabilities: $389,400,000
Net Worth: $188,954,000
Earnings: $19,453,000
Emp.: 3,600
Fiscal Year-end: 12/31/22
Petroleum Reservoir Optimization & Management Services
N.A.I.C.S.: 213112
Mark F. Elvig (Sec, Sr VP & Gen Counsel)

Subsidiaries:

Core Lab de Mexico S.A. de C.V. (1)
Cda Universidad S/N, Villahermosa, 86020, Mexico
Tel.: (52) 9933580451
Oil & Gas Exploration Services
N.A.I.C.S.: 213112

Core Laboratories (U.K.) Limited (1)
Howe Moss Drive Kirkhill Industrial Estate Dyce, Scotland, Aberdeen, AB21 0GL, United Kingdom
Tel.: (44) 1224421000
Web Site: http://www.corel.com
Sales Range: $100-124.9 Million
Emp.: 150
Reservoir Management Services
N.A.I.C.S.: 213112

Core Laboratories Australia PTY LTD (1)
447-449 Belmont Ave, Kewdale, 6105, WA, Australia
Tel.: (61) 893538888
Web Site: http://www.corelab.com

Sales Range: $25-49.9 Million
Emp.: 35
Waste Management Services
N.A.I.C.S.: 924110

Core Laboratories Canada Ltd. (1)
2810 12 Street NE, Calgary, T2E 7P7, AB, Canada
Tel.: (403) 250-4000
Web Site: http://www.corelab.com
Sales Range: $100-124.9 Million
Emp.: 200
Oil & Gas Drilling Services
N.A.I.C.S.: 213111

Core Laboratories International B.V. (1)
Stoomloggerweg 12, 3133 KT, Vlaardingen, Netherlands
Tel.: (31) 104342503
Reservoir Management Services
N.A.I.C.S.: 221310
Arie Kaaden (Gen Mgr)

Core Laboratories LP (1)
6316 Windfern Rd, Houston, TX 77040-4916 (100%)
Tel.: (713) 328-2673
Web Site: http://www.corelab.com
Sales Range: $200-249.9 Million
Emp.: 400
Support Activities for Oil & Gas Operations
N.A.I.C.S.: 213112

Core Laboratories Malaysia SDN BHD (1)
No 17 Jalan Jurutera U1/23 Section U1, HICOM-Glenmarie Industrial Park, 40150, Shah Alam, Selangor Darul Ehsan, Malaysia
Tel.: (60) 350310088
Reservoir Management Services
N.A.I.C.S.: 221310

Owen Oil Tools LP (1)
12001 County Rd 1000, Godley, TX 76044
Tel.: (817) 551-0540
Web Site: http://www.owenoiltools.com
Sales Range: $100-124.9 Million
Emp.: 400
Perforating Equipment Mfr
N.A.I.C.S.: 333132

PT Corelab Indonesia (1)
Cilandak Commercial Estate Building 303 JI Cilandak KKO, Jakarta, 12560, Indonesia
Tel.: (62) 21 7801533
Web Site: http://www.corelab.com
Sales Range: $100-124.9 Million
Emp.: 100
Oil & Gas Exploration Services
N.A.I.C.S.: 213112

Saybolt Belgium N.V. (1)
Zwarte Weg 60 Kaai 371-373, 2030, Antwerp, Belgium
Tel.: (32) 36000150
Oil & Gas Exploration Services
N.A.I.C.S.: 213112

Saybolt Nederland B.V. (1)
Stoomloggerweg 12, 3133 KT, Vlaardingen, Netherlands
Tel.: (31) 104609978
Emp.: 50
Oil & Gas Exploration Services
N.A.I.C.S.: 213112
Andre Hoogland (Mgr-Laboratory)

Saybolt, LP (1)
3113 Red Bluff Rd, Pasadena, TX 77503
Tel.: (713) 477-8171
Sales Range: $1-9.9 Million
Emp.: 10
Oil & Gas Exploration Services
N.A.I.C.S.: 213112

Stim-Lab, Inc. (1)
7406 N Hwy 81, Duncan, OK 73533
Tel.: (580) 252-4309
Web Site: http://www.corelab.com
Oil & Gas Engineering Services
N.A.I.C.S.: 213112

CORE LITHIUM LTD
Level 9 2 Mill Street, Perth, 6000, WA, Australia
Tel.: (61) 883171700
Web Site: https://corelithium.com.au

Year Founded: 2010
CXO—(ASX)
Rev.: $126,531,784
Assets: $216,318,108
Liabilities: $44,795,673
Net Worth: $171,522,435
Earnings: ($138,229,834)
Fiscal Year-end: 06/30/24
Copper & Uranium Exploration Services
N.A.I.C.S.: 212230
Gregory English (Chm)

CORE NICKEL CORP.
Suite 204 75-24th Street East, Saskatoon, S7K 0K3, SK, Canada
Tel.: (306) 668-6927   BC
Web Site: https://www.corenickel.com
Year Founded: 2022
CNCOF—(OTCIQ)
Emp.: 1
Copper Mining Services
N.A.I.C.S.: 212230

CORE ONE LABS INC.
800 1199 West Hastings St, Vancouver, V6E 3T5, BC, Canada
Tel.: (604) 417-6400   BC
Web Site: https://www.core1labs.com
Year Founded: 2010
COOL—(CNSX)
Assets: $7,450,206
Liabilities: $3,231,656
Net Worth: $4,218,550
Earnings: ($42,868,377)
Fiscal Year-end: 12/31/20
Pharmaceuticals Mfr
N.A.I.C.S.: 325412
Robert Hancock (Chm)

CORE SOFTWARE CORPORATION
555 Legget Drive Suite 301, Ottawa, K2K 2X3, ON, Canada
Tel.: (613) 727-5051
Web Site:
   http://www.coremigration.com
Year Founded: 1997
Sales Range: $1-9.9 Million
Computer System Updating & Converting
N.A.I.C.S.: 541519

CORE SPAIN HOLDCO SOCIMI, S.A.U.
Paseo de la Castellana 93 6th floor, 28046, Madrid, Spain
Tel.: (34) 911592402   ES
Web Site:
   https://www.corespainholdco.com
Year Founded: 2022
MLCOE—(EUR)
Rev.: $4,593,222
Assets: $117,196,159
Liabilities: $34,678,221
Net Worth: $82,517,938
Earnings: ($14,190,308)
Fiscal Year-end: 12/31/23
Real Estate Investment Services
N.A.I.C.S.: 531190
Montenegro Klindworth (Co-Chm)

COREAL SA
Str Brestei 4, Dolj, Craiova, Romania
Tel.: (40) 251 413368
Sales Range: Less than $1 Million
Emp.: 40
Restaurant Management Services
N.A.I.C.S.: 722511

COREANA COSMETICS CO., LTD.
6 Samgok 2-gil Seonggeo-eup, Seobuk-gu, Cheonan, 1322-7, Chungcheongnam-do, Korea (South)
Tel.: (82) 317227000

Web Site: https://www.coreana.com
Year Founded: 1988
027050—(KRS)
Rev.: $61,662,152
Assets: $80,940,564
Liabilities: $17,472,537
Net Worth: $63,468,027
Earnings: $1,162,858
Emp.: 173
Fiscal Year-end: 12/31/22
Cosmetic Product Mfr & Distr
N.A.I.C.S.: 325620
Yu Sang Ok (Founder & CEO)

COREM PROPERTY GROUP AB
Riddargatan 13 C, PO Box 56085, 102 17, Stockholm, 102 17, Sweden
Tel.: (46) 104827000
Web Site: https://www.corem.se
Year Founded: 1993
CORE.A—(OMX)
Rev.: $421,307,609
Assets: $6,437,747,048
Liabilities: $4,252,089,735
Net Worth: $2,185,657,313
Earnings: ($794,071,529)
Emp.: 282
Fiscal Year-end: 12/31/23
Real Estate Development Services
N.A.I.C.S.: 531390
Patrik Essehorn (Chm)

COREMAX CORP.
No 11 Wenhua Road Hsinchu Industrial Park, Hsinchu, 303035, Taiwan
Tel.: (886) 35983101
Web Site:
   https://www.coremaxcorp.com
Year Founded: 1992
4739—(TAI)
Rev.: $171,089,009
Assets: $324,413,016
Liabilities: $116,272,437
Net Worth: $208,140,579
Earnings: ($2,433,892)
Emp.: 500
Fiscal Year-end: 12/31/23
Hardware Product Mfr
N.A.I.C.S.: 332510
Chi-Cheng Ho (Chm & Pres)

Subsidiaries:

Coremax (Thailand) Co., Ltd. (1)
64/62 Moo 4, Eastern Seaboard Industrial Estate Tambol Pluakdaeng Amphur Pluakdaeng, Rayong, 21140, Thailand
Tel.: (66) 33012571
Chemical Products Mfr
N.A.I.C.S.: 325998

Coremax (Zhangzhou) Chemical Co., Ltd. (1)
30 Binhai Road Gulei Economic Zone, Zhangzhou, 363216, Fujian, China
Tel.: (86) 5966081866
Chemical Products Mfr
N.A.I.C.S.: 325998

Coremax Ningbo Chemical Co., Ltd. (1)
789 Fengming Road, Zhenhai District, Ningbo, 315204, China
Tel.: (86) 57486502235
Chemical Products Mfr
N.A.I.C.S.: 325998

Coremax Zhuhai Chemical Co., Ltd. (1)
Langwan Road, Nanshui Chemical Industrial Zone Nanshui, Zhuhai, 519050, Guangdong, China
Tel.: (86) 7567269900
Chemical Products Mfr
N.A.I.C.S.: 325998

Hengi Chemical Co., Ltd. (1)
No 440 Jhonghua Rd, Miaoli County, Toufen, 351, Taiwan
Tel.: (886) 37623396
Chemical Products Mfr

N.A.I.C.S.: 325998
Jim C. Ho *(Chm)*

Uranus Chemicals Co., Ltd. (1)
Tel.: (886) 35985750
Chemical Products Mfr
N.A.I.C.S.: 325998

COREMEDIA AG
Ludwig-Erhard-Str 18, Hamburg, 20459, Germany
Tel.: (49) 40 325587 0
Web Site: http://www.coremedia.com
Year Founded: 1996
Sales Range: $10-24.9 Million
Emp.: 150
Web Content Management Software Publisher
N.A.I.C.S.: 513210
Klemens Kleiminger *(CFO)*

Subsidiaries:

CoreMedia Asia Pacific Pte. Ltd. (1)
#03-106 25 International Business Park, Singapore, 609916, Singapore
Tel.: (65) 6562 8866
Web Content Management Software Publisher
N.A.I.C.S.: 513210
Soren Stamer *(CEO)*

CoreMedia Corporation (1)
118 2nd St 5th Fl, San Francisco, CA 94105
Tel.: (415) 371-0400
Web Content Management Software Publisher
N.A.I.C.S.: 513210

CoreMedia UK Ltd. (1)
90 Long Acre Covent Garden, London, WC2E 9RZ, United Kingdom
Tel.: (44) 207 849 3317
Web Content Management Software Publisher
N.A.I.C.S.: 513210
Florian Grebe *(VP-Sls-EMEA)*

CORENTEC CO., LTD.
33-2 Banpo-daero 20-gil, Seocho-gu, Seoul, 6649, Korea (South)
Tel.: (82) 269374993
Web Site: https://www.corentec.com
Year Founded: 2000
104540—(KRS)
Rev.: $49,018,187
Assets: $131,783,568
Liabilities: $74,063,431
Net Worth: $57,720,137
Earnings: $1,365,929
Emp.: 170
Fiscal Year-end: 12/31/22
Medical Device Mfr
N.A.I.C.S.: 339112

COREP LIGHTING GROUP
Radio London Street, 33130, Begles, France
Tel.: (33) 556499600
Web Site: https://corep.com
Year Founded: 1970
MLCOR—(EUR)
Sales Range: $25-49.9 Million
Emp.: 256
Lampshade & Decorative Lamp Mfr
N.A.I.C.S.: 335139
Alain Petit *(CEO)*

Subsidiaries:

COREP IBERICA, Lda (1)
Rua G Lote 33 Zona Industrial Casal Areia, 2460-392, Alcobaca, Portugal
Tel.: (351) 262 545439
Web Site: http://www.corep.pt
Light Equipment Mfr
N.A.I.C.S.: 335139
Filipe Pereira *(Mng Dir)*

Corep France Sarl (1)
2 Rue des Salenques, 31000, Toulouse, France
Tel.: (33) 5 61 22 45 87

Web Site: http://www.corep.fr
Light Equipment Mfr
N.A.I.C.S.: 335139

Corep Lighting India (P) Ltd. (1)
129G/16 NSEZ Phase 2, Noida, 201305, Uttar Pradesh, India
Tel.: (91) 120 246 2584
Web Site: http://www.corepindia.com
Light Equipment Mfr
N.A.I.C.S.: 335139

Forestier SA (1)
4 rue des Fontaines du Temple, 75003, Paris, France
Tel.: (33) 1 40 36 13 10
Web Site: http://www.forestier.fr
Light Equipment Mfr
N.A.I.C.S.: 335139

CORERO NETWORK SECURITY PLC
Salisbury House 29 Finsbury Circus, London, EC2M 5QQ, Buckinghamshire, United Kingdom
Tel.: (44) 1494590404
Web Site: https://www.corero.com
CNS—(LSE)
Rev.: $22,349,000
Assets: $28,436,000
Liabilities: $11,699,000
Net Worth: $16,737,000
Earnings: ($170,000)
Emp.: 81
Fiscal Year-end: 12/31/23
Network Security Software Products Developer
N.A.I.C.S.: 513210
Jens P. Montanana *(Chm)*

Subsidiaries:

Corero Network Security, Inc. (1)
293 Boston Post Rd W Ste 310, Marlborough, MA 01752
Tel.: (978) 212-1500
Web Site: https://www.corero.com
Security Services
N.A.I.C.S.: 561621

CORESA S.A.
San Nicolas N 630, Comuna De San Miguel, Santiago, 8930088, Chile
Tel.: (56) 25108858
Web Site: http://www.coresa.cl
Year Founded: 1966
Sales Range: $25-49.9 Million
Emp.: 700
Container Meshe & Polyethylene Film Mfr
N.A.I.C.S.: 339991
Francisco Javier Vial Herrera *(Pres)*

Subsidiaries:

Coresa Argentina S.A. (1)
General Alvear 21, San Antonio de Areco, Buenos Aires, 2760, Argentina
Tel.: (54) 2326455400
Web Site: http://www.coresa.com.ar
Sales Range: $50-74.9 Million
Emp.: 73
Production & Commercialization of Sacks & Cloths
N.A.I.C.S.: 322220

Coresa Peru S.A. (1)
Av Los Eucaliptus Mz E Lote 8 Y 9 Sta Genoveva, Lurin, Peru
Tel.: (51) 14301880
Packaging Bags Mfr
N.A.I.C.S.: 326111

CORESLAB INTERNATIONAL, INC.
205 Coreslab Drive, Dundas, L9H 0B3, ON, Canada
Tel.: (905) 689-3993
Web Site: http://www.coreslab.com
Year Founded: 1975
Sales Range: $300-349.9 Million
Emp.: 2,700
Precast Concrete Products Mfr

N.A.I.C.S.: 238120
Bob McGee *(VP & Mgr-Sls)*

Subsidiaries:

Coreslab Structures (ALBUQUERQUE) Inc. (1)
2800 2nd St S W, Albuquerque, NM 87103
Tel.: (505) 247-3725
Precast Concrete Products Mfr
N.A.I.C.S.: 327390
Miles Blackman *(Engr-Sls)*

Coreslab Structures (ARIZ) Inc. (1)
PO Box 18150, Phoenix, AZ 85005
Tel.: (602) 237-3875
Precast Concrete Products Distr
N.A.I.C.S.: 423320
Rick Reichenberg *(VP)*

Coreslab Structures (ARK) Inc. (1)
1370 Sturgis Rd, Conway, AR 72034
Tel.: (501) 329-3763
Precast Concrete Products Mfr
N.A.I.C.S.: 327390
Greg Poirier *(Mgr-Sls)*

Coreslab Structures (ATLANTA) Inc. (1)
1655 Noah's Ark Rd, Jonesboro, GA 30236
Tel.: (770) 471-1150
Precast Concrete Products Mfr
N.A.I.C.S.: 327390
Keith Stepp *(Mgr-Sls)*

Coreslab Structures (CONN) Inc. (1)
1023 Waterbury Rd, Thomaston, CT 06787-0279
Tel.: (860) 283-8281
Precast Concrete Products Mfr
N.A.I.C.S.: 327390
Robert Del Vento *(Mgr-Sls)*

Coreslab Structures (KANSAS), Inc. (1)
759 S 65th St, Kansas City, KS 66111
Tel.: (913) 287-5725
Precast Concrete Product Distr
N.A.I.C.S.: 423320
Mark Simpson *(VP & Gen Mgr)*

Coreslab Structures (LA) Inc. (1)
150 W Placentia Ave, Perris, CA 92571
Tel.: (951) 943-9119
Precast Concrete Products Mfr
N.A.I.C.S.: 327390
Jon Clausen *(Mgr-Sls)*

Coreslab Structures (MIAMI) Inc. (1)
10501 NW 121 Way, Medley, FL 33178
Tel.: (305) 823-8950
Precast Concrete Product Distr
N.A.I.C.S.: 423320
Allen Witt *(VP & Mgr-Sls)*

Coreslab Structures (MISSOURI) Inc. (1)
1615 W Arrow St, Marshall, MO 65340
Tel.: (660) 886-3306
Precast Concrete Product Distr
N.A.I.C.S.: 423320
Brian Goebel *(Mgr-Sls)*

Coreslab Structures (ONT) Inc. (1)
205 Coreslab Drive, Dundas, L9H 0B3, ON, Canada
Tel.: (905) 689-3993
Web Site: http://www.coreslab.com
Emp.: 150
Precast Concrete Products Mfr
N.A.I.C.S.: 327390
Anthony E. Franciosa *(VP & Mgr-Sls)*

Coreslab Structures (ORLANDO) Inc. (1)
11041 Rocket Blvd, Orlando, FL 32824
Tel.: (407) 855-3190
Precast Concrete Products Mfr
N.A.I.C.S.: 327390

Coreslab Structures (TAMPA) Inc. (1)
6301 N 56th St, Tampa, FL 33610
Tel.: (813) 626-1141
Precast Concrete Products Mfr
N.A.I.C.S.: 327390
Mark McKeny *(Mgr-Sls)*

Coreslab Structures (TEXAS) Inc. (1)

15916 Anderson Mill Rd, Cedar Park, TX 78630
Tel.: (512) 250-0755
Web Site: http://www.coreslab.com
Precast Concrete Products Mfr
N.A.I.C.S.: 238120
Bob McGee *(VP & Mgr-Sls)*

Coreslab Structures (TULSA) Inc. (1)
3206 N 129th E Ave, Tulsa, OK 74116
Tel.: (918) 438-0230
Precast Concrete Products Mfr
N.A.I.C.S.: 327390
Neil Drews *(VP & Gen Mgr)*

Coreslab Structures, Inc. (1)
7000 S Sunnyland Rd, Oklahoma City, OK 73135-1714
Tel.: (405) 672-2325
Web Site: http://www.coreslab.com
Sales Range: $25-49.9 Million
Emp.: 40
Precast & Prestressed Concrete Products Mfr
N.A.I.C.S.: 327390

Coreslab Structures, Inc. (1)
802 Allied Rd, Bellevue, NE 68123
Tel.: (402) 291-0733
Web Site: http://www.coreslab.com
Sales Range: $50-74.9 Million
Emp.: 200
Precast & Prestressed Concrete Products Mfr & Sales
N.A.I.C.S.: 327390
Todd Ceulp *(Gen Mgr)*

Coreslab Structures, Inc. (1)
1030 S Kitley Ave, Indianapolis, IN 46203-2623
Tel.: (317) 353-2118
Web Site: http://www.coreslab.com
Sales Range: $25-49.9 Million
Emp.: 140
Precast Concrete Mfr
N.A.I.C.S.: 327390
Matt Ballain *(Gen Mgr)*

CORESTATE CAPITAL HOLDING SA
4 rue Jean Monnet, 2180, Luxembourg, Luxembourg
Tel.: (352) 26637220   LU
Web Site: https://www.corestate-capital.com
Year Founded: 2006
CCAP—(DEU)
Rev.: $222,102,310
Assets: $1,525,577,380
Liabilities: $849,773,365
Net Worth: $675,804,015
Earnings: ($215,950,788)
Emp.: 811
Fiscal Year-end: 12/31/21
Real Estate Manangement Services
N.A.I.C.S.: 531210
Thomas Landschreiber *(Co-Chief Investment Officer & Member-Mgmt Bd)*

Subsidiaries:

ATOS Property Management GmbH (1)
Syrlinstrasse 38, 89073, Ulm, Germany
Tel.: (49) 7311592850
Web Site: http://www.atos-pm.com
Property Management Services
N.A.I.C.S.: 531311

CRM Students Ltd. (1)
Hanborough House 5 Wallbrook Court North Hinksey Lane, Botley, Oxford, OX2 0QS, United Kingdom
Tel.: (44) 1865207200
Web Site: https://www.crm-students.com
Investment Advisory Services
N.A.I.C.S.: 523940
Stewart Moore *(CEO)*

Capera Immobilien Service GmbH (1)
Dornhofstrasse 100, 63263, Neu-Isenburg, Germany
Tel.: (49) 610281544100
Web Site: http://www.capera-immobilien.de
Real Estate Manangement Services

CORESTATE Capital Holding SA—(Continued)

N.A.I.C.S.: 531390

Corestate Bank GmbH (1)
Neue Mainzer Strasse 66-68, 60311, Frankfurt am Main, Germany
Tel.: (49) 6999999640
Web Site: https://corestate-bank.com
Real Estate Investment Services
N.A.I.C.S.: 531390

Corestate Capital Advisors GmbH (1)
Friedrich-Ebert-Anlage 35-37 Tower 185, 60327, Frankfurt am Main, Germany
Tel.: (49) 6935356300
Real Estate Manangement Services
N.A.I.C.S.: 531210
Guido Beddig (Mng Dir)

Corestate Capital Partners GmbH (1)
Bahnhofstrasse 17, 8001, Zurich, Switzerland
Tel.: (41) 445678860
Real Estate Manangement Services
N.A.I.C.S.: 531210

Corestate Capital Partners UK Limited (1)
16 Berkeley Street, London, W1J 8DZ, United Kingdom
Tel.: (44) 2071837610
Real Estate Manangement Services
N.A.I.C.S.: 531210
Philipp Rohweder (Dir-Investments)

Genost Consulting GmbH (1)
Petersstrasse 15, 04109, Leipzig, Germany
Tel.: (49) 3413085600
Web Site: http://www.genost.de
Investment Advisory Services
N.A.I.C.S.: 523940

HFS Helvetic Financial Services AG (1)
Sihleggstrasse 23, 8832, Wollerau, Switzerland
Tel.: (41) 438882525
Web Site: http://www.hfs-ag.ch
Investment Advisory Services
N.A.I.C.S.: 523940
Norbert Ketterer (Founder & Chm)

Hannover Leasing Investment GmbH (1)
Wolfratshauser Strasse 49, 82049, Pullach, Germany
Tel.: (49) 89211040
Web Site: https://www.hannover-leasing.de
Investment Advisory Services
N.A.I.C.S.: 523940
Sebastian Hartrott (Mng Dir)

Upartments Real Estate GmbH (1)
Nordstrasse 17-21, 04105, Leipzig, Germany
Tel.: (49) 34198998400
Web Site: https://www.upartments-real-estate.com
Real Estate Manangement Services
N.A.I.C.S.: 531210
David A. Campbell (Mng Dir)

CORESTEM INC.
24 Pangyo-ro 255beon-gil Bundang-gu, Gyeonggi-do, Seongnam, Korea (South)
Tel.: (82) 24973711
Web Site: http://www.corestem.com
166480—(KRS)
Rev.: $35,506,842
Assets: $60,296,973
Liabilities: $28,496,328
Net Worth: $31,800,646
Earnings: ($2,038,090)
Emp.: 376
Fiscal Year-end: 12/31/22
Biopharmaceutical Mfr
N.A.I.C.S.: 325412

Subsidiaries:

ChemOn Inc. (1)
240 Nampyeongro Yangi, Cheoin-gu, Yongin, 17162, Gyeonggi-do, Korea (South) (53%)

Tel.: (82) 313299900
Web Site: http://www.chemon.co.kr
Nonclinical Testing Services
N.A.I.C.S.: 541380
Si Hwan Song (CEO)

CORETRONIC CORPORATION
No 2 Kebei 5th Rd Zhunan Science Park, Miaoli, Chunan, 350401, Taiwan
Tel.: (886) 37777000
Web Site: https://www.coretronic.com
5371—(TPE)
Rev.: $1,291,464,944
Assets: $1,818,368,877
Liabilities: $979,642,888
Net Worth: $838,725,989
Earnings: $39,308,969
Emp.: 10,030
Fiscal Year-end: 12/31/23
Projection & Display Solutions
N.A.I.C.S.: 334118

Subsidiaries:

Boom Power Electronics (Su Zhou) Co. Ltd. (1)
No 158-76 Huashan Road, Suzhou, Jiangsu, China
Tel.: (86) 512 6661 8156
Fluorescent Lamp Driver Mfr & Distr
N.A.I.C.S.: 335139

CORE-FLEX OPTICAL (SUZHOU) CO., LTD. (1)
No 69 Qunxing 3rd Road Suzhou Industrial Park, Suzhou, Jiangsu, China
Tel.: (86) 512 6288 8838
Prism Sheet Mfr
N.A.I.C.S.: 333310

Coretronic (Guangzhou) Co., Ltd. (1)
No 2 1st Road Guangzhou Economic & Technological Development Zone, East Dist, Guangzhou, China
Tel.: (86) 20 3212 7000
Backlight Module Mfr & Distr
N.A.I.C.S.: 335139

Coretronic (Nanjing) Co., Ltd. (1)
No 18 Yinlong Road Jiangning Development Zone, Nanjing, Jiangsu, China
Tel.: (86) 25 5211 5858
Backlight Module Mfr & Distr
N.A.I.C.S.: 335139

Coretronic (Ningbo) Co., Ltd. (1)
No 5 Guanshan Road Ningbo Export Processing Zone, Ningbo, China
Tel.: (86) 574 8682 5600
Backlight Module Mfr & Distr
N.A.I.C.S.: 335139

Coretronic MEMS Corporation (1)
No 2 Kebei 5th Road Zhunan Science Park, Zhunan Town, Miao-li, 350, Taiwan
Tel.: (886) 37777000
Web Site: https://www.coretronicmems.com
Accelerometer Mfr & Distr
N.A.I.C.S.: 334519

Coretronic Projection (Kunshan) Co., Ltd (1)
No 20 3rd Ave Kunshan Free Trade Zone, Kunshan, Jiangsu, China
Tel.: (86) 51257360000
Projector Mfr & Distr
N.A.I.C.S.: 334419

Coretronic System Engineering Corporation (1)
12F No 219 Sec 3 Beixin Road, Xindian District, New Taipei City, 23143, Taiwan (100%)
Tel.: (886) 2 2910 2955
Integrated Imaging Systems Developer
N.A.I.C.S.: 334118

Liuli Gong Fang (U.S.A.), Inc. (1)
398 Lemon Creek Dr Ste F, Walnut, CA 91789
Tel.: (909) 861-0288
Glass & Ceramic Mfr & Distr
N.A.I.C.S.: 327212

Liuli Optoma Technology Corp. (1)
12F No 215 Sec 3 Beixin Road, Xindian District, New Taipei City, 23143, Taiwan
Tel.: (886) 2 8219 1658
Projector Distr
N.A.I.C.S.: 423410

Liuligongfang Hong Kong Co., LTD. (1)
Room 2201 22 Flr Saxon twr No7 Cheungshun St, Central, Hong Kong, China (Hong Kong)
Tel.: (852) 2508 0505
Web Site: http://www.iuli.com
Glass & Ceramic Mfr & Distr
N.A.I.C.S.: 327212
Chang Yi (CEO)

Liuligongfang Shanghai Co., LTD (1)
No 488 Huazhong Road, Qibao Minhang, Shanghai, China
Tel.: (86) 21 6479 0238
Glass & Ceramic Mfr & Distr
N.A.I.C.S.: 327212
Mutzu Huang (Brand Mgr)

Nano Precision (Suzhou) Co., Ltd. (1)
No 69 Qunxing 3rd Road, Suzhou Industrial Park, Jiangsu, China
Tel.: (86) 51262888838
Electronic Component & Lighting Device Mfr & Whslr
N.A.I.C.S.: 335139

Optoma (China & H.K.) Limited (1)
Unit A 4/F Reality Tower 4 Sun On Street, Cheung Sha Wan, Chai Wan, China (Hong Kong)
Tel.: (852) 55287720
Web Site: http://www.optoma.com.hk
Projector Mfr & Distr
N.A.I.C.S.: 334419

Optoma Benelux B.V. (1)
Europalaan 770 D, 1363 BM, Almere, Netherlands
Tel.: (31) 368200250
Pheripheral Equipment Distr & Maintenance Services
N.A.I.C.S.: 423430

Optoma Canada (1)
2420 Meadowpine Blvd Suite 105, Mississauga, L5N 6S2, ON, Canada
Tel.: (905) 285-0685
Projector Repair & Maintenance Services
N.A.I.C.S.: 811210

Optoma Deutschland GmbH (1)
Wiesenstrasse 21, 40549, Dusseldorf, Germany
Tel.: (49) 211 506 6670
Web Site: http://www.optoma.de
Projector Mfr & Distr
N.A.I.C.S.: 334419

Optoma Espana, S.L. (1)
C/ Jose Hierro 36 Of 1C, Rivas-Vaciamadrid, 28529, Madrid, Spain
Tel.: (34) 914990606
Web Site: https://www.optoma.es
Pheripheral Equipment Distr & Maintenance Services
N.A.I.C.S.: 423430

Optoma Europe Limited (1)
1 Bourne End Mills, Hemel Hempstead, HP1 2UJ, Hertfordshire, United Kingdom
Tel.: (44) 192 369 1800
Web Site: https://www.optomaeurope.com
Emp.: 100
Projector Mfr
N.A.I.C.S.: 334419
Eithne Keenan (Mgr-Comm-EMEA)

Optoma France, S.A.S. (1)
Batiment E 81-83 avenue Edouard Vaillant, Boulogne Billancourt, 92100, Boulogne, France
Tel.: (33) 141461220
Web Site: https://www.optoma.fr
Pheripheral Equipment Distr & Maintenance Services
N.A.I.C.S.: 423430

Optoma Scandinavia. A.S. (1)
Kniveveien 29, PO Box 9515, Askollen, 3036, Drammen, Norway
Tel.: (47) 32988990
Web Site: http://www.optoma.no
Projector Mfr & Distr
N.A.I.C.S.: 334419

Optoma Technology, Inc. (1)
47697 Westinghouse Dr, Fremont, CA 94539
Tel.: (510) 897-8600
Web Site: https://www.optomausa.com
Digital Product Mfr & Distr
N.A.I.C.S.: 334118

Optoma USA (1)
47697 Westinghouse Dr, Fremont, CA 94539
Tel.: (510) 897-8600
Web Site: https://www.optomausa.com
Projector Mfr & Distr
N.A.I.C.S.: 334419

Vimax (Kunshan) Co., Ltd. (1)
No 388 Sanjia Road, Zhangpu Town, Kunshan, Jiangsu, China
Tel.: (86) 51257455757
Digital Projector Mfr & Distr
N.A.I.C.S.: 334419

YOUNG Lighting Technology Inc. (1)
No 11 Li Hsing Road Science Park, Hsinchu, 30078, Taiwan (100%)
Tel.: (886) 3 577 2000
Web Site: http://www.younglighting.com
Emp.: 800
Backlight Modules for TVs, Monitors, Tablet PCs & Mobile Phone Screens
N.A.I.C.S.: 334118
Sarah Lin (Pres)

Subsidiary (Domestic):

Coretronic Display Solution Corporation (2)
3F No 2 Ke Bei 5th Road Science Park, Chunan, 350, Miao-Li, Taiwan
Tel.: (886) 37 777 000
Medical Monitors & Clinical Ultrasonic Micro-Imaging Systems
N.A.I.C.S.: 339112

Nano Precision Corporation (2)
No 5 Wen Hua Road Fengshan Vil, Hukou, Hsin-chu, Taiwan (100%)
Tel.: (886) 3 5986 200
Light Guide Plate Mfr
N.A.I.C.S.: 334118

Young Green Energy Co., Ltd. (1)
No 2 Ke Bei 5th Road Science Park, Chunan, 35053, Miai-Li, Taiwan (100%)
Tel.: (886) 37 777000
Energy Saving Technologies Research & Development Services
N.A.I.C.S.: 541715

Young Lighting (Suzhou) Corporation (1)
168 Hongye Road, Suzhou Industrial Park, Suzhou, China
Tel.: (86) 512 6251 5720
Backlight Module Mfr & Distr
N.A.I.C.S.: 335139

YoungOptics Inc. (1)
No 7 Hsin-Ann Rd Hsinchu Science Park, Hsinchu, Taiwan
Tel.: (886) 3 620 6789
Web Site: http://www.youngoptics.com
Optical Lense Mfr & Distr
N.A.I.C.S.: 333310

CORIMON, C.A.
Calle Hans Neumann Edif Corimon Ph, Los Cortijos, Caracas, Venezuela
Tel.: (58) 2124005530
Web Site: http://www.corimon.com
Year Founded: 1949
Emp.: 1,361
Paint Coating & Resin Flexible Packaging Services
N.A.I.C.S.: 325510
Carlos Gill Ramirez (Chm)

Subsidiaries:

Alice Neumaticos de Venezuela, C.A. (1)
Carrera Nacional Valencia-Los Guayos Apdo 194, Valencia, Venezuela
Tel.: (58) 2418747812
Web Site: http://alice.com.ve
Tire Mfr & Sales
N.A.I.C.S.: 326211

Adriana Villalba *(Coord-Dev)*

Corimon Pinturas, C.A. (1)
Urbanizacion Industrial El Bosque, Av Hans
Neumann, Valencia, Edo Carabobo, Ven-
ezuela
Tel.: (58) 2416131777
Web Site: http://www.corimonpinturas.com
Paint & Coatings Mfr
N.A.I.C.S.: 325510

Resimon, C.A. (1)
Carretera Flor Amarillo Km 4, Zona Indus-
trial 1, Valencia, Estado Carabobo, Venezu-
ela
Tel.: (58) 2416131432
Web Site: http://www.resimon.com
Synthetic Resin & Other Chemical Products
Mfr
N.A.I.C.S.: 325211

**CORINEX COMMUNICATIONS
CORP.**
1090 W Georgia St 900, Vancouver,
V6E 3V7, BC, Canada
Tel.: (604) 692-0520
Web Site: https://www.corinex.com
Year Founded: 1999
Sales Range: $25-49.9 Million
IP Communications System Mfr
N.A.I.C.S.: 334290
Sam Shi *(CTO)*

Subsidiaries:

Corinex Communications, a.s. (1)
Nove Zahrady I 13/A, 821 05, Bratislava,
Slovakia
Tel.: (421) 2 59 212 000
Web Site: http://www.corinex.com
Emp.: 15
Communication System Distr
N.A.I.C.S.: 423690

**CORINTHIA HOTELS INTER-
NATIONAL**
22 Europa Centre, Floriana, SRN
1400, Malta
Tel.: (356) 21233141
Web Site: http://www.corinthia.com
Year Founded: 1960
Sales Range: $650-699.9 Million
Emp.: 5,000
Hotel
N.A.I.C.S.: 721110
Alfred Pisani *(Founder & Chm)*

**CORINTHIA PALACE HOTEL
COMPANY LIMITED**
22 Europa Centre Floriana, 1400,
Floriana, Malta
Tel.: (356) 21233141
Web Site:
http://www.corinthiagroup.com
Year Founded: 1966
Hotel Operator
N.A.I.C.S.: 721110
Alfred Pisani *(Founder & Chm)*

Subsidiaries:

**International Hotel Investments
p.l.c.** (1)
22 Europa Centre, Floriana, FRN 1400,
Malta
Tel.: (356) 21233141
Web Site: https://www.ihiplc.com
Rev.: $158,769,672
Assets: $2,082,148,067
Liabilities: $1,052,617,647
Net Worth: $1,029,530,420
Earnings: ($37,250,063)
Emp.: 1,491
Fiscal Year-end: 12/31/2021
Hotel & Real Estate Developer & Operator
N.A.I.C.S.: 721110
Alfred Pisani *(Chm)*

CORLINE BIOMEDICAL AB
Lefflersgatan 5, 754 50, Uppsala,
Sweden
Tel.: (46) 18713090
Web Site: https://www.corline.se

CLBIO—(OMX)
Rev.: $2,205,738
Assets: $9,532,908
Liabilities: $673,429
Net Worth: $8,859,479
Earnings: $218,232
Emp.: 14
Fiscal Year-end: 12/31/22
Biotechnology Products Mfr
N.A.I.C.S.: 325414
Jessica Magnusson *(Mgr-Regulatory
& Quality Assurance)*

**CORMER GROUP INDUS-
TRIES, INC.**
1445 Church Avenue, Winnipeg, R2X
2X9, MB, Canada
Tel.: (204) 987-6400
Web Site:
http://www.cormeraerospace.com
Year Founded: 1988
Rev.: $12,600,000
Emp.: 125
Aircraft Part Mfr
N.A.I.C.S.: 336413
Andrew D. Corner *(CEO & Chm-Fin
& Admin)*

CORNEC SAS
18 rue Jacquard, 77400, Lagny,
Seine Et Marne, France
Tel.: (33) 164022910
Web Site: http://www.cornec.fr
Rev.: $27,100,000
Emp.: 14
Recyclable Material Whslr
N.A.I.C.S.: 423930
Patrick Cornec *(Pres)*

**CORNERSTONE FINANCIAL
HOLDINGS LIMITED**
Room 2703 27th Floor China Re-
sources Building 26 Harbour Road,
Wanchai, China (Hong Kong)
Tel.: (852) 39298800 Ky
Web Site: http://www.cs8112.com
Year Founded: 2004
8112—(HKG)
Rev.: $7,084,967
Assets: $35,834,802
Liabilities: $10,367,884
Net Worth: $25,466,918
Earnings: ($4,156,267)
Emp.: 50
Fiscal Year-end: 12/31/22
Media Investment Holding Company
N.A.I.C.S.: 551112
Patrick Jonathan Hong Gay Wong
(CEO)

Subsidiaries:

Babysteps Limited (1)
25/F 2501-2502 Universal Trade Centre
3-5A Arbuthnot Road, Central, China (Hong
Kong)
Tel.: (852) 28877585
Educational Support Services
N.A.I.C.S.: 624410
Michelle Jones *(Supvr-Academic & Admin)*

**CNP Cosmetics Singapore Pte.,
Limited** (1)
7030 Ang Mo Kio Avenue 5 06-39 Northstar
Amk, Singapore, 569880, Singapore
Tel.: (65) 62882277
Web Site: http://www.cnpcosmetics.com.sg
Cosmetic Product Mfr & Distr
N.A.I.C.S.: 325620
P. J. Wong *(Chm & CEO)*

Cornerstone Securities Limited (1)
Room 802 8/F Lee Garden Five 18 Hysan
Avenue, Causeway Bay, China (Hong
Kong)
Tel.: (852) 21612988
Web Site: https://www.cslsec.com
Security Brokerage Services
N.A.I.C.S.: 523150

**CORNERSTONE MANAGE-
MENT, INC.**
No 6 Zhujiang East Road Zhujiang
New Town Tianhe, 49F Guangzhou
CTF Finance Centre, Guangzhou,
510032, Guangdong, China
Tel.: (86) 20 3891 7643 VG
Web Site: http://www.cscapital.cc
Year Founded: 2015
Sales Range: $1-9.9 Million
Emp.: 31
Investment Management Service
N.A.I.C.S.: 523940
Xu He *(Founder & CEO)*

**CORNERSTONE NETWORKS
CO., LTD.**
A1902 45-14 Sagimakgol-Ro,
JungWon-Gu, Seongnam, 462-806,
Gyeonggido, Korea (South)
Tel.: (82) 317307525
Web Site: http://www.ed.co.kr
Year Founded: 1986
033110—(KRS)
Rev.: $4,834,109
Assets: $36,250,483
Liabilities: $35,161,847
Net Worth: $1,088,637
Earnings: ($33,956,545)
Emp.: 29
Fiscal Year-end: 12/31/20
Electric Equipment Mfr
N.A.I.C.S.: 334419

**CORNERSTONE TECHNOLO-
GIES HOLDINGS LIMITED**
2402 China Merchants Tower Shun
Tak Centre, 168-200 Connaught
Road Central, Hong Kong, China
(Hong Kong)
Tel.: (852) 22832222 Ky
Web Site: http://www.elegance.hk
Year Founded: 1980
8391—(HKG)
Rev.: $10,218,105
Assets: $21,685,073
Liabilities: $15,196,470
Net Worth: $6,488,603
Earnings: ($20,551,343)
Emp.: 181
Fiscal Year-end: 12/31/22
Digital Printing Services
N.A.I.C.S.: 561439
Zihao Liang *(CEO & Compliance
Officer)*

**CORNERSTONECAPITAL VER-
WALTUNGS AG**
Geschaftsstelle Frankfurt Westend-
straSSe 41, 60325, Frankfurt, Ger-
many
Tel.: (49) 697890470
Web Site: http://www.cornerstone-
capital.de
Holding Company
N.A.I.C.S.: 551112
Pieter van Halem *(Mng Partner)*

Subsidiaries:

ELTEC Elektronik AG (1)
Galileo Galilei Strasse 11, Mainz, 55129,
Germany
Tel.: (49) 61319180
Web Site: http://www.eltec.de
Rev.: $13,535,019
Emp.: 40
Electric Device Mfr
N.A.I.C.S.: 334419
Marco Gerhard *(CEO & Mng Dir)*

CORNISH METALS INC.
Suite 960 - 789 West Pender Street,
Vancouver, V6C 1H2, BC, Canada
Tel.: (604) 200-6664
Web Site:
https://www.cornishmetals.com

CUSN—(AIM)
Rev.: $1,280,553
Assets: $78,698,748
Liabilities: $10,668,849
Net Worth: $68,029,899
Earnings: ($2,049,502)
Fiscal Year-end: 12/31/23
Mineral Exploration Services
N.A.I.C.S.: 213114
Richard D. Williams *(Pres & CEO)*

Subsidiaries:

South Crofty Limited (1)
Dudnance Lane Pool, Redruth, TR15 3QT,
United Kingdom
Tel.: (44) 1209715777
Copper Mining Services
N.A.I.C.S.: 212230

CORNU S.A.
Le Moulin En Praz 2, 1424, Cham-
pagne, Switzerland
Tel.: (41) 244361542
Web Site: http://www.cornu.ch
Sales Range: $25-49.9 Million
Emp.: 150
Cookie & Cracker Mfr
N.A.I.C.S.: 311821
Marc-Andre Cornu *(Founder)*

Subsidiaries:

Cornu Sas Fontain (1)
Route de Pugey, 25660, Fontaine, France
Tel.: (33) 381572983
Web Site: http://www.cornu.ch
Rev.: $20,100,000
Emp.: 29
Cookies & Crackers
N.A.I.C.S.: 311821
Daniel Lehmann *(Mgr-Personnel & Admin)*

Roland Murten AG (1)
Freiburgstrasse 49, Murten, 3280, Switzer-
land
Tel.: (41) 266728222
Web Site: http://www.rolandch.ch
Sales Range: $25-49.9 Million
Emp.: 100
Mfr of Cookies, Crackers & Pretzels
N.A.I.C.S.: 311821
Benno Piller *(Mgr-Production)*

CORNWALL GRAVEL CO. LTD.
390 11th Street West, PO Box 67,
Cornwall, K6J 3B2, ON, Canada
Tel.: (613) 932-6571
Web Site:
http://www.cornwallgravel.ca
Year Founded: 1949
Sales Range: $10-24.9 Million
Engineering & Construction Services
N.A.I.C.S.: 236220

CORO ENERGY PLC
1 Park Row, Leeds, LS1 5AB, United
Kingdom
Tel.: (44) 2039657917 UK
Web Site:
https://www.coroenergyplc.com
Year Founded: 2016
CORO—(LSE)
Rev.: $235,000
Assets: $24,871,000
Liabilities: $31,987,000
Net Worth: ($7,116,000)
Earnings: ($5,047,000)
Emp.: 3
Fiscal Year-end: 12/31/23
Oil & Gas Exploration Services
N.A.I.C.S.: 213111

**COROMANDEL AGRO PROD-
UCTS & OILS LTD.**
12-B Skylark Apartments, Basheerb-
agh, Hyderabad, 500 029, India
Tel.: (91) 9849986021
Web Site: https://www.capol.in
Year Founded: 1976

Coromandel Agro Products & Oils Ltd.—(Continued)

507543—(BOM)
Rev.: $16,167,458
Assets: $3,698,076
Liabilities: $1,166,017
Net Worth: $2,532,060
Earnings: $974,213
Emp.: 157
Fiscal Year-end: 03/31/21
Oilseed Processing Services
N.A.I.C.S.: 311224
Kothuri Satyanarayana (CFO)

COROMANDEL ENGINEERING COMPANY LIMITED

BASCON FUTURA SV Ground Floor
No 10/2 Venkatnarayana Road, P B
No 1698, T Nagar, Chennai, 600 017,
India
Tel.: (91) 4425341513
Web Site:
https://www.coromandelengg.com
Year Founded: 1947
533167—(BOM)
Rev.: $14,823,218
Assets: $12,011,399
Liabilities: $13,084,358
Net Worth: ($1,072,958)
Earnings: ($1,089,830)
Emp.: 133
Fiscal Year-end: 03/31/21
Construction & Property Development
Company
N.A.I.C.S.: 541330
M. M. Venkatachalam (Chm)

CORONA CORPORATION

7-7 Higashi-shinbo, Sanjo, 955-8510,
Niigata, Japan
Tel.: (81) 256322111
Web Site: https://www.corona.co.jp
Year Founded: 1937
5909—(TKS)
Rev.: $542,324,060
Assets: $682,773,340
Liabilities: $185,807,100
Net Worth: $496,966,240
Earnings: $8,632,660
Emp.: 2,138
Fiscal Year-end: 03/31/24
Heating Equipment Mfr & Whslr
N.A.I.C.S.: 333414
Tsutomu Uchida (Chm)

CORONADO GLOBAL RESOURCES INC.

Level 33 Central Plaza One 345
Queen St, GPO Box 51, Brisbane,
4000, QLD, Australia
Tel.: (61) 730317777   DE
Web Site: https://coronadoglobal.com
Year Founded: 2011
CRN—(ASX)
Rev.: $2,890,603,000
Assets: $2,678,038,000
Liabilities: $1,432,003,000
Net Worth: $1,246,035,000
Earnings: $156,065,000
Emp.: 1,878
Fiscal Year-end: 12/31/23
Coal Distr
N.A.I.C.S.: 423520
William Koeck (Chm)

CORONATION FUND MANAGERS LIMITED

7th Floor MontClare Place Cnr
Campground & Main Road, PO Box
44684, Claremont, Cape Town, 7708,
South Africa
Tel.: (27) 216802000
Web Site: http://www.coronation.com
Sales Range: $75-99.9 Million
Emp.: 250
Asset Management Services
N.A.I.C.S.: 523999

Anton Pillay (CEO)
Subsidiaries:

Coronation Global Fund Managers
(Ireland) Ltd   (1)
11 Central Hotel Chambers Dame Court,
Dublin, Ireland
Tel.: (353) 16745410
Investment Fund Management Services
N.A.I.C.S.: 523940

COROPLAST FRITZ MULLER GMBH UND CO. KG

Wittener Strasse 271, 42279, Wuppertal, Germany
Tel.: (49) 20226810
Web Site: http://www.coroplast.de
Year Founded: 1928
Rev.: $195,576,089
Emp.: 554
Adhesive Tape Mfr
N.A.I.C.S.: 325520
Natalie Mekelburger (Chm-Mgmt Bd)

Subsidiaries:

Coroplast Harness Technology (Kunshan) Co., Ltd.   (1)
Yuyang Rd 299 Building C & D Plainvim
Industrial Park, Yushan Town, 215300, Kunshan, Jiangsu, China
Tel.: (86) 51236650600
Harness & Automotive Cable Distr
N.A.I.C.S.: 336320
Thomas Mayer (Gen Mgr)

Coroplast Harness Technology (Mianyang) Co., Ltd.   (1)
Chuangxin Rd 18 Building 8 Longsheng
Industrial park, Gaoxin District, 621000, Mianyang, Sichuan, China
Tel.: (86) 8162589596
Harness & Automotive Cable Distr
N.A.I.C.S.: 336320
Thomas Mayer (Gen Mgr)

Coroplast Harness Technology (Taicang) Co., Ltd.   (1)
ChangSheng Road 102, Taicang, 215400,
Jiangsu, China
Tel.: (86) 51253207794
Web Site: http://www.coroplast.cn
Harness & Automotive Cable Distr
N.A.I.C.S.: 336320
Thomas Mayer (Gen Mgr)

Coroplast Spolka z o.o.   (1)
Ul Ozimska 54, 46-043, Dylaki, Poland
Tel.: (48) 774012600
Adhesive Tape Distr
N.A.I.C.S.: 424120
Georg Dittrich (Mng Dir)

Coroplast Tape Corporation   (1)
1230 Galleria Blvd, Rock Hill, SC 29730
Tel.: (803) 207-8334
Adhesive Tape Distr
N.A.I.C.S.: 424120
Robert Alexander (Exec VP)

Coroplast Tunisie Sarl   (1)
Zone Industrielle GP5, BP 73, 7117, El Kef,
Tunisia
Tel.: (216) 78228643
Adhesive Tape Distr
N.A.I.C.S.: 424120
Aymen Zouari (Plant Mgr)

CORPACQ HOLDINGS LIMITED

CorpAcq House, 1 Goose Green, Altrincham, WA14 1DW, United Kingdom
Tel.: (44) 1618044570
Web Site: https://www.corpacq.com
Emp.: 100
Investment Holding Company
N.A.I.C.S.: 551112
Subsidiaries:

CorpAcq Ltd.   (1)
Suite 1 3 20 Market Street, Altrincham,
WA14 1PF, Cheshire, United Kingdom
Tel.: (44) 1619273113

Web Site: http://www.corpacq.com
Emp.: 100
Privater Equity Firm
N.A.I.C.S.: 523999
David Martin (CEO)

Subsidiary (Domestic):

Carrylift Group   (2)
3 Peel Road West Pimbo Industrial Estate,
Skelmersdale, WN8 9PT, Lancashire,
United Kingdom
Tel.: (44) 1695455000
Web Site: http://www.carryliftgroup.com
Material Handling Machinery Distr
N.A.I.C.S.: 423830
Alison Walker (Fin Mgr)

Filtermech Plant Sales Limited   (2)
Unit 6 2 Seckar Wood Industrial Park Barnsley Road, Newmillerdam, Wakefield, WF2
6QW, United Kingdom
Tel.: (44) 1924252252
Web Site: http://www.filtermech.com
Material Handling Machinery Distr
N.A.I.C.S.: 423830

Glasscraft Decorative Limited   (2)
Unit 1 Navigation Park Lockside Rd, Leeds,
LS10 1EP, United Kingdom
Tel.: (44) 1132711400
Web Site: http://www.glasscraft.uk.com
Glass Products Mfr
N.A.I.C.S.: 327215

Hessle Fork Trucks Ltd   (2)
Carrwood Road, Castleford, WF10 4PT,
West Yorkshire, United Kingdom
Tel.: (44) 8707777091
Web Site: http://www.hessle.co.uk
Material Handling Machinery Distr
N.A.I.C.S.: 423830
Tom Baxter (Head-Hire & Logistics)

Metcalfe Plant Hire Limited   (2)
Gilwilly Road Gilwilly Industrial Estate, Penrith, CA11 9BL, Cumbria, United Kingdom
Tel.: (44) 1768868686
Web Site: http://www.metcalfe-plant-hire.co.uk
Construction Engineering Services
N.A.I.C.S.: 541330
Matt Healey (Mgr-Contracting Contracts)

United Forktrucks Ltd   (2)
St Helens House St Helens Way, Thetford,
IP24 1HG, Norfolk, United Kingdom
Tel.: (44) 1842754841
Web Site: http://www.unitedforktrucks.co.uk
Material Handling Machinery Distr
N.A.I.C.S.: 423830
Keith Colborn (Engr-Field Svc)

CORPFIN CAPITAL PRIME RETAIL II SOCIMI SA

Serrano 57 5th Floor, 28006, Madrid,
Spain
Tel.: (34) 917812800
Web Site:
https://www.corpfincapitalprime.com
Year Founded: 2013
PR2—(MAD)
Sales Range: Less than $1 Million
Real Estate Investment Services
N.A.I.C.S.: 531190
Javier Basagoiti Miranda (Chm &
Mng Partner)

CORPFIN CAPITAL PRIME RETAIL III SOCIMI SA

C/ Serrano 57 4 Planta, 28006, Madrid, Spain
Tel.: (34) 910770490
Web Site:
https://www.corpfincapitalprime.com
Year Founded: 2014
PR3—(MAD)
Sales Range: Less than $1 Million
Real Estate Investment Services
N.A.I.C.S.: 531190
Jorge Betegon Alonso (Dir-
Investments)

CORPFIN CAPITAL SA

Serrano 57 5th Planta, 28006, Madrid, Spain
Tel.: (34) 917812800
Web Site:
http://www.corpfincapital.com
Year Founded: 1990
Rev.: $549,380,000
Emp.: 17
Private Equity Fund Services
N.A.I.C.S.: 523999
Javier Maria Esteban (Dir-Funds Admin)

Subsidiaries:

GRUPO BRAVO   (1)
Poligono Industrial Barrio Marron s/n, Ampuero, 39840, Cantabria, Spain
Tel.: (34) 942628460
Web Site: http://www.bravo-e.com
Automotive Spare Parts Distr
N.A.I.C.S.: 423120

INGESPORT   (1)
Campus Empresarial Arbea avenida de Fuencarral 50 edificio 4, planta baja local Alcobendas, 28108, Madrid, Spain
Tel.: (34) 913985990
Web Site: http://www.ingesport.es
Sports Club Facility Operation Services
N.A.I.C.S.: 713940

Logiters Portugal, S.A.   (1)
EN 3 - kM 7 8 Estrada dos Armenios 2/4,
2050-544, Azambuja, Portugal
Tel.: (351) 263857900
Web Site: http://www.logiters.com
Logistics Consulting Servies
N.A.I.C.S.: 541614

Mecanor-Rumania S.R.L.   (1)
Strada Uzinelor N 4, Oradea, 410605, Bihor, Romania
Tel.: (40) 359404600
Automotive Spare Parts Distr
N.A.I.C.S.: 423120

SINAER   (1)
Avda De la Hispanidad s/n Zona Industrial
Aeroportuaria, Aeropuerto de Madrid-Barajas, 28042, Madrid, Spain
Tel.: (34) 3122424
Web Site: http://www.anicefly.com
Aircraft Charter Services
N.A.I.C.S.: 481212
Jesus Suarez (Dir-Quality)

Tecnicos en la Alta Produccion S.A.
de C.V.   (1)
Av Central No 21 Lote 5 Mz 851 Parque
Industrial Tepeji, Tepeji, 42850, Hidalgo,
Mexico
Tel.: (52) 7737339600
Automotive Spare Parts Distr
N.A.I.C.S.: 423120

CORPORACION ACCIONA ENERGIAS RENOVABLES S.A.

Avenida de la Gran Via de Hortaleza
1, 28033, Madrid, Spain
Tel.: (34) 916576460
Web Site: https://www.acciona-energia.com
Year Founded: 2008
CRPAF—(OTCIQ)
Rev.: $3,915,443,206
Assets: $16,196,048,131
Liabilities: $9,198,587,042
Net Worth: $6,997,461,089
Earnings: $625,896,898
Emp.: 3,008
Fiscal Year-end: 12/31/23
Renewable Energy Distribution Services
N.A.I.C.S.: 221210
Jose Manuel Entrecanales Domecq
(Chm)

CORPORACION ACEROS AREQUIPA S.A.

Av Antonio Miro Quesada N 425
Floor 17, Magdalena del Mar, Lima,
Peru
Tel.: (51) 5171800

Web Site:
https://www.acerosarequipa.com
Year Founded: 1997
CORAREC1—(LIM)
Rev.: $1,262,564,434
Assets: $1,705,200,928
Liabilities: $966,402,180
Net Worth: $738,798,747
Earnings: $18,157,234
Emp.: 1,130
Fiscal Year-end: 12/31/23
Steel Products Mfr
N.A.I.C.S.: 331221
Ricardo Cilloniz Champin *(Chm)*

Subsidiaries:

Comercial del Acero S.A.   **(1)**
Av Argentina N 2051 Cercado de, Lima,
Peru
Tel.: (51) 619 3000
Web Site: http://www.comasa.com.pe
Steel Products Mfr
N.A.I.C.S.: 331221
Cesar Cristobal Rosas Zorrilla *(Chm)*

CORPORACION ACTINVER SAB DE CV
Montes Urales No 620 Colonia Lomas de Chapultepec IV Section,
Mayors Office Miguel Hidalgo, CP
11000, Mexico, Mexico
Web Site: http://www.actinver.com
Investment Banking Services
N.A.I.C.S.: 523150
Hector Madero Rivero *(Pres & CEO)*

CORPORACION AMERICA AIRPORTS S.A.
128 Boulevard de la Petrusse,
L-1643, Luxembourg, Luxembourg
Tel.: (352) 26258274   LU
Web Site:
https://investors.corporacion.com
Year Founded: 1998
CAAP—(NYSE)
Rev.: $1,400,038,000
Assets: $2,792,066,000
Liabilities: $1,988,157,000
Net Worth: $803,909,000
Earnings: $226,467,000
Emp.: 6,100
Fiscal Year-end: 12/31/23
Airport Concession Operator
N.A.I.C.S.: 488119
Martin Francisco Antranik Eurnekian *(CEO)*

Subsidiaries:

ACI do Brasil S.A.   **(1)**
Avenida Engenheiro Luiz Carlos Berrini 105
- 5th andar - Conjunto 52, Sao Paulo,
04571-010, SP, Brazil
Tel.: (55) 1133650765
Software Development Services
N.A.I.C.S.: 541511

Alatoscana Spa   **(1)**
Via Aeroporto 208, Marina di Campo,
57034, Livorno, Italy
Tel.: (39) 0565976011
Airport Operation Services
N.A.I.C.S.: 488119

Corporacion America Italia S.p.A. **(1)**
Piazzale Martesana 10, 20128, Milan, Italy
Tel.: (39) 0552337474
Web Site:
https://www.corporacionamericaitalia.com
Holding Company
N.A.I.C.S.: 551112

Holding (Domestic):

Toscana Aeroporti S.p.A.   **(2)**
Via del Termine n 11, 50127, Florence, Fl,
Italy   **(62.28%)**
Tel.: (39) 050 849202
Web Site: http://www.toscana-aeroporti.com
Sales Range: $50-74.9 Million
Airport Operator
N.A.I.C.S.: 488119
Marco Carrai *(Chm)*

Paoletti America S.A.   **(1)**
Avenida 9 de Julio No 260, Coronel Pringles, Buenos Aires, Argentina
Tel.: (54) 2922465463
Logistics Transportation Services
N.A.I.C.S.: 488510

Vola S.R.L   **(1)**
Cross Via Libeccio 48/F, industrial area Cotton, 55044, Viareggio, LU, Italy
Tel.: (39) 058443671
Web Site: https://www.vola.it
Software Development Services
N.A.I.C.S.: 541511

CORPORACION AMERICA S.A.
Honduras 5663, C1414BNE, Buenos
Aires, Argentina
Tel.: (54) 1148526900   Ar
Web Site:
http://www.corporacionamerica.com
Sales Range: $900-999.9 Million
Emp.: 5,000
Investment Holding Company
N.A.I.C.S.: 551112
Ernesto Gutierrez *(CEO)*

Subsidiaries:

Aeropuerto de Punta del Este   **(1)**
Ruta 93 km 113, 20100, Maldonado, Uruguay
Tel.: (598) 42559777
Web Site: http://www.puntadeleste.aero
Airport Management Services
N.A.I.C.S.: 488119

Aeropuertos Argentina 2000   **(1)**
Av Corrientes 441 - Ciudad Autonoma de,
Buenos Aires, C1043AAE, Argentina
Tel.: (54) 11 4852 6900
Web Site: http://www.aa2000.com.ar
Airport Management Services
N.A.I.C.S.: 488119
Raul Francos *(CFO)*

Subsidiary (Domestic):

Terminal de Cargas Argentina   **(2)**
Ezeiza International Airport, B1804EZE,
Buenos Aires, Argentina
Tel.: (54) 1154806400
Web Site: http://www.tca.aero
Airport Management Services
N.A.I.C.S.: 488119

Aeropuertos del Neuquen S.A.   **(1)**
San Martin 5901, Neuquen, Argentina
Tel.: (54) 4440448
Web Site: http://www.anqn.com.ar
Airport Management Services
N.A.I.C.S.: 488119

Airgest S.p.A.   **(1)**
Birgi Aerostazione Civile, 91020, Trapani,
Italy
Tel.: (39) 0923842502
Web Site: http://www.airgest.it
Airport Management Services
N.A.I.C.S.: 488119
Salvatore Castiglione *(Pres)*

Terminal de Cargas Uruguay
S.A.   **(1)**
Aeropuerto Internacional de Carrasco Ruta
101 km 19 950, Carrasco, 14000, Montevideo, Uruguay
Tel.: (598) 26040015
Web Site: http://www.tcu.com.uy
Airport Management Services
N.A.I.C.S.: 488119

CORPORACION ANDINA DE FOMENTO
Ave Luis Roche Torre CAF Altamira,
Caracas, Venezuela
Tel.: (58) 2122092111
Web Site: http://www.caf.com
Sales Range: $400-449.9 Million
Emp.: 400
Banking Services
N.A.I.C.S.: 522110
Luis Enrique Garcia Rodriguez *(CEO & Exec VP)*

CORPORACION CERVESUR S.A.A.
Av Alfonso Ugarte 521, Cercado,
Arequipa, Peru
Tel.: (51) 54205783
Web Site:
https://www.corporacion.com.pe
COCESUC1—(LIM)
Rev.: $213,734,920
Assets: $415,599,007
Liabilities: $122,361,752
Net Worth: $293,237,255
Earnings: $3,494,454
Fiscal Year-end: 12/31/23
Industrial Products Mfr
N.A.I.C.S.: 314999

CORPORACION DE FINANZAS DEL PAIS
Calle 50 Panacredit Building,
Panafoto, Panama, Panama
Tel.: (507) 2643075
Web Site:
https://www.panacredit.com
Year Founded: 2008
CFPA—(PAN)
Sales Range: Less than $1 Million
Financial Services
N.A.I.C.S.: 523999

CORPORACION DERMOESTETICA, S.A.
Calle Pizarro 11-13, 46004, Valencia,
Spain
Tel.: (34) 902252525
Web Site:
http://www.corporacionsa.com
Sales Range: $50-74.9 Million
Emp.: 777
Health Centers, Hospitals & Clinical
Laboratories Owner & Operator
N.A.I.C.S.: 622310
Jose Maria Suescun Verdugo *(Chm & CEO)*

CORPORACION EG S.A.
Niquel # 9204 Ciudad Industrial Mitras, 66000, Villa de Garcia, N.L.,
Mexico
Tel.: (52) 8181585500
Web Site:
http://www.corporacioneg.com
Mfr, Designer & Marketer of Centrifugal Pumps; Operator of Iron & Steel
Foundry; Mfr of Machine Parts for
Industrial & Consumer OEM's
N.A.I.C.S.: 333914

Subsidiaries:

Barnes de Colombia S.A.   **(1)**
Celta Trade Park Bodegas 86 y 93 Autopista Bogota Medellin, Km 7 Costado Occidental, Bogota, Siberia, Colombia
Tel.: (57) 17439090
Web Site: http://www.barnes.com.co
Industrial Pump Mfr
N.A.I.C.S.: 333996

Ruhrpumen India Private Limited   **(1)**
Citi Tower Floor No:7-R 117 Thiyagaraya
Road T Nagar, Chennai, 600017, Tamil
Nadu, India
Tel.: (91) 9840025333
Industrial Pump Distr
N.A.I.C.S.: 423830
Ashwani Shah *(Dir-Sls)*

Ruhrpumpen Inc.   **(1)**
4501 S 86th E Ave, Tulsa, OK 74145
Tel.: (918) 627-8400
Web Site: http://www.ruhrpumpen.com
Sales Range: $25-49.9 Million
Emp.: 100
Industrial Pumps & Parts
N.A.I.C.S.: 333914
Tom Wallbank *(Mgr-IT)*

Subsidiary (Non-US):

Ruhrpumpen GmbH   **(2)**

Stockumer Strasse 28, D 58453, Witten,
Germany
Tel.: (49) 230266103
Web Site: http://www.ruhrpumpen.com
Sales Range: $75-99.9 Million
Mfr of Pumps
N.A.I.C.S.: 333914

Plant (Domestic):

Ruhrpumpen, Inc. - Orland Plant   **(2)**
4050 Airpark Dr, Orland, CA 95963
Tel.: (530) 865-7867
Industrial Pump Mfr
N.A.I.C.S.: 333914

Ruhrpumpen Limited   **(1)**
Salah Nessem St Cross, Suez Canal,
43511, Cairo, Egypt
Tel.: (20) 623365557
Industrial Pump Mfr
N.A.I.C.S.: 333914

Ruhrpumpen Metals, S.A. de
C.V.   **(1)**
Omicron 8110 Parque Industrial Ciudad Mitras, Garcia, Monterrey, 66000, Nuevo
Leon, Mexico
Tel.: (52) 18183810119
Web Site: http://www.fundemex.com
Steel Alloy Mfr
N.A.I.C.S.: 331513

Ruhrpumpen do Brasil Ind. e Com de
Bombas. Hidraulicas Ltda.   **(1)**
Rodovia Washington Luiz 13 721 Chacaras
Rio Petropolis, Duque de Caxias, Rio de
Janeiro, 25230-005, Brazil
Tel.: (55) 2136544063
Industrial Pump Mfr
N.A.I.C.S.: 333914

WDM Pumps, Inc.   **(1)**
4034 Mint Way, Dallas, TX 75237
Tel.: (214) 337-8780
Web Site: http://www.wdmpumps.com
Industrial Pump Mfr
N.A.I.C.S.: 333914

CORPORACION FINANCIERA COLOMBIANA S.A.
Carrera 13 26-45 8th floor8, Bogota,
Colombia
Tel.: (57) 6012863300
Web Site: https://www.corfi.com
Year Founded: 1961
Commercial Banking Services
N.A.I.C.S.: 522110
Maria Lorena Gutierrez Botero *(Pres & CEO)*

CORPORACION FINANCIERA DE DESARROLLO SA
Augusto Tamayo 160, San Isidro, 27,
Lima, 27, Peru
Tel.: (51) 6154000
Web Site: https://www.cofide.com.pe
Year Founded: 1971
COFIDCC1—(LIM)
Rev.: $151,904,299
Assets: $2,920,098,776
Liabilities: $2,325,049,792
Net Worth: $595,048,984
Earnings: $19,394,381
Fiscal Year-end: 12/31/23
Financial Banking Services
N.A.I.C.S.: 522110
Carlos Adrian Linares Penaloza
(Chm)

CORPORACION FINANCIERA DE INVERSIONES SA
Dean Valdivia 111 Suite 901, San
Isidro, Lima, Peru
Tel.: (51) 12027400
Web Site: http://www.cfi.com.pe
Investment Management Service
N.A.I.C.S.: 525990
Alfonso Bustamante Y. Bustamante
(Chm)

CORPORACION GESTAMP SL
Alfonso XII 16, 28014, Madrid, Spain

Corporacion Gestamp SL—(Continued)

Tel.: (34) 91 379 19 99
Web Site: http://www.gestamp.com
Year Founded: 1997
Industrial Holding Company
N.A.I.C.S.: 551112
Francisco Jose Riberas Mera *(Chm)*

Subsidiaries:

Anhui Edscha Automotive Parts, Co. **(1)**
Ltd.
Yulan Road 1, Anhui, Hefei, 230031, China
Tel.: (86) 551 584 2978
Web Site: http://www.edscha.com
Automotive Spare Parts Distr
N.A.I.C.S.: 423120

Gestamp Portugal LTDA. **(1)**
Zona Industrial Polo 2, Vila Nova de Cerveira, Lisbon, Portugal
Tel.: (351) 1 251 70 04 00
Automotive Spare Parts Distr
N.A.I.C.S.: 423120

Gestamp Renewables **(1)**
C/ Ombu 3 - 2nd floor, 28045, Madrid, Spain
Tel.: (34) 91 177 00 10
Web Site: http://www.gestampren.com
Automotive Spare Parts Distr
N.A.I.C.S.: 423120
Oscar Ordonez Ropero *(Head-HR)*

Gestamp Wind **(1)**
Ombu 3 - 10th floor, 28045, Madrid, Spain
Tel.: (34) 91 636 19 94
Web Site: http://www.gestampwind.com
Windmill Mfr
N.A.I.C.S.: 333611
Luis Javier Perez *(Mgr-Treasury)*

Gonvarri Steel Services **(1)**
Calle de Embajadores, 28053, Madrid, Spain
Tel.: (34) 913 791 900
Web Site: http://www.gonvarri.com
Steel Product Distr
N.A.I.C.S.: 428510

Subsidiary (Non-US):

Constructor Group AS **(2)**
Ostensjoveien 27, 0661, Oslo, Norway
Tel.: (47) 67112600
Web Site: http://www.constructor.no
Warehousing, Logistics & Material Handling Services
N.A.I.C.S.: 541614
Kristian Nodeland *(CEO)*

Subsidiary (Non-US):

Constructor Danmark A/S **(3)**
Rorupvej 1, DK 4320, Roskilde, Lejre, Denmark
Tel.: (45) 46328008
Web Site: http://www.constructor.dk
Industrial & Office Storage Products Mfr
N.A.I.C.S.: 337215
Michael Sahl *(Mng Dir)*

Constructor Dexion France **(3)**
SARL
Parc Guilleminot, PB 101413, 60635, Chantilly, Cedex, France
Tel.: (33) 344545200
Web Site: http://www.dexion.fr.pagesperso-orange.fr
Industrial & Office Storage Products Mfr
N.A.I.C.S.: 337215

Constructor Dexion Italia SRL **(3)**
Via Paracelso 26, 20864, Agrate Brianza, MI, Italy
Tel.: (39) 0396091952
Web Site: http://www.dexionitalia.it
Industrial & Office Storage Products
N.A.I.C.S.: 493190

Constructor Finland Oy **(3)**
Sauvonrinne 12, PO Box 100, Lohja, FI-8150, Finland
Tel.: (358) 19 36251
Web Site: http://www.kasten.fi
Industrial & Office Storage Products
N.A.I.C.S.: 493190

Subsidiary (Domestic):

Constructor Norge AS **(3)**

Ostensjoveien 27, 0661, Oslo, Norway
Tel.: (47) 67112600
Web Site: http://www.constructor.no
Industrial & Office Storage Product Mfr
N.A.I.C.S.: 337215

Subsidiary (Non-US):

Constructor Sverige AB **(3)**
Berdsjodalen 60, S 40053, Gothenburg, Sweden
Tel.: (46) 317719600
Web Site: http://www.constructor.se
Industrial & Office Storage Products Mfr
N.A.I.C.S.: 337215

Dexion (Australia) Pty. Ltd. **(3)**
Building E 22 Powers Road, PO Box 6470, Seven Hills, 2147, NSW, Australia
Tel.: (61) 298305000
Web Site: http://www.dexion.com.au
Industrial & Office Storage Products
N.A.I.C.S.: 337215
Mark Barraclough *(Mgr-Natl Bus Dev)*

Dexion Comino Ltd. **(3)**
Murdock Road Dorcan, Swindon, SN3 5HY, Wilts, United Kingdom
Tel.: (44) 800581531
Web Site: http://www.dexion.com
Shelving & Racking Systems Mfr
N.A.I.C.S.: 337215

Dexion GmbH **(3)**
Dexionstrasse 1-5, 35321, Laubach, Germany
Tel.: (49) 6405800
Web Site: http://www.dexion.de
Industrial Storage Products Provider
N.A.I.C.S.: 337215

Dexion Kft. **(3)**
Baross u 89, Budaors, 2040, Budapest, Hungary
Tel.: (36) 623428166
Web Site: http://www.dexion.com
Industrial & Office Storage Products Provider
N.A.I.C.S.: 337215

Dexion NV **(3)**
Buro & Design Center b50 Esplanade Heizel, 1020, Brussels, Belgium
Tel.: (32) 24762635
Web Site: http://www.dexion.be
Commercial Storage Products Provider
N.A.I.C.S.: 337215

Dexion Polska Sp. z.o.o. **(3)**
ul Wenecka Street 12, 03-244, Warsaw, Poland
Tel.: (48) 22295 08 00
Web Site: http://www.dexionpolska.pl
Industrial & Office Storage Products
N.A.I.C.S.: 493190

Dexion s.r.o. **(3)**
Antala Staska 220/77 Krc, 140 00, Prague, 4, Czech Republic
Tel.: (420) 606 729 858
Web Site: http://www.dexion.cz
Industrial & Office Storage Products
N.A.I.C.S.: 337215

Subsidiary (Domestic):

Gonvarri Galicia, S.A. **(2)**
Lugar Muelle Pesquero 0, Marin, 36900, Pontevedra, Spain
Tel.: (34) 986 99 10 00
Automobile Parts Mfr
N.A.I.C.S.: 336390

Gonvauto Asturias, S.L. **(2)**
Plind Canciones 0, Asturias, Corvera de Asturias, Spain
Tel.: (34) 985128200
Web Site: http://www.gonvauto-asturias.pymes.com
Automotive Spare Parts Distr
N.A.I.C.S.: 423120

Gonvauto, S.A. **(2)**
C Prolongaci3 13/16n de Embajadores, 28053, Madrid, Spain
Tel.: (34) 93 773 46 01
Web Site:
    http://www.gonvarristeelservices.com
Automobile Parts Mfr
N.A.I.C.S.: 336390

Industrial Ferro Distribuidora, **(2)**
S.A.
Calle Villa Gris, Sagunto, 46520, Valencia, Spain
Tel.: (34) 962659500
Automobile Parts Mfr
N.A.I.C.S.: 336390

Grupo Gonvarri **(1)**
Prolongacion de Embajadores 5 N, 28053, Madrid, Spain
Tel.: (34) 913791900
Flat Steel Product Mfr
N.A.I.C.S.: 331110

CORPORACION INMOBIL-
IARIA VESTA, S.A.B. DE C.V.

Paseo de los Tamarindos 90 Torre 2 28th Floor, Cuajimalpa de Morelos, C P 05120, Mexico, Mexico
Tel.: (52) 5559500070 MX
Web Site: https://www.vesta.com.mx
Year Founded: 1998
VESTA—(MEX)
Rev.: $213,448,296
Assets: $3,792,216,293
Liabilities: $1,305,247,868
Net Worth: $2,486,968,425
Earnings: $316,637,512
Emp.: 95
Fiscal Year-end: 12/31/23
Industrial Buildings Owner, Developer & Asset Administrator
N.A.I.C.S.: 531390
Lorenzo Manuel Berho Corona *(Chm)*

CORPORACION INTERAMERI-
CANA DE ENTRETENIMIENTO,
S. A. B. DE C. V.

Av Industria Militar S/N Puerta 2 Acceso A Ciudad de, 11600, Mexico, 11600, Mexico
Tel.: (52) 5552019000
Web Site: https://www.cie.com.mx
Year Founded: 1990
CIE—(MEX)
Rev.: $288,720,858
Assets: $830,135,881
Liabilities: $472,412,248
Net Worth: $357,723,634
Earnings: $68,884,875
Emp.: 545
Fiscal Year-end: 12/31/23
Concert Management Services
N.A.I.C.S.: 711310
Luis Alejandro Soberon Kuri *(Chm, Chm, CEO, Mng Dir & Mng Dir)*

CORPORACION MOCTEZUMA
S.A.B. DE C.V.

Monte Elbruz No 134 PH, CP 11000, Lomas de Chapultepec, CP 11000, Mexico
Tel.: (52) 5552795900
Web Site:
    https://www.cmoctezuma.com.mx
CMOCTEZ—(MEX)
Rev.: $1,158,511,233
Assets: $1,009,439,279
Liabilities: $218,434,558
Net Worth: $791,004,721
Earnings: $363,291,098
Emp.: 684
Fiscal Year-end: 12/31/23
Ready-Mix Concrete Mfr & Distr
N.A.I.C.S.: 327320
Jose Maria Barroso *(CEO)*

CORPORACION MULTI INVER-
SIONES SA

5 Av 15-45 Zone 10 Edificio Centro Empresarial, Guatemala, Guatemala
Tel.: (502) 2377 0200
Web Site: http://www.cmi.co
Milling, Fast Food, Livestock & Construction Projects Development & Financial Services

N.A.I.C.S.: 532412

CORPORACION NACIONAL
DEL COBRE DE CHILE

Huerfanos 1270, PO Box 150 D, Santiago, Chile
Tel.: (56) 26903000 CL
Web Site: http://www.codelco.cl
Year Founded: 1976
Sales Range: $1-4.9 Billion
Emp.: 16,800
Copper & Molybdenum Mfr & Sales
N.A.I.C.S.: 212230
Alejandro Rivera Stambuk *(VP-Admin & Fin)*

Subsidiaries:

BioSigma S.A. **(1)**
Carretera General San Martin 16 500 Lote #106 Colina Parque, Industrial Los Libertadores, Santiago, Chile
Tel.: (56) 24379030
Web Site: http://www.biosigma.cl
Sales Range: $25-49.9 Million
Emp.: 70
Mining Proteomics & Bioinformatics Research & Development; Owned by Corporacion Nacional del Cobre de Chile & by JX Holdings, Inc.
N.A.I.C.S.: 541715

CK Metall Agentur GmbH **(1)**
Louise Dumont Str 25, Dusseldorf, 40211, Germany **(100%)**
Tel.: (49) 211173690
Web Site: http://www.codelco.de
Sales Range: $50-74.9 Million
Emp.: 8
N.A.I.C.S.: 212230
Heribert Heitling *(Gen Mgr)*

Codelco Andina Division **(1)**
Ave Santa Teresa 513, Los Andes, Chile **(100%)**
Tel.: (56) 34 4980000
Sales Range: $750-799.9 Million
Emp.: 1,126
Copper Mine
N.A.I.C.S.: 212230

Codelco Chuquicamata Division **(1)**
Casilla 9 D, Chuquicamata, Chile **(100%)**
Tel.: (56) 55323100
Web Site: http://www.codelco.cl
Sales Range: $1-4.9 Billion
Emp.: 7,694
Copper Mine
N.A.I.C.S.: 212230
Hector Espinoza *(Asst Mgr-Control)*

Codelco El Teniente Division **(1)**
Millan 1020, Rancagua, Chile **(100%)**
Tel.: (56) 72292800
Web Site: http://www.teneiente.cl
Sales Range: $200-249.9 Million
Emp.: 300
N.A.I.C.S.: 212230
Jaime Henriquez *(Gen Superintendent-Mine Plng)*

Codelco Salvador Division **(1)**
Av Bernardo O'Higgins No 103, El Salvador, III Region, Chile **(100%)**
Tel.: (56) 52 472 103
Sales Range: $750-799.9 Million
Emp.: 2,247
Copper Mining Operations
N.A.I.C.S.: 212230
Sergio Bustamante *(Gen Superintendent-Mines)*

Codelco Talleres Division **(1)**
Ave Estacion 01200, Rancagua, Chile **(100%)**
Tel.: (56) 26903000
Sales Range: $350-399.9 Million
Emp.: 600
N.A.I.C.S.: 212230
Alex A. Maluenda *(Gen Mgr)*

Codelco-Asia **(1)**
Unit E & F 26 Fl Mirae Asset No-166 Lujiazui Ring Rd, Shanghai, 200120, China
Tel.: (86) 2161090260
Emp.: 20
Sales of Copper
N.A.I.C.S.: 212230

Carlos Alvarado *(Mng Dir)*

Codelco-Kupferhandel GmbH **(1)**
Louise Dumont Strasse 25, 40211, Dussel-
dorf, Germany **(100%)**
Tel.: (49) 211173680
Web Site: http://www.codelco.de
Sales Range: $50-74.9 Million
Emp.: 6
N.A.I.C.S.: 212230
Heriberg Heidiling *(Gen Mgr)*

Complejo Portuario Mejillones
S.A. **(1)**
Coronel Tereira 72, Santiago, Chile
Tel.: (56) 26903850
Web Site: http://www.mejillones.com
Sales Range: $50-74.9 Million
Emp.: 4
Real Estate
N.A.I.C.S.: 531390
Alvaro Arroyo Albala *(Gen Mgr)*

Coppermol S.A. **(1)**
Ricardo Rojas 401 Piso 4, C 1001 AEA,
Buenos Aires, Argentina
Tel.: (54) 11 4312 7086
Sales Range: $50-74.9 Million
Emp.: 8
Sales of Copper & Molybdenum Metals
N.A.I.C.S.: 212230

Corporacion del Cobre (U.S.A.),
Inc. **(1)**
177 Broad St 11th Fl, Stamford, CT 06901-
5003
Tel.: (203) 425-4321
Sales Range: $50-74.9 Million
Emp.: 2
Sales of Copper & Molybdenum
N.A.I.C.S.: 423520

Fundicon Talleres S.A. **(1)**
Avenida Estacion, Rancagua, 01200, Chile
Tel.: (56) 72292083
Web Site: http://www.talleres.cl
Scrap Steel Castings Mfr
N.A.I.C.S.: 331512

Isapre San Lorenzo Ltda **(1)**
Pasaje Cuatro de Julio 694, El Salvador,
Chile
Tel.: (56) 52475315
Web Site: http://www.isl.cl
Financing of Health Care Services & Ben-
efits
N.A.I.C.S.: 525120

Lithium Power International
Limited **(1)**
Level 7 151 Macquarie Street, Sydney,
2000, NSW, Australia
Tel.: (61) 290898723
Web Site:
http://www.lithiumpowerinternational.com
Rev.: $267
Assets: $32,688,729
Liabilities: $611,107
Net Worth: $32,077,622
Earnings: ($9,605,174)
Fiscal Year-end: 06/30/2022
Lithium Exploration Services
N.A.I.C.S.: 212390
Ian Miles *(Mgr-Exploration-Western Austra-
lia)*

Subsidiary (Non-US):

Bearing Lithium Corp. **(2)**
No 503 - 905 West Pender Street, Vancou-
ver, V6C 1L6, BC, Canada
Tel.: (604) 262-8835
Web Site: http://www.bearinglithium.com
Rev.: $1,372
Assets: $14,723,942
Liabilities: $166,805
Net Worth: $14,557,136
Earnings: ($251,950)
Emp.: 1
Fiscal Year-end: 10/31/2019
Mineral Exploration & Development Com-
pany
N.A.I.C.S.: 212290
Benjamin Asuncion *(VP-Bus Dev)*

Sociedad Contractual Minera El
Abra **(1)**
Kilometro 75 Camino Conchi Viejo, Antofa-
gasta, Chile
Tel.: (56) 55818300

Metal Ore Mining
N.A.I.C.S.: 212290

Sociedad Contractual Minera
Puren **(1)**
Los Carrera N 6651, Copiapo, Chile
Tel.: (56) 52221043
Web Site: http://www.codelco.de
Support Activities for Metal Mining
N.A.I.C.S.: 212200

CORPORACION VENEZOLANA
DE GUAYANA
Avenida Guayana con Carrera
Cuchivero Edificio Sede CVG Al-
tavista, Puerto Ordaz, Bolivar, Ven-
ezuela
Tel.: (58) 286 966 1930   VE
Web Site: http://www.cvg.com
Year Founded: 1960
Sales Range: $1-4.9 Billion
Emp.: 22,000
Business & Economic Development
Services
N.A.I.C.S.: 541611
Carlos Osorio *(Pres)*

Subsidiaries:

Complejo Siderurgico de Guayana,
C.A. **(1)**
Parque Industrial CVG-Minorca Sector
Punta Chichillo, 8050, Puerto Ordaz, Boli-
var, Venezuela
Tel.: (58) 2869520080
Web Site: http://www.comsigua.net
Sales Range: $50-74.9 Million
Emp.: 245
Hot Briquette Iron Production & Sales
N.A.I.C.S.: 332111

Rialca **(1)**
Zona Industrial Sur II Avda Henry Ford,
Apartado 1183, Valencia, 46023, Venezuela
Tel.: (58) 2418748411
Sales Range: $200-249.9 Million
Emp.: 530
Aluminum Wheels & Other Aluminum Prod-
ucts Mfr & Sales
N.A.I.C.S.: 331315

CORPORATE & RESOURCE
CONSULTANTS PTY LTD
Level 2 Suite 9 389 Oxford Street,
Hawthorn, 6016, WA, Australia
Tel.: (61) 8 9380 6789
Web Site: http://www.crcpl.com.au
Year Founded: 1996
Sales Range: $10-24.9 Million
Emp.: 15
Financial Management Consulting
Services
N.A.I.C.S.: 541618

CORPORATE DEVELOPMENT
BANK LIMITED
Adarshnagar Main Road Parsa, Bir-
gunj, 44313, Nepal
Tel.: (977) 51531031
Web Site:
https://www.corporatebank.com.np
Year Founded: 2007
CORBL—(NEP)
Rev.: $1,400,224
Assets: $15,047,003
Liabilities: $9,726,101
Net Worth: $5,320,902
Earnings: $4,607
Emp.: 29
Fiscal Year-end: 07/16/23
Banking Services
N.A.I.C.S.: 522110
Jainuddin Ansari *(Chm)*

CORPORATE MERCHANT
BANKERS LIMITED
UG-24 Viswadeep Tower District
Centre Janak Puri, New Delhi, 110
058, Delhi, India
Tel.: (91) 1165382244

Web Site: https://www.cmbl.co.in
540199—(BOM)
Rev.: $23,184
Assets: $501,946
Liabilities: $19,085
Net Worth: $482,861
Earnings: $189
Emp.: 3
Fiscal Year end: 03/31/10
Financial Planning Services
N.A.I.C.S.: 523940
Satyanarayana Kaduri *(CEO)*

Subsidiaries:

Cosmos Industries Limited **(1)**
Unit 6 Technica Complex Narayan Nagar
Near Home Guard, Ghatkopar West, Mum-
bai, 400084, Maharashtra, India
Tel.: (91) 2225021045
Web Site: http://www.cosmosindustries.com
Chemical Products Distr
N.A.I.C.S.: 424690
Ashok Naik *(Founder & CEO)*

CORPORATE SERVICE SYS-
TEMS OAO
Dom 42Str Preobrazhenckaya, Bel-
gorod, 308000, Russia
Tel.: (7) 4722304070
Management Consulting Services
N.A.I.C.S.: 541618
Alexey Alexandrovich Zelensky *(Chm)*

CORPORATE TRAVEL MAN-
AGEMENT LIMITED
Level 9 180 Ann Street, Brisbane,
4000, QLD, Australia
Tel.: (61) 733297400
Web Site: https://au.travelctm.com
Year Founded: 1994
CTMLF—(OTCIQ)
Rev.: $297,804,262
Assets: $1,154,775,518
Liabilities: $326,229,144
Net Worth: $828,546,373
Earnings: $583,837
Emp.: 2,855
Fiscal Year-end: 06/30/22
Travel Services
N.A.I.C.S.: 561599
Jamie Pherous *(Founder & Mng Dir)*

Subsidiaries:

Andrew Jones Travel Pty Ltd. **(1)**
1st Floor 61 Salamanca Place, Hobart,
7000, TAS, Australia
Tel.: (61) 362158799
Web Site: http://www.ajtravel.com.au
Travel Management Services
N.A.I.C.S.: 561510
Monique Dorey *(Specialist-Travel)*

Bees.Travel Limited **(1)**
Room 03 18th Floor Zhongran Building 388
Castle Peak Road, Tsuen Wan, China
(Hong Kong)
Tel.: (852) 82006882
Web Site: http://www.bees.travel
Travel Agency Services
N.A.I.C.S.: 561510

Beijing Westminster Air Service
Limited **(1)**
Unit 16082 16 Floor No 8 Xiaoyunl, Chaoy-
ang District, Beijing, 100125, China
Tel.: (86) 1051645252
Travel Management Services
N.A.I.C.S.: 561510

CTM Overseas Education Centre
Limited **(1)**
Unit 06 18/F CDW Building, Tsuen Wan,
China (Hong Kong)
Tel.: (852) 31965400
Web Site: http://www.edctm.com
Education Consultation Services
N.A.I.C.S.: 611710

Corporate Travel Management (UK)
Limited **(1)**
One Carter Lane, London, EC4V 5ER,
United Kingdom

Tel.: (44) 2074299600
Web Site: http://www.travelctm.co.uk
Travel Management Services
N.A.I.C.S.: 561510
Debbie Carling *(CEO)*

Corporate Travel Management Group
Pty Ltd **(1)**
Level 24 307 Queen Street, Brisbane,
4000, QLD, Australia
Tel.: (61) 73 329 7400
Web Site: https://www.travelctm.com
Sales Range: $25-49.9 Million
Emp.: 140
Travel Management Services
N.A.I.C.S.: 561510

Corporate Travel Management
Limited **(1)**
Unit 01 18/F CDW Building 388 Castle
Peak Road, Tsuen Wan, China (Hong
Kong)
Tel.: (852) 23139722
Web Site: http://www.travelctm.asia
Travel Management Services
N.A.I.C.S.: 561510
Larry Yo *(CEO)*

Corporate Travel Management North
America Inc. **(1)**
2120 S 72nd St, Omaha, NE 68124
Web Site: http://www.us.travelctm.com
Travel Management Services
N.A.I.C.S.: 561510
Kevin O'Malley *(CEO)*

Corporate Travel Planners, Inc. **(1)**
613 NW Loop Ste 140, San Antonio, TX
78216
Tel.: (781) 496-3643
Web Site: https://www.ctp-travel.com
Sales Range: $10-24.9 Million
Emp.: 150
Manager of Travel Agencies
N.A.I.C.S.: 561510
Christine J. Prescott *(Founder & CEO)*

Subsidiary (Domestic):

Rennert Travel **(2)**
613 NW Loop Ste 140, San Antonio, TX
78216
Tel.: (210) 828-4809
Web Site: https://www.ctp-travel.com
Rev.: $25,000,000
Emp.: 50
Provider of Travel Services
N.A.I.C.S.: 561510

ETM Travel Pty Ltd. **(1)**
Level 24 307 Queen Street, Brisbane,
4000, QLD, Australia
Tel.: (61) 732112400
Web Site: https://www.traveletm.com.au
Event Management Services
N.A.I.C.S.: 561920
Tracey Edwards *(Gen Mgr)*

Inspire Travel Management Pty.
Ltd. **(1)**
Level 11 120 Spencer Street, Melbourne,
3000, VIC, Australia
Tel.: (61) 392673260
Web Site: https://www.inspiretm.com.au
Travel Management Services
N.A.I.C.S.: 561510

Jecking Tours & Travel Limited **(1)**
Units 01-06 18/F CDW Building 388 Castle
Peak Road, Tsuen Wan, China (Hong
Kong)
Tel.: (852) 27313100
Web Site: http://www.jeckingtours.com
Travel Management Services
N.A.I.C.S.: 561510
Alan Lee *(Gen Mgr)*

Lotus Tours Limited **(1)**
Units 08 18/F CDW Building 388 Castle
Peak Road, Tsuen Wan, China (Hong
Kong)
Tel.: (852) 23161133
Web Site: https://www.lotustours.com.hk
Travel Management Services
N.A.I.C.S.: 561510

RA Travel, Inc. **(1)**
39 W 14th St Ste 306, New York, NY 10011
Tel.: (212) 633-8300
Web Site: https://ratravel.com

Corporate Travel Management
Limited—(Continued)

Sales Range: $10-24.9 Million
Emp.: 15
Travel Agencies
N.A.I.C.S.: 561510
Rose Aiello (Founder)

Sainten Pty Ltd (1)
L 30 Margaret St, Sydney, 2000, NSW,
Australia
Tel.: (61) 292301000
Travel Management Services
N.A.I.C.S.: 561510
Claire Lesley Gray (Mgr)

Sara Enterprises (1)
2355 Honolulu Ave, Montrose, CA 91020
Tel.: (818) 553-3332
Web Site:
http://www.montroseromancetravel.com
Emp.: 230
Travel Arrangement & Reservation Services
N.A.I.C.S.: 561599
Joseph McClure (Pres)

Tramada Systems Pty. Ltd. (1)
Level 13/255 Elizabeth St, Sydney, 2000,
NSW, Australia
Tel.: (61) 282867470
Web Site: https://www.tramada.com
Software Development Services
N.A.I.C.S.: 541511

Travel Resources Limited (1)
2/F De Tuo Building 1-3 Mody Road, Tsim
Sha Tsui, Kowloon, China (Hong Kong)
Tel.: (852) 28708700
Web Site: https://www.travel-
resources.com.hk
Travel Management Services
N.A.I.C.S.: 561510

Travelcorp Holdings Pty Ltd. (1)
Level 30 60 Margaret Street, Sydney, 2000,
NSW, Australia
Tel.: (61) 292301099
Web Site: http://www.travelcorp.com.au
Travel Management Services
N.A.I.C.S.: 561510
Alex Kouz (Sls Dir)

**Westminster Travel Consultancy
(Guangzhou) Limited** (1)
Units 2307-2310 23/F North Tower Lisheng
Plaza 64 Huadi Road, Liwan District,
Guangzhou, 510375, China
Tel.: (86) 2038114000
Travel Management Services
N.A.I.C.S.: 561510

Westminster Travel Limited (1)
Room 02 18/F China Dye Building 388
Castle Peak Road, Tsuen Wan, China
(Hong Kong)
Tel.: (852) 2 313 9700
Web Site: https://westminstertravel.com
Sales Range: $25-49.9 Million
Emp.: 700
Travel Management Services
N.A.I.C.S.: 561599

Subsidiary (Non-US):

**Corporate Travel Management (S)
Pte. Limited** (2)
1 Changi Business Park Crescent 02-01
Plaza 8 CBP, Singapore, 486025, Singa-
pore
Tel.: (65) 64166716
Web Site:
http://www.westminstertravel.com.sg
Travel Services
N.A.I.C.S.: 561510

**Guangzhou Westminster Travel Ser-
vices Ltd.** (2)
5/F Westminster Plaza Office Tower, 50
Zhongshanqi Road Liwan District,
Guangzhou, 510170, China
Tel.: (86) 20 3811 4000
Travel Services
N.A.I.C.S.: 561510

**Taipei Westminster Travel Limited
(Taiwan)** (2)
4F-1 No 237 Song Jiang Road, Zhongshan,
Taipei, 10483, Taiwan
Tel.: (886) 225027988

Web Site:
http://www.westminstertravel.com.tw
Travel Services
N.A.I.C.S.: 561510

Westminster Travel Limited (1)
4th Floor No 237 Songjiang Road, Zhong-
shan District, Taipei, 10483, Taiwan
Tel.: (886) 225027988
Web Site:
http://www.westminstertravel.com.tw
Travel Management Services
N.A.I.C.S.: 561510

Westminster Travel Limited (1)
Rua Do Dr Pedro Jose Lobo No 17-A Com-
ercial Infante 2 Andar B, Macau, China (Ma-
cau)
Tel.: (853) 28715900
Travel Management Services
N.A.I.C.S.: 561510

CORPORATION AIC-INVEST LLP

office 15 4/3 Otyrar str, Nur-Sultan,
010000, Kazakhstan
Tel.: (7) 7172 21 10 41
Grain Product Whslr
N.A.I.C.S.: 424510

CORPORATION TSESNA JSC

12 Momushuly Street, Almaty district,
Nur-Sultan, 010000, Kazakhstan
Tel.: (7) 7172 770200
Web Site: http://www.tsesna.kz
Rev.: $334,649,532
Assets: $5,163,389,872
Liabilities: $4,713,718,403
Net Worth: $449,671,469
Earnings: $95,369,334
Fiscal Year-end: 12/31/15
Investment Holding Company
N.A.I.C.S.: 551112

Subsidiaries:

Concern Tsesna-Astyk LLP (1)
Akzhol Str 24, Nur-Sultan, 010000, Kazakh-
stan
Tel.: (7) 7172700500
Web Site: http://www.concern.kz
Flour, Cereals, Mixed Feeds, Flakes, Bread,
Bakery Products, Confectionery & Pasta
Mfr, Distr & Retailer
N.A.I.C.S.: 311211
Kalenova Gulnara Tyulyubayevna (Gen Dir)

CORPORATIVO COPAMEX, S.A. DE C.V.

National Army Ave 531 Floor 4 Col
Granada, Del Miguel Hidalgo,
Mexico, 11520, Mexico
Tel.: (52) 5522826900
Web Site: http://www.copamex.com
Year Founded: 1987
Sales Range: $400-449.9 Million
Emp.: 6,800
Paper & Paper Products Mfr
N.A.I.C.S.: 322220
Juan Bosco Maldonado Quiroga
(Chm)

Subsidiaries:

**Copamex Corrugados, S.A. De
C.V.** (1)
Poniente 134 No 649, Col Industrial Vallejo,
02300, Mexico, Mexico (100%)
Tel.: (52) 5550028200
Paperboard Mills
N.A.I.C.S.: 322130

**Copamex Empaque, S.A. De
C.V.** (1)
Montes Apalaches 101-28 Residencial San
Agustin, San Pedro Garza Garcia, Nuevo
Leon, Mexico (100%)
Tel.: (52) 8150006000
Sales Range: $50-74.9 Million
Emp.: 200
Paper Mills
N.A.I.C.S.: 322120

Copamex North America (1)

1201 N Watson Rd Ste 268, Arlington, TX
76006
Tel.: (817) 652-8932
Web Site: http://www.copamex.com
Sales Range: $50-74.9 Million
Emp.: 3
Paper Bag Distr
N.A.I.C.S.: 424130
Raymond A. Radcliffe (Reg Mgr-Sls)

**Higiene Infantil de Mexico, S.A. De
C.V.** (1)
Valdepenas #2030, Anexo Lomas de Za-
popan, 45130, Jalisco, Mexico (100%)
Tel.: (52) 3330033800
Sanitary Paper Product Mfr
N.A.I.C.S.: 322291

**Papelera Mexicana SA de CV,
Industrial** (1)
Blvd Industrial 3201, Colonia La Cofradia,
60000, Uruapan, Michoacan,
Mexico (100%)
Tel.: (52) 4525280173
Sales Range: $125-149.9 Million
Emp.: 360
Mfr of Paper & Paper Products
N.A.I.C.S.: 322120

**Papelera de Chihuahua, S.A. De
C.V.** (1)
Plaza Ferrocarril Kansas No 1, Colonia
Popular, Chihuahua, 31350, Chihuhua,
Mexico
Tel.: (52) 6144394200
Web Site: http://www.copamex.com
Paper Mills
N.A.I.C.S.: 322120

CORPORATIVO FRAGUA, S.A.B. DE C.V.

Enrique Diaz De Leon 261 Norte,
Refugio, 44200, Guadalajara, Jal,
Mexico
Tel.: (52) 3336693333
Year Founded: 1983
FRAGUA—(MEX)
Rev.: $6,422,343
Assets: $3,004,950
Liabilities: $1,649,776
Net Worth: $1,355,173
Earnings: $294,603
Emp.: 55,737
Fiscal Year-end: 12/31/23
Pharmaceutical Preparation Whslr
N.A.I.C.S.: 424210
Javier Arroyo Chavez (Chm)

CORRE ENERGY B.V.

Helperpark 278-3, 9723 ZA, Gronin-
gen, Netherlands
Tel.: (31) 507995060　　　　　Nl
Web Site:
https://www.corre.energy.com
Year Founded: 2018
CORRE—(EUR)
Rev.: $6,141
Assets: $31,413,466
Liabilities: $20,941,492
Net Worth: $10,471,974
Earnings: ($4,847,863)
Emp.: 19
Fiscal Year-end: 12/31/21
Renewable Energy Storage Services
N.A.I.C.S.: 221210
Darren Patrick Green (Pres)

CORREVIO PHARMA CORP.

1441 Creekside Drive 6th Floor, Van-
couver, V6J 4S7, BC, Canada
Tel.: (604) 677-6905　　　　　Ca
Web Site: http://www.correvio.com
Year Founded: 1986
CORV—(NASDAQ)
Rev.: $32,634,000
Assets: $58,893,000
Liabilities: $59,727,000
Net Worth: ($834,000)
Earnings: ($35,184,000)
Emp.: 133
Fiscal Year-end: 12/31/19

Pharmaceutical Developer & Mfr
N.A.I.C.S.: 325412
Sheila M. Grant (COO)

CORROSION & ABRASION SOLUTIONS LTD.

4212 - 97 Street, Edmonton, T6E
5Z9, AB, Canada
Tel.: (780) 461-8333
Web Site: http://www.casltd.ca
Abrasion & Corrosion Control Ser-
vices
N.A.I.C.S.: 213112
Terry Freeman (Chm & CEO)

Subsidiaries:

Christie Corrosion Control Ltd. (1)
6614 - 50 Avenue, Lloydminster, T9V 2W8,
AB, Canada
Tel.: (780) 875-6161
Web Site: https://christiecorrosion.ca
Emp.: 6
Sandblasting Services
N.A.I.C.S.: 213112
Brain Jones (CEO)

Continental Cylinder Inc. (1)
10830 - 181 Street, Edmonton, T5S 1K8,
AB, Canada
Tel.: (780) 486-0776
Web Site:
http://www.continentalcylinder.com
Hydraulic Component Repair Services
N.A.I.C.S.: 811310
Jim Ross (Supvr-Shop)

EnerClear Services Inc. (1)
300 400 - 5 Ave SW, Calgary, T2P 0L6, AB,
Canada
Tel.: (403) 539-8740
Web Site: http://www.enerclear.ca
Pipeline Coating Services
N.A.I.C.S.: 213112
Chad Allan (Mgr-Ops)

**Fuller Western Rubber Linings
Ltd.** (1)
2102 - 5 Street, Nisku, T9E 7X3, AB,
Canada
Tel.: (780) 979-0518
Web Site: http://www.fullerwestern.ca
Industrial Coating Mfr
N.A.I.C.S.: 325510
Ritchie Helm (Mgr-Ops)

**Inotec Coatings & Hydraulics,
Inc.** (1)
4263-95 St NW, Edmonton, T6E 5R6, AB,
Canada
Tel.: (780) 461-8333
Web Site: http://www.inoteccoatings.ca
Hydraulic Equipment Whslr
N.A.I.C.S.: 423830

**MASTERBLASTERS INDUSTRIAL
COATINGS INC.** (1)
55473 - Range Road 220, Fort Saskatch-
ewan, T8L 4C2, AB, Canada
Tel.: (780) 998-9971
Web Site: http://www.masterblasters.ca
Sandblasting Services
N.A.I.C.S.: 213112

Magnum Energy Services Ltd. (1)
-, PO Box 5348, Bonnyville, T9N 2G5, AB,
Canada
Tel.: (780) 826-3092
Web Site:
http://www.magnumenergyservicesltd.com
Industrial Coating Mfr
N.A.I.C.S.: 325510
Moe Blackburn (Pres)

Thermal Spray Industries Ltd. (1)
11205 84 Avenue, Fort Saskatchewan, T8L
4L1, AB, Canada
Tel.: (780) 998-4771
Emp.: 15
Industrial Coating Mfr
N.A.I.C.S.: 325510

CORROSION SERVICE COM-PANY LIMITED

9-280 Hillmount Rd, Markham, L6C
3A1, ON, Canada
Tel.: (416) 630-2600

Web Site:
https://www.corrosionservice.com
Year Founded: 1950
Rev.: $11,859,557
Emp.: 40
Engineeering Services
N.A.I.C.S.: 541330
Brent Dorman *(VP-Western Ops)*

Subsidiaries:

Corrosion Service Company Inc   (1)
300 International Dr Ste 100, Williamsville,
NY 14221
Tel.: (800) 676-4984
Engineeering Services
N.A.I.C.S.: 541330
Alex Wise *(Dir-Corp Strategy)*

CORRUGATED BOX SUPPLIES LIMITED

CBS House Brandon Way, West Bro-
mwich, B70 8JF, United Kingdom
Tel.: (44) 121 525 5555   UK
Web Site:
http://www.cbspackaging.co.uk
Year Founded: 1995
Corrugated Box Mfr & Whslr
N.A.I.C.S.: 322211
Jitha Singh *(CEO)*

Subsidiaries:

Connect Packaging Ltd.   (1)
6-8 Brunel Road, Manor Trading Estate,
Benfleet, SS7 4PS, Essex, United Kingdom
Tel.: (44) 1268 565656
Web Site: http://www.connectpackaging.co.uk
Sales Range: $10-24.9 Million
Emp.: 75
Corrugated Packaging Products Mfr & Com-
mercial Screen Printing Services
N.A.I.C.S.: 322211
Jitha Singh *(CEO)*

CORRUVEN, INC.

355 Ch du Pouvoir, Edmundston,
E3V 4K1, NB, Canada
Tel.: (506) 802-7022   NV
Web Site: http://www.corruven.com
Year Founded: 2010
Sales Range: Less than $1 Million
Composite Panel Mfr
N.A.I.C.S.: 321211
Alain Belanger *(Pres & CEO)*

CORTICEIRA AMORIM, S.G.P.S., S.A.

Rua de Meladas N 380, Apartado 20,
Apartado 20, 4536-902, Lisbon, Por-
tugal
Tel.: (351) 227475400
Web Site: https://www.amorim.pt
Year Founded: 1870
COR—(EUR)
Rev.: $1,087,831,990
Assets: $1,562,230,931
Liabilities: $679,082,680
Net Worth: $883,148,250
Earnings: $110,537,587
Emp.: 3,704
Fiscal Year-end: 12/31/23
Wine Cork Mfr
N.A.I.C.S.: 321999
Antonio Rios de Amorim *(Chm & CEO)*

Subsidiaries:

Agglotap, S.A.   (1)
C/del Suro 8-10 s/n, PO Box 296, 17200,
Palafrugell, Spain
Tel.: (34) 972320066
Web Site: https://www.agglotap.com
Wood Products Mfr
N.A.I.C.S.: 321999

All Closures In, S.A.   (1)
Rua n 1 657, Lourosa, 4535-155, Santa
Maria da Feira, Portugal
Tel.: (351) 227661250
Web Site: https://www.allclosuresin.com
Wood Products Mfr

N.A.I.C.S.: 321999

Amorim & Irmaos, SGPS, S.A.   (1)
Rua dos Corticeiros 850 Apartado 1, Santa
Maria de Lamas, 4536-904, Santa Maria da
Feira, Portugal
Tel.: (351) 227475500
Wood Products Mfr
N.A.I.C.S.: 321999

Amorim (UK) Ltd.   (1)
Unit 9-Horsham Court City Business Centre
6-8 Brighton Road, Horsham, RH13 5BB,
West Sussex, United Kingdom
Tel.: (44) 1403750387
Wood Products Mfr
N.A.I.C.S.: 321999

Amorim Australasia Pty. Ltd.   (1)
27 Tikalara St, Adelaide, 5010, SA, Austra-
lia
Tel.: (61) 883409033
Web Site: http://www.amorimcork.com.au
Wine Distr
N.A.I.C.S.: 445320

Amorim Benelux B.V.   (1)
Slabbecoornweg 27, Postbus 67, 4691 RZ,
Tholen, Netherlands
Tel.: (31) 625407693
Wood Products Mfr
N.A.I.C.S.: 321999

Amorim Cork America, Inc.   (1)
360 Devlin Rd, Napa, CA 94558
Tel.: (707) 224-6000
Cork & Wine Product Whslr
N.A.I.C.S.: 424820

Amorim Cork Beijing Ltd.   (1)
No 6 Fu Xin Center Guo Gong Zhuang,
Hua Xiang Feng Tai District, Beijing, China
Tel.: (86) 1067530804
Wood Products Mfr
N.A.I.C.S.: 321999

Amorim Cork Bulgaria EOOD   (1)
Bulv Bresovsko Shosse 142, 4003, Plovdiv,
4003, Bulgaria
Tel.: (359) 32963913
Wood Products Mfr
N.A.I.C.S.: 321999

Amorim Cork Composites Inc.   (1)
26112 110th St, Trevor, WI 53179
Tel.: (262) 862-2311
Wood Products Mfr
N.A.I.C.S.: 321999

Amorim Cork Composites, S. A.   (1)
Rua Comendador Americo Ferreira Amorim
260, PO Box 20, Mozelos, 4535-186, Santa
Maria da Feira, Portugal
Tel.: (351) 227475300
Web Site:
https://amorimcorkcomposites.com
Emp.: 600
Wood Products Mfr
N.A.I.C.S.: 321999

Amorim Cork Deutschland GmbH &
Co KG   (1)
Am Ockenheimer Graben 38, 55411, Bin-
gen am Rhein, Germany
Tel.: (49) 672191750
Web Site: https://www.amorimcork.de
Wood Products Mfr
N.A.I.C.S.: 321999

Amorim Cork Flooring, S.A.   (1)
Rua do Ribeirinho 202, 4536-907, S Paio
de Oleiros, Portugal
Tel.: (351) 227475600
Web Site:
https://www.amorimcorkflooring.com
Cork Product Mfr & Distr
N.A.I.C.S.: 321999

Amorim Cork Hungary Zrt   (1)
Sport u 2, 2112, Veresegyhaz, Hungary
Tel.: (36) 28385163
Paper & Forest Product Mfr
N.A.I.C.S.: 322299

Amorim Cork Insulation, S.A.   (1)
Rua Comendador Americo Amorim 105,
4535-186, Mozelos, Portugal
Tel.: (351) 227419100
Web Site:
https://www.amorimcorkinsulation.com
Insulation Cork Product Mfr & Distr

N.A.I.C.S.: 321999

Amorim Cork Italia, SPA   (1)
Via Camillo Bianchi 8, 31015, Conegliano,
TV, Italy
Tel.: (39) 0438394971
Web Site: https://www.amorimcorkitalia.com
Paper Products Mfr
N.A.I.C.S.: 322299

Amorim Cork South Africa (Pty)
Ltd.   (1)
R310 Building 2 Stellenbosch Agri Park, PO
Box 130, Lynedoch, Stellenbosch, 7603,
South Africa
Tel.: (27) 218813060
Web Site: https://www.amorimcork.co.za
Wood Products Mfr
N.A.I.C.S.: 321999

Amorim Cork Ventures, Lda.   (1)
Rua de Meladas 105, 4535-186, Mozelos,
Portugal
Tel.: (351) 227475480
Web Site:
https://www.amorimcorkventures.com
Wood Products Mfr
N.A.I.C.S.: 321999

Amorim Deutschland, GmbH   (1)
Berner Strasse 55, D-27751, Delmenhorst,
Germany
Tel.: (49) 422159301
Web Site: https://www.amorim-
deutschland.de
Wood Products Mfr
N.A.I.C.S.: 321999

Amorim Flooring (Switzerland)
AG   (1)
Chamerstrasse 12 b, CH-6300, Zug, Swit-
zerland
Tel.: (41) 417262020
Web Site:
https://www.amorimcorkflooring.ch
Wood Products Mfr
N.A.I.C.S.: 321999

Amorim Flooring Austria GmbH   (1)
Turkenstrasse 25/8, 1090, Vienna, Austria
Tel.: (43) 15451651
Wood Products Mfr
N.A.I.C.S.: 321999

Amorim Flooring North America
Inc.   (1)
7310 Ritchie Hwy Ste 200GB46, Glen Bur-
nie, MD 21061
Tel.: (410) 553-6062
Web Site:
https://www.amorimcorkflooring.us
Wood Products Mfr
N.A.I.C.S.: 321999

Amorim Flooring Sweden AB   (1)
Kungportsavenyen 21, 411 36, Gothenburg,
Sweden
Tel.: (46) 709212012
Wood Products Mfr
N.A.I.C.S.: 321999

Amorim Florestal Espana, SL   (1)
Poligono Industrial S/N, San Vicente de Al-
cantara, 06500, Badajoz, Spain
Tel.: (34) 924413015
Wood Products Mfr
N.A.I.C.S.: 321999

Amorim Florestal Mediterraneo,
SL   (1)
Carretera de Castellar S/N, Estacion de
San Roque, 11368, Cadiz, Spain
Tel.: (34) 924410098
Wood Products Mfr
N.A.I.C.S.: 321999

Amorim Florestal, S.A.   (1)
Rua dos Corticeiros 850 Apartado 1, Santa
Maria de Lamas, 4536-904, Santa Maria da
Feira, Portugal
Tel.: (351) 227475556
Wood Products Mfr
N.A.I.C.S.: 321999

Amorim Isolamentos, S.A.   (1)
Estrada de Lavre Km 6-Apartado 7, 7080-
026, Vendas Novas, Portugal
Tel.: (351) 265809220
Wood Products Mfr
N.A.I.C.S.: 321999

Amorim Japan Corporation   (1)
3-1-27 Umebara Building 2th Floor, Rop-
pongi Minato-ku, Tokyo, 106-0032, Japan
Tel.: (81) 5037123957
Wood Products Mfr
N.A.I.C.S.: 321999

Amorim Revestimentos, S.A.   (1)
Rua do Ribeirinho n 202 Apartado 13, Sao
Paio de Oleiros, 4536-907, Santa Maria da
Feira, Portugal
Tel.: (351) 227475600
Wood Products Mfr
N.A.I.C.S.: 321999

Amorim Sports, Lda.   (1)
Rua Comendador Americo Ferreira Amorim
260, 4535-186, Mozelos, Portugal
Tel.: (351) 227475300
Web Site: https://www.amorim-sports.com
Sports & Recreation Services
N.A.I.C.S.: 611620

Amorim Top Series, S.A.   (1)
Rua Central da Vergada 1055-1085, Argon-
cilhe, 4505-006, Santa Maria da Feira, Por-
tugal
Tel.: (351) 227470420
Web Site: https://www.amorimtopseries.com
Wood Products Mfr
N.A.I.C.S.: 321999

Amorim Tunisie, S.A.R.L.   (1)
Route de Ain Draham, 8110, Tabarka, Tuni-
sia
Tel.: (216) 78670239
Wood Products Mfr
N.A.I.C.S.: 321999

Amosealtex Cork Co., Ltd.   (1)
Room 502-A No 23 Building Gems Park No
487 Tianlin Road, Shanghai, 200233, China
Tel.: (86) 2133674849
Cork Product Mfr
N.A.I.C.S.: 321999

Bouchons Prioux SARL   (1)
3 rue du Clair Marais ZA, Les Forges,
51200, Epernay, France
Tel.: (33) 326544569
Web Site: https://www.bouchons-prioux.com
Wood Products Mfr
N.A.I.C.S.: 321999

Chinamate (Shaanxi) Natural Products Co. Ltd.   (1)
1 Nan Wei Qi Lu Road, Yangling Demonstration Zone, Shaanxi, 712100, China
Tel.: (86) 2987209671
Wood Products Mfr
N.A.I.C.S.: 321999

Comatral - C. de Maroc. de Transf.
du Liege, S.A.   (1)
Km 26-RP n1 From Rabat to Casablanca,
Skhirat, 12050, Casablanca, Morocco
Tel.: (212) 537742162
Wood Products Mfr
N.A.I.C.S.: 321999

Cortex Korkvertriebs GmbH   (1)
Ibisweg 4, 90480, Nuremberg, Germany
Tel.: (49) 911936350
Web Site: https://www.cortex.de
Wood Products Mfr
N.A.I.C.S.: 321999

Corticeira Amorim - France SAS   (1)
19 Rue de Lasserens, 47230, Lavardac,
France
Tel.: (33) 553650030
Wood Products Mfr
N.A.I.C.S.: 321999

Elfverson & Co. AB   (1)
Industrigatan 6, 388 50, Paryd, Sweden
Tel.: (46) 480443630
Web Site: http://www.elfverson.se
Wood Products Mfr
N.A.I.C.S.: 321999

Francisco Oller, S.A.   (1)
Sector Industrial el Trust Crta C65 Km 16 5,
Cassa de la Selva, 17244, Girona, Spain
Tel.: (34) 972460350
Web Site: http://www.ollerfco.com
Bottle Cork Mfr
N.A.I.C.S.: 326160

Herdade de Rio Frio, S.A.   (1)
Lugar de Salteiros de Baixo, Longomel,

CORTICEIRA AMORIM, S.G.P.S., S.A.—(Continued)

7400-402, Ponte de Sor, Portugal
Tel.: (351) 212319661
Web Site: https://www.rio-frio.eu
Agricultural Develpment Services
N.A.I.C.S.: 926140

Hungarocork, Amorim, RT (1)
2112 Veresegyhaz Sport u 2, Budapest,
Hungary
Tel.: (36) 28385163
Wood Products Mfr
N.A.I.C.S.: 321999

Industria Corchera, S.A. (1)
Jorge Caceres 220 Casilla 845, Santiago,
Chile
Tel.: (56) 25255655
Wood Products Mfr
N.A.I.C.S.: 321999

Korken Schiesser Ges.M.B.H. (1)
Margaretengurtel 1a-3a, 1050, Vienna, Aus-
tria
Tel.: (43) 154516530
Web Site: https://www.korken.at
Wine Distr
N.A.I.C.S.: 445320

Korkkitrio Oy (1)
Aurinkokuja 5 A, FI- 33420, Tampere, Fin-
land
Tel.: (358) 405610304
Web Site: https://www.amorimcorkflooring.fi
Cork Product Mfr & Distr
N.A.I.C.S.: 321999

Portocork America, Inc. (1)
164 Gateway Rd E, Napa, CA 94558
Tel.: (707) 258-3930
Web Site: https://www.portocork.com
Cork Product Mfr
N.A.I.C.S.: 321999
Dustin Mowe (Pres & CEO)

Portocork France, S.A.S. (1)
26 rue des Freres Lumiere, Carbon-Blanc,
33560, Bordeaux, France
Tel.: (33) 557771727
Web Site: https://www.portocorkfrance.com
Wine Distr
N.A.I.C.S.: 445320

Portocork Italia, s.r.l. (1)
Corso di Porta Vittoria 28, Milan, Italy
Tel.: (39) 0291761549
Web Site: https://www.portocorkitalia.com
Wood Products Mfr
N.A.I.C.S.: 321999

**SIBL - Societe Industrielle Bois
Liege** (1)
Z I Ouled Salah Taher, BP A74, 18000,
Jijel, 18000, Algeria
Tel.: (213) 34553784
Web Site: https://www.sibl-cork.com
Emp.: 70
Wood Products Mfr
N.A.I.C.S.: 321999

Trefinos, S.L. (1)
Carrer del Suro 8-10, Palafrugell, 17200,
Girona, Spain
Tel.: (34) 972306630
Web Site: https://www.trefinos.net
Wood Products Mfr
N.A.I.C.S.: 321999

CORTINA CAPITAL CORP.
9245 Thimens Street, Pierrefonds,
H8Y 0A1, QC, Canada
Tel.: (514) 866-6743
Private Investment Firm
N.A.I.C.S.: 523999

CORTINA HOLDINGS LIMITED
391B Orchard Road 18-01 Ngee Ann
City Tower B, Singapore, 238874,
Singapore
Tel.: (65) 63399447   **SG**
Web Site: http://www.cortina.com.sg
Year Founded: 1972
C41—(SES)
Rev.: $612,489,811
Assets: $474,620,230
Liabilities: $191,812,523
Net Worth: $282,807,707

Earnings: $61,875,509
Emp.: 613
Fiscal Year-end: 03/31/23
Luxury Watch Distr
N.A.I.C.S.: 423940
Anthony Keen Ban Lim (Co-Founder,
Chm & CEO)

Subsidiaries:

Chronoswiss Asia Pte Ltd (1)
391B Orchard Road 21-01 Ngee Ann City
Tower B, Singapore, 238874, Singapore
Tel.: (65) 63399447
Web Site: http://www.cortina.com.sg
Sales Range: $25-49.9 Million
Emp.: 12
Chronoswiss Watches Whslr
N.A.I.C.S.: 423940

**Cortina Watch (Thailand) Co.,
Ltd.** (1)
26/50 14th Floor Orakarn Building Soi Chid-
lom Ploenchit Road, Lumpini Pathumwan,
Bangkok, 10330, Thailand
Tel.: (66) 22541031
Web Site: https://www.cortinawatch.com
Sales Range: $75-99.9 Million
Emp.: 150
Luxury Watch Distr
N.A.I.C.S.: 423940

Cortina Watch Co., Ltd. (1)
Room C 10F No 3 Section 1 Dunhua S
Road, Songshan District, Taipei,
Taiwan   **(75%)**
Tel.: (886) 225796186
Sales Range: $25-49.9 Million
Emp.: 40
Watches & Clocks Whslr
N.A.I.C.S.: 423940

Cortina Watch HK Limited (1)
3/F Wing Cheong House 53 Queens Road,
Central, China (Hong Kong)
Tel.: (852) 2 537 6231
Web Site: https://www.cortinawatch.com
Sales Range: $50-74.9 Million
Emp.: 8
Luxury Watch Distr
N.A.I.C.S.: 423940

Cortina Watch Pte Ltd. (1)
391B Orchard Road 21-01 Ngee Ann City
Tower B, Singapore, 238874, Singapore
Tel.: (65) 6 339 9447
Web Site: https://www.cortinawatch.com
Sales Range: $25-49.9 Million
Emp.: 30
Luxury Watch Distr
N.A.I.C.S.: 423940
Anthony Keen Ban Lim (Chm & CEO)

Cortina Watch Sdn Bhd (1)
Suite 2206 22nd Floor Wisma Chuang 34
Jalan Sultan Ismail, CP 31, 50250, Kuala
Lumpur, Malaysia
Tel.: (60) 321488354
Web Site: https://www.cortinawatch.com
Luxury Watch Distr
N.A.I.C.S.: 423940

Pacific Time Co., Ltd. (1)
7F1-2 No 21 Section 1 Tunhus South Road,
Taipei, Taiwan   **(100%)**
Tel.: (886) 225706789
Web Site: http://www.cortina.com.sg
Watches & Parts Whslr
N.A.I.C.S.: 423940

Pacific Time Pte Ltd. (1)
391B Orchard Road 18-06 Ngee Ann City
Tower B, Singapore, 238874, Singapore
Tel.: (65) 6 496 9331
Web Site: https://www.pacifictime.sg
Sales Range: $50-74.9 Million
Emp.: 100
Luxury Watch Distr
N.A.I.C.S.: 423940
Sharon Yin Chian Lim (Exec Dir)

CORTUS ENERGY AB
Isafjordsgatan 30C, 16440, Kista,
Sweden
Tel.: (46) 8 588 866 30
Web Site: http://www.cortus.se
Gas Power Distr
N.A.I.C.S.: 221210

CORTUS METALS, INC.
10545-45 Avenue NW 250 South-
ridge Suite 300, Edmonton, T6H
4M9, AB, Canada
Tel.: (780) 701-3215
Web Site:
https://www.cortusmetals.com
CRTS—(TSXV)
Sales Range: Less than $1 Million
Business Consulting Services
N.A.I.C.S.: 522299
Sean Mager (Pres, CEO & Sec)

CORUM GROUP LIMITED
Level 3 120 Sussex Street, Sydney,
2000, NSW, Australia
Tel.: (61) 292894699   **AU**
Web Site:
http://www.corumgroup.com.au
PHX—(ASX)
Rev.: $5,404,647
Assets: $19,936,565
Liabilities: $9,271,501
Net Worth: $10,665,064
Earnings: $63,435
Fiscal Year-end: 06/30/24
Software Development Services
N.A.I.C.S.: 541511
David Clarke (CEO, Mng Dir & Sec)

Subsidiaries:

Corum Health Pty Ltd (1)
120 Sussex Street, Sydney, 2000, NSW,
Australia
Tel.: (61) 1300669865
Web Site: https://www.corumhealth.com.au
Software Services
N.A.I.C.S.: 541511
Julian Sallabank (CEO & Mng Dir)

Corum eCommerce Pty Ltd (1)
Level 3 120 Sussex Street, Sydney, 2000,
NSW, Australia
Tel.: (61) 1300302060
Web Site:
http://www.corumecommerce.com.au
Real Estate Services
N.A.I.C.S.: 531390

CORUM WATCHES S.A.R.L.
Rue du Petit-Chateau 1, 2300, La
Chaux-de-Fonds, Switzerland
Tel.: (41) 329670670   **CH**
Web Site: http://www.corum-
watches.com
Sales Range: $10-24.9 Million
Emp.: 100
Seller of Watches Mfr
N.A.I.C.S.: 334519
Vuillemin Nicolas (Dir-Projects & Dev)

Subsidiaries:

Corum USA LLC (1)
12 H Mauchly, Irvine, CA 92618   **(100%)**
Tel.: (949) 788-6200
Sales Range: $10-24.9 Million
Emp.: 15
Watches & Parts Distr
N.A.I.C.S.: 423940

CORUS ENTERTAINMENT INC.
Corus Quay 25 Dockside Drive, To-
ronto, M5A 0B5, ON, Canada
Tel.: (416) 479-7000   **Ca**
Web Site: https://www.corusent.com
Year Founded: 1999
CJR.B—(OTCIQ)
Rev.: $1,207,435,881
Assets: $3,016,954,347
Liabilities: $2,062,288,779
Net Worth: $954,665,568
Earnings: $152,210,566
Emp.: 3,295
Fiscal Year-end: 08/31/21
Media & Entertainment Services
N.A.I.C.S.: 516120
John Gossling (CFO & Exec VP)

Subsidiaries:

Canadian Broadcast Sales (1)
45 St Clair Avenue West 5th Floor, Toronto,
M4V 1K9, ON, Canada
Tel.: (416) 961-4770
Sales Range: $25-49.9 Million
Emp.: 32
National Radio Advertising Sales Represen-
tation, Owned 50% by Corus Entertainment
Inc. & 50% by Rogers Communications,
Inc.
N.A.I.C.S.: 541840
Jamie Barnes (Grp Dir-Sls-West)

Corus Premium Television Ltd. (1)
25 Dockside Dr, Toronto, M5A 0B5, ON,
Canada   **(100%)**
Tel.: (416) 479-6784
Web Site: http://www.moviecentral.ca
Rev.: $23,628,393
Emp.: 85
Television Programming
N.A.I.C.S.: 516210

Unit (Domestic):

CHEX-TV - Durham (2)
10 Simcoe St N, Oshawa, L1G 4R8, ON,
Canada
Tel.: (905) 434-5030
Web Site: http://www.channel12.ca
Sales Range: $25-49.9 Million
Emp.: 15
Television Broadcasting Network Services
N.A.I.C.S.: 516120

CHEX-TV - Peterborough (2)
743 Monaghan Rd, Peterborough, K9J 5K2,
ON, Canada
Tel.: (705) 742-0451
Web Site: http://www.chextv.com
Sales Range: $25-49.9 Million
Emp.: 60
Television Broadcasting Network Services
N.A.I.C.S.: 516120
Brenda O'Brien (Gen Mgr-Sls)

CKWS-TV (2)
170 Queen St, Kingston, K7K 1B2, ON,
Canada
Tel.: (613) 544-2340
Web Site: http://www.ckwstv.com
Sales Range: $25-49.9 Million
Emp.: 50
Television Broadcasting Network Services
N.A.I.C.S.: 516120

Corus Radio Ltd. (1)
5204 84th St, Edmonton, T6E 5N8, AB,
Canada   **(100%)**
Tel.: (780) 440-6300
Web Site: http://www.corusent.com
Sales Range: $50-74.9 Million
Emp.: 110
Operate Twelve Radio Stations & Three
Radio Networks
N.A.I.C.S.: 516120
John M. Cassaday (CEO)

Unit (Domestic):

CFNY-FM Radio (2)
Corus Quay 25 Dockside Drive, Toronto,
M5A 0B5, ON, Canada
Tel.: (416) 408-3343
Web Site: http://www.edge.ca
Sales Range: $10-24.9 Million
Emp.: 200
Radio Broadcasting
N.A.I.C.S.: 516110

Country Music Television Limited (1)
330 Commerce St, Nashville, TN 37201-
1805
Tel.: (615) 335-8400
Web Site: http://www.cmt.com
Sales Range: $25-49.9 Million
Emp.: 30
Television Broadcasting Network Services
N.A.I.C.S.: 516120

Nelvana Limited (1)
Corus Quay 25 Dockside Drive, Toronto,
M5A 0B5, ON, Canada
Tel.: (416) 479-7000
Web Site: https://www.nelvana.com
Sales Range: $400-449.9 Million
Emp.: 1,200
Animation Programme Production Services

N.A.I.C.S.: 512191
Pam Westman *(Pres)*

Telelatino Network Inc. **(1)**
5125 Steeles Ave W, North York, M9L 1R5,
ON, Canada
Tel.: (416) 744-8200
Web Site: http://www.tlntv.com
Sales Range: $25-49.9 Million
Emp.: 50
Television Broadcasting Network Services
N.A.I.C.S.: 516120
Aldo Di Felice *(Pres)*

Womens Network **(1)**
25 Dockside Dr, Toronto, M5A 0B5, ON,
Canada **(100%)**
Tel.: (416) 479-7000
Web Site: http://www.wnetwork.com
Sales Range: $100-124.9 Million
Emp.: 1,200
Television Service Specialized for Women
N.A.I.C.S.: 516120
Jennifer Savitski *(Chm)*

CORVUS CAPITAL LTD.
3rd Fl 13 charles 2nd St, London,
SW1Y 4QU, United Kingdom
Tel.: (44) 2074519800
Web Site:
http://www.corvuscapital.com
Sales Range: $25-49.9 Million
Emp.: 18
Investment Management Service
N.A.I.C.S.: 523999
Andrew Regan *(CEO)*

COSA RESOURCES CORP.
1723 - 595 Burrard Street, Vancou-
ver, V7X 1L4, BC, Canada
Tel.: (250) 218-2077   BC
Web Site: https://cosaresources.ca
Year Founded: 2020
COSA—(CNSX)
Mineral Exploration Services
N.A.I.C.S.: 212220
Keith Bodnarchuk *(Pres & CEO)*

COSALT PLC
Origin 4 Genesis Park Origin Way,
Grimsby, DN31 3NW, Lincs, United
Kingdom
Tel.: (44) 1472 725560   UK
Web Site: http://www.cosalt.plc.uk
Year Founded: 1873
Holding Company
N.A.I.C.S.: 551112
David Ross *(Chm)*

Subsidiaries:

Cosalt Ballyclare Limited **(1)**
Banner House Greg Street, Reddish, Stock-
port, SK5 7BP, United Kingdom
Tel.: (44) 1614291100
Web Site: http://www.cosalt.com
Sales Range: $50-74.9 Million
Emp.: 40
Personal Protective Equipment & Workwear
Mfr & Distr
N.A.I.C.S.: 423830

COSAN S.A.
Av Brigadeiro Faria Lima 4 100 / 15th
floor, Itaim Bibi, Sao Paulo, 04538-
132, SP, Brazil
Tel.: (55) 1138979797   BR
Web Site: https://www.cosan.com.br
Year Founded: 1936
CSAN—(NYSE)
Rev.: $7,870,873,866
Assets: $27,892,189,052
Liabilities: $17,725,436,634
Net Worth: $10,166,752,418
Earnings: $965,066,308
Emp.: 56,486
Fiscal Year-end: 12/31/23
Sugar Cane & Ethanol Producer
N.A.I.C.S.: 311314

Subsidiaries:

Comma Oil & Chemicals Limited **(1)**
Dering Way, Gravesend, DA12 2QX, Kent,
United Kingdom
Tel.: (44) 1474564311
Web Site: https://www.commaoil.com
Sales Range: $50-74.9 Million
Emp.: 210
Automotive Lubricant Distr
N.A.I.C.S.: 424720

Compass Gas & Energia SA **(1)**
Av Brigadeiro Faria Lima 4100 4 andar
Itaim Bibi, 04538-132, Sao Paulo, Brazil
Tel.: (55) 11992316621
Web Site: https://www.compassbr.com
Natural Gas Distribution Services
N.A.I.C.S.: 221210

Joint Venture (Domestic):

Petrobras Gas S.A. **(2)**
Av Hemmiique Valagaes No 28 18th Floor,
Parte-Centro, 20231030, Rio de Janeiro,
RJ, Brazil **(51%)**
Tel.: (55) 2132241000
Web Site:
http://www.gaspetro.petrobras.com.br
Sales Range: $100-124.9 Million
Emp.: 101
Natural Gas Pipeline Transportation Ser-
vices
N.A.I.C.S.: 486210
Jose Formigle *(Dir-Exploration & Produc-
tion)*

Cosan Cayman Finance Limited **(1)**
494 Shedden Road Suite 2, PO Box 11048,
Georgetown, KY1-1007, Cayman Islands
Tel.: (345) 623 6700
Web Site: http://www.caymanfinances.com
Financial Management Services
N.A.I.C.S.: 523999

Cosan Limited **(1)**
Av Brigadeiro Faria Lima 4 100 16th floor,
Sao Paulo, 04538-132, SP, Brazil
Tel.: (55) 1138979797
Web Site: http://www.cosan.com.br
Rev.: $5,102,972,640
Assets: $16,270,431,245
Liabilities: $12,249,612,959
Net Worth: $4,020,818,286
Earnings: $716,341,287
Emp.: 11,909
Fiscal Year-end: 12/31/2019
Holding Company; Sugar & Ethanol Produc-
tion, Marketing & Distribution
N.A.I.C.S.: 551112
Rubens Ometto Silveira Mello *(Chm)*

Subsidiary (Domestic):

Agricola Ponte Alta S.A. **(2)**
Pte Alta s/n Predio I Barra Bonita, Barra
Bonita, 17340-000, Brazil
Tel.: (55) 1436044400
Sugarcane Farming Services
N.A.I.C.S.: 111930

**Centro de Tecnologia Canavieira
S.A.** **(2)**
Fazenda Santo Antonio S/N, Caixa Postal
162, Piracicaba, 13400-970, Brazil
Tel.: (55) 1934298199
Sugarcane Research & Development Ser-
vices
N.A.I.C.S.: 541715

**Companhia de Gas de Sao Paulo -
Comgas** **(2)**
Av Brigadeiro Faria Lima 4100 4th andar,
Itaim Bibi, Sao Paulo, CEP 04538-132,
Brazil **(99.14%)**
Tel.: (55) 1145045000
Web Site: http://www.comgas.com.br
Sales Range: $1-4.9 Billion
Natural Gas Distr
N.A.I.C.S.: 221210
Marcos Marinho Lutz *(Vice Chm)*

Subsidiary (Domestic):

**CIA de Gas de Sao Paulo - Comgas
ON** **(3)**
Av Brigadeiro Faria Lima 4100 42 59/64
andar, Sao Paulo, 04538-132, Brazil
Tel.: (55) 1145045000

Sales Range: Less than $1 Million
Oil & Gas Distribution Services
N.A.I.C.S.: 221210
Antonio Simoes Rodrigues Jr. *(CEO)*

Subsidiary (Domestic):

**Esso Brasileira de Petroleo
Limitada** **(2)**
Rua Victor Civita 77 Building 1, Rio de Ja-
neiro, 22775-905, Barra da Tijuca, Brazil
Tel.: (55) 2134332000
Web Site: http://www.esso.com
Sales Range: $450-499.9 Million
Emp.: 1,500
Gasoline Service Stations
N.A.I.C.S.: 457110

Rumo S.A. **(2)**
Rua Emilio Bertolini 100 Vila Oficinas,
82920-030, Sao Paulo, 82920-030, Brazil
Tel.: (55) 4121417555
Web Site: https://ri.rumolog.com
Rev.: $1,962,610,031
Assets: $9,163,774,055
Liabilities: $6,090,596,271
Net Worth: $3,073,177,784
Earnings: $102,506,930
Emp.: 7,742
Fiscal Year-end: 12/31/2022
Transportation Related Services
N.A.I.C.S.: 488999
Rubens Ometto Silveira Mello *(Chm)*

Handson Participacoes S.A. **(1)**
Fazenda Pau Dalho S/N Sala 20 B Predio
Administrativo, Barra Bonita, Sao Paulo,
17340-000, Brazil
Tel.: (55) 51 3204 5500
Agricultural Chemical Product Mfr
N.A.I.C.S.: 325320

COSAR PHARMACEUTICAL
COMPANY
Darougar Station 17Km Oldway,
Karaj, Tehran, Iran
Tel.: (98) 21 44922074
Web Site:
http://www.cosarpharm.com
Year Founded: 1974
Emp.: 220
Pharmaceutical Preparation Mfr
N.A.I.C.S.: 325412

COSBOARD INDUSTRIES LIM-
ITED.
New Industrial Estate Phase II, Jag-
atpur, Cuttack, 754021, Orissa, India
Tel.: (91) 6712491966
Web Site: https://www.cosboard.com
Year Founded: 1981
Sales Range: Less than $1 Million
Paperboard Mfr
N.A.I.C.S.: 322130
Anil Kumar Gilra *(Compliance Officer)*

COSCO (INDIA) LIMITED
2/8 Roop Nagar, Delhi, 110007, India
Tel.: (91) 1123843000
Web Site:
https://www.coscoindia.com
Year Founded: 1980
530545—(BOM)
Rev.: $20,325,778
Assets: $14,314,045
Liabilities: $8,346,020
Net Worth: $5,968,026
Earnings: $615,342
Emp.: 430
Fiscal Year-end: 03/31/21
Health & Fitness Equipment Mfr
N.A.I.C.S.: 339920
Pankaj Jain *(CFO)*

COSCO CAPITAL, INC.
3/F New Tabacalera Bldg3/F New
Tabacalera Bldg, No 900 D Romualdez Sr St Paco, Manila, 1007, Philippines
Tel.: (63) 2567106
Web Site:
https://www.coscocapital.com

Year Founded: 1988
COSCO—(PHI)
Rev.: $3,753,862,299
Assets: $3,706,348,381
Liabilities: $1,422,938,317
Net Worth: $2,283,410,064
Earnings: $122,724,035
Emp.: 11,373
Fiscal Year-end: 12/31/20
Oil & Gas Exploration Services
N.A.I.C.S.: 211120
Teodoro A. Polinga *(Comptroller)*

Subsidiaries:

118 Holdings Inc. **(1)**
Gate 5 No 900 D Romualdez Sr St, Paco,
Manila, Philippines
Tel.: (63) 25222312
Real Estate Services
N.A.I.C.S.: 531390

**Alcorn Petroleum & Minerals
Corporation** **(1)**
Tabacalera Bldg 2 No 900 D Romualdez Sr
St, Paco, Manila, Philippines
Tel.: (63) 24375680
Oil & Mineral Exploration Services
N.A.I.C.S.: 213112

Ellimac Prime Holdings Inc. **(1)**
Tabacalera Bldg 1 No 900 D Romualdez Sr
St, Paco, Manila, Philippines
Tel.: (63) 25222312
Real Estate Services
N.A.I.C.S.: 531390

Meritus Prime Distributions Inc. **(1)**
Unit 704 Federal Tower Dasmarinas St, Bi-
nondo, Manila, Philippines
Tel.: (63) 22436630
Spirit & Wine Distr
N.A.I.C.S.: 424820

Montosco Inc. **(1)**
Unit 1501 Federal Tower Dasmarinas
Street, Binondo, Manila, Philippines
Tel.: (63) 22435530
Liquor Distr
N.A.I.C.S.: 424820

**NE Pacific Shopping Centers
Corp.** **(1)**
Km 111 Maharlika Highway, Cabanatuan,
Nueva Ecija, Philippines
Tel.: (63) 449401256
Real Estate Services
N.A.I.C.S.: 531390

Nation Realty Inc. **(1)**
Gate 5 No 900 D Romualdez Sr St, Paco,
Manila, Philippines
Tel.: (63) 22745573
All Merchandise Product Distr
N.A.I.C.S.: 455219

Premier Wine & Spirits Inc. **(1)**
900 N Romualdez St Compound Paco Gate
1, Tabacalera, Manila, Philippines
Tel.: (63) 25242165
Spirit & Wine Distr
N.A.I.C.S.: 424820

Pure Petroleum Corp. **(1)**
Lot Adjacent to Boton Wharf Argonaut High-
way Subic Bay Freeport Zone, Bataan, Phil-
ippines
Tel.: (63) 472502417
Fuel Terminal Services
N.A.I.C.S.: 424710

COSCO SHIPPING HOLDINGS
CO., LTD.
Second Floor Building 12 Tianjin Air-
port Economic Zone, Yuanhang Busi-
ness Center Intersection of Central
Avenue & Dongqi Avenue, Tianjin,
300461, China
Tel.: (86) 2160298620   CN
Web Site:
https://en.hold.coscoshipping.com
Year Founded: 2005
CICOF—(OTCIQ)
Rev.: $54,904,612,923
Assets: $71,853,871,818
Liabilities: $36,259,176,952

COSCO Shipping Holdings Co., Ltd.—(Continued)

Net Worth: $35,594,694,865
Earnings: $15,387,101,777
Emp.: 31,510
Fiscal Year-end: 12/31/22
Holding Company; Container Shipping Services
N.A.I.C.S.: 551112
Yuntei Sun (CFO)

Subsidiaries:

COSCO SHIPPING Container Line
Agencies Limited (1)
7-8/F CHT Tower Terminal 8 East Container
Port Road South, Kwai Chung, China (Hong
Kong)
Tel.: (852) 26161888
Web Site: http://www.coslina.com
Freight Transportation Services
N.A.I.C.S.: 488510
Ada Li (Gen Mgr-Customer Svc)

COSCO SHIPPING Lines (Dalian)
Co., Ltd.
Block B COSCO SHIPPING Plaza No 6
Youhao Square, Zhongshan, Dalian,
116001, China
Tel.: (86) 41182636161
Web Site:
   https://investdl.coscoshipping.com
Logistic Services
N.A.I.C.S.: 541614

COSCO SHIPPING Lines Americas,
Inc. (1)
100 Lighting Way, Secaucus, NJ 07094
Tel.: (201) 422-0500
Web Site: https://na.coscoshipping.com
Container Shipping Mfr
N.A.I.C.S.: 811310

COSCO SHIPPING Ports
Limited (1)
49/F COSCO Tower 183 Queen s Road,
Central, China (Hong Kong) (47.15%)
Tel.: (852) 28098188
Web Site: http://ports.coscoshipping.com
Rev.: $1,441,273,000
Assets: $11,310,812,000
Liabilities: $4,687,221,000
Net Worth: $6,623,591,000
Earnings: $388,847,000
Emp.: 4,855
Fiscal Year-end: 12/31/2022
Holding Company; Marine Terminal Operation, Logistics & Cargo Handling Services
N.A.I.C.S.: 551112
Michelle Man Hung (Gen Counsel & Sec)

Subsidiary (Non-US):

CSP Zeebrugge Terminal NV (2)
Leopold II-dam Kaai 120-122, 8380, Zeebrugge, Belgium (100%)
Tel.: (32) 50502500
Web Site: https://cspterminals.be
Shipping Terminal Operator
N.A.I.C.S.: 488310
Carla Debart (Mng Dir)

Cosco Shipping Lines (Brazil)
S.A. (1)
Paulista Avenue 1337 18 Floor Bela Vista,
Sao Paulo, CEP 01311-200, SP, Brazil
Tel.: (55) 1131772888
Container Shipping Mfr
N.A.I.C.S.: 811310

Tianjin YuanHua Shipping Co.,
Ltd (1)
7-8 Building 4 West District Financial Street
3rd Avenue, Tianjin Economic & Technological Development Zone, Tianjin, 300457,
China
Tel.: (86) 22 66280000
Web Site: http://www.cosbulk.com
Container Shipping Services
N.A.I.C.S.: 488510

Subsidiary (Non-US):

COSCO Container Industries
Limited (2)
49/F COSCO Tower 183 Queen's Road,
Central, China (Hong Kong)
Tel.: (852) 2809 8888
Holding Company

N.A.I.C.S.: 551112

COSEL CO., LTD.

1-6-43 Kami-Akae Machi, Toyama,
930-0816, Japan
Tel.: (81) 764328151
Web Site: https://www.cosel.co.jp
6905—(TKS)
Hev: $273,898,570
Assets: $359,564,170
Liabilities: $47,195,400
Net Worth: $312,368,770
Earnings: $34,167,090
Emp.: 721
Fiscal Year-end: 05/31/24
Industrial Machinery Mfr
N.A.I.C.S.: 335313
Masato Tanikawa (Pres & CEO)

Subsidiaries:

Cosel (Shanghai) Electronics Co.,
Ltd. (1)
Unit 709 Tower 1 Kerry Everbright City 218
Tian Mu Road West, Jingan District, Shanghai, 200070, China
Tel.: (86) 2164400381
Web Site: https://www.coselasia.cn
Sales Range: $25-49.9 Million
Emp.: 10
Power Supplies Mfr
N.A.I.C.S.: 335311

Cosel Asia Ltd. (1)
Room 707 7/F Westin Centre 26 Hung To
Road, Kwun Tong, Kowloon, China (Hong
Kong)
Tel.: (852) 23052712
Web Site: https://www.coselasia.com
Sales Range: $25-49.9 Million
Emp.: 8
Power Supplies Mfr
N.A.I.C.S.: 335311
Toru Takeda (Mng Dir)

Cosel Europe GmbH (1)
Lurgiallee 6-8, D-60439, Frankfurt am Main,
Germany
Tel.: (49) 699500790
Web Site: https://www.coseleurope.eu
Sales Range: $25-49.9 Million
Emp.: 7
Power Supplies Mfr
N.A.I.C.S.: 335311

Powerbox International AB (1)
Vastberga Alle 36A 5tr, 126 30, Hagersten,
Sweden
Tel.: (46) 15870300
Web Site: https://www.prbx.com
Power Supply Product Mfr
N.A.I.C.S.: 335999

COSET INC.

39 Cheomdan venture-ro 60beon-gil,
Buk-gu, Gwangju, 61009, Korea
(South)
Tel.: (82) 629758881
Web Site: https://www.coset.com
Year Founded: 1999
Packaging Solutions & Services
N.A.I.C.S.: 326112

COSHIP ELECTRONICS CO., LTD.

27/F Building 1 Xunmei Science and
Technology Plaza High tech Park,
Nanshan District, Shenzhen, 518057,
China
Tel.: (86) 75526990000
Web Site: https://www.coship.com
Year Founded: 1994
002052—(SSE)
Rev.: $35,775,324
Assets: $61,954,308
Liabilities: $51,290,928
Net Worth: $10,663,380
Earnings: ($6,678,828)
Fiscal Year-end: 12/31/22
Telecommunications Equipment Mfr
N.A.I.C.S.: 334220
Liu Yongteng (Chm)

COSIGO RESOURCES LTD.

3854 Cadboro Bay Road, Victoria,
V8N 4G4, BC, Canada
Tel.: (250) 477-7748
Web Site: https://www.cosigo.com
Gold Exploration Services
N.A.I.C.S.: 212220
Andres M. Rendle (VP-South American Ops)

COSLIGHT TECHNOLOGY INTERNATIONAL GROUP LIMITED

No 68 Dianlan Street Xuefu Road,
Nangang District, Harbin, 150086,
China
Tel.: (86) 451 86677970   BM
Web Site: http://www.cncoslight.com
Year Founded: 1994
Rev.: $464,721,543
Assets: $1,043,644,750
Liabilities: $682,312,798
Net Worth: $361,331,951
Earnings: $32,752,151
Emp.: 6,850
Fiscal Year-end: 12/31/18
Battery Mfr
N.A.I.C.S.: 335910
Dian Quan Song (Chm)

Subsidiaries:

COSLIGHT USA INC. (1)
317 W Main St, Alhambra, CA 91801
Tel.: (626) 348-7878
Battery Distr
N.A.I.C.S.: 423610

COSLIGHT-NEWGEN LTD. (1)
B Novodmitrovskaya Street 14 Office 235,
Moscow, 127015, Russia
Tel.: (7) 9032584300
Battery Distr
N.A.I.C.S.: 423610

Coslight Technology International
Group Limited - Changdu Coslight
Li-Min Pharmaceutical Factory (1)
No 14 Changdu West Road, Chengdu,
854000, Xizang, China
Tel.: (86) 895 4823339
Battery Mfr
N.A.I.C.S.: 335910

Euro-COSLIGHT GmbH (1)
Zonser Strasse 55, 41539, Dormagen, Germany
Tel.: (49) 173 2651905
Emp.: 2
Battery Distr
N.A.I.C.S.: 423610
Christian Wudel (Mgr-Sls & Mktg)

Hangzhou Yuexi Bus Manufacture
Co., Ltd. (1)
No 5588 Jiang Dong Sixth Road Jiang
Dong Industrial Park, Hangzhou, 311222,
Zhejiang, China
Tel.: (86) 57157179693
Web Site: http://www.en.yuexibus.com
Bus Research & Development Mfr
N.A.I.C.S.: 336211

Harbin Coslight Electric Automation
Company Limited (1)
Harbin No 9 Dianchi Street Yingbin Road
Concentration Zone, Daoli District, Shanghai, 150078, China
Tel.: (86) 45151686640
Web Site: http://www.clea.com.cn
Electric Power Automation Product Distr
N.A.I.C.S.: 238210

Harbin Coslight Electric Wire & Cable
Co., Ltd. (1)
No 68 Dianlan Street Xuefu Road, Nangang
District, Harbin, 150086, China
Tel.: (86) 45186600540
Electric Wire & Cable Mfr
N.A.I.C.S.: 335929

Harbin Coslight Power Co., Ltd. (1)
No 8 Taihu South Street Yingbin Road Center Zone, Daoli, Harbin, China
Tel.: (86) 451 86649582

Emp.: 304
Battery Mfr
N.A.I.C.S.: 335910

Harbin Coslight Storage Battery Company Limited (1)
No 68 Dianlan Street Xuefu Road, Nangang
District, Harbin, 150086, China
Tel.: (86) 45186677970
Battery Mfr & Distr
N.A.I.C.S.: 335910

Harbin Coslight Switch Company
Limited (1)
No 68 Dianlan Street Xuefu Road, Nangang
District, Harbin, China
Tel.: (86) 45186661821
Voltage Switch Cabinet Mfr
N.A.I.C.S.: 335999

Shanghai Sino-IC Microelectronics
Company Limited (1)
Room 3401-03 of No 3 Building No 200
Zhangheng Road, Zhangjiang High-tect
Park Pudong District, Shanghai, 201203,
China
Tel.: (86) 2133932402
Battery Mfr & Distr
N.A.I.C.S.: 335910

Shenyang Northeast Storage Battery
Ltd. (1)
No 33 North erzhong Road, Diexi, Shenyang, China
Tel.: (86) 24 25656921
Battery Mfr
N.A.I.C.S.: 335910

Shenzhen Coslight Software Co.,
Ltd. (1)
2nd floor of M-8 Building Ma Que Ling Industrial zone, Nanshan, Shenzhen, 518057,
China
Tel.: (86) 755 26856003
Battery Mfr
N.A.I.C.S.: 335910

Shenzhen Lexel Battery Co., Ltd. (1)
3rd Industrial Park, Luotian Community
Yanluo Baoan, Shenzhen, China
Tel.: (86) 75527066466
Web Site: http://www.lexelbattery.com
Battery Mfr & Distr
N.A.I.C.S.: 335910
Gao Xuefeng (Chm)

Subsidiary (Non-US):

LEXEL BATTERY (JAPAN) CO.,
LTD. (2)
6-2-1 Oka Matsubara city, Osaka, 580-0014, Japan
Tel.: (81) 72 335 6070
Web Site: http://www.nihonlexel.co.jp
Emp.: 8
Battery Distr
N.A.I.C.S.: 423610
Yohji Hayashi (Mgr-Ops)

Tianjin Coslight Electrical Bicycle Co.,
Ltd (1)
No 36 Yuanquan Road Wuqing Economic
Development Zone, Tianjin, China
Tel.: (86) 22 82117700
Web Site: http://www.cosbike.com
Battery Mfr
N.A.I.C.S.: 335910

Yanbian Coslight Storage Battery
Ltd. (1)
No 26 Henan Road, Mingyue Town Antu
County, Jilin, 133600, Yanbian Korean Auton, China
Tel.: (86) 433 5833280
Emp.: 333
Battery Mfr
N.A.I.C.S.: 335910

Zhuhai Coslight Battery Co., Ltd. (1)
No 9 Zhufeng Road Xinqing Science and
Technology Park, Doumen, Zhuhai, 519180,
China
Tel.: (86) 756 6199908
Battery Mfr
N.A.I.C.S.: 335910

Zhuhai Coslight Electric Technology
Co., Ltd. (1)
No 239 Zhufeng Road Xinqing Science and
Technology Park, Doumen, Zhuhai, China

Tel.: (86) 756 6199696
Battery Mfr
N.A.I.C.S.: 335910

COSMAX BTI INC.
255 Pangyo-ro Building E Building F
Pangyo Inno Valley, Bundang-gu,
Seongnam, Gyeonggi-do, Korea
(South)
Tel.: (82) 317893000
Web Site: https://www.cosmax.com
Year Founded: 1992
044820—(KRS)
Rev.: $473,548,695
Assets: $718,016,816
Liabilities: $468,157,343
Net Worth: $249,859,473
Earnings: ($15,520,955)
Emp.: 210
Fiscal Year-end: 12/31/22
Cosmetics Products Mfr
N.A.I.C.S.: 325620
Kyungsoo Lee (Founder & Chm)

COSMAX INC.
255 Pangyoro Pangyo Inno Valley
Building E Building F, Bundang-gu,
Seongnam, Gyeonggi-do, Korea
(South)
Tel.: (82) 317893000
Web Site: https://www.cosmax.com
Year Founded: 1992
192820—(KRS)
Rev.: $1,227,296,466
Assets: $1,071,077,537
Liabilities: $730,340,431
Net Worth: $340,737,106
Earnings: ($12,614,716)
Emp.: 843
Fiscal Year-end: 12/31/22
Cosmetic Product Mfr & Whslr
N.A.I.C.S.: 325620
Kyung-Soo Lee (Founder & Chm)

Subsidiaries:

Cosmax (Thailand) Co., Ltd.   (1)
Moo 7 28/6-7 Bangpla, Bang Phli District,
Samut Prakan, 10540, Samutprakarn, Thailand
Tel.: (66) 21385390
Web Site: https://www.cosmax.co.th
Cosmetic Product Mfr & Distr
N.A.I.C.S.: 325620

COSMAX NBT, INC.
5/6F GB2 Bldg Pangyo ro 256beon
gil 25, Bundang gu, Seongnam,
13487, Gyeonggi do, Korea (South)
Tel.: (82) 3180168527
Web Site:
    https://www.cosmaxnbt.com
Year Founded: 2002
222040—(KRS)
Rev.: $251,735,086
Assets: $233,145,686
Liabilities: $196,901,596
Net Worth: $36,244,090
Earnings: ($9,905,938)
Emp.: 642
Fiscal Year-end: 12/31/22
Food Products Mfr
N.A.I.C.S.: 311999
Yun Won-Il (CEO)

COSMECCA KOREA CO.,LTD.
17-9 17-12 Daegeum-ro 196beon-gil
Daeso-myeon, Eumseong,
Chungcheongbuk-do, Korea (South)
Tel.: (82) 315357161
Web Site: https://www.cosmecca.com
Year Founded: 1999
241710—(KRS)
Rev.: $306,339,215
Assets: $301,243,572
Liabilities: $142,456,501
Net Worth: $158,787,071
Earnings: $2,037,184

Emp.: 520
Fiscal Year-end: 12/31/22
Cosmetic Product Mfr & Distr
N.A.I.C.S.: 325620
Eun Hee Park (Co-CEO)

Subsidiaries:

Cosmecca Foshan, Ltd.   (1)
No 17 West Keji Rd Nanhai District Songxia
Industrial Park, Foshan, 528231, Guang-
dong, China
Tel.: (86) 75781760080
Cosmetics Products Mfr
N.A.I.C.S.: 325620

Cosmecca Suzhou Co., Ltd.   (1)
71 Namho Road Wuzhong qu Economic
Development Zone, Suzhou, Jiangsu, China
Tel.: (86) 51267080143
Cosmetic Product Distr
N.A.I.C.S.: 424210

COSMIC CRF LIMITED
19 Manoharpukur Road, Kolkata,
700029, West Bengal, India
Tel.: (91) 8100862182
Web Site: https://www.cosmiccrf.com
Year Founded: 2021
543928—(BOM)
Iron & Steel Mfr
N.A.I.C.S.: 331210
Aditya Vikram Birla (Mng Dir)

COSMO AM & T CO., LTD.
36 Chungjuhosu-ro, Seo-gu, Chungju,
Chungcheongbuk-do, Korea (South)
Tel.: (82) 438501114
Web Site:
    https://www.cosmoamt.com
Year Founded: 1967
005070—(KRS)
Rev.: $372,459,222
Assets: $346,163,296
Liabilities: $153,489,754
Net Worth: $192,673,542
Earnings: $21,243,620
Emp.: 383
Fiscal Year-end: 12/31/22
Toner & Audio Product Mfr
N.A.I.C.S.: 325992
Dong Hwan Hong (CEO)

COSMO BIO CO., LTD.
Toyo-Ekimae Bldg 2-20 Toyo
2-Chome Koto-ku, Tokyo, 135-0016,
Japan
Tel.: (81) 356329600
Year Founded: 1978
3386—(TKS)
Rev.: $66,220,600
Assets: $77,082,480
Liabilities: $13,088,140
Net Worth: $63,994,340
Earnings: $3,133,780
Emp.: 155
Fiscal Year-end: 12/31/23
Research Reagents Sales & Services
N.A.I.C.S.: 541715
Haruhisa Sakurai (Pres)

Subsidiaries:

Cosmo Bio USA, Inc.   (1)
2792 Loker Ave W Ste 101, Carlsbad, CA
92010
Tel.: (760) 431-4600
Web Site: https://www.cosmobiousa.com
Emp.: 6
Chemical Products Mfr
N.A.I.C.S.: 325998
Haruhisa Sakurai (Pres & CEO)

Proteintech Japan Co., Ltd.   (1)
Toyo Ekimae Building 2-2-20 Toyo, Koto-ku,
Tokyo, 135-0016, Japan
Tel.: (81) 356329712
Biotechnology Research & Development
Services
N.A.I.C.S.: 541714

COSMO CHEMICAL CO., LTD.

55 Wonbong-ro, Onsan-eup, Ulsan,
Korea (South)
Tel.: (82) 522316700
Web Site:
    https://www.cosmochem.com
Year Founded: 1968
005420—(KRS)
Rev.: $550,855,235
Assets: $619,627,773
Liabilities: $313,863,196
Net Worth: $305,764,577
Earnings: $8,623,840
Emp.: 235
Fiscal Year-end: 12/31/22
Titanium Dioxide Mfr
N.A.I.C.S.: 325180
J. K. Ham (CEO)

Subsidiaries:

Cosmo Chemical Co., Ltd. - Onsan
Factory   (1)
55 Wonbong-ro Onsan-eup, Ulju-gun, Ul-
san, Korea (South)
Tel.: (82) 522316712
Basic Inorganic Chemical Mfr
N.A.I.C.S.: 325180

COSMO COMMUNICATIONS CORPORATON
Unit 2 - 55 Travail Road, Markham,
L3S-3J1, ON, Canada
Tel.: (905) 209-0488   FL
Web Site:
    http://www.cosmocanada.ca
Year Founded: 1983
Sales Range: $10-24.9 Million
Emp.: 14
Consumer Electronic Equipment Mfr
N.A.I.C.S.: 334419

COSMO ELECTRONICS COR-PORATION
11F No 258 Liancheng Rd, Zhonghe
Dist, Taipei, 235, Taiwan
Tel.: (886) 282271877
Web Site: https://www.cosmo-ic.com
2466—(TAI)
Rev.: $34,449,130
Assets: $141,863,398
Liabilities: $80,312,270
Net Worth: $61,551,128
Earnings: $983,780
Fiscal Year-end: 12/31/23
Light Emitting Diode Mfr
N.A.I.C.S.: 334413

Subsidiaries:

COSMO Electronics Technology (Kun
Shan)Co., Ltd.   (1)
No 339 Qing Yang Highway, Zhoushi Town
Kuanshan, Jiangsu, China
Tel.: (86) 51257628561
Electronic Components Mfr & Distr
N.A.I.C.S.: 335999

Cosmo Electronics Corp. - Yilan
Plant   (1)
No 396 Lupu Road, Dongshan, Yilan, Tai-
wan
Tel.: (886) 39583455
Web Site: http://www.cosmo.com.tw
Circuit Relays Mfr
N.A.I.C.S.: 335314

COSMO ENERGY HOLDINGS CO., LTD.
1-1-1 Shibaura, Minato-ku, Tokyo,
105-8302, Japan
Tel.: (81) 570783280   JP
Web Site: https://www.cosmo-
    energy.co.jp
Year Founded: 2015
5021—(TKS)
Rev.: $18,042,457,700
Assets: $14,625,193,460
Liabilities: $9,816,980,310
Net Worth: $4,808,213,150
Earnings: $542,416,600

Emp.: 221
Fiscal Year-end: 03/31/24
Holding Company
N.A.I.C.S.: 551112
Yasuhiro Suzuki (Sr Exec Officer)

Subsidiaries:

Cosmo Abu Dhabi Energy Exploration
& Production Co., Ltd.   (1)
Hamamatsucho BLDG 1-1-1 Shibaura,
Minato-ku, Tokyo, Japan
Tel.: (81) 33 798 3144
Oil Exploration Services
N.A.I.C.S.: 213112

Cosmo Business Associates Co.,
Ltd.   (1)
Hamamatsucho BLDG 1-1-1 Shibaura,
Minato-ku, Tokyo, Japan
Tel.: (81) 33 798 3100
Petrochemical Product Distr
N.A.I.C.S.: 424720

Cosmo Eco Power Co., Ltd.   (1)
1-6-1 Osaki TOC Osaki Building 8th Floor
General Reception, Shinagawa-ku, Tokyo,
141-0032, Japan
Tel.: (81) 35 487 8560
Web Site: https://cosmo.eco-power.co.jp
Wind Power Generation Services
N.A.I.C.S.: 221115

Cosmo Energy Exploration & Produc-
tion Co., Ltd.   (1)
1-1-1 Shibaura, Minato-ku, Tokyo, 105-
8528, Japan
Tel.: (81) 37983144
Web Site: http://cep.cosmo-oil.co.jp
Emp.: 21
Petroleum Exploration Strategic Planning
Operations
N.A.I.C.S.: 213112
Yasushi Ohe (Pres)

Cosmo Energy Solutions Co.,
Ltd.   (1)
Tornare Nihonbashi Hamacho 3-3-2,
Nihonbashi-Hamacho Chuo-ku, Tokyo, Ja-
pan
Tel.: (81) 35 642 8755
Petrochemical Product Distr
N.A.I.C.S.: 424720

Cosmo Oil Company, Limited   (1)
1-1-1 Shibaura, Minato-ku, Tokyo, 105-
8528, Japan
Tel.: (81) 570783280
Web Site: http://coc.cosmo-oil.co.jp
Sales Range: $25-49.9 Billion
Emp.: 6,491
Petroleum Trading, Refining & Marketing
Services
N.A.I.C.S.: 324110
Masashi Nakayama (Sr Exec Officer)

Subsidiary (Domestic):

CM Aromatics Co Ltd   (2)
1 1 1 Shibaura, Minato-ku, Tokyo, 105
8528, Japan
Tel.: (81) 337983262
Web Site: http://www.cosmo-oil.co.jp
Sales Range: $50-74.9 Million
Emp.: 3
Oil Refining Services
N.A.I.C.S.: 213112
Keizo Morikawa (Pres)

COSMO COMPUTER CENTER CO.,
LTD.   (2)
3-3-2 Nihonbashi-Hamacho, Chuo-ku, To-
kyo, 103-0007, Japan
Tel.: (81) 356428755
Web Site: http://www.cosmo-oil.co.jp
Sales Range: Less than $1 Million
Computer Software Development Services
N.A.I.C.S.: 541511

COSMO PETRO SERVICE CO.,
LTD.   (2)
2 Goikaigan, Ichihara, 290-8566, Chiba,
Japan
Tel.: (81) 436210452
Web Site: http://www.cosmo-oil.co.jp
Petroleum Refinery Services
N.A.I.C.S.: 324110

Cosmo Business Support Co.,
Ltd.   (2)

Cosmo Energy Holdings, Ltd.—(Continued)

2 2 2 Kaji cho, Tokyo, 101 0044, Chiyo-
daku, Japan
Tel.: (81) 332516714
Web Site: http://www.cosmo-business-
support.co.jp
Sales Range: $50-74.9 Million
Emp.: 60
Brokerage & management of real estate
N.A.I.C.S.: 531210

Cosmo Delivery Service Co.,
Ltd. **(2)**
2 Goikaigan, 1 3 Nakase Mihama-ku,
Chiba, 261-8501, Japan
Tel.: (81) 436210452
Web Site: http://www.cosmo-oil.co.jp
Land Truck Transportation Services
N.A.I.C.S.: 213112

Cosmo Energy Exploration and De-
velopment Ltd. **(2)**
Hamamatsucho Building 1-1-1 Shibaura,
Minato-ku, Tokyo, 140 0002, Japan
Tel.: (81) 367180950
Crude Oil Development
N.A.I.C.S.: 324199

Cosmo Engineering Co., Ltd. **(2)**
2 5 8 Higashi-Shinagawa, Shinagawa ku,
Tokyo, 140-0002, Japan
Tel.: (81) 354620150
Web Site: http://www.cosmoeng.co.jp
Sales Range: $125-149.9 Million
Emp.: 500
General plant & equipment engineering
N.A.I.C.S.: 325110
Fumiharu Ando (Pres & CEO)

Cosmo Kaiun Co., Ltd. **(2)**
No 8 Sawanotsuru Ningyo-cho Building 2 Fl
Ningyo-cho chome 3rd, Nihonbashi, Tokyo,
103 0013, Japan
Tel.: (81) 336620591
Web Site: http://www.cosmo-kaiun.co.jp
Sales Range: $25-49.9 Million
Emp.: 100
Marine Transportation & Shipping Agency
N.A.I.C.S.: 488320
Muramoto Hiroyukikai (Dir)

Cosmo Matsuyama Oil Co., Ltd. **(2)**
3 580 Okaga, Matsuyama, 791 8057,
Ehime, Japan
Tel.: (81) 899511111
Web Site: http://www.cosmo-oil.co.jp
Oil Refining Services
N.A.I.C.S.: 211120

Subsidiary (Non-US):

Cosmo Oil (Shanghai) Co., Ltd. **(2)**
Room 4105A Band Center, 222 Yan An
East Road, Shanghai, 200002, China
Tel.: (86) 21 6335 0206
Web Site: http://www.cosmo-oil.co.jp
Oil Distr
N.A.I.C.S.: 486110

Subsidiary (Domestic):

Cosmo Oil Ashmore, Ltd **(2)**
1-1-1 Shibaura, Minato, Tokyo, 105-0023,
Japan
Tel.: (81) 570783280
Web Site: http://www.cosmo-oil.co.jp
Sales Range: $50-74.9 Million
Emp.: 10
Oil Exploration Services
N.A.I.C.S.: 213112

Subsidiary (Non-US):

Cosmo Oil International Pte Ltd **(2)**
6 Battery Road 15-04, Singapore, 049909,
Singapore
Tel.: (65) 63243722
Sales Range: $50-74.9 Million
Emp.: 13
Crude Oil Merchants & Whslr
N.A.I.C.S.: 213112
Kiyotaka Mannami (Mng Dir)

Subsidiary (Domestic):

Cosmo Oil Lubricants Co., Ltd. **(2)**
5-3-2 Shiba, Minato, Tokyo, 108-0014, Japan
Tel.: (81) 354845301
Web Site: http://www.cosmo-lube.co.jp

Sales Range: $25-49.9 Million
Emp.: 253
Lubricating Oil Mfr
N.A.I.C.S.: 324191
Torigoe Shiyunsuke (Pres)

Subsidiary (Non-US):

Cosmo Oil Sales Co., Ltd. **(2)**
Web Site: http://www.cosmo-sales.com
Sales Range: $750-799.9 Million
Emp.: 1,790
Oil Products Selling
N.A.I.C.S.: 213112

Subsidiary (US):

Cosmo Oil of U.S.A., Inc. **(2)**
1800 W Loop S Ste 1810, Houston, TX
77027 **(100%)**
Tel.: (832) 834-7822
Petroleum Trading
N.A.I.C.S.: 425120

Subsidiary (Domestic):

Cosmo Petroleum Gas Co., Ltd . **(2)**
5-29-14 Shiba Minato-ku, Tokyo, Japan
Tel.: (81) 337983171
Sales Range: $50-74.9 Million
Emp.: 50
Import & Sales of LPG
N.A.I.C.S.: 213112

Cosmo Techno Yokkaichi Co.,
Ltd. **(2)**
1-1 Daikyo-cho, Yokkaichi, 510-8502, Mie,
Japan
Tel.: (81) 593548773
Web Site: http://www.cosmo-oil.co.jp
Petroleum Refinery Services
N.A.I.C.S.: 324110

Cosmo Trade and Service Co.,
Ltd. **(2)**
7F Hamamatsucho Building 1-1-1 Shibaura,
Minato-Ku, Tokyo, 105-8325, Japan
Tel.: (81) 354622800
Web Site: https://www.cosmo-trade.com
Sales Range: $50-74.9 Million
Emp.: 205
General trading
N.A.I.C.S.: 238990

Hokuto Kogyo Co.,Ltd. **(2)**
6 4 1 Nanaehama, Hokuto, 049 0111, Hok-
kaido, Japan
Tel.: (81) 138492021
Web Site: http://www.hokuto-kougyo.co.jp
Emp.: 100
Construction, oil receiving & shipment
works
N.A.I.C.S.: 488320
Hiroo Lura (Gen Mgr)

KANSAI COSMO LOGISTICS CO.,
LTD. **(2)**
3-14, Chikkoshin-machi, Nishi-ku, Sakai,
Osaka, Japan
Tel.: (81) 722470803
Petroleum Refinery Services
N.A.I.C.S.: 324110

Qatar Petroleum Development Co.,
Ltd. **(2)**
Hamamatsucho Bldg 1-1-1, Shibaura
Minato-ku, Tokyo, Japan **(100%)**
Tel.: (81) 337982015
Oil Exploration Services
N.A.I.C.S.: 213112

SAKAIDE COSMO KOSAN CO.,
LTD. **(2)**
1-1 Bannosu-Midori-cho, Sakaide, 762-
0065, Kagawa, Japan
Tel.: (81) 877467119
Web Site: http://www.cosmo-oil.co.jp
Emp.: 100
Marine Transportation Services
N.A.I.C.S.: 483111

Joint Venture (Domestic):

Tozai Oil Terminal Co., Ltd. **(2)**
1-10-2 Nishi-Shimbashi Sumitomo Life
Nishi-Shimbashi Building 8F, Minato-ku, To-
kyo, 105-0003, Japan
Tel.: (81) 33 539 1451
Web Site: https://www.tozai-ot.jp
Emp.: 278

Petroleum Terminal Operator
N.A.I.C.S.: 424710

Cosmo Oil Marketing Co., Ltd. **(1)**
1-1-1 Shibaura, Minato-ku, Tokyo, 105-
0023, Japan
Tel.: (81) 67224700
Web Site: http://com.cosmo-oil.co.jp
Emp.: 305
Oil & Other Petroleum Product Marketing &
Sales
N.A.I.C.S.: 425120
Koji Moriyama (Pres)

Cosmo Oil Property Service Co.,
Ltd. **(1)**
Hamamatsucho BLDG 1-1-1 Shibaura,
Minato-ku, Tokyo, Japan
Tel.: (81) 33 798 8519
Petrochemical Product Distr
N.A.I.C.S.: 424720

Cosmo Refinery Support Sakai Co.,
Ltd. **(1)**
3-14 Chikkoshin-machi, Nishi-ku, Sakai,
Osaka, Japan
Tel.: (81) 72 247 0803
Oil Exploration Services
N.A.I.C.S.: 213112

Eco Power Co., Ltd. **(1)**
Toc Osaki Bldg 1-6-1 Osaki, Shinagawa-ku,
Tokyo, 141-0032, Japan
Tel.: (81) 354878560
Web Site: https://cosmo.eco-power.co.jp
Wind Power Turbine Developer & Operator
N.A.I.C.S.: 221115
Toshiyuki Mizui (Pres)

Hyundai Cosmo Petrochemical Co.,
Ltd. **(1)**
182 Pyeongsin2 i-ro, Daesan-eup, Seosan,
Chungcheongnam-do, Korea (South)
Tel.: (82) 22 004 3960
Petrochemical Mfr & Distr
N.A.I.C.S.: 325110

Maruzen Petrochemical Co., Ltd. **(1)**
1-1 Irifune 2-chome, Chuo-ku, Tokyo, 104-
8502, Japan
Tel.: (81) 33 552 9361
Web Site: https://www.chemiway.co.jp
Petrochemical Product Mfr & Distr
N.A.I.C.S.: 325110
Masaru Nabeshima (Pres)

Yokkaichi Kasumi Power Co.,
Ltd. **(1)**
Hamamatsucho Building 1-1-1 Shibaura,
Minato-ku, Tokyo, 105-0023, Japan
Tel.: (81) 337983207
N.A.I.C.S.: 221111

COSMO FIRST LIMITED
1st Floor Uppal s Plaza M6 Jasola
District Centre, New Delhi, 110 025,
Delhi, India
Tel.: (91) 1149494949
Web Site:
https://www.cosmofilms.com
508814—(BOM)
Rev.: $421,335,915
Assets: $376,678,575
Liabilities: $214,143,930
Net Worth: $162,534,645
Earnings: $54,137,265
Emp.: 1,039
Fiscal Year-end: 03/31/22
Packaging Film Mfr
N.A.I.C.S.: 322220
Ashok Jaipuria (Chm & Mng Dir)

Subsidiaries:

CF (Netherlands) Holdings Limited
B.V. **(1)**
Mercuriusstraat 9, 6468 ES, Kerkrade,
Netherlands
Tel.: (31) 45 535 7676
Packaging Film Mfr & Distr
N.A.I.C.S.: 326112

Cosmo Ferrites Ltd. **(1)**
517 5th Floor DLF Tower-A Jasola New District Centre, Jasola, New Delhi, 110025,
India
Tel.: (91) 1149398800

Web Site: https://www.cosmoferrites.com
Rev.: $15,776,697
Assets: $14,829,920
Liabilities: $10,753,415
Net Worth: $4,076,504
Earnings: $1,942,081
Emp.: 212
Fiscal Year-end: 03/31/2022
Soft Ferrites Mfr
N.A.I.C.S.: 339999
Ambrish Jaipuria (Chm & CEO)

Cosmo Films (Netherlands) Coopera-
tief U.A **(1)**
Weena 327, 1014 BA, Rotterdam, Nether-
lands
Tel.: (31) 205814040
Packaging Film Mfr & Distr
N.A.I.C.S.: 326112

Cosmo Films (Singapore) Pte
Ltd **(1)**
10 Jalan Besar 10-12 Sim Lim Tower, Sin-
gapore, 208787, Singapore
Tel.: (65) 65 6293 8089
Packaging Film Mfr & Distr
N.A.I.C.S.: 326112
Ri Gopalan (Mgr-Sls-APAC)

Cosmo Films Japan, GK **(1)**
Yamatane Nai Tokyo-Danashsoko 6-2-11,
Iriya Adachi-Ku, Tokyo, 121-0836, Japan
Tel.: (81) 3 5837 1805
Packaging Film Mfr & Distr
N.A.I.C.S.: 326112

Cosmo Films Korea Limited **(1)**
811 Sineon-Ri Dogo-Myeon, Choongnam,
Asan, 336-914, Korea (South)
Tel.: (82) 41 531 1830
Packaging Film Mfr & Distr
N.A.I.C.S.: 326112
Steve Hong (Gen Mgr)

Cosmo Films Ltd. - Plant I **(1)**
J-4 MIDC Industrial Area, Chikalthana, Au-
rangabad, 431 210, India
Tel.: (91) 240 2485894
Packaging Film Mfr
N.A.I.C.S.: 326112

Cosmo Films Ltd. - Plant II **(1)**
B-14/8-9 MIDC Industrial Area, Waluj, Au-
rangabad, 431 136, India
Tel.: (91) 240 2554611
Packaging Film Mfr
N.A.I.C.S.: 326112

Cosmo Films Ltd. - Plant III **(1)**
B-21 MIDC Industrial Area, Aurangabad,
431 136, India
Tel.: (91) 240 2551888
Packaging Film Mfr
N.A.I.C.S.: 326112

Cosmo Films Ltd. - Plant IV **(1)**
AL-24/1 MIDC-SEZ Shendra Industrial Area,
Aurangabad, 431 201, India
Tel.: (91) 240 2622205
Packaging Film Mfr
N.A.I.C.S.: 326112

Cosmo Films, Inc. **(1)**
775 Belden Ste D, Addison, IL 60101
Tel.: (302) 328-7780
Packaging Film Mfr & Distr
N.A.I.C.S.: 326112
Dave Scofield (Mgr-Technical)

COSMO LADY (CHINA) HOLD-
INGS COMPANY LIMITED
Unit 909 On 9/F Of China Merchants
Tower Shun Tak Centre, 168-200
Connaught Road, Central, China
(Hong Kong)
Tel.: (852) 31506788
Web Site: http://www.cosmo-
lady.com.hk
Year Founded: 2014
2298—(HKG)
Rev.: $422,429,904
Assets: $488,839,525
Liabilities: $220,370,155
Net Worth: $268,469,370
Earnings: $3,372,970
Emp.: 3,000
Fiscal Year-end: 12/31/22

Holding Company
N.A.I.C.S.: 551112
Yaonan Zheng *(Chm)*

COSMO METALS LIMITED

Level 1 51 Colin Street, West Perth, 6005, WA, Australia
Tel.: (61) 864005301   AU
Web Site:
https://www.cosmometals.com.au
Year Founded: 2021
CMO—(ASX)
Rev.: $4,348
Assets: $7,209,318
Liabilities: $455,670
Net Worth: $6,753,648
Earnings: ($982,425)
Fiscal Year-end: 06/30/24
Metal Exploration Services
N.A.I.C.S.: 213114
Melanie Ross *(CFO & Sec)*

COSMO PHARMACEUTICALS N.V.

Riverside II Sir John Rogersons Quay, Dublin, 2, Ireland
Tel.: (353) 18170370
Web Site:
https://www.cosmopharma.com
Year Founded: 1997
COPN—(SWX)
Rev.: $110,175,912
Assets: $819,762,573
Liabilities: $319,235,916
Net Worth: $500,526,657
Earnings: $18,891,647
Emp.: 295
Fiscal Year-end: 12/31/22
Pharmaceuticals Mfr
N.A.I.C.S.: 456110
Mauro Severino Ajani *(Founder & Chm)*

Subsidiaries:

Cassiopea SpA   **(1)**
Via Cristoforo Colombo 1, Lainate, I-20045, Milan, Italy   **(97.85%)**
Tel.: (39) 0286891124
Rev.: $729,575
Assets: $22,878,426
Liabilities: $3,699,459
Net Worth: $19,178,968
Earnings: ($15,117,178)
Emp.: 12
Fiscal Year-end: 12/31/2020
Pharmaceuticals Mfr
N.A.I.C.S.: 325412

Cosmo Research & Development S.R.L.   **(1)**
Via Cristoforo Colombo 1, Lainate, 20020, Milan, Italy
Tel.: (39) 0293337276
Pharmaceutical Product Whslr
N.A.I.C.S.: 424210

Cosmo S.p.A.,   **(1)**
Via Cristoforo Colombo 1, Lainate, Milan, 20020, Italy
Tel.: (39) 0293337614
Web Site: http://www.cosmopharma.com
Sales Range: $25-49.9 Million
Emp.: 20
Pharmaceutical Product Whslr
N.A.I.C.S.: 424210
Roberto Villa *(Mng Dir)*

Linkverse S.r.l.   **(1)**
Via Ostiense 131/L, 00154, Rome, Italy
Tel.: (39) 0690287198
Web Site: https://www.linkverse.com
Health Information Technology Services
N.A.I.C.S.: 541513

COSMOS EXPLORATION LIMITED

Level 1 338 Barker Road, Subiaco, 6008, WA, Australia
Tel.: (61) 861436720   AU
Web Site:
https://www.cosmosx.com.au

Year Founded: 2021
C1X—(ASX)
Rev.: $38,301
Assets: $5,848,487
Liabilities: $89,071
Net Worth: $5,759,416
Earnings: ($1,527,917)
Fiscal Year-end: 06/30/23
Mineral Exploration Services
N.A.I.C.S.: 212390
Jeremy Robinson *(Exec Chm)*

COSMOS GROUP CO., LTD.

Building No 1 Heming Guangyu Building No 68 Longshe Road, Shangcheng District, Hangzhou, 310006, Zhejiang, China
Tel.: (86) 57187925786
Web Site:
http://www.cosmosgroup.com.cn
Year Founded: 2004
002133—(SSE)
Rev.: $845,917,020
Assets: $2,816,338,356
Liabilities: $2,179,995,012
Net Worth: $636,343,344
Earnings: $15,870,816
Fiscal Year-end: 12/31/22
Real Estate Development Services
N.A.I.C.S.: 531390
Yilei Wang *(Chm)*

COSMOS GROUP HOLDINGS INC.

Rooms 1309-11 13th Floor Tai Yau Building No 181 Johnston Road, Wanchai, China (Hong Kong)
Tel.: (852) 36431111   NV
Web Site: http://www.cosgus.com
Year Founded: 1987
COSG—(OTCIQ)
Rev.: $6,550,670
Assets: $36,681,644
Liabilities: $32,722,316
Net Worth: $3,959,328
Earnings: ($104,119,102)
Emp.: 35
Fiscal Year-end: 12/31/22
Holding Company
N.A.I.C.S.: 551112
Chan Man Chung *(CEO, CFO & Sec)*

COSMOS INSURANCE COMPANY PUBLIC LTD

46 Griva Digeni Avenue, 1080, Nicosia, Cyprus
Tel.: (357) 22796000
Web Site:
https://www.cosmosinsurance.com
Year Founded: 1981
COS—(CYP)
Sales Range: Less than $1 Million
Insurance Services
N.A.I.C.S.: 524298
Elias Nissiotis *(CIO)*

COSMOS MACHINERY ENTERPRISES LIMITED

10th Floor Billion Plaza 2 No 10 Cheung Yue Street Cheung Sha Wan, Kowloon, China (Hong Kong)
Tel.: (852) 23766188
Web Site: https://www.cosmel.com
Year Founded: 1958
0118—(HKG)
Rev.: $298,336,995
Assets: $334,744,875
Liabilities: $138,599,385
Net Worth: $196,145,490
Earnings: $2,401,718
Emp.: 2,381
Fiscal Year-end: 12/31/22
Industrial Machinery Mfr
N.A.I.C.S.: 423830
Yiu Ming Wong *(Vice Chm)*

Subsidiaries:

Cosmos Machinery International Ltd.   **(1)**
10/F Billion Plaza 2 No 10 Cheung Yue Street, Cheung Sha Wan, Kowloon, China (Hong Kong)
Tel.: (852) 23867881
Web Site: http://www.cmil.com.hk
Machine Tool Distr
N.A.I.C.S.: 423830

Cosmos Machinery Limited   **(1)**
10th F Billion Plaza 2 No 10 Cheung Yue St Cheung Sha Wan, Kowloon, New Territories, China (Hong Kong)
Tel.: (852) 24312111
Industrial Machinery Mfr
N.A.I.C.S.: 333248
Tang To *(Mng Dir)*

Cosmos i-Tech Solutions Ltd.   **(1)**
Workshop 2 5/F Gravity No 29 Hing Yip Street, Kwun Tong, Kowloon, China (Hong Kong)
Tel.: (852) 3 619 1195
Web Site: https://www.cits.hk
Information Technology Services
N.A.I.C.S.: 541511

Dongguan Cosmos Plastics Products Company Ltd   **(1)**
No 5 Yinzhu Road Zhouwu Industrial Park, Dongcheng District, Dongguan, 523118, Guangdong Province, China
Tel.: (86) 7692 280 6016
Web Site: https://www.cosmos-plastics.com
Sales Range: $50-74.9 Million
Emp.: 120
Blow Molded Plastic Products Mfr
N.A.I.C.S.: 339991

Donghua Machinery Ltd.   **(1)**
Yinzhu Road, Zhouwu Industrial Zone Dongcheng District, Dongguan, 523118, Guangdong, China
Tel.: (86) 76922806237
Web Site: https://www.donghua-ml.com
Molding Machine & Auxiliary Equipment Mfr & Distr
N.A.I.C.S.: 333511

Great Wall (Holding) Company Limited   **(1)**
Units 1217-1223A 12 /F Trade Square No 681 Cheung Sha Wan Road, Kowloon, New Territories, China (Hong Kong)
Tel.: (852) 23955265
Investment Holding Services
N.A.I.C.S.: 523940

Great Wall (Optical) Plastic Works Ltd.   **(1)**
Units 1110-1123 11/F Trade Square 681 Cheung Sha Wan Road, Kowloon, China (Hong Kong)
Tel.: (852) 23955265
Web Site:
http://www.greatwalloptical.com.hk
Sales Range: $25-49.9 Million
Emp.: 10
Optical Instruments Mfr & Supplier
N.A.I.C.S.: 333310

Guangzhou Melco Industrial Supplies Co,, Ltd.   **(1)**
Room 717 west tower Building 12 Innovation Industry Park, Panyu District, Guangzhou, Guangdong, China
Tel.: (86) 2083266170
Web Site: https://www.melco.com
Industrial Machinery & Tools Mfr & Distr
N.A.I.C.S.: 333248

KFE Hong Kong Co., Limited   **(1)**
Room 1503 15/F CCT Telecom Building 11 Wo Shing Street, Fo Tan, Hong Kong, New Territories, China (Hong Kong)
Tel.: (852) 27304611
Web Site: https://www.kfehk.com
Emp.: 105
Printed Circuit Board Mfr
N.A.I.C.S.: 334412

Subsidiary (Non-US):

KFE (Shenzhen) Co., Ltd.   **(2)**
Block 3 Wan Le Road North, TongFu Yu Industrial District Sha Jing Street Bao An County, Shenzhen, China

Tel.: (86) 75527560272
Industrial Machinery & Consumable Distr
N.A.I.C.S.: 423830

KFE (Suzhou) Co., Ltd.   **(2)**
Room 902 Modern Logistics Building No 88 Modern Avenue, Suzhou Industrial Park Suzhou District Free Trade Experimental Zone, Suzhou, China
Tel.: (86) 51282693199
Industrial Machinery & Consumable Distr
N.A.I.C.S.: 423830

KFE (Thailand) Co., Ltd.   **(2)**
123/131 Fifth Avenue Lad Krabang Chalong Krung road Lam-plating, Ladkra bang, Bangkok, 10520, Thailand
Tel.: (66) 29952988
Industrial Machinery & Consumable Distr
N.A.I.C.S.: 423830

Kyoei Futaba Engineering Co., Ltd.   **(2)**
Kokudo Awajicho Building 7F Kanda Awajicho 1-4-3, Chiyodaku, Tokyo, 101-0063, Japan
Tel.: (81) 335265615
Industrial Machinery & Consumable Distr
N.A.I.C.S.: 423830

Mahorasha Co., Ltd.   **(2)**
12-2 Samuraiharacho, Nara, 630-8425, Nara Prefecture, Japan
Tel.: (81) 742220951
Web Site: https://mahorasha.co.jp
Industrial Machinery & Consumable Distr
N.A.I.C.S.: 423830

Karmay Industrial Limited   **(1)**
10 Cheung Yue St Cheung Sha Wan, Kowloon, China (Hong Kong)
Tel.: (852) 85224312111
Web Site: http://www.cosmel.com
Emp.: 500
Plastics Product Mfr
N.A.I.C.S.: 325211

Karmay Plastic Products (Zhuhai) Co., Ltd   **(1)**
No 7 Airport North Road, Sanzao Town Jinwan District, Zhuhai, 519040, Guangdong, China
Tel.: (86) 756 763 0668
Web Site: https://www.karmay.com.cn
Sales Range: $125-149.9 Million
Emp.: 400
Plastics Product Mfr
N.A.I.C.S.: 325211

Melco Industrial Supplies (Shanghai) Co., Ltd   **(1)**
9/F Datong Commercial Tower 369 Fuxing Road Central, Shanghai, China
Tel.: (86) 2163201250
Fastener Products Import & Distr
N.A.I.C.S.: 423830

Melco Industrial Supplies Co., Limited   **(1)**
10th Floor Billion Plaza 2 No 10 Cheung Yue Street, Cheung Sha Wan, Kowloon, China (Hong Kong)
Tel.: (852) 2 386 7881
Web Site: https://www.melco.com.hk
Fastener Product Distr
N.A.I.C.S.: 423710

Ming Sun Enterprises (China) Limited   **(1)**
10th Floor Billion Plaza 2 No 10 Cheung Yue Street, Kowloon, China (Hong Kong)
Tel.: (852) 24312191
Web Site: http://www.mingsun.com
Sales Range: $400-449.9 Million
Emp.: 1,700
Plastic Injection Molding Machine Mfr
N.A.I.C.S.: 333248

Posh Concept Mannequins Co., Ltd.   **(1)**
No 2 Yinzhu Road, Zhouwu Industrial Park Dongcheng District, Dongguan, Guangdong, China
Tel.: (86) 76923380756
Industrial Machinery Mfr
N.A.I.C.S.: 333248
Jacky Wu *(Sls Mgr)*

Welltec Machinery Limited   **(1)**
10/F Billion Plaza 2 10 Cheung Yue Street,

Cosmos Machinery Enterprises Limited—(Continued)

Cheung Sha Wan, Kowloon, China (Hong Kong)
Tel.: (852) 2 431 2198
Web Site: https://www.welltec.com.hk
Injection Molding Machine Mfr
N.A.I.C.S.: 333248

COSMOS PHARMACEUTICAL CORPORATION
Dai-ichi Fukuoka Building S 4F
2-10-1 Hakata Eki Higashi, Hakata-ku, Fukuoka, 812-0013, Japan
Tel.: (81) 924330660
Web Site:
https://www.cosmospc.co.jp
Year Founded: 1983
3349—(TKS)
Rev.: $6,378,577,290
Assets: $3,149,969,060
Liabilities: $1,620,137,440
Net Worth: $1,529,831,620
Earnings: $161,640,940
Emp.: 5,101
Fiscal Year-end: 05/31/24
Drug Store Operator
N.A.I.C.S.: 456110
Masateru Uno *(Founder & Chm)*

COSMOS TECHNOLOGY INTERNATIONAL BERHAD
No 11 Jalan Mega 2/1 Kawasan Per-industrian Mega 2, 43500, Semenyih, Selangor, Malaysia
Tel.: (60) 387276029
Web Site: https://www.ctib.com
Year Founded: 2019
COSMOS—(KLS)
Rev.: $7,579,259
Assets: $14,243,386
Liabilities: $3,016,085
Net Worth: $11,227,302
Earnings: $485,714
Emp.: 95
Fiscal Year-end: 04/30/24
Fabricated Metal Product Mfr & Distr
N.A.I.C.S.: 332312

COSMOS YATIRIM HOLDING A.S.
Etiler Mah Yanarsu Sk No 44 Dogan Apt Kat 2 D 2 Besiktas, Istanbul, Turkiye
Tel.: (90) 2123527425
Web Site:
http://www.cosmosholding.com
COSMO—(IST)
Rev.: $2,552,282
Assets: $1,975,634
Liabilities: $1,074,462
Net Worth: $901,172
Earnings: $482,068
Fiscal Year-end: 12/31/22
Holding Company
N.A.I.C.S.: 551112
Metin Asik *(Chm)*

COSMOSTEEL HOLDINGS LIMITED
14 Lok Yang Way, Singapore, 628633, Singapore
Tel.: (65) 68631828
Web Site:
https://www.cosmosteel.com
Year Founded: 1984
B9S—(SES)
Rev.: $61,836,236
Assets: $75,529,455
Liabilities: $15,921,452
Net Worth: $59,608,003
Earnings: $2,078,548
Emp.: 61
Fiscal Year-end: 09/30/23
Piping System Components Mfr
N.A.I.C.S.: 237110
Pih Peng Lee *(Sec)*

Subsidiaries:

CosmoSteel (Australia) Pty Ltd **(1)**
Unit 83/37-47 Borec Road, Penrith, 2760, NSW, Australia
Tel.: (61) 297260115
Sales Range: $50-74.9 Million
Emp.: 4
Steel Structures Whslr
N.A.I.C.S.: 423610

Kim Seng Huat Hardware Pte
Ltd **(1)**
14 Lok Yang Way, Singapore, 628633, Singapore
Tel.: (65) 68631828
Web Site: https://www.cosmosteel.com
Sales Range: $25-49.9 Million
Emp.: 100
Hardware Retailer
N.A.I.C.S.: 444140

COSMUR CONSTRUCTION (LONDON) LTD
Cosmur House 72 Salusbury Rd, London, NW6 6NU, United Kingdom
Tel.: (44) 2076042277
Web Site: http://www.cosmur.co.uk
Year Founded: 1973
Rev.: $28,131,956
Emp.: 53
Construction Materials Distr
N.A.I.C.S.: 423390
Paul Godfrey *(Mng Dir)*

COSNINE CO., LTD.
27 Hagunsandan 2-ro, Yangchon-eup, Gimpo, Gyeonggi-do, Korea (South)
Tel.: (82) 316068700
Web Site: https://www.cosnine.com
Year Founded: 2001
082660—(KRS)
Rev.: $6,901,749
Assets: $36,938,511
Liabilities: $18,996,866
Net Worth: $17,941,644
Earnings: ($8,259,002)
Emp.: 68
Fiscal Year-end: 12/31/22
Telecommunication & Broadcasting Equipment Mfr
N.A.I.C.S.: 334419
Gyeong Ho Hong *(CFO)*

COSOL LTD.
Level 3 201 Leichhardt Street, Spring Hill, QLD, Australia
Tel.: (61) 7 3129 3341
Web Site: http://www.cosol.com.au
Digital Services
N.A.I.C.S.: 513210
Scott McGowan *(CEO)*

Subsidiaries:

AddOns, Inc. **(1)**
8040 Southpark Ln, Littleton, CO 80120
Tel.: (303) 406-4000
Web Site: http://www.addonsinc.com
Data Processing, Hosting & Related Services
N.A.I.C.S.: 518210
Chris Long *(CEO)*

COSON CO., LTD.
333 8th Floor Yeongdongdaero, Gangnam-gu, Seoul, Korea (South)
Tel.: (82) 234540276
Web Site: http://www.coson.co.kr
069110—(KRS)
Rev.: $8,136,201
Assets: $55,184,493
Liabilities: $91,371,646
Net Worth: ($36,187,153)
Earnings: ($51,142,248)
Emp.: 30
Fiscal Year-end: 12/31/22
Cosmetics Products Mfr
N.A.I.C.S.: 325620
Dong Gun Lee *(CEO)*

Subsidiaries:

Coson Co., Ltd. - Osan Factory **(1)**
40-20 Gajang Industrial Seobuk-ro, Osan, Gyeonggi, Korea (South)
Tel.: (82) 313787861
Cosmetics Products Mfr
N.A.I.C.S.: 325620

COSONIC INTELLIGENT TECHNOLOGIES CO., LTD.
No 151 Shipai Section Dongyuan Avenue, No 3 Keyuan Road Songshan Lake Park Shipai Town, Dongguan, 523000, Guangdong, China
Tel.: (86) 76922862666
Web Site: https://www.cosonic.cc
Year Founded: 2013
300793—(SSE)
Rev.: $304,983,900
Assets: $494,665,704
Liabilities: $152,713,080
Net Worth: $341,952,624
Earnings: $24,370,632
Fiscal Year-end: 12/31/22
Electronic Products Mfr
N.A.I.C.S.: 334419
Wenhua Yan *(Chm)*

Subsidiaries:

Cosonic Acoustic (HK) Technology
Co., Limited **(1)**
Suite 2401 China Insurance Group Building 141 Des Voeux Road, Central, China (Hong Kong)
Tel.: (852) 3 188 9086
Consumer Electronics Product Mfr
N.A.I.C.S.: 334419

Cosonic Electroacoustic Technology
Co., Ltd. **(1)**
Middle 9th Road Shajing Miaobianwang, Shipai Town, Dongguan, 523343, Guangdong, China
Tel.: (86) 7698 659 6918
Consumer Electronics Product Mfr
N.A.I.C.S.: 334419

COSPOWER ENGINEERING LTD.
403 Chandra-Raj Building Chincholi Bunder Road, Behind Vivanta Hospital Malad West, Mumbai, 400064, India
Tel.: (91) 2240129990
Web Site: https://www.cel.net.in
Year Founded: 2004
543172—(BOM)
Electrical & Mechanical Equipment Mfr
N.A.I.C.S.: 334513
Felix Shridhar Kadam *(Mng Dir)*

COSTA GROUP OF COMPANIES
275 Robinsons Road, Ravenhall, 3023, VIC, Australia
Tel.: (61) 383639000
Web Site:
http://www.costagroup.com.au
Emp.: 1,300
Holding Company; Produce Distr & Logistics Services
N.A.I.C.S.: 551112
Neil Chatfield *(Chm)*

Subsidiaries:

CostaExchange Ltd **(1)**
275 Robinsons Rd, Ravenhall, 3023, VIC, Australia
Tel.: (61) 386451600
Web Site:
http://www.costaexchange.com.au
Sales Range: $250-299.9 Million
Emp.: 2,000
Produce Farming, Packing, Marketing & Distr
N.A.I.C.S.: 424480
Frank A. Costa *(Chm)*

COSTA LEAL EL VICTOR ELECTRONICA-PNEUMATICA, LDA.
Rua Augusto Lessa 269, 4200-100, Porto, Portugal
Tel.: (351) 225508520
Web Site: http://www.clv.pt
Sales Range: $25-49.9 Million
Emp.: 15
Industrial Equipment Distr
N.A.I.C.S.: 423830
Jose Costa *(Gen Mgr)*

COSTA VERDE AERONAUTICA SA
Rosario Norte No 615 Of 1402, Las Condes, Santiago, Chile
Tel.: (56) 27951700
Sales Range: Less than $1 Million
Textile Products Mfr
N.A.I.C.S.: 314999
Juan Jose Cueto Plaza *(Chm)*

COSTAIN GROUP PLC
Costain Building 8 Foundation Park, Maidenhead, SL6 3UD, Berkshire, United Kingdom
Tel.: (44) 1628442444
Web Site: https://www.costain.com
Year Founded: 1875
COST—(LSE)
Rev.: $1,712,076,300
Assets: $580,809,900
Liabilities: $316,542,600
Net Worth: $264,267,300
Earnings: $31,196,550
Fiscal Year-end: 12/31/22
Holding Company; Civil Engineering, Commercial & Residential Building Contractor; Property Management
N.A.I.C.S.: 551112
Alex Vaughan *(CEO)*

Subsidiaries:

Construction Study Centre
Limited **(1)**
6280 Bishops Court, Birmingham Business Park, Solihull, B37 7YB, United Kingdom
Tel.: (44) 783 473 9019
Web Site: https://www.csctraining.co.uk
Training Provider Services
N.A.I.C.S.: 611430
Lisa Pateman *(Gen Mgr)*

Costain (Africa) Limited **(1)**
87 Plymouth Rd, PO Box ST 197, Southerton, Harare, Zimbabwe **(100%)**
Tel.: (263) 4663571
Web Site: http://www.costain.co.zw
Sales Range: $25-49.9 Million
Emp.: 60
Civil Engineering & Construction Contracting
N.A.I.C.S.: 541330

Costain Abu Dhabi Company **(1)**
MN 4 Plot 20 Industrial Area Mussafah, PO Box 3069, Mussafah Industrial Area, Abu Dhabi, United Arab Emirates
Tel.: (971) 25553920
Web Site: http://www.costain-abudhabi.ae
Sales Range: $25-49.9 Million
Emp.: 40
Oil & Gas Industry Construction Services
N.A.I.C.S.: 237120

Costain Civil Engineering Ltd. **(1)**
Costain Ltd Costain House Vanwall Business Park, Maidenhead, SL6 4UP, Berkshire, United Kingdom **(100%)**
Tel.: (44) 1628442196
Sales Range: $25-49.9 Million
Emp.: 1,000
Civil Engineering Contractor
N.A.I.C.S.: 541330
Mike Napier *(Mgr-Bus Dev)*

Costain Engineering & Construction
Ltd. **(1)**
111 Westminster Bridge Rd, London, SE1 7UE, United Kingdom **(100%)**
Tel.: (44) 2077058444

Sales Range: $25-49.9 Million
Emp.: 50
Civil Engineering, Commercial & Residential
Building Contractor
N.A.I.C.S.: 237990

Subsidiary (Domestic):

Costain Building & Civil Engineering
Ltd. **(2)**
Costain House Nicholsons Walk, Maiden-
head, SL6 1LN, Berkshire, United
Kingdom **(100%)**
Tel.: (44) 628842444
Sales Range: $50-74.9 Million
Civil Engineering, Commercial & Residential
Building Contractor
N.A.I.C.S.: 237990

Costain Construction Limited **(2)**
Costain House, Vanwall Bus Pk, Maiden-
head, SL6 4UB, Berks, United
Kingdom **(100%)**
Tel.: (44) 1628842444
Web Site: http://www.costain.com
Sales Range: $50-74.9 Million
Commercial & Residential Building Contrac-
tor
N.A.I.C.S.: 236220

Costain International Limited **(2)**
Costain House, Vanwall Business Park,
Maidenhead, SL6 4UB, Berkshire, United
Kingdom **(100%)**
Tel.: (44) 628842444
Web Site: http://www.costain.com
Sales Range: $75-99.9 Million
Holding Company; Civil Engineering, Com-
mercial & Residential Building Contractor
N.A.I.C.S.: 541330

Joint Venture (Non-US):

NESMA & Partners Contracting
Ltd. **(2)**
PO Box 1498, Al Khobar, 31952, Saudi
Arabia
Tel.: (966) 138519000
Web Site: http://www.nesma-partners.com
Provider of Process Engineering, Procure-
ment, Construction & Project Management
Services
N.A.I.C.S.: 541330

Costain Ltd **(1)**
Costain House, Vanwall Bussiness Park,
Maidenhead, SL6 4UB, Berkshire, United
Kingdom
Tel.: (44) 162 884 2444
Web Site: https://www.costain.com
Sales Range: $25-49.9 Million
Emp.: 300
Construction Engineering Services
N.A.I.C.S.: 541330

Costain Oil, Gas & Process Ltd **(1)**
1500 Aviator Way, Manchester Business
Park, Manchester, M22 5TG, United King-
dom
Tel.: (44) 161 910 3444
Web Site: https://www.costain.com
Sales Range: $200-249.9 Million
Emp.: 300
Oil & Natural Gas Plant Construction Ser-
vices
N.A.I.C.S.: 213112

Division (Domestic):

Costain Oil, Gas & Process Limited
Pipeline & Offshore Division **(2)**
Costain House 1500 Aviator Way, Man-
chester Business Park, Manchester, M22
5TG, United Kingdom **(100%)**
Tel.: (44) 161 910 3444
Web Site: http://www.costain-group.com
Sales Range: $25-49.9 Million
Emp.: 100
Oil & Gas Industry Construction Services
N.A.I.C.S.: 237120

Richard Costain Ltd **(1)**
Costain House Vanwall Business Park,
Maidenhead, SL6 4UB, Berkshire, United
Kingdom
Tel.: (44) 1628842444
Construction Engineering Services
N.A.I.C.S.: 541330

Yahya Costain LLC **(1)**

PO Box 2282, 112, Ruwi, Oman **(60%)**
Tel.: (968) 4591366
Web Site: http://www.costain.com
Civil Engineering & Contract Construction
N.A.I.C.S.: 541330

COSTAMARE INC.
7 rue de Gabian, MC 98000, Mo-
naco, Monaco
Tel.: (377) 93250940   MH
Web Site:
  https://www.costamare.com
CMRE—(NYSE)
Rev.: $1,511,406,000
Assets: $5,287,022,000
Liabilities: $2,848,262,000
Net Worth: $2,438,760,000
Earnings: $381,019,000
Emp.: 2,750
Fiscal Year-end: 12/31/23
Container Vessel Transportation
N.A.I.C.S.: 483111
Konstantinos V. Konstantakopoulos
(Chm & CEO)

Subsidiaries:

Costamare Participations Plc **(1)**
San Sushi Street 28 1st Floor Office 101A,
2003, Nicosia, Cyprus
Tel.: (357) 2 208 0630
Web Site: https://costamare.cy
Container Shipping ervices
N.A.I.C.S.: 488510

Costamare Partners LP **(1)**
60 Zephyrou Street & Syngrou Avenue,
17564, Athens, Greece
Sales Range: $25-49.9 Million
Container Shipping
N.A.I.C.S.: 488510
Konstantinos Konstantakopoulos *(CEO)*

COSTAMP S.R.L
Via Zignola 12, ZI Villanova, 47122,
Forli, FC, Italy
Tel.: (39) 0543 754217   IT
Web Site: http://www.costampsrl.it
Year Founded: 1987
Sales Range: $1-9.9 Million
Emp.: 15
Sheet Metal Products Mfr
N.A.I.C.S.: 332322

COSTAR GROUP CO., LTD.
No 508 Gongye South Road, Nan-
yang, 473003, Henan, China
Tel.: (86) 37763865031
Web Site: http://www.lida-oe.com
Year Founded: 1995
002189—(SSE)
Rev.: $461,229,444
Assets: $510,800,472
Liabilities: $308,382,984
Net Worth: $202,417,488
Earnings: ($26,032,968)
Fiscal Year-end: 12/31/22
Optical Product Mfr
N.A.I.C.S.: 333310
Chen Haibo *(Chm)*

COSUCRA - GROUPE WARCO-
ING
1 rue de la Sucrerie, Warcoing, Pecq,
7740, Belgium
Tel.: (32) 69446600
Web Site: http://www.cosucra.com
Year Founded: 1852
Sales Range: $50-74.9 Million
Emp.: 220
Production of Natural Food Ingredi-
ents Sourced From Locally Grown
Chicory & Peas
N.A.I.C.S.: 311999

COSUMAR SA
8 rue Mouatamid Ibnou Abbad,
Roches Noires, BP 3098, Casablanca, Morocco

Tel.: (212) 522678300
Web Site:
  https://www.cosumar.co.ma
Year Founded: 1929
Rev.: $773,237,643
Earnings: $91,792,047
Fiscal Year-end: 12/31/16
Sugar Mfr
N.A.I.C.S.: 311313
Mohammed Fikrat *(Chm & CEO)*

COSYN LIMITED
Plot No 15 TP House 3rd floor, Jai-
hind Enclave Madhapur, Hyderabad,
500 081, Telangana, India
Tel.: (91) 7330666517
Web Site: https://www.cosyn.in
538922—(BOM)
Rev.: $2,212,569
Assets: $4,701,620
Liabilities: $1,011,165
Net Worth: $3,690,455
Earnings: $21,526
Fiscal Year-end: 03/31/22
IT Solutions
N.A.I.C.S.: 541511
Ravi Vishnu *(Chm & Mng Dir)*

Subsidiaries:

WelltoDesk Inc. **(1)**
20907 Avery Cove Ln, Katy, TX 77450
Tel.: (713) 503-5011
Web Site: http://www.welltodesk.com
Cloud Database & Storage Services
N.A.I.C.S.: 518210

COTA CO., LTD.
77 Tai-Shinarami Kumiyama-cho,
Kuse-gun, Kyoto, 613-0036, Japan
Tel.: (81) 774441681
Web Site: https://www.cota.co.jp
Year Founded: 1979
4923—(TKS)
Sales Range: $50-74.9 Million
Haircare Cosmetic Product Mfr &
Distr
N.A.I.C.S.: 325620
Hiroteru Oda *(Pres)*

COTANA GROUP JOINT
STOCK COMPANY
Lot CC5A - Linh am Peninsula - Ho-
ang Liet Ward, Hoang Mai District,
Hanoi, Vietnam
Tel.: (84) 435632763
Web Site:
  https://www.cotanagroup.vn
Year Founded: 1993
CSC—(HNX)
Rev.: $173,139,000
Assets: $239,307,900
Liabilities: $159,506,000
Net Worth: $79,801,900
Earnings: $26,289,200
Fiscal Year-end: 12/31/22
Building Construction Services
N.A.I.C.S.: 236220
Dao Ngoc Thanh *(Chm-Mgmt Bd)*

Subsidiaries:

Cotabig Joint Stock Company **(1)**
5th Floor-P 508-HH2 Building Bac Ha-Le
Van Luong Extended, Thanh Xuan District,
Hanoi, Vietnam
Tel.: (84) 2466552828
Construction Services
N.A.I.C.S.: 236220

Cotana Capital Housing Investment &
Development Joint Stock
Company **(1)**
6th Floor HCC Building No 28 Ly Thuong
Kiet, Vinh Ninh Ward, Hue, Thua Thien
Hue, Vietnam
Tel.: (84) 2343848998
Construction Services
N.A.I.C.S.: 236220

Cotana Construction Joint Stock
Company **(1)**
5th Floor - Cotana Group Building Lot
CC5A Linh Dam Peninsula, Hoang Liet
Ward Hoang Mai District, Hanoi, Vietnam
Tel.: (84) 2436417108
Construction Work Equipment Distr
N.A.I.C.S.: 423810

Cotana Consultant Construction Joint
Stock Company **(1)**
4th Floor - Cotana Group Building Lot
CC5A Linh Dam Peninsula, Hoang Liet
Ward Hoang Mai District, Hanoi, Vietnam
Tel.: (84) 2436408047
Building Design Consultancy Services
N.A.I.C.S.: 541330

Cotana Green Landscape Architec-
ture Joint Stock Company **(1)**
3rd Floor - Cotana Group Building Lot
CC5A Linh Dam Peninsula, Hoang Liet
Ward Hoang Mai District, Hanoi, Vietnam
Tel.: (84) 2435632763
Construction Services
N.A.I.C.S.: 236220

Cotana Infrastructure Construction
Joint Stock Company **(1)**
4th Floor - Cotana Group Building Lot
CC5A Linh Dam Peninsula, Hoang Liet
Ward Hoang Mai District, Hanoi, Vietnam
Tel.: (84) 2436417376
Construction Services
N.A.I.C.S.: 236220

Cotana Investment Consultancy &
Trading Joint Stock Company **(1)**
5th Floor - Cotana Group Building Lot
CC5A Linh Dam Peninsula, Hoang Liet
Ward Hoang Mai District, Hanoi, Vietnam
Tel.: (84) 2435635793
Construction Work Equipment Distr
N.A.I.C.S.: 423810

COTEC HOLDINGS CORP.
Suite 428 - 755 Burrard Street, Van-
couver, V6Z 1X6, BC, Canada
Tel.: (604) 992-5600   BC
Web Site: https://www.cotec.ca
Year Founded: 1986
CTHCF—(OTCQB)
Rev.: $9,877,671
Assets: $27,103,375
Liabilities: $3,642,679
Net Worth: $23,460,696
Earnings: $7,372,197
Fiscal Year-end: 12/31/23
Mineral Exploration Services
N.A.I.C.S.: 213114
Hendrik Dietrichsen *(CEO)*

COTECCONS CONSTRUCTION
JOINT STOCK COMPANY
Coteccons Building 236/6 Dien Bien
Phu 17 Ward, Binh Thanh Dist, Ho
Chi Minh City, Vietnam
Tel.: (84) 2835142255
Web Site: https://www.coteccons.vn
Year Founded: 2004
CTD—(HOSE)
Rev.: $674,432,800
Assets: $2,137,503,000
Liabilities: $1,310,331,900
Net Worth: $827,171,100
Earnings: $5,222,800
Emp.: 1,800
Fiscal Year-end: 12/31/23
Construction Services
N.A.I.C.S.: 236210
Thanh Liem Vo *(Gen Dir-Acting)*

Subsidiaries:

Unicons Investment Construction Co.,
Ltd. **(1)**
Floor 5-6-7 Coteccons Tower 236/6 Dien
Bien Phu Str Ward 17, Binh Thanh District,
Ho Chi Minh City, Vietnam
Tel.: (84) 2835143366
Web Site: http://www.unicons.vn
Construction Engineering Services
N.A.I.C.S.: 541330

Coteccons Construction Joint Stock Company—(Continued)

COTECNA INSPECTION S.A.
Rue de la Terrassiere 58, 1207, Geneva, Switzerland
Tel.: (41) 22 849 69 00
Web Site: http://www.cotecna.com
Inspection, Testing, Verification & Certification Services
N.A.I.C.S.: 926150
Robert M. Massey *(CEO)*

Subsidiaries:

COINS Portugal UNIP LDA   **(1)**
Rua Pedro Hispano 198, 4100 393, Porto, Portugal
Tel.: (351) 22 6052450
Inspection, Testing, Verification & Certification Services
N.A.I.C.S.: 926150

COTECNA DEL PARAGUAY S.A.   **(1)**
Teniente Heyn 7080 Casa 2 Villa Aurelia, Asuncion, Paraguay
Tel.: (595) 501062063
Inspection & Verification Services
N.A.I.C.S.: 926150

COTECNA DESTINATION INSPECTION LTD   **(1)**
4th Floor Yinka Folawiyo Plaza 38 Warehouse Road, Apapa, Lagos, Nigeria
Tel.: (234) 14617120
Inspection & Verification Services
N.A.I.C.S.: 926150

COTECNA INSPECTION BANGLADESH LIMITED   **(1)**
House - 198 Road - 08 Block - D 1st Floor Mohanagar Project, Rampura, 1219, Dhaka, Bangladesh
Tel.: (880) 1714208133
Inspection & Verification Services
N.A.I.C.S.: 926150

COTECNA INSPECTION KOREA INC.   **(1)**
2nd floor Media Tower Bldg 106 Worldcupbuk Road, Mapo-Gu, 121-844, Seoul, Korea (South)
Tel.: (82) 27141344
Web Site: http://www.cotecna.kr
Inspection & Verification Services
N.A.I.C.S.: 926150

COTECNA INSPECTION SA   **(1)**
4th Floor Graha Mustika Ratu Jl Jenderal Gatot Subroto Kav 74-75, 12870, Jakarta, Indonesia
Tel.: (62) 218306641
Inspection & Verification Services
N.A.I.C.S.: 926150

COTECNA INTERNATIONAL TRADE CONSULTING (SHANGHAI) LTD **(1)**
Suite 2101 No 989 Dong Fang Lu Zhong Da Square, Pudong Xinqu, 200122, Shanghai, China
Tel.: (86) 2168672300
Inspection & Verification Services
N.A.I.C.S.: 926150

COTECNA LATIN AMERICA S.A..   **(1)**
International Business Park Building 3825 Office 201b, Panama Pacifico Blvd, Panama, Panama
Tel.: (507) 8389811
Inspection & Verification Services
N.A.I.C.S.: 926150

COTECNA SENEGAL SARL   **(1)**
Immeuble Carde 5 Avenue Carde 3eme etage, PO Box 11853, Dakar, Senegal
Tel.: (221) 338494959
Inspection & Verification Services
N.A.I.C.S.: 926150

COTECNA SERVICOS LTDA   **(1)**
Rua Artur de Almeida 73, Vila Mariana, 04011-080, Sao Paulo, Brazil
Tel.: (55) 1133831800
Inspection & Verification Services
N.A.I.C.S.: 926150

Cotecna - Beijing   **(1)**
Room 2005 Tower A Jia Tai international Mansion, N 41 East Fourth Ring Road Chaoyang District, Beijing, China
Tel.: (86) 10 6581 3931
Inspection, Testing, Verification & Certification Services
N.A.I.C.S.: 926150

Cotecna Certificadora Services Ltda.   **(1)**
Calle 103 No 14A-43, Oficina 201, Bogota, Colombia
Tel.: (57) 1 7427655
Inspection, Testing, Verification & Certification Services
N.A.I.C.S.: 926150

Cotecna Del Ecuador SA   **(1)**
Av 9 de Octubre 100 y Malecon, Edificio La Previsora Piso 28 Oficina 2801, Guayaquil, Ecuador
Tel.: (593) 4 2523723
Inspection, Testing, Verification & Certification Services
N.A.I.C.S.: 926150

Cotecna El Salvador   **(1)**
Urbanizacion Madre Selva, alle Llama del Bosque Poniente No. 21 Segunda Planta, Santa Elena Antiguo Cuscatlan Dept De la Libertad, San Salvador, El Salvador
Tel.: (503) 2121 4600
Inspection, Testing, Verification & Certification Services
N.A.I.C.S.: 926150

Cotecna Gozetim AS   **(1)**
Istiklal Cad Gurle Is Hani No 84, Bursa, Turkiye
Tel.: (90) 224 5149378
Inspection, Testing, Verification & Certification Services
N.A.I.C.S.: 926150

Cotecna Inspection (Vostok) LLC **(1)**
1 Bol'shaya Yakimanka Street, 119180, Moscow, Russia
Tel.: (7) 4952155585
Inspection, Testing, Verification & Certification Services
N.A.I.C.S.: 926150

Cotecna Inspection Argentina SA **(1)**
Av Paseo Colon 728 Piso 8B, Buenos Aires, Argentina
Tel.: (54) 11 52398888
Inspection, Testing, Verification & Certification Services
N.A.I.C.S.: 926150

Cotecna Inspection Congo Sarl **(1)**
Avenue Denis Sassou Nguesso Immeuble Capinfo, 226, Brazzaville, Congo, Republic of
Tel.: (242) 55500010
Inspection, Testing, Verification & Certification Services
N.A.I.C.S.: 926150

Cotecna Inspection Egypt, S.A.E.   **(1)**
El-Fardous Street El-Ealamien Tower area #4, Behind Moubark City Sport, Semouha, Alexandria, Egypt
Tel.: (20) 3 427 3634
Inspection, Testing, Verification & Certification Services
N.A.I.C.S.: 926150

Cotecna Inspection France Sarl **(1)**
5 Rue du Mail, Cite Expandis Immeuble Le Normandie, Orvault, France
Tel.: (33) 2 51 78 95 95
Inspection, Testing, Verification & Certification Services
N.A.I.C.S.: 926150

Cotecna Inspection GmbH   **(1)**
Martinstrasse 47 - 55, Haus G, 40223, Dusseldorf, Germany
Tel.: (49) 211 178570
Inspection, Testing, Verification & Certification Services
N.A.I.C.S.: 926150

Cotecna Inspection India Pvt. Ltd.   **(1)**
A-302 Delphi Building 3rd Floor A Wing, Hiranandani Business Park Orchard Road, 400076, Mumbai, India

Tel.: (91) 22 42188000
Inspection, Testing, Verification & Certification Services
N.A.I.C.S.: 926150

Cotecna Inspection Japan Limited   **(1)**
4th Floo KY Bldg 3-16-14 Roppongi Minato-Ku, Tokyo, 106-0032, Japan
Tel.: (81) 3 55726960
Web Site: http://www.cotecna.com
Emp.: 4
Inspection, Testing, Verification & Certification Services
N.A.I.C.S.: 926150
Arkadiusz Izdebski *(Mgr)*

Cotecna Inspection Ltd.   **(1)**
4th Floor One Lampton Road, Hounslow, TW3 1JB, United Kingdom
Tel.: (44) 208 2777700
Inspection, Testing, Verification & Certification Services
N.A.I.C.S.: 926150

Cotecna Inspection Philippines, Inc.   **(1)**
Unit 1009 National Life Insurance Company Building, 6762 Ayala Avenue, San Lorenzo Village, 1223, Manila, Makati City, Philippines
Tel.: (63) 2 893 1173
Web Site: http://www.cotecna.com
Emp.: 25
Inspection, Testing, Verification & Certification Services
N.A.I.C.S.: 926150
Fermin Barrenechea *(Gen Mgr)*

Cotecna Inspection SL   **(1)**
C/ Fontsanta N 46 4 B, Sant Joan Despi, 8970, Barcelona, Spain
Tel.: (34) 93 4707990
Web Site: http://www.cotecna.com
Emp.: 20
Inspection, Testing, Verification & Certification Services
N.A.I.C.S.: 926150

Cotecna Inspection South Africa Pty. Ltd.   **(1)**
Suite SF 01 & 02 Second Floor The Square, 250 Umhlanga Rocks Drive La, Durban, South Africa
Tel.: (27) 31 5663231
Inspection, Testing, Verification & Certification Services
N.A.I.C.S.: 926150

Cotecna Inspection Thailand   **(1)**
23/101 Sorachai Building 23rd Floor, Sorachai building 23rd Floor Sukhumvit 63, North Klon, Bangkok, Thailand
Tel.: (66) 2 7143310 16
Inspection, Testing, Verification & Certification Services
N.A.I.C.S.: 926150

Cotecna Inspection Uruguay SA **(1)**
Manuel Oribe 0766 Colonia Dep, 70001, Colonia del Sacramento, Uruguay
Tel.: (598) 5446631
Inspection, Testing, Verification & Certification Services
N.A.I.C.S.: 926150

Cotecna Inspection, Inc.   **(1)**
900 S. Loop W Suite 190, Houston, TX 77054
Tel.: (713) 842-4660
Inspection, Testing, Verification & Certification Services
N.A.I.C.S.: 926150

Cotecna Iraq   **(1)**
Zayouna-Mothana No 714-44, Baghdad, Iraq
Tel.: (964) 771 809 5894
Inspection, Testing, Verification & Certification Services
N.A.I.C.S.: 926150

Cotecna Kazakhstan LLP   **(1)**
VP-9 5th flor 25 Syganak Street, Nur-Sultan, 010000, Kazakhstan
Tel.: (7) 7172 55 06 92
Inspection, Testing, Verification & Certification Services
N.A.I.C.S.: 926150

Cotecna Quality SRL   **(1)**

19 Via Monterosa, Milan, Italy
Tel.: (39) 02 48011300
Inspection, Testing, Verification & Certification Services
N.A.I.C.S.: 926150

Cotecna S.A. - Hong Kong   **(1)**
Sinoswiss Inspection Limited Suite 1527 15/F Star House, 3 Salisbury Road Tsimshatsui, Kowloon, Hong Kong, China (Hong Kong)
Tel.: (852) 21113571 3
Inspection, Testing, Verification & Certification Services
N.A.I.C.S.: 926150

Cotecna Saudi Arabia Co. Ltd. **(1)**
N208 Northern Olaya Centre Al Olaya, Al Khobar, Saudi Arabia
Tel.: (966) 8111474384
Inspection, Testing, Verification & Certification Services
N.A.I.C.S.: 926150

Cotecna Servicos Angola Limitada   **(1)**
Avenida Dr Agostinho Neto, Edificio da Sistec, Cabinda, Angola
Tel.: (244) 231 220101
Inspection, Testing, Verification & Certification Services
N.A.I.C.S.: 926150

Cotecna Servicos Ltda.   **(1)**
Avenida Gabriel de Lara 363, 83.221-370, Parana, Brazil
Tel.: (55) 41 34240307
Inspection, Testing, Verification & Certification Services
N.A.I.C.S.: 926150

Cotecna Singapore Pte. Ltd.   **(1)**
112 Robinson Road Unit 05-04 Robinson, Singapore, 068902, Singapore
Tel.: (65) 6 2782933
Inspection, Testing, Verification & Certification Services
N.A.I.C.S.: 926150

Cotecna Trade Services   **(1)**
Office 409 Mthari Center Building 174, Mecca Stree, Amman, 11941, Jordan
Tel.: (962) 6 554 2255
Web Site: http://www.cotecna.com
Inspection, Testing, Verification & Certification Services
N.A.I.C.S.: 926150

Cotecna Trade Services Malaysia Sdn Bhd   **(1)**
No.9 9-1 Jalan Semerbak 20, Taman Bukit Dahlia, 81700, Pasir Gudang, Malaysia
Tel.: (60) 7 2976038
Inspection, Testing, Verification & Certification Services
N.A.I.C.S.: 926150

Cotecna Ukraine Limited   **(1)**
Piolskiy Spusk 11, Business Centre Morskoy 2, 65026, Odessa, Ukraine
Tel.: (380) 482 33 53 62
Web Site: http://www.cotecna.com
Emp.: 15
Inspection, Testing, Verification & Certification Services
N.A.I.C.S.: 926150
Korchmar Victoria *(CEO)*

Cotecna Vietnam, Co., Ltd.   **(1)**
3 Fl Binadon, 1 Dinh Le Street, Ward 12 District 4, Ho Chi Minh City, Vietnam
Tel.: (84) 8 3943 3299
Inspection, Testing, Verification & Certification Services
N.A.I.C.S.: 926150

Cotecna, Inc.   **(1)**
8285 El Rio Suite 190, Houston, TX 77054
Tel.: (713) 440-0900
Inspection, Testing, Verification & Certification Services
N.A.I.C.S.: 926150

Gateway Services Limited   **(1)**
George Walker Bush Motorway N1 highway, Accra, Ghana
Tel.: (233) 30 702 0169
Inspection, Testing, Verification & Certification Services
N.A.I.C.S.: 926150
Tracy Wright *(CEO)*

COTELSA S.A.
Chiloe 4846, San Miguel, Santiago, Chile
Tel.: (56) 2223520210
Web Site: http://www.cotelsa.cl
Sales Range: $50-74.9 Million
Emp.: 112
Wood Crate Pallet & Spindle Mfr
N.A.I.C.S.: 321920
Carlos Loch Contreras *(CEO)*

COTEMINAS COMPANHIA DE TECIDOS NORTE DE MINAS
Av Magalhaes Pinto 4000, Bairro Planalto, CEP 39404-166, Montes Claros, MG, Brazil
Tel.: (55) 38 3215 7777
Web Site:
http://www.coteminas.com.br
Year Founded: 1967
Sales Range: $550-599.9 Million
Yarn, Textiles, Knitwear, T-Shirts, Underwear, Bathrobes, Towels & Linens Mfr
N.A.I.C.S.: 313310
Joao Batista da Cunha Bomfim *(Dir-IR)*

Subsidiaries:

AMMO Varejo Ltda **(1)**
Av Paulista 1754, Sao Paulo, 01310-200, Brazil
Tel.: (55) 1130322679
Apparel & Accessory Distr
N.A.I.C.S.: 424350

Coteminas Argentina S.A. **(1)**
Cerrito 1136 Piso 12 Frente, C1010AAX, Buenos Aires, Argentina
Tel.: (54) 84 4006 2300
Home Furnishing Whslr
N.A.I.C.S.: 423220

MMartan Textil Ltda. **(1)**
Rodovia Anhanguera 3117 Km 77 5 Capela Vinhedo, Capivari, Sao Paulo, 13280-000, Brazil
Tel.: (55) 8007237222
Web Site: http://www.mmartan.com.br
Apparel & Accessory Distr
N.A.I.C.S.: 424350

Springs Brands, LLC **(1)**
100 5th Ave, New York, NY 10011
Tel.: (212) 556-6000
Home Furnishing Whslr
N.A.I.C.S.: 423220

Springs Global Participacoes S.A. **(1)**
Bairro Planalto Avenida Magalhaes Pinto 4000, 39404-166, Montes Claros, Minas Gerais, Brazil
Tel.: (55) 553832157777
Mfr of Linens, Rugs, Pillows & Window Treatments
N.A.I.C.S.: 313210

Subsidiary (US):

Springs Global US, Inc. **(2)**
205 N White St PO Box 70, Fort Mill, SC 29715
Tel.: (803) 547-3775
Web Site: http://www.springs.com
Sales Range: $650-699.9 Million
Emp.: 100
Mfr of Home Furnishing Products
N.A.I.C.S.: 313210
Janice Louttit *(Mgr-Trade Payables)*

Subsidiary (Domestic):

Espacio LLC **(3)**
7913 McPherson Rd Ste 106, Laredo, TX 78045
Tel.: (956) 791-7183
Web Site: http://www.espaciosonline.com
Office Furniture Whslr
N.A.I.C.S.: 423210
Debra McLennan *(Mgr-Ops)*

Division (Non-US):

Springs Canada, Ltd. **(3)**
110 Matherson Blvd W Ste 200, Missis-

sauga, L5R 3T4, ON, Canada **(100%)**
Tel.: (905) 890-4994
Sales Range: $10-24.9 Million
Emp.: 70
Marketing of Bed & Bath Products
N.A.I.C.S.: 449129

Springs de Mexico, S.A. de C.V. **(3)**
Carretera Acambaro Jerecuaro No 19, Acambaro Guanajuato, CP 38610, Mexico, Mexico **(100%)**
Tel.: (52) 4171727711
Sales Range: $25-49.9 Million
Finished Fabrics, Home Furnishings & Window Treatments Mfr
N.A.I.C.S.: 314910

Subsidiary (Domestic):

Warbird Corporation **(3)**
1105 N Market St, Wilmington, DE 19801
Tel.: (302) 427-9903
Holding Company
N.A.I.C.S.: 551112

COTINGA PHARMACEUTI-CALS INC.
The Canadian Venture Building 82 Richmond Street East 1st Floor, Toronto, M5C 1P1, ON, Canada
Tel.: (860) 798-0816 ON
Web Site:
http://www.cotingapharma.com
Year Founded: 2008
Assets: $914,962
Liabilities: $2,673,655
Net Worth: ($1,758,693)
Earnings: ($1,977,026)
Fiscal Year-end: 04/30/19
Pharmaceutical Product Development Services
N.A.I.C.S.: 325412
John C. Drake *(Chm)*

COTS TECHNOLOGY CO., LTD.
702 Building C Bundang Techno Park 744 Pangyo-ro, Bundang-gu, Seongnam, Gyeonggi-do, Korea (South)
Tel.: (82) 317021665
Web Site: https://www.cotstech.com
Year Founded: 1999
448710—(KRS)
Computer Hardware Product Mfr & Distr
N.A.I.C.S.: 334111

COTTCO HOLDINGS LIMITED
1 Lytton Road, PO Box 2697, Workington, Harare, Zimbabwe
Tel.: (263) 4 749458
Web Site:
http://www.cottcoholdings.com
Year Founded: 2008
Sales Range: $25-49.9 Million
Holding Company; Agro-Industrial Business
N.A.I.C.S.: 551112
Pious Manamike *(Sec & Head-Fin)*

Subsidiaries:

Cottco International (Proprietary) Limited **(1)**
Ebene House 3rd Floor 33 Cybercity, Ebene, Mauritius
Tel.: (230) 467 4693
Holding Company
N.A.I.C.S.: 551112

Olivine Industries (Private) Limited **(1)**
36 Birmingham Road Southerton, PO Box 797, Harare, 797, Zimbabwe **(49%)**
Tel.: (263) 4754556
Web Site: http://www.olivine.co.zw
Sales Range: $550-599.9 Million
Emp.: 1,200
Manufactures Cooking Oils, Fats & Soaps
N.A.I.C.S.: 325611
Jonas Shanji Mushangari *(Mng Dir)*

Seed Co. Limited **(1)**

Shamwari Road Stapleford Westgate, PO Box WGT 64, Harare, Zimbabwe **(51.21%)**
Tel.: (263) 42915408
Web Site: http://www.seedcogroup.com
Rev.: $117,859,127
Assets: $365,644,497
Liabilities: $145,248,563
Net Worth: $220,395,934
Earnings: $43,637,109
Emp.: 230
Fiscal Year-end: 03/31/2023
Seed Farming, Marketing & Production Services
N.A.I.C.S.: 111998
Morgan Nzwere *(Grp CEO)*

Subsidiary (Non-US):

Seed Co International Limited **(2)**
43178 Unit 1, Phakalane, 47143, Gaborone, Botswana
Tel.: (267) 3911907
Web Site: http://www.seedcogroup.com
Sales Range: $25-49.9 Million
Emp.: 5
Farming Seed Production
N.A.I.C.S.: 424590
Olesile Ramaabya *(Country Mgr)*

Subsidiary (Non-US):

Seed Co Limited **(3)**
Area 29 Plot 24 Pvt Bag 421, Kanengo, Lilongwe, Malawi
Tel.: (265) 1712074
Web Site: http://www.seedcogroup.com
Sales Range: $25-49.9 Million
Farming Seed Production
N.A.I.C.S.: 424590

The Cotton Company of Zimbabwe Limited **(1)**
1 Lytton Road Workington, PO Box 2697, Harare, Zimbabwe **(100%)**
Tel.: (263) 4749458
Web Site:
http://www.thecottoncompany.com
Sales Range: $350-399.9 Million
Emp.: 620
Purchaser & Processor of Cotton
N.A.I.C.S.: 115114
Patison Sithole *(Chm)*

COTTON COUNTY RETAIL LIMITED
Focal Point, Ludhiana, 141010, India
Tel.: (91) 161267259091 In
Year Founded: 2001
Menswear Apparel Product Mfr
N.A.I.C.S.: 315990

COUGAR METALS NL
Ground Floor 16 Ord Street, West Perth, 6005, WA, Australia
Tel.: (61) 8 9482 0580
Web Site: http://www.cgm.com.au
Rev.: $1,261
Assets: $270,821
Liabilities: $5,301,712
Net Worth: ($5,030,892)
Earnings: ($2,673,994)
Fiscal Year-end: 06/30/18
Minerals Exploration
N.A.I.C.S.: 213115
Randal Lloyd Swick *(Chm)*

COULSON GROUP OF COMPANIES
4890 Cherry Creek Road, Port Alberni, V9Y 8E9, BC, Canada
Tel.: (250) 724-7600
Web Site:
https://www.coulsongroup.com
Holding Company; Logging & Forestry Operations; Aircraft Operator
N.A.I.C.S.: 551112
Britton Coulson *(Co-Pres)*

Subsidiaries:

Coulson Aircrane (U.S.A.), Inc. **(1)**
610 SW Alder St Ste 910, Portland, OR 97205
Tel.: (503) 227-2933

Aviation Services
N.A.I.C.S.: 481112

Coulson Aircrane Ltd. **(1)**
Port Alberni Airport 7500 Airport Rd, Port Alberni, V9Y 7L7, BC, Canada
Tel.: (250) 723-8100
Aircraft Operator
N.A.I.C.S.: 481219
Wayne Coulson *(Owner)*

Subsidiary (Domestic):

Flying Tankers, Inc. **(2)**
9350 Bomber Base V9Y8Z3, Port Alberni, V9Y 7L7, BC, Canada
Tel.: (250) 723-6225
Web Site: http://www.martinmars.com
Sales Range: $25-49.9 Million
Emp.: 23
Fire Fighting Aircraft Operator
N.A.I.C.S.: 481219
Wayne Coulson *(CEO)*

Coulson Manufacturing Ltd. **(1)**
100 Seizal Rd, Port Alberni, V9Y 1A1, BC, Canada
Tel.: (250) 723-8118
Web Site: http://www.coulsongroup.com
Wood Products Mfr
N.A.I.C.S.: 321912
Foster Coulson *(Gen Mgr)*

COUNT LIMITED
Level 11 45 Clarence Street, Sydney, 2000, NSW, Australia
Tel.: (61) 282188778
Web Site: https://www.count.au
Year Founded: 2007
CUP—(ASX)
Rev.: $74,652,110
Assets: $290,536,190
Liabilities: $209,216,078
Net Worth: $81,320,112
Earnings: $2,269,631
Emp.: 3,455
Fiscal Year-end: 06/30/24
Offices of Other Holding Companies
N.A.I.C.S.: 551112
Raymond John Kellerman *(Chm)*

Subsidiaries:

Count Financial Limited **(1)**
Level 8 1 Chifley Square, Sydney, 2000, NSW, Australia
Tel.: (61) 282188778
Web Site: http://www.count.com.au
Sales Range: $125-149.9 Million
Emp.: 100
Insurance Services
N.A.I.C.S.: 524114
Andrew Kennedy *(Chief Advice Officer)*

Subsidiary (Domestic):

Equity Loan Broking Pty Ltd. **(2)**
PO Box 3323, Sydney, 2001, NSW, Australia
Tel.: (61) 282720291
Web Site:
http://www.equityloanbroking.com.au
Sales Range: $50-74.9 Million
Emp.: 1
Banking Services
N.A.I.C.S.: 523150

finconnect (australia) pty. ltd. **(2)**
Gold Fields House Level 19 1 Alfred St, PO Box 3323, Sydney, 2000, New South Wales, Australia
Tel.: (61) 282720440
Web Site: http://www.finconnect.com.au
Sales Range: $50-74.9 Million
Emp.: 80
Financial Planning Accountants & Advisory Services
N.A.I.C.S.: 523999

Diverger Limited **(1)**
Level 7 115 Pitt Street, Sydney, 2000, NSW, Australia
Tel.: (61) 280748599
Web Site: https://diverger.com.au
Rev.: $86,363,044
Assets: $38,299,537
Liabilities: $13,062,529
Net Worth: $25,237,009

Count Limited—(Continued)

Earnings: $1,846,515
Fiscal Year-end: 06/30/2023
Investment Services
N.A.I.C.S.: 523999
Grahame Evans (Chm-Wealth Svcs)

Subsidiary (Domestic):

Law Central Co. Pty. Ltd. (2)
Level 1 18 Richardson Street, West Perth, 6005, WA, Australia
Tel.: (61) 8 9476 4900
Web Site: http://www.lawcentral.com.au
Legal Document Preparation Services
N.A.I.C.S.: 561410

COUNTRY BIRD HOLDINGS LIMITED

Ground Floor 8 Melville Road, Illovo, Johannesburg, 2196, South Africa
Tel.: (27) 11 447 6044 ZA
Web Site: http://cbh.co.za
Poultry Products Producer
N.A.I.C.S.: 311615
Kevin William James (Founder)

Subsidiaries:

Enterprise Foods (Pty) Limited (1)
28 21st Street, Industria, Polokwane, South Africa
Tel.: (27) 11 821 7000
Web Site: http://www.enterprisefoods.co.za
Processed Meat Mfr
N.A.I.C.S.: 311412

Long Iron Meats (Pty) Limited (1)
12 Tjaart Kruger Rd, Randlespark, Klerksdorp, 2570, North West, South Africa
Tel.: (27) 184641001
Web Site: http://www.longironmeats.com
Sales Range: $25-49.9 Million
Emp.: 140
Beef Slaughtering Services
N.A.I.C.S.: 311611

Nutri Feeds (Pty) Limited (1)
41 Buskus Street, Potchefstroom, 2531, North West, South Africa
Tel.: (27) 180118888
Web Site: http://www.nutrifeeds.co.za
Sales Range: $25-49.9 Million
Emp.: 53
Animal Feed Mfr
N.A.I.C.S.: 311119
Loutjie Dunn (Mgr-Natl Technical)

Plant (Domestic):

Nutri Feeds (Pty) Limited - Bloemfontein Feed Mill (2)
Leon Bartell St 22, Oos Einde, Bloemfontein, 9301, Free State, South Africa
Tel.: (27) 514321313
Web Site: http://www.nutri.co.za
Sales Range: $25-49.9 Million
Animal Feed Mfr
N.A.I.C.S.: 311119
Johan Anderson (Gen Mgr)

Nutri Feeds (Pty) Limited - Mafikeng Feed Mill (2)
Agro Road 2 Industrial Area, Mafikeng, 2745, North West Region, South Africa
Tel.: (27) 183810686
Web Site: http://www.nutrifeeds.co.za
Sales Range: $25-49.9 Million
Animal Feed Mfr
N.A.I.C.S.: 311119

Nutri Feeds (Pty) Limited - Viljoenskroon Feed Mill (2)
Fortuna Street 18, Viljoenskroon, 9520, Free State, South Africa
Tel.: (27) 563442200
Web Site: http://www.nutrifeeds.com
Animal Feed Mfr
N.A.I.C.S.: 311119
Johan Anderson (Gen Mgr)

Ross Breeders (Botswana) (Pty) Limited (1)
Plot 55 Ntowanie St, Gaborone, Botswana
Tel.: (267) 3161629
Web Site: http://www.rossafrica.com
Emp.: 280
Poultry Breeding Services

N.A.I.C.S.: 115210

Subsidiary (Domestic):

OistIns (Pty) Limited (2)
PO Box 285, PO Box 285, Shashis, Botswana
Tel.: (267) 2484274
Sales Range: $25-49.9 Million
Emp.: 120
Broiler Chicken Production Services
N.A.I.C.S.: 112320

Supreme Poultry (Pty) Limited (2)
2 Yellow St Botshabelo Industria, PO Box 6851, Botshabelo, Mpumalanga, Free State, South Africa
Tel.: (27) 514486803
Web Site: http://www.supremechicken.net
Sales Range: $25-49.9 Million
Emp.: 40
Poultry Hatcheries & Breeding Services
N.A.I.C.S.: 112340
Spengler Spengler (Dir-Fin)

COUNTRY CLUB HOSPITALITY & HOLIDAYS LIMITED

Country Club Kool 6-3-1219 4th & 5th Floor, Begumpet, Hyderabad, 500 016, India
Tel.: (91) 4066533618
Web Site:
https://www.countryclubindia.net
Year Founded: 1991
526550—(BOM)
Rev.: $16,301,289
Assets: $79,325,040
Liabilities: $41,339,740
Net Worth: $37,985,301
Earnings: $1,515,341
Emp.: 761
Fiscal Year-end: 03/31/23
Resorts & Hotels
N.A.I.C.S.: 721110
Y. Rajeev Reddy (Chm & Mng Dir)

Subsidiaries:

Jade Resorts Private Limited (1)
No 107 Survey No-211b ECR Road Near Crocodile Park, Vadanemelli Village Kancheepuram District, Chengalpattu, 603 104, India
Tel.: (91) 4437470800
Web Site: http://www.jaderesorts.com
Hotel Operator
N.A.I.C.S.: 721110

COUNTRY CONDOS LTD

7-1-1913 1st Floor I S R Complex Kundanbagh, Begumpet, Hyderabad, 500016, Telangana, India
Tel.: (91) 4066533618
Web Site:
https://www.countrycondos.co.in
COUNCODOS—(NSE)
Rev.: $2,547,701
Assets: $3,976,944
Liabilities: $1,232,672
Net Worth: $2,744,272
Earnings: $96,517
Emp.: 77
Fiscal Year-end: 03/31/23
Pharmaceuticals Mfr
N.A.I.C.S.: 424210
Y. Rajeev Reddy (Chm & Mng Dir)

COUNTRY GARDEN HOLDINGS COMPANY LIMITED

Suite 1702 17/F Dina House Ruttonjee Centre 11 Duddell Street, Central, China (Hong Kong)
Tel.: (852) 75766832635
Web Site:
https://www.countrygarden.com.cn
CTRYF—(OTCIQ)
Rev.: $59,588,363,979
Assets: $241,535,639,123
Liabilities: $198,672,740,363
Net Worth: $42,862,898,759
Earnings: ($410,112,982)

Emp.: 69,932
Fiscal Year-end: 03/30/23
Investment Holding Company; Property Development, Construction & Management
N.A.I.C.S.: 551112
Kwok Keung Yeung (Co/Co-Chm)

Subsidiaries:

Country Garden Danga Bay Sdn. Bhd. (1)
Lot PTB 22056 Danga Bay Jalan Bertingkat Skudai, 80200, Johor Bahru, Johor, Malaysia
Tel.: (60) 72209957
Web Site:
http://www.countrygardendangabay.com
Property Development Services
N.A.I.C.S.: 531390
Yc Ha (Mgr-Pur)

Country Garden Pacificview Sdn. Bhd. (1)
Jalan Forest City 1, Forest City Pulau Satu, 81500, Johor Bahru, Johor, Malaysia
Tel.: (60) 7 505 8888
Web Site: https://www.forestcitycgpv.com
Property Development Services
N.A.I.C.S.: 531390

Guangdong Giant Leap Construction Co., Ltd. (1)
No 18 Industrial Avenue, Shunde District Beijiao Town, Foshan, 528311, Guangdong, China
Tel.: (86) 75726639956
Web Site: https://www.tengyuejz.com
Emp.: 10,000
Garden Apartment Construction Services
N.A.I.C.S.: 236116

Risland (Thailand) Co., Ltd. (1)
Artisan Ratchada Condominium 88/1393 3rd floor Soi Pracha Uthit 24, Huai Khwang, Bangkok, 10310, Thailand
Tel.: (66) 20266888
Web Site: https://www.risland.co.th
Property Development Services
N.A.I.C.S.: 531390
Paul Nie (Deputy Gen Mgr-Sls & Mktg)

COUNTRY GARDEN SERVICES HOLDINGS COMPANY LIMITED

No 1 Country Garden Avenue, Shunde District, Foshan, 528312, Guangdong, China
Tel.: (86) 75766832635 HK
Web Site: https://www.bgy.com.cn
Year Founded: 1992
6098—(HKG)
Rev.: $5,899,910,141
Assets: $9,587,405,018
Liabilities: $4,217,711,149
Net Worth: $5,369,693,869
Earnings: $71,542,839
Emp.: 213,712
Fiscal Year-end: 12/31/23
Holding Company
N.A.I.C.S.: 551112
Changjiang Li (Pres)

Subsidiaries:

Sichuan Languang Justbon Services Group Co., Ltd. (1)
No 9 Xixin Avenue high-Tech Zone West, Chengdu, China (100%)
Tel.: (86) 2887825661
Web Site: http://www.justbon.com
Rev.: $418,854,997
Assets: $738,185,697
Liabilities: $325,831,860
Net Worth: $412,353,837
Earnings: $84,263,049
Emp.: 16,468
Fiscal Year-end: 12/31/2020
Property Management Services
N.A.I.C.S.: 531311
Min Yao (Chm)

Subsidiary (Domestic):

Chengdu Hezhiheli Property Management Co., Ltd. (2)

No 66 Shuangcheng 5th Road, Chenghua District, Chengdu, 610051, China
Tel.: (86) 2884712310
Web Site: http://www.hezhiheli.com
Real Estate Development Services
N.A.I.C.S.: 531390

COUNTRY GROUP DEVELOPMENT PUBLIC COMPANY LIMITED

20th Fl Ploenchit Tower 898 Ploenchit Rd, Bangkok, 10330, Thailand
Tel.: (66) 26587888
Web Site: https://www.cgd.co.th
Year Founded: 2010
CGD—(THA)
Rev.: $130,423,553
Assets: $498,113,331
Liabilities: $363,676,436
Net Worth: $134,436,895
Earnings: $7,497,053
Emp.: 89
Fiscal Year-end: 12/31/23
Real Estate Development Services
N.A.I.C.S.: 531390
Vikrom Koompirochana (Chm)

Subsidiaries:

A-HOST Co., Ltd. (1)
SM Tower 21st Floor 979/53-55 Phaholyothin Rd, Samsennai Phyatai, Bangkok, 10400, Thailand
Tel.: (66) 2298 0625
Web Site: http://www.a-host.co.th
Information Technology & Consulting Services
N.A.I.C.S.: 541512

Subsidiary (Domestic):

ABCS Co., Ltd. (2)
Software Park Building 7 th Floor Unit D 99/28 Chaengwattana Road, Klong Gleua Pak Kret, Nonthaburi, Thailand
Tel.: (66) 2962 0470
Software Development Services
N.A.I.C.S.: 541511

COUNTRY GROUP HOLDINGS PUBLIC COMPANY LIMITED

Level 20 Sindhorn Tower 3 132 Wireless Road Lumpini, Pathumwan, Bangkok, 10330, Thailand
Tel.: (66) 22567999 TH
Web Site:
https://www.cgholdings.co.th
Year Founded: 2014
CGH—(THA)
Rev.: $41,334,918
Assets: $269,861,673
Liabilities: $96,784,860
Net Worth: $173,076,814
Earnings: ($5,671,193)
Emp.: 738
Fiscal Year-end: 12/31/23
Holding Company; Securities Dealing
N.A.I.C.S.: 551112
Sawawut Taechaubol (Chm)

COUNTRY GROUP SECURITIES PUBLIC COMPANY LIMITED

132 Sindhorn Bldg 1 2nd 3rd 9th Fl Wireless Rd, Patumwan, Bangkok, 10330, Thailand
Tel.: (66) 2205 7000 TH
Web Site: http://www.cgsec.co.th
Year Founded: 1966
Sales Range: $50-74.9 Million
Emp.: 915
Financial Services
N.A.I.C.S.: 523999
Surabhon Kwunchaithunya (Co-Chm)

COUNTRY HEIGHTS HOLDINGS BERHAD

8th Floor Block A Mines Waterfront Business Park No 3, Jalan Tasik

Mines Resort City, 43300, Seri Kembangan, Selangor Darul Ehsan, Malaysia
Tel.: (60) 389438811
Web Site:
https://www.countryheights.com.my
CHHB—(KLS)
Rev.: $9,806,984
Assets: $256,185,820
Liabilities: $103,245,714
Net Worth: $152,940,106
Earnings: ($22,771,852)
Emp.: 325
Fiscal Year-end: 12/31/22
Property Development & Investment Services
N.A.I.C.S.: 531311
Cheng Wen Lee *(Deputy Chm)*

Subsidiaries:

Borneo Highlands Hornbill Golf & Jungle Club Berhad **(1)**
Jalan Borneo Heights, Padawan, Kuching, Sarawak, Malaysia
Tel.: (60) 168860790
Web Site:
http://www.borneohighlands.com.my
Resort Services
N.A.I.C.S.: 721110

COUNTRY STYLE COOKING RESTAURANT CHAIN CO., LTD.

16th Floor C1 Building Chongqing Headquarters City District C, No 780 Jingwei Avenue Yuzhong District, Chongqing, China
Tel.: (86) 23 8866 8866   Ky
Web Site: http://www.csc100.com
Year Founded: 1996
Sales Range: $200-249.9 Million
Restaurant Owner & Operator
N.A.I.C.S.: 722513
Xingqiang Zhang *(CEO & Acting CFO)*

COUNTRY STYLE FOODS LIMITED

50 Pontefract Lane, Leeds, LS9 8HY, United Kingdom
Tel.: (44) 1132000000   UK
Web Site:
http://www.countrystyle.co.uk
Year Founded: 1962
Commercial Bakery
N.A.I.C.S.: 311812

COUNTRY VIEW BERHAD

Unit 26-01 Level 26 Menara Landmark No 12 Jalan Ngee Heng, Mail Box 261, 80000, Johor Bahru, Johor, Malaysia
Tel.: (60) 72236799
Web Site:
https://www.countryview.com.my
CVIEW—(KLS)
Rev.: $23,880,061
Assets: $150,818,895
Liabilities: $61,235,743
Net Worth: $89,583,153
Earnings: $1,727,253
Emp.: 100
Fiscal Year-end: 11/30/23
Property Development & Investment Services
N.A.I.C.S.: 531312
Seng Piow Piow Ong *(CFO)*

COUNTY INTERNATIONAL LIMITED

Level 2 27 Macquarie Place, Sydney, 2000, NSW, Australia
Tel.: (61) 2 9251 3311
Web Site:
http://www.countyinternational.com
Rev.: $695
Assets: $1,008,158

Liabilities: $19,014
Net Worth: $989,144
Earnings: ($88,852)
Emp.: 2
Fiscal Year-end: 06/30/18
Coal Mining Services
N.A.I.C.S.: 212115
Rodney J. Ruston *(CEO & Mng Dir)*

COUPANG, INC.

Tower 730 570 Songpa-daero, Songpa-gu, Seoul, 05510, Korea (South)
Tel.: (82) 2063333839   DE
Web Site:
http://www.aboutcoupang.com
Year Founded: 2010
CPNG—(NYSE)
Rev.: $20,582,615,000
Assets: $9,512,903,000
Liabilities: $7,098,990,000
Net Worth: $2,413,913,000
Earnings: ($92,042,000)
Emp.: 63,000
Fiscal Year-end: 12/31/22
Online Shopping Services
N.A.I.C.S.: 423620
Bom Suk Kim *(Founder, Chm & CEO)*

Subsidiaries:

Farfetch Limited **(1)**
The Bower 211 Old Street, London, EC1V 9NR, United Kingdom
Tel.: (44) 2035100670
Web Site: https://www.farfetch.com
Rev.: $2,316,680,000
Assets: $3,675,916,000
Liabilities: $2,770,295,000
Net Worth: $905,621,000
Earnings: $344,855,000
Emp.: 6,728
Fiscal Year-end: 12/31/2022
Online Fashion Retailer
N.A.I.C.S.: 458110
Jose Neves *(Founder, Chm & CEO)*

Subsidiary (Non-US):

Farfetch Portugal - Unipessoal, Lda **(2)**
Rua Da Lionesa N 446 Edificio G12, Leca Do Balio, 4465-671, Porto, Portugal
Tel.: (351) 220430530
Web Site: https://www.farfetch.com
N.A.I.C.S.: 458110

New Guards Group Holding S.p.A **(2)**
Via Filippo Turati 12, 20121, Milan, Italy
Tel.: (39) 0283997000
Web Site: https://newguardsgroup.com
N.A.I.C.S.: 315990

COURAGE INVESTMENT GROUP LIMITED

Suite 1510 15th Floor Great Eagle Centre 23 Harbour Road, Wanchai, China (Hong Kong)
Tel.: (852) 31840755
Web Site: http://www.courageinv.com
1145—(HKG)
Rev.: $12,079,000
Assets: $66,455,000
Liabilities: $5,317,000
Net Worth: $61,138,000
Earnings: $1,123,000
Emp.: 16
Fiscal Year-end: 12/31/22
Marine Transportation Services
N.A.I.C.S.: 488320
Lok Ka Sue *(Chm)*

Subsidiaries:

Courage - New Amego Shipping Corp. **(1)**
5/F Transworld Commercial Center 2 Nanking East Road Section 2, Taipei, 10457, Taiwan
Tel.: (886) 225420122
Web Site: http://www.couragemarine.com

Sales Range: $25-49.9 Million
Marine Shipping Services
N.A.I.C.S.: 488510
Philip Wu *(Gen Mgr)*

Subsidiary (Domestic):

Courage - New Amego Shipping Agency Co. Ltd. **(2)**
5 F No 2 Nanjing E Road, Jhongstan District, Taipei, 104, Taiwan
Tel.: (886) 2 25420122
Ship Management Services
N.A.I.C.S.: 483111
Chu Wu *(Gen Mgr)*

Courage Marine (HK) Company Limited **(1)**
Room 1501 15th Floor Great Eagle Centre 23 Harbour Road, Connaught Road Sheungaan, Wanchai, China (Hong Kong)
Tel.: (852) 31840755
Web Site: http://www.couragemarine.com
Sales Range: $50-74.9 Million
Emp.: 5
Ship Management Services
N.A.I.C.S.: 483111
Wu Chao Huan *(Mng Dir)*

COURANT SAS

241 Route de Dommartin, Manziat, 01570, Lyon, France
Tel.: (33) 385368800   FR
Web Site: http://www.courant.fr
Sales Range: $25-49.9 Million
Emp.: 104
Rubber & Plastic Hoses Mfr
N.A.I.C.S.: 326220
Stephanie Bernard *(Dir-Sls, Admin & Comm)*

COURBET SA

58 avenue Iena, 75116, Paris, France
Tel.: (33) 412290115
Web Site: https://www.courbetsa.com
Year Founded: 1991
MLCOU—(EUR)
Sales Range: Less than $1 Million
Financial Investment Services
N.A.I.C.S.: 523940

COURT CAVENDISH LIMITED

The Care House Randalls Way, Leatherhead, KT22 7TW, Surrey, United Kingdom
Tel.: (44) 800 014 8509   UK
Web Site:
http://www.courtcavendish.com
Year Founded: 1988
Social & Health Care Investment Holding Company
N.A.I.C.S.: 551112
Chai Patel *(Chm)*

Subsidiaries:

HC-One Limited **(1)**
Southgate House Archer Street, Darlington, DL3 6AH, United Kingdom
Tel.: (44) 1325 351 100
Web Site: http://www.hc-one.co.uk
Residential Nursing Care & Specialty Disorder Facilities Operator
N.A.I.C.S.: 623110
Chai Patel *(Chm)*

COURTESY CHEV OLDS LTD.

1635 The Queensway, Toronto, M8Z 1T8, ON, Canada
Tel.: (416) 255-9151
Web Site:
http://www.courtesychevrolet.ca
Year Founded: 1968
Rev.: $36,130,457
Emp.: 75
New & Used Car Dealers
N.A.I.C.S.: 441110
Don Polyschuk *(Owner & Pres)*

COURTESY FORD LINCOLN SALES

684 Wharncliffe Rd S, London, N6J 2N7, ON, Canada
Tel.: (519) 680-1200
Web Site:
https://www.courtesyfordlincoln.com
Year Founded: 1996
Rev.: $35,212,705
Emp.: 70
New & Used Car Dealers
N.A.I.C.S.: 441110
Bill Eansor *(Pres)*

COURTEVILLE BUSINESS SOLUTIONS PLC.

38 Commercial Avenue Sabo Yaba, Lagos, Nigeria
Tel.: (234) 8028994830   NG
Web Site:
http://www.courtevillegroup.com
Year Founded: 2005
COURTVILLE—(NIGE)
Rev.: $2,077,381
Assets: $5,622,461
Liabilities: $1,396,609
Net Worth: $4,225,852
Earnings: ($99,789)
Emp.: 176
Fiscal Year-end: 12/31/23
Business Consulting & Management Services
N.A.I.C.S.: 541618
Adebola Akindele *(Mng Dir-Grp)*

Subsidiaries:

Courteville Loss Adjusters Ltd. **(1)**
5 Stanton Terrace 6 St Andrew, Kingston, Jamaica
Tel.: (876) 9275705
Portfolio Management Services
N.A.I.C.S.: 523940

COURTIERS EN DOUANES CARSON LIMITEE

700 Leigh Capreol, Dorval, H4Y 1G7, QC, Canada
Tel.: (514) 393-9830
Web Site: http://www.carson.ca
Sales Range: $100-124.9 Million
Emp.: 80
Custom house broker
N.A.I.C.S.: 531210
Rick Carrson *(CEO)*

COURTOIS SA

3 rue Mage, BP 48531, 31685, Toulouse, Cedex, France
Tel.: (33) 562267322
Web Site: https://www.courtois-sa.com
COUR—(EUR)
Holding Company
N.A.I.C.S.: 551112
Jean-Louis Courtois de Vicose *(Chm & CEO)*

COURTS (JAMAICA) LIMITED

79-81A Slipe Road, Cross Roads, Kingston, 5, Jamaica
Tel.: (876) 9262110
Web Site: http://www.courts.com.jm
General Merchandise Retailer
N.A.I.C.S.: 455219
Mario Guerrero *(Mng Dir)*

COVALIS CAPITAL LP

802 West Bay Road, Georgetown, KY1-1202, Grand Cayman, Cayman Islands
Tel.: (345) 7693101   Ky
Web Site:
http://www.covaliscapital.com
Privater Equity Firm
N.A.I.C.S.: 523999
John M. Lee *(Mng Partner & COO)*

Subsidiaries:

Covalis Capital (America) LLC **(1)**

Covalis Capital LP—(Continued)

405 Lexington Ave 33rd Fl, New York, NY
10174
Tel.: (212) 303-6633
Web Site: http://www.covaliscapital.com
Privater Equity Firm
N.A.I.C.S.: 523999
John M. Lee (Mng Partner & Grp COO)

Covalis Capital LLP (1)
55 New Bond Street, London, W1S 1DG,
United Kingdom
Tel.: (44) 20 3540 6850
Web Site: http://www.covaliscapital.com
Privater Equity Firm
N.A.I.C.S.: 523999
Dara Heller (Head-IR & Bus Dev)

Joint Venture (Non-US):

Nortegas Energia Distribucion,
S.A.U. (2)
Plaza Euskadi 5- Planta 23, 48009, Bilbao,
Spain
Tel.: (34) 944035700
Web Site: http://www.nortegas.es
Rev.: $109,384,982
Assets: $3,479,107,707
Liabilities: $2,243,707,972
Net Worth: $1,235,399,735
Earnings: $14,359,946
Emp.: 250
Fiscal Year-end: 12/31/2017
Natural Gas Distribution Services
N.A.I.C.S.: 221210
Alejandro Legarda Zaragueta (Chm)

Subsidiary (Domestic):

NED Espana Distribucion Gas,
S.A.U. (3)
Calle General Concha 20, 48010, Bilbao,
Spain
Tel.: (34) 946 140 020
Web Site: http://www.nortegas.es
Gas Distr
N.A.I.C.S.: 221210

COVALON TECHNOLOGIES LTD.

1660 Tech Avenue Unit 5, Missis-
sauga, L4W 5S7, ON, Canada
Tel.: (905) 568-8400
Web Site: https://www.covalon.com
COV—(TSXV)
Rev.: $20,082,524
Assets: $18,802,834
Liabilities: $4,612,079
Net Worth: $14,190,755
Earnings: ($3,368,571)
Emp.: 73
Fiscal Year-end: 09/30/23
Pharmaceutical Products Mfr & Sales
N.A.I.C.S.: 325412
Brian Pedlar (CEO)

Subsidiaries:

Covalon Technologies Inc. (1)
1660 Tech Ave Unit 5, Mississauga, L4W
5S7, ON, Canada
Tel.: (905) 568-8400
Web Site: http://www.covalon.com
Emp.: 50
Surgical & Medical Instrument Mfr
N.A.I.C.S.: 339112

COVE-ITO ADVERTISING LTD.

6F Fukuyoshi-cho Bldg 2-2-6 Rop-
pongi, Minato-ku, Tokyo, 106-0032,
Japan
Tel.: (81) 3 3568 7170 JP
Year Founded: 1975
Emp.: 100
Advetising Agency
N.A.I.C.S.: 541810
Peter Cove (Pres)

Subsidiaries:

Cove-Ito (Thailand) Ltd. (1)
323 United Ctr Bldg 34th Fl Unit 3401, Silom Rd Bangrak, Bangkok, 10500, Thailand
Tel.: (66) 2 233 2610
Advertising Agencies

N.A.I.C.S.: 541810

Cove-Ito Interactive (1)
Pola Aoyama Bldg 2-5-17, Minami-Aoyama,
Minato-ku, Tokyo, 107-0062, Japan
Tel.: (81) 3 3403 7253
Emp.: 34
Advertising Agencies
N.A.I.C.S.: 541810

Cove-Ito International Ltd. (1)
Unit D 5/F Max Share Centre, 367-373
King's Road, North Point, China (Hong
Kong)
Tel.: (852) 2886 1337
Emp.: 10
Advertising Agencies
N.A.I.C.S.: 541810

COVEA GROUPE S.A.S.

86-90 rue Saint Lazare, 75009, Paris,
France
Tel.: (33) 1 5550 6000 FR
Web Site: http://www.covea.eu
Year Founded: 2003
Rev.: $19,485,100,378
Assets: $125,855,565,768
Liabilities: $107,871,974,797
Net Worth: $17,983,590,970
Earnings: $979,594,175
Emp.: 23,000
Fiscal Year-end: 12/31/19
Mutual Insurance Holding Company;
Reinsurance, Health Insurance, Prop-
erty & Casualty Insurance Products &
Services
N.A.I.C.S.: 551112
Thierry Derez (Chm & CEO)

Subsidiaries:

Covea Finance SAS (1)
8-12 rue boissy d'Anglas, 75008, Paris,
France
Tel.: (33) 1 40 06 51 50
Web Site: http://www.covea-finance.com
Portfolio Management Services
N.A.I.C.S.: 523940
Olivier Le Borgne (Chm-Supervisory Bd)

Covea Insurance plc (1)
A&B Mills, Dean Clough, Halifax, HX3 5AX,
United Kingdom
Tel.: (44) 1422 331166
Web Site: http://www.coveainsurance.co.uk
Emp.: 833
General Insurance Services
N.A.I.C.S.: 524210
James Reader (CEO)

Covea Risks S.A. (1)
19-21 allees de l'Europe, 92616, Clichy,
Cedex, France
Tel.: (33) 1 57 64 30 00
Web Site: http://www.covea-risks.fr
Insurance Services
N.A.I.C.S.: 524210

FIDELIA Assistance SA (1)
Departement Gestion Clients 27 Quai Car-
not, 92212, Saint-Cloud, Cedex, France
Tel.: (33) 1 47 11 12 00
Web Site: http://www.fidelia-assistance.fr
General Insurance Services
N.A.I.C.S.: 524210

GMF Assurances S.A. (1)
76 rue de Prony, 75857, Paris, Cedex 17,
France
Tel.: (33) 147541010
Web Site: http://www.gmf.fr
Sales Range: $5-14.9 Billion
Emp.: 6,200
Health, Property & Casualty Insurance
Products & Services
N.A.I.C.S.: 524126
Patrice Forget (Deputy Mng Dir)

MAAF Assurances S.A. (1)
Chaban de Chauray, Niort, F-79036, France
Tel.: (33) 549343536
Web Site: http://www.maaf.fr
Sales Range: $1-4.9 Billion
Emp.: 7,000
Health, Property & Casualty Insurance
Products & Services
N.A.I.C.S.: 524126
Thierry Derez (Pres)

MMA S.A. (1)
14 Boulevard Marie & Alexandre Oyon,
72030, Le Mans, Cedex 9, France
Tel.: (33) 440048882
Web Site: http://www.mma.fr
Sales Range: $5-14.9 Billion
Emp.: 11,800
Insurance Services
N.A.I.C.S.: 524113
Didier Bazzocchi (Deputy Mng Dir
Resources)

Subsidiary (Non-US):

MMA Holdings UK plc (2)
2 Norman Place, Reading, RG1 8DA,
United Kingdom
Tel.: (44) 1189 552 222
Insurance Services
N.A.I.C.S.: 524210

PartnerRe Ltd. (1)
90 Pitts Bay Road, Pembroke, HM 08, Ber-
muda
Tel.: (441) 2920888
Web Site: https://www.partnerre.com
Rev.: $9,122,836,000
Assets: $30,488,489,000
Liabilities: $22,064,068,000
Net Worth: $8,424,421,000
Earnings: $2,308,369,000
Emp.: 1,248
Fiscal Year-end: 12/31/2023
Reinsurance Services
N.A.I.C.S.: 524130
Thierry Derez (Chm)

Subsidiary (Non-US):

Partner Reinsurance Asia Pte.
Ltd. (2)
9 Raffles Place #19-20 Republic Plaza II,
Singapore, 048619, Singapore
Tel.: (65) 6538 2066
Reinsurance Products & Services
N.A.I.C.S.: 524130
James Beedle (CEO)

Subsidiary (Domestic):

Partner Reinsurance Company
Ltd. (2)
Wellesley House South 90 Pitts Bay Road,
Pembroke, HM 08, Bermuda
Tel.: (441) 2920888
Reinsurance Services
N.A.I.C.S.: 524130
David Vwiener (Pres)

Subsidiary (Non-US):

PartnerRe Holdings Europe
Limited (2)
5th Fl Block 1 The Oval 160 Shelbourne
Rd, Dublin, 4, Ireland
Tel.: (353) 16379600
Reinsurance Services
N.A.I.C.S.: 524130
Ted Dziurman (Gen Mgr)

Subsidiary (US):

PartnerRe Connecticut Inc. (3)
200 1st Stamford Pl Ste 400, Stamford, CT
06902
Tel.: (203) 485-4200
Reinsurance Services
N.A.I.C.S.: 524130
Nancy Fico (Mgr-Ops)

Subsidiary (Non-US):

PartnerRe Holdings SA (3)
32 rue Guersant, 75017, Paris, France
Tel.: (33) 144011717
Reinsurance Services
N.A.I.C.S.: 524130

Subsidiary (Non-US):

Partner Reinsurance Europe SE (4)
5th Floor Block 1 The Oval 160 Shelbourne
Road, Dublin, 4, Ireland
Tel.: (353) 16379600
Reinsurance Services
N.A.I.C.S.: 524130
Emmanual Clarke (Gen Mgr)

Subsidiary (US):

PartnerRe Miami Inc. (4)

701 Brickell Ave Ste 2500, Miami, FL 33131
Tel.: (305) 377-1292
Insurance Brokerage Services
N.A.I.C.S.: 524210

Subsidiary (US):

PartnerRe U.S. Corporation (3)
200 1st Stamford Pl Ste 400, Stamford, CT
06902 (100%)
Tel.: (203) 485-4200
Multi-Line Reinsurance Services
N.A.I.C.S.: 524130
Thomas L. Forsyth (Pres & CEO)

Subsidiary (Domestic):

Partner Reinsurance Company of the
U.S. (4)
200 1st Stamford Pl Ste 400, Stamford, CT
06902
Tel.: (203) 485-4200
Reinsurance Services
N.A.I.C.S.: 524130
Jonathan M. Colello (Pres)

PartnerRe Asset Management
Corporation (4)
200 1st Stamford Pl Ste 400, Stamford, CT
06902
Tel.: (203) 485-4200
Investment Management Service
N.A.I.C.S.: 523940

PartnerRe Finance A LLC (4)
200 1st Stamford Pl Ste 400, Stamford, CT
06902
Tel.: (203) 485-4200
Reinsurance Services
N.A.I.C.S.: 524130
Vincent Forgione (Mgr-HR)

PartnerRe Finance B LLC (4)
200 1st Stamford Pl Ste 400, Stamford, CT
06902
Tel.: (203) 485-4200
Reinsurance Services
N.A.I.C.S.: 524130

Subsidiary (Non-US):

PartnerRe Holdings Switzerland
GmbH (2)
Bellerivestrasse 36, 8034, Zurich, Switzer-
land
Tel.: (41) 443853535
Web Site: http://partnerre.com
Investment Management Service
N.A.I.C.S.: 523940
Constantinos Miranthis (CEO)

PartnerRe Life Reinsurance Com-
pany of Canada (2)
95 Wellington Street West 12th Floor, To-
ronto, M5J 2N7, ON, Canada
Tel.: (416) 861-0033
Web Site: http://www.partnerre.com
Reinsurance Products & Services
N.A.I.C.S.: 524130

Santeclair (1)
78 Boulevard de la Republique, 92514,
Boulogne-Billancourt, Cedex, France
Tel.: (33) 1 47 61 21 00
Web Site: http://www.santeclair.fr
Life & Health Insurance Services
N.A.I.C.S.: 524210

COVENTRY BUILDING SOCI-ETY

Economic House High Street, PO
Box 9, Coventry, CV1 5QN, United
Kingdom
Tel.: (44) 2476555255
Web Site:
http://www.coventrybuilding.co.uk
CVB—(LSE)
Rev.: $553,542,444
Assets: $69,920,271,876
Liabilities: $66,925,005,784
Net Worth: $2,995,266,092
Earnings: $137,672,808
Emp.: 1,992
Fiscal Year-end: 12/31/20
Insurance & Financial Services
N.A.I.C.S.: 524128
Peter Ayliffe (Deputy Chm)

Subsidiaries:

Godiva Mortgages Limited (1)
Binley Bus Pk, PO Box 139, Coventry, CV1
5ZT, United Kingdom **(100%)**
Tel.: (44) 8457573612
Web Site:
http://www.coventrybuildingsociety.co.uk
Emp.: 1,000
Mortgage & Nonmortgage Loan Brokers
N.A.I.C.S.: 522310

Godiva Savings Limited (1)
Oakfield House Binley Business Park, PO
Box 600, Coventry, CV3 9YR, West Mid-
lands, United Kingdom
Tel.: (44) 7452266974
Web Site: http://www.godivasavingsltd.com
Financial Investment Services
N.A.I.C.S.: 523999
Green Robert Huelin (Chief Ops & Tech
Officer)

The Property Directory Limited (1)
Binley Bus Pk, 139, CV15WF, Coventry,
United Kingdom **(100%)**
Tel.: (44) 2476653517
Miscellaneous Financial Investment Activi-
ties
N.A.I.C.S.: 523999

**COVENTRY COIL-O-MATIC
(HARYANA) LIMITED**
N H 8 87 km Delhi Jaipur Road vil-
lage Salawas, Sangwari, Rewari, 123
401, Haryana, India
Tel.: (91) 9896033552
Web Site: https://hcoilomatic.com
Year Founded: 1988
523415—(BOM)
Sales Range: $1-9.9 Million
Automobile Parts Mfr & Distr
N.A.I.C.S.: 332613

COVENTRY GROUP LIMITED
235 Settlement Road, PO Box 526,
Thomastown, 3074, VIC, Australia
Tel.: (61) 392058290   AU
Web Site: https://www.cgl.com.au
CYG—(ASX)
Rev.: $247,599,492
Assets: $233,293,268
Liabilities: $137,758,413
Net Worth: $95,534,855
Earnings: $440,037
Emp.: 1,100
Fiscal Year-end: 06/30/24
Industrial & Automotive Products
Supplier
N.A.I.C.S.: 423840
Bruce Carter (Gen Mgr)

Subsidiaries:

Coventry Group (NZ) Limited (1)
11 Bruce Roderick Drive, East Tamaki,
2013, New Zealand
Tel.: (64) 94796260
Web Site: http://www.coventrys.com.au
Sales Range: $25-49.9 Million
Emp.: 30
Automotive Gasket Mfr
N.A.I.C.S.: 339991

**Coventry Group Limited Artia
Division** (1)
17 Main Road, Wivenhoe, Burnie, 7320,
TAS, Australia
Tel.: (61) 364319009
Web Site: https://www.cgl.com.au
Sales Range: $25-49.9 Million
Emp.: 4
Fastener Mfr
N.A.I.C.S.: 339993

**Coventry Group Limited Coventry
Fasteners Division** (1)
6 Nello Place, Wetherill Park, 2164, NSW,
Australia
Tel.: (61) 296166100
Web Site: https://www.cgl.com.au
Sales Range: $50-74.9 Million
Emp.: 10
Fastener Whslr
N.A.I.C.S.: 423710

**Coventry Group Limited Coventrys
Division** (1)
25 Redcliffe Road, Redcliffe, 6104, WA,
Australia
Tel.: (61) 862725333
Web Site: https://www.cgl.com.au
Sales Range: $100-124.9 Million
Emp.: 300
Automotive Parts & Tools Whslr
N.A.I.C.S.: 441330

**Coventry Group Limited Hylton
Parker Fasteners Division** (1)
15-17 William Pickering Drive, Albany,
Auckland, New Zealand
Tel.: (64) 94770480
Sales Range: $25-49.9 Million
Emp.: 100
Fastener Mfr
N.A.I.C.S.: 339993

Nubco Proprietary Limited (1)
46 Formby Rd, Devonport, 7310, TAS, Aus-
tralia
Tel.: (61) 36 423 6211
Web Site: http://web.nubco.com.au
Industrial Machinery & Equipment Whslr
N.A.I.C.S.: 423830

COVER 50 S.P.A.
Via Torino 25, 10044, Pianezza, TO,
Italy
Tel.: (39) 0119661445
Web Site: https://www.pt-torino.com
COV—(ITA)
Apparel Product Mfr & Distr
N.A.I.C.S.: 315990
Pierangelo Fassino (Chm)

COVER CORPORATION
Tokyo Mita Garden Tower 3-5-19
Mita, Minato-ku, Tokyo, 108-0073,
Japan
Tel.: (81) 362804036
Web Site: https://www.cover-
corp.com
Year Founded: 2016
5253—(TKS)
Emp.: 392
Software Development Services
N.A.I.C.S.: 541511
Ikko Fukuda (CTO)

COVER TECHNOLOGIES INC.
145 925 Georgia Street West, Van-
couver, V6C 3L2, BC, Canada
Tel.: (604) 669-4771
Web Site:
https://www.magoneproducts.com
MDD—(CNSX)
Rev.: $7,766
Assets: $105,422
Liabilities: $1,047,231
Net Worth: ($941,809)
Earnings: ($978,044)
Fiscal Year-end: 09/30/19
Magnesium Processing Technology
Developer
N.A.I.C.S.: 332999
Tony Louie (CEO & CFO-Interim)

**COVIDH TECHNOLOGIES LIM-
ITED**
B-2 Plot 797/A Sai Krishna Building
Road No 36 Jubilee Hills, Hyderabad,
500033, Telangana, India
Tel.: (91) 40 64643093
Web Site: http://www.covidh.com
Year Founded: 1993
Rev.: $3,683,239
Assets: $2,533,008
Liabilities: $2,462,436
Net Worth: $70,572
Earnings: ($6,225)
Fiscal Year-end: 03/31/19
Software Development & Highway
Construction Services
N.A.I.C.S.: 541511
Naresh Konda (Exec Dir)

**COVINGTON CAPITAL COR-
PORATION**
36 Distillery Lane Suite 440, Toronto,
M5A 3C4, ON, Canada
Tel.: (416) 365-0060   NS
Web Site:
http://www.covingtonfunds.com
Year Founded: 1994
Sales Range: $75-99.9 Million
Emp.: 15
Privater Equity Firm
N.A.I.C.S.: 523999

COVIVIO
18 Avenue Francois Mitterrand,
57000, Metz, France
Tel.: (33) 158975000
Web Site: https://www.covivio.eu
COV—(EUR)
Rev.: $977,747,680
Assets: $29,852,114,181
Liabilities: $14,644,355,709
Net Worth: $15,207,758,472
Earnings: $1,238,831,211
Emp.: 925
Fiscal Year-end: 12/31/22
Residential & Commercial Real Es-
tate Investment Services
N.A.I.C.S.: 531390
Jean Laurent (Chm)

Subsidiaries:

Acopio Facility GmbH & Co. KG. (1)
Essener Str 66, 46047, Oberhausen, Ger-
many
Tel.: (49) 208970640
Real Estate Services
N.A.I.C.S.: 531390

**Central Societa Di Investimento Per
Azioni A Capitalo Fisso Central Sicaf
S.P.A** (1)
Vla C O Cornaggia 6, 20123, Milan, Italy
Tel.: (39) 023 666 4650
Web Site: https://www.centralsicaf.it
Real Estate Services
N.A.I.C.S.: 531390
Marco Bignami (CEO)

Covivio Immobilien Se (1)
Essener Str 66, 46047, Oberhausen, Ger-
many
Tel.: (49) 20 897 0640
Web Site: https://www.covivio.immo
Real Estate Services
N.A.I.C.S.: 531390

Covivio Office AG (1)
Taunusanlage 8, 60329, Frankfurt am Main,
Germany
Tel.: (49) 6927139730
Web Site: http://www.covivio.eu
Commercial Property Management Services
N.A.I.C.S.: 531312

Covivio Office GmbH (1)
Taunusanlage 8, 60329, Frankfurt am Main,
Germany
Tel.: (49) 6927139730
Web Site: http://www.godewind-ag.com
Real Estate Services
N.A.I.C.S.: 531390

Fonciere des Murs SCA (1)
30 avenue Kleber, 75208, Paris, Cedex 16,
France **(49.9%)**
Tel.: (33) 1 58 97 50 00
Web Site: http://www.foncieredesmurs.fr
Real Estate Development Services
N.A.I.C.S.: 531390
Christophe Kullmann (Chm-Supervisory Bd)

**Real Estate Solution & Technology
Srl** (1)
Via di Santa Teresa 35, 00198, Rome, Italy
Tel.: (39) 0636 2221
Web Site: https://www.resolutiontech.it
Real Estate Services
N.A.I.C.S.: 531390
Massimo Paolini (CEO)

Revalo Spa (1)
Via Cristoforo Colombo 112, 00154, Rome,
Italy
Tel.: (39) 069 972 4444

Web Site: https://www.revalo.it
Property Management Services
N.A.I.C.S.: 531311
David Vichi (CEO)

Urbis Park SAS (1)
13 rue du Coetlosquet, Metz, 57000, Mo-
selle, France
Tel.: (33) 387393220
Web Site: http://www.urbispark.fr
Parking Management Services
N.A.I.C.S.: 812930

COWAY CO., LTD.
136-23 Yugumagoksa-ro, Yugu-eup,
Gongju, 32508, Chungcheongnam-
do, Korea (South)
Tel.: (82) 418507805
Web Site: https://www.cowayir.com
Year Founded: 1989
021240—(KRS)
Rev.: $2,957,653,931
Assets: $3,348,012,429
Liabilities: $1,574,732,424
Net Worth: $1,773,280,006
Earnings: $351,420,213
Emp.: 6,442
Fiscal Year-end: 12/31/22
Water Purification Equipment Mfr
N.A.I.C.S.: 335220
Jun-Hyuk Bang (Chm)

Subsidiaries:

Coway (M) Sdn. Bhd. (1)
Ground Floor Wisma UOA II No 21, Jalan
Pinang, 50450, Kuala Lumpur, Malaysia
Tel.: (60) 3 2059 0188
Web Site: http://www.coway.com.my
Water Purification Equipment Distr
N.A.I.C.S.: 423690

Coway USA Inc. (1)
4221 Wilshire Blvd Ste 210, Los Angeles,
CA 90010
Tel.: (213) 480-1600
Web Site: https://coway-usa.com
Water Purification Equipment Distr
N.A.I.C.S.: 423690
Young Kwan Kim (Dir-Mktg)

COWELL E HOLDINGS INC.
1 Songbai Road Huanan Industrial
Zone, Liaobu Town, Dongguan,
Guangdong, China
Tel.: (86) 76989765000   Ky
Web Site:
http://www.cowellholdings.com
Year Founded: 2006
1415—(HKG)
Rev.: $1,116,210,000
Assets: $631,154,000
Liabilities: $270,557,000
Net Worth: $360,597,000
Earnings: $83,816,000
Emp.: 3,405
Fiscal Year-end: 12/31/22
Holding Company; Electronic Product
Mfr
N.A.I.C.S.: 551112
Yan Meng (CEO)

Subsidiaries:

**Cowell Electronics Company
Limited** (1)
901 Acehightechcity beomgye 29 Simin-
daero 109beon-gil, Dongan-gu, Anyang,
Gyeonggi-do, Korea (South)
Tel.: (82) 314291650
Optical Product Distr
N.A.I.C.S.: 423460
Kyu Beom Cho (CEO)

Cowell Optic Electronics Limited (1)
Suite 1620 16/F Ocean Centre 5 Canton
Road, Tsim Sha Tsui, Kowloon, China
(Hong Kong)
Tel.: (852) 23686620
Web Site: http://www.cowellholdings.com
Optical Product Distr
N.A.I.C.S.: 423460
Lam Wing Yan (Sec)

Cowell e Holdings Inc.—(Continued)

COWELL FASHION CO., LTD.
270 Sinwon-ro, Yeongtong-gu, Suwon, Gyeonggi-do, Korea (South)
Tel.: (82) 312172500
Web Site:
https://www.cowellfashion.co.kr
Year Founded: 1974
033290—(KRS)
Rev.: $915,244,976
Assets: $818,814,885
Liabilities: $438,142,660
Net Worth: $380,672,225
Earnings: $47,274,012
Emp.: 548
Fiscal Year-end: 12/31/22
Electronic Components Mfr
N.A.I.C.S.: 334416
Yong Seok Choi *(CEO)*

COWON PLAY CO., LTD.
540 Eonju-Ro, Gangnam-Gu, Seoul, 06147, Korea (South)
Tel.: (82) 25579482
Web Site:
http://www.cowongames.com
Year Founded: 1996
056000—(KRS)
Rev.: $1,392,685
Assets: $19,503,800
Liabilities: $5,291,134
Net Worth: $14,212,667
Earnings: ($3,258,594)
Emp.: 22
Fiscal Year-end: 12/31/22
Software Development Services
N.A.I.C.S.: 541511
Peter Lee *(CEO)*

COWON SYSTEMS INC.
Cowon Tower 689-3 YeokSam-Dong, Gangnam-Gu, Seoul, 135-080, Korea (South)
Tel.: (82) 269000000
Web Site:
http://www.cowonglobal.com
Year Founded: 1995
Sales Range: $100-124.9 Million
Emp.: 180
Digital Multimedia & Wireless Internet Products
N.A.I.C.S.: 334220
Nam Gyu Park *(CEO)*

Subsidiaries:

Cowon Indonesia   **(1)**
TIFA Bldg 2nd Fl, Jl Kuningan Barat I No 26, Jakarta, 12710, Indonesia
Tel.: (62) 215262409
Web Site: http://www.cowon.com
Sales Range: $25-49.9 Million
Emp.: 30
Electronic Products Mfr
N.A.I.C.S.: 334310

COX & KINGS LIMITED
Turner Morrison Building 4th Floor 16 Bank Street Fort, Mumbai, 400 001, India
Tel.: (91) 2222709100
Web Site:
http://www.coxandkings.com
Year Founded: 1758
533144—(LUX)
Sales Range: $1-4.9 Billion
Travel & Tour Services
N.A.I.C.S.: 561599
Amrita Shah *(Deputy Mgr)*

Subsidiaries:

Cox & Kings (UK) Limited   **(1)**
6th Floor 30 Millbank, London, SW1P 4EE, United Kingdom
Tel.: (44) 20 7873 5000
Web Site: http://www.coxandkings.co.uk
Travel Tour Operator
N.A.I.C.S.: 561520

Mark Stacey *(Mgr-Mktg & Bus Dev)*

Subsidiary (US):

East India Travel Company, Inc.   **(2)**
8060 Melross Ave 3rd Fl, Los Angeles, CA 90046
Tel.: (323) 655-1758
Web Site: http://www.coxandkingsusa.com
Travel Tour Operator
N.A.I.C.S.: 561520
Warren Chang *(COO)*

Cox & Kings Global Services LLC   **(1)**
PO Box 25770, Dubai, United Arab Emirates
Tel.: (971) 321 0334
Web Site: http://www.ckgs.ae
Visa Processing Services
N.A.I.C.S.: 928120

Cox & Kings Global Services Sweden AB   **(1)**
David Bagares Gata 26 B, 111 38, Stockholm, Sweden
Tel.: (46) 84401460
Travel Tour Operator
N.A.I.C.S.: 561520

Cox & Kings GmBH   **(1)**
Landshuter Allee 8 3rd Floor, 80637, Munich, Germany
Tel.: (49) 30 26949750
Web Site: http://www.in.de.coxandkings.com
Visa Processing Services
N.A.I.C.S.: 928120
Peter Ajay *(Mng Dir)*

Cox & Kings Japan Limited   **(1)**
YK Bldg 3F 2-2-16 Sangenjaya, Setagaya-ku, Tokyo, 154-0024, Japan
Tel.: (81) 3 3424 5151
Web Site: http://www.coxandkings.co.jp
Travel Tour Operator
N.A.I.C.S.: 561520
Noriko Ogawa *(Pres & CEO)*

Cox & Kings Tours LLC   **(1)**
S-04 & G-01 AL YAMAMA Near GPO, PO Box 31126, Karama, Dubai, United Arab Emirates
Tel.: (971) 4 357 2628
Web Site: http://www.coxandkings.ae
Travel Tour Operator
N.A.I.C.S.: 561520

Cox and Kings Global Services Private Limited   **(1)**
3A/3B Rushabh Chamber Marol Makwana Road, Andheri E, Mumbai, 400059, India
Tel.: (91) 22 6731 3935
Web Site: http://www.ckgs.com
Business Process Outsourcing Services
N.A.I.C.S.: 561110
Sanjay Bhaduri *(CEO)*

Depot Starvillas SARL   **(1)**
zac la Baume, 34290, Servian, France
Tel.: (33) 9 67 36 67 61
Travel Tour Operator
N.A.I.C.S.: 561520

Eurosites AS   **(1)**
Vester Farimagsgade 7 6 sal, 1606, Copenhagen, Denmark
Tel.: (45) 70 28 71 00
Web Site: http://www.eurocamp.dk
Travel Tour Operator
N.A.I.C.S.: 561520

Eurosites BV   **(1)**
Zuidsingel 22, 3811 HB, Amersfoort, Netherlands
Tel.: (31) 33 460 27 22
Web Site: http://www.eurocamp.nl
Travel Tour Operator
N.A.I.C.S.: 561520

Holidaybreak Ltd.   **(1)**
Hartford Manor, Greenbank Lane, Northwich, CW8 1HW, Cheshire, United Kingdom   **(65.58%)**
Tel.: (44) 1606787000
Web Site: http://www.holidaybreak.co.uk
Sales Range: $750-799.9 Million
Holding Company; Tour Operator of Self-Drive Camping & Mobile-Home Holidays in Europe
N.A.I.C.S.: 561520
Steve Whitfield *(Mng Dir-Camping Div)*

Subsidiary (Non-US):

B.V. Weekendjeweg.nl   **(2)**
Van Heuven Goedhartlaan 935A, Amstelveen, 1181LD, North Holland, Netherlands
Tel.: (31) 204564099
Web Site: http://www.weekendjeweg.nl
Hotel Reservation Services
N.A.I.C.S.: 561520
Karel Vos *(Mng Dir)*

Bookit B.V.   **(2)**
Van Heuven Goedhartlaan 935a, Amstelveen, 1181 LD, North Holland, Netherlands
Tel.: (31) 20 456 42 42
Web Site: http://www.bookit.nl
Sales Range: $25-49.9 Million
Emp.: 70
Hotel & Transportation Reservation Services
N.A.I.C.S.: 561599
Karel Vos *(Mng Dir)*

Business Reservations Centre Holland B.V.   **(2)**
Van Heuven Goedhartlaan 935 A, 1181 LD, Amstelveen, North Holland, Netherlands
Tel.: (31) 204564035
Web Site: http://www.bookit.nl
Sales Range: $25-49.9 Million
Emp.: 57
Hotel & Transportation Reservation Services
N.A.I.C.S.: 561599
Karel Vos *(Mng Dir)*

Camping in Comfort B.V.   **(2)**
Zuidsingel 22, 3811 HB, Amersfoort, Netherlands
Tel.: (31) 334602703
Web Site: http://www.eurocamp.nl
Sales Range: $10-24.9 Million
Emp.: 60
Camping & Touring Services
N.A.I.C.S.: 721214

Djoser B.V.   **(2)**
Breestraat 125, 2311 CM, Leiden, South Holland, Netherlands
Tel.: (31) 71 5126400
Web Site: http://www.djoser.nl
Sales Range: $10-24.9 Million
Emp.: 40
Travel Tour Operating Services
N.A.I.C.S.: 561520
Myra van der Spek *(Gen Mgr)*

Subsidiary (Non-US):

Djoser-Divantoura bvba   **(3)**
Bagattenstraat 176, 9000, Gent, Oost-Vlaanderen, Belgium
Tel.: (32) 92230069
Web Site: http://www.djoser.be
Travel & Tour Operating Agencies
N.A.I.C.S.: 561510

Subsidiary (Non-US):

Easycamp B.V.   **(2)**
Zuidsingel 22, 3811 HB, Amersfoort, Utrecht, Netherlands
Tel.: (31) 334220470
Web Site: http://www.ecamp.nl
Sales Range: $10-24.9 Million
Emp.: 60
Camping Tour Operators
N.A.I.C.S.: 721214

Ecamp GmbH   **(2)**
Barmbeker Str 10, 22303, Hamburg, Germany
Tel.: (49) 408221830
Web Site: http://www.ecamp.de
Emp.: 13
Recreational Camps & Touring Services
N.A.I.C.S.: 721214

Eurocamp Travel AG   **(2)**
Kaspar-Fenner-Str 6, 8700, Zurich, Switzerland
Tel.: (41) 525607000
Web Site: http://www.eurocamp.ch
Camping Tour Operators
N.A.I.C.S.: 721214

Eurocamp Travel B.V.   **(2)**
Zuidsingel 22, 3811 HB, Amersfoort,

Utrecht, Netherlands
Tel.: (31) 334602722
Web Site: http://www.eurocamp.nl
Sales Range: $10-24.9 Million
Emp.: 60
Transportation & Camps Accommodation Services
N.A.I.C.S.: 721214

Subsidiary (Domestic):

European Study Tours Limited   **(2)**
4 Post Office Walk, Fore Street, Hertford, SG14 1DL, Hertfordshire, United Kingdom
Tel.: (44) 844 576 1960
Web Site: http://www.euro-study-tours.co.uk
Sales Range: $10-24.9 Million
Emp.: 22
Educational Tour Operating Services
N.A.I.C.S.: 561520
Laura Michelson *(Mgr-Ops)*

Explore Worldwide Limited   **(2)**
Nelson House, 55 Victoria Road, Farnborough, GU14 7PA, Hampshire, United Kingdom
Tel.: (44) 8450131537
Web Site: http://www.explore.co.uk
Sales Range: $25-49.9 Million
Emp.: 100
Travel Tour Operating Services
N.A.I.C.S.: 561520
Caroline Phillips *(Product Mgr)*

Subsidiary (Non-US):

Holidaybreak Reisevermittlung GmbH   **(2)**
Barmbeker Strasse 10, 22303, Hamburg, Germany
Tel.: (49) 40450970
Web Site: http://www.eurocamp.de
Sales Range: $10-24.9 Million
Emp.: 30
Camping Tour Operators
N.A.I.C.S.: 561520
Carola Thuering *(Mgr-Online Mktg)*

Keycamp Holidays (Ireland) Limited   **(2)**
78-80 South Mall, Cork, Munster, Ireland
Tel.: (353) 21 425 2300
Web Site: http://www.eurocamp.ie
Sales Range: $10-24.9 Million
Emp.: 6
Outdoor Accommodation & Management Services
N.A.I.C.S.: 721214
Colette Forde *(Mgr)*

Keycamp Holidays Netherlands B.V.   **(2)**
Zuidsingel 22, 3811 HB, Amersfoort, Utrecht, Netherlands
Tel.: (31) 334602775
Web Site: http://www.keycamp.nl
Sales Range: $25-49.9 Million
Emp.: 60
Holiday Tour Operators
N.A.I.C.S.: 561520

NST Limited   **(2)**
Unit 22 Northwood Court, Swords Road, Dublin, 9, Ireland
Tel.: (353) 1 8940300
Web Site: http://www.nst.ie
Sales Range: $10-24.9 Million
Emp.: 16
School & College Tour Operating Agencies
N.A.I.C.S.: 561520
Steve Craven *(Mgr-Bus Dev)*

Subsidiary (Domestic):

NST Travel Group Limited   **(2)**
Discovery House Brooklands Way, Whitehills Business Park, Blackpool, FY4 5LW, Lancashire, United Kingdom
Tel.: (44) 1253 833 833
Web Site: http://www.nstgroup.co.uk
Sales Range: $25-49.9 Million
Emp.: 130
School Trips, Tours, Educational Visits & School Group Travel
N.A.I.C.S.: 561520
Steve Craven *(Gen Mgr)*

Own A Holiday Home Limited   **(2)**
Hartford Manor, Greenbank Lane, Northwich, CW8 1HW, Cheshire, United Kingdom

Tel.: (44) 1606787000
Web Site: http://www.ownaholidayhome.com
Sales Range: $25-49.9 Million
Emp.: 3
Mobile Home Sales
N.A.I.C.S.: 459930

PGL Adventure Limited (2)
Alton Court, Penyard Lane, Ross-on-Wye,
HR9 5GL, Herefordshire, United Kingdom
Tel.: (44) 1989764211
Web Site: http://www.pgl.co.uk
Sales Range: $10-24.9 Million
Emp.: 200
Outdoor Accommodation & Recreational
Services
N.A.I.C.S.: 721214
Richard Sanders (Dir-Ops)

PGL Group Limited (2)
Alton Court, Penyard Lane, Ross-on-Wye,
HR9 5GL, Herefordshire, United Kingdom
Tel.: (44) 1989764211
Web Site: http://www.pgl.co.uk
Sales Range: $75-99.9 Million
Emp.: 250
Holding Company; Travel & Tour Operating
Agencies
N.A.I.C.S.: 551112
Patricia Mary Walker (Dir-HR)

PGL Travel Limited (2)
Alton Court, Penyard Lane, Ross-on-Wye,
HR9 5GL, Herefordshire, United Kingdom
Tel.: (44) 1989764211
Web Site: http://www.pgl.co.uk
Sales Range: $25-49.9 Million
Emp.: 250
Residential Activity Holidays & Educational
Tours for Youth
N.A.I.C.S.: 561520
Darren McLean (Mgr-HR Sys)

Regal Diving and Tours Limited (2)
58 Lancaster Way, Ely, CB6 3NW, Cam-
bridgeshire, United Kingdom
Tel.: (44) 1353 659 999
Web Site: http://www.regal-diving.co.uk
Sales Range: $10-24.9 Million
Emp.: 10
Diving Tour Operating Services
N.A.I.C.S.: 611620
Emma Mackenzie (Mgr-Brand Mktg)

Subsidiary (Non-US):

SAS Le Chateau d'Ebblinghem (2)
1934 Route Nationale, 59173, Ebblinghem,
Lille, France   **(100%)**
Tel.: (33) 328442210
Web Site: http://www.nstgroup.co.uk
Sales Range: $10-24.9 Million
Emp.: 20
Residential Hostel
N.A.I.C.S.: 721199

Travelplus Group GmbH (2)
Munsterstr 111, Munster, 48155, Nordrhein-
Westfalen, Germany
Tel.: (49) 2506 8303 0
Web Site: http://www.travelworks.de
Sales Range: $10-24.9 Million
Emp.: 42
Travel Tour Operating Services
N.A.I.C.S.: 561520
Tanja Kuntz (Chm)

Quoprro Global Services Pvt.
Ltd. (1)
Mirror Tower Unit No 102A 61 Mody Road,
Tsim Sha Tsui, Kowloon, China (Hong
Kong)
Tel.: (852) 2723 6278
Web Site: http://www.in.hk.quoprro.com
Visa Processing Services
N.A.I.C.S.: 928120

Superbreak Mini Holidays Group
Ltd. (1)
Eboracum Way, York, YO31 7RE, United
Kingdom   **(49%)**
Tel.: (44) 1904 717 362
Web Site: http://www.superbreak.com
Emp.: 200
Tour Operators & Travel Arrangements
N.A.I.C.S.: 561520
Jane Atkins (Dir-Sls & Product)

Subsidiary (Domestic):

Superbreak Mini-Holidays
Limited (2)

Eboracum Way, York, YO31 7RE, United
Kingdom
Tel.: (44) 1904 717 362
Web Site: http://www.superbreak.com
Emp.: 200
Travel Agency Activities
N.A.I.C.S.: 561599
Christopher Cundall (Head-Partnerships &
Travel Trade Support)

COX CO., LTD.
HF Nihombashi-Hamacho Building
1-2-1 Nihonbashi Hamacho, Chuo-
Ku, Tokyo, 103-0007, Japan
Tel.: (81) 358216070
Web Site: https://www.cox-
online.co.jp
Year Founded: 1973
9876—(TKS)
Rev.: $105,534,650
Assets: $83,895,970
Liabilities: $29,926,890
Net Worth: $53,969,080
Earnings: $8,096,780
Emp.: 773
Fiscal Year-end: 02/29/24
Apparel Clothing Mfr & Whslr
N.A.I.C.S.: 315990
Hideki Miyake (Pres)

COXON PRECISE INDUSTRIAL
CO., LTD.
No 48 Lane 1274 Chung Cheng Rd,
Chung-li, 320, Tao Yuan Hsien, Tai-
wan
Tel.: (886) 34252153
Web Site:
https://www.coxongroup.com
Year Founded: 1989
3607—(TAI)
Rev.: $86,245,590
Assets: $98,166,614
Liabilities: $37,529,741
Net Worth: $60,636,873
Earnings: ($1,324,831)
Fiscal Year-end: 12/31/23
Communication Device Parts Mfr
N.A.I.C.S.: 334220
Hong Huan Chin (CEO)

Subsidiaries:

COXON Industrial Ltd. (1)
Flat V10/F Everest Industrial Centre 396
Kwun Tong Road, Kwun Tong, Kowloon,
999077, China (Hong Kong)
Tel.: (852) 2 412 0080
Web Site: https://www.coxon.com.hk
Injection Molded Plastic Products Mfr
N.A.I.C.S.: 326121
Kevin C. K. Liu (Dir-Engrg)

Plant (Non-US):

COXON Industrial Ltd. - Guangdong
Plastic & Mould Plant (2)
Zhen An 1st Road 6th Industrial District
Shang Sha Village, Chang An Town, Dong-
guan, 523859, Guangdong, China
Tel.: (86) 76985070288
Web Site: http://www.coxon.com.tw
Injection Molded Plastic Products Mfr
N.A.I.C.S.: 322299

Dong Guan CHENSONG Plastic &
Mould (1)
Zhen An 1st Rd, 6th Industrial Dist Shang
Sha Vil Chang An Town, Dongguan,
523859, Guangdong, China
Tel.: (86) 76985070288
Web Site: https://www.coxongroup.com
Molded Plastic Product Mfr & Distr
N.A.I.C.S.: 326291

Dong Guan Cheng Da Metal Product
Company Limited (1)
Zhen An 1st Rd, 6th Industrial Dist Shang
Sha Vil Chang An Town, Dongguan,
523859, Guang Dong, China
Tel.: (86) 76985070288
Plastics Product Mfr
N.A.I.C.S.: 326199

SUN CAN International Ltd. -
SINYON Plastic & Mould Factory (1)
Industrial Area No 3 Xin Hua Road Wu Sha
Jiang Bei Village, Chang An Town, Dong-
guan, 523859, Guangdong, China
Tel.: (86) 76985548081
Injection Molded Plastic Products Mfr
N.A.I.C.S.: 326121

Sinxon Plastic (Dong Guan) Co.,
Ltd. (1)
Bu Bu Gao Da Dao, Jiang BEI Village Wu-
sha Chang An Town, Dongguan, 523859,
Guangdong, China
Tel.: (86) 76985079188
Designing Mold Mfr
N.A.I.C.S.: 333511

Sinyon Plastic Industrial Co., Ltd. (1)
Bu Bu Gao Da Dao, Jiang BEI Village Wu-
sha Chang An Town, Dongguan, 523859,
Guangdong, China
Tel.: (86) 7698 554 8082
Designing Mold Mfr
N.A.I.C.S.: 333511

TECKON Industrial Corporation (1)
6E06 Taipei World Trade Center 5 Xin Yi
Road Section 5, Taipei, 11011, Taiwan
Web Site: http://www.teckon.com.tw
Molded Plastic Product Mfr
N.A.I.C.S.: 326199

VASTECH Plastic (Shanghai) Indus-
trial Co., Ltd. (1)
No 3 Lane 309 Nanle Road Chedun Town,
Songjiang District, Shanghai, 201613, China
Tel.: (86) 2157749216
Injection Molded Plastic Products Mfr
N.A.I.C.S.: 326121

COYOTE SYSTEM SAS
24, quai Gallieni Suresnes, Paris,
92150, France
Tel.: (33) 1 76 49 48 47
Web Site:
http://www.coyotesystems.com
Year Founded: 2005
Urban Planning & Associated Traffic
Information Services
N.A.I.C.S.: 925120
David Audrain (Mgr-Tech)

Subsidiaries:

Traqueur S.A. (1)
25 quai Gallieni, 92150, Suresnes, France
Tel.: (33) 156977000
Web Site: http://www.traqueur.com
Vehicle Tracking & Recovery Systems
N.A.I.C.S.: 561621

CP HOLDINGS LTD.
CP House, Otterspool Way, Watford,
WD25 8JP, United Kingdom
Tel.: (44) 1923 250500
Holding Company
N.A.I.C.S.: 551112
Lilly Schreier (Dir)

Subsidiaries:

Danubius Hotel and Spa Nyrt. (1)
Szent Istvan ter 11, 1051, Budapest, Hun-
gary
Tel.: (36) 1889 4185
Web Site: http://www.danubiushotels.com
Rev.: $189,965,160
Assets: $328,602,120
Liabilities: $119,318,100
Net Worth: $209,284,020
Earnings: $6,145,590
Emp.: 4,119
Fiscal Year-end: 12/31/2014
Home Management Services
N.A.I.C.S.: 561110
Janos Tobias (CFO & Sr VP)

CP2 GROUP LIMITED
Level 32 200 George Street, Sydney,
2000, NSW, Australia
Tel.: (61) 282774131   **AU**
Web Site: http://www.cp2.com
Year Founded: 2007
Investment Holding Company
N.A.I.C.S.: 551112

Sally Holloway (Co-Founder & Chm)

Subsidiaries:

CP2 (UK) Limited (1)
Suite FF10-11 Holland House 4 Bury Street,
London, EC3A 5AW, United Kingdom
Tel.: (44) 207 194 8470
Financial Investment Services
N.A.I.C.S.: 522390

CP2 Limited (1)
Level 8 Aurora St, 88 Phillip St, Sydney,
2000, NSW, Australia
Tel.: (61) 282745900
Web Site: http://www.cp2.com
Sales Range: $50-74.9 Million
Emp.: 20
Investment Management Firm
N.A.I.C.S.: 523999
Sally Holloway (Co-Founder & Chm)

Joint Venture (Domestic):

Airport Link Co. Pty Ltd. (2)
Mascot Station, PO Box 604, Cnr Church
Ave & Bourke Road, Mascot, 2020, NSW,
Australia
Web Site: http://www.airportlink.com.au
Sales Range: $25-49.9 Million
Emp.: 10
Operation & Management of Railway Sta-
tions
N.A.I.C.S.: 488210

Holding (Domestic):

ConnectEast Pty. Limited (2)
2 Hilcrest Ave, Ringwood, 3134, VIC, Aus-
tralia
Tel.: (61) 399551700
Web Site: http://www.connecteast.com.au
Sales Range: $150-199.9 Million
Building Maintaining & Operating Distr
N.A.I.C.S.: 488490
Tony Hudson (Gen Counsel & Sec)

CPC CORPORATION
No 3 Songren Rd, Sinyi District, Tai-
pei, 11010, Taiwan
Tel.: (886) 287898989   **CN**
Web Site: http://www.cpc.com.tw
Year Founded: 1946
Rev.: $33,719,092,131
Assets: $26,664,780,310
Liabilities: $16,488,679,456
Net Worth: $10,176,100,855
Earnings: $1,078,723,732
Emp.: 15,836
Fiscal Year-end: 12/31/19
Petroleum & Natural Gas Exploration
& Production Services
N.A.I.C.S.: 324110
Angela Koju Lin (CEO-Solvent &
Chemical Bus Div)

Subsidiaries:

CPC International Trading Pte
Ltd (1)
6 Battery Road Ste 35-04, Singapore,
049909, Singapore
Tel.: (65) 6327 9881
Oil & Gas Exploration Services
N.A.I.C.S.: 213112

Exploration & Development Research
Institute (1)
No 1 Ta Yuan Wen Shan, Miao-li, 36010,
Taiwan
Tel.: (886) 37356150
Web Site: http://www.cpc.com.tw
Emp.: 150
Commercial Petroleum Research
N.A.I.C.S.: 541715

Exploration & Production Business
Division (1)
No 3 Sungren Road Shinyi Chiu, Taipei,
11010, Taiwan
Tel.: (886) 2 8989
Web Site: http://www.cpc.com.tw
Sales Range: $750-799.9 Million
Emp.: 1,400
Commercial Exploration of Oil-Bearing
Lands
N.A.I.C.S.: 211120

CPC Corporation—(Continued)

Kaohsiung Refinery (1)
Tso Ying Nan Road 2, Kaohsiung, 811, Taiwan
Tel.: (886) 75824141
Web Site: http://www.cpckoa.com.tw
Sales Range: $1-4.9 Billion
Emp.: 3,000
Petroleum Refiner
N.A.I.C.S.: 324110

Northern Project & Construction Division (1)
111 Shalung Village Tayuan Town, Taoyuan, Hsien, Taiwan
Tel.: (886) 3 3832 680
Provider of Petroleum Services
N.A.I.C.S.: 324110

OPIC AFRICA CORPORATION (1)
PO Box 1155, N'djamena, Chad
Tel.: (235) 6221 7816
Oil & Gas Exploration Services
N.A.I.C.S.: 213112

Opicoil America, Inc. (1)
3040 Post Oak Blvd Ste 800, Houston, TX 77056
Tel.: (713) 840-7171
Sales Range: $50-74.9 Million
Emp.: 10
Crude Petroleum & Natural Gas Extraction
N.A.I.C.S.: 211120
Amof Chen (Pres)

Division (Domestic):

Opicoil Houston, Inc. (2)
3040 Post Oak Blvd Ste 800, Houston, TX 77056
Tel.: (713) 840-7171
Sales Range: $50-74.9 Million
Crude Petroleum & Natural Gas Extraction
N.A.I.C.S.: 211120
Mao-Hsiung Chen (Pres)

Overseas Petroleum and Investment Corporation (1)
No 3 Sungren Road Shinyi Chiu, Taipei, 11010, Taiwan
Tel.: (886) 287898989
Web Site: http://www.cpc.com.tw
Sales Range: $400-449.9 Million
Emp.: 1,000
Crude Petroleum & Natural Gas Extraction; Investments
N.A.I.C.S.: 211120

Division (Domestic):

Lubricants Business Division (2)
6th Fl No 15 Cheng Kung 2nd Rd, Kaohsiung, 11010, PRC, Taiwan
Tel.: (886) 75361510
Web Site: http://www.cpc.com.tw
Crude Petroleum & Natural Gas Extraction
N.A.I.C.S.: 211120

Refining & Manufacturing Research Institute (1)
217 Min Sheng South Road, Chiayi, 60036, Taiwan
Tel.: (886) 52224171
Web Site: http://www.cpc.com.tw
Sales Range: $25-49.9 Million
Emp.: 12
Petroleum Manufacturing Research
N.A.I.C.S.: 541715
Yen Shiang Shih (Chm)

Taiwan Marketing & Transportation Division (1)
No 3 Sungren Rd, Taipei, 11010, Shinyi Chu, Taiwan
Tel.: (886) 287898989
Web Site: http://www.cpctmtd.com.tw
Sales Range: $450-499.9 Million
Emp.: 2,500
Provider of Marketing & Transportation of Petroleum & Petrochemicals
N.A.I.C.S.: 486910

CPC INGENIERIA Y CONSTRUCCIONES SA
Av Madero 900, Torre Catalinas Plaza Piso 20, Buenos Aires, C105 4AAF, Argentina
Tel.: (54) 11 5077 6980

Web Site: http://www.cpc-sa.com.ar
Construction Services
N.A.I.C.S.: 237310
Alberto Ealo Artetxe (Dir-Fin)

CPD S.A.
ul Prosta 20, 00-850, Warsaw, Poland
Tel.: (48) 000128353   PL
Web Site: https://www.cpdsa.pl
CPD—(WAR)
Rev.: $43,407
Assets: $38,959,993
Liabilities: $3,838,438
Net Worth: $35,121,555
Earnings: $26,701,366
Fiscal Year-end: 12/31/21
Property Investment & Development Services
N.A.I.C.S.: 236117
Andrew Pegge (Chm-Supervisory Bd)

Subsidiaries:

Celtic Italy SRL (1)
Via Brisa 7, 20123, Milan, Italy
Tel.: (39) 0289095617
Web Site: http://www.celticitaly.it
Property Management Services
N.A.I.C.S.: 531311

Challange Eighteen Sp. z o.o. (1)
Rondo ONZ 1, 00-124, Warsaw, Poland
Tel.: (48) 22 544 81 00
Investment Management Service
N.A.I.C.S.: 523999

Elara Investments Sp. z o.o. (1)
Al Jerozolimskie 56 c, 00-803, Warsaw, Poland
Tel.: (48) 22 379 94 40
Real Estate Development Services
N.A.I.C.S.: 531390

Gaston Investments Sp. z o.o. (1)
Rondo ONZ 1 00-124, Warsaw, Poland
Tel.: (48) 22 544 81 00
Investment Management Service
N.A.I.C.S.: 523999

CPG INTERNATIONAL S.P.A.
Via Martiri d'Italia 26, 10014, Caluso, Italy
Tel.: (39) 011989411   IT
Web Site: http://www.cpg-i.com
Sales Range: $75-99.9 Million
Emp.: 300
Printer Mfr
N.A.I.C.S.: 333248

Subsidiaries:

CPG International (1)
Hector Henneaulaan 105, 1930, Zaventem, Belgium
Tel.: (32) 27126270
Web Site: http://www.cpg-i.com
Rev.: $62,904,650
Emp.: 200
Fiscal Year-end: 12/31/2003
Laser Printers Distr
N.A.I.C.S.: 423430

Subsidiary (Non-US):

CPG International Pty Limited (2)
Unit 17 12th Mars Rd, Lane Cove, 2066, NSW, Australia
Tel.: (61) 294209066
Web Site: http://www.tgcom.com.au
Electronics Whslr
N.A.I.C.S.: 423690

CPG International S.A. (2)
150 Ave Joseph Kessel, Parc De La Grande Ile, 78960, Voisins-le-Bretonneux, France
Tel.: (33) 161085900
Web Site: http://www.cpg-international.com
Emp.: 10
N.A.I.C.S.: 449210

CPG International GmbH (1)
Robert Bosch Strasse 26-28, D-63225, Langen, Germany
Tel.: (49) 610370659
Electronics Whslr

N.A.I.C.S.: 423690

CPH CHEMIE + PAPIER HOLDING AG
Perlenring 1, CH-6035, Perlen, Switzerland
Tel.: (41) 414558000   CH
Web Site: http://www.cph.ch
CPHN—(SWX)
Rev.: $848,232,816
Assets: $738,570,953
Liabilities: $295,592,018
Net Worth: $442,978,936
Earnings: $112,019,956
Emp.: 1,181
Fiscal Year-end: 12/31/22
Holding Company; Chemicals, Paper & Packaging Films Mfr
N.A.I.C.S.: 551112
Tim Talaat (Deputy Chm)

Subsidiaries:

APS Altpapier Service Schweiz AG (1)
Perlenring 1, Perlen, 6035, Root, Switzerland
Tel.: (41) 32 671 4700
Web Site: https://www.aps.swiss
Waste Paper Disposal Services
N.A.I.C.S.: 562119

CU Deutero + Agro AG (1)
Seestrasse 108, 8707, Uetikon, Switzerland
Tel.: (41) 449229357
Web Site: http://www.uetikon.ch
Sales Range: $25-49.9 Million
Emp.: 12
Agricultural Chemical Mfr
N.A.I.C.S.: 325320

CU Immobilien Lahr AG (1)
Seestrasse 108, Uetikon, 8707, Zurich, Switzerland
Tel.: (41) 449229111
Web Site: http://www.uition.ch
Sales Range: $50-74.9 Million
Emp.: 10
Real Estate Property Management Services
N.A.I.C.S.: 531210

Chemie Uetikon AG (1)
Seestrasse 108, 8707, Uetikon, Switzerland
Tel.: (41) 449229111
Web Site: http://www.uetikon.ch
Chemical Plant Manager
N.A.I.C.S.: 531312

Jiangsu Zeochem Technology Co. Ltd. (1)
1089 Jingdu Ave, Donghai County, Lianyungang, 222300, Jiangsu, China
Tel.: (86) 51887797616
Chemicals Mfr
N.A.I.C.S.: 325998

Perlen Converting AG (1)
Perlenring 1, 6035, Perlen, Switzerland
Tel.: (41) 414558820
Web Site: http://www.perlenpackaging.com
Coated Pharma Films Mfr
N.A.I.C.S.: 326113
Wolfgang Grimm (CEO)

Subsidiary (US):

Perlen Converting L.L.C. (2)
135 Algonquin Pkwy, Whippany, NJ 07981
Tel.: (973) 887-0257
Web Site: https://www.perlenpackaging.com
Sales Range: $25-49.9 Million
Emp.: 12
Pharmaceutical Products Distr
N.A.I.C.S.: 424210
Douglas Voreis (Mng Dir & VP)

Subsidiary (Non-US):

ac-Folien GmbH (2)
Neuenburger Strasse 9, 79379, Mullheim, Germany
Tel.: (49) 76318030
Web Site: http://www.ac-folien.com
Sales Range: $50-74.9 Million
Emp.: 140
Plastic Mono Films Mfr
N.A.I.C.S.: 326112

Perlen Deutschland GmbH (1)
Ranertstrasse 6, D-81249, Munich, Bavaria, Germany
Tel.: (49) 89 863 893 0
Web Site: http://www.cph.ch
Paper Product Distr
N.A.I.C.S.: 322299

Perlen France Sarl (1)
1 Ave Sonia Delarmay, 94506, Champigny-sur-Marne, France
Tel.: (33) 148811968
Paper Product Distr
N.A.I.C.S.: 424130
Raoul Gil (Mng Dir)

Perlen Immobilien AG (1)
Perlenring 1, 6035, Perlen, Switzerland
Tel.: (41) 4558000
Web Site: http://www.perlen-immobilien.ch
Sales Range: $50-74.9 Million
Emp.: 2
Apartment Rental Services
N.A.I.C.S.: 531110
Scherer Chtistof (Mgr)

Perlen Packaging (Suzhou) Co., Ltd. (1)
828 Caizi Road, Wujiang Economic and Technological Development Zone, Suzhou, 215200, Jiangsu, China
Tel.: (86) 51263956762
Packaging Services
N.A.I.C.S.: 561910
Colin Tham (Mng Dir)

Perlen Packaging AG (1)
Perlenring 3, 6035, Perlen, Switzerland
Tel.: (41) 414558800
Web Site: https://www.perlenpackaging.com
Emp.: 551
Packaging Services
N.A.I.C.S.: 561910
Wolfgang Grimm (Mng Dir)

Perlen Packaging Anapolis Industria e Comercio Ltda. (1)
Via Primaria 6-DA Quadra 10 Modulos 11/12-B, Distrito Agroindustrial de Anapolis - DAIA, Anapolis, 75132-135, Goias, Brazil
Tel.: (55) 6233131211
Packaging Services
N.A.I.C.S.: 561910
Emma Mckenzie (Mgr)

Perlen Packaging GmbH (1)
Neuenburger Strasse 9, 79379, Mullheim, Germany
Tel.: (49) 76318030
Packaging Services
N.A.I.C.S.: 561910
Reiner Gerlach (Mng Dir)

Perlen Packaging L.L.C. (1)
135 Algonquin Pkwy, Whippany, NJ 07981
Tel.: (973) 887-0257
Packaging Services
N.A.I.C.S.: 561910
Markus Haid (Mng Dir)

Perlen Papier AG (1)
Perlenring 1, 6035, Perlen, Switzerland
Tel.: (41) 414558000
Web Site: https://www.perlen.ch
Sales Range: $125-149.9 Million
Emp.: 400
Magazine & Newsprint Paper Mfr
N.A.I.C.S.: 322120

Zeochem AG (1)
Joweid 5, 8630, Ruti, Switzerland
Tel.: (41) 449229393
Web Site: http://www.zeochem.ch
Sales Range: $25-49.9 Million
Emp.: 100
Molecular Chemicals Mfr
N.A.I.C.S.: 325998
Martin Iseli (CFO)

Subsidiary (US):

Zeochem L.L.C (2)
1600 W Hill St, Louisville, KY 40210
Tel.: (502) 634-7600
Web Site: http://www.zeochem.com
Sales Range: $25-49.9 Million
Emp.: 75
Inorganic Chemical Mfr
N.A.I.C.S.: 325199

Zeochem Pte. Ltd. (1)
Level 30 Singapore Land Tower 50 Raffles

Place, Singapore, 48623, Singapore
Tel.: (65) 85185799
Chemical Distr
N.A.I.C.S.: 424690

Zeochem d.o.o.   (1)
Karakaj 229a, 75400, Zvornik, Bosnia &
Herzegovina
Tel.: (387) 56490830
Chemicals Mfr
N.A.I.C.S.: 325998

CPI COMPUTER PERIPHER-ALS INTERNATIONAL

Rafailidi 1 & Agriniou, Tavros, 177 78,
Athens, Athens, Greece
Tel.: (30) 2104805800
Web Site: https://www.cpi.gr
Year Founded: 1990
CPI—(ATH)
Sales Range: Less than $1 Million
Emp.: 132
Computer Peripheral Equipment
Whslr
N.A.I.C.S.: 423430

CPI IMMOBILIEN AG

Hahngasse 3, 1090, Vienna, Austria
Tel.: (43) 14095440514   AT
Web Site: http://www.cpi.co.at
Year Founded: 1997
Sales Range: $1-9.9 Million
Emp.: 160
Property Developer & Manager
N.A.I.C.S.: 531311

Subsidiaries:

CPI Bautrager und Immobilienverwal-
tung GmbH   (1)
Hahngasse 3, 1090, Vienna, Austria
Tel.: (43) 14095440
Apartment Building Contractors
N.A.I.C.S.: 236116

CPI Marketing GmbH   (1)
Hahngasse 3, 1090, Vienna, Austria
Tel.: (43) 140954400
Real Estate Rental Services
N.A.I.C.S.: 531390

CPI Wachstums Immobilien AG   (1)
Hahngasse 3, 1090, Vienna, Austria
Tel.: (43) 14095440
Real Estate Investment Services
N.A.I.C.S.: 531390

CPI Wertpapier Beratung und Vermit-
tlung GmbH   (1)
Hahngasse 3, 1090, Vienna, Austria
Tel.: (43) 14095440
Web Site: http://www.cpi.co.at
Real Estate Brokerage Services
N.A.I.C.S.: 531390

CPI PROPERTY GROUP, S.A.

40 rue de la Vallee, L-2661, Luxem-
bourg, Luxembourg
Tel.: (352) 26476758   LU
Web Site: http://www.cpigp.com
Year Founded: 1991
O5G—(DEU)
Rev.: $1,827,973,235
Assets: $23,667,494,064
Liabilities: $17,658,860,350
Net Worth: $6,008,633,715
Earnings: ($971,184,977)
Emp.: 4,243
Fiscal Year-end: 12/31/23
Real Estate Investment & Develop-
ment
N.A.I.C.S.: 531390
David Greenbaum (CFO)

Subsidiaries:

Biopark, s.r.o.   (1)
Lipova 270, Lipova, 407 81, Cheb, Czech
Republic
Tel.: (420) 41 239 1280
Web Site: https://www.biohovezi.cz
Organic Food Product Distr
N.A.I.C.S.: 424410

CPI East, s.r.o.   (1)
Vladislavova 1390/17, 110 00, Prague,
Czech Republic
Tel.: (420) 737215667
General Merchandise Product Distr
N.A.I.C.S.: 455219

CPI Energo, A.S.   (1)
Vladislavova 1390/17, 110 00, Prague,
Czech Republic
Tel.: (420) 22 650 6110
Real Estate Services
N.A.I.C.S.: 531390

CPI FIM S.A.   (1)
40 rue de la Vallee, L-2661, Luxembourg,
Luxembourg   (97.31%)
Tel.: (352) 2647671
Web Site: https://www.cpifimsa.com
Rev.: $50,110,080
Assets: $7,411,638,247
Liabilities: $5,556,528,167
Net Worth: $1,855,110,080
Earnings: $194,954,673
Emp.: 7
Fiscal Year-end: 12/31/2022
Real Estate Developer, Manager & Lessor
N.A.I.C.S.: 531190

Subsidiary (Non-US):

Diana Property Sp. z o.o.   (2)
Aleje Jerozolimskie 81, Warsaw, 00-021,
Poland   (100%)
Tel.: (48) 225059197
Real Estate Manangement Services
N.A.I.C.S.: 531390

HAGIBOR OFFICE BUILDING,
a.s.   (2)
Na Poricii 1047/26, 110 00, Prague, Czech
Republic   (100%)
Tel.: (420) 221416311
Real Estate Manangement Services
N.A.I.C.S.: 531390

ORCO Budapest Kft   (2)
70 Andrassy Ave, 1062, Budapest, Hungary
Tel.: (36) 18807200
Sales Range: $50-74.9 Million
Real Estate Property Lessors
N.A.I.C.S.: 531190

CPI Hotels Slovakia, s.r.o.   (1)
Sulekova 20, 811 06, Bratislava, Slovakia
Tel.: (421) 25 910 0200
Web Site:
     https://www.mamaisonsulekova.com
Hotel Operator
N.A.I.C.S.: 721110

CPI Hotels, A.S.   (1)
Vladislavova 17, 110 00, Prague, Czech
Republic
Tel.: (420) 23 471 2444
Web Site: https://www.cpihotels.com
Hotel Operator
N.A.I.C.S.: 721110
Jan Kratina (CEO)

CPI Hungary Kft.   (1)
Dunavirag utca 2-6 3rd tower 4th Floor,
1138, Budapest, Hungary
Tel.: (36) 1 225 6600
Web Site: https://www.cpigroup.hu
Real Estate Services
N.A.I.C.S.: 531390

CPI IMMO, S.a.r.l.   (1)
Parc d'Affaires Edonia-Bat M-Rue des Iles
Kerguelen, BP 76248, 35762, Saint-
Gregoire, Cedex, France
Tel.: (33) 29 930 1033
Web Site: https://www.cpi-immobilier.fr
Real Estate Services
N.A.I.C.S.: 531390

CPI Meteor Centre, s.r.o.   (1)
Thamova 681/32, 186 00, Prague, Czech
Republic
Tel.: (420) 72 452 6433
Web Site: https://www.meteorcentre.cz
Real Estate Services
N.A.I.C.S.: 531390

CPI Poland Sp. z o.o.   (1)
Ul Emilii Plater 53, 00-113, Warsaw, Poland
Tel.: (48) 22 892 0610
Web Site: https://www.cpipg.pl
Real Estate Services
N.A.I.C.S.: 531390

CPI Retail Portfolio I, A.S.   (1)
Vladislavova 1390/17, Nove Mesto, 110 00,
Prague, Czech Republic
Tel.: (420) 281082115
Web Site: https://www.cpiretailportfolio.cz
Real Estate Services
N.A.I.C.S.: 531390

Campona Shopping Center Kft.   (1)
Nagytetenyi ut 37 40, 1222, Budapest, Hun
gary
Tel.: (36) 1 424 3000
Web Site: https://www.campona.hu
General Merchandise Product Distr
N.A.I.C.S.: 455219
Kinga Voith (Mktg Dir)

Eurocentrum Offices Sp. z o.o.   (1)
Al Jerozolimskie 134, 02-305, Warsaw, Po-
land
Tel.: (48) 22 202 6398
Web Site: https://www.eurocentrum.pl
General Merchandise Product Distr
N.A.I.C.S.: 455219
Marcin Marchwinski (Mgr)

GSG Solar Berlin GmbH   (1)
Genststrasse 3 Zufahrt Reichartstrasse 2
Aufgang G 4 OG, 10829, Berlin, Germany
Tel.: (49) 303 909 3141
Web Site: https://www.gsg.solar
Solar Power Generation Services
N.A.I.C.S.: 221114

Gewerbesiedlungs-Gesellschaft
GmbH   (1)
Genststrasse 5 Entrance Reichartstrasse
2 Staircase G 4th Floor, 10829, Berlin, Ger-
many
Tel.: (49) 3 039 0930
Web Site: https://www.gsg.de
Real Estate Services
N.A.I.C.S.: 531390

Hofnetz und IT Services GmbH   (1)
Genststrasse 5, 10829, Berlin, Germany
Tel.: (49) 3044 012 3166
Web Site: https://www.hofnetz.de
Information Technology Services
N.A.I.C.S.: 541511

Hotel U Parku, s.r.o.   (1)
Pod Nadrazim 281/22, 268 01, Horovice,
Czech Republic
Tel.: (420) 60 385 3949
Web Site: https://www.hoteluparku.cz
Hotel Operator
N.A.I.C.S.: 721110

One Crans-Montana SA   (1)
Rue du Grand-Place 14, Crans-Montana,
3963, Sierre, Switzerland
Tel.: (41) 27 775 5050
Web Site: https://www.onecransmontana.ch
Emp.: 41
Apartment Rental Services
N.A.I.C.S.: 531110

Outlet Arena Moravia, s.r.o.   (1)
Hlucinska 1170 Moravian, Ostrava, Czech
Republic
Tel.: (420) 55 230 9812
Web Site:
     https://www.outletarenamoravia.com
General Merchandise Product Distr
N.A.I.C.S.: 455219
Petr Leder (Mgr)

Residence Belgicka, s.r.o.   (1)
Belgicka 318/12, 120 00, Prague, Czech
Republic
Tel.: (420) 22 140 1800
Web Site:
     https://www.mamaisonbelgicka.com
Residential Hotel Operator
N.A.I.C.S.: 531110

Residence Izabella, Zrt.   (1)
Izabella u 61, 1064, Budapest, Hungary
Tel.: (36) 1 475 5900
Web Site:
     https://www.mamaisonizabella.com
Residential Hotel Operator
N.A.I.C.S.: 531110

Statek Blatiny, s.r.o.   (1)
Blatiny 16, Snezne, Zdar nad Sazavou,
Morave, Czech Republic
Tel.: (420) 60 136 5744
Web Site: https://www.statek-blatiny.cz
Accommodation Services

N.A.I.C.S.: 721110

Tower-Service Sp. z o.o.   (1)
Ul Chalubinskiego 8, 00-613, Warsaw, Po-
land
Tel.: (48) 22 430 3563
Web Site: https://www.towerservice.pl
Property Management Services
N.A.I.C.S.: 531311

Zemspol, s.r.o.   (1)
Rymarovska 495, Bridlicna, 793 51, Bruntal,
Czech Republic
Tel.: (420) 60 421 5330
Web Site: https://www.zemspol-bridlicna.cz
Beef Cattle Breeding Services
N.A.I.C.S.: 112111

Zerodix Sarl   (1)
Cableway Route 32, Crans-Montana, 3963,
Sierre, Switzerland
Tel.: (41) 27 481 0090
Web Site: https://www.zerodix.ch
Restaurant Operators
N.A.I.C.S.: 722511

CPL GROUP PUBLIC COM-PANY LIMITED

700 Moo 6 Sukhumvit Road
Bangpoo-Mai Muang, Samut Prakan,
10280, Thailand
Tel.: (66) 27095633   TH
Web Site: http://www.cpl.co.th
Year Founded: 1989
CPL—(THA)
Rev.: $53,756,562
Assets: $72,697,496
Liabilities: $48,811,710
Net Worth: $23,885,786
Earnings: ($4,974,995)
Fiscal Year-end: 12/31/23
Leather Mfr & Distr
N.A.I.C.S.: 316990
Suwatchai Wongcharoensin (Chm)

CPMC HOLDINGS LIMITED

160 Wei Ken Street, Economic & De-
velopment District, Hangzhou, China
Tel.: (86) 57187388300   HK
Web Site: https://www.cofcopack.com
Year Founded: 2000
0906—(DEU)
Rev.: $1,042,808,480
Assets: $1,619,538,686
Liabilities: $873,273,188
Net Worth: $746,265,498
Earnings: $43,865,731
Emp.: 6,692
Fiscal Year-end: 12/31/19
Metal Packaging Product Mfr
N.A.I.C.S.: 332439
Xin Zhang (Chm)

Subsidiaries:

CPMC (Chengdu) Company
Limited   (1)
466 West Liutai Dadao Cross-Strait Tech-
nopark, Wenjiang District, Chengdu, China
Tel.: (86) 2882631818
Metal Packaging Product Mfr
N.A.I.C.S.: 332431

CPMC (Kunshan) Company
Limited   (1)
12 Manshi Road, Qiandeng Town, Kunshan,
Jiangsu, China
Tel.: (86) 51257055002
Metal Packaging Product Mfr
N.A.I.C.S.: 332431

CPMC (Tianjin) Company
Limited   (1)
KaiYuan Road, WuQing District, Tianjin,
China
Tel.: (86) 2282198888
Metal Packaging Product Mfr
N.A.I.C.S.: 332431

CPMC (Wuhan) Company
Limited   (1)
68 Fengshu Nan Road Economic & Development District, Wuhan, China
Tel.: (86) 2784950000

CPMC Holdings Limited—(Continued)

Metal Packaging Product Mfr
N.A.I.C.S.: 332431

CPMC (Zhenjiang) Company Limited (1)
Chuanshan Road, Dagang New District, Zhenjiang, China
Tel.: (86) 51188881105
Metal Packaging Product Mfr
N.A.I.C.S.: 332431

FC Packaging (Harbin) Limited (1)
3 Jingbo Road Haping Road Harbin Development Zone, Central District, Harbin, Heilongjiang, China
Tel.: (86) 45186818968
Metal Packaging Product Mfr
N.A.I.C.S.: 332431

Fujian FC Packaging Limited (1)
No 24 Fuzhou Airport Industrial Zone, Fuzhou, Fujian, China
Tel.: (86) 59128632276
Metal Packaging Product Mfr
N.A.I.C.S.: 332431

Guangzhou Panyu MCP Industries Limited (1)
Lianhuawei Industrial Zone, Hualong Town Panyu District, Guangzhou, China
Tel.: (86) 2084756333
Metal Packaging Product Mfr
N.A.I.C.S.: 332431

Shanghai Pinguan Plastic Industry Company Limited (1)
1111 Jindu Road, Meilong Town Minhang District, Shanghai, China
Tel.: (86) 2164976655
Plastic Packaging Products Mfr
N.A.I.C.S.: 326199

Victoria Package (Suzhou) Company Limited (1)
10 Jianye Road Fuhao Economic Development District, Shuangfeng Town, Taicang, Jiangsu, China
Tel.: (86) 51253375361
Plastic Packaging Products Mfr
N.A.I.C.S.: 326199

Wuxi Huapeng Closures Company Limited (1)
6 Huangshan Road New District, Wuxi, Jiangsu, China **(61.48%)**
Tel.: (86) 51085219898
Metal Packaging Product Mfr
N.A.I.C.S.: 332431

CPN RETAIL GROWTH LEASEHOLD REIT
31st Floor centralwOrld Offices 999/9 Rama1 Rd, Patumwan, Bangkok, 10330, Thailand
Tel.: (66) 26675555
Web Site: https://www.cpnreit.com
Year Founded: 2005
CPNREIT—(THA)
Rev.: $168,635,608
Assets: $2,375,264,172
Liabilities: $1,398,533,365
Net Worth: $976,730,807
Earnings: $63,741,483
Fiscal Year-end: 12/31/23
Real Estate Investment Trust Services
N.A.I.C.S.: 523991
Pirinee Pringsulaka (Board of Directors, CEO & Head-Bus Dev)

CPPGROUP PLC
6 East Parade, Leeds, LS1 2AD, United Kingdom
Tel.: (44) 1134877350 **UK**
Web Site:
https://corporate.cppgroup.com
Year Founded: 2010
CPP—(LSE)
Rev.: $245,749,205
Assets: $69,007,002
Liabilities: $59,439,847
Net Worth: $9,567,155
Earnings: ($10,310,630)

Emp.: 4,558
Fiscal Year-end: 12/31/23
Holding Company; Life Assistance Products & Services
N.A.I.C.S.: 551112
Lorraine Beavis (Sec)

Subsidiaries:

CPP Creating Profitable Partnerships GmbH (1)
Ballindamm 39, 20095, Hamburg, Germany
Tel.: (49) 4087607515
Web Site: http://www.de.cppgroup.com
Sales Range: $25-49.9 Million
Emp.: 75
Bail Bonding Services
N.A.I.C.S.: 812990

CPP Global Assistance Bangladesh Limited (1)
Ventura Iconia Level-8 Plot No-37 Road No-11 Block-H, Banani, Dhaka, 1213, Bangladesh
Tel.: (880) 961 211 4477
Financial Services
N.A.I.C.S.: 523999

Concepts for Travel Limited (1)
M K M House Warwick Road, Manchester, M16 0XX, Greater Manchester, United Kingdom
Tel.: (44) 1618771114
Sales Range: $25-49.9 Million
Emp.: 5
Travel & Tour Operating Agencies
N.A.I.C.S.: 561520

CPR GOMU INDUSTRIAL PUBLIC COMPANY LIMITED
78 Moo 2 Paholyothin Rd km 77 5 Tambon Sanabthub Amphur Wangnoi, Ayutthaya, 13170, Thailand
Tel.: (66) 35352685
Web Site: https://www.cprgomu.co.th
Year Founded: 1975
CPR—(THA)
Rev.: $13,398,238
Assets: $21,591,549
Liabilities: $2,478,982
Net Worth: $19,112,567
Earnings: $1,366,476
Fiscal Year-end: 12/31/23
Synthetics Rubber Part Mfr
N.A.I.C.S.: 325212
Hisashi Motoyama (Chm & Mng Dir)

CPS CAPITAL
41 Industrial St, Suite 201, Toronto, M45 0C7, ON, Canada
Tel.: (416) 860-3639 **Ca**
Web Site: https://cpscapital.com
Year Founded: 2013
Private Equity
N.A.I.C.S.: 523999
Mike Greenwood (VP)

Subsidiaries:

CPS HVAC Partners Inc (1)
1801 Royal Ln, Ste 405, Dallas, TX 75229
Tel.: (214) 206-8464
Web Site:
https://www.royalhousepartners.com
Commercial HVAC, Plumbing & Electrical
N.A.I.C.S.: 238220
Doug Hart (CEO)

Subsidiary (Domestic):

SOS Mechanical LLC (2)
2111 Sam Bass Rd, Round Rock, TX 78681-1828
Tel.: (512) 238-6699
Web Site: http://www.sosmechanical.net
Plumbing, Heating & Air-Conditioning Contractors
N.A.I.C.S.: 238220

Sinak Plumbing Company Inc. (2)
1300 S Laclede Station Rd, Saint Louis, MO 63119
Tel.: (314) 968-1340
Web Site: http://www.sinakplumbing.com

Sales Range: Less than $1 Million
Emp.: 21
Plumbing, Heating & Air-Conditioning Contractors
N.A.I.C.S.: 238220

CloudMD Software & Services, Inc. (1)
Suite 810-789 West Pender Street, Vancouver, V6C 1I I2, DC, Canada
Tel.: (514) 616-5356
Web Site: https://www.cloudmd.ca
Rev.: $84,550,491
Assets: $138,133,264
Liabilities: $52,683,756
Net Worth: $85,449,509
Earnings: ($116,489)
Emp.: 450
Fiscal Year-end: 12/31/2022
Software Development Services
N.A.I.C.S.: 541511
Dhruv Chandra (CTO)

Subsidiary (Domestic):

Oncidium Inc. (2)
3700 Steeles Ave W Suite 600, Vaughan, L4L 8K8, ON, Canada
Tel.: (905) 264-4674
Web Site: https://www.oncidium.ca
Information Technology Services
N.A.I.C.S.: 541519

CPS GMBH
Meisenstr 3, 83101, Rohrdorf, Germany
Tel.: (49) 80319011730
Web Site: http://www.cps-gmbh.net
Sales Range: $10-24.9 Million
Emp.: 50
Mfr of Specialty Plastic Products
N.A.I.C.S.: 326199
Adalbert Loidl (Co-CEO)

Subsidiaries:

cps China CO., LTD (1)
No 95 YingCheng Road ShenTai Industry Area, Shaoxing, 31135, Zhejiang, China
Tel.: (86) 575 88778958
Plastic Product Distr
N.A.I.C.S.: 424610
Peace Peng (Mgr)

CPS GROUP INVESTMENTS PTY. LTD.
Level 4 116 Military Road, Neutral Bay, 2089, NSW, Australia
Tel.: (61) 2 9909 3022 **AU**
Investment Services
N.A.I.C.S.: 523999

Subsidiaries:

ConverterTechnology Inc. (1)
1 Tara Blvd Ste 301, Nashua, NH 03060
Tel.: (603) 880-9118
Web Site:
http://www.convertertechnology.com
IT Services
N.A.I.C.S.: 541519
Shawn Allaway (CEO)

CPT DRIVES & POWER PCL
230/7 Thetsabarnrungruknuer Road Ladyao Jattujak, Bangkok, 10900, Thailand
Tel.: (66) 29542590
Web Site:
https://www.cptthailand.com
Year Founded: 1995
CPT—(THA)
Rev.: $34,354,862
Assets: $34,874,771
Liabilities: $7,570,937
Net Worth: $27,303,833
Earnings: $2,252,160
Fiscal Year-end: 12/31/23
Electronic Products Mfr
N.A.I.C.S.: 334419
Chaiyot Piyawannarat (CEO)

CPT GLOBAL LIMITED
Level 3 818 Bourke Street Dock-

lands, Melbourne, 3008, VIC, Australia
Tel.: (61) 396847900 **AU**
Web Site: https://www.cptglobal.com
CGO—(ASX)
Rev.: $13,831,968
Assets: $4,528,079
Liabilities: $3,826,980
Net Worth: $701,098
Earnings: ($1,061,267)
Emp.: 108
Fiscal Year-end: 06/30/24
IT Consulting Services
N.A.I.C.S.: 541690
Gerry Tuddenham (Founder)

Subsidiaries:

CPT Global Inc (1)
175 Varick St, New York, NY 10014
Tel.: (416) 642-2886
Web Site: https://www.cptglobal.com
Sales Range: $25-49.9 Million
Emp.: 10
Management Consulting Services
N.A.I.C.S.: 541618
Mike Lazorik (Pres)

CPT TECHNOLOGY (GROUP) CO., LTD.
No 6 Rujiang West Road, Mawei District, Fuzhou, 350015, Fujian, China
Tel.: (86) 59167052590
Web Site: http://www.cpttg.com
Year Founded: 1993
000536—(SSE)
Rev.: $329,913,324
Assets: $1,300,206,492
Liabilities: $730,283,580
Net Worth: $569,922,912
Earnings: ($171,712,008)
Fiscal Year-end: 12/31/22
Electronic Products Mfr
N.A.I.C.S.: 334419

CPU SOFTWAREHOUSE AG
August Wessels Strasse 23, 86156, Augsburg, Germany
Tel.: (49) 82146020
Web Site: https://www.cpu-ag.com
Year Founded: 1987
CPU2—(MUN)
Rev.: $3,444,074
Assets: $3,841,468
Liabilities: $816,864
Net Worth: $3,024,604
Earnings: $55,193
Emp.: 44
Fiscal Year-end: 12/31/23
Software Publishing Services
N.A.I.C.S.: 513210
Roger Heinz (Member-Mgmt Bd)

CQS NATURAL RESOURCES GROWTH & INCOME PLC
4th Floor One Strand, London, WC2N 5HR, United Kingdom
Tel.: (44) 2072016900 **UK**
Year Founded: 1999
CYN—(LSE)
Rev.: $6,469,536
Assets: $207,170,422
Liabilities: $23,780,466
Net Worth: $183,389,956
Earnings: $31,905,062
Fiscal Year-end: 06/30/22
Investment Management Service
N.A.I.C.S.: 523999
Helen Green (Chm)

CQV CO., LTD.
144 Seongjung-ro Jincheon-eup, Jincheon-gun, Jincheon, Chungcheong Buk-Do, Korea (South)
Tel.: (82) 435312500
Web Site: https://www.cqv.co.kr
Year Founded: 2000

101240—(KRS)
Rev.: $35,500,412
Assets: $66,249,939
Liabilities: $16,508,426
Net Worth: $49,741,513
Earnings: $4,129,359
Emp.: 167
Fiscal Year-end: 12/31/22
Chemical Products Mfr
N.A.I.C.S.: 325998

CR BASEL
St Jakobs Strasse 185, CH-4002,
Basel, Switzerland
Tel.: (41) 613777171
Web Site: http://www.crbasel.ch
Year Founded: 1968
Sales Range: $10-24.9 Million
Emp.: 20
N.A.I.C.S.: 541810
Peter Frey (Mng Dir)

CR CAPITAL REAL ESTATE AG
Heinrich hertz str 1b, 14532, Berlin,
Germany
Tel.: (49) 3320332070
Web Site: https://cr-energy.de
CRZK—(DEU)
Rev.: $75,681,327
Assets: $446,106,983
Liabilities: $11,767,254
Net Worth: $434,339,729
Earnings: $72,612,569
Emp.: 5
Fiscal Year-end: 12/31/23
Real Estate Manangment Services
N.A.I.C.S.: 531390
Stefan Krach (Chm-Supervisory Bd)

Subsidiaries:

KENT Immobilemanagemnt
GmbH   (1)
Fasanenstrasse 77, 10623, Berlin, Ger-
many
Tel.: (49) 3027499080
Real Estate Services
N.A.I.C.S.: 531390

Terrabau GmbH   (1)
Dreischeibenhaus 1, 40211, Dusseldorf,
Germany
Tel.: (49) 21188250195
Web Site: http://www.terra-bau.de
Construction Services
N.A.I.C.S.: 236220

CR HOLDINGS CO., LTD.
55 Saneop-ro, Gwangyang,
Jeollanam-do, Korea (South)
Tel.: (82) 617988114
Web Site: http://www.chosunref.co.kr
Year Founded: 1947
000480—(KRS)
Rev.: $612,096,383
Assets: $1,242,879,054
Liabilities: $608,521,019
Net Worth: $634,358,035
Earnings: $31,388,634
Emp.: 539
Fiscal Year-end: 12/31/22
Refractory Mfr
N.A.I.C.S.: 327120
Yong-joon Yang (CEO)

Subsidiaries:

Chosun Refractories Eng Co.,
Ltd.   (1)
12 Sapyeong-daero 56-gil, Seocho-gu,
Seoul, Gyeongsangbuk-do, Korea (South)
Tel.: (82) 25093942
Refractory Material Mfr
N.A.I.C.S.: 327120
Kang Nam Won (CEO)

Samhan Co. Ltd.   (1)
40-2 Ungnam-dong, Seongsan-gu,
Changwon, Gyeongsangnam-do, Korea
(South)
Tel.: (82) 552 850 0414

Web Site: https://www.samhanltd.co.kr
Automobile Parts Mfr
N.A.I.C.S.: 336390
Kun Jin Lee (Pres)

CR2 EMPREENDIMENTOS IMOBILIARIOS S.A.
126 Bloco 9 sala 817 Torre 3 Del,
Castilho, Rio de Janeiro, RJ, Brazil
Tel.: (55) 2130954600
Web Site: http://www.cr2.com.br
Year Founded: 2006
FIEI3—(BRAZ)
Rev.: $461,736
Assets: $16,793,407
Liabilities: $2,481,901
Net Worth: $14,311,506
Earnings: ($2,296,169)
Fiscal Year-end: 12/31/23
Real Estate Development Services
N.A.I.C.S.: 531390
Andre Strauss Vasques (CEO, CTO
& Dir-IR)

CRABTREE OF GATESHEAD LTD.
Kingsway Team Valley Trading Es-
tate, Gateshead, NE11 0SU, Tyne &
Wear, United Kingdom
Tel.: (44) 191 487 5071
Web Site: http://www.crabpress.co.uk
Year Founded: 1849
Sales Range: $25-49.9 Million
Emp.: 110
Printing Machinery Mfr
N.A.I.C.S.: 333248
Bill Athey (Dir-Spare Part Sls)

CRADLE RESOURCES LIMITED
Emerald House 1202 Hay Street,
West Perth, 6005, WA, Australia
Tel.: (61) 892003425
Web Site:
     http://www.cradleresources.com.au
CXX—(ASX)
Rev.: $729
Assets: $189,914
Liabilities: $82,191
Net Worth: $107,722
Earnings: $671,202
Emp.: 7
Fiscal Year-end: 06/30/22
Metal Mining
N.A.I.C.S.: 212290
Grant Davey (Exec Dir)

CRAFTPORT CANNABIS CORP.
6111 London Road Suite 105, Rich-
mond, V7E 3S3, BC, Canada
Tel.: (604) 238-0005   BC
Web Site:
     http://www.benchmarkbotanics.com
Year Founded: 2009
BBW0—(DEU)
Rev.: $993,688
Assets: $4,818,094
Liabilities: $7,166,100
Net Worth: ($2,348,006)
Earnings: ($10,230,714)
Fiscal Year-end: 12/31/21
Investment Services
N.A.I.C.S.: 523999
George Dorin (Chm)

CRAFTSMAN AUTOMATION LIMITED
123/4 Sangothipalayam Road, Arasur
Post, Coimbatore, 641407, Tamil
Nadu, India
Tel.: (91) 4227161000
Web Site:
     https://www.craftsmanltd.com
Year Founded: 1986

CRAFTSMAN—(NSE)
Rev.: $214,309,095
Assets: $321,034,350
Liabilities: $188,707,155
Net Worth: $132,327,195
Earnings: $13,289,640
Emp.: 1,989
Fiscal Year-end: 03/31/21
Industrial Machinery Mfr
N.A.I.C.S.: 333248
Srinivasan Ravi (Chm & Mng Dir)

Subsidiaries:

Craftsman Europe B.V.   (1)
Pascalstraat 88, 3316 GR, Dordrecht, Neth-
erlands
Tel.: (31) 78 303 2820
Web Site: https://www.craftsmanmarine.com
Boat Equipment Mfr
N.A.I.C.S.: 336999

CRAIG MANUFACTURING LTD.
96 McLean Avenue, Hartland, E7P
2K5, NB, Canada
Tel.: (506) 375-4493
Web Site: http://www.craig-mfg.com
Year Founded: 1941
Rev.: $13,320,339
Emp.: 140
Heavy Equipment Mfr
N.A.I.C.S.: 333248
Colden Wetmore (Gen Mgr)

CRAILAR TECHNOLOGIES INC.
Suite 305 - 4420 Chatterton Way,
Victoria, V8X 5J2, BC, Canada
Tel.: (250) 658-8582   BC
Web Site: http://www.crailar.com
CL—(OTCIQ)
Sales Range: $1-9.9 Million
Emp.: 27
Fiber Mfr
N.A.I.C.S.: 325220
Jay Nalbach (CMO)

CRAMO PLC
Kalliosolantie 2, FI-01740, Vantaa,
Finland
Tel.: (358) 1066110
Web Site: http://www.cramo.com
CRA1V—(OMX)
Rev.: $120,371
Assets: $80,716,610
Liabilities: $7,541,492
Net Worth: $73,175,118
Earnings: ($17,827,709)
Emp.: 2,753
Fiscal Year-end: 12/31/20
Construction Machinery, Equipment &
Modular Space Rental & Leasing
Services
N.A.I.C.S.: 532412
Tatu Hauhio (Mng Dir-Cramo Finland
& Exec VP-Finland & Eastern Eu-
rope)

Subsidiaries:

ALVA Technika, UAB   (1)
V A Graiciuno g 2A, 02241, Vilnius, Lithu-
ania
Tel.: (370) 8 52108741
Web Site: http://www.alvatechnika.lt
Sales Range: $50-74.9 Million
Emp.: 2
Construction Equipment Rental Services
N.A.I.C.S.: 532412

AS Cramo Estonia   (1)
Kadaka Tee 131, 129 15, Tallinn, Estonia
Tel.: (372) 6830800
Web Site: http://www.cramo.ee
Sales Range: $25-49.9 Million
Emp.: 140
Construction Equipment Rental Services
N.A.I.C.S.: 532412

Cramo A/S   (1)
Hoejvangen 19, 3360, Espergaerde, Denmark

Tel.: (45) 49122100
Web Site: http://www.cramo.dk
Sales Range: $75-99.9 Million
Emp.: 130
Construction Machinery Rental Services
N.A.I.C.S.: 532412

Cramo AB   (1)
Rosenborgsgatan 12, 169 74, Solna, Swe-
den
Tel.: (46) 86235400
Web Site: http://www.cramo.se
Sales Range: $50-74.9 Million
Emp.: 90
Construction Machinery Rental Services
N.A.I.C.S.: 532412

Cramo AG   (1)
Emeranstrasse 49-51, 85622, Feldkirchen,
Germany
Tel.: (49) 89857980
Web Site: http://www.cramo.de
Construction Equipment Rental Services
N.A.I.C.S.: 532412
Anna Kiefer (Head-HR)

Cramo AS   (1)
Smalvollveien 42, Alnabru, 0667, Nor-
way
Tel.: (47) 23375560
Web Site: http://www.cramo.no
Sales Range: $75-99.9 Million
Emp.: 180
Construction Machinery, Equipment & Mod-
ules Rental Services
N.A.I.C.S.: 532490

Cramo Instant AB   (1)
Rosenborgsgatan 12, Solna, 169 04, Swe-
den
Tel.: (46) 86235400
Web Site: http://www.cramo.se
Sales Range: $50-74.9 Million
Emp.: 90
Construction Machinery Rental Services
N.A.I.C.S.: 532412
Jordan Karlson (Gen Mgr)

Cramo Instant AS   (1)
Kobbervikdalen 75, 3036, Drammen, Nor-
way
Tel.: (47) 32 23 50 00
Web Site: http://www.cramo.no
Construction Machinery Rental Services
N.A.I.C.S.: 532412

Cramo Kaliningrad OOO   (1)
St 4 Kiev 33, 236009, Kaliningrad, Russia
Tel.: (7) 4012776222
Web Site: http://www.cramo.no
Construction Equipment Rental Services
N.A.I.C.S.: 532412

Cramo New Holding AB   (1)
Tureberg Rd 11A, 19129, Sollentuna, Swe-
den
Tel.: (46) 86235400
Web Site: http://www.cramo.se
Sales Range: $50-74.9 Million
Emp.: 90
Construction Machinery Rental Services
N.A.I.C.S.: 532412

Cramo S.R.O   (1)
Tlumacovska 1237 32, 155 00, Prague,
Czech Republic
Tel.: (420) 724152152
Web Site: http://www.cramo.cz
Sales Range: $25-49.9 Million
Emp.: 30
Construction Machinery Rental Services
N.A.I.C.S.: 532412

Cramo Sverige AB   (1)
Torshamnsgatan 35, 164 95, Kista, Sweden
Tel.: (46) 86235400
Web Site: http://www.cramo.se
Sales Range: $50-74.9 Million
Emp.: 90
Construction Machinery Rental Services
N.A.I.C.S.: 532412

CRANE GROUP LIMITED
Watling Drive Sketchley Meadows,
Hinckley, LE10 3EY, United Kingdom
Tel.: (44) 1455 25 1488   UK
Web Site: http://www.crane-
     electronics.com
Year Founded: 2006

Crane Group Limited—(Continued)

Holding Company; Industrial Products & Technologies Mfr
N.A.I.C.S.: 551112
Adrian James Duffin (Owner & Mng Dir)

Subsidiaries:

Crane Electronics Ltd. (1)
Watling Drive Sketchley Meadows, Hinckley, LE10 3EY, United Kingdom
Tel.: (44) 1455 25 1488
Web Site: http://www.crane-electronics.com
Torque Management & Control Electronics Mfr & Whslr
N.A.I.C.S.: 334419

Subsidiary (US):

Crane Electronics, Inc. (2)
1260 11th St W, Milan, IL 61264-2234
Tel.: (309) 787-1263
Web Site: http://www.crane-electronics.com
Emp.: 15
Industrial Products Mfr
N.A.I.C.S.: 332911
Richard Haywood (Gen Mgr)

CRANE INFRASTRUCTURE LTD.
D No 25-18-54 Opp Crane Betel Nut Powder Works Office Main Road, Guntur, 522 004, Andhra Pradesh, India
Tel.: (91) 8632223311
Web Site: https://www.cranegroup.in
Year Founded: 2008
538770—(BOM)
Rev.: $74,386
Assets: $3,967,141
Liabilities: $145,595
Net Worth: $3,821,546
Earnings: $25,453
Emp.: 1,000
Fiscal Year-end: 03/31/21
Real Estate Support Services
N.A.I.C.S.: 531390
Kothuri Praveen (Officer-Compliance)

CRANES SOFTWARE INTERNATIONAL LIMITED
82 Presidency Building 3rd & 4th Floor St Marks Road, Bengaluru, 560 001, Karnataka, India
Tel.: (91) 8067644800
Web Site: https://www.cranessoftware.com
Year Founded: 1991
512093—(BOM)
Rev.: $9,738,920
Assets: $41,206,074
Liabilities: $145,485,754
Net Worth: ($104,279,680)
Earnings: ($2,047,282)
Emp.: 6
Fiscal Year-end: 03/31/22
Software Development Services
N.A.I.C.S.: 541511
Asif Khader (Founder)

Subsidiaries:

Caravel Info System Private Limited (1)
88 Times Square MG Road, Bengaluru, 560 001, India
Tel.: (91) 8067650000
Web Site: https://www.caravelindia.com
Software Development Services
N.A.I.C.S.: 541511

Systat Software Gmbh (1)
Schimmelbuschstr 25, 40699, Erkrath, Germany
Tel.: (49) 21154039646
Web Site: https://www.systat.de
Scientific Software Development Services
N.A.I.C.S.: 541511

CRANEWARE PLC

1 Tanfield, Edinburgh, EH3 5DA, United Kingdom
Tel.: (44) 1315503100
Web Site: https://public.craneware.com
CRW—(AIM)
Rev.: $189,268,000
Assets: $543,655,000
Liabilities: $215,063,000
Net Worth: $328,592,000
Earnings: $11,703,000
Emp.: 750
Fiscal Year-end: 06/30/24
Supplier of Business Intelligence & Revenue Cycle Software
N.A.I.C.S.: 513210
Keith Neilson (Co-Founder & CEO)

Subsidiaries:

Craneware InSight, Inc. (1)
545 Brandies Cir, Murfreesboro, TN 37128
Tel.: (615) 869-4000
Web Site: http://www.cranewareinsight.com
Sales Range: $25-49.9 Million
Emp.: 23
Healthcare Software Development Services
N.A.I.C.S.: 541511

Craneware US Holdings, Inc. (1)
3340 Peachtree Rd NE Ste 850, Atlanta, GA 30326
Tel.: (404) 364-2032
Hospital & Health Care Services
N.A.I.C.S.: 622110

Craneware, Inc. (1)
3340 Peachtree Rd NE Ste 850, Atlanta, GA 30326-1072
Tel.: (404) 364-2032
Web Site: https://public.craneware.com
Sales Range: $25-49.9 Million
Emp.: 30
Supplier of Business Intelligence & Revenue Cycle Software
N.A.I.C.S.: 513210

Sentry Data Systems, Inc. (1)
800 Fairway Dr Ste 400, Deerfield Beach, FL 33441
Web Site: https://www.sentryds.com
Professional, Scientific & Technical Services
N.A.I.C.S.: 541990
Travis Leonardi (CEO)

CRANEX LIMITED
57/1 Industrial Area Site IV, Sahibabad, Ghaziabad, 201010, Uttar Pradesh, India
Tel.: (91) 1203240427
Web Site: https://www.cranexltd.com
522001—(BOM)
Rev.: $551,728,663
Assets: $627,172,477
Liabilities: $502,165,526
Net Worth: $125,006,951
Earnings: $10,024,472
Emp.: 142
Fiscal Year-end: 03/31/22
Crane Mfr
N.A.I.C.S.: 333923
Piyush Agrawal (Mng Dir)

CRANFIELD AEROSPACE SOLUTIONS LIMITED
Building 84 College Road, Cranfield, Bedford, MK43 0AL, Beds, United Kingdom
Tel.: (44) 1234754046   UK
Web Site: https://cranfieldaerospace.com
Year Founded: 1989
Emp.: 100
Aircraft & Spacecraft Design & Mfr
N.A.I.C.S.: 336412
Paul Hutton (CEO)

CRANK MEDIA INC.
650 West Georgia Street 1720, Vancouver, V6B 4N7, BC, Canada
Tel.: (604) 558-2515   NV
Web Site: https://crankmedia.com

Year Founded: 2013
CRKM—(OTCIQ)
Rev.: $2,557
Assets: $358
Liabilities: $492,597
Net Worth: ($492,239)
Earnings: ($429,634)
Emp.: 2
Fiscal Year-end: 12/31/20
Sports Software Development Services
N.A.I.C.S.: 513210
Stephen Brown (Chm, Pres, CEO, CFO & Sec)

CRANSWICK PLC
Crane Court Hesslewood Country Office Park Ferriby Road, Hessle, HU13 0PA, Yorkshire, United Kingdom
Tel.: (44) 1482375000
Web Site: https://www.cranswick.plc.uk
CWK—(LSE)
Rev.: $2,726,980,620
Assets: $1,552,009,732
Liabilities: $508,058,824
Net Worth: $1,043,950,908
Earnings: $140,524,020
Emp.: 9,930
Fiscal Year-end: 03/31/22
Pig Farming & Feed & Food Mfr
N.A.I.C.S.: 311999
Martin Davey (Chm)

Subsidiaries:

Cranswick Convenience Foods (1)
Valley Park Industrial Estate Meadowgate, Wombwell, Barnsley, S73 0UN, South Yorkshire, United Kingdom
Tel.: (44) 1226344400
Web Site: http://www.cranswick.plc.uk
Sales Range: $250-299.9 Million
Emp.: 600
Fresh Pork Distr
N.A.I.C.S.: 424470

Cranswick Country Foods plc (1)
Staithes Road, Preston, Hull, HU12 8TB, Yorkshire, United Kingdom
Tel.: (44) 148 289 1001
Web Site: http://www.cranswickcountryfoods.plc.uk
Pork & Pork Products Mfr
N.A.I.C.S.: 311612

Subsidiary (Domestic):

Cranswick Country Foods (Norfolk) Limited (2)
Brandon Road, Watton, Norfolk, IP25 6LW, United Kingdom
Tel.: (44) 1953881555
Web Site: http://www.cranswick.co.uk
Emp.: 800
Fresh Pork Distr
N.A.I.C.S.: 424470

Cranswick Gourmet Bacon Company Limited (2)
Sherburn-in-Elmet, Leeds, LS25 6PL, West Yorkshire, United Kingdom
Tel.: (44) 1977686700
Food Products Mfr
N.A.I.C.S.: 311999

Cranswick Gourmet Pastry Company Limited (2)
Hugden Way Norton, Norton Grove industrial Estate, Malton, YO17 9NE, North Yorkshire, United Kingdom
Tel.: (44) 1653605620
Food Products Mfr
N.A.I.C.S.: 311999

Cranswick Gourmet Sausage Company Limited (2)
76 Helsinki Road Sutton Fields, Hull, HU7 0YW, United Kingdom
Tel.: (44) 1482372000
Food Products Mfr
N.A.I.C.S.: 311999

Crown Chicken Limited (1)

Green Farm Edge Green, Kenninghall, Norwich, NR16 2DR, United Kingdom
Tel.: (44) 1953887736
Food Products Mfr
N.A.I.C.S.: 311999

Delico Limited (1)
Steinbeck Crescent Snelshaw West, Milton Keynes, MK4 4AE, Bucks, United Kingdom
Tel.: (44) 1908522122
Sales Range: $100-124.9 Million
Emp.: 350
Cooked Meat Products Mfr
N.A.I.C.S.: 311612
Trew Drayton (Mng Dir)

CRATER GOLD MINING LIMITED
Level 3 216 St Georges Terrace, Perth, 6000, WA, Australia
Tel.: (61) 861888181
Web Site: http://www.cratergold.com.au
Rev.: $229,469
Assets: $7,131,447
Liabilities: $6,164,721
Net Worth: $966,726
Earnings: ($4,855,130)
Fiscal Year-end: 06/30/19
Gold & Other Metal Mining Services
N.A.I.C.S.: 212220
Thomas M. Fermanis (Deputy Chm)

CRAVATEX LTD.
First Floor Godrej Bhavan 4A Home Street Charanjit Rai Marg Fort, Mumbai, 400001, India
Tel.: (91) 2266667474
Web Site: https://www.cravatex.com
Year Founded: 1951
509472—(BOM)
Rev.: $70,451,417
Assets: $18,653,913
Liabilities: $6,046,281
Net Worth: $12,607,631
Earnings: $8,044,300
Emp.: 6
Fiscal Year-end: 03/31/23
Casual & Sport Wear Mfr
N.A.I.C.S.: 339920
Sudhanshu Namdeo (Compliance Officer & Sec)

CRAVEN HOUSE CAPITAL PLC
776-778 Barking Road, London, E13 9PJ, United Kingdom
Tel.: (44) 2032868130   UK
Web Site: https://www.cravenhousecapital.com
CRV—(AIM)
Assets: $1,180,000
Liabilities: $1,560,000
Net Worth: ($380,000)
Earnings: ($5,520,000)
Fiscal Year-end: 05/31/23
Investment Services
N.A.I.C.S.: 523999
Mark Pajak (Bd of Dirs, Chm & Chm)

CRAVEROLANIS
Av A Moreau De Justo 240 Piso 1, C1107AFP, Buenos Aires, Argentina
Tel.: (54) 11952725050   Ar
Web Site: http://www.cravero.net
Year Founded: 1974
Sales Range: $25-49.9 Million
Emp.: 120
Advetising Agency
N.A.I.C.S.: 541810
Juan Cravero (Dir Gen-Creative & Partner)

CRAWFORD HEALTHCARE HOLDINGS LIMITED
King Edward Court King Edward Road, Knutsford, WA16 0BE, Cheshire, United Kingdom

Tel.: (44) 1565654920　　　UK
Web Site:
　　http://www.crawfordhealthcare.com
Pharmaceuticals Mfr
N.A.I.C.S.: 325412
Richard Anderson *(CEO)*

Subsidiaries:

Patient Plus Limited　　　(1)
79 New Cavendish St, London, W1W 6XB,
United Kingdom
Tel.: (44) 2073887722
Sales Range: $25-49.9 Million
Emp.: 15
Medicine Research & Development Services
N.A.I.C.S.: 541715

CRAWFORD PACKAGING INC.
3036 Page Street, London, N5V 4P2,
ON, Canada
Tel.: (519) 659-0909
Web Site:
　　http://www.crawfordpackaging.com
Year Founded: 1963
Packaging Services
N.A.I.C.S.: 333993
Clarence A. Covey *(Chm)*

CRAWFORD TECHNOLOGIES, INC.
60 St Clair Ave E Ste 1002, Toronto,
M4T 1N5, ON, Canada
Tel.: (416) 923-0080
Web Site:
　　http://www.crawfordtech.com
Software Solutions & Services
N.A.I.C.S.: 513210
Ernie Crawford *(Pres & CEO)*

Subsidiaries:

Composition Research Technologies,
Inc.　　　(1)
235 Waterwood Dr, Moneta, VA 24121-
5230
Tel.: (540) 912-9132
Web Site: http://www.comp-research.com
Custom Computer Programming Services
N.A.I.C.S.: 541511
Philip J. Trzcinski *(CEO)*

CRAYON GROUP AS
Sandakerveien 114 A, 0484, Oslo,
Norway
Tel.: (47) 22 89 10 00
Web Site: http://www.crayon.com
Year Founded: 2002
Software Licensing, Distribution &
Support Services
N.A.I.C.S.: 423430
Glenn Orcutt *(CEO-Crayon USA)*

Subsidiaries:

Crayon A/S　　　(1)
Ellekr 9 1 sal, 2730, Herlev, Denmark
Tel.: (45) 70232088
Information Technology Consulting Services
N.A.I.C.S.: 541511

Crayon AB　　　(1)
Rontgenvagen 3D, Solna, 171 54, Stock-
holm, Sweden
Tel.: (46) 850530730
Web Site: https://www.crayon.com
Emp.: 50
Information Technology Consulting Services
N.A.I.C.S.: 541511

Crayon Austria GmbH　　　(1)
Am Europlatz 2 Euro Plaza Building 4,
1120, Vienna, Austria
Tel.: (43) 720303025
Web Site: https://www.crayon.com
Emp.: 70
Information Technology Consulting Services
N.A.I.C.S.: 541511

Crayon B.V.　　　(1)
Karspeldreef 8, 1101CJ, Amsterdam, Neth-
erlands
Tel.: (31) 202626511
Information Technology Consulting Services

N.A.I.C.S.: 541511

Crayon Channel APAC　　　(1)
Level 19 100 Miller Street, North Sydney,
2060, NSW, Australia
Tel.: (61) 396428695
Web Site: https://apac.crayonchannel.com
Information Technology Services
N.A.I.C.S.: 541511
Mark McLellan *(CFO & COO)*

Subsidiary (Domestic):

Frigrite Refrigeration Pty Ltd　　　(2)
2/13 Abbott Road, Dandenong South, 3175,
VIC, Australia
Tel.: (61) 397066815
Web Site: http://www.frigrite.com.au
Refrigeration Maintenance Services
N.A.I.C.S.: 333415

Crayon France SAS　　　(1)
7 Avenue de la Cristallerie Crisco Duo,
Sevres, 92310, Paris, France
Tel.: (33) 184018500
Information Technology Consulting Services
N.A.I.C.S.: 541511

Crayon Global Services GmbH　　　(1)
Bajuwarenring 1, 82041, Oberhaching, Ger-
many
Tel.: (49) 89200050400
Information Technology Consulting Services
N.A.I.C.S.: 541511

Crayon Iceland　　　(1)
Borgartun 25 6th floor, 105, Reykjavik, Ice-
land
Tel.: (354) 5199600
Web Site: https://www.crayon.com
Information Technology Consulting Services
N.A.I.C.S.: 541511

Crayon India　　　(1)
Jai Antariksha Office No 706 7th floor,
Mumbai, 400059, India
Tel.: (91) 8042679100
Information Technology Consulting Services
N.A.I.C.S.: 541511
Vikas Bhonsle *(CEO)*

Crayon Ltd　　　(1)
York House 18 York Road, Maidenhead,
SL6 1SF, United Kingdom
Tel.: (44) 1628622121
Information Technology Consulting Services
N.A.I.C.S.: 541511
Gareth Johnson *(CEO)*

Crayon Middle East　　　(1)
Building 5 G12 Dubai Internet City, Dubai,
United Arab Emirates
Tel.: (971) 44249977
Information Technology Consulting Services
N.A.I.C.S.: 541511
Joachim Hagstrom *(CEO)*

Crayon OY　　　(1)
Aku Korhosen tie 4 6 krs, 00440, Helsinki,
Finland
Tel.: (358) 104408300
Web Site: https://www.crayon.com
Information Technology Consulting Services
N.A.I.C.S.: 541511

Crayon Portugal　　　(1)
Rua Antonio Champalimaun Lt 1 Lispolis Ed
CID, 1600-546, Lisbon, Portugal
Tel.: (351) 217150378
Information Technology Consulting Services
N.A.I.C.S.: 541511

Crayon Pte Ltd　　　(1)
Singapore Land Tower 50 Raffles Place 05-
00, Singapore, 048623, Singapore
Tel.: (65) 69507678
Information Technology Consulting Services
N.A.I.C.S.: 541511
Sandeep Angresh *(CEO)*

Crayon Software Experts Malaysia
Sdn. Bhd.　　　(1)
Mercu 2 Level 40 No 3 Jalan Bangsar, KL
Eco City, 59200, Kuala Lumpur, Malaysia
Tel.: (60) 340650832
Information Technology Consulting Services
N.A.I.C.S.: 541511

Crayon Spain　　　(1)
Calle la Calendula 93 - Miniparc III Edificio,
28109, Alcobendas, Spain

Tel.: (34) 917902481
Information Technology Consulting Services
N.A.I.C.S.: 541511

Kryptos Networks Pvt ltd　　　(1)
No 29 Sarathy Nagar Narayana Complex
1st floor C Wing, Velachery, Chennai,
600042, India　　　(100%)
Tel.: (91) 4443915151
Information Technology Consulting Services
N.A.I.C.S.: 541511

MAP License AS　　　(1)
Prinsensgate 22, Oslo, 0157, Norway
Tel.: (47) 22700800
Information Technology Consulting Services
N.A.I.C.S.: 541511

CRAYON GROUP HOLDING ASA
Gullhaug Torg 5, 0484, Oslo, Norway
Tel.: (47) 22891000　　　NO
Web Site: https://www.crayon.com
Year Founded: 2002
CRAYN—(OSL)
Rev.: $590,892,296
Assets: $1,528,172,917
Liabilities: $1,299,187,142
Net Worth: $228,985,775
Earnings: ($14,686,865)
Emp.: 4,021
Fiscal Year-end: 12/31/23
Holding Company
N.A.I.C.S.: 551112
Erwin Heinrich *(COO)*

Subsidiaries:

CRAYON, Celovite IT Resitve,
d.o.o.　　　(1)
Smartinska 106, 1000, Ljubljana, Slovenia
Tel.: (386) 59787142
Information Technology Services
N.A.I.C.S.: 541519

Complit As　　　(1)
Gullhaug Torg 5, 0484, Oslo, Norway
Tel.: (47) 23507500
Web Site: https://complit.no
Technical Support Services
N.A.I.C.S.: 518210

Crayon Africa S.A.　　　(1)
Workshop 17 Firestation 16 Baker Street
Rosebank, Johannesburg, 2196, Gauteng,
South Africa
Tel.: (27) 874057017
Information Technology Services
N.A.I.C.S.: 541519

Crayon Czech Republic and Slovakia
s.r.o.　　　(1)
Evropska 2591/33d Dejvice, 160 00,
Prague, 6, Czech Republic
Tel.: (420) 724272966
Information Technology Services
N.A.I.C.S.: 541519

Crayon Deutschland GmbH　　　(1)
Inselkammerstrasse 12, 82008, Unterhach-
ing, Germany
Tel.: (49) 89200050400
Information Technology Consulting Services
N.A.I.C.S.: 541690

Crayon Mauritius Ltd.　　　(1)
Suite 1909 Citadelle Mall Sir Edgar Laurent
Street, Port Louis, Mauritius
Tel.: (230) 27874057017
Information Technology Services
N.A.I.C.S.: 541519

Crayon Poland sp. z o.o.　　　(1)
Domaniewska 39, 02-672, Warsaw, Poland
Tel.: (48) 797676361
Cloud Computing Services
N.A.I.C.S.: 518210

Crayon Schweiz AG　　　(1)
Bahnhofplatz 1, 6460, Altdorf, Switzerland
Tel.: (41) 418747450
Information Technology Consulting Services
N.A.I.C.S.: 541690

Crayon Software Experts India Pvt.
Ltd.　　　(1)
02-903 9th Floor Lodha Supremus Kanjur
Village Road Nehru Nagar, Kanjurmarg

East, Mumbai, 400 042, India
Tel.: (91) 8056522331
Information Technology Services
N.A.I.C.S.: 541519

Crayon Software Experts Philippines
Inc.　　　(1)
11F Net One Center Building 26th Corner
3rd Streets, Bonifacio Global City, Taguig,
1634, Philippines
Tel.: (63) 288718463
Information Technology Services
N.A.I.C.S.: 541519

Crayon Software Experts Romania
S.R.L.　　　(1)
141-143 Calea Floreasca 1st Floor,
014467, Bucharest, Romania
Tel.: (40) 723235012
Information Technology Consulting Services
N.A.I.C.S.: 541519

Crayon Software Experts Spain
S.L.　　　(1)
Av de Europa 24 Edif B 10 B, Alcobendas,
28108, Madrid, Spain
Tel.: (34) 917274966
Information Technology Consulting Services
N.A.I.C.S.: 541519

Crayon Software Licensing Unipes-
soal LDA　　　(1)
Rua Antonio Champalimaud Ed 3 Lispolis,
1600-546, Lisbon, Portugal
Tel.: (351) 217150378
Information Technology Consulting Services
N.A.I.C.S.: 541690

Crayon UK Ltd.　　　(1)
Crayon House Mercury Park, Wooburn
Green, HP10 0HH, Buckinghamshire,
United Kingdom
Tel.: (44) 1494917760
Information Technology Consulting Services
N.A.I.C.S.: 541519

EMT Distribution Pty. Ltd.　　　(1)
83 King William Road, Unley, 5061, SA,
Australia
Tel.: (61) 882733030
Web Site: https://www.emtdist.com
Cybersecurity Artificial Intelligence Services
N.A.I.C.S.: 561990

Navicle Pty. Ltd.　　　(1)
4 Boronia Street, Redfern, 2016, NSW,
Australia
Tel.: (61) 289156219
Web Site: https://www.navicle.com
Information Technology Consulting Services
N.A.I.C.S.: 541519

P.T. Krayon Konsultan Indonesia　　　(1)
Revenue Tower 23rd Floor, District 8 SCBD
Jl Jend Sudirman Kav 52-53, Jakarta,
12190, Indonesia
Tel.: (62) 2150666200
Information Technology Consulting Services
N.A.I.C.S.: 541519

P.T. Rhipe International
Indonesia　　　(1)
WeWork office Revenue Tower 25th Floor Jl
Jend Sudirman Kav 52-53 SCBD, Jakarta
Selatan, 12190, Indonesia
Tel.: (62) 2150610168
Business Consulting Services
N.A.I.C.S.: 541611

Parallo Limited　　　(1)
Level M 17 Albert Street, Auckland, 1010,
New Zealand
Tel.: (64) 99730500
Web Site: https://www.parallo.com
Information Technology Consulting Services
N.A.I.C.S.: 541519

Puzzlepart AS　　　(1)
Gullhaug Torg 5, 0484, Oslo, Norway
Tel.: (47) 99088077
Web Site: https://puzzlepart.com
Microsoft Technology Services
N.A.I.C.S.: 541512

Rhipe Japan KK　　　(1)
1-23-1 Toranomon, Minato-ku Toranomon
Hills Mori Tower 16F, Tokyo, 105-6316,
Japan
Tel.: (81) 344554050
Web Site: https://rhipe.co.jp

Crayon Group Holding ASA—(Continued)

Business Consulting Services
N.A.I.C.S.: 541611

Rhipe Lanka (Pvt.) Limited (1)
Level 06 East Tower World Trade Center,
01, Colombo, Sri Lanka
Tel.: (94) 770632252
Business Consulting Services
N.A.I.C.S.: 541611

Rhipe Malaysia Sdn. Bhd. (1)
WeWork Mercu 2 Level 38 No 3 Jalan
Bangsar Kampung Haji Abdullah Hukum,
Kuala Lumpur, Malaysia
Tel.: (60) 389663558
Cloud Computing Services
N.A.I.C.S.: 518210

Rhipe New Zealand Ltd. (1)
Level M 17 Albert Street, Auckland, 1010,
New Zealand
Tel.: (64) 99730500
Cloud Computing Services
N.A.I.C.S.: 518210

Rhipe Philippines, Inc. (1)
Level 22 Greenfield Towercorner Mayflower
& Williams Street, Greenfield District, Man-
daluyong, 1550, Philippines
Tel.: (63) 288612428
Cloud Computing Services
N.A.I.C.S.: 518210

Rhipe Singapore Pte. Ltd. (1)
3 Fusionopolis Way Symbiosis Tower 12-20,
Singapore, 138633, Singapore
Tel.: (65) 66786596
Cloud Computing Services
N.A.I.C.S.: 518210

Rhipe Technology (Thailand) Co., (1)
Ltd.
173 28/F Asia Center Building South
Sathorn Rd, Thung Maha Mek Sathorn,
Bangkok, 10120, Thailand
Tel.: (66) 21560301
Business Consulting Services
N.A.I.C.S.: 541611

Rhipe Technology Philippines, (1)
Inc.
Level 22 Greenfield Tower corner Mayflower
& Williams Street, Greenfield District, Man-
daluyong, 1550, Philippines
Tel.: (63) 288612428
Business Consulting Services
N.A.I.C.S.: 541611

Sensa Ehf. (1)
Lynghals 4, 110, Reykjavik, Iceland
Tel.: (354) 4251500
Web Site: https://sensa.is
System Integration Services
N.A.I.C.S.: 541512

SmartEncrypt Pty. Ltd. (1)
Level 17 100 Arthur Street, North Sydney,
2060, NSW, Australia
Tel.: (61) 1300732009
Web Site: https://smartencrypt.com
Data Protect Services
N.A.I.C.S.: 541513

CRAZY INFOTECH LTD.
Plot No 51 Anna Salai Sem-
mencherry OMR, West Mambalam,
Chennai, 600 119, India
Tel.: (91) 44 24710737
Web Site:
　　http://www.crazyinfotech.com
Rev.: $18,548
Assets: $23,651
Liabilities: $138,935
Net Worth: ($115,284)
Earnings: ($34,170)
Emp.: 1
Fiscal Year-end: 03/31/18
Information Technology Enabled Ser-
vices
N.A.I.C.S.: 519290

CRAZY SPORTS GROUP LIM-
ITED
Room 3006 30/F 9 Queen s Road,
Central, China (Hong Kong)

Tel.: (852) 28698966　　　　　BM
Web Site: http://www.v1group.com
0082—(HKG)
Rev.: $89,690,513
Assets: $152,952,315
Liabilities: $49,057,283
Net Worth: $103,895,033
Earnings: $2,259,810
Emp.: 133
Fiscal Year-end: 12/31/22
Investment Holding Company
N.A.I.C.S.: 551112
Chun Wang (Co-COO)

CRB SHARE CUSTODIAN
SERVICES LTD.
Room No 15 Basement Floor 3 B
Lalbazar Street, Kolkata, 700001,
West Bengal, India
Tel.: (91) 3322625609
530423—(BOM)
Other Financial Services
N.A.I.C.S.: 523999
Vishal Wason (Compliance Officer &
Sec)

CRCC HIGH-TECH EQUIP-
MENT CORPORATION LIM-
ITED
No 384 Yangfangwang, Jinma Town
China pilot free trade zone, Kunming,
650215, Yunnan, China
Tel.: (86) 87163831998　　　　　CN
Web Site: https://www.crcce.com.cn
Year Founded: 1954
1786—(HKG)
Rev.: $396,197,221
Assets: $1,204,310,808
Liabilities: $373,288,728
Net Worth: $831,022,080
Earnings: $16,240,287
Emp.: 2,009
Fiscal Year-end: 12/31/22
Railway Track Maintenance Services
N.A.I.C.S.: 488210
Changhua Ma (Co-Sec & Deputy
Gen Mgr)

Subsidiaries:

CE cideon engineering GmbH & Co. (1)
KG
Tzschirnerstrasse 5a, 02625, Bautzen, Ger-
many
Tel.: (49) 3591374460
Web Site: https://cideon-engineering.com
Emp.: 110
Rail Vehicle & Rail Road Construction Ser-
vices
N.A.I.C.S.: 488210

CE cideon engineering Schweiz (1)
AG
Aeschengraben 6, 4051, Basel, Switzerland
Tel.: (41) 612057750
Rail Vehicle & Rail Road Construction Ser-
vices
N.A.I.C.S.: 488210

CRDB BANK PLC
Ali Hassan Mwinyi Road, PO Box
268, Dar es Salaam, Tanzania
Tel.: (255) 222197700　　　　　TZ
Web Site: https://crdbbank.co.tz
Year Founded: 1996
CRDB—(DAR)
Rev.: $382,711,180
Assets: $2,836,816,640
Liabilities: $2,461,396,970
Net Worth: $375,419,670
Earnings: $51,662,350
Emp.: 3,196
Fiscal Year-end: 12/31/19
Banking Services
N.A.I.C.S.: 522110
Esther Kileo Kitoka (COO)

CRE LOGISTICS REIT, INC.

2-10-1 Toranomon, Minato-Ku, Tokyo,
105-0001, Japan
Tel.: (81) 363863655
Web Site: https://www.cre-reit.co.jp
3487—(TKS)
Sales Range: $1-4.9 Billion
Real Estate Manangement Services
N.A.I.C.S.: 531390
Tsuyoohi Ito (Exoo Dir)

CRE, INC.
Toranomon Twin Bldg East Tower
19F 10-1 Toranomon 2-chome,
Minato-ku, Tokyo, 105-0001, Japan
Tel.: (81) 355726600
Web Site: https://www.cre-jpn.com
Year Founded: 2009
3458—(TKS)
Rev.: $416,124,220
Assets: $886,704,540
Liabilities: $630,627,140
Net Worth: $256,077,400
Earnings: $27,001,020
Emp.: 222
Fiscal Year-end: 07/31/24
Real Estate Services
N.A.I.C.S.: 531390
Shuhei Yamashita (Chm)

Subsidiaries:

CRE (Thailand) Co., Ltd. (1)
47/4 Soi Nuan Noi Soi Ekamai 28 Klongton
Nua, Wattana, Bangkok, 10110, Thailand
Tel.: (66) 2 275 5472
Web Site: https://cre-th.com
Real Estate Services
N.A.I.C.S.: 531210

CRE Alliance, Inc. (1)
Toranomon Twin Bldg East Tower 18F 10-1
Toranomon 2-chome, Minato-ku, Tokyo,
Japan
Tel.: (81) 335050324
Money Lending Services
N.A.I.C.S.: 522291

CRE Asia Pte. Ltd. (1)
80 Robinson Road 10-01A, Singapore,
068898, Singapore
Tel.: (65) 64206370
Asset Management Services
N.A.I.C.S.: 531390

CRE REIT Advisers, Inc. (1)
Toranomon Twin Bldg East Tower 14F 10-1
Toranomon 2-chome, Minato-ku, Tokyo,
105-0001, Japan
Tel.: (81) 35 575 3600
Logistics Real Estate Services
N.A.I.C.S.: 531390

Hapilogi, Inc. (1)
1-2-19 Kitahorie Asterio Kitahorie 3rd Floor,
Nishi-ku, Osaka, 550-0014, Japan
Tel.: (81) 66 110 8872
Web Site: https://www.hapilogi.co.jp
Warehouse Services
N.A.I.C.S.: 493110

Logicom, Inc. (1)
2-1-3 Tateno, Higashiyamato, 207-0021,
Tokyo, Japan
Tel.: (81) 425652111
Web Site: http://www.logicom.jp
Real Estate Lending Services
N.A.I.C.S.: 531210
Hideo Aoyama (Chm)

Strategic Partners Co., Ltd. (1)
19F Toranomon Twin Building East 2-10-1,
Toranomon Minato-ku, Tokyo, Japan
Tel.: (81) 355753600
Web Site: http://www.strategicpartners.co.jp
Emp.: 17
Real Estate Consulting Service
N.A.I.C.S.: 531210
Yasuyuki Mizuno (Pres)

CRE8 DIRECT (NINGBO) CO.,
LTD.
45W Lushan Road Beilun, Ningbo,
315806, China
Tel.: (86) 57486188166
Web Site: https://www.cre8direct.net

Year Founded: 2001
300703—(CHIN)
Rev.: $191,384,543
Assets: $209,851,443
Liabilities: $89,290,970
Net Worth: $120,560,473
Earnings: $10,808,871
Fiscal Year-end: 12/31/23
Paper Product Mfr & Distr
N.A.I.C.S.: 322230

CREACTIVES GROUP SPA
Piazzale Luigi Cadorna 6, 37126, Ve-
rona, Italy
Tel.: (39) 0456261357
Web Site:
　　https://www.creactivesgroup.com
Year Founded: 2000
CREG—(VIE)
Sales Range: Less than $1 Million
Software Development Services
N.A.I.C.S.: 541511
Paolo Gamberoni (Co-Founder, Pres
& CEO)

CREADES AB
Ingmar Bergmans gata 4 floor 7, Box
55900, 10216, Stockholm, Sweden
Tel.: (46) 841201100
Web Site: http://www.creades.se
CRED.A—(OMX)
Rev.: $53,407,986
Assets: $925,407,525
Liabilities: $14,592,888
Net Worth: $910,814,636
Earnings: $55,393,413
Emp.: 8
Fiscal Year-end: 12/31/23
Investment Services
N.A.I.C.S.: 523999
Sven Hagstromer (Chm)

CREADEV SAS
15 Rue Louis le Grand, Paris, 75002,
France
Tel.: (33) 1 81 90 10 02
Web Site: http://www.creadev.com
Investment Services
N.A.I.C.S.: 523999
Bertrand de Talhouet (CEO)

Subsidiaries:

Groupe Acticall SAS (1)
50-52 Boulevard Haussmann, 75009, Paris,
France
Tel.: (33) 1 53 56 70 00
Web Site: http://www.groupe-acticall.com
Call Center Services
N.A.I.C.S.: 561499
Laurent Uberti (Founder, Chm-Sitel, CEO &
Partner)

Subsidiary (US):

SITEL Worldwide Corporation (2)
3102 W End Ave 2 American Ctr Ste 900,
Nashville, TN 37203
Tel.: (615) 301-7100
Web Site: http://www.sitel.com
Sales Range: $1-4.9 Billion
Emp.: 75,100
Business Outsourcing Services
N.A.I.C.S.: 561499
Pat Tolbert (CFO)

Subsidiary (Non-US):

SITEL France SAS (3)
50-52 50-50 boulevard Haussmann, 75009,
Paris, France
Tel.: (33) 158351000
Web Site: http://www.sitel.com
Emp.: 3,200
Customer Relation Solutions & Services
N.A.I.C.S.: 541511
Nordine Benbekhti (Reg Dir)

SITEL GmbH (3)
Munsterstrasse 100, D-40476, Dusseldorf,
Germany
Tel.: (49) 211 505 3030
Web Site: http://www.sitel.de

Emp.: 4,000
Customer Relation Solutions & Services
N.A.I.C.S.: 541511
Pedro Lozano *(Gen Mgr-Germany & Europe)*

SITEL Iberica Teleservices, S.A. (3)
C/ Retama 7, 28045, Madrid, Spain
Tel.: (34) 913797474
Web Site: http://www.sitel.com
Emp.: 4,000
Customer Relation Solutions & Services
N.A.I.C.S.: 541511

SITEL Netherlands (3)
Twentheplein 11, 7607 GZ, Almelo, Netherlands
Tel.: (31) 402917000
Web Site: http://www.sitel.com
Emp.: 300
Customer Relation Solutions & Services
N.A.I.C.S.: 541511
Marcel Zuurmond *(Site Dir)*

SITEL New Zealand Limited (3)
Level 1 Raphoe House 8 Gloucester Park Road, Onehunga, Auckland, 1061, New Zealand
Tel.: (64) 9 622 4550
Web Site: http://www.sitel.com
Emp.: 140
Customer Relation Solutions & Services
N.A.I.C.S.: 541511
Steve Barker *(COO-Australia & New Zealand)*

SITEL UK Ltd. (3)
Building 600 Leavesden Park, Hercules Way, Watford, WD25 7GS, United Kingdom
Tel.: (44) 800 444 221
Web Site: http://www.sitel.com
Emp.: 2,400
Customer Relation Solutions & Services
N.A.I.C.S.: 541511
Karl Brough *(Reg Dir)*

Subsidiary (Domestic):

Sykes Enterprises, Incorporated (3)
400 N Ashley Dr Ste 2800, Tampa, FL 33602
Tel.: (813) 274-1000
Web Site: http://www.sykes.com
Rev.: $1,710,261,000
Assets: $1,435,805,000
Liabilities: $542,151,000
Net Worth: $893,654,000
Earnings: $56,432,000
Emp.: 61,100
Fiscal Year-end: 12/31/2020
Outsourced Customer Contact Management Solutions & Services in the Business Process Outsourcing (BPO) Arena
N.A.I.C.S.: 541512
Jenna R. Nelson *(Chief HR Officer)*

Subsidiary (Non-US):

Alpine Access Canada, Inc (4)
520 3 Ave Sw Suite 1900, Calgary, T2P0R3, AB, Canada
Tel.: (888) 466-2749
Emp.: 10
Office Management Services
N.A.I.C.S.: 561110
Emily Shaw *(Partner-HR Bus)*

Subsidiary (Domestic):

Clear Link Technologies, LLC (4)
5202 W Douglas Corrigan Way, Salt Lake City, UT 84116
Tel.: (801) 424-0018
Web Site: http://www.clearlink.com
Marketing & Advertising Services
N.A.I.C.S.: 541810
Bruce Westenskow *(CTO)*

Subsidiary (Domestic):

Portent, Inc. (5)
920 5th Ave Ste 1400, Seattle, WA 98104-1189
Tel.: (206) 575-3740
Web Site: http://www.portent.com
Internet Marketing Services
N.A.I.C.S.: 541890
Ian Lurie *(Founder)*

Subsidiary (Non-US):

Qelp B.V. (4)
Kingsfordweg 43-117, 1043 GP, Amsterdam, Netherlands
Tel.: (31) 208202240
Web Site: http://www.qelp.com
Software Development Services
N.A.I.C.S.: 541511
Elena Skoutaki *(Mgr-Key Acct)*

Qelp Do Brasil Software E Contuedo Digital LTDA (4)
Av Doutor Chucri Zaidan 920 920 Andar 9 Vila Cordeiro, Sao Paulo, 04583-904, Brazil
Tel.: (55) 1123135700
Software Development Services
N.A.I.C.S.: 541511

Sykes (Shanghai) Co. Ltd (4)
No 221 3rd Jiangchang Road, Jingan District,, Shanghai, 200436, China
Tel.: (86) 400 880 7953
Web Site: http://www.sykes.com
Contact Center Services
N.A.I.C.S.: 561422
Cherry Wong *(Sr VP-Asia Ops)*

Sykes Asia, Inc. (4)
26 Fl Robinsons Summit Bldg 6783 Ayala Ave, Makati, 1200, Philippines (100%)
Tel.: (63) 28178781
Sales Range: $100-124.9 Million
Outsourcing & Technology Solutions
N.A.I.C.S.: 541512

Sykes Assistance Services Corporation (4)
248 Pall Mall Street, PO Box 5845, London, N6A 4T4, ON, Canada
Web Site: http://www.assistanceservicesgroup.com
Contact Center Services
N.A.I.C.S.: 561422

Sykes Datasvar Support AB (4)
Herrogatan 25, PO Box 202, 84222, Harjedalen, Sveg, Sweden
Tel.: (46) 680716000
Web Site: http://www.sykes.com
Sales Range: $50-74.9 Million
Emp.: 250
Business Process Outsourcing Services
N.A.I.C.S.: 561422

Sykes El Salvador, Ltda (4)
Boulevard de los Heroes entre Avenida, Los Sisimiles y Pasaje Las Palmeras, San Salvador, El Salvador
Tel.: (503) 22613600
Web Site: http://www.sykeselsalvador.com
Contact Center Services
N.A.I.C.S.: 561422

Sykes Enterprises (India) Pvt Ltd (4)
802 7th Cross Mico Layout, HBCS BTM 2nd Stage, Bengaluru, 560076, Karnataka, India
Tel.: (91) 8041374500
Web Site: http://www.sykes.com
Emp.: 3
Business Process Outsourcing Services
N.A.I.C.S.: 561422
Prashanth Krishna Setty *(Mng Dir)*

Sykes Enterprises Berlin GmbH & Co. KG (4)
Zeughofstrasse 1, 10997, Berlin, Germany
Tel.: (49) 30269490
Customer Relationship Management Services
N.A.I.C.S.: 561422

Sykes Enterprises Bochum GmbH & Co. KG (4)
Bessemerstr 85, 44793, Bochum, Germany
Tel.: (49) 2345398000
Business Process Outsourcing Services
N.A.I.C.S.: 561422

Sykes Enterprises Denmark ApS (4)
Agerhatten 27b, 5220, Odense, Denmark
Tel.: (45) 63168200
Web Site: http://www.sykes.com
Sales Range: $25-49.9 Million
Emp.: 50
Business Process Outsourcing Services
N.A.I.C.S.: 561422

Sykes Enterprises Eastern Europe S.R.L. (4)
109 Republicii Street Sigma Business Center 6th Floor, Cluj-Napoca, 400489, Romania
Tel.: (40) 374165000
Web Site: http://www.sykes.com
Emp.: 800
Contact Center Services
N.A.I.C.S.: 561422

Sykes Enterprises Management GmbH (4)
Bessemerstr 85, Bochum, 44793, Germany
Tel.: (49) 2345398000
Office Management Services
N.A.I.C.S.: 561110

Sykes Enterprises Norway AS (4)
Folke Bernadottesvei 50, 5147, Bergen, Fyllingsdalen, Norway
Tel.: (47) 53001102
Business Process Outsourcing Services
N.A.I.C.S.: 561422

Sykes Global Services Ltd. (4)
Nether Road, Galashiels, TD1 3HE, United Kingdom (100%)
Tel.: (44) 1896754866
Web Site: http://www.sykes-gala.com
Sales Range: $100-124.9 Million
Emp.: 400
Call Center Operations
N.A.I.C.S.: 561422

Sykes Kozep-Europa Kft (4)
Vaci ut 43 Advance Tower Office Building, Budapest, 1134, Hungary
Tel.: (36) 13821000
Telecommunication Servicesb
N.A.I.C.S.: 517810

Sykes Latin America, S.A. (4)
700 Parkway Global Park, La Aurona, Heredia, Belen, Costa Rica
Tel.: (506) 22982170
Web Site: http://www.sykescostarica.com
Emp.: 5,000
Business Process Outsourcing Services
N.A.I.C.S.: 561499

Subsidiary (Domestic):

Sykes Realty, Inc. (4)
400 N Ashley Dr Ste 3100, Tampa, FL 33602
Tel.: (813) 274-1000
Emp.: 5
Contact Center Services
N.A.I.C.S.: 561422

Subsidiary (Non-US):

Sykes Slovakia Sro (4)
Letna 45 6th Floor, 040 01, Kosice, Slovakia
Tel.: (421) 557953700
Web Site: http://www.sykes.com
Sales Range: $25-49.9 Million
Emp.: 8
Business Process Outsourcing Services
N.A.I.C.S.: 561422

Sykes Sweden AB (4)
Gotaverksgatan 8, 41755, Gothenburg, Sweden
Tel.: (46) 859009500
Web Site: http://www.sykes.com
Customer Relationship Management Services
N.A.I.C.S.: 561422

CREADOR SDN. BHD.
Lot 8.02B (East Wing) 8th Floor Menara BRDB 285 Jalan Ma'arof, Bukit Bandar Raya, 59000, Kuala Lumpur, Malaysia
Tel.: (60) 3 2182 6888   MY
Web Site: http://www.creador.com
Emp.: 50
Privater Equity Firm
N.A.I.C.S.: 523999
Brahmal Vasudevan *(Founder & CEO)*

Subsidiaries:

ASIAMET Education Group Berhad (1)
G-8 Jalan Kemacahaya 11, Taman Kemacahaya Batu 9, 43200, Cheras, Selangor Darul Ehsan, Malaysia (27.02%)

Tel.: (60) 390805888
Web Site: http://www.aegb.com.my
Sales Range: $1-9.9 Million
Education Services
N.A.I.C.S.: 611710

CTOS Holding Sdn Bhd (1)
Unit A-9-6 9th Floor Megan Avenue 1 No 189 Jalan Tun Razak, 50400, Kuala Lumpur, Malaysia
Tel.: (60) 327228833
Web Site: http://www.ctoscredit.com.my
Financial Investment Management Services
N.A.I.C.S.: 523940
Dennis Martin *(Grp CEO)*

Creador Advisors India Private Limited (1)
Senans Square 4th Floor No 99 Santhome High Road, Chennai, 600028, India
Tel.: (91) 4424934033
Financial Investment Management Services
N.A.I.C.S.: 523940
Anand Narayan Sr. *(Mng Dir)*

PT Creador Indonesia (1)
Indonesia Stock Exchange Building IDX Tower 2 29th Floor Suite 2903, Jalan Jendral Sudirman Kav 52-53, Jakarta, 12190, Indonesia
Tel.: (62) 215155538
Financial Investment Management Services
N.A.I.C.S.: 523940
Cyril Noerhadi Sr. *(Mng Dir)*

CREAS F&C CO., LTD.
Creas F&C 176 Dogok-ro, Gangnam-gu, Seoul, 06261, Korea (South)
Tel.: (82) 234093000
Web Site: https://www.creas.co.kr
Year Founded: 1998
110790—(KRS)
Rev.: $292,163,098
Assets: $461,152,578
Liabilities: $218,810,566
Net Worth: $242,342,012
Earnings: $20,220,130
Emp.: 312
Fiscal Year-end: 12/31/22
Sporting & Recreational Equipment Distr
N.A.I.C.S.: 423910
Woo Jin Seok *(Co-CEO)*

CREAT GROUP CORPORATION
8/F Tower 1 Fusheng Mansion 4 Huixin East Street, Chaoyang District, Beijing, 100029, China
Tel.: (86) 10 8472 1992
Web Site: http://www.creatgroup.com
Year Founded: 1992
Privater Equity Firm
N.A.I.C.S.: 523999
Yuewen Zheng *(Chm)*

CREAT RESOURCES HOLDINGS LIMITED
Murchison Suite Wilmot Street, Burnie, 7320, Tasmania, Australia
Tel.: (61) 36 435 1454   AU
Web Site: http://www.creatresources.com
Year Founded: 1999
Sales Range: Less than $1 Million
Investment Services
N.A.I.C.S.: 523999
Morris R. Hansen *(Sec & Gen Mgr)*

CREATE CORPORATION
1-13-15 Awaza, Nishi-ku, Osaka, Osaka, Japan
Tel.: (81) 665382333
Web Site: https://www.cr-net.co.jp
Year Founded: 1948
3024—(TKS)
Rev.: $237,034,600
Assets: $112,244,410
Liabilities: $79,756,260
Net Worth: $32,488,150
Earnings: $945,230

CREATE CORPORATION—(Continued)

Emp.: 542
Fiscal Year-end: 03/31/24
Pipe Fitting & Coupling Valves Distr
N.A.I.C.S.: 423720
Takanori Yoshinari *(Pres & COO)*

Subsidiaries:

Daipoly System Corporation (1)
1-13-15 Awaza Create Building 8F, Nishi-ku,
Osaka, 550-0011, Japan
Tel.: (81) 665382440
Web Site: https://www.daipoly.co.jp
Emp.: 29
Water Supply Management Services
N.A.I.C.S.: 221310

CREATE MEDIC CO. LTD.

2-5-25 Chigasakiminami, Tsuzuki-ku,
Yokohama, 224-0037, Kanagawa,
Japan
Tel.: (81) 459432741
Web Site:
　　https://www.createmedic.co.jp
Year Founded: 1974
5187—(TKS)
Rev.: $89,227,650
Assets: $136,539,220
Liabilities: $30,586,260
Net Worth: $105,952,960
Earnings: $1,091,860
Emp.: 962
Fiscal Year-end: 12/31/23
Medical Appliances Mfr & Sales
N.A.I.C.S.: 334510
Hidenori Taniguchi *(Sr Mng Dir)*

Subsidiaries:

**Create Medic Dalian International
Trading Co., Ltd.** (1)
No 99 Honggang Road, Ganjingzi-District,
Dalian, 116033, China
Tel.: (86) 41183602266
Web Site: https://www.createmedic.com
Hospital Equipment Distr
N.A.I.C.S.: 423450

**Dalian Create Medical Products Co.,
Ltd.** (1)
No IIB-31 Dalian Export Processing Zone,
Dalian, 116600, Liaoning, China
Tel.: (86) 41187322560
Hospital Equipment Distr
N.A.I.C.S.: 423450

Kyushu Create Medic Co., Ltd. (1)
2-52 Makiyamakaigan, Tobataku, Kitakyu-
ushu, Fukuoka, Japan
Tel.: (81) 938821750
Hospital Equipments Mfr
N.A.I.C.S.: 334510

Vietnam Create Medic Co., Ltd. (1)
Lot 303 Road 7A Amata Industrial Park,
Long Binh Ward, Bien Hoa, Dong Nai, Viet-
nam
Tel.: (84) 2518877055
Web Site: https://www.createmedic.vn
Hospital Equipment Distr
N.A.I.C.S.: 423450

CREATE RESTAURANTS
HOLDINGS INC.

5-10-18 Higashigotanda, Shinagawa-
Ku, Tokyo, 141-0022, Japan
Tel.: (81) 354888001
Web Site:
　　https://www.createrestaurants.com
3387—(TKS)
Rev.: $1,033,431,310
Assets: $927,485,440
Liabilities: $648,345,050
Net Worth: $279,140,390
Earnings: $35,740,690
Emp.: 4,205
Fiscal Year-end: 02/29/24
Restaurant Management Services
N.A.I.C.S.: 722511
Hitoshi Gotoh *(Chm)*

Subsidiaries:

Create Dining inc. (1)
5-10-18 Higashi Gotanda, Shinagawa-ku,
Tokyo, Japan (99.97%)
Tel.: (81) 354888004
Web Site: http://www.createrestaurants.com
Restaurant
N.A.I.C.S.: 722511
Naohiko Harada *(CEO)*

Create Restaurants Asia Pte.Ltd. (1)
51 Cuppage Road 06-04, Singapore,
229469, Singapore
Tel.: (65) 62213114
Web Site:
　　http://www.asia.createrestaurants.com
Food Restaurant Services
N.A.I.C.S.: 722511

**Create Restaurants Taiwan Co.,
Ltd.** (1)
Rm332 12F-1 No 51 Hengyang Rd, Taipei,
10045, Taiwan
Tel.: (886) 223752168
Food Restaurant Services
N.A.I.C.S.: 722511
Hitoshi Ohno *(CEO)*

Eat Walk Co., Ltd (1)
5-10-18 Higashi Gotanda, Shinagawa-ku,
Tokyo, 106-0045, Japan (100%)
Tel.: (81) 354888057
Web Site: http://www.createrestaurants.com
Restaurant Operators
N.A.I.C.S.: 722511
Akira Watanabe *(CEO)*

Gourmet Brands Company Inc. (1)
5-10-18 Higashi Gotanda, Shinagawa-ku,
Tokyo, Japan
Tel.: (81) 354888008
Food Restaurant Services
N.A.I.C.S.: 722511
Katsuji Ishii *(CEO)*

**Hokkaido-Saint-Germain Co.,
Ltd.** (1)
Building 2-43 Hassamu 8-jo 11-chome,
Nishi-ku, Sapporo, 063-0828, Japan
Tel.: (81) 116631936
Web Site: https://www.h-saint-germain.co.jp
Emp.: 820
Baked Goods Mfr & Retailer
N.A.I.C.S.: 311812

Icchou Inc. (1)
319-3 Kiyoharacho, Ota, 373-0012, Gunma,
Japan
Tel.: (81) 276367878
Web Site:
　　https://www.createrestaurants.com
Food Restaurant Services
N.A.I.C.S.: 722511

Il Fornaio (America) Corporation (1)
223 Corte Madera Town Center, Corte Mad-
era, CA 94925
Tel.: (415) 927-4400
Web Site: https://www.ilfornaio.com
Full-Service Italian Restaurant Bakery &
Retail Market Owner & Operator Services
N.A.I.C.S.: 722511
Laurence B. Mindel *(Founder & CEO)*

KR Holdings Corporation (1)
9-1 Toyotsu-cho Belot Esaka Building 19F,
Suita, 564-0051, Osaka, Japan
Tel.: (81) 661701590
Web Site: http://www.food-kr.com
Food Restaurant Services
N.A.I.C.S.: 722511

LG&EW Inc. (1)
5-10-18 Higashi Gotanda, Shinagawa-ku,
Tokyo, Japan
Tel.: (81) 354888057
Food Restaurant Services
N.A.I.C.S.: 722511
Tatsuo Iinuma *(CEO)*

Route 9g Inc. (1)
5-10-18 Higashi Gotanda, Shinagawa-ku,
Tokyo, Japan
Tel.: (81) 354888099
Food Restaurant Services
N.A.I.C.S.: 722511
Shiro Nakanishi *(CEO)*

YUNARI Co., Ltd. (1)
5-10-18 Higashi Gotanda, Shinagawa-ku,
Tokyo, Japan
Tel.: (81) 368538102
Food Restaurant Services
N.A.I.C.S.: 722511
Ken Kojima *(CEO)*

Yuzuru Inc. (1)
5-5 Misono 2-jo 6-chome, Toyohira-ku, Sap-
poro, 060-0002, Hokkaido, Japan
Tel.: (81) 118127826
Web Site:
　　https://www.createrestaurants.com
Food Restaurant Services
N.A.I.C.S.: 722511

**create restaurants hong kong
Ltd.** (1)
Room 604 6th Floor Emperor Group Centre
288 Hennessy Road, Wanchai, China
(Hong Kong)
Tel.: (852) 39000691
Food Restaurant Services
N.A.I.C.S.: 722511
Ken Ng *(Mng Dir)*

create restaurants inc. (1)
5-10-18 Higashi Gotanda, Shinagawa-ku,
Tokyo, 150-0002, Japan
Tel.: (81) 354888002
Web Site:
　　https://www.createrestaurants.com
Food Service Shop Operations
N.A.I.C.S.: 722511

create sports & leisure inc. (1)
5-10-18 Higashi Gotanda, Shinagawa-ku,
Tokyo, Japan
Tel.: (81) 354888020
Food Restaurant Services
N.A.I.C.S.: 722511
Hiroshi Ikeda *(CEO)*

CREATE S.D. HOLDINGS CO.,
LTD.

2-3-2 Edanishi, Aoba-ku, Yokohama,
225-0014, Japan
Tel.: (81) 459148241
Web Site:
　　https://www.createsdhd.co.jp
Year Founded: 1983
3148—(TKS)
Rev.: $2,791,601,300
Assets: $1,430,939,410
Liabilities: $570,033,180
Net Worth: $860,906,230
Earnings: $90,497,510
Emp.: 1,335
Fiscal Year-end: 05/31/24
Pharmaceuticals, Food Products &
Cosmetics Retailer
N.A.I.C.S.: 456110
Taizo Hirose *(Pres)*

CREATE TECHNOLOGY & SCI-
ENCE CO., LTD.

No 37 Sutong Road Industrial Park,
Suzhou, 215021, Jiangsu, China
Tel.: (86) 51268241551
Web Site: https://www.000551.cn
Year Founded: 1993
000551—(SSE)
Rev.: $586,925,352
Assets: $885,133,548
Liabilities: $430,067,664
Net Worth: $455,065,884
Earnings: $23,015,772
Fiscal Year-end: 12/31/22
Electronics Instrument Mfr
N.A.I.C.S.: 334513
Shen Weimin *(Chm)*

CREATIVE CASTINGS LTD.

102 G I D C Phase-II Dolatpara
Rajkot Road, Junagadh, 362 003,
India
Tel.: (91) 2852660040
Web Site: https://www.creative-
cast.com
Year Founded: 1980
539527—(BOM)
Rev.: $4,262,231
Assets: $4,540,926

Liabilities: $622,349
Net Worth: $3,918,577
Earnings: $386,605
Emp.: 138
Fiscal Year-end: 03/31/21
Steel Alloy Casting Services
N.A.I.C.S.: 331513
Dhirubhai H. Dand *(Chm)*

CREATIVE CHINA HOLDINGS
LIMITED

23/F Yue Thai Commercial Building
128 Connaught Road, Sheung Wan,
Central, China (Hong Kong)
Tel.: (852) 21531221 Ky
Web Site: http://www.ntmediabj.com
Year Founded: 2013
8368—(HKG)
Rev.: $21,437,395
Assets: $47,839,054
Liabilities: $22,887,587
Net Worth: $24,951,467
Earnings: $6,879,179
Emp.: 43
Fiscal Year-end: 12/31/22
Television Production Services
N.A.I.C.S.: 512110
Philip Jian Yang *(Chm, Pres, CEO &
Compliance-Officer)*

Subsidiaries:

**New Talent Media Company
Limited** (1)
Bldg C9-A Universal Creative Park 9 Jiuxi-
anqiao North Rd, Chaoyang District, Beijing,
100015, China
Tel.: (86) 1084430339
Investment Holding Services
N.A.I.C.S.: 551112

CREATIVE EYE LIMITED

12- A Kailash Plaza New Link Road
Opp Laxmi Industrial Estate, Andheri
West, Mumbai, 400053, India
Tel.: (91) 2226732613
Web Site:
　　https://www.creativeeye.com
CREATIVEYE—(NSE)
Rev.: $966,340
Assets: $4,597,725
Liabilities: $1,348,188
Net Worth: $3,249,537
Earnings: ($37,448)
Emp.: 11
Fiscal Year-end: 03/31/21
Motion Picture & Video Production
Services
N.A.I.C.S.: 512110
Dheeraj Kumar *(Chm & Mng Dir)*

CREATIVE JAR

Tudor House 24 High St, Twyford,
RG10 9AG, Berkshire, United King-
dom
Tel.: (44) 1189344069
Web Site: http://www.creative-jar.com
Year Founded: 2001
Sales Range: $10-24.9 Million
Emp.: 25
E-Commerce, Graphic Design, Inte-
grated Marketing, Internet/Web De-
sign, Multimedia, Print, Search En-
gine Optimization
N.A.I.C.S.: 541810
Joseph Richardson *(Mng Dir)*

CREATIVE MASTER BER-
MUDA LTD.

Yeung Yiu Chung No 8 Industrial
Building, 20 Wang Hoi Road, Kow-
loon, China (Hong Kong)
Tel.: (852) 23960147 BM
Year Founded: 2002
Sales Range: Less than $1 Million
Emp.: 25
Holding Company
N.A.I.C.S.: 551112

Carl Ka Wing Tong *(CEO)*

Subsidiaries:

Creative Master L&W Limited　　(1)
Foreign Economic District Shang Ling
Chun, Heng Li Zhen, Dongguan, 523478,
China
Tel.: (86) 7693732828
Die-Cast Plastic Molded Products Mfr
N.A.I.C.S.: 326199

Creative Master Northcord
Limited　　(1)
Yeung Yiu Chung No 8 Industrial Building,
20 Wang Hoi Road, Kowloon, China (Hong
Kong)
Tel.: (852) 23960147
Web Site: http://www.cmn.com.hk
Die-Cast Replica Model Mfr & Distr
N.A.I.C.S.: 331523

Creative Master Overseas Holdings
Limited　　(1)
Room D 3 F Yeung Yiu Chung No 8 Indl 20
Wang Hoi Road, Hong Kong, China (Hong
Kong)
Tel.: (852) 23960147
Die Cast Replicas Mfr
N.A.I.C.S.: 331523

Excel Master Limited　　(1)
Room D 3 F Yeung Yiu Chung No 8 Indus-
trial Building 20 Wang Hoi Road, Kowloon
Bay, Kowloon, China (Hong Kong)
Tel.: (852) 23960147
Die Cast Replicas Mfr
N.A.I.C.S.: 331523

CREATIVE NEWTECH LIMITED
Unit No 3rd & 4th Floor Plot No
137AB, Government Industrial Estate
Charkop Kandivali West, Mumbai,
400067, India
Tel.: (91) 2250612700
Web Site:
　https://creativenewtech.com
Year Founded: 1992
CREATIVE—(NSE)
Rev.: $71,842,844
Assets: $26,177,328
Liabilities: $17,757,681
Net Worth: $8,419,648
Earnings: $1,280,670
Emp.: 196
Fiscal Year-end: 03/31/21
Electronic Products Mfr
N.A.I.C.S.: 334111
Ketan C. Patel *(Chm & Mng Dir)*

**CREATIVE SALMON COM-
PANY LTD.**
612 Campbell Street, PO Box 265,
Tofino, V0R 2Z0, BC, Canada
Tel.: (250) 725-2884　　　　　BC
Web Site:
　http://www.creativesalmon.com
Year Founded: 1990
Emp.: 55
Salmon Farming Services
N.A.I.C.S.: 445250
Tim Rundle *(Gen Mgr)*

CREATIVE SENSOR INC.
9F No 501 Sec 6 Nanjing E Rd,
Neihu Dist, Taipei, 114, Taiwan
Tel.: (886) 289121289
Web Site: https://www.csi-
　sensor.com.tw
8249—(TAI)
Rev.: $99,945,187
Assets: $236,165,726
Liabilities: $67,316,522
Net Worth: $168,849,204
Earnings: $8,070,571
Emp.: 416
Fiscal Year-end: 12/31/23
Image Sensors Mfr
N.A.I.C.S.: 334413
Eugene Huang *(Chm)*

Subsidiaries:

NanChang Creative Sensor Technol-
ogy Co., LTD.　　(1)
No 36 HuoJu Wu Road Hi Tech Zone, Nan-
chang, Jiangxi, China
Tel.: (86) 7918851198
Web Site: http://www.csi-sensor.com.tw
Image Sensors Mfr
N.A.I.C.S.: 334413

Wuxi Creative Sensor Technology
Co., LTD　　(1)
A4 No 93 Wuxi National Hi-Tech Industrial
Development Zone, New District, JiangSu,
214028, Jiangsu, China
Tel.: (86) 51085342588
Sensor Module Mfr
N.A.I.C.S.: 334413

CREATIVE TECHNOLOGY LTD.
31 International Business Park 03-01
Lobby C, Singapore, 609921, Singa-
pore
Tel.: (65) 68954000
Web Site: https://us.creative.com
Year Founded: 1981
CREAF—(OTCIQ)
Rev.: $56,236,000
Assets: $91,167,000
Liabilities: $31,089,000
Net Worth: $60,078,000
Earnings: ($16,689,000)
Emp.: 288
Fiscal Year-end: 06/30/23
Digital Entertainment Products Mfr
N.A.I.C.S.: 334118
Wong Hoo Sim *(Founder, Chm &
CEO)*

Subsidiaries:

3D Labs Inc., Ltd.　　(1)
1901 McCarthy Blvd, Milpitas, CA 95035
Tel.: (408) 432-6700
Web Site: http://www.3dlabs.com
Sales Range: $50-74.9 Million
Emp.: 150
Supplier of Integrated Hardware & Software
Graphics Accelerator Solutions
N.A.I.C.S.: 518210

Subsidiary (Non-US):

3DLabs　　(2)
Level 16 Shiroyama Hills, 4-3-1 Toranomon
Minato-Ku, Tokyo, 105, Japan
Tel.: (81) 354034653
Provider of Electronic Products & Compo-
nents
N.A.I.C.S.: 334419

Cambridge SoundWorks, Inc.　　(1)
100 Brickstone Sq, Andover, MA 01810-
1428
Tel.: (978) 623-4400
Sales Range: $50-74.9 Million
Emp.: 250
Online Retailer of Consumer Electronics
N.A.I.C.S.: 449210

Creative Advanced Technology
Center　　(1)
1500 Green Hills Rd Ste 205, Scotts Valley,
CA 95066
Tel.: (831) 440-2800
Sales Range: $25-49.9 Million
Emp.: 50
Integrated Circuits for the Multimedia, Stor-
age & Communications Markets
N.A.I.C.S.: 541330

Creative Labs　　(1)
Av Eng Duarte Pacheco, Torre 2 Amoreiras
Piso 4, Sala 4, 1070, Lisbon, Portugal
Tel.: (351) 21 383 9720
Electronic Products & Components
N.A.I.C.S.: 449210

Creative Labs　　(1)
15th Fl No 163 Sec 1 Keelung Rd, 11, Tai-
pei, Taiwan
Tel.: (886) 227482988
Web Site: http://www.taiwan.creative.com
Electronic Products & Components
N.A.I.C.S.: 449210

Creative Labs (HK) Limited　　(1)
Units 2908 29/F, Tower 1, Metroplaza, 223
Hing Fong Road, Kwai Fong, China (Hong
Kong)　　(100%)
Tel.: (852) 23312930
Web Site: http://www.asia.creative.com
Sales Range: $25-49.9 Million
Emp.: 11
Electronic Products & Components
N.A.I.C.S.: 449210

Creative Labs (Sweden)　　(1)
Spanga Ctr, PO Box 129, Stormbyvagen 2
4, 16329, Spanga, Sweden　　(100%)
Tel.: (46) 856472020
Web Site: http://www.europe.creative.com
Sales Range: $25-49.9 Million
Emp.: 5
Electronic Products & Components
N.A.I.C.S.: 449210

Creative Labs Ireland Ltd.　　(1)
Unit 1 Block 4B Blanchardstown Corporate
Park, Blanchardstown, 15, Dublin,
Ireland　　(100%)
Tel.: (353) 18206444
Web Site: http://en.europe.creative.com
Sales Range: $100-124.9 Million
Emp.: 360
Operations & Technical Center
N.A.I.C.S.: 449210

Creative Labs N.V.　　(1)
Royal House Coremansstraat 34, PO Box
2, 2600, Berchem, Belgium　　(100%)
Tel.: (32) 32878777
Web Site: http://www.europe.creative.com
Sales Range: $25-49.9 Million
Emp.: 11
Electronic Products & Components
N.A.I.C.S.: 449210

Creative Labs Srl　　(1)
Strada 4 Palazzo A/2, Assago Milanofiori,
20090, Assago, MI, Italy
Tel.: (39) 02 822 8161
Web Site: http://www.creative.com
Electronic Products & Components
N.A.I.C.S.: 334419

Creative Labs, Inc.　　(1)
1900 McCarthy Blvd Ste 103, Milpitas, CA
95035-7427　　(100%)
Tel.: (408) 428-6600
Web Site: https://us.creative.com
Sales Range: $75-99.9 Million
Emp.: 120
Computer Peripherals, Consumer Electron-
ics & Home Entertainment Devices Mfr
N.A.I.C.S.: 423430

Creative Labs, Inc.　　(1)
703 Evans Avenue Suite 401, Etobicoke,
M9C 5E9, ON, Canada
Tel.: (405) 742-6655
Provider of Computer Services
N.A.I.C.S.: 541511

Creative Labs, Inc. - Latin
America　　(1)
5200 Blue Lagoon Dr Ste 250, Miami, FL
33126-2034　　(100%)
Tel.: (305) 264-7050
Sales Range: $25-49.9 Million
Emp.: 3
Mfr & Distributor of Electronics
N.A.I.C.S.: 541512
Roger Sanchez *(Mng Dir)*

Creative Media K.K.　　(1)
4F-7 Sotokanda Soft 99 Building 4F,
Chiyoda-ku, Tokyo, 101-0021,
Japan　　(100%)
Tel.: (81) 332565577
Web Site: http://www.jp.creative.com
Sales Range: $25-49.9 Million
Emp.: 30
Electronic Products & Components
N.A.I.C.S.: 449210

Creative Technology (China) Co.,
Ltd.　　(1)
4-12 Building No 1388 Zhangdong Road,
Zhangjiang Hi-tech Park, Pudong New Dis-
trict, Shanghai, 201203, China
Tel.: (86) 21 6100 1100
Web Site: http://www.creative.com
Sales Range: $25-49.9 Million
Emp.: 50
Electronic Products & Components

N.A.I.C.S.: 334419

Branch (Domestic):

Creative Technology (China) Co.,
Ltd.　　(2)
Creative Park 18 Anhuaxili Block 2, Chaoy-
ang District, Beijing, 100011,
China　　(100%)
Tel.: (86) 10 64257312
Sales Range: $25-49.9 Million
Emp.: 20
Electronic Products & Components
N.A.I.C.S.: 334118

Creative Technology (China) Co.,
Ltd.　　(2)
Room 2001 Eastern Tower Building, No 625
Tianhe Road, Tianhe Entertainment Plaza,
Guangzhou, 510630, Guandong, China
Tel.: (86) 2087540677
Web Site: http://www.creative.com
Sales Range: $25-49.9 Million
Emp.: 6
Electronic Products & Components
N.A.I.C.S.: 334419

Creative Technology Centre Pte
Ltd　　(1)
31 International Business Park 03-01, Sin-
gapore, 609921, Singapore
Tel.: (65) 68954000
Web Site: http://www.creative.com
Computer Peripheral Equipment Mfr
N.A.I.C.S.: 334118

E-Mu Systems, Inc　　(1)
1500 Green Hills Rd Ste 205, Scotts Valley,
CA 95066-4945　　(100%)
Tel.: (831) 438-1921
Web Site: http://www.emu.com
Sales Range: $25-49.9 Million
Emp.: 50
Developer of Digital Audio Products Based
on Digital Sampling Technology for the Mu-
sical Instrument & Computer Controlled
Sound Markets
N.A.I.C.S.: 339992

JCHyun Systems, Inc.　　(1)
JCHyun Bldg, 6 1 Shingye Dong Yongsan
Distr, 140090, Seoul, Korea
(South)　　(100%)
Tel.: (82) 27075044
Sales Range: $50-74.9 Million
Emp.: 150
Electronic Products & Components
N.A.I.C.S.: 334419

QMax Communications Pte Ltd.　　(1)
Creative Resource 31 International Busi-
ness Park, 609921, Singapore, Singapore
Tel.: (65) 6895 4899
Web Site: http://www.qmaxcom.com
Telecommunication Equipment Mfr & Whslr
N.A.I.C.S.: 334290

CREATIVE VISTAS INC.
2100 Forbes Street Units 9, Whitby,
L1N 9T3, ON, Canada
Tel.: (905) 666-8676　　　　　AZ
Web Site:
　https://www.creativevistasinc.com
Year Founded: 1983
CVAS—(OTCIQ)
Sales Range: $1-9.9 Million
Emp.: 47
Electronic Security & Surveillance
Products & Solutions
N.A.I.C.S.: 561621
Sayan Navaratnam *(Chm)*

Subsidiaries:

Creative Vistas Acquisition Corp.　(1)
2100 Forbes St, Whitby, L1N 9T3, ON,
Canada
Tel.: (905) 666-8676
Web Site: http://www.actechnical.com
Emp.: 50
Broadband Services
N.A.I.C.S.: 517111
Fairy Lee *(CFO)*

Subsidiary (Domestic):

AC Technical Systems Ltd.　　(2)
2100 Forbes Street Units-8-10, Whitby, L1N

Creative Vistas Inc.—(Continued)

9T3, ON, Canada   **(100%)**
Tel.: (905) 666-8676
Web Site: https://www.actechnical.com
Security Solutions
N.A.I.C.S.: 561621
Chris Daigle (Mgr-Ops)

Dependable HomeTech   **(1)**
2321 Fairview St, Burlington, L7H 2E3, ON,
Canada
Tel.: (905) 634-7152
Web Site:
http://www.dependablehometech.com
Electrical Contractor
N.A.I.C.S.: 238210
Cheryl Lewis (VP)

Subsidiary (Domestic):

XL Digital Services Inc.   **(2)**
2321 Fairview St, Burlington, L7R 2E3, ON,
Canada
Tel.: (905) 634-7152
Cable Subscription Services
N.A.I.C.S.: 516210

Iview Digital Video Solutions Inc. **(1)**
250 Shields Court Units 12-13, Markham,
L3R 9W7, ON, Canada
Tel.: (905) 940-5533
Web Site: https://www.iviewsolutions.com
Electronic Computer Mfr
N.A.I.C.S.: 334111

OSS IM View Inc.   **(1)**
2321 Fairview St Ste 200, Burlington, L7R
2E3, ON, Canada
Tel.: (905) 634-2206
Web Site: http://www.ossimview.com
Software Consulting Services
N.A.I.C.S.: 541512

CREATIVEFORGE GAMES S.A.
ul Bluszczanska 76/PAW 6, 00-712,
Warsaw, Poland
Tel.: (48) 508379738
Web Site:
https://www.creativeforge.pl
Year Founded: 2011
CFG—(WAR)
Software Development Services
N.A.I.C.S.: 541511
Piotr Karbowski (Pres)

CREATOR CAPITAL LTD.
Floor Two 73 Front St, Hamilton, Ber-
muda
Tel.: (441) 6049472555
Software Development Services
N.A.I.C.S.: 541511
Déborah Fortescue-Merrin (Chm,
Pres, CEO & CFO)

CRECER SEGUROS
Av Jorge Basadre 310 Piso 2, San
Isidro, Lima, Peru
Tel.: (51) 14174400
Web Site:
https://www.crecerseguros.pe
CRECERC1—(LIM)
Rev.: $82,897,471
Assets: $110,056,406
Liabilities: $90,167,598
Net Worth: $19,888,808
Earnings: $4,307,344
Fiscal Year-end: 12/31/23
Insurance Services
N.A.I.C.S.: 524210
Carlota Ponce (Chief Risk Officer)

CRED HOLDING CO., LTD.
2F Tower C Changyuan Tiandi Man-
sion No 18 Suzhou Street, Haidian
District, Beijing, 100080, China
Tel.: (86) 108 260 8847
Web Site:
http://www.credholding.com
600890—(SHG)
Rev.: $1,669,989
Assets: $38,665,608
Liabilities: $3,257,245

Net Worth: $35,408,363
Earnings: ($7,790,729)
Fiscal Year-end: 12/31/20
Holding Company
N.A.I.C.S.: 551112
Lei Zhu (Chm)

**CREDENCE SOUND & VISION
LIMITED**
Sky Scraper B Building Ground Floor
4/697 Bhulabhai Desai Road, Mum-
bai, 400026, Maharashtra, India
Tel.: (91) 2223698333
13064—(CSE)
Audio & Video Equipment Whslr
N.A.I.C.S.: 423690
Akshay P. Sanghavi (Mng Dir)

CREDENT CAPITAL CORP.
20 Sixth Street, New Westminster,
V3L 3Y8, BC, Canada
Tel.: (604) 527-8146   **BM**
Year Founded: 2011
Assets: $140,047
Liabilities: $112,588
Net Worth: $27,459
Earnings: ($54,408)
Fiscal Year-end: 04/30/18
Investment Services
N.A.I.C.S.: 523999
John A. Versfelt (Pres & CEO)

**CREDENT GLOBAL FINANCE
LIMITED**
One BKC G-Block C Wing 6th Floor
Unit No 609 BKC, Mumbai, 400051,
Maharashtra, India
Tel.: (91) 7065500007
Web Site: https://credentglobal.com
539598—(BOM)
Rev.: $47,573
Assets: $823,401
Liabilities: $13,114
Net Worth: $810,286
Earnings: $21,807
Emp.: 3
Fiscal Year-end: 03/31/21
Financial Support Services
N.A.I.C.S.: 523999
Ashok Kumar Jain (Mng Dir)

CREDICORP BANK
Calle 50 Edif Plaza Creicorp Bank,
Obarrio, Panama, Panama
Tel.: (507) 210 1111   **Pa**
Web Site:
http://www.credicorpbank.com
Year Founded: 1992
Commericial Banking
N.A.I.C.S.: 522110
Raymond Harari (Chm)

**CREDICORP CAPITAL PERU
S.A.A.**
Av El Derby 055 Torre 3 Piso 7, San-
tiago de Surco, Lima, 33, Peru
Tel.: (51) 14163333
Web Site:
http://www.credicorpcapital.com
Financial Investment Services
N.A.I.C.S.: 523999
Galantino Gallo (Chief Investment
Officer)

CREDICORP LTD.
Calle Centenario 156 La Molina, 33,
Lima, Peru
Tel.: (51) 13132000   **BM**
Web Site: https://www.credicorp.gcs-
web.com
Year Founded: 1995
BAP—(NYSE)
Rev.: $5,050,643,471
Assets: $64,169,851,693
Liabilities: $55,274,885,277
Net Worth: $8,894,966,416

Earnings: $1,332,584,095
Emp.: 37,074
Fiscal Year-end: 12/31/23
Bank Holding Company
N.A.I.C.S.: 551111
Raimundo Morales Dasso (Vice Chm)

Subsidiaries:

Banco de Credito del Peru SA   **(1)**
Tel.: (51) 13119898
Sales Range: $500-549.9 Million
Emp.: 9,336
Banking Services
N.A.I.C.S.: 522110

Subsidiary (Domestic):

**Empresa Financiera Edyficar
S.A.**   **(2)**
Avenida Paseo De La Republica Nro 3717,
3705 Urb Limatambo, San Isidro, Lima,
Peru
Tel.: (51) 1 319 5555
Web Site: http://www.edyficar.com.pe
Sales Range: $150-199.9 Million
Emp.: 30
Financial Management Services
N.A.I.C.S.: 523999
Ana Maria Zegarra (Gen Mgr)

Credicorp Capital USA Inc.   **(1)**
121 Alhambra Plz Ste 1200, Coral Gables,
FL 33134
Tel.: (305) 446-4446
Financial Services
N.A.I.C.S.: 523999

Credicorp Securities Inc.   **(1)**
121 Alhambra Plz Ste 1200, Coral Gables,
FL 33134
Tel.: (786) 999-1603
Web Site: http://www.credisec.com
Security Brokerage Services
N.A.I.C.S.: 523150

**Pacifico Compania De Seguros Y
Reaseguros S.A.**   **(1)**
Av Juan de Arona 830, San Isidro 27, Lima,
Peru
Tel.: (51) 35000
Web Site: https://www.pacifico.com.pe
Chemical Product Mfr & Distr
N.A.I.C.S.: 325314

Sami Shop S.A.C.   **(1)**
Horacio Cachay Diaz 264, Lima 13, Lima,
Peru
Tel.: (51) 934509655
Web Site: https://www.samishop.pe
E-Commerce Platform Services
N.A.I.C.S.: 541511

Ultralat Capital Market Inc.   **(1)**
801 Brickell Ave Ste 1060, Miami, FL 33131
Tel.: (305) 455-0970
Web Site: http://www.ultralat.com
Financial Services
N.A.I.C.S.: 523999
Carlos Coll (COO)

CREDIMO NV
Weversstraat 6-10, 1730, Asse, Bel-
gium
Tel.: (32) 24541010
Web Site: http://www.credimo.be
Investment Management Service
N.A.I.C.S.: 523940
Jozef De Mey (Chm)

**CREDIT AGRICOLE ALPES
PROVENCE**
25 Chemin des Trois Cypres, FR-
13090, Aix-en-Provence, Cedex 2,
France
Tel.: (33) 432407600
Web Site: https://www.credit-
agricole.fr
CRAP—(EUR)
Sales Range: $450-499.9 Million
Financial Consulting Services
N.A.I.C.S.: 541611
Franck Alexandre (Chm)

CREDIT AGRICOLE CIB AO

11b Degtyarny pereulok, 191144,
Saint Petersburg, Russia
Tel.: (7) 8127791144
Web Site: http://www.ca-cib.ru
Rev.: $40,342,812
Assets: $835,773,732
Liabilities: $757,850,706
Net Worth: $77,923,026
Earnings: $1,174,444
Fiscal Year-end: 12/31/18
Investment Banking Services
N.A.I.C.S.: 523150
Gorelov Dmitriy Vyacheslavovich
(Member-Mgmt Bd & Gen Mgr)

**CREDIT AGRICOLE DU MOR-
BIHAN**
Avenue De Keranguen, 56956,
Vannes, Cedex 9, France
Tel.: (33) 2 97 01 77 77
Web Site: http://www.ca-morbihan.fr
Financial Services
N.A.I.C.S.: 522320
Pierre-Louis Boissiere (CEO)

CREDIT ANDORRA, S.A.
Av Meritxell 80, AD500, Andorra La
Vella, Andorra
Tel.: (376) 88 93 00
Web Site:
http://www.comercial.creditandorra.ad
Year Founded: 1949
Sales Range: $75-99.9 Million
Emp.: 250
Banking Services
N.A.I.C.S.: 522110
Josep Peralba Duro (CEO & Sec)

Subsidiaries:

Banco Alcala, SA   **(1)**
Calle Ortega y Gasset 7 4, 28006, Madrid,
Spain
Tel.: (34) 91 175 07 00
Web Site: http://www.bancoalcala.com
Sales Range: $50-74.9 Million
Emp.: 60
Investment Management Service
N.A.I.C.S.: 523940
Francesc Xavier Cornella Castel (Vice
Chm)

**Banque de Patrimoines Prives,
SA**   **(1)**
30 Boulevard Royal, Luxembourg, 2449,
Luxembourg
Tel.: (352) 272071
Web Site: http://www.bbpp.lu
Sales Range: $50-74.9 Million
Emp.: 30
Banking & Financial Services
N.A.I.C.S.: 521110
Ramonda Gosdep (Mgr)

Beta Capital Management LP   **(1)**
777 Brickell Ave Ste 1201, Miami, FL 33131
Tel.: (305) 358-8844
Web Site: http://www.betacap.com
Sales Range: $50-74.9 Million
Emp.: 22
Investment Management Service
N.A.I.C.S.: 523940
Mirta Estrada (Mgr-Ops)

Crediinvest SA   **(1)**
C/Bonaventura Armengol 6-8, Andorra La
Vella, Andorra
Tel.: (376) 88 95 10
Investment Management Service
N.A.I.C.S.: 523940

**Credit Andorra Panama Securities
SA.**   **(1)**
Regus Business Centre Torres de las
Americas Torre A, Piso 10 Punta Pacifica,
Panama, Panama
Tel.: (507) 306 48 00
Securities Brokerage Services
N.A.I.C.S.: 523150

Credit Andorra Private Bankers **(1)**
Av Meritxell 80, AD500, Andorra La Vella,
Andorra
Tel.: (376) 88 86 50

Web Site:
http://www.creditandorrabankers.com
Banking & Financial Services
N.A.I.C.S.: 521110

Credit Asseurances **(1)**
Siter Rossell 22, Escaldes-Engordany,
AD700, Andorra
Tel.: (376) 88 89 00
Web Site: http://www.creditassegurances.ad
Emp.: 25
Insurance Management Services
N.A.I.C.S.: 524298
Joseph Brunet *(Gen Dir)*

Valira Asset Management SL **(1)**
C/ Goya 23 1, Madrid, 28001, Spain
Tel.: (34) 91 429 08 37
Web Site: http://www.valiraam.com
Sales Range: $50-74.9 Million
Emp.: 12
Investment Management Service
N.A.I.C.S.: 523940

CREDIT ASSOCIATION ORDA CREDIT LLP
47 G llaev str, 160011, Shymkent,
Kazakhstan
Tel.: (7) 7252 54 53 34
Mortgage Services
N.A.I.C.S.: 522310

CREDIT BANK OF MOSCOW OJSC
Tel.: (7) 4957774888   RU
Web Site: http://www.mkb.ru
Year Founded: 1992
CBOM—(MOEX)
Rev.: $4,436,019,316
Assets: $50,475,257,269
Liabilities: $46,712,264,023
Net Worth: $3,762,993,246
Earnings: $646,517,740
Emp.: 11,000
Fiscal Year-end: 12/31/23
Commercial Banking Services
N.A.I.C.S.: 522110
Vladimir A. Chubar *(Chm-Mgmt Bd)*

CREDIT BUREAU ASIA LIMITED
6 Shenton Way 17-10 OUE Downtown 2, Singapore, 068809, Singapore
Tel.: (65) 65656161   SG
Web Site:
https://www.creditbureauasia.com
Year Founded: 1993
TCU—(SES)
Rev.: $41,028,428
Assets: $70,986,408
Liabilities: $19,460,166
Net Worth: $51,526,242
Earnings: $16,675,185
Emp.: 183
Fiscal Year-end: 12/31/23
Financial Investment Services
N.A.I.C.S.: 523999
Kevin Koo *(Founder & Chm)*

Subsidiaries:

Credit Bureau (Singapore) Pte.
Ltd.   **(1)**
2 Shenton Way 20-02 SGX Centre 1, Singapore, 068804, Singapore
Tel.: (65) 65656363
Web Site: https://www.creditbureau.com.sg
Credit Bureau Services
N.A.I.C.S.: 561450

Dun & Bradstreet (D&B) Malaysia
Sdn. Bhd.   **(1)**
Suite A-03-07 Level 3 Empire Tower 1 Empire Subang Jalan SS16/1, 47500, Subang
Jaya, Selangor, Malaysia
Tel.: (60) 356235888
Web Site: http://www.dnb.com.my
Credit Reporting Services
N.A.I.C.S.: 561450

CREDIT CLEAR LIMITED
Building 11 41-43 Bourke Road, Alexandria, 2015, NSW, Australia
Tel.: (61) 1300909934   AU
Web Site:
https://www.creditclear.com.au
Year Founded: 2015
CCR—(ASX)
Rev.: $23,445,263
Assets: $50,103,019
Liabilities: $10,142,792
Net Worth: $39,960,227
Earnings: ($7,210,015)
Fiscal Year-end: 06/30/23
Financial Investment Services
N.A.I.C.S.: 523999
Jason Serafino *(CTO & Chief Product Officer)*

Subsidiaries:

ARMA Group Holdings Pty. Ltd.   **(1)**
Locked Bag 5044, Alexandria, 2015, NSW,
Australia
Tel.: (61) 1300363394
Web Site: https://armagroup.com.au
Banking & Finance Services
N.A.I.C.S.: 525910

Force Legal Pty. Ltd.   **(1)**
Building 11 The Mill Level 841-43 Bourke
Road, Alexandria, 2015, NSW, Australia
Tel.: (61) 283206770
Web Site: https://www.forcelegal.com.au
Litigation & Debt Recovery Services
N.A.I.C.S.: 525910

Oakbridge Lawyers Pty. Ltd.   **(1)**
Suite 5 245 Fullarton Road, Eastwood,
5063, SA, Australia
Tel.: (61) 871001885
Web Site: https://oakbridgelawyers.com.au
Debt Recovery & Insolvency Law Services
N.A.I.C.S.: 525910

CREDIT CORP GROUP LIMITED
Level 15 201 Kent Street, Sydney,
2000, NSW, Australia
Tel.: (61) 286515000   AU
Web Site:
https://www.creditcorp.com.au
CCP—(ASX)
Rev.: $51,117,121
Assets: $884,300,878
Liabilities: $332,971,420
Net Worth: $551,329,458
Earnings: $33,858,841
Emp.: 2,231
Fiscal Year-end: 06/30/24
Debt Management & Support Services
N.A.I.C.S.: 523999
Thomas Beregi *(CEO & Co-Sec)*

Subsidiaries:

CashFirst Pty Ltd   **(1)**
138 Queen Street, Campbelltown, 2560,
NSW, Australia
Tel.: (61) 130 067 7514
Web Site: https://www.cashfirst.com.au
Mortgage Loan Services
N.A.I.C.S.: 522310

Credit Corp Australia Pty Limited **(1)**
Level 11 10 Barrack Street, Sydney, 2000,
NSW, Australia
Tel.: (61) 293473600
Web Site: http://www.creditcorp.com.au
Debt Collection Services
N.A.I.C.S.: 561440

Credit Corp Collections Pty
Limited   **(1)**
Level 11 10 Barrack Street, Sydney, 2001,
NSW, Australia
Tel.: (61) 293473600
Debt Collection Services
N.A.I.C.S.: 561440

Credit Corp Facilities Pty Limited **(1)**
Level 11 10 Barrack Street, Sydney, 2000,
NSW, Australia
Tel.: (61) 293473600
Web Site: http://creditcorp.com

Debt Collection Services
N.A.I.C.S.: 561440

Credit Corp Services Pty Limited **(1)**
Level 11 10 Barrack Street, Sydney, 2000,
NSW, Australia
Tel.: (61) 293473600
Web Site: http://www.creditcorp.com.au
Sales Range: $75-99.9 Million
Emp.: 360
Debt Collection Services
N.A.I.C.S.: 561440

Credit Corp Solutions Inc.   **(1)**
63 E 11400 S Ste 408, Sandy, UT 84070
Web Site: https://www.creditcorponline.com
Financial Services
N.A.I.C.S.: 523999

Credit Plan B Pty Limited   **(1)**
GPO Box 4491, Sydney, 2001, NSW, Australia
Tel.: (61) 130 066 3281
Web Site: https://www.creditplanb.com.au
Financial Support Services
N.A.I.C.S.: 523999

National Credit Management
Limited   **(1)**
123 Glen Osmond Road, Eastwood, 5063,
SA, Australia
Tel.: (61) 28 598 3218
Web Site: https://www.ncml.com.au
Debt Collection & Legal Recovery Services
N.A.I.C.S.: 561440

Thorn Australia Pty Ltd   **(1)**
PO Box 6244, Silverwater, 1811, NSW,
Australia
Tel.: (61) 291015000
Web Site: http://www.thorn.com.au
Sales Range: $550-599.9 Million
Emp.: 150
Electrical Equipment Rental Services
N.A.I.C.S.: 423610

CREDIT CORPORATION (PNG) LIMITED
Ground Level Credit House Cuthbertson Street, PO Box 1787, Port
Moresby, 121, Papua New Guinea
Tel.: (675) 321 7066   PG
Web Site:
http://www.creditcorporation.com.pg
Year Founded: 1978
CCP—(PNGX)
Rev.: $60,260,965
Assets: $440,661,075
Liabilities: $177,271,634
Net Worth: $263,389,441
Earnings: $37,735,831
Emp.: 255
Fiscal Year-end: 12/31/19
Financial Services
N.A.I.C.S.: 523999
Syd Yates *(Chm)*

CREDIT IMMOBILIER ET HOTELIER SA
187 Avenue Hassan II, 20 000, Casablanca, Morocco
Tel.: (212) 522479765
Web Site: http://www.cihbank.ma
Year Founded: 1920
CIH—(CAS)
Sales Range: Less than $1 Million
Commercial Banking Services
N.A.I.C.S.: 522110
Ahmad Rahhou *(CEO)*

CREDIT INTELLIGENCE LIMITED
Ground Floor 16 Ord Street, West
Perth, 6005, WA, Australia
Tel.: (61) 297139495   AU
Web Site: https://www.ci1.com.au
CI1—(ASX)
Rev.: $6,388,783
Assets: $8,457,721
Liabilities: $2,596,597
Net Worth: $5,861,124
Earnings: ($7,374,012)

Fiscal Year-end: 06/30/24
Debt-Restructuring & Personal Insolvency Management Services
N.A.I.C.S.: 541611
Jimmie Wong *(Chm, CEO & Mng Dir)*

Subsidiaries:

Chapter Two Holdings Pty. Ltd.   **(1)**
Unit 601 56 Pitt St, Sydney, 2000, NSW,
Australia
Tel.: (61) 1300344433
Web Site: https://chaptertwo.com.au
Debt Solutions Services
N.A.I.C.S.: 522390

Hong Kong I.V.A. Consultants
Limited   **(1)**
5th Floor Double Building 22 Stanley Street,
Central, China (Hong Kong)
Tel.: (852) 61060330
Web Site: https://www.hkiva.com
Other Management Consulting Services
N.A.I.C.S.: 541618

Hup Hoe Credit Pte. Ltd.   **(1)**
1 Rochor Canal 01-01 Sim Lim Square Taxi
Stand, Singapore, 188504, Singapore
Tel.: (65) 63969119
Web Site: https://www.huphoecredit.com.sg
Personal & Business Loan Services
N.A.I.C.S.: 522390

ICS Funding Pte. Ltd.   **(1)**
2 Kallang Avenue 05-06 CT Hub, Singapore, 339407, Singapore
Tel.: (65) 82922088
Web Site: https://icsfunding.com.sg
Business Term Loan Services
N.A.I.C.S.: 522291

CREDIT MOBILIER DE MONACO S.A.
15 avenue de Grande-Bretagne, Monaco, 98000, Monaco
Tel.: (377) 93 50 52 08   MC
Web Site:
http://www.creditmobilier.com
Year Founded: 1907
Sales Range: $10-24.9 Million
Emp.: 6
Pawnbroking & Consumer Lending
Services
N.A.I.C.S.: 522299
Pierpaolo Caretta *(Mng Dir)*

CREDIT ORGANIZATION OF SMALL & MEDIUM-SIZED ENTERPRISES CO., LTD.
1-10-7 Ryogoku, Sumida-ku, 130-0026, Tokyo, Japan
Tel.: (81) 356253190   JP
Year Founded: 1974
Sales Range: $10-24.9 Million
Emp.: 105
Financial Business Credit Services
N.A.I.C.S.: 522299
Takaaki Hiramatsu *(Dir-Gen Affairs)*

CREDIT RATING & COLLECTION COMPANY KSCC
Al-Sharq-Ahmad Al-Jaber St Al-Awadi
Towers Tower No 3 First floor, PO
Box 1432, Safat, Kuwait, 13015, Kuwait
Tel.: (965) 1802230
Web Site: http://www.crckt.com
Year Founded: 1998
TAHSSILAT—(KUW)
Rev.: $1,764,909
Assets: $17,188,888
Liabilities: $655,692
Net Worth: $16,533,196
Earnings: $278,261
Emp.: 31
Fiscal Year-end: 12/31/22
Credit Rating, Risk Management &
Debt Recovery Services
N.A.I.C.S.: 561450

CREDIT SAISON CO., LTD.

Credit Saison Co., Ltd.—(Continued)

Sunshine 60 Bldg 1-1 Higashi-Ikebukuro 3-chome, Toshima-ku, Tokyo, 170-6073, Japan
Tel.: (81) 339882110
Web Site:
https://corporate.saisoncard.co.jp
Year Founded: 1951
8253—(TKS)
Rev.: $647,462,720
Assets: $28,659,981,720
Liabilities: $23,916,573,010
Net Worth: $4,743,408,710
Earnings: $482,444,070
Emp.: 3,783
Fiscal Year-end: 03/31/24
Credit Card Issuer
N.A.I.C.S.: 522210
Tatsunari Okamoto *(Mng Exec Officer & Gen Mgr-Fin Div & Head-Fin Div)*

Subsidiaries:

Casalago Co., Ltd. **(1)**
Room A 7th Floor Kanai Building 2-29-10 Minamiikebukuro, Toshima-ku, Tokyo, 171-0022, Japan
Tel.: (81) 339873302
Web Site: http://www.casalago.jp
Lifestyle Product Retailer
N.A.I.C.S.: 458110

Concerto Inc. **(1)**
3-1-1 Higashiikebukuro Sunshine 60 37F, Toshima-ku, Tokyo, 170-6037, Japan
Tel.: (81) 339887787
Web Site: http://www.concerto-inc.jp
Emp.: 513
Real Estate Services
N.A.I.C.S.: 531390

Idemitsu Credit Co., Ltd. **(1)**
18th floor of Ryogoku City Core 2-10-14 Ryogoku, Sumida-ku, Tokyo, 130-0026, Japan
Tel.: (81) 356247312
Web Site: https://www.idemitsucard.com
Credit Card Services
N.A.I.C.S.: 522210

JPN Holdings Company, Limited **(1)**
3-1-1 Higashiikebukuro Toshima-ku, Tokyo, 170-6039, Japan **(100%)**
Tel.: (81) 359921119
Holding Company
N.A.I.C.S.: 551112

Jpn Collection Service Co., Ltd. **(1)**
Sunshine 60 53F 3-1-1 Higashi-Ikebukuro, Toshima-ku, Tokyo, 170-6053, Japan
Tel.: (81) 368305180
Web Site: https://www.saison-servicer.co.jp
Financial Banking Services
N.A.I.C.S.: 522320

Kurashino Saison Co., Ltd. **(1)**
2-60-3 Higashiikebukuro Grace Rotary Building 6th Floor, Toshima-ku, Tokyo, 170-0013, Japan
Tel.: (81) 359928400
Web Site: http://www.kurashi-saison.co.jp
Emp.: 270
Property Maintenance Services
N.A.I.C.S.: 561790

Omnibus K.K. **(1)**
1-4-4 Higashiyama Meguro Higashiyama Building 3F, Meguro-ku, Tokyo, 153-0043, Japan
Tel.: (81) 357258317
Web Site: http://www.e-omnibus.jp
Marketing Consulting Services
N.A.I.C.S.: 541613

Saison Asset Management Co., Ltd. **(1)**
3-1-1 Higashiikebukuro Sunshine 60 / 48F, Toshima-ku, Tokyo, 170-6048, Japan
Tel.: (81) 339888668
Web Site: http://www.saison-am.co.jp
Asset Management Services
N.A.I.C.S.: 523940

Saison Business Support, Inc. **(1)**
11-25 Kagoshima Fukoku Seimei Takamibaba Building 8F Nishisengokucho, Kagoshima, 892-0847, Japan

Tel.: (81) 992040988
Web Site: https://saison-bs.co.jp
Billing Agency Services
N.A.I.C.S.: 561440

Saison Fundex Corporation **(1)**
3-1-1 Higashiikebukuro Sunshine 60 37th floor, Toshima-ku, Tokyo, 170-6037, Japan
Tel.: (81) 339881883
Web Site: http://www.fundex.co.jp
Real Estate Services
N.A.I.C.S.: 531390

Saison Information Systems Co., Ltd. **(1)**
19F Akasaka Intercity AIR 1-8-1 Akasaka Minato-ku, Tokyo, 107-0052, Japan
Tel.: (81) 363702000
Rev.: $157,676,058
Assets: $149,961,524
Liabilities: $56,003,017
Net Worth: $93,958,507
Earnings: $3,985,344
Emp.: 757
Fiscal Year-end: 03/31/2024
Software Development Services
N.A.I.C.S.: 541511
Kazuhiro Uchida *(Pres & CEO)*

Saison Partners Co., Ltd. **(1)**
49th Floor Sunshine 60 3-1-1 Higashiikuro, Toshima-ku, Tokyo, 170-6049, Japan
Tel.: (81) 367056901
Web Site: https://saison-partners.co.jp
Emp.: 18
Credit Management & Financial Services
N.A.I.C.S.: 541611

Saison Personalplus Co., Ltd. **(1)**
1-33-8 Higashiikebukuro NBF Ikebukuro Tower 6F, Toshima-ku, Tokyo, 170-0013, Japan
Tel.: (81) 339882123
Web Site: http://www.saison-psp.co.jp
Staff Recruitment Services
N.A.I.C.S.: 561311

Stock Point, Inc. **(1)**
1-4-5 Roppongi, Ark Hills South Tower 16F WeWork Minato-ku, Tokyo, 1060032, Japan
Tel.: (81) 358606167
Web Site: https://www.stockpoint.co.jp
Stock Trading Services
N.A.I.C.S.: 512191

Takashimaya Credit Co. Ltd. **(1)**
2-4-1 Nihonbashi, Chuo-Ku, Tokyo, 103-0027, Japan
Tel.: (81) 359961397
Web Site: http://www.t-card.co.jp
Emp.: 161
Credit Card Issuing
N.A.I.C.S.: 522210

Wine&Wine Culture Co., Ltd. **(1)**
4-13-5 Akasaka, Minato-ku, Tokyo, 107-0052, Japan
Tel.: (81) 362291727
Web Site: https://www.wincle.com
Beverage Whslr
N.A.I.C.S.: 424820

CREDITACCESS GRAMEEN LIMITED
No 49 46th Cross 8Th Block Jayanagar, Next To Rajalakshmi Kalayana Mantap, Bengaluru, 560070, Karnataka, India
Tel.: (91) 8022637300
Web Site:
https://www.creditaccessgrameen.in
Year Founded: 1999
541770—(BOM)
Rev.: $336,618,555
Assets: $2,055,586,260
Liabilities: $1,537,380,390
Net Worth: $518,205,870
Earnings: $17,936,100
Emp.: 10,625
Fiscal Year-end: 03/31/21
Financial Services
N.A.I.C.S.: 523999
Udaya Kumar Hebbar *(CEO & Mng Dir)*

Subsidiaries:

Madura Micro Finance Limited **(1)**

634 Karumuttu Centre 6th Floor Anna Salai, Nandanam, Chennai, 600035, India
Tel.: (91) 444 683 8989
Web Site:
https://www.maduramicrofinance.com
Banking Finance Services
N.A.I.C.S.: 523150
Tara Thiagarajan *(Mng Dir & Chm)*

CREDITCHECK PARTNERS PRIVATE LIMITED
104 Shah & Nahar Estate Off E Moses Road, Worli, Mumbai, 400 018, India
Tel.: (91) 9820086712
Web Site:
https://www.creditcheckpartner.com
Year Founded: 2010
Investment Management Service
N.A.I.C.S.: 523999

CREDITO EMILIANO S.P.A.
Via Emilia San Pietro 4, 42121, Reggio Emilia, Italy
Tel.: (39) 0522582111   **IT**
Web Site: https://www.credem.it
Year Founded: 1910
CE—(ITA)
Rev.: $1,452,808
Assets: $69,580,097
Liabilities: $60,684,208
Net Worth: $8,895,889
Earnings: $247,607
Emp.: 6,219
Fiscal Year-end: 12/31/20
Bank Holding Company
N.A.I.C.S.: 551111
Enrico Corradi *(Deputy Chm)*

Subsidiaries:

Abaxbank SpA **(1)**
Corso Monforte 34, 20122, Milan, Italy
Tel.: (39) 02774261
Web Site: http://www.abaxbank.com
Commericial Banking
N.A.I.C.S.: 522110

Anteprima Srl **(1)**
Via Che Guevara 4, 42100, Modena, Reggio Emilia, Italy
Tel.: (39) 0522285260
Web Site: http://www.agenzia-anteprima.it
Insurance Agencies & Brokerages
N.A.I.C.S.: 524210
Ferdinando Rebecchi *(Pres)*

Banca Euromobiliare SpA **(1)**
Via S Margherita 9, 20121, Milan, MI, Italy
Tel.: (39) 0263761
Web Site: http://www.bancaeuro.it
Commericial Banking
N.A.I.C.S.: 522110

Credem International (LUX) S.A. **(1)**
10 12 Ave Pasteur, 2310, Luxembourg, Luxembourg
Tel.: (352) 4759591
Sales Range: $50-74.9 Million
Emp.: 25
Financial Services
N.A.I.C.S.: 522299
Lorenzo Modestini *(Gen Mgr)*

Credem Private Equity Sgr SpA **(1)**
Via Che Guevara 4, 42123, Reggio Emilia, Italy
Tel.: (39) 0522582203
Web Site: http://www.credempriveq.it
Sales Range: $50-74.9 Million
Emp.: 5
Real Estate Investment Trust
N.A.I.C.S.: 525990
Enrico Corradi *(Chm)*

Credemassicurazioni SpA **(1)**
Via Luigi Sani 3, 42121, Reggio Emilia, Italy
Tel.: (39) 0522586050
Web Site: http://www.credemassicurazioni.it
Insurance Agencies & Brokerages
N.A.I.C.S.: 524210

Credemfactor SpA **(1)**
Via E Che Guevara 4/B, 42123, Reggio Emilia, Italy
Tel.: (39) 0522326911

Web Site: http://www.credemfactor.it
Credit Factoring & Loan Management Services
N.A.I.C.S.: 522390

Credemleasing S.p.A. **(1)**
Via Mirabello 2, 42122, Reggio Emilia, Italy
Tel.: (39) 0522402600
Web Site: http://www.credemleasing.it
Saloo Rango: $50-74.0 Million
Emp.: 15
Credit Intermediation
N.A.I.C.S.: 522390

Credemtel SpA **(1)**
via Togliatti 36/1, Montecavolo di Quattro Castella, 42020, Reggio Emilia, Italy
Tel.: (39) 0522203040
Web Site: http://www.credemtel.it
Data Processing Hosting & Related Services
N.A.I.C.S.: 518210

Credemvita SpA **(1)**
Via Luigi Sani 1, 42121, Reggio Emilia, Italy
Tel.: (39) 0522586000
Web Site: http://www.credemvita.it
Sales Range: $50-74.9 Million
Emp.: 35
Direct Life Insurance Carriers
N.A.I.C.S.: 524113

Credito Emiliano SpA **(1)**
Via Emilia San Pietro 4, 42121, Reggio Emilia, Italy
Tel.: (39) 0522582111
Web Site: http://www.credem.it
Commercial Banking
N.A.I.C.S.: 522110

Euromobiliare Alternative Investment Sgr SpA **(1)**
Corso Monforte 34, 20121, Milan, Italy
Tel.: (39) 02620841
Web Site: http://www.euroaisgr.it
Sales Range: $50-74.9 Million
Emp.: 70
Financial Investment Activities
N.A.I.C.S.: 523999
Fulvio Albarelli *(Mng Dir)*

Euromobiliare Asset Management Sgr SpA **(1)**
Corso Monsorpee 34, 20122, Milan, Italy
Tel.: (39) 02620841
Web Site: http://www.eurosgr.it
Sales Range: $50-74.9 Million
Emp.: 16
Open-End Investment Funds
N.A.I.C.S.: 525910
Matteo Mattei Gentili *(Chm)*

Euromobiliare Fiduciaria SpA **(1)**
Corso Monforte 34, 20122, Milan, Italy
Tel.: (39) 026328171
Web Site:
http://www.euromobiliarefiduciaria.it
Holding Company
N.A.I.C.S.: 551112

Magazzini Generali Delle Tagliate (M.G.T.) SpA **(1)**
Via P Togliatti 36/1, Montecavolo di Quattro Castell, Modena, RE, Italy
Tel.: (39) 0522880634
General Warehousing & Storage
N.A.I.C.S.: 493110
William Bizzarri *(Gen Mgr)*

CREDITO REAL S.A.B. DE C.V.
Avenida Insurgentes sur 730, Piso 20 Colonia del Valle Norte, 3103, Mexico, Mexico
Tel.: (52) 5553405200
Web Site: https://www.creal.mx
Year Founded: 1993
CRQDQ—(OTCEM)
Rev.: $525,090,757
Assets: $3,532,016,380
Liabilities: $2,724,894,821
Net Worth: $807,121,559
Earnings: $40,421,839
Emp.: 624
Fiscal Year-end: 12/31/20
Consumer Lending
N.A.I.C.S.: 522291

Angel Francisco Romanos Berrondo
(Chm & CEO)

Subsidiaries:

AFS Acceptance LLC　　　　　　(1)
1475 W Cypress Creek Rd Ste 300, Fort
Lauderdale, FL 33309　　　　　　**(65%)**
Tel.: (954) 615-1400
Web Site: http://www.afsacceptance.com
Sales Range: $10-24.9 Million
Emp.: 78
Automobile Finance Services
N.A.I.C.S.: 522220
Eric Van Eaton *(VP-Loan Servicing)*

CREDITO VALTELLINESE SO-CIETA COOPERATIVA

Piazza Quadrivio 8, 23100, Sondrio,
Italy
Tel.: (39) 0342 522111　　　　　　IT
Web Site: http://www.creval.it
Year Founded: 1908
Sales Range: $650-699.9 Million
Bank Holding Company
N.A.I.C.S.: 551111

Subsidiaries:

Banca Cattolica S.p.A.　　　　　　(1)
Via Cardinal Salotti 6, 01027, Montefias-
cone, VT, Italy
Tel.: (39) 07618381
Web Site: http://www.bancacattolica.it
Commercial Banking Services
N.A.I.C.S.: 522110

Bancaperta S.p.A.　　　　　　　　(1)
Via Ragazzi Del 99 12, 23100, Sondrio,
Italy
Tel.: (39) 0342522111
Commercial Banking Services
N.A.I.C.S.: 522110
Norberto Gualteroni *(Pres)*

Bankadati Servizi Informatici
S.p.A.　　　　　　　　　　　　　　(1)
Via Trento 22, Sondrio, 23100, Italy
Tel.: (39) 0342522111
Emp.: 400
Banking Software Development Services
N.A.I.C.S.: 541511
Giovanni De Censi *(Pres)*

Cassa di Risparmio di Fano
S.p.A.　　　　　　　　　　　　　　(1)
Piazza Xx Settembre 19, 61032, Fano, Pe-
saro e Urbino, Italy
Tel.: (39) 0721886400
Web Site: http://www.creval.it
Sales Range: $200-249.9 Million
Emp.: 350
Banking Services
N.A.I.C.S.: 522110

Credito Artigiano S.p.A.　　　　　(1)
Piazza San Fedele 4, 20121, Milan, Italy
Tel.: (39) 02806371
Web Site: http://www.creval.it
Sales Range: $1-9.9 Million
Emp.: 70
Banking
N.A.I.C.S.: 523150
Luciano Camagni *(Gen Mgr)*

Credito Piemontese S.p.A.　　　　(1)
Corso Re Umberto 21-Bis, 10128, Turin,
Italy
Tel.: (39) 01119782601
Banking Services
N.A.I.C.S.: 522110

Stelline Servizi Immobiliari S.p.A.　(1)
Via Cesura 3, 23100, Sondrio, Italy
Tel.: (39) 0342522111
Web Site: http://www.creval.it
Sales Range: $50-74.9 Million
Emp.: 55
Real Estate Manangement Services
N.A.I.C.S.: 531210
Enzo Rocca *(Gen Dir)*

CREDITOS Y AHORRO CREDI-FINANCIERA S.A., COMPANIA DE FINANCIAMIENTO

Cra 10 64 44, Bogota, 11001, Colombia

Tel.: (57) 14823382
Web Site:
　　http://www.credifinanciera.com.co
Financial Services & Holding Com-
pany
N.A.I.C.S.: 551111
Alba Rico *(Dir-Ops)*

Subsidiaries:

Banco ProCredit Columbia S.A.　(1)
Av Calle 39 No 13a - 16, Bogota, Colombia
Tel.: (57) 15954040
Web Site: http://www.bancoprocredit.com
Finance & Banking Services
N.A.I.C.S.: 522110

CREDITWEST FAKTORING A.S.

Buyukdere cad Enka Binasi No 108
Kat 1, Esentepe, 34394, Istanbul,
Turkiye
Tel.: (90) 2123561910
Web Site:
　　https://www.creditwest.com.tr
CRDFA—(IST)
Sales Range: $75-99.9 Million
Financial Factoring Services
N.A.I.C.S.: 522299
Ali Altinbas *(Chm)*

CREDO BRANDS MARKETING LIMITED

B-8 MIDC Central Road Marol Next
to MIDC Police Station Andheri E,
Mumbai, 400093, Maharashtra, India
Tel.: (91) 61417200
Web Site: https://www.credobrands.in
Year Founded: 1999
544058—(BOM)
Rev.: $13,138,795
Assets: $8,002,230
Liabilities: $5,002,397
Net Worth: $2,999,833
Earnings: $285,947
Emp.: 20
Fiscal Year-end: 03/31/23
Clothing Products Distr
N.A.I.C.S.: 458110

CREDO INTERACTIVE INC.

4612 Strathcona Rd, North Vancou-
ver, V7G 1G3, BC, Canada
Tel.: (604) 291-6717
Web Site:
　　https://www.charactermotion.com
Rev.: $55,000,000
Emp.: 20
Software & Animation Developers
N.A.I.C.S.: 513210
Bart Copeland *(Pres & CEO)*

CREED CORPORATION

19F Hibiya Park Front 2-1-6
Uchisaiwai-cho, Chiyoda-ku, Tokyo,
100-0011, Japan
Tel.: (81) 5017460975
Web Site: http://www.creed-
　　group.com
Year Founded: 1996
Sales Range: $400-449.9 Million
Emp.: 150
Real Estate & Investment Services
N.A.I.C.S.: 531300
Toshihiko Muneyoshi *(Founder & Mng Dir)*

Subsidiaries:

Creed Asia (Cambodia) Co., Ltd.　(1)
17F Phnom Penh Tower 445 Monivong Blvd
St 93/232 Sangkat Boeung Pralit, Prampir
Meakkakra, Phnom Penh, Cambodia
Tel.: (855) 23964016
Real Estate Investment Services
N.A.I.C.S.: 531210

Creed Asia Development (M) Sdn.
Bhd.　　　　　　　　　　　　　　(1)

Suite 13A 02A Level13A Johor Bahru City
Square 106-108, Jalan Wong Ah Fook,
80000, Johor Bahru, Johor, Malaysia
Tel.: (60) 72230362
Real Estate Investment Services
N.A.I.C.S.: 531210
Takashi Eguchi *(VP & Mgr-Fin & Admin)*

Creed Asia Investment Co., Ltd.　(1)
411 Central Park Tower La Tour Shinjuku
6-15-1 Nishi-Shinjuku, Shinjuku, Tokyo,
160-0023, Japan
Tel.: (81) 353216511
Real Estate Investment Services
N.A.I.C.S.: 531210

Creed Capital Management and Re-
search, Inc.　　　　　　　　　　(1)
Kasumigaseki Building 20th Floor, 3-2-5
Kasumigaseki Chiyoda-ku, Tokyo, Japan
Tel.: (81) 335003466
Web Site: http://www.creed.co.jp
Sales Range: $25-49.9 Million
Emp.: 3
Management Consulting Services
N.A.I.C.S.: 541618

Creed Holdings Pte.Ltd.　　　　　(1)
Unit 006 4F Centec Tower 72-74 Nguyen
Thi Minh Khai Street District 3, Ho Chi Minh
City, Vietnam
Tel.: (84) 862994229
Real Estate Investment Services
N.A.I.C.S.: 531210

Creed Hotel Management
Corporation　　　　　　　　　　(1)
Shimbashi 5-chome Building 6th Floor,
5-9-1 Shimbashi Minato-ku, 105-0004, To-
kyo, Japan
Tel.: (81) 354039600
Web Site: http://www.creed.co.jp
Management Consulting Services
N.A.I.C.S.: 541618

Creed Investments Pte. Ltd.　　　(1)
230 Orchard Road 07-232 Faber House,
Singapore, 238854, Singapore
Tel.: (65) 67348007
Real Estate Investment Services
N.A.I.C.S.: 531210

ORO Financecorp PLC.　　　　　(1)
No 147 Monireth Blvd Sangkat Boeng Sa-
lang, Tuol Kouk, Phnom Penh, Cambodia
Tel.: (855) 23955567
Web Site: http://www.orofinancecorp.com
Financial Management Services
N.A.I.C.S.: 523940
Fukada Tsuyoshi *(CEO)*

CREEK & RIVER CO., LTD.

SHINTORA-DORI CORE 4-1-1 Shim-
bashi, Minato-ku, Tokyo, 105-0004,
Japan
Tel.: (81) 345500011
Web Site: http://www.cri.co.jp
4763—(TKS)
Rev.: $353,074,910
Assets: $180,213,620
Liabilities: $68,581,570
Net Worth: $111,632,050
Earnings: $18,845,220
Emp.: 2,176
Fiscal Year-end: 02/29/24
Management Consulting Services
N.A.I.C.S.: 541618
Yukihiro Ikawa *(Pres)*

Subsidiaries:

C&R Legal Agency, Co., Ltd.　　(1)
Shintora-Dori Core 4-1-1, Shinbashi Minato-
ku, Tokyo, 105-0004, Japan
Tel.: (81) 34 550 0095
Agency Business Services
N.A.I.C.S.: 561439

CREEK & RIVER KOREA Co.,
Ltd.　　　　　　　　　　　　　　(1)
4F Namjung B / D 12 Gukhoe-daero 74-gil,
Yeongdeungpo-gu, Seoul, Korea (South)
Tel.: (82) 27618901
Web Site: http://www.crikorea.com
Comic Book Publisher
N.A.I.C.S.: 513120

CREEK & RIVER SHANGHAI Co.,
Ltd.　　　　　　　　　　　　　　(1)
Room 5H Xinda Building No 1399 Beijing
West Road, Jing an District, Shanghai,
200040, China
Tel.: (86) 2161905200
Web Site: https://www.crichina.com.cn
Business Consulting Services
N.A.I.C.S.: 541618

Leading Edge Co., Ltd.　　　　　(1)
13th floor Shintora-dori CORE 4-1-1 Shim-
bashi, Minato-ku, Tokyo, 105-0004, Japan
Tel.: (81) 345500020
Web Site: https://www.leadinge.co.jp
Software Development Services
N.A.I.C.S.: 541511

Medical Principle Co., Ltd.　　　(1)
Shintora-dori CORE 4-1-1 Shimbashi,
Minato-ku, Tokyo, 105-0004, Japan
Tel.: (81) 345656100
Web Site: https://www.medical-
　　principle.co.jp
Medical Staff Recruitment Services
N.A.I.C.S.: 561311

CREEMA LTD.

2-12-5 Kita-Aoyama, Minato-Ku, To-
kyo, 107-0061, Japan
Tel.: (81) 364470105
Web Site: http://www.akamaru-
　　holdings.co.jp
Year Founded: 2009
4017—(TKS)
Rev.: $17,781,720
Assets: $25,438,920
Liabilities: $18,348,920
Net Worth: $7,090,000
Earnings: $560,110
Emp.: 90
Fiscal Year-end: 02/29/24
E Commerce Site Operator
N.A.I.C.S.: 423690
Kotaro Marubayashi *(Founder, Pres & CEO)*

CREEPY JAR S.A.

Czluchowska 9, 01 360, Warsaw,
Poland
Tel.: (48) 223000825
Web Site: https://www.creepyjar.com
Year Founded: 2016
CRJ—(WAR)
Rev.: $13,129,042
Assets: $24,801,498
Liabilities: $886,344
Net Worth: $23,915,153
Earnings: $8,717,413
Fiscal Year-end: 12/31/22
Software Development Services
N.A.I.C.S.: 541511
Krzysztof Kwiatek *(Co-Founder, Pres & CEO)*

CREIGHTONS PLC

1210 Lincoln Road, Werrington, Pe-
terborough, PE4 6ND, Cambridgesh-
ire, United Kingdom
Tel.: (44) 1733281000　　　　　　UK
Web Site:
　　https://www.creightons.com
CRL—(LSE)
Rev.: $80,192,992
Assets: $62,740,920
Liabilities: $33,815,848
Net Worth: $28,925,072
Earnings: $4,077,832
Fiscal Year-end: 03/31/22
Beauty Product Mfr
N.A.I.C.S.: 325620
William O. McIlroy *(Chm & CEO)*

Subsidiaries:

Potter & Moore Innovations
Limited　　　　　　　　　　　　(1)
1210 Lincoln Rd, Werrington, Peterborough,
PE4 6ND, Cambridgeshire, United Kingdom
Tel.: (44) 1733281000
Web Site: http://www.potterandmoore.com

Creightons plc—(Continued)

Emp.: 200
Cosmetics Mfr & Distr
N.A.I.C.S.: 325620
Bernard J. Johnson *(Mng Dir)*

CRELANCO CVBA

Sylvain Dupuislaan 251, 1070, Brussels, Belgium
Tel.: (32) 2 558 7111
Bank Holding Company
N.A.I.C.S.: 551111
Jean-Pierre Dubois *(Chm)*

Subsidiaries:

Crelan SA/NV   (1)
Boulevard Sylvain Dupuis 251, 1070, Anderlecht, Belgium
Tel.: (32) 2 558 7111
Web Site: http://www.crelan.be
Banking Services
N.A.I.C.S.: 522110
Philippe Voisin *(CEO)*

CREMONINI S.P.A.

Via Modena 53, Castelvetro di Modena, 41014, Modena, Italy
Tel.: (39) 059754611   IT
Web Site: http://www.cremonini.com
Year Founded: 1963
Sales Range: $1-4.9 Billion
Emp.: 16,000
Fresh, Canned & Frozen Beef
N.A.I.C.S.: 311421
Luigi Cremonini *(Chm)*

Subsidiaries:

As. Ca. S.p.A.   (1)
Via Trattati di Roma 64, villanova di castenaso, 40055, Bologna, Italy
Tel.: (39) 0516055011
Web Site: http://www.asca-bo.it
Frozen Food Product Distr
N.A.I.C.S.: 424470
Aldo Setti *(Pres)*

Baldini Adriatica Pesca S.r.l.   (1)
Via Pennabilli 6, Riccione, 47838, Rimini, Italy
Tel.: (39) 0541605657
Frozen Food Product Distr
N.A.I.C.S.: 424470

Busseto Foods, Inc.   (1)
1090 West Church St, Fresno, CA 93706
Tel.: (559) 485-9882
Web Site: http://www.busseto.com
Sales Range: $25-49.9 Million
Emp.: 50
Mfr of Salami
N.A.I.C.S.: 311612
Randy Hergenroeder *(CFO & Controller)*

Cremonini Chef Iberica S.A.   (1)
Paseo de la Castellana 151 bis 1, 28046, Madrid, Spain
Tel.: (34) 915064390
Web Site: http://www.cremonini.es
Railway Catering Services
N.A.I.C.S.: 722310
Miguel Nigorra *(Dir Gen)*

Cremonini Rail Iberica s.a.   (1)
Calle Comercio 12, 28045, Madrid, Spain
Tel.: (34) 915064390
Web Site: http://www.cremonini.it
On-Board Railway Catering Services
N.A.I.C.S.: 722511

Cremonini Restauration S.A.S.   (1)
Rue Andree Gide 17, 75015, Paris, France
Tel.: (33) 142797776
Web Site: http://www.cremonini.fr
Catering Services
N.A.I.C.S.: 722320

Cremonini S.p.A. - Administrative
Headquarters   (1)
Via Modena 53, Castelvetro di Modena, 41014, Modena, Italy
Tel.: (39) 059754611
Web Site: http://www.cremonini.com
Office Administrative Services
N.A.I.C.S.: 561110

Frimo S.A.M.   (1)
1 Rue du Gabian Le Thales, Monte Carlo, 98000, Monaco   (51%)
Tel.: (377) 93104193
Sales Range: $50-74.9 Million
Emp.: 10
Meat & Meat Product Whslr
N.A.I.C.S.: 424470
Mirco Albisecci *(Gen Mgr)*

Ges.Car. S.r.l.   (1)
Viale Europa 10, Ospedaletto Lodigiano, Lodi, 26864, Italy
Tel.: (39) 03779791
Sales Range: $25-49.9 Million
Emp.: 100
Rendering & Meat Byproduct Processing
N.A.I.C.S.: 311613

Guardamiglio S.r.l.   (1)
Via Coppalati n 52, Piacenza, 29100, Italy
Tel.: (39) 0523596111
Frozen Meat Product Distr
N.A.I.C.S.: 424470

Inalca S.p.A.   (1)
Via Spilamberto 30/c, Castelvetro di Modena, 41014, Modena, Italy   (71.6%)
Tel.: (39) 059755111
Web Site: http://www.inalca.it
Sales Range: $200-249.9 Million
Emp.: 1,000
Meat Processing Service
N.A.I.C.S.: 311613
Paolo Boni *(Co-CEO)*

Subsidiary (Domestic):

Bell Carni S.r.l.   (2)
Via Eridania 58, Stienta, Rovigo, 45039, Italy
Tel.: (39) 0425746211
Beef Slaughtering Services
N.A.I.C.S.: 311615

Fiorani & C, S.p.A   (2)
Via Coppalati N 52, 29122, Piacenza, Italy
Tel.: (39) 0523 596111
Meat Product Mfr & Distr
N.A.I.C.S.: 311615

Subsidiary (Non-US):

Inalca Algerie S.a.r.l.   (2)
Route de la gare BP N 64, Corso, Boumerdes, Algeria
Tel.: (213) 24 84 00 84
Web Site: http://www.inalca-algerie.com
Meat Product Distr
N.A.I.C.S.: 445240

Inalca Angola L.t.d.a.   (2)
Rua Dom Manuel Nunes Gabrie, Luanda, Angola
Tel.: (244) 222 260601
Web Site: http://www.inalcaangola.com
Food Products Distr
N.A.I.C.S.: 424490
Marco Mucci *(Mgr-Warehouse)*

Inalca Kinshasa S.p.r.l.   (2)
N 935 Avenue Bobozo Quartier Ndolo, BP 5043, Gombe, Kinshasa, Congo, Democratic Republic of
Tel.: (243) 99 99 23 519
Web Site: http://www.avendre.cd
Canned Food Distr
N.A.I.C.S.: 424490
Sunil Dath *(Dir-Fin)*

Subsidiary (Domestic):

Italia Alimentari S.p.A.   (2)
Via Europa 14, 43011, Busseto, Italy
Tel.: (39) 0376 6801
Web Site: http://www.italiaalimentari.it
Meat Products Retailer
N.A.I.C.S.: 445240
Simona Marolla *(Mgr-Mktg)*

Subsidiary (Non-US):

Montana Alimentari GMBH   (3)
Kirschstrasse 20, 80999, Munich, Germany
Tel.: (49) 8945244300
Web Site: http://www.montana-gmbh.de
Preserved Food Product Mfr
N.A.I.C.S.: 311412

Subsidiary (Domestic):

Realbeef S.r.l.   (2)

Strada Consortile Asi Zona Industriale Valle Ufita, Flumeri, 83040, Avellino, Italy
Tel.: (39) 0825474311
Web Site: http://www.fioraniec.com
Meat Product Distr
N.A.I.C.S.: 424470

Interjet S.r.l.   (1)
Via Belvedere 23, Castelvetro di Modena, 41014, Modena, Italy
Tel.: (39) 051406931
Web Site: http://www.interjet.it
Oil Transportation Services
N.A.I.C.S.: 481212

Marr Russia L.l.c.   (1)
5 Vostochnaya str, Odintsovo, 143006, Moscow, Russia
Tel.: (7) 4957853944
Web Site: http://www.marr.ru
Meat Product Mfr & Distr
N.A.I.C.S.: 311615
Pavel Ivanov *(Dir-Logistics)*

Marr S.p.A.   (1)
Via Spagna 20, 47921, Rimini, Italy   (58.8%)
Tel.: (39) 0541746111
Web Site: https://www.marr.it
Rev.: $2,027,709,907
Assets: $1,254,545,651
Liabilities: $886,040,363
Net Worth: $368,505,288
Earnings: $28,653,141
Emp.: 957
Fiscal Year-end: 12/31/2022
Food Products Distr to Foodservice Operators
N.A.I.C.S.: 424410
Pierpaolo Rossi *(Mgr-Fin, Controlling & Admin)*

Subsidiary (Non-US):

Marr Foodservice Iberica S.A.   (2)
Goya - Esc A 3 1 99, Madrid, 28009, Spain
Tel.: (34) 914321212
Frozen Food Product Distr
N.A.I.C.S.: 424470

Subsidiary (Domestic):

Sfera S.p.A.   (2)
Via Della Croseta 51, Arcore, Italy   (100%)
Tel.: (39) 0464513114
Grocery & Related Products Whslr
N.A.I.C.S.: 424490

Montana Alimentari S.p.A.   (1)
Via Marconi 3, 46040, Gazoldo degli Ippoliti, Italy
Tel.: (39) 03766801
Web Site: http://www.montanafood.it
Meat Processing
N.A.I.C.S.: 311613

Moto S.p.A.   (1)
Via V Veneto 9, Introbio, 23815, Lecco, Italy
Tel.: (39) 0341901533
Web Site: http://www.hmmoto.it
Sales Range: $25-49.9 Million
Emp.: 35
Miscellaneous Food Mfr
N.A.I.C.S.: 311999

New Catering S.r.l.   (1)
Via Kolbe Massimiliano 5, 47122, Forli, Italy
Tel.: (39) 0543476565
Web Site: http://www.newcatering.it
Frozen Food Product Distr
N.A.I.C.S.: 424470

Railrest S.A.   (1)
Rue de France 95 Frankrijkstraat, 1070, Brussels, Belgium
Tel.: (32) 2 558 0100
Web Site: https://www.railrest.be
Travel Agency Services
N.A.I.C.S.: 561599

Roadhouse Grill Italia S.r.l.   (1)
Via Modena 53, Castelvetro Di Modena, Modena, Italy
Tel.: (39) 059754611
Web Site: http://www.roadhousegrill.it
Drinking Places
N.A.I.C.S.: 722410
Vincenzo Cremonini *(Mng Dir)*

Tecno-Star Due S.r.l.   (1)
Via Modena 53, Castelvetro Di Modena,

41014, Modena, Italy
Tel.: (39) 059754901
Food Product Machinery Mfr
N.A.I.C.S.: 333241

CREO CO., LTD.

12F Reception Sumitomo Fudosan Shinagawa Building 4-10-27, Higashishinagawa Shinagawa-Ku, Tokyo, 140-0002, Japan
Tel.: (81) 357833530
Web Site: https://www.creo.co.jp
Year Founded: 1974
9698—(TKS)
Rev.: $94,860,110
Assets: $66,476,770
Liabilities: $18,250,210
Net Worth: $48,226,560
Earnings: $4,739,370
Emp.: 1,244
Fiscal Year-end: 03/31/24
Software Development Services
N.A.I.C.S.: 541511
Yuji Anan *(Chm)*

Subsidiaries:

CREATE LAB CO., LTD.   (1)
4F East Square Omori Building 6-20-14 Minami-Ooi, Shinagawa-ku, Tokyo, 140-0013, Japan
Tel.: (81) 337680600
Web Site: http://www.ccl.co.jp
Emp.: 250
Computer Support Services
N.A.I.C.S.: 541512

CREO Marketing CO., LTD.   (1)
14F Reception /8F Riverge Shinagawa 4-1-8 Konan Minato-ku, Tokyo, 108-0075, Japan
Tel.: (81) 357693620
Web Site: http://www.zeem.jp
System Software Development Services
N.A.I.C.S.: 541511

CREO Networks CO., LTD.   (1)
14F Riverge Shinagawa 4-1-8 Konan Minato-ku, Tokyo, 108-0075, Japan
Tel.: (81) 357693630
Web Site: http://www.creo-networks.co.jp
Software Development Services
N.A.I.C.S.: 541511

CREO Solution CO., LTD.   (1)
2F Reception /4F/6F Ichigo Mita Building 5-13-18 Shiba Minato-ku, Tokyo, 108-0014, Japan
Tel.: (81) 364146250
Web Site: http://www.creo-sol.co.jp
Embedded Software Development Services
N.A.I.C.S.: 541511

CREO MEDICAL GROUP PLC

Creo House Unit 2 Beaufort Park Beaufort Park Way, Chepstow, NP16 5UH, United Kingdom
Tel.: (44) 1291606005   UK
Web Site:
    https://www.creomedical.com
Year Founded: 2003
CREO—(AIM)
Rev.: $32,726,265
Assets: $90,747,030
Liabilities: $18,717,930
Net Worth: $72,029,100
Earnings: ($32,449,230)
Emp.: 91
Fiscal Year-end: 12/31/22
Surgical Appliance & Supplies Manufacturing
N.A.I.C.S.: 339113
Charles Alexander Evan Spicer *(Chm)*

Subsidiaries:

Aber Electronics Limited   (1)
17 Angora Business Park Peartree Road, Colchester, CO3 0AB, United Kingdom
Tel.: (44) 1206617580
Web Site: https://aberelectronics.co.uk
Amplifiers Mfr
N.A.I.C.S.: 334220

Boucart Medical SRL **(1)**
Rue des Veterinaires 42, 1070, Brussels,
Belgium
Tel.: (32) 23435001
Web Site: https://boucartmedical.com
Medical Equipment Distr
N.A.I.C.S.: 423450

Creo Medical Limited **(1)**
Creo House Unit 2 Beaufort Park Beaufort
Park Way, Chepstow, NP16 5UH, United
Kingdom
Tel.: (44) 1291637300
Web Site: https://creomedical.com
Medical Device Mfr
N.A.I.C.S.: 339112

CREOTECH INSTRUMENTS S.A.
Ul Jana Pawla II 66, 05-500,
Piaseczno, Poland
Tel.: (48) 222464575
Web Site: https://www.creotech.pl
Year Founded: 2012
CRI—(WAR)
Rev.: $7,806,148
Assets: $43,835,366
Liabilities: $20,621,189
Net Worth: $23,214,177
Earnings: ($3,643,801)
Emp.: 150
Fiscal Year-end: 12/31/23
Electric Equipment Mfr
N.A.I.C.S.: 333414
Jacek Kosiec (VP)

CRESCENDAS PTE. LTD.
63 Ubi Avenue 1 #06-01, Singapore,
408937, Singapore
Tel.: (65) 64884688   SG
Web Site:
http://www.crescendas.com
Year Founded: 1982
Sales Range: $50-74.9 Million
Emp.: 200
Holding Company; International Real
Estate Development, Manufacturing,
Distribution & Technology Services
N.A.I.C.S.: 551112
Lawrence Leow (Chm & CEO)

CRESCENDO CORPORATION BERHAD
18th Floor Public Bank Tower No 19
Jalan Wong Ah Fook, 80000, Johor
Bahru, Johor, Malaysia
Tel.: (60) 7 224 8316
Web Site:
http://www.crescendo.com.my
CRESNDO—(KLS)
Rev.: $53,737,159
Assets: $350,439,783
Liabilities: $110,159,981
Net Worth: $240,279,802
Earnings: $5,935,396
Emp.: 389
Fiscal Year-end: 01/31/22
Investment Services; Real Estate &
Building
N.A.I.C.S.: 523999
Seong Lim Gooi (Chm & Mng Dir)

Subsidiaries:

Crescendo International College Sdn. Bhd. **(1)**
Lebuh Cemerlang Desa Cemerlang, 81800,
Ulu Tiram, Johor, Malaysia
Tel.: (60) 78636888
Web Site: https://www.crescendo.edu.my
College Educational Services
N.A.I.C.S.: 611310

CRESCENDO INDUSTRIES
1030 Avenue Guillibert de la
Lauziere, BP 20140, ZI Les Milles,
F-13794, Aix-en-Provence, Cedex 03,
France
Tel.: (33) 442607000

Web Site: http://www.crescendo-
industries.com
Year Founded: 2004
Holding Company
N.A.I.C.S.: 551112

CRESCENT CAPITAL PARTNERS LTD.
Level 29 Governor Phillip Tower 1
Farrer Place, Sydney, 2000, NSW,
Australia
Tel.: (61) 292208100   AU
Web Site:
http://www.crescentcap.com.au
Year Founded: 2000
Privater Equity Firm
N.A.I.C.S.: 523999
Michael Alscher (Founder & Mng Partner)

Subsidiaries:

Australian Clinical Labs Limited **(1)**
1868 Dandenong Road, Clayton, 3168,
VIC, Australia
Tel.: (61) 395386777
Web Site: http://www.clinicallabs.com.au
Emp.: 3,800
Holding Company; Pathology Laboratory
Testing Services
N.A.I.C.S.: 551112
Christopher Barnes (Natl Dir-Haematology)

Subsidiary (Domestic):

Clinical Laboratories Pty. Ltd. **(2)**
1868 Dandenong Road, Clayton, 3168,
VIC, Australia
Tel.: (61) 3 9538 6777
Web Site: http://www.clinicallabs.com.au
Medical Pathology Laboratories Operator
N.A.I.C.S.: 621511
Anoop Singh (COO)

CSR Building Products Ltd. **(1)**
Triniti 3 39 Delhi Road, North Ryde, 2113,
NSW, Australia   **(100%)**
Tel.: (61) 2 9235 8000
Web Site: http://www.csr.com.au
Sales Range: $50-74.9 Million
Emp.: 210
Flat Glass Mfr
N.A.I.C.S.: 327211

Division (Non-US):

Viridian **(2)**
15 Waiouru, Mount Wellington, Auckland,
2013, New Zealand
Tel.: (64) 95731427
Web Site: http://www.viridianglass.com
Emp.: 50
Glass Mfr
N.A.I.C.S.: 327211
Brett Woods (Gen Mgr)

Nude by Nature Pty Limited **(1)**
Level 6 22 Pitt St, Sydney, 2000, NSW,
Australia
Tel.: (61) 1300 795 003
Web Site: http://www.nudebynature.com.au
Cosmetic Product Distr
N.A.I.C.S.: 424210

Steel-Line Garage Doors **(1)**
51 Perivale St, Darra, 4076, QLD, Australia
Tel.: (61) 7 3717 6666
Web Site: http://www.steel-line.com.au
Garage Door Mfr & Distr
N.A.I.C.S.: 332321
Giles Reynolds (Gen Mgr-Ops & Engrg)

CRESCENT COTTON MILLS LIMITED
New Lahore Road, Nishatabad, Fais-
alabad, Pakistan
Tel.: (92) 418752112
Web Site:
https://www.crescentcotton.com
Year Founded: 1959
CCM—(PSX)
Rev.: $47,611,139
Assets: $42,291,145
Liabilities: $12,067,517
Net Worth: $30,223,628

Earnings: ($362,340)
Emp.: 1,291
Fiscal Year-end: 06/30/19
Sugar Mfr
N.A.I.C.S.: 311313
Muhammad Arshad (CEO)

CRESCENT FIBRES LIMITED
104 Shadman 1, Lahore, 54000,
Pakistan
Tel.: (92) 4235960871
Web Site:
https://www.crescentfibres.com
Year Founded: 1969
CFL—(KAR)
Rev.: $37,978,187
Assets: $36,980,422
Liabilities: $14,359,972
Net Worth: $22,620,450
Earnings: $812,736
Emp.: 1,021
Fiscal Year-end: 06/30/19
Paperboard Mills
N.A.I.C.S.: 322130
Riaz Masood (Exec Dir)

Subsidiaries:

Premier Financial Services (Pvt) Limited **(1)**
B-1004 10th Floor Lakson Square Building
ste 3 Sarwar Shaheed Road, Karachi, Paki-
stan
Tel.: (92) 2135672815
Web Site:
http://www.firstequitymodaraba.com.pk
Trading Services
N.A.I.C.S.: 523160
Adil A. Ghaffar (CEO)

CRESCENT JUTE PRODUCTS LIMITED
1st Floor 65-XX Khayban-e-Iqbal
Road Phase-III DHA, Lahore, 54792,
Pakistan
Tel.: (92) 4237186438
Web Site: https://www.cresjute.com
Year Founded: 1964
Rev.: $273,873
Assets: $1,387,462
Liabilities: $3,301,401
Net Worth: ($1,913,939)
Earnings: ($94,130)
Emp.: 14
Fiscal Year-end: 06/30/19
Jute & Jute Products Mfr
N.A.I.C.S.: 313210
Humayun Mazhar (CEO)

CRESCENT LEASING LTD.
229 A J C Bose Road 9th floor Unit -
9C, Kolkata, 700 020, West Bengal,
India
Tel.: (91) 3346011021
Web Site:
http://www.crescentleasingltd.com
539131—(BOM)
Sales Range: $1-9.9 Million
Financial Support Services
N.A.I.C.S.: 523999
Chanchal Mallick (CFO)

CRESCENT N.V.
Geldenaaksebaan 329, 3001, Leu-
ven, Belgium
Tel.: (32) 16317411
Web Site: https://www.option.com
OPTI—(EUR)
Rev.: $20,380,332
Earnings: ($5,542,187)
Emp.: 57
Fiscal Year-end: 12/31/19
Wireless Technology Products & Ser-
vices
N.A.I.C.S.: 334220
Jan Callewaert (Founder)

Subsidiaries:

Option Germany GmbH **(1)**
Beim Glaspalast 1, 86153, Augsburg, Ger-
many
Tel.: (49) 8216505290
Sales Range: $25-49.9 Million
Emp.: 30
Communication Devices Mfr
N.A.I.C.S.: 334290

Option Wireless Hong Kong Limited **(1)**
35 F Central Plaza 18 Harbour Road Wan
Chai, Hong Kong, China (Hong Kong)
Tel.: (852) 25931111
Wireless Communication Equipment Mfr
N.A.I.C.S.: 334220

Option Wireless Ltd **(1)**
Kilbarry Industrial Park, Dublin Hill, Cork,
Ireland
Tel.: (353) 214946210
Wireless Communication Devices Mfr
N.A.I.C.S.: 334290

CRESCENT STAR INSURANCE LIMITED
2nd Floor Nadir House I I Chundri-
garh Road, Karachi, 74000, Pakistan
Tel.: (92) 2132415471
Web Site:
https://www.cstarinsurance.com
CSIL—(PSX)
Rev.: $713,881
Assets: $6,941,753
Liabilities: $2,569,255
Net Worth: $4,372,498
Earnings: $125,528
Emp.: 42
Fiscal Year-end: 12/31/19
Insurance Services
N.A.I.C.S.: 524126
Naim Anwar (CEO & Mng Dir)

CRESCENT STEEL AND ALLIED PRODUCTS LIMITED
E- Floor IT Tower 73-E/1 Hali Road,
Gulberg III, Lahore, Pakistan
Tel.: (92) 4235783801   PK
Web Site:
https://www.crescent.com.pk
Year Founded: 1987
CSAP—(PSX)
Rev.: $19,004,822
Assets: $40,661,297
Liabilities: $13,945,724
Net Worth: $26,715,572
Earnings: $2,124,603
Emp.: 198
Fiscal Year-end: 06/30/23
Mfr of Cotton Yarn & Coating of Steel
Pipes
N.A.I.C.S.: 331210
Ahsan M. Saleem (CEO & Mng Dir)

Subsidiaries:

Rousch (Pakistan) Power Limited **(1)**
403-C Descon office Evacuee Trust Plaza
F-5/1, Islamabad, 75400, Pakistan
Tel.: (92) 3200001149
Web Site: https://www.rouschpak.com
Power Generation Services
N.A.I.C.S.: 221113

CRESCERA CAPITAL ACQUISITION CORP.
Rua Anibal de Mendonca 27 2nd
floor, Rio de Janeiro, 22410-050,
Brazil
Tel.: (55) 2136871500   Ky
Year Founded: 2021
CREC—(NASDAQ)
Rev.: $295
Assets: $209,135,662
Liabilities: $216,125,623
Net Worth: ($6,989,961)
Earnings: $15,514,272
Emp.: 2

Crescera Capital Acquisition Corp.—(Continued)

Fiscal Year-end: 12/31/22
Investment Services
N.A.I.C.S.: 523999
Rafael Moreira Pereira (CFO)

CRESCITA THERAPEUTICS, INC.
6733 Mississauga Road Suite 800,
Mississauga, L5N 6J5, ON, Canada
Tel.: (905) 673-4295
Web Site:
   https://www.crescitatherapeutic.com
Pharmaceutical Products Distr
N.A.I.C.S.: 424210
Serge Verreault (Pres & CEO)

CRESCO, LTD.
26th floor Shinagawa Intercity Building A 2-15-1 Konan, Minato-ku, Tokyo, 108-6026, Japan
Tel.: (81) 357698011
Web Site: https://www.cresco.co.jp
Year Founded: 1988
4674—(TKS)
Rev.: $348,710,550
Assets: $262,509,540
Liabilities: $79,538,130
Net Worth: $182,971,410
Earnings: $24,642,080
Emp.: 3,088
Fiscal Year-end: 03/31/24
Software Developer
N.A.I.C.S.: 334610
Hiroyuki Nemoto (Pres)

Subsidiaries:

C3 Co., Ltd. (1)
1-27-7 Omika-cho, Hitachi, 319-1221, Ibaraki, Japan
Tel.: (81) 294526900
Web Site: https://www.c3w.co.jp
Emp.: 90
Software Services
N.A.I.C.S.: 541511

CRESCO Communications Inc. (1)
TOC Building 10th Floor 7-22-17 Nishi-Gotanda, Shinagawa-ku, Tokyo, 141-0031, Japan
Tel.: (81) 357193418
Web Site: http://www.cresco-com.jp
Website Designing & Hosting Services
N.A.I.C.S.: 518210

CRESCO Digital Technologies Ltd. (1)
Akesan Takahama Building 2F 2-12-23 Konan, Minato-ku, Tokyo, 108-0075, Japan
Tel.: (81) 354957981
Web Site: https://www.cresco-dt.co.jp
Emp.: 220
Information Technology Services
N.A.I.C.S.: 541511

CRESCO J Cube Co., Ltd. (1)
15th Floor Shinagawa Grand Central Tower 2-16-4 Konan, Minato-ku, Tokyo, 108-0075, Japan
Tel.: (81) 364179995
Web Site: https://www.cresco-jcube.co.jp
Emp.: 226
Information Technology Services
N.A.I.C.S.: 541511

Creative Japan Co, Ltd. (1)
2-12-23 Konan Takahama Building 2nd Floor, Minato- ku, Tokyo, 108-0075, Japan
Tel.: (81) 354957981
Web Site: http://www.creative-japan.co.jp
Software Services
N.A.I.C.S.: 541511

Cresco Hokuriku Ltd. (1)
Kanazawa Fukoku Seimei Ekimae Building 2-11-7 Honmachi, Kanazawa, 920-0853, Ishikawa, Japan
Tel.: (81) 762333240
Web Site: https://www.cresco-hokuriku.jp
Emp.: 83
IT Consulting Services
N.A.I.C.S.: 541611

Cresco ID Systems Inc. (1)
Senryudou Bldg 1st Fl 3-6 Hayabusa-cho, Chiyoda-ku, Tokyo, Japan
Tel.: (81) 332217735
Web Site: http://www.cresco-ids.jp
Sales Range: $25-49.9 Million
Emp.: 8
Security Locker Installation Services
N.A.I.C.S.: 561621

Cresco Vietnam Co., Ltd. (1)
Room 201 2nd Floor Somerset Hoa Binh Building No 106, Hoang Quoc Viet Street Nghia Do Ward Cau Giay District, Hanoi, Vietnam
Tel.: (84) 936172558
Web Site: https://www.cresco-vn.com.vn
Software Services
N.A.I.C.S.: 541511
Atsushi Hirasawa (CEO)

Cresco Wireless, Inc. (1)
9th Floor Yamate Building 2-5-9 Sanno, Ota-ku, Tokyo, 143-0023, Japan
Tel.: (81) 357466800
Web Site: https://wireless-t.jp
Communication Equipment Mfr & Distr
N.A.I.C.S.: 334290

Cresco e-Solution Co. Ltd. (1)
PMO Hatchobori Shinkawa 2-9-11 Shinkawa, Chuo-ku, Tokyo, 104-0033, Japan (100%)
Tel.: (81) 355409560
Web Site: http://www.cresco-es.co.jp
Sales Range: $25-49.9 Million
Emp.: 152
Computer System Design Services
N.A.I.C.S.: 541512

Enisias Co., Ltd. (1)
A-PLACE Gotanda 10F 2-27-3 Nishigotanda, Shinagawa-ku, Tokyo, 141-0031, Japan
Tel.: (81) 364557575
Web Site: https://www.enisias.com
Emp.: 107
Software Services
N.A.I.C.S.: 541511

IOS Co., Ltd. (1)
15th floor South Building World Trade Center Building, 2-4-1 Hamamatsucho Minato-ku, Tokyo, 105-5115, Japan
Tel.: (81) 358437651
Web Site: http://www.ios-net.co.jp
Sales Range: $25-49.9 Million
Emp.: 278
Financial & Business Software Development Services
N.A.I.C.S.: 541511

Japan Software Design Co.,Ltd. (1)
Osaka Sakaisuji Building 3F 2-2-13 Bakurocho, Chuo-ku, Osaka, 541-0059, Japan
Tel.: (81) 662680369
Web Site: https://www.jsdcom.co.jp
Emp.: 121
Software Development Services
N.A.I.C.S.: 541511

Mexess Co., Ltd. (1)
Osaka 2F Nomura Fudosan Midosuji Honmachi Building 4-2-12 Honmachi, Chuo-ku, Osaka, 541-0053, Japan
Tel.: (81) 671759417
Web Site: https://www.mexess.co.jp
Software Services
N.A.I.C.S.: 541511

N-System Corporation (1)
1-16-8 Sotokanda, Chiyoda-ku, Tokyo, 101-0021, Japan
Tel.: (81) 352970361
Web Site: http://www.n-system21.co.jp
Software Services
N.A.I.C.S.: 541511

OEC Ltd. (1)
8th Floor Shinjuku SKY Building 4-1-23 Shinjuku, Shinjuku-ku, Tokyo, 160-0022, Japan
Tel.: (81) 333566591
Web Site: https://www.oec-ltd.co.jp
Financial Services
N.A.I.C.S.: 921130

Wireless Technologies, Inc. (1)
7th floor of Omori Mitsubishi Building 3-10-10 Sanno, Ota-ku, Tokyo, 143-0023, Japan

Tel.: (81) 357466800
Web Site: http://www.wireless-t.jp
Sales Range: $25-49.9 Million
Emp.: 5
Wireless Devices Retailer
N.A.I.C.S.: 517112

ZXY MEQQE Corporation (1)
1-1-1 Akasaka, Minato-ku, Tokyo, 107-0052, Japan
Tel.: (81) 368111350
Web Site: https://zxy-meqqe.co.jp
E-book Brokerage Services
N.A.I.C.S.: 523150

CRESSANDA SOLUTIONS LIMITED
12A 3rd Flr Pl no 207 Embassy Centre Jamnalal Bajaj Marg, Nariman Point, Mumbai, 400 021, Maharashtra, India
Tel.: (91) 8169245676
Web Site:
   https://www.cressanda.com
Year Founded: 1985
512379—(BOM)
Rev.: $12,735
Assets: $3,302,884
Liabilities: $3,627
Net Worth: $3,299,257
Earnings: $617
Fiscal Year-end: 03/31/21
Information Technology Consulting Services
N.A.I.C.S.: 541512
Ramesh Laximan Bhosle (CFO)

CREST BUILDER HOLDINGS BERHAD
Penthouse The Crest 3 Two Square No 2 Jalan 19/1, 46300, Petaling Jaya, Selangor Darul Ehsan, Malaysia
Tel.: (60) 378416000
Web Site:
   https://www.crestbuilder.com.my
CRESBLD—(KLS)
Rev.: $106,298,445
Assets: $278,204,107
Liabilities: $215,590,930
Net Worth: $62,613,177
Earnings: ($8,484,252)
Emp.: 243
Fiscal Year-end: 12/31/23
General Construction, Mechanical & Electrical Engineering Services
N.A.I.C.S.: 541330
Chiang Pooh Heng (Sec)

CREST INVESTMENTS CO., LTD.
1-3 Kamiyama-cho, Kita-ku, Osaka, 530-0026, Japan
Tel.: (81) 677327890
Web Site: http://www.crest-inv.jp
Year Founded: 2000
Sales Range: $150-199.9 Million
Emp.: 191
Consulting & Back Office Services to Small & Medium Size Enterprises
N.A.I.C.S.: 561499
Eiji Tanaka (Pres)

Subsidiaries:

Club Nets Corporation (1)
Aqua Dojima NBF Tower 1 4 16, Kita-Ku, Osaka, Japan
Tel.: (81) 335193411
Web Site: http://www.clubnets.jp
Sales Range: $25-49.9 Million
Emp.: 40
Development & Operation of Point Card System Promotion Programs for Increasing Customers
N.A.I.C.S.: 541512

Cube Planning Corporation (1)
Aqua Dojima Building 1 4 16 Dojimahama Kita-ku, Osaka, 530-0004, Japan
Tel.: (81) 677327875

Web Site: http://www.cubeplanning.com
Interior Design Services for Stores & Bakeries
N.A.I.C.S.: 541410

Yusei Nishi-Kyushu Seika Co.,Ltd. (1)
484 Tasakimachi, Kumamoto, 860-0063, Japan
Tel.: (81) 963232611
Web Site: http://www.b-b-net.com
Non-Durable Goods Whslr
N.A.I.C.S.: 424990

CREST NICHOLSON HOLDINGS PLC
500 Dashwood Lang Road, Bourne Business Park, Addlestone, KT15 2HJ, Surrey, United Kingdom
Tel.: (44) 1932580555 **UK**
Web Site:
   https://www.crestnicholson.com
Year Founded: 1963
CRST—(LSE)
Rev.: $1,240,412,992
Assets: $2,144,111,424
Liabilities: $945,108,892
Net Worth: $1,199,002,532
Earnings: $35,843,808
Emp.: 797
Fiscal Year-end: 10/31/22
Holding Company
N.A.I.C.S.: 551112
Kevin Maguire (Gen Counsel)

CREST NICHOLSON PLC
Pyrcroft Road Crest House, Chertsey, KT16 9GN, Surrey, United Kingdom
Tel.: (44) 1932580555 **UK**
Web Site:
   http://www.crestnicholson.com
Year Founded: 1963
Sales Range: $1-4.9 Billion
Emp.: 790
Residential Housing & Mixed-Use Real Estate Developer
N.A.I.C.S.: 236117
Stephen Stone (Chm)

Subsidiaries:

Crest Nicholson (Chiltern) Ltd. (1)
Crest House Progression Centre Mark Rd, Hemel Hempstead, HP2 7DW, Herts, United Kingdom
Tel.: (44) 01442219921
Web Site: http://www.crestnicholson.com
Sales Range: $25-49.9 Million
Emp.: 75
Residential Development Services
N.A.I.C.S.: 236117

Crest Nicholson (Eastern) Ltd. (1)
1 Myrtle Rd, Brentwood, CM14 5EG, Essex, United Kingdom
Tel.: (44) 1277693230
Web Site: http://www.crestnicholson.com
Sales Range: $25-49.9 Million
Emp.: 50
Residential Housing & Mixed-Use Real Estate Developer
N.A.I.C.S.: 236117
Peter Diffley (Mng Dir)

Crest Nicholson (South West) Ltd. (1)
Crest House Lime Kiln Close, Bristol, BS34 8ST, Avon, United Kingdom
Tel.: (44) 1179236600
Sales Range: $25-49.9 Million
Emp.: 41
Residential Housing & Mixed-Use Real Estate Developer
N.A.I.C.S.: 236117

Crest Nicholson (South) Ltd. (1)
Crest House Pyrcroft Rd, Chertsey, KT16 9GN, Surrey, United Kingdom
Tel.: (44) 1932580444
Web Site: http://www.crestnicholson.com
Sales Range: $25-49.9 Million
Emp.: 60
Residential Housing & Mixed-Use Real Estate Developer Services

N.A.I.C.S.: 236117
Dean Cooke *(Mgr-IT)*

Crest Partnership Homes Ltd. (1)
Crest House, Pyrcroft Road, Chertsey,
KT16 9GN, Surrey, United Kingdom
Tel.: (44) 1932580555
Web Site: http://www.crestnicholson.com
Sales Range: $25-49.9 Million
Emp.: 80
Residential Housing & Mixed-Use Real Estate Developer
N.A.I.C.S.: 236117
Colin Smith *(Mng Dir)*

CREST RADIUS INC.
7 Kaapa, Tsolgo, 65552, Estonia
Tel.: (372) 775 525 3078 NV
Year Founded: 2017
Laundry Washing Machine Distr
N.A.I.C.S.: 423620
Kardo Valbe *(Pres, CEO & CFO)*

CREST RESOURCES, INC.
Suite 2501 - 550 Burrard Street, Vancouver, V6C 2B5, BC, Canada
Tel.: (778) 819-1870
Web Site:
https://www.crestresourcesinc.com
CRSTF—(OTCIQ)
Rev.: $30,630
Assets: $3,722,826
Liabilities: $846,172
Net Worth: $2,876,654
Earnings: ($2,319,953)
Fiscal Year-end: 05/31/24
Oil & Gas Exploration Services
N.A.I.C.S.: 211130
Michael Collins *(Pres & CEO)*

CREST VENTURES LIMITED
111 Maker Chambers IV 11th Floor,
Nariman Point, Mumbai, 400021,
India
Tel.: (91) 2243347000
Web Site: https://www.crest.co.in
511413—(BOM)
Rev.: $7,808,537
Assets: $116,662,209
Liabilities: $36,070,316
Net Worth: $80,591,893
Earnings: $1,651,486
Emp.: 17
Fiscal Year-end: 03/31/22
Real Estate Services
N.A.I.C.S.: 531390
Vijay Choraria *(Mng Dir)*

Subsidiaries:

Crest Finserv Limited (1)
4th Floor Kalpataru Heritage 127 M G
Road, Fort, Mumbai, 400 001, India
Tel.: (91) 224 051 2200
Web Site: https://www.crestfinserv.com
Mutual Fund Services
N.A.I.C.S.: 523940

ITI Securities Limited (1)
4th Floor Kalpataru Heritage 127 M G Road
Fort, Mumbai, 400001, India
Tel.: (91) 2240512500
Sales Range: $50-74.9 Million
Emp.: 80
Securities Brokerage Services
N.A.I.C.S.: 523150

Tamarind Tours Private Limited (1)
401 AJ House Marol Maroshi Road Andheri
East, Bandra West, Mumbai, 400 059, India
Tel.: (91) 2266802500
Web Site: https://www.tamarindglobal.com
Sales Range: $25-49.9 Million
Emp.: 150
Travel Tour Operator
N.A.I.C.S.: 561520
Gufran Qureshi *(Mgr-Bus Dev)*

CRESTCHEM LIMITED
Sr No 550/1 Sub Plot Number 12 Village Indrad Taluka-Kadi, Mehsana,
382715, Gujarat, India

Tel.: (91) 9409119484
Web Site:
https://www.crestchemlimited.in
Year Founded: 1991
526269—(BOM)
Rev.: $1,050,488
Assets: $409,251
Liabilities: $205,525
Net Worth: $203,726
Earnings: $78,371
Fiscal Year-end: 03/31/21
Food Ingredient Mfr & Distr
N.A.I.C.S.: 311999
Dipak Narendraprasad Patel *(Chm, Mng Dir & Officer-Compliance)*

CRESTCHIC PLC
Second Avenue Centrum 100, Burton, DE14 2WF, United Kingdom
Tel.: (44) 1283531645
Web Site:
http://www.northbridgegroup.co.uk
NBI—(LSE)
Rev.: $46,131,252
Assets: $66,175,273
Liabilities: $28,611,234
Net Worth: $37,564,039
Earnings: ($10,199,193)
Emp.: 179
Fiscal Year-end: 12/31/20
Industrial Equipment Sales
N.A.I.C.S.: 424130
Eric W. Hook *(CEO)*

Subsidiaries:

Crestchic (Middle East) FZE (1)
Jebel Ali, PO Box 262519, Dubai, 262519,
United Arab Emirates
Tel.: (971) 48818655
Web Site: http://www.northbridge-me.com
Sales Range: $75-99.9 Million
Emp.: 10
Power Testing & Generation Services
N.A.I.C.S.: 221118

Crestchic Limited (1)
2nd Avenue Centrum 100, Burton-on-Trent,
DE14 2WF, Staffs, United Kingdom
Tel.: (44) 128 353 1645
Web Site: https://crestchicloadbanks.com
Sales Range: $25-49.9 Million
Emp.: 50
Loadbank Mfr & Hiring Services
N.A.I.C.S.: 334515
Paul Brickman *(Dir-Sls & Mktg)*

CRESTEC INC.
69 Higashimikata-cho, Chuo-ku, Hamamatsu, 433-8104, Shizuoka-ken,
Japan
Tel.: (81) 534390315
Web Site: https://www.crestec.co.jp
Year Founded: 1984
7812—(TKS)
Rev.: $118,590,520
Assets: $122,956,960
Liabilities: $65,558,800
Net Worth: $57,398,160
Earnings: $5,660,200
Emp.: 1,428
Fiscal Year-end: 06/30/24
Manual Creation & Document Solutions, Including Technical Writing,
Translations & Printing
N.A.I.C.S.: 561410
Hisashi Tominaga *(Sr Mng Exec Officer, Mng Exec Officer & Dir)*

Subsidiaries:

CRESTEC (MALAYSIA) SDN
BHD (1)
Suite 7-01 Level 7 City Plaza 21 Jalan
Tebrau, 80300, Johor Bahru, Malaysia
Tel.: (60) 73314633
Emp.: 5
Hard Disk Drive Mfr
N.A.I.C.S.: 334112

CRESTEC (SHANGHAI) CO.,
LTD. (1)

2/F Hui Yin Finance Business Center No 20
Lane 599 Yun Ling Road East, Shanghai,
China
Tel.: (86) 2152388383
Emp.: 50
Desktop Publishing Services
N.A.I.C.S.: 561410
Zhao YuHeng *(Engr-Sys)*

CRESTEC (THAILAND) CO.,
LTD. (1)
23/26-27 Sorachai Building 14th Floor
Sukhumvit 63 Road Klongton-Nua, Watthana, Bangkok, 10110, Thailand
Tel.: (66) 27143050
Web Site: http://www.crestec.co.th
Emp.: 40
Printing Services
N.A.I.C.S.: 513199

CRESTEC INFORMATION TECHNOLOGY (SHENZHEN)
LIMITED (1)
Rm 10B6 10/F Guang Cai Xin Tian Di
Building Gui Miao Road Ns District, Shenzhen, China
Tel.: (86) 75583690876
Information Technology Services
N.A.I.C.S.: 541512

CRESTEC PHILIPPINES, Inc. (1)
Block 19 Lot 2 Units 1-4 Building 5 Lima
Technology Center, Lipa, 4217, Batangas,
Philippines
Tel.: (63) 43 455 6907
Web Site: https://www.crestecphil.com.ph
Packaging Material Mfr & Distr
N.A.I.C.S.: 322212

CRESTEC PRINTING (DONGGUAN)
LIMITED (1)
Zhen An Science Technology Industrial
Park, Changan, Dongguan, Guangdong,
China
Tel.: (86) 76985332338
Printing Services
N.A.I.C.S.: 513199

CRESTEC VIETNAM CO., LTD. (1)
126 Nguyen Thi Minh Khai Street, Vo Thi
Sau Ward District 3, Ho Chi Minh City, Vietnam
Tel.: (84) 2839307536
Printing Services
N.A.I.C.S.: 513199

Crestec (Asia) Limited (1)
RM03 14/F Charm Centre 700 Castle Peak
Road, Lai Chi Kok, Kowloon, China (Hong
Kong)
Tel.: (852) 2 865 7723
Web Site: https://crestec-asia.com.cn
Printing Services
N.A.I.C.S.: 513199
Kevin Yeung *(Mgr-Sls Plng)*

Crestec Electronics Technology (Zhuhai) Co., Ltd. (1)
3st Floors Block A No 321 Huawei Road,
Qianshan Industrial Zone XiangZhou District, Zhuhai, 518104, Guangdong, China
Tel.: (86) 756 881 2060
Document Preparation Services
N.A.I.C.S.: 561410

Crestec Europe B.V. (1)
Teleportboulevard 110, 1043 EJ, Amsterdam, Netherlands
Tel.: (31) 205854640
Web Site: http://www.crestec.eu
Emp.: 40
Translation Services
N.A.I.C.S.: 541930
Takuya Miyago *(Pres)*

Crestec Inc. - Surabaya Factory (1)
Kawasan Industri PIER JL Rembang Industri 2/14 Pasuruan, Java, 67152, Timur, Indonesia
Tel.: (62) 343740312
Printing Services
N.A.I.C.S.: 513199

Crestec USA Inc. (1)
2410 Mira Mar Ave, Long Beach, CA 90815
Tel.: (310) 327-9000
Web Site: https://www.crestecusa.com
Printing Services
N.A.I.C.S.: 513199

MINDS Co., Ltd. (1)
NAC Minato Building 9F 2-1-24 Kaigan,
Minato-ku, Tokyo, 105-0022, Japan
Tel.: (81) 33 769 2611
Web Site: https://www.mind-s.jp
Emp.: 20
Digital Marketing Services
N.A.I.C.S.: 541810
Yukifumi Ikeda *(Pres & CEO)*

Navi Co., Ltd. (1)
1021 Sasagase-cho, Higashi-ku, Hamamatsu, 435-0042, Shizuoka-ken, Japan
Tel.: (81) 53 466 8558
Web Site: https://www.japan-navi.com
Advertising Agency Services
N.A.I.C.S.: 541810
Takeshi Nagai *(Chm)*

Ohno Printing Co., Ltd. (1)
1-42-2 Kitamachi, Nerima-ku, Tokyo, 179-
0081, Japan
Tel.: (81) 33 559 4167
Web Site: https://www.ohnoprinting.co.jp
Emp.: 59
Commercial Printing Services
N.A.I.C.S.: 323111

PT CRESTEC INDONESIA (1)
Industrial Town MM 2100 Jalan Lombok I
Blok N-2 17 18 Cikarang Barat, Bekasi,
17520, Indonesia
Tel.: (62) 218980258
Printing Equipment Mfr
N.A.I.C.S.: 333248

Passage Co., Ltd. (1)
7F NMF Shiba Bldg 4-2-3 Shiba, Minato-ku,
Tokyo, 108-0014, Japan
Tel.: (81) 36 435 0324
Web Site: https://passage.co.jp
Software Development Services
N.A.I.C.S.: 541511
Yoichi Yamashita *(Pres)*

SUZHOU CRESTEC PRINTING CO.,
LTD. (1)
596-598 Chang Jiang Road, Suzhou, Jiangsu, China
Tel.: (86) 51266653338
Emp.: 240
Printing Services
N.A.I.C.S.: 513199

ZHUHAI CRESTEC HUAGUANG
ELECTRONICS TECHNOLOGY CO.,
LTD. (1)
Huasheng Industrial Park Wanzai, Zhuhai,
Guangdong, China
Tel.: (86) 7568812060
Hard Disk Drive Mfr
N.A.I.C.S.: 334112

CRESTONE WEALTH MANAGEMENT LIMITED
Level 32 Chifley Tower 2 Chifley
Square, Sydney, 2000, NSW, Australia
Tel.: (61) 2 8422 5500 AU
Web Site:
http://www.crestone.com.au
Rev.: $9,664,340,000
Emp.: 170
Wealth Management Services
N.A.I.C.S.: 523940
Michael Chisholm *(CEO)*

Subsidiaries:

Crestone Wealth Management Limited - Melbourne (1)
Level 18 120 Collins Street, Melbourne,
3000, VIC, Australia
Tel.: (61) 3 9245 6000
Web Site: http://www.crestone.com.au
Wealth Management Services
N.A.I.C.S.: 523940

CRESTVIEW EXPLORATION, INC.
1250 639 5th Avenue SW, Calgary,
T2P 0L3, AB, Canada
Tel.: (604) 803-5229
Web Site:
https://www.crestviewexploration.ca
CRS—(CNSX)

Crestview Exploration, Inc.—(Continued)

Assets: $1,277,315
Liabilities: $246,486
Net Worth: $1,030,829
Earnings: ($644,211)
Fiscal Year-end: 11/30/23
Mineral Exploration & Mining Services
N.A.I.C.S.: 213115
Gisele Joubin (CFO)

CRESUD SOCIEDAD ANONIMA, COMERCIAL, IN-MOBILIARIA, FINANCIERA Y AGROPECUARIA
Carlos M Della Paolera 261 9th Floor, C1001ADA, Buenos Aires, Argentina
Tel.: (54) 1148147800　　　　Ar
Web Site: https://www.cresud.com.ar
Year Founded: 1972
CRESY—(NASDAQ)
Rev.: $780,433,091
Assets: $3,810,280,616
Liabilities: $2,094,546,233
Net Worth: $1,715,734,383
Earnings: $103,103,578
Emp.: 2,867
Fiscal Year-end: 06/30/24
Real Estate Investment Trust; Beef, Dairy Cattle & Grains Farming
N.A.I.C.S.: 525990
Alejandro Gustavo Elsztain (CEO)

CRETA FARM S.A.
15th km Heraklion Hwy, PO Box 115, 741 00, Athens, Greece
Tel.: (30) 2831086700
Web Site: http://www.cretafarm.gr
CRETA—(ATH)
Sales Range: $100-124.9 Million
Emp.: 854
Meat & Meat Products Producer
N.A.I.C.S.: 311612
Emmanouil S. Domazakis (Chm & Mng Dir)

Subsidiaries:

Creta Farm S.A.　　　　　　　　(1)
15th Kilometre Rethymno-Irakleio National Road, Post Box 115, 74100, Rethymno, Greece　　　　　　　　　　　　(80%)
Tel.: (30) 2831086700
Sales Range: $50-74.9 Million
Emp.: 100
Meat & Meat Product Whslr
N.A.I.C.S.: 424470

Eurocreta S.A.　　　　　　　　(1)
15th Klm Rethymno-Iraklio, Rethymno, 74100, Greece　　　　　　　(100%)
Tel.: (30) 2831086700
Web Site: http://www.creatafarm.gr
Hotels & Motels
N.A.I.C.S.: 721110
Domazakis Manos (Mgr)

CRETAN GROUP PLC
Roman House 296 Golders Green Road, London, NW11 9PT, United Kingdom
Tel.: (44) 2084559570　　　　CY
Web Site:
http://www.cretangroup.com
Real Estate Investment Services
N.A.I.C.S.: 531390
Georgios Vlamakis (Chm & CEO)

CRG HOLDINGS CO., LTD.
37th Floor Shinjuku Mitsui Building 2-1-1 Nishi-Shinjuku, Shinjuku-Ku, Tokyo, 163-0437, Japan
Tel.: (81) 333452772
Web Site: https://www.crgh.co.jp
Year Founded: 2013
7041—(TKS)
Rev.: $147,578,350
Assets: $51,253,610
Liabilities: $29,168,260

Net Worth: $22,085,350
Earnings: $311,960
Emp.: 1,987
Fiscal Year-end: 09/30/23
Holding Company
N.A.I.C.S.: 551112
Hiroshi Inoue (Founder & Chm)

CRH PLC
Stonemason's Way, Rathfarnham, Dublin, D16 KH51, Ireland
Tel.: (353) 14041000　　　　IE
Web Site: https://www.crh.com
Year Founded: 1970
CRH—(NYSE)
Rev.: $34,949,000,000
Assets: $47,469,000,000
Liabilities: $26,181,000,000
Net Worth: $21,288,000,000
Earnings: $3,072,000,000
Emp.: 78,500
Fiscal Year-end: 12/31/23
Holding Company; Building Materials Mfr & Distr
N.A.I.C.S.: 551112
Richard P. Boucher (Chm)

Subsidiaries:

AEV CRH Holdings, Inc.　　　(1)
NAC Tower 32nd Street, Bonifacio Global City, Taguig, 1634, Philippines　　(40%)
Tel.: (63) 2 886 2800
Holding Company
N.A.I.C.S.: 551112

Subsidiary (Domestic):

Republic Cement & Building Materials Inc.　　　　　　　　　　　(2)
20F The Salcedo Tower 169 HV Dela Costa Street, Salcedo Village, Makati, 1227, Metro Manila, Philippines
Tel.: (63) 2 885 4599
Web Site: http://www.republiccement.com
Cement Mfr
N.A.I.C.S.: 327310
Mary Margaret L. San Pedro (Treas)

Subsidiary (Domestic):

Republic Cement Services, Inc.　(3)
15/F Menarco Tower 32nd Street, Bonifacio Global City, Taguig, 1632, Philippines
Tel.: (63) 288854599
Cement & Building Materials Mfr
N.A.I.C.S.: 327310

Plant (Domestic):

Republic Cement Services, Inc. - Batangas Plant　　　　　　　(4)
Barrio Mapulo, Taysan, Batangas, Philippines
Tel.: (63) 288854598
Web Site: http://republiccement.com
Cement Mfr
N.A.I.C.S.: 327310

Republic Cement Services, Inc. - Bulacan Cement Plant　　　　(4)
Barrio Minuyan, Norzagaray, Bulacan, Philippines
Tel.: (63) 2 885 4598
Web Site: http://republiccement.com
Cement Mfr
N.A.I.C.S.: 327310

Republic Cement Services, Inc. - Norzagaray Plant　　　　　(4)
Barrio Bigte, Norzagaray, Bulacan, Philippines
Tel.: (63) 288854598
Web Site: http://republiccement.com
Cement Mfr
N.A.I.C.S.: 327310

Republic Cement Services, Inc. - Teresa Plant　　　　　　　(4)
Barangay Dulumbayan, Teresa, Rizal, Philippines
Tel.: (63) 288854598
Web Site: http://republiccement.com
Cement Mfr
N.A.I.C.S.: 327310

Adbri Limited　　　　　　　(1)

　　　　　　　　　　　　　(57.3%)
Tel.: (61) 882238000
Web Site: http://www.adbri.com.au
Rev.: $1,202,305,348
Assets: $1,749,135,151
Liabilities: $776,840,041
Net Worth: $972,295,110
Earnings: $89,414,373
Emp.: 1,500
Fiscal Year-end: 12/31/2021
Construction Materials, Cement & Lime Mfr & Marketer
N.A.I.C.S.: 327310
Marcus R. D. Clayton (Gen Counsel & Sec)

Subsidiary (Domestic):

Adbri Masonry Group Pty. Ltd.　(2)
264 Keilor Road, North Essendon, Melbourne, 3041, VIC, Australia
Tel.: (61) 93050900
Masonry Products
N.A.I.C.S.: 327331

Subsidiary (Domestic):

Adbri Masonry Pty. Ltd.　　　(3)
85 Christensen Road, Stapylton, Beenleigh, 4207, QLD, Australia
Tel.: (61) 73 382 4100
Web Site: https://www.adbrimasonry.com.au
Masonry Product Mfr
N.A.I.C.S.: 327331

Subsidiary (US):

Adelaide Brighton Cement (Florida) Inc.　　　　　　　　　　　(2)
12567 NE 7th Ave, Miami, FL 33161-4811
Tel.: (305) 893-2008
Cement Mfr
N.A.I.C.S.: 327310

Subsidiary (Domestic):

Adelaide Brighton Cement Ltd.　(2)
62 Elder Rd, Birkenhead, 5015, SA, Australia
Tel.: (61) 883000300
Web Site:
http://www.adelaidebrighton.com.au
Sales Range: $25-49.9 Million
Emp.: 100
Cement Mfr
N.A.I.C.S.: 327310

Division (Non-US):

Cockburn Cement　　　　　(2)
　　　　　　　　　　　　　(100%)
Tel.: (61) 89 411 1000
Web Site: https://cockburncement.com.au
Sales Range: $25-49.9 Million
Emp.: 100
Mfr of Cement
N.A.I.C.S.: 327310

Subsidiary (Domestic):

E.B. Mawson and Sons Pty. Ltd.　(2)
141 King George Street, Box 66, Cohuna, 3568, VIC, Australia
Tel.: (61) 35 456 2409
Web Site: https://www.mawsons.com.au
Emp.: 300
Building Materials Distr
N.A.I.C.S.: 444180
Geoff Hall (Project Mgr)

Hurd Haulage Pty. Ltd.　　(2)
Lot 132 Diamond Head Road, Dunbogan, 2443, NSW, Australia
Tel.: (61) 26 559 9834
Web Site:
http://www.adelaidebrighton.com.au
Emp.: 10
Sand & Soil & Gravel Hauling Services
N.A.I.C.S.: 484220

Hy-Tec Industries (Queensland) Pty. Ltd.　　　　　　　　　　　(2)
42-48 Fishermans Rd, Maroochydore, 4558, QLD, Australia
Tel.: (61) 754795100
Concrete Mfr
N.A.I.C.S.: 327320

Northern Cement Ltd.　　　(2)
810 Berrimah Road, East Arm, Darwin, 0828, NT, Australia　　　　(100%)
Tel.: (61) 88 984 0600

Web Site: https://northerncement.com.au
Cement & Quicklime Product Mfr & Distr
N.A.I.C.S.: 327310

Southern Quarries Pty Ltd　　(2)
16 Phillips Street, Thebarton, 5031, SA, Australia
Tel.: (61) 88 334 4745
Web Site:
https://www.southernquarries.com.au
Quarry Material Extraction Services & Distr
N.A.I.C.S.: 212319

Aluminium Verkoop Zuid B.V.　(1)
Kanaaldijk 11, Postbus 37, 5683 CR, Best, Netherlands
Tel.: (31) 499328600
Web Site: https://www.avz.nl
Emp.: 70
Aluminum Component Whslr
N.A.I.C.S.: 444180

Americas Products & Distribution, Inc.　　　　　　　　　　　(1)
12811 Commerce Lakes Dr, Fort Myers, FL 33913
Tel.: (239) 204-9063
Investment Management Service
N.A.I.C.S.: 523999

Ancon Building Products Pty Ltd　(1)
98 Kurrajong Avenue, Mount Druitt, Sydney, 2770, NSW, Australia
Tel.: (61) 1300304320
Web Site: https://www.ancon.com.au
Construction Product Mfr
N.A.I.C.S.: 333120
Jon Bond (Mng Dir)

Arfman Hekwerk B.V.　　　(1)
Ondernemersweg 15, 7451 PK, Holten, Netherlands
Tel.: (31) 548362948
Web Site: http://www.arfman.nl
Emp.: 30
Fencing System Mfr
N.A.I.C.S.: 332999

Ash Grove Cement Company　(1)
11011 Cody St, Overland Park, KS 66210-1567
Tel.: (913) 451-8900
Web Site: https://www.ashgrove.com
Emp.: 2,500
Cement, Lime & Limestone Producer
N.A.I.C.S.: 212312
James M. Gatens (VP-Sls-Texas)

Plant (Domestic):

Ash Grove Cement Company, Cement Plt　　　　　　　　　　　(2)
16215 Hwy 50, Louisville, NE 68037-2881　　　　　　　(100%)
Tel.: (402) 234-2415
Web Site: http://www.ashgrove.com
Cement Mfr
N.A.I.C.S.: 327320

Ash Grove Cement Plant　　(2)
4457 Hwy 108, Foreman, AR 71836
Tel.: (870) 542-6217
Web Site: http://www.ashgrove.com
Cement Mfr
N.A.I.C.S.: 327310

Unit (Domestic):

Ash Grove Materials Corp.　(2)
11011 Cody St, Overland Park, KS 66210
Tel.: (913) 451-8900
Emp.: 2,500
Cement & Lime Mfr
N.A.I.C.S.: 327310

Division (Domestic):

Ash Grove Aggregates, Inc.　(3)
Hwy 52 W, Butler, MO 64730
Tel.: (660) 679-4128
Web Site: http://www.ashgroveagg.com
Cement & Lime Mfr
N.A.I.C.S.: 212312

Division (Domestic):

Ash Grove Aggregates　　　(4)
Hwy 52, Butler, MO 64730　　(100%)
Tel.: (660) 679-4128
Web Site: http://www.ashgroveagg.com
Rock Quarry

N.A.I.C.S.: 212312
Jeff Burton *(Gen Mgr)*

Subsidiary (Domestic):

Fordyce Concrete Company, Inc. **(3)**
11011 Cody St, Shawnee Mission, KS
66210-1507
Tel.: (913) 345-2030
Readymix Concrete Mfr
N.A.I.C.S.: 327320

Precision Packaging **(3)**
315 Phillips Rd, North Little Rock, AR
72117
Tel.: (501) 945-2336
Packaging Ready Mix Concrete Products
Mfr
N.A.I.C.S.: 541618
Dan Hamblen *(Pres)*

Plant (Domestic):

Ash Grove Texas **(2)**
900 Gifco Rd, Midlothian, TX
76065 **(100%)**
Tel.: (972) 723-2301
Web Site: http://www.ashgrove.com
Bulk Cement & Cement Products Mfr &
Whslr
N.A.I.C.S.: 327310
Lary W. Bender *(Reg Mgr-Sls)*

Unit (Domestic):

Cedar Creek Properties LLC **(2)**
25775 W 103rd St, Olathe, KS 66061-7403
Tel.: (913) 829-6500
Real Estate Development
N.A.I.C.S.: 531210

Cedar Creek Realty, LLC **(2)**
25775 W 103rd St, Olathe, KS 66061-7403
Tel.: (913) 829-6500
Real Estate Development
N.A.I.C.S.: 531210
Ken Rosberg *(Pres)*

BR Bauhandel AG **(1)**
Riedmattstrasse 2, 8153, Rumlang, Switzer-
land
Tel.: (41) 432112121
Web Site: https://www.baubedarf-richner-
miauton.ch
Construction Materials Distr
N.A.I.C.S.: 423390
Andreas Niklaus *(Comml Dir-Kriens)*

Bauking AG **(1)**
Buchholzer Str 98, 30655, Hannover, Ger-
many
Tel.: (49) 5111232060
Web Site: http://www.bauking.de
Sales Range: $1-4.9 Billion
Emp.: 3,500
Manufacture And Distribution of Building
Products And Materials
N.A.I.C.S.: 423390
Andreas Strietzel *(Chm & Mng Dir)*

Beton Catalan S.A. **(1)**
C Joaquim Molins n 5, 08028, Barcelona,
Spain
Tel.: (34) 935053600
Web Site: https://www.betonc.com
Sales Range: $25-49.9 Million
Emp.: 60
Readymix Concrete Mfr
N.A.I.C.S.: 327320
Roger Roic *(Mng Dir)*

Betongruppen RBR A/S **(1)**
Industrivege 8, 6800, Varde, Denmark
Tel.: (45) 76951122
Web Site: https://rbrc.dk
Paving Materials Mfr
N.A.I.C.S.: 324121

Bosta Beton Sp. z o.o. **(1)**
Tel.: (48) 225080901
Building Material Mfr & Distr
N.A.I.C.S.: 327120

CPM Development Corporation **(1)**
5111 E Broadway, Spokane, WA 99212
Tel.: (509) 534-6221
Readymix Concrete Mfr
N.A.I.C.S.: 327320
Mike Delaney *(VP)*

CRH (Srbija) d.o.o. **(1)**

Pancevacki put 62, 11000, Belgrade,
Serbia **(100%)**
Tel.: (381) 35 572 200
Web Site: http://www.crhserbia.com
Cement Mfr
N.A.I.C.S.: 327310
Milan Ilic *(Dir-Comml)*

CRH (Wien) GmbH **(1)**
Franzosengraben 7, A-1030, Vienna, Aus-
tria
Tel.: (43) 18890303
Web Site: http://www.crhaustria.com
Cement Mfr & Distr
N.A.I.C.S.: 327310
Josef Nowak *(CEO)*

CRH Agregate Betoane S.A. **(1)**
Sector 1 Str Emanoil Porumbaru no 93-95
Floor 1 and 5, 011857, Bucharest,
Romania **(98.62%)**
Tel.: (40) 213075300
Emp.: 900
Concrete Products Mfr
N.A.I.C.S.: 327390

CRH Bouwmaten B.V. **(1)**
Straatweg 62, 3621 BR, Breukelen, Nether-
lands
Tel.: (31) 346259159
Sales Range: $25-49.9 Million
Emp.: 17
Building Materials Distr
N.A.I.C.S.: 423390

CRH Bouwmaterialenhandel B.V. **(1)**
Stationsweg 2, Geldermalsen, 4191 KK,
Netherlands
Tel.: (31) 886337202
Web Site: http://www.crh-bouwmaterialen.nl
Construction Materials Distr
N.A.I.C.S.: 423390

CRH Canada Group Inc. **(1)**
2300 Steeles Road West, Concord, L4K
5X6, ON, Canada
Tel.: (866) 322-2003
Web Site: http://www.crhcanada.com
Emp.: 3,000
Cement & Concrete; Aggregates; Construc-
tion Services
N.A.I.C.S.: 327310

Plant (Domestic):

CRH Cement - Joliette Plant **(2)**
966 Praries Road, Joliette, J6E 0L4, QC,
Canada
Tel.: (450) 756-1076
Web Site: http://www.crhcanada.com
Cement Mfr
N.A.I.C.S.: 327310

**CRH Cement - Mississauga
Plant** **(2)**
2391 Lakeshore Road West, Mississauga,
L5J 1K1, ON, Canada
Tel.: (905) 822-1653
Web Site: http://www.crhcanada.com
Construction Materials Whslr
N.A.I.C.S.: 423320

Unit (Domestic):

Demix Agregats - Laval **(2)**
1500 St Martin East Boulevard, Laval, H7G
4S8, QC, Canada
Tel.: (450) 669-7475
Web Site: http://www.crhcanada.com
Production & Sale of Concrete Aggregates
N.A.I.C.S.: 212321

Demix Beton - Quebec **(2)**
205 Bl Louis XIV Porte 102, Quebec, G2K
1W6, QC, Canada
Tel.: (800) 463-4518
Web Site: http://www.crhcanada.com
Cement Concrete Aggregates & Construc-
tion Equipment Mfr
N.A.I.C.S.: 327310

Demix Construction - Laval **(2)**
26 Saulnier Street, Laval, H7M 1S8, QC,
Canada
Tel.: (866) 436-8165
Web Site: http://www.crhcanada.com
Road & Bridge Construction; Concrete &
Asphalt Paving
N.A.I.C.S.: 237310

Dufferin Aggregates Butler Pit **(2)**

1180 Cedar Creek Road, Cambridge, N1R
5S5, ON, Canada
Tel.: (905) 761-7500
Web Site: http://www.crhcanada.com
Sand & Gravel Mining
N.A.I.C.S.: 212321

Dufferin Concrete **(2)**
2300 Steeles Avenue West, Concord, L4K
5X6, ON, Canada
Tel.: (905) 761-7000
Web Site: http://www.crhcanada.com
Readymix Concrete Mfr
N.A.I.C.S.: 327320

Branch (Domestic):

Dufferin Concrete - Kitchener **(3)**
26 Forwell Road, Kitchener, N2B 3E8, ON,
Canada
Tel.: (519) 576-5570
Web Site: http://www.crhcanada.com
Retail of Concrete Block & Concrete
N.A.I.C.S.: 444110

Unit (Domestic):

Dufferin Construction Company **(2)**
585 Michigan Drive Suite 1, Oakville, L6L
0G1, ON, Canada
Tel.: (905) 842-2741
Web Site:
http://www.dufferinconstruction.com
Highway Construction
N.A.I.C.S.: 237310
John Serafini *(Mgr-Health & Safety)*

CRH Ciment (Romania) S.A. **(1)**
Sector 1 Str Emanoil Porumbaru no 93-95
Floor 1 and 5, 011857, Bucharest,
Romania **(98.62%)**
Tel.: (40) 213075200
Web Site: https://www.romcim.ro
Cement Mfr
N.A.I.C.S.: 327310

CRH Concrete A/S **(1)**
Vestergade 25, Seeland, 4130, Viby, Den-
mark
Tel.: (45) 70103510
Web Site: https://www.crhconcrete.dk
Concrete Product Distr
N.A.I.C.S.: 423320
Claus Bering *(CEO)*

CRH Europe **(1)**
Einsteinlaan 26, Rijswijk, 2298 CC, Nether-
lands
Tel.: (31) 704142400
Web Site: http://www.crh.com
Sales Range: $25-49.9 Million
Emp.: 60
N.A.I.C.S.: 327991

Division (Domestic):

**CRH Europe - Products &
Distribution** **(2)**
Einsteinlaan 26, 2289 CC, Rijswijk, Nether-
lands
Tel.: (31) 704142400
Web Site: http://www.crh.com
Sales Range: $25-49.9 Million
Operating Division
N.A.I.C.S.: 327331

Subsidiary (Non-US):

Ancon Limited **(3)**
President Way President Pk, Sheffield, S4
7UR, United Kingdom
Tel.: (44) 1142755224
Web Site: https://www.ancon.co.uk
Sales Range: $150-199.9 Million
Emp.: 250
Building Products
N.A.I.C.S.: 332312

CRH Europe-Materials **(1)**
Shrewsbury House Cabinteely, Dublin, 18,
Ireland **(100%)**
Tel.: (353) 012048200
Web Site: http://www.crh.com
Sales Range: $25-49.9 Million
Emp.: 30
N.A.I.C.S.: 327991

CRH Fencing Limited **(1)**
Herons Way Carr Hill, Doncaster, DN4
8WA, United Kingdom
Tel.: (44) 1302 760861

Sales Range: $50-74.9 Million
Emp.: 75
Building Material Mfr & Distr
N.A.I.C.S.: 327120

CRH France SAS **(1)**
86-90 Rue du Dome, 92100, Boulogne-
Billancourt, France
Tel.: (33) 149109916
Holding Company; Construction Materials
Mfr & Distr
N.A.I.C.S.: 551112

Subsidiary (Domestic):

Beton Moule Industriel S.A. **(2)**
47 Ave des Genottes Le Cerame - Bat B,
BP 98318, Cergy-Pontoise, 95803, France
Tel.: (33) 134255555
Concrete Block Mfr
N.A.I.C.S.: 327331

CRH France Distribution SAS **(2)**
88 rue du Dome, 92100, Boulogne-
Billancourt, France
Tel.: (33) 146948000
Web Site: http://www.crh-francedistribution.fr
Building Materials Distr
N.A.I.C.S.: 423320

Subsidiary (Domestic):

**CRH Ile de France Distribution
SAS** **(3)**
69/71 Boulevard de la Republique, 92514,
Boulogne-Billancourt, Cedex, France
Tel.: (33) 1 4609 9500
Web Site: http://www.raboni.fr
Building Materials Distr
N.A.I.C.S.: 423390

Subsidiary (Domestic):

Eqiom S.A.S. **(2)**
49 Avenue Georges Pompidou, 92593,
Levallois-Perret, Cedex, France **(99.99%)**
Tel.: (33) 141061143
Web Site: http://www.eqiom.com
Emp.: 1,500
Cement, Concrete & Aggregate Mfr
N.A.I.C.S.: 327310
Pascal Hildwein *(CFO)*

Plant (Domestic):

Eqiom Betons **(3)**
Port Public, 57270, Uckange, France
Tel.: (33) 3 82 86 37 81
Web Site: http://www.eqiom.com
Construction Materials Whslr
N.A.I.C.S.: 423320

**Eqiom S.A.S. - Grand-Couronne
Grinding Plant** **(3)**
Boulevard Maritime, 76530, Grand
Couronne, France
Tel.: (33) 2 32 11 17 27
Web Site: http://www.eqiom.com
Cement Mfr
N.A.I.C.S.: 327310

Eqiom S.A.S. - Heming Plant **(3)**
Route de Lorquin, BP 1, 57830, Heming,
France
Tel.: (33) 3 87 23 37 00
Web Site: http://www.eqiom.com
Cement Mfr
N.A.I.C.S.: 327310

**Eqiom S.A.S. - La Rochelle Grinding
Center** **(3)**
Grand Port Maritime, 17000, La Rochelle,
France
Tel.: (33) 546525160
Web Site: http://www.eqiom.com
Cement Mfr
N.A.I.C.S.: 327310

Eqiom S.A.S. - Lumbres Plant **(3)**
Rue Jean-Baptiste Macaux, 62380, Lum-
bres, France
Tel.: (33) 3 21 38 11 11
Web Site: http://www.eqiom.com
Cement Mfr
N.A.I.C.S.: 327310

Subsidiary (Domestic):

Heras Cloture S.A.R.L. **(2)**
Allee des Lilas Les Fenieres - Bat A, 01150,
Saint-Vulbas, France

CRH plc—(Continued)

Tel.: (33) 474366711
Web Site: https://www.cloture-mobile.fr
Sales Range: $25-49.9 Million
Emp.: 7
Security System Services
N.A.I.C.S.: 561621

Laubeuf SAS (2)
5 avenue du Général de Gaulle, 94160,
Saint-Mande, France
Tel.: (33) 141743660
Web Site: http://www.laubeuf.com
Roofing System Designer & Mfr
N.A.I.C.S.: 332323

Plakabeton France S.A. (2)
6 Rue de Cabanis L'Union, 31240, Tou-
louse, France
Tel.: (33) 534253925
Building Material Retailer
N.A.I.C.S.: 444180

Stradal SAS (2)
47 Avenue des Genottes, 95800, Cergy-
Pontoise, France
Tel.: (33) 134255555
Sales Range: $550-599.9 Million
Emp.: 1,200
Concrete Product Mfr & Distr
N.A.I.C.S.: 327390

CRH Getaz Holding AG (1)
Avenue Reller 14, Vevey, 1800, Switzerland
Tel.: (41) 219250800
Web Site: http://www.getaz-romang.ch
Concrete Block Mfr
N.A.I.C.S.: 327331

CRH Kleiwaren Beheer B.V. (1)
Engelsmanstraat 56, 6086 BD, Neer, Neth-
erlands
Tel.: (31) 475 51 81 00
Building Material Mfr & Distr
N.A.I.C.S.: 327120

CRH Klinkier Sp. z o.o. (1)
Ul Pszczynska 309, Gliwice, 44-100, Poland
Tel.: (48) 32 239 4105
Web Site: http://www.crh-klinkier.pl
Construction Materials Distr
N.A.I.C.S.: 423390

CRH Structural Concrete B.V. (1)
Boerdijk 30, 7844 TC, Veenoord, Nether-
lands
Tel.: (31) 591551763
Sales Range: $75-99.9 Million
Emp.: 150
Building Materials Distr
N.A.I.C.S.: 423320

CRH Sudamericana S.A. (1)
Manuel Belzu 1939 Olivos, B1636GMI,
Buenos Aires, Argentina
Tel.: (54) 1147904500
Building Materials Mfr & Distr
N.A.I.C.S.: 327991

Cabi S.A. (1)
Joaquim Molins 5, 08028, Barcelona, Spain
Tel.: (34) 935053600
Web Site: http://www.cabi.es
Cement Mfr
N.A.I.C.S.: 327310

Calduran Kalkzandsteen B.V. (1)
Einsteinstraat 5, 3846 BH, Harderwijk,
Netherlands
Tel.: (31) 341 464 000
Web Site: http://www.calduran.nl
Sales Range: $125-149.9 Million
Emp.: 260
Building Materials Mfr
N.A.I.C.S.: 327120

Cantera de Aridos Puig Broca
S.A. (1)
Calle Joaquim Molins 5, Barcelona, 08028,
Spain
Tel.: (34) 972622362
Building Materials Distr
N.A.I.C.S.: 423320

Canteras Cerro Negro S.A. (1)
Manuel Belzu 1939-43, Olivos, B1636GMI,
Buenos Aires, Argentina
Tel.: (54) 11 4790 0200
Web Site: http://www.cerronegro.com.ar
Ceramic Wall & Floor Tile Mfr

N.A.I.C.S.: 327120

Cement Ozarow S.A. (1)
Ul Father Ignacy Skorupka 5, 00-546, War-
saw, Poland
Tel.: (48) 158391100
Web Site: https://ozarow.com.pl
Cement Mfr
N.A.I.C.S.: 327310

Cementbouw B.V. (1)
Bennebroekerdijk 244, Cruquius, 2142 LE,
Netherlands
Tel.: (31) 23 548 14 81
Web Site: http://www.cementbouw.nl
Readymix Concrete Mfr
N.A.I.C.S.: 327320

Comercial Duomo Limitada (1)
Bathroom Fixture & Fittings Mfr
N.A.I.C.S.: 332999

Concrete Specialties Company (1)
8011 Green Bay Rd, Kenosha, WI 53142
Tel.: (262) 694-3166
Web Site:
   http://www.concretespecialtiesco.com
Sales Range: $10-24.9 Million
Emp.: 40
Pre-Cast Concrete Products
N.A.I.C.S.: 327390

Cormela S.A. (1)
Sales Range: $25-49.9 Million
Emp.: 88
Clay Ceramic & Brick Mfr
N.A.I.C.S.: 327120

Danucem Magyarorszag Kft. (1)
Vaci Ut 144-150, 1138, Budapest, Hungary
Tel.: (36) 14725000
Web Site: https://www.danucem.com
Cement Concrete Mfr
N.A.I.C.S.: 327320

Douterloigne N.V. (1)
Vichtsesteenweg 159, 8570, Anzegem, Bel-
gium
Tel.: (32) 56694040
Web Site: https://www.douterloigne.com
Emp.: 25
Prefabricated Concrete Material Distr
N.A.I.C.S.: 423320

Drogomex Sp. Z O O. (1)
ul Stefana Bryly 4, 05-800, Pruszkow, Po-
land
Tel.: (48) 227588981
Road Construction Engineering Services
N.A.I.C.S.: 237310

Dycore B.V. (1)
Ambachtsweg 16, 4906 CH, Oosterhout,
Netherlands
Tel.: (31) 162477477
Web Site: https://www.dycore.nl
Sales Range: $25-49.9 Million
Emp.: 100
Concrete Floor System Mfr
N.A.I.C.S.: 327390

EHL AG (1)
Alte Chaussee 127, 56642, Kruft, Germany
Tel.: (49) 265280080
Web Site: https://www.ehl.de
Concrete Block Mfr
N.A.I.C.S.: 327331

Element AG (1)
Mariahilfstrasse 25, 1712, Tafers, Switzer-
land
Tel.: (41) 264947777
Web Site: https://www.element.ch
Sales Range: $75-99.9 Million
Emp.: 110
Concrete Product Distr
N.A.I.C.S.: 423320

Elpreco SA (1)
Calea Severinului no 44, 200609, Craiova,
Dolj, Romania
Tel.: (40) 251307700
Web Site: https://www.elpreco.ro
Emp.: 400
Building Materials Mfr
N.A.I.C.S.: 327120

Ergon N.V. (1)
Marnixdreef 5, 2500, Lier, Belgium
Tel.: (32) 34900400
Web Site: https://www.ergon.be

Sales Range: $150-199.9 Million
Emp.: 350
Prefabricated Concrete Material Distr
N.A.I.C.S.: 423320

Ergon Poland Sp. z o.o. (1)
Ul Grojecka 19, Badowo Msciska, 96-320,
Mszczonow, Poland
Tel.: (48) 468581800
Web Site: http://www.ergon-
   international.com
Building Materials Distr
N.A.I.C.S.: 423390

F.J. Aschwanden AG (1)
Grenzstrasse 24, 3250, Lyss, Switzerland
Web Site: http://www.aschwanden.com
Emp.: 60
Metal Construction Accessory Mfr
N.A.I.C.S.: 332323

Ferrobeton Beton-es Vasbetonelem
gyarto Zrt (1)
Papirgyari ut 18 - 22, 2400, Dunaujvaros,
Hungary
Tel.: (36) 25284444
Web Site: https://www.ferrobeton.hu
Concrete Brick Distr
N.A.I.C.S.: 423320

Ferrobeton Dunaujvarosi Beton- es
Vasbetonelem-gyarto Zrt (1)
Papirgyari ut 18-22, 2400, Dunaujvaros,
Hungary
Tel.: (36) 25887075
Web Site: https://ferrobeton.hu
Construction Materials Whslr
N.A.I.C.S.: 423320

Ferrobeton Romania (1)
Str Neagoe Basarab no 4, Negoiesti,
107086, Brazi, Romania
Tel.: (40) 344100240
Web Site: https://ferrobeton.ro
Sales Range: $50-74.9 Million
Emp.: 70
Construction Materials Distr
N.A.I.C.S.: 423320

Ferrobeton Slovakia, s.r.o. (1)
Sladkovicova 8, Sturovo, 94302, Slovakia
Tel.: (421) 36 751 1150
Web Site: http://www.ferrobeton.sk
Sales Range: $25-49.9 Million
Emp.: 20
Building Materials Distr
N.A.I.C.S.: 423320

Ferrobeton concrete and reinforced
concrete producer Public Limited
Company (1)
Papirgyari ut 18-22, 2400, Dunaujvaros,
Hungary
Tel.: (36) 25284444
Concrete Block & Brick Mfr
N.A.I.C.S.: 327331

Finnsementti Oy (1)
Hatsinanpuisto 8, PL 115, 02600, Espoo,
Finland
Tel.: (358) 201206200
Web Site: http://www.finnsementti.fi
Cement Mfr & Distr
N.A.I.C.S.: 327310
Miikka Riionheimo (Pres & CEO)

Formigons Girona S.A. (1)
Disseminat S/N Vilatenim Figures, 17484,
Gerona, Spain
Tel.: (34) 972468070
Building Materials Distr
N.A.I.C.S.: 423390

Geoquip Limited (1)
Units 3 & 4 Duffield Road, Little Eaton,
DE21 5DR, Derbyshire, United Kingdom
Tel.: (44) 1629824891
Web Site: http://www.geoquip.com
Sales Range: $25-49.9 Million
Emp.: 40
Electronic Security System Installation Ser-
vices & Mfr
N.A.I.C.S.: 238210

Grupa Ozarow S.A. (1)
Karsy 77, 27-530, Ozarow, Swietokrzyskie,
Poland
Tel.: (48) 158391100
Sales Range: $200-249.9 Million
Emp.: 550
Cement Mfr

N.A.I.C.S.: 327310

Halfen AS (1)
Flintegata 4, 4095, Stavanger, Norway
Tel.: (47) 51 82 34 00
Web Site: http://www.halfen.no
Metal Product Distr
N.A.I.C.S.: 423510

Halfen GmbH (1)
Liebigstr 14, 40764, Langonfold, Rhoinland,
Germany
Tel.: (49) 2173 970 0
Web Site: http://www.halfen.com
Construction Fitting Mfr
N.A.I.C.S.: 332919

Halfen S.R.L. (1)
Via F lli Bronzetti 28, 24124, Bergamo, Italy
Tel.: (39) 035 0760711
Web Site: http://www.halfen.it
Sales Range: $25-49.9 Million
Emp.: 17
Building Fixture Mfr
N.A.I.C.S.: 332999

Hammerl GmbH & Co. KG (1)
Niedere Klinge 15, 74376, Gemmrigheim,
Germany
Tel.: (49) 714384480
Web Site: https://www.hammerl.de
Emp.: 50
Plastic Product Mfr & Distr
N.A.I.C.S.: 326199

Heras Mobilzaun GmbH (1)
Heinrich-Malina-Str 100, Krefeld, 47809,
Germany
Tel.: (49) 2151 32 78 274
Web Site: http://www.heras-mobilzaun.de
Sales Range: $25-49.9 Million
Emp.: 4
Electronic Security System Services
N.A.I.C.S.: 561621

Heras SKS GmbH (1)
Raiffeisenring 44, Bocholt, 46395, Germany
Tel.: (49) 287124414 0
Concrete Block & Brick Mfr
N.A.I.C.S.: 327331
Juergen Busch (Product Dir)

Heras-Adronit GmbH (1)
Raiffeisenring 44, 46395, Bocholt, Germany
Tel.: (49) 2871 24414 0
Web Site: http://www.heras-adronit.de
Security Fencing Services
N.A.I.C.S.: 331222

Hylas B.V. (1)
Tel.: (31) 481371948
Sales Range: $25-49.9 Million
Emp.: 25
Fabric Screen Mfr
N.A.I.C.S.: 332618

Infrastructure Products Australia Pty.
Ltd. (1)
1/1 Reeves Court, Breakwater, 3519, VIC,
Australia
Tel.: (61) 1800065356
Web Site:
   https://www.infrastructureproducts.com.au
Emp.: 200
Polymer Material Mfr
N.A.I.C.S.: 325211

Irish Cement Ltd. (1)
Platin, Drogheda, County Louth,
Ireland (100%)
Tel.: (353) 419876000
Web Site: https://www.irishcement.ie
Sales Range: $125-149.9 Million
Emp.: 150
Mfr of Cement Products
N.A.I.C.S.: 327310
Albert J. Manifold (Pres)

J, De Saegher Steenhandel N.V, (1)
Engelselei 79, 2140, Antwerp, Belgium
Tel.: (32) 32310821
Emp.: 12
Building Materials Distr
N.A.I.C.S.: 423390

JURA-Holding AG (1)
Zurlindeninsel 1, 5000, Aarau, Switzerland
Tel.: (41) 628380505
Emp.: 30
Investment Management Service
N.A.I.C.S.: 523999

Patrick Stapfer *(Mng Dir)*

Jonker Beton B.V. **(1)**
Panovenweg 15, Postbus 6193, 4004 JE,
Tiel, Netherlands
Tel.: (31) 344624488
Building Materials Distr
N.A.I.C.S.: 423390

Kleiwarenfabriek Buggenum B.V. **(1)**
Dorpstraat 60, 6082 AR, Buggenum, Neth-
erlands
Tel.: (31) 475 591666
Sales Range: $25-49.9 Million
Emp.: 20
Building Materials Distr
N.A.I.C.S.: 423390

Kooy Baksteencentrum B.V. **(1)**
Rembrandtlaan 38, 3723 BJ, Bilthoven,
Netherlands
Tel.: (31) 302259800
Web Site: https://www.kooy.nl
Emp.: 15
Building Materials Distr
N.A.I.C.S.: 423390
Michiel van der Kaay *(Mgr-Comml)*

Leviat AG **(1)**
Grenzstrasse 24, 3250, Lyss, Switzerland
Tel.: (41) 800226600
Web Site: https://www.ancon.ch
Emp.: 3,000
Construction Accessories Mfr
N.A.I.C.S.: 333991

Leviat B.V. **(1)**
Oostermaat 3, 7623 CS, Borne, Nether-
lands
Tel.: (31) 742671449
Web Site: https://www.leviat.com
Construction Materials Whslr
N.A.I.C.S.: 423320

Leviat Pty Limited **(1)**
98 Kurrajong Avenue, Mount Druitt, Sydney,
2770, NSW, Australia
Tel.: (61) 288401600
Web Site: https://www.leviat.com
Engineering Consulting Services
N.A.I.C.S.: 541330

Mahalo Acquisition Corp. **(1)**
1081 Makepono St, Honolulu, HI 96819
Tel.: (808) 864-0136
Construction Materials Whslr
N.A.I.C.S.: 423390

Marlux Klaps N.V. **(1)**
Industriezone West - Limburg 4 345 Al-
bertkade 3, 3980, Tessenderlo, Belgium
Tel.: (32) 13679100
Sales Range: $75-99.9 Million
Emp.: 200
Building Materials Distr
N.A.I.C.S.: 423320

Masfalt Sp. z o.o. **(1)**
Ul Stefana Bryly 4, 05-800, Pruszkow, Po-
land
Tel.: (48) 22 758 89 81
Web Site: http://www.masfalt.pl
Building Material Mfr & Distr
N.A.I.C.S.: 327120

Mavotrans B.V. **(1)**
Storkstraat 25, Postbus 81, 2700 AB, Zo-
etermeer, Netherlands
Tel.: (31) 79 344 63 63
Web Site: http://www.mavotrans.nl
Sales Range: $25-49.9 Million
Emp.: 25
Building Material Mfr & Distr
N.A.I.C.S.: 327120

Moravacem d.o.o. **(1)**
Branka Ristica 8, Popovac, 35254, Paracin,
Serbia
Tel.: (381) 35572200
Web Site: https://moravacem.rs
Cement Mfr & Whslr
N.A.I.C.S.: 327310

Mulzer Crushed Stone Inc. **(1)**
534 Mozart St, Tell City, IN 47586
Tel.: (812) 547-7921
Web Site: https://www.mulzer.com
Sales Range: $25-49.9 Million
Crushed & Broken Limestone
N.A.I.C.S.: 212312

N.V.B. Ubbens Bouwstoffen B.V. **(1)**
Slauerhoffweg 6, Postbus 48, 8912 BH,
Leeuwarden, Netherlands
Tel.: (31) 582937777
Web Site: http://www.nvbubbens.nl
Building Materials Distr
N.A.I.C.S.: 423390

Northgate Ready Mix, LLC **(1)**
3500 Petaluma Hill Rd, San Rafael, CA
95404
Tel.: (415) 258-4700
Web Site:
      http://www.northgatereadymix.com
Ready Mix Concrete & Related Products
Mfr
N.A.I.C.S.: 327320

Northstone (NI) Limited **(1)**
99 Kingsway Dunmurry, Belfast, BT17 9NU,
United Kingdom
Tel.: (44) 2890551200
Web Site: https://www.northstone-ni.co.uk
Building Materials Distr
N.A.I.C.S.: 423390
Eamonn Sweeney *(CEO)*

O.K.S.M. Sp. z o.o. **(1)**
ul Budowlana 3, Olsztyn, 10424, Poland
Tel.: (48) 89 521 10 00
Web Site: http://www.oksm.pl
Emp.: 107
Mineral Mining Services
N.A.I.C.S.: 212390

OPTERRA GmbH **(1)**
Goerdelerring 9, 04109, Leipzig,
Germany **(100%)**
Tel.: (49) 34139378510
Web Site: http://www.opterra-crh.com
Emp.: 400
Cement Mfr
N.A.I.C.S.: 327310
Danilo Buscaglia *(Chm)*

Subsidiary (Domestic):

OPTERRA Beton GmbH **(2)**
Dieselstrasse 8, 84088, Neufahrn, Germany
Tel.: (49) 8773 7074 37
Web Site: http://www.opterra-crh.com
Concrete Products Mfr
N.A.I.C.S.: 327390

OPTERRA Zement GmbH **(2)**
Strasse der Einheit 25, 06638, Karsdorf,
Germany **(100%)**
Tel.: (49) 3446173
Web Site: http://www.opterra-crh.com
Cement Mfr
N.A.I.C.S.: 327310

Oeterbeton N.V. **(1)**
Hooggeistersveld 15, 3680, Maaseik, Bel-
gium
Tel.: (32) 89860100
Emp.: 15
Precast Concrete Mfr
N.A.I.C.S.: 327390

Oldcastle, Inc. **(1)**
900 Ashwood Pkwy, Atlanta, GA
30338 **(100%)**
Tel.: (770) 804-3363
Web Site: http://www.oldcastle.com
Sales Range: $5-14.9 Billion
Emp.: 50,000
Holding Company
N.A.I.C.S.: 327320

Subsidiary (Domestic):

MMI Products, Inc. **(2)**
400 N Sam Houston Pkwy E Ste 1200,
Houston, TX 77060
Tel.: (281) 876-0080
Sales Range: $450-499.9 Million
Emp.: 2,500
Fencing & Concrete Construction Products
N.A.I.C.S.: 332312
Glenn Head *(Mgr-Benefits)*

Subsidiary (Domestic):

ADC Manufacturing **(3)**
300 N Industrial Park Rd, Harrison, AR
72601-1197
Tel.: (870) 741-6193
Web Site: http://www.adcmanufacturing.com

Sales Range: $25-49.9 Million
Emp.: 60
Fence Parts & Castings
N.A.I.C.S.: 332618
Kathy Slay *(Plant Mgr)*

Meadow Burke **(3)**
531 S Hwy 301, Tampa, FL 33619
Tel.: (813) 248-1944
Web Site: http://www.meadowburke.com
Custom Constuction Reinforcement Prod-
ucts
N.A.I.C.S.: 423390
Jason Tebeau *(VP-Ops)*

Plant (Domestic):

Meadow Burke **(4)**
5110 Santa Fe Rd, Tampa, FL 33619
Tel.: (813) 247-3663
Web Site: http://www.meadowburke.com
Sales Range: $10-24.9 Million
Emp.: 50
Concrete Forming & Reinforcing Products
N.A.I.C.S.: 331222

Subsidiary (Domestic):

Oldcastle APG, Inc. **(2)**
400 Perimeter Ctr Ter Fl 10, Atlanta, GA
30346
Tel.: (678) 461-2838
Web Site: http://www.oldcastleapg.com
Concrete Building Products Mfr
N.A.I.C.S.: 327390
Tim Ortman *(Pres)*

Subsidiary (Domestic):

Barrette Outdoor Living, Inc. **(3)**
7830 Freeway Cir, Middleburg Heights, OH
44130
Tel.: (440) 891-0790
Web Site:
      http://www.barretteoutdoorliving.com
Wood & Vinyl Products Mfr
N.A.I.C.S.: 321999
Jean DesAutels *(CEO)*

Subsidiary (Domestic):

Alumi-Guard, Inc. **(4)**
2401 Corporate Blvd, Brooksville, FL 34604
Tel.: (352) 754-8555
Web Site: http://www.alumi-guard.com
Sales Range: $10-24.9 Million
Emp.: 120
Fabricated Wire Product Mfr
N.A.I.C.S.: 332618
William Woodard *(Founder)*

Subsidiary (Domestic):

Buckeye Resources, Inc. **(3)**
3815 Springfield Xenia, Springfield, OH
45506
Tel.: (937) 462-8346
Web Site:
      http://www.buckeyeresources.com
Mulch, Soils & Plant Material Mfr & Distr
N.A.I.C.S.: 115112

Calstone, Co. **(3)**
5787 Obata Way, Gilroy, CA 95020
Tel.: (408) 984-8800
Web Site: http://www.calstone.com
Concrete Block & Brick Mfr
N.A.I.C.S.: 327331

USM-RGC, Inc. **(3)**
112 South Santa Fe Dr, Denver, CO 80223
Tel.: (303) 778-7227
Web Site: http://www.usmix.com
Rev.: $3,333,333
Emp.: 30
Concrete Products Mfr
N.A.I.C.S.: 327390
Bruce Peterson *(CEO)*

Subsidiary (Domestic):

**Oldcastle Adams Products
Company** **(2)**
5701 McCrimmon Pkwy, Morrisville, NC
27560 **(100%)**
Tel.: (919) 467-2218
Web Site: http://www.adamsproducts.com
Sales Range: $25-49.9 Million
Emp.: 50
Mfr of Masonry Block & Pavers
N.A.I.C.S.: 327331

Oldcastle Architectural, Inc. **(2)**
375 Northridge Rd Ste 250, Atlanta, GA
30350
Tel.: (770) 804-3363
Web Site: http://www.oldcastle.com
Sales Range: $25-49.9 Million
Emp.: 50
Concrete, Masonry & Brick Products
N.A.I.C.S.: 327331

Subsidiary (Non-US):

APG Canada **(3)**
8145 Bombardier St, Ville d'Anjou, H1J
1A5, QC, Canada
Tel.: (514) 351-2125
Web Site: http://www.permacon.ca
Sales Range: $50-74.9 Million
Concrete Pavers Mfr
N.A.I.C.S.: 327331

Subsidiary (Domestic):

**Advanced Environmental Recycling
Technologies, Inc.** **(3)**
3400 914 Jefferson St, Springdale, AR
72764
Tel.: (479) 756-7400
Recycle Waste Polyethylene Plastics Devel-
oper & Mfr
N.A.I.C.S.: 423930
Richard Shields *(VP-Ops)*

Allied Concrete Company **(3)**
1000 Harris St, Charlottesville, VA
22903-5315 **(100%)**
Tel.: (434) 296-7181
Web Site: http://www.alliedconcrete.com
Sales Range: $10-24.9 Million
Emp.: 50
Concrete Block & Brick Products Mfr
N.A.I.C.S.: 327331

Anchor Block Company **(3)**
5959 Baker Rd Ste 390, Minnetonka, MN
55345
Tel.: (952) 351-9670
Web Site: http://www.anchorblock.com
Concrete Block & Brick Products
N.A.I.C.S.: 327331
Glenn Bolles *(CEO)*

Affiliate (Domestic):

Anchor Wall Systems **(4)**
5959 Baker Rd Ste 390, Minnetonka, MN
55345-5996
Tel.: (952) 933-8855
Web Site: http://www.anchorwall.com
Concrete Block & Brick
N.A.I.C.S.: 533110

Subsidiary (Domestic):

Anchor Concrete Products Inc. **(3)**
1913 Atlantic Ave, Manasquan, NJ 08736
Tel.: (732) 292-2500
Web Site: http://www.oldcastlemasonry.com
Sales Range: $50-74.9 Million
Masonry & Landscape Products Mfr
N.A.I.C.S.: 327331

Big River Industries, Inc. **(3)**
3600 Mansell Rd Ste 575, Alpharetta, GA
30022-1512 **(100%)**
Tel.: (678) 461-2830
Lightweight Aggregates & Fly-Ash Mfr
N.A.I.C.S.: 327992

Bonsal American, Inc. **(3)**
8201 Arrowridge Blvd, Charlotte, NC 28273-
5678
Tel.: (704) 525-1621
Web Site: http://www.bonsalamerican.com
Sales Range: $25-49.9 Million
Packaged Building Materials & Pavement
Maintenance Products Mfr
N.A.I.C.S.: 327390

Subsidiary (Domestic):

Sakrete of North America, LLC **(4)**
8201 Arrowridge Blvd, Charlotte, NC 28273
Tel.: (513) 242-3644
Web Site: https://www.sakrete.com
Sales Range: $10-24.9 Million
Concrete Mix Mfr & Distr
N.A.I.C.S.: 327320

Subsidiary (Domestic):

Northfield Block Co. **(3)**

CRH plc—(Continued)

1 Hunt Ct, Mundelein, IL 60060
Tel.: (847) 949-3600
Web Site: http://www.northfieldblock.com
Emp.: 60
Concrete Blocks
N.A.I.C.S.: 327331

Branch (Domestic):

Northfield Block (4)
6045 Dixie Hwy, Bridgeport, MI 48722
Tel.: (989) 777-0420
Web Site: http://www.northfieldblock.com
Rev.: $42,399,612
Emp.: 19
Stone & Marble Products Distr
N.A.I.C.S.: 423320
Craig Belasco (Pres)

Subsidiary (Domestic):

Oldcastle APG Northeast, Inc. (3)
1231 Willis Rd, North Chesterfield, VA
23237
Tel.: (703) 361-2777
Building Materials Distr
N.A.I.C.S.: 423320

Oldcastle APG South, Inc. (3)
108 Buchanan Church Rd, Greensboro, NC
27405-8631
Tel.: (336) 375-5656
Building Materials Mfr
N.A.I.C.S.: 327120

Oldcastle APG West, Inc. (3)
4150 W Turney, Phoenix, AZ 85019
Tel.: (602) 302-9600
Building Material Mfr & Distr
N.A.I.C.S.: 327120

Supreme Concrete Block Inc. (3)
396 Tyson Dr, Winchester, VA 22603
Tel.: (540) 667-4600
Web Site: http://www.betcosupreme.com
Rev.: $12,000,000
Emp.: 30
Concrete Products, Nec
N.A.I.C.S.: 327332

Subsidiary (Non-US):

Oldcastle Building Envelop Canada, Inc. (2)
3601 72 Ave SE, Calgary, T2C 2K3, AB,
Canada
Tel.: (403) 279-2544
Building Materials Distr
N.A.I.C.S.: 423320

Oldcastle Building Products Canada, Inc. (2)
8145 Rue Bombardier, Anjou, H1J 1A5,
QC, Canada
Tel.: (514) 351-2120
Sales Range: $75-99.9 Million
Emp.: 200
Concrete Block Mfr & Distr
N.A.I.C.S.: 327331
Henri Besnier (VP-Fin & Dev)

Subsidiary (Domestic):

Expocrete Concrete Products Ltd. (3)
16333-137 Ave, Edmonton, T5V 1N8, AB,
Canada
Tel.: (780) 447-2122
Web Site: http://www.expocrete.com
Sales Range: $25-49.9 Million
Emp.: 100
Concrete Products Mfr
N.A.I.C.S.: 327390

Division (Domestic):

Oldcastle Building Products Canada, Inc. - Permacon Division (3)
8140 rue Bombardier, Anjou, H1J 1A5, QC,
Canada
Tel.: (888) 737-6226
Web Site: http://www.permacon.ca
Concrete Panel Mfr
N.A.I.C.S.: 327390

Subsidiary (Domestic):

Oldcastle Building Products, Inc (2)

900 Ashwood Pkwy Ste600, Atlanta, GA
30338
Tel.: (800) 899-8455
Sales Range: $1-4.9 Billion
Emp.: 7,000
Concrete Block Mfr & Whslr
N.A.I.C.S.: 327331

Oldcastle Infrastructure, Inc. (2)
7000 Central Parkway Ste 800, Atlanta, GA
30328
Tel.: (253) 833-2777
Web Site: http://oldcastleinfrastructure.com
Precast Concrete & Composite Products
Mfr
N.A.I.C.S.: 327390

Subsidiary (Domestic):

Amcor Inc. (3)
333 S Redwood Rd, North Salt Lake, UT
84054-2902 (100%)
Tel.: (801) 936-7628
Web Site: https://www.amcormasonry.com
Sales Range: $25-49.9 Million
Emp.: 48
Mfr of Concrete Pipe & Precast Concrete
Products
N.A.I.C.S.: 331210

Granite Precasting & Concrete, Inc. (3)
4030 Bakerview Spur, Bellingham, WA
98226
Tel.: (360) 671-2251
Other Building Material Dealers
N.A.I.C.S.: 444180

Hancock Concrete Products Inc. (3)
17 Atlantic Ave, Hancock, MN 56244
Tel.: (320) 392-5207
Web Site: http://www.hancockconcrete.com
Sales Range: $10-24.9 Million
Emp.: 150
Culvert Pipe, Concrete
N.A.I.C.S.: 327332
Robert Schmidgall (Pres)

Subsidiary (Non-US):

Hydro International Limited (3)
Shearwater House Clevedon Hall Estate,
Clevedon, BS21 7RD, United Kingdom
Tel.: (44) 1275878371
Web Site: http://www.hydro-int.com
Water & Wastewater Management & Treat-
ment Services
N.A.I.C.S.: 221310
Paul Cleaver (CEO)

Subsidiary (US):

Eutek Systems, Inc (4)
2925 NW Aloclek Dr Ste 140, Hillsboro, OR
97124
Tel.: (503) 615-8130
Engineering Services
N.A.I.C.S.: 541330

Subsidiary (Domestic):

N.C. Products (3)
920 Withers Rd, Raleigh, NC
27603-6095 (100%)
Tel.: (919) 772-6301
Sales Range: $50-74.9 Million
Emp.: 60
Mfr of Concrete Pipe, Precast Concrete
Products & Manholes
N.A.I.C.S.: 423390

Division (Domestic):

Oldcastle Precast Building Systems (3)
1401 Trimble Rd, Edgewood, MD 21040
Tel.: (410) 612-1213
Sales Range: $50-74.9 Million
Emp.: 180
Concrete Products
N.A.I.C.S.: 327390

Subsidiary (Domestic):

Oldcastle Precast, Inc. - Portland (3)
28499 SW Boberg Rd, Portland, OR 97070-
0323
Tel.: (503) 682-2844
Web Site: http://www.oldcastleprecast.com
Sales Range: $25-49.9 Million
Emp.: 65

Concrete Pipe Mfr & Precast Concrete Contractor Services
N.A.I.C.S.: 327332

Quality Concrete Products, Inc. (3)
3050 Wilma Dr, Clarkston, WA 99403
Tel.: (509) 758-2655
Web Site:
https://www.qualityconcreteproducts.biz
Precast Concrete Products Mfr
N.A.I.C.S.: 327390

Utility Vault Co., Inc. (3)
2808 A St SE, Auburn, WA 98002 (100%)
Tel.: (253) 839-3500
Web Site: http://www.uvauburn.com
Sales Range: $25-49.9 Million
Emp.: 80
Mfr of Precast Concrete, Concrete Pipe,
Prestressed Concrete Piling
N.A.I.C.S.: 327390

Subsidiary (Domestic):

Oldcastle Lawn & Garden, Inc. (2)
481 Spring Water Rd, Poland Spring, ME
04274
Tel.: (207) 998-5580
Garden Supplies Mfr & Distr
N.A.I.C.S.: 339999
Eoin Lehane (Pres)

Subsidiary (Domestic):

Jolly Gardener Products Inc. (3)
481 Spring Water Rd, Poland Spring, ME
04274
Tel.: (207) 998-5580
Web Site: http://www.jollygardener.com
Rev.: $25,000,000
Emp.: 65
Mulch, Wood & Bark Producer & Distr
N.A.I.C.S.: 321999

Subsidiary (Domestic):

Oldcastle Material Texas Inc. (2)
420 Decker Dr Ste 200, Irving, TX 75062
Tel.: (214) 741-3531
Web Site: https://texasmaterials.com
Asphalt Paving & Construction Services
N.A.I.C.S.: 324121

Oldcastle Materials, Inc. (2)
900 Ashwood Pkwy Ste 600, Atlanta, GA
30338-4780
Tel.: (770) 522-5600
Web Site:
https://www.crhamericasmaterials.com
Sales Range: $5-14.9 Billion
Emp.: 23,000
Holding Company; Construction Materials &
Civil Engineering Construction Services
N.A.I.C.S.: 551112

Subsidiary (Domestic):

APAC Mid-South, Inc. (3)
2700 Corporate Dr Ste 250, Birmingham,
AL 35242
Tel.: (205) 995-5900
Web Site: https://apac-al.com
Construction Sand & Crushed Stone Mining
N.A.I.C.S.: 212321

Unit (Domestic):

APAC-Arkansas - Arkhola Division (3)
755 E Millsap Rd, Fayetteville, AR 72703
Tel.: (479) 785-4271
Construction Materials
N.A.I.C.S.: 327991
Josh Lee (Mgr-HR)

APAC-Arkansas - McClinton Anchor Division (3)
755 E Millsap Rd PO Box 9208, Fayette-
ville, AR 72703
Tel.: (479) 587-3300
Web Site: http://www.oldcastlematerials.com
Sales Range: $25-49.9 Million
Emp.: 50
Hot-Mix Asphalt, Construction Aggregates &
Heavy Highway Construction Services
N.A.I.C.S.: 324121

APAC-Atlantic - Asheville Division (3)
1188 Smokey Park Hwy, Candler, NC
28715

Tel.: (828) 665-1180
Web Site: http://www.apacatlanticinc.com
Sales Range: $125-149.9 Million
Emp.: 500
Asphalt Production Services
N.A.I.C.S.: 324121

APAC-Atlantic - Harrison Division (3)
226 Gill St, Alcoa, TN 37701
Tel.: (865) 003-0100
Web Site: http://www.oldcastlematerials.com
Asphalt Paving & Construction Services
N.A.I.C.S.: 324121

APAC-Kansas - Kansas City Division (3)
7415 W 130th St Ste 300, Overland Park,
KS 66213-2677
Tel.: (913) 814-6700
Web Site: http://www.oldcastlematerials.com
Emp.: 100
Construction Services & Products
N.A.I.C.S.: 237310

APAC-Kansas - Shears Division (3)
1600 N Lorraine St Ste 1, Hutchinson, KS
67501
Tel.: (620) 662-3307
Sales Range: $100-124.9 Million
Emp.: 500
Asphalt Paving & Construction Materials
N.A.I.C.S.: 237310
Chad Girard (Co-Pres)

Subsidiary (Domestic):

APAC-Mississippi, Inc. (3)
5725 Hwy 18 S, Jackson, MS 39209
Tel.: (601) 376-4000
Web Site: http://www.oldcastlematerials.com
Sales Range: $50-74.9 Million
Emp.: 150
Asphalt Paving & Construction Services
N.A.I.C.S.: 324121

APAC-Oklahoma, Inc. (3)
4150 S 100th E Ave Cherokee Bldg Ste
300, Tulsa, OK 74146
Tel.: (918) 438-2020
Web Site: http://www.oldcastlematerials.com
Sales Range: $50-74.9 Million
Emp.: 130
Asphalt & Concrete Paving & Construction
Services
N.A.I.C.S.: 237310
Branden LeFevre (Pres)

Unit (Domestic):

APAC-Southeast - Southern Florida Division (3)
1451 Myrtle St, Sarasota, FL 34234-4723
Tel.: (941) 355-7178
Sales Range: $25-49.9 Million
Emp.: 60
Asphalt Paving & Construction Services
N.A.I.C.S.: 237310

Subsidiary (Domestic):

APAC-Tennessee, Inc. (3)
1210 Harbor Ave, Memphis, TN 38113
Tel.: (901) 947-5600
Web Site: http://www.apac.com
Sales Range: $200-249.9 Million
Emp.: 350
Highway Paving & Heavy Construction Ser-
vices
N.A.I.C.S.: 212319

Unit (Domestic):

APAC-Texas - Trotti & Thomson Division (3)
12907 US Hwy 90, Beaumont, TX 77713
Tel.: (409) 866-1444
Asphalt Paving & Construction Services
N.A.I.C.S.: 324121

Ballenger Paving Division (3)
900 W Lee Rd, Taylors, SC 29687-2521
Tel.: (864) 292-9550
Web Site: http://www.oldcastlematerials.com
Rev.: $55,000,000
Emp.: 150
Concrete Paving & Construction Services
N.A.I.C.S.: 237310

Subsidiary (Domestic):

Best Masonry & Tool Supply, Inc. (3)

16745 W Hardy Rd, Houston, TX 77060
Tel.: (281) 821-9487
Web Site: http://www.isgproducts.com
Brick, Stone & Related Materials Supplier
N.A.I.C.S.: 423320

Callanan Industries, Inc. (3)
8 Southwoods Blvd 4th Fl, Albany, NY
12211 **(100%)**
Tel.: (518) 374-2222
Web Site: http://www.callanan.com
Aggregates Asphalt & Related Construction
Activities
N.A.I.C.S.: 327390
Donald E. Fane *(Pres)*

Conrad Yelvington Distributors, Inc. (3)
2328 Bellvue Ave, Daytona Beach, FL
32114-5614
Tel.: (386) 257-5504
Sales Range: $75-99.9 Million
Emp.: 165
Construction Materials Services
N.A.I.C.S.: 423320

Dolomite Products Company Inc. (3)
800 Parker Hill Dr Ste 400, Rochester, NY
14625
Tel.: (585) 381-7010
Web Site: https://www.dolomitegroup.com
Sales Range: $25-49.9 Million
Emp.: 30
Asphalt & Ready-Mix Concrete Mfr; Construction Sand, Gravel & Crushed Stone
Mining
N.A.I.C.S.: 324121
John H. Odenbach *(Founder)*

Don's Building Supply, L.P. (3)
2327 Langford St, Dallas, TX 75208
Tel.: (214) 742-3045
Sales Range: $25-49.9 Million
Emp.: 15
Supplier of Building Materials
N.A.I.C.S.: 423390

Eugene Sand & Gravel, Inc. (3)
3000 Delta Hwy N, Eugene, OR 97408
Tel.: (541) 683-6400
Web Site: http://www.eugenesand.com
Highway & Street Paving Contractor
N.A.I.C.S.: 212321

Evans Construction Company (3)
7255 S US Hwy 89, Jackson, WY 83001-4309
Tel.: (307) 733-3029
Web Site: https://evansconstruction.com
Sales Range: $25-49.9 Million
Emp.: 50
Heavy Civil Construction Services, Asphalt
& Ready-Mix Concrete Mfr, Construction
Sand & Rock Mining
N.A.I.C.S.: 237310
Mitchell Lewis *(Pres)*

Four Corners Materials (3)
PO Box 1969, Bayfield, CO 81122
Tel.: (970) 247-2172
Web Site: http://www.oldcastlematerials.com
Rev.: $15,000,000
Emp.: 100
Provider of Heavy Construction Services
N.A.I.C.S.: 327390

Helena Sand & Gravel, Inc. (3)
2209 Airport Rd, Helena, MT 59602
Tel.: (406) 442-1185
Web Site: https://helenasandgravel.com
Construction Sand & Gravel Mining
N.A.I.C.S.: 212321

Michigan Paving & Materials Co. (3)
2575 S Hagerty Rd Ste 100, Canton, MI
48188
Tel.: (734) 397-2050
Web Site: http://www.michiganpaving.com
Sales Range: $200-249.9 Million
Emp.: 20
Paving Services; Ready-Mixed Asphalt &
Concrete Mfr
N.A.I.C.S.: 238220
Rick Becker *(Pres)*

Subsidiary (Domestic):

Michigan Materials & Aggregates Company (4)
15203 S Telegraph Rd, Monroe, MI 48161
Tel.: (734) 397-2050

Web Site: http://www.stoneco.net
Construction Sand, Gravel & Crushed Limestone Mining
N.A.I.C.S.: 212321

Subsidiary (Domestic):

Mountain Enterprises, Inc. (3)
2257 Executive Dr, Lexington, KY 40505-4809
Tel.: (859) 299-7001
Web Site: https://mountaincompanies.com
Rev.: $23,300,000
Emp.: 1,500
Highway & Street Paving Contracting Services
N.A.I.C.S.: 237310
Phillip Annis *(Pres)*

Subsidiary (Domestic):

Bizzack, Inc. (4)
3009 Atkinson Ave Ste 200, Lexington, KY
40509
Tel.: (859) 299-8001
Sales Range: $25-49.9 Million
Emp.: 10
Highway Construction Services
N.A.I.C.S.: 237310
Lester Wimpy *(Asst VP)*

Subsidiary (Domestic):

OMG Midwest, Inc. (3)
5550 NE 22nd St Ste 100, Des Moines, IA
50313 **(100%)**
Tel.: (515) 263-3860
Web Site: http://www.omgmidwest.com
Sales Range: $50-74.9 Million
Emp.: 100
Holding Company; Asphalt & Ready-Mix
Concrete Mfr & Paving Services
N.A.I.C.S.: 551112

Division (Domestic):

American Concrete Products (4)
2401 SE Tones Dr Ste 13, Ankeny, IA
50021
Tel.: (515) 263-3860
Web Site: http://www.amerconcrete.com
Sales Range: $25-49.9 Million
Emp.: 75
Readymix Concrete Mfr
N.A.I.C.S.: 327320

Subsidiary (Domestic):

Cessford Construction Company (4)
2320 Zeller Ave, Le Grand, IA 50142
Tel.: (641) 479-2695
Web Site:
http://www.cessfordconstruction.com
Sales Range: $50-74.9 Million
Asphalt & Ready-Mix Concrete Mfr & Paving Services
N.A.I.C.S.: 237310

Division (Domestic):

Des Moines Asphalt & Paving Co. (4)
2401 SE Tones Dr Ste 13, Ankeny, IA
50020
Tel.: (515) 262-8296
Web Site: http://www.desmoinesasphalt.com
Sales Range: $25-49.9 Million
Emp.: 5
Asphalt Mfr & Paving Services
N.A.I.C.S.: 324121
Craig Lamberty *(Pres)*

Subsidiary (Domestic):

Simon Contractors of South Dakota Inc. (4)
3975 Sturgis Rd, Rapid City, SD 57702
Tel.: (605) 394-3300
Asphalt & Ready-Mix Concrete Mfr, Paving
Services, Construction Sand & Rock Mining
N.A.I.C.S.: 327320
Brett Baker *(Pres)*

Southern Minnesota Construction Company (4)
1905 3rd Ave, Mankato, MN 56001-2802
Tel.: (507) 625-4848
Web Site: http://www.smc-co.com
Paving Services, Asphalt & Ready-Mix Concrete Mfr, Construction Sand & Rock Mining
N.A.I.C.S.: 237310

Division (Domestic):

Oldcastle Materials, Inc.-Mid-Atlantic Group (3)
2950 Charles Ave, Dunbar, WV 25064
Tel.: (304) 769-9733
Web Site: http://www.oldcastlematerials.com
Aggregate, Ready Mixed Concrete & Asphalt Products Mfr
N.A.I.C.S.: 327320

Subsidiary (Domestic):

Pennsy Supply, Inc. (4)
2400 Thea Dr Ste 3A, Harrisburg, PA 17110
Tel.: (717) 233-4511
Web Site: https://www.pennsysupply.com
Asphalt & Concrete Mfr; Construction Sand
& Crushed Stone Mining
N.A.I.C.S.: 324121
Dino Faiola *(Pres)*

Subsidiary (Domestic):

McMinn, Inc. (5)
27 Steamwhistle Dr, Ivyland, PA 18974
Tel.: (215) 953-5858
Web Site: http://www.symtechsolutions.com
Emp.: 30
Life Safety Communication Systems Installation Services & Distr
N.A.I.C.S.: 517810

Subsidiary (Domestic):

Binkley & Ober Inc. (6)
RR 72, East Petersburg, PA 17520
Tel.: (717) 569-0441
Web Site: http://www.binkleyandober.com
Sales Range: $10-24.9 Million
Concrete Block & Brick
N.A.I.C.S.: 327331

McMinn's Asphalt Co., Inc. (6)
2743 Lancaster Rd, Manheim, PA 17545
Tel.: (717) 569-2623
Sales Range: $10-24.9 Million
Highway Construction Services & Materials
N.A.I.C.S.: 237310

Prospect Aggregates, Inc. (6)
1001 Paxton St, Harrisburg, PA 17104
Tel.: (717) 233-4511
Building Materials & Hardscape Supply
Whlsr
N.A.I.C.S.: 444180

Subsidiary (Domestic):

P.J. Keating Company (3)
998 Reservoir Rd, Lunenburg, MA 01462
Tel.: (978) 582-5200
Web Site: https://www.pjkeating.com
Sales Range: $25-49.9 Million
Emp.: 300
Hot Mix Asphalt Mfr
N.A.I.C.S.: 324121

Pike Industries, Inc. (3)
3 Eastgate Park Rd, Belmont, NH
03220 **(100%)**
Tel.: (603) 527-5100
Web Site: https://www.pikeindustries.com
Sales Range: $25-49.9 Million
Emp.: 45
Mfr of Paving Mixtures, Guardrail & Fencing
Highway Contractor
N.A.I.C.S.: 237310

Unit (Domestic):

Pike Industries (4)
95 Western Ave, Fairfield, ME 04937
Tel.: (207) 453-9381
Sales Range: $10-24.9 Million
Emp.: 40
Bridge Construction
N.A.I.C.S.: 237310

Subsidiary (Domestic):

Staker & Parson Companies Inc. (3)
2350 S 1900 W, Ogden, UT
84401 **(100%)**
Tel.: (801) 731-1111
Web Site: https://www.stakerparson.com
Sales Range: $75-99.9 Million
Emp.: 225
Asphalt, Gravel, Sand & Concrete Products
Mfr
N.A.I.C.S.: 212321

The Shelly Company (3)
80 Park Dr, Thornville, OH 43076
Tel.: (740) 246-6315
Web Site: https://www.shellyco.com
Sales Range: $1-4.9 Billion
Emp.: 1,600
Sand, Gravel & Limestone Mining, Asphalt
Mfr, Road Construction & Paving Services
N.A.I.C.S.: 324121
Tony Barna *(Sr VP & Gen Mgr-Southern Div)*

Subsidiary (Domestic):

All Ohio Ready Mix (4)
7901 Sylvania Ave, Sylvania, OH 43560-9732
Tel.: (419) 841-3838
Sales Range: $10-24.9 Million
Emp.: 85
Readymix Concrete Mfr
N.A.I.C.S.: 327320
Billy Perry *(VP & Gen Mgr)*

Middleport Terminal, Inc. (4)
1400 State Route 7 N, Gallipolis, OH
45631-9475
Tel.: (740) 441-0004
Sales Range: $25-49.9 Million
Emp.: 20
Asphalt Mfr
N.A.I.C.S.: 324121
Rick Vangundy *(Gen Mgr)*

Shelly Materials, Inc. (4)
80 Park Dr, Thornville, OH 43076-9397
Tel.: (740) 246-6315
Web Site: http://www.shellyco.com
Sales Range: $75-99.9 Million
Emp.: 200
Sand, Gravel & Limestone Mining
N.A.I.C.S.: 212312

Smith Concrete (4)
26650 SR 7, Marietta, OH 45750
Tel.: (740) 373-7441
Sales Range: $25-49.9 Million
Emp.: 80
Readymix Concrete Mfr
N.A.I.C.S.: 327320

Division (Domestic):

The Shelly Co. - Columbus Division (4)
2506 Jackson Pike, Columbus, OH 43223
Tel.: (614) 437-2345
Sales Range: $200-249.9 Million
Emp.: 800
Sand, Gravel & Limestone Mining, Asphalt
Mfr, Road Construction & Paving Services
N.A.I.C.S.: 324121

The Shelly Co. - Northeast Division (4)
8920 Canyon Falls Blvd Ste 120, Twinsburg, OH 44087
Tel.: (330) 425-7861
Sales Range: $125-149.9 Million
Emp.: 356
Sand, Gravel & Limestone Mining, Asphalt
Mfr, Road Construction & Paving Services
N.A.I.C.S.: 324121

The Shelly Co. - Northwest Division (4)
1700 Fostoria Ave, Findlay, OH 45840
Tel.: (419) 422-8854
Emp.: 100
Sand, Gravel & Limestone Mining, Asphalt
Mfr, Road Construction & Paving Services
N.A.I.C.S.: 324121

The Shelly Co. - Southern Division (4)
80 Park Dr, Thornville, OH 43076-0266
Tel.: (740) 246-6315
Sales Range: $200-249.9 Million
Emp.: 787
Sand, Gravel & Limestone Mining & Asphalt
Mfr
N.A.I.C.S.: 324121

Unit (Domestic):

Thompson-Arthur Paving & Construction (3)
300 S Benbow Rd, Greensboro, NC 27401
Tel.: (336) 412-6800
Web Site: https://www.thompsonarthur.com

CRH plc—(Continued)

Sales Range: $150-199.9 Million
Emp.: 250
Asphalt Paving Services; Stone Base; Bridge, Curb & Gutter Construction Services; Site Utilities; Grading & Sand Products
N.A.I.C.S.: 324121
Larry Brickey (Pres)

Subsidiary (Domestic):

Tilcon Connecticut Inc. (3)
642 Black Rock Ave, New Britain, CT 06050
Tel.: (860) 224-6010
Web Site: https://www.tilconct.com
Sales Range: $650-699.9 Million
Emp.: 1,500
Asphalt Mfr & Paving Services; Construction Sand, Gravel & Crushed Stone Mining
N.A.I.C.S.: 324121

Tilcon New York Inc. (3)
162 Old Mill Rd, West Nyack, NY 10994
Tel.: (845) 358-4500
Web Site: http://www.tilconny.com
Emp.: 30
Asphalt Mfr & Paving Services; Construction Sand, Gravel & Crushed Stone Mining
N.A.I.C.S.: 324121
Christopher J. Madden (Pres & CEO)

Division (Domestic):

Tilcon New York Inc. - New Jersey (4)
625 Mount Hope Rd, Wharton, NJ 07885-2807
Tel.: (973) 366-7741
Web Site: http://www.tilconny.com
Sales Range: $125-149.9 Million
Emp.: 500
Asphalt Mfr & Paving Services; Construction Sand, Gravel & Crushed Stone Mining
N.A.I.C.S.: 324121
George W. Thompson (Chm)

Subsidiary (Domestic):

United Companies of Mesa County (3)
2273 River Rd, Grand Junction, CO 81505
Tel.: (970) 243-4900
Web Site: http://www.united-gj.com
Sales Range: $25-49.9 Million
Emp.: 250
General Contractor; Highway & Street Construction
N.A.I.C.S.: 237310

W-L Construction & Paving, Inc. (3)
1484 Hwy 107, Chilhowie, VA 24319
Tel.: (276) 646-3804
Sales Range: $50-74.9 Million
Emp.: 230
Provider of Highway & Street Construction Services
N.A.I.C.S.: 237310

West Virginia Paving, Inc. (3)
2950 Charles Ave, Dunbar, WV 25064-2103
Tel.: (304) 768-9733
Sales Range: $25-49.9 Million
Emp.: 32
Highway & Street Construction Services
N.A.I.C.S.: 237310
Bob Brookover (Pres)

Subsidiary (Domestic):

Southern West Virginia Asphalt, Inc. (4)
651 Ewart Ave, Beckley, WV 25801
Tel.: (304) 252-6528
Web Site: http://www.asphaltwv.com
Sales Range: $25-49.9 Million
Emp.: 8
Highway & Street Construction Services
N.A.I.C.S.: 324121

Subsidiary (Domestic):

Oldcastle SW Group, Inc. (2)
2273 River Rd, Grand Junction, CO 81502
Tel.: (970) 243-4900
Readymix Concrete Mfr
N.A.I.C.S.: 327320

Oldcastle Southern Group, Inc. (2)

13101 Telecom Dr Ste 101, Tampa, FL 33637
Tel.: (813) 384-3030
Web Site: http://www.oldcastlesoutherngroup.com
Asphalt Mix Mfr
N.A.I.C.S.: 324121

Oldcastle Surfaces, Inc. (2)
1400 W Marietta St, Atlanta, GA 30318
Tel.: (404) 355-3108
Web Site: http://www.oldcastlesurfaces.com
Countertop Mfr
N.A.I.C.S.: 337110

Preferred Materials, Inc. (2)
11482 Columbia Park Dr W Ste 3, Jacksonville, FL 32258
Tel.: (904) 288-6300
Web Site: https://preferredmaterials.com
Asphalt Paving & Construction Services
N.A.I.C.S.: 324121

PJSC Mykolaivcement (1)
1 Stryske Shose Str, Mykolaiv, Lviv, 81600, Ukraine
Tel.: (380) 324141105
Cement Mfr
N.A.I.C.S.: 327310
Yevhen Poluliekh (Gen Mgr)

Plaka Ireland Limited (1)
Toughers Business Park Newhall, Naas, Kildare, Ireland
Tel.: (353) 45 438691
Web Site: http://www.plakagroup.ie
Emp.: 10
Construction Materials Distr
N.A.I.C.S.: 423390

Plakabeton N.V. (1)
Industrielaan 2, 1740, Ternat, Belgium
Tel.: (32) 25822945
Web Site: http://www.plakagroup.com
Sales Range: $75-99.9 Million
Emp.: 130
Building Materials Distr
N.A.I.C.S.: 423390

Podilsky Cement PJSC (1)
1A Khmelnytske Shose Str, Gumentsi Kamyanets-Podilskyi district, Khmelnytsky, 32325, Ukraine
Tel.: (380) 384967215
Cement Mfr
N.A.I.C.S.: 327310
Diacova Ana (Gen Mgr)

Polbruk S.A. (1)
ul Nowy Swiat 16 c, 80-299, Gdansk, Poland
Tel.: (48) 585545945
Web Site: https://www.polbruk.pl
Sales Range: $25-49.9 Million
Emp.: 60
Readymix Concrete Mfr
N.A.I.C.S.: 327320

Prefaco N.V. (1)
Tel.: (32) 53767373
Web Site: http://www.prefaco.be
Emp.: 25
Concrete Block & Brick Mfr
N.A.I.C.S.: 327331

Premac spol. s.r.o. (1)
Stara Vajnorska 25, 832 17, Bratislava, Slovakia
Tel.: (421) 249279111
Web Site: http://www.premac.sk
Sales Range: $50-74.9 Million
Emp.: 120
Concrete Paving Services
N.A.I.C.S.: 238990

Premier Cement Limited (1)
Shed E Kings Dock, Swansea, SA1 8QT, United Kingdom - Wales
Tel.: (44) 1792645302
Web Site: https://www.premiercement.co.uk
Sales Range: $25-49.9 Million
Emp.: 5
Cement Mfr
N.A.I.C.S.: 327310
Philip Matthews (Mgr-Area)

Quester Baustoffhandel GmbH (1)
Heiligenstadter Strasse 24, 1190, Vienna, Austria
Tel.: (43) 501616710
Web Site: https://www.quester.at

Sales Range: $250-299.9 Million
Emp.: 500
Building Materials Distr
N.A.I.C.S.: 423390
Rene Rieder (Mng Dir)

RC Beton A/S (1)
Bjerrevej 80, DK-8840, Rodkaersbro, Denmark
Tel.: (45) 86658055
Web Site: https://rbrc.dk
Tiles & Paving Stone Mfr
N.A.I.C.S.: 324121

Regusci S.A. (1)
Via San Gottardo 98, 6500, Bellinzona, Switzerland
Tel.: (41) 918202323
Web Site: https://www.reguscireco.ch
Construction Materials Distr
N.A.I.C.S.: 423390

Remacle NV/SA. (1)
Rue Sous-la-Ville 8, 5150, Floriffoux, Belgium
Tel.: (32) 81448888
Web Site: https://www.remacle.be
Emp.: 82
Building Materials Distr
N.A.I.C.S.: 423390

Reuss-Seifert GmbH (1)
Wuppertaler Strasse 77, 45549, Sprockhovel, Germany
Tel.: (49) 232490460
Emp.: 250
Construction Equipment Whslr
N.A.I.C.S.: 423810

Roadstone Limited (1)
Fortunestown Tallaght, Dublin, D24, PKK2, Ireland
Tel.: (353) 14041200
Web Site: https://www.roadstone.ie
Building Material Mfr & Distr
N.A.I.C.S.: 327120

Romcim S.A. (1)
Str Emanoil Porumbaru no 93-95 Floor 1 and 5 Sector 1, Bucharest, Romania
Tel.: (40) 213075200
Web Site: https://www.romcim.ro
Building Materials Mfr
N.A.I.C.S.: 327120

Royal Roofing Materials B.V. (1)
Bijsterhuizen 24-01, 6604 LK, Wijchen, Netherlands
Tel.: (31) 24 371 73 91
Web Site: http://www.royalroofingmaterials.com
Sales Range: $75-99.9 Million
Emp.: 170
Roofing Material Distr
N.A.I.C.S.: 423390

Rudus Oy Ab (1)
Karvaamokuja 2a, PO Box 49, 380, Helsinki, Finland (100%)
Tel.: (358) 20447711
Web Site: https://www.rudus.fi
Sales Range: $250-299.9 Million
Emp.: 80
Ready-mixed Concrete & Aggregates Mfr
N.A.I.C.S.: 327390

Subsidiary (Domestic):

Lemminkainen Rakennustuotteet Oy (2)
Puusepantie 11, 4360, Tuusula, Finland
Tel.: (358) 2071 50100
Web Site: http://www.lemminkainen.com
Sales Range: $125-149.9 Million
Emp.: 40
Building Materials Mfr & Distr
N.A.I.C.S.: 327331

SAX Sanitair N.V. (1)
Autostradeweg 3, 9090, Melle, Belgium
Tel.: (32) 9 252 44 00
Web Site: http://www.sax-sanitair.be
Emp.: 200
Sanitary & Plumbing Product Retailer
N.A.I.C.S.: 444180

Schelfhout N.V. (1)
Rue de l'Avenir 18, 4530, Villers-le-Bouillet, Belgium
Tel.: (32) 42282800
Web Site: https://www.schelfhout.com

Sales Range: $25-49.9 Million
Emp.: 38
Wall Precast Concrete Mfr
N.A.I.C.S.: 327390

Schrauwen Sanitair en Verwarming BVBA (1)
Kapelsesteenweg 80, 2930, Brasschaat, Belgium
Tel.: (32) 36452479
Sanitary & Heating Material Sales & Installation Services
N.A.I.C.S.: 423720

Struyk Verwo Groep B.V. (1)
Tel.: (31) 162475475
Web Site: http://www.struykverwo.nl
Building Material Dealers
N.A.I.C.S.: 444180

Superglass S.A. (1)
Marcos Sastre 627 El Talar De Pacheco, Buenos Aires, B1618GSZ, Argentina
Tel.: (54) 1141166400
Tempered Glass Product Mfr
N.A.I.C.S.: 327215

TUVAN-stangsel AB (1)
Knut Pals Vag 1, 256 69, Helsingborg, Sweden
Tel.: (46) 42 29 56 50
Web Site: http://www.heras.se
Security System Services
N.A.I.C.S.: 561621

Tarmac Holdings Limited (1)
Portland House Bickenhill Lane, Solihull, B37 7BQ, W Midlands, United Kingdom (100%)
Tel.: (44) 8001218218
Web Site: http://www.tarmac.com
Emp.: 7,000
Holding Company; Construction Materials Mfr & Whslr
N.A.I.C.S.: 551112
Martin Riley (Sr VP)

Joint Venture (Domestic):

ScotAsh Limited (2)
Longannet Power Station, Kincardine, FK104AA, Scotland, United Kingdom
Tel.: (44) 1259730110
Web Site: http://www.scotash.com.net
Recycled Pulverized Fuel Ash Construction Products Mfr
N.A.I.C.S.: 327120
Chris Bennett (Mgr-Sls & Quality)

Subsidiary (Domestic):

Tarmac Aggregates Limited (2)
Portland House Bickenhill Lane, Solihull, B37 7BQ, W Midlands, United Kingdom
Tel.: (44) 8001218218
Web Site: http://www.tarmac.com
Sand & Gravel Quarrying & Distr
N.A.I.C.S.: 212321

Tarmac Building Products Limited (2)
Interchange 10 Railway Drive, Wolverhampton, WV1 1LH, West Midlands, United Kingdom
Tel.: (44) 3444636465
Building Materials Whslr
N.A.I.C.S.: 423320
Bevan Browne (Mng Dir-Building Products & Comml-Natl)

Tarmac Cement & Lime Limited (2)
Portland House Bickenhill Lane, Solihull, B37 7BQ, United Kingdom
Tel.: (44) 8458126300
Web Site: http://www.tarmac.com
Cement & Lime Mfr
N.A.I.C.S.: 327310

Tarmac Trading Limited (2)
Portland House Bickenhill Lane, Solihull, B37 7BQ, W Midlands, United Kingdom
Tel.: (44) 1902353522
Web Site: http://www.tarmac.co.uk
Asphalt, Aggregates & Building Materials Mfr & Whslr
N.A.I.C.S.: 423320
Paul Fleetham (Mng Dir-Contracting)

Co-Headquarters (Domestic):

Tarmac Trading Limited (3)

Millfields Road Ettingshall, Wolverhampton, WV4 6JP, W Midlands, United Kingdom
Tel.: (44) 8001218218
Web Site: http://www.tarmac.co.uk
Asphalt, Aggregates & Building Materials Mfr & Whslr
N.A.I.C.S.: 551114

Teralta **(1)**
2 rue Amiral Bouvet, BP 187, 97825, Le Port, Reunion
Tel.: (262) 26242 69 69
Web Site: http://www.teralta-crh.com
Readymix Concrete Mfr
N.A.I.C.S.: 327320

Transpave, Inc. **(1)**
500 Rue Saint-Eustache, Saint-Eustache, J7R 7E7, QC, Canada
Tel.: (450) 491-7800
Web Site: http://www.transpave.com
Sales Range: $25-49.9 Million
Emp.: 50
Concrete Block Mfr
N.A.I.C.S.: 327331

Unipol Holland B.V. **(1)**
Rijnstraat 15a, 5347 KL, Oss, Netherlands
Tel.: (31) 412643243
Web Site: https://www.unipol.nl
Emp.: 60
Construction Materials Distr
N.A.I.C.S.: 423390

VVM N.V. **(1)**
Kaaistraat 75, 8800, Roeselare, Belgium
Tel.: (32) 51 207313
Web Site: http://www.vvmcem.be
Readymix Concrete Mfr
N.A.I.C.S.: 327320

Van Neerbos Belgie N.V. **(1)**
Koralenhoeve 5, 2160, Wommelgem, Belgium
Tel.: (32) 33552740
Sales Range: $25-49.9 Million
Emp.: 20
Building Materials Distr
N.A.I.C.S.: 423320

Vidrios Dell Orto, S.A. **(1)**
Piloto Lazo 419, Cerrillos, Santiago, Chile
Tel.: (56) 27511800
Web Site: https://www.dellorto.cl
Tempered Glass Product Mfr
N.A.I.C.S.: 327215

Williaam Cox Ltd. **(1)**
Unit AF 40, Cloverhill Industrial Estate, Clondalkin, 22, Dublin, Ireland
Tel.: (353) 14605400
Web Site: https://williaamcox.com
Sales Range: $25-49.9 Million
Emp.: 50
Architectural Glazing, Coxdome Daylight Products, Smoke & Heat Ventilation & Plastic Distr
N.A.I.C.S.: 541310

ZPW Trzuskawica S.A. **(1)**
Sitkowka 24, Sitkowka-Nowiny, 26052, Poland
Tel.: (48) 41 346 91 30
Web Site: http://www.trzuskawica.pl
Limestone Mfr
N.A.I.C.S.: 212311

CRI MIDDLEWARE CO., LTD.
Shibuya Info Tower 11th Floor 20-1 Sakuragaoka-cho, Shibuya-ku, Tokyo, 150-0031, Japan
Tel.: (81) 364187081
Web Site: https://www.cri-mw.co.jp
3698—(TKS)
Rev.: $21,199,100
Assets: $36,577,310
Liabilities: $11,407,810
Net Worth: $25,169,500
Earnings: $1,644,880
Emp.: 161
Fiscal Year-end: 09/30/23
Software Developer
N.A.I.C.S.: 513210
Kenshi Furukawa *(Chm)*

CRICKET AUSTRALIA

60 Jolimont Street, Jolimont, 3002, VIC, Australia
Tel.: (61) 396539999   AU
Web Site: http://www.cricket.com.au
Sales Range: $200-249.9 Million
Emp.: 70
National Cricket Sports League
N.A.I.C.S.: 813990
Earl Eddings *(Chm)*

CRICKET ENERGY HOLDINGS, INC.
20 Floral Parkway, Concord, L4K4R1, ON, Canada
Tel.: (855) 353-2579
Web Site:
   http://www.cricketenergy.com
Holding Company
N.A.I.C.S.: 551112

Subsidiaries:

Sunwave Home Comfort Inc. **(1)**
1 Eglinton Avenue East Suite 202, Toronto, M4P 3A1, ON, Canada
Tel.: (416) 923-4663
Web Site: http://www.homecomfortgroup.ca
Water Heater Distr
N.A.I.C.S.: 423720

CRIE ANABUKI INC.
Anabuki Central Bldg 2-8 Togiyamachi, Takamatsu, 760-0026, Kagawa, Japan
Tel.: (81) 878228898
Web Site: http://www.crie.co.jp
Year Founded: 1986
4336—(TKS)
Rev.: $60,780,720
Assets: $21,809,040
Liabilities: $9,486,400
Net Worth: $12,322,640
Earnings: $1,142,240
Emp.: 102
Fiscal Year-end: 03/31/21
Temporary Staffing Services
N.A.I.C.S.: 561320
Hiroshi Joguchi *(Pres)*

CRIF S.P.A.
Via M Fantin 1-3, 40131, Bologna, Italy
Tel.: (39) 0514176111   IT
Web Site: http://www.crif.com
Year Founded: 1988
Sales Range: $350-399.9 Million
Emp.: 1,500
Credit Reporting, Business Information & Decision Support Systems Mfr
N.A.I.C.S.: 561499
Carlo Gherardi *(Pres & CEO)*

Subsidiaries:

CRIBIS D&B S.r.l. **(1)**
Via dei Valtorta 48, 20127, Milan, Italy
Tel.: (39) 02284551
Web Site: http://www.cribis.com
Credit Management Services
N.A.I.C.S.: 541611
Fabio Lazzarini *(Dir-Mktg)*

CRIBIS Teleservice S.r.l. **(1)**
Via Della Beverara 19, 40131, Bologna, Italy
Tel.: (39) 0516583811
Web Site: http://www.cribisteleservice.it
Debt Collection Services
N.A.I.C.S.: 561440

CRIF (Shanghai) Business Information Service Co. Ltd **(1)**
Suite G23 22/F Tower 3 Jing An Kerry Centre 1228 Yan An Zhong Road, Shanghai, 200040, China
Tel.: (86) 2131063487
Business Support Services
N.A.I.C.S.: 561499

CRIF - Czech Credit Bureau, a. s. **(1)**
Na Vitezne plani 1719/4, 140 00, Prague, Czech Republic

Tel.: (420) 277778530
Web Site: http://www.crif.cz
Credit Management Services
N.A.I.C.S.: 541611
Romana Knyblova *(Project Mgr)*

CRIF - Slovak Credit Bureau, s.r.o. **(1)**
Maly trh 2/A, 811 08, Bratislava, Slovakia
Tel.: (421) 259207511
Web Site: http://www.crif.sk
Credit Processing & Management Services
N.A.I.C.S.: 561450
Synak Pavol *(Mgr-Bus Dev)*

CRIF AG **(1)**
Riesbachstrasse 61, 8008, Zurich, Switzerland
Tel.: (41) 44 305 12 12
Web Site: http://www.ofwi.ch
Credit Reporting, Business Information & Decision Support Systems Mfr
N.A.I.C.S.: 561499
Andreas Dietschweiler *(Mgr-Bus Dev & Risk)*

CRIF Alacak Yonetim Ve Danismanlik Hizmetleri Anonim Sirketi **(1)**
Eski Buyukdere Cad Park Plaza No 14 Kat 18, Maslak, 34398, Istanbul, Türkiye
Tel.: (90) 2123654000
Web Site: http://www.crif.com.tr
Debt Collection Services
N.A.I.C.S.: 561440

CRIF Beijing Ltd. **(1)**
Room 1610-1611 Zhongyu Plaza A6 Gongti North Road, Chaoyang District, 100027, Beijing, China
Tel.: (86) 1065030663
Web Site: http://www.crif.cn
Credit Processing & Management Services
N.A.I.C.S.: 561450

CRIF Corporation **(1)**
280 Interstate N Cir Ste 400, Atlanta, GA 30339
Tel.: (770) 952-4940
Web Site:
   http://www.criflendingsolutions.com
Application Software Development Services
N.A.I.C.S.: 541511
Larry Howell *(Chm)*

CRIF Corporation **(1)**
Level 10-1 Fort Legend Tower 31st Street & 3rd Avenue, Bonifacio Global City, Taguig, 1632, Manila, Philippines
Tel.: (63) 2242158
Web Site: http://www.crif.ph
Credit Processing & Management Services
N.A.I.C.S.: 561450

CRIF Decision Solutions Ltd. **(1)**
Calverley House 55 Calverley Road, Tunbridge Wells, TN1 2TU, Kent, United Kingdom
Tel.: (44) 1892704235
Web Site:
   http://www.crifdecisionsolutions.co.uk
Application Software Development Services
N.A.I.C.S.: 541511
Lynn Young *(Head-UK Sls Consultancy Team)*

CRIF GmbH **(1)**
Diefenbachgasse 35, 1150, Vienna, Austria
Tel.: (43) 189742440
Web Site: http://www.crif.at
Credit Processing & Management Services
N.A.I.C.S.: 561450
Sepp Puwein-Borkowski *(Acct Mgr & Mgr-Bus Dev)*

CRIF Gulf DWC LLC **(1)**
15th floor 48 Burjgate Downtown Burj AreaSheikh Zayed Road, PO Box 72478, Dubai, United Arab Emirates
Tel.: (971) 44069900
Application Software Development Services
N.A.I.C.S.: 541511
Vilveshwar Johari *(Mgr-Ops)*

CRIF High Mark Credit Information Services Pvt. Ltd. **(1)**
3B-01 02 & 03 3rd Floor Phoenix Paragon Plaza CTS No 124/B, Kurla, Mumbai, 400070, India
Tel.: (91) 2271712900
Web Site: http://www.crifhighmark.com

Credit Processing & Management Services
N.A.I.C.S.: 561450
Pinkesh P. Ambavat *(CTO & Chief Info Security Officer)*

CRIF Hong Kong Limited **(1)**
Room 1020-21A Ocean Centre 5 Canton Road, Tsimshatsui, Kowloon, China (Hong Kong)
Tel.: (852) 37524186
Credit Processing & Management Services
N.A.I.C.S.: 561450

CRIF S.A. de S.V. **(1)**
Torre Masaryk - Av Presidente Masaryk 101 Col Chapultepec Morales, Mexico, 11570, Mexico
Tel.: (52) 5555451772
Web Site: http://www.crif.com.mx
Application Software Development Services
N.A.I.C.S.: 541511

CRIF Solutions Private Limited **(1)**
Unit No 701 & 801 7th & 8th Level Survey no - 114 & 115, Icon Towers Baner Road, Pune, 411045, Maharashtra, India
Tel.: (91) 2067157700
Credit Processing & Management Services
N.A.I.C.S.: 561450
Shailja Apte *(Mgr-Admin)*

CRIF Sp. z o. o. **(1)**
ul Trebacka 4, 00-074, Warsaw, Poland
Tel.: (48) 226309624
Web Site: http://www.crif.pl
Application Software Development Services
N.A.I.C.S.: 541511
Dominik Lewandowski *(Mgr-Bus Dev)*

Data4value, Srl **(1)**
via Vincenzo Lamaro 15, 00173, Rome, Italy
Tel.: (39) 0672974201
Web Site: http://www.data4value.com
Application Software Development Services
N.A.I.C.S.: 541511

OOO CRIF **(1)**
10-1 shabolovka St, 119049, Moscow, Russia
Tel.: (7) 4952870105
Web Site: http://www.crif.ru
Application Software Development Services
N.A.I.C.S.: 541511

PT CRIF **(1)**
Cyber 2 Tower 18 Floor Jl H R Rasuna Said Blok X-5, Jakarta, 12950, Indonesia
Tel.: (62) 2157998243
Web Site: http://www.crif.co.id
Credit Processing & Management Services
N.A.I.C.S.: 561450

CRIMSON BIOENERGY LTD.
Suite 202 5752 176th Street, Surrey, V3S 4C8, BC, Canada
Tel.: (604) 574-3100   BC
Web Site:
   http://www.crimsonbioenergy.com
Year Founded: 2009
CSN—(TSXV)
Sales Range: Less than $1 Million
Emp.: 2
Investment Services
N.A.I.C.S.: 523999
William W. Carr *(Pres & CEO)*

CRIMSON METAL ENGINEERING COMPANY LIMITED
163/1 II Floor K Sons Complex Prakasam Salai, Broadway, Chennai, 600108, India
Tel.: (91) 4425224315
Web Site: https://www.crmetal.in
Year Founded: 1985
526977—(BOM)
Rev.: $1,277,476
Assets: $5,292,869
Liabilities: $4,516,567
Net Worth: $776,303
Earnings: $53,385
Emp.: 2
Fiscal Year-end: 03/31/21
Steel Pole Mfr
N.A.I.C.S.: 331110

Crimson Metal Engineering Company
Limited—(Continued)

Vinay Kumar Goyal *(Mng Dir)*

CRIMSON TIDE PLC

Brockbourne House 77 Mount
Ephraim, Tunbridge Wells, TN4 8BS,
Kent, United Kingdom
Tel.: (44) 1892542444   UK
Web Site:
https://www.crimsontide.co.uk
TIDE—(AIM)
Rev.: $7,842,111
Assets: $12,336,048
Liabilities: $2,788,023
Net Worth: $9,548,025
Earnings: ($394,652)
Fiscal Year-end: 12/31/23
Mobile Data Solution Provider
N.A.I.C.S.: 334220
Stephen Keith Goodwin *(Sec & Dir-Fin)*

Subsidiaries:

Crimson Tide (IE) Limited   (1)
3013 Lake Drive, Citywest Campus, Dublin,
Ireland
Tel.: (353) 1 469 3728
Information Technology Services
N.A.I.C.S.: 541511

Crimson Tide mPro Limited   (1)
The Tavern Cellars 39-41 The Pantiles,
Tunbridge Wells, TN2 5TE, Kent, United
Kingdom
Tel.: (44) 1892542444
Web Site: http://www.crimsontide.co.uk
Emp.: 10
Mobile Data & Software Solutions
N.A.I.C.S.: 518210
Barrie Reginald John Whipp *(Founder &
Chm)*

CRIMSONLOGIC PTE LTD

31 Science Park Road The Crimson,
Singapore, 117611, Singapore
Tel.: (65) 68877888
Web Site:
http://www.crimsonlogic.com
Year Founded: 1988
Rev.: $106,200,000
Emp.: 250
Information Technology Services
N.A.I.C.S.: 518210
Chong Kok Keong *(CEO-GeTS)*

Subsidiaries:

CrimsonLogic (North America)
Inc.   (1)
100 York Boulevard Suite 260, Richmond
Hill, L4B 1J8, ON, Canada
Tel.: (905) 763-6887
Web Site: http://www.crimsonlogic.ca
Software Development Services
N.A.I.C.S.: 541511
Winnie Lau *(Mgr-Ops)*

CrimsonLogic (Trinidad and Tobago)
Ltd.   (1)
First Floor Alexandra Court 4A Alexandra
Street St Clair, Port of Spain, Trinidad &
Tobago
Tel.: (868) 8682232588
Software Development Services
N.A.I.C.S.: 541511

CrimsonLogic Bahrain S.P.C   (1)
No 7A Malkiya Road Block No 1032, Ma-
nama, Bahrain
Tel.: (973) 36171223
Software Development Services
N.A.I.C.S.: 541511

CrimsonLogic Chile SpA   (1)
Huerfanos 835 Office 704, Santiago, Chile
Tel.: (56) 32027560
Software Development Services
N.A.I.C.S.: 541511

CrimsonLogic Emirates Information
Technology LLC   (1)
Unit 303 RAK Ceramics Building opposite
ADCB Building, PO Box 105653, Junction

of Salam and Electra Street, Abu Dhabi,
United Arab Emirates
Tel.: (971) 26454031
Software Development Services
N.A.I.C.S.: 541511

CrimsonLogic IT Solutions Private
Limited   (1)
Logix Park A-4 Sector 16, Noida, 201301,
India
Tel.: (91) 1204366000
Software Development Services
N.A.I.C.S.: 541511

CrimsonLogic India Private
Limited   (1)
124 6th Floor Surya Chambers Murugesh-
palya Old Airport Road, Bengaluru, 560
017, India
Tel.: (91) 8041289999
Software Development Services
N.A.I.C.S.: 541511
Somashekar Munikoti *(Sr Mgr-Bus Sys)*

CrimsonLogic Panama Inc.   (1)
Clayton City of Knowledge Building 239 3rd
Floor, Panama, Panama
Tel.: (507) 3170996
Software Development Services
N.A.I.C.S.: 541511

CrimsonLogic Software Technology
(Shanghai) Co., Ltd   (1)
No 998 Jintiandi International Building Ren-
min Road, Shanghai, 200021, China
Tel.: (86) 13003176666
Software Development Services
N.A.I.C.S.: 541511

CrimsonLogic USA, Inc.   (1)
3 Bethesda Metro Ctr Ste 708, Bethesda,
MD 20814
Tel.: (301) 961-1562
Web Site: http://www.crimsonlogic.us
Software Development Services
N.A.I.C.S.: 541511

CRINSURANCE S.A.S.

Calle 44 n 793, 1900, La Plata, Ar-
gentina
Tel.: (54) 92215984673
Web Site: https://crinsurancelife.com
Insurance Services
N.A.I.C.S.: 524298

CRISPR THERAPEUTICS AG

Baarerstrasse 14, 6300, Zug, Swit-
zerland
Tel.: (41) 415613277   CH
Web Site: https://www.crisprtx.com
Year Founded: 2013
CRSP—(NASDAQ)
Rev.: $914,963,000
Assets: $2,751,877,000
Liabilities: $352,417,000
Net Worth: $2,399,460,000
Earnings: $377,661,000
Emp.: 473
Fiscal Year-end: 12/31/21
Genome Editing for Human Thera-
peutics
N.A.I.C.S.: 541715
Rodger Novak *(Co-Founder)*

Subsidiaries:

CRISPR Therapeutics, Inc.   (1)
105 W 1st St, Cambridge, MA 02127
Tel.: (617) 315-4600
Clinical Research Services
N.A.I.C.S.: 541715

ERS Genomics Ltd.   (1)
8th Floor Block E Iveagh Court Harcourt
Road, Dublin, Ireland
Tel.: (353) 15390082
Web Site: https://www.ersgenomics.com
Editing Technology Services
N.A.I.C.S.: 541511
Eric Rhodes *(CEO)*

CRISTALERIAS DE CHILE S.A.

Jose Luis Caro 501, Padre Hurtado,
834-0518, Santiago, Chile
Tel.: (56) 227878888   CL

Web Site: https://www.cristalchile.cl
Year Founded: 1904
Sales Range: $300-349.9 Million
Emp.: 710
Glass & Plastic Containers Mfr
N.A.I.C.S.: 327213
Cirilo Elton Gonzalez *(Gen Mgr)*

Subsidiaries:

S.A. Vina Santa Rita   (1)
Avenida Apoquindo 3669 Piso 6, Santiago,
Chile   (100%)
Tel.: (56) 23622000
Web Site: http://www.santarita.cl
Sales Range: $50-74.9 Million
Emp.: 100
Wine & Distilled Alcoholic Beverage Whslr
N.A.I.C.S.: 424810
Luis Arturo Valverde *(Gen Mgr)*

CRISTALLERIA ARTISTICA LA PIANA S.P.A.

Localita Catarelli, I 53034, Colle di
Val d'Elsa, SI, Italy
Tel.: (39) 0577910111
Web Site: http://www.calp.it
Year Founded: 1967
Sales Range: $150-199.9 Million
Emp.: 793
Crystal, Glass & Related Products
Mfr & Distr
N.A.I.C.S.: 327212
Pearucte Roberto *(Mgr-Mktg)*

CRISTIE SOFTWARE LIMITED

New Mill Chestnut Lane, GL5 3EW,
Stroud, Glos, United Kingdom
Tel.: (44) 1453847000   UK
Web Site: https://www.cristie.com
Emp.: 100
Software Publisher
N.A.I.C.S.: 518210

Subsidiaries:

Storix Inc.   (1)
7801 Mission Ctr Ct Ste 250, San Diego,
CA 92108
Tel.: (619) 543-0200
Web Site: http://www.storix.com
Emp.: 100
Computer System Design Services
N.A.I.C.S.: 541512
Anthony Johnson *(Pres & CEO)*

CRISTIRO S.A.

Str Industriei 5, Bistrita, Bistrita-
Nasaud, Romania
Tel.: (40) 263 238 106
Web Site: http://www.cristiro.ro
Year Founded: 1974
Sales Range: $1-9.9 Million
Household Glassware Mfr
N.A.I.C.S.: 327212

CRITEO S.A.

32 rue Blanche, 75009, Paris, France
Tel.: (33) 140402290   FR
Web Site: https://www.criteo.com
Year Founded: 2005
CRTO—(NASDAQ)
Rev.: $2,017,003,000
Assets: $2,348,894,000
Liabilities: $1,267,788,000
Net Worth: $1,081,106,000
Earnings: $10,875,000
Emp.: 3,716
Fiscal Year-end: 12/31/22
Digital Display Advertising Solutions
N.A.I.C.S.: 541890
Franck Le Ouay *(Co-Founder)*

Subsidiaries:

Criteo Advertising (Beijing) Co.,
Ltd.   (1)
Level 7 Xin Dong Fang South Tower No 2
Haidian Dong San Street, Haidian District,
Beijing, 100080, China
Tel.: (86) 1062602310
Digital Advertising Services

N.A.I.C.S.: 541810
Yang Wang *(Engr-Technical Solution)*

Criteo B.V.   (1)
Herengracht 124-128, 1015 BT, Amster-
dam, Netherlands
Tel.: (31) 442031707027
Emp.: 3
Digital Advertising Services
N.A.I.C.S.: 541810
Vincent Moraal *(Dir-Bus Dev)*

Criteo Canada Corp.   (1)
500 King St W, Toronto, M5V 1L9, ON,
Canada
Tel.: (416) 797-2711
Advertising Agency & Consulting Services
N.A.I.C.S.: 541810
Phil Schlatter *(Dir-Sls)*

Criteo Do Brasil Desenvolvimento De
Servicos De Internet Ltda.   (1)
6th Floor 1017 Renato St Paes De Barros,
04530-001, Sao Paulo, Brazil
Tel.: (55) 1137084400
Digital Advertising Services
N.A.I.C.S.: 541810
Fernando Tassinari *(Mng Dir)*

Criteo Espana, S.L.   (1)
Calle goya 24 - Piso 7, Madrid, 28001,
Spain
Tel.: (34) 911829387
Web Site: http://www.criteo.com
Digital Advertising Services
N.A.I.C.S.: 541810

Criteo France S.A.S.   (1)
32 rue Blanche, 75009, Paris, France
Tel.: (33) 140402290
Digital Advertising Services
N.A.I.C.S.: 541810
Romain Niccoli *(CTO)*

Criteo GmbH   (1)
Gewurzmuhlstr 11, 80538, Munich, Ger-
many
Tel.: (49) 89189285100
Digital Advertising Services
N.A.I.C.S.: 541810
Georg Sobczak *(Dir-Comml)*

Criteo K.K.   (1)
26 Floor Yebisu Garden Place Tower
4-20-3, Ebisu Shibuya-ku, Tokyo, 150-6026,
Japan
Tel.: (81) 364503350
Digital Advertising Services
N.A.I.C.S.: 541810
Sachi Matsuda *(Mgr-Comm-Creative Svcs
APAC)*

Criteo LLC   (1)
9 Lesnaya St, Moscow, 125047, Russia
Tel.: (7) 4957375441
Digital Advertising Services
N.A.I.C.S.: 541810
Sergey Gorobchenko *(Head-Mid-Market
Russia & CIS)*

Criteo S.R.L.   (1)
Bastioni di Porta Nuova 20, 20121, Milan,
Italy
Tel.: (39) 0294753415
Digital Advertising Services
N.A.I.C.S.: 541810
Alberto Torre *(Mng Dir)*

Criteo Singapore PTE. LTD.   (1)
138 Market Street 34-01/02 CapitaGreen,
Singapore, 048946, Singapore
Tel.: (65) 68188900
Digital Advertising Services
N.A.I.C.S.: 541810
Yuko Saito *(Mng Dir-Southeast Asia)*

CRITES & RIDDELL BASICS

8203 Montreal Toronto Blvd, Mon-
treal, H4X 1N1, QC, Canada
Tel.: (514) 368-8641
Web Site: http://www.crites-
riddell.com
Year Founded: 1911
Rev.: $10,939,302
Emp.: 47
Office Supplies & Printing Service
N.A.I.C.S.: 424120
Peter Lai *(Mng Partner)*

CRITICAL CONTROL ENERGY SERVICES CORP.

800 140-10th Avenue SE, Calgary, T2G 0R1, AB, Canada
Tel.: (403) 705-7500   AB
Web Site:
http://www.criticalcontrol.com
Year Founded: 1999
Rev.: $19,694,171
Assets: $12,276,515
Liabilities: $10,457,283
Net Worth: $1,819,232
Earnings: ($14,100,877)
Emp.: 138
Fiscal Year-end: 12/31/18
Business Process & Information Control Solutions
N.A.I.C.S.: 561499
Alykhan A. Mamdani *(Founder & CEO-Spirit Digital Media)*

Subsidiaries:

CriticalControl Energy Services   (1)
800 140 10th Avenue SE, Calgary, T2G 0R1, AB, Canada
Tel.: (403) 705-7500
Web Site: http://www.criticalcontrol.com
Sales Range: $25-49.9 Million
Emp.: 80
Business Management Services
N.A.I.C.S.: 541618

CRITICAL ELEMENTS LITHIUM CORPORATION

80 de la Seigneurie West Blvd Suite 201, Blainville, J7C 5M3, QC, Canada
Tel.: (514) 904-1496   Ca
Web Site: https://www.cecorp.ca
Year Founded: 2006
CRE—(OTCIQ)
Rev.: $45,626
Assets: $23,921,694
Liabilities: $7,280,605
Net Worth: $16,641,090
Earnings: ($1,779,135)
Fiscal Year-end: 08/31/21
Metal Exploration Services
N.A.I.C.S.: 213114
Jean-Sebastien Lavallee *(CEO)*

CRITICAL INFRASTRUCTURE TECHNOLOGIES LTD.

2600 1066 West Hastings Street, Vancouver, V6E 3X1, BC, Canada
Tel.: (614) 117-5119
Year Founded: 2019
CTTT—(CNSX)
Software Development Services
N.A.I.C.S.: 541511

CRITICAL METALS PLC

22 Bishopsgate, London, EC2N 4BQ, United Kingdom   UK
Web Site:
https://www.criticalmetals.co.uk
Year Founded: 2020
CRTM—(LSE)
Assets: $5,914,443
Liabilities: $2,946,313
Net Worth: $2,968,131
Earnings: ($3,408,516)
Emp.: 3
Fiscal Year-end: 06/30/23
Investment Management Service
N.A.I.C.S.: 523999
Russell Fryer *(CEO)*

CRITICAL MINERAL RESOURCES PLC

Eccleston Yards 25 Eccleston Place, London, SW1W 9NF, United Kingdom   UK
Web Site: https://cmrplc.com
Year Founded: 2017
CMRS—(LSE)
Assets: $7,521,329

Liabilities: $798,827
Net Worth: $6,722,502
Earnings: ($1,341,387)
Emp.: 3
Fiscal Year-end: 12/31/21
Mineral Exploration Services
N.A.I.C.S.: 213115

CRITICAL MINERALS GROUP LIMITED

Level 4 Gold Tower 10 Eagle Street, Brisbane, 4000, QLD, Australia
Tel.: (61) 755555077   AU
Web Site:
https://www.criticalminerals.com.au
Year Founded: 2021
CMG—(ASX)
Rev.: $467
Assets: $89,204
Liabilities: $150,665
Net Worth: ($61,461)
Earnings: ($716,283)
Fiscal Year-end: 06/30/22
Mineral Exploration Services
N.A.I.C.S.: 212390
Scott Drelincourt *(CEO)*

CRITTALL WINDOWS LTD.

Francis House Freebournes Road, Witham, CM8 3UN, Essex, United Kingdom
Tel.: (44) 1376530800
Web Site: http://www.crittall-windows.co.uk
Sales Range: $10-24.9 Million
Emp.: 180
Window Mfr
N.A.I.C.S.: 332321
John Pyatt *(Mng Dir)*

CRM COMPANY GROUP SA

29 cite d'Antin, 75009, Paris, Cedex, France
Tel.: (33) 1 5577 2828
Sales Range: $10-24.9 Million
Marketing Consulting Services
N.A.I.C.S.: 541613
Bertrand Frey *(Chm & CEO)*

CRNI MARKO A.D.

Sadine vodenice 6, Pirot, Serbia
Tel.: (381) 10311424
Year Founded: 1953
BLAG—(BEL)
Sales Range: $1-9.9 Million
Emp.: 69
Bread Mfr
N.A.I.C.S.: 311812
Miodrag Rancic *(Exec Dir)*

CROATIA AIRLINES D.D.

Bani 75b Buzin, 10 010, Zagreb, Croatia
Tel.: (385) 16676555
Web Site:
https://www.croatiaairlines.com
Year Founded: 1989
CRAL—(ZAG)
Rev.: $248,412,628
Assets: $251,873,275
Liabilities: $235,127,498
Net Worth: $16,745,778
Earnings: $2,607,352
Emp.: 935
Fiscal Year-end: 12/31/23
Scheduled Passenger Air Transportation
N.A.I.C.S.: 481111
Jasmin Bajic *(Pres, CEO & Member-Mgmt Bd)*

Subsidiaries:

Amadeus Croatia d.d.   (1)
Trg kralja Tomislava 9, Zagreb, 10000, Croatia   (95%)
Tel.: (385) 14839555
Web Site: http://www.amadeus.hr

Sales Range: $25-49.9 Million
Emp.: 8
Scheduled Passenger Air Transportation
N.A.I.C.S.: 481111
Egen Sune *(CEO)*

Obzor putovanja d.o.o   (1)
Teslina 5, Zagreb, 10000, Croatia   (100%)
Tel.: (385) 16160243
Wob Sito: http://www.obzorputovanja.hr
Sales Range: $25-49.9 Million
Emp.: 13
Tour Operator
N.A.I.C.S.: 561520
Jabranka Skelin *(Gen Mgr)*

Pleso prijevoz d.o.o.   (1)
Avenija Marina Drzica 4, 10000, Zagreb, Croatia   (50%)
Tel.: (385) 16331999
Web Site: https://www.plesoprijevoz.hr
Emp.: 70
Other Support Activities for Road Transportation
N.A.I.C.S.: 488490
Zvonka Zuhec *(Gen Mgr)*

CROATIA LLOYD D.D.

Ulica grada Vukovara 62, PO Box 737, 10000, Zagreb, Croatia
Tel.: (385) 16308888
Web Site: http://www.croatialloyd.hr
Sales Range: $25-49.9 Million
Reinsurance Services
N.A.I.C.S.: 524130
Kitica Mioc *(Member-Mgmt Bd)*

CROCODILE GARMENTS LIMITED

25/F Crocodile Centre 79 Hoi Yuen Street, Kwun Tong, Kowloon, China (Hong Kong)
Tel.: (852) 27853898   HK
Web Site:
https://www.crocodile.com.hk
Year Founded: 1971
0122—(HKG)
Rev.: $14,445,760
Assets: $283,835,839
Liabilities: $86,300,260
Net Worth: $197,535,579
Earnings: ($249,318)
Emp.: 157
Fiscal Year-end: 07/31/21
Apparel & Accessories Mfr
N.A.I.C.S.: 315250
Edward Yee Hwa Wan *(Exec Dir)*

CRODA INTERNATIONAL PLC

Cowick Hall, Snaith, Goole, DN14 9AA, East Yorkshire, United Kingdom
Tel.: (44) 1405860551   UK
Web Site: https://www.croda.com
Year Founded: 1925
CRDA—(OTCIQ)
Rev.: $1,887,638,116
Assets: $4,112,398,108
Liabilities: $1,946,698,936
Net Worth: $2,165,699,172
Earnings: $273,716,352
Emp.: 5,684
Fiscal Year-end: 12/31/20
Specialty Chemicals Mfr
N.A.I.C.S.: 325199
Tom Brophy *(Gen Counsel & Sec)*

Subsidiaries:

Avanti Polar Lipids, Inc.   (1)
700 Industrial Park Dr, Alabaster, AL 35007-9105
Tel.: (205) 663-2494
Web Site: https://avantilipids.com
Sales Range: $1-9.9 Million
Emp.: 53
Medicinal & Botanical Mfr
N.A.I.C.S.: 325411
Walter A. Shaw *(Founder)*

Croda (SA) (Pty) Ltd.   (1)
Block G Clearwater Estate Office Park cnr Atlas and Park Road, Parkhaven Ext 8, Boksburg, 1459, South Africa

Tel.: (27) 113972380
Natural Specialty Chemical Mfr
N.A.I.C.S.: 325199

Croda (Thailand) Co., Ltd   (1)
319 Chamchuri Square Building 16th Floor Unit 1613 Payathai Road, Patumwan, Bangkok, 10330, Thailand
Tel.: (66) 2 160 5444
Emp.: 19
Oleochemical Products Whslr
N.A.I.C.S.: 424690
Phairat Tuntisirikul *(Mgr)*

Croda Argentina SA   (1)
Dardo Rocha 2044 Martinez, 1640, Buenos Aires, Argentina   (100%)
Tel.: (54) 11 4898 3000
Web Site: http://www.croda.com
Sales Range: $50-74.9 Million
Emp.: 6
Specialty & Oleochemical Distr
N.A.I.C.S.: 424690

Croda Canada Ltd.   (1)
1700 Langstaff Suite 1000, Vaughan, Toronto, LK4 3S3, ON, Canada   (100%)
Tel.: (905) 886-1383
Web Site: http://www.croda.com
Sales Range: $50-74.9 Million
Emp.: 9
Specialty Chemicals Distr
N.A.I.C.S.: 424690

Croda Chemicals Europe Ltd   (1)
Cowick Hall, Snaith, Goole, DN14 9AA, E Yorkshire, United Kingdom   (100%)
Tel.: (44) 1405860551
Web Site: http://www.croda.com
Sales Range: $125-149.9 Million
Emp.: 300
Mfr of Polymer Additives
N.A.I.C.S.: 325998

Croda Chemicals International (Moscow) Ltd   (1)
Raketnyi Boulevard 16 BC Alekseevskaya Tower, Moscow, 129164, Russia
Tel.: (7) 4956608998
Web Site: http://www.croda.com
Healthcare Chemical Products Whslr
N.A.I.C.S.: 424690

Croda Chemicals International Ltd   (1)
Cowick Hall, Goole, DN14 9AA, North Humberside, United Kingdom
Tel.: (44) 1405 860 551
Chemical Products Mfr
N.A.I.C.S.: 325180

Croda Chemicals SA Pty Ltd   (1)
Block G Clearwater Estate Office Park cnr Atlas and Park Roads, PO Box 1641, Parkhaven Ext 8, Boksburg, 1459, South Africa   (100%)
Tel.: (27) 11 397 2380
Web Site: http://www.croda.com
Sales Range: $25-49.9 Million
Emp.: 35
Specialty Chemicals Distr
N.A.I.C.S.: 325998

Croda Chile Ltda.   (1)
Santa Beatriz 100 12th Floor Office 1205, Providencia, 7500515, Santiago, Chile
Tel.: (56) 228389500
Natural Specialty Chemical Mfr
N.A.I.C.S.: 325199

Croda China Trading Company Ltd.   (1)
Unit BCD 19 Floor Urban City Center No 45 Nan Chang Road, Shanghai, 200030, China
Tel.: (86) 2123159228
Natural Specialty Chemical Mfr
N.A.I.C.S.: 325199

Croda Chocques SAS   (1)
1 Rue De Lapugnoy, Chocques, 62920, Pas-de-Calais, France
Tel.: (33) 321618400
Sales Range: $25-49.9 Million
Emp.: 100
Cosmetics Products Mfr
N.A.I.C.S.: 325620

Croda Colombia   (1)
Calle 90 19 - 41 Office 601 Edificio Quan-

Croda International plc—(Continued)

tum, Bogota, Colombia
Tel.: (57) 1 321 4230
Web Site: http://www.croda.com
Personal Care Products Whslr
N.A.I.C.S.: 424590

Croda Europe Ltd. (1)
Cowick Hall, Snaith, Goole, DN14 9AA,
East Yorkshire, United Kingdom (100%)
Tel.: (44) 140 586 0551
Web Site: https://www.croda.com
Natural Oils, Oxidized Hydrocarbon Waxes
& Strippable Plastic Coatings for Health
Care, Industrial & Personal Care Industries
N.A.I.C.S.: 311225

Subsidiary (Domestic):

Plant Impact plc (2)
Rothamsted West Common, Harpenden,
AL5 2JQ, Herts, United Kingdom
Tel.: (44) 1582 465 540
Web Site: http://www.plantimpact.com
Crop Nutrition & Protection Products Re-
search & Development
N.A.I.C.S.: 541715

Branch (US):

**Plant Impact Plc - Morrisville
Branch** (3)
3005 Carrington Mill Blvd Ste 520, Morris-
ville, NC 27560
Tel.: (984) 465-4188
Web Site: http://www.plantimpact.com
Agriculture Product Distr
N.A.I.C.S.: 424910

Subsidiary (Non-US):

**Plant Impact Tecnologia em Nutricao
Ltda** (3)
Avenida das Nacoes Unidas 18 801- Con-
junto 501 Vila Almeida, Sao Paulo, 04795-
100, Brazil
Tel.: (55) 1130802170
Web Site: http://ww.plantimpact.com
Agricultural Consulting Services
N.A.I.C.S.: 541690

Croda France SAS (1)
Immoparc RN 10, PO Box 49, 78197,
Trappes, France (100%)
Tel.: (33) 130139430
Sales Range: $25-49.9 Million
Emp.: 43
Specialty Chemicals Distr
N.A.I.C.S.: 325998
Nicolas Gadda *(Dir)*

Croda GmbH (1)
Herrenpfad-Sud 33, Kaldenkirchen, 41334,
Nettetal, Germany (100%)
Tel.: (49) 215781730
Web Site: http://www.croda.de
Sales Range: $25-49.9 Million
Emp.: 100
Specialty Chemicals Distr
N.A.I.C.S.: 325998

Croda Holdings France SAS (1)
Immoparc Route Nationale No 10, 78190,
Trappes, France
Tel.: (33) 130139430
Web Site: http://www.croda.com
Sales Range: $25-49.9 Million
Emp.: 14
Chemical Products Distr
N.A.I.C.S.: 424690

Croda Hungary Ltd. (1)
Sasadi Ut 114, 1112, Budapest,
Hungary (100%)
Tel.: (36) 012470910
Web Site: http://www.croda.com
Sales Range: $25-49.9 Million
Emp.: 2
Specialty Chemicals Distr
N.A.I.C.S.: 325998

Croda Iberica SA (1)
Calle Pujades 350 - P 10, 08019, Barce-
lona, Spain
Tel.: (34) 93 322 1193
Web Site: http://www.croda.com
Emp.: 20
Specialty Chemicals Mfr & Distr
N.A.I.C.S.: 325998

Croda Inc. (1)
300-A Columbus Cir, Edison, NJ
08837 (100%)
Tel.: (732) 417-0800
Web Site: http://www.crodausa.com
Sales Range: $25-49.9 Million
Emp.: 4
Specialty Chemicals Distr
N.A.I.C.S.: 325998

**Croda India Company Private
Ltd.** (1)
Plot No 1/1Part TTC Industrial Area Thane
Belapur Road, Koparkhairne, Navi Mumbai,
400 710, Maharashtra, India
Tel.: (91) 2230948400
Natural Specialty Chemical Mfr
N.A.I.C.S.: 325199
Shantanu Das *(Asst Mgr)*

Croda Italiana S.p.A. (1)
Via Petro Grocco 917/919, 27036, Mortara,
Italy (100%)
Tel.: (39) 0384205011
Web Site: http://www.croda.com
Sales Range: $25-49.9 Million
Emp.: 22
Specialty Chemicals Distr
N.A.I.C.S.: 325998

Croda Japan KK (1)
Shinjuku Park Tower 11th Floor 3-7-1 Nishi-
shinjuku, Shinjuku-ku, Tokyo, 163-1011,
Japan
Tel.: (81) 362581910
Natural Specialty Chemical Mfr
N.A.I.C.S.: 325199

**Croda Kimya Ticaret Limited
Sirket** (1)
Nidakule Goztepe Is Merkezi Merdivenkoy
Mah Bora Sok No 1 Kat 2/5, Kadikoy,
34732, Istanbul, Turkiye
Tel.: (90) 2166888152
Natural Specialty Chemical Mfr
N.A.I.C.S.: 325199

Croda Korea Co., Ltd. (1)
Rm 1201 12th Floor 42 Hwang Sae Ul-Ro
360 Beon-Gil, Bundang-Gu, Seongnam,
463-721, Gyeong Gi-Do, Korea (South)
Tel.: (82) 316982540
Emp.: 20
Natural Specialty Chemical Mfr
N.A.I.C.S.: 325199

Croda Magyarorszag Kft. (1)
Croda Hungary Bolcso u 6, 1117, Budapest,
Hungary
Tel.: (36) 12470910
Natural Specialty Chemical Mfr
N.A.I.C.S.: 325199

Croda Mexico, S.A. de C.V. (1)
Hamburgo 213 Piso 10, Parque Indus San
Pablo Xalpa T, Chihuahua, 54090, Colonia
Juarez, Mexico (100%)
Tel.: (52) 5553675760
Web Site: http://www.crodala.com
Sales Range: $10-24.9 Million
Emp.: 18
Specialty Chemicals Distr
N.A.I.C.S.: 424690

Croda Middle East (1)
Office 511 LOB 16 Jebel Ali Free Zone, PO
Box 17916, Dubai, United Arab Emirates
Tel.: (971) 4 887 0100
Sales Range: $50-74.9 Million
Emp.: 6
Specialty Chemicals Distr
N.A.I.C.S.: 424690
Sreek Snieders *(Reg Mgr)*

Croda Nederland B.V. (1)
Buurtje 1, 2802 BE, Gouda, Netherlands
Tel.: (31) 182542911
Web Site: http://www.croda.com
Sales Range: $125-149.9 Million
Emp.: 300
Chemical Products Mfr
N.A.I.C.S.: 325998

Subsidiary (Domestic):

Incotec Group B.V. (2)
Westeinde 107, 1601 BL, Enkhuizen, Neth-
erlands
Tel.: (31) 228 358 000
Web Site: http://www.incotec.com

Agricultural Seed Coating, Pelleting, Enhancement & Analytical Services
N.A.I.C.S.: 541990

Subsidiary (US):

**Incotec Integrated Coating & Seed
Technology, Inc.** (3)
1293 Harkins Rd, Salinas, CA 93901-4408
Tel.: (831) 757-4367
Web Site: http://www.incotec.com
Agricultural Seed Coating, Pelleting, En-
hancement & Analytical Services
N.A.I.C.S.: 541990
Gerard Denny *(Mgr-Integrated Product Res)*

Croda Nordica AB (1)
Geijersgatan 2B, 216 18, Limhamn,
Sweden (100%)
Tel.: (46) 4 036 8550
Web Site: http://www.croda.com
Sales Range: $25-49.9 Million
Emp.: 12
Specialty Chemicals Distr
N.A.I.C.S.: 325998

**Croda Oleochemicals Iberica,
S.A.** (1)
Plz Francesco Macia 7 7B, 08029, Barce-
lona, Spain (100%)
Tel.: (34) 933221193
Web Site: http://www.croda-iberica.com
Specialty Chemicals Mfr & Distr
N.A.I.C.S.: 325998

Croda Overseas Holdings Ltd (1)
Cowick Hall, Goole, DN14 9AA, East York-
shire, United Kingdom
Tel.: (44) 1405 860551
Web Site: http://www.croda.com
Emp.: 300
Investment Management Service
N.A.I.C.S.: 523999

Croda Pars Trading Co (1)
Apt 305 3rd Floor No 14 Golestan Ave
Alikhani Ave Southern Shiraz Str, Tehran,
Iran
Tel.: (98) 2188621301
Natural Specialty Chemical Mfr
N.A.I.C.S.: 325199

Croda Peruana S.A.C (1)
Av Juan de Aliaga 425 Ofc 401-8,
Magdalena del Mar, Lima, Peru
Tel.: (51) 1 500 6773
Web Site: http://www.croda.com
Sales Range: $50-74.9 Million
Emp.: 4
Personal Care Product Distr
N.A.I.C.S.: 424210

Croda Poland Sp. z o.o. (1)
Wadowicka 6, 30-415, Krakow, Poland
Tel.: (48) 12 633 1529
Web Site: http://www.croda.com.pl
Sales Range: $50-74.9 Million
Emp.: 1
Health Care Product Whslr
N.A.I.C.S.: 424210

Croda RUS LLC (1)
Raketnyi bulvar 16 Office 1333, Moscow,
129164, Russia
Tel.: (7) 4956608898
Natural Specialty Chemical Mfr
N.A.I.C.S.: 325199
Andrey Vinogradov *(Mng Dir)*

Croda Singapore Pte. Ltd. (1)
No 30 Seraya Avenue, Singapore, 627884,
Singapore (100%)
Tel.: (65) 6 551 9600
Web Site: http://www.croda.com.sg
Emp.: 200
Specialty Chemicals Mfr & Distr
N.A.I.C.S.: 325998

Subsidiary (Non-US):

Croda Australia (2)
Suite 102 Level 1 447 Victoria Street,
Wetherill Park, 2164, NSW,
Australia (100%)
Tel.: (61) 01300667050
Web Site: http://www.croda.com.au
Sales Range: $25-49.9 Million
Emp.: 10
Specialty Chemicals Distr
N.A.I.C.S.: 325998

Croda Chemicals (India) Pvt Ltd. (2)
501 Glacis Tower Linking Road, Khar W,
Mumbai, 400 052, India (100%)
Tel.: (91) 22 2648 2733
Web Site: http://www.croda.co.in
Sales Range: $25-49.9 Million
Emp.: 7
Specialty Chemicals Distr
N.A.I.C.S.: 325998

Croda Hong Kong (2)
Rm 806 Tower 2 South Seas St, 77 Mody
Rd Psin Sha Psui E, Kowloon, China (Hong
Kong) (100%)
Tel.: (852) 25593327
Sales Range: $25-49.9 Million
Emp.: 11
Specialty Chemicals Distr
N.A.I.C.S.: 325998

**Croda Korea Chemical International
Ltd.** (2)
Rm 1201 42 Hyang Sauel/Ro 360 Beon/Gil
Buntang Gu, Bundang-Ku, Seongnam, 463
721, Kyunggi-Do, Korea (South) (100%)
Tel.: (82) 317061756
Web Site: http://www.croda.com
Sales Range: $25-49.9 Million
Emp.: 19
Specialty Chemicals Distr
N.A.I.C.S.: 325998

Croda Shanghai (2)
Room 531 D5 Building Shanghai Jia Hua
Business Center, No 808 Hong Qiao Road,
Shanghai, 200030, China
Tel.: (86) 2164479516
Sales Range: $25-49.9 Million
Emp.: 3
Specialty Chemicals Distr
N.A.I.C.S.: 325998

Croda Sipo (Sichuan) Co., Ltd. (1)
No 656 East Tangxun Road Economic-
Technological Development Zone, Mian-
yang, 621000, Sichuan, China
Tel.: (86) 8162533796
Natural Specialty Chemical Mfr
N.A.I.C.S.: 325199

Croda Spol. s.r.o. (1)
Pekarska 603/12, 155 00, Prague, Czech
Republic
Tel.: (420) 222513163
Natural Specialty Chemical Mfr
N.A.I.C.S.: 325199

**Croda Trading (Shanghai) Co.,
Ltd** (1)
Rm 531 Rm 301 Building D5 Jiahua Busi-
ness Centre No 808, Shanghai, 200000,
China
Tel.: (86) 2164479516
Sales Range: $25-49.9 Million
Emp.: 2
Personal Care Product Distr
N.A.I.C.S.: 424210
James Lee *(Gen Mgr)*

Croda do Brasil Ltda (1)
Rua Croda 580-Distrito Industrial, Campi-
nas, 13054-710, Sao Paulo, Brazil
Tel.: (55) 193 765 3500
Web Site: http://www.croda.com.br
Emp.: 200
Specialty Chemicals Mfr
N.A.I.C.S.: 325998

Crodarom (1)
Herrenpfad Sud 33, 41334, Nettetal, Ka-
Idenkirchen, Germany (100%)
Tel.: (49) 215781730
Web Site: http://www.croda.co.in
Sales Range: $25-49.9 Million
Emp.: 50
Mfr of Plant Extractss & Additives
N.A.I.C.S.: 325998

Crodarom SAS (1)
Parc d'Activites Les Plaines, 48230,
Chanac, France
Tel.: (33) 46 648 2027
Web Site:
http://www.crodapersonalcare.com
Plant Extraction Mfr
N.A.I.C.S.: 325414

Enza Biotech AB (1)
Scheelevagen 22, 223 63, Lund, Sweden
Tel.: (46) 700905712

Web Site: http://www.enzabiotech.com
Biotechnology-Based Production Services
N.A.I.C.S.: 541714

Flavor Inn Corporation Sdn Bhd   **(1)**
6 Jalan Anggerik Mokara 31/54, Kota Kemuning Section 31, 40460, Shah Alam, Selangor Darul Ehsan, Malaysia
Tel.: (60) 351219598
Web Site: https://www.flavorinn.com
Food Ingredient Mfr
N.A.I.C.S.: 311999

Iberchem South Africa (Pty) Ltd.   **(1)**
383 Roan Crescent Corporate Park, North Randjespark, Midrand, 1685, South Africa
Tel.: (27) 126534447
Chemicals Mfr
N.A.I.C.S.: 325199

Incotec (Beijing) Agricultural Technology Co., Ltd.   **(1)**
2nd Floor Building 21 East Zone of Yongyou, Industrial Park No 9 Yongfeng Road Haidian District, Beijing, 100094, China
Tel.: (86) 1062480309
Natural Specialty Chemical Mfr
N.A.I.C.S.: 325199
Zhang Xiaohui *(Mgr-Sls)*

Incotec (Tianjin) Agricultural Technology Co., Ltd.   **(1)**
No 2 Plant of Yabao Pharmacy No 1 Quanfeng Road, Wuqing Development Zone Wuqing District, Tianjin, 301700, China
Tel.: (86) 2259007360
Natural Specialty Chemical Mfr
N.A.I.C.S.: 325199

Incotec America do Sul Tecnologia em Sementes Ltda.   **(1)**
Rua das Sementes 291 Altura do km 34 da SP 107, Holambra, 13825-000, Sao Paulo, Brazil
Tel.: (55) 1938029600
Seed Quality Development Services
N.A.I.C.S.: 111199

Incotec Argentina S.A   **(1)**
Ruta 8 Km 224 3, Pergamino, 2700, Buenos Aires, Argentina
Tel.: (54) 2477423869
Seed Quality Development Services
N.A.I.C.S.: 111199

Incotec Malaysia Sdn. Bhd.   **(1)**
B-08-13A Gateway Kiaramas No 1 Jalan Desa Kiara, Mont Kiara, 50480, Kuala Lumpur, Malaysia
Tel.: (60) 362033233
Natural Specialty Chemical Mfr
N.A.I.C.S.: 325199

Integrated Coating & Seed Technology India Pvt. Ltd.   **(1)**
46 and 47 Mahagujarat Industrial Estate Opp. Pharmatech Sarkhej-Bavla Highway At- Moraiya Ta- Sanand, Ahmedabad, 382 213, India
Tel.: (91) 9998980829
Natural Specialty Chemical Mfr
N.A.I.C.S.: 325199

PT Croda Cikarang   **(1)**
Cikarang Industrial Estate JL Jababeka IV Block V, Kav 74 75, Jakarta, 17530, Cikarang Bekasi, Indonesia   **(60%)**
Tel.: (62) 218934923
Web Site: http://www.croda.com
Sales Range: $25-49.9 Million
Emp.: 40
Mfr & Distr of Oleochemicals
N.A.I.C.S.: 325998
Erwin Harun *(Mng Dir)*

PT Croda Indonesia Ltd   **(1)**
Cikarang Industrial Estate JL Jababeka IV Block V Kav 74-75, Bekasi, 17530, Cikarang, Indonesia
Tel.: (62) 21 893 4923
Web Site: http://www.croda.com
Chemical Products Mfr
N.A.I.C.S.: 325998

Rewitec GmbH   **(1)**
Dr-Hans-Wilhelmi-Weg 1, 35633, Lahnau, Germany
Tel.: (49) 6441445990
Web Site: https://www.rewitec.com

Lubricant Mfr & Distr
N.A.I.C.S.: 333914

SEDERMA GmbH   **(1)**
Herrenpfad-Sud 33, 41334, Nettetal, Germany
Tel.: (49) 21 57 817318
Web Site: http://www.sederma.de
Cosmetics Products Mfr
N.A.I.C.S.: 325620

SEDERMA Inc.   **(1)**
300 Columbus Cir, Edison, NJ 08837
Tel.: (732) 692-1652
Web Site: http://www.sederma.fr
Cosmetics Products Mfr
N.A.I.C.S.: 325620

Sederma SA   **(1)**
29 Rue Du Chemin Vert, 78612, Yvelines, Cedex, France   **(100%)**
Tel.: (33) 134841010
Web Site: http://www.sederma.fr
Sales Range: $50-74.9 Million
Emp.: 130
Specialty Chemical & Toiletries Mfr
N.A.I.C.S.: 325998

CRODUX PLIN D.O.O.
Savska Opatovina 36, Zagreb, 10090, Croatia
Tel.: (385) 14590580
Web Site: http://crodux-plin.hr
Emp.: 114
Natural Gas Distr Services
N.A.I.C.S.: 221210
Ivan Cermak *(Gen Mgr)*

CROISSANCE LTD.
362 2nd Floor 11th cross 4th Main 2nd Block, RT Nagar, Bengaluru, 560032, KA, India
Tel.: (91) 8023330019
Web Site: https://www.croissance-group.com
Year Founded: 1994
531909—(BOM)
Rev.: $7,849
Assets: $1,085,803
Liabilities: $110,043
Net Worth: $975,760
Earnings: $3,096
Fiscal Year-end: 03/31/21
Real Estate Development Services
N.A.I.C.S.: 531390
M. Jayasimha Reddy *(Chm & Mng Dir)*

CROMA SECURITY SOLUTIONS GROUP PLC
Unit 7 & 8 Fulcrum 4 Solent Way, Whiteley, PO15 7FT, Hampshire, United Kingdom
Tel.: (44) 1489566100
Web Site: https://www.cssgplc.com
CSSG—(AIM)
Rev.: $47,744,224
Assets: $25,852,347
Liabilities: $9,365,553
Net Worth: $16,486,794
Earnings: $85,536
Emp.: 1,000
Fiscal Year-end: 06/30/22
Covert Surveillance Security & Homeland Defense Related Products Designer & Mfr
N.A.I.C.S.: 561621
Sebastian Jake Finch Morley *(Chm)*

Subsidiaries:

RDDS Avionics Limited   **(1)**
Star Lane, Margate, CT9 4ED, Kent, United Kingdom
Tel.: (44) 184 323 3030
Web Site: https://rdds.co.uk
Sales Range: $25-49.9 Million
Emp.: 15
Surveillance Equipment Mfr
N.A.I.C.S.: 334310
Tom Morrison *(Mgr-Sls & Mktg)*

Vigilant Security (Scotland) Limited   **(1)**
First Floor 161 Brooms Road, 23 Loganbarns Rd, Dumfries, DG1 2SH, United Kingdom
Tel.: (44) 138 724 7842
Web Site: http://www.vigilantsecurityservices.com
Security Training Services
N.A.I.C.S.: 561621

CROMEX S/A
Av Prof Celestino Bourroul 273, Limao, Sao Paulo, 02710-000, Brazil
Tel.: (55) 11 3856 1000
Web Site: http://www.cromex.com.br
Color Concentrate Mfr
N.A.I.C.S.: 325130
Marcos Pinhel *(Dir-Comml)*

CROMPTON CONTROLS LTD.
Monckton Rd, Wakefield, WF2 7AL, W Yorkshire, United Kingdom
Tel.: (44) 1924368251   UK
Web Site: http://www.cromptoncontrols.co.uk
Year Founded: 1880
Electric Motor Control Equipment Mfr
N.A.I.C.S.: 335999
Dean Sweeney *(Mng Dir)*

CROMPTON GREAVES CONSUMER ELECTRICALS LIMITED
Equinox Business Park 1st Floor Tower 3 LBS Marg Kurla W, Mumbai, 400070, Maharashtra, India
Tel.: (91) 2261678499
Web Site: https://www.crompton.co.in
Year Founded: 2015
539876—(BOM)
Rev.: $666,018,990
Assets: $493,761,450
Liabilities: $230,121,255
Net Worth: $263,640,195
Earnings: $84,172,725
Emp.: 1,853
Fiscal Year-end: 03/31/21
Household Appliance Mfr & Distr
N.A.I.C.S.: 335210
Shantanu Khosla *(Mng Dir)*

Subsidiaries:

Butterfly Gandhimathi Appliances Limited   **(1)**
No 34 2nd Floor Rajiv Gandhi Salai, Egattur Village, Chennai, 600130, Tamil Nadu, India   **(75%)**
Tel.: (91) 4449005100
Web Site: https://www.butterflyindia.com
Rev.: $145,118,979
Assets: $68,619,260
Liabilities: $29,628,990
Net Worth: $38,990,270
Earnings: $7,052,382
Emp.: 1,349
Fiscal Year-end: 03/31/2023
Kitchen Product Mfr
N.A.I.C.S.: 423440
V. M. Lakshminarayanan *(Chm & Mng Dir)*

Subsidiary (Domestic):

LLM Appliances Limited   **(2)**
Annachi Building No 1/3 2nd Floor Soundararajan Street T Nagar, Chennai, 600 017, Tamil Nadu, India
Tel.: (91) 4442287631
Web Site: http://butterflyindia.com
Sales Range: $50-74.9 Million
Emp.: 250
Home Appliance Mfr
N.A.I.C.S.: 335220

CROMSOURCE S.R.L.
Via Giorgio De Sandre 3, 37135, Verona, MI, Italy
Tel.: (39) 045 8222 811   IT
Web Site: http://www.cromsource.com
Year Founded: 1993

Sales Range: $10-24.9 Million
Emp.: 90
Clinical Research & Testing Services
N.A.I.C.S.: 541715
Oriana Zerbini *(Founder & CEO)*

Subsidiaries:

CROMSOURCE Inc.   **(1)**
1 Alewife Ctr Ste 120, Cambridge, MA 02140
Tel.: (617) 871-1128
Web Site: http://www.cromsource.com
Emp.: 8
Clinical Research & Testing Services
N.A.I.C.S.: 541715
Helen Colquhoun *(Sr VP)*

CROMSOURCE Ltd.   **(1)**
Suite 11 Sabrina Court Longden Coleham, Shrewsbury, SY3 7BF, United Kingdom
Tel.: (44) 1743 243 277
Web Site: http://www.cromsource.com
Clinical Research & Testing Services
N.A.I.C.S.: 541715

CROMWELL EUROPEAN REAL ESTATE INVESTMENT TRUST
50 Collyer Quay 07-02 OUE Bayfront, Singapore, 49321, Singapore
Tel.: (65) 69207539   SG
Web Site: https://www.cromwelleuropean.com
CWBU—(SES)
Rev.: $238,976,708
Assets: $2,613,393,311
Liabilities: $1,227,875,042
Net Worth: $1,385,518,269
Earnings: ($81,575,229)
Emp.: 340
Fiscal Year-end: 12/31/23
Investment Management Service
N.A.I.C.S.: 523940
Elena Arabadjieva *(COO & Head-IR)*

CROMWELL PROPERTY GROUP
Tel.: (61) 732255777
CMW—(ASX)
Rev.: $146,702,478
Assets: $2,058,642,420
Liabilities: $997,069,368
Net Worth: $1,061,573,052
Earnings: ($187,167,522)
Emp.: 390
Fiscal Year-end: 06/30/24
Real Estate Investment Trust
N.A.I.C.S.: 525990
Philip Cowling *(Chief Sustainability Officer)*

Subsidiaries:

CH Janki Sp Zoo   **(1)**
Ul Mszczonowska 3 Janki Near, 05-090, Warsaw, Poland
Tel.: (48) 22 711 3000
Web Site: https://chjanki.pl
Real Estate Services
N.A.I.C.S.: 531390

Cromwell Corporate Secretarial Limited   **(1)**
1st Floor Unit 16, Manor Court Business Park, Scarborough, YO11 3TU, United Kingdom
Tel.: (44) 172 358 5600
Web Site: https://www.cromwellpropertygroup.co.uk
Real Estate Services
N.A.I.C.S.: 531390

Cromwell Corporation Limited   **(1)**
Level 19 200 Mary Street, Brisbane, 4000, QLD, Australia
Tel.: (61) 732257777
Web Site: http://www.cromwell.com.au
Sales Range: $50-74.9 Million
Emp.: 80
Property Management Services
N.A.I.C.S.: 531312

Cromwell Property Group—(Continued)

Subsidiary (Domestic):

Cromwell Property Securities Limited (2)
Level 19 200 Mary Street, Brisbane, 4000, QLD, Australia
Tel.: (61) 732257777
Web Site: http://www.cromwell.com.au
Sales Range: $50-74.9 Million
Emp.: 60
Fund Management Services
N.A.I.C.S.: 525910

Cromwell Property Services Pty. Ltd. (2)
Level 19 200 Mary St, Brisbane, 4000, QLD, Australia
Tel.: (61) 732257777
Web Site: http://www.cromwell.com.au
Sales Range: $50-74.9 Million
Emp.: 90
Property Management Services
N.A.I.C.S.: 531312

Cromwell Denmark A/S (1)
Kay Fiskers Plads 9 St, 2300, Copenhagen, Denmark
Tel.: (45) 7020 5410
Web Site:
　　https://www.cromwellpropertygroup.dk
Investment Management Service
N.A.I.C.S.: 541611

Cromwell European Management Services Limited (1)
Minerva House 29 East Parade, Leeds, LS1 5PS, United Kingdom
Tel.: (44) 1132044520
Residential Property Management Services
N.A.I.C.S.: 531311
Matt Girling (Mgr-Investment)

Cromwell Finland O/Y (1)
Salomonkatu 17B, 00100, Helsinki, Finland
Tel.: (358) 10 387 6000
Web Site:
　　https://www.cromwellpropertygroup.fi
Investment Management Service
N.A.I.C.S.: 541611

Cromwell Property Group Czech Republic s.r.o. (1)
Salvatorsa 931/8, 1 Old Town, 110 00, Prague, Czech Republic
Tel.: (420) 77 716 7376
Web Site:
　　https://www.cromwellpropertygroup.cz
Investment Management Service
N.A.I.C.S.: 523940
David Svoboda (Country Mgr)

Cromwell Property Group Italy SRL (1)
Third Floor Via Giuseppe Sacchi 7, 20121, Milan, Italy
Tel.: (39) 028 295 5320
Web Site:
　　https://www.cromwellpropertygroup.it
Real Estate Services
N.A.I.C.S.: 531390

Cromwell Sweden A/B (1)
Hyllie Stationstorg 31 van 5, 215 32, Malmo, Sweden
Tel.: (46) 40 668 8498
Web Site:
　　https://www.cromwellpropertygroup.se
Real Estate Services
N.A.I.C.S.: 531390

The 10 Group Limited (1)
23 Beaumont Mews, London, W1G6EN, United Kingdom
Tel.: (44) 2076370656
Web Site: https://the10group.com
Marketing Consulting Services
N.A.I.C.S.: 541613

CRONA CORP.
Strada Jean-Louis Calderon 31, Bucharest, 030167, Romania
Tel.: (40) 371700107　　　　　NV
Web Site: http://www.corpcrona.com
Year Founded: 2016
CCCP—(OTCIQ)
Rev.: $78,118

Assets: $102,510
Liabilities: $101,820
Net Worth: $690
Earnings: $45,148
Fiscal Year-end: 12/31/22
Music Recording Services
N.A.I.C.S.: 512250
Demetrios Malamas (Pres, CEO, CFO, Treas & Sec)

CRONEX CO LTD
55 Juseok-ro 778beon-gil, Paltan-myeon, Hwaseong, 18525, Gyeonggi-Do, Korea (South)
Tel.: (82) 313527669
Web Site: http://www.cronex.co.kr
Year Founded: 2012
Bio Technology Services
N.A.I.C.S.: 541714
Son Young-June (Board of Directors & CEO)

CRONIMET HOLDING GMBH
Sudbeckenstrasse 22, 76189, Karlsruhe, Germany
Tel.: (49) 721952250　　　　　De
Web Site: http://www.cronimet.de
Year Founded: 1980
Sales Range: $50-74.9 Million
Emp.: 1,578
Metal Scrap Mfr & Distr
N.A.I.C.S.: 331492
Gunter Pilarsky (Founder & Mng Dir-Cronimet Grp)

Subsidiaries:

Avarus AG (1)
Allmendstr 11, 6312, Steinhausen, Switzerland
Tel.: (41) 41 748 4200
Web Site: http://www.avarus.ch
Steel & Ferroalloy Mfr
N.A.I.C.S.: 331110

CRONIFER U.K. Ltd. (1)
Hardwick View Road, Chesterfield, S42 5UW, United Kingdom
Tel.: (44) 124 68561 11
Web Site: http://www.cronifer.co.uk
Metal Scraper Mfr
N.A.I.C.S.: 333998
Colin Simpson (Mng Dir)

CRONILEG Rohstoffhandelsgesellschaft mbH (1)
Sympherstr 96A, 47138, Duisburg, Germany
Tel.: (49) 203 450370
Steel & Ferroalloy Distr
N.A.I.C.S.: 423510
Stefan Grosskopf (Mgr-Comml)

CRONIMET (Great Britain) Ltd. (1)
Staffordshire, Cannock, WS12 OPL, United Kingdom
Tel.: (44) 1543 877337
Steel & Ferroalloy Distr
N.A.I.C.S.: 423510

CRONIMET (Holland) b.v. (1)
Vlasweg 7, 4782, Moerdijk, Netherlands
Tel.: (31) 168 382038
Steel & Ferroalloy Distr
N.A.I.C.S.: 423510
Thorsten Groening (Mng Dir)

CRONIMET ALFA Ferrolegierungen Handels GmbH (1)
Rupert Bodner Str 25, 81245, Munich, Germany
Tel.: (49) 89 8649500
Web Site: http://www.cronimet-alfa.de
Steel & Ferroalloy Distr
N.A.I.C.S.: 423510

CRONIMET Base Metals GmbH (1)
Sudbeckenstr 22, 76189, Karlsruhe, Germany
Tel.: (49) 721 952250
Steel & Ferroalloy Distr
N.A.I.C.S.: 423510

CRONIMET Belgium NV (1)

Tiendenstraat 10 Zutendaal, 3690, Genk, Belgium
Tel.: (32) 89 5007 70
Web Site: http://www.cronimet.be
Steel & Ferroalloy Distr
N.A.I.C.S.: 423510

CRONIMET Brasil Ltda. (1)
Avenida Engenheiro Roberto Zuccolo 255, Vila Leopoldina, Sao Paulo, 05307-190, Brazil
Tel.: (55) 11 3839 4500
Web Site: http://www.cronimet.com.br
Steel & Ferroalloy Distr
N.A.I.C.S.: 423510
Leandro Pinheiro de Campos (Mng Dir)

CRONIMET Central Africa AG (1)
Allmendstrasse 11 Kanton Zug, 6312, Steinhausen, Switzerland
Tel.: (41) 41 748 42 06
Web Site: http://www.cronimet-mining.com
Metal Ore Mining Services
N.A.I.C.S.: 212290

CRONIMET China (1)
Suite 803 Shanghai Kerry Centre, 1515 Nanjing Road West, Shanghai, 200040, China
Tel.: (86) 21 62790022
Steel & Ferroalloy Distr
N.A.I.C.S.: 423510
Herr Kevin Wang (Mgr)

CRONIMET Corporation (1)
1 Pilarsky Way, Aliquippa, PA 15001
Tel.: (724) 375-5004
Web Site: http://www.cronimetusa.com
Steel & Ferroalloy Distr
N.A.I.C.S.: 423510
David Porco (VP-Quality & Admin)

Subsidiary (Non-US):

CRONIMET MEXICO (2)
Insurgentes Sur 1802-5 Colonia Florida, Mexico, 01030, Mexico
Tel.: (52) 55 56633262
Steel & Ferroalloy Distr
N.A.I.C.S.: 423510
Oscar Roman Galaviz (Gen Mgr)

CRONIMET Fagersta AB (1)
PO Box 123, 73723, Fagersta, Sweden
Tel.: (46) 223 42000
Steel & Ferroalloy Distr
N.A.I.C.S.: 423510

CRONIMET Ferrolegierungen Handelsges. mbH (1)
Sudbeckenstrasse 22, Karlsruhe, 76189, Germany
Tel.: (49) 721952250
Web Site: http://www.cronimet.de
Rev.: $358,550,000
Emp.: 120
Raw Material & Stainless Steel Recycling Company
N.A.I.C.S.: 331110
Thomas Heil (Mng Dir)

CRONIMET France S.A.S. (1)
Rue du 8 Mai 1945 Mitry Mory, 77290, Paris, France
Tel.: (33) 64673200
Steel & Ferroalloy Distr
N.A.I.C.S.: 423510

Subsidiary (Non-US):

ERG Edelstahl Recycling GmbH (2)
Limesstr 20, 63741, Aschaffenburg, Germany
Tel.: (49) 6021 44260
Steel & Ferroalloy Distr
N.A.I.C.S.: 423510

CRONIMET HISPANIA, S. A. (1)
Muelle AZ-2 Zierbena, 48508, Santurce, Spain
Tel.: (34) 94 4831728
Steel & Ferroalloy Distr
N.A.I.C.S.: 423510

CRONIMET India Metals Pvt. Ltd. (1)
C -201 Ashit Apartment Sudhir Pawar Path, Modi Baug Near Agriculture College Shivajinagar, Pune, 411016, India
Tel.: (91) 20 2552 0178
Steel & Ferroalloy Distr

N.A.I.C.S.: 423510
Ramchandra Sapre (Mgr-Comml)

CRONIMET Latvia SIA (1)
Spridisa iela 1, 1084, Riga, Latvia
Tel.: (371) 28659555
Steel & Ferroalloy Distr
N.A.I.C.S.: 423510

CRONIMET Legierungen Dortmund GmbH (1)
Kipperstr 11, 44147, Dortmund, Germany
Tel.: (49) 231 878050
Steel & Ferroalloy Distr
N.A.I.C.S.: 423510
Gunter Pilarsky (Chm)

CRONIMET London Ltd. (1)
72-76 River Road Barking, London, IG11 0DS, United Kingdom
Tel.: (44) 208 5070800
Steel & Ferroalloy Distr
N.A.I.C.S.: 423510

CRONIMET MINING AG (1)
Aygestan 5-te Strasse Haus 15, 0070, Yerevan, Armenia
Tel.: (374) 10 554305
Metal Ore Mining Services
N.A.I.C.S.: 212290

CRONIMET Metal Philippines, Inc. (1)
Purok 2 Bucal National Road, Calamba, 4027, Laguna, Philippines
Tel.: (63) 49 834 1400
Steel & Ferroalloy Distr
N.A.I.C.S.: 423510

CRONIMET Noble Alloys Handelges. mbH (1)
Kasslerfelder Strasse 188-192, 47059, Duisburg, Germany
Tel.: (49) 20345567 30
Steel & Ferroalloy Distr
N.A.I.C.S.: 423510

CRONIMET Nordic OU (1)
Jalaka 60B, 50109, Tartu, Estonia
Tel.: (372) 2 7400510
Steel & Ferroalloy Distr
N.A.I.C.S.: 423510

CRONIMET Ostrava, s.r.o (1)
Polanecka 820 Svinov, 721 00, Ostrava, Czech Republic
Tel.: (420) 596 634 711
Steel & Ferroalloy Distr
N.A.I.C.S.: 423510

CRONIMET PL Sp. Z.o.o. (1)
Klopot 10A, 88-100, Inowroclaw, Poland
Tel.: (48) 52 356 45 00
Web Site: http://www.cronimet.com.pl
Emp.: 110
Steel & Ferroalloy Distr
N.A.I.C.S.: 423510
Andrzej Bartoszak (Mgr-Trade Mktg)

CRONIMET RSA (PTY) LTD (1)
6 Fuchs Street Alrode EXT 2 Alberton, PO BOX 124284, Johannesburg, 1451, Gauteng, South Africa
Tel.: (27) 11 908 1620
Steel & Ferroalloy Distr
N.A.I.C.S.: 423510

Subsidiary (Domestic):

CRONIMET Chrome Mining (Pty.) Ltd. (2)
Building C Willow Wood Office Park 220 Third cnr, Cedar Roads Broadacres, 2021, Johannesburg, South Africa
Tel.: (27) 119580544
Steel & Ferroalloy Distr
N.A.I.C.S.: 423510
Charles Hopkins (Mgr-Legal)

CRONIMET S.A. (1)
Torre Alfa La Sguancia Nr 1, 6900, Lugano, Switzerland
Tel.: (41) 91 9856 990
Steel & Ferroalloy Distr
N.A.I.C.S.: 423510

CRONIMET Shanghai Co., Ltd. (1)
288 Yin Shi Road Shanghai Baoshan Industrial Zone, Shanghai, 200949, China
Tel.: (86) 21 3607 4550
Steel & Ferroalloy Distr

N.A.I.C.S.: 423510

CRONIMET Singapore Pte. Ltd.   (1)
27 Jalan Buroh, Singapore, 619485, Singapore
Tel.: (65) 6225 3946
Web Site: http://www.cronimet.de
Emp.: 25
Steel & Ferroalloy Distr
N.A.I.C.S.: 423510
Mahiar Patel *(Mng Dir)*

Giuliani Metalli s.a.s.   (1)
Via Redi 25, 20129, Milan, Italy
Tel.: (39) 02 29515 799
Steel & Ferroalloy Distr
N.A.I.C.S.: 423510

M & S Alloys Ltd.   (1)
Pleasant Street, West Bromwich, B70 7DP, West Midlands, United Kingdom
Tel.: (44) 121 525 0606
Steel & Ferroalloy Distr
N.A.I.C.S.: 423510

MSP Metall Service Pedack GmbH   (1)
Rheinhafenstr 12, 76189, Karlsruhe, Germany
Tel.: (49) 721 16131 0
Web Site: http://www.metall-service-pedack.de
Steel & Ferroalloy Mfr
N.A.I.C.S.: 331110

Metalloy Metalle-Legierungen GmbH   (1)
Oststrasse 134, 22844, Norderstedt, Germany
Tel.: (49) 40526780
Steel & Ferroalloy Distr
N.A.I.C.S.: 423510
Helmut Kappen *(Plant Mgr)*

Metals & Alloys International Ltd.   (1)
Chorley New Road Ennerdale Suite Paragon House, Paragon Business Park, Bolton, BL6 6HG, United Kingdom
Tel.: (44) 1204 692 200
Steel & Ferroalloy Distr
N.A.I.C.S.: 423510

NICHEL LEGHE Spa   (1)
Via M L King 12/14 Vittuone, 20010, Milan, Italy
Tel.: (39) 02 90111 925
Steel & Ferroalloy Distr
N.A.I.C.S.: 423510
Luca Stinchelli *(CEO)*

OJSC Plant of Pure Iron   (1)
75 Artsakhi Ave, 0053, Yerevan, Armenia
Tel.: (374) 104 74260
Web Site: http://www.pureironplant.com
Steel & Ferroalloy Distr
N.A.I.C.S.: 423510
Karen Sahakyan *(Head-Comml Dept)*

Schach Matt Handels + Vertriebs GmbH   (1)
Am Ortsguterbahnhof 9, 59063, Hamm, Germany
Tel.: (49) 2381 9029 0
Web Site: http://www.schach-matt-gmbh.de
Steel & Ferroalloy Distr
N.A.I.C.S.: 423510

TSR Recycling GmbH & Co. KG   (1)
Hafenstr 98, 46242, Bottrop, Germany
Tel.: (49) 204170600
Web Site: http://www.tsr.eu
Steel Scrap & Non-Ferrous Metals Recycling
N.A.I.C.S.: 423930

Subsidiary (Non-US):

HKS Metals B.V.   (2)
Graanweg 18, 4782 PP, Moerdijk, Netherlands   **(100%)**
Tel.: (31) 886065200
Web Site: http://www.hks.nl
Emp.: 2,600
Holding Company; Scrap Metal Recycling Services
N.A.I.C.S.: 551112

Subsidiary (Domestic):

HKS Scrap Metals B.V.   (3)

Graanweg 18, 4782 PP, Moerdijk, Netherlands
Tel.: (31) 886065000
Web Site: http://www.hksmetals.eu
Emp.: 70
Scrap Metal Recycling
N.A.I.C.S.: 562920
Wouter Kusters *(Mng Dir)*

United Alloys & Metals. Inc   (1)
9600 John St, Santa Fe Springs, CA 90670
Tel.: (562) 273-7004
Web Site: http://www.uametals.com
Steel & Ferroalloy Distr
N.A.I.C.S.: 423510
Allan R. Sacks *(Sr VP)*

Zangezur Copper & Molybdenum Combine CJSC   (1)
Lernagortsneristr 18 Syunik Marz, 3309, Kajaran, Armenia
Tel.: (374) 285 33557
Web Site: http://www.zcmc.am
Metal Ore Mining Services
N.A.I.C.S.: 212290
Armen Barikyan *(Dir-Comml)*

CRONOS GROUP INC.
111 Peter St Ste 300, Toronto, M5V 2H1, ON, Canada
Tel.: (416) 504-0004   ON
Web Site: http://thecronosgroup.com
CRON—(NASDAQ)
Rev.: $91,904,000
Assets: $1,213,009,000
Liabilities: $72,045,000
Net Worth: $1,140,964,000
Earnings: ($168,734,000)
Emp.: 447
Fiscal Year-end: 12/31/22
Medicinal & Botanical Mfr
N.A.I.C.S.: 325411
Shannon Buggy *(Sr VP & Head-People-Global)*

CROOKES BROTHERS LIMITED
2nd floor Ridge 6 K20 Ncondo Place Umhlanga Ridge, PO Box 611, Mt Edgecombe, Durban, 4300, Kwa-Zulu Natal, South Africa
Tel.: (27) 310015400
Web Site: https://www.cbl.co.za
CKS—(JSE)
Rev.: $32,516,714
Assets: $99,844,686
Liabilities: $46,578,175
Net Worth: $53,266,511
Earnings: ($9,369,976)
Emp.: 987
Fiscal Year-end: 03/31/23
Sugar Products Producers
N.A.I.C.S.: 111930
Guy S. Clarke *(Mng Dir)*

Subsidiaries:

Crookes Plantations Ltd   (1)
PO Box 35, Big Bend, Eswatini
Tel.: (268) 23636523
Web Site: http://www.cbl.co.za
Sugarcane Farming Services & Sugar Exports
N.A.I.C.S.: 111930
Christo Bothma *(Gen Mgr)*

Mthayiza Farming (Pty) Ltd   (1)
Mtata Farm, Malelane, 1320, Mpumalanga, South Africa
Tel.: (27) 137937196
Web Site: http://www.crookesbrothers.co.za
Emp.: 250
Citrus Groves Farming Services
N.A.I.C.S.: 115112

CROOZ, INC.
Roppongihills Mori Tower F38 6-10-1 Roppongi, Minato-ku, Tokyo, 106-6138, Japan
Tel.: (81) 357867080
Web Site: http://crooz.co.jp
Year Founded: 2001

2138—(TKS)
Rev.: $94,324,700
Assets: $179,025,240
Liabilities: $107,584,360
Net Worth: $71,440,880
Earnings: $6,662,880
Fiscal Year-end: 03/31/24
Online Game Development Services
N.A.I.C.S.: 513210

Subsidiaries:

Cloud9, Inc.   (1)
1-8-1 Shimomeguro Arco Tower 12th Floor, Meguro Ward, Tokyo, 153-0064, Tokyo Prefecture, Japan
Tel.: (81) 362805121
Web Site: https://www.cloud9-plus.com
Emp.: 50
Game Application Development Services
N.A.I.C.S.: 541511

CROP LIFE SCIENCE LIMITED
209 Primate Nr Judges Bunglow Cross Road, Bodakdev, Ahmedabad, 380 015, Gujarat, India
Tel.: (91) 7940373967   In
Web Site:
https://www.croplifescience.com
Year Founded: 2006
CLSL—(NSE)
Emp.: 185
Agricultural Chemical Product Mfr
N.A.I.C.S.: 325199
Rajesh Lunagariya *(Mng Dir)*

CROPLOGIC LIMITED
45 Ventnor Avenue, West Perth, 6005, WA, Australia
Tel.: (61) 893894403   AU
Web Site: http://www.croplogic.com
Year Founded: 2010
Rev.: $1,615,679
Assets: $6,740,731
Liabilities: $1,679,861
Net Worth: $5,060,870
Earnings: ($2,683,993)
Fiscal Year-end: 03/31/18
Business Application Management Services
N.A.I.C.S.: 541513
Daniel Bramich *(CFO)*

CROPPER MOTORS
Highway 6 North, Naicam, S0K 2Z0, SK, Canada
Tel.: (306) 874-2011
Web Site:
http://www.croppermotors.com
Sales Range: $10-24.9 Million
New & Used Car & Truck Dealers
N.A.I.C.S.: 441110
Kevin Cropper *(Gen Mgr & Mgr-Vehicle & RV Sls)*

CROPS CORPORATION
KDX Nagoya Ekimae Building 26-8 Meieki 3-chome, Nakamura-ku, Nagoya, 450-0002, Japan
Tel.: (81) 525865145
Web Site: https://www.crops.co.jp
9428—(NGO)
Rev.: $360,006,506
Assets: $220,548,336
Liabilities: $133,207,759
Net Worth: $87,340,577
Earnings: $7,968,283
Emp.: 259
Fiscal Year-end: 03/31/24
Mobile Communications Retailer
N.A.I.C.S.: 449210

Subsidiaries:

Tenpo Innovation Co., Ltd.   (1)
JR Shinjuku Miraina Tower 10th floor 4-1-6 Shinjuku Shinjuku-ku, Tokyo, Japan
Tel.: (81) 333593111
Web Site: http://www.tenpo-r.co.jp
Rev.: $94,278,430

Assets: $90,537,170
Liabilities: $68,565,530
Net Worth: $21,971,640
Earnings: $4,402,260
Fiscal Year-end: 03/31/2024
Commercial Property Rental Services
N.A.I.C.S.: 531120
Yasuo Hara *(Pres & CEO)*

CROPSTER AGRO LIMITED
B 2 207 West Gate Business Bay Opp Andaj Party Plot Bodakdev, Ahmedabad, 3800054, India
Tel.: (91) 9023517216   In
Web Site:
https://www.planterspolysacks.com
Year Founded: 1985
523105—(BOM)
Assets: $8,297
Liabilities: $75,715
Net Worth: ($67,418)
Earnings: ($13,992)
Fiscal Year-end: 03/31/23
Chemical & Plastic Product Whslr
N.A.I.C.S.: 424690
Kanhaiyalal Satyanarain Basotia *(Exec Dir)*

CROSBY VOLKSWAGEN INC
1175 Weber Street E, Kitchener, N2A 1C1, ON, Canada
Tel.: (519) 894-9300
Web Site: http://www.crosbyvw.com
Year Founded: 1937
Rev.: $14,103,200
Emp.: 37
New & Used Car Dealers
N.A.I.C.S.: 441110
Steve Hummel *(Mgr-Parts)*

CROSS CAT CO., LTD.
1-2-70 Konan Minato-ku Shinagawa Season Terrace, Tokyo, 108-0075, Japan
Tel.: (81) 334745251
Web Site: https://www.xcat.co.jp
Year Founded: 1973
2307—(TKS)
Rev.: $98,652,103
Assets: $62,543,755
Liabilities: $28,959,358
Net Worth: $33,584,398
Earnings: $8,662,039
Emp.: 876
Fiscal Year-end: 03/31/24
System Development Services
N.A.I.C.S.: 541512
Yutaka Ushijima *(Chm & Co-CEO)*

CROSS EQUITY PARTNERS AG
Unterdorfstrasse 12, 8808, Pfaffikon, Switzerland
Tel.: (41) 44 269 93 93
Web Site: http://crossequity.ch
Year Founded: 2008
Privater Equity Firm
N.A.I.C.S.: 523999
Michael Petersen *(Co-Mng Partner)*

CROSS MARKETING GROUP INC.
24F 3-20-2 Nishishinjuku Opera City Tower, Shinjuku-ku, Tokyo, 163-1424, Japan
Tel.: (81) 368592269
Web Site: https://www.cm-group.co.jp
Year Founded: 2013
3675—(TKS)
Rev.: $162,870,700
Assets: $103,438,600
Liabilities: $59,388,560
Net Worth: $44,050,040
Earnings: $7,420,460
Emp.: 1,156
Fiscal Year-end: 06/30/24

Cross Marketing Group Inc.—(Continued)

Holding Company; Marketing Research, Consulting & Information Services
N.A.I.C.S.: 551112
Susumu Kamei (*Exec Officer*)

Subsidiaries:

Cross J Tech Inc. **(1)**
Tokyo Opera City Tower 3-20-2 Nishi-Shinjuku, Shinjuku-ku, Tokyo, 163-1424, Japan
Tel.: (81) 368592313
Web Site: http://www.cjt.co.jp
Computer Software Development Services
N.A.I.C.S.: 541511

Cross Marketing Asia Pte. Ltd. **(1)**
11-01 RB Capital Building 22 Malacca Street, Singapore, 048980, Singapore
Tel.: (65) 63728481
Web Site: http://www.cross-m.asia
Marketing Research Service
N.A.I.C.S.: 541910

Cross Marketing Inc. **(1)**
Tokyo Opera City Tower 24F 3-20-2 Nishi-ishinjuku, Shinjuku-ku, Tokyo, 163-1424, Japan
Tel.: (81) 368592250
Web Site: http://global.cross-m.co.jp
Sales Range: $25-49.9 Million
Emp.: 120
Marketing Research & Consulting Services
N.A.I.C.S.: 541910
Miki Igarashi (*Pres & CEO*)

Subsidiary (Domestic):

EC Research Corp. **(2)**
Ginza COM Building 6F 8-15-2 Ginza, Chuo-ku, Tokyo, 104-0061, Japan **(100%)**
Tel.: (81) 335490262
Web Site: http://www.ec-r.co.jp
Sales Range: $75-99.9 Million
Information Technology Market Research & Consulting Services
N.A.I.C.S.: 541910

Cross Propworks Inc. **(1)**
Goryokakucho 1-14 Goryokaku 114 Building 2F, Hokkaido, 040-0001, Hakodate, Japan
Tel.: (81) 138881177
Web Site: https://www.propworks.co.jp
Marketing Research Service
N.A.I.C.S.: 541910

D&M, Inc. **(1)**
Tokyo Opera City Tower 24F 3-20-2, Nishi-Shinjuku Shinjuku-ku, Tokyo, 163-1424, Japan
Tel.: (81) 368592296
Web Site: https://www.d-and-m.co.jp
Marketing Research Service
N.A.I.C.S.: 541910

Envirosell Japan Inc. **(1)**
Tokyo Opera City Tower 24F 3-20-2, Nishi-ishinjuku Shinjuku-ku, Tokyo, 163-1424, Japan
Tel.: (81) 368592267
Web Site: https://www.envirosilljapan.com
Consulting Management Services
N.A.I.C.S.: 541613

Subsidiary (US):

Envirosell Inc. **(2)**
907 BRdway, New York, NY 10010
Tel.: (212) 673-9100
Web Site: https://www.envirosell.com
Fiscal Year-end: 12/31/2010
Marketing Research Service
N.A.I.C.S.: 541910
Paco Underhill (*Founder & CEO*)

Fittio Inc. **(1)**
Tokyo Opera City Tower 24F 3-20-2 Nishi-Shinjuku, Shinjuku-ku, Tokyo, 163-1424, Japan
Tel.: (81) 36 859 2313
Web Site: https://fittio.co.jp
Employment Agency Business Services
N.A.I.C.S.: 561311

Jupiter MR Solutions Co., Ltd. **(1)**
128/226 Phayathai Plaza 21st Floor Phayathai Road, Thung Phayathai Ratchathewi, Bangkok, 10400, Thailand

Tel.: (66) 21293272
Web Site: https://www.jupitermrsolutions.com
Marketing Research Service
N.A.I.C.S.: 541910

Kadence International (Thailand) Co., Ltd. **(1)**
140 One Pacific Place 19th Floor Unit 1910 Sukhumvit Rd, Kolngtoey, Bangkok, 10110, Thailand
Tel.: (66) 2 116 7590
Market Research Services
N.A.I.C.S.: 541910

Kadence International Business Research Pte. Ltd. **(1)**
22 Malacca Street 11-00 RB Capital Building, Singapore, 048980, Singapore
Tel.: (65) 6 372 8710
Market Research Services
N.A.I.C.S.: 541910

Kadence International Inc. **(1)**
J 4 28/F Cyberscape Gamma Topaz and Ruby Streets Ortigas Center, Metro Manila, Pasig, Philippines
Tel.: (63) 917 630 8970
Market Research Services
N.A.I.C.S.: 541910

Kadence International Limited **(1)**
Jl Prof DR Satrio Blok C4 No 5 Kuningan Timur, Setiabudi, Jakarta Selatan, 12950, Indonesia
Tel.: (62) 212 788 3500
Market Research Services
N.A.I.C.S.: 541910

Kadence International Ltd. **(1)**
10 Valentine Place, London, SE1 8QH, United Kingdom
Tel.: (44) 207 620 8360
Market Research Services
N.A.I.C.S.: 541910

Kadence International Pvt., Ltd. **(1)**
Times of India Building 23a Shivaji Marg Main Najafgarh Road, New Delhi, 110015, India
Tel.: (91) 114 556 8400
Market Research Services
N.A.I.C.S.: 541910

Markelytics Solutions India Private Limited **(1)**
No 1873/38 5th Main Road RPC Layout, Bengaluru, 560040, India
Tel.: (91) 8061126112
Web Site: http://www.markelytics.com
Marketing Research Service
N.A.I.C.S.: 541910
Rachan K (*Dir-Assoc*)

Medilead Inc. **(1)**
Nishi-Shinjuku 3-20-2 Tokyo Opera City Tower 24F, Tokyo, 163-1424, Japan
Tel.: (81) 368592295
Web Site: http://www.medi-l.com
Emp.: 19
Marketing Research Service
N.A.I.C.S.: 541910
Susumu Kamei (*CEO & Mng Dir*)

Norfre Food Inc. **(1)**
Saito Studio Court 1F 1-16 Minami 10 Nishi 15, Chuo-ku, Sapporo, 064-0810, Japan
Tel.: (81) 112000822
Web Site: https://www.norfre.com
Food Product Mfr & Distr
N.A.I.C.S.: 311999

Research & Development, Inc. **(1)**
Tokyo Opera City Tower 24F 3-20-2 Nishi-Shinjuku, Shinjuku, Tokyo, 163-1424, Japan
Tel.: (81) 368592285
Web Site: http://www.rad.co.jp
Emp.: 110
Marketing Research Service
N.A.I.C.S.: 541910
Takehisa Matsuda (*Pres & Dir-Rep*)

Supotant Co., Ltd.
Tokyo Opera City Tower 24F 3-20-2 Nishi-Shinjuku, Shinjuku-ku, Tokyo, 163-1424, Japan
Tel.: (81) 368591191
Web Site: http://www.supotant.com
Employment Placement Services

N.A.I.C.S.: 561311

CROSS PLUS INC.
3-9-13 Hananoki nishiku, Nagoya, 451-8560, Japan
Tel.: (81) 525322211
Web Site: https://www.crossplus.co.jp
Year Founded: 1951
0020—(TKG)
Rev.: $426,747,100
Assets: $201,143,300
Liabilities: $91,078,140
Net Worth: $110,065,160
Earnings: $14,633,760
Emp.: 679
Fiscal Year-end: 01/31/24
Clothing Mfr & Sales
N.A.I.C.S.: 424350
Hironori Yamamoto (*Pres*)

Subsidiaries:

Nakahatsu Co., Ltd. **(1)**
3-3-2 Nihonbashihamacho Tornare Nihonbashihamacho 12F, Chuo-ku, Tokyo, 103-0007, Japan
Tel.: (81) 33 669 5271
Web Site: https://www.nakahatsu.co.jp
Fashion Accessories Mfr & Distr
N.A.I.C.S.: 315990

CROSS RIVER VENTURES CORP.
1430-800 West Pender Street, Vancouver, V6C 2V6, BC, Canada
Tel.: (604) 227-6610
Web Site:
https://www.crossriverventures.com
CRVC—(OTCIQ)
Rev.: $2,786
Assets: $4,921,844
Liabilities: $326,125
Net Worth: $4,595,718
Earnings: ($2,074,233)
Fiscal Year-end: 01/31/22
Mineral Exploration & Mining Services
N.A.I.C.S.: 213115
John Fraser (*Pres*)

CROSSFOR CO., LTD.
7-11-4 Kokubo, Kofu, 400-0043, Yamanashi, Japan
Tel.: (81) 570889640
Web Site: https://www.crossfor.co.jp
Year Founded: 1987
7810—(TKS)
Rev.: $21,228,860
Assets: $32,455,960
Liabilities: $21,322,160
Net Worth: $11,133,800
Earnings: $174,160
Emp.: 75
Fiscal Year-end: 07/31/24
Jewelry Mfr & Distr
N.A.I.C.S.: 339910
Hidetaka Dobashi (*Pres*)

Subsidiaries:

Crossfor HK Limited **(1)**
Unit 211 2/F Mirror Tower 61 Mody Road Tsimshatsui East, Kowloon, China (Hong Kong)
Tel.: (852) 23120059
Jewelry Mfr
N.A.I.C.S.: 339910

CROSSJECT SA
6 Rue Pauline Kergomard, 21000, Dijon, France
Tel.: (33) 380549850   FR
Web Site: https://www.crossject.com
Year Founded: 2001
ALCJ—(EUR)
Rev.: $7,039,043
Assets: $41,256,582
Liabilities: $34,348,960
Net Worth: $6,907,622
Earnings: ($12,089,566)

Emp.: 94
Fiscal Year-end: 12/31/20
Needle-Free Injection Systems Mfr
N.A.I.C.S.: 339112
Patrick Alexandre (*Founder, Chm-Mgmt Bd & CEO*)

CROSSLAND STRATEGIC METALS LIMITED
Level 2 470 Collins Street, Melbourne, 3000, VIC, Australia
Tel.: (61) 3 9867 7199
Web Site:
http://www.crosslandstrategic.com
Rev.: $4,100
Assets: $3,731,429
Liabilities: $1,789,941
Net Worth: $1,941,488
Earnings: ($272,956)
Emp.: 20
Fiscal Year-end: 12/31/18
Rare Earth Metals Mining
N.A.I.C.S.: 212290
Eric Vesel (*CEO*)

CROSSLOG SA
151 avenue Jean Jaures, 75019, Paris, France
Tel.: (33) 142463282
Web Site: http://www.crosslog.com
Logistics Management & Transportation Services
N.A.I.C.S.: 541614
Luc Murard de Saint Romain (*Chm & CEO*)

CROSSTEC GROUP HOLDINGS LIMITED
20/F 625 Kings Road, North Point, China (Hong Kong)
Tel.: (852) 26901223   Ky
Web Site:
http://www.crosstec.com.hk
3893—(HKG)
Rev.: $5,159,974
Assets: $6,251,919
Liabilities: $7,854,366
Net Worth: ($1,602,448)
Earnings: ($2,823,114)
Emp.: 36
Fiscal Year-end: 06/30/22
Interior Design Services
N.A.I.C.S.: 541410
Wai Sang Lee (*Chm & CEO*)

CROSSWOOD SA
8 Rue de Seze, 75009, Paris, France
Tel.: (33) 33158361450
Web Site: https://www.crosswood.fr
CROS—(EUR)
Sales Range: Less than $1 Million
Real Estate Manangement Services
N.A.I.C.S.: 531390
Jacques Lacroix (*Chm & CEO*)

CROSSWORD CYBERSECURITY PLC
60 Gracechurch St 6th Floor, London, EC3V 0HR, United Kingdom
Tel.: (44) 3330902587   UK
Web Site:
https://www.crosswordsecurity.com
Year Founded: 2014
CCS—(AIM)
Rev.: $2,947,796
Assets: $9,341,640
Liabilities: $4,447,268
Net Worth: $4,894,373
Earnings: ($3,086,945)
Emp.: 44
Fiscal Year-end: 12/31/21
Cyber Security Services
N.A.I.C.S.: 561621
Mary Dowd (*CFO*)

CROW TECHNOLOGIES 1977 LTD.
12 Kineret Street, Airport City, 70100, Israel
Tel.: (972) 39726000
Industrial Equipment Mfr
N.A.I.C.S.: 333248
Shmuel Melman *(CEO)*

CROWDCUBE LIMITED
The Innovation Centre University of Exeter Rennes Drive, Exeter, EX4 4RN, United Kingdom
Tel.: (44) 1392 241 319　　　　UK
Web Site: http://www.crowdcube.com
Year Founded: 2010
Investment Services
N.A.I.C.S.: 523940
Darren Westlake *(Co-Founder)*

CROWDSPARK LTD
Level 1 Office F 1139 Hay Street, West Perth, 6005, WA, Australia
Tel.: (61) 8 9321 0715
Web Site:
　　http://www.newzululimited.com
Sales Range: Less than $1 Million
Emp.: 8
Internet Kiosks Developer, Distr & Operator
N.A.I.C.S.: 334118

CROWDWORKS INC.
6F Yebisu Garden Place Tower 4-20-3 Ebisu, Shibuya-ku, Tokyo, 150-6006, Japan
Tel.: (81) 364278187
Web Site: https://crowdworks.co.jp
Year Founded: 2011
3900—(TKS)
Rev.: $93,658,900
Assets: $70,864,550
Liabilities: $28,048,040
Net Worth: $42,816,510
Earnings: $7,770,640
Fiscal Year-end: 09/30/23
Internet Crowd Sourcing Services
N.A.I.C.S.: 513199
Koichiro Yoshida *(Pres & CEO)*

CROWELL DEVELOPMENT CORP.
6F No 747 Wenzhong Rd, Taoyuan Dist, Taoyuan, 330, Taiwan
Tel.: (886) 32171111
Web Site: http://www.crowell.com.tw
2528—(TAI)
Rev.: $60,498,314
Assets: $700,863,115
Liabilities: $527,770,640
Net Worth: $173,092,475
Earnings: $7,900,814
Emp.: 34
Fiscal Year-end: 12/31/23
Construction Engineering Services
N.A.I.C.S.: 236220
Yung-Ping Su *(Chm, Pres & Gen Mgr)*

CROWN ADVANCED MATE-RIAL CO., LTD.
No 32 Jingfa Avenue, Economic and Technological Development Zone, Yichun, 336000, Jiangxi, China
Tel.: (86) 7957029699
Web Site: https://www.mg-crown.com
Year Founded: 2007
688560—(SHG)
Rev.: $244,511,374
Assets: $526,398,224
Liabilities: $84,142,310
Net Worth: $442,255,914
Earnings: $14,727,721
Fiscal Year-end: 12/31/22
Electrical Equipment Mfr & Distr
N.A.I.C.S.: 335999

Hongjia Yan *(Chm & Gen Mgr)*

CROWN ASIA CHEMICALS CORPORATION
KM 33 MacArthur Highway Bo Tuktukan, Guiguinto, Bulacan, Philippines
Tel.: (63) 447940268
Web Site:
　　https://www.crownpvc.com.ph
Year Founded: 1989
CROWN—(PHI)
Rev.: $36,209,625
Assets: $41,633,470
Liabilities: $8,584,751
Net Worth: $33,048,719
Earnings: $4,665,568
Fiscal Year-end: 12/31/21
Industrial Chemicals Mfr
N.A.I.C.S.: 325998
Walter H. Villanueva *(Pres, Chief Risk Mgmt Officer & Gen Mgr-PVC Roof Div)*

CROWN CAPITAL PARTNERS, INC.
700 2nd Street SW19th Floor Calgary, Calgary, T2P 2W3, AB, Canada
Tel.: (403) 775-2554
Web Site:
　　https://www.crowncapital.ca
CRWN—(TSX)
Rev.: $35,064,919
Assets: $252,268,872
Liabilities: $188,682,807
Net Worth: $63,586,065
Earnings: ($10,400,413)
Fiscal Year-end: 12/31/20
Asset Management Services
N.A.I.C.S.: 523940
Christopher A. Johnson *(Pres & CEO)*

CROWN CONFECTIONERY CO., LTD.
131-1 Namyeong-dong, Yongsan-gu, Seoul, 140-160, Korea (South)
Tel.: (82) 27919123
Web Site: http://www.crown.co.kr
Year Founded: 1968
Sales Range: $50-74.9 Million
Emp.: 500
Bakery & Confectionery Product Mfr
N.A.I.C.S.: 311812
Su Jang Wang *(CEO)*

Subsidiaries:

Crown Confectionery Co., Ltd.　　**(1)**
1337 31 Socho Dong, Sucho Gu, Seoul, 137 070, Korea (South)　　**(100%)**
Tel.: (82) 27919133
Confectionery Mfr
N.A.I.C.S.: 311352

Crown Snack Co., Ltd.　　**(1)**
131-1 Namyeong-Dong Yongsan-Gu, Seoul, 80708, Korea (South)
Tel.: (82) 27919103
Rev.: $33,000,000
Emp.: 200
Bakery & Snack Food Mfr
N.A.I.C.S.: 311812
Jang Wan-Soo *(Pres)*

CROWN EQUITIES, INC.
Crown Center 158 N Garcia corner Jupiter Sts, Bel Air, Makati, 1209, Philippines
Tel.: (63) 28990081　　　　PH
Web Site:
　　https://www.crownequitiesinc.com
Year Founded: 1969
CEI—(PHI)
Rev.: $4,357,616
Assets: $51,077,709
Liabilities: $4,185,627
Net Worth: $46,892,082
Earnings: $1,968,761
Emp.: 75

Fiscal Year-end: 12/31/21
Metal Mining Services
N.A.I.C.S.: 212290
George L. Go *(Chm)*

CROWN INTERNATIONAL CORPORATION LIMITED
Room 2707 27th Floor China Resources Building 26 Harbour Road, Wanchai, China (Hong Kong)
Tel.: (852) 21210988
Web Site:
　　https://www.crownicorp.com
0727—(HKG)
Rev.: $1,788,437
Assets: $468,553,256
Liabilities: $216,655,445
Net Worth: $251,897,811
Earnings: ($13,656,660)
Emp.: 50
Fiscal Year-end: 03/31/21
Investing & Financial Services
N.A.I.C.S.: 523940
Hong Shen Liu *(Vice Chm)*

CROWN INVESTMENTS CORPORATION OF SASKATCH-EWAN
400 - 2400 College Avenue, Regina, S4P 1C8, SK, Canada
Tel.: (306) 787-6851　　　　SK
Web Site: http://www.cicorp.sk.ca
Year Founded: 1947
Rev.: $4,852,936,562
Assets: $16,886,435,326
Liabilities: $11,918,826,685
Net Worth: $4,967,608,641
Earnings: $282,433,589
Emp.: 3,525
Fiscal Year-end: 03/31/22
Holding Company
N.A.I.C.S.: 551112
Cindy Ogilvie *(CFO & VP-Fin & Admin)*

Subsidiaries:

101069101 Saskatchewan Ltd.　　**(1)**
903 Hwy 55, Meadow Lake, S9X 1V7, SK, Canada
Tel.: (306) 236-2444
Asset Management Services
N.A.I.C.S.: 531390

HARO Financial Corporation　　**(1)**
1874 Scarth Street Suite 2000, Regina, S4P 4B3, SK, Canada
Tel.: (306) 777-0600
Financial Consulting Services
N.A.I.C.S.: 523940

SaskEnergy Inc.　　**(1)**
1777 Victoria Avenue, Regina, S4P 4K5, SK, Canada
Tel.: (306) 777-9200
Web Site: https://www.saskenergy.com
Natural Gas Distr
N.A.I.C.S.: 221210
Susan B. Barber *(Chm)*

Saskatchewan Government Insurance　　**(1)**
2260 - 11th Ave, Regina, S4P 0J9, SK, Canada　　**(100%)**
Tel.: (306) 751-1200
Web Site: http://www.sgi.sk.ca
Sales Range: $500-549.9 Million
Emp.: 2,000
Provider of Propery & Casualty Insurance Products in Saskatchewan
N.A.I.C.S.: 524126
Arlene Wiks *(Chm)*

Subsidiary (Domestic):

SGI CANADA Insurance Services Ltd.　　**(2)**
2260 11th Avenue, Regina, S4P 0J9, SK, Canada　　**(83%)**
Tel.: (306) 775-6590
Web Site: http://www.sgi.sk.ca
Sales Range: $25-49.9 Million
Emp.: 50

Provider of Property & Casualty Insurance Products Outside Saskatchewan
N.A.I.C.S.: 524128

Saskatchewan Opportunities Corporation　　**(1)**
Innovation Pl 114 - 15 Innovation Blvd, Saskatoon, S7N 2X8, SK, Canada
Tel.: (306) 933-6295
Web Site: http://www.oooo.ck.oa
Emp.: 50
Business Support Services
N.A.I.C.S.: 541611
Mark Regier *(Chm)*

Saskatchewan Power Corporation　　**(1)**
2025 Victoria Avenue, Regina, S4P 0S1, SK, Canada　　**(100%)**
Tel.: (306) 566-2031
Web Site: http://www.saskpower.com
Rev.: $1,997,343,250
Assets: $8,657,841,640
Liabilities: $6,796,097,840
Net Worth: $1,861,743,800
Earnings: $144,395,090
Emp.: 3,167
Fiscal Year-end: 03/31/2019
Public Utility & Electricity Supplier
N.A.I.C.S.: 221122
Bryan Leverick *(Vice Chm)*

Subsidiary (Domestic):

SaskPower International　　**(2)**
2025 Victoria Ave, Regina, S4P 0S1, SK, Canada　　**(100%)**
Tel.: (306) 566-2121
Web Site: http://www.saskpower.com
Sales Range: $50-74.9 Million
Emp.: 15
Power Marketing Services
N.A.I.C.S.: 221118

Saskatchewan Telecommunications Holdings Corporation　　**(1)**
Cornwall Centre - Main Floor 2121 Saskatchewan Drive, Regina, S4P 3Y2, SK, Canada
Tel.: (306) 777-3706
Web Site: https://www.sasktel.com
Emp.: 3,300
Communications Services Including Wireline, Wireless, Internet & Digitial Network E-Business Solutions
N.A.I.C.S.: 517112
Doug Burnett *(Pres & CEO)*

Saskatchewan Transportation Company　　**(1)**
1717 Saskatchewan Drive, Regina, S4P 2E2, SK, Canada
Tel.: (306) 787-3347
Web Site: http://www.stcbus.com
Emp.: 240
Freight Forwarding & Transportation Services
N.A.I.C.S.: 488510
Jonathan Abrametz *(Chm)*

Saskatchewan Water Corporation　　**(1)**
200-111 Fairford St E, Moose Jaw, S6H 1C8, SK, Canada
Web Site: http://www.saskwater.com
Emp.: 115
Waste Water Treatment Services
N.A.I.C.S.: 221320
Doug Matthies *(Pres & CEO)*

CROWN LIFTERS LTD.
104 Raheja Plaza Veera Desai Road Andheri W, Shah Industrial Estate, Mumbai, 400053, India
Tel.: (91) 2240062829
Web Site:
　　https://www.crownlifters.com
Year Founded: 1986
CROWN—(NSE)
Rev.: $1,717,479
Assets: $4,752,092
Liabilities: $2,152,463
Net Worth: $2,599,629
Earnings: $353,198
Emp.: 73
Fiscal Year-end: 03/31/21
Lift Equipment Distr

Crown Lifters Ltd.—(Continued)

N.A.I.C.S.: 423830
Karim Kamruddin Jaria *(Chm & Mng Dir)*

CROWN PAINTS KENYA LTD.
Likoni Road Industrial Area, PO Box 78848, 00507, Nairobi, Kenya
Tel.: (254) 206533604
Web Site:
http://www.crownpaints.co.ke
Sales Range: $25-49.9 Million
Paint & Coating Mfr
N.A.I.C.S.: 325510
Patrick Mwati *(Dir-Fin)*

CROWN PAINTS KENYA PLC
Likoni Road Industrial Area, PO Box 78848, 00507, Nairobi, Kenya
Tel.: (254) 202165703　　　　　KE
Web Site:
https://www.crownpaints.co.ke
Year Founded: 1958
BERG—(NAI)
Sales Range: $75-99.9 Million
Paint Product Mfr
N.A.I.C.S.: 325510
Mhamud Charania *(Chm)*

Subsidiaries:

Regal Paints Uganda Limited　　(1)
Plot 74 Block 111, Mawotto Namanve, Kampala, Uganda
Tel.: (256) 752228951
Web Site: http://www.regalpaints.co.ug
Paint Product Mfr
N.A.I.C.S.: 325510
Sanjay Babuta *(Deputy Gen Mgr)*

CROWN POINT ENERGY INC.
Station M, PO Box 1562, Calgary, T2P 3B9, AB, Canada
Tel.: (403) 232-1150
Web Site:
https://www.crownpointenergy.com
Year Founded: 1966
CWVLF—(OTCIQ)
Rev.: $21,995,428
Assets: $67,785,665
Liabilities: $49,953,578
Net Worth: $17,832,087
Earnings: ($8,127,632)
Fiscal Year-end: 12/31/23
Oil & Gas Exploration Services
N.A.I.C.S.: 211120
Brian J. Moss *(Pres & CEO)*

Subsidiaries:

Crown Point Energia S.A.　　(1)
Tel.: (54) 1150325600
Natural Gas Extraction Services
N.A.I.C.S.: 211130

CROWN TOURS LIMITED
Opp Rajputana Palace Sheraton, New Panel Raigarh, Jaipur, 410206, Rajasthan, India
Tel.: (91) 1415102311
Web Site: http://www.crownjaipur.org
538521—(BOM)
Rev.: $307,300
Assets: $522,175
Liabilities: $5,180
Net Worth: $516,995
Earnings: ($452,857)
Emp.: 7
Fiscal Year-end: 03/31/21
Tour Operator
N.A.I.C.S.: 561520
Bharat Raj Bhandari *(Mng Dir)*

CROWN WORLDWIDE HOLDINGS LTD.
Suite 2001 China Evergrande Centre 38 Gloucester Road, Wanchai, China (Hong Kong)
Tel.: (852) 25286111　　　　　HK

Web Site:
http://www.crownworldwide.com
Year Founded: 1965
Sales Range: $550-599.9 Million
Emp.: 5,000
Holding Company; Mobility, Relocation, Record Management, Warehousing, Freight Forwarding & Third-Party Logistics Services
N.A.I.C.S.: 551112
James Edward Thompson *(Founder & Chm)*

Subsidiaries:

Crown Relocations　　(1)
5252 Argosy Ave, Huntington Beach, CA 92649-1074
Tel.: (714) 898-0955
Web Site: http://www.crownrelo.com
Sales Range: $25-49.9 Million
Emp.: 35
Freight Transportation Services
N.A.I.C.S.: 488510
James E. Thompson *(Chm)*

Crown Wine Cellars Ltd　　(1)
18 Deep Water Bay Drive, Hong Kong, China (Hong Kong)
Tel.: (852) 2580 6287
Web Site: http://www.crownwinecellars.com
Wine Whslr
N.A.I.C.S.: 424820
Noelle Shek *(Mgr-Events & Catering)*

Crown Worldwide Oy　　(1)
Vanha Porvoontie 231, 1380, Vantaa, Finland
Tel.: (358) 10 545 8200
Air Frieght & Logistic Services
N.A.I.C.S.: 481112
Timo Matilainen *(Mgr-Bus Dev)*

Crown Worldwide Srl.　　(1)
Via Fleming 3, Settimo Milanese, Milan, Italy
Tel.: (39) 02 45 31 375
Air Frieght & Logistic Services
N.A.I.C.S.: 481112
Elisa Ghidini *(Supvr-Fine Art)*

The Crown Group　　(1)
200 Mac Lane, Keasbey, NJ 08832
Tel.: (800) 879-3326
Air Frieght & Logistic Services
N.A.I.C.S.: 481112

CROWN-BAELE NV/SA
Nijverheidsstraat 15, 1840, Londerzeel, Belgium
Tel.: (32) 5231 9090　　　　　BE
Web Site: http://www.crown-baele.com
Sales Range: $1-9.9 Million
Bottling & Packaging Process Optimization Services & Custom Packaging Systems Mfr
N.A.I.C.S.: 541690
Wilfried Van Welden *(CEO)*

CROWNIA HOLDINGS LTD.
1980-1075 West Georgia Street, Vancouver, V6E 3C9, BC, Canada
Tel.: (604) 488-8878　　　　　BC
Web Site: http://crowniaholdings.com
Year Founded: 2012
Steel Investment Services
N.A.I.C.S.: 523999
Xizhou Tong *(Pres & CEO)*

CROYDON CLOCKTOWER
Katharine Street, Croydon, CR9 1ET, United Kingdom
Tel.: (44) 2082531030
Web Site:
http://www.croydonclocktower.org.uk
Sales Range: $10-24.9 Million
Emp.: 100
Cultural Services; Exhibitions, Museum, Live Performances, Art House Films, Library, Cinema, Cafe & Tourist Services
N.A.I.C.S.: 611620

CRP RISK MANAGEMENT LIMITED
C110 Calsssique Centre Plot No 26, Off Mahakali Caves Road Near Paper Box Andheri East, Mumbai, 400 093, India
Tel.: (91) 2242116000
Web Site: https://www.crp.co.in
Rev.: $11,942,036
Assets: $15,399,952
Liabilities: $5,591,267
Net Worth: $9,808,686
Earnings: $1,098,657
Emp.: 120
Fiscal Year-end: 03/31/19
Risk Managemeng Srvices
N.A.I.C.S.: 524291
Hitesh Asrani *(Founder & CFO)*

CRRC CORPORATION LIMITED
No 16 West Fourth Ring Middle Road, Haidian District, Beijing, 100036, China
Tel.: (86) 1051862188　　　　　CN
Web Site: https://www.crrcgc.cc
Year Founded: 2007
601766—(SHG)
Rev.: $32,994,579,338
Assets: $66,449,539,941
Liabilities: $38,770,199,884
Net Worth: $27,679,340,058
Earnings: $2,052,062,952
Emp.: 154,292
Fiscal Year-end: 12/31/23
Rolling Railroad Stock Mfr
N.A.I.C.S.: 336510
Zheng Li *(CFO)*

Subsidiaries:

Beijing CSR Times Locomotive and Rolling Stock Mechanics Co., Ltd.　　(1)
W Rwy Sta 500 Meters Zhong Guan Cun Hi-Tech Park, Changping, Beijing, 102249, China
Tel.: (86) 1060753721
Web Site: http://www.teg.cn
Railway Locomotives Mfr
N.A.I.C.S.: 488210

Blue Engineering S.R.L.　　(1)
Via Albenga 98, 10098, Rivoli, TO, Italy
Tel.: (39) 0119504211
Web Site: http://www.blue-group.it
Engineeering Services
N.A.I.C.S.: 541330

CNR Dalian Locomotive Research Institute Co., Ltd.　　(1)
No 49 Zhongchang Street, Shahekou District, Dalian, Liaoning, China
Tel.: (86) 411 84601010
Railway Transportation Equipment Mfr
N.A.I.C.S.: 336999

CRRC Changchun Railway Vehicle Co., Ltd.　　(1)
435 Qingyin Road, Changchun, 130062, Jilin, China
Tel.: (86) 431 87831651
Web Site: http://www.cccar.com.cn
Railway Vehicle Mfr
N.A.I.C.S.: 336510

CRRC Dalian R&D Co., Ltd.　　(1)
No 1 Haoyang North Street, Lvshun Economic Development Zone, Dalian, 116052, China
Tel.: (86) 41162685200
Rail Transit Equipment Mfr
N.A.I.C.S.: 336510

CRRC Datong Co., Ltd.　　(1)
Qianjin Street No 1, Datong, 037038, Shanxi, China
Tel.: (86) 3527162133
Emp.: 6,000
Rail Transit Equipment Mfr
N.A.I.C.S.: 336510

CRRC Nanjing Puzhen Co., Ltd.　　(1)
No 5 LonghuLane Puzhen, Nanjing,

210031, Jiangsu, China
Tel.: (86) 2585847400
Rail Transit Equipment Mfr
N.A.I.C.S.: 336510
Xuming Zhang *(Project Mgr)*

CRRC Qingdao Sifang Co., Ltd.　　(1)
No 88 Jinhongdong Road, Chengyang District, Qingdao, 266111, China
Tel.: (86) 53287801188
Rail Transit Equipment Mfr
N.A.I.C.S.: 336510

CRRC Sifang Co., Ltd.　　(1)
No 9 Hongping Road, Chengyang District, Qingdao, 266111, Shandong, China
Tel.: (86) 53268017016
Rail Transit Equipment Mfr
N.A.I.C.S.: 336510

CRRC Tangshan Co., Ltd.　　(1)
No 3 Changqian Road, Fengrun District, Tangshan, 064000, Hebei, China
Tel.: (86) 3153089963
Web Site: https://www.crrcgc.cc
N.A.I.C.S.: 336510

CRRC Yangtze Group.	(1)
Daqiao New Area Jiangxia Economic Development Zone, Wuhan, 430212, China
Tel.: (86) 2751170152
Web Site: https://www.crrcgc.cc
N.A.I.C.S.: 336510

CRRC Yongji Electric Co., Ltd.　　(1)
Jieli Mansion No 15 Wenjing North Road, Xi'an, 710016, China
Tel.: (86) 2986498411
Web Site: https://www.crrcgc.cc
Electronic Product Mfr & Distr
N.A.I.C.S.: 334419

CRRC Zhuzhou Institute Co., Ltd.　　(1)
Shidai Road, Zhuzhou, 412001, Hunan, China
Tel.: (86) 73128498304
Web Site: https://www.crrcgc.cc
N.A.I.C.S.: 336510
Ding Rongjun *(Chm)*

CRRC Ziyang Co., Ltd.　　(1)
No 6 Chenfeng Road, Yanjiang Disitrict, Ziyang, 641301, Sichuan, China
Tel.: (86) 2826286175
Web Site: https://www.crrcgc.cc
N.A.I.C.S.: 336510

CSR Feb. 7th Rolling Stock Co., Ltd　　(1)
No A1 Zhang Guo Zhuang, Fengtai, Beijing, 10072, China
Tel.: (86) 1083804132
Web Site: http://www.csrgc.com.cn
Sales Range: $800-899.9 Million
Emp.: 3,500
Rolling Stock Mfr
N.A.I.C.S.: 336510
Shuozhi Shi *(Pres)*

CSR Meishan Rolling Stock Co., Ltd　　(1)
Chongren Town Dongpo, Meishan, 620032, Sichuan, China
Tel.: (86) 2838502013
Web Site: http://www.msrsco.com
Sales Range: $800-899.9 Million
Emp.: 5,000
Rolling Stock Mfr
N.A.I.C.S.: 336510

CSR Qishuyan Locomotive Co., Ltd　　(1)
No 358 Yanling Rd, Changzhou, Jiangsu, China
Tel.: (86) 51985051291
Web Site: http://www.qscn.cn
Sales Range: $1-4.9 Billion
Emp.: 6,000
Locomotive Mfr
N.A.I.C.S.: 488210

CSR Ziyang Locomotive Co., Ltd　　(1)
Songshuping, Yanjiang District, Ziyang, 641301, Sichuan, China
Tel.: (86) 2826286177
Web Site: http://www.cccme.org.cn
Railway Locomotives Equipment Mfr
N.A.I.C.S.: 336510

LORIC Import & Export Corp., Ltd.　　(1)

Room 502 CNR Mansion 15 Area One Fangchengyuan, Fengtai District, Beijing, China
Tel.: (86) 1051897299
Locomotive & Rolling Stock Distr
N.A.I.C.S.: 425120

Qiqihar Railway Rolling Stock Co., Ltd. **(1)**
36 ChangQian 1 Lu, Qiqihar, 161002, Heilongjiang, China
Tel.: (86) 4522938472
Web Site: http://www.qrrs.com.cn
Railway Wagons & Cranes Mfr
N.A.I.C.S.: 333923

Taiyuan Railway Rolling Stock Co., Ltd. **(1)**
10 Jiefang North Road, Taiyuan, 030006, Shanxi, China **(100%)**
Tel.: (86) 3517026319
Web Site: http://www.railway-vehicle.com
Railroad Rolling Stock Mfr
N.A.I.C.S.: 336510

Tianjin JL Railway Transport Equipment Ltd.
No 22 Nankou Road, Hebei District, Tianjin, 300232, China
Tel.: (86) 22 26243376
Web Site: http://www.tlr.cn
Emp.: 3,000
Locomotives & Freight Cars Mfr
N.A.I.C.S.: 339999

Vossloh Locomotives GmbH **(1)**
Doktor-Hell-Strasse 6, 24107, Kiel, Germany
Tel.: (49) 4 313 9990
Web Site: https://www.vl-rs.com
Locomotive Mfr
N.A.I.C.S.: 333618

Subsidiary (Non-US):

Vossloh Locomotives France SAS **(2)**
153 Boulevard Haussmann, 75008, Paris, France
Tel.: (33) 1 55 59 09 82
Web Site: http://www.vossloh-locomotives.com
Sales Range: $25-49.9 Million
Emp.: 12
Locomotives Repair & Maintenance Services
N.A.I.C.S.: 811198

CRS HOLDING AG
Burgstrasse 28, Glarus, 8750, GL, Switzerland
Tel.: (41) 556402147
Year Founded: 1989
Holding Company
N.A.I.C.S.: 551112

Subsidiaries:

Filtrox AG **(1)**
Moosmuhlen Strasse 6, Saint Gallen, 9001, Switzerland **(100%)**
Tel.: (41) 712729111
Web Site: http://www.filtrox.ch
Sales Range: $25-49.9 Million
Emp.: 100
Mfr of Industrial Machinery
N.A.I.C.S.: 333310
Peter Keller *(Mgr-Fin)*

Subsidiary (Domestic):

A. Sutter AG **(2)**
Moosmuhlestrasse 6, CH 9000, Saint Gallen, Switzerland **(100%)**
Tel.: (41) 712729500
Web Site: http://www.sutterag.ch
Sales Range: $25-49.9 Million
Consulting, Designing & Producing Equipment for the Production of Wine & Fruit Juice
N.A.I.C.S.: 333241

CRT CONSTRUCTION INC.
870 Archimede Street, Levis, G6V 7M5, QC, Canada
Tel.: (418) 833-8073

Web Site:
http://www.crtconstruction.ca
Year Founded: 1966
Rev.: $31,726,263
Emp.: 250
Highway Street & Bridge Construction Services
N.A.I.C.S.: 237310
Jean-Francois Turgeon *(Exec VP)*

CRUCIAL INNOVATIONS, CORP.
Xibahe Beili 25, Beijing, 100096, China
Tel.: (86) 17024259229   NV
Web Site:
http://www.learningplatform.com
Year Founded: 2018
CINV—(OTCIQ)
Liabilities: $429
Net Worth: ($429)
Earnings: ($30,558)
Emp.: 1
Fiscal Year-end: 12/31/20
Online Educational Training Services
N.A.I.C.S.: 611710
Laura De Leon Castro *(Chm, Pres, CEO, Principal Acctg Officer, Treas & Sec)*

CRUCIALTEC CO., LTD.
20 79beon-gil Hoseo-ro Baebang-eup, Asan, Chungcheongnam-do, Korea (South)
Tel.: (82) 315466655
Web Site: http://www.crucialtec.com
Year Founded: 2001
114120—(KRS)
Rev.: $22,235,068
Assets: $17,998,043
Liabilities: $16,130,618
Net Worth: $1,867,425
Earnings: ($5,625,440)
Emp.: 79
Fiscal Year-end: 12/31/22
Mobile Device Mfr
N.A.I.C.S.: 334220
Charles Keon-Joon Ahn *(Founder & CEO)*

Subsidiaries:

Crucialtec USA, Inc. **(1)**
820 Gessner Rd Ste 1275, Houston, TX 77024
Tel.: (832) 767-5453
Electric Device Mfr
N.A.I.C.S.: 334419

CRUDECORP ASA
Haraldsgaten 90, 5528, Haugesund, Norway
Tel.: (47) 52719500   NO
Web Site: http://www.crudecorp.no
Year Founded: 2007
Petroleum Extraction
N.A.I.C.S.: 211310
Sigurd Aase *(Chm)*

CRUDELI SA
47 boulevard des Acieries, 13010, Marseille, France
Tel.: (33) 491177070
Web Site: http://www.crudeli.com
Year Founded: 1965
Sales Range: $25-49.9 Million
Emp.: 160
Plumbing, Heating & Air-Conditioning Services
N.A.I.C.S.: 238220
Christophe Sebroville *(Mgr-Fin)*

CRUNCHFISH AB
Stora Varvsgatan 6A, 211 19, Malmo, Sweden
Tel.: (46) 406267700
Web Site:
https://www.crunchfish.com

Year Founded: 2010
CFISH—(OMX)
Rev.: $579,767
Assets: $6,227,580
Liabilities: $723,070
Net Worth: $5,504,510
Earnings: ($2,250,695)
Emp.: 23
Fiscal Year-end: 12/31/22
Mobile Application Development Services
N.A.I.C.S.: 541511
Joakim Nydemark *(CEO)*

CRUST CRAFT INC.
13211-146 Street NW, Edmonton, T5L 4S8, AB, Canada
Tel.: (780) 466-1333
Web Site: https://www.crustcraft.com
Year Founded: 1989
Rev.: $10,349,230
Emp.: 70
Flour & Other Grain Products Supplier
N.A.I.C.S.: 311211
Paul Flesher *(Pres)*

CRUZ BATTERY METALS CORP.
2905 - 700 West Georgia Street, PO Box 10112, Pacific Centre, Vancouver, V7Y 1C6, BC, Canada
Tel.: (604) 899-9150   BC
Web Site:
https://www.cruzbatterymetals.com
Year Founded: 2007
BKTPF—(OTCIQ)
Rev.: $9,918
Assets: $3,293,999
Liabilities: $450,380
Net Worth: $2,843,619
Earnings: ($694,004)
Fiscal Year-end: 07/31/21
Investment Services
N.A.I.C.S.: 523999
James Nelson *(Pres, CEO & Sec)*

CRUZADOS S.A.D.P.
Av Las Flores 13000, Las Condes, Santiago, Chile
Tel.: (56) 224124710
Web Site: https://www.cruzados.cl
CRUZADOS—(SGO)
Sales Range: Less than $1 Million
Sporting & Recreational Activity Provider
N.A.I.C.S.: 611620
Juan Tagle Quiroz *(Pres)*

CRVENI SIGNAL A.D.
Karadordeva 11, Belgrade, Serbia
Tel.: (381) 112633149
Web Site:
http://www.crvenisignal.co.rs
Year Founded: 1969
CRSG—(BEL)
Sales Range: Less than $1 Million
Emp.: 3
Driver Training Services
N.A.I.C.S.: 611692
Igor Markicevic *(Exec Dir & Dir)*

CRVENI SIGNAL A.D.
Ul Koste Stamenkovica 22, Leskovac, Serbia
Tel.: (381) 16213101
Year Founded: 1992
CSLE—(BEL)
Sales Range: Less than $1 Million
Emp.: 2
Driving School Operator
N.A.I.C.S.: 611692
Svetlana Kostic *(Exec Dir)*

CRVENKA FABRIKA SECERA A.D.

Masarikova 7, Crvenka, Serbia
Tel.: (381) 25 731 122
Year Founded: 1989
CRFS—(BEL)
Sales Range: $50-74.9 Million
Emp.: 202
Sugar Mfr
N.A.I.C.S.: 311314
Aristeidis Vasilopoulos *(Mng Dir)*

CRYO-SAVE (INDIA) PVT. LTD.
No 183 Gayatri Tech Park Road 1B, EPIP KIADB, Bengaluru, 560 066, India
Tel.: (91) 80 42430100   In
Year Founded: 2008
Sales Range: $10-24.9 Million
Stem Cell Storage Services
N.A.I.C.S.: 621511
Arun Kumar *(Mgr-Laboratory)*

CRYOCORD HOLDINGS SDN. BHD.
Suite 1-1 1st Floor Bio-X Centre Persiaran Cyberpoint Selatan Cyber 8, Block D1 Dataran Prima, 63000, Cyberjaya, Selangor, Malaysia
Tel.: (60) 386898888   MY
Web Site:
http://www.cryocord.com.my
Year Founded: 2003
Human Stem Cell & Tissue Cryopreservation Research Services
N.A.I.C.S.: 551112
Soon Keng Cheong *(Dir-Medical)*

Subsidiaries:

CryoCord Sdn. Bhd. **(1)**
Suite 1-1 1st Floor Bio X Centre Persiaran Cyberpoint Selatan Cyber 8, Block D1 Dataran Prima, 47301, Cyberjaya, Selangor, Malaysia
Tel.: (60) 3 7880 2929
Web Site: http://www.cryocord.com.my
Emp.: 320
Stem Cell Crogenic Storage & Services
N.A.I.C.S.: 621511
Soon Keng Cheong *(Dir-Medical)*

Subsidiary (Domestic):

Stemtech International Sdn. Bhd. **(2)**
UM-PKNS Innotech Park Block E&F Jalan Teknologi 3/4 Selangor Science, Park Sec 3 Kota Damansara, 47810, Petaling Jaya, Selangor DE, Malaysia **(100%)**
Tel.: (60) 361418881
Web Site: http://www.stemtech-international.com
Sales Range: $10-24.9 Million
Emp.: 20
Stem Cell Research
N.A.I.C.S.: 621511
Guat Eng Kua *(Dir-Laboratory Svcs)*

CRYOFOCUS MEDTECH (SHANGHAI) CO., LTD.
No 15 Lane 3399 Kangxin Road, Pudong New District, Shanghai, 200120, China
Tel.: (86) 2120977850   CN
Web Site: https://www.cryofocus.com
Year Founded: 2013
6922—(HKG)
Rev.: $4,159,498
Assets: $48,086,950
Liabilities: $8,345,962
Net Worth: $39,740,989
Earnings: ($18,127,194)
Emp.: 375
Fiscal Year-end: 12/31/22
Medical Device Mfr
N.A.I.C.S.: 339112
Jun Zhu *(CEO)*

Subsidiaries:

Ningbo SensCure Biotechnology Co., Ltd. **(1)**
Building 3 Area B No 777 Binhai 4th Road,

Cryofocus Medtech (Shanghai) Co.,
Ltd.—(Continued)

Hangzhou Bay New District, Ningbo,
315336, Zhejiang, China
Tel.: (86) 57463729798
Web Site: https://www.senscure.net
Medical Device Mfr & Distr
N.A.I.C.S.: 339112

CRYOMAX COOLING SYSTEM CORP.
No 3 Gongqu 6th Rd, Fangyuan,
Chang-Hua, Taiwan
Tel.: (886) 48967892
Web Site:
https://www.cryomaxcooling.com
Year Founded: 1984
1587—(TAI)
Rev.: $69,396,021
Assets: $109,040,481
Liabilities: $64,172,894
Net Worth: $44,867,587
Earnings: $1,375,486
Emp.: 382
Fiscal Year-end: 12/31/23
Automobile Equipment Mfr
N.A.I.C.S.: 336110
Yen-Chiu Liu (Chm)

Subsidiaries:

Cool Max Auto Parts Co., Ltd.   (1)
No 6 Industrial Park Wu Sha, Changan
Township, Dongguan, Guangdong, China
Tel.: (86) 76986068933
Radiator Part Mfr
N.A.I.C.S.: 336390

Nanjing Cryomax Auto Parts Co.,
Ltd.   (1)
No 78 FengShan Road, Gaochun EDZ
county, Nanjing, Jiangsu, China
Tel.: (86) 2568618600
Radiator Part Mfr
N.A.I.C.S.: 336390

CRYONIC MEDICAL
6 rue Berthelot, 25000, Besancon,
France
Tel.: (33) 3 81 54 35 40
Web Site: http://www.cryonic-
medical.com
Medical Equipment Mfr
N.A.I.C.S.: 334510
Gerald Brothier (CEO)

CRYOSITE LIMITED
13a Ferndell Street, Sydney, 2142,
NSW, Australia
Tel.: (61) 288652000   AU
Web Site: https://www.cryosite.com
Year Founded: 2002
CTE—(ASX)
Rev.: $8,421,474
Assets: $13,163,061
Liabilities: $12,195,513
Net Worth: $967,548
Earnings: $1,228,632
Emp.: 25
Fiscal Year-end: 06/30/24
Temperature Critical Biological Prod-
ucts Distribution
N.A.I.C.S.: 325412
Bryan Dulhunty (Chm & Sec)

Subsidiaries:

Cryosite Distribution Pty Limited   (1)
13A Ferndell St, South Granville, Sydney,
2066, NSW, Australia
Tel.: (61) 294201400
Web Site: http://www.cryosite.com
Emp.: 30
Logistic Services
N.A.I.C.S.: 541614

CRYPTO BLOCKCHAIN INDUSTRIES S.A.
38 rue de Berri, 75008, Paris, France
Web Site: https://www.cbicorp.io
Year Founded: 2021

CBIBS—(EUR)
Rev.: $52,577,270
Assets: $335,598,156
Liabilities: $119,194,551
Net Worth: $216,403,606
Earnings: $48,214,561
Fiscal Year-end: 03/31/22
Investment Management Service
N.A.I.C.S.: 523999
Frederic Chesnais (Founder)

CRYPTO FLOW TECHNOLOGY LIMITED
50th Floor Bank of China Tower 1
Garden Road, Central, China (Hong
Kong)
Tel.: (852) 25963098   Ky
Web Site: http://www.lotoie.com
Year Founded: 2002
8198—(HKG)
Rev.: $3,767,625
Assets: $13,988,790
Liabilities: $4,176,263
Net Worth: $9,812,528
Earnings: ($7,253,985)
Emp.: 10
Fiscal Year-end: 12/31/22
Financial Investment Services
N.A.I.C.S.: 523999
Huang Lilan (Exec Dir)

CRYPTOBLOX TECHNOLOGIES INC.
6th Floor 905 West Pender St, Van-
couver, V6C 1L6, BC, Canada
Tel.: (236) 259-0279
Web Site: https://cryptoblox.ca
BLOX—(CNSX)
Rev.: $18,073
Assets: $5,408,012
Liabilities: $3,129,584
Net Worth: $2,278,428
Earnings: ($1,671,649)
Fiscal Year-end: 01/31/24
Software Development Services
N.A.I.C.S.: 541511
Bryson Goodwin (CEO)

CRYPTOSTAR CORP.
181 Bay Street Suite 4400, Toronto,
M5J 2T3, ON, Canada
Tel.: (614) 199-3694
Web Site: https://www.cryptostar.com
CSTR—(TSXV)
Rev.: $3,626,809
Assets: $12,713,650
Liabilities: $5,190,777
Net Worth: $7,522,873
Earnings: ($5,613,000)
Emp.: 5
Fiscal Year-end: 12/31/23
Data Processing Services
N.A.I.C.S.: 518210
David Jellins (Founder & CEO)

CRYSTAL AMBER ASSET MANAGEMENT (GUERNSEY) LLP
Heritage Hall Le Marchant Street,
Saint Peter Port, GY1 4HY, Guernsey
Tel.: (44) 1481742742   GY
Web Site:
http://www.crystalamber.com
Year Founded: 2008
Investment Fund Management & Ad-
visory Services
N.A.I.C.S.: 523940
Richard Bernstein (Principal)

Subsidiaries:

Crystal Amber Fund Limited   (1)
Floor 2 Trafalgar Court, PO Box 286, Saint
Peter Port, GY1 4HY, Guernsey   (4.77%)
Tel.: (44) 1481716000
Web Site: http://www.crystalamber.com
Rev.: $9,172,375
Assets: $164,257,811

Liabilities: $372,068
Net Worth: $163,885,743
Earnings: $11,922,790
Emp.: 2,800
Fiscal Year-end: 06/30/2022
Closed-End Investment Fund
N.A.I.C.S.: 525990
Christopher Waldron (Chm)

CRYSTAL CLAIRE COSMETICS INC.
20 Overlea Boulevard, Toronto, M4H
1A4, ON, Canada
Tel.: (416) 421-1882
Web Site:
http://www.crystalclaire.com
Rev.: $15,642,363
Emp.: 150
Cosmetics Products Mfr
N.A.I.C.S.: 456120
Wendy Tung (Dir-Sls)

CRYSTAL CLEAR ELECTRONIC MATERIAL CO., LTD
No 168 Shanfeng Road Wuzhong
Economic Development Zone, Su-
zhou, 215124, Jiangsu, China
Tel.: (86) 51266037938
Web Site: http://www.jingrui-
chem.com.cn
Year Founded: 2001
300655—(CHIN)
Rev.: $183,022,617
Assets: $709,759,883
Liabilities: $230,361,485
Net Worth: $479,398,398
Earnings: $2,087,791
Fiscal Year-end: 12/31/23
Organic Chemical Mfr & Distr
N.A.I.C.S.: 325180
Li Qing (Chm)

CRYSTAL GLOBE LIMITED
No 2 Baowang Road, Baodi Eco-
nomic Development Zone, Tianjin,
301800, China
Tel.: (86) 2222533666   VG
Holding Company; Tourmaline Health
Products Mfr & Whslr
N.A.I.C.S.: 551112

CRYSTAL INTERNATIONAL GROUP LIMITED
Crystal Industrial Building 71 How
Ming Street Kwun Tong, Kowloon,
China (Hong Kong)
Tel.: (852) 22618888   BM
Web Site:
http://www.crystalgroup.com
Year Founded: 1970
2232—(HKG)
Rev.: $2,490,966,000
Assets: $1,894,965,000
Liabilities: $549,666,000
Net Worth: $1,345,299,000
Earnings: $173,229,000
Emp.: 73,000
Fiscal Year-end: 12/31/22
Clothing Product Mfr & Distr
N.A.I.C.S.: 315250
Kenneth Lok Fung Lo (Co-Founder &
Chm)

Subsidiaries:

Crystal Martin (Vietnam) Company
Limited   (1)
Lot R R1 Quang Chau IZ, Viet Yen, Bac
Giang, Vietnam
Tel.: (84) 2043818188
Web Site:
https://www.crystalmartinvietnam.com
Lingerie Mfr & Distr
N.A.I.C.S.: 315250

CRYSTAL LAKE MINING CORPORATION

13236 Cliffstone Court Lake Country,
Kelowna, V4V 2R1, BC, Canada
Tel.: (604) 261-4466   BC
Web Site:
http://www.crystallakeminingcorp.com
Year Founded: 2009
Iron Ore Mining
N.A.I.C.S.: 212210

CRYSTAL MANAGEMENT JSC
21 Utegen batyr Street, Business
Centre Almaty Towers, 50062, Al-
maty, Kazakhstan
Tel.: (7) 3132006
Web Site: https://www.crystal-
management.kz
Year Founded: 2008
CRMG—(KAZ)
Rev.: $15,367,981
Assets: $128,945,370
Liabilities: $60,052,425
Net Worth: $68,892,945
Earnings: ($6,335,190)
Fiscal Year-end: 12/31/20
Eletric Power Generation Services
N.A.I.C.S.: 221111
Daulet Sajzinuly (Gen Dir)

CRYSTALGENOMICS, INC.
5F Tower A Korea Bio Park 700
Daewangpangyo-ro, Bundang-gu,
Seongnam, 463-400, Gyeonggi-do,
Korea (South)
Tel.: (82) 316282700
Web Site: http://www.cgxinc.com
Year Founded: 2000
083790—(KRS)
Rev.: $29,638,445
Assets: $247,444,220
Liabilities: $99,088,757
Net Worth: $148,355,463
Earnings: ($18,307,482)
Emp.: 55
Fiscal Year-end: 12/31/22
Drug Discovery & Development Ser-
vices
N.A.I.C.S.: 325412
Joong Myung Cho (Chm & CEO)

Subsidiaries:

CG Pharmaceuticals, Inc.   (1)
Pine Grove Business Center 100-D 4
Orinda Way, Orinda, CA 94563
Tel.: (925) 257-7036
Web Site: https://www.cgpharma.com
Pharmaceutical Development Services
N.A.I.C.S.: 325412

CRYSTALVUE MEDICAL CORPORATION
No 116 Lane 956 Zhongshan Road,
Taoyuan District, Taoyuan, 33072,
Taiwan
Tel.: (886) 33607711
Web Site:
https://www.crystalvue.com.tw
Year Founded: 2009
6527—(TPE)
Rev.: $24,871,182
Assets: $31,672,482
Liabilities: $7,420,255
Net Worth: $24,252,228
Earnings: $3,596,442
Fiscal Year-end: 12/31/22
Diagnostic Medical Care Services
N.A.I.C.S.: 621512
William Wang (Chm)

CRYSTALWISE TECHNOLOGY, INC.
No 8 Ke bei 5th Rd Chunan Science
Park, Miaoli County, Chunan, 35053,
Taiwan
Tel.: (886) 37585166
Web Site: http://www.crystalwise.com
4944—(TPE)
Rev.: $13,198,462

Assets: $53,730,192
Liabilities: $34,913,982
Net Worth: $18,816,210
Earnings: ($4,751,974)
Fiscal Year-end: 12/31/20
Electronic Components Mfr
N.A.I.C.S.: 334419
Chung-Hsien Kao *(VP)*

CS BEARING CO., LTD.
8F CS Wind B/D 723 Eonju-ro,
Gangnam-gu, Seoul, 52002,
Gyeongsangnam-do, Korea (South)
Tel.: (82) 262851257
Web Site: https://www.cs-
bearing.co.kr
Year Founded: 2007
297090—(KRS)
Rev.: $37,588,106
Assets: $119,570,870
Liabilities: $52,746,568
Net Worth: $66,824,302
Earnings: ($13,331,718)
Emp.: 24
Fiscal Year-end: 12/31/22
Bearing Mfr
N.A.I.C.S.: 332991
Man-Je Cho *(Co-CEO)*

CS CORPORATION
Wins-Building 8F 15 Pangyo-ro
228beon-gil, Bundang-Gu, Seong-
nam, 13487, Gyeonggi-do, Korea
(South)
Tel.: (82) 316223333
Web Site: https://cs-holdings.com
Year Founded: 1999
065770—(KRS)
Rev.: $26,985,081
Assets: $26,167,985
Liabilities: $12,235,650
Net Worth: $13,932,335
Earnings: ($2,669,382)
Emp.: 63
Fiscal Year-end: 12/31/22
Wireless Telecommunication Compo-
nents Mfr & Supplier
N.A.I.C.S.: 334220
Kyu-Hoon Choi *(CEO)*

Subsidiaries:

CS MACROLITE   **(1)**
8F Suite 808 West Tower Phillipine Stock
Exchange Bldg Exchange Rd, Ortigas Cen-
tre, Pasig, 1605, Philippines
Tel.: (63) 2637 1488
Web Site: http://www.macrolite-phil.com
Sales Range: $25-49.9 Million
Emp.: 2
Industrial Machinery Distr
N.A.I.C.S.: 423830
Mario Jan-Sen T. Coloma *(Bus Mgr)*

CS HOLDINGS CO., LTD.
43 Goedong-ro, Nam-gu, Pohang,
Gyeongsangbuk-do, Korea (South)
Tel.: (82) 542858221
Web Site:
https://www.chosunwelding.com
Year Founded: 1949
000590—(KRS)
Rev.: $134,429,369
Assets: $279,281,245
Liabilities: $25,842,854
Net Worth: $253,438,391
Earnings: $10,900,669
Emp.: 5
Fiscal Year-end: 12/31/22
Holding Company Management Ser-
vices
N.A.I.C.S.: 551114
Won Young Chang *(Chm & CEO)*

Subsidiaries:

Chosun Welding Japan Co., Ltd. **(1)**
9F TTN Bldg 7-2 1-Chome Kawaramachi,
Chuo-ku, Osaka, 541-0048, Japan
Tel.: (81) 66 209 0280

Welding Material Distr
N.A.I.C.S.: 423830

Chosun Welding Pohang Co.,
Ltd.   **(1)**
43 Goedong-ro, Nam-gu, Pohang,
Gyeongsangbuk-do, Korea (South)
Tel.: (82) 542898200
Web Site: http://www.chosunwelding.com
Rev.: $51,370,715
Assets: $111,317,238
Liabilities: $7,093,354
Net Worth: $104,223,885
Earnings: $8,070,478
Emp.: 125
Fiscal Year-end: 12/31/2022
Welding Material Mfr
N.A.I.C.S.: 333992
Chang Won Young *(Chm)*

CS MEDICA A/S
Indiakaj 10, 2100, Copenhagen, Den-
mark
Tel.: (45) 70707337
Web Site: https://www.cs-
medica.com
Year Founded: 2016
8G8—(DEU)
Rev.: $158,033
Assets: $3,828,394
Liabilities: $2,286,411
Net Worth: $1,541,983
Earnings: ($2,148,924)
Emp.: 9
Fiscal Year-end: 09/30/23
Medical Device Mfr
N.A.I.C.S.: 339112
Gitte Henriksen *(CFO)*

Subsidiaries:

Cannordic A/S   **(1)**
Fruebjergvej 3, DK-2100, Copenhagen,
Denmark
Tel.: (45) 70707337
Web Site: https://www.cannordic.com
Medical Device Mfr & Distr
N.A.I.C.S.: 339112

CS WIND CORPORATION
723 CS Wind Headquarters, Eonju-
ro, Seoul, 31109, Chungcheongnam-
do, Korea (South)
Tel.: (82) 264801800
Web Site: https://www.cswind.com
112610—(KRS)
Rev.: $1,054,543,175
Assets: $1,364,907,295
Liabilities: $655,686,275
Net Worth: $709,221,020
Earnings: ($752,856)
Emp.: 103
Fiscal Year-end: 12/31/22
Wind Tower Construction
N.A.I.C.S.: 237130
Seong Gon Gim *(Chm & CEO)*

Subsidiaries:

CS Wind Canada Inc.   **(1)**
9355 Anchor Drive, Windsor, N8N 5A8, ON,
Canada
Tel.: (519) 735-0973
Transportation Tool & Steel Parts Mfr
N.A.I.C.S.: 336999
James Won *(Gen Dir)*

CS Wind China Co., Ltd.   **(1)**
30 Yunyang Road, Lian Yungang Economic
& Technical Development Area, Lianyun-
gang, Jiangsu, China
Tel.: (86) 51882320456
Transportation Tool & Steel Parts Mfr
N.A.I.C.S.: 336999

CS Wind Malaysia Sdn. Bhd.   **(1)**
Lot 138A Jalan Gebeng 2/5, Gebeng Indus-
trial Estate, 26080, Kuantan, Pahang, Ma-
laysia
Tel.: (60) 95833368
Transportation Tool & Steel Parts Mfr
N.A.I.C.S.: 336999

CS Wind Taiwan Ltd.   **(1)**
No 201 Sec 2 Zhongnan 1st Rd, Wuqi Dist,

Taichung, 45341, Taiwan
Tel.: (886) 47524131
Transportation Tool & Steel Parts Mfr
N.A.I.C.S.: 336999

CS Wind Turkey Imalati Enerji Ve Ce-
lik San. Tic. A.S.   **(1)**
Coraklar Mah 5013 Sok No 4-B Aliaga
OSB, Aliaga, 35800, Izmir, Türkiye
Tel.: (90) 23262150
Transportation Tool & Steel Parts Mfr
N.A.I.C.S.: 336999

CS Wind UK Limited   **(1)**
PO Box 9263, Campbeltown, PA28 6WA,
United Kingdom
Tel.: (44) 1586555000
Transportation Tool & Steel Parts Mfr
N.A.I.C.S.: 336999

CS Wind Vietnam Co., Ltd.   **(1)**
Road 2B Phu My I Industrial Zone, Phu My
Ward Phu My Town, Ho Chi Minh City,
Baria-Vungtau, Vietnam
Tel.: (84) 643921612
Transportation Tool & Steel Parts Mfr
N.A.I.C.S.: 336999

CSA COSMIC CO., LTD.
20 Hakdong-ro 30-gil, Gangnam-Gu,
Seoul, 06105, Korea (South)
Tel.: (82) 262035370
Web Site:
https://www.csacosmic.com
Year Founded: 1989
083660—(KRS)
Rev.: $46,939,678
Assets: $26,556,636
Liabilities: $24,321,725
Net Worth: $2,234,911
Earnings: ($9,397,398)
Fiscal Year-end: 12/31/22
Water Storage Systems Mfr
N.A.I.C.S.: 221310

CSA GROUP
178 Rexdale Blvd, Toronto, M9W
1R3, ON, Canada
Tel.: (416) 747-4000
Web Site: http://www.csagroup.org
Sales Range: $200-249.9 Million
Emp.: 1,200
Business Services
N.A.I.C.S.: 561499
Paul Keane *(Exec VP-HR, Health,
Safety & Environment)*

Subsidiaries:

CSA America, Inc.   **(1)**
8501 E Pleasant Valley Rd, Cleveland, OH
44131-5575
Tel.: (216) 524-4990
Web Site: http://www.csa-america.org
Sales Range: $25-49.9 Million
Emp.: 50
Holding Company
N.A.I.C.S.: 551112
Richard Papa *(VP)*

Subsidiary (Domestic):

OnSpeX   **(2)**
8503 E Pleasant Valley Rd, Cleveland, OH
44131-5516
Tel.: (216) 524-4990
Web Site: http://www.onspex.com
Sales Range: $50-74.9 Million
Emp.: 175
Consumer Product Evaluation, Data Man-
agement & Consulting Services
N.A.I.C.S.: 541380

CSA Group Europe GmbH   **(1)**
Weismullerstrasse 45, 60314, Frankfurt,
Germany
Tel.: (49) 69 509 571 500
Business Support Services
N.A.I.C.S.: 561499

CSA Group Italy S.r.l.   **(1)**
Via Marco Fabio Quintiliano 43, 20138, Mi-
lan, Italy
Tel.: (39) 02 5801 3290
Business Support Services
N.A.I.C.S.: 561499

Alberto Carelli *(Country Mgr)*

CSA Group Netherlands   **(1)**
Utrechtseweg 310, 6812 AR, Arnhem, Neth-
erlands
Tel.: (31) 263562856
Web Site: http://www.csagroup.org
Testing Laboratories
N.A.I.C.S.: 541380
Ralf Schunk *(Reg VP)*

CSA Group Switzerland GmbH   **(1)**
Reusswehrstrasse 1, 5412, Gebenstorf,
Switzerland
Tel.: (41) 56 201 9500
Business Support Services
N.A.I.C.S.: 561499
Oliver Bosl *(Mng Dir)*

CSA International   **(1)**
178 Rexdale Blvd, Toronto, M9W 1R3, ON,
Canada
Tel.: (416) 747-4000
Web Site: http://www.csagroup.org
Sales Range: $150-199.9 Million
Emp.: 600
Testing Laboratories
N.A.I.C.S.: 541380
David Weinstein *(CEO)*

Subsidiary (Non-US):

CSA International - Asia   **(2)**
Room 1604 Concordia Plaza 1 Science Mu-
seum Road, Tsimshatsui East, Kowloon,
China (Hong Kong)
Tel.: (852) 26642872
Web Site: http://www.csa-international.org
Sales Range: $25-49.9 Million
Emp.: 20
Testing Laboratories
N.A.I.C.S.: 541380

Canadian Standards Association   **(1)**
5060 Spectrum Way Ste 100, Mississauga,
L4W 5N6, ON, Canada
Tel.: (416) 747-4000
Web Site: http://www.csagroup.com
Sales Range: $25-49.9 Million
Emp.: 215
Testing Laboratories
N.A.I.C.S.: 541380
Gianluca Arcari *(Exec Dir)*

Canadian Standards Association (Far
East Operations) Ltd.   **(1)**
Suite 811 Tsimshatsui Center East Wing 66
Mody Road, Tsimshatsui East, Kowloon,
China (Hong Kong)
Tel.: (852) 2268 6888
Business Support Services
N.A.I.C.S.: 561499

Sira Consulting Limited   **(1)**
Kelvin House Worsley Bridge Road, Lon-
don, SE26 5BX, United Kingdom
Tel.: (44) 20 8461 5555
Business Support Services
N.A.I.C.S.: 561499

Sira Environmental Limited   **(1)**
12 Acorn Industrial Park Crayford Road,
Dartford, Crayford, DA1 4AL, Kent, United
Kingdom
Tel.: (44) 1322 520500
Web Site: http://www.siraenvironmental.com
Automotive Emission Testing Services
N.A.I.C.S.: 811198

Sira Test and Certification
Limited   **(1)**
Unit 6 Hawarden Industrial Park, Eccleston,
Chester, CH5 3US, Cheshire, United King-
dom
Tel.: (44) 1244 670 900
Web Site: http://www.siracertification.com
Testing & Certification Services
N.A.I.C.S.: 541380

mi Technology Group Ltd.   **(1)**
Aston Way, Leyland, PR26 7TZ, Lan-
cashire, United Kingdom
Tel.: (44) 1772 422911
Web Site: http://www.mi-technology.com
Vehicle Testing Services
N.A.I.C.S.: 423120
Paul Wilkinson *(Dir-Technical)*

CSB-SYSTEM AG

CSB-System AG—(Continued)

An Furthenrode 9-15, 52511, Geilen-
kirchen, Germany
Tel.: (49) 2451 6250
Web Site: http://www.csb.com
Year Founded: 1977
Sales Range: $75-99.9 Million
Emp.: 600
IT Services
N.A.I.C.S.: 541512
Peter Schimitzek (Founder & Chm)

Subsidiaries:

CSB Services Asia Pacific Pvt.
Ltd　　　　　　　　　　　　　　**(1)**
No 2 8th Cross Street Dandeswaram Na-
gar, Velachery, Chennai, 600042, India
Tel.: (91) 4442132123
Information Technology Consulting Services
N.A.I.C.S.: 541512

CSB-Automation AG　　　　　　**(1)**
Gaustrasse 52, 4703, Kestenholz, Switzer-
land
Tel.: (41) 623898989
Web Site: http://www.csb-automation.com
Information Technology Consulting Services
N.A.I.C.S.: 541512
Max Studer (CEO)

CSB-System Austria GmbH　　　**(1)**
Hietzinger Kai 13 Top 9, 1130, Vienna, Aus-
tria
Tel.: (43) 18158283
Information Technology Consulting Services
N.A.I.C.S.: 541512

CSB-System Benelux BV　　　　**(1)**
Tramsingel 13, 4814 AB, Breda, Nether-
lands
Tel.: (31) 765307676
Information Technology Consulting Services
N.A.I.C.S.: 541512
Jacques Jobse (Mgr-Sis)

CSB-System Bulgaria EGmbH　　**(1)**
Preslav Str 19, 4000, Plovdiv, Bulgaria
Tel.: (359) 32648988
Information Technology Consulting Services
N.A.I.C.S.: 541512

CSB-System Espana S.L.　　　　**(1)**
Cami de Corbins N7, 25005, Lleida, Spain
Tel.: (34) 973289420
Information Technology Consulting Services
N.A.I.C.S.: 541512

CSB-System Hungary Kft.　　　　**(1)**
A Lepcsohaz II/1 Lechner Odon fasor 3,
1098, Budapest, Hungary
Tel.: (36) 12176382
Information Technology Consulting Services
N.A.I.C.S.: 541512
Kovacs Anita (Mgr)

CSB-System INTERNATIONAL,
Inc.　　　　　　　　　　　　　　**(1)**
625 Plainfield Rd Ste 322, Willowbrook, IL
60527
Tel.: (800) 852-9977
Information Technology Consulting Services
N.A.I.C.S.: 541512

CSB-System INTERNATIONAL,
Inc.　　　　　　　　　　　　　　**(1)**
41 River Road East Unit 2, Kitchener, N2B
2G3, ON, Canada
Tel.: (519) 579-7272
Information Technology Consulting Services
N.A.I.C.S.: 541512

CSB-System POLSKA Sp.Z.o.o.　**(1)**
Ul Chorwacka 45, 51-107, Wroclaw, Poland
Tel.: (48) 713267180
Information Technology Consulting Services
N.A.I.C.S.: 541512

CSB-System Romania SRL　　　　**(1)**
Str Dobrogea nr 12, 500204, Brasov, Ro-
mania
Tel.: (40) 368446235
Information Technology Consulting Services
N.A.I.C.S.: 541512
Daniel Turcu (Mgr)

CSB-System S.r.l.　　　　　　　　**(1)**
Via del Commercio 3-5, Bussolengo, 37012,
Verona, Italy

Tel.: (39) 0458905593
Information Technology Consulting Services
N.A.I.C.S.: 541512
Andre Andre (Mng Dir)

CSB-System d.o.o.　　　　　　　**(1)**
Ulica Zvonka i Vladimira Milkovica 13,
42000, Varazdin, Croatia
Tel.: (385) 42242050
Information Technology Consulting Services
N.A.I.C.S.: 541512
Predrag Makaj (CEO)

OOO CSB-System　　　　　　　**(1)**
Ul Pyatnizkaya 73 Office 8, 115054, Mos-
cow, Russia
Tel.: (7) 4956415156
Information Technology Consulting Services
N.A.I.C.S.: 541512

CSBC CORP. TAIWAN
No 3 Jhonggang Rd, Siaogang Dis-
trict, Kaohsiung, 81234, Taiwan
Tel.: (886) 78059888
Web Site:
　　https://www.csbcnet.com.tw
Year Founded: 1972
2208—(TAI)
Rev.: $696,344,099
Assets: $1,264,710,080
Liabilities: $1,045,979,881
Net Worth: $218,730,199
Earnings: ($131,809,603)
Emp.: 2,847
Fiscal Year-end: 12/31/23
Commercial & Naval Ships Mfr
N.A.I.C.S.: 336611
Kuo-Cheng Tseng (Pres)

Subsidiaries:

CSBC Coating Solutions Co.,
Ltd.　　　　　　　　　　　　　　**(1)**
No 3 Jhonggang Road, Siaogang District,
Kaohsiung, 81234, Taiwan
Tel.: (886) 78010111
Web Site: https://www.csbc-coating.com.tw
Engineeering Services
N.A.I.C.S.: 541330

CSC FINANCIAL CO., LTD
CITIC Tower Guanghualu, Chaoyang
District, Beijing, 100020, China
Tel.: (86) 1064660088　　　　**CN**
Web Site: https://www.group.citic
Year Founded: 2005
601066—(SHG)
Rev.: $4,770,712,253
Assets: $73,394,407,195
Liabilities: $59,701,699,652
Net Worth: $13,692,707,543
Earnings: $989,447,378
Emp.: 13,901
Fiscal Year-end: 12/31/23
Investment Management Service
N.A.I.C.S.: 523940
Changqing Wang (Chm)

Subsidiaries:

China Capital Management Co.,
Ltd.　　　　　　　　　　　　　　**(1)**
12/F Block B Kaiheng Center Building
Dongcheng District, Beijing, China
Tel.: (86) 1085130648
Web Site: http://ccmc.csc108.com
Investment Management Service
N.A.I.C.S.: 523940

China Fund Management Co.,
Ltd.　　　　　　　　　　　　　　**(1)**
17 and 19/F Block B Kaiheng Center Build-
ing Dongcheng District, Beijing, China
Tel.: (86) 1059100211
Web Site: http://www.cfund108.com
Fund Management Service
N.A.I.C.S.: 523940

China Futures Co., Ltd.　　　　　**(1)**
Room 808 Chamtime International Finance
Center No 1589 Century Avenue, Pudong,
Shanghai, China
Tel.: (86) 2158302346
Web Site: http://www.cfc108.com
Futures Brokerage Services

N.A.I.C.S.: 523160

China Securities (International) Fi-
nance Holding Company Limited　**(1)**
18/F Two Exchange Square, Central, China
(Hong Kong)
Tel.: (852) 3 465 5600
Web Site: https://www.csci.hk
Investment Banking Services
N.A.I.C.S.: 523150

CSC HOLDINGS LIMITED
Rooms 3206-3210 32nd Floor China
Resources Building 26 Harbour
Road, Wanchai, China (Hong Kong)
Tel.: (852) 25862666　　　　　**HK**
Web Site: http://www.cshldgs.com
0235—(HKG)
Rev.: $54,686,746
Assets: $407,571,899
Liabilities: $96,203,860
Net Worth: $311,368,038
Earnings: ($462,173,647)
Emp.: 48
Fiscal Year-end: 12/31/21
Holding Company
N.A.I.C.S.: 551112
Ching Fai Or (Chm)

Subsidiaries:

CS Wealth Securities Limited　　**(1)**
Rooms 3206 32nd Floor China Resources
Building 26 Harbour Road, Wanchai, China
(Hong Kong)
Tel.: (852) 25211261
Web Site: https://www.cswsec.com.hk
Securities Services
N.A.I.C.S.: 523150

CSC HOLDINGS LIMITED
No 2 Tanjong Penjuru Crescent, Sin-
gapore, 608968, Singapore
Tel.: (65) 62626266
Web Site: https://www.cschl.com.sg
C06—(SES)
Rev.: $196,200,159
Assets: $283,712,730
Liabilities: $191,503,498
Net Worth: $92,209,233
Earnings: ($20,097,616)
Emp.: 1,300
Fiscal Year-end: 03/31/23
Civil Engineering Services
N.A.I.C.S.: 541330
Yeow Beng Lim (Dir-Contracts)

Subsidiaries:

Borneo Geotechnic Sdn. Bhd.　　**(1)**
B-3-01 B-3A-01 B-5-01 Neo Damansara
Jalan PJU 8/1, Bandar Damansara Per-
dana, Petaling Jaya, 47820, Selangor, Ma-
laysia
Tel.: (60) 377106266
Web Site:
　　http://www.borneogeotechnic.com.my
Sales Range: $25-49.9 Million
Emp.: 50
Geotechnical Engineering Services
N.A.I.C.S.: 541330
Soon Teck Tee (Gen Mgr)

CS Bored Pile System Pte. Ltd.　**(1)**
2 Tanjong Penjuru Crescent, Singapore,
608968, Singapore
Tel.: (65) 63627088
Sales Range: $50-74.9 Million
Emp.: 200
Bored Piling Contractors
N.A.I.C.S.: 238910

CS Construction & Geotechnic Pte.
Ltd.　　　　　　　　　　　　　　**(1)**
2 Tanjong Penjuru Crescent, Singapore,
608968, Singapore
Tel.: (65) 63670933
Construction Engineering Services
N.A.I.C.S.: 541330
Koh Seng Lim (Mgr-HR)

Subsidiary (Domestic):

CS Geotechnic Pte. Ltd.　　　　**(2)**
2 Tanjong Penjuru Crescent, Singapore,

608968, Singapore
Tel.: (65) 63626866
Web Site: http://www.cschl.com.sg
Sales Range: $75-99.9 Million
Emp.: 300
Geotechnical Engineering Services
N.A.I.C.S.: 541330
Poh Chee Kuan (CEO)

G Pilo Siotom Sdn. Bhd.　　　　**(1)**
B-3-01 B-3A-01 Neo Damansara Jalan PJU
8/1 Bandar Damansara Perdana, Bandar
Damansara Perdana, 47820, Petaling Jaya,
Selangor, Malaysia
Tel.: (60) 37 710 8477
Web Site: https://www.g-pile.com.my
Infrastructure Construction Services
N.A.I.C.S.: 236220
Lim Leong Koo (Mng Dir)

ICE Far East (HK) Limited　　　**(1)**
DD 125 Lot 1953 P Ping Ha Road, Ha
Tsuen, Yuen Long, New Territories, China
(Hong Kong)
Tel.: (852) 24726363
Equipment Rental Services
N.A.I.C.S.: 532490

ICE Far East (Thailand) Co., Ltd.　**(1)**
99/750 Nouvelle Condominium Block D
Thanacity Bangna-Trad Road km 14 5, Tam-
bol Bangchalong Amphur, Bang Phli,
10540, Samutprakarn, Thailand
Tel.: (66) 23360920
Equipment Rental Services
N.A.I.C.S.: 532490

ICE Far East Pte. Ltd.　　　　　**(1)**
13 Pioneer Sector 2, Singapore, 628374,
Singapore
Tel.: (65) 68613733
Equipment Rental Services
N.A.I.C.S.: 532490

ICE Far East Sdn. Bhd.　　　　　**(1)**
No 46-1 & Mezzanine Jalan Tengah,
Cheras Selatan 118, 43200, Cheras, Selan-
gor, Malaysia
Tel.: (60) 390821126
Equipment Rental Services
N.A.I.C.S.: 532490

IMT-THL India Private Limited　　**(1)**
Plot No W-233, TTC-MIDC Industrial Area
Village Khairane, Navi Mumbai, 400 709,
Maharashtra, India
Tel.: (91) 2232039009
Equipment Rental Services
N.A.I.C.S.: 532490

L&M Foundation Specialist Pte.
Ltd.　　　　　　　　　　　　　　**(1)**
2 Tanjong Penjuru Crescent, Singapore,
608968, Singapore
Tel.: (65) 62626266
Sales Range: $100-124.9 Million
Emp.: 400
Foundation Engineering Services
N.A.I.C.S.: 238140
Yen Tarn See (Pres & CEO)

Soil Investigation Pte. Ltd.　　　**(1)**
120 Pioneer Road 04-01/02/03, Singapore,
639597, Singapore
Tel.: (65) 6 745 6765
Web Site:
　　https://www.soilinvestigation.com.sg
Emp.: 200
Geotechnical Engineering Services
N.A.I.C.S.: 541380
Joo Sheun Ng (Mgr-Contracts & Assets)

Subsidiary (Domestic):

Wisescan Engineering Services Pte.
Ltd.　　　　　　　　　　　　　　**(2)**
14 Little Road 02-01, Singapore, 536987,
Singapore
Tel.: (65) 6 841 0880
Web Site: https://www.wisescan.com
Emp.: 170
Land & Tunnel Surveying Services
N.A.I.C.S.: 541370
Keng Guan Chua (Founder & Mng Dir)

THL Foundation Equipment (Myan-
mar) Company Limited　　　　　**(1)**
Unit 508 No 29 Kanbawza Avenue Street,
Bahan Township, Yangon, Myanmar
Tel.: (95) 12306228

Equipment Rental Services
N.A.I.C.S.: 532490

THL Foundation Equipment (Philippines) Inc. (1)
Cityland Pasong Tamo Tower Unit 812 2210 Don Chino Roces Ave, Makati, 1231, Philippines
Tel.: (63) 27100807
Equipment Rental Services
N.A.I.C.S.: 532490

THL Foundation Equipment Pte. Ltd. (1)
4 Benoi Place, Singapore, 629925, Singapore
Tel.: (65) 6 861 0089
Web Site: https://www.thlfe.com.sg
Sales Range: $50-74.9 Million
Emp.: 55
Foundation & Geotechnical Equipment Rental Services
N.A.I.C.S.: 532412

THL Vietnam Company Limited (1)
Floor 10 Lilama 10 Building No 56 To Huu Street, Trung Van Ward Nam Tu Liem District, Hanoi, Vietnam
Tel.: (84) 91292606
Equipment Rental Services
N.A.I.C.S.: 532490

CSC STEEL HOLDINGS BERHAD

180 Kawasan Industri Ayer Keroh, 75450, Melaka, Malaysia
Tel.: (60) 62310169
Web Site:
https://www.cscmalaysia.com
CSCSTEL—(KLS)
Rev.: $359,498,433
Assets: $198,627,139
Liabilities: $16,299,918
Net Worth: $182,327,221
Earnings: $3,091,638
Emp.: 677
Fiscal Year-end: 12/31/22
Steel Mfrs
N.A.I.C.S.: 331110
Ling Piew Ten (VP)

CSCEC SCIMEE SCI & TECH CO., LTD.

No 3 Wuxing 1st Road, Wuhou District, Chengdu, 610045, Sichuan, China
Tel.: (86) 2885001657
Web Site: https://www.scimee.com
Year Founded: 2002
300425—(CHIN)
Rev.: $223,910,287
Assets: $581,287,933
Liabilities: $250,406,424
Net Worth: $330,881,509
Earnings: $27,631,424
Fiscal Year-end: 12/31/21
Magnetic Separation Water Treatment Equipment Mfr
N.A.I.C.S.: 333310
Wang Zhexiao (Sec & Gen Mgr)

CSD WATER SERVICE CO., LTD.

2F Building 2 Area D No 66 Xixiaokou Road, Haidian District, Beijing, 100192, China
Tel.: (86) 1082800999
Web Site: http://www.zchb-water.net
Year Founded: 2009
603903—(SHG)
Rev.: $201,540,016
Assets: $637,815,326
Liabilities: $386,449,301
Net Worth: $251,366,025
Earnings: $16,890,752
Fiscal Year-end: 12/31/22
Sewage Treatment Services
N.A.I.C.S.: 221320
Zhang Yifei (Chm)

CSE GLOBAL LTD.

202 Bedok South Avenue 1 Building C 01-21, Singapore, 469332, Singapore
Tel.: (65) 65120333
Web Site: https://www.cse-global.com
544—(OTCIQ)
Rev.: $379,590,611
Assets: $303,399,794
Liabilities: $158,718,853
Net Worth: $144,680,941
Earnings: $21,139,160
Emp.: 1,400
Fiscal Year-end: 12/31/20
System Integration Services
N.A.I.C.S.: 541512
Boon Kheng Lim (CEO & Mng Dir)

Subsidiaries:

Bus Communications Pty Ltd (1)
40 Arthur Street, Balmain, 2041, NSW, Australia
Tel.: (61) 1300800997
Web Site: http://www.businessca.com.au
Telecommunication Servicesb
N.A.I.C.S.: 517810

CC American Oilfield, LLC (1)
4826 Santa Elena St, Corpus Christi, TX 78405
Tel.: (361) 884-6774
Web Site: http://www.aos-tx.com
Industrial Pressure Vessel Mfr
N.A.I.C.S.: 332420
Gayle Miller (Mgr)

CSE Communications & Security Sdn Bhd (1)
Suite 07-07 7th Floor Menara Sey Hoy Chan No 374 Jalan Tun Razak, 50400, Kuala Lumpur, Malaysia
Tel.: (60) 321663988
System Integration Services
N.A.I.C.S.: 541512

CSE Comsource Pty Ltd (1)
45 King Edward Road, Osborne Park, 6017, WA, Australia
Tel.: (61) 89 204 8001
Web Site: https://www.cse-australia.com
Telecommunications Integration Services
N.A.I.C.S.: 517112
Ben Marshall (Gen Mgr)

Subsidiary (Domestic):

CSE-Transtel Pty Ltd (2)
45 King Edward Road, Osborne Park, 6017, WA, Australia
Tel.: (61) 892048000
Web Site: http://www.cse-transtel.com
Emp.: 30
Telecommunication Engineering Services
N.A.I.C.S.: 541330
Roy Rowe (CEO)

CSE Crosscom Pty Ltd (1)
664 Lorimer Street, Port Melbourne, 3207, VIC, Australia
Tel.: (61) 393221500
Web Site: https://csecrosscom.net
Telecommunication Servicesb
N.A.I.C.S.: 517810

CSE Icon, Inc. (1)
2829 Technology Forest Blvd Ste 460, The Woodlands, TX 77381
Tel.: (281) 670-1010
Web Site: https://www.cse-icon.com
Industrial Automation & System Integration Services
N.A.I.C.S.: 541512

CSE Semaphore Australia Pty Ltd (1)
Unit 8/3-5 Gilda Ct, Mulgrave, 3170, VIC, Australia
Tel.: (61) 385448544
Web Site: http://www.cse-semaphore.com
Electronic Components Mfr
N.A.I.C.S.: 334419

CSE Semaphore Belgium SA (1)
Waterloo Office Park Building M Dreve Richelle 161, 1410, Waterloo, Belgium
Tel.: (32) 2 387 42 59

Electronic Components Mfr
N.A.I.C.S.: 334419

CSE Semaphore Inc (1)
1200 Chantry Place, Lake Mary, FL 32746
Tel.: (407) 333-3235
Web Site: http://www.cse-semaphore.com
Electronic Components Mfr
N.A.I.C.S.: 334419

CSE Systems & Engineering (India) Pvt Limited (1)
No 3 3rd Floor 100ft Road 2nd Stage 1st Phase BTM Layout, Bengaluru, 560 076, India
Tel.: (91) 8026783302
Emp.: 20
Industrial Automation Solutions
N.A.I.C.S.: 238210
Ravindra D. (Country Mgr)

CSE W-Industries Nigeria Ltd. (1)
10 Estate Road Rumuogba, Port Harcourt, Rivers, Nigeria
Tel.: (234) 8064456174
System Integration Services
N.A.I.C.S.: 541512

CSE-EIS (Malaysia) Sdn Bhd (1)
Suite 3 02 3rd Floor Mercu PICORP Lot 10 Jalan Astaka U8/84, Bukit Jelutong Business Technology Centre, 40150, Shah Alam, Selangor, Malaysia
Tel.: (60) 378468580
Sales Range: $25-49.9 Million
Emp.: 30
System Integration Services
N.A.I.C.S.: 541512

CSE-EIS Pte Ltd (1)
202 Bedok South Avenue 1 Building C 01-21, Singapore, 469332, Singapore
Tel.: (65) 65120333
Industrial Automation Solutions
N.A.I.C.S.: 238210

CSE-Global (Australia) Pty Ltd (1)
45 King Edward Road, Osborne Park, 6017, WA, Australia
Tel.: (61) 89 204 8000
Web Site: https://www.cse-australia.com
Sales Range: $25-49.9 Million
Emp.: 50
Industrial Automation & Telecommunication Support Services
N.A.I.C.S.: 238210
Roy Row (CEO)

CSE-Global (Australia), Ltd. (1)
10 Columbia Way, Baulkham Hills, 2153, NSW, Australia
Tel.: (61) 288534200
Web Site: http://www.cse-uniserve.com.au
Sales Range: $25-49.9 Million
Emp.: 30
System Integration Services
N.A.I.C.S.: 541512
Greg Swinton (Mng Dir)

Subsidiary (Domestic):

CSE-Uniserve Pty Limited (2)
10 Columbia Way, Baulkham Hills, 2153, NSW, Australia
Tel.: (61) 288534200
Sales Range: $10-24.9 Million
System Integration Services
N.A.I.C.S.: 541512

CSE-Global (UK) Limited (1)
Rotherside Road, Eckington, Sheffield, S21 4HL, United Kingdom
Tel.: (44) 1246437400
Web Site: http://www.cse-globaluk.com
Business Consultancy Services
N.A.I.C.S.: 561499

Subsidiary (Non-US):

CSE-Controls s.r.o. (2)
Piaristickai 2, Nitra, 94901, Slovakia
Tel.: (421) 37 6519 529
Sales Range: $25-49.9 Million
Emp.: 37
Industrial Control System Mfr
N.A.I.C.S.: 335314
Peter Rozek (Mng Dir)

Subsidiary (Domestic):

CSE-Healthcare Systems Limited (2)

Rotherside Road, Sheffield, S21 4HL, United Kingdom
Tel.: (44) 1246437500
Web Site: http://www.cse-healthcare.com
Emp.: 100
Health Care Srvices
N.A.I.C.S.: 621999
Alan Stubbs (CEO)

Servelec Controls - Aberdeen (2)
The Technology Centre Claymore Drive, Aberdeen, AB23 8GD, United Kingdom
Tel.: (44) 1224707700
Web Site: http://www.serveleccontrols.com
Sales Range: $25-49.9 Million
Emp.: 40
Oil & Gas Exploration Services
N.A.I.C.S.: 213112
Andrew Mills (Mng Dir)

CSE-Hankin (China) Co., Ltd. (1)
05-07 1/F Tower 2 Zone 2 Hanwei International, No 186 South 4th Ring Xi Lu Fengtai District, Beijing, 100070, China
Tel.: (86) 1082014593
System Integration Services
N.A.I.C.S.: 541512

CSE-Hankin (Taiwan) Ltd. (1)
3F-2 No 11 Minquan W Rd, Zhongshan Dist, Taipei, 104026, Taiwan
Tel.: (886) 225080660
Property Investment Services
N.A.I.C.S.: 531390

CSE-Hankin Inc (1)
1 Harvard Way Ste 6, Hillsborough, NJ 08844
Tel.: (908) 722-9595
Web Site: https://www.hankines.com
Sales Range: $75-99.9 Million
Emp.: 13
Waste Water Treatment Services
N.A.I.C.S.: 221510
David Chen (Pres & CEO)

CSE-IAP Pte Ltd (1)
202 Bedok South Avenue 1 Building C 01-21, Singapore, 469332, Singapore
Tel.: (65) 6 512 0333
Web Site: https://www.cse-global.com
Industrial Automation Solutions
N.A.I.C.S.: 238210

CSE-ITS Pte Ltd (1)
202 Bedok South Avenue 1 Building C 01-21, Singapore, 469332, Singapore
Tel.: (65) 6 512 0333
Web Site: https://www.cse-global.com
Emp.: 50
Telecommunication Servicesb
N.A.I.C.S.: 517810

CSE-Servelec Limited (1)
The Straddle Victoria Quays, Sheffield, S2 5SY, United Kingdom
Tel.: (44) 1144334800
Web Site: http://www.servelec.co.uk
Sales Range: $25-49.9 Million
Emp.: 200
System Integration Services
N.A.I.C.S.: 541512

CSE-Servelec s.r.o. (1)
Piaristicka 2, 949 01, Nitra, Slovakia
Tel.: (421) 376519529
Web Site: http://www.cse-control.sk
Sales Range: $25-49.9 Million
Emp.: 33
Pipeline Management Services
N.A.I.C.S.: 486990
Peter Yalis (Gen Mgr)

CSE-Uniserve Corporation Pty Ltd (1)
10 Columbia Way, Baulkham Hills, 2153, NSW, Australia
Tel.: (61) 288534200
Web Site: http://www.cseuniserve.com.au
Sales Range: $25-49.9 Million
Emp.: 30
Industrial Automation & Telecommunication Support Services
N.A.I.C.S.: 238210
Rob Roye (Gen Mgr)

Subsidiary (Non-US):

CSE-W Arthur Fisher Limited (2)
15 Polaris Place, East Tamaki, 2013, Auckland, New Zealand

CSE Global Ltd.—(Continued)

Tel.: (64) 9 271 3810
Web Site: https://cse-waf.nz
Sales Range: $25-49.9 Million
Emp.: 25
Instrumentation & Control System Whslr
N.A.I.C.S.: 423690
Harry Singh (Mng Dir)

Chatterbox Limited (1)
1 Guards Avenue The Village, Caterham-on-the-Hill, Caterham, CR3 5XL, Surrey, United Kingdom
Tel.: (44) 2071834391
Web Site: http://www.cse-chatterbox.com
Radio System Distr
N.A.I.C.S.: 423690

Gulf Coast Power & Control of Louisi-ana LLC (1)
64080 LA-1090, Pearl River, LA 70452
Tel.: (985) 863-2336
Web Site: http://www.gulfcoastpwr.com
Measuring & Testing Electricity & Electrical Signals Instrument Mfr
N.A.I.C.S.: 334515

Industrias W de Mexico, SA de C.V. (1)
Avenida del Mar No 46 Col Bibalvo, 24158, Ciudad del Carmen, Campeche, Mexico
Tel.: (52) 9381182631
Web Site:
  https://www.industriaswmexico.com
System Integration Services
N.A.I.C.S.: 541512
Gilberto Lopez Rivero (Mgr-Admin)

P.T. Communications & Security (1)
Gedung Menara Topas Lantai 12 Jl M H Thamrin Kav 9, Kel Gondangdia Kec Menteng Kota Adm, Jakarta Pusat, Jakarta, Indonesia
Tel.: (62) 2121231711
Telecommunication Servicesb
N.A.I.C.S.: 517810

RCS Telecommunications Pty Ltd (1)
Level 1-The Annexe 133 Mary Street, Brisbane, 4000, QLD, Australia
Tel.: (61) 732280800
Web Site: http://www.rcst.com.au
Emp.: 80
Wireless Telecommunication Services
N.A.I.C.S.: 517112
Brad Clark (Ops Mgr)

RTUnet (Australia) Pty Ltd. (1)
Ste 8 3-5 Gilda Court, Mulgrave, 3170, VIC, Australia
Tel.: (61) 385448544
Web Site: http://www.cse-semaphore.com
Sales Range: $25-49.9 Million
Emp.: 50
System Integration Services
N.A.I.C.S.: 541512

TransTel Engineering (Nigeria) Ltd. (1)
10 Rumuogba Estate Road, Port Harcourt, Rivers, Nigeria
Tel.: (234) 8064456174
System Integration Services
N.A.I.C.S.: 541512

TransTel Engineering Arabian Limited Co. (1)
1st Floor Euro Village Office Building, PO Box 691, Al Khobar, 31932, Saudi Arabia
Tel.: (966) 38595378
System Integration Services
N.A.I.C.S.: 541512

TransTel Engineering Pte Ltd. (1)
1 Jalan Kilang, Dynasty Bldg 06-00, Singapore, 159402, Singapore
Tel.: (65) 62767600
Web Site: http://www.transtel-engineering.com
Sales Range: $50-74.9 Million
Emp.: 170
System Integration Services
N.A.I.C.S.: 541512
Leong Say Haur (Mng Dir)

Subsidiary (Non-US):

CSE Systems & Engineering (Thailand) Limited (2)

283/46 Unit No 1001-2 Homeplace Office Building 10th Floor, Soi Sukhumvit 55 Sukhumvit Road Kwaeng Klongton Nur Khet Wattana, Bangkok, 10110, Thailand
Tel.: (66) 2 7127331
Web Site: http://www.cse-global.com
Sales Range: $25-49.9 Million
Emp.: 1
Engineeering Services
N.A.I.C.S.: 541330
Lee Wahlian (Mng Dir)

PT TransTel Engineering (2)
MidPlaza Building I 10th Floor Jl Jend Sudirman Kav 10-11, Jakarta, 10220, Indonesia
Tel.: (62) 2157905515
Sales Range: $25-49.9 Million
Emp.: 26
Telecommunication Servicesb
N.A.I.C.S.: 517810

TransTel Engineering (Thailand) Co Limited (2)
283/46 Unit No 1001-2 Homeplace Office Bldg 10th Floor, Soi Sukhumvit 55 Sukhumvit Road Kwaeng Klongton Nur Khet Wattana, Bangkok, 10110, Thailand
Tel.: (66) 27127331
Web Site:
  http://www.transtelengineering.com
Sales Range: $25-49.9 Million
Emp.: 10
Telecommunication Servicesb
N.A.I.C.S.: 517810

TransTel Engineering Arabia Limited Co (2)
1st Floor Air Line Center Building, PO Box 691, Al Khobar, 31932, Saudi Arabia
Tel.: (966) 38870230
Telecommunication Engineering Services
N.A.I.C.S.: 541330

TransTel Engineering PNG Ltd (2)
Waigani, PO Box 981, National Capital District, Port Moresby, Papua New Guinea
Tel.: (675) 3520356
Web Site: http://www.transtel-engineering.com
Telecommunication Servicesb
N.A.I.C.S.: 517810

Volta, LLC (1)
1616 Gears Rd, Houston, TX 77067
Tel.: (832) 369-2420
Web Site: https://www.volta-us.com
Electric Equipment Mfr
N.A.I.C.S.: 335999
Bradley Davis (Pres)

W-Industries, Inc. (1)
11500 Charles Rd, Houston, TX 77041
Tel.: (713) 466-9463
Web Site: https://w-industries.com
Sales Range: $100-124.9 Million
Emp.: 400
System Integration Services
N.A.I.C.S.: 541512
Greg Hanson (Pres & CEO)

Subsidiary (Domestic):

W-Industries - Louisiana LLC (2)
7620 Johnston St, Maurice, LA 70555
Tel.: (337) 993-7425
Web Site: https://w-industries.com
Sales Range: $25-49.9 Million
Emp.: 50
Industrial Control Systems Distr
N.A.I.C.S.: 423830

CSEPEL HOLDING PLC
Varrogepgyar ut 1, 1211, Budapest, Hungary
Tel.: (36) 12785800
Web Site: https://www.csepel-holding.hu
Sales Range: $10-24.9 Million
Emp.: 121
Industrial Machinery Mfr
N.A.I.C.S.: 333248

CSF GROUP PLC
Block B Annex Building Jalan Impact 7118, 63000, Cyberjaya, Selangor Darul Ehsan, Malaysia

Tel.: (60) 3 8322 0245   JE
Web Site: http://www.csf-group.com
Sales Range: $1-9.9 Million
Emp.: 161
Data Center Design, Construction & Maintenance Services
N.A.I.C.S.: 236220
Billy Kok Chi Lee (Chm & CEO-CSF Advioors)

Subsidiaries:

Atlas CSF Sdn Bhd (1)
MY01 Block B Annex Building 7118 Jalan Impact, 63000, Cyberjaya, Selangor, Malaysia
Tel.: (60) 383119563
Web Site: http://www.atlas-csf.com
Computer Facility Management Services
N.A.I.C.S.: 541513

CSG HOLDINGS LIMITED
Brooklyn Office Park Block D 1109 Jan Shoba Street, Brooklyn, Pretoria, 0011, South Africa
Tel.: (27) 123629778   ZA
Web Site:
  http://www.csgholdings.co.za
Year Founded: 1980
CSG—(JSE)
Rev.: $119,489,493
Assets: $51,328,542
Liabilities: $25,092,674
Net Worth: $26,235,868
Earnings: ($5,406,613)
Emp.: 8,938
Fiscal Year-end: 03/31/20
Holding Company
N.A.I.C.S.: 551112
Mark Nico Hattingh (Sec)

Subsidiaries:

Afriboom Proprietary Limited (1)
Block B Unit 7 9 Zeiss Road Laser Park, Kimbult Industrial Park, Honeydew, South Africa
Tel.: (27) 117945199
Web Site: http://www.afriboom.co.za
Cleaning Service
N.A.I.C.S.: 561720

CSG Food Solutions Proprietary Limited (1)
Brooklyn Office Park Block D 1109 Jan Shoba Street, Brooklyn, 0181, Pretoria, South Africa
Tel.: (27) 861306093
Web Site: http://www.csgfoods.co.za
Food Service
N.A.I.C.S.: 722310
Gary Davis (CEO)

CSG Resourcings Proprietary Limited (1)
Brooklyn Office Park Block D 1109 Jan Shoba Street, Brooklyn, Pretoria, 0181, South Africa
Tel.: (27) 123629778
Web Site: http://www.csgresourcing.co.za
Temporary Employment Services
N.A.I.C.S.: 561311

CSG Skills Institute Proprietary Limited (1)
1490 Schooner Avenue Laser Park, Honeydew, 2040, Gauteng, South Africa
Tel.: (27) 117942000
Web Site: http://www.csgskills.co.za
Skill Development Services
N.A.I.C.S.: 611430
Odette Page (CEO)

Hi-Tech Asset Protection Proprietary Limited (1)
8 Nel Street, Nelspruit, South Africa
Tel.: (27) 137525806
Emp.: 600
Security Guard Services
N.A.I.C.S.: 561612

Hi-Tech Nelspruit Proprietary Limited (1)
17 Hendrik Potgieter Street, Nelspruit, 1200, South Africa
Tel.: (27) 137524470

Security Guard Services
N.A.I.C.S.: 561612

Revert Risk Management Solutions (Pty) Ltd. (1)
Cnr Jones & Springbok Road, Bartlett, Boksburg, 1459, South Africa
Tel.: (27) 861738 378
Web Site: http://www.revert.co.za
Integrated Seourity Servioos
N.A.I.C.S.: 561621
Gideon Joubert (Gen Mgr)

Safety Adherence Technology (Pty) Ltd (1)
Cnr of Nelson Mandela Drive and PDP Kruger St Fundu Park, Secunda, 2303, South Africa
Tel.: (27) 17 638 0140
Web Site: https://www.safetyadtechsa.co.za
Electronic Surveillance Equipment Rental Services
N.A.I.C.S.: 532210
Coenie Deysel (Mgr-Contract)

CSG SMART SCIENCE & TECHNOLOGY CO., LTD.
No 777 sizhuan Road, Dongjing Town Songjiang District, Shanghai, 201619, China
Tel.: (86) 2150804882
Web Site: http://www.csg.com.cn
Year Founded: 2002
300222—(CHIN)
Rev.: $436,907,404
Assets: $766,583,252
Liabilities: $531,871,643
Net Worth: $234,711,609
Earnings: ($18,004,841)
Emp.: 3,200
Fiscal Year-end: 12/31/23
Electricity Distribution & Usage Automatic Systems Mfr
N.A.I.C.S.: 334515
Mingsong Huang (Chm, Pres & Gen Mgr)

Subsidiaries:

CSG Intelligence Technology (Hefei) Co., Ltd. (1)
No 5111 Wangjiang West Road, Hefei, China
Tel.: (86) 551 65322333
Automation Technology Developer
N.A.I.C.S.: 334513

CSG Intelligent Electrical Technology Co., Ltd. (1)
No 5111 Wangjiang West Road, Hefei, 230088, China
Tel.: (86) 551 653223
Automation Technology Developer
N.A.I.C.S.: 334513

CSG Smart Electric Technology Co., Ltd. (1)
No 5111 Wangjiang West Road, Hefei, China
Tel.: (86) 55165322333
Power Distribution Services
N.A.I.C.S.: 221122

CSG Smart Robot Technology Co., Ltd. (1)
No 777 Sizhuan Road, Shanghai, China
Tel.: (86) 2150809880
Information Technology Services
N.A.I.C.S.: 541511

Huaxiao Precision (Suzhou) Co., Ltd. (1)
No 110 Kejing Road, New District, Suzhou, China
Tel.: (86) 51268088856
Web Site: https://www.huaxiao.com.cn
Industrial Machinery Mfr & Distr
N.A.I.C.S.: 333248

Huaxiao Precision Industry (Suzhou) Co., Ltd. (1)
No 110 Kejing Road, New District, Suzhou, 215163, Jiangsu, China
Tel.: (86) 51268088856
Web Site: https://en.huaxiao.com.cn
Automation Technology Developer

N.A.I.C.S.: 334513

Shanghai Guanzhi Industrial Automation Co., Ltd. (1)
Building 4 No 1218 Xinda Road Qingpu District, Shanghai, 201799, China
Tel.: (86) 21 6921 0777
Automation Technology Developer
N.A.I.C.S.: 334513

Shanghai Yongqian Electrical and Mechanical Co., Ltd. (1)
No 99 Lianxing Road Jiading District, Shanghai, 201804, China
Tel.: (86) 21 5959 0800
Automation Technology Developer
N.A.I.C.S.: 334513

Shenzhen HW Automation Equipment Co., Ltd. (1)
Building 26 Yutang Street Changxing Science, Technology Industrial Park
Changzhen Community Guangming District, Shenzhen, 518101, China
Tel.: (86) 75526722801
Web Site: https://www.sz-hw.com.cn
Emp.: 200
Industrial Automation Product Mfr & Distr
N.A.I.C.S.: 334512

Yantai CSG Zhengxin Electric Technology Co., Ltd. (1)
No 12 Xiangtan Road Guxian Industrial Park, Yantai Development Zone, Yantai, 264006, China
Tel.: (86) 535 2161678
Automation Technology Developer
N.A.I.C.S.: 334513

Yantai Keda Zhengxin Electric Co., Ltd. (1)
No 12 Xiangtan Road, Guxian Industrial Park, Yantai, China
Tel.: (86) 5352161678
Information Technology Services
N.A.I.C.S.: 541511

Zhejiang New Yuhong Intelligent Equipment Co., Ltd. (1)
No 1 Lingshang Road, Fengdu Industrial Zone Pingyao Town Yuhang District, Hangzhou, China
Tel.: (86) 57188546558
Web Site: https://en.yhjg.com
Sanitary Paper Product Mfr & Distr
N.A.I.C.S.: 322291

CSH ALLIANCE BERHAD
No 5-G Jalan Panglima Persiaran Mahkota, Bandar Mahkota Cheras, 43200, Cheras, Malaysia
Tel.: (60) 390117577
Web Site:
   https://www.velocitymy.com
VELOCITY—(KLS)
Rev.: $7,951,300
Assets: $87,793,244
Liabilities: $5,914,261
Net Worth: $81,878,984
Earnings: ($5,810,946)
Emp.: 80
Fiscal Year-end: 06/30/23
Ceramic Related Product Retailer, Exporter & Mfr
N.A.I.C.S.: 327110
Melvin Mun Shung Lim (Exec Dir)

Subsidiaries:

Asian Porcelain Sdn. Bhd. (1)
80 Jalan Pahang, Kuala Lumpur, 53000, Federal Territory, Malaysia
Tel.: (60) 340421355
Web Site: http://www.intracopallet.com
Sales Range: $75-99.9 Million
Emp.: 120
Porcelain Products Import & Distr
N.A.I.C.S.: 423320
Sung Chai Cheah (Mgr)

Asian Pottery (Penang) Sdn. Bhd. (1)
Plot 58 Jalan Logam 3 Kamunting Raya Estet Perindustrian Kamunting 3, 34600, Kamunting, Perak, Malaysia
Tel.: (60) 58911319
Web Site: https://asian-pottery.com

Pottery & Porcelain Product Mfr
N.A.I.C.S.: 327110
Kathrina Goh (Mng Dir)

Asian Pottery Home & Garden Sdn. Bhd. (1)
547-P Jalan Wee Hein Tze, Tanjung Bungah, 11200, George Town, Penang, Malaysia
Tel.: (60) 48998669
Web Site: http://www.asian-pottery.com
Sales Range: $75-99.9 Million
Emp.: 6
Flower Pots & Vases Distr
N.A.I.C.S.: 424930

Oriwina Sdn. Bhd. (1)
Plot 53-58 Jalan Logam 3, Kawasan Perindustrian Kamunting Raya, 34600, Kamunting, Perak, Malaysia
Tel.: (60) 58911319
Web Site: https://oriwina.business.site
Sales Range: $25-49.9 Million
Emp.: 55
Flower Pots & Vases Mfr
N.A.I.C.S.: 327110

CSI PROPERTIES LIMITED
31/F Bank of America Tower 12 Harcourt Road, Central, China (Hong Kong)
Tel.: (852) 2 878 2800   BM
Web Site: http://www.csigroup.hk
0497—(HKG)
Rev.: $102,613,392
Assets: $3,694,496,284
Liabilities: $1,776,405,684
Net Worth: $1,918,090,601
Earnings: $53,978,775
Emp.: 105
Fiscal Year-end: 03/31/21
Financial Investment Services
N.A.I.C.S.: 523999
Mico Cho Yee Chung (Chm)

Subsidiaries:

ICC Financial Limited (1)
1605 Bonham Strand Trade Centre 135 Bonham Strand, Hong Kong, China (Hong Kong)
Tel.: (852) 25814212
Web Site: https://www.iccfinancial.com
Financial Services
N.A.I.C.S.: 523940

CSI-GMBH
Freight Center Module C, 85356, Munich, Germany
Tel.: (49) 89973304410
Web Site: http://www.csi-spedition.com
Sales Range: $10-24.9 Million
Transportation Services
N.A.I.C.S.: 488999
Martin Brummer (Co-Mng Dir)

CSL LIMITED
655 Elizabeth Street, Melbourne, 3000, VIC, Australia
Tel.: (61) 393891911   AU
Web Site: https://www.csl.com
Year Founded: 1916
CMXHF—(OTCQX)
Rev.: $13,310,000,000
Assets: $36,234,000,000
Liabilities: $18,408,000,000
Net Worth: $17,826,000,000
Earnings: $2,244,000,000
Emp.: 31,792
Fiscal Year-end: 06/30/23
Biotechnology Research & Development Services
N.A.I.C.S.: 325414
Karen Etchberger (Exec VP-Quality & Bus Svcs)

Subsidiaries:

CSL Behring (Australia) Pty Ltd. (1)
189-209 Camp Road, Broadmeadows, 3047, VIC, Australia
Tel.: (61) 392465200

Web Site: https://www.cslbehring.com.au
Plasma Product Mfr
N.A.I.C.S.: 325414
Paul Perreault (Pres, Exec VP-Comml Ops & Bus Dev-Worldwide)

CSL Behring AG (1)
Wankdorfstrasse 10, 3014, Bern, Switzerland
Tel.: (41) 31 344 4444
Web Site: https://www.cslbehring.ch
Sales Range: $200-249.9 Million
Emp.: 1,200
Plasma Mfr & Distr
N.A.I.C.S.: 325414

CSL Behring Canada Inc. (1)
55 Metcalfe Suite 1460, Ottawa, K1P 6L5, ON, Canada
Tel.: (613) 232-3111
Web Site: https://www.cslbehring.ca
Sales Range: $25-49.9 Million
Emp.: 30
Pharmaceutical Products Mfr & Distr
N.A.I.C.S.: 325412

CSL Behring GmbH (1)
Emil-von-Behring-Strasse 76, 35041, Marburg, Germany
Tel.: (49) 64213912
Plasmas Retailer
N.A.I.C.S.: 424210

Subsidiary (Non-US):

CSL Behring AB (2)
Berga Backe 2, Box 712, 182 17, Danderyd, Stockholm, Sweden
Tel.: (46) 85 449 6670
Web Site: https://www.cslbehring.se
Emp.: 24
Plasmas Retailer
N.A.I.C.S.: 424210

CSL Behring B.V. (2)
Bijster 14, 4817 HX, Breda, Netherlands
Tel.: (31) 851119600
Plasmas Retailer
N.A.I.C.S.: 424210
Patrick Reygaert (Gen Mgr)

CSL Behring GmbH (2)
Austria Campus 6 Walcherstrasse 1A / Stiege 1, 1020, Vienna, Austria
Tel.: (43) 180 101 1040
Web Site: https://www.cslbehring.at
Plasmas Mfr & Distr
N.A.I.C.S.: 325414

CSL Behring Lda. (2)
Mar Vermelho Building Av D Joao II lot 1 06 2 5 Floor 3 Front, 1990-095, Lisbon, Portugal
Tel.: (351) 217826230
Web Site: http://www.cslbehring.com
Emp.: 7
Plasmas Mfr & Sales
N.A.I.C.S.: 325414
Paulo Roberto Morisson (Mng Dir)

CSL Behring MEPE (2)
5 Hatziyianni Mexi Str, 11528, Athens, Greece
Tel.: (30) 210 725 5660
Web Site: http://www.cslbehring.gr
Emp.: 11
Plasmas Retailer
N.A.I.C.S.: 424210

CSL Behring N.V. (2)
Bedrijvenlaan 11, 2800, Mechelen, Flemish Brabant, Belgium
Tel.: (32) 1 528 8920
Web Site: https://www.cslbehring.be
Plasmas Mfr & Distr
N.A.I.C.S.: 325414

CSL Behring S.A. (2)
Calle Tarragona 149-157 planta 18, 08014, Barcelona, Spain
Tel.: (34) 93 367 1870
Web Site: https://www.cslbehring.es
Plasmas Retailer
N.A.I.C.S.: 424210

CSL Behring S.p.A. (2)
viale del Ghisallo n 20, 20151, Milan, Italy
Tel.: (39) 0234 9641
Web Site: https://www.cslbehring.it
Plasmas Mfr
N.A.I.C.S.: 325414

CSL Behring LLC (1)
1020 1st Ave, King of Prussia, PA 19406-0901
Tel.: (610) 878-4000
Web Site: https://www.cslbehring.com
Plasma-Derived & Recombinant Products Mfr
N.A.I.C.S.: 325414
Paul McKenzie (CEO)

Subsidiary (Non-US):

CSL Behring K.K. (2)
1-2-3 Kita Aoyama okyo Aoyama Building 8th floor, Minato-ku, Tokyo, 135-0062, Japan
Tel.: (81) 34 213 0180
Web Site: https://www.cslbehring.co.jp
Pharmaceutical Products Distr
N.A.I.C.S.: 424210

CSL Behring S.A. (2)
Crystal Tower 7/11 Quai Andre Citroen, 75015, Paris, France
Tel.: (33) 153585400
Sales Range: $25-49.9 Million
Emp.: 30
Plasmas Mfr & Sales
N.A.I.C.S.: 325414

CSL Biotherapies GmbH. (2)
Emil-von-Behring-Strasse 76, 35041, Marburg, Germany
Tel.: (49) 8003601010
Web Site: https://www.cslseqirus.de
Pharmaceutical Products Mfr & Distr
N.A.I.C.S.: 325412

Subsidiary (Domestic):

CSL Plasma Inc. (2)
5201 Congress Ave Ste 220, Boca Raton, FL 33487
Tel.: (561) 981-3700
Web Site: http://www.cslplasma.com
Emp.: 100
Blood Plasma Collection Services
N.A.I.C.S.: 621991

Calimmune Inc. (2)
51551 E Broadway Ste 1020, Tucson, AZ 85711-3776
Tel.: (310) 806-6240
Investment Advice
N.A.I.C.S.: 523940
Alan Wills (Pres)

ZLB Bioplasma Inc. (2)
5201 Congress Ave Ste 220, Boca Raton, FL 33487   (100%)
Tel.: (561) 981-3700
Web Site: http://www.clsplasma.com
Plasma Collection Services
N.A.I.C.S.: 325414

CSL Behring UK Ltd. (1)
4 Milton Road, Haywards Heath, RH16 1AH, West Sussex, United Kingdom
Tel.: (44) 144 444 7400
Web Site: https://www.cslbehring.co.uk
Sales Range: $25-49.9 Million
Emp.: 30
Plasmas Mfr & Sales
N.A.I.C.S.: 325414
Emil von Behring (Founder)

CSL Biotherapies Ltd. (1)
45 Poplar Road, Parkville, 3052, VIC, Australia   (100%)
Tel.: (61) 393891911
Web Site: http://www.cslbiotherapies.com.au
Sales Range: $250-299.9 Million
Emp.: 1,000
Vaccines & Pharmaceutical Products Mfr & Marketer
N.A.I.C.S.: 325414
Paul Perreault (Mng Dir)

CSL Finance PLC (1)
4 Milton Road, Haywards Heath, RH16 1AH, West Sussex, United Kingdom
Tel.: (44) 1444635021
Web Site: https://www.cslfinance.co.uk
Financial Banking Services
N.A.I.C.S.: 921130

CSL Plasma GmbH (1)
Emil-von-Behring-Strasse 76, 35041, Marburg, Germany
Tel.: (49) 64213912

CSL Limited—(Continued)

Sales Range: $25-49.9 Million
Emp.: 40
Plasmas Mfr & Sales
N.A.I.C.S.: 325414

Seqirus (1)
50 Hampshire St 9th Fl, Cambridge, MA 02139
Tel.: (617) 245-4300
Web Site: https://www.seqirus.us
Vaccine Distr
N.A.I.C.S.: 424210

Seqirus Pty Ltd. (1)
63 Poplar Road, Parkville, 3052, VIC, Australia
Tel.: (61) 393892000
Web Site: http://www.seqirus.com.au
Cell Based Vaccine Mfr
N.A.I.C.S.: 325414

Seqirus UK Limited (1)
Point Level 3 29 Market Street, Maidenhead, SL6 8AA, United Kingdom
Tel.: (44) 1628641500
Web Site: http://www.seqirus.com
Cell Based Vaccine Mfr
N.A.I.C.S.: 325414
Chris Larkins (Sr VP-Global Ops)

Seqirus USA Inc. (1)
475 Green Oaks Pkwy, Holly Springs, NC 27540
Web Site: https://www.cslseqirus.us
Pharmaceuticals Product Mfr
N.A.I.C.S.: 325412

Vifor Pharma Ltd. (1)
Rechenstrasse 37, 9014, Saint Gallen, Switzerland
Tel.: (41) 58 851 80 00
Web Site: http://www.viforpharma.com
Rev.: $1,931,540,832
Assets: $5,902,093,899
Liabilities: $1,352,282,427
Net Worth: $4,549,811,472
Earnings: $519,350,742
Emp.: 2,429
Fiscal Year-end: 12/31/2020
Pharmaceutical Products Mfr & Marketer
N.A.I.C.S.: 325412
Jacques Theurillat (Chm)

Subsidiary (Domestic):

Alloga AG (2)
Buchmattstrasse 10, 3401, Burgdorf, Switzerland
Tel.: (41) 58 851 4545
Web Site: https://www.alloga.ch
Sales Range: $25-49.9 Million
Emp.: 200
Distribution & Logistics Services for the Pharmaceutical Industry
N.A.I.C.S.: 541614

Amavita Apotheken GaleniCare AG (2)
Untermattweg 8, 3027, Bern, Switzerland
Tel.: (41) 588528400
Web Site: https://www.amavita.ch
Emp.: 300
Pharmaceuticals Product Mfr
N.A.I.C.S.: 325412

Amavita Pharmacy (2)
Bundesplatz 10, 6300, Zug, Switzerland
Tel.: (41) 588782450
Web Site: https://www.amavita.ch
Pharmacy Operations
N.A.I.C.S.: 456110
Patricia Schelbert (Mng Dir)

Subsidiary (Non-US):

Aspreva International Limited (2)
1203-4464 Markham Street, Victoria, V8Z 7X8, BC, Canada
Tel.: (250) 744-2488
Web Site: http://www.viforpharma.com
Sales Range: $25-49.9 Million
Emp.: 27
Pharmaceuticals Product Mfr
N.A.I.C.S.: 325412

Subsidiary (Domestic):

Cophar Ltd. (2)
Vifor SA Route de Moncor 10, Villars-sur-

Glane, 1752, Fribourg, Switzerland
Tel.: (41) 588516111
Sales Range: $50-74.9 Million
Emp.: 200
Pharmaceuticals Product Mfr
N.A.I.C.S.: 325412
Frederic Zwahlen (Gen Mgr)

Corviglia-Apotheke AG (2)
Via Maistra 11, Saint Moritz, 7500, Switzerland
Tel.: (41) 81 833 41 34
Pharmaceuticals Product Mfr
N.A.I.C.S.: 325412

Dauf SA (2)
via Figino 6 Barbengo, Barbengo, 6917, Lugano, Switzerland
Tel.: (41) 91 985 6611
Web Site: https://www.dauf.ch
Pharmaceutical Management Software Development Services
N.A.I.C.S.: 541511

Documed Ltd. (2)
Elisabethenanlage 11, 4051, Basel, Switzerland
Tel.: (41) 58 851 21 11
Web Site: http://www.documed.ch
Pharmaceutical Management Software Development Services
N.A.I.C.S.: 541511

Etrea SA (2)
Rue du Bois-du-Lan 22, Postfach 88, 1217, Meyrin, Switzerland
Tel.: (41) 227831111
Pharmaceutical Products Distr
N.A.I.C.S.: 424210

Subsidiary (Non-US):

Fresenius Medical Care Nephrologica Deutschland GmbH (2)
Else-Kroner-Strasse 1, 61352, Bad Homburg, Germany
Tel.: (49) 89324918600
N.A.I.C.S.: 621492

Subsidiary (Domestic):

G-Pharma AG (2)
Industriestrasse 2, 4704, Niederbipp, Switzerland
Tel.: (41) 588517258
Pharmaceutical Products Distr
N.A.I.C.S.: 424210

Subsidiary (Non-US):

Galenica Finance Limited (2)
La Motte Chambres, Saint Helier, JE1 1PB, Jersey
Tel.: (44) 1534 78 97 15
Financial Investment Management Services
N.A.I.C.S.: 523999

Subsidiary (Domestic):

Galexis AG (2)
Industriestrasse 2, 4704, Niederbipp, Switzerland
Tel.: (41) 58 851 7111
Web Site: https://www.galexis.com
Sales Range: $75-99.9 Million
Emp.: 400
Distribution & Logistics Services for the Pharmaceutical Industry
N.A.I.C.S.: 541614
Christoph Metzler (Member-Exec Bd & Head-Market)

HCI Solutions Ltd. (2)
Untermattweg 8, 3000, Bern, Switzerland
Tel.: (41) 58 851 2600
Web Site: https://www.hcisolutions.ch
Pharmaceutical Management Software Development Services
N.A.I.C.S.: 541511

Medichemie Bioline AG (2)
Postfach 3650, 4002, Basel, Switzerland
Tel.: (41) 61 726 22 00
Pharmaceuticals Product Mfr
N.A.I.C.S.: 325412

Subsidiary (Non-US):

Potters Limited (2)
1 Botanic Court Martland Park, Wigan, WN5 0JZ, United Kingdom

Tel.: (44) 1202449752
Web Site: http://www.pottersherbals.co.uk
Herbal Medicine Mfr
N.A.I.C.S.: 325412

Renapharma-Vifor AB (2)
Riddargatan 16, 114 51, Stockholm, Sweden
Tel.: (46) 107001140
Web Site: https://www.renapharma.se
Sales Range: $25-49.9 Million
Emp.: 17
Pharmaceutical Products Distr
N.A.I.C.S.: 424210

Subsidiary (Domestic):

S-OM SA (2)
Rue du Bois-du-Lan 22, Meyrin, 1217, Geneva, Switzerland
Tel.: (41) 227831111
Sales Range: $50-74.9 Million
Emp.: 200
Pharmaceuticals Product Mfr
N.A.I.C.S.: 325412

St. Jakob-Apotheke AG (2)
Saint Jakob-Strasse 38, Saint Gallen, 9000, Switzerland
Tel.: (41) 712447130
Health Care Srvices
N.A.I.C.S.: 621999

Stern Apotheke AG (2)
Collegegasse 17, 2502, Biel, Switzerland
Tel.: (41) 588513235
Pharmaceuticals Product Mfr
N.A.I.C.S.: 325412

Triamun AG (2)
Worbstrasse 201, 3073, Gumligen, Switzerland
Tel.: (41) 31 950 05 00
Web Site: http://www.triamun.ch
Pharmaceutical Software Development Services
N.A.I.C.S.: 541511

Unione Farmaceutica Distribuzione SA (2)
Via Figino 6, Barbengo, 6917, Lugano, Switzerland
Tel.: (41) 91 985 6111
Web Site: https://www.ufd.swiss
Pharmaceutical Products Distr
N.A.I.C.S.: 424210
Daniele Graziano (Gen Mgr)

Vifor AG (2)
Route de Moncor 10, 1752, Villars-sur-Glane, Switzerland
Tel.: (41) 588516111
Web Site: http://www.viforpharma.ch
Sales Range: $125-149.9 Million
Emp.: 350
Pharmaceuticals Mfr
N.A.I.C.S.: 325412

Subsidiary (Domestic):

Vifor (International) Inc. (3)
Rechenstrasse 37, 9014, Saint Gallen, 9001, Switzerland
Tel.: (41) 588518484
Web Site: http://www.viforpharma.com
Sales Range: $50-74.9 Million
Emp.: 250
Pharmaceuticals Mfr
N.A.I.C.S.: 325412

Subsidiary (Non-US):

Vifor Pharma Aspreva International Ltd. (3)
1203-4464 Markham St, Victoria, V8Z 7X8, BC, Canada
Tel.: (250) 744-2488
Web Site: http://www.viforpharma.com
Sales Range: Less than $1 Million
Emp.: 133
Pharmaceuticals Mfr
N.A.I.C.S.: 325412

Subsidiary (US):

Vifor Pharma Aspreva Pharmaceuticals Inc. (3)
106 Allen Rd, Basking Ridge, NJ 07920
Tel.: (908) 212-1020
Web Site: http://www.viforpharma.com

Sales Range: $25-49.9 Million
Emp.: 2
Pharmaceutical Mfr & Sales
N.A.I.C.S.: 325412

Subsidiary (Non-US):

Vifor Pharma Aspreva Pharmaceuticals Limited (3)
The Old Stables Bagshot Park, Surrey, Bagshot, GU19 5PJ, United Kingdom
Tel.: (44) 1276853600
Web Site: http://www.viforpharma.co.uk
Sales Range: $25-49.9 Million
Emp.: 20
Pharmaceutical Mfr & Sales
N.A.I.C.S.: 325412

Subsidiary (Domestic):

Vifor Pharma Aspreva Pharmaceuticals SA (3)
Rue des Beaux-Arts 8, Case postale 1611, 2001, Neuchatel, Switzerland
Tel.: (41) 32 720 0550
Pharmaceutical Mfr & Sales
N.A.I.C.S.: 325412
Dario Eklund (Head-Intl Bus Ops)

Subsidiary (Non-US):

Vifor France SA (2)
100-101 Terrasse Boieldieu Tour Franklin La Defense 8, Paris, La Defense, 92042, Paris, Cedex, France (100%)
Tel.: (33) 141065890
Web Site: https://www.viforpharma.com
Sales Range: $25-49.9 Million
Emp.: 10
Pharmacies & Drug Stores
N.A.I.C.S.: 456110

Vifor Fresenius Kabi (Beijing) Pharmaceutical Consulting Co. Ltd. (2)
12F Unit 1203 GrandyVic Building 16 Taiyanggong Mid Street, Chaoyang District, Beijing, 100028, China
Tel.: (86) 1050865525
N.A.I.C.S.: 541690

Subsidiary (US):

Vifor Pharma (2)
200 Cardinal Way, Redwood City, CA 94063
Tel.: (650) 421-9500
Web Site: https://www.viforpharma.com
Sales Range: $10-24.9 Million
Emp.: 406
Pharmaceuticals Mfr
N.A.I.C.S.: 325412
Phung Osborn (VP)

Subsidiary (Non-US):

Vifor Pharma America Latina S.A. (2)
Los Crisantemos 265 Edificio Skyglass Piso 2 Oficina 306, 1669, Buenos Aires, Argentina
Tel.: (54) 2320477272
N.A.I.C.S.: 325412

Vifor Pharma Asia Pacific Pte. Limited (2)
20 McCallum Street 20-01 Tokio Marine Centre, Singapore, 069046, Singapore
Tel.: (65) 63275937
Web Site: https://www.viforpharma.com
Pharmaceuticals Product Mfr
N.A.I.C.S.: 325412

Vifor Pharma Belgie NV (2)
Uitbreidingstraat 84, 2600, Antwerp, Belgium
Tel.: (32) 32182070
Web Site: http://www.galenica.com
Pharmaceuticals Product Mfr
N.A.I.C.S.: 325412

Vifor Pharma Deutschland GmbH (2)
Baierbrunner Strasse 29, 81379, Munich, Germany
Tel.: (49) 8932 491 8600
Web Site: http://www.viforpharma.com
Pharmaceutical Products Distr
N.A.I.C.S.: 325412

Vifor Pharma Espana, S.L. (2)

Avinguda Diagonal 611 - 613 Planta 10, 08028, Barcelona, Spain
Tel.: (34) 902121111
N.A.I.C.S.: 325412

Vifor Pharma Italia S.r.l. **(2)**
Via Paolo di Dono 73, 00142, Rome, RM, Italy
Tel.: (39) 064 565 0120
Web Site: https://www.viforpharma.it
Pharmaceutical Product Mfr & Distr
N.A.I.C.S.: 325412

Subsidiary (Domestic):

Vifor Pharma Management Ltd. **(2)**
Flughofstrasse 61, 8152, Glattbrugg, Switzerland
Tel.: (41) 588518000
N.A.I.C.S.: 325412

Subsidiary (Non-US):

Vifor Pharma Nederland B.V. **(2)**
Westbroek 43, 4822, Breda, Netherlands
Tel.: (31) 888484300
Sales Range: $25-49.9 Million
Emp.: 19
Pharmaceutical Products Distr
N.A.I.C.S.: 424210

Vifor Pharma Nordiska AB **(2)**
Gustav III s Boulevard 46, 169 73, Solna, Sweden
Tel.: (46) 85 580 6600
Web Site: https://www.viforpharma.se
Pharmaceutical Product Mfr & Distr
N.A.I.C.S.: 325412

Vifor Pharma Osterreich GmbH **(2)**
Linzer Strasse 221, 1140, Vienna, Austria
Tel.: (43) 14164777
N.A.I.C.S.: 325412

Vifor Pharma Pty Ltd. **(2)**
Level 9 140 William Street, Southbank, Melbourne, 3000, VIC, Australia
Tel.: (61) 39 686 0111
Web Site: https://www.viforpharma.com
Emp.: 5
Pharmaceuticals Product Mfr
N.A.I.C.S.: 325412

Vifor Pharma Romania S.R.L. **(2)**
Cladirea A The Office Bd 21 Decembrie 1989 nr 77 camera 6 5, 400604, Cluj-Napoca, Romania
Tel.: (40) 264449556
Web Site: https://www.viforpharma.com
Sales Range: $25-49.9 Million
Emp.: 14
Pharmaceuticals Product Mfr
N.A.I.C.S.: 325412

Vifor Pharma UK Limited **(2)**
2nd Floor Waterfront Lotus Park The Causeway, Watermans Business Park Kingsbury Crescent, Staines-upon-Thames, TW18 3AG, Surrey, United Kingdom
Tel.: (44) 1276853600
Emp.: 40
Pharmaceutical Products Mfr & Distr
N.A.I.C.S.: 325412

Subsidiary (Domestic):

Winconcept AG **(2)**
Untermattweg 8, 3027, Bern, Switzerland
Tel.: (41) 588528200
Pharmaceutical Products Distr
N.A.I.C.S.: 424210

e-mediat AG **(2)**
Untermatt Weg 8, CH-3027, Bern, Switzerland
Tel.: (41) 588512600
Web Site: http://www.e-mediat.ch
Sales Range: $50-74.9 Million
Emp.: 70
Health Care Information Services
N.A.I.C.S.: 519290
Ulrich Schaefer *(CEO)*

bioCSL (NZ) Ltd **(1)**
Level 2 347-351 Parnell Road, Parnell, Auckland, 1052, New Zealand
Tel.: (64) 93771520
Web Site: https://www.cslseqirus.co.nz
Sales Range: $25-49.9 Million
Emp.: 19
Pharmaceutical Products Distr

N.A.I.C.S.: 424210
Mary Sontrop *(Dir-CSL)*

CSP CHINA STEEL PLC
Thames House Portsmouth Road, Esher, KT10 9AD, Surrey, United Kingdom
Tel.: (44) 20 341 10465
Web Site: http://www.cspchinasteel.com
Steel
N.A.I.C.S.: 331110
Hugo Benz *(Dir)*

CSP INTERNATIONAL FASHION GROUP S.P.A.
Via Piubega 5/C, Ceresara Mantova, 46040, Mantua, Italy
Tel.: (39) 03768101 IT
Web Site: https://www.iubenda.com
CSP—(ITA)
Sales Range: $150-199.9 Million
Emp.: 635
Mfr & Distr of Various Hosiery & Underwear Products
N.A.I.C.S.: 315120
Francesco Bertoni *(Pres & CEO)*

Subsidiaries:

Le Bourget S.A. **(1)**
68 Rue Henri Matisse, Fresnoy-le-Grand, Le Bourget, 02230, France
Tel.: (33) 3 23 09 33 00
Web Site: http://www.lebourget.com
Sales Range: $25-49.9 Million
Emp.: 150
Sheer Hosiery Mills
N.A.I.C.S.: 315120

Sanpellegrino Polska Sp. z o.o. **(1)**
Ul Lodzka 27, Konstantynow Lodzki, 95-050, Pabianice, Poland
Tel.: (48) 422111334
Sheer Hosiery Mills
N.A.I.C.S.: 315120

CSP STEEL CENTER PUBLIC COMPANY LIMITED
No 475 Outer Alley Rama III Road, Bang Kho Laem, Bangkok, 10120, Thailand
Tel.: (66) 2291631421
Web Site: https://www.cspsteel.com
Year Founded: 1987
CSP—(THA)
Rev.: $69,477,081
Assets: $58,784,985
Liabilities: $38,993,232
Net Worth: $19,791,752
Earnings: ($2,652,091)
Emp.: 364
Fiscal Year-end: 12/31/23
Rolled Steel Mfr
N.A.I.C.S.: 331221
Supachai Chaisupat *(Chm, Pres & CEO)*

CSPC PHARMACEUTICAL GROUP LIMITED
Suite 3206 32/F Central Plaza 18 Harbour Road, Wanchai, China (Hong Kong)
Tel.: (852) 28023011
Web Site: https://www.cspc.com.hk
1093—(OTCIQ)
Rev.: $4,283,465,884
Assets: $5,783,364,809
Liabilities: $1,402,289,959
Net Worth: $4,381,074,850
Earnings: $862,877,991
Emp.: 24,837
Fiscal Year-end: 12/31/22
Pharmaceuticals Mfr
N.A.I.C.S.: 325412
Carmelo Ka Sze Lee *(Sec)*

Subsidiaries:

Bioworkops Limited **(1)**

No 5 Dongwang Road, Suzhou Industrial Park, Suzhou, China
Tel.: (86) 51267999700
Web Site: https://www.bioworkops.com
Pharmaceuticals Product Mfr
N.A.I.C.S.: 325412

CSPC Dermay Europe GMBH **(1)**
Bremer Strasse 27-29, 21073, Hamburg, Germany
Tel.: (49) 403 251 8744
Web Site: https://cspceu.com
Premier Ingredient Distr
N.A.I.C.S.: 424690

CSPC Dophen Corporation **(1)**
4070 Truxel Rd, Sacramento, CA 95834
Tel.: (916) 928-3010
Web Site: https://www.dophen.com
Pharmaceutical Research & Development Services
N.A.I.C.S.: 541714

CSPC Healthcare Inc. **(1)**
1221 W State St, Ontario, CA 91762
Tel.: (909) 395-5272
Web Site: https://cspcusa.com
Health Care Srvices
N.A.I.C.S.: 622110
Gary Gao *(Pres)*

CSPC Hebei Zhongnuo Pharmaceutical (Shijiazhuang) Co., Ltd.
No 188 Gongnong Road, Shijiazhuang, 050051, Hebei, China
Tel.: (86) 31183805386
Web Site: http://www.cspczhongnuo.com
Emp.: 4,500
Pharmaceuticals Product Mfr
N.A.I.C.S.: 325412
Han Xiaoyan *(Mgr-Market)*

CSPC Weisheng Pharmaceutical (Shijiazhuang) Co., Ltd **(1)**
No 236 Huanghe Street, Shijiazhuang, 050035, Hebei, China
Tel.: (86) 31185388577
Web Site: https://www.e-wspc.com
Pharmaceuticals Product Mfr
N.A.I.C.S.: 325412

Megalith Pharmaceuticals Inc. **(1)**
302 Carnegie Ctr Ste 100, Princeton, NJ 08540
Tel.: (609) 356-0210
Web Site: https://www.megalithpharma.com
Pharmaceuticals Product Mfr
N.A.I.C.S.: 325412

CSR LIMITED
Triniti 3 39 Delhi Road, North Ryde, 2113, NSW, Australia
Tel.: (61) 292358000 AU
Web Site: https://www.csr.com.au
Year Founded: 1855
CSR—(ASX)
Rev.: $1,771,124,804
Assets: $1,874,866,930
Liabilities: $1,147,446,144
Net Worth: $727,420,786
Earnings: $213,537,153
Emp.: 2,573
Fiscal Year-end: 03/31/22
Concrete Pipe Manufacturing
N.A.I.C.S.: 327332
Andrew Rottinger *(Exec Gen Mgr-Construction Sys-Building Products)*

Subsidiaries:

Burnbridge Glass Pty Limited **(1)**
1 A Pennant Street, Cardiff, 2285, New South Wales, Australia
Tel.: (61) 4956 9811
Web Site: http://www.burnbridgeglass.com.au
Sales Range: $25-49.9 Million
Emp.: 25
Glass Mfr
N.A.I.C.S.: 327211

CSR Building Products (NZ) Ltd. **(1)**
14 The Furlong, Takanini, Auckland, 2112, New Zealand
Tel.: (64) 92972800
Web Site: http://www.csr.co.nz
Building Product Mfr & Distr

N.A.I.C.S.: 332311

CSR Fricker Ceiling Systems **(1)**
20 Loftus Street, Sydney, 2000, NSW, Australia
Tel.: (61) 2 9247 5333
Ceiling Tile Mfr
N.A.I.C.S.: 337215

Unit (Domestic):

CSR Fricker Ceiling Systems QLD **(2)**
Unit 2 151 Robinson Road, Banyo Geebung, Brisbane, 4034, QLD, Australia
Tel.: (61) 736218888
Web Site: http://www.comprador.com.au
Emp.: 10
Commercial Interior Products Mfr
N.A.I.C.S.: 337215

Subsidiary (Non-US):

Potter Interior Systems Ltd. **(2)**
393 Church Street, Penrose, 1061, New Zealand
Web Site: http://www.potters.co.nz
Sales Range: $25-49.9 Million
Emp.: 45
Interior Partition & Ceiling Tile Mfr
N.A.I.C.S.: 337215
Craig Hawkins *(Gen Mgr)*

CSR Martini Pty Limited **(1)**
4 MacDonald Rd, Ingleburn, 2565, NSW, Australia
Tel.: (61) 1300767776
Web Site: https://www.csrmartini.com.au
Acoustic Product Mfr
N.A.I.C.S.: 332323

PGH Bricks & Pavers Pty Limited **(1)**
75 Townson Road, Schofields, 2762, NSW, Australia
Tel.: (61) 298526807
Web Site: http://www.pghbricks.com.au
Clay Brick Mfr
N.A.I.C.S.: 327120

CSS HOLDINGS, LTD.
10-1 Kodenma-cho Nihonbashi, Chuo-Ku, Tokyo, 103-0001, Japan
Tel.: (81) 366617840
Web Site: https://www.css-holdings.jp
Year Founded: 1984
2304—(TKS)
Rev.: $105,158,880
Assets: $40,413,000
Liabilities: $23,779,860
Net Worth: $16,633,140
Earnings: $1,630,700
Emp.: 5,768
Fiscal Year-end: 09/30/23
Holding Company
N.A.I.C.S.: 551111
Midori Noguchi *(Chm)*

Subsidiaries:

Yamato Foods Co., Ltd. **(1)**
Kumagaya Transport Building 5F, 3-193 Tsukuba, Kumagaya, Saitama, Japan
Tel.: (81) 485262521
Web Site: https://www.ymtfds.co.jp
Emp.: 1,313
Food Franchisee; Manages Franchised Stores & Restaurants
N.A.I.C.S.: 722513

CSSC OFFSHORE & MARINE ENGINEERING COMPANY LTD.
15/F Marine Tower No 137 Gexin Road, Guangzhou, 510250, Guangdong, China
Tel.: (86) 2081891712
Web Site: https://comec.cssc.net.cn
Year Founded: 1954
600685—(SHG)
Rev.: $1,778,532,268
Assets: $5,965,617,021
Liabilities: $3,276,606,519
Net Worth: $2,689,010,502
Earnings: $555,666,654
Emp.: 7,618

CSSC Offshore & Marine Engineering Company Ltd.—(Continued)

Fiscal Year-end: 12/31/20
Ship Building & Shipping Services
N.A.I.C.S.: 336611
Guangde Han (Chm)

Subsidiaries:

Guangzhou Hongfan Technology Co.,
Ltd. (1)
Room 311-314 Tianyi Daxia 115 Shuiyin
Road Shahe Street, Tianhe District,
Guangzhou, China
Tel.: (86) 2061246666608
Web Site: http://www.hongfan.cn
System Integration Services
N.A.I.C.S.: 541512

Guangzhou United Steel Structures
Limited (1)
No 138 Gexin Road, Haizhu District,
Guangzhou, China
Tel.: (86) 208 159 2405
Web Site: https://www.ussl.com
Steel Products Mfr
N.A.I.C.S.: 331210

Guangzhou Wenchong Shipyard Co.,
Ltd. (1)
No 1 Wenchuan Road Hongshan Street,
Huang Pu, Guangzhou, 510727, China
Tel.: (86) 2082389933
Web Site: https://www.gws.cssc.net.cn
Building Container Vessel Mfr
N.A.I.C.S.: 336611

CST CANADA COAL LIMITED
Suite 500 800 5th AVE sw, Calgary,
T2P 3T6, AB, Canada
Tel.: (403) 767-6534
Web Site: http://www.cstcoal.ca
Coal Mining
N.A.I.C.S.: 213113
Arpad Koltai (Pres & CEO)

Subsidiaries:

Grande Cache Coal Corporation (1)
800 5th Avenue Southwest Suite 1610, Cal-
gary, T2P 3T6, AB, Canada
Tel.: (403) 543-7070
Web Site: http://www.gccoal.com
Coal Mining
N.A.I.C.S.: 212115

CST GROUP LIMITED
Rooms 4503-05 45F China Re-
sources Building, 26 Harbour Road,
Wanchai, China (Hong Kong)
Tel.: (852) 28569300 Ky
Web Site: http://www.cstgrouphk.com
Year Founded: 1993
0985—(HKG)
Rev.: $227,130,000
Assets: $688,696,000
Liabilities: $558,916,000
Net Worth: $129,780,000
Earnings: ($174,132,000)
Fiscal Year-end: 03/31/23
Holding Company
N.A.I.C.S.: 551112
Tao Chiu (Chm & Exec Dir)

Subsidiaries:

CST Minerals Lady Annie Pty
Limited (1)
Mcnamara Road, Mount Isa, 4825, QLD,
Australia
Tel.: (61) 7 4748 0000
Sales Range: $100-124.9 Million
Emp.: 20
Copper Mining Services
N.A.I.C.S.: 212230
Tracey Pile (Mgr-Tenement)

CSTONE PHARMACEUTICALS
C1 Building No 218 Xinghu Street,
Suzhou Industrial Park, Suzhou,
215123, China
Tel.: (86) 51287186550

Web Site:
http://www.cstonepharma.com
Year Founded: 2015
2616—(HKG)
Rev.: $67,583,365
Assets: $230,035,151
Liabilities: $166,949,780
Net Worth: $63,085,370
Earnings: ($126,735,991)
Emp.: 476
Fiscal Year-end: 12/31/22
Pharmaceuticals Product Mfr
N.A.I.C.S.: 325412

CSU CARDSYSTEM S.A.
R Piaui 136 - Bloco A/b, 06440-182,
Barueri, SP, Brazil
Tel.: (55) (11) 2627 8500
Web Site: http://www.csu.com.br
Year Founded: 1992
CARD3—(BRAZ)
Sales Range: $100-124.9 Million
Payment Processing Services
N.A.I.C.S.: 522320
Antonio Kandir (Chm)

CSUN MFG. LTD.
No 2-1 Gongba Road Gonger Indus-
trial Zone, Linkou Dist, Taipei, 24450,
Taiwan
Tel.: (886) 226017706
Web Site: https://www.csun.com.tw
2467—(TAI)
Rev.: $118,571,597
Assets: $261,755,705
Liabilities: $150,091,528
Net Worth: $111,664,177
Earnings: $17,336,112
Fiscal Year-end: 12/31/23
Printed Circuit Board Mfr
N.A.I.C.S.: 334412

Subsidiaries:

Csun Technology (Guangzhou) Co.,
Ltd. (1)
No 6 Lihe Road, Shiling Town Huadu Dis-
trict, Guangzhou, 510850, China
Tel.: (86) 2086846341
Printed Circuit Board Mfr & Distr
N.A.I.C.S.: 334418

CT AUTOMOTIVE GROUP PLC
1000 Lakeside North Harbour West-
ern Road, Portsmouth, PO6 3EN,
Hampshire, United Kingdom
Tel.: (44) 2392819059 UK
Web Site: https://www.ct-
automotive.net
Year Founded: 2000
CTA—(LSE)
Rev.: $142,974,000
Assets: $84,404,000
Liabilities: $67,437,000
Net Worth: $16,967,000
Earnings: $6,553,000
Emp.: 2,200
Fiscal Year-end: 12/31/23
Motor Vehicle Gasoline Engine & En-
gine Parts Manufacturing
N.A.I.C.S.: 336310

Subsidiaries:

CT Automotive Japan KK (1)
WCT-C1702 4-6-8 Konan, Minato-Justin,
Tokyo, 108-0075, Japan
Tel.: (81) 334713798
Automotive Industry Interior Component
Services
N.A.I.C.S.: 541410

CT DEVELOPERS LTD.
1 1764 Rathburn Road East, Missis-
sauga, L4W 2NB, ON, Canada
Tel.: (416) 884-8601 ON
Year Founded: 2011
DEV.H—(TSXV)

Assets: $1,811
Liabilities: $29,402
Net Worth: ($27,591)
Earnings: ($57,141)
Fiscal Year-end: 06/30/19
Investment Services
N.A.I.C.S.: 523999
Jason Jessup (CEO)

**CT ENVIRONMENTAL GROUP
LIMITED**
Room 807 8/F Empire Centre 68
Mody Road Tsim Sha Tsui, Kowloon,
China (Hong Kong)
Tel.: (852) 25279777
Web Site: http://www.chongto.com
Wastewater & Industrial Water Supply
Services
N.A.I.C.S.: 221310
Xiao'an Lu (Exec Dir)

**CT GLOBAL MANAGED PORT-
FOLIO TRUST PLC**
6th Floor Quartermile 4 7a Nightin-
gale Way, Edinburgh, EH3 9EG,
United Kingdom
Tel.: (44) 800136420
Web Site:
https://www.columbianeedle.co.uk
Year Founded: 2008
CMPG—(LSE)
Rev.: $6,522,343
Assets: $202,009,594
Liabilities: $9,508,962
Net Worth: $192,500,631
Earnings: $18,189,851
Fiscal Year-end: 05/31/24
Investment Management Service
N.A.I.C.S.: 523940
Peter Hewitt (Dir & Portfolio Mgr)

CT INGENIEROS AAISL
Business Park La Carpetania Av.
Leonardo da Vinci 22, 28906, Getafe,
Madrid, Spain
Tel.: (34) 916832030
Web Site: http://www.ctingenieros.es
Technological Engineering Company
& Mfr
N.A.I.C.S.: 541330
Vicente Egea (Mng Dir)

Subsidiaries:

Bertin Pharma SAS (1)
Parc d'activites du Pas du Lac 10 Bis Av-
enue Ampere, 78180, Montigny-le-
Bretonneux, France
Tel.: (33) 1 39 306 220
Web Site: http://www.bertinpharma.com
Pharmaceutical Research & Development
Services
N.A.I.C.S.: 541715
Philippe Demigne (Pres)

**CT PRIVATE EQUITY TRUST
PLC**
Quartermile 4 7a Nightingale Way,
Edinburgh, EH3 9EG, United King-
dom
Tel.: (44) 1315738300
Web Site: http://www.bmogam.com
Year Founded: 2001
CTPE—(LSE)
Rev.: $100,963,141
Assets: $711,191,618
Liabilities: $57,726,584
Net Worth: $653,465,034
Earnings: $83,716,233
Fiscal Year-end: 12/31/22
Investment Management Service
N.A.I.C.S.: 523940
Richard Gray (Chm)

**CT REAL ESTATE INVEST-
MENT TRUST**
2180 Yonge Street, Toronto, M4P
2V8, ON, Canada

Tel.: (416) 480-2029 ON
Web Site: https://www.ctreit.com
Year Founded: 2013
CRT.UN—(TSX)
Rev.: $374,212,308
Assets: $4,610,197,563
Liabilities: $2,058,807,053
Net Worth: $2,551,390,510
Earnings: $235,076,371
Emp.: 37
Fiscal Year-end: 12/31/19
Real Estate Investment Services
N.A.I.C.S.: 523999
Kenneth Silver (Pres & CEO)

**CT UK CAPITAL AND INCOME
INVESTMENT TRUST PLC**
Cannon Place 78 Cannon Street,
London, EC4N 6AG, United Kingdom
Tel.: (44) 1315738300 UK
Web Site: http://www.bmogam.com
Year Founded: 1992
BCI—(LSE)
Rev.: $20,422,873
Assets: $430,854,582
Liabilities: $33,547,084
Net Worth: $397,307,498
Earnings: $48,375,410
Fiscal Year-end: 09/30/23
Investment Trust Management Ser-
vices
N.A.I.C.S.: 523940

**CT UK HIGH INCOME TRUST
PLC**
Web Site:
http://www.bmoukhighincome.com
CHIB—(LSE)
Rev.: $1,017,702
Assets: $153,350,316
Liabilities: $24,064,929
Net Worth: $129,285,387
Earnings: ($719,838)
Fiscal Year-end: 03/31/23
Investment Management Service
N.A.I.C.S.: 525990
Andrew Watkins (Chm)

CT VISION INVESTMENT LTD
Room 09 27 F Ho King Commercial
Center 2 16 Fa Yuen Street, Kow-
loon, Mongkok, China (Hong Kong)
Tel.: (852) 53153737
Web Site:
http://www.ctvisionholdings.com
Investment Services
N.A.I.C.S.: 523999
Lam Cheng-Chiang (Chm)

Subsidiaries:

CT Vision (International) Holdings
Limited (1)
Room Nos 808-814 8th Floor Sun Hung Kai
Centre 30 Harbour Road, Wanchai, China
(Hong Kong) (51.9%)
Tel.: (852) 2 3793 385
Web Site: http://www.ctvision994.com
Rev.: $31,701,861
Assets: $66,483,250
Liabilities: $36,405,904
Net Worth: $30,077,346
Earnings: ($13,886,001)
Emp.: 130
Fiscal Year-end: 12/31/2019
Construction Management Services
N.A.I.C.S.: 236220
Kai Lun Lee (Exec Dir)

CT&T CO., LTD.
113-5 Banpo 4-dong, Seocho-gu,
Seoul, Korea (South)
Tel.: (82) 15992227
Web Site: http://www.ctco.lv
Year Founded: 2002
Electric Vehicles Mfr & Sales
N.A.I.C.S.: 336211
Young Gi Lee (CEO)

CTA HOLDING
ZA du Caillou 3 rue Jules Verne,
69630, Chaponost, France
Tel.: (33) 478567070
Web Site: http://www.cta.fr
Year Founded: 1987
Sales Range: $1-9.9 Million
Air Compressor Mfr
N.A.I.C.S.: 333912

CTAC N.V.
Meerendonkweg 11, 5216 TZ, 's-
Hertogenbosch, Netherlands
Tel.: (31) 736920692
Web Site: http://www.ctac.nl
CTAC—(EUR)
Rev.: $126,993,309
Assets: $81,564,861
Liabilities: $48,182,603
Net Worth: $33,382,258
Earnings: $5,102,525
Emp.: 385
Fiscal Year-end: 12/31/22
IT Consulting Services
N.A.I.C.S.: 541690

Subsidiaries:

Ctac Belgie N.V.   (1)
Uilenbaan 82, 2160, Wommelgem, Belgium
Tel.: (32) 33540979
Web Site: https://www.ctac.be
Information Technology Services
N.A.I.C.S.: 541512

Ctac Belgium BVBA   (1)
Uilenbaan 82, 2160, Wommelgem, Belgium
Tel.: (32) 3 354 09 79
Web Site: http://www.ctac.be
Emp.: 60
Information Technology Consulting Services
N.A.I.C.S.: 541512

Ctac Deutschland GmbH   (1)
Kaiserswerther Str 115, 40880, Ratingen,
Germany
Tel.: (49) 2102 420 675
Information Technology Consulting Services
N.A.I.C.S.: 541512

Ctac France SAS   (1)
54-56 Avenue Hoche, 75008, Paris, France
Tel.: (33) 1 56 60 53 89
Web Site: http://www.ctacfrance.fr
Information Technology Consulting Services
N.A.I.C.S.: 541512
Jean-Claude Gandon *(Mng Dir)*

Persity Resourcing B.V.   (1)
Minister Hartsenlaan 10, Hilversum, 1217
LS, Netherlands
Tel.: (31) 35 8200988
Web Site: http://www.persity.nl
Human Resource Consulting Services
N.A.I.C.S.: 541612
Tesca Dijkstra *(Office Mgr)*

Purple Square Management Partners
BV   (1)
Schoolstraat 11, 5301 NV, Zaltbommel,
Netherlands
Tel.: (31) 85 782 0440
Web Site: https://purplesqr.com
Portfolio Management Services
N.A.I.C.S.: 523940

CTBC FINANCIAL HOLDING CO., LTD.
27 29F No 168 Jingmao 2nd Rd,
Nangang Dist, Taipei, 115, Taiwan
Tel.: (886) 233277777   TW
Web Site: https://ir.ctbcholding.com
Year Founded: 2002
2891—(TAI)
Rev.: $6,890,750,711
Assets: $259,642,148,360
Liabilities: $245,092,376,638
Net Worth: $14,549,771,722
Earnings: $1,800,148,391
Emp.: 27,000
Fiscal Year-end: 12/31/23
Holding Company
N.A.I.C.S.: 551112

Winston Hsia *(Chief Investment Officer)*

Subsidiaries:

CTBC Asia Limited   (1)
Room 2809 Phase 2 International Finance
Centre 8 Finance Street, Central, 518000,
China (Hong Kong)
Tel.: (852) 29161772
Web Site: https://www.ctbcasia.com.hk
N.A.I.C.S.: 523999

CTBC Asset Management Co.,
Ltd.   (1)
19F No 168 Jingmao 2nd Rd, Nangang
Dist, Taipei, Taiwan
Tel.: (886) 281705377
Investment Banking Business Services
N.A.I.C.S.: 523150

CTBC Bank (Philippines) Corp.   (1)
16th to 19th Floors Fort Legend Towers
31st Street corner 3rd Avenue, Bonifacio
Global City, Taguig, 1634, Philippines
Tel.: (63) 27 717 5287
Web Site: https://www.ctbcbank.com.ph
Investment Banking Business Services
N.A.I.C.S.: 523150
Wen-Hung Lee *(Chm)*

CTBC Bank Co., Ltd.   (1)
No 166 168 170 186 188 Jingmao 2nd Rd,
Nangang Dist, Taipei, Taiwan
Tel.: (886) 233277777
Web Site: http://www.chinatrust.com.tw
Sales Range: $300-349.9 Million
Emp.: 416
National Commercial Banks & Bank Holding
Companies
N.A.I.C.S.: 551111

Subsidiary (US):

CTBC Bank Corp. (USA)   (2)
801 S Figueroa St Ste 2300, Los Angeles,
CA 90017
Tel.: (310) 791-2828
Web Site: http://www.ctbcbankusa.com
Rev.: $85,327,000
Emp.: 100
Banking Services
N.A.I.C.S.: 522110
Peter Yam *(Exec VP)*

Subsidiary (Non-US):

Chinatrust (Philippines) Commercial
Bank Corporation   (2)
16th to 19th Floors Fort Legend Towers
31st Street corner 3rd Avenue, Bonifacio
Global City, 1634, Taguig,
Philippines   (99.41%)
Tel.: (63) 29889287
Web Site: http://www.chinatrust.com.ph
Sales Range: $25-49.9 Million
Emp.: 575
Commercial Banking Services
N.A.I.C.S.: 522110

The Tokyo Star Bank, Limited   (2)
2-3-5 Akasaka, Minato-ku, Tokyo, 107-8480,
Japan   (98.2%)
Tel.: (81) 335863111
Web Site: http://www.tokyostarbank.co.jp
Rev.: $308,695,440
Assets: $21,856,388,400
Liabilities: $20,601,005,040
Net Worth: $1,255,383,360
Earnings: $110,849,040
Emp.: 1,708
Fiscal Year-end: 03/31/2018
Retail Banking & Corporate Finance Services
N.A.I.C.S.: 522110
Hiroyuki Shimizu *(Exec Officer-Compliance & Legal)*

CTBC Bank Corp.   (1)
2799 Granville Street, Vancouver, V6H 3J1,
BC, Canada
Tel.: (604) 683-3882
Web Site: https://www.ctbcbank.ca
Investment Banking Business Services
N.A.I.C.S.: 523150

CTBC Investments Co., Ltd.   (1)
12F No 188 Jingmao 2nd Rd, Nangang
Dist, Taipei, Taiwan
Tel.: (886) 226526688

Investment Banking Business Services
N.A.I.C.S.: 523150
Min Fang *(Mgr-Fund)*

CTBC Life Insurance Co,, Ltd.   (1)
No 42 Sec 2 Zhongshan N Rd, Taipei, Taiwan
Tel.: (886) 2 25116411
Web Site: http://www.twlife.com.tw
Fire Insurance Services
N.A.I.C.S.: 524298
Shu-Po Hsu *(Chm & Gen Mgr)*

CTBC Security Co., Ltd.   (1)
5F No 188 Jingmao 2nd Rd, Nangang Dist,
Taipei, Taiwan
Tel.: (886) 226530355
Emp.: 400
Investment Banking Business Services
N.A.I.C.S.: 523150

CTBC Venture Capital Co., Ltd.   (1)
21F No 168 Jingmao 2nd Rd, Nangang
Dist, Taipei, 115, Taiwan
Tel.: (886) 226522277
Investment Banking Business Services
N.A.I.C.S.: 523150

Chinatrust Insurance Brokers Co.,
Ltd.   (1)
13F No 16 Young Ji Road, 11070, Taipei,
Taiwan
Tel.: (886) 227680505
Web Site: http://www.chinatrust.com.tw
Insurance & Brokerage Services
N.A.I.C.S.: 524210

Chinatrust Life Insurance Co.,
Ltd.   (1)
8th Floor 1 Sec 5 Nanjing South Rd, Taipei,
105, Taiwan
Tel.: (886) 227607988
Sales Range: $50-74.9 Million
Emp.: 50
Personal & Group Life & Health Insurance,
Personal Annuities & Personal & Group Accident Services
N.A.I.C.S.: 524298

Chinatrust Securities Co., Inc.   (1)
3rd Floor No 168 Jingmao 2nd Road, Taipei, Taiwan
Tel.: (886) 800024365
Web Site: http://www.win168.com.tw
Sales Range: $50-74.9 Million
Securities Brokerage Services
N.A.I.C.S.: 523150

Chinatrust Securities Co., Ltd.   (1)
3F No 168 Jingmao 2nd Rd, Nangang, Taipei, Taiwan
Tel.: (886) 266392345
Web Site: http://www.ctbcsec.com
Securities Brokerage Services
N.A.I.C.S.: 523150

PT Bank CTBC Indonesia   (1)
Tamara Center 15th - 17th Floor Jl Jend
Sudirman Kav 24, Jakarta, 12920, Indonesia
Tel.: (62) 2125578787
Web Site: http://www.ctbcbank.co.id
Investment Banking Business Services
N.A.I.C.S.: 523150
Iwan Satawidinata *(Pres)*

Taiwan Life Insurance Co., Ltd.   (1)
8F No 188 Jingmao 2nd Rd, Nangang Dist,
Taipei, Taiwan
Tel.: (886) 281709888
Investment Banking Business Services
N.A.I.C.S.: 523150
Jasmine Ku *(Head-Fin Dept)*

Subsidiary (Domestic):

TLG Insurance Co., Ltd.   (2)
18F 1 No 17 Xuchang St, Zhongzheng Dist,
Taipei, 100, Taiwan
Tel.: (886) 223700789
Web Site: http://www.tlg-insurance.com
Insurance Services
N.A.I.C.S.: 524210
Gary Chen *(Chief Compliance Officer)*

Taiwan Lottery Co., Ltd.   (1)
15th Floor No 188 Economic and Trade 2nd
Road, Nangang District, Taipei, 11568, Taiwan
Tel.: (886) 809077168
Web Site: https://www.taiwanlottery.com.tw

Sales Range: $75-99.9 Million
Emp.: 180
Lottery Operating Services
N.A.I.C.S.: 713290

Taiwan Lottery Corporation   (1)
15F No 188 Jingmao 2nd Rd, Nangang
Dist, Taipei, Taiwan
Tel.: (886) 281705228
Investment Banking Business Services
N.A.I.C.S.: 523150

Tokyo Star Business Finance,
Ltd.   (1)
10th Floor Shinjuku Daiichi Life Building
2-7-1 Nishi-Shinjuku, Shinjuku-ku, Tokyo,
163-0710, Japan
Tel.: (81) 353395321
Web Site: https://www.tokyostar-bf.co.jp
N.A.I.C.S.: 522110
Osamu Kanamori *(Pres)*

CTC BIO., INC.
27 Dongtancheomdansaneop 1-ro,
Songpa-gu, Hwaseong, 138-858,
Gyeonggi-do, Korea (South)
Tel.: (82) 7040330200
Web Site: http://www.ctcbio.com
Year Founded: 1995
060590—(KRS)
Rev.: $126,712,629
Assets: $144,118,937
Liabilities: $70,515,287
Net Worth: $73,603,650
Earnings: $5,178,724
Emp.: 255
Fiscal Year-end: 12/31/22
Pharmaceuticals Product Mfr
N.A.I.C.S.: 325412
Min-Goo Lee *(CEO)*

Subsidiaries:

CTC International, Inc   (1)
363 Cliffwood Park Street Ste D, Brea, CA
92821
Tel.: (714) 782-7690
Web Site: http://www.ctc-intl.com
Emp.: 43
Pharmaceutical Product Mfr & Distr
N.A.I.C.S.: 325412
Joshua Lee *(Mgr-Bus Dev)*

CTC MEDIA, INC.
31A Leningradsky Prospekt, 125284,
Moscow, Russia
Tel.: (7) 4957974100   RU
Web Site: http://www.ctcmedia.ru
Year Founded: 1996
Emp.: 1,085
Commercial Television Broadcasting
Services
N.A.I.C.S.: 516210
Jean-Pierre Morel *(CEO, CFO & Sec)*

CTCI ADVANCED SYSTEMS INC.
11F 16 Fushan Rd, Beitou Dist, Taipei, 112037, Taiwan
Tel.: (886) 227853839
Web Site: https://www.asi.ctci.com
Year Founded: 1987
5209—(TPE)
Rev.: $122,766,532
Assets: $109,203,452
Liabilities: $87,381,609
Net Worth: $21,821,843
Earnings: $7,607,760
Emp.: 189
Fiscal Year-end: 12/31/22
Engineeering Services
N.A.I.C.S.: 541330
Han-Chung Chen *(Pres)*

CTCI CORPORATION
89 Sec 6 Zhongshan N Rd, Taipei,
111046, Taiwan
Tel.: (886) 228339999   TW
Web Site: https://www.ctci.com
Year Founded: 1979

CTCI Corporation—(Continued)

9933—(TAI)
Rev.: $3,385,565,162
Assets: $3,618,142,085
Liabilities: $2,873,223,607
Net Worth: $744,918,478
Earnings: $93,375,385
Emp.: 2,512
Fiscal Year-end: 12/31/23
Engineering & Construction Services
N.A.I.C.S.: 237990
John T. Yu *(Chm)*

Subsidiaries:

Advanced Control & Systems Inc. (1)
5F No 52 Sec 3 Nangang Road, Taipei, 11510, Taiwan
Tel.: (886) 227853839
Web Site: http://www.acs.com.tw
Sales Range: $50-74.9 Million
Emp.: 230
System Integrator of Computer, Communication, Control & Information Technologies
N.A.I.C.S.: 541519

CINDA Engineering & Construction Pvt. Ltd. (1)
Corenthum 6th Floor Tower-B Plot No A-41 Sector-62, Noida, 201 301, Uttar Pradesh, India
Tel.: (91) 1204722300
Web Site: https://www.cinda.in
Emp.: 7,400
Construction Engineering Services
N.A.I.C.S.: 541330

CIPEC Construction Inc. (1)
Unit 1202 Global Tower Gen Mascardo ST, Bangkal, Makati, Philippines
Tel.: (63) 84438335513
Procurement Services
N.A.I.C.S.: 541990

CTAS Corporation (1)
11757 Katy Fwy Ste 1520, Houston, TX 77079
Tel.: (281) 870-9998
Petroleum Refinery Services
N.A.I.C.S.: 324110

CTCI (Thailand) Co., Ltd. (1)
19 Fl Phairojkijja Tower 825 Debaratana Road KM 4 Bangna Nua, Bangna, Bangkok, 10260, Thailand
Tel.: (66) 2 769 6888
Web Site: https://www.thailand.ctci.com
Sales Range: $200-249.9 Million
Emp.: 200
Construction & Engineering Services
N.A.I.C.S.: 237990

CTCI Advanced Systems Shanghai Inc. (1)
8F No 26 Lane 168 Daduhe Road, Putuo District, Shanghai, 200062, China
Tel.: (86) 592 252 0958
Web Site: https://www.asi.ctci.com
Computer Software Development Services
N.A.I.C.S.: 541511

CTCI Americas, Inc. (1)
3rd Fl 15721 Park Row, Houston, TX 77084
Tel.: (281) 870-9998
Web Site: https://www.americas.ctci.com
Stationary Equipment Mfr
N.A.I.C.S.: 322230
Abe Fatemizadeh *(Chm & CEO)*

CTCI Arabia Ltd. (1)
Room 301 Al-Mohammdia Tower Dhahran Road, PO Box 1962, Al Khobar, 31952, Saudi Arabia
Tel.: (966) 138656145
Procurement Services
N.A.I.C.S.: 541990

CTCI Chemicals Corp. (1)
808 Baiyu South Rd, Guanyin Dist, Taoyuan, 32842, Taiwan
Tel.: (886) 34736999
Web Site: http://www.ctci.com
Sales Range: $25-49.9 Million
Emp.: 50
Chemicals Mfr & Supplier
N.A.I.C.S.: 325998

CTCI Corporation (1)
R 303 3 Fl Sheikh Sultan Suroor Al Dhahiri Bldg LuLu Center, PO Box 44924, Al Salam St, Abu Dhabi, United Arab Emirates
Tel.: (971) 26711572
Engineering & Construction Services
N.A.I.C.S.: 541330

CTCI Engineering & Construction Sdn Bhd (1)
7 Fl Wisma MIE 2 Jalan Industri PBP 2 Taman Industri, Pusat Bandar Puchong, 47100, Puchong, Selangor Darul Ehsan, Malaysia
Tel.: (60) 38 074 6900
Web Site: http://www.ctci.com.tw
Sales Range: $25-49.9 Million
Emp.: 60
Planning, Design, Procurement, Construction & Maintenance of Refinery, Petrochemical & Power Plants
N.A.I.C.S.: 237990

Subsidiary (Domestic):

MIE Industrial Sdn.Bhd. (2)
Wisma Mie 2 Jalan Industri PBP 2 Taman Industri Pusat Bandar, 47100, Puchong, Selangor, Malaysia
Tel.: (60) 380746888
Emp.: 3,500
Electrical, Instrument & Control Panel Mfr
N.A.I.C.S.: 423830
Khairuddin B. Othman *(CEO)*

Subsidiary (Domestic):

Seremban Engineering Berhad (3)
Lot 1A-1C Lorong Bunga Tanjung 1/3, Senewang Industrial Park Seremban, 70400, Negeri Sembilan, Darul Khusus, Malaysia **(72.66%)**
Tel.: (60) 66775898
Web Site: https://www.seb.net.my
Rev.: $58,163,765
Assets: $36,795,392
Liabilities: $29,555,749
Net Worth: $7,239,644
Earnings: $977,896
Emp.: 300
Fiscal Year-end: 06/30/2023
Engineeering Services
N.A.I.C.S.: 541330
Ahmad Fuzi Abdul Razak *(Chm)*

CTCI Machinery Corporation (1)
No 5 Xinggong Rd, Dashe Dist, Kaohsiung, 81567, Taiwan
Tel.: (886) 7 351 2141
Web Site: https://www.mac.ctci.com
Sales Range: $150-199.9 Million
Emp.: 450
Power Plant Machinery Mfr, Maintenance & Inspection Services
N.A.I.C.S.: 333248

CTCI Shanghai Co., Ltd. (1)
602R 6F No 26 Lane 168 Da Du He Road, Putuo District, Shanghai, 200062, China
Tel.: (86) 2152519888
Web Site: https://www.shanghai.ctci.com
Emp.: 7,400
Procurement Services
N.A.I.C.S.: 541990

CTCI Singapore Pte. Ltd. (1)
80 Robinson Road 02-00, Singapore, 068896, Singapore
Tel.: (65) 62952997
Emp.: 100
Petrochemical Refinery Services
N.A.I.C.S.: 324110
Steve Wu *(Mng Dir)*

CTCI Vietnam Company Limited (1)
6 Floor Charmvit Tower 117 Tran Duy Hung Road, Cau Giay District, Hanoi, Vietnam **(50%)**
Tel.: (84) 2438335513
Web Site: https://www.vietnam.ctci.com
Sales Range: $50-74.9 Million
Emp.: 200
Engineering & Construction Services
N.A.I.C.S.: 541330

CTCI Vietnam Company Limited (1)
6 Floor Charmvit Tower 117 Tran Duy Hung Road, Cau Giay District, Hanoi, Vietnam
Tel.: (84) 2438335513
Web Site: https://www.vietnam.ctci.com

Emp.: 200
Procurement Services
N.A.I.C.S.: 541990

Ctci Trading Shanghai Co., Ltd. (1)
8 Fl 26 Lane 168 Daduhe Rd, Putuo District, Shanghai, 200062, China
Tel.: (86) 2152519888
Engineering Consulting Services
N.A.I.C.S.: 541000

Ctci-Hdec (Chungli) Corp. (1)
No 95 Dunhua S Rd Sec 2, Daan District, Taipei, 106, Taiwan
Tel.: (886) 237015000
Construction Services
N.A.I.C.S.: 236210

E&C Engineering Corporation (1)
5th Floor 16 Lane 270 Sec 3 Pei Shen Road, Shenkang, Taipei, 222, Taiwan **(100%)**
Tel.: (886) 226625858
Web Site: http://www.eandc.com.tw
Sales Range: $200-249.9 Million
Emp.: 650
Engineering & Construction Services
N.A.I.C.S.: 541330

Fortune Energy Corporation (1)
5th Fl 132 Xingshan Road, Neihu District, Taipei, 114, Taiwan **(75%)**
Tel.: (886) 2 2612 1689
Waste Treatment Services
N.A.I.C.S.: 562219

Jingding Engineering & Construction Co., Ltd. (1)
10F Building B Royal City International Centre No 138, Andingmenwai Street Dongcheng District, Beijing, 100011, China
Tel.: (86) 10 64827878
Web Site: http://www.jdec.com.cn
Sales Range: $75-99.9 Million
Emp.: 450
Construction Engineering Services
N.A.I.C.S.: 541330

KD Holding Corporation (1)
2F No 132 Xing Shan Road, Neihu District, Taipei, 114, Taiwan
Tel.: (886) 226121689
Web Site: https://www.ecove.com
Sales Range: $100-124.9 Million
Emp.: 8
Holding Company; Professional Investments
N.A.I.C.S.: 551112

Subsidiary (Domestic):

HD Resources Management Corporation (2)
5th Fl 132 Xingshan Road, Neihu District, Taipei, 114, Taiwan
Tel.: (886) 2 2612 1689
Sales Range: $1-9.9 Million
Waste Management Services
N.A.I.C.S.: 562119

Leading Energy Corporation (2)
5th Fl 132 Xingshan Road, Neihu District, Taipei, 114, Taiwan
Tel.: (886) 226121689
Waste Management
N.A.I.C.S.: 562213

PT CTCI International Indonesia (1)
Menara Global 10Fl Suite C Jl Jend Gatot Subroto Kav 27, Jakarta, 12950, Indonesia
Tel.: (62) 215270201
Procurement Services
N.A.I.C.S.: 541990

Resources Engineering Services Inc. (1)
4FL 48 Nan Kang Rd Sec 3, Taipei, 11510, Taiwan
Tel.: (886) 227838250
Web Site: http://www.res.com.tw
Planning, Design, Engineering & Construction Services
N.A.I.C.S.: 237990

Sino Environmental Services Corp. (1)
5F No 132 Xingshan Road, Neihu District, Taipei, 114, Taiwan
Tel.: (886) 226121689
Web Site: http://www.sesc.com.tw

Winson Hsie *(Chm)* (...)

Sales Range: $250-299.9 Million
Emp.: 580
Waste Management Services
N.A.I.C.S.: 562998

Subsidiary (Domestic):

Innovest Investment Corp (2)
10 Fl 89 Sec 6 Zhongshan North Rd, Taipei, Taiwan
Tel.: (886) 2 2833 9999
Investment Management Service
N.A.I.C.S.: 523999

CTEAM CONSULTING & ANLAGENBAU GMBH
Im Stocken 6, 88444, Ummendorf, Germany
Tel.: (49) 7351440980
Web Site: http://www.cteam.de
Year Founded: 2002
Sales Range: $50-74.9 Million
Emp.: 200
Power & Communication Line Engineering Consulting Services
N.A.I.C.S.: 541690
Martina Buck *(Mng Dir & Head-Bus Mgmt)*

CTEK AB
Rostugnsvagen 3, 776 70, Vikmanshyttan, Sweden
Tel.: (46) 103448800
Web Site: https://www.ctekgroup.com
Year Founded: 1977
CTEK—(OMX)
Rev.: $84,108,386
Assets: $142,028,904
Liabilities: $73,178,042
Net Worth: $68,850,862
Earnings: ($24,061,742)
Emp.: 211
Fiscal Year-end: 12/31/23
Battery Mfr
N.A.I.C.S.: 335910
Hans Straberg *(Chm)*

CTI ENGINEERING CO., LTD.
Nihombashi Hamacho F Tower
3-21-1 Nihombashi Hamacho, Chuoku, Tokyo, 103-8430, Japan
Tel.: (81) 336680451
Web Site: https://www.ctie.co.jp
Year Founded: 1945
9621—(TKS)
Rev.: $659,774,130
Assets: $566,590,260
Liabilities: $175,980,890
Net Worth: $390,609,370
Earnings: $53,416,060
Emp.: 2,188
Fiscal Year-end: 12/31/23
Construction Consulting Services
N.A.I.C.S.: 541330
Masahiro Emori *(Mng Exec Officer)*

Subsidiaries:

CTI AURA Co., Ltd. (1)
Cti Saitama Bldg 1-14-6 Kamikizaki, Urawa, 330-0071, Saitama, Japan
Tel.: (81) 488332049
Environmental Engineering Services
N.A.I.C.S.: 541330

CTI Ascend Co., Ltd. (1)
74 Machi Tamano, Minamisoma, 976-0154, Fukushima, Japan
Tel.: (81) 244342050
Agricultural Product Mfr
N.A.I.C.S.: 311221

CTI Engineering International Co., Ltd. (1)
Tachibana Annex Building 2-25-14 Kameido, Koto-ku, Tokyo, 136-0071, Japan **(70%)**
Tel.: (81) 336382561
Web Site: http://www.ctii.co.jp
Sales Range: $25-49.9 Million
Emp.: 157
Engineering Consulting Services

N.A.I.C.S.: 541330
Norio Tomonaga *(Chm)*

CTI Ground Planning Co., Ltd. **(1)**
Cti Fukuoka Bldg 2-4-12 Daimyo, Chuo-Ku, Fukuoka, 810-0041, Japan
Tel.: (81) 927375333
Web Site: http://www.ctie.co.jp
Sales Range: $25-49.9 Million
Emp.: 55
Environmental Engineering Services
N.A.I.C.S.: 541330

CTI Myanmar Co., Ltd. **(1)**
Strand Condo Unit 1 4F No 33/49 Mahabandoola Garden St, Kyauktada Township, Yangon, Myanmar **(95%)**
Tel.: (95) 1377868
Web Site: http://www.cti-mm.com
Civil Construction Management Services
N.A.I.C.S.: 237310
Hnin Wityi *(COO)*

CTI Pilipinas, Inc. **(1)**
S & L Building 1500 Roxas Boulevard, Ermita, Manila, Philippines
Tel.: (63) 84051194
Engineering Consulting Services
N.A.I.C.S.: 541330

CTI Reed Co., Ltd. **(1)**
CTI Saitama Building 1-14-6 Kamikizaki, Urawa-ku, Saitama, 330-0071, Japan
Tel.: (81) 488332049
Web Site: https://www.reed.ctie.co.jp
Emp.: 82
Information Technology Services
N.A.I.C.S.: 541511

Chi-ken Sogo Consultants Co., Ltd. **(1)**
2-26-2-Nishinippori, Arakawa-ku, Tokyo, 116-0013, Japan
Tel.: (81) 363115135
Web Site: http://www.chiso-con.co.jp
Emp.: 93
Geological Surveying Services
N.A.I.C.S.: 541360
Yabe Masayuki *(Pres)*

Environmental Research & Solutions Co., Ltd. **(1)**
No 23 Uji Kozaki, Uji, 611-0021, Kyoto, Japan
Tel.: (81) 774252522
Web Site: http://www.ctiers.co.jp
Environmental Consulting Services
N.A.I.C.S.: 541620
Hiroshi Sugiyama *(Pres)*

NISSOKEN Architects/Engineers Inc. **(1)**
1-34-14 Hatagaya, Shibuya-ku, Tokyo, 151-0072, Japan
Tel.: (81) 354789700
Web Site: https://www.nissoken.co.jp
Emp.: 127
Architectural Planning & Designing Services
N.A.I.C.S.: 541310

Waterman Group PLC **(1)**
Picksford Wharf Clink Street, London, SE1 9DG, United Kingdom
Tel.: (44) 2079287888
Web Site: http://www.watermangroup.com
Engineering & Environmental Consultant Services
N.A.I.C.S.: 541611
Nicholas Taylor *(CEO)*

Subsidiary (Non-US):

Moylan Engineering Limited **(2)**
Block S East Point Business Park, Dublin, D03 H3F4, Ireland **(100%)**
Tel.: (353) 16648900
Engineeering Services
N.A.I.C.S.: 541330

Subsidiary (Domestic):

Waterman Aspen Limited **(2)**
Picksford Wharf Clink Street, London, SE1 9DG, United Kingdom **(100%)**
Tel.: (44) 2079287888
Web Site: http://www.watermanaspen.co.uk
Engineeering Services
N.A.I.C.S.: 541330
Chris Chaplin *(Mng Dir)*

Waterman Building Services Limited **(2)**
Picksford Wharf Clink Street, London, SE1 9DG, United Kingdom **(100%)**
Tel.: (44) 2079287888
Engineeering Services
N.A.I.C.S.: 541330

Waterman Energy, Environment & Design Limited **(2)**
Pickfords Wharf Clink Street, London, SE1 9DG, United Kingdom
Tel.: (44) 20 7928 7888
Consulting Engineering Services
N.A.I.C.S.: 541330

Waterman Infrastructure & Environment Limited **(2)**
Pickfords Wharf Clink Street, London, SE1 9DG, United Kingdom **(100%)**
Tel.: (44) 2079287888
Heavy & Civil Engineering Construction
N.A.I.C.S.: 237990

Waterman International Holdings Limited **(2)**
Pickfords Wharf clink St, Clink Street, London, SE1 9DG, United Kingdom **(100%)**
Tel.: (44) 2079287888
Holding Company
N.A.I.C.S.: 551112

Subsidiary (Non-US):

Waterman International (Asia) Pty Limited **(3)**
Suite 4 Level 8 20 Bridge Street, Sydney, 2000, NSW, Australia **(100%)**
Tel.: (61) 294119900
Engineering Consulting Services
N.A.I.C.S.: 541330

Subsidiary (Domestic):

Waterman AHW Pty Limited **(4)**
Suite 4 Level 8 20 Bridge Street, Sydney, 2000, NSW, Australia
Tel.: (61) 294119900
Engineeering Services
N.A.I.C.S.: 541330

Waterman Group (Aus) Pty Limited **(4)**
60 Park Street, Melbourne, 3205, VIC, Australia
Tel.: (61) 396859900
Web Site: http://www.watermangroup.com
Engineering Consulting Services
N.A.I.C.S.: 541330

Subsidiary (Domestic):

Waterman International Limited **(3)**
Pickfords Wharf Clink Street, London, SE1 9DG, United Kingdom **(100%)**
Tel.: (44) 2079287888
Management Consulting Services
N.A.I.C.S.: 541618

Subsidiary (Domestic):

Waterman Structures Limited **(2)**
Pickfords Wharf, Clink Street Southwark, London, SE19DG, United Kingdom **(100%)**
Tel.: (44) 2079287888
Web Site: http://www.watermangroup.com
Scientific & Technical Consulting Services
N.A.I.C.S.: 541690

CTI LOGISTICS LIMITED
1 Drummond Place, West Perth, 6005, WA, Australia
Tel.: (61) 894221100
Web Site: http://www.ctilogistics.com
CLX—(ASX)
Rev.: $214,451,465
Assets: $188,372,237
Liabilities: $107,282,243
Net Worth: $81,089,994
Earnings: $10,572,867
Emp.: 1,000
Fiscal Year-end: 06/30/24
Transportation & Warehousing Logistics
N.A.I.C.S.: 488510
David Robert Watson *(Chm)*

Subsidiaries:

Action Logistics (WA) Pty Ltd **(1)**
339 Collier Road, Bassendean, 6054, WA, Australia
Tel.: (61) 89 270 5678
Web Site:
  https://www.actioncouriers.com.au
Logistic Services
N.A.I.C.S.: 541614

Ausplastics Pty Ltd **(1)**
32 Denninup Way, Malaga, 6090, WA, Australia
Tel.: (61) 892491500
Web Site: http://www.ausplastics.com
Sales Range: $25-49.9 Million
Emp.: 25
Plastic Plumbing Fittings Mfr
N.A.I.C.S.: 326122
Coaire Rimson *(Gen Mgr)*

Australian Fulfilment Services Pty Ltd **(1)**
87 Grose Street, Parramatta, 2150, NSW, Australia
Tel.: (61) 29 890 2777
Web Site: https://fulfilmentaustralia.com.au
Logistic Services
N.A.I.C.S.: 541614

Bring Transport Industries Pty Ltd **(1)**
1 Drummond Place, West Perth, 6005, WA, Australia
Tel.: (61) 89 427 4888
Web Site: https://www.bringcouriers.com.au
Transportation Services
N.A.I.C.S.: 488490

CTI Business Investment Company Pty Ltd **(1)**
339 Collier Road, Bassendean, 6054, WA, Australia
Tel.: (61) 892705678
Web Site:
  https://www.actioncouriers.com.au
Transportation Services
N.A.I.C.S.: 488490

CTI Couriers Pty Ltd **(1)**
1 Drummond Place, West Perth, 6005, WA, Australia
Tel.: (61) 89 427 4700
Web Site: https://www.cticouriers.com.au
Courier Service
N.A.I.C.S.: 492110

CTI Fleet Management Pty Ltd **(1)**
316 Bushmead Road, Hazelmere, 6055, WA, Australia
Tel.: (61) 892378877
Web Site: https://www.ctilogistics.com
Fleet Leasing Services
N.A.I.C.S.: 532112

CTI Freight Systems Pty Ltd **(1)**
54 Miguel Rd, Bibra Lake, 6163, WA, Australia
Tel.: (61) 894221100
Web Site: http://www.ctilogistics.com
Freight Transportation Services
N.A.I.C.S.: 481212
Neil Raspi *(Gen Mgr)*

CTI Freightlines Pty Ltd **(1)**
841 Abernethy Road, Forrestfield, 6058, WA, Australia
Tel.: (61) 89 479 2555
Web Site: https://www.ctifreightlines.com.au
Freight Services
N.A.I.C.S.: 488510

CTI Logistics Ltd - Fleet Management Division **(1)**
316 Bushmead Road, Hazelmere, Perth, 6055, WA, Australia
Tel.: (61) 89 237 8877
Web Site: https://www.ctilogistics.com
Sales Range: $25-49.9 Million
Emp.: 20
Logistic Services
N.A.I.C.S.: 541614

CTI Logistics Ltd - General & Container Transport Division **(1)**
54 Miguel Road, Bibra Lake, 6163, WA, Australia
Tel.: (61) 894998888
Web Site: http://www.ctitaxitrucks.com.au

Sales Range: $25-49.9 Million
Emp.: 20
Logistic Services
N.A.I.C.S.: 541614

CTI Records Management Pty Ltd **(1)**
54 Miguel Road, 1585, Bibra Lake, 6163, WA, Australia
Tel.: (61) 894343433
Web Site: http://www.ctitaxitrucks.com.au
Taxi Fleet Operators
N.A.I.C.S.: 485310

CTI Records Management Pty Ltd **(1)**
1 Drummond Place, West Perth, 6005, WA, Australia
Tel.: (61) 89 427 4747
Web Site: https://www.ctirecordsmgt.com
Sales Range: $25-49.9 Million
Emp.: 1,000
Record Management & Document Storage Services
N.A.I.C.S.: 561439

CTI Security Services Pty Ltd **(1)**
1 Drummond Place, West Perth, 6872, WA, Australia
Tel.: (61) 894274800
Web Site: https://www.armsecurity.com.au
Security Consulting Services
N.A.I.C.S.: 561621
Glen Brown *(CEO)*

CTI Security Systems Pty Ltd **(1)**
1 Drummond Pl, West Perth, 6005, WA, Australia
Tel.: (61) 894221111
Web Site: https://www.securus.com.au
Security Services
N.A.I.C.S.: 561621

CTI Taxi Trucks Pty. Ltd. **(1)**
841 Abernethy Road, Forrestfield, 6058, WA, Australia
Tel.: (61) 892378888
Web Site: https://www.ctitaxitrucks.com.au
Transportation Services
N.A.I.C.S.: 926120

CTI Transport Systems Pty Ltd **(1)**
841 Abernethy Road, Forrestfield, 6058, WA, Australia
Tel.: (61) 89 237 8888
Web Site: https://www.ctitaxitrucks.com.au
Sales Range: $200-249.9 Million
Transportation Services
N.A.I.C.S.: 488490

CTI Xpress Systems Pty Ltd **(1)**
50 Railway Parade, Welshpool, 6106, WA, Australia
Tel.: (61) 89 311 7700
Web Site: https://www.ctixpress.com.au
Parcel Delivery Services
N.A.I.C.S.: 492110

Consolidated Transport Industries Pty Ltd **(1)**
1 Drummond Pl, West Perth, 6005, WA, Australia
Tel.: (61) 894221100
Web Site: http://www.ctilogistics.com.au
Emp.: 100
Transportation Services
N.A.I.C.S.: 488490

Subsidiary (Domestic):

Foxline Logistics Pty Ltd **(2)**
339 Collier Road, Bassendean, 6054, WA, Australia
Tel.: (61) 89 377 9377
Web Site: https://www.foxline.com.au
Courier & Taxi Truck Services
N.A.I.C.S.: 492110

Mercury Messengers Pty Ltd **(1)**
1 Drummond Place, West Perth, 6005, WA, Australia
Tel.: (61) 89 427 4777
Web Site: https://mercuryonline.com.au
Emp.: 10
Courier Service
N.A.I.C.S.: 492110

CTK COSMETICS
234 Hyoryeong-ro, Seocho-gu, Seoul, Korea (South)

CTK Cosmetics—(Continued)

Tel.: (82) 262387200
Web Site:
http://www.ctkcosmetics.com
Year Founded: 2001
260930—(KRS)
Rev.: $53,200,211
Assets: $137,063,062
Liabilities: $21,234,146
Net Worth: $115,828,915
Earnings: ($16,237,433)
Emp.: 143
Fiscal Year-end: 12/31/22
Cosmetics Products Mfr
N.A.I.C.S.: 325620
Christine Ansari *(Exec Dir)*

CTM SA
Km 13 5 Casa-Rabat Highway Sidi
Bernoussi, Casablanca, Morocco
Tel.: (212) 800090030
Web Site: https://www.ctm.ma
Year Founded: 1919
CTM—(CAS)
Sales Range: $50-74.9 Million
Passenger Transportation Services
N.A.I.C.S.: 485999
Ezzoubeir Errhaimini *(Chm, CEO & Mng Dir)*

CTNETWORKS CO., LTD.
12 Shinhawa-gil Ansim-ri Yeonmu-eup, Ch'ung-Nam, Chungcheongnam-do, Korea (South)
Tel.: (82) 41 742 0609
Web Site:
http://www.ctnetworks.co.kr
Year Founded: 2007
Fiber Optic Cable Mfr
N.A.I.C.S.: 335921

CTP N.V.
Apollolaan 151, 1077 AR, Amster-dam, Netherlands
Tel.: (31) 852731294   Nl
Web Site: https://www.ctp.eu
Year Founded: 2021
CTPNV—(EUR)
Rev.: $727,174,617
Assets: $16,051,370,602
Liabilities: $9,395,963,738
Net Worth: $6,655,406,864
Earnings: $995,683,143
Emp.: 732
Fiscal Year-end: 12/31/23
Real Estate Services
N.A.I.C.S.: 531190
Remon Vos *(Founder & CEO)*

CTR HOLDINGS LIMITED
21 Woodlands Close 08-11 12 Primz Bizhub, Singapore, 737854, Singapore
Tel.: (65) 63686026   Ky
Web Site: https://www.chianteck.com
Year Founded: 2006
1416—(HKG)
Rev.: $66,509,818
Assets: $57,452,390
Liabilities: $20,641,719
Net Worth: $36,810,671
Earnings: $5,094,479
Emp.: 479
Fiscal Year-end: 02/28/23
Holding Company
N.A.I.C.S.: 551112
Xuping Xu *(Chm & CEO)*

CTS CO., LTD.
115 Furusato, Ueda, 386-0005, Nagano, Japan
Tel.: (81) 268263700
Web Site: https://www.cts-h.co.jp
Year Founded: 1990
4345—(TKS)
Rev.: $73,304,900

Assets: $110,453,100
Liabilities: $29,612,800
Net Worth: $80,840,300
Earnings: $12,281,380
Emp.: 323
Fiscal Year-end: 03/31/24
System Equipment Rental & Leasing
N.A.I.C.S.: 532420
Taizo Yokoshima *(Pres & CEO)*

CTS EVENTIM AG & CO. KGAA
Contrescarpe 75 A, 28195, Bremen, Germany
Tel.: (49) 42136660   De
Web Site: https://www.eventim.de
Year Founded: 1999
EVD—(DEU)
Rev.: $2,603,532,588
Assets: $3,527,239,966
Liabilities: $2,537,278,311
Net Worth: $989,961,655
Earnings: $303,166,857
Emp.: 3,733
Fiscal Year-end: 12/31/23
Ticket Retailer
N.A.I.C.S.: 713990
Klaus-Peter Schulenberg *(CEO & Member-Mgmt Bd)*

Subsidiaries:

ALL IN ONE Communication AG   **(1)**
Tellstrasse 22a, 8004, Zurich, Switzerland
Tel.: (41) 582258450
Web Site:
https://www.allinonecommunication.ch
Event Management Services
N.A.I.C.S.: 711310

ARGO Konzerte GmbH   **(1)**
Friedrich-Bergius-Ring 26, 97076, Wurzburg, Germany
Tel.: (49) 93123000
Web Site: http://www.argo-konzerte.de
Online Ticket Booking Services
N.A.I.C.S.: 561599

Act Entertainment AG   **(1)**
Paulusgasse 16, PO Box 4, Basel, 4051, Switzerland
Tel.: (41) 612269000
Web Site: http://www.topact.ch
Sales Range: $50-74.9 Million
Emp.: 25
Concert Organizing Services
N.A.I.C.S.: 711310
Thomas Durr *(CEO)*

All Artists Agency GmbH   **(1)**
Tel.: (49) 3076758335
Web Site: http://www.allartists.agency
Concert Agency Services
N.A.I.C.S.: 711320

Arcadia Live GmbH   **(1)**
Porzellangasse 7a, 1090, Vienna, Austria
Tel.: (43) 19580505
Web Site: http://www.arcadia-live.com
Live Concert Entertainment Services
N.A.I.C.S.: 711310
Filip Potocki *(Mng Partner-Booking)*

Arena Berlin Betriebs GmbH   **(1)**
Eichenstrasse 4, 12435, Berlin, Germany
Tel.: (49) 305332030
Web Site: http://www.arena.berlin
Event Entertainment Services
N.A.I.C.S.: 711310

Arena Management GmbH   **(1)**
Willy-Brandt-Platz 3, 50679, Cologne, Germany
Web Site: http://www.lanxess-arena.de
Online Ticket Booking Services
N.A.I.C.S.: 561599

Barracuda Music GmbH   **(1)**
Alser Strasse 24/Top 13, 1090, Vienna, Austria
Tel.: (43) 1522522011
Web Site: https://www.barracudamusic.at
Event Management Services
N.A.I.C.S.: 711310

Big Tours S.L.   **(1)**

Ronda Sant Pere 38 5, 08010, Barcelona, Spain
Tel.: (34) 932682828
Web Site: https://www.doctormusic.com
Concert Organizing Services
N.A.I.C.S.: 561920

CTS Eventim Austria GmbH   **(1)**
Mariahilferstrasse 41-43, 1060, Vienna, Austria
Tel.: (43) 9009496096
Web Site: http://www.oeticket.com
Online Ticket Booking Services
N.A.I.C.S.: 561599

CTS Eventim Israel Ltd.   **(1)**
Brodeskey 43, Tel Aviv, 69052, Israel
Tel.: (972) 35111777
Event Ticketing Agency Services
N.A.I.C.S.: 711310
Shauly Yonay *(Mgr-Full Stack Dev)*

CTS Eventim Nederland B.V.   **(1)**
PO Box 69507, 1060, Amsterdam, Netherlands
Tel.: (31) 206167895
Web Site: http://www.eventim.nl
Sales Range: $25-49.9 Million
Emp.: 25
Ticketing & Entertainment Event Management Services
N.A.I.C.S.: 561599

CTS Eventim RU o.o.o.   **(1)**
Leningradsky Prospect 31A Building 1 Room 1 Floor 25, Moscow, 125284, Russia
Tel.: (7) 4952580000
Web Site: http://www.parter.ru
Event Ticketing Agency Services
N.A.I.C.S.: 711310
Igor Denisov *(Mktg Dir)*

CTS Eventim Schweden AB   **(1)**
Arenavagen 41, Stockholm, 12128, Sweden
Tel.: (46) 855668980
Web Site: http://www.eventim.se
Sales Range: $25-49.9 Million
Emp.: 6
Ticketing & Event Management Services
N.A.I.C.S.: 541618
Lars Aadde *(CEO)*

CTS Eventim Solutions GmbH   **(1)**
Contrescarpe 75 A, 28195, Bremen, Germany
Tel.: (49) 42120315512
Web Site: https://www.eventim.de
Emp.: 300
Ticketing Software Development Services
N.A.I.C.S.: 541511

CTS Eventim Sports GmbH   **(1)**
Hohe Bleichen 11, 20354, Hamburg, Germany
Tel.: (49) 806991155
Web Site: https://www.eventimsports.de
Sales Range: $25-49.9 Million
Emp.: 30
Software Solutions & Consulting Services
N.A.I.C.S.: 541511

DERTICKETSERVICE DE GmbH & Co. KG   **(1)**
Grosse Neugasse 2, 50667, Cologne, Germany
Tel.: (49) 221280271710
Web Site: https://www.derticketservice.de
Event Management Services
N.A.I.C.S.: 711310

Di & Gi S.R.L.   **(1)**
Via Dei Girasoli 30, 55041, Camaiore, LU, Italy
Tel.: (39) 058446477
Web Site: http://www.dalessandroegalli.com
Online Ticket Booking Services
N.A.I.C.S.: 561599

Dirk Becker Entertainment GmbH   **(1)**
Schanzenstrasse 37, 51063, Cologne, Germany
Tel.: (49) 2219681060
Web Site: https://www.dirkbecker-entertainment.de
Event Organizing Services
N.A.I.C.S.: 561920

DreamHaus GmbH   **(1)**
Kurfurstendamm 59, 10707, Berlin, Germany

Tel.: (49) 3040361320
Web Site: https://www.dreamhaus.com
Event Management Services
N.A.I.C.S.: 711310

Entradas Eventim S.A.   **(1)**
Serrano Anguita street 8, 28004, Madrid, Spain
Tel.: (34) 902488488
Web Site: https://www.entradas.com
Online Ticket Booking Services
N.A.I.C.S.: 561599

Eventim BG o.o.d.   **(1)**
10 Nikola Vaptzapov Blvd, 1407, Sofia, Bulgaria
Tel.: (359) 29615370
Web Site: http://www.eventim.bg
Sales Range: $25-49.9 Million
Emp.: 3
Ticketing & Entertainment Event Management Services
N.A.I.C.S.: 561599

Eventim Marketing und Sponsoring GmbH   **(1)**
Hohe Bleichen 11, 20345, Hamburg, Germany
Tel.: (49) 403807883090
Web Site: http://www.eventim-brand-connect.com
Event Marketing & Sponsoring Services
N.A.I.C.S.: 541613
Milan Goltz *(Dir-Video Content & Streaming)*

Eventim Norge AS   **(1)**
Kongens Gate 24, 0153, Oslo, Norway
Tel.: (47) 21959200
Web Site: https://www.eventim.no
Online Ticket Booking Services
N.A.I.C.S.: 561599

Eventim Popkurs Hamburg gemeinnutzige GmbH   **(1)**
Harvestehuder Weg 12, 20148, Hamburg, Germany
Tel.: (49) 40428482574
Web Site: http://www.popkurs-hamburg.de
Event Entertainment Services
N.A.I.C.S.: 711310

Eventim SI d.o.o.   **(1)**
Celovska Cesta 25, 1000, Ljubljana, Slovenia
Tel.: (386) 14302405
Web Site: http://www.eventim.si
Online Ticket Booking Services
N.A.I.C.S.: 561599
Robert Zagar *(Head-Mktg)*

Eventim SK, s.r.o.   **(1)**
29 Augusta 5, 81108, Bratislava, Slovakia
Tel.: (421) 252632425
Web Site: http://www.eventim.sk
Emp.: 6
Ticketing & Entertainment Event Management Services
N.A.I.C.S.: 561599

Eventim Sp. z o.o.   **(1)**
Mokotowska 49, 00-542, Warsaw, Poland
Tel.: (48) 225918383
Web Site: https://www.eventim.pl
Event Management Services
N.A.I.C.S.: 561920
Ditta Sadowska *(Project Mgr-Sls)*

Eventim Sports Consulting GmbH   **(1)**
Hohe Bleichen 11, Hamburg, 20354, Germany
Tel.: (49) 40380788599
Web Site: http://www.eventimsports.de
Sales Range: $25-49.9 Million
Emp.: 20
Business Management Services
N.A.I.C.S.: 541618
Arndt Scheffler *(Mng Dir)*

Eventim Sverige AB   **(1)**
Avagen 24, 412 51, Gothenburg, Sweden
Tel.: (46) 771130150
Web Site: https://www.eventim.se
Online Ticket Booking Services
N.A.I.C.S.: 561599

Eventim UK Limited   **(1)**
1 Chamberlain Square Cs, Birmingham, B3 3AX, United Kingdom

Tel.: (44) 3333446250
Web Site: http://www.eventim.co.uk
Online Ticket Booking Services
N.A.I.C.S.: 561599
John Gibson *(Mng Dir)*

Eventim d.o.o.   **(1)**
Kupinecka 4, Zagreb, 10020, Croatia
Tel.: (385) 16552860
Web Site: http://www.eventim.hr
Sales Range: $25-49.9 Million
Emp.: 7
Ticketing & Entertainment Event Manage-
ment Services
N.A.I.C.S.: 561599
Damir Vranic *(Mng Dir)*

Eventim ru S.R.L.   **(1)**
Polona St No 15, 010502, Bucharest, Ro-
mania
Tel.: (40) 212501008
Web Site: http://www.eventim.ro
Sales Range: $25-49.9 Million
Emp.: 25
Ticketing & Event Management Services
N.A.I.C.S.: 561599

FKP Area One GmbH   **(1)**
Kastanienallee 4, 10435, Berlin, Germany
Tel.: (49) 3044049977
Web Site: https://fkpareaone.de
Music & Entertainment Services
N.A.I.C.S.: 711130

FKP Scorpio Belgium B.V.   **(1)**
Waterloostraat 35, 2600, Antwerp, Belgium
Tel.: (32) 34891835
Web Site: https://fkpscorpio.be
Event Management Services
N.A.I.C.S.: 711310

FKP Scorpio Entertainment Ltd.   **(1)**
16a Crane Grove, London, N7 8LE, United
Kingdom
Tel.: (44) 7802498905
Web Site: https://fkpscorpio.co.uk
Music & Entertainment Services
N.A.I.C.S.: 713940

**FKP Scorpio Konzertproduktionen
GmbH**   **(1)**
Grosse Elbstrasse 277a, 22767, Hamburg,
Germany
Tel.: (49) 4085388888
Web Site: https://www.fkpscorpio.com
Emp.: 250
Event Entertainment Services
N.A.I.C.S.: 327910
Folkert Koopmans *(Co-CEO & Exec Dir)*

Subsidiary (Non-US):

FKP Poland Sp. z o. o.   **(2)**
ul Spacerowa 32, Pomieczyno, 83-305,
Gdansk, Poland
Tel.: (48) 587317001
Web Site: http://www.fkp.gda.pl
Building Construction Services
N.A.I.C.S.: 236220

FKP Scorpio Norge AS   **(1)**
Brenneriveien 11, 0182, Oslo, Norway
Tel.: (47) 22903010
Web Site: https://www.fkpscorpio.no
Concert Organizing Services
N.A.I.C.S.: 561920
Hedda Eline Gilberg *(Project Mgr-Intl)*

FKP Scorpio Poland Sp. z o.o.   **(1)**
Tel.: (48) 505985644
Web Site: http://www.fkpscorpio.pl
Event Entertainment Services
N.A.I.C.S.: 711310
Folkert Koopmans *(Co-CEO)*

FKP Scorpio Sverige AB   **(1)**
Pyramidvagen 7, 169 91, Stockholm, Swe-
den
Tel.: (46) 771130150
Web Site: https://www.fkpscorpio.se
Concert Organizing Services
N.A.I.C.S.: 561920

FKP Show Creations GmbH   **(1)**
Grosse Elbstrasse 277a, 22767, Hamburg,
Germany
Tel.: (49) 4085388888
Web Site: https://fkpshowcreations.com
Event Management Services
N.A.I.C.S.: 711310

Friends & Partners S.p.A.   **(1)**
Via dei Sormani 3, 20144, Milan, Italy
Tel.: (39) 024805731
Web Site: https://www.friendsandpartners.it
Live Concert Entertainment Services
N.A.I.C.S.: 327910

Subsidiary (Domestic):

Vivo Concerti S.r.l.   **(2)**
Via dei Sormani 3, 20144, Milan, MI, Italy
Tel.: (39) 0230515029
Web Site: https://www.vivoconcerti.com
Concert Organizing Services
N.A.I.C.S.: 561920

Fullsteam Agency Oy   **(1)**
Tel.: (358) 929050805
Web Site: http://www.fullsteam.fi
Event Ticketing Agency Services
N.A.I.C.S.: 711310
Anna Makela *(Mgr-Mktg & PR)*

Subsidiary (Domestic):

Seinajoki Festivals Oy   **(2)**
Rytmikorjaamo/Vaasantie 11, 60100, Seina-
joki, Finland
Tel.: (358) 503091117
Web Site: http://www.provinssi.fi
Event Ticketing Booking Services
N.A.I.C.S.: 711320

**Gadget abc Entertainment Group
AG**   **(1)**
Lagerstrasse 119, 8004, Zurich, Switzerland
Tel.: (41) 582258585
Web Site: https://www.gadget.ch
Event Management Services
N.A.I.C.S.: 711310

**HOI Productions Germany
GmbH**   **(1)**
Amelungstrasse 5, 20354, Hamburg, Ger-
many
Tel.: (49) 403807887980
Event Entertainment Services
N.A.I.C.S.: 711310

Holiday on Ice Productions B.V.   **(1)**
Marktplein 108 4th Floor, 2132 DD, Hoofd-
dorp, Netherlands
Tel.: (31) 880235127
Web Site: http://www.holidayonice.com
Event Entertainment Services
N.A.I.C.S.: 711310
Bogdan Lewko *(Sr Mgr-Technical)*

JetTicket Software GmbH   **(1)**
Spitalstrasse 5, Oberpullendorf, 7350,
Eisenstadt, Austria
Tel.: (43) 261243440
Web Site: http://www.jetticket.at
Online Ticket Booking Services
N.A.I.C.S.: 561599

K.B. Hallen Management A/S   **(1)**
Peter Bangs Vej 147, 2000, Frederiksberg,
Denmark
Tel.: (45) 70263267
Web Site: http://www.kbhallen.dk
Concert Organizing Services
N.A.I.C.S.: 561920
Kasper Busch Lund *(CEO)*

Kinoheld GmbH   **(1)**
Tel.: (49) 38712114040
Web Site: http://www.kinoheld.de
Online Ticket Booking Services
N.A.I.C.S.: 561599

Lippupiste Oy   **(1)**
Televisiokatu 4A, 00240, Helsinki, Finland
Tel.: (358) 600900900
Web Site: http://www.lippu.fi
Online Ticket Booking Services
N.A.I.C.S.: 561599

**Marek Lieberberg Konzertagentur
GmbH & Co. KG**   **(1)**
Morikestr 14, 60320, Frankfurt am Main,
Germany
Tel.: (49) 699562020
Web Site: http://www.mlk.com
Sales Range: $50-74.9 Million
Emp.: 100
Ticketing & Event Management Services
N.A.I.C.S.: 711310

**Marek Lieberberg Konzertagentur
Holding GmbH**   **(1)**

Morikestr 14, Frankfurt am Main, 60320,
Hessen, Germany
Tel.: (49) 699562020
Web Site: http://www.mlk.com
Sales Range: $25-49.9 Million
Emp.: 18
Ticketing & Event Management Services
N.A.I.C.S.: 541618
Marek Lieberberg *(CEO)*

**OTS Gesellschaft zum Vertrieb
elektronischer Eintrittskarten
mbH**   **(1)**
Brandstrasse 16, 8510, Stainz, Styria, Aus-
tria
Tel.: (43) 34633323
Web Site: http://www.oeticket.com
Sales Range: $25-49.9 Million
Emp.: 10
Ticketing & Event Management Services
N.A.I.C.S.: 561599
Claudia Sallene *(Mgr-Styria)*

OpenAir St.Gallen AG   **(1)**
Heiligkreuzstrasse 9, 9008, Saint Gallen,
Switzerland
Tel.: (41) 582258500
Web Site: https://www.openairsg.ch
Event Management Services
N.A.I.C.S.: 561920

**PGM Promoters Group Munich Konz-
ertagentur GmbH**   **(1)**
Ganghoferstrasse 68a, 80339, Munich, Ger-
many
Tel.: (49) 897907800
Web Site: https://promoters-group-
munich.de
Event Management Services
N.A.I.C.S.: 711310

**PGM Promotors Group Munich Konz-
ertagentur GmbH**   **(1)**
Ganghoferstrasse 68a, 80339, Munich, Ger-
many
Tel.: (49) 897907800
Web Site: http://www.promoters-group-
munich.de
Sales Range: $50-74.9 Million
Emp.: 4
Concert Promoter Services
N.A.I.C.S.: 711310
Peter Pracht *(Mgr)*

Palazzo Producties B.V.   **(1)**
ArenA Blvd 61-75 1101 DL A'dam, Amster-
dam, Zuidoost, Netherlands
Tel.: (31) 204353010
Web Site: http://www.palazzo.nl
Sales Range: $50-74.9 Million
Emp.: 6
Dining & Entertainment Services
N.A.I.C.S.: 711110

Palazzo Produktionen GmbH   **(1)**
Grosse Elbstrasse 277A, 22767, Hamburg,
Germany
Tel.: (49) 4085388730
Web Site: http://www.palazzo.org
Sales Range: $25-49.9 Million
Emp.: 50
Dining & Entertainment Services
N.A.I.C.S.: 711110

Subsidiary (Domestic):

**Palazzo Produktionen Berlin
GmbH**   **(2)**
Grosse Elbstrasse 277-279, 22767, Ham-
burg, Germany
Tel.: (49) 40 853 88 730
Web Site: http://www.palazzo.org
Sales Range: $50-74.9 Million
Emp.: 25
Dining & Entertainment Services
N.A.I.C.S.: 711110
Oliver Jauk *(Mng Dir)*

Subsidiary (Non-US):

Palazzo Produktionen GmbH   **(2)**
Phorusgasse 2/8, 1040, Vienna, Austria
Event Entertainment Services
N.A.I.C.S.: 711310

**Peter Rieger Konzertagentur GmbH
& Co. KG**   **(1)**
Sulzburgstrasse 13, Cologne, 50937, Ger-
many
Tel.: (49) 2219420020

Web Site: http://www.prknet.de
Entertainment Agency Services
N.A.I.C.S.: 561599

**Peter Rieger Konzertagentur Holding
GmbH**   **(1)**
Sulzburgstr 13, North Rhine-Westphalia,
50937, Cologne, Germany
Tel.: (49) 2219420020
Web Site: http://www.prknet.de
Sales Range: $25-49.9 Million
Emp.: 10
Entertainment Agency Services
N.A.I.C.S.: 561599
Klaus Matziol *(Mgr)*

Peter Rieger Verwaltungs GmbH   **(1)**
Sulzburgstrasse 13, 50937, Cologne,
Nordrhein-Westfalen, Germany
Tel.: (49) 2219420020
Web Site: http://www.prknet.de
Sales Range: $25-49.9 Million
Emp.: 15
Entertainment Agency Services
N.A.I.C.S.: 561599
Klaus Peter Matziol *(CEO)*

**Production Service Switzerland
AG**   **(1)**
Tellstrasse 22a, 8004, Zurich, Switzerland
Tel.: (41) 582258470
Web Site: https://www.productionservice.ch
Event Management Services
N.A.I.C.S.: 561920

Seaside Festival AG   **(1)**
Thunstrasse 17, 3005, Bern, Switzerland
Tel.: (41) 582258410
Web Site: https://seasidefestival.ch
Event Management Services
N.A.I.C.S.: 711310

Seekers Event GmbH   **(1)**
Philosophenweg 9, 07743, Jena, Germany
Tel.: (49) 3641666472
Web Site: http://www.seekers-event.com
Event Marketing Services
N.A.I.C.S.: 711310

**Semmel Concerts Entertainment
GmbH**   **(1)**
Am Muhlgraben 70, 95445, Bayreuth, Ger-
many
Tel.: (49) 921746000
Web Site: https://www.semmel.de
Emp.: 150
Online Ticket Booking Services
N.A.I.C.S.: 561599

**Show-Factory Entertainment
GmbH**   **(1)**
Mehrerauerstrabe 3, 6900, Bregenz, Austria
Tel.: (43) 557454750
Web Site: http://www.showfactory.at
Sales Range: $50-74.9 Million
Emp.: 25
Family Entertainment Services
N.A.I.C.S.: 711410

Stargarage AG   **(1)**
Solothurnerstrasse 235, 4600, Olten, Swit-
zerland
Tel.: (41) 622852000
Web Site: http://www.stargarage.ch
Online Ticket Booking Services
N.A.I.C.S.: 561599

SummerDays Festival AG   **(1)**
Heiligkreuzstrasse 9, CH-9008, Saint Gal-
len, Switzerland
Tel.: (41) 582258500
Web Site: https://summerdays.ch
Event Management Services
N.A.I.C.S.: 561920

Swiss Gadget Entertainment AG   **(1)**
Culmannstrasse 33, 8006, Zurich, Switzer-
land
Tel.: (41) 435010888
Web Site: http://www.gadget.ch
Event Ticketing Agency Services
N.A.I.C.S.: 711310

TEX Hungary Kft.   **(1)**
Bajcsy-Zsilinszky ut 31, Budapest, 1065,
Hungary
Tel.: (36) 305050666
Web Site: http://www.eventim.hu
Online Ticket Booking Services
N.A.I.C.S.: 561599

CTS Eventim AG & Co. KGAA—(Continued)

Attila Morocz *(Supvr-Sls Ops)*

Ticket Express Hungary Kft. (1)
Andrassy ut 18, H-1061, Budapest, Hungary
Tel.: (36) 303030999
Web Site: https://www.eventim.hu
Ticketing & Entertainment Event Management Services
N.A.I.C.S.: 561499

TicketOne S.p.A. (1)
Via Fabio Filzi n 29, 20124, Milan, Italy
Tel.: (39) 02392261
Web Site: https://www.ticketone.it
Online Ticket Booking Services
N.A.I.C.S.: 327910
Germana Solcia *(Mgr-HR)*

Subsidiary (Domestic):

CREA Informatica S.r.l. (2)
Via Roberto Lepetit 8/10, 20124, Milan, Italy
Tel.: (39) 02466565
Web Site: http://www.creaweb.it
Online Ticket Booking Services
N.A.I.C.S.: 561599
Simone Pera *(Head-IT)*

T.O.S.C. - Ticketone Sistemi Culturali S.r.l. (2)
Via Giovanni Giolitti 287/c, 00185, Rome, Italy
Tel.: (39) 063264971
Web Site: http://www.tosc.it
Online Ticket Booking Services
N.A.I.C.S.: 561599

Ticketcorner AG (1)
Riedmatt Center, 8153, Rumlang, Switzerland (50%)
Tel.: (41) 900 800 800
Web Site: http://www.ticketcorner.ch
Sales Range: $25-49.9 Million
Emp.: 130
International & Local Ticket & Event Retailer
N.A.I.C.S.: 711310
Andreas Angehrn *(CEO)*

Vaddi Concerts GmbH (1)
Kaiser-Joseph-Strasse 263, 79098, Freiburg, Germany
Tel.: (49) 7618879500
Web Site: https://www.vaddi-concerts.de
Online Ticket Booking Services
N.A.I.C.S.: 561599

Vertigo S.r.l. (1)
Via Lepetit 8/10, 20124, Milan, Italy
Tel.: (39) 028936221
Web Site: http://www.vertigo.co.it
Event Entertainment Services
N.A.I.C.S.: 711310

Wepromote Entertainment Group Switzerland AG (1)
Heiligkreuzstrasse 9, 9008, Saint Gallen, Switzerland
Tel.: (41) 712723434
Web Site: http://www.wepromote.ch
Event Entertainment Services
N.A.I.C.S.: 711310
Christof Huber *(Pres)*

You Are Special Events AG (1)
Tellstrasse 22a, 8004, Zurich, Switzerland
Tel.: (41) 582258440
Web Site: https://youarespecial.ch
Event Management Services
N.A.I.C.S.: 711310

eventimpresents GmbH & Co. KG (1)
Contrescarpe 75a, 28195, Bremen, Germany
Tel.: (49) 3040361320
Web Site: https://www.rock-am-ring.com
Event Management Services
N.A.I.C.S.: 561920

getgo consulting GmbH (1)
Hohe Bleichen 11, 20354, Hamburg, Germany
Tel.: (49) 1806570080
Web Site: http://www.getgo.de
Event & Show Management Services
N.A.I.C.S.: 711320

nolock Softwarelosungen GmbH (1)
Strobachgasse 6, 1050, Vienna, Austria
Tel.: (43) 158510061006
Web Site: https://www.nolock.at
Computer Software Development Services
N.A.I.C.S.: 541511
Clemens Geistler *(Co-CEO)*

simply-X GmbH (1)
Liegnitzer Str 2, 37581, Bad Gandersheim, Germany
Tel.: (49) 53829179180
Web Site: https://www.simply-x.com
Industrial Mold Mfr
N.A.I.C.S.: 333511

tour-house Veranstaltungs-, Konzert-, TV- und Media-Consulting GmbH (1)
Semmel Concert Hohepleichen 11, 20354, Hamburg, Germany
Tel.: (49) 4075118580
Web Site: http://www.tour-house.de
Sales Range: $25-49.9 Million
Emp.: 5
Ticketing & Entertainment Event Management Services
N.A.I.C.S.: 561599

CTS GLOBAL EQUITY GROUP, INC.

Unit 2701-A East Tektite Towers Ortigas Center, Manila, Pasig, Philippines
Tel.: (63) 286355735
Web Site:
https://www.ctsglobalgroup.com
Year Founded: 1986
CTS—(PHI)
Rev.: $1,872,509
Assets: $39,750,541
Liabilities: $3,469,961
Net Worth: $36,280,580
Earnings: $415,228
Emp.: 73
Fiscal Year-end: 12/31/23
Securities Brokerage Services
N.A.I.C.S.: 523150
Edmund C. Lee *(CFO)*

CTS INTERNATIONAL LOGISTICS CORPORATION LIMITED

20F Tian'an Center No 338 Nanjing West Road, Shanghai, 200003, China
Tel.: (86) 4001603128   CN
Web Site: https://www.ctsfreight.com
Year Founded: 1984
603128—(SHG)
Rev.: $3,098,654,620
Assets: $1,372,034,655
Liabilities: $527,492,796
Net Worth: $844,541,858
Earnings: $124,722,402
Emp.: 2,033
Fiscal Year-end: 12/31/22
Logistic Services
N.A.I.C.S.: 541614
Wu Chunquan *(Chm)*

Subsidiaries:

CTS Global Supply Chain Solutions (1)
1137 Senoia Rd Ste, Tyrone, GA 30290
Tel.: (770) 907-0736
Web Site: http://www.ctsglobalsolutions.com
Emp.: 3
Logistics Consulting Servies
N.A.I.C.S.: 541614

CTS International Logistics (HK) Co., Ltd. (1)
3/F China Travel Cargo Logistics Centre 1 Cheong Tung Road, Hung Hom, Kowloon, China (Hong Kong)
Tel.: (852) 2773 9613
Logistics Consulting Servies
N.A.I.C.S.: 541614
Lawrence Luk *(Gen Mgr)*

CTS International Logistics (Singapore) Pte Ltd. (1)
Logistics Consulting Servies
N.A.I.C.S.: 541614

China Special Article Logistics Co., Ltd. (1)
Building 36 Zone 12 No 188 South 4th Ring Road West, Fengtai Dist, Beijing, China
Tel.: (86) 1051122800
Web Site: https://www.csalc.cn
Cargo Logistics Services
N.A.I.C.S.: 488320

Cts Global Logistics(Canada) Inc. (1)
315-5508 Hollybridge Way, Richmond, V7C 0E2, BC, Canada
Tel.: (647) 717-1696
Warehouse & Transportation Services
N.A.I.C.S.: 561910

Cts Global Logistics(Thailand)Co., Ltd. (1)
47 Soi Suk-Chai Yak Ban Kluay Tai Sukhumvit 42 Road, Prakanong Klongtoey, Bangkok, 10110, Thailand
Tel.: (66) 643628365
Warehouse & Transportation Services
N.A.I.C.S.: 561910

Cts International Freight (Spain) S.L. (1)
Edificio Regus La Moraleja Avda De Europa 19 3A, 28108, Madrid, Spain
Tel.: (34) 686070955
Warehouse & Transportation Services
N.A.I.C.S.: 561910

Cts International Logistics (Germany) GmbH (1)
Cargo City South Building 571, 60549, Frankfurt, Germany
Tel.: (49) 6924743510
Logistic Services
N.A.I.C.S.: 541614

Cts International Logistics (Japan) Co., Ltd. (1)
Asahi-Jimbocho-Plaza 502 2-14-4 Jimbocho Kanda, Chiyoda-ku, Tokyo, 101-0051, Japan
Tel.: (81) 362616613
Warehouse & Transportation Services
N.A.I.C.S.: 561910

Cts International Logistics (Netherlands) B.V. (1)
Westersingel 87, 3015 LC, Rotterdam, Netherlands
Tel.: (31) 613901643
Logistic Services
N.A.I.C.S.: 541614

Cts International Logistics (Viet Nam) Co., Ltd. (1)
9Fl Paragon Building 03 Nguyen Luong Bang Street, District 7, Ho Chi Minh City, Vietnam
Tel.: (84) 965566728
Warehouse & Transportation Services
N.A.I.C.S.: 561910

Cts International Logistics Tanzania Limited (1)
PO Box 25266, Dar es Salaam, Tanzania
Tel.: (255) 768621780
Warehouse & Transportation Services
N.A.I.C.S.: 561910

Zhengzhou CTS International Logistics Corporation Limited (1)
RM358 Xinzheng International Airport Cargo Terminal, Zhengzhou, 451162, Henan, China
Tel.: (86) 371 6851 2927
Logistics Consulting Servies
N.A.I.C.S.: 541614
Pan Hui *(Mgr)*

CTS SPEDITION GMBH

Ludwig-Erhard-Strasse 8, Bremen, 28197, Germany
Tel.: (49) 421437 72 87 0
Web Site: http://www.cts-bremen.de
Emp.: 160
Trucking Service
N.A.I.C.S.: 484230
Holger Schulz *(Mng Dir)*

Subsidiaries:

EKB Container Logistik GmbH & Co. KG (1)
Richard-Dunkel-Strasse 120, 28199, Bremen, Germany
Tel.: (49) 421 5236 0
Web Site: http://www.ekb-containerlogistik.de
Sales Range: $100-124.9 Million
Emp.: 60
Transportation Services
N.A.I.C.S.: 488490
Wolfgang Weber *(Mng Dir)*

CTT - CORREIOS DE PORTUGAL SA

Avenida D Joao II N 13, 1999-001, Lisbon, Portugal
Tel.: (351) 210471836
Web Site: https://www.ctt.pt
CTT—(EUR)
Rev.: $978,442,688
Assets: $4,378,899,416
Liabilities: $4,136,152,302
Net Worth: $242,747,114
Earnings: $39,221,007
Emp.: 12,081
Fiscal Year-end: 12/31/22
Postal Service
N.A.I.C.S.: 491110
Antonio Pedro Ferreira Vaz da Silva *(Exec Dir)*

CTT SYSTEMS AB

Brukslagarvagen 5, PO Box 1042, 611 39, Nykoping, Sweden
Tel.: (46) 104573200
Web Site: https://www.ctt.se
CTT—(OMX)
Rev.: $24,661,178
Assets: $35,319,902
Liabilities: $10,096,753
Net Worth: $25,223,149
Earnings: $6,209,784
Emp.: 73
Fiscal Year-end: 12/31/22
Aircraft Humidity Control Systems Mfr
N.A.I.C.S.: 336413
Tomas Torlof *(Chm)*

Subsidiaries:

Broderna Ingemar och Bo Mekaniska AB (1)
Diabasvagen 1, Nybro, 39222, Sweden
Tel.: (46) 48148280
Web Site: http://www.bribo.se
Emp.: 9
Machine Tools Mfr
N.A.I.C.S.: 333515
Tony Rosendahl *(Mgr)*

CTX HOLDINGS JOINT STOCK COMPANY

2nd floor HH2 building Duong Dinh Nghe street Yen Hoa ward, Cau Giay district, Hanoi, Vietnam
Tel.: (84) 462812000
Web Site: http://www.ctx.vn
Year Founded: 1982
CTX—(HNX)
Rev.: $13,867,632
Assets: $81,005,050
Liabilities: $39,096,246
Net Worth: $41,908,805
Earnings: $1,472,035
Emp.: 53
Fiscal Year-end: 12/31/23
Holding Company
N.A.I.C.S.: 551112

CTY GROUP AS

Prumyslova 1472/11 Hostivar, 102 00, Prague, Czech Republic
Tel.: (420) 296781490
Web Site: http://www.cty.cz
Year Founded: 2001
1HUS01AE—(BRA)
Sales Range: Less than $1 Million
Financial Support Services
N.A.I.C.S.: 541611
Juraj Kamaras *(Chm)*

CU MEDICAL SYSTEMS INC.
130-1 Dongwhagongdan-ro Munmak-eup, Wonju, Gangwon-do, Korea (South)
Tel.: (82) 337477657
Web Site: https://www.cu911.com
Year Founded: 2001
115480—(KRS)
Rev.: $36,016,295
Assets: $67,558,479
Liabilities: $22,358,904
Net Worth: $45,199,575
Earnings: $7,041,687
Emp.: 108
Fiscal Year-end: 12/31/22
Emergency Medical Device Mfr & Sales
N.A.I.C.S.: 339112
Kim Hyung Soo (CEO)

Subsidiaries:

Healthwell Medical Inc.   (1)
101-2 Donghwagongdan-ro Munmak-eup, Wonju, 26365, Gangwon, Korea (South)
Tel.: (82) 338131102
Web Site: https://www.hwm911.com
Medical Device Mfr
N.A.I.C.S.: 339112

CUB ELECPARTS INC.
No 6 Lane 546 Sec 6 Changlu Rd Fuhsin Township, Taipei, 50648, Changhua, Taiwan
Tel.: (886) 47782010
Web Site: http://www.cubelec.com.tw
2231—(TAI)
Rev.: $143,810,911
Assets: $335,322,235
Liabilities: $163,584,153
Net Worth: $171,738,082
Earnings: $10,907,322
Fiscal Year-end: 12/31/23
Electric Automotive Parts Mfr
N.A.I.C.S.: 336320
Shan-Chuan Yu (Chm, Pres & Gen Mgr)

Subsidiaries:

Cub Elecparts Inc. - Shanghai Facility   (1)
No 51 Jinwen Rd, Zhuqiqo Town Pudong New District, Shanghai, 201323, China
Tel.: (86) 213 375 6999
Web Site: http://www.cubelec.com.tw
Automobile Electronic Parts Mfr
N.A.I.C.S.: 336110

Cubtek Inc.   (1)
Rooms 7 and 8 6th Floor No 38 Taiyuan Street, Hsinchu County, Zhubei, 302, Taiwan
Tel.: (886) 35600289
Web Site: https://www.cubtek.com
Automotive Interior Switch Mfr & Distr
N.A.I.C.S.: 336390

Harbinger Technology Corp.   (1)
7th Floor No 166 Jianyi Road, Zhonghe District, New Taipei City, Taiwan
Tel.: (886) 28 226 3456
Web Site: https://www.harbinger.com.tw
Electrical Equipment Mfr & Distr
N.A.I.C.S.: 335999

CUBE BIO-ENERGY PVT LTD.
501, KK Plaza, 100 Feet Rd, Ayyappa Society, Chanda Naik Nagar, Madhapur,, Hyderabad, Telangana, 500081, India
Tel.: (91) 4040057965
Environmental Services
N.A.I.C.S.: 541620

CUBE LABS S.P.A.
Giulio Caccini 1, 00186, Rome, Italy
Tel.: (39) 0692090183
Web Site: https://www.cube-labs.com
Year Founded: 2013
CUBE—(ITA)
Healthcare Technology Services

N.A.I.C.S.: 541512
Filippo Surace (CEO)

CUBE SYSTEM INC.
Osaki Wiz Tower 2-11-1 Osak, Shinagawa-ku, Tokyo, 141-0032, Japan
Tel.: (81) 354876030
Web Site: https://www.cubesystem.co.jp
Year Founded: 1972
2335—(TKS)
Rev.: $119,118,810
Assets: $89,149,070
Liabilities: $22,169,940
Net Worth: $66,979,130
Earnings: $7,052,870
Emp.: 952
Fiscal Year-end: 03/31/24
Information Technology Services
N.A.I.C.S.: 541512
Osamu Sakiyama (Chm)

Subsidiaries:

Cube System Vietnam Co., Ltd.   (1)
6th Floor JVPE Building Quang Trung Software Park, Tan Chanh Hiep Ward District 12, Ho Chi Minh City, Vietnam
Tel.: (84) 837155701
Web Site: https://vn-cubesystem.com
Information Technology Consulting Services
N.A.I.C.S.: 541512
Hoai Vu Dinh (Mgr-Sys Dev)

Hokkaido Cube System Inc.   (1)
7-4-4 Kita 1 West Pacific Marks Sapporo Kita 1 6F, Chuo-ku, Sapporo, 060-0001, Hokkaido, Japan
Tel.: (81) 11 271 5600
Web Site: https://www.h-cube.co.jp
Emp.: 79
Information Technology Services
N.A.I.C.S.: 541511

CUBE.ITG SA
Dlugosza Street 60, 51-1116, Wroclaw, Poland
Tel.: (48) 71 79 72 666
Web Site: http://www.cubeitg.pl
Emp.: 400
IT Services
N.A.I.C.S.: 541519
Marek Girek (Chm-Mgmt Bd)

CUBEX TUBINGS LIMITED
1-7-27 to 34 2nd Floor Shyam Towers United Building Complex, Sarojini Devi Road, Secunderabad, 500 003, India
Tel.: (91) 4027817440
Web Site: https://www.cubextubings.com
526027—(BOM)
Rev.: $26,339,108
Assets: $13,279,566
Liabilities: $4,448,153
Net Worth: $8,831,414
Earnings: $361,397
Fiscal Year-end: 03/31/23
Copper Alloy Product Mfr
N.A.I.C.S.: 331420
Pushparaj Bhandari (Mng Dir)

CUBIC DIGITAL TECHNOLOGY CO., LTD.
Intersection of Gaocheng East Road and Jing'er Road, Economic and Technological Development Zone, Lu'an, 237009, Anhui, China
Tel.: (86) 5643336150
Web Site: http://www.taikongintel.com
Year Founded: 1999
300344—(CHIN)
Rev.: $26,916,238
Assets: $73,898,629
Liabilities: $20,584,298
Net Worth: $53,314,331
Earnings: ($17,819,117)

Fiscal Year-end: 12/31/23
Foam Cement Composites Mfr
N.A.I.C.S.: 327310
Guo Linsheng (Chm)

CUBIC KOREA INC.
39 Salmak-gil, Danwon-gu, Ansan, 425-839, Gyeonggi-do, Korea (South)
Tel.: (82) 314915325
Web Site: https://www.cubic.co.kr
Year Founded: 1989
021650—(KRS)
Rev.: $161,108,270
Assets: $121,445,592
Liabilities: $60,192,851
Net Worth: $61,252,741
Earnings: $5,007,800
Emp.: 146
Fiscal Year-end: 12/31/22
Cubic Printing Services
N.A.I.C.S.: 323111
Bong Gyun Oh (CEO)

Subsidiaries:

Cubic Korea INC. - Busan Factory   (1)
5-13BL Daechi-ri Chilseo-myeon, Hamangun, Busan, Gyeongsangnam-do, Korea (South)
Tel.: (82) 55 586 5325
Printing Equipment Mfr
N.A.I.C.S.: 333248

THAI CUBIC TECHNOLOGY CO., LTD.   (1)
85/30 Moo4, Sub-district Bueng Sriracha, Chon Buri, 20230, Thailand
Tel.: (66) 33 047 3156
Web Site: https://www.cubic.co.th
Cubic Printing Services
N.A.I.C.S.: 323113

Plant (Domestic);

THAI CUBIC TECHNOLOGY CO., LTD. - SRIRACHA FACTORY   (2)
Sahapattana Indestrial Park 620/2 Moo 11, Nongkham, Si Racha, 20232, Chonburi, Thailand
Tel.: (66) 38 481 236
Printing Equipment Mfr
N.A.I.C.S.: 333248

CUBIC SENSOR & INSTRUMENT CO., LTD.
Fenghuang No 3 Road FenghuangIndustrial Park, Eastlake HitechDevelopment Zone, Wuhan, 430205, Hubei, China
Tel.: (86) 2781628827
Web Site: https://www.gassensor.com.cn
Year Founded: 2003
688665—(SHG)
Rev.: $84,583,222
Assets: $158,926,721
Liabilities: $33,529,149
Net Worth: $125,397,572
Earnings: $20,423,047
Fiscal Year-end: 12/31/22
Gas Sensor Mfr
N.A.I.C.S.: 334513
Youhui Xiong (Chm & Gen Mgr)

Subsidiaries:

Hubei Cubic-Ruiyi Instrument Co., Ltd.   (1)
No 6 Fenghuangyuan Middle Road Fenghuang Industrial Park, Eastlake Hi-tech Development Zone, Wuhan, 430205, China
Tel.: (86) 2781628831
Web Site: https://www.gas-analyzers.com
Electronic Appliance Mfr & Distr
N.A.I.C.S.: 335210

CUBICAL FINANCIAL SERVICES LIMITED
456 Aggarwal Metro Heights Netaji Subhash Place Pitam Pura, Delhi, 110034, India

Tel.: (91) 47057757
Web Site: https://www.cubical90.com
Year Founded: 1990
511710—(BOM)
Rev.: $179,070
Assets: $1,813,392
Liabilities: $13,785
Net Worth: $1,799,607
Earnings: $28,014
Emp.: 6
Fiscal Year-end: 03/31/21
Investment Management Service
N.A.I.C.S.: 523999
Ashwani Kr Gupta (Mng Dir)

CUBICFARM SYSTEMS CORP.
7170 Glover Road, Langley, V2Y 2R1, BC, Canada   BC
Web Site: https://cubicfarms.com
Year Founded: 2015
7CU—(DEU)
Rev.: $3,252,420
Assets: $10,237,532
Liabilities: $28,344,254
Net Worth: ($18,106,723)
Earnings: ($12,442,955)
Fiscal Year-end: 12/31/23
Agricultural & Vertical Farming Automation Services
N.A.I.C.S.: 111998
John de Jonge (Interim CEO)

Subsidiaries:

Hydrogreen Inc.   (1)
25781 Cottonwood Ave, Sioux Falls, SD 57107
Tel.: (605) 277-7271
Web Site: https://www.hydrogreenglobal.com
Hydro Green Farm Research Services
N.A.I.C.S.: 115116
John de Jonge (Pres)

CUBO COMMUNICATIONS GROUP PLC
Holden House 57 Rathbone Place, London, W1T 1JU, United Kingdom
Tel.: (44) 20 7612 1111
Web Site: http://www.cubogroup.com
Year Founded: 1995
Rev.: $10,340,006
Assets: $10,237,195
Liabilities: $2,854,880
Net Worth: $7,382,316
Earnings: $1,129,665
Emp.: 49
Fiscal Year-end: 12/31/16
Marketing & Advertising Agency
N.A.I.C.S.: 541810
Kerry Simpson (CEO)

Subsidiaries:

Cubo Brand Communications Limited   (1)
Holden House 57 Rethbone Pl, London, W1T 1JU, United Kingdom
Tel.: (44) 2076121111
Web Site: http://www.cubo.com
Sales Range: $25-49.9 Million
Communication Agency
N.A.I.C.S.: 517810
Toby Hartwell (Mng Dir)

The Media Foundry International Limited   (1)
Holden House 57 Rathbone Pl, London, W1T 1JU, United Kingdom
Tel.: (44) 2076121155
Web Site: http://www.themediafoundry.com
Sales Range: $25-49.9 Million
Emp.: 10
Public Relations Consulting Services
N.A.I.C.S.: 541820
Neil Foster (Mng Dir)

CUBOX CO., LTD.
Pyongbang Building 12 Teheran-ro 22-gil, Gangnam-gu, Seoul, Korea (South)

CUBOX Co., Ltd.—(Continued)

Tel.: (82) 262777800
Web Site: https://www.cubox.ai
Year Founded: 2010
340810—(KRS)
Software Development Services
N.A.I.C.S.: 541511

CUBUS LUX PLC

Ixl House 18 Ixl House 18 Heddon
Street, London, W1B 4DA, United
Kingdom
Tel.: (44) 2074676347
Year Founded: 2004
Building Projects Developer; Leisure
& Tourism Company
N.A.I.C.S.: 721110
Stephen John McCann *(Sec)*

Subsidiaries:

Cubus Lux d.o.o **(1)**
Verudela 17, Pula, 52100, Istria, Croatia
Tel.: (385) 52 380350
Sales Range: $25-49.9 Million
Casino Operator
N.A.I.C.S.: 713210

Duboko Plavetnilo Ugljan Projektant
d.o.o. **(1)**
Obala kneza Trpimira 33, Zadar, 23000,
Croatia
Tel.: (385) 23335811
Sales Range: $50-74.9 Million
Emp.: 1
Real Estate & Development Services
N.A.I.C.S.: 531390

CUCINA BELLA S.A.

Av del Libertador 13 570, Martinez,
B1640 AOT, Buenos Aires, Argentina
Tel.: (54) 1147985800 **Ar**
Web Site:
http://www.cucinabella.com.ar
Year Founded: 1978
Kitchen Cabinet Mfr
N.A.I.C.S.: 337110

CUCKOO HOLDINGS CO., LTD.

14 Yusangongdan 2-gil, Yangsan,
626-610, Gyeongsangnam-do, Korea
(South)
Tel.: (82) 553800734
Web Site:
http://www.cuckooworld.com
Year Founded: 1978
192400—(KRS)
Sales Range: $400-449.9 Million
Emp.: 33
Household Electronic Appliances
N.A.I.C.S.: 335210
Bon Hak Koo *(CEO)*

CUCKOO HOMESYS CO LTD.

349 Emtibeuibuk-Ro, Siheung,
Gyeonggi-do, Korea (South)
Tel.: (82) 553800734
Year Founded: 2017
284740—(KRS)
Rev.: $821,782,859
Assets: $891,861,186
Liabilities: $248,159,513
Net Worth: $643,701,673
Earnings: $139,953,828
Emp.: 620
Fiscal Year-end: 12/31/21
Personal & Household Goods Rental
Services
N.A.I.C.S.: 532289
Jae-Young Hur *(Mng Dir)*

CUESTA COAL LIMITED

Suite 3B 165 Moggill Road, Taringa,
Brisbane, 4068, QLD, Australia
Tel.: (61) 7 3327 8100 **AU**
Web Site:
http://www.cuestacoal.com.au
Year Founded: 2011

Coal Exploration
N.A.I.C.S.: 212115
Matthew Crawford *(CEO)*

CUFE LTD

32 Harrogate Street, West Leeder-
ville, 6007, WA, Australia
Tel.: (61) 861819793
Web Site: https://cufe.com.au
CUF—(ASX)
Rev.: $64,191,968
Assets: $23,027,945
Liabilities: $19,348,074
Net Worth: $3,679,870
Earnings: ($9,096,174)
Fiscal Year-end: 06/30/24
Gold Ore & Silver Ore Mining
N.A.I.C.S.: 212220
Antony William Paul Sage *(Chm)*

CUHADAROGLU METAL SANAYI VE PAZARLAMA AS

Yakuplu Mh Hurriyet Bul No 6 Beylik-
duzu, 34524, Istanbul, Turkiye
Tel.: (90) 2122242020
Web Site:
https://www.cuhadaroglu.com
Year Founded: 1954
CUSAN—(IST)
Rev.: $59,317,674
Assets: $51,057,435
Liabilities: $33,203,071
Net Worth: $17,854,364
Earnings: $6,273,486
Fiscal Year-end: 12/31/22
Metals Mfr
N.A.I.C.S.: 331441
Murat Ruhi Cuhadaroglu *(Chm)*

CUKIERMAN & CO. INVESTMENT HOUSE LTD.

28 Haarbaa St, Tel Aviv, 64731, Is-
rael
Tel.: (972) 36950666
Web Site: http://www.cukierman.co.il
Year Founded: 1993
Holding Company; Investment Bank-
ing, Real Estate & Private Equity
Services
N.A.I.C.S.: 551112
Edouard Cukierman *(Chm)*

Subsidiaries:

Catalyst Investments, L.P. **(1)**
3 Daniel Frish St Fl 11, Tel Aviv, 64731-04,
Israel
Tel.: (972) 36950666
Web Site: http://www.catalyst-fund.com
Sales Range: $50-74.9 Million
Emp.: 15
Privater Equity Firm
N.A.I.C.S.: 523999
Edouard Cukierman *(Founder, Mng Partner)*

Holding (Domestic):

Onset Technology Inc. **(2)**
2 Maskit Bldg D 3rd Fl, Herzliya Pituach,
46733, Israel
Tel.: (972) 99561615
Web Site: http://www.onsettechnology.com
Sales Range: $1-9.9 Million
Emp.: 45
Mobile Technologies Software Developer
N.A.I.C.S.: 513210

Holding (US):

harmon.ie Corporation **(2)**
1521 California Cir, Milpitas, CA 95035
Tel.: (408) 907-1339
Web Site: http://www.harmon.ie
Sales Range: $25-49.9 Million
Interoperable Computer Software Devel-
oper, Publisher & Whslr
N.A.I.C.S.: 513210
Yaacov Cohen *(Co-Founder, Pres & CEO)*

Branch (Domestic):

harmon.ie Corp. - Boston Office **(3)**
31 Milk St Ste 717, Boston, MA 02109

Web Site: http://www.harmon.ie
Sales Range: $1-9.9 Million
Emp.: 25
Interoperable Computer Software Whslr
N.A.I.C.S.: 423430

Branch (Non-US):

harmon.ie Corp. - Israel Office **(3)**
18 Abba Hillel Silver, North Industrial Area,
Lod, 71294, Israel
Tel.: (972) 8 978 1300
Web Site: http://www.harmon.ie
Interoperable Computer Software Devel-
oper, Publisher & Whslr
N.A.I.C.S.: 513210

Cukierman & Co. Life Sciences **(1)**
3 Daniel Frish St, Tel Aviv, 64731, Israel
Tel.: (972) 36950666
Web Site: http://www.cukierman.co.il
Sales Range: $75-99.9 Million
Emp.: 15
Life Sciences Industry Corporate Interme-
diation
N.A.I.C.S.: 523910

Cukierman & Co. Real Estate
Ltd. **(1)**
3 Daniel Frish St, Tel Aviv, 64731, Israel
Tel.: (972) 36950666
Web Site: http://www.cukierman.co.il
Sales Range: $50-74.9 Million
Emp.: 15
Real Estate Investment Trust
N.A.I.C.S.: 525990
Edouard Cukierman *(Gen Mgr)*

Cukierman & Co. S.A. **(1)**
56 Rue Lafayette, F-75009, Paris, France
Tel.: (33) 147700184
Investment Banking, Real Estate & Private
Equity Investment Services
N.A.I.C.S.: 523150

CUKUROVA HOLDING A.S.

Levent Mahallesi Comert Sokak, Yapi
Kredi Plaza A-Blok No 1/A Kat 16
Besiktas, 34330, Istanbul, Turkiye
Tel.: (90) 2123701200
Web Site:
http://www.cukurovaholding.com.tr
Holding Company
N.A.I.C.S.: 551112
Ali Samsa Karamehmet *(Vice Chm)*

Subsidiaries:

Cukurova Insaat Makinalari San. ve
Tic. A.S. **(1)**
Garden Fur Mah Adana Road No 53 Medi-
terranean, 33115, Mersin, Turkiye
Tel.: (90) 3242218400
Web Site: http://www.cimsatas.com
Industrial Machinery Mfr
N.A.I.C.S.: 333120

Cukurova Kimya Endustrisi A.S. **(1)**
50 Yil Caddesi No 10 Organize Sanayi
Bolgesi, 45030, Manisa, Turkiye
Tel.: (90) 2362332320
Web Site: http://www.cukurovakimya.com.tr
Plastics Product Mfr
N.A.I.C.S.: 325211

Cukurova Ziraat Endustri ve Tic.
A.S. **(1)**
Icmeler Mah D-100 Karayolu Tersaneler
Kavsagi No 36, Tuzla, Istanbul, Turkiye
Tel.: (90) 2166251500
Web Site: http://www.cukurovaziraat.com.tr
Agricultural Machinery Distr
N.A.I.C.S.: 423820

Kaplamin Ambalaj Sanayi ve Ticaret
A.S. **(1)**
Izmir Ankara Karayolu 25 Km No 158, Ke-
malpasa, Izmir, Turkiye
Tel.: (90) 2328770855
Web Site: http://www.kaplamin.com.tr
Packaging Products Mfr
N.A.I.C.S.: 326140

Noksel A.S. **(1)**
Yukari Ovecler Mah Lizbon Cad No 10 Can-
kaya, Ovecler, 6460, Ankara,
Turkiye **(52%)**
Tel.: (90) 3124725959

Sales Range: $200-249.9 Million
Emp.: 50
Spiral Welded Steel Pipe Mfr
N.A.I.C.S.: 331210

Subsidiary (Non-US):

Noksel Espana S.A. **(2)**
Av Mediterraneo 5 - 1 G, Pozuelo de Alar-
con, 28007, Madrid, Spain
Tel.: (34) 915351790
Web Site: https://nokselspain.com
Spiral Welded Steel Pipe Mfr
N.A.I.C.S.: 331210

Selkasan Kagit ve Paketleme Malze-
meleri Imalati San. ve Tic. A.S. **(1)**
Manisa OIZ 2nd Section Kecilikoy OSB
Neighborhood, Mustafa Kemal Bulvari No 8
Yunusemre, 45030, Manisa,
Turkiye **(51%)**
Tel.: (90) 236 213 0273
Web Site: https://www.selkasan.com
Sales Range: $25-49.9 Million
Paperboard Mfr
N.A.I.C.S.: 322299

Turkcell Holding AS **(1)**
Turkcell Plaza Mesrutiyet Caddesi 153, Te-
pebasi, 80050, Istanbul, Turkiye **(52.91%)**
Tel.: (90) 2123131000
Web Site: http://www.turkcell.com.tr
Sales Range: $25-49.9 Million
Emp.: 50
Holding Company; Communications
N.A.I.C.S.: 517112
Sureyya Ciliv *(CEO)*

YALOVA AMBALAJ SANAYI VE TI-
CARET A.S. **(1)**
Kaytazdere Balci Mevkii Altinova, Yalova,
Turkiye
Tel.: (90) 2264629672
Web Site: http://www.yalovaambalaj.com.tr
Packaging Products Mfr
N.A.I.C.S.: 326140

CULINARY DESTINATIONS LIMITED

35 Jutland Road, Toronto, M8Z 2G6,
ON, Canada
Tel.: (416) 201-0707
Web Site:
http://www.culinarydestinations.com
Year Founded: 1997
Rev.: $17,194,390
Emp.: 60
Food Products Mfr
N.A.I.C.S.: 424450
Keith Chen *(Pres)*

CULLEN INVESTMENTS LIMITED

8 Airpark Drive Mangere, Auckland,
2022, New Zealand
Tel.: (64) 92570711
Web Site:
http://www.culleninvestments.com
Privater Equity Firm
N.A.I.C.S.: 523999
Eric Watson *(Founder & Exec VP)*

CULLEN RESOURCES LIMITED

Unit 4 7 Hardy Street, South Perth,
6151, WA, Australia
Tel.: (61) 894745511 **AU**
Web Site:
https://cullenresources.com.au
CUL—(ASX)
Rev.: $80,045
Assets: $3,248,793
Liabilities: $109,678
Net Worth: $3,139,115
Earnings: ($762,143)
Emp.: 1
Fiscal Year-end: 06/30/24
Support Activities for Nonmetallic
Minerals
N.A.I.C.S.: 212390
Chris Ringrose *(Mng Dir)*

Subsidiaries:

Cullen Exploration Pty Ltd   **(1)**
Northern Territory, Saint Leonards, 2065,
WA, Australia
Tel.: (61) 894096951
Mineral Exploration Services
N.A.I.C.S.: 213115

CULLINAN HOLDINGS LIMITED
The Travel House 6 Hood Avenue,
Rosebank, 2196, Johannesburg,
South Africa
Tel.: (27) 11 770 7511
Web Site: http://www.cullinan.co.za
Year Founded: 1901
CUL—(JSE)
Tour & Travel Operator
N.A.I.C.S.: 561520
Michael Tollman (CEO)

Subsidiaries:

Central Boating (Pty) Ltd   **(1)**
85 Bree Street, Cape Town, 8001, South
Africa
Tel.: (27) 214248026
Web Site: http://centralboating.co.za
Boating Equipment Distr
N.A.I.C.S.: 441222
David Barnes (Mng Dir)

Cullinan Namibia (Pty) Ltd   **(1)**
Wasserberg Park Unit 7 1 Jan Jonker Klein
Windhoek, Windhoek, Namibia
Tel.: (264) 61247417
Web Site: http://www.cullinannamibia.com
Tour Operator
N.A.I.C.S.: 561520
Birgit Louw (Mgr-Product & Relationship)

Eastgate Safaris & Transfers   **(1)**
PO Box 1426, Hoedspruit, 1380, South
Africa
Tel.: (27) 157933678
Web Site: http://www.eastgatesafaris.co.za
Travel Tour Operator
N.A.I.C.S.: 561520

Glacier Enterprises (Pty) Ltd   **(1)**
Chiappini Square 17 Chiappini Stre, Cape
Town, 8001, South Africa
Tel.: (27) 214091630
Web Site: http://www.glacier-
    enterprises.co.za
Emp.: 6
Trade Financing Services
N.A.I.C.S.: 522299
Lance Tollman (CEO)

Hylton Ross Tours (Pty) Ltd   **(1)**
PO Box 287, Paarden Eiland, Cape Town,
7420, South Africa
Tel.: (27) 215062575
Web Site: http://hyltonross.co.za
Tour & Travel Operator
N.A.I.C.S.: 561520
Jacqui Le Sueur (Branch Mgr)

Ikapa Coach Charters   **(1)**
92 Maple Street Pomona Kempton Park,
Johannesburg, 1619, South Africa
Tel.: (27) 113961053
Web Site: http://www.ikapacoaches.co.za
Transport Services
N.A.I.C.S.: 561520
Jacqui Mitchell (Branch Mgr)

Ikapa Tours & Travel (Pty) Ltd.   **(1)**
94 Voortrekker Road Salt River, PO Box
102, Observatory, Cape Town, 7925, South
Africa
Tel.: (27) 215063700
Web Site: http://www.ikapa.co.za
Tour Operator
N.A.I.C.S.: 561520
Karen Tollman (Mktg Mgr)

Manex & Power Marine Ltd   **(1)**
PO Box 173, Paarden Eiland, Cape Town,
7420, South Africa
Tel.: (27) 215117292
Web Site: http://www.manex.co.za
Recreational Boat Distr
N.A.I.C.S.: 423910
David Barnes (Mng Dir)

Pentravel (Pty) Ltd   **(1)**

41 The Blvd, Westville, 3629, South Africa
Tel.: (27) 312752000
Web Site: http://www.pentravel.co.za
Emp.: 25
Travel Tour Operator
N.A.I.C.S.: 561510
Sean Hough (Mng Dir)

Silverton Travel (Pty) Ltd   **(1)**
20 The Boulevard West End Office Park
Spine Road, Westville, Kwazulu Natal,
South Africa
Tel.: (27) 312650040
Web Site: http://www.edusport.co.za
Tour & Travel Operator
N.A.I.C.S.: 561520
Nicky Bell (CEO)

Springbok Atlas Namibia (Pty)
Ltd   **(1)**
24,-26 Nguni Street Northern Industrial
Area, Windhoek, Namibia
Tel.: (264) 61215943
Web Site: http://www.springbokatlas.co.za
Bus Charter Services
N.A.I.C.S.: 485510
Suzette Vorster (Mgr-Sls-Natl)

Springbok Atlas Tours & Safaris Pty
Ltd   **(1)**
17 Chiappini Street, PO Box 819, Cape
Town, 8000, South Africa
Tel.: (27) 214604700
Web Site: http://www.springbokatlas.com
Tour Operator
N.A.I.C.S.: 561520
Glenn McKeag (CEO)

Thompsons Gateway (PTE) Ltd   **(1)**
801 Mountbatten Road, Singapore, 437801,
Singapore
Tel.: (65) 63449866
Tour & Travel Operator
N.A.I.C.S.: 561520

CULLINAN METALS CORP.
Suite 610 - 700 W Pender, Vancou-
ver, V6C 1G8, BC, Canada
Tel.: (403) 852-4869   BC
Web Site:
    https://www.cullinanmetals.com
Year Founded: 2021
CMT—(CNSX)
Rev.: $36,702
Assets: $320,910
Liabilities: $118,025
Net Worth: $202,885
Earnings: ($814,303)
Fiscal Year-end: 06/30/24
Metal Exploration Services
N.A.I.C.S.: 213114
John Bean (CFO)

CULLITON BROTHERS LIMITED
473 Douro St, PO Box 850, Stratford,
N5A 6W3, ON, Canada
Tel.: (519) 271-1981
Web Site:
    http://www.cullitonbrothers.com
Year Founded: 1932
Rev.: $23,475,137
Emp.: 120
Multi Trade Contractor Services
N.A.I.C.S.: 811210
Tim Culliton (Pres)

CULPEO MINERALS LIMITED
Level 48 152-158 St Georges Ter-
race, Perth, 6000, WA, Australia
Tel.: (61) 892005812   AU
Web Site:
    https://www.culpeominerals.com.au
Year Founded: 2018
CPO—(ASX)
Rev.: $2,079
Assets: $3,817,336
Liabilities: $191,115
Net Worth: $3,626,221
Earnings: ($1,582,798)
Fiscal Year-end: 06/30/22
Mineral Exploration Services

N.A.I.C.S.: 212390
Max Tuesley (Mng Dir)

CULT FOOD SCIENCE CORP.
Suite 810 - 789 West Pender Street,
Vancouver, V6C 1H2, BC,
Canada   BC
Web Site:
    https://www.cultfoodscience.com
Year Founded: 1983
CULT—(CNSX)
Assets: $5,043,926
Liabilities: $170,668
Net Worth: $4,873,258
Earnings: ($1,996,106)
Fiscal Year-end: 12/31/21
Food Service Contracting Services
N.A.I.C.S.: 722310
Lejjy Gafour (CEO)

CULTI MILANO S.P.A.
via dell Aprica 12, 20122, Milan, Italy
Tel.: (39) 0249784974
Web Site: https://www.culti.com
CULT—(ITA)
Sales Range: Less than $1 Million
Fragrance Product Mfr
N.A.I.C.S.: 339999
Pierpaolo Manes (CEO)

**CULTURAL INVESTMENT
HOLDINGS CO., LTD.**
22 Baisong Roa Sujiatun District,
Shenyang, 110101, China
Tel.: (86) 10 5704 2692
Automobile Mfr
N.A.I.C.S.: 336110

Subsidiaries:

Framestore Limited   **(1)**
19-23 Wells Street, London, W1T 3PQ,
United Kingdom
Tel.: (44) 20 7244 8000
Web Site: http://www.framestore.com
Emp.: 1,000
Motion Picture, Video & TV Post Production
N.A.I.C.S.: 512110
William Sargent (CEO)

Subsidiary (US):

Framestore Inc.   **(2)**
135 Spring St, New York, NY 10012
Tel.: (212) 775-0600
Web Site: http://www.framestore.com
Industrial Design Services
N.A.I.C.S.: 541420
Jonathan Shipman (Mng Dir-Integrated Ad-
vertising)

**CULTURE CONVENIENCE
CLUB CO., LTD.**
Shibuya Garden Tower 6F 16-17
Nanpeidai-cho, Shibuya-ku, Tokyo,
150-0036, Japan
Tel.: (81) 3 6800 4500
Web Site: http://www.ccc.co.jp
Year Founded: 1983
Sales Range: $1-4.9 Billion
Emp.: 2,259
DVDs, CDs, Books, Magazines &
Video Games Retailer; E-Commerce;
Marketing Services
N.A.I.C.S.: 459999
Muneaki Masuda (Pres & CEO)

Subsidiaries:

Culture Publishers Inc   **(1)**
16th Floor Yebisu Garden Place Tower,
4-20-3 Ebisu Shibuya-ku, 150-6021, Tokyo,
Japan
Tel.: (81) 354756910
Web Site: http://www.culture-pub.jp
Sales Range: $800-899.9 Million
Music Publishers
N.A.I.C.S.: 512230

Esquire Magazine Japan, Inc.   **(1)**
4th Floor SI Bldg, 1-3-6 Kita-Aoyama
Minato-ku, 107-0061, Tokyo, Japan

Tel.: (81) 357755690
Web Site: http://www.esquire.co.jp
Sales Range: $25-49.9 Million
Emp.: 45
Publisher
N.A.I.C.S.: 513199

Kitamura Co., Ltd.   **(1)**
1-30 Akabori, Kohoku-ku, Yokohama, 222-
0033, Kanagawa, Japan   **(94.6%)**
Tel.: (81) 45 4760777
Web Site: http://www.kitamura.jp
Sales Range: $1-4.9 Billion
Electronic Equipment Distr
N.A.I.C.S.: 423620
Masashi Kitamura (Pres & CEO)

Photocreate Co., Ltd.   **(1)**
6-16-6 Nishishinjuku, Shinjuku-ku, Tokyo,
160-0023, Japan   **(27.39%)**
Tel.: (81) 3 5909 5870
Web Site: http://www.photocreate.co.jp
Emp.: 698
Internet Photoservices
N.A.I.C.S.: 541922

T Card & Marketing Co., Ltd.   **(1)**
24th Floor Yebisu Garden Place Tower,
4-20-3 Ebisu Shibuya-ku, 150-6023, Tokyo,
Japan
Tel.: (81) 354242361
Web Site: http://www.tcard.jp
Credit Card Issuing
N.A.I.C.S.: 522210

Tsutaya Online Co., Ltd.   **(1)**
26th Floor Yebisu Garden Place Tower,
4-20-3 Ebisu Shibuya-ku, 150-6021, Tokyo,
Japan
Tel.: (81) 354241674
Web Site: http://www.tsutaya.co.jp
Sales Range: $1-4.9 Billion
Electronic Shopping & Mail-Order Houses
N.A.I.C.S.: 425120

Tsutaya Stores Holdings Co., Ltd   **(1)**
7th Floor Shionogi Shibuya Bldg, 2-17-5
Shibuya Shibuya-ku, 150-0002, Tokyo, Ja-
pan
Tel.: (81) 354594281
Web Site: http://www.ccc.co.jp
Prerecorded Compact Disc Tape & Record
Reproducing
N.A.I.C.S.: 334610

CULTURECOM HOLDINGS LTD
Room 1502 15/F Far East Finance
Centre 16 Harcourt Road, Admiralty,
Hong Kong, China (Hong Kong)
Tel.: (852) 2 950 8888
Web Site:
    http://www.culturecom.com.hk
0343—(HKG)
Rev.: $26,647,913
Assets: $31,692,708
Liabilities: $9,434,113
Net Worth: $22,258,595
Earnings: ($9,066,649)
Emp.: 162
Fiscal Year-end: 03/31/21
Printing & Publishing Industry
N.A.I.C.S.: 513120
Kin Chung Kwan (Mng Dir)

Subsidiaries:

Citicomics Limited   **(1)**
Suite 1102 Chinachem Tower 37 Corner
Road Central, Hong Kong, China (Hong
Kong)
Tel.: (852) 29508888
Sales Range: $25-49.9 Million
Emp.: 50
Books Publishing Services
N.A.I.C.S.: 513120
Cheung Wai Tung (Mng Dir)

Culturecom Centre Limited   **(1)**
Rm 610c 612-613 Level 6 Core D 100 Cy-
berport Rd, Hong Kong, China (Hong Kong)
Tel.: (852) 29508888
Property Holding Services
N.A.I.C.S.: 531312

**CUMBERLAND BUILDING SO-
CIETY**
Cumberland House Cooper Way,

Cumberland Building Society—(Continued)

Parkhouse, Carlisle, CA3 0JF, United Kingdom
Tel.: (44) 1228 403141
Web Site:
   http://www.cumberland.co.uk
Rev.: $83,712,173
Assets: $3,270,015,812
Liabilities: $3,035,078,332
Net Worth: $234,937,480
Earnings: $14,468,097
Emp.: 343
Fiscal Year-end: 03/31/19
Mortgage Lending
N.A.I.C.S.: 522310
Trevor Hebdon (Co-Chm)

CUMICA CORPORATION
389-1 Kimmei-cho, Soka, 340-0052, Saitama, Japan
Tel.: (81) 489441849
Web Site: https://www.cumica.co.jp
Year Founded: 1983
88870—(TKS)
Sales Range: Less than $1 Million
Emp.: 36
Real Estate Development Services
N.A.I.C.S.: 531311
Junji Kawai (Pres & CEO)

CUMULEX N.V.
Grensstraat 7, Vlaams-Brabant, 1831, Machelen, Belgium
Tel.: (32) 32853966
Web Site: https://www.cumulex.be
Year Founded: 1956
CLEX—(EUR)
Investment Management Service
N.A.I.C.S.: 523999

CUNDARI INTEGRATED ADVERTISING
26 Duncan St, Toronto, M5V 2B9, ON, Canada
Tel.: (416) 510-1771
Web Site: http://www.cundari.com
Emp.: 100
Advertising Agencies
N.A.I.C.S.: 541810
Maria Orsini (VP-Admin & Fin)

CUONGTHUAN INVESTMENT CORPORATION
168 KP11, Bien Hoa, Dong Nai, Vietnam
Tel.: (84) 616291081
Web Site: https://www.cuongthuan.vn
Year Founded: 2000
CTI—(HOSE)
Rev.: $33,552,786
Assets: $186,047,458
Liabilities: $127,930,038
Net Worth: $58,117,420
Earnings: $3,297,401
Fiscal Year-end: 12/31/23
Precast Concrete Products Mfr
N.A.I.C.S.: 327331
Nguyen Xuan Quang (Gen Mgr)

CUP INTERACTIVE SAS
122 rue Edouard Vaillant, 92300, Levallois-Perret, France
Tel.: (33) 1 4639 5500   FR
Web Site:
   http://www.cupinteractive.com
Sales Range: $10-24.9 Million
Online Media Publisher
N.A.I.C.S.: 516210
Jean-Philippe Caste (Dir Gen)

CUPRUM S.A. DE C.V.
Avenida Diego Diaz de Berlanga No 95-A Norte, Fraccionamiento El Nogalar, San Nicolas, CP 66480, NL, Mexico
Tel.: (52) 81 8385 8500   MX

Web Site: http://www.cuprum.com
Year Founded: 1948
Emp.: 6,000
Aluminum Extruder & Products Mfr
N.A.I.C.S.: 331318
Arnulfo Muzquiz Tamez (Pres)

Subsidiaries:

Escaleras, S. de R.L. de C.V.
Avenida Diego Diaz de Berlanga No 95-A Norte, Fraccionamiento El Nogalar, San Nicolas, CP 66480, NL, Mexico
Tel.: (52) 81 8305 8500
Web Site: http://www.escaleras.mx
Aluminum Ladder Mfr
N.A.I.C.S.: 332999

Louisville Ladder Inc.   (1)
7765 National Tpke Unit 190, Louisville, KY 40214
Tel.: (502) 636-2811
Web Site: http://www.louisvilleladder.com
Emp.: 100
Aluminum Ladders & Scaffolding Mfr
N.A.I.C.S.: 332999
Jorge A. Viramontes Medina (Pres)

Subsidiary (Non-US):

Featherlite Industries Ltd.   (2)
100 Engelhard Drive, Aurora, L4G 3V2, ON, Canada
Tel.: (905) 727-0031
Web Site: http://www.featherliteladders.com
Sales Range: $10-24.9 Million
Emp.: 85
Aluminum Ladder Mfr & Distr
N.A.I.C.S.: 332999

CURA TECHNOLOGIES LTD.
3rd Floor 1-98-9/3/9 & 10 Plot 25 & 26 Sy No 71 Part, Hyderabad, 500 081, India
Tel.: (91) 4023111793
Web Site: https://curasoftware.com
Year Founded: 1994
Rev.: $449,550
Assets: $1,682,390
Liabilities: $1,517,454
Net Worth: $164,936
Earnings: ($195,239)
Fiscal Year-end: 03/31/18
Software Development Services
N.A.I.C.S.: 541511
Bala Reddy Gopu (Chm & Mng Dir)

Subsidiaries:

CURA Risk Management Software (PTY) Limited   (1)
13 Scott Street Waverly, Johannesburg, 2090, South Africa
Tel.: (27) 11 321 7500
Web Site: http://www.curasoftware.com
Sales Range: $50-74.9 Million
Emp.: 200
Management Software Publisher
N.A.I.C.S.: 513210

CURA Risk Management Software (PTY) Limited   (1)
Level 10 390 St Kilda Road, Melbourne, 3004, VIC, Australia
Tel.: (61) 3 9948 0020
Web Site: http://www.curasoftware.com
Emp.: 12
Software Development Services
N.A.I.C.S.: 541511

Subsidiary (Non-US):

CURA Software Solutions UK Limited   (2)
Suite 125 Berkeley Square House, London, W1J 6BD, United Kingdom
Tel.: (44) 20 7887 1584
Software Development Services
N.A.I.C.S.: 541511

CURACHEM CO., LTD.
207 Osongsaengmyeong 1-ro Osong-eup, Heungdeok-gu, Cheongju, 28161, Chungcheongbuk-do, Korea (South)
Tel.: (82) 432367387

Web Site: https://www.curachem.com
Year Founded: 2009
456190—(KRS)
Biotechnology Research & Development Services
N.A.I.C.S.: 541714

CURACLE CO., LTD.
23-1 Hyoryeong-ro, Seocho-gu, Seoul, 06694, Gyeonggi-do, Korea (South)
Tel.: (82) 234870077
Web Site: https://www.curacle.com
Year Founded: 2016
365270—(KRS)
Research & Experimental Development Services
N.A.I.C.S.: 541715
Ji-Hye Kang (Head-Clinical Dev)

CURASAN AG
Lindigstrasse 4, D-63801, Kleinostheim, Germany
Tel.: (49) 6027409000
Web Site: http://www.curasan.de
Regenerative Medicinal Products Mfr
N.A.I.C.S.: 325412
Gregor Siebert (Head-Mktg & Sls)

CURATIS HOLDING AG
Weierweg 7 CH, Liestal, Switzerland
Tel.: (41) 619278777   CH
Web Site: https://curatis.com
Year Founded: 2017
CURN—(SWX)
Rev.: $317,092
Assets: $154,016
Liabilities: $607,004
Net Worth: ($452,988)
Earnings: ($161,943)
Fiscal Year-end: 12/31/21
Pharmaceutical Product Mfr & Distr
N.A.I.C.S.: 325412
Roland Rutschmann (CEO)

CURCAS OIL N.V.
Haaksbergweg 71, 1101 BR, Amsterdam, Netherlands
Tel.: (31) 203121212
Alternative Energy Services
N.A.I.C.S.: 213112
Kurt Stuessi (Founder, CEO & Mng Dir)

CURETIS NV
Max-Eyth-Str 42, 71088, Holzgerlingen, Germany
Tel.: (49) 703149195
Year Founded: 2007
CURE—(EUR)
Molecular Diagnostic System Mfr
N.A.I.C.S.: 334510
Werner Schafer (Vice Chm)

CUREVAC N.V.
Friedrich-Miescher-Strasse 15, 72076, Tubingen, Germany
Tel.: (49) 707198830   NL
Web Site: https://www.curevac.com
Year Founded: 2020
CVAC—(NASDAQ)
Rev.: $82,807,941
Assets: $1,056,866,129
Liabilities: $401,903,465
Net Worth: $654,962,665
Earnings: ($305,867,379)
Emp.: 904
Fiscal Year-end: 12/31/22
Holding Company
N.A.I.C.S.: 551112
Franz-Werner Haas (CEO)

Subsidiaries:

CureVac Netherlands B.V.   (1)
Science Park 106, 1098 XG, Amsterdam, Netherlands
Tel.: (31) 202374970

Messenger Ribonucleic Acid Vaccine Mfr & Distr
N.A.I.C.S.: 325414

CureVac SE   (1)
Friedrich Miescher Str 15, 72076, Tubingen, Germany
Tel.: (49) 707198830
Prophylactic & Therapeutic Medicine Mfr
N.A.I.C.S.: 325412

CureVac Swiss AG   (1)
Wartenbergstrasse 40, CH-4052, Basel, Switzerland
Tel.: (41) 707198830
Messenger Ribonucleic Acid Vaccine Mfr & Distr
N.A.I.C.S.: 325414

CUREXO INC.
3rd & 4th Floor 480 480 Wiryesunhwan-ro, Songpa-gu, Seoul, 137-904, Korea (South)
Tel.: (82) 262028500
Web Site: https://www.curexo.com
Year Founded: 1992
060280—(KRS)
Rev.: $49,847,829
Assets: $75,471,165
Liabilities: $12,822,193
Net Worth: $62,648,972
Earnings: ($2,332,359)
Emp.: 77
Fiscal Year-end: 12/31/22
Medical Equipment Mfr
N.A.I.C.S.: 339113
Jaejun Lee (CEO)

CURIOX BIOSYSTEMS CO., LTD.
Samsung Harrington IT Tower 202 204-213 9 Gil 41 Digital-Ro, Geumchun-Gu, Seoul, 8511, Korea (South)
Tel.: (82) 220397160
Web Site: https://www.curiox.com
Year Founded: 2018
445680—(KRS)
Medical Equipment Mfr
N.A.I.C.S.: 339112

CURIUM SAS
63 Avenue des Champs-Elysees, 75008, Paris, France
Tel.: (33) 1 6985 7070   FR
Web Site:
   http://www.curiumpharma.com
Year Founded: 2012
Radiopharmaceutical Molecular Imaging Equipment Developer, Mfr & Distr
N.A.I.C.S.: 334510
Renaud Dehareng (CEO)

Subsidiaries:

Curium Netherlands Holdings B.V.   (1)
Stationsplein 105, 5211 BM, 's-Hertogenbosch, Netherlands
Tel.: (31) 800 2500008
Holding Company
N.A.I.C.S.: 551112

Branch (Non-US):

Curium Netherlands Holding B.V. - Czech Branch   (2)
Prosecka 852/66, 190 00, Prague, 9, Czech Republic
Tel.: (420) 236081296
Radiopharmaceutical Products Whslr
N.A.I.C.S.: 424210

Subsidiary (Domestic):

Mallinckrodt Medical B.V.   (2)
Westerduinweg 3, 1755 LE, Petten, Netherlands
Tel.: (31) 224 56 78 90
Radiopharmaceuticals Mfr
N.A.I.C.S.: 325412

Curium Sweden AB   (1)

Kungsgatan 50, 111 35, Stockholm, Sweden
Tel.: (46) 8 5025 2209
Radiopharmaceutical Products Whslr
N.A.I.C.S.: 424210

Curium US LLC (1)
111 W Port Plz Ste 800, Saint Louis, MO 63146
Tel.: (314) 384-8009
Radiopharmaceutical Products Developer, Mfr & Distr
N.A.I.C.S.: 325412
Dan Brague (CEO-North America)

Mallinckrodt Belgium BVBA (1)
Schalienhoevedreef 20T, 2800, Mechelen, Belgium
Tel.: (32) 1579 6780
Radiopharmaceutical Products Whslr
N.A.I.C.S.: 424210

CURO CO., LTD.
260-37 Cheoyong-ro, Nam-gu, Ulsan, 680-110, Korea (South)
Tel.: (82) 522789000
Web Site: http://www.dkme.com
Year Founded: 1981
015590—(KRS)
Rev.: $81,051,887
Assets: $147,791,126
Liabilities: $63,553,856
Net Worth: $84,237,270
Earnings: $8,650,229
Emp.: 193
Fiscal Year-end: 12/31/22
Chemical Equipment Mfr
N.A.I.C.S.: 332410
Sang Hun Suh (Pres & CEO)

CURRENT MOTOR CORPORATION
4-1-19 Utsukushigaoka, Aoba-Ku, Yokohama, 225-0002, Kanagawa, Japan
Tel.: (81) 459051008
Web Site:
https://www.currentmotor.co.jp
Year Founded: 2000
7690—(TKS)
Rev.: $63,975,120
Assets: $19,166,400
Liabilities: $13,861,760
Net Worth: $5,304,640
Earnings: $813,120
Emp.: 103
Fiscal Year-end: 10/31/22
Automobile Parts Distr
N.A.I.C.S.: 423120
Tomohiko Takeshita (Sr Mng Dir)

Subsidiaries:

Current Tech Center Co., Ltd. (1)
2-17-10 Mizusawa, Miyamae-ku, Kawasaki, 216-0012, Kanagawa, Japan
Tel.: (81) 44 978 5678
Web Site: https://www.current-tech.co.jp
Automotive Repair & Maintenance Services
N.A.I.C.S.: 811198

ICIN Co., Ltd. (1)
1-4-3 Azamino Mihashi Building 3F, Aoba-ku, Yokohama, 225-0011, Kanagawa, Japan
Tel.: (81) 45 903 0911
Web Site: https://www.icin.co.jp
Automotive Repair & Maintenance Services
N.A.I.C.S.: 811198

CURRENT TECHNOLOGY CORPORATION
850 West Hastings Street Suite 302, Vancouver, V6C 1E1, BC, Canada
Tel.: (604) 684-2727
Web Site: http://www.current-technology.com
Sales Range: Less than $1 Million
Emp.: 4
Applied Research Solutions
N.A.I.C.S.: 541690
Robert K. Kramer (Chm, Pres, CEO & Treas)

CURRENT WATER TECHNOLOGIES INC.
70 Southgate Drive Unit 4, Guelph, N1G 4P5, ON, Canada
Tel.: (519) 836-6155   ON
Web Site:
https://www.currentwatertech.com
Year Founded: 1996
WATR—(TSXV)
Rev.: $1,839,313
Assets: $877,512
Liabilities: $1,147,728
Net Worth: ($270,216)
Earnings: $15,280
Fiscal Year-end: 12/31/19
Waste Water Treatment Services
N.A.I.C.S.: 562998
Gene S. Shelp (Co-Founder, Pres & CEO)

Subsidiaries:

Blue Print Technologies (Pty) Ltd. (1)
394 Aries Street Waterkloof Ridge, Pretoria, 0181, South Africa
Tel.: (27) 12 460 8922
Waste Treatment Services
N.A.I.C.S.: 221310

CURRIE & BROWN HOLDINGS LIMITED
12 Dumaresq Street, Saint Helier, JE2 3RL, Jersey
Tel.: (44) 20 7920 9220   JE
Web Site:
http://www.curriebrown.com
Year Founded: 1919
Holding Company; Construction Project & Asset Management Consulting Services
N.A.I.C.S.: 551112
David Broomer (Chm)

Subsidiaries:

Currie & Brown (Australia) Pty. Limited (1)
Level 2 179 Queen Street, Melbourne, 3000, VIC, Australia
Tel.: (61) 3 9691 0000
Web Site: http://www.curriebrown.com
Construction Project & Asset Management Consulting Services
N.A.I.C.S.: 541690
Ray Bongiorno (Mng Dir)

Currie & Brown (CI) Limited (1)
12 Dumaresq Street, Saint Helier, JE2 3RL, Channel Islands, Jersey
Tel.: (44) 1534 720 326
Web Site: http://www.curriebrown.com
Construction Project & Asset Management Consulting Services
N.A.I.C.S.: 541990
James O'Mahony (Dir-Ops)

Currie & Brown UK Limited (1)
Dashwood House 69 Old Broad Street, London, EC2M 1QS, United Kingdom
Tel.: (44) 845 287 8800
Web Site: http://www.curriebrown.com
Construction Project & Asset Management Consulting Services
N.A.I.C.S.: 541990
Stuart McEwan (Dir-Ops)

Currie & Brown, Inc. (1)
821 Alexander Rd Ste 206, Princeton, NJ 08540
Tel.: (609) 759-7000
Web Site: http://www.curriebrown.com
Construction Project & Asset Management Consulting Services
N.A.I.C.S.: 541990
Paul Wood (COO)

CURRIE ROSE RESOURCES INC.
2704-401 Bay Street, Toronto, M5H 2Y4, ON, Canada
Tel.: (905) 688-9115   ON
Web Site: https://www.currierose.com

CUI—(TSXV)
Assets: $1,422,444
Liabilities: $300,960
Net Worth: $1,121,484
Earnings: ($54,307)
Emp.: 1
Fiscal Year-end: 12/31/19
Gold Exploration & Mining Services
N.A.I.C.S.: 212220
Michael Griffiths (Pres & CEO)

CURRO HOLDINGS LTD.
38 Oxford Street Durbanville, Cape Town, 7550, South Africa
Tel.: (27) 219791204   ZA
Web Site: https://www.curro.co.za
COH—(JSE)
Rev.: $259,447,440
Assets: $670,402,600
Liabilities: $282,211,720
Net Worth: $388,190,880
Earnings: $1,742,720
Emp.: 6,756
Fiscal Year-end: 12/31/23
Holding Company
N.A.I.C.S.: 551112
Santie L. Botha (Chm)

Subsidiaries:

Curro Education Botswana (Pty) Ltd. (1)
Plot 18580 Gaborone West Phase II, Gaborone, Botswana
Tel.: (267) 3923397
School Education Services
N.A.I.C.S.: 611710

Curro Education Namibia (Pty) Ltd. (1)
1 Sossusvlei Street, Kleine Kuppe, Windhoek, Namibia
Tel.: (264) 61381450
School Education Services
N.A.I.C.S.: 611710

Northriding College (Pty) Ltd. (1)
358 Valley Road, Northriding, Randburg, 2164, South Africa
Tel.: (27) 870877586
School Education Services
N.A.I.C.S.: 611710

Waterstone College (Pty) Ltd. (1)
Main Service Road, Kibler Park, Johannesburg, 2053, South Africa
Tel.: (27) 872854740
School Education Services
N.A.I.C.S.: 611710

Woodhill College Property Holdings (Pty) Ltd. (1)
De Villebois Mareuil Drive, Pretoria, South Africa
Tel.: (27) 129981774
School Education Services
N.A.I.C.S.: 611710

CURRYS PLC
1 Portal Way, London, W3 6RS, United Kingdom
Tel.: (44) 3713842089   UK
Web Site: https://www.currysplc.com
Year Founded: 1989
CURY—(LSE)
Rev.: $12,005,806,614
Assets: $7,383,236,556
Liabilities: $4,994,950,770
Net Worth: $2,388,285,786
Earnings: ($607,169,907)
Emp.: 28,166
Fiscal Year-end: 04/29/23
Telecommunication Servicesb
N.A.I.C.S.: 517112
Tony Denunzio (Deputy Chm)

Subsidiaries:

Alfa s.r.l. (1)
Via Caduti di Ustica 28, 40012, Calderara di Reno, BO, Italy
Tel.: (39) 0510828494
Web Site: http://www.alfadispenser.com
Paints Mfr

N.A.I.C.S.: 325510

Connected World Services Netherlands BV (1)
Watermanweg 96, 3067 GG, Rotterdam, Netherlands
Tel.: (31) 107421018
Web Site:
http://www.connectedworldservices.nl
Insurance Services
N.A.I.C.S.: 524210

DSG International Belgium BVBA (1)
Vluchtenburgstraat 11, 2630, Aartselaar, Belgium
Tel.: (32) 38273422
Web Site: http://www.dsg-belgium.com
Electrical Contractor Services
N.A.I.C.S.: 238210

DSG Retail Limited (1)
1 Portal Way, London, W3 6RS, United Kingdom   (100%)
Tel.: (44) 208 896 5000
Web Site: http://www.currys.co.uk
Consumer Electronics Retailer
N.A.I.C.S.: 449210

Dixons Carphone CoE s.r.o. (1)
Trnita 491/5, 602 00, Brno, Czech Republic
Tel.: (420) 543123100
Web Site: http://www.dixonscarphone.cz
Electronic Retail Services
N.A.I.C.S.: 449210
Kristina Sabakova (Mgr-Recruitment & Branding)

Dixons Deutschland GmbH (1)
Wittenberger Str 9, 04129, Leipzig, Germany
Tel.: (49) 34190980000
Tube & Hose Fitting Mfr
N.A.I.C.S.: 332912

ElGiganten A/S (1)
Arne Jacobsens Alle 16 2nd Floor, 2300, Copenhagen, Denmark
Tel.: (45) 70807070
Web Site: https://www.elgiganten.dk
N.A.I.C.S.: 334290

Elgiganten Aktiebolag (1)
Franzengatan 6, 11251, Stockholm, Sweden
Tel.: (46) 771115115
Web Site: https://www.elgiganten.se
N.A.I.C.S.: 449210

Elkjop Nordic AS (1)
Nydalsveien 18a, 0484, Oslo, Norway
Tel.: (47) 23007000
Web Site: http://www.elkjopnordic.com
Electronic Retail Services
N.A.I.C.S.: 449210
Erik G. Sonsterud (CEO)

Epoq Logistic DC k.s. (1)
Evropska 868, 664 42, Modrice, Czech Republic
Tel.: (420) 295509910
Web Site: https://www.epoqlogistics.cz
N.A.I.C.S.: 541614

Simplify Digital Limited (1)
1 Portal Way, London, W3 6RS, United Kingdom
Tel.: (44) 8005424704
Web Site: http://www.simplifydigital.co.uk
Comparison Software Development Services
N.A.I.C.S.: 541511
Charlie Ponsonby (CEO)

The Carphone Warehouse Limited (1)
1 Portal Way, London, W3 6RS, United Kingdom
Tel.: (44) 3701116565
Web Site:
https://www.carphonewarehouse.com
N.A.I.C.S.: 484220

CURT BAUER GMBH
Bahnhofstrasse 16, 08280, Aue, Germany
Tel.: (49) 37715000
Web Site: http://www.curt-bauer.de
Rev.: $18,968,026

Curt Bauer GmbH—(Continued)

Emp.: 123
Broadwoven Fabric Mfr
N.A.I.C.S.: 313210
Michael Bauer (Mng Dir)

CURT GEORGI GMBH & CO. KG

Otto-Lilienthal-Str 35-37, 71034, Boblingen, Germany
Tel.: (49) 7031640101
Web Site: http://www.curtgeorgi.de
Year Founded: 1875
Sales Range: $10-24.9 Million
Emp.: 50
Food Products Mfr
N.A.I.C.S.: 311999
Andreas Landgraf (Owner & Co-Mng Dir)

Subsidiaries:

Hungary Curt Georgi KFT   (1)
Hegyalja Utca 38, Csopak, Hungary
Tel.: (36) 87456287
Food Products Distr
N.A.I.C.S.: 456191

Poland Curt Georgi Poland   (1)
ul Brzozowa 75B, Komorow, Nowa Wies, Poland
Tel.: (48) 227580435
Web Site: http://www.curtgeorgi.pl
Food Products Distr
N.A.I.C.S.: 456191

Romania Curt Georgi Romania S.R.L.   (1)
Str Independentei nr 24 jud Bihor, Oradea, Romania
Tel.: (40) 259437707
Food Products Distr
N.A.I.C.S.: 456191

Serbia Curt Georgi Novi Sad   (1)
Svetozara Miletica 54, Kac, Serbia
Tel.: (381) 63508511
Food Products Distr
N.A.I.C.S.: 456191

Spain Curt Georgi Aromas y Esencias S.A.   (1)
Consejo de Ciento 138 entlo 4a, Barcelona, Spain
Tel.: (34) 933251908
Food Products Distr
N.A.I.C.S.: 456191

CURTIS INTERNATIONAL LTD.

315 Attwell Dr, Etobicoke, Toronto, M9W 5C1, ON, Canada
Tel.: (800) 968-9853   ON
Web Site: http://www.curtisint.com
Consumer Electronic Products Mfr & Distr
N.A.I.C.S.: 423620
Aaron Herzog (Pres)

CURVES HOLDINGS CO., LTD.

11F Shibaura Renesite Tower 3-9-1 Shibaura, Minato-ku, Tokyo, 108-0023, Japan
Tel.: (81) 354189922
Web Site:
https://www.curvesholdings.co.jp
Year Founded: 2008
7085—(TKS)
Rev.: $220,592,300
Assets: $257,346,280
Liabilities: $136,622,300
Net Worth: $120,723,980
Earnings: $22,180,520
Emp.: 695
Fiscal Year-end: 08/31/24
Holding Company
N.A.I.C.S.: 551112
Takeshi Masumoto (Pres)

Subsidiaries:

Curves Japan Co., Ltd.   (1)
Shibaura Rene Site Tower 11F 3-9-1

Shibaura, Minato-ku, Tokyo, 108-0023, Japan
Tel.: (81) 35 418 9900
Web Site: https://www.curves.co.jp
Heath Gymnastic Services
N.A.I.C.S.: 713940

HighStandard Co., Ltd.   (1)
3-9-1 Shibaura Shibaura Rene Site Tower 11F, Minato-ku, Tokyo, Japan
Tel.: (81) 35 418 9920
Web Site: https://high-standard.co.jp
Heath Gymnastic Services
N.A.I.C.S.: 713940

CURZON ENERGY PLC

71-91 Aldwych House, London, WC2B 4HN, United Kingdom
Tel.: (44) 2077479980   UK
Web Site:
https://www.curzonenergy.com
Year Founded: 2016
CZN—(LSE)
Assets: $213,887
Liabilities: $1,920,853
Net Worth: ($1,706,966)
Earnings: ($617,574)
Emp.: 3
Fiscal Year-end: 12/31/20
Oil & Gas Exploration Services
N.A.I.C.S.: 213112
Scott Kaintz (CEO)

CUSCAL LTD.

1 Margaret Street, Sydney, 2000, NSW, Australia
Tel.: (61) 282999000   AU
Web Site: http://www.cuscal.com.au
Rev.: $157,732,246
Assets: $1,639,416,786
Liabilities: $1,459,533,110
Net Worth: $179,883,676
Earnings: $15,611,484
Emp.: 450
Fiscal Year-end: 06/30/19
Wholesale & Transactional Banking Services
N.A.I.C.S.: 522110
Craig N. Kennedy (Mng Dir)

Subsidiaries:

Credit Union Dispute Resolution Centre Pty Limited   (1)
1 Margaret Street, Sydney, 2000, NSW, Australia   (100%)
Tel.: (61) 2 8299 9000
Web Site: http://www.cuscal.com.au
Trust Fiduciary, Credit Union & Custody Activities
N.A.I.C.S.: 523991

Credit Union Foundation Australia Pty Limited   (1)
Level 1 No 1 Margireg St, 10 Queen Rd, 3004, Sydney, Australia   (100%)
Tel.: (61) 282999059
Web Site: http://www.cufa.com.au
Sales Range: $50-74.9 Million
Emp.: 25
Trust Fiduciary & Custody Activities
N.A.I.C.S.: 523991

Cuscal Management Pty Limited   (1)
1 Margaret St Level 2, Sydney, 2000, NSW, Australia
Tel.: (61) 282999000
Web Site: http://www.cuscal.com.au
Emp.: 370
Trust Fiduciary & Custody Activities
N.A.I.C.S.: 523991
Craig Kennedy (Mng Dir)

Integris Securitisation Services Pty Limited   (1)
1 Margaret St Level 3, Sydney, 2000, NSW, Australia
Tel.: (61) 282999000
Web Site: http://www.cuscal.com.au
Mortgage & Nonmortgage Loan Brokers
N.A.I.C.S.: 522310
Craig N. Kennedy (Mng Dir)

CUSCAPI BERHAD

Level 27 and 28 Block N Empire City Damansara, No 8 Jalan Damansara PJU 8, 47820, Petaling Jaya, Selangor, Malaysia
Tel.: (60) 376237777   MY
Web Site: https://www.cuscapi.com
Year Founded: 1978
CUSCAPI—(KLS)
Rev.: $6,007,622
Assets: $13,625,341
Liabilities: $2,319,850
Net Worth: $11,305,491
Earnings: $404,707
Emp.: 40
Fiscal Year-end: 12/31/23
Software Development Services
N.A.I.C.S.: 513210
Panneer Selvam (Chm)

Subsidiaries:

Cuscapi (Thail) Co. Ltd.   (1)
CTI Tower 191/86 10th Floor Ratchadapisek Road, Klongtoey, Bangkok, 10110, Thailand
Tel.: (66) 22588673
Tape Distr
N.A.I.C.S.: 424130
Eric Chai (Gen Mgr)

Cuscapi Beijing Co. Ltd.   (1)
Room 1205 Tongguang Tower, Haoyang District, Beijing, 100027, China
Tel.: (86) 1065069779
Software Publisher
N.A.I.C.S.: 513210

Cuscapi Singapore Pte. Ltd.   (1)
2 Kallang Avenue CT HUB 07-26, Singapore, 339407, Singapore
Tel.: (65) 62381080
Tape Distr
N.A.I.C.S.: 424130

Cuscapi Suzhou Co. Ltd.   (1)
Room 1726 Zhong Heng Building No111 Ba Da Street, Suzhou Industry Park, Suzhou, 215100, Jiangsu, China
Tel.: (86) 51262929368
Software Publisher
N.A.I.C.S.: 513210

PT Cuscapi Indonesia   (1)
JI Cideng Timur No 11 D RT5/RW 1 Petojo Utara Kecamatan Gambir, Kota Jakarta Pusat Daerah Khusus Ibukota, 10130, Jakarta, Indonesia
Tel.: (62) 2129772902
Tape Distr
N.A.I.C.S.: 424130

CUSPIS CAPITAL LTD.

77 King Street West TD North Tower Suite 700, Toronto, M5K 1G8, ON, Canada
Tel.: (416) 214-4810
CUSP.P—(TSXV)
Rev.: $28,693
Assets: $1,687,183
Liabilities: $14,253
Net Worth: $1,672,929
Earnings: ($216,043)
Fiscal Year-end: 12/31/19
Asset Management Services
N.A.I.C.S.: 523940
William Ollerhead (CEO)

CUSTODIAN INVESTMENT PLC

16A Commercial Avenue Sabo, Yaba, Lagos, Nigeria
Tel.: (234) 127740009
Web Site:
https://www.custodianplc.com.ng
Year Founded: 1991
CUSTODIAN—(NIGE)
Rev.: $76,296,220
Assets: $157,808,255
Liabilities: $104,008,621
Net Worth: $53,799,634
Earnings: $8,262,067
Emp.: 362
Fiscal Year-end: 12/31/22
General Insurance Services

N.A.I.C.S.: 524210
Omobola Johnson (Chm)

Subsidiaries:

Crusader Sterling Pension Limited   (1)
14B Keffi Street Off Awolowo Road Ikoyi, Lagos, Nigeria
Tel.: (234) 12714605
Web Site: https://crusaderpensions.com
Fund Security & Management Services
N.A.I.C.S.: 524292

CrusaderSterling Pensions Ltd.   (1)
14B Keffi Street Off Awolowo Road Ikoyi, Lagos, Nigeria
Tel.: (234) 127138004
Web Site:
https://www.crusaderpensions.com
Emp.: 200
Insurance Agency Services
N.A.I.C.S.: 524210
Adeniyi Falade (Mng Dir)

UPDC Plc.   (1)
UAC House 1-5 Odunlami Street, PO Box 156, Lagos, Nigeria   (51%)
Tel.: (234) 9023488511
Web Site: https://updcplc.com
Rev.: $4,339,091
Assets: $58,183,874
Liabilities: $33,018,807
Net Worth: $25,165,067
Earnings: ($1,581,443)
Emp.: 266
Fiscal Year-end: 12/31/2020
Real Estate Manangement Services
N.A.I.C.S.: 531390
Wole Oshin (Chm)

CUSTOJUSTO UNIPESSOAL, LDA

Rua Castilho 44 8 Floor, Lisbon, 1250 071, Portugal
Tel.: (351) 214028274
Web Site: http://www.custojusto.pt
Sales Range: $25-49.9 Million
Emp.: 8
Advertising Agencies
N.A.I.C.S.: 541810
Pedro Furtado (Mng Dir)

CUSTOM ELECTRIC LTD.

1725 - 27th Avenue NE, Calgary, T2E 7E1, AB, Canada
Tel.: (403) 291-3303
Web Site:
https://www.customelectric.com
Year Founded: 1970
Rev.: $27,058,737
Emp.: 150
Electrical Contractor
N.A.I.C.S.: 238210
Brian Phelps (VP-Bus Dev)

CUSTOM PLASTICS INTERNATIONAL LTD.

887 D Arcy Street, Cobourg, K9A 4B4, ON, Canada
Tel.: (905) 372-2281
Web Site:
http://www.customplastics.ca
Year Founded: 1965
Rev.: $13,277,500
Emp.: 90
Plastic Injection Molding Material Mfr
N.A.I.C.S.: 333248
Richard B. Gadd (VP-Sls)

CUSTOM SPA

Via Berettine 2, Fontevivo, 43010, Parma, Italy
Tel.: (39) 0521 680111   IT
Web Site: http://www.custom.it
Year Founded: 1992
Holding Company
N.A.I.C.S.: 551112
Carlo Stradi (Pres & CEO)

Subsidiaries:

Custom America, Inc.   (1)

12 Creek Pkwy Ste 100, Boothwyn, PA 19061
Tel.: (302) 384-6931
Web Site: https://www.custom.biz
Software & Hardware Solutions
N.A.I.C.S.: 423430
Nicholas Ciarlante *(CEO)*

Subsidiary (Domestic):

POS-X, LLC   **(2)**
1975 Midway Ln Ste O, Bellingham, WA 98226
Tel.: (360) 302-2222
Web Site: http://www.pos-x.com
Sales Range: $1-9.9 Million
Emp.: 9
Computer Hardware Mfr
N.A.I.C.S.: 334118
Mark Dunlop *(VP-Sls)*

CUTIX PLC.
No 17 Osita Onyejianya Street Umuanuka Otolo Nnewi, Ajao Estate, Lagos, Nigeria
Tel.: (234) 7046236426
Web Site:
   https://www.cutixplc.com.ng
Year Founded: 1982
CUTIX—(NIGE)
Rev.: $6,845,353
Assets: $4,324,239
Liabilities: $1,979,329
Net Worth: $2,344,910
Earnings: $584,745
Emp.: 258
Fiscal Year-end: 04/30/23
Electronic Cable Mfr
N.A.I.C.S.: 237130
Gilbert Obiajulu Uzodike *(Founder)*

CUTLER FOREST PRODUCTS INC.
81 Royal Group Crescent Unit A, Vaughan, L4X 1X9, ON, Canada
Tel.: (905) 212-1414
Web Site: http://www.cutlergroup.com
Year Founded: 2001
Rev.: $31,626,797
Emp.: 80
Wood Products Whslr
N.A.I.C.S.: 321999
Jonathan Glick *(Pres)*

Subsidiaries:

Cutler Distribution & Fabrication   **(1)**
81 Royal Group Crescent Unit A, Vaughan, L4H 1X9, ON, Canada
Tel.: (905) 212-1414
Web Site: http://www.cutlerpanels.com
Panel Distr
N.A.I.C.S.: 423310

CUU LONG PETRO URBAN DEVELOPMENT & INVEST-MENT CORPORATION
No 02 Block KTM06 Road No 6 Urban Area 5A Ward 4, Soc Trang, Vietnam
Tel.: (84) 793627999
Web Site: https://www.pvcl.com.vn
CCL—(HOSE)
Rev.: $13,044,785
Assets: $46,929,602
Liabilities: $18,672,376
Net Worth: $28,257,226
Earnings: $2,377,158
Fiscal Year-end: 12/31/23
Real Estate Development Services
N.A.I.C.S.: 531390

CUU LONG PHARMACEUTI-CAL JOINT STOCK CORPO-RATION
No 150 14/9 Street Ward 5, Vinh Long, Vietnam
Tel.: (84) 703822533
Web Site:
   https://www.pharimexco.com.vn

DCL—(HOSE)
Rev.: $47,130,575
Assets: $93,831,352
Liabilities: $34,058,722
Net Worth: $59,772,630
Earnings: $2,559,921
Fiscal Year-end: 12/31/23
Pharmaceutical Preparation Mfr
N.A.I.C.S.: 325412
Luong Van Hoa *(Exec Dir)*

CUULONG FISH JOINT STOCK COMPANY
90 Hung Vuong street My Tho Hamlet My Quy Ward, Long Xuyen, An Giang, Vietnam
Tel.: (84) 76931000
Web Site: https://www.clfish.com
ACL—(HOSE)
Rev.: $46,008,081
Assets: $72,066,216
Liabilities: $39,141,566
Net Worth: $32,924,650
Earnings: $405,944
Emp.: 3,000
Fiscal Year-end: 12/31/23
Fish Farming Services
N.A.I.C.S.: 112511
Hai Xuan Nguyen *(Member-Mgmt Bd)*

CVA S.P.A. A S.U.
Via Stazione n 31, 11024, Chatillon, Italy
Tel.: (39) 0166823111   IT
Web Site: https://www.cvaspa.it
Holding Company
N.A.I.C.S.: 551112

Subsidiaries:

CVA EOS S.r.l.   **(1)**
Via Stazione n 31, 11024, Chatillon, Italy
Tel.: (39) 0166823111
Web Site: https://www.cvaspa.it
Electric Power Distr
N.A.I.C.S.: 221122

CVC BRASIL OPERADORA E AGENCIA DE VIAGENS S.A.
Rua da Catequese 227, Jardim Santo Andre, Sao Paulo, 09090-401, SP, Brazil
Tel.: (55) 983850696   BR
Web Site: http://ww2.cvc.com.br
Year Founded: 1972
CVCB3—(BRAZ)
Rev.: $295,247,810
Assets: $830,681,914
Liabilities: $705,394,125
Net Worth: $125,287,789
Earnings: ($94,153,529)
Fiscal Year-end: 12/31/23
Tour Operator
N.A.I.C.S.: 561520
Felipe Pinto Gomes *(Dir-Investor Relations)*

Subsidiaries:

Submarino Viagens Ltda   **(1)**
600-1 andar Rooms 108-B and 109-B, Grand Plaza Shopping Business Center, Santo Andre Bairro Jardim Avenida Industrial, 09080-970, Sao Paulo, Brazil
Tel.: (55) 1130032989
Web Site:
   http://www.submarinoviagens.com.br
Tourism & Travel Agency Services
N.A.I.C.S.: 561510

Visual Turismo Ltda   **(1)**
Rua das Esmeraldas 387/395, Jardim Santo Andre, Sao Paulo, Brazil
Tel.: (55) 1132352000
Web Site: http://www.visualturismo.com.br
Tourism & Travel Agency Services
N.A.I.C.S.: 561510

CVC CAPITAL PARTNERS SICAV-FIS S.A.

20 Avenue Monterey, 2163, Luxembourg, Luxembourg
Tel.: (352) 26478368   LU
Web Site: http://www.cvc.com
Year Founded: 1981
Holding Company; Private Equity Investment Firms
N.A.I.C.S.: 551112
Steve Koltes *(Co-Founder & Co-Chm)*

Subsidiaries:

CVC Advisers Ltd.   **(1)**
111 Strand, London, WC2R 0AG, United Kingdom
Tel.: (44) 205204950
Web Site: http://www.cvc.com
Privater Equity Firm
N.A.I.C.S.: 523999
John Clark *(Mng Partner)*

Holding (Non-US):

AR Packaging Group AB   **(2)**
Maskinvagen 1, PO Box 177, 22100, Lund, Sweden
Tel.: (46) 46 287 33 00
Web Site: http://www.ar-packaging.com
Sales Range: $600-649.9 Million
Emp.: 3,200
Packaging Mfr
N.A.I.C.S.: 322212
Stig Gustavson *(Chm)*

Subsidiary (Domestic):

A&R Carton AB   **(3)**
Adelgatan 6, SE 211 22, Malmo, Sweden
Tel.: (46) 406615660
Web Site: http://www.ar-carton.com
Folding Cartons & Packaging Machinery Mfr
N.A.I.C.S.: 322211

Subsidiary (Non-US):

A&R Carton   **(4)**
Romuvos str 32 C, 47197, Kaunas, Lithuania
Tel.: (370) 37460626
Web Site: http://www.ar-carton.com
Emp.: 1
Folding Cartons & Packaging Machinery Mfr
N.A.I.C.S.: 322211
Rimantas Putrius *(Mgr-Sls)*

A&R Carton A/S   **(4)**
Bredmyra 4 N, Box 33, Borgenhaugen, 1739, Sarpsborg, Norway
Tel.: (47) 69973803
Web Site: http://www.ar-carton.com
Sales Range: $25-49.9 Million
Folding Cartons & Packaging Machinery Mfr
N.A.I.C.S.: 322211

Subsidiary (Domestic):

A&R Carton Lund AB   **(4)**
Maskinvagen 1, 221 00, Lund, Sweden
Tel.: (46) 46183020
Web Site: http://www.ar-carton.com
Sales Range: $50-74.9 Million
Folding Cartons & Packaging Machinery Mfr
N.A.I.C.S.: 322211

Subsidiary (US):

A&R Carton North America Inc.   **(4)**
1400 N Brook Pkwy Ste 350, Suwanee, GA 30052
Tel.: (770) 623-8235
Web Site: http://www.ar-carton.com
Sales Range: $50-74.9 Million
Emp.: 2
Folding Cartons & Packaging Machinery Solutions
N.A.I.C.S.: 322211

Subsidiary (Non-US):

A&R Carton Oy   **(4)**
Luvalahdentie 1, PO Box 120, Kauttua, 27500, Finland
Tel.: (358) 10430500
Web Site: http://www.ar-carton.com
Folding Cartons & Packaging Machinery Mfr
N.A.I.C.S.: 322212
Rauno Viljakainen *(VP & Bus Area Mgr)*

A&R Carton St Petersburg ZAO   **(4)**

Volkhonskoye Shosse 4, Lomonosov District, Poselok Gorelovo, 198323, Saint Petersburg, Russia
Tel.: (7) 8123466167
Web Site: http://www.ar-carton.com
Sales Range: $25-49.9 Million
Folding Cartons & Packaging Machinery Mfr
N.A.I.C.S.: 322211

A&R Carton cdf SA   **(4)**
Boulevard Du Cormier, Cholet, 49302, France
Tel.: (33) 241462940
Web Site: http://www.ar-carton.com
Folding Cartons & Packaging Machinery Mfr
N.A.I.C.S.: 322211
Olivier Moisan *(Mgr)*

BSC Drukarnia Opakowan SA   **(4)**
Ul Zmigrodzka 37, PL 60-171, Poznan, Poland   **(98.17%)**
Tel.: (48) 618676061
Web Site: http://www.bsc-packaging.com
Rev.: $60,401,437
Assets: $84,884,365
Liabilities: $12,507,260
Net Worth: $72,377,105
Earnings: $6,289,609
Emp.: 470
Fiscal Year-end: 12/31/2018
Packaging Products Mfr
N.A.I.C.S.: 322220
Janusz Schwark *(Chm-Mgmt Bd)*

Subsidiary (Domestic):

POSBAU S.A.   **(5)**
Ul Zmigrodzka 41/49, 60-171, Poznan, Poland
Tel.: (48) 618676011
Web Site: http://www.posbau.pl
Construction Services
N.A.I.C.S.: 236220

Subsidiary (Non-US):

Graphic Packaging International Europe Netherlands B.V.   **(4)**
Steenhouwersstraat 4, 8601 WD, Sneek, Netherlands
Tel.: (31) 515422922
Sales Range: $75-99.9 Million
Emp.: 110
Beverage Packaging Mfr
N.A.I.C.S.: 322211
Joseph P. Yost *(Sr VP-Europe)*

Subsidiary (Domestic):

Flextrus AB   **(3)**
Lund Business Park Maskinvagen 1, PO Box 22, SE-221 00, Lund, Sweden
Tel.: (46) 46183000
Flexible Packaging Mfr
N.A.I.C.S.: 322220

Subsidiary (Non-US):

Istragrafika d.d.   **(3)**
Obala Vladimira Nazora 1, 52210, Rovinj, Croatia
Tel.: (385) 52844800
Web Site: http://www.istragrafika.hr
Emp.: 160
General Packaging Products Mfr
N.A.I.C.S.: 326112

Joint Venture (Domestic):

Acromas Holdings Ltd.   **(2)**
Enbrook Park, Folkestone, CT20 3SE, Kent, United Kingdom
Tel.: (44) 1303776023
Web Site: http://www.acromas.com
Sales Range: $1-4.9 Billion
Emp.: 31,302
Holding Company; Financial, Insurance, Travel, Healthcare & Lifestyle Products & Services
N.A.I.C.S.: 551112
John Andrew Goodsell *(Chm & CEO)*

Subsidiary (Domestic):

Saga Group Limited   **(3)**
Enbrook Park, Middleburg Square, Folkestone, CT20 3SE, Kent, United Kingdom
Tel.: (44) 1303771111
Web Site: http://www.saga.co.uk
Sales Range: $125-149.9 Million
Emp.: 6,000

CVC Capital Partners SICAV-FIS S.A.—(Continued)

Holding Company; Insurance, Travel, Financial & Lifestyle Products & Services
N.A.I.C.S.: 551112
Roger Ramsden *(CEO-Saga Svcs)*

Subsidiary (Domestic):

Acromas Holidays Limited (4)
Enbrook Park, Middleburg Square, Folkestone, CT20 3SE, Kent, United Kingdom
Tel.: (44) 1303 771 111
Web Site: http://www.travel.saga.co.uk
Vacation & Tour Travel Agency
N.A.I.C.S.: 561510
Susan Hooper *(CEO)*

Acromas Shipping Limited (4)
Enbrook Park, Middleburg Square, Folkestone, CT20 3SE, Kent, United Kingdom
Tel.: (44) 1303 771 111
Web Site: http://www.saga.co.uk
Cruise Vacation Travel Agency
N.A.I.C.S.: 561510

Allied Healthcare (4)
Beaconsfield Court Beaconsfield Road, Hatfield, AL10 8HU, Herts, United Kingdom
Tel.: (44) 8458501435
Web Site: http://www.alliedhealthcare.com
Holding Company; Health & Social Care Staffing
N.A.I.C.S.: 551112
John Rennocks *(Chm)*

Subsidiary (Domestic):

Nestor Primecare Services Ltd. (5)
Beaconfields Court Beaconsfield Road, Hatfield, AL10 8HU, Herts, United Kingdom
Tel.: (44) 1707 286800
Web Site: http://www.nestor-healthcare.co.uk
Sales Range: $10-24.9 Million
Health Care Srvices
N.A.I.C.S.: 621999

Subsidiary (US):

Allied Healthcare International Inc. (4)
245 Park Ave 39th Fl, New York, NY 10167
Tel.: (212) 750-0064
Web Site: http://www.alliedhealthcare.com
Sales Range: $250-299.9 Million
Emp.: 1,160
Holding Company; Healthcare Staffing
N.A.I.C.S.: 551112

Subsidiary (Non-US):

Allied Healthcare Group Holdings Limited (5)
Stone Business Park, Brooms Road, Stone, ST15 0TL, Staffs, United Kingdom
Tel.: (44) 1785810600
Web Site: http://www.alliedhealthcare.co.uk
Holding Company
N.A.I.C.S.: 551112

Subsidiary (Domestic):

Allied Healthcare Holdings Limited (6)
Stone Business Park, Brooms Road, Stone, ST15 0TL, Staffs, United Kingdom
Tel.: (44) 1785810600
Web Site: http://www.alliedhealthcare.co.uk
Sales Range: $150-199.9 Million
Emp.: 200
Holding Company; Healthcare Staffing Services
N.A.I.C.S.: 551112

Subsidiary (Domestic):

Allied Healthcare Group Limited (7)
Stone Business Park, Brooms Road, Stone, ST15 0TL, Staffordshire, United Kingdom
Tel.: (44) 1785810600
Web Site: http://www.alliedhealthcare.co.uk
Sales Range: $25-49.9 Million
Nursing & Healthcare Services
N.A.I.C.S.: 621610

Subsidiary (Domestic):

Saga Services Limited (4)
Enbrook Park, Middleburg Square, Folkestone, CT20 1AZ, Kent, United Kingdom

20 Avenue Momas
Tel.: (44) 1303771111
Web Site: http://www.saga.co.uk
Financial Information & Advisory Services
N.A.I.C.S.: 525990
Andrew Goodsell *(CEO)*

Subsidiary (Domestic):

The Automobile Association Limited (3)
Fanum House Basingview, Basingstoke, RG21 4EA, Hants, United Kingdom
Tel.: (44) 8705448866
Web Site: http://www.theaa.com
Sales Range: $300-349.9 Million
Automobile Services Club
N.A.I.C.S.: 561599
Michael Cutbill *(Dir-Mktg & Sls)*

Holding (Non-US):

April Group SA (2)
Immeuble Aprilium 114 boulevard Marius Vivier Merle, 69439, Lyon, Cedex 03, France (88.8%)
Tel.: (33) 4 72 36 73 73
Web Site: http://www.april.com
Sales Range: $1-4.9 Billion
Holding Company; Life Insurance, Property & Casualty Insurance Services
N.A.I.C.S.: 551112
Bruno Rousset *(Chm)*

Subsidiary (Domestic):

Amt Assurances Sarl (3)
14 Quai Marmoutier, 37072, Tours, France
Tel.: (33) 810125750
Web Site: http://www.amt.tm.fr
Insurance Agencies & Brokerages
N.A.I.C.S.: 524210
Philips Annoncera *(Mng Dir)*

April Corporate Broking Sarl (3)
33 Rue Maurice Flandin, 69003, Lyon, France
Tel.: (33) 472755471
Web Site: http://www.aprilcorporate.com
Real Estate Agents & Brokers
N.A.I.C.S.: 531210

April Cover Sarl (3)
114 Boulevard Marius Vivier Merle, Lyon, 69003, France
Tel.: (33) 472367342
Web Site: http://www.april.fr
Sales Range: $50-74.9 Million
Insurance Agencies & Brokerages
N.A.I.C.S.: 524210
Bruno Rousset *(CEO)*

Subsidiary (Non-US):

April Deutschland AG (3)
Richard Reitzner Allee 1, 85540, Haar, Germany
Tel.: (49) 8943607120
Web Site: http://www.april.de
Sales Range: $1-9.9 Million
Financial & Insurance Services
N.A.I.C.S.: 525990
Lutz Goehler *(Chm-Mgmt Bd & CEO)*

Subsidiary (Domestic):

April Entreprise Lyon (3)
90 Avenue Felix Faure, CS 73344, 69439, Lyon, France
Tel.: (33) 469732691
Web Site: http://april-entreprise.fr
Sales Range: $50-74.9 Million
Insurance Agencies & Brokerages
N.A.I.C.S.: 524210

Subsidiary (Non-US):

April Germany AG (3)
Richard-Reitzner-Allee 1, 85540, Haar, Germany
Tel.: (49) 89436070
Web Site: http://www.april.de
Sales Range: $25-49.9 Million
Direct Life Insurance Carriers
N.A.I.C.S.: 524113

Subsidiary (Domestic):

April Iard Sarl (3)
27 Rue Maurice Flandin, 69404, Lyon, France
Tel.: (33) 437911133

Web Site: http://www.axeria-iard.fr
Sales Range: $50-74.9 Million
Insurance Agencies & Brokerages
N.A.I.C.S.: 524210

Subsidiary (Non-US):

April Iberia Sarl (3)
C-Serrano 93 2 E, 28006, Madrid, Spain
Tel.: (34) 915643170
Web Site: http://www.april-iberia.es
Sales Range: $50-74.9 Million
Emp.: 2
Insurance Agencies & Brokerages
N.A.I.C.S.: 524210

Subsidiary (Domestic):

April Marine (3)
12 rue Paul Doumer, BP 47, 850002, La Roche-sur-Yon, France
Tel.: (33) 251372260
Web Site: http://www.aprilmarine.fr
Sales Range: $50-74.9 Million
Marine Insurance Agencies & Brokerages
N.A.I.C.S.: 524210

April Marketing Solutions Sarl (3)
Le Bois Des Cotes Bat A 300 Route Nationale 6, 69576, Limonest, France
Tel.: (33) 426294316
Web Site: http://www.aprilgroup.com
Sales Range: $75-99.9 Million
Insurance Agencies & Brokerages
N.A.I.C.S.: 524210

April Mon Assurance Lyon (3)
152 bis avenue Felix Faure, 69003, Lyon, France
Tel.: (33) 4 72 68 65 68
Web Site: http://agence.april.fr
Insurance Agencies
N.A.I.C.S.: 524210

April Patrimoine Sarl (3)
27 Rue Maurice Flandin, 69395, Lyon, France
Tel.: (33) 472367500
Web Site: http://www.april-patrimoine.fr
Insurance Agencies & Brokerages
N.A.I.C.S.: 524210

Axeria Prevoyance Sarl (3)
33 Rue Maurice Flandin, 69003, Lyon, France
Tel.: (33) 472361794
Sales Range: $50-74.9 Million
Direct Life Insurance Carrier Services
N.A.I.C.S.: 524113

Cgca Sarl (3)
1 Avenue De La Fosse aux Mats, 17304, Rochefort, France
Tel.: (33) 546993160
Web Site: http://www.cgca.fr
Sales Range: $50-74.9 Million
Insurance Agencies & Brokerages
N.A.I.C.S.: 524210

Subsidiary (Non-US):

Dierrevi SpA (3)
Via Carducci 38, 20123, Milan, Italy
Tel.: (39) 0243319588
Sales Range: $50-74.9 Million
Emp.: 6
Insurance Agencies & Brokerages
N.A.I.C.S.: 523160

Subsidiary (Domestic):

Europassur Sarl (3)
33 Rue De Chateaudun, 75009, Paris, France
Tel.: (33) 149680720
Sales Range: $50-74.9 Million
Emp.: 9
Insurance Agencies & Brokerages
N.A.I.C.S.: 524210

Subsidiary (Non-US):

Moral Caraibes Sarl (3)
Immeuble Mirador, 97122, La Baie Mahault, Guadeloupe
Tel.: (590) 380636
Sales Range: $25-49.9 Million
Insurance Agencies & Brokerages
N.A.I.C.S.: 524210

Subsidiary (Domestic):

Mutant Assurances Sarl (3)
Mlle Frederique Millet-Perriol 41 Rue Garibaldi, Lyon, 69006, France
Tel.: (33) 472822010
Web Site: http://www.mutant-assurances.fr
Sales Range: $150-199.9 Million
Insurance Agencies & Brokerages
N.A.I.C.S.: 524210
Catherine Lafont *(Dir-Mktg)*

Resolution Sarl (3)
27 Rue Maurice Flandin, 69444, Lyon, France
Tel.: (33) 472755460
Sales Range: $50-74.9 Million
Insurance Agencies & Brokerages
N.A.I.C.S.: 524210

Sasco Sarl (3)
81 Rue des Carts, BP 70030, 74373, Pringy, Cedex, France
Tel.: (33) 40 50523860
Sales Range: $25-49.9 Million
Insurance Agencies & Brokerages
N.A.I.C.S.: 524210

Solucia Protection Juridique Sarl (3)
14 Rue Scandicci, 93500, Pantin, France
Tel.: (33) 148105400
Web Site: http://www.soluciapj.fr
Direct Health & Medical Insurance Carriers
N.A.I.C.S.: 524114

TMS Contact Sarl (3)
110 Ave de la Republique, 75011, Paris, France
Tel.: (33) 73034101
Web Site: http://www.tmscontact.com
Sales Range: $25-49.9 Million
Insurance Agencies & Brokerages
N.A.I.C.S.: 524210

Holding (Domestic):

Autobar Group Ltd. (2)
East Wing 14th Floor 389 Chiswick High Road, London, W4 4AJ, United Kingdom
Tel.: (44) 20 8987 6500
Web Site: http://www.autobar.com
Sales Range: $900-999.9 Million
Vending Machine Services
N.A.I.C.S.: 445132

Subsidiary (Non-US):

BIP - Business Integration Partners S.p.A. (2)
Piazza San Babila 5, 20122, Milan, Italy
Tel.: (39) 024541521
Web Site: http://www.bipconsulting.com
Management Consulting Services (for Energy & Telecommunications Industries)
N.A.I.C.S.: 541690
Carlo Maria Cape *(Mng Dir)*

Subsidiary (Non-US):

Verco Advisory Services Ltd. (3)
Office 125 Metal Box Factory 30 Great Guilford Street, London, SE1 0HS, United Kingdom
Tel.: (44) 2035989770
Web Site: http://www.vercoglobal.com
Sales Range: $25-49.9 Million
Emp.: 30
Environmental Consulting Services
N.A.I.C.S.: 541620
Dave Worthington *(Mng Dir)*

Subsidiary (Domestic):

The Edinburgh Centre for Carbon Management Limited (4)
Tower Mains Studios, 18F Liberton Brae, Edinburgh, EH16 6AE, United Kingdom
Tel.: (44) 1316665070
Sales Range: $25-49.9 Million
Emp.: 10
Environmental Consulting Services
N.A.I.C.S.: 541620

Holding (Non-US):

Breitling S.A. (2)
Schlachthausstrasse 2, PO Box 1132, Grenchen, 2540, Switzerland
Tel.: (41) 326545454
Web Site: http://www.breitling.com
Watch Mfr

N.A.I.C.S.: 334519
D. Kennedy Frierson Jr. *(Pres, Pres-Masland Residential & Gen Mgr-Dixie Home)*

Subsidiary (Non-US):

BREITLING CHINA LIMITED **(3)**
Westgate Mall Office Tower 27th Floor Unit 2704-06A 1038 Nanjing West, 200041, Shanghai, China
Tel.: (86) 21 6352 2670
Chronograph Wrist Watch Distr
N.A.I.C.S.: 423940

BREITLING FRANCE S.A.R.L. **(3)**
2 Rue De la Paix, 75002, Paris, France
Tel.: (33) 1 42 61 18 84
Chronograph Wrist Watch Distr
N.A.I.C.S.: 423940

BREITLING ITALIA SRL **(3)**
Via Della Moscova 3, 20121, Milan, Italy
Tel.: (39) 02 00 69 10 10
Web Site: http://www.breitling.com
Chronograph Wrist Watch Distr
N.A.I.C.S.: 423940

BREITLING JAPAN LTD **(3)**
6-6-19 Ginza, Chuo-ku, Tokyo, 104-0061, Japan
Tel.: (81) 3 32 891884
Chronograph Wrist Watch Distr
N.A.I.C.S.: 423940

Subsidiary (US):

BREITLING USA INC. **(3)**
206 Danbury Rd Ste 1, Wilton, CT 06897-4004
Tel.: (203) 762-1180
Chronograph Wrist Watch Distr
N.A.I.C.S.: 423940

Subsidiary (Domestic):

Universal Geneve S.A. **(3)**
Chemin du Grand-Puits 38, Meyrin, 1217, Switzerland
Tel.: (41) 223077880
Web Site: http://www.universal.ch
Sales Range: $25-49.9 Million
Emp.: 45
Watch Clock & Part Mfr
N.A.I.C.S.: 334519
Nicolas Vernier *(CEO)*

Holding (US):

ConvergeOne Holdings, Inc. **(2)**
10900 Nesbitt Ave S, Eagan, MN 55437
Tel.: (888) 321-6227
Web Site: http://www.convergeone.com
Holding Company
N.A.I.C.S.: 551112
John A. McKenna Jr. *(Chm, Pres & CEO)*

Subsidiary (Domestic):

ConvergeOne, Inc. **(3)**
10900 Nesbitt Ave S, Bloomington, MN 55437 **(100%)**
Tel.: (888) 321-6227
Web Site: http://www.convergeone.com
Investment Management Service
N.A.I.C.S.: 523940
Paul K. Maier *(Pres-Svcs Org)*

Unit (Domestic):

ConvergeOne Advanced Services **(4)**
1255 Crescent Green Ste 145, Cary, NC 27518
Tel.: (919) 858-8898
Web Site: http://www.converge-one.com
Systems Integration & Software Development
N.A.I.C.S.: 513210
Bruce Calhoon *(Exec VP)*

Subsidiary (Domestic):

ConvergeOne Unified Technology Solutions, Inc. **(4)**
1290 Ave of the Americas, New York, NY 10020-1095
Tel.: (212) 282-2222
Web Site: http://www.c1uts.com
Telecommunications & Data Services
N.A.I.C.S.: 517121

John T. Tarduno *(VP)*

Venture Technologies, Inc. **(4)**
860 Ctr St, Ridgeland, MS 39157-4501
Tel.: (601) 956-5440
IT Solutions Provider
N.A.I.C.S.: 423430
Joe Rucker *(COO)*

Subsidiary (Domestic):

Whitelight Group, LLC **(5)**
N14 W24200 Tower Pl Ste 203, Waukesha, WI 53188
Tel.: (262) 522-8450
Web Site: http://www.whitelightgrp.com
Enterprise It Software Sales & Consulting Srvcs
N.A.I.C.S.: 541690
Paul Demes *(Partner)*

Holding (Non-US):

Deoleo, S.A. **(2)**
C/ Marie Curie 7 4 plta, Rivas Vaciamadrid, 28521, Madrid, Spain
Tel.: (34) 915589505
Web Site: https://deoleo.com
Rev.: $863,553
Assets: $1,106,675
Liabilities: $496,460
Net Worth: $610,215
Earnings: $75,321
Emp.: 650
Fiscal Year-end: 12/31/2021
Olive Oil, Biscuits, Rice, Confectionery & Condiment Producer
N.A.I.C.S.: 311224
Manuel Pacheco Manchado *(Co-Sec)*

Holding (Domestic):

Domestic & General Group Limited **(2)**
Swan Court, London, SW19 4JS, United Kingdom
Tel.: (44) 2089467777
Web Site: http://www.domgen.com
Warranty Protection Services on Household Appliances, Pet Health Insurance Services & Call Center Services
N.A.I.C.S.: 525990
Tom Hinton *(CFO)*

Subsidiary (Domestic):

Domestic & General Insurance PLC **(3)**
Swan Court 11 Worple Road, Wimbledon, London, SW19 4JS, United Kingdom
Tel.: (44) 2089467777
Sales Range: $150-199.9 Million
Insurance Services
N.A.I.C.S.: 524298

Domestic & General Insurance Services Limited **(3)**
Swan Court 11 Worple Road, Wimbledon, London, SW19 4JS, United Kingdom
Tel.: (44) 870 5500 500
Warranty Protection Services on Household Appliances
N.A.I.C.S.: 524298

Subsidiary (Non-US):

Domestic & General Service Gmbh **(3)**
Hagenauer Str 44, 65203, Wiesbaden, Germany
Tel.: (49) 611 308 78 0
Web Site: http://www.domesticandgeneral.de
Sales Range: $10-24.9 Million
Emp.: 80
Appliance Warranty & Repair Cost Insurance Services
N.A.I.C.S.: 524298
Carlos Bermudez *(Mng Dir)*

Subsidiary (Domestic):

Domestic & General Services Limited **(3)**
Swan Court 11 Worple Road, Wimbledon, London, SW19 4JS, United Kingdom
Tel.: (44) 208 946 7777
Web Site: http://www.domgen.com

Sales Range: $50-74.9 Million
Emp.: 350
Warranty Service Plans & Support Services
N.A.I.C.S.: 524298

Holding (Non-US):

Kirk Beauty One GmbH **(2)**
Luise-Rainer-Strasse 7-11, 40235, Dusseldorf, Germany
Tel.: (49) 211 16847 9
Holding Company
N.A.I.C.S.: 551112
Isabelle Parize *(CEO)*

Subsidiary (Domestic):

Douglas Cosmetics GmbH **(3)**
Konigsallee 46, 40212, Dusseldorf, Germany
Tel.: (49) 211327608
Perfume & Cosmetics Stores
N.A.I.C.S.: 456120
Manuel Koelman *(Head-Product Mgmt-Desktop & Mobile Innovations)*

Douglas Einkaufs- und Servicegesellschaft mbH & Co. KG **(3)**
Zum Konigsgraben 1, 15806, Zossen, Germany
Tel.: (49) 3377200570
Cosmetics & Beauty Supplies Purchasing Activities
N.A.I.C.S.: 561499
Beatrix Eisermann *(Gen Mgr)*

Douglas GmbH **(3)**
Luise-Rainer-Strasse 7-11, 40235, Dusseldorf, Germany
Tel.: (49) 211 16847 9
Web Site: http://www.douglas.de
Sales Range: $1-4.9 Billion
Emp.: 20,000
Cosmetics & Beauty Supplies Stores
N.A.I.C.S.: 456120
Henning Kreke *(Chm-Supervisory Bd)*

Parfumerie Douglas GmbH **(3)**
Luise-Rainer-Strasse 7-11, 40235, Dusseldorf, Germany **(100%)**
Tel.: (49) 2331 690 0
Web Site: http://www.douglas.de
Perfume & Beauty Cosmetics Stores
N.A.I.C.S.: 456120
Isabelle Parize *(CEO)*

Subsidiary (Non-US):

Douglas Polska Sp. z o.o. **(4)**
Klif Tower Ul Okopowa 58/72, 01-042, Warsaw, Poland **(100%)**
Tel.: (48) 223309898
Web Site: http://www.douglas.pl
Sales Range: $75-99.9 Million
Cosmetic & Perfume Distr
N.A.I.C.S.: 456120
Agnieszka Zagorska *(Mgr-Pur Dept-ecommerce)*

Douglas parfumerije d.o.o. **(4)**
Krese Golika 3a, 10000, Zagreb, Croatia
Tel.: (385) 1 5625 630
Web Site: http://www.douglas.hr
Cosmetics & Perfume Products Distr
N.A.I.C.S.: 456120
Adrijana Bokan *(Exec Dir)*

Nocibe France SAS **(4)**
2 rue de Ticleni, 59493, Villeneuve d'Ascq, France **(100%)**
Tel.: (33) 810 49 49 49
Web Site: http://www.nocibe.fr
Perfume Stores
N.A.I.C.S.: 456120
Sandrine Israel *(Mgr-Mktg-Comml)*

Parfumerie Douglas AG **(4)**
Lindenstrasse 16, 6340, Baar, Switzerland **(100%)**
Tel.: (41) 41 768 21 31
Web Site: http://www.douglas.ch
Sales Range: $10-24.9 Million
Emp.: 20
Perfume Retailer
N.A.I.C.S.: 456120
Claudia Reinery *(Mng Dir)*

Parfumerie Douglas Ges.m.b.H. **(4)**
Rotenturmstrasse 11, 1010, Vienna, Austria **(100%)**
Tel.: (43) 1 532 10 91

Web Site: http://www.douglas.at
Sales Range: $50-74.9 Million
Perfume Whslr
N.A.I.C.S.: 456120
Rebekka Panzenbock *(Mng Dir)*

Subsidiary (Domestic):

Parfumerie Douglas International GmbH **(4)**
Kabeler Strasse 4, 58099, Hagen, Germany **(100%)**
Tel.: (49) 23316900
Web Site: http://www.douglas.de
Perfume Stores
N.A.I.C.S.: 456120
Frank Hoffmann *(Dir-Strategic Pur)*

Subsidiary (Non-US):

Parfumerie Douglas Monaco S.A.M. **(4)**
20 Boulevard Des Moulins, 98000, Monaco, Monaco **(100%)**
Tel.: (377) 93505271
Sales Range: $10-24.9 Million
Emp.: 12
Perfume & Beauty Supply Stores
N.A.I.C.S.: 456120

Parfumerie Douglas Nederland B.V. **(4)**
St Annastraat 265, PO Box 479, Nijmegen, 6525 GR, Netherlands **(100%)**
Tel.: (31) 243515151
Web Site: http://www.douglas.nl
Sales Range: $10-24.9 Million
Emp.: 50
Perfume & Beauty Supply Stores
N.A.I.C.S.: 456120
William Butler *(Mng Dir)*

Parfumerie Douglas s.r.o. **(4)**
Na Prikope 17/1047, Prague, 110 00, Czech Republic
Tel.: (420) 222222800
Web Site: http://www.douglas.cz
Cosmetic & Perfume Distr
N.A.I.C.S.: 456120
Michal Kocman *(Mng Dir)*

Perfumaria Douglas Portugal Lda. **(4)**
Avenida D Joao II n 46 Edificio D Joao II 3 andar, Parque das Nacoes, 1990 095, Lisbon, Portugal
Tel.: (351) 218943065
Web Site: http://www.douglas.pt
Cosmetic Products & Perfume Retail Stores
N.A.I.C.S.: 456120

Profumerie Douglas S.p.A. **(4)**
Viale Postumia 58, 37069, Villafranca di Verona, VR, Italy
Tel.: (39) 045 6313111
Web Site: http://www.douglas.it
Sales Range: $25-49.9 Million
Perfume & Cosmetic Products Retail Stores
N.A.I.C.S.: 456120
Joerg Mingers *(Mng Dir)*

SIA Douglas Latvia **(4)**
G Astras 8B, 1082, Riga, Latvia
Tel.: (371) 67788100
Web Site: http://www.douglas.lv
Sales Range: $25-49.9 Million
Emp.: 22
Cosmetics & Perfumes Distr
N.A.I.C.S.: 456120
Sarmite Zvirbule *(Head-HR)*

UAB Douglas LT **(4)**
Svitrigailos g 11M, 03228, Vilnius, Lithuania **(100%)**
Tel.: (370) 8 5 210 6888
Web Site: http://www.douglas.lt
Cosmetic Products & Perfume Distr
N.A.I.C.S.: 456120

Subsidiary (Domestic):

inter-moda GmbH **(3)**
Burgermeister-Mittenmeier-Strasse 1-3, 93077, Bad Abbach, Germany
Tel.: (49) 9405 7317
Web Site: http://www.intermoda.de
Fashion Accessories Mfr
N.A.I.C.S.: 315990
Martin Dobler *(Mng Dir)*

CVC Capital Partners SICAV-FIS S.A.—(Continued)

Holding (US):

Ontic Engineering & Manufacturing, Inc. (2)
20400 Plummer St, Chatsworth, CA 91311
Tel.: (818) 678-6555
Web Site: http://www.ontic.com
Legacy Aircraft Parts Mfr & Whslr
N.A.I.C.S.: 423860
Gareth Hall (Pres & Mng Dir)

Subsidiary (Non-US):

Ontic Engineering & Manufacturing UK Limited (3)
Cleeve Business Park, Bishops Cleeve, Cheltenham, GL52 8TW, Gloucestershire, United Kingdom
Tel.: (44) 3332408600
Web Site: http://www.ontic.com
Metal Tank & Gauge Mfr & Whslr
N.A.I.C.S.: 332420

Holding (Non-US):

Ortel Mobile Holding B.V. (2)
Rijswijkseweg 66, Hague, 2516 EH, Netherlands
Tel.: (31) 703634565
Investment Management Service
N.A.I.C.S.: 523999

Subsidiary (Domestic):

RiverStone Insurance (UK) Limited (2)
Park Gate 161-163 Preston Road, Brighton, BN16AU, United Kingdom
Tel.: (44) 1273792604
Insurance Services
N.A.I.C.S.: 524298
Luke Tanzer (CEO)

Subsidiary (US):

E.R. Quinn Co., Inc. (3)
119 N Park Ave 4th Fl, Rockville Centre, NY 11570
Tel.: (516) 594-1500
Web Site: http://www.erquinnco.com
Insurance Services
N.A.I.C.S.: 524298
Edward R. Quinn Jr. (Pres & CEO)

Holding (Non-US):

STARK Group A/S (2)
C. F. Richs Vej, 115 2000, Frederiksberg, Denmark
Tel.: (45) 82522600
Web Site: https://starkgroup.dk
Building Materials Distr & Whslr
N.A.I.C.S.: 423390

Subsidiary (Non-US):

Saint-Gobain Building Distribution Ltd. (3)
Aldwych House 81 Aldwych, London, WC2B 4HQ, United Kingdom
Tel.: (44) 2074008888
Web Site: http://www.saint-gobain.co.uk
Importer & Distributor of Wood Products & Building Materials
N.A.I.C.S.: 423310

Joint Venture (Non-US):

Sebia SA (2)
Parc Technologique Leonard de Vinci, Lisses, 91008, France
Tel.: (33) 69 89 80 80
Web Site: http://www.sebia.com
Sales Range: $125-149.9 Million
Emp.: 400
Medical Diagnostic Equipment Mfr
N.A.I.C.S.: 339112
Benoit Adelus (Chm & CEO)

Subsidiary (Non-US):

ORGENTEC Diagnostika GmbH (3)
Carl-Zeiss-Strasse 49-51, 55129, Mainz, Germany
Tel.: (49) 6131 9258 0
Web Site: http://www.orgentec.com
Emp.: 120
Diagnostic Services
N.A.I.C.S.: 621511

Ralf Wehen (Mng Dir)

Subsidiary (US):

Corgenix Medical Corporation (4)
11575 Main St Ste 400, Broomfield, CO 80020
Tel.: (303) 457-4345
Web Site: http://www.corgenix.com
Sales Range: $10-24.9 Million
Specialized Diagnostic Test Kits Developer & Marketer for Vascular Diseases & immunological Disorders
N.A.I.C.S.: 325413
James F. Widergren (Pres)

Subsidiary (US):

Sebia, Inc. (3)
1705 Corporate Dr, Norcross, GA 30093
Tel.: (770) 446-3707
Web Site: http://www.sebia-usa.com
Rev.: $3,300,000
Emp.: 22
Medical Diagnostic Equipment Mfr
N.A.I.C.S.: 339112
Theresa Heslin (CEO)

Zeus Scientific, Inc. (3)
199 & 200 Evans Way, 08876, Branchburg, NJ
Tel.: (908) 526-3744
Web Site: http://www.zeusscientific.com
Surgical & Medical Instrument Mfr
N.A.I.C.S.: 339112
Mark Kopnitsky (VP-Science & Quality)

Holding (Non-US):

Syntegon Technology GmbH (2)
Stuttgarter Strasse 130, 71332, Waiblingen, Germany
Tel.: (49) 7118110
Web Site: https://www.syntegon.com
Packaging Services
N.A.I.C.S.: 333993
Klaus Aibeck (Member-Mgmt Bd)

Subsidiary (Non-US):

Bosch Inspection Technology (Shanghai) Co., Ltd. (3)
F-Room 5 F 2272 Hongqiao Road, Shanghai, 200336, China
Tel.: (86) 21 5216 1341
Sales Range: $25-49.9 Million
Emp.: 15
Inspection Machinery Mfr
N.A.I.C.S.: 334519

Subsidiary (Domestic):

Bosch Inspection Technology GmbH (3)
Mathias-Brueggen-Str 142, D 50829, Cologne, Germany (100%)
Tel.: (49) 2219564590
Sales Range: $25-49.9 Million
Emp.: 20
Inspection Machinery Mfr
N.A.I.C.S.: 334519

Subsidiary (US):

Bosch Inspection Technology Inc. (3)
90 Boroline, Allendale, NJ 07401
Tel.: (201) 760-5100
Sales Range: $25-49.9 Million
Emp.: 25
Inspection Machinery Mfr
N.A.I.C.S.: 334519
Peter Spinelli (Pres)

Subsidiary (Non-US):

Bosch Packaging Systems AG (3)
Industriestrasse 8, CH-8222, Beringen, Switzerland
Tel.: (41) 58 674 10 00
Sales Range: $450-499.9 Million
Emp.: 1,500
Packaging Mfr & Services
N.A.I.C.S.: 322220

Subsidiary (US):

Bosch Packaging Services (4)
2440 Sumner Blvd, Raleigh, NC 27616
Tel.: (919) 877-0886

Web Site: http://www.boschpackagingservices.com
Sales Range: $25-49.9 Million
Emp.: 50
Packaging Equipment Mfr
N.A.I.C.S.: 333993
Gary Anderson (Gen Mgr)

Subsidiary (Non-US):

Bosch Packaging Systems Kft. (3)
Hatar ua3, Pecei, 2119, Hungary
Tel.: (36) 28547520
Packaging Products Mfr
N.A.I.C.S.: 326112

Subsidiary (US):

Bosch Packaging Technology (3)
8700 Wyoming Ave N, Minneapolis, MN 55445-1836
Tel.: (763) 424-4700
Web Site: http://www.boschpackaging.com
Sales Range: $50-74.9 Million
Emp.: 180
Packaging Machinery
N.A.I.C.S.: 333248
Stefan Konig (Member-Mgmt Bd)

Subsidiary (Non-US):

Bosch Packaging Technology (Chengdu) Co., Ltd. (3)
Printing Technology Park Shouan, Pujian, Chengdu, 611630, China
Tel.: (86) 2880598888
Packaging Machinery Mfr
N.A.I.C.S.: 333993

Bosch Packaging Technology (Hangzhou) Co., Ltd. (3)
680 Road No 23 Hangzhou Economic and Technological Development Area, Hangzhou, 310018, China
Tel.: (86) 571 8726 5000
Web Site:
    http://www.boschpackaging.com.cn
Packaging Machinery Mfr & Distr
N.A.I.C.S.: 333993

Bosch Packaging Technology (Singapore) Pte. Ltd. (3)
11 Bishan Street 21, Singapore, 573943, Singapore
Tel.: (65) 62585511
Web Site: http://www.bosch.com.sg
Sales Range: $25-49.9 Million
Packaging Technology Mfr
N.A.I.C.S.: 333993
Jon Lim (Reg Sls Mgr)

Bosch Packaging Technology B.V. (3)
Conradstraat 4, 3125 BC, Schiedam, Netherlands
Tel.: (31) 104885899
Packaging Products Mfr
N.A.I.C.S.: 326112
Letty Oostdijk (Mgr-HR)

Bosch Packaging Technology K.K. (3)
3-6-7 Shibuya, Shibuya ku, Tokyo, 150 0002, Japan
Tel.: (81) 3 5466 2550
Web Site: http://www.boschpackaging.co.jp
Sales Range: $25-49.9 Million
Emp.: 30
Packaging Machinery Mfr
N.A.I.C.S.: 333993

Unit (Domestic):

Bosch Packaging Technology K.K. (4)
Sumitomo Seisen Koishikawa Building 5F 3-5-10 Otsuka Bunkyo-ku, Tokyo, 112 0012, Japan
Tel.: (81) 353192202
Sales Range: $25-49.9 Million
Inspection Machinery Mfr
N.A.I.C.S.: 334519

Subsidiary (Non-US):

Bosch Packaging Technology Ltd. (3)
Unit 2A Meteor Business Park Meteor Centre Mansfield Road GB, Derby, DE21 4SU, Merseyside, United Kingdom

Tel.: (44) 1332 626 262
Web Site: http://www.boschpackaging.com
Sales Range: $50-74.9 Million
Emp.: 145
Packaging Machinery Mfr
N.A.I.C.S.: 333993

Bosch Packaging Technology Ltd. (3)
Unit 2A Meteor Business Park Meteor Centre Mansfield Road, Derby, DE21 4SU, United Kingdom
Tel.: (44) 1332626262
Web Site: http://www.boschpackaging.com
Sales Range: $10-24.9 Million
Emp.: 40
Packaging Solutions
N.A.I.C.S.: 561910
Frank Tarr (Mng Dir)

Bosch Packaging Technology SA (3)
44 Av du Tir-Federal, 1024, Ecublens, Switzerland
Tel.: (41) 216335200
Packaging Products Mfr
N.A.I.C.S.: 326112

Bosch Packaging Technology SAS (3)
Europarc Sainte Victoire BAT 4, Meyreuil, 13590, Aix-en-Provence, France
Tel.: (33) 442298330
Packaging Products Mfr
N.A.I.C.S.: 326112

Subsidiary (US):

Bosch Packaging Technology, Inc. (3)
869 S Knowles Ave, New Richmond, WI 54017
Tel.: (715) 246-6511
Web Site: http://www.boschpackaging.com
Sales Range: $100-124.9 Million
Emp.: 275
Packaging Machinery Mfr
N.A.I.C.S.: 333993

Osgood Industries, Inc. (3)
601 Burbank Rd, Oldsmar, FL 34677
Tel.: (813) 855-7337
Web Site: http://www.osgoodinc.com
Food & Beverage Packaging Machinery Mfr & Whslr
N.A.I.C.S.: 333993

Subsidiary (Non-US):

Robert Bosch Tecnologia de Embalagem Ltda. (3)
Av Jurua 606 Alphaville, Barueri, 06455-010, Sao Paulo, Brazil
Tel.: (55) 1121176800
Web Site:
    http://www.boschpackaging.com.br
Sales Range: $1-9.9 Million
Emp.: 40
Small Arms Manufacturing
N.A.I.C.S.: 332994

Sapal S.A. (3)
Avenue du Tir Federal 44, 1024, Ecublens, Switzerland
Tel.: (41) 216335300
Web Site: http://www.sapal.ch
Sales Range: $25-49.9 Million
Emp.: 80
Pakckaging System Mfr
N.A.I.C.S.: 333248

CVC Advisors (U.S.) Inc. (1)
712 5th Ave 43rd Fl, New York, NY 10019
Tel.: (212) 265-6222
Web Site: http://www.cvc.com
Privater Equity Firm
N.A.I.C.S.: 523999
David Rous (Mng Dir)

Joint Venture (Domestic):

Anchor Glass Container Corporation (2)
3001 N Rocky Point Dr E Ste 300, Tampa, FL 33607
Tel.: (813) 884-0000
Web Site: http://www.anchorglass.com
Glass Container Products Mfr
N.A.I.C.S.: 327213
Robert Stewart (Chief Compliance Officer)

Holding (Domestic):

BOLT Solutions, Inc. (2)
100 Park Ave 16th Fl, New York, NY
10017 **(70%)**
Tel.: (212) 209-0866
Web Site: http://www.boltinc.com
Software Publisher
N.A.I.C.S.: 513210
Eric Gewirtzman *(CEO)*

Subsidiary (Domestic):

**Business Owners Liability Team
LLC** (3)
10 Waterside Dr Ste 202, Farmington, CT
06032
Tel.: (800) 216-4171
Web Site: http://www.boltinsurance.com
Insurance Brokerage Services
N.A.I.C.S.: 524210
Eric Gewirtzman *(CEO)*

**Superior Access Insurance Services,
Inc.** (3)
3721 Executive Center Dr Ste 100, Irvine,
CA 78731
Tel.: (800) 272-7550
Web Site: http://www.superioraccess.com
Insurance Agents, Brokers & Services
N.A.I.C.S.: 524210
Ballard Ingram *(Mgr-Svc)*

Subsidiary (Domestic):

**CVC Capital Partners Advisory (U.S.),
Inc.** (2)
712 5th Ave 43rd Fl, New York, NY 10019
Tel.: (212) 265-6222
Private Equity Investment Advisory & Port-
folio Management Services
N.A.I.C.S.: 523940
Cameron Breitner *(Mng Partner)*

Joint Venture (Domestic):

Messer Industries USA, Inc. (2)
200 Somerset Corporate Blvd Ste 7000,
Bridgewater, NJ 08807
Web Site: http://www.messer-us.com
Holding Company; Industrial Gas Mfr
N.A.I.C.S.: 551112

Subsidiary (Domestic):

Messer Gas LLC (3)
200 Somerset Corporate Blvd Ste 7000,
Bridgewater, NJ 08807
Web Site: http://www.messer-us.com
Industrial Gas Mfr
N.A.I.C.S.: 325120

Subsidiary (Domestic):

Messer Gas Puerto Rico, Inc. (4)
Rd 869 Km 2 0 Esq Calle 19 Barrio Pal-
mas, Catano, PR 00962
Tel.: (787) 641-7445
Web Site: http://www.messer-us.com
Industrial & Medical Gases, Specialty
Gases, Cutting & Welding, Sales & Rent of
Scaffolding & Construction Equipment,
Safety Equipment & Accessories
N.A.I.C.S.: 424690

Holding (Domestic):

OANDA Corp. (2)
795 Folsom St, San Francisco, CA 94107
Tel.: (212) 858-7690
Web Site: http://www.oanda.com
Forex Trading Services
N.A.I.C.S.: 523150
David Hodge *(CEO-EMEA & CMO)*

Joint Venture (Domestic):

Petco Holdings, Inc. (2)
10850 Via Frontera, San Diego, CA 92127
Tel.: (858) 453-7845
Web Site: http://www.petco.com
Sales Range: $1-4.9 Billion
Emp.: 17,000
Holding Company; Pet Food, Supplies &
Services Retailer
N.A.I.C.S.: 551112
Justin Tichy *(Chief Stores Officer)*

Subsidiary (Domestic):

Petco Animal Supplies, Inc. (3)

10850 Via Frontera, San Diego, CA 92127
Tel.: (858) 453-7845
Web Site: http://www.petco.com
Sales Range: $1-4.9 Billion
Emp.: 9,900
Pet Food, Supplies & Services Retailer
N.A.I.C.S.: 459910
Justin Tichy *(Chief Stores Officer)*

Subsidiary (Domestic):

Petco Wellness, LLC (4)
2253 Air Park Rd, Rhinelander, WI 54501
Web Site: http://www.drsfostersmith.com
Emp.: 115
Pet Food, Supplies & Services Retailer
N.A.I.C.S.: 459910
Spencer Insolia *(Pres)*

Holding (Domestic):

Radwell International, Inc. (2)
1 Millennium Dr, Willingboro, NJ 08046
Tel.: (609) 288-9393
Web Site: http://www.radwell.com
Sales Range: $25-49.9 Million
Emp.: 900
Industrial Machinery Distr
N.A.I.C.S.: 423830
Brian Radwell *(Pres & CEO)*

VelocityEHS Holdings, Inc. (2)
222 Merchandise Mart Plz Ste 1750, Chi-
cago, IL 60654
Tel.: (888) 362-2007
Web Site: http://www.ehs.com
Environmental, Health & Safety Software
Publisher
N.A.I.C.S.: 513210
Glenn Trout *(Founder)*

Subsidiary (Domestic):

Chem-Tel Inc. (3)
1305 N Florida Ave, Tampa, FL 33602-2902
Tel.: (813) 248-0573
Web Site: http://www.chemtelinc.com
Chemical Transportation & Compliance Ser-
vices
N.A.I.C.S.: 541620
Tammy Gillis *(Dir-IT)*

Humantech, Inc. (3)
1161 Oak Valley Dr, Ann Arbor, MI 48108
Tel.: (734) 663-6707
Web Site: http://www.humantech.com
Engineering Services
N.A.I.C.S.: 541330
James Mallon *(Pres)*

MSDSonline, Inc. (3)
222 Merchandise Mart Plaza Ste 1750, Chi-
cago, IL 60654
Tel.: (312) 881-2000
Web Site: http://www.msdsonline.com
Business Support Services
N.A.I.C.S.: 561499
Mike Flynn *(VP-Product Dev & Strategy)*

CVC Asia Pacific Ltd. (1)
Suite 901-3 ICBC Tower Citibank Plaza, 3
Garden Road, Central, China (Hong Kong)
Tel.: (852) 35186360
Web Site: http://www.cvc.com
Sales Range: $50-74.9 Million
Emp.: 30
Privater Equity Firm
N.A.I.C.S.: 523999
Roy Kuan *(Mng Partner-Asia)*

Holding (Non-US):

Asia Timber Products Group (2)
9th Floor Shanghai Oriental Centre No 31
Wujiang Road, Jing'an District, Shanghai,
200041, China
Tel.: (86) 21 5200 1188
Web Site: http://www.atpgroup.com.cn
Sales Range: $200-249.9 Million
Lumber & Other Wood Materials Distr
N.A.I.C.S.: 423310
Paul Weatherall *(CEO)*

Subsidiary (Non-US):

CVC Asia Pacific (Australia) Ltd. (2)
Level 45 Citigroup Centre 2 Park St, Syd-
ney, 2000, NSW, Australia
Tel.: (61) 292609800
Web Site: http://www.cvc.com

Sales Range: $50-74.9 Million
Emp.: 4
Privater Equity Firm
N.A.I.C.S.: 523999

Holding (Domestic):

Stella Group Pty Ltd. (3)
77 Berry St Level 3, North Sydney, 2060,
NSW, Australia **(65%)**
Tel.: (61) 282294000
Web Site:
http://www.jetsettravelworld.com.au
Sales Range: $75-99.9 Million
Travel Agency & Hotel Operator
N.A.I.C.S.: 561510

Subsidiary (Non-US):

**CVC Asia Pacific (Beijing)
Limited** (2)
1625 1629 China World Tower 11 Jian-
guomenwai Avenue, Beijing, 100004, China
Tel.: (86) 10 6535 1800
Financial Investment Services
N.A.I.C.S.: 523910
Sunny Sun *(Sr Mng Dir)*

**CVC Asia Pacific (Japan) Kabushiki
Kaisha** (2)
Kasumigaseki Building 32F 3-2-5 Kasumi-
gaseki, Chiyoda-ku, Tokyo, 100-6032, Ja-
pan
Tel.: (81) 3 4563 9300
Web Site: http://www.cvc.com
Privater Equity Firm
N.A.I.C.S.: 523999

Holding (Domestic):

TechnoPro Holdings, Inc. (3)
Roppongi Hills Mori Tower 35F 6-10-1 Rop-
pongi, Minato-ku, Tokyo, 106-6135, Japan
Tel.: (81) 363857998
Web Site:
https://www.technoproholdings.com
Rev.: $1,363,535,960
Assets: $949,489,220
Liabilities: $440,089,880
Net Worth: $509,399,340
Earnings: $91,334,480
Emp.: 31,623
Fiscal Year-end: 06/30/2024
Engineering Staffing Services
N.A.I.C.S.: 561311
Tatsunori Okumura *(Exec Officer-Mgmt
Plng)*

Subsidiary (Domestic):

Hitec, Inc. (4)
Tokyo Minato-ku 6-10-1 Roppongi Roppongi
Hills Mori Tower 35F, Tokyo, 106 6135,
Japan
Tel.: (81) 354101012
Web Site: http://www.hitec.co.jp
Emp.: 770
Biotechnology Research & Development
Company
N.A.I.C.S.: 541714
Masami Hayafune *(Pres)*

TechnoPro Engineering Inc. (4)
Tokyo Minato-ku 6-10-1 Roppongi, Rop-
pongi Hills Mori Tower 35F, Tokyo, 106
6135, Japan
Tel.: (81) 363117924
Web Site: http://www.technopro-eg.com
Engineering Services
N.A.I.C.S.: 541330
Kouichirou Asai *(Pres)*

TechnoPro Smile, Inc. (4)
Minato-ku Roppongi Hills Mori Tower 35F,
6-10-1 Roppongi, Tokyo, 106 6135, Japan
Tel.: (81) 363616055
Web Site: http://www.technopro-smile.com
Sales Range: $25-49.9 Million
Emp.: 30
Staffing Services
N.A.I.C.S.: 561330
Akito Sonohara *(Pres)*

Subsidiary (Non-US):

**CVC Asia Pacific (Shanghai)
Limited** (2)
Room 4708 Plaza 66 Tower 2 No 1266
Nanjing West Road, Shanghai, 200040,
China

Tel.: (86) 21 2230 1200
Financial Investment Services
N.A.I.C.S.: 523910
Bo Liu *(Sr Mng Dir)*

**CVC Asia Pacific (Singapore) Pte
Ltd** (2)
Suite 2921 Level 29 The Offices at Central-
world 999/9 Rama No 1 Road, Khwaeng
Pathumwan Khet Pathumwan, Bangkok,
10330, Thailand
Tel.: (66) 2207 2328
Financial Investment Services
N.A.I.C.S.: 523910

Holding (Non-US):

**Da Niang Dumplings Holdings
Limited** (2)
No 7 Gucun, Changzhou, Jiangsu, China
Tel.: (86) 519 88122910
Web Site: http://www.cnddr.com
Restaurant Operators
N.A.I.C.S.: 492210
Vincent Huang *(Mng Dir)*

**CVC Capital Partners (Benelux)
SA/NV** (1)
Chaussee de la Hulpe 166, Brussels, BE-
1170, Belgium
Tel.: (32) 26638090
Web Site: http://www.cvc.com
Sales Range: $50-74.9 Million
Emp.: 10
Privater Equity Firm
N.A.I.C.S.: 523999
Rolly van Rappard *(Founder & Chm)*

Holding (Domestic):

Betafence NV (2)
Deerlijkstraat 58A, 8550, Zwevegem, Bel-
gium
Tel.: (32) 56734500
Web Site: http://www.betafence.com
Sales Range: $100-124.9 Million
Fencing Mfr & Distr
N.A.I.C.S.: 332999
Michele Volpi *(CEO)*

Subsidiary (Non-US):

Betafence (3)
Shepcote Ln, PO Box 119, Sheffield, S9
1TY, United Kingdom
Tel.: (44) 1142561561
Web Site: http://www.betafence.com
Wire & Steel Products
N.A.I.C.S.: 332618
Chris Morris *(Mng Dir)*

Betafence Deutschland GmbH (3)
Werk Rosler Draht, Postfach 67, 41364,
Schwalmtal, Germany
Tel.: (49) 21633390
Web Site: http://www.betafence.com
Emp.: 2,000
Security Fence Mfr
N.A.I.C.S.: 332618
Egon Vonken *(Mng Dir)*

Betafence France SA (3)
Rte Du Guindal 15, BP 20, F 59630, Bour-
bourg, France
Tel.: (33) 328658300
Web Site: http://www.betafence.com
Sales Range: $50-74.9 Million
Mfr of Security Fencing Systems
N.A.I.C.S.: 332618

Betafence Sp Zoo (3)
Ul Debowa 4, 47 246, Kotlarnia, Poland
Tel.: (48) 774062200
Web Site: http://www.betafence.com
Sales Range: $25-49.9 Million
Fabricated Wire Products
N.A.I.C.S.: 332618

Hesco Group Limited (3)
Unit 41 Knowsthorpe Way, Cross Green
Industrial Estate, Leeds, LS9 0SW, W
Yorks, United Kingdom
Tel.: (44) 113 248 6633
Web Site: http://www.hesco.com
Emp.: 200
Holding Company; Barrier Systems Design
& Mfr
N.A.I.C.S.: 551112
Michael Hughes *(CEO)*

CVC Capital Partners SICAV-FIS S.A.—(Continued)

Subsidiary (US):

Hesco Armor, Inc.   **(4)**
2210 Port Industrial Rd, Aberdeen, WA
98520-4558
Tel.: (360) 637-6867
Web Site: http://www.hesco.com
Ballistic Resistant Armor Plates Design &
Mfr
N.A.I.C.S.: 339999
Ryan Reed *(COO)*

Subsidiary (Domestic):

Hesco Bastion Ltd.   **(4)**
Unit 41 Knowsthorpe Way Cross Green Ind
Est, Leeds, LS9 0SW, United Kingdom
Tel.: (44) 1132486633
Web Site: http://www.hesco.com
Emp.: 200
Steel Wire Mesh & Polypropylene Lined
Protective Barrier Developer & Mfr
N.A.I.C.S.: 332618
Kevin Lyons *(COO)*

Subsidiary (US):

Hesco Bastion, Inc.   **(5)**
2821 Azalea Dr, Charleston, SC 29405
Tel.: (843) 637-3409
Web Site: http://www.hesco.com
Barrier Systems Mfr
N.A.I.C.S.: 444180
Hamish Russell *(Mgr-Global Bus Dev)*

Subsidiary (US):

SecureUSA Inc.   **(3)**
1649 NW 136th Ave Bldg J, Sunrise, FL
33323
Tel.: (888) 222-4559
Web Site: http://www.secureusa.net
Security Consulting, Engineering & Project
Management Services
N.A.I.C.S.: 561621
Tammy Herslebs *(CFO & Exec VP)*

Subsidiary (Non-US):

CVC Capital Partners Nederland   **(2)**
World Trade Ctr Schiphol Airport Twr D 6th
Fl Schiphol Boulevard 285, Luchthaven
Schiphol, 1118 BH, Amsterdam, Nether-
lands
Tel.: (31) 203548051
Web Site: http://www.cvc.com
Emp.: 5
Privater Equity Firm
N.A.I.C.S.: 523999
Bas Becks *(Mng Dir)*

Holding (Domestic):

Acordis BV   **(3)**
Westervoortsedijk 73, 6827 AV, Arnhem,
Netherlands
Tel.: (31) 263664444
Web Site: http://www.acordis.com
Sales Range: $100-124.9 Million
Fiber & Specialty Material Mfr
N.A.I.C.S.: 325220

Subsidiary (Non-US):

Acetate Products Ltd.   **(4)**
1 Holme Ln, PO Box 5, Spondon, Derby,
Ds21 7BP, United Kingdom
Tel.: (44) 332661422
Man-Made Fiber & Specialty Material Mfr
N.A.I.C.S.: 325220

Joint Venture (Non-US):

Century Enka Ltd.   **(4)**
Plot No 72 & 72-A MIDC, Bhosari, Pune,
411 026, Maharashtra, India
Tel.: (91) 2066127300
Web Site: http://www.centuryenka.com
Rev.: $169,917,930
Assets: $182,830,830
Liabilities: $34,197,345
Net Worth: $148,633,485
Earnings: $9,680,580
Emp.: 1,656
Fiscal Year-end: 03/31/2021
Synthetic Fiber Mfr
N.A.I.C.S.: 314999
B. K. Birla *(Chm)*

Holding (Domestic):

ChemicalInvest Holding B.V.   **(3)**
Poststraat 1, 6135 KR, Sittard,
Netherlands   **(65%)**
Tel.: (31) 46 477 0111
Holding Company; Specialty Chemicals &
Resin Products Mfr & Distr
N.A.I.C.S.: 551112
Pierre Winand *(CEO)*

Subsidiary (Non-US):

Aliancys AG   **(4)**
Stettemerstrasse 28, 8207, Schaffhausen,
Switzerland
Tel.: (41) 52 644 1212
Web Site: http://www.aliancys.com
Resin Products Mfr & Distr
N.A.I.C.S.: 325211
Bert Bakker *(CEO)*

Subsidiary (Non-US):

AOC Nederland B.V.   **(5)**
Nieuw Amsterdamseweg 31a, 7764 AN,
Schoonebeek, Netherlands   **(100%)**
Tel.: (31) 524 53 7200
Web Site: http://www.aocresins.com
Resin Products Mfr & Distr
N.A.I.C.S.: 325211

Aliancys France SAS   **(5)**
Avenue du Vermandois, 60200, Compiegne,
France
Tel.: (33) 3 4440 7575
Web Site: http://www.aliancys.com
Resin Product Distr
N.A.I.C.S.: 424690

Aliancys Italia S.r.l.   **(5)**
Via Rodi 5, 24040, Filago, Bergamo, Italy
Tel.: (39) 0526441212
Web Site: http://www.aliancys.com
Resin Product Distr
N.A.I.C.S.: 424690

Subsidiary (Domestic):

**Aliancys Holding International
B.V.**   **(4)**
Poststraat 1, 6135 KR, Sittard, Netherlands
Tel.: (31) 46 477 0111
Web Site: http://www.aliancys.com
Holding Company; Resin Mfr & Distr
N.A.I.C.S.: 551112
Bert Bakker *(CEO)*

Subsidiary (Domestic):

Aliancys (China) Holding B.V.   **(5)**
Poststraat 1, 6135 KR, Sittard, Netherlands
Tel.: (31) 46 477 0035
Holding Company
N.A.I.C.S.: 551112
Eric Gao *(Mng Dir)*

Subsidiary (Domestic):

AnQore B.V.   **(4)**
Poststraat 1, 6135 KR, Sittard, Netherlands
Tel.: (31) 46 477 3886
Web Site: http://www.anqore.com
Organic Chemical Distr
N.A.I.C.S.: 424690
Pieter Boon *(CEO)*

Holding (Domestic):

Lucardie BV   **(3)**
Lauren, NL 2521 DD, Hague, Netherlands
Tel.: (31) 573401800
Web Site: http://www.lucardie.nl
Sales Range: $25-49.9 Million
Walk-in Jewelers
N.A.I.C.S.: 458310
Andrea Wuestman *(Gen Mgr)*

Perry Sport BV   **(3)**
Oosteinderweg 247 B, NL 1432 AT, Aals-
meer, Netherlands
Tel.: (31) 297330600
Web Site: http://www.perrysport.nl
Sales Range: $25-49.9 Million
Emp.: 100
Sportswear & Sports & Camping Equipment
Retailer
N.A.I.C.S.: 459110

Retail Network BV   **(3)**

Erasmuslaan 82, 3707 ZE, Zeist, Nether-
lands
Tel.: (31) 30 234 0490
Sales Range: $25-49.9 Million
Emp.: 6
Holding Company; Non-Food Retailer
N.A.I.C.S.: 551112
Tom Heidman *(CEO)*

Subsidiary (Domestic):

Het Huis Opticiens   **(4)**
Edisonweg 21 Paelan Papland 21,
Gorinchem, 4206CK, Netherlands
Tel.: (31) 183697588
Web Site: http://www.hethuisopticiens.nl
Sales Range: $50-74.9 Million
Opticians
N.A.I.C.S.: 339115
Onno Hillers *(Mgr-Fin)*

Holding (Domestic):

TMF Group   **(3)**
Luna Aren A Herikerbergweg 238, Amster-
dam, 1101 CM, North Holland, Netherlands
Tel.: (31) 205755600
Web Site: http://www.tmf-group.com
Global Management & Accounting Out-
sourcing
N.A.I.C.S.: 541611
Mark Weil *(CEO)*

Subsidiary (Non-US):

KCS Limited   **(4)**
36/F Tower Two Times Square 1 Matheson
Street, Causeway Bay, China (Hong Kong)
Tel.: (852) 35898899
Web Site: http://www.kcs.com
Sales Range: $75-99.9 Million
Emp.: 150
Holding Company; Corporate Accounting,
Payroll Outsourcing, Corporate Secretarial,
Trust & Estate Administration Services
N.A.I.C.S.: 561621
Tom Corkhill *(Dir Client Svcs-Global)*

Division (Domestic):

KCS Hong Kong Ltd.   **(4)**
Causeway Bay Times Square Tower 2 26th
Floor C-6, Hong Kong, China (Hong
Kong)   **(100%)**
Tel.: (852) 35898899
Corporate Accounting, Payroll Outsourcing
& Corporate Secretarial Services
N.A.I.C.S.: 561499
Lydia Tye *(Head-Payroll Outsourcing &
Corp Acctg)*

Affiliate (Domestic):

UNIVEG Group   **(2)**
Strijbroek 10, 2860, Saint-Katelijne-Waver,
Belgium
Tel.: (32) 15324200
Web Site: http://www.univeg.com
Emp.: 5,550
Holding Company; Fruit & Vegetables,
Flowers, Prepared Meals & Meal Compo-
nents Distr
N.A.I.C.S.: 551112
Hein Deprez *(Founder & Chm)*

Subsidiary (US):

Seald Sweet LLC   **(3)**
1991 74th Ave, Vero Beach, FL 32966-5110
Tel.: (772) 569-2244
Web Site: https://www.sealdsweet.com
Sales Range: $25-49.9 Million
Emp.: 25
Citrus Products Marketer & Distr
N.A.I.C.S.: 424480

Subsidiary (Domestic):

Univeg Fruit & Vegetables B.V.   **(3)**
Strijbroek 10, 2860, Saint-Katelijne-Waver,
Belgium   **(100%)**
Tel.: (32) 15324200
Web Site: http://www.univeg.com
Sales Range: $25-49.9 Million
Emp.: 30
Fruit & Vegetables Distr
N.A.I.C.S.: 424480
Theo de Kool *(CFO)*

Subsidiary (Non-US):

UNIVEG Deutschland GmbH   **(4)**

Universitatsallee 16, D 2859, Bremen, Ger-
many
Tel.: (49) 421 30 92 1
Web Site: http://www.univeg.de
Fruit & Vegetables Distr
N.A.I.C.S.: 424480
Hein Deprez *(Mng Dir)*

**CVC Capital Partners (Deutschland)
GmbH**   **(1)**
WestendDuo Bockenheimer Landstrasse
24, 60323, Frankfurt am Main, 60323, Ger-
many
Tel.: (49) 699758350
Web Site: http://www.cvc.com
Privater Equity Firm
N.A.I.C.S.: 523999
Alexander C. Dibelius *(Mng Partner)*

**CVC Capital Partners (Espana)
SL**   **(1)**
Calle de Serrano 42, Madrid, 28001, Spain
Tel.: (34) 914364280
Web Site: http://www.cvc.com
Sales Range: $50-74.9 Million
Emp.: 9
Privater Equity Firm
N.A.I.C.S.: 523999
Javier de Jaime *(Mng Partner)*

**CVC Capital Partners (France)
SA**   **(1)**
63 Ave Des Champselysee, 75008, Paris,
France
Tel.: (33) 145022300
Web Site: http://www.cvc.com
Sales Range: $50-74.9 Million
Emp.: 9
Privater Equity Firm
N.A.I.C.S.: 523999
Geert Duyck *(Mng Partner-Belgium &
France)*

Holding (Domestic):

Condat SAS   **(2)**
23 avenue Georges Haupinot, BP 24,
24570, Le Lardin-Saint-Lazare, France
Tel.: (33) 5 53 51 43 33
Web Site: http://www.condat-pap.com
Paper Mfr
N.A.I.C.S.: 322120

Subsidiary (Domestic):

Nord Papier SA   **(3)**
25 rue Luyot, 59113, Seclin, Cedex, France
Tel.: (33) 3 20 62 55 88
Tape Distr
N.A.I.C.S.: 424110

Holding (Domestic):

Delachaux SA   **(2)**
119 ave Louis Roche, BP 152, 92231,
Gennevilliers, Cedex, France
Tel.: (33) 146881500
Web Site: http://www.delachaux.fr
Sales Range: $1-4.9 Billion
Industrial Machinery, Railroad, Electricity &
Cast Iron Molded Steel Mfr
N.A.I.C.S.: 333248

Subsidiary (Non-US):

CONDUCTIX-WAMPFLER AG   **(3)**
Rheinstrasse 27-33, 79576, Weil am Rhein,
Baden-Wurttemberg, Germany
Tel.: (49) 76216620
Web Site: http://www.conductix.de
Sales Range: $125-149.9 Million
Power Transmission Equipments Mfr & Distr
N.A.I.C.S.: 333613

Subsidiary (Non-US):

CONDUCTIX-WAMPFLER AB   **(4)**
Tumstockvagen 17, Taby, 187 66, Sweden
Tel.: (46) 8 630 12 90
Web Site: http://www.conductix.se
Power Transmission Equipment Distr
N.A.I.C.S.: 423690

CONDUCTIX-WAMPFLER B.V.   **(4)**
A Hofmanweg 75, 2031 BH, Haarlem, North
Holland, Netherlands
Tel.: (31) 235421200
Web Site: http://www.conductix.nl
Sales Range: $25-49.9 Million
Emp.: 10
Power Transmission Equipment Mfr

N.A.I.C.S.: 333612
Jan Soede *(Principal)*

CONDUCTIX-WAMPFLER Ltd. **(4)**
Lathaleere, Baltinglass, W901PR64, Wicklow, Ireland
Tel.: (353) 59 648 12 08
Web Site: http://www.conductix.ie
Sales Range: $10-24.9 Million
Emp.: 42
Energy & Data Transmission Equipments Mfr
N.A.I.C.S.: 332312
Marian Roberts *(Gen Mgr)*

CONDUCTIX-WAMPFLER Ltda **(4)**
Rua Luiz Pionti Vila Progresso, Camargo, Itu, 13313534, Sao Paulo, Brazil
Tel.: (55) 11 4813 7330
Web Site: http://www.conductix.com
Emp.: 35
Data Transmission Systems Distr
N.A.I.C.S.: 423610
Alessandro Ceazar *(Gen Mgr)*

CONDUCTIX-WAMPFLER O.O.O. **(4)**
Tverskaya Street Building 16/1 Office 901 B, Floor 7, Moscow, 125009, Russia
Tel.: (7) 499 922 24 06
Web Site: http://www.conductix.ru
Sales Range: $25-49.9 Million
Emp.: 4
Data Transmission System Mfr
N.A.I.C.S.: 334210
Borris Moskovskiy *(Gen Mgr)*

CONDUCTIX-WAMPFLER Sdn Bhd **(4)**
678076 U 28A Jalan SS4C 5, 47301, Petaling Jaya, Selangor, Malaysia
Tel.: (60) 378055663
Web Site: http://www.conductix.my
Sales Range: $50-74.9 Million
Emp.: 9
Data Transmission Equipments Distr
N.A.I.C.S.: 221121

Subsidiary (Non-US):

CONDUCTIX-WAMPFLER Pte Ltd **(3)**
3 Raffles Place 07-01 Baharat Building, Singapore, 48617, Singapore
Tel.: (65) 63296405
Web Site: http://www.conductix.com
Data Transmission Systems Mfr
N.A.I.C.S.: 221121

CONDUCTIX-WAMPFLER Pvt Ltd **(3)**
4/24 Goodwill Enclave Road No 9 Kalyani Nagar, Pune, 411 006, Maharashtra, India
Tel.: (91) 2040046409
Web Site: http://www.conductix.com
Data Transmission Equipments Distr
N.A.I.C.S.: 423840

CONDUCTIX-WAMPFLER Srl **(3)**
Via de Capitani 14/16, Agrate Brianza, Monza e Brianza, Italy
Tel.: (39) 039 60743 1
Web Site: http://www.wampfler.it
Sales Range: $25-49.9 Million
Emp.: 70
Power Transmission Equipment Distr
N.A.I.C.S.: 423690

Subsidiary (US):

Conductix Inc. **(3)**
10102 F St, Omaha, NE 68127-1104
Tel.: (402) 339-9300
Web Site: http://www.conductix.us
Sales Range: $50-74.9 Million
Emp.: 125
Electrical Conductors Mfr & Distr
N.A.I.C.S.: 335999
Lon Miller *(CEO)*

Subsidiary (Non-US):

CONDUCTIX-WAMPFLER Ltd. **(4)**
1 Michigan Avenue Off-Broadway, Salford, M50 2GY, Lancashire, United Kingdom
Tel.: (44) 1618480161
Web Site: http://www.conductix.co.uk
Sales Range: $10-24.9 Million
Emp.: 30
Power Transmission Equipment Mfr

N.A.I.C.S.: 333613
Alen Jones *(Mng Dir)*

CONDUCTIX-WAMPFLER Pty Ltd **(4)**
14 England Street, Dandenong, 3175, VIC, Australia
Tel.: (61) 397068844
Web Site: http://www.conductix.com.au
Sales Range: $25-49.9 Million
Emp.: 25
Mobile Electrification Systems Mfr
N.A.I.C.S.: 335999

CONDUCTIX-WAMPFLER S.de RL de C.V. **(4)**
Calle Trevino 983-C Zona Centroe, 66600, Apodaca, Nuevo Leon, Mexico
Tel.: (52) 8110909013
Web Site: http://www.conductix.mx
Power Transmission Equipment Distr
N.A.I.C.S.: 423610

Subsidiary (US):

DELACHAUX METAL Inc. **(3)**
25 Interstate Dr, Napoleon, OH 43545
Tel.: (419) 599-1754
Material Handling Machinery Distr
N.A.I.C.S.: 423830

Subsidiary (Domestic):

ETS RAOUL LENOIR SAS **(3)**
ZI du Bearn, 54400, Cosnes-et-Romain, France
Tel.: (33) 382252300
Web Site: http://www.raoul-lenoir.com
Sales Range: $25-49.9 Million
Emp.: 100
Magnetic Separation & Lifting Equipment Mfr
N.A.I.C.S.: 333998

Subsidiary (Non-US):

MEC DELACHAUX S.R.L. **(4)**
Via Isorella 5, 25010, Visano, Brescia, Italy
Tel.: (39) 030 9958561
Web Site: http://www.mec-delachaux.it
Sales Range: $25-49.9 Million
Emp.: 20
Magnetic Separation & Lifting Equipments Mfr
N.A.I.C.S.: 333998

Subsidiary (Domestic):

FONDERIES NICOLAS SAS **(3)**
5 Rue de la Haillette, 08700, Nouzonville, Ardennes, France
Tel.: (33) 324538210
Web Site: http://www.delachaux.fr
Sales Range: $25-49.9 Million
Emp.: 33
Foundry Machinery Distr
N.A.I.C.S.: 423830

Subsidiary (Non-US):

IAT Ltda **(3)**
Av Severo Dullius 2015, Porto Alegre, 90200-310, Brazil
Tel.: (55) 5133734300
Web Site: http://www.iatltda.com.br
Rail Fastening Systems Mfr
N.A.I.C.S.: 331110

PANDROL AUSTRALIA Pty Limited **(3)**
7 Bessemer Street, Blacktown, 2148, NSW, Australia
Tel.: (61) 298522500
Web Site: http://www.pandrol.com.au
Sales Range: $25-49.9 Million
Emp.: 80
Rail Joints & Fastenings Mfr
N.A.I.C.S.: 332999
Mark Pittendrigh *(Mgr-Sls & Mktg)*

PT PANDROL INDONESIA **(3)**
Jalan Abdul Muis No 80A, Jakarta, 10160, Indonesia
Tel.: (62) 21 344 3333
Rail Joints & Fastenings Mfr
N.A.I.C.S.: 331110

ROLF PLOTZ GmbH & Co. KG **(3)**
Wiesenstrasse 12, 51580, Reichshof, Nordrhein-Westfalen, Germany
Tel.: (49) 2261913480

Web Site: http://www.ploetz-group.com
Rail Fastenings Mfr
N.A.I.C.S.: 331110
Rolf Plotz *(Founder)*

Railtech Deutschland GmbH **(3)**
Wiesenstrasse 12, 51580, Reichshof, Nordrhein-Westfalen, Germany
Tel.: (49) 22619134828
Web Site: http://www.railtech-deutschland.de
Sales Range: $25-49.9 Million
Emp.: 23
Rail Joints & Fastenings Mfr.
N.A.I.C.S.: 331110
Joachim Kraegeloh *(Mng Dir)*

Holding (Domestic):

Railtech International **(3)**
205 R De Sin Le Noble, BP 261, 59504, Douai, France
Tel.: (33) 327996400
Web Site: http://www.pandrol.com
Railroad & Other Heavy Manufacturing
N.A.I.C.S.: 336510

Subsidiary (Non-US):

Les Industries RAILWEL Inc. **(4)**
175 Rue John F Kennedy, Saint-Jerome, J7Y 4B5, QC, Canada
Tel.: (450) 565-9100
Railway Track Welding Product Mfr
N.A.I.C.S.: 333992

Subsidiary (US):

RT CONTRACTING Corp. **(4)**
25 Interstate Dr, Napoleon, OH 43545
Tel.: (419) 592-5050
Rail Fastenings Mfr
N.A.I.C.S.: 331110

Subsidiary (Domestic):

Railtech Alu Singen SAS **(4)**
119 Avenue Louis Roche, BP 152, 92231, Gennevilliers, Hauts-de-Seine, France
Tel.: (33) 146881772
Web Site: http://www.railtech.fr
Sales Range: $25-49.9 Million
Emp.: 5
Rail Joints & Fastenings Mfr
N.A.I.C.S.: 331110

Subsidiary (Non-US):

Railtech Australia Ltd. **(4)**
52 Lysaght Street, Acacia Ridge, 4110, QLD, Australia
Tel.: (61) 733445444
Web Site: http://www.railtech.com.au
Aluminothermic Rail Welding Materials Distr
N.A.I.C.S.: 423840

Subsidiary (US):

Railtech Boutet Inc. **(4)**
25 Interstate Dr, Napoleon, OH 43545
Tel.: (419) 592-5050
Web Site: http://www.railtechboutet.com
Railway Track Welding Supplies Mfr.
N.A.I.C.S.: 333514
Jeff Hoff *(Mgr-Sls & Distr)*

Subsidiary (Non-US):

Railtech Calomex S. de R. L. de C. V. **(4)**
Marconi No 6 Fracc Industrial San Nicolas, Tlalnepantla, 54030, Mexico
Tel.: (52) 5553109371
Web Site: http://www.railtech.com.mx
Emp.: 30
Railway Track Components Mfr
N.A.I.C.S.: 332323
Genaro De la Cruz *(Gen Mgr)*

Railtech Pandrol China Ltd. **(4)**
HanZhengJie Industrial Zone Building A122 21 Jiefang Avenue, Wuhan, Hubei, China
Tel.: (86) 2783499999
Sales Range: $25-49.9 Million
Rail Fastening Systems Mfr
N.A.I.C.S.: 331110

Railtech Pandrol Italia SRL **(4)**
Via Facii Zona Industriale le S Atto, Teramo, 64020, Italy
Tel.: (39) 0861587149

Web Site: http://www.railtech.fr
Sales Range: $25-49.9 Million
Emp.: 15
Rail Joints & Fastenings Mfr
N.A.I.C.S.: 331110
Monica Melasecca *(Controller)*

Railtech Porsol Lda. **(4)**
Rua Jose Afonso No 4C 1st Floor, 1600-130, Lisbon, Portugal
Tel.: (351) 213866234
Rail Joints & Fastenings Mfr
N.A.I.C.S.: 331110
Rkuem Amaro *(Mgr)*

Subsidiary (Domestic):

Railtech Schlatter Systems, S.A.S. **(4)**
9 Rue Debarcadere, 927007, Colombes, France
Tel.: (33) 146881730
Web Site: http://www.railtech.fr
Sales Range: $25-49.9 Million
Emp.: 5
Railroad Systems; Joint Venture of Railtech International (51%) & Schaltter AG (49%)
N.A.I.C.S.: 333992
Seewald Sabrace *(Mng Dir)*

Subsidiary (Non-US):

Railtech Stedef Ltd **(3)**
16th Floor Chartered Square Building 152 North Sathorn Road, SILOM, Bangkok, 10500, Thailand
Tel.: (66) 26378127
Web Site: http://www.pandrol.co.th
Rail Fastenings Mfr
N.A.I.C.S.: 331110
Baptiste Destailleurs *(Mng Dir)*

Railtech UK Ltd **(3)**
Unit 100 Catesby Park Kings Norton, Birmingham, B38 8SE, West Midlands, United Kingdom
Tel.: (44) 1214864444
Web Site: http://www.railtech-uk.com
Sales Range: $25-49.9 Million
Emp.: 5
Rail Fastenings Mfr
N.A.I.C.S.: 331110
Steve Kettle *(Mgr-Bus Dev)*

Subsidiary (Domestic):

TAMARIS INDUSTRIES SAS **(3)**
212 rue de Pressense, 30319, Ales, Gard, France
Tel.: (33) 4 66 54 27 00
Web Site: http://www.delachaux.fr
Industrial Machinery Mfr
N.A.I.C.S.: 333248

Holding (Domestic):

Lecta S.A. **(2)**
15 Avenue Galilee, 92350, Le Plessis-Robinson, France
Tel.: (33) 146017070
Web Site: http://www.lecta.com
Sales Range: $1-4.9 Billion
Coated Woodfree Paper Mfr
N.A.I.C.S.: 322220
Santiago Ramirez Larrauri *(Chm & CEO)*

Subsidiary (Non-US):

Lecta Deutschland GmbH **(3)**
Tel.: (49) 89350497
Tape Distr
N.A.I.C.S.: 424110

Lecta HQ SA **(3)**
Gran Via De Les Corts Catalanes 678, Barcelona, 08010, Spain
Tel.: (34) 0934 82 11
Tape Distr
N.A.I.C.S.: 424110

Polyedra SpA **(3)**
Via Riccardo Lombardi 19/10, 20153, Milan, Italy **(100%)**
Tel.: (39) 02335511
Web Site: http://www.polyedra.com
Sales Range: $150-199.9 Million
Emp.: 365
Graphics Solutions & Paper Products Distr
N.A.I.C.S.: 424130
Renato Panfilo *(Mgr-Customer Svc & Telemarketing)*

CVC Capital Partners SICAV-FIS S.A.—(Continued)

Subsidiary (Domestic):

Carthago Srl (4)
Via Quattro Novembre 18, Trecasali, 43010, Parma, Italy
Tel.: (39) 0521372160
Paper & Cardboard Distr
N.A.I.C.S.: 424130

Subsidiary (Non-US):

Torraspapel, S.A. (3)
Llull 331, 08019, Barcelona, Spain
Tel.: (34) 93 482 10 00
Sales Range: $1-4.9 Billion
Paper Mfr
N.A.I.C.S.: 322299

Subsidiary (Non-US):

Cartiere del Garda SpA (4)
Viale Rovereto 15, 38066, Rome, Trentino, Italy
Tel.: (39) 0464 579111
Web Site: http://www.gardacartiere.com
N.A.I.C.S.: 322130
Giovanni Lo Presti (Gen Dir-Industrial)

Lecta Benelux SA (4)
Boulevard du Souverain 100, 1170, Brussels, Belgium
Tel.: (32) 2 675 24 42
Tape Distr
N.A.I.C.S.: 424110

Lecta Maroc Sarl (4)
4 Rue de la Bastille 1er etage Residence Mervet, Casablanca, 20 100, Morocco
Tel.: (212) 522 951 500
Tape Distr
N.A.I.C.S.: 424110

Lecta Mexico S. de R.L. de C.V. (4)
Av Presidente Masaryk No 101-Of 801A, Col Chapultepec Morales Delegacion Miguel Hidalgo, Mexico, 11570, Mexico
Tel.: (52) 55 5020 34 20
Tape Distr
N.A.I.C.S.: 424110

Subsidiary (US):

Lecta North America Inc (4)
2975 Westchester Ave Ste 412, Purchase, NY 10577
Tel.: (914) 253-8150
Tape Distr
N.A.I.C.S.: 424110

Subsidiary (Non-US):

Lecta Paper UK Ltd (4)
4 Shenley Pavilions Chalkdell Drive, Shenley Wood, Milton Keynes, MK5 6LB, United Kingdom
Tel.: (44) 190 828 80 00
Web Site: http://www.lecta.com
Emp.: 10
N.A.I.C.S.: 424110
Jonathan Howard (Gen Mgr)

Torraspapel Portugal Lda (4)
Rua Mario Sampaio Ribeiro 1, 1600-504, Lisbon, Portugal
Tel.: (351) 707 91 99 91
Web Site: http://www.torraspapel.pt
Tape Distr
N.A.I.C.S.: 424110

CVC Capital Partners Denmark A/S (1)
31 Bredgade 3rd Floor, 1260, Copenhagen, Denmark
Tel.: (45) 33 12 00 10
Financial Investment Services
N.A.I.C.S.: 523910
Christoffer Sjoqvist (Mng Dir)

CVC Capital Partners Jersey Limited (1)
3rd Floor Sir Walter Raleigh House 48-50 The Esplanade, Saint Helier, JE2 3QB, Channel Islands, Jersey
Tel.: (44) 1534 828 750
Web Site: http://www.cvc.com
Financial Investment Services
N.A.I.C.S.: 523910
Carl Hansen (Sr Mng Dir)

CVC Capital Partners Svenska AB (1)
Hamngatan 13, 111 47, Stockholm, Sweden
Tel.: (46) 8 407 8790
Financial Investment Services
N.A.I.C.S.: 523910
Jakob Eliasson (Dir-Investment)

CVC Capital Partners Switzerland GmbH (1)
Bahnhofstrasse 94, 8001, Zurich, Switzerland
Tel.: (41) 44 217 7000
Financial Investment Services
N.A.I.C.S.: 523910
Gregor Hilverkus (Mng Dir)

CVC Capital Partners srl (1)
Via dell'Orso 8, 20121, Milan, Italy
Tel.: (39) 02 7607 571
Financial Investment Services
N.A.I.C.S.: 523910
Giorgio De Palma (Mng Dir)

CVC Credit Partners Limited (1)
111 Strand, London, WC2R 0AG, United Kingdom
Tel.: (44) 20 7520 4950
Web Site: http://www.cvc.com
Investment Fund Management Services
N.A.I.C.S.: 523940
Brandon Bradkin (Partner & COO)

Subsidiary (US):

CVC Credit Partners, LLC (2)
712 5th Ave 42nd Fl, New York, NY 10019
Tel.: (212) 506-3858
Web Site: http://www.cvc.com
Investment Fund Management Services
N.A.I.C.S.: 523940
Oscar Anderson (Mng Dir & Portfolio Mgr)

Joint Venture (Non-US):

Ideal Standard International NV (2)
Ikaroslaan 18, 1930, Zaventem, Belgium
Tel.: (32) 23256600
Web Site: http://www.idealstandard.be
Emp.: 60
Shower Enclosure & Bathroom Fixture Mfr
N.A.I.C.S.: 325620
Torsten Tuerling (CEO)

Subsidiary (Non-US):

Ideal Standard (UK) Ltd. (3)
The Bathroom Works National Avenue, Kingston upon Hull, HU5 4HS, United Kingdom
Tel.: (44) 1482346461
Web Site: http://www.ideal-standard.co.uk
Shower Enclosure & Bathroom Fixture Mfr & Distr
N.A.I.C.S.: 327110
Keith Boad (Mng Dir)

Ideal Standard France (3)
165 Avenue Du Bois De La Pie, 95920, Roissy-en-France, France
Tel.: (33) 149382800
Web Site: http://www.idealstandard.com
Sales Range: $25-49.9 Million
Shower Enclosure & Bathroom Fixture Mfr & Distr
N.A.I.C.S.: 327110

Ideal Standard GmbH (3)
Euskirchener Strasse 80, PO Box 1809, 53121, Bonn, Germany
Tel.: (49) 2285210
Web Site: http://www.idealstandard.de
Sales Range: $25-49.9 Million
Shower Enclosure & Bathroom Fixture Mfr & Distr
N.A.I.C.S.: 327110

Branch (Non-US):

Ideal Standard GmbH Zweigniederlassung Osterreich (4)
Murbangasse 4, 1108, Vienna, Austria
Tel.: (43) 125662220
Web Site: http://www.idealstandard.de
Shower Enclosure & Bathroom Fixture Mfr & Distr
N.A.I.C.S.: 327110

Subsidiary (Non-US):

Ideal Standard Italia S.r.l. (3)

Via Domodossola 19, 20145, Milan, Italy
Web Site: http://www.idealstandard.it
Shower Enclosure & Bathroom Fixture Mfr & Distr
N.A.I.C.S.: 327110

Ideal Standard S.A.I. (3)
265 Messogion Avenue, 15451, Athens, Greece
Tel.: (30) 2106790800
Web Site: http://www.idealstandard.gr
Sales Range: $25-49.9 Million
Emp.: 60
Shower Enclosure & Bathroom Fixture Mfr & Distr
N.A.I.C.S.: 327110

Ideal Standard s.r.o. (3)
Zemska 623, Teplice, 41501, Czech Republic
Tel.: (420) 417592111
Web Site: http://www.idealstandard.cz
Sales Range: $50-74.9 Million
Kitchen & Bathroom Products Mfr & Distr
N.A.I.C.S.: 332913
Jiri Tourek (Gen Mgr)

Quality Ceramic (Arklow) Limited (3)
South Quay, Co Wicklow, Arklow, Ireland
Tel.: (353) 40231288
Sales Range: $25-49.9 Million
Emp.: 50
Vitreous China Plumbing Fixture & China & Earthenware Bathroom Accessories Mfr
N.A.I.C.S.: 327110

Subsidiary (Domestic):

Quality Ceramics (Sales) Limited (4)
South Quay, Co Wicklow, Arklow, Wicklow, Ireland
Tel.: (353) 40 231288
Bathroom Fixtures Whslr
N.A.I.C.S.: 423720
John O'Loughlin (Mng Dir)

Subsidiary (Non-US):

Quay Bathrooms Limited (3)
South Quay, Arklow, Wicklow, Ireland
Tel.: (353) 40 231288
Bathroom Fixture Mfr
N.A.I.C.S.: 327110

Shires (Ireland) Limited (3)
Broomhill Road, Tallaght, Dublin, 24, Ireland
Tel.: (353) 1 4047600
Sales Range: $25-49.9 Million
Emp.: 45
Plumbing & Heating Equipment & Supplies Hydronics Merchant Whslr
N.A.I.C.S.: 423720

Icario, Inc. (1)
123 N 3rd St Ste 300, Minneapolis, MN 55401
Tel.: (855) 612-6688
Web Site: http://icariohealth.com
Information & Technology Services
N.A.I.C.S.: 519290
Steve Wigginton (CEO)

Subsidiary (Domestic):

ChipRewards, Inc. (2)
2901 2nd Ave S Ste 210, Birmingham, AL 35233
Tel.: (205) 323-4008
Web Site: http://www.chiprewards.com
Supermarkets & Grocery Stores
N.A.I.C.S.: 445110
William R. Dexheimer (Founder & CEO)

Stock Spirits Group PLC (1)
Solar House Mercury Park, Wooburn Green, HP10 0HH, Buckinghamshire, United Kingdom
Tel.: (44) 162 864 8500
Web Site: http://www.stockspirits.com
Rev.: $462,966,227
Assets: $851,431,643
Liabilities: $380,150,738
Net Worth: $471,280,905
Earnings: $26,554,288
Emp.: 1,120
Fiscal Year-end: 09/30/2020
Spirits Mfr & Distr
N.A.I.C.S.: 312140
Richard Hayes (Dir-Sls & Mktg)

Subsidiary (US):

Distillerie Stock USA Ltd. (2)

400 E 77th St Apt 11b, New York, NY 10075-2325
Tel.: (718) 651-9800
Web Site: http://www.grangala.com
Sales Range: $1-9.9 Million
Mfr & Importer of Liqueurs & Wines
N.A.I.C.S.: 424820

TechInsights Inc. (1)
1891 Robertson Road Suite 500, Ottawa, K2H 5B7, ON, Canada
Tel.: (613) 599-6500
Web Site: http://www.techinsights.com
Consulting & Management Software Solutions
N.A.I.C.S.: 513210
Mike McLean (Sr VP-Intellectual Property Rights)

Subsidiary (US):

Strategy Analytics, Inc. (2)
199 Wells Ave Ste 108, Newton, MA 02459
Tel.: (617) 614-0700
Web Site: http://www.strategyanalytics.com
Marketing Research & Consulting Services
N.A.I.C.S.: 541910
Harvey Cohen (Founder & Pres)

Subsidiary (Non-US):

Strategy Analytics (3)
19 Rue Pierre Lescot, 75001, Paris, France
Tel.: (33) 1 53 40 99 50
Marketing Research & Consulting Services
N.A.I.C.S.: 541910

Strategy Analytics GmbH (3)
Sebastiansplatz 5, Munich, 80331, Germany
Tel.: (49) 89 51 51 35 0
Marketing Research & Consulting Services
N.A.I.C.S.: 541910

Strategy Analytics Inc. (3)
59-2-102 Beijing Suncity No 30 Litang Road, Xiaotangshan Changping District, Beijing, 102209, China
Tel.: (86) 10 8975 5246
Marketing Research & Consulting Services
N.A.I.C.S.: 541910

Strategy Analytics Inc. (3)
Level 18 Yebisu Garden Place Tower 4-20-3 Ebisu, Shibuya-ku, Tokyo, 150-6018, Japan
Tel.: (81) 3 5789 5935
Marketing Research & Consulting Services
N.A.I.C.S.: 541910

Strategy Analytics Inc. (3)
14F 631 Gangam-daero, Seocho-gu, Seoul, 06524, Korea (South)
Tel.: (82) 2 310 9122
Marketing Research & Consulting Services
N.A.I.C.S.: 541910

Strategy Analytics Ltd. (3)
Bank House 171 Midsummer Boulevard, Milton Keynes, MK9 1EB, United Kingdom
Tel.: (44) 1908 423600
Web Site: http://www.strategyanalytics.com
Marketing Research & Consulting Services
N.A.I.C.S.: 541910
Chris Webber (VP-Global Automotive Practice)

Subsidiary (US):

VLSI Research, Inc. (2)
2880 Lakeside Dr Ste 350, Santa Clara, CA 95054
Tel.: (408) 453-8844
Web Site: http://www.vlsiresearch.com
Sales Range: $1-9.9 Million
Emp.: 23
Marketing Research & Public Opinion Polling
N.A.I.C.S.: 541910
Dan G. Hutcheson (Chm & CEO)

Teneo Holdings LLC (1)
280 Park Ave, New York, NY 10017
Tel.: (212) 886-1600
Web Site: http://www.teneoholdings.com
Professional, Scientific & Technical Services
N.A.I.C.S.: 541990
John Crean (Mng Dir-Canada)

Holding (Domestic):

Goldin Associates, LLC (2)

350 Fifth Ave, New York, NY 10018
Tel.: (212) 593-2255
Web Site: http://www.goldinassociates.com
Management Consulting Services
N.A.I.C.S.: 541611
Harrison Goldin *(Founder & Sr Mng Dir)*

Subsidiary (Non-US):

Teneo Blue Rubicon Limited **(2)**
5th floor 6 More London Place, London,
SE1 2DA, United Kingdom
Tel.: (44) 20 7260 2700
Web Site: http://www.teneobluerubicon.com
Emp.: 200
Professional, Scientific & Technical Services
N.A.I.C.S.: 541990
Fraser Hardie *(Chm)*

Subsidiary (Non-US):

Teneo Blue Rubicon - Singapore **(3)**
Asia Square Tower 2 #23-01 12 Marina
View, Singapore, 018961, Singapore
Tel.: (65) 9154 2225
Web Site: http://www.teneobluerubicon.com
Professional Scientific & Technical Services
N.A.I.C.S.: 541990

Zabka Polska sp. Z o. o. **(1)**
Anders Square 7, 61 894, Poznan, Poland
Tel.: (48) 61 856 37 00
Web Site: http://www.zabka.pl
Convenience Store Operator
N.A.I.C.S.: 445131
Kasia Kazior *(Chief Digital Officer)*

CVC INCOME & GROWTH LIMITED
IFC1 The Esplanade, Saint Helier,
JE1 4BP, Jersey
Tel.: (44) 1534815200　JE
Web Site: https://ig.cvc.com
Year Founded: 2013
CVCG—(LSE)
Rev.: $21,998,675
Assets: $276,072,741
Liabilities: $275,912,714
Net Worth: $160,026
Earnings: $35,038,781
Fiscal Year-end: 12/31/23
Financial Investment Services
N.A.I.C.S.: 523940
David Alan Wood *(Partner)*

CVC LIMITED
Suite 40 04 Level 40 Governor Phillip
Tower 1 Farrer Place, Sydney, 2000,
NSW, Australia
Tel.: (61) 290878000　AU
Web Site: https://www.cvc.com.au
Year Founded: 1984
CVC—(ASX)
Rev.: $15,766,514
Assets: $224,914,513
Liabilities: $104,446,390
Net Worth: $120,468,123
Earnings: ($3,126,249)
Emp.: 10
Fiscal Year-end: 06/30/24
Miscellaneous Financial Investment
Activities
N.A.I.C.S.: 523999
John Douglas Read *(Chm)*

Subsidiaries:

Biomedical Systems Pty Limited **(1)**
PO Box 2513, Carlingford, 2118, NSW,
Australia
Tel.: (61) 29 871 0580
Web Site:
　https://www.biomedsystems.com.au
Medical Diagnostic Services
N.A.I.C.S.: 621511

CVC Managers Pty. Limited **(1)**
Level 37 Gateway 1 Macquarie Place, Sydney, 2000, NSW, Australia
Tel.: (61) 290878000
Investment Management Service
N.A.I.C.S.: 523940
John Andrew Hunter *(Controller-Fin)*

Eildon Capital Limited **(1)**

Suite 3703 Level 37 Gateway 1 Macquarie
Place, Sydney, 2000, NSW, Australia
Tel.: (61) 2 9087 8000
Web Site: http://www.eildonfunds.com
Rev.: $5,937,127
Assets: $33,844,885
Liabilities: $2,017,947
Net Worth: $31,826,938
Earnings: $3,610,914
Fiscal Year-end: 06/30/2017
Closed-End Venture Capital Private Equity
Fund
N.A.I.C.S.: 525990
John Hunter *(Co-Sec)*

CVC TECHNOLOGIES, INC.
No 190 Gongye 9th Rd, Dali Dist,
Taichung, 412, Taiwan
Tel.: (886) 424963666
Web Site: https://www.cvcusa.com
Year Founded: 1979
4744—(TPE)
Rev.: $28,228,496
Assets: $66,753,369
Liabilities: $33,329,331
Net Worth: $33,424,038
Earnings: $1,758,903
Fiscal Year-end: 12/31/22
Pharmaceutical Packaging Equipment
Mfr
N.A.I.C.S.: 333993
Te-Hsin Yen *(Chm)*

Subsidiaries:

C V C Technologies, Inc. **(1)**
10861 Business Dr, Fontana, CA 92337
Tel.: (909) 355-0311
Web Site: http://www.cvcusa.com
Sales Range: $1-9.9 Million
Emp.: 19
Labelling Equipment Mfr & Distr
N.A.I.C.S.: 333993
Yulie Luo *(Mgr-Acctg)*

CVF TECHNOLOGIES CORP.
2967 Dundas Street 627, Toronto,
M6P 1Z2, ON, Canada
Tel.: (613) 703-5790　NV
CNVT—(OTCIQ)
Sales Range: Less than $1 Million
Investment Management Service
N.A.I.C.S.: 531390
Peter M. Claus *(CEO)*

CVI DOM MAKLERSKI SP. Z O.O.
Piekna 24/26A, 00-549, Warsaw,
Poland
Tel.: (48) 22 185 55 44
Web Site: http://cvi.pl
Year Founded: 2012
Investment Company
N.A.I.C.S.: 523999
Dorota Dubyk *(Compliance Officer)*

Subsidiaries:

Exact Systems S.A. **(1)**
53/5 Ferdynanda Focha St, 42-200, Czesto- **(69%)**
chowa, Poland
Tel.: (48) 34 365 58 26
Web Site: http://www.exactsystems.com
Automotive Parts Repair & Sorting; Quality
Process Improvement & Resident Engineering
N.A.I.C.S.: 811198
Pawel Gos *(Gen Mgr)*

Subsidiary (Non-US):

Exact Systems Czech Republic
s.r.o. **(2)**
Daliborova 426/25, Marianske Hory, 709 00,
Ostrava, Czech Republic
Tel.: (420) 553 034 361
Web Site: http://www.exactsystems.cz
Automotive Part Whslr
N.A.I.C.S.: 423120
Radovan Meles *(Gen Mgr)*

Exact Systems GmbH **(2)**
Girbigsdorfer Str 17, 02828, Gorlitz, Germany

Tel.: (49) 35 81 421 707
Web Site: http://www.exactsystems.de
Automotive Part Whslr
N.A.I.C.S.: 423120

Exact Systems Slovakia s.r.o. **(2)**
Jana Kalinciaka 22, 010 01, Zilina, Slovakia
Tel.: (421) 41 7231333
Web Site: http://www.exactsystems.sk
Emp.: 500
Automotive Part Whslr
N.A.I.C.S.: 423120
Stanislav Novak *(Mgr-Sls & Dev)*

ZAO Exact Systems **(2)**
3RD floor 38A 2nd Khutorskaya str bld 9,
127287, Moscow, Russia
Tel.: (7) 495 662 10 68
Automotive Engineering Services
N.A.I.C.S.: 541330

CVILUX CORPORATION
9F No 9 Lane 3 Sec 1 ChungCheng
East Road, Tamshui, New Taipei City,
25147, Taiwan
Tel.: (886) 226201000
Web Site: https://www.cvilux.com
8103—(TAI)
Rev.: $99,165,567
Assets: $164,149,475
Liabilities: $63,662,936
Net Worth: $100,486,539
Earnings: $7,031,557
Emp.: 2,700
Fiscal Year-end: 12/31/23
Computer Communication Equipment
Mfr
N.A.I.C.S.: 334417
Chao-Chun Yang *(Chm & CEO)*

Subsidiaries:

CviLux (Singapore) Corporation **(1)**
Block 52 Ubi Avenue 3 04-36 Froniter, Singapore, Singapore
Tel.: (65) 67420946
Electronic Components Distr
N.A.I.C.S.: 423690

CviLux Electronics (Dongguan) Co.,
Ltd. **(1)**
Tai He Road, Gao Long Development Zone
Huan Zhu Li Village Chang Ping Town,
Dongguan, Guangdong, China
Tel.: (86) 76983397111
Electronic Connector Mfr
N.A.I.C.S.: 334417

CviLux Korea Corporation **(1)**
14 Baranmanse-gil Hyangnam-eup,
Hwaseong, Gyeonggi, Korea (South)
Tel.: (82) 313527764
Electronic Connector Mfr
N.A.I.C.S.: 334417

CviLux Lao Co., Ltd. **(1)**
Lot 329 and 330 Savan-Seno Special Economic Zone C KM10 Route No 9, Nongdeun Village Kaysone Phomvihane Dist,
Savannakhet, Lao People's Democratic
Republic
Tel.: (856) 309889303
Electronic Connector Mfr
N.A.I.C.S.: 334417

CviLux Sdn Bhd **(1)**
No 4-5 Jalan 3/137B 5th Mile off Old Klang
Road, 58200, Kuala Lumpur, Malaysia
Tel.: (60) 379819199
Electronic Connector Mfr
N.A.I.C.S.: 334417

CviLux Technology (Chongqing)
Corporation **(1)**
No 2609 Hing Dragon Ave Phoenix Lake
Industrial Park, Yongchuan Chongqing
Yongchuan Industrial Park, Chongqing,
402160, China
Tel.: (86) 2361162111
Electronic Components Mfr & Distr
N.A.I.C.S.: 334419

CviLux Technology (Shenzhen)
Corporation **(1)**
C-27D Qianhai Haoyuan No 220 Xuefu
Road Nantou Street, Daxin community Nanshan District, Shenzhen, China
Tel.: (86) 76983397111

Electronic Connector Mfr
N.A.I.C.S.: 334417

CviLux Technology (Suzhou) Co.,
Ltd. **(1)**
No 245 Tonggang Road Fenhu Economic
Development Zone, Luxu Town, Wujiang,
215200, Jiangsu, China
Tel.: (86) 51263272111
Electronic Components Mfr & Distr
N.A.I.C.S.: 334417

CviLux USA Corporation **(1)**
6000 Bothell - Everett Hwy Ste 170, Mill
Creek, WA 98012
Tel.: (425) 379-7097
Electronic Connector Mfr
N.A.I.C.S.: 334417

Dongguan Qunhan Electronics
Co.,Ltd. **(1)**
Tai-He Road Gao-Long Development Zone,
Huan-Zhu-Li Village, Chang-Ping Town,
Dongguan, 523560, Guangdong, China
Tel.: (86) 76983824816
Connector Mfr
N.A.I.C.S.: 334417

CVO PETROCHEMICAL REFINERY LIMITED
37 Katalgonj Panchlaish, Chittagong,
Bangladesh
Tel.: (880) 31650525
Web Site: https://www.cvopetro.com
Year Founded: 1984
CVOPRL—(CHT)
Rev.: $398,768
Assets: $6,803,001
Liabilities: $3,419,996
Net Worth: $3,383,006
Earnings: ($730,176)
Fiscal Year-end: 06/30/21
Soybean Oil Mfr
N.A.I.C.S.: 311224
Shamsul Alam Shamim *(Chm)*

CVR MEDICAL CORP.
Suite 409 221 West Esplanade, North
Vancouver, V7M 3J3, BC, Canada
Tel.: (757) 909-0491　BC
Web Site: https://www.cvrmed.com
CRRVF—(OTCEM)
Assets: $1,219,211
Liabilities: $3,905,420
Net Worth: ($2,686,209)
Earnings: ($173,400)
Fiscal Year-end: 12/31/20
Medical Equipment Mfr
N.A.I.C.S.: 339112
Paul Blunden *(Pres)*

CVS BAY AREA INC.
26th floor CVS Bay Area Building
SCEC Building, 1-7-1 Nakase Mihama Ward, Chiba, 261-0023, Japan
Tel.: (81) 432966621
Web Site: https://www.cvs-
　bayarea.co.jp
Year Founded: 1951
2687—(TKS)
Rev.: $53,309,710
Assets: $72,892,290
Liabilities: $49,076,980
Net Worth: $23,815,310
Earnings: $4,941,730
Emp.: 202
Fiscal Year-end: 02/29/24
Convenience Store Operator
N.A.I.C.S.: 445131
Yutaka Izumisawa *(Chm)*

CVS GROUP PLC
CVS House Owen Road, Diss, IP22
4ER, Norfolk, United Kingdom
Tel.: (44) 1379644288
Web Site: https://www.cvsukltd.co.uk
CVSG—(LSE)
Rev.: $818,124,367
Assets: $872,093,022
Liabilities: $542,846,308

CVS Group Plc—(Continued)

Net Worth: $329,246,713
Earnings: $33,367,037
Emp.: 9,000
Fiscal Year-end: 06/30/24
Veterinary Services
N.A.I.C.S.: 541940
Simon Innes (CEO)

Subsidiaries:

Albavet Limited (1)
24 Nicol Street, Kirkcaldy, KY1 1NY, Fife,
United Kingdom
Tel.: (44) 1592641333
Web Site: http://www.albavet.co.uk
Veterinary Care Services
N.A.I.C.S.: 541940
Tom Henderson (Dir-Clinical)

Animal Health Centre Limited (1)
43 Moor Lane, Torquay, TQ2 8NU, United
Kingdom
Tel.: (44) 1803313400
Web Site:
  https://www.animalhealthcentre.co.uk
Animal Health Centre Services
N.A.I.C.S.: 541940

Animed Direct Limited (1)
CVS House Owen Road, Diss, IP22 4ER,
Norfolk, United Kingdom
Tel.: (44) 1379640052
Web Site: https://www.animeddirect.co.uk
Pet Care Product Whslr
N.A.I.C.S.: 424990

Axiom Veterinary Laboratories
Limited (1)
Manor House Brunel Road, Newton Abbot,
TQ12 4PB, Devon, United Kingdom
Tel.: (44) 162 635 5655
Web Site: https://www.axiomvetlab.com
Sales Range: $10-24.9 Million
Emp.: 50
Clinical Pathology Services
N.A.I.C.S.: 621511
Katherine James (Mgr-Fin & Facilities)

CVS (UK) Limited (1)
CVS House Owen Road, Diss, IP22 4ER,
Norfolk, United Kingdom
Tel.: (44) 1379644288
Web Site: http://www.cvsukltd.co.uk
Sales Range: $25-49.9 Million
Emp.: 45
Veterinary Services
N.A.I.C.S.: 541940
Simon Innes (CEO)

Campsie Veterinary Centre
Limited (1)
25 Knockanmoe Road, Killyclogher,
Omagh, BT79 7LB, Tyrone, United Kingdom
Tel.: (44) 2882246644
Web Site:
  https://www.campsievetcentre.com
Veterinary Services
N.A.I.C.S.: 541940
Cathal McNamee (Dir-Clinical)

Coen Dierenarts B.V. (1)
Oldenzaalsestraat 324, 7557 GE, Hengelo,
Netherlands
Tel.: (31) 742590786
Web Site: http://www.coendierenarts.nl
Veterinary Care Services
N.A.I.C.S.: 541940

Dierenartsenpraktijk NOP B.V (1)
Bedrijfsweg 92, 8304 AA, Emmeloord, Neth-
erlands
Tel.: (31) 527615544
Web Site: http://www.dapnoplvv.nl
Veterinary Services
N.A.I.C.S.: 541940

Dierenartsenpraktijk Zuid-West Fries-
land B.V (1)
Albert Koopmanstraat 3, 8531 HC, Lemmer,
Netherlands
Tel.: (31) 514561577
Web Site: http://www.dierenartsenpraktij.nl
Veterinary Services
N.A.I.C.S.: 541940

Dierenziekenhuis Drachten B.V. (1)
De Bolder 74, 9206 AR, Drachten, Netherlands

Tel.: (31) 512513627
Web Site:
  http://www.dierenziekenhuisdrachten.nl
Veterinary Services
N.A.I.C.S.: 541940

Endell Veterinary Group Limited (1)
49 Endless Street, Salisbury, SP1 3UH,
United Kingdom
Tel.: (44) 1722333291
Web Site:
  https://www.endeliveterinarygroup.co.uk
Veterinary Services
N.A.I.C.S.: 541940
Theresa Smith (Mgr-Practice)

Greenacres Pet Crematorium
Limited (1)
Messingham Lane, East Butterwick,
Scunthorpe, DN17 3AL, Lincolnshire, United
Kingdom
Tel.: (44) 1724784081
Web Site:
  https://www.greenacrespetcremator.co.uk
Pet Cremation Services
N.A.I.C.S.: 812220

Greendale Veterinary Diagnostics
Limited (1)
Lansbury Estate, Knaphill, Woking, GU21
2EP, United Kingdom
Tel.: (44) 1483797707
Web Site: https://www.greendale.co.uk
Emp.: 20
Veterinary Services
N.A.I.C.S.: 541940
Arlene Nubi (Gen Mgr)

Rossendale Pet Crematorium
Limited (1)
Crawshawbooth, Crawshawbooth, Rossend-
ale, BB4 8UE, Lancashire, United Kingdom
Tel.: (44) 170 621 3810
Web Site:
  https://www.rossendalepetcrem.co.uk
Sales Range: $25-49.9 Million
Emp.: 10
Pet Cremation Services
N.A.I.C.S.: 812220
Allison Morris (Gen Mgr)

Silvermere Haven Limited (1)
Byfleet Road, Cobham, KT11 1DZ, Surrey,
United Kingdom
Tel.: (44) 1932868847
Web Site:
  https://www.silvermerehaven.co.uk
Pet Cremation Services
N.A.I.C.S.: 812220

St Elmo Veterinary Clinic Limited (1)
Unit 2 Northwest Business Park Be-
raghmore Road, Skeoge Industrial Estate,
Derry, BT48 8SE, United Kingdom
Tel.: (44) 2871353538
Web Site:
  https://www.stelmoveterinaryclinic.co.uk
Veterinary Services
N.A.I.C.S.: 541940
Kimberley Somers (Bus Mgr)

The Pet Crematorium Limited (1)
The Willows Langley Park Industrial Estate,
Witton Gilbert, Durham, DH7 6TX, United
Kingdom
Tel.: (44) 1913735551
Web Site: https://www.pet-
  crematorium.co.uk
Pet Cremation Services
N.A.I.C.S.: 812220

Valley Pet Crematorium Limited (1)
Owen Road, Diss, IP22 4ER, Norfolk,
United Kingdom
Tel.: (44) 1647253053
Web Site:
  http://www.valleypetcrematorium.co.uk
Pet Cremation Services
N.A.I.C.S.: 812220

Whitley Brook Crematorium for Pets
Limited (1)
Davy Road, Astmoor Industrial Estate, Run-
corn, WA7 1PZ, Cheshire, United Kingdom
Tel.: (44) 1928560211
Web Site: https://www.whitleybrook.co.uk
Pet Cremation Services
N.A.I.C.S.: 812220

CVTECH-IBC INC.

300 Labonte St, Drummondville, J2C
6X9, QC, Canada
Tel.: (819) 477-3232
Web Site: http://www.cvtech-ibc.com
Sales Range: $25-49.9 Million
Emp.: 10
Power Transmission System Mfr
N.A.I.C.S.: 333613
Monia Coto (Controller)

CVW CLEANTECH INC.

Suite 305 505 - 8th Ave SW, Calgary,
T2P 1G2, AB, Canada
Tel.: (403) 460-8135   ON
Web Site: https://cvwcleantech.com
Year Founded: 2001
CVW—(TSXV)
Rev.: $225,614
Assets: $4,750,300
Liabilities: $512,920
Net Worth: $4,237,380
Earnings: ($2,794,940)
Fiscal Year-end: 12/31/23
Titanium Exploration & Mining Ser-
vices
N.A.I.C.S.: 212290
Scott Nelson (Pres & CEO)

CW GROUP HOLDINGS LIM-
ITED

68 Kallang Pudding Road, #05-01
SYH Logistics Building, Singapore,
349327, Singapore
Tel.: (65) 6259 2289
Web Site: http://www.cwgroup-
  int.com
Sales Range: $250-299.9 Million
Holding Company; Precision Machine
Tool Mfr
N.A.I.C.S.: 551112
William Koon Lup Wong (Chm &
CEO)

Subsidiaries:

CW Advanced Technologies Pte.
Ltd. (1)
50 Kallang Avenue 05-01/02, Singapore,
339505, Singapore
Tel.: (65) 6747 3996
Industrial Equipment Distr
N.A.I.C.S.: 423830
Jimmy Tay (Gen Mgr)

CW Group Pte. Ltd. (1)
50 Kallang Avenue 05-01/02, Singapore,
339505, Singapore
Tel.: (65) 6259 2289
Industrial Machinery & Equipment Whslr
N.A.I.C.S.: 423830

CW Tech Pte. Ltd. (1)
50 Kallang Avenue 05-01/02, Singapore,
339505, Singapore
Tel.: (65) 6259 2289
Emp.: 20
Investment Management Service
N.A.I.C.S.: 523940
William Wong (CEO)

SG Tech Holdings Limited (1)
50 Kallang Avenue 05-01/02, Singapore,
339505, Singapore
Tel.: (65) 6259 2289
Web Site: http://www.sgtechholdings.com
Investment Management Service
N.A.I.C.S.: 523940

CWB AUTOMOTIVE ELEC-
TRONICS CO., LTD.

No 1098 East Xingfu Road,
Hongqiao, Yueqing, 325608, Zheji-
ang, China
Tel.: (86) 57762338888
Web Site: https://www.cwb.com.cn
Year Founded: 2006
605005—(SHG)
Rev.: $205,089,160
Assets: $278,877,531
Liabilities: $54,003,596
Net Worth: $224,873,934

Earnings: $26,730,658
Emp.: 2,000
Fiscal Year-end: 12/31/22
Electronic Product Mfr & Distr
N.A.I.C.S.: 334419
Wenbao Chen (Chm)

Subsidiaries:

CWB Automotive Electronics (Ta-
icang) Co., Ltd. (1)
No 117 East Guangzhou Road, Taicang,
215413, Jiangsu, China
Tel.: (86) 51233066711
Automobile Parts Mfr
N.A.I.C.S.: 336390

CWG HOLDINGS BERHAD

6428 Lorong Mak Mandin Tiga Mak
Mandin Industrial Estate, 13400, But-
terworth, Malaysia
Tel.: (60) 43329299   MY
Web Site:
  https://www.cwgholdings.com.my
CWG—(KLS)
Rev.: $19,603,060
Assets: $26,840,392
Liabilities: $4,690,235
Net Worth: $22,150,157
Earnings: $1,266,320
Emp.: 465
Fiscal Year-end: 06/30/23
Holding Company
N.A.I.C.S.: 551112
Ooi Chin Soon (Deputy Chm)

Subsidiaries:

Campap Mareketing Sdn. Bhd. (1)
6428 Lorong Mak Mandin Tiga, Mak Mandin
Industrial Estate, 13400, Butterworth, Pen-
ang, Malaysia
Tel.: (60) 43329299
Web Site: http://campap.com
Stationery Mfr
N.A.I.C.S.: 322230
Ooi Chin Soon (Deputy Chm)

Campap Marketing Sdn. Bhd. (1)
6428 Lorong Mak Mandin Tiga, Mak Mandin
Industrial Estate, 13400, Butterworth, Ma-
laysia
Tel.: (60) 43329299
Web Site: https://campap.com
Stationery Product Mfr
N.A.I.C.S.: 322230
Ooi Chin Soon (Deputy Chm)

Future Ace E-Commerce Sdn.
Bhd. (1)
6428 Lorong Mak Mandin Tiga, Mak Mandin
Industrial Estate, 13400, Butterworth, Pen-
ang, Malaysia
Tel.: (60) 43329299
Stationery Distr
N.A.I.C.S.: 424120

CWG INTERNATIONAL LTD

6 Eu Tong Sen Street #04-08 The
Central, Singapore, 059817, Singa-
pore
Tel.: (65) 6224 0669   SG
Web Site: http://www.chiwayland.com
Year Founded: 1996
Real Estate Development
N.A.I.C.S.: 531390

CWG PLC

Block 54A Plot 10 Off Rufus Giwa
Street Off Adebayo Doherty Road,
Off Admiralty Way Lekki Phase 1,
Lagos, Nigeria
Tel.: (234) 12706065   NG
Web Site: https://www.cwg-plc.com
Year Founded: 1992
CWG—(NIGE)
Rev.: $10,515,797
Assets: $10,757,321
Liabilities: $9,667,798
Net Worth: $1,089,522
Earnings: $352,929

Emp.: 544
Fiscal Year-end: 12/31/22
Cloud & Software Services; IT Infra-
structure Services
N.A.I.C.S.: 518210
Austin Okere *(Founder)*

CWI REAL ESTATE AG
Klostergasse 5, 95444, Leipzig, Ger-
many
Tel.: (49) 34160076790
Web Site: http://www.cwi.de
Year Founded: 2006
Sales Range: $50-74.9 Million
Emp.: 2
Immovable Property Trading Services
N.A.I.C.S.: 531312
Jochen Pooten *(Mng Dir)*

**CWT INTERNATIONAL LIM-
ITED**
Suites 1101-3 & 12 11th Floor Tower
2 The Gateway Harbour, Wan Chai,
Kowloon, China (Hong Kong)
Tel.: (852) 25581580   HK
Web Site:
      https://www.hnaholdinghk.com
Year Founded: 1983
591—(HKG)
Rev.: $7,069,725,570
Assets: $3,179,197,455
Liabilities: $2,576,975,558
Net Worth: $602,221,898
Earnings: $36,893,273
Emp.: 6,074
Fiscal Year-end: 12/31/22
Logistics Management Services
N.A.I.C.S.: 541614
Quan Zhao *(Exec Dir)*

Subsidiaries:

CWT Europe B.V. Group   **(1)**
De Entree 159 Oval Tower, 1101 HE, Am-
sterdam, Netherlands
Tel.: (31) 202000200
Financial Services
N.A.I.C.S.: 523999

CWT Globelink Pte Ltd   **(1)**
11 Keppel Road 12-01/2 ABI Plaza, Singa-
pore, 089057, Singapore
Tel.: (65) 6 225 1833
Web Site: https://www.globelink-group.com
Freight Forwarding Services
N.A.I.C.S.: 488510

Globelink-Trans (Tianjin) International
Forwarding Co., Ltd.   **(1)**
6 Floor Gong Shang Lian Bldg No 59 Yan
An Dong Road, Shanghai, 200002, China
Tel.: (86) 2163373006
Freight Forwarding Services
N.A.I.C.S.: 488510
Wang Fei *(Deputy Gen Mgr)*

Straits Financial Group Pte Ltd   **(1)**
9 Temasek Boulevard 28-02 Suntec Tower
Two, Singapore, 038989, Singapore
Tel.: (65) 66729669
Web Site: http://www.straitsfinancial.com
Financial Brokerage Services
N.A.I.C.S.: 523999

Straits Financial LLC   **(1)**
425 S Financial Pl Ste 3990, Chicago, IL
60605
Tel.: (312) 462-4499
Financial Brokerage Services
N.A.I.C.S.: 523999

CX ADVISORS LLP
305 3rd Floor Wordmark 2, New
Delhi, 110037, India
Tel.: (91) 11 4764 0000   In
Web Site: http://www.cxpartners.in
Emp.: 100
Investment Advisory Services
N.A.I.C.S.: 523940
Ajay Relan *(Founder & Chm)*

Subsidiaries:

CX Capital Management Limited   **(1)**
D-15 1st Floor Defence Colony, New Delhi,
10024, India
Tel.: (91) 11 4764 0000
Web Site: http://www.cxcapital.net
Investment Fund Management Services
N.A.I.C.S.: 523940

Holding (Domestic):

Transaction Solutions International
(India) Private Limited   **(2)**
11 A&B 4th Floor D2 Southern Park Saket
Place, Saket, New Delhi, 110 017,
India   **(75%)**
Tel.: (91) 1142658401
Web Site: http://www.tsiplc.com
Electronic Transactions Processing Services
N.A.I.C.S.: 522320
Mohnish Kumar *(CEO)*

**CX TECHNOLOGY CORPORA-
TION**
20F 179 Liaoning Street, Taipei,
10041, Taiwan
Tel.: (886) 223898686
Web Site:
      https://www.cxtechnology.com
2415—(TAI)
Rev.: $74,031,424
Assets: $275,806,556
Liabilities: $188,972,360
Net Worth: $86,834,197
Earnings: $335,557
Emp.: 900
Fiscal Year-end: 12/31/23
Magnetic Induction Speaker Parts Mfr
N.A.I.C.S.: 334310
Albert K. Ting *(Chm & Gen Mgr)*

Subsidiaries:

CX Technology (Shanghai) Corp.   **(1)**
245 Pan Qiao Road Xu Han Town, Jia Ding
District, Shanghai, 201809, China
Tel.: (86) 2139533308
Metal Stamping Mfr
N.A.I.C.S.: 332119

Merrimack River Precision Industrial
Corporation   **(1)**
8F No 4 Section 1 Zhongxiao West Road,
Zhongshan District, Taipei, 10041, Taiwan
Tel.: (886) 223898686
Web Site: https://merrimack-river.com
Electronic Connector Mfr
N.A.I.C.S.: 334417

**CXI HEALTHCARE TECHNOL-
OGY GROUP LIMITED**
3F Century Yard Cricket Square, PO
Box 902, Georgetown, KY1-1103,
Grand Cayman, Cayman Islands
Tel.: (345) 27820560
Web Site: https://www.ckhfnh.co.kr
Year Founded: 2009
900120—(KRS)
Rev.: $52,203,260
Assets: $318,115,980
Liabilities: $2,696,924
Net Worth: $315,419,055
Earnings: $5,487,202
Emp.: 257
Fiscal Year-end: 06/30/23
Holding Company
N.A.I.C.S.: 551112
Jinsheng Lin *(CEO)*

CXJ GROUP CO., LIMITED
C290 DoBe E-Manor Dongning Road
No 553, Jianggan District, Hangzhou,
310026, Zhejiang, China
Tel.: (86) 18668175727   NV
Web Site: https://www.ecxj.net
Year Founded: 1998
ECXJ—(OTCIQ)
Emp.: 33
Automobile Parts Mfr & Distr
N.A.I.C.S.: 336110

**CXR ANDERSON JACOBSON
SAS**
Rue de l'Ornette, 28410, Abondant,
France
Tel.: (33) 237628790   FR
Web Site: http://www.cxr.com
Year Founded: 1973
Telecommunication & Computer Pe-
ripheral Equipment Mfr
N.A.I.C.S.: 334290
Eric Piaget *(Dir-Mktg)*

CY BIOTECH
3F 1 No 3-1 Park St, Nangang Dist,
Taipei, 115, Taiwan
Tel.: (886) 226557339
Web Site:
      http://www.cybiotech.com.tw
6566—(TPE)
Rev.: $6,757,055
Assets: $13,002,293
Liabilities: $8,897,053
Net Worth: $4,105,240
Earnings: $2,472,791
Fiscal Year-end: 12/31/20
Pharmaceutical Product Mfr & Distr
N.A.I.C.S.: 325411
Robbin Shih *(Chm)*

CY4GATE S.P.A.
Via Coponia 8, 00131, Rome, Italy
Tel.: (39) 0691503700
Web Site: https://www.cy4gate.com
Year Founded: 2014
CY4—(ITA)
Rev.: $73,395,577
Assets: $197,425,508
Liabilities: $74,757,112
Net Worth: $122,668,396
Earnings: ($9,822,462)
Emp.: 456
Fiscal Year-end: 12/31/23
Computer System Design Services
N.A.I.C.S.: 541512
Domitilla Benigni *(Pres)*

Subsidiaries:

Azienda Informatica Italiana S.r.l.   **(1)**
Corso Vittorio Emanuele II 74, 10121, Turin,
Italy
Tel.: (39) 01119214520
Web Site: https://www.azinit.it
Core Network Design & Maintenance Ser-
vices
N.A.I.C.S.: 541512

RCS ETM Sicurezza S.p.A.   **(1)**
Caldera Park Via Caldera 21, 20153, Milan,
Italy
Tel.: (39) 02397771
Web Site: https://rcslab.it
Cybercrime Security Services
N.A.I.C.S.: 541690

CYAN AG
Theatinerstrabe 11, 80333, Munich,
Germany
Tel.: (49) 89710422073
Web Site:
      http://www.cyansecurity.com
Business Segment Services; IT-
Security
N.A.I.C.S.: 513210
Markus Cserna *(CTO)*

Subsidiaries:

I-New Unified Mobile Solutions
AG   **(1)**
Am Anger 1, 7210, Mattersburg,
Austria   **(81.71%)**
Tel.: (43) 262620720
Web Site: http://www.inew-cs.com
Mobile Software Development Services
N.A.I.C.S.: 513210
Peter Nussbaumer *(CEO)*

**CYANCONNODE HOLDINGS
PLC**
The Jeffreys Building Suite 2 Ground
Floor Cowley Road, St Johns Innova-
tion Park, Cambridge, CB4 0DS,
United Kingdom
Tel.: (44) 1223865750
Web Site:
      https://www.cyanconnode.com
CYAN—(AIM)
Rev.: $14,568,798
Assets: $25,389,843
Liabilities: $7,048,457
Net Worth: $18,341,386
Earnings: ($2,987,771)
Emp.: 64
Fiscal Year-end: 03/31/23
Semiconductor Mfr
N.A.I.C.S.: 334413
John James Cronin *(Chm)*

**CYBA-STEVENS MANAGE-
MENT GROUP**
100 5735 7th Street NE, Calgary,
T2E 8V3, AB, Canada
Tel.: (403) 291-3288
Web Site:
      http://www.cybastevens.com
Sales Range: $400-449.9 Million
Emp.: 50
Grocery Merchant Whslr
N.A.I.C.S.: 424410

CYBELE CO., LTD.
2-1-3 Zao Matsugaoka, Yamagata,
990-2338, Japan
Tel.: (81) 23 6891131
Web Site: http://www.cybele.co.jp
Year Founded: 1981
Confectionary Product Mfr
N.A.I.C.S.: 311352
Tatsuo Kuroda *(Mng Dir)*

CYBELE INDUSTRIES LIMITED
138 179 Sidco Industrial Estate, Am-
battur, Chennai, 600 098, Tamil
Nadu, India
Tel.: (91) 9500147550
Web Site: https://www.cybele.co.in
531472—(BOM)
Rev.: $4,473,797
Assets: $5,610,443
Liabilities: $2,310,113
Net Worth: $3,300,330
Earnings: $38,343
Fiscal Year-end: 03/31/23
Electronic Cable Mfr
N.A.I.C.S.: 332618
P. A. Joykutty *(Chm)*

CYBER BAY CORPORATION
Suite 2402 Discovery Center 25 ADB
Avenue, Ortigas Center, 1226, Pasig,
1226, Philippines
Tel.: (63) 286339757   PH
Year Founded: 1989
CYBR—(PHI)
Rev.: $18
Assets: $12,987,614
Liabilities: $38,648,569
Net Worth: ($25,660,955)
Earnings: ($47,648)
Fiscal Year-end: 12/31/23
Real Estate Development Services
N.A.I.C.S.: 531390
Raul G. Gerodias *(Pres)*

CYBER BUZZ, INC.
Sumitomo Fudosan Shibuya Info An-
nex 4 5 6F 12-10 Sakuragaoka-cho,
Shibuya-Ku, Tokyo, 150-0031, Japan
Tel.: (81) 357844113
Web Site:
      https://www.cyberbuzz.co.jp
Year Founded: 2006
7069—(TKS)
Rev.: $40,817,130
Assets: $36,166,090

Cyber Buzz, Inc.—(Continued)

Liabilities: $20,156,870
Net Worth: $16,009,220
Earnings: $1,453,450
Fiscal Year-end: 09/30/23
Media Advertising Services
N.A.I.C.S.: 541840
Akihiko Okabe (Exec Officer)

CYBER MEDIA INDIA LTD.
Cyber House B-35 Sector-32, Gurgaon, 122 001, India
Tel.: (91) 1244822222
Web Site:
    https://www.cybermedia.co.in
532640—(BOM)
Rev.: $9,427,792
Assets: $4,352,209
Liabilities: $4,203,021
Net Worth: $149,188
Earnings: $484,168
Emp.: 46
Fiscal Year-end: 03/31/23
Magazine Publishing Services
N.A.I.C.S.: 513120
Sankaranarayanan V. V. (CFO)

CYBER SECURITY CLOUD, INC.
VORT Ebisu maxim 3F 3-9-19 Higashi, Shibuya-ku, Tokyo, 150-0011, Japan
Tel.: (81) 364169996
Web Site: https://www.cscloud.co.jp
Year Founded: 2010
4493—(TKS)
Rev.: $21,695,400
Assets: $19,717,290
Liabilities: $6,799,310
Net Worth: $12,917,980
Earnings: $3,027,430
Fiscal Year-end: 12/31/23
Software Development Services
N.A.I.C.S.: 541511
Masafumi Kurata (CFO)

CYBER_FOLKS S.A.
Franklina Roosevelta 22, 60-829, Poznan, Poland
Tel.: (48) 616229018
Web Site: https://cyberfolks.pl
Year Founded: 1999
CBF—(WAR)
Rev.: $79,966,326
Assets: $156,178,602
Liabilities: $81,193,591
Net Worth: $74,985,012
Earnings: $8,904,949
Emp.: 453
Fiscal Year-end: 12/31/21
Software Publisher
N.A.I.C.S.: 513210
Jakub Dwernicki (CEO)

Subsidiaries:

Gazduire Web S.R.L   (1)
Str Calea Floreasca no 169 IPA Building Floor 2 Room 4 Sector 1, 14459, Bucharest, Romania
Tel.: (40) 376448020
Web Site: http://www.gazduire.ro
Web Hosting Services
N.A.I.C.S.: 518210

Kei.pl Sp. z o.o.   (1)
ul Marcik 27 CD, 30-443, Krakow, Poland
Tel.: (48) 123492200
Web Site: http://www.kei.pl
Web Hosting Services
N.A.I.C.S.: 518210

Oxylion S.A.   (1)
ul Daszynskiego 3B, Olesnica, Poland
Tel.: (48) 612786445
Web Site: http://www.oxylion.pl
Telecommunication Operator
N.A.I.C.S.: 517121

Redgroup Sp. z o.o.   (1)

Baltyk ul Roosevelta 22, 60-829, Poznan, Poland
Tel.: (48) 616222404
Web Site: http://www.redsales.pl
Advertising & Consulting Services
N.A.I.C.S.: 541810

Seofabryka Sp. z o.o.   (1)
Warszawska 67, 81-309, Gdynia, Poland
Tel.: (48) 585858701
Web Site: http://seofabryka.pl
Advertising & Consulting Services
N.A.I.C.S.: 541810

Serwer SMS Polska Sp. z o.o.   (1)
Ul Ogrodowskiego 27, 44-203, Rybnik, Poland
Tel.: (48) 327500001
Web Site: http://www.serwersms.pl
Advertising & Consulting Services
N.A.I.C.S.: 541810
Daniel Zawilinski (Mng Dir)

CYBERAGENT, INC.
Abema Towers 40-1 Udagawacho, Shibuya-ku, Tokyo, 150-0042, Japan
Tel.: (81) 354590202
Web Site:
    https://www.cyberagent.co.jp
Year Founded: 1998
4751—(TKS)
Rev.: $5,588,852,160
Assets: $3,622,102,320
Liabilities: $1,852,626,720
Net Worth: $1,769,475,600
Earnings: $113,072,160
Emp.: 11,623
Fiscal Year-end: 09/30/24
Internet Related Services Including E-Commerce, Online Gaming, Website Development & Advertising Services
N.A.I.C.S.: 541890
Susumu Fujita (Pres & CEO)

Subsidiaries:

AMoAd, Inc.   (1)
2-11-1 Dogenzaka Shibuya Mark City West 13f, Shibuya-Ku, Tokyo, 150-0043, Japan
Tel.: (81) 354596760
Web Site: http://www.amoad.com
Emp.: 5
Mobile Platform Software & Development Services
N.A.I.C.S.: 541511
Kazushi Fujita (Mgr)

CA Mobile Ltd.   (1)
40-1 Udagawa-cho, Shibuya-ku, Tokyo, 150-0042, Japan
Tel.: (81) 364153400
Web Site: https://cam-inc.co.jp
Sales Range: $75-99.9 Million
Emp.: 189
Mobile Marketing Services
N.A.I.C.S.: 561422

CASM, Inc.   (1)
219 S William Dillard Dr Bldg 1 Ste 101, Gilbert, AZ 85233
Tel.: (480) 680-8528
Web Site: https://www.casm-inc.com
Heating Contractor Services
N.A.I.C.S.: 238220

Ca Design, Inc.   (1)
180 Crosby Rd, Dover, NH 03820
Tel.: (603) 749-6755
Web Site: https://www.c-a-design.com
Engineeering Services
N.A.I.C.S.: 541330

CyberAgent Ventures (Beijing) Co., Ltd   (1)
Room 121 5th Floor Gate 5 Block C Yingke Center, No 2 Worker Stadium North Road Chaoyang District, Beijing, 100022, China
Tel.: (86) 1051235061
Web Site: https://www.cyberagent.co.jp
Emp.: 1
Online Game Software Development Services
N.A.I.C.S.: 541511
Nobuaki Kitagawa (CEO & Mng Dir)

CyberAgent Ventures Inc.   (1)

Akasaka DS bldg 3F 8-5-26 Akasaka, Minato-ku, Tokyo, 107-0052, Japan
Tel.: (81) 3 5772 1234
Web Site:
    http://www.cyberagentventures.com
Sales Range: $50-74.9 Million
Emp.: 1
Venture Capital Services
N.A.I.C.S.: 523910
Nobuaki Kitagawa (Mng Dir)

CyberZ Inc.   (1)
Tel.: (81) 354596276
Sales Range: $25-49.9 Million
Emp.: 45
Internet Service Provider
N.A.I.C.S.: 517810
Takahiro Yamauchi (Mng Dir)

Gcrest, Inc.   (1)
Abema Towers 40-1, Udagawa-cho Shibuya-ku, Tokyo, 150-0042, Japan
Tel.: (81) 57 000 8018
Web Site: https://www.gcrest.com
Information Technology Services
N.A.I.C.S.: 541519
Junpei Otsuji (Pres & CEO)

Makuake, Inc.   (1)
Shibuya 2-16-1 Daiwa Shibuya Miyamasuzaka Building 10F, Shibuya-ku, Tokyo, 150-0002, Japan
Tel.: (81) 363284038
Web Site: https://www.makuake.co.jp
Software Development Services
N.A.I.C.S.: 541511
Ryotaro Nakayama (Chm, Pres & CEO)

MicroAd, Inc.   (1)
Shibuya Infos Tower 13F 20-1 Sakuragaoka-cho, Shibuya-ku, Tokyo, 150-0031, Japan
Tel.: (81) 501 746 3333
Web Site: https://www.microad.co.jp
Data Platform Business Services
N.A.I.C.S.: 518210

Tapple, Inc.   (1)
40-1 Udagawa-cho, Shibuya-ku, Tokyo, 150-0042, Japan
Tel.: (81) 36 328 2692
Web Site: https://www.tapple.co.jp
Software Development Services
N.A.I.C.S.: 541511

Trenders Inc.   (1)
8F F Nissay Ebisu Building 3-16-3, Shibuya-Ku, Tokyo, 150-0011, Higashi, Japan
Tel.: (81) 357748871
Web Site: https://www.trenders.co.jp
Rev.: $37,498,530
Assets: $44,868,680
Liabilities: $17,523,110
Net Worth: $27,345,570
Earnings: $3,166,190
Emp.: 222
Fiscal Year-end: 03/31/2024
Marketing Consulting Services
N.A.I.C.S.: 541613
Ikuo Okamoto (Chm)

VOYAGE BB Inc   (1)
First Place 8-16 Shinsen-Cho Shibuya 7 Floor, Shibuya-Ku, Tokyo, 150-0045, Japan
Tel.: (81) 3 5459 1168
Web Site: http://www.voyage-bb.com
Internet Application Systems Development Services
N.A.I.C.S.: 541511

Zucks Inc   (1)
Shibuya First Place Bldg 8F Shinsen-cho 8-16, Shibuya, Tokyo, 150-0045, Japan
Tel.: (81) 3 5459 2061
Web Site: http://www.zucks.co.jp
Sales Range: $25-49.9 Million
Emp.: 15
Online Advertising Services
N.A.I.C.S.: 541890
Masashi Nishizono (Pres & CEO)

CYBERARK SOFTWARE LTD.
9 Hapsagot St, PO Box 3143, Park Ofer 2, 4951040, Petah Tikva, 4951040, Israel
Tel.: (972) 39180000
Web Site: https://www.cyberark.com
Year Founded: 1999

CYBR—(NASDAQ)
Rev.: $591,710,000
Assets: $1,819,401,000
Liabilities: $1,141,257,000
Net Worth: $678,144,000
Earnings: ($130,368,000)
Emp.: 2,768
Fiscal Year-end: 12/31/22
Information Technology Security Software Developer, Publisher & Marketer
N.A.I.C.S.: 513210
Joshua Siegel (CFO)

Subsidiaries:

CyberArk Software (UK) Limited   (1)
Abbey House 1650 Arlington Business Park, Reading, RG7 4SA, United Kingdom
Tel.: (44) 118 929 8430
Web Site: http://www.cyber-ark.com
Information Technology Security Software Marketer
N.A.I.C.S.: 423430

CyberArk Software, Inc.   (1)
60 Wells Ave Ste 103, Newton, MA 02459
Tel.: (617) 965-1544
Web Site: http://www.cyberark.com
Emp.: 80
Information Technology Security Software Developer, Publisher & Marketer
N.A.I.C.S.: 513210
Ernie Rhyne (VP-Pub Sector)

Vaultive, Inc.   (1)
470 Atlantic Ave 12th Fl, Boston, MA 02210
Tel.: (617) 614-6862
Software Publisher
N.A.I.C.S.: 513210

Venafi, Inc.   (1)
175 E 400 S Ste 300, Salt Lake City, UT 84111
Tel.: (801) 676-6900
Web Site: http://www.venafi.com
Software Publisher
N.A.I.C.S.: 513210
Jeff Hudson (CEO)

CYBERCATCH HOLDINGS, INC.
1095 West Pender Street Suite 750, Vancouver, V6E 2M6, BC, Canada   BC
Web Site:
    https://www.cybercatch.com
Year Founded: 2021
CYBE—(TSXV)
Assets: $2,274,922
Liabilities: $26,428
Net Worth: $2,248,494
Earnings: $468,190
Emp.: 12
Fiscal Year-end: 04/30/22
Holding Company
N.A.I.C.S.: 551112
Bryan Rho (CTO)

CYBERDYNE INC.
2-2-1 Gakuen-Minami, Tsukuba, 305-0818, Ibaraki, Japan
Tel.: (81) 298553189
Web Site: https://www.cyberdyne.jp
Year Founded: 2004
7779—(TKS)
Rev.: $28,779,940
Assets: $330,493,390
Liabilities: $62,940,420
Net Worth: $267,552,970
Earnings: ($9,756,360)
Fiscal Year-end: 03/31/24
Medical Device Mfr
N.A.I.C.S.: 339112
Yoshiyuki Sankai (Founder, Pres & CEO)

Subsidiaries:

Cyberdyne Care Robotics GmbH   (1)
Hunscheidtstrasse 34, 44789, Bochum, Germany
Tel.: (49) 2345873000
Web Site: https://www.cyberdyne.eu

Fitness Training Services
N.A.I.C.S.: 812990
Shinji Uga *(Mng Dir)*

**Shonan Robo Care Center Co.,
Ltd.** (1)
2-2-1 Tsujidokandai, Fujisawa, 251-0041,
Kanagawa, Japan
Tel.: (81) 466302360
Health Care Srvices
N.A.I.C.S.: 622110

**Suzuka Robo Care Center Co.,
Ltd.** (1)
3500-3 Minamitamagakicho, Suzuka, 513-
0816, Mie, Japan
Tel.: (81) 593897762
Nursing Care Insurance Services
N.A.I.C.S.: 524210

CYBERGUN SA
ZI Les Bordes 9-11 rue Henri Dunant,
91070, Bondoufle, France
Tel.: (33) 169117100
Web Site: http://www.cybergun.com
ALCYB—(EUR)
Sales Range: $50-74.9 Million
Emp.: 160
Toy Gun Mfr
N.A.I.C.S.: 339930
Eric Gruau *(CFO)*

Subsidiaries:

Verney-Carron S.A. (1)
54 Boulevard Thiers, BP 80072, 42002,
Saint-Etienne, Cedex 1, France (65%)
Tel.: (33) 477791500
Web Site: https://www.verney-carron.com
Sales Range: $1-9.9 Million
Gun Mfr & Whslr
N.A.I.C.S.: 332994
Jean Verney-Carron *(Chm-Supervisory Bd)*

CYBERJAYA EDUCATION GROUP BERHAD
Level 8 Tower Block University of Cy-
berjaya Campus Persiaran Bestari,
Cyber 11, 63000, Cyberjaya, Selan-
gor, Malaysia
Tel.: (60) 388005290 MY
Web Site: https://cyberjaya.education
CYBERE—(KLS)
Rev.: $26,709,210
Assets: $110,805,255
Liabilities: $60,657,053
Net Worth: $50,148,203
Earnings: $866,745
Emp.: 531
Fiscal Year-end: 12/31/21
Educational Support Services
N.A.I.C.S.: 611710
Leong Tuck Yee *(Grp CFO)*

Subsidiaries:

**Cyberjaya College Central Sdn.
Bhd.** (1)
Persiaran Bestari Cyber 11, 63000, Cyber-
jaya, Selangor, Malaysia
Tel.: (60) 383137000
Web Site: https://college.cyberjaya.edu.my
Educational Support Services
N.A.I.C.S.: 611710

SMR HR Group Sdn. Bhd. (1)
8th Floor University of Cyberjaya Persiaran
Bestari Cyber 11, 63000, Cyberjaya, Selan-
gor, Malaysia
Tel.: (60) 327709199
Web Site: https://www.smrhrgroup.com
Educational Institution Services
N.A.I.C.S.: 611710

UOC Sdn. Bhd. (1)
Persiaran Bestari Cyber 11, 63000, Cyber-
jaya, Selangor, Malaysia
Tel.: (60) 383137000
Web Site: http://www.cyberjaya.edu.my
Educational Institution Services
N.A.I.C.S.: 611710
Mohd Amin Jalaludin *(Chm)*

CYBERLINK CORP.

15F No 100 Minquan Rd, Xindian
Dist, New Taipei City, 231, Taiwan
Tel.: (886) 286671298
Web Site: https://www.cyberlink.com
5203—(TAI)
Rev.: $60,990,285
Assets: $187,298,073
Liabilities: $41,730,500
Net Worth: $145,567,574
Earnings: $7,261,061
Emp.: 458
Fiscal Year-end: 12/31/23
Digital Entertainment & Multimedia
Solutions Provider
N.A.I.C.S.: 513210
Jau-Hsiung Huang *(Founder, Chm &
CEO)*

Subsidiaries:

CyberLink Europe B.V. (1)
Burgemeester de Hesselleplein 31, 6411
CH, Heerlen, Netherlands
Tel.: (31) 45 799 2146
Web Site: http://www.cyberlink.com
Sales Range: $200-249.9 Million
Video Playback Software Publishing Ser-
vices
N.A.I.C.S.: 513210

CyberLink Inc. (1)
Shibadaimon 116 Bldg 3F 1-16-3 Shiba-
daimon, Minato-ku, Tokyo, 105-0012, Japan
Tel.: (81) 336628005
Web Site: http://jp.cyberlink.com
Emp.: 16
Multimedia Software Sales & Support Ser-
vice
N.A.I.C.S.: 541511

CyberLink USA (1)
3031 Tisch Way 110 Plz W, San Jose, CA
95128
Tel.: (408) 217-1850
Web Site: http://www.cyberlink.com
Multimedia Software Retailer
N.A.I.C.S.: 423430

CYBERLINK PACIFIC TELE-COMMUNICATIONS LIMITED
202 1128 W Broadway, Vancouver,
V6H 1G5, BC, Canada
Tel.: (604) 668-9898
Year Founded: 1994
Rev.: $27,100,000
Emp.: 140
Communication Service
N.A.I.C.S.: 517111
David Lopes *(Pres)*

CYBERLINKS CO., LTD.
849-3 Kimiidera, Wakayama, 641-
0012, Japan
Tel.: (81) 734483600
Web Site: https://www.cyber-l.co.jp
3683—(TKS)
Rev.: $106,513,070
Assets: $92,545,770
Liabilities: $39,888,340
Net Worth: $52,657,430
Earnings: $3,155,050
Emp.: 883
Fiscal Year-end: 12/31/23
Cloud-Based Software
N.A.I.C.S.: 513210
Tsuneo Murakami *(Pres)*

Subsidiaries:

**Minamiosaka Computing Center Co.,
Ltd.** (1)
4-2-22 Wakihama, Kaizuka, 597-0073, Ja-
pan
Tel.: (81) 724323663
Web Site: https://www.mcc-osaka.co.jp
Emp.: 199
Software Development Services
N.A.I.C.S.: 541511

SYNERGY Ltd. (1)
3F Proto Ginowan Daini Building 7-10-14
Oyama, Ginowan, 901-2223, Okinawa, Japan
Tel.: (81) 989880184

Web Site: https://synergy-spirit.co.jp
Emp.: 85
Software Development Services
N.A.I.C.S.: 541511

CYBERNAUT INTERNATIONAL HOLDINGS COMPANY LIM-ITED
Unit 1002 Capital Centre 151 Glouc-
ester Road, Wanchai, China (Hong
Kong)
Tel.: (852) 85235496353 Ky
Web Site:
http://www.cybernaut.com.hk
Year Founded: 2005
1020—(HKG)
Rev.: $7,994,376
Assets: $47,875,558
Liabilities: $27,961,222
Net Worth: $19,914,336
Earnings: $1,516,882
Emp.: 47
Fiscal Year-end: 12/31/22
Steel Flow Control Product Mfr
N.A.I.C.S.: 332999
Min Zhu *(Chm)*

Subsidiaries:

VT Zero Limited (1)
Room 19-20 16/F Metro Centre 2 21 Lam
Hing Street, Kowloon Bay, China (Hong
Kong)
Tel.: (852) 2 345 3353
Web Site: https://www.vtzero.com
Electronic Product Distr
N.A.I.C.S.: 423690

CYBERNORTH VENTURES INC.
365 Bay Street Suite 400, Toronto,
M5H 2V1, ON, Canada
Web Site:
http://www.cybernorthventures.com
Sales Range: Less than $1 Million
Privater Equity Firm
N.A.I.C.S.: 523999
Gary Bartholomew *(Founder, Pres &
Mng Partner)*

Subsidiaries:

United Royale Holdings Corp. (1)
2 Campbell Dr Ste 307C, Uxbridge, L9P
1H6, ON, Canada (77.6%)
Tel.: (647) 400-6927
Web Site: http://www.unitedroyale.com
Assets: $70,178
Liabilities: $104,405
Net Worth: ($34,227)
Earnings: ($127,068)
Emp.: 4
Fiscal Year-end: 12/31/2020
Planting & Cultivation Services
N.A.I.C.S.: 115112
Gary Bartholomew *(Chm, Pres, CEO, Treas
& Sec)*

CYBERONE CO., LTD.
39 Hyoryeong-Ro, Seocho-Gu, Seoul,
06694, Korea (South)
Tel.: (82) 234754900
Web Site: https://www.cyberone.kr
Year Founded: 2005
356890—(KRS)
Rev.: $17,452,233
Assets: $25,024,028
Liabilities: $2,988,181
Net Worth: $22,035,847
Earnings: $1,600,913
Emp.: 241
Fiscal Year-end: 12/31/22
Software Development Services
N.A.I.C.S.: 541511
Jieun Kim *(Asst Mgr)*

CYBEROO S.P.A.
Via Brigata Reggio 37, 42124, Reg-
gio Emilia, Italy
Tel.: (39) 0522385011

Web Site: https://www.privacylab.it
CYB—(ITA)
Sales Range: Less than $1 Million
Software Development Services
N.A.I.C.S.: 541511
Fabio Leonardi *(CEO)*

CYBERPORT GMBH
Am Brauhaus 5, 01099, Dresden,
Germany
Tel.: (49) 351 33 95 60
Web Site: http://www.cyberport.de
Rev.: $514,784,880
Emp.: 700
Computer Products Online Retailer
N.A.I.C.S.: 423430
Danilo Frasiak *(Member-Mgmt Bd)*

CYBERPOWER SYSTEMS, INC.
11F No 26 Jinzhuang Rd, Neihu Dist,
Taipei, 114, Taiwan
Tel.: (886) 287929510
Web Site:
https://www.cyberpower.com
Year Founded: 1997
3617—(TAI)
Rev.: $383,634,768
Assets: $418,395,942
Liabilities: $179,874,875
Net Worth: $238,521,068
Earnings: $48,228,685
Emp.: 357
Fiscal Year-end: 12/31/23
Power Supply Systems & Computer
Peripherals Mfr & Distr
N.A.I.C.S.: 335999

Subsidiaries:

Cyber Energy Co., Ltd. (1)
2F -1 No 26 Jinzhuang Rd, Neihu Dist, Tai-
pei, 11469, Taiwan
Tel.: (886) 28 792 9628
Web Site: https://www.cyberenergy.com
Electronic Product Mfr & Distr
N.A.I.C.S.: 334111

Cyber Power Systems France (1)
ZI Saint Severin, Cloyes-sur-le-Loir, 28220,
France
Tel.: (33) 237986150
Web Site: http://www.cyberpower-eu.com
Sales Range: $25-49.9 Million
Emp.: 14
Power Management Systems Distr
N.A.I.C.S.: 423610

**Cyber Power Systems S.A. DE
C.V.** (1)
Aniceto Ortega 634 Col Del Valle Centro,
Del Benito Juarez, 03100, Mexico, Mexico
Tel.: (52) 554 622 8654
Web Site: https://www.cyberpower.com
Electric Equipment Mfr
N.A.I.C.S.: 335999

**CyberPower Systems (USA),
Inc.** (1)
4241 12th Ave E Ste 400, Shakopee, MN
55379
Tel.: (952) 403-9500
Web Site:
https://www.cyberpowersystems.com
Sales Range: $25-49.9 Million
Emp.: 90
Uninterruptible Power Supply System Mfr
N.A.I.C.S.: 335999

CyberPower Systems B.V. (1)
Flight Forum 3545, Eindhoven, 5657DW,
Netherlands
Tel.: (31) 402348170
Sales Range: $50-74.9 Million
Emp.: 9
Power Management Systems Distr
N.A.I.C.S.: 423610
Douglas Wu *(Gen Mgr)*

CyberPower Systems GmbH (1)
Edisonstr 16, 85716, Unterschleissheim,
Germany
Tel.: (49) 891 222 1660
Web Site: https://www.cyberpower.com
Electric Equipment Mfr

CyberPower Systems, Inc.—(Continued)

N.A.I.C.S.: 335999

CyberPower Systems K.K. (1)
9F Cosmo Kourakuen BL 1-3-10 Koishikawa, Bunkyoku, 112-0002, Tokyo, Japan
Tel.: (81) 358405025
Web Site: http://www.cpsww.co.jp
Sales Range: $50-74.9 Million
Emp.: 3
Power Management Systems Distr
N.A.I.C.S.: 423610

CYBERSCAPE MULTIMEDIA LTD.
50 5th Cross 6th Main 7th Block 4th Phase, Banashankari 3rd Stage, Bengaluru, 560 085, India
Tel.: (91) 80 26693925
Web Site: http://cyberscapeindia.com
Year Founded: 1996
Sales Range: Less than $1 Million
Information Technology Services
N.A.I.C.S.: 541511

CYBERSTEP, INC.
4F Asahi Seimei Daitabashi Bldg
1-22-19 Izumi, Suginami-Ku, Tokyo, 168-0063, Japan
Tel.: (81) 353552085
Web Site: http://www.cyberstep.com
Year Founded: 2000
3810—(TKS)
Rev.: $19,737,460
Assets: $13,517,450
Liabilities: $5,902,730
Net Worth: $7,614,720
Earnings: ($9,637,380)
Emp.: 239
Fiscal Year-end: 05/31/24
Online Game Developer
N.A.I.C.S.: 513210

CYBERTAN TECHNOLOGY, INC.
No 99 Park Ave 3 Science Based Park, Hsin-chu, 308, Taiwan
Tel.: (886) 35777777
Web Site:
https://www.cybertan.com.tw
3062—(TAI)
Rev.: $124,444,647
Assets: $231,338,263
Liabilities: $75,351,186
Net Worth: $155,987,077
Earnings: ($10,361,032)
Emp.: 1,300
Fiscal Year-end: 12/31/23
Broadband & Wireless Networking Equipment Mfr
N.A.I.C.S.: 334210
Teddy Chen *(Chm)*

Subsidiaries:

CyberTAN Corporation (1)
1595 N Main St, Orange, CA 92867
Tel.: (714) 258-2583
Sales Range: $25-49.9 Million
Emp.: 10
Internet Service Provider
N.A.I.C.S.: 517810

CYBIN INC.
100 King Street West Suite 5600, Toronto, M5X 1C9, ON, Canada
Tel.: (908) 764-8385   Ca
CYBN—(NYSEAMEX)
Rev.: $552,672
Assets: $220,793,186
Liabilities: $7,380,656
Net Worth: $213,412,530
Earnings: ($57,080,196)
Emp.: 50
Fiscal Year-end: 03/31/24
Mineral Exploration Services
N.A.I.C.S.: 212220

CYBIRD HOLDINGS CO., LTD.
Roppongi Hills Mori Tower 22F
6-10-1 Roppongi, Tokyo, 106-6161, Japan
Tel.: (81) 357856111
Web Site: http://www.cybird.co.jp
Year Founded: 1998
Sales Range: $150-199.9 Million
Emp.: 670
Holding Company: Mobile Content & Platforms Developer & Marketer
N.A.I.C.S.: 551112
Yasuharu Kishitani *(Auditor)*

Subsidiaries:

BottleCube inc. (1)
Mansard Daikanyama 10-1 Sarugaku-cho, Shibuya-Ku, Tokyo, 150-0033, Japan
Tel.: (81) 3 6415 4360
Web Site: http://www.bottlecube.co.jp
Mobile Software Development Services
N.A.I.C.S.: 541511
Tatsuya Kawaguchi *(Pres)*

Gigaflops Japan Inc. (1)
Roppongi Hills Mori Tower 22nd Floor, Minato-Ku, Tokyo, Japan
Tel.: (81) 357856149
Web Site: http://www.gigaflops.co.jp
Sales Range: $25-49.9 Million
Emp.: 35
Data Processing Services
N.A.I.C.S.: 518210

Plus Mobile Communications Co., Ltd. (1)
Roppongi Hills Mori Tower 22nd Floor C-O Cybird Co Ltd, Minato-Ku, Tokyo, Japan
Tel.: (81) 334052510
Advertising Agencies
N.A.I.C.S.: 541810

CYBOZU INC.
27th Floor Tokyo Nihonbashi Tower
2-7-1, Nihombashi Chuo-ku, Tokyo, 103-6027, Japan
Tel.: (81) 343060808
Web Site: https://www.cybozu.com
Year Founded: 1997
4776—(TKS)
Rev.: $180,312,880
Assets: $136,468,320
Liabilities: $56,684,550
Net Worth: $79,783,770
Earnings: $17,639,920
Emp.: 1,276
Fiscal Year-end: 12/31/23
Software Services
N.A.I.C.S.: 513210

Subsidiaries:

BRING UP Co.,Ltd. (1)
2-10-5 Toridoe Paito-ku, Tokyo, Japan
Tel.: (81) 358336322
Web Site: http://www.bringup.co.jp
Human Resource Development Services
N.A.I.C.S.: 541612

Cybozu IT Shanghai Inc. (1)
Room E 11th Floor 726 West Yan'an Road, Huamin Hanzun International Market, Shanghai, 200050, China
Tel.: (86) 2152392626
Web Site: http://www.cybozu.net.cn
Sales Range: $25-49.9 Million
Emp.: 30
Software Development Services
N.A.I.C.S.: 541511
Huang Yuan *(Gen Mgr)*

Cybozu Media and Technology Co.,Ltd. (1)
7-3-16 Kikunakohoku-ku, Yokohama, 222-0011, Japan
Tel.: (81) 454318951
Web Site: http://www.tc3.jp
Sales Range: $25-49.9 Million
Emp.: 10
Computer Servers Mfr
N.A.I.C.S.: 334111

Cybozu Research Institute, Inc. (1)
1-4-14 Kouraku Bunkyo-Ku, Tokyo, 112-0004, Japan

Tel.: (81) 363612501
Web Site: http://www.cybozu-ri.co.jp
Sales Range: $25-49.9 Million
Emp.: 30
Business Research Services
N.A.I.C.S.: 541720

Cybozu Vietnam Co., Ltd. (1)
7th Fl E Town 3 Bldg 364 Cong Hoa Ward 13, Tan Binh Dist, Ho Chi Minh City, Vietnam
Tel.: (84) 838131101
Web Site: http://www.cybozu.com
Sales Range: $25-49.9 Million
Emp.: 24
Software Development Services
N.A.I.C.S.: 541511
Huynx Trieu *(Mng Dir)*

J-Yado Inc. (1)
Shinjuku-ku Yotsuya 2-4-1 Rune Yotuya Bldg 8F, Tokyo, 160-0004, Japan
Tel.: (81) 359191220
Web Site: http://www.j-yado.com
Sales Range: $25-49.9 Million
Emp.: 13
Tour Operating Services
N.A.I.C.S.: 561520
Takahashi Hiroyuki *(Pres)*

YMIRLINK Inc. (1)
Ebisu East 438 Bldg 4F 4-3-8 Ebisu, Shibuya-ku, Tokyo, 150-0013, Japan
Tel.: (81) 368200088
Web Site: http://www.ymir.co.jp
Sales Range: $25-49.9 Million
Emp.: 57
Software Development Services
N.A.I.C.S.: 541511
Wataru Shimizu *(Pres)*

CYBRID TECHNOLOGIES, INC.
No 369 Yegang Road, Wujiang Economic& Development Zone, Suzhou, 215200, China
Tel.: (86) 51282878808
Web Site: https://www.cybrid.com.cn
Year Founded: 2008
603212—(SHG)
Rev.: $577,785,930
Assets: $698,391,945
Liabilities: $281,651,723
Net Worth: $416,740,222
Earnings: $24,042,938
Fiscal Year-end: 12/31/22
Electronic Product Mfr & Distr
N.A.I.C.S.: 334419
Xiaoping Wu *(Chm, CEO & Gen Mgr)*

CYCLIQ GROUP LIMITED
Level 3 101 St Georges Tce, Perth, 6000, WA, Australia
Tel.: (61) 865580886   AU
Web Site: http://cycliq.com
CYQ—(ASX)
Rev.: $3,077,013
Assets: $1,069,508
Liabilities: $1,077,507
Net Worth: ($7,999)
Earnings: ($587,420)
Fiscal Year-end: 06/30/24
Oil & Gas Exploration
N.A.I.C.S.: 211120
Timothy Slate *(CFO & Sec)*

CYCLONE METALS LIMITED
32 Harrogate Street, Leederville, 6007, WA, Australia
Tel.: (61) 893809555
Web Site:
http://www.capelam.com.au
CLEDA—(ASX)
Rev.: $9,822
Assets: $8,087,591
Liabilities: $2,538,014
Net Worth: $5,549,577
Earnings: ($3,513,634)
Fiscal Year-end: 06/30/24
Gold & Iron Ore Mining
N.A.I.C.S.: 212220
Antony William Paul Sage *(Chm)*

Subsidiaries:

Scarborough Minerals International BV (1)
Martinus Nijhofflaan 2, 2624 ES, Delft, Netherlands
Tel.: (31) 152569251
Sales Range: $50-74.9 Million
Emp.: 30
Mineral Exploration Services
N.A.I.C.S.: 213115

Thrace Investments BV (1)
Martinus Nijhofflaan 2, 2624 ES, Delft, Netherlands
Tel.: (31) 152569251
Mineral Exploration Services
N.A.I.C.S.: 213115

CYCLONE MFG. INC.
7300 Rapistan Court, Mississauga, L5N 5S1, ON, Canada
Tel.: (905) 567-5601
Web Site:
https://www.cyclonemfg.com
Year Founded: 1964
Emp.: 500
Aircraft Parts & Equipment Mfr
N.A.I.C.S.: 336413
Andrew Sochaj *(Pres)*

CYCLOPHARM LIMITED
Unit 4 1 The Crescent, Kingsgrove, 2208, NSW, Australia
Tel.: (61) 295410411   AU
Web Site:
https://www.cyclomedica.com
CYC—(ASX)
Rev.: $21,936,553
Assets: $31,274,565
Liabilities: $9,300,938
Net Worth: $21,973,627
Earnings: ($3,201,966)
Emp.: 87
Fiscal Year-end: 12/31/23
Nuclear Medicine Mfr
N.A.I.C.S.: 621511
James M. McBrayer *(CEO, Mng Dir & Sec)*

Subsidiaries:

Cyclomedica Australia Pty Ltd (1)
Unit 4 / 1 The Crescent, Kingsgrove, 2208, NSW, Australia
Tel.: (61) 295410411
Sales Range: $25-49.9 Million
Emp.: 20
Medical Equipment & Pharmaceutical Mfr
N.A.I.C.S.: 325412

Cyclomedica Canada Limited (1)
Suite 23- 35 Main St N, PO Box 120, Waterdown, L0R 2H0, ON, Canada
Tel.: (905) 690-0345
Pharmaceutical Product Mfr
N.A.I.C.S.: 325412

Cyclomedica Europe Limited (1)
Unit A5 Calmount Business Park, Ballymount, Dublin, 12, Ireland
Tel.: (353) 14050506
Web Site: http://www.cyclomedica.com.au
Sales Range: $25-49.9 Million
Emp.: 15
Medical Equipment Mfr
N.A.I.C.S.: 339112

Cyclomedica Germany GmbH (1)
Marie-Curie Strasse 8, 51377, Leverkusen, Germany
Tel.: (49) 21484051202
Web Site: http://www.cyclopharm.com
Sales Range: $25-49.9 Million
Emp.: 4
Medical Equipment Mfr
N.A.I.C.S.: 339112

Cyclomedica Nordic AB (1)
Gustavslundsvagen 145, 167 51, Bromma, Sweden
Tel.: (46) 85 648 4530
Medical Equipment Mfr & Distr
N.A.I.C.S.: 339112

Cyclopet Pty Ltd (1)

Unit 4 / 1 The Crescent, Kingsgrove, 2208,
NSW, Australia
Tel.: (61) 29 541 0411
Pharmaceuticals Product Mfr
N.A.I.C.S.: 325412

CYCOS AG
Joseph-von-Fraunhofer-Strasse 5,
52477, Alsdorf, Germany
Tel.: (49) 24049010
Web Site: http://www.cycos.com
Sales Range: $10-24.9 Million
Emp.: 83
Communication Service
N.A.I.C.S.: 517810
Wolfgang Schiffer *(COO)*

CYDSA S.A.B. DE C.V.
Av Ricardo Margain Zozaya 335
Torre 2 Piso 6 Col Valle Del Campes-
tre, San Pedro, 66265, Garza Garcia,
Nuevo Leon, Mexico
Tel.: (52) 8181524500
Web Site: https://cydsa.com
Year Founded: 1945
CYDSASA—(MEX)
Rev.: $557,081,140
Assets: $1,377,088,460
Liabilities: $872,019,940
Net Worth: $505,068,520
Earnings: $69,350,160
Emp.: 1,696
Fiscal Year-end: 12/31/19
Chemicals Mfr
N.A.I.C.S.: 325998

Subsidiaries:

Celulosa y Derivados de Monterrey,
S.A. **(1)**
Av Ricardo Margain No 565 Santa Engra-
cia, Garza Garcia, 66265, Nuevo Leon,
Mexico
Tel.: (52) 8181524500
Rayon Filament Weaving Mfr
N.A.I.C.S.: 314999
Tomas Gonzalez Sada *(Gen Mgr)*

Cydsa S.A. de C.V. - Altamira
Plant **(1)**
Km 32 Carr Tampico-Mante, 89600, Alta-
mira, Tamps, Mexico
Tel.: (52) 833 229 1300
Plastics Product Mfr
N.A.I.C.S.: 326199

Cydsa S.A. de C.V. - Environmental
Services Division **(1)**
Av Ricardo Margain Zozaya 325 565, Col
Valle Del Campestre, 66267, Garza Garcia,
NL, Mexico
Tel.: (52) 8181524699
Web Site: http://www.cydsa.com
Environmental Projects & Services
N.A.I.C.S.: 325220

Cydsa S.A. de C.V. - La Presa
Plant **(1)**
Av La Presa 8 Col Lazaro Cardenas, San
Juan Ixhuatepec, 54180, Tlalnepantla,
Mexico
Tel.: (52) 55 5747 5500
Chemical Products Mfr
N.A.I.C.S.: 325998

Cydsa S.A. de C.V. - Packaging
Division **(1)**
Av Ricardo Margain Zozaya 325 565, Col
Valle del Campestre, 66265, Garza Garcia,
Mexico
Tel.: (52) 8181524500
Web Site: http://www.cydsa.com
Sales Range: $25-49.9 Million
Emp.: 100
Flexible Packaging Mfr
N.A.I.C.S.: 326119

Derivados Acrilicos S.A. de C.V. -
AGUASCALIENTES PLANT **(1)**
Av Adolfo Lopez Mateos 1502 Pte, Col Cir-
cunvalacion Pte, Aguascalientes, 20210,
Mexico
Tel.: (52) 449 910 3300
Web Site: http://www.cydsa.com
Synthetic & Natural Fiber Yarn Mfr

N.A.I.C.S.: 313110

Industria Quimica del Istmo, S.A. de
C.V. **(1)**
Complejo Indus Pajaritos SN, PO Box 850,
96400, Coatzacoalcos, Veracruz,
Mexico **(100%)**
Tel.: (52) 9212113410
Web Site: http://www.asertec.com.mx
Sales Range: $125-149.9 Million
Emp.: 300
Mfr of Chlorine, Caustic Soda & Basic
Chemical Products
N.A.I.C.S.: 325998

Plant (Domestic):

Industria Quimica del Istmo, S.A. de
C.V. - Coatzacoalcos Plant **(2)**
Complejo Industrial Pajaritos, 96400, Coat-
zacoalcos, Veracruz, Mexico
Tel.: (52) 9212113410
Web Site: http://www.cydsa.com
Chlorine & Caustic Soda Mfr
N.A.I.C.S.: 325998

Industria Quimica del Istmo, S.A. de
C.V. - Hermosillo Plant **(2)**
Calle del Plomo 45 Parque Industrial,
83299, Hermosillo, Sonora, Mexico
Tel.: (52) 6622511024
Web Site: http://www.cydsa.com
Chlorine & Caustic Soda Mfr
N.A.I.C.S.: 325998

Industrias Cydsa Bayer, S.A. de
C.V. **(1)**
Rio Becerra 287, Col Napoles Del Benito
Juarez, 03810, Mexico, DP,
Mexico **(60%)**
Tel.: (52) 5553401800
Web Site: http://www.icb.com.mx
Sales Range: $25-49.9 Million
Emp.: 70
Mfr of Toluene Di-Isocyanate
N.A.I.C.S.: 325110
Jenea Isgenere *(Mgr)*

Inversiones Meximex, S.A. de
C.V **(1)**
Ricardo Margain Zozaya 325 Valle del
Campestre, Garza Garcia, 66220, Nuevo
Leon, Mexico
Tel.: (52) 8181524500
Investment Management Service
N.A.I.C.S.: 523999

Quimica Empresarial De Mexico, SA
De CV **(1)**
Av Ricardo Margain Zozaya No 565-B,
Garza Garcia, 66267, Mexico
Tel.: (52) 8181524500
Web Site: http://www.cydsa.com
Emp.: 20
Chemical Products Distr
N.A.I.C.S.: 424690

Quimobasicos, S.A. de C.V. **(1)**
Av Adolfo Ruiz Cortines No 2333 Poniente,
PO Box 1730, Col Pedro Lozano, 64400,
Monterrey, Nuevo Leon, Mexico **(60%)**
Tel.: (52) 8183054600
Web Site: http://www.quimobasicos.com
Sales Range: $75-99.9 Million
Emp.: 200
Refrigeration & Repellent Gases
N.A.I.C.S.: 423740

Sales del Istmo, S.A. de C.V. **(1)**
(100%)
Tel.: (52) 5553401800
Web Site: http://www.salesdelistmo.com.mx
Sales Range: $75-99.9 Million
Emp.: 250
Refined Table & Industrial Salt Mfr
N.A.I.C.S.: 424690

CYFIELD DEVELOPMENT CO.
LTD.
132 Limassol Avenue Cyfield Tower
5th Floor, 2015, Strovolos, Cyprus
Tel.: (357) 22427230
Web Site:
http://www.cyfieldgroup.com
Year Founded: 1990
Land Development & Residential
Housing Construction
N.A.I.C.S.: 237210

CYFROWY POLSAT S.A.
Lubinowa 4a, 03-878, Warsaw, Po-
land
Tel.: (48) 223566000
Web Site:
https://www.grupapolsatplus.pl
Year Founded: 1996
CPS—(WAR)
Rev.: $3,244,561,121
Assets: $8,116,012,661
Liabilities: $4,144,048,636
Net Worth: $3,971,964,026
Earnings: $226,096,568
Emp.: 7,648
Fiscal Year-end: 12/31/22
Satellite Television & Wireless Tele-
communications Services
N.A.I.C.S.: 516210
Maciej Stec *(Vice Chm-Mgmt Bd)*

Subsidiaries:

Netia SA **(1)**
Netia Tower Tasmowa 7A, 02-677, Warsaw,
Poland **(99.9%)**
Tel.: (48) 2235220
Web Site: http://www.netia.pl
Fixed Line Telecommunication Services
N.A.I.C.S.: 517810

Subsidiary (Domestic):

Petrotel Sp. z o.o **(2)**
Ul Chemikow 7, 09-411, Plock, Poland
Tel.: (48) 24 365 22 30
Web Site: http://www.petrotel.pl
Telecommunication Servicesb
N.A.I.C.S.: 517112

Telefonia Dialog S.A. **(2)**
Pl Jana Pawla II 1-2, 50-136, Wroclaw,
Poland
Tel.: (48) 71 7811601
Web Site: http://www.dialog.pl
Telecommunications
N.A.I.C.S.: 517810

Polkomtel S.A. **(1)**
ul Konstruktorska 4, 02-673, Warsaw, Po-
land
Tel.: (48) 224261000
Web Site: https://www.plus.pl
Sales Range: $1-4.9 Billion
Mobile Telecommunications Services
N.A.I.C.S.: 517112
Wojciech Dylewski *(Dir-Ops)*

Subsidiary (Domestic):

MIDAS S.A. **(2)**
Al Stanow Zjednoczonych 61a, 04-028,
Warsaw, Poland
Tel.: (48) 22 249 83 10
Web Site: http://www.midasnfi.pl
Telecommunication Servicesb
N.A.I.C.S.: 517121

CYFUSE BIOMEDICAL K.K.
West Wing-1F Sumitomo Fudosan
Mita Twin Bldg 3-5-27 Mita, Minato-
ku, Tokyo, 108-6301, Japan
Year Founded: 2010
4892—(TKS)
Biotechnology Research & Develop-
ment Services
N.A.I.C.S.: 541714
Shizuka Akieda *(CEO)*

CYGAM ENERGY INC.
Central Park Plaza 340 12 Ave SW,
Calgary, T2R 1L5, AB, Canada
Tel.: (403) 802-6983 **AB**
Year Founded: 1996
Oil & Natural Gas Exploration Ser-
vices
N.A.I.C.S.: 213112

Subsidiaries:

Rigo Oil Company Tunisia Ltd **(1)**
Rue du Lac Turkana - Les Berges du Lac
Immeuble Nour el Bouhaira, App B4, 1053,
Tunis, Tunisia
Tel.: (216) 71 962 562
Oil & Gas Exploration Services

N.A.I.C.S.: 213112

CYGNUS METALS LIMITED
Level 2 8 Richardson Street West
Perth, Perth, 6005, WA, Australia
Tel.: (61) 861181627 **AU**
Web Site:
https://www.cygnusmetals.com
CY5—(ASX)
Rev.: $1,958,521
Assets: $23,898,360
Liabilities: $5,522,639
Net Worth: $18,375,721
Earnings: ($9,195,761)
Fiscal Year-end: 12/31/23
Mineral Exploration Services
N.A.I.C.S.: 213114
Michael Naylor *(Co-Sec)*

CYIENT LIMITED
Plot No 11 Software Units Layout In-
focity, Madhapur, Hyderabad, 500
081, Telangana, India
Tel.: (91) 4067641000
Web Site: https://www.cyient.com
532175—(BOM)
Rev.: $634,247,250
Assets: $653,466,450
Liabilities: $228,487,350
Net Worth: $424,979,100
Earnings: $71,293,950
Emp.: 12,780
Fiscal Year-end: 03/31/22
Engineering, Geographic Information
Systems & Information Technology
Services
N.A.I.C.S.: 541511
B. V. R. Mohan Reddy *(Founder &
Chm)*

Subsidiaries:

Ansem BV **(1)**
Hengelosestraat 565, 7521 AG, Enschede,
Netherlands
Tel.: (31) 532032500
Fabless Analog ASIC Design Services
N.A.I.C.S.: 541490

Ansem NV **(1)**
Researchpark Haasrode 1113 Esperanto-
laan 9, 3001, Heverlee, Belgium
Tel.: (32) 16386500
Web Site: http://www.ansem.com
Fabless Analog ASIC Design Services
N.A.I.C.S.: 541490
Domenica Visalli *(Mgr-Quality)*

Blom Aerofilms Ltd. **(1)**
The Astrolabe Cheddar Business Park,
Cheddar, BS27 3EB, United Kingdom
Tel.: (44) 1934311000
Web Site: http://www.blom-uk.co.uk
Geophysical Surveying Services
N.A.I.C.S.: 541360

CERTON Software, Inc. **(1)**
1450 S Babcock St, Melbourne, FL 32901
Tel.: (321) 674-2155
Web Site: http://www.certon.com
Software Development Services
N.A.I.C.S.: 541511
Christina Dalton *(Mgr-Fin)*

Celfinet - Consultoria em Telecomuni-
cacoes, S.A. **(1)**
Edificio Porto Inova Rua Eng Ferreira Dias
N 728 Sala 1 05, 4100-246, Porto, Portugal
Tel.: (351) 226192915
Web Site: https://cotecportugal.pt
Software Development Services
N.A.I.C.S.: 541511

Citec Information & Engineering
GmbH **(1)**
Schwarzwiesen 13, 61440, Oberursel, Ger-
many
Tel.: (49) 8920190300
Engineering & Consultancy Services
N.A.I.C.S.: 541330

Citec Norway AS **(1)**
Strandveien 37, 1366, Lysaker, Norway
Tel.: (47) 90887748
Oil & Gas Services

Cyient Limited—(Continued)

N.A.I.C.S.: 211130

Citec Oy Ab (1)
Silmukkatie 2, PO Box 109, 65101, Vaasa, Finland
Tel.: (358) 63240700
Engineering & Consultancy Services
N.A.I.C.S.: 541330

Cyient Australia Pty Limited (1)
45 Ventnor Ave, West Perth, 6005, WA, Australia
Tel.: (61) 893894410
Engineering & Technology Services
N.A.I.C.S.: 541330

Cyient Benelux BV
Minervum 7491 Breda Oost, 4817 ZP, Breda, Netherlands
Tel.: (31) 765722966
Engineering & Technology Services
N.A.I.C.S.: 541330

Cyient DLM Private Limited (1)
Tel.: (91) 8214280000
Web Site: https://www.cyientdlm.com

Subsidiary (US):

Altek Electronics Inc. (1)
89 Commercial Blvd, Torrington, CT 06790-7215
Tel.: (860) 482-7626
Electronics Stores
N.A.I.C.S.: 449210
David Altschuler *(Treas & VP)*

Cyient Europe Limited (1)
Apex Forbury Road, Reading, RG1 1AX, United Kingdom
Tel.: (44) 1183043720
Engineering & Technology Services
N.A.I.C.S.: 541330

Cyient GmbH (1)
Mollenbachstr 37, 71229, Leonberg, Baden-Wurttemberg, Germany
Tel.: (49) 715294520
Web Site: http://www.cyient.com
Advanced Graphic Software & IT Management Services
N.A.I.C.S.: 513210

Cyient KK (1)
Sho-Building 6F 3-14-5, Nihonbashi Chuo-ku, Tokyo, 103-0027, Japan
Tel.: (81) 335279825
Information Technology Services
N.A.I.C.S.: 541519

Cyient N.V. (1)
Researchpark Haasrode 1113 Esperantolaan 9, Heverlee, 3001, Leuven, Belgium
Tel.: (32) 16386500
Information Technology Services
N.A.I.C.S.: 541519

Cyient SRO (1)
Classic 7 Business Park Jankovcova 1603/47a, 170 00, Prague, 7, Czech Republic
Tel.: (420) 277008200
Engineering & Technology Services
N.A.I.C.S.: 541330

Cyient Schweiz GmbH (1)
Christoffeigasse 6, 3011, Bern, Switzerland
Tel.: (41) 313825082
Engineering & Technology Services
N.A.I.C.S.: 541330

Cyient Singapore Pte Limited (1)
1 North Bridge Road 19-04/05 High Street Centre, Singapore, 179094, Singapore
Tel.: (65) 63372472
Engineering & Technology Services
N.A.I.C.S.: 541330

Infotech Enterprises America Inc. (1)
99 E River Dr 5th Fl, East Hartford, CT 06108
Tel.: (860) 528-5430
Web Site: http://www.infotech-enterprises.com
Sales Range: $200-249.9 Million
Emp.: 700
Software Publishing Services
N.A.I.C.S.: 513210

Division (Domestic):

Infotech Enterprises America Inc. (2)

5301 Linwood Dr, Paragould, AR 72450
Tel.: (870) 236-1080
Web Site: http://www.infotech-enterprises.com
Sales Range: $50-74.9 Million
Emp.: 180
Engineering & Telecommunication Services
N.A.I.C.S.: 541330
Betty Ellis *(Mgr-IT Svcs)*

Infotech Enterprises Europe Ltd (1)
First Fl W High Holborn House, 52-54 High Holborn, London, WC1V 6RL, United Kingdom
Tel.: (44) 2074040640
Web Site: http://www.infotech-enterprises.com
Sales Range: $25-49.9 Million
Emp.: 35
Software Publishing Services
N.A.I.C.S.: 513210

Infotech Enterprises Europe Ltd. (1)
Minervum 7491, 4817 ZP, Breda, North Brabant, Netherlands
Tel.: (31) 765722966
Web Site: http://www.infotech-enterprises.com
Sales Range: $25-49.9 Million
Emp.: 8
Software Publishing Services
N.A.I.C.S.: 513210

Infotech Enterprises GmbH France (1)
18 Rue Saint Vincent, 78100, Saint Germain-en-Laye, Yvelines, France
Tel.: (33) 130611673
Web Site: http://www.infotech-enterprises.com
Sales Range: $25-49.9 Million
Emp.: 3
Software Publishing Services
N.A.I.C.S.: 513210

Infotech Enterprises Japan KK (1)
Sho- Bldg 6F 3-14-5 Nihonbashi Chuo-Ku, Minato-ku, Tokyo, 1030027, Japan
Tel.: (81) 357787686
Emp.: 10
Software Publishing Services
N.A.I.C.S.: 513210

Infotech Enterprises Ltd (1)
Level 8 350 Collins St, Melbourne, 3000, VIC, Australia
Tel.: (61) 386054815
Web Site: http://www.infotech-enterprises.com
Sales Range: $25-49.9 Million
Emp.: 30
Computer Integrated Systems Design Services
N.A.I.C.S.: 541512
Sanjay Krishna *(Assoc VP)*

Infotech Enterprises Ltd (1)
Unit 10-197 Block 7 Lorang 7, Toapayoh, Singapore, 310007, Singapore
Tel.: (65) 63372472
Web Site: http://www.infotechsw.com
Software Publishing Services
N.A.I.C.S.: 513210

Infotech Enterprises Ltd - Software & Engineering Divisions (1)
Infotech IT Park Plot No 110A & 110B Phase 1, Electronics City Hosur Rd, Bengaluru, 560 100, Karnataka, India
Tel.: (91) 80 285 22341
Web Site: http://www.infotech-enterprises.com
Software Publishing Services
N.A.I.C.S.: 513210

Infotech Enterprises Ltd. (1)
Dubai Airport Free Zone Authority (DAFZA), PO Box 54713, Dubai, United Arab Emirates
Tel.: (971) 50 6867045
Web Site: http://www.infotech-enterprises.com
Sales Range: $25-49.9 Million
Emp.: 20
Software Publishing Services
N.A.I.C.S.: 513210

Infotech Software Solutions Canada Inc (1)
7575 Trans-Canada Hwy Suite 500, Saint

Laurent, H4B 1V6, QC, Canada
Tel.: (514) 489-0370
Emp.: 50
Software Publishing Services
N.A.I.C.S.: 513210

Workforce Delta Pty. Ltd. (1)
Level 2 10 Queens Rd, Melbourne, 3004, VIC, Australia
Tel.: (61) 1300189144
Web Site: https://www.workforcedelta.com.au
Management Consultancy Services
N.A.I.C.S.: 541611

CYL CORPORATION BERHAD
12 Jalan Teluk Gadung 27/93 Section 27, 40000, Shah Alam, Selangor Darul Ehsan, Malaysia
Tel.: (60) 351913888
Web Site: https://www.cylcorporation.com
CYL—(KLS)
Rev.: $12,264,620
Assets: $18,663,473
Liabilities: $2,944,088
Net Worth: $15,719,385
Earnings: $334,732
Fiscal Year-end: 01/31/22
Plastics Product Mfr
N.A.I.C.S.: 238350
Wai Ying Tham *(Co-Sec)*

Subsidiaries:

Perusahaan Jaya Plastik (M) Sdn. Bhd. (1)
Lot 12 Jalan Teluk Gadung 27/93 Section 27, 40000, Shah Alam, Selangor Darul Ehsan, Malaysia
Tel.: (60) 351913888
Web Site: https://www.jayaplastik.com
Plastics Product Mfr
N.A.I.C.S.: 326199
Chen Yat Lee *(Founder & Mng Dir)*

CYMAT TECHNOLOGIES LTD.
6320-2 Danville Road, Mississauga, L5T 2L7, ON, Canada
Tel.: (905) 696-9900
Web Site: https://www.cymat.com
CYM—(TSXV)
Rev.: $3,248,089
Assets: $5,149,579
Liabilities: $2,899,835
Net Worth: $2,249,745
Earnings: ($424,776)
Emp.: 11
Fiscal Year-end: 04/30/21
Materials Technology Services
N.A.I.C.S.: 541990
Michael M. Liik *(Founder, Chm & CEO)*

CYMBRIA CORPORATION
150 Bloor Street West Suite 500, Toronto, M5S 2X9, ON, Canada
Tel.: (416) 963-9353   ON
Web Site: https://www.cymbria.com
Year Founded: 2008
CYB—(TSX)
Rev.: $156,336,236
Assets: $960,644,799
Liabilities: $36,436,903
Net Worth: $924,207,897
Earnings: $130,442,045
Emp.: 41
Fiscal Year-end: 12/31/19
Investment Services
N.A.I.C.S.: 523999
Diane Rossi *(Sec)*

CYMECHS INC.
46 Dongtansandan 2-gil, Dongtan-myeon, Hwaseong, 18487, Gyeonggi-do, Korea (South)
Tel.: (82) 313718600
Web Site: https://www.cymechs.com
160980—(KRS)
Rev.: $149,607,834

Assets: $173,379,183
Liabilities: $55,187,597
Net Worth: $118,191,586
Earnings: $5,989,153
Emp.: 234
Fiscal Year-end: 12/31/22
Semiconductor Tool Automation Mfr
N.A.I.C.S.: 334413
KooRyong Jung *(Co-CEO)*

CYMOT (PTY) LTD.
15 Newcastle St, PO Box 726, Windhoek, 9000, Namibia
Tel.: (264) 612956000
Web Site: http://www.cymot.com
Year Founded: 1948
Sales Range: $200-249.9 Million
Emp.: 360
Automotive Refinishing Products, Workshop Equipment, Tools, Safety Products & Sports Equipment Distr
N.A.I.C.S.: 425120
Axel Theissen *(CEO & Mng Dir)*

CYNATA THERAPEUTICS LIMITED
Level 3 100 Cubitt Street, Cremorne, 3121, VIC, Australia
Tel.: (61) 370676940
Web Site: https://www.cynata.com
CYP—(ASX)
Rev.: $6,003,232
Assets: $20,340,834
Liabilities: $1,982,857
Net Worth: $18,357,978
Earnings: ($4,172,036)
Fiscal Year-end: 06/30/22
Therapeutic Stem Cell Products
N.A.I.C.S.: 325413
Ross Alexander MacDonald *(CEO & Mng Dir)*

CYNERGY CAPITAL LTD.
97 Park Lane Mayfair, London, W1K 7TG, United Kingdom
Year Founded: 2018
Holding Company
N.A.I.C.S.: 551112
Nick Fahy *(CEO)*

Subsidiaries:

Cynergy Bank Ltd. (1)
4th Floor, One New Change, London, EC4M 9AF, United Kingdom
Tel.: (44) 0345850555
Web Site: https://www.cynergybank.co.uk
Commercial Banking
N.A.I.C.S.: 522110

CYNOTECH HOLDINGS LIMITED
Level 4 20 Kent St, PO Box 9846, Newmarket, 1149, Auckland, New Zealand
Tel.: (64) 95206073
Web Site: http://www.cynotech.co.nz
Sales Range: $1-9.9 Million
Emp.: 80
Investment Management & Satellite Phones Mfr
N.A.I.C.S.: 523940
Allan Hawkins *(Chm)*

Subsidiaries:

Budget Loans Ltd (1)
15a Saleyards Road, Otahuhu, Auckland, New Zealand
Tel.: (64) 95206073
Web Site: http://www.budgetloans.co.nz
Financial Lending Services
N.A.I.C.S.: 522291

CYPARK RESOURCES BERHAD
Unit 13A-09 Block A Phileo Damansara II, No 15 Jalan 16/11, 46350, Petaling Jaya, Selangor, Malaysia

Tel.: (60) 376606170
Web Site: https://www.cypark.com
Year Founded: 1999
CYPARK—(KLS)
Rev.: $66,028,571
Assets: $580,112,593
Liabilities: $363,583,704
Net Worth: $216,528,889
Earnings: ($56,155,556)
Emp.: 124
Fiscal Year-end: 04/30/23
Landscaping & Engineering Services
N.A.I.C.S.: 541320
Daud Ahmad *(CEO-Grp)*

CYPHER METAVERSE INC.
1780-355 Burrard St, Vancouver,
V6C 2G8, BC, Canada
Tel.: (604) 343-2977   BC
Web Site: https://www.cypher-
meta.com
Year Founded: 2013
CODE—(CNSX)
Rev.: $33,883
Assets: $1,594,691
Liabilities: $67,472
Net Worth: $1,527,219
Earnings: ($2,397,745)
Fiscal Year-end: 12/31/22
Investment Services
N.A.I.C.S.: 523999
George Tsafalas *(Pres & CEO)*

CYPHERPUNK HOLDINGS INC.
217 Queen St W 401, PO Box 99,
Toronto, M5V 0R2, ON, Canada
Tel.: (647) 946-1300
Web Site:
https://cypherpunkholdings.com
Year Founded: 2018
CYFRF—(OTCIQ)
Rev.: $120,516
Assets: $12,877,932
Liabilities: $171,016
Net Worth: $12,706,916
Earnings: ($4,743,886)
Fiscal Year-end: 09/30/23
Minerals Exploration
N.A.I.C.S.: 213115
Antanas Guoga *(CEO)*

CYPRESS DEVELOPMENT CORP.
1610 - 777 Dunsmuir Street, Vancou-
ver, V7Y 1K4, BC, Canada
Tel.: (604) 687-3376   BC
Web Site:
https://www.centurylithium.com
Year Founded: 1991
CYP—(OTCIQ)
Gold, Silver & Base Metal Mining &
Exploration Services
N.A.I.C.S.: 212220
Donald G. Myers *(Dir-Corp Comm)*

CYPRESS HILLS RESOURCE CORP.
Web Site:
http://www.cypresshillsresource.com
Year Founded: 1983
CHY—(TSXV)
Rev.: $244
Assets: $192,913
Liabilities: $31,757
Net Worth: $161,155
Earnings: ($83,187)
Fiscal Year-end: 12/31/21
Oil & Gas Exploration Services
N.A.I.C.S.: 211120

CYPRIUM METALS LIMITED
Level 1 437 Roberts Road, Subiaco,
6008, WA, Australia
Tel.: (61) 863741550

Web Site:
https://www.cypriummetals.com
CYM—(ASX)
Rev.: $122,171
Assets: $103,145,535
Liabilities: $49,483,847
Net Worth: $53,661,688
Earnings: ($18,341,642)
Emp.: 100
Fiscal Year-end: 12/31/22
Gold Ore & Silver Ore Mining
N.A.I.C.S.: 212220
Barry Cahill *(Exec Dir)*

Subsidiaries:

PT Indonusa Mining Services   **(1)**
Perkantoran CBD/BIDEX Blok F No 5 Jl
Pahlawan Seribu BSD City, Tangerang,
15321, Indonesia
Tel.: (62) 2153160118
Gold Ore Mining Services
N.A.I.C.S.: 212220

CYPRUS AIRWAYS PUBLIC LIMITED
1 Spartis Str Antoniou Building 5th-
6th Floor, Larnaca, Cyprus
Tel.: (357) 24000053
Web Site:
http://www.cyprusairways.com
Sales Range: $300-349.9 Million
Emp.: 1,226
Oil Transportation Services
N.A.I.C.S.: 481111
Aharon Karaoghlanian *(CEO & Mgr-
Acctg)*

Subsidiaries:

Cyprus Airways (Duty Free Shops)
Ltd.   **(1)**
Larnaca Airport, PO Box 43027, CY-6650,
Larnaca, Cyprus
Tel.: (357) 24841400
Web Site: http://www.cydutyfree.com
General Retailer
N.A.I.C.S.: 455219

Eurocypria Airlines Ltd   **(1)**
97 Artemidos Ave Artemis Building, PO Box
40970, 6308, Larnaca, Cyprus   **(100%)**
Tel.: (357) 24658005
Web Site: http://www.eurocypria.com
Sales Range: $50-74.9 Million
Emp.: 180
Charter Flight Operations
N.A.I.C.S.: 481211

ZENON National Distribution Centre
Ltd.   **(1)**
Alkaiou 24, PO Box 25326, Engomi, 1308,
Nicosia, Cyprus   **(100%)**
Tel.: (357) 22664515
Web Site: http://www.zenonndc.com
Travel Industry Electronic Information Distr
N.A.I.C.S.: 561599

CYPRUS FOREST INDUS-TRIES PUBLIC LTD
Ayias Sofias1, PO Box 24043, Pa-
liometocho, 2682, Nicosia, Cyprus
Tel.: (357) 22872700
Web Site: https://www.cfi.com.cy
Year Founded: 1970
CFI—(CYP)
Emp.: 110
Industrial Wood Panels Mfr
N.A.I.C.S.: 321999
Charis Charalambous *(Gen Mgr)*

CYPRUS LIMNI RESORTS & GOLFCOURSES PLC
Shacolas House 200 Lemesos Av-
enue, 2025, Strovolos, Cyprus
Tel.: (357) 22740000
Web Site: http://www.limnibay.com
Building Construction Services
N.A.I.C.S.: 236220

CYPRUS STOCK EXCHANGE

71-73 Lordou Vironos Ave, Nicosia,
1096, Cyprus
Tel.: (357) 22712300
Web Site: http://www.cse.com.cy
Sales Range: $1-9.9 Million
Emp.: 93
Stock Exchange Services
N.A.I.C.S.: 523210
Marios A. Pilavakis *(Chm)*

CYPRUS TELECOMMUNICA-TIONS AUTHORITY
Telecommunications Str, Strovolos,
Nicosia, 1396, Cyprus
Tel.: (357) 22701000
Web Site: http://www.cyta.com.cy
Sales Range: $400-449.9 Million
Emp.: 2,485
Telecommunication Administration
Organization Services
N.A.I.C.S.: 926130
Photios Savvides *(CEO)*

Subsidiaries:

Actel Kft.   **(1)**
105-113 Bartok Bela Street, 1115, Buda-
pest, Hungary
Tel.: (36) 14814646
Data Transmission, Telephony & Multimedia
Services
N.A.I.C.S.: 517810

CytaGlobal   **(1)**
Telecommunications Street, PO Box 24929,
1396, Nicosia, Cyprus
Tel.: (357) 22702550
Web Site: http://www.cytaglobal.com
Sales Range: $25-49.9 Million
Emp.: 35
Electronic Communication Products & Ser-
vices
N.A.I.C.S.: 517810
Constantinos A. Michaelides *(Sr Mgr-
Infrastructure Support)*

Cytacom Solutions Limited   **(1)**
18 Makarios Arch III Avenue Latsia, 2220,
Nicosia, Cyprus
Tel.: (357) 70006000
Web Site: http://www.cytacom.com
Sales Range: $25-49.9 Million
Emp.: 20
Telecommunications Equipment & Consult-
ing Services
N.A.I.C.S.: 517810

Cytaglobal Hellas AE   **(1)**
21 Aegialias and Halepa 1, 15125, Ma-
roussi, Athens, Greece
Tel.: (30) 2169006777
Web Site: https://www.cytaglobalhellas.com
Telecommunication Servicesb
N.A.I.C.S.: 513199

Iris Gateway Satellite Services
Limited   **(1)**
Telecommunications Street, PO Box 24929,
Nicosia, 1396, Cyprus
Tel.: (357) 22701730
Web Site: http://www.irissat.com
Satellite Turnaround Services
N.A.I.C.S.: 517410

CYRELA BRAZIL REALTY S.A.
Avenida Brigadeiro Faria Lima 3600 -
12th Floor - Itaim Bibi, 04538-132,
Sao Paulo, 04538-132, SP, Brazil
Tel.: (55) 1145023000   BR
Web Site: https://www.cyrela.com.br
Year Founded: 1962
CYRBY—(OTCIQ)
Rev.: $1,117,730,973
Assets: $3,105,271,543
Liabilities: $1,585,844,687
Net Worth: $1,519,426,856
Earnings: $197,654,667
Emp.: 10,000
Fiscal Year-end: 12/31/23
Real Estate Development Services
N.A.I.C.S.: 531390
Efraim Schmuel Horn *(Vice Chm-
Exec Bd)*

Subsidiaries:

Living Salinas Empreendimentos Imo-
biliarios Ltda.   **(1)**
Rua Senador Theotonio Vilela 190-Edf Em-
presarial Convention Center, Sala 304 Bro-
tas, 40279-901, Salvador, Bahia, Brazil
Tel.: (55) 7132373139
Web Site: http://www.salinasltda.com.br
Real Estate Services
N.A.I.C.S.: 531210

Plano Pitangueiras Empreendimentos
Imobiliarios Ltda.   **(1)**
Rua Samuel Morse 74-13 Andar, Brooklin,
Sao Paulo, 04576-060, Brazil
Tel.: (55) 1140957400
Web Site: http://www.planoplano.com.br
Apartment Rental Services
N.A.I.C.S.: 531311

CYSTECH ELECTRONICS CORP.
15F-7 No 716 Chung Cheng Rd,
Zhong Ho District, New Taipei City,
235, Taiwan
Tel.: (886) 282273827
Web Site:
https://www.en.cystekec.com
6651—(TAI)
Electronic Product Distr
N.A.I.C.S.: 449210
Chien-Ching Li *(Chm)*

CYTOGEN CO., LTD
A-8F SK V1 GL Metrocity 128
Beobwon-ro, Songpa-gu, Seoul, Ko-
rea (South)
Tel.: (82) 0269251070
Web Site:
https://www.cytogenlab.com
Year Founded: 2010
217330—(KRS)
Research & Development on the
Physical, Engineering & Life Sciences
N.A.I.C.S.: 541715
Jung YunYoung *(CFO)*

Subsidiaries:

Expertox Inc   **(1)**
1803 Center St, Deer Park, TX 77536
Tel.: (281) 476-4600
Web Site: http://www.expertox.com
Rev.: $1,100,000
Emp.: 12
Testing Laboratories
N.A.I.C.S.: 541380
Loretta Anderson *(Pres)*

CYTOMED THERAPEUTICS LIMITED
08-22 One Commonwealth 1 Com-
monwealth Lane, Singapore, 149544,
Singapore
Tel.: (65) 62507738   SG
Web Site: https://w2.cytomed.sg
Year Founded: 2018
GDTC—(NASDAQ)
Rev.: $366,443
Assets: $3,946,272
Liabilities: $3,503,635
Net Worth: $442,637
Earnings: ($2,364,152)
Emp.: 28
Fiscal Year-end: 12/31/22
Biopharmaceutical Developer & Mfr
N.A.I.C.S.: 325412
Tien Wee Lucas Luk *(Chief Clinical
Officer)*

CYTORI THERAPEUTICS K.K.
Otemachi Park Building 7F 1-1-1
Otemachi, Chiyoda-ku, Tokyo, 100
0004, Japan
Tel.: (81) 3 6860 5700
Sales Range: $10-24.9 Million
Emp.: 25
Stem Cell Preservation Services
N.A.I.C.S.: 541715

Cytori Therapeutics K.K.—(Continued)

Seijiro Shirahama (Pres)

CYTOTOOLS AG
Klappacher Strasse 126, 64285,
Darmstadt, Germany
Tel.: (49) 61519515812
Web Site: https://bloxxmed.ag
Year Founded: 2000
T5O—(DEU)
Rev.: $10,792
Assets: $23,321,822
Liabilities: $205,051
Net Worth: $23,116,771
Earnings: ($895,748)
Fiscal Year-end: 12/31/22
Medical Device Mfr
N.A.I.C.S.: 339112
Bruno Rosen (Member-Exec Bd)

CYVIZ AS
Grenseveien 21, 4313, Sandnes,
Norway
Tel.: (47) 51635580
Web Site: https://www.cyviz.com
Year Founded: 1998
CYVIZ—(OSL)
Rev.: $54,075,189
Assets: $25,413,449
Liabilities: $16,466,377
Net Worth: $8,947,072
Earnings: $341,400
Emp.: 153
Fiscal Year-end: 12/31/23
Information Technology Services
N.A.I.C.S.: 541512
Espen Gylvik (CEO)

Subsidiaries:

Cyviz Pte. Ltd. **(1)**
78 Shenton Way 14-04, Singapore, 079120,
Singapore
Tel.: (65) 68141000
Software Development Services
N.A.I.C.S.: 541511

CYXONE AB
Adelgatan 21, 211 22, Malmo, Swe-
den
Tel.: (46) 708882172
Web Site: https://www.cyxone.com
Year Founded: 2015
CYXO—(DEU)
Rev.: $599,342
Assets: $4,919,779
Liabilities: $522,727
Net Worth: $4,397,052
Earnings: ($3,977,540)
Emp.: 7
Fiscal Year-end: 12/31/22
Pharmaceuticals Product Mfr
N.A.I.C.S.: 325412
Bert Junno (Chm)

CZECH AIRLINES, A.S.
ul K Letisti, 6 16008, Prague, Czech
Republic
Tel.: (420) 220104111
Web Site: http://www.csa.cz
Sales Range: $1-9.9 Million
Emp.: 5,303
Air Transportation
N.A.I.C.S.: 481111
Josef Adam (VP-Legal Affairs, HR &
IT)

CZECH MEDIA INVEST AS
Parizka 130/26, Josefov, Prague, 110
00, Czech Republic CZ
Web Site:
http://www.czechmediainvest.cz
Media Holding Company
N.A.I.C.S.: 551112
Daniel Kretinsky (Owner & Chm)

Subsidiaries:

EVROPA 2, spol. s r.o. **(1)**
Wenzigova 4, 120 00, Prague, Czech Re-
public
Tel.: (420) 257 001 111
Web Site: http://www.evropa2.cz
Internet Radio Broadcasting Services
N.A.I.C.S.: 516210

Editis SAS **(1)**
30 place d Italie, 75702, Paris, Cedex 13,
France
Tel.: (33) 0153533000
Web Site: http://www.editis.com
Trade, Education & Reference Books & Pe-
riodicals Publisher
N.A.I.C.S.: 513130

Subsidiary (Domestic):

Editions Bordas **(2)**
25 avenue Pierre de Coubertin, 75211,
Paris, Cedex 13, France
Tel.: (33) 153552627
Sales Range: $25-49.9 Million
Emp.: 100
Educational Texts & Reference Material
Publisher
N.A.I.C.S.: 513130

Editions Nathan **(2)**
25 Avenue Pierre de Coubertin, 75211,
Paris, Cedex 13, France
Tel.: (33) 145875324
Web Site: http://www.nathan.fr
Sales Range: $25-49.9 Million
Emp.: 100
Educational Book Publisher
N.A.I.C.S.: 513130

Subsidiary (Non-US):

Interforum Canada Inc. **(2)**
1001 Boul de Maisonneuve E. 10e etage
Bureau 1001, Montreal, H2L 4P9, QC,
Canada **(100%)**
Tel.: (514) 281-1050
Web Site: https://interforumcanada.com
Sales Range: $50-74.9 Million
Emp.: 10
Publisher
N.A.I.C.S.: 513199

Hachette Filipacchi Presse SA **(1)**
149 rue Anatole France, 92300, Levallois-
Perret, France
Tel.: (33) 141346000
Newspaper & Magazine Publishing Services
N.A.I.C.S.: 513110

Lagardere Publicite SAS **(1)**
10 rue Thierry le Ludon, 92300, Levallois-
Perret, France **(100%)**
Tel.: (33) 141349000
Web Site: http://www.lagardere-active-
pub.com
Sales Range: $800-899.9 Million
Emp.: 3,000
Periodical Publishers
N.A.I.C.S.: 513120
Constance Benque (Pres)

Radio Music RRM SRL **(1)**
Pipera Road, no. 46D-46E-48 Building B of
Oregon Park Sector 2, Bucharest, Romania
Tel.: (40) 372069500
Web Site: http://www.rrm.ro
Radio Station Broadcasting Services
N.A.I.C.S.: 516110

Radio Plus Polska Sp. z o.o. **(1)**
ul Zurawia 8, 00-503, Warsaw, Poland
Tel.: (48) 22 583 35 75
Web Site: http://www.radioplus.pl
Radio Station Broadcasting Services
N.A.I.C.S.: 516110
Marcin Jedlinski (Mgr)

CZERWONA TOREBKA SA
ul Ogrodowa 12, 61-821, Poznan,
Poland
Tel.: (48) 616232800
Web Site:
https://www.czerwonatorebka.pl
CZT—(WAR)
Rev.: $3,671,748
Assets: $51,769,817
Liabilities: $21,563,770

Net Worth: $30,206,047
Earnings: ($3,857,978)
Fiscal Year-end: 12/31/23
Shopping Centers & Retail Chain
Stores
N.A.I.C.S.: 459999
Mateusz Switalski (Pres & CEO)

CZR RESOURCES LIMITED
Suite 9 Level 3 47 Havelock Street,
West Perth, 6005, WA, Australia
Tel.: (61) 894682050 AU
Web Site:
http://www.czrresources.com
CZR—(ASX)
Rev.: $694,953
Assets: $28,474,038
Liabilities: $10,064,131
Net Worth: $18,409,907
Earnings: $7,007,593
Fiscal Year-end: 06/30/24
Metal Ore Mining Development
N.A.I.C.S.: 213114
Trevor O'Connor (CFO & Co-Sec)

D & H INDIA LIMITED
Plot A Sector A Industrial Area
Sanwer Road, Indore, 452 015,
Madhya Pradesh, India
Tel.: (91) 7316633501
Web Site: https://www.dnhindia.com
517514—(BOM)
Rev.: $12,454,178
Assets: $9,001,411
Liabilities: $4,708,649
Net Worth: $4,292,761
Earnings: $327,641
Emp.: 90
Fiscal Year-end: 03/31/22
Welding Electrode & Material Mfr
N.A.I.C.S.: 333992
Harsh Kumar Vora (Mng Dir)

Subsidiaries:

D & H India Limited - Unit II **(1)**
Village Sejvaya Dhar Road, Ghatabillod,
Dhar, Madhya Pradesh, India
Tel.: (91) 7292277030
Web Site: https://www.dnhindia.com
Welding Consumables Mfr
N.A.I.C.S.: 325998

**D & O GREEN TECHNOLO-
GIES BERHAD**
Lot 6 Batu Berendam FTZ Phase III,
75350, Melaka, Malaysia
Tel.: (60) 62833566
Web Site: https://www.do.com.my
D&O—(KLS)
Rev.: $221,291,686
Assets: $386,658,905
Liabilities: $181,136,266
Net Worth: $205,522,640
Earnings: $10,381,367
Emp.: 2,700
Fiscal Year-end: 12/31/23
Semiconductor Components Mfr
N.A.I.C.S.: 334413
Tek Beng Low (COO)

Subsidiaries:

Dominant Opto Technologies (Shang-
hai) Co., Ltd. **(1)**
Room 305 Hongwell International Plaza No
1600 Zhong Shan West Road, Xuhui Dis-
trict, Shanghai, 200235, China
Tel.: (86) 2154035655
Semiconductor & Related Device Mfr
N.A.I.C.S.: 334413

Dominant Opto Technologies Japan
KK **(1)**
Three One Building 703 3-20-5 ShinYoko-
hama, Kouhoku-ku, Yokohama, 222-0033,
Japan
Tel.: (81) 456249345
Semiconductor Component Distr
N.A.I.C.S.: 423690

Dominant Opto Technologies Korea
Inc. **(1)**
6F Dojin Bldg 30 Samhaksa-ro, Songpa-gu,
Seoul, 05692, Korea (South)
Tel.: (82) 24255203
Semiconductor & Related Device Mfr
N.A.I.C.S.: 334413

Dominant Opto Technologies North
America, Inc. **(1)**
10381 Citation Dr Ste 200, Brighton, MI
48116
Tel.: (616) 893-5456
Semiconductor & Related Device Mfr
N.A.I.C.S.: 334413

Omega Semiconductor Sdn.
Bhd. **(1)**
8760 Lot 8 Kawasan Perdagangan Bebas
Fasa III Batu Berendam, 75350, Melaka,
Malaysia
Tel.: (60) 62822672
Web Site:
http://www.omegasemicon.com.my
Sales Range: $200-249.9 Million
Emp.: 800
Semiconductor Mfr
N.A.I.C.S.: 334413

Subsidiary (Domestic):

Dominant Opto Technologies Sdn.
Bhd. **(2)**
Lot 6 Batu Berendam FTZ Phase III, 75350,
Melaka, Malaysia
Tel.: (60) 6 283 3566
Web Site: https://www.dominant-semi.com
Emp.: 2,500
Opto Semiconductors Mfr
N.A.I.C.S.: 334413

Subsidiary (Non-US):

Dominant Semiconductors (Europe
GmbH) **(3)**
Raiffeisenstr 38, 74906, Bad Rappenau,
Germany
Tel.: (49) 726 489 0100
Web Site: http://www.dominant-semi.com
Emp.: 15
Light Emitting Diode Mfr
N.A.I.C.S.: 334413

Dominant Semiconductors Korea
Inc. **(3)**
Room 211 Sunteak City Apartment 513 15
Sangdaewon-dong, Jungwon-gu, Seong-
nam, 462 725, Gyeonggi-do, Korea (South)
Tel.: (82) 317015203
Web Site: http://www.dominant-semi.com
Semiconductor Device Distr
N.A.I.C.S.: 423690

**D ALEX MACDONALD FORD
LINCOLN**
25 Water Street, Summerside, C1N
1A3, PE, Canada
Tel.: (902) 436-2138
Web Site:
http://dalexmacdonald.dealer.com
Rev.: $15,727,375
Emp.: 35
New & Used Car Dealers
N.A.I.C.S.: 441110
Mike MacDonald (Mgr-Bodyshop)

**D AND O HOME COLLECTION
CO., LTD.**
15th Floor Building A New Hope In-
ternational Building, No 19 Tianfu 3rd
Street Middle Section of Tianfu Av-
enue High-tech Zone, Chengdu,
610041, Sichuan, China
Tel.: (86) 2882801234
Web Site: http://www.monarch-
sw.com
Year Founded: 1994
002798—(SSE)
Rev.: $577,329,854
Assets: $1,109,014,419
Liabilities: $710,937,401
Net Worth: $398,077,019
Earnings: ($228,197,680)
Fiscal Year-end: 12/31/22

Sanitary Ware Mfr & Distr
N.A.I.C.S.: 332999
Jin Liu *(Chm)*

D B CORP LTD.
6 Dwarka Sadan Press Complex M P
Nagar Zone I, Bhopal, 462 011,
Madhya Pradesh, India
Tel.: (91) 7554730000
Web Site: https://www.dbcorpltd.com
Year Founded: 2005
533151—(BOM)
Rev.: $207,778,799
Assets: $337,969,496
Liabilities: $89,148,560
Net Worth: $248,820,936
Earnings: $19,303,557
Emp.: 7,453
Fiscal Year-end: 03/31/21
Newspaper Printing & Publishing
Services
N.A.I.C.S.: 513110
P. G. Mishra *(Grp CFO)*

D C SECURITY INC
397 Humberline Drive Unit 5, Etobi-
coke, M9W 5T5, ON, Canada
Tel.: (416) 213-1995
Web Site: http://www.dc-security.com
Rev.: $24,653,724
Emp.: 100
Security Services
N.A.I.C.S.: 561612
Clement G. Dennis *(Pres)*

D HLM NOTRE LOGIS
1 Place des Bleuets, BP 126, 59433,
Halluin, Cedex, France
Tel.: (33) 320030201
Web Site: http://www.notre-logis.fr
Rev.: $23,900,000
Emp.: 51
Apartment Building Operator
N.A.I.C.S.: 531110
Alain Leurent *(Dir)*

D MECATRONICS, INC.
7669 Kimbel Street, Mississauga, L58
1A7, ON, Canada
Tel.: (905) 672-7669
Web Site:
http://www.dmecatronics.com
DMTA—(OTCIQ)
Sales Range: Less than $1 Million
Automobile Component Distr
N.A.I.C.S.: 441330

D NALOZBE D.D.
Smartinska 52, 1000, Ljubljana, Slo-
venia
Tel.: (386) 31326879
Investment Fund Services
N.A.I.C.S.: 525910
Danilo Peteh *(CEO)*

D P WIRES LTD.
16 - 18A Industrial Area, Ratlam,
Ujjain, 457001, Madhya Pradesh,
India
Tel.: (91) 7412261130
Web Site: https://www.dpwires.co.in
Year Founded: 1998
DPWIRES—(NSE)
Rev.: $64,052,338
Assets: $20,980,241
Liabilities: $4,236,755
Net Worth: $16,743,486
Earnings: $3,286,606
Emp.: 60
Fiscal Year-end: 03/31/21
Fabricated Metal Products Mfr
N.A.I.C.S.: 332999
Praveen Kataria *(Mng Dir)*

**D&D PLATFORM REIT CO.,
LTD.**
7F 382 Gangnam-daero, Gangnam-

Gu, Seoul, Korea (South)
Tel.: (82) 262019500
Web Site:
http://www.dndplatformreit.com
Year Founded: 2020
377190—(KRS)
Real Estate Services
N.A.I.C.S.: 531210
Yeon-Seok Yoo *(Gen Mgr)*

**D&E AIR CONDITIONING PTY.
LIMITED**
Level 1 11 Corporate Avenue, PO
Box 2010, Rowville, 3178, VIC, Aus-
tralia
Tel.: (61) 397514222   AU
Web Site: http://www.de-air.com.au
Year Founded: 1989
Sales Range: $50-74.9 Million
Emp.: 250
Air-Conditioning & Mechanical Con-
tractor
N.A.I.C.S.: 238220
Brad Alexander *(Mgr-Ops)*

D&E BEARINGS AB
Himmelsbodavagen 9, 147 39,
Tumba, Sweden
Tel.: (46) 84474050   SE
Web Site: http://www.debearings.com
Year Founded: 1966
Bearing Component Mfr
N.A.I.C.S.: 332991

D&E BEARINGS OY
Takasenkatu 55, 08150, Lohja, Fin-
land
Tel.: (358) 207118670   FI
Web Site: http://www.debearings.fi
Bearing Component Mfr
N.A.I.C.S.: 332991

**D&G TECHNOLOGY HOLDING
CO., LTD.**
7/F Hing Lung Commercial Building
68-74 Bonham Strand, Sheung Wan,
China (Hong Kong)
Tel.: (852) 25422872   Ky
Web Site:
http://www.dgtechnology.com
Year Founded: 1999
1301—(HKG)
Rev.: $48,492,335
Assets: $120,476,959
Liabilities: $32,623,765
Net Worth: $87,853,194
Earnings: ($5,726,635)
Emp.: 384
Fiscal Year-end: 12/31/22
Asphalt Product Mfr & Distr
N.A.I.C.S.: 324121
Hung Nang Choi *(Founder & Chm)*

Subsidiaries:

Langfang D&G Machinery Technology
Company Limited   (1)
No 12 Ying Hua Road Yongqing Industrial
Zone, Langfang, 065601, Hebei, China
Tel.: (86) 1081571866
Web Site:
https://www.dgmachinery.hzyjmx.com
Asphalt Mixing Equipment Mfr
N.A.I.C.S.: 324121

Primach Technology Pte Ltd   (1)
60 Paya Lebar Road 10-26 Paya Lebar
Square, Singapore, 409051, Singapore
Tel.: (65) 63853361
Web Site: http://www.primach-tech.com
Construction Machinery Equipment Distr
N.A.I.C.S.: 423810

D&L INDUSTRIES, INC.
65 Calle Industria, Bagumbayan,
Quezon City, 1110, Philippines
Tel.: (63) 286350680
Web Site: https://www.dnl.com.ph

DLNDY—(OTCIQ)
Rev.: $604,898,035
Assets: $769,615,335
Liabilities: $392,843,188
Net Worth: $376,772,147
Earnings: $41,444,669
Emp.: 1,097
Fiscal Year-end: 12/31/23
Holding Company; Food Ingredients,
Plastic Products, Chemicals Mfr
N.A.I.C.S.: 551112
Yin Yong L. Lao *(Chm)*

Subsidiaries:

Oleo-Fats Inc   (1)
5 Mercury Avenue, Bagumbayan, Quezon
City, 1100, Philippines
Tel.: (63) 286350680
Web Site: https://www.oleofats.com
Oil & Specialty Ingredient Mfr
N.A.I.C.S.: 311225
Jeoffrey Balomit *(Mgr-Technical)*

D&R HENDERSON PTY. LTD.
PO Box 6307, Wetherill Park, 1851,
NSW, Australia
Tel.: (61) 281183600
Web Site:
http://www.drhenderson.com.au
Year Founded: 1964
Emp.: 400
Plywood Mfr
N.A.I.C.S.: 321211
Richard Kaine *(Gen Mgr-Mfg)*

D&S ANASTOPOULOS SA
Antoniou Kiousi 56 Thesi Prari,
19400, Koropi, Greece
Tel.: (30) 2106020586
Web Site: https://www.anastopoulos-
sa.gr
Year Founded: 1976
Paper Product Distr
N.A.I.C.S.: 424130
Spyros Anastopoulos *(Owner)*

**D'AMICO INTERNATIONAL
SHIPPING S.A.**
Corso d Italia 35/B, 198, Rome, Italy
Tel.: (39) 06845611
Web Site: https://en.damicoship.com
Year Founded: 1952
DIS—(ITA)
Rev.: $479,619,000
Assets: $1,054,885,000
Liabilities: $576,471,000
Net Worth: $478,414,000
Earnings: $134,869,000
Emp.: 617
Fiscal Year-end: 12/31/22
Marine Transportation Services
N.A.I.C.S.: 483111
Paolo d'Amico *(Chm)*

Subsidiaries:

d'Amico Tankers Ltd   (1)
The Anchorage 17-19 Sir John Rogerson's
Quay, Dublin, 32, Ireland
Tel.: (353) 16740100
Web Site: http://www.damicoship.com
Emp.: 40
Marine Transportation Services
N.A.I.C.S.: 483111

Subsidiary (Non-US):

DM shipping Ltd   (2)
Salamons Way, Rainham, RM13 9UL,
United Kingdom
Tel.: (44) 1708551000
Marine Transportation Services
N.A.I.C.S.: 483111

Subsidiary (Domestic):

High Pool Tankers Ltd   (2)
The Anchorage 17-19 Sir John Rogerson's
Qua, Dublin, 2, Ireland
Tel.: (353) 16761840
Web Site: http://www.damicoship.com
Marine Transportation Services

N.A.I.C.S.: 483111

Subsidiary (Non-US):

d'Amico Tankers Monaco SAM   (2)
20 Bd de Suisse, Monte Carlo, 98000, Mo-
naco
Tel.: (377) 93105270
Web Site: http://www.damico.com
Marine Transportation Services
N.A.I.C.S.: 483111

d'Amico Tankers UK Ltd   (2)
2 Queen Annes Gate Building Dartmouth
Street, London, 1H 9BP, United Kingdom
Tel.: (44) 2073402000
Web Site: http://www.damicoship.com
Emp.: 10
Marine Transportation Services
N.A.I.C.S.: 483111
Flemming Carlsen *(CEO)*

D'LIVE CO., LTD.
239-1 Nonhyeon Dong, Gangnam-gu,
Seoul, 135-010, Korea (South)
Tel.: (82) 2 2056 7777
Web Site: http://www.dlive.kr
TV Cable Services
N.A.I.C.S.: 516210
Gyu-Seok Oh *(Pres)*

D'NONCE TECHNOLOGY BHD.
51-14-B and C Menara BHL Jalan
Sultan Ahmad Shah, 10050, Penang,
Malaysia
Tel.: (60) 42281198
Web Site: https://www.dnonce.com
Year Founded: 1989
DNONCE—(KLS)
Rev.: $37,329,718
Assets: $70,726,145
Liabilities: $20,257,973
Net Worth: $50,468,172
Earnings: ($1,846,848)
Fiscal Year-end: 03/31/24
Electronic Components Mfr
N.A.I.C.S.: 334417
Peter Lim Oon Jin *(Head-Southern
Reg)*

Subsidiaries:

AV Plastics Sdn. Bhd.   (1)
No 137 & 138 Jalan Suasa 7 Taman Suasa,
9000, Kulim, Kedah, Malaysia
Tel.: (60) 44892255
Web Site: http://www.dnoncetech.com
Sales Range: $50-74.9 Million
Emp.: 50
Plastic Products Mfr & Whslr
N.A.I.C.S.: 326199
Ak Teoh *(Mgr)*

Attractive Venture (JB) Sdn. Bhd.   (1)
No 3312 Lot 58830 Jalan Tanjung 27/2 Ka-
wasan Perindustrian Indahpura, 81000, Ku-
lai, Johor, Malaysia
Tel.: (60) 76615188
Web Site:
http://www.attractivepackaging.com.my
Sales Range: $25-49.9 Million
Emp.: 90
Industrial Packaging Materials Mfr
N.A.I.C.S.: 322220

Attractive Venture (KL) Sdn.
Bhd.   (1)
Tel.: (60) 390748646
Web Site: http://www.dnoncetech.com.my
Sales Range: $25-49.9 Million
Emp.: 60
Industrial Packaging Materials Mfr
N.A.I.C.S.: 322220

Attractive Venture Sdn. Bhd.   (1)
No 2733 MK 1 Tingkat Perusahaan 6A Ka-
wasan Perusahaan Prai, Zone Perdagan-
gan Bebas, 13600, Prai, Penang, Malaysia
Tel.: (60) 43997968
Web Site:
http://www.attractivepackaging.com.my
Emp.: 200
Industrial Packaging Materials Mfr
N.A.I.C.S.: 322220

D'nonce (Johore) Sdn. Bhd.   (1)

D'nonce Technology Bhd.—(Continued)

1218-1220 Jalan Sri Putri 3/4 Taman Putri
Kulai, Kulai, Johor, Malaysia
Tel.: (60) 7 355 7969
Sales Range: $25-49.9 Million
Emp.: 100
Security Control Equipment Mfr
N.A.I.C.S.: 334419

D'nonce (K.L) Sdn. Bhd. (1)
Lot 20 Jln CJ 1/1 Kawasan Perusahaan
Cheras Jaya, Batu 11, Cheras, 43200,
Kuala Lumpur, Malaysia
Tel.: (60) 123583011
Adhesive Tape Mfr
N.A.I.C.S.: 322230

D'nonce (Kelantan) Sdn. Bhd. (1)
PT 4110-A B Padang Tembak Kawasan
Perindustrian Pengkalan Chepa 2, Padang
Tembak, 16100, Kota Baharu, Kelantan,
Malaysia
Tel.: (60) 97743312
Sales Range: $25-49.9 Million
Emp.: 50
Adhesive Tape Mfr
N.A.I.C.S.: 322230

D'nonce (M) Sdn. Bhd. (1)
PMT 3089 Jalan Jelawat Taman Perindus-
trian Seberang Jaya, 13700, Prai, Penang,
Malaysia
Tel.: (60) 43841292
Sales Range: $25-49.9 Million
Emp.: 20
Adhesive Tape Mfr
N.A.I.C.S.: 322230

**ISCM Technology (Thailand) Co.,
Ltd.** (1)
101/47/20 Navanakorn Industrial Estate,
Klongnueng, Pathumthani, 12120, Thailand
Tel.: (66) 25292180
Web Site: http://www.iscmtechnology.com
Disk Drives Mfr
N.A.I.C.S.: 334112

Richmond Technology Sdn. Bhd. (1)
PT 4110-A B C Kawasan Perindustrian
Pengkalan Chepa 2, Padang Tembak,
16100, Kota Baharu, Kelantan, Malaysia
Tel.: (60) 97743312
Web Site:
http://www.attractivepackaging.com.my
Emp.: 35
Industrial Packaging Materials Mfr
N.A.I.C.S.: 326112

D-BOX TECHNOLOGIES INC.
2172 rue de la Province, Longueuil,
J4G 1R7, QC, Canada
Tel.: (450) 442-3003   Ca
Web Site: https://www.d-box.com
DBOXF—(TSX)
Rev.: $16,672,734
Assets: $17,483,958
Liabilities: $8,226,456
Net Worth: $9,257,502
Earnings: ($1,460,517)
Emp.: 90
Fiscal Year-end: 03/31/22
Motion Simulation System Mfr
N.A.I.C.S.: 334419
David Montpetit (CFO)

D-LINK CORPORATION, INC.
No 289 Xinhu 3rd Road, Neihu Dis-
trict, Taipei, 114, Taiwan
Tel.: (886) 266000123
Web Site: https://www.dlinktw.com.tw
Year Founded: 1986
2332—(TAI)
Rev.: $521,314,510
Assets: $543,535,707
Liabilities: $164,330,286
Net Worth: $379,205,421
Earnings: $22,815,592
Emp.: 717
Fiscal Year-end: 12/31/23
Data Network Equipment Mfr
N.A.I.C.S.: 334210
Victor Kuo (Chm)

Subsidiaries:

D-Link (Deutschland) GmbH (1)
Schwalbacher Str 74, 65760, Eschborn,
Germany
Tel.: (49) 61 967 7990
Web Site: https://eu.dlink.com
Information Technology Services
N.A.I.C.S.: 541511

D-Link (India) Ltd (1)
Kalpataru Square 2nd Floor Unit 24 Kondi-
vita Lane, Off Andheri Kurla Road Next to
VITS Hotel Andheri East, Mumbai, 400059,
India   **(60.37%)**
Tel.: (91) 2229215700
Web Site: https://www.dlink.co.in
Rev.: $100,108,363
Assets: $58,859,387
Liabilities: $22,509,396
Net Worth: $36,349,991
Earnings: $4,279,125
Emp.: 284
Fiscal Year-end: 03/31/2021
Telecommunications Equipment Mfr
N.A.I.C.S.: 334220
C. M. Gaonkar (CFO)

D-Link Malaysia Sdn. Bhd. (1)
Strata Office SO-20-08 Menara 1 KL Eco
City, Jalan Bangsar Kg Hj Abdullah Hukum,
59200, Kuala Lumpur, Malaysia
Tel.: (60) 32 202 0032
Web Site: https://www.dlink.com.my
Networking Equipment Mfr
N.A.I.C.S.: 334210
Wah Cheong (Mgr)

D-Link Systems, Inc. (1)
14420 Myford Rd Ste 100, Irvine, CA 92606
Tel.: (714) 885-6000
Web Site: https://us.dlink.com
Networking Connectivity & Data Communi-
cations Products Mfr
N.A.I.C.S.: 423430

D-MARKET ELECTRONIC SERVICES & TRADING
Kustepe Mahallesi Mecidiyekoy Yolu
Cadde No 12 Trump Towers Kule 2
K2, Sisli, 34387, Istanbul, Turkiye
Tel.: (90) 2123042000   TR
Year Founded: 2000
HEPS—(NASDAQ)
Rev.: $2,178,527,745
Assets: $1,364,833,486
Liabilities: $1,087,906,274
Net Worth: $276,927,212
Earnings: ($394,162,997)
Emp.: 3,834
Fiscal Year-end: 12/31/22
Online Shopping Services
N.A.I.C.S.: 541511
Hanzade Vasfiye Dogan Boyner
(Founder & Chm)

D-PHARM LTD.
Kiryat Weizmann Science Park Bldg
7, PO Box 2313, 76123, Rehovot,
Israel
Tel.: (972) 4848316 30
Web Site: http://www.dpharm.com
Year Founded: 1993
Rev.: $208,101
Assets: $491,038
Liabilities: $130,963
Net Worth: $360,075
Earnings: ($169,244)
Emp.: 90
Fiscal Year-end: 12/31/17
Pharmaceuticals Mfr
N.A.I.C.S.: 325412

D-WAVE QUANTUM INC.
3033 Beta Avenue, Burnaby, V5G
4M9, BC, Canada
Tel.: (604) 630-1428
Web Site: https://www.dwavesys.com
QBTS—(NYSE)
Rev.: $7,173,000
Assets: $26,947,000
Liabilities: $32,861,000

Net Worth: ($5,914,000)
Earnings: ($51,529,000)
Emp.: 215
Fiscal Year-end: 12/31/22
Quantum Computing Systems, Soft-
ware & Services
N.A.I.C.S.: 513210

Subsidiaries:

D-Wave Systems Inc. (1)
3033 Beta Avenue, Burnaby, V5G 4K4, BC,
Canada
Tel.: (604) 630-1428
Web Site: https://www.dwavesys.com
Emp.: 100
Quantum Computing Systems, Software &
Services
N.A.I.C.S.: 513210

DPCM Capital, Inc. (1)
382 NE 191 St Ste 24148, Miami, FL 33179
Tel.: (305) 857-5086
Investment Services
N.A.I.C.S.: 523999

D. D. LITVATRANS BANOVICI
Armije BiH br 4, 75 290, Banovici,
Bosnia & Herzegovina
Tel.: (387) 35 876 865
Web Site: http://www.litvatrans.ba
Year Founded: 1946
Rev.: $1,575,351
Assets: $4,763,744
Liabilities: $1,500,205
Net Worth: $3,263,539
Earnings: $62,306
Emp.: 119
Fiscal Year-end: 12/31/18
Passenger Transportation Services
N.A.I.C.S.: 485999

D. LAZZARONI & C. S.P.A.
Via Novara 55, I-21047, Saronno, VA,
Italy
Tel.: (39) 029375391   IT
Web Site:
http://www.lazzaronisaronno.com
Year Founded: 1870
Sales Range: $25-49.9 Million
Emp.: 115
Baked Goods
N.A.I.C.S.: 311812
Stefano Tombetti (Mng Dir)

D. P. ABHUSHAN LTD.
19 Chandni Chowk, 2nd Floor, Rat-
lam, 457001, India
Tel.: (91) 7412490966
Web Site:
https://www.dpjewellers.com
Year Founded: 1940
DPABHUSHAN—(NSE)
Rev.: $166,295,711
Assets: $53,930,372
Liabilities: $40,679,034
Net Worth: $13,251,338
Earnings: $3,740,359
Emp.: 475
Fiscal Year-end: 03/31/21
Jewelry Product Retailer
N.A.I.C.S.: 458310
Vikas Kataria (Mng Dir)

D. WESTERN THERAPEUTICS INSTITUTE, INC.
7th Floor CK21 Hirokoujifushimi Bldg
1-18-11 Nishiki, Naka-ku, Nagoya,
460-0003, Aichi, Japan
Tel.: (81) 522188785
Web Site: https://www.dwti.co.jp
Year Founded: 1999
4576—(TKS)
Rev.: $3,034,520
Assets: $16,824,570
Liabilities: $7,756,460
Net Worth: $9,068,110
Earnings: ($5,757,080)
Emp.: 19

Fiscal Year-end: 12/31/23
Pharmaceutical Mfr & Researcher
N.A.I.C.S.: 325412
Hiroyoshi Hidaka (Chm)

D.C. THOMSON & CO. LTD.
2 Albert Square, Dundee, DD1 1DD,
United Kingdom
Tel.: (44) 1382 223 131
Web Site:
http://www.dcthomson.co.uk
Year Founded: 1905
Sales Range: $400-449.9 Million
Emp.: 2,170
News Publishing Services
N.A.I.C.S.: 513110
Richard Neville (Head-Newspapers)

Subsidiaries:

DC Thomson Ventures (1)
185 Fleet Street, London, EC4A 2HS,
United Kingdom
Tel.: (44) 2074001030
Web Site: http://www.dctventures.com
Venture Capital Funding Services
N.A.I.C.S.: 523910
Jayne Mould (Principal)

Findmypast Limited (1)
6 Chapel Place Rivington Street, London,
EC2A 3DQ, United Kingdom
Tel.: (44) 2079940147
Web Site: http://www.findmypast.com
Software Development Services
N.A.I.C.S.: 541511
Katie Spinks Seabrook (Head-Mktg)

My Family Club Limited (1)
45 Moorfields, London, EC2Y 9AE, United
Kingdom
Tel.: (44) 2071833741
Web Site: http://www.myfamilyclub.co.uk
Electronic Store Operator
N.A.I.C.S.: 449210
Gemma Johnson (CEO)

Parragon Books Ltd (1)
Chartist House 15-17 Trim Street, Bath,
BA1 1HA, United Kingdom
Tel.: (44) 1225 478888
Web Site: http://www.parragon.com
Book Publishers
N.A.I.C.S.: 513130
Mike Symons (CEO)

Puzzler Media Limited (1)
Stonecroft 69 Station Road, Redhill, RH1
1EY, United Kingdom
Tel.: (44) 1737378700
Web Site: http://www.puzzler.com
Book Publishers
N.A.I.C.S.: 513130
Lynda Newland (Dir-Sls & Mktg)

brightsolid (1)
Gateway House Technology Park, Dundee,
DD2 1TP, United Kingdom
Tel.: (44) 1382429000
Web Site: http://www.brightsolid.com
Software Development Services
N.A.I.C.S.: 541511
Elaine Maddison (CEO)

D.G.S. CONSTRUCTION COM-PANY LTD.
A101 - 13761 - 116th Ave, Surrey,
V3R 0T2, BC, Canada
Tel.: (604) 584-2214
Web Site:
https://www.dgsconstruction.com
Year Founded: 1982
Emp.: 10
Building Construction Services
N.A.I.C.S.: 236220

D.I. SYSTEM CO., LTD.
4-10-1 Nakano, Nakano-Ku, Tokyo,
164-0001, Japan
Tel.: (81) 353186940
Web Site: https://www.di-system.co.jp
Year Founded: 1997
4421—(TKS)
Rev.: $44,248,690

Assets: $19,660,570
Liabilities: $10,727,170
Net Worth: $8,933,400
Earnings: $1,701,600
Emp.: 747
Fiscal Year-end: 09/30/23
Application Development Services
N.A.I.C.S.: 541511
Kentaro Tomita *(Pres & CEO)*

D.ID CORPORATION
27 3 Sam Gongdan 2 i-Ro, Seobuk-gu, Cheonan, 330220,
Chungcheongnam-do, Korea (South)
Tel.: (82) 41 621 7541
Web Site: http://www.didsp.co.kr
Year Founded: 1998
Sales Range: $150-199.9 Million
Emp.: 690
Liquid Crystal Display Module Mfr
N.A.I.C.S.: 334419
Seong-su Park *(Exec Dir)*

D.K FORD SALES
6559 Sparrow Drive, Leduc, T9E 7L1,
AB, Canada
Tel.: (855) 804-9622
Web Site: http://www.dkford.com
Year Founded: 1993
New & Used Car Dealers
N.A.I.C.S.: 441110
Jerry Maciuk *(Gen Mgr)*

**D.K. ENTERPRISES GLOBAL
LIMITED**
Plot Number-235 Industrial Area
Phase-2, Panchkula, 134109, Haryana, India
Tel.: (91) 1722591548
Web Site:
https://www.dkenterprises.co.in
Year Founded: 2019
DKEGL—(NSE)
Rev.: $12,861,344
Assets: $5,733,846
Liabilities: $3,089,118
Net Worth: $2,644,728
Earnings: $473,641
Emp.: 77
Fiscal Year-end: 03/31/22
Packaging Materials Mfr
N.A.I.C.S.: 322220

D.L.G.L. LTD.
850 Michele Bohec, Blainville, J7C
5E2, QC, Canada
Tel.: (450) 979-4646
Web Site: http://www.dlgl.com
Year Founded: 1980
Sales Range: $10-24.9 Million
Human Capital Management Software Programming Services
N.A.I.C.S.: 541511
Jacques Guenette *(Pres)*

D.M. TEXTILE MILLS LIMITED
Westridge Industrial Area, Rawalpindi, Pakistan
Tel.: (92) 51518197778
Web Site:
https://www.dmtextile.com.pk
Year Founded: 1958
DMTX—(PSX)
Rev.: $178,576
Assets: $4,713,235
Liabilities: $987,923
Net Worth: $3,725,312
Earnings: ($54,025)
Emp.: 26
Fiscal Year-end: 06/30/19
Textile Products Mfr
N.A.I.C.S.: 314999
Habib Ullah *(CEO)*

D.S. INDUSTRIES LIMITED
20-K Gulberg II, Lahore, Pakistan

Tel.: (92) 4235714810
Web Site: https://dsil.com.pk
Year Founded: 1980
DSIL—(PSX)
Rev.: $133,754
Assets: $1,072,421
Liabilities: $398,797
Net Worth: $673,624
Earnings: ($51,807)
Emp.: 13
Fiscal Year-end: 06/30/23
Textile Spinning Mill Operator
N.A.I.C.S.: 313110
Pervez Ahmad *(CEO)*

Subsidiaries:

Pervez Ahmed Securities Limited **(1)**
20-K Gulberg II, Lahore, Pakistan
Tel.: (92) 4235714809
Web Site: https://www.pervezahmed.net
Shares Brokerage Services
N.A.I.C.S.: 523150

**D.T.C. ENTERPRISE PUBLIC
COMPANY LIMITED**
63 Soi Sukhumvit 68 Sukhumvit Rd,
Bangna Nuea Bangna, Bangkok,
10260, Thailand
Tel.: (66) 1176
Web Site: https://dtc.co.th
Year Founded: 1996
DTCENT—(THA)
Rev.: $21,294,374
Assets: $50,961,882
Liabilities: $7,509,342
Net Worth: $43,452,539
Earnings: $2,914,234
Emp.: 400
Fiscal Year-end: 12/31/23
Software Development Services
N.A.I.C.S.: 541511
Apisit Rujikeatkamjorn *(Vice Chm)*

**D.T.C. INDUSTRIES PUBLIC
COMPANY LIMITED**
176 SOI Phongwetanuson Sukhumvit
64 Road, Phra Khanong, Bangkok,
10260, Thailand
Tel.: (66) 23111371
Web Site: http://www.lancerpen.com
Year Founded: 1963
DTCI—(THA)
Rev.: $4,276,332
Assets: $13,374,009
Liabilities: $1,724,662
Net Worth: $11,649,348
Earnings: $217,480
Fiscal Year-end: 12/31/23
Stationery Product Mfr & Whslr
N.A.I.C.S.: 339940
Sathit Uthaisri *(Chm & Pres)*

D2 LITHIUM CORP.
202 8661 201st Street, Langley, V2Y
0G9, BC, Canada
Tel.: (604) 681-6151   BC
Web Site: https://www.heliosx.ca
Year Founded: 2022
DTWO—(TSXV)
Assets: $3,766,964
Liabilities: $832,320
Net Worth: $2,934,644
Earnings: ($15,189,631)
Emp.: 70
Fiscal Year-end: 11/30/22
Mineral Mining Services
N.A.I.C.S.: 213115

D2L GROUP SA
Le favrot - 842 route de Neuville,
01390, Saint-Andre-de-Corcy, France
Tel.: (33) 481762500
Web Site: http://www.gelgroupe.com
MLGEL—(EUR)
Sales Range: $200-249.9 Million
Human Resource Management Services

N.A.I.C.S.: 541612
Guilhem Dufaure de Lajarte *(Chm &
CEO)*

D4T4 SOLUTIONS PLC
Elmbrook House 18-19 Station Road,
Sunbury-on-Thames, TW16 6SB,
United Kingdom
Tel.: (44) 1932893333
Web Site:
https://www.d4t4solutions.com
D4T4—(AIM)
Rev.: $33,208,473
Assets: $73,162,100
Liabilities: $29,871,198
Net Worth: $43,290,902
Earnings: $2,301,335
Emp.: 149
Fiscal Year-end: 03/31/22
Computer-Related Consulting, Development, Creative Design, Training &
Support Services; Software Products
Distr
N.A.I.C.S.: 541690
John Lythall *(Co-Founder)*

Subsidiaries:

D4t4 Solutions Inc.   **(1)**
215 E Chatham St Ste 115, Cary, NC
27511
Tel.: (984) 465-0550
Information Technology Services
N.A.I.C.S.: 541511

D8
90 Mitchell St, Glasgow, G1 3NQ,
United Kingdom
Tel.: (44) 1415720810
Web Site: http://www.weared8.com
Year Founded: 1999
Sales Range: $10-24.9 Million
Emp.: 40
N.A.I.C.S.: 541810
Adrian Carroll *(Dir-Creative)*

DA AN GENE CO., LTD.
No 19 Xiangshan Road, Huangpu
District, Guangzhou, 510665, Guangdong, China
Tel.: (86) 2032290789
Web Site: https://en.daangene.com
002030—(SSE)
Rev.: $1,691,278,056
Assets: $2,071,892,628
Liabilities: $441,018,864
Net Worth: $1,630,873,764
Earnings: $759,892,536
Emp.: 2,500
Fiscal Year-end: 12/31/22
Biological Products Mfr & Distr
N.A.I.C.S.: 325414
Yunshao He *(Chm & CEO)*

Subsidiaries:

Hangzhou AGS Med Tech Co.
Ltd.   **(1)**
Building 5 Building 6 No 597 Kangxin Road,
LinPing District, Hangzhou, 311106, Zhejiang, China
Tel.: (86) 57187671223
Web Site: https://www.bioags.com
Biological Product Mfr
N.A.I.C.S.: 325414
Gary Zhang *(CEO & Gen Mgr)*

Zhongshan Bio-Tech Co., Ltd.   **(1)**
NO 1 Shengwugu Avenue National Health
Base, Torch Development Area, Zhongshan,
528437, Guangdong, China
Tel.: (86) 76085310089
Web Site: https://www.en.bio-kit.com
Biological Product Mfr
N.A.I.C.S.: 325414

**DA CIN CONSTRUCTION CO.,
LTD.**
9F No 92 Sec 2 Dunhua S Rd, Da-an
District, Taipei, 106, Taiwan
Tel.: (886) 227062929

Web Site: https://www.dacin.com.tw
Year Founded: 1967
2535—(TAI)
Rev.: $474,394,959
Assets: $783,320,713
Liabilities: $480,907,075
Net Worth: $302,413,638
Earnings: $37,995,813
Emp.: 530
Fiscal Year-end: 12/31/23
Commercial Construction Services
N.A.I.C.S.: 236115
Eric Chen *(VP-Bus Dev Grp & Bus
Dev Div)*

DA GROUP
70 Mitchell St, Glasgow, G1 3LX,
United Kingdom
Tel.: (44) 1415820600
Web Site: http://www.digital-animations.com
Year Founded: 1990
Sales Range: $10-24.9 Million
Emp.: 40
Computer Software
N.A.I.C.S.: 541511
Angie Collins *(Office Mgr)*

DA HUI LIMITED
3rd Floor No 27 Alley 16 Lane 337
Section 1 Datong Road, Xizhi District,
New Taipei City, 22161, Taiwan
Tel.: (886) 226497298
Web Site: https://www.da-hui.com.tw
Year Founded: 1994
5276—(TPE)
Rev.: $24,645,656
Assets: $25,415,658
Liabilities: $9,024,544
Net Worth: $16,391,114
Earnings: $712,910
Emp.: 109
Fiscal Year-end: 12/31/21
Automobile Parts Mfr
N.A.I.C.S.: 336390
Hsu Hung-Chun *(Chm)*

**DA LUE INTERNATIONAL
HOLDING CO., LTD.**
No 225 Pioneer Building Hongj,
Shanghai, China
Tel.: (86) 2134318322
Web Site: http://www.dalue.com.tw
4804—(TPE)
Rev.: $50,534,327
Assets: $223,870,452
Liabilities: $145,814,553
Net Worth: $78,055,899
Earnings: ($4,786,893)
Fiscal Year-end: 12/31/20
Photographic Services
N.A.I.C.S.: 541921
Lin Shixiong *(Gen Mgr)*

**DA MING INTERNATIONAL
HOLDINGS LIMITED**
Suite 1007 Central Plaza 18 Harbour
Road, Wanchai, China (Hong Kong)
Tel.: (852) 25110744   Ky
Web Site: http://www.dmssc.net
1090—(HKG)
Rev.: $7,037,173,588
Assets: $1,794,034,991
Liabilities: $1,301,977,217
Net Worth: $492,057,774
Earnings: ($22,300,153)
Emp.: 7,060
Fiscal Year-end: 12/31/22
Stainless Steel Processor & Distr
N.A.I.C.S.: 331110
Keming Zhou *(Co-Founder & Chm)*

DA NANG PORT JSC
26 Bach Dang Thach Thang Ward,
Hai Chau District, Da Nang, Vietnam
Tel.: (84) 2363822163

Da Nang Port JSC—(Continued)

Web Site:
https://www.danangport.com
Year Founded: 1901
CDN—(HNX)
Rev.: $123,531,900
Assets: $220,227,900
Liabilities: $51,169,600
Net Worth: $169,058,300
Earnings: $27,532,400
Fiscal Year-end: 12/31/23
Port Transportation Services
N.A.I.C.S.: 488310
Tran Le Tuan *(Gen Dir)*

DA RETAILGROEP B.V.
Benj Fralklinstraat 2, Zwolle, 8000
AB, Netherlands
Tel.: (31) 384697200
Web Site: http://www.da.nl
Year Founded: 1991
Sales Range: $350-399.9 Million
Emp.: 400
Drugstore Supplier & Operator
N.A.I.C.S.: 456110
Henk Castelijns *(Mng Dir)*

DA SEN HOLDINGS GROUP LIMITED
Room Nos Unit 1604 16th Floor Emperor Group Centre, No 288 Hennessy Road, Wanchai, China (Hong Kong)
Tel.: (852) 26092338   Ky
Web Site: http://www.msdscn.com
1580—(HKG)
Year Founded: 2011
Rev.: $8,351,975
Assets: $20,790,151
Liabilities: $17,129,923
Net Worth: $3,660,228
Earnings: ($7,268,508)
Emp.: 32
Fiscal Year-end: 03/31/23
Wood Product Mfr & Distr
N.A.I.C.S.: 321999
Mingcai Ke *(Chm)*

DA TECHNOLOGY CO., LTD.
15 Ssanghak-gil, Bibong-myeon,
Hwaseong, 445-862, Gyeonggi-Do,
Korea (South)
Tel.: (82) 313698800
Web Site: https://www.dat21.co.kr
Year Founded: 2000
196490—(KRS)
Rev.: $40,808,843
Assets: $100,778,526
Liabilities: $39,959,959
Net Worth: $60,818,568
Earnings: ($19,138,539)
Emp.: 153
Fiscal Year-end: 12/31/22
Battery Equipment Mfr
N.A.I.C.S.: 333248
Jong-Wook Lee *(CEO)*

DA VINCI CAPITAL LLC
Capital City Northern Block 13th Floor Office 19, Presnenskaya Embankment 8, 123112, Moscow, Russia
Tel.: (7) 495 7756222
Web Site: http://dvcap.com
Year Founded: 2007
Private Investment Firm
N.A.I.C.S.: 523999
Oleg Jelezko *(Mng Partner)*

Subsidiaries:

ITI Capital Limited   **(1)**
Tel.: (44) 2075628001
Web Site: https://www.iticapital.com
Securities Brokerage Services
N.A.I.C.S.: 523150

DA YU FINANCIAL HOLDINGS LTD.
Room 1801 18th Floor Allied Kajima Building 138 Gloucester Road, Hong Kong, China (Hong Kong)
Tel.: (852) 28270183   Ky
1073—(HKG)
Holding Company
N.A.I.C.S.: 551112
Shaoning Wu *(Chm & CEO)*

Subsidiaries:

Morton Securities Ltd.   **(1)**
1804-05 18/F Union Kajima Building 138 Gloucester Road, Wanchai, China (Hong Kong)
Tel.: (852) 85226527100
Web Site: http://www.mortonsec.hk
Transportation Agency Services
N.A.I.C.S.: 541614

DA-LI DEVELOPMENT CO., LTD.
10F No 96 Sec 1 Jianguo N Rd,
Zongshan District, Taipei, 104, Taiwan
Tel.: (886) 225061966
Web Site: https://www.da-li.com.tw
6177—(TAI)
Rev.: $74,815,911
Assets: $1,132,191,855
Liabilities: $933,069,643
Net Worth: $199,122,212
Earnings: $5,317,573
Fiscal Year-end: 12/31/20
Residential Buildings & Home Construction Services
N.A.I.C.S.: 236116
Chih Chang Hsieh *(Chm)*

Subsidiaries:

Da Li Development LLC   **(1)**
450 S Main St Ste 168, Seattle, WA 98104
Tel.: (206) 618-9361
Web Site: https://da-li.us
Real Estate Development Services
N.A.I.C.S.: 531390

Da Li Development USA LLC   **(1)**
450 S Main St Ste 168, Seattle, WA 98104
Tel.: (206) 618-9361
Web Site: https://da-li.us
Residential Services
N.A.I.C.S.: 531110

DAAR COMMUNICATIONS PLC
1 Ladi Lawal Drive Off Gen T Y Danjuma, Abuja, Nigeria
Tel.: (234) 17730968
Web Site: https://daargroup.com
Year Founded: 1994
DAARCOMM—(NIGE)
Rev.: $3,543,519
Assets: $9,215,621
Liabilities: $7,577,337
Net Worth: $1,638,285
Earnings: ($568,521)
Emp.: 586
Fiscal Year-end: 12/31/22
Media Advertising Services
N.A.I.C.S.: 541840
Raymond Dokpesi Jr. *(Chm)*

DABACO GROUP JOINT STOCK COMPANY
35 Ly Thai To Street, Bac Ninh, Bac Ninh, Vietnam
Tel.: (84) 2413826077
Web Site: https://www.dabaco.com.vn
Rev.: $238,388,305
Assets: $279,568,638
Liabilities: $179,463,974
Net Worth: $100,104,664
Earnings: $8,004,209
Fiscal Year-end: 12/31/17
Animal Feed Mfr
N.A.I.C.S.: 311119

Subsidiaries:

DABACO Real Estate   **(1)**
Nguyen Cao street, Ninh Xa ward, Bac Ninh, Vietnam
Tel.: (84) 241 3875636
Real Estate Development Services
N.A.I.C.S.: 531390

DABACO Substructure Development & Building Investment Company Limited   **(1)**
Huyen Quang Str, Ninh Xa ward, Bac Ninh, Vietnam
Tel.: (84) 241 3813713
Web Site: http://www.dabaco.com.vn
Civil Engineering Services
N.A.I.C.S.: 541330

Dabaco High - Tech Agriculture Company Limited   **(1)**
Ho Ve Village Lac Ve Commune, Tien Du District, Bac Ninh, Vietnam
Tel.: (84) 241 3724138
Web Site: http://www.dabaco.com.vn
Animal Feed Mfr
N.A.I.C.S.: 311119
Viet Chuong Nguyen *(Dir)*

Hiep Quang Trading Co., Ltd   **(1)**
Khac Niem Industrial clusters, Bac Ninh, Vietnam
Tel.: (84) 241 3717256
Plastic Packaging Product Mfr & Distr
N.A.I.C.S.: 326199

Investment And Development Breed Processing Company Limited   **(1)**
Lac Ve Commune Industrial Clusters, Tien Du District, Bac Ninh, Vietnam
Tel.: (84) 241 3723523
Egg Production Services
N.A.I.C.S.: 112310

DABBAGH GROUP HOLDING COMPANY LTD.
PO Box 1039, Jeddah, 21431, Saudi Arabia
Tel.: (966) 26697220
Web Site: http://www.dabbagh.com
Year Founded: 1962
Diverse Holding Company
N.A.I.C.S.: 551112
M. H. Jazeel *(CEO & CFO)*

Subsidiaries:

Advance Petroleum Services Ltd.   **(1)**
Third Floor Adham Center Madinah Road, PO Box 2120, Jeddah, 21451, Saudi Arabia
Tel.: (966) 2 614 2424
Web Site: http://www.apsl-ksa.com
Petroleum & Lubricants Distr
N.A.I.C.S.: 424720

Agricultural Development Company Ltd.   **(1)**
PO Box 86909, Riyadh, 11632, Saudi Arabia
Tel.: (966) 14775192
Web Site: http://www.adc-ksa.com
Animal Feeds, Broiler Chicks, Hatching Eggs, Animal Health Products, Livestock Equipment & Technology Producer & Distr
N.A.I.C.S.: 112320

Al Jazira Oil & Gas Services Company EC   **(1)**
PO Box 1039, Jeddah, 21431, Saudi Arabia
Tel.: (966) 26697220
Web Site: http://www.al-jazira.com
Oil & Gas Investment Services
N.A.I.C.S.: 523999
M. H. Jazeel *(CFO)*

Consulting Engineering Bureau Abdullah Dabbagh Partners   **(1)**
PO Box 1039, Jeddah, 21431, Saudi Arabia
Tel.: (966) 26678662
Web Site: http://www.dabbaghceb.com
Sales Range: $25-49.9 Million
Emp.: 10
Engine Services
N.A.I.C.S.: 541330

DG International Oil Company Ltd.   **(1)**

PO Box 1039, Jeddah, 21431, Saudi Arabia
Tel.: (966) 26697220
Web Site: http://www.dgoil.com
Sales Range: $200-249.9 Million
Emp.: 500
Oil & Gas Investment Services
N.A.I.C.S.: 523999

DGH Investment Company Ltd.   **(1)**
PO Box 1039, Jeddah, 21431, Saudi Arabia
Tel.: (966) 26697220
Investment Services
N.A.I.C.S.: 523999

Gulf Co-Operation Insurance Company Ltd., EC   **(1)**
PO Box 5248, Jeddah, 21422, Saudi Arabia
Tel.: (966) 26515808
Sales Range: $125-149.9 Million
Emp.: 150
Insurance Services
N.A.I.C.S.: 524126

Gulf Power International Ltd.   **(1)**
PO Box 1039, Jeddah, 21432, Saudi Arabia
Tel.: (966) 2 6905883
Web Site: http://www.gpi.com.sa
Sales Range: $100-124.9 Million
Emp.: 500
Power Facilities Construction & Engineering
N.A.I.C.S.: 541330

International Project Developers Ltd.   **(1)**
PO Box 1039, Jeddah, 21431, Saudi Arabia
Tel.: (966) 26697220
Web Site: http://www.ipd-intl.com
Turnkey Project Development Services
N.A.I.C.S.: 237990

Marketing and Commercial Agencies Company Ltd.   **(1)**
PO Box 5248, Jeddah, 21422, Saudi Arabia
Tel.: (966) 26515808
Sales Range: $50-74.9 Million
Emp.: 100
Insurance Services
N.A.I.C.S.: 524210

National Scientific Company Ltd.   **(1)**
Al-Salam Building Tahlia Street, PO Box 1039, Jeddah, 21431, Saudi Arabia
Tel.: (966) 26644466
Web Site: http://www.nsc-ksa.com
Industrial Chemicals, Laboratory Equipment & Scientific Instruments Distr
N.A.I.C.S.: 424690

Petromin Corporation   **(1)**
PO Box 1432, Jeddah, 21431, Saudi Arabia
Tel.: (966) 12 215 7000
Web Site: http://www.petromin.com
Petroleum Product Mfr
N.A.I.C.S.: 324191
Kashif Zia *(Gen Mgr)*

Subsidiary (Non-US):

Petromin Egypt   **(2)**
44 Elnady St, PO Box 1120, Maadi, 11511, Cairo, Egypt
Tel.: (20) 2 2750 7703
Petroleum Product Mfr
N.A.I.C.S.: 324191
Saleem Waked *(Mgr-Fin & Mgr-Admin)*

Red Sea Housing Services Company (Papua New Guinea) Limited   **(1)**
PO Box 317, Konedobu, Papua New Guinea
Tel.: (675) 340 4585
Modular Building Mfr
N.A.I.C.S.: 321991

Red Sea International Company   **(1)**
Tel.: (966) 133613451
Web Site: http://www.redseaintl.com
Rev.: $111,870,151
Assets: $207,637,382
Liabilities: $182,660,979
Net Worth: $24,976,403
Earnings: ($52,731,369)
Emp.: 1,700
Fiscal Year-end: 12/31/2022
Modular Building Mfr
N.A.I.C.S.: 321991
Jamal Abdullah Al Dabbagh *(Deputy Chm)*

Subsidiary (Non-US):

Red Sea Housing Services Company   **(2)**

PO Box 8352, Wynnum North, Brisbane, 4178, QLD, Australia
Tel.: (61) 7 3137 6800
Web Site: http://www.redseahousing.com
Emp.: 2
Modular Building Mfr
N.A.I.C.S.: 321991
Brett Mcdonald (Pres)

Subsidiary (Non-US):

Red Sea Housing Services (Ghana) Limited (3)
Private Mail Bag, Tema, Ghana
Tel.: (233) 22 251 033
Modular Building Mfr
N.A.I.C.S.: 321991

Red Sea Housing Services (Mozambique), LDA (3)
Rua 1301 n 97 Largo Do Comite, Central Sommerschield, Maputo, Mozambique
Tel.: (258) 21 493465
Modular Building Mfr
N.A.I.C.S.: 321991

Red Sea Housing Services LLC (3)
PC 131 Al Wattayah, PO Box 971, Muscat, Oman
Tel.: (968) 2466 7648
Modular Building Mfr
N.A.I.C.S.: 321991

Subsidiary (Domestic):

Red Sea Housing Services Pty Ltd (3)
PO Box 8352, Wynnum North, Brisbane, 4178, QLD, Australia
Tel.: (61) 7 3137 6800
Modular Building Mfr
N.A.I.C.S.: 321991

Subsidiary (Non-US):

SARL Red Sea Housing Services Algeria Limited (3)
Route d'El Borma, Hassi Messaoud, Ouargla, Algeria
Tel.: (213) 2975 0822
Modular Building Mfr
N.A.I.C.S.: 321991

Saudi Egyptian Logistics and Electronics Company, S.A.E. (1)
8278th Street, Maadi, Cairo, Egypt
Tel.: (20) 225229222
Web Site: http://www.salec.com
Data Network & Telecommunication Infrastructure Designer & Mfr
N.A.I.C.S.: 541519

Supreme Foods Processing Company Ltd. (1)
PO Box 86909, Riyadh, 11632, Saudi Arabia
Tel.: (966) 14775192
Web Site: http://www.sfgarabia.net
Food Processor
N.A.I.C.S.: 311991

Tanmiah Commercial Group Ltd. (1)
PO Box 1039, Jeddah, 21431, Saudi Arabia
Tel.: (966) 26697220
Web Site: http://www.tanmiah.com
Sales Range: $50-74.9 Million
Emp.: 100
Investment Services
N.A.I.C.S.: 523999

Tanmiah Food Group (1)
PO Box 86909, Riyadh, 11632, Saudi Arabia
Tel.: (966) 11 477 5192
Web Site: http://www.sfgarabia.net
Emp.: 1,800
Food Product Mfr & Distr
N.A.I.C.S.: 311991

DABOMB PROTEIN CORP.
No 52 Gungye 3rd Rd, Annan Dist, Tainan City, 709, Taiwan
Tel.: (886) 63840771
Web Site:
   https://www.dabombprotein.com
Year Founded: 2001
6578—(TPE)
Rev.: $13,558,140

Assets: $40,023,950
Liabilities: $17,286,777
Net Worth: $22,737,173
Earnings: ($1,396,492)
Fiscal Year-end: 12/31/22
Food Mfr
N.A.I.C.S.: 311999
Yu-Fen Liu (Chm & Pres)

Subsidiaries:

Fujian DaBomb Protein Biotech Corp. (1)
Gang Yuan Industrial Park Zhangtai, Chenxiang Township, Zhengzhou, Fujian, China
Tel.: (86) 5968331768
Soybean Protein Powder Mfr
N.A.I.C.S.: 311224

DABUR INDIA LTD
8/3 Asaf Ali Road, New Delhi, 110002, India
Tel.: (91) 1203962100
Web Site: https://www.dabur.com
Year Founded: 1884
DABUR—(NSE)
Rev.: $1,349,567,310
Assets: $1,480,633,245
Liabilities: $429,553,215
Net Worth: $1,051,080,030
Earnings: $231,360,675
Emp.: 5,070
Fiscal Year-end: 03/31/21
Health, Personal Care & Food Products Mfr
N.A.I.C.S.: 325620
P. D. Narang (Dir-Corp Affairs)

Subsidiaries:

African Consumer Care Ltd. (1)
18 Burma Road Apapa, Lagos, Nigeria
Tel.: (234) 17902781
Food Products Mfr
N.A.I.C.S.: 311999

Asian Consumer Care Private Limited (1)
245 Tejgaon, Industrial Area, Dhaka, 1208, Bangladesh (76%)
Tel.: (880) 29885694
Ayurvedic Product Distr
N.A.I.C.S.: 456199

Dabur (UK) Limited (1)
2 Gayton Road, Harrow, HA1 2XU, United Kingdom
Tel.: (44) 2089017620
Ayurvedic Product Distr
N.A.I.C.S.: 456199

Dabur Egypt Ltd (1)
2 Saudi Co Bldgs El Nozha St, Heliopolis, Cairo, Egypt
Tel.: (20) 2 22900264
Cosmetics Mfr
N.A.I.C.S.: 325620

Dabur India Ltd - Baddi - Oral Care Unit (1)
601 Malkhumajra Nalagarh Road, Baddi, Himachal Pradesh, India
Tel.: (91) 1795 246363
Web Site: http://www.dabur.com
Oral Care Product Mfr
N.A.I.C.S.: 325412

Dabur India Ltd - Jammu Unit I , II & III (1)
Lane No 3 Phase II Sidco Industrial Complex, Bari Brahmana, Jammu and Kashmir, India
Tel.: (91) 1923 220123
Personal Care Product Mfr
N.A.I.C.S.: 325620

Dabur India Ltd - Nashik Unit (1)
D-55 M I D C, Ambad, Nashik, 422 010, India
Tel.: (91) 253 662 3222
Web Site: http://www.dabur.com
Pharmaceuticals Product Mfr
N.A.I.C.S.: 325412

Dabur International Ltd. (1)

PO Box 16944, Jebel Ali, Dubai, United Arab Emirates
Tel.: (971) 4 8817756
Web Site: http://www.dabur.com
Sales Range: $25-49.9 Million
Emp.: 150
Food Products Mfr
N.A.I.C.S.: 311999
Krishan Kumar Chutani (CEO)

Subsidiary (Non-US):

Dabur International Limited (2)
1 Olympic Way, Wembley, HA9 0NP, United Kingdom
Tel.: (44) 208 795 5774
Web Site: http://www.daburinternational.com
Personal Care Product Mfr
N.A.I.C.S.: 325620
Rahul Chaudhary (Head-Bus-Europe)

Dabur Nepal Pvt. Ltd. (2)
TNT Building Tinkune Koteshwor, Kathmandu, 14375, Nepal
Tel.: (977) 12054533
Personal Care Product Mfr
N.A.I.C.S.: 325620
Rukma Rana (Mng Dir)

Hobi Kozmetik Imalat Sanayi Ve (2)
Cevizli Mahallesi Tugayyolu Caddesi No 20/A Ofisim istanbul Plazalari, A Blok Kat 11 No 49-50-51 Maltepe, Istanbul, 34846, Turkiye
Tel.: (90) 2166300030
Web Site: http://www.hobikozmetik.com
Cosmetic Product Distr
N.A.I.C.S.: 424210

H&B Stores Ltd. (1)
Hindi Bhavan 11-Rouse Avenue ITO, Near Bal Bhavan, New Delhi, 110002, India
Tel.: (91) 11 42786084
Health Care & Cosmetic Products Distr
N.A.I.C.S.: 424210

DACARTO BENVIC S.A.
Estrada De Alpina 59 Sitio Cachoeira, 06278, Sao Paulo, Brazil
Tel.: (55) 1136589400   BR
Web Site:
   http://www.dacartobenvic.com.br
Year Founded: 1968
Polyvinyl Chloride Products Developer, Mfr & Whslr
N.A.I.C.S.: 326199
Jose Antonio Almeida (Mgr-HR)

DACHAN FOOD (ASIA) LIMITED
Suite 1806 Tower 1 The Gateway 25 Canton Road Tsimshatsui, Kowloon, China (Hong Kong)
Tel.: (852) 27375300
Web Site:
   http://www.dachanfoodasia.com
3999—(HKG)
Rev.: $869,802,570
Assets: $501,407,291
Liabilities: $175,243,068
Net Worth: $326,164,223
Earnings: $17,196,192
Emp.: 7,936
Fiscal Year-end: 12/31/22
Food Industry
N.A.I.C.S.: 311615
Chia-Yin Han (Exec Dir)

DACHAN GREAT WALL GROUP
No 3 Niaosong 2nd St, Yongkang Dist, T'ainan, 71042, Taiwan
Tel.: (886) 62531111
Web Site: https://www.dachan.com
Rev.: $2,365,986,192
Assets: $1,388,908,337
Liabilities: $663,117,144
Net Worth: $725,791,194
Earnings: $78,828,372
Emp.: 30,000
Fiscal Year-end: 12/31/18
Animal Food Mfr & Distr
N.A.I.C.S.: 311119

DACHSER GMBH & CO.
Thomas Dachser Str 2, 87439, Kempten, Germany
Tel.: (49) 83159160
Web Site: http://www.dachser.com
Year Founded: 1930
Sales Range: $1-4.9 Billion
Emp.: 12,000
International Freight Forwarding
N.A.I.C.S.: 488510
Michael Schilling (COO-Road Logistics)

Subsidiaries:

DACHSER (Bangladesh) Ltd. (1)
House 28 Road 28 Block-E Niketan, Gulshan, 1212, Dhaka, Bangladesh
Tel.: (880) 2 8833251 59
Logistics Consulting Servies
N.A.I.C.S.: 541614
Ferdausur Rhaman (Asst Mgr)

DACHSER (Thailand) Co., Ltd. (1)
89/2 Amornpan Tower 1 Building 6th Floor Ratchada Soi 7 Ratchada Road, 10400, Bangkok, Thailand
Tel.: (66) 2 692 2481
Logistics Consulting Servies
N.A.I.C.S.: 541614

DACHSER Belgium Air & Sea Logistics NV (1)
Wayenborgstraat 21, 2800, Mechelen, Belgium
Tel.: (32) 15 2151 60
Logistics Consulting Servies
N.A.I.C.S.: 541614
Linda Thijs (Branch Mgr)

DACHSER Belgium N.V. (1)
Avenue de I Eau Vive 1, 7700, Mouscron, Belgium
Tel.: (32) 56 39 25 11
Web Site: http://www.dachser.be
Emp.: 180
Logistics Consulting Servies
N.A.I.C.S.: 541614

DACHSER Brasil Logistica Ltda. (1)
Avenida Jose de Souza Campos n 894 2 andar-salas 22 23 24 e 25, Campinas, 13.092-123, Sao Paulo, Brazil
Tel.: (55) 19 3312 6200
Web Site: http://www.dachser.com.br
Logistics Consulting Servies
N.A.I.C.S.: 541614
Patricia Kirschnik (Mgr-Sls)

DACHSER Chile S.A. (1)
Edificio Aube Oficina 902 Av Camino el Alba 8760, Las Condes, Chile
Tel.: (56) 2 2206 0310
Web Site: http://www.dachser.cl
Emp.: 20
Logistics Consulting Servies
N.A.I.C.S.: 541614
Carola Sandoal (Mgr-Customer Svcs & Ops)

DACHSER Czech Republic a.s. (1)
Hutska 272, 272 01, Kladno, Czech Republic
Tel.: (420) 312 291 811
Web Site: http://www.dachser.cz
Logistics Consulting Servies
N.A.I.C.S.: 541614

DACHSER Denmark A/S (1)
Helsholmen 11, 2650, Hvidovre, Denmark
Tel.: (45) 36 34 77 77
Web Site: http://www.dachser.dk
Emp.: 100
Logistics Consulting Servies
N.A.I.C.S.: 541614
Finn Peterson (Gen Mgr)

DACHSER Far East Ltd (1)
18/F 625 King s Road, North Point, China (Hong Kong)
Tel.: (852) 2796 2111
Web Site: http://www.dachser.com.hk
Logistics Consulting Servies
N.A.I.C.S.: 541614
Nadia Chouf-Feng (Mgr-Route-Europe & Africa)

DACHSER France S.A.S. (1)
1 Avenue de I Europe, BP 80007, 85130,

Dachser GmbH & Co.—(Continued)

La Verriere, France
Tel.: (33) 2 51 66 54 10
Web Site: http://www.dachser.fr
Logistics Consulting Servies
N.A.I.C.S.: 541614
Renaud Harrison (Mgr-Ops)

DACHSER Hong Kong Ltd. (1)
Unit 3 1st Floor Global Gateway 168 Yeung
Uk Road, Tsuen Wan, New Territories,
China (Hong Kong)
Tel.: (852) 2 7515728
Logistics Consulting Servies
N.A.I.C.S.: 541614
David Boehme (Gen Mgr)

DACHSER India Private Limited (1)
Rajaskaran Tech Park 2nd Floor Tower 1
Phase II Andheri-Kurla Road, Nr Sakinaka
Metro Station Andheri E, Mumbai, 400 072,
Maharashtra, India
Tel.: (91) 22 4232 8200
Web Site: http://www.dachser.in
Logistics Consulting Servies
N.A.I.C.S.: 541614
Ashish Vakil (Mgr-Bus Dev)

DACHSER Ltd. (1)
Thomas Dachser Way Brackmills,
Northampton, NN4 7HT, United Kingdom
Tel.: (44) 1604 433100
Web Site: http://www.dachser.co.uk
Emp.: 150
Logistics Consulting Servies
N.A.I.C.S.: 541614
Mark Rollinson (Mng Dir)

DACHSER Malaysia Sdn. Bhd. (1)
Suite 801-3 Level 8 Tower 1 Wisma Am-
FirstJalan SS7/15 Jalan Stadium Ke,
47301, Petaling Jaya, Selangor Darul Eh-
san, Malaysia
Tel.: (60) 3 7803 0102
Web Site: http://www.dachser.my
Emp.: 25
Logistics Consulting Servies
N.A.I.C.S.: 541614
Thomas Murugan Andrew (Mgr-Sls)

DACHSER Netherlands B.V. (1)
Handelsweg 2, 2742 RD, Waddinxveen,
Netherlands
Tel.: (31) 180 635311
Web Site: http://www.dachser.nl
Logistics Consulting Servies
N.A.I.C.S.: 541614
Tim Regelink (Mgr-Facility)

DACHSER Norway AS (1)
Nesoddveien 22, 1407, Vinterbro, Norway
Tel.: (47) 23 29 95 00
Web Site: http://www.dachser.com
Logistics Consulting Servies
N.A.I.C.S.: 541614
Benjamin Fjellheim (Mgr-Sls)

DACHSER OOO (1)
3rd Rybinskaya Str 18, Moscow, 107113,
Russia
Tel.: (7) 495 2870107
Web Site: http://www.dachser.com
Emp.: 45
Logistics Consulting Servies
N.A.I.C.S.: 541614
Pavel Voronov (Dir-Ops)

DACHSER Romania SRL (1)
Bd Iuliu Maniu 600A Sector 6, Bucharest,
061129, Romania
Tel.: (40) 21 300 35 36
Web Site: http://www.dachser.ro
Logistics Consulting Servies
N.A.I.C.S.: 541614
Vlad Tudor (Mgr-Controlling)

DACHSER S.a.r.l. (1)
10 Rue Op der Ahlkerrech, 6776, Greven-
macher, Luxembourg
Tel.: (352) 270771 0
Web Site: http://www.dachser.lu
Logistics Consulting Servies
N.A.I.C.S.: 541614

DACHSER Shenzhen Co. Ltd. (1)
No 18 Zimao West St Qianhai, Shenzhen,
518026, China
Tel.: (86) 75582934748
Web Site: http://www.dachser.cn
Logistics Consulting Servies

DACHSER Spedition AG (1)
Althardstr 355, 8105, Regensdorf, Switzer-
land
Tel.: (41) 44 8721 100
Web Site: http://www.dachser.ch
Logistics Consulting Servies
N.A.I.C.S.: 541614

DACHSER Sweden AB (1)
Arendals Alle 5, 418 79, Gothenburg, Swe-
den
Tel.: (46) 31 70934 00
Web Site: http://www.dachser.se
Emp.: 30
Logistics Consulting Servies
N.A.I.C.S.: 541614

DACHSER Taiwan, Inc. (1)
10F No 35 Sec 3 Min Quan E Road, Taipei,
10476, Taiwan
Tel.: (886) 2 2517 1588
Web Site: http://www.dachser.com.tw
Logistics Consulting Servies
N.A.I.C.S.: 541614
Helena Gmail (Gen Mgr)

DACHSER Tanger SARL (1)
Agence Tanger/Tangier Km 7 Route de Tet-
ouan, Tangiers, 90001, Morocco
Tel.: (212) 539 359600
Web Site: http://www.dachser.ma
Logistics Consulting Servies
N.A.I.C.S.: 541614

**DACHSER de Mexico S.A. de
C.V.** (1)
Calle Leibnitz 11-103 Col Anzures Del
Miguel Hidalgo, 11590, Mexico, Mexico
Tel.: (52) 55 11661500
Web Site: http://www.dachser.com
Logistics Consulting Servies
N.A.I.C.S.: 541614

DACHSER s.r.o. (1)
Jana Opletala 3506, 69002, Breclav, Czech
Republic
Tel.: (420) 519 827 224
Web Site: http://www.dachser.cz
Logistics Consulting Servies
N.A.I.C.S.: 541614
Jan Lacina (Mgr-Key Acct)

Dachser Singapore Pte Ltd. (1)
21 Bukit Batok Crescent 25-77/78/79
WCEGA Tower, 658065, Singapore, Singa-
pore
Tel.: (65) 6659 3648
Web Site: http://www.dachser.com.sg
N.A.I.C.S.: 541614
Matthew Ong (Mng Dir)

Dachser South Africa (Pty.) Ltd. (1)
9 Sim Road - Pomona - Kempton Park, Jo-
hannesburg, 1620, South Africa (100%)
Tel.: (27) 11 396 1113
Web Site: http://www.dachser.co.za
Logistics Consulting Servies
N.A.I.C.S.: 541614
Detlev Duve (Mng Dir)

**Dachser Transport of America
Inc.** (1)
20 W Lincoln Ave, Valley Stream, NY
11580-5730 (100%)
Tel.: (516) 561-7800
Web Site: http://www.dachser.us
Sales Range: $25-49.9 Million
Emp.: 25
Freight Forwarding
N.A.I.C.S.: 488510
Frank Guenzerodt (Pres & CEO)

Dachser Vietnam Co., Ltd. (1)
9th Floor Dinh Le Building 01 Dinh Le
Street Ward 12 Dist 4, Ho Chi Minh City,
Vietnam
Tel.: (84) 838255666
Web Site: http://www.dachser.vn
Logistics Consulting Servies
N.A.I.C.S.: 541614
Michael Deisemann (Mng Dir)

Frigoscandia AB (1)
Landskronavagen 11, 252 32, Helsingborg,
Sweden
Tel.: (46) 42178140
Web Site: https://frigoscandia.com
Food & Home Goods Delivery Services

N.A.I.C.S.: 722513
Peter Haveneth (CEO)

**LIEGL & DACHSER Szallitmanyo-
szasi es Logisztikai Kft.** (1)
Ipartelep u 1, Pilisvorosvar, 2085, Hungary
Tel.: (36) 26 532 000
Web Site: http://www.dachser.hu
Logistics Consulting Servies
N.A.I.C.S.: 541614

MGI & DACHSER, Inc. (1)
3F 22 World Cup buk-ro, Mapo-gu, 121-
819, Seoul, Korea (South)
Tel.: (82) 2 3140 7300
Web Site: http://www.dachser.kr
Logistics Consulting Servies
N.A.I.C.S.: 541614

DACOME INTERNATIONAL
LTD.
2F 29 Hai Bian Road, Kaohsiung,
Taiwan
Tel.: (886) 75369536
9960—(TPE)
Rev.: $29,670,481
Assets: $40,297,846
Liabilities: $21,445,737
Net Worth: $18,852,109
Earnings: $3,804,896
Fiscal Year-end: 12/31/22
Golf Product Distr
N.A.I.C.S.: 459110
Johnny Wu (Chm)

DACRO INDUSTRIES INC.
9325 51 Avenue NW, Edmonton, T6E
4W8, AB, Canada
Tel.: (780) 434-8900
Web Site: https://www.dacro.com
Year Founded: 1974
Fabricated Metal Equipment Mfr
N.A.I.C.S.: 332311

DAD CO., LTD.
13 Doyama Maigi-cho, Okazaki, 444-
3511, Aichi, Japan
Tel.: (81) 564483073
Web Site: http://www.dad.co.jp
Year Founded: 1971
Emp.: 557
Automobile Parts Mfr
N.A.I.C.S.: 336390
Chikuo Kubota (Pres & CEO)

DADA NEXUS LIMITED
22/F Oriental Fisherman's Wharf No
1088 Yangshupu Road, Yangpu Dis-
trict, Shanghai, 200082, China
Tel.: (86) 2131657167   Ky
Web Site: https://ir.imdada.cn
Year Founded: 2014
DADA—(NASDAQ)
Rev.: $1,315,210,338
Assets: $1,270,030,180
Liabilities: $287,269,492
Net Worth: $982,760,688
Earnings: ($281,923,902)
Emp.: 2,631
Fiscal Year-end: 12/31/22
Holding Company
N.A.I.C.S.: 551112
Beck Zhaoming Chen (CFO)

DADABHAI GROUP
Building 600 Road 2808 Seif District,
PO Box 20143, Manama, Bahrain
Tel.: (973) 17587575
Web Site: http://www.dadabhai.com
Sales Range: $125-149.9 Million
Emp.: 500
Construction Services, Travel Ser-
vices & Neon Sign Mfr & Sales
N.A.I.C.S.: 236220
Mohammed Dadabhai (Founder &
Chm)

Subsidiaries:

Arabian Neon W.L.L. (1)

PO Box 11587, Manama, Bahrain
Tel.: (973) 1746 9999
Neon Signs & Billboards Design & Manu-
facture
N.A.I.C.S.: 339950

**DADABHAI CONSTRUCTION
W.L.L.** (1)
Building No 192 Road 907 Block 309, PO
Box 20531, Manama, Bahrain
Tel.: (973) 17 255 209
Web Site:
http://www.dadabhaiconstruction.com
Construction Engineering Services
N.A.I.C.S.: 541330
Unni Krishnan (Mgr-Pur)

Dadabhai Travel LLC (1)
SR1&2 Ground Floor Gulf Towers next to
Canadian Hospital Oud, Metha Road,
Dubai, United Arab Emirates
Tel.: (971) 4 3885566
Web Site: http://www.dadabhaitravel.ae
Emp.: 220
Travel Tour Operator
N.A.I.C.S.: 561520
Farzana Sameer (Sr Mgr-HR & Bus Dev)

DADAM INVESTMENT CORP.
3rd floor Hakdong-ro 523, Gangnam-
gu, 0607, Seoul, Korea (South)
Tel.: (82) 025634050
Web Site: http://ddinvest.co.kr
Venture Investment Company
N.A.I.C.S.: 523999

DADCO ALUMINA & CHEMI-
CALS LTD.
Hamilton House St Julians Avenue,
Saint Peter Port, Guernsey
Tel.: (44) 1481740605
Web Site:
http://www.dadcoalumina.com
Year Founded: 1915
Private Equity Firm & Trading Ser-
vices
N.A.I.C.S.: 523999
Victor Phillip Michael Dahdaleh
(Owner & Chm)

Subsidiaries:

Aluminium Oxid Stade GmbH (1)
JohannRathjeKoser-Strasse, 21683, Stade,
Germany (100%)
Tel.: (49) 4146921
Web Site: http://www.aos-stade.de
Sales Range: $200-249.9 Million
Emp.: 530
Alumina Refinery Mfr
N.A.I.C.S.: 331313
Victor Phillip M. Dahdaleh (Chm-
Supervisory Bd)

Dadco (Suisse) S.A. (1)
Avenue d'Ouchy 61, 1006, Lausanne, Swit-
zerland
Tel.: (41) 21 613 13 70
Chemical Products Distr
N.A.I.C.S.: 424690

DADEX ETERNIT LIMITED
34-A/1 Block-6 PECHS Shahrah-e-
Faisal, Karachi, 75400, Pakistan
Tel.: (92) 2134313860   PK
Web Site: https://www.dadex.com
DADX—(KAR)
Rev.: $23,976,878
Assets: $24,241,504
Liabilities: $16,294,026
Net Worth: $7,947,477
Earnings: ($1,403,891)
Emp.: 404
Fiscal Year-end: 06/30/19
Fibre Cement Sheets, Malidar
Beams, Fibre Cement, PVC Pressure
Pipes, Building Pipes & Other Re-
lated Products Mfr & Distr
N.A.I.C.S.: 327310
Sikander Dada (Chm)

DADI EARLY-CHILDHOOD
EDUCATION GROUP LTD.

Rm 217 11F No 51 Hengyang Rd,
Zhongzheng Dist, Taipei, 100504,
Taiwan
Tel.: (886) 223826998
8437—(TPE)
Rev.: $17,391,364
Assets: $107,833,849
Liabilities: $25,903,761
Net Worth: $81,930,088
Earnings: $5,779,133
Fiscal Year-end: 12/31/22
Management Consulting Services
N.A.I.C.S.: 541618
Cheng Dar-Kuen *(Chm & CEO)*

DADI EDUCATION HOLDINGS LIMITED

Units Nos 702 and 703 7th Floor 700
Nathan Road, Mong kok, Kowloon,
China (Hong Kong)
Tel.: (852) 2 314 8312   Ky
Web Site: http://www.dadi.com.hk
Year Founded: 1990
8417—(HKG)
Rev.: $3,087,265
Assets: $10,910,547
Liabilities: $865,198
Net Worth: $10,045,349
Earnings: $904,795
Fiscal Year-end: 03/31/21
Educational Consulting Services
N.A.I.C.S.: 611710
Patrick Mok *(CEO & Compliance Officer)*

DADI INTERNATIONAL GROUP LIMITED

Unit 1504-1506 15th Floor Office
Tower Convention Plaza 1 Harbour
Road, 141 Des Voeux Road Central,
Wanchai, China (Hong Kong)
Tel.: (852) 2 718 8128   BM
Web Site: http://www.dadi-
international.com.hk
8130—(HKG)
Rev.: $79,444,070
Assets: $172,951,604
Liabilities: $125,166,061
Net Worth: $47,785,542
Earnings: ($25,296,589)
Emp.: 80
Fiscal Year-end: 03/31/21
Marketing & Advertising Services
N.A.I.C.S.: 541613
Xiaoming Wu *(Vice Chm & CEO)*

DAE HWA PHARM CO., LTD.

2145 Nambusunhwan-ro, Seocho-gu,
Seoul, Korea (South)
Tel.: (82) 267161071
Web Site: https://www.dhpharm.co.kr
Year Founded: 1984
067080—(KRS)
Rev.: $100,598,193
Assets: $161,043,043
Liabilities: $81,782,789
Net Worth: $79,260,254
Earnings: ($2,284,512)
Emp.: 368
Fiscal Year-end: 12/31/20
Pharmaceuticals Product Mfr
N.A.I.C.S.: 325412
Eun-Seok Kim *(CEO)*

DAE HWA PHARMACEUTICAL CO., LTD.

2145 Nambusunhwan-ro, Seocho-gu,
Seoul, Korea (South)
Tel.: (82) 267161071
Web Site: http://www.dhpharm.co.kr
Year Founded: 1989
067080—(KRS)
Rev.: $101,176,268
Assets: $152,676,315
Liabilities: $90,019,100
Net Worth: $62,657,215

Earnings: $936,628
Emp.: 412
Fiscal Year-end: 12/31/22
Pharmaceuticals Mfr
N.A.I.C.S.: 325412
Byung-Tae No *(Co-CEO)*

DAE HYUN CO., LTD.

619 Eonju-ro, Gangnam-gu, Seoul,
137-860, Korea (South)
Tel.: (82) 234857000
Web Site: http://www.daehyun.co.kr
Year Founded: 1982
016090—(KRS)
Rev.: $244,907,149
Assets: $228,297,412
Liabilities: $42,184,035
Net Worth: $186,113,377
Earnings: $19,505,680
Emp.: 460
Fiscal Year-end: 12/31/22
Apparel Product Mfr & Distr
N.A.I.C.S.: 315990
Hyun-Kyun Shin *(Chm & CEO)*

DAE SUNG MICROBIOLOGI-CAL LABS. CO., LTD.

103 Deogyeong-Daero, Uiwang,
Gyeonggi-Do, Korea (South)
Tel.: (82) 314617103
Web Site: https://www.dsmbio.com
Year Founded: 1968
036480—(KRS)
Rev.: $19,558,550
Assets: $49,938,837
Liabilities: $20,150,544
Net Worth: $29,788,294
Earnings: $1,306,347
Fiscal Year-end: 12/31/22
Pharmaceutical Preparation Mfr
N.A.I.C.S.: 325412
Hang Won Cho *(CEO)*

DAE WOONG CO., LTD.

12 Bongeunsa-ro 114-gil,
Gangnam-gu Samseong-dong, Seoul,
Korea (South)
Tel.: (82) 25508800
Web Site:
   https://www.daewoongholdings.com
Year Founded: 1945
003090—(KRS)
Rev.: $1,301,858,616
Assets: $1,655,880,217
Liabilities: $674,506,937
Net Worth: $981,373,280
Earnings: $92,245,590
Emp.: 325
Fiscal Year-end: 12/31/22
Holding Company
N.A.I.C.S.: 551112
Seo Tae Won *(Mgr)*

DAE YOUNG PACKAGING CO., LTD.

837-4 5 Nae-ri Guji-myeon,
Dalseong-gun, Daegu, Korea (South)
Tel.: (82) 314909300
Web Site: http://www.dypc.co.kr
Year Founded: 1979
014160—(KRS)
Rev.: $232,058,954
Assets: $189,722,729
Liabilities: $61,621,248
Net Worth: $128,101,481
Earnings: $9,857,899
Emp.: 340
Fiscal Year-end: 12/31/22
Corrugated & Solid Fiber Box Mfr
N.A.I.C.S.: 322211

DAE YU CO., LTD.

Daeyu Building 26 Hakdong-ro 77-gil,
Gangnam-gu, Seoul, 135-950, Korea
(South)
Tel.: (82) 25566293

Web Site: https://www.dae-yu.co.kr
Year Founded: 1977
290380—(KRS)
Rev.: $27,116,565
Assets: $109,195,486
Liabilities: $27,490,000
Net Worth: $81,705,486
Earnings: ($13,505,540)
Emp.: 157
Fiscal Year-end: 12/31/22
Crop Farming Services
N.A.I.C.S.: 111998

DAE-IL CORPORATION

680 Bonggea-ri, Dudong-Myeon Ulju-
Gun, Ulsan, Korea (South)
Tel.: (82) 522550500
Web Site: https://www.dicorp.co.kr
Year Founded: 1976
092200—(KRS)
Rev.: $533,747,800
Assets: $497,195,151
Liabilities: $387,090,405
Net Worth: $110,104,746
Earnings: $3,632,841
Emp.: 700
Fiscal Year-end: 12/31/22
Automobile Parts Mfr
N.A.I.C.S.: 336350
Sung-Moon Kim *(Chm & CEO)*

Subsidiaries:

Dae-Il Corporation-Dudong 2
Plant   (1)
680 Bongged-ri Dudong-myeon, Ulju-gun,
Ulsan, Korea (South)
Tel.: (82) 5225505005
Transmission Gear & Component Mfr
N.A.I.C.S.: 336350

Dae-Il Corporation-Heavy Machinery
Plant   (1)
302 Jeoneub-ri Duseo-myeon, Ulju-gun,
Ulsan, Korea (South)
Tel.: (82) 5226263325
Transmission Gear & Component Mfr
N.A.I.C.S.: 336350

Dae-Il Corporation-Unyang Plant   (1)
216 Yangdeung-ri Sangbug-myeon, Ulju-
gun, Ulsan, Korea (South)
Tel.: (82) 522550700
Transmission Gear & Component Mfr
N.A.I.C.S.: 336350

Dae-Il USA, Inc.   (1)
18225 Serene Dr Ste 150, Morgan Hill, CA
95037
Tel.: (408) 825-5000
Transmission Gear & Component Mfr
N.A.I.C.S.: 336350
Jolene Ramirez *(Mgr-Fin)*

Daeho Machinery Ind. Co., Ltd.   (1)
825 Palbong-dong, Iksan, Chollabuk-do,
Korea (South)
Tel.: (82) 638303200
Transmission Gear & Component Mfr
N.A.I.C.S.: 336350

Daeil Automotive Parts Co., Ltd.   (1)
Korea Industrial Park, Fenghuang Town,
Zhangjiagang, Jiangsu, China
Tel.: (86) 51282597700
Transmission Gear & Component Mfr
N.A.I.C.S.: 336350

Daeil Innotech Corporation   (1)
San 122-5 745-22 Sinjang-ri Eumam-
Myeon, Seosan, Chungchongnam-do, Ko-
rea (South)
Tel.: (82) 416610500
Transmission Gear & Component Mfr
N.A.I.C.S.: 336350

Jungwon Machinery Ind. Co.,
Ltd.   (1)
154-7 Sangpyung-dong, Jinju,
Gyeongsangnam-do, Korea (South)
Tel.: (82) 557528480
Transmission Gear & Component Mfr
N.A.I.C.S.: 336350

DAE-JIN SEMICONDUCTOR CO., LTD.

1209 SJ-Technoville 278 Beotkkot-ro,
Geumcheon-gu, Seoul, 08511, Korea
(South)
Tel.: (82) 233973610   KR
Web Site: http://www.semidj.com
Year Founded: 1993
Semiconductor Product Distr
N.A.I.C.S.: 423690
Park Sung-Seo *(CEO)*

DAEATI CO., LTD.

Daea Building 139 Sudo-ro, Ojeong-
Gu, Bucheon, 14490, Gyeonggi-Do,
Korea (South)
Tel.: (82) 326800800
Web Site: https://www.daeati.co.kr
Year Founded: 1996
045390—(KRS)
Rev.: $80,955,099
Assets: $153,107,636
Liabilities: $68,797,932
Net Worth: $84,309,704
Earnings: $6,454,490
Emp.: 304
Fiscal Year-end: 12/31/22
Communication Equipment Mfr
N.A.I.C.S.: 334290
Jin-Woo Choi *(Pres & CEO)*

DAEBO MAGNETIC CO., LTD.

25-13 Hyundaekia-Ro, Paltan-Myeon,
Hwaseong, 18576, Gyeonggi-Do, Ko-
rea (South)
Tel.: (82) 313543960
Web Site: http://www.daebo.com
Year Founded: 1994
290670—(KRS)
Rev.: $83,265,595
Assets: $77,431,080
Liabilities: $16,340,653
Net Worth: $61,090,427
Earnings: $16,787,485
Emp.: 111
Fiscal Year-end: 12/31/22
Industrial Machinery Maintenance
Services
N.A.I.C.S.: 811310
Jun-Gak Lee *(Board of Directors & CEO)*

DAEBONG LS CO., LTD.

123 Neungheodae-ro 649 beon-gil,
Namdong-ku, Incheon, 21697, Korea
(South)
Tel.: (82) 327128800
Web Site:
   https://www.daebongls.co.kr
Year Founded: 1986
078140—(KRS)
Rev.: $71,717,839
Assets: $142,767,006
Liabilities: $28,913,157
Net Worth: $113,853,848
Earnings: $9,045,893
Emp.: 129
Fiscal Year-end: 12/31/22
Pharmaceuticals Product Mfr
N.A.I.C.S.: 325412
Jong-Ho Park *(Founder & CEO)*

Subsidiaries:

Daebong LS Co., Ltd. - Incheon
Factory   (1)
123 Neungheodae-ro 649 Beon-gil,
Namdong-gu, Incheon, 21697, Korea
(South)
Tel.: (82) 327128800
Cosmetic & Laboratory Product Mfr
N.A.I.C.S.: 325620

Daebong LS Co., Ltd. - Jeju
Factory   (1)
Bio-Convergence Center Building No 2
Suite 105 Jeju Techno Park 102,
Jejudaehang-ro, Jeju, 63243, Korea (South)
Tel.: (82) 647518773
Cosmetic & Laboratory Product Mfr
N.A.I.C.S.: 325620

Daebong LS Co., Ltd.—(Continued)

P&K Skin Research Center Co., Ltd. (1)
Education Facility Disaster Relief Society Building 4F, National Assembly Road 62 -25 Yeongdeungpo-gu, Seoul, 07236, Korea (South)
Tel.: (82) 269 251 5013
Web Site: https://www.pnkskin.com
Cosmetic & Laboratory Product Mfr
N.A.I.C.S.: 325620

UCL Co., Ltd. (1)
2nd floor Dongseong Building 21 Gukhoe-daero 62-gil, Yeongdeungpo-gu, Seoul, 07236, Korea (South)
Tel.: (82) 22 135 7000
Web Site: https://www.e-ucl.co.kr
Cosmetic & Laboratory Product Mfr
N.A.I.C.S.: 325620
Lee Ji-won (CEO)

Plant (Domestic):

UCL Co., Ltd. - Incheon Factory (2)
119 Neungheodaero 649-gil, Namdong-gu, Incheon, 21697, Korea (South)
Tel.: (82) 328175000
Cosmetic & Laboratory Product Mfr
N.A.I.C.S.: 325620

UCL Co., Ltd. - Jeju Factory (2)
67 Eoeum 10-gil Aewol-eup, Jeju, 63038, Korea (South)
Tel.: (82) 648058505
Cosmetic & Laboratory Product Mfr
N.A.I.C.S.: 325620

DAECHANG CO., LTD.
506 4Na Sihwa Industrial Complex 1292-4 Jeongwang-dong, Siheung, Gyeonggi-do, Korea (South)
Tel.: (82) 314963000
Web Site: https://www.brassone.com
Year Founded: 1974
012800—(KRS)
Rev.: $1,105,456,004
Assets: $644,397,979
Liabilities: $432,156,672
Net Worth: $212,241,306
Earnings: $2,803,884
Emp.: 396
Fiscal Year-end: 12/31/22
Metal Products Mfr
N.A.I.C.S.: 331410
Si-Young Cho (CEO)

DAECHANG FORGING CO., LTD.
115-92 Bongnim-ro Saengnim-myeo, Saengnim-myeon, Gimhae, 50800, Gyeongsangnam-do, Korea (South)
Tel.: (82) 553293911
Web Site: https://www.dcf.co.kr
Year Founded: 1955
015230—(KRS)
Rev.: $323,288,704
Assets: $259,421,252
Liabilities: $73,502,507
Net Worth: $185,918,745
Earnings: $28,151,636
Emp.: 103
Fiscal Year-end: 12/31/22
Heavy Machinery Component & Automobile Parts Mfr
N.A.I.C.S.: 332111
Kwon Il Park (Pres & CEO)

Subsidiaries:

Delta (Vancouver), B.C. (1)
1519 Derwent Way Annacis Island, Delta, V3M 6K8, BC, Canada
Tel.: (604) 526-8735
Iron & Steel Forging Mfr
N.A.I.C.S.: 332111

DAECHANG SOLUTION CO., LTD.
387 22 Samdong-ro, Samdong-myeon Ulju-gun, Ulsan, Korea (South)

Tel.: (82) 527117700
Web Site: https://www.dsol.co.kr
Year Founded: 1953
096350—(KRS)
Rev.: $40,463,928
Assets: $95,244,797
Liabilities: $73,046,924
Net Worth: $22,197,873
Earnings: ($5,359,127)
Emp.: 145
Fiscal Year-end: 12/31/22
Marine Engine Component Mfr
N.A.I.C.S.: 333618
Park Jung Ho (Co-CEO)

Subsidiaries:

Daechang Solution Co., Ltd. - Ulju Factory (1)
387-22 Samdong-ro Samdong-myeon, Ulju-gun, Ulsan, Korea (South)
Tel.: (82) 527117700
Engine Equipment Mfr
N.A.I.C.S.: 333618

DAECHANG STEEL CO., LTD.
1213 Aam-daero, Namdong-gu, Incheon, Korea (South)
Tel.: (82) 328167700
Web Site: http://www.dcsteel.com
Year Founded: 1980
140520—(KRS)
Rev.: $305,662,021
Assets: $184,011,357
Liabilities: $56,007,909
Net Worth: $128,003,447
Earnings: $42,749,978
Emp.: 91
Fiscal Year-end: 12/31/22
Steel Product Mfr & Whlsr
N.A.I.C.S.: 331221
Chang Bok Moon (Pres & CEO)

DAEDONG CORPORATION
35 Nongongjungang-ro 34-gil, Nongong-eup Dalseong-gun, Daegu, 42984, Korea (South)
Tel.: (82) 536103000
Web Site: https://daedong-kioti.com
Year Founded: 1947
000490—(KRS)
Rev.: $1,122,686,992
Assets: $1,314,464,049
Liabilities: $952,447,139
Net Worth: $362,016,910
Earnings: $29,643,317
Emp.: 1,343
Fiscal Year-end: 12/31/22
Farming Machinery & Equipment Mfr
N.A.I.C.S.: 333111
Joon-Sik Kim (Co-CEO)

Subsidiaries:

Daedong USA Inc. (1)
6300 Kioti Dr, Wendell, NC 27591
Tel.: (919) 374-5100
Web Site: https://www.kioti.com
Agricultural Machinery Distr
N.A.I.C.S.: 423820

Hankuk Chain Industrial Co., Ltd. (1)
4867-11 Seodong-daero, Daedeok-myeon, Anseong, Gyeonggi-do, Korea (South)
Tel.: (82) 3167355447
Web Site: http://www.hanchain.co.kr
Roller Chain Mfr
N.A.I.C.S.: 333613
Seung Won Lee (CEO)

Kioti Golf Co., Ltd. (1)
410-6 Deokbongseowon-ro, Yangseong-myeon, Anseong, Gyeonggi-do, Korea (South)
Tel.: (82) 312646680
Web Site: https://www.kiotigolf.com
Golf Equipment Distr
N.A.I.C.S.: 423910

DAEDONG GEAR CO., LTD.
177 Geonji-ri,Daedeokmyeon,

Sanam-myeon, 52528, Anseong-si, Gyeonggi-do, Korea (South)
Tel.: (82) 316735544
Web Site: https://www.daedonggear.com
Year Founded: 1973
008830—(KRS)
Rev.: $185,688,838
Assets: $188,583,988
Liabilities: $131,594,908
Net Worth: $56,989,080
Earnings: $3,240,919
Emp.: 251
Fiscal Year-end: 12/31/22
Axle Assemblies Mfr
N.A.I.C.S.: 336110
Gyeong Gyu Kang (CEO)

DAEDONG KOREA GINSENG CO., LTD.
586 Gunbuk-ro Gunbuk-myeon Geumsan-gun, Ch'ung-Nam, Korea (South)
Tel.: (82) 417538803
Web Site: https://www.ddkorea.co.kr
Year Founded: 2002
Ginseng Products
N.A.I.C.S.: 325411
Sung-Geun Chol (CEO)

DAEDONG METALS CO., LTD.
602 Nongong-ro Nongong-eub, Dalsung-gun, Daegu, Korea (South)
Tel.: (82) 536105000
Web Site: https://www.daedongmetals.co.kr
Year Founded: 1987
020400—(KRS)
Rev.: $112,695,890
Assets: $77,498,638
Liabilities: $41,569,824
Net Worth: $35,928,813
Earnings: $1,673,617
Emp.: 143
Fiscal Year-end: 12/31/22
Casting Machine Parts Services
N.A.I.C.S.: 331511
Lee Pung-Woo (CEO)

DAEDONG STEEL CO., LTD.
165 Block Lot 1 Namdong Industrial Complex, Angogae-ro, Seoul, Korea (South)
Tel.: (82) 27804448
Web Site: https://www.daedongsteel.co.kr
Year Founded: 1973
048470—(KRS)
Rev.: $139,941,181
Assets: $73,255,590
Liabilities: $18,413,211
Net Worth: $54,842,378
Earnings: ($3,522,256)
Emp.: 47
Fiscal Year-end: 12/31/22
Steel Products Mfr
N.A.I.C.S.: 331221
Jong Wung Lee (Mng Dir)

Subsidiaries:

Daedong Steel Co., Ltd. - Incheon Plant (1)
Lot 1 Block 165 Namdong Industrial Complex 29 Aenggogae-ro, Gojan-dong Namdong-gu, Incheon, Korea (South)
Tel.: (82) 27804448
Web Site: https://www.daedongsteel.co.kr
Steel Product Mfr & Distr
N.A.I.C.S.: 332111

Daedong Steel Co., Ltd. - Pohang Plant (1)
506 Cheolgang-ro, Nam-gu, Pohang, Gyeonsangbuk, Korea (South)
Tel.: (82) 542784664
Steel Product Mfr & Distr
N.A.I.C.S.: 332111

DAEDUCK CO., LTD.
2536-10 Hamma-daero, Naeseo-eup Masanhoewon-gu, Changwon, Gyeongsangnam-do, Korea (South)
Tel.: (82) 552310013   KR
Web Site: https://www.idaeduck.co.kr
Year Founded: 1972
008060—(KRS)
Rev.: $1,312,906,506
Assets: $1,503,647,345
Liabilities: $331,075,878
Net Worth: $1,172,571,467
Earnings: $105,382,446
Emp.: 16
Fiscal Year-end: 12/31/22
Holding Company; Printed Circuit Board Mfr & Services
N.A.I.C.S.: 551112
Shin Yeong Hwan (CEO)

Subsidiaries:

Daeduck Electronics Co., Ltd. (1)
230 Gangchon-ro, Ansan, Gyeonggi-do, Korea (South)
Tel.: (82) 31 8040 8000
Web Site: http://eng.daeduck.com
Printed Circuit Board Mfr
N.A.I.C.S.: 334412
Yeong Hwan Shin (CEO)

Plant (Domestic):

Daeduck Electronics Co., Ltd. - Ansan Plant #1 (2)
390-1 Mocknae-dong, Danwon-gu, 425-100, Ansan, Gyeonggi-do, Korea (South)
Tel.: (82) 31 599 8800
Web Site: http://www.daeduck.com
Electronic Components Mfr
N.A.I.C.S.: 334419

Nakor Inc. (1)
215 Sanders St Suite 202, Kemptville, K0G 1J0, ON, Canada
Tel.: (613) 258-4775
Electronic Components Mfr
N.A.I.C.S.: 334419
Bill Ballantyne (Gen Mgr)

DAEGU DEPARTMENT STORE CO., LTD.
Daegu Department Store Dong-seongno 2-ga, Jung-gu, Daegu, Korea (South)
Tel.: (82) 534231234
Web Site: https://www.debec.co.kr
Year Founded: 1969
006370—(KRS)
Rev.: $58,215,080
Assets: $360,756,350
Liabilities: $183,256,924
Net Worth: $177,499,426
Earnings: ($14,267,278)
Emp.: 1,555
Fiscal Year-end: 12/31/22
Departmental Store Operator
N.A.I.C.S.: 455110
Pung-Woo Lee (Pres)

DAEHAN FLOUR MILLS CO., LTD
14F KCCI Bldg 39 Sejong-daero, Jung-gu, Seoul, Korea (South)
Tel.: (82) 234550200
Web Site: http://www.dhflour.co.kr
Year Founded: 1952
001130—(KRS)
Rev.: $1,049,386,429
Assets: $1,011,237,266
Liabilities: $306,093,451
Net Worth: $705,143,815
Earnings: $31,710,659
Emp.: 344
Fiscal Year-end: 12/31/22
Flour Product Mfr
N.A.I.C.S.: 311211
Boonghee Han (Mng Dir)

Subsidiaries:

Daehan Livestock & Feed Co. Ltd. - CHANGWON PLANT (1)

986 Uichang-daero Songjeong-ri, Dong-eup, Changwon, 634-860, Gyeongsang-nam, Korea (South)
Tel.: (82) 5512913124
Pet Food Mfr
N.A.I.C.S.: 311119

Daehan Livestock & Feed Co. Ltd. - INCHON PLANT (1)
13 Bukseongpo-gil, Jung-gu, Incheon, 400-201, Korea (South)
Tel.: (82) 3277011002
Pet Food Mfr
N.A.I.C.S.: 311119

Daehan Livestock & Feed Co. Ltd. - JEONJU PLANT (1)
186 Seogwi-ro, Deokjin-gu, Jeonju, Jeollabuk-do, Korea (South)
Tel.: (82) 632100806
Pet Food Mfr
N.A.I.C.S.: 311119

Korea Silo Co., Ltd. (1)
52 Wolmi-ro, Jung-gu, Incheon, Korea (South)
Tel.: (82) 327601600
Grain Storage Services
N.A.I.C.S.: 493130

DAEHAN NEW PHARM CO., LTD.
66 Jeyakgongdan 1-gil, Hyangnam-eup, Hwaseong, 18622, Gyeonggi-do, Korea (South)
Tel.: (82) 313536141
Web Site: https://www.dhnp.co.kr
Year Founded: 1984
054670—(KRS)
Rev.: $151,833,287
Assets: $129,898,087
Liabilities: $50,928,607
Net Worth: $78,969,480
Earnings: $18,651,296
Emp.: 345
Fiscal Year-end: 12/31/22
Pharmaceutical Product Mfr & Distr
N.A.I.C.S.: 325412
Kim Sung Jo (Mgr)

DAEHAN STEEL CO., LTD.
S tower 12F Saemunan-ro 82, Jongno-gu, Seoul, Korea (South)
Tel.: (82) 16703300
Web Site: https://www.idaehan.com
Year Founded: 1954
084010—(KRS)
Rev.: $1,642,619,703
Assets: $936,121,053
Liabilities: $323,712,298
Net Worth: $612,408,755
Earnings: $105,544,615
Emp.: 406
Fiscal Year-end: 12/31/22
Steel Products Mfr
N.A.I.C.S.: 331110
Kyungbaek Lee (Co-CEO)

Subsidiaries:

Angkasa Amsteel Pte Ltd (1)
20 Woodlands Loop, Singapore, 738321, Singapore (50%)
Tel.: (65) 6759 5973
Web Site: http://www.angkasa.com.sg
Sales Range: $25-49.9 Million
Emp.: 100
Steel Reinforcement Bars Mfr & Distr
N.A.I.C.S.: 314994

Daehan Networks Co., Ltd (1)
Tel.: (82) 514421108
Web Site: http://www.idhnetworks.com
Logistics Consulting Servies
N.A.I.C.S.: 541614

Daehan Steel Co., Ltd. - Noksan Plant (1)
333 Noksan Saneop Buk-ro, Gangseo-gu, Busan, Korea (South).
Tel.: (82) 5116703300
Steel Products Mfr
N.A.I.C.S.: 331110

Daehan Steel Co., Ltd. - Pyeongtaek Plant (1)
Road 268 Pyeongtaek Hang-ro, Poseung-eup, Pyeongtaek, Gyeonggi, Korea (South)
Tel.: (82) 16703300
Steel Products Mfr
N.A.I.C.S.: 331110

STAZ Singapore Pte. Ltd. (1)
21 Woodlands Close 04-33, Singapore, 737854, Singapore
Tel.: (65) 65587063
Steel Product Mfr & Distr
N.A.I.C.S.: 331110

Staz USA Inc. (1)
1800E Lambert Rd Ste 215, Brea, CA 92821
Tel.: (714) 990-4000
Steel Product Mfr & Distr
N.A.I.C.S.: 331110
Young Kim (Mgr)

Staz Vietnam Co. Ltd. (1)
B Lot 4B6 CN Myphuoc 3 Industrial Park, BenCat District, Ben Cat, Binh Duong, Vietnam
Tel.: (84) 6502220480
Steel Product Mfr & Distr
N.A.I.C.S.: 331110

YK Steel Corp. (1)
760 Eulsukdo-daero, Saha-Gu, Busan, 49456, Korea (South) (51%)
Tel.: (82) 51 260 2114
Web Site: https://www.yk-steel.co.kr
Emp.: 336
Concrete & Steel Mfr
N.A.I.C.S.: 331110
Jong Woong Lee (Pres)

DAEHO AL CO., LTD.
211 Nongongjungang-ro, Nongong-eup Dalseong-gun, Daegu, Korea (South)
Tel.: (82) 536105400
Web Site: https://www.daeho-al.com
Year Founded: 2002
069460—(KRS)
Rev.: $133,486,180
Assets: $120,431,507
Liabilities: $62,427,231
Net Worth: $58,004,276
Earnings: $4,544,447
Emp.: 160
Fiscal Year-end: 12/31/22
Aluminium Products Mfr
N.A.I.C.S.: 331315
Ji Dae-Hyun (CEO)

DAEHO TECHNOLOGY KOREA CO., LTD.
7 Jukjeon-ro, Uichang-gu, Changwon, Gyeongsangnam-do, Korea (South)
Tel.: (82) 55 292 0560
Web Site: http://www.daehoteck.co.kr
Optical & Robotic Equipment Mfr
N.A.I.C.S.: 333310
Young Hwa Jung (CEO)

DAEJOO CO.,LTD
20F G TOWER 549 Cheonho-daero, Gwangjin-gu, Seoul, Korea (South)
Tel.: (82) 264167203
Web Site: http://www.daejooind.co.kr
Year Founded: 1962
003310—(KRS)
Rev.: $76,113,861
Assets: $80,613,362
Liabilities: $27,761,926
Net Worth: $52,851,436
Earnings: $3,326,603
Emp.: 158
Fiscal Year-end: 12/31/22
Animal Feed Mfr
N.A.I.C.S.: 311111
Lim Hyun Ae (Mgr)

DAEJOO ELECTRONIC MATERIALS CO., LTD.
148 Seohaean-Ro, Siheung, 15094, Gyeonggi-do, Korea (South)
Tel.: (82) 314982901
Web Site: https://www.daejoo.co.kr
Year Founded: 1981
078600—(KRS)
Rev.: $133,533,478
Assets: $251,490,803
Liabilities: $158,921,814
Net Worth: $92,568,989
Earnings: $765,905
Emp.: 292
Fiscal Year-end: 12/31/22
Electronic Materials Mfr
N.A.I.C.S.: 334416
Moo-Hyun Lim (CEO)

Subsidiaries:

Dongguan Daejoo Electronic Materials Co., Ltd. (1)
Building A Xianyon-Fenxi Industrial Zone, Wanjiang District, Dongguan, Guangdong, China
Tel.: (86) 76922775941
Web Site: https://en.daejoocn.com
Electronic Components Mfr
N.A.I.C.S.: 334419

Qingdao Daejoo Electronic Materials Co., Ltd. (1)
Zhong Huang Bu, Xia Zhuang Town Cheng Yang District, Qingdao, Shandong, China
Tel.: (86) 53287796815
Electronic Components Mfr
N.A.I.C.S.: 334419

Shanghai Daejoo Electronic Materials Co., Ltd. (1)
No 3405 Jindu Road, Xinzhuang Industrial Zone, Shanghai, 201108, China
Tel.: (86) 2164588585
Web Site: https://www.daejoo.com.cn
Electronic Components Mfr
N.A.I.C.S.: 334419

Taiwan Daejoo Electronic Materials Co., Ltd. (1)
3F No 59 Lane 229 Sec 3 Changxing Rd, Luzhu Township, Taoyuan, 33852, Taiwan
Tel.: (886) 3 324 7321
Electronic Components Mfr
N.A.I.C.S.: 334419

DAEJOO ENERGY INNOVATION TECHNOLOGY CO LTD
4F 4 Sinpo-ro Jung-gu, Incheon, Korea (South)
Web Site: http://www.daejooent.co.kr
Steel Pipe Mfr & Distr
N.A.I.C.S.: 331210
Park Joo-Bong (Chm)

DAEJUNG CHEMICALS & METALS CO., LTD.
186 Seohaean-ro, Siheung, Gyeonggi-do, Korea (South)
Tel.: (82) 314888822
Web Site: https://www.daejungchem.co.kr
Year Founded: 1968
120240—(KRS)
Rev.: $74,098,246
Assets: $133,304,150
Liabilities: $20,835,803
Net Worth: $112,468,347
Earnings: $10,540,320
Emp.: 196
Fiscal Year-end: 12/31/22
Chemicals Mfr
N.A.I.C.S.: 325998
Young Jun Song (CEO)

Subsidiaries:

Daejung EM Co., Ltd. (1)
116B 6L Namdong Industrial Complex Gojan-dong, Namdong-gu, Incheon, Korea (South)
Tel.: (82) 12691456
Medicines Mfr & Sales
N.A.I.C.S.: 325412

DAEKYO CO LTD
Daekyo Tower 23 Boramae-ro 3-gil, Gwanak-gu, Seoul, 08708, Korea (South)
Tel.: (82) 28291114
Web Site: https://www.daekyo.com
Year Founded: 1975
019680—(KRS)
Rev.: $523,919,556
Assets: $511,377,146
Liabilities: $201,209,909
Net Worth: $310,167,237
Earnings: ($104,445,840)
Emp.: 2,354
Fiscal Year-end: 12/31/22
Education Services
N.A.I.C.S.: 611710
Young-Joong Kang (Founder, Founder, Chm & Chm)

Subsidiaries:

Daekyo Eye Level Singapore Pte. Ltd. (1)
3501 Jalan Bukit Merah 01-02 Rubikon, Singapore, 159460, Singapore
Tel.: (65) 63976117
Education Services
N.A.I.C.S.: 611710

Daekyo Malaysia Snd. Bhd. (1)
50-G-2 Wisma UOA Jalan Dungun, Bukit Damasara, 50490, Kuala Lumpur, Malaysia
Tel.: (60) 320931909
Education Services
N.A.I.C.S.: 611710

Daekyo Vietnam Co., Ltd. (1)
191 Hoa Lan Street Ward2 Phu Nhuan Street, Ho Chi Minh City, Vietnam
Tel.: (84) 838270661
Education Services
N.A.I.C.S.: 611710

P.T. Daekyo Indonesia (1)
JL Gatot Subroto Kav 27 Menera Global 17B, 12950, Jakarta Selatan, Indonesia
Tel.: (62) 2152920911
Education Services
N.A.I.C.S.: 611710

Sanghai Daekyo Co., Ltd. (1)
716 Xuanrunguojidasha Wuzhong Road No 1100, Minhangqu, Shanghai, China
Tel.: (86) 21614583234
Education Services
N.A.I.C.S.: 611710

DAELIM B&CO., LTD.
52 Gongdan-ro, Seongsangu, Changwon, Gyeongsangnam-do, Korea (South)
Tel.: (82) 552808400
Web Site: https://www.daelimbath.com
Year Founded: 1966
005750—(KRS)
Rev.: $194,427,561
Assets: $258,932,153
Liabilities: $137,775,568
Net Worth: $121,156,585
Earnings: ($659,456)
Emp.: 723
Fiscal Year-end: 12/31/22
Bathroom Product Mfr
N.A.I.C.S.: 327110
Tae-Sik Kang (Exec Mng Dir)

Subsidiaries:

Daelim B&Co., Ltd. - Jecheon Plant (1)
1-3 Jupo-ri Bongyang-eup, Jecheon, Chungbuk, Korea (South)
Tel.: (82) 234291470
Bathroom Ware Mfr
N.A.I.C.S.: 326191

DAELIM INDUSTRIAL CO., LTD.
Daelim Building 36 Jong-ro 1gil, Jongno-gu, Seoul, 03152, Korea (South)

Daelim Industrial Co., Ltd.—(Continued)

Tel.: (82) 220117114
Web Site: http://www.daelim.co.kr
Year Founded: 1939
000210—(KRS)
Rev.: $3,969,186,976
Assets: $9,218,568,313
Liabilities: $5,676,742,580
Net Worth: $3,541,825,734
Earnings: $55,449,771
Emp.: 39
Fiscal Year-end: 12/31/22
Civil Engineering Construction, Architectural Services & Production of Petrochemical Products
N.A.I.C.S.: 541330

Subsidiaries:

DL Chemical Co. Ltd.   (1)
26 Fl Donuimun Gate D Tower 134 Tongil-ro, Jongno-gu, Seoul, 03181, Korea (South)
Tel.: (82) 237083000
Web Site: https://dlchemical.co.kr
Petrochemical Distr
N.A.I.C.S.: 325110

Subsidiary (US):

Kraton Corporation   (2)
15710 John F Kennedy Blvd Ste 300, Houston, TX 77032
Tel.: (281) 504-4700
Web Site: http://www.kraton.com
Rev.: $1,970,129,000
Assets: $2,654,608,000
Liabilities: $1,806,604,000
Net Worth: $848,004,000
Earnings: $170,226,000
Emp.: 1,751
Fiscal Year-end: 12/31/2021
Holding Company; Polymer Mfr
N.A.I.C.S.: 551112
Holger R. Jung (Pres- & Sr VP)

Subsidiary (Non-US):

KRATON Formosa Polymers Corporation   (3)
11F 32 Songren Road, Xinyi District, Taipei, 11073, Taiwan
Tel.: (886) 227225412
Synthetic Rubber Mfr & Distr
N.A.I.C.S.: 325520
David Brooks (VP-Ops)

KRATON Polymers do Brasil Industria E Comercio de Produtos Petroquimicos Ltda.
Av Roberto Simonsen 1500, PO Box 57, Bairro Recanto dos Passaros Sao Paulo, 13148-901, Paulinia, SP, Brazil
Tel.: (55) 1938747250
Web Site: http://www.kraton.com.br
Mfr of Engineered Polymers
N.A.I.C.S.: 325211

Kraton Chemical A.B.   (3)
Massvagen 15, Gavleborg, Soderhamn, 826 73, Sweden
Tel.: (46) 27062500
Chemical Products Mfr
N.A.I.C.S.: 325998

Kraton Chemical B.V.   (3)
Transistorstraat 16, Almere, Netherlands
Tel.: (31) 365462800
Chemical Products Mfr
N.A.I.C.S.: 325998

Subsidiary (Domestic):

Kraton Chemical, LLC   (3)
9000 Southside Blvd, Jacksonville, FL 32256
Tel.: (904) 928-8700
Chemical Products Mfr
N.A.I.C.S.: 325998

Subsidiary (Non-US):

Kraton Polymers Japan Ltd,   (3)
2-16-2 Konan Taiyoseimeishihagawa Bldg 9F, Minato-ku, Tokyo, 108-0075, Japan
Tel.: (81) 354617430
Chemical Products Mfr
N.A.I.C.S.: 325998

Subsidiary (Domestic);

Kraton Polymers U.S. LLC   (3)
15710 John F Kennedy Blvd Ste 300, Houston, TX 77032
Tel.: (281) 504-4700
Web Site: https://www.kraton.com
Sales Range: $1-4.9 Billion
Emp.: 800
Engineered Polymers Mfr & Supplier
N.A.I.C.S.: 325211
Torsten Schmidt (Pres)

DL E&C Co., Ltd.   (1)
Donuimun D Tower 134 Tongil-ro, Jongno-gu, Seoul, 3181, Korea (South)
Tel.: (82) 220117114
Web Site: https://www.dlenc.co.kr
Construction Services
N.A.I.C.S.: 236220

Daelim (Malaysia) Sdn. Bhd.   (1)
, 9th Fl Menarahapseng Jalan P R, 50250, Kuala Lumpur, Malaysia   (100%)
Tel.: (60) 321459911
Web Site: http://www.daelim.com
Sales Range: $25-49.9 Million
Emp.: 4
N.A.I.C.S.: 541330

Daelim (Nanjing) Construction Project Management Co., Ltd.   (1)
A Room 12F Chang Fa Shu Ma Building No 188, North of HongWu Road Xuanwu District, Nanjing, 210008, China
Tel.: (86) 25 8453 0090
Construction Services
N.A.I.C.S.: 236210

Daelim Concrete Products Co., Ltd.   (1)
5th FL & 6th FL 16 Eulji-ro 5-gil, Seoul, Korea (South)
Tel.: (82) 23113300
Web Site: http://www.daelimcorp.co.kr
Concrete Products Mfr
N.A.I.C.S.: 327332

Daelim Corporation   (1)
11th Fl The Korea Chamber of Commerce & Industry Building 45 4-ga, Namdaemunro Jung-gu, Seoul, 100 743, Korea (South)
Tel.: (82) 27083114
Web Site: http://www.daelimcorp.co.kr
Sales Range: $50-74.9 Million
Emp.: 115
Distr Petrochemical Products
N.A.I.C.S.: 325110
Sang-Ki Lee (CEO)

Daelim I&S Co., Ltd.   (1)
19F KBS MEDIA CENTER 45 Maebongsan-ro, Mapo-gu, Seoul, Korea (South)
Tel.: (82) 2 3704 8400
Web Site: http://www.daelimins.com
System Integration & Consulting; Software Development & Software Package; Networking & System Management
N.A.I.C.S.: 541512

Daelim Motor Co., Ltd.   (1)
602 Gongdanro, Sungsan-gu, Changwon, 642938, Gyungnam, Korea (South)   (100%)
Tel.: (82) 552397000
Web Site: https://www.dlmotors.co.kr
Sales Range: $200-249.9 Million
Emp.: 800
Motorcycles & Scooters Mfr
N.A.I.C.S.: 336991

Daelim Philippines Inc.   (1)
Unit No 902 1 Corporate Centre Dona Julia Vargas Ave, Cnr Meralco Avenue Ortigas Centre, Pasig, 1605, Philippines
Tel.: (63) 2 584 7010
Construction Services
N.A.I.C.S.: 236210

Daelim Saudi Arabia Co., Ltd.   (1)
Al Raja Tower 1st FL King Abdulaziz Rd, PO Box 2346, Al Khobar, 31451, Dammam, Saudi Arabia   (100%)
Tel.: (966) 38879303
Web Site: http://www.daelimsaudiarabia.com
Sales Range: $25-49.9 Million
Emp.: 25
Engineering & Project Management Services

N.A.I.C.S.: 541330
Sung In Kin (Mng Dir)

Daelim-Dar Co., Ltd.   (1)
Al-Khereji B/D 6th Floor King Faisal Bin Abdulaziz Road, PO Box 20753, Al Khobar, 31952, Saudi Arabia
Tel.: (966) 3 849 3850
Construction Services
N.A.I.C.S.: 236210

Korea Development Corporation   (1)
17F G SQUARE 180 Citizen-daero, Dongan-gu, Anyang, Gyeonggi-do, Korea (South)
Tel.: (82) 314209000
Web Site: http://www.kdc.co.kr
Engineering & Construction
N.A.I.C.S.: 541330

Ora Resort Co., Ltd.   (1)
263 15 Yon Dong, Cheju, 690723, Korea (South)   (100%)
Tel.: (82) 647475000
Web Site: http://www.oraresort.com
Sales Range: $50-74.9 Million
Emp.: 350
Operation of Hotel & Leisure Facilities
N.A.I.C.S.: 721199

PT. Daelim Utama Construction   (1)
Korea Center Building 4th Floor, JL Gatot Subroto Kav 58, 12950, Jakarta, Selatan, Indonesia
Tel.: (62) 21 5296 1060
Sales Range: $25-49.9 Million
Emp.: 2
Engineering & Construction Services
N.A.I.C.S.: 541330

Yeochun NCC Co., Ltd.   (1)
Centropolis B 7F 26 Ujeongguk-ro, Jongno-gu, Seoul, 03161, Korea (South)
Tel.: (82) 26 370 5300
Web Site: https://www.yncc.co.kr
Emp.: 981
Petrochemical Mfr; Owned 50% by Hanwha Chemical Corporation & 50% by Daelim Industrial Co., Ltd.
N.A.I.C.S.: 325110

DAELIM PAPER CO., LTD.
169 Nueup-dong, Hwangsae-ro, Osan, Gyeonggi-Do, Korea (South)
Tel.: (82) 313737670
Web Site: https://www.daelimpaper.co.kr
Year Founded: 2001
017650—(KRS)
Rev.: $143,699,931
Assets: $228,153,416
Liabilities: $38,752,196
Net Worth: $189,401,220
Earnings: $18,727,394
Emp.: 167
Fiscal Year-end: 12/31/22
Corrugated Board Mfr
N.A.I.C.S.: 322211
Ryu Chang-Seung (CEO)

DAELIM TRADING CO., LTD.
142 Yeonhui-ro, Seodaemun-gu, Seoul, Korea (South)
Tel.: (82) 27309811
Web Site: https://daelimtrading.co.kr
Year Founded: 1970
006570—(KRS)
Rev.: $133,544,105
Assets: $131,764,938
Liabilities: $70,151,908
Net Worth: $61,613,030.
Earnings: $2,906,609
Emp.: 271
Fiscal Year-end: 12/31/22
Architecture & Interior Material Whslr
N.A.I.C.S.: 423390
Ji Yong Lee (CEO)

Subsidiaries:

DAELIM TRADING Co., Ltd. - DOBI-DOS Plant   (1)
56 Gajaeul-ro, Seo-gu, Incheon, Korea (South)
Tel.: (82) 20325844901

Bidet Mfr
N.A.I.C.S.: 327110

DAELIM TRADING Co., Ltd. - Faucet Plant   (1)
258 Wanjeong-ro, Seo-gu, Incheon, Korea (South)
Tel.: (82) 2 564 2201
Faucet Mfr
N.A.I.C.S.: 327110

DAELIM TRADING Co., Ltd. - Jeungpyeong Plant   (1)
23 Jeungpyeong-sandanro, Jeungpyeong, Chungcheongbuk-do, Korea (South)
Tel.: (82) 438388510
Faucet Mfr
N.A.I.C.S.: 327110

PT DAELIM INDONESIA   (1)
Kawasan Industri Jababeka Jalan Jababeka Raya blok E Nomor 6-8, Cibitung, Bekasi, Jawa Barat, Indonesia
Tel.: (62) 21 8934518
Web Site: http://www.daelimindonesia.com
Bidet Mfr
N.A.I.C.S.: 327110

DAEMO ENGINEERING CO.
2611-2 Jungwang-Dong, Siheung, 15118, Gyeonggi-do, Korea (South)
Tel.: (82) 314886000
Web Site: https://www.daemo.co.kr
Year Founded: 1989
317850—(KRS)
Rev.: $42,031,377
Assets: $53,398,970
Liabilities: $16,921,236
Net Worth: $36,477,734
Earnings: $988,930
Emp.: 109
Fiscal Year-end: 12/31/22
Hydraulic Attachment Mfr
N.A.I.C.S.: 332912
Nam Gung Pyong (Mng Dir)

DAEMYUNG SONOSEASON CO., LTD.
262 Hanchigol-gil, Seomyeon, Hongcheon, Gangwon, Korea (South)
Tel.: (82) 222227500
Web Site: https://daemyungsonoseason.com
Year Founded: 1972
007720—(KRS)
Rev.: $131,136,023
Assets: $129,592,564
Liabilities: $41,549,013
Net Worth: $88,043,551
Earnings: ($14,067,595)
Emp.: 181
Fiscal Year-end: 12/31/22
Image Security Equipment Mfr
N.A.I.C.S.: 334290
Kwon Kwang-Soo (CEO)

DAERYUK CAN CO., LTD.
5th floor Women's Economic Association Building 221 Yeoksam-ro, Seoul, Gangnam, Korea (South)
Tel.: (82) 260030600
Web Site: https://www.drcc.co.kr
Year Founded: 1958
004780—(KRS)
Rev.: $211,676,368
Assets: $142,084,293
Liabilities: $41,991,200
Net Worth: $100,093,093
Earnings: $7,442,399
Emp.: 438
Fiscal Year-end: 12/31/22
Metal Container Mfr
N.A.I.C.S.: 332439
Bong Jun Park (Pres & CEO)

Subsidiaries:

Dae Ryuk International Inc   (1)
140 Rte 70 N 301, Paramus, NJ 07652
Tel.: (201) 655-6337
Industrial Machinery Distr

N.A.I.C.S.: 423830

DAESANG CORPORATION

Jongno Place 120 Changgyunggung-ro, Jongno-gu, Seoul, 03130, Korea (South)
Tel.: (82) 222209500
Web Site: https://www.daesang.com
Year Founded: 1956
001680—(KRS)
Rev.: $3,132,497,243
Assets: $2,446,880,676
Liabilities: $1,432,426,149
Net Worth: $1,014,454,527
Earnings: $63,713,755
Emp.: 4,913
Fiscal Year-end: 12/31/22
Food Products Mfr
N.A.I.C.S.: 311999
Jung-Bae Lim (CEO)

Subsidiaries:

Chlorella Supply Co., Ltd (1)
1372-17 Nagohamacho, Izumo, Shimane, Japan
Tel.: (81) 853282780
Food Products Distr
N.A.I.C.S.: 424490

Daesang (Beijing) Foods Co Ltd. (1)
Room 3A02 Block A Boya International Center No 1 Lizezhongyi Road, Chaoyang Dist, Beijing, China
Tel.: (86) 108 472 0420
Web Site: https://www.daesang.com
Food Product Mfr & Distr
N.A.I.C.S.: 311941

Plant (Domestic):

Daesang (Beijing) Foods Co Ltd. - Beijing Factory (2)
No 12 Keji Road Miyun Economc Development B, Beijing, China
Tel.: (86) 1069076639
Food Products Mfr
N.A.I.C.S.: 311941

Daesang (H.K.) Limited (1)
Unit 901 9th Floor No 88 Hing Fat Street, Causeway Bay, China (Hong Kong)
Tel.: (852) 25449795
Web Site: http://www.chungjungone.com.hk
Food Products Distr
N.A.I.C.S.: 424490
Helen Lam (Officer-Sls & Mktg)

Daesang Corporation - Tay Ninh Tapioca Starch Factory (1)
B2 Phuoc Minh W, Duong Minh Chau Dist, Tay Ninh, Tay Ninh Prov, Vietnam
Tel.: (84) 663775201
Food Products Mfr
N.A.I.C.S.: 311999

Daesang Europe B.V. (1)
Van Heuven Goedhartlaan 935, 1181 LD, Amstelveen, Netherlands
Tel.: (31) 20 640 6080
Web Site: https://daesangeurope.com
Food Products Distr
N.A.I.C.S.: 424490

Daesang FNF Corporation (1)
Gyeongyeong Bldg 8th Floor 101-2 Sinseol-dong Dongdaeum-gu, Seoul, 130-110, Korea (South)
Tel.: (82) 232908730
Web Site: http://www.daesangfnf.com
Food Product Mfr & Distr
N.A.I.C.S.: 311941

Daesang Japan Inc. (1)
Hama Rikyu Parkside Place 14F 5-6-10 Tsukiji, Chuo-ku, Tokyo, 104-0045, Japan
Tel.: (81) 33 580 8880
Web Site: https://www.daesang.co.jp
Food Products Distr
N.A.I.C.S.: 424490

Daesang Ricor Corporation (1)
6th Floor Legaspi Tower 200 107 Paseo De Roxas, Makati, 1200, Philippines
Tel.: (63) 9157496601
Food Product Mfr & Distr
N.A.I.C.S.: 311941

Plant (Domestic):

Daesang Ricor Corporation - Cagayan De Oro Factory (2)
PRK 6 Tablon, Cagayan de Oro, Philippines
Tel.: (63) 7047085032
Food Products Mfr
N.A.I.C.S.: 311941

Dongseo Construction Co., Ltd. (1)
Saeshin Bldg 8th Floor 129-11 Chungdam-dong Gangnam-gu, Seoul, 135-765, Korea (South)
Tel.: (82) 221565600
Web Site: http://www.dongseoi.com
Civil Engineering Services
N.A.I.C.S.: 541330

Lucky Foods LLC (1)
7774 SW Nimbus Ave, Beaverton, OR 97008-6423
Tel.: (503) 641-6602
Web Site: http://www.luckyfood.com
Food Mfr
N.A.I.C.S.: 311999

Miwon Vietnam Co., Ltd. (1)
22 Pham Hung Mai Dich Cau Giay, Hanoi, Vietnam
Tel.: (84) 2437680216
Web Site: https://www.miwon.com.vn
Food Product Mfr & Distr
N.A.I.C.S.: 311941

Plant (Domestic):

Miwon Vietnam Co., Ltd. - Tay Ninh Tapioca Starch Factory (2)
B2 Phuoc Minh W Duong Minh Chau Dist, Tay Ninh, Vietnam
Tel.: (84) 663775201
Food Products Mfr
N.A.I.C.S.: 311221

Miwon Vietnam Co., Ltd. - Viet Tri Factory (2)
Song Thao Str Tho Son W, Viet Tri, Phu Tho, Vietnam
Tel.: (84) 2103848717
Food Products Mfr
N.A.I.C.S.: 311941

PT Jico Agung (1)
Jl Perintis Kemerdekaan No 1-3, Puloga-dung, Jakarta, 13260, Indonesia
Tel.: (62) 214892908
Web Site: https://jicoagung.foodmate.com
Food Products Mfr
N.A.I.C.S.: 311999

PT Miwon Indonesia (1)
Jl Perintis Kemerdekaan No 1-3, Jakarta, 13260, Indonesia
Tel.: (62) 214892904
Web Site: https://daesang.id
Food Flavor Mfr & Distr
N.A.I.C.S.: 311942

Plant (Domestic):

PT Miwon Indonesia - Gresik Factory (2)
Kec Driyorejo, Gresik, 61177, Jawa Timur, Indonesia
Tel.: (62) 317507888
Food Flavor Mfr
N.A.I.C.S.: 311942

PT. Aneka Boga Nusantara (1)
Jl Surya Utama KAV-I 25B Kawasan Industri Surya Cipta Ciampel, Karawang, 41361, Indonesia
Tel.: (62) 2678638006
Food Product & Beverage Mfr
N.A.I.C.S.: 311421
Syaiful Bahri (Supvr-Maintenance)

Sang Am & Associates, Inc. (1)
3435 Wilshire Blvd Ste 1400, Los Angeles, CA 90010
Tel.: (213) 252-6320
Web Site: https://sang-am.com
Fiscal Year-end: 12/31/2006
Advertising Agency Services
N.A.I.C.S.: 541810
C.K. Han (Pres)

Tianjin Defeng Foods Co., Ltd. (1)
668 Baoshan Road ED-Area, Tanggu, Tianjin, China
Tel.: (86) 2225215155

Food Products Distr
N.A.I.C.S.: 424490

DAESANG HOLDINGS CO., LTD.

2F Olive tower 135 Seosomun-dong, Jung-gu, Seoul, 100-737, Korea (South)
Tel.: (82) 222116500
Year Founded: 2005
084690—(KRS)
Rev.: $4,008,848,082
Assets: $3,079,756,153
Liabilities: $1,886,993,783
Net Worth: $1,192,762,370
Earnings: $59,872,558
Emp.: 46
Fiscal Year-end: 12/31/22
Holding Company
N.A.I.C.S.: 551112
Kim Haeryong (Mgr)

Subsidiaries:

Daesang America, Inc. (1)
1 University Plz Ste 510, Hackensack, NJ 07601
Tel.: (201) 488-4010
Web Site: http://www.daesangamerica.com
Convenience Food Mfr & Distr
N.A.I.C.S.: 311412

Daesang Information Technology Co., Ltd. (1)
8th and 9th floors G Tower 549 Cheonho-daero, Gwangjin-gu, Seoul, Korea (South)
Tel.: (82) 234080114
Web Site: https://www.daesangit.com
Health & Food Science Services
N.A.I.C.S.: 541714

Daesang Life Science Corp. (1)
Daesang Building 470 Myeonmok-ro, Jungnang-gu, Seoul, 02154, Korea (South)
Tel.: (82) 22 220 9414
Web Site: https://www.daesanglifescience.co.kr
Health & Food Science Services
N.A.I.C.S.: 541714

Jeong Poong Co., Ltd. (1)
62-21 Pungse Industrial Complex 4 -ro Pungse-myeon, Dongnam-gu, Cheonan, Chungnam, Korea (South)
Tel.: (82) 415507900
Web Site: https://www.jeongpoong.com
Food Products Mfr
N.A.I.C.S.: 333241
I. M. Dong-Man (CEO)

DAESUNG FINE TECH. CO., LTD.

627 Nammyeon-ro, Seongsan-gu, Changwon, Gyeongsangnam-do, Korea (South)
Tel.: (82) 552894883
Web Site: https://www.dsfinetec.com
Year Founded: 1988
104040—(KRS)
Rev.: $20,904,725
Assets: $61,432,461
Liabilities: $21,787,357
Net Worth: $39,645,103
Earnings: ($2,367,154)
Emp.: 116
Fiscal Year-end: 12/31/22
Automotive Product Mfr
N.A.I.C.S.: 339999
Lee Chang Gyu (Gen Mgr)

DAESUNG HOLDINGS CO., LTD.

85 Myeongdeok-ro Jung-gu, Daegu, Korea (South)
Tel.: (82) 536061300
Web Site: http://www.daesung-holdings.com
Year Founded: 1983
016710—(KRS)
Rev.: $961,181,327
Assets: $1,067,162,442
Liabilities: $603,277,667

Net Worth: $463,884,775
Earnings: $3,760,108
Emp.: 39
Fiscal Year-end: 12/31/22
Holding Company
N.A.I.C.S.: 551112
David Younghoon Kim (Chm & CEO)

Subsidiaries:

Daesung Energy Co., Ltd. (1)
85 Myeongdeok-ro, Jung-gu, Daegu, 700-725, Korea (South)
Tel.: (82) 536061000
Web Site: https://www.daesungenergy.com
Rev.: $783,058,260
Assets: $640,053,798
Liabilities: $399,374,158
Net Worth: $240,679,640
Earnings: ($579,403)
Emp.: 414
Fiscal Year-end: 12/31/2022
Natural Gas Distr
N.A.I.C.S.: 221210
Jung Bon Woo (Pres)

Daesung Private Equity, Inc. (1)
4F Haesung Building 165 Yeoksam-ro, Gangnam-gu, Seoul, Korea (South)
Tel.: (82) 25592900
Web Site: https://www.daesungpe.com
Rev.: $9,176,600
Assets: $64,072,238
Liabilities: $1,030,637
Net Worth: $63,041,601
Earnings: $1,616,801
Emp.: 27
Fiscal Year-end: 12/31/2023
Financial Investment Services
N.A.I.C.S.: 523999
David Younghoon Kim (Chm & CEO)

DAETWYLER GLOBAL TEC HOLDING AG

Flugplatz, Bleienbach, I-3368, Bern, Switzerland
Tel.: (41) 62 919 34 34   CH
Web Site: http://www.daetwyler.com
Year Founded: 1952
Holding Company
N.A.I.C.S.: 551112
Peter Daetwyler (Chm)

Subsidiaries:

Max Daetwyler Corp. (1)
13420 Reese Blvd W, Huntersville, NC 28078
Tel.: (704) 875-1200
Web Site: http://www.daetwyler-usa.com
Printing Trades Machinery, Equipment & Supplies Mfr
N.A.I.C.S.: 423830
Roger Heid (CEO)

DAEWON CABLE CO., LTD.

92 Hoeumdeongnyeong-gil Godeok-myeon, Yesan, Chungcheongnam, Korea (South)
Tel.: (82) 413393400
Web Site: https://www.daewoncable.co.kr
Year Founded: 1964
006340—(KRS)
Rev.: $431,382,321
Assets: $188,650,194
Liabilities: $118,393,849
Net Worth: $70,256,345
Earnings: $1,038,569
Emp.: 153
Fiscal Year-end: 12/31/22
Cable & Wire Mfr
N.A.I.C.S.: 331491

Subsidiaries:

Kumsung Industrial Co., Ltd. (1)
115-1 Bukchang-ro Sunseong-myeon, Dangjin, Chungnam, Korea (South)
Tel.: (82) 413620903
Plastic Injection Molding Mfr
N.A.I.C.S.: 333511

Daewon Cable Co., Ltd.—(Continued)

DAEWON CHEMICAL CO., LTD.
538-38 Seobong-ro, Hyangnam-uep, Hwaseong, Korea (South)
Tel.: (82) 313537905
Web Site:
https://www.daewonchemical.co.kr
Year Founded: 1974
024890—(KRS)
Rev.: $112,599,576
Assets: $100,410,614
Liabilities: $52,506,397
Net Worth: $47,904,217
Earnings: ($7,379,955)
Emp.: 158
Fiscal Year-end: 12/31/22
Synthetic Leather Mfr & Distr
N.A.I.C.S.: 316990
Sungyuk Won *(Pres)*

Subsidiaries:

DAEWON Chemical Co., Ltd. - Osan
Factory (1)
496 Yoisammi-Dong, Osan, Kyounggi-Do, Korea (South)
Tel.: (82) 31 372 3992
Synthetic Leather Mfr
N.A.I.C.S.: 316990

did Co., Ltd. (1)
10-13th floor Gungdo Bldg 327 Bongeunsa-ro, Gangnam-gu, Seoul, Korea (South)
Tel.: (82) 221413930
Web Site: https://www.didwallpaper.com
Emp.: 150
Wallpaper Mfr
N.A.I.C.S.: 322220

DAEWON CO., LTD.
15 Jikji-Daero 435Beon-Gil, Heungdeok-gu, Cheongju, Chungbuk, Korea (South)
Tel.: (82) 432641115
Web Site: https://www.daewon.co.kr
Year Founded: 1972
007680—(KRS)
Rev.: $274,825,162
Assets: $413,709,439
Liabilities: $135,216,956
Net Worth: $278,492,483
Earnings: $14,964,847
Emp.: 225
Fiscal Year-end: 12/31/22
Commercial Building Construction Services
N.A.I.C.S.: 236220
Jincheol Bae *(Office Mgr)*

DAEWON KANG UP CO., LTD.
114-41 Osong 1 gil Seonggeo-Eup, Seobuk-Gu, Cheonan, 31042, Chungnam, Korea (South)
Tel.: (82) 415207500
Web Site: https://www.dwku.com
Year Founded: 1946
000430—(KRS)
Rev.: $785,753,533
Assets: $774,991,239
Liabilities: $316,316,125
Net Worth: $458,675,114
Earnings: $14,462,560
Emp.: 714
Fiscal Year-end: 12/31/22
Automobile Parts Mfr
N.A.I.C.S.: 336360
Chai Chul Hur *(Chm & CEO)*

Subsidiaries:

Beijing Daewon Asia Automobile Science & Technology Co., Ltd. (1)
M2-6, Xinggu Industrial Development Pinggu District, Beijing, China
Tel.: (86) 1069956571
Suspension & Coil Spring Mfr
N.A.I.C.S.: 332613

Contitech Daewon Airspring Systems Co. Ltd. (1)
302-1 sinbang-ro Seonghwan-eup, Seobuk-gu, Cheonan, 330-807, Chungman-do, Korea (South)
Tel.: (82) 415822800
Air Spring Mfr
N.A.I.C.S.: 332613

Daewon Europe Co., Ltd. (1)
16 Frezerow, 20-209, Lublin, Poland
Tel.: (48) 817491900
Suspension & Coil Spring Mfr
N.A.I.C.S.: 332613

Daewon India Autoparts Private Limited (1)
Survey No 477 and 489 No 99 Thiruvallur Taluk, Papparambakkam Village, Thiruvallur, 602 025, Tamilnadu, India
Tel.: (91) 4437670700
Suspension & Coil Spring Mfr
N.A.I.C.S.: 332613

Daewon Mexico S. de R.L. de C.V. (1)
Del Parque 1165, Monterrey Technology Park, 65550, Cienega de Flores, Nuevo Leon, Mexico
Tel.: (52) 7075253643
Suspension & Coil Spring Mfr
N.A.I.C.S.: 332613

Daewon Spring & Seat LLC (1)
AutoZavodskaya St 5 Udmurt Republic, 426013, Izhevsk, Russia
Tel.: (7) 3412246206
Suspension & Coil Spring Mfr
N.A.I.C.S.: 332613

Jiangsu Daewon Asia Automobile Spring Co., Ltd. (1)
No 56 Ganjiang Road Yancheng Economic Development Zone, Yancheng, Jiangsu, China
Tel.: (86) 51589021500
Suspension & Coil Spring Mfr
N.A.I.C.S.: 332613

DAEWON MEDIA CO., LTD.
Hangang-daero 23-gil 55 I-PARK MALL Theme Park 6th floor 1-1, Yongsan-gu, Seoul, 4377, Korea (South)
Tel.: (82) 263733000
Web Site:
https://www.daewonmedia.com
Year Founded: 1973
048910—(KRS)
Rev.: $232,749,107
Assets: $147,514,161
Liabilities: $50,168,184
Net Worth: $97,345,977
Earnings: $5,536,472
Emp.: 177
Fiscal Year-end: 12/31/22
Animation Services
N.A.I.C.S.: 512191
Wook Jung *(Pres)*

Subsidiaries:

Daewon C.I. Inc. (1)
9-12 Hangang-daero 15-gil, Yongsan-gu, Seoul, Korea (South)
Tel.: (82) 22 071 2000
Web Site: https://www.dwci.co.kr
Book Publishers
N.A.I.C.S.: 513130

Haksan Publishing Co., Ltd. (1)
282 Sangdo-ro, Dongjak-gu, Seoul, 156-031, Korea (South)
Tel.: (82) 28288988
Web Site: https://www.haksanpub.co.kr
Motion Picture Production Services
N.A.I.C.S.: 512110

DAEWON PHARMACEUTICAL CO., LTD.
386 Cheonhodaero, Sungdong-gu, Seoul, Korea (South)
Tel.: (82) 222047000
Web Site:
https://www.daewonpharm.com

Year Founded: 1958
003220—(KRS)
Rev.: $367,304,531
Assets: $347,872,900
Liabilities: $157,069,993
Net Worth: $190,802,908
Earnings: $24,501,317
Emp.: 1,087
Fiscal Year-end: 12/31/22
Pharmaceutical Product Mfr & Whslr
N.A.I.C.S.: 325412
Seung Ryel Baek *(CEO)*

Subsidiaries:

Daewon Pharmaceutical Co., Ltd. - Hyangnam Factory (1)
24 Jeyakgongdan 1-gil, Hyangnam-eup, Hwaseong, Gyeonggi-do, Korea (South)
Tel.: (82) 313534451
Pharmaceuticals Mfr
N.A.I.C.S.: 325412
Seung Ryel Baek *(CEO)*

DAEWON SANUP CO., LTD.
179 Wonsi-ro, Danwon-gu, Ansan, Gyeonggi-do, Korea (South)
Tel.: (82) 314952301
Web Site: http://www.dwsu.co.kr
Year Founded: 1968
005710—(KRS)
Rev.: $565,310,150
Assets: $428,994,189
Liabilities: $108,647,158
Net Worth: $320,347,032
Earnings: $28,883,588
Emp.: 529
Fiscal Year-end: 12/31/22
Automobile Seats Mfr
N.A.I.C.S.: 336360
Nam Kyung Pyo *(Mgr)*

DAEWON SEMICONDUCTOR PACKAGING INDUSTRIAL CORPORATION
622-33 Hanam-daero, Hanam, 465-816, Gyeonggi-do, Korea (South)
Tel.: (82) 317942001
Web Site:
http://www.daewonspic.com
Year Founded: 1975
Sales Range: $25-49.9 Million
Emp.: 250
Plastic Injection Molding Products Mfr
N.A.I.C.S.: 326199

Subsidiaries:

Daewon Semiconductor Packaging Industrial Corporation - IMS Daewon Factory (1)
854-27 Seoicheon-ro, Icheon, 467-841, Gyeonggi-do, Korea (South)
Tel.: (82) 31 645 9900
Semiconductor Components Mfr
N.A.I.C.S.: 334413

S&G Company, Ltd. (1)
Unit F 19/F CDW Building, 388 Castle Peak Road, Tsuen Wan, China (Hong Kong)
Tel.: (852) 31936000
Web Site: http://www.peakf.com
Sales Range: $25-49.9 Million
Emp.: 20
Semiconductor Plastic Extrusion & Thermoform Molded Products
N.A.I.C.S.: 326199

Subsidiary (Domestic):

Peak International, Inc. (2)
Ste F 19/F CDW Bldg, 388 Castle Peak Rd, Tsuen Wan, China (Hong Kong)
Tel.: (852) 31936000
Web Site: http://www.peak.com.hk
Sales Range: $50-74.9 Million
Emp.: 20
Engineered Plastics & Packaging Products Mfr
N.A.I.C.S.: 326199
Michael Cho Nae Eul *(Pres)*

Subsidiary (Non-US):

Peak International Singapore (3)
150 Kmpong Ampag KA Ctr 0404A, Singapore, 368324, Singapore
Tel.: (65) 68462002
Web Site: http://www.peak.com.hk
Sales Range: $10-24.9 Million
Emp.: 3
Semiconductor Precision-Engineered Packaging
N.A.I.C.S.: 326199
Bj Ng *(Gen Mgr)*

Subsidiary (US):

Peak International, Inc. (3)
2350 Mission College Blvd Ste 900, Santa Clara, CA 95054-1532
Tel.: (408) 213-6200
Web Site: http://www.peakinternational.com
Engineered Plastics & Packaging Mfr
N.A.I.C.S.: 326140

DAEWOO ELECTRONIC COMPONENTS CO., LTD.
3 Gongdan 2-gil, Jeongeup, Jeallabuk-do, Korea (South)
Tel.: (82) 635308114
Web Site: https://www.dwecc.com
Year Founded: 1973
009320—(KRS)
Rev.: $77,084,984
Assets: $69,982,023
Liabilities: $50,301,874
Net Worth: $19,680,149
Earnings: ($6,706,638)
Emp.: 269
Fiscal Year-end: 12/31/22
Electronic Components Mfr
N.A.I.C.S.: 334419
Joong-Kyo Seo *(Co-CEO)*

Subsidiaries:

Ajin USA LLC (1)
1500 County Rd 177, Cusseta, AL 36852
Tel.: (334) 756-8601
Web Site: https://wooshinusa.com
Automotive Products Mfr
N.A.I.C.S.: 336390
Jung Ho Sea *(CEO)*

DAEWOO ELECTRONIC EQUIPMENT CO., LTD (1)
Ben Cat District, Tan Dinh, Binh Duong, Vietnam
Tel.: (84) 650 3560 101
Electric Equipment Mfr
N.A.I.C.S.: 334416

Daewoo Electronic Components Suzhou A&T Technology Co., Ltd. (1)
No 777 Kang Yuan Rd, Xiang Cheng Economic Development Zone, Suzhou, Jiangsu, China
Tel.: (86) 5126 579 8217
Electronic Parts Mfr & Distr
N.A.I.C.S.: 334419
Joong Ho Seo *(Co-CEO)*

Daewoo Electronic Components Vietnam Corporation (1)
Tan Dinh Viliage, Ben Cat, Binh Duong, Vietnam
Tel.: (84) 94 285 6500
Electronic Parts Mfr & Distr
N.A.I.C.S.: 334419
Joong Ho Seo *(CEO)*

DAEWOO MOTOR SALES CORPORATION
426-1 Chongchon-2Dong, Bupyong-gu, Incheon, Korea (South)
Tel.: (82) 32510414
Web Site: http://www.dm.co.kr
Year Founded: 1993
Automobile Parts Mfr
N.A.I.C.S.: 336110
Dongho Lee *(Pres & Co-CEO)*

DAEWOO SPECIAL PURPOSE ACQUISITION 2 CO., LTD.
Daewoo Security Bldg Yeouido-dong,

Yeongdeungpo-gu, Seoul, Korea (South)
Tel.: (82) 27683420
Year Founded: 2014
Assets: $9,799,332
Liabilities: $703,166
Net Worth: $9,096,166
Earnings: ($118,240)
Financial Investment Management Services
N.A.I.C.S.: 523940
Jang Ju Woong-Joo *(CEO)*

DAEWOO SPECIAL PURPOSE ACQUISITION 3 CO., LTD.
56 Gukjegeumyung-ro, Yeongdeungpo-gu, Seoul, Korea (South)
Tel.: (82) 27683488
Year Founded: 2015
Financial Investment Management Services
N.A.I.C.S.: 523940
Se Hun Jeon *(CEO)*

DAEWOONG PHARMACEUTI-CAL CO., LTD.
12 Bongeunsa-ro 114-gil, Gangnam-gu, Seoul, Korea (South)
Tel.: (82) 25508800
Web Site:
　https://www.daewoong.co.kr
Year Founded: 1945
069620—(KRS)
Rev.: $981,830,450
Assets: $1,199,082,251
Liabilities: $630,564,212
Net Worth: $568,518,039
Earnings: $30,038,151
Emp.: 1,419
Fiscal Year-end: 12/31/22
Pharmaceuticals Product Mfr
N.A.I.C.S.: 325412

Subsidiaries:

Daewoong Vietnam Co., Ltd.　(1)
Hamlet 4, Dong Thanh Village Hoc Mon District, Ho Chi Minh City, Vietnam
Tel.: (84) 837110022
Web Site: https://www.daewoong.vn
Gift Product Mfr
N.A.I.C.S.: 339940
Ho Woong Hyun *(Pres)*

PT Daewoong Pharmaceutical Company　(1)
27th Floor UOB Plaza Thamrin Nine MH Thamrin No 10, Jakarta, 10230, Indonesia
Tel.: (62) 213 048 2266
Web Site: https://www.daewoong.co.id
Pharmaceuticals Product Mfr
N.A.I.C.S.: 325412
Jeon Sengho *(CEO)*

DAEYANG ELECTRIC CO., LTD.
245 Jangpyeong-ro, Saha-gu, 49438, Busan, Korea (South)
Tel.: (82) 512005282
Web Site: https://www.daeyang.co.kr
Year Founded: 1977
108380—(KRS)
Rev.: $100,013,753
Assets: $200,273,305
Liabilities: $32,707,446
Net Worth: $167,565,859
Earnings: ($5,749,701)
Emp.: 382
Fiscal Year-end: 12/31/22
Electrical Lighting, Components & Instruments Mfr
N.A.I.C.S.: 335132

Subsidiaries:

Bogo Co., Ltd.　(1)
305 NakDongDaeRo-388 306 Rich-W B/D DangRi-Dong, SaHa-Gu, Busan, Korea (South)

Tel.: (82) 51 294 7771
Web Site: https://www.bogoco.co.kr
Emp.: 20
Marine Equipment Mfr
N.A.I.C.S.: 336611
Kim Ja-Won *(Pres)*

DAEYANG INSTRUMENT CO., LTD　(1)
45-10 Noksansandan 261-ro 14 beon-gil, Gangseo-gu, Busan, Korea (South)
Tel.: (82) 512009720
Web Site: https://dmc.daeyang.co.kr
Sales Range: $50-74.9 Million
Emp.: 24
Measuring Instruments Mfr
N.A.I.C.S.: 334513
Young Woo Seo *(CEO)*

Daeyang Electric Co., Ltd. - ELECTRICAL / ELECTRONIC DIVISON　(1)
504 Sinpyong-Dong, Saha-Ku, Busan, 604836, Korea (South)
Tel.: (82) 51 200 5283
Sales Range: $100-124.9 Million
Emp.: 40
Communication System Mfr
N.A.I.C.S.: 334290

Daeyang Electric Co., Ltd. - LIGHTING DIVISON　(1)
245 Jangpyeongro, Saha-Gu, Pusan, 49438, Korea (South)
Tel.: (82) 512005281
Sales Range: $100-124.9 Million
Emp.: 367
Electronic Lighting Mfr
N.A.I.C.S.: 335139
Young Woo Seo *(Pres)*

Elcome International LLC　(1)
Dubai Investments Park 598-1121 DIP Phase 1, PO Box 1788, Dubai, United Arab Emirates
Tel.: (971) 4 812 1333
Web Site: https://elcome.com
Maritime Transportation Services
N.A.I.C.S.: 488390

Essem Corporation Sdn Bhd　(1)
C-7-1 Melawati Corporate Centre, Jalan Bandar Melawati Taman Melawati, 53100, Kuala Lumpur, Malaysia
Tel.: (60) 34 101 0200
Web Site: https://www.essemgroup.net
Oil & Gas Extraction Services
N.A.I.C.S.: 213112

Hai Cheung Trading Co.　(1)
Rm 1106 Building A Biyun Mansion No 289 Zheqiao Road, Pudong, Shanghai, China
Tel.: (86) 216 168 2673
Lighting Equipment Mfr
N.A.I.C.S.: 335139

Hans Bell Equipment Ltd.　(1)
Rm 7-401 1st Building 118 Fuma Rd, Fuzhou, 350011, China
Tel.: (86) 5918 785 0152
Web Site: https://www.hansbell.com
Marine Equipment Mfr & Distr
N.A.I.C.S.: 333618

Hongkong Great International Enterprise Co., Limited　(1)
Room 1920 Building A4 The Wanda Plaza, Gangzha District, Nantong, 226000, Jiangsu, China
Tel.: (86) 1589 627 6111
Lighting Equipment Mfr
N.A.I.C.S.: 335139

KIMPEX, INC　(1)
235 Anthony Trail, Northbrook, IL 60062
Tel.: (847) 412-4600
Web Site: http://www.kimpexusa.com
Emp.: 5
Electronic Components Distr
N.A.I.C.S.: 423690
James Kim *(Gen Mgr)*

Kyokuyo Electric Co., Ltd.　(1)
19-1-1 Chiyozaki, Nishi-ku, Osaka, 550-0023, Japan
Tel.: (81) 66 581 5815
Web Site: https://www.kyokuyoe.co.jp
Electrical Equipment Distr
N.A.I.C.S.: 423610
Teppei Kamiya *(Pres)*

LEADERS INTERNATIONAL UK LTD
42 Purley Bury Avenue, Purley, CR8 1JD, Surrey, United Kingdom - England
Tel.: (44) 7831324625
Lighting Equipment Mfr
N.A.I.C.S.: 335139

LS Marine Co., Ltd.　(1)
Room 1006 Building 3 Forte Pujiang Center Lane 1505, Pujiang Lianhang Road Minhang District, Shanghai, 200122, China
Tel.: (86) 215 835 8980
Marine Equipment Mfr & Distr
N.A.I.C.S.: 333618

M&O Partners A/S　(1)
Vestre Stromkaien 7 8th Floor, Bergen, Norway
Tel.: (47) 9 301 7941
Lighting Equipment Mfr
N.A.I.C.S.: 335139

M&O Partners Ltda　(1)
Av Rio Branco 89/802, Centro, Rio de Janeiro, 20040-004, Brazil
Tel.: (55) 213 239 4850
Web Site: https://mopartners.global
Sale Development Services
N.A.I.C.S.: 541613
Erik Hannisdal *(Mng Partner)*

Nippon Diesel Service GmbH　(1)
Hermann-Blohm-Strasse 1, 20457, Hamburg, Germany
Tel.: (49) 40 317 7100
Web Site: https://nds-marine.com
Marine Spare Parts Mfr
N.A.I.C.S.: 333618

Nti Ltd.　(1)
Nakhimova St house 20 lit A 10th floor, 199226, Saint Petersburg, Russia
Tel.: (7) 8124244846
Web Site: http://www.nticorp.ru
Emp.: 80
Marine Equipment Mfr
N.A.I.C.S.: 336611

Offshoremarine Trading LLC　(1)
Dubai Investment Park, PO Box 33297, Dubai, United Arab Emirates
Tel.: (971) 4 812 4390
Lighting Equipment Mfr
N.A.I.C.S.: 335139

Penta Electromec Pvt. Ltd.　(1)
602 Rajhans Opp Gaon Devi Bus Depot Naupada Thane W, Mumbai, 400 602, Maharashtra, India
Tel.: (91) 222 537 8734
Web Site: https://www.pentaindia.co.in
Standard Professional Services
N.A.I.C.S.: 541990

Petromar Energy Services LLC　(1)
ADDAX Tower Office No 4803/4/5 City of Lights Al Reem Island, PO Box 47858, Abu Dhabi, United Arab Emirates
Tel.: (971) 2 644 4557
Web Site: https://www.petromar-thecompany.com
Oil & Gas Extraction Services
N.A.I.C.S.: 213112
Salim Shaikh *(CEO)*

Samhwa Trading Co., Ltd.　(1)
189 Bosu-daero, Seo-gu, Busan, 49216, Korea (South)
Tel.: (82) 51 831 1660
Web Site: https://www.shtc.kr
Ship Building Services
N.A.I.C.S.: 336611
Sung Yee Kim *(Pres)*

Shanghai Know-How Technologies Co., Ltd.　(1)
Floor 5th G10 Lane 3188 Xiu Pu Road, Kang Qiao Pudong, Shanghai, 201315, China
Tel.: (86) 216 443 9428
Lighting Equipment Mfr
N.A.I.C.S.: 335139

Sinhoo Group Co., Ltd.　(1)
Room 1510 Sinopec Material Tower No 139 Futexiyi Road, Pudong New District, Shanghai, 200129, China
Lighting Equipment Mfr
N.A.I.C.S.: 335139

Uzushio Enterprise Co., Ltd.　(1)
Ko-105 Noma, Imabari, Ehime, Japan
Tel.: (81) 89 823 8888
Web Site: https://www.bemac-uzushio.com
Electric Equipment Mfr
N.A.I.C.S.: 333618

ZIRCON ENGINEERING PTE LTD　(1)
7 Kaki Bukit Crescent Fullion Building, Singapore, 416239, Singapore
Tel.: (65) 6 288 8889
Web Site: https://www.zircon.com.sg
Emp.: 30
Marine Equipment Distr
N.A.I.C.S.: 423860

DAEYANG PAPER MFG. CO., LTD.
1062-1 Shingil-dong, Ansan, Kyounggi-do, Korea (South)
Tel.: (82) 314909302
Web Site:
　https://dygroup.gobizkorea.com
Year Founded: 1970
006580—(KRS)
Rev.: $94,602,621
Assets: $170,959,519
Liabilities: $60,013,888
Net Worth: $110,945,632
Earnings: ($2,398,190)
Emp.: 56
Fiscal Year-end: 12/31/22
Corrugated Cardboard Material Mfr
N.A.I.C.S.: 322130
Park Deuk Cheol *(CEO)*

DAFA PROPERTIES GROUP LTD.
Room 2805-06 28th Floor Bank of America Tower No 12 Harcourt Road, Central, China (Hong Kong)
Tel.: (852) 2123100338　Ky
Web Site: http://www.dafaland.com
Year Founded: 1996
6111—(HKG)
Rev.: $1,407,769,166
Assets: $5,373,143,185
Liabilities: $4,026,953,102
Net Worth: $1,346,190,083
Earnings: $109,596,322
Emp.: 1,029
Fiscal Year-end: 12/31/20
Real Estate Development Services
N.A.I.C.S.: 531390
Yiyang Ge *(Chm)*

DAFENG PORT HESHUN TECHNOLOGY COMPANY LIMITED
Unit 1009 Exchange Tower 33 Wang Chiu Road, Kowloon Bay, Kowloon, China (Hong Kong)
Tel.: (852) 25487800　Ky
Web Site: http://www.dfport.com.hk
8310—(HKG)
Rev.: $101,485,793
Assets: $96,811,898
Liabilities: $160,790,505
Net Worth: ($63,978,608)
Earnings: ($8,190,728)
Emp.: 95
Fiscal Year-end: 12/31/22
Freight Forwarding & Logistics
N.A.I.C.S.: 488510
Jing Xu *(Sec)*

Subsidiaries:

Win Top Shipping Company Limited　(1)
Rm 1903-6 Sterling Centre 11 Cheung Yue Street, Cheung Sha Wan, Kowloon, China (Hong Kong)
Tel.: (852) 2 541 9178
Web Site: https://www.wintop.com.hk
Logistics Consulting Servies
N.A.I.C.S.: 541614

Dafeng Port Heshun Technology Company
Limited—(Continued)

DAFENG TV LTD.

5F No 207 Sec 2 Zhonghua Rd,
Tucheng Dist, New Taipei City, Tai-
wan
Tel.: (886) 282538888
Web Site: http://www.dafeng.tv
6184—(TAI)
Rev.: $67,648,155
Assets: $222,152,122
Liabilities: $75,336,110
Net Worth: $146,816,012
Earnings: $17,055,724
Fiscal Year-end: 12/31/23
Digital Cable TV Services
N.A.I.C.S.: 516120
M. C. Chang *(Chm & Gen Mgr)*

DAFFODIL COMPUTERS LIM-
ITED

64/3 Lake Circus 2nd floor Mirpur Rd,
Dhaka, 1205, Bangladesh
Tel.: (880) 1713493161
Web Site: https://www.daffodil-
bd.com
Year Founded: 1990
DAFODILCOM—(CHT)
Rev.: $5,584,658
Assets: $9,230,950
Liabilities: $1,439,578
Net Worth: $7,791,371
Earnings: $403,533
Emp.: 172
Fiscal Year-end: 06/30/21
Software Development Services
N.A.I.C.S.: 541511
Mohammad Sabur Khan *(CEO &
Mng Dir)*

DAFORA S.A.

P-ta Regele Ferdinand I nr 15 Me-
dias, 551002, Sibiu, Romania
Tel.: (40) 259841668
Web Site: https://www.dafora.ro
DAFR—(BUC)
Rev.: $11,605,312
Assets: $19,486,483
Liabilities: $27,842,127
Net Worth: ($8,355,644)
Earnings: ($3,337,114)
Emp.: 183
Fiscal Year-end: 12/31/20
Oil, Gas & Geothermal Water On-
shore Drilling Services
N.A.I.C.S.: 213112

DAG DVERGSTEN AS

Munkedamsv 45 Entrance A 5th Floor
Vika Atrium, 0250, Oslo, Norway
Tel.: (47) 22 94 77 00
Web Site: http://www.dvergsten.com
Year Founded: 1994
Investment & Asset Management
Services
N.A.I.C.S.: 523999

Subsidiaries:

CellCura ASA   **(1)**
Uniongata 18, 3732, Skien, Norway
Tel.: (47) 22 94 77 00
Web Site: http://www.cellcura.com
Assisted Reproductive Technology & Stem
Cell Research Equipment Developer
N.A.I.C.S.: 339112
Tore Viana-Roenningen *(CEO)*

Subsidiary (Non-US):

CellCura Solutions A/S   **(2)**
Slotsmarken 18 2 sal, DK-2970, Horsholm,
Denmark
Tel.: (45) 70206750
Web Site: http://www.cellcurasolutions.com
Medical Software Solutions
N.A.I.C.S.: 513210

Subsidiary (US):

CellCura, Inc.   **(2)**
505 S Rosa Rd, Madison, WI 53719
Tel.: (608) 441-8075
Web Site: http://www.cellcura.com
Medical Diagnostic Equipment Distr
N.A.I.C.S.: 423450

DAGANG HOLDING GROUP
CO. LTD.

No 10 Biyuan 3rd Road High-tech
Zone, Xi'an, 710019, China
Tel.: (86) 2988328410
Web Site: https://www.sxdagang.com
300103—(CHIN)
Rev.: $55,150,524
Assets: $243,985,716
Liabilities: $102,741,912
Net Worth: $141,243,804
Earnings: ($47,427,120)
Fiscal Year-end: 12/31/22
Road Construction Machinery Mfr
N.A.I.C.S.: 333120
Jianxi Sun *(Chm)*

DAGANG NEXCHANGE BER-
HAD

Dagang Net Tower Block 10A&B Cor-
porate Park Star Central, Lingkaran
Cyberpoint Timur Cyber 12, 63000,
Cyberjaya, Selangor, Malaysia
Tel.: (60) 382306900
Web Site: https://www.dnex.com.my
Year Founded: 1970
DNEX—(KLS)
Rev.: $360,702,788
Assets: $1,144,843,425
Liabilities: $568,411,470
Net Worth: $576,431,955
Earnings: $175,050,315
Emp.: 1,729
Fiscal Year-end: 06/30/22
Information Technology Services
N.A.I.C.S.: 541512
Kek Siang Lim *(CFO-Grp)*

Subsidiaries:

DNeX Drilling Tech & Oilfield Ser-
vices Sdn. Bhd.   **(1)**
C3-3-15 Block C3 Solaris Dutamas No 1
Jalan Dutamas 1, 50480, Kuala Lumpur,
Malaysia
Tel.: (60) 364130669
Trade Facilitation Services
N.A.I.C.S.: 522299

DNeX Semiconductor Sdn. Bhd.   **(1)**
Dagang Net Tower Block 10 A & B Corpo-
rate Park, Star Central Lingkaran Cyber-
point Timur Cyber 12, 63000, Cyberjaya,
Selangor, Malaysia
Tel.: (60) 82306900
Semiconductor Mfr & Distr
N.A.I.C.S.: 334413

DNeX Technology Sdn. Bhd.   **(1)**
Tower 3 Avenue 5 The Horizon Bangsar
South No 8 Jalan Kerinchi, 59200, Kuala
Lumpur, Malaysia
Tel.: (60) 327300300
Trade Facilitation Services
N.A.I.C.S.: 522299

Dagang Net Technologies Sdn.
Bhd.   **(1)**
Dagang Net Tower Block 10 A and B Cor-
porate Park Star Central, Lingkaran Cyber-
point Timur Cyber 12, 63000, Cyberjaya,
Selangor, Malaysia
Tel.: (60) 382306900
Web Site: http://www.dagangnet.com
Ecommerce Services
N.A.I.C.S.: 541511
Asvinder Kaur *(COO)*

Subsidiary (Domestic):

Genaxis Group Sdn. Bhd.   **(2)**
Level 10-01-02 PJX-HM Shah Tower 16A
Persiaran Barat, 46050, Petaling Jaya, Se-
langor, Malaysia
Tel.: (60) 32 714 6105

Web Site: https://www.genaxis.com.my
Management Consulting Firm Services
N.A.I.C.S.: 541611
Nuraslina Zainal Abidin *(Mng Dir)*

Global eCommerce Limited   **(2)**
Brumby Centre Lot 42 Jalan Muhibbah,
87000, Labuan, Malaysia
Tel.: (60) 87593828
Trade Facilitation Services
N.A.I.C.S.: 522299

Subsidiary (Non-US):

PT Dagang Net Indonesia   **(2)**
Menara Kadin 30th Floor Jl HR Rasuna
Said Kav 2-3, Kav E 3 2 No 1, Jakarta,
12950, Indonesia
Tel.: (62) 2152994558
Trade Facilitation Services
N.A.I.C.S.: 522299

Subsidiary (Domestic):

SealNet Sdn. Bhd.   **(2)**
24 Jalan Astaka L U8/L, Bukit Jelutong,
40150, Shah Alam, Selangor, Malaysia
Tel.: (60) 378326583
Web Site: http://www.sealnet.com.my
Application & System Development Ser-
vices
N.A.I.C.S.: 541511

Forward Energy Generation Ltd.   **(1)**
Level 2 Lot 19 Lazenda Commercial Centre
Phase 3, 87007, Labuan, Malaysia
Tel.: (60) 87421644
Trade Facilitation Services
N.A.I.C.S.: 522299

OGPC Sdn. Bhd.   **(1)**
No 1 & 3 Jalan Riyal U3/37 iPARC 3 Shah
Alam Seksyen U3, 40150, Shah Alam, Se-
langor, Malaysia
Tel.: (60) 35 870 0100
Web Site: https://www.ogpc.com.my
Oil & Gas Operation Services
N.A.I.C.S.: 213112

Ping Petroleum UK PLC   **(1)**
H1 Hill of Rubislaw Anderson Drive, Aber-
deen, United Kingdom
Tel.: (44) 1224047954
Web Site: https://www.pingpetroleum.com
Oil & Gas Services
N.A.I.C.S.: 213112

Silterra Malaysia Sdn Bhd   **(1)**
Lot 8 Phase II Kulim Hi-Tech Park, 09090,
Kulim, Kedah Darul Aman, Malaysia
Tel.: (60) 4 401 5111
Web Site: https://www.silterra.com
Semiconductor Equipment Mfr
N.A.I.C.S.: 334413
Arjun Kumar Kanthimahanti *(Sr VP-Tech
Dev)*

Subsidiary (US):

SilTerra USA Inc.   **(2)**
2880 Zanker Rd Ste 203, San Jose, CA
95134
Tel.: (408) 530-0888
Semiconductor Equipment Distr
N.A.I.C.S.: 423690

Subsidiary (Non-US):

Silterra Sales & Marketing (L)
Ltd.   **(2)**
20F-3 No 295 Sec 2 Kuang-Fu Road, Jalan
Desa Bahagia, Hsin-chu, Taiwan
Tel.: (886) 3 516 5577
Web Site: http://www.silterra.com
Semiconductor Equipment Distr
N.A.I.C.S.: 423690
Lai Yit Loong *(Exec VP-Sls & Mktg-World
Wide)*

DAGESTAN ENERGOSBYT
COMPANY

st Dakhadaeva 73, Makhachkala,
367000, Russia
Tel.: (7) 8722663659
Web Site: https://dag-esk.ru
Year Founded: 2005
DASB—(MOEX)
Sales Range: Less than $1 Million
Electric Power Distribution Services

N.A.I.C.S.: 221122

DAGI GIYIM SANAYI VE TI-
CARET A.S.

Birahane Sokak Plaza 3/1, Bomonti
Sisli, Istanbul, Turkiye
Tel.: (90) 2122404065
Web Site: http://www.dagi.com.tr
Sales Range: $10-24.9 Million
Emp.: 180
Underwear, Nightwear, Sportswear,
Maternity & Other Clothing Mfr
N.A.I.C.S.: 315120
Mahmut Nedim Koc *(Chm)*

DAGI YATIRIM HOLDING A.S.

Birahane St KOC Plaza No 3 F 4/5,
Bomonti Sisli, Istanbul, Turkiye
Tel.: (90) 2123461515
Web Site:
    https://www.dagiholding.com
Year Founded: 1994
DAGHL—(IST)
Rev.: $16,870,249
Assets: $4,230,966
Liabilities: $3,208,443
Net Worth: $1,022,523
Earnings: ($1,522,005)
Fiscal Year-end: 12/31/23
Holding Company
N.A.I.C.S.: 551112
Mahmut Nedim Koc *(Chm)*

DAGMAR OY

Lonnrotinkatu 25 A, 00180, Helsinki,
Finland
Tel.: (358) 9693011
Web Site: http://www.dagmar.fi
Year Founded: 1973
Sales Range: $200-249.9 Million
Emp.: 135
Fiscal Year-end: 08/31/12
N.A.I.C.S.: 541810
Tuula Kallio *(CEO & Mng Dir)*

DAH SAN ELECTRIC WIRE &
CABLE CO., LTD.

No 369 Sec 3 Yun-Lin Rd, Douliu,
640101, Yunlin, Taiwan
Tel.: (886) 55222331
Web Site: http://www.dahsan.com.tw
1615—(TAI)
Rev.: $161,698,676
Assets: $147,196,862
Liabilities: $50,641,517
Net Worth: $96,555,345
Earnings: $17,169,462
Fiscal Year-end: 12/31/23
Power & Communication Cables Mfr
N.A.I.C.S.: 335929
Wen-Pin Su *(Chm, Pres & Gen Mgr)*

Subsidiaries:

Dah San Electric Wire & Cable Co.,
Ltd. - Second Factory   **(1)**
No 369 Xiping Rd, Douliu, 640009, Yunlin,
Taiwan
Tel.: (886) 5 551 8868
Web Site: http://www.dahsan.com.tw
Electrical Cables Mfr
N.A.I.C.S.: 331318

DAH SING FINANCIAL HOLD-
INGS LIMITED

26 th Floor Dah sing Financial Center
248 Queen s Road East, Hong Kong,
China (Hong Kong)
Tel.: (852) 25078866
Web Site: https://www.dahsing.com
DSFGY—(OTCIQ)
Rev.: $895,617,979
Assets: $33,208,517,387
Liabilities: $28,460,150,293
Net Worth: $4,748,367,094
Earnings: $202,398,175
Emp.: 3,047
Fiscal Year-end: 12/31/22

Bank Holding Company
N.A.I.C.S.: 551111
David Shou-Yeh Wong *(Chm)*

Subsidiaries:

Banco Comercial de Macau, S.A. (1)
Avenida Da Praia Grande 572, Macau, China (Macau)
Tel.: (853) 87910000
Web Site: https://www.bcm.com.mo
Banking Services
N.A.I.C.S.: 522110
Mariana Cheang *(Mgr-PMD)*

Bank Consortium Trust Company Limited (1)
18/F Cosco Tower 183 Queen's Road, Central, China (Hong Kong)
Tel.: (852) 22989800
Web Site: https://www.bcthk.com
Pension Plan Services
N.A.I.C.S.: 525110

Dah Sing Bank Limited (1)
26th Floor Dah Sing Financial Centre 248 Queen's Road East, Wan Chai, Hong Kong, China (Hong Kong) (100%)
Tel.: (852) 28288168
Web Site: https://www.dahsing.com
Rev.: $959,561,446
Emp.: 1,000
Fiscal Year-end: 12/31/2019
N.A.I.C.S.: 522299

Dah Sing Banking Group Limited (1)
26th Floor Dah Sing Financial Centre 248 Queen's Road East, 108 Gloucester Rd, Wanchai, China (Hong Kong)
Tel.: (852) 25078866
Web Site: https://www.dahsing.com
Commericial Banking
N.A.I.C.S.: 522110
David Shou-Yeh Wong *(Chm)*

Dah Sing Company Limited (1)
36th Floor Dah Sing Financial Centre, 108 Gloucester Rd, Wanchai, China (Hong Kong)
Tel.: (852) 25078866
Holding Company
N.A.I.C.S.: 551112
David Shou-Yeh Wong *(Chm)*

Dah Sing Finance Limited (1)
36th Floor Dah Sing Financial Centre, 108 Gloucester Rd, Wanchai, China (Hong Kong)
Tel.: (852) 25078866
Nondepository Credit Intermediation
N.A.I.C.S.: 522299

Dah Sing General Insurance Company Limited (1)
2703 27/F Island Place Tower 510 King's Road, North Point, China (Hong Kong) (100%)
Tel.: (852) 2 808 5000
Web Site:
  https://www.dahsinginsurance.com
Sales Range: $50-74.9 Million
Emp.: 30
Insurance Agencies & Brokerages
N.A.I.C.S.: 524210

Dah Sing Insurance Company (1976) Limited (1)
2703 27/F Island Place Tower 510 King's Road, North Point, China (Hong Kong)
Tel.: (852) 28085000
Web Site:
  https://www.dahsinginsurance.com
Insurance Services
N.A.I.C.S.: 524210

Dah Sing Nominees Ltd (1)
36th Floor Dah Sing Financial Centre, 108 Gloucester Road, Wanchai, China (Hong Kong)
Tel.: (852) 25078866
Real Estate Investment Trust
N.A.I.C.S.: 525990
David Shou-Yeh Wong *(Chm)*

Macau Insurance Company Limited (1)
Avenida da Praia Grande No 594 Edf BCM 11/F, Macau, China (Macau)
Tel.: (853) 2 855 5078

Web Site: https://www.mic.com.mo
Sales Range: $50-74.9 Million
Emp.: 60
Insurance Agencies & Brokerages
N.A.I.C.S.: 524210
Diamond Lo *(CEO)*

Mevas Bank Limited (1)
33rd Floor Dah Sing Financial Centre, PO Box 141, 108 Gloucester Road, Wanchai, China (Hong Kong) (74.9%)
Tel.: (852) 31013101
Sales Range: $50-74.9 Million
Emp.: 35
Commericial Banking
N.A.I.C.S.: 522110

DAHENG NEW EPOCH TECHNOLOGY, INC.
15F North Block Daheng Technology Building No 3 Suzhou Street, Haidian District, Beijing, 100080, China
Tel.: (86) 1082827855
Web Site: http://www.dhxjy.com.cn
Year Founded: 1998
600288—(SHG)
Rev.: $326,031,067
Assets: $504,459,166
Liabilities: $193,931,880
Net Worth: $310,527,285
Earnings: $9,763,233
Fiscal Year-end: 12/31/22
Information Technology Equipment Mfr & Whslr
N.A.I.C.S.: 334220
Lu Yongzhi *(Chm & Pres)*

Subsidiaries:

Beijing DVT Technology Co., Ltd. (1)
12F Daheng Scitech Mansion No 3 Suzhou Street, Haidian District, Beijing, 100080, China
Tel.: (86) 1082827795
Electronic Device Mfr & Distr
N.A.I.C.S.: 334413

Beijing Daheng Electric Co., Ltd. (1)
Floor 11A Zhongke Building 22 Zhongguan-cun Street, Haidian District, Beijing, 100080, China
Tel.: (86) 1062628380
Electro Mechanical Product Mfr & Distr
N.A.I.C.S.: 334513

Beijing Daheng Laser Equipment Co., Ltd. (1)
No 8 Kechuang 3 street East Road, Yizhuang Economic and Technology Development Area, Beijing, 100076, China
Tel.: (86) 106 789 2150
Web Site: https://www.dahenglaser.com
Laser Cutting Machine Mfr & Distr
N.A.I.C.S.: 333517

Beijing Daheng Medical Equipment Co., Ltd. (1)
9th Floor North Block Daheng Technology Building No 3 Suzhou Street, Haidian District, Beijing, 100080, China
Tel.: (86) 4006805120
Web Site: http://www.dahengmedical.com
Medical Equipment Mfr & Distr
N.A.I.C.S.: 334510

Beijing Gaoneng Daheng Accelerator Technology Co. Ltd. (1)
616B Lingxiu Building 1 Gucheng Street, Shijingshan District, Beijing, 100043, China
Tel.: (86) 1088233118
Electronic Device Mfr & Distr
N.A.I.C.S.: 334413

Bejing Daheng Creative Technology Co., Ltd. (1)
11/F Daheng Scitech Mansion No 3 Suzhou Street, Haidian District, Beijing, 100080, China
Tel.: (86) 1082828800
Web Site: http://www.dahengit.com
Display Product Mfr & Distr
N.A.I.C.S.: 334419

Dayang Technology Development Inc. (1)
Dayang Building Zhongguancun Software

Park 11, Haidian District, Beijing, 100193, China
Tel.: (86) 1058985588
Web Site: http://www.en.dayang.com.cn
Communication Equipment Mfr
N.A.I.C.S.: 334220

Subsidiary (Non-US):

Dayang International (Singapore) Pte Ltd (2)
90 middle road 19-05 Fortune Centre, Singapore, 188979, Singapore
Tel.: (65) 85224051
Communication Equipment Distr
N.A.I.C.S.: 423690

Dayang International (Thailand) Co., Ltd (2)
Floor 20 Room 2002 Le Concorde Building Ratchadapisek Road, Huaykwang District, Bangkok, 10320, Thailand
Tel.: (66) 26941919
Communication Equipment Distr
N.A.I.C.S.: 423690

Taizhou Mingxin Microelectronics Co., Ltd. (1)
No 76 East Phoenix Road, Hailing District, Taizhou, 225300, Jiangsu, China
Tel.: (86) 5238 687 5801
Web Site: http://www.china-mingxin.com
Electronic Device Mfr & Distr
N.A.I.C.S.: 334413

DAHER GROUP
1 Allee Maryse Bastie, 91325, Wissous, Cedex, France
Tel.: (33) 149759800
Web Site: http://www.daher.com
Year Founded: 1863
Sales Range: $750-799.9 Million
Emp.: 5,000
Aerospace Equipment Manufacturing & Services
N.A.I.C.S.: 336412
Patrick Daher *(Chm)*

Subsidiaries:

DAHER Industry & Defence (1)
10 Pl de la Joliette, BP 32312, 13567, Marseilles, France
Tel.: (33) 491397500
Sales Range: $25-49.9 Million
Emp.: 50
Industrial Parts Mfr
N.A.I.C.S.: 336419

DAHER Support Management (1)
10 Place de la Joliette, 13567, Marseilles, France
Tel.: (33) 491397500
Support Services
N.A.I.C.S.: 561499

Quest Aircraft Company, LLC (1)
1200 Turbine Dr, Sandpoint, ID 83864
Tel.: (208) 263-1111
Web Site: http://www.questaircraft.com
Aircraft Mfr
N.A.I.C.S.: 336411
Nicholas Newby *(Sr VP-Sls, Mktg & Customer Svc)*

DAHU AQUACULTURE COMPANY LIMITED
No 348 Jianshe East Road Jianminxiang Community Danyang Street, Changde, 415000, Hunan, China
Tel.: (86) 7367252796
Web Site: http://www.dhszgf.com
Year Founded: 1999
600257—(SHG)
Rev.: $153,697,677
Assets: $303,527,433
Liabilities: $162,934,790
Net Worth: $140,592,643
Earnings: ($10,037,912)
Fiscal Year-end: 12/31/22
Fish Farming Services
N.A.I.C.S.: 112511
Dingkun Luo *(Chm & Gen Mgr)*

Subsidiaries:

Hunan Dehai Pharmaceutical Co., Ltd. (1)
Group 3 Chongde Neighborhood Committee, Economic & Technological Development Zone Deshan Town, Changde, China
Tel.: (86) 7367321988
Web Site: http://www.hndhzy.com
Medicinal Material Mfr
N.A.I.C.S.: 325412

Hunan Xiangyun Biotechnology Co., Ltd. (1)
No 1183 Shanju Road, Dingcheng District, Changde, 415101, Hunan, China
Tel.: (86) 7367301999
Web Site: https://www.xiang-yun.com
Aquatic Product Food Services
N.A.I.C.S.: 424460
Yang Zhen *(Gen Mgr)*

DAHUA GROUP DALIAN CHEMICAL INDUSTRY CO., LTD.
Songmudao Chemical Industrial Park Puwan New Area, Dalian, 116038, Liaoning, China
Tel.: (86) 411 86893436
Web Site: http://www.dahuagf.com
Rev.: $46,229,825
Assets: $107,964,668
Liabilities: $100,237,565
Net Worth: $7,727,102
Earnings: ($20,157,256)
Fiscal Year-end: 12/31/18
Chemical Product Mfr & Distr
N.A.I.C.S.: 325180
Wei Zhang *(Chm-Interim)*

DAHUA INC.
8th Floor Officer Tower 3 Henderson Center, 18 Jianguomennei Street Dongcheng District, Beijing, 100005, China
Tel.: (86) 1064801527   DE
Year Founded: 2002
DHUA—(OTCIQ)
Sales Range: Less than $1 Million
Emp.: 65
Residential Construction
N.A.I.C.S.: 236115

DAI CHAU JSC
Group 23 Section 4 Nhat Tan Ward, Tay Ho District, Hanoi, Vietnam
Tel.: (84) 437194353
Web Site:
  http://www.daichaugroup.com
Rev.: $5,986,633
Assets: $26,770,050
Liabilities: $1,472,300
Net Worth: $25,297,750
Earnings: ($108,251)
Emp.: 70
Fiscal Year-end: 12/31/17
Wooden Furniture Mfr
N.A.I.C.S.: 337211

DAI HAN PHARMACEUTICAL CO., LTD.
3 Seonyu-ro 45-gil Yeongdeungpo-gu, Seoul, 07209, Korea (South)
Tel.: (82) 226783911   KR
Web Site: https://www.daihan.com
Year Founded: 1945
023910—(KRS)
Rev.: $151,743,220
Assets: $227,913,250
Liabilities: $35,844,920
Net Worth: $192,068,330
Earnings: $22,017,603
Emp.: 708
Fiscal Year-end: 12/31/23
Pharmaceutical Developer, Mfr & Whslr
N.A.I.C.S.: 325412
Yoonwoo Lee *(CEO)*

Dai Han Pharmaceutical Co., Ltd.—(Continued)

DAI NIPPON PRINTING CO., LTD.

1-1-1 Ichigaya Kagacho, Shinjuku-ku,
Tokyo, 162-8001, Japan
Tel.: (81) 332662111
Web Site: https://www.dnp.co.jp
Year Founded: 1876
7912—(TKS)
Rev.: $9,418,073,420
Assets: $12,926,707,690
Liabilities: $4,752,206,620
Net Worth: $8,174,501,070
Earnings: $733,240,690
Emp.: 36,911
Fiscal Year-end: 03/31/24
Printing Materials Distr
N.A.I.C.S.: 424110
Masato Yamaguchi *(Sr Mng Dir)*

Subsidiaries:

2Dfacto, Inc. (1)
1-1-1 Ichigaya Kagacho, Shinjuku-ku, To-
kyo, 162-8001, Japan
Tel.: (81) 358607565
Web Site: https://www.2dfacto.co.jp
N.A.I.C.S.: 513130
Ikko Suzuki *(Pres)*

Aseptic Systems Co., Ltd. (1)
1-1-1 Ichigaya-Kagacho, Shinjuku-ku, Tokyo, 162-8001, Japan
Tel.: (81) 367350809
N.A.I.C.S.: 561910

CP Design Consulting Co., Ltd. (1)
3-5-20 Nishigotanda DNP Gotanda Building,
Shinagawa-ku, Tokyo, 141-8001, Japan
Tel.: (81) 363867332
Web Site: https://www.cpdc.co.jp
Environmental Consulting Services
N.A.I.C.S.: 541620

D.N.K. Co., Ltd. (1)
2-21-8 Kichijoji Honmachi, Musashino, 180-
0004, Tokyo, Japan
Tel.: (81) 42 222 7787
Web Site: https://www.chuos.com
Machine Tools Repair & Maintenance Ser-
vices
N.A.I.C.S.: 811310
Saito Maoru *(Pres)*

DNP (Singapore) Pte. Ltd. (1)
456 Alexandra Road 05-01/02/03 Fragrance
Empire Building, Singapore, 119962,
Singapore **(100%)**
Tel.: (65) 64697611
Web Site: http://www.dnp.co.jp
Sales Range: $25-49.9 Million
Emp.: 17
Sales of Printed Matter
N.A.I.C.S.: 541890

DNP (UK) Co. Ltd. (1)
4th Fl 27 Throgmorton St, London, EC2N
2AQ, United Kingdom **(100%)**
Tel.: (44) 2075882088
Web Site: http://www.dnp.co.jp
Sales Range: $25-49.9 Million
Emp.: 3
Sales of Printed Matter
N.A.I.C.S.: 541890

DNP AV Center Co., Ltd. (1)
DNP Ichigaya Sanaimachi Building 1-1-1
Ichigaya Kagacho, Shinjuku-ku, Tokyo, 162-
8001, Japan
Tel.: (81) 364313510
Web Site: https://www.dnp-cd.co.jp
Emp.: 70
Graphic Software Development Services
N.A.I.C.S.: 541511
Jun Itou *(Mng Dir)*

**DNP Art Communications Co.,
Ltd.** (1)
1-1-1 Ichigaya Kagacho, Shinjuku-ku, To-
kyo, 162-8001, Japan
Tel.: (81) 367356515
Web Site: https://www.dnpartcom.jp
Arts & Graphic Design Services
N.A.I.C.S.: 541430

**DNP Business Consulting (Shanghai)
Co., Ltd.** (1)

Suite 602 Shanghai Centre No 6 Building
1376 Nanjing Xi Lu, Shanghai, China
Tel.: (86) 2162797807
Plastics Product Mfr & Distr
N.A.I.C.S.: 326199

DNP Chubu Co., Ltd. (1)
3-902 Seko, Moriyama-ku, Nagoya, 463-
8543, Aichi, Japan
Tel.: (81) 527582215
Web Site: http://www.dnp-chubu.co.jp
Books Publishing Services
N.A.I.C.S.: 513130

**DNP Color Techno Kameyama Co.,
Ltd.** (1)
464 Shiraki-cho, Kameyama, 519-0169,
Mie, Japan
Tel.: (81) 595842650
Color Filters Mfr
N.A.I.C.S.: 334419

DNP Corporation USA (1)
335 Madison Ave Lbby 3, New York, NY
10017-4646 **(100%)**
Tel.: (212) 503-1850
Web Site: http://www.dnp.co.jp
Sales Range: $25-49.9 Million
Emp.: 14
Printing & Publishing Services
N.A.I.C.S.: 424110

Subsidiary (Domestic):

DNP America, LLC (2)
335 Madison Ave 3rd Fl, New York, NY
10017
Tel.: (212) 503-1060
Web Site: http://www.dnpamerica.com
Precision Electronic Component Whslr
N.A.I.C.S.: 423830

Subsidiary (Domestic):

DNP (AMERICA), Inc. (3)
101 Uhland Rd Ste 210, San Marcos, TX
78666 **(100%)**
Tel.: (512) 753-7280
Web Site: http://www.dnpphoto.com
Sales Range: $25-49.9 Million
Emp.: 50
Printing Whslr
N.A.I.C.S.: 424110

Subsidiary (Domestic):

DNP Electronics America, LLC (2)
2391 Fenton St, Chula Vista, CA 91914
Tel.: (619) 397-6700
Web Site: http://www.dnpamerica.com
Precision Electronic Component Mfr &
Whslr
N.A.I.C.S.: 334419
Toshiyuki Suzuki *(Pres)*

**DNP Imagingcomm America
Corporation** (2)
4524 Enterprise Dr NW, Concord, NC
28027
Tel.: (704) 784-8100
Web Site: https://www.dnpphoto.com
Inked Ribbon Mfr
N.A.I.C.S.: 339940
Shinichi Yamashita *(Pres)*

Subsidiary (Domestic):

**DNP Imagingcomm America
Corporation** (3)
1001 Technology Dr, Mount Pleasant, PA
15666-1766
Tel.: (724) 696-7500
Sales Range: $25-49.9 Million
Emp.: 200
Inked Ribbon Mfr
N.A.I.C.S.: 339940

Foto Fantasy, Inc. (3)
8A Industrial Way, Salem, NH 03079-2837
Tel.: (603) 324-3240
Web Site: http://wp.innovativefoto.com
Sales Range: $2-4.9 Million
Emp.: 110
Photo Booth Mfr & Operator
N.A.I.C.S.: 333310
Dale Valvo *(Pres & CEO)*

DNP Data Techno Co., Ltd. (1)
1650-70 Okubaracho, Ushiku, 300-1283,
Ibaraki, Japan
Tel.: (81) 298752211

Plastic Parts Mfr
N.A.I.C.S.: 326199

**DNP Data Techno Kansai Co.,
Ltd.** (1)
712-10 Toin Kawanishicho, Shiki-gun, Nara,
636-0204, Japan
Tel.: (81) 745441121
Commercial Printing Services
N.A.I.C.S.: 323111

DNP Denmark A/S (1)
Skruegangen 2, 2690, Karlslunde, Denmark
Tel.: (45) 4 616 5100
Web Site: https://www.dnp-screens.com
Sales Range: $50-74.9 Million
Emp.: 75
Optical Projection Screens Distr
N.A.I.C.S.: 423410
Niels Hermansen *(COO)*

DNP Digital Solutions Co., Ltd. (1)
1-1-1 Ichigaya Kagacho, Shinjuku-ku, Tokyo, 162-8001, Japan
Tel.: (81) 332662111
N.A.I.C.S.: 541519

DNP Digitalcom Co., Ltd. (1)
DNP Gotanda Bldg 3-5-20 Nishi Gotanda,
Shinagawa-ku, Tokyo, 141-8001, Japan
Tel.: (81) 364316000
Web Site: http://www.dnp-digi.com
Sales Range: $75-99.9 Million
Emp.: 436
Web Consulting Services
N.A.I.C.S.: 541512

DNP Ellio Co., Ltd. (1)
4013 Nakatsu, Aikawa, Aiko, 243-0303, Ka-
nagawa, Japan
Tel.: (81) 462857743
N.A.I.C.S.: 332322
Kenji Yasuda *(Pres)*

DNP Engineering Co., Ltd. (1)
1-1-3 Midorigahara, Tsukuba, 300-2646,
Ibaraki, Japan
Tel.: (81) 298470589
N.A.I.C.S.: 513130
Toshiyuki Ogihara *(Pres)*

DNP Facility Services Co., Ltd. (1)
DNP Facility Service Ichigaya Building 2-1
Ichigaya Takajocho, Shinjuku-ku, Tokyo,
162-0848, Japan
Tel.: (81) 332664743
Web Site: https://www.dnp.co.jp
Emp.: 705
Building Facility Management Services
N.A.I.C.S.: 561210

DNP Fine Chemicals Co., Ltd. (1)
450 Aotocho, Midori-ku, Yokohama, 226-
0022, Kanagawa, Japan
Tel.: (81) 459325121
Emp.: 332
Chemical Products Mfr
N.A.I.C.S.: 325199
Itsuo Totsuka *(Pres)*

**DNP Fine Chemicals Utsunomiya
Co., Ltd.** (1)
1062-8 Honjo, Nishikata, Tochigi, 322-0606,
Tochigi, Japan
Tel.: (81) 282920321
N.A.I.C.S.: 513130
Hideaki Fujii *(Pres)*

DNP Fine Electronics Co., Ltd. (1)
2-2-1 Fukuoka, Fujimino, 356-0011, Sai-
tama, Japan
Tel.: (81) 492782458
Semiconductor Devices Mfr
N.A.I.C.S.: 334413

DNP Fotolusio Co., Ltd. (1)
3-35-13 Yayoi-cho, Nakano-ku, Tokyo, 164-
0013, Japan
Tel.: (81) 367020810
Web Site: http://www.fotolusio.jp
Commercial Printing Services
N.A.I.C.S.: 323111

DNP Graphica Co., Ltd. (1)
1-1-1 Ichigaya Kagacho, Shinjuku Ward,
Tochigi, 322-0606, Japan
Tel.: (81) 282921200
Web Site: https://www.dnp.co.jp
Emp.: 1,194
Commercial Printing Services
N.A.I.C.S.: 323111

DNP Hokkaido Co., Ltd. (1)
11-1-1 Kita7johigashi, Higashi-Ku, Sapporo,
065-0007, Hokkaido, Japan
Tel.: (81) 11 750 2205
Web Site: http://www.dnp.co.jp
Packaging Product Mfr & Distr
N.A.I.C.S.: 322299

DNP Holding USA Corporation (1)
335 Madison Ave Fl 3, New York, NY 10017
Tel.: (212) 503-1860
Investment Management Service
N.A.I.C.S.: 523999

DNP Hoso Co., Ltd. (1)
2-10-25 Akabane Minami, Kita-ku, Tokyo,
115-0044, Japan
Tel.: (81) 339038900
Packaging Product Distr
N.A.I.C.S.: 423840

DNP Human Services Co., Ltd. (1)
DNP Ichigaya Sanaicho Building 1-1-1 Ichi-
gaya Kagacho, Shinjuku-ku, Tokyo, 162-
8001, Japan
Tel.: (81) 367356990
N.A.I.C.S.: 513130
Masahiko Kawamura *(Pres)*

DNP HyperTech Co., Ltd (1)
ASTEM Kyoto Research Park Chudoji
Minami-machi 134 Shimogyo-ku, Kyoto,
600-8813, Japan
Tel.: (81) 753221228
Web Site: https://www.hypertech.co.jp
Software Publishing Services
N.A.I.C.S.: 513210

DNP ID System Co., Ltd. (1)
Forecast Shinjuku South 6F 4-3-17 Shin-
juku, Shinjuku-ku, Tokyo, 160-0022, Japan
Tel.: (81) 333504611
Precision Electronic Component Whslr
N.A.I.C.S.: 423830

**DNP Imaging Communication
(Shanghai) Co., Ltd.** (1)
1376 Nanjing Xi Lu Suite 603, Shanghai,
200040, China
Tel.: (86) 2162797809
Web Site: https://www.dnpphoto.com
Printer Mfr & Distr
N.A.I.C.S.: 334112

**DNP Imagingcomm Asia Sdn.
Bhd.** (1)
Plo 676 Jalan Nikel 4, Kawasan Perindus-
trian Pasir Gudang, 81700, Pasir Gudang,
Johor, Malaysia
Tel.: (60) 7 257 8400
Web Site: https://asia-dnpribbons.com
Thermal Transfer Ribbon Mfr
N.A.I.C.S.: 333248
Yosuke Ogawa *(Mng Dir)*

DNP Imagingcomm Europe B.V. (1)
Oudeweg 42, 2031 CC, Haarlem, Nether-
lands
Tel.: (31) 235533060
Web Site: http://www.eu.dnpribbons.com
Thermal Transfer Ribbon Mfr
N.A.I.C.S.: 333248

**DNP Information Systems Co.,
Ltd.** (1)
3-5-20 Nishigotonda, Shinagawa-ku, Tokyo,
141-8001, Japan **(100%)**
Tel.: (81) 3 6431 4840
Web Site: http://www.dnp-is.co.jp
Emp.: 874
Computer Software Development Services
N.A.I.C.S.: 541511
Koji Yoshifuku *(Pres & Dir)*

**DNP International Trading (Shanghai)
Co., Ltd.** (1)
1376 Nanjing Xi Lu Suite 603B, Shanghai,
200040, China
Tel.: (86) 2162798511
Commercial Printing Services
N.A.I.C.S.: 323111

DNP LSI Design Co., Ltd. (1)
2-2-1 Fukuoka, Fujimino, 356-8507, Sai-
tama, Japan
Tel.: (81) 49 278 1912
Web Site: http://www.dnp.co.jp
Semiconductor Components Mfr
N.A.I.C.S.: 334413
Sakamoto Hiromasa *(Pres)*

DNP Logistics Co., Ltd. **(1)**
2-20-7 Akabaneminami, Kita-ku, Tokyo, 115-
8585, Japan
Tel.: (81) 339038940
Web Site: http://www.dnp.co.jp
Warehouse Management Services
N.A.I.C.S.: 493110

DNP Media Art Co., Ltd. **(1)**
1-1-1 Ichigaya Kaga-cho, Shinjuku-ku, To-
kyo, 162-0062, Japan
Tel.: (81) 367356030
Web Site: https://www.dnp.co.jp
Commercial Printing Services
N.A.I.C.S.: 323111

DNP Media Create Co., Ltd. **(1)**
7 Enokicho, Shinjuku-ku, Tokyo, 162-0806,
Japan
Tel.: (81) 352616444
Commercial Photography Services
N.A.I.C.S.: 541922

DNP Media Support Co., Ltd. **(1)**
2-11-1 Shinomiya, Kadoma, 571-0017,
Osaka, Japan
Tel.: (81) 728850373
N.A.I.C.S.: 513130
Shoichi Goto *(Pres)*

DNP Micro Technica Co., Ltd. **(1)**
2-2-1 Fukuoka, Fujimino, 356-0011, Sai-
tama, Japan
Tel.: (81) 492781658
Industrial Machinery Mfr
N.A.I.C.S.: 333248

DNP Multi Print Co., Ltd. **(1)**
1-1-1 DNP Ichigayasanai Building
Ichigayakaga-cho, Shinjuku-ku, Tokyo, 162-
0842, Japan **(100%)**
Tel.: (81) 367350822
Web Site: http://www.dnp.co.jp
Commercial Printing Services
N.A.I.C.S.: 323111
Ido Takashi *(Pres)*

DNP Nishi Nippon Co., Ltd. **(1)**
2-16-36 Shimizu, Minami-ku, Fukuoka, 815-
0031, Japan
Tel.: (81) 925534144
Packaging Product Mfr & Distr
N.A.I.C.S.: 322220

DNP Photo Imaging Co., Ltd. **(1)**
3-35-13 Yayoicho, Nakano-ku, Tokyo, 164-
0013, Japan
Tel.: (81) 367020420
Books Publishing Services
N.A.I.C.S.: 513130

DNP Photo Imaging Europe SAS **(1)**
Z I Paris Nord 2 22 Avenue des Nations,
CS 51077, Roissy CDG, 95948, Roissy-en-
France, Cedex, France
Tel.: (33) 14 938 6550
Web Site: https://www.dnpphoto.eu
Sales Range: $25-49.9 Million
Emp.: 47
Photo Imaging Products Distr
N.A.I.C.S.: 423410
Roch Hollande *(Pres & Mng Editor)*

**DNP Photo Imaging Japan Co.,
Ltd.** **(1)**
1-1-1 Ichigaya Kagacho, Shinjuku-ku, To-
kyo, 162-8001, Japan
Tel.: (81) 120372010
N.A.I.C.S.: 513130

DNP Photo Imaging Russia LLC **(1)**
3rd Yamskogo Polya St 2 Building 7 Room
1 Office 17, Moscow, 125124, Russia
Tel.: (7) 4958990474
Web Site: https://www.dnpphoto.eu
N.A.I.C.S.: 513130

DNP Photomask Europe S.p.A. **(1)**
Via Camillo Olivetti 2/A, 20041, Agrate Bri-
anza, MB, Italy
Tel.: (39) 0396549300
Web Site: www.dnp-europe.it
Photomasks Mfr & Whslr
N.A.I.C.S.: 325992

DNP Planning Network Co., Ltd. **(1)**
2-3-12 Higashi-Shinagawa Seafort Square
Center Building 6th floor, Shinagawa-ku,
Tokyo, 140-0002, Japan
Tel.: (81) 357962831
Web Site: https://www.dnpplanet.co.jp

Emp.: 167
Content Production Services
N.A.I.C.S.: 512110

**DNP Plastic Molding (Shanghai) Co.,
Ltd.** **(1)**
888-2-1-A Taishunlu Anting Zhen Jiading
Qu, Shanghai, China
Tel.: (86) 21 3958 7045
Plastics Product Mfr
N.A.I.C.S.: 326199

DNP Precision Devices Co., Ltd. **(1)**
2-2-1 Fukuoka, Fujimino, 356-0011, Sai-
tama, Japan
Tel.: (81) 492782456
Electronic Components Mfr
N.A.I.C.S.: 334419

DNP SP Tech Co., Ltd. **(1)**
3-10-17 Nishigotanda, Shinagawa-ku, To-
kyo, 141-0031, Japan
Tel.: (81) 334924825
Web Site: http://www.dnp.co.jp
Outdoor Advertising Services
N.A.I.C.S.: 541850

DNP Shikoku Co., Ltd. **(1)**
1-15 Nakashimadacho, Tokushima, 770-
0052, Japan
Tel.: (81) 886313279
Web Site: https://www.dnp.co.jp
Emp.: 181
Commercial Printing Services
N.A.I.C.S.: 323111

DNP Tamura Plastic Co., Ltd. **(1)**
3-41 Kokihigashi, Komaki, 485-8532, Aichi,
Japan
Tel.: (81) 568774165
Web Site: https://www.tamura.co.jp
Emp.: 210
Plastic Product Mfr & Distr
N.A.I.C.S.: 326199

DNP Techno Polymer Co., Ltd. **(1)**
409 Toyofuta, Kashiwa, 277-0872, Chiba,
Japan
Tel.: (81) 471321731
Web Site: http://www.dnp.co.jp
Molded Plastic Product Mfr
N.A.I.C.S.: 326199

DNP Technopack Co., Ltd. **(1)**
2-6-1 Hirosedai, Sayama, 350-1328, Sai-
tama, Japan
Tel.: (81) 429550582
Containers & Packaging Products Mfr &
Distr
N.A.I.C.S.: 322220

DNP Technopack Tokai Co., Ltd. **(1)**
1646-39 Nasubigawa, Nakatsugawa, 509-
9132, Gifu, Japan
Tel.: (81) 573686122
Packaging Paper Products Mfr
N.A.I.C.S.: 322299

**DNP Technopack Yokohama Co.,
Ltd.** **(1)**
3500 Ikonobecho, Tsuzuki-ku, Yokohama,
224-0053, Kanagawa, Japan
Tel.: (81) 459331111
Commercial Printing Services
N.A.I.C.S.: 323111

DNP Tohoku Co., Ltd. **(1)**
3-5-1 Nigatake, Miyagino-ku, Sendai, 983-
0036, Miyagi, Japan
Tel.: (81) 227834700
Web Site: http://www.dnp-tohoku.co.jp
Packaging Product Mfr & Distr
N.A.I.C.S.: 322220

**DNP Total Process Maebashi Co.,
Ltd.** **(1)**
1-2-12 Honmachi, Maebashi, 371-0023,
Gunma, Japan
Tel.: (81) 272353366
Commercial Printing Services
N.A.I.C.S.: 323111

**DNP Total Process Nagaoka Co.,
Ltd.** **(1)**
1-6-22 Fukuzumi, Nagaoka, 940-0034, Nii-
gata, Japan
Tel.: (81) 258325400
Commercial Printing Services
N.A.I.C.S.: 323111

DNP Trading Co., Ltd. **(1)**

2-1-11 Iidabashi Dmp Logistics Iidabashi
Bldg, Chiyoda-ku, Tokyo, 102-0072, Japan
Tel.: (81) 332887630
Paper Product Whslr
N.A.I.C.S.: 424130

DNP Uniprocess Co., Ltd. **(1)**
Dainipponinsatsuhonsha Bldg, Shinjuku-ku,
Tokyo, 162-0062, Japan
Tel.: (81) 332663565
Web Site: http://www.dnp.co.jp
Commercial Printing Services
N.A.I.C.S.: 323111

DT Fine Electronics Co., Ltd. **(1)**
Saiwai Komukaitoshiba-cho address 1,
Kanagawa-ku, Kawasaki, 212-8583, Japan
Tel.: (81) 44 549 8393
Web Site: http://www.dtf.co.jp
Semiconductor Components Mfr
N.A.I.C.S.: 334413

**Dai Nippon Printing (Europa)
GmbH** **(1)**
(100%)
Tel.: (49) 2118620180
Web Site: http://www.dnp.co.jp
Sales Range: $25-49.9 Million
Emp.: 13
Sales of Printed Matter
N.A.I.C.S.: 541890
Kenzaburo Osawa *(Mng Dir)*

**Dai Nippon Printing Co. (Australia)
Pty. Ltd.** **(1)**
Ste 1002 Level 10 St Martins Tower 31
Market St, Sydney, 2000, NSW,
Australia **(100%)**
Tel.: (61) 292678166
Web Site: http://www.dnp.co.jp
Sales Range: $25-49.9 Million
Emp.: 3
Sales of Printed Matter
N.A.I.C.S.: 541890
Kazunori Daimaru *(Mng Dir)*

**Dai Nippon Printing Co. (Taiwan),
Ltd.** **(1)**
RM D 6F 44 Chung-Shan North Road Sec-
tion 2, Taipei, 104, Taiwan **(100%)**
Tel.: (886) 223278311
Web Site: http://www.dnp.co.jp
Sales of Precision Electronic Components &
Information Media Supplies
N.A.I.C.S.: 334419

Dai Nippon Shoji Co., Ltd. **(1)**
Kanaba Jinbo, Chochiyo Daku, Tokyo, 101
8424, Japan **(94.3%)**
Tel.: (81) 332887630
Web Site: http://www.dnp.co.jp
Sales Range: $75-99.9 Million
Emp.: 240
Wholesaler, Trade & Broker of Materials
N.A.I.C.S.: 425120
Masatoshi Omatsu *(Gen Mgr)*

Direc Co., Ltd. **(1)**
5-6-30 Kojimashimonocho, Kurashiki, 711-
0906, Okayama, Japan
Tel.: (81) 864725222
Educational Equipment & Books Distr
N.A.I.C.S.: 424920

**Hokkaido Coca-Cola Bottling Co.,
Ltd.** **(1)**
1-2-1 Kiyota 1-jo, Kiyota-ku, Sapporo, 004-
8588, Hokkaido, Japan **(53%)**
Tel.: (81) 0118882001
Web Site: http://www.hokkaido.ccbc.co.jp
Sales Range: $100-124.9 Million
Emp.: 481
Mfr & Sale of Beverages
N.A.I.C.S.: 311930

**LIFESCAPE MARKETING
CORPORATION** **(1)**
1-11-11 Kudan-kita No 2 Funato Bldg,
Chiyoda-ku, Tokyo, 102-0073, Japan
Tel.: (81) 335157088
Information Technology Consulting Services
N.A.I.C.S.: 541512

M's Communicate Co., Ltd **(1)**
3rd floor of G-FRONT AOYAMA 2-12-15
Kita-Aoyama, Minato-ku, Tokyo, 107-0061,
Japan
Tel.: (81) 334047111
Web Site: https://www.emscom.co.jp

Customer Relationship Management Services
N.A.I.C.S.: 541611

Maruzen CHI Holdings Co., Ltd. **(1)**
31-2 Ichigaya Sanai-cho, Shinjuku-ku, To-
kyo, 162-0846, Japan **(52.3%)**
Tel.: (81) 367350785
Web Site: https://www.maruzen-chi.co.jp
Rev.: $1,155,152,430
Assets: $913,872,640
Liabilities: $575,211,700
Net Worth: $338,660,940
Earnings: $15,555,460
Fiscal Year-end: 01/31/2024
Holding Company
N.A.I.C.S.: 551112

Subsidiary (Domestic):

**Maruzen-Yushodo Company,
Limited** **(2)**
1-9-18 Kaigan, Minato-ku, Tokyo, 105-0022,
Japan
Tel.: (81) 120010335
Web Site:
http://www.yushodo.maruzen.co.jp
Academic Books, Journals & Online Infor-
mation Publisher, Importer, Exporter &
Sales; Stationery & Apparel Sales; Library
Designing & Engineering Services
N.A.I.C.S.: 513130
Masaya Yano *(Pres)*

Subsidiary (Domestic):

Junkudo Co., Ltd. **(3)**
1-6-18 Sannomiyacho, Chuo-ku, Kobe, 650-
0021, Japan
Tel.: (81) 7 8392 1001
Web Site: http://www.junkudo.co.jp
Books & Magazines Retailer
N.A.I.C.S.: 459210

Maruzen Bookmates Co., Ltd. **(3)**
9-2 Nihombashi 3-chome, Chuo-ku, Tokyo,
103 8244, Japan **(100%)**
Tel.: (81) 3 3273 3601
Web Site: http://www.maruzen.co.jp
Sales Range: $75-99.9 Million
Emp.: 200
Import, Export & Domestic Sales of Books,
Journals, Stationery, Office Furniture & Sun-
dries
N.A.I.C.S.: 424920

Maruzen Bookstores Co., Ltd. **(3)**
27-5 Sakamachi, Shinjuku-ku, Tokyo, 160-
0002, Japan
Tel.: (81) 3 6380 1291
Books & Magazines Retailer
N.A.I.C.S.: 459210

Branch (Non-US):

**Maruzen Co., Ltd. - London
Office** **(3)**
1st Fl 2 Thayer St, London, W1U 3JB,
United Kingdom
Tel.: (44) 2074873865
Web Site: http://www.maruzen.co.jp
Sales Range: $25-49.9 Million
Emp.: 3
Publishing Services
N.A.I.C.S.: 561410

Subsidiary (US):

Maruzen International Co., Ltd. **(3)**
110B Meadowlands Pkwy Ste 205, Secau-
cus, NJ 07094-1878 **(100%)**
Tel.: (201) 865-4400
Web Site: http://www.maruzenusa.com
Sales Range: $50-74.9 Million
Emp.: 7
Publisher
N.A.I.C.S.: 424920

Subsidiary (Non-US):

Maruzen Kyoei Prince **(3)**
Wisma Kyoei Prince Bldg 7th Fl 1 Jalan
Jenderal, Sudirman Kav 3-4, Jakarta,
10220, Pusat, Indonesia
Tel.: (62) 215723171
Publishing Services
N.A.I.C.S.: 513130

Maruzen Mega Pasaraya **(3)**
Mega Pasaraya 8th Fl Jalan Iskandarsyah
II 2 Blok M, Kebayoran Baru, Jakarta, Sela-

Dai Nippon Printing Co., Ltd.—(Continued)

tan, Indonesia
Tel.: (62) 217260170
Web Site: http://www.pasaraya.co.id
Sales Range: $150-199.9 Million
Provider of Publishing Services
N.A.I.C.S.: 561410

Maruzen Pasaraya Manggarai (3)
Pasara Manggarai 6th Fl, Jalan Sultan
Agung 1, Manggarai, Jakarta, 12970,
Indonesia (100%)
Provider of Publishing Services
N.A.I.C.S.: 561410

Subsidiary (Domestic):

Maruzen Publishing Co., Ltd. (3)
3-10 Nihonbashi 2-Chome, Chuo-ku, Tokyo,
Japan
Tel.: (81) 3 6367 6035
Web Site: http://www.pub.maruzen.co.jp
Books Publishing Services
N.A.I.C.S.: 513130

**Maruzen System Service Co.,
Ltd.** (3)
2 17 Kandajinbocho, Chiyoda-ku, Tokyo,
105-0022, Japan (100%)
Tel.: (81) 335123256
Web Site: http://www.maruzen.co.jp
Sale, Lease, Service & Customer Support
of Computer & Information Technology
Equipment; Applications Software Develop-
ment
N.A.I.C.S.: 532420

NexantiS Corporation (3)
26-8 Nandomachi Yokoi Bldg 2F, Shinjuku-
ku, Tokyo, 115-8001, Japan
Tel.: (81) 352494810
Web Site: http://www.nexantis.co.jp
Business Software Development Services
N.A.I.C.S.: 541511

**OGUCHI BOOK BINDING & PRINT-
ING CO., LTD.** (1)
3-6 Chikumazawa-higashi Miyoshimachi,
Iruma-gun, Saitama, 354-0046, Japan
Tel.: (81) 492597577
Web Site: http://www.obp1949.co.jp
Emp.: 150
Books Binding & Printing Services
N.A.I.C.S.: 323117

**P.T. Dai Nippon Printing
Indonesia** (1)
Jl Pulogadung No16-18 Kav II H2 danII H3
Kawasan Industri Pulogadung, Block H No
2 3, Jakarta, 13930, Timur,
Indonesia (51%)
Tel.: (62) 14605790
Web Site: http://www.dnp.co.jp
Sales Range: $400-449.9 Million
Emp.: 2,000
Mfr, Printing & Sale of Printed Matter
N.A.I.C.S.: 513130

SHUFUNOTOMO Co., Ltd. (1)
Meguro Central Square 3-1-1 Kamiosaki,
Shinagawa, Tokyo, 141-0021, Japan
Tel.: (81) 35 280 7500
Web Site: https://www.shufunotomo.co.jp
Emp.: 126
Magazine Publishing Services
N.A.I.C.S.: 513120
Yoshiyuki Ogino (Pres)

Sagami Yoki Co., Ltd. (1)
1000 Narita, Odawara, 250-0862, Kanagawa, Japan
Tel.: (81) 465366633
N.A.I.C.S.: 326122

TRC Library Service Inc. (1)
3-1-1 Otsuka, Bunkyo-ku, Tokyo, 112-8632,
Japan
Tel.: (81) 339432221
Web Site: https://www.trc.co.jp
Emp.: 9,591
Library Management Services
N.A.I.C.S.: 611710

TRC, Inc. (1)
1-1-25 Shin-Urashimacho Techno Wave 100
Bldg 8F, Kanagawa-ku, Yokohama, 221-
0031, Kanagawa, Japan
Tel.: (81) 454503391
Book Distr

N.A.I.C.S.: 424920

TWP Sendirian Berhad (1)
89 Jalan Tampoi, Kawasan Perindustrian
Tampoi, 80350, Johor Bahru,
Malaysia (100%)
Tel.: (60) 72369899
Web Site: http://www.twpsip.com
Sales Range: $450-499.9 Million
Emp.: 2,000
Provider of Corrugated & Solid Fiber Boxes
N.A.I.C.S.: 322211

Tien Wah Press (Pte.) Ltd. (1)
No 25 New Industrial Road 5th Floor, Sin-
gapore, 536211, Singapore (84.6%)
Tel.: (65) 64666222
Web Site: http://www.twp-global.com
Sales Range: $200-249.9 Million
Emp.: 850
Mfr & Sale of Printed Matter; Printing Ser-
vices
N.A.I.C.S.: 513130
Yoichi Sanada (Mng Dir)

**Toshokan Ryutsu Center Co.,
Ltd.** (1)
6-1-1 Heiwajima, Ota-ku, Tokyo, 143-0006,
Japan
Tel.: (81) 337672111
Web Site: http://www.trc-inc.co.jp
Building Logistic Services
N.A.I.C.S.: 541614

Uzumine Country Club Co., Ltd. (1)
1 Miyata Shiota, Sukagawa, 962-0711, Fu-
kushima, Japan
Tel.: (81) 248792101
Web Site: http://www.uzumine-cc.com
Golf Course Management Services
N.A.I.C.S.: 713910

VISUALJAPAN Inc. (1)
1-29-4 Jinbo-cho, Kanda Chiyoda-ku, To-
kyo, 101-0051, Japan
Tel.: (81) 5038525510
Web Site: https://www.visualjapan.co.jp
Emp.: 30
Software Development Services
N.A.I.C.S.: 541511

Yushodo (Kyoto) CO., Ltd. (1)
Kyoto Asahi Building Oike-dori
Yanaginobamba-kado, Nakagyo-ku, Kyoto,
604-8101, Japan
Tel.: (81) 75 222 0165
Books Publishing Services
N.A.I.C.S.: 513130

mobileBook.jp, Inc. (1)
3-2-3 Kanda Jimbocho 6F Daiwa Jimbocho
3-chome, Chiyoda-ku, Tokyo, 101-0051,
Japan
Tel.: (81) 35210230
Web Site: http://www.mobilebook.jp
Emp.: 126
Books Publishing Services
N.A.I.C.S.: 513130

DAI NIPPON TORYO CO., LTD.
1-18-11 Minamisenba, Chuo-ku,
Osaka, 542-0081, Japan
Tel.: (81) 662663100   **JP**
Web Site: https://www.dnt.co.jp
Year Founded: 1929
4611—(TKS)
Rev.: $475,523,400
Assets: $671,694,980
Liabilities: $258,636,080
Net Worth: $413,058,900
Earnings: $30,406,000
Emp.: 685
Fiscal Year-end: 03/31/24
Industrial, Automobile, Refinishing,
Marine & Home Paints & Coating Mfr;
Paint Creation Machinery Mfr
N.A.I.C.S.: 325510
Takayuki Sato (Pres)

Subsidiaries:

**AJISCO-DNT (Ningbo) Paint
Co.,Ltd.** (1)
Building 2 No 25 Gangxi Avenue West
Area, Ningbo Free Trade Zone, Ningbo,
315806, Zhejiang, China
Tel.: (86) 57486822006

Paint Mfr & Sales
N.A.I.C.S.: 325510

BO Chemical Co., Ltd. (1)
3-10-5 Chojabaruhigashi Kasuya-cho,
Kasuya-gun, Fukuoka, 811-2317, Japan
Tel.: (81) 929382321
Web Site: http://www.bochemical.co.jp
Emp.: 49
Paints Mfr
N.A.I.C.S.: 325510

Chiba Kako Co., Ltd. (1)
4-1 Yakoshimmei Sakae-machi, Imba-gun,
Chiba, 270-1501, Japan
Tel.: (81) 476957711
Paint & Coating Mfr
N.A.I.C.S.: 325510

DN LIGHTING Co., Ltd. (1)
1-13-5 Nishigotanda, Shinagawa-ku, Tokyo,
141-0031, Japan
Tel.: (81) 334924460
Web Site: https://www.dnlighting.co.jp
Emp.: 214
Fluorescent Lamp Sales
N.A.I.C.S.: 423610

DNT (Shanghai) Co.,Ltd. (1)
No 8 Dongye Road Dongjing Town, Songji-
ang District, Shanghai, 201619, China
Tel.: (86) 2157670682
Paint Mfr & Sales
N.A.I.C.S.: 325510

DNT Business Service Co., Ltd. (1)
6-1-124 Nishikujo, Konohana-ku, Osaka,
554-0012, Japan
Tel.: (81) 664666665
Sales Range: $25-49.9 Million
Emp.: 23
Accounting Services
N.A.I.C.S.: 541219
Norihiro Nagata (Gen Mgr)

**DNT Kansai Mexicana S.A. de
C.V.** (1)
Prolongacion Av Juarez Sur 801-3 Colonia
La, Trinidad San Francisco de los Romo,
20300, Aguascalientes, Mexico
Tel.: (52) 4659670975
Coating Mfr
N.A.I.C.S.: 325510

DNT Paint (Malaysia) Sdn. Bhd. (1)
Plo 33 Jalan Teknologi 2 Taman Teknologi
Johor Johor Darul Takzim, 81400, Senai,
Malaysia
Tel.: (60) 75991399
Coating Mfr
N.A.I.C.S.: 325510

DNT Sanyo Chemical Co., Ltd. (1)
3-4-1 Ozu, Minami-ku, Hiroshima, 732-
8765, Japan
Tel.: (81) 822815221
Coating Mfr
N.A.I.C.S.: 325510

DNT Service Co., Ltd. (1)
2-9-45 Mizuhai, Higashi-osaka, 578-0921,
Osaka, Japan
Tel.: (81) 729607200
Paint Tinting Services
N.A.I.C.S.: 561990

DNT Singapore Pte. Ltd. (1)
21 Bukit Batok Crescent 07-75 WCEGA
Tower, Singapore, 658065,
Singapore (100%)
Tel.: (65) 62653344
Web Site: https://www.dnt.com.sg
Sales Range: $25-49.9 Million
Emp.: 40
Paints & Coating Mfr; Paint Creation Ma-
chinery Mfr
N.A.I.C.S.: 325510

**Dai Nippon Toryo Hanbai Co.,
Ltd.** (1)
6-1-124 Nishikujo, Konohana-Ku, Osaka,
554-0012, Japan
Tel.: (81) 664666653
Paint Sales
N.A.I.C.S.: 424950

**Dai Nippon Toryo Hokkaido Co.,
Ltd.** (1)
1-5-1 Chuo Nijo, Shiroishi-ku, Sapporo,
003-0012, Japan
Tel.: (81) 118231641
Paint Sales
N.A.I.C.S.: 424950

Coating Mfr
N.A.I.C.S.: 325510

**Dai Nippon Toryo Mexicana S. A. DE
C. V.** (1)
South Juarez Extension Avenue 801-3 La
Trinidad, 20300, San Francisco de los
Romo, Aguascalientes, Mexico
Tel.: (52) 4659672454
Web Site: https://dainippon.com.mx
Paint Mfr & Distr
N.A.I.C.S.: 325510
Wataru Fujie (Gen Mgr)

**Japan Powder Coatings Manufactur-
ing Co., Ltd.** (1)
878 Nishinomon Mitsubuchi, Komaki, 485-
0075, Aichi, Japan
Tel.: (81) 568582957
Coating Mfr
N.A.I.C.S.: 325510

Nippo Denko Co., Ltd. (1)
81-1 Shioguchi Kitano Tenno, Katagami,
010-0201, Akita, Japan
Tel.: (81) 188785151
Coating Mfr
N.A.I.C.S.: 325510

Nitto Chemical Co., Ltd. (1)
Shiba SIA Building 6F 1-6-10 Shiba,
Minato-ku, Tokyo, 105-0014, Japan
Web Site: http://www.nitto-c.co.jp
Emp.: 60
Paints Mfr
N.A.I.C.S.: 325510
Hisashi Masaoka (Pres)

Nitto Engineering Co., Ltd. (1)
8F Kanegen Bldg 5-10 Shinkawadori,
Kawasaki-ku, Kawasaki, 210-0013, Japan
Tel.: (81) 445895441
Engineeering Services
N.A.I.C.S.: 541330

Nitto Fudohsan Co., Ltd. (1)
Dai Nippon Toryo Co Limited 6-1-124 Nishi-
kujo, Konohana-ku, Osaka, 554-0012, Ja-
pan
Tel.: (81) 664666682
Real Estate Manangement Services
N.A.I.C.S.: 531390

Nitto Sanwa Toryo Co., Ltd. (1)
3-3-1 Ishibeguchi, Konan, 520-3114, Shiga,
Japan
Tel.: (81) 748778825
Web Site: http://www.dnt.co.jp
Paints Mfr
N.A.I.C.S.: 325510

Nitto Service Co., Ltd (1)
4-12-24 Mokuzaidori, Mihara-ku, Sakai,
587-0042, Osaka, Japan
Tel.: (81) 723622123
Paint Mfr & Sales
N.A.I.C.S.: 325510

Okayama Kako Co., Ltd. (1)
152-6 Nishi Kibichuo-cho, Kaga-gun,
Okayama, 716-1554, Japan
Tel.: (81) 866556234
Web Site: http://www.dnt.co.jp
Paints Mfr
N.A.I.C.S.: 325510
Hideyoshi Noda (Pres)

Pt. DNT INDONESIA (1)
Jl Sungkai 2 Blok F26 No 15C and 16A
Delta Silicon 3, lippo cikarang, Bekasi,
17530, Indonesia
Tel.: (62) 2189909901
Coating Mfr
N.A.I.C.S.: 325510

SINLOIHI Co., Ltd. (1)
12-19-2 Dai, Kamakura, 247-8550, Kana-
gawa, Japan
Tel.: (81) 467432121
Web Site: http://www.sinloihi.co.jp
Emp.: 51
Fluorescent Pigment Mfr
N.A.I.C.S.: 325130
Shunsuke Tamura (Pres)

Sunday Paint Co., Ltd. (1)
SR Bldg Nagahori 1-18-11 Minamisemba,
Chuo-ku, Osaka, 542-0081, Japan
Tel.: (81) 662663150
Paint Sales
N.A.I.C.S.: 424950

Thai DNT Paint Manufacturing Co., Ltd. (1)
38/25 Moo 5 Laem Chabang Industrial Estate Sukhumvit Road, Thung Sukhla Si Racha, Chon Buri, 20230, Thailand
Tel.: (66) 384948658
Web Site: https://www.thaidnt.com
Paint & Coating Mfr
N.A.I.C.S.: 325510

DAI THIEN LOC CORPORATION
Lot A street 22 song Than Industrial zone, Di An, Thu Dau Mot, Binh Duong, Vietnam
Tel.: (84) 3719999
Web Site:
https://www.daithienloc.com.vn
Year Founded: 2001
DTL—(HOSE)
Rev.: $81,229,673
Assets: $85,399,525
Liabilities: $54,281,082
Net Worth: $31,118,442
Earnings: ($6,432,762)
Emp.: 491
Fiscal Year-end: 12/31/23
Steel Sheet Mfr
N.A.I.C.S.: 331110
Thanh Nghia Nguyen (Pres & Gen Dir)

DAI-DAN CO LTD
1-9-25 Edobori, Nishi-ku, Osaka, 550-8520, Japan
Tel.: (81) 664478000
Web Site: https://www.daidan.co.jp
1980—(TKS)
Rev.: $1,305,018,910
Assets: $1,061,255,330
Liabilities: $440,001,260
Net Worth: $621,254,070
Earnings: $60,065,070
Emp.: 1,901
Fiscal Year-end: 03/31/24
Engineeering Services
N.A.I.C.S.: 238210
Shohei Kitano (Chm)

Subsidiaries:

DAI-DAN Co Ltd - Technical Development Division (1)
390 Kitanagai Miyoshi, Iruma, 354-0044, Saitama, Japan
Tel.: (81) 492581511
Emp.: 70
Air Conditioner Mfr
N.A.I.C.S.: 333415
Yoji Sasaki (Mgr)

DAI-DAN Service Kanto Co., Ltd. (1)
2nd Floor Ugai Building 2-30-9 Fukagawa, Koto-ku, Tokyo, 135-0033, Japan
Tel.: (81) 356390721
Sales Range: $25-49.9 Million
Emp.: 14
Air Conditioning Equipment Mfr
N.A.I.C.S.: 333415

Dai-Dan Philippines, Inc. (1)
7th Fl Mobile Entertainment Ctr 104 Rada St, Legaspri Vlg, Makati, Philippines
Tel.: (63) 27522431
Web Site: http://www.daidan.co.jp
Sales Range: $25-49.9 Million
Emp.: 3
Electrical & Plumbing Services
N.A.I.C.S.: 238210

Merino-ODD Sdn. Bhd. (1)
57-3A Jalan SS 23 15 Taman SEA, 47400, Petaling Jaya, Selangor, Malaysia
Tel.: (60) 378048877
Sales Range: $25-49.9 Million
Emp.: 12
Air Conditioner Mfr
N.A.I.C.S.: 333415

DAI-ICHI CUTTER KOGYO K.K.
833 Hagisono, Chigasaki, 253-0071, Kanagawa, Japan
Tel.: (81) 467853939

Web Site: https://www.daiichi-cutter.co.jp
Year Founded: 1967
1716—(TKS)
Rev.: $130,109,960
Assets: $135,956,760
Liabilities: $22,224,060
Net Worth: $113,732,700
Earnings: $12,272,060
Emp.: 629
Fiscal Year-end: 06/30/24
Construction Engineering Services
N.A.I.C.S.: 237990
Shunichi Hirose (Chm)

DAI-ICHI HIGH FREQUENCY CO., LTD.
Yoshino Dai-ichi Bldg 4F 1-6-2, Nihonbashi Bakurocho Chuo-ku, Tokyo, 103-0002, Japan
Tel.: (81) 356493725
Web Site: https://dhf.co.jp
Year Founded: 1950
Emp.: 484
Heating Equipment Mfr
N.A.I.C.S.: 333414

DAI-ICHI KARKARIA LIMITED
3rd Floor Liberty Building Sir Vithaldas Thackersey Marg, Mumbai, 400 020, India
Tel.: (91) 2269117130
Web Site: https://www.dai-ichiindia.com
Year Founded: 1960
526821—(BOM)
Rev.: $139,721,400
Assets: $326,275,950
Liabilities: $93,584,400
Net Worth: $232,691,550
Earnings: $69,178,200
Emp.: 162
Fiscal Year-end: 03/31/21
Specialty Chemical Mfr & Distr
N.A.I.C.S.: 325199
Shernaz Firoze Vakil (Chm & Mng Dir)

DAI-ICHI LIFE HOLDINGS, INC.
1-13-1 Yurakucho, Chiyoda-ku, Tokyo, 100-8411, Japan
Tel.: (81) 332161222   JP
Web Site: https://www.dai-ichi-life-hd.com
Year Founded: 1902
8750—(TKS)
Rev.: $72,896,177,260
Assets: $446,441,442,490
Liabilities: $420,780,384,720
Net Worth: $25,661,057,770
Earnings: $746,930
Emp.: 997
Fiscal Year-end: 03/31/24
Holding Company
N.A.I.C.S.: 551112
Shigeo Tsuyuki (Vice Chm)

Subsidiaries:

Asset Management One Co., Ltd. (1)
Tekko Building 1-8-2 Marunouchi, Chiyoda-ku, Tokyo, 100-0005, Japan (49%)
Tel.: (81) 36 774 5000
Web Site: https://www.am-one.co.jp
Asset Management Services
N.A.I.C.S.: 523940
Akira Sugano (Pres & CEO)

Subsidiary (Non-US):

Asset Management One Hong Kong Limited (2)
12/F K11 Atelier 18 Salisbury Road Tsim Sha Tsui, Hong Kong, China (Hong Kong)
Tel.: (852) 29189030
Asset Management Services
N.A.I.C.S.: 523940

Asset Management One Singapore Pte. Ltd. (2)
2 Shenton Way 12-01 SGX Centre I, Singapore, 068804, Singapore
Tel.: (65) 65325470
Asset Management Services
N.A.I.C.S.: 523940

DLI Asia Pacific Pte. Ltd. (1)
12 Marina View 24 03/04 Asia Square Tower 2, Singapore, 018961, Singapore
Tel.: (65) 68050550
N.A.I.C.S.: 524113

Dai-ichi Life Insurance (Cambodia) PLC. (1)
Ground Floor 1st Floor & 2nd Floor Samaky Tower St 315 Phum 6, Sangkat Boeung Kork II Khan Toul Kork, Phnom Penh, Cambodia
Tel.: (855) 23955333
Web Site: https://dai-ichilife.com.kh
N.A.I.C.S.: 524113

Dai-ichi Life Insurance Company of Vietnam, Limited (1)
149-151 Nguyen Van Troi Street, Ward 11 Phu Nhuan District, Ho Chi Minh City, Vietnam
Tel.: (84) 2838100888
Web Site: https://www.dai-ichi-life.com.vn
Sales Range: $200-249.9 Million
Fire Insurance Services
N.A.I.C.S.: 524113

Dai-ichi Life Insurance Myanmar Ltd. (1)
Level 20 Sule Square Office Tower No 221 Sule Pagoda Road, Kyauktada Township, Yangon, Myanmar
Tel.: (95) 9778801000
Web Site: http://www.dai-ichi-life.com.mm
Fire Insurance Services
N.A.I.C.S.: 524113
Daw Zarchi Tin (CEO)

Dai-ichi Life International (AsiaPacific) Limited (1)
Suite 902 Central Plaza 18 Harbour Road, Wanchai, China (Hong Kong) (100%)
Tel.: (852) 25881331
Web Site: http://www.dai-ichi-life.co.jp
Sales Range: $50-74.9 Million
Emp.: 100
Fire Insurance Services
N.A.I.C.S.: 524113

Dai-ichi Life International (Europe) Limited (1)
6th Floor 6 Gracechurch Street, London, EC3V 0AT, United Kingdom (100%)
Tel.: (44) 2072201770
Web Site: https://www.dai-ichi-life-hd.com
Sales Range: $50-74.9 Million
Fire Insurance Services
N.A.I.C.S.: 524113

Dai-ichi Life International (U.S.A.) Inc. (1)
400 Park Ave Fl 4, New York, NY 10022 (100%)
Tel.: (212) 350-7600
Web Site: http://www.dai-ichi-life.co.jp
Fire Insurance Services
N.A.I.C.S.: 524113
Toshiya Kaname (Pres)

Dai-ichi Life Realty Asset Management Co., Ltd. (1)
Web Site: http://www.dai-ichi-life-realty.co.jp
Asset Management Services
N.A.I.C.S.: 523940

Dai-ichi Life Research Institute Inc., (1)
13-1 Yurakucho 1-chome, Chiyoda-ku, Tokyo, 100-0006, Japan
Tel.: (81) 352214505
Insurance Management Services
N.A.I.C.S.: 524298
Masayuki Koyama (Pres)

Ocean Life Insurance Co., Ltd. (1)
170/74-83 Ocean Tower 1 Ratchadaphisek Rd, Khlong Toei, Bangkok, 10110, Thailand
Tel.: (66) 22612300
Web Site: http://www.Ocean.co.th
Sales Range: $350-399.9 Million
Fire Insurance Services
N.A.I.C.S.: 524113

Kirati Assakul (Chm)

Protective Life Corporation (1)
2801 Hwy 280 S, Birmingham, AL 35223
Tel.: (205) 268-1000
Web Site: http://www.protective.com
Rev.: $5,040,954,000
Assets: $89,938,754,000
Liabilities: $84,171,020,000
Net Worth: $5,767,734,000
Earnings: $302,361,000
Emp.: 2,948
Fiscal Year-end: 12/31/2018
Holding Company; Life Insurance & Pension Products & Services
N.A.I.C.S.: 551112
Steven Glen Walker (CFO & Exec VP)

Subsidiary (Domestic):

Interstate National Corporation (2)
200 Galleria Pkwy SE Ste 1000, Atlanta, GA 30339
Tel.: (877) 738-6567
Web Site: http://www.revolos.com
Emp.: 100
Insurances Solutions Services
N.A.I.C.S.: 524298
Richard Holland (CEO)

Subsidiary (Domestic):

Interstate National Dealer Services, Inc. (3)
PO Box 724707, Atlanta, GA 31139
Tel.: (678) 894-3500
Web Site: http://www.inds.com
Sales Range: $75-99.9 Million
Marketer & Distr of Service Contracts & Warranties for New & Used Motor Vehicles & Recreational Vehicles
N.A.I.C.S.: 524128
Breanne Morley (Exec VP-Sls)

Subsidiary (Domestic):

Protective Life Insurance Company (2)
2801 Hwy 280 S, Birmingham, AL 35223 (100%)
Tel.: (205) 268-1000
Web Site: http://www.protective.com
Rev.: $6,413,000,000
Assets: $131,572,000,000
Liabilities: $118,808,000,000
Net Worth: $12,764,000,000
Earnings: $285,000,000
Emp.: 3,510
Fiscal Year-end: 12/31/2021
Life & Health Insurance Services
N.A.I.C.S.: 524130
Steven Glen Walker (CFO & Exec VP)

Subsidiary (Domestic):

A U L Corp. (3)
1325 W Imola Ave Ste 318, Napa, CA 94559
Tel.: (707) 257-9700
Web Site: http://www.aulcorp.com
Sales Range: $1-9.9 Million
Emp.: 40
Business Services, Nec, Nsk
N.A.I.C.S.: 711410
Gina Eagerton (Mgr-Compliance)

Concourse Financial Group Agency, Inc. (3)
2801 US Hwy 280 S, Birmingham, AL 35223 (100%)
Tel.: (833) 504-1774
Web Site:
http://www.concoursefinancial.com
Fire Insurance Services
N.A.I.C.S.: 524128
Darren Guerrera (CFO)

Lyndon Property Insurance Company (3)
14755 N Outer Forty Dr Ste 400, Saint Louis, MO 63017
Tel.: (636) 536-5600
Web Site:
http://www.protectiveassetprotection.com
Dealership Warranty Services
N.A.I.C.S.: 524128
Gregg Cariolano (CFO)

Protective Life & Annuity Insurance Company (3)

Dai-ichi Life Holdings, Inc.—(Continued)

PO Box 1928, Birmingham, AL 35282-8238
Tel.: (800) 456-6330
Web Site: http://www.protective.com
Fire Insurance Services
N.A.I.C.S.: 524113

**West Coast Life Insurance
Company** (3)
PO Box 12687, Birmingham, AL 35202-6687
Web Site: https://www.protective.com
Fire Insurance Services
N.A.I.C.S.: 524113

QOLead, Limited (1)
Shibuya Daiichi Seimei Building 8th Floor
3-8-12, Shibuya Shibuya-ku, Tokyo, 150-0002, Japan
Tel.: (81) 337970916
Web Site: https://qolead.com
Healtcare Services
N.A.I.C.S.: 621610
Shin Nakayama (Co-CEO)

Sohgo Housing Co. Ltd. (1)
2-2 Osaki 1-Chome, Shinagawa-ku, Tokyo, 141-0032, Japan
Tel.: (81) 334946771
Web Site: https://www.sohgo-jyutaku.co.jp
N.A.I.C.S.: 531210
Masao Taketomi (Pres)

**Star Union Dai-ichi Life Insurance
Company Limited** (1)
11th Floor Vishwaroop I T Park Plot No 34
35 and 38 Sector 30A of IIP, Vashi Navi,
Mumbai, 400 703, India (44%)
Tel.: (91) 2271966200
Web Site: http://www.sudlife.in
Fire Insurance Services
N.A.I.C.S.: 524113
Girish Kulkarni (Co-CEO & Mng Dir)

**TAL Dai-ichi Life Australia Pty
Ltd.** (1)
Level 16 363 George Street, Sydney, 2000,
NSW, Australia
Tel.: (61) 294489000
N.A.I.C.S.: 524113

TAL Life Limited (1)
GPO Box 5380, Sydney, 2001, NSW, Australia
Tel.: (61) 294489000
Web Site: https://www.tal.com.au
Fire Insurance Services
N.A.I.C.S.: 524113

TAL Services Limited (1)
363 George Street Level 16, Sydney, 2000,
NSW, Australia (100%)
Tel.: (61) 294489100
Web Site: http://www.tal.com.au
Sales Range: $900-999.9 Million
Emp.: 650
Insurance Services
N.A.I.C.S.: 524298
Brett Clark (CEO-Grp & Mng Dir)

Subsidiary (Domestic):

**Asteron Advisory Services
Limited** (2)
Level 10 321 10 Kent Street, Sydney, 2000,
NSW, Australia (100%)
Tel.: (61) 282753411
Web Site: www.asteron.com.au
Investment Banking & Securities Dealing
N.A.I.C.S.: 523150
Geoff Summerhays (CEO)

Asteron Limited (2)
Level 10 321 Kent Street, Sydney, 2001,
NSW, Australia
Tel.: (61) 282753411
Web Site: http://www.asteron.com.au
Asset Administration & Management Services
N.A.I.C.S.: 523999
David Carter (Gen Mgr-Brisbane)

**Asteron Portfolio Services
Limited** (2)
L 10 321 Kent St, Sydney, 2000, NSW,
Australia (100%)
Tel.: (61) 282753500
Web Site: www.asteron.com.au
Health & Welfare Funds

N.A.I.C.S.: 525120
Garry Grinsfield (Mng Dir)

GIO General Limited (2)
Reply Paid 3999, Sydney, NSW, Australia
Tel.: (61) 3 8650 4196
Web Site: http://www.gio.com.au
General Insurance Services
N.A.I.C.S.: 524210

**Pivotal Financial Advisers
Limited** (2)
363 George St, Sydney, 2001, NSW, Australia
Tel.: (61) 299540325
Web Site: http://www.pivfin.com.au
Sales Range: $50-74.9 Million
Emp.: 15
General Insurance Services
N.A.I.C.S.: 524113
Craig Parker (Gen Mgr)

TAL Direct Pty Limited (2)
Level 16 363 George St, Sydney, 2000,
NSW, Australia
Tel.: (61) 299968400
Web Site: http://www.tal.com.au
Sales Range: $150-199.9 Million
General Insurance Services
N.A.I.C.S.: 524113

Branch (Domestic):

TAL Limited-Victoria (2)
Level 6 390 Latrobe St, PO Box 142, Melbourne, 3000, VIC, Australia
Tel.: (61) 294489000
Web Site: http://www.tal.com.au
Sales Range: $10-24.9 Million
Emp.: 5
Provider of Insurance Services
N.A.I.C.S.: 524113

The Dai-ichi Building Co., Ltd. (1)
Art Village Osaki Central Tower 11F 1-2-2
Osaki, Shinagawa-ku, Tokyo, 141-0032,
Japan
Tel.: (81) 367737220
Web Site: https://www.dai-ichi-building.co.jp
Emp.: 480
Real Estate Services
N.A.I.C.S.: 531390

**The Dai-ichi Frontier Life Insurance
Co., Ltd.** (1)
Hibiya Fort Tower 1-1-1 Nishi-Shinbashi,
Minato-ku, Tokyo, 105-0003, Japan
Tel.: (81) 120876126
Web Site: https://www.d-frontier-life.co.jp
N.A.I.C.S.: 524113
Akashi Mamoru (Pres)

**The Dai-ichi Life Information Systems
Co., Ltd** (1)
1-13-1 Yurakucho, Chiyoda-ku, Tokyo, 183-0044, Japan
Tel.: (81) 423306500
Emp.: 1,799
Insurance Management Services
N.A.I.C.S.: 524113

The Neo First Life Insurance Company, Limited (1)
Osaki With Tower 2-11-1 Osaki, Shinagawa-ku, Tokyo, 141-0032, Japan
Tel.: (81) 120581201
Web Site: https://neofirst.co.jp
N.A.I.C.S.: 524113
Takashi Uehara (Pres)

DAICEL CORPORATION

Grand Front Osaka Tower-B 3-1
Ofuka-cho, Kita-ku, Osaka, 530-0011,
Japan
Tel.: (81) 676397171   JP
Web Site: https://www.daicel.com
Year Founded: 1919
4202—(TKS)
Rev.: $3,688,750,160
Assets: $5,546,907,090
Liabilities: $3,065,446,990
Net Worth: $2,481,460,100
Earnings: $369,062,740
Emp.: 11,134
Fiscal Year-end: 03/31/24
Cellulosic Derivatives, Organic
Chemicals, Plastics, Films, Membranes, Medical Products & Rocket
Propellants Mfr

N.A.I.C.S.: 325199
Kotaro Sugimoto (Sr Mng Exec Officer & Gen Mgr-Corp Support)

Subsidiaries:

**Arbor Biosciences (BioDiscovery
LLC)** (1)
5840 Interface Dr Ste 101, Ann Arbor, MI
48103
Tel.: (734) 998-0751
Web Site: https://www.arborbiosci.com
Biological Product Mfr
N.A.I.C.S.: 325414
Jean-Marie Rouillard (Co-Founder & Dir-Tech)

**Chiral Technologies-Europe
S.A.R.L.** (1)
Parc d Innovation - 160 Bd Gonthier d Andernach, PO Box 80140, 67404, Illkirch-Graffenstaden, Cedex, France (100%)
Tel.: (33) 388795200
Web Site: http://chiraltech.com
Sales Range: $25-49.9 Million
Emp.: 30
Sale of Optical Separation Columns & Provision of Services Related to the Separation
of Optical Active Compounds
N.A.I.C.S.: 325998

**DAICEL CHIRAL TECHNOLOGIES
(CHINA) CO., LTD.** (1)
Part C FL5 No 16th Building No 69 Xiya
Road WaiGaoQiao Free Trade Zone,
Shanghai, 200131, China
Tel.: (86) 2150460086
Web Site: http://www.daicelchiral.com
Sales Range: $25-49.9 Million
Emp.: 32
Medical Equipment Mfr
N.A.I.C.S.: 334510

DM Novafoam Ltd. (1)
361-1 Oaza Karita, Obuse-machi Kamitakai-gun, Nagano, 381-0211, Japan
Tel.: (81) 262472557
Web Site: https://www.dmnovafoam.com
Cushioning Material Mfr
N.A.I.C.S.: 326111

Daicel (Asia) Pte. Ltd. (1)
78 Shenton Way 15-01/01B, Singapore,
079120, Singapore (100%)
Tel.: (65) 63272038
Web Site: http://www.daicel.com
Sales Range: $25-49.9 Million
Emp.: 10
Asian Chemical Marketing Operations
N.A.I.C.S.: 325998

**Daicel (China) Investment
Co.,Ltd.** (1)
4F No 32 Hexiang Road, Pilot Free Trade
Zone, Shanghai, 200131, China
Tel.: (86) 2158780737
Chemical Product Mfr & Distr
N.A.I.C.S.: 325998

Daicel (U.S.A.) Inc. (1)
1 Parker Plz Sixth Fl 400 Kelby St, Fort
Lee, NJ 07024
Tel.: (201) 461-4466
Web Site: http://www.daicel.com
Sales Range: $50-74.9 Million
Emp.: 4
U.S. Marketing Operations
N.A.I.C.S.: 424690

Subsidiary (Domestic):

Chiral Technologies Inc. (2)
800 N 5 Points Rd, West Chester, PA
19380 (100%)
Tel.: (610) 594-2100
Web Site: http://www.chiraltech.com
Sales Range: $10-24.9 Million
Develops & Supplies Bulk Chiral Stationary
Phase Media for Process Scale Chromatographic Separations
N.A.I.C.S.: 423450
Joseph Barendt (Pres)

**Daicel Safety Systems America
LLC** (2)
3431 N Reseda Cir, Mesa, AZ 85215
Tel.: (480) 990-5411
Web Site: http://www.daicelssa.com
Sales Range: $1-4.9 Billion
Automotive Air Bag Inflator Mfr
N.A.I.C.S.: 336390

Wayne Thomas (Pres)

Special Devices, Incorporated (2)
2655 1st St Ste 300, Simi Valley, CA 93065
Tel.: (805) 387-1000
Web Site: https://www.specialdevices.com
Sales Range: $100-124.9 Million
Pyrotechnic Devices Designer & Mfr
N.A.I.C.S.: 325998

Daicel Aboshi Sangyo Co. Ltd. (1)
1239 Shinzaike Aboshi Ku Himeji Shi,
Hyogo, 671-1281, Japan (45%)
Tel.: (81) 792743621
Web Site: https://www.daicel.co.jp
Mfr & Distributor of Magnesium Hydroxide
N.A.I.C.S.: 325180

Daicel America Holdings,Inc. (1)
21515 Hawthorne Blvd Ste 600, Torrance,
CA 90503
Tel.: (424) 290-7390
Web Site: https://www.daicelamerica.com
Chemical Products Mfr
N.A.I.C.S.: 325998

Daicel Arai Chemical Ltd. (1)
1 1 Shinko Cho Myoko shi, Niigata,
9448550, Japan (100%)
Tel.: (81) 255723123
Sales Range: $125-149.9 Million
Emp.: 400
Mfr of Chlorinated Compounds
N.A.I.C.S.: 325180
Tran Nitra Naito (Plant Mgr)
Mashaho Naito (Plant Mgr)

Daicel Beyond Ltd. (1)
10 Shindo Amarube-Cho, Kameoka, Kyoto,
621-0806, Japan
Tel.: (81) 771242600
Chemical Product Mfr & Distr
N.A.I.C.S.: 325998

Daicel ChemTech, Inc. (1)
1 Parker Plz 400 Kelby St, Fort Lee, NJ
07024
Tel.: (201) 461-4466
Web Site: https://www.daicelchemtech.com
Chemical Products Distr
N.A.I.C.S.: 424690

**Daicel Chemical (China) Investment
Co., Ltd.** (1)
4th floor No 32 Hexiang Road, Pudong,
Shanghai, 200131, China
Tel.: (86) 2158780737
Web Site: http://www.daicelchina.com
Investment Management Service
N.A.I.C.S.: 523999
Yanase Fumito (Gen Mgr)

Daicel Chemicals Co Ltd (1)
1 Teppo Cho Sakai Shi, Osaka, 590 8501,
Japan (100%)
Tel.: (81) 722273088
Sales Range: $125-149.9 Million
Emp.: 400
Mfr & Distribution of Oligomer Products,
Acryl Resins & Polyesther Resins
N.A.I.C.S.: 325211

**Daicel Chiral Technologies (India) Pvt
Ltd.** (1)
Survey No 542/2 IKP Knowledge Park
Turkapally Shamirpet Mandal, Medchal-Malkajgiri District, Hyderabad, 500 101, Telangana, India
Tel.: (91) 8418660700
Web Site: http://chiraltech.com
Sales Range: $25-49.9 Million
Emp.: 24
Chromatography Analytical Services
N.A.I.C.S.: 541380

Daicel Europe GmbH (1)
Mergenthalerallee 77, 65760, Eschborn,
Germany (100%)
Tel.: (49) 6196470350
Sales Range: $1-9.9 Million
Emp.: 6
Management of Marketing Operations
N.A.I.C.S.: 424690

Daicel Finance Ltd. (1)
3 13 Azuchi Machi 2 Chome, Chuo Ku,
Osaka, Japan (100%)
Tel.: (81) 662634806
Web Site: http://www.daicel.co.jp
Sales Range: $50-74.9 Million
Emp.: 3
Fund Manager

N.A.I.C.S.: 523940

Daicel Logistics Service Co., Ltd. (1)
Grand Front Osaka Tower-B 3-1 Ofuka-cho,
Kita-ku, Osaka, 530-0011, Japan
Tel.: (81) 676397441
Cargo Storage Services
N.A.I.C.S.: 493110

Daicel Micro Optics Co. Ltd. (1)
14F 7 No 295 Sec 2 Kuangfu Rd, East Dist,
Hsinchu, 30017, Taiwan
Tel.: (886) 35736700
Optical Product Mfr & Retailer
N.A.I.C.S.: 333310

**Daicel Miraizu (Thailand) Co.,
Ltd.** (1)
388 Exchange Tower Level 22 Unit 2201
2202-1 Sukhumvit Road, Klongtoey Subdistrict Klongtoey District, Bangkok, 10110,
Thailand
Tel.: (66) 26618818
Resin Compound Product Mfr & Distr
N.A.I.C.S.: 325211

Daicel Miraizu Ltd. (1)
JR Shinagawa East Building 2-18-1 Konan,
Minato-ku, Tokyo, 108-0075, Japan
Tel.: (81) 367118510
Web Site: https://www.daicelmiraizu.com
Emp.: 140
Chemical Products Mfr
N.A.I.C.S.: 325998
Seiji Yamakado *(Pres)*

**Daicel Nanning Food Ingredients Co.,
Ltd.** (1)
29 Jinkai Road Nanning, Nanning, 530031,
Guangxi, China
Tel.: (86) 7714810970
Web Site: http://www.daicelnn.com.cn
Food Ingredient Mfr
N.A.I.C.S.: 311999

Daicel Novafoam Ltd. (1)
361-1 Oaza Karita Obuse Cho, Kamitakai
Gun, Nagano, 381-0211, Japan   **(100%)**
Tel.: (81) 262472557
Web Site: http://www.daicel.com
Sales Range: $25-49.9 Million
Emp.: 80
Manufacture & Sale of Foam Packaging
Materials
N.A.I.C.S.: 326140
Yasuo Okada *(Gen Mgr-Sls)*

Daicel Ohtake Sangyo Co., Ltd. (1)
1-4 Higashisakae 2-chome, Otake, 739-
0695, Hiroshima, Japan
Tel.: (81) 827536721
Emp.: 200
Chemical Products Mfr
N.A.I.C.S.: 325199
Takayuki Nakamura *(Mgr)*

Daicel Pack Systems Ltd. (1)
Suda-cho MK Bldg 8-1 Kanda Suda-cho
2-chome, Chiyoda-ku, Tokyo, 101-0041,
Japan
Tel.: (81) 352097900
Web Site: http://www.daicel.com
Emp.: 23
Plastics Molded Products Mfr
N.A.I.C.S.: 322220

Daicel Packsystems Ltd. (1)
25 Kasumigaseki, 3 Chome Chiyoda K, Tokyo, 100 6077, Japan   **(100%)**
Tel.: (81) 335073188
Vacuum & Pressure-Molded Plastic Products Mfr
N.A.I.C.S.: 326199

**Daicel Polymer (Hong Kong)
Limited.** (1)
Suite 23A01 23A/F Tower 2 The Gateway
Harbour City 25 Canton Road, Kowloon,
China (Hong Kong)
Tel.: (852) 27302129
Thermoplastic Resin Mfr
N.A.I.C.S.: 325211

Daicel Polymer Ltd. (1)
JR Shinagawa East Bldg 2-18-1 Kohnan,
Minato-ku, Tokyo, 108-8230,
Japan   **(100%)**
Tel.: (81) 367118401
Web Site: http://www.daicelpolymer.com
Resin, Polymer Alloy & Polystyrene Sheet
Mfr & Sales

N.A.I.C.S.: 325211

Daicel Polymer, Ltd. (1)
JR Shinagawa East Bldg 14 Fl 2-18-1
Kohnan Minato-Ku, Minato ku, Tokyo, 108
8230, Japan   **(100%)**
Tel.: (81) 367118401
Web Site: http://www.daicelpolymer.com
Sales Range: $50-74.9 Million
Emp.: 160
Mfr & Sales of Polymer Alloys
N.A.I.C.S.: 326199
Mikio Yagi *(Pres)*

Daicel Prosperity (China) Ltd. (1)
Unit 3 3/F 17 Wang Hoi Road, Shun Fat
Industrial Building, Kowloon, China (Hong
Kong)
Tel.: (852) 23574368
Web Site: http://www.dpchk.com.hk
Optical Frame Mfr & Retailer
N.A.I.C.S.: 339115

**Daicel Safety Systems (Jiangsu) Co.,
Ltd.** (1)
Chenshan, Danbei Town, Danyang, 212312,
Jiangsu, China
Tel.: (86) 51186391999
Automotive Airbag Inflator Mfr & Retailer
N.A.I.C.S.: 333996

**Daicel Safety Systems (Thailand)
Co.,Ltd.** (1)
241 Moo 4 304 Industrial Park T Thatoom A
Srimahapote, Tambol Dong-Kee-Lek,
25140, Prachinburi, Thailand
Tel.: (66) 37270900
Web Site: http://www.daicelsst.com
Sales Range: $200-249.9 Million
Emp.: 1,300
Automobile Parts Mfr
N.A.I.C.S.: 336390

**Daicel Safety Systems Americas,
Inc.** (1)
4558 E Virginia St, Mesa, AZ 85215
Tel.: (480) 990-5300
Chemical Product Mfr & Distr
N.A.I.C.S.: 325998

**Daicel Safety Systems Europe
Sp.z.o.o** (1)
ul Strefowa 6, 58-130, Zarow, Poland
Tel.: (48) 74 641 9900
Web Site: https://www.daicelsse.com
Emp.: 350
Automotive Airbag Inflator Mfr
N.A.I.C.S.: 336390
Atsushi Hatomoto *(Pres)*

**Daicel Safety Systems India Pvt.
Ltd.** (1)
Unit412 4th Floor MGF Metropolis Mall MG
Road, Gurgaon, Haryana, India
Tel.: (91) 1244313670
Airbag Inflator Retailer
N.A.I.C.S.: 423120

**Daicel Safety Systems Korea,
Inc.** (1)
285 Yeongcheonsandan-ro, Geumho-eup,
Yeongcheon, 38899, Gyeongsangbuk-do,
Korea (South)
Tel.: (82) 543324212
Automotive Airbag Inflator Mfr & Retailer
N.A.I.C.S.: 333996

Daicel Safety Systems, Inc. (1)
805 Umaba Ibogawa-cho, Tatsuno-shi, Tatsuno, 671-1681, Hyogo, Japan
Tel.: (81) 791725411
Web Site: https://www.daicel.com
Sales Range: $200-249.9 Million
Emp.: 655
Automobile Airbag Inflators Mfr
N.A.I.C.S.: 336360

**Daicel Safety Technologies (Thailand)
Co., Ltd.** (1)
241 Moo 4 304 Industrial Park T Thatoom A
Srimahapote, Tambol Dong-Kee-Lek,
25140, Prachinburi, Thailand
Tel.: (66) 37270900
Web Site: http://www.daicelsst-stt.com
Emp.: 1,300
Automobile Parts Mfr
N.A.I.C.S.: 336390

Daicel Sakai Jitsugyo Co. Ltd. (1)

1 Teppo Cho Sakai Shi, Osaka, 590 0905,
Japan   **(50%)**
Tel.: (81) 22273271
Sales Range: $25-49.9 Million
Emp.: 100
Administrative Operations & Management of
Buildings; Manufacturer & Distribution of
Mats.
N.A.I.C.S.: 561110

Daicel Trading (Shanghai) Ltd. (1)
No 88 Wangdong Middle Road, Sijing Town
Songjiang District, Shanghai, 201601, China
Tel.: (86) 2157619381
Web Site: https://www.daiceltrading.com
Chemical Product Retailer
N.A.I.C.S.: 424690

Daicel-Allnex Ltd. (1)
Nihonbashi Front Bldg 3-6-2 Nihonbashi,
Chuo-ku, Tokyo, 103-0027, Japan
Tel.: (81) 355421626
Electron Beam Curable Resin Mfr & Distr
N.A.I.C.S.: 325998

Daicel-Cytec Company, Ltd. (1)
3-5-7 Ariake Toc Ariake E Tower 9f, Koto,
Tokyo, 135-0063, Japan
Tel.: (81) 3 3527 7890
Web Site: http://www.daicel-cytec.com
Polyester Resin Mfr
N.A.I.C.S.: 325211

Daicel-Evonik Ltd. (1)
Shinjuku Monolith 13F 2-3-1 Nishi-shinjuku,
Shinjuku-ku, Tokyo, 163-0913,
Japan   **(50%)**
Tel.: (81) 353246331
Web Site: https://www.pp-evonik.com
Sales Range: $25-49.9 Million
Polymers Mfr & Distr
N.A.I.C.S.: 325211

Daicen Membrane-Systems Ltd. (1)
Shinjuku Estate Bldg 34 15, Shinjuku 1
Chome, Tokyo, 160 0022, Japan   **(100%)**
Tel.: (81) 333545081
Web Site: http://www.daicen.co.jp
Sales Range: $25-49.9 Million
Emp.: 68
Mfr, Processing & Marketing of Separation
Membranes
N.A.I.C.S.: 325998

Dainichi Chemical Corp. (1)
28-11 Kuidesaku Jyobanshimofunaomachi,
Iwaki, 972-8312, Fukushima, Japan
Tel.: (81) 246445255
Emp.: 50
Specialty Chemicals Mfr & Distr
N.A.I.C.S.: 325199
Mottomi Takadi *(Pres)*

Hayashi Shipping, Co., Ltd. (1)
827-7 Oeshima, Aboshi-ku, Himeji, 671-
1231, Hyogo, Japan
Tel.: (81) 792721112
Shipping Transportation Services
N.A.I.C.S.: 488510

Japan Shotshell Ltd. (1)
760 Hamagawa-machi, Takasaki, 370 0081,
Gunma, Japan   **(100%)**
Tel.: (81) 27 343 8700
Web Site: http://www.daicel.com
Sales Range: $25-49.9 Million
Emp.: 60
Mfr & Distr of Shell Cartridges for Hunting
N.A.I.C.S.: 332992
Koji Kamimura *(Pres)*

Kyodo Sakusan Co. Ltd. (1)
JR Shinagawa East Bldg 2-18-1, Konan
Minato-ku, Tokyo, 108-8230,
Japan   **(54%)**
Tel.: (81) 367118421
Sales Range: $25-49.9 Million
Emp.: 3
Acetic Acid Mfr & Distr
N.A.I.C.S.: 325199

Kyoei Shokusan Co. Ltd. (1)
2 15 Kawara Machi 3 Chome, Chuo Ku,
Osaka, 541-0048, Japan   **(45%)**
Tel.: (81) 662034770
Sales Range: $50-74.9 Million
Emp.: 10
Insurance & Travel Agency
N.A.I.C.S.: 524298

Kyoudou Polymer Co., Ltd. (1)

JR Shinagawa East Bldg 2-18-1, Konan
Minato-ku, Tokyo, 108-8231, Japan
Tel.: (81) 367118401
ABS Resin Mfr
N.A.I.C.S.: 325211

Kyouei Shokusan Co., Ltd. (1)
Grand Front Osaka Tower-B 3-1 Ofuka-cho,
Kita-ku, Osaka, 530-0011, Japan
Tel.: (81) 676397431
Insurance Agency Services
N.A.I.C.S.: 524210

**LCP Leuna Carboxylation Plant
GmbH** (1)
Am Haupttor Bau 7629, 06237, Leuna, Germany
Tel.: (49) 346 143 4350
Web Site: https://www.lcp-carboxy.com
Chemical Products Mfr
N.A.I.C.S.: 325998
Felix Huhnerschulte *(Mng Dir)*

Lomapharm GmbH (1)
Langes Feld 5, 31860, Emmerthal, Germany
Tel.: (49) 51 552 7910
Web Site: https://www.lomapharm.de
Emp.: 165
Pharmaceuticals Product Mfr
N.A.I.C.S.: 325412
Ulrich Wollstadt *(Head-Sls & Mktg)*

**Ningbo Da-An Chemical Industries
Co., Ltd.** (1)
No 198 Da-an Road, Zhaobaoshan Subdistrict Zhenhai, Ningbo, 315200, China
Tel.: (86) 57486668890
Cellulose Acetate Mfr & Retailer
N.A.I.C.S.: 325220

PI-CRYSTAL Inc. (1)
273-1 Kashiwa 36 Rooms in Kashiwa Office, Kashiwa, 277-0005, Chiba, Japan
Tel.: (81) 471362036
Semiconductor Devices Mfr
N.A.I.C.S.: 334413

Polyplastics (Nantong) Ltd. (1)
No 171 Minxing Road, Economic and Technology Development Area, Nantong,
226009, Jiangsu, China
Tel.: (86) 51385922000
Polymer Product Mfr & Retailer
N.A.I.C.S.: 325211

Polyplastics Co., Ltd. (1)
JR Shinagawa East Bldg 18-1 Konan
2-chome, Minato-ku, Tokyo, 108-8280,
NSW, Japan   **(55%)**
Tel.: (81) 36 711 8600
Web Site: https://www.polyplastics.com
Sales Range: $1-4.9 Billion
Emp.: 1,500
Mfr & Distirbutor of Acetal Polymers & PBT
Resins; Joint Venture of Daicel Chemical
Industries, Ltd. (55%) & Ticona GmbH
(45%)
N.A.I.C.S.: 325211
Toshio Shiwaku *(Pres & CEO)*

Subsidiary (Non-US):

**Polyplastics Asia Pacific Sdn.
Bhd.** (2)
50-5-13A 5th Fl Wisma UOA Damansara 50
Jalan Dungun, Damansara Heights, 50490,
Kuala Lumpur, Malaysia   **(100%)**
Tel.: (60) 32 773 6600
Web Site: http://www.polyplastics.com
Plastic Materials Mfr
N.A.I.C.S.: 325211
Yoshimitsu Shirai *(Mng Dir)*

**Polyplastics Asia Pacific Singapore
Pte. Ltd.** (2)
6 Temasek Boulevard 25-01 Suntec Tower
4, Singapore, 038986, Singapore   **(100%)**
Tel.: (65) 67373693
Web Site: http://www.polyplastics.com
Sales Range: $10-24.9 Million
Emp.: 19
Provider of Plastic Materials
N.A.I.C.S.: 325211
Yoshitake Kawazu *(Mng Dir)*

Polyplastics China Ltd. (2)
17th Fl Soundwill Plz, 38 Russell St,
Causeway Bay, China (Hong Kong)
Tel.: (852) 28029488

Daicel Corporation—(Continued)

Web Site: http://www.polyplastics.com
Sales Range: $25-49.9 Million
Emp.: 30
Provider of Plastic Materials
N.A.I.C.S.: 325211

Subsidiary (Non-US):

Polyplastics Shanghai Ltd. (3)
3rd Floor Tower 2 Enterprise Centre 209
Gonghe Rd, Jing'an District, Shanghai,
200070, China
Tel.: (86) 213 256 8600
Web Site: http://www.polyplastics.com
Sales Range: $25-49.9 Million
Emp.: 50
Plastic Product Distr
N.A.I.C.S.: 424610
Masaaki Nakamura *(Mng Dir)*

Subsidiary (Non-US):

Polyplastics Marketing (T) Ltd. (2)
Lake Rajada Office Complex 15th Fl 193
Ratchadaphisek Road, Kwang Klong Toey
Khate Klong-Toey, Bangkok, 10110,
Thailand **(100%)**
Tel.: (66) 2 264 0447
Web Site: http://www.polyplastics.com
Sales Range: Less than $1 Million
Emp.: 42
Provider of POM Products
N.A.I.C.S.: 326199
Tomoaki Tanaka *(Mng Dir)*

Polyplastics Taiwan Co., Ltd. (2)
12th Fl Union Commercial Building No137
Section 2 Nanjing East Road, Zhongshan
District, Taipei, Taiwan **(75%)**
Tel.: (886) 225157111
Web Site: http://www.polyplastics.com
Sales Range: $50-74.9 Million
Emp.: 160
PVC Resin Mfr
N.A.I.C.S.: 325211

**Polyplastics Trading (Shanghai)
Ltd.** (2)
3rd Floor Tower 2 Enterprise Center 209
Gonghe Rd, Jing an District, Shanghai,
200070, China **(100%)**
Tel.: (86) 21 3256 8600
Web Site: http://www.polyplastics.com
Sales Range: $25-49.9 Million
Emp.: 10
Importing & Selling Various Engineering
Plastics
N.A.I.C.S.: 326199

Joint Venture (Domestic):

WinTech Polymer Ltd. (2)
JR Shinagawa East Building 18-1 Konan
2-chome, Minato-ku, Tokyo, 108 8280,
Japan **(60%)**
Tel.: (81) 367118610
Web Site: http://www.wintechpolymer.co.jp
Sales Range: $50-74.9 Million
Emp.: 150
Polymer Plastic Products Distr & Mfr
N.A.I.C.S.: 326199

Polyplastics Europe GmbH (1)
Am Prime Parc 9, 65479, Raunheim, Ger-
many
Tel.: (49) 69945158000
Web Site: http://www.polyplastics.com
Polymer Product Mfr & Retailer
N.A.I.C.S.: 325211

Polyplastics Korea Ltd. (1)
1713 Hanshin Inter Valley 24 707-34,
Yeoksam-dong Gangnam-gu, Seoul, 06211,
Korea (South)
Tel.: (82) 221832270
Polymer Product Mfr & Retailer
N.A.I.C.S.: 325211

**Polyplastics Marketing (India) Pvt
Ltd.** (1)
818 -C Wing 215 Atrium Near Hotel Court-
yard Marriott, Andheri Kurla Road Andheri
East, Mumbai, 400 059, India
Tel.: (91) 226 758 7668
Web Site: https://www.polyplastics.com
Sales Range: $50-74.9 Million
Emp.: 6
Poly Plastic Products Distr
N.A.I.C.S.: 424610

Jun Uchida *(Mng Dir)*

**Polyplastics Marketing Mexico, S.A.
de C.V.** (1)
Blvd Miguel de Cervantes Saavedra No 301
Torre Terret Norte Piso 15, Colonia Amplia-
cion Granada Del Miguel Hidalgo, 11520,
Mexico, Mexico
Tel.: (52) 5572521360
Polymer Product Mfr & Retailer
N.A.I.C.S.: 325211

Polyplastics USA, Inc. (1)
27240 Haggerty Rd Ste E-20, Farmington
Hills, MI 48331
Tel.: (248) 479-8928
Polymer Product Mfr & Retailer
N.A.I.C.S.: 325211

Shanghai Daicel Polymers, Ltd. (1)
East Industrial Development Zone, Sijing
Town, Shanghai, Songjiang, China
Tel.: (86) 2157619381
Web Site: http://www.daicelpolymers.cn
Sales Range: $50-74.9 Million
Emp.: 200
Mfr & Sale of Flame-Retardant ABS Resins
& ABS Alloy Resin
N.A.I.C.S.: 325211

**Special Devices (Thailand) Co.,
Ltd.** (1)
76 Moo 1 T Pukhamjarn A Praputthabaht,
Saraburi, 18120, Thailand
Tel.: (66) 36236320
Air Bag Initiator Mfr
N.A.I.C.S.: 336390

Special Devices Japan Ltd. (1)
JR Shinagawa East Building 15F 2-18-1,
Konan Minato-ku, Tokyo, 108-8230, Japan
Tel.: (81) 367118235
Air Bag Initiator Mfr
N.A.I.C.S.: 336390

**Topas Advanced Polymers
GmbH** (1)
Am Prime Parc 9, 65479, Raunheim, Ger-
many
Tel.: (49) 6994 515 8000
Web Site: https://www.topas.com
Polymer Product Mfr & Retailer
N.A.I.C.S.: 325211
Gregor Bommel *(Mng Dir)*

Toyo Styrene Co., Ltd. (1)
CJ Building 4F 7-4 Nishi-Shinbashi
2-chome, Minato-ku, Tokyo, 105-0003, Ja-
pan
Tel.: (81) 33 519 5600
Web Site: https://www.toyo-st.co.jp
Emp.: 150
Polystyrene Resin Mfr & Distr
N.A.I.C.S.: 325211
Sanshiro Matsushita *(Pres)*

Toyoshina Film Co., Ltd. (1)
5050 Toyoshina, Azumino, 399-8205, Na-
gano, Japan
Tel.: (81) 263727300
Polypropylene Film Mfr
N.A.I.C.S.: 326113

**Xi'an Huida Chemical Industries Co.,
Ltd.** (1)
Yuxia Town, Huxian County, Xi'an, 710302,
Shaanxi, China
Tel.: (86) 2984969846
Acetate Tow Mfr & Retailer
N.A.I.C.S.: 325220

Y.S. Logistics Service Co., Ltd. (1)
13 4 Matsuya Yamatogawa Dori 1 Chome,
Sakai Shi, Osaka, 590 0902,
Japan **(60%)**
Tel.: (81) 55370367
Web Site: http://www.ys-butsuyu.co.jp
Sales Range: $10-24.9 Million
Emp.: 40
Warehousing Packing & Transporting
N.A.I.C.S.: 493190

DAIDO GROUP LTD
Unit No 1301 Level 13 Tower 1 Kow-
loon Commerce Centre, No 51 Kwai
Cheong Road, Kwai Chung, New Ter-
ritories, China (Hong Kong)
Tel.: (852) 31078600
Web Site: http://www.daidohk.com

0544—(HKG)
Rev.: $34,846,770
Assets: $36,565,343
Liabilities: $34,184,153
Net Worth: $2,381,190
Earnings: $606,900
Emp.: 220
Fiscal Year-end: 12/31/22
Construction & Building Material Mfr
N.A.I.C.S.: 423390
Ivan Hon Chung Ho *(Exec Dir)*

Subsidiaries:

**Brilliant Cold Storage Management
Limited** (1)
8 Kwai Hei Street, Kwai Chung, New Terri-
tories, China (Hong Kong)
Tel.: (852) 2 614 8383
Web Site: http://www.b-coldstorage.com.hk
Sales Range: $75-99.9 Million
Refrigerated Warehousing Services
N.A.I.C.S.: 493120

Brilliant Top In Logistics Limited (1)
8 Kwai Hei Street, Kwai Chung, China
(Hong Kong)
Tel.: (852) 26141017
Cross Border Cargo Transportation Ser-
vices
N.A.I.C.S.: 488320

Daido Home International Ltd. (1)
50 Wang Lee Street, Yuen Long Industrial
Estate, Yuen Long, China (Hong Kong)
Tel.: (852) 26673630
Web Site: http://www.daidohk.com
Construction & Building Materials Mfr
N.A.I.C.S.: 423390

Diamond Sparkling Limited (1)
Room 1906 19th Floor Shun Tak Center
West Twr, Sheung Wan, China (Hong
Kong) **(100%)**
Tel.: (852) 31078600
Sales Range: $50-74.9 Million
Emp.: 25
Real Estate Property Lessors
N.A.I.C.S.: 531190

DAIDO KOGYO CO., LTD.
I-197 Kumasaka-machi, Kaga, 922-
8686, Ishikawa, Japan
Tel.: (81) 761721234
Web Site: https://www.did-daido.co.jp
Year Founded: 1933
6373—(TKS)
Rev.: $370,431,010
Assets: $522,989,810
Liabilities: $280,501,960
Net Worth: $242,487,850
Earnings: $2,260,620
Emp.: 2,480
Fiscal Year-end: 03/31/24
Industrial Machinery Mfr
N.A.I.C.S.: 333248
Kozo Araya *(Chm)*

Subsidiaries:

Atlas DID (Private) Ltd. (1)
2nd Floor Federation House Shahra-e-
Firdousi Clifton, Karachi, Pakistan
Tel.: (92) 2132 575 5615
Motorcycle Chain Mfr & Distr
N.A.I.C.S.: 336991

D.I.D Asia Co., Ltd. (1)
Siam Eastern Industrial Park 60/12 M 3
Mabyangporn, Pluakdaeng, Rayong, 21140,
Thailand
Tel.: (66) 38891206
Web Site: http://www.didasia.co.th
Motorcycle Chain Mfr & Distr
N.A.I.C.S.: 333613
Nobuyuki Koshino *(Pres)*

D.I.D Co., Ltd. (1)
3-5-4 Nihonbashi ningyo-cho, Chuo-ku, To-
kyo, 103-0013, Japan
Tel.: (81) 338080781
Web Site: http://www.did-coltd.com
Motorcycle Chain Mfr & Distr
N.A.I.C.S.: 333613
Shigeki Kimura *(Pres)*

D.I.D Philippines Inc. (1)

R1-B Lot 13 Phase 1B FPIP-SEZ Brgy,
Pantay Bata, Tanauan, 4232, Batangas,
Philippines
Tel.: (63) 43 455 7650
Web Site: https://www.did-philippines.com
Chain & Sprocket Mfr
N.A.I.C.S.: 333998

D.I.D Vietnam Co., Ltd. (1)
Standard factory 7D Lot H-1, Thang Long
Industrial Park II Di Su Commune My Hao
District, Hung Yen, Vietnam
Tel.: (84) 2213766825
Web Site: http://www.didvietnam.com.vn
Motorcycle Chain Mfr & Distr
N.A.I.C.S.: 333613

DID Europe S.R.L. (1)
Via del Fondatore 16, 40138, Bologna, Italy
Tel.: (39) 051531543
Web Site: https://www.dideu.it
Motorcycle Chain Distr
N.A.I.C.S.: 423830
Noriyasu Goya *(Mng Dir)*

DID Malaysia Sdn. Bhd. (1)
Empire Gallery Subang No B03-06 Empire
Soho Jalan 16/1, 47500, Subang Jaya, Se-
langor, Malaysia
Tel.: (60) 38 601 2270
Web Site: https://www.didmalaysia.com.my
Motorcycle Chain Mfr & Distr
N.A.I.C.S.: 336991

**Daido Chain (Changshu) Co.,
Ltd.** (1)
No 16 Zhujing Road, High-tech Industrial
Development Zone, Changshu, 215533,
Jiangsu, China
Tel.: (86) 51252836019
Web Site: https://www.did-daido.cn
Conveying Equipment Mfr & Distr
N.A.I.C.S.: 333922

Daido Corporation of America (1)
1031 Fred White Blvd, Portland, TN 37148
Tel.: (615) 323-4020
Web Site: https://www.daidocorp.com
Conveyor Chain Mfr & Distr
N.A.I.C.S.: 333613

Daido General Service Co., Ltd. (1)
35-1 Kumasaka-cho, Kaga, 922-0842,
Ishikawa, Japan
Tel.: (81) 761723990
Web Site: https://did-general.co.jp
Emp.: 60
Industrial Machinery Mfr
N.A.I.C.S.: 333248
Tatsuyoshi Oomoto *(Pres)*

Daido India Pvt. Ltd. (1)
SP2-96 New Industrial Complex Majrakath,
Neemrana Dist, Alwar, 301 705, Rajasthan,
India
Tel.: (91) 1494670700
Emp.: 300
Industrial Machinery Distr
N.A.I.C.S.: 423830
Bhim Sen Verma *(Officer-IT)*

**Daido Industria De Correntes Da
Amazonia Ltda.** (1)
Avenida Solimoes 1825 Distrito Industrial 1,
Manaus, 69075-200, Brazil
Tel.: (55) 9232114700
Web Site: https://daido.com.br
Motorcycle Chain Mfr & Distr
N.A.I.C.S.: 333613

**Daido Industrial E Comercial
Ltda.** (1)
Avenida Independencia 3 300, Taubate,
12032-000, Brazil
Tel.: (55) 1221258000
Web Site: http://www.daido.com.br
Motorcycle Chain Mfr & Distr
N.A.I.C.S.: 333613

Daido Kensetsu Co., Ltd. (1)
32 Ni Kumasakamachi, Kaga, 922-0842,
Japan
Tel.: (81) 761 72 0697
Web Site: http://www.daidokensetsu.co.jp
Industrial Machinery Mfr
N.A.I.C.S.: 333248

Daido Sittipol Co., Ltd. (1)
60/12 M 3 Mabyangporn, Siam Eastern Industrial Park, Pluak Daeng, 21140, Rayong,
Thailand

Tel.: (66) 3 889 1206
Web Site: https://www.ds.co.th
Motorcycle Chain Mfr & Distr
N.A.I.C.S.: 336991

Interface Solutions Co., Ltd. (1)
693/5-6 Moo1, Nongkham Subdistrict, Si
Racha, 20230, Chon Buri, Thailand
Tel.: (66) 38 340 2425
Web Site: https://www.interface.co.th
Emp.: 250
Automobile Parts Mfr
N.A.I.C.S.: 336390

Interface Systech Co., Ltd. (1)
75/5 Moo 11 Phahonyothin Road, T Klong-
nueng A Klongluang, Pathumthani, 12120,
Thailand
Tel.: (66) 2 529 0817
Web Site: https://www.interfacesystech.co.th
Information Technology Services
N.A.I.C.S.: 541511

Izumi Shoko Co., Ltd. (1)
1-7-20 Kyomachibori, Nishi-ku, Osaka, 550-
0003, Japan
Tel.: (81) 66 441 2651
Web Site: https://www.izumishoko.co.jp
Transmission Equipment Distr
N.A.I.C.S.: 423830

**P.T. Daido Indonesia
Manufacturing** (1)
Indotaisei Industrial Park Kota Bukit Indah
Sector IA Block P-2, Cikampek, Karawang,
41373, West Java, Indonesia
Tel.: (62) 264350180
Web Site: https://www.daido.co.id
Motorcycle Chain Mfr & Distr
N.A.I.C.S.: 333613

Shinsei Kogyo., Ltd. (1)
4-75 Chugo, Nakagawa-ku, Nagoya, 454-
0921, Aichi, Japan
Tel.: (81) 52 351 0501
Web Site: https://www.shinsei-kogyo.co.jp
Hard Steel Wire Mfr
N.A.I.C.S.: 331110

**Tsukiboshi Manufacturing Co.,
Ltd.** (1)
71-1-1 Nagai-machi, Kaga, 922-8611,
Ishikawa, Japan
Tel.: (81) 76 173 8282
Web Site: https://www.tsukiboshi.co.jp
Emp.: 510
Old-Formed Parts Mfr
N.A.I.C.S.: 336390

iwis-Daido LLC (1)
3500 N US Hwy 641, Murray, KY 42071
Tel.: (270) 767-6151
Industrial Automotive Product Distr
N.A.I.C.S.: 423120

DAIDO METAL CORPORATION
13F Nagoya-Hirokoji Bldg 2-3-1 Sa-
kaè, Naka-ku, Nagoya, 460-0008,
Japan
Tel.: (81) 522051400
Web Site:
https://www.daidometal.com
Year Founded: 1939
7245—(NGO)
Rev.: $827,991,600
Assets: $1,242,682,890
Liabilities: $737,527,710
Net Worth: $505,155,180
Earnings: ($15,831,360)
Emp.: 6,984
Fiscal Year-end: 03/31/23
Bearing Mfr
N.A.I.C.S.: 332991

Subsidiaries:

**ATA Casting Technology Co.,
Ltd.** (1)
361 Moo1 Rattanaraj Rd Bangna-Trad Rd
Km 27, Tambon Bangbor Amphur Bangbor,
Samut Prakan, 10560, Thailand
Tel.: (66) 23381389
Emp.: 695
Aluminium Products Mfr
N.A.I.C.S.: 331524

**ATA Casting Technology Japan Co.,
Ltd.** (1)

17th Tennoz Central Tower 2-2-24 Higash-
ishinagawa, Shinagawa-ku, Tokyo, 140-
0002, Japan
Tel.: (81) 367124455
Emp.: 707
Aluminium Product Distr
N.A.I.C.S.: 423510
Ichiro Nakamura *(Pres)*

Asia Kelmet Co., Ltd. (1)
3-29-1 Yaguchi, Ohta-ku, Tokyo, 146-0093,
Japan
Tel.: (81) 337594571
Web Site: http://www.daidometal.com
Sales Range: $25-49.9 Million
Emp.: 4
Automobile Plain Bearing Mfr
N.A.I.C.S.: 336390

BBL Daido Private Limited (1)
RS No 19 Vandalur Kelambakkam Road,
Pudupakkam Village Kancheepuram Dis-
trict, Kelambakkam, 603103, India
Tel.: (91) 4467402828
Automotive Bearing Mfr
N.A.I.C.S.: 332991

Bimetal Bearings Ltd (1)
18 Race Course Road, Coimbatore,
641018, India
Tel.: (91) 4222220054
Web Site: http://www.bimite.co.in
Sales Range: $25-49.9 Million
Emp.: 100
Ball & Roller Bearing Mfr
N.A.I.C.S.: 332991

**Chung Yuan Daido (Guangzhou) Co.,
Ltd.** (1)
B01 4th Floor Jianfa Plaza No 111 Airport
Road, Guangzhou, 510405, China
Tel.: (86) 2086347509
Automobile Engine Bearing Distr
N.A.I.C.S.: 423120

Chung Yuan Daido Co., Ltd. (1)
6th Floor No 700 Zhongzheng Road Build-
ing K Far East Century Plaza, Taipei
County, Zhonghe, 235, Taiwan
Tel.: (886) 282262160
Automobile Engine Bearing Distr
N.A.I.C.S.: 423120

DAIDO METAL CZECH s.r.o. (1)
Svedske valy 1309/6, 627 00, Brno, Czech
Republic
Tel.: (420) 545425511
Web Site: https://www.daidometal.cz
Sales Range: $25-49.9 Million
Emp.: 314
Automotive Bearing Mfr
N.A.I.C.S.: 332991

DAIDO METAL EUROPE LTD (1)
Winterhay Lane, Ilminster, TA19 9PH, Som-
ersetshire, United Kingdom
Tel.: (44) 146053221
Web Site: http://www.daidometal.com
Sales Range: $150-199.9 Million
Emp.: 200
Automobile Bearing Distr
N.A.I.C.S.: 423840

**DAIDO METAL GERMANY
GmbH** (1)
Solitudestrasse 49, 71638, Ludwigsburg,
Germany
Tel.: (49) 7141 6889340
Web Site: http://www.daidometal.com
Plain Bearings Distr
N.A.I.C.S.: 423840

DAIDO METAL KOTOR AD (1)
Industrijska zona bb, 85330, Kotor, Monte-
negro
Tel.: (382) 32331513
Web Site: https://daidokotor.com
Sales Range: $50-74.9 Million
Emp.: 181
Automobile Plain Bearing Mfr & Distr
N.A.I.C.S.: 423840
Esaki Shibuya *(Mng Dir)*

DAIDO METAL RUSSIA LLC (1)
Zavolzhye Sovetskaya str 1A premises P1,
606522, Nizhniy Novgorod, Russia
Tel.: (7) 8316121230
Web Site: http://www.daidorussia.ru
Plain Bearings Distr
N.A.I.C.S.: 423840

**DAIDO PRECISION METAL (SU-
ZHOU) CO., LTD.** (1)
No 246 QingQiu Str Suzhou Industrial Park,
Suzhou, China
Tel.: (86) 512 6283 3531
Web Site: http://www.dpmsz.cn
Automotive Bearing Mfr & Distr
N.A.I.C.S.: 336390

**DAIDO REBUILD SERVICES
INC.** (1)
665 A Bonifacio Street Balintawak, Quezon
City, Philippines
Tel.: (63) 23668476
Web Site: http://www.daidometal.com
Engine Rebuilding Services
N.A.I.C.S.: 811114

**DM Casting Technology (Thailand)
Co., Ltd.** (1)
88/7 Moo 3, Klongsuan Sub district Bang-
bor District, Samut Prakan, 10560, Thailand
Tel.: (66) 23260322
Emp.: 125
Aluminium Products Mfr
N.A.I.C.S.: 331524

DMS Korea Co., Ltd. (1)
325-1 Uijeon-ri Jinyeong-eup, Gimhae,
Gyeongsangnam, Korea (South)
Tel.: (82) 55 342 0780
Web Site: https://www.dmskr.com
Automobile Engine Bearing Distr
N.A.I.C.S.: 423120
Seo Jong-Hee *(CEO)*

DONGSUNG METAL CO., LTD. (1)
160 Yongsan-myun, Youngdong-kun, Bekja-
jun, 370-912, Chungbuk, Korea (South)
Tel.: (82) 5 730 36 88
Sales Range: $50-74.9 Million
Emp.: 190
Automobile Plain Bearing Mfr
N.A.I.C.S.: 336390

**Daido Industrial Bearings Europe
Ltd.** (1)
Winterhay Lane, Ilminster, TA19 9PH, Som-
erset, United Kingdom
Tel.: (44) 146053221
Web Site: http://www.daidometal.com
Sales Range: $50-74.9 Million
Emp.: 180
Ball & Roller Bearing Mfr
N.A.I.C.S.: 332991

**Daido Industrial Bearings Japan Co.,
Ltd.** (1)
8 Iwata Tonoji, Inuyama, 484-0094, Aichi,
Japan
Tel.: (81) 568633915
Non-Automobile Bearing Mfr
N.A.I.C.S.: 332991

Daido Logitech Co., Ltd. (1)
Tendoh Shinden Maehara, Inuyama, 484-
0061, Aichi, Japan
Tel.: (81) 568611214
Warehousing Services
N.A.I.C.S.: 493190

Daido Metal Co., Ltd (1)
13F Nagoya-Hirokoji Bldg, Nagoya, 460-
0008, Japan
Tel.: (81) 568613111
Web Site: http://www.daidometal.com
Sales Range: $400-449.9 Million
Emp.: 1,200
Motor Vehicle Electrical & Electronic Equip-
ment Mfr
N.A.I.C.S.: 336320

**Daido Metal Corporation - Bimetal
Division** (1)
Tendoh Shinden Maehara, Inuyama, 484-
0061, Aichi, Japan
Tel.: (81) 568611354
Web Site: http://www.daidometal.com
Automotive Bearing Mfr
N.A.I.C.S.: 332991

**Daido Metal Corporation - Gifu
Factory** (1)
135 Ohara Minami Gujo, Gifu, 501-4107,
Japan
Tel.: (81) 575792221
Web Site: http://www.daidometal.com
Automotive Metal Bearings Mfr
N.A.I.C.S.: 332991

**Daido Metal Corporation - Inuyama
Factory** (1)
Tendoh Shinden Maehara, Inuyama, 484-
0061, Aichi, Japan
Tel.: (81) 568611353
Web Site: http://www.daidometal.com
Automotive Bearing Mfr
N.A.I.C.S.: 332991

**Daido Metal Corporation - Maehara
Factory** (1)
Tendoh Shinden Maehara, Inuyama, 484-
0061, Aichi, Japan
Tel.: (81) 568613112
Web Site: http://www.daidometal.com
Sales Range: $200-249.9 Million
Emp.: 900
Automotive Bearing Mfr
N.A.I.C.S.: 332991

Daido Metal Europe GmbH (1)
Solitudestrasse 49, 71638, Ludwigsburg,
Germany
Tel.: (49) 71416889340
Web Site: http://www.daidometal.com
Emp.: 5
Motor Vehicle Supplies & New Parts Whslr
N.A.I.C.S.: 423120
Michitoshi Inagaki *(Mng Dir)*

**Daido Metal Mexico Sales, S.A. de
C.V.** (1)
Carretera Retono No 100 Col, Santa Cruz
de las Flores, 45640, Tlajomulco de Zuniga,
Jalisco, Mexico
Tel.: (52) 3314545000
Automotive Engine Distr
N.A.I.C.S.: 423120

**Daido Metal Mexico, S.A. de
C.V.** (1)
Carretera San Isidro Mazatepec No 7501
Col, Santa Cruz de las Flores Tlajomulco
de Zuniga, 45640, Mexico, Jalisco, Mexico
Tel.: (52) 3314545000
Web Site:
https://www.daidometalmexico.com
Emp.: 500
Automotive Bearing Mfr
N.A.I.C.S.: 332991

Daido Metal Saga Co., Ltd. (1)
5088-9 Osaki Oaza, Kitagata-cho, Takeo,
849-2204, Saga, Japan
Tel.: (81) 954278250
Automotive Bearing Mfr
N.A.I.C.S.: 332991

Daido Metal Sales Co., Ltd (1)
Tendoh Shinden Maehara Inuyama, Na-
goya, 484-0061, Japan
Tel.: (81) 568611367
Web Site: http://www.daidometalsales.jp
Sales Range: $25-49.9 Million
Emp.: 25
Ball & Roller Bearing Mfr
N.A.I.C.S.: 332991
Yoshihiko Miwa *(Pres)*

Daido Metal U.S.A. Inc (1)
1215 S Greenwood St, Bellefontaine, OH
43311-1628
Tel.: (847) 590-8520
Web Site: http://www.daidometal.com
Sales Range: $25-49.9 Million
Emp.: 100
Ball & Roller Bearing Mfr
N.A.I.C.S.: 332991

Daido Plain Bearings Co., Ltd. (1)
8-1 Nozomigaoka Seki, Gifu, 501-3219,
Japan
Tel.: (81) 575234083
Web Site: http://www.daidometal.com
Emp.: 100
Automobile Plain Bearing Mfr
N.A.I.C.S.: 336390

Dyna Metal Co., Ltd. (1)
101 Moo 9 Wellgrow Rd 14 Bangwoa,
Bangpakong Dist, Chachoengsao, 24180,
Thailand
Tel.: (66) 38570 611 0614
Web Site: https://www.dynametal.co.th
Emp.: 494
Automobile Engine Bearing Distr
N.A.I.C.S.: 423120
Hakakoshi Shigemasa *(Pres)*

**IINO (Foshan) Technology Co.,
Ltd.** (1)

Daido Metal Corporation—(Continued)

1-3 A Danheng Road Nanhai Japanese
Medium-sized Enterprizes Park, Danzao
Nanhai District, Foshan, Guangdong, China
Tel.: (86) 75785437068
Automobile Parts Mfr
N.A.I.C.S.: 336390

ISS America, Inc. (1)
760 Challenger St, Brea, CA 92821-2924
Tel.: (714) 580-8124
Web Site: https://www.issamerica.com
Automobile Parts Mfr
N.A.I.C.S.: 336390

ISS Mexico Manufacturing, S.A. de C.V. (1)
Rio Danubio 801 Parque Technoindustrial
Castro del Rio, 36810, Irapuato, Guanajuato, Mexico
Tel.: (52) 4626937118
Automobile Parts Mfr
N.A.I.C.S.: 336390

Iino Manufacturing Co., Ltd. (1)
17th Floor Tennozu Central Tower 2-2-24
Higashi-Shinagawa, Shinagawa-ku, Tokyo, 140-0002, Japan
Tel.: (81) 35 781 6777
Web Site: https://www.iinoseisakusho.co.jp
Emp.: 1,471
Automobile Engine Bearing Distr
N.A.I.C.S.: 423120
Sokichi Kimpara (Mng Dir)

KOREA DRY BEARING CO., LTD. (1)
163-12 Okcheon-eup, Okcheon-gun, Dongan, 373-800, Chungcheongbuk-do, Korea (South)
Tel.: (82) 437339361
Polymer Bearings Mfr & Distr
N.A.I.C.S.: 332991

NDC Co., Ltd. (1)
2-39-1 Mimomi, Narashino, 2750002, Chiba, Japan
Sales Range: $100-124.9 Million
Emp.: 400
Engine Bearings, Bushings & Thrust Washers Mfr & Sales
N.A.I.C.S.: 336310
Yasushi Shibuya (Pres)

NDC Sales Co., Ltd. (1)
2-39-1 Mimomi Narashino, Chiba, 275-0002, Japan
Tel.: (81) 474771122
Web Site: http://www.ndc-sales.co.jp
Automotive Plain Bearing Distr
N.A.I.C.S.: 423120
Hisao Anraku (CEO)

PT. Daido Metal Indonesia (1)
Web Site: http://www.daidometal.com
Copper Foundries
N.A.I.C.S.: 331529

PT. IINO Indonesia (1)
Jalan Jababeka IVC Blok T2M Kawasan
Industri Jababeka I, Desa Pasir Gombong
Cikarang Utara, Bekasi, 17530, Indonesia
Tel.: (62) 21 893 6645
Web Site: https://www.iinoseisakusho.co.id
Automobile Parts Distr
N.A.I.C.S.: 441330
Takashi Okumoto (Pres)

Philippine Iino Corporation (1)
Dinagyang Street Mactan Economic Zone
II, Special Economic Zone Basak, Lapu-Lapu, 6015, Cebu, Philippines
Tel.: (63) 32 340 8610
Web Site: https://www.phillino.com
Precision Turned Product Mfr
N.A.I.C.S.: 332721

Shippo Asahi Moulds (Thailand) Co., Ltd. (1)
438 Moo 17 Bangplee Industrial Estate Soi 7, Bang Sao Thong Subdistrict Bang Sao Thong District, Samut Prakan, 10570, Thailand
Tel.: (66) 27067800
Web Site: https://www.samt.co.th
Emp.: 86
Die-Casting Mold Mfr
N.A.I.C.S.: 333514

DAIDO SIGNAL CO., LTD.

Shin-Onarimon-Building 6-17-19
Shimbashi, Minato-ku, Tokyo, 105-8650, Japan
Tel.: (81) 334384111
Web Site: https://www.daido-signal.co.jp
Year Founded: 1929
6743—(TKS)
Rev.: $137,276,480
Assets: $295,255,480
Liabilities: $105,237,810
Net Worth: $190,017,670
Earnings: $3,767,700
Emp.: 904
Fiscal Year-end: 03/31/24
Synthetic Resin Mfr & Whslr
N.A.I.C.S.: 325612
Toru Imai (Pres & CEO)

DAIDO STEEL CO., LTD.

1-10 Higashisakura 1-chome,
Higashi-ku, Nagoya, 461-8581, Aichi, Japan
Tel.: (81) 529637501   JP
Web Site: https://www.daido.co.jp
Year Founded: 1916
5471—(NGO)
Rev.: $3,822,688,061
Assets: $5,211,323,285
Liabilities: $2,189,764,831
Net Worth: $3,021,558,454
Earnings: $201,882,996
Emp.: 11,941
Fiscal Year-end: 03/31/24
Integrated Specialty Steel
N.A.I.C.S.: 331513
Tadashi Shimao (Chm)

Subsidiaries:

DAIDO AMISTAR (M) SDN. BHD. (1)
No 8 Jalan Perusahaan Utama Taman Industri Selesa Jaya Off Jalan, 43300, Balakong, Selangor, Malaysia
Tel.: (60) 389617566
Web Site: http://www.amistar.com.my
Sales Range: $25-49.9 Million
Emp.: 60
Stainless Steel Products Mfr
N.A.I.C.S.: 331110
Koichi Hayashi (Mng Dir)

DAIDO AMISTAR(S) PTE LTD (1)
No 21 Senoko South Road Woodlands
East, Singapore, 758079, Singapore
Tel.: (65) 67581611
Web Site: http://www.amistar.com.sg
Sales Range: $25-49.9 Million
Emp.: 54
Steel Product Distr
N.A.I.C.S.: 423510

DAIDO DMS (Thailand) Co., Ltd. (1)
120 Moo 5 Bangna-Trad Rd Km 36, Wellgrow Industrial Estate Bang Samak Bang Pakong, Chachoengsao, 24180, Thailand
Tel.: (66) 33599700
Web Site: https://www.daidopdm.co.th
Emp.: 207
Moulding Product Mfr & Distr
N.A.I.C.S.: 333511

DAIDO PDM (Thailand) CO., LTD. (1)
120 Moo 5 Wellgrow Industrial Estate
Bangna-Trad Rd KM 36 Bangsamak, Bang
Pakong, Chachoengsao, 24180, Thailand
Tel.: (66) 38545999
Web Site: http://www.daidopdm.co.th
Sales Range: $75-99.9 Million
Emp.: 207
Tool Steel Distr
N.A.I.C.S.: 423510

DAIDO Steel Group Europe GmbH (1)
Insterburger Strasse 16, 60487, Frankfurt
am Main, Germany
Tel.: (49) 697474870
Steel Product Mfr & Distr
N.A.I.C.S.: 332313

DMS Moldes Mexico S.A. de C.V. (1)
Av Mina de Guadalupe No 902 Parque Industrial Santa IV, CP Puerto Interior Guanajuato, 36275, Silao, Mexico
Tel.: (52) 4727489390
Steel Product Mfr & Distr
N.A.I.C.S.: 332313

Daido Amistar Co., Ltd. (1)
152 Hino 3-chome, Daito, 574-0062, Osaka, Japan
Tel.: (81) 728718601
Web Site: http://www.amistar.co.jp
Sales Range: $25-49.9 Million
Emp.: 100
Metal Stamping Mfr
N.A.I.C.S.: 332119

Daido Bunseki Research Inc. (1)
2-30 Daido-cho, Minami-ku, Nagoya, 457-8545, Aichi, Japan
Tel.: (81) 526119434
Sales Range: $25-49.9 Million
Emp.: 228
Biotechnology Research & Development Services
N.A.I.C.S.: 541714
Nobuyuki Tukamoto (Dir-Personnel & Gen Affairs Div)

Daido Castings Co., Ltd. (1)
10 Ryugu-cho, Minato-ku, Nagoya, 455-0022, Aichi, Japan
Tel.: (81) 526915191
Web Site: https://www.d-cast.jp
Sales Range: $100-124.9 Million
Emp.: 474
Steel Casting Mfr
N.A.I.C.S.: 331513

Daido D.M.S. India Pvt. Ltd. (1)
Plot No 255 Sector-24, Faridabad, 121 005, Haryana, India
Tel.: (91) 1294100255
Web Site: http://www.daidodmsi.co.in
Steel Product Mfr & Distr
N.A.I.C.S.: 331210
Tadashi Wakao (Mng Dir)

Daido DMS Malaysia Sdn. Bhd. (1)
Lot 5302 Jalan Semenyih Batu 19 Kawasan
Perindustrian Kajang Jaya, 43500, Semenyih, Selangor, Malaysia
Tel.: (60) 387247566
Web Site: https://m.dmsm.com.my
Metal Product Mfr & Distr
N.A.I.C.S.: 332312
Takuya Kawasaki (Mng Dir)

Daido DMS Phils., Inc. (1)
Ominworth Bldg Unit 7 Lot5 121 East Main
Avenue Laguna Technopark, Binan, 4024, Philippines
Tel.: (63) 493071581
Steel Product Mfr & Distr
N.A.I.C.S.: 332313

Daido DMS Vietnam Co., Ltd. (1)
F Building-IDE International Plant B2 Street
Section B, Pho Noi A Industrial Park, Hung
Yen, Vietnam
Tel.: (84) 2213967604
Steel Product Mfr & Distr
N.A.I.C.S.: 332313

Daido Die & Mold Steel Solutions Co., Ltd. (1)
3-152 Hino, Daito, 574-0062, Osaka, Japan
Tel.: (81) 728718601
Web Site: https://www.daidodms.co.jp
Emp.: 600
Metal Dies Mfr
N.A.I.C.S.: 333517
Kazuhito Koto (Pres)

Daido Dms Mexico, S.A. de C.V. (1)
Av Mina de Guadalupe No 902 Parque Industrial Santa IV, CP Puerto Interior Guanajuato, 36275, Silao, Mexico
Tel.: (52) 4727489389
Steel Product Mfr & Distr
N.A.I.C.S.: 332313

Daido Dms Singapore Pte. Ltd. (1)
No 39 Senoko Way, Singapore, 758052, Singapore
Tel.: (65) 67581611
Steel Product Mfr & Distr
N.A.I.C.S.: 332313

Daido EcoMet Co., Ltd. (1)

39 Motohama-cho, Tokai, 477-0035, Aichi, Japan
Tel.: (81) 562335946
Web Site: https://www.d-ecomet.co.jp
Emp.: 162
Steel Wastes Recycling Services
N.A.I.C.S.: 325612

Daido Electronics (GuangDong) Co., Ltd. (1)
No 5 NanMei Road Xin Er ShaJing, Baoan
Region, Shenzhen, 518125, Guangdong, China
Tel.: (86) 75527415292
Machinery Parts Mfr & Distr
N.A.I.C.S.: 333248
Naoki Makino (Chm)

Daido Electronics (Suzhou) Co., Ltd. (1)
No 98 Longtan Road, Suzhou Industrial
Park, Suzhou, 215126, Jiangsu, China
Tel.: (86) 51262896801
Electronic Components Mfr
N.A.I.C.S.: 334419
Minoru Aizaki (Chm)

Daido Electronics (Thailand) Co., Ltd. (1)
43 Moo 9 Rojana Industrial Park Rojana
Road, Tambol Tanuu Amphur U-Thai, Ayutthaya, 13210, Thailand
Tel.: (66) 35330735
Web Site: http://www.daido-electronics.co.jp
Sales Range: $100-124.9 Million
Emp.: 450
Spindle Motor Magnets Mfr
N.A.I.C.S.: 332999

Daido Electronics Co., Ltd. (1)
1642-144 Nasubigawa, Nakatsugawa, 509-9132, Gifu, Japan
Tel.: (81) 573686177
Web Site: http://www.daido-electronics.co.jp
Magnet Mfr
N.A.I.C.S.: 334610
Hajime Amano (Pres)

Daido Environment Engineering Co.,Ltd. (1)
9 Takiharu-cho, Minami-ku, Nagoya, 457-0819, Aichi, Japan
Tel.: (81) 526136851
Web Site: http://www.daido-kankyo.co.jp
Ash Melting Contract Operation & Maintenance Services
N.A.I.C.S.: 561990

Daido IT Solutions Co., Ltd. (1)
21st Floor Urban Net Nagoya Building
1-1-10 Higashisakura, Higashi-ku, Nagoya, 461-0005, Japan
Tel.: (81) 523085801
Web Site: http://www.daido-its.co.jp
Software Development Services
N.A.I.C.S.: 541511

Daido Kogyo (Thailand) Co., Ltd. (1)
22F Silom Complex Bldg 191 Silom Road,
Bangrak, Bangkok, 10500, Thailand
Tel.: (66) 26320072
Web Site: http://www.fact-link.com
Steel Product Mfr & Distr
N.A.I.C.S.: 331210

Daido Kogyo India Pvt. Ltd. (1)
Unit No 302 and 309 Plam Spring Plaza 3rd
Foolr Golf Course Road, Gurgaon, 122011, Haryana, India
Tel.: (91) 1246250000
Steel Product Mfr & Distr
N.A.I.C.S.: 332313

Daido Life Service Co., Ltd. (1)
4-7 Daido-cho, Minami-ku, Nagoya, 457-0811, Aichi, Japan
Tel.: (81) 526118841
Web Site: https://www.daidolife.co.jp
Emp.: 317
Apartment Building Construction Services
N.A.I.C.S.: 236116

Daido Machinery Co., Ltd. (1)
9 Takiharu-cho, Minami-ku, Nagoya, 457-8577, Aichi, Japan
Tel.: (81) 526117171
Web Site: http://www.dm-daido.co.jp
Emp.: 350
Metal Cutting Machinery Mfr
N.A.I.C.S.: 333517

Daido Matex Co., Ltd. **(1)**
16-1 Minami-machi, Kawasaki, 210-0015,
Kanagawa, Japan
Tel.: (81) 442211070
Web Site: http://www.daidomatex.co.jp
Sales Range: $50-74.9 Million
Emp.: 70
Steel Product Distr
N.A.I.C.S.: 423510

Daido Plant Industries Co., Ltd. **(1)**
9 Takiharu-cho, Minami-ku, Nagoya, 457-
0819, Japan
Tel.: (81) 526136861
Web Site: http://www.daido-plant.co.jp
Machinery Equipment Mfr
N.A.I.C.S.: 333248
Jun Maeda *(Pres)*

Daido Precision Industries Ltd. **(1)**
3-1-15 Nishi-Ikebukuro TS building 3F,
Toshima-ku, Tokyo, 171-0021, Japan
Tel.: (81) 359569176
Web Site: https://www.daidoseimitu.co.jp
Sales Range: $50-74.9 Million
Emp.: 200
Precision Machine Parts Mfr & Distr
N.A.I.C.S.: 331513

Daido Shizai Service Co., Ltd. **(1)**
4-7 Daido Buld 4F Daido Cho, Minami Ku,
Nagoya, 457-0811, Aichi, Japan
Tel.: (81) 52 611 8801
Web Site: http://www.daido.co.jp
Sales Range: $25-49.9 Million
Emp.: 45
Industrial Materials & Equipments Procure-
ment Services
N.A.I.C.S.: 533110
Takashi Murase *(Pres)*

Daido Star Techno Co., Ltd. **(1)**
500 Ishihara, Shibukawa, 377-0007,
Gunma, Japan
Tel.: (81) 279 23 1375
Web Site: http://www.dsteku.jp
Emp.: 260
Steel Products Mfr
N.A.I.C.S.: 331513

Daido Star Tekuno Co., Ltd. **(1)**
500 Ishihara, Shibukawa, 377-0007, Japan
Tel.: (81) 279231375
Web Site: https://www.dsteku.jp
Emp.: 260
Structural Steel Mfr & Distr
N.A.I.C.S.: 332312

Daido Steel (America) Inc **(1)**
1051 Perimeter Dr Ste 1175, Schaumburg,
IL 60173
Tel.: (847) 517-7950
Web Site: http://www.daidosteel.com
Sales Range: $50-74.9 Million
Emp.: 10
Electronic Components Mfr
N.A.I.C.S.: 324199

Daido Steel (Shanghai) Co., Ltd. **(1)**
Room 1402 Ruijin Building No 205 Maom-
ing South Road, Shanghai, 200020, China
Tel.: (86) 2154662020
Web Site: https://daidosteel.net
Emp.: 50
Steel Mfrs
N.A.I.C.S.: 332111
Matsuzaki Shinji *(Chm)*

**Daido Steel Co., Ltd. - Chita
Plant** **(1)**
39 Motohama-machi, Tokai, 477-0035,
Aichi, Japan
Tel.: (81) 562333101
Web Site: http://www.daido.co.jp
Steel Products Mfr
N.A.I.C.S.: 327910

**Daido Steel Co., Ltd. - Kawasaki
Plant** **(1)**
4-1 Yako 2-chome, Kawasaki-ku, Kawasaki,
210-0863, Kanagawa, Japan
Tel.: (81) 44 266 3760
Web Site: http://www.daido.co.jp
Reinforcing Bars & Rails Mfr
N.A.I.C.S.: 331110

**Daido Steel Co., Ltd. - Kimitsu
Plant** **(1)**
1 Kimitsu, Kimitsu, 299-1141, Chiba, Japan
Tel.: (81) 439521541

Sales Range: $800-899.9 Million
Emp.: 3,000
Steel Forging Mfr
N.A.I.C.S.: 331110
Isaki Masahiro *(Project Mgr)*

Daido Steel Co., Ltd. - Oji Plant **(1)**
9-3 Kamiya 3-chome, Kita-ku, Tokyo, 115-
0043, Japan
Tel.: (81) 339014161
Steel Alloys Mfr
N.A.I.C.S.: 331110

**Daido Steel Co., Ltd. - Shibukawa
Plant** **(1)**
500 Ishihara, Shibukawa, 377-0007,
Gunma, Japan
Tel.: (81) 279252000
Web Site: http://www.daido.co.jp
Sales Range: $200-249.9 Million
Emp.: 600
Steel Forging Mfr
N.A.I.C.S.: 332111

**Daido Steel Materials Technology
Shanghai Co.,Ltd.** **(1)**
RM801 Building 3 Sino Agriculture Invest-
ment Tower, No 58 Yaoyuan Road, Shang-
hai, 200126, China
Tel.: (86) 2161909501
Structural Steel Distr
N.A.I.C.S.: 423510

Daido Technica Co., Ltd. **(1)**
39 Motohamamachi, Tokai, 477-0035, Aichi,
Japan
Tel.: (81) 562331231
Web Site: http://www.daido-technica.co.jp
Emp.: 500
Stainless Steel Products Mfr
N.A.I.C.S.: 331110

Daido Tienwen Steel Co., Ltd. **(1)**
No 1 Dachang Road, Pingzhen District,
Taoyuan, Taiwan
Tel.: (886) 34936621
Web Site: http://www.daidosteel.com.tw
Tool Steels Mfr
N.A.I.C.S.: 331110

Fuji Oozx Mexico, S.A. de C.V. **(1)**
Av Mina de Guadalupe No 902 Parque In-
dustrial Santa Fe IV, 36275, Silao, Guana-
juato, Mexico
Tel.: (52) 4721352100
Steel Product Mfr & Distr
N.A.I.C.S.: 332313

**Fuji Valve (Guangdong)
Corporation** **(1)**
Fiez No 6 Yinhai Road, Nanhai Eco-
Industrial Park Danzao Nanhai, Foshan,
China
Tel.: (86) 75785405516
Engine Parts Mfr & Distr
N.A.I.C.S.: 336310

Izumi Denki Kogyo Co., Ltd. **(1)**
8-1 Narihara 4-chome, Sumida-Ku, Tokyo,
130-0002, Japan
Tel.: (81) 336248331
Web Site: https://www.izumidenki.com
Emp.: 59
Steel Products Mfr
N.A.I.C.S.: 331110

Japan Drop Forge Co., Ltd. **(1)**
2-1-1 Ohamacho, Amagasaki, 660-0095,
Hyogo, Japan **(100%)**
Tel.: (81) 664161051
Web Site: https://www.j-d-f.co.jp
Emp.: 127
Forged Products Mfr
N.A.I.C.S.: 332111

Kawaichi Sangyo Co., Ltd. **(1)**
5-9 Ogimachi, Kawasaki-ku, Kawasaki, 210-
0867, Japan
Tel.: (81) 443552715
Web Site: http://www.kawaichi.jp
Emp.: 192
General Freight Trucking Services
N.A.I.C.S.: 484110
Iwata Syuuiti *(Pres)*

**Kisokomakogen Kankokaihatsu Co.,
Ltd.** **(1)**
4898-8 Higi Kiso-cho, Kiso-gun, Nagano,
399-6101, Japan
Tel.: (81) 264237550

Web Site: https://www.kisokoma.co.jp
Emp.: 87
Golf Course Construction Services
N.A.I.C.S.: 237990

Maruta Transport Co., Ltd. **(1)**
22-20 Shinkaicho, Mizuho-ku, Nagoya, 467-
0856, Japan
Tel.: (81) 528723311
Web Site: https://www.maruta.co.jp
Emp.: 487
Cargo Handling Services
N.A.I.C.S.: 488320

Nippon Seisen Co., Ltd. **(1)**
Kogin Building 9F 4-1-1 Koraibashi, Chuo-
ku, Osaka, 541-0043, Osaka,
Japan **(50.83%)**
Tel.: (81) 662225433
Web Site: https://www.n-seisen.co.jp
Rev.: $295,645,470
Assets: $352,987,220
Liabilities: $91,964,930
Net Worth: $261,022,290
Earnings: $17,133,120
Emp.: 596
Fiscal Year-end: 03/31/2024
Stainless Steel Wire Mfr
N.A.I.C.S.: 331110
Motoshi Shinkai *(Pres & CEO)*

Subsidiary (Non-US):

**Daido Stainless Steel (Dalian) Co.,
Ltd.** **(2)**
IC-43 Bonded Area, Dalian, 116600, China
Tel.: (86) 41187316559
Stainless Steel Wire Distr
N.A.I.C.S.: 423510

NASLON Korea Co., Ltd. **(2)**
1517 Gwanghwamun Officia 92 Saemunan-
ro, Jongno-gu, Seoul, 03186, Korea (South)
Tel.: (82) 232762929
Stainless Steel Wire Distr
N.A.I.C.S.: 423510

**Naslon Fuji Filter (Changshu) Co.,
Ltd.** **(2)**
No 13 Xin An Jiang Road, Changshu, Ji-
angsu, China
Tel.: (86) 51281586999
Stainless Steel Wire Distr
N.A.I.C.S.: 423510

Plant (Domestic):

**Nippon Seisen Co., Ltd. - Hirakata
Factory** **(2)**
4-17 1 Ikenomiya, Hirakata-shi, Osaka, 573-
8522, Japan
Tel.: (81) 72 840 1261
Stainless Steel Wire Mfr
N.A.I.C.S.: 331110

**Nippon Seisen Co., Ltd. - Nagoya
Factory** **(2)**
Minato-ku, Nagoya, Nagoya, 455-0022,
Aichi, Japan
Tel.: (81) 52 692 3374
Stainless Steel Wire Mfr
N.A.I.C.S.: 331110

**Nippon Seisen Co., Ltd. - Osaka
Factory** **(2)**
4-3-27 Nishikonoike-cho, Higashi, Osaka,
578-0976, Japan
Tel.: (81) 6 6745 0025
Stainless Steel Wire Mfr
N.A.I.C.S.: 331110

Subsidiary (Non-US):

Thai Seisen Co., Ltd. **(2)**
Bangpoo Industrial Estate 533 Soi 8 Moo 4
Sukhumvit Road, Samut Prakan, 10280,
Thailand
Tel.: (66) 23240414
Stainless Steel Wire Mfr
N.A.I.C.S.: 331110

Nissei Seiko Co., Ltd. **(1)**
2-1-3 Tango-dori, Minami-ku, Nagoya, 457-
0801, Japan
Tel.: (81) 52 611 6271
Web Site: http://www.nssy.co.jp
Emp.: 85
Fastener Mfr
N.A.I.C.S.: 339993
Kazuya Sakaguchi *(Pres)*

Ohio Star Forge Co. **(1)**
4000 Mahoning Ave NW, Warren, OH
44483 **(100%)**
Tel.: (330) 847-6360
Web Site: http://www.ohiostar.com
Sales Range: $25-49.9 Million
Emp.: 100
Bearing Lace & Automobile Parts by Steel
Bar Hot-Forming
N.A.I.C.S.: 000110
William J. Orbach *(Pres & CEO)*

**Oriental Shimomura Drawing (M)
Sdn. Bhd.** **(1)**
1046 Jaran Perusahaan Prai Industrial Es-
tate Phase 4, Penang, 13600, Prai, Malay-
sia
Tel.: (60) 45070981
Emp.: 56
Steel Products Mfr
N.A.I.C.S.: 331210
Fumitoshi Ogura *(Mng Dir)*

PT. Daido DMS Indonesia **(1)**
Jl Industri I Lot MM-6c, Kawasan Industri
KIIC Desa Margamulya Kecamatan Teluk-
jambe Barat, Karawang, 41361, West Java,
Indonesia
Tel.: (62) 267407099
Moulding Product Mfr & Distr
N.A.I.C.S.: 333511

PT. Fuji Oozx Indonesia **(1)**
Jl Mitra Barat II Blok H2, Kawasan Industri
Mitra Karawang Desa Parungmulya Kec
Ciampel Keb, Karawang, 41361, Indonesia
Tel.: (62) 2678637999
Steel Product Mfr & Distr
N.A.I.C.S.: 332313

Riken Seiko Co., Ltd. **(1)**
10F Central Building 1-1-5 Kyobashi, Chuo-
ku, Tokyo, 104-0031, Japan
Tel.: (81) 352043141
Web Site: https://www.rkn.co.jp
Sales Range: $50-74.9 Million
Emp.: 240
Stainless Steel Products Mfr
N.A.I.C.S.: 333515

Sakurai Kosan Co., Ltd. **(1)**
3 Tsurumidori 3-chome, Minami-ku, Nagoya,
457-0807, Aichi, Japan
Tel.: (81) 526115151
Web Site: https://www.sakuraikosan.co.jp
Emp.: 66
Steel Products Mfr
N.A.I.C.S.: 331110

**Shimomura Tokushu Seiko Co.,
Ltd.** **(1)**
1-3-18 Ichikawa, Ichikawa, 272-0034,
Chiba, Japan
Tel.: (81) 473213841
Web Site: https://www.sts-shimomura.com
Sales Range: $50-74.9 Million
Emp.: 313
Steel Products Mfr
N.A.I.C.S.: 331513
Yoshiaki Mori *(Pres)*

Star Info Tech Co., Ltd. **(1)**
21st floor of Urbannet Nagoya Building
1-1-1 Higashisakura, Chome 1-10, Nagoya,
461-0005, Aichi, Japan
Tel.: (81) 52 308 5801
Web Site: http://www.d-sit.co.jp
Sales Range: $25-49.9 Million
Emp.: 217
Enterprise Management Software Devel-
oper & Publisher
N.A.I.C.S.: 513210

Toyo Sangyo Co., Ltd. **(1)**
16 Ohira Kajiyashiki, Ohira Village, Ohira,
981-3602, Miyagi, Japan
Tel.: (81) 223450151
Web Site: https://www.ring-roll-toyo.co.jp
Emp.: 72
Mfr of Automobile & Industrial Equipment
Parts
N.A.I.C.S.: 336110

DAIDOH LIMITED
3-1-16 Sotokanda, Chiyoda-ku, Tokyo, 101-8619, Japan
Tel.: (81) 332575050
Web Site: https://www.daidoh-
limited.com

Daidoh Limited—(Continued)

Year Founded: 1879
3205—(TKS)
Rev.: $189,687,170
Assets: $270,230,020
Liabilities: $173,419,960
Net Worth: $96,810,060
Earnings: $1,923,510
Emp.: 635
Fiscal Year-end: 03/31/24
Apparel Mfr & Whslr
N.A.I.C.S.: 315250
Masahiro Yamada (Chm)

Subsidiaries:

NEWYORKER LTD. (1)
4-5F Daidoh Limited Building 1-16 Soto-kanda 3 Chome, Chiyoda-ku, Tokyo, Japan
Tel.: (81) 3 5294 5700
Web Site: http://www.newyorker-corp.jp
Emp.: 679
Men & Women Apparel Distr
N.A.I.C.S.: 458110

Pontetorto S.p.A. (1)
Capitale Sociale Euro 1 549 500 00 I v Via Roma 15/17/19/21/23a, PO Box 184, Montemurlo, 59013, Prato, PO, Italy
Tel.: (39) 0574 6851
Web Site: https://pontetorto.it
Fabrics Whslr
N.A.I.C.S.: 424310

DAIDONG ELECTRONICS CO., LTD.
327-18 Gasan-Dong, Geumcheon-gu, Seoul, Korea (South)
Tel.: (82) 28555121
Web Site: http://www.daidong.com
Year Founded: 1972
008110—(KRS)
Rev.: $31,374,979
Assets: $196,975,987
Liabilities: $19,945,683
Net Worth: $177,030,305
Earnings: $13,497,643
Emp.: 108
Fiscal Year-end: 03/31/23
Electronic Components Mfr
N.A.I.C.S.: 334419
Lee Kyungman (Mgr-Accounting)

Subsidiaries:

Daidong Electronics (Thailand) Co., Ltd. (1)
63/2 MU 5 Banbung Bankai Road, Tumbol Banbung Amper BanBung, Chon Buri, 20170, Thailand
Tel.: (66) 384439813
Emp.: 270
Mold Mfr
N.A.I.C.S.: 333511

Daidong Engineering Malaysia Sdn Bhd (1)
Lot Pt 11647 Jalan Techvalley 1/2, Kawasan Perindustrian Sendayan Techvalley Seremban, 71950, Bandar Sri Sendayan, Negeri Sembilan, Malaysia
Tel.: (60) 66662500
Emp.: 192
Mold Repairing Services
N.A.I.C.S.: 811210

Daidong Mold & Plastics (Shanghai) Co., Ltd. (1)
3702 Chuansha Road, Pu Dong New Area, Shanghai, China
Tel.: (86) 2158387558
Emp.: 86
Mold Mfr
N.A.I.C.S.: 333511

Wuxi Daidong Electronics Co., Ltd. (1)
82-C Block, Wuxi New Hi-Tec Industrial Development Zone, Wuxi, Jiang-su, China
Tel.: (86) 51085204016
Emp.: 152
Mold Mfr
N.A.I.C.S.: 333511

DAIEI KANKYO CO., LTD.
6F & 7F Kobe Fashion Plaza 2-9-1 Koyochonaka, Higashinada-Ku Kobe, Hyogo, 658-0032, Japan
Tel.: (81) 788576600
Web Site: https://www.dinsgr.co.jp
Year Founded: 1979
9336—(TKS)
Rev.: $482,761,350
Assets: $1,142,181,560
Liabilities: $560,448,680
Net Worth: $581,732,880
Earnings: $89,836,510
Emp.: 2,675
Fiscal Year-end: 03/31/24
Waste Treatment & Disposal Services
N.A.I.C.S.: 562211
Fumio Kaneko (Pres)

Subsidiaries:

Asahikouseki Co., Ltd. (1)
13-4 Biwanokubo Iitanicho, Tokushima, 771-4265, Japan
Tel.: (81) 886450169
Waste Recycling & Management Services
N.A.I.C.S.: 562998

Ashiya Josui Co., Ltd. (1)
3-13 Kusunokicho, Ashiya, 659-0015, Hyogo, Japan
Tel.: (81) 797225672
Waste Recycling & Management Services
N.A.I.C.S.: 562998

DINS Hokkaido Co., Ltd. (1)
562-14 Abira Abiracho, Yufutsu, Hokkaido, 059-1511, Japan
Tel.: (81) 145232515
Waste Oil Management & Recycling Services
N.A.I.C.S.: 562998

DINS Kansai Co., Ltd. (1)
1-5-38 Chikko Shinmachi, Nishi-ku, Sakai, 592-8331, Osaka, Japan
Tel.: (81) 722457777
Web Site: https://www.dinskansai.co.jp
Bioethanol Mfr & Distr
N.A.I.C.S.: 325193

DINS Mirai Co., Ltd. (1)
6F Kobe Fashion Plaza 2-9-1 Koyochonaka, Higashinada-ku, Kobe, 658-0032, Hyogo, Japan
Tel.: (81) 788559261
Waste Disposal & Recycling Services
N.A.I.C.S.: 562211

Daiei Amet Co., Ltd. (1)
2nd floor Eco Building 1-38 Hajinomiya-cho, Fukuchiyama, 620-0856, Kyoto, Japan
Tel.: (81) 773202020
Web Site: https://www.daiei-amet.jp
Waste Disposal Services
N.A.I.C.S.: 562211

Daiei Kankyo Research Institute Co., Ltd. (1)
6F HO Kanda Higashimatsushitacho, Chiyoda City, Tokyo, 101-0042, Japan
Tel.: (81) 362252385
Waste Disposal & Consulting Services
N.A.I.C.S.: 562211

Fukuchiyama Golf Co., Ltd. (1)
194 Hatakenaka, Fukuchiyama, 620-0967, Kyoto, Japan
Tel.: (81) 773341234
Web Site: https://www.fukuchiyama.golf
Golf Course Management Services
N.A.I.C.S.: 713910

Green Arrows Kansai Co., Ltd. (1)
4-2-3 Chikko Shinmachi, Nishi-ku, Sakai, 592-8331, Osaka, Japan
Tel.: (81) 722805681
Waste Gypsum Board Recycling Services
N.A.I.C.S.: 562920

Kobe Port Recycle Co., Ltd. (1)
9-13 Minatojima, Chuo-ku, Kobe, 650-0045, Hyogo, Japan
Tel.: (81) 783030505
Waste Recycling & Management Services
N.A.I.C.S.: 562998

Kouki Corp. (1)
6-23 Hamawakicho, Nishinomiya, 662-0941,

Hyogo, Japan
Tel.: (81) 798381312
Web Site: https://www.kouki-corp.com
Environmental Equipment Design & Maintenance Services
N.A.I.C.S.: 541620

Kyodoh Doboku Co., Ltd. (1)
26-1 Harashinmachi, Ageo, 362-0016, Saitama, Japan
Tel.: (81) 5035330212
Web Site: https://www.kyodohdoboku.co.jp
Emp.: 198
Waste Oil Management & Recycling Services
N.A.I.C.S.: 562998

Kyoto Kankyo Co., Ltd. (1)
8 Saiin Higashinakasui-cho, Ukyo-ku, Kyoto, 615-0042, Japan
Tel.: (81) 753126671
Web Site: https://kyoto-kankyo.jp
Emp.: 171
Freight Truck Transportation Services
N.A.I.C.S.: 532120

Makinosato Agricultural Producers Cooperative Corporation (1)
132-8 Tani Kitsushoji Kuchiyokawacho, Miki, 673-0752, Hyogo, Japan
Tel.: (81) 794881250
Waste Disposal & Recycling Services
N.A.I.C.S.: 562211

Mie Chuo Kaihatsu Co., Ltd. (1)
4713 Hachiya, Yono, Iga, 518-1152, Mie, Japan
Tel.: (81) 595201119
Food Scraps Recycle Services
N.A.I.C.S.: 562111

Negibozu Agricultural Producers' Co-operative Corporation (1)
11654 Kakinokigawa, Yono, Iga, 518-1152, Mie, Japan
Tel.: (81) 595390898
Waste Disposal & Recycling Services
N.A.I.C.S.: 562211

Omihachiman Eco Service Co., Ltd. (1)
1143 Takecho, Omihachiman, 523-0036, Shiga, Japan
Tel.: (81) 748378087
Waste Disposal & Recycling Services
N.A.I.C.S.: 562211

Plafactory Co., Ltd. (1)
4-2-3 Chikkoshinmachi, Nishi-ku, Sakai, 592-8331, Osaka, Japan
Tel.: (81) 722758651
Plastic Pallet Mfr
N.A.I.C.S.: 326199

Safety Island Co., Ltd. (1)
16-7 Uozakihamacho, Higashinada-ku, Kobe, 658-0024, Japan
Tel.: (81) 784124477
Web Site: https://www.golila.co.jp
Emp.: 19
Construction Waste Recycling Services
N.A.I.C.S.: 562211

Settsu Seiun Co., Ltd. (1)
2-4-27 Higashitsukaguchicho, Amagasaki, 661-0011, Hyogo, Japan
Tel.: (81) 664298236
Web Site: https://settsu-seiun.jp
Waste Recycling & Management Services
N.A.I.C.S.: 562998

DAIFUKU CO., LTD.
3-2-11 Mitejima, Nishiyodogawa-ku, Osaka, 555-0012, Japan
Tel.: (81) 664721261   JP
Web Site: https://www.daifuku.com
Year Founded: 1937
6383—(TKS)
Rev.: $4,041,862,970
Assets: $4,271,077,940
Liabilities: $1,899,707,390
Net Worth: $2,371,370,550
Earnings: $300,497,210
Emp.: 13,071
Fiscal Year-end: 03/31/24
Material Handling System Mfr
N.A.I.C.S.: 333248

Yoshiyuki Horiba (Mng Officer-Cleanroom Automation)

Subsidiaries:

ATS Co., Ltd. (1)
678-11 Kojan-dong, Namdong-gu, Incheon, Korea (South)
Tel.: (82) 326650300
Web Site: http://www.daifukukorea.com
Sales Range: $25-49.9 Million
Emp.: 53
Materials Handling Equipment
N.A.I.C.S.: 333248
Imasato Tetsushi (Chm)

BCS Airport Systems Pty Limited (1)
151 Wedgewood Road, Hallam, 3803, VIC, Australia
Tel.: (61) 397031364
Airport Maintenance Services
N.A.I.C.S.: 488119

BCS Integration Solutions Sdn. Bhd. (1)
Unit 23-15 Level 23 Q Sentral 2A Jalan Stesen Sentral 2 KL Sentral, 50470, Kuala Lumpur, Malaysia
Tel.: (60) 327806806
Airport Maintenance Services
N.A.I.C.S.: 488119

CLEAN FACTOMATION, INC. (1)
14 Dongtanjiseong-ro, Hwaseong, 18453, Gyeonggi-do, Korea (South)
Tel.: (82) 3180157800
Web Site: http://www.cfinc.co.kr
Material Handling Equipment Mfr
N.A.I.C.S.: 333248

Plant (Domestic):

CLEAN FACTOMATION, INC. - Asan Plant (2)
1110-22 Chungmu-ro, Eumbong-myeon, Asan, 31413, Chungcheongnam-do, Korea (South)
Tel.: (82) 41 538 1000
Web Site: http://www.cfinc.co.kr
Material Handling Equipment Mfr
N.A.I.C.S.: 333248

Contec (Shanghai) Co., Ltd. (1)
Room 1002 Qilai Building No 889 Yishan Road, Xuhui District, Shanghai, 200233, China
Tel.: (86) 2154012288
Peripheral Device Distr
N.A.I.C.S.: 423430

Contec Americas Inc. (1)
3991 Sarno Rd, Melbourne, FL 32934
Tel.: (321) 728-0172
Web Site: https://www.contec.com
Peripheral Device Distr
N.A.I.C.S.: 423430

Contec Co., Ltd. (1)
3-9-31 Himesato, Nishi-yodogawa-ku, Osaka, 555-0025, Japan
Tel.: (81) 66 472 7130
Web Site: http://www.contec.com
Rev.: $249,119,437
Assets: $208,947,669
Liabilities: $98,667,853
Net Worth: $110,279,816
Earnings: $15,562,091
Emp.: 604
Fiscal Year-end: 03/31/2021
Computer & Electronic Products Mfr & Distr
N.A.I.C.S.: 334118
Tetsuya Akakuma (Corp Officer)

Subsidiary (Non-US):

BEIJING CONTEC MICROELECTRONICS CORPORATION (2)
B-806 Huatong Building No B19 Chegongzhuang West Road, Haidian District, Beijing, 100044, China
Tel.: (86) 10 8801 8228
Web Site: http://www.daifuku.com
Computer Peripheral Device Distr
N.A.I.C.S.: 423430

Subsidiary (US):

CONTEC DTx INC. (2)
3991 Sarno Road, Melbourne, FL 32934
Tel.: (321) 728-0172

Sales Range: $25-49.9 Million
Emp.: 75
Systems Design, Engineering & Computing Services
N.A.I.C.S.: 541512
Gene Garafalo *(VP-Bus Dev)*

Subsidiary (Non-US):

CONTEC SOLUTION CHINA CORPORATION (2)
Room 1002 Qilai Building 889 Yishan Road, Shanghai, 200233, China
Tel.: (86) 21 5401 2288
Web Site: http://www.contecsolution.com.cn
Electronic Software Development Services
N.A.I.C.S.: 541511

CONTEC SOLUTION CO., LTD. (2)
2FL-3 No 738 Zhongzheng Road, Zhonghe District, Taipei, 23511, Taiwan
Tel.: (886) 2 8227 8669
Web Site: http://www.contec.com
Computer Peripheral Equipment Distr
N.A.I.C.S.: 423430

Subsidiary (Domestic):

Contec EMS Co., Ltd. (2)
1500 Komakihara-shinden, Komaki, 485-8653, Aichi, Japan
Tel.: (81) 568 74 1500
Web Site: http://www.contec.com
Sales Range: $50-74.9 Million
Emp.: 110
Electronic Components Mfr
N.A.I.C.S.: 334417

Subsidiary (Non-US):

TAIWAN CONTEC CO., LTD. (2)
9FL No 738 Zhongzheng Road, Zhonghe District, Xinbei City, 23511, Taiwan
Tel.: (886) 282278669
Computer Peripheral Device Mfr
N.A.I.C.S.: 334118

DAIFUKU (CHINA) AUTOMATION CO., LTD. (1)
15 Mocheng Avenue, Mocheng District, Changshu, 215556, Jiangsu, China
Tel.: (86) 51252490111
Web Site: https://www.daifuku.com
Automobile Spare Parts Mfr
N.A.I.C.S.: 336390

DAIFUKU (CHINA) MANUFACTUR-ING CO., LTD. (1)
388 Tangming Road, Shihudang Town Songjiang District, Shanghai, 201617, China
Tel.: (86) 2167742436
Material Handling Machinery Mfr
N.A.I.C.S.: 333248

DAIFUKU INDIA PRIVATE LIMITED (1)
Tel.: (91) 1244246027
Material Handling Equipment Mfr
N.A.I.C.S.: 333248
Toshio Minoshima *(Mng Dir)*

DAIFUKU KOREA CO., LTD. (1)
Tel.: (82) 326650300
Material Handling Machinery Mfr & Distr
N.A.I.C.S.: 333248
Imasato Tetsushi *(Chm)*

Division (Domestic):

DAIFUKU KOREA CO., LTD. - Car-wash Division (2)
5FL Ungjin Bldg 682-2 Deungchon-dong, Gangseo-gu, Seoul, 157-033, Korea (South)
Tel.: (82) 2 3663 1326
Web Site: http://www.daifuku.com
Material Handling Machinery Mfr
N.A.I.C.S.: 333248

DAIFUKU KOREA CO., LTD. - Over-seas Division (2)
114B-2L Namdong Industrial Estate 684-1 Gojan-dong, Namdong-gu, Incheon, 405-820, Korea (South)
Tel.: (82) 32 818 0033
Web Site: http://www.daifuku.com
Material Handling Machinery Mfr
N.A.I.C.S.: 333248
Julia Kwon *(Gen Dir)*

Daifuku (China) Co., Ltd. (1)

Room 901 Shanghai International Trade Center 2201 Yan An West Road, Changn-ing District, Shanghai, 200336, China
Tel.: (86) 2162368600
Car Wash Machines Mfr
N.A.I.C.S.: 333248

Daifuku (Malaysia) Sdn. Bhd. (1)
Unit 9-1 Level 9 Tower 2B No1 Jalan Peng-aturcara U1/51A Seksyen U1, UOA Busi-ness Park, 40150, Shah Alam, Selangor Darul Ehsan, Malaysia
Tel.: (60) 358880850
Sales Range: $25-49.9 Million
Emp.: 17
Material Handling Systems
N.A.I.C.S.: 333248
Akinori Sasaki *(Mng Dir)*

Daifuku (Suzhou) Cleanroom Auto-mation Co., Ltd. (1)
75 Songbei Road, Suzhou Industrial Park, Suzhou, 215024, Jiangsu, China
Tel.: (86) 51267084570
Material Handling Equipment Mfr & Distr
N.A.I.C.S.: 333998

Daifuku (Thailand) Ltd. (1)
150/46 Moo 9 Pinthong Industrial Estate, Nongkham Sriracha, Chon Buri, 20230, Thailand
Tel.: (66) 38347151
Material Handling Systems
N.A.I.C.S.: 333248

Daifuku Automation (Tianjin) Co., Ltd. (1)
Room 1206 12FL China Overseas Plaza Weijinnan Road, Wujiayao Street Cross Hexi District, Tianjin, 300074, China
Tel.: (86) 2258181600
Automotive Assembly Systems
N.A.I.C.S.: 333248

Daifuku Business Service Corporation (1)
3-2-11 Mitejima, Nishiyodogawa-Ku, Osaka, 555-0012, Japan
Tel.: (81) 664721261
Security Support Services
N.A.I.C.S.: 561621

Daifuku Canada Inc. (1)
216a Matheson Blvd, Mississauga, L4Z 1X1, ON, Canada
Tel.: (905) 507-1133
Web Site: http://www.daifuku.com
Sales Range: $10-24.9 Million
Emp.: 9
Automotive Assembly Systems
N.A.I.C.S.: 333248

Daifuku Cleanroom Automation America Corporation (1)
7406 W Detroit St, Chandler, AZ 85226
Tel.: (480) 726-2522
Material Handling Equipment Mfr & Distr
N.A.I.C.S.: 333998

Daifuku Co., Ltd. - Shiga Works (1)
1225 Nakazaiji Hino-cho, Gamo-gun, Shiga, 529-1692, Japan
Tel.: (81) 748 53 0321
Web Site: http://www.daifuku.com
Material Handling Equipment Mfr
N.A.I.C.S.: 333248

Daifuku Design & Engineering Co., Ltd. (1)
3-2-11 Mitejima, Nishiyodogawa-Ku, Osaka, 555-0012, Japan
Tel.: (81) 664762951
Material Handling System Mfr
N.A.I.C.S.: 333248

Daifuku Europe Ltd. (1)
Unit 5 Dunfermline Court, Kingston, Milton Keynes, MK10 0BY, United Kingdom
Tel.: (44) 1908288780
Web Site: http://www.daifuku.com
Sales Range: $25-49.9 Million
Emp.: 35
Material Handling Systems
N.A.I.C.S.: 333248
Haruki Ishimoto *(Mng Dir)*

Daifuku Institute of Technology & Training Co., Ltd. (1)
1225 Nakazaiji Hino-cho, Gamo-gun, Shiga, 529-1692, Japan

Tel.: (81) 748 52 5942
Web Site: http://www.daifuku.co.jp
Sales Range: $25-49.9 Million
Emp.: 25
Material Handling Equipment Research & Professional Training Services
N.A.I.C.S.: 541715
Tatsuo Inoue *(Chm)*

Daifuku Intralogistics Vietnam Co., Ltd. (1)
Unit 703 7th floor Zen Plaza 54-56 Nguyen Trai Street, Ben Thanh Ward District 1, Ho Chi Minh City, Vietnam
Tel.: (84) 2838228280
Material Handling Equipment Distr
N.A.I.C.S.: 423830

Daifuku Logistic Technology Co., Ltd. (1)
4-103 Komakihara, Komaki, 485-0829, Ja-pan
Tel.: (81) 568741558
Material Handling System Mfr
N.A.I.C.S.: 333248

Daifuku Manufacturing Technology Co., Ltd. (1)
5-3-50 Ayukawa, Ibaraki, 567-0831, Osaka, Japan
Tel.: (81) 726344341
Web Site: http://www.daifuku.com
Material Handling System Mfr
N.A.I.C.S.: 333248

Daifuku Mechatronics (Singapore) Pte. Ltd. (1)
Blk 4010 Ang Mo Kio Ave 10 07-01 Tech-place 1, Singapore, 569626, Singapore
Tel.: (65) 65526166
Sales Range: $25-49.9 Million
Emp.: 70
Material Handling Systems
N.A.I.C.S.: 333248
Yutaka Chimura *(Mng Dir)*

Daifuku North America Holding Company (1)
30100 Cabot Dr, Novi, MI 48377
Tel.: (248) 553-1000
Web Site: http://www.daifuku.com
Material Handling Equipment Mfr & Distr
N.A.I.C.S.: 333998
Seiji Sato *(Pres)*

Daifuku Oceania Limited (1)
8 Antares Place Rosedale, Auckland, 0632, New Zealand
Tel.: (64) 94141350
Material Handling Equipment Distr
N.A.I.C.S.: 423830

Daifuku Pioneer Co., Ltd. (1)
6F 202 Sec 2 Yen Ping North Road, Taipei, Taiwan
Tel.: (886) 225533653
Web Site: http://www.taiwandaifuku.com
Material Handling Systems
N.A.I.C.S.: 333248

Daifuku Plusmore Co., Ltd. (1)
Tens Building 1F 2-11-2 Koyanagi-cho, Fuchu-shi, Tokyo, 183-0013, Japan
Tel.: (81) 423065960
Web Site: https://www.daifuku-carwash.jp
Car Wash Machinery Distr
N.A.I.C.S.: 423830

Daifuku Software Development Co., Ltd. (1)
3-9-31 Himesato, Nishiyodogawa-Ku, Osaka, 555-0025, Japan
Tel.: (81) 664762381
Material Handling Software Development Services
N.A.I.C.S.: 541511

Daifuku Webb Holding Company (1)
34375 W 12 Mile Rd, Farmington Hills, MI 48331
Tel.: (248) 553-1000
Web Site: http://www.daifukuwebb.com
Sales Range: $350-399.9 Million
Holding Company
N.A.I.C.S.: 551112
Tetsuya Hibi *(CFO & Sr VP)*

Subsidiary (Domestic):

Daifuku America Corporation (2)

6700 Tussing Rd, Reynoldsburg, OH 43068-5083
Tel.: (614) 863-1888
Mfr & Distribution Machinery
N.A.I.C.S.: 333248
Scott Stegert *(Pres)*

Elite Line Services, Inc. (2)
1505 Luna Rd Ste 100, Carrollton, TX 75006
Tel.: (972) 389-6200
Web Site: http://www.elitelineservices.com
Industrial Machinery Maintenance & Repair Services
N.A.I.C.S.: 811310

Jervis B. Webb Company (2)
30100 Cabot Dr, Novi, MI 48377
Tel.: (248) 553-1000
Sales Range: $300-349.9 Million
Emp.: 500
Material Handling Systems
N.A.I.C.S.: 333248

Plant (Domestic):

Jervis B. Webb Company (3)
156 Webb Forging Rd, Carlisle, SC 29031-0400
Tel.: (864) 427-8421
Web Site: http://www.jervisbwebb.com
Sales Range: $25-49.9 Million
Emp.: 80
Forgings & Machining
N.A.I.C.S.: 332111

Jervis B. Webb Company (3)
8212 M-119, Harbor Springs, MI 49740-9070
Tel.: (231) 347-3931
Web Site: http://www.jervisbwebb.com
Sales Range: $25-49.9 Million
Emp.: 150
Heavy Duty Roller Conveyors, Gravity Roller, Chain Driven Live Roller, Accumula-tion Conveyors, Chain Transfer Conveyors
N.A.I.C.S.: 333924

Subsidiary (Non-US):

Jervis B. Webb Company Ltd. (3)
Unit 5 Dumfermline Court, Kingston, Milton Keynes, MK10 0BY, United Kingdom
Tel.: (44) 1908512480
Sales Range: $25-49.9 Million
Emp.: 10
Custom-Designed Material Handling Sys-tems, Conveyors
N.A.I.C.S.: 333922

Jervis B. Webb Company of Canada Ltd. (3)
1647 Burlington Street East Station C, PO Box 3428, Hamilton, L8H 7M5, ON, Canada
Tel.: (905) 547-0411
Web Site: http://www.jervisbwebb.com
Sales Range: $25-49.9 Million
Emp.: 200
Custom-Designed Material Handling Sys-tems, Conveyors
N.A.I.C.S.: 333922

Jervis Webb China Co., Ltd. (3)
2908 New Town Center 83 Loushanguan Road, Shanghai, 200336, China
Tel.: (86) 21 5879 9020
Web Site: http://www.webb-china.com
Automotive Spare Parts Distr
N.A.I.C.S.: 423120

Subsidiary (Domestic):

Logan Teleflex, Inc. (2)
4620-C Proximity Dr, Louisville, KY 40213
Tel.: (502) 964-4929
Web Site: http://www.loganteleflex.com
Sales Range: $25-49.9 Million
Emp.: 15
Airport Baggage Handling Services
N.A.I.C.S.: 488119
Mike Prentice *(VP-Ops)*

Subsidiary (Non-US):

Daifuku Logan Ltd (3)
Sutton Road, Hull, HU7 0DR, United King-dom
Tel.: (44) 1482785600
Baggage Handling System Mfr
N.A.I.C.S.: 333248
Ron Osborne *(Mng Dir)*

Daifuku Co., Ltd.—(Continued)

LOGAN TELEFLEX (FRANCE) S.A. (3)
Tel.: (33) 149597474
Web Site: http://www.loganteleflex.com
Sales Range: $25-49.9 Million
Airport Baggage Handling Services
N.A.I.C.S.: 488119
Daniel Bordes (Gen Mgr)

Subsidiary (Domestic):

Wynright Corporation (2)
2500 York Rd, Elk Grove Village, IL 60007
Tel.: (847) 595-9400
Web Site: http://www.wynright.com
Sales Range: $100-124.9 Million
Emp.: 200
Material Handling Systems & Solutions
N.A.I.C.S.: 423830
Joe O'Connor (Dir-Mktg)

Daifuku de Mexico, S.A. de C.V. (1)
Blvd Bernardo Quintana No 300 INT 1201
Edificio Torre 57 Centro Sur, 76090, Queretaro, Mexico
Tel.: (52) 4421894040
Web Site: http://www.daifuku.com
Automotive Equipment Distr
N.A.I.C.S.: 423120

ForgePro India Private Limited (1)
Plot 2 3 and 4 Harohalli Industrial Area, Bangalore Rural Dt, Bengaluru, 562112, Karnataka, India
Tel.: (91) 8028014200
Web Site: http://www.forgepro.net
Material Handling Equipment Mfr & Distr
N.A.I.C.S.: 333998

Hallim Machinery Co., Ltd. (1)
32 Cheongwonsandan 2-gil Mado-myeon, Hwaseong, Gyeonggi-do, Korea (South)
Tel.: (82) 314983981
Web Site: https://www.hallims.co.kr
Car Washing Services
N.A.I.C.S.: 811192

Hiniaratakan Corporation (1)
1225 Nakazaiji, Hino-cho Gamo-gun, Shiga, 529-1692, Japan
Tel.: (81) 748 53 3970
Web Site: http://www.daifuku.co.jp
Material Handling Equipment Mfr
N.A.I.C.S.: 333248

Intersystems (Asia Pacific) Pty. Ltd. (1)
1/747 Lytton Road, Murarrie, 4172, QLD, Australia
Tel.: (61) 739097777
Web Site: https://www.inter-systems.com
Software Development Services
N.A.I.C.S.: 541511

Iwasaki Seisakusho Co., Ltd. (1)
5th Fl Ikebukuro Nishiguchi Sky Bldg 2-14-4 Ikebukuro, Toshima-ku, Tokyo, 171-0014, Japan
Tel.: (81) 359282552
Web Site: http://www.iwasakiss.co.jp
Emp.: 30
Flat-panel Display Mfr & Distr
N.A.I.C.S.: 334118
Masahiro Niki (Pres)

Jiangsu Daifuku Rixin Automation Co., Ltd. (1)
Changrui Village Mocheng Management Zone Yushan Town, Changshu, 215556, China
Tel.: (86) 51252490198
Automobile Parts Mfr
N.A.I.C.S.: 336390

P.T. DAIFUKU INDONESIA (1)
Gedung Menara Bidakara 1 Lt 12 Jl Jend Gatot Subroto Kav 71-73, Kel Menteng Dalam Kec Tebet Kota Adm Jakarta Selatan Prov DKI, Jakarta, 12870, Indonesia
Tel.: (62) 2183793162
Material Handling System Mfr
N.A.I.C.S.: 333248

Scarabee Aviation Group - Japan Co., Ltd. (1)
15F Tennoz Ocean Square 2-2-20 Higashi, Shinagawa Shinagawa-ku, Tokyo, 140-0002, Japan

---

Tel.: (81) 5038506421
Airport Maintenance Services
N.A.I.C.S.: 488119

Scarabee Aviation Group B.V. (1)
Hoeksteen 131, 2132 MX, Hoofddorp, Netherlands
Tel.: (31) 857608620
Web Site: https://www.scarabee.com
Material Handling Equipment Distr
N.A.I.C.S.: 423830

Singapore Contec Pte. Ltd. (1)
Blk 4010 Ang Mo Kio Ave 10 07-01 Techplace 1, Singapore, 569626, Singapore
Tel.: (65) 64591667
Peripheral Device Distr
N.A.I.C.S.: 423430

TAIWAN DAIFUKU CO., LTD. (1)
No 7 Daye 1st Road Southern Taiwan Science Park, Sinshih District, T'ainan, 74146, Taiwan
Tel.: (886) 65055993
Material Handling System Mfr & Distr
N.A.I.C.S.: 333248

Plant (Domestic):

TAIWAN DAIFUKU CO., LTD. - Taichung Plant (2)
4FL No 46 Keya Road Central Taiwan Science Park, Daya District, Taichung, 42881, Taiwan
Tel.: (886) 4 2567 5885
Web Site: http://www.taiwandaifuku.com
Material Handling Machinery Mfr
N.A.I.C.S.: 333248

Vega Conveyors & Automation Private Limited (1)
24 Phase - III Industrial Park, Pashamylaram Sangareddy District, Hyderabad, 502307, India
Tel.: (91) 8455223625
Web Site: http://www.vegaindia.com
Material Handling Equipment Mfr & Distr
N.A.I.C.S.: 333998

DAIHAN SCIENTIFIC CO., LTD.
326 Shinpyeongseokhwa-ro Jijeong-myeon, Wonju, 26358, Gangwon-do, Korea (South)
Tel.: (82) 29675235
Web Site: https://mall.daihan-sci.com
131220—(KRS)
Rev: $55,438,521
Assets: $45,600,276
Liabilities: $11,523,419
Net Worth: $34,076,857
Earnings: $3,606,448
Emp.: 116
Fiscal Year-end: 12/31/22
Laboratory Instrument Mfr
N.A.I.C.S.: 334516
Chong Ku Shu (Chm & Co-CEO)

Subsidiaries:

SciLab Korea Co., Ltd. (1)
25-38 Hwarangro 18, Seongbuk-gu, Seoul, Korea (South)
Tel.: (82) 7050201658
Web Site: https://www.scilab.kr
Glassware Product Mfr & Distr
N.A.I.C.S.: 327215

DAIHEN CORPORATION
2-1-11 Tagawa, Yodogawa-ku, Osaka, 532-8512, Japan
Tel.: (81) 663011212
Web Site: http://www.daihen.co.jp
Year Founded: 1919
Emp.: 3,783
Robotics
N.A.I.C.S.: 541490
Tetsuya Tajiri (Pres & CEO)

Subsidiaries:

DAIHEN Advanced Component, Inc. (1)
1223 E Arques Ave, Sunnyvale, CA 94085
Tel.: (408) 736-2000
Web Site: http://www.daihen-ac.com

Semiconductor Product Distr
N.A.I.C.S.: 423690
Toyokazu Kitano (Mgr)

DAIHEN Advanced Machinery (Changshu) Co., Ltd. (1)
No 17 Maqio Factory Area Riverside Industrial Park, Economic Development Zone, Changshu, 215513, Jiangsu, China
Tel.: 61260201008
Semiconductoior Product Mfr & Distr
N.A.I.C.S.: 334413

DAIHEN ELECTRIC Co., Ltd. (1)
258-259 Moo 6 Tambon Thasa-a, Bang Pakong, 24130, Chachoengsao, Thailand
Tel.: (66) 385302307
Web Site: http://www.daihen.co.th
Transformer Mfr & Distr
N.A.I.C.S.: 334416
Rawee Sakdarak (Mgr-Quality Assurance)

DAIHEN Engineering Co., Ltd. (1)
2-17-10 Juso-Motoimazato, Yodogawa-ku, Osaka, 532-0028, Japan
Tel.: (81) 663085757
Transformer Mfr
N.A.I.C.S.: 334416

DAIHEN Inc. (1)
1400 Blauser Dr, Tipp City, OH 45371
Tel.: (937) 667-0800
Web Site: http://www.daihen-usa.com
Welding Machine Mfr & Distr
N.A.I.C.S.: 333517
Scott Thayer (Reg Mgr-Sls)

DAIHEN Industrial Machinery Corporation (1)
1041 Azo, Mochigase, Tottori, 689-1227, Japan
Tel.: (81) 858872811
Welding Machinery Mfr
N.A.I.C.S.: 333517

DAIHEN Korea Co., Ltd. (1)
85 Hyeongoksandan-ro, Cheongbuk-myeon, Pyeongtaek, Gyeonggi-do, Korea (South)
Tel.: (82) 316867445
Web Site: http://www.daihen.co.kr
Welding Machine Distr
N.A.I.C.S.: 423830

DAIHEN OTC (Beijing) Co., Ltd. (1)
No 5 Leyuan South Znd Road, Yangi Economic Development Zone, Beijing, 101407, China
Tel.: (86) 1058696915
Transformer Mfr & Distr
N.A.I.C.S.: 334416

DAIHEN Technos Co., Ltd. (1)
5-1 Minami-Senrioka, Settsu, 566-0021, Japan
Tel.: (81) 663172560
Welding Machinery Mfr
N.A.I.C.S.: 333517

DAIHEN VARSTROJ welding cutting and robotics d.d. (1)
Industrijska ulica 4, 9220, Lendava, Slovenia
Tel.: (386) 25788821
Welding Machine Mfr & Distr
N.A.I.C.S.: 333517

DAIHEN Welfare Enterprise Co., Ltd. (1)
1-5-15 Tagawa, Yodogawa-Ku, Osaka, 532-0027, Japan
Tel.: (81) 663022104
Employee Benefit Services
N.A.I.C.S.: 525120

DAIHOKU Industry Co., Ltd. (1)
347-11 Toiso, Eniwa, 061-1405, Hokkaido, Japan
Tel.: (81) 123333889
Transformer Mfr
N.A.I.C.S.: 334416

Daihen Corporation - Chitose Plant (1)
770-7 Kitashinano, Chitose, 066-0075, Hokkaido, Japan
Tel.: (81) 123235171
Transformer Mfr
N.A.I.C.S.: 334416

Daihen Corporation - Kanehira Plant (1)

6-2-10 Noda, Fukushima, 553-0005, Osaka, Japan
Tel.: (81) 664615771
Transformer Mfr
N.A.I.C.S.: 334416

Daihen Corporation - Mie Plant (1)
800 Higashi-Ikebe, Taki-cho, Taki, 519-2155, Mie, Japan
Tel.: 59392313 1
Transformer Mfr
N.A.I.C.S.: 334416

Daihen Corporation - Rokko Plant (1)
4-1 Koyo-cho Nishi, Higashinada-ku, Kobe, 658-0033, Hyogo, Japan
Tel.: (81) 782752000
Welding Machinery Mfr
N.A.I.C.S.: 333517

KYUHEN Co., Inc. (1)
2-1-1 Hanamigaoka, Fukutsu, 811-3292, Fukuoka, Japan
Tel.: (81) 940 42 1364
Web Site: http://www.kyuhen.jp
Emp.: 322
Transformer Mfr & Distr
N.A.I.C.S.: 334416
Masataka Tadokoro (Pres & CEO)

Mudanjiang OTC Welding Machines Co., Ltd. (1)
No 18 Xingye Road, Yangming, Mudanjiang, 157013, Heilongjiang, China
Tel.: (86) 4536500690
Welding Machinery Mfr
N.A.I.C.S.: 333517

OTC (TAIWAN) Co., Ltd. (1)
2F NO 153 Huanbei RD, Chung Li, Taoyuan, Taiwan
Tel.: (886) 34613962
Welding Machine Distr
N.A.I.C.S.: 423830

OTC DAIHEN Asia Co., Ltd. (1)
60/86 Moo 19 Navanakorn Industrial Estate Phase 3, Tambol Klongnueng, Khlong Luang, 12120, Pathumthani, Thailand
Tel.: (66) 25292130
Welding Machinery Mfr
N.A.I.C.S.: 333517
Sawasdee Krub (Pres)

OTC DAIHEN EUROPE GmbH (1)
Krefelder Str 677, 41066, Monchengladbach, Germany
Tel.: (49) 21616949760
Web Site: http://www.otc-daihen.de
Emp.: 250
Welding Machinery Mfr
N.A.I.C.S.: 333517
Keitaro Takahashi (Mng Dir)

OTC DAIHEN INDIA PVT. LTD. (1)
V M Tower Plot No 54A Ground Floor Unit-1 Sector-18, Gurgaon, 122015, Haryana, India
Tel.: (91) 1244239364
Welding Machine Distr
N.A.I.C.S.: 423830
Annu Priya (Coord-Sls)

OTC Industrial (Qingdao) Co., Ltd. (1)
588 Sanjiang Road Economic & Technical Development Area, Qingdao, 266555, China
Tel.: (86) 53286720555
Welding Machinery Mfr
N.A.I.C.S.: 333517

OTC Industrial (Shanghai) Co., Ltd. (1)
17F Majesty Building 138 Pu Dong Da Dao, Shanghai, 200120, China
Tel.: (86) 2158826833
Web Site: http://www.otc-china.com
Welding Machine Distr
N.A.I.C.S.: 423830

Osaka Fuse Co., Ltd. (1)
2-39 Shikinai-cho, Izumiotsu, 595-0035, Osaka, Japan
Tel.: (81) 725325604
Power Distribution Equipment Mfr & Distr
N.A.I.C.S.: 335311

PT. OTC DAIHEN INDONESIA (1)
Blok G1A-20 Jl Kenari II Delta Silicon V,

Lippo Cikarang Industrial Park, Bekasi, 17550, Indonesia
Tel.: (62) 2129577566
Web Site: http://www.otc.co.id
Welding Machine Distr
N.A.I.C.S.: 423830

SHIHEN TECHNICAL
Corporation   (1)
2-1-97 Sakuragawa, Tadotsu-cho Nakatado, Kagawa, 764-8507, Japan
Tel.: (81) 877331212
Web Site: http://www.shihen.co.jp
Power Transformer Mfr
N.A.I.C.S.: 335311

DAIHO CORPORATION
24-4 Shinkawa 1-Chome, Chuo-ku, Tokyo, 104-8289, Japan
Tel.: (81) 332977008
Web Site: https://www.daiho.co.jp
Year Founded: 1949
1822—(TKS)
Rev.: $1,078,897,420
Assets: $1,091,185,410
Liabilities: $635,630,820
Net Worth: $455,554,590
Earnings: ($13,695,920)
Emp.: 1,056
Fiscal Year-end: 03/31/24
Construction Services
N.A.I.C.S.: 541330

Subsidiaries:

Daiho Toso Kogyo Corp.   (1)
Higashi Ueno 2-chome bldg 4F 2-10-12, Higashiueno Taito- Ku, Tokyo, 110-0015, Japan
Tel.: (81) 338358415
Civil Engineering Services
N.A.I.C.S.: 541330

Madagascar Daiho Company
Limited   (1)
Lot Pr II J 133F Ambodiboanjo, Ivandry, 101, Antananarivo, Madagascar
Tel.: (261) 202204010
Civil Engineering Services
N.A.I.C.S.: 541330

Shinwa Machinery Co., Ltd.   (1)
2-28-4 Arakawa, Higashiosaka, 577-0843, Japan
Tel.: (81) 667240106
Web Site: https://www.shinwa01.co.jp
Construction Machinery Distr
N.A.I.C.S.: 423810

Thai Daiho Company Limited   (1)
42 Tower 19th Floor No 65 Sukhumvit 42 Rd, Prakanong Klongtoey, Bangkok, 10110, Thailand
Tel.: (81) 271225412
Web Site: https://www.thaidaiho.com
Building Construction Services
N.A.I.C.S.: 236220

DAIICHI CHUO KISEN KAISHA
Mita Kokusai Building 25F 4-28 Mita 1-chome, Minato-ku, Tokyo, 108-0073, Japan
Tel.: (81) 364367100   JP
Web Site: http://www.firstship.co.jp
Year Founded: 1892
Deep Sea Freight Transportation Services
N.A.I.C.S.: 483111
Ken Shimizu *(Exec Officer)*

DAIICHI CO., LTD.
11447 Nishi 20jo Minami, Obihiro, 080-2470, Hokkaido, Japan
Tel.: (81) 155383456   JP
Web Site: https://www.daiichi-d.co.jp
Year Founded: 1958
7643—(TKS)
Sales Range: $350-399.9 Million
Emp.: 6,184
Supermarket Operating Services
N.A.I.C.S.: 445110
Tatsuo Suzuki *(Pres)*

DAIICHI JITSUGYO CO. LTD.
Ochanomizu Sola City 17F 4-6 Kandasurugadai, Chiyoda-Ku, Tokyo, 101 8222, Japan
Tel.: (81) 363708600
Web Site: https://www.djk.co.jp
Year Founded: 1948
8059—(TKS)
Rev.: $1,241,291,900
Assets: $1,280,984,950
Liabilities: $795,539,940
Net Worth: $485,445,010
Earnings: $49,317,210
Emp.: 1,455
Fiscal Year-end: 03/31/24
Machinery Distr
N.A.I.C.S.: 423830
Daisuke Ozono *(Mng Exec Officer)*

Subsidiaries:

Asano Laboratories Co., Ltd.   (1)
158 Kitayama Oaza Morowa Togo-cho, Aichi-gun, Nagoya, 470-0151, Aichi, Japan
Tel.: (81) 56 138 1211
Web Site: https://www.asano-lab.co.jp
Emp.: 120
Thermoforming Machine Mfr & Distr
N.A.I.C.S.: 333993
Toshihiro Takai *(Pres)*

DAIICHI ENGINEERING CO.,
LTD.   (1)
PMO Ochanomizu 6F 4-4-1 Kandasurugadai, Chiyoda-ku, Tokyo, 101-0062, Japan
Tel.: (81) 363708500
Web Site: http://www.djkeng.com
Emp.: 15
Industrial Engineering Equipment Mfr
N.A.I.C.S.: 333248

DAIICHI JITSUGYO VISWILL CO.,
LTD.   (1)
4-26 Yoshinocho, Suita, 564-0054, Osaka, Japan
Tel.: (81) 66 378 6115
Web Site: http://www.viswill.jp
Emp.: 90
Inspection System Mfr
N.A.I.C.S.: 334519

DC Energy GmbH   (1)
Mergenthalerallee 79-81, 65760, Eschborn, Germany
Tel.: (49) 6196 779 6390
Web Site: https://www.d-c-energy.com
Lithium-Ion Battery Distr
N.A.I.C.S.: 441330
Iraka Aoki *(Mng Dir)*

DJK (Taiwan) Corp.   (1)
12F-1 23 Sec 1 Bade Road, Chang-An E Road, Taipei, 10058, Taiwan   **(100%)**
Tel.: (886) 223278831
Sales Range: $25-49.9 Million
Emp.: 14
Industrial Machinery & Equipment Whslr
N.A.I.C.S.: 423830

DJK EUROPE GMBH   (1)
Mergenthalerallee 79-81, 65760, Eschborn, Germany
Tel.: (49) 6196776140
Industrial Supplies Distr
N.A.I.C.S.: 423840
Keisuke Nishii *(Mng Dir)*

DJK FACTORY SOLUTIONS (PHILIPPINES), INC.   (1)
Lot 3281-1 Laguna Technopark Phase 6A, Laguna Techno Park, Binan, 4024, Laguna, Philippines
Tel.: (63) 495721638
Industrial Equipment Repair Services
N.A.I.C.S.: 811310
Chris Rey Geneciran *(VP)*

DJK Global Mexico, S.A. de C.V.   (1)
Avenida Antea No 1090 Piso 3 Oficina 308 Edificio Business Park II, Col Jurica, 76100, Queretaro, Mexico   **(99%)**
Tel.: (52) 4422174975
Web Site: http://en.djk-latinoamerica.com
Sales Range: $75-99.9 Million
Emp.: 150
Industrial Machinery & Equipment Whslr
N.A.I.C.S.: 423830

DJK INNOVALUE
CORPORATION   (1)
Kowa Nibancho Bldg 11-19 Nibancho, Chiyoda-ku, Tokyo, 1020084, Japan
Tel.: (81) 3 5214 8728
Web Site: http://www.djk.co.jp
Emp.: 400
Industrial Machinery Mfr
N.A.I.C.S.: 333248
Masatoshi Ueno *(Gen Mgr)*

DJK Solar Solution Co., Ltd.   (1)
Ochanomizu Sola City 4-6 Kandasurugadai, Chiyoda-ku, Tokyo, 101-8222, Japan
Tel.: (81) 363708797
Photovoltaic Power Repair Services
N.A.I.C.S.: 221114

Dai-ichi Jitsugyo (Malaysia) Sdn.
Bhd.   (1)
31st Floor UBN Tower No 10 Jalan P Ramlee, Box No 80, 50250, Kuala Lumpur, Malaysia
Tel.: (60) 320706913
Web Site: http://www.daichijitsugyo.com.my
Sales Range: $25-49.9 Million
Emp.: 20
Industrial Machinery & Equipment Whslr
N.A.I.C.S.: 423830

Dai-ichi Jitsugyo (Thailand) Co.,
Ltd.   (1)
33/4 The 9th Towers Grand Rama 9 Tower B TNB05 23rd Floor Rama 9 Road, Huay Khwang, Bangkok, 10310, Thailand
Tel.: (66) 27961555
Web Site: https://www.djk-thai.co.th
Sales Range: $25-49.9 Million
Emp.: 35
Steel Products Mfr
N.A.I.C.S.: 331110

Daiichi Jitsugyo (America), Inc.   (1)
939 AEC Dr, Wood Dale, IL 60191   **(100%)**
Tel.: (630) 875-0101
Web Site: https://djausa.com
Industrial Machinery & Equipment Whslr
N.A.I.C.S.: 423830
Taka Sagawa *(Mgr-Coordination)*

Daiichi Jitsugyo (Guangzhou), Trading Co., Ltd.   (1)
Unit No 1308-1309 Goldlion Digital Network Center 138 Tiyu Road East, Guangzhou, 510620, China   **(100%)**
Tel.: (86) 2038772405
Industrial Machinery & Equipment Whslr
N.A.I.C.S.: 423830

Daiichi Jitsugyo (Hong Kong),
Limited   (1)
Suite 1611A 16th Floor Exchange Tower No 33 Wang Chiu Road, Kowloon Bay, China (Hong Kong)   **(100%)**
Tel.: (852) 28028233
Web Site: https://www.djk.co.jp
Sales Range: $25-49.9 Million
Emp.: 30
Industrial Machinery & Equipment Whslr
N.A.I.C.S.: 423830

Daiichi Jitsugyo (Vietnam) Co.,
Ltd.   (1)
6th Floor Detech Tower 8 Ton That Thuyet Street, My Dinh 2 Ward Nam Tu Liem District, Hanoi, Vietnam
Tel.: (84) 2437665990
Web Site: https://djk-vietnam.com
Industrial Machinery & Equipment Distr
N.A.I.C.S.: 423830

Daiichi Jitsugyo Asia Pte Ltd   (1)
1 Kaki Bukit View 04-30/31 Techview, Singapore, 415941, Singapore   **(100%)**
Tel.: (65) 63383732
Web Site: https://www.djkasiagroup.com
Sales Range: $25-49.9 Million
Emp.: 36
Industrial Machinery & Equipment Whslr
N.A.I.C.S.: 423830

Daiichi Jitsugyo India Pvt. Ltd.   (1)
Unit No 002 Ground Floor Time Tower MG Road, Gurgaon, 122002, Haryana, India
Tel.: (91) 1244266080
Web Site: https://djkindia.co.in
Industrial Machinery & Equipment Distr
N.A.I.C.S.: 423830

Daiichi Jitsugyo Philippines, Inc.   (1)

Unit No 1204 Frabelle Business Center 111 Rada Street, Legaspi Village, Makati, 1229, Philippines   **(100%)**
Sales Range: $25-49.9 Million
Emp.: 30
Industrial Machinery & Equipment Whslr
N.A.I.C.S.: 423830

Daiichi Jitsugyo Puerto Rico, Inc   (1)
106 Gautier Benitez Ave, Caguas, PR 00725   **(100%)**
Tel.: (787) 746-5396
Web Site: http://www.dja-global.com
Industrial Machinery & Equipment Whslr
N.A.I.C.S.: 423830

Daiichi Jitsugyo do Brasil Comercio de Maquinas Ltda.   (1)
Avenida Brigadeiro Luis Antonio 2729 Edificio Torre Brigadeiro, Conjunto 507 - 8 Andar Jardim Paulista, Sao Paulo, 01401-000, SP, Brazil
Tel.: (55) 1132841500
Web Site: https://djausa.com
Industrial Machinery & Equipment Distr
N.A.I.C.S.: 423830

Daiichi Mecha-Tech Corporation   (1)
   (100%)
Tel.: (81) 482221692
Sales Range: $25-49.9 Million
Emp.: 130
Engineering Services
N.A.I.C.S.: 541330
Osamu Fukawa *(Auditor)*

Daiichi Project Service Co., Ltd.   (1)
TNB04-05 23rd Floor Tower B The 9th Towers 33/4 Rama 9 Road, Huay Khwang, Bangkok, 10310, Thailand
Tel.: (66) 26438118
Building Contracting Services
N.A.I.C.S.: 236220

PT. DJK Indonesia   (1)
Mid Plaza 2 14th Floor Jalan Jenderal Sudirman Kavling 10-11, Jakarta, 10220, Indonesia
Tel.: (62) 215739370
Web Site: https://djk.co.id
Industrial Machinery & Equipment Whslr
N.A.I.C.S.: 423830

Shanghai Yishi Trading Co., Ltd.   (1)
2001-2003 the PLACE Tower C 150 Zunyi Road, Changning District, Shanghai, 200051, China   **(100%)**
Tel.: (86) 2162375800
Web Site: https://www.djksh.com
Emp.: 135
Industrial Machinery & Equipment Whslr
N.A.I.C.S.: 423830

Sulzer Daiichi K.K.   (1)
PMO Ochanomizu 6F 4-4-1 Kandasurugadai, Chiyoda-ku, Tokyo, 101-0062, Japan   **(40%)**
Tel.: (81) 363708550
Web Site: http://www.sulzerpumps.com
Sales Range: $25-49.9 Million
Emp.: 8
Joint Venture of Sulzer Ltd. & Daichi Jitsugyo Co. Ltd.; Pulp & Paper Machinery & Equipment Sales
N.A.I.C.S.: 333243

DAIICHI KENSETSU CORPORATION
1-4-34 Yachiyo, Chuo-ku, Niigata, 950-8582, Japan
Tel.: (81) 252418111
Web Site: https://www.daiichi-kensetsu.co.jp
Year Founded: 1942
1799—(TKS)
Sales Range: Less than $1 Million
Emp.: 1,038
Real Estate Development Services
N.A.I.C.S.: 531390
Mikio Uchida *(Pres & CEO)*

DAIICHI KIGENSO KAGAKU KOGYO CO., LTD.
4-4-9 Kitahama, Chuo-ku, Osaka, 541-0041, Japan
Tel.: (81) 662063311

Daiichi Kigenso Kagaku Kogyo Co.,
Ltd.—(Continued)

Web Site: https://www.dkkk.co.jp
Year Founded: 1956
4082—(TKS)
Rev.: $232,804,200
Assets: $433,649,050
Liabilities: $193,600,290
Net Worth: $240,048,760
Earnings: $7,535,400
Emp.: 642
Fiscal Year-end: 03/31/24
Zirconium Compounds Researcher &
Developer
N.A.I.C.S.: 325998
Tsuyoshi Inoue *(Pres & Exec Officer)*

Subsidiaries:

DKK (Shanghai) Materials Trading
Co., Ltd. **(1)**
Room 607 No 3009 Gudai Road, Minhang
District, Shanghai, China
Tel.: (86) 2154961280
Chemical Products Distr
N.A.I.C.S.: 424690

DKK America Materials, Inc. **(1)**
19500 Victor Pkwy Ste 290, Livonia, MI
48152
Tel.: (734) 743-2440
Web Site: https://www.zr-dkk.com
Chemical Products Distr
N.A.I.C.S.: 424690

DKK Logistics Corporation **(1)**
4-4-9 Kitahama, Chuo-ku, Osaka, 541-
0041, Japan
Tel.: (81) 662063311
Web Site: https://dkk-log.com
Warehousing Logistic Services
N.A.I.C.S.: 493110

DKK Thai Materials Trading Co.,
Ltd. **(1)**
98 Sathorn Square Office Tower 29th Floor
Unit 2905 North Sathorn Road, Silom, Ban-
grak, 10500, Thailand
Tel.: (66) 20594460
Web Site: https://www.zr-dkk.com
Chemical Products Distr
N.A.I.C.S.: 424690

DAIICHI KOUTSU SANGYO CO., LTD.

2-6-8 Basyaku, Kokurakita-ku, Kitaky-
ushu, 802-8515, Fukuoka, Japan
Tel.: (81) 935118811
Web Site: http://www.daiichi-
koutsu.co.jp
Year Founded: 1960
Sales Range: $800-899.9 Million
Emp.: 10,600
Holding Company; Taxicab Services;
Real Estate; Car Sales; Financial
Services
N.A.I.C.S.: 551112
Hajime Kurotsuchi *(Chm)*

Subsidiaries:

(Kushikino) Daiichi Traffic Co.,
Ltd. **(1)**
163 Sakae, Kagoshima, 896 0013, Kush-
ikino, Japan
Tel.: (81) 996322128
Web Site: http://www.daiichi-koutsu.co.jp
Hired Car Enterprise
N.A.I.C.S.: 485310

(Masuda) Daiichi Traffic Co., Ltd. **(1)**
1-15 Akebono-Hon, Masuda, 698-0026, Shi-
mane, Japan
Tel.: (81) 856 22 1402
Web Site: http://www.daiichi-koutsu.co.jp
Taxicab Operating Services
N.A.I.C.S.: 485310

(Matsumoto) Daiichi Traffic Co.,
Ltd. **(1)**
2-269-1 Nagisa, Matsumoto, 390-0841, Na-
gano, Japan
Tel.: (81) 263 26 9333
Taxicab Operating Services
N.A.I.C.S.: 485310

(Saku) Daiichi Traffic Ltd. **(1)**
47-1 Atobe Oaza, 385-0054, Saku, Nagano,
Japan
Tel.: (81) 267 64 0808
Web Site: http://www.daiichi-koutsu.co.jp
Taxicab Operating Services
N.A.I.C.S.: 485310

(Takashima) Daiichi Traffic Ltd. **(1)**
2-1249-1 Takashima, 392-0022, Suwa, Na-
gano, Japan
Tel.: (81) 266 58 5151
Taxicab Operating Services
N.A.I.C.S.: 485310

(Tokyo) Daiichi Traffic Co., Ltd. **(1)**
1-17-3 Senju Midori town, Adachi-ku, Tokyo,
120-0044, Japan
Tel.: (81) 338707111
Web Site: http://www.daiichi-koutsu.co.jp
Hired Car Enterprise
N.A.I.C.S.: 485310
Hiromi Tagashira *(Pres)*

Ajigaura Daiichi Traffic Ltd. **(1)**
185-22 Maeyama Aza, Ajigaura-town, 311-
1201, Hitachinaka, Ibaraki, Japan
Tel.: (81) 29 265 8545
Taxicab Operating Services
N.A.I.C.S.: 485310

Akashina Daiichi Traffic Ltd. **(1)**
6833 Nakagawate, Oaza Akashina-town
Higashi Chikuma-gun, Nagano, 399-7102,
Japan
Tel.: (81) 263 82 2306
Web Site: http://www.daiichi-koutsu.co.jp
Taxicab Operating Services
N.A.I.C.S.: 485310

Atami Daiichi Traffic Co., Ltd. **(1)**
14-16 Chuo-Town, Atami, 413-0015, Shi-
zuoka, Japan
Tel.: (81) 557818285
Web Site: http://www.daiichi-koutsu.co.jp
Emp.: 9
Hired Car Enterprise
N.A.I.C.S.: 485310
Daiichi Takshi *(Pres)*

Daiichi Koutsu Sangyo Co., Ltd. - Fukuoka Branch **(1)**
2-17-15 Higashi Hie, Hakata-ku, Fukuoka,
812-0007, Japan
Tel.: (81) 92 475 1567
Taxicab Operating Services
N.A.I.C.S.: 485310

Daiichi Koutsu Sangyo Co., Ltd. - Ka-
goshima Branch **(1)**
2-11-3 Usuki, Kagoshima, 890-0073, Japan
Tel.: (81) 99 286 5802
Taxicab Operating Services
N.A.I.C.S.: 485310

Daiichi Koutsu Sangyo Co., Ltd. - Kitakyushu Headquarters Traffic Enterprise Division **(1)**
2-6-8 Basyaku, Kokurakita-ku, Kitakyushu,
802-8515, Fukuoka, Japan
Tel.: (81) 93 511 8850
Web Site: http://www.daiichi-koutsu.co.jp
Taxicab Operating Services
N.A.I.C.S.: 485310

Daiichi Koutsu Sangyo Co., Ltd. - Miyazaki Banch **(1)**
4238-1 Ko Minami Hamada, Yoshimura-
town, Miyazaki, 880-0841, Japan
Tel.: (81) 985 27 5513
Taxicab Operating Services
N.A.I.C.S.: 485310

Fuji Daiichi Traffic Co., Ltd. **(1)**
I-281 Oda, Oda, 694-0064, Shimane, Japan
Tel.: (81) 854 82 0660
Web Site: http://www.daiichi-koutsu.co.jp
Taxicab Operating Services
N.A.I.C.S.: 485310

Fukugawa Daiichi Traffic Ltd **(1)**
3 11 6 Fukugawa, Shunan, 746 0038,
Yamaguchi, Japan
Tel.: (81) 834630735
Web Site: http://www.daiichi-koutsu.co.jp
Hired Car Enterprise
N.A.I.C.S.: 485310

Fuyo Daiichi Traffic Co., Ltd. **(1)**
2-36-15 Minami Rokugo, Ota-ku, Tokyo,

144-0045, Japan
Tel.: (81) 337387186
Web Site: http://www.daiichi-koutsu.co.jp
Sales Range: $50-74.9 Million
Emp.: 153
Hired Car Enterprise Distr
N.A.I.C.S.: 485310

Gobo Daiichi Traffic Co., Ltd. **(1)**
158 Sono, Gobo, 644-0002, Wakayama,
Japan
Tel.: (81) 738 22 3366
Web Site: http://www.daiichi-koutsu.co.jp
Taxicab Operating Services
N.A.I.C.S.: 485310

Gunhoku Daiichi Traffic Co., Ltd. **(1)**
1830-45, Shibukawa, 377-0008, Gunma,
Japan
Tel.: (81) 279 22 2247
Taxicab Operating Services
N.A.I.C.S.: 485310

Higo Daiichi Traffic Ltd **(1)**
2 17 28 Shimasaki, Kumamoto, 860 0073,
Kumamoto, Japan
Tel.: (81) 963542765
Web Site: http://www.daiichi-koutsu.co.jp
Hired Car Enterprise
N.A.I.C.S.: 485310

Himeji Daiichi Traffic Co., Ltd. **(1)**
867 Megakita Town, Shikama ku, Himeji,
672 8031, Hyogo, Japan
Tel.: (81) 792452440
Web Site: http://www.daiichi-koutsu.co.jp
Hired Car Enterprise
N.A.I.C.S.: 485310

Hiratsuka Daiichi Traffic & Co.,
Ltd. **(1)**
1 Kotohira-cho, Akune, 899-1615, Ka-
goshima, Japan
Tel.: (81) 996721135
Web Site: http://www.daiichi-koutsu.co.jp
Taxi & Car Enterprise
N.A.I.C.S.: 485310

Hiroshima Daiichi Traffic Co.,
Ltd. **(1)**
1 9 54 Kusatsu port Nishi ku, Hiroshima,
733 0832, Hiroshima, Japan
Tel.: (81) 822785522
Web Site: http://www.daiichi-koutsu.co.jp
Sales Range: $25-49.9 Million
Emp.: 100
Hired Car Enterprise
N.A.I.C.S.: 485310
Kazuyuki Noguchi *(Pres)*

Ibaraki Daiichi Traffic Ltd. **(1)**
1-1233-1 Migawa, Mito, 310-0912, Ibaraki,
Japan
Tel.: (81) 29 243 1231
Taxicab Operating Services
N.A.I.C.S.: 485310

Idsumo Daiichi Traffic Co., Ltd. **(1)**
1248-1 Zenkoji Aza, Enya Town, Izumo,
693-0021, Shimane, Japan
Tel.: (81) 853212556
Web Site: http://www.daiichi-koutsu.co.jp
Hired Car Enterprise
N.A.I.C.S.: 485310

Iwakuni Daiichi Traffic Ltd **(1)**
4 65 28 Minami Iwakuni Town, Iwakuni, 740
0032, Yamaguchi, Japan
Tel.: (81) 827312418
Web Site: http://www.daiichi-koutsu.co.jp
Hired Car Enterprise
N.A.I.C.S.: 485310

Izu Daiichi Traffic Co., Ltd. **(1)**
9 1 B 201 Tawara Hon, Atami, 413 0011,
Shizuoka, Japan
Tel.: (81) 557822410
Web Site: http://www.daiichi-koutsu.co.jp
Hired Car Enterprise
N.A.I.C.S.: 485310

Kaga First Transport Service Co.
Ltd. **(1)**
2-96-1 Yamashiro Onsen, Kaga, 922 0842,
Ishikawa, Japan
Tel.: (81) 761731113
Web Site: http://www.daiichi-koutsu.co.jp
Hired Car Enterprise
N.A.I.C.S.: 485310

Kanko Daiichi Traffic Co., Ltd. **(1)**

1-4002-38 Ishikawa, Mito, 310-0905, Iba-
raki, Japan
Tel.: (81) 29 253 1125
Web Site: http://www.daiichi-koutsu.co.jp
Taxicab Operating Services
N.A.I.C.S.: 485310

Kento Daiichi Traffic Co., Ltd. **(1)**
2-4-4 Soja, Maebashi, 371-0853, Gunma,
Japan
Tel.: (81) 27 251 4789
Taxicab Operating Services
N.A.I.C.S.: 485310

Koa Daiichi Traffic Co., Ltd. **(1)**
10-1-25 Kita Nijuyonjo Higashi, Higashi-ku,
Sapporo, 065-0024, Hokkaido, Japan
Tel.: (81) 11 731 2413
Web Site: http://www.daiichi-koutsu.co.jp
Taxicab Operating Services
N.A.I.C.S.: 485310

Kobe Daiichi Traffic Co., Ltd. **(1)**
80 Fukaehama Higashi Nada ku, Kobe, 658
0023, Hyogo, Japan
Tel.: (81) 78 411 2137
Web Site: http://www.daiichi-koutsu.co.jp
Hired Car Enterprise
N.A.I.C.S.: 485310

Koshu Daiichi Traffic Co., Ltd. **(1)**
3-32-10 Marunouchi, Kofu, 400-0031, Ya-
manashi, Japan
Tel.: (81) 55 223 0288
Taxicab Operating Services
N.A.I.C.S.: 485310

Kumamoto Daiichi Traffic Ltd **(1)**
2 3421 Yamanokami, Kumamoto, 862 0915,
Kumamoto, Japan
Tel.: (81) 963606622
Web Site: http://www.daiichi-koutsu.co.jp
Hired Car Enterprise
N.A.I.C.S.: 485310

Kumano Daiichi Traffic Co., Ltd. **(1)**
3 1 1 Ikeda, Shingu, 647 0021, Wakayama,
Japan
Tel.: (81) 735226313
Web Site: http://www.daiichi-koutsu.co.jp
Hired Car Enterprise
N.A.I.C.S.: 485310

Kyoe Daiichi Traffic Industrial Ltd **(1)**
3 2 39 Yatsue, Yahata Nishi ku, Kitakyushu,
807 0851, Fukuoka, Japan
Tel.: (81) 936027200
Web Site: http://www.daiichi-koutsu.co.jp
Hired Car Enterprise
N.A.I.C.S.: 485310

Matsue Daiichi Traffic Ltd **(1)**
281 Higashi Asahi Town, Matsue, 690 0001,
Shimane, Japan
Tel.: (81) 852252323
Web Site: http://www.daiichi-koutsu.co.jp
Hired Car Enterprise
N.A.I.C.S.: 485310

Matsushima Wakaba Daiichi Traffic
Ltd. **(1)**
6-14 Konashiya Aza, Miyagi-gun, Matsu-
shima, 981-0200, Japan
Tel.: (81) 22 354 2068
Taxicab Operating Services
N.A.I.C.S.: 485310

Mikage Daiichi Traffic Co., Ltd. **(1)**
3 1 5 Sumiyoshimiya town, Higashi Nada
ku, Kobe, 658 0053, Japan
Tel.: (81) 788111814
Web Site: http://www.daiichi-koutsu.co.jp
Hired Car Enterprise
N.A.I.C.S.: 485310

Minato Daiichi Traffic Co., Ltd. **(1)**
882 Asai town, Hamada, 697 0022, Shi-
mane, Japan
Tel.: (81) 855226567
Web Site: http://www.daiichi-koutsu.co.jp
Hired Car Enterprise
N.A.I.C.S.: 485310

Nagoya Daiichi Traffic Co., Ltd. **(1)**
3 6 45 Yanagihara, Kita ku, Nagoya, 462
0845, Aichi, Japan
Tel.: (81) 529131112
Web Site: http://www.daiichi-koutsu.co.jp
Transportation Services
N.A.I.C.S.: 485310

Numazu Daiichi Traffic Co., Ltd. (1)
10-9 Shinsawada-town, Numazu, 410-0003,
Shizuoka, Japan
Tel.: (81) 559 23 5811
Taxicab Operating Services
N.A.I.C.S.: 485310

Okubo Daiichi Traffic Ltd. (1)
2-22-2 Fujimi, 350-1306, Sayama, Saitama,
Japan
Tel.: (81) 42 959 5161
Web Site: http://www.daiichi-koutsu.co.jp
Taxicab Operating Services
N.A.I.C.S.: 485310

Osaka Daiichi Traffic Co., Ltd. (1)
1-45-1 Kan-nabe-town, Sakai, 590-0984,
Osaka, Japan
Tel.: (81) 72 232 6764
Taxicab Operating Services
N.A.I.C.S.: 485310

Saitama Daiichi Traffic Co., Ltd. (1)
1-3-28 Irumagawa, Sayama, 350-1305, Sai-
tama, Japan
Tel.: (81) 42 959 5161
Web Site: http://www.daiichi-koutsu.co.jp
Taxicab Operating Services
N.A.I.C.S.: 485310

Sakai Daiichi Traffic Co., Ltd. (1)
1 45 1 Kan Nabe, Sakai, 590 0984, Osaka,
Japan
Tel.: (81) 722326764
Web Site: http://www.daiichi-koutsu.co.jp
Hired Car Enterprise
N.A.I.C.S.: 485310

San Daiichi Traffic Ltd. (1)
2-22-2 Fujimi, Sayama, 350-1306, Saitama,
Japan
Tel.: (81) 42 959 5161
Web Site: http://www.daiichi-koutsu.co.jp
Taxicab Operating Services
N.A.I.C.S.: 485310

Sapporo Daiichi Traffic Co., Ltd. (1)
1-1-1 Ichijo Higashi Sapporo, Shiraishi-ku,
003-0001, Sapporo, Hokkaido, Japan
Tel.: (81) 11 811 6024
Web Site: http://www.daiichi-koutsu.co.jp
Taxicab Operating Services
N.A.I.C.S.: 485310

Sawara Daiichi Traffic Ltd (1)
3 25 10 Noke, Sawara ku, Fukuoka, 814
0171, Fukuoka, Japan
Tel.: (81) 928745131
Web Site: http://www.daiichi-koutsu.co.jp
Hired Car Enterprise
N.A.I.C.S.: 485310

Sen Nari Daiichi Traffic Co., Ltd. (1)
1-63 Nakagiri cho, Kita-ku, Nagoya, 462-
0051, Aichi, Japan
Tel.: (81) 525311126
Web Site: http://www.daiichi-koutsu.co.jp
Hired Car Enterprise
N.A.I.C.S.: 485310

Sendai Daiichi Traffic Co., Ltd. (1)
58 Yomogidamae Aza Gamo, Miyagino-ku,
983-0002, Sendai, Miyagi, Japan
Tel.: (81) 22 254 2224
Web Site: http://www.daiichi-koutsu.co.jp
Taxicab Operating Services
N.A.I.C.S.: 485310

Shimabara Daiichi Traffic Ltd. (1)
18 Shimo Kawashiri Shimabara, Nagasaki,
855 0861, Japan
Tel.: (81) 957 62 2262
Web Site: http://www.daiichi-koutsu.co.jp
Hired Car Enterprise
N.A.I.C.S.: 485310

**Shirahama Daiichi Traffic Co.,
Ltd.** (1)
3086 Shirahama town, Nishi Muro gun, Wa-
kayama, 649 2211, Japan
Tel.: (81) 739423666
Web Site: http://www.daiichi-koutsu.co.jp
Hired Car Enterprise
N.A.I.C.S.: 485310

Shunan Daiichi Traffic Co., Ltd. (1)
4-2-4 Nishi Matsubara, Tokuyama, 745-
0054, Yamaguchi, Japan
Tel.: (81) 834212288
Web Site: http://www.daiichi-koutsu.co.jp
Hired Car Enterprise

N.A.I.C.S.: 485310

Suwa Daiichi Traffic Ltd. (1)
2-1249-1 Takashima, Suwa, 392-0022, Na-
gano, Japan
Tel.: (81) 266 58 5151
Web Site: http://www.daiichi-koutsu.co.jp
Taxicab Operating Services
N.A.I.C.S.: 485310

Taiyo Daiichi Traffic Co., Ltd. (1)
4 15 16 Wakunami, Kanazawa, 920 0953,
Ishikawa, Japan
Tel.: (81) 76 231 5556
Web Site: http://www.daiichi-koutsu.co.jp
Taxi Operator
N.A.I.C.S.: 485310

Takasaki Daiichi Traffic Co., Ltd. (1)
1842-2 Shibaduka, Takasaki, 370-0064,
Gunma, Japan
Tel.: (81) 27 325 5454
Taxicab Operating Services
N.A.I.C.S.: 485310

**Tobata Daiichi Traffic Industrial Co.,
Ltd.** (1)
2 5 27 Yomiya, Tobata ku, Kitakyushu, 804
0042, Fukuoka, Japan
Tel.: (81) 938814380
Web Site: http://www.daiichi-koutsu.co.jp
Hired Car Enterprise
N.A.I.C.S.: 485310

Tohoku Daiichi Traffic Co., Ltd. (1)
3-6-14 Ogi-town, Miyagino-ku, Sendai, 983-
0034, Miyagi, Japan
Tel.: (81) 22 231 7259
Taxicab Operating Services
N.A.I.C.S.: 485310

**Tokushima Daiichi Traffic Co.,
Ltd.** (1)
3 36 2 Minamijosanjlma, Tokushima, 770
0814, Tokushima, Japan
Tel.: (81) 886547651
Web Site: http://www.daiichi-koutsu.co.jp
Hired Car Enterprise
N.A.I.C.S.: 485310

Tokuyama Daiichi Traffic Ltd (1)
4233 3 Shimo Ogushibara, Yunoaza Oaza,
Tokuyama, 745-1132, Yamaguchi, Japan
Tel.: (81) 834 83 3901
Web Site: http://www.daiichi-koutsu.co.jp
Hired Car Enterprise
N.A.I.C.S.: 485310

**Tokyo Daiichi Hire(Chauffeur driven
hired car) Ltd** (1)
1 17 3 Senju Midori Town, Adachi ku, To-
kyo, 120 0044, Japan
Tel.: (81) 338707733
Web Site: http://www.daiichi-koutsu.co.jp
Sales Range: $125-149.9 Million
Emp.: 400
Hired Car Enterprise
N.A.I.C.S.: 485310

**Yamanaka Daiichi Traffic Co.,
Ltd.** (1)
1 YA 25 Honmachi Yamanaka, Enuma, Ka-
nazawa, 922 0115, Ishikawa, Japan
Tel.: (81) 761781324
Web Site: http://www.daiichi-koutsu.co.jp
Hired Car Enterprise Services
N.A.I.C.S.: 485310

**Yamanashi Daiichi Traffic Co.,
Ltd.** (1)
3-10-12 Satoyoshi, Kofu, 400-0822, Yama-
nashi, Japan
Tel.: (81) 55 223 0285
Web Site: http://www.daiichi-koutsu.co.jp
Taxicab Operating Services
N.A.I.C.S.: 485310

**Yamashiro Daiichi Traffic Co.,
Ltd.** (1)
2-96-1 Yamashiro Onsen Kikyogaoka,
Kaga, 922-0257, Ishikawa, Japan
Tel.: (81) 761 76 0111
Web Site: http://www.daiichi-koutsu.co.jp
Taxicab Operating Services
N.A.I.C.S.: 485310

DAIICHI SANKYO CO., LTD.

3-5-1 Nihonbashi-honcho, Chuo-ku,
Tokyo, 103-8426, Japan

Tel.: (81) 362251111   JP
Web Site:
https://www.daiichisankyo.com
Year Founded: 2005
D4S—(DEU)
Rev.: $10,587,157,680
Assets: $22,878,102,350
Liabilities: $11,716,436,520
Net Worth: $11,161,665,830
Earnings: $1,326,831,910
Emp.: 18,726
Fiscal Year-end: 03/31/24
Pharmaceutical Product Development
& Mfg Services
N.A.I.C.S.: 551112
Toshiaki Sai *(CFO, Exec VP & Head-
Corp Strategy & Mgmt Div)*

Subsidiaries:

Asubio Pharma Co., Ltd. (1)
6-4-3 Minatojima-Minamimachi, Chuo-ku,
Kobe, Hyogo, Japan
Tel.: (81) 783065500
Web Site: http://www.asubio.co.jp
Emp.: 150
Pharmaceuticals Research & Development
Services
N.A.I.C.S.: 325412
Yoshiharu Minamitake *(Pres & CEO)*

**Daiichi Sankyo (China) Holdings Co.,
Ltd.** (1)
51st Floor Wheelock Square 1717 Nanjing
West Road, Jing'an District, Shanghai,
200040, China
Tel.: (86) 4006563228
Web Site: http://www.daiichisankyo.com.cn
Pharmaceuticals Product Mfr
N.A.I.C.S.: 325412

Daiichi Sankyo (Thailand) Ltd. (1)
24th Floor United Center Bldg 323 Silom
Road Silom, Bangrak, Bangkok, 10500,
Thailand
Tel.: (66) 2 631 2070
Web Site: https://www.daiichisankyo.co.th
Emp.: 90
Pharmaceutical Products Mfr & Distr
N.A.I.C.S.: 325412

Daiichi Sankyo Biotech Co., Ltd. (1)
6-111 Arai, Kitamoto, 364-0026, Saitama,
Japan
Tel.: (81) 485933939
Web Site: http://www.daiichisankyo-bt.co.jp
Vaccines Mfr
N.A.I.C.S.: 325414

**Daiichi Sankyo Brasil Farmaceutica
Ltda.** (1)
Av das Nacoes Unidas 12 901 - Complexo
das Nacoes Unidas, Torre Norte - 5 andar
cj 501/502, Sao Paulo, 04578-000, Brazil
Tel.: (55) 8000556596
Web Site: http://www.daiichisankyo.com.br
Pharmaceutical Products Mfr & Whslr
N.A.I.C.S.: 325412

**Daiichi Sankyo Business Associe Co.,
Ltd.** (1)
3-5-1 Nihonbashihoncho, Chuo-ku, Tokyo,
103-8426, Japan
Tel.: (81) 33 243 8002
Web Site: https://www.daiichisankyo-
ba.co.jp
Emp.: 210
Business Support Services
N.A.I.C.S.: 561499

**Daiichi Sankyo Chemical Pharma
Co., Ltd.** (1)
Nihonbashihoncho 3-5-1, Chuo-ku, Tokyo,
103-8426, Japan
Tel.: (81) 33 243 9270
Web Site: https://www.daiichisankyo-
cp.co.jp
Emp.: 750
Pharmaceutical Ingredient Mfr
N.A.I.C.S.: 325412

**Daiichi Sankyo Co., Ltd. - Akita
Plant** (1)
1-10-1 Mukaihama, Akita, 010-1601, Japan
Tel.: (81) 18 863 7701
Web Site: http://www.daiichisankyo.com
Pharmaceuticals Product Mfr

N.A.I.C.S.: 325412

**Daiichi Sankyo Co., Ltd. - Hiratsuka
Plant** (1)
1-12-1 Shinomiya, Hiratsuka, 254-0014,
Kanagawa, Japan
Tel.: (81) 46 331 6111
Web Site: http://www.daiichisankyo.com
Pharmaceuticals Product Mfr
N.A.I.C.S.: 325412

**Daiichi Sankyo Co., Ltd. - Odawara
Plant** (1)
477 Takada, Odawara, 250-0216, Kana-
gawa, Japan
Tel.: (81) 46 542 2174
Web Site: http://www.daiichisankyo.com
Pharmaceuticals Product Mfr
N.A.I.C.S.: 325412

**Daiichi Sankyo Co., Ltd. - Onahama
Plant** (1)
389-4 Izumimachi Shimokawa Aza Otsurugi,
Iwaki, 971-8183, Fukushima, Japan
Tel.: (81) 24 656 1981
Web Site: http://www.daiichisankyo.com
Pharmaceuticals Product Mfr
N.A.I.C.S.: 325412

**Daiichi Sankyo Co., Ltd. - Takatsuki
Plant** (1)
4-38 Aketacho, Takatsuki, 569-0806, Osaka,
Japan
Tel.: (81) 72 682 1181
Pharmaceuticals Product Mfr
N.A.I.C.S.: 325412

Daiichi Sankyo Espha Co., Ltd. (1)
3-5-1 Nihonbashihoncho, Chuo-ku, Tokyo,
103-8426, Japan
Tel.: (81) 33 243 6051
Web Site: https://www.daiichisankyo-
ep.co.jp
Emp.: 330
Pharmaceuticals Product Mfr
N.A.I.C.S.: 325412
Ichiro Ishizuka *(Exec VP & Gen Mgr-Sls
Div)*

Daiichi Sankyo Europe GmbH (1)
Zielstattstrasse 48, 81379, Munich, Ger-
many
Tel.: (49) 897 8080
Web Site: https://www.daiichi-sankyo.eu
Sales Range: $125-149.9 Million
Emp.: 30
Holding Company; Pharmaceutical Devel-
oper, Mfr & Distr
N.A.I.C.S.: 551112
Martin Hesse *(Mng Dir & CFO)*

Subsidiary (Non-US):

Daiichi Sankyo (Schweiz) AG (2)
Vulkanstrasse 106, 8010, Zurich, Switzer-
land
Tel.: (41) 434333300
Web Site: https://www.daiichi-sankyo.ch
Emp.: 34
Importer & Marketer of Pharmaceuticals
N.A.I.C.S.: 424210
Ralf Goeddertz *(Mng Dir)*

Daiichi Sankyo Altkirch Sarl (2)
39 rue du 3eme Zouaves, 68130, Altkirch,
France
Tel.: (33) 38 908 9632
Web Site: https://www.daiichisankyo.com
Sales Range: $1-9.9 Million
Mfr & Exporter of Raw Materials for Phar-
maceuticals
N.A.I.C.S.: 325412

Daiichi Sankyo Austria GmbH (2)
Europlaza Gebaude J Kranichberggasse 2,
1120, Vienna, Austria
Tel.: (43) 14 858 6420
Web Site: https://www.daiichi-sankyo.at
Sales Range: $10-24.9 Million
Drug Distr
N.A.I.C.S.: 424210

Daiichi Sankyo Belgium NV/SA (2)
Boulevard de France 3-5, 1420, Braine-
l'Alleud, Belgium
Tel.: (32) 2 227 1880
Web Site: https://www.daiichi-sankyo.be
Drug Distr
N.A.I.C.S.: 424210

Daiichi Sankyo Co., Ltd.—(Continued)

Subsidiary (Domestic):

Daiichi Sankyo Deutschland GmbH (2)
Zielstattstrasse 48, 81379, Munich, Germany
Tel.: (49) 897 8080
Web Site: https://www.daiichi-sankyo.de
Sales Range: $100-124.9 Million
Pharmaceutical Research & Development; Mfr & Marketer of Pharmaceuticals
N.A.I.C.S.: 325412

Subsidiary (Non-US):

Daiichi Sankyo Development Ltd. (2)
Chiltern Place Chalfont Park, Gerrards Cross, SL9 0BG, Buckinghamshire, United Kingdom
Tel.: (44) 17 53 89 36 00
Web Site: http://www.daiichisankyo.com
Pharmaceuticals Product Mfr
N.A.I.C.S.: 325412

Daiichi Sankyo Espana, S.A. (2)
C / Acanto 22 planta 9, 28045, Madrid, Spain
Tel.: (34) 91 539 9911
Web Site: https://www.daiichi-sankyo.es
Importer & Marketer of Pharmaceuticals
N.A.I.C.S.: 424210

Daiichi Sankyo France S.A.S. (2)
Immeuble le Corosa 1 rue Eugene et Armand Peugeot, 92508, Rueil-Malmaison, France
Tel.: (33) 15 562 1460
Web Site: https://www.daiichi-sankyo.fr
Pharmaceutical Product Whslr
N.A.I.C.S.: 424210

Daiichi Sankyo Italia S.p.A. (2)
Via Paolo di Dono 73, 00142, Rome, Italy
Tel.: (39) 0685 2551
Web Site: https://www.daiichi-sankyo.it
Sales Range: $25-49.9 Million
Importer & Marketer of Pharmaceuticals
N.A.I.C.S.: 424210

Daiichi Sankyo Nederland B.V. (2)
Kabelweg 37, 1014 BA, Amsterdam, Netherlands
Tel.: (31) 20 407 2072
Web Site: https://www.daiichi-sankyo.nl
Sales Range: $25-49.9 Million
Emp.: 30
Importer & Marketer of Pharmaceuticals
N.A.I.C.S.: 424210
Curd Lejaegere (Mng Dir)

Daiichi Sankyo Portugal, Lda. (2)
Tagus Park - Parque de Ciencia e Tecnologia Avenida, Professor Doutor Cavaco Silva Edificio Tecnologia IV n 81 a 83, 2740-257, Porto Salvo, Portugal
Tel.: (351) 21 423 2010
Web Site: https://www.daiichi-sankyo.pt
Sales Range: $25-49.9 Million
Importer & Marketer of Pharmaceuticals
N.A.I.C.S.: 424210
Isabel Borges (Mng Dir)

Daiichi Sankyo UK Limited (2)
Building 4 Uxbridge Business Park Sanderson Road, Uxbridge, UB8 1DH, United Kingdom
Tel.: (44) 189 591 0500
Web Site: https://www.daiichi-sankyo.co.uk
Sales Range: $25-49.9 Million
Emp.: 240
Importer & Marketer of Pharmaceuticals
N.A.I.C.S.: 424210

Subsidiary (Domestic):

U3 Pharma GmbH (2)
Fraunhoferstrasse 22, 82152, Martinsried, Germany
Tel.: (49) 89 8103 9100
Web Site: http://www.u3pharma.com
Pharmaceutical Products Research Services
N.A.I.C.S.: 541715
Johannes Bange (Chief Scientific Officer)

Daiichi Sankyo Happiness Co., Ltd. (1)
1-12-1 Shinomiya, Hiratsuka, 254-0014, Kanagawa, Japan

Tel.: (81) 46 331 7194
Web Site: https://www.daiichisankyo.co.jp
Emp.: 90
Business Support Services
N.A.I.C.S.: 561499
Nakazawa Hisao (Pres, CEO & Mng Dir)

Daiichi Sankyo Healthcare Co., Ltd. (1)
3-14-10 Nihonbashi, Chuo-ku, Tokyo, 103 8234, Japan
Tel.: (81) 35 255 6222
Web Site: https://www.daiichisankyo-hc.co.jp
Personal Care Products Mfr & Whslr
N.A.I.C.S.: 325620

Daiichi Sankyo Hong Kong Limited (1)
Room 1801 18/F One Hysan Avenue, Causeway Bay, China (Hong Kong)
Tel.: (852) 2868 9072
Web Site: http://www.daiichisankyo.com.hk
Pharmaceuticals Products Distr
N.A.I.C.S.: 424210

Daiichi Sankyo Ilac Ticaret Ltd. Sti. (1)
Unalan Mah Libadiye Cad Emaar Square Sit F Blok Apt No 82 F/17, Uskudar, 34700, Istanbul, Turkiye
Tel.: (90) 2165776505
Web Site: http://www.daiichi-sankyo.com.tr
Pharmaceuticals Product Mfr
N.A.I.C.S.: 325412

Daiichi Sankyo India Pvt. Ltd. (1)
Village Sarhaul Sector-18, Udyog Vihar Industrial Area, Gurgaon, 122015, Haryana, India
Tel.: (91) 124 284 8500
Web Site: http://www.dsin.co.in
Emp.: 200
Pharmaceutical Research, Development & Marketing Services
N.A.I.C.S.: 325412
Takahide Nishi (Pres & CEO-DSIN)

Daiichi Sankyo Ireland Ltd. (1)
Unit 29 Block 3 Northwood Court Northwood Avenue, Santry, Dublin, Ireland
Tel.: (353) 14893000
Web Site: http://www.daiichi-sankyo.ie
Emp.: 17,000
Pharmaceuticals Product Mfr
N.A.I.C.S.: 325412

Daiichi Sankyo Korea Co., Ltd. (1)
15th floor Mirae Asset Center One Building East Building, 26 Eulji-ro 5-gil Jung-gu, Seoul, 04539, Korea (South)
Tel.: (82) 234533300
Web Site: http://www.daiichi-sankyo.co.kr
Pharmaceutical Products Distr
N.A.I.C.S.: 424210

Daiichi Sankyo Logistics Co., Ltd. (1)
1-8 Nihonbashi koamicho, Chuo-ku, Tokyo, 103-8541, Japan
Tel.: (81) 3 3664 0941
Web Site: http://www.daiichisankyo.com
Pharmaceutical Freight Transportation & Logistics Services
N.A.I.C.S.: 488510

Daiichi Sankyo Nordics ApS (1)
Amagerfaelledvej 106 2, 2300, Copenhagen, Denmark
Tel.: (45) 8978080
Web Site: https://nordics.daiichi-sankyo.eu
Pharmaceuticals Mfr
N.A.I.C.S.: 325412

Daiichi Sankyo Northern Europe GmbH (1)
Zielstattstrasse 48, 81379, Munich, Germany
Tel.: (49) 897808267
Web Site: https://www.daiichi-sankyo.eu
Pharmaceutical Product Mfr & Distr
N.A.I.C.S.: 325412

Daiichi Sankyo Pharmaceutical (Beijing) Co., Ltd. (1)
No 5 Yong Chang Zhong Lu Beijing Economic Technological Development, Beijing, China
Tel.: (86) 10 8525 1088
Pharmaceutical Products Mfr & Whslr

N.A.I.C.S.: 424210

Daiichi Sankyo Pharmaceutical (Shanghai) Co., Ltd. (1)
500 Juli Road Zhangjiang Hi-Tech Park, Pudong New Area, Shanghai, 201203, China
Tel.: (86) 2160362000
Web Site: http://www.daiichisankyo-sh.com.cn
Pharmaceutical Products Mfr & Whslr
N.A.I.C.S.: 424210

Daiichi Sankyo Portugal, Unipessoal Lda. (1)
Rua das Lagoas Pequenas Edificio 5B Piso 3, 2740-245, Porto Salvo, Portugal
Tel.: (351) 214232010
Pharmaceuticals Product Mfr
N.A.I.C.S.: 325412

Daiichi Sankyo Propharma Co., Ltd. (1)
3-5-1 Nihonbashihoncho, Chuo-ku, Tokyo, 103-8426, Japan
Tel.: (81) 33 243 9091
Web Site: https://www.daiichisankyo-pp.co.jp
Emp.: 800
Pharmaceuticals Product Mfr
N.A.I.C.S.: 325412

Daiichi Sankyo RD Novare Co., Ltd. (1)
1-16-13 Kitakasai, Edogawa-ku, Tokyo, 134-8630, Japan
Tel.: (81) 35 696 8301
Web Site: https://www.daiichisankyo-rdn.co.jp
Chemical Products Mfr
N.A.I.C.S.: 325998

Daiichi Sankyo Taiwan Ltd. (1)
13F No 223 Songjiang Rd, Zhongshan Dist, Taipei, 104, Taiwan
Tel.: (886) 2 8772 2250
Web Site: http://www.daiichi-sankyo.com.tw
Pharmaceutical Product Whslr
N.A.I.C.S.: 424210
Sharon Lin (Pres)

Daiichi Sankyo Vietnam Co., Ltd. (1)
6th Floor Havana Building No 132 Ham Nghi St, Ben Thanh Ward Dist 1, Ho Chi Minh City, Vietnam
Tel.: (84) 839147441
Web Site: https://daiichisankyo.com.vn
Emp.: 64
Pharmaceutical Product Mfr & Distri
N.A.I.C.S.: 325412

Daiichi Sankyo, Inc. (1)
211 Mt Airy Rd, Basking Ridge, NJ 07920-2311
Tel.: (908) 992-6400
Web Site: https://daiichisankyo.us
Pharmaceuticals Product Mfr
N.A.I.C.S.: 325412
Ken Keller (Pres & CEO)

Subsidiary (Domestic):

American Regent, Inc. (2)
5 Ramsey Rd, Shirley, NY 11967
Tel.: (631) 924-4000
Web Site: https://americanregent.com
Pharmaceuticals Developer & Mfr
N.A.I.C.S.: 325412
James Sherry (Sr Mgr-Quality Assurance)

Branch (Domestic):

Luitpold Pharmaceuticals, Inc. - Norristown Office (3)
1000 Madison Ave, Norristown, PA 19403
Tel.: (610) 650-4200
Web Site: http://www.luitpold.com
Emp.: 20
Pharmaceutical Preparation Mfr
N.A.I.C.S.: 325412
Todd Koch (Sr Mgr-Clinical Project)

Subsidiary (Domestic):

Asubio Phamaceuticals, Inc. (2)
115 W Century Rd 3rd Fl, Paramus, NJ 07652
Tel.: (201) 368-5020
Web Site: http://www.asubio.com

Pharmaceutical Products Research & Development Services
N.A.I.C.S.: 541715

Kitasato Daiichi Sankyo Vaccine Co., Ltd. (1)
6-111 Arai, Kitamoto, 364-0026, Saitama, Japan (80%)
Tel.: (81) 48 593 3939
Web Site: http://www.daiichisankyo-kv.co.jp
Emp.: 478
Vaccine Mfr & Whslr
N.A.I.C.S.: 541715
Ken Ogita (Pres & CEO)

DAIICHI SOGYO CO. LTD.
Okigin Kohakura Shiten 3F 3 8 8, Kohakura, Naha, 900 0024, Japan
Tel.: (81) 988535353
Office Equipmemt
N.A.I.C.S.: 337214

DAIICHIKOUSHO CO., LTD.
5-5-26 Kitashinagawa, Shinagawa, Tokyo, 141-8701, Japan
Tel.: (81) 332802151
Web Site: https://www.dkkaraoke.co.jp
Year Founded: 1973
7458—(TKS)
Rev.: $969,991,060
Assets: $1,397,261,460
Liabilities: $676,830,950
Net Worth: $720,430,510
Earnings: $83,074,480
Emp.: 3,411
Fiscal Year-end: 03/31/24
Music Software Publishers
N.A.I.C.S.: 513210
Tatsuya Kumagai (Sr Mng Dir)

Subsidiaries:

DK KOREA Co., Ltd. (1)
Dae-O B/D Room No 1006 53-1 Yeouinaru-ro, Yeongdeungpo-gu, Seoul, 07327, Korea (South)
Tel.: (82) 27804007
Karaoke Equipment Distr
N.A.I.C.S.: 449210

DK Music Publishing Co., Ltd. (1)
Gotenyama Building 6-5-27 Kitashinagawa, Shinagawa-Ku, Tokyo, 141-0001, Japan
Tel.: (81) 363817820
Web Site: https://www.dkmp.co.jp
Karaoke Equipment Mfr
N.A.I.C.S.: 334310

Nippon Crown Co., Ltd. (1)
6-5-27 Kitashinagawa Gotenyama Building 3F, Shinagawa-ku, Tokyo, 141-0001, Japan
Tel.: (81) 364325440
Music Production & Artist Management Services
N.A.I.C.S.: 512230

Tri-M, Inc. (1)
7542 Darrow Rd, Hudson, OH 44236
Tel.: (330) 342-1400
Karaoke Equipment Mfr & Distr
N.A.I.C.S.: 339999

DAIKAFFIL CHEMICALS INDIA LIMITED.
E/4 MIDC Tarapur Boisar, 401506, Palghar, 401506, Maharashtra, India
Tel.: (91) 2525272674
Web Site: https://www.daikaffil.com
530825—(BOM)
Rev.: $1,176,985
Assets: $3,593,813
Liabilities: $246,505
Net Worth: $3,347,308
Earnings: ($341,714)
Emp.: 34
Fiscal Year-end: 03/31/22
Specialty Chemicals Mfr
N.A.I.C.S.: 325998
Amit J. Patel (Co-Mng Dir)

DAIKEN CO., LTD.

2-7-13 Niitaka, Yodogawa-ku, Osaka, 532-0033, Japan
Tel.: (81) 663925551
Web Site: https://www.daiken.ne.jp
Year Founded: 1948
59000—(TKS)
Sales Range: Less than $1 Million
Emp.: 310
Architectural Product Mfr
N.A.I.C.S.: 337212

DAIKEN CORPORATION
1 1 Inami, Nanto, 932-0298, Toyama, Japan
Tel.: (81) 66 452 6000
Web Site: http://www.daiken.jp
Year Founded: 1945
7905—(TKS)
Rev.: $2,162,289,360
Assets: $1,775,224,880
Liabilities: $898,575,040
Net Worth: $876,649,840
Earnings: $76,200,960
Emp.: 3,965
Fiscal Year-end: 03/31/22
Residential & Construction Building Materials Mfr
N.A.I.C.S.: 236220
Masanori Okuda *(Pres)*

Subsidiaries:

Dai-Wood Corporation   (1)
2782-23 Saimyoji, Iga-shi, Mie, 518-0809, Japan
Tel.: (81) 595238872
Sales Range: $25-49.9 Million
Emp.: 40
Hardwood Veneer & Plywood Mfr
N.A.I.C.S.: 321211
Ono Toshio *(Mgr)*

Dai-tac Corporation   (1)
2-5-8 Kaigandori, Minami-ku, Okayama, 702-8045, Japan
Tel.: (81) 862625450
Door & Window Mfr
N.A.I.C.S.: 321911

Daifit Co., Ltd   (1)
776-1 Wada, Kurayoshi, 682-0912, Tottori, Japan
Tel.: (81) 858235155
Door & Window Mfr
N.A.I.C.S.: 321911

Daiken (Shanghai) Corporation,   (1)
Room 2302 Ruijin Building 205 Maoming Roads, Shanghai, 200020, China
Tel.: (86) 2164731201
Building Materials Mfr
N.A.I.C.S.: 327120

Daiken Corporation - Mie Plant   (1)
1945-3 Moricho, Kawage-cho, Tsu, 514-1254, Mie, Japan
Tel.: (81) 592550611
Web Site: http://www.daiken.jp
Wood Flooring Mfr
N.A.I.C.S.: 321918

Daiken Corporation - Okayama   (1)
2-5-8 Kaigandori, Minami-ku, Okayama, 702-8045, Japan
Tel.: (81) 862621137
Web Site: http://www.daiken.jp
Insulation Board Mfr
N.A.I.C.S.: 238310

Daiken Corporation - Takahagi Plant   (1)
160-1 Akahama, Takahagi, 318-8501, Ibaraki, Japan
Tel.: (81) 293 23 6511
Web Site: http://www.daiken.jp
Wood Fiber Board Mfr
N.A.I.C.S.: 321999

Daiken Engineering Corporation   (1)
3-2-4 Nakanoshima Nakanoshima Festival Tower West 14th floor, Kita-ku, Osaka, 530-8210, Japan
Tel.: (81) 662025650
Web Site: https://www.daiken.jp
Emp.: 70
Specialty Trade Contractors

N.A.I.C.S.: 238990

Daiken Industries (Ningbo) Corporation   (1)
Industry Park Zone Simen, Yuyao, Ningbo, Zhejiang, China
Tel.: (86) 57462159777
Custom Architectural Woodwork & Millwork Mfr
N.A.I.C.S.: 337212

Daiken Miri Sdn. Bhd.   (1)
Lot 825 Block 1, Kuala Baram Industrial Estate CDT No 121, 98009, Miri, Sarawak, Malaysia
Tel.: (60) 85605099
Web Site: https://www.daiken-ad.com
Sales Range: $50-74.9 Million
Emp.: 200
Reconstituted Wood Product Mfr
N.A.I.C.S.: 321219

Daiken New Zealand Limited   (1)
166 Upper Sefton Road Ashley RD7, Rangiora, 7477, New Zealand
Tel.: (64) 33136819
Web Site: https://www.customwood.co.nz
Wood Products Mfr
N.A.I.C.S.: 321999

Daiken New Zeland Limited   (1)
166 Upper Sefton Road Ashley RD7, Rangiora, 7477, New Zealand
Tel.: (64) 33136819
Web Site: https://www.customwood.co.nz
Air Conditioning Installation Services
N.A.I.C.S.: 238220

Subsidiary (Domestic):

Daiken Southland Limited   (2)
301 Pioneer Highway 4RD, PO Box 189, Gore, Wellington, 9774, New Zealand
Tel.: (64) 32093100
Web Site:
   https://www.daikensouthland.co.nz
Wood Panel & Fibreboard Mfr
N.A.I.C.S.: 321211

Daiken Sarawak Sdn. Bhd.   (1)
Lot 2069 Block 26, PO Box 1117, Kidurong Industrial Estate, 97008, Bintulu, Sarawak, Malaysia
Tel.: (60) 86251000
Web Site: https://www.daiken-ad.com
Emp.: 200
Reconstituted Wood Product Mfr
N.A.I.C.S.: 321219
Kazuyoshi Katsumata *(CEO)*

Inami Daiken Corporation   (1)
1-1 Inami, Nanto, 932-0298, Toyama, Japan
Tel.: (81) 763825850
Web Site: http://www.daiken.jp
Door & Window Mfr
N.A.I.C.S.: 321911

Inami Daiken Products Corporation   (1)
1-1 Inami, Nanto, Toyama, Japan
Tel.: (81) 763825850
Web Site: http://www.daiken.com
Custom Architectural Woodwork & Millwork Mfr
N.A.I.C.S.: 337212

Koukou Sangyo Corporation   (1)
3-12-8 Sotokanda, Chiyoda-ku, Tokyo, 101-0021, Japan
Tel.: (81) 362717880
Door & Window Mfr
N.A.I.C.S.: 321911

Pacific Woodtech Corporation   (1)
1850 Park Ln, Burlington, WA 98233   **(51%)**
Tel.: (360) 707-2200
Web Site: https://www.pacificwoodtech.com
Engineered Wood Products Mfr
N.A.I.C.S.: 321211

Sanki Co Ltd   (1)
4-18 Higashishimbo, Sanjo, 955-0863, Niigata, Japan
Tel.: (81) 256340209
Industrial Machinery & Equipment Mfr
N.A.I.C.S.: 333248

Toyama Daiken Corporation   (1)
6 Horiesengoku, Imazu, Shiga, Japan
Tel.: (81) 766860585

Hardwood Veneer & Plywood Mfr
N.A.I.C.S.: 321211

Toyama Juki Co., Ltd.   (1)
614 Takanami, Tonami, 939-1341, Toyama, Japan
Tel.: (81) 763335523
Web Site: http://www.daiken.jp
Wood Household Furniture Mfr
N.A.I.C.S.: 337122
Masaru Morikawa *(Pres)*

DAIKEN MEDICAL CO., LTD.
2-6-2 Ayumino, Izumi, 594-1157, Osaka, Japan
Tel.: (81) 725303150
Web Site: https://www.daiken-iki.co.jp
Year Founded: 1968
7775—(TKS)
Sales Range: $50-74.9 Million
Medical Devices & Equipment Mfr & Distr
N.A.I.C.S.: 339112
Keiichi Yamada *(Pres & COO)*

DAIKI ALUMINIUM INDUSTRY CO., LTD.
Nichiei Bldg 1-4-8 Tosabori, Nishi-ku, Osaka, 550-0001, Japan
Tel.: (81) 664442743
Web Site:
   https://www.daikialuminium.com
Year Founded: 1922
5702—(TKS)
Rev.: $1,736,255,310
Assets: $916,668,190
Liabilities: $440,338,370
Net Worth: $476,329,820
Earnings: $21,442,840
Fiscal Year-end: 03/31/24
Aluminium Alloy Ingot Mfr
N.A.I.C.S.: 331313
Takaaki Yamamoto *(Pres & Chm)*

Subsidiaries:

Anglo Asia Alloys Vietnam Co., Ltd.   (1)
Thon Thang Tri Xa Minh Tri Huyen Soc Son Thanh Pho, Hanoi, Vietnam
Tel.: (84) 45997026
Metal Products Mfr
N.A.I.C.S.: 332999

DAIKI ALUMINIUM INDUSTRY (MALAYSIA) SDN. BHD.   (1)
Lot 3 Jalan Waja Kawasan Taman Perindustrian Bukit Raja, 41050, Klang, Selangor Darul Ehsan, Malaysia
Tel.: (60) 333419500
Web Site: https://www.dik-my.com
Aluminium Alloy Ingot Mfr & Distr
N.A.I.C.S.: 331313

Daiki (Foshan) Trading Ltd.   (1)
Room 03 10F 18 Chengmentou Road, Chancheng District, Foshan, China
Tel.: (86) 75782037002
Aluminium Alloy Ingot Distr
N.A.I.C.S.: 423510

Daiki Aluminium Industry Thailand Co., Ltd.   (1)
Amata City Chonburi Industrial Estate 700/99 Moo 1 T Bankao, Panthong, Chon Buri, 20160, Thailand
Tel.: (66) 38468441
Web Site: https://www.dik-th.in.th
Aluminium Alloy Ingot Mfr & Distr
N.A.I.C.S.: 331313
Masao Montani *(Chm)*

Subsidiary (Domestic):

Daiki Aluminium Industry Thailand Co., Ltd. - Amata City Factory   (2)
Amata City Rayong Industrial Estate 7/412 Moo 6, Mabyangphon Sub-district Pluak Daeng District, Rayong, 21140, Thailand
Tel.: (66) 38027513
Aluminium Alloy Ingot Mfr
N.A.I.C.S.: 331313

Daiki Aluminium Vietnam Co., Ltd.   (1)

No 1643 16th Floor Icon 4 Tower 243A De La Thanh, Lang Thuong Ward Dong Da, Hanoi, Vietnam
Tel.: (84) 2437606671
Metal Products Mfr
N.A.I.C.S.: 332999

Daiki Engineering (SEA) Sdn Bhd   (1)
No 20 Jalan TPK 1/6 Taman Perindustrian Kinrara, Seksyen 1, 47100, Puchong, Malaysia
Tel.: (60) 3 8070 1948
Web Site:
   http://www.daikiengineeringsea.com
Emp.: 6
Industrial Furnace Mfr & Distr
N.A.I.C.S.: 333994
Morikawa Takamitsu *(Mng Dir)*

Daiki Engineering Co., Ltd.   (1)
7-37 5-chome Kanou, Higashiosaka, 578-0901, Osaka, Japan
Tel.: (81) 72 816 1070
Web Site: http://www.dik-eng.com
Emp.: 9
Industrial Furnace Mfr
N.A.I.C.S.: 333994
Norio Nishi *(Mng Dir)*

Daiki Engineering Thai Co., Ltd.   (1)
No 333/33 Soi Project TIP8 Moo6 T Bangpla, Bangplee, Samut Prakan, 10540, Thailand
Tel.: (66) 21800123
Industrial Furnace Mfr & Distr
N.A.I.C.S.: 333994

Daiki International Trading Corporation   (1)
3528 Torrance Blvd Ste 214, Torrance, CA 90503
Tel.: (424) 237-1010
Emp.: 5
Aluminium Alloy Ingot Distr
N.A.I.C.S.: 423510
Hide Nawa *(Mgr)*

Daiki Material Co., Ltd.   (1)
1291-1 Aza Jizoso, Kawasaki-cho, Kameyama, 519-0211, Mie, Japan
Tel.: (81) 595852311
Aluminium Alloy Ingot Mfr
N.A.I.C.S.: 331313

Daiki Om Aluminium Industry (Philippines) ,Inc.   (1)
Lot 5 Block 21 Phase 3 Cavite Economic Zone, Rosario, Cavite, 4106, Philippines
Tel.: (63) 464370416
Web Site: https://www.daiki-om.com
Metal Products Mfr
N.A.I.C.S.: 332999

Daiki-Sigma Engineering (China) Inc.   (1)
No 1677 Siyi Road, Malu Town Jiading District, Shanghai, 201801, China
Tel.: (86) 2160767770
Industrial Furnace Mfr & Distr
N.A.I.C.S.: 333994

Delta Metal Recycling (Holdings) Ltd.   (1)
Room 1201 12F Tower 1 China Hong Kong City 33 Canton Road, Kowloon, Tsim Tsa Tsui, China (Hong Kong)
Tel.: (852) 31029305
Aluminium Alloy Ingot Distr
N.A.I.C.S.: 423510

Kyushu Daiki Aluminium Co,, Ltd.   (1)
3-8-1 Kifune, Umi-machi Kasuya-gun, Fukuoka, 811-2131, Japan
Tel.: (81) 929320742
Emp.: 12
Aluminium Alloy Ingot Mfr
N.A.I.C.S.: 331313
Osamu Naito *(Pres)*

PT. Daiki Aluminium Industry Indonesia   (1)
Jl Maligi VIII Lot T-02, Karawang International Industrial City, Karawang, 41361, West Java, Indonesia
Tel.: (62) 2129286994
Web Site: https://dik-id.co.id
Emp.: 20
Aluminium Alloy Ingot Mfr & Distr

Daiki Aluminium Industry Co., Ltd.—(Continued)

N.A.I.C.S.: 331313
Tisna Wijaya (Dir-HR)

PT.Daiki Trading Indonesia (1)
Jl maligi VIII lot t-2 Teluk jambe Barat,
Karawang International Industrial City, Kara-
wang, 41361, Jawa Barat, Indonesia
Tel.: (62) 2129286994
Web Site: https://dik-ld.co.id
Metal Products Mfr
N.A.I.C.S.: 332999

Seishin (Thailand) Co., Ltd. (1)
Amata Nakorn Industrial Estate 700/183
Moo 1, Bankao Panthong, Chon Buri,
20160, Thailand
Tel.: (66) 38458272
Web Site: https://www.seishin.co.th
Die Cast Mfr
N.A.I.C.S.: 333511

Seishin Seisakusyo Co., Ltd. (1)
1592-1 Fukaya, Shibahara Minami-cho,
Higashi-omi, 527-0066, Shiga, Japan
Tel.: (81) 748203755
Web Site: https://seishinss.co.jp
Emp.: 145
Aluminium Alloy Ingot Mfr
N.A.I.C.S.: 331313

DAIKI AXIS CO., LTD.
1-9-1 Misawa, Matsuyama, 791-8022,
Ehime, Japan
Tel.: (81) 899273330
Web Site: https://www.daiki-axis.com
4245—(TKS)
Rev.: $302,608,290
Assets: $241,563,390
Liabilities: $174,038,230
Net Worth: $67,525,160
Earnings: $1,453,450
Emp.: 1,052
Fiscal Year-end: 12/31/23
Water Treatment Equipment Mfr
N.A.I.C.S.: 221310
Hiroshi Ogame (Pres & CEO)

Subsidiaries:

A.C.R. ThuKhaChanThar Co.,
Ltd. (1)
47-J Insein Road 9 Quarter Near Bu Thar
Yone Bus Stop, Hlaing, Yangon, Myanmar
Tel.: (95) 9778783464
Web Site: https://www.acrtkct.com
Waste Water Treatment Services
N.A.I.C.S.: 562219

Crystal Clear Contractor Pte.
Ltd. (1)
1032 Eunos Avenue 5A 01-30, Singapore,
409702, Singapore
Tel.: (65) 62512126
Web Site: https://crystalclear-sg.com
Emp.: 40
Swimming Pool Maintenance Services
N.A.I.C.S.: 561790

DA Invent Co., Ltd. (1)
No 86 Ashiharacho Aichi, Nishi-ku, Nagoya,
452-0823, Japan
Tel.: (81) 8525056700
Web Site: www.da-invent.com
Hydrothermal Processing Distr
N.A.I.C.S.: 423830
Hiroshi Ogame (Chm)

DAITEC Co., Ltd. (1)
225-9 Otsu Yamada-cho, Matsuyama,
Ehime, Japan
Tel.: (81) 899895245
Waste Water Treatment Services
N.A.I.C.S.: 221310

Daiki Axis India Pvt. Ltd. (1)
701 The Capital Bandra Kurla Complex,
Plot C-70 Bandra East, Mumbai, 400051,
Maharashtra, India
Tel.: (91) 2249055836
Web Site: https://daikiaxis.in
Construction & Management Water Treat-
ment Equipment Distr
N.A.I.C.S.: 423830

Daiki Axis Singapore Pte. Ltd. (1)
18 Robinson Road Level 15, 18 Robinson,

Singapore, 048547, Singapore
Tel.: (65) 69557664
Construction & Management Water Treat-
ment Equipment Distr
N.A.I.C.S.: 423830

Daiki-Usafi Ltd. (1)
The Atrium Building 5th Floor Chaka Road,
PO Box 2945-00100, Kilimani, Nairobi, Ke-
nya
Tel.: (254) 790546473
Web Site: https://usafi.co
Waste Management Services
N.A.I.C.S.: 562998
Rachel Njeri (Project Mgr)

Daqi Environmental Protection Engi-
neering (Dalian) Co., Ltd. (1)
No 8 Tieshan West Road, Dalian Economic
and Technological Development Zone, Lia-
oning, 116600, China
Tel.: (86) 4118 761 3229
Web Site: https://www.dldaiki.com
Wastewater Treatment Equipment Mfr &
Distr
N.A.I.C.S.: 333310

Environmental Analysis Center Co.,
Ltd. (1)
225 Yamagata-cho, Ehime, Matsuyama,
Japan
Tel.: (81) 899895251
Web Site: http://www.ehimekankyou.co.jp
Water Quality Inspection Agency Distr
N.A.I.C.S.: 423830

LEC Industries Co., Ltd. (1)
PMO Higashi-Nihonbashi Bldg 9F 2-15-4
Higashi- Nihonbashi, Chuo-ku, Tokyo, 103-
0004, Japan
Tel.: (81) 3 5835 5885
Web Site: http://www.leci.co.jp
Emp.: 18
Wastewater Treatment Equipment Mfr &
Distr
N.A.I.C.S.: 333310
Takehiko Ito (Pres & CEO)

PT. Daiki Axis Indonesia (1)
Tel.: (62) 2183791186
Wastewater Treatment Equipment Mfr &
Distr
N.A.I.C.S.: 333310
Hiroshi Ogame (Pres & CEO)

Sanei Ecohome Inc. (1)
1-5-6 Kugenumaishigami Watanabe Build-
ing 2nd Floor, Fujisawa, 251-0025, Kana-
gawa, Japan
Tel.: (81) 46 621 7412
Web Site: https://sanei-ecohome.co.jp
Emp.: 20
Solar Electric Power Generation Services
N.A.I.C.S.: 221114

Sylphid Inc. (1)
PMO Higashi-Nihonbashi Bldg 2-15-4
Higashi-Nihonbashi, Chuo-ku, Tokyo, 103-
0004, Japan
Tel.: (81) 35 825 4951
Web Site: https://www.sylphid.co.jp
Water Quality Inspection Agency Distr
N.A.I.C.S.: 423830

TOBU Co., Ltd. (1)
86 Ashihara, Nishi-ku, Nagoya, 452-0823,
Aichi, Japan
Tel.: (81) 525028211
Web Site: http://www.daiki-axis.com
Emp.: 50
Wastewater Treatment Equipment Mfr &
Distr
N.A.I.C.S.: 333310

DAIKIN INDUSTRIES, LTD.
Osaka Umeda Twin Towers South
1-13-1 Umeda, Kita-ku, Osaka, 530-
0001, Japan
Tel.: (81) 663734312　　　　JP
Web Site: https://www.daikin.com
Year Founded: 1924
6367—(TKS)
Rev.: $29,053,045,370
Assets: $32,258,320,300
Liabilities: $14,495,254,080
Net Worth: $17,763,066,220
Earnings: $1,720,655,710
Emp.: 98,162

Fiscal Year-end: 03/31/24
Household Products Mfr
N.A.I.C.S.: 333415
Noriyuki Inoue (Chm & Chief Global
Grp Officer)

Subsidiaries:

AAF-Lufttechnik GmbH (1)
Odonwaldstrasse 4, 64646, Heppenheim,
Germany
Tel.: (49) 6252699770
Air Conditioning & Refrigeration Whslr
N.A.I.C.S.: 423730

AC World Electronics Ltd. (1)
Urban Centre Point 400 New Eskaton Road
4th Floor, Dhaka, 1000, Bangladesh
Tel.: (880) 1919561801
Air Conditioning & Refrigeration Whslr
N.A.I.C.S.: 423730

AHT Cooling Systems GmbH (1)
Werksgasse 57, Rottenmann, 8786, Liezen,
Austria
Tel.: (43) 36 142 4510
Web Site: https://www.aht.at
Air Conditioning & Refrigeration Mfr & Whslr
N.A.I.C.S.: 333415

Abbar & Zainy Daikin Airconditioning
Company Ltd. (1)
PO Box 5700, Jeddah, 21432, Saudi Arabia
Tel.: (966) 26473367
Web Site: http://www.daikin.com
Air Conditioning Equipment Installation Ser-
vices
N.A.I.C.S.: 238220

Access International Projects (Pvt)
Ltd. (1)
278 Access Tower Union Place, Colombo,
Sri Lanka
Tel.: (94) 773125500
Air Conditioning & Refrigeration Whslr
N.A.I.C.S.: 423730

Aitken Spence Engineering Solutions
(Pvt) Ltd. (1)
315 Vauxhall St, Colombo, Sri Lanka
Tel.: (94) 773380589
Air Conditioning & Refrigeration Whslr
N.A.I.C.S.: 423730

All World Machinery Supply, Inc. (1)
6164 All World Way, Roscoe, IL 61073
Tel.: (815) 943-9111
Web Site: http://www.allworldmachinery.com
Industrial Machinery Product Distr
N.A.I.C.S.: 423830
David J. Koepp (Pres & CEO)

All World Machinery Supply, Inc. (1)
Jaigon Business Park Bodega 36 Prolonga-
cion Bernardo Quintana 2481, Delegacion
Felipe Carrillo Puerto, 76138, Queretaro,
QRO, Mexico
Tel.: (52) 4422910597
Air Conditioning & Refrigeration Whslr
N.A.I.C.S.: 423730

American Air Filter Manufacturing
Sdn. Bhd. (1)
Lot 6 Jalan Pengapit 15/19 Seksyen 15,
40000, Shah Alam, Selangor, Malaysia
Tel.: (60) 350397777
Air Conditioning & Refrigeration Mfr & Whslr
N.A.I.C.S.: 333415

Baridi Baridi Tanzania Ltd. (1)
Tanzanite Park Victoria, PO Box 33758, Dar
es Salaam, Tanzania
Tel.: (255) 222224000
Web Site: https://baridibaridi.co.tz
N.A.I.C.S.: 811412
Hiroki Asada (CEO)

Bibus Italia Srl (1)
Via Robert Fulton 27, 40017, San Giovanni
in Persiceto, BO, Italy
Tel.: (39) 05 189 3958
Web Site: https://www.bibus.it
Engineering Services
N.A.I.C.S.: 541330
Giuseppe Lodi (Mng Dir)

Civimech (Pvt) Ltd (1)
118 Dutugemunu Street, Kohuwala,
Dehiwala-Mount Lavinia, Sri Lanka
Tel.: (94) 772440880

Air Conditioning & Refrigeration Whslr
N.A.I.C.S.: 423730

Confidence Trade Limited (1)
09-05 Navana Tower 45 Gulshan Avenue,
Dhaka, 1212, Bangladesh
Tel.: (880) 1711541545
Air Conditioning & Refrigeration Whslr
N.A.I.C.S.: 423730

Cooltooh Engineering Services (Pvt)
Ltd. (1)
No 21 St Peter's Road, Moratuwa, Sri
Lanka
Tel.: (94) 777308807
Air Conditioning & Refrigeration Whslr
N.A.I.C.S.: 423730

Cri-Tech Inc. (1)
85 Winter St, Hanover, MA 02339
Web Site: http://www.critechinc.com
Chemical Products Mfr
N.A.I.C.S.: 325180
Richard Park (Dir-Bus Sys)

DAI Funding Corporation (1)
20 Olympic Dr, Orangeburg, NY 10962
Tel.: (845) 365-9500
Web Site: http://www.daikin-america.com
Sales Range: $50-74.9 Million
Emp.: 75
Financial Management Services
N.A.I.C.S.: 523999
Lisa Strassman (Controller)

DAIKIN McQUAY AR CONDICIO-
NADO BRASIL LTDA. (1)
Av Vital Brasil 305, Butanta, Sao Paulo,
05503-001, Brazil
Tel.: (55) 11 3123 2525
Web Site: http://www.daikin.com.br
Air Conditioning Equipment Mfr
N.A.I.C.S.: 333415

Daikin (CHINA) Investment Co.,
Ltd. (1)
20th Floor East Third Office Building Orien-
tal Plaza 1 East, Changan Street
Dongcheng District, Beijing, 100738, China
Tel.: (86) 10 8518 1117
Web Site: http://www.daikin-china.com.cn
Air Conditioning Equipment Mfr
N.A.I.C.S.: 333415

Daikin AC (Americas), Inc. (1)
1645 Wallace Dr Ste 100, Carrollton, TX
75006　　　　(100%)
Tel.: (972) 245-1510
Web Site: http://www.daikinac.com
Air Conditioning Solutions for Residential,
Commercial & Industrial Applications
N.A.I.C.S.: 333415

Daikin AC Spain, S.A. (1)
C/ Via de los Poblados 1 Parque Empre-
sarial Alvento Edificio, A y B Planta 4,
28033, Madrid, Spain
Tel.: (34) 91 334 5600
Web Site: https://www.daikin.es
Air Conditioning Equipment Mfr
N.A.I.C.S.: 333415

Daikin Accounting Solutions Co.,
Ltd (1)
2-4-12 Nakazakinishi Umeda Center Bldg,
Kita-Ku, Osaka, 530-0015, Japan
Tel.: (81) 663734321
Financial Management Services
N.A.I.C.S.: 523999
Ikura Keiichi (Mgr)

Daikin Air Conditioning (M) Sdn.
Bhd. (1)
1 Floor Lot 4 Lorong 191A Seksyen 19,
46300, Petaling Jaya, Selangor,
Malaysia　　　　(100%)
Tel.: (60) 379559090
Web Site: http://www.daikin.com
Sales Range: $25-49.9 Million
Emp.: 50
Air Conditioning
N.A.I.C.S.: 333415

Daikin Air Conditioning (Vietnam)
Joint Stock Company (1)
Floor 12 - 14 - 15 201-203 CMT8, Ward 4
District 3 City, Ho Chi Minh City, Vietnam
Tel.: (84) 86 250 4888
Web Site: https://www.daikin.com.vn
Air Conditioning & Refrigeration Whslr

N.A.I.C.S.: 423730

Daikin Air Conditioning Argentina S.A. (1)
Marcelo T de Alvear 1430 1er Piso, C1060AAB, Buenos Aires, Argentina
Tel.: (54) 11 4816 3274
Web Site: http://www.daikin-argentina.com
Air Conditioning Equipment Whslr
N.A.I.C.S.: 423730

Daikin Air Conditioning Egypt S.A.E. (1)
Maddi Nile Corniche in front of Water Police Club, the tower of Foreign countries Workers/286029, Cairo, 11728, Egypt
Tel.: (20) 102 929 2330
Web Site: https://www.daikinegypt.com
Air Conditioning & Refrigeration Whslr
N.A.I.C.S.: 423730

Daikin Air Conditioning Singapore Pte. Ltd. (1)
10 Ang Mo Kio Industrial Park 2, Singapore, 569501, Singapore
Tel.: (65) 6 583 8888
Web Site: https://www.daikin.com.sg
Sales Range: $100-124.9 Million
Emp.: 300
Mfr of Air Conditioning Products
N.A.I.C.S.: 333415
Ching Khim Huat *(Mng Dir)*

Daikin Air-Conditioning (Shanghai) Co., Ltd. (1)
No 318-398 Shenfu Road, Xinzhuang Industrial Park, Shanghai, 201108, China (100%)
Tel.: (86) 2154421118
Web Site: http://www.daikin-dis.com
Emp.: 500
Air Conditioning Mfr
N.A.I.C.S.: 333415
Hiroshi Danno *(Chm)*

Branch (Domestic):

Daikin Air-Conditioning (Shanghai) Co., Ltd. - Huizhou Branch (2)
Dongjiang High-tech Industrial Zone Shuikou Street, Maan Town, Huizhou, 516257, Guangdong, China (100%)
Tel.: (86) 7523619401
Web Site: http://www.daikin.com
Air Conditioning Equipment Mfr
N.A.I.C.S.: 333415

Daikin Air-Conditioning Technology (Beijing), Ltd. (1)
20th Floor East Third Office Building Oriental Plaza 1 East, Changan Street Dongcheng District, Beijing, 100738, China
Tel.: (86) 1085182872
Web Site: http://www.daikin.com
Air Conditioning Equipment Maintenance Services
N.A.I.C.S.: 811310
Wang Fan *(Gen Mgr)*

Daikin Air-Conditioning Technology (Shanghai), Ltd. (1)
Dongjiang High-tech Industrial Zone Shuikou Street, Huizhou, Guangdong, China
Tel.: (86) 7523619401
Web Site: http://www.daikin.com
Air Conditioning Equipment Mfr
N.A.I.C.S.: 333415

Daikin Airconditioning (Hong Kong) Ltd. (1)
3/F 17-18/F Futura Plaza 111-113 How Ming Street, Kwun Tong, Kowloon, China (Hong Kong) (100%)
Tel.: (852) 2 570 2786
Web Site: https://www.daikin.com.hk
Sales Range: $25-49.9 Million
Emp.: 50
HVAC Equipment Mfr & Services
N.A.I.C.S.: 333415

Daikin Airconditioning (Malaysia) Sdn., Bhd. (1)
1st Floor Lot 4 Lorong 19/1A Seksyen 19, 46300, Petaling Jaya, Selangor, Malaysia
Tel.: (60) 3 7955 9090
Web Site: http://www.daikin.com.my
Air Conditioning Product Distr
N.A.I.C.S.: 423730

Daikin Airconditioning (Thailand) Ltd. (1)
700/444 Moo 7 Bangna-Trad Rd Km 57 Tambol Donhualor, Amata Nakorn Industrial Estate Amphur Muang, Chon Buri, 20000, Thailand
Tel.: (66) 387 170 6670
Web Site: https://www.daikinthai.com
Sales Range: $25-49.9 Million
Emp.: 100
Industrial Air Conditioning Mfr
N.A.I.C.S.: 333415
Hiroo Yoshioka *(Pres)*

Daikin Airconditioning Argentina (1)
Marcelo T de Alvear 1430, C1060 AAB, Buenos Aires, Argentina
Tel.: (54) 01148163274
Web Site: http://www.daikin-argentina.com
Sales Range: $25-49.9 Million
Emp.: 36
Air Conditioning Equipment & Supplies Sales & Distr
N.A.I.C.S.: 423730

Daikin Airconditioning Belgium NV (1)
Avenue Franklin 1B, 1300, Wavre, Belgium (100%)
Tel.: (32) 1 023 7223
Web Site: http://www.daikin.de
Sales Range: $25-49.9 Million
Emp.: 100
Air Conditioning Equipment Mfr
N.A.I.C.S.: 333415
Roderik Desiere *(Mng Dir)*

Daikin Airconditioning Central Europe GmbH (1)
Lembockgasse 59/1/1, 1230, Vienna, Austria (100%)
Tel.: (43) 1 253 2111
Web Site: https://www.daikin.at
Emp.: 80
N.A.I.C.S.: 333415

Daikin Airconditioning Chile S.A. (1)
Av Del valle Sur 577- Oficina 603, Huechuraba, Santiago, Chile
Tel.: (56) 227223900
Air Conditioning & Refrigeration Whslr
N.A.I.C.S.: 423730

Daikin Airconditioning Colombia S.A.S (1)
Av Carrera 45 Autopista Norte No 108A-50 Oficina 401, Bogota, Colombia
Tel.: (57) 17456388
Air Conditioning & Refrigeration Whslr
N.A.I.C.S.: 423730

Daikin Airconditioning France SAS (1)
ZA du petit Nanterre rue des Hautes Patures 31, 92737, Nanterre, Cedex, France (100%)
Tel.: (33) 14 669 9569
Web Site: http://www.daikin.fr
Sales Range: $25-49.9 Million
Emp.: 70
Air Conditioning Equipment Mfr
N.A.I.C.S.: 333415
Kazuhide Horimoto *(Gen Mgr)*

Daikin Airconditioning Germany GmbH (1)
Inselkammerstrasse 2, 82008, Unterhaching, Germany (100%)
Tel.: (49) 8 974 4270
Web Site: https://www.daikin.de
Sales Range: $50-74.9 Million
Emp.: 40
Air Conditioning Equipment Mfr
N.A.I.C.S.: 333415
Gunther Gamst *(Mng Dir)*

Daikin Airconditioning Greece S. A. (1)
St Konstantinou 50, 151 24, Maroussi, Greece
Tel.: (30) 210 876 1300
Web Site: https://www.daikin.gr
Sales Range: $25-49.9 Million
Emp.: 21
Air Conditioning Equipment Whslr
N.A.I.C.S.: 423730
Ilias Katsoulis *(Gen Mgr)*

Daikin Airconditioning India Private Limited (1)

12th Floor Building No 9 Tower A DLF Cyber City Building DLF Phase-III, Gurgaon, 122002, Haryana, India
Tel.: (91) 124 455 5444
Web Site: https://www.daikinindia.com
Emp.: 300
Air Conditioning Equipment & Supplies Sales & Distr
N.A.I.C.S.: 423730
Toshio Nakano *(Chm)*

Plant (Domestic):

Daikin Airconditioning India Pvt. Ltd. - Rajasthan Factory (2)
SP2-12 to SP2-15 & SP2-24 to SP2-27 RIICO New Industrial Complex, Majrajath Neemrana, 301 705, Alwar, Rajasthan, India
Tel.: (91) 1494 229 100
Air Conditioning Equipment Mfr
N.A.I.C.S.: 333415

Daikin Airconditioning Italy S.p.A. (1)
Via Ripamonti 85, 20141, Milan, Italy
Tel.: (39) 0251 6191
Web Site: https://www.daikin.it
Air Conditioning Equipment Mfr
N.A.I.C.S.: 333415

Daikin Airconditioning Korea Co., Ltd. (1)
3F Nashil Building 604-1 Yeoksam-dong, Gangnam-gu, Seoul, Korea (South)
Tel.: (82) 2 568 1722
Web Site: http://www.daikin-korea.co.kr
Air Conditioning Equipment Whslr
N.A.I.C.S.: 423730

Daikin Airconditioning Mexico, S. de R.L. de C.V. (1)
Damas No 130 Col San Jose Insurgentes Delegacion Benito Juarez, 03900, Mexico, Mexico
Tel.: (52) 5551470148
Air Conditioning & Refrigeration Whslr
N.A.I.C.S.: 423730

Daikin Airconditioning Netherlands B.V. (1)
Fascinatio Boulevard 562, 2909 VA, Capelle aan den IJssel, Netherlands
Tel.: (31) 88 324 5460
Web Site: https://www.daikin.nl
Air Conditioning Equipment Mfr
N.A.I.C.S.: 333415

Daikin Airconditioning Peru S.A.C. (1)
Av El Derby 250 Oficina 1403 33, Lima, Peru
Tel.: (51) 16136130
Air Conditioning & Refrigeration Whslr
N.A.I.C.S.: 423730

Daikin Airconditioning Philippines, Inc. (1)
18th Floor Exxa Tower Bridgetowne C5 Road, Brgy Ugong Norte, Quezon City, 1103, Philippines (60%)
Tel.: (63) 25 318 6800
Web Site: https://www.daikin.com.ph
Sales Range: $25-49.9 Million
Emp.: 100
Air Conditioning Equipment Mfr
N.A.I.C.S.: 333415

Daikin Airconditioning Poland Sp. z o.o. (1)
The Park Warsaw Ul Krakowiakow 36, 02-255, Warsaw, Poland
Tel.: (48) 22 319 9000
Web Site: https://www.daikin.pl
Sales Range: $25-49.9 Million
Emp.: 45
Air Conditioning Equipment & Supplies Sales & Distr
N.A.I.C.S.: 423730

Daikin Airconditioning Portugal S.A. (1)
Edificio D Maria I Piso 0 ala A/B Quinta da Fonte, Paco de Arcos, 2770-229, Oeiras, Portugal
Tel.: (351) 21 426 87 00
Web Site: http://www.daikin.pt
Air Conditioning Equipment Distr
N.A.I.C.S.: 423730

Daikin Airconditioning Saudi Arabia LLC (1)

King Abdul Aziz Road Al Sahafa Area, PO Box 14949, Riyadh, 11434, Saudi Arabia
Tel.: (966) 115108500
Web Site: https://www.daikin-ksa.com
N.A.I.C.S.: 811412

Daikin Airconditioning South Africa Pty. Ltd. (1)
Unit 1 and 2 Edison Way Century Gate Business Park, Century City, Cape Town, 7441, South Africa (100%)
Tel.: (27) 21 528 3500
Web Site: https://www.daikin.co.za
Sales Range: $1-9.9 Million
Emp.: 20
Air-Conditioning Mfr & Installer
N.A.I.C.S.: 333415
Neil Stander *(Gen Mgr)*

Daikin Airconditioning U.K., Ltd. (1)
The Heights Brooklands, Weybridge, KT13 0NY, Surrey, United Kingdom
Tel.: (44) 1932879000
Web Site: http://www.daikin.co.uk
Emp.: 50
Air Conditioning Mfr & Whslr
N.A.I.C.S.: 333415
Taja Johnson *(Mgr-HR)*

Daikin Airtechnology & Engineering Co., Ltd. (1)
Sumitomo Real Estate Ryogoku Building 2-10-8 Ryogoku, Sumida-ku, Tokyo, 130-0026, Japan
Tel.: (81) 356246301
Web Site: https://www.daikin-at.co.jp
N.A.I.C.S.: 811412

Daikin America, Inc. (1)
20 Olympic Dr, Orangeburg, NY 10962-2511
Tel.: (845) 365-9500
Web Site: https://daikin-america.com
Sales Range: $25-49.9 Million
Emp.: 60
HVAC Equipment Mfr & Services
N.A.I.C.S.: 333415
Kazuhito Kitsuki *(Chm)*

Daikin Applied (Malaysia) Sdn. Bhd. (1)
1 Jalan PJU 1a/5a Ara Damansara, 47301, Petaling Jaya, Selangor, Malaysia
Tel.: (60) 700817740
Air Conditioning & Refrigeration Whslr
N.A.I.C.S.: 423730

Daikin Applied (UK) Ltd. (1)
Bassington Industrial Estate, Cramlington, NE23 8AF, Northumberland, United Kingdom
Tel.: (44) 345 565 2700
Web Site: https://www.daikinapplied.uk
Air Conditioning & Refrigeration Mfr & Whslr
N.A.I.C.S.: 333415
Clive Parkman *(Mng Dir)*

Daikin Applied Europe S.p.A. (1)
Via Piani Di S Maria 72 00072 Ariccia, 00040, Rome, Italy
Tel.: (39) 0693 7311
Web Site: https://www.daikinapplied.eu
Air Conditioning & Refrigeration Mfr
N.A.I.C.S.: 333415

Daikin Applied Germany GmbH (1)
Herriotstrasse 1, 60528, Frankfurt am Main, Germany
Tel.: (49) 6967734360
Air Conditioning & Refrigeration Whslr
N.A.I.C.S.: 423730

Daikin Applied Latin America, L.L.C. (1)
7255 Corporate Ctr Dr Ste A, Miami, FL 33126
Tel.: (305) 716-8631
Web Site: https://daikinlatam.com
Air Conditioning & Refrigeration Whslr
N.A.I.C.S.: 423730

Daikin Applied Systems Co., Ltd. (1)
MS Shibaura Building 4-13-23 Shibaura, Minato-Ku, Tokyo, 108-0023, Japan
Tel.: (81) 36 414 5580
Web Site: https://www.daps.co.jp
Emp.: 520
Air Conditioning Equipment Mfr
N.A.I.C.S.: 333415

Daikin Industries, Ltd.—(Continued)

Daikin Ar Condicionado Brasil Ltda. (1)
Av Doutor Vital Brasil 305 - Torre Europa
Butanta, Sao Paulo, 05503-001, SP, Brazil
Tel.: (55) 1131232525
Web Site: https://www.daikin.com.br
N.A.I.C.S.: 811412

Daikin Arkema Refrigerants Asia Ltd. (1)
Unit 1201A 12/F Wing On Plaza 62 Mody
Road Tsim Sha, Causeway Bay, Kowloon,
China (Hong Kong)
Tel.: (852) 2295 6608
Specialty Chemicals Mfr
N.A.I.C.S.: 325199

Daikin Arkema Refrigerants Trading (Shanghai) Co., Ltd. (1)
3F United Plaza 1468 Nanjing Road W,
Jing An District, Shanghai, 200040, China
Tel.: (86) 2152135599
Air Conditioning & Refrigeration Whslr
N.A.I.C.S.: 423730

Daikin Asia Servicing Pte., Ltd. (1)
9 Tampines Grande 03-11, Singapore,
528735, Singapore (100%)
Tel.: (65) 6 546 8678
Web Site: http://www.daikinasia.com.sg
Sales Range: $25-49.9 Million
Emp.: 30
Air Conditioning Mfr & Whslr
N.A.I.C.S.: 333415
Carol Lin (Mgr-HR)

Daikin Australia Pty. Ltd. (1)
62-66 Governor Macquarie Drive, PO Box
120, Chipping Norton, 2170, NSW,
Australia (100%)
Tel.: (61) 297258888
Web Site: http://www.daikin.com.au
Sales Range: $50-74.9 Million
Emp.: 300
HVAC Equipment Mfr & Services
N.A.I.C.S.: 333415
Robert Woodhouse (Gen Mgr)

Daikin Chemical Europe GmbH (1)
Am Wehrhahn 50, 40211, Dusseldorf,
Germany (100%)
Tel.: (49) 211 179 2250
Web Site: https://www.daikinchem.de
Sales Range: $25-49.9 Million
Emp.: 40
Air Conditioning Mfr & Whslr
N.A.I.C.S.: 333415
Yasuhiko Hiray (Pres)

Daikin Chemical France S.A.S. (1)
Chemin de la Volta, BP 52, 69492, Pierre-
Benite, France
Tel.: (33) 4 7239 4930
Sales Range: $25-49.9 Million
Emp.: 42
Chemical Products Mfr
N.A.I.C.S.: 325180
Tetsuia Higuchi (Gen Mgr)

Daikin Chemical International Trading (Shanghai) Co., Ltd (1)
37F United Plaza 1468 Nanjing Road W,
Jing An District, Shanghai, 200040, China
Tel.: (86) 212 213 9700
Web Site: http://www.daikin.com
Specialty Chemicals Distr
N.A.I.C.S.: 424690

Daikin Chemical Netherlands B.V. (1)
Maaskade 16, 5347 KD, Oss, Netherlands
Tel.: (31) 41 269 7580
Web Site: http://www.daikin.com
Sales Range: $25-49.9 Million
Emp.: 15
Chemical Products Mfr
N.A.I.C.S.: 325180
Herman Pietersma (Gen Mgr)

Daikin Chemical Southeast Asia Co., Ltd. (1)
4345 Bhiraj Tower at Bitec 16th Floor Unit
1609 Sukhumvit Road, Bangnatai Sub-
district Bangna District, Bangkok, Thailand
Tel.: (66) 23995922
Air Conditioning & Refrigeration Whslr
N.A.I.C.S.: 423730

Daikin Compressor Industries, Ltd. (1)
7/202 Moo 6 T Mabyangporn A, Pluak-
daeng, Rayong, 21140, Thailand
Tel.: (66) 3 865 0060
Web Site: https://www.dci.co.th
Emp.: 1,652
Air Conditioner Equipment Mfr
N.A.I.C.S.: 333415

Daikin Device Czech Republic s.r.o. (1)
Svedske valy 1227/2, 627 00, Brno, Czech
Republic
Tel.: (420) 51 754 7310
Web Site: https://www.daikindevice.cz
Sales Range: $100-124.9 Million
Emp.: 500
Air Conditioning Equipment Mfr
N.A.I.C.S.: 333415
Hiroyuki Kubota (Pres)

Daikin Electronic Devices Malaysia Sdn. Bhd. (1)
Lot 3 Jalan Asam Jawa 16/15, PO Box
7354, 40712, Shah Alam, Selangor, Malay-
sia
Tel.: (60) 355413150
Air Conditioning & Refrigeration Mfr
N.A.I.C.S.: 333415

Daikin Europe Coordination Center NV (1)
Zandvoordestraat 300, Oostende, 8400,
West Vlaanderen, Belgium (100%)
Tel.: (32) 59558111
Web Site: http://www.daikineurope.com
Sales Range: $400-449.9 Million
Emp.: 1,500
N.A.I.C.S.: 333415
Dirk Salembier (Dir-HR)

Daikin Europe N.V. (1)
Zandvoordestraat 300, 8400, Oostende,
Belgium (100%)
Tel.: (32) 5 955 8111
Web Site: https://www.daikin.eu
Sales Range: $400-449.9 Million
Emp.: 1,500
HVAC Equipment Mfr & Services
N.A.I.C.S.: 333415
Morita Shigeki (Mng Dir)

Subsidiary (Non-US):

Rotex Heating Systems GmbH (2)
Langwiesenstrasse 10, 74363, Guglingen,
Germany
Tel.: (49) 7135 103 0
Web Site: http://www.rotex-heating.com
Sales Range: $75-99.9 Million
Emp.: 350
Heating Equipment Mfr
N.A.I.C.S.: 333414
Filip De Graeve (Co-CEO)

Daikin Facilities Co., Ltd. (1)
5-29-3 Toyo Sumitomofudosan No 2 Toyo
Bldg 2f, Koto-Ku, Tokyo, 135-0016, Japan
Tel.: (81) 336489531
Web Site: http://www.daikin-dfc.com
Sales Range: $25-49.9 Million
Emp.: 150
Facilities Management Services
N.A.I.C.S.: 561210

Daikin Fluoro Coatings (Shanghai) Co., Ltd. (1)
No 388 Chun Guang Road, Xinzhuang In-
dustry Zone, Shanghai, 201108, China
Tel.: (86) 2154421840
Air Conditioning & Refrigeration Mfr & Whslr
N.A.I.C.S.: 333415

Daikin Fluorochemicals (China) Co., Ltd. (1)
No 8 Xijinyu Road, Changshu New Material
Industrial Park, Changshu, 215522, Ji-
angsu, China
Tel.: (86) 5125 232 2266
Web Site: https://www.daikinchem.com.cn
Air Conditioning Equipment Mfr
N.A.I.C.S.: 333415

Daikin Fukushi Service Co., Ltd. (1)
2-4-12 Nakazakinishi Umeda Center Bldg
18f, Kita-Ku, Osaka, 530-0015, Japan
Tel.: (81) 663734301
Air Conditioning Equipment Whslr

Daikin Fuoro Coatings (Shanghai) Co., Ltd. (1)
No 388 Chun Guang Road, Xinzhuang In-
dustry Zone, Shanghai, 201108, China
Tel.: (86) 215 442 1840
Web Site: http://www.daikinchem.com
Sales Range: $25-49.9 Million
Emp.: 100
Air Conditioning Equipment Mfr
N.A.I.C.S.: 333415

Daikin HVAC Solution Hokkaido Co., Ltd. (1)
19-1-12 Kita16iohigashi, Higashi-Ku, Sap-
poro, 065-0016, Hokkaido, Japan
Tel.: (81) 117846661
Sales Range: $25-49.9 Million
Emp.: 3
Air Conditioning Equipment Mfr
N.A.I.C.S.: 333415
Hiroki Kasai (Pres)

Daikin HVAC Solution Kinki Co., Ltd. (1)
2-10-70 Nambanaka Namba Parks Parks
Bldg 12f, Naniwa-Ku, Osaka, 556-0011,
Japan
Tel.: (81) 666472355
Chemical Products Mfr
N.A.I.C.S.: 325998

Daikin HVAC Solution Kyushu Co., Ltd. (1)
1-10-21 Enokida Daikin Kogyo Fukuoka
Bldg, Hakata-Ku, Fukuoka, 812-0004, Ja-
pan
Tel.: (81) 924756204
Chemical Products Mfr
N.A.I.C.S.: 325998

Daikin HVAC Solution Niigata Co., Ltd. (1)
3-5-114 Yoneyama, Chuo-Ku, Niigata, 950-
0916, Japan
Tel.: (81) 252457200
Web Site: http://www.daikin.co.jp
Air Conditioning Equipment Mfr
N.A.I.C.S.: 333415
Tomomi Watanabe (Pres)

Daikin HVAC Solution Tohoku Co., Ltd. (1)
3-1-33 Oroshimachihigashi, Wakabayashi-
Ku, Sendai, 984-0002, Miyagi, Japan
Tel.: (81) 222880222
Air Conditioning Equipment Whslr
N.A.I.C.S.: 423730

Daikin HVAC Solution Tokai Co., Ltd. (1)
1-17 Shirakabe Daikin Kogyo, Higashi-Ku,
Nagoya, 461-0011, Aichi, Japan
Tel.: (81) 529550700
Chemical Products Mfr
N.A.I.C.S.: 325998

Daikin Holdings (USA), Inc. (1)
475 5th Ave 21th Fl, New York, NY 10017
Tel.: (212) 340-7400
Web Site: http://www.daikin.com
Air Conditioning Equipment Distr
N.A.I.C.S.: 423730

Daikin Hydraulic Engineering Co., Ltd. (1)
4-6-16 Hommachi Torikai, Settsu, 566-0052,
Osaka, Japan
Tel.: (81) 72 653 1111
Web Site: http://www.daikinpmc.com
Hydraulic Equipment Mfr
N.A.I.C.S.: 333248

Daikin Industries (Thailand) Ltd. (1)
700/11 Moo 1 Bangna-trad Rd km 57 Tam-
bol Klongtamru, Amphur Muang, Chon Buri,
20000, Thailand (100%)
Tel.: (66) 3 846 9700
Web Site: https://www.daikinthai.com
Sales Range: $300-349.9 Million
Emp.: 4,000
HVAC Equipment Mfr & Services
N.A.I.C.S.: 333415

Daikin Industries Czech Republic s.r.o. (1)
U Nove Hospody 1, 301 00, Plzen, Czech
Republic
Tel.: (420) 378773111

Web Site: https://www.daikinczech.cz
N.A.I.C.S.: 811412
Martin Loskot (Engr-Reliability)

Daikin Industries, Ltd. - Kanaoka Factory (1)
1304 Kanaoka-cho, Kita-ku, Sakai, 591-
8511, Osaka, Japan
Tel.: (81) 72 252 1151
Air Conditioning & Refrigeration System Mfr
N.A.I.C.S.: 333415

Daikin Industries, Ltd. - Kashima Plant (1)
Sunayama 21, Kamisu, 314-0255, Ibaraki,
Japan
Tel.: (81) 479 46 2441
Web Site: http://www.daikin.com
Specialty Chemicals Mfr
N.A.I.C.S.: 325180

Daikin Industries, Ltd. - Rinkai Factory (1)
12 Chikko Shin-machi 3-chome, Nishi-ku,
Sakai, 592-8331, Osaka, Japan
Tel.: (81) 72 241 1151
Air Conditioning Equipment Mfr
N.A.I.C.S.: 333415

Daikin Industries, Ltd. - Shiga Plant (1)
Okamoto-cho 1000-2, Kusatsu, 525-8526,
Shiga, Japan
Tel.: (81) 77 563 1151
Web Site: http://www.daikin.com
Air Conditioning Equipment Mfr
N.A.I.C.S.: 333415

Daikin Industries, Ltd. - Yodogawa Plant (1)
1-1 Nishi-Hitotsuya, Settsu, 566-8585,
Osaka, Japan
Tel.: (81) 6 6349 7361
Specialty Chemicals Mfr
N.A.I.C.S.: 325998

Daikin Information Systems Co., Ltd. (1)
28-18 Nakanoshima Festival Tower 2-3-18
Nakanoshima, Kita-ku, Osaka, 530-0005,
Japan
Tel.: (81) 662085130
Web Site: http://www.dki.co.jp
Information System Development Services
N.A.I.C.S.: 519290
Hiroshi Matsuo (Gen Mgr)

Daikin Isitma Ve Sogutma Sistemleri Sanayi Ticaret A.S. (1)
AkademiZumrutevler Mah Guroudag Sok
No 2, Maltepe, Istanbul, Turkiye
Tel.: (90) 850 200 7632
Web Site: https://www.daikin.com.tr
Air Conditioning & Refrigeration Mfr & Whslr
N.A.I.C.S.: 333415

Daikin Korea Co., Ltd. (1)
Room 602 6th Floor Keungil Tower 223
Teheran-Ro, Gangnam-gu, Seoul, 06142,
Korea (South)
Tel.: (82) 25681722
Web Site: https://www.daikin-korea.co.kr
N.A.I.C.S.: 333415

Daikin Lubrication Products & Engi-neering Co., Ltd. (1)
3-21-10 Tarumi-Cho 7th Floor Daikin Kogyo
Esaka Building, Suita, 564-0062, Osaka,
Japan
Tel.: (81) 66 337 2123
Web Site: https://www.daikin-
lubrication.co.jp
Industrial Machinery Mfr
N.A.I.C.S.: 333248

Daikin MR Engineering Co., Ltd. (1)
11F Shin-osaka Central-tower 5-5-15 Nishi-
nakajima, Yodogawa-ku, Osaka, 532-0011,
Japan
Tel.: (81) 64 805 7291
Web Site: https://www.dmre.daikin.co.jp
Sales Range: $25-49.9 Million
Emp.: 121
Marine Air Conditioning Equipment Mfr &
Whslr
N.A.I.C.S.: 333415
Ryoji Sanou (Pres)

Daikin Malaysia Sales & Service Sdn. Bhd. (1)

Lot 9 Jalan 13/6 Seksyen 13, 46200, Petaling Jaya, Selangor, Malaysia
Tel.: (60) 37 953 8388
Web Site: https://www.daikin.com.my
Air Conditioning & Refrigeration Whslr
N.A.I.C.S.: 423730
Lawrence Song *(Gen Mgr)*

Daikin Malaysia Sdn. Bhd. (1)
Lot 60334 Persiaran Bukit Rahman Putra 3, PO Box 79, Taman Perindustrian Bukit Rahman Putra, 47000, Sungai Buloh, Selangor, Malaysia
Tel.: (60) 36 145 8600
Web Site: https://www.daikinmalaysia.com
Air Conditioning & Refrigeration Mfr
N.A.I.C.S.: 333415

Daikin Manufacturing Germany GmbH (1)
Langwiesenstrasse 10, 74363, Guglingen, Germany
Tel.: (49) 7 135 1030
Web Site: https://www.daikin-manufacturing.de
Air Conditioning & Refrigeration Mfr & Whslr
N.A.I.C.S.: 333415

Daikin Marine (Shanghai) Co., Ltd. (1)
19G No 1 Plaza 800 Nanjing Road E, Shanghai, China
Tel.: (86) 2163224198
Web Site: http://www.daikin-marine.com
Air Conditioning & Refrigeration Mfr & Whslr
N.A.I.C.S.: 333415

Daikin McQuay Middle East FZE (1)
Plot MO0426 Jafza North Jebel Ali Free Zone, PO Box 18674, Dubai, 18674, United Arab Emirates
Tel.: (971) 48159300
Web Site: http://www.daikinmea.com
Air Conditioning Equipment Distr
N.A.I.C.S.: 423730
Francois Boueri *(Gen Mgr)*

Daikin Middle East & Africa FZE (1)
Plot MO0426 Jafza North Jebel Ali Free Zone, PO Box 18674, Dubai, United Arab Emirates
Tel.: (971) 800324546
Web Site: https://www.daikinafrica.com
N.A.I.C.S.: 333415

Daikin Refrigerants Europe GmbH (1)
Industriepark Hochst Gebaude D821, 65926, Frankfurt am Main, Germany
Tel.: (49) 69257885500
Refrigerant Gas Whslr
N.A.I.C.S.: 424690

Daikin Refrigeration Malaysia Sdn. Bhd. (1)
5 Jalan Gangsa Kawasan Perindustrian Banting, 42700, Banting, Selangor, Malaysia
Tel.: (60) 331872911
Air Conditioning & Refrigeration Mfr
N.A.I.C.S.: 333415

Daikin Research & Development Malaysia Sdn. Bhd. (1)
Lot 4739 Persiaran Bukit Rahman Putra 3, Taman Perindustrian Bukit Rahman Putra, 47000, Sungai Buloh, Selangor, Malaysia
Tel.: (60) 361570846
Air Conditioning & Refrigeration Mfr
N.A.I.C.S.: 333415

Daikin Steel Malaysia Sdn. Bhd. (1)
Lot 1 Jalan Asam Jawa 16/15 Seksyen 16, 40000, Shah Alam, Selangor, Malaysia
Tel.: (60) 355196700
Air Conditioning & Refrigeration Mfr
N.A.I.C.S.: 333415

Daikin Sunrise Settsu Co., Ltd. (1)
4-9-9 Higashibefu, Settsu, 566-0042, Osaka, Japan
Tel.: (81) 663493173
Emp.: 126
Specialty Chemicals Mfr
N.A.I.C.S.: 325998
Ealeisaku Shibuya *(Pres)*

Daikin Sweden A.B. (1)
Svardvagen 19 4th floor, Box 619, Danderyd, 18215, Stockholm, Sweden

Tel.: (46) 10 722 2400
Web Site: https://www.daikin.se
Heat Pump Mfr
N.A.I.C.S.: 333914

Daikin Trading (Thailand) Ltd. (1)
283/77 Home Place Office Building 15th Floor Soi Thonglor 13, Sukhumvit 55 Road Klongtonnua Watthana, Bangkok, 10110, Thailand (100%)
Tel.: (66) 27127314
Web Site: https://www.daikinthai.com
Sales Range: $25-49.9 Million
Emp.: 40
Air Conditioning Equipment Mfr
N.A.I.C.S.: 333415
Sajime Iida *(Pres)*

Daikin U.S. Corporation (1)
475 5th Ave 21th Fl, New York, NY 10017-420 (100%)
Tel.: (212) 340-7400
Web Site: http://www.daikin.com
Sales Range: $25-49.9 Million
Emp.: 24
Mfr of Air Conditioning Equipment
N.A.I.C.S.: 423730
Kelvin Williams *(Gen Counsel & Dir-Gen Affairs)*

Daikin-Sauer-Danfoss Manufacturing Ltd. (1)
1-1 Nishi Hitotsuya, Settsu, 566-0044, Osaka, Japan
Tel.: (81) 6 6349 7264
Hydraulic Components Mfr
N.A.I.C.S.: 332912

Dukin Industries Co., Ltd. (1)
17-9 4Gil Gongdanro Waegwan, Chilgok, 718-802, Kyungbuk, Korea (South)
Tel.: (82) 549750700
Air Conditioning & Refrigeration Whslr
N.A.I.C.S.: 423730

Electro Mart Limited (1)
Noor Holdings 8th Floor 33 South Gulshan Avenue, Gulshan1, Dhaka, Bangladesh
Tel.: (880) 1755696111
Air Conditioning & Refrigeration Whslr
N.A.I.C.S.: 423730

Elite Radio & Engineering Co., Ltd. (1)
No 35/3 Nawala Road, Narahenpita, Colombo, Sri Lanka
Tel.: (94) 777384400
Air Conditioning & Refrigeration Whslr
N.A.I.C.S.: 423730

Enhance Technologies (Pvt) Ltd. (1)
No 255 Colombo Road, Peradeniya, Kandy, Sri Lanka
Tel.: (94) 81 206 6665
Web Site: https://www.ithurukaramu.lk
Computer Software Development Services
N.A.I.C.S.: 541511

Fresco EME Limited (1)
Bashati Condominium House-15 Road-17, Banani, Dhaka, 1213, Bangladesh
Tel.: (880) 1755577333
Air Conditioning & Refrigeration Whslr
N.A.I.C.S.: 423730

Goodman Global, Inc. (1)
5151 San Felipe St Ste 500, Houston, TX 77056
Tel.: (713) 861-2500
Web Site: http://www.goodmanmfg.com
Sales Range: $1-4.9 Billion
Emp.: 4,331
Air-Conditioners & Heating Units Mfr
N.A.I.C.S.: 333415
Lawrence M. Blackburn *(CFO & Exec VP)*

Subsidiary (Domestic):

Goodman Distribution Southeast, Inc. (2)
8925 NW 27th St, Doral, FL 33172
Tel.: (305) 696-0830
Sales Range: $150-199,9 Million
Emp.: 60
Air Heating & Air Conditioning Equipment Whslr
N.A.I.C.S.: 423730
Eliud Chevres *(Plant Mgr)*

Subsidiary (Domestic):

CCOM Group, Inc. (3)

275 Wagaraw Rd, Hawthorne, NJ 07506
Tel.: (973) 427-8224
Web Site: http://www.colonialcomm.com
Rev.: $101,936,300
Assets: $37,629,755
Liabilities: $20,725,905
Net Worth: $16,903,850
Earnings: $1,053,885
Emp.: 162
Fiscal Year-end: 12/31/2020
Air Conditioning Equipment & Appliances Distr
N.A.I.C.S.: 423710
William Salek *(CFO & Sec)*

Subsidiary (Domestic):

S&A Supply Company Inc. (4)
20 Maple Ave, Great Barrington, MA 01230
Tel.: (413) 528-3470
Web Site: http://www.sasupplyinc.com
Sales Range: $10-24.9 Million
Emp.: 55
Plumbing, Heating, Indrustrial Equipment Fittings & Supplies
N.A.I.C.S.: 444180

Subsidiary (Domestic):

Goodman Distribution (3)
2123 Park Central Blvd N, Pompano Beach, FL 33064
Tel.: (954) 984-4848
Sales Range: $25-49.9 Million
Emp.: 12
Air Heating & Air Conditioning Equipment Whslr
N.A.I.C.S.: 423730
Matt Gawflin *(Mgr)*

Goodman Distribution (3)
13200 Automobile Blvd, Clearwater, FL 33762
Tel.: (727) 573-2772
Air Heating & Air Conditioning Equipment Whslr
N.A.I.C.S.: 423730
Stacy Redmond *(Mgr)*

Goodman Distribution (3)
4401 Shader Rd, Orlando, FL 32808
Tel.: (407) 296-4499
Sales Range: $25-49.9 Million
Emp.: 15
Air Heating & Air Conditioning Equipment Whslr
N.A.I.C.S.: 423730
Jim Weber *(Mgr)*

Subsidiary (Domestic):

Goodman Manufacturing Company, L.P. (2)
19001 Kermier Rd, Waller, TX 77484
Tel.: (713) 861-2500
Web Site: https://www.goodmanmfg.com
Air-Conditioning, Ventilation & Heating Equipment Mfr
N.A.I.C.S.: 333415
Lawrence M. Blackburn *(CFO & Exec VP)*

Guangzhou Newly Mechanical & Electrical Co., Ltd. (1)
1st Floor Building 5 No 98 DaLong Tai An Road, Panyu District, Guangzhou, China
Tel.: (86) 2038398032
Air Conditioning & Refrigeration Whslr
N.A.I.C.S.: 423730

HVAC Engineering Limited (1)
House-290/01 Road-8A, Dhaka, Bangladesh
Tel.: (880) 1755628315
Air Conditioning & Refrigeration Whslr
N.A.I.C.S.: 423730

Haroon Engineering Ltd. (1)
No 18 Kamal Ataturk Avenue, Banani, Dhaka, Bangladesh
Tel.: (880) 1781244444
Air Conditioning & Refrigeration Whslr
N.A.I.C.S.: 423730

Heng Yi Da Machine (Yinchuan) Co., Ltd. (1)
Yinchuan Chengxin Street Of, Economy And Technology Development Zone, Yinchuan, China
Tel.: (86) 9512031122
Air Conditioning & Refrigeration Whslr

N.A.I.C.S.: 423730

Heroflon S.p.A. (1)
Via Alcide de Gasperi No 4, Collebeato, 25060, Brescia, Italy
Tel.: (39) 0302510211
Air Conditioning & Refrigeration Mfr & Whslr
N.A.I.C.S.: 333415

Himal Refrigeration & Electrical Industries Pvt. Ltd. (1)
Sanepa Lalitpur, PO Box 13417, Kathmandu, Nepal
Tel.: (977) 9851038787
Air Conditioning & Refrigeration Whslr
N.A.I.C.S.: 423730

Hotai Development Co., Ltd. (1)
No 18 Lane 36 Xinhu 1st Road, Neihu District, Taipei, Taiwan
Tel.: (886) 22 514 8886
Web Site: https://www.hotaidev.com.tw
Air Conditioning & Refrigeration Whslr
N.A.I.C.S.: 423730

Humak Engineering (Pvt) Ltd. (1)
Plot 2 Industrial Triangle Kahuta Road Sector A Model Town Humak, Islamabad, Pakistan
Tel.: (92) 51111000135
N.A.I.C.S.: 423730

IRS International Pty. Ltd. (1)
2 James Street, Brooklyn, Laverton, 3026, VIC, Australia
Tel.: (61) 39 349 6400
Web Site: https://www.irs-worldwide.com
Emp.: 150
Refrigerated Container Repair Services
N.A.I.C.S.: 811310

Idac (Private) Limited (1)
21 Sri Sunandarama Road, Kalubowila, Colombo, Sri Lanka
Tel.: (94) 777750180
Air Conditioning & Refrigeration Whslr
N.A.I.C.S.: 423730

Inaire (Pvt) Ltd. (1)
No 14 4th Lane Nawala, Rajagiriya, Colombo, Sri Lanka
Tel.: (94) 11 280 5326
Web Site: https://www.inaire.com.lk
Air Conditioning & Refrigeration Mfr
N.A.I.C.S.: 333415
Wimal Jayakody *(Chm & Mng Dir)*

J&E Hall International Ltd. (1)
Questor House 191 Hawley Road, Dartford, DA1 1PU, Kent, United Kingdom
Tel.: (44) 1322394420
Web Site: https://www.jehall.com
N.A.I.C.S.: 335220

J.S.S Enterprises (Pvt) Ltd. (1)
121 Union place, Colombo, Sri Lanka
Tel.: (94) 778590647
Air Conditioning & Refrigeration Whslr
N.A.I.C.S.: 423730

JiangXi DaTang Chemicals Co., Ltd. (1)
GuTang Town, LianXi District, Jiujiang, JiangXi, China
Tel.: (86) 7928318666
Chemical Product Mfr & Whslr
N.A.I.C.S.: 325180

K D Hydraulics, Ltd. (1)
Room 1606 Ace Hi-Tech City 775 Gyeongin-ro, Yeongdeungpo-gu, Seoul, Korea (South)
Tel.: (82) 26 309 7600
Web Site: https://www.kdhyd.com
Air Conditioning & Refrigeration Whslr
N.A.I.C.S.: 423730

K.S Trading (Pvt) Ltd. (1)
494/1 Nawala Road, Rajagiriya, Colombo, Sri Lanka
Tel.: (94) 11 288 7134
Web Site: https://www.kstrading.lk
Engineeering Services
N.A.I.C.S.: 541330

Kailing Hydraulic Technology (Shanghai) Co., Ltd. (1)
Room 408 Block D Oriental International Building, No 85 Loushanguan Road Changning District, Shanghai, 200050, China
Tel.: (86) 216 466 2121

Daikin Industries, Ltd.—(Continued)

Web Site: https://www.klyysh.com
Air Conditioning & Refrigeration Whslr
N.A.I.C.S.: 423730

Lin Chi Hydraulics Co., Ltd. (1)
No 67 Kai'an 2nd Street, Annan District,
Tainan City, 709, Taiwan
Tel.: (886) 6 355 5106
Web Site: https://www.linchi.com.tw
Air Conditioning & Refrigeration Whslr
N.A.I.C.S.: 423730

M.K. Electronics Limited (1)
Plot No- 01/A 11th Floor Sector-4, Uttara,
Dhaka, 1230, Bangladesh
Tel.: (880) 9613333111
Air Conditioning & Refrigeration Whslr
N.A.I.C.S.: 423730

MIA Corporation (Pvt) Ltd. (1)
Plot 384 Street 16 Industrial Area Sector
I-9, Islamabad, Pakistan
Tel.: (92) 5144454825
Air Conditioning & Refrigeration Whslr
N.A.I.C.S.: 423730

Mechanical Services Ltd. (1)
Government Buildings 18 Matua Street
Walubay, PO Box 2430, Suva, Fiji
Tel.: (679) 331 4933
Web Site:
https://www.mechanicalservicesfiji.com
Refrigeration Mechanical Services
N.A.I.C.S.: 238220
Shiv Nand Sharma *(Mng Dir)*

Moritani Daikin Co, Ltd. (1)
67 MBR99 5F Kanda Sakumagashi,
Chiyoda-ku, Tokyo, 101-0026, Japan
Tel.: (81) 33 851 2181
Web Site: https://www.gmdk.co.jp
Emp.: 102
Air Conditioning Equipment Mfr
N.A.I.C.S.: 333415

Nandee Inter-Trade Co., Ltd. (1)
Soi Chan 32 Chan Road, Thung Wat Don
Sathorn, Bangkok, 10120, Thailand
Tel.: (66) 2 675 8230
Web Site: https://www.nandee.co.th
Air Conditioning & Refrigeration Whslr
N.A.I.C.S.: 423730

Nippon Muki Co., Ltd. (1)
Nisshin Ueno Bldg 5-1-5 Higashi-ueno,
Taito-ku, Tokyo, 110-0015, Japan
Tel.: (81) 36 860 7500
Web Site: https://www.nipponmuki.co.jp
Sales Range: $75-99.9 Million
Emp.: 249
Fiberglass Mfr & Whslr
N.A.I.C.S.: 326199
Michihiro Hiroto *(Pres)*

**O.Y.L. Manufacturing Company Sdn.
Bhd. (OYLM)** (1)
Lot 60334 Persiaran Bukit Rahman Putra 3
Taman Perindustrian Bukit, Raman Putra,
47000, Sungai Buloh, Selangor, Malaysia
Tel.: (60) 361458600
Web Site: http://www.oyl.com.my
Sales Range: $1-4.9 Billion
Emp.: 1,600
Heating & Air Conditioning Products Mfr
N.A.I.C.S.: 333415
Tan Yong Cheem *(Gen Mgr)*

Subsidiary (US):

**American Air Filter International,
Inc.** (2)
9920 Corporate Campus Dr Ste 2200, Lou-
isville, KY 40223-5000
Tel.: (502) 637-0516
Web Site: https://www.aafintl.com
Sales Range: $800-899.9 Million
Emp.: 200
Commercial, Industrial & Institutional Heat-
ing, Ventilating, Air-Conditioning, Filtration &
Air Pollution Control Products, Systems &
Controls
N.A.I.C.S.: 333415

Subsidiary (Non-US):

AAF International B.V. (3)
Egelenburg 2, 1081 GK, Amsterdam, Neth-
erlands
Tel.: (31) 205494411

Web Site: http://www.aafeurope.com
Sales Range: $25-49.9 Million
Emp.: 25
Air Pollution Control Equipment Mfr
N.A.I.C.S.: 333413
Quekleng Chan *(Mng Dir)*

Dinair Group AB (3)
Tel.: (46) 1 431 2580
Web Site: https://www.dinair.se
Emp.: 350
Holding Company; Air Filters Mfr
N.A.I.C.S.: 551112
Niels-Erik Kongste *(CEO)*

Subsidiary (Non-US):

Dinair Clean Air Oy (4)
Koivuvaarankuja 2, 01640, Vantaa, Finland
Tel.: (358) 10 322 2610
Web Site: https://dinair.fi
Air Filtration Equipment Mfr & Whslr
N.A.I.C.S.: 333413
Matti Siltala *(Mgr-Production)*

Dinair Ekonomifilter AS (4)
Prof Birkelands vei 36, 1081, Oslo, Norway
Tel.: (47) 22905900
Web Site: http://www.dinair.se
Air Filter Equipment Distr
N.A.I.C.S.: 423730
Hans Petter Faye *(Dir)*

Dinair Filton SIA (4)
Rupnicu iela 4, Olaine, 2114, Latvia
Tel.: (371) 6 706 9823
Web Site: https://www.dinair.lv
Air Filter Equipment Distr
N.A.I.C.S.: 423730
Kent Petersson *(CEO & Mng Dir-Sls)*

Subsidiary (Domestic):

STF Svenska Textilfilter AB (4)
Anasvagen 18, SE-511 56, Kinna, Sweden
Tel.: (46) 320209070
Web Site: http://www.textilfilter.se
Air Filter Equipment Mfr
N.A.I.C.S.: 333413
Mikael Niemi *(Service Officer)*

Subsidiary (Domestic):

**National Air Filter Service Co of New
Jersey** (3)
325 Washington Ave, Carlstadt, NJ 07072
Tel.: (201) 438-0800
Web Site: http://www.nationalairfilter.com
Sales Range: $1-9.9 Million
Emp.: 31
Plumbing/Heating/Air Cond Contractor
N.A.I.C.S.: 238220
Donald Borghoff *(Pres)*

Northeast Air Solutions Inc (3)
3 Lopez Rd, Wilmington, MA 01887
Tel.: (978) 988-2000
Web Site: http://www.nas-hvac.com
Sales Range: $10-24.9 Million
Emp.: 30
Providers of Air Engineering
N.A.I.C.S.: 423840

Subsidiary (US):

Daikin Applied Americas Inc. (2)
13600 Industrial Park Blvd, Minneapolis,
MN 55441
Tel.: (763) 553-5330
Web Site: https://www.daikinapplied.com
Heating, Ventilating & Air Conditioning
Equipment Mfr
N.A.I.C.S.: 333415
Jeff Drees *(Pres & CEO)*

Subsidiary (Domestic):

CM3 Building Solutions, Inc. (3)
185 Commerce Dr, Fort Washington, PA
19034-9034 (100%)
Tel.: (215) 322-8400
Web Site: http://www.cm3web.com
Plumbing, Heating & Air-Conditioning Con-
tractors
N.A.I.C.S.: 238220
Bruce Michelson *(Pres)*

Carroll Air Systems Inc. (3)
3711 W Walnut St, Tampa, FL 33607
Tel.: (813) 879-5790

Web Site: https://www.carrollair.com
Rev.: $16,000,000
Emp.: 29
Warm Air Heating & Air Conditioning
N.A.I.C.S.: 423730
Phillip R. Carroll *(CEO)*

Dynamic Controls, Inc. (3)
727 Sabrina Dr, East Peoria, IL 61611-3578
Tel.: (309) 692-8810
Web Site: https://dciusa.com
Electrical Contractor
N.A.I.C.S.: 238210
Karen Hall *(Pres)*

**McQuay International-Chiller
Products** (3)
207 Laurellhill Rd, Verona, VA 24482-2510
Tel.: (540) 248-0711
Web Site: http://www.mcquay.com
Refrigeration Products
N.A.I.C.S.: 333415

OK Kizai Co., Ltd. (1)
1-7-4 Higashinodamachi Wakita Kyobashi
No 2 Building, Miyakojima-ku, Osaka, 534-
0024, Japan
Tel.: (81) 66 354 3013
Web Site: https://www.ok-kizai.co.jp
Emp.: 208
Air Conditioning Equipment Whslr
N.A.I.C.S.: 423730

**PT. Daikin Airconditioning
Indonesia** (1)
Jl BKR No 23 Regol Pasirluyu, Bandung,
40254, Indonesia
Tel.: (62) 22 522 5150
Web Site: https://www.daikin.co.id
Air Conditioning & Refrigeration Whslr
N.A.I.C.S.: 423730

**PT. Daikin Applied Solutions
Indonesia** (1)
Jl Opak 33, Surabaya, 69241, Indonesia
Tel.: (62) 319 953 9777
Web Site: https://www.daikinapplied.co.id
Air Conditioning & Refrigeration Whslr
N.A.I.C.S.: 423730

**PT. Daikin Manufacturing
Indonesia** (1)
Bekasi International Industrial Estate Lippo
Cikarang Block C-2 No 12A, Jln Raya Ciba-
rusah Lemah Abang, Bekasi, 17550, Jawa
Barat, Indonesia
Tel.: (62) 218972915
Air Conditioning & Refrigeration Mfr
N.A.I.C.S.: 333415

PT. Eterna Karya Sejahtera (1)
Komplek Duta Merlin Blok C No 31-32 Jl
Gajah Mada No 3-5, Jakarta, 10130, Indo-
nesia
Tel.: (62) 21 634 1749
Web Site: https://www.eterna.co.id
Air Conditioning & Refrigeration Whslr
N.A.I.C.S.: 423730

Penguin Engineering Limited (1)
H84 4th Floor R7A, Dhanmondi, Dhaka,
1205, Bangladesh
Tel.: (880) 1711523716
Air Conditioning & Refrigeration Whslr
N.A.I.C.S.: 423730

Port Enterprises (Guam) Inc. (1)
PO Box BX, Agana, GU 96910
Tel.: (671) 646-1722
Air Conditioning & Refrigeration Whslr
N.A.I.C.S.: 423730

**Power Fluidtronics & Industries Sdn.
Bhd.** (1)
Lot 12 Jalan 31/47 Kota Kemuning, 40460,
Shah Alam, Selangor, Malaysia
Tel.: (60) 351220188
Air Conditioning & Refrigeration Whslr
N.A.I.C.S.: 423730

Premier Engineering Ltd. (1)
Planners Tower 13/A 13th Floor, My-
mensingh Road Room No 4-5, Dhaka,
1000, Bangladesh
Tel.: (880) 1710000000
Air Conditioning & Refrigeration Whslr
N.A.I.C.S.: 423730

ROTEX Polska SP. Z O.O. (1)
ul Tasmowa 7, 02-677, Warsaw, Poland
Tel.: (48) 22 319 90 00

Web Site: http://www.rotex.com.pl
Heating Equipment Mfr
N.A.I.C.S.: 333414

SEM Daikin Co, Ltd. (1)
2-1-1 Awaza Urban Ace Awaza Building,
Nishi-ku, Osaka, 550-0011, Japan
Tel.: (81) 66 606 9000
Web Site: https://www.sem-daikin.co.jp
Emp.: 46
Air Conditioning Equipment Whslr
N.A.I.C.S.: 423730
Takuji Ogawa *(Gen Mgr)*

Sauer Bibus GmbH (1)
Lise-Meitner-Ring 13, 89231, Neu-Ulm,
Germany
Tel.: (49) 7 311 8960
Web Site: https://www.sauerbibus.de
Engineering Services
N.A.I.C.S.: 541330
Ralf Schrempp *(Mng Dir)*

Scan Engineering (Pvt) Ltd. (1)
Suite 705 Hilton Colombo Residence 200
Union Place, Colombo, Sri Lanka
Tel.: (94) 777777426
Air Conditioning & Refrigeration Whslr
N.A.I.C.S.: 423730

**Shanghai Hongkai Hydlaulics Equip-
ment Co., Ltd.** (1)
No 5 Lane 121 Xiangyin Road, Yangpu Dis-
trict, Shanghai, 200433, China
Tel.: (86) 2165489969
Air Conditioning & Refrigeration Whslr
N.A.I.C.S.: 423730

Siam Daikin Sales Co., Ltd. (1)
22 Soi On Nut 55 1 On Nut Road, Prawet
Subdistrict Prawet District, Bangkok, 10250,
Thailand
Tel.: (66) 2 838 3200
Web Site: https://www.daikin.co.th
Air Conditioning Equipment Distr
N.A.I.C.S.: 423730

Singhagiri (Pvt) Ltd. (1)
No 515 T B Jayah Mawatha, Colombo, Sri
Lanka
Tel.: (94) 11 541 3413
Web Site: https://www.singhagiri.lk
Air Conditioning & Refrigeration Mfr
N.A.I.C.S.: 333415

Taicin Sy Co., Ltd. (1)
2F No 366 Sec 1 Jhonghua N Rd, North
Dist, Tainan City, 70459, Taiwan
Tel.: (886) 63507723
Air Conditioning & Refrigeration Whslr
N.A.I.C.S.: 423730

**Taiwan Daikin Advanced Chemicals,
Inc.** (1)
Room B 12th Floor No 170 Dunhua North
Road, Songshan District, Taipei, 10549,
Taiwan
Tel.: (886) 22 547 1269
Web Site: https://www.taiwandaikin.com
Air Conditioning & Refrigeration Whslr
N.A.I.C.S.: 423730

Techno HVAC System Ltd. (1)
101 1st Floor, Kakrail, Dhaka, 1000, Ban-
gladesh
Tel.: (880) 1713438601
Air Conditioning & Refrigeration Whslr
N.A.I.C.S.: 423730

Toho Kasei Co., Ltd. (1)
6-2 Imagoucho-cho, Yamato-koriyama, 639-
1031, Nara, Japan
Tel.: (81) 74 359 2361
Web Site: https://www.toho-kasei.co.jp
Semiconductor Equipment Mfr & Distr
N.A.I.C.S.: 334413
Yoshihiko Misugi *(Gen Mgr)*

Transcom Electronics Limited (1)
Sadar Road Mohakhali, Dhaka, 1206, Ban-
gladesh
Tel.: (880) 1730340627
Air Conditioning & Refrigeration Whslr
N.A.I.C.S.: 423730

Venstar, Inc. (1)
9250 Owensmouth Ave, Chatsworth, CA
91311
Tel.: (818) 341-8760
Web Site: http://www.venstar.com

Sales Range: $1-9.9 Million
Emp.: 15
Air-Conditioning & Warm Air Heating Equipment & Commercial & Industrial Refrigeration Equipment Mfr
N.A.I.C.S.: 333415
Steve Dushane *(Founder, Pres & CEO)*

Vivasa (Pvt) Ltd. (1)
31/24 Dawson Street, Colombo, Sri Lanka
Tel.: (94) 773897107
Air Conditioning & Refrigeration Whslr
N.A.I.C.S.: 423730

Xi'an Daikin Qing'an Compressor Co., Ltd. (1)
No 10 Gaoxin 2 nd Road, Hi-Tec Industrial Development Area, Xi'an, 710075, Shaanxi, China (51%)
Tel.: (86) 2988310966
Web Site: http://www.xadaikin.com
Emp.: 1,500
Commercial Airconditioning Scroll Compressors Mfr
N.A.I.C.S.: 333415

Zanotti S.p.A. (1)
Via ML King 30, 46020, Pegognaga, MN, Italy
Tel.: (39) 0376 5551
Web Site: https://www.zanotti.com
Air Conditioning & Refrigeration Mfr & Whslr
N.A.I.C.S.: 333415

Zhuhai Gree Daikin Device Co., Ltd. (1)
No 8 Longshan No 3 Rd Longshan Area Fushan Industrial Park, Zhuhai, 519110, Guangdong, China
Tel.: (86) 7565790174
Web Site: http://www.daikin.com
Printed Circuit Board Mfr
N.A.I.C.S.: 334412
Tao Li *(Gen Mgr)*

Zicom Private Ltd. (1)
9 Tuas Avenue 9, Singapore, 639198, Singapore
Tel.: (65) 6 513 0618
Web Site: https://www.zicom.com.sg
Electric Equipment Mfr
N.A.I.C.S.: 335999

DAIKO DENSHI TSUSHIN, LTD.
Karukozaka MN Building 2-1 Agebacho, Shinjuku-ku, Tokyo, 162-8565, Japan
Tel.: (81) 332668111
Web Site: https://privacymark.jp
Year Founded: 1953
8023—(TKS)
Rev.: $286,728,580
Assets: $183,943,080
Liabilities: $106,401,170
Net Worth: $77,541,910
Earnings: $12,149,180
Fiscal Year-end: 03/31/24
Computer & Computer Related Product Whslr
N.A.I.C.S.: 423430
Koichiro Matsuyama *(Pres & COO)*

DAIKO TSUSAN CO., LTD.
791-8012 6-11 Himehara 3-chome Matsuyama City Ehime Prefecture, Matsuyama, 791-8012, Japan
Tel.: (81) 899232288
Web Site: https://www.daiko-tsusan.co.jp
7673—(TKS)
Sales Range: Less than $1 Million
Communication Equipment Mfr
N.A.I.C.S.: 334290
Akira Kawada *(Chm & Pres)*

DAIKOKU DENKI CO., LTD.
1-43-5 Nagono, Nakamura-ku, Nagoya, 450-8640, Aichi, Japan
Tel.: (81) 525817113
Web Site: https://www.daikoku.co.jp
Year Founded: 1964
6430—(TKS)
Rev.: $356,021,210

Assets: $391,847,410
Liabilities: $122,688,210
Net Worth: $269,159,200
Earnings: $55,947,040
Fiscal Year-end: 03/31/24
Computer System Mfr & Whslr
N.A.I.C.S.: 334111
Masakatsu Kayamori *(Chm)*

Subsidiaries:

Aloft Co., Ltd. (1)
8th floor Soft 99 Building 4-7-7 Sotokanda, Chiyoda-ku, Tokyo, 101-0021, Japan
Tel.: (81) 35 289 7178
Web Site: https://a-loft.co.jp
Emp.: 35
Lighting Equipment Mfr
N.A.I.C.S.: 335139

Daikoku Denki Co., Ltd. - Kasugai Division (1)
1-26 Kagiya-cho, Kasugai, 480-0304, Aichi, Japan
Tel.: (81) 568887771
Computer System Mfr
N.A.I.C.S.: 334118

Daikoku Denki Co., Ltd. - Kozoji Division (1)
2-Kibukicho 1-chome, Kasugai, 487-0014, Japan
Tel.: (81) 568 51 7111
Computer System Mfr
N.A.I.C.S.: 334118

Daikoku Denki Co., Ltd. - Sakashita Division (1)
1-875 Sakashita-cho, Kasugai, 480-0395, Aichi, Japan
Tel.: (81) 568887111
Computer System Mfr
N.A.I.C.S.: 334118

Genki Co., Ltd. (1)
Harmony Tower 1-32-2 Hon-cho, Nakano-ku, Tokyo, 164-8721, Japan
Tel.: (81) 3 5365 3306
Web Site: http://www.genki.co.jp
Emp.: 151
Game Software Development Services
N.A.I.C.S.: 541511
Takashi Hoshino *(Pres)*

DAIKOKUTENBUSSAN CO., LTD.
297-1 Nishinakashinden, Kurashiki, 710-0833, Okayama, Japan
Tel.: (81) 864351100
Web Site: https://www.e-dkt.co.jp
Year Founded: 1986
2791—(TKS)
Rev.: $1,785,208,970
Assets: $689,766,720
Liabilities: $322,938,160
Net Worth: $366,828,560
Earnings: $41,682,660
Emp.: 2,044
Fiscal Year-end: 05/31/24
Supermarket Operator
N.A.I.C.S.: 445110
Shoji Oga *(Pres & CEO)*

Subsidiaries:

Nishigen Company (1)
2-9-25 Koyaminami, Matsumoto, 399-0038, Nagano, Japan
Tel.: (81) 263578800
Food Products Distr
N.A.I.C.S.: 424490

DAIKOKUYA HOLDINGS CO., LTD.
2-15-8 Takanawa, Minato-ku, Tokyo, 108-0074, Japan
Tel.: (81) 334487300
Web Site:
http://www.daikokuyajp.com
Year Founded: 1935
6993—(TKS)
Rev.: $72,491,870
Assets: $43,083,980
Liabilities: $38,886,630

Net Worth: $4,197,350
Earnings: ($3,562,790)
Emp.: 162
Fiscal Year-end: 03/31/24
Electronic Appliance Mfr & Whslr
N.A.I.C.S.: 335220
Kohei Ogawa *(Pres)*

DAILY MAIL & GENERAL TRUST PLC
Northcliffe House 2 Derry Street, London, W8 5TT, United Kingdom
Tel.: (44) 2079386000   UK
Web Site: https://www.dmgt.com
Year Founded: 1896
Rev.: $1,201,989,516
Assets: $5,006,185,184
Liabilities: $821,556,372
Net Worth: $4,184,628,812
Earnings: $81,191,656
Emp.: 4,034
Fiscal Year-end: 09/30/21
Newspaper & Business-to-Business Information Publisher; Conference & Trade Show Organizer; Radio Station Operator
N.A.I.C.S.: 513110
Fran L. Sallas *(Sec)*

Subsidiaries:

Associated Newspapers Ltd. (1)
Northcliffe House 2 Derry Street, London, W8 5TT, United Kingdom (100%)
Tel.: (44) 2079386000
Web Site: http://www.dmgmedia.co.uk
Newspaper Publishers
N.A.I.C.S.: 513110
Paul Dacre *(Chm & Editor-in-Chief)*

British Pathe PLC (1)
The Media Centre, 3-8 Carburton St, London, W1W 5AJ, United Kingdom (100%)
Tel.: (44) 02076658340
Web Site: http://www.britishpathe.com
Newsreel Archive Services
N.A.I.C.S.: 513110

Coral Mint Ltd. (1)
4 Mary's Abbey, Dublin, Ireland
Tel.: (353) 16708688
Web Site: http://www.coralmint.com
Media Production Services
N.A.I.C.S.: 512110
Naoise McNally *(Co-Founder & Mng Dir)*

DMG Events (USA) Inc. (1)
3 Stamford Landing Ste 400 46 Southfield Ave, Stamford, CT 06902
Tel.: (203) 973-2940
Web Site: http://www.dmgevents.com
Sales Range: $75-99.9 Million
Emp.: 8
Consumer Exhibitions Organizer
N.A.I.C.S.: 561920
Suresh Kavan *(Chm)*

Subsidiary (Non-US):

DMG Events (Canada) Inc. (2)
1510 140 10th Ave SE, Calgary, T2G 0R1, AB, Canada (100%)
Tel.: (403) 209-3555
Web Site: http://www.dmgevents.com
Rev.: $1,764,720
Emp.: 50
Consumer Exhibitions Organizer
N.A.I.C.S.: 561920

DMG Events (Dubai) Limited (2)
5th Floor The Palladium Cluster C Jumeirah Lakes Towers, PO Box 33817, Dubai, United Arab Emirates
Tel.: (971) 4 4380 355
Web Site: http://www.dmgeventsme.com
Emp.: 300
Consumer Exhibitions Organizer
N.A.I.C.S.: 561920

Unit (Domestic):

DMG Events (USA) Inc. - Digital Marketing (2)
221 Main St Ste 920, San Francisco, CA 94105-1923
Tel.: (415) 537-8500

Web Site:
http://www.dmgdigitalmarketing.com
Sales Range: $25-49.9 Million
Emp.: 20
Consumer Exhibitions Organizer & Digital Marketing Services
N.A.I.C.S.: 561920

Subsidiary (Non-US):

DMG Events Limited (2)
Northcliffe House 2 Derry Street, London, W8 5TT, United Kingdom (100%)
Tel.: (44) 20 7938 6000
Web Site: http://www.gastech.co.uk
Sales Range: $300-349.9 Million
Consumer Exhibitions Organizer
N.A.I.C.S.: 561920
Nick Ratcliffe *(CFO)*

DMG Events Asia Pacific Pte Ltd. (1)
138 Market Street 05-01 Capitagreen, Singapore, 048946, Singapore
Tel.: (65) 68565205
Event & Exhibition Services
N.A.I.C.S.: 561920
Mel Shah *(VP-Energy)*

DMG Events Egypt Ltd. (1)
Office B2 Plaza 2 between Halls 3 and 4, Egypt International Exhibition Centre El Moushir Tantawy Axis, New Cairo, Egypt
Tel.: (20) 222614503
Event & Exhibition Services
N.A.I.C.S.: 561920

DMG Events, LLC (1)
Office 408 Sakura Plaza Al Madinah Al Munawarah Road, PO Box 3650, As Salamah District, Jeddah, Saudi Arabia
Tel.: (966) 920009623
Event & Exhibition Services
N.A.I.C.S.: 561920

DMG Information US Inc. (1)
3 Stamford Landing Ste 400 46 Southfield Ave, Stamford, CT 06902
Tel.: (203) 973-2940
Web Site: http://www.dmginfo.com
Sales Range: $125-149.9 Million
Emp.: 10
Group Investment Services
N.A.I.C.S.: 517810

Subsidiary (Non-US):

Decision Insight Information Group (Europe) Limited (2)
42 Kings Hill Avenue, Kings Hill, West Malling, ME19 4AJ, Kent, United Kingdom
Tel.: (44) 870 787 7625
Holding Company
N.A.I.C.S.: 551112

Subsidiary (Domestic):

Millar & Bryce Limited (3)
Floor 4 Ocean Point 1 94 Ocean Drive, Leith, Edinburgh, EH6 6JH, United Kingdom
Tel.: (44) 131 556 1313
Web Site: http://www.millar-bryce.com
Legal Advisory Services
N.A.I.C.S.: 541611
Richard Hepburn *(Mng Dir)*

SearchFlow Limited (3)
42 Kings Hill Avenue, Kings Hill, West Malling, ME19 4AJ, Kent, United Kingdom
Tel.: (44) 1732523900
Web Site: http://www.searchflow.co.uk
Real Estate Information Services
N.A.I.C.S.: 519290
Katriona O'Hare *(Mgr-Customer Svcs)*

Environmental Data Resources, Inc. (1)
6 Armstrong Rd 4th Fl, Shelton, CT 06484
Tel.: (203) 255-6606
Web Site: http://www.edrnet.com
Geographic-Based Information Publishing, Consulting & Analytic Services to the Real Estate, Municipal & Telecommunications Markets
N.A.I.C.S.: 541690

Hobsons plc (1)
IDT House 44 Featherstone Street, London, EC1Y 8RN, United Kingdom
Tel.: (44) 2072506600
Web Site: http://www.hobsons.com

Daily Mail & General Trust plc—(Continued)

Sales Range: $25-49.9 Million
Emp.: 50
Publisher of Educational & Career Information
N.A.I.C.S.: 513199

Subsidiary (US):

Hobsons, Inc. (2)
3033 Wilson Blvd Ste 500, Arlington, VA 22201
Tel.: (703) 234-5910
Web Site: https://www.hobsons.com
Custom Computer Programming Services
N.A.I.C.S.: 541511
Kate Cassino (CEO)

Landmark FAS Ltd. (1)
Imperium Imperial Way, Reading, RG2 0TD, Berkshire, United Kingdom
Tel.: (44) 8448449967
Web Site: http://www.landmarkfas.co.uk
Financial Assets Management Services
N.A.I.C.S.: 523940

Landmark Information Group (1)
7 Abbey Ct Eagle Way, Sowton Industrial Estate, Exeter, EX2 7HY, Devon, United Kingdom (100%)
Tel.: (44) 392441700
Web Site: http://www.landmark.co.uk
Sales Range: $25-49.9 Million
Emp.: 100
Produces Site-Specific Environmental Reports for Firms of Environmental & Geo-Technical Consultants, Civil Engineers & Large Industrial Owners
N.A.I.C.S.: 541620
Ian Clarke (CTO)

Lawlink (UK) Ltd. (1)
Bible House 27 Howard Street, Belfast, BT1 6NB, United Kingdom
Tel.: (44) 2890230095
Web Site: http://www.lawlink.co.uk
Title Insurance Services
N.A.I.C.S.: 524127

Northcliffe Media Holdings Limited (1)
Northcliffe House 2 Derry Street, London, W8 5TT, United Kingdom (100%)
Tel.: (44) 2074001401
Web Site: http://www.thisisnorthcliffe.co.uk
Sales Range: $800-899.9 Million
Emp.: 6,350
Regional Newspaper Publisher
N.A.I.C.S.: 513110

Ochresoft Technologies Ltd. (1)
Imperium Imperial Way, Reading, RG2 0TD, Berkshire, United Kingdom
Tel.: (44) 3300366700
Web Site: http://www.ochresoft.com
Software Development Services
N.A.I.C.S.: 541511
Julia O'Reilly (Project Mgr)

Teletext Limited (1)
10 Chiswick Park, 566 Chiswick High Road, London, W4 5TS, United Kingdom (100%)
Tel.: (44) 2083235000
Web Site: http://www.teletext.co.uk
Sales Range: $50-74.9 Million
Emp.: 200
Television Information Services
N.A.I.C.S.: 516210

Trepp UK Ltd. (1)
King's Gate 1 Bravington Walk, London, N1 9AE, United Kingdom
Tel.: (44) 2036372791
Financial Mortgage Services
N.A.I.C.S.: 522292

Trepp, LLC (1)
600 5th Ave 7th Fl, New York, NY 10020
Tel.: (212) 754-1010
Web Site: http://www.trepp.com
Financial Mortgage Services
N.A.I.C.S.: 522292
Tom Fink (Mng Dir & Sr VP)

Zoopla Property Group Ltd. (1)
2nd Floor Union House, 182-194 Union Street, London, SE1 0LH, United Kingdom (52.6%)
Tel.: (44) 20 7620 4618

Web Site: http://www.zooplapropertygroup.com
Online Property Website Services
N.A.I.C.S.: 531390
Holly Westall (Head-Product-Property Mktg)

DAILY POLYMER CO., LTD.
No 10 Yonghong Ln, Renwu Dist, Kaohsiung, 814, Taiwan
Tel.: (886) 73711321
Web Site: https://www.daily-polymer.com
Year Founded: 1970
4716—(TPE)
Rev.: $29,686,082
Assets: $56,605,209
Liabilities: $26,416,416
Net Worth: $30,188,793
Earnings: $652,532
Fiscal Year-end: 12/31/20
Paint & Coating Mfr
N.A.I.C.S.: 325510
Chiu Chih-Hsiang (Chm)

DAIMAN DEVELOPMENT BER-HAD
Level 32 and 33 Menara Landmark No 12 Jalan Ngee Heng, 80000, Johor Bahru, Johor, Malaysia
Tel.: (60) 72255888
Web Site: http://www.daiman.com.my
Rev.: $42,322,268
Assets: $384,830,908
Liabilities: $93,283,552
Net Worth: $291,547,356
Earnings: $10,112,337
Fiscal Year-end: 06/30/18
Property Development Services
N.A.I.C.S.: 531312
Thiam Song Tay (Mng Dir)

Subsidiaries:

Atlantic Dynamics Sdn. Bhd. (1)
Level 32 & 33 Menara Landmark No 12 Jalan Ngee Heng, 80000, Johor Bahru, Johor, Malaysia
Tel.: (60) 72255888
Web Site: http://www.daiman.com.my
Sales Range: $50-74.9 Million
Emp.: 100
Property Development Services
N.A.I.C.S.: 531390

Daiman Bowl Sdn. Bhd. (1)
No 2 Jalan Dedap 3 Taman Johor Jaya, 81100, Johor Bahru, Johor, Malaysia
Tel.: (60) 73513399
Sales Range: $50-74.9 Million
Emp.: 21
Ten Pin Bowling Center Operation Services
N.A.I.C.S.: 713950
Tay Siowee (Mgr)

Daiman Golf Berhad (1)
No 18 Jalan Pesona Taman Johor Jaya, 81100, Johor Bahru, Johor, Malaysia
Tel.: (60) 73516813
Sales Range: $50-74.9 Million
Emp.: 20
18 Holes Golf Course Operation Services
N.A.I.C.S.: 713910
Tay Tian Liang (Mng Dir)

Daiman Johor Jaya Sports Complex Berhad (1)
No 1 Jalan Dedap 3 Taman Johor Jaya, 81100, Johor Bahru, Johor, Malaysia
Tel.: (60) 73551888
Sales Range: $50-74.9 Million
Emp.: 26
Sports Club Facilities Operation Services
N.A.I.C.S.: 713940

Daiman Trading Sdn. Bhd. (1)
Level 32 & 33 Menara Landmar, No 12 Jalan Ngee Heng, 80000, Johor Bahru, Johor, Malaysia
Tel.: (60) 7 225 5990
Building Materials Distr
N.A.I.C.S.: 444180
Elaine Lee (Officer-HR)

DAIMARU ENAWIN CO., LTD.

1-4-39 Midorigi, Suminoe-ku, Osaka, 559-0022, Japan
Tel.: (81) 666855101
Web Site: https://www.gas-daimaru.co.jp
Year Founded: 1951
9818—(TKS)
Rev.: $197,672,050
Assets: $144,283,080
Liabilities: $50,857,340
Net Worth: $93,425,740
Earnings: $4,845,130
Emp.: 642
Fiscal Year-end: 03/31/24
Liquefied Petroleum Gas Distr
N.A.I.C.S.: 424720
Kiyokazu Iuchi (Co-Mng Dir)

DAIMLER TRUCK HOLDING AG
Fasanenweg 10, 70771, Leinfelden-Echterdingen, Germany
Tel.: (49) 71184850 De
Web Site: https://www.daimlertruck.com
Year Founded: 2019
DTG—(DEU)
Rev.: $60,317,289,014
Assets: $76,853,011,008
Liabilities: $52,868,551,694
Net Worth: $23,984,459,314
Earnings: $4,074,034,103
Emp.: 101,475
Fiscal Year-end: 12/31/23
Holding Company
N.A.I.C.S.: 551112

Subsidiaries:

Banco Mercedes-Benz do Brasil S.A. (1)
Avenida Alfred Jurzykowski No 562 Predio 20 2 Andar, Pauliceia, Sao Bernardo do Campo, 09680-900, Brazil
Tel.: (55) 8007228499
Web Site: https://www.bancomercedes-benz.com.br
Automobile Finance & Insurance Services
N.A.I.C.S.: 524128

Daimler Truck Australia Pacific Pty. Ltd. (1)
Level 4 631 Springvale Road, Mulgrave, 3170, VIC, Australia
Tel.: (61) 800033557
Web Site: https://www.daimlertruck.com.au
Truck Mfr & Distr
N.A.I.C.S.: 333924

Daimler Truck Financial Services Belgium N.V. (1)
Tollaan 68, 1200, Brussels, Belgium
Tel.: (32) 28821910
Web Site: https://en-be.dtfs.be
Automobile Finance & Insurance Services
N.A.I.C.S.: 524128

Daimler Truck Financial Services Canada Corporation (1)
2680 Matheson Blvd East Suite 202, Mississauga, L4W 0A5, ON, Canada
Web Site: https://daimler-truckfinancial.com
Automobile Finance & Insurance Services
N.A.I.C.S.: 524128

Daimler Truck Financial Services Italia S.p.A. (1)
Via Giulio Vincenzo Bona 110, 00156, Rome, Italy
Tel.: (39) 0642989100
Automobile Finance & Insurance Services
N.A.I.C.S.: 524128

Daimler Truck Financial Services Nederland B.V. (1)
Ravenswade 4, 3439 LD, Nieuwegein, Netherlands
Tel.: (31) 302471601
Web Site: https://en-nl.dtfs.nl
Automobile Finance & Insurance Services
N.A.I.C.S.: 524128

Daimler Truck Financial Services UK Limited (1)

Delaware Drive Tongwell, Milton Keynes, MK15 8BA, Buckinghamshire, United Kingdom
Tel.: (44) 8000389991
Automobile Finance & Insurance Services
N.A.I.C.S.: 524128

Daimler Truck Nederland B.V. (1)
Ravenswade 4, 3439 LD, Nieuwegein, Netherlands
Tel.: (31) 885850000
Web Site: https://nl.daimlertruck.com
Automobile Finance & Insurance Services
N.A.I.C.S.: 524128

Daimler Truck Southern Africa Ltd. (1)
Highway Business Park 1 Park Ave, Rooihuiskraal, Centurion, 0154, South Africa
Tel.: (27) 126499670
Web Site: https://dtsa.daimlertruck.com
Truck Mfr & Distr
N.A.I.C.S.: 333924

DAIMYO AS
Uranienborg Terrasse 9, 0351, Oslo, Norway
Tel.: (47) 22374300
Web Site: http://www.daimyo.no
Sales Range: $10-24.9 Million
Emp.: 25
Investment Services
N.A.I.C.S.: 523999
Karsten Aubert (Chm)

Subsidiaries:

SC Casa de Compensare Bucuresti SA (1)
Blvd Carol I nr 34-36 Fl 3 sector 2, 020922, Bucharest, Romania
Tel.: (40) 21 315 7312
Web Site: http://www.casadecompensare.ro
Electric Power Distribution Services
N.A.I.C.S.: 221122

DAINICHI CO., LTD.
1-33 Himegaoka, Kani, 509-0249, Gifu, Japan
Tel.: (81) 574634484
Web Site: https://www.kk-dainichi.co.jp
Year Founded: 1948
5951—(TKS)
Sales Range: Less than $1 Million
Fabricated Structural Metal Mfr
N.A.I.C.S.: 332312
Hisakazu Inoue (CEO)

DAINICHISEIKA COLOR & CHEMICALS MFG. CO., LTD.
1-7-6 Nihonbashi-Bakurocho, Chuo-ku, Tokyo, 103-8383, Japan
Tel.: (81) 336627111 JP
Web Site: https://www.daicolor.co.jp
Year Founded: 1931
4116—(TKS)
Rev.: $792,036,640
Assets: $1,287,971,720
Liabilities: $500,284,460
Net Worth: $787,687,260
Earnings: $24,192,600
Emp.: 1,437
Fiscal Year-end: 03/31/24
Mfr & Sales of Inorganic & Organic Pigments, Printing Inks, Coloring Agents for Plastics & Synthetic Fibers, Printing Agents for Textile, Synthetic Resin & High Polymer Products
N.A.I.C.S.: 325211
Koji Takahashi (Pres)

Subsidiaries:

Aeolian Corporation (1)
No 47 San De St, Lu Jwu Dist, Taoyuan, 338, Taiwan
Tel.: (886) 33543151
Emp.: 20
Plastic Colored Pellet Mfr & Distr
N.A.I.C.S.: 325211

DAINICHI COLOR VIETNAM CO., LTD. (1)
Tel.: (84) 2223714800
Web Site: http://www.daicolor.co.jp
Coloring Pigment Mfr
N.A.I.C.S.: 325199

Daicolor Italy S.R.L. (1)
Via Vittor Pisani 28, 20124, Milan, Italy (100%)
Tel.: (39) 0267076688
Web Site: http://www.daicolor.co.jp
Sales Range: $25-49.9 Million
Emp.: 6
Mfr of Inks, Pigments & Other Coloring Agents
N.A.I.C.S.: 325910

Daicolor Shanghai Mfg. Co., Ltd. (1)
125 Chu Hua Road Shanghai Chemical Industrial Zone Feng Xian Sub Zone, Shanghai, China
Tel.: (86) 2157448220
Specialty Chemicals Mfr
N.A.I.C.S.: 325998

Daicolor do Brasil Ind. e Com. Ltda. (1)
Av Piramide 692, Eldorado Diadema, Sao Paulo, 09970-330, Brazil (100%)
Tel.: (55) 1140597721
Web Site: http://www.daicolor.com.br
Sales Range: $25-49.9 Million
Emp.: 60
Plastic Compounding & Plastics Materials Mfr
N.A.I.C.S.: 325211

Dainichi Color (Thailand) Ltd. (1)
No 60/78 Village No 19 Phaholyothin Road, Khlong Nueng Sub-district Khlong Luang District, Pathumthani, 12120, Thailand
Tel.: (66) 25292709
Web Site: https://www.dainichi-color.com
Emp.: 280
Plastic Colored Pellet Mfr
N.A.I.C.S.: 325211

Dainichi Color India Private Ltd. (1)
SP2-28 Majrakath, Riico New Industrial Complex, Neemrana, 301705, Rajasthan, India
Tel.: (91) 1494246188
Plastic Colored Pellet Mfr & Distr
N.A.I.C.S.: 325211

Dainichiseika (H.K.) Ltd. (1)
RM 2204 22/F Windsor House 311 Gloucester Road, Causeway Bay, China (Hong Kong) (100%)
Tel.: (852) 25778923
Web Site: https://www.dns-hk.com.hk
Sales Range: $1-9.9 Million
Emp.: 360
Plastics Compounding Mfr
N.A.I.C.S.: 325211
Takebayashi Fumitoshi *(Mng Dir)*

Subsidiary (Domestic):

Dainichiseika (H.K.) Colouring Co., Ltd. (2)
RM 2204 22/F Windsor House 311 Gloucester Road, Causeway Bay, China (Hong Kong) (100%)
Tel.: (852) 28390558
Web Site: https://www.dns-hk.com.hk
Plastics Compounding Mfr
N.A.I.C.S.: 325211

Subsidiary (Non-US):

Dong Guan Dainichi Chemical Manufacturing Co., Ltd. (2)
Dabandi Industrial Estate, Daning District Humen Town, Dongguan, Guangdong, China (90%)
Tel.: (86) 76985556675
Web Site: http://www.dns-hk.com.hk
Emp.: 210
Plastic Compounding & Plastics Materials Mfr
N.A.I.C.S.: 325211

Dainichiseika (Shanghai) Trading Ltd. (1)
1606-841 Yan An Middle Road OOCL Plaza, Shanghai, 200040, China (100%)
Tel.: (86) 2162792737
Web Site: http://www.daicolor.co.jp

Sales Range: $25-49.9 Million
Emp.: 14
Plastics Compounding Mfr
N.A.I.C.S.: 325211
Sang Ping Fan *(Mng Dir)*

Dainichiseika Color & Chemicals S.A. (1)
4 Rue Agrippa Daubigne, 78540, Vernouillet, France (100%)
Tel.: (33) 139280956
Sales Range: $25-49.9 Million
Emp.: 1
Chemical Mfg
N.A.I.C.S.: 325510

Dainichiseika Ink (Guangzhou) Ltd. (1)
No 3 Xinye Road Yonghe Economic Zone Getdd, Guangzhou, 511356, China
Tel.: (86) 2082976870
Sales Range: $25-49.9 Million
Emp.: 3
Printing Ink Mfr
N.A.I.C.S.: 325910
Hikita Tomohisa *(Gen Mgr)*

E & S Home of Color B.V. (1)
Ir. E.L.C. Schiffstraat 246, 7547, Enschede, Netherlands
Tel.: (31) 53 4601010
Sells Inorganic & Organic Pigments & Printing Inks
N.A.I.C.S.: 325211

Esta Fine Color Corporation (1)
37 Arturo Drive First Avenue Bagumbayan, Taguig, 1630, Metro Manila, Philippines
Tel.: (63) 28661337
Web Site: https://www.estatrading.net
Sales Range: $25-49.9 Million
Coloring Pigment Mfr
N.A.I.C.S.: 325130

Filpassion SA (1)
10 Rue Des Moissons, 51110, Caurel, France
Tel.: (33) 326828694
Web Site: http://www.filpassion.fr
Sales Range: $25-49.9 Million
Emp.: 30
Sells Inorganic & Organic Pigments & Printing Inks
N.A.I.C.S.: 325211
Virgile Deghaye *(Gen Mgr)*

Hi-Tech Color (Shanghai) Co., Ltd. (1)
125 Chu Hua Road Shanghai Chemical Industrial Zone Feng Xian Sub Zone, Shanghai, China
Tel.: (86) 2157448222
Sales Range: $75-99.9 Million
Emp.: 13
Packaging & Building Materials Mfr
N.A.I.C.S.: 326199

Hi-Tech Color, Inc. (1)
1721 Midway Rd, Odenton, MD 21113
Tel.: (410) 551-9871
Web Site: https://www.htcolor.com
Sales Range: $25-49.9 Million
Emp.: 12
Mfr of Printing Inks
N.A.I.C.S.: 325910

Kanto Dainichiseika Kogyo Co., Ltd. (1)
2-2-1 Furukawa, Kazo, 3400113, Saitama, Japan
Tel.: (81) 480684600
Chemical Products Mfr
N.A.I.C.S.: 325998

Kyushu Dainichiseika Kogyo Co., Ltd (1)
1-15-50 Nishitsukiguma, Hakata-Ku, Fukuoka, 812-0857, Japan
Tel.: (81) 924112020
Specialty Chemicals Mfr
N.A.I.C.S.: 325199

Midbec AB (1)
Analysvagen 1, 435 33, Molnlycke, Sweden
Tel.: (46) 31880550
Web Site: https://www.midbectapeter.se
Sales Range: $25-49.9 Million
Emp.: 20
Sells Inorganic & Organic Pigments & Printing Inks

N.A.I.C.S.: 325211

Oy. Avane Trading Ltd. (1)
Kuortaneenkatu 7, 00520, Helsinki, Finland
Tel.: (358) 8929509610
Sells Inorganic & Organic Pigments & Printing Inks
N.A.I.C.S.: 325211

P.T. Hi-Tech Ink Indonesia (1)
Delta Silicone Industrial Park Jl Akasia I Blok A8 No 2, Lippo Cikarang, Bekasi, 17550, Indonesia (100%)
Tel.: (62) 218973890
Web Site: http://www.daicolor.co.jp
Sales Range: Less than $1 Million
Emp.: 150
Adhesives & Gravure & Offset Printing Inks Mfr & Sales
N.A.I.C.S.: 325520

Plalloy Mtd B.V. (1)
Mercuriusstraat 2, 6468 ER, Kerkrade, Netherlands (60%)
Tel.: (31) 455464653
Web Site: https://www.plalloy.com
Sales Range: $10-24.9 Million
Emp.: 100
Plastics Compounding Mfr
N.A.I.C.S.: 325211
M. Vermeulen *(Mgr-QA)*

Puylaert Designs Of The Time N.V. (1)
Europark-Zuid 15, Sint-Niklaas, 9100, Saint-Niklaas, Belgium
Tel.: (32) 37809470
Web Site: https://www.designsofthetime.be
Sells Inorganic & Organic Pigments & Printing Inks
N.A.I.C.S.: 325211

Sambo Fine Chemicals Mfg. Co., Ltd. (1)
39-37 Hakjang-ro, Sasang-gu, Busan, Korea (South) (100%)
Tel.: (82) 513113001
Web Site: http://www.sambofine.co.kr
Sales Range: $1-9.9 Million
Emp.: 100
C-Acid, Dye Intermediates & Inorganic Pigments Mfr
N.A.I.C.S.: 325130

Shanghai Daicolor & Fuji Co., Ltd. (1)
1033 Xin Miao San Road, Xinqiao Songjiang, Shanghai, China
Tel.: (86) 2157680930
Sales Range: $25-49.9 Million
Emp.: 3
Specialty Chemicals Mfr
N.A.I.C.S.: 325998

Shanghai Mitsui Plastic Compounds Ltd. (1)
No 511 Yutang Rd, Songjiang Industrial Zone, Shanghai, 201600, China (33%)
Tel.: (86) 2157741111
Web Site: http://www.shmpc.com.cn
Sales Range: $1-9.9 Million
Emp.: 150
Plastics Compounding Mfr
N.A.I.C.S.: 325211

Tai Chin Chemical Industry Co., Ltd. (1)
NO 402 Fengren Road, Renwu Dist, Kaohsiung, Hsin, Taiwan (100%)
Tel.: (886) 73711621
Web Site: https://www.taichin.com
Sales Range: $25-49.9 Million
Emp.: 85
Plastics Compounding Mfr
N.A.I.C.S.: 325211

DAIO PAPER CORPORATION
Iidabashi Grand Bloom 2 Chome-10-2 Fujimi, Chiyoda-ku, Tokyo, 102-0071, Japan
Tel.: (81) 368567624   JP
Web Site: https://www.daio-paper.co.jp
Year Founded: 1943
3880—(TKS)
Rev.: $4,439,857,680
Assets: $6,211,714,450
Liabilities: $4,492,545,990

Net Worth: $1,719,168,460
Earnings: $29,791,270
Emp.: 12,372
Fiscal Year-end: 03/31/24
Paper, Paperboard, Stationery & Office Supplies Mfr
N.A.I.C.S.: 322120
Masayoshi Sako *(Pres & CEO)*

Subsidiaries:

Akabira Paper Corporation (1)
199-5 Kyowa-cho, Akabira-shi, Hokkaido, 079-1101, Japan
Tel.: (81) 125322250
Web Site: http://www.elleair-akabira.com
Sanitary Paper Mfr & Whslr
N.A.I.C.S.: 322291

Dainichi Paper Corporation (1)
9-1 Shinbashicho, Fuji, 417-0004, Shizuoka Prefecture, Japan
Tel.: (81) 545512511
Web Site: https://www.dainichi-paper.co.jp
Emp.: 115
Sanitary Paper Mfr & Whslr
N.A.I.C.S.: 322291

Daio Engineering Co., Ltd. (1)
Tel.: (81) 896239129
Web Site: http://www.daio-eng.co.jp
Environment Related Equipment Mfr
N.A.I.C.S.: 334512

Daio Logistics Co., Ltd. (1)
1695 Nakanoshocho, Shikokuchuo, 799-0422, Ehime Prefecture, Japan
Tel.: (81) 896247737
Web Site: https://www.daio-logistics.co.jp
Emp.: 720
Freight Transportation Services
N.A.I.C.S.: 484121

Daio Mill Support Co., Ltd. (1)
5-1 Mishima Kamiyacho, Shikokuchuo, 799-0402, Ehime Prefecture, Japan
Tel.: (81) 896241904
Web Site: https://www.daio-dms.co.jp
Emp.: 560
Specialty Paper Mfr
N.A.I.C.S.: 322120

Daio Mill Support Tokai Corporation (1)
50-4 Shimokawabe, Kawabe-cho Kamo, Gifu, 509-0306, Japan
Tel.: (81) 574535591
Web Site: https://www.daio-mill-support-tokai.com
Emp.: 220
Packaging Product Mfr & Distr
N.A.I.C.S.: 326112

Daio Package Corporation (1)
2-5-2 Kanda Suda-cho, Chiyoda-ku, Tokyo, 101-0041, Japan
Tel.: (81) 352090750
Web Site: https://www.daio-package.co.jp
Packaging Machinery Mfr
N.A.I.C.S.: 333993

Daio Paper Products Corporation (1)
Yodabashi-cho 7-34, Fuji, 417-0003, Shizuoka, Japan
Tel.: (81) 545523132
Web Site: http://www.daio-pp.co.jp
Household Paper Mfr & Distr
N.A.I.C.S.: 322291

Daio Postal Chemical Corporation (1)
1-13-4 Kitaotsuka Oak Otsuka Building 3rd Floor, Toshima-ku, Tokyo, 170-0004, Japan
Tel.: (81) 359801021
Web Site: http://www.postal.co.jp
Labeling Machine Mfr
N.A.I.C.S.: 333993

Daio Printing Corporation (1)
1-13-4 Kitaotsuka Oak Otsuka Building 3F, Toshima-ku, Tokyo, 170-0004, Japan
Tel.: (81) 359072320
Web Site: http://www.daio-printing.co.jp
Commercial Printing Services
N.A.I.C.S.: 811310

Daio Pulp & Paper Co., Ltd. (1)
6th Floor Tsukamoto Building 1-6-5 Nihonbashihoncho, Chuo-ku, Tokyo, 103-0023, Japan

Daio Paper Corporation—(Continued)

Tel.: (81) 355421635
Web Site: http://www.dpps.co.jp
Special Paper Mfr & Whslr
N.A.I.C.S.: 322120

Daiwa Shiko Co., Ltd. (1)
3-13-10 Kyobashi 6F, Chuo-ku, Tokyo, 104-0031, Japan
Tel.: (81) 355246675
Web Site: http://www.daiwa-shiko.co.jp
Warehouse Business Services
N.A.I.C.S.: 493110

Elleair Business Support Co., Ltd (1)
1-13-4 Kitaotsuka Oak Otsuka Building 2nd Floor, Toshima-ku, Tokyo, 170-0004, Japan
Tel.: (81) 368658001
Web Site: http://www.elleair-bs.co.jp
Industrial Wipe Whslr
N.A.I.C.S.: 423840

Elleair International (Thailand) Co., Ltd. (1)
7/320 M 6 Mabyangporn, Amata City Industrial Estate, Pluak Daeng, 21140, Rayong, Thailand
Tel.: (66) 3803633641
Web Site: https://www.elleair.co.th
Emp.: 500
Sanitary Products Mfr
N.A.I.C.S.: 322291

Elleair International Korea Co., Ltd. (1)
1108-1112 West Building 24 Hanshin Intervalley 322 Teheran-ro, Gangnam-gu, Seoul, Korea (South)
Tel.: (82) 7078262344
Web Site: https://www.elleairgoo-n.co.kr
Sanitary Products Mfr
N.A.I.C.S.: 322291

Elleair Paper Co., Ltd. (1)
6-Nanryo, Fujinomiya, 418-0019, Shizuoka Prefecture, Japan
Tel.: (81) 544234521
Web Site: https://www.elleair-paper.co.jp
Emp.: 540
Specialty Paper Mfr
N.A.I.C.S.: 322120

Elleair Product Co., Ltd. (1)
4765-11 Samukawa-cho, Shikokuchuo, 799-0431, Ehime, Japan
Tel.: (81) 896252022
Web Site: https://www.elleair-product.com
Secure Product Mfr
N.A.I.C.S.: 334290

Elleair Texel Corporation (1)
677-1 Ima Higashiyama, Kani, 509-0246, Gifu Prefecture, Japan
Tel.: (81) 574651240
Web Site: http://www.e-texel.jp
Specialty Paper Mfr
N.A.I.C.S.: 322120

Forestal Anchile Ltda. (1)
Avenida Juan Mackenna 1673, Tenth Region of Los Lagos, Osorno, Chile
Tel.: (56) 642453700
Web Site: https://www.anchile.cl
Wood Chip Whslr
N.A.I.C.S.: 423310

Harima Paper Tech. Corporation (1)
2-34 Nishiwaki Befucho, Kakogawa, 675-0125, Hyogo Prefecture, Japan
Tel.: (81) 794351333
Web Site: http://www.hptech.co.jp
Corrugated Board Mfr & Whslr
N.A.I.C.S.: 322211

Iwaki Daio Paper Corporation (1)
4-3-6 Minamidai, Iwaki, 974-8242, Fukushima Prefecture, Japan
Web Site: http://www.iwaki-daio.co.jp
Newspaper & Corrugated Board Mfr
N.A.I.C.S.: 322211

Marubishi Paper Tec. Corporation (1)
2012 Kinseicho Shimobun, Shikokuchuo, 799-0111, Ehime Prefecture, Japan
Tel.: (81) 896564464
Web Site: http://www.marubisi-pt.co.jp
Specialty Paper Mfr
N.A.I.C.S.: 322120

Otsu Paper Board Co., Ltd. (1)
1-15-15 Banba, Otsu, 520-0802, Shiga Prefecture, Japan
Tel.: (81) 775224171
Web Site: https://www.otsu-itagami.co.jp
Emp.: 163
Corrugated Board Mfr & Whslr
N.A.I.C.S.: 322211

Taisei Paper Corporation (1)
200-1 Kawasaki, Tsuyama, 708-0841, Okayama Prefecture, Japan
Tel.: (81) 868261114
Web Site: http://www.taisei-seisi.co.jp
Corrugated Board Mfr
N.A.I.C.S.: 322211

DAIOHS CORPORATION

Sapia Tower 14th FL 1-7-12 Marunouchi, Chiyoda-ku, Tokyo, 100-0005, Japan
Tel.: (81) 334385511
Web Site: http://www.daiohs.com
Year Founded: 1969
4653—(TKS)
Rev.: $278,619,440
Assets: $216,241,520
Liabilities: $95,280,240
Net Worth: $120,961,280
Earnings: $3,659,040
Emp.: 1,148
Fiscal Year-end: 03/31/22
Office Administrative Services
N.A.I.C.S.: 561110

Subsidiaries:

DAIOHS SINGAPORE PTE. LTD. (1)
Blk 211 Henderson Road 14-02, Singapore, 159552, Singapore
Tel.: (65) 6 264 2991
Web Site: https://www.daiohs.sg
Coffee Distr
N.A.I.C.S.: 424490

Daiohs Coffee Commercial Trade (Shanghai) Co., Ltd. (1)
Room 818 No 1 Building Chang An Building Chang An Road 1001, Zhabei District, Shanghai, 1001, China
Tel.: (86) 216 381 0190
Web Site: https://www.daiohs.cn
Tea Server Mfr
N.A.I.C.S.: 311920
Shinichi Ohkubo *(Pres & CEO)*

Daiohs Hong Kong Limited (1)
Room A2 & A7 5/F Mai Wah Ind'l Building 1-7 Wah Sing Street, Kwai Chung, China (Hong Kong)
Tel.: (852) 2 877 7229
Web Site: https://www.daiohs.com.hk
Coffee Distr
N.A.I.C.S.: 424490

Daiohs Korea Co. Ltd. (1)
4th FL Jinsung-bldg 157 Dongjakdaero, Dongjak-Gu, Seoul, Korea (South)
Tel.: (82) 2 508 1155
Web Site: https://www.daiohs.co.kr
Coffee Distr
N.A.I.C.S.: 424490

Taiwan Daiohs Co., Ltd. (1)
2F No 111 Sec 1 Keelung Rd, Xinyi Dist, Taipei, Taiwan
Tel.: (886) 22 753 5105
Web Site: https://www.daiohs.com.tw
Coffee Distr
N.A.I.C.S.: 424490

DAIOS PLASTICS S.A

12th KM Veria, 59200, Naousa, Greece
Tel.: (30) 2332042412
Web Site:
   https://www.daiosplastics.com
Year Founded: 1977
DAIOS—(ATH)
Sales Range: Less than $1 Million
Emp.: 139
Polyethylene Film Mfr
N.A.I.C.S.: 326130
Dimitrios A. Daios *(Bd of Dirs & VP)*

DAIREI CO., LTD.

2-3-1 Tsukishima Chuo-ku, Tokyo, 104-0052, Japan
Tel.: (81) 3 3536 1551
Web Site: http://www.dai-rei.co.jp
Year Founded: 1972
2883—(TKS)
Sales Range: $1-4.9 Billion
Emp.: 155
Frozen Food Mfr & Distr
N.A.I.C.S.: 311412
Osamu Saitou *(Pres)*

DAIRIBORD HOLDINGS LIMITED

1225 Rekayi Tangwena Rd, PO Box 2512, Harare, Zimbabwe
Tel.: (263) 4790801
Web Site: https://www.dairibord.com
Year Founded: 1952
DZL—(ZIM)
Rev.: $36,353,105
Assets: $16,810,413
Liabilities: $7,446,526
Net Worth: $9,363,887
Earnings: $167,298
Emp.: 434
Fiscal Year-end: 12/31/21
Holding Company
N.A.I.C.S.: 551112
Anthony S. Mandiwanza *(CEO-Grp)*

Subsidiaries:

Dairibord Malawi Limited (1)
Along Ali Hassan Mwinyi/Corner Makata Road Behind Kamuzu Stadium, Blantyre, Malawi
Tel.: (265) 1871450561
Dairy Product Mfr & Distr
N.A.I.C.S.: 311511
Theodora Nyamandi *(Mng Dir)*

Dairibord Zimbabwe (Private) Limited (1)
Rekayi Tangwena Avenue, Harare, Zimbabwe
Tel.: (263) 477903542
Web Site: https://www.dairibord.com
Dairy Product Mfr & Distr
N.A.I.C.S.: 311511

DAIRYGOLD CO-OPERATIVE SOCIETY LTD

Clonmel Road, Mitchellstown, P67 DD36, Co Cork, Ireland
Tel.: (353) 2524411
Web Site: http://www.dairygold.ie
Year Founded: 1990
Rev.: $1,135,654,222
Assets: $750,808,919
Liabilities: $364,324,566
Net Worth: $386,484,353
Earnings: $10,553,750
Emp.: 1,252
Fiscal Year-end: 12/31/18
Dairy Products Mfr
N.A.I.C.S.: 311514
Jim Woulfe *(CEO)*

Subsidiaries:

Agricola Properties Limited (1)
6 Thomas Davis Street West End, Mallow, Co Cork, Ireland
Tel.: (353) 25 24411
Web Site: http://www.dairygold.ie
Real Estate Development Services
N.A.I.C.S.: 531390

Co-Operative Animal Health Limited (1)
Indust Est, R93 W0D8, Tullow, Carlow, Ireland
Tel.: (353) 599151251
Web Site: http://www.cahl.ie
Sales Range: $25-49.9 Million
Emp.: 100
Animal Health Products Whslr; Owned 50% by Glanbia plc & 50% by Dairygold Co-op Society Limited
N.A.I.C.S.: 311119

Donald O'Sullivan *(Mng Dir)*

Dairygold Deutschland Handlesgesellschaft mbH (1)
An der Brunnenstube 25, 55120, Mainz, Germany
Tel.: (49) 6131 9687 10
Web Site: http://www.irish-land.de
Dairy Products Distr
N.A.I.C.S.: 424490

Dairygold Finance Limited (1)
Clonmel Rd, Mitchelstown, P67 DD36, Cork, Ireland (100%)
Tel.: (353) 2524411
Web Site: http://www.dairygold.ie
Sales Range: $100-124.9 Million
Emp.: 300
Cheese Mfr
N.A.I.C.S.: 311513

Dairygold Food Ingredients (France) SAS (1)
ZI du Chateau Rouge, 44522, Mesanger, France
Tel.: (33) 2 40967808
Dairy Products Distr
N.A.I.C.S.: 424490
Chris Harnett *(Gen Mgr)*

Dairygold Food Ingredients (UK) Limited (1)
Lancaster Fields, Crewe Gates Farm, Crewe, CW16FU, United Kingdom (100%)
Tel.: (44) 1270589136
Sales Range: $25-49.9 Million
Emp.: 150
Cheese Mfr
N.A.I.C.S.: 311513

Dairygold Food Ingredients Limited (1)
Clonmel Rd, Mitchelstown, P67 DD36, Cork, Ireland (100%)
Tel.: (353) 2524411
Web Site: http://www.dairygold.ie
Sales Range: $750-799.9 Million
Emp.: 1,000
Cheese Mfr
N.A.I.C.S.: 311513
Eugene O'Connor *(Mgr-Production)*

Dairygold Trading Limited (1)
Dairygold Trading, Mallow, Ireland (100%)
Tel.: (353) 2221204
Non-Durable Goods Whslr
N.A.I.C.S.: 424990

Dan Dairies (UK) Limited (1)
19 Astley Way, Swillington, Leeds, LS26 8XT, West Yorkshire, United Kingdom (100%)
Tel.: (44) 1132877788
Web Site: http://www.dairygold.co.uk
Sales Range: $25-49.9 Million
Emp.: 50
Dairy Product Whslr
N.A.I.C.S.: 424430

Diarygold Asia Limited (1)
Suite 1111 Rui Jin Mansion, 205 South Mao Ming Road Huang Pu District, Shanghai, China
Tel.: (86) 8516039999
Agriculture Business Services
N.A.I.C.S.: 423820

Diarygold Deutschland Handlesgesellschaft mbH (1)
An der Brunnenstube 25, 55120, Mainz, Germany
Tel.: (49) 613196870
Dairy Product Mfr & Distr
N.A.I.C.S.: 311514

Munster Cattle Breeding Group Limited (1)
Ballyvorisheen, Mallow, P51YF57, Co Cork, Ireland
Tel.: (353) 22 43228
Web Site: http://www.munsterai.ie
Cattle Breeding Services
N.A.I.C.S.: 112990
Pat Mulvehill *(Mng Dir)*

DAISAN CO., LTD.

Sun Marion NBF Tower 3rd Floor, 2-6-12 Minami Honmachi Chuo-ku, Osaka, 541-0054, Japan

Tel.: (81) 662438002
Web Site: https://www.daisan-g.co.jp
Year Founded: 1975
4750—(TKS)
Rev.: $68,790,270
Assets: $68,558,920
Liabilities: $33,168,980
Net Worth: $35,389,940
Earnings: $396,600
Emp.: 435
Fiscal Year-end: 04/30/24
Construction Equipment Mfr & Sales
N.A.I.C.S.: 333120
Taketoshi Fujita *(Pres)*

DAISEKI CO. LTD.

1-86 Funami-cho, Minato-ku, Nagoya,
455-8505, Aichi, Japan
Tel.: (81) 526116322
Web Site: https://www.daiseki.co.jp
9793—(TKS)
Rev.: $490,754,591
Assets: $770,285,332
Liabilities: $136,181,279
Net Worth: $634,104,052
Earnings: $74,581,709
Emp.: 1,215
Fiscal Year-end: 02/29/24
Environmental Service & Petroleum
Mfr
N.A.I.C.S.: 324110
Yoshihiro Miyachi *(Mng Exec Officer)*

Subsidiaries:

Daiseki Co. Ltd. - Chiba Works   **(1)**
23-8 Minami Sode, Sodegaura, 299-0268,
Chiba, Japan
Tel.: (81) 438628798
Web Site: https://www.daiseki.co.jp
Industrial Waste & Water Treatment Services
N.A.I.C.S.: 562211

Daiseki Co. Ltd. - Hokuriku Unit   **(1)**
631-1 Aikawa Shinmachi, Hakusan, 924-
0028, Ishikawa, Japan
Tel.: (81) 762756585
Emp.: 600
Industrial Wastes Treatment Services
N.A.I.C.S.: 221320
Hideki Hashira *(Pres)*

Daiseki Co. Ltd. - Kansai Unit   **(1)**
21-6 Minamifutami Futami-cho, Akashi, 674-
0093, Hyogo, Japan
Tel.: (81) 789491180
Web Site: http://www.daiseki.co.jp
Sales Range: $75-99.9 Million
Industrial Wastes Treatment Services
N.A.I.C.S.: 221320

Daiseki Co. Ltd. - Kanto Second
Plant   **(1)**
3-4 Sakae-cho, Sano, 327-0816, Tochigi,
Japan
Tel.: (81) 283228862
Web Site: http://www.daiseki.co.jp
Industrial Wastes Treatment Services
N.A.I.C.S.: 562211

Daiseki Co. Ltd. - Kanto Third
Plant   **(1)**
570-1 Nishiura-cho, Sano, 327-0814,
Tochigi, Japan
Tel.: (81) 283248006
Web Site: http://www.daiseki.co.jp
Sales Range: $75-99.9 Million
Industrial Wastes Treatment Services
N.A.I.C.S.: 562219

Daiseki Co. Ltd. - Kyushu Unit   **(1)**
4-6-1 Minamifutajima, Wakamatsu-ku, Kita-
kyushu, 808-0109, Kyushu, Japan
Tel.: (81) 937012016
Industrial Wastes Treatment Services
N.A.I.C.S.: 562219

Daiseki Co. Ltd. - Nagoya Unit   **(1)**
1-86 Funami-cho, Minato-ku, Nagoya, 455-
8505, Aichi, Japan
Tel.: (81) 526116321
Web Site: http://www.daiseki.co.jp
Sales Range: $500-549.9 Million
Industrial Wastes Treatment Services
N.A.I.C.S.: 221320

Daiseki Co. Ltd.- Kanto First
Plant   **(1)**
14-10 Sakae-machi, Sano, 327-0816,
Tochigi, Japan
Tel.: (81) 283248006
Web Site: http://www.daiseki.co.jp
Sales Range: $150-199.9 Million
Industrial Wastes Treatment Services
N.A.I.C.S.: 562219

Daiseki MCR Co., Ltd.   **(1)**
38-25 Hiraide Industrial Park, Utsunomiya,
321-0905, Tochigi, Japan
Tel.: (81) 286642228
Web Site: http://www.daiseki-mcr.com
Sales Range: $25-49.9 Million
Metal Smelting & Industrial Waste Process-
ing Services
N.A.I.C.S.: 562119

Hokuriku Daiseki Co., Ltd.   **(1)**
302-2 Higashi Takicho, Kanazawa, 920-
0377, Ishikawa, Japan
Tel.: (81) 762496363
Web Site: https://www.hokuriku-daiseki.com
Sales Range: $25-49.9 Million
Emp.: 16
Lubricating Oil Refining Services & Petro-
leum Products Sales
N.A.I.C.S.: 324110

System Kikou Co., Ltd.   **(1)**
MA Shibaura Bldg 1F 8-10 Shibaura
3-chome, Minato-ku, Tokyo, 108-0023, Ja-
pan
Tel.: (81) 35 730 4020
Web Site: https://system-kk-english.cts-
co.net
Emp.: 83
Industrial Waste Collector & Transporter
Services
N.A.I.C.S.: 562119
Junichi Inagaki *(Chm)*

DAISEKI ECO. SOLUTION CO., LTD.

8-18 Meizen-cho, Mizuho-ku, Na-
goya, 467-0852, Aichi, Japan
Tel.: (81) 528195310
Web Site: https://www.daiseki-
eco.co.jp
Year Founded: 1996
1712—(TKS)
Rev.: $171,223,500
Assets: $193,918,590
Liabilities: $68,609,930
Net Worth: $125,308,660
Earnings: $12,627,290
Emp.: 200
Fiscal Year-end: 02/29/24
Recyclable Material Collection Ser-
vices
N.A.I.C.S.: 562111
Ryuji Suzuki *(VP)*

Subsidiaries:

Green Arrows Central Co., Ltd.   **(1)**
213-7 Honowari Minami Shibata-cho, Tokai,
476-0001, Aichi, Japan
Tel.: (81) 5268935011
Waste Recycling Services
N.A.I.C.S.: 562920

DAISHI HOKUETSU FINAN-CIAL GROUP, INC.

1071-1 Higashiborimae-dori
7-bancho, Chuo-ku, Niigata, Niigata,
Japan
Tel.: (81) 252247111   JP
Web Site: https://www.dhfg.co.jp
Year Founded: 2018
7327—(TKS)
Rev.: $1,203,403,380
Assets: $73,622,239,490
Liabilities: $70,317,887,270
Net Worth: $3,304,352,220
Earnings: $495,750
Emp.: 3,463
Fiscal Year-end: 03/31/24
Commercial Banking Services
N.A.I.C.S.: 551112
Fujio Namiki *(Pres)*

Subsidiaries:

Daishi Hokuetsu Career Bridge, Co.,
Ltd.   **(1)**
Hokuetsu Daiichi Bldg 2nd Floor 2-25
Higashi-Odori1-Chome, Chuo-ku, Niigata,
Japan
Tel.: (81) 252825704
Web Site: https://k-agent.biz
N.A.I.C.S.: 561311

Daishi Hokuetsu Securities Co.,
Ltd.   **(1)**
2-3-10 Ote-Dori, Nagaoka, 940-0062, Japan
Tel.: (81) 25835211
Web Site: https://www.dh-sec.co.jp
N.A.I.C.S.: 524210

The Daishi Bank, Ltd.   **(1)**
1071-1 Higashiborimae-dori 7 bancho,
Chuo-ku, Niigata, 951-8066, Japan **(100%)**
Tel.: (81) 252224111
Web Site: http://www.daishi-bank.co.jp
Rev.: $883,036,080
Assets: $52,903,372,560
Liabilities: $49,918,573,680
Net Worth: $2,984,798,880
Earnings: $122,330,880
Emp.: 2,260
Fiscal Year-end: 03/31/2018
Banking Services
N.A.I.C.S.: 522110
Kouichi Masuda *(Auditor)*

Subsidiary (Domestic):

The Daishi Business Service Co.,
Ltd.   **(2)**
9-15 Shichikuyama 3-chome, Chuo-ku, Nii-
gata, 950 0914, Japan   **(100%)**
Tel.: (81) 252857221
Custody & Management of Housing Loan
Documents; Assessment of Secured Prop-
erty
N.A.I.C.S.: 523991

The Daishi Cash Business Co.,
Ltd.   **(2)**
1-20 Horinouchi Minami 3-chome, Niigata,
950 0982, Japan   **(100%)**
Tel.: (81) 252818181
Sales Range: $50-74.9 Million
Emp.: 100
Cash Settlements & Processing Services
N.A.I.C.S.: 522320

The Daishi Computer Service Co.,
Ltd.   **(2)**
1-17 Abumi 1-chome, Chuo-ku, Niigata,
950-0913, Japan   **(5%)**
Tel.: (81) 252224111
Web Site: https://www.daishi-dcs.co.jp
Emp.: 88
Computer Related Services
N.A.I.C.S.: 541511

The Daishi DC Card Co., Ltd.   **(2)**
Daishi Marine Building 2-1-18 Higashi
Odori, Chuo-ku, Niigata, 950-0087, Japan
Tel.: (81) 252501640
Web Site: https://www.daishidc.co.jp
Emp.: 15
Credit Card Services
N.A.I.C.S.: 522210
Junio Taneda *(Pres & Dir)*

Affiliate (Domestic):

The Daishi Guaranty Co., Ltd.   **(2)**
224-1 Honcho-dori 5-Bancho, Chuo-ku, Nii-
gata, 951 8067, Japan   **(5%)**
Tel.: (81) 252224111
Web Site: http://www.daishibank.co.jp
Credit Guarantee Business
N.A.I.C.S.: 522299

Subsidiary (Domestic):

The Daishi JCB Card Co., Ltd.   **(2)**
Daishi Marine Building 2-1-18 Higashi
Odori, Chuo-ku, Niigata, 950-0087,
Japan   **(5%)**
Tel.: (81) 252501550
Web Site: https://www.daishi-jcb.co.jp
Emp.: 43
Credit Card & Credit Guaranty Businesses
N.A.I.C.S.: 522210

The Daishi Lease Co., Ltd.   **(2)**

2 10 Akashi 2-chome, Niigata, 950 0084,
Japan   **(26%)**
Tel.: (81) 252433636
General Leasing Business
N.A.I.C.S.: 531110

The Daishi Staff Service Co.,
Ltd.   **(2)**
224-1 Honcho-dori 5-bancho, Chuo-ku, Nii-
gata, 951 8067, Japan   **(100%)**
Tel.: (81) 252281411
Sales Range: $150-199.9 Million
Emp.: 1,000
Temporary Staff for Banking Businesses
N.A.I.C.S.: 561320

The Daishi Hokuetsu Bank, Ltd.   **(1)**
1071-1 Higashiborimae-Dori 7-Bancho,
Chuo-ku, Niigata, 951-8066, Japan
Tel.: (81) 252224111
Web Site: https://www.dhbk.co.jp
N.A.I.C.S.: 522110
Kazuyoshi Hirokawa *(Chm)*

The Hokuetsu Bank, Ltd.   **(1)**
2-14 Otedori 2-chome, Nagaoka, 940-8650,
Niigata, Japan   **(100%)**
Tel.: (81) 258353111
Web Site: http://www.hokuetsubank.co.jp
Rev.: $432,393,840
Assets: $24,883,944,480
Liabilities: $23,816,843,760
Net Worth: $1,067,100,720
Earnings: $60,970,080
Emp.: 1,437
Fiscal Year-end: 03/31/2018
Commericial Banking
N.A.I.C.S.: 522110
Katsuya Sato *(Pres & CEO)*

Subsidiary (Domestic):

The Hokuetsu Leasing Co., Ltd.   **(2)**
5F Hokuetsu Higashi Build 1-9-20 Mihonbai,
Nagaoka, 940-0033, Niigata, Japan
Tel.: (81) 258 33 6511
Web Site: http://www.hokuetsulease.co.jp
Equipment Finance Leasing Services
N.A.I.C.S.: 525990
Nobuo Saito *(Dir)*

The Hokugin Economic Research
Institute Ltd   **(2)**
2-14 Otedori 2-chome, Nagaoka, 940 8650,
Niigata, Japan
Tel.: (81) 258353111
Research & Investigation & Provision of In-
formation on Socioeconomic Issues
N.A.I.C.S.: 541720

The Hokuetsu Card Co., Ltd.   **(1)**
Hokuetsu Higashi Building 4F 1-9-20 Kes-
ashiro, Nagaoka, Niigata, Japan
Tel.: (81) 258337011
Web Site: https://www.hokuetsucard.co.jp
N.A.I.C.S.: 522210
Katsutoshi Sakai *(Pres)*

DAISHIN BALANCE 4TH SPE-CIAL PURPOSE ACQUISITION CO LTD

343 Samil-daero Jung-gu, Seoul,
04538, Korea (South)
Tel.: (82) 27693921
Emp.: 1
Investment Services
N.A.I.C.S.: 523999
Im Byung-Wan *(CEO)*

DAISHIN CHEMICAL CO., LTD.

1-9-9 Shibadaimon, Minato-Ku, To-
kyo, 105-0012, Japan
Tel.: (81) 334324786
Web Site: https://www.daishin-
chemical.co.jp
Year Founded: 1952
46290—(TKS)
Sales Range: Less than $1 Million
Thinner Product Mfr
N.A.I.C.S.: 325510
Hisaki Sugiura *(Pres)*

DAISHIN INFORMATION & COMMUNICATIONS CO.,LTD.

6F hausD gasan FIRSTAR 169-16

Daishin Information & Communications
Co.,Ltd.—(Continued)

Gasan digital 2-ro, Geumcheon-gu,
Seoul, 08500, Korea (South)
Tel.: (82) 221075000
Web Site: https://www.dsic.co.kr
Year Founded: 1987
020180—(KRS)
Assets: $64,662,199
Liabilities: $42,937,435
Net Worth: $21,724,764
Earnings: ($36,751)
Emp.: 660
Fiscal Year-end: 03/31/23
Software Development Services
N.A.I.C.S.: 541511
Lee Jae-Won (CEO)

DAISHINKU CORP.

1389 Shinzaike Hiraoka-cho Ka-
kogawa, Hyogo, 675-0194, Japan
Tel.: (81) 794263211
Web Site: https://www.kds.info
Year Founded: 1959
6962—(TKS)
Rev.: $260,057,230
Assets: $601,933,040
Liabilities: $290,945,760
Net Worth: $310,987,280
Earnings: $12,400,360
Emp.: 3,278
Fiscal Year-end: 03/31/24
Electronic Components & Equipment
Mfr & Sales
N.A.I.C.S.: 334419
Sohei Hasegawa (Pres)

Subsidiaries:

DAISHINKU (AMERICA) CORP (1)
17800 Newhope St Ste F, Fountain Valley,
CA 92708
Tel.: (714) 641-2600
Web Site: http://www.kds.info
Quartz Crystal Mfr
N.A.I.C.S.: 334419
Yoko Kermane (Gen Mgr)

DAISHINKU (THAILAND) CO.,
LTD. (1)
2098 M Tower 2nd Floor Room 204-205
Sukhumvit Road, Phra Khanong Tai Sub-
district Phra Khanong District, Bangkok,
10260, Thailand
Tel.: (66) 23913291
Web Site: http://www.kds.info
Quartz Crystal Mfr
N.A.I.C.S.: 334419

Daishinku (Deutschland) GmbH (1)
Wiesenstrasse 70A2, 40549, Dusseldorf,
Germany
Tel.: (49) 2115065300
Web Site: http://www.kds.info.com
Sales Range: $25-49.9 Million
Emp.: 14
Other Electronic & Precision Equipment Re-
pair & Maintenance
N.A.I.C.S.: 811210
kenichi Hieida (Mng Dir)

Daishinku (Deutschland) GmbH (1)
Brook House 54a Cowley Mill Road, Ux-
bridge, UB8 2QE, Middlesex, United King-
dom
Tel.: (44) 2034054913
Electronic Components & Electronic Equip-
ment Mfr & Whslr
N.A.I.C.S.: 334419

Daishinku (HK) Ltd (1)
Units 1-2 22/F Futura Plaza 111-113 How
Ming Street, Kwun Tong, Kowloon, China
(Hong Kong)
Tel.: (852) 23302541
Web Site: http://www.kds.info
Emp.: 14
Other Electronic Parts & Equipment Whslr
N.A.I.C.S.: 423690
Rock Tsang Kwok Ming (Chm & CEO)

Daishinku (Singapore) Pte. Ltd (1)
12 Little Road 03- 01, Lian Cheong Industrial Building, Singapore, 536986, Singapore
Tel.: (65) 62867646

Web Site: http://www.kds.info
Sales Range: $25-49.9 Million
Emp.: 10
Other Electronic Component Mfr
N.A.I.C.S.: 334419

Daishinku Corp. - Kanzaki Plant (1)
629 Sawa Ichikawa-cho, Kanzaki, 679-
2336, Hyogo, Japan
Tel.: (81) 790281241
Synthetic Quartz Crystals Mfr
N.A.I.C.S.: 334419

Daishinku Corp. - Nishiwaki
Plant (1)
2082 Maesaka Kurodasho-cho, Nishiwaki,
679-0303, Hyogo, Japan
Tel.: (81) 795282491
Synthetic Quartz Crystals Mfr
N.A.I.C.S.: 334419

Daishinku Corp. - Tokushima Production Division (1)
1939-11 Ushinoshima Kamojima-cho, Yoshi-
nogawa, 776-0001, Tokushima, Japan
Tel.: (81) 883245161
Synthetic Quartz Crystals Mfr
N.A.I.C.S.: 334419

Daishinku Corp. - Tottori Production
Division (1)
7-3-21Wakabadai minami, Tottori, 689-1112,
Japan
Tel.: (81) 857524501
Web Site: http://www.kds.info
Quartz Crystal Mfr
N.A.I.C.S.: 334419

Harmony Electronics (DongGuan)
Co., Ltd. (1)
Building A1 Huazhi Industrial Park No 38
Jingfu East Road, Dalang Town, Dongguan,
Guangdong, China
Tel.: (86) 76981068668
Electronic Components & Electronic Equip-
ment Mfr
N.A.I.C.S.: 334419

Harmony Electronics (Thailand) Co
Ltd (1)
66 Moo 5 Kaongu-Beokprai Road T Beokp-
rai, A Banpong, Ratchaburi, 70110, Thailand
Web Site: http://www.hele.com.tw
Sales Range: $100-124.9 Million
Emp.: 450
Quartz Frequency Component Mfr
N.A.I.C.S.: 334419

Harmony Electronics Corp (1)
5F No 80 Zhouzi Street, Neihu, Taipei,
114064, Taiwan
Tel.: (886) 226588883
Web Site: https://www.hele.com.tw
Sales Range: $25-49.9 Million
Emp.: 32
Other Electronic Component Mfr
N.A.I.C.S.: 334419
Yang Juisyang (Gen Mgr)

Kyushu Daishinku Corp (1)
20013-2 Kawaminami Kawaminami-cho,
Koyu, 889-1301, Miyazaki, Japan
Tel.: (81) 983 47 0345
Web Site: http://www.kds.info
Tuning Fork Crystal Mfr
N.A.I.C.S.: 334419

Pt. Kds Indonesia (1)
Blok O-20 O-21, Kawasan Berikat MM2100
Industrial Town Cikarang Barat, Bekasi,
17520, Jawa Barat, Indonesia
Tel.: (62) 218980120
Web Site: https://www.ptkds.co.id
Other Electronic Parts & Equipment Mer-
chant Whslr
N.A.I.C.S.: 423690

Shanghai Daishinku International
Trading Co., Ltd (1)
906 1 No 641 Tianshan Road, Shanghai,
200336, China
Tel.: (86) 2162368701
Web Site: http://www.kds.info
Sales Range: $50-74.9 Million
Emp.: 60
Other Electronic Parts & Equipment Mer-
chant Whslr
N.A.I.C.S.: 423690

Tianjin KDS Corp. (1)

No 8 Fuyuan Road, Wuqing Development
Zone, Tianjin, 301700, China
Tel.: (86) 2260686800
Electronic Components & Electronic Equip-
ment Mfr
N.A.I.C.S.: 334419

DAISHO CO., LTD.

1-17-3 Kamezawa, Sumida-ku, To-
kyo, 130-0014, Japan
Tel.: (81) 336269321
Web Site: https://www.daisho.co.jp
Year Founded: 1966
2816—(TKS)
Sales Range: Less than $1 Million
Food Product Mfr & Whslr
N.A.I.C.S.: 311941
Yosuke Matsumoto (Chm & CEO)

Subsidiaries:

DAISHO Co., Ltd. - Fukuoka
Factory (1)
1-11-17 Matsuda, Higashi-ku, Fukuoka,
812-0064, Japan
Tel.: (81) 92 611 9321
Web Site: https://www.daisho.co.jp
Food Products Mfr
N.A.I.C.S.: 311941

DAISHO Co., Ltd. - Fukuoka Second
Factory (1)
1-9-30 Matsuda, Higashi-ku, Fukuoka, 812-
0064, Japan
Tel.: (81) 92 624 1511
Food Products Mfr
N.A.I.C.S.: 311941

DAISHO Co., Ltd. - Kanto
Factory (1)
1689 Saigochi, Omitama, 319-0102, Ibaraki,
Japan
Tel.: (81) 299 48 2461
Food Products Mfr
N.A.I.C.S.: 311941

DAISHO Co., Ltd. - Kyushu
Factory (1)
3034 Yamada Hisayama, Kasuya-gun, Fu-
kuoka, 811-2502, Japan
Tel.: (81) 92 962 9321
Food Products Mfr
N.A.I.C.S.: 311941

DAISHO MICROLINE HOLD-
INGS LIMITED

Unit 303A 3rd Floor Shui Hing Cen-
tre, 13 Sheung Yuet Road, Kowloon,
China (Hong Kong)
Tel.: (852) 2953 0333   BM
Web Site: http://www.daisho-
microline.com
Sales Range: $25-49.9 Million
Emp.: 689
Holding Company; Printed Circuit
Board Mfr & Sales
N.A.I.C.S.: 551112
Harry Sik Ming Chan (Chm)

DAISO SANGYO CO., LTD.

1-4-14 Higashi Saijoyoshi, Hiroshima,
739-8501, Hiroshima, Japan   JP
Web Site: http://www.daiso-
sangyo.co.jp
Year Founded: 1977
All Other Miscellaneous Store Retail-
ers
N.A.I.C.S.: 459999
Seiji Yano (Pres)

DAISUE CONSTRUCTION CO.,
LTD.

2-5-28 Kyutarocho, Chuo-ku, Osaka,
541-0056, Japan
Tel.: (81) 661217121
Web Site: https://www.daisue.co.jp
Year Founded: 1947
1814—(TKS)
Rev.: $514,357,150
Assets: $390,697,270
Liabilities: $241,635,160

Net Worth: $149,062,110
Earnings: $8,163,350
Emp.: 595
Fiscal Year-end: 03/31/24
Construction Engineering Services
N.A.I.C.S.: 541330
Mitsuaki Hidaka (Chm)

DAISUI CO., LTD.

Noda, Fukushima-ku, Osaka, 553-
8550, Japan
Tel.: (81) 664693000
Web Site: https://www.daisui.co.jp
Year Founded: 1939
7538—(TKS)
Rev.: $650,820,600
Assets: $163,564,450
Liabilities: $97,186,830
Net Worth: $66,377,620
Earnings: $6,669,490
Emp.: 424
Fiscal Year-end: 03/31/24
Marine Product Whslr
N.A.I.C.S.: 332510
Eiichiro Yamahashi (Pres & Chm)

DAISY GROUP LIMITED

Daisy House Unit 16 & 20 Lindred
Road Lomeshaye Industrial Estate,
Nelson, BB9 5SR, Lancashire, United
Kingdom
Tel.: (44) 1282882421   UK
Web Site: http://www.daisygroup.com
Year Founded: 2000
Sales Range: $550-599.9 Million
Emp.: 1,389
Holding Company; Commercial Tele-
communications Products & Services
N.A.I.C.S.: 551112
Matthew Riley (Founder)

Subsidiaries:

Daisy Communications Ltd. (1)
Daisy House Lindred Road Business Park,
Nelson, BB9 5SR, Lancs, United Kingdom
Tel.: (44) 1282 882 421
Web Site: http://www.daisygroupplc.com
Wireless Telecommunications Reseller
N.A.I.C.S.: 517121
Kate O'Brien (Mktg Dir)

Subsidiary (Domestic):

Anglia Telecom Centres Limited (2)
Communications House 166 Handford
Road, Ipswich, IP1 2BH, United Kingdom
Tel.: (44) 1473 382 000
Web Site: http://www.daisydistribution.com
Emp.: 40
Mobile Telecommunications Distr
N.A.I.C.S.: 517121
Dave McGinn (Mng Dir)

Daisy Corporate Services
Limited (2)
Daisy House Unit 16 & 20, Lomeshaye In-
dustrial Estate, Nelson, BB9 5SR, Lancs,
United Kingdom
Tel.: (44) 1282 882 421
Web Site: http://www.daisygroup.com
Information Communications Technology
Services
N.A.I.C.S.: 541990

Daisy Wholesale Limited (2)
Mitchell House Southampton Road, Eastle-
igh, SO50 9XD, Hampshire, United King-
dom
Tel.: (44) 1282 882 421
Web Site: http://www.daisywholesale.com
Wireless Telecommunications Whslr
N.A.I.C.S.: 517121
Terry O'Brien (Mng Dir)

Daisy Worldwide Limited (2)
Daisy House Lindred Road Business Park,
Nelson, BB9 5SR, Lancs, United Kingdom
Tel.: (44) 344 241 2000
Web Site: http://www.daisyworldweldltd.com
Wireless Telecommunications Retailer
N.A.I.C.S.: 517121
Andrew Fryatt (Mng Dir)

Daisy Corporate Services Trading Limited (1)
Daisy House Unit 16 & 20 Lindred Road, Lomeshaye Industrial Estate, Nelson, BB9 5SR, Lancs, United Kingdom
Tel.: (44) 1282 882 421
Web Site: http://daisygroup.com
Sales Range: $150-199.9 Million
Telecommunication Servicesb
N.A.I.C.S.: 517121
Steve Smith *(CFO & Member-Exec Bd)*

Subsidiary (Domestic):

Aurora Kendrick James Limited (2)
7 Sherwood House Walderslade Centre, Chatham, ME5 9UD, Kent, United Kingdom
Tel.: (44) 1634673800
Web Site: http://www.aurora-billing.co.uk
Emp.: 200
Billing Software Solutions
N.A.I.C.S.: 518210
Derek Watson *(Mng Dir)*

Ecsc Group PLC (2)
28 Campus Road Listerhills Science Park, Bradford, BD7 1HR, United Kingdom
Tel.: (44) 1274736223
Web Site: http://www.ecsc.co.uk
Rev.: $8,341,832
Assets: $4,714,004
Liabilities: $4,413,948
Net Worth: $300,056
Earnings: ($715,518)
Emp.: 87
Fiscal Year-end: 12/31/2021
Information Technology Management Services
N.A.I.C.S.: 541512
Lucy Sharp *(COO)*

O-bit Telecom Limited (1)
2 Fagnall Farm Barns Fagnall Lane, Winchmore Hill, Loudwater, HP7 0PG, Buckinghamshire, United Kingdom
Tel.: (44) 8008 494 949
Emp.: 200
Telecommunications Products & Services
N.A.I.C.S.: 517810
David Breith *(CEO)*

Servassure Limited (1)
Unit 4 Cramond Park, Lovet Road, Harlow, CM19 5TF, Essex, United Kingdom
Tel.: (44) 8700843030
Web Site: http://www.servassure.co.uk
Sales Range: $25-49.9 Million
Emp.: 50
Information & Communication Technology Services
N.A.I.C.S.: 541990
Jamie Pailthorpe *(Ops Mgr)*

DAISY WHOLESALE LIMITED
4th Floor Eastleigh House, Upper Market Street, Eastleigh, SO50 9RD, Hants, United Kingdom
Tel.: (44) 3301001233   UK
Web Site:
http://www.daisywholesale.com
Year Founded: 2001
Sales Range: $50-74.9 Million
Emp.: 49
Telecommunications Connectivity & Hosting Solutions
N.A.I.C.S.: 517810
Richard Jay *(CEO)*

DAISYO CORPORATION
1 Chome1-10 Omori City Building Omorikita, Ota-ku, Tokyo, 143-0016, Japan
Tel.: (81) 337632181
Web Site: https://www.daisyo.co.jp
Year Founded: 1971
9979—(TKS)
Rev.: $314,644,920
Assets: $208,519,280
Liabilities: $143,818,840
Net Worth: $64,700,440
Earnings: $8,291,260
Emp.: 1,328
Fiscal Year-end: 08/31/24
Restaurant Operators
N.A.I.C.S.: 722511

Kouichi Ishimura *(Sr Exec Mng Dir)*
Subsidiaries:

Yonekawa Suisan Corporation (1)
3F DS L Headquarters Haneda 6-1-27 Higashikojidani, Ota-ku, Tokyo, 144-0033, Japan
Tel.: (81) 364236376
Web Site: https://www.yonekawa-suisan.co.jp
Emp.: 43
Food Products Distr
N.A.I.C.S.: 424490

DAITO CHEMIX CORPORATION
3-1-7 Matta-Omiya, Tsurumi-ku, Osaka, 538-0031, Japan
Tel.: (81) 669119310
Web Site:
https://www.daitochemix.co.jp
Year Founded: 1938
4366—(TKS)
Rev.: $104,510,710
Assets: $165,117,800
Liabilities: $69,034,840
Net Worth: $96,082,960
Earnings: ($6,643,050)
Emp.: 243
Fiscal Year-end: 03/31/24
Chemical Products Mfr
N.A.I.C.S.: 325992
Shuichi Minami *(Mng Exec Officer & Mng Exec Officer)*

Subsidiaries:

Daito Chemix Corporation - Fukui Plant (1)
31-118 Ishibashi-cho, Fukui, 910-3137, Japan
Tel.: (81) 776851841
Electronic Materials Mfr
N.A.I.C.S.: 334419

Daito Chemix Corporation - Shizuoka Plant (1)
3110 Hamano, Kakegawa, 437-1424, Shizuoka, Japan
Tel.: (81) 537722888
Electronic Materials Mfr
N.A.I.C.S.: 334419

Japan Ecology Corporation (1)
2-2-40 Katamachi 603 Daide Building, Osaka, 534-0025, Japan
Tel.: (81) 66 881 0251
Web Site: https://www.nihon-ecology.co.jp
Emp.: 45
Waste Treatment Services
N.A.I.C.S.: 562219

DAITO KOUN CO., LTD.
7th Floor Tamachi First Building 468 Shibaura, Minato-Ku, Tokyo, 108-0023, Japan
Tel.: (81) 354769701
Web Site: https://www.daito-koun.co.jp
Year Founded: 1957
9367—(TKS)
Rev.: $106,097,110
Assets: $97,404,960
Liabilities: $36,824,310
Net Worth: $60,580,650
Earnings: $3,529,740
Emp.: 417
Fiscal Year-end: 03/31/24
Logistics Consulting Servies
N.A.I.C.S.: 541614

DAITO ME HOLDINGS CO., LTD.
190 Elgin Avenue, Grand Cayman, Georgetown, KY1-9005, Cayman Islands
Tel.: (345) 227133220
Year Founded: 1957
8455—(TPE)
Rev.: $45,443,361
Assets: $50,410,374

Liabilities: $29,545,165
Net Worth: $20,865,210
Earnings: ($341,838)
Fiscal Year-end: 12/31/22
Electronic Components Distr
N.A.I.C.S.: 423690
Okuyama One-Inch Mage *(Pres)*

DAITO PHARMACEUTICAL CO., LTD.
326 Yokamachi, Toyama, 939-8567, Toyama, Japan
Tel.: (81) 764215665
Web Site: https://www.daitonet.co.jp
Year Founded: 1942
4577—(TKS)
Rev.: $309,975,950
Assets: $513,649,880
Liabilities: $168,178,230
Net Worth: $345,471,650
Earnings: $21,779,950
Emp.: 821
Fiscal Year-end: 05/31/24
Pharmaceuticals Mfr
N.A.I.C.S.: 325412
Yasunobu Otsuga *(Pres & CEO)*

Subsidiaries:

Daito Pharmaceutical (China) Co., Ltd. (1)
Economy and Technology Development Zone, Hefei, 230601, Anhui, China
Tel.: (86) 55163822206
Pharmaceutical Product Mfr & Retailer
N.A.I.C.S.: 325412

Daito Pharmaceuticals America, Inc. (1)
707 Skokie Blvd Ste 210, Northbrook, IL 60062
Tel.: (847) 205-0800
Pharmaceutical Product Mfr & Retailer
N.A.I.C.S.: 325412

DAITO TRUST CONSTRUCTION CO., LTD.
2-16-1 Konan, Minato-ku, Tokyo, 108-8211, Japan
Tel.: (81) 367189111   JP
Web Site: https://www.kentaku.co.jp
Year Founded: 1974
DITTF—(OTCIQ)
Rev.: $11,444,996,870
Assets: $7,139,256,090
Liabilities: $4,456,918,090
Net Worth: $2,682,338,000
Earnings: $493,667,850
Emp.: 8,172
Fiscal Year-end: 03/31/24
Land Developer Specializing in Commerical & Residential Use Properties
N.A.I.C.S.: 237210
Takeshi Nakagawa *(Gen Mgr-Bus Strategy Dept)*

Subsidiaries:

Care Partner Co Ltd (1)
6-20-14 Minamioi, Shinagawa-ku, Tokyo, 140-0013, Japan
Tel.: (81) 36 404 8111
Web Site: https://www.care-partner.com
Sales Range: $10-24.9 Million
Emp.: 2,855
Nursing Homes Operation Services
N.A.I.C.S.: 623110

Daito Asia Development (Malaysia) Sdn. Bhd. (1)
7th Floor Le Meridien KL No 2 Jalan Stesen Sentral, 50480, Kuala Lumpur, Malaysia
Tel.: (60) 322735387
Emp.: 200
Hotel Operating Services
N.A.I.C.S.: 721110
Michael Delargy *(Gen Mgr)*

Daito Building Management Co Ltd (1)
Konan 2-16-1, Minato-ku Shinagawa, Tokyo, 108-8211, Japan
Tel.: (81) 3 6718 9111

Web Site: http://www.kentaku.co.jp
Sales Range: $1-9.9 Million
Emp.: 420
Building Management & Rental Services
N.A.I.C.S.: 541618

Daito Construction Co., Ltd. (1)
7F NS3 Building 2-51-3, Akabane Kita-ku, Tokyo, 115-0045, Japan
Tel.: (81) 359393500
Web Site: http://www.daito-j.com
Emp.: 92
Building Construction of Condominiums & Apartments
N.A.I.C.S.: 236116

Daito Corporate Service Co., Ltd. (1)
Higashi-Shinagawa 2-2-4 Tennozu First Tower, Shinagawa-ku, Tokyo, 140-0002, Japan
Tel.: (81) 367189300
Web Site: https://www.daito-copo.com
N.A.I.C.S.: 532412
Kazunori Fukuda *(Pres)*

Daito Finance Co., Ltd. (1)
22nd Floor Shinagawa East One Tower 1-16-1 Konan, Minato-ku, Tokyo, 108-0075, Japan
Tel.: (81) 367189090
Web Site: https://www.daitofinance.com
N.A.I.C.S.: 532412
Yasuhiro Fujisawa *(CEO)*

Daito Gas Partner Corporation (1)
2nd Floor East Court II 608-2 Kyozuka, Urasoe, 901-2111, Okinawa, Japan
Tel.: (81) 988797611
N.A.I.C.S.: 424710
Masaki Ikeda *(Pres)*

Daito Kentaku Partners Co., Ltd. (1)
Shinagawa East One Tower 1-16-1 Konan 2-Chome, Minato-ku, Tokyo, 108-0075, Japan
Tel.: (81) 367189102
N.A.I.C.S.: 561730
Yoshihiro Mori *(Pres)*

Daito Mirai Trust Co., Ltd. (1)
2-16-1 Konan, Minato-ku, Tokyo, 108-0075, Japan
Tel.: (81) 367189290
Web Site: https://www.daitomirai.com
Real Estate Trust Services
N.A.I.C.S.: 525920

Daito Steel Co., Ltd. (1)
901-1 Hamatome, Yaizu, 425-0012, Shizuoka, Japan
Tel.: (81) 546262700
Web Site: http://www.daito-steel.com
Emp.: 37
Steel Materials Distr
N.A.I.C.S.: 423390

Gaspal Co Ltd (1)
2-2-24 Higashi-Shinagawa Tennozu Central Tower 11th floor, Shinagawa-ku, Tokyo, 140-0002, Japan
Tel.: (81) 36 718 9080
Web Site: https://www.gas-pal.com
Sales Range: $125-149.9 Million
Emp.: 993
Petroleum Distr
N.A.I.C.S.: 457210

Gaspal Kyushu Corporation (1)
1-1-29 Takasago 1-chome KF Building 2nd Floor, Chuo-ku, Fukuoka, 810-0011, Japan
Tel.: (81) 925230661
Gas Distr
N.A.I.C.S.: 221210

House Leave Co., Ltd. (1)
2-16-1 Konan, Minato-ku, Tokyo, 108-0075, Japan
Tel.: (81) 120753010
Web Site: https://www.house-leave.com
N.A.I.C.S.: 561730
Chihiro Bushi *(CEO)*

House Payment Co., Ltd. (1)
2-16-1 Konan, Minato-ku Shinagawa East One Tower, Tokyo, 108-0075, Japan
Tel.: (81) 36719266
Web Site: https://www.housepayment.co.jp
N.A.I.C.S.: 522210
Yoki Matsumoto *(Pres)*

Daito Trust Construction Co., Ltd.—(Continued)

Housecom Corporation (1)
2-16-1 Konan Shinagawa East One Tower 9th floor, Minato-ku, Tokyo, 108-0075, Japan
Tel.: (81) 367176900
Web Site: https://www.housecom.co.jp
Rev.: $89,426,690
Assets: $71,262,410
Liabilities: $23,406,010
Net Worth: $47,856,400
Earnings: $2,710,100
Fiscal Year-end: 03/31/2024
Real Estate Brokerage & Rental Management Services
N.A.I.C.S.: 531210
Tamura Ho (Pres & CEO)

Housecom Technologies Co., Ltd. (1)
9F Shinagawa East One Tower 2-16-1 Konan, Minato-ku, Tokyo, 108-0075, Japan
Tel.: (81) 367176922
Web Site: https://technologies.housecom.co.jp
Digital Marketing Services
N.A.I.C.S.: 541613

Invalance Ltd. (1)
17th Floor Shinjuku Maynds Tower 2-1-1 Yoyogi, Shibuya-ku, Tokyo, 151-0053, Japan
Tel.: (81) 353027177
Web Site: https://www.invalance.jp
Real Estate Development Services
N.A.I.C.S.: 531390

JU-SEE Publishing Co., Ltd. (1)
Kounan 2 16 1, Minato ku Shinagawa, 108-8211, Tokyo, Japan
Tel.: (81) 3 6718 9111
Web Site: http://www.jsee.com
Sales Range: $25-49.9 Million
Emp.: 12
Publisher of Rental Apartment Information Magazine
N.A.I.C.S.: 513199
Koichi Ebihara (Gen Mgr & Exec Officer)

SHIMA Co., Ltd. (1)
73-2 Gongeshita Shidoke, Haramachi-ku Fukushima, Minamisoma, 975-0042, Japan
Tel.: (81) 244221555
Web Site: https://goodtruck.jp
Emp.: 206
Machinery Spare Parts Mfr & Distr.
N.A.I.C.S.: 333248

DAITOBO CO., LTD.
Nihonbashi Honmachi 1-6-1, Chuo-ku, Tokyo, 103-0023, Nihonbashi, Japan
Tel.: (81) 362626565
Web Site: https://www.daitobo.co.jp
Year Founded: 1896
3202—(TKS)
Rev.: $26,658,130
Assets: $134,506,890
Liabilities: $101,886,540
Net Worth: $32,620,350
Earnings: $1,011,330
Fiscal Year-end: 03/31/24
Apparel Product Mfr & Distr
N.A.I.C.S.: 315250
Kazuhiro Yamauchi (Co-Pres & CEO)

DAITRON CO., LTD.
6-11 Miyahara 4-chome, Yodogawa-ku, Osaka, 532-0003, Japan
Tel.: (81) 663967731
Web Site: https://www.daitron.co.jp
Year Founded: 1952
7609—(TKS)
Rev.: $653,386,040
Assets: $480,616,920
Liabilities: $271,809,330
Net Worth: $208,807,590
Earnings: $28,459,260
Emp.: 1,003
Fiscal Year-end: 12/31/23
Electronic Components & Semiconductor Equipment Mfr, Sales, Importer & Exporter
N.A.I.C.S.: 334413

Isayuki Mae (Pres & COO)

Subsidiaries:

Daito Denso Co., Ltd. (1)
689-1 Nogami Iseochi, Ritto, 520-3044, Shiga, Japan
Tel.: (81) 775537600
Web Site: http://www.daitodenso.co.jp
Electronic Products Mfr & Sales
N.A.I.C.S.: 423690

Daito Electron Co., Ltd. - EM Machida Factory (1)
2-5-6 Oyamagaoka 2 Chome, Machida-City, Tokyo, 194-0215, Japan
Tel.: (81) 42 798 5161
Web Site: http://www.daitron.co.jp
Electronic Components Mfr
N.A.I.C.S.: 334419

Daito Electron Co., Ltd. - Machida Factory (1)
2-5-6 Oyamagaoka 2-chome, Machida, 194-0215, Tokyo, Japan
Tel.: (81) 427985161
Sales Range: $25-49.9 Million
Emp.: 30
Power Supplies Mfr
N.A.I.C.S.: 335999

Daito-Tec Co., Ltd. (1)
4-6-11 Miyahara, Yodogawa-ku, Osaka, 532-0003, Japan
Tel.: (81) 663967731
Industrial Cable Harnesses Mfr
N.A.I.C.S.: 335931

Daitron (H.K.) Co., Ltd. (1)
Room 806-807 8/F 9 Wing Hong Street, Cheung Sha Wan, Kowloon, China (Hong Kong) (100%)
Tel.: (852) 28380682
Web Site: https://www.daitron.com.hk
Semiconductor & Electronic Components & Equipment Mfr, Importer, Exporter & Sales
N.A.I.C.S.: 334413

Daitron (Korea) Co., Ltd. (1)
7th Floor EnC Venture Dream Tower 6 Cha 41 Digital-Ro 31-gil, Guro-gu, Seoul, 08375, Korea (South)
Tel.: (82) 69103337
Web Site: https://www.daitron.co.kr
Sales Range: $100-124.9 Million
Emp.: 372
Software Development & Electronic Equipment Sales
N.A.I.C.S.: 541511

Daitron (Malaysia) Sdn. Bhd. (1)
Suite 808 8th Floor Central Tower Wisma Consplant 1 No 2, Jalan SS16 4, 47500, Subang Jaya, Selangor Darul Ehsan, Malaysia (100%)
Tel.: (60) 358805300
Web Site: http://www.daitron.com.my
Sales Range: $25-49.9 Million
Emp.: 11
Semiconductor & Electronic Equipment & Components Mfr, Importer, Exporte & Sales
N.A.I.C.S.: 334413

Daitron (Netherlands) B.V. (1)
High Tech Campus 5 5 053-5 055, 5656AE, Eindhoven, Netherlands
Tel.: (31) 402180085
Electronic Equipment Mfr & Distr
N.A.I.C.S.: 333413

Daitron (Shanghai) Co., Ltd. (1)
Tel.: (86) 2160932193
Web Site: http://www.daitron.com.cn
Electronic Components Mfr & Distr
N.A.I.C.S.: 334419

Daitron (Shenzhen) Co., Ltd. (1)
Room 1617 16/F Pacific Commercial Trade Building No 4028 Jiabin Road, Luohu District, Shenzhen, 518010, China
Tel.: (86) 75525904712
Electronic Equipment Distr
N.A.I.C.S.: 423690

Daitron (Taiwan) Co., Ltd. (1)
13F No 80 Section 2 Zhongxiao East Road, Zhongzheng District, Taipei, 10050, Taiwan
Tel.: (886) 223945134
Electronic Equipment Distr
N.A.I.C.S.: 423690

Daitron (Thailand) Co., Ltd. (1)
75/105 38th floor Ocean Tower 2 Soi Sukhumvit 19 Sukhumvit Road, Khlong Toey Nua Wattana, Bangkok, 10110, Thailand
Tel.: (66) 26617265
Web Site: https://th.daitron.net
Electronic Components Sales & Maintenance Services
N.A.I.C.S.: 423690

Daitron Inc. (1)
9720 SW Hillman Ct Ste 805, Wilsonville, OR 97070
Tel.: (503) 682-7560
Web Site: http://www.daitron.com
Sales Range: $25-49.9 Million
Emp.: 14
Electronic Component Mfr & Distr
N.A.I.C.S.: 334419

Daitron Technology Co., Ltd. (1)
1-1-3 Shimamachi Chuo-ku, Osaka, 540-0034, Japan (100%)
Tel.: (81) 669431911
Web Site: http://www.dtc-daitron.com
Sales Range: $50-74.9 Million
Emp.: 127
Semiconductor Manufacturing & Inspection Equipment & water Pressure-Resistant Connectors Mfr & Sales
N.A.I.C.S.: 333242

DAIUN CO., LTD.
1-3 4-chome Kyutaroumachi, Chuou-ku, Osaka, 541-0056, Japan
Tel.: (81) 665324101
Web Site: https://www.daiunex.co.jp
Year Founded: 1945
9363—(TKS)
Sales Range: $50-74.9 Million
Marine Transportation Services
N.A.I.C.S.: 488320
Kenichi Takahashi (Pres)

DAIWA CAN COMPANY
9F JP Tower 2-7-2 Marunouchi, Chiyoda-ku, Tokyo, 100-7009, Japan
Tel.: (81) 362129722
Web Site: http://www.daiwa-can.com
Year Founded: 1939
Sales Range: $1-4.9 Billion
Emp.: 1,330
Metal & Plastic Cans Mfr
N.A.I.C.S.: 332431
Hirohisa Yamaguchi (Pres)

Subsidiaries:

DS Containers Inc. (1)
1789 Hubbard Ave, Batavia, IL 60510
Tel.: (630) 406-9600
Web Site: http://www.dscontainers.com
Can Mfr
N.A.I.C.S.: 332431

Daiwa Yoki Co., Ltd. (1)
5-10 Tsukubamachi, Isahaya, Nagasaki, 854-0065, Japan
Tel.: (81) 957251211
Can Distr
N.A.I.C.S.: 423840

Fountain Can Corporation (1)
12F Huei-Fong Bldg No27 Chung-Shan N Rd Sec 3, Taipei, Taiwan
Tel.: (886) 225972192
Web Site: http://www.fountaincan.com.tw
Can Distr
N.A.I.C.S.: 423840

Fountain Can Corporation Tainan Factory (1)
1 Industrial South Road Kuantien Industrial Area, Kuantien, T'ainan, Taiwan
Tel.: (886) 66984541
Can Mfr
N.A.I.C.S.: 332431

Hangzhou Dahui Foam Pump Company Ltd (1)
Nanxing Village Xingqiao Street, Yuhang District, Hangzhou, Zhejiang, China
Tel.: (86) 57188267221
Can Distr
N.A.I.C.S.: 423840

Shanghai Daiwa Can Trading Company (1)
Room No 1506,15F Xietai Center Bldg No 88 Zunyi South Road, Changning District, Shanghai, China
Tel.: (86) 2161257645
Can Distr
N.A.I.C.S.: 423840

DAIWA CO., LTD.
5F Katamachi Kirara 2-2-5 Katamachi, Kanazawa, 920-8561, Ishikawa, Japan
Tel.: (81) 762201111
Web Site: https://www.daiwa-dp.co.jp
Year Founded: 1943
8247—(TKS)
Rev.: $117,247,330
Assets: $195,698,180
Liabilities: $163,913,710
Net Worth: $31,784,470
Earnings: $4,622,680
Fiscal Year-end: 02/29/24
Departmental Store Operator
N.A.I.C.S.: 455110
Jiro Miya (Pres & CEO)

DAIWA COMPUTER CO., LTD.
36-18 Wakamatsucho, Takatsuki, 569-0054, Osaka, Japan
Tel.: (81) 726762221
Web Site: https://www.daiwa-computer.co.jp
Year Founded: 1977
3816—(TKS)
Rev.: $20,470,020
Assets: $38,072,620
Liabilities: $6,344,400
Net Worth: $31,728,220
Earnings: $2,127,240
Emp.: 180
Fiscal Year-end: 07/31/24
Software Development Services
N.A.I.C.S.: 541511
Kenji Nakamura (Pres)

Subsidiaries:

fit.com Co., Ltd. (1)
2-25-7 Shirokanedai, Minato-ku, Tokyo, 108-0071, Japan
Tel.: (81) 5031627281
Information Technology Consulting Services
N.A.I.C.S.: 541512

DAIWA CYCLE CO., LTD.
5F Esaka Soliton Building 1-12-38 Esaka-cho, Osaka, 564-0063, Japan
Tel.: (81) 663803338
Web Site: https://www.daiwa-cycle.co.jp
Year Founded: 1980
5888—(TKS)
Emp.: 797
Bicycle Mfr & Distr
N.A.I.C.S.: 336991
Yoshihiro Wakumoto (Pres & CEO)

DAIWA HEAVY INDUSTRY CO., LTD.
1-21-23 Kabe, Asakita, Hiroshima, 731-0221, Japan
Tel.: (81) 828142101
Web Site: https://www.daiwajuko.co.jp
Year Founded: 1831
5610—(TKS)
Industrial Machinery Mfr
N.A.I.C.S.: 333998
Hironori Tanaka (Pres)

DAIWA HOUSE INDUSTRY CO., LTD.
3-3-5 Umeda, Kita-ku, Osaka, 530-8241, Japan
Tel.: (81) 352142813
Web Site: https://www.daiwahouse.co.jp

JP

Year Founded: 1947
1925—(TKS)
Rev.: $34,391,294,590
Assets: $43,187,895,810
Liabilities: $26,505,828,990
Net Worth: $16,682,066,820
Earnings: $1,974,750,720
Emp.: 48,483
Fiscal Year-end: 03/31/24
Real Estate Manangement Services
N.A.I.C.S.: 551112
Tamio Ishibashi *(Exec VP-Info Sys)*

Subsidiaries:

Baoye Daiwa Industrialized House
Manufacturing Co., Ltd.   **(1)**
No 567Shanyin West Road, Keqiao, Shaox-
ing, Zhejiang, China
Tel.: (86) 57584889737
Web Site: https://www.baoyedaiwa.com
N.A.I.C.S.: 333120
Yukikazu Kataoka *(Chm)*

Cosmos Initia Co., Ltd.   **(1)**
Shintamachi Bldg Shiba 5-34-6, Minato-ku,
Tokyo, 108-8416, Japan   **(63.25%)**
Tel.: (81) 335711111
Web Site: https://www.cigr.co.jp
Rev.: $823,526,680
Assets: $1,145,731,130
Liabilities: $844,301,910
Net Worth: $301,429,220
Earnings: $28,277,580
Emp.: 612
Fiscal Year-end: 03/31/2024
Real Estate Brokerage
N.A.I.C.S.: 531210
Koji Kashiwagi *(Sr Mng Officer)*

Subsidiary (Non-US):

Cosmos Australia Pty Ltd   **(2)**
Unit 6 123 Buxton St North, Adelaide, 5006,
SA, Australia
Tel.: (61) 493213263
Web Site: https://www.cosmos.com.au
N.A.I.C.S.: 531390

Subsidiary (Domestic):

Cosmos Hotel Management Co.,
Ltd.   **(2)**
Shintamachi Bldg Shiba 5-34-6, Minato-ku,
Tokyo, 108-8416, Japan
Tel.: (81) 354443600
Web Site: https://www.cigr.co.jp
N.A.I.C.S.: 721110
Hideki Fujioka *(Pres)*

Cosmos More Co., Ltd.   **(2)**
New Horizon Ebisu 3-14-20 Higashi,
Shibuya-ku, Tokyo, 150-0011, Japan
Tel.: (81) 368922010
Web Site: http://www.cosmosmore.co.jp
Sales Range: Less than $1 Million
Emp.: 169
Apartment Sale Services
N.A.I.C.S.: 236117
Hisao Edahiro *(CEO)*

DDInnovation Co., Ltd.   **(1)**
6-3-9 Minami Aoyama MA Building 10th
Floor, Minato-ku, Tokyo, 107-0062, Japan
Tel.: (81) 36 451 1041
Web Site: https://www.ddinnovation.jp
Outsourcing Business Services
N.A.I.C.S.: 561990

DH (Dalian) Administrative Manage-
ment Consulting Center Co., Ltd.   **(1)**
143 Zhongshan Road, Dalian, 116011, Lia-
oning, China
Tel.: (86) 4118 360 8905
Web Site: https://www.daiwa-cn.com
Outsourcing Business Services
N.A.I.C.S.: 561990

DH Asia Investment Pte. Ltd.   **(1)**
8 Marina View 14-09 Asia Square Tower 1,
Singapore, Singapore
Tel.: (65) 6 202 0488
Real Estate Services
N.A.I.C.S.: 531210

DH Logistic Property Vietnam Co.,
Ltd.   **(1)**
Lot I Loc An-Binh Son IP, Long An Com-
mune, Long Thanh, Dong Nai, Vietnam

Tel.: (84) 2513686515
N.A.I.C.S.: 236220

DT Development Vietnam LLC   **(1)**
Unit 1103 11 Floor Viglacera Office Building
No 1 Thang Long Avenue, Nam Tu Liem
Dist, Hanoi, Vietnam
Tel.: (84) 2432018988
N.A.I.C.S.: 531390

Daiwa Baoye (Nantong) Real Estate
Development Co., Ltd.   **(1)**
Building 20 Hefeng Yasong Garden No 330
Fuxing East Road, Development Zone,
Nantong, Jiangsu, China
Tel.: (86) 51351085666
N.A.I.C.S.: 531390

Daiwa Cosmos Construction Co.,
Ltd.   **(1)**
5-1-31 Akasaka 6th Seiko Building 2nd
Floor, Minato-ku, Tokyo, 107-0052, Japan
Tel.: (81) 35 549 7023
Web Site: https://www.dcconst.jp
Condominium Operator
N.A.I.C.S.: 813990

Daiwa Energy Co., Ltd.   **(1)**
Abeno Harukas 33F 1-43 Abenosuji, Abeno-
ku, Osaka, 145-6033, Japan
Tel.: (81) 647033208
Web Site: http://www.daiwa-energy.com
Sales Range: $25-49.9 Million
Emp.: 40
Development of Business & Housing Envi-
ronmental Products
N.A.I.C.S.: 334512

Daiwa Estate Co., Ltd.   **(1)**
7F Daiwa House Tokyo Building 3-13-1 Iida-
bashi, Chiyoda-ku, Tokyo, 102-0072, Japan
Tel.: (81) 120998181
Web Site: https://www.daiwaestate.jp
Sales Range: $1-9.9 Million
Emp.: 35
Real Estate Brokerage
N.A.I.C.S.: 531210

Daiwa House (Changzhou) Real Es-
tate Development Co., Ltd.   **(1)**
East of Longjin Road North of Zhulin North
Road Langyue Longzhou, Tianning District,
Changzhou, China
Tel.: (86) 5198 188 5568
Real Estate Services
N.A.I.C.S.: 531210

Daiwa House (Suzhou) Real Estate
Development Co., Ltd.   **(1)**
1902 Zhongyin Huilong Building 8 Suhui
Road Suzhou Industrial Park, Suzhou, Ji-
angsu, China
Tel.: (86) 51288852001
Sales Range: $50-74.9 Million
Emp.: 56
Real Estate Development Services
N.A.I.C.S.: 531390

Daiwa House Asset Management
Co., Ltd.   **(1)**
7th Floor Nissei Nagatacho Building 2-4-8
Nagatacho, Chiyoda-Ku, Tokyo, 100-0014,
Japan
Tel.: (81) 335951151
Web Site: https://www.dh-am.com
Sales Range: $10-24.9 Million
Emp.: 37
Asset Management Services
N.A.I.C.S.: 523940
Koichi Tsuchida *(Pres & CEO)*

Daiwa House Chintai Reform Co.,
Ltd.   **(1)**
3-5-1 Bakuromachi, Chuo-ku, Osaka, 541-
0059, Japan
Tel.: (81) 66 743 4860
Web Site: https://www.daiwahouse-chintai-
reform.jp
Remodeling Construction Services
N.A.I.C.S.: 236118

Daiwa House Construction Manage-
ment Inc.   **(1)**
222 W Las Colinas Blvd Ste 1540 E, Irving,
TX 75039
Tel.: (469) 834-5176
Construction Services
N.A.I.C.S.: 236220

Daiwa House Europe B.V.   **(1)**

Strawinskylaan 831, 1077XX, Amsterdam,
Netherlands
Tel.: (31) 202382980
Web Site: https://www.daiwahouse.eu
N.A.I.C.S.: 541910
Kazuya Sawamoto *(CEO)*

Daiwa House Financial Co., Ltd.   **(1)**
Web Site:
http://www.daiwahousefinancial.co.jp
Sales Range: $50-74.9 Million
Emp.: 13
Credit Card & Consumer Finance Services
N.A.I.C.S.: 522210

Daiwa House Industry India Pvt.
Ltd.   **(1)**
3rd Floor Building No 9-A DLF Cyber City
Phase-III, Gurgaon, India
Tel.: (91) 124 454 5010
Real Estate Services
N.A.I.C.S.: 531210

Daiwa House Industry(Thailand)Co.,
Ltd.   **(1)**
399 Interchange Building 23rd Floor Unit 12
Sukhumvit Road, Klongtoey-Nua Wattana,
Bangkok, 10110, Thailand
Tel.: (66) 2 262 1747
Real Estate Services
N.A.I.C.S.: 531210

Daiwa House Insurance Co., Ltd.   **(1)**
6th floor Yamato House Bingomachi Build-
ing 1-2-5 Bigocho, Chuo-ku, Osaka, 541-
0051, Japan
Tel.: (81) 6 6229 7260
Web Site: http://www.daiwahouse-ins.jp
Sales Range: $75-99.9 Million
Emp.: 127
Insurance Agents
N.A.I.C.S.: 524210
Shigeru Sasashita *(Pres)*

Daiwa House Life Support Co.,
Ltd.   **(1)**
3-1-7 Mita Toho Building 6th Floor, Minato-
ku, Tokyo, 108-0073, Japan
Tel.: (81) 33 456 4165
Web Site: https://www.dhls.jp
Nursing Care Facilities Services
N.A.I.C.S.: 623110

Daiwa House Malaysia Sdn.
Bhd.   **(1)**
No 2-19 & 2-20 Citrine Hub Persiaran Me-
dini 3, Sunway Citrine Sunway Iskandar
Bandar Medini Iskandar, 79250, Iskandar
Puteri, Johor, Malaysia
Tel.: (60) 75096607
N.A.I.C.S.: 236220

Daiwa House Morimoto Asset Man-
agement Co., Ltd.   **(1)**
2-4-8 Nagatacyo, Chiyoda-ku, Tokyo, Japan
Tel.: (81) 3 3595 1151
Web Site: http://www.daiwahouse-resi-
reit.co.jp
Emp.: 35
Asset Management Services
N.A.I.C.S.: 523940
Koichi Tsuchida *(Pres)*

Daiwa House Parking Co., Ltd.   **(1)**
2-16-1 Minamikamata Technoport Kamata
Center Building 10F, Ota-ku, Tokyo, 144-
0035, Japan
Tel.: (81) 33 737 3777
Web Site: https://www.dh-parking.co.jp
Parking System Services
N.A.I.C.S.: 812930

Daiwa House Property Management
Co., Ltd.   **(1)**
2-18-2 Iidabashi Yamato House Kudan
Building 5th Floor, Chiyoda-ku, Tokyo, 102-
0072, Japan
Tel.: (81) 35 214 2540
Web Site: https://www.daiwahouse-pm.com
Remodeling Construction Services
N.A.I.C.S.: 236118

Daiwa House REIT Management Co.,
Ltd.   **(1)**
7th Floor Nissei Nagatacho Building 2 4-8
Nagatacho, Chiyoda-ku, Tokyo, 100-0014,
Japan
Tel.: (81) 335951151
Web Site: https://www.dh-am.com

Sales Range: $50-74.9 Million
Emp.: 7
Investment Trust Management
N.A.I.C.S.: 525990

Daiwa House Real Asset Manage-
ment Vietnam, Co., Ltd.   **(1)**
Road N3-3 Long Duc Industrial Park, Long
Thanh, Dong Nai, Vietnam
Tel.: (84) 2513682934
N.A.I.C.S.: 236220

Daiwa House Real Estate Develop-
ment Co., Ltd.   **(1)**
Long Duc Industrial Park, Long Thanh Dis-
trict, Dong Nai, Vietnam
Tel.: (84) 251 368 1272
Real Estate Services
N.A.I.C.S.: 531210

Daiwa House Real Estate Investment
Management Co., Ltd.   **(1)**
3-2-2 Iidabashi, Chiyoda-ku, Tokyo, Japan
Tel.: (81) 33 239 5960
Web Site: https://www.dh-reim.co.jp
Real Estate Services
N.A.I.C.S.: 531210

Daiwa House Renew Co., Ltd.   **(1)**
Web Site: http://www.daiwahouse-
reform.co.jp
Sales Range: $10-24.9 Million
Emp.: 500
Home Renovation
N.A.I.C.S.: 236118

Daiwa House Texas Inc.   **(1)**
222 W Las Colinas Blvd Ste 1540 E, Irving,
TX 75039
Tel.: (469) 834-5176
N.A.I.C.S.: 531390

Daiwa Information Service Co.,
Ltd.   **(1)**
Daiwa House Kudan Building 2-18-2 Iida-
bashi, Chiyoda-ku, Tokyo, 102-0072,
Japan   **(100%)**
Tel.: (81) 352142950
Web Site: http://www.daiwainfo.jp
Sales Range: $10-24.9 Million
Emp.: 166
Property Leasing & Shopping Center Op-
eration; Property Management for Commer-
cial Facilities, Office Buildings & Hotels
N.A.I.C.S.: 531190
Fujita Katsuyuki *(Pres)*

Daiwa Lantec Co., Ltd.   **(1)**
1-5-2 Bingo-machi, Chuo-ku, Osaka, 541-
0051, Japan
Tel.: (81) 662297270
Web Site: http://www.daiwalantec.jp
Sales Range: $150-199.9 Million
Emp.: 353
Geological Surveying Services
N.A.I.C.S.: 541360

Daiwa Lease Co., Ltd.   **(1)**
Pippu Bldg 2-1-36 Noninbashi, Chuo-ku,
Osaka, 540-0011, Japan   **(100%)**
Tel.: (81) 669428011
Web Site: https://www.daiwalease.co.jp
Emp.: 2,357
Housing & Commercial Facilities Leasing
Services
N.A.I.C.S.: 531390
Shunsaku Morita *(Pres)*

Daiwa LifeCosmo Co., Ltd.   **(1)**
2-7-26 Minamisenba Osaka Shinsei Build-
ing 7F, Chuo-ku, Osaka, 542-0081, Japan
Tel.: (81) 66 262 7536
Web Site: https://www.dlcosmo.jp
Cleaning Equipment Maintenance Services
N.A.I.C.S.: 811310

Daiwa LifeNext Co., Ltd.   **(1)**
5-1-33 Akasaka, Minato-Ku, Tokyo, 107-
0052, Japan
Tel.: (81) 355497111
Web Site: https://www.daiwalifenext.co.jp
Emp.: 8,176
Property Management Services
N.A.I.C.S.: 531311

Daiwa Living California Inc.   **(1)**
348 S Clover Ave, San Jose, CA 95128
Tel.: (408) 850-7802
Web Site: https://daiwalivingca.com
Rental House Business Services

Daiwa House Industry Co., Ltd.—(Continued)

N.A.I.C.S.: 532310

Daiwa Living Co., Ltd. (1)
Ariake central tower 7F 3-7-18 Ariake, Koto-ku, Tokyo, 135-0063, Japan (100%)
Tel.: (81) 355006500
Web Site: http://www.daiwaliving.co.jp
Sales Range: $1-4.9 Billion
Emp.: 1,281
Management & Operation of Rental Housing, Subcontractor for Renovation Work & Insurance Services
N.A.I.C.S.: 236118
Masaru Akashi (Pres)

Daiwa Living Nesuto Holdings Pty Ltd (1)
110 - 114 James Ruse Drive, Rosehill, Sydney, 2142, NSW, Australia
Tel.: (61) 28 837 8000
Web Site: https://www.nesuto.com
Real Estate Services
N.A.I.C.S.: 531210
Mark Ronfeldt (CEO)

Daiwa LogiTech Inc. (1)
2F MA Building 6-3-9 Minami Aoyama, Minato-ku, Tokyo, 107-0062, Japan
Tel.: (81) 36 868 0495
Web Site:
https://www.daiwahousegroup.com
Logistic Services
N.A.I.C.S.: 541614

Daiwa Logistics Co., Ltd. (1)
1-5-16 Awaza, Nishi-ku, Osaka, 550-0011, Japan (100%)
Tel.: (81) 649686355
Web Site: https://www.daiwabutsuryu.co.jp
Emp.: 1,404
Trucking Services, Storage & Packing of Goods
N.A.I.C.S.: 541614
Tsutomu Aoyagi (CEO)

Daiwa Logistics Vietnam Co., Ltd. (1)
0510 Floor 5 CJ Building 2Bis-4-6 Le Thanh Ton, Ben Nghe Ward District 1, Ho Chi Minh City, Vietnam
Tel.: (84) 286 255 6770
Web Site: https://www.daiwabutsuryu.co.jp
Freight Forwarding Services
N.A.I.C.S.: 488510
Kazuya Hirota (Gen Dir)

Daiwa Monthly Co., Ltd. (1)
Daiwa House Tokyo Building 3-13-1 Iidabashi, Tokyo, 1020072, Chiyoda-ku, Japan
Tel.: (81) 352142706
Web Site: http://www.daiwamonthly.co.jp
Sales Range: $1-9.9 Million
Emp.: 23
Rental Housing Management; Non-Life Insurance Services
N.A.I.C.S.: 531311

Daiwa Resort Co., Ltd. (1)
Ariake Central Tower 10F 3-7-18 Ariake, Koto-ku, Tokyo, 135-0063, Japan (100%)
Tel.: (81) 364571551
Web Site: http://www.daiwaresort.jp
Sales Range: $200-249.9 Million
Emp.: 2,011
Resort Hotels & Golf Courses
N.A.I.C.S.: 721110
Yoshinari Shibayama (Pres)

Daiwa Royal Co., Ltd. (1)
Daiwa House Kudan Building 2-18-2 Iidabashi, Chiyoda-ku, Tokyo, 102-0072, Japan (100%)
Tel.: (81) 352142950
Web Site: https://www.dh-realty.co.jp
Sales Range: $100-124.9 Million
Emp.: 1,282
Real Estate Brokerage & Property Management Services
N.A.I.C.S.: 531210
Ken Harada (Pres)

Daiwa Royal Golf Co., Ltd. (1)
1055 Yamashita-cho, Kameyama, 519-0147, Mie, Japan (100%)
Tel.: (81) 595831212
Web Site: http://www.daiwaroyalgolf.jp
Sales Range: $350-399.9 Million
Emp.: 119
Operation & Management of Golf Courses

N.A.I.C.S.: 713910
Seishu Umaoka (Pres)

Daiwa Royal Hotel City Co., Ltd. (1)
2-18-2 Iidabashi, Chiyoda-ku, Tokyo, 102-0072, Japan
Tel.: (81) 35 214 2950
Hotel Operator
N.A.I.C.S.: 721110
Mitsuhiro Ito (Pres & CEO)

Daiwa Service Co., Ltd. (1)
Daiwa Building 1-5-16 Awaza, Nishi-ku, Osaka, Japan
Tel.: (81) 665366270
Web Site: http://www.daiwaservice.co.jp
Sales Range: $200-249.9 Million
Emp.: 3,000
Commercial Building Management, Maintenance & Repair Services; Residential Remodeling
N.A.I.C.S.: 531312
Yamne Hirme (CEO)

Daiyoshi Trust Co., Ltd. (1)
(94%)
Web Site: http://www.daiyoshi.com
Sales Range: $25-49.9 Million
Emp.: 30
Parking Facilities & Real Estate Services
N.A.I.C.S.: 812930

Dalian Acacia Town Villa Co., Ltd. (1)
West Liaohe Road Dalian Development Zone, Dalian, 116600, China
Tel.: (86) 41187641171
Web Site: https://www.dlacacia.com
Emp.: 44
Management of Rental Housing & Lot-Division Houses
N.A.I.C.S.: 531311
Xin'an Yuan (Chm)

Dalian Yihe Property Management Co., Ltd. (1)
No 18A Bulao Street, Xigang District, Dalian, Liaoning, China
Tel.: (86) 4113 987 8358
Real Estate Services
N.A.I.C.S.: 531210

DesignArc Co., Ltd. (1)
1-5-16 Awaza, Nishi-ku, Osaka, 550-0014, Japan
Tel.: (81) 66 546 6111
Web Site: https://www.designarc.co.jp
Construction Machinery Equipment Mfr & Distr
N.A.I.C.S.: 333120
Kaichi Tatsumi (Pres)

DiceNext Inc. (1)
2-12 Kanda Tsukasamachi 4th Floor Kanda Tsukasamachi Building, Chiyoda-ku, Tokyo, 101-0048, Japan
Tel.: (81) 33 526 2426
Web Site: https://www.saikoro.co.jp
Real Estate Services
N.A.I.C.S.: 531210

Eneserve Corporation (1)
2-19-6 Tsukiwa, Otsu, 520-2152, Shiga, Japan (51.4%)
Tel.: (81) 775436330
Web Site: http://www.eneserve.co.jp
Sales Range: $50-74.9 Million
Emp.: 197
Energy Management Services
N.A.I.C.S.: 811310

Frameworx Inc. (1)
6-3-9 Minami Aoyama 2nd Floor MA Building, Minato-ku, Tokyo, 107-0062, Japan
Tel.: (81) 36 427 7818
Web Site:
https://www.daiwahousegroup.com
Logistic Services
N.A.I.C.S.: 541614

Fujita (China) Construction Co., Ltd. (1)
No 88 Xuhui North Road 1608 and 801 Rooms, Xuhui District, Shanghai, China
Tel.: (86) 216 841 5522
Web Site: https://www.fujita-china.biz
Construction Services
N.A.I.C.S.: 236220

Fujita Corporation (1)

4-25-2 Sendagaya, Shibuya-ku, Tokyo, 151-8570, Japan (97.1%)
Tel.: (81) 334021911
Web Site: https://www.fujita.com
Emp.: 3,494
Construction & Civil Engineering Services
N.A.I.C.S.: 237990
Yoji Okumura (Pres & CEO)

Subsidiary (Domestic):

FBS Co., Ltd. (1)
4-25-2 Sendagaya, Shibuya-ku, Tokyo, 151-0051, Japan
Tel.: (81) 354743273
Web Site: http://www.fbsys.net
Sales Range: $25-49.9 Million
Emp.: 12
Information Technology Services
N.A.I.C.S.: 541519

Subsidiary (US):

Fujita Americas, Inc. (2)
15821 Ventura Blvd Ste 245, Encino, CA 91436
Tel.: (818) 981-2657
Web Site: https://www.fjtamericas.com
Construction Management Services
N.A.I.C.S.: 236220

Unit (Domestic):

Fujita Research (Encino Office) (3)
6345 Balboa Blvd Bldg 3 Ste 370, Encino, CA 91316
Tel.: (818) 981-2657
Construction Technology Development & Transfer Services
N.A.I.C.S.: 541690

Subsidiary (Domestic):

Fujita Building Maintenance Inc. (2)
1st floor Iwao Building 5-8-10 Sendagaya, Shibuya-ku, Tokyo, 151-0051, Japan
Tel.: (81) 353613861
Web Site: http://www.fujita.com
Facility Management Services
N.A.I.C.S.: 561210

Subsidiary (Non-US):

Fujita Philippines Inc. (2)
14A Chatham House 116 Valero St corner Rufino St, Salcedo Village, Makati, Metro Manila, Philippines
Tel.: (63) 288560621
Sales Range: $150-199.9 Million
Construction Contractor
N.A.I.C.S.: 236210

Subsidiary (Domestic):

Fujita Road Construction Co., Ltd. (2)
Harumi Island Triton Square Office Tower X 3F 1-8-10 Harumi, Chuo-ku, Tokyo, 104-6003, Japan
Tel.: (81) 358590670
Web Site: https://www.fujitaroad.co.jp
Sales Range: $200-249.9 Million
Emp.: 213
Road, Bridge & Other Civil Engineering Construction Services
N.A.I.C.S.: 237310

Fujita Shoji Co., Ltd. (2)
15th floor Koraku Mori-Building 1-4-14 Koraku, Bunkyo-ku, Tokyo, 112-0004, Japan
Tel.: (81) 367576751
Sales Range: $100-124.9 Million
Emp.: 70
Export & Import Trading Services
N.A.I.C.S.: 425120
Usuda Kunihiko (Gen mgr)

KOKANKYO Engineering Corporation (EAE) (2)
5F Yoyogi TR Building 4-30-3 Sendagaya, Shibuya-ku, Tokyo, 151-0051, Japan
Tel.: (81) 354136222
Web Site: https://www.eae.co.jp
Sales Range: $250-299.9 Million
Emp.: 33
Environmental Engineering & Technology-Consulting Construction Services
N.A.I.C.S.: 237990

Technomaterial Corporation (2)
4-12-1 Higashi-ueno, Taito-ku, Tokyo, 110-

0015, Japan
Tel.: (81) 358301080
Sales Range: $100-124.9 Million
Precast Concrete Product Mfr & Contractor Services
N.A.I.C.S.: 327390

Fujita Corporation (M) Sdn. Bhd. (1)
A-39-2 Level 39 Tower A Menara UOA Bangsar, No 5 Jalan Bangsar Utama 1, 59000, Kuala Lumpur, Malaysia
Tel.: (60) 32 287 6188
Construction Services
N.A.I.C.S.: 236220

Fujita Corporation (Thailand) Ltd. (1)
29 Bangkok Business Center Building 19th Floor Room 1905, Sukhumvit 63 Ekamai Road Klongton Nua Wattana, Bangkok, 10110, Thailand
Tel.: (66) 2 714 7325
Construction Services
N.A.I.C.S.: 236220

Fujita Corporation Singapore Pte. Ltd. (1)
3 Shenton Way 25-01A Shenton House, Singapore, 068805, Singapore
Tel.: (65) 6 337 3336
Construction Services
N.A.I.C.S.: 236220

Fujita Corporation Vietnam Co., Ltd. (1)
19-01 19th Floor Gelex Tower 52 Le Dai Hanh Street, Hai Ba Trung District, Hanoi, Vietnam
Tel.: (84) 243 726 2452
Construction Services
N.A.I.C.S.: 236220

Fujita Engineering India Pvt., Ltd. (1)
Door No 3 Ashirwad Illam First Floor 3rd East Street Kamaraj Nagar, Thiruvanmiyur, Chennai, 600041, Tamil Nadu, India
Tel.: (91) 444 857 4048
Construction Services
N.A.I.C.S.: 236220

Fujita Integral Mexico S.A. de C.V. (1)
Independencia 2100 1B y 2B Col Granjas de San Miguerito, 36557, Irapuato, Guanajuato, Mexico
Tel.: (52) 462 607 0101
Construction Services
N.A.I.C.S.: 236220

Fujita Philippines Construction & Development, Inc. (1)
14A Chatham House 116 Valero St corner Rufino St, Salcedo Village, Makati, Philippines
Tel.: (63) 2 856 0621
Construction Services
N.A.I.C.S.: 236220

Global Community Co., Ltd. (1)
3-3-7 Bakuromachi Building Hirotake, Chuo-ku, Osaka, 541-0059, Japan
Tel.: (81) 12 076 8720
Web Site: https://www.glob-com.co.jp
Real Estate Services
N.A.I.C.S.: 531210

JUST Logistics, Inc. (1)
2848 Miyanagamachi, Hakusan, 924-0017, Ishikawa, Japan
Tel.: (81) 76 274 7171
Web Site: https://just-buturyu.com
Freight Transportation Services
N.A.I.C.S.: 484121

Jan Snel HD B.V. (1)
Willeskop 94, Postbus 200, 3417 ME, Montfoort, Netherlands
Tel.: (31) 34 847 9090
Building Architectural Design Services
N.A.I.C.S.: 541310

Jiuxin(Changzhou)Real Estate Development Co., Ltd. (1)
East Side of Longjin Road North Side of Zhulin North Road, Langyue Longzhou Field Office Tianning District, Changzhou, China
Tel.: (86) 51981230868
N.A.I.C.S.: 531390

Jukeikai Co., Ltd.   (1)
17-2 Izumi, Atami, 413-0000, Shizuoka, Japan
Tel.: (81) 465 63 6432
Web Site: http://www.daiwahouse.com
Rev.: $9,277,360
Emp.: 79
Private Nursing Home with Assisted Living Services
N.A.I.C.S.: 623110
Toshinori Inaguchi (Pres)

Media Tech Inc.   (1)
1010-3 EDGE Honmachi Building 2-3-12 Minamihonmachi, Chuo-ku, Osaka, 541-0054, Japan   (100%)
Tel.: (81) 647087770
Web Site: http://www.mediatech.jp
Information Communications Services
N.A.I.C.S.: 541519
Masayuki Honda (Pres)

Nihon Jyutaku Ryutu Co., Ltd.   (1)
1-3-800 Station 3rd Building 8F, Umeda Kita-ku, Osaka, 530-0001, Japan   (100%)
Tel.: (81) 647993144
Web Site: http://www.jyutaku.co.jp
Sales Range: $150-199.9 Million
Emp.: 395
Real Estate Brokerage; Rental Housing
N.A.I.C.S.: 531210

Nippon Athletic Service Co., Ltd.   (1)
26th floor of Shiroyama Trust Tower 4-3-1 Toranomon, Minato-ku, Tokyo, 105-6026, Japan
Tel.: (81) 120744115
Web Site: https://www.nas-club.co.jp
Sales Range: $75-99.9 Million
Emp.: 340
Operation & Management of Sports Facilities
N.A.I.C.S.: 713940

Nishiwaki Royal Hotel Co., Ltd.   (1)
991 Nishiwaki, Nishiwaki, 677-0015, Hyogo, Japan
Tel.: (81) 79 523 2000
Web Site: https://www.nishiwaki-royalhotel.jp
Home Management Services
N.A.I.C.S.: 721110

Osaka Marubiru Co., Ltd.   (1)
1-9-20 Umeda, Kita-ku, Osaka, 530-0001, Japan
Tel.: (81) 663414411
Web Site: http://www.marubiru.com
Sales Range: $10-24.9 Million
Emp.: 70
Operation of Hotels
N.A.I.C.S.: 721110
Haruyuki Yoshimoto (Pres)

PT Daiwa House Indonesia   (1)
Wisma Argo Manunggal Lantai 9 Jl Jendral Gatot Subroto Kav 22, Jakarta, 12930, Indonesia
Tel.: (62) 21 252 2720
Management Consulting Services
N.A.I.C.S.: 541611

PT Daiwa Life Next Indonesia   (1)
RDTX Place Lt 18 - Zona 8 Jl Prof Dr Satrio Kav 3, Jakarta Selatan, 12940, DKI Jakarta, Indonesia
Tel.: (62) 2139720853
Web Site: https://www.daiwalifenext.co.id
N.A.I.C.S.: 531390

PT. Nas Fitness Indonesia   (1)
RDTX Place 18th Floor Zone 8 Jl Prof Dr Satrio Kav 3 RT 017 RW 004, Karet Kuningan Setiabudi, South Jakarta, 12940, Indonesia
Tel.: (62) 2139720850
N.A.I.C.S.: 236220

Parking Solutions Co., Ltd.   (1)
1-9-12 Omorinishi, Ota-ku, Tokyo, 143-8539, Japan
Tel.: (81) 33 762 5151
Web Site: https://www.parking-s.co.jp
Parking Lot Services
N.A.I.C.S.: 812930

Royal Gate Inc.   (1)
4th Floor Akasaka Hinoki Building 2-10-5 Akasaka, Minato-ku, Tokyo, 107-0052, Japan
Tel.: (81) 33 568 4321

Web Site: https://www.royalgate.co.jp
Cashless Payment Services
N.A.I.C.S.: 522320

Royal Home Center Co., Ltd.   (1)
5th floor Yamato Building 1-5-16 Awaza, Nishi-ku, Osaka, 550-0011, Japan   (100%)
Tel.: (81) 643918830
Web Site: https://www.royal-hc.co.jp
Sales Range: $550-599.9 Million
Emp.: 4,002
Home Center Operator
N.A.I.C.S.: 444110

Shanghai Hebao Property Service Co., Ltd.   (1)
66 Miaojing Road, Minhang District, Shanghai, China
Tel.: (86) 215 263 7165
Real Estate Services
N.A.I.C.S.: 531210

Shanghai International Realty Co., Ltd.   (1)
3081 Hong Mei Rd, Shanghai, 201103, China   (30%)
Tel.: (86) 2162759646
Web Site: http://www.hongqiao-villa.com
Sales Range: $50-74.9 Million
Emp.: 30
Management of Rental Housing
N.A.I.C.S.: 531311

Sports Club NAS Co., Ltd.   (1)
1-8-1 Marunouchi Trust Tower N Building 13th Floor, Chiyoda-ku, Tokyo, 100-0005, Japan
Tel.: (81) 12 074 4115
Web Site: https://www.nas-club.co.jp
Fitness Club Services
N.A.I.C.S.: 713940

Stanley Martin Holdings, LLC   (1)
11710 Plaza America Dr Ste 1100, Reston, VA 20190
Tel.: (703) 964-5000
Web Site: https://www.stanleymartin.com
Residential Construction
N.A.I.C.S.: 236115

Taiwan Daiwa House Construction Co., Ltd.   (1)
9F No 6 Sec 1 Zhongxiao W Rd, Zhongzheng Dist, Taipei, 10041, Taiwan
Tel.: (886) 22 311 1038
Real Estate Services
N.A.I.C.S.: 531210

Tianjin Jiuhe International Villa Co., Ltd.   (1)
No 140 Weiguo Road, Hedong District, Tianjin, 300161, China
Tel.: (86) 2224514888
Web Site: https://www.kyuka.net
Sales Range: $50-74.9 Million
Emp.: 70
Rental Housing Management
N.A.I.C.S.: 531311

Wakamatsu Konpou Unyu Soko, Inc.   (1)
855 Kita Fukumasu-Cho, Kanazawa, 920-0376, Ishikawa, Japan
Tel.: (81) 762747200
Web Site: https://www.wakamatsugr.jp
N.A.I.C.S.: 493190
Shuichi Eda (CEO)

acca international Co., Ltd.   (1)
MA Building 3F 6-3-9 Minamiaoyama, Minato-ku, Tokyo, 107-0062, Japan
Tel.: (81) 364526613
Web Site: https://acca-int.jp
N.A.I.C.S.: 541614
Yoichi Hide (CEO)

DAIWA HOUSE REIT INVESTMENT CORPORATION
2-4-8 Nagatacho, Chiyoda-ku, Tokyo, 100-0014, Japan
Tel.: (81) 335951265
Web Site: https://www.daiwahouse-reit.co.jp
Year Founded: 2005
8984—(TKS)
Sales Range: Less than $1 Million
Real Estate Investment Services
N.A.I.C.S.: 531390

Tsuyoshi Saito (Exec Dir)

Subsidiaries:

DAIWA CORE FACTORY CO., LTD.   (1)
Daiwa House Okayama Plant 2056 Taga, Akaiwa, 701-2216, Okayama, Japan
Tel.: (81) 86 957 9008
Emp.: 298
Housing Component Mfr
N.A.I.C.S.: 321999

Daiwa Homes Online Co., Ltd.   (1)
13-1 Iidabashi 3-chome, Chiyoda-ku, Tokyo, 102-8112, Japan
Tel.: (81) 3 5214 2705
Web Site: http://www.dhol.co.jp
Emp.: 34
Real Estate Brokerage Services
N.A.I.C.S.: 531210
Norio Togashi (Pres)

Daiwa House (Wuxi) Real Estate Development Co., Ltd.   (1)
Moonlit Garden 43 518 Hongshan Road Hongshan Street, New District, Wuxi, 214115, Jiangsu, China
Tel.: (86) 510 8899 3086
Web Site: http://www.daiwahouse-wx.com
Emp.: 38
Real Estate Investment Services
N.A.I.C.S.: 531390
Yukikaze Kataoka (Chm)

Daiwa House Australia Pty Ltd.   (1)
Suite 402 Level 4 2 Elizabeth Plaza, North Sydney, 2060, NSW, Australia
Tel.: (61) 2 8036 4551
Real Estate Investment Services
N.A.I.C.S.: 531390

Daiwa House California   (1)
101 Metro Dr Ste 325, San Jose, CA 95110
Tel.: (408) 878-6076
Emp.: 6
Real Estate Investment Services
N.A.I.C.S.: 531390

Daiwa House Reform Co., Ltd.   (1)
Daiwa House Osaka Bldg 3-3-5 Umeda, Kita-ku, Osaka, Japan
Tel.: (81) 6 6342 4410
Web Site: http://www.daiwahouse-reform.co.jp
Emp.: 1,826
Housing Renovation Services
N.A.I.C.S.: 236118
Junichi Sugiura (Pres)

Daiwa House Vietnam Co., Ltd.   (1)
6 Floor Lotus Building D2-Lot C-D11 Cau Giay New Urban, Cau Giay District Dich Vong Hau Ward, Hanoi, Vietnam
Tel.: (84) 4 3736 7847
Emp.: 38
Real Estate Investment Services
N.A.I.C.S.: 531390

DAIWA INDUSTRIES LTD.
Daiwa Reiki Uehonmachi DRK Bldg 3-13 Obase-cho, Tennoji-ward, Osaka, 543-0028, Japan
Tel.: (81) 667678171
Web Site: https://www.daiwa-inds.com
Year Founded: 1950
6459—(TKS)
Sales Range: $250-299.9 Million
Heating & Cooling Equipment Mfr & Distr
N.A.I.C.S.: 333415
Atsushi Ozaki (Pres)

DAIWA MOTOR TRANSPORTATION CO., LTD.
2-16-31 Sarue, Koto-ku, Tokyo, 135-0003, Japan
Tel.: (81) 367577161
Web Site: https://www.daiwaj.com
Year Founded: 1939
9082—(TKS)
Rev.: $121,471,970
Assets: $199,595,560
Liabilities: $138,519,160
Net Worth: $61,076,400

Earnings: ($3,516,520)
Emp.: 2,506
Fiscal Year-end: 03/31/24
Passenger Automobile Transportation Services
N.A.I.C.S.: 485113
Kinya Maejima (Chm)

DAIWA OFFICE INVESTMENT CORPORATION
6-2-1 Ginza, Chuo-ku, Tokyo, Japan
Tel.: (81) 362159500
Web Site: https://www.daiwa-office.co.jp
Year Founded: 2005
8976—(TKS)
Sales Range: $75-99.9 Million
Investment Management Service
N.A.I.C.S.: 523999
Toshisuke Tanaka (Exec Dir)

DAIWA SECURITIES GROUP INC.
GranTokyo North Tower 9-1 Marunouchi 1-chome, Chiyoda-ku, Tokyo, 100-6751, Japan
Tel.: (81) 355551111   JP
Web Site: https://www.daiwa-grp.jp
Year Founded: 1999
DSE—(DEU)
Rev.: $8,444,156,020
Assets: $211,700,446,390
Liabilities: $199,877,417,010
Net Worth: $11,823,029,380
Earnings: $803,491,770
Emp.: 15,529
Fiscal Year-end: 03/31/24
Holding Company; Securities Brokerage, Investment Banking, Portfolio Management & Trust Services
N.A.I.C.S.: 551112
Akihiko Ogino (Pres, CEO & Corporate Exec Officer)

Subsidiaries:

Connect Co. Ltd.   (1)
1-2-1 Kyobashi, Chuo-ku, Tokyo, Japan
Tel.: (81) 366703917
Web Site: http://www.connect-sec.co.jp
Brokerage Security Services
N.A.I.C.S.: 523150

DCS Advisory LLC   (1)
605 Third Ave 11th Fl, New York, NY 10158
Tel.: (212) 904-9400
Web Site: http://us.dcadvisory.com
Emp.: 75
Investment Banking & Securities Dealing
N.A.I.C.S.: 523150
Herald L. Ritch (Founder)

DIR Information Systems Co., Ltd.   (1)
1-14-6 Eitai, Koto-ku, Tokyo, Japan
Tel.: (81) 363652580
Web Site: http://www.dir-is.co.jp
Software Development Services
N.A.I.C.S.: 541511

Daiwa (Shanghai) Corporate Strategic Advisory Co. Ltd.   (1)
44/F Hang Seng Bank Tower 1000 Lujiazui Ring Road, Pudong, Shanghai, China
Tel.: (86) 2168598000
Financial Advisory Services
N.A.I.C.S.: 523940

Daiwa Asset Management Co. Ltd.   (1)
1-9-1 Marunouchi GranTokyo North Tower, Chiyoda-ku Marunouchi, Tokyo, 100-6753, Japan   (88%)
Tel.: (81) 355553111
Web Site: http://www.daiwa-am.co.jp
Sales Range: $200-249.9 Million
Emp.: 671
Investment Trust
N.A.I.C.S.: 525910
Junichi Aizawa (Deputy Pres)

Daiwa Capital Markets Deutschland GmbH   (1)

Daiwa Securities Group Inc.—(Continued)

Neue Mainzer Strasse 1, 60311, Frankfurt
am Main, Germany
Tel.: (49) 69271398100
Web Site: http://www.de.daiwacm.com
Securities Trading Bank Services
N.A.I.C.S.: 523150
Manabu Takahashi (Co-Mng Dir)

Daiwa Corporate Advisory GmbH (1)
Neue Mainzer Strasse 1, 60311, Frankfurt
am Main, Germany
Tel.: (49) 699720040
Financial Advisory Services
N.A.I.C.S.: 523940

Subsidiary (Non-US):

IBI Corporate Finance Limited (2)
33 Fitzwilliam Place, Dublin 2, Dublin, D02
W899, Ireland
Tel.: (353) 19631200
Web Site: http://www.ibicorporatefinance.ie
Corporate Finance Adviser
N.A.I.C.S.: 523940
Ted Webb (Mng Dir)

**Daiwa Corporate Advisory
Limited** (1)
5 King William Street, London, EC4N 7DA,
United Kingdom
Tel.: (44) 2078560999
Financial Advisory Services
N.A.I.C.S.: 523940

Daiwa Corporate Advisory S.r.l. (1)
Via Manzoni 5, 20121, Milan, Italy
Tel.: (39) 0209942669
Financial Advisory Services
N.A.I.C.S.: 523940

Daiwa Corporate Advisory SAS (1)
17 rue de Surene, 75008, Paris, France
Tel.: (33) 142124900
Financial Advisory Services
N.A.I.C.S.: 523940

Daiwa Corporate Advisory SLU (1)
Calle Montalban 9, 28014, Madrid, Spain
Tel.: (34) 915241123
Financial Advisory Services
N.A.I.C.S.: 523940

**Daiwa Corporate Investment Co.,
Ltd.** (1)
Sumitomo Fudosan Kudan Building 12F,
8-10 Kudankita 1-chome, Chiyoda-ku, To-
kyo, 102-0073, Japan (100%)
Tel.: (81) 369102600
Sales Range: $250-299.9 Million
Emp.: 185
Private Equity Investment Firm
N.A.I.C.S.: 523999

**Daiwa Energy & Infrastructure Co.
Ltd.** (1)
Gran Tokyo North Tower 1-9-1, Marunouchi
Chiyoda-ku, Tokyo, 100-6730, Japan
Tel.: (81) 355556100
Web Site: http://www.daiwa-ei.jp
Asset Management Services
N.A.I.C.S.: 523940
Akira Yamanouchi (Chm)

Daiwa Facilities Co., Ltd. (1)
Daiwa Yaesu Building 6th Floor 2-1 Kyo-
bashi 1-chome, Chuo-ku, Tokyo, 104-0031,
Japan
Tel.: (81) 355554700
Securities Brokerage Services
N.A.I.C.S.: 523150

Daiwa Fund Consulting Co. Ltd. (1)
GranTokyo North Tower 9-1 Marunouchi
1-chome, Chiyoda-ku, Tokyo, 100-6756,
Japan
Tel.: (81) 355556550
Web Site: http://www.daiwa-fc.co.jp
Financial Advisory Services
N.A.I.C.S.: 523940
Tetsuo Akuzawa (Pres)

**Daiwa Institute of Research Holdings
Ltd.** (1)
15-6 Fuyuki, Koto-ku, Tokyo, 135-8460,
Japan
Tel.: (81) 35 620 5100
Web Site: https://www.dir.co.jp
Business Research & Consulting Services
N.A.I.C.S.: 523720

Takehiko Mizutani (Sr Exec Mng Dir)

Subsidiary (Domestic):

**Daiwa Institute of Research Business
Innovation Ltd.** (2)
1-14-5 Eitai Koto-ku, Tokyo, 135-0034, Ja-
pan
Tel.: (81) 3 5931 8600
System Integration & Consulting Services
N.A.I.C.S.: 541618
Yasuharu Okanoya (Sr Exec Mng Dir)

Daiwa Institute of Research Ltd. (1)
15-6 Fuyuki, Koto-ku, Tokyo, 135-8460,
Japan (100%)
Tel.: (81) 356205100
Web Site: http://www.dir.co.jp
Sales Range: $550-599.9 Million
Emp.: 1,500
Research & System Integration Services
N.A.I.C.S.: 541512
Takehiko Mizutani (Sr Exec Mng Dir)

Subsidiary (US):

**Daiwa Institute of Research America
Inc.** (2)
32 Old Slip 11th Fl, New York, NY
10005-3504 (100%)
Tel.: (212) 612-6100
Rev.: $1,000,000
Emp.: 21
Investment Research
N.A.I.C.S.: 523940

Subsidiary (Non-US):

**Daiwa Institute of Research Europe
Ltd.** (2)
5 King William Street, London, EC4N 7DA,
United Kingdom
Tel.: (44) 207 597 8503
Web Site: http://www.uk.daiwacm.com
Sales Range: $100-124.9 Million
Emp.: 500
Research, System Solutions & Consulting
Services
N.A.I.C.S.: 541611

**Daiwa Institute of Research Hong
Kong Ltd.** (2)
One Pacific Place 88 26th Fl, Queensway,
Central, China (Hong Kong)
Tel.: (852) 28484970
Web Site: http://www.daiwast.com
Sales Range: $25-49.9 Million
Emp.: 25
Research, System Solutions & Consulting
Services
N.A.I.C.S.: 541715

**Daiwa Interenational Holdings
Ltd.** (1)
GranTokyo North Tower 9-1 Marunouchi
1-chome, Chiyoda-ku, Tokyo, 100-6751,
Japan
Tel.: (81) 355551111
Securities Brokerage Services
N.A.I.C.S.: 523150

Daiwa International Holdings Inc. (1)
9-1 Marunouchi 1-chome, Chiyoda-ku, To-
kyo, 100-6751, Japan
Tel.: (81) 355551111
Securities Brokerage Services
N.A.I.C.S.: 523150

**Daiwa Investment Management
Inc.** (1)
GranTokyo North Tower 9-1 Marunouchi
1-chome, Chiyoda-ku, Tokyo, 100-6730,
Japan
Tel.: (81) 355556060
Securities Brokerage Services
N.A.I.C.S.: 523150

**Daiwa Investor Relations Co.
Ltd.** (1)
Daiwa Yaesu Building 7th Floor 1-2-1 Kyo-
bashi, Chuo-ku, Tokyo, 104-0031, Japan
Tel.: (81) 355554111
Web Site: http://www.daiwair.co.jp
Research & Consulting Services
N.A.I.C.S.: 541690
Jun Suzuki (Pres)

Daiwa Next Bank, Ltd. (1)
Gran Tokyo North Tower 9-1 Marunouchi

1-chome, Chiyoda-ku, Tokyo, 100-6756,
Japan (100%)
Tel.: (81) 3 5555 6500
Commercial Banking Services
N.A.I.C.S.: 522110
Kusaba Shinya (Pres)

Daiwa PI Partners Co. Ltd (1)
1-9-1 Marunouchi, Chiyoda-Ku, Tokyo, 100-
6730, Japan
Tel.: (81) 355556001
Web Site: https://www.dpipartners.co.jp
Sales Range: $50-74.9 Million
Emp.: 50
Investment Management Service
N.A.I.C.S.: 523999
Yuki Hayakawa (Pres)

Daiwa Property Co., Ltd. (1)
1-2-1kyoubashi, Chuo-ku, Tokyo, 104-0031,
Japan (100%)
Tel.: (81) 3 5555 4721
Web Site: http://www.daiwa-property.co.jp
Sales Range: $25-49.9 Million
Emp.: 45
Property Manager for Group Holdings
N.A.I.C.S.: 531311

**Daiwa Real Estate Asset Manage-
ment Co. Ltd** (1)
Daiwa Ginza Building 5F 6-2-1 Ginza,
Chuo-Ku, Tokyo, 104-0061, Japan
Tel.: (81) 36 215 9500
Web Site: https://www.daiwareal.co.jp
Real Estate Management Services
N.A.I.C.S.: 531390
Akira Yamanouchi (Mng Dir)

**Daiwa Securities Business Center
Co., Ltd.** (1)
Toyocho Center Building 2-3-2 Toyo, Koto-
ku, Tokyo, 135-0016, Japan (100%)
Tel.: (81) 356336100
Web Site: http://www.daiwa-dsc.co.jp
Sales Range: $1-9.9 Million
Emp.: 608
Business Services
N.A.I.C.S.: 561499

**Daiwa Securities Capital Markets Ko-
rea Co., Ltd.** (1)
21 Fl One IFC 10 Gukjegeumyung-Ro,
Yeongdeungpo-Gu, Seoul, 07326, Korea
(South)
Tel.: (82) 27879100
Financial Advisory Services
N.A.I.C.S.: 523940

Daiwa Securities Co., Ltd. (1)
GranTokyo North Tower 1-9-1, Chiyoda-ku
Marunouchi, Tokyo, 100-6752,
Japan (99.98%)
Tel.: (81) 35 555 2111
Web Site: https://www.daiwa.jp
Sales Range: $350-399.9 Million
Emp.: 744
Securities Brokerage Services
N.A.I.C.S.: 523150
Seiji Nakata (Pres)

Subsidiary (Non-US):

**DBP-Daiwa Capital Markets Philip-
pines, Inc.** (2)
18th Fl Citibank Tower 8741 Paseo de
Roxas, Salcedo Village, 1226, Makati,
Metro Manila, Philippines (60%)
Tel.: (63) 28137344
Sales Range: $50-74.9 Million
Emp.: 30
Investment Banking & Securities Brokerage
Services
N.A.I.C.S.: 523150

Subsidiary (US):

**Daiwa Capital Markets America Hold-
ings Inc.** (2)
32 Old Slip Financial Sq, New York, NY
10005-3504 (100%)
Tel.: (212) 612-7000
Sales Range: $75-99.9 Million
Emp.: 250
Holding Company; Investment Banking, Se-
curities Brokerage & Trust Services
N.A.I.C.S.: 551112
Masaaki Goto (Chm & CEO)

Subsidiary (Domestic):

**Daiwa Capital Markets America
Inc.** (3)

Financial Sq 32 Old Slip 14th Fl, New York,
NY 10005-3538 (100%)
Tel.: (212) 612-7000
Web Site: https://www.us.daiwacm.com
Sales Range: $200-249.9 Million
Emp.: 300
Investment Banking & Securities Brokerage
Services
N.A.I.C.S.: 523150
Masaaki Goto (Chm & CEO)

Daiwa Securities Trust Company (3)
1 Evertrust Plz, Jersey City, NJ
07302-3051 (100%)
Tel.: (201) 333-7300
Web Site: http://www.daiwast.com
Sales Range: $50-74.9 Million
Emp.: 30
Trust Company
N.A.I.C.S.: 522110

Subsidiary (Non-US):

**Daiwa Capital Markets Australia
Limited** (2)
Level 34 Rialto North Tower 525 Collins
Street, Melbourne, 3000, VIC,
Australia (100%)
Tel.: (61) 399161300
Web Site: http://www.au.daiwacm.com
Sales Range: $50-74.9 Million
Emp.: 20
Investment Banking & Securities Brokerage
Services
N.A.I.C.S.: 523150
Dean Stanford (Mng Dir)

**Daiwa Capital Markets Europe
Limited** (2)
5 King William Street, London, EC4N 7DA,
United Kingdom (100%)
Tel.: (44) 2075978000
Web Site: http://www.uk.daiwacm.com
Sales Range: $150-199.9 Million
Emp.: 435
Investment Banking & Securities Brokerage
Services
N.A.I.C.S.: 523150
Wilfried Schmidt (Vice Chm)

**Daiwa Capital Markets Hong Kong
Limited** (2)
Level 28 One Pacific Place 88 Queensway,
Hong Kong, 852, China (Hong
Kong) (100%)
Tel.: (852) 25250121
Web Site: http://www.hk.daiwacm.com
Sales Range: $50-74.9 Million
Emp.: 100
Investment Banking & Securities Brokerage
Services
N.A.I.C.S.: 523150

**Daiwa Capital Markets India Private
Limited** (2)
10th Floor 3 North Avenue Maker Maxity
Bandra East, Mumbai, 400 051, India
Tel.: (91) 22 6622 1000
Emp.: 5
Financial Management Services
N.A.I.C.S.: 523999

**Daiwa Capital Markets Philippines,
Inc.** (2)
Citibank Tower 18th Floor Paseo de Roxas
Salcedo Village, 8741, Makati, Philippines
Tel.: (63) 2 813 7344
Financial Management Services
N.A.I.C.S.: 523999

**Daiwa Capital Markets Singapore
Limited** (2)
7 Straits View Marina One East Tower 16-
05/06, Singapore, 018936,
Singapore (100%)
Tel.: (65) 6 387 8888
Web Site: https://www.sg.daiwacm.com
Sales Range: $100-124.9 Million
Emp.: 120
Investment Banking & Securities Brokerage
Services
N.A.I.C.S.: 523150

**Daiwa-Cathay Capital Markets Co.,
Ltd.** (2)
14th Floor 200 Keelung Road Sec 1, 1071,
Taipei, Taiwan (90%)
Tel.: (886) 22 723 9698
Web Site: http://www.jp.daiwacm.com

Sales Range: $100-124.9 Million
Emp.: 110
Investment Banking & Securities Brokerage Services
N.A.I.C.S.: 523150

Daiwa Securities Realty Co. Ltd. (1)
2-1 Ginza 6-Chome, Chuo-ku, Tokyo, 104-0061, Japan
Tel.: (81) 362159580
Web Site: https://daiwarealty.co.jp
N.A.I.C.S.: 531390
Toshio Fukushima *(Pres)*

Daiwa Securities SMBC Principal Investments Co. Ltd. (1)
Gran Tokyo North Tower 1-9-1 Marunouchi, Chiyoda-ku, Tokyo, 100-6754, Japan
Tel.: (81) 35 555 6111
Web Site: https://www.daiwasmbcpi.co.jp
Sales Range: $50-74.9 Million
Emp.: 65
Private Equity, Real Estate & Other Investment Services; Owned 60% by Daiwa Securities Group Inc. & 40% by Sumitomo Mitsui Financial Group, Inc.
N.A.I.C.S.: 523999
Shinya Nishio *(Chm)*

Fintertech Co. Ltd. (1)
6th Floor Atlas Building 5 Ichibancho, Chiyoda-ku, Tokyo, 102-0082, Japan
Tel.: (81) 332227333
Investment Brokerage Services
N.A.I.C.S.: 523999

Good Time Living Co. Ltd. (1)
2-15-15 Shiba, Minato-Ku, Tokyo, 105-0014, Japan
Tel.: (81) 354392200
Web Site: http://www.gtl-daiwa.co.jp
Housing Management Services
N.A.I.C.S.: 236117

IFIS Japan Ltd. (1)
Mfpr Roppongi Azabudai Bldg 1-8-7 Roppongi, Minato-ku, Tokyo, 106-0032, Japan
Tel.: (81) 368246440
Web Site: https://www.ifis.co.jp
Rev.: $39,377,860
Assets: $43,894,190
Liabilities: $5,473,480
Net Worth: $38,420,710
Earnings: $3,176,320
Emp.: 211
Fiscal Year-end: 12/31/2023
Document Preparation Services
N.A.I.C.S.: 561410
Kazuharu Osawa *(Chm & Pres)*

Myanmar Securities Exchange Centre Co., Ltd. (1)
21-25 Sule Pagoda Road 1st Floor of MEB, Pabedan Township, Yangon, Myanmar
Tel.: (95) 1378647
Web Site: http://www.msecmyanmar.com
Securities Brokerage Services
N.A.I.C.S.: 523150
U. Yin Zaw Myo *(Chm)*

Retela Crea Securities Co., Ltd. (1)
1-2-1 Kyobashi, Chuo-ku, Tokyo, 104-0031, Japan
Tel.: (81) 363850611
Web Site: http://www.retela.co.jp
Brokerage Security Services
N.A.I.C.S.: 523150

Sumitomo Mitsui DS Asset Management Company, Limited (1)
Toranomon Hills Business Tower 26F 1-17-1 Toranomon, Minato-ku, Tokyo, 105-6426, Japan
Tel.: (81) 36 205 0200
Web Site: https://www.smd-am.co.jp
Emp.: 1,009
Financial Advisory Services
N.A.I.C.S.: 523940
Takashi Saruta *(Pres & CEO)*

DAIWA SECURITIES LIVING INVESTMENT CORPORATION
6-2-1 Ginza, Chuo-ku, Tokyo, 104-0061, Japan
Tel.: (81) 367579680
Web Site: https://www.daiwa-securities-living.co.jp
Year Founded: 2005

8986—(TKS)
Sales Range: $50-74.9 Million
Real Estate Investment Management Services
N.A.I.C.S.: 523999
Tetsuo Akuzawa *(Exec Dir)*

DAIWABO HOLDINGS CO., LTD.
Nakanoshima Festival Tower West 3-2-4 Nakanoshima, Kita-ku, Osaka, 530-0005, Japan
Tel.: (81) 677397307
Web Site: https://www.daiwabo-holdings.com
Year Founded: 1941
3107—(TKS)
Rev.: $6,396,893,600
Assets: $2,678,742,160
Liabilities: $1,739,243,030
Net Worth: $939,499,130
Earnings: $28,310,630
Emp.: 2,867
Fiscal Year-end: 03/31/24
Textile Products Mfr
N.A.I.C.S.: 314999
Yoshihiro Nogami *(Chm-Daiwabo Information System Co Ltd)*

Subsidiaries:

Asahi Kako Co., Ltd. (1)
3-9-8 Tomobuchi-cho, Miyakojima-ku, Osaka, 534-0016, Japan
Tel.: (81) 66 923 5567
Web Site: https://www.asahi-kakou.co.jp
Home Electronic Product Mfr
N.A.I.C.S.: 334419
Satoshi Yoshimoto *(Pres)*

Asahi Processing Co., Ltd. (1)
8-14-8-1 Minamihonmachi, Chuo-ku, Osaka, Japan
Tel.: (81) 6 6271 2046
Textile Products Mfr
N.A.I.C.S.: 314999

DAIWA DO BRASIL TEXTIL LTDA. (1)
Av Jose Andraus Gassani 2215-Distrito Industrial, Uberlandia, 38402-322, Minas Gerais, Brazil
Tel.: (55) 34 3292 6000
Textile Products Mfr
N.A.I.C.S.: 314999

DIS Service & Solution Co., Ltd. (1)
3-2-4 Nakanoshima Festival Tower West 10F, Kita-ku, Osaka, 530-0005, Japan
Tel.: (81) 64 707 8300
Web Site: https://www.dis-sas.co.jp
System Integration Services
N.A.I.C.S.: 541512

Daiwa Maruesu Inc. (1)
73-1 Uozumicho Shimizu, Akashi, 674-0074, Hyogo, Japan
Tel.: (81) 789467501
Web Site: http://www.daiwa-maruesu.jp
Baseball & Softball Apparel Mfr & Distr
N.A.I.C.S.: 314999
Yasuaki Ochiai *(Pres)*

Daiwabo Information System Co., Ltd. (1)
3-2-4 Nakanoshima, Kita-ku, Osaka, 530-0005, Japan
Tel.: (81) 647078000
Emp.: 1,660
Personal Computer & Office Automation Machine Sales
N.A.I.C.S.: 423430
Yoshihiro Nogami *(Pres & CEO)*

Subsidiary (Domestic):

DIS Artworks Co., Ltd. (2)
Oi 1-20-10 Sumitomo Oimachibiru South Bldg Shinagawa-ku, Tokyo, 1400014, Japan
Tel.: (81) 364296069
Web Site: http://www.disart.co.jp
Commercial Printing & Promotional Products
N.A.I.C.S.: 323111
Kaoru Kikui *(Pres)*

DIS Service & Support Co., Ltd. (2)
Osaka International Building 22F 2-3-3 Azuchicho, Chuo-ku, Osaka, 541-0052, Japan (100%)
Tel.: (81) 662651630
Web Site: http://www.dis-sas.co.jp
Emp.: 256
Warehousing, Computer-Controlled Inventory, Logistics & Delivery Systems Services
N.A.I.C.S.: 493110
Kaoru Kikui *(Pres)*

DIS Solution Co., Ltd. (2)
1-20-10 Oi Sumitomo Oimachi Building South Building, Shinagawa-Ku, Tokyo, 140-0014, Japan
Tel.: (81) 364296088
Web Site: http://www.dsol.co.jp
Sales Range: $25-49.9 Million
Emp.: 147
Custom Computer Programming Services
N.A.I.C.S.: 541511

ZOA Corporation (2)
719 Ozuwa, Numazu City, Shizuoka, 410-0873, Japan
Tel.: (81) 559221975
Web Site: http://www.zoa.co.jp
Sales Range: Less than $1 Million
Emp.: 128
Computer Retail Operations
N.A.I.C.S.: 449210
Motofumi Ii *(Pres)*

Daiwabo Lifesupport Co., Ltd. (1)
7th Floor Sakaisuji Honmachi Building 1-8-14 Minamihonmachi, Chuo-ku, Osaka, 541-0054, Japan
Tel.: (81) 66 266 0314
Web Site: https://www.life-daiwabo.jp
Insurance Services
N.A.I.C.S.: 524210

Daiwabo Neu Co., Ltd. (1)
Midsuji Daiwa Bldg 6-8 Kyutaromachi 3-chome, Chuo-ku, Osaka, 541-0056, Japan
Tel.: (81) 662812405
Web Site: http://www.daiwabo.co.jp
Emp.: 82
Textile Products Mfr
N.A.I.C.S.: 314999
Kiyokazu Saito *(Pres)*

Daiwabo Rayon Co., Ltd. (1)
Midosuji Daiwa Bldg 6-8 Kyutaromachi 3-chome, Chuo-ku, Osaka, 541-0056, Japan
Tel.: (81) 676353290
Sales Range: $100-124.9 Million
Emp.: 161
Textile Products Mfr
N.A.I.C.S.: 314999
Kazunari Fukushima *(Pres)*

Subsidiary (Domestic):

Daiwabo Rayon Co., Ltd. - Masuda Mill (2)
3-1 Suko-cho, Masuda, 698-0036, Shimane, Japan
Tel.: (81) 856310550
Cotton Yarn Mfr
N.A.I.C.S.: 313110

Daiwabo Spintec Co., Ltd. (1)
75-2 Sasou Shinji-cho, Matsue, 699-0406, Shimane, Japan
Tel.: (81) 85 266 0221
Textile Product Mfr & Distr
N.A.I.C.S.: 313310

Daiwabo Tex Inc (1)
Nittsu Nigyocho Building 6F 26-5 Nihonbashiningyocho 2-Chome, Chuo-Ku, Tokyo, 103-0013, Japan
Tel.: (81) 3 4332 5226
Web Site: http://www.daiwabo-tex.co.jp
Textile Products Mfr
N.A.I.C.S.: 314999
Ken Hariya *(Mgr)*

Daiwaboadvance co., ltd. (1)
Web Site: http://www.daiwaboadvance.co.jp
Innerwear Mfr
N.A.I.C.S.: 315990

Daiwabouasoshie Inc. (1)
8-6-3 Kyutaromachi, Chuo-ku, Osaka, Japan

Tel.: (81) 662812512
Textile Products Mfr
N.A.I.C.S.: 314999

Daiwabouporitekku Inc. (1)
8-6-3 Kyutaromachi, Chuo-ku, Osaka, 541-0056, Japan
Tel.: (81) 662812414
Textile Products Mfr
N.A.I.C.S.: 314999

Plant (Domestic):

Daiwabouporitekku Inc. - Harima Plant (2)
877 Komiya Harima-cho, Kako-gun, Hyogo, Japan
Tel.: (81) 789421521
Sales Range: $25-49.9 Million
Emp.: 150
Textile Products Mfr
N.A.I.C.S.: 314999
Osamu Hamasaki *(Gen Mgr)*

Daiwabouraifusapoto Inc. (1)
8-4-1 Minamihonmachi, Chuo-ku, Osaka, 541-0054, Japan
Tel.: (81) 662660314
Textile Products Mfr
N.A.I.C.S.: 314999

Dienupurodakutsu Inc. (1)
Uozumicho Nishioka, Akashi, 674-0084, Japan
Tel.: (81) 78 944 6753
Textile Products Mfr
N.A.I.C.S.: 314999

Kanbo Pras Corporation (1)
1-8-14 Minamihonmachi Sakaisuji Honmachi Building 8th Floor, Chuo-ku, Osaka, 541-0054, Japan
Tel.: (81) 66 261 6836
Web Site: https://kanbo.co.jp
Emp.: 144
Resin Product Mfr & Distr
N.A.I.C.S.: 325211
Shinji Nakamura *(Pres)*

Kebi Industry Co., Ltd. (1)
1-5-24 Tadaokakita Tadaoka-cho, Senboku-gun, Osaka, Japan
Tel.: (81) 725203151
Textile Products Mfr
N.A.I.C.S.: 314999

O-M (U.S.A.), Inc. (1)
1104 Heinz Dr, East Dundee, IL 60118
Tel.: (847) 930-5893
Web Site: https://www.o-musa.com
Machinery Products Mfr
N.A.I.C.S.: 333248

O-M Machinery Ltd. (1)
10-10 Ueno 1-chome Usagiya Building, Taito-ku, Tokyo, 110-0005, Japan
Tel.: (81) 33 837 1271
Emp.: 137
Automatic Packaging Machinery Mfr & Distr
N.A.I.C.S.: 333993
Junji Oka *(Pres)*

O-M Shanghai Co., Ltd. (1)
Block E 8th Floor Feizhou International 899 Lingling Road, Xuhui District, Shanghai, 200030, China
Tel.: (86) 216 875 0633
Web Site: https://www.omltd.com.cn
Industrial Machinery Distr
N.A.I.C.S.: 423830

OMK Ltd. (1)
75 Sasou Shinji-cho, Matsue, 699-0406, Shimane, Japan
Tel.: (81) 85 266 0320
Automatic Packaging Machinery Mfr & Distr
N.A.I.C.S.: 333993

OMTEC Ltd. (1)
2-1 Kitazono-cho, Nagaoka, 940-0014, Niigata, Japan
Tel.: (81) 25 824 2131
Automatic Packaging Machinery Mfr & Distr
N.A.I.C.S.: 333993

Oji Fiber Co., Ltd. (1)
7F OJI Holdings 1st Building 5-12-9, Ginza Chuo-Ku, Tokyo, 104-0061, Japan
Tel.: (81) 35 550 3003
Web Site: https://www.ojifiber.co.jp
Textile Product Mfr & Distr

Daiwabo Holdings Co., Ltd.—(Continued)

N.A.I.C.S.: 313310
Hiroyuki Shiraishi (Pres & CEO)

P.T. Daiwabo Nonwoven Indonesia (1)
Suryacipta City of Industry Jl Surya Lestari Kavling I-2K, Desa Kutamekar Kecamatan Ciampel Kabupaten, Karawang, 41363, Jawa Barat, Indonesia
Tel.: (62) 267 863 7565
Nonwoven Fabric Mfr & Distr
N.A.I.C.S.: 313230

P.T. Primatexco Indonesia (1)
I Irip Srimoharjo Street, Sambong Batang Regency, 51212, East Java, Indonesia
Tel.: (62) 28 539 1300
Web Site: https://www.primatexco.com
Emp.: 1,710
Fabric Production Mfr
N.A.I.C.S.: 313310

PT DAIWABO INDUSTRIAL FAB-RICS INDONESIA (1)
Jl Raya Cirebon Bandung Km 12 Desa Plumbon, Kecamatan Plumbon, Cirebon, Jawa Barat, Indonesia
Tel.: (62) 231324002
Sales Range: $25-49.9 Million
Emp.: 129
Textile Products Mfr
N.A.I.C.S.: 314999
Harif Yasuka (Gen Mgr)

PT DAYANI GARMENT INDONESIA (DGI) (1)
Jl Raya Narogong Km 11 Bantar Gebang, Bekasi, Indonesia
Tel.: (62) 21 8250092
Web Site: http://www.daiwabo.co.jp
Textile Products Mfr
N.A.I.C.S.: 314999
Sinada Gorda (Gen Mgr)

PT Daiwabo Sheetec Indonesia (1)
Jalan Raya Cirebon-Bandung Km 12 Desa Plumbon Kecamatan, Kabupaten Cirebon, Karawang, Jawa Barat, Indonesia
Tel.: (62) 231 833 0115
Sewing Machine Services
N.A.I.C.S.: 811412

PT TOKAI TEXPRINT INDONESIA (TTI) (1)
Jl Jababaka Laya Kav B4 10 Cikarang Industrial Estate, Desa Pasir Gombong Kecamatan Cikarang Utara, Bekasi, 17530, West Java, Indonesia
Tel.: (62) 218934142
Web Site: https://tokaitexprint.blogspot.com
Textile Products Mfr
N.A.I.C.S.: 314999
Masaru Kasai (Gen Mgr)

DAIWASYSTEM CO., LTD.
3-6-1 Dosyo-machi Chuo-ku, Osaka, 541-0045, Japan
Tel.: (81) 662057011
Web Site: http://www.daiwasys.co.jp
Sales Range: $350-399.9 Million
Emp.: 240
Industrial & Commercial Construction Services; Other Real Estate Services
N.A.I.C.S.: 236220
Kazuhiko Hiromoto (Pres)

DAIYANG METAL CO., LTD.
222 kaechon-ri Sinam-myun, Yesan, 340-861, Chungcheong, Korea (South)
Tel.: (82) 413334675
Web Site: https://www.daiyangmetal.com
Year Founded: 1973
009190—(KRS)
Rev.: $195,560,187
Assets: $307,472,729
Liabilities: $173,631,943
Net Worth: $133,840,786
Earnings: $6,702,005
Emp.: 234
Fiscal Year-end: 12/31/22
Stainless Steel Mfr

N.A.I.C.S.: 331110
Lee YunSung (Exec Dir)

DAJIN HEAVY INDUSTRY CORPORATION
No 155 Xinqiu Street, Xinqiu District, Fuxin, 123005, Liaoning, China
Tel.: (86) 4186602618
Web Site: http://www.djse.com.cn
Year Founded: 2000
002487—(SSE)
Rev.: $716,897,844
Assets: $1,580,777,640
Liabilities: $667,190,628
Net Worth: $913,587,012
Earnings: $63,219,312
Emp.: 715
Fiscal Year-end: 12/31/22
Steel Structure Products Mfr & Distr
N.A.I.C.S.: 331110
Xin Jin (Chm)

DAKA SERVIS A.D.
Venizeloseva 29, Belgrade, Serbia
Tel.: (381) 11 3392 014
Year Founded: 1997
Sales Range: Less than $1 Million
Emp.: 61
Electrical Contracting Services
N.A.I.C.S.: 238210

DAKERYN INDUSTRIES LTD.
233 W 1st St #210, North Vancouver, V7M 1B3, BC, Canada
Tel.: (604) 986-0323
Web Site: http://www.dakeryn.com
Year Founded: 1991
Dimension Lumber Supplier
N.A.I.C.S.: 423310
Rob Chimko (Pres)

DAKOTA MINERALS LIMITED
25-27 Jewell Parade, Fremantle, 6159, WA, Australia
Tel.: (61) 89 335 3565　　　AU
Web Site: http://www.dakotaminerals.com.au
DKO—(ASX)
Sales Range: Less than $1 Million
Metal Mineral Exploration Services
N.A.I.C.S.: 212290
Mathew Whyte (Sec)

DALA ENERGI AB
Overmovagen 15, Box 254, 793 35, Leksand, Sweden
Tel.: (46) 24773800
Web Site: https://www.dalaenergi.se
Year Founded: 1897
DE—(NASDAQ)
Emp.: 80
Electricity Distribution Services
N.A.I.C.S.: 237990
Ake Soderman (Chm)

DALAL STREET INVEST-MENTS LIMITED
409 Dev Plaza 68 SV Road, Mumbai, 400058, Maharashtra, India
Tel.: (91) 2226201233
Web Site: https://www.dalalinvestments.com
Year Founded: 1977
501148—(BOM)
Rev.: $189,860
Assets: $1,191,670
Liabilities: $557,706
Net Worth: $633,964
Earnings: $18,868
Emp.: 3
Fiscal Year-end: 03/31/21
Securities Trading Services
N.A.I.C.S.: 523150
Megha Mehul Unadkat (CFO)

DALAROO METAL LIMITED

Suite 1 346 Barker Road, Subiaco, 6008, WA, Australia
Tel.: (61) 863809675　　　　AU
Web Site: https://www.dalaroometals.com.au
Year Founded: 2021
DAL—(ASX)
Rev.: $62,090
Assets: $1,307,289
Liabilities: $304,144
Net Worth: $1,003,145
Earnings: ($1,612,246)
Fiscal Year-end: 06/30/23
Metal Exploration Services
N.A.I.C.S.: 213114
Harjinder Singh Kehal (Mng Dir)

DALAT REAL ESTATE JOINT STOCK COMPANY
25 Tran Phu, Ward 3, Da Lat, Vietnam
Tel.: (84) 2633822243
Web Site: https://www.dalatreal.com.vn
Year Founded: 1992
Sales Range: $1-9.9 Million
Emp.: 180
Construction & Real Estate Services
N.A.I.C.S.: 236220
Dinh Thanh Tam (Chm)

DALATA HOTEL GROUP PLC
Termini 3 Arkle Road Sandyford Business Park, Sandyford, Dublin, D18 C9C5, Ireland
Tel.: (353) 12069400　　　　IE
Web Site: https://www.dalatahotelgroup.com
Year Founded: 2007
DAL—(LSE)
Rev.: $602,482,193
Assets: $2,459,431,254
Liabilities: $1,139,804,662
Net Worth: $1,319,626,592
Earnings: $104,387,006
Emp.: 5,487
Fiscal Year-end: 12/31/22
Hotel Owner & Operator
N.A.I.C.S.: 721110
Pat McCann (CEO)

Subsidiaries:

Pillo Hotels Limited (1)
The Rath, Co Meath, Ashbourne, A84 KR91, Ireland
Tel.: (353) 18350800
Web Site: https://www.pillohotelashbourne.com
Hotel Operator
N.A.I.C.S.: 721110
Andre Konings (Mgr-Guest Rels)

DALDRUP & SOHNE AG
Ludinghauser Str 42-46, 59387, Ascheberg, Westfalen, Germany
Tel.: (49) 259395930
Web Site: https://www.daldrup.eu
4DS—(DEU)
Rev.: $54,222,094
Assets: $45,865,798
Liabilities: $22,673,490
Net Worth: $23,192,309
Earnings: $982,444
Emp.: 133
Fiscal Year-end: 12/31/23
Drilling Services
N.A.I.C.S.: 213111
Josef Daldrup (Chm-Supervisory Bd)

Subsidiaries:

Daldrup Bohrtechnik AG (1)
Stationsstrasse 90, 6023, Rothenburg, Switzerland
Tel.: (41) 415111440
Drilling & Environmental Services
N.A.I.C.S.: 811310

GeoEnergie Taufkirchen GmbH & Co. KG (1)
Bavariafilmplatz 7, Geiselgasteig, 82031, Grunwald, Germany
Tel.: (49) 89215367762
Web Site: http://geoenergie-taufkirchen.de
Geothermal Energy Drilling Services
N.A.I.C.S.: 237110
Joerg Uhde (Gen Mgr)

Geothermie Neuried Verwaltungs GmbH (1)
Kirchstr 21, 77743, Neuried, Baden-Wurttemberg, Germany
Tel.: (49) 89 4524379 11
Geothermal Energy Drilling Services
N.A.I.C.S.: 237110

DALE ALCOCK HOMES PTY. LTD.
1 Pearson Way, Osborne Park, 6017, WA, Australia
Tel.: (61) 865580733
Web Site: http://www.dalealcock.com.au
Year Founded: 1987
Emp.: 150
Housing Construction Services
N.A.I.C.S.: 236116
Dale Alcock (Owner & Mng Dir)

DALE CAPITAL GROUP LIM-ITED
C/O NWT Trust 6/7th Floor Dias Pier Building, Le Caudan Waterfront Caudan, 11307, Port Louis, 11307, Mauritius
Tel.: (230) 2126946　　　　MU
Web Site: https://www.dale-capital.com
Year Founded: 2000
DCPL—(MAU)
Sales Range: $1-9.9 Million
Investment Management Service
N.A.I.C.S.: 523999
Norman Theodore Noland (Founder & CEO)

DALE DOWNIE NISSAN
1111 Oxford St E, London, N5Y 3C7, ON, Canada
Tel.: (519) 451-4560
Web Site: http://www.daledownienissan.ca
Year Founded: 1995
Sales Range: $25-49.9 Million
New & Used Car Dealers
N.A.I.C.S.: 441110
Richard Voakes (Gen Mgr)

DALEKOVOD D.D.
Marijana Cavica 4, 10000, Zagreb, Croatia
Tel.: (385) 12411111
Web Site: https://www.dalekovod.com
Year Founded: 1949
DLKV—(ZAG)
Rev.: $183,011,370
Assets: $152,256,320
Liabilities: $83,648,306
Net Worth: $68,608,014
Earnings: ($3,530,191)
Emp.: 1,029
Fiscal Year-end: 12/31/23
Engineeering Services
N.A.I.C.S.: 541330
Ivan Kurobasa (Member-Mgmt Bd)

Subsidiaries:

DALEKOVOD d.d. - Velika Gorica Factory (1)
Vukomericka bb, 10 410, Velika Gorica, Zagreb, Croatia
Tel.: (385) 16229900
Web Site: http://www.dalekovod-pro.com
Sales Range: $100-124.9 Million
Emp.: 300
Electricity Transmission Equipments Mfr

N.A.I.C.S.: 335311

Dalcom Engineering GmbH (1)
Muenchener Strasse 67 D, 83395, Freilass-ing, Bavaria, Germany
Tel.: (49) 8654608645
Eletric Power Generation Services
N.A.I.C.S.: 221111

Dalekovod AG (1)
Muenchener Strasse 67 D, Freilassing, 83395, Bavaria, Germany
Tel.: (49) 8654608645
Web Site: http://www.dalekovod.com
Emp.: 1
Eletric Power Generation Services
N.A.I.C.S.: 221111
Nenad Martinovic (Gen Mgr)

Dalekovod EMU d.o.o. (1)
43 Street no 36, 20 270, Vela Luka, Dubrovnik-Neretva, Croatia
Tel.: (385) 12411111
Sales Range: $25-49.9 Million
Emp.: 6
Electricity Meters Mfr
N.A.I.C.S.: 334515

Dalekovod Kazakhstan (1)
Prospekt Kabanbay-Batyra 11, Nur-Sultan, 010000, Kazakhstan
Tel.: (7) 7172688894
Web Site: http://www.dalekovod.com
Eletric Power Generation Services
N.A.I.C.S.: 221111

Dalekovod Professio d.o.o (1)
Marijana Cavica 4, 10 000, Zagreb, Croatia
Tel.: (385) 12459708
Web Site: http://www.dalekovod.com
Real Estate Consulting Service
N.A.I.C.S.: 531210

Dalekovod Skopje (1)
Ulica Jani Lukrovski br 8, 10 000, Skopje, North Macedonia
Tel.: (389) 1 241 1111
Web Site: http://www.dalekovod.com
Eletric Power Generation Services
N.A.I.C.S.: 221111

Dalekovod TKS a.d. (1)
Rudanka 28 PP 246, 74000, Doboj, Bosnia & Herzegovina
Tel.: (387) 53288100
Web Site: http://www.dalekovod-tks.com
Sales Range: $100-124.9 Million
Emp.: 256
Power Transmission Line & Structure Mfr
N.A.I.C.S.: 237130
Savo Malesevic (Vice Chm-Mgmt Bd)

Dalekovod Ukrajina d.o.o. (1)
19 Yevhena Sverstiuka Street building No 6A rooms 506 506A 506V, 02002, Kiev, Ukraine
Tel.: (380) 445783605
Construction Services
N.A.I.C.S.: 236220

Dalekovod d.o.o., Ljubljana (1)
Zavetiska Ulica 1, 1000, Ljubljana, Slovenia
Tel.: (386) 12561597
Eletric Power Generation Services
N.A.I.C.S.: 221111

Dalekovod-Cincaonica d.o.o., (1)
Trnoscica bb, 10 370, Dugo Selo, Croatia
Tel.: (385) 12784110
Web Site: http://www.dalekovod.com
Steel Products Mfr
N.A.I.C.S.: 331110

Dalekovod-projekt d.o.o. (1)
Marijana Cavica 4, 10000, Zagreb, Croatia
Tel.: (385) 12411111
Web Site: https://www.dalekovod-projekt.com
Emp.: 99
Electrical Engineering Services
N.A.I.C.S.: 541330
Davor Durdevic (Co-Pres)

Proizvodnja MK d.o.o. (1)
Vukomericka 9, Velika Gorica, 10410, Croatia
Tel.: (385) 1 622 9900
Construction Services
N.A.I.C.S.: 236220

DALETH PARTICIPACOES S.A.

Av Rio Branco 311 - Sala 523, 20040903, Rio de Janeiro, Brazil
Tel.: (55) 21 2196 7200
Year Founded: 1998
Emp.: 6,820
Investment Management Service
N.A.I.C.S.: 523940
Alberto Ribeiro Guth (Dir-IR)

DALI FOODS GROUP CO. LTD.
Room 2601 26th Floor One Harbour-front 18 Tak Fung Street, Hunghom, Kowloon, China (Hong Kong)
Tel.: (852) 59587335077   Ky
Web Site: http://www.dali-group.com
Year Founded: 1989
3799—(HKG)
Rev.: $2,801,990,740
Assets: $3,791,275,114
Liabilities: $1,166,625,158
Net Worth: $2,624,649,955
Earnings: $419,808,355
Emp.: 39,518
Fiscal Year-end: 12/31/22
Snack Food & Beverage Mfr & Distr
N.A.I.C.S.: 311919
Shihui Xu (Founder, Chm & Pres)

Subsidiaries:

Chengdu Dali Foods Co., Ltd. (1)
No 669 Xinban Road, Zhuzhuyuan Town Xindu District, Chengdu, 610506, Sichuan, China
Tel.: (86) 2883989809
Food & Beverage Product Mfr & Distr
N.A.I.C.S.: 311999

Gansu Dali Foods Co., Ltd. (1)
Dali Road, Laingzhou District, Wuwei, 733000, Gansu, China
Tel.: (86) 9356311530
Food & Beverage Product Mfr & Distr
N.A.I.C.S.: 311999

Guangdong Dali Foods Co., Ltd. (1)
No 70 Xingang East Road Wanshengwei, Haizhu, Guangdong, 526238, China
Tel.: (86) 7583637828
Food & Beverage Product Mfr & Distr
N.A.I.C.S.: 311999

Hebei Dali Foods Co., Ltd. (1)
No 2 Jiacun Hanchuan City, Xiaogan, 431600, Hubei, China
Tel.: (86) 7128413736
Food & Beverage Product Mfr & Distr
N.A.I.C.S.: 311999

Henan Dali Foods Co., Ltd. (1)
Dali Food Co Ltd Shenzhou Road East Xin-zheng City, Zhengzhou, 451100, Henan, China
Tel.: (86) 37155929556
Food & Beverage Product Mfr & Distr
N.A.I.C.S.: 311999

Jiangsu Dali Foods Co., Ltd. (1)
No 66 Lushan Avenue Hubin New City, Suqian, 223800, Jiangsu, China
Tel.: (86) 52788262208
Food & Beverage Product Mfr & Distr
N.A.I.C.S.: 311999

Jilin Dali Foods Co., Ltd. (1)
Near Haraha Gas Station, Zhuchengzi Town, Jilin, 130306, China
Tel.: (86) 43187300777
Food & Beverage Product Mfr & Distr
N.A.I.C.S.: 311999

Jinan Dali Foods Co., Ltd. (1)
Near No 42 Zhongxing Avenue, Jinan, 251402, China
Tel.: (86) 53184552809
Food & Beverage Product Mfr & Distr
N.A.I.C.S.: 311999

Ma'anshan Dali Foods Co., Ltd. (1)
No 166 Hunan Road Economic and Tech-nological Development Zone, Ma'anshan, 243000, Anhui, China
Tel.: (86) 5552106999
Food & Beverage Product Mfr & Distr
N.A.I.C.S.: 311999

Nanchang Dali Foods Co., Ltd. (1)

No 133 Yinhu 2nd Road Xiaolan Economic Development Zone, Liantang Town Nan-chang County, Nanchang, 330200, China
Tel.: (86) 79187176888
Food & Beverage Product Mfr & Distr
N.A.I.C.S.: 311999

Quanzhou Dali Foods Co., Ltd. (1)
102 Wanan Road Yutou Village, Huian County, Quanzhou, 362121, Fujian, China
Tel.: (86) 59587485068
Food & Beverage Product Mfr & Distr
N.A.I.C.S.: 311999

Shanxi Dali Foods Co., Ltd. (1)
183 Taihang North Road, Yinzhou District, Changzhi, 046011, Shanxi, China
Tel.: (86) 3553769198
Food & Beverage Product Mfr & Distr
N.A.I.C.S.: 311999

Yunnan Dali Foods Co., Ltd. (1)
1602 Building 5 Runcheng 1 District Qian-wei West Road, Xishan District, Kunming, 653100, Yunnan, China
Tel.: (86) 8772791806
Food & Beverage Product Mfr & Distr
N.A.I.C.S.: 311999

DALI PHARMACEUTICAL CO., LTD.
No 118 West Huancheng Road, Xi-aguan Town, Dali, 671000, China
Tel.: (86) 8728880055
Web Site: https://www.daliyaoye.cn
Year Founded: 1996
603963—(SHG)
Rev.: $18,581,098
Assets: $70,689,505
Liabilities: $14,367,146
Net Worth: $56,322,359
Earnings: ($2,485,291)
Emp.: 300
Fiscal Year-end: 12/31/22
Pharmaceutical Product Mfr & Distr
N.A.I.C.S.: 325412
Yang Junxiang (Chm & Gen Mgr)

DALIA LTD.
6 Sazaklyatie Str, Gabrovo, 5300, Bulgaria
Tel.: (359) 888 205 930
Web Site: http://www.dalia.bg
Woodworking & Furniture Products Mfr
N.A.I.C.S.: 449110

DALIAN BIO-CHEM COMPANY LIMITED
Floor 11 Yifang Financial Plaza No 12 Gangdong Street, Zhongshan District, Liaoning, 116001, China
Tel.: (86) 41182735006
Web Site: https://www.biofc.com
Year Founded: 2003
603360—(SHG)
Rev.: $176,435,050
Assets: $246,316,679
Liabilities: $41,154,216
Net Worth: $205,162,462
Earnings: $56,520,196
Emp.: 600
Fiscal Year-end: 12/31/22
Antiseptic Mfr & Distr
N.A.I.C.S.: 325412
Liu Xianwu (Chm)

Subsidiaries:

Dalian Bio-Chem Company Limited - Lvshun Factory (1)
No 325 Shunle Street Economic Develop-ment Zone Lvshunkou District, Dalian, 116052, China
Tel.: (86) 41186227111
Chemical Products Mfr
N.A.I.C.S.: 325320

Dalian Bio-Chem Company Limited - Songmudao Factory (1)
Songmudao Chemical Industrial Zone Wa-fangdian, Dalian, Liaoning, China
Tel.: (86) 41185316000

Chemical Products Mfr
N.A.I.C.S.: 325320

DALIAN DAFU HOLDINGS CO., LTD.
No 411 Houge Street, Ganjingzi Dis-trict, Dalian, 116035, Liaoning, China
Tel.: (86) 411 66888775
Sales Range: $50-74.9 Million
Holding Company
N.A.I.C.S.: 551112
Shengjun Dou (Chm-Interim)

DALIAN ENERGAS GAS-SYSTEM CO., LTD.
42 Fuquan North Road, Dalian, 116600, China
Tel.: (86) 41162493333
Web Site: http://www.energas.cn
Year Founded: 2002
603318—(SHG)
Rev.: $543,284,258
Assets: $611,257,908
Liabilities: $357,331,310
Net Worth: $253,926,598
Earnings: $6,265,561
Emp.: 500
Fiscal Year-end: 12/31/22
Gas Distribution Equipment Mfr & Distr
N.A.I.C.S.: 333248
Fan Dengzhao (Pres)

DALIAN FRIENDSHIP (GROUP) CO., LTD.
No 1 Qiyi Street, Zhongshan District, Dalian, 116023, Liaoning, China
Tel.: (86) 41182691470
Web Site: https://www.sz000679.com
Year Founded: 1992
000679—(SSE)
Rev.: $20,984,184
Assets: $137,191,860
Liabilities: $92,868,984
Net Worth: $44,322,876
Earnings: ($7,042,464)
Fiscal Year-end: 12/31/22
Departmental Store Operator
N.A.I.C.S.: 455110
Li Jian (Chm)

DALIAN HAOSEN EQUIPMENT MANUFACTURING CO., LTD.
No 9 Yinghui Road, Ganjingzi District, Dalian, Liaoning, China
Tel.: (86) 41139516666
Web Site:
https://www.haosen.com.cn
Year Founded: 2002
688529—(SHG)
Rev.: $219,975,729
Assets: $583,080,723
Liabilities: $414,364,682
Net Worth: $168,716,040
Earnings: $12,666,102
Emp.: 1,900
Fiscal Year-end: 12/31/22
Automation Equipment Mfr
N.A.I.C.S.: 334512

Subsidiaries:

Dalian Haosen Software Co., Ltd. (1)
No 9 Yinghui Road, Ganjingzi District, Da-lian, Liaoning, China
Tel.: (86) 41139030116
Web Site: https://www.haosen-soft.com
Industrial Machinery Mfr & Distr
N.A.I.C.S.: 333248

Dalian Haosenread Equipment Manu-facture Co., Ltd. (1)
No 9 Yinghui Road, Ganjingzi District, Da-lian, Liaoning, China
Tel.: (86) 41139516666
Industrial Machinery Mfr & Distr
N.A.I.C.S.: 333248

Dalian Haosen Equipment Manufacturing Co.,
Ltd.—(Continued)

Haosen Automation GmbH (1)
Friedrich-Ebert-Anlage 36, 60325, Frankfurt
am Main, Germany
Tel.: (49) 15204563139
Industrial Machinery Mfr & Distr
N.A.I.C.S.: 333248

**Haosen Automation India Private
Limited** (1)
275/1 276/1 Raisoni Industrial Park Hinje-
wadi Phase II Village Maan, Tal Mulshi,
Pune, 411057, India
Tel.: (91) 8390926596
Industrial Machinery Mfr & Distr
N.A.I.C.S.: 333248

**Haosen Automation North America,
Inc.** (1)
691N Squirrel Rd Ste 288, Auburn Hills, MI
48326
Tel.: (248) 556-6398
Industrial Machinery Mfr & Distr
N.A.I.C.S.: 333248

Haosen Hong Kong Limited (1)
Room 1702 17/F Hong Kong Trade Centre
Nos 161-167 Des Voeux Road, Central,
China (Hong Kong)
Tel.: (852) 35903426
Industrial Machinery Mfr & Distr
N.A.I.C.S.: 333248

**Haosen Intelligent Equipment (Shen-
zhen) Co., Ltd.** (1)
Unit E/F 16th Floor Building 2 Phase 3,
North Region of Baoneng Science & Tech
Park Qinghu Community Longhua, Shen-
zhen, China
Tel.: (86) 75523779424
Industrial Machinery Mfr & Distr
N.A.I.C.S.: 333248

**Haosen Runbo Intelligent Manufactur-
ing Changzhou Co., Ltd.** (1)
No 366 Jingye Road, Wujin District,
Changzhou, Jiangsu, China
Tel.: (86) 51968025866
Automotive Equipment Mfr & Distr
N.A.I.C.S.: 336320

Haosen Ultra-precision Co., Ltd. (1)
Room 1203 Block B Building 11 Shenzhen
Bay Ecological Park No 16 South, Science
& Technology Road Yuehai Sub-district
Nanshan District, Shenzhen, China
Tel.: (86) 75586660270
Electric Equipment Mfr
N.A.I.C.S.: 334419

**DALIAN HUARUI HEAVY IN-
DUSTRY GROUP CO., LTD.**
No 169 Bayi Road, Xigang District,
Dalian, 116013, Liaoning, China
Tel.: (86) 41186427861
Web Site: http://www.dhidcw.com
Year Founded: 1993
002204—(SSE)
Rev.: $1,454,174,748
Assets: $3,042,962,208
Liabilities: $2,106,796,068
Net Worth: $936,166,140
Earnings: $40,459,068
Emp.: 5,430
Fiscal Year-end: 12/31/22
Industrial Machinery Mfr & Distr
N.A.I.C.S.: 333248
Changnan Shao *(Chm)*

Subsidiaries:

DHHI Germany GmbH (1)
Wasserstr 221, 44799, Bochum, Germany
Tel.: (49) 23452861880
Web Site: https://www.dhhi.de
Gearbox Mfr & Retailer
N.A.I.C.S.: 333612
Yuan Wang *(Mng Dir)*

**Dalian Huarui Heavy Industry India
Company Priviate Limited** (1)
704 Suryakiran Building 19 KG Marg, New
Delhi, 10001, India
Tel.: (91) 1143404228
Web Site: http://www.dhhiindia.com

Heavy Industrial Equipment Mfr & Retailer
N.A.I.C.S.: 333248

STX Heavy Industry Co. Ltd. (1)
381 Nammyeon-ro, Seongsan-gu, 642-050,
Changwon, Gyeongsangnam, Korea
(South)
Tel.: (82) 552800700
Web Site: http://www.stxhi.co.kr
Engine Equipment Mfr
N.A.I.C.S.: 333618

**DALIAN INSULATOR GROUP
CO., LTD.**
No 88 East Liaohe Road DD Port,
Dalian Econ & Tech Dev Area, Da-
lian, 116600, China
Tel.: (86) 41162272888
Web Site: https://www.insulators.cn
Year Founded: 1915
002606—(SSE)
Rev.: $169,325,208
Assets: $291,363,696
Liabilities: $78,473,772
Net Worth: $212,889,924
Earnings: $25,373,088
Emp.: 2,060
Fiscal Year-end: 12/31/22
Porcelain & Ceramic Insulator Mfr
N.A.I.C.S.: 327110
Ying Jian *(Chm)*

Subsidiaries:

Dalian Insulator (Fujian) Co., Ltd. (1)
No 128 Bosan Bosan Block, ChiYuan Town
MinQing County, Fuzhou, 350807, Minqing,
China
Tel.: (86) 59162302693
Insulator Mfr
N.A.I.C.S.: 327110

**DALIAN MORNINGSTAR NET-
WORK TECHNOLOGY CO.,
LTD.**
No 9 4th Floor Unit 1 No 52 Changji-
ang East Road, Zhongshan District,
Dalian, 116308, Liaoning, China
Tel.: (86) 411 82952526
Web Site:
   http://www.morningstarnet.com
Year Founded: 2001
002447—(SSE)
Sales Range: $100-124.9 Million
Mobile Device-based Games De-
signer
N.A.I.C.S.: 513210
Xiaohui Song *(CFO & Deputy Gen
Mgr)*

**DALIAN MY GYM EDUCATION
TECHNOLOGY CO., LTD.**
No 39 Torch Road Qixianling Industri-
alization Base, High-Tech Zone, Da-
lian, 116024, Liaoning, China
Tel.: (86) 41184798808
Web Site: http://www.slsj.com.cn
002621—(SSE)
Rev.: $21,603,348
Assets: $378,365,364
Liabilities: $192,249,720
Net Worth: $186,115,644
Earnings: ($61,780,212)
Emp.: 340
Fiscal Year-end: 12/31/22
Plastic Pipe Equipment Mfr
N.A.I.C.S.: 333248
Xin Chen *(Chm)*

**DALIAN SHIDE GROUP CO.,
LTD.**
38 Gao Er Ji Road, XiGang District,
Dalian, 116011, Liaoning, China
Tel.: (86) 41183622218   **CN**
Web Site: http://www.shide.com
Year Founded: 1992
Sales Range: $800-899.9 Million
Emp.: 5,500

Holding Company; Chemical Building
Materials, Petrochemicals & Home
Appliances Mfr & Distr
N.A.I.C.S.: 551112
Chunguo Chen *(Pres)*

Subsidiaries:

**Chengdu Building Materials
Company** (1)
No 24 Xingguang West Road, Longquanyi
District, Chengdu, China
Tel.: (86) 2884868269
Building Material Mfr & Distr
N.A.I.C.S.: 327120

**Dalian Building Materials
Company** (1)
No 55 Mosquito Street Changxing Island,
Shide Industrial Park Lingang Industrial
Zone, Dalian, China
Tel.: (86) 41139923335
Building Material Mfr & Distr
N.A.I.C.S.: 327120

**Dalian Shide Plastics Industry Co.,
Ltd.** (1)
38 Gao Er Ji Road, XiGang District, Dalian,
116011, Liaoning, China
Tel.: (86) 41183622218
Web Site: http://www.shide-global.com
Chemical & Plastic Building Materials Mfr &
Distr
N.A.I.C.S.: 325998
Chunguo Chen *(Pres)*

**Jiangxi Building Materials
Company** (1)
Industrial Park, Anyi County, Nanchang,
Jiangxi, China
Tel.: (86) 79183499377
Building Material Mfr & Distr
N.A.I.C.S.: 327120

**Jiaxing Building Materials
Company** (1)
No 383 Binhai Avenue Economic Develop-
ment Zone, Shide Industrial Park Daqiao
New District Haiyan County, Jiaxing, China
Tel.: (86) 57386863082
Building Material Mfr & Distr
N.A.I.C.S.: 327120

**Luohe Building Materials
Company** (1)
North Section of Taihang Mountain Road,
Shide Industrial Park Yancheng District,
Luohe, China
Tel.: (86) 3953226695
Building Material Mfr & Distr
N.A.I.C.S.: 327120

**Yinchuan Building Materials
Company** (1)
No 218 Wenchang South Road, Xixia Dis-
trict, Yinchuan, Ningxia Hui, China
Tel.: (86) 9517680114
Building Material Mfr & Distr
N.A.I.C.S.: 327120

**DALIAN SUNAISA TOURISM
HOLDINGS CO., LTD.**
No 608-6-8 Zhongshan Road, Sha-
hekou District, Dalian, 116023, Liaon-
ing, China
Tel.: (86) 41184685225
Web Site: http://www.sunasia.com
Year Founded: 1993
600593—(SHG)
Rev.: $22,072,621
Assets: $285,740,297
Liabilities: $242,768,532
Net Worth: $42,971,765
Earnings: ($10,958,739)
Fiscal Year-end: 12/31/22
Holding Company
N.A.I.C.S.: 551112
Yang Ziping *(Chm)*

**DALIAN THERMAL POWER
CO., LTD.**
No 32 Kunming Street, Zhongshan
District, Dalian, 116011, Liaoning,
China

Tel.: (86) 41184438700
Web Site: https://www.dlrd.com
600719—(SHG)
Rev.: $113,297,788
Assets: $375,320,650
Liabilities: $313,382,347
Net Worth: $61,938,302
Earnings: ($21,979,171)
Emp.: 3,000
Fiscal Year-end: 12/31/22
Electric Power Generation & Distribu-
tion Services
N.A.I.C.S.: 221116
Tian Luwei *(Chm)*

Subsidiaries:

**Hangzhou Caizhixin Technology Co.,
Ltd.** (1)
Rm 1314-1315 Jinjun Plaza 341 Shuixiang
Rd, Jiangang, Hangzhou, 310020, China
Tel.: (86) 57186539522
Web Site: https://www.hzkaixin.com
Chemical Mfr & Distr
N.A.I.C.S.: 325998

**Montessori Academy Group Holdings
Pty Ltd.** (1)
60 - 70 Parramatta Road, Summer Hill,
2130, NSW, Australia
Tel.: (61) 1300000162
Web Site:
   https://montessoriacademy.com.au
Child Care Services
N.A.I.C.S.: 624410

**DALIAN TIANBAO GREEN
FOODS CO., LTD.**
No 624 Sanli Village Yongzheng
Street, Jinzhou District, Dalian,
116001, China
Tel.: (86) 411 3995 9288
Web Site: http://www.cn-tianbao.com
Year Founded: 1997
Rev.: $151,060,210
Assets: $722,588,300
Liabilities: $347,191,320
Net Worth: $375,396,980
Earnings: ($23,989,350)
Fiscal Year-end: 12/31/18
Aquatic & Agricultural Product Mfr
N.A.I.C.S.: 311710
Hongze Li *(Pres)*

**DALIAN TONGHAI MACHIN-
ERY & ELECTRONIC EQUIP-
MENT CO., LTD.**
38 Anshan Rd, Dalian, 116022, Sha-
hekou District, China
Tel.: (86) 411 844 22299
Year Founded: 1948
Machine Tools Mfr
N.A.I.C.S.: 333517

Subsidiaries:

ICM (1)
3505 Centennial Dr, Midland, MI 48642-
6940
Tel.: (989) 495-5000
Web Site: http://www.teamicms.com
Sales Range: $25-49.9 Million
Emp.: 50
Design & Mfr of Crankshaft & Camshaft
Processing
N.A.I.C.S.: 333517
Lee Anne Rise *(Controller)*

Ingersoll Production Systems (1)
1301 Eddy Ave, Rockford, IL 61103-3173
Tel.: (815) 637-8500
Web Site: http://www.ingersollprodsys.com
Sales Range: $25-49.9 Million
Emp.: 60
Machine Tool Services
N.A.I.C.S.: 333517
Scott Kuhar *(Engr-Design Controls)*

**DALIAN TOP-EASTERN
GROUP CO., LTD.**
218 Zhenxing Road, Ganjingzi District, Dalian, 116113, China

Tel.: (86) 41187103820   CN
Web Site: http://www.top-
eastern.com
Year Founded: 2003
Sales Range: $50-74.9 Million
Emp.: 4,000
Holding Services
N.A.I.C.S.: 551112
Shumin Qi *(CEO)*

Subsidiaries:

Greenfield Industries, Inc.   **(1)**
2501 Davis Creek Rd, Seneca, SC 29678
Tel.: (706) 863-7708
Web Site: http://www.gfii.com
Sales Range: $50-74.9 Million
Emp.: 200
Industrial Cutting Tools Mfr & Supplier
N.A.I.C.S.: 333517
Ty Taylor *(Pres & CEO)*

Subsidiary (Non-US):

Greenfield Industries Canada
Inc.   **(2)**
1305 Meyerside Dr, Mississauga, L5T 1C9,
ON, Canada
Tel.: (905) 696-8561
Cutting Tools Mfr & Whslr
N.A.I.C.S.: 333517

Herramientas Cleveland, S.A. de
C.V.   **(2)**
Calz Azcapotzalco La Villa No 1001, Col
Industrial Vallejo, Mexico, 02300, DF,
Mexico
Tel.: (52) 5555877400
Web Site:
http://www.herramientascleveland.com
Sales Range: $50-74.9 Million
Emp.: 150
Cutting Tools, Machine Tool Accessories &
Machinists Precision Measuring Devices
N.A.I.C.S.: 333515

DALIAN WANDA GROUP COR-
PORATION LTD.
Tower B Wanda Plaza No 93 Jianguo
Road, Chaoyang District, Beijing,
100022, China
Tel.: (86) 10 8585 3888   CN
Web Site: http://www.wanda-
group.com
Year Founded: 1988
Sales Range: $5-14.9 Billion
Investment Holding Company
N.A.I.C.S.: 551112
Jianlin Wang *(Chm)*

Subsidiaries:

AMC Entertainment Holdings,
Inc.   **(1)**
1 AMC Way 11500 Ash St, Leawood, KS
66211   **(75%)**
Tel.: (913) 213-2000
Web Site: http://www.amctheatres.com
Rev.: $4,812,600,000
Assets: $9,009,200,000
Liabilities: $10,857,100,000
Net Worth: ($1,847,900,000)
Earnings: ($396,600,000)
Emp.: 2,881
Fiscal Year-end: 12/31/2023
Holding Company; Motion Picture Theaters
Owner & Operator
N.A.I.C.S.: 551112
Kevin M. Connor *(Gen Counsel, Sec & Sr
VP)*

Subsidiary (Domestic):

AMC Entertainment Inc.   **(2)**
1 AMC Way 11500 Ash St, Leawood, KS
66211   **(100%)**
Tel.: (913) 213-2000
Web Site: http://www.amctheatres.com
Rev.: $2,946,900,000
Assets: $5,109,989,000
Liabilities: $3,570,018,000
Net Worth: $1,539,971,000
Earnings: $103,856,000
Emp.: 970
Fiscal Year-end: 12/31/2015
Motion Picture Theaters Owner & Operator
N.A.I.C.S.: 512131

Craig R. Ramsey *(CFO & Exec VP)*

Carmike Cinemas, LLC   **(2)**
11500 Ash St, Leawood, KS 66211
Tel.: (913) 213-2000
Holding Company; Motion Picture Theaters
Owner & Operator
N.A.I.C.S.: 551112

Subsidiary (Domestic):

Seth Childs 12 of Kansas L.L.C.   **(3)**
2610 Farm Bureau Rd, Manhattan, KS
66502   **(100%)**
Tel.: (785) 776-9811
Theater Operator
N.A.I.C.S.: 711110

Start Media LLC   **(3)**
101 Hudson St 37th Fl Ste 3705, Jersey
City, NJ 07302
Tel.: (212) 620-5700
Web Site: http://start-alternative.com
Theater Operator
N.A.I.C.S.: 711110
Michael J. Maher *(CEO)*

Subsidiary (Domestic):

Cinetopia, LLC   **(2)**
12345 SW Horizon Blvd Ste 231, Beaver-
ton, OR 97007
Tel.: (360) 213-2800
Restaurant Operating Services
N.A.I.C.S.: 722410
Bryan Monahan *(Gen Mgr)*

Dalian Wanda Commercial Properties
Co., Ltd.   **(1)**
Floor 21-25 Tower B Wanda Plaza No 93
Jianguo Road, Chaoyang District, Beijing,
100022, China
Tel.: (86) 10 85853888
Web Site: http://www.wandaplazas.com
Commercial Properties Construction Ser-
vices & Owner
N.A.I.C.S.: 236220
Jie Qi *(Chm)*

Infront Sports & Media AG   **(1)**
Grafenauweg 2, PO Box 44426, 6304, Zug,
Switzerland
Tel.: (41) 41 723 15 15
Web Site: http://www.infrontsports.com
Emp.: 1,000
Sports Event Management Services
N.A.I.C.S.: 711310
Philippe Blatter *(Pres & CEO)*

Subsidiary (Non-US):

Infront Austria GmbH   **(2)**
Innsbrucker Bundesstrasse 126, 5020,
Salzburg, Austria
Tel.: (43) 662 83 18 18 0
Sports Event Management Services
N.A.I.C.S.: 711310
Stefan Krauss *(Co-Mng Dir)*

Infront Finland Oy   **(2)**
Areenankuja 1 E, 00240, Helsinki, Finland
Tel.: (358) 204 1997
Sports Event Management Services
N.A.I.C.S.: 711310
Mikko Vanni *(Mng Dir)*

Infront France SAS   **(2)**
48 avenue Marceau, 75008, Paris, France
Tel.: (33) 1 55 19 55 00
Web Site: http://www.infrontsports.com
Emp.: 20
Sports Event Management Services
N.A.I.C.S.: 711310
Jean-Francois Jeanne *(Mng Dir)*

Infront Germany GmbH   **(2)**
Zentrale Frankfurt Barckhausstrasse 1,
60325, Frankfurt am Main, Germany
Tel.: (49) 69 7079 836 0
Advertising Services
N.A.I.C.S.: 541810
Reinhardt Weinberger *(Mng Dir)*

Infront Italy S.r.l.   **(2)**
Via Deruta 20, 20132, Milan, Italy
Tel.: (39) 02 771121
Web Site: http://www.infrontsports.com
Emp.: 250
Medical Consulting Services
N.A.I.C.S.: 512191
Luigi de Siervo *(Pres & CEO)*

Infront Netherlands BV   **(2)**
Beech Avenue 101, 1119 RB, Schiphol-Rijk,
Netherlands
Tel.: (31) 20 201 1233
Sports Event Management Services
N.A.I.C.S.: 711310
Barbara Peeters *(Mng Dir)*

Infront Pan-Asia Pte. Ltd.   **(2)**
600 North Bridge Road 24-06/07 Parkview
Square, Singapore, 188778, Singapore
Tel.: (65) 6829 2500
Web Site: http://www.infrontsports.com
Emp.: 9
Sports Event Management Services
N.A.I.C.S.: 711310
Ian Mathie *(Mng Dir)*

Infront Sportif Pazarlama Anonim
Sirketi   **(2)**
Sinanpasa Mahallesi Suleyman Seba Cad-
desi Akaretler Siraevler No 14 F1, Besiktas,
Istanbul, Turkiye
Tel.: (90) 212 260 30 30
Sports Event Management Services
N.A.I.C.S.: 711310
Ender Uslu *(Mng Dir)*

Infront Sports & Media (China) Co.,
Ltd   **(2)**
707 South Area China National Convention
Center No 7 Tianchen East, Chaoyang Dis-
trict, 100105, Beijing, China
Tel.: (86) 10 8889 0888
Web Site: http://www.infront.com
Emp.: 70
Sports Event Management Services
N.A.I.C.S.: 711310
Anne Zhao *(Mng Dir)*

Legendary Entertainment, LLC   **(1)**
2900 W Alameda Ave 15th Fl, Burbank, CA
91505
Tel.: (818) 688-7003
Web Site: http://www.legendary.com
Holding Company; Motion Picture, Television & Digital Content Production & Distribution Services; Comic Book Publisher; Entertainment Fan Website Publisher
N.A.I.C.S.: 513199
Thomas Tull *(Founder)*

Subsidiary (Domestic):

Legendary Pictures Productions,
LLC   **(2)**
2900 W Alameda Ave 15th Fl, Burbank, CA
91505
Tel.: (818) 688-7003
Web Site: http://www.legendary.com
Motion Picture Production Services
N.A.I.C.S.: 512110
Thomas Tull *(Founder, Chm & CEO)*

Legendary Television, LLC   **(2)**
2900 W Alameda Ave 15th Fl, Burbank, CA
91505
Tel.: (818) 688-7003
Web Site: http://www.legendary.com
Television Program Production Services
N.A.I.C.S.: 512110
Bruce Rosenblum *(Pres)*

Wanda Hotel Development Company
Limited   **(1)**
Unit 3007 30th Floor Two Exchange Square
8 Connaught Place, Central, China (Hong
Kong)   **(65%)**
Tel.: (852) 21533600
Web Site: http://www.wanda-hotel.com.hk
Rev.: $104,139,450
Assets: $670,803,638
Liabilities: $264,399,555
Net Worth: $406,404,083
Earnings: $29,704,440
Emp.: 1,342
Fiscal Year-end: 12/31/2022
Real Estate Development Services
N.A.I.C.S.: 531312
Benxi Ding *(Chm)*

Wanda Sports Group Company
Limited   **(1)**
93 Jianguo Road 9/F Tower B Wanda
Plaza, Chaoyang District, Beijing, 100022,
China   **(88.5%)**
Tel.: (86) 10 8585 7456
Web Site: http://www.wsg.cn
Rev.: $1,153,545,389
Assets: $2,011,336,871

Liabilities: $1,755,993,113
Net Worth: $255,343,758
Earnings: ($306,657,983)
Emp.: 1,850
Fiscal Year-end: 12/31/2019
Holding Company
N.A.I.C.S.: 551112
Edith Kwan *(Gen Mgr-Securities Dept)*

World Triathlon Corporation   **(1)**
3407 W Martin Luther King Blvd Ste 100,
Tampa, FL 33607
Tel.: (813) 868-5940
Web Site: http://www.ironman.com
Sporting Event Organizer & Promoter
N.A.I.C.S.: 711320
Andrew Messick *(Pres & CEO)*

Subsidiary (Domestic):

Competitor Group, Inc.   **(2)**
3407 W Dr Martin Luther King Jr Blvd Ste
100, Tampa, FL 33607
Tel.: (858) 650-4510
Web Site: http://www.competitorgroup.com
Media & Event Entertainment Services; Pe-
riodical Publisher
N.A.I.C.S.: 711320

DALIAN ZEUS ENTERTAIN-
MENT CO., LTD.
East Tower 2403 No 9 Zhongshan No
2 Xinglin Street, Zhongshan District,
Dalian, 116001, Liaoing, China
Tel.: (86) 41188858282
Web Site:
http://www.tianshenhudong.com
Year Founded: 2003
002354—(SSE)
Rev.: $244,669,366
Assets: $388,056,516
Liabilities: $51,012,880
Net Worth: $337,043,636
Earnings: ($34,245,062)
Emp.: 700
Fiscal Year-end: 12/31/22
Web & Mobile Game Developer
N.A.I.C.S.: 513210

DALIAN ZHIYUN AUTOMATION
CO., LTD.
No 32 Yingri Road Yingchengzi In-
dustrial Park, Gan Jing Zi District,
Dalian, 116011, Liaoning, China
Tel.: (86) 41186705656
Web Site: https://www.zhiyun-cn.com
Year Founded: 1999
300097—(CHIN)
Rev.: $63,213,696
Assets: $198,476,460
Liabilities: $126,136,764
Net Worth: $72,339,696
Earnings: ($40,252,680)
Fiscal Year-end: 12/31/22
Automation Equipment Mfr & Sales
N.A.I.C.S.: 334513

DALIPAL HOLDINGS LIMITED
Room 4006 40th Floor Jardine House
1 Connaught Place, Hong Kong,
China (Hong Kong)   Ky
Web Site: https://www.dalipal.com
Year Founded: 1998
1921—(HKG)
Rev.: $647,741,544
Assets: $641,395,280
Liabilities: $426,242,477
Net Worth: $215,152,803
Earnings: $23,224,185
Emp.: 1,777
Fiscal Year-end: 12/31/22
Holding Company
N.A.I.C.S.: 551112
Hongyao Zhang *(Vice Chm)*

DALLAH AL BARAKA HOLD-
ING COMPANY E.C.
Jeddah Dallah Street Dallah Tower,
PO Box 430, Jeddah, 21411, Saudi
Arabia

Dallah Al Baraka Holding Company
E.C.—(Continued)

Tel.: (966) 126710000
Web Site: http://www.dallah.com
Sales Range: $1-4.9 Billion
Emp.: 38,250
Holding Company; Industrial Investment; Agriculture; Real Estate Development; Tourism; Transportation; Media; Construction; Communications; Finance & Insurance
N.A.I.C.S.: 551112
Saleh Abdullah Kamel *(Founder & Chm)*

Subsidiaries:

Islamic Arab Insurance Co.
(P.S.C.)   (1)
4th Floor Block A Spectrum Building Oud
Metha Sheikh Rashid Road, PO Box
10214, Dubai, United Arab Emirates
Tel.: (971) 800725262
Web Site: https://www.salama.ae
Rev.: $302,495,376
Assets: $983,892,684
Liabilities: $804,952,908
Net Worth: $178,939,776
Earnings: ($37,934,819)
Emp.: 275
Fiscal Year-end: 12/31/2023
Insurance Services
N.A.I.C.S.: 524298
Jassim Mohammed Alseddiqi *(Chm)*

DALLAH ALMUTAQDMAH BUSES & EQUIPMENT CO. LTD.
Dallah Tower Philistine St, Jeddah,
Saudi Arabia
Tel.: (966) 126710000   SA
Transportation Services
N.A.I.C.S.: 485999

DALLAH HEALTH COMPANY
King Fahed Road Nakheel, Riyadh,
12381, Saudi Arabia
Tel.: (966) 112255065
Web Site:
https://www.dallahhealth.com
Year Founded: 1987
4004—(SAU)
Rev.: $351,051,039
Assets: $1,061,809,012
Liabilities: $569,223,743
Net Worth: $492,585,269
Earnings: $26,658,363
Emp.: 2,000
Fiscal Year-end: 12/31/20
Hospital Owner & Operator
N.A.I.C.S.: 622110
Ahmad Saleh Babaeer *(CEO)*

DALLI-WERKE GMBH & CO. KG
Zweifaller Strasse 120, 52224, Stolberg, Germany
Tel.: (49) 24028900   De
Web Site: http://www.dalli-group.com
Year Founded: 1845
Sales Range: $250-299.9 Million
Emp.: 1,750
Private Label Brand Mfr
N.A.I.C.S.: 339999
Hermann Wirtz *(Mng Dir)*

Subsidiaries:

DALLI-WIN IBERICA SL   (1)
Av Maresme 45, Sant Adria de Besos,
08930, Barcelona, Spain
Tel.: (34) 93462 7140
Detergent Product Mfr
N.A.I.C.S.: 325611

Dalli-De Klok B.V.   (1)
Kamperweg 1, 8181 CR, Heerde, Netherlands
Tel.: (31) 578 698 500
Detergent Product Mfr
N.A.I.C.S.: 325611

WIN AEROSOL GmbH & Co.
KG   (1)
Langenhahner Strasse 33, 56457, Westerburg, Germany
Tel.: (49) 2663 982 212
Cosmetics Products Mfr
N.A.I.C.S.: 325620

WIN COSMETIC GmbH & Co.
KG   (1)
Wilhelm-Ternis-Strasse 21-25, 67592, Florsheim, Germany
Tel.: (49) 6243 90 60 0
Cosmetics Products Mfr
N.A.I.C.S.: 325620

WIN WARTH GmbH   (1)
Marktstrasse 25, 2831, Warth, Austria
Tel.: (43) 2629 23 61 312
Detergent Product Mfr
N.A.I.C.S.: 325611

DALLMEIER ELECTRONIC GMBH & CO. KG
Cranachweg 1, Regensburg, 93051,
Germany
Tel.: (49) 94187000
Web Site: http://www.dallmeier.com
Year Founded: 1984
Rev.: $29,657,100
Emp.: 108
Software Technology Solution Service
N.A.I.C.S.: 541511
Dieter Dallmeier *(Founder & CEO)*

Subsidiaries:

Dallmeier International Ltd.   (1)
5C Anson House 13-19 Lock Road, Tsimshatsui, Kowloon, China (Hong Kong)
Tel.: (852) 27353811
Photographic Equipment Distr
N.A.I.C.S.: 423410

Dallmeier International Ltd.   (1)
Unit J K - 10th Floor Zhu Kuan Mansion
Avenida Xian Xing Hai No 81-121, Macau,
China (Macau)
Tel.: (853) 28728901
Photographic Equipment Distr
N.A.I.C.S.: 423410
Craig Graham *(Gen Mgr-Asia)*

Dallmeier Italia Srl   (1)
Via della Previdenza Sociale 9, 42124,
Reggio Emilia, Italy
Tel.: (39) 0522232465
Photographic Equipment Distr
N.A.I.C.S.: 423410
Daniele Sisinio *(Dir-Branch Office)*

Dallmeier Korea Co., Ltd   (1)
Room 201-1104 Chunui Technopark,
Chunui-dong Wonmi-gu, Bucheon,
Gyeonggi-do, Korea (South)
Tel.: (82) 326230535
Digital Video Equipment Mfr
N.A.I.C.S.: 334310
Jeon Yongwan *(Gen Mgr)*

Dallmeier Switzerland Divinet
GmbH   (1)
Bosch 73, 6331, Hunenberg, Switzerland
Tel.: (41) 417831979
Photographic Equipment Distr
N.A.I.C.S.: 423410
Roland Deja *(Mgr-Sls)*

Dallmeier Turkey NI-TI Elektronik Guvenlik Sist San.Tic. Ltd   (1)
Ceyhun Atuf Kansu Cad No 145/22, Cankaya, Ankara, Turkiye
Tel.: (90) 3122299100
Photographic Equipment Distr
N.A.I.C.S.: 423410

Dallmeier electronic Espana,
S.L.   (1)
C/ Princesa 25 6 1 Edificio Hexagono,
28008, Madrid, Spain
Tel.: (34) 915902287
Photographic Equipment Mfr
N.A.I.C.S.: 333310

Dallmeier electronic UK Ltd   (1)
Dallmeier House 3 Beaufort Trade Park,
Pucklechurch, Bristol, BS16 9QH, United
Kingdom

Tel.: (44) 1173039303
Photographic Equipment Distr
N.A.I.C.S.: 423410
James Walker *(Mng Dir)*

Dallmeier electronic USA Inc.   (1)
2953 W Cypress Creek Rd Ste 200, Fort
Lauderdale, FL 33309
Tel.: (702) 487-8500
Photographic Equipment Distr
N.A.I.C.S.: 423410
Marcel Zangger *(Dir-Ops)*

DALLMER GMBH & CO. KG
Wiebelsheidestrasse 25, 59757, Arnsberg, Germany
Tel.: (49) 293296160
Web Site: http://www.dallmer.de
Year Founded: 1913
Rev.: $19,984,500
Emp.: 170
Sanitary Ware Products Mfr
N.A.I.C.S.: 322291
Johannes Dallmer *(Gen Mgr)*

Subsidiaries:

Dallmer Ltd.   (1)
4 Norman Way Lavenham, Sudbury, C010
9PY, Suffolk, United Kingdom
Tel.: (44) 1787248244
Web Site: http://www.dallmer.com
Bathroom Fitting & Accessory Mfr
N.A.I.C.S.: 332999

DALMAR MOTORS LTD.
475 Wharncliffe Rd South, London,
N6J 2N1, ON, Canada
Tel.: (519) 433-3181   ON
Web Site: http://www.dalmarvw.ca
Year Founded: 1953
New & Used Car Dealers
N.A.I.C.S.: 441110
Ken Oesch *(Mgr-Svs)*

DALMIA BHARAT LIMITED
11th & 12th Floor Hansalaya Building,
15 Barakhamba Road, New Delhi,
110 001, India
Tel.: (91) 1123310121   In
Web Site:
http://www.dalmiabharat.com
Year Founded: 1935
Rev.: $1,373,636,800
Assets: $1,205,277,600
Liabilities: $36,254,800
Net Worth: $1,169,022,800
Earnings: $45,435,200
Emp.: 2,658
Fiscal Year-end: 03/31/18
Cement Mfr
N.A.I.C.S.: 327310
Jai Hari Dalmia *(Mng Dir)*

Subsidiaries:

Dalmia Bharat Sugar and Industries
Ltd   (1)
11th and 12th Floors Hansalaya Building 15
Barakhamba Road, New Delhi, 110 001,
India
Tel.: (91) 11123465100
Web Site: https://www.dalmiasugar.com
Rev.: $420,723,030
Assets: $521,739,855
Liabilities: $199,725,435
Net Worth: $322,014,420
Earnings: $40,367,145
Emp.: 2,648
Fiscal Year-end: 03/31/2022
Cement & Sugar Mfr
N.A.I.C.S.: 327310
Jai Hari Dalmia *(Vice Chm)*

Dalmia Cement (Bharat) Limited   (1)
Hansalaya Bldg 11th & 12th Fl 15 Barakhamba Rd, New Delhi, 110 001, India
Tel.: (91) 1123465100
Web Site: http://www.dalmiacement.com
Cement Mfr
N.A.I.C.S.: 327310
Jai Hari Dalmia *(Vice Chm)*

Subsidiary (Domestic):

OCL India Limited   (2)
Narain Manzil 17th Floor 23 Barakhamba
Road, New Delhi, 110001, India   (100%)
Tel.: (91) 11 4363 1200
Web Site: http://www.ocl.in
Rev.: $571,314,964
Assets: $828,453,300
Liabilities: $401,527,356
Net Worth: $426,925,944
Earnings: $65,753,448
Fiscal Year-end: 03/31/2018
Cement & Concrete Product Mfr
N.A.I.C.S.: 327310
Pradip Kumar Khaitan *(Chm)*

Subsidiary (Domestic):

Landmark Property Development
Company Limited   (3)
11th Floor Narain Manzil Building 23 Barakhamba Road, New Delhi, 110 001,
India   (100%)
Tel.: (91) 1143621200
Web Site: https://www.landmarkproperty.in
Rev.: $256,087
Assets: $8,591,320
Liabilities: $124,096
Net Worth: $8,467,224
Earnings: $54,710
Fiscal Year-end: 03/31/2021
Real Estate Development Services
N.A.I.C.S.: 531390
Gaurav Dalmia *(Chm & Mng Dir)*

Subsidiary (Non-US):

OCL China Limited   (3)
Nanlau Economic Development Zone Chenjia Village, Dashiqiao, 115103, Liaoning,
China
Tel.: (86) 13840759468
Web Site: http://www.oclindialtd.in
Sales Range: $10-24.9 Million
Refractory Product Mfr & Distr
N.A.I.C.S.: 327120
Mayadhar Mishra *(Asst Exec Dir)*

Dalmia Refractories Limited   (1)
4 Scindia House Connaught Place, New
Delhi, 110 001, India
Tel.: (91) 11 23457100
Web Site: http://www.dalmiarefractories.com
Rev.: $28,614,249
Assets: $46,984,198
Liabilities: $13,389,800
Net Worth: $33,594,398
Earnings: ($992,308)
Emp.: 373
Fiscal Year-end: 03/31/2018
Refractory Products Mfr
N.A.I.C.S.: 327310
C. N. Maheshwari *(CEO)*

DALMIA INDUSTRIAL DEVELOPMENT LIMITED
9th Floor Room No 8E 2A Ganesh
Chandra Avenue, Kolkata, 700 013,
West Bengal, India
Tel.: (91) 3340014000
Web Site:
https://www.dalmiaindustry.in
Year Founded: 1956
Rev.: $886,248
Assets: $3,030,989
Liabilities: $81,258
Net Worth: $2,949,731
Earnings: $18,943
Fiscal Year-end: 03/31/19
Textile Product Mfr & Distr
N.A.I.C.S.: 313240
Raj Mohta *(Exec Dir)*

DALMORE CAPITAL LIMITED
Watling House 5th Floor 33 Cannon
Street, London, EC4M 5SB, United
Kingdom
Tel.: (44) 20 3372 0490   UK
Web Site:
http://www.dalmorecapital.com
Year Founded: 2009
Emp.: 30
Investment Fund Management Services

N.A.I.C.S.: 523940
Michael Ryan *(Co-Founder, CEO & Partner)*

DALOL OIL SHARE COMPANY
New Bright Tower 3rd Floor Room 301, PO Box 8049, Addis Ababa, Ethiopia
Tel.: (251) 11 667 25 01   ET
Web Site: http://www.daloloil.com
Year Founded: 2009
Sales Range: $25-49.9 Million
Emp.: 8
Petroleum Products & Lubricants Supplier; Oil & Gas Exploration Services; Gas Station Owner & Operator
N.A.I.C.S.: 424720
Dereje Walelign *(Chm)*

DALRYMPLE BAY INFRA-STRUCTURE LIMITED
Level 15 One Eagle Waterfront Brisbane 1 Eagle St, Brisbane, 4000, QLD, Australia
Tel.: (61) 730023100   AU
Web Site:
   https://www.dbinfrastructure.com.au
Year Founded: 2020
DBI—(ASX)
Rev.: $446,011,171
Assets: $2,630,751,311
Liabilities: $1,881,336,421
Net Worth: $749,414,890
Earnings: $50,355,562
Fiscal Year-end: 12/31/23
Construction Services
N.A.I.C.S.: 237120
Stephanie Commons *(CFO)*

Subsidiaries:

Dalrymple Bay Infrastructure Management Pty. Ltd.   **(1)**
Level 15 Waterfront Place 1 Eagle St, Brisbane, QLD 4000, NT, Australia
Tel.: (61) 30023100
Web Site: https://dbinfrastructure.com.au
Telecommunication Infrastructure Services
N.A.I.C.S.: 517111

DAM PHU MY PACKAGING JSC
1B Street Phu My 1 Industrial Zone Phu My Ward, Phu My, Ba Ria Vung Tau, Vietnam
Tel.: (84) 937979075
Web Site: https://dpmp.vn
Year Founded: 2004
PMP—(HNX)
Rev.: $54,974,100
Assets: $23,954,000
Liabilities: $17,199,400
Net Worth: $6,754,600
Earnings: $714,200
Fiscal Year-end: 12/31/22
Plastics Bag Mfr
N.A.I.C.S.: 326111

DAM SEN WATER PARK CORPORATION
03 Hoa Binh Ward 3 District 11, Ho Chi Minh City, Vietnam
Tel.: (84) 838588418
Web Site:
   https://www.damsenwaterpark.com
Year Founded: 1999
DSN—(HOSE)
Rev.: $10,255,257
Assets: $14,276,130
Liabilities: $1,220,344
Net Worth: $13,055,786
Earnings: $4,635,288
Fiscal Year-end: 12/31/23
Amusement Park Operator
N.A.I.C.S.: 713110

DAMABOIS, INC.
441 County Road 7 East, Saint-Damase-de-Matapédia, G0J 2J0, QC, Canada
Tel.: (418) 776-5455
Web Site: https://damabois.com
Wooden Pallets Mfr
N.A.I.C.S.: 321920

Subsidiaries:

Pallets, Inc.   **(1)**
99 1/2 East St, Fort Edward, NY 12828
Tel.: (518) 747-4177
Web Site:
   http://www.palletsincorporated.com
Sales Range: $1-9.9 Million
Emp.: 45
Wooden Pallets, Skids & Crates Mfr
N.A.I.C.S.: 321920
Arthur Binley *(Chm)*

DAMAC GROUP
Damac Exec Heights Opp Emmar Bus Park, PO Box 2195, Dubai, United Arab Emirates
Tel.: (971) 43731000
Web Site:
   http://www.damacgroup.com
Sales Range: $150-199.9 Million
Emp.: 1,900
Holding Company; Investments; Fast Food; Industrial Catering; Property Development; & Commercial Trading
N.A.I.C.S.: 551112
Hussain Sajwani *(Founder & Chm)*

Subsidiaries:

Al Amana Building Materials Co. L.L.C   **(1)**
PO Box 1429, Ruwi, Oman
Tel.: (968) 24815080
Web Site: http://www.damacholding.com
Sales Range: $25-49.9 Million
Emp.: 85
Building Material Dealers
N.A.I.C.S.: 444180
R. Murali *(Gen Mgr)*

Al-Jazeira Services Co. SAOG   **(1)**
408 4th Floor International Medical Centre, PO Box 2865, Near Al Hamriya Roundabout, 112, Ruwi, Oman
Tel.: (968) 24706499
Web Site: https://www.aljazeiraservices.com
Rev.: $26,632,240
Assets: $53,616,707
Liabilities: $7,493,566
Net Worth: $46,123,141
Earnings: $5,937,770
Emp.: 1,040
Fiscal Year-end: 12/31/2023
Business Services
N.A.I.C.S.: 561499
Hussain Ali Habib Sajwani *(Chm)*

Blues Seafood Restaurant LLC   **(1)**
Unit 3 Marina Walk, PO Box 2195, Dubai Marina, Dubai, United Arab Emirates
Tel.: (971) 43674747
Web Site: http://www.damacholding.com
Full-Service Restaurants
N.A.I.C.S.: 722511

DAMAC Invest Co. LLC   **(1)**
Tecom Executive Heights Damac Building, PO Box 2195, Dubai, United Arab Emirates
Tel.: (971) 43322005
Web Site: http://www.damacgroup.com
Real Estate Property Lessors
N.A.I.C.S.: 531190

DAMAC Properties Dubai Co PJSC   **(1)**
Executive Heights 20th Floor Barsha Heights, PO Box 2195, Dubai, United Arab Emirates
Tel.: (971) 43731000
Web Site: http://www.damacproperties.com
Rev.: $1,197,510,860
Assets: $6,485,303,077
Liabilities: $2,654,532,034
Net Worth: $3,830,771,043
Earnings: ($10,038,833)
Fiscal Year-end: 12/31/2019
Property Development Services
N.A.I.C.S.: 531311

Farooq Mahmood Arjomand *(Chm)*

Subsidiary (Non-US):

Roberto Cavalli S.p.A.   **(2)**
Piazza San Babila 3, 20122, Milan, Italy
Tel.: (39) 02 7630 371
Web Site: http://www.robertocavalli.com
Men's & Women's Clothing Designer
N.A.I.C.S.: 315990
Roberto Cavalli *(Founder)*

de Grisogono SA   **(2)**
Route de Saint Julien 176 bis, Plan-les-Ouates, 1228, Switzerland
Tel.: (41) 228178100
Web Site: http://www.degrisogono.com
Sales Range: $100-124.9 Million
Emp.: 160
Watch & Jewelry Mfr
N.A.I.C.S.: 334519
Fawaz Gruosi *(Founder & Pres)*

Damac Al Jazeira Catering WLL   **(1)**
PO Box 5113, Doha, Qatar
Tel.: (974) 4447387
Web Site: http://www.dohadamac.qa
Sales Range: $10-24.9 Million
Emp.: 50
Caterers
N.A.I.C.S.: 722320

Draieh Genera Trading Co. WLL   **(1)**
PO Box 2415, Kuwait, Safat, Kuwait
Tel.: (965) 25313860
Web Site: http://www.damacholding.com
Full-Service Restaurants
N.A.I.C.S.: 722511

DAMANSARA REALTY BERHAD
Lot 10 3 Level 10 Wisma Chase Perdana Off Jalan Semantan, Damansara Heights, 50490, Kuala Lumpur, Malaysia
Tel.: (60) 3 2081 2688   MY
Web Site: http://www.dbhd.com.my
DBHD—(KLS)
Sales Range: $50-74.9 Million
Emp.: 1,379
Property Development Services
N.A.I.C.S.: 531312
Safiah Adnan *(Head-Operation)*

Subsidiaries:

Damansara Realty Management Services Sdn. Bhd.   **(1)**
Level 4 Block C Pusat Bandar Damansara, 50490, Kuala Lumpur, Malaysia
Tel.: (60) 3 2732 2695
Property Management Services
N.A.I.C.S.: 531311

Damansara Technology Sdn. Bhd.   **(1)**
Lot 10 3 Level 10 Wisma Chase Perdana Off Jalan Semantan, Damansara Heights, 50490, Kuala Lumpur, Malaysia
Tel.: (60) 320812688
Web Site: http://www.damansaratech.com
Software Services
N.A.I.C.S.: 541511

HC Duraclean Sdn. Bhd.   **(1)**
No 2 Jalan Garuda 1 Off Jalan Cenderawasih Larkin Jaya, 80350, Johor Bahru, Malaysia
Tel.: (60) 72217970
Web Site: http://www.hcduraclean.com.my
Cleaning & Water Disposal Services
N.A.I.C.S.: 562998

Metro Parking (M) Sdn. Bhd.   **(1)**
Lot 10 2 Level 10 Wisma Chase Perdana Off Jalan Semantan, Damansara Heights, 50490, Kuala Lumpur, Malaysia
Tel.: (60) 320812777
Web Site: http://www.metro-parking.com
Consultancy Services
N.A.I.C.S.: 541618
Azrul Abdul Karim *(Head-Bus Compliance)*

Metro Parking (S) Pte. Ltd.   **(1)**
Block 1004 Toa Payoh North 03-11/12/14/15, Singapore, 318995, Singapore
Tel.: (65) 63347773
Web Site: http://www.metroparking.com.sg

Other Commercial Services
N.A.I.C.S.: 561499

Metro Parking Management (Philippines) Inc.   **(1)**
4th Floor Salustiana D Ty Tower104 Paseo de Roxas Street, Makati, Philippines
Tel.: (63) 7521026
Web Site: http://www.metro-parking.com.ph
Transport Services
N.A.I.C.S.: 485999

TMR Urusharta (M) Sdn. Bhd.   **(1)**
Suite 6 1a Level 6 Wisma Chase Perdana Off Jalan Semantan Damansara, 50490, Kuala Lumpur, Malaysia
Tel.: (60) 320812692
Web Site: http://www.tmrurusharta.com
Mechanical & Electrical Installation Services
N.A.I.C.S.: 238290
Brian Iskandar Zulkarim *(Chm)*

DAMARA GOLD CORP.
301 - 1665 Ellis Street, Kelowna, V1Y 2B3, BC, Canada
Tel.: (250) 717-1840
Web Site:
   https://www.damaragoldcorp.com
Year Founded: 1989
DMR—(TSXV)
Sales Range: Less than $1 Million
Gold Exploration Services
N.A.I.C.S.: 212220
David M. R. Stone *(Pres & COO)*

DAMARIS SA
9 chemin du Jublin, 69570, Dardilly, France
Tel.: (33) 478645151
Web Site: https://damaris.fr
MLDAM—(EUR)
Sales Range: Less than $1 Million
Software Publishing Services
N.A.I.C.S.: 513210
Artak Abedi *(Chm & CEO)*

DAMARTEX SA
160 boulevard de Fourmies, 59100, Roubaix, France
Tel.: (33) 320114500   FR
Web Site: https://www.damartex.com
Year Founded: 1953
ALDAR—(EUR)
Sales Range: $800-899.9 Million
Emp.: 3,300
Thermal Underwear & Related Cold Weather Clothing Mfr & Marketer
N.A.I.C.S.: 313310
Bruno Defache *(CFO & Member-Mgmt Bd)*

Subsidiaries:

3 Pagen Versand und Handelsgesellschaft mbH   **(1)**
St Joeris Strasse 16-28, 52477, Alsdorf, Germany
Tel.: (49) 1805 70 70 70
Web Site: http://www.3pagen.de
Mail Order Catalog Company; Sales of Kitchen, Household & Decorative Items
N.A.I.C.S.: 425120

Subsidiary (Non-US):

3 Pagen Handelsgesellschaft mbH   **(2)**
Pflegerplatz 4, Hallein, 5400, Salzburg, Austria
Tel.: (43) 820 89 99 11
Web Site: http://www.3pagen.at
Mail Order Catalog Company; Sales of Kitchen, Household & Decorative Items
N.A.I.C.S.: 423320

Damart   **(1)**
Bowling Green Mills, Bingley, BD97 1AD, West Yorkshire, United Kingdom   **(100%)**
Tel.: (44) 1274 510900
Web Site: http://www.damartonline.co.uk
Sales Range: $100-124.9 Million
Emp.: 350
Provider of Clothing by Mail Order
N.A.I.C.S.: 313310

Damartex SA—(Continued)

Damart Serviposte S.A. (1)
25 Ave De La Fosse Aux Chenes, Roubaix, 59100, France (100%)
Tel.: (33) 320114530
Web Site: http://www.damart.com
Sales Range: $650-699.9 Million
Emp.: 300
Mail-Order Houses
N.A.I.C.S.: 315250

Damart Swiss AG (1)
Swissair IATA Center Route de l'Aeroport 29, CP 230, 1215, Geneva, Switzerland
Tel.: (41) 848000873
Ecommerce Services
N.A.I.C.S.: 813910

Damartex UK Ltd (1)
Bowling Green Mills, Bingley, BD97 1AD, West Yorkshire, United Kingdom
Tel.: (44) 8714230000
Ecommerce Services
N.A.I.C.S.: 813910
Fiona Mannion (Mng Dir)

Labels by Andres NV (1)
Nijverheidsstraat 20, 9070, Destelbergen, Belgium
Tel.: (32) 92181811
Web Site: http://www.labelsbyandres.be
Emp.: 160
Fashion & Apparel Distr
N.A.I.C.S.: 458110
Tine Naessens (Mktg Dir)

DAMAVAND MINING COMPANY
No1 2nd alley Pakistan av Dr Beheshti av, Tehran, Iran
Tel.: (98) 88500267
Web Site:
    https://damavandmining.co.ir
Year Founded: 1983
DMVN—(THE)
Sales Range: Less than $1 Million
Emp.: 40
Metal Mining Services
N.A.I.C.S.: 212290

DAMEN SHIPYARDS GROUP
Avelingen-West 20, Gorinchem, 4202, Netherlands
Tel.: (31) 183639911
Web Site: http://www.damen.com
Year Founded: 1927
Ship & Shipyards Designing & Construction Services; Maritime Services
N.A.I.C.S.: 336611
Kommer Damen (Chm)

Subsidiaries:

AMELS (1)
Glacisstraat 165, 4381 SE, Vlissingen, Netherlands
Tel.: (31) 118 485 002
Web Site: http://www.amels-holland.com
Ship Building & Repair Services
N.A.I.C.S.: 336611
Rob Luijendijk (Mng Dir)

Brixham Marine Services Ltd (1)
Unit 21 Northfield Industrial Est, Brixham, Devon, TQ5 8UA, United Kingdom
Tel.: (44) 1803 856 633
Web Site: http://www.bmslimited.co.uk
Marine Engineering Services
N.A.I.C.S.: 541330
Mike Rankin (Mng Dir)

DAMEN Shipyards Cape Town (Pty) Ltd. (1)
Corner of Duncan & Eastern Mole Roads, Table Bay Harbour, Cape Town, 8001, South Africa
Tel.: (27) 21 447 17 14
Web Site: http://www.damen.co.za
Ship Building & Repair Services
N.A.I.C.S.: 336611
Gary Atkins (Mgr-Bus Dev-Repairs & Svcs)

DAMEX Shipbuilding & Engineering (1)
KM 7 Carretera de Punta Gorda, Santiago

de Cuba, Havana, Cuba
Tel.: (53) 22686101
Web Site: http://www.damex.biz
Sales Range: $50-74.9 Million
Emp.: 200
Shipbuilding, Engineering & Repairing Services
N.A.I.C.S.: 336611

Damen Dredging Equipment BV (1)
Edisonstraat 32, 3861 NE, Nijkerk, Netherlands
Tel.: (31) 332474040
Web Site: http://www.damen.com
Sales Range: $25-49.9 Million
Emp.: 80
Ship Building & Repairing
N.A.I.C.S.: 336611
Trimpe Burger (Mng Dir)

Damen Engineering Gdansk Sp. z o. o. (1)
C K Norwida 4, 80-280, Gdansk, Poland
Tel.: (48) 58 760 76 70
Ship Building & Repair Services
N.A.I.C.S.: 336611
Bert Nieuwenhuizen (Mng Dir)

Damen Marine Components (Suzhou) Co., Ltd.
111 Tianshangjiang road, 215128, Suzhou, Jiangsu, China
Tel.: (86) 512 659 85 166
Marine Component Mfr
N.A.I.C.S.: 332999
Rikkers Rikkers (Gen Mgr)

Damen Marine Components BV (1)
Nijverheidsstraat 8, PO Box 96, 3371 XE, Hardinxveld-Giessendam, Netherlands
Tel.: (31) 184676262
Web Site: http://www.damenmc.com
Sales Range: $25-49.9 Million
Emp.: 25
Ship Building & Repairing
N.A.I.C.S.: 336611
Steef Staal (Gen Mgr)

Damen Marine Components Gdansk sp. z o.o. (1)
Sztutowska 21, 80722, Gdansk, Poland
Tel.: (48) 58 301 2264
Marine Equipment Mfr
N.A.I.C.S.: 332999
Slawomir Gieron (Mng Dir)

Damen Marine Services BV (1)
Rivierdijk 561, PO Box 1, 3371, Hardinxveld-Giessendam, Netherlands
Tel.: (31) 184616000
Web Site: http://www.dms.nl
Sales Range: $25-49.9 Million
Emp.: 11
Inland Water Passenger Transportation
N.A.I.C.S.: 483212
Wim Crum (Mng Dir)

Damen Oskarshamnsvarvet Sweden AB (1)
Grondalsgatan 17, 572 35, Oskarshamn, Sweden
Tel.: (46) 491 576 50
Web Site: http://www.oskarshamnsvarvet.se
Emp.: 30
Ship Building & Repair Services
N.A.I.C.S.: 336611
Flip van der Waal (Mng Dir)

Damen Schelde Gears BV (1)
Koningsweg 2, 4381 NA, Vlissingen, Netherlands
Tel.: (31) 118 48 28 12
Web Site: http://www.damengears.com
Marine Engineering Services
N.A.I.C.S.: 541330

Damen Schelde Marine Services Pte Ltd. (1)
24 Gul Drive, Singapore, 629472, Singapore
Tel.: (65) 6265 1270
Marine Engine Spare Parts Mfr & Distr
N.A.I.C.S.: 333618
Alex Chen (Mgr-Sls)

Damen Services Brisbane Pty Ltd. (1)
Unit 20 Bridgemark Centre 93 Rivergate Place, Murarrie, 4172, QLD, Australia
Tel.: (61) 419 175 796

Ship Building & Repair Services
N.A.I.C.S.: 336611

Damen Shiprepair (1)
Adm de Ruyterstraat 24, PO Box 22, Schiedam, 3115HB, Netherlands
Tel.: (31) 102041222
Web Site: http://www.damenshiprepair.com
Sales Range: $100-124.9 Million
Emp.: 260
Ship Building & Repairing
N.A.I.C.S.: 336611
Mark Wethshaens (Mng Dir)

Subsidiary (Domestic):

Damen Verolme Rotterdam B.V. (2)
Prof Gerbrandyweg 25, 3197 KK, Rotterdam, Netherlands
Tel.: (31) 181 234300
Web Site: http://www.damenshiprepair.com
Offshore Marine Services
N.A.I.C.S.: 488330
Praveen Badloo (Mgr-Comml)

Damen Shiprepair Brest S.A.S. (1)
Rue Emile de Carcaradec, 29200, Brest, France
Tel.: (33) 2 98 43 43 43
Web Site:
    http://www.damenshiprepairbrest.com
Emp.: 200
Ship Building & Repair Services
N.A.I.C.S.: 336611
Robert Magueur (Head-Mktg & Sls)

Damen Shiprepair Dunkerque (1)
Route de Docks, BP 2074, 59376, Dunkerque, France
Tel.: (33) 3 28 66 48 00
Ship Building & Repair Services
N.A.I.C.S.: 336611

Damen Shiprepair Vlissingen B.V. (1)
Ritthemsestraat 500, 4389 PA, Ritthem, Netherlands
Tel.: (31) 118 48 30 00
Web Site: http://www.scheldepoort.com
Ship Building & Repair Services
N.A.I.C.S.: 336611

Damen Shipyards Bergum (1)
Damsingel 4, 9262 NC, Sumar, Netherlands
Tel.: (31) 511 46 72 22
Web Site: http://www.damen-bergum.nl
Ship Building & Repair Services
N.A.I.C.S.: 336611
Frederik Dijkstra (Mgr-Engrg)

Damen Shipyards Den Helder B.V. (1)
Zwarte Pad 1, 1781 AH, Den Helder, Netherlands
Tel.: (31) 223 61 66 41
Web Site: http://www.damen.com
Ship Building & Repair Services
N.A.I.C.S.: 336611
Jelle Loosman (Mng Dir)

Damen Shipyards Galati (1)
Strada Alexandru Moruzzi 132, 800223, Galati, Romania
Tel.: (40) 236307230
Web Site: http://www.damen.com
Sales Range: $800-899.9 Million
Emp.: 2,500
Ship Building & Repairing Mfr
N.A.I.C.S.: 336611

Damen Shipyards Gdynia S.A. (1)
1st Indyjska Str, 81-336, Gdynia, Poland
Tel.: (48) 58 622 14 10
Web Site: http://www.damen.pl
Ship Building & Repair Services
N.A.I.C.S.: 336611
Jacek Duch (Co-Founder)

Damen Shipyards Hardinxveld BV (1)
Rivierdijk 544, 3371 EB, Hardinxveld-Giessendam, Netherlands
Tel.: (31) 184 61 30 88
Web Site: http://www.damen.com
Ship Building & Repair Services
N.A.I.C.S.: 336611
Peter Baars (Dir-Product)

Damen Shipyards Kozle Sp Z.o.o. (1)

Stoczniowcow 2, Kedzierzyn-Kozle, 47-200, Rybnik, Opolskie, Poland
Tel.: (48) 774825914
Web Site: http://www.damenkozle.eu
Sales Range: $50-74.9 Million
Emp.: 200
Boat Building
N.A.I.C.S.: 336612

Damen Shipyards Oostende NV (1)
Industrieterrein Plassendale 1, Esperantolaan 10, 8400, Oostende, Belgium
Tel.: (32) 59251898
Web Site: http://www.damen-shipyards.be
Specialty Trade Contractors
N.A.I.C.S.: 238990

Damen Shipyards Singapore Pte Ltd (1)
29 Tuas Crescent, Singapore, 638720, Singapore
Tel.: (65) 68614180
Web Site: http://www.damen.com.sg
Emp.: 300
Ship Building & Repairing
N.A.I.C.S.: 336611
Maarten Jongen (Mng Dir)

Damen Shipyards Yichang (1)
14 Heping Rd Xiba, 443002, Yichang, Hubei, China
Tel.: (86) 7176271909
Emp.: 200
Ship Building & Repairing
N.A.I.C.S.: 336611

Damen Trading & Chartering (1)
Avelingen-West 20, PO Box 1, Gorinchem, Netherlands
Tel.: (31) 183639522
Web Site: http://www.damentrading.nl
Sales Range: $25-49.9 Million
Emp.: 3
Management Consulting Services
N.A.I.C.S.: 541618
Michel Radjiman (Sr Mgr-Sls)

Damen Trading (Suzhou) Co., Ltd. (1)
111 Tian Shangjiang Road Wuzhong Economic Development Zone, 215128, Suzhou, Jiangsu, China
Tel.: (86) 512 6635 0716
Ship Building & Repair Services
N.A.I.C.S.: 336611
Palade Petrut (Mgr-Quality Control)

Damen Yichang Shipyard Ltd. (1)
14 Heping Road Xiba, 443002, Yichang, Hubei, China
Tel.: (86) 717 627 19 09
Emp.: 438
Ship Building & Repair Services
N.A.I.C.S.: 336611
Zhiping Deng (Mgr)

Gotaverken Cityvarvet AB (1)
Pumpgorthen 10, PO Box 8045, Gothenburg, 41755, Sweden (100%)
Tel.: (46) 31502000
Web Site: http://www.damenshiprepair.se
Sales Range: $10-24.9 Million
Emp.: 130
Shipbuilding & Repairing
N.A.I.C.S.: 336611
Monica Svennes (Mng Dir)

Maaskant Shipyards BV (1)
Deltahaven 40, 3251 LC, Stellendam, Netherlands
Tel.: (31) 187 49 14 77
Web Site: http://www.maaskant-shipyards.nl
Ship Building & Repair Services
N.A.I.C.S.: 336611

Marine Engineering Galati (1)
Alexandru Moruzzi nr 132 Cladire Obiectiv nr 325, Parter si Etaj 1 Zona Nord, 800223, Galati, Romania
Tel.: (40) 236 30 75 00
Web Site: http://www.marineengineering.ro
Marine Engineering Services
N.A.I.C.S.: 541330
Mihut Tetic (Mgr-Hull Dept)

Shipdock B.V. (1)
t t Vasumweg 131, 1033 SG, Amsterdam, Netherlands
Tel.: (31) 20 631 82 18
Web Site: http://www.shipdock.nl

Ship Building & Repair Services
N.A.I.C.S.: 336611
Flip van der Waal *(Mng Dir)*

DAMIANI S.P.A.

Via Montenapoleone 10, 20121, Milan, Italy
Tel.: (39) 02 467161
Web Site: http://www.damiani.it
Year Founded: 1924
Sales Range: $150-199.9 Million
Emp.: 584
Mfr & Retailer of Luxury Jewelry
N.A.I.C.S.: 458310
Paola Burzi *(IR Officer)*

Subsidiaries:

Damiani International B.V.   (1)
Via Cantonele Centro Gallerie 3, 6928,
Manno, Switzerland
Tel.: (41) 916101500
Sales Range: $25-49.9 Million
Emp.: 30
Jewelry Whslr
N.A.I.C.S.: 423940

Damiani Japan K.K.   (1)
Renai Aoyama Bldg 3 FL 3-3-11 Kita
aoyoma, Minato-Ku, Tokyo, 107 0061, Japan
Tel.: (81) 3 5785 1080
Jewellery Distr
N.A.I.C.S.: 423940

Rocca International S.A.   (1)
Riva Albertolli 1, 6900, Lugano, Switzerland
Tel.: (41) 91 922 99 40
Jewelry Mfr
N.A.I.C.S.: 339910

Rocca S.p.A.   (1)
Via Pagano Mario 40, 20145, Milan, Italy
Tel.: (39) 024677881
Watch Mfr
N.A.I.C.S.: 334519

DAMLORAN RAZAK PHARMACEUTICAL COMPANY

No 4-Western Doctor Fatemi St-
Parvin Alley, 14186 43415, Tehran,
Iran
Tel.: (98) 2166945732
Year Founded: 1983
DAML1—(THE)
Sales Range: Less than $1 Million
Emp.: 177
Pharmaceutical Preparation Mfr
N.A.I.C.S.: 325412

DAMM & BIERBAUM AGENTUR FUR MARKETING UND KOMMUNIKATION GMBH

Hanauer Landstrasse 135-137,
60314, Frankfurt, Germany
Tel.: (49) 69 7891 050
Web Site:
    http://www.dammbierbaum.de
Year Founded: 1982
Rev.: $13,280,500
Emp.: 48
Full Service
N.A.I.C.S.: 541810
Dirk Damm *(Mng Dir)*

DAMODAR INDUSTRIES LIMITED

19/22 & 27/30 Madhu Estate Pan-
durang Budhkar Marg Worli, Mumbai,
400 013, India
Tel.: (91) 49763203
Web Site:
    https://www.damodargroup.com
Year Founded: 1987
DAMODARIND—(NSE)
Rev.: $83,502,860
Assets: $53,686,889
Liabilities: $39,902,692
Net Worth: $13,784,198
Earnings: $95,522
Emp.: 627

Fiscal Year-end: 03/31/23
Synthetic Blended Yarn Mfr
N.A.I.C.S.: 313110
Arun Kumar Biyani *(Chm)*

Subsidiaries:

Shri Damodar Yarn Manufacturing
Pvt. Ltd.   (1)
161 Mittal Estate Bldg No 6 1st Floor Sir M
V Road, Andheri, Mumbai, 400 059, India
Tel.: (91) 9324722000
Web Site: https://damodaryarn.com
Apparel & Polyester Yarn Mfr
N.A.I.C.S.: 313110

DAMON TECHNOLOGY GROUP CORP., LTD.

7F-8F Software Building 56 No 461
Hongcao Road, Xuhui, Shanghai,
China
Tel.: (86) 2164856600
Web Site: https://www.damon-
    group.com
Year Founded: 2001,
688360—(SHG)
Rev.: $214,776,563
Assets: $242,065,325
Liabilities: $102,538,613
Net Worth: $139,526,712
Earnings: $11,467,647
Emp.: 1,000
Fiscal Year-end: 12/31/22
Conveyor & Conveying Equipment
Mfr
N.A.I.C.S.: 333922
Harry Zhuo *(CEO)*

DAMPSKIBSSELSKABET NORDEN A/S

52 Strandvejen, 2900, Hellerup, Denmark
Tel.: (45) 33150451
Web Site: https://www.ds-norden.com
DNORD—(CSE)
Rev.: $53,124,000,000
Assets: $27,554,000,000
Liabilities: $14,247,000,000
Net Worth: $13,307,000,000
Earnings: $7,435,000,000
Emp.: 425
Fiscal Year-end: 12/31/22
Cargo Transportation Services
N.A.I.C.S.: 488320
Martin Badsted *(CFO)*

Subsidiaries:

NORDEN Shipping (Singapore) Pte.
Ltd   (1)
Web Site: http://www.ds-norden.com
Emp.: 40
Shipping Services
N.A.I.C.S.: 483111

Subsidiary (Non-US):

NORDEN Tankers & Bulkers India
Pvt. Ltd   (2)
Office No 12 First Floor Ground Level Kal-
pataru Square Off Kurla Road, Kondivita
Lane, Mumbai, 400059, Maharashtra, India
Tel.: (91) 2228329188
Sales Range: $25-49.9 Million
Emp.: 4
Shipping Services
N.A.I.C.S.: 483111
Adam Nielsen *(Gen Mgr)*

NORDEN Shipping Abidjan
SARLU   (1)
Batiment Arc-en-ciel apt 4-8 Rue du Canal
zone 4, Abidjan, Cote d'Ivoire
Tel.: (225) 70719555
Freight Shipping Services
N.A.I.C.S.: 541614

NORDEN Shipping Middle East
DMCC   (1)
Office 1101 Swiss Tower Cluster Y, Dubai,
United Arab Emirates
Tel.: (971) 42733844
Freight Shipping Services

N.A.I.C.S.: 541614
NORDEN Tankers & Bulkers do Bra-
zil Ltda   (1)
Edificio Argentina Praia De Botafogo 228-
801 Andar-Sala 801 B, Rio de Janeiro,
22359-900, Brazil
Tel.: (55) 2125540055
Sales Range: $25-49.9 Million
Emp.: 6
Ship Management Services
N.A.I.C.S.: 336611
Rasmus Saltofte *(Mgr)*

DAMS FORD LINCOLN SALES LTD.

19330 Langley Bypass, Surrey,
V3S7R2, BC, Canada
Tel.: (604) 532-9921
Web Site: http://dams.net
Year Founded: 1974
Sales Range: $50-74.9 Million
Emp.: 200
New & Used Car Dealer
N.A.I.C.S.: 441110
Ike Penner *(Mgr-Svc)*

DAMSTRA HOLDINGS LTD.

38-40 Garden Street Level 1, South
Yarra, 3141, VIC, Australia
Tel.: (61) 300722801
Web Site:
    http://www.damstratechnology.com
DTC—(ASX)
Rev.: $22,211,082
Assets: $100,082,036
Liabilities: $23,990,175
Net Worth: $76,091,861
Earnings: ($51,451,191)
Emp.: 90
Fiscal Year-end: 06/30/22
Holding Company
N.A.I.C.S.: 551112

Subsidiaries:

Damstra Technology Pty Ltd   (1)
Suite 3 Level 3 299 Toorak Road, South
Yarra, 3141, VIC, Australia
Tel.: (61) 300722801
Web Site:
    https://www.damstratechnology.com
Workforce & Human Capital Management
Technologies Services
N.A.I.C.S.: 541618
Christian Damstra *(CEO)*

Vault Intelligence Limited   (1)
145-147 Bouverie Street, Carlton, 3053,
VIC, Australia
Tel.: (61) 1300 723240
Web Site: http://www.vaultintel.com
Investment Services
N.A.I.C.S.: 523999
Brent Melhop *(CFO)*

Subsidiary (Non-US):

Vault IQ NZ Ltd.   (2)
Level 1 106 Wrights Road, Christchurch,
8024, New Zealand
Tel.: (64) 5084752846
Intelligent Software Development Services
N.A.I.C.S.: 541511

DAN HOTELS LTD.

111 Hayarkon Street, Tel Aviv, 63571,
Israel
Tel.: (972) 37408966
Web Site: https://www.danhotels.com
Year Founded: 1947
DANH—(TAE)
Rev.: $446,354,738
Assets: $654,588,193
Liabilities: $317,077,216
Net Worth: $337,510,977
Earnings: $34,037,574
Emp.: 3,500
Fiscal Year-end: 12/31/23
Hotels (except Casino Hotels) & Mo-
tels
N.A.I.C.S.: 721110

Ami Federmann *(Deputy Chm-Mgmt
Bd)*

DAN KANE CHEVROLET CADILLAC

500 Division Rd, PO Box 510, Wind-
sor, N9A 6M9, ON, Canada
Tel.: (519) 969-6000
Web Site:
    http://www.dankanechev.com
Rev.: $49,100,000
Emp.: 83
New & Used Car Dealers
N.A.I.C.S.: 441110
Dan Kane *(Pres)*

DAN LACHS GMBH

Lise Meithner Str 16, 24223, Schwen-
tinental, Germany
Tel.: (49) 43078233382
Web Site: http://www.danlachs.de
Year Founded: 1973
Sales Range: $25-49.9 Million
Emp.: 20
Fish & Seafood Distr
N.A.I.C.S.: 424460
Hans Christian Petersen *(Gen Mgr)*

DANA GAS PJSC

Crescent Tower 11th Floor Al Buhaira
Corniche, PO Box 2011, Sharjah,
United Arab Emirates
Tel.: (971) 65569444   AE
Web Site: https://www.danagas.com
Year Founded: 2005
DANA—(ABU)
Rev.: $422,270,623
Assets: $2,790,089,838
Liabilities: $424,176,422
Net Worth: $2,365,913,417
Earnings: $159,542,608
Emp.: 86
Fiscal Year-end: 12/31/23
Natural Gas Pipeline Transportation,
Processing & Marketing Services
N.A.I.C.S.: 486210
Hamid Dhiya Jafar *(Chm)*

Subsidiaries:

Centurion Energy International
Inc.   (1)
Ste 1700 Bow Valley Square II, 205 5th Ave
SW, Calgary, T2P 2V7, AB, Canada
Tel.: (403) 263-6002
Sales Range: $75-99.9 Million
Emp.: 140
Petroleum & Natural Gas Exploration, De-
velopment, Drilling & Extraction
N.A.I.C.S.: 211120

Subsidiary (Non-US):

Centurion Petroleum Corporation   (2)
El Safa Office Towers Lot No 42 6th district,
Zahraa El Maadi subdivision, Cairo,
Egypt   (100%)
Tel.: (20) 2 7545499
Web Site:
    http://centurion.stagingserver.co.uk
Sales Range: $50-74.9 Million
Emp.: 75
Petroleum & Natural Gas Exploration, De-
velopment, Drilling & Extraction
N.A.I.C.S.: 211120

United Gas Transmissions Company
Limited   (1)
PO Box 61213, Sharjah, United Arab Emir-
ates
Tel.: (971) 65727000
Oil & Natural Gas Extraction Services
N.A.I.C.S.: 211130

DANA INSURANCE COMPANY

No 25 15th Street Gandi Avenue,
Tehran, 15178 91197, Iran
Tel.: (98) 21 877 7716
Web Site: http://www.dana-
    insurance.com
Year Founded: 1989

Dana Insurance Company—(Continued)

BDAN1—(THE)
Sales Range: Less than $1 Million
Insurance Agency Services
N.A.I.C.S.: 524210

DANA-Y STEEL JOINT STOCK COMPANY
Road No 11B Thanh Vinh Industrial Zone Hoa Khanh Bac Ward, Lien Chieu District, Da Nang, Vietnam
Tel.: (84) 511 3841000
Web Site: http://www.thepdana-y.com
Year Founded: 2000
DNY—(HNX)
Sales Range: $50-74.9 Million
Emp.: 400
Iron & Steel Construction Material Mfr
N.A.I.C.S.: 331110
Huynh Van Tan *(Chm, Gen Dir & Member-Mgmt Bd)*

DANAKALI LIMITED
Level 1 2A / 300 Fitzgerald St, Perth, 6006, WA, Australia
Tel.: (61) 862668368
Web Site:
  https://www.danakali.com.au
DNK—(OTCIQ)
Rev.: $58,345
Assets: $42,298,367
Liabilities: $622,585
Net Worth: $41,675,782
Earnings: ($3,010,477)
Fiscal Year-end: 12/31/22
Potash Mining
N.A.I.C.S.: 212390
Seamus Ian Cornelius *(Chm)*

DANAL CO., LTD
9th floor First Tower 55 Bundang-ro, Bundang-gu, Seongnam, 463-824, Gyeonggi-do, Korea (South)
Tel.: (82) 316971004
Web Site: https://www.danal.co.kr
Year Founded: 1997
064260—(KRS)
Rev.: $226,225,333
Assets: $574,785,869
Liabilities: $319,580,283
Net Worth: $255,205,586
Earnings: ($11,737,932)
Emp.: 250
Fiscal Year-end: 12/31/22
Mobile Payment Services
N.A.I.C.S.: 522320
Seong-Chan Park *(Chm)*

DANAMECO MEDICAL JOINT STOCK CORPORATION
12 Trinh Cong Son Street Hoa Cuong Nam Ward, Hai Chau District, Da Nang, Vietnam
Tel.: (84) 2363690777
Web Site:
  https://www.danameco.com
DNM—(HNX)
Rev.: $31,790,000
Assets: $39,111,500
Liabilities: $34,741,300
Net Worth: $4,370,200
Earnings: ($10,018,700)
Fiscal Year-end: 12/31/22
Medical Supplies Mfr & Distr
N.A.I.C.S.: 339113
Thi Minh Trang Pham *(Vice Chm)*

DANANG AIRPORT SERVICES COMPANY
Danang International Airport, Haichau District Hoa Thuan Tay, Da Nang, Vietnam
Tel.: (84) 236830340
Web Site: https://www.masco.com.vn
MAS—(HNX)
Rev.: $1,803,446

Assets: $3,030,468
Liabilities: $1,924,430
Net Worth: $1,106,038
Earnings: ($593,491)
Emp.: 641
Fiscal Year-end: 12/31/21
Airport Operations
N.A.I.C.S.: 488119

DANANG BOOKS & SCHOOL EQUIPMENT JOINT STOCK COMPANY
76-78 Bach Dang, Hai Chau District, Da Nang, Vietnam
Tel.: (84) 2363821009
Web Site:
  https://www.danangbook.com
BED—(HNX)
Rev.: $2,948,937
Assets: $2,036,868
Liabilities: $418,008
Net Worth: $1,618,860
Earnings: $220,713
Fiscal Year-end: 12/31/21
Stationery Product Whslr
N.A.I.C.S.: 459410
Nguyen Van Can *(Chm)*

DANANG EDUCATION INVEST-MENT & DEVELOPMENT JOINT STOCK COMPANY
145 Le Loi Street Hai Chau 1 ward, Hai Chau District, Da Nang, Vietnam
Tel.: (84) 2363889954
Web Site:
  http://www.dautugiaoduc.com.vn
DAD—(HNX)
Rev.: $36,653,100
Assets: $16,744,500
Liabilities: $7,299,000
Net Worth: $9,445,500
Earnings: $1,446,100
Fiscal Year-end: 12/31/22
Books Publishing Services
N.A.I.C.S.: 513130
Nguyen Van Nam *(Member-Mgmt Bd)*

DANANG HOUSING DEVELOP-MENT JOINT STOCK COM-PANY
31 Nui Thanh Hoa Thuan Dong ward, Hai Chau district, Da Nang, Vietnam
Tel.: (84) 2363631157
Web Site: https://www.ndx.com.vn
Year Founded: 2008
NDX—(HNX)
Rev.: $4,851,712
Assets: $8,108,168
Liabilities: $3,189,271
Net Worth: $4,918,897
Earnings: $183,069
Fiscal Year-end: 12/31/21
Civil Engineering Construction Ser-vices
N.A.I.C.S.: 237990
Trung Quang Nguyen *(Chm-Mgmt Bd)*

DANANG HOUSING INVEST-MENT AND DEVELOPMENT JOINT STOCK COMPANY
38 Nguyen Chi Thanh, Thach Thang Ward Hai Chau District, Da Nang, Vietnam
Tel.: (84) 2363561577
Web Site: https://www.ndn.com.vn
NDN—(HNX)
Rev.: $342,400
Assets: $149,721,800
Liabilities: $60,056,400
Net Worth: $89,665,400
Earnings: ($14,296,100)
Emp.: 100
Fiscal Year-end: 12/31/22
Real Estate Investment Services
N.A.I.C.S.: 531390

DANANG PLASTIC JOINT-STOCK COMPANY
Floor 06 Indochina Riverside 74 Bach Dang Hai Chau dist, Da Nang, Viet-nam
Tel.: (84) 5113822630
Web Site: https://www.pcdanang.com
Year Founded: 1976
DPC—(HNX)
Rev.: $2,156,700
Assets: $8,258,200
Liabilities: $4,879,700
Net Worth: $3,378,500
Earnings: ($1,563,800)
Fiscal Year-end: 12/31/22
Plastic Packaging Product Mfr & Distr
N.A.I.C.S.: 326112
Linh Ngoc Pham *(Chm-Mgmt Bd)*

DANAOS CORPORATION
14 Akti Kondyli, 185 45, Piraeus, Greece
Tel.: (30) 2104196480   MH
Web Site: https://www.danaos.com
Year Founded: 1972
DAC—(NYSE)
Rev.: $993,344,000
Assets: $3,400,228,000
Liabilities: $839,814,000
Net Worth: $2,560,414,000
Earnings: $559,210,000
Emp.: 1,722
Fiscal Year-end: 12/31/22
International Owner of Containerships
N.A.I.C.S.: 483111
Iraklis Prokopakis *(COO, Treas & Sr VP)*

Subsidiaries:

Danaos Germany   **(1)**
Neuer Wall 9, Hamburg, 20354, Germany
Tel.: (49) 4041349718
Web Site: http://web2.danaos.gr
Maritime Shipping Management Services
N.A.I.C.S.: 488330

Danaos Management Consultants SA   **(1)**
14 Akti Kondyli Street, 18545, Piraeus, Greece
Tel.: (30) 2104196600
Web Site: https://www.danaos.gr
Sales Range: $25-49.9 Million
Emp.: 70
Management Services
N.A.I.C.S.: 541611
Dimitris Theodossiou *(Co-Founder)*

Danaos Nordic A.S.   **(1)**
PO Box 111, Sagvag, N-5408, Norway
Tel.: (47) 4000 1819
Maritime Navigation Management Services
N.A.I.C.S.: 488330

Danaos Peripherals S.A.   **(1)**
14 Akti Kondyli, 18545, Piraeus, Greece
Tel.: (30) 2104196560
Web Site: http://www.danaos.gr
Sales Range: $25-49.9 Million
Emp.: 100
Information System Management Services
N.A.I.C.S.: 541512

Danaos SeaRoutes Ltd.   **(1)**
14 Akti Kondyli, 185 45, Piraeus, Greece
Tel.: (30) 2104196600
Marine Navigation System & Management Services
N.A.I.C.S.: 488330

Danaos Shipping Co., Ltd.   **(1)**
14 Akti Kondyli, 18545, Piraeus, Athens, Greece
Tel.: (30) 2104196400
Sales Range: $25-49.9 Million
Emp.: 100
Management Services
N.A.I.C.S.: 541611

Danaos Software Services Pte Ltd.   **(1)**
3 Brady Gladys Plaza, 1/447 S.B. Marg, Lower Parel, Mumbai, 400 013, India
Tel.: (91) 2256611439

Maritime Navigation Management Services
N.A.I.C.S.: 488330

Danaos Systems (Cyprus) Ltd.   **(1)**
145-149 Chr Hadjipavlou Str Christiel Build-ing, Christiel Building, CY3036, Limassol, Cyprus
Tel.: (357) 25889000
Web Site: https://www.danaoscy.eu
Sales Range: $50-74.9 Million
Maritime Navigation Management Services
N.A.I.C.S.: 488330

DANBY PRODUCTS LTD.
5070 Whitelaw Road, Guelph, N1H 6Z9, ON, Canada
Tel.: (519) 837-0920
Web Site: http://www.danby.com
Year Founded: 1947
Sales Range: $10-24.9 Million
Emp.: 100
Household Appliance Distr
N.A.I.C.S.: 335220
Jim Estill *(Pres & CEO)*

Subsidiaries:

Intirion Corp.   **(1)**
2 Annette Rd, Foxboro, MA 02035
Tel.: (508) 660-9200
Web Site: http://www.microfridge.com
Household Appliances Mfr
N.A.I.C.S.: 335220
Jim Russo *(Mng Dir-Sls)*

DANCANN PHARMA A/S
Rugvaenget 5, 6823, Ansager, Den-mark
Tel.: (45) 69160393
Web Site: https://www.dancann.com
Year Founded: 2018
DAN—(DEU)
Rev.: $878,731
Assets: $2,516,821
Liabilities: $1,141,352
Net Worth: $1,375,468
Earnings: ($9,008,696)
Emp.: 12
Fiscal Year-end: 12/31/23
Pharmaceutical Product Mfr & Distr
N.A.I.C.S.: 325412
Carsten Trads *(Chm)*

Subsidiaries:

CannGros ApS   **(1)**
Rugaenget 5, 6823, Ansager, Denmark
Tel.: (45) 69166101
Web Site: https://canngros.dk
Medical Product Mfr & Distr
N.A.I.C.S.: 339112

DANCAP PRIVATE EQUITY INC.
197 Sheppard Ave. W, Toronto, M2N 1M9, ON, Canada
Tel.: (416) 590-9444
Web Site: https://dancap.ca
Private Equity
N.A.I.C.S.: 523940
Elias Toby *(CFO & COO)*

DANCOMECH HOLDINGS BERHAD
No 19 Jalan Pelukis U1/46 Seksyen U1, 40150, Shah Alam, Selangor, Malaysia
Tel.: (60) 355692929   MY
Web Site:
  https://www.dancomech.com.my
Year Founded: 1989
DANCO—(KLS)
Rev.: $44,859,775
Assets: $61,501,070
Liabilities: $15,139,359
Net Worth: $46,361,711
Earnings: $4,048,819
Fiscal Year-end: 12/31/22
Measurement Instrument Distr
N.A.I.C.S.: 423120

Swee Tong Aik *(Co-Founder & Mng Dir)*

Subsidiaries:

Arah Edar (M) Sdn. Bhd. **(1)**
C4B 2nd Floor Jalan Prima 1 Block A Taman Rasa Sayang, 43200, Kuala Selangor, Malaysia
Tel.: (60) 90823377
Coal Mining Services
N.A.I.C.S.: 213113

Jusev Charging Network Sdn. Bhd. **(1)**
No 24-1 1st Floor Jalan Penguasa B U1/53B, Seksyen U1 Temasya Square Glenmarie, 40150, Shah Alam, Selangor, Malaysia
Tel.: (60) 128188547
Web Site: https://jusev.com.my
Electric Vehicle Charging Services
N.A.I.C.S.: 926130

Mechpump Sdn. Bhd. **(1)**
15 & 15A Lorong Raja Nong 18A Off Jalan Penghulu Abu Bakar, Taman Bunga Raya, 41000, Klang, Selangor, Malaysia
Tel.: (60) 333701416
Web Site: https://www.mechpump.com
Pump Distr
N.A.I.C.S.: 423830

UTC Engineering Sdn. Bhd. **(1)**
3 & 5 Jalan USJ 21/11, 47630, Subang Jaya, Selangor, Malaysia
Tel.: (60) 380136708
Web Site: https://utcesb.n.my
Electrical Engineering Services
N.A.I.C.S.: 541330

DANDONG XINTAI ELECTRIC COMPANY LIMITED

No 159 Dongpin Street, Zhen'an District, Dandong, 118006, China
Tel.: (86) 415 4139770
Web Site: http://www.xintaidianqi.com
Sales Range: $50-74.9 Million
Emp.: 620
Energy Efficient Transformers & Electric Power Transmission Equipment Mfr
N.A.I.C.S.: 335311

DANDOT CEMENT CO., LTD.

5-Zafar Ali Road, Gulberg, Lahore, Pakistan
Tel.: (92) 111184184   PK
Web Site:
   https://www.dandotcement.com
Year Founded: 1980
Rev.: $14,373,355
Assets: $33,934,109
Liabilities: $29,642,784
Net Worth: $4,291,325
Earnings: $4,022,068
Emp.: 567
Fiscal Year-end: 06/30/19
Cement Mfr
N.A.I.C.S.: 327310
Taha Muhamamd Naseem *(CEO)*

DANEL (ADIR YEHOSHUA) LTD.

Abba Hillel 12, Ramat Gan, Israel
Tel.: (972) 37564111
Web Site: https://www.danel-jobs.co.il
Year Founded: 1974
DANE—(TAE)
Rev.: $694,521,884
Assets: $359,212,040
Liabilities: $225,551,868
Net Worth: $133,660,172
Earnings: ($3,689,184)
Emp.: 30,000
Fiscal Year-end: 12/31/23
Human Resource Consulting Services
N.A.I.C.S.: 541612

DANEN TECHNOLOGY CORPORATION

No 599 Huan Nan Rd Taoyuan High Tech Industrial Park, Guanyin Dist, Taoyuan, 328, Taiwan
Tel.: (886) 34738788
Web Site:
   https://www.danentech.com
Year Founded: 2007
3686—(TAI)
Rev.: $1,339,906
Assets: $23,270,512
Liabilities: $222,604
Net Worth: $23,047,908
Earnings: ($959,940)
Emp.: 600
Fiscal Year-end: 12/31/23
Silicon Ingots & Wafer Mfr
N.A.I.C.S.: 335999
James Fang *(Chm & Pres)*

DANESCO INC.

18111 Trans Canada Hwy, Kirkland, H9J 3K1, QC, Canada
Tel.: (514) 694-9111
Web Site:
   http://www.danescoinc.com
Year Founded: 1963
Housewares Distr
N.A.I.C.S.: 423220
William R. Ferguson *(Chm)*

DANFOSS A/S

Nordborgvej 81, 6430, Nordborg, Denmark
Tel.: (45) 74882222   DK
Web Site: https://www.danfoss.com
Year Founded: 1933
Rev.: $11,760,679,988
Assets: $12,934,098,688
Liabilities: $6,925,709,240
Net Worth: $6,008,389,448
Earnings: $904,073,297
Emp.: 40,954
Fiscal Year-end: 12/31/23
Holding Company; Heating, Ventilation, Air Conditioning, Refrigeration & Motion Control Systems & Components Mfr
N.A.I.C.S.: 551112
Jens Bjerg Sorensen *(Vice Chm)*

Subsidiaries:

Danfoss (Anshan) Controls Co. Ltd. **(1)**
No 1 Huimin Street, Qianshan District, 114041, Anshan, China
Tel.: (86) 412 8253 111
Electronic Components Mfr
N.A.I.C.S.: 334419

Danfoss (Australia) Pty. Ltd. **(1)**
2 National Drive, Dandenong South, 3175, VIC, Australia
Tel.: (61) 3 9538 4444
Web Site: http://www.danfoss.com
Emp.: 50
Electronic Components Mfr
N.A.I.C.S.: 334419

Danfoss (New Zealand) Ltd. **(1)**
6 George Bourke Drive Penrose Mount Wellington, PO Box 12422, 1006, Auckland, New Zealand
Tel.: (64) 9 259 25 10
Electronic Components Distr
N.A.I.C.S.: 423690

Danfoss (Pty) Ltd. **(1)**
20 Woodlands Dr, Woodlands, Johannesburg, 2191, South Africa **(100%)**
Tel.: (27) 117857600
Web Site: http://www.danfoss.co.za
Sale of Commercial Refrigeration Equipment
N.A.I.C.S.: 423740

Danfoss (Thailand) Co. Ltd. **(1)**
3rd Floor SP Arcade Building 71 Ramkhamhaeng Road, Khwang Huamark Khet Bangkapi, Bangkok, 10240, Thailand

Tel.: (66) 2 308 6700
Electronic Components Mfr
N.A.I.C.S.: 334419

Danfoss (Tianjin) Ltd. **(1)**
No 5 Fu Yuan Road, Wuqing Development Area, Tianjin, 301700, China **(100%)**
Tel.: (86) 2282126400
Web Site: http://www.danfoss.com.cn
Sales Range: $1-9.9 Million
Emp.: 2,000
Sales & Servicer of Valves & Controls
N.A.I.C.S.: 423840

Danfoss A/S - Comfort Controls Division **(1)**
Haarupvaenget 11, Haarup, DK 8600, Silkeborg, Denmark **(100%)**
Tel.: (45) 74888000
Web Site: http://www.heating.danfoss.com
Sales Range: $50-74.9 Million
Emp.: 130
Temperature Controls Mfr
N.A.I.C.S.: 334512
Soren K. Petersen *(Dir-Fin)*

Danfoss A/S Appliance Controls Div. **(1)**
Nordborgvej 81, 6430, Nordborg, Denmark **(100%)**
Tel.: (45) 74882222
Web Site: http://www.bc.danfoss.com
Sales Range: $400-449.9 Million
Emp.: 2,500
Mfr of Appliance Controls
N.A.I.C.S.: 334512

Danfoss A/S Building Controls Div. **(1)**
Nordborgvej 81, 6430, Nordborg, Denmark **(100%)**
Tel.: (45) 74882222
Web Site: http://www.bc.danfoss.com
Sales Range: $1-4.9 Billion
Emp.: 7,000
Mfr of Regulating Controls
N.A.I.C.S.: 334512

Danfoss A/S Flow Div. **(1)**
Nordborg Vej 81, Nordborg, 6340, Denmark **(100%)**
Tel.: (45) 74882222
Web Site: http://www.flow.danfoss.com
Sales Range: $100-124.9 Million
Emp.: 300
Mfr of Flowmeter Components
N.A.I.C.S.: 334513

Danfoss A/S Industrial Controls Div. **(1)**
Albuen 29, 6000, Kolding, Denmark **(100%)**
Tel.: (45) 76356565
Web Site: http://www.danfoss.com
Sales Range: $200-249.9 Million
Emp.: 550
Mfr of Industrial Controls
N.A.I.C.S.: 334513

Danfoss A/S Refrigeration & A/C Controls Division **(1)**
Nordborgvej 81, Nordborg, 6430, Denmark **(100%)**
Tel.: (45) 74882222
Web Site: http://www.bc.danfoss.com
Sales Range: $1-4.9 Billion
Emp.: 7,000
Mfr of Temperature Controls
N.A.I.C.S.: 334512

Danfoss A/S Water Hydraulics Division **(1)**
Nordborgvej 81, 6430, Nordborg, Denmark **(100%)**
Tel.: (45) 74882222
Web Site: http://www.danfoss.com
Sales Range: $1-4.9 Billion
Emp.: 7,000
Supplier of Hydraulic, Humidification, Lumber Drying & Fire Fighting Products
N.A.I.C.S.: 332912
Peter Clausen *(Mng Dir)*

Danfoss AB **(1)**
Industrigatan 5, Ostergotland, 581 99, Linkoping, Sweden
Tel.: (46) 13258500
Web Site: http://www.danfoss.se
Sales Range: $25-49.9 Million
Emp.: 60
Mfr of Industrial & Temperature Controls

N.A.I.C.S.: 334512

Danfoss AG **(1)**
Parkstrasse 6, Basel-Landschaft, 4402, Frenkendorf, Switzerland
Tel.: (41) 615100019
Web Site: http://www.danfoss.ch
Emp.: 30
Electronic Components Mfr
N.A.I.C.S.: 334419
Benno Kollmann *(Mng Dir)*

Danfoss AS **(1)**
A H Tammsaare road 47, 11316, Tallinn, Estonia
Tel.: (372) 6593 300
Web Site: http://www.danfoss.com
Emp.: 6
Electronic Components Mfr
N.A.I.C.S.: 334419

Danfoss AS **(1)**
Arenga 2 1340 Skui, Skui, Baerum, Norway
Tel.: (47) 67 17 72 00
Electronic Components Mfr
N.A.I.C.S.: 334419
Mona Oddevald *(Gen Mgr)*

Danfoss Automatic Controls Management (Shanghai) Co. Ltd. **(1)**
20th Floor Block C Hi-Tech Building, 900 Yi Shan Road, 200233, Shanghai, China
Tel.: (86) 21 6151 3000
Electronic Components Distr
N.A.I.C.S.: 423690

Danfoss Bauer GmbH **(1)**
Eberhard Bauer Strasse 36 60, PO Box 100208, Esslingen, 73734, Germany **(100%)**
Tel.: (49) 71135180
Web Site: http://www.danfoss-bauer.com
Sales Range: $50-74.9 Million
Emp.: 200
Mfr of Gear Motors
N.A.I.C.S.: 333612
Hanspeteno Simon *(Mgr)*

Danfoss Co. Ltd. **(1)**
12F-5 No 736 Zhongzheng Rd, Zhonghe, New Taipei City, 235, Taiwan
Tel.: (886) 2 82263263
Web Site: http://www.danfoss.com
Electronic Components Mfr
N.A.I.C.S.: 334419

Danfoss Commercial Compressors Ltd. **(1)**
1775G Mac Leod Dr, Lawrenceville, GA 30043-5718
Tel.: (678) 337-5100
Web Site: http://www.danfoss.com
Sales Range: $50-74.9 Million
Emp.: 150
Compressor Mfr
N.A.I.C.S.: 333415

Danfoss Commercial Compressors S.A. **(1)**
ZI De Reyrieux, B P 331, 20 Rue Du Pou Du Ciel, 01603, Trevoux, Cedex, France
Tel.: (33) 474002829
Web Site: http://www.danfoss.com
Sales Range: $100-124.9 Million
Emp.: 500
Mfr of Compressors
N.A.I.C.S.: 333912
Noel Ryan *(Pres)*

Danfoss Distribution Services A/S **(1)**
Kometvej 40, 6230, Rodekro, Denmark
Tel.: (45) 7474 4969
Electronic Components Mfr
N.A.I.C.S.: 334419

Danfoss District Heating S.r.l. **(1)**
Bd Tudor Vladimirescu no 22 Green Gate Office Building et 10 Sector 5, Bucharest, 050883, Romania
Tel.: (40) 312222101
Web Site: http://www.danfoss.com
Industrial Machinery Mfr
N.A.I.C.S.: 333310

Danfoss Drives A/S **(1)**
Ulsnas 1, Grasten, 6300, Denmark **(100%)**
Tel.: (45) 74882222
Sales Range: $400-449.9 Million
Emp.: 1,200
Mfr of Drives for Motors

Danfoss A/S—(Continued)

N.A.I.C.S.: 333613
Patrick Appleby (VP-Indus Sls)

Danfoss EOOD (1)
5 Rezbarska Street, 1510, Sofia, Bulgaria
Tel.: (359) 2 942 49 10
Electronic Components Mfr
N.A.I.C.S.: 334419

Danfoss Electronic Drives (1)
4401 N Bell School Rd, Loves Park, IL
61111-5600
Tel.: (815) 639-8600
Web Site: http://www.danfossdrives.com
Sales Range: $50-74.9 Million
Mfr of Refrigeration Controls
N.A.I.C.S.: 335314

Subsidiary (Domestic):

Danfoss Graham (2)
8800 W Bradley Rd, Milwaukee, WI 53224-9541
Tel.: (414) 355-8800
Web Site: http://www.danfossdrives.com
Sales Range: $50-74.9 Million
Emp.: 200
AC Variable Frequency Drives Mfr
N.A.I.C.S.: 335314

Danfoss Esslingen GmbH (1)
Eberhard-Bauer-Str 36-60, Esslingen am
Neckar, 73734, Baden-Wurttember, Germany
Tel.: (49) 698 9020
Electronic Components Mfr
N.A.I.C.S.: 334419

Danfoss FZCO (1)
PO Box 61248, Jebel Ali Free Zone, Dubai,
United Arab Emirates
Tel.: (971) 4812 3000
Web Site: http://www.danfoss.com
Emp.: 50
Electronic Components Mfr
N.A.I.C.S.: 334419
Ziad Al Bawaliz (Pres-Turkey, Middle East &
Africa)

Danfoss Gesellschaft m.b.H. (1)
Danfoss-Strasse 8, 2353, Guntramsdorf,
Austria
Tel.: (43) 720548000
Web Site: http://www.danfoss.at
Emp.: 30
Heating Equipment Mfr
N.A.I.C.S.: 333414

Danfoss GmbH (1)
Carl-Legien-Strasse 8, Offenbach, 63004,
Germany
Tel.: (49) 69 8902 960
Heating Equipment Mfr
N.A.I.C.S.: 333414

Danfoss Heat Pumps UK Ltd. (1)
Parkwood Road, Unit 3 Parkwood Business
Park, Sheffield, S3 8AL, S Yorkshire, United
Kingdom
Tel.: (44) 114 270 3900
Heating Equipment Mfr
N.A.I.C.S.: 333414

Danfoss Heating Division (1)
Nordborgvej 81, Nordborg, 6430, Denmark
Tel.: (45) 74882222
Web Site: http://www.danfoss.com
Mfr of Heating Systems & Components
N.A.I.C.S.: 333414
Mads Pinnerup (VP-Bus Admin)

Division (Domestic):

**Danfoss Burner Components
Division** (2)
Nordborgvej 81, 6430, Nordborg,
Denmark (100%)
Tel.: (45) 74882222
Web Site: http://www.danfoss.com
Sales Range: $550-599.9 Million
Emp.: 2,000
Mfr of Oil Burner Nozzles, Pumps, Ignition
Components, Preheaters, Controls & Thermostats
N.A.I.C.S.: 334512

Subsidiary (US):

Danfoss Hago Inc. (3)

1120 Globe Ave, Mountainside, NJ 07092
Tel.: (908) 232-8687
Web Site: http://www.hago.danfoss.com
Sales Range: $10-24.9 Million
Emp.: 60
Mfr of Oil Burner Nozzles
N.A.I.C.S.: 333414

Danfoss IXA A/S (1)
Ulvehavevej 61, Vejle, 7100, Denmark
Tel.: (45) 74888590
Electronic Components Mfr
N.A.I.C.S.: 334419

Danfoss Inc. (1)
11655 Crossroads Cir, Baltimore, MD
21220
Tel.: (410) 931-8250
Web Site: http://www.danfoss.com
Sales Range: $125-149.9 Million
Emp.: 300
Mfr of Refrigeration & Air Conditioning Compressors & Components, Heating Systems
& Components & Motion Control Components
N.A.I.C.S.: 333414
John Galyen (Pres-North America)

Subsidiary (Domestic):

AAIMControls, Inc. (2)
11885 Mutual Dr, Waynesboro, PA 17268
Tel.: (717) 765-9100
Web Site: http://www.aaimcontrols.com
Engineeering Services
N.A.I.C.S.: 541330
Arthur J. Marshall (Pres)

Danfoss Industries Limited (1)
8th Floor Glouchester Tower Landmark, 15
Queens Road, Central, China (Hong Kong)
Tel.: (852) 25 173872
Electronic Components Mfr
N.A.I.C.S.: 334419

Danfoss Industries Pte. Ltd. (1)
25 International Business Park German
Centre Ste 03-57/58, Singapore, Singapore
Tel.: (65) 6885 9788
Electronic Components Mfr
N.A.I.C.S.: 334419

Danfoss Industries Pvt. Limited (1)
10th Floor 4A Campus RMZ Milennia Business Park, No 143 MGR Salai Perungudi,
Chennai, India
Tel.: (91) 44 66 50 1555
Electronic Components Mfr
N.A.I.C.S.: 334419

Danfoss Industries Sdn Bhd (1)
Unit Ste 2 02 Mercu Picorp Lot 10 Jalan
Astaka U8/84 Section U8, Bukit Jelutong,
Shah Alam, Selangor, Malaysia
Tel.: (60) 3 7845 1608
Emp.: 35
Electronic Components Mfr
N.A.I.C.S.: 334419
Eric Lim (Mgr-Sls)

Danfoss Industries, SA de CV (1)
Carretera Miguel Aleman 162, 66634, Apodaca, Mexico (100%)
Tel.: (52) 8181565685
Web Site: http://www.danfoss.com
Sales & Servicer of Compressors
N.A.I.C.S.: 423830

Danfoss Kft. (1)
Vaci ut 91, 1139, Budapest, Hungary
Tel.: (36) 14502531
Web Site: http://www.danfoss.hu
Emp.: 20
Electronic Components Mfr
N.A.I.C.S.: 334419

Danfoss LLC (1)
11655 Crossroads Cir, Baltimore, MD
21220
Tel.: (410) 931-8250
Electronic Components Mfr
N.A.I.C.S.: 334419

Danfoss LLP (1)
Arai Building 20A Kazibek Bi Street, Almaty,
050010, Kazakhstan
Tel.: (7) 27 293 95 05
Electronic Components Mfr
N.A.I.C.S.: 334419

Danfoss Lda. (1)

C/ Calendula 93 Ed I Miniparc II, Alcobendas, 28109, Spain
Tel.: (34) 707 782 518
Electronic Components Mfr
N.A.I.C.S.: 334419

Danfoss Limited (1)
Capswood Oxford Road, Denham, UB9
4LH, Bucks, United Kingdom
Tel.: (44) 870 608 0008
Electronic Components Mfr
N.A.I.C.S.: 334419
Gerhard Strauss (Mng Dir)

Danfoss Ltd. (1)
3/4F Korean Judical Agent Association Bldg
151-31 Nonheyon-dong, Gangnam-gu,
Seoul, 135824, Korea (South)
Tel.: (82) 2 567 0090
Electronic Components Mfr
N.A.I.C.S.: 334419

Danfoss Micro Channel Heat Exchanger (Jiaxing) Co., Ltd. (1)
No 90 Chengbei East Rd Wuyuan Street,
Jiaxing, 314300, Zhejiang, China
Tel.: (86) 57386165008
Heating Equipment Mfr
N.A.I.C.S.: 333414

**Danfoss Otomasyon ve Urunleri Tic
Ltd.** (1)
Pakdil Sok No 5 Bir Plaza B Blok Yukaridudullu, Umraniye, Istanbul, Türkiye
Tel.: (90) 216 526 40 96
Web Site: http://www.danfoss.com
Heating Equipment Mfr
N.A.I.C.S.: 333414
Levenc Taskin (Gen Mgr)

Danfoss Poland Sp.z.o.o. (1)
Ul Chrzanowska 5, 05-825, Grodzisk Mazowiecki, Poland
Tel.: (48) 22 755 0700
Electronic Components Mfr
N.A.I.C.S.: 334419

Danfoss Power Electronics A/S (1)
Ulsnaes 1, Grasten, 6300, Denmark
Tel.: (45) 7488 2222
Electronic Components Mfr
N.A.I.C.S.: 334419

**Danfoss Power Solutions GmbH &
Co. OHG** (1)
Krokamp 35, 24539, Neumunster, Germany
Tel.: (49) 4321 8710
Web Site:
http://www.powersolutions.danfoss.de
Electronic Components Mfr
N.A.I.C.S.: 334419

Danfoss Power Solutions Ltda. (1)
Rua Americo Vespucio 85, Osasco, Sao
Paulo, 06273-070, Brazil
Tel.: (55) 11 3658 6800
Electronic Components Mfr
N.A.I.C.S.: 334419
Antonio Datti (Gen Mgr)

Danfoss Power Solutions Oy Ab (1)
Niittytaival 13, 02200, Espoo, Finland
Tel.: (358) 20 7010600
Web Site: http://www.danfoss.fi
Emp.: 30
Electronic Components Mfr
N.A.I.C.S.: 334419

**Danfoss Power Solutions Pte.
Ltd.** (1)
22 Boon Lay Way Ste 01-59 Tradehub 21,
Singapore, 609968, Singapore
Tel.: (65) 6262 3833
Hydraulic & Electronic Component Whslr
N.A.I.C.S.: 423830

**Danfoss Power Solutions Pty.
Ltd.** (1)
17 Healey Circuit NSW, Huntingwood,
2148, NSW, Australia
Tel.: (61) 9853 0600
Electronic Components Mfr
N.A.I.C.S.: 334419

Danfoss Power Solutions S.r.l. (1)
Via Giovanni Rinaldi 111, Reggio Emilia,
42100, Italy
Tel.: (39) 0522915511
Pumps Mfr
N.A.I.C.S.: 333914

Danfoss Power Solutions, Inc. (1)
2800 E 13th St, Ames, IA 50010 (100%)
Tel.: (515) 239-6000
Web Site: http://powersolutions.danfoss.com
Hydraulic, Electronic, Electrical & Mechanical Components & Systems for Mobile
Equipment Designer, Mfr & Whslr
N.A.I.C.S.: 333996
Eric Alstrom (Pres)

Subsidiary (Non-US):

Daiken-Dauer-Danfoss Ltd. (2)
1-1 Nishi Hitotsuya, Yodogawa-ku, Osaka,
566-0044, Japan
Tel.: (81) 663497264
Web Site: http://www.daikin-sauer-danfoss.com
Emp.: 20
Automotive Hydraulic Component Mfr
N.A.I.C.S.: 334419
Yukihiro Hagiwara (Pres)

Danfoss Power Solutions (1)
S Pos Pavlo Suburban D Leshkovo 217,
Moscow, 143581, Istra, Russia
Tel.: (7) 495 792 57 57
Web Site: http://www.danfoss.com
Emp.: 15
Hydraulic System & Electronic Component
Mfr
N.A.I.C.S.: 334419
Eric Alstrom (Reg Pres)

Hydro-Gear Europe BVBA (2)
Industrielaan 32 bus 4, Hoeselt, 3730, Tongeren, Belgium
Tel.: (32) 12670631
Web Site: http://www.hydro-gear.com
Precision Drive System Design & Mfr
N.A.I.C.S.: 336310

Subsidiary (Domestic):

Hydro-Gear, Inc. (2)
1411 S Hamilton St, Sullivan, IL 61951
Tel.: (217) 728-2581
Web Site: http://www.hydro-gear.com
Precision Drive System Design & Mfr
N.A.I.C.S.: 336310

Subsidiary (Non-US):

**Sauer-Danfoss (Shanghai) Co.
Ltd.** (2)
No 626 Rong Qiao Jin Hai Road Jin Qiao
Export Processing Zone, Pudong New District, Shanghai, 201206, China
Tel.: (86) 2120358100
Web Site:
http://www.powersolutions.danfoss.com
Emp.: 250
Hydraulic System & Electronic Component
Mfr
N.A.I.C.S.: 336390
Jason Zhan (Reg Mgr-Category)

Subsidiary (Domestic):

Sauer-Danfoss (US) Company (2)
2800 E 13th St, Ames, IA 50010
Tel.: (515) 239-6000
Hydraulic System & Mechanical Component
Mfr
N.A.I.C.S.: 336390
Will Miller (Mgr-Supply Chain)

Subsidiary (Non-US):

Sauer-Danfoss AB (2)
Vretenvagen 13, 171 54, Solna, Sweden
Tel.: (46) 86290730
Web Site: http://www.sauer-danfoss.se
Hydraulic Product & Electrical Component
Mfr
N.A.I.C.S.: 336310

Sauer-Danfoss AS (2)
Arenga 2 1309 Rud, Skui, 1340, Baerum,
Norway
Tel.: (47) 67177373
Web Site: http://www.sauer-danfoss.no
Hydraulic System & Electronic Component
Mfr
N.A.I.C.S.: 336310

Sauer-Danfoss ApS (2)
Nordborgvej 81, Nordborg, 6430, Denmark
Tel.: (45) 74884444
Web Site: http://www.sauer-danfoss.dk
Motors Steering Component & Valve Mfr

N.A.I.C.S.: 334419
Rasmus Bunten *(Mgr-Global Acct)*

Sauer-Danfoss BVBA (2)
Gossetlaan 28, 1740, Groot-Bijgaarden, Belgium
Tel.: (32) 25825880
Web Site: http://www.sauer-danfoss.com
Sales Range: $25-49.9 Million
Emp.: 38
Hydraulic, Electronic, Electrical & Mechanical Components & Systems Whslr
N.A.I.C.S.: 423120

Sauer-Danfoss China Holding Company ApS (2)
Nordborgvej 81, 6430, Nordborg, Denmark
Tel.: (45) 74882222
Investment Management Service
N.A.I.C.S.: 551112
Niels Chiastiansen *(CEO)*

Sauer-Danfoss GmbH (2)
Krokamp 35, Neumunster, 24539, Germany
Tel.: (49) 43218710
Web Site: http://www.danfoss.com
Emp.: 50
Hydraulic Component & System Design & Mfr
N.A.I.C.S.: 333996
Joachim Hergt *(Portfolio Mgr-Product)*

Sauer-Danfoss Gmbh & Co. OHG (2)
Krokamp 35, Neumunster, 24539, Germany
Tel.: (49) 43218710
Web Site: http://www.sauer-danfoss.de
Sales Range: $250-299.9 Million
Emp.: 900
Electrohydraulic Products, Hydrostatic Transmissions Systems & Components Mfr
N.A.I.C.S.: 333996

Sauer-Danfoss Hidraulica Mobil Ltda. (2)
Rua Domingos Chies 973 Bairro Interlagos, Caxias do Sul, 95052-160, Rio Grande do Sul, Brazil
Tel.: (55) 5430259750
Sales Range: $25-49.9 Million
Emp.: 184
Spool Valve Mfr
N.A.I.C.S.: 332911

Sauer-Danfoss S.A.S. (2)
322 Rue de Seine, F-77190, Dammarie, Cedex, France
Tel.: (33) 164379133
Web Site: http://www.sauer-danfoss.com
Sales Range: $25-49.9 Million
Emp.: 20
Hydraulic, Electronic, Electrical & Mechanical Components & Systems Whslr
N.A.I.C.S.: 423120

Sauer-Danfoss a.s. (2)
Kukucinova 2148, 017 01, Povazska Bystrica, Slovakia
Tel.: (421) 8224301111
Web Site: http://www.danfoss.com
Hydraulic Electrical & Electronic Component Mfr
N.A.I.C.S.: 334419

Sauer-Danfoss-Daikin Ltd. (2)
401-2 4th FL Korean Judicial Agent Association Bldg, Nonhyeon-dong Gangnam-gu, Seoul, 151-31, Korea (South)
Tel.: (82) 25087834
Web Site: http://www.sauer-danfoss-daikin.com
Hydraulic Component & System Design & Mfr
N.A.I.C.S.: 336390
Joakim Fahlstedt *(Country Mgr)*

Sauer-Danfoss-Daikin Mobile Hydraulics (Shanghai) Co., Ltd. (2)
900 Yishan Road Block C 22F Caohejing Development Zone, Shanghai, 200233, China
Tel.: (86) 2134185200
Web Site: http://www.sauer-danfoss-daikin.com
Hydraulic & Electronic Product Mfr
N.A.I.C.S.: 336390
Steven Chou *(Gen Mgr)*

Sauer-Danfoss-Daikin Pte. Ltd. (2)
22 Boon Lay Way 01-59 Tradehub 21, Singapore, 609968, Singapore
Tel.: (65) 62623833
Web Site: http://www.sauer-danfoss-daikin.com
Sales Range: $25-49.9 Million
Emp.: 10
Mobile Power & Control System Mfr & Supplier
N.A.I.C.S.: 336390
Francis Cheng *(Mgr-Sls)*

Subsidiary (Domestic):

UQM Technologies, Inc. (2)
4120 Specialty Pl, Longmont, CO 80504
Tel.: (303) 682-4900
Web Site: http://www.uqm.com
Rev.: $14,174,784
Assets: $14,014,017
Liabilities: $10,000,244
Net Worth: $4,013,773
Earnings: ($6,503,562)
Emp.: 66
Fiscal Year-end: 12/31/2018
Permanent Magnet Electric Motors & Controls for Electric & Hybrid Vehicles
N.A.I.C.S.: 334419
Adrian P. Schaffer *(Sr VP-Sls & Bus Dev)*

Danfoss Randall Limited (1)
Ampthill Road, Bedford, MK42 9ER, Bedfordshire, United Kingdom
Tel.: (44) 01234364621
Web Site: http://www.danfoss-randall.co.uk
Sales Range: $50-74.9 Million
Emp.: 200
Supplier of Domestic & Commercial Heating Controls
N.A.I.C.S.: 334512

Danfoss Redan A/S (1)
Harupvaenget 11, 8600, Silkeborg, Denmark
Tel.: (45) 86851897
Web Site: http://www.redan.danfoss.dk
Electronic Components Mfr
N.A.I.C.S.: 334419
Michael Hvid Petersen *(Mgr-Sls Support)*

Danfoss S.A. (1)
Edificio I Miniparc III Calrendula 93 El Soto de la Moraleja, Alcobendas, Madrid, 28109, Spain
Tel.: (34) 902 611 623
Valve Mfr
N.A.I.C.S.: 332919

Danfoss S.A. de C.V. (1)
Carr Miguel Aleman Ste 162 Col El Milagro, Apodaca, 66600, Nuevo Leon, Mexico
Tel.: (52) 81 8156 5600
Electronic Components Mfr
N.A.I.C.S.: 334419

Danfoss S.a.r.l. (1)
2 rue Rene Caudron Batiment E, 78960, Voisins-le-Bretonneux, France **(100%)**
Tel.: (33) 130625000
Web Site: http://www.danfoss.fr
Sales Range: $50-74.9 Million
Emp.: 150
Supplier of Industrial Controls
N.A.I.C.S.: 334513

Danfoss S.r.l. (1)
Corso Enrico Tazzoli 221, 10137, Turin, Italy **(100%)**
Tel.: (39) 0694809900
Web Site: http://www.danfoss.com
Sales Range: $25-49.9 Million
Emp.: 70
Industrial Controls & Related Products Mfr & Sales
N.A.I.C.S.: 334512

Danfoss Semco A/S (1)
Middelfartvej 9, 5000, Odense, Denmark
Tel.: (45) 74887800
Web Site: http://www.danfoss-semco.com
Fire Protection Services
N.A.I.C.S.: 922160

Danfoss Silicon Power GmbH (1)
Husumer Strasse 251, Schleswig-Holstein, 24941, Flensburg, Germany **(100%)**
Tel.: (49) 461430140
Web Site:
   http://www.siliconpower.danfoss.com
Sales Range: $100-124.9 Million
Emp.: 300
Supplier of Industrial Controls

N.A.I.C.S.: 334513

Danfoss Sp. z.o.o. (1)
Ul Chrzanowska 5, 05-825, Grodzisk Mazowiecki, Poland **(100%)**
Tel.: (48) 227550700
Web Site: http://www.danfoss.com.pl
Sales Range: $200-249.9 Million
Emp.: 800
Mfr & Sales of Industrial & Household Controls
N.A.I.C.S.: 334513
Adam Jedrzejczak *(Pres-Eastern Europe & Poland)*

Danfoss T.o.v. (1)
15/15/6 Vikentiya Khvoiky Str, Kiev, 04080, Ukraine
Tel.: (380) 44 4618700
Web Site: http://www.danfoss.com
Emp.: 8
Electronic Components Mfr
N.A.I.C.S.: 334419

Danfoss Trata d.o.o. (1)
Ulica Jozeta Jame 16, Sentvid, Ljubljana, 1210, Slovenia
Tel.: (386) 3861582036
Electronic Components Mfr
N.A.I.C.S.: 334419

Danfoss Turbocor Compressors Inc. (1)
1769 E Paul Dirac Dr, Tallahassee, FL 32310
Tel.: (850) 504-4800
Web Site: http://www.turbocor.com
Compressor Mfr
N.A.I.C.S.: 333912
Ricardo Schneider *(Pres & CEO)*

Danfoss UAB (1)
Smolensko 6, Vilnius, 3201, Lithuania
Tel.: (370) 8 5 2105 740
Electronic Components Mfr
N.A.I.C.S.: 334419

Danfoss d.o.o. (1)
Ulica Jozeta Jame 16, Ljubljana, 1210, Sentvid, Slovenia **(100%)**
Tel.: (386) 1 582 0200
Sales Range: $25-49.9 Million
Emp.: 12
Sales & Servicer of Valves & Controls
N.A.I.C.S.: 332919

Danfoss do Brasil Industria e Comercio Ltda. (1)
Rod Anhanguera Km 16 5 Jd Platina-Osasco-SP, Osasco, Brazil
Tel.: (55) 11 2135 5400
Electronic Components Mfr
N.A.I.C.S.: 334419

Danfoss hf. (1)
Skutuvogi 6, Reykjavik, 104, Iceland
Tel.: (354) 510 4100
Electronic Components Mfr
N.A.I.C.S.: 334419

Danfoss s.r.o. (1)
Jihlavska 1558/21, Praha 4, 140 00, Prague, Czech Republic
Tel.: (420) 2 83 014 111
Web Site: http://www.danfoss.cz
Emp.: 30
Electronic Components Mfr
N.A.I.C.S.: 334419

Danfoss spol. S.r.o. (1)
Tovarenska 49, Zlate Moravce, 953 01, Slovakia
Tel.: (421) 37 6406280
Web Site: http://www.danfoss.com
Emp.: 220
Electronic Components Mfr
N.A.I.C.S.: 334419

Gemina Termix Production A/S (1)
Navervej 15-17, 7451, Sunds, Denmark
Tel.: (45) 9714 1444
Web Site: http://www.termix.dk
Emp.: 90
Heating Equipment Mfr
N.A.I.C.S.: 333414
Christian Bentzen-Bilkvist *(Gen Mgr)*

N.V. Danfoss S.A. (1)
Alfons Gossetlaan 28, Vlaams Brabant, 1702, Dilbeek, Belgium
Tel.: (32) 25889988

Web Site: http://www.danfoss.com
Pump & Valve Distr
N.A.I.C.S.: 423730

OOO Danfoss (1)
House 28 Nekrasova St, 150000, Yaroslavl, Russia
Tel.: (7) 4957925757
Web Site: http://www.danfoss.ru
Emp.: 500
Electronic Components Mfr
N.A.I.C.S.: 334419

PT Danfoss Indonesia (1)
JL MT Haryono Road Kav 15 RT 010 RW 005 Tebet Barat Tebet, Gd Graha Pratama 18th Floor, Jakarta, 12810, Indonesia
Tel.: (62) 21 83790621
Electric Equipment Mfr
N.A.I.C.S.: 335999

SIA Danfoss (1)
Tiraines street 1, Riga, 1058, Latvia
Tel.: (371) 67339166
Web Site: http://www.danfoss.lv
Electronic Components Mfr
N.A.I.C.S.: 334419

Scroll Technologies (1)
1 Scroll Dr, Arkadelphia, AR 71923-8813
Tel.: (870) 246-0700
Sales Range: $125-149.9 Million
Emp.: 750
Compressor Mfr
N.A.I.C.S.: 333912

Vacon Ltd (1)
Runsorintie 7, 65380, Vaasa, Finland
Tel.: (358) 2012121
Web Site: http://www.danfoss.fi
AC Drives Developer & Mfr
N.A.I.C.S.: 333612

Subsidiary (Non-US):

VACON AT Antriebssysteme GmbH (2)
Aumuhlweg 21, Leobersdorf, 2544, Austria
Tel.: (43) 225665166
Web Site: http://www.eanfoff.com
Emp.: 20
Power Transmission Systems Mfr
N.A.I.C.S.: 221121
Johann Goldfuss *(Mng Dir)*

Vacon AB (2)
Anderstorpsvagen 16, Solna, 171 54, Sweden
Tel.: (46) 8293055
Web Site: http://drives.danfoss.com
Generator Electric Drives Mfr
N.A.I.C.S.: 335312
Thomas Thorewik *(VP-Northern & Eastern Europe)*

Vacon Benelux B.V. (2)
Weide 40, 4206 CJ, Gorinchem, Netherlands
Tel.: (31) 183642970
Web Site: http://drives.danfoss.com
Frequency Converters Mfr & Distr
N.A.I.C.S.: 335312

Vacon Benelux N.V./S.A. (2)
Interleuvenlaan 62, 3001, Heverlee, Belgium
Tel.: (32) 16394825
Web Site: http://www.nl.vacon.com
Frequency Converters Mfr & Distr
N.A.I.C.S.: 335312
Daniel De Coster *(Mng Dir)*

Vacon Drives & Controls Pvt. Ltd. (2)
352 Kapaleeshwar Nagar East Coast Road Neelangarai, Chennai, Tamil Nadu, India
Tel.: (91) 44 2449 0024
Electric Drives & Controls Mfr
N.A.I.C.S.: 335311

Vacon Drives A/S (2)
Jyllandsgade 30, 6400, Sonderborg, Denmark
Tel.: (45) 88437000
Web Site: http://drives.danfoss.com
Frequency Converters Mfr
N.A.I.C.S.: 335312
John Wind *(Mng Dir)*

Vacon Drives UK Ltd. (2)
18 Maizefield, Hinckley, LE10 1YF, Leices-

Danfoss A/S—(Continued)

tershire, United Kingdom
Tel.: (44) 1455611515
Web Site: http://www.drives.danfoss.com
Frequency Converters Mfr
N.A.I.C.S.: 335312

Vacon France s.a.s. (2)
Siege Social 33 rue de la Mare a Tissier,
BP 72, 91280, Saint-Pierre-du-Perray,
France
Tel.: (33) 169896030
Web Site: http://drives.danfoss.com
Frequency Converters Mfr
N.A.I.C.S.: 334419

Vacon GmbH (2)
Gladbecker Str 425, Essen, 45329, Germany
Tel.: (49) 201806700
Web Site: http://drives.danfoss.com
Generator Mfr
N.A.I.C.S.: 335312
Vladimir Kozak (Mng Dir)

Vacon Pacific Pty Ltd (2)
2 National Drive, Dandenong South, Melbourne, 3175, VIC, Australia
Tel.: (61) 392389300
Web Site: http://drives.danfoss.com
Emp.: 40
Frequency Converters Mfr
N.A.I.C.S.: 335312
Mike Smith (Gen Mgr)

Vacon S.p.A. (2)
Via Fratelli Guerra 35, 42124, Reggio
nell'Emilia, Italy
Tel.: (39) 0522276811
Web Site: http://drives.danfoss.com
Frequency Converters Mfr
N.A.I.C.S.: 335312

ZAO Danfoss (1)
Pavlovskaya Sloboda 217, Leshkovo village
Istra District, 143581, Moscow,
Russia (100%)
Tel.: (7) 4957925757
Web Site: http://www.danfoss.ru
Sales Range: $50-74.9 Million
Emp.: 200
Mfr of Regulators
N.A.I.C.S.: 335313

ZAO Ridan (1)
16 Kominterna Str, Nizhniy Novgorod,
603014, Russia
Tel.: (7) 831 2778855
Electronic Components Mfr
N.A.I.C.S.: 334419

Zheijang Holip Electronic Technology
Co. Ltd. (1)
C1 7th Floor Donghai Chuangyi Centre No
7 Tianmushan Road, Hangzhou, China
Tel.: (86) 571 28891883
Electronic Components Mfr
N.A.I.C.S.: 334419

DANGEE DUMS LTD.

4/A Ketan Society Opp BD Patel
House Nr Sardar Patel Colony
Naranpura, Ahmedabad, 380 013,
Gujarat, India
Tel.: (91) 919898088885
Web Site:
https://www.dangeedums.com
Year Founded: 2010
DANGEE—(NSE)
Rev.: $2,207,355
Assets: $7,633,039
Liabilities: $5,048,343
Net Worth: $2,584,696
Earnings: ($1,371,102)
Emp.: 208
Fiscal Year-end: 03/31/21
Bakery Products Mfr
N.A.I.C.S.: 311812
Nikul Jagdishchandra Patel (Chm &
Mng Dir)

DANGOTE GROUP LIMITED

Union Marble House 1 Alfred Rewane
Road, PO Box 40032, Falomo Ikoyi,
Lagos, Nigeria

Tel.: (234) 14480815
Web Site: http://www.dangote-group.com
Sales Range: $700-749.9 Million
Emp.: 7,000
Diversified Mfr, Importer & Exporter
N.A.I.C.S.: 425120
Knut Ulvmoen (Exec Dir)

Subsidiaries:

Dangote BAIL Limited (1)
Federal Ocean Terminal Drive Trans Amadi
Layout, PO Box 2464, Port Harcourt, Rivers
State, Nigeria
Tel.: (234) 84 830360
Cement Mfr
N.A.I.C.S.: 327310

Dangote Cement PLC (1)
Leadway Marble House 1 Alfred Rewane
Road, Lagos, Nigeria
Tel.: (234) 1460643
Web Site: https://dangotecement.com
Rev.: $1,197,879,333
Assets: $1,936,102,414
Liabilities: $1,137,468,079
Net Worth: $798,634,335
Earnings: $282,985,810
Emp.: 19,112
Fiscal Year-end: 12/31/2022
Cement Product Mfr
N.A.I.C.S.: 327310
Knut Ulvmoen (Dir-Supply Chain)

Subsidiary (Non-US):

Sephaku Cement (Pty) Limited (2)
Southdowns Office Park Block A Ground
Floor Cnr, John Vorster & Karee St X54,
Irene, 0062, South Africa
Tel.: (27) 12 684 6300
Web Site: http://www.sephakucement.co.za
Cement Mfr
N.A.I.C.S.: 327310
Duncan Leith (Mgr-Comml)

Dangote Global Services Limited (1)
75 Davies Street, London, W1K 5JN, United
Kingdom
Tel.: (44) 207 399 3070
Cement Mfr
N.A.I.C.S.: 327310

Dangote Sugar Refinery PLC (1)
3rd Floor GDNL Building Terminal E Shed
20 NPA Wharf, Port Complex Apapa, Lagos, Nigeria
Tel.: (234) 8150983259
Web Site: https://sugar.dangote.com
Rev.: $298,481,845
Assets: $364,498,898
Liabilities: $237,757,464
Net Worth: $126,741,434
Earnings: $40,520,014
Emp.: 3,003
Fiscal Year-end: 12/31/2022
Food Mfr
N.A.I.C.S.: 311314
Gcon Aliko Dangote (Chm)

Dansa Foods Limited (1)
Dansa drive off Lagos-Badagry Expressway, Abule Oshun, Lagos, Nigeria
Tel.: (234) 8060769770
Web Site: http://www.dansa-foods.com
Food Product & Beverage Mfr & Whslr
N.A.I.C.S.: 312111
Erasmus Akhabue (Mgr-Key Accts)

Green View Development Services
Limited (1)
Administration Building Former N P A Container Terminal, P M B 1079, Apapa, Lagos,
Nigeria
Tel.: (234) 1 7615460
Business Support Services
N.A.I.C.S.: 561110

DANHUA CHEMICAL TECH-
NOLOGY CO., LTD.

C1 Building No 888 South Third Ring
Road, High-tech Innovation Park,
Danyang, 212300, Jiangsu, China
Tel.: (86) 51180265777
Web Site: https://www.600844.com
Year Founded: 1993

900921—(SHG)
Rev.: $131,108,230
Assets: $261,446,211
Liabilities: $81,256,317
Net Worth: $180,189,894
Earnings: ($41,134,926)
Emp.: 361
Fiscal Year-end: 12/31/22
Chemical Component Mfr
N.A.I.C.S.: 325998

DANI INSTRUMENTS SPA

Viale Brianza 87, Cologno Monzese,
20093, Milan, Italy
Tel.: (39) 022539941 IT
Web Site: http://www.dani-instruments.com
Year Founded: 1975
Gas Chromatographic Instrumentation
N.A.I.C.S.: 333132
Umberto Saini Fasanotti (Pres)

Subsidiaries:

DANI Instruments S.A. (1)
Via A Ramel 29, Contone, 6594, Gambarogno, Switzerland
Tel.: (41) 91 924 93 00
Gas Chromatographic Instrumentation
N.A.I.C.S.: 333132
Umberto Saini Fasanotti (Mng Dir)

Spectra Analysis Instruments,
Inc. (1)
257 Simarano Dr, Marlborough, MA 01752
Tel.: (508) 281-6232
Web Site: http://www.spectra-analysis.com
Printing Ink Mfr
N.A.I.C.S.: 325910
Ming Zhou (Dir-Applications Engrg)

DANIEL STEWART SECURI-
TIES PLC

Becket House 36 Old Jewry, London,
EC2R 8DD, United Kingdom
Tel.: (44) 20 7776 6550 UK
Web Site:
http://www.danielstewart.co.uk
Year Founded: 1989
Sales Range: $1-9.9 Million
Emp.: 39
Investment Banking, Securities Dealing & Brokerage Services
N.A.I.C.S.: 523150
Peter Shea (Founder & CEO)

Subsidiaries:

Daniel Stewart & Company plc (1)
Becket House 36 Old Jewry, London, EC2R
8DD, United Kingdom
Tel.: (44) 20 7776 6550
Sales Range: $50-74.9 Million
Emp.: 50
Investment Banking Services
N.A.I.C.S.: 523150
Martin Lampshire (Head-Corp Broking)

DANIEL THWAITES PLC

Penny Street, Blackburn, BB1 5BU,
Lancs, United Kingdom
Tel.: (44) 1254686868 UK
Web Site:
http://www.danielthwaites.com
Year Founded: 1807
Sales Range: $150-199.9 Million
Emp.: 300
Holding Company; Breweries, Retail
Pubs & Hotels Owner & Operator
N.A.I.C.S.: 551112
John Yerburgh (Pres)

Subsidiaries:

Daniel Thwaites Brewery (1)
Penny Street, Blackburn, BB1 6HL, Lancs,
United Kingdom
Tel.: (44) 1254686868
Web Site: http://www.thwaitesbeers.co.uk

Sales Range: $100-124.9 Million
Emp.: 500
Brewery
N.A.I.C.S.: 312120
Joe Calling (Dir-HR)

Shire Hotels Limited (1)
The Old Wine Warehouse Larkhill St, Blackburn, BB1 5DF, Lancs, United
Kingdom (100%)
Tel.: (44) 1254267444
Web Site: http://www.shirehotels.com
Sales Range: $10-24.9 Million
Emp.: 30
Hotel Owner & Operator
N.A.I.C.S.: 721110

DANIELI & C. OFFICINE MEC-
CANICHE S.P.A.

Via Nazionale 41, Buttrio, 33042,
Udine, Italy
Tel.: (39) 04321958111
Web Site: https://www.danieli.com
DAN—(ITA)
Rev.: $4,426,997,626
Assets: $7,059,071,876
Liabilities: $4,460,643,212
Net Worth: $2,598,428,664
Earnings: $260,411,181
Emp.: 9,643
Fiscal Year-end: 06/30/23
Machinery & Plants Mfr
N.A.I.C.S.: 333519
Gianpietro Benedetti (Chm &
Member-Exec Bd)

Subsidiaries:

ABS Centre Metallurgique Sarl (1)
Rue Pierre Simon Delaplace n 10, 57075,
Metz, Cedex, France
Tel.: (33) 355944009
Steelmaking Product Mfr
N.A.I.C.S.: 331110

ABS SPA (1)
Via Buttrio 28, Cargnacco, 33050, Udine,
Italy
Tel.: (39) 0432613211
Steelmaking Product Mfr & Whslr
N.A.I.C.S.: 331110

ABS Sisak Doo (1)
Via B Kavurica n 12, 40010, Sisak, Croatia
Tel.: (385) 44565202
Steelmaking Product Mfr
N.A.I.C.S.: 331110

Danieli Automation SPA (1)
Via B Stringher 4, Buttrio, 33042, Udine,
Italy
Tel.: (39) 0432518111
Web Site: https://www.dca.it
Steelmaking Product Mfr & Whslr
N.A.I.C.S.: 331110
Antonello Mordeglia (Co-Pres)

Danieli Centro Combustion SPA (1)
Via Galileo Galilei 40, Cinisello Balsamo,
20092, Milan, Italy
Tel.: (39) 02262451
Web Site:
https://www.danielicentrocombustion.it
Steel Heat Treatment Services
N.A.I.C.S.: 332811

Danieli Co., Ltd. (1)
64/210 Moo 4, The Eastern Seaboard Ind
Estate Tambol Pluakdaeng Amphur Pluakdaeng, 21140, Rayong, 21140, Thailand
Tel.: (66) 38929000
Steelmaking Product Mfr & Whslr
N.A.I.C.S.: 331110

Danieli Constr International SPA (1)
Via Nazionale 41, Buttrio, 33042, Udine,
Italy
Tel.: (39) 04321953766
Steelmaking Product Mfr & Whslr
N.A.I.C.S.: 331110

Danieli Corporation (1)
600 Cranberry Woods Dr Ste 200, Cranberry Township, PA 16066 (100%)
Tel.: (724) 778-5400
Web Site: https://www.danieli-usa.com
Sales Range: $25-49.9 Million
Emp.: 36

Distr & Service of Custom Steel-Making Equipment
N.A.I.C.S.: 333519

Danieli Corus Technical Services BV **(1)**
Rooswijkweg 291, Noord, 1951 ME, Velsen, Netherlands **(50%)**
Tel.: (31) 251500500
Web Site: https://www.danieli-corus.com
Emp.: 250
Engineeering Services
N.A.I.C.S.: 541330
Peter Zonneveld *(Mng Dir)*

Subsidiary (US):

Danieli Corus, Inc. **(2)**
8300 Mississippi Street, Merrillville, IN 46410
Tel.: (219) 650-5500
Web Site: http://www.danieli-corus.com
Metals Industry Equipment Mfr
N.A.I.C.S.: 541330

Danieli Do Brazil SA **(1)**
Rod Raimundo Antunes Soares 2289, Capoavinha, Sao Paulo, 18115-120, Brazil
Tel.: (55) 1139953150
Web Site: http://www.danieli.com.br
Steelmaking Product Mfr & Whslr
N.A.I.C.S.: 331110

Danieli Engineering & Service GMBH **(1)**
Max-Planck Strasse 5, 9100, Volkermarkt, Austria
Tel.: (43) 4232514406101
Steelmaking Product Mfr & Whslr
N.A.I.C.S.: 331110

Danieli Engineering Japan Ltd. **(1)**
42F Yokohama Landmark Tower 2-2-1 Minatomirai, Nishi-ku, Yokohama, 220-8142, Japan
Tel.: (81) 456517077
Steelmaking Product Mfr & Whslr
N.A.I.C.S.: 331110

Danieli Finance Solution SA **(1)**
126 rue Cents, 1319, Luxembourg, Luxembourg
Tel.: (352) 27125465
Web Site: https://www.danieli.lu
Financial Investment Services
N.A.I.C.S.: 523999
Alessandro Brussi *(Chm)*

Danieli Germany GMBH **(1)**
Schifferstasse 166, 47059, Duisburg, Germany
Tel.: (49) 20398567000
Steelmaking Product Mfr & Whslr
N.A.I.C.S.: 331110

Danieli Germany GmbH. **(1)**
Brunsnosstrasse 12, 45470, Mulheim an der Ruhr, Germany **(100%)**
Tel.: (49) 2083780000
Web Site: http://www.danieli-ht.de
Sales Range: $25-49.9 Million
Emp.: 11
N.A.I.C.S.: 333519
Joerg Schroeder *(Mng Dir)*

Danieli Henschel SAS **(1)**
Rue Copernic 490 Savoie Hexapole, 73420, Mery, France
Tel.: (33) 479622644
Steelmaking Product Mfr & Whslr
N.A.I.C.S.: 331110

Danieli Metall Equipment & Service Co., Ltd. **(1)**
No 19 Xing Gang Road, CEDZ Changshu, Jiangsu, 215513, China
Tel.: (86) 51252267000
Steelmaking Product Mfr & Whslr
N.A.I.C.S.: 331110

Danieli Middle East Eng. & Serv.CO. **(1)**
76 Al-moltaka Sheraton Zone Heliopolis, Al-Arabi Dist, 11799, Cairo, Egypt
Tel.: (20) 222699491
Steelmaking Product Mfr & Whslr
N.A.I.C.S.: 331110

Danieli Morgardshammar SA **(1)**
Avenida Zugazarte 8 Fl 2 El Abra 4, 48930, Las Arenas, Vizcaya, Spain **(100%)**

Tel.: (34) 944804343
Web Site: http://www.morgardshammar.org
Sales Range: $25-49.9 Million
Emp.: 16
N.A.I.C.S.: 333519
Anders Eriksson *(Mng Dir)*

Danieli Procome Iberica SA **(1)**
Poligono Sondikalde Calle Portu Bidea 2, 48150, Sondika, Vizcaya, Spain
Tel.: (34) 944872800
Web Site: http://www.danieliprocome.com
Steelmaking Product Mfr & Whslr
N.A.I.C.S.: 331110

Danieli Systec Doo **(1)**
Vinez 601, 52220, Labin, Croatia
Tel.: (385) 52884130
Web Site: https://www.danieli-systec.com
Emp.: 300
Steelmaking Product Mfr & Whslr
N.A.I.C.S.: 331110

Danieli UK Holding LTD. **(1)**
4 Ignite Magna Way, Rotherham, S60 1FD, United Kingdom
Tel.: (44) 1709724300
Steelmaking Product Mfr & Whslr
N.A.I.C.S.: 331110

Danieli Volga LLC **(1)**
Avtozavodskoe shosse 48, Nizhny Novgorod region, 606016, Dzerzhinsk, Russia
Tel.: (7) 8313310310
Web Site: http://www.danielivolga.ru
Steelmaking Product Mfr & Whslr
N.A.I.C.S.: 331110

FATA SpA **(1)**
Strada Statale 24 km 12, 10044, Pianezza, Turin, Italy
Tel.: (39) 01196681
Web Site: http://www.fatagroup.it
Industrial Plant Engineering, Contracting & Mfg Services
N.A.I.C.S.: 237990
Carlos Lemos *(Engr-Project & Design)*

Subsidiary (US):

Danieli FATA Hunter, Inc. **(2)**
1040 Iowa Ave Ste 100, Riverside, CA 92507
Tel.: (951) 328-0200
Web Site: http://www.fatahunter.com
Coil & Sheet Processing Equipment Mfr
N.A.I.C.S.: 333517
Raymond Sanchez *(CFO)*

Subsidiary (Non-US):

Fata Gulf CO WLL **(2)**
Al Mana Tower-15th Floor Office No 15-D C-Ring Road, PO Box 22851, Suhaim Bin Hamad Street, Doha, Qatar
Tel.: (974) 44192300
Procurement Services
N.A.I.C.S.: 541990

Industrielle Beteiligung Co., Ltd. **(1)**
Lot A4B Industrial Park In Tan Thuan Export Processing Zone, Tan Thuan Dong Ward District 7, Ho Chi Minh City, Vietnam
Tel.: (84) 907563119
Web Site: https://danieli.com.vn
Emp.: 300
Steelmaking Product Mfr & Whslr
N.A.I.C.S.: 331110

Innoval Technology LTD. **(1)**
Beaumont Close, Banbury, OX16 1TQ, Oxfordshire, United Kingdom
Tel.: (44) 1295702800
Web Site: https://www.innovaltec.com
Aluminum Consultant Services
N.A.I.C.S.: 541611

More SRL **(1)**
Via Santa Lucia 7 - Centro affari, Gemona del Friuli, 33013, Udine, Italy
Tel.: (39) 0432973511
Web Site: https://www.more-oxy.com
Steelmaking Product Mfr & Whslr
N.A.I.C.S.: 331110

Morgardshammar AB **(1)**
Nya Agatan 23, PO Box 502, 777 50, Smedjebacken, Sweden
Tel.: (46) 240668500
Web Site: https://www.morgardshammar.se

Sales Range: $50-74.9 Million
Emp.: 250
Mfr of Hot Rolling Mill Machinery, Mining Equipment & Wire Drawing Equipment
N.A.I.C.S.: 333131

Rotelec SA **(1)**
85 Boucle de La Ramee, 38070, Saint-Quentin-Fallavier, Cedex, France
Tel.: (33) 474959670
Web Site: https://www.rotelec.fr
Steelmaking Product Mfr & Whslr
N.A.I.C.S.: 331110

Sund Birsta AB **(1)**
Heffners Alle 51, 856 33, Sundsvall, Sweden
Tel.: (46) 60139400
Web Site: http://www.sundbirsta.com
Steel Binding Machine Mfr
N.A.I.C.S.: 333517

Telerobot Labs SRL **(1)**
Corso Ferdinando Maria Perrone 47 R, 16152, Genoa, Italy
Tel.: (39) 0105341731
Web Site: http://www.telerobotlabs.it
Industrial Automation Machinery Mfr
N.A.I.C.S.: 333998

DANIR RESOURCES AB
Dockplatsen 1, 211 19, Malmo, Sweden
Tel.: (46) 40 665 90 00
Web Site: http://www.danir.se
Year Founded: 1986
Emp.: 3,400
Holding Services
N.A.I.C.S.: 551112
Dan Olofsson *(Owner)*

Subsidiaries:

Sigma AB **(1)**
Dockplatsen 1, 211 19, Malmo, Sweden
Tel.: (46) 771550500
Web Site: http://www.sigma.se
Emp.: 3,100
IT Management & Information Logistics Services
N.A.I.C.S.: 541990

Subsidiary (Non-US):

Eclipse SP LLC **(2)**
10A Ac Proskura str 96, Kharkiv, 61085, Ukraine
Tel.: (380) 577164585
Web Site: http://www.eclipse-sp.com
Sales Range: $25-49.9 Million
Emp.: 40
IT Consulting Services
N.A.I.C.S.: 541519
Vladimir Beck *(Mng Dir)*

Subsidiary (Domestic):

Sigma Adactum AB **(2)**
Teknikringen 10, Linkoping, 583 30, Sweden
Tel.: (46) 771550500
Web Site: http://www.sigma.se
Sales Range: $25-49.9 Million
Emp.: 100
IT Consulting Services
N.A.I.C.S.: 541519
Jonas Steffensson *(CEO)*

Sigma Civil AB **(2)**
Marieviksgatan 19 C 3 tr, Box 47 137, SE-100 74, Stockholm, Sweden
Tel.: (46) 771 550 500
Web Site: http://sigmacivil.se
Emp.: 500
Consulting Services; Infrastructure, Construction & Project Management
N.A.I.C.S.: 541618
Jonas Wallberg *(CEO)*

Subsidiary (Non-US):

Sigma Consulting Solutions Ltd **(2)**
Ropewalks Newton St, Macclesfield, SK11 6QJ, Cheshire, United Kingdom
Tel.: (44) 1625427718
Web Site: http://www.wearesigma.com
Sales Range: $25-49.9 Million
Emp.: 40
IT Consulting Services

N.A.I.C.S.: 541519

Subsidiary (Domestic):

Sigma Emprove AB **(2)**
Eastern Vittusgatan 36, 37133, Karlskrona, Sweden
Tel.: (46) 733600110
IT Consulting Services
N.A.I.C.S.: 541519

Subsidiary (Non-US):

Sigma Kudos Finland Oy **(2)**
Kalevantie 7, 33100, Tampere, Finland
Tel.: (358) 32255257
Web Site: http://www.sigmakudos.com
Sales Range: $25-49.9 Million
Emp.: 20
Logistics Management Services
N.A.I.C.S.: 541614

Sigma Maxiflex Oy **(2)**
Kalevantie 7, 33100, Tampere, Finland
Tel.: (358) 331234800
Web Site: http://www.sigmasolutions.fi
Sales Range: $25-49.9 Million
Emp.: 12
IT Consulting Services
N.A.I.C.S.: 541519

Subsidiary (Domestic):

Sigma Solutions AB **(2)**
Lindholmspiren 9, 417 56, Gothenburg, Sweden
Tel.: (46) 317254700
IT Consulting Services
N.A.I.C.S.: 541519

Subsidiary (Non-US):

Sigma Technology Hungary Ltd. **(2)**
Kozraktar Str 30-32 Building K32 4th Floor, H-1093, Budapest, Hungary
Tel.: (36) 1215 7553
Web Site: http://www.sigmatechnology.se
Sales Range: $25-49.9 Million
Emp.: 30
Supplier of Product Information, Software & Embedded Solutions & Offshore Development
N.A.I.C.S.: 541519
Gyordy Nagy *(Mng Dir)*

Subsidiary (Domestic):

Sigma iMal Projektledning AB **(2)**
Dockplatsen 1, 211 19, Malmo, Sweden
Tel.: (46) 40 662 20 00
Web Site: http://www.sigma.se
IT Consulting Services
N.A.I.C.S.: 541519

DANISH AEROTECH A/S
Herningvej 30, 7470, Karup, Denmark
Tel.: (45) 99626262
Web Site: http://www.aerotech.dk
Year Founded: 1992
Sales Range: $25-49.9 Million
Emp.: 100
Development, Production, Installation & Support of Electrical, Electronic & Mechanical Components for Aircraft, Helicopters, Missiles & Targeting Systems
N.A.I.C.S.: 336413
Jan Jorgensen *(CEO)*

DANISH AGRO AMBA
Kogevej 55, 4653, Karise, Denmark
Tel.: (45) 7215 8000
Web Site: http://www.danishagro.com
Year Founded: 1901
Sales Range: $1-4.9 Billion
Emp.: 4,500
Agricultural & Industrial Cooperative Services
N.A.I.C.S.: 111998
Jorgen H. Mikkelsen *(Chm-Supervisory Bd)*

Subsidiaries:

Hedegaard A/S **(1)**
Nordre Havnegade 3, 9400, Norresundby, Denmark **(100%)**

Danish Agro AmbA—(Continued)

Tel.: (45) 99 36 17 00
Web Site: http://www.hedegaard-as.dk
Sales Range: $300-349.9 Million
Emp.: 164
Grain, Feed & Fertilizer Mfr
N.A.I.C.S.: 424910
Soren Rathcke (CEO)

DANISH CROWN AMBA
Marsvej 43, 8960, Randers, Denmark
Tel.: (45) 89191919   DK
Web Site:
    http://www.danishcrown.com
Year Founded: 1990
Rev.: $10,599,474,840
Assets: $4,845,794,920
Liabilities: $3,496,677,810
Net Worth: $1,349,117,110
Earnings: $359,852,600
Emp.: 26,641
Fiscal Year-end: 09/30/22
Slaughtering, Meat Processing
N.A.I.C.S.: 311611
Preben Sunke (Grp COO)

Subsidiaries:

DAT-Schaub A/S   (1)
Flaesketorvet 41, 1711, Copenhagen,
Denmark   (100%)
Tel.: (45) 33266600
Web Site: http://dat-schaub.dk
Sales Range: $150-199.9 Million
Emp.: 580
Holding Company; Natural Casings & Ingredients Distr
N.A.I.C.S.: 551112
Morten Fredborg Andreasen (CFO)

Subsidiary (Non-US):

Argental S.A.R.L.   (2)
Sortie Sud R N 82, Bourg Alandroal, 42220,
Bourg-en-Bresse, France
Tel.: (33) 477391168
Sales Range: $10-24.9 Million
Emp.: 20
Hotels & Motels
N.A.I.C.S.: 721110
Patrich Vidal (Mng Dir)

Boyauderie Orleanaise SA   (2)
45 rue de Curembourg, BP 92226, 45402,
Fleury-les-Aubrais, France
Tel.: (33) 238864545
Holding Company
N.A.I.C.S.: 551112

Boyaux Bressans SA   (2)
Cenord-10 rue Jacquard, BP 8303, 01008,
Bourg-en-Bresse, France
Tel.: (33) 474233432
Holding Company
N.A.I.C.S.: 551112

CKW Pharma-Extrakt GmbH & Co.
KG   (2)
Enshedestrasse 12, 48529, Nordhorn, Germany
Tel.: (49) 59212011
Web Site: http://www.dif-kuepers.de
Sales Range: $25-49.9 Million
Emp.: 15
Pharmaceutical Preparation Mfr
N.A.I.C.S.: 325412
Walter Koop (Mng Dir)

DAT-Schaub (Deutschland)
GmbH   (2)
Fuchtenfelder Stasse 26, Wietmarschen,
Lingen, 49835, Germany
Tel.: (49) 594691330
Web Site: http://www.dif-kuepers.de
Sales Range: $25-49.9 Million
Emp.: 180
Management Consulting Services
N.A.I.C.S.: 541618

DAT-Schaub (Porto) SA   (2)
Rua Do Eirado 350, Arcozelo, 4410-429,
Vila Nova de Gaia, Portugal
Tel.: (351) 227537100
Web Site: http://www.dat-schaub.dk
Sales Range: $75-99.9 Million
Emp.: 360

Mayonnaise Dressing & Prepared Sauce
Mfr
N.A.I.C.S.: 311941

DAT-Schaub AB   (2)
Varnemovagen 6A, 43232, Varberg, Sweden
Tel.: (46) 40592170
Web Site: http://www.dat-schaub.se
Grocery & Related Products Merchant
Whslr
N.A.I.C.S.: 424490
Bengt Landquist (Mgr)

DAT-Schaub Casings (Australia) Pty
Ltd   (2)
Nott Road, PO Box 525, Ararat, 3377, VIC,
Australia
Tel.: (61) 408 503 794
Meat Product Whslr
N.A.I.C.S.: 424470

DAT-Schaub Polska Sp. z o.o.   (2)
Ul Obornicka 85, 62 002, Suchy Las, Poland
Tel.: (48) 61 652 23 75
Web Site: http://www.dat-schaub.com.pl
Meat Product Whslr
N.A.I.C.S.: 424470

DS-France S.A.S.   (2)
13 rue des Alouettes, Thiais, 94320, France
Tel.: (33) 149785800
Web Site: http://www.soussana.com
Sales Range: $25-49.9 Million
Emp.: 92
Holding Company
N.A.I.C.S.: 551112

Dif Organveredlung Gerhard Kupers
GmbH & Co. Kg   (2)
Fuchtenfelder Stasse 26, Wietmarschen,
49835, Lingen, Germany
Tel.: (49) 594691330
Web Site: http://www.dif-kuepers.de
Sales Range: $50-74.9 Million
Emp.: 200
Meat & Meat Product Merchant Whslr
N.A.I.C.S.: 424470

Oriental Sino Limited   (2)
2804 28/F Universal Trade Centre, 3 Arbuthnot Road, Central, China (Hong Kong)
Tel.: (852) 28107321
Web Site: http://www.osl-grp.com
Sales Range: $25-49.9 Million
Emp.: 4
Holding Company
N.A.I.C.S.: 551112

Oy DAT - Schaub Finland Ab   (2)
Mahlamaentie 44, Tuusula, 04310, Finland
Tel.: (358) 9862 44629
Meat Product Whslr
N.A.I.C.S.: 424470

Subsidiary (Domestic):

Thomeko Oy   (3)
Asentajankatu 5, PO Box 236, 00811, Helsinki, Finland
Tel.: (358) 207 921 200
Web Site: http://www.thomeko.fi
Emp.: 14
Industrial Machinery Mfr
N.A.I.C.S.: 333310
Juha Pikkarainen (Mng Dir)

Subsidiary (Non-US):

Thomeko Eesti OU   (4)
Parnu Mnt 533 Saku Vald, 76404, Harjumaa, Estonia
Tel.: (372) 6 800 880
Web Site: http://www.thomeko.ee
Industrial Machinery Mfr
N.A.I.C.S.: 333310

Subsidiary (Non-US):

Soussana S.A.   (2)
13 rue des Alouettes, Boves, 94320, Thiais,
France
Tel.: (33) 149785800
Web Site: http://www.soussana.com
Sales Range: $25-49.9 Million
Emp.: 21
Grocery & Related Products Merchant
Whslr
N.A.I.C.S.: 424490

DC Trading Co., Ltd   (1)
9F Toranomon 40MT Building 5-13-1,
Minato-ku, Tokyo, 105-0001, Japan
Tel.: (81) 3 5404 4224
Meat Product Whslr
N.A.I.C.S.: 424470

DCW Casing LLC   (1)
1129 Close Ave, Bronx, NY 10472
Tel.: (718) 842-7151
Veal Product Mfr
N.A.I.C.S.: 311615

Danish Crown - Beef Division
S.A.   (1)
Piazza Indipendenza 3, 6830, Chiasso,
Switzerland
Tel.: (41) 916957080
Meat Product Whslr
N.A.I.C.S.: 424470

Danish Crown Beef Company
A/S   (1)
Erhvervsparken 57, 8882, Farvang, Denmark
Tel.: (45) 89 19 24 00
Meat Product Whslr
N.A.I.C.S.: 424470
Christina Veissing (Office Mgr)

Danish Crown Espana S.A.   (1)
Guetaria 79, Madrid, 28041, Spain
Tel.: (34) 913411557
Meat Product Whslr
N.A.I.C.S.: 424470

Danish Crown Foods France
S.A.S.   (1)
Actipole - Batiment A 130 Avenue Joseph
Kessel, 78960, Voisins-le-Bretonneux,
France
Tel.: (33) 13 930 5500
Meat Mfr & Distr
N.A.I.C.S.: 311612

Danish Crown Foods Germany
GmbH   (1)
Christoph-Probst-Weg 26, 20251, Hamburg,
Germany
Tel.: (49) 405 543 6030
Web Site: https://www.tulip.de
Meat Mfr & Distr
N.A.I.C.S.: 311612

Danish Crown Foods Haarlem
B.V.   (1)
Oudeweg 10, 2031 CC, Haarlem, Netherlands
Tel.: (31) 23 531 0223
Meat Mfr & Distr
N.A.I.C.S.: 311612

Danish Crown Foods Italy S.r.l.   (1)
Via G Rossini 1/A, 20020, Lainate, MI, Italy
Tel.: (39) 02 890 4601
Web Site: https://www.tulipfood.it
Meat Mfr & Distr
N.A.I.C.S.: 311612

Danish Crown Foods Jonkoping
AB   (1)
Barnarpsvagen 102, 556 52, Jonkoping,
Sweden
Tel.: (46) 36 585 1700
Meat Mfr & Distr
N.A.I.C.S.: 311612

Danish Crown Foods Norway AS   (1)
Kabelgaten 1, 0580, Oslo, Norway
Tel.: (47) 7 394 9400
Web Site: https://www.tulip.no
Meat Mfr & Distr
N.A.I.C.S.: 311612

Danish Crown Foods Sweden
AB   (1)
Lisa Sass gata 1, Box 4103, Hisings Backa,
Sweden
Tel.: (46) 3 165 5050
Web Site: https://www.tulip.se
Meat Mfr & Distr
N.A.I.C.S.: 311612

Danish Crown France S.A.S.   (1)
1 place Jean Monnet, BP 4529, 45045, Orleans, France
Tel.: (33) 23 843 2929
Pet Care Services
N.A.I.C.S.: 812910

Danish Crown GmbH   (1)
Waldstrasse 7, 49632, Oldenburg,
Germany   (100%)
Tel.: (49) 5434850
Web Site: http://www.danishcrown.de
Sales Range: $25-49.9 Million
Emp.: 1,300
Packaged Frozen Meat & Meat Products
Whslr
N.A.I.C.S.: 424470

Subsidiary (Non-US):

Danish Crown Sp.z o.o.   (2)
Ul Torunska 262, 62 600, Kolo, Poland
Tel.: (48) 632626506
Meat Product Whslr
N.A.I.C.S.: 424470

Danish Crown K-Pack AB   (1)
Barnarpsvagen 102 Torsvik, 556 52, Jonkoping, Sweden
Tel.: (46) 36 585 1700
Emp.: 160
Packaged Frozen Food Distr
N.A.I.C.S.: 424420
Rasmus Hansen (Mgr-Factory)

Danish Crown Korea LLC   (1)
5F Daehan Paper Bldg 563, Achasan-ro
Gwangjin-gu, Seoul, 04983, Korea (South)
Tel.: (82) 2 754 0212
Pet Care Services
N.A.I.C.S.: 812910

Danish Crown Schlachtzentrum Nord-
friesland GmbH   (1)
Schlachtzentrum Maas 10-12, Postfach
1747, 25813, Husum, Germany
Tel.: (49) 4841 6950
Web Site: http://www.danishcrown.de
Meat Product Whslr
N.A.I.C.S.: 424470
Uwe Follscher (Mng Dir)

Danish Crown Teterower Fleisch
GmbH   (1)
Koppelbergstr 2, 17166, Teterow, Germany
Tel.: (49) 3 996 1660
Meat Mfr & Distr
N.A.I.C.S.: 311612

Danish Crown UK Limited   (1)
57 Stanley Road, Whitefield, M45 8GZ,
Manchester, United Kingdom
Tel.: (44) 1617661144
Emp.: 36
Frozen Food Whslr
N.A.I.C.S.: 424420
Allan Hansen (Gen Mgr)

Danish Crown USA Inc.   (1)
200 S Ave E, Cranford, NJ 07016-5001
Tel.: (908) 931-9733
Emp.: 12
Meat Product Whslr
N.A.I.C.S.: 424470
Stig Kjaeroe (Pres)

ESS-FOOD (Shanghai) Trading Co.
Ltd   (1)
27/F World Plaza 855 Podong Road South
Suite F, Shanghai, 200120, China
Tel.: (86) 21 50203200
Meat Product Whslr
N.A.I.C.S.: 424470
Alex Wang (Area Mgr)

ESS-FOOD A/S   (1)
Vesterbrogade 4A 2, 1620, Copenhagen,
Denmark
Tel.: (45) 43 46 90 00
Web Site: http://www.ess-food.com
Emp.: 65
Meat Product Whslr
N.A.I.C.S.: 424470

ESS-FOOD Brazil Servicos de Consultoria Ltda   (1)
Rua Antonio Lapa 178 6 Ander Salas 609 E
610, Campinas, 13025-240, Brazil
Tel.: (55) 19 2115 4545
Meat Product Whslr
N.A.I.C.S.: 424470
Philippe Nelson (Area Mgr-Export)

ESS-FOOD Holding A/S   (1)
Vesterbrogade 4A 2, 1620, Copenhagen,
Denmark
Tel.: (45) 4 346 9000

Web Site: https://www.ess-food.com
Meat Mfr & Distr
N.A.I.C.S.: 311612

ESS-Food AmbA (1)
Vesterbrogade 4A, 1620, Copenhagen,
Denmark (100%)
Tel.: (45) 43469000
Web Site: http://www.ess-food.com
Sales Range: $250-299.9 Million
Emp.: 100
Beef & Pork Distr
N.A.I.C.S.: 445240

**Elaboradora de Subprodutos de Ori-
gem Animal do Brasil Ltda.** (1)
R Vereador Mario Pezzi 1057 Sala 02 Cen-
tro, Caxias do Sul, 95084-180, Brazil
Tel.: (55) 543 537 2013
Web Site: https://www.esbdobrasil.com
Meat Mfr & Distr
N.A.I.C.S.: 311612
Jens Kongensholm (Mng Dir)

Foodane A/S (1)
Marsvej 43, 8960, Randers,
Denmark (100%)
Tel.: (45) 89191919
Web Site: http://www.danishcrown.dk
Sales Range: $25-49.9 Million
Emp.: 15
Meat Product Whslr
N.A.I.C.S.: 445240

Friland Deutschland GmbH (1)
Fraunhoferstr 2, 24118, Kiel, Germany
Tel.: (49) 4315 302 0300
Web Site: https://www.friland.com
Meat Mfr & Distr
N.A.I.C.S.: 311612

KLS Ugglarps (1)
Sodra vagen 60, 392 45, Kalmar, Sweden
Tel.: (46) 480 707000
Web Site: http://www.klsugglarps.se
Meat Production Services
N.A.I.C.S.: 424470

Leivers Brothers Ltd. (1)
86 Brookfield Road, Arnold, Nottingham,
NG5 7ER, Nottinghamshire, United King-
dom
Tel.: (44) 115 926 4256
Web Site: https://www.leiversbros.com
Refrigerated Vehicles Services
N.A.I.C.S.: 484230

SPF-Danmark A/S (1)
Drejervej 7, 6600, Vejen, Denmark
Tel.: (45) 7 696 4600
Web Site: https://www.spf.dk
Pet Care Services
N.A.I.C.S.: 812910

Scan-hide A.m.b.a. (1)
Industrivej 15, 5762, Vester Skerninge,
Denmark
Tel.: (45) 62 24 10 57
Emp.: 105
Meat Product Whslr
N.A.I.C.S.: 424470

Sokolow (1)
al 550-lecia 1, 08-300, Sokolow, Poland
Tel.: (48) 256408200
Web Site: http://www.sokolow.pl
Emp.: 8,000
Food Products Processing Services
N.A.I.C.S.: 311999

Sokolow-Logistyka Sp. z o.o. (1)
Aleja 550-lecia 2, Sokolow Podlaski, 08-
300, Warsaw, Poland
Tel.: (48) 25 781 2839
Web Site: https://sokolow-logistyka.pl
Pet Care Services
N.A.I.C.S.: 812910

Sunhill Food of Vermont, Inc. (1)
14 Jonergin Dr, Swanton, VT 05488-1312
Tel.: (802) 868-7314
Sales Range: $25-49.9 Million
Emp.: 70
Processing & Packaging of Meat
N.A.I.C.S.: 311612

**Tulip Fleischwaren Oldenburg
GmbH** (1)
Georg-Bolts Str 10, 26135, Oldenburg, Ger-
many
Tel.: (49) 441 2007 0

Web Site: http://www.tulips.de
Emp.: 500
Veal Product Mfr
N.A.I.C.S.: 311999
Walter Breitenbach (Gen Mgr)

Tulip Food Company (1)
Tulipvej 1, Randers, 8940, Denmark
Tel.: (45) 89 10 50 00
Web Site: http://www.tulip.dk
Emp.: 250
Meat Product Whslr
N.A.I.C.S.: 424470
Kasper Lenbroch (CEO)

Subsidiary (Non-US):

Polsemannen AB (2)
Kalendegatan 18, 211 35, Malmo, Sweden
Tel.: (46) 40974044
Web Site: http://www.polsemannen.se
Meat Product Whslr
N.A.I.C.S.: 424470

Tulip Food Company AB (2)
Lisa Sass Gata 1, PO Box 4103, 422 04,
Hisings Backa, Sweden
Tel.: (46) 31655050
Web Site: http://www.tulip.se
Meat Product Whslr
N.A.I.C.S.: 424470

**Tulip Food Company France
S.A.** (2)
130 Avenue Joseph Kessel, Voisins-le-
Bretonneux, 78960, France
Tel.: (33) 139305500
Web Site: http://www.tulip.dk
Emp.: 11
Meat Product Whslr
N.A.I.C.S.: 424470
Marc Ouellet (Gen Mgr)

Tulip Food Company GmbH (2)
Christoph-Probst-Weg 26, 20251, Hamburg,
Germany
Tel.: (49) 40 5543 6030
Web Site: http://www.tulip.de
Meat Product Whslr
N.A.I.C.S.: 424470

**Tulip Food Company Italiana
S.r.L.** (2)
Via G Rossini 1 A, 20020, Lainate, Italy
Tel.: (39) 028904601
Web Site: http://www.tulipfood.it
Meat Product Whslr
N.A.I.C.S.: 424470

**Tulip Food Company Japan Co.
Ltd** (2)
9F Nissay Naha Building 3-1-1 Kumoji,
Naha, 900-0015, Okinawa, Japan
Tel.: (81) 98 860 4100
Web Site: http://www.tulip-okinawa.com
Emp.: 3
Meat Product Whslr
N.A.I.C.S.: 424470
Ito Kazu (Branch Mgr)

Tulip Norge AS (2)
Kabelgaten 1, 0580, Oslo, Norway
Tel.: (47) 7394 9400
Web Site: http://www.tulip.no
Food Product Whslr
N.A.I.C.S.: 445298

DANKOTUWA PORCELAIN
PLC
Kurunegala Road, Dankotuwa, Put-
talam, Sri Lanka
Tel.: (94) 315500500
Web Site:
https://www.dankotuwa.com
Year Founded: 1984
DPL—(COL)
Rev.: $12,940,465
Assets: $25,692,337
Liabilities: $13,653,926
Net Worth: $12,038,412
Earnings: ($2,116,267)
Emp.: 643
Fiscal Year-end: 03/31/21
Porcelain Tableware Mfr
N.A.I.C.S.: 327110

DANMAGI GROUP APS

Skodsborg Strandvej 123, Skodsborg,
2942, Valby, Denmark
Tel.: (45) 70252829
Web Site: http://www.danmagi.info
Internet Access Services
N.A.I.C.S.: 513210
Daniel Lister (CEO)

Subsidiaries:

Danmagi India Pvt. Ltd (1)
Dlf City Club - Phase IV, Gurgaon, 122001,
India
Tel.: (91) 1246540333
Internet Service Provider
N.A.I.C.S.: 517112

**Danmagi Servicos de Informatica
Ltda.** (1)
Rua Mexico n 90 es 610 - Centro, 20031-
141, Rio de Janeiro, Brazil
Tel.: (55) 2135531619
Internet Service Provider
N.A.I.C.S.: 517112

DANMARKS NATIONALBANK
Havnegade 5, 1093, Copenhagen,
Denmark
Tel.: (45) 33 63 63 63 DK
Web Site:
http://www.nationalbanken.dk
Year Founded: 1818
Rev.: $20,821,968
Assets: $76,121,772,025
Liabilities: $64,836,269,514
Net Worth: $11,285,502,512
Earnings: ($3,709,599)
Emp.: 420
Fiscal Year-end: 12/31/18
Central Bank
N.A.I.C.S.: 521110
Bent Jensen (Co-CEO)

DANONE
17 boulevard Haussmann, 15 rue du
Helder, 75009, Paris, France
Tel.: (33) 144352020 FR
Web Site: https://www.danone.com
Year Founded: 1966
DANOY—(OTCQX)
Rev.: $30,487,912,577
Assets: $49,106,965,456
Liabilities: $31,199,911,694
Net Worth: $17,907,053,761
Earnings: $1,012,253,008
Emp.: 88,843
Fiscal Year-end: 12/31/23
Holding Company; Fresh Dairy Prod-
ucts, Bottled Water, Baby Food &
Clinical Nutrition Products Mfr
N.A.I.C.S.: 551112
Henri Bruxelles (Chief Sustainability
& Strategic Bus Dev Officer)

Subsidiaries:

Al Safi Danone Co. (1)
PO Box 15025, Riyadh, 11443, Saudi Ara-
bia
Tel.: (966) 1 211 9999
Web Site: http://www.alsafidanone.com.sa
Dairy Products; Owned by Group Danone
SA & Al Faisaliah Group
N.A.I.C.S.: 112120

Bagley Latinoamerica S.A. (1)
Edificio International Plaza, Moreno 877
Piso 12, 1091, Buenos Aires, Argentina
Tel.: (54) 114 341 09500
Web Site: http://www.arcor.com.ar
Sales Range: $250-299.9 Million
Emp.: 4,900
Cookies, Snacks, Cereal Bars & Cereals
Mfr
N.A.I.C.S.: 311230

Bledina SA (1)
383 rue Philippe Heron, PO Box 432,
69400, Villefranche-sur-Saone, Cedex,
France (100%)
Tel.: (33) 474626364
Web Site: http://www.bledina.com
Sales Range: $450-499.9 Million
Emp.: 500

Baby Foods, Health Foods, Packaged
Bread Products, Diet Foods & Clinical Nutri-
tion
N.A.I.C.S.: 311423

Clover S.A. (PTY) Ltd (1)
200 Constantia Drive Constantia Kloof,
Roodepoort, 1709, South Africa (100%)
Tel.: (27) 114711400
Web Site: https://www.clover.co.za
Sales Range: $600-649.9 Million
Emp.: 560
Dairy Products Mfr
N.A.I.C.S.: 311514
Johann Vorster (CEO)

Club Restauration (1)
3 Rue Saarinen, PO Box 60347, 94618,
Rungis, France (100%)
Tel.: (33) 156344900
Sales Range: $50-74.9 Million
Emp.: 80
Grocery Wholesaler
N.A.I.C.S.: 424490

Danone (UK) Limited (1)
International House 7 High Street, Ealing
Broadway, London, W5 5DW, United
Kingdom (100%)
Tel.: (44) 8081449451
Web Site: http://www.danone.co.uk
Mfr of Dairy Products
N.A.I.C.S.: 311514

Danone AS (1)
Solsortevej 15 Brande, 4690, Ringkobing,
Denmark
Tel.: (45) 76405380
Web Site: http://www.danone.dk
Emp.: 2
Mfr of Dairy Products
N.A.I.C.S.: 445298
Fredrick Leroy (Gen Mgr)

Danone Asia Pte. Ltd. (1)
1 Temasek Ave, Singapore, 49483,
Singapore (100%)
Tel.: (65) 63383484
Web Site: http://www.danone.com
Sales Range: $25-49.9 Million
Emp.: 40
Biscuits, Sweet & Salted Snacks Mfr
N.A.I.C.S.: 311812

**Danone Baby & Medical Nutrition
B.V.** (1)
Schiphol Boulevard 105, Schiphol Airport,
NL-1118 BG, Schiphol,
Netherlands (100%)
Tel.: (31) 204569000
Web Site: http://www.danone.com
Sales Range: $1-4.9 Billion
Emp.: 13,000
Holding Company; Baby Food & Clinical
Nutrition Products Mfr
N.A.I.C.S.: 551112

Subsidiary (Non-US):

**Danone Asia-Pacific Holdings Pte.
Ltd.** (2)
47 Scotts Road 06-00 Goldbell Towers, Sin-
gapore, 228233, Singapore (100%)
Tel.: (65) 62139088
Web Site: http://www.dumex.com.sg
Holding Company; Baby Food & Clinical
Nutrition Products Mfr & Distr
N.A.I.C.S.: 551112

Subsidiary (Non-US):

Danone Dumex (3)
188 Ning Qiao Lu Pu Dong Jin Qiao, Export
Processing Zone, Shanghai, 201206,
China (100%)
Tel.: (86) 21 5899 0899
Web Site: http://www.dumex.com.cn
Sales Range: $200-249.9 Million
Emp.: 800
Baby Nutritional Products Mfr & Distr
N.A.I.C.S.: 311999

Danone Dumex Ltd. (3)
359 Moo 17 Theparak Road Bangplee In-
dustrial Estate, Bangsaothong, Samut Pra-
kan, 10540, Thailand (100%)
Tel.: (66) 27403300
Web Site: http://www.dumex.co.th
Sales Range: $125-149.9 Million
Emp.: 400

Danone—(Continued)

Baby & Infant Nutritional Products Mfr &
Distr
N.A.I.C.S.: 311999

Subsidiary (Domestic):

Danone Beheer B.V. **(2)**
Schiphol Boulevard 105, Schiphol Airport,
NL-1118 BG, Schiphol,
Netherlands **(100%)**
Tel.: (31) 204569120
Web Site: http://www.nutricia.nl
Sales Range: $50-74.9 Million
Emp.: 80
Holding Company; Nutritional Products
N.A.I.C.S.: 551112

Danone Financial Center B.V. **(2)**
Schiphol Boulevard 105, Schiphol Airport,
Schiphol, 1118 BG, Netherlands **(100%)**
Tel.: (31) 204569000
Web Site: http://www.danone.com
Sales Range: $50-74.9 Million
Emp.: 600
Corporate Financial Services
N.A.I.C.S.: 522299
Philip Valvan Randwjk *(Mng Dir)*

Danone Research B.V. **(2)**
Uppsalalaan 12, 3584 CT, Utrecht,
Netherlands **(100%)**
Tel.: (31) 30 209 5000
Web Site: https://www.danone.nl
Sales Range: $25-49.9 Million
Emp.: 200
Baby & Clinical Nutrition Product Research
& Development
N.A.I.C.S.: 541715

Subsidiary (Non-US):

Kasdorf S.A. **(2)**
Av Panamericana y General Savio Parque
Industrial OKS, Estafeta No 1, B1619BSA,
Garin, Buenos Aires, Argentina **(100%)**
Tel.: (54) 3327452134
Web Site: http://www.kasdorf.com.ar
Sales Range: $25-49.9 Million
Emp.: 100
Baby Milk Formula & Clinical Nutrition Prod-
ucts Mfr & Distr
N.A.I.C.S.: 311511

Joint Venture (Domestic):

Nutricia Bago S.A. **(3)**
Marcelo T de Alvear 590 Piso 1,
C1058AAF, Buenos Aires, Argentina
Tel.: (54) 1153545400 **(3)**
Web Site: https://nutriciaoverseas.com.ar
Sales Range: $10-24.9 Million
Emp.: 40
Newly Developed Baby & Clinical Nutrition
Products Marketer; Owned 51% by Danone
Baby & Medical Nutrition B.V. & 49% by
Laboratorios Bago S.A.
N.A.I.C.S.: 541613
Sandra Slavkis *(Gen Mgr-Bus Dev)*

Subsidiary (Non-US):

Milupa Commercial S.A. **(2)**
Zona Industrial De Carnaxide, PT-2790 076,
Carnaxide, Portugal
Tel.: (351) 214246880
Web Site: http://www.milupa.pt
Infant Nutritional Milk Products Marketer &
Whslr
N.A.I.C.S.: 424490

Milupa GmbH **(2)**
Halleiner Landesstrasse 264, 5412, Puch,
Austria **(100%)**
Tel.: (43) 62457940
Web Site: http://www.milupa.at
Sales Range: $25-49.9 Million
Emp.: 70
Baby & Infant Nutritional Products Mfr &
Distr
N.A.I.C.S.: 311514

Milupa GmbH **(2)**
Bahnstrasse 14-30, D-61381, Frie-
drichsdorf, Germany **(100%)**
Tel.: (49) 6172990
Web Site: http://www.milupa-gmbh.de
Sales Range: $100-124.9 Million
Emp.: 400

Infant Nutritional Products Developer, Mfr &
Distr
N.A.I.C.S.: 311999
Susann Luick-Nijboer *(Chm-Mgmt Bd &
Mng Dir)*

Milupa N.V. **(2)**
Hingenesteenweg 67, 2880, Bornem,
Belgium **(100%)**
Tel.: (32) 3 890 2378
Web Site: http://www.milupa.be
Sales Range: $25-49.9 Million
Emp.: 15
Provider of Nutritional Products
N.A.I.C.S.: 456191

**Numil Gida Urunleri Sanayi ve Ticaret
A.S.** **(2)**
Comert Sokak Yapi Kredi Bloks B Blok No
1B Floor 8-9, Kat 9 No 24, Levent Mah Be-
siktas, 34330, Istanbul, Turkiye **(100%)**
Web Site: https://www.nutricia.com.tr
Sales Range: $25-49.9 Million
Emp.: 75
Baby Food & Clinical Nutrition Products
Distr
N.A.I.C.S.: 424490
Gamze Emre *(Gen Mgr)*

Numil Hellas S.A. **(2)**
Side road 17 km E O Athens Lamias Ka-
lamatas 2, Nea Kifisia Attica, 14564, Kifis-
sia, Greece **(100%)**
Tel.: (30) 2106248500
Web Site: https://www.danone.gr
Sales Range: $25-49.9 Million
Emp.: 40
Baby Nutritional Products Distr
N.A.I.C.S.: 424490
Myrto Siappa *(Mgr-Fin)*

**Numil Hungary Tapszerkereskedelni
Kft.** **(2)**
Robert Karoly Korut 82-84, Budapest, 1134,
Hungary **(100%)**
Tel.: (36) 14527770
Web Site: http://www.nutricia.hu
Sales Range: $25-49.9 Million
Emp.: 70
Clinical Nutrition Products Distr
N.A.I.C.S.: 424490
Beatrix Katona *(Gen Mgr)*

Numil Nutricion S.R.L. **(2)**
Carretera de Andalucia Km 25 600, ES-
28340, Valdemoro, Madrid, Spain
Tel.: (34) 918096300 **(2)**
Web Site: http://www.milupa.es
Sales Range: $50-74.9 Million
Emp.: 125
Baby Nutritional Products Mfr & Distr
N.A.I.C.S.: 311511

Nutricia (Russia) LLC **(2)**
ul Moskovskaya 48, Istra, 143500,
Russia **(100%)**
Tel.: (7) 4959946636
Web Site: http://www.nutricia.ru
Sales Range: $150-199.9 Million
Emp.: 480
Holding Company; Baby Nutrition Products
Mfr
N.A.I.C.S.: 551112

Division (Domestic):

OAO Istra-Nutricia **(3)**
ul Moskovskaya 48, Istra, 143500,
Russia **(100%)**
Tel.: (7) 4959945282
Web Site: http://www.nutricia.ru
Sales Range: $75-99.9 Million
Emp.: 300
Baby Formulas Mfr
N.A.I.C.S.: 311514

Subsidiary (Non-US):

Nutricia A/S **(2)**
Rormosevej 2A, 3450, Allerod, Denmark
Tel.: (45) 70210709
Web Site: https://pro.nutricia.dk
Sales Range: $25-49.9 Million
Emp.: 12
Clinical Nutrition Products Marketer & Distr
N.A.I.C.S.: 424490
Ken Tinebo *(Mng Dir-Denmark & Nordics)*

Nutricia Australia Pty. Ltd. **(2)**
Talavera Corporate Centre Level 4 Bldg D,

12-18 Talavera Road, Macquarie, 2113,
NSW, Australia **(100%)**
Tel.: (61) 288700400
Web Site: http://www.nutricia.com.au
Sales Range: $25-49.9 Million
Emp.: 150
Baby Food & Clinical Nutrition Products
Distr
N.A.I.C.S.: 424490

Subsidiary (Non-US):

Nutricia (New Zealand) Ltd. **(3)**
37 Banks Rd, Mount Wellington, Auckland,
1060, New Zealand **(100%)**
Tel.: (64) 95700970
Web Site: http://www.nutricia.com.au
Sales Range: $25-49.9 Million
Emp.: 75
Baby Food & Clinical Nutrition Products
Distr
N.A.I.C.S.: 424490
Corine Tap *(Mng Dir)*

Subsidiary (Non-US):

Nutricia Baby Oy **(2)**
Hitsaajankatu 20, PL 275, FI-00811, Hel-
sinki, Finland **(100%)**
Tel.: (358) 106808600
Web Site: http://www.nutriciababy.fi
Baby Food Developer, Mfr & Distr
N.A.I.C.S.: 311999
Pia Hogstrom *(Product Mgr)*

Nutricia Belgie N.V. **(2)**
Romeinsesteenweg 564/c, Strombeek-
Bever, 1853, Belgium **(100%)**
Tel.: (32) 24621211
Web Site: http://www.nutricia.be
Sales Range: $50-74.9 Million
Emp.: 115
Baby Food & Clinical Nutrition Products
Distr
N.A.I.C.S.: 424490
Selena Levointurier *(Mng Dir)*

Subsidiary (Domestic):

Nutricia Cuijk B.V. **(2)**
Grotestraat 91, 5431 DJ, Cuijk,
Netherlands **(100%)**
Tel.: (31) 485394911
Web Site: http://www.nutricia.nl
Sales Range: $75-99.9 Million
Emp.: 300
Special Baby & Clinical Nutrition Products
Mfr
N.A.I.C.S.: 311514
Bart Graat *(Dir-Fin)*

Subsidiary (Non-US):

Nutricia France S.A. **(2)**
Immeuble l'Europeen Batiment D, 4 Rue
Joseph Monier, F-92859, Rueil-Malmaison,
France **(100%)**
Tel.: (33) 147102525
Web Site: http://www.nutricia.fr
Sales Range: $50-74.9 Million
Emp.: 125
Baby Food & Clinical Nutrition Products
Distr
N.A.I.C.S.: 424490

Nutricia GmbH **(2)**
Allee am Rothelheimpark 11, 91052, Erlan-
gen, Germany **(100%)**
Tel.: (49) 697191350
Web Site: https://www.nutricia.de
Sales Range: $100-124.9 Million
Emp.: 290
Clinical Nutrition Products Mfr & Distr
N.A.I.C.S.: 311999
Meurisse Bruno *(Co-Mng Dir)*

Nutricia Holdings Ltd. **(2)**
White Horse Business Park, Newmarket
Avenue, Trowbridge, BA14 0XQ, Wilts,
United Kingdom **(100%)**
Tel.: (44) 1225711688
Web Site: http://www.nutricia.co.uk
Sales Range: $200-249.9 Million
Emp.: 400
Holding Company; Baby Food & Clinical
Nutrition Products Mfr, Marketer & Distr
N.A.I.C.S.: 551112

Division (Domestic):

**Nutricia Ltd. - Advanced Medical
Nutrition** **(3)**

Newmarket House Newmarket Avenue,
White Horse Business Park, Trowbridge,
BA14 0XQ, Wiltshire, United
Kingdom **(100%)**
Tel.: (44) 1225711688
Web Site: http://www.nutricia-clinical-
care.co.uk
Sales Range: $125-149.9 Million
Emp.: 350
Clinical Nutrition Products Mfr & Distr
N.A.I.C.S.: 311999
Mark Lane *(Dir-Comml)*

Nutricia Ltd. - Baby Nutrition **(3)**
Newmarket House Newmarket Avenue,
White Horse Business Park, Trowbridge,
BA14 0XQ, Wilts, United Kingdom
Tel.: (44) 1225711511 **(3)**
Web Site: http://www.nutricia.co.uk
Sales Range: $125-149.9 Million
Emp.: 400
Baby Milk Formula & Nutritional Products
Mfr & Distr
N.A.I.C.S.: 311511
Simon Tozey *(Dir-Sls)*

Subsidiary (Domestic):

SHS International Ltd. **(3)**
100 Wavertree Boulevard, Wavertree Tech-
nology Park, Liverpool, L7 9PT, United
Kingdom **(100%)**
Tel.: (44) 1512288161
Web Site: http://www.nutricia.co.uk
Sales Range: $100-124.9 Million
Emp.: 220
Clinical Nutrition Products Mfr
N.A.I.C.S.: 311999
Joanne Carlin *(Mgr-HR)*

Subsidiary (Non-US):

Nutricia Italia S.p.A. **(2)**
Via Bonnet Nino 6/A, 20154, Milan,
Italy **(100%)**
Tel.: (39) 02 6369511
Web Site: http://www.nutricia.it
Sales Range: $50-74.9 Million
Emp.: 150
Clinical Nutrition Products Distr
N.A.I.C.S.: 456191

Nutricia Medical Oy **(2)**
Linnankatu 26 A, Turku, 20100,
Finland **(100%)**
Tel.: (358) 22744111
Web Site: http://www.nutricia.fi
Sales Range: $25-49.9 Million
Emp.: 18
Clinical Nutrition Products Distr
N.A.I.C.S.: 424490
Paivi Pakarinen *(Mng Dir)*

Subsidiary (Domestic):

Nutricia N.V. **(2)**
Albert Einsteinlaan 20, NL-2712 HM, Zo-
etermeer, Netherlands **(100%)**
Tel.: (31) 793539000
Web Site: http://www.nutricia.nl
Sales Range: $150-199.9 Million
Emp.: 1,000
Baby & Clinical Nutrition Products Mfr
N.A.I.C.S.: 311999
Harold Diender *(Mng Dir & Gen Mgr-
Sls/Mktg-Clinical Nutrition Div)*

Division (Domestic):

Nutricia Nederland B.V. **(3)**
Einsteinlaan 20, 2719 EP, Zoetermeer,
Netherlands **(100%)**
Tel.: (31) 683651133
Web Site: https://www.nutricia.nl
Sales Range: $150-199.9 Million
Emp.: 500
Baby & Clinical Nutrition Products Marketer
& Whslr
N.A.I.C.S.: 424490

Subsidiary (Non-US):

**Nutricia Nahrungsmittel GmbH & Co.
KG** **(2)**
Technologiestrasse 10 Euro Plaza / Building
E, A-1230, Vienna, Austria **(100%)**
Tel.: (43) 168826260
Web Site: http://www.nutricia.at
Sales Range: $25-49.9 Million
Emp.: 35

Clinical Nutrition Products Developer &
Whslr
N.A.I.C.S.: 424490
Steffen Dreher *(Mng Dir)*

Subsidiary (Domestic):

Nutricia Netherlands B.V.   **(2)**
Einsteinlaan 20, 2719 EP, Zoetermeer,
Netherlands   **(100%)**
Tel.: (31) 79 353 9000
Holding Company
N.A.I.C.S.: 551112

Holding (Non-US):

Nutricia Polska Sp. z o.o.   **(3)**
ul Bobrowiecka 8, 00-728, Warsaw,
Poland   **(100%)**
Tel.: (48) 225500155
Web Site: https://www.nutricia.pl
Sales Range: $150-199.9 Million
Emp.: 400
Baby Milk Formula & Food Products Mfr,
Marketer & Distr
N.A.I.C.S.: 424490
Malgorzata Kolodrub *(Mgr-Comm)*

Subsidiary (Non-US):

Nutricia Nordica AB   **(2)**
Gardsvagen 14, 169 70, Solna,
Sweden   **(100%)**
Tel.: (46) 8241530
Web Site: https://www.nutricia.se
Sales Range: $25-49.9 Million
Emp.: 30
Clinical Nutrition Products Distr
N.A.I.C.S.: 424490

Nutricia Norge AS   **(2)**
Holbergs gt 21, NO-0166, Oslo,
Norway   **(100%)**
Tel.: (47) 23002100
Web Site: http://www.nutricia.no
Sales Range: $25-49.9 Million
Emp.: 25
Clinical Nutrition Products Distr
N.A.I.C.S.: 424490

**Nutricia Pharmaceutical (Wuxi) Co.,
Ltd.**   **(2)**
Room 3905 Kerry Parkside Office Tower No
1155 Fangdian Road, Pudong, Shanghai,
China   **(100%)**
Tel.: (86) 216 179 8605
Web Site: https://www.nutriciachina.com
Sales Range: $25-49.9 Million
Emp.: 60
Clinical Nutrition Products Mfr & Distr
N.A.I.C.S.: 311999

Nutricia Portugal L.D.A.   **(2)**
Zona Industrial de Carnaxide, PT-2790 076,
Carnaxide, Portugal
Tel.: (351) 214259600
Web Site: http://www.nutricia.pt
Sales Range: $25-49.9 Million
Emp.: 15
Baby Food & Clinical Nutrition Products
Distr
N.A.I.C.S.: 424490
Rosa Pena *(Mng Dir)*

Nutricia S.A.   **(2)**
Rue De Vevey 218, CH-1630, Bulle,
Switzerland   **(100%)**
Tel.: (41) 266752529
Web Site: http://www.nutricia.ch
Sales Range: $50-74.9 Million
Emp.: 6
Holding Company; Baby & Clinical Nutrition
Products Distr
N.A.I.C.S.: 551112

Division (Domestic):

Milupa S.A.   **(3)**
Rue de l Industrie 24, CH-1564, Domdidier,
Switzerland   **(100%)**
Tel.: (41) 266769600
Web Site: http://www.milupa.ch
Sales Range: $25-49.9 Million
Baby Milk Formula & Products Distr
N.A.I.C.S.: 424490
Sany Jerome *(Mng Dir)*

Subsidiary (Non-US):

Nutricia S.R.L.   **(2)**
Calle Torrelaguna 77 6a Planta, ES-28043,

Madrid, Spain   **(100%)**
Tel.: (34) 900211088
Web Site: http://www.nutriciaclinico.es
Sales Range: $50-74.9 Million
Emp.: 150
Baby Food & Clinical Nutrition Products
Distr
N.A.I.C.S.: 424490

Nutricia a.s.   **(2)**
Na Hrebenech 1718 10, Prague, 4, Czech
Republic   **(100%)**
Tel.: (420) 296332700
Web Site: http://www.nutricia.cz
Sales Range: $25-49.9 Million
Emp.: 100
Baby Food & Clinical Nutrition Products
Marketer & Distr
N.A.I.C.S.: 424490
Beatrix Katona *(Gen Mgr)*

Nutricia s.r.o.   **(2)**
Prievozska 4, Bratislava, 821 09, Slovakia
Tel.: (421) 257107111
Web Site: http://www.nutricia.sk
Sales Range: $25-49.9 Million
Emp.: 70
Baby Food & Clinical Nutrition Products
Distr
N.A.I.C.S.: 424490

PT Nutricia Indonesia Sejahtera   **(2)**
RDTX Place Lt 5-9 Jl Prof DR Satrio Kav 3,
Kel Karet Kuningan Kec Setiabudi, Jakarta
Selatan, 12940, Indonesia   **(100%)**
Tel.: (62) 2125508255
Web Site: https://nutricia.co.id
Sales Range: $100-124.9 Million
Emp.: 476
Baby & Toddler Nutritional Products Mfr &
Distr
N.A.I.C.S.: 311511
Marc de Rouw *(Pres)*

PT Sari Husada Tbk   **(2)**
Jalan Kusumanegara 173, Yogyakarta,
55165, Indonesia   **(100%)**
Tel.: (62) 274512990
Web Site: http://www.sarihusada.co.id
Sales Range: $150-199.9 Million
Emp.: 800
Baby Formula & Food Products Developer,
Mfr & Whslr
N.A.I.C.S.: 311511

**Support Produtos Nutricionais
Ltda.**   **(2)**
Al Vicente Pinzon 173 Fl 2, Edificio Midas
Vila Olimpia, 04547 130, Sao Paulo, SP,
Brazil   **(100%)**
Tel.: (55) 1138967600
Web Site: http://www.supportnet.com.br
Sales Range: $50-74.9 Million
Emp.: 170
Clinical Nutrition Products Mfr & Distr
N.A.I.C.S.: 311999

Danone Eaux France   **(1)**
3 Rue Saarinen, PO Box 342, 94628, Run-
gis, France   **(100%)**
Tel.: (33) 156343000
Web Site: http://www.evian.fr
Sales Range: $150-199.9 Million
Emp.: 1,000
Still & Carbonated Water
N.A.I.C.S.: 312112

Danone Finland   **(1)**
PL 1191, 00101, Helsinki, Finland   **(100%)**
Tel.: (358) 201427777
Web Site: http://www.danone.fi
Sales Range: $25-49.9 Million
Emp.: 30
Mfr of Dairy Products
N.A.I.C.S.: 445298

Danone Foods Inc.   **(1)**
1 Maple Ave, White Plains, NY 10605
Tel.: (914) 872-8400
Web Site:
    http://www.danonenorthamerica.com
Yogurt & Other Dairy Products Mfr
N.A.I.C.S.: 311511

Subsidiary (Non-US):

Aguas Danone de Argentina   **(2)**
Moreno 877, C1091AAQ, Buenos Aires,
Argentina
Tel.: (54) 1143414000

Bottled Water
N.A.I.C.S.: 445298

Danone Argentina SA   **(2)**
Moreno 877 Piso 14, 1091, Buenos Aires,
Argentina
Tel.: (54) 11434140
Web Site: http://corporate.danone.com.ar
Dairy Products Mfr
N.A.I.C.S.: 311514
Boris Bourdin *(CEO)*

Danone Inc.   **(2)**
100 Rue De Lauzon, Boucherville, J4B 1E6,
QC, Canada   **(100%)**
Tel.: (450) 655-7331
Web Site: https://www.danone.ca
Sales Range: $75-99.9 Million
Mfr of Yogurts, Cream & Cottage Cheese
N.A.I.C.S.: 311511

Branch (Domestic):

Danone Inc. - Mississauga   **(3)**
1310 Aimco Blvd, Mississauga, L4W 1B2,
ON, Canada
Tel.: (905) 625-0733
Web Site: http://www.danone.ca
Sales Range: $25-49.9 Million
Emp.: 50
Mfr of Fluid Milk
N.A.I.C.S.: 311511

Subsidiary (Non-US):

Danone S.A.   **(2)**
Caixa Postal 66275, CEP 05389 970, Sao
Paulo, Brazil   **(55.1%)**
Tel.: (55) 1137419110
Web Site: http://www.danone.com.br
Dairy Products Mfr
N.A.I.C.S.: 311514

Subsidiary (Domestic):

Danone US, Inc.   **(2)**
12002 Airport Way, Broomfield, CO 80021
Tel.: (303) 635-4000
Web Site:
    http://www.danonenorthamerica.com
Holding Company; Dairy & Plant-Based Or-
ganic Foods & Beverages Mfr & Distr
N.A.I.C.S.: 551112
Carlos Veraza *(Pres)*

Subsidiary (Non-US):

Alpro Holdings, BVBA   **(3)**
Kortrijksesteenweg 1093C, 9051, Gent,
Belgium
Tel.: (32) 92602211
Web Site: http://www.alpro.com
Holding Company; Soy-Based Non-Dairy
Food Products Mfr
N.A.I.C.S.: 551112

Subsidiary (Domestic):

Alpro Comm.VA   **(4)**
Vlamingstraat 28, 8560, Wevelgem, Bel-
gium
Tel.: (32) 473800655
Web Site: https://www.alpro.com
Non-Dairy Food Products Mfr
N.A.I.C.S.: 311999

Subsidiary (Non-US):

Alpro (UK) Limited   **(5)**
Latimer Business Park Altendiez Way, Bur-
ton Latimer, Kettering, NN15 5YT,
Northamptonshire, United Kingdom
Web Site: https://www.alpro.com
Non-Dairy Food Products Mfr & Distr
N.A.I.C.S.: 311999

Alpro GmbH   **(5)**
Johannstrasse 37, 40476, Dusseldorf, Ger-
many
Tel.: (49) 2115 504 9811
Web Site: https://www.alpro.com
Non-Dairy Food Products Mfr & Distr
N.A.I.C.S.: 311999

Alpro Soja Nederland B.V.   **(5)**
Hoge Mosten 22, 4822 NH, Breda, Nether-
lands
Tel.: (31) 765967070
Web Site: http://www.alpro.com
Non-Dairy Food Products Mfr & Distr
N.A.I.C.S.: 311999

Subsidiary (Domestic):

Earthbound Farm, LLC   **(3)**
1721 San Juan Hwy, San Juan Bautista,
CA 95045
Tel.: (831) 623-7880
Web Site: http://www.ebfarm.com
Organic Produce Distr
N.A.I.C.S.: 111219

Horizon Organic Dairy, LLC   **(3)**
12002 Airport Way, Broomfield, CO 80021-
2546
Tel.: (303) 635-4000
Web Site: http://www.horizondairy.com
Organic Dairy Products Mfr
N.A.I.C.S.: 311511

So Delicious Dairy Free   **(3)**
PO Box 72060, Springfield, OR 97475
Tel.: (866) 388-7853
Web Site:
    http://www.sodeliciousdairyfree.com
Packaged Food Product Mfr
N.A.I.C.S.: 311991
Charles F. Marcy *(Owner)*

WWF Operating Company LLC   **(3)**
12002 Airport Way, Broomfield, CO 80021
Tel.: (303) 635-4000
Web Site: http://www.whitewave.com
Organic Food Distr
N.A.I.C.S.: 445298
Jarod Ballentine *(Coord-Comm)*

Wallaby Yogurt Company, LLC   **(3)**
110B Mezzetta Ct, American Canyon, CA
94503
Tel.: (855) 925-4636
Web Site: http://www.wallabyyogurt.com
Dairy Yogurt Products Mfr & Distr
N.A.I.C.S.: 424430

Subsidiary (Non-US):

Danone de Mexico SA de CV   **(2)**
Mario Pani 150 Col Lomas de Santa Fe,
Deleg Cuajimalpa de Morelos, 053 00,
Mexico, Mexico   **(100%)**
Tel.: (52) 5552587200
Web Site: http://www.danone.com.mx
Sales Range: $25-49.9 Million
Emp.: 100
Yogurts, Fresh Cheeses, Desserts
N.A.I.C.S.: 311513

Subsidiary (Domestic):

Nurture Inc.   **(2)**
40 Fulton St Fl 19, New York, NY 10038
Tel.: (212) 374-2779
Sales Range: $10-24.9 Million
Emp.: 68
Perishable Prepared Food Mfr
N.A.I.C.S.: 311991
Shazi Visram *(Founder & CEO)*

The Dannon Company, Inc.   **(2)**
Fl 3 100 Hillside Ave, White Plains, NY
10603-2862   **(89.3%)**
Tel.: (914) 872-8400
Web Site: http://www.dannon.com
Mfr of Yogurt & Frozen Yogurt
N.A.I.C.S.: 311511
Philippe Caradec *(VP-Regulatory & Corp
Affairs)*

Unit (Domestic):

The Dannon Co.   **(3)**
1300 W Peter Smith St, Fort Worth, TX
76104-2116
Tel.: (817) 332-1264
Web Site: http://www.dannon.com
Sales Range: $25-49.9 Million
Emp.: 250
Mfr of Dairy Products
N.A.I.C.S.: 311511

The Dannon Co.   **(3)**
216 S Gate Dr, Minster, OH
45865-9406   **(100%)**
Tel.: (419) 628-3861
Web Site: http://www.dannon.com
Sales Range: $100-124.9 Million
Emp.: 400
Mfr of Yogurt
N.A.I.C.S.: 311511

The Dannon Co.   **(3)**

Danone—(Continued)

6165 W Dannon Way, West Jordan, UT 84088-8102
Tel.: (801) 280-7414
Web Site: http://www.dannon.com
Sales Range: $25-49.9 Million
Emp.: 100
Preparation of Yogurt
N.A.I.C.S.: 311511
John McQuade *(Office Mgr)*

Subsidiary (Domestic):

The Yofarm Company, Inc. **(2)**
80 Rado Dr, Naugatuck, CT 06770-2921
Tel.: (203) 720-0000
Web Site: http://www.yocrunch.com
Yogurt Mfr
N.A.I.C.S.: 311999

YoCream International Inc. **(2)**
5858 NE 87th Ave, Portland, OR 97220-1312 **(95%)**
Tel.: (503) 256-3754
Web Site: http://www.yocream.com
Sales Range: $50-74.9 Million
Emp.: 100
Produces, Markets & Sells Frozen Dessert, Snack & Beverage Items
N.A.I.C.S.: 311520
Terry Lusetti *(Dir-IR)*

Danone GmbH **(1)**
Richard Reitzner Allee 1, 85540, Hanner, Germany **(100%)**
Tel.: (49) 89627330
Web Site: http://www.danone.de
Sales Range: $25-49.9 Million
Emp.: 200
Mfr of Dairy Products
N.A.I.C.S.: 311514
Albert Ragon *(Gen Dir)*

Danone India **(1)**
Neville House Currimbhoy Road, Ballard Est, 400038, Mumbai, India
Tel.: (91) 8222621641
Mfr of Dairy Products
N.A.I.C.S.: 311514
Manjari Upadhye *(Mgr-Dairy Bus)*

Danone Industria **(1)**
Leningrad Port 15, 125040, Moscow, Russia **(100%)**
Tel.: (7) 957779040
Mfr of Biscuits
N.A.I.C.S.: 311821

Danone Japan **(1)**
2-1-1 Nakameguro GT Tower 13F Kamimeguro, Meguro-ku, Tokyo, 153-0051, Japan **(50%)**
Tel.: (81) 120409610
Web Site: https://www.danone.co.jp
Emp.: 392
Fresh Dairy Products Mfr & Distr
N.A.I.C.S.: 311511

Danone Kft. **(1)**
Vaci ut 35, 1134, Budapest, Hungary **(100%)**
Tel.: (36) 18037275
Web Site: https://www.danone.hu
Sales Range: $100-124.9 Million
Emp.: 400
Mfr of Dairy Products
N.A.I.C.S.: 311514
Yann Trevian *(Dir-Mktg)*

Danone Ltd. **(1)**
Block 1 Deansgrange Business Park Deansgrange, Tallaght, 24, Dublin, Ireland **(100%)**
Tel.: (353) 14510299
Sales Range: $25-49.9 Million
Emp.: 35
Mfr of Dairy Products
N.A.I.C.S.: 311514
Donald Courtney *(Mng Dir)*

Danone Nederland B.V. **(1)**
Zonnebaan 21, 3542 EB, Utrecht, Netherlands
Tel.: (31) 307105000
Web Site: https://www.danone.nl
Sales Range: $50-74.9 Million
Emp.: 60
Holding Company
N.A.I.C.S.: 551112

Division (Domestic):

Danone Nederland B.V. - Foodservice **(2)**
Zonnebaan 21, 3542 EB, Utrecht, Netherlands **(99.9%)**
Tel.: (31) 30 710 5000
Web Site: https://www.danone.nl
Sales Range: $25-49.9 Million
Emp.: 45
Marketing of Fresh Cheeses, Yogurts & Desserts
N.A.I.C.S.: 424450

Danone Oesterreich GmbH **(1)**
Dr Hans Lechner Strasse 504. Siezenheim, 5071, Salzburg, Austria **(99.9%)**
Tel.: (43) 66289610
Web Site: http://www.danone.at
Sales Range: $25-49.9 Million
Emp.: 40
Mfr of Dairy Products
N.A.I.C.S.: 311514

Danone Portugal, S.A. **(1)**
Torre Zen - Avenida D Joao II n 41 3 andar, 1990-084, Lisbon, Portugal **(52.9%)**
Tel.: (351) 808297919
Web Site: https://www.danone.pt
Sales Range: $100-124.9 Million
Emp.: 398
Dairy Products Mfr
N.A.I.C.S.: 311514

Danone Produits Frais France **(1)**
150 Blvd Victor Hugo, 93400, Saint-Ouen, Cedex, France **(100%)**
Tel.: (33) 810111213
Sales Range: $550-599.9 Million
Emp.: 2,500
Yogurts, Fresh Cheeses & Desserts
N.A.I.C.S.: 424430

Danone Romania **(1)**
Str Hip Nicolae Canea no 140-160 sector 2, Bucharest, 023076, Romania **(100%)**
Tel.: (40) 37 152 0005
Web Site: http://www.danone.ro
Sales Range: $150-199.9 Million
Emp.: 600
Mfr of Dairy Products
N.A.I.C.S.: 311514
Dieter Schultz *(Gen Mgr)*

Danone S.p.A. **(1)**
Via C Farini 41, 20159, Milan, Italy **(100%)**
Tel.: (39) 026 074 6111
Sales Range: $100-124.9 Million
Emp.: 300
Yogurt, Fresh Cheeses & Desserts
N.A.I.C.S.: 311513

Danone SA **(1)**
Rue Jules Cockx 6, 1160, Brussels, Belgium **(100%)**
Tel.: (32) 27766811
Web Site: http://www.danone.be
Sales Range: $25-49.9 Million
Emp.: 100
Yogurts, Fresh Cheeses, Dessert & Refrigerated Pastry Dough
N.A.I.C.S.: 311513
Bruno Fromage *(Mng Dir)*

Danone SA Espana **(1)**
Calle Buenos Aires 21, 08029, Barcelona, Spain **(98.4%)**
Tel.: (34) 900180957
Web Site: https://www.danone.es
Emp.: 400
Yogurt, Fresh Cheeses & Desserts Mfr
N.A.I.C.S.: 311511
Javier Robles *(COO)*

Danone Serdika S.A. **(1)**
3 Ohrid Lake Street, 1330, Sofia, Bulgaria **(100%)**
Tel.: (35) https://www.danone.bg
Sales Range: $100-124.9 Million
Emp.: 150
Dairy Products
N.A.I.C.S.: 445298
Daniela Uzunova *(Mng.Dir)*

Danone Sp. z o.o. **(1)**
ul Redutowa 9/23, 01-103, Warsaw, Poland **(100%)**
Tel.: (48) 228608200

Web Site: https://danone.pl
Sales Range: $150-199.9 Million
Emp.: 3,000
Dairy Products Mfr
N.A.I.C.S.: 311514

Danone Water Brands Benelux **(1)**
Jules Cockx St 6, Brussels, 1160, Belgium **(100%)**
Tel.: (32) 16251560
Web Site: http://www.evian.be
Sales Range: $25-49.9 Million
Emp.: 25
Bottled Water
N.A.I.C.S.: 445298
Stephan Gelders *(Mng Dir)*

Danone Waters Deutschland GmbH **(1)**
Am Hauptbahnhof 18, 60329, Frankfurt am Main, Germany **(100%)**
Tel.: (49) 697191350
Web Site: http://www.volvic.de
Sales Range: $25-49.9 Million
Emp.: 75
Bottled Water
N.A.I.C.S.: 445298

Danone Waters UK & Ireland Ltd. **(1)**
566 Chiswick High Road, 7 Chiswick Business Park, London, W4 5YG, United Kingdom **(100%)**
Tel.: (44) 2087995800
Web Site: https://www.danone.co.uk
Sales Range: $50-74.9 Million
Emp.: 200
Bottled Water
N.A.I.C.S.: 445298

Font Vella SA **(1)**
Buenos Aires 21, 8036, Barcelona, Spain **(77%)**
Tel.: (34) 932272500
Web Site: http://www.fontvella.es
Sales Range: $100-124.9 Million
Emp.: 300
Bottlers of Still & Sparkling Mineral Water
N.A.I.C.S.: 312112

Galbani **(1)**
Via Flavio Gioia 8, 20149, Milan, Italy **(85%)**
Tel.: (39) 0800328468
Web Site: https://www.galbani.it
Sales Range: $1-4.9 Billion
Emp.: 5,647
Yogurt & Fresh Cheeses
N.A.I.C.S.: 311513

Galbani France **(1)**
126 rue Jules-Guesde, BP 63, 92302, Levallois-Perret, Cedex, France **(100%)**
Tel.: (33) 1 40 87 20 00
Web Site: http://www.danone.com
Dairy Products
N.A.I.C.S.: 311513
Arnaud Roche *(Dir-Fin)*

Griesson de Beukelaer GmbH & Co. KG **(1)**
August-Horch-Str 23, PO Box 1147, 56751, Polch, Germany **(100%)**
Tel.: (49) 26544010
Web Site: https://www.griesson-debeukelaer.de
Sales Range: $600-649.9 Million
Emp.: 2,124
Biscuit Mfr
N.A.I.C.S.: 311821
A. Land *(Member-Mgmt Bd)*

Griesson de Beukelaer Osterreich GmbH **(1)**
Aichhorngasse 8/Loft, 1120, Vienna, Austria **(60%)**
Tel.: (43) 18908544
Biscuits & Packaged Bread Products
N.A.I.C.S.: 311821

SA des Eaux Minerales d'Evian **(1)**
11 avenue du General Dupas, 74500, Evian-les-Bains, Cedex, France **(100%)**
Tel.: (33) 14 435 2020
Web Site: http://www.evian.com
Still & Sparkling Mineral Water, Skin Care Spray & Sports Drinks Mfr
N.A.I.C.S.: 312112
Frederic Guichard *(CMO)*

SAPY Danone **(1)**
Fond Nicolas, 97231, Le Robert, Martinique **(100%)**
Tel.: (596) 596652060
Sales Range: $25-49.9 Million
Emp.: 42
Dairy Products
N.A.I.C.S.: 445298

SGPY **(1)**
Z I Plus Jaula, 97129, Lamentin, Martinique **(100%)**
Tel.: (596) 590283232
Sales Range: $25-49.9 Million
Emp.: 46
Dairy Products
N.A.I.C.S.: 445298

Semoulerie de Bellevue **(1)**
4 Chemin Du Littoral, BP 2338, 13213, Marseilles, Cedex, France **(100%)**
Tel.: (33) 491101150
Web Site: http://www.panzani.com
Sales Range: $250-299.9 Million
Emp.: 1,000
Grocery
N.A.I.C.S.: 424490
Jean Victor Bregliano *(Gen Mgr)*

Societe D'Exploitation D'Activites Touristiques **(1)**
Chateau De Blonay BP 8, Evian-les-Bains, 74501, France **(100%)**
Tel.: (33) 450268500
Web Site: http://www.evianroyalresort.com
Sales Range: $100-124.9 Million
Emp.: 700
Hotels & Leisure
N.A.I.C.S.: 721110

Star Stabilianto Alimentare S.p.A. **(1)**
via G Matteotti 142, Agrate Brianza, 20864, Milan, MB, Italy **(50%)**
Tel.: (39) 0800274094
Web Site: https://www.star.it
Sales Range: $350-399.9 Million
Emp.: 1,657
Sauces, Condiments, Olive Oil, Margarine, Stocks, Canned Tuna, Herb Tea, Tomato Products, Ready-to-Serve Dishes & Cooking Preparations & Baby Foods
N.A.I.C.S.: 311941

VMC **(1)**
41 Rue Pierre Maitre, PO Box 67, 51100, Reims, France **(99.7%)**
Tel.: (33) 326879600
Sales Range: $450-499.9 Million
Emp.: 1,393
Glass Tableware, Glass Jars for Food Products & Glass Containers
N.A.I.C.S.: 327213

DANSK GENERATIONSSKIFTE A/S

Filippavej 57, 5762, Faborg, Vester Skerninge, Denmark
Tel.: (45) 62241741
Web Site:
http://www.generationsskifte.com
Year Founded: 2005
Emp.: 5
Plumbing Fixture Mfr
N.A.I.C.S.: 326191
Jens Heimburger *(Mng Dir)*

DANSK INDUSTRI INVEST A/S

Marienlystvej 65, 7800, Skive, Denmark
Tel.: (45) 96 14 37 00 **DK**
Web Site: http://www.dantherm.com
Year Founded: 1958
Holding Company
N.A.I.C.S.: 551112

Subsidiaries:

Dantherm Cooling Inc. **(1)**
671 Springfield Rd, Spartanburg, SC 29303
Tel.: (864) 595-9800
Web Site: http://danthermcooling.com
Air Dehumidification, Heating, Air conditioning, Ventilation & Electronics Cooling Equipment Design, Manufacturing & Installation Services

N.A.I.C.S.: 333415
Rick Schmidt *(CTO)*

DANSK TRAEEMBALLAGE A/S
Banevej 3, 5600, Faborg, Denmark
Tel.: (45) 62681323
Web Site: http://www.dte.dk
Sales Range: $25-49.9 Million
Emp.: 265
Wooden Packaging Mfr
N.A.I.C.S.: 321999
Peter Jensen *(Mgr)*

Subsidiaries:

DTE Stampen A/S   **(1)**
Anne Juels Vej 10 Flauenskjold, Copenhagen, 9330, Denmark
Tel.: (45) 98861511
Emp.: 55
Molding Timber Mfr
N.A.I.C.S.: 321113

DANSKE ANDELSKASSERS BANK A/S
Baneskellet 1, 8830, Hammershoj, 8830, Tjele, Denmark
Tel.: (45) 87993000
Web Site:
   https://www.andelskassen.dk
Year Founded: 1969
DAB—(CSE)
Rev.: $84,723,127
Assets: $2,018,814,660
Liabilities: $1,688,048,212
Net Worth: $330,766,448
Earnings: $21,595,694
Emp.: 313
Fiscal Year-end: 12/31/22
Banking Services
N.A.I.C.S.: 522110

DANSKE BANK A/S
Bernstorffsgade 40, 1577, Copenhagen, V, Denmark
Tel.: (45) 33440000   DK
Web Site:
   https://www.danskebank.com
Year Founded: 1871
DANSKE—(CSE)
Rev.: $10,622,584,640
Assets: $678,310,761,170
Liabilities: $650,466,918,640
Net Worth: $27,843,842,530
Earnings: $757,506,230
Emp.: 22,376
Fiscal Year-end: 12/31/20
Retail & Commercial Banking, Insurance, Mortgage Finance & Asset Management Services
N.A.I.C.S.: 522110
Martin Norkjaer Larsen *(Vice Chm)*

Subsidiaries:

Danica Life Ltd.   **(1)**
3rd Floor International House 3 Harbourmaster Place, Dublin, Ireland
Tel.: (353) 1 484 2000
Web Site: http://www.danicalife.ie
Sales Range: $50-74.9 Million
Emp.: 8
Pension Fund Management Services
N.A.I.C.S.: 523940

Danica Pension   **(1)**
Parallelvej 17, 2800, Lyngby, Denmark
Tel.: (45) 7 011 2525
Web Site: https://danicapension.dk
Pension Insurance
N.A.I.C.S.: 525110

Danske Bank International S.A.   **(1)**
13 Rue Edward Steishen, PO Box 173, 2011, Luxembourg, Luxembourg
Tel.: (352) 4612751
Web Site: https://www.danskebank.lu
Sales Range: $100-124.9 Million
Emp.: 95
Commericial Banking
N.A.I.C.S.: 522110

Danske Capital AS   **(1)**
Narva mnt 11, 15015, Tallinn, Estonia
Tel.: (372) 6752295
Web Site: http://www.danskecapital.ee
Emp.: 10
Fund Management Services
N.A.I.C.S.: 525910

Danske Invest Asset Management AS   **(1)**
Bryggetorget 4, 0250, Oslo, Norway
Tel.: (47) 85409800
Web Site: https://www.danskeinvest.no
N.A.I.C.S.: 525190

Danske Invest Management A/S   **(1)**
Parallelvej 17, Kongens Lyngby, 2800, Copenhagen, Denmark
Tel.: (45) 33337171
Web Site: https://www.danskeinvest.dk
Financial Investment Services
N.A.I.C.S.: 523999

Danske Leasing A/S   **(1)**
Birkerod Kongevej 25, 2100, Birkerod, Denmark
Tel.: (45) 45121212
Web Site: http://www.nordalia.dk
Commercial Banking Services
N.A.I.C.S.: 522110

Danske Markets Inc.   **(1)**
575 5th Ave 33rd FL, New York, NY 10017
Tel.: (212) 293-0600
Web Site:
   https://www.danskemarketsinc.com
Investment Banking Services
N.A.I.C.S.: 523150
Anders Iversen *(CEO)*

Danske Mortgage Bank Plc   **(1)**
Televisiokatu 1, 00075, Helsinki, Finland
Tel.: (358) 2002590
Investment Banking Services
N.A.I.C.S.: 523150

Danske Private Equity   **(1)**
Parallelvej 17, 2800, Kongens Lyngby, Denmark
Tel.: (45) 33446300
Web Site: https://danskeprivateequity.com
Sales Range: $50-74.9 Million
Emp.: 15
Private Equity
N.A.I.C.S.: 523150

Fokus Bank ASA   **(1)**
Vestre Rosten 77, 7466, Trondheim, Norway
Tel.: (47) 91585400
Web Site: http://www.fokus.no
Sales Range: $650-699.9 Million
Emp.: 1,000
Banking Services
N.A.I.C.S.: 522110

MobilePay Denmark A/S   **(1)**
Vester Sogade 10 6, 1601, Copenhagen, Denmark
Tel.: (45) 45144447
Web Site: http://www.mobilepay.dk
Financial Services
N.A.I.C.S.: 541611

MobilePay Finland OY   **(1)**
Keskuskatu 4, 00100, Helsinki, Finland
Tel.: (358) 20031331
Web Site: http://www.mobilepay.fi
Financial Services
N.A.I.C.S.: 523999

National Irish Bank Limited   **(1)**
3 Harbourmaster Place IFSC, Dublin, 1, Ireland
Tel.: (353) 14840000
Web Site: http://www.danskebank.ie
Sales Range: $200-249.9 Million
Emp.: 800
Retail & Commercial Banking & Other Financial Services
N.A.I.C.S.: 522110

Nordania Leasing   **(1)**
Birkerod Kongevej 25, 3460, Birkerod, Denmark
Tel.: (45) 4 512 1212
Web Site: https://www.nordania.dk
Emp.: 150
Business Equipment Leasing
N.A.I.C.S.: 532420

Northern Bank Limited   **(1)**
Tel.: (44) 2890245277
Web Site: http://www.danskebank.co.uk
Sales Range: $700-749.9 Million
Emp.: 2,000
Banking Services
N.A.I.C.S.: 522110

Realkredit Danmark A/S   **(1)**
Lerso Parkalle 100, 2100, Copenhagen, Denmark
Tel.: (45) 70125300
Web Site: https://rd.dk
Emp.: 300
Mortgage Lending
N.A.I.C.S.: 522310

Sampo Bank plc   **(1)**
Hiililaiturinkuja 2 1548, 00180, Helsinki, Finland
Tel.: (358) 105460000
Web Site: http://www.sampopankki.fi
Rev.: $368,250,240
Emp.: 2,000
Commercial & Investment Banking
N.A.I.C.S.: 523150

ZAO Danske Bank   **(1)**
Marata Street 69-71 A, 191119, Saint Petersburg, Russia
Tel.: (7) 8123327300
Web Site: http://www.danskebank.ru
Sales Range: $50-74.9 Million
Emp.: 45
Commercial Banking Services
N.A.I.C.S.: 522110

home a/s   **(1)**
Soren Frichs Vej 36F 1st floor, Abyhoj, 8230, Aarhus, Denmark
Tel.: (45) 86152700
Web Site: https://www.home.dk
Emp.: 900
Real Estate Services
N.A.I.C.S.: 531390

DANTAX A/S
Bransagervej 15, 9490, Pandrup, Denmark
Tel.: (45) 98247677
Web Site: https://www.dantaxradio.dk
Year Founded: 1971
DANT—(OMX)
Rev.: $4,939,535
Assets: $11,719,964
Liabilities: $870,977
Net Worth: $10,848,987
Earnings: $908,455
Emp.: 12
Fiscal Year-end: 06/30/19
Audio Equipment Mfr & Distr
N.A.I.C.S.: 334310
Peter Bogh Jensen *(CEO)*

Subsidiaries:

Dantax Radio A/S   **(1)**
Bransagervej 15, 9490, Pandrup, Denmark
Tel.: (45) 98247677
Loudspeaker Parts Mfr & Distr
N.A.I.C.S.: 334310

DANTO HOLDINGS CORPORATION
Umeda Daibiru 3F 3-3-10 Umeda, Kita-ku, Osaka, 530-0001, Japan
Tel.: (81) 647955000
Web Site: https://www.danto.co.jp
Year Founded: 1885
5337—(TKS)
Rev.: $39,377,860
Assets: $84,789,310
Liabilities: $18,965,750
Net Worth: $65,823,560
Earnings: ($6,770,950)
Emp.: 199
Fiscal Year-end: 12/31/23
Holding Company
N.A.I.C.S.: 551112
Tomohiko Kato *(Chm)*

Subsidiaries:

Elemus LLC   **(1)**
39-79 Saigonaka, Myodaiji-cho, Okazaki,

444-0867, Aichi, Japan
Tel.: (81) 564736322
Web Site: https://elemus.co.jp
Tableware & Accessory Product Retailer
N.A.I.C.S.: 423220

Touchstone Capital Management Co., Ltd.   **(1)**
Hulic JP Akasaka Building 12F 5-8 Akasaka 2-Chome, Minato-ku, Tokyo, 107-0052, Japan
Tel.: (81) 351146622
Web Site: https://www.touchstone-cm.com
Asset Management Services
N.A.I.C.S.: 531390

DANU INVESTMENT PARTNERS LTD.
72 Merrion Square, Dublin, 2, Ireland
Tel.: (353) 1 696 4456
Web Site: http://www.danupartners.ie
Private Investment Firm
N.A.I.C.S.: 523999
Michael ORourke *(Principal)*

Subsidiaries:

The Smith & Wollensky Restaurant Group, Inc.   **(1)**
260 Franklin St Ste 204, Boston, MA 02110
Tel.: (617) 600-3500
Web Site:
   http://www.smithandwollensky.com
Management Services-Restaurants
N.A.I.C.S.: 722511
Fortunato N. Valenti *(CEO)*

DANUBE INDUSTRIES LIMITED
Office A-2101 Privilon Bh Iscon Temple Ambli-bopal Road, Vejalpur, Ahmedabad, India
Tel.: (91) 7940323856
Web Site:
   https://danubeindustries.com
Year Founded: 1980
540361—(BOM)
Rev.: $4,659,951
Assets: $4,555,573
Liabilities: $4,017,011
Net Worth: $538,563
Earnings: $47,398
Emp.: 4
Fiscal Year-end: 03/31/21
Paper Product Mfr & Distr
N.A.I.C.S.: 322120
Manisha Jain *(Compliance Officer)*

DANZER AG
Schutzengelstr 36, PO Box 2461, Baar, 6340, Switzerland
Tel.: (41) 7670303   CH
Web Site:
   http://www.danzergroup.com
Year Founded: 1936
Sales Range: $400-449.9 Million
Emp.: 3,200
Holding Company; Hardwood Veneer, Lumber & Vinterio Products Mfr & Distr
N.A.I.C.S.: 551112
Hans-Joachim Danzer *(CEO & Member-Mgmt Bd)*

Subsidiaries:

Danzer Services Europe GmbH   **(1)**
Storlach Str 1, Reutlingen, 72760, Germany   **(100%)**
Tel.: (49) 71213070
Web Site: http://www.danzergroup.com
Sales Range: $50-74.9 Million
Emp.: 20
Executive & Legislative Office; Hardwood Veneer & Lumber Products Distr
N.A.I.C.S.: 921140

Division (Non-US):

Danzer Europe Veneer AG   **(2)**
Schutzengelstr 36, PO Box 2461, Baar, 6340, Switzerland   **(100%)**
Tel.: (41) 5607813

Danzer AG—(Continued)

Web Site: http://www.danzergroup.com
Sales Range: $50-74.9 Million
Emp.: 10
Holding Company; Hardwood Veneer Mfr &
Whslr
N.A.I.C.S.: 551112

Subsidiary (Non-US):

Danzer Bohemia-Dyharna s.r.o. (3)
Krivenice 1, 27703, Horni Pocaply, Czech
Republic (100%)
Tel.: (420) 315630700
Web Site: http://www.danzer.cz
Sales Range: $125-149.9 Million
Emp.: 480
Hardwood Veneer Mfr & Distr
N.A.I.C.S.: 321211
Radim Vrablik (Gen Mgr)

Danzer UK Limited (3)
46 Market Hill, Maldon, CM9 4QA, Essex,
United Kingdom (100%)
Tel.: (44) 1621851002
Web Site: http://www.danzer.co.uk
Sales Range: $25-49.9 Million
Lumber Sawmill & Products Distr
N.A.I.C.S.: 321113
Ken Walsh (Mng Dir)

Karl Danzer Ges.m.b.H. (3)
Gollstrasse 20, Grodig, 5082,
Austria (100%)
Tel.: (43) 624672155
Web Site: http://www.danzer.at
Sales Range: $25-49.9 Million
Hardwood Veneer Mfr & Whslr
N.A.I.C.S.: 321211
Walter Mooslechner (Mng Dir)

Subsidiary (Non-US):

Danzer Forestacion S.A. (2)
Casilla de Correo 449, 3300 WAI, Posadas,
Misiones, Argentina (100%)
Tel.: (54) 3752480295
Sales Range: $25-49.9 Million
Timberland Management Services
N.A.I.C.S.: 113110

Group (US):

Danzer Services, Inc. (2)
119 AID Dr, Darlington, PA 16115
Tel.: (724) 827-3700
Web Site: http://www.danzergroup.com
Sales Range: $50-74.9 Million
Executive Office; Hardwood Veneer & Lum-
ber Products Distr
N.A.I.C.S.: 921110
Greg Lottes (Pres/CEO-Veneer-Americas)

Division (Domestic):

Bradford Forest, Inc. (3)
444 High St, Bradford, PA 16701 (100%)
Tel.: (814) 368-3701
Web Site: http://www.bradfordforest.com
Sales Range: $50-74.9 Million
Lumber Sawmill & Products Distr
N.A.I.C.S.: 321113
Mark Conolly (Pres)

Danzer Forestland, Inc. (3)
119 AID Dr, Darlington, PA 16115
Tel.: (724) 827-3700
Web Site: http://www.danzerforestland.com
Timberland Acquisition & Management Ser-
vices
N.A.I.C.S.: 113110

Danzer Veneer Americas, Inc. (3)
119 AID Dr, Darlington, PA 16115
Tel.: (724) 827-8366
Web Site: http://www.danzer.com
Sales Range: $25-49.9 Million
Emp.: 100
Hardwood Veneer Products Mfr & Distr
N.A.I.C.S.: 321211
Greg Lottes (Pres & CEO)

Subsidiary (Domestic):

David R. Webb Company, Inc. (4)
206 S Holland St, Edinburgh, IN 46124
Tel.: (812) 526-2601
Web Site: http://www.davidrwebb.com

Sales Range: $25-49.9 Million
Emp.: 120
Hardwood Veneer Mfr & Distr
N.A.I.C.S.: 321211
Ed Pendleton (Mgr-HR)

DAODAOQUAN GRAIN AND OIL CO LTD
10th Floor Building 9 Kaile Interna-
tional City Xiangjiang Middle Road,
Kaifu District, Changsha, 410000,
Hunan, China
Tel.: (86) 7308318506
Web Site: http://www.ddqly.com
Year Founded: 1999
002852—(SSE)
Rev.: $986,778,936
Assets: $682,564,428
Liabilities: $397,027,332
Net Worth: $285,537,096
Earnings: ($58,681,584)
Emp.: 850
Fiscal Year-end: 12/31/22
Vegetable Oil Mfr & Distr
N.A.I.C.S.: 311224
Jianjun Liu (Chm & Gen Mgr)

DAOHE GLOBAL GROUP LIM-ITED
6/F YHC Tower 1 Sheung Yuet Road
Kowloon Bay, Hong Kong, China
(Hong Kong)
Tel.: (852) 29935328
Web Site:
http://www.daoheglobal.com.hk
0915—(HKG)
Rev.: $62,639,000
Assets: $30,848,000
Liabilities: $19,889,000
Net Worth: $10,959,000
Earnings: $4,086,000
Emp.: 301
Fiscal Year-end: 12/31/21
Garment Mfr & Sales
N.A.I.C.S.: 315120
Dennis Hing Lin Wong (Pres & CEO)

Subsidiaries:

Linmark (HK) Limited (1)
6/F YHC Tower 1 Sheung Yuet Road, Kow-
loon Bay, China (Hong Kong)
Tel.: (852) 27340888
Web Site: https://www.linmark.com
Business Consulting Services
N.A.I.C.S.: 541618

Linmark International (Hong Kong)
Limited (1)
6/F YHC Tower 1 Sheung Yuet Road, Kow-
loon Bay, China (Hong Kong)
Tel.: (852) 27340888
Web Site: https://www.linmark.com
Supply Chain Management Services
N.A.I.C.S.: 541614

Tamarind Trading (Shanghai)
Limited (1)
31/F No 500 North Chengdu Road Lucky
Target, Huang Pu District, Shanghai,
200003, China
Tel.: (86) 2160293088
Supply Chain Management Services
N.A.I.C.S.: 541614

DAOJIA LIMITED
8/F Building 5 Beijing Cultural Cre-
ative Building No 30 Beiyuan Road,
Chaoyang District, Beijing, 100012,
China
Tel.: (86) 10 8347 6824
Year Founded: 2014
JIA—(NYSE)
Rev.: $108,944,720
Assets: $142,115,757
Liabilities: $321,932,513
Net Worth: ($179,816,755)
Earnings: ($94,118,588)
Emp.: 2,733
Fiscal Year-end: 12/31/20

Home & Personal Services
N.A.I.C.S.: 561790
Xiaohua Chen (Founder, Chm &
CEO)

DAOMING OPTICS AND CHEMICAL CO., LTD.
No 581 Dongwu Road Economic De-
velopment Zone, Yongkang, 321399,
Zhejiang, China
Tel.: (86) 57987311626
Web Site:
https://www.chinadaoming.com
Year Founded: 2007
002632—(SSE)
Rev.: $180,638,640
Assets: $393,287,076
Liabilities: $64,447,812
Net Worth: $328,839,264
Earnings: $44,077,176
Emp.: 900
Fiscal Year-end: 12/31/22
Reflective Films, Fabrics, Apparel &
Other Reflective Products Mfr
N.A.I.C.S.: 325998
Hu Zhibiao (Chm)

DAOU DATA CORP.
5th 11th floor Dongmakro 311
Jaehwa Square, Mapo-gu, Seoul,
04156, Korea (South)
Tel.: (82) 234105100
Web Site: https://www.daoudata.co.kr
Year Founded: 1992
032190—(KRS)
Rev.: $7,670,401,489
Assets: $40,036,713,929
Liabilities: $35,793,825,834
Net Worth: $4,242,888,094
Earnings: $328,738,177
Emp.: 216
Fiscal Year-end: 12/31/23
Management Cousulting Service
N.A.I.C.S.: 541611

Subsidiaries:

Daou Japan KK (1)
19F Toranomon Towers Office 4-1-28 Tora-
nomon, Minato-ku, Tokyo, 105-0001, Japan
Tel.: (81) 364530337
Web Site: https://www.daou.co.jp
Software Development Services
N.A.I.C.S.: 541511

Kiwoom Investment Co., Ltd. (1)
3rd Floor Sindoricoh Building 943-27
Daechi-dong, Gangnam-Gu, Seoul, 135-
845, Korea (South)
Tel.: (82) 2 3430 4800
Financial Investment Services
N.A.I.C.S.: 523940

PT. Kiwoom Securities Indonesia (1)
Treasury Tower Lt 27A District 8 Kawasan
SCBD Lot 28, Jl Jend Sudirman Kav 52-53,
Jakarta, 12190, Indonesia
Tel.: (62) 2127085695
Web Site: https://www.kiwoom.co.id
Investment Banking Services
N.A.I.C.S.: 523150
Ratnawati Wibowo (Dir-Mktg)

DAOU TECHNOLOGY, INC.
7F 10F 4F Daou Digital Square 69
Geumto-ro, Sujeong-gu, Seongnam,
Gyeonggi-do, Korea (South)
Tel.: (82) 7087071000
Web Site: http://www.daou.co.kr
Year Founded: 1986
023590—(KRS)
Rev.: $7,314,951,678
Assets: $39,593,292,557
Liabilities: $35,473,424,799
Net Worth: $4,119,867,757
Earnings: $363,712,829
Emp.: 617
Fiscal Year-end: 12/31/23
IT Solution Development Services
N.A.I.C.S.: 541512
Sang-Beom Shin (Vice Chm)

DAP CO., LTD.
474-22 Anseongmatchum-daero
Miyang-myeon, Anseong, Gyeonggi-
do, Korea (South)
Tel.: (82) 316770005
Web Site: http://www.dap.co.kr
Year Founded: 1987
066900—(KRS)
Rev.: $255,917,222
Assets: $202,804,251
Liabilities: $117,543,081
Net Worth: $85,261,170
Earnings: $4,084,793
Emp.: 1,045
Fiscal Year-end: 12/31/22
Printed Circuit Board Mfr
N.A.I.C.S.: 334412
Bong Yoon Choi (Pres & CEO)

DAPAI INTERNATIONAL HOLDINGS CO. LTD.
Chengbei Industrial Zone, Luocheng
Town Huian County, Quanzhou, Fu-
jian, China
Tel.: (86) 59527301555
Web Site: http://www.chinazaino.com
Sales Range: $150-199.9 Million
Emp.: 2,800
Backpacks & Luggage Developer, Mfr
& Sales
N.A.I.C.S.: 316990
Xizhong Chen (Chm)

DAPD MEDIA HOLDING AG
Reinhardtstrasse 52, D-10117, Berlin,
Germany
Tel.: (49) 30 23122 0
Holding Company; News Syndicate &
Media Publishing Services
N.A.I.C.S.: 551112
Martin Vorderwulbecke (CEO)

Subsidiaries:

dapd nachrichtenagentur GmbH (1)
Reinhardtstrasse 52, D-10117, Berlin, Ger-
many
Tel.: (49) 30 23122 0
Web Site: http://www.dapd.de
Sales Range: $10-24.9 Million
Emp.: 300
News Agency
N.A.I.C.S.: 516210

DAPHNE INTERNATIONAL HOLDINGS LIMITED
Unit 2605 26/F The Metropolis Tower
10 Metropolis Drive, Hung Hom,
Kowloon, China (Hong Kong)
Tel.: (852) 23679021
Web Site:
http://www.daphneholdings.com
0210—(OTCIQ)
Rev.: $46,938,531
Assets: $110,752,288
Liabilities: $28,524,056
Net Worth: $82,228,232
Earnings: ($31,177,691)
Emp.: 150
Fiscal Year-end: 12/31/20
Footwear Industry
N.A.I.C.S.: 316210
Chih-Kai Chang (Chm)

Subsidiaries:

Gentlefit Trading Limited (1)
17 F Fung House 19-20 Connaught Rd,
Central, China (Hong Kong)
Tel.: (852) 23679021
Web Site: http://www.daphne.com.cn
Emp.: 30
Footwear Distr
N.A.I.C.S.: 424340

DAPS ADVERTISING LTD.
9-B IInd Floor 128 Clyde House Opp
Heer Palace The Mall, Kanpur,
208001, Uttar Pradesh, India

Tel.: (91) 9935430555
Web Site:
https://www.dapsadvertising.com
Year Founded: 1993
543651—(BOM)
Advertising Agency Services
N.A.I.C.S.: 541810

DAQIAN ECOLOGY & ENVIRONMENT GROUP CO., LTD.
Room 4505 45th Floor Building E-06 Suning Ruicheng Huigu, No 270 Jiqingmen Street Gulou District, Nanjing, 210036, Jiangsu, China
Tel.: (86) 2583751401
Web Site: http://www.daqianjg.com
Year Founded: 1988
603955—(SHG)
Rev.: $35,377,262
Assets: $472,087,039
Liabilities: $216,244,431
Net Worth: $255,842,608
Earnings: $1,509,005
Fiscal Year-end: 12/31/22
Urban Landscaping & Architecture Design Services
N.A.I.C.S.: 561730
Xu Feng (Chm)

DAQIN RAILWAY CO., LTD.
No 14 Zhanbei St, Datong, 037005, Shanxi, China
Tel.: (86) 3527121248   CN
Web Site: http://www.daqintielu.com
601006—(SHG)
Rev.: $10,636,377,107
Assets: $28,402,502,240
Liabilities: $8,719,936,608
Net Worth: $19,682,565,632
Earnings: $1,571,954,553
Emp.: 40,388
Fiscal Year-end: 12/31/22
Railway Transportation & Freight Services
N.A.I.C.S.: 482111

DAQING HUAKE COMPANY LIMITED
No 293 Jianshe Road Daqing High-tech Industrial Development Zone, Daqing, 163316, Heilongjiang, China
Tel.: (86) 4596291758
Web Site: https://www.huake.com
Year Founded: 1998
000985—(SSE)
Rev.: $366,309,216
Assets: $99,132,228
Liabilities: $14,447,160
Net Worth: $84,685,068
Earnings: $2,163,564
Fiscal Year-end: 12/31/22
Petrochemical Products Mfr
N.A.I.C.S.: 325110
Wang Hongtao (Chm)

DAQO NEW ENERGY CORP.
29th Floor Huadu Building No 838 Zhangyang Road, Shanghai, 200122, China
Tel.: (86) 2150752918   Ky
Web Site:
https://stage.investorroom.com
DQ—(NYSE)
Rev.: $4,608,350,000
Assets: $7,594,096,000
Liabilities: $989,490,000
Net Worth: $6,604,606,000
Earnings: $1,819,801,000
Emp.: 4,099
Fiscal Year-end: 12/31/22
Polysilicon, Silicon Wafer & Solar Module Mfr
N.A.I.C.S.: 325998
Guangfu Xu (Chm)

Subsidiaries:

Chongqing Daqo New Energy Co., Ltd.   **(1)**
666 Longdu Avenue, Wanzhou, Chongqing, 404000, China
Tel.: (86) 2364866666
Polysilicon Product Mfr
N.A.I.C.S.: 334413

Xinjiang Daqo New Energy Co. Ltd.   **(1)**
Block D 29th Floor Huadu Building 838 Zhangyang Road, Pudong New District, Shanghai, 200122, China
Tel.: (86) 2150560970
Web Site: https://www.dqsolar.com
Rev.: $2,260,894,093
Assets: $7,019,142,460
Liabilities: $943,704,226
Net Worth: $6,075,438,234
Earnings: $797,892,141
Fiscal Year-end: 12/31/2023
Solar Cell Product Mfr
N.A.I.C.S.: 334413

DAR AL AMAN FOR ISLAMIC FINANCE PLC
AbduAllah Ghousheh Street Alhusseini Building Number 53, PO Box 4544, Tilaa ali, Amman, 11953, Jordan
Tel.: (962) 65538450
DAIF—(AMM)
Rev.: $1,132,627
Assets: $15,895,615
Liabilities: $892,665
Net Worth: $15,002,950
Earnings: ($34,377)
Emp.: 14
Fiscal Year-end: 12/31/20
Financial Management Services
N.A.I.C.S.: 523999
Nabil Mazaq (Gen Mgr)

DAR AL ARKAN REAL ESTATE DEVELOPMENT COMPANY
PO Box 105633, Riyadh, 11656, Saudi Arabia
Tel.: (966) 112069888
Web Site:
https://www.daralarkan.com
4300—(SAU)
Rev.: $1,046,660,179
Assets: $8,935,569,391
Liabilities: $3,708,498,867
Net Worth: $5,227,070,524
Earnings: $117,776,296
Emp.: 391
Fiscal Year-end: 12/31/22
Real Estate Investment, Management & Development Services
N.A.I.C.S.: 531390
Yousef Abdullah Al Shelash (Chm)

DAR AL DAWA DEVELOPMENT & INVESTMENT CO.
PO Box 9364, Naour, Amman, 11191, Jordan
Tel.: (962) 62222200
Web Site: https://www.dadgroup.com
Year Founded: 1975
DADI—(AMM)
Rev.: $74,967,810
Assets: $143,303,251
Liabilities: $98,297,084
Net Worth: $45,006,167
Earnings: $12,037,703
Emp.: 792
Fiscal Year-end: 12/31/20
Pharmaceutical Product Mfr & Whslr
N.A.I.C.S.: 325412
Osama Mohammed Mortada Yaish (Vice Chm)

Subsidiaries:

Hamad Medical Corporation   **(1)**
PO Box 3050, Doha, Qatar
Tel.: (974) 44395777

Web Site: https://www.hamad.qa
Pharmaceutical Product Mfr & Distr
N.A.I.C.S.: 325412

Kambal International Co.   **(1)**
PO Box 10336, Khartoum, Sudan
Tel.: (249) 183779337
Pharmaceutical Product Mfr & Distr
N.A.I.C.S.: 325412

SADCO Sami Dandan & Co.   **(1)**
SADCO Bldg Beer Hassan Street No 76, PO Box 11-4486, Beirut, Lebanon
Tel.: (961) 1855560
Web Site: https://sadco.com.lb
Healthcare & Hospital Services
N.A.I.C.S.: 622110

SC. Dar Al DawaPharma SRL   **(1)**
Strada Claudiu NR 7 Sector 2, Bucharest, Romania
Tel.: (40) 213268690
Pharmaceuticals Product Mfr
N.A.I.C.S.: 325412

Zenad Group Co. For Trading & Contracting. & Pharmasom Ltd.   **(1)**
Hawlwadag Street - Bakare Market, Mogadishu, Somalia
Tel.: (252) 615502696
Pharmaceutical Product Mfr & Distr
N.A.I.C.S.: 325412

DAR AL TAKAFUL HOUSE PJSC
Al Andalus Building, 235353, Dubai, United Arab Emirates
Tel.: (971) 42623240
Web Site: http://www.takafulhouse.ae
Year Founded: 2008
DARTAKAFUL—(DFM)
Sales Range: $10-24.9 Million
Insurance Services
N.A.I.C.S.: 524298

Subsidiaries:

National Takaful Company (Watania) PJSC   **(1)**
4th Floor Al Jazira Sports Complex Tower A Al Muroor Rd, PO Box 6457, Opposite to Dusit Thani Hotel, Abu Dhabi, United Arab Emirates
Tel.: (971) 26138888
Web Site: http://www.watania.ae
Rev.: $53,865,731
Assets: $129,659,067
Liabilities: $104,153,535
Net Worth: $25,505,533
Earnings: $3,574,662
Fiscal Year-end: 12/31/2019
Insurance Management Services
N.A.I.C.S.: 524298
Ali Saeed Harmel Aldhaheri (Chm)

DAR AL THURAYA REAL ESTATE CO KSCP
Qebla Block 13 b 28 Reem Realestate complex - 14th floor, PO Box 1376, Kuwait, 13014, Kuwait
Tel.: (965) 22061060
Web Site:
https://www.daralthuraya.com
Year Founded: 2004
THURAYA—(KUW)
Rev.: $42,953
Assets: $68,091,917
Liabilities: $10,864,752
Net Worth: $57,227,165
Earnings: $1,036,045
Emp.: 13
Fiscal Year-end: 12/31/23
Real Estate Manangement Services
N.A.I.C.S.: 531390
Ahmad Al-Bahar (Vice Chm)

DAR AL-MAAL AL-ISLAMI TRUST
84 Avenue Louis Casai, PO Box 64, 1216, Cointrin, Switzerland
Tel.: (41) 22 7917111
Web Site: http://www.dmitrust.com
Year Founded: 1981

Sales Range: $400-449.9 Million
Banking Services
N.A.I.C.S.: 522110
Mohamed Al Faisal Al Saud (Chm)

Subsidiaries:

DMI Administrative Services S.A.   **(1)**
84 Avenue Louis-Casai, PO Box 64, 1216, Geneva, Switzerland
Tel.: (41) 227917111
Financial Consulting Services
N.A.I.C.S.: 523940
Ladane Samii Guionneau (Head-HR)

Islamic Investment Company of the Gulf (Bahamas) Limited   **(1)**
Waly Al-Ahad Street Tamlik Tower 2nd & 3rd floor, PO Box 9707, Jeddah, 21423, Saudi Arabia
Tel.: (966) 126516900
Investment Advisory Services
N.A.I.C.S.: 523940

Ithmaar Holding B.S.C.   **(1)**
Seef Tower Seef District, PO Box 2820, Manama, Bahrain
Tel.: (973) 17584000
Web Site: https://www.ithmaarholding.com
Rev.: $358,518,342
Assets: $6,125,986,048
Liabilities: $5,915,548,659
Net Worth: $210,437,389
Earnings: $22,132,039
Emp.: 52
Fiscal Year-end: 12/31/2022
Holding Company; Banking Services
N.A.I.C.S.: 551111
Ahmed Abdul Rahim (CEO)

Subsidiary (Non-US):

Faysal Bank Limited   **(2)**
Faysal House ST-02 Shahrah-e-Faisal, Karachi, Pakistan   **(66.94%)**
Tel.: (92) 111747747
Web Site: https://www.faysalbank.com
Rev.: $183,393,052
Assets: $4,056,301,833
Liabilities: $3,700,778,883
Net Worth: $355,522,950
Earnings: $38,666,024
Emp.: 6,118
Fiscal Year-end: 12/31/2019
Retail, Commercial & Investment Banking Services
N.A.I.C.S.: 522110
Farooq Rahmatullah Khan (Chm)

Subsidiary (Domestic):

Shamil Bank of Bahrain B.S.C.   **(2)**
PO Box 2820, 1714, Manama, Bahrain
Tel.: (973) 17585000
Web Site: http://www.shamilbank.net
Sales Range: $100-124.9 Million
Emp.: 251
Banking Services
N.A.I.C.S.: 522110

Sakana Holistic Housing Solutions B.S.C.   **(1)**
Ground Floor128 Bahrain Car Park Company Building, 383, Manama, Bahrain
Tel.: (973) 17201919
Web Site: http://www.sakanaonline.com
Financial Consulting Services
N.A.I.C.S.: 523940
Abdul Hakim Al Mutawa (Chm)

Subsidiary (Non-US):

AEL Textiles Limited   **(2)**
404-405 4th Floor Business Center Mumtaz Hassan Road, Karachi, Pakistan
Tel.: (92) 2132416553
Web Site: http://www.arshadenergy.com
Rev.: $115,658
Assets: $240,933
Liabilities: $3,264
Net Worth: $237,669
Earnings: $8,771
Emp.: 1
Fiscal Year-end: 06/30/2023
Eletric Power Generation Services
N.A.I.C.S.: 221118
Muhammad Arshad (Chm)

DAR AL-SHIFA'A FOR THE

DAR AL-SHIFA'A FOR THE —(CONTINUED)

MANUFACTURING OF PHAR-MACEUTICALS
PO Box 677, Ramallah, Palestine
Tel.: (970) 22900680
Year Founded: 1986
PHARMACARE—(PAL)
Sales Range: Less than $1 Million
Pharmaceutical Preparation Mfr & Whslr
N.A.I.C.S.: 325412
Bassim Subhi Farah Khoury Nasr
(Chm & CEO)

DAR ES SALAM INVESTMENT BANK
Al Sadoun Park Section 103 Street
41 Building 3, PO Box 3067, Elawiya, Baghdad, Iraq
Tel.: (964) 1 7196488
Web Site: http://desiraq.com
Year Founded: 1998
Sales Range: $10-24.9 Million
Banking Services
N.A.I.C.S.: 522110

DARAB CEMENT COMPANY
Tel.: (98) 7191001335
Web Site:
http://www.darabcement.com
Year Founded: 1987
SDAB—(THE)
Sales Range: Less than $1 Million
Cement Mfr
N.A.I.C.S.: 327310
Alireza Bostanian *(CEO)*

DARAG GROUP LIMITED
Whitehall Mansions Ta Xbiex Seafront, Ta' Xbiex, XBX 1026, Malta
Tel.: (356) 21378349
Web Site: http://www.darag-group.com
Reinsurance Services
N.A.I.C.S.: 524130
Stuart Davies *(Chm)*

Subsidiaries:

SOBC DARAG Holdings Ltd.   (1)
8200 Beckett Park Dr Ste 201, West Chester, OH 45069
Tel.: (513) 889-5663
Web Site: http://sobcdarag.com
Run-Off Acquisition & Management Solutions
N.A.I.C.S.: 561499
Stephanie Mocatta *(CEO)*

DARAT JORDAN HOLDINGS
Arjan Area - Near Ministry of Interior, PO Box 212466, Amman, 11121, Jordan
Tel.: (962) 65664109
Web Site: https://www.ase.com
Year Founded: 2008
DARA—(AMM)
Rev.: $1,263,770
Assets: $15,470,833
Liabilities: $76,257
Net Worth: $15,394,576
Earnings: $820,043
Emp.: 6
Fiscal Year-end: 12/31/20
Investment Development Services
N.A.I.C.S.: 523999

DARCO WATER TECHNOLO-GIES LIMITED
1 Commonwealth Lane09-06 One Commonwealth, Singapore, 149544, Singapore
Tel.: (65) 63633886   SG
Web Site:
https://www.darcowater.com
Year Founded: 1999

BLR—(SES)
Rev.: $53,205,332
Assets: $56,225,858
Liabilities: $33,815,799
Net Worth: $22,410,058
Emp.: 450
Fiscal Year-end: 12/31/23
Water Treatment & Waste Management Services
N.A.I.C.S.: 924110
Chun Sem Teh *(Controller-Fin)*

Subsidiaries:

Darco Engineering Pte Ltd.   (1)
41 Loyang Drive, Singapore, 508952, Singapore
Tel.: (65) 65453800
Sales Range: $50-74.9 Million
Emp.: 100
Waste Treatment Services
N.A.I.C.S.: 924110

Subsidiary (Non-US):

Darco Environmental (Philippines)
Inc.   (2)
Unit 502 Caresma Building No 50 Polaris No 27 Badajos Street, Corner P Burgos Street, Makati, 1261, Philippines
Tel.: (63) 28969375
Web Site: http://www.darcophil.com.ph
Sales Range: $25-49.9 Million
Emp.: 56
Environmental Engineering Solutions
N.A.I.C.S.: 541620

Shanghai Darco Engineering Co Ltd   (2)
Tel.: (86) 2157749731
Web Site: http://www.darcowater.com.cn
Waste Treatment Services
N.A.I.C.S.: 221310

Shanghai Darco Envirotech Company Limited   (2)
No 200 Lane 1276 Nanle Road, Songjiang Industrial Zone, Shanghai, China
Tel.: (86) 2157749731
Web Site: http://www.darcowater.com.cn
Water & Wastewater Engineering Services & Solutions
N.A.I.C.S.: 924110

Darco Industrial Water Sdn. Bhd.   (1)
20 Hujong Perusahaan 2 Kawasan MIEL Prai Industrial Estate Phase 2, Arab Malaysian Industrial Park, Pulau Penang, 13600, Perai, Malaysia
Tel.: (60) 43902455
Web Site: http://www.darcowaters.com
Sales Range: $25-49.9 Million
Emp.: 40
Water Treatment & Waste Management Services
N.A.I.C.S.: 924110
Dhanalaraj Sundaram *(Gen Mgr)*

Darco Water Systems Sdn. Bhd.   (1)
Lot 10645 Jalan Permata 1/6, Arab Malaysian Industrial Park, 71800, Nilai, Negeri Sembilan, Malaysia
Tel.: (60) 6 799 6773
Web Site: http://www.darcowater.com
Sales Range: $50-74.9 Million
Emp.: 91
Water Treatment & Waste Management Services
N.A.I.C.S.: 924110

Darco-EnviDan Sdn Bhd   (1)
Lot 10645 PT 16724 Jalan Permata 1/6 Arab Malaysian Industrial Park, 71800, Nilai, Negeri Sembilan, Malaysia
Tel.: (60) 6 799 6773
Web Site: http://www.darcowater.com
Sales Range: $75-99.9 Million
Emp.: 6
Waste Management Services
N.A.I.C.S.: 221310
Thye Kim Sah *(Gen Mgr)*

Grober Industrial Services Sdn. Bhd.   (1)
20 Hujong Perusahaan Kaw MIEL Phase 2, Prai Industrial Estate, 13600, Prai, Penang, Malaysia

Tel.: (60) 43902455
Industrial Equipment Distr
N.A.I.C.S.: 423830

Ness Plus Trading Sdn. Bhd.   (1)
Lot 10645 Jalan Permata 1/6, Arab Malaysian Industrial Park, 71800, Nilai, Negeri Sembilan, Malaysia
Tel.: (60) 67996773
Water System Assembly & Installation Services
N.A.I.C.S.: 237110

PV Vacuum Engineering Pte Ltd   (1)
21 Marsiling Industrial Estate Rd 9, Singapore, 739175, Singapore
Tel.: (65) 67556169
Web Site: http://www.pvsin.com.sg
Sales Range: $25-49.9 Million
Emp.: 16
Total Vacuum Application Solutions
N.A.I.C.S.: 335210
K M Thye *(Chm)*

Singaway FluidControls Pte Ltd.   (1)
41 Loyang Drive, Singapore, 508952, Singapore
Tel.: (65) 6545 0334
Fluid Control Solutions
N.A.I.C.S.: 334513

Vietnam Darco Environment Company Limited   (1)
10th Floor Thanh Dung Building 179 Nguyen Cu Trinh St, Nguyen Cu Trinh Ward District 1, Ho Chi Minh City, Vietnam
Tel.: (84) 2839208967
Water System Assembly & Installation Services
N.A.I.C.S.: 237110

Wuhan Kaidi Water Services Co., Ltd.   (1)
Building 20 Guanggu Witpark Financial Harbour 1st Road Guanggu Road, East Lake New-Tech Development Zone, Wuhan, Hubei, China
Tel.: (86) 2767848947
Water System Assembly & Installation Services
N.A.I.C.S.: 237110
Jiangtao Fu *(Engr-Professional)*

DARCOR LIMITED
7 Staffordshire Place, Toronto, M8W 1T1, ON, Canada
Tel.: (416) 255-8563
Web Site: http://www.darcor.com
Year Founded: 1931
Rev.: $17,041,210
Emp.: 95
Office Equipments Mfr
N.A.I.C.S.: 333310
Vaughn Pipe *(Dir-Mktg)*

DARDANEL ONENTAS GIDA SANAYI AS
Mah Haydar Aliyev Cad No 142, Tarabya, Istanbul, Turkiye
Tel.: (90) 2122238830
Web Site:
https://www.dardanel.com.tr
Year Founded: 1984
DARDL—(IST)
Rev.: $127,969,803
Assets: $91,242,090
Liabilities: $75,058,538
Net Worth: $16,183,552
Earnings: $12,454,927
Fiscal Year-end: 12/31/20
Fish Production & Distribution Services
N.A.I.C.S.: 114111
Osman Niyazi Onen *(Chm)*

DARE FOODS LIMITED
2481 Kingsway Dr, PO Box 1058, Kitchener, N2G 4G4, ON, Canada
Tel.: (519) 893-5500   ON
Web Site: http://www.darefoods.com
Year Founded: 1892
Sales Range: $150-199.9 Million
Emp.: 300

Biscuits, Candy & Crackers Mfr
N.A.I.C.S.: 311821

DARE POWER DEKOR HOME CO., LTD.
Daya Industrial Park No 99 Qiliang Road Economic Development Zone, Danyang City Economic & Technological Development Zne, Danyang, 212310, Jiangsu, China
Tel.: (86) 51186981046
Web Site:
http://www.dareglobal.com.cn
Year Founded: 1000
000910—(SSE)
Rev.: $1,033,760,988
Assets: $1,340,768,052
Liabilities: $411,068,736
Net Worth: $929,699,316
Earnings: $59,011,524
Fiscal Year-end: 12/31/22
Wood-Based Product Mfr
N.A.I.C.S.: 321999
Chen Jianjun *(Chm, Pres & Gen Mgr)*

DARELLE ONLINE SOLU-TIONS INC.
4907 Fillinger Crescent, Nanaimo, V9V 1H9, BC, Canada
Tel.: (778) 840-3325   Ca
Web Site: https://www.darelle.com
Year Founded: 2001
DAR—(TSXV)
Rev.: $202,059
Assets: $156,208
Liabilities: $822,156
Net Worth: ($665,948)
Earnings: ($100,032)
Fiscal Year-end: 08/31/21
Investment Services
N.A.I.C.S.: 523999

Subsidiaries:

Darelle Media Inc.   (1)
Suite 527 2818 Main Street, Vancouver, V5T 0C1, BC, Canada
Tel.: (604) 628-2008
Web Site: https://darelle.com
Online Raffle Distr
N.A.I.C.S.: 519290
Kyle Kotapski *(Pres)*

DAREWAY SOFTWARE CO., LTD.
No 1579 Wenbo Road, Zhangqiu, Jinan, 250200, Shandong, China
Tel.: (86) 53158215506
Web Site:
http://www.dareway.com.cn
Year Founded: 1992
688579—(SHG)
Rev.: $63,728,838
Assets: $236,878,556
Liabilities: $54,810,180
Net Worth: $182,068,375
Earnings: $8,692,515
Fiscal Year-end: 12/31/22
Software Development Services
N.A.I.C.S.: 541511
Qingzhong Li *(Chm)*

DARI COUSPATE S.A
Quartier Industriel, EzZahra El Oulja Sale, Casablanca, Morocco
Tel.: (212) 537808721
Web Site:
https://www.couscousdari.com
Year Founded: 1995
DRI—(CAS)
Sales Range: $50-74.9 Million
Couscous Pasta Mfr
N.A.I.C.S.: 311824
Mohammed Khalil *(Chm & CEO)*

DARJEELING ROPEWAY COM-PANY LTD.
104-Shreejee Darshan Tata Road No

2 Opera House, Mumbai, 400004, India
Tel.: (91) 6358262367
Web Site:
http://www.darjeelingropeway.com
539770—(BOM)
Rev.: $35,476
Assets: $960,728
Liabilities: $297,461
Net Worth: $663,267
Earnings: ($723)
Fiscal Year-end: 03/31/21
Electrical Transport Support Services
N.A.I.C.S.: 488999
Dilipbhai Ramanlal Doshi *(CFO)*

DARK HORSE TECHNOLOGY GROUP CO., LTD.
Block B Building 2 Dentsu Creative Plaza No 7 Jiuxianqiao North Road, Chaoyang District, Beijing, 100015, China
Tel.: (86) 1062691933
Web Site: http://www.iheima.com
Year Founded: 2011
300688—(SSE)
Rev.: $48,735,648
Assets: $112,409,856
Liabilities: $32,972,940
Net Worth: $79,436,916
Earnings: ($11,727,612)
Fiscal Year-end: 12/31/22
Business Consulting Services
N.A.I.C.S.: 541611
Niu Wenwen *(Chm & Gen Mgr)*

DARK STAR MINERALS, INC.
1056 Handsworth Road, North Vancouver, V7R 2A6, BC, Canada
Tel.: (604) 816-2555   BC
Web Site:
https://www.darkstarminerals.com
Year Founded: 2021
BATT—(CNSX)
Mineral Exploration Services
N.A.I.C.S.: 213115

DARKHAN GURIL TEJEEL JOINT STOCK COMPANY
6th Team Darkhan Sum, Darkhan, Mongolia
Tel.: (976) 11 453269
DAR—(MONG)
Sales Range: Less than $1 Million
Grain & Oilseed Farming Services
N.A.I.C.S.: 111191

DARKOM INVESTMENT CO.
Sharaf Street Building No 124 5th Floor, PO Box 930419, Shmeisani Sharif Abdul Hamid, Amman, 11193, Jordan
Tel.: (962) 65679555
Web Site: https://darkom-jo.com
Rev.: $61,650
Assets: $7,926,689
Liabilities: $2,333,926
Net Worth: $5,592,763
Earnings: $632
Emp.: 8
Fiscal Year-end: 12/31/15
Investment Management Service
N.A.I.C.S.: 523999

DARLINGTON BUILDING SOCIETY
Sentinel House Morton Road, Darlington, DL1 4PT, Durham, United Kingdom
Tel.: (44) 1325 366366
Web Site: http://www.darlington.co.uk
Year Founded: 1856
Rev.: $22,172,598
Assets: $873,267,215
Liabilities: $813,294,305
Net Worth: $59,972,910

Earnings: $1,855,914
Emp.: 122
Fiscal Year-end: 12/31/19
Mortgage Lending & Other Financial Services
N.A.I.C.S.: 522310
Robert Cuffe *(Vice Chm)*

DARMON IMPRESSIONS
Zac Du Moulin Rue Du Noyer, 95700, Roissy-en-France, Val D Oise, France
Tel.: (33) 134293740
Web Site: http://www.groupe-darmon.com
Rev.: $23,500,000
Emp.: 75
Commercial Printing
N.A.I.C.S.: 323111

DAROU PAKHSH PHARMACEUTICAL MFG CO.
Darou Pakhsh St Km 18 Tehran-Karaj highway, Tehran, Iran
Tel.: (98) 44986815
Web Site: http://www.dppharma.ir
Year Founded: 1956
DPAK—(THE)
Sales Range: $1-9.9 Million
Pharmaceuticals Product Mfr
N.A.I.C.S.: 325412
Kambiz Amjadi *(Mng Dir)*

DAROUPAKHSH HOLDING COMPANY
No 81 Nahid Gharbi St Africa Ave, Tehran, Iran
Tel.: (98) 21 22650124
Web Site: http://www.dpholding.com
Year Founded: 1956
DARO—(THE)
Sales Range: $1-9.9 Million
Emp.: 3,443
Pharmaceutical Preparation Mfr
N.A.I.C.S.: 325412
Hossein Attar *(CEO)*

DARSHAN ORNA LIMITED
2018/1 First Floor Nr Rupa Surchand Ni Pole M G Haveli Road, Manek Chowk, Ahmedabad, 380 001, India
Tel.: (91) 7922142568   In
Web Site:
https://www.darshanorna.com
Year Founded: 2011
539884—(BOM)
Rev.: $1,103,599
Assets: $1,683,133
Liabilities: $32,390
Net Worth: $1,650,743
Earnings: $251,248
Emp.: 12
Fiscal Year-end: 03/31/21
Jewelry Product Distr
N.A.I.C.S.: 423940
Ritesh M. Sheth *(Chm, Mng Dir & CFO)*

DART MINING NL
204 Melbourne Road, Wodonga, 3690, VIC, Australia
Tel.: (61) 295971198   AU
Web Site:
https://www.dartmining.com.au
DTM—(ASX)
Rev.: $201,205
Assets: $14,245,417
Liabilities: $644,580
Net Worth: $13,600,837
Earnings: ($1,173,233)
Emp.: 4
Fiscal Year-end: 06/30/24
Gold & Base-Metals Exploration & Development
N.A.I.C.S.: 212220
James Chirnside *(Chm & Mng Dir)*

DARWIN PRECISIONS CORPORATION
No 20-1 Guangfu N Rd, Hukou Township, Hsinchu, 303, Taiwan
Tel.: (886) 425692188
Web Site:
https://www.darwinprecisions.com
Year Founded: 1989
6120—(TAI)
Rev.: $581,117,150
Assets: $596,010,148
Liabilities: $294,438,133
Net Worth: $301,572,015
Earnings: $3,749,599
Emp.: 5,870
Fiscal Year-end: 12/31/23
Optoelectronic Product Mfr
N.A.I.C.S.: 334413
Kuo-Hsin Tsai *(Chm)*

Subsidiaries:

Forhouse Corporation - Da-Ya Factory   (1)
No 45 Lane 313 Sec 3 Minsheng Road, Daya District, Taichung, 42844, Taiwan
Tel.: (886) 4 2569 2188
Web Site: http://www.forhouse.com.tw
Optronic Products Mfr
N.A.I.C.S.: 334413

Forhouse Corporation - Malaysian Factory   (1)
1727 Jalan Industri 2 Taman Perindustrian Bukit Panchor, Nibong Tebal, 14300, Penang, Malaysia
Tel.: (60) 4 5937860
Electronic Products Mfr & Sales
N.A.I.C.S.: 334419

Forhouse Corporation - Xiamen Factory   (1)
No 18 Xiangming Road, Xiangan District, Xiamen, 361101, Fujian, China
Tel.: (86) 5927829666
Web Site: http://www.forhouse.com.tw
Optoelectronic Product Mfr
N.A.I.C.S.: 334413

DARWIN PRIVATE EQUITY LLP
21-22 New Row, London, WC2N 4LE, United Kingdom
Tel.: (44) 2074200750   UK
Web Site: http://www.darwinpe.com
Year Founded: 2007
Privater Equity Firm
N.A.I.C.S.: 523999
Derek Elliott *(Partner-Bus Svcs, Media & Tech)*

DASAN NETWORKS, INC.
Dasan Tower 49 Daewangpangyo-ro644Beon-gil, Bundang-gu, Seongnam, 463-400, Gyeonggi-do, Korea (South)
Tel.: (82) 7070101000   KR
Web Site:
http://www.dasannetworks.com
Year Founded: 1993
Sales Range: $100-124.9 Million
Emp.: 349
Networking Solution Services
N.A.I.C.S.: 334413

DASAN SOLUETA CO.,LTD.
498-42 Haeun-ro, Mado-myeon, Hwaseong, 18544, Gyeonggi-do, Korea (South)
Tel.: (82) 315082655
Web Site: https://www.solueta.com
Year Founded: 2003
154040—(KRS)
Rev.: $121,088,149
Assets: $116,089,853
Liabilities: $85,312,310
Net Worth: $30,777,543
Earnings: $3,087,420
Emp.: 132
Fiscal Year-end: 12/31/22

Electromagnetic Compatibility & Electromagnetic Interference Material Components Mfr
N.A.I.C.S.: 334419
Samju Yang *(CEO)*

Subsidiaries:

Solueta Vina Co., Ltd.   (1)
LK1-C11 Splendora New Uraban Area, Bac Ankhanh Ward Hoai Duc District, Hanoi, Vietnam
Tel.: (84) 2462538650
Electromagnetic Wave Shielding Product Mfr
N.A.I.C.S.: 334510
Tien Pham *(Mgr-Mdse)*

DASCAN INDUSTRIAL CONTROLS
300 Wildcat Rd, Toronto, M3J 2N5, ON, Canada
Tel.: (416) 665-1511
Web Site: http://www.dascan.com
Year Founded: 1982
Sales Range: $10-24.9 Million
Emp.: 20
Industrial Control Apparatus Mfg
N.A.I.C.S.: 335314
Anil Seth *(Controller)*

Subsidiaries:

Dascan Industrial Controls, Inc.   (1)
301 N Cattlemen Rd Ste 102, Sarasota, FL 34232
Tel.: (877) 269-7723
Industrial Control Equipment Distr
N.A.I.C.S.: 423610

Electrical Design & Control Co. Inc.   (1)
2200 Stephenson Hwy, Troy, MI 48083-2153
Tel.: (248) 743-2400
Web Site: http://www.edandc.com
Mfr of Switchgear & Switchboard Apparatus
N.A.I.C.S.: 541330

DASHANG GROUP CO., LTD.
No 1 Qingsan Street, Zhongshan District, Dalian, 116001, Liaoning, China
Tel.: (86) 41183643215
Web Site: http://www.dsjt.com
Year Founded: 1992
600694—(SHG)
Rev.: $1,021,640,270
Assets: $2,547,760,681
Liabilities: $1,386,640,607
Net Worth: $1,161,120,074
Earnings: $77,105,827
Emp.: 250,000
Fiscal Year-end: 12/31/22
Department Stores, Supermarkets, Shopping Malls & Specialty Stores Operator
N.A.I.C.S.: 455110
Gang Niu *(Chm)*

DASHENG TIMES CULTURAL INVESTMENT CO., LTD.
6th Floor Postal Complex Building 28-1 Jingtian North 1st Street, Futian District, Shenzhen, 518023, Guangdong, China
Tel.: (86) 75582600892
Web Site:
https://www.600892.com.cn
Year Founded: 1996
600892—(SHG)
Rev.: $29,221,129
Assets: $53,616,612
Liabilities: $24,604,609
Net Worth: $29,012,003
Earnings: $3,462,938
Fiscal Year-end: 12/31/22
Steel Products Trading Services
N.A.I.C.S.: 331512

DASHENLIN PHARMACEUTI-

DASHENLIN PHARMACEUTI—(CONTINUED)

CAL GROUP CO., LTD.

No 410 Longxi Avenue Liwan District, Guangzhou, 510378, China
Tel.: (86) 2081284688
Web Site: https://www.dslyy.com
603233—(SHG)
Rev.: $2,983,231,373
Assets: $2,926,110,545
Liabilities: $1,962,383,548
Net Worth: $963,726,997
Earnings: $145,415,622
Fiscal Year-end: 12/31/22
Pharmaceutical Product Mfr & Whslr
N.A.I.C.S.: 325412

DASHTESTAN CEMENT IN-DUSTRIES COMPANY

Square Argentin Alund Street Lane
31 No 9 First And Second Floors, Tehran, 15166 69114, Iran
Tel.: (98) 2188881410
Year Founded: 1992
SDST1—(THE)
Sales Range: Less than $1 Million
Emp.: 559
Cement Mfr
N.A.I.C.S.: 327310

DASIN RETAIL TRUST MAN-AGEMENT PTE LTD.

190 Middle Road 16-06 Fortune Centre, Singapore, 188979, Singapore
Tel.: (65) 65098626
Web Site: https://www.dasintrust.com
CEDU—(SES)
Rev.: $75,122,107
Assets: $1,883,422,606
Liabilities: $1,057,635,559
Net Worth: $825,787,047
Earnings: ($36,270,473)
Emp.: 4,000
Fiscal Year-end: 12/31/21
Real Estate Investment Management Services
N.A.I.C.S.: 531120
Zhang Zhencheng (Chm)

DASSAS COMMUNICATION

37 rue Pierre L'homme, 92411, Courbevoie, Cedex, France
Tel.: (33) 146917000
Web Site: http://www.dassas.com
Year Founded: 1980
Rev.: $60,000,000
Emp.: 25
Advetising Agency
N.A.I.C.S.: 541810
Pierre Dassas (Pres)

DASSAULT SYSTEMES S.A.

10 rue Marcel Dassault Paris Campus, CS 40501, 78140, Velizy-Villacoublay, France
Tel.: (33) 161626162   FR
Web Site: https://www.3ds.com
Year Founded: 1981
DSY—(EUR)
Rev.: $5,194,474,880
Assets: $15,196,946,560
Liabilities: $8,558,629,760
Net Worth: $6,638,316,800
Earnings: $827,037,440
Emp.: 20,496
Fiscal Year-end: 12/31/21
3D Software for Product Design & Development
N.A.I.C.S.: 513210
Dominique Florack (Pres)

Subsidiaries:

3D PLM Software Solutions Limited   (1)
Unit No 703-B 7th Fl B Wing Reliable Tch Pk Airoli, Vikhroli West, Mumbai, 400 708, India

Tel.: (91) 2267056500
Web Site: http://www.3dplmsoftware.com
Emp.: 2,000
3D Design & Product Lifecycle Management Software Developer & Market Support Services
N.A.I.C.S.: 513210

DS Deutschland GmbH   (1)
Meitnerstrasse 8, D-70563, Stuttgart, Germany   (99%)
Tel.: (49) 711273000
Web Site: http://www.3ds.com
3D Software for Product Design & Development
N.A.I.C.S.: 334610

Dassault Data Services   (1)
22 Quai Gallieni, 92156, Suresnes, France   (95%)
Tel.: (33) 141384138
Web Site: http://www.dassault-data-services.fr
Sales Range: $100-124.9 Million
Emp.: 370
Provider of Information Services
N.A.I.C.S.: 519290

Dassault Systemes (Suisse) S.A.   (1)
Grosspeteranlage 29, 4052, Basel, Switzerland
Tel.: (41) 615880395
Software Development Services
N.A.I.C.S.: 541511

Dassault Systemes 3DExcite GmbH   (1)
St-Martin-Strasse 82, 81541, Munich, Germany
Tel.: (49) 892002750
Web Site: https://www.3dexcite.com
Software Development Services
N.A.I.C.S.: 541511
Dominic Kurtaz (Mng Dir)

Dassault Systemes AB   (1)
Rosenholmvn 25, 1410, Kolbotn, Norway
Tel.: (47) 9164 5932
Web Site: http://www.3ds.com
Software Development Services
N.A.I.C.S.: 541511

Dassault Systemes Americas Corp.   (1)
175 Wyman St, Waltham, MA 02451
Tel.: (781) 810-3000
Sales Range: $75-99.9 Million
Emp.: 185
Holding Company; Regional Managing Office
N.A.I.C.S.: 551112

Subsidiary (Domestic):

Accelrys, Inc.   (2)
5005 Wateridge Vista Dr, San Diego, CA 92121
Tel.: (858) 799-5000
Web Site: http://www.accelrys.com
Rev.: $168,526,000
Assets: $392,566,000
Liabilities: $144,107,000
Net Worth: $248,459,000
Earnings: $5,690,000
Emp.: 735
Fiscal Year-end: 12/31/2013
Molecular Modeling & Simulation Software
N.A.I.C.S.: 334610
Judith Ohrn Hicks (Sr VP-HR)

Subsidiary (Non-US):

Accelrys K.K.   (3)
Nishi Shimbashi TS Building 11F Nishi Shimbashi 3 3 1 Minato ku, Tokyo, 105 0003, Japan   (100%)
Tel.: (81) 335783861
Web Site: http://www.accelrys.com
Sales Range: $10-24.9 Million
Emp.: 30
Developer of Molecular Modeling Software
N.A.I.C.S.: 513210

Accelrys Limited   (3)
334 Cambridge Science Park, Cambridge, CB4 0WN, United Kingdom
Tel.: (44) 1223228500
Web Site: http://www.accelrys.com
Sales Range: $50-74.9 Million
Emp.: 100
Developer of Molecular Modeling Software

N.A.I.C.S.: 513210

Accelrys SARL   (3)
Parc Club Orsay Universite 20, 20 Rue Jean Rostand, 91898, Orsay, Cedex, France   (100%)
Tel.: (33) 169353232
Web Site: http://www.accelrys.com
Rev.: $3,000,000
Emp.: 9
Marketing of Molecular Modeling Software
N.A.I.C.S.: 513210

Subsidiary (Domestic):

Accelrys Software Incorporated   (3)
5005 Wateridge Vista Dr, San Diego, CA 92121
Tel.: (858) 799-5000
Emp.: 240
Lifecycle Management Software Provider
N.A.I.C.S.: 513210
Max Carnecchina (Pres)

Subsidiary (Domestic):

Aegis Analytical Corporation   (4)
1380 Forest Park Cir Ste 200, Lafayette, CO 80026
Tel.: (303) 926-0317
Web Site: http://www.aegiscorp.com
Sales Range: $1-9.9 Million
Emp.: 40
Enterprise Manufacturing Process Intelligence Software Developer
N.A.I.C.S.: 513210

Subsidiary (Domestic):

ChemSW, Inc.   (3)
4771 Mangels Blvd, Fairfield, CA 94534-1464
Tel.: (707) 864-0845
Web Site: http://www.chemsw.com
Sales Range: $10-24.9 Million
Emp.: 25
Chemical Inventory Management Software Publisher
N.A.I.C.S.: 513210
David J. Hessler (CTO & VP-Software R&D)

Unit (Domestic):

Dassault Systemes Americas - Woodland Hills   (2)
Trillium E Tower 6320 Canoga Ave Ste 300, Woodland Hills, CA 91367-2402
Tel.: (818) 999-2500
Sales Range: $25-49.9 Million
Emp.: 80
Provider of 3D Software for Product Design & Development
N.A.I.C.S.: 541511
Al Bunshaft (Mng Dir)

Subsidiary (Domestic):

Dassault Systemes DELMIA Corp.   (2)
900 N Skuirrel, Auburn Hills, MI 48326-2615   (100%)
Tel.: (248) 267-9696
Web Site: http://www.delmia.com
Sales Range: $50-74.9 Million
Emp.: 200
Provider of Software
N.A.I.C.S.: 423430

Dassault Systemes Enovia Corp.   (2)
900 Chelmsford St Tower 2 Fl 5, Lowell, MA 01851
Tel.: (978) 442-2500
Web Site: http://www.3ds.com
Sales Range: $100-124.9 Million
Emp.: 200
Product Lifecycle Management Application Software Mfr
N.A.I.C.S.: 334610

Dassault Systemes Simulia Corp.   (2)
1301 Atwood Ave, Johnston, RI 02919-2499
Tel.: (401) 276-4400
Web Site: https://www.hks.com
Computer Software Development
N.A.I.C.S.: 541511
Colin Mercer (VP-R&D)

Spatial Corp.   (2)

310 Interlocken Pkwy, Ste 200, Broomfield, CO 80021-3468   (100%)
Tel.: (303) 544-2900
Web Site: https://www.spatial.com
Sales Range: $25-49.9 Million
Emp.: 100
Developer & Retailer of 3D Software Components for Technical Applications
N.A.I.C.S.: 541511
Connie King (Dir-HR)

Dassault Systemes ApS   (1)
Silkeborgvej 2 Stuen, 8000, Arhus, Denmark
Tel.: (45) 40 49 25 62
Sales Range: $25-49.9 Million
Emp.: 6
Software Development Services
N.A.I.C.S.: 541511
Bjarne Jorgensen (Gen Mgr)

Dassault Systemes Australia Pty Ltd   (1)
Level 12 15 William Street, Melbourne, 3004, VIC, Australia
Tel.: (61) 392742203
Software Development Services
N.A.I.C.S.: 541511
Craig Law (Sr Dir-Enterprise Sls)

Dassault Systemes Austria GmbH   (1)
Euro Plaza Wienerbergstrasse 51, 1120, Vienna, Austria
Tel.: (43) 1 227 07 0
Emp.: 20
Computer Software Distr
N.A.I.C.S.: 423430
Andria Barth (Mgr)

Dassault Systemes BV   (1)
Crosspoint Office Building Safariweg 14-16, 3605 MA, Maarssen, Netherlands
Tel.: (31) 346 585 710
Sales Range: $25-49.9 Million
Emp.: 3
Software Development Services
N.A.I.C.S.: 541511

Dassault Systemes CZ s.r.o.   (1)
Praha City Center Klimentska 46, 11000, Prague, Czech Republic
Tel.: (420) 222 191 107
Emp.: 6
Software Development Services
N.A.I.C.S.: 541511

Dassault Systemes Canada Innovation Technologies Inc.   (1)
300-393 Saint-Jacques St, Montreal, H2Y 1N9, QC, Canada
Tel.: (514) 940-2949
Computer System Designing Services
N.A.I.C.S.: 541512

Dassault Systemes China   (1)
China Central Place Tower 2 Room 707-709 No 79 Jianguo Road, Chaoyang District, Beijing, China
Tel.: (86) 10 6536 2288
Software Development Services
N.A.I.C.S.: 541511

Dassault Systemes Deutschland GmbH   (1)
Meitnerstr 8, Vaihingen, 70563, Stuttgart, Germany
Tel.: (49) 711273000
Web Site: https://www.3dsevents.de
Software Development Services
N.A.I.C.S.: 541511

Dassault Systemes Inc.   (1)
393 St-Jacques West Suite 300, Montreal, H2Y 1N9, QC, Canada
Tel.: (514) 940-2949
Web Site: http://www.3ds.com
Sales Range: $75-99.9 Million
Emp.: 30
Software Development Services
N.A.I.C.S.: 541511

Dassault Systemes India Pvt. Ltd (1)
DLF Cyber City Building 10 C 12 F Phase 11, Gurgaon, 122002, Haryana, India
Tel.: (91) 1244577100
Emp.: 65
Software Development Services
N.A.I.C.S.: 541511
Samson Khauo (Mng Dir)

Dassault Systemes Israel Ltd. **(1)**
5 HaGavish St, 44641, Kfar Saba, Israel
Tel.: (972) 9 764 4000
Web Site: http://www.3ds.com
Emp.: 15
Software Development Services
N.A.I.C.S.: 541511

Dassault Systemes Italia Srl **(1)**
Via Rossini 1/A, 20020, Lainate, Milan, Italy
Tel.: (39) 02 3343061
Web Site: http://www.3ds.com
Emp.: 87
Software Development Services
N.A.I.C.S.: 541511

Dassault Systemes Japan **(1)**
Pier City Shibaura Bldg 3-18-1 Kaigan,
Minato-Ku, Tokyo, 108-0022, Japan
Tel.: (81) 3 5442 40 11
Web Site: http://www.3ds.com
Software Development Services
N.A.I.C.S.: 541511

Dassault Systemes Korea Corp. **(1)**
ASEM Tower 9F 517 Yeongdong-daero,
Gangnam-gu, Seoul, 06164, Korea (South)
Tel.: (82) 232707800
Sales Range: $25-49.9 Million
Emp.: 15
Software Development Services
N.A.I.C.S.: 541511

Dassault Systemes Mexico **(1)**
Av Paseo de la Reforma No 505 Piso 41,
Cuauhtemoc, Mexico, 6500, Mexico
Tel.: (52) 5552560780
Software Development Services
N.A.I.C.S.: 541511

Dassault Systemes Oy **(1)**
Falcon Business Park - Lago Vaisalantie
2-8, 02130, Espoo, Finland
Tel.: (358) 50 301 6393
Web Site: http://www.3ds.com
Software Development Services
N.A.I.C.S.: 541511

Dassault Systemes Provence **(1)**
53 ave de l'Europe, 13092, Aix-en-
Provence, Cedex 2, France **(100%)**
Tel.: (33) 413108020
Sales Range: $25-49.9 Million
Emp.: 90
Provider of 3D Software for Product Design
& Development
N.A.I.C.S.: 334610

Dassault Systemes Russia Corp. **(1)**
Kuntsevo Plaza Yartsevskaya Street 19,
121552, Moscow, Russia
Tel.: (7) 4959358928
Emp.: 3
Software Development Services
N.A.I.C.S.: 541511

Dassault Systemes Schweiz AG **(1)**
Balz-Zimmermannstrasse 7, 8302, Kloten,
Switzerland
Tel.: (41) 44 200 367 0
Sales Range: $25-49.9 Million
Emp.: 8
Software Development Services
N.A.I.C.S.: 541511
Daniel Nick *(Mng Dir)*

Dassault Systemes Singapore Pte.
Ltd. **(1)**
9 Tampines Grande Level 6, Singapore,
528735, Singapore
Tel.: (65) 65117988
Software Development Services
N.A.I.C.S.: 541511
Josephine Ong *(Head-Strategy & Mktg)*

Dassault Systemes SolidWorks
Corporation **(1)**
175 Wyman St, Waltham, MA 02451
Tel.: (781) 810-5011
Web Site: https://www.solidworks.com
Software Development Services
N.A.I.C.S.: 541511
Gian Paolo Bassi *(CEO)*

Dassault Systemes Sp. z o.o. **(1)**
ul Ilzecka 26, 02-135, Warsaw, Poland
Tel.: (48) 22 575 70 00
Web Site: http://www.3ds.com
Software Development Services
N.A.I.C.S.: 541511

Dassault Systemes Taiwan **(1)**
Room 607 No 205 Tun Hwa North Road,
Shunsan District, Taipei, Taiwan
Tel.: (886) 227180286
Software Development Services
N.A.I.C.S.: 541511

Dassault Sytemes Australia Pty
Ltd **(1)**
236A Lennox Street Ground Floor, Rich-
mond, 2121, VIC, Australia
Tel.: (61) 3 9421 2900
Web Site: http://www.3ds.com
Software Development Services
N.A.I.C.S.: 541511

Delmia GmbH **(1)**
Raiffeisenplatz 4, 70736, Fellbach,
Germany **(97%)**
Tel.: (49) 711273000
Web Site: http://www.delmia.de
Sales Range: $50-74.9 Million
Emp.: 150
Provider of Software
N.A.I.C.S.: 334610

Exalead S.A. **(1)**
10 place de la Madeleine, 75008, Paris,
France **(69%)**
Tel.: (33) 155352626
Web Site: http://www.exalead.com
Sales Range: $10-24.9 Million
Emp.: 150
Enterprise & Web Search Software & Ser-
vices
N.A.I.C.S.: 513210
Morgan Zimmermann *(VP-Sls-Worldwide)*

Subsidiary (US):

Exalead Inc. **(2)**
221 Main St Ste 750, San Francisco, CA
94105
Tel.: (415) 230-3800
Web Site: http://www.exalead.com
Enterprise & Web Search Software & Ser-
vices
N.A.I.C.S.: 513210

IQMS Inc. **(1)**
2231 Wisteria Ln, Paso Robles, CA 93446
Tel.: (805) 227-1122
Web Site: http://www.iqms.com
Sales Range: $25-49.9 Million
Emp.: 200
Fiscal Year-end: 12/31/2015
Custom Computer Programming Services
N.A.I.C.S.: 541511
Randy Flamm *(Chief Product Officer)*

Medidata Solutions, Inc. **(1)**
350 Hudson St 9th Fl, New York, NY 10014
Tel.: (212) 918-1800
Web Site: http://www.medidata.com
Rev.: $635,696,000
Assets: $913,212,000
Liabilities: $281,764,000
Net Worth: $631,448,000
Earnings: $51,921,000
Emp.: 1,998
Fiscal Year-end: 12/31/2018
Medical Technology Software
N.A.I.C.S.: 541512
Glen M. de Vries *(Pres)*

Subsidiary (Domestic):

CHITA Inc. **(2)**
1200 Park Pl Ste 210, San Mateo, CA
94403
Tel.: (650) 425-6400
Software Publisher
N.A.I.C.S.: 513210
Kevin Barrett *(CEO)*

Subsidiary (Non-US):

MDSOL Europe Ltd. **(2)**
12 Hammersmith Grove 9th floor, Hammer-
smith, London, W6 7AP, United Kingdom
Tel.: (44) 2086006400
Web Site: https://www.mdsol.com
Medical Technology
N.A.I.C.S.: 541512

Medidata Solutions K.K. **(2)**
JP Tower 29th Floor, Tokyo, 100-0005, Ja-
pan
Tel.: (81) 345880800
Web Site: http://www.mdsol.com
Medical Technology

N.A.I.C.S.: 541512
Jim Xu *(Gen Mgr)*

Subsidiary (Domestic):

SHYFT Analytics, Inc. **(2)**
110 High St 6th Fl, Boston, MA 02110
Tel.: (781) 547-7500
Web Site: http://www.shyftanalytics.com
Computer Facility Management Services
N.A.I.C.S.: 541513
Zackary King *(Pres & Exec VP)*

No Magic Inc. **(1)**
700 Central Expy S Ste 110, Allen, TX
75013
Tel.: (214) 291-9100
Web Site: https://www.3ds.com
Computer Software Development
N.A.I.C.S.: 541511
Gary Duncanson *(Pres & CEO)*

Outscale SAS **(1)**
1 rue Royale-319 Bureaux de la Colline,
92210, Saint-Cloud, France
Tel.: (33) 153275270
Web Site: https://en.outscale.com
Cloud Computing Services
N.A.I.C.S.: 541512
Laurent Seror *(Head-Publication)*

SmarTeam Corp **(1)**
5 Hagavish St Ovadia House, PO Box
7020, 44641, Kfar Saba, Israel **(84%)**
Tel.: (972) 97644000
Web Site: http://www.smarteam.com
Sales Range: $25-49.9 Million
Emp.: 20
Provider of Software
N.A.I.C.S.: 334610

DAT XANH GROUP JOINT STOCK COMPANY
2 WUngVan Khiem Ward 25 Binh TH,
Binh Thanh District, Ho Chi Minh
City, Vietnam
Tel.: (84) 862525252
Web Site: https://www.datxanh.vn
Year Founded: 2003
DXG—(HOSE)
Rev.: $153,462,831
Assets: $1,186,001,369
Liabilities: $601,523,008
Net Worth: $584,478,362
Earnings: $6,189,888
Emp.: 3,773
Fiscal Year-end: 12/31/23
Real Estate Development Services
N.A.I.C.S.: 531390
Luong Tri Thin *(Chm)*

Subsidiaries:

Dat Xanh Dong Nam Bo Services &
Investment JSC **(1)**
11 lot C1 Highway No 51, Long Binh Tan
Ward, Bien Hoa, Dong Nai, Vietnam
Tel.: (84) 616266288
Real Estate Services
N.A.I.C.S.: 531210

Dat Xanh Mien Bac Services & Real
Estate JSC **(1)**
18 Floor Center Building No 1 Nguyen Huy
Tuong, Thanh Xuan, Hanoi, Vietnam
Tel.: (84) 2473038181
Web Site:
   http://www.datxanhmienbac.com.vn
Real Estate Services
N.A.I.C.S.: 531210
Tran Dong Duong *(Fin Dir)*

Dat Xanh Mien Nam Investment &
Services JSC **(1)**
27 Dinh Bo Linh, Ward 24 Binh Thanh Dis-
trict, Ho Chi Minh City, Vietnam
Tel.: (84) 1900232427
Web Site:
   http://www.datxanhmiennam.com.vn
Construction Design Services
N.A.I.C.S.: 541310

Dat Xanh Mien Tay Service and In-
vestment Joint Stock Company **(1)**
139 Tran Hung Dao, P An Phu Q Ninh
Kieu, Can Tho, Vietnam
Tel.: (84) 2923636468

Web Site: https://datxanhmientay.net
Real Estate Brokerage Services
N.A.I.C.S.: 531210

Dat Xanh Mien Trung JSC **(1)**
52-54 Vo Van Kiet Street, An Hai Dong
Ward Son Tra District, Da Nang, Vietnam
Tel.: (84) 2366266266
Web Site: http://www.datxanhmientrung.com
Real Estate Services
N.A.I.C.S.: 531210
Tran Ngoc Thanh *(CEO)*

HCMC Invesment & Development
JSC **(1)**
27 Dinh Bo Linh, Ward 24 Binh Thanh Dis-
trict, Ho Chi Minh City, Vietnam
Tel.: (84) 862525252
Real Estate Services
N.A.I.C.S.: 531210

Ha Thuan Hung Construction - Trade
- Service Ltd. Company **(1)**
27 Dinh Bo Linh, Ward 24 Binh Thanh Dis-
trict, Ho Chi Minh City, Vietnam
Tel.: (84) 862525252
Real Estate Services
N.A.I.C.S.: 531210

Indochine Real estate Joint Stock
Company **(1)**
Tang 5 toa nha Van Gia Phat So 1 Tran
Khanh Du, Phuong Tan Dinh Quan 1, Ho
Chi Minh City, Vietnam
Tel.: (84) 1800646428
Web Site: https://datxanhindochine.com
Real Estate Brokerage Services
N.A.I.C.S.: 531210

Saigon Real Investment and Service
Joint Stock Company **(1)**
21 Nguyen Cuu Van, Phuong 17 Quan Binh
Thanh, Ho Chi Minh City, Vietnam
Tel.: (84) 2835114114
Web Site:
   https://saigonreal.datxanhmiennam.com.vn
Real Estate Brokerage Services
N.A.I.C.S.: 531210

Viethomes Real estate Joint Stock
Company **(1)**
6th Floor MHDI Tower No 26 Nguyen Co
Thach Street, South Tu Liem District, Hanoi,
Vietnam
Tel.: (84) 912353635
Web Site: https://www.viethomes.vn
Real Estate Brokerage Services
N.A.I.C.S.: 531210

DATA APPLICATIONS CO., LTD.
27F Tokyo Midtown Yaesu Central
Tower 2-2-1 Yaesu, Chuo-ku, Tokyo,
104-0028, Japan
Tel.: (81) 363700909
Web Site: https://www.dal.co.jp
Year Founded: 1982
3848—(TKS)
Rev.: $18,850,384
Assets: $39,930,836
Liabilities: $9,417,411
Net Worth: $30,513,425
Earnings: $1,624,092
Emp.: 136
Fiscal Year-end: 03/31/23
Prepackaged Software
N.A.I.C.S.: 334610
Takaaki Kaneko *(Operating Officer &*
Officer-Admin & Corp Strategic Plng)

DATA CENTER DYNAMICS LTD
102-108 Clifton Street, London, EC28
4HW, United Kingdom
Tel.: (44) 207 377 1907
Web Site:
   http://www.datacenterdynamics.com
Sales Range: $1-9.9 Million
Emp.: 70
B2B Information Services
N.A.I.C.S.: 519290
Dan Scarbrough *(Co-Founder)*

Data Center Dynamics Ltd—(Continued)

Subsidiaries:

Data Center Dynamics Asia
Limited   **(1)**
38/F Tower One Lippo Center 89 Queensway, Hong Kong, China (Hong Kong)
Tel.: (852) 8191 0837
Web Site:
   http://www.datacenterdynamics.com
B2B Information Services
N.A.I.C.S.: 519290
Dedric Lam *(Gen Mgr)*

Data Center Dynamics Inc.   **(1)**
The Monadnock Bldg 685 Market St Ste 590, San Francisco, CA 94105
Tel.: (415) 735-2800
B2B Information Services
N.A.I.C.S.: 519290

Data Center Dynamics MEA
FZ-LLC   **(1)**
1705 Shatha Tower, PO Box 502520, Dubai, United Arab Emirates
Tel.: (971) 4 434 8450
B2B Information Services
N.A.I.C.S.: 519290
Praveen Balachandran *(Gen Mgr)*

Data Center Dynamics Sarl   **(1)**
5 rue de Castiglione, 75001, Paris, France
Tel.: (33) 805 08 0016
B2B Information Services
N.A.I.C.S.: 519290

Data Center Dynamics Shanghai Co.
Ltd.   **(1)**
Crystal Century Tower 5/F Suite 5B, 567 Weihai Road, Shanghai, 200041, China
Tel.: (86) 21 6170 3777
Web Site:
   http://www.datacenterdynamics.com
Emp.: 5
B2B Information Services
N.A.I.C.S.: 519290
Dedric Lam *(Gen Mgr)*

Data Centre Dynamics (Holland)
BV   **(1)**
Newtonlaan 115, 3584 BH, Utrecht, Netherlands
Tel.: (31) 30 210 6534
B2B Information Services
N.A.I.C.S.: 519290

Data Centre Dynamics Mexico S. de
RL de CV   **(1)**
Avda Ejercito Nacional 843-B Torre Corporativa 1 piso 5, Col Granada-Antara, Polanco, 11520, Mexico
Tel.: (52) 55 8000 1733
Data Processing Services
N.A.I.C.S.: 518210

Data Centre Dynamics Spain
S.L.U.   **(1)**
Paseo de la Castellana 121 Esc Izq 5oC, 28046, Madrid, Spain
Tel.: (34) 911331762
Web Site:
   http://www.datacenterdynamics.es
Emp.: 5
B2B Information Services
N.A.I.C.S.: 519290
Jose Luis Friebel *(Gen Mgr)*

Datacentre Dynamics India Pvt.
Ltd   **(1)**
3rd Floor Kitab Mail Bn Road Sn 5 Fort, 40001, Mumbai, India
Tel.: (91) 22 4922 0300
Web Site: http://www.datacentre.com
Emp.: 9
Data Processing Services
N.A.I.C.S.: 518210
Praveen Nair *(CEO)*

DATA COMMUNICATIONS MANAGEMENT CORP.
9195 Torbram Road, Brampton, L6S 6H2, ON, Canada
Tel.: (905) 791-3151
Web Site: http://www.datacm.com
Data Processing Services
N.A.I.C.S.: 518210
Steve Livingstone *(Sr VP-Digital)*

Subsidiaries:

Moore Canada Corporation   **(1)**
6100 Vipond Drive, Mississauga, L5T 2X1, ON, Canada
Tel.: (905) 362-3100
Web Site: http://www.rrd.com
Emp.: 350
Commercial Printing Services
N.A.I.C.S.: 323111
Rael Fisher *(Chief Integration Officer)*

Perennial Inc.   **(1)**
15 Waulron St, Toronto, M9C 1B4, ON, Canada
Tel.: (416) 251-2180
Web Site: http://www.perennialinc.com
Advetising Agency
N.A.I.C.S.: 541810
Chris Lund *(CEO)*

DATA HORIZON CORPORATION
Hiroshima Mixis Building 1-21-35 Kusatsu Shinmachi, Nishi-ku, Hiroshima, 733-0834, Japan
Tel.: (81) 822795550
Web Site: https://www.dhorizon.co.jp
Year Founded: 1982
3628—(TKS)
Rev.: $31,143,540
Assets: $41,425,200
Liabilities: $21,421,680
Net Worth: $20,003,520
Earnings: ($5,019,540)
Emp.: 276
Fiscal Year-end: 06/30/24
Communication Service
N.A.I.C.S.: 517810
Yoshio Utsumi *(Pres)*

DATA INFRASTRUCTURE TRUST
Unit-1 9 th Floor Tower-4 Equinox Business Park L B S Marg, Kurla W, Mumbai, 400070, India
Tel.: (91) 2269075252
Web Site: https://datainfratrust.com
Year Founded: 1882
543225—(BOM)
Rev.: $1,127,421,750
Assets: $5,657,365,350
Liabilities: $2,914,698,150
Net Worth: $2,742,667,200
Earnings: ($134,179,500)
Fiscal Year-end: 03/31/21
Investment Trust Services
N.A.I.C.S.: 525920
Kapil Jain *(Compliance Officer)*

Subsidiaries:

Summit Digitel Infrastructure Private
Limited   **(1)**
Unit 2 9th Floor Tower 4 LBS Marg Kurla W, Equinox Business Park, Mumbai, 400070, India
Tel.: (91) 226 907 5252
Web Site: https://www.summitdigitel.com
Mobile Network Operator
N.A.I.C.S.: 517112
Dhananjay Joshi *(CEO & Mng Dir)*

DATA INTEGRITY INC.
30 Via Renzo Dr, Richmond Hill, L4S 0B8, ON, Canada
Tel.: (416) 638-0111
Web Site: http://www.dataintegrity.ca
Year Founded: 1980
Rev.: $22,208,384
Emp.: 40
Information Technology Services
N.A.I.C.S.: 541512
Norm Filicetti *(Founder & Pres)*

Subsidiaries:

Skipton Group Inc.   **(1)**
30 Via Renzo Drive, Richmond Hill, L4S 0B8, ON, Canada
Tel.: (905) 780-9514
Web Site: http://www.skipton.ca

Information Technology Consulting Services
N.A.I.C.S.: 541512

DATA MODUL AG
Landsberger Str 322, D-80687, Munich, Germany
Tel.: (49) 89560170
Web Site: https://www.data-modul.com
Year Founded: 1972
DAM—(MUN)
Rev.: $312,660,139
Assets: $241,990,381
Liabilities: $81,222,755
Net Worth: $160,767,627
Earnings: $15,995,076
Emp.: 525
Fiscal Year-end: 12/31/23
Flat Display Monitors Mfr
N.A.I.C.S.: 334118
Kristin D. Russell *(Chm-Supervisory Bd)*

Subsidiaries:

Conrac GmbH   **(1)**
Lindenstrasse 8, 97990, Weikersheim, Baden-Wurttemberg, Germany
Tel.: (49) 79341010
Web Site: http://www.conrac.de
Sales Range: $50-74.9 Million
Emp.: 196
Flat Panel Displays Mfr
N.A.I.C.S.: 334118

Subsidiary (Non-US):

CONRAC Ltda.   **(2)**
Carrera 16 No 79-76 Officina 702, Bogota, Cundinamarca, Colombia
Tel.: (57) 13465338
Sales Range: $25-49.9 Million
Emp.: 10
Flat Panel Displays Mfr
N.A.I.C.S.: 334118

Conrac Asia Display Products PTE
Ltd.   **(2)**
82 Genting Ln No 05-04, Singapore, Singapore
Tel.: (65) 67427988
Web Site: http://www.conrac-asia.com
Sales Range: $25-49.9 Million
Emp.: 2
Flat Panel Displays Mfr
N.A.I.C.S.: 334118

Conrac MENA FZE   **(2)**
Unit WB 03 Block I Warehouse 11 Airport FZE, PO Box 54592, Dubai, United Arab Emirates
Tel.: (971) 42994009
Web Site: http://www.conrac.ae
Sales Range: $25-49.9 Million
Emp.: 20
Flat Panel Displays Mfr
N.A.I.C.S.: 334118

Conrac South Africa (Pty) Ltd.   **(2)**
1st Fl Kiepersol House Stone Mill Ofc Park 300 Acacia Rd Darrenwood, Randburg, Johannesburg, 2194, Gauteng, South Africa
Tel.: (27) 836350369
Web Site: http://www.conrac.co.za
Flat Panel Displays Mfr
N.A.I.C.S.: 334118

Data Modul Electronic Technology
(Shanghai) Co., Ltd.   **(1)**
Room 202 Building 2 Xinguang Technology Innovation Park, No 177 Jiangkai Road Pujiang Town Minhang District, Shanghai, 201114, China
Tel.: (86) 2150313935
Touch Display Product Mfr
N.A.I.C.S.: 334419

Data Modul France, S.A.R.L   **(1)**
7 Rue Saint Christophe, 60300, Baron, France
Tel.: (33) 344549699
Web Site: http://www.data-modul.com
Sales Range: $25-49.9 Million
Emp.: 7
Flat Panel Displays Mfr
N.A.I.C.S.: 334118

Data Modul France, S.A.R.L.   **(1)**
Bat B Hall 204 1-3 rue des Campanules, 77185, Lognes, Seine-et-Marne, France
Tel.: (33) 160378100
Web Site: http://www.datamodul.com
Sales Range: $50-74.9 Million
Emp.: 3
Electronic Components Distr
N.A.I.C.S.: 423690
Jerome Bly *(Gen Mgr)*

Data Modul Iberia S.L.   **(1)**
Edificio Las Americas III Oficina 13 c/ Adolfo Perez Esquivel 3, 28230, Las Rozas, Madrid, Spain
Tel.: (34) 016366458
Sales Range: $25-49.9 Million
Emp.: 4
Liquid Crystal Display Screens Mfr
N.A.I.C.S.: 334419

Data Modul Inc.   **(1)**
275 Marcus Blvd Unit R, Hauppauge, NY 11788-2022
Tel.: (631) 951-0800
Web Site: http://www.datamodul.com
Sales Range: $25-49.9 Million
Emp.: 6
Flat Panel Displays Mfr
N.A.I.C.S.: 334118

Data Modul Ltd.   **(1)**
Surestore Business Hub Gallan Park Watling Street, Cannock, Birmingham, WS11 0XG, Staffordshire, United Kingdom
Tel.: (44) 1922457358
Information System Solutions
N.A.I.C.S.: 541512

Data Modul Polska sp. z o.o   **(1)**
Jozefa Franczaka Lalka 16, 20-325, Lublin, Poland
Touch Display Product Mfr
N.A.I.C.S.: 334419
Rafal Ufnal *(Supvr-Production & Quality Assurance)*

DATA PATTERNS (INDIA) LTD.
Plot No H9 4th Main Road SIPCOT IT Park, Off Rajiv Gandhi Salai OMR Siruseri, Chennai, 603103, Tamil Nadu, India
Tel.: (91) 4447414000
Web Site:
   https://www.datapatternsindia.com
Year Founded: 1998
543428—(BOM)
Software Development Services
N.A.I.C.S.: 541511
Manvi Bhasin *(Compliance Officer & Sec)*

DATA STREAMS CORPORATION
Data Streams 6th floor 28 Saimdangro, Seocho-gu, Seoul, 136-876, Korea (South)
Tel.: (82) 234739077
Web Site:
   https://www.datastreams.co.kr
Sales Range: $10-24.9 Million
Emp.: 100
Data Integration, Analysis & Management Software & Consulting
N.A.I.C.S.: 513210

DATA SYSTEMS CONSULTING CO., LTD.
222 Sec 1 Jungshing Rd, Hsindian, Taipei, 231, Taiwan
Tel.: (886) 289111688
Web Site: http://www.dsc.com.tw
Year Founded: 1982
Sales Range: $100-124.9 Million
Emp.: 1,380
IT Services
N.A.I.C.S.: 518210
Sun Ge Bin *(Chm)*

DATA TEXTILES LIMITED
3-A Race View Jail Road, Lahore, Pakistan

Tel.: (92) 42 7569711
Textile Spinning Mill Operator
N.A.I.C.S.: 313110

DATA#3 LIMITED
Level 1 555 Coronation Drive,
Toowong, 4066, QLD, Australia
Tel.: (61) 300232823
Web Site: https://www.data3.com
DTL—(ASX)
Rev.: $544,660,121
Assets: $578,356,702
Liabilities: $528,332,663
Net Worth: $50,024,038
Earnings: $28,920,272
Emp.: 1,480
Fiscal Year-end: 06/30/24
Software Licensing & Software Asset
Management
N.A.I.C.S.: 541511
Richard A. Anderson *(Chm)*

Subsidiaries:

Business Aspect (ACT) Pty Ltd   (1)
Level 1 555 Coronation Drive, Toowong,
4066, QLD, Australia
Tel.: (61) 73 831 7600
Web Site:
  https://www.businessaspect.com.au
Business Consulting Services
N.A.I.C.S.: 541611
Laurence Baynham *(CEO & Mng Dir)*

Business Aspect Pty Ltd   (1)
Level 1 555 Coronation Drive, Toowong,
4066, QLD, Australia
Tel.: (61) 73 831 7600
Web Site:
  https://www.businessaspect.com.au
Business Consulting Services
N.A.I.C.S.: 541611

Data#3 Business Systems Pty.
Ltd.   (1)
67 High Street, Toowong, 4066, QLD, Aus-
tralia
Tel.: (61) 733718088
Web Site: http://www.data3.com.au
Sales Range: $50-74.9 Million
Emp.: 200
Data Processing Services
N.A.I.C.S.: 518210
John Grant *(Mng Dir)*

Discovery Technology Pty Ltd   (1)
Level 8 / 100 Arthur Street North, Sydney,
2060, NSW, Australia
Tel.: (61) 28 977 8400
Web Site: https://discovery.com.au
Software Development Services
N.A.I.C.S.: 541511

DATABARRACKS LIMITED
Ground Floor Mill Court, La Charrote-
rie, Saint Peter Port, Guernsey
Tel.: (44) 20 3177 1910   UK
Web Site:
  http://www.databarracks.com
Business Continuity & IT Disaster
Recovery Provider
N.A.I.C.S.: 518210
Peter Groucutt *(Mng Dir)*

Subsidiaries:

4sl Consulting Limited   (1)
4 Snow Hill, London, EC1AÂ 2DJ, United
Kingdom
Tel.: (44) 203 307 1030
Web Site: http://www.4sl.com
Sales Range: $1-9.9 Million
Emp.: 28
Information Technology Support Services
N.A.I.C.S.: 518210
Barnaby Mote *(Founder & CEO)*

DATABLE TECHNOLOGY
CORP.
1062 Homer Street Unit 301, Vancouver, V6B 2W9, BC, Canada
Tel.: (604) 639-5440
Web Site:
  https://www.datablecorp.com

TTMZF—(OTCIQ)
Rev.: $1,194,517
Assets: $664,046
Liabilities: $1,201,922
Net Worth: ($537,876)
Earnings: ($1,694,350)
Fiscal Year-end: 12/31/19
Software Development Services
N.A.I.C.S.: 541511
Robert Craig *(Pres & CEO)*

DATACOLOR AG
Habsburgerstrasse 26, CH-6003, Lu-
cerne, Switzerland
Tel.: (41) 444884019
Web Site: http://www.datacolor.com
Year Founded: 1834
DCN—(SWX)
Rev.: $93,212,000
Assets: $95,605,000
Liabilities: $38,699,000
Net Worth: $56,906,000
Earnings: $10,875,000
Emp.: 426
Fiscal Year-end: 09/30/23
Color Measurement Systems Mfr
N.A.I.C.S.: 541512
Werner Dubach *(Chm)*

Subsidiaries:

Datacolor Asia Pacific (HK)
Limited   (1)
Unit E 15/Floor Billion Plaza 2 No 10 Ch-
eung Yue Street, Cheung Sha Wan, Kow-
loon, China (Hong Kong)   **(51%)**
Tel.: (852) 24208283
Web Site: https://www.datacolor.com
Sales Range: $25-49.9 Million
Emp.: 100
Ink Mfr
N.A.I.C.S.: 325910

Datacolor Belgium BVBA   (1)
Jan Samijnstraat 17, 9050, Gentbrugge,
Belgium
Tel.: (32) 92438720
Color Measurement Instrument Mfr & Whslr
N.A.I.C.S.: 334516

Datacolor Color Technologies Trading
& Service Company LLC   (1)
Ataturk Mah 62 Ada Gardenya 4-2 D 1,
Atasehir, 34758, Istanbul, Turkiye
Tel.: (90) 2164553085
Color Measurement Instrument Mfr & Whslr
N.A.I.C.S.: 334516

Datacolor GmbH   (1)
Elbestr 10, 45768, Marl, Germany
Tel.: (49) 236551090
Color Measurement Instrument Mfr & Whslr
N.A.I.C.S.: 334516

Datacolor Inc.   (1)
5 Princess Rd, Lawrenceville, NJ
08648   **(100%)**
Tel.: (609) 924-2189
Emp.: 380
Mfr of Color Measuring & Testing Devices
N.A.I.C.S.: 333310

Datacolor International France
SAS   (1)
Tour Ariane 5 Place de la Pyramide, La De-
fense, 92088, Paris, Cedex, France
Tel.: (33) 14 818 5480
Color Measurement Instrument Mfr & Whslr
N.A.I.C.S.: 334516

Datacolor International Ltd.   (1)
Suite 11 Unit 16 Leeway Estate, Newport,
NP19 4SL, United Kingdom
Tel.: (44) 161 929 9441
Color Measurement Instrument Mfr & Whslr
N.A.I.C.S.: 334516

Datacolor Solutions Private Ltd.   (1)
802 Jay Antariksha Makwana Road, Marol
Andheri East, Mumbai, 400 059, India
Tel.: (91) 2220880444
Color Measurement Instrument Mfr & Whslr
N.A.I.C.S.: 334516

Datacolor Trading (Shanghai) Co.,
Ltd.   (1)

Unit 2701-2702 World Trade Tower No 500
Guangdong Road, Huangpu District,
Shanghai, 200001, China
Tel.: (86) 2153086988
Color Measurement Instrument Mfr & Whslr
N.A.I.C.S.: 334516

Datacolor Vietnam Co., Ltd.   (1)
Room 2111 21st Floor Saigon Trade Center
37 Ton Duc Thang Street, Ben Nghe Ward
District 1, 700000, Ho Chi Minh City, Viet-
nam
Tel.: (84) 2838247968
Color Measurement Instrument Mfr & Whslr
N.A.I.C.S.: 334516

DATADOT TECHNOLOGY LTD
8 Ethel Avenue, Brookvale, 2100,
NSW, Australia
Tel.: (61) 289774900
Web Site:
  https://www.datadotdna.com
DDT—(ASX)
Rev.: $1,992,851
Assets: $6,935,618
Liabilities: $701,544
Net Worth: $6,234,073
Earnings: $48,277
Emp.: 41
Fiscal Year-end: 06/30/24
Asset Identification System Mfr
N.A.I.C.S.: 334519
Patrick Raper *(CFO & Sec)*

Subsidiaries:

DataDot Technology (UK) Ltd.   (1)
4 Twickenham Rd, Union Park Indust, Nor-
wich, NR6 6NG, Norfolk, United Kingdom
Tel.: (44) 1603407171
Web Site: http://www.ddotdna.eu
Sales Range: $25-49.9 Million
Emp.: 12
Theft Prevention Systems Mfr
N.A.I.C.S.: 561621
Andrew Winfield *(Mng Dir-UK & Europe)*

Subsidiary (Domestic):

Data Traceid (Europe) Limited   (2)
4 Twickenham Rd, Union Park Indust, Nor-
wich, NR6 6NG, Norfolk, United Kingdom
Tel.: (44) 1603407171
Web Site: http://www.datadotdna.eu
Sales Range: $25-49.9 Million
Emp.: 10
Theft Prevention Systems Mfr
N.A.I.C.S.: 561621
Andrew Winfield *(Mng Dir)*

DataDot Technology - Taiwan   (1)
1F No 19 Lane 66 Xingzhong Road, Neihu
District, Taipei, Taiwan
Tel.: (886) 227946777
Web Site: https://www.datadot.com.tw
Sales Range: $25-49.9 Million
Emp.: 10
Theft Prevention Systems Mfr
N.A.I.C.S.: 561621

DATAGATE BILGISAYAR
MALZEMELERI TICARET A.S.
Ayazaga Mah Mimar Sinan Sok No
21 Seba Office Boulevard D, Blok Kat
1 Bolum No 10, 34485, Istanbul, Tur-
kiye
Tel.: (90) 2123312727
Web Site:
  https://www.datagate.com.tr
Year Founded: 1992
DGATE—(IST)
Rev.: $174,444,837
Assets: $56,647,939
Liabilities: $45,654,030
Net Worth: $10,993,909
Earnings: ($6,019,381)
Fiscal Year-end: 12/31/23
Computer Peripheral Equipment Distr
N.A.I.C.S.: 423430
Nevres Erol Bilecik *(Chm)*

DATAGROUP SE

Wilhelm-Schickard-Strasse 7, 72124,
Pliezhausen, Germany
Tel.: (49) 7114900500   De
Web Site: https://www.datagroup.de
Year Founded: 2005
D6H—(MUN)
Rev.: $549,506,486
Assets: $513,619,672
Liabilities: $350,909,234
Net Worth: $162,710,438
Earnings: $30,996,670
Emp.: 3,250
Fiscal Year-end: 09/30/23
Holding Company; Information Tech-
nology Services
N.A.I.C.S.: 551112
Hans-Hermann Schaber *(CEO, CFO
& Member-Exec Bd)*

Subsidiaries:

DATAGROUP Financial IT Services
GmbH   (1)
Georg-Glock-Str 18, 40474, Dusseldorf,
Germany
Tel.: (49) 211822116
Web Site: http://www.datagroup.de
IT Outsourcing & Data Security
N.A.I.C.S.: 518210

DATALAB TEHNOLOGIJE D.D.
Hajdrihova ulica 28c, SI-1000, Lju-
bljana, Slovenia
Tel.: (386) 12528900
Web Site: https://www.datalab.si
Year Founded: 1997
DATG—(LJU)
Rev.: $17,126,614
Assets: $21,420,687
Liabilities: $9,361,960
Net Worth: $12,058,726
Earnings: $3,934,209
Emp.: 157
Fiscal Year-end: 12/31/23
Software & Computer Operating Sys-
tems Designer
N.A.I.C.S.: 513210
Vanya Cigoj *(Asst Dir-DL Academy)*

Subsidiaries:

Datalab AL sh.p.k.   (1)
Rr Perlat Rexhepi Pallati Unicom hyrja 1 ap
8, 1001, Tirana, Albania
Tel.: (355) 44 516 368
Web Site: http://www.datalab.al
Information Technology Consulting Services
N.A.I.C.S.: 541512

Datalab Automotive, d.o.o.   (1)
Bulevar dr Zorana Dindica 4a, Novi Beo-
grad, 11000, Belgrade, Serbia
Tel.: (381) 11 214 6727
Web Site: https://www.dl-automotive.rs
Computer Services
N.A.I.C.S.: 541519
Persida Pandurovic *(Mng Dir)*

Datalab BH, d.o.o.   (1)
Vilsonovo setaliste 10, 71000, Sarajevo,
Bosnia & Herzegovina
Tel.: (387) 33652101
Web Site: https://www.datalab.ba
Computer Services
N.A.I.C.S.: 541519
Nedim Pasic *(Mng Dir)*

Datalab Bulgaria, Ltd.   (1)
13 Tintyava Str, 1113, Sofia, Bulgaria
Tel.: (359) 29609750
Web Site: https://www.datalab.bg
Computer Services
N.A.I.C.S.: 541519

Datalab HR d.o.o.   (1)
Avenija V Holjevca 40, 10000, Zagreb,
Croatia
Tel.: (385) 13535595
Web Site: https://www.datalab.hr
Information Technology Services
N.A.I.C.S.: 541519

Datalab MK, d.o.o.   (1)
st Louis Pasteur 5/4-5, 1000, Skopje, North
Macedonia

Datalab Tehnologije d.d.—(Continued)

Tel.: (389) 23079231
Web Site: https://www.datalab.com.mk
Emp.: 20
Computer Services
N.A.I.C.S.: 541519
Irina Rizinsta *(Mng Dir)*

Datalab SI d.o.o.　　　　　　**(1)**
Hajdrihova ulica 28c, SI-1000, Ljubljana, Slovenia
Tel.: (386) 12528900
Web Site: https://www.datalab.si
Computer Services
N.A.I.C.S.: 541519

Datalab SR, d.o.o.　　　　　　**(1)**
Bulevar Arsenija Carnojevica 99V, 11000, Belgrade, Serbia
Tel.: (381) 13119439
Web Site: https://www.datalab.rs
Computer Services
N.A.I.C.S.: 541519
Miodrag Ranisavljevic *(Mng Dir)*

Datalab Tehnologije d.o.o.　　　**(1)**
Trg 1 Istarske brigade 6, 52100, Pula, Croatia
Tel.: (385) 52 380 147
Web Site: http://www.datalab.hr
Computer Services
N.A.I.C.S.: 541519
Tihomir Stricevic *(Mng Dir)*

Datalab.MN, d.o.o.　　　　　　**(1)**
Marka Radovica 59/1, 81000, Podgorica, Montenegro
Tel.: (382) 20212121
Web Site: https://www.datalab.me
Emp.: 8
Computer Services
N.A.I.C.S.: 541519
Danko Obradovic *(Mng Dir)*

DATALEX PLC

Marina House Block V EastPoint, Dublin, D03 AX24, Ireland
Tel.: (353) 18063500
Web Site: https://www.datalex.com
Year Founded: 1985
DLE—(ISE)
Rev.: $28,070,000
Assets: $20,816,000
Liabilities: $44,514,000
Net Worth: ($23,698,000)
Earnings: ($6,477,000)
Emp.: 140
Fiscal Year-end: 12/31/20
Holding Company; Ecommerce Software Development Services
N.A.I.C.S.: 511210
Ryan Estes *(VP-Tech & Academy)*

Subsidiaries:

Datalex Netherlands B.V.　　　**(1)**
Tel.: (31) 205030200
Emp.: 6
Software Development Services
N.A.I.C.S.: 541511

Datalex Solutions (UK) Limited　**(1)**
4th Floor 55 Spring Gardens, Manchester, M2 2BY, United Kingdom
Tel.: (44) 1612447200
Software Development Services
N.A.I.C.S.: 541511

Datalex USA Inc.　　　　　　**(1)**
1105 Sanctuary Pkwy 190, Alpharetta, GA 30009
Tel.: (770) 255-2400
Sales Range: $1-9.9 Million
Emp.: 42
Commerce Software Development Services
N.A.I.C.S.: 541511
Gianni Cataldo *(VP & Gen Mgr)*

DATALINER AB

PO Box 5070, 630 05, Eskilstuna, Sweden
Tel.: (46) 16147140
Web Site: http://www.dataliner.se
Automotive Dataline Equipment Mfr
N.A.I.C.S.: 336390
Johnny Carlson *(Mng Dir)*

DATALINKS CORPORATION

25F Odakyu Daiichi Seimei Bldg
2-7-1 Nishi Shinjuku, Shinjuku-Ku, Tokyo, 163-0725, Japan
Tel.: (81) 3 59627621
Web Site: http://www.datalinks.co.jp
Year Founded: 1982
Business Process Outsourcing Services
N.A.I.C.S.: 561422
Isao Yokoo *(Pres)*

DATALOG TECHNOLOGY INC.

10707 50th Street SE, Calgary, T2C 3E5, AB, Canada
Tel.: (403) 243-2024
Web Site:
http://www.datalogtechnology.com
Rev.: $19,677,774
Emp.: 700
Petroleum Services
N.A.I.C.S.: 213112
Ian Underdown *(Founder & CEO)*

Subsidiaries:

Datalog LWT Inc.　　　　　　**(1)**
228 NW 59th St, Oklahoma City, OK 73118
Tel.: (405) 286-0418
Petroleum Reserve Management Services
N.A.I.C.S.: 213112
Gustavo Murillo *(Mgr-Ops)*

Datalog Technology Inc.　　　**(1)**
Jl Raya Hankam No 10 Jati Melati, Bekasi, 17431, Jawa Barat, Indonesia
Tel.: (62) 2184301440
Petroleum Reserve Management Services
N.A.I.C.S.: 213112

DATALOGIC S.P.A.

Via Candini 2 Lippo di Calderara di Reno, 40012, Bologna, Italy
Tel.: (39) 0513147011　　　　IT
Web Site: https://www.datalogic.com
Year Founded: 1972
DAL—(ITA)
Rev.: $709,551,268
Assets: $916,443,746
Liabilities: $426,993,280
Net Worth: $489,450,466
Earnings: $32,653,371
Emp.: 3,069
Fiscal Year-end: 12/31/22
Laser-Based Bar Code Readers, Mobile Computers & Warehouse Management Systems Mfr
N.A.I.C.S.: 335999
Romano Volta *(Chm)*

Subsidiaries:

Datalogic ADC S.r.L.　　　　　**(1)**
Via S Vitalino 13, Lippo di Calderara di Reno, 40012, Bologna, Italy
Tel.: (39) 0513147011
Web Site: http://www.datalogic.com
Mobile Computers Mfr & Marketer
N.A.I.C.S.: 334118

Datalogic Australia Pty Ltd　　**(1)**
25 Hardner Road, Mount Waverley, 3149, VIC, Australia
Tel.: (61) 385144900
Computer Parts Mfr
N.A.I.C.S.: 334111

Datalogic Automation S.r.l.　　**(1)**
Via Lavino 265, Monte San Pietro, 40050, Bologna, Italy
Tel.: (39) 0516765611
Web Site: http://www.datalogic.com
Sales Range: $125-149.9 Million
Industrial Automation Products Mfr & Marketer
N.A.I.C.S.: 334118

Datalogic Holdings, Inc.　　　**(1)**
959 Terry St, Eugene, OR 97402
Tel.: (541) 683-5700
Web Site: http://www.datalogic.com
Sales Range: $150-199.9 Million
Emp.: 740

Holding Company; Automatic Data Collection Systems & Components Mfr
N.A.I.C.S.: 551112

Subsidiary (Domestic):

Datalogic Automation, Inc.　　**(2)**
5775 W Old Shakopee Rd Ste 160, Bloomington, MN 55437
Tel.: (952) 996-9500
Web Site: http://www.datalogic.com
Machine Vision & Laser Marking Systems Mfr
N.A.I.C.S.: 334513

Datalogic Hungary Kft　　　　**(1)**
Klapka Gy u 37, Balatonboglar, H-8630, Balatonfured, Hungary
Tel.: (36) 516765611
Computer Parts Mfr
N.A.I.C.S.: 334111

Datalogic Japan Co., Ltd.　　　**(1)**
R408 Q Plaza Shinjuku 3-chome 3-5-6 Shinjuku, Shinjuku-ku, Tokyo, 160-0022, Japan
Tel.: (81) 364570860
Computer System Design Services
N.A.I.C.S.: 541512

Datalogic Singapore Asia Pacific Pte Ltd.　　　　　　　　　　　**(1)**
750A Chai Chee Road 07-11 ESR BizPark Chai Chee, Singapore, 469001, Singapore
Tel.: (65) 64351311
Computer Parts Mfr
N.A.I.C.S.: 334111

Datalogic Slovakia S.r.o.　　　**(1)**
Prilohy 47, Zavar, 91926, Trnava, Slovakia
Tel.: (421) 335908911
Computer Parts Mfr
N.A.I.C.S.: 334111

Datalogic Technologia de Mexico S.r.l.　　　　　　　　　　　　**(1)**
Antonio Dovali Jaime no 75 Piso 5 Col, Lomas de Santa Fe Alvaro Obregon, 01219, Mexico, Distrito Federal, Mexico
Tel.: (52) 8802272633
Computer Parts Mfr
N.A.I.C.S.: 334111

Datalogic USA, Inc.　　　　　**(1)**
959 Terry St, Eugene, OR 97402
Computer Parts Mfr
N.A.I.C.S.: 334111

Datalogic Vietnam LLC　　　　**(1)**
F04 Lot I-4a Saigon Hi-Tech Park Le Van Viet Street, District 9, 700000, Ho Chi Minh City, Vietnam
Tel.: (84) 837308481
Computer Parts Mfr
N.A.I.C.S.: 334111

Datalogic do Brazil Comercio de Equipamentos e Automacao Ltda.　　**(1)**
Rua Arandu 281 CJ 32, Brooklin Novo, Sao Paulo, 04562-030, Brazil
Tel.: (55) 1129232600
Computer Parts Mfr
N.A.I.C.S.: 334111

Datasensing S.r.l.　　　　　　**(1)**
Strada S Caterina 235, 41122, Modena, Italy
Tel.: (39) 059420411
Web Site: https://www.datasensing.com
Sensor Mfr & Distr
N.A.I.C.S.: 333995

Pekat S.r.o.　　　　　　　　**(1)**
Pekat Odstepny Zavod Botanicka 68a, 602 00, Brno, Czech Republic
Tel.: (420) 702072595
Web Site: https://www.pekatvision.com
Software Development Services
N.A.I.C.S.: 541511

Suzhou Mobydata Smart System Co. Ltd.　　　　　　　　　　　　**(1)**
3f Building E Yida Science Park 11 Jinpu Road, Industrial Park, Suzhou, China
Tel.: (86) 51268234699
Web Site: https://www.mobydata.com
Scanner Product Mfr
N.A.I.C.S.: 334118

Wasp Barcode Technologies Ltd.　**(1)**
Dunstable Road, Redbourn, Saint Albans,

AL3 7PR, United Kingdom
Tel.: (44) 8454301971
Computer Software Services
N.A.I.C.S.: 541511

DATAMARS SA

Via Industria 16, 6814, Lamone, Switzerland
Tel.: (41) 91 935 73 80　　　CH
Web Site: http://www.datamars.com
Emp.: 1,500
Livestock Management, Pet Identification & Reunification Services
N.A.I.C.S.: 115210
Klaus Ackerstaff *(CEO)*

Subsidiaries:

Datamars, Inc.　　　　　　　**(1)**
1110 Industrial Blvd, Temple, TX 76504
Tel.: (254) 598-3440
Web Site: http://www.datamars.com
RFID Microchip Mfr
N.A.I.C.S.: 115210
Klaus Ackerstaff *(CEO)*

Subsidiary (Non-US):

Simcro Limited　　　　　　　**(2)**
13 Kaimiro St, Hamilton, 3200, New Zealand
Tel.: (64) 7 846 7723
Web Site: http://www.simcro.com
Veterinary Instrument Mfr
N.A.I.C.S.: 541940
Nigel Hazelwood *(Fin Dir-Asia Pacific)*

Subsidiary (Non-US):

Simcro (UK) Limited　　　　　**(3)**
PO Box 9020, Bournemouth, BH1 9YU, United Kingdom
Tel.: (44) 7825 129 123
Veterinary Instrument Mfr
N.A.I.C.S.: 541940
Mark Hoare *(Sls Mgr-UK/Europe)*

DATAMATICS GLOBAL SERVICES LTD.

Knowledge Center Street No 17 MIDC, Andheri East, Mumbai, 400093, India
Tel.: (91) 2261020000
Web Site:
https://www.datamatics.com
532528—(BOM)
Rev.: $167,537,234
Assets: $151,479,647
Liabilities: $34,987,544
Net Worth: $116,492,103
Earnings: $21,496,293
Emp.: 6,459
Fiscal Year-end: 03/31/22
Information Technology & BPO Services
N.A.I.C.S.: 541513
Divya Kumat *(Chief Legal Officer, Compliance Officer, Sec & Exec VP)*

Subsidiaries:

CIGNEX Datamatics Corporation　**(1)**
4633 Old Ironsides Dr Ste 109, Santa Clara, CA 95054
Tel.: (510) 205-5125
Web Site: http://www.cignex.com
Sales Range: $75-99.9 Million
Emp.: 325
Open Source Solutions
N.A.I.C.S.: 541512
Vidur V. Bhogilal *(Chm)*

CIGNEX Datamatics Pte. Limited　**(1)**
4 Shenton Way 08-03 SGX Centre 2, Singapore, 068807, Singapore
Tel.: (65) 90175519
Software Development Services
N.A.I.C.S.: 541511

CIGNEX Datamatics Technologies Limited　　　　　　　　　　　**(1)**
Ground Floor President Plaza S G Highway, Ahmedabad, 380054, Gujarat, India
Tel.: (91) 9372899091

Software Development Services
N.A.I.C.S.: 541511

Datamatics Global Services Corp. (1)
Bernaldo Directo and PO Law Offices U180 City Land 10 Tower I H V Dela, Costa St Bel-Air Salcedo Village, Makati, 1227, Philippines
Tel.: (63) 2840053538
Software Development Services
N.A.I.C.S.: 541511

Datamatics Global Services FZ-LLC (1)
320 I 32nd Floor Shatha Tower Dubai Media City, PO Box 501755, Dubai, United Arab Emirates
Tel.: (971) 44310172
Software Development Services
N.A.I.C.S.: 541511

Datamatics Staffing Services Limited (1)
Eucharistic Congress Bldg No III 6th Floor 5 Convent Street Colaba, Mumbai, 400 001, India **(97.42%)**
Tel.: (91) 2266517000
Web Site: http://www.datamaticsindia.com
Software Development Services
N.A.I.C.S.: 541511
Lalit S. Kanodia *(Founder & Chm)*

Datamatics Technologies GmbH (1)
Wilhelm-Leuschner-St Hessen 8-10, 64347, Griesheim, Germany
Tel.: (49) 6155848614
Sales Range: $10-24.9 Million
Emp.: 30
Business Solutions Provider
N.A.I.C.S.: 561499

Datamatics Technologies U.K. Limited (1)
8 The Square Stockley Park, Uxbridge, UB11 1FW, Middlesex, United Kingdom
Tel.: (44) 2086106105
Web Site: http://www.datamatics.co.uk
Business Management Services
N.A.I.C.S.: 561499

Lumina Datamatics Limited (1)
Unit 117 - 120 Sdf - IV Seepz - Sez Andheri E, Mumbai, 400 096, Maharashtra, India
Tel.: (91) 2240340515
Software Development Services
N.A.I.C.S.: 541511

Lumina Datamatics, Inc. (1)
600 Cordwainer Dr Unit 103, Norwell, MA 02061
Tel.: (508) 746-0300
Software Development Services
N.A.I.C.S.: 541511

DATAMETREX AI LIMITED
2300 Yonge Street Suite 2802, Toronto, M4P 1E4, ON, Canada
Tel.: (416) 901-5611   ON
Web Site:
https://www.datametrex.com
Year Founded: 2011
DTMXF—(OTCIQ)
Rev.: $9,683,081
Assets: $7,821,493
Liabilities: $5,281,933
Net Worth: $2,539,560
Earnings: ($3,916,310)
Fiscal Year-end: 12/31/20
Investment Services
N.A.I.C.S.: 523999
Andrew Ryu *(Chm)*

DATANG HUAYIN ELECTRIC POWER CO., LTD.
Huayin Shihaoyuan Office Building No 35 Heishipu Road, Tianxin District, Changsha, 410007, Hunan, China
Tel.: (86) 73189687188
Web Site:
http://www.hypower.com.cn
Year Founded: 1993
600744—(SHG)
Rev.: $1,362,222,225

Assets: $3,014,919,611
Liabilities: $2,803,202,757
Net Worth: $211,716,854
Earnings: $3,799,435
Fiscal Year-end: 12/31/22
Electric Power Distribution Services
N.A.I.C.S.: 221122
Zhihui Liu *(Pres)*

Subsidiaries:

Dalian University of Technology Science Park Co., Ltd (1)
No 2 Linggong Road, Ganjingzi District, Dalian, 116024, Liaoning, China
Tel.: (86) 411 84708320
Educational Support Services
N.A.I.C.S.: 611710

DATANG TELECOM TECHNOLOGY CO., LTD.
No 6 Yongjia North Road, Haidian District, Beijing, 100094, China
Tel.: (86) 1058919172
Web Site: http://www.datang.com
Year Founded: 2007
600198—(SHG)
Rev.: $150,921,660
Assets: $495,595,952
Liabilities: $244,161,314
Net Worth: $251,434,638
Earnings: $5,260,016
Fiscal Year-end: 12/31/22
Communication Equipment Distr
N.A.I.C.S.: 423690
Liu Xin *(Chm)*

Subsidiaries:

Datang NXP Semiconductors Co., Ltd. (1)
No 99 Jinggangshan Rd Rudong Economic Development Zone, Nantong, 226400, Jiangsu, China
Tel.: (86) 51368926010
Web Site: http://www.datangnxp.com
Semiconductor Product Mfr
N.A.I.C.S.: 334413
Henning M. Hauenstein *(CEO & Gen Mgr)*

DATAPLOT GMBH
Gutenbergstrasse 15, 24558, Henstedt-Ulzburg, Germany
Tel.: (49) 41939950
Web Site: http://www.dataplot.de
Year Founded: 1979
Rev.: $30,002,821
Emp.: 56
Computer Equipment Mfr
N.A.I.C.S.: 423430
Karsten Werther *(Co-CEO)*

DATAPOINT CUSTOMER SOLUTIONS LTD.
1000 Great West Road, Brentford, TW8 9HH, Middlesex, United Kingdom
Tel.: (44) 845 850 2277
Web Site: http://www.datapoint.com
Sales Range: $50-74.9 Million
Emp.: 200
Call Centre Equipment Design & Distr
N.A.I.C.S.: 423430
Martin Hill Wilson *(Dir-Strategy)*

Subsidiaries:

Datapoint France (1)
64 rue de Tiquetonne, 75002, Paris, France **(100%)**
Tel.: (33) 170392950
Web Site: http://www.datapoint.com
Call Centre Equipment Design & Distr
N.A.I.C.S.: 423430

Datapoint Iberica S.A. (1)
Costa Brava 13 Mirasierra Bldg 2 Fl, Edificio Mirasierra, 28034, Madrid, Spain **(100%)**
Tel.: (34) 917341011
Rev.: $91,592
Emp.: 70

Call Centre Equipment Design & Distr
N.A.I.C.S.: 423430
Enrique Amat *(Dir-Mktg & Comm)*

Datapoint Nederland B.V. (1)
Maliebaan 6, 3581 CM, Utrecht, Netherlands **(100%)**
Tel.: (31) 307999010
Web Site: http://www.datapoint.com
Rev.: $5,133,396
Emp.: 77
Call Centre Equipment Design & Distr
N.A.I.C.S.: 423430

DATAPROCES GROUP A/S
Skalhuse 13, 9240, Nibe, Denmark
Tel.: (45) 41210500
Web Site: https://www.dataproces.dk
Year Founded: 2011
DATA—(NASDAQ)
Information Technology Services
N.A.I.C.S.: 541512
Hans Christian R. Maarup *(Chm)*

DATAPULSE TECHNOLOGY LTD.
8 Shenton Way 09-01 AXA Tower, Singapore, 068811, Singapore
Tel.: (65) 63827989
Web Site:
https://www.datapulse.com.sg
BKW—(SES)
Rev.: $3,556,132
Assets: $46,590,589
Liabilities: $2,175,621
Net Worth: $44,414,969
Earnings: ($867,729)
Emp.: 26
Fiscal Year-end: 07/31/23
Computer-Related Storage Products Mfr
N.A.I.C.S.: 334112
Kam Seng Lee *(Interim CEO & Co-Sec)*

DATASEA INC.
20th Floor Tower B Guorui Plaza 1 Ronghua South Road, Technological Development Zone, Beijing, 100176, China
Tel.: (86) 1056145240   NV
Web Site:
https://www.dataseainc.com
Year Founded: 2014
DTSS—(NASDAQ)
Rev.: $23,975,867
Assets: $3,291,704
Liabilities: $3,599,982
Net Worth: ($308,278)
Earnings: ($11,377,064)
Emp.: 36
Fiscal Year-end: 06/30/24
Business Services
N.A.I.C.S.: 561499
Xingzhong Sun *(Founder)*

DATASECTION INC.
Gotanda PLACE 8th floor 1-3-8 Nishigotanda, Shinagawa-ku, Tokyo, 141-0031, Japan
Tel.: (81) 364272565   JP
Web Site:
https://www.datasection.co.jp
Year Founded: 2000
3905—(TKS)
Rev.: $14,733,690
Assets: $25,025,460
Liabilities: $11,924,440
Net Worth: $13,101,020
Earnings: ($8,335,210)
Fiscal Year-end: 03/31/24
SaaS & Technical Consulting Services
N.A.I.C.S.: 518210

Subsidiaries:

Solid Intelligence Inc. (1)
Barbizon22 9F 5-8-11 Hiroo, Shibuya-ku,

Tokyo, 150-0012, Japan
Tel.: (81) 354226355
Web Site: https://www.solid-i.co.jp
Internet Marketing Services
N.A.I.C.S.: 541613

d-ss Inc. (1)
1-3-8 Nishigotanda Place 8th Floor, Shinagawa-ku Gotanda, Tokyo, 141-0031, Japan
Tel.: (81) 359627755
Web Site: http://www.d-ss.co.jp
Building Maintenance Services
N.A.I.C.S.: 561790

DATASOLUTION, INC.
06101 10th floor Hyundai Intelex 620 Eonjuro, Gangnam-Gu, Seoul, Korea (South)
Tel.: (82) 234677200
Web Site: https://www.datasolution.kr
Year Founded: 2011
263800—(KRS)
Rev.: $76,024,088
Assets: $53,353,619
Liabilities: $29,313,482
Net Worth: $24,040,138
Earnings: $1,839,633
Emp.: 201
Fiscal Year-end: 12/31/22
Software Development Services
N.A.I.C.S.: 541511
Jin-Chan Lee *(Deputy Gen Mgr)*

DATASONIC GROUP BERHAD
Level 6 Bangunan Setia 1 No 15 Lorong Dungun, Damansara Heights, 50490, Kuala Lumpur, Malaysia
Tel.: (60) 320876000
Web Site:
https://www.datasonic.com.my
DSONIC—(KLS)
Rev.: $77,948,994
Assets: $99,106,878
Liabilities: $21,376,931
Net Worth: $77,729,946
Earnings: $19,520,000
Emp.: 832
Fiscal Year-end: 03/31/24
Computer Related Services
N.A.I.C.S.: 541519
Abu Hanifah Noordin *(CEO & Mng Dir)*

Subsidiaries:

Datasonic Innovation Sdn. Bhd. (1)
Level 6 Bangunan Setia 1 No 15 Lorong Dungun, Damansara Heights, 50490, Kuala Lumpur, Malaysia
Tel.: (60) 326329699
Information Technology Services
N.A.I.C.S.: 541511

Datasonic Manufacturing Sdn. Bhd. (1)
No 1 Lebuh 1 Bandar Sultan Sulaiman Taiwanese Industrial Park, Port Klang, 42000, Selangor, Malaysia **(99.45%)**
Tel.: (60) 3 3176 6700
Sales Range: $50-74.9 Million
Emp.: 200
Mfr of Smart Cards & Electronic Modules for Smart Cards
N.A.I.C.S.: 334419
Eddie Huo Shao Wei *(Gen Mgr)*

Datasonic Smart Solutions Sdn Bhd (1)
No A1-3 Block A Jalan Radius 1/1B, Radius Business Park, 63000, Cyberjaya, Selangor Darul Ehsan, Malaysia
Tel.: (60) 388008000
Communication Equipment Distr
N.A.I.C.S.: 423690

Datasonic Technologies Sdn Bhd (1)
No 20A Jalan 51A/223 Seksyen 51A, 46100, Petaling Jaya, Selangor, Malaysia
Tel.: (60) 379541697
Communication Equipment Distr
N.A.I.C.S.: 423690
Ramesh Selvaraja *(Sr Mgr-Ops)*

Datasonic Group Berhad—(Continued)

DATATEC LIMITED
3rd Floor Sandown Chambers Sandown Village Office Park 81 Maude Street, Sandown, Johannesburg, 2196, South Africa
Tel.: (27) 112331000   **ZA**
Web Site: https://www.datatec.co.za
Year Founded: 1986
DTC—(JSE)
Rev.: $5,457,947,000
Assets: $3,633,336,000
Liabilities: $3,064,192,000
Net Worth: $560,144,000
Earnings: $50,938,000
Emp.: 11,000
Fiscal Year-end: 02/29/24
Networking, Conferencing & IT Services
N.A.I.C.S.: 517810
Jens P. Montanana (CEO)

Subsidiaries:

Analysys Mason AS   (1)
Tjuvholmen Alle 19, Oslo, 0252, Norway
Tel.: (47) 92049000
Telecommunication Management Consulting Services
N.A.I.C.S.: 541618
Finn Terje Schoyen (Partner)

Analysys Mason FZ LLC   (1)
Al Shatha Tower 2605 Dubai Media City, PO Box 502064, Dubai, United Arab Emirates
Tel.: (971) 44467473
Telecommunication Management Consulting Services
N.A.I.C.S.: 541618

Analysys Mason Group Limited   (1)
Bush House North West Wing Aldwych, London, WC2B 4PJ, United Kingdom
Tel.: (44) 2073959000
Web Site: https://www.analysysmason.com
Sales Range: $25-49.9 Million
Network Integration Services
N.A.I.C.S.: 541512

Subsidiary (Non-US):

Analysys Mason Pte Limited   (2)
17-03 Robinson Point 39 Robinson Road, Singapore, 068911, Singapore
Tel.: (65) 64936029
Web Site: http://www.analysysmason.com
Telecommunications Consulting Services
N.A.I.C.S.: 541611
Amrish Kacker (Partner)

Subsidiary (Domestic):

Mason Group Ltd.   (2)
5 Exchange Quay, Manchester, M5 3EF, United Kingdom
Tel.: (44) 01618777808
Web Site: http://www.mason.biz
Sales Range: $25-49.9 Million
Emp.: 70
Provider of Telecommunications Consulting Services
N.A.I.C.S.: 517111

Analysys Mason India Pvt. Limited   (1)
1st Floor Tower C Building No 10 DLF Cyber City Phase II, Gurgaon, 122002, Haryana, India
Tel.: (91) 1244501860
Telecommunication Management Consulting Services
N.A.I.C.S.: 541618
Rohan Dhamija (Partner)

Analysys Mason Limited   (1)
Suite 242 The Capel Building, Dublin, Ireland
Tel.: (353) 16024755
Telecommunication Management Consulting Services
N.A.I.C.S.: 541618
Patrick Kidney (Partner)

Analysys Mason Limited   (1)
G/F 5-13 New Street, Sai Ying Pun, Hong Kong, China (Hong Kong)

Tel.: (852) 93137552
Telecommunication Management Consulting Services
N.A.I.C.S.: 541618

Analysys Mason S.R.L.   (1)
Corso Venezia 37, 20121, Milan, Italy
Tel.: (39) 0276318834
Telecommunication Management Consulting Services
N.A.I.C.S.: 541618
Fabio Fradella (Partner)

Analysys Mason SAS   (1)
25 rue d'Artois 4th Floor, 75008, Paris, France
Tel.: (33) 172719696
Telecommunication Management Consulting Services
N.A.I.C.S.: 541618
Stephane Piot (Partner)

Analysys Mason Spain S.L.   (1)
Calle Jose Abascal 57 7 D, 28003, Madrid, Spain
Tel.: (34) 913995016
Telecommunication Management Consulting Services
N.A.I.C.S.: 541618
Fran Gonzalez (Partner)

Analysys Mason Ventures Fund Nordic 1 AS   (1)
Tjuvholmen alle 19, Oslo, 252, Norway
Tel.: (47) 90559075
Management Consulting Services
N.A.I.C.S.: 541611

Cilnet - Comunicacoes e Projectos Especiais S.A.   (1)
Lagoas park edificio 5 Torre A piso 5, 2740-265, Porto Salvo, Portugal
Tel.: (351) 214702130
Web Site: https://www.pt.logicalis.com
IT Services
N.A.I.C.S.: 541519

Coasin Chile S.A.   (1)
Av El Bosque Norte 177 Oficina 801 - Edificio Torre del Bosque, 755-0155, Las Condes, Santiago, Chile
Tel.: (56) 28994200
IT Services
N.A.I.C.S.: 541519

Datatec Management Services (Pty) Limited   (1)
Ground Floor Sand Own Chamber 16 Maude St, Sandown, Johannesburg, 2146, Gauteng, South Africa
Tel.: (27) 112331221
Web Site: http://www.datatec.com
Sales Range: $25-49.9 Million
Emp.: 12
Information Technology Consulting Services
N.A.I.C.S.: 541512
Jens Montanana (CEO)

ITUMA GmbH   (1)
Kleinhulsen 29, 40721, Hilden, Germany
Tel.: (49) 2103280990
Web Site: https://www.ituma.de
IT Services
N.A.I.C.S.: 541519
Simon Marg (CEO)

Logicalis Argentina S.A.   (1)
Av Belgrano 955, C1092AAJ, Buenos Aires, Argentina
Tel.: (54) 1152820300
IT Services
N.A.I.C.S.: 541519

Logicalis Chile S.A.   (1)
Av Del Valle Norte 732 Ciudad Empresarial, 8580659, Huechuraba, Santiago, Chile
Tel.: (56) 224108000
IT Services
N.A.I.C.S.: 541519

Logicalis Ecuador S.A.   (1)
Av Naciones Unidas E2-30 and Office 602, Nunez de Vela Building Metropolitan Floor 6, Quito, Ecuador
Tel.: (593) 23828580
IT Services
N.A.I.C.S.: 541519

Logicalis Group Ltd.   (1)
The Urban Building Part 6th Floor West 3 - 9 Albert Street, Slough, SL1 2BE, Berk-

shire, United Kingdom   **(100%)**
Tel.: (44) 1753 797100
Web Site: http://www.logicalis.com
Sales Range: $1-4.9 Billion
Emp.: 6,500
IT Network Integration Services
N.A.I.C.S.: 541512
Jens Montanana (Chm)

Subsidiary (Domestic):

Inca Software Limited   (2)
110 Buckingham Avenue, Slough, SL1 4PF, Berkshire, United Kingdom
Tel.: (44) 1753 491 310
Software Developer
N.A.I.C.S.: 513210

Subsidiary (Non-US):

Logicalis Andina S.A.C.   (2)
Av La Floresta 497 Of 201, Miraflores, Lima, 41, Peru
Tel.: (51) 16119696
Logistics Consulting Servies
N.A.I.C.S.: 541614

Logicalis Australia Pty Limited   (2)
Level 3 Tower B 112-118 Talavera Road, Sydney, 2113, NSW, Australia
Tel.: (61) 298059805
Web Site: http://www.au.logicalis.com
Sales Range: $10-24.9 Million
Emp.: 48
Information Technology & Consulting Services
N.A.I.C.S.: 541512
Paul Crilly (CFO)

Logicalis Brasil Importacao Exportacao Ltda   (2)
Web Site: http://www.br.promonlogicalis.com
Logistics Consulting Servies
N.A.I.C.S.: 541614

Logicalis Deutschland GmbH   (2)
Siemensstrasse 10, 63263, Neu-Isenburg, Germany
Tel.: (49) 610277860
Web Site: https://www.de.logicalis.com
Information Technology Consulting Services
N.A.I.C.S.: 541512

Logicalis Hong Kong Limited   (2)
Suites 1401-03 14/F 1063 King s Road, Quarry Bay, Hong Kong, China (Hong Kong)   **(100%)**
Tel.: (852) 21728888
Web Site: http://www.ap.logicalis.com
Logistics Consulting Servies
N.A.I.C.S.: 541614
James Tay (CEO)

Logicalis Ireland Limited   (2)
Donnybrook House 36-42 Donnybrook Road, Sandyford Industrial Estate, D04 C6X9, Dublin, 2, Ireland
Tel.: (353) 16582800
Web Site: http://www.ie.logicalis.com
Sales Range: $25-49.9 Million
IT & Analytics Services
N.A.I.C.S.: 541519

Logicalis Spain SL   (2)
Avda Diagonal 569 2A Planta Edificio L'Illa Diagonal, 08029, Barcelona, Spain
Tel.: (34) 93 363 25 90
Web Site: http://www.logicalis.com
Sales Range: $25-49.9 Million
IT & Analytic Services
N.A.I.C.S.: 541519
Alex Zaragoza (CEO)

Subsidiary (Domestic):

Logicalis UK Limited   (2)
Building 8 Ground Floor Foundation Park Roxborough Way, Maidenhead, SL6 3UD, Berkshire, United Kingdom
Tel.: (44) 1753777200
Web Site: http://www.uk.logicalis.com
Sales Range: $50-74.9 Million
IT Network Integration Services
N.A.I.C.S.: 541519

Subsidiary (US):

Logicalis, Inc.   (2)
1 Penn Plz 51st Fl Ste 5130, New York, NY 10119
Tel.: (212) 596-7160

Web Site: http://www.us.logicalis.com
Information Technology Solutions & Managed Services
N.A.I.C.S.: 541512
Mike Martin (Sr VP-Solutions & Svcs)

Branch (Domestic):

Logicalis US   (3)
2600 S Telegraph Rd Ste 200, Bloomfield Hills, MI 48302
Tel.: (248) 957-5600
Web Site: https://www.us.logicalis.com
Emp.: 77
Information Technology Solutions & Managed Services
N.A.I.C.S.: 541519
Nancy Saltzman (Gen Counsel, Sec & Sr VP)

Subsidiary (Non-US):

Logicalis-Minters GmbH   (2)
Max Planck Strasse 35, 50858, Cologne, Germany
Tel.: (49) 2234954180
Information Technology Consulting Services
N.A.I.C.S.: 541512

NetstarLogicalis Malaysia Sdn Bhd   (2)
Suite 3b-20-6 20th Floor Block 3b Plaza Sentral Jalan Stesen Sentral 5, Kuala Lumpur, 50470, Malaysia
Tel.: (60) 322723388
Sales Range: $25-49.9 Million
Emp.: 15
Information Technology Consulting Services
N.A.I.C.S.: 541512

Siticom GmbH   (2)
Gutenbergstrasse 10, 64331, Weiterstadt, Germany
Tel.: (49) 8921540440
Web Site: http://www.siticom.de
Telecommunication Servicesb
N.A.I.C.S.: 517810
Ruth Colmie-Konig (Mktg Mgr)

Logicalis Guernsey Limited   (1)
Pitronnerie Road, Saint Peter Port, GY1 2RF, Guernsey
Tel.: (44) 1481737000
IT Services
N.A.I.C.S.: 541519
Rene Brun (Gen Mgr)

Logicalis Jersey Limited   (1)
Rue A La Dame Five Oaks, Saint Saviour, JE2 7NH, Jersey
Tel.: (44) 1534288000
Web Site: http://www.je.logicalis.com
IT Services
N.A.I.C.S.: 541519
Jonathan Crichard (Mng Dir)

Logicalis Malaysia Sdn. Bhd.   (1)
Suites 6-02 Level 6 Menara Sunway Visio Lingkaran SV Sunway Velocity, 55100, Kuala Lumpur, Malaysia
Tel.: (60) 327282713
IT Services
N.A.I.C.S.: 541519

Logicalis Mexico, S. de R.L. de C.V.   (1)
Av Ejercito Nacional 769 Floor 8 of the Miyana Business and, Commercial Center, 11570, Mexico, Mexico
Tel.: (52) 5568238872
IT Services
N.A.I.C.S.: 541519

Logicalis Paraguay S.A.   (1)
Torre 1 del Paseo La Galeria - Piso 15, Avda Santa Teresa between Aviadores del Chaco and Herminio Maldonado, Asuncion, 1827, Paraguay
Tel.: (595) 21695636
IT Services
N.A.I.C.S.: 541519

Logicalis Pte. Limited   (1)
Room 902 Shen Tian Building No 42-46 Shen Tian Road, Siming District, Xiamen, 361003, Fujian, China
Tel.: (86) 5925155052
IT Services
N.A.I.C.S.: 541519

Logicalis Puerto Rico Inc.   (1)

1225 Ave Juan Ponce de Leon Ste PH 5
Workshop Ste 5, San Juan, PR 00907
Tel.: (939) 260-9756
IT Services
N.A.I.C.S.: 541519

Logicalis SA (Pty) Ltd
Ground Floor Bergzicht Building Tygerberg
Office Park, 163 Uys Krige Drive Plattek-
loof, Cape Town, South Africa
Tel.: (27) 219356600
Web Site: https://www.za.logicalis.com
IT Services
N.A.I.C.S.: 541519
Frikkie Grobler *(CEO)*

Logicalis Shanghai Limited **(1)**
Suites 2201-02 22F Eton Place West A
Tower 69 Dong Fang Road, Pu Dong New
Area, Shanghai, 200120, China
Tel.: (86) 2151088393
IT Services
N.A.I.C.S.: 541519

Logicalis Singapore Pte. Limited **(1)**
80 Pasir Panjang Road 17-84 Mapletree
Business City II, Singapore, 117372, Singa-
pore
Tel.: (65) 63273368
IT Services
N.A.I.C.S.: 541519

Orange Networks GmbH **(1)**
Sachsentor 26, Bergedorf, 21029, Ham-
burg, Germany
Tel.: (49) 4073923720
Web Site: https://www.orange-networks.com
IT Services
N.A.I.C.S.: 541519

**PT Westcon International
Indonesia** **(1)**
MD Place Tower 1 5th Floor Unit 2 Jl Setia-
budi Selatan No 7, Jakarta, 12910, Indone-
sia
Tel.: (62) 2180621400
Web Site: https://www.westconcomstor.com
IT Services
N.A.I.C.S.: 541519

PT iZeno Teknologi Indonesia **(1)**
World Trade Center 3 Lt 29 Jl Jend
Sudirman Kav 29-31, Jakarta Selatan,
12920, Indonesia
Tel.: (62) 2129608211
Information Technology Services
N.A.I.C.S.: 541511

PT. Packet Systems Indonesia **(1)**
Manhattan Square Mid Tower - 25/f Jl TB
Simatupang kav 1s, Jakarta, 12560, Indo-
nesia
Tel.: (62) 2129710500
Web Site: https://www.packet-systems.com
IT Services
N.A.I.C.S.: 541519

**Redbox Consulting Services
Limited** **(1)**
3 Sceptre House Hornbeam Square North,
Harrogate, HG2 8PB, North Yorkshire,
United Kingdom
Tel.: (44) 1423810985
Web Site: https://redboxcs.com
Research & Consulting Services
N.A.I.C.S.: 541618

**Thomas Duryea Logicalis Asia Pacific
MSC Sdn. Bhd.** **(1)**
L2-01 CoPlace3 Block 3740 Persiaran
APEC Cyber 8, 63500, Cyberjaya, Selan-
gor, Malaysia
Tel.: (60) 1800651484
IT Services
N.A.I.C.S.: 541519

WG Services, Inc. **(1)**
PO Box 7605, Porter Ranch, CA 91327
Tel.: (818) 858-0044
Web Site: http://wgservicesinc.com
Cardboard Box Whslr
N.A.I.C.S.: 424130

WGEO Switzerland GmbH **(1)**
Balz-Zimmermann-Strasse 7, 8302, Kloten,
Switzerland
Tel.: (41) 582698131
Web Site: https://www.westconcomstor.com
IT Services
N.A.I.C.S.: 541519

Walter Ludwig *(Mng Dir)*

Westcon Africa (Kenya) Limited **(1)**
LR No 209/18559 Chiromo Road 5th Floor
Tower 2 The Mirage, Westlands, 00100,
Nairobi, Kenya
Tel.: (254) 204201000
IT Services
N.A.I.C.S.: 541519

**Westcon Africa (Mauritius)
Limited** **(1)**
25 Vishnu Kchetra Street, 11411, Port
Louis, Mauritius
Tel.: (230) 2101200
IT Services
N.A.I.C.S.: 541519

Westcon Africa (Morocco) SARL **(1)**
16 Rue des Asphodeles Angle Boulevard
Ghandi, Casablanca, 20190, Morocco
Tel.: (212) 522234750
IT Services
N.A.I.C.S.: 541519

Westcon Africa Angola Limited **(1)**
Centro de Logistica do Talatona Armazem
F06, Talatona, Luanda, Angola
Tel.: (244) 226431377
IT Services
N.A.I.C.S.: 541519

**Westcon Africa Distribution (Nigeria)
Limited** **(1)**
17A Remi Fani Kayode Avenue, Ikeja, La-
gos, Nigeria
Tel.: (234) 16322936
IT Services
N.A.I.C.S.: 541519

Westcon Denmark ApS **(1)**
Egegardsvej 39C, 2610, Rodovre, Denmark
Tel.: (45) 44928600
IT Services
N.A.I.C.S.: 541519

**Westcon Group (Thailand) Co.
Limited** **(1)**
9th Floor 444 Olympia Thai Tower Ratch-
adaphisek Road Samsen Nok, Huai
Khwang, Bangkok, 10310, Thailand
Tel.: (66) 293894779
IT Services
N.A.I.C.S.: 541519

**Westcon Group (Vietnam) Co.
Limited** **(1)**
5th Floor 68 Nguyen Du Street, Hoan Kiem
District, Hanoi, Vietnam
Tel.: (84) 439367905
IT Services
N.A.I.C.S.: 541519

Westcon Group Austria GmbH **(1)**
Brown-Boveri-Strasse 6/15, 2351, Wiener
Neudorf, Austria
Tel.: (43) 22368644440
IT Services
N.A.I.C.S.: 541519

Westcon Group Germany GmbH **(1)**
Franklinstr 28/29, 10587, Berlin, Germany
Tel.: (49) 3034603300
IT Services
N.A.I.C.S.: 541519

Westcon Group Italia S.R.L. **(1)**
Via Paracelso 6 Palazzo Liocorno, 20864,
Agrate Brianza, MB, Italy
Tel.: (39) 039607221
IT Services
N.A.I.C.S.: 541519

Westcon Group Netherlands B.V. **(1)**
Loodsboot 19, 3991 CJ, Houten, Nether-
lands
Tel.: (31) 302489411
Information Technology Services
N.A.I.C.S.: 541511

**Westcon Group Poland Sp.
Z.O.O.** **(1)**
Budynek Business Garden III Pietro ul
Zwirki i Wigury 16A, 02-092, Warsaw, Po-
land
Tel.: (48) 222253172
IT Services
N.A.I.C.S.: 541519

**Westcon Group Portugal, Sociedade
Unipessoal, Limitada** **(1)**

Rua Ivone Silva - Edificio Arcis 6-6oD,
1050-124, Lisbon, Portugal
Tel.: (351) 210310210
IT Services
N.A.I.C.S.: 541519

Westcon Group Pte. Limited **(1)**
150 Kampong Ampat 06-09 KA Centre, Sin-
gapore, 368324, Singapore
Tel.: (65) 64248442
IT Services
N.A.I.C.S.: 541519

Westcon International, Limited **(1)**
Chandler's House Wilkinson Road,
Cirencester, GL7 1YT, Gloucestershire,
United Kingdom
Tel.: (44) 1285647000
IT Services
N.A.I.C.S.: 541519

Westcon LLC **(1)**
Office G28 Ground Floor PC 118 Regus
Business Center, PO Box 395, Bait
Mahmyiat Al Qurum Shatti Al Qurum, Mus-
cat, Oman
Tel.: (968) 90402055
IT Services
N.A.I.C.S.: 541519

**Westcon Middle East Bahrain
WLL** **(1)**
21st Floor Office No 2223 Building 2504
Almoayyed Tower, Road 2832 Block 428 Al
Seef District, Manama, Bahrain
Tel.: (973) 17566705
Information Technology Services
N.A.I.C.S.: 541511

Westcon Saudi Company LLC **(1)**
2nd Floor Unit 2 Building 8894 King Abdul
Aziz Branch Road, PO Box 325151, Al Wa-
zarath, Riyadh, 12622, Saudi Arabia
Tel.: (966) 112054325
Information Technology Services
N.A.I.C.S.: 541511

Westcon Solutions (HK) Limited **(1)**
Unit 11-13 8/F Global Gateway Tower 63
Wing Hong Street, Cheung Sha Wan, Kow-
loon, China (Hong Kong)
Tel.: (852) 23977002
IT Services
N.A.I.C.S.: 541519

**Westcon Solutions (M) Sdn.
Bhd.** **(1)**
Suite 506 Block C Pusat Dagangan Phileo
Damansara 1 No 9 Jalan 16/11, 46350,
Petaling Jaya, Selangor, Malaysia
Tel.: (60) 379318393
IT Services
N.A.I.C.S.: 541519

**Westcon Solutions Philippines,
Inc.** **(1)**
Unit 6and7 9F Wilcon IT Hub 2251 Chino
Roces Avenue, Makati, 1223, Philippines
Tel.: (63) 26838199
IT Services
N.A.I.C.S.: 541519

iZeno Private Limited **(1)**
351 Braddell Road 04-02, Singapore,
579713, Singapore
Tel.: (65) 61002788
Web Site: https://www.izeno.com
Information Technology Services
N.A.I.C.S.: 541511

DATAVAN INTERNATIONAL CORP.
10F No 186 Jian 1st Rd, Zhonghe,
New Taipei City, 235, Taiwan
Tel.: (886) 282272556
Web Site:
    https://www.datavan.com.tw
Year Founded: 1986
3521—(TPE)
Rev.: $7,987,149
Assets: $38,313,291
Liabilities: $22,473,845
Net Worth: $15,839,446
Earnings: ($2,686,865)
Fiscal Year-end: 12/31/22
Electronic Products Mfr
N.A.I.C.S.: 334111

Chuan Yung Lin *(Chm)*

Subsidiaries:

Maincon Corporation **(1)**
11F No 186 Jian 1st Rd, Zhonghe Dist,
New Taipei City, 23552, Taiwan
Tel.: (886) 282278229
Web Site: https://maincon.com.tw
Electronic Product Mfr & Distr
N.A.I.C.S.: 336320

DATAWALK S.A.
Rzezicza 32-33, 50-130, Wroclaw,
Poland
Tel.: (48) 717072174
Web Site: http://www.datawalk.pl
DAT—(WAR)
Rev.: $6,545,732
Assets: $13,276,169
Liabilities: $10,122,713
Net Worth: $3,153,455
Earnings: ($7,151,677)
Fiscal Year-end: 12/31/23
Software Development Services
N.A.I.C.S.: 541511
Gabe Gotthard *(CEO)*

DATAWORDS DATASIA SARL
18 bis rue de Villiers, Levallois-
Perret, France
Tel.: (33) 1 74 33 80 80
Web Site:
    http://www.datawordsgroup.com
Year Founded: 2000
Multilingual Technology Services
N.A.I.C.S.: 513210
Stanislas De Nervo *(Mng Dir)*

Subsidiaries:

Vanksen Group **(1)**
7 rue des Merovingiens - 1er Etage, ZA du
Bourmicht, Bertrange, L-8070, Luxembourg
Tel.: (352) 48 90 90
Web Site: http://www.vanksengroup.com
Emp.: 75
Communications, Production (Ad, Film,
Broadcast), Promotions, Viral/Buzz/Word of
Mouth, Web (Banner Ads, Pop-ups, etc.)
N.A.I.C.S.: 541810

DATBIM SA
432 rue du Bourg, 38620, Montferrat,
France
Tel.: (33) 476374293
Web Site: http://www.datbim.com
Engineering Consulting Services
N.A.I.C.S.: 541330

DATECS LTD.
115A Tsarigradsko shosse, 1784, So-
fia, Bulgaria
Tel.: (359) 29740055
Web Site: http://www.datecs.bg
Year Founded: 1990
Sales Range: $25-49.9 Million
Emp.: 250
Office Equipment Mfr & Distr
N.A.I.C.S.: 333310
Nikolay Iliev *(Pres)*

DATELINE RESOURCES LTD.
Level 29 2 Chifley Square, Sydney,
2000, NSW, Australia
Tel.: (61) 439449999
Web Site:
    https://www.datelineresources.com
DTR—(ASX)
Assets: $6,696,711
Liabilities: $4,302,437
Net Worth: $2,394,275
Earnings: ($11,510,035)
Fiscal Year-end: 06/30/24
Gold Mining Services
N.A.I.C.S.: 212220
John Smith *(CFO & Sec)*

DATELINE UK LTD.

Dateline UK Ltd.—(Continued)

1 Cooks Barn, Turkey Mill, Maidstone, ME14 5PP, Kent, United Kingdom
Tel.: (44) 1622753311   UK
Web Site: http://www.dateline.co.uk
Year Founded: 1967
Sales Range: $10-24.9 Million
Emp.: 80
Online Dating Services
N.A.I.C.S.: 812990
Conrad Morris *(Mng Dir)*

DATENTECHNIK AG
Richardstraut St 43, Vienna, 1230, Austria
Tel.: (43) 1740700
Web Site: http://www.datentechnik.com
Year Founded: 1979
Sales Range: $150-199.9 Million
Emp.: 600
Computer Peripherals & Software Mfr
N.A.I.C.S.: 334118
George Szlatinay *(CEO)*

Subsidiaries:
Datentechnik d.o.o.   (1)
Dinarska 67, 10000, Zagreb, Croatia
Tel.: (385) 13014081
Web Site: http://www.datentechnik.com
Custom Computer Programming Services
N.A.I.C.S.: 541511

DATEV EG
Paumgartnerstrasse 6 14, 90429, Nuremberg, Germany
Tel.: (49) 911 319 0
Web Site: http://www.datev.de
Year Founded: 1966
Sales Range: $900-999.9 Million
Emp.: 5,844
Accounting Software Developer
N.A.I.C.S.: 513210
Robert Mayr *(Chm-Exec Bd)*

Subsidiaries:
DATEV Hungary   (1)
Galagonya u 5, 1036, Budapest, Hungary
Tel.: (36) 14360500
Web Site: http://www.datev.hu
Software Development Services
N.A.I.C.S.: 541511

DATEV KOINOS s.r.l.   (1)
Via A Bertani 6, 20154, Milan, Italy
Tel.: (39) 023183021
Web Site: http://www.datevkoinos.it
Software Development Services
N.A.I.C.S.: 541511
Massimo Barba *(Dir-Sls)*

DATEV.at GmbH   (1)
Strohgasse 14C, 1030, Vienna, Austria
Tel.: (43) 150360610
Web Site: http://www.datev.at
Software Development Services
N.A.I.C.S.: 541511

DATEV.cz s.r.o.   (1)
Veveri 9, 602 00, Brno, Czech Republic
Tel.: (420) 541428911
Web Site: http://www.datev.cz
Software Development Services
N.A.I.C.S.: 541511

DATEV.pl Sp. z o.o.   (1)
ul Plocka 15, 01-231, Warsaw, Poland
Tel.: (48) 228621700
Web Site: http://www.datev.pl
Software Development Services
N.A.I.C.S.: 541511
Piotr Marcin Franciszkowski *(Chm-Mgmt Bd)*

DATIWARE MARITIME INFRA LTD.
Adam s Court 1st Floor Baner Road, Pune, 411045, Maharashtra, India
Tel.: (91) 7410090100
Web Site: https://www.datiware.com

Year Founded: 1992
519413—(BOM)
Rev.: $509,527
Assets: $947,345
Liabilities: $893,490
Net Worth: $53,855
Earnings: $180,934
Emp.: 7
Fiscal Year-end: 03/31/21
Aquaculture Farming Services
N.A.I.C.S.: 112512
Ashok Bhalchandra Patil *(Chm)*

DATONG COAL INDUSTRY CO., LTD.
Xinpingwang, Yungang District, Datong, 037003, Shanxi, China
Tel.: (86) 3527010476
Web Site: https://dtmy.jnkgjtnews.com
Year Founded: 2001
601001—(SHG)
Rev.: $2,257,869,501
Assets: $5,927,124,771
Liabilities: $2,952,051,776
Net Worth: $2,975,072,995
Earnings: $427,348,551
Emp.: 22,200
Fiscal Year-end: 12/31/22
Coal Mining & Production Services
N.A.I.C.S.: 212115
Wangguo Wu *(Chm)*

DATONG COAL MINE GROUP CO., LTD.
Xinpingwang, Datong, 037003, China
Tel.: (86) 352 7868200
Web Site: http://www.dtcoalmine.com
Year Founded: 1949
Sales Range: $25-49.9 Billion
Coal Product Mfr & Distr
N.A.I.C.S.: 325998
Zhang Youxi *(Chm)*

Subsidiaries:
Datong Coal Industry Jinyu Kaolin Chemical Co., Ltd.   (1)
Datong Coal Mine Group Tashan Recycling Economy Park, Datong, Shanxi, China.
Tel.: (86) 51255110065
Web Site: http://www.jinyukaolin.com
Coal Mining Services
N.A.I.C.S.: 212115

Foreign Trade & Economic Cooperation Co., Ltd.   (1)
Xinping Wang Mine Area, Datong, 037003, China
Tel.: (86) 3527868435
Coal Mining Services
N.A.I.C.S.: 212115

DATRIX S.P.A.
Foro Buonaparte 71, 20121, Milan, Italy
Tel.: (39) 0276281064
Web Site: https://www.datrixgroup.com
Year Founded: 2010
DATA—(EUR)
Software Development Services
N.A.I.C.S.: 541511
Claudio Zamboni *(Chief Revenue Officer)*

Subsidiaries:
ByTek S.r.l.   (1)
Foro Buonaparte 71, 20121, Milan, Italy
Tel.: (39) 0276281064
Web Site: https://bytek.ai
Information Technology Services
N.A.I.C.S.: 518210

FinScience S.r.l.   (1)
Foro Buonaparte 71, 20121, Cusano Milanino, Italy
Tel.: (39) 0276281064
Web Site: https://datrixgroup.com
Software Solution & Finance Services

N.A.I.C.S.: 518210

DATRON AG
In den Gansackern 5, Muhltal, D-64367, Hessen, Germany
Tel.: (49) 615114190
Web Site: https://www.datron.de
Year Founded: 1969
DAR—(MUN)
Rev.: $70,448,983
Assets: $62,479,042
Liabilities: $15,321,716
Net Worth: $47,157,326
Earnings: $5,099,879
Emp.: 311
Fiscal Year-end: 12/31/23
Automation Systems & Electronic Component Mfr & Sales
N.A.I.C.S.: 333248

Subsidiaries:
Datron Austria GmbH   (1)
Ramsau 149, Ramsau am Dachstein, 8972, Liezen, Austria
Tel.: (43) 368781811
Web Site: http://www.datron.at
Metal Machinery Distr
N.A.I.C.S.: 423830

Datron France SAS   (1)
Primavera Park 54 Allee Primavera Promery, 74370, Pringy, France
Tel.: (33) 480730026
Web Site: http://www.datron.fr
CNC Machine Tool Mfr
N.A.I.C.S.: 333517

Datron Technology CZ s.r.o.   (1)
Podnikatelska 2902/4, Brno, Czech Republic
Tel.: (420) 455458480
Web Site: http://www.datrontechnology.cz
CNC Machine Tool Mfr
N.A.I.C.S.: 333517

Datron Technology s.r.o.   (1)
A Hlinku 2, Detva, 962 12, Banska Bystrica, Slovakia
Tel.: (421) 455458480
Web Site: http://www.datron.sk
CNC Machine Tool Mfr
N.A.I.C.S.: 333517

Datron Tool Technology GmbH   (1)
Am Raupenstein 12, 64678, Lindenfels, Germany
Tel.: (49) 6255968909
Web Site: http://www.datron-tool-technology.de
CNC Machine Tool Mfr
N.A.I.C.S.: 333517

DATRONIX HOLDINGS LIMITED
19/Floor 499 Kings Road North Point Industrial Building, Hong Kong, China (Hong Kong)
Tel.: (852) 25648477   BM
Web Site: https://www.datronixhldgs.com.hk
Year Founded: 2000
0889—(HKG)
Rev.: $33,459,060
Assets: $118,202,828
Liabilities: $9,792,383
Net Worth: $108,410,445
Earnings: $3,554,063
Emp.: 1,114
Fiscal Year-end: 12/31/22
Conglomerates & Holding Companies
N.A.I.C.S.: 551112
Nina Margaret Siu *(Exec Dir)*

Subsidiaries:
Datatronic Distribution, Inc.   (1)
28151 Highway 74, Menifee, CA 92585
Tel.: (951) 928-7700
Web Site: https://www.datatronics.com
Industrial Electronic Mfr
N.A.I.C.S.: 334419

DATUM VENTURES INC.

19335 96 Avenue Unit 103, Surrey, V4N 4C4, BC, Canada
Tel.: (604) 562-5737   BC
Year Founded: 2011
DAT.H—(TSXV)
Assets: $186,916
Liabilities: $39
Net Worth: $186,877
Earnings: ($12,518)
Fiscal Year-end: 03/31/23
Investment Services
N.A.I.C.S.: 523999
James T. Gillis *(CFO)*

DAULAT SECURITIES LIMITED
3rd Floor 86 Canning Street, Kolkata, 700 001, West Bengal, India
Tel.: (91) 9038397090
Web Site: https://www.daulatsec.com
Year Founded: 1992
530171—(BOM)
Rev.: $288,972
Assets: $2,083,923
Liabilities: $256,172
Net Worth: $1,827,751
Earnings: $188,448
Fiscal Year-end: 03/31/21
Security Brokerage Services
N.A.I.C.S.: 523150
Jitendra Kochar *(Mng Dir)*

DAUN & CIE. AG
Bahnhofstrasse 21, 26180, Rastede, Germany
Tel.: (49) 440299800
Web Site: http://www.daun-ag.de
Sales Range: $1-4.9 Billion
Emp.: 6
Holding Company; Textile Mfr
N.A.I.C.S.: 551112
Claas E. Daun *(Chm)*

DAUNAT BRETAGNE
ZI de Bellevue, 22202, Guingamp, France
Tel.: (33) 296401060
Web Site: http://www.daunat.com
Emp.: 330
Commercial Bakery
N.A.I.C.S.: 311812
Bruno Merel *(Pres)*

DAUPHIN HUMANDESIGN GROUP GMBH & CO. KG
Espanstrasse 36, Offenhausen, 91238, Germany
Tel.: (49) 915817700   De
Web Site: http://www.dauphin-group.in
Year Founded: 1992
Sales Range: $150-199.9 Million
Emp.: 800
Holding Company; Office Furniture Mfr
N.A.I.C.S.: 551112
Friedrich-Wilhelm Dauphin *(Founder, CEO & Mng Dir)*

Subsidiaries:
Burositzmobelfabrik Friedrich- W. Dauphin GmbH & Co. KG   (1)
Espanstrasse 29, 91238, Offenhausen, Germany   (100%)
Tel.: (49) 9158170
Web Site: http://www.dauphin.de
Sales Range: $50-74.9 Million
Emp.: 300
Office Furniture Mfr
N.A.I.C.S.: 337211
Friedrich-Wilhelm Dauphin *(Founder & Mng Dir)*

Dauphin (SEA) Pte. Ltd.   (1)
52 Genting Lane, 07 02 03 Hiang Kie Complex 1, 349560, Singapore, Singapore
Tel.: (65) 67481600
Mfr of Office Furniture
N.A.I.C.S.: 337127

Dauphin Espana S.A. (1)
Galileo Galilei 14, Poligono Industrial La Garena, 28806, Madrid, Alcala de Henares, Spain
Tel.: (34) 918845555
Web Site:
http://www.wdauphinespanasa.com
Sales Range: $25-49.9 Million
Emp.: 22
Mfr of Office Furniture
N.A.I.C.S.: 337127

Dauphin France S. A. (1)
6 Allee Du Parc De Garlande, F-92220, Bagneux, France
Tel.: (33) 146541590
Web Site: http://www.dauphin-france.com
Sales Range: $25-49.9 Million
Emp.: 10
Mfr of Office Furniture
N.A.I.C.S.: 337127
Elke Dauphin (Mng Dir)

Dauphin HumanDesign AG (1)
Kirschgartenstrasse 7, CH-4051, Basel, Switzerland
Tel.: (41) 612838000
Web Site: http://www.dauphin.ch
Sales Range: $10-24.9 Million
Emp.: 5
Office Furniture Mfr
N.A.I.C.S.: 337127
Claude Frey (Mgr)

Dauphin HumanDesign B.V. (1)
Staalweg 1-3, 4104 AS, Culemborg, Netherlands
Tel.: (31) 345533292
Web Site: http://www.dauphin.nl
Sales Range: $25-49.9 Million
Emp.: 13
Office Furniture Mfr
N.A.I.C.S.: 337127

Dauphin HumanDesign Belgium NV/SA (1)
Terbekehofdreef 46, Wilrijk, 2610, Antwerp, Belgium
Tel.: (32) 38877850
Web Site: http://www.dauphinnv-sa.be
Sales Range: $1-9.9 Million
Emp.: 3
Mfr of Ergonomic Office Furniture
N.A.I.C.S.: 337127

Dauphin HumanDesign UK Limited (1)
Clerkenwell 3rd Floor 11 Northburgh Street, London, EC1V 0AH, United Kingdom
Tel.: (44) 207 2537774
Office Furniture Distr
N.A.I.C.S.: 423210

Dauphin Industry (Schweiz) uniq solution gmbh (1)
Malzgasse 20, 4052, Basel, Switzerland
Tel.: (41) 61 3338800
Web Site: http://www.uniq.ch
Office Furniture Distr
N.A.I.C.S.: 423210

Dauphin Italia (1)
Via Gaetano Crespi 12, 20134, Milan, Italy
Tel.: (39) 0276018394
Web Site: http://www.dauphin.it
Sales Range: $25-49.9 Million
Emp.: 6
Mfr of Office Furniture
N.A.I.C.S.: 337127
Friedrich-Wilhelm Dauphin (Pres)

Dauphin North America (1)
100 Fulton St, Boonton, NJ 07005
Tel.: (973) 263-1100
Web Site: http://www.dauphin.com
Sales Range: $75-99.9 Million
Emp.: 85
Furniture Mfr & Distr
N.A.I.C.S.: 423210
Nick Bayvel (CEO)

Dauphin Office Seating S.A. (Pty) Ltd. (1)
62 Hume Rd Dunkeld, PO Box 55551, Northlands, 2116, Johannesburg, South Africa
Tel.: (27) 114479888
Web Site: http://www.dauphin.co.za
Sales Range: $25-49.9 Million
Emp.: 10
Mfr of Office Furniture

N.A.I.C.S.: 337127

Dauphin Scandinavia A/S (1)
Frederikssuntsvej 272, DK-2700, Herlev, Scandinavia, Denmark
Tel.: (45) 44537053
Web Site: http://www.dauphin.dk
Mfr of Office Furniture
N.A.I.C.S.: 337127

Dauphin-RIM Polska Sp. z o.o. (1)
ulica Walicow 11 (Aurum Building), PL-00-851, Warsaw, Poland
Tel.: (48) 225839138
Mfr of Office Furniture
N.A.I.C.S.: 337127
Anna Jaworska (Mgr)

Trendline Office Interiors Ltd. (1)
Peter St, Blackburn, BB1 5LH, Lancashire, United Kingdom
Tel.: (44) 25452220
Web Site: http://www.trendline-interiors.co.uk
Sales Range: $25-49.9 Million
Emp.: 41
Office Furniture Designer & Mfr
N.A.I.C.S.: 337127

DAURA CAPITAL CORP.
543 Granivillle Street Suite 501, Vancouver, V6C 1X8, BC, Canada
Tel.: (604) 669-0660
Year Founded: 2018
DUR.P—(TSXV)
Assets: $1,056
Liabilities: $327,850
Net Worth: ($326,795)
Earnings: ($17,165)
Fiscal Year-end: 12/31/23
Business Consulting Services
N.A.I.C.S.: 522299
Mark D. Sumner (CEO)

DAVANGERE SUGAR COMPANY LIMITED
73/1 Shamanur Road, Post Box No 312, Davangere null, Bengaluru, 577004, Karnataka, India
Tel.: (91) 8192201623
Web Site:
https://www.davangeresugar.com
Year Founded: 1970
543267—(BOM)
Rev.: $16,990,155
Assets: $81,035,955
Liabilities: $46,740,330
Net Worth: $34,295,625
Earnings: $775,320
Emp.: 207
Fiscal Year-end: 03/31/22
Sugar Products Mfr
N.A.I.C.S.: 311314

DAVENHAM GROUP PLC
55 King Street, Manchester, M2 4LQ, United Kingdom
Tel.: (44) 1618328484
Web Site:
http://www.davenhamasset.co.uk
Year Founded: 1991
Emp.: 250
Financial & Leasing Services
N.A.I.C.S.: 522320

Subsidiaries:

Davenham Group Holdings plc (1)
The Chancery 58 Spring Gardens, Manchester, M2 1EW, United Kingdom
Tel.: (44) 1618328484
Management & Leasing Services
N.A.I.C.S.: 525990
David Coates (CEO)

Subsidiary (Domestic):

Davenham Trade Finance Limited (2)
55 King Street, Manchester, M2 4LG, United Kingdom
Tel.: (44) 161 832 8484

Web Site:
http://www.davenhamtradefinance.co.uk
Emp.: 200
Trade Finance Services
N.A.I.C.S.: 522299
Vince Tovey (Mng Dir)

DAVI II FARMACEUTICA S.A.
Estrada Consiglieri Pedroso 69 B-Queluz de Baixo, 2730-055, Barcarena, Portugal
Tel.: (351) 214340000
Web Site: http://www.davi.pt
Pharmaceuticals Product Mfr
N.A.I.C.S.: 325412

DAVIAN CONSTRUCTION LTD.
740 Logan Avenue, Winnipeg, R3E 1M9, MB, Canada
Tel.: (204) 783-7251
Web Site:
https://www.davianconstruction.com
Year Founded: 1974
Rev.: $10,346,449
Emp.: 36
Building Construction Services
N.A.I.C.S.: 238190
Ian A. Balcain (Owner & Pres)

Subsidiaries:

Heather Painting & Decorating Ltd (1)
270 Lulu St, Winnipeg, R3E 1X9, MB, Canada
Tel.: (204) 783-2690
Painting & Decorating Services
N.A.I.C.S.: 238320

DAVICOM SEMICONDUCTOR, INC.
No 6 Li-Hsin Road 6, Science Park, Hsin-chu, Taiwan
Tel.: (886) 35798797
Web Site:
https://www.davicom.com.tw
Year Founded: 1996
3094—(TAI)
Rev.: $7,932,633
Assets: $37,673,402
Liabilities: $3,878,446
Net Worth: $33,794,956
Earnings: $1,659,439
Emp.: 74
Fiscal Year-end: 12/31/23
Semiconductor Mfr
N.A.I.C.S.: 334413
Ting Herh (Founder, Chm & Gen Mgr)

DAVICTUS PLC
No 9A 1st Floor Jalan SS15 2A Darul Ehsan, 47500, Subang Jaya, Selangor, Malaysia
Tel.: (60) 356320878
Web Site: https://www.davictus.co.uk
Year Founded: 2015
DVT—(LSE)
Rev.: $381,922
Assets: $621,959
Liabilities: $232,194
Net Worth: $389,766
Earnings: $115,081
Fiscal Year-end: 12/31/23
Investment Management Service
N.A.I.C.S.: 525990
Robert Logan Pincock (CEO)

DAVID CHEVROLET CORVETTE BUICK GMC LTD.
915 Niagara Street, Welland, L3C 1M4, ON, Canada
Tel.: (888) 682-8140
Web Site: http://www.davidchev.com
Year Founded: 1992
New Car Dealers
N.A.I.C.S.: 441110
Greg Sims (Mgr-Internet)

DAVID MORRIS FINE CARS LTD.
17407 111th Ave, Edmonton, T5S 0A1, AB, Canada
Tel.: (780) 484-9000
Web Site:
http://www.davidmorrisfinecars.com-benz.ca
Year Founded: 1986
Rev.: $19,997,339
Emp.: 42
New & Used Car Dealers
N.A.I.C.S.: 441110
David Morris (Pres)

DAVID OPPENHEIMER & COMPANY
11 Burbidge Street, Coquitlam, V3K 7B2, BC, Canada
Tel.: (604) 461-6779
Web Site: https://oppy.com
Year Founded: 1858
Produce Distr
N.A.I.C.S.: 424480
John Anderson (Chm, CEO & Mng Partner)

Subsidiaries:

David Oppenheimer & Company I, LLC (1)
180 Nickerson St Ste 211, Seattle, WA 98109
Tel.: (206) 284-1705
Sales Range: $50-74.9 Million
Emp.: 10
Produce Distr
N.A.I.C.S.: 424480

Oppy Argentina (1)
Juan Segundo Fernandez 256 1 Floor of 9, San Isidro, B1642AMP, Argentina
Tel.: (54) 114 7636398
Fruit Distr
N.A.I.C.S.: 424480

Oppy Chile (1)
Avenida Kennedy 5757 of 302, Las Condes, Chile
Tel.: (56) 2 2430 8500
Emp.: 15
Fruit Distr
N.A.I.C.S.: 424480
Ray Reey (Gen Mgr)

Oppy Costa Rica (1)
Calle 40 Avenida 16 Casa 57, Sabana Sur, San Jose, Costa Rica
Tel.: (506) 2 288 4667
Fruit Distr
N.A.I.C.S.: 424480

Oppy Peru (1)
Calle Monterrey 341 of 501 Urb Chacarilla Del Estanque - Surco, Lima, Peru
Tel.: (51) 1 682 6877
Fruit Distr
N.A.I.C.S.: 424480

DAVID PAJIC DAKA A.D.
Venizelosova 29, 11000, Belgrade, Serbia
Tel.: (381) 11 33 919 66
Web Site: http://www.daka.rs
Year Founded: 1947
Sales Range: $1-9.9 Million
Emp.: 55
Lifting Equipment Mfr
N.A.I.C.S.: 333998

DAVID WOOD BAKING LIMITED
214 Leeds Road, Rothwell, Leeds, LS26 8JD, West Yorkshire, United Kingdom
Tel.: (44) 3453011115
Web Site: http://www.dwbaking.com
Sales Range: $75-99.9 Million
Emp.: 780
Commercial Bakeries
N.A.I.C.S.: 311812
David Wood (Founder)

David Wood Baking Limited—(Continued)

Subsidiaries:

Creative Foods   **(1)**
Unit 19 Aber Park Industrial Estate, Flint,
CH6 5EX, Wales, United Kingdom
Tel.: (44) 1352 897644
Web Site: http://www.creative-foods.co.uk
Sales Range: $25-49.9 Million
Emp.: 142
Grocery Product Distr
N.A.I.C.S.: 424490
Glen Annison (Dir-Site)

DAVIDSON ENMAN LUMBER LTD.
452 42 Avenue SE, Calgary, T2G
1Y5, AB, Canada
Tel.: (403) 243-2566
Web Site: http://www.delumber.com
Year Founded: 1948
Rev.: $14,335,392
Emp.: 75
Lumber & Building Materials Supplier
N.A.I.C.S.: 423310
Greg Davidson (Owner)

DAVIDSTEA INC.
5430 Ferrier street, Mount-Royal,
H4P 1M2, QC, Canada   Ca
Web Site: https://www.davidstea.com
Year Founded: 2008
DAT—(DEU)
Rev.: $45,792,742
Assets: $33,019,132
Liabilities: $16,778,011
Net Worth: $16,241,121
Earnings: ($10,441,044)
Fiscal Year-end: 02/03/24
Tea Mfr & Retailer
N.A.I.C.S.: 311920
Jane Silverstone Segal (Chm)

Subsidiaries:

DavidsTea (USA) Inc.   **(1)**
1124 3rd Ave, New York, NY 10065
Tel.: (212) 717-1116
Tea Accessory Retailer
N.A.I.C.S.: 424490

DAVIE YARDS ASA
Lysaker Torg 12, PO Box 465, 1327,
Lysaker, Norway
Tel.: (47) 67200300
Web Site: http://www.davie.ca
Shipyard Owner & Operator; Water
Transportation Services
N.A.I.C.S.: 336611
Sigurd Lange (CEO)

Subsidiaries:

Chantier Davie Canada Inc.   **(1)**
22 George D Davie, Levis, G6V 0K4, QC,
Canada   **(100%)**
Tel.: (418) 837-5841
Web Site: http://www.davie.ca
Shipyard Owner & Operator
N.A.I.C.S.: 336611
James Davies (Pres)

DAVIS COMMODITIES LIMITED
10 Bukit Batok Crescent 10-01, The
Spire, Singapore, 658079, Singapore
Tel.: (65) 68965333   Ky
Web Site: https://www.daviscl.com
Year Founded: 2022
DTCK—(NASDAQ)
Rev.: $190,724,000
Assets: $29,878,000
Liabilities: $19,620,000
Net Worth: $10,258,000
Earnings: $1,086,000
Emp.: 22
Fiscal Year-end: 12/31/23
Agriculture Product Distr
N.A.I.C.S.: 424510
Abbie Jillia Lee (Chief Admin Officer)

DAVOLINK INC.
112 Beolmal-ro, Dongan-Gu, Anyang,
Gyeonggi-do, Korea (South)
Tel.: (82) 313873240
Web Site: https://www.davolink.co.kr
Year Founded: 2000
340360—(KRS)
Emp.: 64
Wireless Telecommunication Services
N.A.I.C.S.: 517112
Yong-Hwa Lee (CEO)

DAWN CORPORATION
5F Sannomiya Grand Bldg 2 2 21
Isogami Dori, Chuo-ku, Kobe, 651-
0086, Hyogo, Japan
Tel.: (81) 782229700
Web Site: https://www.dawn-
corp.co.jp
Year Founded: 1997
23030—(TKS)
Sales Range: Less than $1 Million
Software Development Services
N.A.I.C.S.: 541511
Masanobu Miyazaki (Pres & CEO)

DAWN PROPERTIES LIMITED
8th Floor Beverley Court 100 Nelson
Mandela Avenue, Harare, Zimbabwe
Tel.: (263) 4707101
Web Site:
   http://www.dawnpropertiesltd.co.zw
Year Founded: 2003
Investment Property Holding Com-
pany
N.A.I.C.S.: 551112
Phibion Gwatidzo (Chm)

Subsidiaries:

Dawn Property Consultancy   **(1)**
8th Floor Beverly Court 100 Nelson Mandela Ave Fourth Street, Harare, Zimbabwe
Tel.: (263) 4707101
Web Site:
   http://www.dawnpropertyconsult.co.zw
Commercial Real Estate Brokerage, Property Management & Valuation Advisory Services
N.A.I.C.S.: 531210
John Kondo (Mng Dir)

DAWNEY & CO., LTD.
Level 8 1 Eagle Street, Brisbane,
4000, QLD, Australia
Tel.: (61) 730240000
Web Site:
   http://www.dawneyco.com.au
Year Founded: 2009
DWY—(NSXA)
Rev.: $1,495,734
Assets: $3,099,130
Liabilities: $211,844
Net Worth: $2,887,286
Earnings: $861,655
Fiscal Year-end: 06/30/21
Investment Services
N.A.I.C.S.: 523999
Mitchell David Dawney (Mng Dir &
Co-Sec)

**DAWNING INFORMATION IN-
DUSTRY CO., LTD.**
Building 36 No 8 Dongbeiwang West
Road, Haidian District, Beijing,
100193, China
Tel.: (86) 1056308016
Web Site: http://www.sugon.com
Year Founded: 1993
603019—(SHG)
Rev.: $1,826,316,910
Assets: $4,466,148,430
Liabilities: $1,975,369,832
Net Worth: $2,490,778,597
Earnings: $216,808,348
Fiscal Year-end: 12/31/22
Computer System Development Ser-
vices

N.A.I.C.S.: 334111
Guo Jie Li (Chm)

**DAWNRAYS PHARMACEUTI-
CAL (HOLDINGS) LTD**
Units 3001-02 30/F CNT Tower 338
Hennessy Road, Wanchai, China
(Hong Kong)
Tel.: (852) 21119708
Web Site: http://www.dawnrays.com
2348—(HKG)
Rev.: $179,386,553
Assets: $515,639,077
Liabilities: $143,597,750
Net Worth: $372,041,327
Earnings: $49,961,480
Emp.: 1,106
Fiscal Year-end: 12/31/22
Pharmaceutical Industry
N.A.I.C.S.: 325412
Yung Lai Hung (Co-Founder)

Subsidiaries:

Suzhou Dawnrays Pharmaceutical
Co., Ltd.   **(1)**
22 Tianling Road Wuzhong Economic De-
velopment District, Suzhou, Jiangsu, China
Tel.: (86) 51265626868
Pharmaceutical Product Mfr & Distr
N.A.I.C.S.: 325412

DAWON NEXVIEW CO.,LTD.
485 Shihwa Hosu-Ro, Danwon-Gu,
Ansan, 15616, Gyeonggi-do, Korea
(South)
Tel.: (82) 3180857899
Web Site: https://www.nexview.co.kr
Year Founded: 2009
323350—(KRS)
Laser Soldering Equipment Mfr
N.A.I.C.S.: 334510
Gi-Jung Nam (Pres & CEO)

DAWONSYS CO., LTD.
485 Shihwa hosu-ro Danwon-gu, An-
san, Gyeonggi-do, Korea (South)
Tel.: (82) 3180853000
Web Site: http://www.dawonsys.co.kr
Year Founded: 1996
068240—(KRS)
Rev.: $160,447,640
Assets: $516,097,452
Liabilities: $358,492,684
Net Worth: $157,604,768
Earnings: ($116,529,970)
Emp.: 548
Fiscal Year-end: 12/31/22
Inductive Heating Systems & Other
Power Supply Products Mfr
N.A.I.C.S.: 334416
Sun-Soon Park (CEO)

Subsidiaries:

Dawonsys Co., Ltd. - Gimcheon
Factory   **(1)**
447 Eomo Ro Eomo Myeon, Gimcheon,
Gyeong Sang Buk do, Korea (South)
Tel.: (82) 544202800
Rail Stock Mfr
N.A.I.C.S.: 336510

**DAWOOD CORPORATION
(PVT.) LTD.**
35-A Empress Rd, 54000, Lahore,
Pakistan
Tel.: (92) 426301601   In
Holding Company
N.A.I.C.S.: 551112

Subsidiaries:

Dawood Hercules Corporation
Limited   **(1)**
Dawood Centre MT Khan Road, Karachi,
Pakistan
Tel.: (92) 2135686001
Web Site: https://www.dawoodhercules.com
Rev.: $1,454,922,069
Assets: $3,694,236,609

Liabilities: $2,354,429,552
Net Worth: $1,339,807,057
Earnings: $191,828,518
Emp.: 39
Fiscal Year-end: 12/31/2019
Fertilizer & Anhydrous Ammonia Mfr
N.A.I.C.S.: 325314
Hussain Dawood (Chm)

Plant (Domestic):

Dawood Hercules Chemicals -
Sheikhupura   **(2)**
28-KM Lahore Sheikhupura Road, Chichoki
Mallian, Sheikhupura, Pakistan
Tel.: (92) 4237360760
Chemicals Mfr
N.A.I.C.S.: 325998

Dawood Lawrencepur Limited   **(1)**
Dawood Centre M T Khan Road, Karachi,
75530, Pakistan
Tel.: (92) 21356322009
Web Site: https://dawoodlawrencepur.com
Rev.: $34,941,962
Assets: $180,592,650
Liabilities: $83,398,859
Net Worth: $97,193,791
Earnings: $11,119,446
Emp.: 183
Fiscal Year-end: 12/31/2020
Yarn & Fabric Mfr & Sales
N.A.I.C.S.: 313240
Shahid Hamid Pracha (Chm)

DAWOOD EQUITIES LIMITED
17th floor Saima trade Tower-A I I
Chundrighar Road, Karachi, 74000,
Pakistan
Tel.: (92) 2132271881
Web Site:
   https://www.dawoodequities.com
DEL—(KAR)
Rev.: $117,843
Assets: $1,701,984
Liabilities: $93,374
Net Worth: $1,608,611
Earnings: $3,443
Emp.: 10
Fiscal Year-end: 06/30/19
Stock Brokerage Services
N.A.I.C.S.: 523150
Abdul Aziz Habib (CEO)

**DAWSON INTERNATIONAL
PLC**
Burnfoot Industrial Estate, Hawick,
TD9 8RJ, Scotland, United Kingdom
Tel.: (44) 1450 365555   UK
Web Site: http://www.dawson-
international.co.uk
Year Founded: 1974
Sales Range: $250-299.9 Million
Emp.: 623
Holding Company; Specialty Textile
Yarns & Apparel Mfr & Distr
N.A.I.C.S.: 551112
David John Bolton (Chm)

Subsidiaries:

Dawson Cashmere LLC   **(1)**
8A Pleasant St, South Natick, MA 01760
Tel.: (508) 651-7910
Web Site: http://www.kinrosscashmere.com
Sales Range: $50-74.9 Million
Emp.: 11
Cashmere Apparel Whslr
N.A.I.C.S.: 424350
Erin Spencer (Office Mgr)

Dawson Fabrics Ltd.   **(1)**
Greenside Mills, Saville Rd Skelmanthorpe,
Huddersfield, HD8 9EE, United
Kingdom   **(100%)**
Tel.: (44) 1484868600
Web Site: http://www.dawson-fab.co.uk
Sales Range: $50-74.9 Million
Emp.: 200
Fabric Mills
N.A.I.C.S.: 313210

DAX-AUTO SA
2034 Avenue De La Resistance,

40990, Saint-Paul-les-Dax, Landes, France
Tel.: (33) 558911178
Web Site:
http://www.daxauto.peugeot.fr
Sales Range: $25-49.9 Million
Emp.: 60
New Car Dealers
N.A.I.C.S.: 441110
Brigitte Maucorps *(DP Mgr)*

DAXIN MATERIALS CORPO-RATION

No 15 Keyuan 1st Rd Central Taiwan Science Park, Taichung, 40763, Taiwan
Tel.: (886) 424608889
Web Site: https://www.daxinmat.com
5234—(TAI)
Rev.: $139,446,052
Assets: $151,805,514
Liabilities: $49,295,953
Net Worth: $102,509,562
Earnings: $17,114,817
Emp.: 431
Fiscal Year-end: 12/31/23
Chemicals Mfr
N.A.I.C.S.: 325998
Cheng-Yih Lin *(Chm)*

DAY LEWIS PLC.

Day Lewis House 2 Peterwood Way, Croydon, CR0 4UQ, Surrey, United Kingdom
Tel.: (44) 208 256 6200
Web Site:
http://www.daylewisplc.co.uk
Year Founded: 1975
Sales Range: $300-349.9 Million
Emp.: 1,267
Pharmaceutical Product Whslr
N.A.I.C.S.: 424210
J. C. Patel *(Co-Founder)*

DAY'S MOTOR GROUP

Swansea Road Garngoch, Swansea, SA4 4LL, United Kingdom
Tel.: (44) 1792 222 111
Web Site: http://www.days.co.uk
Year Founded: 1926
Sales Range: $250-299.9 Million
Emp.: 525
New & Used Car Dealer
N.A.I.C.S.: 441110
Graham M. Day *(Chm & CEO)*

DAYA BUMIMAJU SDN. BHD.

Lot 13B Kawasan Perindustrian MIEL Jakar Phase IV, 24000, Kemaman, Terengganu, Malaysia
Tel.: (60) 98681241
Web Site:
http://www.dayabumimaju.com
Year Founded: 2004
Emp.: 20
Industrial Machinery Repair & Maintenance Services
N.A.I.C.S.: 811310
Azlan Abu Bakar *(Mng Dir)*

DAYA CMT SDN. BHD.

Plot 81 Lebuhraya Kampung Jawa, 11900, Bayan Lepas, Penang, Malaysia
Tel.: (60) 46422280
Emp.: 70
Construction Engineering Services
N.A.I.C.S.: 541330

DAYANG ENTERPRISE HOLD-INGS BERHAD

Sublot 5-10 Lot 46 Block 10 Jalan Taman Raja, PO Box 1134, Miri Concession Land District, 98000, Miri, Sarawak, Malaysia
Tel.: (60) 85420185

Web Site: https://www.desb.net
Year Founded: 1980
DAYANG—(KLS)
Rev.: $208,292,698
Assets: $499,844,444
Liabilities: $150,554,497
Net Worth: $349,289,947
Earnings: $26,526,349
Emp.: 2,161
Fiscal Year-end: 12/31/22
Holding Company; Marine Vessel Mfr, Maintenance & Chartering Services
N.A.I.C.S.: 551112
Yusof Ahmad Shahruddin *(Mng Dir)*

Subsidiaries:

Fortune Triumph Sdn. Bhd.　　　**(1)**
Sublot 5-10 Lot 46 Block 10, Jalan Taman Raja-Hilltop, Miri, 98000, Malaysia
Tel.: (60) 85420185
Emp.: 200
Marine Engineering Services
N.A.I.C.S.: 541330

Perdana Petroleum Berhad　　　**(1)**
Level 18 Block 2 VSQ PJCC Jalan Utara, 46200, Petaling Jaya, Selangor, Malaysia
Tel.: (60) 379318524
Web Site: https://perdana.my
Rev.: $41,614,392
Assets: $174,130,794
Liabilities: $50,251,640
Net Worth: $123,879,153
Earnings: $2,409,524
Emp.: 1,221
Fiscal Year-end: 12/31/2022
Offshore Marine Oil & Gas Services
N.A.I.C.S.: 211120
Oi Wah Leong *(Sec)*

Subsidiary (Domestic):

Intra Oil Services Berhad　　　**(2)**
No 6-8 Jalan 3/3C Batu 7 Jalan Ipoh, Kuala Lumpur, 68100, Malaysia
Tel.: (60) 362578833
Web Site: http://www.intraoil.com.my
Oil & Gas Field Support Services
N.A.I.C.S.: 213112

Subsidiary (Non-US):

Perdana Marine Offshore Pte Ltd　**(2)**
21 Ubi Road 1 05-02A/B, 408724, Singapore, Singapore
Tel.: (65) 65437088
Web Site: http://www.perdana.my
Marine Support Services
N.A.I.C.S.: 483111

DAYDREAM ENTERTAINMENT CO., LTD.

15th floor New Building Hoseong Building 65-gil 20, Yeouido-dong Yeongdeungpo-gu, Seoul, Korea (South)
Tel.: (82) 27618836
Web Site: https://www.daydream.kr
348840—(KRS)
Broadcasting Services
N.A.I.C.S.: 516120

DAYMEN CANADA

55 Valleywood Dr, Markham, L3R 5L9, ON, Canada
Tel.: (905) 944-9400
Web Site: http://www.daymen.ca
Year Founded: 1981
Rev.: $15,472,337
Emp.: 90
Photographic & Digital Imaging Products Distr
N.A.I.C.S.: 423410
Rick Zebryk *(Controller)*

DAYOU PLUS CO., LTD.

509 Dunchondaero, Jungwon-gu, Seongnam, 462-806, Gyeonggi-do, Korea (South)
Tel.: (82) 317377000
Web Site: https://dayouplus.co.kr
Year Founded: 1967

000300—(KRS)
Rev.: $411,631,070
Assets: $416,642,282
Liabilities: $331,311,645
Net Worth: $85,330,637
Earnings: ($18,627,226)
Emp.: 169
Fiscal Year-end: 12/31/22
Motor Vehicle Parts Mfr
N.A.I.C.S.: 336330
Yeong-Woo Park *(Chm)*

DAYTHREE DIGITAL BERHAD

Level 8 Tower 7 UOA Business Park No 1 Jalan Pengaturcara U1/51A, Seksyen U1, 40150, Shah Alam, Selangor, Malaysia
Tel.: (60) 355672388
Web Site: https://www.daythree.co
Year Founded: 2016
DAY3—(KLS)
Rev.: $19,563,473
Assets: $19,104,746
Liabilities: $4,820,933
Net Worth: $14,283,813
Earnings: $1,648,673
Fiscal Year-end: 12/31/23
Investment Management Service
N.A.I.C.S.: 523999
Raymond Devadass *(Founder)*

DAYTONA CORPORATION

4805 Ichinomiya Mori-machi, Shuchi-gun, Shizuoka, 437-0226, Japan
Tel.: (81) 538842220
Web Site: https://www.daytona-global.com
Year Founded: 1972
7228—(TKS)
Rev.: $98,983,490
Assets: $73,246,790
Liabilities: $18,965,750
Net Worth: $54,281,040
Earnings: $8,373,290
Fiscal Year-end: 12/31/23
Motorcycle Parts Mfr
N.A.I.C.S.: 336991
Tetsuji Oda Tetsu *(Pres)*

Subsidiaries:

PT Daytona Azia　　　　　　　**(1)**
I Flores III Blok C3-3 Kawasan Industri MM2100, Cikarang Barat, Bekasi, 17845, Indonesia
Tel.: (62) 2189983135
Web Site: http://www.daytonaindonesia.com
Emp.: 8
Motorcycle Parts Mfr
N.A.I.C.S.: 336991

DAYTONA HOMES

11504 170 Street, Edmonton, T5S 1J7, AB, Canada
Tel.: (780) 452-2288
Web Site:
https://www.daytonahomes.ca
Year Founded: 1993
Rev.: $13,041,743
Emp.: 60
Building Construction Services
N.A.I.C.S.: 236117
Tally Hutchinson *(Pres)*

DAYU IRRIGATION GROUP CO., LTD.

F33-35 BLD No B Courtyard 24 Lize Road, Fengtai District Next to Entrance C of Dongguantou Subway Station, Beijing, 735009, China
Tel.: (86) 15201752855
Web Site: https://www.cndayu.com
Year Founded: 1999
300021—(CHIN)
Rev.: $486,295,330
Assets: $1,120,328,210
Liabilities: $798,201,006
Net Worth: $322,127,204

Earnings: $7,061,712
Fiscal Year-end: 12/31/23
Irrigation System Distr
N.A.I.C.S.: 221310
Wang Dong *(Founder)*

DAZHENG PROPERTY GROUP CO., LTD.

A 19F Mingyi Floor No 9 Shangqingsi Road, Yuzhong, Chongqing, 400042, China
Tel.: (86) 2363809676
Web Site: https://www.dzwy.com
Year Founded: 1998
002968—(SSE)
Rev.: $430,271,255
Assets: $282,390,428
Liabilities: $114,474,870
Net Worth: $167,915,558
Earnings: $22,033,975
Fiscal Year-end: 12/31/23
Property Management Services
N.A.I.C.S.: 531311
Maoshun Li *(Chm)*

DAZHONG TRANSPORTATION (GROUP) CO., LTD.

1515 Zhongshan West Road 12F Dazhong Building, 12th floo, Shanghai, 200232, China
Tel.: (86) 2164289122
Web Site: http://www.96822.com
Year Founded: 1992
600611—(SHG)
Rev.: $331,359,627
Assets: $2,810,935,975
Liabilities: $1,384,024,099
Net Worth: $1,426,911,876
Earnings: ($38,483,261)
Fiscal Year-end: 12/31/22
Taxi Transportation Services
N.A.I.C.S.: 485310
Guoping Yang *(Chm, Pres, CEO & Sec-Party Committee)*

DAZZEL CONFINDIVE LTD.

SBG-4 Behind Air India Nehru Place Lal Kothi Tonk Road, Jaipur, 302 015, Rajasthan, India
Tel.: (91) 141 3947425
Web Site:
http://www.dazzelconfindive.com
Year Founded: 1992
Rev.: $185,121
Assets: $2,819,601
Liabilities: $447,237
Net Worth: $2,372,364
Earnings: $52,596
Fiscal Year-end: 03/31/18
Civil Engineering Services
N.A.I.C.S.: 237990
Atul Vijayvargiya *(Exec Dir)*

DAZZLE FASHION CO., LTD.

Building 8 Xuhui Century Plaza No 1-2 Lane 28 Danba Road, Putuo District, Shanghai, 200062, China
Tel.: (86) 2131085111
Web Site: http://www.dazzle-fashion.com
Year Founded: 2002
603587—(SHG)
Rev.: $337,012,173
Assets: $612,176,166
Liabilities: $105,159,558
Net Worth: $507,016,608
Earnings: $53,990,315
Fiscal Year-end: 12/31/22
Women Clothing Distr
N.A.I.C.S.: 458110
Rui Min Ma *(Chm & Gen Mgr)*

DB (INTERNATIONAL) STOCK BROKERS LTD.

114 New Delhi House 27 Bara-

DB (International) Stock Brokers Ltd.—(Continued)

khamba Road, New Delhi, 110001,
India
Tel.: (91) 1143606162　　　　　In
Web Site: https://www.dbonline.in
Year Founded: 1992
DBSTOCKBRO—(NSE)
Rev.: $3,545,261
Assets: $11,988,331
Liabilities: $5,130,048
Net Worth: $6,858,283
Earnings: $764,344
Emp.: 56
Fiscal Year-end: 03/31/23
Financial Services
N.A.I.C.S.: 523999
Shiv Narayan Daga (Mng Dir)

DB BROADCAST LTD.

Sedgeway Business Park Witchford,
Ely, CB6 2HY, Cambridgeshire,
United Kingdom
Tel.: (44) 1353 661117
Web Site:
　http://www.dbbroadcast.co.uk
Year Founded: 1989
Sales Range: $25-49.9 Million
Emp.: 54
Television Broadcasting Services
N.A.I.C.S.: 516120
David Bird (Mng Dir)

DB CORP LIMITED

Plot no 280 Sarkhej Gandhi Nagar
Highway Near YMCA Club Makarba,
Ahmedabad, 380051, Gujarat, India
Tel.: (91) 79 49088888
Web Site: http://www.dbcorpltd.com
DBCORP—(BOM)
Rev.: $207,778,799
Assets: $337,969,496
Liabilities: $89,148,560
Net Worth: $248,820,936
Earnings: $19,303,557
Emp.: 7,453
Fiscal Year-end: 03/31/21
Newspaper Publisher; Radio Station
Operator
N.A.I.C.S.: 513110
Pradyumna Gopalkrishna Mishra (Grp
CFO)

Subsidiaries:

I Media Corp Ltd.　　　　　　　(1)
D-143 Sector-63, Noida, 201 301, Uttar
Pradesh, India
Tel.: (91) 1203341200
Web Site: http://www.imcl.in
Sales Range: $25-49.9 Million
Emp.: 100
Integrated Internet & Mobile Interactive Ser-
vices
N.A.I.C.S.: 513199
Gyan Gupta (COO)

DB ELETTRONICA TELECO-
MUNICAZIONI SPA

Riviera Maestri del Lavoro 20 1, Pa-
dova, Italy
Tel.: (39) 0498700588
Web Site:
　http://www.dbbroadcast.com
Telecommunication Servicesb
N.A.I.C.S.: 517810
Didier Muragwabugabo (Mng Dir-
D&M Broadcast Engrg)

Subsidiaries:

Screen Future S.r.l.　　　　　　(1)
Via Gian Battista Cacciamali, 71 - 25125,
Brescia, Italy
Tel.: (39) 0393057831
Web Site: http://www.screen.it
Sales Range: $75-99.9 Million
Television Broadcasting Equipment Mfr.
N.A.I.C.S.: 334220
Carla Sora (CFO)

Subsidiary (US):

Screen Service America LLC　　(2)
6095 NW 167 th St Ste D 10, Miami, FL
33015
Tel.: (305) 826-2212
Marketing Consulting Services
N.A.I.C.S.: 541613

Subsidiary (Non-US):

Screen Service do Brasil Ltda.　(2)
Av Dos Alecrins 740 Dist Industrial CEP,
37550-000, Pouso Alegre, Minas Gerais,
Brazil
Tel.: (55) 553534713697
Broadcasting Equipment Wnsir
N.A.I.C.S.: 423690

DB ENERGY SA

al Armii Krajowej 45, 50-541, Wro-
claw, Poland
Tel.: (48) 713371325
Web Site: https://www.dbenergy.pl
Year Founded: 2009
DBE—(WAR)
Rev.: $13,238,274
Assets: $23,735,450
Liabilities: $15,960,092
Net Worth: $7,775,357
Earnings: $1,122,570
Fiscal Year-end: 06/30/23
Electricity Distribution Services
N.A.I.C.S.: 237990
Dominik Brach (VP)

DBA GROUP SRL

Viale Felissent 20/D, 31020, Villorba,
Treviso, Italy
Tel.: (39) 0422 318811
Web Site: http://www.dbagroup.it
Sales Range: $10-24.9 Million
Emp.: 233
Holding Company; Civil Engineering,
Plant Design, Architecture & Project
Management
N.A.I.C.S.: 551112
Francesco De Bettin (Chm)

Subsidiaries:

Actual I.T., d.d.　　　　　　　(1)
Ferrarska ulica 14, 6000, Koper,
Slovenia　　　　　　　　(73.77%)
Tel.: (386) 56622700
Web Site: http://www.actual-it.si
IT Outsourcing Services
N.A.I.C.S.: 541519
Gregor Veselko (Chm-Mgmt Bd)

OOO DBA PROEKT　　　　　　(1)
Pl Karla Faberge 8 Russkie Samozvety of-
fice 722, Saint Petersburg, Russia
Tel.: (7) 8126470363
Web Site: http://www.dbaproekt.ru
Construction Management Services
N.A.I.C.S.: 236220

Weez Srl　　　　　　　　　(1)
Via Natale Battaglia 10, 20127, Milan, Italy
Tel.: (39) 0228511010
Web Site: http://www.weez.it
Project Management Services
N.A.I.C.S.: 561110

DBA TELECOMMUNICATION
(ASIA) HOLDINGS LIMITED

Unit 1301 13th Floor Henan Building,
90-92 Jaffe Road, Wanchai, China
(Hong Kong)
Tel.: (852) 31063068
Web Site: http://www.dba-asia.com
Sales Range: $1-4.9 Billion
Emp.: 798
Telecommunications Equipment Mfr
N.A.I.C.S.: 517810
Mingqiang Mo (Exec Dir)

DBAPP SECURITY CO., LTD.

No 188 Lianhui Street Xixing Street,
Binjiang District, Hangzhou, 310051,
Zhejiang, China

Tel.: (86) 57128898076
Web Site:
　http://www.dbappsecurity.com
Year Founded: 2007
688023—(SHG)
Rev.: $277,993,741
Assets: $704,007,720
Liabilities: $293,544,080
Net Worth: $410,463,640
Earnings: $35,583,776
Fiscal Year-end: 12/31/22
Application Development Services
N.A.I.C.S.: 541511
Frank Fan (Chm & Pres)

DBAY ADVISORS LIMITED

3rd floor Exchange House 54-62
Athol Street, Douglas, IM1 1JD, Isle
of Man
Tel.: (44) 1624602130　　　　IM
Web Site:
　http://www.dbayadvisors.com
Year Founded: 2008
Investment Advisory & Asset Man-
agement Services
N.A.I.C.S.: 523940
Alex Paiusco (Founder & CEO)

Subsidiaries:

Eddie Stobart Logistics Plc　　(1)
Stretton Green Distribution Park Langford
Way, Appleton, Warrington, WA4 4TQ,
Cheshire, United Kingdom　　(51%)
Tel.: (44) 1925605400
Web Site: http://www.eddiestobart.com
Holding Company; Logistics Services
N.A.I.C.S.: 551112
David Pickering (COO)

Subsidiary (Domestic):

AutoLogic Holdings Limited　　(2)
Autologic House 5 Grange Park Court, Ro-
man Way, Northampton, NN4 5EA, United
Kingdom
Tel.: (44) 1604 664400
Web Site: http://www.autologic.co.uk
Sales Range: $200-249.9 Million
Emp.: 1,215
Holding Company; Automotive Industry Lo-
gistics Services
N.A.I.C.S.: 551112

Subsidiary (Non-US):

Walon B.V.　　　　　　　　(3)
Ramshoorn 4, Breda, 4824 AG, Nether-
lands
Tel.: (31) 765482150
Web Site: http://www.eddiestobart.com
Sales Range: $25-49.9 Million
Emp.: 30
Vehicle Logistics Services, Including Vehicle
Import, Processing, Distribution, Technical
Services & Transport
N.A.I.C.S.: 541614
Theo Dexters (Mng Dir)

Walon CZ s.r.o.　　　　　　(3)
Pripotocni 1519/10a, 101 00, Prague, 10,
Czech Republic
Tel.: (420) 267216670
Web Site: http://www.walon.com
Sales Range: $25-49.9 Million
Emp.: 30
Motor Vehicle Transport & Logistics Ser-
vices
N.A.I.C.S.: 541614

Subsidiary (Domestic):

Eddie Stobart Limited　　　　(2)
Solway Business Centre, Carlisle, CA6 4BY,
Cumbria, United Kingdom
Tel.: (44) 1228 882300
Web Site: http://www.stobartgroup.com
Freight Trucking Services
N.A.I.C.S.: 484121

Eddie Stobart Promotions
Limited　　　　　　　　　(2)
Kingstown Industrial Estate, Carlisle, CA3
0EH, United Kingdom
Tel.: (44) 1228 517800
Web Site: http://www.clubstobart.co.uk
Corporate Merchandising Services

N.A.I.C.S.: 561499

O'Connor Container Transport
Limited　　　　　　　　　(2)
Widnes Intermodal Rail Depot Desoto Road
West Bank Dock Estate, Widnes, WA8 0PB,
United Kingdom
Tel.: (44) 15 1424 6724
Sales Range: $25-49.9 Million
Emp.: 40
Deep Sea Freight Container Handling Ser-
vices
N.A.I.C.S.: 488320

Subsidiary (Non-US):

Stobart (Ireland) Limited　　　(2)
Stobart Ireland Distribution Centre Tolka
Quay Road, Dublin Port, Dublin, 1, Ireland
Tel.: (353) 1 886 0020
Web Site: http://www.stobart.com
Sales Range: $25-49.9 Million
Emp.: 40
Logistics & Air Freight Transportation Ser-
vices
N.A.I.C.S.: 541614
David O'Neill (Gen Mgr)

Subsidiary (Domestic):

Stobart Rail Freight Limited　　(2)
15 Stratford Place 3rd Floor, London, W1C
1BE, Cheshire, United Kingdom
Tel.: (44) 1228882300
Web Site: http://www.stobartrail.com
Sales Range: $125-149.9 Million
Emp.: 500
Rail Freight Transportation & Logistics Ser-
vices
N.A.I.C.S.: 488210

Finsbury Food Group plc　　　(1)
Maes Y Coed Road, Cardiff, CF14 4XR,
United Kingdom
Tel.: (44) 2920357500
Web Site: http://www.finsburyfoods.co.uk
Rev.: $484,445,358
Assets: $329,829,562
Liabilities: $168,459,109
Net Worth: $161,370,453
Earnings: $15,733,259
Emp.: 3,208
Fiscal Year-end: 07/02/2022
Baked Goods Mfr
N.A.I.C.S.: 311813
Laura Nuttall (Sec)

Subsidiary (Domestic):

Campbells Cake Company Ltd.　(2)
73 Bothwell Rd, Twechar, Hamilton, ML3
0DW, United Kingdom　　　(100%)
Tel.: (44) 1236826633
Sales Range: $25-49.9 Million
Emp.: 50
Frozen Cakes Pies & Pastries Mfr
N.A.I.C.S.: 311813
Patrick Campell (Mgr-Ops)

Fletchers Bakeries Limited　　(2)
Claywheels Lane, Wadsley Bridge, Shef-
field, S6 1LY, United Kingdom
Tel.: (44) 1142348171
Web Site: http://finsburyfoods.co.uk
Emp.: 400
Specialty Breads & Confectionary Products
Mfr
N.A.I.C.S.: 311812

Lees Foods Limited　　　　　(2)
North Caldeen Road, Coatbridge, ML5 4EF,
Scotland, United Kingdom
Tel.: (44) 1236441600
Web Site: http://www.leesfoods.co.uk
Sales Range: $25-49.9 Million
Emp.: 200
Confectionery & Cake Products Mfr
N.A.I.C.S.: 311352
David Simson (Sec & Dir-Fin)

Subsidiary (Domestic):

Lees of Scotland Limited　　　(3)
N Caldeen Rd, Coatbridge, ML5 4EF,
United Kingdom
Tel.: (44) 1236441600
Web Site: https://www.leesofscotland.co.uk
Sales Range: $25-49.9 Million
Emp.: 250
Confectionary Product Mfr
N.A.I.C.S.: 311340

Bert Croll *(Sls Dir)*

Subsidiary (Domestic):

Lightbody Group Ltd. (2)
73 Bothwell Road, Hamilton, ML3 0DW,
United Kingdom
Tel.: (44) 1698285227
Sales Range: $150-199.9 Million
Emp.: 1,100
Frozen Cakes Mfr & Whslr
N.A.I.C.S.: 311813

Affiliate (Non-US):

Lightbody Europe SARL (3)
14 allee Coysevox, CS 56939, 35069,
Rennes, Cedex, France (50%)
Tel.: (33) 299316344
Web Site: http://www.otoogood.com
Sales Range: $25-49.9 Million
Emp.: 18
Children's Novelty Cake & Beverage Whslr
N.A.I.C.S.: 424490
Philippe Stretez *(Mng Dir)*

Subsidiary (Domestic):

Memory Lane Cakes Limited (2)
Maes Y Coed Road, Cardiff, CF14 4XR,
Glamorgan, United Kingdom (100%)
Tel.: (44) 2920357500
Web Site: http://www.finsburyfoods.co.uk
Sales Range: $150-199.9 Million
Emp.: 850
Mfr of Cakes & Confections
N.A.I.C.S.: 311812

Nicholas & Harris Ltd. (2)
Brunel House Brunel Road, Churchfields
Industrial Estate, Salisbury, SP2 7PU,
United Kingdom
Tel.: (44) 1722327152
Web Site: http://www.finsburyfoods.co.uk
Sales Range: $100-124.9 Million
Emp.: 350
Mfr of Premium & Speciality Breads
N.A.I.C.S.: 311813

Subsidiary (Non-US):

Ultraeuropa Sp. z o.o. (2)
Ul Bielska 41, Rybarzowice, 43-378, Zgor-
zelec, Poland
Tel.: (48) 334322867
Web Site: https://www.ultraeuropa.eu
Bread Product Mfr
N.A.I.C.S.: 311812

Harvey Nash Group Ltd (1)
3 Noble Street, London, EC2V 7EE, United
Kingdom
Tel.: (44) 2073330033
Web Site: http://www.harveynash.com
Rev.: $755,160,807
Assets: $357,042,584
Liabilities: $280,007,994
Net Worth: $77,034,590
Earnings: $794,407
Emp.: 2,809
Fiscal Year-end: 01/31/2019
Holding Company; Employment Recruiting
Services
N.A.I.C.S.: 551112
Simon Wassall *(Mng Dir-Europe)*

Subsidiary (Non-US):

Alumni AB (2)
World Trade Center Kungsbron 1, Box 843,
101 36, Stockholm, Sweden
Tel.: (46) 8 796 17 00
Web Site: http://www.alumni.se
Sales Range: $25-49.9 Million
Emp.: 47
Executive Search Consulting Services
N.A.I.C.S.: 541612
Magnus Tegborg *(CEO & Partner)*

Bjerke & Luther AS (2)
Haakon VII gate 6 3 etg, 0160, Oslo,
Norway (100%)
Tel.: (47) 22 40 40 80
Recruitment Consulting Services
N.A.I.C.S.: 541612

Harvey Nash (Ireland) Ltd (2)
100 Mount Street Lower Grand Canal Dock,
Dublin, DO2 TY46, Ireland
Tel.: (353) 1 6741400
Web Site: http://www.harveynash.ie

Recruitment Consulting Services
N.A.I.C.S.: 541612
Sonya Curley *(Mng Dir)*

Harvey Nash (Vietnam) Ltd (2)
6th Floor HITC Building 239 Xuan Thuy
Road, Cau Giay District, Hanoi, Vietnam
Tel.: (84) 2473003388
Web Site: http://www.harveynash.vn
Recruitment Consulting Services
N.A.I.C.S.: 561311
Tam Truong *(Dir-Exec Search & HR Svcs)*

Harvey Nash AG (2)
Badenerstrasse 15, Postfach 8021, 8004,
Zurich, Switzerland (100%)
Tel.: (41) 442968844
Web Site: http://www.harveynash.ch
Employment Agencies
N.A.I.C.S.: 561311
Simon Hindle *(Dir-Sls)*

Harvey Nash BV (2)
Industrieweg 4, Maarssen, 3606 AS,
Netherlands (100%)
Tel.: (31) 346581070
Web Site: http://www.harveynash.nl
Employment Agencies
N.A.I.C.S.: 561311
Matt Nabil *(Bus Mgr)*

Harvey Nash GmbH (2)
5th Floor-Red Rocks Grafenberger Allee
337 b, D-40235, Dusseldorf,
Germany (100%)
Tel.: (49) 2111793920
Web Site: http://www.harveynash.de
Computer System Design Services
N.A.I.C.S.: 541512
Mark Hayes *(Country Mgr)*

Harvey Nash IT Consulting NV (2)
Nieuwe Gentsesteenweg 21/3, 1702, Groot-
Bijgaarden, Belgium (100%)
Tel.: (32) 24631430
Web Site: http://www.harveynash.be
Employment Placement Agencies
N.A.I.C.S.: 561311

Subsidiary (US):

Harvey Nash Inc (2)
225 Bush St Ste 1840, San Francisco, CA
94104 (100%)
Tel.: (415) 901-0910
Web Site: http://www.harveynash.com
Employment Agencies
N.A.I.C.S.: 561311

Subsidiary (Domestic):

Harvey Nash Limited (2)
110 Bishopsgate, London, EC2N 4AY,
United Kingdom (100%)
Tel.: (44) 2073330033
Web Site: http://www.harveynash.com
Employment Agencies
N.A.I.C.S.: 561311

Subsidiary (Non-US):

Harvey Nash NV (2)
Nieuwe Gentsesteenweg 21/3, 1702, Groot-
Bijgaarden, Belgium (100%)
Tel.: (32) 24631430
Web Site: http://www.harveynash.be
Management Consulting Services
N.A.I.C.S.: 541618
Nadia Van Sande *(Mgr-HR)*

Impact Executives Ltd (2)
WTC Kungsbron 1, Stockholm, 10136SE,
Sweden (100%)
Tel.: (46) 812225440
Web Site: http://www.impactexecutives.com
Employment Agencies
N.A.I.C.S.: 561311
Anna Hjertstedt *(Mng Dir)*

Subsidiary (US):

Latitude 36, Inc. (2)
810 Crescent Centre Ste 120, Franklin, TN
37067
Tel.: (615) 468-0188
Web Site: http://www.lat36.com
Human Resource Consulting Services
N.A.I.C.S.: 541612
Jason Pyle *(Pres & COO)*

Subsidiary (Domestic):

Spinks (2)
110 Bishopsgate, London, EC2N 4AY,
United Kingdom
Tel.: (44) 2071706400
Web Site: http://www.mortimerspinks.com
Employment Agencies
N.A.I.C.S.: 561311
Robin Beattie *(Mng Dir)*

Proactis Holdings PLC (1)
Riverview Court Castle Gate, Wetherby,
LS22 6LE, United Kingdom
Tel.: (44) 1937545070
Web Site: http://www.proactis.com
Sales Range: $50-74.9 Million
B2B E-commerce Sales Software Applica-
tions
N.A.I.C.S.: 513210
Tim Sykes *(CEO)*

SQLI SA (1)
166 rue Jules Guesde, 92300, Levallois-
Perret, France (96.44%)
Tel.: (33) 185642020
Web Site: https://www.sqli.com
Rev.: $139,825,490
Assets: $202,171,146
Liabilities: $113,316,230
Net Worth: $88,854,916
Earnings: $11,806,859
Emp.: 2,116
Fiscal Year-end: 12/31/2023
IT Design, Integration & Consulting Ser-
vices
N.A.I.C.S.: 541512
Nathalie Mensy *(Partner-Brand & Retail)*

Subsidiary (Domestic):

ALCYONIX (2)
Empasse 31300, ZAC Grande Plaine,
31500, Toulouse, France
Tel.: (33) 562477070
Web Site: http://www.alcyonix.com
Sales Range: $25-49.9 Million
Emp.: 50
Information Technology Consulting Services
N.A.I.C.S.: 541519
Eric Galtier *(Mng Dir)*

Subsidiary (Non-US):

CDLX GmbH (2)
Oranienstrasse 183, 10999, Berlin, Ger-
many
Tel.: (49) 3069506906
Web Site: http://www.cdlx.de
Computer Integrated Systems Design Ser-
vices
N.A.I.C.S.: 541512
Martin Christel *(Mng Dir)*

Inventcommerce Ltd. (2)
Floor 3 8a Great Newport Street, London,
WC2H 7JA, United Kingdom
Tel.: (44) 2030115000
E-Commerce Consulting Services
N.A.I.C.S.: 541512

Inventcommerce Proprietary Ltd. (2)
1st Floor Office 4A The Planet Art One 32
Jamieson Street, Cape Town, 8001, South
Africa
Tel.: (27) 213003108
E-Commerce Consulting Services
N.A.I.C.S.: 541512
Narriman Richards *(Mgr-Fin)*

Osudio Nordics APS (2)
Adelgade 15, 1304, Copenhagen, Denmark
Tel.: (45) 406935912
Business Consulting Services
N.A.I.C.S.: 541618

Subsidiary (Domestic):

SQLI Agency (2)
Immeuble le Pressense 268 Ave du Presi-
dent Wilson, Saint-Denis, 93210, Paris,
France
Tel.: (33) 155932600
Web Site: http://www.sqli.com
Information Technology Consulting Services
N.A.I.C.S.: 541519

Subsidiary (Non-US):

SQLI Belgium SA (2)
Lambroekstraat 5C, 1831, Diegem, Belgium

Tel.: (32) 23115838
Information Technology Management Ser-
vices
N.A.I.C.S.: 541511

Subsidiary (Domestic):

SQLI Conseil IT (2)
Immeuble le Pressense 268 Ave du Presi-
dent Wilson, Saint-Denis, 93210, Paris,
France
Tel.: (33) 155932600
Information Technology Consulting Services
N.A.I.C.S.: 541519
Didier Fauque *(Pres)*

SQLI Immobilier (2)
268 Ave du President Wilson, Saint-Denis,
Paris, 93210, France
Tel.: (33) 155932600
Web Site: http://www.sqli-immobilier.com
Emp.: 500
Real Estate & Asset Management Services
N.A.I.C.S.: 531390

SQLI Institut (2)
Immeuble le Pressense 268 Ave du Presi-
dent Wilson, Saint-Denis, Saint-Denis,
Paris, France
Tel.: (33) 155932600
Web Site: http://www.sqli.com
Information Technology Consulting Services
N.A.I.C.S.: 541519

Subsidiary (Non-US):

SQLI Luxembourg SA (2)
204 Route d Arlon, 8010, Strassen, Luxembourg
Tel.: (352) 26313749
Information Technology Management Services
N.A.I.C.S.: 541511

Subsidiary (Domestic):

SQLI NewBI (2)
Building the Pressense 268 Ave du Presi-
dent Wilson, Saint-Denis, 93210, Paris,
France
Tel.: (33) 155932600
Web Site: http://www.sqli.com
Emp.: 50
Information Technology Consulting Services
N.A.I.C.S.: 541519

Subsidiary (Non-US):

Star Republic AB (2)
Ekelundsgatan 9, 411 18, Gothenburg,
Sweden
Tel.: (46) 317620200
Web Site: http://www.starrepublic.com
E-Commerce Consulting Services
N.A.I.C.S.: 541512
Bengt Wessborg *(Partner)*

Subsidiary (Domestic):

Urbanys (2)
Immeuble Le Pressense 268 Ave du Presi-
dent Wilson, Saint-Denis, 93210, Paris,
France
Tel.: (33) 155930240
Web Site: http://www.urbanys.fr
Information Technology Consulting Services
N.A.I.C.S.: 541519

Telit Communications PLC (1)
Cannon Place 78 Cannon Street, London,
EC4N 6AF, United Kingdom (100%)
Tel.: (44) 2032893831
Web Site: http://www.telit.com
Mobile Communication & Mobile Data Mod-
ule Technologies Developer
N.A.I.C.S.: 334210
Yossi Moscovitz *(Chief Strategy Officer)*

Subsidiary (Non-US):

Dai Telecom Ltd. (2)
3 Nirim St, Tel Aviv, 67060, Israel
Tel.: (972) 37914040
Web Site: http://www.daitelecom.co.il
Sales Range: $25-49.9 Million
Emp.: 30
Mobile Communication Equipment Mfr &
Sales
N.A.I.C.S.: 334220

DBAY Advisors Limited—(Continued)

Subsidiary (US):

ILS Technology LLC   **(2)**
5300 Broken Sound Blvd Ste 150, Boca
Raton, FL 33487
Tel.: (561) 982-9898
Web Site: http://www.ilstechnology.com
Emp.: 56
Enterprise Intelligent Devices Software Applications Services
N.A.I.C.S.: 513210
Fred Yentz (Pres & CEO)

Subsidiary (Non-US):

Telit Communications S.p.A.   **(2)**
Via Stazione di Prosecco 5/B, 34010,
Sgonico, TS, Italy
Tel.: (39) 0404 19 22 00
Develops Mobile Communication & Mobile
Data Module Technologies
N.A.I.C.S.: 334210
Antonino Sgroi (Mgr-R&D-Cellular-EMEA)

Telit Wireless Solutions (Pty) Ltd. **(2)**
W Wing Birchwood Ct Montrose St Vorna
Valley, Midrand, 1685, South Africa
Tel.: (27) 11 655 7190
Data Communication Equipment Sales
N.A.I.C.S.: 423690

Telit Wireless Solutions Co., Ltd. **(2)**
8th Floor Shinyoung Securities Building 6
Gukjegeumyung-ro8-gil, Yeongdeungpo-gu,
Seoul, 150-884, Korea (South)
Tel.: (82) 2 368 4600
Telecommunication Servicesb
N.A.I.C.S.: 334220

Subsidiary (US):

Telit Wireless Solutions Inc.   **(2)**
Churchill Hall at imperial Ctr 5425 Page Rd
Ste 120, Durham, NC 27703
Tel.: (919) 439-7977
Web Site: http://www.telit.com
Cellular Phone Mfr & Sales
N.A.I.C.S.: 334220

Subsidiary (Non-US):

Telit Wireless Solutions Ltd.   **(2)**
10 Habarzel St, Tel Aviv, 69710, Israel
Tel.: (972) 37914000
Web Site: http://www.telit.com
Sales Range: $50-74.9 Million
Emp.: 100
Data Communication Equipment Sales
N.A.I.C.S.: 423690

DBG CANADA LIMITED
110 Ambassador Dr, Mississauga,
L5T 2X8, ON, Canada
Tel.: (905) 670-1555
Web Site: http://www.debiasi.com
Year Founded: 1976
Rev.: $41,557,856
Emp.: 320
Design Tools Mfr
N.A.I.C.S.: 333517
Mike De Biasi (Pres)

DBG TECHNOLOGY CO., LTD.
No 5 Yongda Road Xiang Shui River
Industrial Area Daya Bay, Huizhou,
516083, Guangdong, China
Tel.: (86) 7525108688
Web Site: https://www.dbg.ltd
Year Founded: 1994
300735—(CHIN)
Rev.: $760,934,942
Assets: $1,061,317,976
Liabilities: $331,245,269
Net Worth: $730,072,707
Earnings: $55,880,632
Emp.: 25,000
Fiscal Year-end: 12/31/23
Computer Equipment Mfr & Whslr
N.A.I.C.S.: 334111

Subsidiaries:

DBG Technology (India) Private
Limited   **(1)**

Plot No2 Sector-8, Industrial Area, Bawal,
123501, Haryana, India
Tel.: (91) 1284270000
Web Site: http://www.dbgindia.in
Electronic Products Mfr
N.A.I.C.S.: 334419
Avinash Kumar (Mgr-IT)

DBH FINANCE PLC
Landmark Building 9th Floor 12-14
Gulshan North C/A, Gulshan-2,
Dhaka, 1212, Bangladesh
Tel.: (880) 9612334455
Web Site: https://dbhfinance.com
DBH—(DHA)
Rev.: $58,621,466
Assets: $699,231,909
Liabilities: $615,199,989
Net Worth: $84,031,921
Emp.: $12,109,112
Emp.: 316
Fiscal Year-end: 12/31/21
Housing Financial Services
N.A.I.C.S.: 522310
Nasir A. Choudhury (Chm)

DBS GROUP HOLDINGS LTD.
12 Marina Boulevard Level 41 DBS
Asia Central, Marina Bay Financial
Centre Tower 3, Singapore, 018982,
Singapore
Tel.: (65) 68788888
Web Site: https://www.dbs.com
Year Founded: 1968
DBSDF—(OTCIQ)
Rev.: $21,102,779,660
Assets: $559,949,253,670
Liabilities: $512,803,150,535
Net Worth: $47,146,103,134
Earnings: $7,621,752,628
Emp.: 3,000
Fiscal Year-end: 12/31/23
Bank Holding Company
N.A.I.C.S.: 551111
Alvin Zhuang (Asst Sec)

Subsidiaries:

DBS Bank (Taiwan) Limited   **(1)**
Songren Road No 36 17F, Xinyi District,
Taipei, 110, Taiwan
Tel.: (886) 266129888
Banking Services
N.A.I.C.S.: 522110

DBS Securities (Japan) Co., Ltd. **(1)**
Otemachi First Square East Tower 15th
Floor 1-5-1 Otemachi, Chiyoda-ku, Tokyo,
100-0004, Japan
Tel.: (81) 332134660
Securities & Financial Product Mediation
Services
N.A.I.C.S.: 523210

DBSN Services Pte. Ltd.   **(1)**
12 Marina Boulevard DBS Asia Central at
Marina Bay, Financial Centre Tower 3, Singapore, 018982, Singapore
Tel.: (65) 65339688
Banking Services
N.A.I.C.S.: 522110

P.T. DBS Vickers Sekuritas
Indonesia   **(1)**
DBS Bank Tower Ciputra World 1 Floor
32nd Jl Prof Dr Satrio Kav 3-5, Jakarta,
12940, Indonesia
Tel.: (62) 2130034950
Financial Advisory Services
N.A.I.C.S.: 523999

The Development Bank of Singapore,
Ltd.   **(1)**
6 Shenton Way DBS Bldg Tower 1, Singapore, 068809, Singapore
Tel.: (65) 68351234
Web Site: http://www.dbs.com
Sales Range: $1-4.9 Billion
Emp.: 11,454
Banking & Financial Services
N.A.I.C.S.: 522110
Joyce Tee (Grp Head-SME Banking)

Subsidiary (Non-US):

DBS Asia Ltd.   **(2)**
39-41 Des Voeux Rd, Central, Hong Kong,
China (Hong Kong)   **(100%)**
Tel.: (852) 36682080
Web Site: http://www.dbs.com
Sales Range: $50-74.9 Million
Emp.: 20
Selective Financial Services
N.A.I.C.S.: 522220

DBS Bank (Hong Kong) Limited **(2)**
11th Floor The Center 99 Queen's Road,
Central, China (Hong Kong)   **(100%)**
Tel.: (852) 36680808
Commercial & Retail Banking
N.A.I.C.S.: 522110

Subsidiary (Domestic):

DBS Asia Capital Limited   **(3)**
73th Floor The Center 99 Queen's Road,
Central, China (Hong Kong)   **(100%)**
Tel.: (852) 36681148
Web Site: https://www.dbs.com.hk
Sales Range: $50-74.9 Million
Emp.: 70
Investment Banking & Corporate Finance
N.A.I.C.S.: 523150

Subsidiary (Non-US):

DBS Bank India Limited   **(2)**
Express Towers Ground Floor Nariman
Point, Mumbai, 400021, Maharashtra, India
Tel.: (91) 2266388888
Web Site: https://www.dbs.com
Banking & Financial Services
N.A.I.C.S.: 522110

Subsidiary (Domestic):

DBS Bank Ltd.   **(2)**
12 Marina Boulevard, DBS Asia Central Marina Bay Financial Centre Tower 3, Singapore, 018982, Singapore   **(100%)**
Tel.: (65) 6 878 8888
Web Site: http://www.dbs.com.sg
Group Financing
N.A.I.C.S.: 522210
Raof Latiff (Head-Digital-Institutional Banking Grp)

Subsidiary (Domestic):

AXS Pte Ltd   **(3)**
61 Mohamed Sultan Road Floor 01-11 Sultan Link, Singapore, 239001,
Singapore   **(87.7%)**
Tel.: (65) 6 560 2727
Web Site: https://www.axs.com.sg
Sales Range: $25-49.9 Million
Emp.: 100
Telecommunication Servicesb
N.A.I.C.S.: 517810
Joey Chang (Founder & CEO)

DBS Asset Management (United
States) Pte Ltd   **(3)**
8 Cross Street 08-01 PWC Building, Singapore, 048424, Singapore
Tel.: (65) 65358025
Fund Management Services
N.A.I.C.S.: 524292

Subsidiary (Non-US):

DBS Vickers (Hong Kong)
Limited   **(3)**
16/F One Island East 18 Westlands Road
Island East, Hong Kong, China (Hong
Kong)
Tel.: (852) 3 668 3288
Web Site: http://www.dbsvickers.com
Securities Brokerage Services
N.A.I.C.S.: 523150
Josephine Lam (CEO)

DBS Vickers Securities (Hong Kong)
Limited   **(3)**
18-19 f Man Yee Bldg 68 Des Voeux Rd,
Hong Kong, China (Hong Kong)
Tel.: (852) 28204888
Securities Brokerage Services
N.A.I.C.S.: 523150

Subsidiary (Domestic):

DBS Vickers Securities Holdings Pte
Ltd   **(3)**

12 Marina Boulevard 10-01 Marina Bay Financial Centre Tower 3, Singapore, 018982,
Singapore
Tel.: (65) 63272288
Securities Brokerage Services
N.A.I.C.S.: 523150

Subsidiary (Domestic):

DBS Vickers Securities (Singapore)
Pte Ltd   **(4)**
12 Marina Boulevard 10-01 Marina Bay Financial Centre Tower 3, Singapore, 018982,
Singapore
Tel.: (65) 6 327 2288
Web Site: http://www.dbsvickers.com
Futures Trading
N.A.I.C.S.: 523160

Subsidiary (Non-US):

DBS Vickers Securities (Thailand)
Co. Ltd.   **(4)**
989 Siam Piwat Tower 9th 14th-15th Floor
Rama 1 Road, Pathumwan, Bangkok,
10330, Thailand
Tel.: (66) 2 857 7000
Web Site: https://www.dbsvitrade.com
Securities Brokerage Services
N.A.I.C.S.: 523150

DBS Vickers Securities (UK) Ltd **(4)**
4th Floor Paternoster House 65 St Pauls
Churchyard, London, EC4M 8AB, United
Kingdom
Tel.: (44) 2076181888
Securities Brokerage Services
N.A.I.C.S.: 523150

Subsidiary (Domestic):

DBS Vickers Securities Online Holdings Pte Ltd   **(3)**
12 Marina Blvd #10-01 Marina Bay Financial Ctr Tower 3, Singapore, 018982, Singapore
Tel.: (65) 63272288
Web Site: http://www.dbsvonline.com
Investment Banking Services
N.A.I.C.S.: 523150

Branch (Non-US):

DBS Bank-London Branch   **(2)**
4th Fl Paternoster House 65 St Pauls
Church Yard, London, EC4M8AB, United
Kingdom   **(100%)**
Tel.: (44) 2074896550
Sales Range: $25-49.9 Million
Emp.: 55
Banking Services
N.A.I.C.S.: 541910

Subsidiary (Domestic):

DBS Card Centre Pte. Ltd.   **(2)**
12 Marina Boulevard Marina Bay Financial
Centre Tower 3, Singapore, 018982, Singapore
Tel.: (65) 68788888
Web Site: http://www.dbs.com
Sales Range: $75-99.9 Million
Emp.: 212
Credit & Charge Card Operations
N.A.I.C.S.: 522210

DBS Trustee Ltd.   **(2)**
12 Marina Boulevard, DBS Asia Central Marina Bay Financial Centre Tower 3, Singapore, 018982, Singapore
Tel.: (65) 6 878 8888
Web Site: http://www.dbs.com
Trust Services
N.A.I.C.S.: 523991

DBS Vickers Research (Singapore)
Pte Ltd   **(2)**
8 Cross Street 02-01 Pwc Building, Singapore, 048424, Singapore
Tel.: (65) 65339688
Investment Banking Services
N.A.I.C.S.: 523150

DBS Vickers Securities Nominees
(Singapore) Pte Ltd   **(2)**
6 Shenton Way Tower 1 Dbs Building, Singapore, 068809, Singapore
Tel.: (65) 65339688
Investment Banking Services
N.A.I.C.S.: 523150

Subsidiary (Non-US):

PT Bank DBS Indonesia **(2)**
DBS Bank Tower 37th Floor Ciputra World
1 Jalan Prof Dr Satrio Kav 3-5, Jakarta,
12940, Indonesia **(99%)**
Tel.: (62) 2129885000
Web Site: https://www.dbs.com
Sales Range: $75-99.9 Million
Emp.: 150
Commercial Banking Services
N.A.I.C.S.: 522110

DBT

Parc Horizon 2000, 62117, Brebieres,
France
Tel.: (33) 321509292
Web Site: https://www.dbt.fr
Year Founded: 1990
ALDBT—(EUR)
Sales Range: Less than $1 Million
Electric Power Distribution Services
N.A.I.C.S.: 221122

DBTEL

8F-3 No 51 Chung Yang Rd Sec 4,
Tucheng, Taiwan
Tel.: (886) 77158588
Mobile Phone Mfr
N.A.I.C.S.: 334210
Mo Hao-Jan (CEO)

DBUB GROUP, INC.

108 ShangCheng Road Suite 1-1003,
Shanghai, China
Tel.: (86) 156 18521412 **NV**
Year Founded: 2005
DBUB—(OTCIQ)
Sales Range: Less than $1 Million
Computers & Consumer Electronic
Product Mfr & Distr
N.A.I.C.S.: 334111
Zinan Zhou (Chm & CEO)

DBV TECHNOLOGIES S.A.

177-181 avenue Pierre Brossolette,
92120, Montrouge, France
Tel.: (33) 155427878 **FR**
Web Site: http://www.dbv-
technologies.com
Year Founded: 2002
DBVT—(NASDAQ)
Rev.: $15,728,000
Assets: $182,986,000
Liabilities: $42,799,000
Net Worth: $140,187,000
Earnings: ($72,726,000)
Emp.: 104
Fiscal Year-end: 12/31/23
Pharmaceuticals Mfr
N.A.I.C.S.: 325412
Virginie Boucinha (CFO & Principal
Acctg Officer)

DC D.D.

Krasevo br 68, 74 266, Tesanj, Bos-
nia & Herzegovina
Tel.: (387) 32692388
Web Site: http://www.dct.ba
DCTKR—(SARE)
Rev.: $3,546,394
Assets: $7,321,753
Liabilities: $420,827
Net Worth: $6,900,926
Earnings: $917,944
Emp.: 9
Fiscal Year-end: 12/31/21
Vehicle Parking Services
N.A.I.C.S.: 812930

DC GRADACAC D.D.

Sarajevska bb, 76 250, Gradacac,
Bosnia & Herzegovina
Tel.: (387) 62341139
DCGDR—(SARE)
Rev.: $71,636
Assets: $2,568,482
Liabilities: $1,352,761

Net Worth: $1,215,721
Earnings: ($16,386)
Fiscal Year-end: 12/31/20
Grocery Distr
N.A.I.C.S.: 445110

**DC HEALTHCARE HOLDINGS
BERHAD**

Suite 22 01 22 02 & 22 05 Level 22
Centrepoint South, Mid Valley City
Lingkaran Syed Putra Wilayah Perse-
kutuan, 59200, Kuala Lumpur, Malay-
sia
Tel.: (60) 322016707 **MY**
Web Site:
https://www.dchealthcare.com
Year Founded: 2016
DCHCARE—(KLS)
Rev.: $14,736,728
Assets: $21,585,814
Liabilities: $7,571,010
Net Worth: $14,014,804
Earnings: $545,074
Fiscal Year-end: 12/31/23
Investment Management Service
N.A.I.C.S.: 523999
Tze Sheng Chong (Mng Dir)

**DC INFOTECH & COMMUNI-
CATION LTD.**

Unit No 2 Aristocrate Lajjya Com-
pund, Opp Madhu Ind Estate Mogra
Pada Andheri-East, Mumbai, 400069,
India
Tel.: (91) 8898059812
Web Site:
https://www.dcinfotech.com
Year Founded: 1998
DCI—(NSE)
Rev.: $23,988,694
Assets: $9,934,012
Liabilities: $7,415,720
Net Worth: $2,518,292
Earnings: $3,001,420
Emp.: 53
Fiscal Year-end: 03/12/21
Security Services
N.A.I.C.S.: 561612
Chetankumar Timbadia (Mng Dir)

DCB BANK LIMITED

6th Floor Tower A Peninsula Business
Park Senapati Bapat Marg, Lower
Parel, Mumbai, 400013, India
Tel.: (91) 2266187000
Web Site: https://www.dcbbank.com
DCBBANK—(NSE)
Rev.: $541,195,773
Assets: $6,120,679,328
Liabilities: $5,568,014,811
Net Worth: $552,664,517
Earnings: $167,353,627
Emp.: 8,029
Fiscal Year-end: 03/31/22
Commercial Banking Services
N.A.I.C.S.: 522110
Murali M. Natrajan (CEO & Mng Dir)

DCC PLC

DCC House Leopardstown Road,
Foxrock, Dublin, Ireland
Tel.: (353) 12799400 **IE**
Web Site: https://www.dcc.ie
Year Founded: 1976
DCCPF—(OTCIQ)
Rev.: $25,067,865,476
Assets: $11,970,738,468
Liabilities: $7,952,773,302
Net Worth: $4,017,965,166
Earnings: $429,863,671
Emp.: 16,600
Fiscal Year-end: 03/31/24
Holding Company; Energy, IT & En-
tertainment, Healthcare, Environmen-
tal, Food & Beverage Products &
Services

N.A.I.C.S.: 551112
Donald Murphy (CEO)

Subsidiaries:

Advent Data Limited **(1)**
Unit H4 Premier Way Lowfields Business
park, Elland, HX5 9HF, United Kingdom
Tel.: (44) 871 222 3844
Web Site: http://www.adventdata.co.uk
Sales Range: $75-99.9 Million
Emp.: 100
Printer & Data Storage Media Supplies Distr
N.A.I.C.S.: 423430
Raj Advani (Gen Mgr)

Allied Foods Limited **(1)**
Second Ave, Cookstown Industrial Estate,
Dublin, Ireland **(100%)**
Tel.: (353) 14662600
Web Site: http://www.alliedfoods.ie
Sales Range: $150-199.9 Million
Emp.: 350
Frozen & Chilled Foods Distr
N.A.I.C.S.: 424420

Almo Corporation **(1)**
2709 Commerce Way, Philadelphia, PA
19154-1011
Tel.: (215) 698-4000
Web Site: https://www.almo.com
Emp.: 800
Wholesale Distr of Major Appliances
N.A.I.C.S.: 423620
Warren Chaiken (Pres & CEO)

Subsidiary (Domestic):

Almo Professional A/V **(2)**
2709 Commerce Way, Philadelphia, PA
19154-1011
Tel.: (410) 560-2890
Web Site: http://www.almoproav.com
Audio & Video Equipment Distr
N.A.I.C.S.: 423690
Sam Taylor (Exec VP)

Amacom Holding BV **(1)**
De Tweeling 24a, 5215 MC, 's-
Hertogenbosch, Netherlands
Tel.: (31) 735430775
Web Site: https://www.amazingcompany.eu
Electronic Product Distr
N.A.I.C.S.: 423690

Banque Magnetique SAS **(1)**
Paris Nord II - 99 Avenue de la Pyramide,
BP 64060, 95972, Roissy-en-France,
France
Tel.: (33) 1 49 90 93 93
Web Site: http://www.banquemagnetique.fr
Computer Accessories Distr
N.A.I.C.S.: 423430

Bottle Green Limited **(1)**
19 New Street, Leeds, LS18 4BH, United
Kingdom
Tel.: (44) 1132054500
Web Site: http://www.bottlegreen.com
Sales Range: $25-49.9 Million
Emp.: 25
Wine & Distilled Alcoholic Beverage Whslr
N.A.I.C.S.: 424810

Certas Energy **(1)**
302 Bridgewater Place Birchwood Park,
Birchwood, Warrington, WA3 6XG, United
Kingdom
Tel.: (44) 3456004040
Web Site: http://www.certasenergy.co.uk
Sales Range: $75-99.9 Million
Emp.: 2,300
Oil & Liquefied Petroleum Gas Sales, Mar-
keting & Distribution
N.A.I.C.S.: 424710
Tony Stewart (Dir)

Certas Energy France SAS **(1)**
9 Avenue Edouard Belin, 92500, Rueil-
Malmaison, France
Tel.: (33) 155940628
Web Site: https://www.certasenergyretail.fr
Petroleum Product Distr
N.A.I.C.S.: 424710

Certas Energy Norway AS **(1)**
Elias Smiths vei 24, 1337, Sandvika, Nor-
way
Tel.: (47) 67522400
Web Site: https://www.certasretail.no
Emp.: 23

Petroleum Product Distr
N.A.I.C.S.: 424710

Comm-Tec GmbH **(1)**
Siemensstrasse 14, 73066, Uhingen, Ger-
many
Tel.: (49) 716130000
Web Site: https://www.exertisproav.de
Electronic Equipment Distr
N.A.I.C.S.: 423690
Eric Maurice Bousquet (Gen Mgr)

Comtrade SAS **(1)**
300 R Du Pdt Salvador Allende, 92700, Co-
lombes, Hauts-de-Seine, France
Tel.: (33) 156470593
Sales Range: $50-74.9 Million
Emp.: 60
Multimedia Device & Accessories Distr
N.A.I.C.S.: 423690

DCC Energi Danmark A/S **(1)**
Naerum Hovedgade 8, 2850, Naerum, Den-
mark
Tel.: (45) 70102010
Web Site: https://www.dccenergi.dk
Petroleum Product Distr
N.A.I.C.S.: 424710

DCC Energy **(1)**
DCC House Brewery Rd, Stillorgan Black-
rock, CO, Dublin, Ireland
Tel.: (353) 12799400
Web Site: http://www.dcc.ie
Holding Company
N.A.I.C.S.: 551112

Subsidiary (Non-US):

Butagaz SAS **(2)**
47/53 rue Raspail, 92594, Levallois-Perret,
Cedex, France
Tel.: (33) 970818122
Web Site: https://www.butagaz.fr
Liquefied Petroleum Gas, Butane & Pro-
pane Products Distr
N.A.I.C.S.: 424720
Emmanuel Trivin (Pres)

Subsidiary (US):

Hicksgas, LLC **(2)**
204 N State Rte 54, Roberts, IL 60962
Tel.: (217) 395-2281
Web Site: http://www.hicksgas.com
Crude Petroleum & Natural Gas Extracting
Services
N.A.I.C.S.: 211120

DCC Energy Limited **(1)**
40-48 Airport Road West, Sydenham, Bel-
fast, BT3 9ED, United Kingdom
Tel.: (44) 2890732611
Lubricant Oil Distr
N.A.I.C.S.: 424720
Pat O'Neill (Gen Mgr)

DCC Environmental **(1)**
DCC House Brewery Road, Stillorgan
Blackrock, Dublin, Ireland
Tel.: (353) 12799400
Web Site: http://www.dcc.ie
Sales Range: $50-74.9 Million
Emp.: 55
Holding Company
N.A.I.C.S.: 551112
Tommy Breen (CEO & Mng Dir)

DCC Food & Beverage **(1)**
DCC House Brewery Rd, Stillorgan Black-
rock, Dublin, Ireland
Tel.: (353) 12799400
Web Site: http://www.dcc.ie
Sales Range: $25-49.9 Million
Emp.: 35
Holding Company
N.A.I.C.S.: 551112
Frank Fenn (Mng Dir)

DCC Health And Beauty Solutions
Limited **(1)**
9-11 Hardwick Road, Astmoor, Runcorn,
WA7 1PH, Cheshire, United Kingdom
Tel.: (44) 1928573734
Web Site:
https://www.dcchealthandbeauty.com
Sales Range: $50-74.9 Million
Emp.: 160
Pharmaceutical Preparation Mfr
N.A.I.C.S.: 325412

DCC plc—(Continued)

Subsidiary (US):

Amerilab Technologies, Inc. (2)
2765 Niagara Ln N, Minneapolis, MN 55447
Tel.: (763) 525-1262
Web Site: http://www.amerilabtech.com
Pharmaceutical Preparation Mfr
N.A.I.C.S.: 325412
Fred Wehling (Founder)

Ion Labs, Inc. (2)
8031 114th Ave Ste 4000, Largo, FL 33773
Tel.: (727) 527-1072
Web Site: http://www.ionlabs.com
Herbal & Vitamin Products Mfr & Distr
N.A.I.C.S.: 325411
Clayton Desjardine (CEO)

DCC Healthcare (1)
DCC House Leopardstown Road, Foxrock,
Dublin, D18 PK00, Ireland
Tel.: (353) 12799400
Web Site: http://www.dcc.ie
Sales Range: $25-49.9 Million
Emp.: 60
Drugs & Druggists Sundries Whslr
N.A.I.C.S.: 424210
Conor Costigan (Mng Dir)

DCC LPG Ltd. (1)
DCC House Leopardstown Road Foxrock,
Dublin, 18, Ireland
Tel.: (353) 12799400
Gas Distr
N.A.I.C.S.: 333912
Donal Murphy (CEO)

DCC Propane LLC (1)
1001 Warrenville Rd Ste 350, Lisle, IL
60532
Tel.: (630) 658-9501
Web Site: http://www.dccpropane.com
N.A.I.C.S.: 424720
Matt Danntine (CEO)

DCC SerCom (1)
Leopardstown Road Foxrock, Stillorgan
Blackrock, Dublin, 18, Ireland
Tel.: (353) 12799400
Sales Range: $25-49.9 Million
Emp.: 35
Computer Related Services
N.A.I.C.S.: 541519
Niall Ennis (Mng Dir)

DCC Technology Limited (1)
DCC House Leopardstown Road Foxrock,
Dublin, D18 PK00, Ireland
Tel.: (353) 12799400
Computer Services
N.A.I.C.S.: 541519
Tim Griffin (Mng Dir)

Subsidiary (Non-US):

Jam Industries Ltd. (2)
21000 Trans-Canadienne, Baie-d'Urfe, H9X
4B7, QC, Canada
Tel.: (514) 457-2555
Web Site: https://www.jamindustries.com
Sales Range: $50-74.9 Million
Emp.: 300
Musical Instruments, Audio & Lighting
Equipment & Consumer Electronics Distr
N.A.I.C.S.: 339992
Martin Szpiro (Pres & CEO)

Subsidiary (US):

American Music & Sound LLC (3)
925 Broadbeck Dr Ste 220, Newbury Park,
CA 91320
Tel.: (800) 431-2609
Web Site:
   http://www.americanmusicandsound.com
Musical Instrument Distr
N.A.I.C.S.: 459140
Tim Schaeffer (Sr VP-Allen & Health USA)

Division (Domestic):

American Audio & Video (4)
4325 Executive Dr Ste 300, Southaven, MS
38672
Tel.: (866) 916-4667
Web Site:
   http://www.americanaudiovideo.com
Musical Instrument Distr
N.A.I.C.S.: 459140

Melanie Robitaille (Mgr-Credit)

Subsidiary (US):

Ashly Audio Inc (3)
847 Holt Rd, Webster, NY, 14580-9103
Tel.: (585) 872-0010
Web Site: http://www.ashly.com
Emp.: 50
Signal Processing Equipment Mfr.
N.A.I.C.S.: 334515
Anthony Errigo (Dir-Mktg Comm)

U.S. Music Corporation (3)
444 E Courtland St, Mundelein, IL
60060   **(100%)**
Tel.: (847) 949-0444
Web Site: http://www.usmusiccorp.com
Sales Range: $50-74.9 Million
Emp.: 140
Musical Instrument & Sound Equipment Mfr;
Guitars, Amplifiers & Sound Engineering
Equipment
N.A.I.C.S.: 339992
Barry Ryan (Pres)

Subsidiary (US):

Jeff Burgess & Associates, Inc. (2)
1050 Northgate Dr Ste 200, San Rafael, CA
94903
Tel.: (415) 256-2800
Web Site: http://www.jbanda.com
Sales Range: $10-24.9 Million
Emp.: 11
Video Broadcasting & Post-Production Services
N.A.I.C.S.: 512199
Jeffrey Burgess (CEO)

DCC Vital Limited (1)
Fannin House, South County Business Park
Leopardstown, Dublin, D18 Y0C9, Ireland
Tel.: (353) 12907000
Web Site: http://www.dccvital.com
Emp.: 1,000
Pharmaceuticals Distr
N.A.I.C.S.: 424210
Harry Keenan (Mng Dir)

DSG Energy Limited (1)
Room 2201-02 22/F Landmark East AIA
Kowloon Building, 100 How Ming Street
Kwun Tong, Kowloon, China (Hong Kong)
Tel.: (852) 24358388
Web Site: https://dsg-energy.com
N.A.I.C.S.: 213112

Emo Oil Limited (1)
Clonminam Indus Estate, Portlaoise, Laois,
Ireland
Tel.: (353) 818366425
Web Site: http://www.emo.ie
Sales Range: $50-74.9 Million
Emp.: 50
Crude Petroleum & Natural Gas Extraction
N.A.I.C.S.: 211120

**Energie Direct
MineralolhandelsgesmbH** (1)
Alte Poststrasse 400, 8055, Graz, Austria
Tel.: (43) 316 210
Web Site: http://www.energiedirect.at
Sales Range: $50-74.9 Million
Emp.: 100
Petroleum Product Distr
N.A.I.C.S.: 424720

Enva Ireland Limited (1)
Clonminam Industrial Estate, Portlaoise,
Laois, R32 XD95, Ireland
Tel.: (353) 578678600
Web Site: http://www.enva.ie
Sales Range: $25-49.9 Million
Emp.: 200
Nonhazardous Waste Treatment & Disposal
N.A.I.C.S.: 562219
Tom Walsh (CEO)

EuroCaps Limited (1)
Crown Business Park, South Wales, Trede-
gar, NP22 4EF, United Kingdom
Tel.: (44) 1495308900
Web Site: https://www.eurocaps.co.uk
Sales Range: $50-74.9 Million
Emp.: 300
Chemical Product & Preparation Mfr
N.A.I.C.S.: 325998
Brett Tomlin (Mng Dir)

Exertis (UK) Limited (1)

St George House Parkway, Harlow Busi-
ness Park, Harlow, CM19 5QF, Essex,
United Kingdom
Tel.: (44) 1279822800
Web Site: http://www.expertisgem.co.uk
Sales Range: $1-4.9 Billion
Emp.: 1,000
Technology Distribution Network Services
N.A.I.C.S.: 519290
Gerry O'Keeffe (Mng Dir-Intl)

Subsidiary (Domestic):

Exertis (UK) Ltd. (2)
Technology House Magnesium Way, Hap-
ton, Burnley, BB12 7BF, United Kingdom
Tel.: (44) 1282776776
Web Site: https://www.exertis.co.uk
Wireless Communication Services
N.A.I.C.S.: 517112

Exertis (UK) Ltd (1)
Shorten Brook Way Altham Business Park,
Altham, Accrington, BB5 5YJ, Lancashire,
United Kingdom   **(100%)**
Tel.: (44) 1282776776
Web Site: http://www.exertis.co.uk
IT, Communication & Home Entertainment
Products Distr
N.A.I.C.S.: 423420
Paul Bryan (Mng Dir-IT & Mobile)

Exertis Arc Telecom Limited (1)
Unit No 702 X3 Building, Jumeirah Lakes
Towers, Dubai, United Arab Emirates
Tel.: (971) 44537255
Memory & Accessory Product Distr
N.A.I.C.S.: 423690

Exertis CapTech AB (1)
Aminogatan 17, Molndal, 431 53, Gothen-
burg, Sweden
Tel.: (46) 31450400
Web Site: http://www.exertis.se
Computer Distr
N.A.I.C.S.: 423430

Exertis France SAS (1)
5 rue Pleyel, 93200, Saint Denis, France
Tel.: (33) 156470470
Web Site: https://www.exertis.fr
Emp.: 180
Computer Peripheral & Accessory Distr
N.A.I.C.S.: 423430

Exertis Hammer Limited (1)
Intec 1 Intec Business Park Wade Road,
Basingstoke, RG24 8NE, Hampshire,
United Kingdom
Tel.: (44) 1256841000
Web Site: http://www.exertisenterprise.com
Software Services
N.A.I.C.S.: 541511
James Stidwill (Mng Dir)

Exertis Ireland Limited (1)
21 Fonthill Business Park, Ballymount Road
Upper, Dublin, D22 FR82, Ireland
Tel.: (353) 14087171
Web Site: https://www.exertis.ie
IT & Home Entertainment Products Mfr
N.A.I.C.S.: 541614

Subsidiary (Non-US):

Janson Computers Plc (2)
The Technology Park Colindeep Lane, Lon-
don, NW9 6BX, United Kingdom
Tel.: (44) 2082008282
Web Site: http://www.unlimited.com
Computer Products Distr
N.A.I.C.S.: 423430
James Sanson (Chm & CEO)

**Exertis Supply Chain Services
Limited** (1)
Unit 21 Fonthill Business Park Fonthill
Road, Clondalkin, Dublin, D22 FR82, Ire-
land
Tel.: (353) 14056500
Web Site:
   https://www.exertissupplychain.com
Supply Chain Services
N.A.I.C.S.: 541614

Fannin Limited (1)
Fannin House South County Business Park,
Leopardstown, Dublin, 18, Ireland **(100%)**
Tel.: (353) 12907000
Web Site: https://www.fannin.eu

Sales Range: $25-49.9 Million
Emp.: 100
Pharmacies & Drug Stores
N.A.I.C.S.: 456110

Flogas Ireland Limited (1)
Knockbrack House Matthews Lane Donore
Road, Drogheda, A92 T803, Louth, Ireland
Tel.: (353) 412149600
Web Site: https://www.flogas.ie
Sales Range: $25-49.9 Million
Emp.: 80
Liquefied Petroleum Gas, Bottled Gas,
Dealers
N.A.I.C.S.: 457210
John Rooney (Mng Dir)

Flogas Norge AS (1)
Sandakerveien 116 building D, 0484, Oslo,
Norway
Tel.: (47) 90248000
Web Site: http://www.flogas.no
Natural Gas Distribution Services
N.A.I.C.S.: 221210

Flogas Sverige AB (1)
Brannkyrkag 63, 118 22, Stockholm, Swe-
den
Tel.: (46) 86750080
Web Site: https://www.flogas.se
Natural Gas Distribution Services
N.A.I.C.S.: 221210

Flogas UK Limited (1)
Rayns Way Watermead Business Park,
Syston, Leicester, LE7 1PF, United King-
dom
Tel.: (44) 3457200100
Web Site: http://www.flogas.co.uk
Sales Range: $100-124.9 Million
Emp.: 150
Crude Petroleum & Natural Gas Extraction
N.A.I.C.S.: 211120
Gannon Lee (Mng Dir)

Subsidiary (Non-US):

Benegas B.V. (2)
Zuiderzeestraatweg 1, Well, 3882 NC, Put-
ten, Netherlands
Tel.: (31) 341723350
Web Site: http://benegas.com
Sales Range: $50-74.9 Million
Emp.: 27
Liquefied Petroleum Gas Distr
N.A.I.C.S.: 221210

Subsidiary (Domestic):

**Dieselec Thistle Generators
Limited** (2)
Cadder House 160 Clober Road, Milngavie,
Glasgow, G62 1 LW, United Kingdom
Tel.: (44) 1419567764
Web Site: http://www.dieselecthistle.co.uk
Generator Distribution Services
N.A.I.C.S.: 423610
Paul Moore (Mng Dir)

Subsidiary (Non-US):

LP Gas B.V. (2)
Zuiderzeestraatweg 1, Putten, 3882 NC,
Netherlands
Tel.: (31) 341723400
Web Site: http://www.lpgas.nl
Sales Range: $50-74.9 Million
Emp.: 60
Petroleum & Gas Products Whslr
N.A.I.C.S.: 424720
Jan van Dijk (Head-Sls)

Fuel Card Services Limited (1)
Alexandra House Lawnswood Business
Park Redvers Close, Leeds, LS16 6QY,
United Kingdom
Tel.: (44) 1132981000
Web Site: https://www.fuelcardservices.com
Sales Range: $50-74.9 Million
Emp.: 48
Fossil Fuel Electric Power Generation
N.A.I.C.S.: 221112

Gaz de Paris SAS (1)
47/53 rue Raspail, 92300, Levallois-Perret,
France
Tel.: (33) 810109610
Web Site: https://www.gaz-europeen.com
Natural Gas Distribution Services
N.A.I.C.S.: 221210

Go Telecom BV (1)
Laan van Copenhagen 100, 3317 DM, Dordrecht, Netherlands
Tel.: (31) 788800700
Web Site: http://www.exertis.nl
Communication Tool Distr
N.A.I.C.S.: 423690

Great Gas Petroleum (Ireland) Limited (1)
Market House, Churchtown, Mallow, Cork, Ireland
Tel.: (353) 22 23 989
Web Site: http://www.greatgas.com
Sales Range: $50-74.9 Million
Emp.: 1
Petroleum Product Distr
N.A.I.C.S.: 424720
Ray O'Sullivan *(Mng Dir)*

Hypertec Limited (1)
2 Swangate Charnham Park, Hungerford, RG17 0YX, Berkshire, United Kingdom
Tel.: (44) 1488686844
Memory & Accessory Product Distr
N.A.I.C.S.: 423690

Kelkin Limited (1)
Merrywell Industrial Estate Ballymount, Ballymount Cross, Dublin, D12 A590, Ireland
Tel.: (353) 14051500
Web Site: http://www.kelkin.ie
Sales Range: $25-49.9 Million
Emp.: 65
Specialty Food Stores
N.A.I.C.S.: 445298

Laleham Healthcare Limited (1)
Sycamore Park, Mill Lane, Alton, GU34 2PR, Hampshire, United Kingdom
Tel.: (44) 1420566500
Web Site: http://www.laleham-healthcare.com
Sales Range: $50-74.9 Million
Emp.: 200
Pharmaceutical Preparation Mfr
N.A.I.C.S.: 325412

MTR Group Limited (1)
Unit 10 Spire Green Centre The Pinnacles, Harlow, CM19 5TR, Essex, United Kingdom
Tel.: (44) 8446931663
Web Site: https://mtr.co.uk
N.A.I.C.S.: 449210

Medisource Ireland Limited (1)
Unit 24-26 Bullford Business Campus, Kilcoole, Wicklow, A63 YX52, Ireland
Tel.: (353) 12866366
Web Site: http://www.medisource.ie
Pharmaceuticals Distr
N.A.I.C.S.: 424210

Pace Fuelcare Limited (1)
Hanover House 18 The Avenue, Egham, TW20 9AB, Surrey, United Kingdom
Tel.: (44) 1784 484444
Web Site: http://www.pacefuelcare.co.uk
Fuel Distr
N.A.I.C.S.: 424720

Qstar Forsaljning AB (1)
Spargatan 5, Box 633, 601 14, Norrkoping, Sweden
Tel.: (46) 11280000
Web Site: https://www.qstar.se
Petroleum Product Distr
N.A.I.C.S.: 424710

Robert Roberts Limited (1)
79 Broomhill Road Tallaght, Dublin, 24, Ireland
Tel.: (353) 14047300
Web Site: http://www.robert-roberts.ie
Sales Range: $75-99.9 Million
Emp.: 200
Confectionery Whslr
N.A.I.C.S.: 424450
Tom Gray *(Mng Dir)*

SerCom Distribution Limited (1)
DCC House Brewery Road, Stillorgan, Dublin, Ireland
Tel.: (353) 1 2799 400
Web Site: http://www.dcc.ie
Emp.: 5
Software & Consumer Electronics Distr
N.A.I.C.S.: 423430
Niall Ennis *(Mng Dir)*

SerCom Solutions Limited (1)

M50 Business Park, Ballymount Road Upper, Dublin, 12, Ireland
Tel.: (353) 14056500
Web Site: http://www.sercomsolutions.ie
Sales Range: $25-49.9 Million
Emp.: 20
Management Consulting Services
N.A.I.C.S.: 541618
Neil Ennis *(CEO)*

Sharptext Limited (1)
M50 Business Park, Ballymount Road Upper, Dublin, 12, Ireland
Tel.: (353) 14087171
Web Site: http://www.sharptext.com
Sales Range: $25-49.9 Million
Emp.: 60
Computer Related Services
N.A.I.C.S.: 541519
John Dunne *(Mng Dir)*

Squadron Medical Limited (1)
Greaves Close Markham Vale, Chesterfield, S44 5FB, United Kingdom
Tel.: (44) 1246822822
Web Site: http://www.squadronmedical.co.uk
Healthcare Logistics Services
N.A.I.C.S.: 541614

Swea Energi AB (1)
Storgatan 35, SE-434 32, Kungsbacka, Sweden
Tel.: (46) 3007 5600
Web Site: http://www.sweaenergi.se
Sales Range: $50-74.9 Million
Emp.: 54
Heating Oil & Transport Fuels Distr
N.A.I.C.S.: 424720
Maria Utell *(VP & Controller)*

Technische Gase und Gasetechnik GmbH (1)
Werner-von-Siemens-Strasse 18, 97076, Wurzburg, Germany
Tel.: (49) 93120930
Web Site: https://www.tega.de
Natural Gas Distribution Services
N.A.I.C.S.: 221210

Tega-Technische Gase und Gasetechnik GmbH (1)
Werner-von-Siemens-Strasse 18, 97076, Wurzburg, Germany **(100%)**
Tel.: (49) 93120930
Web Site: https://www.tega.de
Emp.: 100
Industrial Gas Mfr
N.A.I.C.S.: 325120

The TPS Healthcare Group Limited (1)
27-35 Napier Place Wardpark North, Cumbernauld, G68 0LL, United Kingdom
Tel.: (44) 1236 739 668
Web Site: http://www.tpshealthcare.co.uk
Sales Range: $25-49.9 Million
Emp.: 79
Healthcare Logistics Services
N.A.I.C.S.: 541614

Thompson & Capper Limited (1)
9-12 Hardwick Road, Astmoor Industrial Estate, Runcorn, WA7 1PH, Cheshire, United Kingdom
Tel.: (44) 1928573734
Web Site: https://www.thompsonandcapper.com
Sales Range: $50-74.9 Million
Emp.: 200
Pharmaceutical Preparation Mfr
N.A.I.C.S.: 325412
Matthew Dyal *(Mng Dir)*

Virtus Inc. (1)
1896 Lammers Pke, Batesville, IN 47006
Tel.: (812) 933-1121
Sales Range: $25-49.9 Million
Emp.: 100
Mattress Mfr
N.A.I.C.S.: 337910
John Miller *(Mng Dir)*

Wastecycle Ltd. (1)
Enviro Building Private Rd Number 4, Colwick Industrial Estate, Nottingham, NG4 2JT, United Kingdom
Tel.: (44) 01159403111
Web Site: http://www.wastecycle.co.uk

Sales Range: $1-9.9 Million
Emp.: 200
Recycling & Waste Management Services
N.A.I.C.S.: 562998

William Tracey Limited (1)
49 Burnbrae Road Linwood, Paisley, PA33BD, United Kingdom
Tel.: (44) 1505321000
Web Site: http://www.williamtraceygroup.com
Emp.: 200
Waste Management Services
N.A.I.C.S.: 562998
Michael Tracey *(Pres)*

Williams Medical Supplies Limited (1)
Craiglas House, The Maerdy Industrial Estate, Rhymney, NP22 5PY, Gwent, United Kingdom
Tel.: (44) 1685846666
Web Site: https://www.wms.co.uk
Pharmaceuticals Distr
N.A.I.C.S.: 424210

DCD MEDIA PLC
6th Floor 2 Kingdom Street, London, W2 6JP, United Kingdom
Tel.: (44) 2038690190
Web Site: http://www.dcdmedia.co.uk
DCD—(LSE)
Rev.: $14,845,310
Assets: $16,877,817
Liabilities: $13,207,900
Net Worth: $3,669,917
Earnings: ($211,804)
Emp.: 17
Fiscal Year-end: 03/31/20
Arts, Entertainment, Music & Drama
TV Programming Producer & Distr
N.A.I.C.S.: 512110
Nicky Davies Williams *(CEO-DCD Rights-Distr Div)*

Subsidiaries:

Box TV Limited (1)
151 Wardour Street, London, W1F 8WE, United Kingdom
Tel.: (44) 2072978040
Web Site: http://www.box-tv.co.uk
Television Program Producers
N.A.I.C.S.: 512110

DCD Publishing Limited (1)
Glen House 22 Glenthorne Road, London, W6 0NG, United Kingdom
Tel.: (44) 208 563 9393
Web Site: http://www.dcdpublishing.co.uk
Emp.: 30
Media & Public Relations Agency
N.A.I.C.S.: 541830

Prospect Pictures Limited (1)
Glen House, 22 Glenthorne Rd, London, W6 0NG, United Kingdom
Tel.: (44) 2076361234
Web Site: http://www.prospect-uk.com
Motion Picture Production Services
N.A.I.C.S.: 512110

September Films Limited (1)
Glen House, 22 Glenthorne Rd, London, W6 0NG, United Kingdom
Tel.: (44) 2085639393
Motion Picture Production Services
N.A.I.C.S.: 512110

Subsidiary (US):

September Films USA, Inc. (2)
Raleigh Studios 650 N Bronson Ave Ste B114, Los Angeles, CA 90004
Tel.: (323) 960-8085
Motion Picture Production Services
N.A.I.C.S.: 512110

DCD-DORBYL (PTY) LTD.
Ring Road, Duncanville, 1939, Vereeniging, South Africa
Tel.: (27) 164280000   **ZA**
Web Site: http://www.dcd.com
Year Founded: 2002
Sales Range: $25-49.9 Million
Emp.: 100

Holding Company; Heavy Mechanical Engineering Products & Services
N.A.I.C.S.: 551112
Dirk Els *(Exec Dir-Mktg)*

Subsidiaries:

DCD-Dorbyl Heavy Engineering Vereeniging (1)
Ring Road, Duncanville, Vereeniging, 1939, South Africa **(100%)**
Tel.: (27) 164280000
Web Site: http://www.dcd-dorbyl.com
Emp.: 503
Mining, Steel & Power Industry Equipment Mfr
N.A.I.C.S.: 333131
Dawie Marais *(Gen Mgr)*

DCD-Dorbyl Rolling Stock Division (1)
54 Victor Street Industrial Park, East Rand, Boksburg, 1406, South Africa
Tel.: (27) 119141400
Web Site: http://www.dcd-dorbyl.com
Sales Range: $100-124.9 Million
Emp.: 200
Railroad Rolling Stock & Specialty Vehicle Designer, Mfr & Refurbishment Services
N.A.I.C.S.: 336510
Gary Steinmetz *(Gen Mgr)*

DCI ADVISORS LIMITED
Tortola Pier Park Building 1 Second Floor Wickhams Cay 1, Road Town, Tortola, Virgin Islands (British)
Web Site: https://www.dciadvisorsltd.com
DCI—(LSE)
Rev.: $339,878
Assets: $184,568,934
Liabilities: $55,728,301
Net Worth: $128,840,634
Earnings: ($6,194,765)
Emp.: 27
Fiscal Year-end: 12/31/22
Real Estate Investment Services
N.A.I.C.S.: 531390
Nicholas Paris *(Mng Dir)*

DCI DATABASE FOR COMMERCE AND INDUSTRY AG
Enzianstrasse 2, 82319, Starnberg, Germany
Tel.: (49) 81512650
Web Site: https://www.dci.de
DCIK—(MUN)
Rev.: $1,379,838
Assets: $6,060,246
Liabilities: $397,393
Net Worth: $5,662,853
Earnings: $386,354
Emp.: 1
Fiscal Year-end: 12/31/23
Database & Information Management Services
N.A.I.C.S.: 519290
Thomas Friedbichler *(Chm-Supervisory Bd)*

DCK CONCESSIONS LTD.
DCK House Station Court Radford Way, Billericay, CM12 0DZ, Essex, United Kingdom
Tel.: (44) 1277 650655
Web Site: http://www.dckconcessions.com
Year Founded: 1992
Sales Range: $300-349.9 Million
Emp.: 2,457
Jewelry Product Whslr
N.A.I.C.S.: 423940
Alan Witzenfeld *(Founder & CEO)*

DCM CORP.
55 Ungsangnonggongdanji-gil, Yangsan, Gyeongsangnam-do, Korea (South)
Tel.: (82) 553669991
Web Site: https://www.dcmcorp.co.kr

DCM Corp.—(Continued)

Year Founded: 1972
024090—(KRS)
Rev.: $184,543,424
Assets: $235,435,499
Liabilities: $31,903,421
Net Worth: $203,532,078
Earnings: $28,871,793
Emp.: 180
Fiscal Year-end: 12/31/22
Steel Products Mfr
N.A.I.C.S.: 331110
Yon-Taek Jeong (CEO)

DCM DECOMETAL GMBH
Grazerplatz 5, A-8280, Fuerstenfeld,
Austria
Tel.: (43) 3382 520 52
Web Site: http://www.dcm-
vienna.com
Metal Ore Mining Services
N.A.I.C.S.: 212290
Herbert H. Depisch (Chm & Founder)

Subsidiaries:

DCM Austria　　　　　　　　　　(1)
Urban-Loritz-Platz 4/16, 1070, Vienna, Aus-
tria
Tel.: (43) 6601433376
Web Site: http://www.dcm.at
Metal Ore Mining Services
N.A.I.C.S.: 212210

DCM HOLDINGS CO., LTD.
Omori Bellport E Building 6-22-7
Minami-Oi, Shinagawa-ku, Tokyo,
140-0013, Japan
Tel.: (81) 357645211　　　　　　JP
Web Site: https://www.dcm-
hldgs.co.jp
Year Founded: 2006
3050—(TKS)
Rev.: $3,464,266,170
Assets: $4,415,184,060
Liabilities: $2,633,651,400
Net Worth: $1,781,532,660
Earnings: $152,052,140
Fiscal Year-end: 02/29/24
Household Products Retailer
N.A.I.C.S.: 449129
Toshihiro Hisada (Chm & CEO)

Subsidiaries:

DCM Daiki Co., Ltd.　　　　　　(1)
1-9-1 Misawa, Matsuyama, 791-8517,
Ehime, Japan
Tel.: (81) 89 925 1111
Household Product Distr
N.A.I.C.S.: 449129
Masashi Kojima (Pres)

Subsidiary (Domestic):

Daiki Real Estate Information Co.,
Ltd.　　　　　　　　　　　　　(2)
3-20-33 Takewara, Matsuyama, 790-0053,
Ehime, Japan
Tel.: (81) 899215111
Household Product Distr
N.A.I.C.S.: 449129

Home Center Sanko Co., Ltd.　(2)
1-1-1 Midorigaoka, Arao, 864-0033, Kuma-
moto, Japan
Tel.: (81) 968693535
Household Product Distr
N.A.I.C.S.: 449129

DCM Homac Corp.　　　　　　　(1)
3-2 Atsubetsu-Chuo, Atsubetsu-Ku, Sap-
poro, 004-8611, Hokkaido, Japan
Tel.: (81) 11 892 6611
Web Site: http://www.homac.co.jp
Household Product Distr
N.A.I.C.S.: 449129
Yasunori Ishiguro (Pres)

Subsidiary (Domestic):

Homac Nicot Corp.　　　　　　(2)
2-1-40 3jo Atsubetsuchuo, Atsubetsu-Ku,
Sapporo, 004-0053, Hokkaido, Japan

Tel.: (81) 118023810
Web Site: http://www.homac-nicot.co.jp
Household Product Distr
N.A.I.C.S.: 449129

DCM Kahma Co., Ltd.　　　　　(1)
3-411 Hidaka-cho, Kariya, 448-8535, Aichi,
Japan
Tel.: (81) 566 25 2511
Web Site: http://www.kahma.co.jp
Household Product Distr
N.A.I.C.S.: 449129
Yoshiyuki Toyoda (Pres)

Subsidiary (Domestic):

Kahya Co., Ltd.　　　　　　　(2)
3-4-11 Tarumicho, Suita, 564-0062, Osaka,
Japan
Tel.: (81) 663689730
Household Product Distr
N.A.I.C.S.: 449129

DCM Kuroganeya Co., Ltd.　　(1)
1-13-18 Nakagogahara, Kofu, 400-0855,
Yamanashi, Japan
Tel.: (81) 55 2412471
Web Site: http://www.kuroganeya.co.jp
Household Appliance Store Operator
N.A.I.C.S.: 444110
Mikio Akai (Pres)

DCM Nicot Co., Ltd.　　　　　(1)
Atsubetsu Chuo 3-2-1-40, Atsubetsu, Sap-
poro, 004-0053, Japan
Tel.: (81) 11 802 3810
Web Site: https://www.homac-nicot.co.jp
Household Product Distr
N.A.I.C.S.: 449129

DCM Sanwa Co., Ltd.　　　　　(1)
69-1 Aza-Miyoshi Oaza-Ishie, Aomori, 004-
8611, Japan
Tel.: (81) 17 782 3200
Web Site: http://www.sanwado.com
Household Product Distr
N.A.I.C.S.: 449129

DCM advanced technologies Co.,
Ltd.　　　　　　　　　　　　　(1)
6-22-7 Minamioi Omori Bellport E Building,
Shinagawa-ku, Tokyo, 140-0013, Japan
Tel.: (81) 357645231
Web Site: https://www.dcm-at.co.jp
System Planning & Development Services
N.A.I.C.S.: 541511

XPRICE Inc.　　　　　　　　　(1)
1F Lucid Square Toyocho 2-7-5 Mina-
misuna, Koto-ku, Tokyo, 136-0076, Japan
Tel.: (81) 570076406
Web Site: https://www.xprice.co.jp
Household Appliance Distr
N.A.I.C.S.: 423620

DCM LIMITED
Unit Nos 2050 to 2052 Floor Plaza -II
Central Square Bara Hindu Rao, 20
Manohar Lal Khurana Marg, New
Delhi, 110006, India
Tel.: (91) 1141539170
Web Site: https://www.dcm.in
502820—(BOM)
Rev.: $7,067,369
Assets: $17,158,992
Liabilities: $19,761,624
Net Worth: ($2,602,632)
Earnings: ($2,435,310)
Emp.: 728
Fiscal Year-end: 03/31/21
Yarn Mfr & Software Development
Services
N.A.I.C.S.: 313110
Vinay Bharat Ram (Chm & Mng Dir)

Subsidiaries:

DCM Data Systems Limited　　(1)
316 Udyog Vihar Phase-II, Gurgaon, 122
016, India
Tel.: (91) 124 412 2800
Web Site: http://www.dcmds.com
Information Technology Consulting Services
N.A.I.C.S.: 541512

DCM Engineering Limited　　　(1)
Phagwara-Mohali Express Hwy, Shahid
Bhagat Singh Nagar, Tehsils, 144533, Pun-

jab, India
Tel.: (91) 1881270802
Web Site: https://www.dcmengg.com
Emp.: 1,700
Automotive Products Mfr
N.A.I.C.S.: 336110

DCM Financial Services Ltd.　(1)
UGF South Tower NBCC Place Bhisham
Pitamah Marg, New Delhi, 110020, India
Tel.: (91) 1120818570
Web Site: http://www.dfslonline.in
Rev.: $348,194
Assets: $5,450,452
Liabilities: $11,359,383
Net Worth: ($5,908,931)
Earnings: ($42,941)
Fiscal Year-end: 03/31/2020
Financial Services
N.A.I.C.S.: 523999
Shantanu Deveshwar (Exec Dir)

DCM Infotech Limited　　　　　(1)
Unit No 2050-2052 Plaza-II Central Square
20 Manohar Lal Khurana Marg, Bara Hindu
Rao, Delhi, 110006, India
Tel.: (91) 1141539140
Web Site: https://www.dcminfotech.com
Software Development Services
N.A.I.C.S.: 541511

DCM Textiles Limited　　　　　(1)
Near Mela Ground, PO Box 59, Hisar,
125001, Haryana, India
Tel.: (91) 1662 259801
Web Site: http://www.dcmnvl.com
Emp.: 1,000
Textile Mill Operator
N.A.I.C.S.: 313310
Vinay Bharat Ram (Chm)

DCM SHRIRAM INDUSTRIES LIMITED
5th Floor Kanchenjunga Building Ba-
rakhamba Road, Connaught Place,
New Delhi, 110 001, India
Tel.: (91) 1143745000
Web Site: https://www.dcmsr.com
Year Founded: 1990
DCMSRIND—(NSE)
Rev.: $283,967,628
Assets: $233,927,187
Liabilities: $148,000,995
Net Worth: $85,926,191
Earnings: $7,213,009
Emp.: 2,367
Fiscal Year-end: 03/31/23
Sugar Mfr & Distr
N.A.I.C.S.: 311314
Tilak Dhar (Dir-Corp Affairs)

Subsidiaries:

DCM Shriram Industries Limited -
CHEMICAL & ALCOHOL
DIVISION　　　　　　　　　　　(1)
5th Floor Kanchenjunga Road Bara-
khamba Road Connaught Place, New Delhi,
110 001, India
Tel.: (91) 114 374 5000
Web Site: https://dcmsr.com
Chemical Products Mfr
N.A.I.C.S.: 325998
Anand Gujral (CEO)

DCM Shriram Industries Limited -
RAYONS DIVISION　　　　　　(1)
Akashdeep Building 5th Floor 26A Bara-
khamba Road, New Delhi, 110001, India
Tel.: (91) 11 2331413
Rayon Fiber Mfr
N.A.I.C.S.: 325220

DCM Shriram Industries Limited -
SUGAR DIVISION　　　　　　　(1)
Kanchenjunga Building 10th Floor 18 Bara-
khamba Road, New Delhi, 110001, India
Tel.: (91) 11 23321413
Cane Sugar Mfr
N.A.I.C.S.: 311314

DCM Shriram Industries Limited -
Shriram Rayons Works　　　　(1)
Shriram Nagar, Kota, 324004, Rajasthan,
India
Tel.: (91) 744 2480001
Rayon Fiber Mfr

N.A.I.C.S.: 325220

DCM SHRIRAM LIMITED
2nd Floor West Wing World Mark 1,
Aerocity, Delhi, 110037, India
Tel.: (91) 1142100200
Web Site:
　　https://www.dcmshriram.com
DCMSHRIRAM—(NSE)
Rev.: $1,356,988,815
Assets: $1,279,126,485
Liabilities: $528,130,785
Net Worth: $750,995,700
Earnings: $145,693,275
Emp.: 5,357
Fiscal Year-end: 03/31/22
Fertilizer, Cement & Sugar Mfr
N.A.I.C.S.: 325312
Ajay S. Shriram (Chm & Sr Mng Dir)

Subsidiaries:

Bioseed Research India Private
Limited　　　　　　　　　　　　(1)
Plot no 234 B Block Phase II, Kavuri Hills,
Hyderabad, 500 033, India
Tel.: (91) 4067066696
Web Site: http://bioseed.com
Sales Range: $25-49.9 Million
Emp.: 150
Seed Breeding Services
N.A.I.C.S.: 541690

Bioseed Research Philippines
Inc　　　　　　　　　　　　　　(1)
NH Katangawan, General Santos, 9500,
Philippines
Tel.: (63) 83 552 9305
Web Site: http://bioseed.com
Emp.: 28
Hybrid Seed Mfr
N.A.I.C.S.: 111199

Bioseed Vietnam Limited　　　(1)
6th Floor Unit 2 Hong Ha Building 25 Ly
Thuong Kiet Street, Phan Chu Trinh Ward
Hoan Kiem District, Hanoi, 100000, Vietnam
Tel.: (84) 2439344625
Web Site: http://bioseed.com
Emp.: 20
Farm Seed Mfr
N.A.I.C.S.: 311224

Hariyali Insurance Broking
Limited　　　　　　　　　　　　(1)
LGF A - 6 Sector 16, Noida, 201301, India
Tel.: (91) 1203968500
Web Site: http://www.dscl.com
Insurance Brokerage Services
N.A.I.C.S.: 524210

Shriram Bioseed (Thailand)
Limited　　　　　　　　　　　　(1)
54 BB Building Room No 1312 Soi
Sukhumvit 21 Asoke Road, Klongtoey Nua
Wattana, Bangkok, 10110, Thailand
Tel.: (66) 26642216
Seed Research & Development Services
N.A.I.C.S.: 541714

DCODR DIGITAL AGENCY
78 River Street, South Yarra, 3141,
VIC, Australia
Tel.: (61) 3 8530 1000
Web Site: http://www.dcodr.com
Year Founded: 2011
Sales Range: $1-9.9 Million
Emp.: 10
Strategy, Creative Design, Web De-
velopment & Branding
N.A.I.C.S.: 541890
Jamie Silver (Mng Dir & Founder)

DCON PRODUCTS PUBLIC COMPANY LIMITED
Elephant Tower B 8th Floor
3300/57 Phaholyothin Road, Chom
Phon Chatuchak, Bangkok, 10900,
Thailand
Tel.: (66) 29373312
Web Site:
　　https://www.dconproduct.com

DCON—(THA)
Rev.: $41,834,278
Assets: $111,726,293
Liabilities: $31,201,561
Net Worth: $80,524,732
Earnings: $6,564,167
Emp.: 340
Fiscal Year-end: 12/31/23
Construction Product Mfr
N.A.I.C.S.: 212321
Wittawat Pornkul *(CEO)*

Subsidiaries:

DCON Products Public Company
Limited - Lopburi Factory 1   **(1)**
33 Moo 8 Chongsarika, Phattananikom,
Lopburi, 15140, Thailand
Tel.: (66) 36 491 484
Construction Materials Mfr
N.A.I.C.S.: 327390

DCON Products Public Company
Limited - Lopburi Factory 2   **(1)**
280 Moo 1 Chongsarika, Phattananikom,
Lopburi, 15140, Thailand
Tel.: (66) 36 436 500 1
Construction Materials Mfr
N.A.I.C.S.: 327390

DCON Products Public Company
Limited - Surat Thani Factory   **(1)**
3300/57 Elephant Building Building B, Surat
Thani, 10900, Thailand
Tel.: (66) 29373312
Web Site: http://www.dconproduct.com
Construction Materials Mfr
N.A.I.C.S.: 327390

Orrada Co., Ltd.   **(1)**
No 330059 Elephant Building Building B 8th
Floor Phahonyothin Road, Chomphon Sub-
District Chatuchak District, Bangkok, 10900,
Thailand
Tel.: (66) 2 937 4337
Web Site: https://www.orrada.com
Real Estate Services
N.A.I.C.S.: 531210

Rompo Products Co. Ltd.   **(1)**
170 Moo 4 Pasak District A Meaung, Lamp-
hun, Thailand
Tel.: (66) 2 937 3312
Flooring Product Mfr & Distr
N.A.I.C.S.: 327120

**DCT CHAMBERS TRUCKING
LTD.**
600 Waddington Drive, Vernon, V1T
8T6, BC, Canada
Tel.: (250) 549-2157
Web Site:
http://www.dctchambers.com
Year Founded: 1964
Rev.: $774,656,542
Emp.: 85
Transportation Services
N.A.I.C.S.: 488999
Robbie Donaldson *(VP)*

DCW LIMITED
Nirmal 3rd Floor Nariman Point,
Mumbai, 400 021, India
Tel.: (91) 22871914
Web Site: https://www.dcwltd.com
DCW—(NSE)
Rev.: $201,418,526
Assets: $255,970,588
Liabilities: $162,168,402
Net Worth: $93,802,186
Earnings: $517,758
Emp.: 1,740
Fiscal Year-end: 03/31/21
Specialty Chemicals Mfr
N.A.I.C.S.: 325180
Pramod Kumar Jain *(Chm & Mng Dir)*

Subsidiaries:

DCW Limited - SAHUPURAM
UNIT   **(1)**
Arumuganeri, Thiruchendur, 628 229, India
Tel.: (91) 4639 280231
Petrochemical Mfr

N.A.I.C.S.: 325110

DCX SYSTEMS LIMITED
Aerospace SEZ Sector Plot No 29 30
& 107, Hi-Tech Defence & Aerospace
Pk KIADB Industrial Area Kavadada-
sanahalli, Bengaluru, 562110, Karna-
taka, India
Tel.: (91) 8067119555
Web Site: https://www.dcxindia.com
Year Founded: 2011
543650—(BOM)
Rev.: $153,472,001
Assets: $128,666,948
Liabilities: $112,615,913
Net Worth: $16,051,035
Earnings: $8,955,492
Fiscal Year-end: 03/31/22
Aerospace Equipment Mfr
N.A.I.C.S.: 335991

DD DOBOJPUTEVI
Usorska 130, Matuzici, 74203, Doboj,
Bosnia & Herzegovina
Tel.: (387) 32691474
Web Site: http://www.dobojputevi-
doboljug.com.ba
DBJPR—(SARE)
Rev.: $6,905,401
Assets: $8,225,490
Liabilities: $6,124,663
Net Worth: $2,100,827
Earnings: $431,627
Emp.: 151
Fiscal Year-end: 12/31/21
Road Construction & Maintenance
Services
N.A.I.C.S.: 237310
Prnjavorac Saca *(Member-Mgmt Bd)*

DD HOLDINGS CO., LTD.
18F Mita NN Bldg 4-1-23 Shiba,
Minato-ku, Tokyo, 108-0014, Japan
Tel.: (81) 368586080   JP
Web Site: http://www.dd-
holdings.com
Year Founded: 1996
3073—(TKS)
Rev.: $262,890,110
Assets: $243,130,280
Liabilities: $174,087,860
Net Worth: $69,042,420
Earnings: $24,212,350
Emp.: 1,191
Fiscal Year-end: 02/29/24
Holding Company
N.A.I.C.S.: 551112
Atsuhisa Matsumura *(Founder &
Pres)*

Subsidiaries:

Diamond Dining Co., Ltd.   **(1)**
4-1-23 Shiba Mita NN Building 18F, Minato-
ku, Tokyo, Japan
Tel.: (81) 368582192
Web Site: https://www.diamond-dining.com
Restaurant Owner & Operator
N.A.I.C.S.: 722511
Taiichi Sawada *(Pres)*

DD MAPEX MAGLAJ
Ul Sulejmana Omerovica, 74250,
Maglaj, Bosnia & Herzegovina
Tel.: (387) 32 603 116
Web Site: http://www.mapex.com.ba
Year Founded: 1978
MPKSRK2—(SARE)
Rev.: $23,855
Assets: $2,651,707
Liabilities: $432,227
Net Worth: $2,219,479
Earnings: ($16,595)
Emp.: 2
Fiscal Year-end: 12/31/19
Catering Services
N.A.I.C.S.: 722320

**DD'S DELUXE ROD HOLDER,
INC.**
Room 402 Unit 1 Building 1 No 1
Huaxing Street, Hengyang, 421000,
Hunan, China
Tel.: (86) 18974731107   NV
Year Founded: 2014
DDLX—(OTCIQ)
Sales Range: Less than $1 Million
Fishing Rod Holder Mfr & Distr
N.A.I.C.S.: 339920
Jun Gu Quan *(Chm, Pres, CEO, CFO
& Sec)*

DD3 ACQUISITION CORP.
Pedregal 24 4th Floor, Colonia Molino
del Rey Del Miguel Hidalgo, Mexico,
11040, Mexico
Tel.: (52) 55 8647 0417   VG
Year Founded: 2018
DDMXU—(NASDAQ)
Emp.: 3
Investment Services
N.A.I.C.S.: 523999
Martin M. Werner *(Chm & CEO)*

DDC ENTERPRISE LIMITED
Room 1601-1602 16/F Hollywood
Centre 233 Hollywood Road, Sheung
Wan, China (Hong Kong)
Tel.: (852) 28030688   Ky
Web Site: https://ir.daydaycook.com
Year Founded: 2012
DDC—(NYSEAMEX)
Rev.: $25,213,884
Assets: $35,855,039
Liabilities: $244,699,972
Net Worth: ($208,844,933)
Earnings: ($32,448,581)
Emp.: 104
Fiscal Year-end: 12/31/22
Food Products Distr
N.A.I.C.S.: 424420

DDD LTD.
94 Rickmansworth Road, Watford,
WD18 7JJ, Herts, United Kingdom
Tel.: (44) 1923229251
Web Site: http://www.dddltd.co.uk
Year Founded: 1912
Sales Range: $10-24.9 Million
Emp.: 250
Pharmaceutical Toiletry & Household
Product Mfr
N.A.I.C.S.: 325412
Amy Allison *(Acct Mgr-Cosmetics)*

Subsidiaries:

Dendron Ltd.   **(1)**
94 Rickmansworth Road, Watford, WD18
7JJ, Herts, United Kingdom
Tel.: (44) 1923229251
Web Site: http://www.ddd.co.uk
Emp.: 150
Markets, Sells & Distributes Branded OTC
Pharmaceutical & Toiletry
N.A.I.C.S.: 325412

Fleet Laboratories Inc.   **(1)**
Caxton Court Caxton Way, Watford Busi-
ness Park, WG1D 8RH, Watford, Herts,
United Kingdom
Tel.: (44) 01923229251
Web Site: http://www.fleetlabs.co.uk
Pharmaceutical & Toiletry Product Mfr
N.A.I.C.S.: 325412

Trinity Scientific Ltd   **(1)**
31 Greenhill Crescent Watford Business
Park, Watford, WD18 8YB, Herts, United
Kingdom
Tel.: (44) 1923 205748
Web Site: http://www.trinityscientific.co.uk
Laboratory Testing Services
N.A.I.C.S.: 541380
Tom Horner *(Mng Dir)*

**DDEV PLASTIKS INDUSTRIES
LIMITED**

2B Pretoria Street, Kolkata, 700071,
West Bengal, India
Tel.: (91) 3322823744   In
Web Site: https://www.ddevgroup.in
Year Founded: 1977
543547—(BOM)
Rev.: $307,021,069
Assets: $126,837,029
Liabilities: $73,342,774
Net Worth: $53,494,254
Earnings: $7,477,593
Emp.: 350
Fiscal Year-end: 03/31/22
Plastics Material Mfr
N.A.I.C.S.: 325211

DDM HOLDING AG
DDM Group Landis Gyr Strasse 1,
CH-6340, Zug, Switzerland
Tel.: (41) 417661420
Web Site: https://www.ddm-group.ch
Year Founded: 2007
DDM—(OMX)
Rev.: $25,304,200
Assets: $304,841,799
Liabilities: $263,193,408
Net Worth: $41,648,390
Earnings: $8,386,423
Emp.: 11
Fiscal Year-end: 12/31/21
Holding Company; Financial & Invest-
ment Services
N.A.I.C.S.: 551112
Fredrik Olsson *(CFO)*

Subsidiaries:

DDM Invest VII d.o.o.   **(1)**
Dunajska Cesta 9, 1000, Ljubljana, Slove-
nia
Tel.: (386) 59339252
Financial Management Services
N.A.I.C.S.: 523940

Finalp Zrt.   **(1)**
7-13 Hegyalja ut, 1016, Budapest, Hungary
Tel.: (36) 614551100
Web Site: http://www.finalp.hu
Financial Management Services
N.A.I.C.S.: 523940
Balazs Toth *(CFO)*

DDMP REIT, INC.
10th Floor Tower 1 DoubleDragon
Plaza DD Meridian Park Corner,
Macapagal Avenue & EDSA Exten-
sion Bay Area, Pasay, Philippines
Tel.: (63) 288567111
Web Site: https://www.ddmpreit.com
Year Founded: 2014
DDMPR—(PHI)
Rev.: $200,294,057
Assets: $1,117,658,090
Liabilities: $45,584,840
Net Worth: $1,072,073,250
Earnings: $181,164,085
Fiscal Year-end: 12/31/23
Real Estate Manangement Services
N.A.I.C.S.: 531311
Tony Tan Caktiong *(Co-Chm)*

DDOR NOVI SAD A.D.O.
8 Mihajlo Pupin Blvd, 21000, Novi
Sad, Serbia
Tel.: (381) 214886000
Web Site: http://www.ddor.co.rs
Sales Range: $150-199.9 Million
Emp.: 2,054
Insurance & Reinsurance Services
N.A.I.C.S.: 524126
Veroljub Dugalic *(Chm-Supervisory
Bd)*

**DDS WIRELESS INTERNA-
TIONAL INC.**
11920 Forge Place, Richmond, V7A
4V9, BC, Canada
Tel.: (604) 241-1441   BC

DDS Wireless International Inc.—(Continued)

Web Site:
http://www.ddswireless.com
Year Founded: 1987
Sales Range: $1-9.9 Million
Emp.: 197
Holding Company; Wireless Mobile
Data Solutions
N.A.I.C.S.: 551112
Vari Ghai *(Founder)*

Subsidiaries:

DDS eFleet Services Inc   **(1)**
11920 Forge Pl, Richmond, V7A 4V9, BC,
Canada
Tel.: (604) 214-7299
Web Site: http://www.efleetservices.com
Mobile Software Development Services
N.A.I.C.S.: 541511

DW Digital Wireless Inc   **(1)**
11920 Forge Pl, Richmond, V7A 4V9, BC,
Canada
Tel.: (604) 241-1441
Web Site: http://www.dw-wireless.com
Emp.: 100
Communication Equipment Mfr & Distr
N.A.I.C.S.: 334290
Markus Pauli *(Pres)*

Digital Dispatch (Intl) Ltd   **(1)**
Bar Hill Business Park, Saxon Way Bar Hill,
Cambridge, CB23 8SL, United Kingdom
Tel.: (44) 01954780888
Web Site: http://www.digital-dispatch.com
Sales Range: $1-9.9 Million
Emp.: 8
Wireless Mobile Data Services
N.A.I.C.S.: 517112

Subsidiary (Non-US):

MobiSoft Oy   **(2)**
Hatanpaan Valtatie 26, 33100, Tampere,
Finland
Tel.: (358) 102170800
Web Site: http://www.mobisoft.fi
Mobile Data Software Development Ser-
vices
N.A.I.C.S.: 541511

Digital Dispatch (Itl) Pte Ltd   **(1)**
12 Arumugam Rd Lion Building B Ste 03-
12B, Singapore, 409958, Singapore
Tel.: (65) 64551713
Web Site: http://www.digital-dispatch.com
Sales Range: $1-9.9 Million
Emp.: 1
Wireless Mobile Data Services
N.A.I.C.S.: 517112
Vari Ghai *(Chm)*

Digital Dispatch India Pvt. Ltd   **(1)**
215 2nd floor Sikanderpur, Mahatma Gan-
dhi Rd, Gurgaon, 122002, Haryana, India
Tel.: (91) 9810396658
Web Site: http://www.ddswireless.com
Sales Range: $1-9.9 Million
Emp.: 2
Wireless Mobile Data Services
N.A.I.C.S.: 517112

Digital Dispatch Limited
Partnership   **(1)**
11920 Forge Pl, Richmond, V7A 4V9, BC,
Canada
Tel.: (604) 241-1441
Web Site: http://www.ddswireless.com
Emp.: 110
Application Software Development Services
N.A.I.C.S.: 541511
Vari Ghai *(CEO)*

Digital Dispatch Ltd   **(1)**
14833 W 95th St, Lenexa, KS
66215   **(100%)**
Tel.: (913) 599-0419
Web Site: http://www.digitaldispatch.com
Sales Range: $10-24.9 Million
Emp.: 10
Wireless Mobile Data Services
N.A.I.C.S.: 517112

Digital Dispatch Scandinavia AB   **(1)**
Radmansgatan 48, SE-113 57, Stockholm,
Sweden
Tel.: (46) 86741250
Web Site: http://www.digitaldespatch.com

Sales Range: $1-9.9 Million
Emp.: 4
Wireless Mobile Data Services
N.A.I.C.S.: 517112

StrataGen Systems, Inc.   **(1)**
4040 Lake Washington Blvd NE Ste 201,
Kirkland, WA 98033
Tel.: (425) 821-8454
Web Site: http://www.stratagen.com
Sales Range: $10-24.9 Million
Emp.: 20
Wireless Mobile Data Services
N.A.I.C.S.: 517112
Ramond Fast *(Pres)*

DDS, INC.
3-6-41 Marunouchi, Naka-ku, Na-
goya, 460-0002, Japan
Tel.: (81) 529556600
Web Site: http://www.dds.co.jp
Year Founded: 1992
3782—(TKS)
Rev.: $11,190,080
Assets: $34,770,560
Liabilities: $6,350,080
Net Worth: $28,420,480
Earnings: ($1,674,640)
Fiscal Year-end: 12/31/20
Computer Peripherals Mfr
N.A.I.C.S.: 334118

Subsidiaries:

DDS Korea, Inc.   **(1)**
Business Center 17F Keungil Tower 677-25
Yeoksam-dong GangNam-gu, Seoul, Korea
(South)
Tel.: (82) 25495502
Electronic Product Distr
N.A.I.C.S.: 423690

DE AGOSTINI S.P.A.
Via G Da Verrazzano 15, 28100, No-
vara, Italy
Tel.: (39) 026249951   IT
Web Site:
http://www.gruppodeagostini.it
Year Founded: 1901
Sales Range: $5-14.9 Billion
Emp.: 6,427
Holding Company; Publishing, Gam-
ing, Media & Finance Services
N.A.I.C.S.: 551112
Paolo Ceretti *(Gen Mgr)*

Subsidiaries:

Adventure Line Productions S.A   **(1)**
23 Rue Linois, 75015, Paris, France
Tel.: (33) 141861400
Web Site: https://www.alp.tv
Television Broadcasting Services
N.A.I.C.S.: 516120
Delphine Plantive *(Chief Creative Officer)*

De Agostini Communications
S.p.A   **(1)**
Via G da Verrazano 15, Novara, Italy
Tel.: (39) 0321.4241
Web Site: http://www.deagostinigroup.com
Sales Range: $700-749.9 Million
Media Content Production, Broadcasting &
Distribution
N.A.I.C.S.: 512110
Paolo Ceretti *(CEO)*

Subsidiary (Non-US):

Zodiak Media Group - London   **(2)**
Gloucester Building Kensington Village,
Avonmore Road, London, W14 8RF, United
Kingdom
Tel.: (44) 2070134000
Web Site: http://www.zodiakmedia.com
Sales Range: $700-749.9 Million
Emp.: 511
Producer & Distr of Television Shows
N.A.I.C.S.: 512110
Joely Fether *(COO)*

Subsidiary (Domestic):

IWC Media   **(3)**
St Georges Studios 93-97 St Georges
Road, Glasgow, G3 6JA, United Kingdom

Tel.: (44) 3700421404
Web Site: https://www.iwcmedia.co.uk
Sales Range: $25-49.9 Million
Emp.: 50
Television Show Production Services
N.A.I.C.S.: 512110
Peter Langenberg *(Interim Mng Dir & COO)*

Subsidiary (Non-US):

Magnolia Italy   **(3)**
Via Tito Speri 8, 20154, Milan, Italy
Tel.: (39) 02455071
Web Site: http://www.magnoliatv.it
Television Program Production Services
N.A.I.C.S.: 516120

Magnolia Spain   **(3)**
Padre Damian 40 1 B, 28036, Madrid,
Spain
Tel.: (34) 917452643
Web Site: http://www.magnoliatv.es
Television Broadcasting Services
N.A.I.C.S.: 516120
Alfredo Ereno *(CEO)*

Sol Production Pvt. Ltd   **(3)**
B - 40 3rd Floor Shree Babanagar St Pe-
ters Rd Off Hill Road Bandra W, Mumbai,
400 050, Maharashtra, India
Tel.: (91) 2226451352
Web Site: http://www.solworld.co.in
Television Broadcasting Services
N.A.I.C.S.: 516120
Fazila Allana *(Mng Dir)*

Subsidiary (Domestic):

The Comedy Unit   **(3)**
Unit D Glasgow North Trading Estate 24
Craigmont Street, 6th Floor, Glasgow, G20
9BT, United Kingdom
Tel.: (44) 1416748222
Web Site: https://www.comedyunit.co.uk
Sales Range: $25-49.9 Million
Emp.: 40
Television Show Production Services
N.A.I.C.S.: 512110
April Chamberlain *(Mng Dir)*

The Foundation   **(3)**
4th floor Avon house Kensington village
Avonmore, New Cut Road, London, W14
8TS, United Kingdom
Tel.: (44) 1622524053
Web Site: http://www.foundationtv.co.uk
Sales Range: $25-49.9 Million
Emp.: 200
Television Show Production Services
N.A.I.C.S.: 512110
Michael Carrington *(CEO)*

Touchpaper Television   **(3)**
21 John Adam Street, London, WC2N 6JG,
United Kingdom
Tel.: (44) 2073172233
Web Site: http://www.touchpapertv.com
Sales Range: $25-49.9 Million
Emp.: 6
Television Show Production Services
N.A.I.C.S.: 512110
Rob Pursey *(Mng Dir)*

Subsidiary (Non-US):

Zodiak Active S.p.A   **(3)**
Via Deruta 20, 20132, Milan, Italy
Tel.: (39) 02455071
Web Site: http://www.zodiakactive.com
Television Broadcasting Services
N.A.I.C.S.: 516120
Alberto Pillon *(Dir-Entertainment)*

Subsidiary (US):

Zodiak Americas   **(3)**
520 Broadway Ste 500, Santa Monica, CA
90401
Tel.: (310) 460-4490
Television Broadcasting Services
N.A.I.C.S.: 516120
Andy Lennon *(CFO & COO)*

Subsidiary (Domestic):

Zodiak New York   **(4)**
100 6th Ave Ste 12-50, New York, NY
10013
Tel.: (212) 488-1699
Television Broadcasting Services
N.A.I.C.S.: 516120

Mike Gamson *(CEO)*

Subsidiary (Non-US):

Zodiak Belgium   **(3)**
Fabriekstraat 38 Bus 6, 2547, Lint, Belgium
Tel.: (32) 32911100
Web Site: http://www.zodiakbelgium.com
Television Broadcasting Services
N.A.I.C.S.: 516120
Peter Langenberg *(Mng Dir)*

Subsidiary (Domestic):

Zodiak Kids   **(3)**
Avon House Kensington Village Avonmore
Road, London, W14 8TS, United Kingdom
Tel.: (44) 2070134300
Web Site: http://www.zodiakkids.com
Entertainment Services
N.A.I.C.S.: 713940
Cecile Cau *(VP-Sls)*

Subsidiary (Non-US):

Marathon Media   **(4)**
131 Avenue Charles de Gaulle, 92200,
Neuilly-sur-Seine, France
Tel.: (33) 144346600
Television Broadcasting Services
N.A.I.C.S.: 512191
Ambroise Delorme *(COO)*

Subsidiary (Non-US):

Zodiak Nederland   **(3)**
Mediapark Gateway A Sumatralaan 45,
1217 GP, Hilversum, Netherlands
Tel.: (31) 356773796
Web Site: http://www.zodiaknederland.nl
Television Broadcasting Services
N.A.I.C.S.: 516120
Jan Schots *(CFO)*

De Agostini Editore S.p.A   **(1)**
via G da Verrazano 15, 28100, Novara,
Italy
Tel.: (39) 03214241
Web Site: http://www.deagostinieditore.com
Emp.: 300
Book, Periodical & Multimedia Publishing
N.A.I.C.S.: 513130
Stefano Di Bella *(Mng Dir)*

Subsidiary (Domestic):

De Agostini Libri S.p.A   **(2)**
Via Borgonuovo 16, Milan, 20121, Italy
Tel.: (39) 02380861
Web Site: http://www.deagostinilibri.it
Books Publishing Services
N.A.I.C.S.: 513130

De Agostini Publishing Italia
S.p.A   **(2)**
Via Giovanni da Verrazzano 15, Novara,
28100, Italy
Tel.: (39) 03214241
Web Site: http://www.deagostinipassion.com
Books Publishing Services
N.A.I.C.S.: 513130
Davide Ardizio *(Mgr-IT)*

Subsidiary (Non-US):

Editions Atlas (France) S.A.S.   **(2)**
89 Rue La Boetie, 75008, Paris,
France   **(100%)**
Tel.: (33) 0140743838
Web Site: http://www.editionsatlas.fr
Sales Range: $50-74.9 Million
Emp.: 200
Publishing & Communications
N.A.I.C.S.: 513130

Editorial Planeta de Agostini, SA   **(2)**
Avenida Diagonal 662, Barcelona, 08034,
Spain
Tel.: (34) 933440600
Web Site: http://www.planetadeagostini.es
Sales Range: $50-74.9 Million
Emp.: 200
Printing & Publishing
N.A.I.C.S.: 513130
Javier Rey *(Dir-Fin)*

DeA Capital SpA   **(1)**
Via Brera 21, 20121, Milan, Italy   **(51%)**
Tel.: (39) 026249951
Web Site: http://www.deacapital.it
Rev.: $33,931,694

Assets: $657,619,126
Liabilities: $133,195,789
Net Worth: $524,423,337
Earnings: $27,514,443
Emp.: 242
Fiscal Year-end: 12/31/2021
Equity Investment Services
N.A.I.C.S.: 523999
Paolo Ceretti (CEO)

DeA Communications SA (1)
2 rue de la Roquette-Cour Sainte
Marguerite-Esc B, 75011, Paris, France
Tel.: (33) 14 807 3077
Web Site: https://www.deacommunication.fr
Restaurant Services
N.A.I.C.S.: 722511

GTV Productions (1)
115-123 avenue Charles de Gaulle, 92200,
Neuilly-sur-Seine, France
Tel.: (33) 153109500
Web Site: http://www.geteve.fr
Television Broadcasting Services
N.A.I.C.S.: 516120

IDeA Capital Funds SGR (1)
Via Brera 21, 20121, Milan, Italy
Tel.: (39) 022906631
Web Site: http://www.ideasgr.com
Emp.: 23,000
Private Equity Fund Management Services
N.A.I.C.S.: 523940
Chicco Testa (Vice Chm)

IDeA Fimit SGR (1)
Via Mercadante 18, 00198, Rome, Italy
Tel.: (39) 06681631
Web Site: http://www.ideafimit.it
Real Estate Asset Management Services
N.A.I.C.S.: 531390
Alberto Meloni (Dir-Asset Mgmt Div)

Mastiff Norway (1)
Hammersborggata 9, 0181, Oslo, Norway
Tel.: (47) 22389800
Web Site: http://www.mastiff.no
Television Broadcasting Services
N.A.I.C.S.: 516120
Gustav Jansen (COO)

Mona Lisa Production (1)
3 et 4 Place Chazette, 69001, Lyon, France
Tel.: (33) 478390404
Web Site: http://www.monalisa-prod.com
Television Broadcasting Services
N.A.I.C.S.: 516120
Thierry Berrod (Mng Dir)

RDF Television (1)
Shepherds Building Central, Charecroft
Way, London, W14 0EE, United Kingdom
Tel.: (44) 3700420042
Web Site: https://www.rdftelevision.com
Television Broadcasting Services
N.A.I.C.S.: 516120
Jane Wilson (Dir-Production)

RDF Television West (1)
Regent House Regent Street, Clifton, Bris-
tol, BS8 4HG, United Kingdom
Tel.: (44) 1179707600
Television Broadcasting Services
N.A.I.C.S.: 516120
Jim Allen (Mng Dir)

TeleAlliance (1)
Lenin Hills 1 pp 44, Moscow, Russia
Tel.: (7) 4952323139
Web Site: http://www.telealliance.ru
Television Broadcasting Services
N.A.I.C.S.: 516120
Tatiana Golm (CFO)

Yellow Bird (1)
Magasin 1 Frihamnen, PO Box 270 34, 102
51, Stockholm, Sweden
Tel.: (46) 850307700
Web Site: https://www.yellowbird.se
Television Broadcasting Services
N.A.I.C.S.: 516120
Cecilia Colling (CFO & Chief Comml Offi-
cer)

Zodiak Finland Oy (1)
Kornetintie 3, 00380, Helsinki, Finland
Tel.: (358) 207533000
Web Site: http://www.zodiakfinland.fi
Television Broadcasting Services
N.A.I.C.S.: 516120
Anssi Rimpela (Chief Creative Officer)

DE BOERTIEN GROEP B.V.
Scheepmakerij 320, 3331 MC, Zwijn-
drecht, Netherlands
Tel.: (31) 786841800   NI
Web Site:
   http://www.boertiengroep.nl
Sales Range: $25-49.9 Million
Emp.: 220
Holding Company
N.A.I.C.S.: 551112
Xander Ferdinadusse (CEO)

DE CONSTRUCTII NAPOCA S.A.
Str Piata 1 Mai Nr 1-2, Cluj-Napoca,
Romania
Tel.: (40) 264425861
Web Site: http://sccnapoca.ro
NAPO—(BUC)
Rev.: $17,845,985
Assets: $44,409,298
Liabilities: $38,080,987
Net Worth: $6,328,311
Earnings: $2,758,794
Emp.: 181
Fiscal Year-end: 12/31/22
Building Construction
N.A.I.C.S.: 236220

DE DIETRICH PROCESS SYSTEMS S.A.
Glass-Lining plant, PO Box 8, 67110,
Zinswiller, France
Tel.: (33) 388532300   FR
Web Site: http://www.dedietrich.com
Year Founded: 1684
Sales Range: $400-449.9 Million
Emp.: 3,400
Railways Heating Equipment Chemi-
cal Equipment & Sundries Mfr
N.A.I.C.S.: 333414
Daniel Steck (CEO)

Subsidiaries:

**DE DIETRICH PROCESS
SYSTEMS** (1)
Pavlovskaya street Build 6 2nd floor Office
2 2, 125167, Moscow, Russia
Tel.: (7) 495 663 9904
Web Site: http://www.ddps.ru
Industrial Laboratory Equipment Distr
N.A.I.C.S.: 423490

**DE DIETRICH PROCESS SYSTEMS
(Wuxi) Co, Ltd.** (1)
B31-D Mei Yu Road Mei Cun National Hi-
Tech Industrial Development Zone, Wuxi,
214112, Jiangsu, China
Tel.: (86) 510 6696 7500
Web Site: http://www.ddps.cn
Industrial Laboratory Equipment Distr
N.A.I.C.S.: 423490
Yimin Han (Mgr-HR)

**DE DIETRICH PROCESS SYSTEMS
AG** (1)
Gestadeckplatz 6, 4410, Liestal, Switzer-
land
Tel.: (41) 61 925 11 11
Web Site: http://www.rosenmund.com
Industrial Laboratory Equipment Distr
N.A.I.C.S.: 423490
Max Volkart (Mgr-Sls)

**DE DIETRICH PROCESS SYSTEMS
INDIA PRIVATE LIMITED** (1)
B-803 Sagar Tech Plaza Sakinaka Junction
Andheri-Kurla Road, Andheri, Mumbai, 400
072, India
Tel.: (91) 22 6742 42 70
Web Site: http://www.dedietrich.co.in
Emp.: 25
Industrial Laboratory Equipment Distr
N.A.I.C.S.: 423490
Manish Shah (Exec Dir)

**DE DIETRICH PROCESS SYSTEMS
N.V.** (1)
Technologielaan 7, Heverlee, 3001, Leuven,
Belgium
Tel.: (32) 16 40 50 00
Web Site: http://www.ivia.be

Emp.: 7
Industrial Laboratory Equipment Distr
N.A.I.C.S.: 423490
Huib Van Klinken (Mng Dir-Sls Sys Ben-
elux)

**DE DIETRICH PROCESS SYSTEMS
SEMUR SAS** (1)
Zone Industrielle, 21140, Semur-en-Auxois,
France
Tel.: (33) 3 80 97 12 23
Web Site: http://www.dedietrich-semur.com
Industrial Laboratory Equipment Distr
N.A.I.C.S.: 423490
Jerome Poupom (Mgr)

**DE DIETRICH PROCESS SYSTEMS
Srl.** (1)
Via Iseo 22, 30027, San Dona di Piave,
Italy
Tel.: (39) 0421 222 128
Industrial Laboratory Equipment Distr
N.A.I.C.S.: 423490

De Dietrich Do Brasil Ltda (1)
Rua Costa Barros n 3000, Vila Alpina,
03210-001, Sao Paulo, SP, Brazil
Tel.: (55) 1127037380
Web Site: http://www.dedietrichddz.com
Industrial Machinery & Equipment Whslr
N.A.I.C.S.: 423830
Marcos Piloso (Mgr-Sls)

**De Dietrich Equipos Quimicos
SL** (1)
Av Princep dAsturies 43-45-1 5a, 8012,
Barcelona, Spain
Tel.: (34) 932188613
Web Site: http://www.dedietrich.es
Sales Range: $25-49.9 Million
Emp.: 25
Industrial Machinery & Equipment Whslr
N.A.I.C.S.: 423830

**De Dietrich Process Systems
GmbH** (1)
Hattenbergstrasse 36, 55122, Mainz, Ger-
many
Tel.: (49) 613197040
Industrial Machinery Mfr
N.A.I.C.S.: 333248

**De Dietrich Process Systems Ireland
Ltd.** (1)
Western Bus Pk, Shannon, Ireland
Tel.: (353) 61366925
Web Site: http://www.dietrich.com
Sales Range: $50-74.9 Million
Emp.: 3
Electrical Apparatus & Equipment Wiring
Supplies & Construction Material Whslr
N.A.I.C.S.: 423610
Martin Corner (Mng Dir)

**De Dietrich Process Systems S.A. -
Glass-Lining Plant** (1)
Glass-Lining Plant, BP 8, 67110, Zinswiller,
France
Tel.: (33) 388532300
Industrial Machinery Mfr
N.A.I.C.S.: 333248

**De Dietrich Process Systems S.A.-
Courcouronnes Site** (1)
8 -10 Ruaduboissaugaga, 91055, Evry,
France
Tel.: (33) 169470400
Web Site: http://www.dedietrichddz.com
Sales Range: $25-49.9 Million
Emp.: 13
Industrial Supplies Whslr
N.A.I.C.S.: 423840

**De Dietrich Process Systems,
Inc.** (1)
244 Sheffield St, Mountainside, NJ 07092
Tel.: (908) 317-2585
Web Site: http://www.ddpsinc.com
Rev.: $14,100,000
Emp.: 90
Mfr of Glass Lined Vessels
N.A.I.C.S.: 333248
Helen Wilson (CFO)

Subsidiary (Domestic):

**De Dietrich Process Systems-
Rosenmund Division** (2)
9110 Forsyth Park Dr, Charlotte, NC 28273-
3881

Tel.: (704) 587-0440
Web Site: http://www.ddpsinc.com
Sales Range: $25-49.9 Million
Emp.: 20
Mfr of General Line Industrial Filters
N.A.I.C.S.: 333998

De Dietrich Singapore (Pte) Ltd. (1)
20 Bukit Batok Crescent 03-05 Enterprise
Ctr, Singapore, 658080, Singapore
Tel.: (65) 68611232
Web Site: http://www.dedietrich.com
Sales Range: $25-49.9 Million
Emp.: 8
Surgical & Medical Instrument Mfr
N.A.I.C.S.: 339112
Allan Ong (Gen Mgr)

**De Dietrich South Africa (Pty)
Ltd.** (1)
PO BOX 6245, PO Box 6245, Johannes-
burg, 1508, South Africa
Tel.: (27) 119184131
Web Site: http://www.dietrich.com
Sales Range: $25-49.9 Million
Emp.: 11
Surgical & Medical Instrument Mfr
N.A.I.C.S.: 339112

QVF Engineering GmbH (1)
Hattenbergstrasse 36, 55122, Mainz, Ger-
many
Tel.: (49) 613197040
Web Site: http://www.qvf.com
Sales Range: $100-124.9 Million
Emp.: 260
Industrial Machinery Mfr
N.A.I.C.S.: 333248
Manfred Pertlea (Mgr-Sls)

QVF Process Systems Ltd. (1)
Tollgate Drive, Tollgate Industrial Estate,
Stafford, ST16 3HS, United Kingdom
Tel.: (44) 1785609900
Web Site: http://www.qvf.co.uk
Emp.: 25
Industrial Machinery Mfr
N.A.I.C.S.: 333248
Peter McElvaney (Gen Mgr)

DE ENK GROEN & GOLF B.V.
Bennekomseweg 128, 6871 KH, Ren-
kum, Netherlands
Tel.: (31) 317 727 000
Web Site:
   http://www.deenkgroenengolf.nl
Year Founded: 1958
Sales Range: $25-49.9 Million
Emp.: 104
Golf Course & Sports Field Grounds-
keeping Services
N.A.I.C.S.: 561730
Gerard van der Werf (Co-Owner &
Mng Dir)

DE GOUDSE N.V.
Tel.: (31) 182544544
Web Site: https://www.goudse.nl
Year Founded: 1924
Sales Range: $200-249.9 Million
Emp.: 800
Insurance Services
N.A.I.C.S.: 524298
G. W. Bouwmeester (Dir-Special
Distr)

Subsidiaries:

**Algemene Zeeuwse Verzekering
Maatschappij N.V.** (1)
Houtkaai 11, 4331 JR, Middelburg,
Netherlands   **(100%)**
Tel.: (31) 118683300
Web Site: http://www.algemenezeeuwse.nl
Sales Range: $75-99.9 Million
Emp.: 35
N.A.I.C.S.: 522210
Aan Kole (Mgr-Admin)

DE GREY MINING LIMITED
Ground Floor 2 Kings Park Road,
West Perth, 6005, WA, Australia
Tel.: (61) 861179328

De Grey Mining Limited—(Continued)

Web Site:
https://www.degreymining.com.au
DGD—(DEU)
Rev.: $649,657
Assets: $238,750,576
Liabilities: $17,979,711
Net Worth: $220,770,865
Earnings: ($8,073,122)
Emp.: 5
Fiscal Year-end: 06/30/22
Support Activities for Nonmetallic
Minerals (except Fuels) Mining
N.A.I.O.S.: 213115
Simon Lill *(Chm)*

DE LA RUE PLC
2 Gresham Street, Basingstoke,
RG22 4BS, Hampshire, United King-
dom
Tel.: (44) 1256605000
Web Site: https://www.delarue.com
Year Founded: 1813
DLUEY—(OTCIQ)
Rev.: $434,257,460
Assets: $432,891,480
Liabilities: $389,428,480
Net Worth: $43,463,000
Earnings: ($71,030,960)
Emp.: 2,138
Fiscal Year-end: 03/25/23
Mfr of Currency Paper, Secure
Printed Products & Cash Handling
Equipment
N.A.I.C.S.: 323111
Edward Peppiatt *(Gen Counsel &
Sec)*

Subsidiaries:

De La Rue (Malaysia) Sdn. Bhd. **(1)**
4rd Floor Wisma Able Match Lot 271, Jalan
Chan Sow Lin, Kuala Lumpur, 56100, Ma-
laysia
Tel.: (60) 392210952
Web Site: http://www.delarue.com
Sales Range: $25-49.9 Million
Emp.: 9
Cash Handling Equipment Mfr
N.A.I.C.S.: 333310
Terence Ho *(Reg Mgr-Sls)*

De La Rue (Thailand) Limited **(1)**
18th Fl Ste B 2 Ploenchit Center Bldg,
Sukhumvit Road, Bangkok, 10110, Thailand
Tel.: (66) 265689614
Sales Range: $25-49.9 Million
Emp.: 10
Cash Handling Equipment Mfr
N.A.I.C.S.: 333310

De La Rue Authentication Solutions
Inc. **(1)**
1750 N 800 W, Logan, UT 84321,
Tel.: (435) 753-5775
Printing Material Mfr
N.A.I.C.S.: 325211

De La Rue BV **(1)**
Sportlaan 14, 4131 NN, Vianen, Nether-
lands
Tel.: (31) 347 329 000
Warm Air Heating & Air Conditioning Equip-
ment Merchant Whslr
N.A.I.C.S.: 423730

De La Rue CIS **(1)**
212v Building 102 Prospect Red Army, Ser-
giev Posad, 141300, Moscow, Russia
Tel.: (7) 96 547 3745
Cash Handling Equipment Mfr
N.A.I.C.S.: 333310

De La Rue Holdings plc **(1)**
De La Rue House Jays Close, Basingstoke,
RG22 4BS, Hants, United Kingdom
Tel.: (44) 1256 329122
Sales Range: $200-249.9 Million
Emp.: 450
Investment Management Service
N.A.I.C.S.: 523999

De La Rue International Limited **(1)**
Frenchs Avenue, Dunstable, LU6 1BJ, Bedfordshire, United Kingdom

Tel.: (44) 1582679600
Sales Range: $25-49.9 Million
Emp.: 70
Commercial Printing Services
N.A.I.C.S.: 323111

De La Rue Mexico, S.A. de C.V **(1)**
Sanchez Azcona 239 Colonia Narvarte Pte,
03020, Mexico, Mexico
Tel.: (52) 55 5286 4190
Sales Range: $25-49.9 Million
Emp.: 30
Commercial Printing Services
N.A.I.C.S.: 323111

De La Rue North America Inc. **(1)**
6401 Commerce Dr, Irving, TX 75063
Tel.: (972) 582-1100
Financial Transaction Processing Services
N.A.I.C.S.: 522320

De La Rue Security Products **(1)**
De La Rue House Jays Close, Viables,
Basingstoke, RG22 4BS, Hants, United
Kingdom **(100%)**
Tel.: (44) 256605000
Web Site: http://www.delarue.com
Sales Range: $125-149.9 Million
Emp.: 300
Security Printers
N.A.I.C.S.: 323111

Subsidiary (Domestic):

De La Rue Currency (Divisional Engi-
neering Unit) **(2)**
Kingsway S Team Vly Trading Est, Gates-
head, NE11 0SQ, United Kingdom **(100%)**
Tel.: (44) 1914958000
Sales Range: $25-49.9 Million
Emp.: 100
Security Printing Equipment Mfr
N.A.I.C.S.: 333248

Subsidiary (Non-US):

De La Rue Currency And Security
Print **(2)**
B40 43 Bulebel Industrial Estate, Zejtun,
ZTN 3000, Malta **(100%)**
Tel.: (356) 21693757
Web Site: http://www.mtdelarue.com
Security Printers
N.A.I.C.S.: 323111

De La Rue Currency and Security
Print **(2)**
Villa 2178 Road 2755, Adliya, 327, Bahrain
Tel.: (973) 712667
Security Printers
N.A.I.C.S.: 323111

De La Rue Currency and Security
Print Limited **(2)**
Noordin Rd Off Thika Rd, PO Box 38622,
Ruaraka, Nairobi, Kenya **(100%)**
Tel.: (254) 2860086
Sales Range: $50-74.9 Million
Emp.: 250
Security Printers
N.A.I.C.S.: 323111

De La Rue Ltd. **(2)**
Hedwig Van Steenhuyze House, Seatown
Business Campus, Swords, Co Dublin, Ire-
land
Tel.: (353) 18907707
Web Site: http://www.delarue.com
Sales Range: $25-49.9 Million
Emp.: 20
Cash Handling Equipment Mfr
N.A.I.C.S.: 333310
Keith Brown *(Mng Dir-Currency)*

De La Rue Malaysia Sdn. Bhd. **(2)**
3rd Fl Wisma Able Match, Lot 271 Jalan
Dua, Off Jalan Chan Sow Lin, 55200, Kuala
Lumpur, Malaysia **(100%)**
Tel.: (60) 392210952
Sales Range: $25-49.9 Million
Emp.: 12
Security Printers
N.A.I.C.S.: 323111
Ghansyam Dass *(Reg Dir)*

Subsidiary (Domestic):

De La Rue Security Papers **(2)**
Bathford Mill, Bath, BA1 7QG, Avon, United
Kingdom **(100%)**

Tel.: (44) 1225859903
Web Site: http://www.delarue.com
Sales Range: $25-49.9 Million
Emp.: 85
Mfr of Cotton-Based Banknote Security
Papers
N.A.I.C.S.: 561621
Andrew Nash *(Gen Mgr)*

Subsidiary (US):

De La Rue Security Print Inc. **(2)**
100 Powers Ct, Dulles, VA
20166-9321 **(100%)**
Tel.: (703) 450-1300
Web Site: http://www.delarue.com
Sales Range: $25-49.9 Million
Emp.: 100
Security Printers
N.A.I.C.S.: 323111

Subsidiary (Domestic):

De La Rue Security Products **(2)**
Frenchs Ave, Dunstable, LU6 1BJ, Beds,
United Kingdom **(100%)**
Tel.: (44) 1582679600
Sales Range: $50-74.9 Million
Emp.: 200
Security Printers
N.A.I.C.S.: 323111

De La Rue Security Products **(2)**
Padholme Rd E, Peterborough, PE1 5XL,
United Kingdom **(100%)**
Tel.: (44) 1733564164
Web Site: http://www.delarue.com
Sales Range: $50-74.9 Million
Emp.: 145
Security Printers
N.A.I.C.S.: 323111

Subsidiary (Non-US):

De La Rue Smurfit Limited **(2)**
Pinewood Close Boghall Rd, Bray, Co
Wicklow, Ireland **(50%)**
Tel.: (353) 012768600
Web Site: http://www.smurfitkappa.ie
Sales Range: $25-49.9 Million
Emp.: 100
Security Printers
N.A.I.C.S.: 323111

De La Rue Systems Limited **(1)**
Room 1705-6 17/F Tai Yau Building 181
Johnston Road, Wanchai, China (Hong
Kong)
Tel.: (852) 2586 1660
Sales Range: $25-49.9 Million
Emp.: 20
Currency Counting & Sorting Machines Mfr
N.A.I.C.S.: 333310

DE LICACY INDUSTRIAL CO.,
LTD.
No 240 Sanshe, Xinshi Dist, T'ainan,
74444, Taiwan
Tel.: (886) 65011200
Web Site:
https://www.delicacy.com.tw
Year Founded: 1982
1464—(TAI)
Rev.: $321,463,541
Assets: $493,733,982
Liabilities: $311,917,938
Net Worth: $181,816,043
Earnings: $3,790,510
Emp.: 2,393
Fiscal Year-end: 12/31/23
Yarn Dyed Fabrics Mfr
N.A.I.C.S.: 313310
Ye Jiaming *(Chm)*

Subsidiaries:

Apex (Nantong) Textile Co., Ltd. **(1)**
No 777 Lifa Avenue East, Hai an Economic
& Technological Development Area, Nan-
tong, 226601, Jiangsu, China
Tel.: (86) 51366968888
Textile Material Mfr & Distr
N.A.I.C.S.: 313310

DE NEDERLANDSCHE BANK
N.V.

Westeinde 1, 1017 ZN, Amsterdam,
Netherlands
Tel.: (31) 205249111 **NI**
Web Site: http://www.dnb.nl
Year Founded: 1814
Rev.: $1,671,950,980
Assets: $337,175,287,820
Liabilities: $328,279,119,980
Net Worth: $8,896,167,840
Earnings: $1,316,955,360
Emp.: 1,813
Fiscal Year-end: 12/31/19
Banking Services
N.A.I.C.S.: 521110
Klaas H. W. Knot *(Pres)*

DE NEERS TOOLS LIMITED
468 Fie Patparganj Industrial Area,
Delhi, 110092, India
Tel.: (91) 9810664401
Web Site:
https://www.deneerstools.com
Year Founded: 1952
DENEERS—(NSE)
Emp.: 92
Hand Tools Mfr & Distr
N.A.I.C.S.: 333515
Nisha Shaw *(Chief Compliance Offi-
cer)*

DE POAN PNEUMATIC CORP.
No 81 Museum Rd, Bali, New Taipei
City, 24947, Taiwan
Tel.: (886) 226195619
Web Site: https://www.depoan.com
Year Founded: 1983
1570—(TPE)
Rev.: $20,042,335
Assets: $32,775,162
Liabilities: $4,254,072
Net Worth: $28,521,089
Earnings: $3,380,421
Fiscal Year-end: 12/31/22
Pneumatic Tool Mfr
N.A.I.C.S.: 333991

DE RAJ GROUP AG
Christophstrasse 15-17, 50670, Co-
logne, Germany
Tel.: (49) 2212998507
Web Site:
http://www.thederajgroup.com
DRJ—(VIE)
Oil & Gas Distribution Services
N.A.I.C.S.: 221210
Nagendran Nadarajah *(Chm)*

DE RIGO S.P.A.
Zona Industriale Villanova 12, 32013,
Longarone, Belluno, Italy
Tel.: (39) 04377777
Web Site: http://www.derigo.com
Year Founded: 1978
Sales Range: $650-699.9 Million
Emp.: 4,760
Eyeglass & Sunglass Frames De-
signer, Distr & Mfr
N.A.I.C.S.: 339115
Maurizio Dessolis *(Vice Chm)*

Subsidiaries:

De Rigo D.A.C.H. GmbH **(1)**
Babenhauser Strasse 50, 63762, Grossos-
theim, Germany
Tel.: (49) 6026 991 2222
Web Site: https://www.derigo-dach.de
High Quality Eyewear Mfr & Distr
N.A.I.C.S.: 339115

De Rigo France SAS **(1)**
8 Rue Francois Rochaix, 01100, Arbent,
France
Tel.: (33) 47 481 4284
Luxury Goods & Jewelry Whslr
N.A.I.C.S.: 423940

De Rigo Hellas S.A. **(1)**
11 Sorou ke Geor Zikou, Marousi, 151 25,
Athens, Greece

Tel.: (30) 210 682 6326
Luxury Goods & Jewelry Whslr
N.A.I.C.S.: 423940

De Rigo Hong Kong Ltd. (1)
Unit 06-11 28Fl 9 Wing Hong St Cheung
Sha Wan, Kowloon, China (Hong Kong)
Tel.: (852) 21 483883
Web Site: http://www.derigo.com
Sales Range: $25-49.9 Million
Emp.: 50
Exporter of Sunglasses, Metal Frames &
Other Optical Products
N.A.I.C.S.: 339115
Jacky Fong (Accountant)

De Rigo Japan Co., Ltd. (1)
1-17-4 JPR Ningyocho Building 6F, Nihon-
bashi Ningyocho Chuo-ku, Tokyo, Japan
Tel.: (81) 36 661 9422
Web Site: https://derigo.co.jp
Luxury Goods & Jewelry Whslr
N.A.I.C.S.: 423940

De Rigo Portugal, Lda. (1)
Rua das Vigias N2 - R/C - Letra A Parque
das Nacoes, 1990-506, Lisbon, Portugal
Tel.: (351) 21 893 4190
Luxury Goods & Jewelry Whslr
N.A.I.C.S.: 423940

De Rigo Rem Inc. (1)
10941 La Tuna Canyon Rd, Sun Valley, CA
91352
Tel.: (818) 504-3950
Web Site: https://www.derigo.us
Eyewear Mfr & Distr
N.A.I.C.S.: 339115
Alessandro Baronti (Pres & CEO)

De Rigo UK Ltd (1)
Suite 6 Bld 2 Marlins Meadow Croxley buis-
ness Park, Century Court, Watford, WD18
8YA, Hertfordshire, United Kingdom
Tel.: (44) 1923249491
Sales Range: $25-49.9 Million
Emp.: 8
Ophthalmic Goods Mfr
N.A.I.C.S.: 339115
Paul Clipton (Gen Mgr)

De Rigo Vision Australia Pty Ltd (1)
Locked Bag 3640 Lane Cove Dc, Lane
Cove, 2066, NSW, Australia
Tel.: (61) 29 428 1500
Luxury Goods & Jewelry Whslr
N.A.I.C.S.: 423940

De Rigo Vision Espana SA (1)
Carrer de Sabino Arana 34 Bis, 08028, Bar-
celona, Spain
Tel.: (34) 93 264 3838
Luxury Goods & Jewelry Whslr
N.A.I.C.S.: 423940

**De Rigo Vision Middle East
FZCO** (1)
605 Tower A The Opus by Omniyat Busi-
ness Bay, Dubai, United Arab Emirates
Tel.: (971) 4 363 1100
Luxury Goods & Jewelry Whslr
N.A.I.C.S.: 423940

De Rigo Vision S.p.A. (1)
Zona Industriale Villanova 12, Longarone,
32013, Belluno, Italy
Tel.: (39) 04377777
Web Site: http://www.derigovision.com
Emp.: 200
Ophthalmic Goods Mfr
N.A.I.C.S.: 339115
Michele Aracri (CEO)

De Rigo Vision Trading Co., Ltd. (1)
Rm 2101 Baohua Center No 355 West
Guangzhong Rd, Jing An District, Shanghai,
China
Tel.: (86) 212 601 8270
Luxury Goods & Jewelry Whslr
N.A.I.C.S.: 423940

**De Rigo ve Sesa Grup Gozluk San
Ve Tic AS** (1)
Darulaceze Cad Nadide Sok No 34 Sesa
Plaza, Sisli, 34384, Istanbul, Turkiye
Tel.: (90) 212 314 0099
Web Site: https://www.derigo.com.tr
Eyewear Mfr & Distr
N.A.I.C.S.: 339115

Derigo Oy (1)

Kappelikuja 6, 02200, Espoo, Finland
Tel.: (358) 9 509 5500
Luxury Goods & Jewelry Whslr
N.A.I.C.S.: 423940

General Optica S.A. (1)
Andrade 128, Barcelona, 08020, Spain
Tel.: (34) 933037970
Web Site: http://www.generaloptica.es
Emp.: 1,000
Optical Goods Stores
N.A.I.C.S.: 456130
Jordi Fontcuberta (Mng Dir)

DE RUCCI HEALTHY SLEEP CO., LTD.
No 1 Houjie Science and Technology
Avenue, Houjie, Dongguan, 523900,
Guangdong, China
Tel.: (86) 76985035088
Web Site: https://www.derucci.com
Year Founded: 2007
001323—(SSE)
Rev.: $816,100,272
Assets: $816,122,736
Liabilities: $204,210,396
Net Worth: $611,912,340
Earnings: $99,532,368
Fiscal Year-end: 12/31/22
Mattress Mfr
N.A.I.C.S.: 337910
Wang Bingkun (Chm & Gen Mgr)

DE VERE GROUP LIMITED
17 Portland Place, London, W1B
1PU, United Kingdom
Tel.: (44) 844 346 3370   UK
Web Site:
   http://www.deveregroup.co.uk
Year Founded: 1999
Sales Range: $550-599.9 Million
Emp.: 8,500
Holding Company; Hotel & Resort
Owner & Operator
N.A.I.C.S.: 551112
Robert Barclay Cook (CEO-Hotels &
Village Urban Resorts)

DE&T CO., LTD.
40-56 Gajangsaneopseobuk-ro,
Osan, Gyeonggi-do, Korea (South)
Tel.: (82) 415293456
Web Site: https://www.i-det.com
Year Founded: 2001
079810—(KRS)
Rev.: $38,470,108
Assets: $68,302,858
Liabilities: $50,314,655
Net Worth: $17,988,203
Earnings: ($4,275,093)
Emp.: 145
Fiscal Year-end: 12/31/22
Flat Display Panel Mfr
N.A.I.C.S.: 334220
Sung-min Bae (CEO)

DE'LONGHI S.P.A.
Via Lodovico Seitz 47, 31100, Tre-
viso, Italy
Tel.: (39) 04224131   IT
Web Site:
   https://www.delonghigroup.com
DLG—(ITA)
Rev.: $3,408,626,160
Assets: $3,835,210,447
Liabilities: $2,040,055,040
Net Worth: $1,795,155,407
Earnings: $194,089,143
Emp.: 9,450
Fiscal Year-end: 12/31/22
Holding Company; Household Appli-
ances Mfr
N.A.I.C.S.: 551112
Giuseppe De'Longhi (Founder)

Subsidiaries:

De'Longhi America Inc. (1)

Park 80 W Plz 1 Fl 4, Saddle Brook, NJ
07663   (100%)
Tel.: (201) 909-4000
Web Site: http://www.delonghiusa.com
Rev.: $95,000,000
Emp.: 65
Electric Household Appliances Mfr
N.A.I.C.S.: 423620

De'Longhi Switzerland AG (1)
Lattichstrasse 6, 6340, Baar, Switzerland
Tel.: (41) 417668727
Kitchen Product Whslr
N.A.I.C.S.: 423620

Eversys Digitronics AG (1)
Sudstrasse 1, 3110, Munsingen, Switzer-
land
Tel.: (41) 317221030
Web Site: https://delisys.ch
Coffee Machine Mfr
N.A.I.C.S.: 333241

Eversys S.A. (1)
Ecoparc de Daval A 2, Sierre, Switzerland
Tel.: (41) 273052121
Coffee Machine Mfr & Distr
N.A.I.C.S.: 333310

Subsidiary (US):

La Marzocco International, LLC (2)
5601 1st Ave S, Seattle, WA 98108
Tel.: (206) 706-9104
Web Site: http://www.lamarzocco.com
Sales Range: $1-9.9 Million
Emp.: 25
Commercial & Service Industry Machinery
Mfr
N.A.I.C.S.: 333310
Amy Brunet (Admin)

Kenwood Limited (1)
1 Kenwood Business Park New Lane, Ha-
vant, PO9 2NH, Hampshire, United
Kingdom   (100%)
Tel.: (44) 3452220458
Web Site: http://www.kenwoodworld.com
Sales Range: $100-124.9 Million
Mfr of Food Mixers, Liquidisers, Waste Dis-
posal Units; Rotary Ironers
N.A.I.C.S.: 335210

Subsidiary (Non-US):

Kenwood Manufacturing GmbH (2)
12 Sud Strasse 2A, PO Box 55, 2355, Wie-
ner Neudorf, Austria   (100%)
Tel.: (43) 223664500
Web Site: http://www.kenwood.at
Sales Range: $10-24.9 Million
Emp.: 16
Food Mixers & Blenders, Waste Disposal
Units, Rotary Ironers
N.A.I.C.S.: 335210

DE.MEM LIMITED
Level 4 96-100 Albert Road, South
Melbourne, 3205, VIC, Australia
Tel.: (61) 396927222   AU
Web Site:
   http://www.demembranes.com
DEM—(ASX)
Rev.: $15,943,737
Assets: $12,737,552
Liabilities: $4,854,574
Net Worth: $7,882,978
Earnings: ($2,134,732)
Emp.: 75
Fiscal Year-end: 12/31/23
Waste Water Treatment Services
N.A.I.C.S.: 221320
Andreas Kroell (CEO)

Subsidiaries:

Akwa-Worx Pty. Ltd. (1)
32 Cessna Drive, Caboolture, 4510, QLD,
Australia
Tel.: (61) 754283265
Web Site: http://www.akwaworx.com
Waste Water Treatment Services
N.A.I.C.S.: 221310
Greg Horton (Project Mgr)

DEA GENERAL AVIATION HOLDING CO., LTD.

Gongye Ave West Songxia Industrial
Park, Songgang Nanhai, Foshan,
528234, Guangdong, China
Tel.: (86) 7578 837 4888
Web Site: http://www.elecpro.com
Year Founded: 1993
002260—(SSE)
Rev.: $77,018,667
Assets: $139,506,898
Liabilities: $18,080,312
Net Worth: $121,426,586
Earnings: $3,220,474
Fiscal Year-end: 12/31/20
Holding Company
N.A.I.C.S.: 551112

Subsidiaries:

Elecpro USA Inc. (1)
1650 S Amphlett Blvd Ste 101, San Mateo,
CA 94402
Tel.: (650) 627-8118
Market Research Services
N.A.I.C.S.: 541910

DEAG DEUTSCHE ENTER-TAINMENT AG
Potsdamer Strasse 58, 10785, Berlin,
Germany
Tel.: (49) 30810750   De
Web Site: http://www.deag.de
Year Founded: 1998
Rev.: $207,411,510
Assets: $207,373,435
Liabilities: $179,202,237
Net Worth: $28,171,198
Earnings: ($1,329,274)
Emp.: 263
Fiscal Year-end: 12/31/19
Entertainment Services
N.A.I.C.S.: 516210
Christian Diekmann (COO, Chief
Digital Officer & Member-Exec Bd)

Subsidiaries:

C 2 Concerts GmbH (1)
Kolner Strasse 28, 70376, Stuttgart, Ger-
many
Tel.: (49) 71184961670
Web Site: http://www.c2concerts.de
Event Management Services
N.A.I.C.S.: 561920
Christian Doll (CEO)

Subsidiary (Domestic):

Kessel Festival GmbH (2)
Kol-ner Str 28, 70376, Stuttgart, Germany
Tel.: (49) 71189466140
Web Site: http://www.kesselfestival.de
Event Management Services
N.A.I.C.S.: 561920

**Christmas Garden Deutschland
GmbH** (1)
Potsdamer Strasse 58, 10785, Berlin, Ger-
many
Tel.: (49) 30810750
Web Site: http://www.christmas-garden.de
Event Management Services
N.A.I.C.S.: 561920
Sebastian Stein (Mng Dir)

**Concert Concept
Veranstaltungs-GmbH** (1)
Postdamer Str 58, 10758, Berlin, Germany
Tel.: (49) 30810750
Web Site: http://www.concert-concept.de
Sales Range: $50-74.9 Million
Emp.: 3
Concert Organizing Services
N.A.I.C.S.: 711310
Peter Schwenkow (Founder)

DEAG Classics AG (1)
Potsdamer Strasse 58, 10785, Berlin, Ger-
many
Tel.: (49) 30810750
Sales Range: $25-49.9 Million
Emp.: 50
Concerts & Event Organizing Services
N.A.I.C.S.: 711310
Peter Schwenkow (Mng Dir)

DEAG Concerts GmbH (1)

DEAG Deutsche Entertainment AG—(Continued)

Potsdamer Str 58, 10785, Berlin, Germany
Tel.: (49) 30810750
Web Site: http://www.deag.com
Sales Range: $25-49.9 Million
Emp.: 45
Concert Organizing Services
N.A.I.C.S.: 711310

DEAG Music GmbH (1)
Potsdamer Strasse 58, 10785, Berlin, Germany
Tel.: (49) 30810750
Web Site: http://www.deag.de
Music Publishing Services
N.A.I.C.S.: 512230

EM Event Marketing AG (1)
Thurgauerstrasse 105 Glattpark, 8152, Zurich, Switzerland
Tel.: (41) 448096666
Web Site: http://www.goodnews.ch
Sales Range: $50-74.9 Million
Emp.: 3
Event Management Services
N.A.I.C.S.: 711310

Friedrichsbau Variete Betriebs- und Verwaltungs GmbH (1)
Friedrichsstrasse 24, 70174, Stuttgart, Germany
Tel.: (49) 7112257070
Web Site: http://www.deag-friedrichsbau.de
Sales Range: $25-49.9 Million
Emp.: 12
Entertainment Ticketing & Marketing Services
N.A.I.C.S.: 561599
Timo Steinhauer (Mng Dir)

Global Concerts GmbH (1)
Atelierstr 1, 81671, Munich, Germany
Tel.: (49) 894900940
Web Site: http://www.globalconcerts.de
Sales Range: $50-74.9 Million
Emp.: 8
Concert Organizing Services
N.A.I.C.S.: 711310
Christian Diekmann (Mng Dir)

Global Concerts Touring GmbH (1)
Jensenstrasse 4, 81679, Munich, Germany
Tel.: (49) 894900940
Web Site: http://www.globalconcerts.de
Entertainment Facility Services
N.A.I.C.S.: 711310

I-Motion GmbH (1)
Am Hohen Stein 8, 56218, Mulheim-Karlich, Germany (50.1%)
Tel.: (49) 261 921 584 0
Web Site: http://www.i-motion.ag
Emp.: 40
Live Events & Entertainment Services
N.A.I.C.S.: 711320
Sheldon Finkel (Exec Dir)

I-Motion GmbH Events & Communication (1)
Am Hohen Stein 8, 56218, Mulheim-Karlich, Germany
Tel.: (49) 2619215840
Web Site: http://www.i-motion.ag
Event Management Services
N.A.I.C.S.: 561920

KBK Konzert- und Kunstleragentur GmbH (1)
Potsdamer Str 58, 10785, Berlin, Germany
Tel.: (49) 3026391430
Web Site: http://www.kb-k.com
Sales Range: $50-74.9 Million
Emp.: 6
Concert Organizing Services
N.A.I.C.S.: 711310
Klaus Boenisch (CEO & Mng Dir)

Kultur im Park GmbH (1)
Potsdamer Str 58, 10785, Berlin, Germany
Tel.: (49) 3081075230
Web Site: http://www.potsdamer-schloessernacht.de
Event Management Services
N.A.I.C.S.: 561920

Kultur- und Kongresszentrum Jahrhunderthalle (1)
Pfaffenwiese 301, 65929, Frankfurt am Main, Germany

Tel.: (49) 693601236
Web Site: http://www.jahrhunderthalle.de
Sales Range: $50-74.9 Million
Emp.: 15
Concerts & Event Management Services
N.A.I.C.S.: 711310
Ursel Ottersberg (Mng Dir)

Live Music Production SA (1)
211 route de Ferney, Grand-Saconnex, 1218, Geneva, Switzerland
Tel.: (41) 229943131
Web Site: http://www.livemusic.ch
Entertainment Facility Services
N.A.I.C.S.: 711310
Camille Bodson (Mar-Mkta & Promo)

MEWES Entertainment Group GmbH (1)
Friedrich-Ebert-Damm 145, 22047, Hamburg, Germany
Tel.: (49) 4071140584
Web Site: http://www.kuenstlershow.de
Event Management Services
N.A.I.C.S.: 561920
Jan Mewes (Gen Mgr)

Pro Media GmbH (1)
Basler Str 18, 79588, Efringen-Kirchen, Germany
Tel.: (49) 76282258
Web Site: http://www.pro-media-gmbh.de
Marketing Services
N.A.I.C.S.: 541810

River Concerts GmbH (1)
Johannisbollwerk 20, 20459, Hamburg, Germany
Tel.: (49) 4041330180
Web Site: http://www.riverconcerts.de
Sales Range: $50-74.9 Million
Emp.: 5
Concert Organizing Services
N.A.I.C.S.: 711310
Moritz Schwenkow (Mng Dir)

Subsidiary (Domestic):

Elbklassik Konzerte GmbH (2)
Feldbrunnenstrasse 8, 20148, Hamburg, Germany
Tel.: (49) 40413301830
Web Site: http://www.elbklassik.de
Sales Range: $50-74.9 Million
Emp.: 5
Concert Organizing Services
N.A.I.C.S.: 711310
Moritz Schwenkow (Mng Dir)

Wizard Promotions Konzertagentur GmbH (1)
Bruehlstrasse 37, 60439, Frankfurt am Main, Germany
Tel.: (49) 699043590
Web Site: http://www.wizpro.com
Event Management Services
N.A.I.C.S.: 561920
Tobias Dietermann (Head-Press)

coco tours Veranstaltungs GmbH (1)
Podtagrmm St 58, Berlin, 10785, Germany
Tel.: (49) 30810750
Sales Range: $25-49.9 Million
Emp.: 50
Concert Tour Operation Services
N.A.I.C.S.: 711310
Peter Schwenkow (CEO)

handwerker promotion e. GmbH (1)
Morgenstr 10, 59423, Unna, Germany
Tel.: (49) 2303254640
Web Site: http://www.handwerker-promotion.de
Entertainment Facility Services
N.A.I.C.S.: 711310
Fred Handwerker (Founder & CEO)

mytic myticket AG (1)
Johannisbollwerk 20, 20459, Hamburg, Germany
Tel.: (49) 1806777111
Web Site: http://www.myticket.de
Event Management Services
N.A.I.C.S.: 561920
Michael Wolfram (Sr Mgr)

DEALT LIMITED
6/57 59 Oxford St, Bulimba, Brisbane, 4171, QLD, Australia

Tel.: (61) 1300887623 AU
Web Site:
http://www.velocityproperty.com.au
Rev.: $27,018,579
Assets: $67,715,358
Liabilities: $53,556,612
Net Worth: $14,158,746
Earnings: $1,610,850
Fiscal Year-end: 06/30/19
Property Management Services
N.A.I.C.S.: 531311
Brendon Ansell (Founder & Mng Dir)

DEAN COOLEY GM
1600 Main Street South, Dauphin, R7N 3B3, MB, Canada
Tel.: (204) 638-4026
Web Site:
http://www.deancooleygm.ca
Year Founded: 1995
New & Used Car Dealers
N.A.I.C.S.: 441110
Dean Cooley (Principal)

DEAP CAPITAL MANAGEMENT & TRUST PLC
5th Floor 94 Broad Street, Lagos, Nigeria
Tel.: (234) 14751756
Web Site:
https://www.deapcapital.com
DEAPCAP—(NIGE)
Assets: $222,642
Liabilities: $2,388,382
Net Worth: ($2,165,740)
Earnings: ($134,525)
Emp.: 3
Fiscal Year-end: 09/30/23
Investment Services
N.A.I.C.S.: 523940
Joel Omole (Mng Dir)

Subsidiaries:

Resort Developers Limited (1)
Second Fl Resort House, 12 Boyle St, Lagos, Nigeria
Tel.: (234) 7098141711
Real Estate Services
N.A.I.C.S.: 531210

DEAR LIFE CO., LTD.
2F Hulic Kudan Building 1-13-5 Kudan-Kita, Chiyoda-ku, Tokyo, 102-0073, Japan
Tel.: (81) 352103721
Web Site: https://www.dear-life.co.jp
Year Founded: 2004
3245—(TKS)
Rev.: $308,436,270
Assets: $295,752,260
Liabilities: $124,443,680
Net Worth: $171,308,580
Earnings: $30,515,360
Fiscal Year-end: 09/30/23
Real Estate Services
N.A.I.C.S.: 531390

Subsidiaries:

ID Property Co., Ltd. (1)
Id Shinagawa 2F 3-27-4 Higashioi, Shinagawa-ku, Tokyo, 140-0011, Japan
Tel.: (81) 367121461
Web Site: https://idg-p.jp
Building Rental Services
N.A.I.C.S.: 531110

DEARBORN MOTORS
2555 East Trans Canada HWY, Kamloops, V2C 4B1, BC, Canada
Tel.: (250) 372-7101
Web Site:
https://www.dearbornford.com
Year Founded: 1939
New & Used Car Dealers
N.A.I.C.S.: 441110
Michael Bacon (Dealer Principal)

DEAUVILLE DIAMOND PROPERTIES SA
23 rue Balzac, 75008, Paris, France
Tel.: (33) 231140150
Web Site: http://www.81lhotel.com
Real Estate Support Services
N.A.I.C.S.: 531390
Gilles Boyer (Chm & CEO)

DEBENHAMS PLC
200 Aldersgate Street, London, EC1A 4HD, United Kingdom
Tel.: (44) 2074084444 UK
Web Site:
http://www.debenhams.com
Year Founded: 1778
Sales Range: $1-4.9 Billion
Online Retail Store
N.A.I.C.S.: 458110
Daniel Finley (CEO)

Subsidiaries:

Debenhams Properties Limited (1)
West Orchard Shopping Centre, Coventry, CV1 1QL, West Midlands, United Kingdom
Tel.: (44) 1823337979
Property Management Services
N.A.I.C.S.: 531311

DEBFLEX SA
3 Avenue du Moulin, 80210, Feuquieres-en-Vimeu, France
Tel.: (33) 322603737
Web Site: http://www.debflex.fr
Year Founded: 1948
Electric Equipment Mfr
N.A.I.C.S.: 335999
Jean-Eric Riche (Chm & CEO)

DEBITUM INVEST REIT
2 Enos Street 5th Floor, Sofia, 1408, Bulgaria
Tel.: (359) 28106447
Web Site:
http://www.debituminvest.bg
Year Founded: 2011
Financial Management Services
N.A.I.C.S.: 522110
Borislav Niklev (Chm)

DEBOCK SALES & MARKETING LTD.
51 Lohiya Colony 200 Feet Bye Pass, Vaishali Nagar, Jaipur, 302021, India
Tel.: (91) 1412358161
Web Site:
https://www.debockgroup.com
Year Founded: 2007
DSML—(NSE)
Rev.: $4,201,436
Assets: $7,421,729
Liabilities: $3,930,856
Net Worth: $3,490,873
Earnings: $295,305
Emp.: 21
Fiscal Year-end: 03/31/21
Digital Marketing Services
N.A.I.C.S.: 541613
Mukesh Manveer Singh (Chm & Mng Dir)

DEBOFFE
Route departementale 1029, 80480, Saleux, France
Tel.: (33) 322332470
Web Site: http://deboffe.claas-partner.fr
Year Founded: 1942
Farm Machinery Retailer
N.A.I.C.S.: 423820
Thierry Pecourt (CEO)

DEBRO CHEMICALS LTD
11 Automatic Road, Brampton, L6S 4K6, ON, Canada

Tel.: (905) 799-8200
Web Site: http://www.debro.com
Year Founded: 1920
Sales Range: $25-49.9 Million
Emp.: 35
Specialty Chemicals Distr
N.A.I.C.S.: 424690
Brian Imrie *(Chm)*

DEBUSCHERE SA
23 Avenue des Temps Modernes ZI,
BP 32, 86361, Chasseneuil-du-
Poitou, France
Tel.: (33) 549528020
Rev.: $23,800,000
Emp.: 216
Painting & Paper Hanging
N.A.I.C.S.: 238320
Laurent Trommenschlager *(Dir)*

DEBUT DIAMONDS INC.
82 Richmond Street East, The Cana-
dian Venture Building, Toronto, M5C
1P1, ON, Canada
Tel.: (773) 236-7972   ON
Web Site:
http://www.wesanahealth.com
Year Founded: 2007
DDI—(CNSX)
Assets: $199,388
Liabilities: $35,591
Net Worth: $163,797
Earnings: ($142,129)
Emp.: 5
Fiscal Year-end: 04/30/21
Diamond Exploration Services
N.A.I.C.S.: 212390
Frank C. Smeenk *(Mng Dir)*

DECA CABLES INC.
150 N Murray St, Trenton, K8V 6R8,
ON, Canada
Tel.: (613) 392-3585
Web Site:
http://www.decacables.com
Rev.: $35,615,880
Emp.: 90
Wire & Cable Mfr
N.A.I.C.S.: 335921

DECA INVESTMENTS AIFM
49 Agiou Konstantinou Str, Maroussi,
151 24, Athens, Greece
Tel.: (30) 13) 010 9200
Web Site:
http://www.decainvestments.eu
Investment Services
N.A.I.C.S.: 523940
Nicos J. Koulis *(CEO & Partner)*

Subsidiaries:

Minerva S.A. Edible Oils & Food
Enterprises   (1)
165 Tatoiou Ave & Odysseos St, Metamor-
phosi, 14452, Athens, Greece
Tel.: (30) 210 285 4200
Web Site: http://www.minerva.com.gr
Oilseed (except Soybean) Farming
N.A.I.C.S.: 111120
D. Takas *(Pres)*

DECA SYSTEM INC.
514-1 Yatap-dong, Bundang-gu,
Seongnam, Gyeonggi-do, Korea
(South)
Tel.: (82) 70 8270 7814
Web Site: http://www.golfbuddy.kr
Golf GPS System Mfr
N.A.I.C.S.: 334220
Steve Jeong *(Pres & CEO)*

DECADE RESOURCES LTD.
611-8th Street, Box 211, Stewart,
V0T 1W0, BC, Canada
Tel.: (250) 636-2264
Web Site:
https://www.decaderesources.ca

Year Founded: 2006
DECXF—(OTCIQ)
Rev.: $178,147
Assets: $12,773,468
Liabilities: $1,257,439
Net Worth: $11,516,029
Earnings: ($1,488,310)
Fiscal Year-end: 04/30/24
Mineral Exploration Services
N.A.I.C.S.: 213114
Edward R. Kruchkowski *(Pres)*

DECAMA CAPITAL LTD.
Habarzel St 38, Tel Aviv, 67910, Is-
rael
Tel.: (972) 36849333
DCMA—(TAE)
Rev.: $1,654,761
Assets: $31,909,656
Liabilities: $7,654,939
Net Worth: $24,254,717
Earnings: ($1,789,216)
Fiscal Year-end: 12/31/20
Real Estate Manangement Services
N.A.I.C.S.: 531210
Nathaniel Lorenzi *(CEO)*

DECATHLON SA
4 boulevard de Mons, PO Box 299,
59650, Villeneuve d'Ascq, France
Tel.: (33) 320335000
Web Site: http://www.decathlon.com
Year Founded: 1976
Sales Range: $5-14.9 Billion
Emp.: 50,000
Sporting Goods Designer, Mfr & Re-
tailer
N.A.I.C.S.: 459110
Jimena Almendares *(Global Chief
Digital Officer)*

Subsidiaries:

Bergfreunde GmbH   (1)
Bahnhofstr 26, 72138, Kirchentellinsfurt,
Germany
Tel.: (49) 712170120
Web Site: https://www.bergfreunde.de
Online Mountain Sport Equipment Retailer
N.A.I.C.S.: 541830
Ronny Hohn *(Mng Dir)*

Decathlon USA   (1)
326 Ballardvale St, Wilmington, MA 01887-
1012
Tel.: (978) 657-0100
Web Site: http://www.decathlon-usa.com
Sales Range: $250-299.9 Million
Emp.: 1,000
Sporting Goods & Bicycle Shops
N.A.I.C.S.: 459110

DECCAN BEARINGS LIMITED
Office No 64A Floor No 4 Plot No
327 Nawab Building, Dadabhai
Nawroji Road Hutatma Chowk Fort,
Mumbai, 400 001, Maharashtra, India
Tel.: (91) 2222852552   In
Web Site:
https://www.deccanbearings.in
Year Founded: 1985
505703—(BOM)
Rev.: $11,145
Assets: $123,725
Liabilities: $4,464
Net Worth: $119,261
Earnings: ($56,279)
Emp.: 6
Fiscal Year-end: 03/31/22
Bearing Mfr & Whslr
N.A.I.C.S.: 332991
Kiran Nagindas Vora *(Mng Dir)*

DECCAN CEMENTS LIMITED
Deccan Chambers 6-3-666/B Somajiguda, Hyderabad, 500082, Telangana, India
Tel.: (91) 4023310168

Web Site:
https://www.deccancements.com
Year Founded: 1979
DECCANCE—(NSE)
Rev.: $104,839,862
Assets: $117,592,034
Liabilities: $40,472,550
Net Worth: $77,119,483
Earnings: $15,714,904
Emp.: 379
Fiscal Year-end: 03/31/21
Cement Mfr
N.A.I.C.S.: 327310
M. B. Raju *(Chm)*

DECCAN CHRONICLE HOLD-
INGS LTD.
36 Sarojini Devi Road, Secundera-
bad, 500 003, India
Tel.: (91) 40 2780 3930
Web Site:
http://www.deccanchronicle.com
Sales Range: $100-124.9 Million
Daily Magazine Publisher
N.A.I.C.S.: 513120
T. Venkattram Reddy *(Chm)*

Subsidiaries:

Asian Age Holdings Ltd.   (1)
S-7&8 Green Park Main Mkt, New Delhi,
110 016, India
Tel.: (91) 1126530001
Web Site: http://www.asianage.com
Sales Range: $50-74.9 Million
Emp.: 250
Newspaper & Magazine Publishing Services
N.A.I.C.S.: 513110
P. Venkatesh *(Gen Mgr-Fin)*

Odyssey India Ltd.   (1)
No 45 & 47 Odyssey Tower 3rd Fl First
Main Rd Gandhinagar, Adyar, Chennai, 600
020, Tamil Nadu, India
Tel.: (91) 4443910300
Web Site: http://www.odyssey.in
Sales Range: $125-149.9 Million
Emp.: 500
Book Stores Management Services
N.A.I.C.S.: 459210

DECCAN GOLD MINES LTD.
No 77 16 th Cross Road 4 th Sector
HSR Layout, Bengaluru, 560 102,
India
Tel.: (91) 8047762900
Web Site:
https://www.deccangoldmines.com
Year Founded: 2003
512068—(BOM)
Rev.: $5,678
Assets: $6,203,748
Liabilities: $99,017
Net Worth: $6,104,730
Earnings: ($438,807)
Emp.: 16
Fiscal Year-end: 03/31/21
Gold Exploration Services
N.A.I.C.S.: 212220
Sundaram Subramaniam *(Compli-
ance Officer, Sec & Head-Legal)*

DECCAN HEALTH CARE LTD.
6-3-347 17 5 A Dwarkapuri Colony
Punjagutta, Hyderabad, 500 082,
India
Tel.: (91) 4040144508
Web Site:
https://www.deccanhealthcare.co.in
542248—(BOM)
Rev.: $4,617,959
Assets: $12,594,541
Liabilities: $2,135,624
Net Worth: $10,458,917
Earnings: $53,221
Emp.: 47
Fiscal Year-end: 03/31/21
Pharmaceuticals Product Mfr
N.A.I.C.S.: 325412

Sreya Mitra *(Officer-Compliance &
Sec)*

DECCAN POLYPACKS LIM-
ITED
Plot No A-40 Road No 7 IDA Kukat-
pally, Hyderabad, 502 325, Telan-
gana, India
Tel.: (91) 8458279577   In
Web Site:
https://www.deccanpolypacks.com
Year Founded: 1984
Rev.: $132,758
Assets: $721,486
Liabilities: $1,081,482
Net Worth: ($359,996)
Earnings: $31,929
Fiscal Year-end: 03/31/18
Woven Sack Mfr
N.A.I.C.S.: 314910
D. V. Prudvi Raju *(Exec Dir)*

DECEUNINCK NV
Bruggesteenweg 360, BE-8830,
Hooglede, Belgium
Tel.: (32) 51239211   BE
Web Site:
https://www.deceuninck.com
Year Founded: 1937
DECB—(EUR)
Rev.: $1,051,266,998
Assets: $765,808,332
Liabilities: $420,869,847
Net Worth: $344,938,485
Earnings: $8,203,108
Emp.: 3,939
Fiscal Year-end: 12/31/22
Mfr, Designer & Extruder of PVC Sys-
tems
N.A.I.C.S.: 326199
Ann Bataillie *(Gen Counsel)*

Subsidiaries:

DECEUNINCK ITALIA SRL   (1)
Via Padre Eugenio Barsanti 1, 56025, Pont-
edera, Pisa, Italy
Tel.: (39) 058759920
Web Site: https://www.deceuninck.it
Sales Range: $25-49.9 Million
Emp.: 8
Plastic Profile Systems Mfr
N.A.I.C.S.: 326121

Decalu NV   (1)
Bruggesteenweg 360 Gits, 8830, Hooglede,
Belgium
Tel.: (32) 51239211
Plastic Tank Mfr
N.A.I.C.S.: 326122

Decalu Solutions Sp. z o.o.   (1)
Ul Dunska 4, 05-152, Czosnow, Poland
Tel.: (48) 2273259121
Window & Door Mfr & Distr
N.A.I.C.S.: 321911

Deceuninck (Thailand) Co., Ltd.   (1)
79/74 Moo 12 Bangna-Trad, Bang Kaeo
Bang Phli District, Samut Prakan, 10540,
Thailand
Tel.: (66) 275195445
Web Site: https://www.deceuninck.co.th
Plastic Tank Mfr
N.A.I.C.S.: 326122

Deceuninck Baltic UAB   (1)
V Kuzmos 6 1, 44280, Kaunas, Lithuania
Tel.: (370) 37338844
Plastic Profile Systems Mfr
N.A.I.C.S.: 326121

Deceuninck Beheer BV   (1)
Krekelveen 629, Spijkenisse, 3205 RD,
Zuid-Holland, Netherlands
Tel.: (31) 647912727
Plastic Household Product Mfr
N.A.I.C.S.: 326199

Subsidiary (Non-US):

Deceuninck Holding Germany
GmbH   (2)

Deceuninck NV—(Continued)

Bayerwaldstr 18, D-94327, Bogen, Germany
Tel.: (49) 94228210
Web Site: https://www.deceuninck.de
Investment Management Service
N.A.I.C.S.: 523999
Peter Laubenstein (Gen Mgr)

Deceuninck Bulgaria EOOD (1)
Blvd Saint Petersburg No 41, 4000, Plovdiv, Bulgaria
Tel.: (359) 32637295
Web Site: https://www.deceuninck.bg
Plastic Profile Systems Mfr
N.A.I.C.S.: 326121
Asparuh Schterev (Gen Mgr)

Deceuninck Germany GmbH (1)
Bayerwaldstrasse 18, 94327, Bogen, Germany
Tel.: (49) 94228210
Web Site: https://www.deceuninck.de
Window & Door Distr
N.A.I.C.S.: 449122

Deceuninck Germany Produktions GmbH & Co. KG (1)
Bayerwaldstrasse 18, 94327, Bogen, Germany
Tel.: (49) 94228210
Web Site: https://www.deceuninck.de
Window & Door Mfr & Distr
N.A.I.C.S.: 332321

Deceuninck Holdings UK Ltd (1)
Unit 2 Stanier Road Porte Marsh, Calne, SN11 9PX, Wiltshire, United Kingdom
Tel.: (44) 1249816969
Web Site: https://www.deceuninck.com
Emp.: 55
Plastic Profile Systems Mfr
N.A.I.C.S.: 326121

Deceuninck Importadora Limitada (1)
El Otono 472, Lampa, 9380000, Santiago, Chile
Tel.: (56) 957727836
Web Site: https://www.deceuninck.cl
Plastic Tank Mfr
N.A.I.C.S.: 326122

Deceuninck Kunststof B.V. (1)
Jeugdland 1A, 4851 AT, Houten, Netherlands
Tel.: (31) 765617834
Sales Range: $25-49.9 Million
Emp.: 3
Retailer of PVC-U Profiles for the Building Industry
N.A.I.C.S.: 326199

Deceuninck Ltd. (1)
Stanier Road, Porte Marsh, Calne, SN11 9PX, Wiltshire, United Kingdom (100%)
Tel.: (44) 249816969
Web Site: https://www.deceuninck.co.uk
Sales Range: $50-74.9 Million
Emp.: 130
Mfr of Door & Window Systems; Roofline Products; External Building Products; Interior Wall Panelling; Ceiling Systems
N.A.I.C.S.: 326199

Deceuninck NV Sucursal em Portugal (1)
Avenida Da Liberdade 110 Fl 1, 1269-046, Lisbon, Portugal (100%)
Tel.: (351) 214160813
Retailer of PVC-U Profiles for the Building Industry
N.A.I.C.S.: 326199

Deceuninck NV Sucursal en Espana (1)
Avda de La Industria 1007 Pol Ind Antonio Del Rincon, Borox, 45222, Toledo, Spain (100%)
Tel.: (34) 925527241
Web Site: https://www.deceuninck.es
Sales Range: $25-49.9 Million
Emp.: 30
Mfr, Designer & Extrudrer of PVC Systems
N.A.I.C.S.: 326199

Deceuninck North America Inc. (1)
351 N Garver Rd, Monroe, OH 45050
Tel.: (513) 539-4444

Web Site: https://www.deceuninckna.com
Sales Range: $125-149.9 Million
Emp.: 300
Mfr of Door & Window Systems; External Building Products; Interior Wall Panelling; Ceiling Systems
N.A.I.C.S.: 326121
Darwin G. Brown (Pres & CEO)

Subsidiary (Domestic):

Deceuninck North America LLC (2)
203 N Garver Rd, Monroe, OH 45050
Tel.: (513) 539-4444
Web Site: https://www.deceuninck-americas.com
Sales Range: $75-99.9 Million
Window & Door Mfr
N.A.I.C.S.: 332321

Deceuninck Poland Sp. z o.o. (1)
Jasin ul Poznanska 34, 62-020, Swarzedz, Poland
Tel.: (48) 618187000
Web Site: https://www.deceuninck.pl
Window & Door Mfr & Distr
N.A.I.C.S.: 332321

Deceuninck Profiles India Private Limited (1)
Building 09 Casa Grande Distripark, Satharai Village Tiruvallur Taluk Tiruvallur District, Chennai, 631 203, Tamil Nadu, India
Tel.: (91) 7358413331
Web Site: https://www.deceuninck.in
Plastic Tank Mfr
N.A.I.C.S.: 326122

Deceuninck Pty. Ltd. (1)
71 Premier Dve, Campbellfield, 3061, VIC, Australia
Tel.: (61) 393575033
Web Site: http://www.deceuninck.com.au
Sales Range: $25-49.9 Million
Emp.: 3
Plastic Windows & Door Mfr
N.A.I.C.S.: 326199

Deceuninck Romania SRL (1)
Str Traian nr 2 bl F1 sc 4 ap 24 Sector 3, Bucharest, Romania
Tel.: (40) 213274962
Plastics Product Mfr
N.A.I.C.S.: 326199

Deceuninck Rus OOO (1)
Tel.: (7) 84991100522
Web Site: https://www.deceuninck.ru
Sales Range: $50-74.9 Million
Emp.: 150
Plastic Profile Systems Mfr
N.A.I.C.S.: 326121
Volker Guth (Gen Dir)

Deceuninck S.A.S. (1)
Variante Turbaco Cll 1 Cra 2-5 Dup 1 Zona Franca Parque Central, Warehouse 15, Cartagena, Colombia
Tel.: (57) 3023992771
Web Site: https://www.deceuninck.co
Plastic Tank Mfr
N.A.I.C.S.: 326122

Deceuninck SA (1)
Zone Industrielle Impasse des bleuets, 80700, Roye, France (100%)
Tel.: (33) 322876666
Web Site: http://www.deceuninck.fr
Mfr & Retailer of PVC-U Profiles for the Building Industry
N.A.I.C.S.: 326199

Deceuninck Sp. z o.o. (1)
Jasin ul Poznanska 34, 62-020, Swarzedz, Poland
Tel.: (48) 618187000
Web Site: http://www.deceuninck.pl
Plastic Tank Mfr
N.A.I.C.S.: 326122

Deceuninck d.o.o. (1)
Industrijska Ulica 3, 10370, Dugo Selo, Croatia
Tel.: (385) 12781353
Web Site: http://www.deceuninck.com
Plastic Profile Systems Mfr
N.A.I.C.S.: 326121

Deceuninck d.o.o. (1)
Kruzni put bb, Lestane, 11309, Belgrade, Serbia

Tel.: (381) 113443217
Plastic Tank Mfr
N.A.I.C.S.: 326122

Deceuninck de Mexico S.A. De C.V. (1)
No 809 Huajuapan Road Int 2 C Colonia, San Francisco Ocotlan Town Coronango Municipality, 72680, Mexico, Puebla, Mexico
Tel.: (52) 2221443552
Web Site: https://deceuninck.com.mx
Window & Door Mfr & Distr
N.A.I.C.S.: 332321

Deceuninck do Brazil Ltda. (1)
Estrada Boa Vista 575, Jardim Atalaia - Condominio Boa Vista - Galpao 10, Cotia, 06701-475, Brazil
Tel.: (55) 1123389190
Web Site: https://deceuninck.com.br
Window & Door Mfr & Distr
N.A.I.C.S.: 332321

Ege Profil AS (1)
10003 Sokak 5, AOSB 35620, Izmir, Turkiye (97.16%)
Tel.: (90) 2323767160
Sales Range: $50-74.9 Million
Emp.: 250
Mfr & Retailer of PVC-U Profiles for the Building Industry
N.A.I.C.S.: 326122
Ergun Cicekci (Gen Mgr)

Ege Profil Tic. ve San. A.S. (1)
Building 09 Casa Grande Distripark, Satharai Village Thiruvallur Taluk, 631 203, Chennai, India
Tel.: (91) 9717707732
Plastic Tank Mfr
N.A.I.C.S.: 326122

Ege Profil Ticaret ve Sanayi AS (1)
Ataturk Plastik OSB Mahallesi 1 Cadde No 5 Menemen, O S B Mahallesi 5 Cadde No 4 Menemen, Izmir, Turkiye
Tel.: (90) 2323989898
Web Site: https://www.egeprofil.com.tr
Plastic Tank Mfr
N.A.I.C.S.: 326122
Sadi Godek (Mgr-HR)

Inoutic / Deceuninck, spol. s r.o. (1)
Areal Slatina- Turanka 115, 627 00, Popovky, Czech Republic (100%)
Tel.: (420) 547427777
Web Site: http://www.inoutic.cz
Sales Range: $25-49.9 Million
Emp.: 50
Window & Door Systems; Window Boards, Conservatories, Claddings, Fences, Roofline Products; External Building Products; Interior Wall Paneling; Ceiling Systems
N.A.I.C.S.: 326199
Robert Lovecky (Gen Mgr)

Inoutic Deceuninck GmbH (1)
Bayerwaldstrasse 18, Bogen, 1164, Germany
Tel.: (49) 94228210
Web Site: http://www.inoutic.com
Sales Range: $125-149.9 Million
Emp.: 500
Plastic Profile Systems Mfr
N.A.I.C.S.: 326121

Subsidiary (Non-US):

Deceuninck d.o.o. (2)
Prvog marta bb, 75270, Zivinice, Bosnia & Herzegovina
Tel.: (387) 35773313
Web Site: https://www.deceuninck.ba
Plastic Profile Systems Mfr
N.A.I.C.S.: 326121

Inoutic d.o.o. (1)
Industrijska ulica 3, 10370, Dugo Selo, Croatia
Tel.: (385) 12781350
Web Site: http://www.deceuninck.hr
Plastic Tank Mfr
N.A.I.C.S.: 326122

Pimas Plastik Insaat Malzemeleri A.S. (1)
Beylikbagi Mah Istanbul Cad No 29, 41420, Gebze, Turkiye (81.23%)
Tel.: (90) 2626777777

Web Site: http://www.pimas.com.tr
Sales Range: $125-149.9 Million
Emp.: 484
Plastics Product Mfr
N.A.I.C.S.: 326199

Plastics Deceuninck NV (1)
Bruggesteenweg 374, 8800, Roeselare, Belgium
Tel.: (32) 51239206
Plastic Door & Window Mfr
N.A.I.C.S.: 326199

Range Valley Extrusions Ltd (1)
Unit 2 Stanier Road Trading Address Porte Marsh Industrial Estate, Calne, SN11 9PX, Wiltshire, United Kingdom
Tel.: (44) 1249816969
Sales Range: $25-49.9 Million
Emp.: 63
Plastic Profile Systems Mfr
N.A.I.C.S.: 326121

Rep. Office Deceuninck NV (1)
128 Xiang Gang Dong Lu Shuang Long Yuan 3-2-402, Laoshan, Qingdao, 266071, Shandong, China
Tel.: (86) 53285890357
Plastic Tank Mfr
N.A.I.C.S.: 326122

SA Detajoint NV (1)
ZI Barriere De Fer, Avenue Du Bois Jacquet, B 7711, Dottignies, Belgium (75%)
Tel.: (32) 56484461
Sales Range: $25-49.9 Million
Emp.: 19
Mfr of Complex Tri-extrusion Profiles
N.A.I.C.S.: 326199

Solardec CVBA (1)
Bruggesteenweg 360 Gits, 8830, Hooglede, Belgium
Tel.: (32) 51239211
Solar Panel Mfr
N.A.I.C.S.: 334413

DECHELETTE MALLEVAL SA
Boulevard Jean Monnet, BP 42, 69490, Maurepas, France
Tel.: (33) 474057800
Web Site: http://www.dechelette-malleval.fr
Rev.: $23,400,000
Emp.: 115
Textile Goods
N.A.I.C.S.: 313110
Georges Dechelette (Dir-Personnel)

DECIBEL CANNABIS COMPANY, INC.
1440-140 4th Ave SW, Calgary, T2P 3N3, AB, Canada
Tel.: (416) 459-6006   AB
Web Site: https://decibelcc.com
Year Founded: 2018
DB—(TSXV)
Rev.: $53,110,554
Assets: $98,511,738
Liabilities: $58,822,762
Net Worth: $39,688,976
Earnings: $1,363,514
Fiscal Year-end: 12/31/21
Cannabis Product Mfr
N.A.I.C.S.: 325412
Stephen Mason (Co-Founder & Exec Chm)

DECIDEBLOOM LTD.
Omega Boulevard Thorne, Doncaster, DN8 5TX, N Lincs, United Kingdom
Tel.: (44) 8451 254 848
Web Site: http://www.stoneacre.co.uk
Year Founded: 1994
Sales Range: $350-399.9 Million
Emp.: 1,155
New & Used Car Dealer
N.A.I.C.S.: 441110
Mike Cain (Gen Mgr-Regional)

DECILLION FINANCE LTD.
Jajodia Tower 3 Bentinck Street 4th

Floor Room No D-8, Kolkata, 700001, India
Tel.: (91) 3322485664
Web Site: https://www.decillion.co.in
Rev.: $491,209
Assets: $1,948,257
Liabilities: $130,577
Net Worth: $1,817,680
Earnings: $12,169
Emp.: 4
Fiscal Year-end: 03/31/18
Financial Support Services
N.A.I.C.S.: 523999
Ishu Maskara *(Sec)*

DECIMAL TECHNOLOGIES INC.
793 Jean-Paul-Vincent Blvd Ste 202, Longueuil, J4G 1R3, QC, Canada
Tel.: (450) 640-1222
Web Site: http://www.decimal.ca
Sales Range: $10-24.9 Million
Emp.: 20
Financial Performance Management Services
N.A.I.C.S.: 541611

DECISIVE DIVIDEND CORPO-RATION
260 - 1855 Kirschner Rd, Kelowna, V1Y 4N7, BC, Canada
Tel.: (250) 870-9146   BC
Web Site:
    https://www.decisivedividend.com
Year Founded: 2012
DE—(TSXV)
Rev.: $36,264,724
Assets: $45,448,369
Liabilities: $28,716,396
Net Worth: $16,731,973
Earnings: $580,817
Fiscal Year-end: 12/31/19
Investment Services
N.A.I.C.S.: 523999
James Paterson *(Chm & CEO)*

Subsidiaries:

Blaze King Industries Canada
Ltd.   (1)
1290 Commercial Way, Penticton, V2A 3H5, BC, Canada
Tel.: (250) 493-7444
Web Site: http://www.blazeking.com
Emp.: 80
Wood Stove Distr
N.A.I.C.S.: 423720

Blaze King Industries Inc.   (1)
146 A St, Walla Walla, WA 99362
Tel.: (509) 522-2730
Wood Stove Distr
N.A.I.C.S.: 423720
Chris Neufeld *(VP-Ops)*

Slimline Manufacturing Ltd.   (1)
559 Okanagan Ave East, Penticton, V2A 3K4, BC, Canada
Web Site: https://slimlinemfg.com
Farm Equipment Mfr
N.A.I.C.S.: 333111

Unicast Inc.   (1)
1200 Mayfair Rd, Kelowna, V1X 7W7, BC, Canada   (100%)
Tel.: (250) 807-7999
Web Site: https://www.unicast.ca
Steel, Iron & Metal Alloy Wear Parts Designer, Mfr & Distr
N.A.I.C.S.: 332999
Gerry L'Esperance *(Founder)*

DECKLAR RESOURCES INC.
120 Adelaide Street West Suite 2500, Toronto, M5H 1T1, ON, Canada
Tel.: (416) 360-3412
Web Site:
    http://www.asianmineralres.com
ASN—(TSXV)
Sales Range: Less than $1 Million
Emp.: 196

Mineral Exploration Services
N.A.I.C.S.: 213114
Christopher D. Castle *(Chm)*

DECKMA HAMBURG GMBH
Kieler Strasse 316, 22525, Hamburg, Germany
Tel.: (49) 405488760
Web Site: http://www.deckma.com
Rev.: $10,345,500
Emp.: 18
Oil & Water Supplier
N.A.I.C.S.: 213112
Gunthor Sohulzo *(Foundor & Mng Dir)*

DECLAN RESOURCES INC.
1558 West Hastings St, Vancouver, V6G 3J4, BC, Canada
Tel.: (604) 639-4452   BC
Web Site:
    https://canadianpalladium.com
Year Founded: 2005
LAN—(CNSX)
Sales Range: Less than $1 Million
Gold Exploration Services
N.A.I.C.S.: 212220

DECLOET GREENHOUSE MANUFACTURING LTD.
1805 Charlotteville West Qtr Line, Simcoe, N3Y 4J9, ON, Canada
Tel.: (519) 582-3081   ON
Web Site:
    http://www.decloetgreenhouse.com
Year Founded: 1986
Greenhouse Mfr
N.A.I.C.S.: 332311
Ben DeCloet *(Owner)*

DECO&E CO., LTD.
27 Wiryeseong-daero 22-gil, Songpa-gu, Seoul, Korea (South)
Tel.: (82) 2 2145 1300
Web Site: http://www.deco.co.kr
Year Founded: 1978
Rev.: $46,459,131
Assets: $59,880,871
Liabilities: $32,849,713
Net Worth: $27,031,158
Earnings: ($9,519,848)
Emp.: 100
Fiscal Year-end: 12/31/18
Women's Apparel Mfr & Distr
N.A.I.C.S.: 315250
Jae-Chun Kim *(Exec Dir)*

DECO-MICA LIMITED
306 3rd Floor Iskon Mall Star Bazar Building, Jodhpur Char Rasta, Ahmedabad, 380015, India
Tel.: (91) 7926730412
Web Site:
    https://www.decomicaltd.com
531227—(BOM)
Rev.: $7,313,097
Assets: $6,603,638
Liabilities: $4,066,472
Net Worth: $2,537,166
Earnings: $181,449
Emp.: 177
Fiscal Year-end: 03/31/21
Decorative Laminated Sheet Mfr & Distr
N.A.I.C.S.: 326130
Vijaykumar Dindayal Agarwal *(Chm, CEO & Mng Dir)*

Subsidiaries:

DECO-MICA LIMITED - RAJPUR
FACTORY   (1)
Plot No 1195 Chhatral Mehsana Highway, Rajpur, 382 715, India
Tel.: (91) 2764 278501
Decorative Laminated Sheet Mfr
N.A.I.C.S.: 326130

DECOR CABINETS LTD.
239 Mountain St S, PO Box 2110, Morden, R6M 1B8, MB, Canada
Tel.: (204) 822-6151
Web Site:
    http://www.decorcabinets.com
Year Founded: 1977
Rev.: $10,286,554
Emp.: 23
Cabinetry Mfr
N.A.I.C.S.: 321999
Larry Dyck *(Pres)*

DECOR PRODUCTS INTERNA-TIONAL, INC.
6 Economic Zone, Wushaliwu, Chang'an Town, Dongguan, Guang-dong, China
Tel.: (86) 76985533948   FL
Sales Range: $10-24.9 Million
Emp.: 75
Interior Decorating
N.A.I.C.S.: 541410
Rui Sheng Liu *(Pres & CEO)*

DECOR-REST FURNITURE LTD.
511 Chrislea Road, Woodbridge, L4L 8N6, ON, Canada
Tel.: (905) 856-5956
Web Site: http://www.decor-rest.com
Year Founded: 1972
Furniture Mfr
N.A.I.C.S.: 337211
Angelo Marzilli Jr. *(Pres)*

DECORA S.A.
ul Ignacego Pradzynskiego 24 a, 63-000, Sroda Wielkopolska, Poland
Tel.: (48) 612864200
Web Site: https://www.decora.pl
DCR—(WAR)
Rev.: $145,054,878
Assets: $118,780,488
Liabilities: $42,167,683
Net Worth: $76,612,805
Earnings: $17,007,622
Emp.: 600
Fiscal Year-end: 12/31/23
Decorating Products & Home Decor Accessories Mfr
N.A.I.C.S.: 337920
Wlodzimierz Lesinski *(Chm-Supervisory Bd)*

Subsidiaries:

Decora Balt uab   (1)
Savanoriu pr 174 A, 03153, Vilnius, Lithuania
Tel.: (370) 52040116
Sales Range: $25-49.9 Million
Emp.: 9
Decorating Products Distr
N.A.I.C.S.: 459420

Decora Hungaria kft   (1)
Europa u 9 BILK logisztikai koezpont, I epuelet Wegry, 1239, Budapest, Hungary
Tel.: (36) 18025555
Sales Range: $25-49.9 Million
Emp.: 30
Decorating Products Distr
N.A.I.C.S.: 459420

Decora Nova s.r.o.   (1)
Tesinska 288, Senov, 739 34, Frydek-Mistek, Senov, Czech Republic
Tel.: (420) 596 411 890
Decorating Products Distr
N.A.I.C.S.: 459420

Decora Ru ooo   (1)
ul 4-ta Tverskaya-Yamskaya 2/11 2, 125047, Moscow, Russia
Tel.: (7) 4956633369
Decorating Products Distr
N.A.I.C.S.: 459420

Decora Ukraina TOB   (1)
Str Kuthozova No 100 134, 07400, Brovary, Ukraine

Tel.: (380) 444985890
Sales Range: $50-74.9 Million
Emp.: 60
Decorating Products Distr
N.A.I.C.S.: 424990

E. Wicklein GmbH   (1)
Am Fluegelbahnhof 4, 96317, Kronach, Bavaria, Germany
Tel.: (49) 9261 50490 40
Acoustic Insulation Materials Distr
N.A.I.C.S.: 423330

Ewifoam E. Wicklein GmbH   (1)
Stockumer Str 28, 58453, Witten, Germany
Tel.: (49) 2302 430 9290
Web Site: https://ewifoam.de
Plastic Fabrication Mfr
N.A.I.C.S.: 326111

IP Decora East   (1)
ul Gorkogo 145/5/1, 210604, Vitsyebsk, Belarus
Tel.: (375) 296795570
Sales Range: $25-49.9 Million
Emp.: 52
Window & Ceiling Decor Products
N.A.I.C.S.: 449122

Trans Sp. z o.o.   (1)
Aleja Milenijna 21, 66-470, Kostrzyn, Lubusz, Poland
Tel.: (48) 957283100
Decorating Products Mfr
N.A.I.C.S.: 321918

DECORINT SA
Take Ionescu Nr 77, Cluj-Napoca, 400473, Romania
Tel.: (40) 264 406450
Web Site: http://www.decorint.ro
Year Founded: 1994
Emp.: 50
Real Estate Development
N.A.I.C.S.: 531390
Tibor Konti *(CEO)*

DECOROUS INVESTMENT & TRADING CO. LTD.
R-489 GF-B New Rajinder Nagar, New Delhi, 110 060, India
Tel.: (91) 9910003638
Web Site: https://www.ditco.in
539405—(BOM)
Rev.: $40,324
Assets: $474,809
Liabilities: $3,225
Net Worth: $471,584
Earnings: $85
Fiscal Year-end: 03/31/21
Jewelry Mfr & Distr
N.A.I.C.S.: 541490
Raj Kumar Gupta *(CFO)*

DECOTEX JSC
42 Hadzhi Dimitar str, 8800, Sliven, Bulgaria
Tel.: (359) 44662382
Web Site: https://www.decotex.org
Year Founded: 1909
DEX—(BUL)
Sales Range: Less than $1 Million
Textile Products Mfr
N.A.I.C.S.: 314110

DEDALO GRUPO GRAFICO, S.L.
Carretera de Pinto a Fuenlabrada km 20.8, ES-28320, Pinto, Spain
Tel.: (34) 915069300   ES
Web Site:
    http://www.dedalogrupografico.es
Year Founded: 2003
Sales Range: $125-149.9 Million
Emp.: 500
Holding Company; Commercial Printing Services
N.A.I.C.S.: 551112
Oscar Gomez Barbero *(Pres)*

Dedalo Grupo Grafico, S.L.—(Continued)

Subsidiaries:

Dedalo Heliocolor **(1)**
Pol Ind N1 Francois Marina E Mindosa No
5 & 6, Poligono Cabanillas del Compo, ES-
19171, Guadalajara, Spain
Tel.: (34) 94 933 3100
Web Site: http://www.dedalogrupografico.com
Sales Range: $125-149.9 Million
Emp.: 380
Commercial Lithographic & Gravure Printing
Services
N.A.I.C.S.: 323111

Graficas Integradas S.A. **(1)**
Santa Leonor N 63 2 planta, Madrid,
28037, Spain
Tel.: (34) 913273695
Web Site: http://www.dedalogrupografico.es
Digital Printing Services
N.A.I.C.S.: 323111
Luis Lopez Mendiola *(Mng Dir)*

DEDICARE AB
Ringvagen 100 Entrance E 10 Floor,
118 60, Stockholm, Sweden
Tel.: 855565600
Web Site: https://www.dedicare.se
Year Founded: 1996
DEDI—(OMX)
Rev.: $167,528,543
Assets: $69,561,194
Liabilities: $44,969,607
Net Worth: $24,591,587
Earnings: $9,487,669
Emp.: 1,230
Fiscal Year-end: 12/31/22
Medical Staffing Services
N.A.I.C.S.: 561311
Krister Widstrom *(Pres & CEO)*

Subsidiaries:

Dedicare AS **(1)**
Kjopmannsgata 24C, PB 41, 7500, Stjordal,
Norway
Tel.: (47) 74804070
Web Site: http://www.dedicare.no
Staffing & Recruiting Services
N.A.I.C.S.: 561311

DEDIENNE MULTIPLASTURGY GROUP SAS
ZAC les Champs Chouette N2, 1 rue
des Houssieres, Paris, France
Tel.: (33) 2 32 22 38 38
Web Site: http://www.dedienne.com
Year Founded: 1947
Plastic Materials Mfr
N.A.I.C.S.: 326199
Nicolas Jacquemin *(Mng Dir)*

Subsidiaries:

Met2Plastic LLC **(1)**
701 Lee St, Elk Grove Village, IL 60007
Tel.: (847) 228-5070
Web Site: http://www.metplastics.com
Sales Range: $1-9.9 Million
All Other Plastics Product Mfr
N.A.I.C.S.: 326199
Mike Walter *(Pres)*

DEDINJE A.D.
Koste Glavinica 2, 11000, Belgrade,
Serbia
Tel.: (381) 112650534
Year Founded: 1948
DEDI—(BEL)
Rev.: $58,550
Assets: $537,567
Liabilities: $365,258
Net Worth: $172,309
Earnings: ($88,031)
Emp.: 1
Fiscal Year-end: 12/31/23
Building Cleaning Services
N.A.I.C.S.: 561790

DEE TECH SA

2 rue Alfred de Vigny, 75008, Paris,
France
Web Site: https://www.deetech.eu
Year Founded: 2021
DEE—(EUR)
Asset Management Services
N.A.I.C.S.: 523999

DEEP DIAMOND INDIA LIMITED
408 Corporate Avenue Wing-A
Sonawala Road Goregaon East, NR
Udyog Bhavan, Mumbai, 400 063,
Maharashtra, India
Tel.: (91) 2246065770
Web Site: http://deepdiamondltd.com
Year Founded: 1993
539559—(BOM)
Rev.: $104,765
Assets: $1,037,255
Liabilities: $15,677
Net Worth: $1,021,578
Earnings: ($6,405)
Fiscal Year-end: 03/31/21
Diamond Jewelry Mfr & Distr
N.A.I.C.S.: 339910
Prakash Rikhabchand Solanki *(Chm & CFO)*

DEEP ENERGY RESOURCES LTD.
12A and 14 Abhishree Corporate
Park Ambli Bopal Road, Ambli,
Ahmedabad, 380058, Gujarat, India
Web Site:
    https://www.deepenergy.ooo
532760—(BOM)
Rev.: $327,791
Assets: $66,942,658
Liabilities: $7,850,729
Net Worth: $59,091,928
Earnings: $81,436
Emp.: 2
Fiscal Year-end: 03/31/21
Oil & Gas Exploration Services
N.A.I.C.S.: 211120
Rupesh K. Savla *(Mng Dir)*

Subsidiaries:

Deep Energy LLC **(1)**
4133 N Lincoln Blvd, Oklahoma City, OK
73105
Tel.: (405) 209-5560
Oil & Gas Exploration Services
N.A.I.C.S.: 213112

Deep Natural Resources Limited **(1)**
601 6th Floor Astron Tower Opp Fun Republic Cinema Satellite, Ahmedabad,
380015, India
Tel.: (91) 7926862076
Oil & Gas Exploration Services
N.A.I.C.S.: 213112

Prabha Energy Private Limited **(1)**
12A Abhishree Corporate Park Opp Swagat
Bungalows BRTS Bus Stop, Ambli Bopal
Road Ambli, Ahmedabad, 380058, India
Tel.: (91) 2717298510
Web Site: http://www.prabhaenergy.com
Oil & Gas Exploration Services
N.A.I.C.S.: 213112
Paras Savla *(Chm & Mng Dir)*

DEEP POLYMERS LTD.
Block No 727 Rakanpur Santej, Gan-
dhinagar, Kalol, Gujarat, India
Tel.: (91) 2764286032
Web Site: https://deeppoly.com
Year Founded: 2004
541778—(BOM)
Rev.: $5,501,452
Assets: $4,312,667
Liabilities: $587,362
Net Worth: $3,725,305
Earnings: $248,969
Fiscal Year-end: 03/31/21
Chemical Product Mfr & Distr

N.A.I.C.S.: 325199
Rameshbhai Bhimjibhai Patel *(Mng Dir)*

DEEP SPACE MEDIA GROUP AG
Reberastr. 5, FL-9494, Schaan,
Liechtenstein
Tel.: (423) 399 02 47
Web Site:
    http://www.deepspacemedia.com
Emp.: 30
Interactive Media, TV & Mobile Ser-
vices
N.A.I.C.S.: 517810
Benjamin Wordehoff *(COO)*

DEEP VALUE DRILLER AS
Munkedamsveien 45 F, 0250, Oslo,
Norway
Web Site:
    https://www.deepvaluedriller.no
Year Founded: 2021
DVD—(OSL)
Rev.: $12,632,138
Assets: $141,563,188
Liabilities: $109,340,422
Net Worth: $32,222,766
Earnings: ($24,302,667)
Fiscal Year-end: 12/31/23
Investment Management Service
N.A.I.C.S.: 523999
Einar J. Greve *(Chm)*

DEEP WELL OIL & GAS, INC.
Suite 700 10150 - 100 Street, Ed-
monton, T5J 0P6, AB, Canada
Tel.: (780) 409-8144   NV
Web Site:
    https://www.deepwelloil.com
Year Founded: 1988
DWOG—(OTCIQ)
Rev.: $7,694
Assets: $22,677,977
Liabilities: $571,384
Net Worth: $22,106,593
Earnings: ($197,135)
Emp.: 3
Fiscal Year-end: 09/30/19
Oil & Gas Exploration Services
N.A.I.C.S.: 213112
Horst A. Schmid *(Chm, Pres & CEO)*

Subsidiaries:

Northern Alberta Oil Ltd. **(1)**
10150 100 St Nw, Edmonton, AB, Canada
Tel.: (780) 409-8144
Oil & Gas Exploration Services
N.A.I.C.S.: 213112

DEEP YELLOW LIMITED
Level 1 502 Hay Street, Subiaco,
6008, WA, Australia
Tel.: (61) 892866999   AU
Web Site:
    https://www.deepyellow.com.au
Year Founded: 2000
DYLLF—(OTCQX)
Rev.: $394,568
Assets: $92,644,471
Liabilities: $4,396,992
Net Worth: $88,247,479
Earnings: ($5,229,484)
Emp.: 60
Fiscal Year-end: 06/30/22
Metallic Mineral Exploration & Mining
N.A.I.C.S.: 213114
Mark Pitts *(CFO & Sec)*

Subsidiaries:

Reptile Uranium Namibia (Pty.)
Ltd. **(1)**
48 Hidipo Hamutenya St, PO Box 2538,
Swakopmund, 9000, Namibia
Tel.: (264) 64415200
Web Site: http://www.reptile.com.na

N.A.I.C.S.: 212290
Greg Cochran *(Dir)*

Superior Uranium Pty. Ltd. **(1)**
Level 4 502 Hay St, Subiaco, 6008, WA,
Australia
Tel.: (61) 892866999
Web Site: http://www.deepyellow.com.au
Sales Range: $50-74.9 Million
Emp.: 2
Uranium Ore Mining Services
N.A.I.C.S.: 212290
Greg Cochran *(Mng Dir)*

Vimy Resources Limited **(1)**
First Floor 1209 Hay Street, West Perth,
6005, WA, Australia
Tel.: (61) 893892700
Web Site: http://www.vimyresources.com.au
Rev.: $237,446
Assets: $23,688,470
Liabilities: $1,822,561
Net Worth: $21,865,909
Earnings: ($5,263,243)
Fiscal Year-end: 06/30/2021
Uranium Exploration
N.A.I.C.S.: 212290
Tony Chamberlain *(COO)*

DEEP-SOUTH RESOURCES INC.
Suite 888 700 West Georgia, Van-
couver, V7Y 1G5, BC, Canada
Tel.: (819) 340-0140
Web Site:
    https://www.deepsouthresources.com
Year Founded: 1987
DSD—(DEU)
Assets: $705,415
Liabilities: $80,443
Net Worth: $624,971
Earnings: ($1,052,251)
Emp.: 2
Fiscal Year-end: 08/31/23
Mineral Exploration Services
N.A.I.C.S.: 213114
John H. Akwenye *(Chm)*

DEEPAK FASTENERS LIMITED
4th Floor First Mall Mall Road, Ludhi-
ana, 141 001, Punjab, India
Tel.: (91) 1613911111
Web Site:
    http://www.deepakfasteners.com
Year Founded: 1958
Sales Range: $550-599.9 Million
Emp.: 5,000
Industrial Fastener Mfr
N.A.I.C.S.: 332722

Subsidiaries:

Deepak Fasteners (Australia) Pty
Ltd. **(1)**
67-69 Licola Crescent, Dandenong, 3175,
VIC, Australia
Tel.: (61) 398940026
Web Site:
    http://www.deepakfasteners.com.au
Sales Range: $10-24.9 Million
Emp.: 16
Industrial Fastener Mfr
N.A.I.C.S.: 339993

Deepak Fasteners (Shannon)
Ltd. **(1)**
BAYS 25-30 Shannon Industrial Estate,
Shannon, County Clare, Ireland **(100%)**
Tel.: (353) 61716500
Web Site: http://www.unvrako.com
Sales Range: $75-99.9 Million
Emp.: 150
Industrial Fastener Mfr
N.A.I.C.S.: 332722

Deepak Fasteners (U.K.) Ltd. **(1)**
12-14 Tower Street, Newtown, Birmingham,
B19 3RR, United Kingdom
Tel.: (44) 1213334610
Web Site: http://www.deepakfasteners.co.uk
Sales Range: $25-49.9 Million
Emp.: 5
Industrial Fastener Mfr

N.A.I.C.S.: 332722
Adesh Gupta *(CEO)*

DEEPAK FERTILISERS & PETROCHEMICALS CORPORATION LIMITED

Sai Hira Survey No 93 Mundhwa,
Pune, 411 036, Maharashtra, India
Tel.: (91) 2066458000
Web Site: https://www.dfpcl.com
500645—(BOM)
Rev.: $797,318,340
Assets: $975,049,530
Liabilities: $502,004,130
Net Worth: $382,145,400
Earnings: $55,479,060
Fiscal Year-end: 03/31/21
Chemicals, Petrochemicals & Fertilizers Mfr
N.A.I.C.S.: 325998
Sailesh Chimanlal Mehta *(Chm & Mng Dir)*

Subsidiaries:

Performance Chemiserve
Limited   (1)
Plot 32 Sector 16, Vashi, Navi Mumbai,
400703, India
Tel.: (91) 2241518888
Web Site: http://www.pclindia.co.in
Agricultural Chemical Mfr
N.A.I.C.S.: 325320
Sailesh Chimanlal Mehta *(Chm)*

Platinum Blasting Services Pty.
Limited   (1)
GPO Box 785, Brisbane, 4000, QLD, Australia
Tel.: (61) 1300656760
Web Site: http://www.platinumblasting.com
Mining Services
N.A.I.C.S.: 213114

Smartchem Technologies Limited (1)
W-46 M I D C Baramati, Pune, 413 133,
Maharashtra, India
Tel.: (91) 2024334654
Fertilizer Mfr
N.A.I.C.S.: 325314

DEEPAK NITRITE LIMITED

2nd floor Fermenter house Alembic
Avenue Road, Vadodara, 390 004,
Gujarat, India
Tel.: (91) 2652765200
Web Site: https://www.godeepak.com
Year Founded: 1970
506401—(BOM)
Rev.: $598,043,355
Assets: $485,980,950
Liabilities: $165,663,225
Net Worth: $320,317,725
Earnings: $105,898,065
Emp.: 1,532
Fiscal Year-end: 03/31/21
Specialty Chemicals Mfr
N.A.I.C.S.: 325998
Sanjay Upadhyay *(CFO & Dir-Fin)*

DEEPAK SPINNERS LIMITED

Plot No 194-195 Fourth Floor Industrial Area Phase II, Chandigarh,
160002, India
Tel.: (91) 1722650973
Web Site: https://www.dsl-india.com
514030—(BOM)
Rev.: $54,385,490
Assets: $36,630,089
Liabilities: $14,924,391
Net Worth: $21,705,698
Earnings: $2,141,685
Emp.: 3,130
Fiscal Year-end: 03/31/21
Synthetic Fiber Mfr
N.A.I.C.S.: 313110
Puneeta Arora *(Compliance Officer & Sec)*

DEEPMARKIT CORP.

Suite 202 615-15th Ave SW, Calgary,
T2R 0R4, AB, Canada
Tel.: (403) 537-0067
Web Site:
   https://www.deepmarkit.com
Year Founded: 2007
MKTDF—(OTCQB)
Rev.: $2,352
Assets: $506,917
Liabilities: $290,665
Net Worth: $216,253
Earnings: ($3,727,351)
Fiscal Year-end: 12/31/21
Investment Services
N.A.I.C.S.: 523999
Alex Parken *(Sec)*

DEEPMATTER GROUP PLC

Office 3B Centrum Building 38 Queen
Street, Glasgow, G1 3DX, United
Kingdom
Tel.: (44) 1415488156   UK
Web Site:
   http://www.deepmattergroup.com
Year Founded: 2006
DMTR—(LSE)
Rev.: $1,790,833
Assets: $13,414,274
Liabilities: $1,330,566
Net Worth: $12,083,708
Earnings: ($3,276,178)
Emp.: 41
Fiscal Year-end: 12/31/20
Software Publisher; Chemicals, Materials & Formulations in Pharmaceutical Research, Fine Chemicals, Scientific Publications & Teachings.
N.A.I.C.S.: 513210
Mark Warne *(CEO)*

DEEPMIND PLATFORM CO., LTD.

PangyoInnovalley 1002 10F 255
Pangyo-ro, Bundang-gu, Seongnam,
Gyeonggi, Korea (South)
Tel.: (82) 7044903133
Web Site: http://www.deepmind.im
Year Founded: 2011
223310—(KRS)
Rev.: $15,897,393
Assets: $21,140,817
Liabilities: $2,793,028
Net Worth: $18,347,789
Earnings: ($1,737,355)
Emp.: 39
Fiscal Year-end: 12/31/22
Dash Camera Mfr
N.A.I.C.S.: 334220

DEEPNOID INC.

1305 55 Digital-Ro 33-Gil, Guro-Gu,
Seoul, 08376, Korea (South)
Tel.: (82) 269526001
Web Site: https://www.deepnoid.com
Year Founded: 2008
315640—(KRS)
Emp.: 110
Software Development Services
N.A.I.C.S.: 541511
T. G. Kim *(CTO)*

DEEPROCK MINERALS, INC.

1518 - 800 West Pender Street, Vancouver, V6C 2V6, BC, Canada
Tel.: (778) 302-2257
Web Site:
   https://www.deeprockminerals.com
DEEP—(CNSX)
Assets: $304,982
Liabilities: $289,459
Net Worth: $15,523
Earnings: ($142,241)
Fiscal Year-end: 11/30/23
Mineral Exploration Services
N.A.I.C.S.: 213114
Keith Margetson *(CFO)*

DEEPSPATIAL INC.

Suite 2502 Scotia Plaza 40 King St
West, Toronto, M5H 3Y2, ON,
Canada
Tel.: (416) 304-1231   Ca
Web Site:
   http://www.aylencapital.com
Year Founded: 2010
DSAIF—(OTCQB)
Rev.: $13,739
Assets: $886,830
Liabilities: $835,360
Net Worth: $51,470
Earnings: ($1,123,815)
Fiscal Year-end: 06/30/23
Investment Services
N.A.I.C.S.: 523999
John D. Pennal *(Pres & CEO)*

Subsidiaries:

Grapevine Solutions Inc.   (1)
11 Allstate Parkway Suite 200, Markham,
L3R 9T8, ON, Canada
Tel.: (905) 946-6629
Web Site:
   http://www.grapevinesolutions.com
Financial Investment Services
N.A.I.C.S.: 523999

DEEPVERGE PLC

York Biotech Campus Sand Hutton,
York, YO41 1LZ, United Kingdom
Tel.: (44) 1904404036   UK
Year Founded: 2016
DVRG—(LSE)
Rev.: $12,622,723
Assets: $42,500,709
Liabilities: $10,238,567
Net Worth: $32,262,143
Earnings: ($3,637,332)
Emp.: 73
Fiscal Year-end: 12/31/21
Pharmaceutical Product Mfr & Distr
N.A.I.C.S.: 325412

Subsidiaries:

DeepVerge Ireland Limited   (1)
12 St James's Terrace, Malahide, Dublin,
K36N996, Ireland
Tel.: (353) 2032393716
Software Development Services
N.A.I.C.S.: 541511

Modern Water plc   (1)
12th Floor 6 New Street Square, London,
EC4A 3BF, United Kingdom
Tel.: (44) 20 3827 3439
Web Site: http://www.modernwater.com
Sales Range: $1-9.9 Million
Developing & Deploying technology For
Fresh Water & Treatment Of Wastewater
N.A.I.C.S.: 237110

Subsidiary (US):

Modern Water Inc.   (2)
15 Reads Way Ste 100, New Castle, DE
19720
Tel.: (302) 669-6900
Waste Water Services
N.A.I.C.S.: 237110
Sejal Patel *(Mgr-Ops)*

Subsidiary (Domestic):

Modern Water Monitoring
Limited   (2)
Unit 22 South Cambridge Business Park
Babraham Road, Sawston, Cambridge,
CB22 3JH, United Kingdom
Tel.: (44) 1483696030
Waste Water Services
N.A.I.C.S.: 237110

Subsidiary (Non-US):

Modern Water Technology (Shanghai)
Co., Ltd.   (2)
1702 Xinyin Building No 888 Yishan Road,
Xuhui District, Shanghai, 200233, China
Tel.: (86) 2162306747
Waste Water Services
N.A.I.C.S.: 237110

Rinocloud Limited   (1)
The Rubicon Centre CIT Campus, Bishopstown, Cork, Ireland
Tel.: (353) 212427009
Web Site: http://www.rinocloud.com
Information Technology Development Services
N.A.I.C.S.: 541519

DEER BRIDGE PLUMBING & HEATING LTD.

4522 - 112th Ave SE, Calgary, T2C
2K2, AB, Canada
Tel.: (403) 252-1101
Year Founded: 1986
Sales Range: $10-24.9 Million
Emp.: 40
Plumbing Contract Services
N.A.I.C.S.: 332913

DEER CONSUMER PRODUCTS, INC.

Area 2 1/F Building M-6 Ctr HighTech Industrial Park, Nanshan, Shenzhen, 518057, China
Tel.: (86) 75586028285   NV
Web Site: http://www.deerinc.com
Year Founded: 2006
Sales Range: $200-249.9 Million
Emp.: 890
Home & Kitchen Electric Appliances
Designer, Mfr & Sales
N.A.I.C.S.: 335220
Ying He *(Chm & CEO)*

DEERA INVESTMENT & REAL ESTATE DEVELOPMENT CO.

Arjan Area Near Ministry of Interior,
PO Box 212466, Amman, 11121, Jordan
Tel.: (962) 65544826
Web Site: http://www.deera.jo
DERA—(AMM)
Rev.: $6,045,291
Assets: $124,108,184
Liabilities: $43,952,120
Net Worth: $80,156,064
Earnings: ($3,760,316)
Emp.: 121
Fiscal Year-end: 12/31/20
Real Estate Investment Services
N.A.I.C.S.: 531390
Mohammed Yousef Al Tarawneh
(Chm)

DEERLAND FARM EQUIPMENT (1985) LTD.

8599 112 Street, Fort Saskatchewan,
T8L 3V3, AB, Canada
Tel.: (780) 998-3249
Web Site: https://www.deerland.ca
Year Founded: 1978
Rev.: $12,630,950
Emp.: 35
Farm Equipment Supplier
N.A.I.C.S.: 423820

DEERNS RAADGEVENDE INGENIEURS B.V

Fleminglaan 10, 2289, Rijswijk, Netherlands
Tel.: (31) 88 374 0000
Web Site: http://www.deerns.com
Year Founded: 1928
Emp.: 500
Engineering Consulting Services
N.A.I.C.S.: 541690

Subsidiaries:

Deerns Italia SpA   (1)
via Guglielmo Silva 36, 20149, Milan, Italy
Tel.: (39) 02 3616 7888
Web Site: http://www.deerns.com
Engineering Consulting Services
N.A.I.C.S.: 541330

DEEWIN TIANXIA CO., LTD.

Deewin Tianxia Co., Ltd.—(Continued)

16th Fl Unit 1 Building 1 Jingwei
Centre 29 West Section of Xijin Rd,
Economic & Technological Develop-
ment Zone Jingwei New City, Xi'an,
Shaanxi, China
Tel.: (86) 2986060733　　　　CN
Web Site: https://www.deewintx.com
Year Founded: 2014
2418—(HKG)
Rev.: $431,911,414
Assets: $1,274,483,274
Liabilities: $814,901,279
Net Worth: $459,581,995
Earnings: $20,941,792
Emp.: 1,694
Fiscal Year-end: 12/31/23
Logistic Services
N.A.I.C.S.: 541614
Lulu Liu *(Fin Dir)*

DEFACTO OZON GIYIM SANAYI VE TICARET A.S.

DeFacto Plaza Basin Ekspres Yolu
Bahariye Cad No 31, Halkali, 34303,
Istanbul, Turkiye
Tel.: (90) 212 705 12 12　　　TR
Web Site:
　http://www.defactokurumsal.com
Year Founded: 2003
Women's & Men's Apparel Mfr &
Whslr
N.A.I.C.S.: 458110
Ihsan Ates *(Vice Chm & Pres-Retail Grp)*

DEFENCE TECH HOLDING S.P.A. SB

Via Giacomo Peroni 452, 00131,
Rome, Italy
Tel.: (39) 0645752720
Web Site: https://www.defencetech.it
Year Founded: 2015
DTH—(ITA)
Rev.: $20,746,845
Assets: $65,002,237
Liabilities: $24,907,098
Net Worth: $40,095,139
Earnings: $4,479,010
Emp.: 246
Fiscal Year-end: 12/31/22
Offices of Other Holding Companies
N.A.I.C.S.: 551112
Enrico Remondini *(CTO)*

DEFENCE THERAPEUTICS INC.

1680-200 Burrard Street, Vancouver,
V6C 3L6, BC, Canada
Tel.: (514) 947-2272　　　BC
Web Site:
　https://defencetherapeutics.com
Year Founded: 2020
DTCFF—(OTCIQ)
Assets: $536,871
Liabilities: $825,989
Net Worth: ($289,118)
Earnings: ($5,478,623)
Fiscal Year-end: 06/30/22
Biotechnology Research & Develop-
ment Services
N.A.I.C.S.: 541714
Joseph Meagher *(CFO)*

DEFENSE INDUSTRIES INTER-NATIONAL, INC.

12 Hamefalsim Street, Petah Tiqwa,
49514, Israel
Tel.: (972) 37168383　　　NV
Sales Range: $10-24.9 Million
Emp.: 201
Security & Defense Products Mfr
N.A.I.C.S.: 332994
Uri Nissani *(Chm, Pres & CEO)*

Subsidiaries:

Achidatex Nazareth Elite (1977) Ltd　　　　　　　　　(1)
12 Hamefalsim St, Kiryat Arieh, Petah
Tiqwa, 52121, Israel
Tel.: (972) 39213431
Web Site: http://www.achidatex.com
Military Equipment Mfr
N.A.I.C.S.: 336992

DEFENSE METALS CORP.

1020-800 West Pender Street, Van-
couver, V6C 2V6, BC, Canada
Tel.: (770) 994-0072
Web Site:
　https://www.defensemetals.com
DFMTF—(OTCQB)
Assets: $24,426,717
Liabilities: $489,765
Net Worth: $23,936,953
Earnings: ($2,021,822)
Emp.: 1
Fiscal Year-end: 03/31/23
Mineral Exploration Services
N.A.I.C.S.: 213114
Luisa Moreno *(Pres)*

DEFENX PLC

105 Victoria Street, London, SW1E
6QT, United Kingdom
Tel.: (44) 20 3709 0687
Web Site: http://www.defenx.com
Rev.: $1,802,008
Assets: $7,543,055
Liabilities: $5,550,693
Net Worth: $1,992,361
Earnings: ($4,804,510)
Emp.: 9
Fiscal Year-end: 12/31/18
Mobile Phone Security
N.A.I.C.S.: 561621
Anthony Henry Reeves *(Chm)*

DEFI COMMUNICATION MAR-KETING INC.

209 St Paul St W Ste 200, Montreal,
H2Y 2A1, QC, Canada
Tel.: (514) 288-3334
Sales Range: $10-24.9 Million
Emp.: 10
N.A.I.C.S.: 541810
Claude Dutil *(Pres)*

DEFI GROUP SAS

54 rue Klock, 92110, Clichy, France
Tel.: (33) 1 41 40 42 00　　　FR
Web Site: http://www.defi-group.com
Year Founded: 1977
Sales Range: $50-74.9 Million
Emp.: 300
Outdoor Advertising Services
N.A.I.C.S.: 541850
Lucas Su *(CFO)*

Subsidiaries:

DEFI Deutschland GmbH　　　(1)
Magdalenenstrasse 8, 20148, Hamburg,
Germany
Tel.: (49) 403697360
Web Site: http://www.defi-group.com
Sales Range: $25-49.9 Million
Emp.: 3
Outdoor Advertising Services
N.A.I.C.S.: 541850

DEFI France SAS　　　　　　(1)
21 rue Georges Boisseau, 92110, Clichy,
France
Tel.: (33) 1 41 40 42 00
Web Site: http://www.defi-group.com
Sales Range: $25-49.9 Million
Emp.: 15
Outdoor Advertising Services
N.A.I.C.S.: 541850

DEFI Group Asia Ltd.　　　　(1)
12/F Ruttonjee House, 11 Duddell Street,
Central, China (Hong Kong)
Tel.: (852) 25213661

Outdoor Advertising
N.A.I.C.S.: 541850
Christophe Thery *(Head-Ops)*

DEFI Hungary Kft　　　　　　(1)
Alkotas Ut 50, H 1123, Budapest, Hungary
Tel.: (36) 1 489 52 40
Emp.: 6
Outdoor Advertising Services
N.A.I.C.S.: 541850
Bertalan Hamvai *(Head-Ops)*

DEFI Italia S.p.A.　　　　　　(1)
Via lattanzio 77, Milan, 20137, Italy
Tel.: (39) 02 551 3722
Web Site: http://www.defi-group.com
Emp.: 20
Outdoor Advertising
N.A.I.C.S.: 541850
Giorgio Fallica *(Gen Mgr)*

DEFI Neolux　　　　　　　　(1)
Av Casal Ribeiro 18 9 Dt, 1000-103, Lis-
bon, Portugal
Tel.: (351) 21 351 40 10
Outdoor Advertising
N.A.I.C.S.: 541850
Delfim Costa *(Pres)*

DEFI Poland Sp. z o.o.　　　(1)
ul Krucza 16/22, 00-526, Warsaw, Poland
Tel.: (48) 224342177
Sales Range: $25-49.9 Million
Emp.: 13
Outdoor Advertising Services
N.A.I.C.S.: 541850

Iberdefi　　　　　　　　　　(1)
Calle Arturo Soria 336 1 Planta, 28033, Ma-
drid, Spain
Tel.: (34) 91 716 02 91
Outdoor Advertising Services
N.A.I.C.S.: 541850
Cyrille Leclerc *(Head-Ops-Western Europe)*

ZAO DEFI Russie　　　　　(1)
Usacheva Street 62/1 Office 18, 119048,
Moscow, Russia
Tel.: (7) 495 925 75 70
Emp.: 25
Outdoor Advertising Services
N.A.I.C.S.: 541850
Sergey Kluchkin *(Pres)*

DEFIANCE SILVER CORP.

Suite 2900-550 Burrard Street, Van-
couver, V6C 0A3, BC, Canada
Tel.: (604) 343-4677
Web Site:
　https://www.defiancesilver.com
Year Founded: 2007
DNCVF—(OTCQX)
Sales Range: Less than $1 Million
Silver Exploration & Development
Services
N.A.I.C.S.: 212220
Darrell A. Rader *(Founder)*

DEFINITY FINANCIAL CORP.

111 Westmount Road South, PO Box
2000, Waterloo, N2L 2L6, ON,
Canada
Tel.: (519) 570-8200　　　Ca
Web Site:
　https://www.definityfinancial.com
Year Founded: 2021
DFY—(TSX)
Rev.: $2,695,894,800
Assets: $6,204,332,800
Liabilities: $4,353,954,400
Net Worth: $1,850,378,400
Earnings: $188,439,600
Emp.: 3,500
Fiscal Year-end: 12/31/22
Investment Management Service
N.A.I.C.S.: 523999
Liam McFarlane *(Chief Risk Officer)*

DEFRAQ VENTURES AG

Thurn-und Taxis-Platz 6, 60313,
Frankfurt, Germany
Web Site: https://www.defraq.com
Year Founded: 2013
FKEK—(DEU)

Emp.: 8
Holding Company
N.A.I.C.S.: 551112

DEGAMA SOFTWARE SOLU-TIONS, INC.

1 Yonge St, Toronto, M5E 1W7, ON,
Canada
Tel.: (416) 306-2492
Year Founded: 1997
Software Development Services
N.A.I.C.S.: 541511
Seijin Ki *(Pres & CEO)*

DEGELMAN INDUSTRIES LTD.

272 Industrial Dr, PO Box 830, Re-
gina, S4P 3B1, SK, Canada
Tel.: (306) 543-4447　　　Ca
Web Site: http://www.degelman.com
Year Founded: 1962
Farm Equipment
N.A.I.C.S.: 333111
Wilfred Degelman *(Mgr)*

Subsidiaries:

Hylar Metal Products　　　　(1)
272 Industrial Dr, PO Box 830, Regina, S4P
3B1, SK, Canada　　　　　　(100%)
Tel.: (306) 543-4447
Web Site: http://www.degelman.com
Sales Range: $25-49.9 Million
Emp.: 10
Custom Machining & Fabrication Metals
N.A.I.C.S.: 333248
Roland Degelman *(Mgr-Admin)*

DEGEM BERHAD

No 40-46 Jalan Ma arof Bangsar
Baru, 59100, Kuala Lumpur, Malaysia
Tel.: (60) 3 2282 3618
Web Site: http://www.degembhd.com
Rev.: $38,976,701
Assets: $75,611,976
Liabilities: $15,724,140
Net Worth: $59,887,836
Earnings: $25,989
Fiscal Year-end: 12/31/18
Jewelry Mfr & Distr
N.A.I.C.S.: 339910
Kai Fatt Choong *(CEO)*

DEGETEL

54 Avenue du General Leclerc,
92100, Boulogne-Billancourt, France
Tel.: (33) 141860200
Web Site: http://www.degetel.com
Year Founded: 1999
Rev.: $20,300,000
Emp.: 450
Custom Computer Programming Ser-
vices
N.A.I.C.S.: 541511
Denis Klenkle Lallemand *(Founder)*

Subsidiaries:

Degetel Benelux　　　　　　(1)
Avenue Louise 137, 1050, Brussels, Bel-
gium
Tel.: (32) 2 535 76 88
Custom Computer Programming Services
N.A.I.C.S.: 541511
Guillaume Aubert *(Mgr)*

**Degetel Portugal - Sociedade Unipes-
soal Lda.**　　　　　　　　　(1)
Avenida da Liberdade n 110, 1269-046, Lis-
bon, Portugal
Tel.: (351) 1 213 404 514
Custom Computer Programming Services
N.A.I.C.S.: 541511
Pedro Passos *(Mgr)*

DEHUA TB NEW DECORATION MATERIAL CO., LTD.

No 588 Linxi Street, Fuxi Subdistrict
Deqing County, Huzhou, 313200,
Zhejiang, China
Tel.: (86) 5728405635
Web Site: http://www.tubaobao.com

Year Founded: 1993
002043—(SSE)
Rev.: $1,252,001,556
Assets: $738,004,176
Liabilities: $390,045,240
Net Worth: $347,958,936
Earnings: $62,531,352
Fiscal Year-end: 12/31/22
Decoration Material Mfr
N.A.I.C.S.: 321999
Ding Hongmin *(Founder & Chm)*

DEICHMANN SE
Deichmannweg 9, 45359, Essen,
Germany
Tel.: (49) 201867600　　　　De
Web Site: http://www.deichmann.com
Year Founded: 1913
Sales Range: $1-4.9 Billion
Emp.: 21,000
Shoe Mfr
N.A.I.C.S.: 316210
Heinrich O. Deichmann *(CEO & Mng Partner)*

Subsidiaries:

Deichmann Obuv s.r.o.　　　　(1)
Brno Business Park Londynske namesti
853/1- Budova 1, Styria, 639 00, Brno,
Czech Republic
Tel.: (420) 543420430
Web Site: http://www.deichmann.com
Emp.: 50
Shoe Retailer
N.A.I.C.S.: 458210
Heinrich O. Deichmann *(CEO)*

Deichmann Sko ApS　　　　(1)
Vesterbrogade 6D 1 Sal, 1620, Copenha-
gen, Denmark
Tel.: (45) 33343800
Web Site: http://www.deichmann.com
Emp.: 500
Shoe Retailing Services
N.A.I.C.S.: 458210

Deichmann-Obuwie Sp.z. o.o.　　(1)
Street Lotnicza 12, 54-155, Wroclaw,
Poland　　　　　　　　　　　(100%)
Tel.: (48) 713901427
Web Site: http://www.deichmann.com
Sales Range: $25-49.9 Million
Emp.: 75
Shoe Retailer Distr
N.A.I.C.S.: 458210
Heinrich O. Deichmann *(CEO)*

Deichmann-
Schuhvertriebsgesellschaft
m.b.H.　　　　　　　　　　　(1)
Modecenterstrasse 14 A4, 1030, Vienna,
Austria
Tel.: (43) 017986400
Web Site: http://www.deichmann.at
Shoe Retailer
N.A.I.C.S.: 458210
Heinrich O. Deichmann *(CEO)*

Deichmann-Shoes UK Ltd.　　(1)
18 Main Street, Lubenham, Market Harbor-
ough, LE16 9TF, Leicestershire, United
Kingdom
Tel.: (44) 3 1858 468 546
Web Site: http://www.deichmann-
　　shoes.co.uk
Shoe Retailer
N.A.I.C.S.: 458210
Heinrich O. Deichmann *(Chm & CEO)*

Dosenbach Ochsner AG　　　(1)
Schuhe und Sport, Allmendstrasse 25,
8953, Dietikon, Switzerland
Tel.: (41) 447454511
Web Site: http://www.ochsner-shoes.com
Sales Range: $350-399.9 Million
Emp.: 2,000
Shoe Retailer
N.A.I.C.S.: 458210

Rack Room Shoes Inc.　　　(1)
8310 Technologie Dr, Charlotte, NC 28262
Tel.: (704) 547-8110
Web Site: http://www.rackroomshoes.com
Sales Range: $250-299.9 Million
Emp.: 500
Shoe Stores

N.A.I.C.S.: 458210
Ernie Shore *(CFO)*

Snipes SE　　　　　　　　(1)
Schanzenstrasse 41, 51063, Cologne, Ger-
many
Tel.: (49) 221977790
Sneakers & Street Wear Mfr
N.A.I.C.S.: 458210
Carolin Schriebl *(Mgr-Social Media)*

Subsidiary (US):

Mr. Alan's Men's Bootery Inc.　(2)
14157 Telegraph Rd, Redford, MI 48239
Tel.: (313) 387-4100
Web Site: http://www.kicksusa.com
Men's Shoes
N.A.I.C.S.: 458210

DEINOVE SA
Cap Sigma-ZAC Euromedecine II
1682 rue de la Valsiere Grabels,
34790, Montpellier, France
Tel.: (33) 4 48 19 01 00
Web Site: http://www.deinove.com
Year Founded: 2006
ALDEI—(EUR)
Rev.: $713,351
Assets: $11,630,866
Liabilities: $19,026,421
Net Worth: ($7,395,555)
Earnings: ($11,475,205)
Emp.: 60
Fiscal Year-end: 12/31/19
Chemicals & Biofuel Developer & Mfr
N.A.I.C.S.: 325998
Philippe Pouletty *(Co-Founder)*

DEJIN RESOURCES GROUP COMPANY LIMITED
8/F Rykadan Capital Tower 135 Hoi
Bun Road, Kwun Tong, Kowloon,
China (Hong Kong)
Tel.: (852) 2984 0888　　　BM
Web Site:
　http://www.dejinresources.com
Sales Range: $1-9.9 Million
Emp.: 35
Gold Mining, Timber-Related Services
& Lighting Product Mfr
N.A.I.C.S.: 212220
Hao Tang *(CEO)*

Subsidiaries:

Whole Bright Industries (HK)
Limited　　　　　　　　　　(1)
Rm 1909 Block B Ming Pao Indus Ctr 18
Ka Yip St, Chai Wan, China (Hong Kong)
Tel.: (852) 28892013
Emp.: 4
Electric Lighting Products Sales
N.A.I.C.S.: 423220
John Pak *(Gen Mgr)*

DEJMARK GROUP S.R.O.
Podebradska 55/88, 190 00, Prague,
9, Czech Republic
Tel.: (420) 724 554 417
Web Site: http://www.dejmark.com
Year Founded: 2012
Sales Range: $10-24.9 Million
Emp.: 70
Decorative Paints & Industrial Coat-
ings Whslr
N.A.I.C.S.: 424950

Subsidiaries:

Dejmark Kft.　　　　　　　(1)
Gyali ut 27-29, Budapest, 1097, Hungary
Tel.: (36) 1 348 3040
Web Site: http://www.dejmark.hu
Paints Mfr
N.A.I.C.S.: 325510
Haar Magdolano *(Mgr-Fin)*

Dejmark Partners SRL　　　(1)
Str Cernat nr 27, 525400, Targu Secuiesc,
Romania
Tel.: (40) 734 542 253
Web Site: http://www.dejmark.ro

Paint
N.A.I.C.S.: 424950
Nagy Lehel *(Sls Dir)*

Dejmark spol. s r.o.　　　　(1)
Priekopska 3706/104, Priekopa, 036 01,
Martin, Slovakia
Tel.: (421) 43 40 100 40
Web Site: http://www.dejmark.sk
Emp.: 20
Decorative Paint & Industrial Coating Distr
N.A.I.C.S.: 424950
Dusan Pavlov *(Exec Dir)*

DEKABANK
Mainzer Landstrasse 16, 60325,
Frankfurt, Germany
Tel.: (49) 69 7147 0　　　　De
Web Site: http://www.dekabank.de
Year Founded: 1918
Rev.: $2,919,363,034
Assets: $108,942,220,520
Liabilities: $102,770,112,130
Net Worth: $6,172,108,390
Earnings: $234,386,698
Emp.: 4,108
Fiscal Year-end: 12/31/19
Investment Banking, Securities Bro-
kerage, Real Estate Investment &
Sales Financing Services
N.A.I.C.S.: 523150
Georg Stocker *(Chm-Mgmt Bd)*

Subsidiaries:

Bevestor GmbH　　　　　　(1)
Hamburger Allee 14, 60486, Frankfurt am
Main, Germany
Tel.: (49) 8003377299
Web Site: http://www.bevestor.de
Financial Consulting Services
N.A.I.C.S.: 541611

DKC Deka Kommunal Consult
GmbH　　　　　　　　　　　(1)
Hans-Bockler-Strasse 33 Postfach 10 42
39, Dusseldorf, 40476, Germany
Tel.: (49) 21188288811
Commercial Banking Services
N.A.I.C.S.: 522110

Deka Immobilien Investment
GmbH　　　　　　　　　　　(1)
Taunusanlage 1, 60329, Frankfurt am Main,
Germany　　　　　　　　　　(100%)
Tel.: (49) 69 7147 0
Web Site: http://www.deka.de
Emp.: 47
Real Estate Investment Fund Management
Services
N.A.I.C.S.: 531390
Torsten Knapmeyer *(Mng Dir)*

Subsidiary (Domestic):

Deka Immobilien GmbH　　　(2)
Taunusanlage 1, 60329, Frankfurt am Main,
Germany　　　　　　　　　　(100%)
Tel.: (49) 69 7147 0
Web Site: http://www.deka.de
Commercial Real Estate Investment Man-
agement, Financing & Property Manage-
ment Services
N.A.I.C.S.: 531390

Subsidiary (Domestic):

Deka Beteiligungs GmbH　　(3)
Taunusanlage 1, 60329, Frankfurt am Main,
Germany　　　　　　　　　　(100%)
Tel.: (49) 69 7147 0
Real Estate Holding Company
N.A.I.C.S.: 551112

Deka Grundstucksverwaltungsgesell-
schaft I (GbR)　　　　　　(3)
Taunusanlage 1, 60329, Frankfurt am Main,
Germany　　　　　　　　　　(100%)
Tel.: (49) 69 7147 0
Commercial Property Management Services
N.A.I.C.S.: 531312

Deka Vermogensverwaltungs
GmbH　　　　　　　　　　　(3)
Taunusanlage 10, 60329, Frankfurt am
Main, 60329, Germany　　　　(100%)
Tel.: (49) 69 7147 0

Commercial Real Estate Asset Management
Services
N.A.I.C.S.: 523940

Subsidiary (Domestic):

WestInvest Gesellschaft fur Invest-
mentfonds mbH　　　　　　(2)
Hamborner Str 55, 40472, Dusseldorf, Ger-
many
Tel.: (49) 211 882 88 500
Web Site: http://www.deka.de
Real Estate Investment Fund Management
Services
N.A.I.C.S.: 523940

Deka International (Ireland) Ltd.　(1)
Fleming Court Fleming Place, Dublin, 4,
Ireland　　　　　　　　　　(100%)
Tel.: (353) 12815720
Web Site: http://www.deka.ie
Sales Range: $50-74.9 Million
Emp.: 15
International Banking Institution
N.A.I.C.S.: 522299
Grainne Walts *(Gen Mgr)*

Deka International S.A.　　　(1)
6 rue Lou Hemmer, Luxembourg-Findel,
1748, Luxembourg, Luxembourg　(100%)
Tel.: (352) 34092739
Web Site: http://www.deka.de
Financial Services
N.A.I.C.S.: 523940

Deka Investment GmbH　　(1)
Mainzer Landstrasse 16, 60325, Frankfurt
am Main, Germany　　　　　(100%)
Tel.: (49) 69 7147 652
Web Site: http://www.deka.de
Investment Banking & Asset Management
Services
N.A.I.C.S.: 523150

DekaBank Deutsche Girozentrale
Luxembourg S.A.　　　　　(1)
6 rue Lou Hemmer, Luxembourg-Findel,
1748, Luxembourg, Luxembourg
Tel.: (352) 34093500
Web Site: http://www.deka.de
Sales Range: $200-249.9 Million
Emp.: 352
Financial Services
N.A.I.C.S.: 523940
Patrick Weydert *(Mng Dir)*

ExFin AG　　　　　　　　(1)
Thurgauerstrasse 54, 8050, Zurich, Switzer-
land
Tel.: (41) 443088888
Emp.: 60
Investment Advisory & Banking Services
N.A.I.C.S.: 523940
Michael Albanus *(Mng Dir)*

Privates Institut fur quantitative Kapi-
talmarktforschung der DekaBank
GmbH　　　　　　　　　　　(1)
Mainzer Landstrasse 16, 60325, Frankfurt
am Main, Germany
Tel.: (49) 6971473499
Web Site: http://www.iq-kap.de
Asset Management Services
N.A.I.C.S.: 541611

S Broker AG & Co. KG　　(1)
Carl-Bosch-Strasse 10, 65203, Wiesbaden,
Germany　　　　　　　　　　(30.6%)
Tel.: (49) 61120441911
Web Site: http://www.sbroker.de
Securities Broker
N.A.I.C.S.: 523150
Thomas Pfaff *(Chm-Mgmt Bd)*

DEKAPRINT S.A.
Larrea 50, 1609-Boulogne, Buenos
Aires, 1609, Argentina
Tel.: (54) 1147356200
Web Site:
　http://www.dekaprint.com.ar
Sales Range: $10-24.9 Million
Emp.: 4
Mfr & Supplier of Box Making, Con-
verting & Packaging Machinery
N.A.I.C.S.: 333993

DEKEL AGRI-VISION PLC

Dekel Agri-Vision PLC—(Continued)

First Floor 18-19 Pall Mall, London,
SW1Y 5LU, United Kingdom
Tel.: (44) 2070248391　　　　　CY
Web Site:
　https://www.dekelagrivision.com
Year Founded: 2007
DKL—(LSE)
Rev.: $33,351,904
Assets: $58,441,984
Liabilities: $42,061,555
Net Worth: $16,380,429
Earnings: ($1,430,054)
Emp.: 300
Fiscal Year-end: 12/31/22
Oil Palm Production
N.A.I.C.S.: 311224
Benjamin Adon *(Dir-Agriculture)*

DEKOMTE DE TEMPLE KOMPENSATOR-TECHNIK GMBH

Walinusstrasse 13, 63500, Seligenstadt, Germany
Tel.: (49) 618221014
Web Site: http://www.dekomte.com
Year Founded: 1978
Rev.: $11,143,136
Emp.: 300
Prefabricated Metal Buildings
N.A.I.C.S.: 332311
Ulrich Stohrer *(Mng Dir)*

Subsidiaries:

DEKOMTE Benelux Bvba.　　　(1)
Simon Stevinstraat 8, 8400, Oostende, Belgium
Tel.: (32) 59510755
Web Site: http://www.dekomte.eu
Industrial Supplies Whslr
N.A.I.C.S.: 423840
Johnny Verkempinck *(Gen Mgr)*

DEKOMTE Bohemia, s.r.o.　　(1)
Hulvacka 2018/4, Zabreh, 70030, Ostrava, Czech Republic
Tel.: (420) 596244026
Industrial Supplies Whslr
N.A.I.C.S.: 423840

DEKOMTE France Sarl.　　　(1)
27 rue Louis de Broglie, 95500, Le Thillay, France
Tel.: (33) 134387960
Industrial Supplies Whslr
N.A.I.C.S.: 423840

DEKOMTE Polska sp. z o.o.　　(1)
ul Zdrojowa 2, 43-200, Pszczyna, Poland
Tel.: (48) 322104278
Web Site: http://www.dekomte.com
Industrial Supplies Whslr
N.A.I.C.S.: 423840

DEKOMTE de Temple Iberia S.L.　(1)
C/Mallorca 628 L 28, 8026, Barcelona, Spain
Tel.: (34) 934676021
Industrial Supplies Whslr
N.A.I.C.S.: 423840

DEKOMTE de Temple Kompensator-Technik (S) Pte. Ltd.　　(1)
24 Boon Lay Way 01-65 Trade Hub 21, 609969, Singapore, Singapore
Tel.: (65) 66864991
Industrial Supplies Whslr
N.A.I.C.S.: 423840

DEKOMTE de Temple Kompensator-Technik (UK) Ltd.　　(1)
Cotswold Business Village London Road, Moreton-in-Marsh, GL56OJQ, Gloucestershire, United Kingdom
Tel.: (44) 8454588125
Industrial Supplies Whslr
N.A.I.C.S.: 423840
Jake Waterhouse *(Mng Dir)*

DEKOMTE de Temple Kompensator-Technik LLC　　(1)
PO Box 29370, Dubai, United Arab Emirates
Tel.: (971) 43596629

Industrial Supplies Whslr
N.A.I.C.S.: 423840
Pramod Karunakaran *(Gen Mgr)*

DEKOMTE de Temple Kompensator-Technik OOO　　(1)
Solnechnaya 48 office 211, 443125, Samara, Russia
Tel.: (7) 8462716961
Industrial Supplies Whslr
N.A.I.C.S.: 423840

DEKOMTE de Temple Kompensator-Technik Saudi Arabia　　(1)
Prince Salman & Ali Bin Talib 2187, 11451, Riyadh, Saudi Arabia
Tel.: (966) 14482410
Industrial Supplies Whslr
N.A.I.C.S.: 423840

DEKOMTE de Temple LLC.　　(1)
885 Franklin Rd Ste 335, Marietta, GA 30067
Tel.: (888) 255-3520
Industrial Supplies Whslr
N.A.I.C.S.: 423840

DEKPOL S.A.

ul Gajowa 31, Pinczyn, 83 251, Starogard Gdanski, Poland
Tel.: (48) 585601060
Web Site: https://www.dekpol.pl
Year Founded: 1993
DEK—(WAR)
Rev.: $348,401,748
Assets: $348,384,414
Liabilities: $228,563,031
Net Worth: $119,821,384
Earnings: $19,793,750
Emp.: 938
Fiscal Year-end: 12/31/22
Commercial Construction
N.A.I.C.S.: 236220
Mariusz Grzegorz Tuchlin *(Chm-Mgmt Bd)*

Subsidiaries:

Betpref Sp. z o.o.　　　(1)
ul Gajowa 31, Pinczyn, 83-251, Starogard Gdanski, Poland
Tel.: (48) 9999999
Web Site: https://www.betpref.pl
Building Materials Mfr
N.A.I.C.S.: 332311

Dekpol Steel Sp. z o.o.　　(1)
Ul Gajowa 31, Pinczyn, 83-251, Starogard Gdanski, Poland
Tel.: (48) 585601067
Web Site: http://www.dekpol.pl
Construction Equipment Whslr
N.A.I.C.S.: 423810
Olga Murach Nowak *(Mgr-Customer Svc)*

Intek Sp. z o.o.　　　(1)
Grunwaldzka 18, 14-260, Lubawa, Poland
Tel.: (48) 896453173
Web Site: https://www.intek.eu.com
Industrial Automation Design Services
N.A.I.C.S.: 238210

Kombet Dzialdowo Sp. z o.o　　(1)
Komorniki 15, 13-200, Dzialdowo, Warminsko-mazurskie, Poland
Tel.: (48) 236972271
Web Site: https://kombet-dzialdowo.com.pl
Construction Material Mfr & Distr
N.A.I.C.S.: 333120

Smartex Sp. z o.o.　　　(1)
ul Braniborska 58-68, 53-680, Wroclaw, Poland
Tel.: (48) 713550023
Web Site: http://www.smartex.com.pl
Rental Services
N.A.I.C.S.: 532310

DEKRA E.V.

Handwerkstrasse 15, 70565, Stuttgart, Germany
Tel.: (49) 711 7861 0
Web Site: http://www.dekra.com
Year Founded: 1925
Sales Range: $1-4.9 Billion
Emp.: 35,000

Automotive Industrial & Personnel Training Safety Inspection & Regulation Organization
N.A.I.C.S.: 926150
Stefan Kolbl *(Chm-Mgmt Bd)*

Subsidiaries:

DEKRA (India) Pvt. Ltd.　　(1)
Muskaan Complex Plot 3 B-2, Vasant Kunj, New Delhi, 110070, India
Tel.: (91) 1146025992
Web Site: http://www.dekra.in
Automotive Inspection Services
N.A.I.C.S.: 811198

DEKRA Arbeit (Schweiz) Holding AG　　(1)
Grossfeldstrasse 33, 7320, Sargans, Switzerland
Tel.: (41) 817200020
Placement Oriented Personnel Services
N.A.I.C.S.: 561311

DEKRA Arbeit (Schweiz) Verwaltungs AG　　(1)
Grossfeldstrasse 33, 7320, Sargans, Switzerland
Tel.: (41) 817200090
Placement Oriented Personnel Services
N.A.I.C.S.: 561311

DEKRA Arbeit AG　　　(1)
St LeonhardStrasse 51, 9000, Saint Gallen, Switzerland
Tel.: (41) 712260909
Placement Oriented Personnel Services
N.A.I.C.S.: 561311

DEKRA Arbeit Austria GmbH　　(1)
Linke Wienzeile 4/III/2DG, 1060, Vienna, Austria
Tel.: (43) 1890890411
Web Site: http://www.dekra-arbeit.at
Job Placement Services
N.A.I.C.S.: 561320

DEKRA Arbeit Bulgaria EOOD　(1)
88 Bulgaria Blvd, 1680, Sofia, Bulgaria
Tel.: (359) 29077734
Web Site: http://www.dekra-arbeit.bg
Human Resource Employment Services
N.A.I.C.S.: 541612

DEKRA Automotive Ltd.　　(1)
Stokenchurch House Oxford Road, Stokenchurch, HP14 3SX, Buckinghamshire, United Kingdom
Tel.: (44) 8003345678
Automotive Services
N.A.I.C.S.: 811198

DEKRA Automotive Pty. Ltd.　　(1)
97 Willem Cruywagen Ave, Klerksoord Rosslyn, Pretoria, 0200, South Africa
Tel.: (27) 813729724
Web Site: http://www.dekraauto.co.za
Automotive Inspection Services
N.A.I.C.S.: 811198
Marius Schutte *(Officer-Information)*

DEKRA Automotive S.a r.l.　　(1)
12 rue Gabriel Lippmann, 5365, Munsbach, Luxembourg
Tel.: (352) 27400790
Web Site: http://www.dekra-automotive.lu
Automotive Inspection Services
N.A.I.C.S.: 811198

DEKRA Belgium N.V.　　　(1)
Leuvensesteenweg 510 b 30, 1930, Zaventem, Belgium
Tel.: (32) 27101010
Web Site: http://www.dekra.be
Insurance Claims Services
N.A.I.C.S.: 524291

DEKRA CZ a.s.　　　(1)
Turkova 1001/9, Chodov, 149 00, Prague, Czech Republic
Tel.: (420) 267288111
Web Site: http://www.dekra.cz
Road & Home Safety Services
N.A.I.C.S.: 561990

DEKRA Claims Services Maroc S.A.R.L.　　(1)
Ave Mers Sultan 196 Resid Al Khansaa 2nd Floor Apt 19, 20120, Casablanca, Morocco
Tel.: (212) 522293853

Web Site: http://www.dekra-claims-services.ma
Claims Management Services
N.A.I.C.S.: 524291

DEKRA Fyn ApS　　　(1)
Hans Egedes Vej 4, 5210, Odense, Denmark
Tel.: (45) 70606500
Web Site: http://www.dekra-fyn.dk
Automotive Inspection Services
N.A.I.C.S.: 811198

DEKRA Hasar Servisi Ltd. Sti.　(1)
Ataturk Mh Vatan Cad No 37/8, Atasehir, Istanbul, Turkiye
Tel.: (90) 2165377531
Web Site: http://www.dekra.com.tr
Automotive Component Testing Services
N.A.I.C.S.: 541380

DEKRA Hovedstaden A/S　　(1)
Kirkebjerg Alle 90, Brondby, Denmark
Tel.: (45) 70606500
Web Site: http://www.dekra-hovedstaden.dk
Transport Training Services
N.A.I.C.S.: 611692

DEKRA Industrial (Guangzhou) Co., Ltd.　　(1)
Building 5 No 3 Qiyun Road, Huangpu District, Guangzhou, 510663, Guangdong, China
Tel.: (86) 2066612000
Automotive Inspection Services
N.A.I.C.S.: 811198

DEKRA Inspecoes Portugal - Unipessoal Lda　　(1)
Avenida Dom Joao II n 45 10, 1990-084, Lisbon, Portugal
Tel.: (351) 217900310
Web Site: http://www.dekrainspecoes.pt
Automotive Inspection Services
N.A.I.C.S.: 811198

DEKRA Job ApS　　　(1)
Vibevej 20 3rd Floor, 2400, Copenhagen, Denmark
Tel.: (45) 88336686
Job Consulting Services
N.A.I.C.S.: 561311

DEKRA Middle East FZE　　(1)
Street N100 Building No 22 Jebel Ali Free Zone, PO Box 261142, Dubai, United Arab Emirates
Tel.: (971) 48830424
Automotive Inspection Services
N.A.I.C.S.: 811198

DEKRA Midtjylland ApS　　(1)
Arnborgvej 1B, Skjern, Denmark
Tel.: (45) 88779311
Web Site: http://www.dekra-midtjylland.dk
Transport Training Services
N.A.I.C.S.: 611692

DEKRA Nordjylland A/S　　(1)
Kjeldgaardsvej 4, Saeby, Denmark
Tel.: (45) 70606500
Web Site: http://www.dekra-nordjylland.dk
Automotive Inspection Services
N.A.I.C.S.: 811198

DEKRA Organisational Reliability Ltd.　　(1)
14 Abercrombie Court Prospect Road Arnhall Business Park, Westhill, AB32 6FE, Aberdeenshire, United Kingdom
Tel.: (44) 1224766700
Automotive Inspection Services
N.A.I.C.S.: 811198

DEKRA Quality Management AB　(1)
FE 1122, 838 83, Froson, Sweden
Tel.: (46) 104551000
Web Site: http://www.dekra-qualitymanagement.se
Automotive Inspection Services
N.A.I.C.S.: 811198

DEKRA Rail B.V.　　　(1)
Concordiastraat 67, 3551 EM, Utrecht, Netherlands
Tel.: (31) 303005100
Web Site: http://www.dekra-rail.com
Automotive Inspection Services
N.A.I.C.S.: 811198
Eric Mohringer *(Acct Mgr-Infrastructure & Light Rail)*

DEKRA SE **(1)**
Handwerkstrasse 15, 70565, Stuttgart,
Germany **(100%)**
Tel.: (49) 71178610
Web Site: http://www.dekra.de
Rev.: $3,817,560,185
Assets: $3,085,689,121.
Liabilities: $2,193,926,685
Net Worth: $891,762,436
Earnings: $132,822,115
Emp.: 43,961
Fiscal Year-end: 12/31/2019
Automotive Testing & Industrial Inspection
Services; Personnel Training, Placement &
Human Resource Consulting Services
N.A.I.C.S.: 488490
Stefan Kolbl (Chm-Mgmt Bd)

Subsidiary (Domestic):

AP Arbeitpartner GmbH & Co.
KG **(2)**
Heinz-Nixdorf-Strasse 27, 41179, Mon-
chengladbach, Germany
Tel.: (49) 2161 549888 0
Human Resource Consulting Services
N.A.I.C.S.: 541612

Subsidiary (Non-US):

AUTOTEST-TOUR s.r.o. **(2)**
Brezolupy 475, 687 13, Prague, Czech Re-
public
Tel.: (420) 572 580 118
Testing & Consulting Services
N.A.I.C.S.: 811198

Amedes Belgium N.V. **(2)**
Steenweg 3-1, 3540, Herk-de-Stad, Belgium
Tel.: (32) 78 35 36 36
Web Site: http://www.amedes.be
Human Resource Consulting Services
N.A.I.C.S.: 541612

Automobile Controle Technique
S.A.R.L. **(2)**
172 rue Colombier, 37100, Tours, France
Tel.: (33) 2 47 42 59 29
Automotive Engineering Consulting Ser-
vices
N.A.I.C.S.: 541330

BST Consultants Pte. Ltd. **(2)**
41 Science Park Road The Gemini Singapore, Science Park 2 04-03C, Singapore,
117610, Singapore
Tel.: (65) 6777 9210
Security Consulting Services
N.A.I.C.S.: 541690

Subsidiary (US):

Behavioral Science Technology (BST)
Inc. **(2)**
1000 Town Center Dr Ste 600, Oxnard, CA
93036
Tel.: (805) 646-0166
Web Site: http://www.bstsolutions.com
Security Consulting Services
N.A.I.C.S.: 541690
Andrew Goodman (Exec VP & Gen Mgr-
Asia Pacific)

Subsidiary (Non-US):

Behavioral Sciene Technology Con-
sultores do Brasil Ltda. **(2)**
Av Eng Luis Carlos Berrini 801, 8 Andar
Brooklin, 04571-010, Sao Paulo, Brazil
Tel.: (55) 11 2507 9772
Security Consulting Services
N.A.I.C.S.: 541690

C.T.A. S.A.R.L. **(2)**
Zone Artisanale Bois De L Arc, 76760,
Paris, France
Tel.: (33) 235567774
Human Resource Consulting Services
N.A.I.C.S.: 541612

Cabinet d'expertise R.TANFERRI
S.A.S. **(2)**
104 rue Thionville, Vitry-sur-Orne, 57185,
Paris, France
Tel.: (33) 3 87 67 17 55
Web Site: http://www.tanferri-expertise.net
Automotive Engineering Consulting Ser-
vices
N.A.I.C.S.: 541330

Centro Revisione Auto s.c.a.r.l. **(2)**
Via del Lavoro 68, Casalecchio, Bologna,
Italy
Tel.: (39) 051 613 22 35
Web Site: http://www.centrorevisioniauto.it
Automotive Engineering Consulting Ser-
vices
N.A.I.C.S.: 541330
Federico Caselli (Founder)

Chilworth Amalthea S.L. **(2)**
C/ Charles Robert Darwin 20 Paterna,
46980, Valencia, Spain
Tel.: (34) 961 366 814
Web Site: http://www.chilworth.es
Security Consulting Services
N.A.I.C.S.: 541690

Chilworth France S.A.S. **(2)**
Sunstone-Bat 2A 22 avenue Lionel Terray,
69330, Jonage, France
Tel.: (33) 4 72 44 05 52
Web Site: http://www.chilworth.fr
Emp.: 15
Security Consulting Services
N.A.I.C.S.: 541690
Joseph-Marc Francois (Mng Dir)

Subsidiary (US):

Chilworth Pacific Fire Laboratories
Inc. **(2)**
2401 B Tally Way, Kelso, WA 98626
Tel.: (360) 423-1220
Web Site: http://www.chilworthpacific.com
Security Consulting Services
N.A.I.C.S.: 541690

Chilworth Technology Inc. **(2)**
113 Campus Dr, Princeton, NJ 08540
Tel.: (609) 799-4449
Web Site: http://www.chilworth.com
Security Consulting Services
N.A.I.C.S.: 541690
Miriam Valentin (Office Mgr)

Subsidiary (Non-US):

Chilworth Technology Ltd. **(2)**
Phi House Southampton Science Park,
Southampton, SO16 7NS, United Kingdom
Tel.: (44) 23 8076 0722
Web Site: http://www.chilworth.co.uk
Emp.: 100
Security Consulting Services
N.A.I.C.S.: 541690
Stephen Rowe (Mng Dir)

Chilworth Vassallo S.r.l. **(2)**
Via Fratelli Gracchi 27 Torre Nord, Cinisello
Balsamo, 20092, Milan, Italy
Tel.: (39) 02 89929600
Web Site: http://www.chilworth.it
Security Consulting Services
N.A.I.C.S.: 541690

Consorzio DEKRA Revisioni **(2)**
Via dei Missaglia 89, 20142, Milan, Italy
Tel.: (39) 03316674971
Automotive Engineering Consulting Ser-
vices
N.A.I.C.S.: 541330

D Akademie S.r.l. **(2)**
Palazzina EurOffice 1-scala A 5 piano, Via
Sommacampagna 63H Interporto Quad-
rante Europa, 37137, Verona, Italy
Tel.: (39) 045 4950264
Web Site: http://www.dakademie.it
Automotive Engineering Consulting & Train-
ing Services
N.A.I.C.S.: 541330

DEKRA (Shanghai) Co., Ltd. **(2)**
10F Building No 16 250 jiangchangsan
Road, Shanghai, 200436, China
Tel.: (86) 21 6056 7666
Automotive Engineering Consulting Ser-
vices
N.A.I.C.S.: 541330
Pan Gao (Sr Mgr-Used Car Mgmt)

DEKRA AMBIO S.A.U. **(2)**
Montnegre 18-24 Esc A Ent 1a, 08029, Bar-
celona, Spain
Tel.: (34) 93 494 00 01
Web Site: http://www.dekra-ambio.es
Weather Forecasting Services
N.A.I.C.S.: 541990
Eduard Sanchez-Fortun (Dir-Comml)

DEKRA Arbeit Isgucu Secme ve yer-
lestirme Hizmetleri Ltd. **(2)**
Yuzer Havuz Sokak 1A Blok Kat 9 Buro
1131, Okmeydani Sisli, 34384, Istanbul,
Turkiye
Tel.: (90) 212 213 0601
Web Site: http://www.dekra-arbeit.de
Human Resource Consulting Services
N.A.I.C.S.: 541612

DEKRA Austria Automotive
GmbH **(2)**
MAN-Str 1, 2333, Vienna, Austria
Tel.: (43) 2235 40 900
Web Site: http://www.dekra-austria.at
Used Car Dealers
N.A.I.C.S.: 441120

DEKRA Automotive AB **(2)**
Drottninggatan 8, 632 20, Eskilstuna, Swe-
den
Tel.: (46) 10 455 10 00
Web Site: http://www.dekra-automotive.se
Emp.: 60
Automotive Engineering Consulting Ser-
vices
N.A.I.C.S.: 541330
Yojan Martinsson (Gen Mgr)

DEKRA Automotive Maroc S.A. **(2)**
B85 Boulevard Oued Sebou Oulfa, 20220,
Casablanca, Morocco
Tel.: (212) 522 91 69 57
Used Car Dealers
N.A.I.C.S.: 441120
Khalid Benmansour (Mgr-Dev)

DEKRA Automotive OOD **(2)**
Man Base 425 Slivnitsa, Sofia, Bulgaria
Tel.: (359) 28263447
Automotive Engineering Consulting Ser-
vices
N.A.I.C.S.: 541330

DEKRA Automotive S.A. **(2)**
11-13 avenue Georges Politzer, 78190,
Trappes, France
Tel.: (33) 1 30 69 58 38
Automotive Engineering Consulting Ser-
vices
N.A.I.C.S.: 541330

Subsidiary (Domestic):

DEKRA Automotive Solutions Ger-
many GmbH **(2)**
Lyoner Str 14, 60528, Frankfurt am Main,
Germany
Tel.: (49) 69 5870960
Automotive Engineering Consulting Ser-
vices
N.A.I.C.S.: 541330

Subsidiary (Non-US):

DEKRA Automotive Solutions Italy
S.r.l. **(2)**
Via Polesine 1/4 Cambiano, 10020, Turin,
Italy
Tel.: (39) 011 198 20810
Automotive Testing & Consulting Services
N.A.I.C.S.: 811198

DEKRA Automotive Solutions Portu-
gal Lda. **(2)**
Avenida Dom Joao Ii Lote 1 17 03 Piso, 10
Escritorio C/d, 1990-084, Lisbon, Portugal
Tel.: (351) 21 898 1020
Web Site: http://www.dekra-
automotivesolutions.pt
Emp.: 50
Used Car Dealers
N.A.I.C.S.: 441120
Sofia Silva (Dir-Remarketing)

DEKRA Automotive Solutions
S.A.S.U. **(2)**
9 avenue Reaumur, 92350, Le Plessis-
Robinson, France
Tel.: (33) 1 57 75 98 50
Web Site: http://www.dekra-automotive.fr
Used Car Dealers
N.A.I.C.S.: 441120

DEKRA Automotive Solutions Spain
S.L. **(2)**
Francisco Gervas 4, Alcobendas, Madrid,
28108, Spain
Tel.: (34) 902367045
Used Car Dealers

N.A.I.C.S.: 441120
Pedro Arroyo (Dir-Networks)

DEKRA CTI Testing and Certification
Ltd. **(2)**
Block A3 No 3 Qiyun Road Science City,
Guangzhou, 510630, China
Tel.: (86) 20 6661 2000
Audit & Certification Services
N.A.I.C.S.: 926150

DEKRA Canada Inc. **(2)**
480 University Avenue Suite 1500, Toronto,
M5G 1V2, ON, Canada
Tel.: (416) 598-7101
Web Site: http://www.dekra-na.com
Vehicle Testing Services
N.A.I.C.S.: 811198

DEKRA Caribbean B.V. **(2)**
Barentslaan 5, Willemstad, Curacao
Tel.: (599) 9 76 61 454
Web Site: http://www.dekra-claims-and-
expertise.nl
Testing & Consulting Services
N.A.I.C.S.: 811198
Jos Dijk (Mng Dir)

DEKRA Certification **(2)**
Business partner CSA International, 178
Rexdale Boulevard, Toronto, M9W 1R3,
ON, Canada
Tel.: (416) 747-2661
Audit & Certification Services
N.A.I.C.S.: 926150

DEKRA Certification (Proprietary)
Ltd. **(2)**
Tuinhof Office Park 265 West Ave, Die Hoe-
wes, Centurion, 0163, South Africa
Tel.: (27) 12 663 4956
Web Site: http://www.dekracertification.co.za
Audit & Certification Services
N.A.I.C.S.: 926150

DEKRA Certification B.V. **(2)**
Meander 1051, 6825, Arnhem, Netherlands
Tel.: (31) 88 96 83000
Web Site: http://www.dekra-certification.com
Emp.: 400
Audit & Certification Services
N.A.I.C.S.: 926150
Henry Dwars (Acct Mgr)

DEKRA Certification Hong Kong
Ltd. **(2)**
Unit 1-14 6/F Fuk Shing Commercial Build-
ing, Fanling 28 On Lok Mun Street On Lok
Tsuen, Hong Kong, China (Hong Kong)
Tel.: (852) 26 695 740
Audit & Certification Services
N.A.I.C.S.: 926150
Christina Lai (Gen Mgr)

Subsidiary (US):

DEKRA Certification Inc. **(2)**
1120 Wolves Rd, Chalfont, PA 18914
Tel.: (800) 768-5362
Web Site: http://www.dekra-certification.us
Audit & Certification Services
N.A.I.C.S.: 926150
Chris Carson (Dir-Bus Dev & Mktg)

Subsidiary (Domestic):

AQS Management Systems, Inc. **(3)**
2167 Northdale Blvd NW, Minneapolis, MN
55433-3006
Tel.: (763) 746-0505
Web Site: http://www.aqsperformance.com
Rev.: $1,500,000
Emp.: 9
Administrative Management & General
Management Consulting Service
N.A.I.C.S.: 541611
Ben Ames (VP)

Subsidiary (Non-US):

DEKRA Certification K.K. **(2)**
West Wing 7F 1-28-10 Akebono-Cho,
Tachikawa-shi, Tokyo, 190-0012, Japan
Tel.: (81) 42 595 7326
Web Site: http://www.dekra-certification.com
Emp.: 15
Audit & Certification Services
N.A.I.C.S.: 926150

DEKRA Certification Ltd. **(2)**

DEKRA e.V.—(Continued)

Atir Yeda st 17 4th floor, 44643, Kfar Saba, Israel
Tel.: (972) 54 540 6006
Audit & Certification Services
N.A.I.C.S.: 926150

DEKRA Certification S.A.S. (2)
5 Avenue de Garlande, 92220, Bagneux, France
Tel.: (33) 1 4117 1120
Web Site: http://www.dekra-certification.fr
Audit & Certification Services
N.A.I.C.S.: 926150

DEKRA Cortification S.R.L. (2)
Strada Constantin Brancusi Nr 131, 400458, Cluj-Napoca, Romania
Tel.: (40) 264 443598
Web Site: http://www.dekra-certification.ro
Emp.: 6
Audit & Certification Services
N.A.I.C.S.: 926150
Ionut Muntean (Mgr)

DEKRA Certification Sp. z o.o. (2)
Plac Solny 20, 50-063, Wroclaw, Poland
Tel.: (48) 71 780 47 77
Web Site: http://www.dekra-certification.com.pl
Audit & Certification Services
N.A.I.C.S.: 926150
Aleksandra Wilk (Mgr-Bus Dev)

DEKRA Certification, S.L.U. (2)
C/ Napoles 249 4a Planta, 8013, Barcelona, Spain
Tel.: (34) 934 792 269
Web Site: http://www.dekra-certification.es
Audit & Certification Services
N.A.I.C.S.: 926150
Alfonso Abadal de Bufala (Mgr-Product)

DEKRA Claims Services Austria GmbH (2)
Petersplatz 3, 1010, Vienna, Austria
Tel.: (43) 1 532 42 46
Claim Processing Services
N.A.I.C.S.: 524292
Vincent Jacobs (Mgr)

DEKRA Claims Services CZ s.r.o. (2)
Turkova 1001, 14900, Prague, Czech Republic
Tel.: (420) 261 219 038
Claim Processing Services
N.A.I.C.S.: 524292

DEKRA Claims Services Finland (2)
Vilhonvuorenkatu 11 C 8, 00500, Helsinki, Finland
Tel.: (358) 9 47 63 63 00
Claim Processing Services
N.A.I.C.S.: 524292

DEKRA Claims Services International BVBA (2)
Lenneke Marelaan 12, 1932, Brussels, Belgium
Tel.: (32) 2 710 10 00
Claim Processing Services
N.A.I.C.S.: 524292

DEKRA Claims Services Luxembourg S.A. (2)
13a Avenue Guillaume, 1651, Luxembourg, Luxembourg
Tel.: (352) 45 59 43
Claim Processing Services
N.A.I.C.S.: 524292

DEKRA Claims Services Portugal S.A. (2)
Avenida D Joao II 45 Piso 10, Parque das Nacoes, Lisbon, 1990-084, Portugal
Tel.: (351) 213 242 010
Web Site: http://www.dekra-claims-services.pt
Claim Processing Services
N.A.I.C.S.: 524292

DEKRA Claims Services Spain, S.A. (2)
Avenida Diagonal 622 4a Planta, 08021, Barcelona, Spain
Tel.: (34) 932419750
Web Site: http://www.dekra-claims-services.es

Claim Processing Services
N.A.I.C.S.: 524292

DEKRA Claims Services Turkey Ltd. (2)
Ataturk Mah Vatan Cad 37/8, 34758, Istanbul, Turkiye
Tel.: (90) 216 537 75 30
Claim Processing Services
N.A.I.C.S.: 524292
Alain Kunz (Gen Mgr)

DEKRA Claims Services UK Ltd. (2)
14 New St, London, EC2M 4HE, United Kingdom
Tel.: (44) 207 972 9003
Claim Processing Services
N.A.I.C.S.: 524292

DEKRA Claims Services Ukraine (2)
Av Bazhana-Prospekt 5-e ap 40, 02121, Kiev, Ukraine
Tel.: (380) 44 560 04 51
Claim Processing Services
N.A.I.C.S.: 524292

Subsidiary (Domestic):

DEKRA EXAM GmbH (2)
Dinnendahlstr 9, 44809, Bochum, Germany
Tel.: (49) 234 3 69 60
Web Site: http://www.dekra-exam.de
Emp.: 125
Audit & Certification Services
N.A.I.C.S.: 926150
Jochen Titze (Mng Dir)

Subsidiary (Non-US):

Chilworth Technology (Pvt) Ltd. (3)
Muskaan Complex Plot 3 B-2 Vasant Kunj, New Delhi, 110070, India
Tel.: (91) 11 2613 6979
Web Site: http://www.chilworth.co.in
Emp.: 20
Security Consulting Services
N.A.I.C.S.: 541690
Martin Paff (Sr Project Mgr)

Subsidiary (Domestic):

DEKRA Akademie GmbH (3)
Handwerkstrasse 15, 70565, Stuttgart, Germany (100%)
Tel.: (49) 71178610
Web Site: http://www.dekra-akademie.de
Professional Training Services
N.A.I.C.S.: 611430

Subsidiary (Non-US):

DEKRA Akademie Kft. (3)
Vermezo ut 4, Budapest, 1012, Hungary
Tel.: (36) 1 487 1090
Web Site: http://www.dekra-akademie.hu
Human Resource Training & Consulting Services
N.A.I.C.S.: 541612
Andras Decsi (CFO)

Subsidiary (US):

DEKRA America, Inc. (3)
3901 Rowell Rd, Marietta, GA 30062
Tel.: (770) 971-3788
Web Site: http://www.dekra-na.com
Emp.: 500
Vehicle Inspection & Certification Services
N.A.I.C.S.: 811198
Shannon Flanagan (VP-Sls-North America)

Subsidiary (Domestic):

DEKRA Arbeit GmbH (3)
Handwerkstr 15, 70565, Stuttgart, Germany (100%)
Tel.: (49) 71178613203
Web Site: http://www.dekra-arbeit.de
Sales Range: $10-24.9 Million
Emp.: 16
Employment Placement Agency Services
N.A.I.C.S.: 561311
Suzana Bernhard (Mng Dir)

Subsidiary (Non-US):

DEKRA Arbeit Magyaroszag Szolgaltato Kft. (3)
Benczur u 42, Budapest, 1068, Hungary
Tel.: (36) 1 461 9080
Web Site: http://www.dekra-arbeit.hu

Human Resource Consulting Services
N.A.I.C.S.: 541612
Gabor Behina (Head-Bus Dev)

Subsidiary (Domestic):

DEKRA Automobil GmbH (3)
Handwerkstrasse 15, Stuttgart, 70765, Germany (100%)
Tel.: (49) 71178610
Web Site: http://www.dekra.com
Sales Range: $200-249.9 Million
Automotive Vehicle Testing & Safety Inspection Services
N.A.I.C.S.: 488490
Stefan Kolb (Mng Dir)

Subsidiary (Non-US):

DEKRA Claims Services Hungary Service Ltd. (3)
Haller street 2, 1096, Budapest, Hungary
Tel.: (36) 1 372 3006
Claim Processing Services
N.A.I.C.S.: 524292

Subsidiary (Domestic):

DEKRA Industrial GmbH (3)
Handwerkstrasse 15, D-70565, Stuttgart, Germany (100%)
Tel.: (49) 71178612631
Web Site: http://www.dekra.de
Industrial Plant Safety, Inspection & Certification Services
N.A.I.C.S.: 541350

Subsidiary (Non-US):

DEKRA Industrial AB (4)
Kvarnbergsgatan 2, 411 05, Gothenburg, Sweden (100%)
Tel.: (46) 104551000
Web Site: http://www.dekra-industrial.se
Sales Range: $50-74.9 Million
Emp.: 450
Industrial Safety Testing & Inspection Services
N.A.I.C.S.: 541350
Staffan Lindbom (Controller)

Subsidiary (Domestic):

DEKRA International GmbH (3)
Handwerkstrasse 15, Stuttgart, 70565, Germany (100%)
Tel.: (49) 71178612065
Web Site: http://www.dekra.de
Holding Company; Automobile Safety Testing & Inspection Services
N.A.I.C.S.: 551112
Rolf Krokel (Mng Dir)

DEKRA Personaldienste GmbH (3)
Handwerkstrasse 15, D-70565, Stuttgart, Germany (100%)
Tel.: (49) 71178613650
Web Site: http://www.dekra-pd.de
Sales Range: $25-49.9 Million
Emp.: 20
Human Resource Consulting Services
N.A.I.C.S.: 541612
Thorsten Machner (Mng Dir)

Subsidiary (Non-US):

Plurel bv (3)
Concordiastraat 67, 3551 EM, Utrecht, Netherlands
Tel.: (31) 30 3005 100
Web Site: http://www.plurel.nl
Emp.: 7
Rail Management & Operations
N.A.I.C.S.: 488210
H. Eric Mohringer (Acct Mgr)

Subsidiary (Non-US):

DEKRA Ekspert d.o.o. (2)
Betinska 1, 10000, Zagreb, Croatia
Tel.: (385) 1 2040 690
Web Site: http://www.dekra.hr
Automotive Engineering Consulting Services
N.A.I.C.S.: 541330
Matija Ferencak (Head-Metrology Dept)

DEKRA Empleo ETT S.L. (2)
C/Pau Claris n 100 1 1a, 08009, Barcelona, Spain
Tel.: (34) 902 15 19 04

Web Site: http://www.dekra-empleo.es
Human Resource Consulting Services
N.A.I.C.S.: 541612

DEKRA Employment Ltd. (2)
Crvena voda Str 7/1, 1000, Skopje, North Macedonia
Tel.: (389) 2 32 30 952
Web Site: http://www.dekra.mk
Human Resource Consulting Services
N.A.I.C.S.: 541612

DEKRA Endustri Yatirimlari A.S. (2)
E Blok 5 Keresteciler Sitesi, Ankara, 6370, Turkiye
Tel.: (90) 312 385 9530
Human Resource Consulting Services
N.A.I.C.S.: 541612

Subsidiary (Domestic):

DEKRA Event & Logistic Services GmbH (2)
Kaistr 5, 40221, Dusseldorf, Germany
Tel.: (49) 211 22 95 07 40
Event Management Services
N.A.I.C.S.: 711310

Subsidiary (Domestic):

DEKRA INCOS GmbH (3)
Bunsenstrasse 29, 85053, Ingolstadt, Germany
Tel.: (49) 841 96698 0
Security Consulting Services
N.A.I.C.S.: 541690

Subsidiary (Non-US):

DEKRA Expertise S.A.S. (2)
7 bis rue de Navarre ZAC de la Porte d Espagne, 14123, Cormelles-le-Royal, France
Tel.: (33) 2 31 35 85 15
Web Site: http://www.dekra-expertise.net
Audit & Certification Services
N.A.I.C.S.: 926150

DEKRA Expertise Spain S.L.U. (2)
C/ Isla del Hierro 7 2a Planta, San Sebastian de los Reyes, 28703, Madrid, Spain
Tel.: (34) 91 659 01 14
Web Site: http://www.dekra-expertise.es
Automotive Consulting Services
N.A.I.C.S.: 541330
Marta Gutierrez Abarquero (Acct Mgr)

DEKRA Expertises Ltda. (2)
Rua dos Tres Irmaos 62 Cj 207 Morumbi, Sao Paulo, 05615-190, Brazil
Tel.: (55) 11 3721 1165
Automotive Engineering Consulting Services
N.A.I.C.S.: 541330

DEKRA Experts B.V. (2)
Rivium Boulevard 301, 2909, Capelle aan den IJssel, Netherlands
Tel.: (31) 10 20 77 260
Web Site: http://www.dekra-claims-and-expertise.nl
Emp.: 200
Claim Processing Services
N.A.I.C.S.: 524292
Angela Wessels (Mgr)

DEKRA Experts NV (2)
Port Arthurlaan 16, 9000, Gent, Belgium
Tel.: (32) 9 255 58 10
Claim Processing Services
N.A.I.C.S.: 524292

DEKRA France S.A.S. (2)
au 11/13 avenue Georges Politzer, BP 152, 78190, Trappes, Cedex, France
Tel.: (33) 1 30 69 52 00
Emp.: 18
Automotive Engineering Consulting Services
N.A.I.C.S.: 541330
Bonnet Kifene (Mgr-Mktg)

DEKRA Industrial (Pty) Ltd. (2)
265 West Ave, Centurion, 163, South Africa
Tel.: (27) 12 663 9413
Security Consulting Services
N.A.I.C.S.: 541690

DEKRA Industrial Oy (2)
Laajaniityntie 3, 01620, Vantaa, Finland
Tel.: (358) 9 878 020
Web Site: http://www.dekra.fi

Testing & Consulting Services
N.A.I.C.S.: 811198
Matti Savolainen *(Mgr-Technical-Metals Laboratory)*

DEKRA Industrial RSA. **(2)**
Vaal Branch Edison Boulevard, Vanderbijl-park, 1900, South Africa
Tel.: (27) 16 981 1160
Web Site: http://www.dekrarsa.com
Emp.: 500
Testing & Consulting Services
N.A.I.C.S.: 811198

DEKRA Industrial s.r.o. **(2)**
Motoristu 77, 530 06, Pardubice, Czech Republic
Tel.: (420) 466 310 354
Web Site: http://www.dekra-industrial.cz
Inspection & Testing Services
N.A.I.C.S.: 926150
Jiri Stastny *(Dir-Operating)*

DEKRA Insight AB **(2)**
Gamlestadsvagen 2, PO Box 13007, 402 51, Gothenburg, Sweden
Tel.: (46) 70 3804579
Security Consulting Services
N.A.I.C.S.: 541690

DEKRA Inspection S.A. **(2)**
18 rue Soukaina Bent El Houcine, Belvedere, 20300, Casablanca, Morocco
Tel.: (212) 5 22 40 19 92
Web Site: http://www.dekra-industrial.ma
Audit & Certification Services
N.A.I.C.S.: 926150

Subsidiary (Domestic):

DEKRA Media GmbH **(2)**
Dahlener Strasse 570, 41239, Monchengladbach, Germany
Tel.: (49) 2166 62198 0
Web Site: http://www.dekra-media.de
Media Support Services
N.A.I.C.S.: 541840

Subsidiary (Non-US):

DEKRA POLSKA Sp. z o.o. **(2)**
ul Rzymowskiego 28, 02-697, Warsaw, Poland
Tel.: (48) 22 577 36 00
Web Site: http://www.dekra.pl
Used Car Dealers
N.A.I.C.S.: 441120
Arnold Olszewski *(Mgr-Used Car)*

DEKRA People B.V. **(2)**
Wognumsebuurt 1, 1817, Alkmaar, Netherlands
Tel.: (31) 72 57 57 704
Claim Processing Services
N.A.I.C.S.: 524292

DEKRA Portugal Expertises-Peritagem Automovel S.A. **(2)**
Avenida Doutor Francisco Sa Carneiro 261 Urbanizacao Quinta De Santo A, Quinta De Santo Antonio 1 Lt 53 Huaedos Irgoeeros Zonr Indostreal Vale, Leiria, 2415644, Portugal
Tel.: (351) 244 820 890
Automotive Engineering Consulting Services
N.A.I.C.S.: 541330

DEKRA Praca Sp. z o.o. **(2)**
ul Puszkarska 9, 30-644, Krakow, Poland
Tel.: (48) 12 442 01 92
Web Site: http://www.dekrapraca.pl
Human Resource Consulting Services
N.A.I.C.S.: 541612

DEKRA Russ O.O.O. **(2)**
Gorokhovskiy Pereulok 12 bld 4, 105064, Moscow, Russia
Tel.: (7) 4956415279
Web Site: http://www.dekrarus.ru
Claim Processing Services
N.A.I.C.S.: 524292
Ramaneset Roseilae *(CEO)*

DEKRA Sertifikasyon A.S. **(2)**
Ekinciler Cad Erturk Sok No 4/5 34810 Kavacik, Beykoz, Istanbul, Turkiye
Tel.: (90) 216 537 07 60
Audit & Certification Services
N.A.I.C.S.: 926150

DEKRA Servicios Recursos Humano S.L. **(2)**
Avda Diagonal n 622 7a planta, 08021, Barcelona, Spain
Tel.: (34) 93 414 54 33
Web Site: http://www.dekra-rrhh.es
Human Resource Consulting Services
N.A.I.C.S.: 541612

DEKRA Solutions B.V. **(2)**
Utrechtseweg 310, 6812, Arnhem, Netherlands
Tel.: (31) 26 356 2025
Audit & Certification Services
N.A.I.C.S.: 926150
Martin de jong *(Mgr-Ops-AIM Svcs)*

DEKRA Solutions Sp. z o.o. **(2)**
ul Chiod na 64, 00-872, Warsaw, Poland
Tel.: (48) 22 654 43 10
Human Resource Training & Consulting Services
N.A.I.C.S.: 541612

DEKRA Test Center S.A. **(2)**
3 rue du Castellas, Paris, France
Tel.: (33) 4 68 42 22 32
Vehicle Inspection Services
N.A.I.C.S.: 811198

DEKRA Testing & Certification spol s r.o. **(2)**
Krizkovskeho 33a, 603 00, Brno, Czech Republic
Tel.: (420) 543 242 886
Web Site: http://www.dekra-certification.com.cz
Audit & Certification Services
N.A.I.C.S.: 926150

DEKRA Testing Services (Zhejiang) Ltd. **(2)**
No 5 Changjiang Road Great Bridge Industrial Park, North Baixiang, Wenzhou, 325603, Zhejiang, China
Tel.: (86) 577 62 86 80 00
Audit & Certification Services
N.A.I.C.S.: 926150

DEKRA Testing and Certification China Ltd. **(2)**
No 48 DongZhiMen Wai Street 23A Beijing, Oriental Kenzo DongCheng, Beijing, China
Tel.: (86) 10 51 39 61 52
Audit & Certification Services
N.A.I.C.S.: 926150
Vicky Zhang *(Project Mgr)*

Subsidiary (Domestic):

DEKRA Testing and Certification GmbH **(2)**
Enderstrasse 92 b, 1277, Dresden, Germany
Tel.: (49) 351 211 814 10
Web Site: http://www.dekra-certification.de
Audit & Certification Services
N.A.I.C.S.: 926150

Subsidiary (Non-US):

DEKRA Vrabotuvanje dooel **(2)**
Mitropolit Teodosij Gologanov 42, 1000, Skopje, North Macedonia
Tel.: (389) 23 23 09 51
Human Resource Consulting Services
N.A.I.C.S.: 541612

DEKRA WIT (Hangzhou) Certification Co. Ltd. **(2)**
Floor 14th International Sunyard No 1750 Jianghong, Avenue Binjiang District, Hangzhou, China
Tel.: (86) 571 87711 500
Web Site: http://www.dekra-wit.com
Audit & Certification Services
N.A.I.C.S.: 926150

DEKRA Zaposljavanje d.o.o. **(2)**
Bulevar Sv Petra Cetinskog 130, 81 000, Podgorica, Montenegro
Tel.: (382) 77 27 22 42
Human Resource Consulting Services
N.A.I.C.S.: 541612

DEKRA Zaposljavanje d.o.o. **(2)**
Bulevar Zorana Dindica 64/A, 11070, Novi Beograd, Serbia
Tel.: (381) 11 2120 454
Web Site: http://www.dekra.rs

Human Resource Consulting Services
N.A.I.C.S.: 541612

DEKRA kvalifikacia a poradenstvo s.r.o. **(2)**
Panonska cesta 47, 851 01, Bratislava, Slovakia
Tel.: (421) 908 818 896
Web Site: http://www.dekraslovakia.sk
Human Resource Consulting Services
N.A.I.C.S.: 541612

DEKRA savjetovanje doo **(2)**
Fra Andela Zvizdovica 1/10 B, 71 000, Sarajevo, Bosnia & Herzegovina
Tel.: (387) 33 29 52 52
Human Resource Consulting Services
N.A.I.C.S.: 541612

DEKRA za privremeno zaposljavanje d.o.o. **(2)**
Horvatova 82/6, 10000, Zagreb, Croatia
Tel.: (385) 1 60 64 420
Web Site: http://www.dekra.hr
Human Resource Consulting Services
N.A.I.C.S.: 541612
Daniele Divjanovic *(Chm)*

DEKRA zaposlitev d.o.o. **(2)**
Smartinska cesta 152, 1000, Ljubljana, Slovenia
Tel.: (386) 1 81 09 038
Web Site: http://www.dekra-zaposlitev.si
Human Resource Consulting Services
N.A.I.C.S.: 541612

DEKRA-Formare Profesionala SRL **(2)**
Str Jiului nr 2A et 1 camera 14 Sector 1, 013219, Bucharest, Romania
Tel.: (40) 722 260 761
Human Resource Consulting Services
N.A.I.C.S.: 541612

Dekra Automotive Solutions Belgium NV **(2)**
Wolfgang-Amadeus Mozartlaan 2, 1620, Drogenbos, Belgium
Tel.: (32) 2 334 01 70
Used Car Dealers
N.A.I.C.S.: 441120

Dekra Claims & Expert Services (Switzerland) SA **(2)**
135 rue de Geneve, 1226, Bern, Switzerland
Tel.: (41) 22 789 14 24
Web Site: http://www.dekra-switzerland.ch
Claim Processing Services
N.A.I.C.S.: 524292

Dekra Expert Ltd **(2)**
Axis 40 Oxford Road, Stokenchurch, HP14 3SX, Buckinghamshire, United Kingdom
Tel.: (44) 800 334 5678
Web Site: http://www.dekra-expert.co.uk
Vehicle Inspection Services
N.A.I.C.S.: 811198

Subsidiary (Domestic):

Deutsches Institut fur Betriebswirtschaft GmbH **(2)**
Wachtersbacher Strasse 83, 60386, Frankfurt am Main, Germany
Tel.: (49) 69 13389485 23
Web Site: http://www.dib.de
Human Resource Training & Consulting Services
N.A.I.C.S.: 541612
Michael Schweitzer *(Mgr-HR Transition)*

Subsidiary (Non-US):

European Road Stars Academy (ERSA) SPRL **(2)**
Rue d Arlon 53 bte 3, 1040, Brussels, Belgium
Tel.: (32) 2 375 22 50
Human Resource Training & Consulting Services
N.A.I.C.S.: 541612

Subsidiary (Domestic):

GKK Gutachterzentrale GmbH **(2)**
Lindemannstrasse 47, 40237, Dusseldorf, Germany
Tel.: (49) 211 68 78 06
Web Site: http://www.gkk.eu

Vehicle Inspection Services
N.A.I.C.S.: 811198

Subsidiary (Non-US):

John Chubb Instrumentation Ltd. **(2)**
Unit 30 Lansdown Industrial Estate, Gloucester Road, Cheltenham, GL51 8PL, United Kingdom
Tel.: (44) 1242 573347
Automotive Accessory Mfr
N.A.I.C.S.: 336390

MERMOZ BASTIE S.C.I. **(2)**
Pa Limoges Sud Orange 19 r, Stuart Mill Cs 70308, 87008, Limoges, France
Tel.: (33) 555584445
Security Consulting Services
N.A.I.C.S.: 541690

PRO - M s.r.o. **(2)**
Na Vybezku 688/11, 190 00, Prague, Czech Republic
Tel.: (420) 284818927
Used Car Dealers
N.A.I.C.S.: 441120

Subsidiary (Domestic):

PRO-LOG IV GmbH **(2)**
Zerrennerstr 30, 75172, Pforzheim, Germany
Tel.: (49) 7231 424790
Human Resource Consulting Services
N.A.I.C.S.: 541612

PRO-LOG Niederrhein GmbH **(2)**
Lohengrinstrasse 3, 47533, Kleve, Germany
Tel.: (49) 28 21 719 34 0
Web Site: http://www.prolog-kleve.de
Human Resource Consulting Services
N.A.I.C.S.: 541612

PRO-LOG Rosenheim GmbH **(2)**
Herzog-Otto-Strasse 6, 83022, Rosenheim, Germany
Tel.: (49) 8031 9012970
Human Resource Consulting Services
N.A.I.C.S.: 541612

PRO-LOG Ruhr GmbH **(2)**
Herner Str 265, 44809, Bochum, Germany
Tel.: (49) 234 610 09 80
Web Site: http://www.pro-log.jobs
Human Resource Consulting Services
N.A.I.C.S.: 541612

Subsidiary (Non-US):

Road Safety Consulting N.V. **(2)**
Aarlenstraat 53, 1040, Brussels, Belgium
Tel.: (32) 2 287 09 11
Web Site: http://www.roadsafetyconsulting.com
Road Transport Support Services
N.A.I.C.S.: 926120

STK - Stanice Technicko Koitroly s.r.o. **(2)**
Fugnerova 404, 336 01, Blovice, Czech Republic
Tel.: (420) 371 522 754
Web Site: http://www.stk-blovice.cz
Vehicle Inspection Services
N.A.I.C.S.: 811198

STK DEKRA Rychnov s.r.o. **(2)**
Pod Budinem 1699 Jestetice, Prague, 516 01, Czech Republic
Tel.: (420) 494 620 226
Automotive Engineering Consulting Services
N.A.I.C.S.: 541330

STK Slavkov s.r.o. **(2)**
Ceskoslovenske armady 217, 684 01, Slavkov u Brna, Czech Republic
Tel.: (420) 544 220 044
Testing & Consulting Services
N.A.I.C.S.: 811198

Subsidiary (US):

Safety Consulting Engineers Inc. **(2)**
2131 Hammond Dr, Schaumburg, IL 60173
Tel.: (847) 925-8100
Security Consulting Services
N.A.I.C.S.: 561612

Subsidiary (Non-US):

TUC AMU Center TUC Midtjylland ApS **(2)**

DEKRA e.V.—(Continued)

Arnborgvej 1B, 6900, Skjern, Denmark
Tel.: (45) 97 36 17 71
Business Support Services
N.A.I.C.S.: 541611

TUC AMU Center TUC SYD A/S (2)
Gamstvej 1a, 6600, Vejen, Denmark
Tel.: (45) 75 55 77 66
Web Site: http://www.tucsyd.dk
Human Resource Training & Consulting Services
N.A.I.C.S.: 541612

TUC DUCAS ApS (2)
Kirkebjorg Parkvoj 7, 2605, Brondby, Denmark
Tel.: (45) 88 33 66 86
Web Site: http://www.ducas.dk
Human Resource Consulting Services
N.A.I.C.S.: 541612

TUC Dansk Vognmandsskole A/S (2)
Logistikparken 5, 8220, Brabrand, Denmark
Tel.: (45) 75 72 47 00
Web Site: http://www.dv-dk.dk
Human Resource Training & Consulting Services
N.A.I.C.S.: 541612

TUC Fyn ApS (2)
Ellestedvej 5a Ellested, 5853, Copenhagen, Denmark
Tel.: (45) 63 33 15 00
Web Site: http://www.tucfyn.dk
Automobile Driving Training Services
N.A.I.C.S.: 611692

TUC Strandens Uddannelses-Center ApS (2)
Industrigrenen 4, 2635, Ishoj, Denmark
Tel.: (45) 43 425 425
Web Site: http://www.stranden.dk
Automobile Driving Training Services
N.A.I.C.S.: 611692

UAB DEKRA Industrial (2)
Taikos pr 7, 31107, Vilnius, Lithuania
Tel.: (370) 386 31608
Web Site: http://www.dekra-industrial.lt
Testing & Consulting Services
N.A.I.C.S.: 811198
Jurij Saburov (Dir Gen)

Subsidiary (Domestic):

UPDOWN Ingenieurtechnik fur Fordertechnik GmbH (2)
Wichmannstrasse 4 Haus 1, 22607, Hamburg, Germany
Tel.: (49) 40 85 17 73 0
Web Site: http://www.updown-ingenieure.de
Engineering Consulting Services
N.A.I.C.S.: 541330
Swang Reuter (Mng Dir)

Subsidiary (Non-US):

Vehicle Testing New Zealand Ltd. (2)
Level 5 15 Willeston Street, Wellington, 6011, New Zealand
Tel.: (64) 4 495 2500
Web Site: http://www.vtnz.co.nz
Emp.: 5
Testing & Consulting Services
N.A.I.C.S.: 811198
Mike Walsh (Exec VP)

Vianorm B.V. (2)
Structuurbaan 19, Postbus 1476, 3439 MA, Nieuwegein, Netherlands
Tel.: (31) 30 608 7970
Audit & Certification Services
N.A.I.C.S.: 926150

Subsidiary (Domestic):

Werkstoffprufung Peters GmbH (2)
Mausegatt 12, 47228, Duisburg, Germany
Tel.: (49) 2065 99 74 0
Human Resource Consulting Services
N.A.I.C.S.: 541612

DEKRA Sjaelland A/S (1)
Bassinbuen 2, Naestved, Denmark
Tel.: (45) 70606500
Web Site: http://www.dekra-sjaelland.dk
Transport Training Services

N.A.I.C.S.: 611692

DEKRA Slovensko s.r.o. (1)
Panonska cesta 47, Petrzalka, 851 04, Bratislava, Slovakia
Tel.: (421) 264288096
Web Site: http://www.dekra.sk
Automotive Inspection Services
N.A.I.C.S.: 811198

DEKRA Sydjylland A/S (1)
Arnfredsvej 8, 6600, Vejen, Denmark
Tel.: (45) 70606500
Web Site: http://www.dekra-sydjylland.dk
Transport Training Services
N.A.I.C.S.: 611692

DEKRA Testing & Certification (Shanghai) Ltd. (1)
Room 2901 Building C Xintian Century Business Center, North of Shixia Second Street Futian District, Shenzhen, 518017, Guangdong, China
Tel.: (86) 75583257286
Web Site: http://www
Automotive Inspection Services
N.A.I.C.S.: 811198

DEKRA Testing & Certification (Suzhou) Co., Ltd. (1)
No 99 Hongye Road, Suzhou Industrial Park, Suzhou, 310052, Jiangsu, China
Tel.: (86) 51262515088
Automotive Inspection Services
N.A.I.C.S.: 811198

DEKRA Testing & Certification Co., Ltd. (1)
No 6 Ln 75 Wenlin St, Linkou Dist, New Taipei City, 244017, Taiwan
Tel.: (886) 226026888
Web Site: http://www.dekra.com.tw
Automotive Inspection Services
N.A.I.C.S.: 811198

DEKRA Testing & Certification Ltda. (1)
Rosario Sur 91 9th Floor, Las Condes, Santiago, Chile
Tel.: (56) 225778009
Automotive Inspection Services
N.A.I.C.S.: 811198

DEKRA Testing & Certification, S.A.U (1)
Parque Tecnologico de Andalucia C/ Severo Ochoa 2, 29590, Malaga, Spain
Tel.: (34) 952619100
Automotive Inspection Services
N.A.I.C.S.: 811198

DEKRA UK Ltd. (1)
Phi House Enterprise Road Southampton Science Park, Southampton, SO16 7NS, United Kingdom
Tel.: (44) 2380760722
Web Site: http://www.dekra-uk.co.uk
Automotive Inspection Services
N.A.I.C.S.: 811198

DEKRA Visatec GmbH (1)
Gewerbepark 7, 87477, Sulzberg, Germany
Tel.: (49) 8376921527
Web Site: http://www.dekra-visatec.com
Inspection Camera Mfr
N.A.I.C.S.: 333310

DEKRA Zaposljavanje d.o.o. (1)
Fra Andela Zvizdovica 1, 71 000, Sarajevo, Bosnia & Herzegovina
Tel.: (387) 33295253
Web Site: http://www.dekra-zapo.ba
Management Consulting Services
N.A.I.C.S.: 541618

DEKRA agencija d.o.o. (1)
Fra Andela Zvizdovica 1, 71 000, Sarajevo, Bosnia & Herzegovina
Tel.: (387) 33295252
Management Consulting Services
N.A.I.C.S.: 541611

DEKRA iST Reliability Services Inc. (1)
No 22 Puding Rd, East Dist, Hsinchu, 300047, Taiwan
Tel.: (886) 35795766
Automotive Inspection Services
N.A.I.C.S.: 811198

DEKRA iST Reliability Services Limited (1)

No 351 Kunjia Road, Kunshan, 215300, Jiangsu, China
Tel.: (86) 51257639600
Automotive Inspection Services
N.A.I.C.S.: 811198

Juan A. Calzado S.A.R.L. (1)
196 Residence AlKhansaa 2eme etage Appt 19, Mers Sultan, Casablanca, 20000, Morocco
Tel.: (212) 522 44 69 03
Claim Processing Services
N.A.I.C.S.: 524292

QC Plzen s.r.o. (1)
Teslova 1239/5 B1, 301 00, Plzen, Czech Republic
Tel.: (420) 3774206356
Web Site: http://www.qcp.cz
Educational Support Services
N.A.I.C.S.: 611710

Regulatory Consultants, Inc. (1)
10433 Montgomery Pkwy NE Ste 100, Albuquerque, NM 87111
Tel.: (505) 944-0058
Web Site: http://www.regconinc.com
Investment Banking & Financial Services
N.A.I.C.S.: 523150
Ron Demaray (CEO)

DEKRO PAINTS (PTY) LTD
24 Fabriek Street, Kuils River, 7580, Cape Town, South Africa
Tel.: (27) 210008609 ZA
Web Site: http://www.dekro.co.za
Sales Range: $25-49.9 Million
Emp.: 65
Paint & Resin Mfr & Distr
N.A.I.C.S.: 325510
Greg Meaker (Mng Dir)

DEKSON CASTINGS LIMITED
Plot No E-21 MIDC Chikhalthana, Aurangabad, 431 210, India
Tel.: (91) 2406617716
Web Site: http://www.dekson.co.in
Year Founded: 1993
Aluminum Casting Services
N.A.I.C.S.: 331523
Vikram Ashok Dekate (Chm & Mng Dir)

DEL GAUDIO
10 Ave De Bourgogne 94184, Rungis, Cedex, France
Tel.: (33) 146876561
Web Site: http://www.delgaudiofr.com
Rev.: $22,200,000
Emp.: 17
Fresh Fruits & Vegetables
N.A.I.C.S.: 424480
Sweet Pandae (Mng Dir)

DELAGRAVE SA
8 rue Sainte Claire Deville, 77185, Lognes, France
Tel.: (33) 1 60 37 51 51
Web Site: http://www.delagrave.fr
Wood Office Furniture Mfr & Distr
N.A.I.C.S.: 337211

DELANCE LIMITED
Leningradskoye shosse 21, 141410, Khimki, Moscow, Russia
Tel.: (7) 495 785 1978 CY
Web Site: http://www.rolf.ru
Year Founded: 2004
Sales Range: $1-4.9 Billion
Emp.: 5,500
Holding Company; Motor Vehicle Sales & Related Services
N.A.I.C.S.: 551112
Igor Salita (CEO)

Subsidiaries:

ROLF LLC (1)
21 Leningradskoe Shosse, 141410, Khimki, Russia
Tel.: (7) 4957851978
Web Site: http://www.rolf.ru

New & Used Car Dealerships Operator
N.A.I.C.S.: 441110

DELANCEY REAL ESTATE ASSET MANAGEMENT LTD.
Lansdowne House Berkeley Square, London, W1J 6ER, United Kingdom
Tel.: (44) 20 7448 1448
Web Site: http://www.delancey.com
Year Founded: 2003
Sales Range: $25-49.9 Million
Emp.: 45
Real Estate Investment Services
N.A.I.C.S.: 523999
Paul Goswell (Mng Dir)

Subsidiaries:

Minerva Ltd. (1)
42 Wigmore Street, London, W1U 2RY, United Kingdom
Tel.: (44) 2075351000
Web Site: http://www.minervaproperty.com
Real Estate Investment & Development Services
N.A.I.C.S.: 531390
Ivan Ezekiel (Co-CEO)

DELATTRE LEVIVIER MAROC
KM 9 Route de Rabat Ain Sebaa, 20250, Casablanca, Morocco
Tel.: (212) 5 22 66 96 00
Web Site: http://www.dlm.ma
Year Founded: 1950
DLM—(CAS)
Sales Range: $25-49.9 Million
Emp.: 1,400
Steel Pipe & Tube Mfr
N.A.I.C.S.: 331210
Mustapha Bouzit (Mgr-Quality & Safety)

DELAVACO RESIDENTIAL PROPERTIES CORP.
The Exchange Tower 130 King Street West Suite 2210, Toronto, M5X 1A9, ON, Canada
Tel.: (416) 362-4441
Web Site: http://www.delavacoproperties.com
DVO—(OTCIQ)
Real Estate Investment Services
N.A.I.C.S.: 523999
Michael Galloro (CFO)

DELAWARE THIRTEEN LTD.
Level 12 225 George Street, Sydney, 2000, NSW, Australia
Tel.: (61) 0894894890
Web Site: http://www.department13.com
Year Founded: 2010
Communication Service
N.A.I.C.S.: 517810
Jonathan Hunter (Mng Dir-Americas)

DELEGAT'S GROUP LIMITED
Tel.: (64) 93597300
DGL—(NZX)
Rev.: $228,135,167
Assets: $635,949,163
Liabilities: $310,129,187
Net Worth: $325,819,976
Earnings: $38,770,933
Emp.: 468
Fiscal Year-end: 06/30/23
Wine Producer & Distr
N.A.I.C.S.: 312130
Jakov Nikola Delegat (Chm)

Subsidiaries:

Delegat (1)
4th Fl Kenilworth House 79/80 Margaret St, London, W1W 8TA, United Kingdom
Tel.: (44) 2031307050
Web Site: http://www.delegats.co.uk
Emp.: 8
Wine Mfr
N.A.I.C.S.: 312130

Delegat Limited (1)
Level 31 15 Customs Street West, PO Box 91681, 1142, Auckland, New Zealand
Tel.: (64) 93597300
Web Site: http://www.delegatsgroup.co.nz
Sales Range: $1-9.9 Million
Grapes Production & Vineyard Services
N.A.I.C.S.: 115112
Jakov Delegat (Mng Dir)

Delegat Limited (1)
Level 31 15 Customs Street West, Auckland, 1010, New Zealand
Tel.: (64) 9 359 7300
Web Site: https://www.delegat.com
Wine Distr
N.A.I.C.S.: 424820
Steven Carden (Mng Dir)

Oyster Bay Wines Australia Pty Limited (1)
5G /12 Lord Street Botany, Mascot, Sydney, 2019, NSW, Australia
Tel.: (61) 293179800
Web Site: http://www.oysterbaywines.com
Sales Range: $25-49.9 Million
Emp.: 20
Wine Distr
N.A.I.C.S.: 424820
John Freeman (Gen Mgr)

Oyster Bay Wines USA, Inc (1)
Ste 9-G The Soho Bldg 110 Greene St, New York, NY 10012
Tel.: (877) 613-9858
Web Site: http://www.oysterbaywines.com
Emp.: 10
Grape Wine Mfr
N.A.I.C.S.: 312130

DELEK GROUP LTD.
19 Abba Eban Blvd, POB 2054, Herzliyya, 4612001, Israel
Tel.: (972) 98638444
Web Site: https://ir.delek-group.com
Year Founded: 1951
DLKGF—(OTCIQ)
Rev.: $3,343,094,192
Assets: $11,886,828,263
Liabilities: $7,837,427,471
Net Worth: $4,049,400,792
Earnings: $646,114,636
Emp.: 23
Fiscal Year-end: 12/31/23
Holding Company
N.A.I.C.S.: 551112
Gabriel Last (Chm)

Subsidiaries:

Cohen Development Gas & Oil Ltd (1)
Giboreyi Isra'el 7, Netanya, 4250407, Israel
Tel.: (972) 733208860
Rev.: $26,468,000
Assets: $34,218,000
Liabilities: $5,443,000
Net Worth: $28,775,000
Earnings: $22,084,000
Emp.: 1
Fiscal Year-end: 12/31/2023
Support Activities for Oil & Gas Operations
N.A.I.C.S.: 213112
Tgar Swarye (Chm)

Delek Benelux BV (1)
Princenhagelaan 9, 4813 DA, Breda, Netherlands
Tel.: (31) 76 523 94 50
Fuel Station Operating Services
N.A.I.C.S.: 457210
Boaz Chechik (CEO)

Delek France BV (1)
Princenhagelaan 9, 4813 DA, Breda, Netherlands
Tel.: (31) 76 523 94 50
Sales Range: $50-74.9 Million
Emp.: 117
Fuel Station Operating Services
N.A.I.C.S.: 457210
Kobi Shmerler (Chief Strategy Officer)

Delek Investments & Properties Ltd. (1)
7 Giborei Israel St, PO Box 8464, Netanya, 42504, Israel

Tel.: (972) 98638444
Web Site: http://www.delek-group.com
Sales Range: $75-99.9 Million
Emp.: 70
Fuel Dealers & Investments
N.A.I.C.S.: 523999
Asaf Joseph Bartfeld (Mng Dir)

Subsidiary (Domestic):

Delek Automotive Systems, Ltd. (2)
PO Box 200, Nir Tzvi, 72905, Israel
Tel.: (972) 8913999
Web Site: https://delek-motors.co.il
Rev.: $1,603,607,379
Assets: $2,820,947,324
Liabilities: $2,097,108,408
Net Worth: $723,838,917
Earnings: $72,248,928
Emp.: 368
Fiscal Year-end: 12/31/2023
Automobile & Other Motor Vehicle Merchant Wholesalers
N.A.I.C.S.: 423110
Avinoam Finkelman (Chm)

Subsidiary (Domestic):

Delek Motors Ltd. (3)
PO Box 200, Nir Tzvi, 72905, Israel
Tel.: (972) 89139999
Web Site: http://www.delekmotors.co.il
Sales Range: $50-74.9 Million
Emp.: 150
Automobile Importer
N.A.I.C.S.: 423110
Shahar Shemesh (CEO)

Subsidiary (Domestic):

Delek Capital Ltd. (2)
7 Giborei Israel Street, PO Box 8464, Netanya, 42504, Israel
Tel.: (972) 98638444
International Financial Services
N.A.I.C.S.: 523999
Danny Guttman (CEO)

Holding (Domestic):

The Phoenix Holdings Ltd. (3)
Derech HaShalom 53, Givatayim, Israel (52.3%)
Tel.: (972) 37332997
Web Site: https://www.fnx.co.il
Rev.: $6,409,790,057
Assets: $43,512,104,707
Liabilities: $40,545,387,493
Net Worth: $2,966,717,214
Earnings: $240,968,345
Emp.: 4,938
Fiscal Year-end: 12/31/2023
Holding Company
N.A.I.C.S.: 551112
Benjamin Gabbay (Chm)

Subsidiary (Domestic):

Excellence Investments Ltd. (4)
25 Efal St, Petah Tiqwa, 4951125, Israel
Tel.: (972) 37532000
Web Site: http://www.xnes.co.il
Sales Range: $125-149.9 Million
Emp.: 585
Financial Investment Services
N.A.I.C.S.: 523999
Tzvika Beck (VP)

The Phoenix Insurance Company Ltd. (4)
53 Derech Hashalom, Givatayim, 53454, Israel
Tel.: (972) 3 733 2222
Web Site: http://www.fnx.co.il
Insurance
N.A.I.C.S.: 524113

Holding (US):

The Republic Group (3)
4455 LBJ Fwy Ste 700, Dallas, TX 75244
Tel.: (972) 788-6001
Web Site: http://www.republicgroup.com
Sales Range: $250-299.9 Million
Emp.: 320
Insurance Services
N.A.I.C.S.: 524126
Kelly Alexander (CIO & VP)

Subsidiary (Domestic):

Delek Infrastructures Ltd. (2)

14 Shenkar St, Herzliya Pituach, 46733, Israel
Tel.: (972) 99712424
Sales Range: $50-74.9 Million
Emp.: 4
Electricity Generation, IPP Power Stations, Water Desalination & Sewage Treatment
N.A.I.C.S.: 213112
Gabriel Last (Chm)

Gadot Biochemical Industries Ltd. (2)
117 Hahistadrut Ave, PO Box 10636, 2629213, Haifa Bay, Israel
Tel.: (972) 48461555
Web Site: http://www.gadotbio.com
Sales Range: $125-149.9 Million
Food Ingredients & Fine Chemicals
N.A.I.C.S.: 325998
Nissim Guigi (CTO)

Subsidiary (Non-US):

Gadot Bio-Chem (Europe) B.V. (3)
Hoefsmidstraat 41, Hoogvliet, 3194 AA, Netherlands
Tel.: (31) 10 296 1090
Web Site: http://www.gadotbio.com
Food Ingredients & Fine Chemicals
N.A.I.C.S.: 325998

Delek Petroleum Ltd. (1)
7 Giborei Israel St, PO Box 8464, South Industrial Area, Netanya, 42504, Israel
Tel.: (972) 98638598
Web Site: http://www.delek.co.il
Sales Range: $300-349.9 Million
Emp.: 550
Refined Oil Products & Lubricants Sales
N.A.I.C.S.: 424720
Gabriel Last (Chm)

Subsidiary (Domestic):

Delek Europe Holdings Ltd. (2)
Bet Adar Building 7 Giborei Israel Street, Netanya, 42504, Israel
Tel.: (972) 98638680
Investment Management Service
N.A.I.C.S.: 523999

Delek The Israel Fuel Corporation Ltd. (2)
Bet Adar Building 7 Giborei Israel St, PO Box 8464, Netanya, 42504, Israel
Tel.: (972) 98638531
Web Site: http://www.delek-group.com
Sales Range: $1-4.9 Billion
Emp.: 200
Fuel Sales
N.A.I.C.S.: 457210
Avi Ben Assayag (CEO)

Affiliate (US):

Delek US Holdings, Inc. (2)
310 7 Springs Way Ste 400 and 500, Brentwood, TN 37027
Tel.: (615) 771-6701
Web Site: https://www.delekus.com
Rev.: $16,917,400,000
Assets: $7,171,800,000
Liabilities: $6,212,100,000
Net Worth: $959,700,000
Earnings: $19,800,000
Emp.: 3,591
Fiscal Year-end: 12/31/2023
Holding Company; Petroleum Refining, Marketing & Supply & Convenience Stores
N.A.I.C.S.: 551112
Ezra Uzi Yemin (Exec Chm)

Subsidiary (Domestic):

Alon USA Energy, Inc. (3)
12700 Park Central Dr Ste 1600, Dallas, TX 75251 (100%)
Tel.: (972) 367-3600
Web Site: http://www.alonusa.com
Sales Range: $1-4.9 Billion
Oil & Gas Refining; Marketing Services
N.A.I.C.S.: 324110

Subsidiary (Domestic):

Alon Assets, Inc. (4)
12700 Park Central Dr Ste 1600, Dallas, TX 75251
Tel.: (972) 367-3600
Asset Management Services
N.A.I.C.S.: 541618

Alon Brands, Inc. (4)
Park Central III Ste 1600 12700 Park Central Dr, Dallas, TX 75251
Tel.: (800) 969-3462
Web Site: http://www.alonbrands.com
Oil Refiner
N.A.I.C.S.: 324110
Judge A. Dobrient (Sr VP-Branded Wholesale Mktg)

Alon Refining Krotz Springs, Inc. (4)
12700 Park Central Dr Ste 1600, Dallas, TX 75251-7030
Tel.: (972) 367-3600
Sales Range: $1-9.9 Million
Crude Oil Refining Services
N.A.I.C.S.: 211120

Alon USA Partners, LP (4)
12700 Park Central Dr Ste 1600, Dallas, TX 75251 (100%)
Tel.: (972) 367-3600
Web Site: http://www.alonpartners.com
Sales Range: $1-4.9 Billion
Petroleum Products Refineries
N.A.I.C.S.: 324110
David Wiessman (Chm)

Wright Asphalt Products Company LLC (4)
11931 Wickchester Ste 101, Houston, TX 77043
Tel.: (281) 452-9084
Web Site: http://www.wrightasphalt.com
Asphalt Product Research & Development Services
N.A.I.C.S.: 541715

Subsidiary (Domestic):

Delek Crude Logistics, LLC (3)
425 Mcmurrey Dr, Tyler, TX 75702
Tel.: (615) 435-1402
Petroleum Product Transportation Services
N.A.I.C.S.: 486910

Delek Finance, Inc. (3)
7102 Commerce Way, Brentwood, TN 37027
Tel.: (615) 771-6701
Web Site: http://www.delekus.com
Emp.: 200
Financial Management Services
N.A.I.C.S.: 541611

Delek Logistics Partners, LP (3)
310 7 Springs Way Ste 500, Brentwood, TN 37027 (60.4%)
Tel.: (615) 771-6701
Web Site: https://www.deleklogistics.com
Rev.: $1,020,409,000
Assets: $1,642,246,000
Liabilities: $1,804,115,000
Net Worth: ($161,869,000)
Earnings: $126,236,000
Fiscal Year-end: 12/31/2023
Crude Petroleum Logistics
N.A.I.C.S.: 486110
Ezra Uzi Yemin (Exec Chm)

Division (Domestic):

Delek Marketing & Supply, Inc. (3)
7102 Commerce Way, Brentwood, TN 37027
Tel.: (615) 771-6701
Web Site: http://www.delekus.com
Fuel Sales
N.A.I.C.S.: 457210

Subsidiary (Domestic):

Delek Marketing & Supply, LP (3)
4008 N US Hwy 67, San Angelo, TX 76905
Tel.: (325) 655-2123
Petroleum Product Transportation Services
N.A.I.C.S.: 486910

Delek Marketing-Big Sandy, LLC (3)
Attn Vanessa Goodspeed 425 Mcmurrey Dr, Tyler, TX 75702
Tel.: (903) 579-3428
Petroleum Product Whslr
N.A.I.C.S.: 424720

Division (Domestic):

Delek Refining, Inc. (3)
7102 Commerce Way, Brentwood, TN 37027
Tel.: (615) 771-6701

Delek Group Ltd.—(Continued)

Sales Range: $125-149.9 Million
Emp.: 271
Fuel Refining Operations
N.A.I.C.S.: 324110
Frederec C. Green (Pres & COO)

Subsidiary (Domestic):

Delek Refining, Ltd. (4)
425 Mcmurrey Dr, Tyler, TX 75702-6326
Tel.: (903) 579-3400
Oil & Gas Refinery Operator
N.A.I.C.S.: 324110
Fred Green (Pres & COO)

Subsidiary (Domestic):

Delek Renewables, LLC (3)
3102 Windmill Rd, Joshua, TX 76058
Tel.: (817) 558-9255
Biodiesel Refinery Operator
N.A.I.C.S.: 324110

Lion Oil Company (3)
1000 McHenry, El Dorado, AR
71730 (100%)
Tel.: (870) 862-8111
Web Site: https://www.lionoil.com
Refiner of Petroleum & Marketer of Petroleum & Petroleum Products
N.A.I.C.S.: 324110

Subsidiary (Domestic):

J. Christy Construction Co., Inc. (4)
1333 Robert E Lee St, El Dorado, AR
71730-6935
Tel.: (870) 862-9348
Rev.: $6,300,000
Emp.: 177
Industrial Buildings & Warehouses
N.A.I.C.S.: 236220
Mark Boggs (Office Mgr)

Lion Oil Trading & Transportation, LLC (4)
1001 School St, El Dorado, AR 71730
Tel.: (870) 864-1280
Sales Range: $25-49.9 Million
Emp.: 80
Petroleum Product Transportation Services
N.A.I.C.S.: 486910
Lydia Smith (Div Mgr-Acctg-Order & Crude Oil)

Subsidiary (Domestic):

Paline Pipeline Company, LLC (3)
7636 US Hwy 190, Jasper, TX 75951
Tel.: (409) 331-0611
Petroleum Pipeline Transportation Services
N.A.I.C.S.: 486910

Delek Pi Glilot - Limited Partnership (1)
Neft St Northern Industrial Zone, PO Box
292, Ashdod, 77102, Israel
Tel.: (972) 8 8513200
Web Site: http://www.delek.co.il
Emp.: 43
Fuel Extraction Storage & Distr
N.A.I.C.S.: 324199
Moshe Karadi (CEO)

Delek Transportation Ltd. (1)
Neft Street, PO Box 12018, Ashdod, 31600,
Israel
Tel.: (972) 8 8534462
Sales Range: $25-49.9 Million
Emp.: 7
Fuel Transportation Services
N.A.I.C.S.: 488999
Yehuda Ochayon (Gen Mgr)

Ithaca Energy Inc. (1)
8 Rubislaw Terrace, Aberdeen, AB10 1XE,
United Kingdom (100%)
Tel.: (44) 1224 638 582
Web Site: http://www.ithacaenergy.com
Sales Range: $125-149.9 Million
Oil & Gas Exploration
N.A.I.C.S.: 213111
Graham Forbes (CFO)

Subsidiary (Domestic):

Ithaca Energy (UK) Limited (2)
Hill of Rubislaw, Aberdeen, AB15 6XL,
United Kingdom (100%)

Tel.: (44) 1224334000
Oil & Gas Exploration Services
N.A.I.C.S.: 213112

Subsidiary (Domestic):

Chevron North Sea Limited (3)
Chevron House Hill of Rubislaw, Aberdeen,
AB15 6XL, United Kingdom
Tel.: (44) 1224334000
Crude Oil & Natural Gas Extraction Services
N.A.I.C.S.: 211120

DELEUM BERHAD
No 2 Jalan Bangsar Utama 9 Bangsar Utama, 59000, Kuala Lumpur,
Malaysia
Tel.: (60) 322957788
Web Site: https://www.deleum.com
DELEUM—(KLS)
Rev.: $147,735,206
Assets: $151,072,082
Liabilities: $63,337,463
Net Worth: $87,734,618
Earnings: $10,844,759
Emp.: 592
Fiscal Year-end: 12/31/22
Oil & Gas Exploration Services
N.A.I.C.S.: 211120
Jayanthi Gunaratnam (CFO-Grp)

Subsidiaries:

Delcom Oilfield Services Sdn. Bhd. (1)
2 Jalan Bangsar Utama 9 Bangsar Utama,
59000, Kuala Lumpur, Malaysia
Tel.: (60) 322957788
Web Site: http://www.deleum.com
Emp.: 150
Oil & Gas Field Engineering Services
N.A.I.C.S.: 213112
Dato Izham (Dir)

Deleum Primera Sdn. Bhd. (1)
No 1-2 Jalan Tasik Utama 8 Medan Niaga
Tasik Damai, Sungai Besi, 57100, Kuala
Lumpur, Malaysia
Tel.: (60) 390544441
Machinery & Oilfield Services
N.A.I.C.S.: 333132

Deleum Rotary Services Sdn. Bhd. (1)
No 3 Jalan P4/8 Seksyen 4 Bandar
Teknologi Kajang, 43500, Kajang, Selangor,
Malaysia
Tel.: (60) 387237070
Machinery & Oilfield Services
N.A.I.C.S.: 333132
Mohd Qayyum (Mgr-Sls)

Deleum Technology Solutions Sdn. Bhd. (1)
Lot PT 8777 Telok Kalong Industrial Area,
24000, Kemaman, Terengganu, Malaysia
Tel.: (60) 98626666
Oil & Gas Industry Inspection Services
N.A.I.C.S.: 213112

Penaga Dresser Sdn. Bhd. (1)
Business Suite 19A-9-1 Level 9 UOA Centre No 19 Jalan Pinang, 50450, Kuala Lumpur, Malaysia
Tel.: (60) 321632322
Web Site: http://www.penagadresser.com
Sales Range: $25-49.9 Million
Emp.: 40
Ball & Safety Valves Distr
N.A.I.C.S.: 423840

Turboservices Sdn. Bhd. (1)
No 2 Jalan Bangsar Utama 9, 59000, Kuala
Lumpur, Malaysia (90%)
Tel.: (60) 322957788
Web Site: https://www.deleum.com
Sales Range: $25-49.9 Million
Emp.: 200
Turbine Engines, Turbine Powered Natural-
Gas Compressor Sets, Generator Sets &
Mechanical-Drive Packages Mfr
N.A.I.C.S.: 333611

DELFI LIMITED
TripleOne Somerset 111 Somerset

Road 1612, Singapore, 238164, Singapore
Tel.: (65) 64775600
Web Site:
https://www.delfilimited.com
P34—(SES)
Rev.: $538,153,000
Assets: $420,944,000
Liabilities: $154,724,000
Net Worth: $266,220,000
Earnings: $46,255,000
Emp.: 2,706
Fiscal Year-end: 12/31/23
Chocolate & Confectionery Mfr
N.A.I.C.S.: 311351
John Tiong Choon Chuang (CEO-Grp)

Subsidiaries:

Delfi Marketing Sdn. Bhd. (1)
Level 6 Block A Sky Park One City Jalan
USJ 25/1, 47650, Subang Jaya, Selangor,
Malaysia
Tel.: (60) 351233300
Web Site:
https://www.delfimarketing.com.my
Consumer & Pharmaceutical Product Distr
N.A.I.C.S.: 424210
Pauline Chin (Brand Mgr)

DELFINGEN INDUSTRY, S.A.
Rue Emile Streit, 25340, Anteuil,
France
Tel.: (33) 381907300
Web Site: https://www.delfingen.com
Year Founded: 1954
ALDEL—(EUR)
Rev.: $445,289,900
Assets: $376,173,485
Liabilities: $220,797,226
Net Worth: $155,376,260
Earnings: $8,815,342
Emp.: 3,934
Fiscal Year-end: 12/31/22
Automotive Suppliers
N.A.I.C.S.: 441330
Bernard Streit (Chm)

Subsidiaries:

Delfingen Automotive parts (Wuhan) Co., Ltd. (1)
No 9 Jinghe road, Dongxihu district,
430047, Wuhan, China
Tel.: (86) 27 8323 2647
Motor Vehicle Parts Distr
N.A.I.C.S.: 423120
Xia Su (Gen Mgr)

Delfingen BR-Sao Paulo Ltda (1)
Avenida Independencia 1544, Bairro do
Eden, Sorocaba, 18087101, Brazil
Tel.: (55) 15 3238 1510
Web Site: http://www.delfingen.com
Motor Vehicle Parts Distr
N.A.I.C.S.: 423120
Andrea Costa (Gen Dir)

Delfingen India Private Limited (1)
S No 2 Vadgaon Sheri Mahavir Nagar,
Pune, 411 014, Maharashtra, India
Tel.: (91) 20270 30520
Motor Vehicle Parts Distr
N.A.I.C.S.: 423120

Delfingen MA-Casablanca Sarl (1)
Complexe Ind Sous traitance Somaca KM
12 autoroute de Rabat, Casablanca, Morocco
Tel.: (212) 522 76 67 74
Motor Vehicle Parts Distr
N.A.I.C.S.: 423120

Delfingen MA-Tanger Sarl (1)
Lot 29 Local no 3 Zone Franche d exportation de Tanger, Tangiers, Morocco
Tel.: (212) 539 39 39 06
Motor Vehicle Parts Distr
N.A.I.C.S.: 423120

Delfingen MX-Coahuila SRL (1)
Av Industria Metalurgica 1024 parque industrial saltillo ramos arizpe, 25900, Coahuila, Mexico
Tel.: (52) 488 64 95

Motor Vehicle Parts Distr
N.A.I.C.S.: 423120

Delfingen PH-Filipinas, Inc (1)
Lot 3 Block 2 Phase II Peza Compound
FCIE, Barangay Langkaan Dasmarinas,
4114, Manila, Philippines
Tel.: (63) 46 402 2362
Motor Vehicle Parts Distr
N.A.I.C.S.: 423120

Delfingen PT-Porto S.A. (1)
Alameda da Bela Vista 99, Lugar Seixezelo,
4415-939, Vila Nova de Gaia, Portugal
Tel.: (351) 227 634 025
Motor Vehicle Parts Distr
N.A.I.C.S.: 423120
Manuel Sosa (Mgr-Client)

Delfingen RO-Transilvania S.r.l (1)
STR 1 NR5 Zona insutriala N V, Arad, Romania
Tel.: (40) 257 227 363
Motor Vehicle Parts Distr
N.A.I.C.S.: 423120
Gabriela Cristina Zagrean (Mgr-Logistic)

Delfingen RO-Valahia S.r.l (1)
Zona Industriala Dibo Hala NR 6-16 17,
107086, Negoiesti, Romania
Tel.: (40) 244 481 076
Motor Vehicle Parts Distr
N.A.I.C.S.: 423120

Delfingen SK-Nitra S.r.o. (1)
Tovarenska 58, 953 01, Zlate Moravce,
Slovakia
Tel.: (421) 137 69 241 22
Motor Vehicle Parts Distr
N.A.I.C.S.: 423120

Delfingen TN-Tunis (1)
13 Avenue de l environnement Borj Cedria,
Bir El Bey, 2055, Hammam, Tunisia
Tel.: (216) 71 410 770
Motor Vehicle Parts Distr
N.A.I.C.S.: 423120
Ala Rouabeh (Mgr-Quality & Environment)

Delfingen TR-Marmara Plastik San. Ve Dis Tic. Ltd. Sti. (1)
Osman Yilmaz mah E 5 Yanyol, 41400,
Gebze, 41400, Kocaeli, Turkiye
Tel.: (90) 262 643 92 26
Web Site: http://www.delfingen.com
Emp.: 20
Motor Vehicle Parts Distr
N.A.I.C.S.: 423120
Alter Kandimir (Gen Mgr)

Delfingen US, Inc (1)
3985 W Hamil Rd, Rochester, MI 48309
Tel.: (248) 519-0534
Web Site: http://www.delfingen.com
Sales Range: $25-49.9 Million
Emp.: 20
All Other Plastics Product Mfr
N.A.I.C.S.: 326199
Bernard Streit (Pres)

Subsidiary (Non-US):

Delfingen HN-Cortes (2)
Edificio 35 ZIP Bufalo, Villanueva, Honduras
Tel.: (504) 574 9150
Motor Vehicle Parts Distr
N.A.I.C.S.: 423120

Subsidiary (Domestic):

Delfingen US-New York, Inc. (2)
2221 Niagara Falls Blvd Ste 12, Niagara
Falls, NY 14304
Tel.: (716) 215-0300
Web Site: http://www.delfingen.com
Sales Range: $25-49.9 Million
All Other Miscellaneous Electrical Equipment & Component Mfr
N.A.I.C.S.: 335999
Diana Bollinger (Mgr-HR)

Delfingen US-Texas LP (1)
12270 Rojas Dr Ste 300, El Paso, TX
79936-7713
Tel.: (915) 858-5577
Web Site: http://www.delfingen.com
Motor Vehicle Parts Distr
N.A.I.C.S.: 423120
Silvia Escobedo (Engr-Quality)

Hilec, LLC (1)
11 Railroad Ave, Arcade, NY 14009
Tel.: (585) 492-2212
Web Site: http://www.hilec.com
Sales Range: $25-49.9 Million
Emp.: 40
Electrical Apparatus & Equipment, Wiring
Supplies & Related Equipment Merchant
Whslr
N.A.I.C.S.: 423610

**DELFONT MACKINTOSH THE-
ATRES LIMITED**
Novello Theatre, London, WC2B 4LD,
United Kingdom
Tel.: (44) 2073794431
Web Site:
  http://www.delfontmackintosh.co.uk
Year Founded: 1991
Sales Range: $25-49.9 Million
Emp.: 120
Theatre Owners
N.A.I.C.S.: 561311

DELFORTGROUP AG
Fabrikstrasse 20, 4050, Traun, Aus-
tria
Tel.: (43) 7229 776 0   AT
Web Site:
  http://www.delfortgroup.com
Sales Range: $500-549.9 Million
Emp.: 1,750
Holding Company; Specialty Papers
Developer, Mfr & Distr
N.A.I.C.S.: 551112
Martin Zahlbruckner (CEO)

Subsidiaries:

Dr. Franz Feurstein GmbH (1)
Fabrikstrasse 20, Traun, 4050, Austria
Tel.: (43) 7229 776 0
Web Site: http://www.delfortgroup.com
Sales Range: $50-74.9 Million
Emp.: 300
Specialty Paper Mill
N.A.I.C.S.: 322120
Jurgen Scheiblehner (Mgr-Sls)

Dunafin Kft. (1)
Papirgyari ut 42-46, 2400, Dunaujvaros,
Hungary
Tel.: (36) 25 511 400
Specialty Paper Mill
N.A.I.C.S.: 322120

OP Papirna, s.r.o. (1)
Olsany 18, 78962, Olsany, Czech Republic
Tel.: (420) 583 384 501
Specialty Paper Mill
N.A.I.C.S.: 322120

Papierfabrik Wattens GmbH & Co.
KG (1)
Ludwig-Lassl-Strasse 15, Wattens, 6111,
Austria
Tel.: (43) 5224 595 0
Specialty Paper Mill
N.A.I.C.S.: 322120

Tervakoski Oy (1)
Vahikkalantie 1, 12400, Tervakoski, Finland
Tel.: (358) 19 771 1
Web Site: http://www.delfortgroup.com
Emp.: 300
Specialty Paper Mill
N.A.I.C.S.: 322120
Andreas Rauscher (Gen Mgr)

Wattens Vietnam Co. Ltd. (1)
No 8 Dan Chu Street V S I P II, Hoa Phu
Ward, Thu Dau Mot, 820000, Binh Duong,
Vietnam
Tel.: (84) 650 3589 558 0
Paper Mfr
N.A.I.C.S.: 322120
Thang Le Toan (Engr-Automation)

DELHIVERY PRIVATE LIMITED
Plot 5 Sector 44, Gurgaon, 122002,
Haryana, India
Tel.: (91) 124 671 9500   In
Web Site: http://www.delhivery.com
Year Founded: 2011
E-Commerce Solutions Services

N.A.I.C.S.: 513210
Ajay Kumar Sharma (Sr Mgr)

**DELICA FOODS HOLDINGS
CO., LTD.**
4-12-12 Rokucho, Adachi-ku, Tokyo,
121-0073, Japan
Tel.: (81) 338581037
Web Site: https://www.delica.co.jp
Year Founded: 1977
3392—(TKS)
Rev.: $349,160,030
Assets: $190,685,280
Liabilities: $132,847,780
Net Worth: $57,837,500
Earnings: $6,695,930
Emp.: 601
Fiscal Year-end: 03/31/24
Vegetable Distr
N.A.I.C.S.: 424480
Isatake Tachimoto (Chm)

Subsidiaries:

Delica Foods Co., Ltd. (1)
4-12-12 Roku-cho, Adachi-ku, Tokyo, 121-
0073, Japan
Tel.: (81) 338581166
Fruit & Vegetable Mfr & Distr
N.A.I.C.S.: 311411

Delica Foods Hokkaido Co., Ltd. (1)
3-1-70 Chuo Ichijo, Shiroishi-ku, Sapporo,
003-0011, Japan
Tel.: (81) 118155105
Fruit & Vegetable Mfr & Distr
N.A.I.C.S.: 311411

Delica Foods Nagasaki Co., Ltd. (1)
5-70 Tsukuba-machi, Isahaya, 854-0065,
Japan
Tel.: (81) 957263350
Fruit & Vegetable Mfr & Distr
N.A.I.C.S.: 311411

Designer Foods Co., Ltd. (1)
4-12-12 Roku-cho, Adachi-ku, Tokyo, 121-
0073, Japan
Tel.: (81) 338585831
Fruit & Vegetable Mfr & Distr
N.A.I.C.S.: 311411

DELICE DE FRANCE LIMITED
Delice House, 149 Brent Rd Southall,
London, UB2 5LJ, United Kingdom
Tel.: (44) 2089179600
Year Founded: 1985
Frozen Bakery Products Mfr
N.A.I.C.S.: 311813
Nick Dint (Gen Mgr)

DELIGNIT AG
Konigswinkel 2-6, 32825, Blomberg,
Germany
Tel.: (49) 5235966100
Web Site: https://www.delignit-ag.de
Year Founded: 1799
DLX—(MUN)
Rev.: $94,988,013
Assets: $53,515,618
Liabilities: $12,826,969
Net Worth: $40,688,648
Earnings: $3,576,539
Emp.: 471
Fiscal Year-end: 12/31/23
Wood Products Mfr
N.A.I.C.S.: 321999
Markus Buscher (CEO & Member-
Exec Bd)

Subsidiaries:

Blomberger Holzindustrie B. Haus-
mann GmbH & Co. KG (1)
Konigswinkel 2, D-32825, Blomberg, Ger-
many
Tel.: (49) 52359660
Web Site: http://www.delignit.com
Emp.: 250
Plywood Products Mfr
N.A.I.C.S.: 321211

DELIMOBIL HOLDING S.A.

---

10 Rue C M Spoo, 2546, Luxem-
bourg, Luxembourg
Tel.: (352) 2 697 6304   LU
Year Founded: 2021
DMOB—(NYSE)
Emp.: 1,057
Holding Company
N.A.I.C.S.: 551112
Vincenzo Trani (Founder & Chm)

DELIVEROO PLC
1 Cousin Lane, London, EC4R 3TE,
United Kingdom   UK
Web Site:
  https://www.deliveroo.co.uk
Year Founded: 2013
ROO—(LSE)
Rev.: $2,562,484,221
Assets: $1,290,078,263
Liabilities: $647,816,208
Net Worth: $642,262,055
Earnings: ($40,141,378)
Emp.: 3,630
Fiscal Year-end: 12/31/23
Food Products Distr
N.A.I.C.S.: 424420
Dan Winn (CTO)

DELIVERY HERO SE
Oranienburger Strasse 70, 10117,
Berlin, Germany
Tel.: (49) 30544459000   De
Web Site:
  https://www.deliveryhero.com
Year Founded: 2010
DHER—(MUN)
Rev.: $10,974,565,153
Assets: $11,577,167,786
Liabilities: $9,751,918,741
Net Worth: $1,825,249,045
Earnings: ($2,536,141,325)
Emp.: 47,981
Fiscal Year-end: 12/31/23
Online Food Ordering & Delivery Ser-
vices
N.A.I.C.S.: 519290
Markus Fuhrmann (Co-Founder)

Subsidiaries:

Donesi D.O.O. (1)
Mladena Stojanovica 117A, 78000, Banja
Luka, Bosnia & Herzegovina
Tel.: (387) 66266391
Web Site: https://www.donesi.com
Food Delivery Services
N.A.I.C.S.: 492210

Donesi D.O.O. (1)
Josipa Broza Tita 65a, 81000, Podgorica,
Montenegro
Tel.: (382) 68302957
Web Site: https://www.donesi.com
Food Delivery Services
N.A.I.C.S.: 492210

E-Table Online Restaurant Reserva-
tion Services Single Member
P.C. (1)
Eleftheriou Venizelou 82 & Artemidos, 183-
45, Moschato, Greece
Tel.: (30) 2113115555
Web Site: https://www.e-table.gr
Restaurant Reservation Services
N.A.I.C.S.: 561599

Foodora AB (1)
Ringvagen 100, 118 69, Stockholm, Swe-
den
Tel.: (46) 5590075643
Web Site: https://www.foodora.com
Food Delivery Services
N.A.I.C.S.: 492210

Foodora Norway AS (1)
Waldemar Thranes gate 98, 0175, Oslo,
Norway
Tel.: (47) 996691349
Web Site: https://www.foodora.no
Food Delivery Services
N.A.I.C.S.: 492210

InstaShop DMCC (1)

Swiss Tower Jlt, PO Box 24645, Dubai,
United Arab Emirates
Tel.: (971) 48795000
Web Site: https://instashop.com
Grocery Products Retailer
N.A.I.C.S.: 445110

Plotun D.O.O. (1)
Obiliceva 33, 37000, Krusevac, Serbia
Tel.: (381) 648670001
Food Delivery Services
N.A.I.C.S.: 492210

S.A.R.L. Room Service (1)
6 Boulevard des Moulins, Monte Carlo, Mo-
naco
Tel.: (377) 97772727
Web Site: https://www.mrroomservice.fr
Hotel & Restaurant Management Services
N.A.I.C.S.: 721110

Talabat Electronic & Delivery Ser-
vices LLC (1)
PO Box 3360, PC 111, Muscat, Oman
Tel.: (968) 80072345
Web Site: https://www.talabat.com
Food Delivery Services
N.A.I.C.S.: 492210

Talabat General Trading & Contract-
ing Company W.L.L (1)
PO Box 156001, Daiya, 35456, Kuwait
Tel.: (965) 1800200
Web Site: https://www.talabat.com
Food Delivery Services
N.A.I.C.S.: 492210

Talabat Services Company
L.L.C. (1)
PO Box 15307, Doha, Qatar
Tel.: (974) 41407776
Web Site: https://www.talabat.com
Food Delivery Services
N.A.I.C.S.: 492210

Woowa Brothers Corp. (1)
2 Wiryeseong-daero, Songpa-gu, Seoul,
5544, Korea (South)
Tel.: (82) 16007001
Web Site: https://www.woowahan.com
Food Delivery Services
N.A.I.C.S.: 492210

**DELIXI XINJIANG TRANSPOR-
TATION GROUP CO., LTD**
No 236 High-speed Railway North
5th Road, Toutunhe District Economic
and Technological Development
Zone, Urumqi, 830000, Xinjiang,
China
Tel.: (86) 9915878240
Web Site: http://www.xjdlxky.cn
Year Founded: 2003
603032—(SHG)
Sales Range: $10-24.9 Million
Transportation Services
N.A.I.C.S.: 541614
Zhongming Wang (Chm)

DELKO S.A.
ul Gostynska 51, 63-100, Srem, Po-
land
Tel.: (48) 612837731
Web Site: https://www.delko.com.pl
Year Founded: 1995
DEL—(WAR)
Rev.: $321,863,030
Assets: $81,982,369
Liabilities: $44,830,772
Net Worth: $37,151,597
Earnings: $9,542,959
Emp.: 379
Fiscal Year-end: 06/30/23
Cleaning Products & Cosmetics Distr
N.A.I.C.S.: 424990
Miroslaw Jan Dabrowski (Vice Chm-
Mgmt Bd)

DELLNER BRAKES AB
Teknikergatan 1, 781 70, Borlange,
Sweden
Tel.: (46) 23 78 30 50

DELLNER BRAKES AB

Dellner Brakes AB—(Continued)

Web Site: http://www.dellner-brakes.com
Year Founded: 1941
Rail Vehicle & Other Industrial Components Mfr
N.A.I.C.S.: 333924
Marcus Aberg (CEO)

Subsidiaries:

Silentbloc UK Ltd (1)
Wellington Road, Burton-on-Trent, DE14 2AP, Staffordshire, United Kingdom
Tel.: (44) 1283741741
Industrial Machinery Mfr
N.A.I.C.S.: 333998
Robert Downes (Head-Sls)

DELLOYD VENTURES SDN BHD

Lot 33004/5 Jalan Kebun Kampung Jawa, 42450, Klang, Selangor Darul Ehsan, Malaysia
Tel.: (60) 3 51636888 MY
Web Site: http://www.delloyd.com
Sales Range: $100-124.9 Million
Motor Vehicles & Automotive Parts Distr
N.A.I.C.S.: 423130
Soo Seong Chua (Deputy CEO-Ops)

Subsidiaries:

Delloyd Industries (M) Sdn Bhd (1)
Lot 33004/5 Batu 5 Jalan Kebun Kampung Jawa, 42450, Port Klang, Selangor, Malaysia
Tel.: (60) 351612288
Sales Range: $200-249.9 Million
Emp.: 1,000
Automotive Parts & Accessories Mfr
N.A.I.C.S.: 336360

Delloyd Plantation Sdn. Bhd. (1)
Sungai Rambai Estate, Batang Berjuntai, Kuala Selangor, 45600, Selangor, Malaysia
Tel.: (60) 332719001
Sales Range: $25-49.9 Million
Emp.: 120
Oil Palm Cultivation Services
N.A.I.C.S.: 115112
Tee Boon Kee (Mng Dir)

Premier Asian Auto Publications (M) Sdn Bhd (1)
Lot 33004/5 Jalan Kebun, Kampung Jawa, 42450, Kelang, Selangor, Malaysia
Tel.: (60) 351636856
Web Site: http://www.asianauto.com
Automobile Magazine Publishing Services
N.A.I.C.S.: 513120

DELMAR INTERNATIONAL, INC.

10636 Chemin de la Cote-de-Liesse, Lachine, H8T 1A5, QC, Canada
Tel.: (514) 636-8800
Web Site:
http://www.delmarcargo.com
Logistic Services
N.A.I.C.S.: 541614
Robert Cutler (CEO)

Subsidiaries:

Rotra, LLC (1)
841 Sivert Dr, Wood Dale, IL 60191
Tel.: (630) 766-8080
Web Site: http://www.rotra.com
Freight Transportation Arrangement
N.A.I.C.S.: 488510
Joerg Frede (Pres & COO)

DELMON POULTRY CO. B.S.C.

17 th Floor Diplomat commercial office Tower, PO Box 787, Manama, Bahrain
Tel.: (973) 17608282
Web Site: http://www.dawajen.bh
POLTRY—(BAH)
Rev.: $49,888,276
Assets: $43,815,519

Liabilities: $6,299,125
Net Worth: $37,516,395
Earnings: $65,362
Emp.: 181
Fiscal Year-end: 12/31/22
Poultry Processing Services
N.A.I.C.S.: 311615
Abdul Rahman Mohamed Jamsheer (Chm)

DELNOR CONSTRUCTION LTD.

3609-74 Avenue, Edmonton, T6B 2T7, AB, Canada
Tel.: (780) 469-1304
Web Site: https://www.delnor.ca
Year Founded: 1983
Rev.: $40,776,945
Emp.: 70
Building Construction Services
N.A.I.C.S.: 236220
Dave Lamash (Principal & Sr Project Mgr)

Subsidiaries:

Delnor Construction 2012 Ltd. (1)
7056K - Farrell Road SE, Calgary, T2H 0T2, AB, Canada
Tel.: (403) 294-1650
Building Construction Services
N.A.I.C.S.: 236220

DELO GROUP

Donskaya Str 15, 119049, Moscow, Russia
Tel.: (7) 4959331916
Web Site: http://www.delo-group.com
Year Founded: 1993
Holding Company; Transportation & Logistics
N.A.I.C.S.: 551112
Sergey Shishkarev (Pres)

Subsidiaries:

Delo-Center LLC (1)
15 Donskaya Street Office 818, Moscow, 119049, Russia
Tel.: (7) 4959331916
Transportation & Logistics
N.A.I.C.S.: 541614

Subsidiary (Non-US):

Global Ports Investments Plc (2)
BG WAYWIN PLAZA Office 302 62 Agiou Athanasiou Avenue, Limassol, 4102, Cyprus (61.5%)
Tel.: (357) 25313475
Web Site: http://www.globalports.com
Rev.: $502,790,000
Assets: $1,443,468,000
Liabilities: $944,077,000
Net Worth: $499,391,000
Earnings: $143,858,000
Emp.: 2,786
Fiscal Year-end: 12/31/2021
Container Terminal Operator
N.A.I.C.S.: 488320
Alexander Iodchin (Chief Strategy & Bus Dev Officer-Global Ports)

Subsidiary (Non-US):

Multi-Link Terminals Ltd Oy (3)
Kumpulantie 3 3rd floor, 00520, Helsinki, Finland
Tel.: (358) 207 460 200
Web Site: http://www.mlt.fi
Emp.: 50
Marine Cargo Handling Services
N.A.I.C.S.: 488320
Dirk van Assendelft (Mng Dir)

OJSC Petrolesport (3)
Gladky island 1, 198095, Saint Petersburg, Russia
Tel.: (7) 812 332 30 22
Web Site: http://www.petrolesport.ru
Container Terminal Operator
N.A.I.C.S.: 488320

VOSTOCHNAYA STEVEDORING COMPANY (3)
14A Vnutriportovaya St Vrangel-1, 692941,

Nakhodka, Russia
Tel.: (7) 4236 665 305
Web Site: http://www.vscport.ru
Marine Cargo Handling Services
N.A.I.C.S.: 488320

Subsidiary (Domestic):

PJSC Center for Cargo Container Traffic TransContainer (2)
Oruzheyniy Pereulok 19, 125047, Moscow, 125047, Russia (100%)
Tel.: (7) 4957881717
Web Site: https://trcont.com
Rev.: $1,394,104,590
Assets: $1,449,843,450
Liabilities: $1,146,647,220
Net Worth: $303,196,230
Earnings: $170,516,730
Emp.: 3,439
Fiscal Year-end: 12/31/2020
Container Transportation Services
N.A.I.C.S.: 488510
Alexander Urudzhev (Dir-Transportation Mgmt)

DELO PRODAJA, D.D.

Dunajska 5, 1000, Ljubljana, Slovenia
Tel.: (386) 14738600 SI
Web Site: http://www.delo-prodaja.si
DPRG—(LJU)
Sales Range: $50-74.9 Million
Emp.: 140
General Merchandise Store Owner & Operator
N.A.I.C.S.: 455219
Rok Gorjup (Chm)

DELOITTE BULGARIA EOOD

103 Alexander Stambolijski Blvd Sofia Tower, Sofia, 1303, Bulgaria
Tel.: (359) 28023300 BG
Web Site: http://www.deloitte.com
Year Founded: 1992
Holding Company; Accounting & Consulting Services
N.A.I.C.S.: 551112
Borislav Stratev (Sr Partner)

Subsidiaries:

Deloitte Audit OOD (1)
103 Alexander Stambolijski Blvd, Sofia Tower, Sofia, 1303, Bulgaria
Tel.: (359) 28023300
Web Site: https://www2.deloitte.com
Corporate Auditing Services
N.A.I.C.S.: 541211

DELOITTE CHILE

Av Provendcia 1760 7th Floor, Santiago, Chile
Tel.: (56) 22703126
Emp.: 34
Accounting Services
N.A.I.C.S.: 541211
Carolina Araneda M. (Atty)

DELOITTE HOLDING B.V.

Wilhelminakade 1, 3072 AP, Rotterdam, Netherlands
Tel.: (31) 882882888 NI
Web Site: https://www2.deloitte.com
Holding Company; Accounting & Consultancy Services
N.A.I.C.S.: 551112

Subsidiaries:

Deloitte Legal BV (1)
Gustav Mahlerlaan 2970, 1081 LA, Amsterdam, Netherlands
Tel.: (31) 882882888
Legal Management Services
N.A.I.C.S.: 541199
Frederieke Leeflang (Partner)

DELOITTE LLP

2 New Street Square, London, EC4A 3BZ, United Kingdom
Tel.: (44) 2079363000 UK
Web Site: https://www2.deloitte.com
Rev.: $4,025,308,760

Assets: $1,704,384,360
Liabilities: $2,306,685,600
Net Worth: ($602,301,240)
Earnings: $576,671,400
Emp.: 18,480
Fiscal Year-end: 05/31/15
Audit, Tax, Consulting & Financial Advisory Services
N.A.I.C.S.: 541211
Richard Houston (CEO & Sr Partner)

DELOITTE TOUCHE TOHMATSU LIMITED

Hill House 1 Little New Street, London, EC4A 3TR, United Kingdom
Tel.: (44) 20 7936 3000 UK
Web Site: http://www2.deloitte.com
Year Founded: 1845
Sales Range: $25-49.9 Billion
Emp.: 334,800
Accounting, Auditing, Tax Preparation & Management Consulting Services Organization
N.A.I.C.S.: 813920
Punit Renjen (Global CEO)

Subsidiaries:

Deloitte Consulting LLP (1)
25 Broadway, New York, NY 10004
Tel.: (212) 618-4000
Web Site: http://www.deloitte.com
Sales Range: $100-124.9 Million
Emp.: 1,100
Financial Consultant
N.A.I.C.S.: 541618
Andrew Vaz (Principal & Chief Innovation Officer)

Subsidiary (Domestic):

BIAS Corporation (2)
1100 Abernathy Rd Ste 950, Atlanta, GA 30328
Tel.: (678) 578-4280
Web Site: http://www.biascorp.com
Sales Range: $25-49.9 Million
Emp.: 160
Information Technology Consulting Services
N.A.I.C.S.: 541512
Jeff Harvey (Co-Founder & Pres)

Unit (Domestic):

Bersin by Deloitte (2)
180 Grand Ave Ste 320, Oakland, CA 94612
Tel.: (510) 251-4400
Web Site: http://www.bersin.com
Sales Range: $10-24.9 Million
Emp.: 57
Research Based People Strategies & Advisory Services
N.A.I.C.S.: 541612
Josh Bersin (Founder & Principal)

Casey Quirk by Deloitte (2)
17 Old Kings Hwy S Ste 200, Darien, CT 06820
Tel.: (203) 899-3000
Web Site: http://www.caseyquirk.com
Corporate Consultancy Services
N.A.I.C.S.: 541611
Kevin P. Quirk (Founder & Principal)

Subsidiary (Domestic):

Deloitte Development LLC (2)
837 N 34th St Ste 100, Seattle, WA 98103
Tel.: (206) 633-1167
Web Site: http://www.deloittedigital.com
Digital Marketing Services
N.A.I.C.S.: 541511
Alicia Hatch (CMO)

Subsidiary (Domestic):

Heat (3)
1100 Sansome St, San Francisco, CA 94111
Tel.: (415) 477-1999
Web Site: http://www.thisisheat.com
Sales Range: $1-9.9 Million
Emp.: 79
Advetising Agency
N.A.I.C.S.: 541810
Steve Stone (Chief Creative Officer)

Subsidiary (Domestic):

Gryphon Scientific, LLC (2)
973 Hale St, Beverly, MA 01915-2235
Tel.: (978) 922-0383
Web Site: http://www.gryphonscientific.com
Scientific & Technical Consulting Services
N.A.I.C.S.: 541690
Kimberly Legrow (Bus Mgr)

National Teleconsultants Inc. (2)
700 N Brand Blvd Ste 10, Glendale, CA
91203-1202
Tel.: (818) 265-4400
Web Site: http://www.ntc.com
Electronics Stores
N.A.I.C.S.: 449210
Elliot Graham (Pres)

Optimal Design Co. (2)
1699 Wall St, Mount Prospect, IL 60056
Tel.: (847) 545-6800
Rev.: $1,500,000
Emp.: 20
Engineering Services
N.A.I.C.S.: 541330

PricewaterhouseCoopers Lanka (Private) Limited (1)
No 100 Braybrooke Place, Colombo,
00200, Sri Lanka
Tel.: (94) 117719838
Web Site: https://www.deloitte.com
Emp.: 400
Accounting, Tax Preparation, Risk Management, Business Assurance, Human Resource, Regulatory, Operational Management & Advisory Services
N.A.I.C.S.: 541211
Channa Manoharan (COO)

DELONG COMPOSITE ENERGY GROUP CO., LTD.
No 55 Jianshe Road, Chengdu,
610051, Sichuan, China
Tel.: (86) 2868539558
Web Site: http://www.dtrq.com
Year Founded: 1987
000593—(SSE)
Rev.: $206,258,832
Assets: $331,018,272
Liabilities: $162,563,544
Net Worth: $168,454,728
Earnings: $6,779,916
Fiscal Year-end: 12/31/22
Department Store Operator & Pipeline Gas Distribution Services
N.A.I.C.S.: 455110

DELONG HOLDINGS LIMITED
50 Raffles Place Singapore Land
Tower Level 30-01, Singapore,
048623, Singapore
Tel.: (65) 66323626
Web Site: http://www.dlholdings.com
Rev.: $2,077,252,792
Assets: $1,912,203,447
Liabilities: $1,027,125,538
Net Worth: $885,077,909
Earnings: $247,290,362
Fiscal Year-end: 12/31/18
Steel Coils Mfr & Whslr
N.A.I.C.S.: 331221
Lee Luang Yeo (Officer-Compliance,
Sec & Mgr-Fin)

Subsidiaries:

Asia Paragon International
Limited (1)
Bharat Building No 07-01, Singapore,
048617, Singapore
Tel.: (65) 6329 6426
Holding Company
N.A.I.C.S.: 551112

DELOREAN CORPORATION LIMITED
Ground Floor 1205 Hay St, West
Perth, 6005, WA, Australia
Tel.: (61) 861477575   AU
Web Site:
  https://www.deloreancorp.com.au

Year Founded: 2014
DEL—(ASX)
Rev.: $12,849,932
Assets: $11,681,010
Liabilities: $10,266,965
Net Worth: $1,414,045
Earnings: ($6,532,441)
Fiscal Year-end: 06/30/23
Natural Gas Exploration Service
N.A.I.C.S.: 211130
David McArthur (Sec)

Subsidiaries:

Cleantech Energy Pty. Ltd. (1)
Ground Floor 1205 Hay Street, West Perth,
6005, WA, Australia
Tel.: (61) 861477555
Renewable Gas Mfr & Distr
N.A.I.C.S.: 333912

DELOTA CORP.
51-7600 Weston Rd, Woodbridge,
L4L 8B7, ON, Canada
Tel.: (905) 330-1602   AB
Web Site:
  http://corporate.spydercannabis.com
Year Founded: 2014
SYDRF—(OTCIQ)
Rev.: $25,726,557
Assets: $10,372,068
Liabilities: $10,081,802
Net Worth: $290,265
Earnings: ($1,504,626)
Emp.: 123
Fiscal Year-end: 01/31/24
Investment Services
N.A.I.C.S.: 523999
Daniel Pelchovitz (CEO-Cannabis
Div)

DELPHA CONSTRUCTION CO., LTD.
16F No 460 Sec 5 Chenggong Rd,
Neihu Dist, Taipei, 114705, Taiwan
Tel.: (886) 226328877
Web Site: https://www.delpha.com.tw
Year Founded: 1960
2530—(TAI)
Rev.: $63,816,767
Assets: $775,955,005
Liabilities: $426,756,483
Net Worth: $349,198,522
Earnings: $16,468,916
Emp.: 83
Fiscal Year-end: 12/31/23
Construction Engineering Services
N.A.I.C.S.: 236220
Cheng Ssu-Tsung (Chm)

DELPHARM S.A.S.
6-8 rue du Quartre Septembre,
92130, Issy-les-Moulineaux, France
Tel.: (33) 1 41 09 19 70   FR
Web Site: http://www.delpharm.com
Sales Range: $125-149.9 Million
Emp.: 870
Pharmaceuticals & Cosmetics Mfr
N.A.I.C.S.: 325412
Sebastien Aguettant (CEO)

Subsidiaries:

Delpharm Evreux SAS (1)
5 rue du Guesclin, 27002, Evreux, Cedex,
France
Tel.: (33) 232295800
Web Site: http://www.delpharm.com
Pharmaceuticals & Cosmetics Mfr
N.A.I.C.S.: 325411

Delpharm S.A.S. - Bretigny Plant (1)
Rue du Petit Paris, 91731, Bretigny-sur-
Orge, Cedex, France
Tel.: (33) 1 69 88 79 00
Pharmaceuticals Product Mfr
N.A.I.C.S.: 325412

Delpharm S.A.S. - Dijon Plant (1)
6 boulevard de l Europe, 21800, Quetigny,
France

Tel.: (33) 3 80 48 30 30
Pharmaceuticals Product Mfr
N.A.I.C.S.: 325412

Delpharm S.A.S. - Drogenbos
Plant (1)
Rue du Grand Bigard 128, Drogenbos,
1620, Belgium
Tel.: (32) 2 334 95 70
Pharmaceuticals Product Mfr
N.A.I.C.S.: 325412

Delpharm S.A.S. - Gaillard Plant (1)
33 rue de l Industrie, 74240, Gaillard,
France
Tel.: (33) 4 56 66 00 50
Emp.: 300
Pharmaceuticals Product Mfr
N.A.I.C.S.: 325412
Nicolas Leforestier (CEO)

Delpharm S.A.S. - Huningue
Plant (1)
Site Industriel de Huningue 26 rue de la
Chapelle, BP 90241, 68330, Huningue, Ce-
dex, France
Tel.: (33) 3 89 89 55 55
Pharmaceuticals Product Mfr
N.A.I.C.S.: 325412

Delpharm S.A.S. - Lille Plant (1)
Parc d Activites Roubaix-Est 22 rue de
Toufflers, CS 50070, 59452, Lys-Lez-
Lannoy, Cedex, France
Tel.: (33) 3 20 20 80 00
Pharmaceuticals Product Mfr
N.A.I.C.S.: 325412

Delpharm S.A.S. - Lyon Biotech
Plant (1)
2 rue Alexander Fleming, 69007, Lyon,
France
Tel.: (33) 4 81 07 73 33
Pharmaceuticals Product Mfr
N.A.I.C.S.: 325412

Delpharm S.A.S. - Reims Plant (1)
10 rue Colonel Charbonneaux, PO Box
50034, 51721, Reims, Cedex, France
Tel.: (33) 3 26 88 81 10
Web Site: http://www.delpharm.com
Emp.: 450
Pharmaceuticals Product Mfr
N.A.I.C.S.: 325412
Otautau Mathieu (Gen Mgr)

Delpharm Tours SAS (1)
rue Paul Langevin La Baraudiere, BP
90241, Tours, 37172, Cedex, France
Tel.: (33) 2 47 48 43 00
Web Site: http://www.delpharm.com
Sales Range: $25-49.9 Million
Emp.: 200
Pharmaceuticals & Cosmetics Mfr
N.A.I.C.S.: 325411
Vincent Declerck (Gen Mgr)

DELPHX CAPITAL MARKETS, INC.
15 Prince Arthur Ave, Toronto, M5R
1B2, ON, Canada
Tel.: (416) 347-0197
Web Site: https://www.delphx.com
DELX—(TSXV)
Rev.: $413,275
Assets: $179,021
Liabilities: $1,966,785
Net Worth: ($1,787,764)
Earnings: ($1,543,059)
Fiscal Year-end: 12/31/23
Financial Management Services
N.A.I.C.S.: 523940
Larry Fondren (Founder)

Subsidiaries:

DelphX Corporation (1)
5 Great Valley Pkwy, Malvern, PA 19355
Tel.: (610) 640-7546
Capital Financial Services
N.A.I.C.S.: 523940

DELSBO CANDLE AB
Fredriksfors, Delsbo, 820 60, Sweden
Tel.: (46) 65323150

Web Site:
http://www.delsbocandle.se
Sales Range: $10-24.9 Million
Emp.: 20
Candle Mfr
N.A.I.C.S.: 339999
Torbjorn Jonsson (Mng Dir)

DELSOLE CORPORATION
7th floor TFT Building West Wing
3-4-10 Ariake, Koto-ku, Tokyo, 135-
0063, Japan
Tel.: (81) 367365690
Web Site: https://www.del-sole.co.jp
Year Founded: 1964
2876—(TKS)
Sales Range: Less than $1 Million
Food Product Mfr & Whslr
N.A.I.C.S.: 311991
Merle Aiko Okawara (Chm)

Subsidiaries:

JC Comsa Corporation - Foods
Manufacturing Division (1)
2231 Omaru Inagi-shi, Tokyo, Japan
Tel.: (81) 423707545
Food Mfr
N.A.I.C.S.: 311412

DELTA 9 CANNABIS, INC.
Osborne Village, PO Box 68096,
Winnipeg, R3L 2V9, MB, Canada
Tel.: (204) 224-7323
Web Site: https://www.delta9.ca
Year Founded: 2012
DN—(STU)
Rev.: $40,715,369
Assets: $59,767,322
Liabilities: $34,002,648
Net Worth: $25,764,673
Earnings: ($5,020,301)
Emp.: 190
Fiscal Year-end: 12/31/20
Biotechnology Research & Development Services
N.A.I.C.S.: 541714
James Lawson (CFO)

Subsidiaries:

Delta 9 Lifestyle Cannabis Clinic
Inc. (1)
202-478 River Ave, Winnipeg, R3L 0C8,
MB, Canada
Tel.: (204) 410-3424
Web Site: https://www.delta9life.com
Medical Clinic Services
N.A.I.C.S.: 621111

DELTA BANK JSC
36b Shchorsa str, Kiev, 01133,
Ukraine
Tel.: (380) 44 428 95 95
Web Site: http://deltabank.com.ua
Year Founded: 2006
Banking Services
N.A.I.C.S.: 522110
Nikolai Lagun (Chm)

DELTA CEDAR PRODUCTS LTD
10104 River Road, Delta, V4C 2R3,
BC, Canada
Tel.: (604) 583-3818
Web Site:
  http://www.deltacedarproducts.com
Year Founded: 1958
Rev.: $96,484,160
Emp.: 400
Cedar & Sawmills Mfr
N.A.I.C.S.: 321113
Brian Dysserinck (Mgr-Ops)

DELTA CLEANTECH INC.
2308 Palisade Dr S W, Calgary, T2V
3V1, AB, Canada
Tel.: (306) 530-6025   AB

Delta CleanTech Inc.—(Continued)

Web Site:
https://www.deltacleantech.com
Year Founded: 2020
DCTIF—(OTCQB)
Rev.: $14,036
Assets: $4,039,589
Liabilities: $399,565
Net Worth: $3,640,023
Earnings: ($2,087,614)
Fiscal Year-end: 12/31/22
Information Technology Services
N.A.I.C.S.: 541512
Donato Sferra *(Offioor)*

Subsidiaries:

Carbon RX Inc.   **(1)**
002 - 2305 Victoria Avenue, Regina, S4P
0S7, SK, Canada
Tel.: (306) 352-6132
Web Site: https://carbonrx.com
Natural Gas & Oil Reservoir Mfr
N.A.I.C.S.: 333618

DELTA CORP HOLDINGS LIMITED

Suite 3016-3017 The Leadenhall
Building 122 Leadenhall Street, City
of London, EC3V 4AB, United Kingdom
Tel.: (44) 45 52712421
Web Site:
https://www.wearedelta.com
Emp.: 100
Transportation, Logistics, Supply
Chain & Storage Services
N.A.I.C.S.: 541614
Joseph Nelson *(Executives)*

DELTA CORP LTD.

Delta House Hornby Vellard Estate
Dr Annie Besant Road, Next to Copper Chimney Worli, Mumbai, 400018,
India
Tel.: (91) 2240794700   In
Web Site: https://www.deltacorp.in
532848—(BOM)
Rev.: $62,016,045
Assets: $295,186,710
Liabilities: $29,957,655
Net Worth: $265,229,055
Earnings: ($3,482,115)
Emp.: 1,710
Fiscal Year-end: 03/31/21
Textile & Real Estate Development
Consultancy Services
N.A.I.C.S.: 531390
Ashish Kapadia *(Mng Dir)*

Subsidiaries:

AAA Aviation Private Limited   **(1)**
16 Ali Chambers 2nd Fl Nagindas Master
Rd, Fort, Mumbai, 400001, Maharastra,
India
Tel.: (91) 22 40794700
Sales Range: $25-49.9 Million
Emp.: 40
Air Freight Services
N.A.I.C.S.: 481212
Ashok Masurkar *(Mgr-Mktg)*

Deltatech Gaming Limited   **(1)**
801/802 8th Floor Kamat Grand St Inez Behind Caculo Mall, Panaji, 403001, Goa,
India
Tel.: (91) 18005720611
Web Site: https://www.deltatech.gg
Online Game Operator
N.A.I.C.S.: 713290

Highstreet Cruises & Entertainment
Private Limited   **(1)**
Peninsula Ctr 850 Off N H 17, Porvorim
Bardez, Goa, 403 521, India
Tel.: (91) 8326659400
Web Site: https://www.casinoroyalegoa.com
Gambling Cruise Management Services
N.A.I.C.S.: 713210

DELTA CORPORATION LIMITED

Sable House Northridge Close, PO
Box BW 294, Borrowdale, Harare,
Zimbabwe
Tel.: (263) 242883865
Web Site: http://www.delta.co.zw
Year Founded: 1978
DLTA—(ZIM)
Rev.: $722,384,000
Assets: $1,349,911,000
Liabilities: $546,914,000
Net Worth: $802,997,000
Earnings: $143,234,000
Emp.: 4,800
Fiscal Year-end: 03/31/19
Soft Drink, Beer & Distilled Beverage
Mfr & Distr
N.A.I.C.S.: 312111
Canaan Farirai Dube *(Chm)*

Subsidiaries:

African Distillers Limited   **(1)**
22km Peg Lomagundi Road, Harare, Zimbabwe
Tel.: (263) 772235008
Web Site: https://www.africandistillers.co.zw
Rev.: $167,127
Assets: $225,770
Liabilities: $57,303
Net Worth: $168,467
Earnings: $49,832
Fiscal Year-end: 06/30/2019
Wine Product Mfr & Distr
N.A.I.C.S.: 312130
R. H. M. Maunsell *(Chm)*

Delta Beverages (Pvt) Limited   **(1)**
9 Telford Rd, Harare, Zimbabwe
Tel.: (263) 4870839
Beer Mfr
N.A.I.C.S.: 312120

Subsidiary (Domestic):

Mega Pak Zimbabwe (Pvt) Ltd   **(2)**
211 Chihombe Rd, PO Box 52, Ruwa,
Mashonaland East, Zimbabwe
Tel.: (263) 27329358
Web Site: https://www.megapak.co.zw
Mfr of Addis Domestic Storage Wares &
Plastic Furniture
N.A.I.C.S.: 326199

United National Breweries (SA) Pty
Ltd.   **(1)**
Richards Drive Gallagher House, Gallagher
Estate, Midrand, 1683, South Africa
Tel.: (27) 11 990 6300
Web Site: http://www.unbreweries.co.za
Brewery
N.A.I.C.S.: 312120
Rajan Ranganathan *(CEO & Mng Dir)*

DELTA CREDIT SPV

Bul Hristofor Kolumb 43, 1592, Sofia,
Bulgaria
Tel.: (359) 29651653
Web Site: https://www.deltacredit-bg.com
DLC—(BUL)
Sales Range: Less than $1 Million
Insurance Services
N.A.I.C.S.: 524210
Milena Stoyanova *(Dir-IR)*

DELTA DJAKARTA TBK

Jalan Inspeksi Tarum Barat Timur,
Tambun, Bekasi, 17510, Indonesia
Tel.: (62) 218822520
Web Site: https://www.deltajkt.co.id
Year Founded: 1932
DLTA—(INDO)
Rev.: $47,850,300
Assets: $78,450,768
Liabilities: $17,769,906
Net Worth: $60,680,862
Earnings: $12,962,793
Emp.: 369
Fiscal Year-end: 12/31/23
Food & Beverage Distr
N.A.I.C.S.: 424810

Jose Daniel A. Javier *(Chm)*

DELTA DRONE SA

27 chemin des Peupliers, 69570,
Dardilly, France
Tel.: (33) 457386335
Web Site: http://www.deltadrone.com
ALDR—(EUR)
Rev.: $21,226,444
Assets: $27,624,346
Liabilities: $12,184,141
Net Worth: $15,440,205
Earnings: ($13,341,143)
Emp.: 449
Fiscal Year-end: 12/31/20
Civilian Drones Mfr
N.A.I.C.S.: 334511
Frederic Serre *(Founder)*

DELTA ELECTRONICS, INC.

186 Ruey Kuang Road, Neihu District, Taipei, 114501, Taiwan
Tel.: (886) 287972088   TW
Web Site: https://www.deltaww.com
Year Founded: 1971
2308—(TAI)
Rev.: $10,052,277,386
Assets: $11,966,324,768
Liabilities: $5,613,891,237
Net Worth: $6,352,433,530
Earnings: $974,060,938
Emp.: 8,776
Fiscal Year-end: 12/31/20
Semiconductor Mfr & Distr
N.A.I.C.S.: 334413
Bruce C. H. Cheng *(Founder)*

Subsidiaries:

Cyntec Co., Ltd.   **(1)**
2 R D 2nd road, Science-Based Industry
Park, Hsinchu, 30076, Taiwan
Tel.: (886) 35799829
Web Site: https://www.cyntec.com
Emp.: 2,000
Inductor & Power Module Mfr
N.A.I.C.S.: 334413
Steven Liu *(Chm)*

DEI Logistics (USA) Corp.   **(1)**
4405 Cushing Pkwy, Fremont, CA 94538-6475
Tel.: (510) 668-5588
Warehousing & Logistics Services
N.A.I.C.S.: 493110

DELTA ELECTRONICS (France)
S.A.S.   **(1)**
ZI du bois Chaland 2 15 rue des Pyrenees,
Lisses, 91056, Evry, Cedex, France
Tel.: (33) 169778260
Electronic Component Mfr & Distr
N.A.I.C.S.: 334419

DELTA Electronics (Germany)
GmbH   **(1)**
Ferdinand-Porsche-Str 45, 60386, Frankfurt
am Main, Germany
Tel.: (49) 69420020
Power Electronic Component Distr
N.A.I.C.S.: 423610

DelSolar (Wujiang) Ltd.   **(1)**
No 1688 Jiangxing East Road Wujiang Economic Deve District, Suzhou, 215200, Jiangsu, China
Tel.: (86) 512 6316 8558
Solar Cell Mfr
N.A.I.C.S.: 334413

Delta America Ltd.   **(1)**
46101 Fremont Blvd, Fremont, CA 94538
Tel.: (510) 668-5100
N.A.I.C.S.: 523150

Delta Electronics (Argentina)
S.R.L.   **(1)**
Jose Roque Funes 1761 PB E, X5009LFS,
Cordoba, Argentina
Tel.: (54) 3514813054
Power Supply Equipment Distr
N.A.I.C.S.: 423610

Delta Electronics (Automotive) Americas Inc.   **(1)**

39209 6 Mile Rd Ste 105, Livonia, MI
48152
Tel.: (734) 464-0068
N.A.I.C.S.: 334419

Delta Electronics (Colombia)
S.A.S   **(1)**
Carrera 72 95-51 Bodega 7, Parque Industrial Los Lagartos, Bogota, Colombia
Tel.: (57) 7049435
Power Supply Equipment Distr
N.A.I.C.S.: 423610

Delta Electronics (Hong Kong)
Ltd.   **(1)**
21F Prosperity Center 25 Chong Yip Street,
Kwun Tong, Kowloon, China (Hong Kong)
Tel.: (852) 23181038
Web Site: http://www.delta.com.tw
Power Supply & Computer Peripherals Mfr
N.A.I.C.S.: 334112

Subsidiary (Non-US):

Delta Electronics (Chenzhou) Co.,
Ltd.   **(2)**
Chenzou Export Processing Zone, Bailutang Town Suxian District, Chenzhou,
423038, Hunan, China
Tel.: (86) 7352661008
Web Site: http://www.deltaww.com
Electronic Components Distr
N.A.I.C.S.: 423690

Delta Electronics (Dongguan) Co.,
Ltd.   **(2)**
Delta Industrial Estate, Shijie Town, Dongguan, 523308, Guangdong, China
Tel.: (86) 76986635008
Power Supplies Mfr
N.A.I.C.S.: 335999

Delta Electronics (Shanghai) Co.,
Ltd.   **(2)**
No 182 Minyu Road, Pudong, Shanghai,
201209, China
Tel.: (86) 21 6872 3988
Web Site: http://www.deltaww.com
Electronic Components Mfr
N.A.I.C.S.: 335999

Delta Electronics (Switzerland)
AG   **(2)**
Freiburgstrasse 251, Bern-Bumpliz, 3018,
Bern, Switzerland   **(100%)**
Tel.: (41) 319985311
Web Site:
http://www.deltaenergysystems.com
Motor & Generator Mfr
N.A.I.C.S.: 335312

Subsidiary (Non-US):

Delta Electronics (Poland) Sp.
z.o.o.   **(3)**
23 Poleczki Str, 02-822, Warsaw,
Poland   **(100%)**
Tel.: (48) 223352600
Web Site:
http://www.deltapowersolutions.com
Electrical Equipment & Component Mfr
N.A.I.C.S.: 335999

Delta Electronics Solutions (Spain)
SLU   **(3)**
Ctra De Villaverde a Vallecas 265 1 Dcha
Ed Hormigueras, Pl de Vallecas, 28031,
Madrid, Spain   **(100%)**
Tel.: (34) 912237420
Web Site:
http://www.deltapowersolutions.com
Electrical Equipment & Component Mfr
N.A.I.C.S.: 335999

Delta Energy Systems (Czech Republic) Spol. s.r.o.   **(3)**
Strasnicka 3165 1B, 10200, Prague, 10,
Czech Republic
Tel.: (420) 271751800
Web Site: http://www.energysystems.com
Sales Range: $25-49.9 Million
Emp.: 30
Communications Holding Company
N.A.I.C.S.: 334290

Delta Energy Systems (France)
S.A.   **(3)**
Route de Longjumeau, 91380, Orly, Chilly-Mazarin, France   **(100%)**

Tel.: (33) 169101805
Sales Range: $25-49.9 Million
Emp.: 12
Motor & Generator Mfr
N.A.I.C.S.: 335312

Delta Energy Systems (Italy)
s.r.l. (3)
Via Leonida Bissolati 54, 00187, Rome,
Italy (100%)
Tel.: (39) 0669941209
Web Site:
  http://www.deltapowersolutions.com
Sales Range: $25-49.9 Million
Emp.: 8
Electrical Equipment & Component Mfr
N.A.I.C.S.: 335999

Delta Energy Systems (Sweden)
AB (3)
Annavagen 3, PO Box 3096, Vaxjo, 30533,
Sweden (100%)
Tel.: (46) 470706800
Web Site:
  http://www.deltapowersolutions.com
Sales Range: $25-49.9 Million
Emp.: 12
Motor & Generator Mfr
N.A.I.C.S.: 335312

Delta Greentech (Brasil) S.A. (3)
Rua Almirante Alexandrino 3100 Bairro
Afonso Pena, Sao Jose dos Pinhais, 3045-
210, PR, Brazil (100%)
Tel.: (55) 4121416363
Web Site:
  http://www.deltaenergysystems.com
Electrical Equipment & Component Mfr
N.A.I.C.S.: 335999

Subsidiary (Non-US):

Delta Electronics (Wuhu) Co.,
Ltd. (2)
No 138 Jiuhua North Road LongShan
Street, Wuhu Economic and Technological
Development Zone, Wuhu, 241009, Anhui,
China
Tel.: (86) 5535773008
Web Site: http://www.delta.com.tw
Power Supply & Computer Peripherals Mfr
N.A.I.C.S.: 335311

Delta Electronics Components (Dong-
guan) Co., Ltd. (2)
Delta Industrial Estate, ShiJie Town, Dong-
guan, 523308, Guangdong, China
Tel.: (86) 76986635008
Web Site: http://www.deltaww.com
Electronic Components Mfr
N.A.I.C.S.: 335314

Delta Electronics Power (Dongguan)
Co., Ltd. (2)
Delta Industrial Zone, Shijie Town, Dong-
guan, 523308, Guangdong, China
Tel.: (86) 76986631008
Power Supplies Mfr
N.A.I.C.S.: 335999

Delta Video Display System (Wuji-
ang) Ltd. (2)
No 1688 Jiangxing East Road Yundong De-
velopment Zone, Wujiang, Jiangsu, China
Tel.: (86) 51263403008
Power Supply & Computer Peripherals Mfr
N.A.I.C.S.: 335311

Delta Electronics (Italy) S.r.l. (1)
Building Spaces Eur Arte Unit 508 - 5F Vi-
ale dell'Arte 25, 144, Rome, Italy
Tel.: (39) 0699310867
Electronic Product Distr
N.A.I.C.S.: 423690

Delta Electronics (Japan) Inc. (1)
2-1-14 Shibadaimon, Minato-ku, Tokyo,
105-0012, Japan (94%)
Tel.: (81) 357331111
Web Site: http://www.dej.co.jp
Sales Range: $75-99.9 Million
Emp.: 225
Electronic Products Sales
N.A.I.C.S.: 423690

Subsidiary (Non-US):

Delta Electronics (Korea), Inc. (2)
186 Ruey Kuang Rd, Neihu, Taipei, 11491,
Taiwan

Tel.: (886) 287972088
Web Site: http://www.deltakor.co.kr
Power Supplies & Computer Peripherals
Mfr
N.A.I.C.S.: 335311

Delta Electronics (Jiangsu) Ltd. (1)
No 1688 Jiangxing East Rd, Wujiang Eco-
nomic and Technological Development
Zone, Suzhou, 215200, Jiangsu, China
Tel.: (86) 51263401008
Power Supply Equipment Mfr
N.A.I.C.S.: 335999

Delta Electronics (Netherlands)
B.V. (1)
Zandsteen 15, 2132 MZ, Hoofddorp, Neth-
erlands
Tel.: (31) 208003900
Web Site: http://www.delta-emea.com
Emp.: 50
Power Supply & Computer Peripherals Mfr
N.A.I.C.S.: 335999

Subsidiary (US):

Amerlux, LLC (2)
178 Bauer Dr, Oakland, NJ 07436
Tel.: (973) 882-5010
Web Site: https://www.amerlux.com
Commercial, Industrial & Institutional Elec-
tric Lighting Fixture Mfr
N.A.I.C.S.: 335132
Chuck Campagna (Pres & CEO)

Subsidiary (Non-US):

Eltek AS (2)
Graaterudveien 8, 3036, Drammen, Norway
Tel.: (47) 32203200
Web Site: https://www.eltek.com
Emp.: 1,000
Power Solutions & Services for Telecom,
Rail & Infrastructure, Power Generation &
Distribution, Solar Energy & Electric Ve-
hicles Industries
N.A.I.C.S.: 335311
Frode Vagen (Chief Quality Officer)

Subsidiary (Non-US):

Eltek Australia Pty Ltd. (3)
20-21/45 Normanby Road, Notting Hill,
3168, VIC, Australia
Tel.: (61) 294794200
Web Site: http://www.eltek.com
Sales Range: $25-49.9 Million
Emp.: 50
Power Supplies Sales & Installation Ser-
vices
N.A.I.C.S.: 423690

Eltek Deutschland GmbH (3)
Ferdinand-Porsche-Str 45, 60386, Frankfurt
am Main, Germany
Tel.: (49) 69 420 02 0
Web Site: http://www.eltek.de
Emp.: 150
Power Electronics & Energy Conversion
Products Mfr & Distr
N.A.I.C.S.: 335311
Volker Rossmann (CEO)

Subsidiary (Domestic):

Eltek Montage GmbH (4)
Ferdinand-Porsche-Str 45, 60386, Frankfurt
am Main, Germany
Tel.: (49) 69 42002 0
Installation & Maintenance of Power Sup-
plies
N.A.I.C.S.: 811210
Volker Rossmann (Mng Dir)

Subsidiary (Non-US):

Eltek Egypt ASA (3)
15 Salah Salem Road Entrance 1 4th Floor,
11371, Cairo, Egypt
Tel.: (20) 224033055
Web Site: http://www.eltek.com
Emp.: 9
Power Electronics & Energy Conversion
Products Distr
N.A.I.C.S.: 423690
Mahmoud Morsy (Mng Dir)

Eltek Energy Technology Ltd. (3)
Guancheng Science & Technology Park
Shilong Road, Guanlong Roads Section,
Dongguan, 523119, Guangdong, China

Tel.: (86) 769 2265 1108
Sales Range: $100-124.9 Million
Emp.: 400
Power Supplies Mfr & Sales
N.A.I.C.S.: 335311
Colin Huang (Office Mgr)

Subsidiary (US):

Eltek Inc. (3)
2925 E Plano Pkwy, Plano, TX 75074
Tel.: (469) 330-9100
Web Site: http://www.eltek.com
Sales Range: $500-549.9 Million
Emp.: 135
Power Electronics & Energy Conversion
Products Mfr & Distr
N.A.I.C.S.: 423690

Subsidiary (Non-US):

Eltek Argentina S.R.L. (4)
Jose Roque Funes 1761 Complejo, Vista
Office Torre 1 - PB C, X5009LFS, Cordoba,
Argentina
Tel.: (54) 351 4813054
Web Site: http://www.eltek.com
Power Electronics & Energy Conversion
Products Distr
N.A.I.C.S.: 423690

Eltek Energy International de Mexico
S. de R.L. de C.V. (4)
Gustavo Baz 309 Edificio E PB Col La
Loma, Tlalnepantla, Mexico
Tel.: (52) 55 52 20 6455
Web Site: http://www.eltek.com
Power Electronics & Energy Conversion
Products Mfr & Distr
N.A.I.C.S.: 335311

Eltek Peru SRL (4)
Calle Enrique Palacios No 335 Oficina 503
Edificio Burgos, Miraflores, Lima,
Peru (100%)
Tel.: (51) 12 42 77 66
Power Supplies Sales
N.A.I.C.S.: 423690
Gina Gonzales Marquez (Reg Mgr-Peru,
Ecuador & Bolivia)

Eltek Sistemas de Energia Industria e
Comercio S.A. (4)
Av Dr Sebastiao Henrique da Cunha Pon-
tes 8000, Chacaras Reunidas, Sao Jose
dos Campos, SP, Brazil
Tel.: (55) 1239322300
Web Site: http://www.eltek.com
Power Supplies Mfr & Distr
N.A.I.C.S.: 335311

Subsidiary (Non-US):

Eltek Italia S.r.l. (3)
Via Leonida Bissolati 54, 00187, Rome,
Italy
Tel.: (39) 06 41 91 227
Web Site: http://www.eltek.com
Sales Range: $25-49.9 Million
Emp.: 6
Power Supplies Sales
N.A.I.C.S.: 423690
Alessandro Casicci (CEO)

Eltek Pakistan (Pvt) Ltd. (3)
House 231 Street 13,E11/4, Islamabad,
44000, Pakistan (100%)
Tel.: (92) 51 111 537 537
Web Site: http://www.eltek.com
Sales Range: $1-9.9 Million
Emp.: 160
Power Supplies Sales
N.A.I.C.S.: 423690
Naveed Ahmed Farooqi (CEO & CFO)

Eltek Polska Sp. z o.o. (3)
ul Gorlicka 2, 71-042, Szczecin,
Poland (51%)
Tel.: (48) 914852440
Web Site: http://www.eltek.com.pl
Sales Range: $25-49.9 Million
Emp.: 60
Power Supplies & Systems Mfr & Sales
N.A.I.C.S.: 423690
Maciej Stypinski (Dir-Comml-Railways)

Eltek Power (Malaysia) Sdn. Bhd (3)
Suite C-05-08 Level 5 Block C, Sky Park
One City Jalan USJ 25/1, 47650, Subang
Jaya, Selangor, Malaysia

Tel.: (60) 350223298
Web Site: http://www.eltek.com
Sales Range: $25-49.9 Million
Emp.: 30
Power Electronics & Energy Conversion
Products Distr
N.A.I.C.S.: 423690

Eltek Power (UK) Ltd. (3)
Cleveland Road, Hemel Hempstead, HP2
7EY, Hertfordshire, United Kingdom
Tel.: (44) 1442 219355
Web Site: http://www.eltek.com
Sales Range: $25-49.9 Million
Emp.: 50
Power Electronics & Energy Conversion
Products Mfr & Distr
N.A.I.C.S.: 335311

Eltek Power France SAS (3)
Z I de Bastillac-Nord, 65000, Tarbes,
France
Tel.: (33) 5623 40930
Web Site: http://www.eltek.com
Emp.: 40
Power Electronics & Energy Conversion
Products Mfr & Distr
N.A.I.C.S.: 335311

Eltek Power Oy (3)
Juvan Teollisuuskatu 15, 02920, Espoo,
Finland (100%)
Tel.: (358) 207 798 820
Web Site: http://www.eltek.com
Sales Range: $25-49.9 Million
Emp.: 5
Power Supplies Sales
N.A.I.C.S.: 423690
Allan Christiansen (Mng Dir)

Eltek Power Pte. Ltd. (3)
No 3 Teban Gardens Crescent, Singapore,
608920, Singapore
Tel.: (65) 67732326
Web Site: http://www.eltek.com
Sales Range: $100-124.9 Million
Emp.: 80
Power Electronics & Energy Conversion
Products Distr
N.A.I.C.S.: 423690

Subsidiary (Non-US):

Eltek Power Inc. (4)
0302 3rd Floor Orient Square Building Em-
erald Avenue, Ortigas, Pasig, Manila, Philip-
pines
Tel.: (63) 29106355
Sales Range: $25-49.9 Million
Emp.: 18
Power Supplies Sales
N.A.I.C.S.: 423690
Thadeo Pulian (Country Mgr)

Subsidiary (Non-US):

Eltek Power Sweden AB (3)
Hammarbacken 4 A, 191 49, Sollentuna,
Sweden (100%)
Tel.: (46) 8 62 66420
Emp.: 32
Power Supplies Sales
N.A.I.C.S.: 423690
Lars Dousa (Dir-Indus Bus Unit)

Eltek SGS Pvt. Ltd. (3)
Plot No 43 Sector 35 HSIIDC, Gurgaon,
122 001, Haryana, India (100%)
Tel.: (91) 1246783333
Power Systems & Supplies Sales & Installa-
tion
N.A.I.C.S.: 423690
Akshaye Barbuddhe (Country Mgr)

Eltek s.r.o. (3)
Palenica 53/79, 033 17, Liptovsky Hradok,
Slovakia
Tel.: (421) 4452 33211
Web Site: http://www.eltek.com
Power Supplies Mfr
N.A.I.C.S.: 335311
Stefan Kuric (Mng Dir)

OOO Eltek (3)
2nd Sovyetskaya House 7 Office 102,
193036, Saint Petersburg, Russia (100%)
Tel.: (7) 8123321117
Web Site: http://www.eltek.ru
Sales Range: $25-49.9 Million
Emp.: 35

Delta Electronics, Inc.—(Continued)

Power Supplies Sales & Power Systems
Installation Service
N.A.I.C.S.: 423690

Delta Electronics (Peru) Inc.
S.R.L. **(1)**
Av Pardo y Aliaga 699 Of 601 San Isidro,
Lima, Peru
Tel.: (51) 995622632
Power Supply Equipment Distr
N.A.I.C.S.: 423610

Delta Electronics (Sweden) AB **(1)**
Hammarbacken 4 A, Box 404, 191 24, Sol-
lentuna, Sweden
Tel.: (46) 86266420
Power Electronic Component Mfr & Distr
N.A.I.C.S.: 334416

Delta Electronics (UK) Ltd. **(1)**
Cleveland Road, Hemel Hempstead, HP2
7EY, Hertfordshire, United Kingdom
Tel.: (44) 1442219355
Power System Maintenance Services
N.A.I.C.S.: 561730

Delta Electronics Europe Ltd. **(1)**
1 Redwood Court, Peel Park, East Kilbride,
G74 5PF, United Kingdom
Tel.: (44) 1355588888
Web Site: https://www.delta-emea.com
Sales Range: $25-49.9 Million
Emp.: 50
Electronic Components Mfr
N.A.I.C.S.: 334419
Jackie Chang (Pres & Gen Mgr-EMEA)

Delta Electronics Int'l (Singapore) Pte
Ltd **(1)**
Tel.: (65) 67475155
Switching Power Supply Mfr; Visual Dis-
plays & Electronic Components Supplier
N.A.I.C.S.: 221118

Holding (Non-US):

Delta Electronics (Thailand) Public
Company Limited **(2)**
909 Soi 9 Moo 4 EPZ Bangpoo Industrial
Estate Tambon Prakasa, Amphur Muang
Samut Prakan, Samut Prakan, 10280,
Thailand **(42.85%)**
Tel.: (66) 27092800
Web Site: https://www.deltathailand.com
Rev.: $4,325,286,516
Assets: $3,156,965,329
Liabilities: $1,185,381,964
Net Worth: $1,971,583,365
Earnings: $537,790,235
Emp.: 21,245
Fiscal Year-end: 12/31/2023
Switching Power Supply Mfr; Video Dis-
plays & Electronic Components Supplier
N.A.I.C.S.: 221122
Chin-Ming Chen (CIO)

Subsidiary (US):

DET Logistics (USA) Corporation **(3)**
46101 Fremont Blvd, Fremont, CA 94538
Tel.: (510) 668-5100
Power Management Equipment Distr
N.A.I.C.S.: 423830

Subsidiary (Non-US):

Delta Electronics (Slovakia) s.r.o. **(3)**
Priemyselna 4600/1, 018 41, Dubnica nad
Vahom, Slovakia **(100%)**
Tel.: (421) 424661111
Web Site: https://www.deltaelectronics.sk
Sales Range: $25-49.9 Million
Emp.: 900
Electronic Components Mfr
N.A.I.C.S.: 334419

Delta Electronics International (Singa-
pore) Pte Ltd **(3)**
4 Kaki Bukit Avenue 1 05-04, Singapore,
417939, Singapore **(54.83%)**
Tel.: (65) 674 751 55
Investment Management Service
N.A.I.C.S.: 523999
Patrick Chang (Mng Dir)

Delta Energy Systems (Germany)
GmbH **(3)**
Coesterweg 45, 59494, Soest, Germany
Tel.: (49) 29219870

Web Site:
http://www.deltaenergysystems.com
Power Supply Systems
N.A.I.C.S.: 332410

Delta Energy Systems (India) Private
Ltd. **(3)**
Plot No 43 Sector 35 HSIIDC, 122001, Gur-
gaon, Haryana, India **(100%)**
Tel.: (91) 1244874900
Web Site:
http://www.deltaenergysystems.com
Electronic Coil Transformer & Other Induc-
tor Mfr
N.A.I.C.S.: 334416

Delta Energy Systems (Singapore)
Pte. Ltd. **(3)**
Ruby Warehouse Complex No 8 Kaki Bukit
Road 2 04-18, Singapore, 417841, Singa-
pore
Tel.: (65) 67475155
Investment Management Service
N.A.I.C.S.: 523940

Delta Green Tianjin Industries Co.,
Ltd. **(3)**
168 No 15 Coastal Way, Tianjin Port Free
Trade Zone, Tianjin, China **(100%)**
Tel.: (86) 2225760351
Sales Range: $400-449.9 Million
Emp.: 1,500
Wireless Communication Equipment Mfr
N.A.I.C.S.: 334220

Delta Electronics International
Ltd. **(1)**
Rm A & R 17 Fl Edif Fu Tat Fa Yuen
Alameda Dr Carlos Dassumpcao, Macau,
China (Macau)
Tel.: (853) 28755808
Power Supply & Computer Peripherals Mfr
N.A.I.C.S.: 334112

Delta Electronics Mexico S.A. de
C.V. **(1)**
Av Gustavo Baz 309 Edificio E Planta Baja,
Col La Loma, Tlalnepantla, 54030, Mexico,
Mexico
Tel.: (52) 15536039200
Web Site: http://www.delta.com.tw
Computer Peripheral Equipment Distr
N.A.I.C.S.: 423430

Delta Energy Systems (UK)
Limited **(1)**
1 Redwood Court Peel Park, Scotland, East
Kilbride, G74 5PF, United Kingdom
Tel.: (44) 1355588888
N.A.I.C.S.: 334419

Delta Greentech (China) Co.,
Ltd. **(1)**
No 238 Min-Xia Road, Pudong District,
Shanghai, China
Tel.: (86) 2158635678
Electronic Product Distr
N.A.I.C.S.: 423690

Delta Networks, Inc. **(1)**
186 Ruey Kuang Rd, Neihu, Taipei, 11491,
Taiwan **(59.03%)**
Tel.: (886) 287972088
Web Site: http://www.dninetworks.com
Sales Range: $400-449.9 Million
Emp.: 2,400
Networking Systems & Peripherals Mfr
N.A.I.C.S.: 334118

Subsidiary (Non-US):

Delta Networks (Dongguan) Co.,
Ltd. **(2)**
Delta Industrial Estate, Shijie Town, Dong-
guan, 523308, Guangdong,
China **(59.51%)**
Tel.: (86) 76986635008
Mfr & Sales of Radio Transmission Appara-
tus
N.A.I.C.S.: 334419

Delta Networks (Shanghai) Ltd. **(2)**
No 238 Minxia Road, Pudong New District,
Shanghai, China
Tel.: (86) 2168723988
Power Supplies & Computer Peripherals
Mfr
N.A.I.C.S.: 423610

Delta Solutions (Finland) Oy **(1)**

Rajatorpantie 8, 1600, Vantaa, Finland
Tel.: (358) 9849660
Electronic Product Distr
N.A.I.C.S.: 423690

Digital Projection Ltd. **(1)**
Unit 3 Aniseed Park Broadgate, Oldham,
OL9 9XA, United Kingdom
Tel.: (44) 1619473300
Web Site: https://www.digitalprojection.com
Projector Mfr & Distr
N.A.I.C.S.: 339992

Eltek Power Co., Ltd. **(1)**
173/13 Moo 9, Bangpla Sub-District Bang
Phli District, Samut Prakan, 10540, Thai-
land
Tel.: (66) 20161481
Power System Maintenance Services
N.A.I.C.S.: 561730

March Networks (Australia) Pty
Limited **(1)**
Unit 7 65 Doody Street Sydney Corporate
Park, Alexandria, 2015, NSW, Australia
Tel.: (61) 1300089419
Software Development Services
N.A.I.C.S.: 541511

March Networks (France) SAS **(1)**
3-5 Rue Saint-Georges, 75009, Paris,
France
Tel.: (33) 881562409727
Software Development Services
N.A.I.C.S.: 541511

March Networks S.r.l. **(1)**
Via dei Lavoratori Autobianchi n 1 Edificio
23, 20832, Desio, Monza e Brianza, Italy
Tel.: (39) 036217935
Video Surveillance System Software Ser-
vices
N.A.I.C.S.: 532282

PreOptix Co., Ltd. **(1)**
8F 428 Tun Hua Road, Taichung, Taiwan
Tel.: (886) 422969779
Sales Range: $25-49.9 Million
Emp.: 30
Optical Equipment Mfr
N.A.I.C.S.: 333310

Subsidiary (Non-US):

PreOptix (Jiang Su) Co., Ltd. **(2)**
No 35 Huayang North Road Jurong Eco-
nomic Development Zone, Zhenjiang, Ji-
angsu, China
Tel.: (86) 51185978455
Lenses & Optical Engines Mfr & Distr
N.A.I.C.S.: 333310

Trihedral UK Limited **(1)**
Glover Pavilion Campus 3, Aberdeen Inno-
vation Park Balgownie Drive, Aberdeen,
B22 8GW, United Kingdom
Tel.: (44) 1224258910
Software Development Services
N.A.I.C.S.: 541511

**DELTA FLEISCH HANDELS
GMBH**
Lagerstrasse 11, Hamburg, 20357,
Germany
Tel.: (49) 40431610
Web Site: http://www.delta-
hamburg.de
Rev.: $53,106,900
Emp.: 110
Meat Product Whslr
N.A.I.C.S.: 424470
Ludmilla Kreuz (Mng Dir)

**DELTA FOR CONSTRUCTION
& REBUILDING**
Smouha-rotation Ibn Abi Taleb inter-
sevtion Albert 1 St with Kamal El-D,
Salah Delta life Towers, Alexandria,
Egypt
Tel.: (20) 3423 88 22
Web Site: http://www.deltaegypt.com
Year Founded: 1986
DCRC.CA—(EGX)
Sales Range: Less than $1 Million
Real Estate Investment Services
N.A.I.C.S.: 523999

Ali Elba (Chm)

DELTA GROUP PTY LTD
577 Plummer Street, Port Melbourne,
3207, VIC, Australia
Tel.: (61) 9646 8277 **AU**
Web Site:
http://www.deltagroup.com.au
Holding Companies; Landscape &
Excavation Services
N.A.I.C.S.: 551112
Con Petropoulos (Founder & Mng
Dir)

Subsidiaries:

CMA Contracting Pty Limited **(1)**
Level 5 160 Sussex St, Sydney, 2000, New
South Wales, Australia
Tel.: (61) 292003500
Web Site:
http://www.cmacontracting.com.au
Demolition Contracting Services
N.A.I.C.S.: 238910

Delta Group Pty Ltd - Concrete Recy-
cling Division **(1)**
473 Somerville Road, Sunshine, 3020, VIC,
Australia
Tel.: (61) 3 9315 2555
Concrete Recycling Services
N.A.I.C.S.: 423930

Delta Group Pty Ltd - Metal Recy-
cling Division **(1)**
42-50 Pinnacle Road, Altona, 3025, VIC,
Australia
Tel.: (61) 3 9369 2374
Metal Recycling Services
N.A.I.C.S.: 423930

DELTA HOLDING
Autoput Za Zagreb 35, Novi, 11000,
Belgrade, Serbia
Tel.: (381) 112012400
Web Site: http://www.deltaholding.rs
Year Founded: 1991
Sales Range: $350-399.9 Million
Emp.: 1,300
Holding Company
N.A.I.C.S.: 551112
Miroslav Miskovic (Pres)

Subsidiaries:

Delta Agrar d.o.o. **(1)**
Autoput za Zagreb 35, Novi Beograd,
11070, Belgrade, Serbia
Tel.: (381) 11 201 23 00
Web Site: http://www.deltaagrar.rs
Sales Range: $350-399.9 Million
Food Products Mfr
N.A.I.C.S.: 311991
Ivan Kostic (CEO)

Subsidiary (Domestic):

DANUBIUS d.o.o. Novi Sad **(2)**
Kanalska 1, 21000, Novi Sad, Serbia
Tel.: (381) 21 48 08 900
Web Site: http://www.addanubius.rs
Pasta Mfr
N.A.I.C.S.: 311824

Yuhor A.D. **(2)**
Kablovska bb, 35000, Jagodina, Serbia
Tel.: (381) 35 200 300
Web Site: http://www.yuhor.rs
Canned Meat Product Mfr
N.A.I.C.S.: 311999

Delta Foundation **(1)**
Vladimira Popovica 6, Belgrade, 11070,
Serbia
Tel.: (381) 112012663
Web Site: http://www.deltafondacija.rs
Employee Benefit Services
N.A.I.C.S.: 525120

Delta Motors **(1)**
Radnicka 8, 11030, Belgrade, Serbia
Tel.: (381) 11 353 99 00
Web Site: http://www.deltaauto.rs
Automotive Distr
N.A.I.C.S.: 441110

Delta Real Estate D.O.O. **(1)**
Milentija Popovica 7b, 11000, Belgrade,
Serbia

Tel.: (381) 11 201 26 00
Web Site: http://www.deltarealestate.rs
Emp.: 50
Real Estate Manangement Services
N.A.I.C.S.: 531390
Dayan Earamich *(VP)*

Subsidiary (Non-US):

Standard Furniture Factory d.d.   **(2)**
Bosanski put 103, Llijas, 71380, Sarajevo,
Bosnia & Herzegovina
Tel.: (387) 3 397 3222
Web Site: http://www.standard-furniture.ba
Rev.: $25,489,769
Assets: $17,942,327
Liabilities: $13,818,030
Net Worth: $4,124,297
Earnings: $76,302
Emp.: 446
Fiscal Year-end: 12/31/2020
Wooden Furniture Mfr
N.A.I.C.S.: 321999

DELTA INDUSTRIAL RE-SOURCES LIMITED

unit no 111 Aggarwal City Square
Plot 10, District Center Mangalam
Place Sector 3 Rohini, Delhi, 110
085, India
Tel.: (91) 1127860681   In
Web Site: https://delta.ind.in
Year Founded: 1984
539596—(BOM)
Rev.: $434,317
Assets: $951,600
Liabilities: $282,715
Net Worth: $668,886
Earnings: ($15,939)
Emp.: 3
Fiscal Year-end: 03/31/21
Textile Products Distr
N.A.I.C.S.: 424310
Rohit Mittal *(Mng Dir)*

DELTA INSURANCE COMPANY LTD.

15 Al Hussein Bin Ali Street, PO Box
3055, Amman, 11181, Jordan
Tel.: (962) 64640008
Web Site: https://www.delta-ins.com
Year Founded: 1976
DICL—(AMM)
Rev.: $25,089,900
Assets: $43,293,271
Liabilities: $28,301,525
Net Worth: $14,991,746
Earnings: $862,868
Emp.: 115
Fiscal Year-end: 12/31/20
General Insurance Services
N.A.I.C.S.: 524298
Ghassan Elia Costandi Nuqul *(Chm)*

DELTA LEASING & FINANCE LIMITED

55 F I E Patparganj Industrial Area,
Delhi, 110092, India
Tel.: (91) 11 42420164   In
Web Site: http://www.deltaleasing.in
Year Founded: 1983
Rev.: $185,477
Assets: $3,426,023
Liabilities: $108,643
Net Worth: $3,317,380
Earnings: $193
Emp.: 7
Fiscal Year-end: 03/31/18
Financial Services
N.A.I.C.S.: 523999
Seema Khandelwal *(Exec Dir)*

DELTA LIFE INSURANCE COMPANY LIMITED

Delta Life Tower Plot 37 Road 90,
Gulshan Circle - 2, Dhaka, 1212,
Bangladesh
Tel.: (880) 9613666000
Web Site: https://www.deltalife.org

Year Founded: 1986
DELTALIFE—(DHA)
Sales Range: $25-49.9 Million
Insurance Agency Services
N.A.I.C.S.: 524210
Uttam Kumar Sadhu *(Deputy Mng Dir)*

DELTA MANUFACTURING LTD

B-87 MIDC Ambad, Nashik, 422 010,
Maharashtra, India
Tel.: (91) 2532382238
Web Site:
https://www.deltamagnets.com
DELTAMAGNT—(NSE)
Sales Range: $10-24.9 Million
Magnet Mfr
N.A.I.C.S.: 331110
Ram H. Shroff *(Vice Chm & Mng Dir)*

Subsidiaries:

Arrow Textiles Ltd.   **(1)**
Plot No 101 - 103 19th Street MIDC Satpur,
Nasik, 422 007, India
Tel.: (91) 2533918200
Web Site: http://www.arrowtextiles.com
Rev.: $6,173,490
Assets: $5,899,508
Liabilities: $1,176,883
Net Worth: $4,722,625
Earnings: $148,604
Emp.: 303
Fiscal Year-end: 03/31/2019
Fabric Woven Label Mfr
N.A.I.C.S.: 313310
Ulhas J. Kale *(CFO)*

MMG India Pvt Ltd   **(1)**
B-87 MIDC Industrial Area, AMBAD, Nasik,
422 010, India   **(100%)**
Tel.: (91) 2532382238
Web Site:
http://www.deltamagnetsgroup.com
Emp.: 200
Electronic Components Mfr
N.A.I.C.S.: 335999

DELTA N.V.

Poelendaelesingel 10, 4335 JA, Mid-
delburg, Netherlands
Tel.: (31) 11388400
Web Site: http://www.delta.nl
Year Founded: 1991
Sales Range: $1-4.9 Billion
Emp.: 1,786
Utilities Operator
N.A.I.C.S.: 221122
Frank Verhagen *(CFO)*

Subsidiaries:

DELTA Energy B.V.   **(1)**
Poelendaelesingel 10, Middelburg, 4335 JA,
Zeeland, Netherlands
Tel.: (31) 118 883 883
Web Site: http://www.delta.nl
Sales Range: $500-549.9 Million
Emp.: 3,000
Elictric Power Generation Services
N.A.I.C.S.: 221118
Gerard Uytdewilligen *(CEO)*

Subsidiary (Domestic):

Deltius B.V.   **(2)**
Europaweg Zuid Haven 9890, 4389 PD,
Ritthem, Zeeland, Netherlands
Tel.: (31) 113 741900
Waste Management Services
N.A.I.C.S.: 924110
Frank Verhagen *(Gen Mgr)*

Litro Energie Nederland B.V.   **(2)**
Poelendaelesingel 10, 4335 JA, Middelburg,
Netherlands
Tel.: (31) 30 2903840
Waste Management Services
N.A.I.C.S.: 924110

DELTA Infra B.V.   **(1)**
Anthony Fokkerstraat 8, Goes, 4330 KA,
Netherlands
Tel.: (31) 113741902
Web Site: http://www.delta.nl

Sales Range: $75-99.9 Million
Emp.: 250
Waste Management Services
N.A.I.C.S.: 924110
Erik Duim *(Bus Dir)*

DELTA Investerings Maatschappij
B.V.   **(1)**
Poelendaelesingel 10, Middelburg, 4335 JA,
Zeeland, Netherlands
Tel.: (31) 118 616888
Waste Management Services
N.A.I.C.S.: 924110

DELTA Milieu Groencompost
B.V.   **(1)**
IJslandweg 6Â , 4455 SR, Nieuwdorp,
Netherlands
Tel.: (31) 113613960
Waste Management Services
N.A.I.C.S.: 924110

DELTA Milieu Recycling B.V.   **(1)**
Deltastraat 47, 4301 RC, Zierikzee, Zee-
land, Netherlands
Tel.: (31) 111 412051
Waste Management Services
N.A.I.C.S.: 924110

DELTA Netwerkbedrijf B.V.   **(1)**
Stationspark 28, Goes, 4462, Netherlands
Tel.: (31) 113 74 11 00
Web Site: http://www.deltanetwerkbedrijf.nl
Emp.: 200
Electric Power Distr
N.A.I.C.S.: 221122

Indaver Nederland B.V.   **(1)**
Polenweg 4, 4455 SX, Nieuwdorp, Nether-
lands
Tel.: (31) 113 67 67 67
Web Site: http://www.indaver.nl
Emp.: 50
Waste Management Services
N.A.I.C.S.: 924110
Peter Louwman *(Mng Dir)*

Internetplatform Zeeland B.V.   **(1)**
Het Rip 9, 4493 RL, Kamperland, Zeeland,
Netherlands
Tel.: (31) 113 377778
Waste Management Services
N.A.I.C.S.: 924110

Stichting DELTA Zeeland Fonds   **(1)**
Poelendaelesingel 10, 4335 JA, Middelburg,
Netherlands
Tel.: (31) 118 88 30 96
Web Site: http://www.deltazeelandfonds.nl
Investment Management Service
N.A.I.C.S.: 523940

Stortplaats Koegorspolder B.V.   **(1)**
Finlandweg 19, 4538 BL, Terneuzen, Neth-
erlands
Tel.: (31) 115 678800
Waste Management Services
N.A.I.C.S.: 924110

Stortplaats Noord en Midden Zeeland
B.V.   **(1)**
Moldiepweg 7, 3313 LN, Dordrecht, Nether-
lands
Tel.: (31) 113676767
Web Site: http://www.indaver.nl
Real Estate Manangement Services
N.A.I.C.S.: 531390

Windpark Kreekraksluis B.V.   **(1)**
Poelendaelesingel 10, 4335 JA, Middelburg,
Netherlands
Tel.: (31) 118 882000
Web Site:
http://www.windparkkreekraksluis.nl
Elictric Power Generation Services
N.A.I.C.S.: 221115

DELTA OIL & GAS, INC.

Suite 604 700 West Pender Street,
Vancouver, V6C 1G8, BC, Canada
Tel.: (604) 602-1500   CO
Web Site:
http://www.deltaoilandgas.com
Year Founded: 2001
Sales Range: Less than $1 Million
Oil & Gas Exploration
N.A.I.C.S.: 211120

DELTA PLUS GROUP

ZAC La Peyroliere, BP 140, 84405,
Apt, Cedex, France
Tel.: (33) 490742033   FR
Web Site: https://www.deltaplus.eu
Year Founded: 1977
DLTA—(EUR)
Rev.: $354,592,888
Assets: $457,273,752
Liabilities: $264,317,248
Net Worth: $192,956,504
Earnings: $35,496,136
Emp.: 1,943
Fiscal Year-end: 12/31/20
Protection Equipment Mfr
N.A.I.C.S.: 335999

Subsidiaries:

Alpic Biotech Ltd.   **(1)**
Signature 1 510 Sarkhej - Gandhinagar
Highway Near YMCA Club, Makarba,
Ahmedabad, 380054, India
Tel.: (91) 8460825777
Web Site: https://alpicbiotechltd.com
Pharmaceutical Products Distr
N.A.I.C.S.: 424210

Alpic S.A.   **(1)**
Technology Park 691 Chemin des Fon-
taines, 38190, Bernin, France
Tel.: (33) 476133030
Web Site: http://www.alpic.fr
Personal Protective Equipment Distr
N.A.I.C.S.: 423450

Aspreseg SAS   **(1)**
Calle 17A No 68 D, Montevideo Industrial
Zone, Bogota, Colombia
Tel.: (57) 14845845
Personal Protective Equipment Mfr & Distr
N.A.I.C.S.: 339113
Luis David Perez Merchan *(Gen Mgr)*

DELTA PLUS BENELUX N.V.   **(1)**
Peter Benoitlaan 49, 8200, Brugge, Belgium
Tel.: (32) 50 45 49 00
Personal Protective Equipment Distr
N.A.I.C.S.: 423990

DELTA PLUS INDIA PVT. Ltd.   **(1)**
EN 12 5th Floor Sector V, Bidhannagar,
700 091, West Bengal, India
Tel.: (91) 3174 222723
Personal Protective Equipment Distr
N.A.I.C.S.: 423990
Sugata Dutta *(Mgr-Pur)*

DELTA PLUS UKRAINA SARL   **(1)**
21 Tsentralna str, Gora Borylspil District,
Kiev, 08324, Ukraine
Tel.: (380) 44 364 19 73
Personal Protective Equipment Distr
N.A.I.C.S.: 423990

Degil Safety Products, Inc.   **(1)**
200 Zenway Blvd Unit 1, Woodbridge, L4H
0L6, ON, Canada
Tel.: (905) 856-1511
Web Site: http://www.degilsafety.com
Safety Equipment Mfr & Distr
N.A.I.C.S.: 339113
Tino Dente *(Pres)*

Delta Plus (U.K.) Ltd.   **(1)**
Unit 1 Point 5 Walker Ind Park, Blackburn,
BB1 2QE, United Kingdom
Tel.: (44) 1254 686 100
Web Site: http://www.lhsafety.co.uk
Personal Protective Equipment Distr
N.A.I.C.S.: 423990

Delta Plus Centroamerica S.A.   **(1)**
La Uruca In Front of the Entrance to
Pueblo, Antiguo of the Amusement Park
Local 2, San Jose, Costa Rica
Tel.: (506) 40002580
Personal Protective Equipment Mfr & Distr
N.A.I.C.S.: 339113

Delta Plus Ceska Republika
S.ro.   **(1)**
Vrsovika 9, 101 00, Prague, 10, Czech Re-
public
Tel.: (420) 267 227 241
Protection Equipment Mfr
N.A.I.C.S.: 334419

Delta Plus China Co., Ltd.   **(1)**

Delta Plus Group—(Continued)

2 Ousheng Ave, Pingwang Zhonglu Park
Wujiang Dist, Suzhou, 215221, Jiangsu,
China
Tel.: (86) 51263647000
Personal Protective Equipment Mfr & Distr
N.A.I.C.S.: 339113
Yuga Yao *(Mgr-Supply Chain)*

Delta Plus Croatia d.o.o. **(1)**
Poslovni centar Zitnjak Slavonska avenija
24/6, 10000, Zagreb, Croatia
Tel.: (385) 1 2929 111
Protection Equipment Mfr
N.A.I.C.S.: 334419

Delta Plus Hellas SRL
34 KM Athinon Lavriou Avenue, Markopou-
lon, 19003, Attikis, Greece
Tel.: (30) 22 990 26001
Web Site: http://www.deltaplus.fr
Protection Equipment Mfr
N.A.I.C.S.: 334419
George Kakos *(Gen Mgr)*

Delta Plus Iberia S.A.U. **(1)**
Mecanicos 39, Poligono Industrial IN 2C
Santa Pola, 03130, Alicante, Spain
Tel.: (34) 965415011
Personal Protective Equipment Mfr & Distr
N.A.I.C.S.: 339113

Delta Plus Magyarorszag Kft **(1)**
Mester Utca 87, Budapest, 1095, Hungary
Tel.: (36) 1 377 8124
Web Site: http://www.deltaplus.eu
Emp.: 6
Protection Equipment Mfr
N.A.I.C.S.: 335999
Geza Szalai *(Mng Dir)*

Delta Plus Middle East FZE **(1)**
A2 50/51 SAIF Zone, PO Box 121220,
Sharjah, 121220, United Arab Emirates
Tel.: (971) 6 5575 004
Web Site: http://www.deltaplus.eu
Emp.: 15
Protection Equipment Mfr
N.A.I.C.S.: 335999
Arun Parasnis *(Mng Dir)*

**Delta Plus Personel Giyim Ve Is Gu-
venligi Ekipmanlari Sanayi Ve Ticaret
Limited Sirket** **(1)**
9 Yapi Sanayi Sitesi Akcaburgaz Mah 3028
Sok No 1 D 5 6, Esenyurt, Istanbul, Turkiye
Tel.: (90) 2125033994
Personal Protective Equipment Mfr & Distr
N.A.I.C.S.: 339113

Delta Plus Peru SAC **(1)**
Los Eucaliptos 371 Avenue, Surquillo, Lima,
16, Lima, Peru
Tel.: (51) 1 225 4114
Web Site: http://www.deltaplus.eu
Emp.: 26
Protection Equipment Mfr
N.A.I.C.S.: 335999
Antonio Dulong *(Mgr-Supply Chain)*

Delta Plus Philippines, Inc. **(1)**
No 0671 Formerly 1425 Quirino Avenue,
San Dionisio, Paranaque, 1700, Philippines
Tel.: (63) 283560901
Personal Protective Equipment Mfr & Distr
N.A.I.C.S.: 339113
Michael Del Rosario *(Reg Sls Mgr)*

Delta Plus Polska SP zo.o **(1)**
Ul Sokolska 68B, 41-219, Sosnowiec, Po-
land
Tel.: (48) 3229 64750
Web Site: http://www.deltaplus.com.eu
Protection Equipment Mfr
N.A.I.C.S.: 334419
Adam Krzycki *(Gen Mgr)*

Delta Plus Romania SRL **(1)**
Dudesti Pantelimon nr 42, Sector 2, Bucha-
rest, 21838, Romania
Tel.: (40) 21 250 0556
Protection Equipment Mfr
N.A.I.C.S.: 335999

Delta Plus Russie OOO **(1)**
Business Center Rosso Riva Shluzovaya
Embankment 4, 115114, Moscow, Russia
Tel.: (7) 9066494848
Web Site: http://www.deltaplus-cei.com
Safety Equipment Mfr

N.A.I.C.S.: 339113

Delta Plus SAS **(1)**
Z A C La Peyroliere, BP 140, 84405, Apt,
Cedex, France
Tel.: (33) 490742033
Personal Protective Equipment Mfr & Distr
N.A.I.C.S.: 339113

Delta Plus Sicurex SRL **(1)**
Via E Fermi 265, Vicenza, 36100, Italy
Tel.: (39) 0 444 822 822
Web Site: http://www.deltaplus.it
Protection Equipment Mfr
N.A.I.C.S.: 334419

Delta Plus Slovensko SRO **(1)**
Mlynske Nivy 71, 82105, Bratislava, Slova-
kia
Tel.: (421) 2 3266 2611
Web Site: http://www.delta-plus.sk
Protection Equipment Mfr
N.A.I.C.S.: 334419

Delta Plus-E SA **(1)**
Poligono Industrial IN-2C/Mecanicos 39,
Santa Pola, Alicante, 03130, Spain
Tel.: (34) 96 541 5011
Web Site: http://www.deltaplus.eu
Protective Products Mfr
N.A.I.C.S.: 334419

ESLINGAR S.A. **(1)**
Amancio Alcorta 1647, Buenos Aires,
CP1283AAC, Argentina
Tel.: (54) 11 6009 0099
Web Site: http://www.eslingar.com.ar
Personal Protective Equipment Distr
N.A.I.C.S.: 423990

Elvex Corporation **(1)**
2 Mountain View Dr, Shelton, CT
06484 **(100%)**
Tel.: (203) 743-2488
Web Site: http://www.elvex.com
All Other Miscellaneous Electrical Equip-
ment & Component Mfr
N.A.I.C.S.: 335999
Martin Salon *(VP)*

ODCO SAS **(1)**
5 rue de la condamine, 38610, Gieres,
France
Tel.: (33) 476633030
Web Site: http://www.odco.fr
Waterproofing Accessory Mfr
N.A.I.C.S.: 315990

Ontario Glove & Safety, Inc. **(1)**
5 Washburn Drive Unit A, Kitchener, N2R
1S1, ON, Canada
Tel.: (519) 886-3590
Web Site: http://www.ontarioglove.com
Safety Equipment Mfr & Distr
N.A.I.C.S.: 339113

Societe Delta Batiment **(1)**
66 Rue du Vieux Moulin Extended, 93130,
Noisy-le-Sec, France
Tel.: (33) 141553097
Web Site: http://www.deltabatiment.com
Home Renovation Services
N.A.I.C.S.: 236118

**Suzhou Delta Plus Personal
Protection** **(1)**
Zhonglu Ecologic Park Pingwang Town,
Wujiang, 215221, Jiangsu, China
Tel.: (86) 512 67 128700
Web Site: http://www.deltaplus.com.cn
Protection Equipment Mfr
N.A.I.C.S.: 334419

Vertic International, SA **(1)**
Parc technologique 691 Chemin des Fon-
taines, 38190, Bernin, France
Tel.: (33) 476131215
Web Site: http://www.vertic-safety.co.uk
Personal Protective Equipment Mfr
N.A.I.C.S.: 339113

Vertic Nederland BV **(1)**
Goudstraat 36, 2718 RC, Zoetermeer, Neth-
erlands
Tel.: (31) 883218000
Web Site: http://www.vertic.nl
Fall Protection System Mfr
N.A.I.C.S.: 339113

Vertic Suisse Sarl **(1)**
Route du Stand 11, 1880, Bex, Switzerland

Tel.: (41) 244662274
Web Site: http://www.vertic.shop
Personal Protective Equipment Distr
N.A.I.C.S.: 423450

**DELTA PROPERTY FUND LIM-
ITED**
Building 3 Silver Stream Office Park
10 Muswell Road South, Bryanston
Sandton, Johannesburg, South Africa
Tel.: (27) 878033582
Web Site:
    https://www.deltafund.co.za
Year Founded: 2002
Rev.: $112,488,299
Assets: $872,044,708
Liabilities: $399,705,139
Net Worth: $472,339,568
Earnings: $18,191,998
Fiscal Year-end: 02/28/19
Investment Management Service
N.A.I.C.S.: 525990
Sandile Hopeson Nomvete *(CEO)*

DELTA PUBLICIDAD
Av Gonzalez Suarez 335 Y San Igna-
cio, Quito, 17-1200659, Ecuador
Tel.: (593) 2 250 5555
Year Founded: 1984
Rev.: $10,000,000
Emp.: 75
N.A.I.C.S.: 541810
Pablo Salazar *(Pres)*

Subsidiaries:

Delta Publicidad - Guayaquil **(1)**
Francisco de Orellana Y Justino Cornejo,
Pichincha Towers, Guayaquil, Ecuador
Tel.: (593) 4 269 2280
N.A.I.C.S.: 541810
Mario Bajona *(Dir)*

DELTA RESOURCES LIMITED
1718 Christine Cr, Kingston, K7L
4V4, ON, Canada
Tel.: (613) 328-1581   ON
Web Site:
    https://www.deltaresources.ca
Year Founded: 1945
DLTA—(TSXV)
Rev.: $1,488
Assets: $1,557,744
Liabilities: $393,837
Net Worth: $1,163,907
Earnings: ($1,499,161)
Fiscal Year-end: 12/31/20
Gold Mining Services
N.A.I.C.S.: 212220
Frank Candido *(Chm & VP-Corp
Comm)*

DELTA SPINNERS LIMITED
254-B Khilgaon Chowdhury Para,
Dhaka, 1219, Bangladesh
Tel.: (880) 47213597
Web Site: https://www.delta-
    spinners.com
Year Founded: 1979
DELTASPINN—(DHA)
Sales Range: $10-24.9 Million
Cotton Yarn Mfr
N.A.I.C.S.: 313110
R. A. Howlader *(Chm)*

DELTA SUGAR COMPANY
Plot 17 - Services Center Street, PO
Box 12566/79, Fourth District, 6th of
October City, Egypt
Tel.: (20) 238308214
Web Site:
    https://www.deltasugar.com
Year Founded: 1978
SUGR.CA—(EGX)
Sales Range: Less than $1 Million
Food Mfr
N.A.I.C.S.: 311314

Ahmed Abo El Yazeed *(Chm & Mng
Dir)*

DELTA TECHNOLOGIES PLC
Robert Karoly krt 70-74, 1134, Buda-
pest, Hungary
Tel.: (36) 14375200
Web Site:
    https://www.deltatechnologies.hu
Year Founded: 1996
DELTA—(BUD)
Emp.: 250
Electrical Product Mfr & Distr
N.A.I.C.S.: 336320
Zoltan Csontos *(Chm)*

DELTA WIRE & MFG.
29 Delta Drive, Harrow, N0R 1G0,
ON, Canada
Tel.: (519) 738-3514
Web Site: http://www.deltawire.com
Rev.: $20,372,500
Emp.: 80
Fabricated Wire Product Mfr
N.A.I.C.S.: 332618
Kerry J. Stomp *(VP-Mfg)*

DELTA-FLY PHARMA, INC.
37-5 Nishikino Miyajima Kawauchi-
cho, Tokushima, 771-0116, Japan
Tel.: (81) 362311278
Web Site: https://www.delta-
    flypharma.co.jp
4598—(TKS)
Sales Range: Less than $1 Million
Biological Product Mfr
N.A.I.C.S.: 325414
Kiyoshi Eshima *(Pres & CEO)*

**DELTAMAC (TAIWAN) CO.,
LTD.**
10F 53 Ming Chuan W Rd, Taipei,
104, Taiwan
Tel.: (886) 25962866
6144—(TPE)
Rev.: $7,037,113
Assets: $12,906,262,702
Liabilities: $12,895,219,648
Net Worth: $11,043,054
Earnings: ($229,716)
Fiscal Year-end: 12/31/22
Video Disc Product Distr
N.A.I.C.S.: 532282
Jason Wu *(Chm)*

**DELTEX MEDICAL GROUP
PLC**
Terminus Road, Chichester, PO19
8TX, West Sussex, United Kingdom
Tel.: (44) 1243774837
Web Site:
    https://www.deltexmedical.com
DEMG—(LSE)
Rev.: $3,255,813
Assets: $7,513,622
Liabilities: $3,927,884
Net Worth: $3,585,739
Earnings: ($1,065,810)
Emp.: 50
Fiscal Year-end: 12/31/20
Medical Devices
N.A.I.C.S.: 339112
Nigel Keen *(Chm)*

Subsidiaries:

Deltex Medical Espana **(1)**
Calle Del Mirador 3, Santa Cristina d Aro,
Castell-Platja d'Aro, 17249, Spain
Tel.: (34) 972835954
Web Site: https://www.deltexmedical.com
Sales Range: $25-49.9 Million
Emp.: 3
Medical Equipment Mfr
N.A.I.C.S.: 339112

Deltex Medical Limited **(1)**
Terminus Road, Chichester, PO19 8TX,
West Sussex, United Kingdom

Tel.: (44) 124 377 4837
Web Site: https://www.deltexmedical.com
Sales Range: $25-49.9 Million
Emp.: 60
Medical Equipment Mfr
N.A.I.C.S.: 339112

Deltex Medical SC Inc. (1)
330 E Coffee St, Greenville, SC 29601
Tel.: (864) 527-5913
Web Site: https://www.deltexmedical.com
Sales Range: $25-49.9 Million
Emp.: 2
Medical Equipment Mfr
N.A.I.C.S.: 339112

DELTIC ENERGY PLC
1st Floor 150 Waterloo Road, London, SE1 8SB, United Kingdom
Tel.: (44) 2078872630   UK
Web Site:
   https://www.delticenergy.com
Year Founded: 2012
DELT—(AIM)
Rev.: $163,218
Assets: $38,724,108
Liabilities: $8,185,487
Net Worth: $30,538,620
Earnings: ($3,773,547)
Emp.: 8
Fiscal Year-end: 12/31/22
Coal Gasification Services
N.A.I.C.S.: 211130
Graham Swindells (CEO)

DELTICOM AG
Bruhlstr 11, 30169, Hannover, Germany
Tel.: (49) 1805335842
Web Site: https://www.delti.com
DEX—(MUN)
Rev.: $525,099,920
Assets: $211,457,337
Liabilities: $158,868,970
Net Worth: $52,588,367
Earnings: $8,864,076
Emp.: 169
Fiscal Year-end: 12/31/23
Tire Retailer
N.A.I.C.S.: 423130
Philip Von Grolman (Member-Mgmt Bd)

Subsidiaries:

DeltiLog Ltd. (1)
6 Langdale Court Market Square, Witney, OX28 6FG, Oxfordshire, United Kingdom
Tel.: (44) 8081891233
Web Site: https://www.mytyres.co.uk
Tire Retailer
N.A.I.C.S.: 441340

Delticom O.E. S.R.L. (1)
Str Anca Popa nr 3 Ap P, 300318, Timisoara, Romania
Tel.: (40) 17776100
Web Site: https://www.gume.com.hr
Tire Retailer
N.A.I.C.S.: 441340

Extor GmbH (1)
Hagenstrasse 3, 30559, Hannover, Germany
Tel.: (49) 5118745530
Web Site: https://www.extor.de
Emp.: 50
Tire 3D Printing Services
N.A.I.C.S.: 323111
Jorn Von der Lippe (Mng Dir)

Giga GmbH (1)
Bornitzstrasse 73-75 House D, 10365, Berlin, Germany
Tel.: (49) 30509307930
Web Site: https://giga-gmbh.de
Auto Parts Retailer
N.A.I.C.S.: 441330

Gourmondo Food GmbH (1)
Sudliche Munchner Strasse 56, 82031, Grunwald, Germany
Tel.: (49) 89642572320
Web Site: https://www.gourmondo.de
Beverage & Food Product Distr

N.A.I.C.S.: 424490

MobileMech GmbH (1)
Bruhlstr 11, 30169, Hannover, Germany
Tel.: (49) 51187989280
Web Site: http://www.mobilemech.de
Tire Retailer
N.A.I.C.S.: 441340

Netix S.R.L. (1)
Str Izlaz Nr 103 Ap Camera 5, Timisoara, 300299, Timis, Romania
Tel.: (40) 256270016
Web Site: http://www.netix.ro
Sales Range: $150-199.9 Million
Online Tire Sales
N.A.I.C.S.: 423130
Freumzache Leonpin (Mng Dir)

Tirendo Deutschland GmbH (1)
Pappelallee 78/79, 10437, Berlin, Germany
Tel.: (49) 5118 798 9141
Web Site: https://www.tirendo.de
Tire Retailer
N.A.I.C.S.: 441340

Tirendo GmbH (1)
Pappelallee 78/79, 10437, Berlin, Germany
Tel.: (49) 51187989141
Web Site: https://www.tirendo.de
Motorcycle Tire & Accessory Distr
N.A.I.C.S.: 423130

TyresNet GmbH (1)
Franz-Joseph-Str 11, 80801, Munich, Germany
Tel.: (49) 51187989259
Web Site: https://www.reifen.de
Tire Retailer
N.A.I.C.S.: 441340

DELTON AG
Gunther Quandt Haus Seedammweg 55, 61352, Bad Homburg, Germany
Tel.: (49) 61724040
Web Site: http://www.delton.de
Sales Range: $1-4.9 Billion
Emp.: 30,077
Diversified Holding Company
N.A.I.C.S.: 551112
Antonius Wagner (Chm-Mgmt Bd)

Subsidiaries:

Biologische Heilmittel Heel GmbH (1)
Dr Reckeweg Strasse 2-4, 76532, Baden-Baden, Germany
Tel.: (49) 772150100
Web Site: http://www.heel.de
Mfr of Homeopathic Medications
N.A.I.C.S.: 325412
Rainer Hopfgarten (CFO & Member-Mgmt Bd)

Subsidiary (Non-US):

Heel Belgium NV (2)
Industriepark Drongen Booiebos 25, 9031, Drongen, Belgium
Tel.: (32) 9 265 95 65
Web Site: http://www.heel.be
Emp.: 50
Pharmaceutical Products Distr
N.A.I.C.S.: 424210
Karin Blaaser (Head-Acctg)

Heel Biologische Geneesmiddelen B.V. (2)
Wilhelmina Straase 5456, 4571 JN, Axel, Netherlands   (100%)
Tel.: (31) 115 563 200
Web Site: http://www.heelbv.nl
Sales Range: $25-49.9 Million
Emp.: 20
Homeopathic Medicines Distr
N.A.I.C.S.: 424210

Heel Polska Sp. z o.o. (2)
ul Poleczki 21, 02-822, Warsaw, Poland
Tel.: (48) 22 545 07 00
Web Site: http://www.heel.pl
Pharmaceutical Products Distr
N.A.I.C.S.: 424210
Katarzyna Miler (Mgr-Mktg)

Heel do Brasil Biomedica Ltda. (2)
Alameda Tocantins 630 - G8 - Alphaville, 06455-020, Barueri, Sao Paulo, Brazil

Tel.: (55) 11 4208 3585
Web Site: http://www.heel.com
Homeopathic Medicine Mfr
N.A.I.C.S.: 325412

Laboratorios Heel Espana, S.A.U. (2)
C/ Madrono s/n Poligono La Mina, Colmenar Viejo, 28770, Madrid, Spain
Tel.: (34) 91 847 39 10
Web Site: http://www.heel.es
Pharmaceutical Products Distr
N.A.I.C.S.: 424210
Jose Manuel Villanueva Quiros (Dir-Mktg)

Productos Farmaceuticos Heel Chile Ltda. (2)
Encomenderos N 260 piso 6 Las Condes, Santiago, Chile
Tel.: (56) 2 2335 4811
Web Site: http://www.heel.cl
Pharmaceutical Products Distr
N.A.I.C.S.: 424210

DELTON Health AG (1)
Gunther-Quandt-Haus Seedammweg 55, 61352, Bad Homburg, Germany
Tel.: (49) 61724040
Web Site: http://www.delton-health.de
Pharmaceuticals Product Mfr
N.A.I.C.S.: 325412

DELTON Logistics Sarl (1)
5 an de Langten, 6776, Grevenmacher, Luxembourg
Tel.: (352) 71969060
Web Site: http://www.delton-logistics.de
Logistic Services
N.A.I.C.S.: 541614
Antonius Wagner (Mng Dir)

DELTON Technology SE (1)
Gunther-Quandt-Haus Seedammweg 55, 61352, Bad Homburg, Germany
Tel.: (49) 61724040
Web Site: http://www.delton-technology.de
Strategic Investment Services
N.A.I.C.S.: 523940

Logwin AG (1)
5 an de Langten ZIR Potaschberg, 6776, Grevenmacher, Luxembourg
Tel.: (352) 7196900
Web Site: https://www.logwin-logistics.com
Rev.: $1,388,138,602
Assets: $806,354,958
Liabilities: $420,331,619
Net Worth: $386,023,339
Earnings: $87,525,852
Emp.: 3,790
Fiscal Year-end: 12/31/2023
Logistics & Transport Services
N.A.I.C.S.: 561499
Antonius Wagner (Chm & CEO)

Subsidiary (Non-US):

Logwin Air & Ocean Far East Ltd. (2)
Suite 2708 27/F Skyline Tower 39 Wang Kwong Road Kowloon Bay, Hong Kong, China (Hong Kong)
Tel.: (852) 2827 8318
Freight Forwarding & Logistics Consulting Services
N.A.I.C.S.: 488510
Alex Szeto (CFO & Reg Dir-Fin)

Logwin Air & Ocean India Pvt. Ltd. (2)
Jeena House Plot No 170 Om Nagar Sahar Pipeline Road, Andheri East, 400099, Mumbai, India
Tel.: (91) 22 6617 9100
Freight Forwarding & Logistics Consulting Services
N.A.I.C.S.: 488510
Tarun Kapoor (Mgr-Sls)

Logwin Air & Ocean Korea Co. Ltd. (2)
Mirae B/D 10/F 166 Yanghwa-ro, Mapo-gu, 121-753, Seoul, Korea (South)
Tel.: (82) 2 330 7200
Freight Forwarding & Logistics Consulting Services
N.A.I.C.S.: 488510

Logwin Air & Ocean Middle East (LLC) (2)

901 AC Musalla Tower 18th Floor Khalid Bin Al Waleed Road, PO Box 119796, Dubai, United Arab Emirates
Tel.: (971) 4 3979 333
Freight Forwarding & Logistics Consulting Services
N.A.I.C.S.: 488510
Sheeja Mukundan (Asst Mgr-Ops)

Logwin Air & Ocean Spain S.L. (2)
Avda Sur del Aeropuerto de Barajas 28 Oficina 3 - Planta 5a, 28042, Madrid, Spain
Tel.: (34) 91 748 1481
Freight Forwarding & Logistics Consulting Services
N.A.I.C.S.: 488510

Logwin Air + Ocean (Thailand) Ltd. (2)
8th Floor Vibulthani 1 Esso Tower 3195/13 Rama IV Road, Klong Ton Klong Toey, 10110, Bangkok, Thailand
Tel.: (66) 2 6615 735 44
Freight Forwarding & Logistics Consulting Services
N.A.I.C.S.: 488510
Wilfried Wedemeyer (Mng Dir)

Logwin Air + Ocean Australia Pty. Ltd. (2)
Unit 9 2 Southridge Street Eastern Creek, Sydney, 2766, NSW, Australia
Tel.: (61) 2 9620 2588
Freight Forwarding & Logistics Consulting Services
N.A.I.C.S.: 488510
Thomas Kilian (Mng Dir)

Logwin Air + Ocean Austria GmbH (2)
Siezenheimerstrase 39a, 5020, Salzburg, Austria
Tel.: (43) 662 4680 0
Web Site: http://www.logwin-logistics.com
Emp.: 300
Freight Forwarding & Logistics Consulting Services
N.A.I.C.S.: 488510
Raimund Klein (Gen Mgr)

Logwin Air + Ocean Belgium N.V. (2)
Haven 190 Noorderlaan 149, 2030, Antwerp, Belgium
Tel.: (32) 3 545 9200
Freight Forwarding & Logistics Consulting Services
N.A.I.C.S.: 488510
Barbara Aertssens (Mgr-Export)

Logwin Air + Ocean Brazil Ltda (2)
Rua Vieira de Moraes 670, Campo Belo, 04617-001, Sao Paulo, Brazil
Tel.: (55) 11 5098 0644
Web Site: http://www.logwin-logistics.com
Emp.: 20
Freight Forwarding & Logistics Consulting Services
N.A.I.C.S.: 488510
Fabricio Liza (Mgr-Fin)

Logwin Air + Ocean Chile S.A. (2)
Apoquindo 3001 Piso 11, Las Condes, Santiago, Chile   (100%)
Tel.: (56) 2 754 1100
Freight Forwarding & Logistics Consulting Services
N.A.I.C.S.: 488510
Eduardo Vergara (Mng Dir)

Logwin Air + Ocean China Ltd. (2)
25th Floor Ocean Towers No 550 Yan An Road East, 200001, Shanghai, China
Tel.: (86) 21 2326 2000
Web Site: http://www.logwin-logistics.cn
Freight Forwarding & Logistics Consulting Services
N.A.I.C.S.: 488510
Fabrizio Stanig (Deputy Mng Dir)

Logwin Air + Ocean Czech s.r.o. (2)
Vinecka 317, 293 01, Mlada Boleslav, Czech Republic
Tel.: (420) 326 718 016
Logistics & Warehousing Services
N.A.I.C.S.: 493110

Logwin Air + Ocean Deutschland GmbH (2)
Airport Tegel Freight Building 12 13, 13405,

Delton AG—(Continued)

Berlin, Germany
Tel.: (49) 30 4101 2735
Web Site: http://www.logwinair.com
Freight Forwarding & Logistics Consulting
Services
N.A.I.C.S.: 488510
Oliva Dihel (Gen Mgr)

Logwin Air + Ocean Hungary Kft. (2)
Lorinci ut 59 - 61, Vecses, 2220, Budapest,
Hungary
Tel.: (36) 29 551 800
Web Site: http://www.logwin-logistics.com
Emp.: 11
Freight Forwarding & Logistics Consulting
Services
N.A.I.C.S.: 488510
Peter Borda (Gen Mgr)

**Logwin Air + Ocean Indonesia
P.T.** (2)
Wisma Soewarna 3rd Floor Suite I-J Taman
Niaga Soewarna, Cengkareng, 19110, Ja-
karta, Indonesia
Tel.: (62) 21 559 11741
Freight Forwarding & Logistics Consulting
Services
N.A.I.C.S.: 488510

**Logwin Air + Ocean International
GmbH** (2)
Weichertstrasse 5, 63741, Aschaffenburg,
Germany
Tel.: (49) 6021 343 0
Freight Forwarding & Logistics Consulting
Services
N.A.I.C.S.: 488510

Logwin Air + Ocean Italy S.r.l. (2)
Via G di Vittorio n 21 Caleppio di Settala,
20090, Milan, Italy
Tel.: (39) 02 216 9161
Web Site: http://www.logwin-logistics.com
Emp.: 25
Freight Forwarding & Logistics Consulting
Services
N.A.I.C.S.: 488510

**Logwin Air + Ocean Philippines
Inc.** (2)
Unit 1 Ground Floor Carlos Perez Building
A C Cortes Avenue, Mandaue, Cebu, 6014,
Philippines
Tel.: (63) 32 345 4446
Freight Forwarding & Logistics Consulting
Services
N.A.I.C.S.: 488510

**Logwin Air + Ocean Poland Sp. z
o.o.** (2)
ul Jana Pawla II 66, 05-500, Piaseczno,
Poland
Tel.: (48) 22 701 1300
Web Site: http://www.logwin-logistics.pl
Freight Forwarding & Logistics Consulting
Services
N.A.I.C.S.: 488510

**Logwin Air + Ocean Shanghai
Ltd.** (2)
168 Rijing Road Wai Gao Qiao Free Trade
Zone, 200131, Shanghai, China
Tel.: (86) 21 5046 3432
Freight Forwarding & Logistics Consulting
Services
N.A.I.C.S.: 488510

**Logwin Air + Ocean Singapore Pte.
Ltd.** (2)
No 01-12 Cargo Agents Building E, PO Box
523, Changi Airfreight Centre, 918101, Sin-
gapore, Singapore
Tel.: (65) 6542 5166
Web Site: http://www.logwin-logistics.sg
Freight Forwarding & Logistics Consulting
Services
N.A.I.C.S.: 488510

**Logwin Air + Ocean South Africa
(Pty.) Ltd.** (2)
Johann Birkart Road, 1619, Johannesburg,
South Africa
Tel.: (27) 11 976 7600
Web Site: http://www.logistics.com
Emp.: 100
Freight Forwarding & Logistics Consulting
Services
N.A.I.C.S.: 488510

Owen Shaw (Mng Dir)

**Logwin Air + Ocean Switzerland
AG** (2)
Hohenrainstr 10, 4133, Pratteln, Switzerland
Tel.: (41) 61 4657 180
Web Site: http://www.logwin-logistics.ch
Freight Forwarding & Logistics Consulting
Services
N.A.I.C.S.: 488510

Logwin Air + Ocean Taiwan Ltd. (2)
16/Fl Shin Kong International Busines Build-
ing 287, Sec 3 Nan Jing East Road, 105
95, Taipei, Taiwan
Tel.: (886) 2 2713 0265
Freight Forwarding & Logistics Consulting
Services
N.A.I.C.S.: 488510
Simon Kuan (Gen Mgr- Sls & Mktg)

**Logwin Air + Ocean The Netherlands
B.V.** (2)
Aalsmeerderdijk 154, Oude Meer, 1438 AX,
Amsterdam, Netherlands
Tel.: (31) 20 3540035
Freight Forwarding & Logistics Consulting
Services
N.A.I.C.S.: 488510

Logwin Air + Ocean UK Limited (2)
Suite B 3rd Floor Block C South Court
Sharston Road, Manchester, M22 4BB,
United Kingdom
Tel.: (44) 161 947 2450
Freight Forwarding & Logistics Consulting
Services
N.A.I.C.S.: 488510

**Logwin Air + Ocean Vietnam Com-
pany Ltd.** (2)
Kimdo Business Centre 4th Floor 123 Le
Loi Street, District 1, Ho Chi Minh City, Viet-
nam
Tel.: (84) 83 8213 070
Freight Forwarding & Logistics Consulting
Services
N.A.I.C.S.: 488510
Duy Pham Anh (Mgr-Natl Sls)

**Logwin Air and Ocean Kenya
Limited** (2)
3rd Floor Suite No 4 Jubilee Insurance
Building Moi Avenue, PO Box 88586-80100,
Mombasa, Kenya
Tel.: (254) 721678558
Freight Forwarding & Logistics Consulting
Services
N.A.I.C.S.: 488510
Lemmy Mweri (Branch Mgr)

**Logwin Air and Ocean Lojistik
Hizmetleri ve Ticaret Limited
Sirketi** (2)
Agaoglu My office 212 Mahmutbey Mah
Tasocagi Yolu Cad No 3 24th Floor,
Bagcilar, 34217, Istanbul, Turkiye
Tel.: (90) 212 500 3461
Freight Forwarding & Logistics Consulting
Services
N.A.I.C.S.: 488510

Logwin Croatia d.o.o. (2)
Jankomir 25 Bld 34 1st floor, 10090, Za-
greb, Croatia
Tel.: (385) 719690 0
Freight Forwarding & Logistics Consulting
Services
N.A.I.C.S.: 488510

Logwin Road + Rail Trier GmbH (2)
Monaiser Str 13, 54294, Trier, Germany
Tel.: (49) 651 81003 0
Freight Forwarding & Logistics Consulting
Services
N.A.I.C.S.: 488510

**Logwin Solutions Liechtenstein
AG** (2)
Essanestr 10, 9492, Eschen, Liechtenstein
Tel.: (423) 377 65 49
Freight Forwarding & Logistics Consulting
Services
N.A.I.C.S.: 488510

**Logwin Solutions Logistics Services
GmbH** (2)
Westerwaldstr 3-13, 64646, Heppenheim,
Germany
Tel.: (49) 6252 688 155

Freight Forwarding & Logistics Consulting
Services
N.A.I.C.S.: 488510

**Logwin Solutions Neckartenzlingen
GmbH** (2)
Stuttgarter Strasse 45-51, 72654, Neck-
artenzlingen, Germany
Tel.: (49) 7127 14 1916
Freight Forwarding & Logistics Consulting
Services
N.A.I.C.S.: 488510

Logwin Solutions Spain S.A. (2)
Antigua Ctra Ajalvir Km 2 200, 28806, Al-
cala de Henares, Madrid, Spain
Tel.: (34) 91 877 2660
Web Site: http://www.logwin-logistics.es
Freight Forwarding & Logistics Consulting
Services
N.A.I.C.S.: 488510
Cristina Busto Pacin (Branch Mgr)

DELTON CABLES LIMITED
Delton House 4801 Bharat Ram
Road 24 Daryaganj, New Delhi,
110002, India
Tel.: (91) 7428231517
Web Site:
https://www.deltoncables.com
Year Founded: 1948
504240—(BOM)
Rev.: $17,022,110
Assets: $19,544,097
Liabilities: $12,016,286
Net Worth: $7,527,811
Earnings: $85,067
Emp.: 180
Fiscal Year-end: 03/31/21
Telecom Cables Distr
N.A.I.C.S.: 517111
Vivek Gupta (Mng Dir)

Subsidiaries:

**Delton Cables Limited -
DHARUHERA WORKS** (1)
70th Milestone Delhi-Jaipur Highway,
Dharuhera, 122106, Haryana, India
Tel.: (91) 1274 242229
Electronic & Electrical Product Mfr
N.A.I.C.S.: 335999

**Delton Cables Limited - FARIDABAD
WORKS** (1)
17/4 Mathura Road, Faridabad, 121002,
Haryana, India
Tel.: (91) 129 2288225
Electrical & Electronic Component Mfr
N.A.I.C.S.: 335999
Safi Sharma (Gen Mgr)

**Delton Cables Limited - NEW DELHI
WORKS** (1)
24 Shivaji Marg, New Delhi, 110 015, India
Tel.: (91) 11 25928280
Electrical & Electronic Product Mfr
N.A.I.C.S.: 335999

DELTRON LTD.
132 Industrial Area Phase I, Chandi-
garh, 160 002, India
Tel.: (91) 1722650558   In
Web Site: https://www.deltron.in
Year Founded: 1982
504256—(BOM)
Sales Range: Less than $1 Million
Electronic Components Mfr
N.A.I.C.S.: 334419
Gurpreet Singh (Chm)

DELUXE FAMILY CO., LTD.
Room 202 No 1 Lane 968 Quxi
Road, Huangpu District, Shanghai,
201103, China
Tel.: (86) 2162376199
Web Site: http://www.deluxe-
family.com
Year Founded: 1996
600503—(SHG)
Rev.: $29,688,886
Assets: $684,670,231
Liabilities: $167,440,240

Net Worth: $517,229,992
Earnings: $10,737,736
Fiscal Year-end: 12/31/22
Real Estate Development Services
N.A.I.C.S.: 561730
Weilin Wang (Chm)

**DEM. TH. BERTZELETOS &
BROS. SA**
22 Fleming Street, 182 33, Agios Io-
annis Rentis, Greece
Tel.: (30) 210 4832 466   GR
Web Site: http://www.dtb.gr
Year Founded: 1893
Sales Range: $100-124.9 Million
Emp.: 300
Holding Company
N.A.I.C.S.: 551112
Theodoros Bertzeletos (Chm & CEO)

Subsidiaries:

Perla Greek Salt Ltd. (1)
22 Fleming Street, 182 33, Agios Ioannis
Rentis, Greece
Tel.: (30) 2104832466
Salt Producer
N.A.I.C.S.: 325998

DEMAE-CAN CO., LTD.
Midosuji Daiwa Building 8F 3-6-8
Kyutaromachi, Chuo-ku, Osaka, 541-
0056, Japan
Tel.: (81) 647045311
Web Site:
http://www.yumenomachi.co.jp
Year Founded: 1999
2484—(TKS)
Rev.: $313,598,765
Assets: $298,245,732
Liabilities: $70,886,472
Net Worth: $227,359,260
Earnings: ($23,048,212)
Fiscal Year-end: 08/31/24
Software Services
N.A.I.C.S.: 541512
Rie Nakamura (Chm)

DEMANT A/S
Kongebakken 9, D-2765, Smorum,
Denmark
Tel.: (45) 39177300
Web Site: https://www.demant.com
WILLF—(OTCIQ)
Rev.: $3,323,165,757
Assets: $4,522,988,068
Liabilities: $3,140,297,615
Net Worth: $1,382,690,453
Earnings: $378,322,350
Emp.: 21,623
Fiscal Year-end: 12/31/23
Developer, Mfr & Marketer of Modular
Hearing Aids, Assistance Listening
Devices, Audio & Public Address Sys-
tems
N.A.I.C.S.: 551112
Niels Bjorn Christiansen (Chm)

Subsidiaries:

ACS Sluchmed Sp. z o.o. (1)
Ul Orla 5, 20-022, Lublin, Poland
Tel.: (48) 815349797
Web Site: http://www.sluchmed.pl
Hearing Aid Clinical Services
N.A.I.C.S.: 621340

AD Styla Sp. z o.o. (1)
Krakowska 91, Andrychow, 34 120, Poland
Tel.: (48) 338705876
Hearing Aid Mfr
N.A.I.C.S.: 334510

AccuQuest Hearing Center LLC (1)
2501 Cottontail Ln, Somerset, NJ 08873
Web Site: http://www.hearinglife.com
Hearing Care Services
N.A.I.C.S.: 456199

Acoustic Metrology Limited (1)
Cadzow Industrial Estate Low Waters Road,

Hamilton, ML3 7QE, Lanarkshire, United Kingdom
Tel.: (44) 1698208250
Web Site: http://www.acousticmetrology.com
Audiometric Calibration & Repair Services
N.A.I.C.S.: 811210
David Canning (Dir-Technical)

Adelaide Digital Hearing Solutions Pty. Ltd. (1)
121 Sir Donald Bradman Drive, Hilton, Adelaide, 5033, SA, Australia
Tel.: (61) 881541090
Web Site: http://www.digitalhearing.com.au
Sales Range: $25-49.9 Million
Emp.: 50
Hearing Testing Services & Hearing Aids Retailer
N.A.I.C.S.: 423450

Akoustica Medica M EPE (1)
Sq Omonias 12, 105 64, Athens, Greece
Tel.: (30) 210 321 4463
Web Site: https://www.akousticamedica.gr
Emp.: 20
Hearing Aid Mfr
N.A.I.C.S.: 334510

American Hearing Aid Associates, Inc. (1)
225 Wilmington W Chester Pike Ste 300, Chadds Ford, PA 19317
Tel.: (610) 455-3010
Web Site: http://www.ahaanet.com
Sales Range: $25-49.9 Million
Emp.: 70
Hearing Impairment Support Services
N.A.I.C.S.: 561990
Tina Soika (Pres)

Amplivox Ltd. (1)
3800 Parkside Solihull Parkway Birmingham Business Park, Birmingham, B37 7YG, West Midlands, United Kingdom (100%)
Tel.: (44) 1865880846
Web Site: https://www.amplivox.com
Sales Range: $25-49.9 Million
Emp.: 11
Audiological Equipment Mfr
N.A.I.C.S.: 334510

Audika AB (1)
Lofstroms alle 5, 172 66, Sundbyberg, Sweden
Tel.: (46) 200111450
Web Site: https://www.audika.se
Hearing Aid Clinical Services
N.A.I.C.S.: 621340

Audika AG (1)
In der Luberzen 40, 8902, Urdorf, Switzerland
Tel.: (41) 435215588
Web Site: https://www.audika.ch
Hearing Device Retailer
N.A.I.C.S.: 456199

Audika ApS (1)
Kongebakken 9, 2765, Smorum, Denmark
Tel.: (45) 70400200
Web Site: https://www.audika.dk
Hearing Aid Clinical Services
N.A.I.C.S.: 621340

Audika Groupe SA (1)
231 rue des Caboeufs, 92230, Gennevilliers, France (100%)
Tel.: (33) 155373030
Web Site: https://www.audika.fr
Hearing Correction Solutions
N.A.I.C.S.: 621999
Alain Tonnard (Founder)

Audio Seleccion S.L. (1)
Avda Fuencarral 24 Edif Europa I, Alcobendas, 28108, Madrid, Spain
Tel.: (34) 913439155
Web Site: https://www.audika.es
Hearing Aid Clinical Services
N.A.I.C.S.: 621340

Audiology Services Company LLC (1)
111 S Spruce St Ste 102, Nazareth, PA 18064
Tel.: (610) 694-0141
Web Site: https://www.audiologyservicespa.com
Hearing Aid Clinical Services
N.A.I.C.S.: 621340

Blaise Delfino (Dir-Ops)

Audmet OY (1)
Tel.: (358) 92786200
Web Site: https://www.audmet.fi
Hearing Aid Clinical Services
N.A.I.C.S.: 621340

Bernafon A/S (1)
Kongebakken 9, 2765, Smorum, Denmark
Tel.: (45) 70227218
Web Site: https://www.bernafon.dk
Hearing Device Distr
N.A.I.C.S.: 423450

Bernafon AG (1)
Morgenstrasse 131, 3018, Bern, Switzerland
Tel.: (41) 319981515
Sales Range: $50-74.9 Million
Emp.: 150
Hearing Aid Mfr
N.A.I.C.S.: 334510

Subsidiary (Non-US):

Acustica Sp. z o.o. (2)
ul Abrahama 1A lok 3 09, 80-307, Gdansk, Poland
Tel.: (48) 585110803
Web Site: https://www.bernafon.pl
Sales Range: $10-24.9 Million
Emp.: 20
Hearing Impairment Support Services
N.A.I.C.S.: 621399

Bernafon (UK) Ltd. (2)
Cadzow Industrial Estate, Hamilton, ML3 7QE, Lanarkshire, United Kingdom
Tel.: (44) 1698283363
Web Site: https://www.bernafon.co.uk
Sales Range: $25-49.9 Million
Emp.: 60
Hearing Aid Mfr
N.A.I.C.S.: 334510

Bernafon Australia Pty. Ltd. (2)
629 Nudgee Road, Nundah, Brisbane, 4012, QLD, Australia
Tel.: (61) 73 250 0300
Web Site: https://www.bernafon.com.au
Hearing Aid Distr
N.A.I.C.S.: 423450

Bernafon Canada Ltd. (2)
500 Trillium Drive Unit 15, Kitchener, N2R 1A7, ON, Canada (100%)
Tel.: (519) 748-6669
Web Site: https://www.bernafon.ca
Sales Range: $1-9.9 Million
Emp.: 150
Mfr of Hearing Aids Products
N.A.I.C.S.: 334510

Bernafon Horgerate GmbH (2)
Nunsdorfer Ring 14, 12277, Berlin, Germany
Tel.: (49) 307239370
Web Site: https://www.bernafon.de
Emp.: 60
Hearing Aid Mfr
N.A.I.C.S.: 334510
Klaus-Peter Lipfert (Mng Dir)

Bernafon Nederland B.V. (2)
Kuiperij 5, 1185 XS, Amstelveen, Netherlands
Tel.: (31) 20 545 1090
Web Site: https://www.bernafon.nl
Sales Range: $25-49.9 Million
Emp.: 7
Hearing Aid Mfr
N.A.I.C.S.: 334510

Bernafon New Zealand Ltd. (2)
Level 1 Building F 27-29 William Pickering Drive, Auckland, 0632, New Zealand
Tel.: (64) 94157917
Sales Range: $25-49.9 Million
Emp.: 2
Hearing Aid Distr
N.A.I.C.S.: 423450
Devah Jackson (Mgr-Sls)

Bernafon S.r.l. (2)
Piazza delle Crociate 16B, 00162, Rome, Italy
Tel.: (39) 064 424 6852
Web Site: https://www.bernafon.it
Hearing Aid Distr
N.A.I.C.S.: 423450

Subsidiary (US):

Bernafon, LLC (2)
580 Howard Ave, Somerset, NJ 08873
Tel.: (732) 560-9996
Web Site: https://www.bernafon.us
Sales Range: $25-49.9 Million
Emp.: 50
Hearing Aid Mfr
N.A.I.C.S.: 334510

Subsidiary (Non-US):

Kuulopiiri Oy (2)
Linnanrakentajantie 2, 00880, Helsinki, Finland
Tel.: (358) 927862020
Web Site: https://www.bernafon.fi
Emp.: 4
Hearing Aids Retailer
N.A.I.C.S.: 423450

Phonic Ear A/S (2)
Kongebakken 9, 2765, Smorum, Nordsjaelland, Denmark
Tel.: (45) 4 445 2530
Web Site: https://www.phonicear.dk
Hearing Aids Retailer
N.A.I.C.S.: 423450

Prodition S.A. (2)
17 avenue des Louvresses Batiment A1, 92230, Gennevilliers, Cedex, France
Tel.: (33) 141880080
Web Site: https://www.prodition.fr
Hearing Aid Distr
N.A.I.C.S.: 423450

Bernafon Iberica S.L.U. (1)
Avenida de Fuencarral 24 Edificio Europa I Portal 3 3 4, Alcobendas, 28108, Madrid, Spain
Tel.: (34) 916573586
Web Site: https://www.bernafon.es
Hearing Device Distr
N.A.I.C.S.: 423450

Centro Auditivo Telex S.A. (1)
Av Venezuela 27 - sala 901, Botafogo, Rio de Janeiro, 20081-311, RJ, Brazil
Tel.: (55) 2121049100
Web Site: https://www.telex.com.br
Hearing Aid Distr
N.A.I.C.S.: 423450

DGS Business Services Sp. Z o.o. (1)
ul Malczewskiego 26, 71-612, Szczecin, Poland
Tel.: (48) 166277000
Hearing Health Care Services
N.A.I.C.S.: 621999

Demant Schweiz AG (1)
Morgenstrasse 131, 3018, Bern, Switzerland
Tel.: (41) 319903415
Web Site: https://www.demant.com
Hearing Device Mfr
N.A.I.C.S.: 334510

Demant Technology Centre Sp. z o.o. (1)
Q22 Al Jana Pawla II 22 9th Floor, 00-133, Warsaw, Poland
Tel.: (48) 221646600
Web Site: http://www.demantwarsaw.pl
Software Services
N.A.I.C.S.: 541511

Diagnostic Group LLC (1)
3406 College St, Beaumont, TX 77701
Tel.: (409) 813-1677
Web Site: https://www.dgihcs.com
Diagnostic Medical Care Services
N.A.I.C.S.: 621512

Diatec AG (1)
Im Schorli 5, 8600, Dubendorf, Switzerland
Tel.: (41) 448221212
Web Site: https://www.diatec-diagnostics.ch
Emp.: 9
Diagnostic Equipment Distr
N.A.I.C.S.: 423450

Diatec Diagnostics GmbH (1)
Hohenbuschei-Allee 2, 44309, Dortmund, Germany
Tel.: (49) 2319253140
Web Site: https://www.diatec-diagnostics.de
Diagnostic Equipment Distr

N.A.I.C.S.: 423450

Diatec Spain, S.L.U. (1)
Avda Fuencarral 24, Alcobendas, 28108, Madrid, Spain
Tel.: (34) 916633908
Web Site: https://www.diatec-diagnostics.es
Diagnostic Equipment Distr
N.A.I.C.S.: 423450

Digital Hearing (UK) Ltd. (1)
6 Auchingramont Road, Hamilton, ML3 6JT, South Lanarkshire, United Kingdom
Tel.: (44) 1698307272
Web Site: http://www.digitalhearinguk.co.uk
Hearing Aid Mfr
N.A.I.C.S.: 334510

EPOS Group A/S (1)
Industriparken 27, 2750, Ballerup, Denmark
Tel.: (45) 56180000
Web Site: https://www.eposaudio.com
Audio & Video Equipment Mfr
N.A.I.C.S.: 334510
Jeppe Dalberg-Larsen (Pres)

Grason-Stadler, Inc. (1)
10393 W 70th St, Eden Prairie, MN 55344
Tel.: (952) 278-4402
Web Site: https://www.grason-stadler.com
Sales Range: $25-49.9 Million
Emp.: 90
Hearing Testing Equipments Mfr
N.A.I.C.S.: 334510

Guymark UK Limited (1)
Veronica House Old Bush Street, Brierley Hill, DY5 1UB, West Midlands, United Kingdom
Tel.: (44) 1384890600
Web Site: https://www.guymark.com
Hearing Device Mfr
N.A.I.C.S.: 334510
Philip Baxter (Gen Mgr)

Hearing Healthcare Management, Inc. (1)
3700 Corporate Dr Ste 140, Columbus, OH 43231
Tel.: (614) 942-1190
Web Site: http://www.avada.com
Sales Range: $25-49.9 Million
Emp.: 13
Hearing Aid Mfr
N.A.I.C.S.: 334510

Hearing Holding Belgium NV (1)
Thonissenlaan 92a, 3500, Hasselt, Belgium
Tel.: (32) 80030929
Web Site: http://www.audika.be
Hearing Aid Clinical Services
N.A.I.C.S.: 621340

Hearing Screening Associates LLC (1)
3333 N Kennicott Ave, Arlington Heights, IL 60004
Web Site: https://www.hearingscreeningassocs.com
Infants Hearing Screening Services
N.A.I.C.S.: 621340

HearingLife Canada Ltd. (1)
4950 Yonge St Unit 1600, North York, M2N 6K1, ON, Canada
Tel.: (416) 925-9223
Web Site: https://www.hearinglife.ca
Hearing Aid Clinical Services
N.A.I.C.S.: 621340

Hidden Hearing (Portugal), Unipessoal Lda. (1)
Rua Vitor Camara Edif D Maria I - 1 Floor - Wing B Quinta da Fonte, Paco De Arcos, 2770-229, Paco d'Arcos, Portugal
Tel.: (351) 218426800
Web Site: https://www.acusticamedica.pt
Sales Range: $25-49.9 Million
Emp.: 50
Hearing Aid Mfr
N.A.I.C.S.: 621340

Hidden Hearing (UK) Ltd. (1)
24 Hanover Street, Midlothian, Edinburgh, EH2 2EN, United Kingdom
Tel.: (44) 1312207640
Web Site: http://www.hiddenhearing.co.uk
Emp.: 2
Hearing Testing & Hearing Aids Distr
N.A.I.C.S.: 423450

Demant A/S—(Continued)

Hidden Hearing Limited　(1)
238 Merrion Road, Ballsbridge, Dublin, D04
X026, Ireland
Tel.: (353) 12180886
Web Site: https://www.hiddenhearing.ie
Sales Range: $10-24.9 Million
Emp.: 20
Hearing Testing Services
N.A.I.C.S.: 621340
Stephen Leddy *(Mng Dir)*

**IDEA Isitme Sistemleri Sanayi ve Ti-
caret A.S.**　(1)
Sahrayicedit Mahallesi Batman Sokak Royal
Plaza No 18/7 Kat 3-4-5, Kadikoy, Istanbul,
Turkiye
Tel.: (90) 4444347
Web Site: https://www.idis.com.tr
Hearing Device Retailer
N.A.I.C.S.: 456199

Inmed Sp. z o.o.　(1)
ul Czapinskiego 3, 30 048, Krakow, Poland
Tel.: (48) 12 63113 80
Hearing Testing Services
N.A.I.C.S.: 621340

Interacoustics A/S　(1)
Audiometer Alle 1, 5500, Middelfart, Den-
mark
Tel.: (45) 63713555
Web Site: https://www.interacoustics.com
Sales Range: $50-74.9 Million
Emp.: 190
Hearing Aids Mfr & Audiologic Diagnostic
Software Development Services
N.A.I.C.S.: 334510

Subsidiary (Non-US):

Interacoustics Pty. Ltd.　(2)
Level 5 11 Khartoum Road, Macquarie
Park, 2113, NSW, Australia
Tel.: 288991200
Web Site: https://interacoustics.com.au
Sales Range: $25-49.9 Million
Emp.: 7
Hearing Aid Mfr
N.A.I.C.S.: 334510

**Interacoustics do Brasil. Com. de
Equip. Medicos Ltda.**　(2)
Rua Assuncao, 119 Parte, 22251 030, Rio
de Janeiro, Brazil
Tel.: (55) 2121049106
Hearing Aid Mfr
N.A.I.C.S.: 334510

LeDiSo Italia S.r.l.　(1)
Via Panciatichi 94/20, 50127, Florence, Italy
Tel.: (39) 0554288392
Web Site: https://www.diatec-diagnostics.it
Hearing Device Distr
N.A.I.C.S.: 423450

Maico Diagnostic GmbH　(1)
Sickingenstr 70-71, 10553, Berlin, Germany
Tel.: (49) 30 707 1460
Web Site: https://www.maico-
diagnostics.com
Emp.: 25
Hearing Aid Mfr
N.A.I.C.S.: 334510
Norbert Bottcher *(Gen Mgr)*

Maico S.r.l.　(1)
Via Panciatichi 96, 50127, Florence, Italy
Tel.: (39) 0554369504
Web Site: https://www.maicoitalia.com
Sales Range: $50-74.9 Million
Emp.: 10
Hearing Aid Distr
N.A.I.C.S.: 423450

Medton Ltd.　(1)
IMI 6, Ramat Gan, Israel
Tel.: (972) 772702700
Web Site: http://www.medton-hedim.co.il
Hearing Aid Clinical Services
N.A.I.C.S.: 621340

Neurelec S.A.S.　(1)
2720 Chemin Saint-Bernard, 06220, Vallau-
ris, France
Tel.: (33) 493951818
Web Site: https://www.oticonmedical.com
Emp.: 14,500
Hearing Device Mfr
N.A.I.C.S.: 334510

OTIX GLOBAL, INC.　(1)
4246 Riverboat Rd Ste 300, Salt Lake City,
UT 84123
Tel.: (801) 312-1700
Web Site: http://www.otixglobal.com
Sales Range: $75-99.9 Million
Emp.: 700
Digital Hearing Aids Mfr, Designer & Mar-
keter
N.A.I.C.S.: 334510

Subsidiary (Non-US):

Sonic Innovations Canada Ltd.　(2)
500 Trillium Drive Unit 15, Kitchener, N2R
1A7, ON, Canada
Tel.: (450) 965-8213
Web Site: https://www.sonici.com
Digital Hearing Aid Distr
N.A.I.C.S.: 423450

Sonic Innovations Pty Ltd.　(2)
629 Nudgee Road, Nundah, Brisbane,
4012, QLD, Australia　(100%)
Tel.: (61) 73 250 0369
Web Site: https://www.sonici.com.au
Sales Range: $50-74.9 Million
Emp.: 150
Digital Hearing Aid Mfr & Distr
N.A.I.C.S.: 339112

Oticon A/S　(1)
Kongebakken 9, 2765, Smorum, Denmark
Tel.: (45) 39177100
Web Site: https://www.oticon.global
Sales Range: $200-249.9 Million
Emp.: 686
Hearing Aid Mfr
N.A.I.C.S.: 334510

Subsidiary (Non-US):

Oticon AB　(2)
Lofstroms alle 5, PO Box 1262, 172 25,
Sundbyberg, Sweden
Tel.: (46) 854522750
Web Site: https://www.oticon.se
Hearing Aid Distr
N.A.I.C.S.: 423450
Hakan Hansson *(CEO)*

Oticon AS　(2)
Hegdehaugsveien 31, 0352, Oslo, Norway
Tel.: (47) 23256100
Web Site: https://www.oticon.no
Sales Range: $25-49.9 Million
Emp.: 25
Hearing Aid Mfr
N.A.I.C.S.: 334510

Oticon Australia Pty. Ltd.　(2)
Suite 4 Level 4 Building B 11 Talavera
Road, Ryde, 2113, NSW, Australia
Tel.: (61) 29 857 8288
Web Site: https://www.oticon.com.au
Hearing Aid Mfr
N.A.I.C.S.: 423450

Oticon Canada Ltd.　(2)
6950 Creditview Rd Unit 1, Mississauga,
L5N 0A6, ON, Canada
Tel.: (905) 677-3231
Web Site: http://www.oticon.ca
Hearing Aid Mfr
N.A.I.C.S.: 334510

Oticon Espana S.A.　(2)
Avenida de Fuencarral 24, Edificio Europa,
28108, Alcobendas, Madrid, Spain
Tel.: (34) 91 663 3900
Web Site: https://www.oticon.es
Sales Range: $25-49.9 Million
Emp.: 43
Hearing Aid Mfr
N.A.I.C.S.: 334510

Oticon Italia S.r.l.　(2)
Via Panciatichi 94 Int 11/20, 50127, Flor-
ence, Italy
Tel.: (39) 080 086 3197
Web Site: https://www.oticon.it
Sales Range: $10-24.9 Million
Emp.: 70
Hearing & Medical Support Services
N.A.I.C.S.: 621340

Oticon K.K.　(2)
Solid Square West Tower 16F 580
Horikawa-cho, Saiwai-ku, Kawasaki, 212-
0013, Kanagawa, Japan
Tel.: (81) 44 543 0615

Web Site: https://www.oticon.co.jp
Sales Range: $25-49.9 Million
Emp.: 100
Hearing Aids Retailer
N.A.I.C.S.: 423450

Oticon Korea Co. Ltd.　(2)
Level 7 Seoyoung B/D 57-9 Seosomun-
Dong, Jung-gu, Seoul, 100-814, Korea
(South)
Tel.: (82) 22 022 3900
Web Site: http://www.oticonkorea.com
Sales Range: $25-49.9 Million
Emp.: 45
Hearing Aid Distr
N.A.I.C.S.: 423450

Oticon Limited　(2)
Cadzow Industrial Estate Low Waters Road,
Hamilton, ML3 7QE, Lanarkshire, United
Kingdom
Tel.: (44) 1698283363
Web Site: https://www.oticon.co.uk
Sales Range: $25-49.9 Million
Emp.: 10
Hearing Aid Mfr
N.A.I.C.S.: 334510

Subsidiary (Domestic):

Oticon Medical A/S　(2)
Kongebakken 9, 2765, Smorum, Hovedsta-
den, Denmark
Tel.: (45) 39177100
Web Site: https://www.oticonmedical.com
Sales Range: $200-249.9 Million
Hearing Aids Retailer
N.A.I.C.S.: 423450
John Sparacio *(Pres-US)*

Subsidiary (Non-US):

Oticon Medical AB　(3)
Datavagen 37B, Askim, 436 32, Gothen-
burg, Sweden
Tel.: (46) 317486100
Sales Range: $25-49.9 Million
Emp.: 12
Hearing Aid Mfr
N.A.I.C.S.: 334510

Subsidiary (Non-US):

Oticon Nederland B.V.　(2)
Kuiperij 5, 1180, Amstelveen, Netherlands
Tel.: (31) 205455780
Web Site: http://www.oticon.nl
Sales Range: $25-49.9 Million
Emp.: 30
Hearing Aid Mfr
N.A.I.C.S.: 334510

Oticon New Zealand Ltd.　(2)
142 Lambton Quay, Te Aro, Wellington,
6011, New Zealand
Tel.: (64) 44733330
Web Site: http://www.oticon.co.nz
Sales Range: $25-49.9 Million
Emp.: 20
Hearing Aid Distr
N.A.I.C.S.: 423450

**Oticon Polska Production Sp. z
o.o.**　(2)
ul Lubieszynska 59 Mierzyn, 72 006, Szc-
zecin, Poland
Tel.: (48) 914417700
Web Site: https://www.ddf.com
Hearing Aid Mfr
N.A.I.C.S.: 334510

Oticon Polska Sp. z o.o.　(2)
Aleja Jana Pawla II 22, 00-133, Warsaw,
Poland
Tel.: (48) 221646500
Web Site: https://www.oticon.pl
Sales Range: $25-49.9 Million
Emp.: 30
Hearing Aids Retailer
N.A.I.C.S.: 423450

Oticon S.A.　(2)
Morgenstrasse 131 B, Postfach 1262, 3018,
Bern, Switzerland
Tel.: (41) 319903400
Web Site: http://www.oticon.ch
Hearing Aid Distr
N.A.I.C.S.: 423450
Martin Hofer *(Mng Dir)*

Oticon Singapore Pte. Ltd.　(2)

23A Serangoon North Avenue 5 04 08, Sin-
gapore, 554369, Singapore
Tel.: (65) 63519450
Web Site: http://www.oticon.com.sg
Sales Range: $25-49.9 Million
Emp.: 26
Hearing Aid Distr
N.A.I.C.S.: 423450

Oticon South Africa (Pty) Ltd.　(2)
Warich Office Close 39 Van Vuuren Street,
Constantia Kloof, Johannesburg, 1709,
Gauteng, South Africa
Tel.: (27) 11 675 6104
Web Site: https://www.oticon.co.za
Sales Range: $10-24.9 Million
Emp.: 50
Hearing Impairment Support Services
N.A.I.C.S.: 813212

Subsidiary (US):

Oticon, Inc.　(2)
580 Howard Ave, Somerset, NJ 08873-6724
Tel.: (732) 560-1220
Web Site: https://www.oticonusa.com
Sales Range: $75-99.9 Million
Emp.: 450
Hearing Aid Mfr
N.A.I.C.S.: 334510
Gary Rosenblum *(Pres)*

Subsidiary (Non-US):

Oy Oticon Ab　(2)
Laivalahdenkatu 2b A, PO Box 408, 00811,
Helsinki, Finland
Tel.: (358) 92786200
Web Site: http://www.oticon.fi
Sales Range: $25-49.9 Million
Emp.: 20
Hearing Aid Mfr
N.A.I.C.S.: 334510

Oticon Denmark A/S　(1)
Kongebakken 9, 2765, Smorum, Denmark
Tel.: (45) 44452500
Web Site: https://www.oticon.dk
Hearing Device Mfr
N.A.I.C.S.: 334510

Oticon GmbH　(2)
Offakamp 7 - 9 b, PO Box 54 04 64, 22529,
Hamburg, Germany
Tel.: (49) 408488840
Web Site: https://www.oticon.de
Hearing Device Mfr
N.A.I.C.S.: 334510

Oticon Malaysia Sdn　(1)
K-02-06 Solaris Mont Kiara No 2 Jalan So-
laris, 50480, Kuala Lumpur, Malaysia
Tel.: (60) 362030690
Hearing Device Mfr
N.A.I.C.S.: 334510

Oticon Medical Maroc　(1)
223 Angle Boulevard Abdelmoumen Place
du Dr Charles Nicolle 5th floor, 20000,
Casablanca, Morocco
Tel.: (212) 522278604
Hearing Device Mfr
N.A.I.C.S.: 334510

**Oticon Shanghai Hearing Technology
Co. Ltd.**　(1)
No 2 Lane 67 Li Bing Rd, Zhangjiang Hi-
Tech Park Pudong New Area, Shanghai,
201203, China
Tel.: (86) 2151320788
Hearing Device Mfr
N.A.I.C.S.: 334510

Phonic Ear Inc.　(1)
1690 Corporate Cir, Petaluma, CA 94954
Tel.: (707) 769-1110
Web Site: https://www.gofrontrow.com
Emp.: 35
Hearing Aids Mfr & Distr
N.A.I.C.S.: 334510
Jens Holstebro *(Pres)*

Sennheiser Communications A/S　(1)
Industriparken 27, 2750, Solrod, Denmark
Tel.: (45) 56180000
Web Site:
　http://www.sennheisercommunications.com
Sales Range: $25-49.9 Million
Emp.: 80
Wireless & Wired Headset Mfr; Joint Ven-
ture of Sennheiser Electronic GmbH & Co.
KG (50%) & William Demant Holding A/S
(50%)

N.A.I.C.S.: 334310
Jane Craven *(Dir-Sls-UK Telecom)*

Udicare S.r.l. (1)
Via Alessandro Manzoni 44, 20095, Cusano
Milanino, MI, Italy
Tel.: (39) 0282940914
Web Site: https://www.audika.it
Hearing Aid Clinical Services
N.A.I.C.S.: 621340

Van Boxtel Hoorwinkels B.V. (1)
Steenweg 17b, 4181 AJ, Waardenburg,
Netherlands
Tel.: (31) 885252052
Web Site:
    https://www.vanboxtelhoorwinkels.nl
Hearing Device Retailer
N.A.I.C.S.: 456199

Workplace Integra Inc. (1)
4140 Mendenhall Oaks Pkwy Ste 101, High
Point, NC 27265
Tel.: (336) 834-8775
Web Site: https://www.workplaceintegra.com
Healthcare Data Management Services
N.A.I.C.S.: 518210
Jeremy Suits *(Gen Mgr)*

Your Hearing Network LLC (1)
580 Howard Ave, Somerset, NJ 08873
Web Site:
    http://www.yourhearingnetwork.com
Hearing Aid Clinical Services
N.A.I.C.S.: 621340
Cindy Beyer *(VP-Contracting & Compliance)*

e3 diagnostics Inc. (1)
3333 N Kennicott Ave, Arlington Heights, IL
60004
Web Site: https://www.e3diagnostics.com
Audiology Equipment Distr
N.A.I.C.S.: 456199

DEMARAIS INDUSTRIES
6 Rue Honore De Balzac, Montoire
Sur Le Loir, 41800, Tours, France
Tel.: (33) 254864440
Web Site: http://www.demarais.com
Sales Range: $10-24.9 Million
Emp.: 159
Motor Vehicles & Car Bodies
N.A.I.C.S.: 336110
Pierre Masson *(Mng Dir)*

DEMCO PUBLIC COMPANY LIMITED
59 Moo 1 Tamboi Suanphrikthai Amphur Muang Pathumthani, Pathumthani, 12000, Thailand
Tel.: (66) 29595811
Web Site: https://www.demco.co.th
Year Founded: 1992
DEMCO—(THA)
Rev.: $67,162,695
Assets: $187,388,889
Liabilities: $82,659,194
Net Worth: $104,729,695
Earnings: ($16,053,569)
Fiscal Year-end: 12/31/23
Engineeering Services
N.A.I.C.S.: 541330
Praphee Puipunthavong *(Chm)*

Subsidiaries:

Demco Power Co., Ltd. (1)
59 Moo 1 Suan Prik Thai, Muang Pathumthani, Pathumthani, 12000, Thailand
Tel.: (66) 2959581115
Web Site: http://www.demcopower.com
Electrical Equipment & Steel Tower Mfr
N.A.I.C.S.: 335999

DEMERARA DISTILLERS LTD.
Block A Plantation Diamond East
Bank, Demerara, Guyana
Tel.: (592) 2655019
Web Site:
    http://www.demeraradistillers.com
Year Founded: 1952
Sales Range: $600-649.9 Million
Emp.: 1,200

Distilled Liquor & Soft Drink Mfr
N.A.I.C.S.: 312140
Komal R. Samaroo *(Chm)*

Subsidiaries:

Demerara Distillers (USA) Inc. (1)
499 NW 70th Ave Ste 120, Plantation, FL
33317
Tel.: (786) 275-0253
Web Site: http://www.theeldoradorum.com
Sales Range: $50-74.9 Million
Emp.: 2
Rum & Beverage Sales
N.A.I.C.S.: 424810

Demerara Distillers Europe BV (1)
Peperstraat 147, 1502 E, Zaandam, Netherlands
Tel.: (31) 756700575
Web Site: http://www.del-europe.nl
Rum & Beverage Sales
N.A.I.C.S.: 424810

DEMESNE ELECTRICAL SALES LIMITED
The Square Industrial Complex, Tallaght, Dublin, Ireland
Tel.: (353) 1 404 7700
Web Site: http://www.demesne.ie
Year Founded: 1977
Electrical Component Supplier, Importer & Distr
N.A.I.C.S.: 335999
Michael Devins *(Mng Dir)*

Subsidiaries:

Demesne Electrical Sales Uk Limited (1)
Unit 4 41 Windmill Rd, Luton, LU13XL,
Bedfordshire, United Kingdom
Tel.: (44) 1582728087
Emp.: 4
Electronic Product Distr
N.A.I.C.S.: 423610
Michael Devins *(Mng Dir)*

DEMESNE RESOURCES LTD.
335-1632 Dickson Avenue, Kelowna,
V1Y 7T2, BC, Canada
Tel.: (647) 328-8227   BC
Web Site:
    https://demesneresourcesltd.com
Year Founded: 2019
DEMRF—(OTCIQ)
Assets: $97,943
Liabilities: $49,170
Net Worth: $48,772
Earnings: ($463,111)
Fiscal Year-end: 12/31/23
Mineral Exploration Services
N.A.I.C.S.: 213115
Adam Virani *(CEO)*

DEMETER CORPORATION PUBLIC COMPANY LIMITED
191/43 CTI Tower 21st Floor, Ratchadapisek Road Klongtoey, Bangkok,
10110, Thailand
Tel.: (66) 22042601   TH
Web Site:
    http://www.demetercorporation.com
Year Founded: 1978
DV8—(THA)
Rev.: $5,881,227
Assets: $20,445,154
Liabilities: $3,701,029
Net Worth: $16,744,126
Earnings: $47,865
Emp.: 95
Fiscal Year-end: 12/31/20
Television Program Production Services
N.A.I.C.S.: 512110
Cholapan Vongsing *(CFO)*

Subsidiaries:

Hinoki Wood Work Company Limited (1)
88/292 Moo 9 Khlong Ha, Khlong Luang,

Pathumthani, 12120, Thailand
Tel.: (66) 891539566
Web Site: http://www.hinokiwoodwork.com
Wood & Cork Product Mfr
N.A.I.C.S.: 321999

DEMETRA HOLDINGS PLC
13 Lemesou Avenue 5th Floor,
Aglantzia, 2112, Nicosia, Cyprus
Tel.: (357) 22818222
Web Site:
    https://www.demetra.com.cy
DEM—(CYP)
Sales Range: $1-9.9 Million
Investment Banking Services
N.A.I.C.S.: 523150
Nearchos Ioannou *(Mng Dir)*

DEMIRE DEUTSCHE MITTELSTAND REAL ESTATE AG
Robert Bosch StraSSe 11, 63225,
Langen, Germany
Tel.: (49) 6103372490   De
Web Site: https://www.demire.ag
DMRE—(DUS)
Rev.: $112,064,882
Assets: $1,465,420,541
Liabilities: $1,130,296,648
Net Worth: $335,123,893
Earnings: ($162,478,625)
Emp.: 33
Fiscal Year-end: 12/31/23
Real Estate Investment Trust
N.A.I.C.S.: 525990
Volkswirt Frank Holzle *(Vice Chm-Supervisory Bd)*

Subsidiaries:

DEMIRE Leipzig Am alten Flughafen 1 GmbH (1)
Building 33 1st Floor Am alten Flughafen 1,
04356, Leipzig, Germany
Tel.: (49) 61033724949
Real Estate Services
N.A.I.C.S.: 531390

Fair Value REIT-AG (1)
Robert-Bosch-Strasse 11, 63225, Langen,
Germany   (77.7%)
Tel.: (49) 61034400160
Web Site: https://www.fvreit.de
Rev.: $26,735,731
Assets: $320,343,074
Liabilities: $161,032,556
Net Worth: $159,310,518
Earnings: ($8,301,102)
Emp.: 2
Fiscal Year-end: 12/31/2023
Real Estate Investment Trust
N.A.I.C.S.: 525990
Thomas Wetzel *(Deputy Chm-Supervisory Bd)*

DEMISAS DOKUM EMAYE MAMULLERI SANAYI AS
Asiroglu Cad No 147, Emek Mah
Darica, 41700, Kocaeli, Turkiye
Tel.: (90) 2626774600
Web Site: https://www.demisas.com
Year Founded: 1974
DMSAS—(IST)
Rev.: $63,661,036
Assets: $51,363,786
Liabilities: $30,250,262
Net Worth: $21,113,524
Earnings: $2,728,169
Emp.: 630
Fiscal Year-end: 12/31/19
Iron Casting Product Mfr
N.A.I.C.S.: 331511
Emre Giray *(Gen Mgr)*

DEMMEL AG
Gruntenweg 14, 88175, Lindau, Germany
Tel.: (49) 838191900
Web Site: http://www.demmel.ag
Sales Range: $10-24.9 Million
Emp.: 400

Industrial Electronics Manufacturing
N.A.I.C.S.: 335999
Thomas Holderried *(Chm-Mgmt Bd)*

Subsidiaries:

Angell-Demmel Europe GmbH (1)
Zechwaldstrasse 1, 88131, Lindau, Germany
Tel.: (49) 8382963512
Automobile Parts Mfr
N.A.I.C.S.: 336390

DEMNER, MERLICEK & BERGMANN WERBEGESELLSCHAFT MBH
Lehargasse 9-11, A-1061, Vienna,
Austria
Tel.: (43) 1 588 460   AT
Web Site: http://www.dmb.at
Year Founded: 1969
Sales Range: Less than $1 Million
Emp.: 120
Full Service, Print, Production, Public
Relations, T.V.
N.A.I.C.S.: 541810
Mariusz Jan Demner *(Mng Partner)*

DEMOS LLC
6 1 Ovchinnikovskaya Nab, 115035,
Moscow, Russia
Tel.: (7) 4959566080
Web Site: http://www.demos.su
Year Founded: 1989
Sales Range: $50-74.9 Million
Emp.: 250
Holding Company; Internet Services,
Corporate Information Solutions, Information Security & Computer Products
N.A.I.C.S.: 551112

Subsidiaries:

Demos-Internet (1)
36 -1 Berzarina Street, Moscow, 123060,
Russia
Tel.: (7) 4957370404
Web Site: http://www.demos-internet.ru
Sales Range: $25-49.9 Million
Emp.: 100
Internet Web Hosting
N.A.I.C.S.: 518210

DEMOS S.A.
20 rue de l'Arcade, 75008, Paris,
France
Tel.: (33) 1 4494 1616
Web Site:
    http://www.demosgroup.com
Year Founded: 1972
Sales Range: $100-124.9 Million
Emp.: 800
Professional Training Services
N.A.I.C.S.: 611430
Jean Wemaere *(Chm & CEO)*

Subsidiaries:

Demos (Beijing) Management & Technical Training Co., Ltd. (1)
No 34 Chongwenmenwai Street Room 1116
South Office Tower, Beijing New World Center Chongwen District, 100062, Beijing,
China
Tel.: (86) 10 67 08 16 35
Professional Training Services
N.A.I.C.S.: 611430

Demos Benelux (1)
67 rue de la Loi, Brussels, 1040, Belgium
Tel.: (32) 2 234 62 41
Professional Training Services
N.A.I.C.S.: 611430

Demos Gmbh (1)
MesseTurm Friedrich-Ebert-Anlage 49,
60308, Frankfurt, Germany
Tel.: (49) 69 9203 7568 17
Web Site: http://www.demos.com.de
Professional Training Services
N.A.I.C.S.: 611430

Demos Middle East Fz (1)

Demos S.A.—(Continued)

Knowledge Village, PO Box 502221, Dubai, United Arab Emirates
Tel.: (971) 4 365 8506
Web Site: http://www.demos.ae
Professional Training Services
N.A.I.C.S.: 611430

Demos Polska Sp. z o.o. (1)
Al Krakowska 110/114 lok B-26, 02-256, Warsaw, Poland
Tel.: (48) 22 646 69 90
Web Site: http://www.demos.pl
Emp.: 20
Professional Training Services
N.A.I.C.S.: 611430
Marcin Rokita (Gen Mgr)

FormaDemos Rabat (1)
1 rue Ghafsa Place Al Joulane, 10000, Rabat, Morocco
Tel.: (212) 5 37 72 76 15
Web Site: http://www.demos.ma
Professional Training Services
N.A.I.C.S.: 611430

Hemsley Fraser Australia Pty Ltd (1)
PO Box 487, Brighton, 5048, SA, Australia
Tel.: (61) 8 8121 5646
Web Site: http://www.hemsleyfraser.com.au
Professional Training Services
N.A.I.C.S.: 611430

Hemsley Fraser Group Limited (1)
St James Court 74-94 Fore Street, Saltash, Plymouth, PL12 6JW, United Kingdom
Tel.: (44) 845 071 2801
Web Site: http://www.hemsleyfraser.co.uk
Professional Training Services
N.A.I.C.S.: 611430
Jean Wemaere (Chm)

Hemsley Fraser US (1)
1215 17th St NW Ste 400, Washington, DC 20036
Tel.: (888) 559-0074
Web Site: http://www.hemsleyfraser.com
Professional Training Services
N.A.I.C.S.: 611430
Remi Blet (CFO)

Pragoeduca A.S. (1)
Na Perstyne 1, 110 00, Prague, Czech Republic
Tel.: (420) 257 003 460
Web Site: http://www.pragoeduca.cz
Professional Training Services
N.A.I.C.S.: 611430

DEN HARTOGH HOLDING BV
Willingestraat 6, 3087 AN, Rotterdam, Netherlands
Tel.: (31) 88 1620000
Web Site:
http://www.denhartogh.com
Year Founded: 1920
Holding Company; Logistics Services
N.A.I.C.S.: 551112
Pieter den Hartogh (Mng Dir)

Subsidiaries:

Den Hartogh Logistics Latin America Ltda. (1)
Ave Rio Branco 4 - 11 Andar, 20090-000, Rio de Janeiro, Brazil
Tel.: (55) 2122333330
Web Site: http://www.denhartogh.com
Tank Container Operating Services
N.A.I.C.S.: 484121

InterBulk Group Limited (1)
Phoenix House Surtees Business Park, Stockton-on-Tees, TS18 3HR, United Kingdom
Tel.: (44) 1642669018
Web Site: http://www.denhartogh.com
Holding Company; Bulk Transportation & Logistics Services
N.A.I.C.S.: 551112

Subsidiary (Non-US):

Den Hartogh Asia Pacific Pte Ltd. (2)
200 Cantonment Road 02-01 Southpoint, Singapore, 089763, Singapore
Tel.: (65) 63720137

Web Site: http://www.denhartogh.com
Container Trucking Services
N.A.I.C.S.: 484110

Subsidiary (Domestic):

Den Hartogh Dry Bulk Logistics Limited (2)
4 Beacon Way, Hull, HU3 4AE, United Kingdom
Tel.: (44) 1482223428
Web Site: http://www.denhartogh.com
Logistics Services Provider
N.A.I.C.S.: 541614

Subsidiary (Non-US):

Den Hartogh Logistics AB (2)
Drakegatan 7A, 41764, Gothenburg, Sweden
Tel.: (46) 313049470
Web Site: http://www.denhartogh.com
Logistic Services
N.A.I.C.S.: 541614

DEN NETWORKS LIMITED
Unit No 116 1st Floor C Wing Bldg No 2 Kailas, Industrial Complex LBS Marg Park Site Vikhroli W, Mumbai, 400079, Maharashtra, India
Tel.: (91) 2261289999
Web Site:
https://www.dennetworks.com
533137—(BOM)
Rev.: $148,981,716
Assets: $450,653,438
Liabilities: $60,259,936
Net Worth: $390,393,502
Earnings: $28,338,589
Emp.: 612
Fiscal Year-end: 03/31/23
Cable Television
N.A.I.C.S.: 517111
Sameer Manchanda (Mng Dir & Chm)

Subsidiaries:

Crystal Vision Media Private Limited (1)
G-31 Basement Kalka Ji, New Delhi, 110019, India
Tel.: (91) 1149848435
Web Site: http://www.cvmpl.com
Cable Network Services
N.A.I.C.S.: 516210

DEN Ambey Cable Networks Private Limited (1)
11/9 Silver Line Civil Line, Kanpur, 208001, Uttar Pradesh, India
Tel.: (91) 9793884433
Web Site: https://www.denambey.com
Cable Network Services
N.A.I.C.S.: 516210

DEN Broadband Private Limited (1)
236 Okhla Phase 3, New Delhi, 110020, India
Tel.: (91) 1206175000
Web Site: https://www.denbroadband.in
Broadband Services
N.A.I.C.S.: 517111
Dheeraj Singh Bhadoria (Officer-Nodal)

Den ADN Network Private Limited (1)
11/15 East Patel Nagar, New Delhi, 110008, India
Tel.: (91) 1149206868
Web Site: https://www.denadn.com
Cable Broadcasting Services
N.A.I.C.S.: 516210

Den Enjoy Cable Networks Private Limited (1)
8 BN Road Shri Raj Complex Near Jai Hind Market, Kaisharbagh, Lucknow, India
Tel.: (91) 5224076502
Web Site: https://www.denenjoy.com
Digital Cable Services
N.A.I.C.S.: 516210

DENA CO., LTD.
Shibuya Scramble Square 2-24-12

Shibuya, Shibuya-ku, Tokyo, 150-6140, Japan
Tel.: (81) 366265225   **JP**
Web Site: https://dena.com
Year Founded: 1999
2432—(TKS)
Rev.: $903,805,130
Assets: $2,219,029,880
Liabilities: $764,664,630
Net Worth: $1,454,365,250
Earnings: ($189,588,020)
Emp.: 2,897
Fiscal Year-end: 03/31/24
Online Advertising, e-Commerce & Mobile Portal Services
N.A.I.C.S.: 541890
Isao Moriyasu (Pres & CEO)

Subsidiaries:

DeNA Global, Inc. (1)
1 Waters Park Dr Ste 165, San Mateo, CA 94403
Tel.: (650) 638-1026
Web Site: http://www.denaglobal.com
Sales Range: $25-49.9 Million
Emp.: 10
Mobile Entertainment & Mobile Social Networking Services
N.A.I.C.S.: 513210

Mobaoku Co., Ltd. (1)
Shibuya Scramble Square 2-24-12 Shibuya, Shibuya-ku, Tokyo, 150-6140, Japan
Tel.: (81) 358430584
Web Site: https://www.mbok.co.jp
Online Auction Services
N.A.I.C.S.: 513210

PAYGENT Co., Ltd. (1)
Shibuya Prime Plaza 19-1 Maruyamacho, Shibuya-ku, Tokyo, 150-0044, Japan
Tel.: (81) 343667270
Web Site: https://www.paygent.co.jp
Sales Range: $50-74.9 Million
Emp.: 60
Online Payment Gateway Services
N.A.I.C.S.: 522320

The Yokohama BayStars Baseball Club, Inc. (1)
7th floor Kannai Arai Building 1-8 Onoe-cho, Naka-ku, Yokohama, 231-0015, Japan   **(66.92%)**
Tel.: (81) 456810811
Web Site: https://www.baystars.co.jp
Sales Range: $50-74.9 Million
Emp.: 80
Professional Basketball Team
N.A.I.C.S.: 711211

ngmoco Inc. (1)
475 Brannan St Ste 420, San Francisco, CA 94107
Tel.: (415) 375-3170
Web Site: http://www.ngmoco.com
Mobile Device Application Developer
N.A.I.C.S.: 513210

DENEL SOC LTD.
Denel Building Nellmapius Drive, Irene, Centurion, Gauteng, South Africa
Tel.: (27) 126712700   **ZA**
Web Site: http://www.denel.co.za
Year Founded: 1992
Rev.: $267,695,680
Assets: $608,858,320
Liabilities: $729,335,600
Net Worth: ($120,477,280)
Earnings: ($124,388,880)
Emp.: 3,968
Fiscal Year-end: 03/31/19
Holding Company; Military Aircraft Components, Munitions & Other Defense Equipment Mfr & Support Services
N.A.I.C.S.: 551112
Themba Zwelibanzi (Mgr-Risk)

Subsidiaries:

Denel Aeronautics (1)
Atlas Road Bonaero Park, Kempton Park, 1619, Gauteng, South Africa

Tel.: (27) 119272620
Web Site: http://www.denelaeronautics.co.za
Aircraft Maintenance, Repair & Overhaul Services
N.A.I.C.S.: 811310
Abdul Karim (CFO)

Rheinmetall Denel Munition (Pty.) Ltd. (1)
Reeb Road Firgrove, Somerset West, Cape Town, 7130, South Africa   **(49%)**
Tel.: (27) 218502911
Sales Range: $200-249.9 Million
Emp.: 700
Ammunition Mfr
N.A.I.C.S.: 332993
Norbert Shoulze (Gen Mgr)

DENGE VARLIK YONETIM A.S.
Esentepe Mah Buyukdere Cad Ercan Han No 121 Kat 4 No 5, Sisli, Istanbul, Turkiye
Tel.: (90) 8504550800
Web Site:
http://www.dengevarlik.com.tr
Year Founded: 2013
Asset Management Services
N.A.I.C.S.: 531390

DENHAM FORD SALES LTD.
45th Avenue & 56th Street, Wetaskiwin, T9A 2G2, AB, Canada
Tel.: (780) 352-6043
Web Site: http://www.denhamford.ca
Year Founded: 1960
Rev.: $40,435,200
Emp.: 55
New & Used Car Dealers
N.A.I.C.S.: 441110
Dan Anderson (Mgr-Sls)

DENIS CHEM LAB LIMITED
401 Abhishree Complex Opp OM Tower Satellite Road, Ahmedabad, 380 015, Gujarat, India
Tel.: (91) 7926925716
Web Site:
https://www.denischemlab.com
Year Founded: 1982
537536—(BOM)
Rev.: $14,968,953
Assets: $12,593,986
Liabilities: $4,198,616
Net Worth: $8,395,369
Earnings: $309,091
Emp.: 191
Fiscal Year-end: 03/31/21
Pharmaceuticals Product Mfr
N.A.I.C.S.: 325412
Dinesh B. Patel (Chm)

DENISON MINES CORP.
1100 40 University Avenue, Toronto, M5J 1T1, ON, Canada
Tel.: (416) 979-1991   **ON**
Web Site:
https://www.denisonmines.com
DNN—(NYSEAMEX)
Rev.: $13,255,735
Assets: $403,496,895
Liabilities: $62,410,298
Net Worth: $341,086,596
Earnings: $11,228,847
Emp.: 76
Fiscal Year-end: 12/31/22
Uranium Exploration & Mining Services
N.A.I.C.S.: 212290
David D. Cates (Pres & CEO)

Subsidiaries:

Denison Mines Corp. - Vancouver Office (1)
885 West Georgia Street Suite 2000, Vancouver, V6C 3E8, BC, Canada
Tel.: (604) 689-7842
Web Site: http://www.denisonmines.com

Sales Range: $50-74.9 Million
Emp.: 40
Uranium Exploration & Mining Services
N.A.I.C.S.: 212290

DENIZ FINANSAL KIRALAMA A.S.

Buyukdere Cad No 141 Kat 16
Esentepe, Sisli, 34394, Istanbul, Turkiye
Tel.: (90) 2123489400
Web Site:
http://www.denizleasing.com.tr
DNFIN—(IST)
Rev.: $86,096,719
Assets: $742,180,622
Liabilities: $534,349,179
Net Worth: $207,831,442
Earnings: $86,333
Fiscal Year-end: 12/31/23
Financial Investment Services
N.A.I.C.S.: 523999
Belgin Sen *(Exec VP-Fin Affairs, Ops & Budget Reporting)*

DENIZ GAYRIMENKUL YATIRIM ORTAKLIGI AS

Buyukdere Cad No 141 K 22,
Esentepe-Sisli, 34394, Istanbul, Turkiye
Tel.: (90) 2123485745
Web Site:
https://www.denizgyo.com.tr
Year Founded: 1995
DZGYO—(IST)
Sales Range: Less than $1 Million
Real Estate Manangement Services
N.A.I.C.S.: 531390
Tanju Kaya *(Chm & Vice Chm)*

DENIZ YATIRIM MENKUL KIYMETLER A.S.

Buyukdere Cad No 141 K 9
Esentepe, Sisli, 34394, Istanbul, Turkiye
Tel.: (90) 2123489191
Web Site:
http://www.denizyatirim.com
DZY—(IST)
Rev.: $41,948,625
Assets: $174,937,923
Liabilities: $97,938,195
Net Worth: $76,999,729
Earnings: $30,847,637
Fiscal Year-end: 12/31/22
Asset Management Services
N.A.I.C.S.: 523999
Melih Akosman *(Gen Mgr)*

DENIZBANK MOSCOW JSC

13 Bld 42 2nd Zvenigorodskaya Str
6th Floor, 123022, Moscow, Russia
Tel.: (7) 4957251020
Web Site: http://www.denizbank.ru
Year Founded: 2003
Sales Range: Less than $1 Million
Electronic Financial Transaction Services
N.A.I.C.S.: 522320
Oguz Yalcin *(Pres & CEO)*

DENIZLI CAM SANAYII VE TICARET A.S.

Is Kuleleri Kule 3 4 Levent, 34330,
Istanbul, Turkiye
Tel.: (90) 212 350 31 56
Web Site:
http://www.denizlicam.com.tr
Year Founded: 1935
DENCM—(IST)
Glass Products Mfr
N.A.I.C.S.: 327215
Cemil Tokel *(Pres)*

DENKI COMPANY LIMITED

Nihonbashi Mitsui Tower 1-1
Nihonbashi-Muromachi, 2-chome
Chuo-ku, Tokyo, 103-8338, Japan
Tel.: (81) 352905055   JP
Web Site: https://www.denka.co.jp
Year Founded: 1915
4061—(TKS)
Rev.: $2,573,028,430
Assets: $4,073,372,840
Liabilities: $1,978,564,690
Net Worth: $2,094,808,150
Earnings: $78,969,670
Emp.: 6,514
Fiscal Year-end: 03/31/24
Chemical Products Mfr
N.A.I.C.S.: 325199
Shinsuke Yoshitaka *(Chm)*

Subsidiaries:

Akros Trading Co., Ltd.   (1)
12F Wing B Shiba Park Building 2-4-1
Shibakoen, Minato-ku, Tokyo, 105-8568,
Japan
Tel.: (81) 354056111
Web Site: https://www.yk-akros.com
Chemical Products Distr
N.A.I.C.S.: 424690
Toyoki Yokoyama *(Exec VP)*

Denka Advanced Materials (Suzhou)
Co. Ltd.   (1)
Unit 9B Modern Indus Sq, No 333 Xingpu
Rd Suzhou Indu, Suzhou, China
Tel.: (86) 51262871088
Sales Range: $25-49.9 Million
Emp.: 60
Organic Chemical Mfr
N.A.I.C.S.: 325199

Denka Advanced Materials Vietnam
Co., Ltd.   (1)
Plot D-5, Thang Long Industrial Park II Lieu
Xa Commune, Yen My, Hung Yen, Vietnam
Tel.: (84) 2213974805
Chemical Products Mfr
N.A.I.C.S.: 325998

Denka Advantech Private Limited (1)
4 Shenton Way 29-02 SGX Centre 2, Singapore, 68807, Singapore
Tel.: (65) 68610004
Web Site: http://www.denka.com.sg
Sales Range: $50-74.9 Million
Emp.: 150
Organic Chemical Mfr
N.A.I.C.S.: 325199
Masaharu Suzuki *(Mng Dir)*

Denka Chemicals Development Suzhou Co., Ltd.   (1)
Unit 1D No 333 Xingpu Road, Modern Industrial Square Suzhou Industrial Park, Suzhou, 215126, Jiangsu, China
Tel.: (86) 51262806808
Chemical Products Mfr
N.A.I.C.S.: 325998

Denka Chemicals GmbH   (1)
Wehrhahn-Center Cantadorstr 3, Dusseldorf, 40211, Germany
Tel.: (49) 211130990
Web Site: http://www.denka.co.jp
Sales Range: $50-74.9 Million
Emp.: 10
Industrial Supplies Whslr
N.A.I.C.S.: 423840
Kazumi Matsubara *(Mng Dir)*

Denka Chemicals Holdings Asia Pacific Pte. Ltd   (1)
8 Jurong Town Hall Road 07-01 The JTC
Summit, Singapore, 609434, Singapore
Tel.: (65) 6 224 1305
Web Site: https://www.denka.com.sg
Sales Range: $25-49.9 Million
Chemical Products Mfr
N.A.I.C.S.: 325998
Masaharu Suzuki *(Chm)*

Denka Chemicals Hong Kong
Ltd.   (1)
Unit 1010 East Wing Tsim Sha Tsui Centre
66 Mody Rd, 1 Science Museum Road,
Kowloon, China (Hong Kong)
Tel.: (852) 36918636
Industrial Supplies Whslr

N.A.I.C.S.: 423840
Denka Chemicals Shanghai Co.,
Ltd.   (1)
1802A Gubei Fortune Center Phase II No
1438 Hongqiao Rd, Changning District,
Shanghai, 200336, China
Tel.: (86) 2162369090
Web Site: http://www.denka.se
Industrial Supplies Whslr
N.A.I.C.S.: 423840

Denka Construction Solutions Malaysia Sdn. Bhd.   (1)
No 18 Jalan Utas 15/7 Seksyen 15, Darul
Ehsan, 40200, Shah Alam, Selangor, Malaysia
Tel.: (60) 355108810
Web Site: http://www.denka-cs.com
Concrete Structure & Repair Services
N.A.I.C.S.: 238110
Tokuzo Kamada *(Mng Dir)*

Denka Consultant & Engineering Co.,
Ltd.   (1)
6-5 Goiminamikaigan, Ichihara, 290-0045,
Chiba, Japan
Tel.: (81) 436215171
Web Site: https://www.denkaeng.co.jp
Chemical Products Mfr
N.A.I.C.S.: 325998

Denka Corporation   (1)
780 3rd Ave 8th Fl, New York, NY 10017
Tel.: (212) 688-8700
Web Site: http://www.denka.co.jp
Sales Range: $50-74.9 Million
Chemical & Allied Products Merchant Whslr
N.A.I.C.S.: 424690

Denka Elastlution Co., Ltd.   (1)
306 Koyagi-machi, Takasaki, 370-0071,
Gunma, Japan
Tel.: (81) 273627510
Web Site: https://www.des.co.jp
Industrial Rubber Product Mfr & Distr
N.A.I.C.S.: 326299
Hideaki Nagasaka *(Pres & Exec Officer)*

Denka Electronics Materials Dalian
Co., Ltd.   (1)
No 41-10 Wanda Road, Dalian Economic
and Technological Development Zone, Dalian, 116600, Liaoning, China
Tel.: (86) 41162634377
Chemical Products Mfr
N.A.I.C.S.: 325998

Denka Infrastructure Technologies
Shanghai Co,. Ltd.   (1)
1802B Gubei Fortune Center Phase II No
1438 Hongqiao Rd, Changning District,
Shanghai, 200336, China
Tel.: (86) 2162365510
Chemical Products Mfr
N.A.I.C.S.: 325998

Denka Inorganic Materials (Tianjin)
Co., Ltd.   (1)
No 3 Saida Mechanical Park, Xiqing Economic Development Area, Tianjin, 300385,
China
Tel.: (86) 2287920488
Chemical Products Mfr
N.A.I.C.S.: 325998

Denka Korea Co., Ltd.   (1)
1615-1617 Hansin Intervalley24 West Bldg
322 Teheran-Ro, Gangnam-gu, Seoul,
06211, Korea (South)
Tel.: (82) 221831025
Web Site: https://www.denka.co.kr
Chemical Products Mfr
N.A.I.C.S.: 325998

Denka Life Innovation Research Pte.
Ltd.   (1)
21 Biopolis Road 03-21/22 Nucleos, Singapore, 138567, Singapore
Tel.: (65) 62652154
Chemical Products Mfr
N.A.I.C.S.: 325998

Denka Performance Elastomer
LLC   (1)
560 Hwy 44, La Place, LA 70068
Tel.: (985) 536-7400
Web Site: https://www.denka-pe.com
Emp.: 235
Polychloroprene Mfr & Distr

N.A.I.C.S.: 325212
Mikio Shimizu *(Pres & CEO)*

Denka Seiken (Shanghai) Co.,
Ltd.   (1)
Room 2505 Metro Plaza No 555 Loushanguan Rd, Changning Area, Shanghai,
200051, China
Tel.: (86) 2162526277
Chemical Products Mfr
N.A.I.C.S.: 325998

Denka Seiken Co., Ltd.   (1)
Nihonbashi Mitsui Tower, 1-1 Nihonbashi-Muromachi 2-chome Chuo-ku, Tokyo, 103-8338, Japan   (100%)
Tel.: (81) 362143236
Web Site: http://www.denka-seiken.co.jp
Sales Range: $100-124.9 Million
Emp.: 377
Human Vaccines & Diagnostic Reagents
Mfr, Importer, Exporter & Marketer
N.A.I.C.S.: 325413
Mitsukuni Ayabe *(Pres)*

Subsidiary (Non-US):

Denka Seiken UK Limited   (2)
Unit 12 Business Innovation Centre Binley
Business Park, Harry Weston Road, Coventry, CV3 2TX, Derbyshire, United Kingdom
Tel.: (44) 2476430350
Pharmaceutical Sales & Distr
N.A.I.C.S.: 456110

Denka Seiken USA Incorporated   (1)
2540 N 1st St Ste 290, San Jose, CA
95131
Tel.: (408) 371-8819
Chemical Products Mfr
N.A.I.C.S.: 325998

Denka Singapore Private Limited (1)
4 Shenton Way #29-02 SGX Centre 2, Singapore, 68807, Singapore
Tel.: (65) 62241305
Web Site: http://www.denka.com.sg
Emp.: 14
Industrial Gas Mfr
N.A.I.C.S.: 325120
Mitsukuni Ayabe *(Mng Dir)*

Denka Taiwan Corporation   (1)
4F-2 No 76 Nanjing W Rd, Datong District,
Taipei, 103-52, Taiwan
Tel.: (886) 225582026
Chemical Products Mfr
N.A.I.C.S.: 325998

Hissan Trading Co., Ltd.   (1)
14th Floor B Wing Shiba Park Building 2 4
1 Shiba koen, Minato-ku, Tokyo, 105-8568,
Japan
Tel.: (81) 3 5405 6105
Web Site: http://www.hissan.co.jp
Chemical Products Mfr
N.A.I.C.S.: 325199

PT. ESTOP Indonesia   (1)
18 Office Park 15th Floor Suite A Jl TB Simatupang Kav 18, Jakarta Selatan, 12520,
Jakarta, Indonesia
Tel.: (62) 2122784182
Construction Material Mfr & Distr
N.A.I.C.S.: 327390

Toyo Adtec Co., Ltd.   (1)
6-16-12 Ginza, Chuo-Ku, Tokyo, Japan
Tel.: (81) 335421331
Web Site: http://www.toyo-adtec.co.jp
Semiconductor Equipment Import & Distr
N.A.I.C.S.: 423690

DENKIRO SERVICE CO., LTD.

Shimizu Bldg 3f, Chiyoda-Ku, Tokyo,
101 0033, Japan
Tel.: (81) 332545626
Web Site: http://www.denkiro.co.jp
Industrial Furnace Mfr
N.A.I.C.S.: 333994

Subsidiaries:

Yamazaki Denki Co., Ltd.   (1)
123 Koyama Sakado, Saitama, 350 0257,
Japan
Tel.: (81) 492833511
Web Site: http://www.yamazaki-denki.co.jp

Denkiro Service Co., Ltd.—(Continued)

Sales Range: $25-49.9 Million
Emp.: 60
Electric Furnaces Mfr
N.A.I.C.S.: 333994
Kazuo Yoshida (Pres)

DENKYO GROUP HOLDINGS CO.,LTD.

2-1-3 Nihonbashi Higashi, Naniwa-ku, Osaka, 556-0006, Japan
Tel.: (81) 666315634
Web Site: https://www.dg-hd.jp
Year Founded: 1919
8144—(TKS)
Rev.: $360,925,830
Assets: $262,423,610
Liabilities: $85,982,880
Net Worth: $176,440,730
Earnings: $555,240
Emp.: 524
Fiscal Year-end: 03/31/24
Electrical & Household Product Whlsr
N.A.I.C.S.: 423610
Ichiro Takase (Pres & CEO)

Subsidiaries:

Apix International Co., Ltd. (1)
5F 4-7-7 Nipponbashi, Naniwa-ku, Osaka, 556-0005, Japan
Tel.: (81) 666320811
Household Products Mfr
N.A.I.C.S.: 337126

Daiwa Musen Denki Co., Ltd. (1)
Yushima Fuji Building 9F 3-13-8 Yushima, Bunkyo-ku, Tokyo, 113-0034, Japan
Tel.: (81) 358468955
Electronic Parts & Equipment Distr
N.A.I.C.S.: 423690

Kajihara Industrial Co., Ltd. (1)
3-3-3 Aramoto Kita Higashi, Osaka, 577-0011, Japan
Tel.: (81) 667445881
Emp.: 96
Household Appliance Distr
N.A.I.C.S.: 423620

DENNEMEYER SA

55 rue des Bruyeres, 1274, Howald, Luxembourg
Tel.: (352) 4998411
Web Site: https://www.dennemeyer.com
Year Founded: 1962
Law firm
N.A.I.C.S.: 541199

DENNY ANDREWS FORD SALES INC.

18208 Stony Plain Road, Edmonton, T5S 1A7, AB, Canada
Tel.: (780) 489-9999
Web Site: https://www.dennyandrewsford.ca
Year Founded: 1984
Sales Range: $75-99.9 Million
New & Used Car Dealers
N.A.I.C.S.: 441110
Kevin Hildebrand (Ops Mgr)

DENOX ENVIRONMENTAL & TECHNOLOGY HOLDINGS LIMITED

1507 Building 2 Nuode Center No. 128 South 4th Ring Western Road, Fengtai District, Beijing, 100070, China
Tel.: (86) 1088829058
Web Site: http://www.china-denox.com
Year Founded: 2010
1452—(HKG)
Rev.: $8,815,856
Assets: $44,141,620
Liabilities: $17,651,650
Net Worth: $26,489,970
Earnings: ($3,303,752)

Emp.: 182
Fiscal Year-end: 12/31/22
Environmental Consulting Services
N.A.I.C.S.: 541620
Shu Zhao (Chm)

DENSAN CO., LTD.

451 Minaminagano Agata-Machi, Nagano, 380-0838, Japan
Tel.: (81) 262340151
Web Site: http://www.ndensan.co.jp
Year Founded: 1966
3640—(TKS)
Rev.: $167,522,080
Assets: $201,082,640
Liabilities: $129,334,480
Net Worth: $71,748,160
Earnings: $8,315,120
Emp.: 730
Fiscal Year-end: 03/31/22
Data Processing Services
N.A.I.C.S.: 518210
Kazuta Todoroki (Pres)

DENSAN SYSTEM CO., LTD.

1-58 Hiokie, Gifu, 501-6196, Japan
Tel.: (81) 582793456   JP
Web Site: https://www.densan-s.co.jp
Year Founded: 1967
Rev.: $368,652,340
Assets: $339,510,080
Liabilities: $239,804,670
Net Worth: $99,705,410
Earnings: $14,296,030
Emp.: 779
Fiscal Year-end: 12/31/19
Computer System Integration & Data Services
N.A.I.C.S.: 541512
Masanao Miyachi (Chm & CEO)

Subsidiaries:

DS Technologies Inc. (1)
Hachobori Tokyu Bldg 5F 2-20-8 Hachobori, Chuo-ku, Tokyo, 104-0032, Japan
Tel.: (81) 3 3537 6980
Web Site: http://www.ds-tech.co.jp
Computer System Maintenance Services
N.A.I.C.S.: 811210
Yasuhiro Sakamoto (Pres & CEO)

Garden Network, Ltd. (1)
2-20-8 Hatchobori Tokyu Building, Chuo-Ku, Tokyo, 104-0032, Japan
Tel.: (81) 3 6701 3630
Web Site: http://www.garden-network.jp
Sales Range: $1-9.9 Million
Gas Station Management Services
N.A.I.C.S.: 541618
Fukumoto Hiroyuki (Pres & CEO)

System Engineering Co., Ltd. (1)
No 37 Thiri Street, Ward 2 Hlaing Township, Yangon, Myanmar
Tel.: (95) 1505969
Web Site: http://www.secmyanmar.com
Construction Services
N.A.I.C.S.: 236220

System IC Co., Ltd. (1)
1-58 Hikie, Gifu, 501-6133, Japan
Tel.: (81) 58 270 0270
Web Site: http://www.system-ic.co.jp
Software Development Services
N.A.I.C.S.: 541511

DENSO CORPORATION

1-1 Showa-cho, Kariya, 448-8661, Aichi, Japan
Tel.: (81) 566255511   JP
Web Site: https://www.denso.com
Year Founded: 1949
DNO—(DEU)
Rev.: $47,226,685,130
Assets: $60,107,175,700
Liabilities: $22,122,777,650
Net Worth: $37,984,398,050
Earnings: $2,067,548,510
Emp.: 162,029
Fiscal Year-end: 03/31/24

Advanced Automotive Technologies, Systems & Components
N.A.I.C.S.: 336390
Yasuhisa Sakurai (Sr Exec Officer & Head-OEM Sls, Marketing, and Corp Strategy Div)

Subsidiaries:

3D Incorporated (1)
4F-KDX Shin-Yokohama Bldg 2-3-8 Shin-Yokohama, Kohoku-ku, Yokohama, 222-0033, Japan
Tel.: (81) 505 533 3380
Web Site: https://www.ddd.co.jp
Software Development Services
N.A.I.C.S.: 541511
Takashi Hikosakai (Pres)

AMERICAN INDUSTRIAL MANU-FACTURING SERVICES, INC. (1)
41673 Corning Pl, Murrieta, CA 92562
Tel.: (951) 698-3379
Web Site: http://www.globaldenso.com
Sales Range: $25-49.9 Million
Emp.: 100
Automotive Electrical Component Mfr
N.A.I.C.S.: 336390

ANDEN CO., LTD. (1)
1-10 Sasamecho, Anjo, 446-8503, Aichi, Japan
Tel.: (81) 566730022
Web Site: http://www.anden.jp
Sales Range: $450-499.9 Million
Emp.: 1,516
Electronic Products Mfr & Distr
N.A.I.C.S.: 334419

ASAHI MANUFACTURING CO., LTD. (1)
5-120 Toshincho, Kariya, 448-0031, Aichi, Japan
Tel.: (81) 566 21 5861
Web Site: http://www.kk-asahi-ss.co.jp
Wiper Linkage Mfr
N.A.I.C.S.: 336390

ASMO CO., LTD (1)
390 Umeda, Kosai, 431-0493, Shizuoka, Japan
Tel.: (81) 535723311
Web Site: http://www.asmo.co.jp
Sales Range: $25-49.9 Billion
Emp.: 15,367
Automobile Motor System Mfr & Distr
N.A.I.C.S.: 336390
Shingo Kuwamura (Pres)

ASMO DETROIT, INC (1)
39575 Lewis Dr Ste 800, Novi, MI 48377
Tel.: (248) 359-4440
Web Site: http://www.globaldenso.com
Sales Range: $25-49.9 Million
Emp.: 38
Automotive Engineering Services
N.A.I.C.S.: 541330

ASMO GREENVILLE OF NORTH CAROLINA, INC. (1)
1125 Sugg Pkwy, Greenville, NC 27834
Tel.: (252) 754-1000
Web Site: http://www.globaldenso.com
Sales Range: $100-124.9 Million
Emp.: 425
Automobile Parts Mfr
N.A.I.C.S.: 336390
Melvin Collins (Engr-Maintenance)

ASMO NORTH CAROLINA, INC. (1)
470 Crawford Rd, Statesville, NC 28625-8504
Tel.: (704) 878-6663
Web Site: http://www.asmo-na.com
Sales Range: $100-124.9 Million
Emp.: 370
Electric Motor Mfr
N.A.I.C.S.: 335312
David Clifton (VP)

Anden (Thailand) Co., Ltd. (1)
700/87 Moo 1 Amata Nakorn Industrial Estate, Bangna-Trdad KM 57 T Bankao, A Panthon, Chon Buri, 20160, Thailand (100%)
Tel.: (66) 38214649
Sales Range: $25-49.9 Million
Emp.: 232
Relays & Flashers Mfr

N.A.I.C.S.: 336350

Apines Inc. (1)
390 Umeda, Kosai, 431-0425, Shizuoka, Japan
Tel.: (81) 535772626
N.A.I.C.S.: 336390

Asmo Czech S.R.O. (1)
Modra 1080, 285 22, Zruc nad Sazavou, Czech Republic
Tel.: (420) 327533711
Web Site: https://www.asmo.cz
Sales Range: $50-74.9 Million
Emp.: 400
Automobile Parts Mfr
N.A.I.C.S.: 336390
Karel Simek (Sr Mgr-Production & Production Control)

Aubass Co., Ltd. (1)
9th floor Taiyoseimeishinagawa building 2-16-2 Konan, Minato-ku, Tokyo, 108-0075, Japan
Tel.: (81) 35 781 2300
Web Site: https://www.aubass.jp
Emp.: 182
Software Development Services
N.A.I.C.S.: 541511
Shoji Izumi (Pres)

CTR S.R.L. (1)
Via Tito ed Ettore Manzini 9, 43126, Parma, Italy
Tel.: (39) 052 195 7611
Web Site: https://www.ctrgroup.it
Sales Range: $25-49.9 Million
Emp.: 24
Heat Exchanger Mfr
N.A.I.C.S.: 332410
Aldo Adamo (Gen Mgr)

DAISHINSEIKI CO., LTD. (1)
200 Ohayashi Kume, Tokoname, 479-8511, Aichi, Japan
Tel.: (81) 569440077
Web Site: http://www.daishinseiki.co.jp
Sales Range: $200-249.9 Million
Emp.: 745
Fuel Injection System Mfr
N.A.I.C.S.: 336310
Akio Shikamura (Pres)

DENSO (CHANGZHOU) FUEL INJECTION SYSTEM CO., LTD. (1)
No 301 Hehai West Road, Xinbei District, Changzhou, Jiangsu, China
Tel.: (86) 5198 515 2130
Web Site: http://www.globaldenso.com
Sales Range: $100-124.9 Million
Emp.: 369
Automotive Parts Mfr & Distr
N.A.I.C.S.: 336390

DENSO (CHINA) INVESTMENT CO., LTD. (1)
No 518 Development Building No 5 Dongsanhuan North Road, Chaoyang District, Beijing, 100004, China
Tel.: (86) 106 590 8337
Web Site: http://www.globaldenso.com
Sales Range: $250-299.9 Million
Emp.: 582
Automobile Component Distr
N.A.I.C.S.: 423120

DENSO (GUANGZHOU NANSHA) CO., LTD (1)
No 33 Shinan Avenue, Huangge Town Nansha District, Guangzhou, China
Tel.: (86) 203 497 2888
Web Site: http://www.globaldenso.com
Emp.: 2,200
Fuel Injection System Mfr & Distr
N.A.I.C.S.: 336390

DENSO (THAILAND) CO., LTD - Wellgrow Plant (1)
Wellgrow Industrial Estate 85 Moo 9 Bangna Trad Rd KM 36, T Bangwua A Bangpakong, Chachoengsao, 24180, Thailand
Tel.: (66) 3857 1717
Sales Range: $800-899.9 Million
Emp.: 2,987
Automobile Parts Mfr
N.A.I.C.S.: 336390

DENSO (TIANJIN) THERMAL PRODUCTS CO., LTD. (1)

No 15 Saida 2nd Street Xiqing Economic Development Area, Tianjin, China
Tel.: (86) 2223889288
Sales Range: $200-249.9 Million
Emp.: 803
Car Air Conditioner Mfr & Distr
N.A.I.C.S.: 336390

DENSO ABASHIRI TEST CENTER CORPORATION (1)
708 Katayama, Abashiri, 093-0133, Hokkaido, Japan
Tel.: (81) 152 61 8700
Sales Range: $25-49.9 Million
Emp.: 8
Product Testing Services
N.A.I.C.S.: 541380
Masahiko Miyaki (CEO)

DENSO ACE CORPORATION (1)
2-15-13 Shoto Denso Shibuya Bldg 4f, Shibuya-Ku, Tokyo, 150-0046, Japan
Tel.: (81) 363673810
Web Site: http://www.denso-ace.com
Sales Range: $50-74.9 Million
Emp.: 99
Air Conditioner Distr
N.A.I.C.S.: 423730

DENSO AIR SYSTEMS CORPORATION (1)
89-8 Hoden Noderacho, Anjo, 444-1165, Aichi, Japan
Tel.: (81) 566 99 0101
Sales Range: $200-249.9 Million
Emp.: 983
Air Conditioning Parts Mfr
N.A.I.C.S.: 334512

Subsidiary (US):

DENSO AIR SYSTEMS MICHIGAN, INC. (2)
300 Fritz Keiper Blvd, Battle Creek, MI 49037
Tel.: (269) 962-9676
Web Site: http://www.denso-asmi.com
Sales Range: $25-49.9 Million
Emp.: 229
Automotive Air Conditioning Parts Mfr
N.A.I.C.S.: 333415
Jerry McGuire (Pres)

Joint Venture (Non-US):

TBMECA Poland Sp. z o.o. (2)
ul Jaworzynska 291 a, 59-220, Legnica, Poland (20%)
Tel.: (48) 768508120
Web Site: http://www.tbmeca.pl
Emp.: 115
Automotive Components Mfr
N.A.I.C.S.: 336390

DENSO AIR SYSTEMS CZECH s.r.o (1)
Newtonova 484 Zona Liberec Jih, 462 02, Liberec, Czech Republic
Tel.: (420) 488100100
Sales Range: $50-74.9 Million
Emp.: 243
Car Air Conditioning Component Mfr
N.A.I.C.S.: 333415
Makoto Morimoto (Gen Mgr)

DENSO AIR SYSTEMS TOYOSHINA CORPORATION (1)
1086-1 Toyoshinatakibe, Azumino, 399-8204, Nagano, Japan
Tel.: (81) 263 72 8870
Sales Range: $50-74.9 Million
Emp.: 137
Automotive Air Conditioner Mfr
N.A.I.C.S.: 333415

DENSO AIR SYSTEMS YASAKA CORPORATION (1)
707 Yasaka, Omachi, 399-7301, Nagano, Japan
Tel.: (81) 261 26 2007
Sales Range: $25-49.9 Million
Emp.: 57
Automotive Air Conditioning Parts Mfr
N.A.I.C.S.: 336390

DENSO AUTOMOTIVE SYSTEMS AUSTRALIA PTY. LTD. (1)
46 Merrindale Drive, Croydon, 3136, VIC, Australia
Tel.: (61) 38 761 1100

Web Site: https://www.denso.com.au
Sales Range: $100-124.9 Million
Emp.: 350
Automotive Cooling System Mfr
N.A.I.C.S.: 336390
Russell Jopson (Pres & CEO)

DENSO AgriTech Solutions, Inc. (1)
1-8-15 Kounan, Minato-ku, Tokyo, Japan
Tel.: (81) 34 231 2730
Web Site: https://www.denso-agri.com
Greenhouse Material Retailer
N.A.I.C.S.: 444240
Osamu Shimizu (CEO)

DENSO CHUGOKU CORPORATION (1)
4-21 Higashihiratsukacho, Naka-Ku, Hiroshima, 730-0025, Japan
Tel.: (81) 822425210
Web Site: http://www.denso-chugoku.com
Sales Range: $50-74.9 Million
Emp.: 84
Automotive Distr & Repair Services
N.A.I.C.S.: 423110

DENSO COMMUNICATIONS CORPORATION (1)
1-1 Showa-cho, Kariya, 448-8661, Aichi, Japan
Tel.: (81) 566 25 6447
Web Site: http://www.d-coms.co.jp
Sales Range: $25-49.9 Million
Emp.: 5
Travel Information Services
N.A.I.C.S.: 561599
Hiroyasu Nakagawa (Gen Mgr)

DENSO DO BRASIL LTDA. (1)
Rua Joao Chede 891 CIC, Caixa Postal 6501, Curitiba, 81170-220, Parana, Brazil
Tel.: (55) 4121414300
Web Site: https://www.denso.com
Sales Range: $400-449.9 Million
Emp.: 1,654
Bus Air Conditioner Mfr
N.A.I.C.S.: 336390

DENSO E & TS TRAINING CENTER CORPORATION (1)
1 Shinmichi Takatana-cho, Anjo, 446-8507, Aichi, Japan
Tel.: (81) 566 73 2612
Web Site: http://www.denso-ets.com
Sales Range: $25-49.9 Million
Emp.: 174
Industrial Training Services
N.A.I.C.S.: 611430
Koichi Hagino (Pres)

DENSO ELECTRONICS CORPORATION (1)
1007-195 Izumisawa, Chitose, 066-0051, Hokkaido, Japan
Tel.: (81) 123 47 8800
Web Site: http://www.denso-electronics.co.jp
Sales Range: $100-124.9 Million
Emp.: 1,000
Automotive Semiconductor Product Mfr
N.A.I.C.S.: 334413
Seiji Nehashi (Pres)

DENSO EMC ENGINEERING SERVICE CORPORATION (1)
1-1 Showa-cho, Kariya, 448-8661, Aichi, Japan
Tel.: (81) 56 625 5955
Web Site: https://www.emces.co.jp
Sales Range: $25-49.9 Million
Emp.: 60
Electromagnetic Compatibility Testing Services
N.A.I.C.S.: 541380
Takashi Morr (Gen Mgr)

DENSO FACILITIES CORPORATION (1)
2-1 Maruta-machi, Kariya, 448-0033, Aichi, Japan
Tel.: (81) 56 625 7511
Web Site: http://www.densofacilities.co.jp
Sales Range: $200-249.9 Million
Emp.: 504
Power Plant Construction & Management Services
N.A.I.C.S.: 237130

DENSO FINANCE & ACCOUNTING CENTER CO., LTD. (1)

1-1 Showacho Kk Denso Honshanai, Kariya, 448-0029, Aichi, Japan
Tel.: (81) 566 25 6775
Sales Range: $50-74.9 Million
Emp.: 9
Financial Management Services
N.A.I.C.S.: 523999

DENSO FINANCE HOLLAND B.V. (1)
Hogeweyselaan 165, 1382 JL, Weesp, Netherlands
Tel.: (31) 294493493
Web Site: http://www.globaldenso.com
Financial Management Services
N.A.I.C.S.: 523999

DENSO HARYANA PVT. LTD. (1)
Plot No 3 Sector-3, IMT Manesar, Gurgaon, 122050, Haryana, India
Tel.: (91) 124 229 0611
Web Site: http://www.globaldenso.com
Sales Range: $200-249.9 Million
Emp.: 545
Fuel Pump Mfr & Distr
N.A.I.C.S.: 336310
Hichore Shibata (Gen Mgr)

DENSO HOKKAIDO CORPORATION (1)
7-2-27 2jo Yamanote, Nishi-Ku, Sapporo, 063-0002, Hokkaido, Japan
Tel.: (81) 11 614 3511
Sales Range: $25-49.9 Million
Emp.: 156
Automotive Repair & Maintenance Services
N.A.I.C.S.: 811198

DENSO INTERNATIONAL EUROPE B.V. (1)
World Trade Centre Tower-I floor 4 Strawinskylaan 1865, 1077 XX, Amsterdam, Netherlands
Tel.: (31) 294493493
Automotive Components Mfr
N.A.I.C.S.: 336390

DENSO INTERNATIONAL INDIA PVT. LTD. (1)
Plot No 3 Sector-3 IMT-Manesar, Gurgaon, 122 050, Haryana, India
Tel.: (91) 124 480 3200
Web Site: http://www.globaldenso.com
Sales Range: $75-99.9 Million
Emp.: 180
Automobile Parts Distr
N.A.I.C.S.: 423120
Yoshitaka Kajita (Mng Dir)

DENSO INTERNATIONAL UK LTD. (1)
1 Bishop Square, Hatfield, AL10 9NE, Herts, United Kingdom
Tel.: (44) 1707282400
Web Site: http://www.globaldenso.com
Sales Range: $25-49.9 Million
Emp.: 50
Automobile Parts Distr
N.A.I.C.S.: 423120
Alan William Richards (Gen Mgr)

DENSO IT Solutions, Inc. (1)
1-27-2 Meiekiminami 11th Floor Nihonseimei Sasashima Building, Nakamura-ku, Nagoya, 450-0003, Aichi, Japan (100%)
Tel.: (81) 52 586 5400
Web Site: http://www.dnitsol.com
Emp.: 375
Information Technology Consulting Services
N.A.I.C.S.: 541512
Toshiyuki Sugiura (Pres & Dir)

DENSO KANSAI CORPORATION (1)
1-7-19 Higashitemma Denso Osaka Shiten 3f, Kita-Ku, Osaka, 530-0044, Japan
Tel.: (81) 6 6355 3800
Web Site: http://www.denso-kansai.com
Sales Range: $25-49.9 Million
Emp.: 147
Automotive Repair Services
N.A.I.C.S.: 811198

DENSO KATSUYAMA CO., LTD. (1)
220 Sanden, Maniwa, 717-0022, Okayama, Japan
Tel.: (81) 867 44 2653
Sales Range: $50-74.9 Million
Emp.: 157
Molded Plastic Product Mfr

N.A.I.C.S.: 326199

DENSO KIKO CO., LTD. (1)
5-1-5 Shindencho, Takahama, 444-1301, Aichi, Japan
Tel.: (81) 566 53 5115
Web Site: http://www.denso-kiko.co.jp
Sales Range: $50-74.9 Million
Emp.: 200
Car Air Conditioning Prototype Mfr
N.A.I.C.S.: 336390

DENSO KYUSHU CORPORATION (1)
2-6-35 Sanno, Hakata-Ku, Fukuoka, 812-0015, Japan
Tel.: (81) 924121177
Web Site: http://www.denso-kyushu.com
Sales Range: $25-49.9 Million
Emp.: 161
Automotive Repair & Maintenance Services
N.A.I.C.S.: 811198

DENSO LOGITEM CORPORATION (1)
1 Sumisaki Shimohasumicho Kk Denso Nishio Seisakusho Nai, Nishio, 445-0012, Aichi, Japan
Tel.: (81) 563 55 1201
Sales Range: $50-74.9 Million
Emp.: 183
Cargo Handling Services
N.A.I.C.S.: 488320

DENSO MANUFACTURING ARGENTINA S.A. (1)
Avenida Las Malvinas Km 4 5 5012, 5012, Cordoba, Argentina
Tel.: (54) 3514968500
Web Site: http://www.globaldenso.com
Emp.: 376
Car Air Conditioner Mfr
N.A.I.C.S.: 336390
Ariel Roldin (Pres)

DENSO MANUFACTURING ATHENS TENNESSEE, INC. (1)
2400 Denso Dr, Athens, TN 37303
Tel.: (423) 746-0000
Sales Range: $200-249.9 Million
Emp.: 400
Hydraulic Components Mfr
N.A.I.C.S.: 332912
Hugh Cantrell (Sr Mgr-HR)

DENSO MANUFACTURING CANADA, INC (1)
900 Southgate Drive, Guelph, N1L 1K1, ON, Canada
Tel.: (519) 837-6600
Web Site: http://www.densocorp-na-dmon.com
Sales Range: $100-124.9 Million
Emp.: 315
Automobile Parts Mfr
N.A.I.C.S.: 336390
Steve Milam (Pres)

DENSO MANUFACTURING KITAKYUSHU CO.,LTD. (1)
5-4-1 Honjo, Yahatanishi-Ku, Kitakyushu, 807-0801, Fukuoka, Japan
Tel.: (81) 93 693 1111
Web Site: http://www.denso-kitakyushu.jp
Sales Range: $200-249.9 Million
Emp.: 894
Automobile Parts Mfr
N.A.I.C.S.: 336310

DENSO MANUFACTURING TENNESSEE, INC. (1)
1720 Robert C Jackson Dr, Maryville, TN 37801
Tel.: (865) 982-7000
Web Site: https://www.denso.com
Sales Range: $400-449.9 Million
Emp.: 2,500
Automotive Components Mfr
N.A.I.C.S.: 336390
Christopher Brinley (Mgr)

DENSO MAQUINAS ROTANTES do BRASIL LTDA. (1)
Avenida Campo de Ourique No 401, Dom Bosco, Betim, 32670-575, MG, Brazil
Tel.: (55) 312 191 1410
Web Site: http://www.denso-dmbr.com.br
Sales Range: $50-74.9 Million
Emp.: 100
Motor Mfr & Distr

Denso Corporation—(Continued)

N.A.I.C.S.: 335312
Francesco Momaco *(Gen Mgr)*

DENSO MEXICO S.A. DE C.V (1)
Boulevard Parque Industrial Monterrey No
502, Parque Industrial Monterrey, 66603,
Apoduca, Nuevo Leon, Mexico
Tel.: (52) 8181567000
Web Site: http://www.globaldenso.com
Sales Range: $800-899.9 Million
Emp.: 3,487
Automotive Cluster & Valves Mfr
N.A.I.C.S.: 336390

**DENSO OTOMOTIV PARCALARI
SANAYI ANONIM SIRKET** (1)
Tsob-Taysad Organize Sanayi Bolgesi 5
Cadde No 1, Sekerpinar, 41480, Gebze,
Turkiye
Tel.: (90) 2626795700
Sales Range: $50-74.9 Million
Emp.: 127
Car Air Conditioner Mfr
N.A.I.C.S.: 336390

DENSO PREAS CO., LTD. (1)
2-58 Nishisakuragicho, Toyokawa, 442-
0063, Aichi, Japan
Tel.: (81) 533862181
Web Site: http://www.densopreas.co.jp
Sales Range: $50-74.9 Million
Emp.: 131
Automotive Parts Mfr & Whslr
N.A.I.C.S.: 336390

DENSO PS CORPORATION (1)
47 Sungsan-Dong Sungsangu, Changwon,
Kyungnam, Korea (South)
Tel.: (82) 556009510
Web Site: http://www.densops.co.kr
Rev.: $438,480,000
Emp.: 1,238
Automotive Electrical Component Mfr
N.A.I.C.S.: 336390

Plant (Domestic):

**DENSO PS CORPORATION - Hong-
seong Factory** (2)
524 Gyunguk-lee Eunha-myeon, Hongseong, chungcheongnam-do, Korea (South)
Tel.: (82) 56428795
Automotive Components Mfr
N.A.I.C.S.: 336390

**DENSO REMANI
CORPORATION** (1)
2-1 Nagane Sato-cho, Anjo, 446-8511,
Aichi, Japan
Tel.: (81) 56 696 0295
Web Site: https://www.densoremani.co.jp
Emp.: 52
Automotive Parts Mfr & Whslr
N.A.I.C.S.: 336390

DENSO SALES CANADA, INC. (1)
195 Brunel Rd, Mississauga, L4Z 1X3, ON,
Canada
Tel.: (905) 890-0890
Sales Range: $25-49.9 Million
Emp.: 30
Automobile Parts Distr
N.A.I.C.S.: 423120
Masaki Fukutomi *(Pres)*

**DENSO SALES FRANCE
S.A.R.L.** (1)
Immeuble Selene 12 Parc Ariane, Guyan-
court, 78280, France
Tel.: (33) 161372222
Web Site: http://www.denso-europe.com
Sales Range: $25-49.9 Million
Emp.: 46
Automobile Component Distr
N.A.I.C.S.: 423120

DENSO SALES RUS L.L.C. (1)
Vodny Business Center 8th floor Golovin-
skoye shosse 5 building 1, 125212, Mos-
cow, Russia
Tel.: (7) 4959705757
Web Site: http://www.globaldenso.com
Sales Range: $25-49.9 Million
Emp.: 11
Automobile Product Distr
N.A.I.C.S.: 423120
Kenji Horibe *(Gen Mgr)*

DENSO SEIBI CO., LTD. (1)

12 Kawarazaki Shimoaonocho, Okazaki,
444-0244, Aichi, Japan
Tel.: (81) 564 43 1945
Sales Range: $25-49.9 Million
Emp.: 53
Waste Material Recycling Services
N.A.I.C.S.: 562920

**DENSO SERVICE NISHISAITAMA
CO., LTD.** (1)
295-2 Higashiaraicho, Tokorozawa, 359-
0034, Saitama, Japan
Tel.: (81) 42 992 0071
Sales Range: $25-49.9 Million
Emp.: 15
Automotive Repair Services
N.A.I.C.S.: 811198

**DENSO SERVICE OKINAWA CO.,
LTD.** (1)
409 Minatogawa, Urasoe, 901-2134, Oki-
nawa, Japan
Tel.: (81) 98 877 4655
Web Site: https://www.ds-okinawa.com
Sales Range: $25-49.9 Million
Emp.: 34
Automotive Parts Repair Services
N.A.I.C.S.: 811198

DENSO SI CORPORATION (1)
1-11-9 Mikawaanjo Minamicho, Anjo, 446-
0058, Aichi, Japan
Tel.: (81) 56 675 7500
Web Site: https://www.denso-si.jp
Sales Range: $25-49.9 Million
Emp.: 105
Information Technology Consulting Services
N.A.I.C.S.: 541512

**DENSO SISTEMAS TERMICOS ES-
PANA S.A.** (1)
Parque Tecnologico y Logistico de Vigo
Calle 1-Parcela 7, Calle 1 Parcela 7, 36312,
Vigo, Pontevedra, Spain
Tel.: (34) 98 682 3601
Web Site: http://www.denso-europe.com
Emp.: 335
Heaters & Cooling Modules Mfr & Distr
N.A.I.C.S.: 333414

**DENSO SOFTWARE SHANGHAI
CO., LTD.** (1)
18401-18404 Room 498 Guoshoujing
Road, Pudong New Area, Shanghai,
201203, China
Tel.: (86) 21 5131 4061
Web Site: http://www.globaldenso.com
Sales Range: $25-49.9 Million
Emp.: 116
Software Development Services
N.A.I.C.S.: 541511

DENSO TAIWAN CORP. (1)
525 Sec 2 Mei Su Road, Yang Mei Town
Hsien, Taoyuan, Taiwan
Tel.: (886) 3 482 8001
Web Site: http://www.denso.com.tw
Sales Range: $125-149.9 Million
Emp.: 417
Automotive Electrical Component Mfr &
Whslr
N.A.I.C.S.: 336390

DENSO TAIYO CO., LTD. (1)
28-1 Kitahama Katahara-cho, Gamagori,
443-0103, Aichi, Japan
Tel.: (81) 533 57 1636
Sales Range: $50-74.9 Million
Emp.: 189
Instrument Cluster Mfr & Whslr
N.A.I.C.S.: 336390

DENSO TECHNO CO., LTD. (1)
2-188 Chuo-cho, Obu, 474-0025, Aichi,
Japan
Tel.: (81) 56 244 1111
Web Site: https://www.densotechno.co.jp
Sales Range: $350-399.9 Million
Emp.: 2,239
Software Development Services
N.A.I.C.S.: 541511

**DENSO TECHNO PHILIPPINES,
INC.** (1)
25/F BPI Buendia Center Sen Gil Puyat
Ave, Makati, Philippines
Tel.: (63) 27519663
Software Development Services
N.A.I.C.S.: 541511

DENSO TEN Limited (1)
2-28 Gosho-dori 1-chome, Hyogo-ku, Kobe,
652-8510, Hyogo, Japan
Tel.: (81) 786715081
Web Site: https://www.denso-ten.com
Emp.: 3,533
Automotive Electronics & Audio Visual
Equipment Mfr & Distr
N.A.I.C.S.: 336320
Yukihiro Kato *(Pres & CEO)*

Subsidiary (Non-US):

DENSO TEN (CHINA) Limited (2)
Room 1805 Tianxin Building No 125 Weidi
road, Hexi District, Tianjin, 300074, China
Tel.: (86) 2228408388
Web Site: http://www.denso-ten.com
Automotive Electric Parts Distr
N.A.I.C.S.: 423120

DENSO TEN (CHINA) Limited (2)
Room 1805 Tianxin Building No 125 Weidi
road, Hexi District, Tianjin, 300457, China
Tel.: (86) 2228408388
Business Management Services
N.A.I.C.S.: 561499

**DENSO TEN (THAILAND)
Limited** (2)
888 Moo 1 Bangna-Trad Road KM 27.5
Tumbol Bangbo, Amphur Bangbo Samut-
prakarn, 10560, Bangkok, Thailand
Tel.: (66) 21050240
Sales Range: $200-249.9 Million
Emp.: 60
Automotive Electronics & Audio Visual
Products Mfr & Distr
N.A.I.C.S.: 336320

Plant (Domestic):

**DENSO TEN (THAILAND)
Limited** (3)
253 Moo 11 Rojana Industrial Park Bankhai
Banbung Rd T Nongbua A, Bankhai, Ray-
ong, 21120, Thailand
Tel.: (66) 33017300
Automotive Electronics & Audio Visual
Products Mfr
N.A.I.C.S.: 336320

Subsidiary (US):

DENSO TEN AMERICA Limited (2)
20200 S Western Ave, Torrance, CA 90501
Tel.: (310) 327-2151
Automotive Audio, Video, Navigation & Con-
trol Systems
N.A.I.C.S.: 423620

Subsidiary (Domestic):

**DENSO TEN AMERICA Limited - Los
Angeles** (3)
20200 S Western Avenue, Torrance, CA
90501
Tel.: (310) 327-2151
Automobile Related Equipment & Parts De-
velopment & Design
N.A.I.C.S.: 336320

Eclipse Mobile Electronics (3)
19600 S Vermont Ave, Torrance, CA 90502-
1122
Tel.: (310) 327-2151
Web Site: http://www.eclipse-web.com
Mfr of Automobile Audio Systems
N.A.I.C.S.: 423620

Subsidiary (Non-US):

**DENSO TEN ELECTRONICS (WUXI)
Limited** (2)
No 19 Xinhua Road, Xinwu District, Wuxi,
214028, China
Tel.: (86) 510 8866 2288
Automotive Infotainment Mfr
N.A.I.C.S.: 336320

DENSO TEN ESPANA, S.A. (2)
Pol Ind Guadalhorce C/Cesar Vallejo 16,
29004, Malaga, Spain
Tel.: (34) 95 213 3000
Web Site: http://www.ftesa.es
Automotive Electronic Product Mfr
N.A.I.C.S.: 336320

Plant (Domestic):

**DENSO TEN Limited - Nakatsugawa
Plant** (2)

2110 Naegi, Nakatsugawa, 508-0101, Gifu,
Japan
Tel.: (81) 573 66 5121
Web Site: http://www.denso-ten.com
Automotive Electronic Parts Mfr
N.A.I.C.S.: 336320

Subsidiary (Non-US):

**DENSO TEN MINDA INDIA Private
Limited** (2)
Plot No 383 Industrial Growth Center Phase
II, Sector 3 Bawal Dsitrict, Rewari, 123501,
Haryana, India
Tel.: (91) 1284266666
Car Infotainment Equipment & Accessory
Mfr
N.A.I.C.S.: 336390

**DENSO TEN PHILIPPINES
CORPORATION** (2)
100 South Science Avenue Laguna Tech-
nopark, 4026, Santa Rosa, Laguna, Philip-
pines
Tel.: (63) 2 793 2900
Automotive Electronics & Audio Visual
Products Mfr & Distr
N.A.I.C.S.: 336320

**DENSO TEN RESEARCH AND DE-
VELOPMENT (TIANJIN) Limited** (2)
No 280 Huang Hai Road TEDA, Tianjin,
300457, China
Tel.: (86) 22 6527 0088
Software Development Services
N.A.I.C.S.: 541511

**DENSO TEN SINGAPORE Private
Limited** (2)
51 Science Park Road #01-18 The Aries
Singapore Science Park II, Singapore,
117586, Singapore
Tel.: (65) 6773 4933
Electronic Device Distr
N.A.I.C.S.: 423690

Subsidiary (Domestic):

DENSO TEN STAFF Limited (2)
2-28 Gosho-dori 1-chome, Hyogo-ku, Kobe,
652-8510, Hyogo, Japan
Tel.: (81) 78 682 2257
Human Resource Consulting Services
N.A.I.C.S.: 541612

**DENSO TEN TECHNOSEPTA
Limited** (2)
6-4 Murotani 1-chome, Nishi-ku, Kobe, 651-
2241, Hyogo, Japan
Tel.: (81) 78 996 0200
Automotive Resin Parts Mfr
N.A.I.C.S.: 325211

Subsidiary (Non-US):

**DENSO TEN de MEXICO, S.A. de
C.V.** (2)
Avenida Industrial Del Norte Manzana 8
Lote 2 Parque, Industrial Del Norte, Rey-
nosa, Tamaulipas, Mexico
Tel.: (52) 8999218700
Audio Visual Products & Automotive Elec-
tronics Mfr & Distr
N.A.I.C.S.: 334310

Subsidiary (Domestic):

Denso Ten Staff Limited (2)
2-28 Gosho-dori 1-chome, Hyogo-ku, Kobe,
652-8510, Hyogo, Japan
Tel.: (81) 786822257
Human Resouce Services
N.A.I.C.S.: 541612

Denso Ten Technology Limited (2)
64-Nishiwaki Okubo-cho, Akashi, 674-8555,
Hyogo, Japan
Tel.: (81) 789645246
Automotive Electronic Design Services
N.A.I.C.S.: 541420

Denso Ten Technosepta Limited (2)
6-4 Murotani 1-chome, Nishi-ku, Kobe, 651-
2241, Hyogo, Japan
Tel.: (81) 789960200
Automobile Parts Mfr
N.A.I.C.S.: 336310

**DENSO THERMAL SYSTEMS PUNE
PVT. LTD.** (1)

No 116 Gat No 1228/2 Sanaswadi Nagar Road, Taluka-Shirur, 412208, Pune, Maharashtra, India
Tel.; (91) 2137 618 901
Sales Range: $25-49.9 Million
Emp.: 44
Automotive Air Conditioner Mfr & Distr
N.A.I.C.S.: 336390

DENSO TOHOKU CORPORATION (1)
2-6-1 Nigatake, Miyagino-Ku, Sendai, 983-0036, Miyagi, Japan
Tel.: (81) 22 238 9911
Web Site: http://www.denso-tohoku.com
Sales Range: $25-49.9 Million
Emp.: 96
Automotive Repair Services
N.A.I.C.S.: 811198

DENSO TOKYO CORPORATION (1)
2-15-13 Shoto, Shibuya-Ku, Tokyo, 150-0046, Japan
Tel.: (81) 35 478 7711
Web Site: http://www.denso-sales.co.jp
Sales Range: $75-99.9 Million
Emp.: 365
Automotive Repair Services
N.A.I.C.S.: 811198

DENSO UNITY SERVICE CORPORATION (1)
1-1-1 Showa-cho, Kariya, 448-8661, Aichi, Japan
Tel.: (81) 56 625 9860
Web Site: https://www.denso-unity.co.jp
Sales Range: $150-199.9 Million
Emp.: 767
Security Consulting Services
N.A.I.C.S.: 561612

DENSO WELL CORPORATION (1)
1-1 Showacho, Kariya, 448-8661, Aichi, Japan
Tel.: (81) 566 25 5660
Sales Range: $25-49.9 Million
Emp.: 232
Payroll Management Services
N.A.I.C.S.: 541214

DENSO WIRELESS SYSTEMS AMERICA, INC. (1)
3250 Business Park Dr, Vista, CA 92081
Tel.: (760) 734-4600
Sales Range: $50-74.9 Million
Emp.: 154
Car Navigation System Mfr
N.A.I.C.S.: 336390

DENSO YUSEN TRAVEL CORPORATION (1)
1-1-1 Showa-cho Denso Corporation Building No 2, Kariya, 448-8661, Aichi, Japan
Tel.: (81) 56 625 9977
Web Site: https://www.denso-yusen.co.jp
Sales Range: $25-49.9 Million
Emp.: 10
Travel Arrangement Services
N.A.I.C.S.: 561991
Tomoyuki Matsuzawa (Gen Mgr)

DENSOTRIM CO., LTD. (1)
2460 Ogohara Akasaka Komono-cho, Mie-gun, Mie, 510-1222, Japan
Tel.: (81) 59 391 0011
Web Site: https://www.densotrim.co.jp
Sales Range: $200-249.9 Million
Emp.: 526
Automobile Spare Parts Mfr
N.A.I.C.S.: 336991

Denso Aircool Corporation (1)
2027-9 Kitahotaka, Hotaka, Azumino, 399-8386, Nagano, Japan
Tel.: (81) 26 381 1100
Web Site: https://www.denso-aircool.co.jp
Emp.: 657
Air Conditioner Mfr
N.A.I.C.S.: 333415
Hiroshi Nishiyama (Pres)

Denso Blossom Co., Ltd. (1)
1-1 Showa-cho, Kariya, 448-8661, Aichi, Japan
Tel.: (81) 566873120
Web Site: http://www.denso-blossom.co.jp
Internet Mail Services
N.A.I.C.S.: 561431

Denso Create Inc.. (1)
2-14-19 Nishiki, Naka-Ku, Nagoya, 460-0003, Japan
Tel.: (81) 52 728 0771
Web Site: https://www.denso-create.jp
Emp.: 208
Software Development Services
N.A.I.C.S.: 541511
Shukichi Hayashi (Pres & CEO)

Denso Europe B.V. (1)
Hogeweyselaan 165, 1382 JL, Weesp, Netherlands
Tel.: (31) 29.449 3493
Web Site: http://www.denso-europe.com
Sales Range: $150-199.9 Million
Emp.: 300
Automotive Products Supplier
N.A.I.C.S.: 423120
Shigehiro Nishimura (Pres & CEO)

Subsidiary (Non-US):

Denso Automotive Deutschland GmbH (2)
Freisinger Strasse 21-23, 85386, Eching, Germany
Tel.: (49) 81659440
Web Site: http://www.denso-europe.com
Sales Range: $125-149.9 Million
Motor Vehicle Parts & Supplies Whslr
N.A.I.C.S.: 423120
Yuji Ishizuka (Pres)

Denso Barcelona S.A. (2)
Calle Sakura No 1, Poligono Industrial Pla de Santa Anna Sant Fruitos Del Bages, 08272, Barcelona, Spain
Tel.: (34) 93 877 7900
Web Site: http://www.denso.com.es
Sales Range: $150-199.9 Million
Electronic Control Unit & Engine Management System Components Mfr
N.A.I.C.S.: 333618
Masati Ito (Pres)

Denso Manufacturing Czech s.r.o. (2)
Heyrovskeho 476, Doubi, 463 12, Liberec, Czech Republic
Tel.: (420) 488101111
Web Site: https://www.denso.cz
Emp.: 2,719
HVAC Units, Evaporators, Condensors & Radiators Mfr
N.A.I.C.S.: 333415
Karel Balatka (Pres)

Denso Manufacturing Hungary Ltd. (2)
Holland Fasor 14, 8000, Szekesfehervar, Hungary
Tel.: (36) 30 404 9000
Web Site: https://www.denso.com
Diesel Injection Pumps & System Control Panel Products Mfr
N.A.I.C.S.: 333996

Denso Manufacturing Italia SpA (2)
Viale Marisa Bellisario 75, 66050, San Salvo, Chieti, Italy
Tel.: (39) 0873388311
Web Site: http://www.denso-europe.com
Sales Range: $550-599.9 Million
Starters, Alternators, Blowers, Fans & Wipers Mfr & Sales
N.A.I.C.S.: 423120

Denso Manufacturing Midlands Ltd. (2)
Unit 1 Maybrook Road, Maybrook Business Park, Minworth, Sutton Coldfield, B76 1AL, United Kingdom
Tel.: (44) 1213136900
Web Site: http://www.denso-midlands.co.uk
Sales Range: $75-99.9 Million
Starters & Alternators Mfr
N.A.I.C.S.: 336390

Denso Manufacturing UK Ltd. (2)
Queensway Campus Hortonwood, Telford, TF1 7FS, Shropshire, United Kingdom
Tel.: (44) 195 260 8400
Web Site: http://www.globaldenso.com
Sales Range: $200-249.9 Million
Air Conditioners, Heaters, Blowers & Panels Mfr
N.A.I.C.S.: 336390
Mark Hayward (Mng Dir)

Denso Marston Ltd. (2)
Marston House Otley Road, Shipley, BD17 7JR, West Yorkshire, United Kingdom
Tel.: (44) 127 458 2266
Sales Range: $200-249.9 Million
Radiators, Oil Coolers & Inter-Coolers Mfr & Sales
N.A.I.C.S.: 336390

Denso Otomotiv Parcalari Sanayi A.S. (2)
TOSB-TAYSAD Organize Sanayi Bolgesi 5 Cadde No 1, Sekerpinar/cayirova, 41480, Kocaeli, Turkiye
Tel.: (90) 262 679 5700
Web Site: http://www.globaldenso.com
Sales Range: $25-49.9 Million
Emp.: 136
Automotive Air Conditioners & Heaters Mfr
N.A.I.C.S.: 336390

Denso Sales Belgium N.V. (2)
Medialaan 50, 1800, Vilvoorde, Belgium
Tel.: (32) 2 257 8900
Web Site: https://www.denso.com
Sales Range: $25-49.9 Million
Emp.: 45
Air Conditioners, Radiators, Meters & Electric Parts Sales
N.A.I.C.S.: 423730
Zangerelst Maxime (Head-HR)

Denso Sales Italia Srl (2)
Frazione Masio 24, Turin, 10046, Italy
Tel.: (39) 0119458811
Sales Range: $25-49.9 Million
Emp.: 26
Automotive Components Sales & Marketer
N.A.I.C.S.: 423120
Gianluca Mrostica (Pres)

Denso Sales Sweden AB (2)
Gotavertksgatan 6A, 41 755, Gothenburg, Sweden
Tel.: (46) 317011890
Web Site: http://www.denso-europe.com
Sales Range: $50-74.9 Million
Emp.: 5
Original Equipment Sales & Engineering Services
N.A.I.C.S.: 423120

Denso Sales UK Ltd. (2)
1 Bishop Sq, Hatfield, AL10 9NE, Herts, United Kingdom
Tel.: (44) 2476842500
Web Site: http://www.denso-europe.com
Sales Range: $25-49.9 Million
Emp.: 50
Automotive Products Sales
N.A.I.C.S.: 423120
Shiro Shimada (Mng Dir)

Denso Thermal Systems Polska Sp.z.o.o. (2)
Ul Turynska 100, 43-100, Tychy, Poland
Tel.: (48) 32 217 9611
Web Site: http://www.globaldenso.com
Emp.: 500
Manufacture & Sales of Car Air Conditioners & Cockpit Modules
N.A.I.C.S.: 333415
J. Gwozdz (Mng Dir)

Denso Thermal Systems SpA (2)
Frazione Masio 24, 10046, Poirino, TO, Italy
Tel.: (39) 011 941 7111
Web Site: https://www.denso-ts.com
Sales Range: $400-449.9 Million
Air Conditioners, Heaters, Radiators, Charge Coolers, Front-End Modules & Cockpit Modules Mfr & Sales
N.A.I.C.S.: 336390

Joao de Deus & Filhos S.A. (2)
Estrada dos Arados 5, Arados Samora Correja, 2135-113, Samora Correia, Portugal
Tel.: (351) 263650240
Web Site: https://www.jdeus.com
Emp.: 480
Radiators, Inter-Coolers & Heater Cores Mfr & Sales
N.A.I.C.S.: 333415
Paolo Etzid (Gen Mgr)

Denso Fukushima Corporation (1)
26 Koyodai, Funehiki-machi, Tamura, Fukushima, Japan
Tel.: (81) 247657700

Web Site: http://www.denso-fukushima.co.jp
Thermal Equipment Product Mfr
N.A.I.C.S.: 333414

Denso IT Laboratory, Inc. (1)
Shibuya Cross Tower 28th floor 2 15 1 Shibuya, Shibuya ku, Tokyo, 150-0002, Japan (100%)
Tel.: (81) 36 419 2300
Web Site: https://www.d-itlab.co.jp
Emp.: 50
IT Services
N.A.I.C.S.: 541519
Yuji Harabayash (Pres)

Denso Industrial da Amazonia Ltda. (1)
Avenida Buriti 3600, Distrito Industrial, Manaus, 69075-000, Amazonas, Brazil
Tel.: (55) 922 121 4200
Web Site: http://www.denso-dnaz.com.br
Sales Range: $100-124.9 Million
Emp.: 334
Automotive Parts Mfr & Distr
N.A.I.C.S.: 336390

Denso International America (1)
Tel.: (248) 350-7500
Web Site: http://www.densocorp-na.com
Sales Range: $300-349.9 Million
Emp.: 1,000
Supplier of Automotive Technology, Systems & Components
N.A.I.C.S.: 423120
Terry Helgesen (Sr VP-Mktg & Sls)

Joint Venture (Domestic):

Associated Fuel Pump Systems Corp. (2)
110 Scotts Br Rd, Anderson, SC 29622 (50%)
Tel.: (864) 224-0012
Web Site: http://www.afco.com
Sales Range: $75-99.9 Million
Emp.: 350
Automotive Gasoline Pumps Mfr
N.A.I.C.S.: 333914
Kevin Hardy (Supvr-Acctg)

Subsidiary (Domestic):

DENSO MANUFACTURING ARKANSAS, INC. (2)
100 Denso Rd, Osceola, AR 72370
Tel.: (870) 622-9500
Web Site: https://www.denso.com
Sales Range: $75-99.9 Million
Emp.: 414
Automobile Parts Mfr
N.A.I.C.S.: 336390
George Harguess (Pres)

DENSO MANUFACTURING MICHIGAN, INC. (2)
1 Denso Rd, Battle Creek, MI 49037-7356
Tel.: (269) 965-3322
Web Site: https://www.denso.com
Sales Range: $350-399.9 Million
Car Air Conditioner Mfr
N.A.I.C.S.: 336390
Yoshi Yoshikawa (VP-Acctg, Bus Plng & Pur)

Denso International Asia Pte. Ltd. (1)
51 Science Park Road The Aries 01-19, Science Park II, Singapore, 117586, Singapore (100%)
Tel.: (65) 67768268
Web Site: https://www.denso.com
Sales Range: $50-74.9 Million
Emp.: 77
Holding Company-Sales of Aftermarket Products
N.A.I.C.S.: 551112
Bruce Eng (Gen Mgr)

Denso International Australia Pty. Ltd. (1)
46 Merrindale Drive, Croydon, 3136, VIC, Australia (100%)
Tel.: (61) 38 761 1100
Web Site: http://www.denso.com.au
Sales Range: $50-74.9 Million
Emp.: 350
Holding Company-Aftermarket Sales & Services
N.A.I.C.S.: 551112

Denso Corporation—(Continued)

Subsidiary (Domestic):

DENSO Australian Automotive Air Pty. Ltd. (2)
2-46 Merrindale Dr, Croydon, 3136, VIC, Australia **(100%)**
Tel.: (61) 387611100
Web Site: http://www.globaldenso.com
Sales Range: $10-24.9 Million
Automotive Air Conditioners, Radiators & Instrument Clusters Mfr
N.A.I.C.S.: 333618

Denso Iwate Corporation (1)
4-2 Nishine Moriyama Kanegasaki-cho, Isawa-gun Central Iwate Kanegasaki Industrial Park, Iwate, 029-4593, Japan
Tel.: (81) 197445311
Web Site: http://www.denso-iwate.co.jp
Electronic Device Part Mfr & Retailer
N.A.I.C.S.: 334419

Denso MTEC Corporation (1)
1 Yoshiike Kusagi Agui-cho, Chita, 470-2298, Aichi Prefecture, Japan
Tel.: (81) 569491631
Web Site: https://www.denso-mtec.co.jp
Emp.: 154
Measurement Equipment Mfr
N.A.I.C.S.: 334515

Denso Miyazaki, Inc. (1)
4188 Kiwaki Kunitomi-Cho, Higashimorokata-gun, Miyazaki, 880-1113, Japan
Tel.: (81) 985751236
N.A.I.C.S.: 336390

Denso Powertrain Technologies Corporation (1)
2430-1 Nabesaka Daian-cho, Inabe, Mie, Japan
Tel.: (81) 594871177
Web Site: http://www.denso-ptc.com
Power Train Control Services
N.A.I.C.S.: 221121

Denso Press Tech Co., Ltd. (1)
11-16 Genzau Hagicho, Toyokawa, 441-0201, Aichi Prefecture, Japan
Tel.: (81) 533568185
Web Site: http://www.denso-presstech.co.jp
Automotive Part Mfr & Distr
N.A.I.C.S.: 336310

Denso Sales California, Inc. (1)
3900 Via Oro Ave, Long Beach, CA 90810-1868
Tel.: (310) 834-6352
Sales Range: $500-549.9 Million
Emp.: 213
Automobile Parts Distr
N.A.I.C.S.: 423120

Denso Solution Japan Corporation (1)
1-1 Showa-cho, Kariya, 448-8661, Aichi, Japan
Tel.: (81) 363679666
Web Site: http://www.denso-solution.com
Automotive Paint Retailer
N.A.I.C.S.: 441330

Denso Tool And Die (Thailand) Co., Ltd. (1)
369 Moo 3 Teparak Road T Teparak, A Muang, Samut Prakan, 10270, Thailand **(100%)**
Tel.: (66) 23843501
Sales Range: $1-9.9 Million
Emp.: 138
Mfr & Sales of Dyes & Jigs for Automotive Equipment
N.A.I.C.S.: 336110

Denso Wave Inc. (1)
1 Yoshiike Kusagi, Agui-cho, Chita, 470-2297, Aichi, Japan **(75%)**
Tel.: (81) 56 949 5000
Web Site: https://www.denso-wave.com
Emp.: 1,282
Automatic Data Capture Equipment, Industrial Robots, Programmable Controllers & Other Apparatus & Systems Developer, Mfr & Sales
N.A.I.C.S.: 334512

Denso Wiper Systems, Inc. (1)

390 Umeda, Kosai, 431-0493, Shizuoka, Japan
Tel.: (81) 535773320
N.A.I.C.S.: 336390

Denso Wisetech Corporation (1)
3-1 Himegaoka, Kani, 509-0249, Gifu Prefecture, Japan
Tel.: (81) 574605220
Web Site: http://www.denso-wisetech.co.jp
Electrical Component Mfr & Retailer
N.A.I.C.S.: 335999

Denso Yamagata Co., Ltd. (1)
3893-1 Hagyu, Iide-cho Nishiokitama, Yamagata, 999-0602, Japan
Tel.: (81) 238722290
Web Site: http://www.denso-yamagata.co.jp
Automotive Turn Signal Flasher Mfr
N.A.I.C.S.: 334290

GAC CORPORATION (1)
1000 Toyoshina, Azumino, 399-8286, Nagano-ken, Japan
Tel.: (81) 263 73 8000
Web Site: http://www.gacjp.com
Sales Range: $200-249.9 Million
Emp.: 620
Air Conditioner & Heat Exchanger Mfr
N.A.I.C.S.: 333415
Akitoshi Sugiura (Pres)

Plant (Domestic):

GAC CORPORATION - Anjo Plant (2)
60 Thouhai Nesaki-cho, Anjo, Aichi-ken, Japan
Tel.: (81) 566 73 8681
Sales Range: $25-49.9 Million
Emp.: 1
Air Conditioner Mfr
N.A.I.C.S.: 333415

GUANGZHOU DENSO CO., LTD. (1)
No 171 Chuangqiang Road Yongning Street, Zengcheng, Guangzhou, 511356, Guangdong, China
Tel.: (86) 208 298 0288
Web Site: http://www.globaldenso.com
Sales Range: $200-249.9 Million
Emp.: 814
Car Air Conditioner Mfr & Distr
N.A.I.C.S.: 336390

Hamanakodenso Co., Ltd. (1)
136 Washizu, Kosai, 431-0431, Shizuoka, Japan
Tel.: (81) 53 576 1331
Web Site: https://www.hamanakodenso.co.jp
Emp.: 4,513
Automotive Parts & Accessories Mfr
N.A.I.C.S.: 336310
Akio Tajima (Pres)

Affiliate (Domestic):

HAMADEN P.S CO., LTD. (2)
141-2 Yamagami Iwasaki-cho, Iwasaki-cho, Toyohashi, 440-0022, Aichi, Japan
Tel.: (81) 53 261 8010
Web Site: https://www.hamanakodenso.co.jp
Auto Parts Mfr
N.A.I.C.S.: 336310

IPICS CORPORATION (1)
2-13-19 Nishiki Takisada Building 6th floor, Naka-ku, Nagoya, 460-0003, Aichi, Japan
Tel.: (81) 52 220 1100
Web Site: https://www.ipics.jp
Emp.: 76
Patent Application Filing Services
N.A.I.C.S.: 541199

Jeco Co., Ltd. (1)
1-4-1 Fujimicho, Gyoda, 361-8511, Saitama, Japan **(100%)**
Tel.: (81) 485567111
Web Site: http://www.jeco.co.jp
Rev.: $248,832,900
Assets: $189,335,880
Liabilities: $55,628,400
Net Worth: $133,707,480
Earnings: $4,194,780
Emp.: 471
Fiscal Year-end: 03/31/2019
Automobile Parts Mfr

N.A.I.C.S.: 336390
Satoshi Sugiura (Pres)

Subsidiary (Domestic):

Nagano Jeco Co., Ltd. (2)
616-1 Wakaho Kawada, Nagano, Japan
Tel.: (81) 262823553
Emp.: 164
Automobile Parts Mfr
N.A.I.C.S.: 336390

KYOSAN DENKI AMERICA, INC. (1)
65 Clarence Dr, Mount Sterling, KY 40353
Tel.: (859) 497-2040
Web Site: http://www.globaldenso.com
Sales Range: $100-124.9 Million
Emp.: 400
Fuel Pump Module Mfr
N.A.I.C.S.: 336390
Mary Grider (Mgr-HR & IT)

KYOSAN DENKI CO., LTD. (1)
11-3 Okazato, Koga, 306-0206, Ibaraki, Japan
Tel.: (81) 28 098 3370
Web Site: https://www.kyosan-denki.co.jp
Rev.: $862,920,000
Emp.: 1,677
Mechanical Fuel Pump Mfr
N.A.I.C.S.: 333914
Hitoshi Iwai (Sr Mng Dir)

Plant (Domestic):

KYOSAN DENKI CO., LTD - Yuki Plant (2)
8-36 Wakamiya, Yuki, 307-0017, Ibaraki, Japan
Tel.: (81) 296 34 0500
Fuel Injection Control System Mfr
N.A.I.C.S.: 336310

KYOSAN DENKI CO., LTD. - Plant 2 (2)
12-1 Okazato, Koga, 306-0206, Ibaraki, Japan
Tel.: (81) 280 98 1531
Web Site: http://www.kyosan-denki.co.jp
Diesel Fuel Filter Mfr
N.A.I.C.S.: 336390

KYOSAN DENSO MANUFACTURING KENTUCKY, LLC. (1)
65 Clarence Dr Mt, Mount Sterling, KY 40353
Tel.: (859) 497-2040
Sales Range: $100-124.9 Million
Emp.: 324
Injection Molding Machine Mfr
N.A.I.C.S.: 333248

KYOSAN SERVICE CORPORATION (1)
11-3 Okasato, Koga, 306-0206, Ibaraki, Japan **(100%)**
Tel.: (81) 280 98 2342
Web Site: http://www.denso.com
Emp.: 21
Consumer Goods Distr
N.A.I.C.S.: 424990

LIPLASTEC s.r.o (1)
Newtonova 478 XXIII - Doubi, 463 12, Liberec, Czech Republic
Tel.: (420) 48 901 9412
Web Site: https://www.liplastec.cz
Emp.: 170
Automotive Plastic Product Mfr
N.A.I.C.S.: 326199

MARCON DENSO CO., LTD. (1)
3893-1 Oka Hagyu Idemachi Nishi, Okitama-Gun, Yamagata, 999-0602, Japan
Tel.: (81) 238 72 2290
Web Site: http://www.marcon.co.jp
Sales Range: $50-74.9 Million
Emp.: 200
Electronic Components Mfr
N.A.I.C.S.: 334419
Hiroshi Natsume (Pres)

MAULTECH CORPORATION (1)
4978-1 Kamitonno, Nogata, 822-0003, Fukuoka, Japan
Tel.: (81) 9492 6 8333
Sales Range: $25-49.9 Million
Emp.: 55
Automotive Air Conditioning Equipment Mfr

N.A.I.C.S.: 333415

MIYAZAKI ASMO CO., LTD. (1)
4188 Kiwaki Kunitomi-Cho, Higashimorokata, Miyazaki, 880-1113, Japan **(100%)**
Tel.: (81) 985 75 1236
Web Site: http://www.globaldenso.com
Emp.: 293
Automobile Parts Mfr
N.A.I.C.S.: 336390

MOBILE MEDIANET INC. (1)
1-21-2 Dogenzaka Shinnampeidaitokyu Bldg 6f, Shibuya-Ku, Tokyo, 150-0043, Japan
Tel.: (81) 454707330
Web Site: http://www.mmnet.co.jp
Satellite Communication Services
N.A.I.C.S.: 517410

Nippon Soken, Inc. (1)
500-20 Minamiyama, Komenoki-cho, Nisshin, 470-0111, Aichi, Japan
Tel.: (81) 561570400
Web Site: https://www.soken-labs.com
Emp.: 441
Vehicle Safety & Pollution Prevention; Owned 75% by Denso Corporation & 25% by Toyota Motor Corporation
N.A.I.C.S.: 541715
Kato Yoshifumi (Pres & CEO)

Nippon Wiper Blade Co., Ltd. (1)
311 Shimo Takayanagi, Kazo, 347 8585, Saitama, Japan **(70%)**
Tel.: (81) 480671101
Web Site: http://www.nwb.co.jp
Sales Range: $300-349.9 Million
Emp.: 1,500
Wiper Arms & Blades Mfr & Sales
N.A.I.C.S.: 336390
Shinji Maki (Pres)

OTARI GAC CO., LTD (1)
1480 Chikuniotsu Otarimura, Kitaazumi-gun, Nagano, Japan
Tel.: (81) 261833051
Sales Range: $25-49.9 Million
Emp.: 2
Sheet Metal Mfr
N.A.I.C.S.: 332322

PHILIPPINE AUTO COMPONENTS, INC. (1)
109 Unity Avenue Carmelray Industrial Park 1, PO Box 109, Canlubang, Calamba, 4037, Laguna, Philippines
Tel.: (63) 495493030
Web Site: http://www.denso.com.ph
Car Air Conditioner Mfr
N.A.I.C.S.: 336390

PT. HAMADEN INDONESIA MANUFACTURING (1)
Jl Gaya Motor 1 No 6 Sunter 2, Tanjung Priok, Jakarta, 14330, Indonesia
Tel.: (62) 21 652 1206
Web Site: http://www.globaldenso.com
Sales Range: $100-124.9 Million
Emp.: 300
Horns Mfr
N.A.I.C.S.: 336390
Yasuyuki Takai (Pres)

SHIMIZU INDUSTRY CO., LTD. (1)
1 Chasenboshita Hitotsugi-cho, Kariya, 448-8534, Aichi, Japan
Tel.: (81) 56 623 2335
Web Site: https://www.shimizu-industry.co.jp
Sales Range: $200-249.9 Million
Emp.: 642
Automobile Parts Mfr
N.A.I.C.S.: 336390

SUAB CO., LTD. (1)
390 Umeda, Kosai, 431-0425, Shizuoka, Japan
Tel.: (81) 53 577 2626
Sales Range: $25-49.9 Million
Emp.: 26
Automobile Parts Mfr
N.A.I.C.S.: 336390

SYSTEX JAPAN INC. (1)
5-16 Akemi-cho, Toyohashi, 441-8074, Aichi, Japan **(100%)**
Tel.: (81) 532 23 3355
Web Site: http://www.denso.com
Emp.: 43
Automotive Plastic Parts Mfr

N.A.I.C.S.: 326199

SYSTEX PRODUCTS ARKANSAS COMPANY **(1)**
101 Denso Rd, Osceola, AR 72370
Tel.: (870) 563-7950
Web Site: http://www.densocorp-na.com
Sales Range: $25-49.9 Million
Emp.: 52
Car Air Conditioner Plastics Mfr
N.A.I.C.S.: 326199
Tokue Yamamoto *(Pres)*

Sankyo Radiator Co., Ltd. **(1)**
108-8 Sayamagahara, Iruma, 358-0032, Saitama, Japan
Tel.: (81) 429352500
Web Site: http://www.sankyo-rad.co.jp
Sales Range: $100-124.9 Million
Emp.: 344
Automobile Radiator Mfr
N.A.I.C.S.: 336390
Atsushi Fukuda *(Pres)*

Siam Denso Manufacturing Co., Ltd. **(1)**
Amata Nakorn Industrial Estate 700/618, T Bankao A Panthong, Chon Buri, 20160, Thailand **(100%)**
Tel.: (66) 3 821 0100
Sales Range: $650-699.9 Million
Emp.: 2,665
Fuel Injection System Products Mfr
N.A.I.C.S.: 333996
Motomi Kato *(Pres)*

TD Mobile Corporation **(1)**
Hamamatsucho Square 1-30-5 Hamamatsucho, Minato-ku, Tokyo, 105-0013, Japan
Tel.: (81) 36 830 2500
Web Site: https://www.tdmobile.co.jp
Emp.: 1,807
Mobile Phone Distr
N.A.I.C.S.: 423690
Tomihiro Hirano *(Pres)*

TECHMA CORPORATION **(1)**
3-1 Himegaoka, Kani, 509-0249, Gifu, Japan
Tel.: (81) 574 60 5220
Web Site: http://www.techma.co.jp
Sales Range: $100-124.9 Million
Emp.: 450
Electronic Components Mfr
N.A.I.C.S.: 334419

TIANJIN ASMO AUTOMOTIVE SMALL MOTOR CO., LTD. **(1)**
No 2 Saida 4th Road Xiqing Economic Development Area, Tianjin, China
Tel.: (86) 2283961808
Web Site: http://www.globaldenso.com
Sales Range: $200-249.9 Million
Emp.: 905
Windshield Wiper System Mfr & Distr
N.A.I.C.S.: 336320

TIANJIN DENSO AIR-CONDITIONER CO., LTD. **(1)**
Qiansang Yuan Yangliu Qing, Xiqing Ward, Tianjin, 300380, China
Tel.: (86) 2287992171
Web Site: http://www.globaldenso.com
Sales Range: $50-74.9 Million
Emp.: 128
Automotive Air Conditioner Mfr
N.A.I.C.S.: 336390

TIANJIN DENSO ENGINE ELECTRICAL PRODUCTS CO., LTD **(1)**
No 3 Liujing Road, Dong i Economic Development District, Tianjin, 300300, China
Tel.: (86) 225 888 5600
Web Site: http://www.globaldenso.com
Sales Range: $200-249.9 Million
Emp.: 942
Automotive Electrical Parts Mfr & Distr
N.A.I.C.S.: 336320

TIANJIN FAWER DENSO AIR-CONDITIONER CO., LTD. **(1)**
No 22 Saida Century Road, Xiqing Economic Development Zone, Tianjin, China
Tel.: (86) 222 388 9188
Web Site: http://www.globaldenso.com
Sales Range: $100-124.9 Million
Emp.: 499
Automotive Air Conditioner Mfr & Distr
N.A.I.C.S.: 336390

Tohoku Pioneer EG Corporation **(1)**
2-1-57 Ishidorii, Tendo, 994-0057, Yamagata, Japan
Tel.: (81) 236555566
Automated Assembly Lines & Inspection Systems on Technologies
N.A.I.C.S.: 541990

Toyota Boshoku Filtration System (Thailand) Co., Ltd. **(1)**
64/42 Moo 4 Hemaraj Road, Eastern Seaboard Industrial Estate Plauk Daeng Sub district, Rayong, 21140, Thailand **(100%)**
Tel.: (66) 3 895 5618
Web Site: https://www.tbfst.co.th
Sales Range: $75-99.9 Million
Emp.: 817
Oil Filter Mfr
N.A.I.C.S.: 811191
Tadahiro Inoue *(Pres)*

Yasaka GAC Co., Ltd. **(1)**
Kanote Yasaka, Omachi, Nagano, Japan
Tel.: (81) 261262007
Web Site: http://www.gacjp.com
Sales Range: $25-49.9 Million
Emp.: 50
Automotive Air Conditioner Mfr
N.A.I.C.S.: 336390

DENT STEEL SERVICES LTD
Low Moor Steel Works New Works Road, Bradford, BD12 0QN, United Kingdom
Tel.: (44) 1274420200
Web Site: http://www.dentsteel.co.uk
Year Founded: 1977
Rev.: $44,151,877
Emp.: 4,347
Steel Supplier
N.A.I.C.S.: 238120
Mark Stafford *(Office Mgr-Sls-Bradford)*

DENTAL CORPORATION PUBLIC COMPANY LIMITED
No 157 2nd Floor Ratchadaphisek Road, Din Daeng District, Bangkok, 10400, Thailand
Tel.: (66) 22457197
Web Site:
　https://www.dentalcorpthailand.com
D—(THA)
Rev.: $27,584,368
Assets: $31,373,194
Liabilities: $14,298,227
Net Worth: $17,074,967
Earnings: $2,079,928
Fiscal Year-end: 12/31/23
Dental Care Services
N.A.I.C.S.: 621210
Pornsak Tantapakul *(CEO)*

DENTAS CO., LTD.
48 Toiyacho, Tokushima, 770-8056, Japan
Tel.: (81) 886573115　　　　　　JP
Web Site: https://www.dentas.jp
Year Founded: 1996
6174—(TKS)
Rev.: $5,677,990
Assets: $3,714,820
Liabilities: $3,609,060
Net Worth: $105,760
Earnings: ($284,230)
Emp.: 50
Fiscal Year-end: 03/31/24
Dental Equipment & Supplies Mfr
N.A.I.C.S.: 339114
Kyosuke Kono *(Pres)*

DENTATUS AB
Bromstensvagen 172, PO Box 8093, 163 08, Spanga, Sweden
Tel.: (46) 854650900
Web Site: http://www.dentatus.com
Sales Range: $10-24.9 Million
Emp.: 40
Dental Equipment Mfr
N.A.I.C.S.: 339114

Bernard Weissman *(Founder)*

Subsidiaries:

Dentatus USA, Ltd. **(1)**
54 W 39th St Ste 5, New York, NY 10018
Tel.: (212) 481-1010
Web Site: http://www.dentatus.com
N.A.I.C.S.: 423450
Thomas J. Murphy *(CEO)*

DENTELLE SOPHIE HALLETTE
2 Rue Alfred Melayers, PO Box 80082, 59542, Caudry, France
Tel.: (33) 327765576
Web Site:
　http://www.sophiehallette.com
Sales Range: $25-49.9 Million
Emp.: 270
Lace Mfr
N.A.I.C.S.: 313240
Bruno Lescroart *(Mng Dir)*

DENTIS CO., LTD.
99 Seongseoseo-Ro, Dalseo-Gu, Daegu, 42718, Korea (South)
Tel.: (82) 535893519
Web Site: https://www.dentis.co.kr
Year Founded: 2016
261200—(KRS)
Rev.: $66,795,833
Assets: $100,530,763
Liabilities: $75,794,827
Net Worth: $24,735,935
Earnings: $942,617
Emp.: 343
Fiscal Year-end: 12/31/22
Medical & Dental Instrument Mfr & Distr
N.A.I.C.S.: 339112
Tae-Hwan Park *(Mgr)*

DENTIUM CO., LTD
2F Dentium 76 Changnyong-daero 256beon-gil, Yeongtong-gu, Suwon, Gyeonggi-do, Korea (South)
Tel.: (82) 7070989122　　　　　KR
Web Site: https://globaldentium.com
Year Founded: 2000
145720—(KRS)
Rev.: $272,949,203
Assets: $517,405,901
Liabilities: $231,189,321
Net Worth: $286,216,580
Earnings: $66,072,308
Emp.: 1,265
Fiscal Year-end: 12/31/22
Dental Implant Mfr
N.A.I.C.S.: 339116
Lee In Jae *(Dir)*

Subsidiaries:

Cideas S.R.L. **(1)**
C/ Fray Luis De Leon 195 Covima La Molina, Lima, Peru
Tel.: (51) 13481874
Web Site: http://www.cideas.net
Dental Equipment Distr
N.A.I.C.S.: 423450

DentalHolding Sp. z o.o. **(1)**
ul Grzybowska 80/82, 00-844, Warsaw, Poland
Tel.: (48) 22 313 0880
Web Site: https://www.dentalholding.com
Dental Equipment Distr
N.A.I.C.S.: 423450

Dentium Baltic, SIA **(1)**
Valnu Street 5, Riga, 1050, Latvia
Tel.: (371) 2 701 1118
Web Site: https://www.dentiumbaltic.eu
Dental Equipment Distr
N.A.I.C.S.: 423450

Dentium China Co., Ltd. **(1)**
Building 13 Baonenghui Valley No 22 Linhe Street, Linhe Economic Development Zone Shunyi District, Beijing, China
Tel.: (86) 1084763053
Dental Equipment Distr

Dentium Iberia SL **(1)**
C/Moreto N1 7 Piso 1 Derecha, Madrid, Spain
Tel.: (34) 669642808
Dental Equipment Distr
N.A.I.C.S.: 423450

Dentium Kft. **(1)**
Aradi utca 14, 1St Em Door 3, 1062, Budapest, Hungary
Tel.: (36) 70 629 8369
Web Site: https://dentium.hu
Dental Equipment Distr
N.A.I.C.S.: 423450

Dentium Shanghai Co., Ltd. **(1)**
No 16 3 4F building Lane 500 FuRongHua Rd, Pudong, Shanghai, 201318, China
Tel.: (86) 2158786737
Web Site: http://www.dentium.com.cn
Dental Equipment Distr
N.A.I.C.S.: 423450

Dentium Singapore Pte Ltd. **(1)**
20 Harbour Drive 06-02 PSA Vista, Singapore, 117612, Singapore
Tel.: (65) 68733705
Dental Equipment Distr
N.A.I.C.S.: 423450

Dentium USA Inc. **(1)**
6761 Katella Ave, Cypress, CA 90630
Tel.: (714) 226-0229
Web Site: https://www.dentiumusa.com
Implant Mfr
N.A.I.C.S.: 339113

Dentium-Com S.R.L **(1)**
Str Tadeus Malinovschi Nr 14/2 Of 4, Chisinau, Moldova
Tel.: (373) 68554402
Web Site: http://www.dentium-com.md
Dental Equipment Distr
N.A.I.C.S.: 423450

ICT Europe GmbH **(1)**
Hubert-Wollenberg-Str 1, 40878, Ratingen, Germany
Tel.: (49) 21021237750
Web Site: https://www.icteurope.de
Dental Equipment Distr
N.A.I.C.S.: 423450

Implantium & Medical Company Srl **(1)**
Str Stefan Negulescu Nr 34 Et 1 Ap 2 Sect 1, 011654, Bucharest, Romania
Tel.: (40) 724325245
Dental Equipment Distr
N.A.I.C.S.: 423450

Implantium Co..Ltd **(1)**
3886/2 Rama4 Rd Phrakanong Klong-toey, Bangkok, 10110, Thailand
Tel.: (66) 26352347
Dental Equipment Distr
N.A.I.C.S.: 423450

Implantium Hongkong Ltd **(1)**
Room A 16/F Capitol Centre Tower II 28 Jardine's Crescent, Causeway Bay, China (Hong Kong)
Tel.: (852) 23503777
Dental Equipment Distr
N.A.I.C.S.: 423450

Implantium India Pvt. Ltd. **(1)**
510 Global Foyer Building Golf course Road, Sector 43, Gurgaon, 122 002, Haryana, India
Tel.: (91) 1244038845
Dental Equipment Distr
N.A.I.C.S.: 423450

Implantium Malaysia Sdn. Bhd. **(1)**
B-11-8 Plaza Mont Kiara No2 Jalan Kiara Mont Kiara, 50480, Kuala Lumpur, Malaysia
Tel.: (60) 362112860
Web Site: http://www.dentium.com
Emp.: 10
Dental Equipment Distr
N.A.I.C.S.: 423450

Implantium UK Ltd. **(1)**
Siren House March Way Battlefield Enterprise Park, Shrewsbury, SY1 3JE, Shropshire, United Kingdom
Tel.: (44) 3300585818
Web Site: https://implantiem.co.uk

Dentium Co., Ltd—(Continued)

Dental Equipment Distr
N.A.I.C.S.: 423450
Jason Buglass *(Mng Dir)*

Implantium de Mexico SA de Cv (1)
Av Revolucion 980-5 Zona Centro, 22000,
Tijuana, BC, Mexico
Tel.: (52) 664 638 3398
Web Site: https://implantiumdemexico.com
Dental Equipment Distr
N.A.I.C.S.: 423450

Minimax Implant Pty Ltd (1)
Suite 203 394 Lane Cove Rd, Macquarie
Park, 2113, NSW, Australia
Tel.: (61) 28 084 2900
Web Site:
    https://www.minimaximplant.com.au
Dental Equipment Distr
N.A.I.C.S.: 423450

PT. ICT Worldwide Indonesia (1)
Office 88 Floor 25 Unit H Kota Kasablanka
Jl Kasablanka No 88, Jakarta Selatan, In-
donesia
Tel.: (62) 7070986366
Dental Equipment Distr
N.A.I.C.S.: 423450

SARL Dentium Maroc (1)
Rue Ibnou Arif H3 1er Etage, Casablanca,
Morocco
Tel.: (212) 66115
Dental Equipment Distr
N.A.I.C.S.: 423450

T&C Bio technology (1)
69 4F Dunhua S Rd Sec 1, Taipei, 105,
Taiwan
Tel.: (886) 225771900
Web Site: http://www.dentiumtaiwan.com.tw
Dental Equipment Distr
N.A.I.C.S.: 423450

Varvan Ltda. (1)
Luis Thayer Ojeda 0115 of 38 Metro To-
balaba, Santiago, Chile
Tel.: (56) 2232450801
Web Site: http://www.dentium.cl
Dental Equipment Distr
N.A.I.C.S.: 423450

iCT FZCO (1)
I-7 LIU sector Dubai Airport Free Zone, PO
Box 54822, Dubai, United Arab Emirates
Tel.: (971) 42522302
Dental Equipment Distr
N.A.I.C.S.: 423450

DENTSU GROUP INC.
1-8-1 Higashi-shimbashi, Minato-ku,
Tokyo, 105-7050, Japan
Tel.: (81) 362176600　　　　　　JP
Web Site:
    https://www.group.dentsu.com
Year Founded: 1901
DNTUY—(OTCIQ)
Rev.: $9,091,872,240
Assets: $32,722,388,160
Liabilities: $24,781,371,120
Net Worth: $7,941,017,040
Earnings: ($1,544,889,280)
Emp.: 66,400
Fiscal Year-end: 12/31/20
Holding Company; Advertising Agen-
cies
N.A.I.C.S.: 551112
Jacki S. Kelley *(Chief Global Client
Officer & CEO-Americas)*

Subsidiaries:

3P Corp, (1)
7th Floor Ginza SC Bldg 8-18-11 Ginza,
Chuo-ku, Tokyo, 104-0061, Japan
Tel.: (81) 3 3545 3931
Web Site: http://www.dentsu.com
Sales Promotion Services
N.A.I.C.S.: 561990

47CLUB Inc. (1)
4th Floor Tsukiji Eto Bldg 1-12-6 Tsukiji,
Chuo-ku, Tokyo, 104-0045, Japan
Tel.: (81) 351484747
Web Site: https://www.47club.co.jp
Advertising Communication Services

N.A.I.C.S.: 541810

Action Click Co., Ltd. (1)
5F TKK Dai2 Shimbashi Bldg 3-15-4 Shimbashi, Minato-ku, Tokyo, 105-0004, Japan
Tel.: (81) 3 5408 5901

Ad Area Co., Ltd. (1)
1st Floor Niban-cho Sankyo Bldg 6-3
Niban-cho, Chiyoda-ku, Tokyo, 102-0084,
Japan
Tel.: (81) 3 5211 7160
Web Site: http://www.ad-area.jp
Internet Advertising Services
N.A.I.C.S.: 541810

Ad Dentsu Osaka Inc. (1)
17th Floor Nakanoshima Festival Tower
West Building 3-2-4 Nakanoshima, Kita-ku,
Osaka, 530-8228, Japan
Tel.: (81) 664848810
Web Site: https://www.addentsu-osaka.co.jp
Sales Range: $25-49.9 Million
Emp.: 68
Advertising Services
N.A.I.C.S.: 541810

Advertisement EDI Center Inc. (1)
7th Floor Matsuoka Ginnana Bldg 7-17-14
Ginza, Chuo-ku, Tokyo, 104-0061, Japan
Tel.: (81) 355517568
Web Site: https://www.ad-edi.com
Advertising Communication Services
N.A.I.C.S.: 541810

BI.Garage, Inc. (1)
Digital Gate Building 3-5-7 Ebisu Minami,
Shibuya-ku, Tokyo, Japan
Tel.: (81) 363671200
Web Site: https://bi.garage.co.jp
Advertising Communication Services
N.A.I.C.S.: 541810

BUILD creativehaus inc. (1)
9F Hamamatsucho DS Bldg 1-27-16 Ha-
mamatsucho, Minato-ku, Tokyo, 105-0013,
Minato-ku, Japan
Tel.: (81) 3 5733 5461
Sales Range: $25-49.9 Million
Emp.: 6
N.A.I.C.S.: 541810
Keita Yamada *(Dir-Creative)*

**Barnes, Catmur & Friends
Limited** (1)
Level 2 109 Cook St, PO Box 6292, Auck-
land, 6292, New Zealand (51%)
Tel.: (64) 93585688
Web Site: http://bcfdentsu.com
Emp.: 31
Advertising Agencies
N.A.I.C.S.: 541810

Blogwatcher Inc. (1)
4th Floor PMO Nihonbashi Kayabacho
3-11-10 NihonbashiKayabacho, Chuo-ku,
Tokyo, 103-0025, Japan
Tel.: (81) 367059210
Advertising Communication Services
N.A.I.C.S.: 541810

Boardwalk Inc. (1)
8th Floor Sogo Hanzomon Bldg 1-7 Koji-
machi, Chiyoda-ku, Tokyo, 102-0083, Japan
Tel.: (81) 362656633
Web Site: https://www.boardwalk-inc.jp
Emp.: 50
Entertainment Ticket Booking Services
N.A.I.C.S.: 711320

Cacdo Co., Ltd. (1)
7-2-21 Akasaka Sogetsu Kaikan 6F, Minato-
ku, Tokyo, 107-0052, Japan
Tel.: (81) 364470510
Web Site: http://www.cacdo.jp
Business Design & Planning Services
N.A.I.C.S.: 541320

Carat Japan Co., Ltd. (1)
Nomura Ginza Bldg 12F 6-18-2 Ginza,
Chuo-ku, Tokyo, 104-0061, Japan
Tel.: (81) 362643251
Web Site: http://www.carat-japan.jp
Advertising Communication Services
N.A.I.C.S.: 541810

Creative Associates Ltd. (1)
Ginza Showa-dori Bldg F5 8-14-14 Ginza,
Chuo-ku, Tokyo, 104-0061, Japan
Tel.: (81) 335452911

Web Site: https://www.cal-net.co.jp
Sales Range: Less than $1 Million
Emp.: 28
Television Program Production Services
N.A.I.C.S.: 512110

D Sports Merchandising Inc. (1)
Toranomon Seiwa Building 6F 1-2-3 Tora-
nomon, Minato-ku, Tokyo, 105-0001, Japan
Tel.: (81) 364579158
Web Site: http://www.dsportsm.co.jp
Sport Good Mfr & Retailer
N.A.I.C.S.: 339920

DENTSU TEC INC. (1)
Shinsaiwaibashi Bldg 1-5-3 Uchisaiwai-cho,
Chuo-ku, Tokyo, 100-8508, Japan
Tel.: (81) 362578000
Web Site: http://www.dentsutec.co.jp
Rev.: $23,720,150
Emp.: 1,252
Media Buying Services
N.A.I.C.S.: 541810
Yasuhiro Matsubara *(Pres & CEO)*

Daifu & Co., Ltd. (1)
1-2-3 Kaigan, Minato-ku, Tokyo, 105-0022,
Japan
Tel.: (81) 367213501
Emp.: 12,436
Advertising Communication Services
N.A.I.C.S.: 541810

Dentsu Ad-Gear Inc. (1)
Sumitomo Fudosan Shiodome Hamarikyu
Bldg 8-21-1 Ginza, Chuo-ku, Tokyo, 104-
0061, Japan
Tel.: (81) 355655510
Web Site: https://www.dentsu-adgear.co.jp
Media Advertising Services
N.A.I.C.S.: 541890

Dentsu Aegis Japan Inc. (1)
12F Nomura Ginza Building 6-18-2 Ginza,
Chuo-ku, Tokyo, 104-0061, Japan (100%)
Tel.: (81) 362643300
Web Site: http://www.dentsuaegisjp.com
Holding Company
N.A.I.C.S.: 551112
Koichi Kanai *(Pres & CEO)*

**Dentsu Casting and Entertainment
Inc.** (1)
1-8-1 Higashi-Shimbashi, Minato-ku, Tokyo,
105-7001, Japan
Tel.: (81) 362171501
Web Site: https://www.dentsucasting.co.jp
Advertising Consulting Services
N.A.I.C.S.: 541890

**Dentsu Communication Institute
Inc.** (1)
1-8-1 Higashi-Shimbashi, Minato-ku, Tokyo,
105-7001, Japan
Tel.: (81) 3 6217 6111
Sales Range: $25-49.9 Million
Emp.: 24
N.A.I.C.S.: 541810

Dentsu Consulting Inc. (1)
1-8-1 Higashi-shimbashi, Minato-ku, Tokyo,
105-7001, Japan
Tel.: (81) 362172400
Web Site: https://www.dentsuconsulting.co.jp
Sales Range: $25-49.9 Million
Emp.: 30
Management Strategy Consulting Services
N.A.I.C.S.: 541618

Dentsu Corporate One Inc. (1)
1-8-1 Higashi-shimbashi, Minato-ku, Tokyo,
105-7001, Japan
Tel.: (81) 362168877
Advertising Services
N.A.I.C.S.: 541810

Dentsu Creative Force Inc. (1)
1-8-1 Higashi-shimbashi, Minato-ku, Tokyo,
105-7001, Japan
Tel.: (81) 335755700
Web Site: https://www.dcf-d.co.jp
Emp.: 137
Creative Production Services
N.A.I.C.S.: 541890

Dentsu Creative X Inc. (1)
1-8-1 Higashi-shimbashi, Minato-ku, Tokyo,
105-7001, Japan
Tel.: (81) 362168600
Web Site: https://www.dentsu-crx.co.jp
Emp.: 360

Graphic Design Services
N.A.I.C.S.: 541430

**Dentsu Customer Access Center
Inc** (1)
9th Floor Nomura Ginza Building 6-18-2
Ginza, Chuo-ku, Tokyo, 104-0061, Japan
Tel.: (81) 3 5551 8855
Web Site: http://www.dentsucac.co.jp
Customer Relationship Management Ser-
vices
N.A.I.C.S.: 541618

Dentsu Digital Co., Ltd. (1)
5F Hamarikyu Kensetsu Plz 5-5-12 Tsukiji,
Chuo-ku, Tokyo, 104-0045, Japan
Tel.: (81) 3 5551 1030
Web Site: http://www.dentsu-em1.co.jp
Sales Range: $25-49.9 Million
N.A.I.C.S.: 541810
Nagahama Kaoru *(Pres & CEO)*

Dentsu Digital Drive Inc. (1)
1-8-1 Higashi-shimbashi, Minato-ku, Tokyo,
105-7077, Japan
Tel.: (81) 362176038
Web Site: https://www.japan.dentsu.com
Marketing Consulting Services
N.A.I.C.S.: 541613

Dentsu Digital Holdings Inc. (1)
1-8-1 Higashi Shimbashi, Minato-ku, Tokyo,
105-7001, Japan
Tel.: (81) 3 6252 1703
Web Site: http://www.dentsu-digital.co.jp
Digital Communication Services
N.A.I.C.S.: 517810
Ryuhei Akiyama *(Pres & CEO)*

Dentsu Digital Inc (1)
1-8-1 Higashi-Shinbashi, Shiodome Minato-
ku, Tokyo, 105-7077, Japan
Tel.: (81) 367220100
Web Site: https://www.dentsudigital.co.jp
Emp.: 70
Marketing Solution Consulting Services
N.A.I.C.S.: 541613
Satoru Yamamoto *(Pres & CEO)*

Subsidiary (Domestic):

Dentsu Isobar, Inc. (2)
Tsukiji Shochiku Building 1-13-1 Tsukiji,
Chuo-ku, Tokyo, 104-0045, Japan
Tel.: (81) 355519885
Web Site: http://www.isobar.com
Emp.: 332
Online Advertising Services
N.A.I.C.S.: 541890
Hidetoshi Tokumaru *(Pres & CEO)*

Dentsu Digital Networks Inc. (1)
Tsukiji Shochiku Building 1-13-1 Tsukiji,
Chuo-ku, Tokyo, 104-0045, Japan
Tel.: (81) 368376006
Web Site: http://www.ddnws.co.jp
Advertising Communication Services
N.A.I.C.S.: 541810

Dentsu East Japan Inc. (1)
Shimbashi Tokyu Bldg 4-21-3 Shimbashi,
Minato-ku, Tokyo, 105-0004, Japan
Tel.: (81) 354029555
Web Site: https://ssl.dentsu-east.co.jp
Emp.: 584
Advertising Agency Services
N.A.I.C.S.: 541810

Dentsu Event Operations Inc. (1)
Shinsaiwaibashi Bldg 1-5-3 Uchisaiwai-cho,
Chiyoda-ku, Tokyo, 100-0011, Japan
Tel.: (81) 362066300
Web Site: https://www.dentsu-eo.co.jp
Emp.: 69
Advertising Communication Services
N.A.I.C.S.: 541810

Dentsu Facility Management Inc. (1)
Dentsukosan No3 Bldg, Chuo-ku, Tokyo,
104-0061, Japan
Tel.: (81) 355518111
Facility Management Services
N.A.I.C.S.: 561210

Dentsu Hokkaido Inc. (1)
Nishi 5-11-1 Odori, Chuo-ku Hokkaido, Sap-
poro, 060-8545, Japan
Tel.: (81) 112145111
Web Site: https://www.dentsu-hokkaido.jp
Emp.: 143
Advertising Services

N.A.I.C.S.: 541810

Dentsu Innovation Partners Inc. (1)
1-8-1 Higashi-shimbashi, Minato-ku, Tokyo, 105-7001, Japan
Tel.: (81) 362168615
Web Site: https://www.dentsu-ip.co.jp
Capital Fund Management Services
N.A.I.C.S.: 523940

Dentsu International Limited (1)
Regents Place 10 Triton Street, Regent's Place, London, NW1 3BF, United Kingdom
Tel.: (44) 020 7070 7700
Web Site: https://www.dentsu.com
Holding Company; Media Buying & Advertising Agencies
N.A.I.C.S.: 551112
Wendy Clark (Global Chief Executive Officer)

Subsidiary (Domestic):

BJL Group Limited (2)
Sunlight House Quay St, Manchester, M3 3JZ, United Kingdom
Tel.: (44) 161 831 7141
Web Site: http://www.bjl.co.uk
Sales Range: $10-24.9 Million
Emp.: 85
Advertising Services
N.A.I.C.S.: 541810
Nicky Unsworth (CEO)

Subsidiary (Non-US):

Beijing Dentsu Advertising Co., Ltd. (2)
3-5/F East Tower Genesis Beijing No 8 Xinyuan South Road, Chaoyang District, Beijing, 100027, China
Tel.: (86) 1059167997
Sales Range: $25-49.9 Million
Emp.: 554
Advertising Agency Services
N.A.I.C.S.: 541810
Akimasa Baba (CEO)

Beijing Dentsu Advertising Co., Ltd. (2)
22/F 5 Corporate Avenue No 150 Hu Bin Road, Shanghai, 200021, China
Tel.: (86) 2123109888
Web Site: http://www.beijingdentsu.com.cn
Sales Range: $25-49.9 Million
Emp.: 304
Advertising Agency Services
N.A.I.C.S.: 541810
Keita Ishikawa (CEO)

Beijing Dentsu Advertising Co., Ltd. (2)
42/F Yuexiu Financial Tower 28 Zhujiang Dong Road, Tianhe District, Guangzhou, 510623, China
Tel.: (86) 2083977888
Emp.: 157
Advertising Agency Services
N.A.I.C.S.: 541810
Akimasa Baba (CEO)

Beijing Dentsu Qingdao (2)
Room 1302 Building A Fulai Mansion No 18 Xiang Gang Zhong Road, Qingdao, 266071, Shandong, China
Tel.: (86) 8532 5761 227
N.A.I.C.S.: 541810

Belgiovane Williams Mackay Pty Ltd (2)
Level 2 44 Mountain St, Ultimo, Sydney, 2007, NSW, Australia (51%)
Tel.: (61) 02 8204 3800
Web Site: http://www.bwmdentsu.com
Emp.: 140
Advetising Agency
N.A.I.C.S.: 541810
Jamie Mackay (Partner & Chief Strategy Officer)

Subsidiary (Domestic):

Belgiovane Williams Mackay Pty Ltd - Melbourne (3)
Level 1 116-122 Chapel St, Windsor, 3181, VIC, Australia
Tel.: (61) 396926333
Web Site: http://www.bwmdentsu.com
Sales Range: $10-24.9 Million
Emp.: 50

Online Marketing & Communications Agency
N.A.I.C.S.: 541810

Subsidiary (Non-US):

BlueChip Agentur for Public Relations & Strategy GmbH (2)
Wilhelm-Beckmann-Str 6, 45327, Essen, Germany
Tel.: (49) 201 83012 4
Web Site: http://www.bluechip-pr.de
Sales Range: $10-24.9 Million
Emp.: 14
N.A.I.C.S.: 541820
Ulrich Herzog (Mng Dir & Partner)

Subsidiary (Domestic):

Carat - Edinburgh (2)
Raeburn House 32 York Place, Edinburgh, EH1 3HU, United Kingdom
Tel.: (44) 131 555 2554
Web Site: http://www.carat.com
Emp.: 70
Media Buying Agency
N.A.I.C.S.: 541830
Sue Holloway (Chm)

Subsidiary (Non-US):

Carat Asia Pacific (2)
27/F 625 Kings Road, North Point, China (Hong Kong)
Tel.: (852) 2523 4222
Web Site: http://www.carat-asiapacific.com
Advertising Services
N.A.I.C.S.: 541830
Sean O'Brien (CEO)

Carat Austria GmbH (2)
Trabrennstrasse 2A, Vienna, 1020, Austria
Tel.: (43) 193435000
Web Site: http://www.carat.com
Sales Range: $10-24.9 Million
Emp.: 130
Advertising Agencies
N.A.I.C.S.: 541810

Carat Beijing (2)
6/F East Tower Genesis Beijing No 8 Xinyuan South Road, Chao Yang District, Beijing, 100027, China
Tel.: (86) 1085005000
Web Site: http://www.carat.com
Sales Range: $50-74.9 Million
Emp.: 150
N.A.I.C.S.: 541870
Gary Pan (Mng Dir)

Carat Belgium (2)
Avenue Herrmann-Debroux 54 Herrmann-Debrouxlaan, Auderghem, 1160, Brussels, 1160, Belgium
Tel.: (32) 26635111
Web Site: http://www.carat.be
Sales Range: $25-49.9 Million
Emp.: 140
Advertising Agencies
N.A.I.C.S.: 541810
Bruno Liesse (Mng Dir)

Subsidiary (Domestic):

Carat Business Ltd. (2)
Parker Tower, 43 49 Parker St, London, WC2B 5PS, United Kingdom (100%)
Tel.: (44) 74306399
Web Site: http://www.carat.co.uk
Sales Range: $75-99.9 Million
Emp.: 400
Business Consultants
N.A.I.C.S.: 541810
Gabriela Merrick (Mng Dir-Brisbane)

Subsidiary (Non-US):

Carat Expert - Milan (2)
Via Durini 28, Milan, 20122, Italy
Tel.: (39) 02 77 69 61
Advertising Agencies
N.A.I.C.S.: 541810

Carat France (2)
4 Place De Saverne, Courbevoie, Paris, 92400, France
Tel.: (33) 141161718
Web Site: http://www.carat.com
Sales Range: $25-49.9 Million
Emp.: 20

Business-To-Business, Consumer Marketing, Media Buying Services
N.A.I.C.S.: 541810
William Multrier (CEO)

Subsidiary (Domestic):

Aposition (3)
4 pl de Saverne La Defense, La defence, 92971, Paris, France
Tel.: (33) 141165400
Web Site: https://www.aposition.com
Sales Range: $10-24.9 Million
Emp.: 50
Search Engine Services
N.A.I.C.S.: 541890
Sebastien Langlois (Partner)

Subsidiary (Non-US):

Carat Guangzhou (2)
Room 2703-05 Guangzhou International Electronic Tower, 403 Huan Shi East Road, Guangzhou, 510095, China
Tel.: (86) 2087321091
Web Site: http://www.carat.com
Media Planning & Buying Specialists
N.A.I.C.S.: 541830

Carat Hong Kong (2)
27/F 625 Kings Road, North Point, 999077, China (Hong Kong)
Tel.: (852) 25234222
Web Site: http://www.carat.com.hk
Sales Range: $25-49.9 Million
Emp.: 40
Business-To-Business, Consumer Marketing, Media Buying Services
N.A.I.C.S.: 541870

Carat International Hellas (2)
Chimarras 5, Marousi, 15125, Athens, Greece
Tel.: (30) 2106008200
Web Site: http://www.carat.com
Sales Range: $10-24.9 Million
Emp.: 50
Advertising Agencies
N.A.I.C.S.: 541810
Angliki Giannopoulou (CEO)

Carat Ireland (2)
Two Haddington Buildings 20-38 Haddington Road, Dublin, D04 HE94, Ireland
Tel.: (353) 12712100
Web Site: https://www.carat.com
Sales Range: $200-249.9 Million
Emp.: 50
Advertising Agencies
N.A.I.C.S.: 541810

Carat Italia-Florence (2)
Via L II Magnifico 10, 50129, Florence, Italy
Tel.: (39) 055 46 22 31
Advertising Agencies
N.A.I.C.S.: 541810

Carat Italia-Rome (2)
Viale dell'Arte 68, 00144, Rome, Italy
Tel.: (39) 064522361
Web Site: https://www.carat.com
Advertising Agencies
N.A.I.C.S.: 541810

Carat Italia-Turin (2)
Via De Sonnaz 14, Turin, 10121, Italy
Tel.: (39) 011 56366 1
Advertising Agencies
N.A.I.C.S.: 541810

Carat Korea (2)
10th Fl JS Tower 6 Teheran-ro 79 gil, Gangnam-Gu, Seoul, 6158, Korea (South)
Tel.: (82) 260050400
Web Site: http://www.carat.com
Media Buying Services
N.A.I.C.S.: 541830
Woohyun Nam (Co-CEO)

Carat Mumbai (2)
601 Poonam Chambers B Wing 6th Floor Dr A B Road, Worli, Mumbai, 400 018, India
Tel.: (91) 2230248100
Media Buying Services
N.A.I.C.S.: 541830
Anita Kotwani (CEO)

Carat New Delhi (2)
8th Floor Tower A Building No-5 DLF Cyber City Phase - III, Gurgaon, 122022, Haryana, India

Tel.: (91) 1247118100
Web Site: http://www.carat.com
Rev.: $32,031,296
Media Buying Services
N.A.I.C.S.: 541830

Carat Nordic AB (2)
Asogatan 108, PO Box 4125, Stockholm, 102 63, Sweden
Tel.: (46) 86986800
Web Site:
    http://www.dentsuaegisnetwork.com
Emp.: 300
Financial Management Services
N.A.I.C.S.: 523999

Carat Norge AS (2)
Pilestredet 8, Oslo, 0180, Norway
Tel.: (47) 22828282
Web Site: http://www.carat.com
Sales Range: $25-49.9 Million
Emp.: 190
Provider of Media Services to Advertisers
N.A.I.C.S.: 541830
Nick Stravs (Exec VP)

Carat Shanghai (2)
15/F 5 Corporate Avenue No 150 Hubin Road, Shanghai, 200021, China
Tel.: (86) 2133350000
Web Site: http://www.carat.com
Sales Range: $50-74.9 Million
Emp.: 241
N.A.I.C.S.: 541870
Wan-Gyn Ang (CEO)

Carat Sweden AB (2)
Asogatan 108, PO Box 4125, 102 63, Stockholm, 102 63, Sweden
Tel.: (46) 86986800
Web Site: http://www.carat.se
Sales Range: $25-49.9 Million
Emp.: 60
Provider of Media Services to Advertisers
N.A.I.C.S.: 541830
Henrik Hannemann (Mng Dir)

Cayenne S.R.L. (2)
Via Volturno 46, 20124, Milan, MI, Italy
Tel.: (39) 02725331
Web Site: https://www.cayenne.it
Sales Range: $10-24.9 Million
Emp.: 50
N.A.I.C.S.: 541810
Peter Grosser (CEO & Partner)

Subsidiary (US):

Character SF, LLC (2)
447 Battery St 3rd Fl, San Francisco, CA 94111
Tel.: (415) 227-2100
Web Site: http://www.character.co
Graphic Design Services
N.A.I.C.S.: 541430

Subsidiary (Non-US):

Dentsu (Malaysia) Sdn. Bhd. (2)
45-24 Plaza Level Block C Plaza Damansara Jalan Medan Setia 1, Damansara Heights, 50490, Kuala Lumpur, 50490, Malaysia
Tel.: (60) 3 2711 5555
Web Site: http://www.dentsu.com
Sales Range: $10-24.9 Million
Emp.: 50
N.A.I.C.S.: 541810

Dentsu (Taiwan) Inc. (2)
13F 68 Sec 3 Nanjing East Road, Taipei, 104, Taiwan
Tel.: (886) 2 2506 9201
Web Site: http://www.dentsu.com.tw
Emp.: 170
Advertising Services
N.A.I.C.S.: 541810

Dentsu (Thailand) Ltd. (2)
27th Fl U-Chu Liang Bldg 968 Rama IV Rd, Silom Bangrak, Bangkok, 10500, Thailand
Tel.: (66) 26324555
Web Site: http://www.dentsu.co.th
Sales Range: $25-49.9 Million
Emp.: 229
N.A.I.C.S.: 541810
Peabporn Prayudthanakul (Asst Dir-Creative)

Subsidiary (Domestic):

Dentsu Media (Thailand) Ltd. (3)

Dentsu Group Inc.—(Continued)

15th Floor U-Chu Liang Bldg 968 Rama IV
Road Silom, Bangrak, Bangkok, 10500,
Thailand
Tel.: (66) 2 632 4020
Web Site: http://www.dentsu.com
Sales Range: $10-24.9 Million
Emp.: 60
Media Advertising Agency Services
N.A.I.C.S.: 541810
Sarnchatt Chansrakao (CEO)

Subsidiary (Non-US):

Dentsu 24/7 Search Holdings
B.V. (2)
Weena 327, 3013 AL, Rotterdam, Nether-
lands
Tel.: (31) 102064600
Advertising Services
N.A.I.C.S.: 541890

Branch (Domestic):

Dentsu Aegis Network (2)
Regent's Place 10 Triton Street, London,
NW1 3BF, United Kingdom (100%)
Tel.: (44) 2074051050
Web Site: http://www.aemedia.com
Sales Range: $75-99.9 Million
Emp.: 400
Provider of Media Services to Advertisers
N.A.I.C.S.: 541830
Robert Harvey (CEO-New Zealand)

Subsidiary (Non-US):

Dentsu Aegis Network (Deutschland)
GmbH (2)
Kreuzberger Ring 19, 65205, Wiesbaden,
Germany
Tel.: (49) 61197880
Web Site:
http://www.dentsuaegisnetwork.com
Emp.: 380
Marketing Consulting Services
N.A.I.C.S.: 541613

Group (US):

Dentsu Aegis Network Americas (2)
150 E 42nd St, New York, NY 10017
Tel.: (212) 591-9100
Web Site:
http://www.dentsuaegisnetwork.com
Advertising Agency Managing Office
N.A.I.C.S.: 551114
Jacki S. Kelley (CEO-Americas)

Subsidiary (Non-US):

Carat Argentina S.A. (3)
Manuel Ugarte 1674 2nd 3rd and 6th Floor,
Ciudad de Buenos Aires, Buenos Aires, CP
1428, Argentina
Tel.: (54) 1151945100
Web Site: http://www.carat.com
Sales Range: $10-24.9 Million
Emp.: 44
Media Buying Services
N.A.I.C.S.: 541830

Carat Canada (3)
127 rue Saint-Pierre, Montreal, H2Y 2L6,
QC, Canada
Tel.: (514) 284-4446
Web Site: http://www.carat.com
Sales Range: $25-49.9 Million
Emp.: 100
Advetising Agency
N.A.I.C.S.: 541810

Carat Mexicana (3)
440 Avenida Santa Fe 10th 11th floors, Col
Santa Fe Cuajimalpa, 05348, Mexico,
Mexico
Tel.: (52) 5530027200
Web Site: http://www.carat.com
Sales Range: $25-49.9 Million
Emp.: 133
Media Buying Services
N.A.I.C.S.: 541830

Subsidiary (Domestic):

Dentsu America LLC (3)
32 Avenue of the Americas 16th Fl, New
York, NY 10013
Tel.: (212) 397-3333

Web Site: http://www.dentsuamerica.com
Rev.: $122,000,000
Emp.: 1,500
N.A.I.C.S.: 541810
Scott Daly (Exec VP & Exec Media Dir)

Subsidiary (Non-US):

Dentsu Argentina S.A. (3)
Vuelta de Obligado 1947 Piso 5, Belgrano,
C1428ADC, Buenos Aires, Argentina
Tel.: (54) 1157774900
Web Site: http://www.dentsu-ar.com.ar
Sales Range: $10-24.9 Million
Emp.: 38
Advertising Agency Services
N.A.I.C.S.: 541810
Guillermo Munro (Gen Mgr)

Dentsu Latin America Propaganda
Ltda. (3)
Rua Joaquim Floriano 413 6 Andar, Itaim
Bibi, 04534-011, Sao Paulo, Brazil
Tel.: (55) 1135285341
Web Site: http://www.dentsubrasilcases.com
Advertising Agency Services
N.A.I.C.S.: 541810

DentsuBos (3)
1 University Avenue, Toronto, M5J 2P1,
ON, Canada
Tel.: (416) 929-9700
Web Site: http://www.dentsubos.com
Sales Range: $25-49.9 Million
Emp.: 200
Advertising Agency Services
N.A.I.C.S.: 541810
Sebastien Rivest (Chief Creative Officer,
Exec VP & Gen Mgr)

Division (Domestic):

DentsuBos - Antibody Healthcare
Communications Division (4)
1 University Ave 8th Floor, Toronto, M5J
2P1, ON, Canada
Tel.: (416) 926-2126
Web Site: http://antibodyhc.com
Emp.: 55
Healthcare Advertising & Marketing Ser-
vices
N.A.I.C.S.: 541890
James Cran (Co-Founder & CEO)

Branch (Domestic):

DentsuBos Montreal (4)
3970 St-Ambroise Street, Montreal, H4C
2C7, QC, Canada
Tel.: (514) 848-0010
Web Site: http://www.dentsubos.com
Sales Range: $10-24.9 Million
Advetising Agency
N.A.I.C.S.: 541810

Subsidiary (Non-US):

Grip Limited (3)
1 University Avenue, Toronto, M5J 2P1,
ON, Canada
Tel.: (416) 340-7111
Web Site: https://www.dentsuone.com
Emp.: 150
Advetising Agency
N.A.I.C.S.: 541810
David Chiavegato (Partner-Creative)

Happy McGarryBowen (3)
No 40 City Center CMH Road, Indiranagar,
Bengaluru, 560038, India
Tel.: (91) 80 4125 0744
Web Site: http://www.happymgb.com
Advetising Agency
N.A.I.C.S.: 541810
Kartik Iyer (CEO)

Subsidiary (Domestic):

Merkle Inc. (3)
7001 Columbia Gateway Dr, Columbia, MD
21046 (68.3%)
Tel.: (443) 542-4000
Web Site: https://www.merkle.com
Marketing & Advertising Agency
N.A.I.C.S.: 541810
David S. Williams (Chm)

Subsidiary (Domestic):

4Cite Marketing, LLC (4)

30 S Pearl St, Albany, NY 12207
Tel.: (844) 545-7110
Web Site: http://www.4cite.com
Custom Computer Programming Services
N.A.I.C.S.: 541511
Jim Finnerty (COO)

Axis41, Inc. (4)
175 W 200 S Ste 4100, Salt Lake City, UT
84101
Tel.: (801) 303-6300
Web Site: http://www.axis41.com
Website & Mobile App Developer
N.A.I.C.S.: 541511
Ron Pynes (Partner-Strategic Svcs)

HelloWorld, Inc. (4)
3000 Town Ctr Ste 2100, Southfield, MI
48075
Tel.: (248) 543-6800
Web Site: http://www.helloworld.com
Online Marketing Services
N.A.I.C.S.: 541613
Jen Todd Gray (Sr VP-Brand Mktg & Cre-
ative Svcs)

Subsidiary (Non-US):

Dentsu Aegis Network Asia
Pacific (2)
1 Raffles Place Suite 28-61 One Raffles
Place Tower 2, Singapore, 48616,
Singapore (100%)
Tel.: (65) 63965280
Sales Range: $25-49.9 Million
Emp.: 25
Media Buying Services
N.A.I.C.S.: 541810
Ashish Bhasin (CEO)

Dentsu Aegis Network Australia (2)
105 York Street, Melbourne, 3205, VIC,
Australia
Tel.: (61) 3 9693 6322
Web Site: http://www.aegismedia.com.au
Sales Range: $200-249.9 Million
Emp.: 300
Direct Response Marketing, Media Buying
Services, Media Planning, Public Relations,
Sports Marketing
N.A.I.C.S.: 541810
Catherine Krantz (Head-Diversity &
Inclusion-Australia & New Zealand)

Unit (Domestic):

Oddfellows/Dentsu Holdings Pty
Ltd. (3)
47 Ridge Street, North Sydney, 2060, NSW,
Australia (51%)
Tel.: (61) 2 9923 3000
Web Site: http://www.oddfellows.com.au
Sales Range: $1-9.9 Million
Emp.: 30
Advertising Services
N.A.I.C.S.: 541810

Subsidiary (Non-US):

Dentsu Aegis Network Iberia S.L (2)
Julian Hernandez 15, Madrid, 28043, Spain
Tel.: (34) 91 353 62 00
Sales Range: $100-124.9 Million
Emp.: 300
Media Communication & Marketing Re-
search Services
N.A.I.C.S.: 517810
Andre Andrade (Gen Mgr)

Dentsu Aegis Network India (2)
Poonam Chambers B Wing 6th Floor, Dr
Annie Besant Road Worli, Mumbai, 400018,
India
Tel.: (91) 22 3024 8100
Web Site:
http://www.dentsuaegisnetwork.com
Communications & Advertising Services
N.A.I.C.S.: 541810
Ashish Bhasin (CEO-Asia Pacific)

Subsidiary (Domestic):

Perfect Relations Pvt. Ltd. (3)
S 27 Star City Mahatta Towers District Cen-
tre Mayur Vihar Phase I, New Delhi,
110091, India
Tel.: (91) 11 49998999
Web Site: http://www.perfectrelations.com
Public Relations Agency
N.A.I.C.S.: 541820

Bobby Kewalramani (Co-Founder)

Subsidiary (Non-US):

Dentsu Aegis Network Italia Srl (2)
Via Bracco 6, 20159, Milan, Italy
Tel.: (39) 0287334100
Web Site:
http://www.dentsuaegisnetwork.com
Advertising Agency Services
N.A.I.C.S.: 541810

Dentsu Aegis Network Netherlands
B.V. (2)
Piet Heinkade 55, 1019 GM, Amsterdam,
Netherlands (100%)
Tel.: (31) 205304500
Sales Range: $25-49.9 Million
Emp.: 75
Holding Company
N.A.I.C.S.: 551112
Julius Minnaar (CEO)

Dentsu Asia Pte. Ltd. (2)
77 Robinson Road 24-01 Robinson 77, Sin-
gapore, 068896, Singapore
Tel.: (65) 683722
Web Site: http://www.dentsuasia.net
Sales Range: $75-99.9 Million
Emp.: 200
Regional Administration Management Ser-
vices
N.A.I.C.S.: 925120
Ted Lim (Chief Creative Officer)

Dentsu Australia Pty Ltd (2)
47 Ridge St, North Sydney, 2060, NSW,
Australia
Tel.: (61) 2 9923 3091
Web Site: http://www.dentsu.com
Advertising Agency Services
N.A.I.C.S.: 541810

Dentsu Brussels Group (2)
Rue Fourmois 15, 1050, Brussels, Belgium
Tel.: (32) 25433900
Web Site:
http://www.dentsubrusselsgroup.com
Sales Range: $10-24.9 Million
Emp.: 35
N.A.I.C.S.: 541810

Dentsu China Limited (2)
Kings Rd 625 254, 510 King's Road, North
Point, China (Hong Kong)
Tel.: (852) 21023333
Web Site: http://www.dentsu.com.jp
Sales Range: $25-49.9 Million
Emp.: 60
N.A.I.C.S.: 541810
Kong Siu Ngan (Pres)

Dentsu Creative Impact Pvt. Ltd. (2)
Rz-1 Bhwani Kunji, Vasant Kunji, New
Delhi, 110070, India
Tel.: (91) 11 4604 7666
Web Site: http://www.dentsu.in
Advertising Agency Services
N.A.I.C.S.: 541810
Benny Augustine (COO)

Dentsu Holdings (Thailand) Ltd. (2)
27th Floor U-Chu Liang Bldg 968 Rama IV
Road Silom, Bangrak, Bangkok, 10500,
Thailand
Tel.: (66) 26324555
Sales Range: $75-99.9 Million
Emp.: 230
Investment Management Service
N.A.I.C.S.: 523999
Amonsak Sakpuaram (Pres)

Dentsu Holdings Philippines Inc. (2)
4/F United Life Building 837 A Arnaiz Ave,
Makati, 1229, Philippines
Tel.: (63) 2 652 7800
Holding Company; Advertising Agency
N.A.I.C.S.: 551112

Subsidiary (Domestic):

DM9 Jayme Syfu Inc. (3)
4/F United Life Building 837 A Arnaiz Ave,
Makati, 1229, Philippines (70%)
Tel.: (63) 26527800
Web Site: https://www.dentsucreative.ph
Emp.: 84
Advetising Agency
N.A.I.C.S.: 541810
Merlee Cruz Jayme (Chm)

Subsidiary (Non-US):

Dentsu Hong Kong Ltd. (2)
Room 1A-10A 7/F Island Place Tower Is-
land Place 510 Kings Road, North Point,
China (Hong Kong)
Tel.: (852) 2102 3333
Telecommunication Network Services
N.A.I.C.S.: 517111
Cecilia Chan (Dir-Client Svc)

Dentsu Korea Inc (2)
35th Floor Asem Tower 159-1 Samsung-
Dong, Gangnam-Gu, Seoul, 135-798, Korea
(South)
Tel.: (82) 12270270
Advertising Services
N.A.I.C.S.: 541810

Dentsu Kuohua (2)
13F 188 Sec 5 Nanjing East Road, Taipei,
105, Taiwan
Tel.: (886) 2 2747 9494
Web Site: http://www.dentsu-kuohua.com
Sales Range: $25-49.9 Million
Emp.: 100
Advertising Services
N.A.I.C.S.: 541810

Dentsu Marcom Pvt. Ltd. (2)
7A Khullar Farms New Mangla Puri, Maandi
Road Mehrauli, New Delhi, 110030, India
Tel.: (91) 11 2612 2938
N.A.I.C.S.: 541810
Harjot Narang (Pres)

Dentsu Media Hong Kong Ltd. (2)
Unit 1901 19/F AIA Hong Kong Tower Me-
dia Palette, North Point, Quarry Bay, China
(Hong Kong)
Tel.: (852) 3971 8500
Web Site: http://www.dentsu.com
Sales Range: $25-49.9 Million
Emp.: 20
Media Advertising Services
N.A.I.C.S.: 541890

Dentsu Media Korea Inc. (2)
20th Floor Glass Tower 946-1 Daechi-Dong,
Gangnam-Gu, Seoul, 135-708, Korea
(South)
Tel.: (82) 2 3011 2500
Web Site: http://www.dentsumedia.com
Emp.: 10
Media Advertising Services
N.A.I.C.S.: 541810
Sunkyoung Kwak (Gen Mgr)

Dentsu Media Vietnam Ltd (2)
19th Floor Vincom Center 72 Le Thanh Ton
Str, Dist 1, Ho Chi Minh City, Vietnam
Tel.: (84) 8 3936 9180
Web Site: http://www.dentsumedia.com.vn
Advetising Agency
N.A.I.C.S.: 541810
Takeshi Gotoda (CEO & Gen Dir)

Dentsu New Ideas LLC (2)
9th Floor 23 Osenny Blvd, Moscow,
121609, Russia
Tel.: (7) 495 781 0068
Web Site: http://www.de-n-i.ru
Sales Range: $25-49.9 Million
Emp.: 25
Advertising Agency Services
N.A.I.C.S.: 541810
Alexander Romanov (Pres)

Dentsu Plus Co., Ltd (2)
323 United Center Bldg 16th Floor Unit
1601-21602 A Silom Road Silom, Bangrak,
Bangkok, 10500, Thailand
Tel.: (66) 2 234 3535
Web Site: http://www.dentsuplus.com
Emp.: 90
Advertising Services
N.A.I.C.S.: 541810

Dentsu Singapore Pvt. Ltd. (2)
Guoco Tower 1 Wallich Street 21-01, Singa-
pore, 078881, Singapore
Tel.: (65) 69119546
Web Site: https://www.dentsu.com.sg
Sales Range: $25-49.9 Million
Emp.: 80
Advertising Agency Services
N.A.I.C.S.: 541810
Andy Greenaway (Exec Creative Dir)

Dentsu Sports Asia, Pte. Ltd. (2)
1 Wallich Street 21-02 Guoco Tower, Singa-
pore, 78881, Singapore
Tel.: (65) 63868322
Web Site: http://asia.dentsusports.com
Sports Event Operating Services
N.A.I.C.S.: 711310

Branch (Domestic):

Dentsu Sports Europe, Ltd. (2)
Berger House 1st Floor 38, Berkeley
Square, London, W1J 5AH, United Kingdom
Tel.: (44) 2074999124
Global Sports Consulting Services
N.A.I.C.S.: 541618

Subsidiary (Non-US):

Dentsu TOP Co., Ltd. (2)
Room 4E3-F 4th Floor Shi Ye Building 18
Cao Xi Road, Shanghai, 200030, China
Tel.: (86) 21 64271008
Web Site: http://www.dentsutop.com
Advertising Services
N.A.I.C.S.: 541810

Dentsu Utama Sdn. Bhd. (2)
Unit 1-1 Level 1 Block B Plaza Damansara
45 Medan Setia 1, Bukit Damansara,
50490, Kuala Lumpur, Malaysia
Tel.: (60) 3 2096 2212
Web Site: http://www.dentsutama.com.my
Integrated Communication Services
N.A.I.C.S.: 517810
Omar Shaari (CEO)

Dentsu Vietnam Ltd. (2)
16th Floor Vincom Center 72 Le Thanh Ton
Street, District 1, Ho Chi Minh City, Vietnam
Tel.: (84) 838219005
Web Site: http://www.dentsu.com.vn
Sales Range: $25-49.9 Million
Emp.: 25
Advertising Agency Services
N.A.I.C.S.: 541810

Dentsu-Smart LLC (2)
11 Osennyaya Str 6th Floor, 121609, Mos-
cow, Russia
Tel.: (7) 495 781 88 18
Web Site: http://www.dentsusmart.ru
Emp.: 20
Advertising Agency Services
N.A.I.C.S.: 541810

Subsidiary (US):

E-Nor LLC (2)
5201 Great America Pkwy Ste 320, Santa
Clara, CA 95054
Tel.: (408) 988-0003
Web Site: http://www.e-nor.com
Digital Analytics & Marketing Consulting
Services
N.A.I.C.S.: 541613
Feras Alhlou (CEO)

Subsidiary (Non-US):

E-Nor EMEA (3)
Boomsesteenweg 690, 2610, Wilrijk, Bel-
gium
Tel.: (32) 473 342121
Digital Analytics & Marketing Consulting
Services
N.A.I.C.S.: 541613

Subsidiary (Non-US):

Indigo Werbeagentur GmbH (2)
Johannstrasse 37, 40476, Dusseldorf, Ger-
many
Tel.: (49) 211977690
Web Site: http://www.indigo-wa.de
Emp.: 30
Advertising & Communication Services
N.A.I.C.S.: 541810

Iprospect (2)
Beim Strohhause 31, 20097, Hamburg,
Germany
Tel.: (49) 4027159200
Web Site: https://www.iprospect.com
Advetising Agency
N.A.I.C.S.: 541810

Branch (Domestic):

Isobar (2)
10 Triton Street Regents Place, London,
NW1 3BF, United Kingdom
Tel.: (44) 20 3535 9700

Web Site: http://www.isobar.com
Sales Range: $25-49.9 Million
Emp.: 150
Advetising Agency
N.A.I.C.S.: 541810
Gary Chi (CEO-Taiwan)

Subsidiary (US):

Digital Evolution Group LLC (3)
6601 College Blvd 6th Fl, Overland Park,
KS 66211
Tel.: (913) 498-9988
Web Site: http://www.degdigital.com
Digital Marketing Consulting Services
N.A.I.C.S.: 541613
Neal A. Sharma (Co-Founder)

Subsidiary (Non-US):

Dentsu Creative GmbH (4)
Johannstrasse 37, 40476, Dusseldorf, Ger-
many
Tel.: (49) 211977690
Web Site: http://www.isobar.com
Advetising Agency
N.A.I.C.S.: 541810

Soap Linked by Isobar (4)
Level 3/20 Windmill St, Walsh Bay, 2000,
NSW, Australia
Tel.: (61) 280947567
Web Site: http://www.soap.com.au
Advetising Agency
N.A.I.C.S.: 541810
Ashley Ringrose (Founder)

Unit (Domestic):

Isobar (3)
31 Old Nichol Street, Shoreditch, London,
E2 7HR, United Kingdom
Tel.: (44) 20 7739 2345
Web Site: http://www.isobar.com
Advetising Agency
N.A.I.C.S.: 541810

Subsidiary (Non-US):

Isobar Australia (2)
Level 3/20 Windmill St, Walsh Bay, 2000,
NSW, Australia
Tel.: (61) 280947567
Web Site: http://www.isobar.com
Sales Range: $25-49.9 Million
Emp.: 100
Advertising, Interactive, Internet/Web De-
sign, Multimedia, Viral/Buzz/Word of Mouth,
Web (Banner Ads, Pop-ups, etc.)
N.A.I.C.S.: 541810
Shamsuddin Jasani (Mng Dir-South Asia)

Isobar Hong Kong (2)
16/F 633 King's Rd, North Point, China
(Hong Kong)
Tel.: (852) 39624500
N.A.I.C.S.: 541810
Jean Lin-Baden (CEO-Asia Pacific)

Isosbar (2)
Suite 103-106, Block G Red Town, 570
Huai Hai West Road, Shanghai, 200052,
China
N.A.I.C.S.: 541830
Jean Lin-Baden (Chief Strategy Officer-
Global)

Division (Domestic):

wwwins Isobar (3)
Suite 103 1st Floor, Block G Huai Hai Xi
Road, Shanghai, 200052, China
Tel.: (86) 21 5238 1333
Advertising, Digital/Interactive, Local Mar-
keting, Media Buying Services, Media Plan-
ning, Strategic Planning/Research
N.A.I.C.S.: 541810
Jean Lin (CEO-Asia/Pacific & Chief Strat-
egy Officer-Global)

Subsidiary (Domestic):

John Brown Media Group Ltd. (2)
8 Baldwin Street, London, EC1V 9NU,
United Kingdom
Tel.: (44) 2075653000
Web Site: http://www.johnbrownmedia.com
Advertising Services
N.A.I.C.S.: 541890
Andrew Hirsch (CEO)

Subsidiary (Non-US):

Kirowski Isobar Zrt (2)
15-23 Kacsa Utca, 1027, Budapest, Hun-
gary
Tel.: (36) 1 4112200
Web Site: http://www.isobar.com
Sales Range: $25-49.9 Million
Emp.: 117
Advetising Agency
N.A.I.C.S.: 541810

Media Palette (Taiwan) Inc. (2)
4F No 10 Section 3, Minsheng East Road,
Taipei, 104, Taiwan
Tel.: (886) 2 2517 8866
Sales Range: $25-49.9 Million
Emp.: 82
Media Buying Services, Merchandising,
Planning & Consultation, Sports Marketing
N.A.I.C.S.: 541810

Subsidiary (US):

MuteSix, LLC (2)
5800 Bristol Pkwy, Culver City, CA 90230
Tel.: (877) 570-5939
Web Site: http://www.mutesix.com
Digital Marketing Services
N.A.I.C.S.: 541810
Christian Vollerslev (CEO)

Subsidiary (Non-US):

PT Dentsu Media Indonesia (2)
Graha Niaga 22nd Floor JI Jendral
Sudirman Kav 58, Jakarta, 12190, Indone-
sia
Tel.: (62) 2505020
Web Site: http://www.dentsumedia.co.id
Media Communication Services
N.A.I.C.S.: 541840

**PT. Dentsu Consultants
Indonesia** (2)
22nd Floor Graha Niaga JI Jenderal
Sudirman Kav 58, Jakarta, 12190, Indone-
sia
Tel.: (62) 21 250 5020
Web Site: http://www.dentsu.com
Management Consulting Services
N.A.I.C.S.: 541618

PT. Dentsu Strat (2)
Bapindo Plaza 12th Floor Citibank Tower JI
Jend Sudirman Kav 54-55, Jakarta, 12190,
Indonesia
Tel.: (62) 21 5273844
Web Site: http://www.dentsustrat.com
Advertising Agency Services
N.A.I.C.S.: 541810
Janoe Arijanto (Pres)

Planete Interactive (2)
4 Place de Saverne, La Defense, Courbev-
oie, 92 971, France　　　　　　　　**(100%)**
Tel.: (33) 141166769
Web Site: http://www.planete-
interactive.com
Interactive Marketing Services
N.A.I.C.S.: 541830

**RPM Radar Reklam Pazarlama
Musavirlik A.S.** (2)
Suleyman Seba Caddesi BJK Plaza Blok
No 48 Kat 7 Besiktas, 34357, Istanbul, Tur-
kiye
Tel.: (90) 212 227 97 77
Web Site: http://www.rpm.com.tr
Sales Range: $10-24.9 Million
Emp.: 50
N.A.I.C.S.: 541810

Smile Vun Group Pvt Ltd. (2)
AIHP Palms Plot No 242 & 243 LGF, Udyog
Vihar Phase-IV, New Delhi, 122015, Guru-
gram, India
Tel.: (91) 0124 6090100
Web Site: http://svgmedia.in
Holding Company; Digital Media Services
N.A.I.C.S.: 551112
Chirag Shah (CEO-SVG Mobile)

Subsidiary (Domestic):

SVG Media Pvt. Ltd. (3)
AIHP Palms Plot No 242 & 243 LGF, Udyog
Vihar Phase IV, New Delhi, 122016, Guru-
gram, India
Tel.: (91) 01246090100

Dentsu Group Inc.—(Continued)

Web Site: http://www.svgmedia.in
Digital Media Services
N.A.I.C.S.: 541890
Deven Dharamdasani (CEO)

Division (Domestic):

Tyroo Media Pvt. Ltd.   (4)
Plot No 241 Udyog Vihar Phase 1, Gurugram, Delhi, 122016, India
Tel.: (91) 911244343500
Web Site: http://www.tyroo.com
Digital Media Services
N.A.I.C.S.: 541890

Subsidiary (Domestic):

DGM India Internet Marketing Private Limited   (5)
Plot No. 926, Udyog Vihar Phase 3, New Delhi, 110020, Gurugram, India
Tel.: (91) 124 473 4600
Online Marketing Services
N.A.I.C.S.: 541613

Subsidiary (Domestic):

Steak Group Ltd.   (2)
62-70 Shorts Gardens, Covent Garden, London, WC2H 9AH, United Kingdom
Tel.: (44) 20 7420 3500
Web Site: http://www.steakgroup.com
Emp.: 40
Digital Marketing Services
N.A.I.C.S.: 541613
Phil Burgss (Mng Dir)

Vizeum UK Ltd.   (2)
10 Triton Street Regents Place, London, NW1 3BF, United Kingdom
Tel.: (44) 2073799000
Web Site: http://www.vizeum.co.uk
Sales Range: $300-349.9 Million
Emp.: 150
Media Buying Agency
N.A.I.C.S.: 541830
Louise Martell (Chief Plng Officer)

Subsidiary (Non-US):

Vizeum Canada Inc.   (3)
1 University Avenue, Toronto, M5J 2P1, ON, Canada
Tel.: (416) 967-7282
Web Site: http://www.vizeum.ca
Sales Range: $25-49.9 Million
Emp.: 25
Advertising Services
N.A.I.C.S.: 541810

Branch (Domestic):

Vizeum Canada Inc. - Vancouver   (4)
1066 W Hastings St, Vancouver, V6E 3X1, BC, Canada
Tel.: (604) 646-7282
Sales Range: $25-49.9 Million
Emp.: 25
Advertising Services
N.A.I.C.S.: 541810
Jim Gordon (Mng Dir & Sr VP)

Subsidiary (US):

Vizeum USA   (3)
32 Avenue of the Americas 25th Fl, New York, NY 10013
Tel.: (212) 784-3800
Web Site: http://www.vizeum.com
Sales Range: $25-49.9 Million
Emp.: 5
Advetising Agency
N.A.I.C.S.: 541810
Kesy Lee (Gen Mgr-Taiwan)

Branch (Domestic):

Whitespace (Scotland) Limited   (2)
Norloch House 36 King's Stables Road, Edinburgh, EH1 2EU, United Kingdom
Tel.: (44) 1316255500
Web Site: http://www.whitespacers.com
Advetising Agency
N.A.I.C.S.: 541810
Phillip Lockwood-Holmes (Mng Partner)

Subsidiary (Non-US):

X-Line Hypermedia Ltd.   (2)
3rd Floor 26 Section 3 Nanjing East Road,

Taipei, 10489, Taiwan
Tel.: (886) 2 2509 0577
Web Site: http://www.dentsu.com
Advertising Services
N.A.I.C.S.: 541810

Zhongying Dentsu Tec Advertising Co., Ltd.   (2)
100027 Room B Floor 13 Tower F Fuhua Tower No 8 Chaoyangmen Beidajie, Dongcheng District, Beijing, China
Tel.: (86) 10 6554 5354
Web Site: http://www.zydentsutec.com
Advertising Services
N.A.I.C.S.: 541810
Sheng Xuan (CEO)

Dentsu Kyushu Inc.   (1)
1-16-10 Akasaka, Chuo-ku, Fukuoka, 810-8675, Japan
Tel.: (81) 927132555
Web Site: https://www.dentsu-kyu.co.jp
Emp.: 282
Advertising Services
N.A.I.C.S.: 541810

Dentsu Macromill Insight, Inc.   (1)
Dentsu Ginza Bldg 7-4-17 Ginza, Chuo-ku, Tokyo, 104-8171, Japan
Tel.: (81) 332896711
Web Site: https://www.dm-insight.jp
Emp.: 214
Data Analyst & Planning Services
N.A.I.C.S.: 541618
Toshiyuki Suzuki (Pres)

Dentsu Management Services Inc.   (1)
JEI Hamamatsucho Bldg 2-2-12 Hamamatsu-cho, Minato-ku, Tokyo, 105-0013, Japan
Tel.: (81) 354081811
Web Site: http://www.dentsu-ms.co.jp
Payroll Management Services
N.A.I.C.S.: 541214

Dentsu Marketing East Asia Inc.   (1)
2nd Floor Creglanz Shimbashi III 3-4-8 Shimbashi, Minato-ku, Tokyo, 105-0004, Japan
Tel.: (81) 3 3539 3188
Web Site: http://www.dentsumarketing.com
Marketing Research Service
N.A.I.C.S.: 541910

Dentsu Medical Communications, Inc.   (1)
1-8-1 Higashi-shimbashi, Minato-ku, Tokyo, 105-7070, Japan
Tel.: (81) 362171900
Web Site: https://www.dentsu-mc.co.jp
Ethical Drug Distr
N.A.I.C.S.: 424210

Dentsu Meitetsu Communications Inc.   (1)
4-8-18 Meieki, Nakamura-ku, Nagoya, 450-0002, Aichi, Japan
Tel.: (81) 525710550
Web Site: https://www.dm-c.co.jp
Sales Range: $25-49.9 Million
Emp.: 167
Advertising Services
N.A.I.C.S.: 541810
Ishikawa Masahiro (Pres & CEO)

Dentsu Music and Entertainment Inc.   (1)
11F Higashi-Shimbashi 1-8-1, Minato-ku, Tokyo, 105-7001, Japan
Tel.: (81) 362171230
Web Site: https://www.dentsumusic.co.jp
Emp.: 37
Music Production Services
N.A.I.C.S.: 711130

Dentsu Okinawa Inc.   (1)
Kokuba Bldg 3-21-1 Kumoji, Naha, 900-0015, Okinawa, Japan
Tel.: (81) 988620012
Web Site: https://www.dentsu-ok.co.jp
Emp.: 32
Motion Picture & Video Advertising Services
N.A.I.C.S.: 512110

Dentsu On-Demand Graphics Inc.   (1)
1-8-3 Higashi-shimbashi, Minato-ku, Tokyo, 105-0021, Japan
Tel.: (81) 3 6217 1270

Web Site: http://www.dodg.co.jp
Graphic Production Services
N.A.I.C.S.: 541430

Dentsu Operation Partners Inc.   (1)
1-8-1 Higashi-Shimbashi, Minato-ku, Tokyo, 105-0021, Japan
Tel.: (81) 362171200
Web Site: https://www.dentsu-op.co.jp
Emp.: 115
Advertising Communication Services
N.A.I.C.S.: 541810

Dentsu Operations Development Inc.   (1)
Dentsu Tsukiji Bldg 2 1-7-11 Tsukiji, Chuo-ku, Tokyo, 104-0045, Japan
Tel.: (81) 3 6226 2760
Business Support Services
N.A.I.C.S.: 561499

Dentsu Promotion Plus Inc.   (1)
1-8-1 Higashi-shimbashi, Minato-ku, Tokyo, 105-7001, Japan
Tel.: (81) 362578000
Advertising Services
N.A.I.C.S.: 541810

Dentsu Research Inc.   (1)
Dentsu Ginza Bldg 7-4-17 Ginza, Chuo-ku, Tokyo, 104-8171, Japan
Tel.: (81) 3 3289 6711
Emp.: 115
N.A.I.C.S.: 541810
Andrew Powell (Mng Dir)

Dentsu Retail Marketing Inc.   (1)
5-31-17 Shiba PMO Tamachi, Minato-ku, Tokyo, 108-0014, Japan
Tel.: (81) 354396141
Web Site: http://www.dentsu-rm.co.jp
Data Analyst & Planning Services
N.A.I.C.S.: 541618

Dentsu Runway Inc.   (1)
1-8-1 Higashi-shimbashi, Minato-ku, Tokyo, 105-7001, Japan
Tel.: (81) 362171800
Advertising Services
N.A.I.C.S.: 541810

Dentsu ScienceJam Inc.   (1)
4-2-28 Akasaka TRES Akasaka 102, Minato-ku, Tokyo, 107-0052, Japan
Tel.: (81) 364355316
Web Site: https://www.dentsusciencejam.com
Research Science Field Services
N.A.I.C.S.: 541713

Dentsu Soken Inc   (1)
2-17-1 Konan, Minato-ku, Tokyo, 108-0075, Japan
Tel.: (81) 367136111
Web Site: https://www.dentsusoken.com
Rev.: $1,011,090,720
Assets: $945,330,970
Liabilities: $357,066,580
Net Worth: $588,264,390
Earnings: $103,960,670
Emp.: 3,652
Fiscal Year-end: 12/31/2023
Information Technology Consulting Services
N.A.I.C.S.: 541512
Akira Kobayashi (Sr Mng Dir)

Subsidiary (Non-US):

ISI-Dentsu Shanghai Co., Ltd   (2)
Room 1101-1106 Hongyi Plaza 288 Jiujiang Road, Shanghai, 200001, China
Tel.: (86) 21 6360 0216
Web Site: http://www.isid.com.cn
Computer Software Distr
N.A.I.C.S.: 423430

ISI-Dentsu South East Asia Pte. Ltd.   (2)
80 Robinson Road 15-01, Singapore, 68898, Singapore
Tel.: (65) 65117088
Web Site: https://www.isidsea.com
Sales Range: $25-49.9 Million
Emp.: 15
Information Technology Consulting Services
N.A.I.C.S.: 541512

ISI-Dentsu of Europe, Ltd.   (2)
City Point 1 Ropemaker Street, London, EC2Y 9HT, United Kingdom
Tel.: (44) 2071531650

Web Site: https://www.iside.co.uk
Financial Software Development Services
N.A.I.C.S.: 541511

ISI-Dentsu of Hong Kong, Ltd.   (2)
Unit A - B 22/F AXA Southside 38 Wong Chuk Hang Road, Hong Kong, 999077, China (Hong Kong)
Tel.: (852) 28290829
Web Site: http://www.isid.hk
Sales Range: $25-49.9 Million
Emp.: 20
Information Technology Consulting Services
N.A.I.C.S.: 519290

Subsidiary (Domestic):

ISID Assist, Ltd.   (2)
2-17-1 Konan, Minato-ku, Tokyo, 108-0075, Japan
Tel.: (81) 367139800
Web Site: http://www.dentsu.com
Business Support Services
N.A.I.C.S.: 561499

ISID Fairness, Ltd.   (2)
1F Komatsu Building 3-3-2 Kyobashi, Chuo-ku, Tokyo, 104-0031, Japan
Tel.: (81) 352021010
Web Site: https://www.fairness.co.jp
Online Financial Information Services
N.A.I.C.S.: 513199

ISID InterTechnologies, Ltd.   (2)
2-17-1 Konan, Minato-ku, Tokyo, 108-0075, Japan
Tel.: (81) 367135111
Web Site: https://www.isid-intertech.co.jp
Emp.: 503
Software Development Services
N.A.I.C.S.: 541511

ISID-AO, Ltd.   (2)
Keio Shinagawa Building 2-17-1 Konan, Minato, Tokyo, 108-0075, Japan
Tel.: (81) 367135900
Web Site: https://www.isid-ao.co.jp
Emp.: 476
IT Support & Resource Management Services
N.A.I.C.S.: 561990
Takeshi Ichikawa (Pres)

iTiD Consulting, Ltd.   (2)
2-17-1 Konan, Minato-ku, Tokyo, 108-0075, Japan
Tel.: (81) 3 6713 5700
Web Site: http://www.itid.co.jp
Information Technology Consulting Services
N.A.I.C.S.: 541512
Atsushi Yoshimoto (Pres & CEO)

Dentsu Solari Inc.   (1)
1-8-1 Higashi-shimbashi, Minato-ku, Tokyo, 105-7001, Japan
Tel.: (81) 362172222
Web Site: https://www.dentsu-sol.co.jp
Emp.: 123
Investment Holding Company Services
N.A.I.C.S.: 551112

Dentsu Sports Partners Inc.   (1)
1-8-1 Higashi-shimbashi, Minato-ku, Tokyo, 105-7001, Japan
Tel.: (81) 362171230
Web Site: http://www.dentsu-sp.co.jp
Sporting Events Operation Services
N.A.I.C.S.: 711310

Dentsu Table Media Communications Inc   (1)
6th Floor Table Media Center 2-21 Ichigaya Honmura-cho, Shinjuku-ku, Tokyo, 162-0845, Japan
Tel.: (81) 3 5227 5450
Web Site: http://www.dentsu.com
Advertising Consulting Services
N.A.I.C.S.: 541890

Dentsu West Japan Inc.   (1)
16th Floor Nakanoshima Festival Tower West Building 3-2-4 Nakanoshima, Kita-ku, Osaka, 530-8228, Japan
Tel.: (81) 664848840
Web Site: https://www.dentsu-west-j.co.jp
Emp.: 167
Advertising Agency
N.A.I.C.S.: 541810

Dentsu Works Inc.   (1)
4th Floor Kosan Building 3 2-16-7 Ginza,

Chuo-ku, Tokyo, 104-8106, Japan
Tel.: (81) 3 5551 8111
Web Site: http://www.dentsu-works.co.jp
Real Estate Manangement Services
N.A.I.C.S.: 531390

Dentsu, Sudler & Hennessey Inc. (1)
Tsukiji Eto Bldg 1-12-6 Tsukiji, Chuo-ku, Tokyo, 104-8427, Japan
Tel.: (81) 335460463
Web Site: http://www.dsh.co.jp
Rev.: $98,000,000
Emp.: 77
Marketing Communication in General Healthcare
N.A.I.C.S.: 541613

Digital Egg Inc. (1)
3-15-8 Ginza, Chuo-ku, Tokyo, 104-0061, Japan
Tel.: (81) 355650801
Web Site: https://www.digitalegg.co.jp
Emp.: 65
Advertising Communication Services
N.A.I.C.S.: 541810

Drill Inc. (1)
19-5 Udagawa-cho, Shibuya-ku, Tokyo, 150-0042, Japan
Tel.: (81) 354288771
Web Site: https://www.drill-inc.jp
Emp.: 10
Strategy, Advertising, Promotion, Content, Product, Event & Public Relations
N.A.I.C.S.: 541810
Jun Nishida *(Chief Content Officer)*

Estech Corp. (1)
6-50-1 Hon-cho, Naka-ku, Yokohama, 231-8315, Kanagawa, Japan
Tel.: (81) 456611661
Web Site: https://www.estech.co.jp
Emp.: 75
Software Services
N.A.I.C.S.: 541511

Hokkaido Ballpark Corporation (1)
1 Hitsujigaoka, Toyohira-ku, Sapporo, 062-0045, Hokkaido, Japan
Tel.: (81) 18573111
Advertising Communication Services
N.A.I.C.S.: 541810

IPG Inc. (1)
Shiodome East Side Building 6F Tsukiji 5-4-18, Chuo-ku, Tokyo, 104-0045, Japan
Tel.: (81) 335442811
Web Site: https://www.ipg.co.jp
Emp.: 67
Advertising Communication Services
N.A.I.C.S.: 541810

ISID Business Consulting, Ltd. (1)
2-17-1 Konan, Minato-ku, Tokyo, 108-0075, Japan
Tel.: (81) 367135555
Web Site: http://www.isidbc.co.jp
Digital Business Services
N.A.I.C.S.: 561439

Interlogics, Inc. (1)
4th Floor Hamarikyu Kensetsu Plaza 5-5-12 Tsukiji, Chuo-ku, Tokyo, 104-0045, Japan
Tel.: (81) 3 3544 0931
Web Site: http://www.interlogics.co.jp
Marketing Information Technology Consulting Services
N.A.I.C.S.: 541512

JEB Co., Ltd. (1)
9F Sumitomo Hamamatsucho Bldg 1-18-16 Hamamatsucho, Minato-ku, Tokyo, 105-0013, Japan
Tel.: (81) 364309588
Web Site: http://www.jeb.co.jp
Sales Range: $25-49.9 Million
Emp.: 5
Entertainment Event Planning Services
N.A.I.C.S.: 711310
Hisao Noguchi *(Pres & CEO)*

Kanagawa Kaihatsu Kankou (1)
26 Oike-cho, Asahi-ku, Yokohama, 241-0834, Kanagawa, Japan
Tel.: (81) 453511241
Advertising Communication Services
N.A.I.C.S.: 541810

Kyodo News PR Wire (1)
9th Floor Shiodome Media Tower 1-7-1

Higashi-shimbashi, Minato-ku, Tokyo, 105-7208, Japan
Tel.: (81) 362526040
Advertising Communication Services
N.A.I.C.S.: 541810

Live Board, Inc. (1)
7th Floor Daiwa Aoyama Building 3-1-30 Jingumae, Shibuya-ku, Tokyo, 150-0001, Japan
Tel.: (81) 358430932
Web Site: https://corp.liveboard.co.jp
Emp.: 47
Advertising Communication Services
N.A.I.C.S.: 541810

Magaport, Inc. (1)
7th Floor Alive Nanpeidai Bldg 16-11 Nanpeidai, Shibuya-ku, Tokyo, 150-0036, Japan
Tel.: (81) 354597076
Advertising Communication Services
N.A.I.C.S.: 541810

My Data Intelligence Inc. (1)
M-Square Bright 11F 1-9-5 Shimbashi, Minato-ku, Tokyo, 105-0004, Japan
Tel.: (81) 362578550
Web Site: http://www.mydata-intelligence.co.jp
Management Consulting Services
N.A.I.C.S.: 541618

My Theater D.D. Inc. (1)
MG Shirokanedai Bldg 7F 5-12-7 Shirokanedai, Minato-ku, Tokyo, 108-0071, Japan
Tel.: (81) 366811074
Web Site: https://www.mytheaterdd.com
Advertising Communication Services
N.A.I.C.S.: 541810

Nagano Ad Bureau Inc. (1)
1-53 Nakagosho, Nagano, 380-0935, Japan
Tel.: (81) 262918600
Advertising Communication Services
N.A.I.C.S.: 541810

Nakahata Inc. (1)
602 ARK Hills Front Tower Rop 2-23-1 Akasaka, Minato-ku, Tokyo, 107-0052, Japan
Tel.: (81) 3 3587 2008
Web Site: http://www.dentsu.com
Advertising Services
N.A.I.C.S.: 541810

OOH Media Solution, Inc. (1)
1-8-1 Higashi-shimbashi, Minato-ku, Tokyo, 105-7001, Japan
Tel.: (81) 362171100
Web Site: https://www.ooh-ms.co.jp
Outdoor Advertising Services
N.A.I.C.S.: 541850
Brendon Cook *(CEO)*

One Sky Inc. (1)
Root Azabujuban 902 1-4-1 Azabujuban, Minato-ku, Tokyo, 106-0045, Japan
Tel.: (81) 369133130
Web Site: https://www.oneskyinc.com
Emp.: 3
N.A.I.C.S.: 541810
Jun Nakagawa *(Gen Mgr)*

PR Consulting Dentsu Inc. (1)
1-8-1, Higashi-shimbashi,, Minato-ku, Tokyo, 105-7001, Japan
Tel.: (81) 362168980
Web Site: https://www.dentsuprc.com
Emp.: 280
Public Relations Agency
N.A.I.C.S.: 541820
Takamasa Yamaguchi *(Pres & CEO)*

Pict Inc. (1)
Shiodome Eastside Bldg 8F 5-4-18 Tsukiji, Chuo-ku, Tokyo, 104-0045, Japan
Tel.: (81) 3 5551 9250
Web Site: http://www.pict-inc.co.jp
Motion Picture & Video Production Services
N.A.I.C.S.: 512110

REWIND INC. (1)
Azabu KF Bldg 1-9-7 Azabu Juban, Minato-ku, Tokyo, 106 0045, Japan
Tel.: (81) 3 5574 8531
Sales Range: $25-49.9 Million
Emp.: 5
N.A.I.C.S.: 541810
Tom Fenwick-Smith *(Dir-Creative)*

Shingata Inc. (1)

5F Minami Aoyama Building 6-12-1 Minami-aoyama, Minato-ku, Tokyo, 107-0062, Japan
Tel.: (81) 3 3407 3261
Sales Range: $25-49.9 Million
Graphic Design, Production
N.A.I.C.S.: 541810
Hiroshi Sasaki *(Pres)*

Shiodome Urban Energy Corp. (1)
3rd Floor Shiodome Annex Bldg 1-8-3 Higashi-shimbashi, Minato-ku, Tokyo, 105-0021, Japan
Tel.: (81) 355680881
Advertising Communication Services
N.A.I.C.S.: 541810

Supership Holdings Co., Ltd. (1)
Tatsumura Aoyama Building 5-4-35 Minami-aoyama, Minato-ku, Tokyo, 107-0062, Japan
Tel.: (81) 363656758
Advertising Communication Services
N.A.I.C.S.: 541810

TVer Inc (1)
6th Floor Shimbashi Marine Bldg 2-19-10 Shimbashi, Minato-ku, Tokyo, 105-0004, Japan
Tel.: (81) 335691800
Web Site: https://tver.co.jp
Advertising Communication Services
N.A.I.C.S.: 541810

Tag Worldwide Group Limited (1)
55 Wells Street, London, W1A 3AE, United Kingdom
Tel.: (44) 2072514571
Web Site: https://www.tagww.com
Software Development Services
N.A.I.C.S.: 541511

Subsidiary (Domestic):

Tag Creative Limited (2)
Ground Floor 44 Pear Tree Street, London, EC1V 3SF, United Kingdom
Tel.: (44) 20 3217 2325
Web Site: http://www.tagcreative.com
Emp.: 2
Advertising Agencies
N.A.I.C.S.: 541810
Liam Church *(Mng Dir)*

Tag Europe Limited (2)
29 Clerkenwell Road, London, EC1M 5TA, United Kingdom
Tel.: (44) 20 7251 4571
Production & Design Agency Services
N.A.I.C.S.: 541490

Subsidiary (Non-US):

Tag Germany GmbH (2)
Ganghofer Strasse 70, 80339, Munich, Germany
Tel.: (49) 89 3090757 25
Web Site: http://www.tagworldwide.com
Sales Range: $25-49.9 Million
Emp.: 30
Video Production Services
N.A.I.C.S.: 512199

Tag India Private Limited (2)
6th Floor DLF Plaza Tower DLF Phase 1, Gurgaon, 122002, India
Tel.: (91) 124 484 3950
Sales Range: $25-49.9 Million
Video Production Services
N.A.I.C.S.: 512199

Tag MENA FZE (2)
Units No 2702 & 2703 Tiffany Tower Plot No W2 Jum00eirah Lake Towers, PO Box 211274, Dubai, 211274, United Arab Emirates
Tel.: (971) 4 4214602
Web Site: http://www.tagworldwide.com
Emp.: 20
Advertising Agencies
N.A.I.C.S.: 541810

Subsidiary (Domestic):

Tag NewCo Limited (2)
29 Clerkenwell Rd, London, EC1M 5TA, United Kingdom
Tel.: (44) 20 7251 4571
Web Site: http://www.tagworldwide.com
Financial Investment Services
N.A.I.C.S.: 523999

Tag Print Services Limited (2)
3-4 Bakers Yard Baker's Row, London, EC1R 3DD, United Kingdom
Tel.: (44) 20 7837 0123
Graphic Design Services
N.A.I.C.S.: 541430

Tag Response Limited (2)
All Gate Tower 2 Leman Street Floor 11, London, E18FA, United Kingdom
Tel.: (44) 20 7833 6370
Web Site: http://www.tag-response.com
Production Design Agency Services
N.A.I.C.S.: 541490
Mikael Pasco *(Mng Dir)*

Subsidiary (Non-US):

Tag Sao Paulo Servico de Consultoria Ltda. (2)
Rua Fidalga 593 - cj 4 e 6 Vila Madalena, Sao Paulo, 05432-070, Brazil
Tel.: (55) 11 3093 8040
Web Site: http://www.tagworlwide.com
Sales Range: $25-49.9 Million
Emp.: 13
Graphic Design Services
N.A.I.C.S.: 541430
Juliana d'Alambert *(Dir-Client Svcs)*

Tag Worldwide (Shanghai) Co Ltd (2)
Unit 201-202 Building D Red Town 570 Huai Hai Xi Road, Shanghai, 200052, China
Tel.: (86) 21 5254 0158
Web Site: http://www.tagworldwide.com
Sales Range: $10-24.9 Million
Emp.: 20
Advertising Agencies
N.A.I.C.S.: 541810

Tag Worldwide (Singapore) Pte. Ltd. (2)
51 Cantonment Road, Singapore, 89752, Singapore
Tel.: (65) 6227 9177
Web Site: http://www.tagworlwide.com
Sales Range: $25-49.9 Million
Video Production Services
N.A.I.C.S.: 512199
Melissa Chan *(Dir-Bus-APAC)*

Subsidiary (US):

Tag Worldwide (USA) Inc. (2)
75 Spring St 3nd Fl, New York, NY 10012
Tel.: (212) 625-6250
Web Site: http://www.tagworldwide.com
Sales Range: $25-49.9 Million
Production & Design Agency Services
N.A.I.C.S.: 541490
Nick Smart *(VP)*

Subsidiary (Non-US):

Tag Worldwide Australia Pty Ltd. (2)
Level 1 4 Bank Place, Melbourne, VIC, Australia
Tel.: (61) 3 9822 3091
Advertising Services
N.A.I.C.S.: 541810

Subsidiary (Domestic):

Tag Worldwide Holdings Limited (2)
82 St John Street, London, EC1M 4JN, United Kingdom
Tel.: (44) 20 7336 6316
Investment Management Service
N.A.I.C.S.: 523940

World Writers Limited (2)
29 Clerkenwell Road, London, EC1M 5TA, United Kingdom
Tel.: (44) 20 3217 2220
Web Site: http://www.worldwriters.com
Sales Range: $150-199.9 Million
Advertising Agencies
N.A.I.C.S.: 541810

The Goal Inc. (1)
kojun Building 6F 6-8-7 Ginza, Chuo-ku, Tokyo, 104-0061, Japan
Tel.: (81) 355375006
Web Site: https://www.thegoal.jp
Emp.: 70
Media Buying Services
N.A.I.C.S.: 541810
Taketsugu Akatsuka *(Pres)*

Video Research Interactive Inc. (1)

Dentsu Group Inc.—(Continued)

7F 6-17 Sanbancho, Chiyoda-ku, Tokyo, 102-0075, Japan
Tel.: (81) 352263281
Web Site: https://www.videoi.co.jp
Advertising Communication Services
N.A.I.C.S.: 541810

Video Research Ltd. (1)
6-17 Sanban-cho, Chiyoda-ku, Tokyo, 102-0075, Japan
Tel.: (81) 358601711
Web Site: https://www.videor.co.jp
Emp.: 346
Advertising Communication Services
N.A.I.C.S.: 541810

Watson-Crick Inc. (1)
4-14-12 Nishi-azabu, Minato-ku, Tokyo, 106-0031, Japan
Tel.: (81) 3 6419 1958
Advertising Campaign Planning Services
N.A.I.C.S.: 541890
Masaki Akama (Office Mgr)

Wunderman Dentsu Inc. (1)
Comodio Shiodome 2-14-1 Higashi-shimbashi Minataku, Minato-ku, Tokyo, 105-0021, Japan
Tel.: (81) 3 6430 8000
Web Site: http://www.wunderman-d.com
Emp.: 40
Direct & Relationship Marketing Services
N.A.I.C.S.: 541613
Kensuke Noguchi (Pres)

Yamagata Ad Bureau Corp. (1)
4-16-18 Nanoka-cho, Yamagata, 990-0042, Japan
Tel.: (81) 236412160
Web Site: https://www.y-ab.co.jp
Emp.: 27
Advertising Communication Services
N.A.I.C.S.: 541810

Yokohama Super Factory Co., Ltd. (1)
1-11 Suehiro-cho, Tsurumi-ku, Yokohama, 230-0045, Kanagawa, Japan
Tel.: (81) 45 506 8181
Web Site: http://www.y-s-f.co.jp
Emp.: 103
Film Studio Operating Services
N.A.I.C.S.: 541921

bless you inc. (1)
Nishirei Higashi Ginza Residence 1907 6-19-21 Tsukiji, Chuo-ku, Tokyo, 104-0045, Japan
Tel.: (81) 335451081
Sales Range: $25-49.9 Million
Emp.: 8
N.A.I.C.S.: 541810
Nobuo Hirano (Mgr)

dof inc. (1)
1-9-1 Shimbashi Kitagawa Bldg 6F, Minato-ku, Tokyo, 105-0004, Japan
Tel.: (81) 355375125
Web Site: https://www.dof.jp
Emp.: 8
Advertising Services
N.A.I.C.S.: 541810
Taro Saito (CEO)

DENYO CO., LTD.

Denyo Co Ltd 2-8-5 Nihonbashi Horidome-cho, Chuo-ku, Tokyo, 103-8566, Japan
Tel.: (81) 368611111
Web Site: https://www.denyo.co.jp
Year Founded: 1948
6517—(TKS)
Rev.: $483,455,400
Assets: $664,569,400
Liabilities: $163,247,170
Net Worth: $501,322,230
Earnings: $33,677,950
Emp.: 1,408
Fiscal Year-end: 03/31/24
Engine-Driven Generators, Welders & Air Compressors Mfr & Sales
N.A.I.C.S.: 335312
Shoichi Shiratori (Pres)

Subsidiaries:

Denyo America Corporation (1)

1450 Minor Rd, Danville, KY 40422
Tel.: (859) 236-7009
Emp.: 2
Other Holding Companies Offices
N.A.I.C.S.: 551112

Denyo Europe B.V. (1)
Naamrijk 1, 3454 PX, De Meern, Netherlands
Tel.: (31) 30 666 8314
Diesel Engine Driven Generator Mfr
N.A.I.C.S.: 333618
Kenichi Otomo (Pres)

Denyo Kosan Co., Ltd. (1)
2-8-5 Nihombashi Horidome-cho, Chuo-Ku, Tokyo, 103-8566, Japan
Tel.: (81) 368610011
Web Site: https://www.denyo.co.jp
Emp.: 36
Industrial Machinery Distr
N.A.I.C.S.: 423830

Denyo Manufacturing Corporation (1)
1450 Minor Rd, Danville, KY 40422
Tel.: (859) 236-3405
Web Site: https://www.denyo.co.jp
Sales Range: $25-49.9 Million
Emp.: 196
Motor & Generator Mfr
N.A.I.C.S.: 335312
Kenji Yamamichi (Pres, CEO & Chm)

Denyo Trading Co Ltd (1)
2-8-5 Nihombashi-horidomecho, Chuo-ku, Tokyo, 103-0012, Japan (100%)
Tel.: (81) 368610055
Web Site: http://www.denyo.co.jp
Sales Range: $75-99.9 Million
Emp.: 200
Electrical Apparatus & Equipment Wiring Supplies & Construction Material Whslr
N.A.I.C.S.: 423610
Shigeru Koga (Chm & Pres)

Denyo United Machinery Pte Ltd. (1)
No 9 Neythal Road, Singapore, 628614, Singapore
Tel.: (65) 68622301
Web Site: https://sg.denyogroup.com
Sales Range: $25-49.9 Million
Emp.: 30
Industrial Machinery Whslr
N.A.I.C.S.: 423830
Sebastian Koh (Mgr-Sls)

Denyo Vietnam Co., Ltd. (1)
Plot A3Thang Long Industrial Park II, Lieu Xa Commune Yen My District, Hung Yen, Vietnam
Tel.: (84) 221 397 4777
Emp.: 218
Electric Motor Mfr
N.A.I.C.S.: 335312
Taizo Mizuno (Gen Dir)

New Japan Machinery Co. Ltd. (1)
Dai-ichi Life Building 3-6-5 Shin-Yokohama, Kohoku-ku, Yokohama, 222-0033, Kanagawa, Japan
Tel.: (81) 454734011
Web Site: https://www.njm.co.jp
Sales Range: $100-124.9 Million
Emp.: 240
Sales & Rental Service of Industrial Electrical Machinery
N.A.I.C.S.: 532490

Nishihatsu Co., Ltd. (1)
140 Chichika, Karatsu, 847-0831, Saga, Japan
Tel.: (81) 95 578 1115
Web Site: https://nishihatsu.co.jp
Emp.: 197
Electrical Appliance Whslr
N.A.I.C.S.: 423620

Nishinihon Generator Mfg. Co., Ltd. (1)
140 Chichika, Karatsu, 847-0831, Japan
Tel.: (81) 955781115
Web Site: http://www.nishihatsu.co.jp
Sales Range: $50-74.9 Million
Emp.: 140
Industrial Electrical Machinery Mfr & Distr
N.A.I.C.S.: 333248

P.T. Dein Prima Generator (1)
Jl Sultan Agung Km 28 Medan Satria

Bekasi Barat, 17132, Bekasi, Jawa Barat, Indonesia
Tel.: (62) 21 885 4410
Web Site: https://dein.co.id
Electric Motor Mfr
N.A.I.C.S.: 335312

DEODATO GALLERY S.P.A.

Via Santa Marta 6 MM Duomo, Milan, Italy
Tel.: (39) 0280886294
Web Site: https://www.deodato.art
Year Founded: 2010
ART—(EUR)
Online Shopping Services
N.A.I.C.S.: 459999
Deodato Salafia (Chm)

DEOGYUSAN RESORT CO., LTD.

Manseon-lo 185 Seolcheon-myeon, Muju-gun, Jeonbuk, 568-811, Korea (South)
Tel.: (82) 633229000
Web Site: http://www.mdysresort.com
Emp.: 300
Resort
N.A.I.C.S.: 721110
Kimto Yeal (Mgr-Sls)

DEP DISTRIBUTION EXCLUSIVE LTEE

7255 Rue Alexandra Ste 200, Montreal, H2R 2Y9, QC, Canada
Tel.: (514) 274-2040
Compact Discs, Cassettes, Videos & DVDs Distr
N.A.I.C.S.: 423990
Maurice Courtois (Pres)

DEPA PLC

Dubai Investment Park 1 Plot No 598 655, PO Box 213537, Dubai, United Arab Emirates
Tel.: (971) 48216666   AE
Web Site: https://www.depa.com
Year Founded: 1996
DEPA—(NASDAQDBAI)
Rev.: $249,825,160
Assets: $310,117,460
Liabilities: $195,058,520
Net Worth: $115,058,940
Earnings: $16,087,020
Emp.: 2,800
Fiscal Year-end: 12/31/22
Interior Design Services
N.A.I.C.S.: 541410
David Holiday (Chief Legal Officer & Sec)

Subsidiaries:

Carrara Mid-East Industrial Co. LLC (1)
Street No 36 Community 599, PO Box 3565, Jebel Ali, Dubai, United Arab Emirates
Tel.: (971) 42858277
Emp.: 1,000
Construction Materials Mfr
N.A.I.C.S.: 327999

DSG (Thailand) Co., Ltd. (1)
Bhiraj Tower at Sathon No 33 31 Unit B 1 4 B 1 5 South Sathorn Rd, Yannawa Sathorn, Bangkok, 10120, Thailand
Tel.: (66) 22128100
Wood Raw Material Mfr
N.A.I.C.S.: 321999

DSG Manufacturing Malaysia Sdn. Bhd. (1)
PLO 44 Kawasan Perindustrian Senai, Senai, Johor Bahru, Malaysia
Tel.: (60) 75986363
Wood Raw Material Mfr
N.A.I.C.S.: 321999

DSG Projects Malaysia Sdn. Bhd. (1)
10th Floor South Block Wisma Golden

Eagle Realty 142A Jalan Ampang, 50450, Kuala Lumpur, Malaysia
Tel.: (60) 321819339
Real Estate Management
N.A.I.C.S.: 321999
AKRizal Arashid (Country Mgr-Bus Dev)

Deco Emirates Company LLC (1)
PO Box 19238, Dubai, 1, United Arab Emirates
Tel.: (971) 48854660
Web Site: https://www.decoemirates.com
Sales Range: $100-124.9 Million
Emp.: 30
Interior Contracting Services & Furniture Mfr
N.A.I.C.S.: 541410

Decolight Trading Co. LLC (1)
PO Box 62162, Dubai, United Arab Emirates
Tel.: (971) 42834346
Web Site: http://www.decolightllc.com
Emp.: 50
Lighting Fixture Supplier
N.A.I.C.S.: 423220

Depa Al Barakah L.L.C. (1)
5th Floor NASA Bldg Al Maktoum St, PO Box 117357, Dubai, United Arab Emirates
Tel.: (971) 42222259
Sales Range: $75-99.9 Million
Emp.: 40
Interior Designing Services
N.A.I.C.S.: 541410
Yasser Abdel Azeem (Gen Mgr)

Depa Egypt (1)
2 W El Mosheer Ahmed Ismail St 1158 Sheraton Heliopolis, Cairo, Egypt
Tel.: (20) 2 2268 6770
Emp.: 4
Interior Designing Services
N.A.I.C.S.: 541410
Essam Shoukry (Gen Mgr)

Depa India Pvt. Ltd. (1)
203 Satellite Silver Bldg Andheri-Kurla Rd Marol, Andheri E, Mumbai, 400 059, India
Tel.: (91) 2240521234
Sales Range: $25-49.9 Million
Emp.: 25
Interior Designing Services
N.A.I.C.S.: 541410
Ali Malas (Mng Dir)

Depa Interiors L.L.C. (1)
1604 16th Floor Al Reem Tower Al Maktoum Street, Dubai, United Arab Emirates
Tel.: (971) 42243800
Web Site: http://www.depa.com
Sales Range: $25-49.9 Million
Emp.: 20
Interior Design Services
N.A.I.C.S.: 541410

Depa Jordan (1)
3rd Floor 165 Abu Tawileh Plaza Mecca St, PO Box 3233, Amman, 11953, Jordan
Tel.: (962) 6 551 6511
Sales Range: $25-49.9 Million
Emp.: 6
Interior Designing Services
N.A.I.C.S.: 541410
Fuad Azab (Gen Mgr)

Depa Qatar Co. W.L.L. (1)
Al Jassim Commercial Tower 7th Floor Suhaim Bin Hamad Street, C Ring Road, Doha, 22931, Qatar
Tel.: (974) 44436759
Web Site: http://www.depa.com
Sales Range: $75-99.9 Million
Emp.: 310
Interior Designing Services
N.A.I.C.S.: 541410

Depa Saudi Arabia (1)
Hail Street Abu ALHasan Building 2nd Floor, PO Box 136528, Jeddah, 21313, Saudi Arabia
Tel.: (966) 2 614 5866
Emp.: 25
Interior Designing Services
N.A.I.C.S.: 541410
Amer Rihawi (Gen Mgr)

Depa UK Limited (1)
4 River Court Brighouse Business Village River Park Industrial Estate, Middlesbrough, TS2 1RT, United Kingdom
Tel.: (44) 1642243857

Web Site: http://www.depa.com
Interior Designing Services
N.A.I.C.S.: 541410

**Eldiar Furniture Manufacturing and
Decoration L.L.C.** (1)
Sector 21 Plot 22 Street 10, PO Box 6687,
Mussafah Industrial Area, Abu Dhabi,
United Arab Emirates
Tel.: (971) 25555656
Web Site: https://www.eldiarfurniture.com
Emp.: 50
Wooden Furniture Mfr
N.A.I.C.S.: 337122

Mivan Depa Contracting L.L.C. (1)
306-310 Wing A Dubai Silicon Oasis Head-
quarters Bldg Nad Al Sheeba, PO Box
182605, Dubai, United Arab Emirates
Tel.: (971) 4 3724085
Web Site: http://www.depa.com
Interior Designing Services
N.A.I.C.S.: 541410

Vedder GmbH (1)
Industriestr 3, 59348, Ludinghausen, Ger-
many
Tel.: (49) 25919290
Web Site: https://www.vedder.net
Emp.: 400
Interior Designing Services
N.A.I.C.S.: 541410
Nicolas Held (Mng Dir)

DEPO AUTO PARTS IND. CO., LTD.
No 20-3 Nan Shin lane Lu kang
Chen, Chang-Hua, 10084, Taiwan
Tel.: (886) 47722311
Web Site: https://www.depo.com.tw
Year Founded: 1977
6605—(TAI)
Rev.: $606,726,620
Assets: $1,042,797,796
Liabilities: $471,036,968
Net Worth: $571,760,827
Earnings: $76,751,101
Emp.: 4,000
Fiscal Year-end: 12/31/23
Automotive Products Mfr
N.A.I.C.S.: 334419

Subsidiaries:

Maxzone Auto Parts Corp. (1)
15889 Slover Ave Unit A, Fontana, CA
92337
Tel.: (909) 822-3288
Web Site: https://www.maxzone.com
Warehouse Product Distr
N.A.I.C.S.: 493110

DEPORTES CLUB GOLF SAN-TIAGO SA
Presidente Riesco 3700, Santiago,
3700, Chile
Tel.: (56) 12313406
Year Founded: 1985
GOLF—(SGO)
Sales Range: Less than $1 Million
Sport Club & Recreation Centre Ser-
vices
N.A.I.C.S.: 713940
Felix Julio Bacigalupo Vicuna (Chm)

DEPOSIT INSURANCE COR-PORATION OF JAPAN
9th Floor Shin-Yurakucho Bldg 1-12-1
Yurakucho, Chiyoda-ku, Tokyo, 100-
0006, Japan
Tel.: (81) 332126030
Web Site: http://www.dic.go.jp
Year Founded: 1971
Sales Range: $5-14.9 Billion
Emp.: 412
Financial Safety Net Provider & Fi-
nancial Assistance Operator Services
N.A.I.C.S.: 541611
Masanori Tanabe (Deputy Governor)

Subsidiaries:

Corporation for Revitalizing
Earthquake-Affected Business (1)

4-6-1 Ichibancho Sendai Daiichi Seimei
Tower Bldg1, Aoba-ku, Sendai, 980-0811,
Japan
Tel.: (81) 223938808
Finance & Banking Services
N.A.I.C.S.: 522110
Norito Ikeda (Pres)

**Regional Economy Vitalization Corpo-
ration of Japan** (1)
9th Floor Otemachi Building 1-6-1
Otemachi, Chiyoda-ku, Tokyo, 100-0004,
Japan
Tel.: (81) 3 6266 0310
Investment Advisory Services
N.A.I.C.S.: 523940

DEPOTS PETROLIERS DE FOS
Z I Secteur 81 818 l'Audience,
13270, Fos-sur-Mer, France
Tel.: (33) 442476577
Rev.: $21,600,000
Emp.: 70
General Warehousing & Storage
N.A.I.C.S.: 493110
Claire Jourdan (Mgr)

DEPPON LOGISTICS CO., LTD.
No 1018 Mingzhu Road Xujing Town,
Qingpu District, Shanghai, 201702,
China
Tel.: (86) 95353
Web Site: https://www.deppon.com
Year Founded: 1996
603056—(SHG)
Rev.: $4,407,372,735
Assets: $2,109,554,731
Liabilities: $1,137,368,550
Net Worth: $972,186,181
Earnings: $91,086,564
Emp.: 120,000
Fiscal Year-end: 12/31/22
Logistic Services
N.A.I.C.S.: 541614
Hu Wei (Chm)

DERDAP TURIST A.D.
Dunavska 5, 19320, Kladovo, Serbia
Tel.: (381) 19 80 10 10
Web Site:
  http://www.hoteldjerdap.com
Year Founded: 1972
DJTR—(BEL)
Sales Range: $1-9.9 Million
Home Management Services
N.A.I.C.S.: 721110
Zeljko Bolbotinovic (Exec Dir)

DEREK POBJOY INVEST-MENTS LTD.
Millennia House Kingswood Park
Bonsor Dr, Kingswood, KT20 6AY,
Surrey, United Kingdom
Tel.: (44) 737818181
Web Site: http://www.pobjoy.com
Sales Range: $25-49.9 Million
Emp.: 45
Holding Company
N.A.I.C.S.: 551112
Derek Pobjoy (Chm)

Subsidiaries:

Pobjoy Mint Ltd. (1)
Millennia House Kingswood Pk Bonsor Dr,
Kingswood, KT20 6AY, Surrey, United King-
dom
Tel.: (44) 1737818181
Web Site: http://www.pobjoy.com
Sales Range: $25-49.9 Million
Emp.: 40
Precious Metal Jewelry Mfr
N.A.I.C.S.: 339910
Taya Pobjoy (Mng Dir)

DERICHEBOURG S.A.
119 Av du General Michel Bizot,
75579, Paris, Cedex 12, France
Tel.: (33) 144754040

Web Site:
  https://www.derichebourg.com
DBG—(EUR)
Rev.: $4,446,597,272
Assets: $3,027,980,072
Liabilities: $2,164,404,528
Net Worth: $863,575,544
Earnings: $215,556,120
Emp.: 41,337
Fiscal Year-end: 09/30/21
Environmental & Recycling Services;
Airport Support Services; Facilities
Management Services
N.A.I.C.S.: 562998
Daniel Derichebourg (Founder)

Subsidiaries:

**Atis Iberica Derichebourg Aero-
nautique SL** (1)
Edificio Renta Sevilla 3 D Avenida de la
Innovacion, 41020, Sevilla, Spain
Tel.: (34) 954519135
Web Site: https://www.derichebourg-
  aeroservices.com
Emp.: 700
Aeronautic Services
N.A.I.C.S.: 481219
Pablo Gonzalez Moyano (Mng Dir)

Bartin Recycling Group S.A.S. (1)
61 Rue Maurice Berteaux, La Courneuve,
93122, France
Tel.: (33) 1 49 92 69 00
Web Site: http://www.derichebourg.com
Waste Material Recycling Services
N.A.I.C.S.: 562998

CRS S.p.A. (1)
Corso Italia 1, 28010, Fontaneto D'Agogna,
NO, Italy
Tel.: (39) 0322864300
Plumbing Fixture Fitting & Trim Product Mfr
N.A.I.C.S.: 332913

DAL Zeitarbeit GmbH (1)
Butendeichsweg 2, 21129, Hamburg, Ger-
many
Tel.: (49) 40319770015
Web Site: http://www.dal-zeitarbeit.de
Employment Agency Services
N.A.I.C.S.: 561311
Ansgar Lauterbach (Mng Dir)

**Derichebourg Aeronautics Services
Germany GmbH** (1)
Butendeichsweg 2, 21129, Hamburg, Ger-
many
Tel.: (49) 4031977000
Web Site: https://derichebourg-
  aeroservices.com
Aeronautic Services
N.A.I.C.S.: 488190

Derichebourg Aqua SAS (1)
60 boulevard de L'Esches, 60110, Meru,
France
Tel.: (33) 139718717
Web Site: http://www.derichebourg-
  aqua.com
Waste Water Treatment Services
N.A.I.C.S.: 221320

Derichebourg Belgium NV (1)
Rue Georges Tourneur 194, Marchienne-
au-Pont, 6030, Charleroi, Belgium
Tel.: (32) 71298899
Web Site:
  http://www.derichebourgbelgium.be
Waste Management Services
N.A.I.C.S.: 562998

**Derichebourg Canada Environnement
Inc.** (1)
9000 boulevard Ray Lawson, Montreal, H1J
1K8, QC, Canada
Tel.: (514) 353-4372
Environmental Services
N.A.I.C.S.: 541620

Derichebourg Environnement (1)
119 Av du General Michel Bizot, 75579,
Paris, Cedex 12, France
Tel.: (33) 144754040
Web Site: http://www.derichebourg-
  environnement.com
Sales Range: $1-4.9 Billion
Emp.: 4,900
Scrap Metal Collector & Recycling Services

N.A.I.C.S.: 562998

Subsidiary (Domestic):

AFM Recyclage S.A. (2)
Siege Social Prairies de Courrejean, BP 8,
Chemin de Guitteronde, 33886, Villenave-
d'Ornon, France (99.81%)
Tel.: (33) 556877320
Scrap Metal Collector & Recycling Services
N.A.I.C.S.: 562998

Subsidiary (Domestic):

AFM Transport S.A. (3)
230 route de Roquefort RD 932, BP 96,
40090, Saint-Avit, France (99.81%)
Tel.: (33) 558754343
Web Site: http://www.derichebourg.com
Scrap Metal Collector & Recycling Services
N.A.I.C.S.: 562998

Subsidiary (Domestic):

Eco - PHU Holding (2)
119 Avenue Bizot, 75012, Paris, France
Tel.: (33) 144754040
Web Site: http://www.derichebourg.com
Holding Company
N.A.I.C.S.: 551112

Eska S.A.S. (2)
Siege Social - 56 rue de Metz, Jouy-aux-
Arches, 57130, Metz, France
Tel.: (33) 387604222
Sales Range: $75-99.9 Million
Emp.: 318
Scrap Metal Recycling
N.A.I.C.S.: 562998

Subsidiary (Domestic):

Marx Spaenlin SA (3)
42 Avenue de Suisse, BP 283, Illzach,
68316, France (100%)
Tel.: (33) 389310202
Sales Range: $10-24.9 Million
Emp.: 40
Scrap Metal Collection
N.A.I.C.S.: 562998
Thierry Konzem (Mng Dir)

Rohr SA (3)
172 rue du Ladhof, BP 1305, Colmar,
68013, France (50%)
Tel.: (33) 389210950
Scrap Metal Collection Services
N.A.I.C.S.: 562998
Thierry Kentzinger (Gen Mgr)

Subsidiary (Domestic):

Ferrotrade Sas (2)
Siege Social - 56 rue de Metz, Metz,
57130, France (100%)
Tel.: (33) 387604222
Web Site: http://www.derichebourg.com
Emp.: 2
Scrap Metal Collection Services
N.A.I.C.S.: 562998

Fricom Recycling (2)
26/28 Chemin Pave, 95340, Bernes-sur-
Oise, France
Tel.: (33) 134700320
Scrap Metal Collector & Recycling Services;
Owned 50% by Oeko-Service SA & 50% by
Derichebourg Environment
N.A.I.C.S.: 562998

Inorec S.A.S. (2)
54 Rue Ernest Macarez, 59300, Valenci-
ennes, 59300, France
Tel.: (33) 327303437
Scrap Metal Collector & Recycling Services
N.A.I.C.S.: 562998

Purfer SAS (2)
RD 147, Quartier de la Gare Saint-Pierre-
de-Chandieu, '69780, Saint-Symphorien-
d'Ozon, France (99.89%)
Tel.: (33) 472481250
Web Site: http://www.purfer.com
Waste Recovery Services
N.A.I.C.S.: 562920

Revival S.A.S. (2)
3 Av Marcellin Berthelot, ZI du Val de
Seine, 92390, Villeneuve-la-Garenne,
France
Tel.: (33) 140857700
Scrap Metal Collector & Recycling Services

Derichebourg S.A.—(Continued)

N.A.I.C.S.: 562998

Subsidiary (Domestic):

Bolton SARL (3)
90 Rue Des Rosiers, St Ouen sur Seine,
93400, Paris, France
Tel.: (33) 140115405
Scrap Metal Collector & Recycling Services
N.A.I.C.S.: 562998

Corepa S.N.C. (3)
119 Avenue Du Generale, 75579, Paris,
France
Tel.: (33) 144754040
Scrap Metal Collector & Recycling Services
N.A.I.C.S.: 562998

Fradena Transport (3)
3 Av Marcellin Berthelot ZI du Val de Seine,
92390, Villeneuve-la-Garenne,
France (100%)
Tel.: (33) 147984859
Transportation Support Services
N.A.I.C.S.: 488999
Alain Siebert (Chm)

Sas Du Petit Lac (3)
65 Boulevard Marechal Foch, Saint Gratien,
France
Tel.: (33) 391 923 356
Scrap Metal Collector & Recycling Services
N.A.I.C.S.: 562998

Valme Technologies SAS (3)
Zone Industrielle Route de la Hoguette, Fal-
aise, 14700, Caen, France
Tel.: (33) 231903040
Waste Management Services
N.A.I.C.S.: 562998

Subsidiary (Domestic):

SCI Quai De Norvege (3)
Activites Immobilieres, D'Autres Biens im-
mobiliers, 59880, Valenciennes, France
Tel.: (33) 327228402
Scrap Metal Collector & Recycling Services
N.A.I.C.S.: 562998

Strap Transport S.A.S. (2)
BP 8 Zone Industrielle No 4, Rue President
Lecuyer, Valenciennes, 59880, France
Tel.: (33) 327228400
Sales Range: $25-49.9 Million
Emp.: 200
Scrap Metal Collector & Recycling Services
N.A.I.C.S.: 562998

**Derichebourg Evolution Formation
EURL** (1)
3 rue Jules Vedrines, CS 24011, 31028,
Toulouse, Cedex, France
Tel.: (33) 562715180
Environmental Services
N.A.I.C.S.: 541620

**Derichebourg Medio Ambiente
SA** (1)
C/Quince nave 17 Pl La Red Sur, Alcala de
Guadaira, 41500, Seville, Spain
Tel.: (34) 955631345
Environmental Services
N.A.I.C.S.: 541620

Derichebourg Multiservices SAS (1)
DERICHEBOURG Tower 51 Chemin des
Meches, 94000, Creteil, Cedex,
France (100%)
Tel.: (33) 145134200
Web Site: https://www.derichebourg-
multiservices.com
Sales Range: $700-749.9 Million
Emp.: 20,700
Holding Company; Cleaning, Temporary
Staffing & Business Support Services
N.A.I.C.S.: 551112

Subsidiary (Domestic):

**Derichebourg Atis Aeronautique
SAS** (2)
Avenue Normangi Niemen, D'Activite De
L'Aeroport, 31700, Blagnac, France
Tel.: (33) 534606140
Web Site: http://www.derichebourg-atis.com
Sales Range: $500-549.9 Million
Emp.: 1,200

Aircraft Construction Process Services;
Manufacturing Preparation, Construction,
Assembly, Logistics, Quality Control & Tech-
nical Assistance
N.A.I.C.S.: 336411
Pascal Lannette (Mng Dir)

Subsidiary (Non-US):

Derichebourg Atis GmbH (3)
Klosterstrasse 22, 40211, Dusseldorf, Ger-
many
Tel.: (49) 21 11 64 11 44
Web Site: http://www.derichebourgde.com
Emp.: 10
Temp Services
N.A.I.C.S.: 561320
Dertela Cohen (Gen Mgr)

Subsidiary (Domestic):

Derichebourg Energie SA (2)
35 rue de Valenton, 94046, Creteil, Cedex,
France (99.8%)
Tel.: (33) 145134200
Sales Range: $50-74.9 Million
Emp.: 140
Electrical Engineering & Air Conditioning
Engineering
N.A.I.C.S.: 541330
Boris Derichebourg (Chm & CEO)

**Derichebourg Entreprises-Valerco -
Valren - Ecoval** (2)
119 Av du General Michel Bizot, 75579,
Paris, France
Tel.: (33) 144754040
Web Site: http://www.derichebourg.com
Metal Container Mfr
N.A.I.C.S.: 332439

Derichebourg Proprete SAS (2)
6 allee des Coquelicots, Boissy-Saint Leger,
Cedex, F-94478, France (100%)
Tel.: (33) 145106400
Cleaning Services; Hospital & Nuclear Facility Sanitation, Hotel, Transport & Workshops Cleaning & Waste Collection & Sorting
N.A.I.C.S.: 561210

Subsidiary (Domestic):

**Derichebourg Espaces Verts
SAS** (3)
Hameau de Saulxier 36-38 Grande Rue,
91160, Paris, France (100%)
Tel.: (33) 144926740
Landscaping Services
N.A.I.C.S.: 561730

Derichebourg Interim SAS (3)
41 rue La Fayette, 75009, Paris,
France (100%)
Tel.: (33) 142851802
Holding Company; Aeronautic Industry Tem-
porary Help Services
N.A.I.C.S.: 561320
Boris Derichebourg (Chm)

Subsidiary (Domestic):

**Derichebourg Interim Aeronautique
SAS** (4)
20 avenue Didier Daurat CS 14434, 31400,
Toulouse, Cedex, France
Tel.: (33) 5 62 71 51 80
Web Site: http://www.derichebourg.com
Aeronautic Industry Temporary Help Ser-
vices
N.A.I.C.S.: 561320

Subsidiary (Domestic):

ULTEAM Sarl (3)
31 avenue de Segur, 75007, Paris,
France (99.98%)
Tel.: (33) 970460045
Web Site: https://ulteam.eu
Public & Private Reception Services;
Switchboard & Mail Management
N.A.I.C.S.: 561210
Boris Derichebourg (Mgr)

**Derichebourg Recycling Mexico
SA** (1)
Av de las Torres No 258 antes 6 Col, Valle
de San Lorenzo-Iztapalapa, 09970, Mexico,
Mexico
Tel.: (52) 5558419801

Environmental Services
N.A.I.C.S.: 541620

**Derichebourg Recycling USA,
Inc.** (1)
8202 W Montgomery, Houston, TX 77088
Tel.: (281) 445-1132
Environmental Services
N.A.I.C.S.: 541620

Derichebourg SNG SAS (1)
84 bd de l'Europe, 69310, Pierre-Benite,
France
Tel.: (33) 472768935
Environmental Services
N.A.I.C.S.: 541620

**Derichebourg Sourcing Aero & En-
ergy SAS** (1)
27/29 avenue de Saint-Mande CS 71270,
Viviers du lac, 75579, Paris, France
Tel.: (33) 140052390
Environmental Services
N.A.I.C.S.: 541620

Subsidiary (Non-US):

**Derichebourg Aviation & Energy Re-
sources Ltd.** (2)
1 London Road, Ipswich, IP1 2HA, Suffolk,
United Kingdom
Tel.: (44) 1473252759
Environmental Services
N.A.I.C.S.: 541620

Derichebourg Technologies SAS (1)
22 Rue Alexandre Parodi, 75010, Paris,
France
Tel.: (33) 826101550
Environmental Services
N.A.I.C.S.: 541620

Derichebourg Umwelt GmbH (1)
Oststrasse 10, 40211, Dusseldorf, Germany
Tel.: (49) 21116410
Web Site: https://www.derichebourg-
umwelt.de
Recycling Material Distr
N.A.I.C.S.: 423930

Ecorec Srl (1)
Via Marzaghette, Adro, 25030, Brescia,
Lombardia, Italy
Tel.: (39) 0307450573
Web Site: https://www.ecorecsrl.it
Environmental Services
N.A.I.C.S.: 541620

Ereco Zrt. (1)
Granatos U 1-3, 1106, Budapest, Hungary
Tel.: (36) 14339999
Web Site: https://www.ereco.hu
Waste Management Services
N.A.I.C.S.: 562998

Grupo Net SLU (1)
C/ Petrel 23, Pol Ind Carrus, 03206, Elche,
Spain
Tel.: (34) 902884477
Web Site: http://www.grupo-net.com
Environmental Cleaning Services
N.A.I.C.S.: 562910

Le Bison Gourmand Sarl (1)
97 Avenue de Bobigny, 93130, Noisy-le-
Sec, France
Tel.: (33) 149420495
Web Site: http://www.lebison-gourmand.com
Restaurant Services
N.A.I.C.S.: 722511

Refinal Industries SAS (1)
Rue Pelouze, CS 40902, 59465, Lomme,
France
Tel.: (33) 320081780
Environmental Services
N.A.I.C.S.: 541620

Romrecycling Srl (1)
Soseaua de Centura Nr 41, Jilava, Roma-
nia
Tel.: (40) 214570263
Web Site: https://romrecycling.ro
Waste Management Services
N.A.I.C.S.: 562998

Safira Facility Services SA (1)
Rua Nova do Arquinho 382, Milheiros,
4475-365, Maia, Portugal
Tel.: (351) 229619530
Web Site: https://www.safira-fs.com

Facility Support Services
N.A.I.C.S.: 561210

**DERIMOD KONFEKSIYON AY-
AKKABI DERI SANAYI VE TI-
CARET A.S.**
Imrahor Street Premier Campus Of-
fice Block No 29/A, Gursel District
Kagithane, Istanbul, Turkiye
Tel.: (90) 2127033000
Web Site: https://www.derimod.com.tr
Year Founded: 1974
DERIM—(IST)
Sales Range: Less than $1 Million
Leather Product Mfr
N.A.I.C.S.: 316990
Nesli Uz (Mgr-Investor Relations)

**DERKWOO ELECTRONICS
CO., LTD.**
185-26 Cheomdangieop-ro Sandong-
myeon, Gumi, Gyeongsangbuk-do,
Korea (South)
Web Site: http://www.derkwoo.com
Year Founded: 1992
263600—(KRS)
Rev.: $160,279,002
Assets: $161,392,798
Liabilities: $73,821,793
Net Worth: $87,571,005
Earnings: $10,261,219
Emp.: 251
Fiscal Year-end: 12/31/22
Electronic Products Mfr
N.A.I.C.S.: 334111
Lee Jun Yong (CEO)

**DERLUKS YATIRIM HOLDING
A.S**
Kazlicesme mah Demirhane Cad
Haci Resit Bey sok No 11, 34020,
Istanbul, Turkiye
Tel.: (90) 2124165996
Web Site:
  http://www.derluksleather.com
Year Founded: 2002
DERHL—(IST)
Rev.: $19,462,958
Assets: $12,635,269
Liabilities: $7,450,884
Net Worth: $5,184,384
Earnings: $2,291,130
Fiscal Year-end: 12/31/22
Leather Product Mfr & Distr
N.A.I.C.S.: 316990
Cemal Guzelci (Chm & Gen Mgr)

Subsidiaries:

**Boran Mesrubat Sanayi ve Ticaret
A.S.** (1)
Yenibosna Merkez Mah Arif Aga Sok 29,
Bahcelievler, Istanbul, Turkiye
Tel.: (90) 2124460070
Web Site: http://www.boranmesrubat.com
Soft Drink Distr
N.A.I.C.S.: 424490

DERMAPHARM HOLDING SE
Lil-Dagover-Ring 7, 82031, Grunwald,
Germany
Tel.: (49) 89641860
Web Site: https://dermapharm.com
Year Founded: 1991
DMP—(MUN)
Rev.: $1,253,278,804
Assets: $2,385,098,793
Liabilities: $1,789,881,050
Net Worth: $595,217,743
Earnings: $68,848,372
Emp.: 3,497
Fiscal Year-end: 12/31/23
Pharmaceuticals Product Mfr
N.A.I.C.S.: 325412
Hans-Georg Feldmeier (Chm-Mgmt
Bd & CEO)

Subsidiaries:

AB Cernelle (1)
Hoganasvagen 365, 262 94, Angelholm, Sweden
Tel.: (46) 4269230
Web Site: https://cernelle.com
Pollen Extracts Pharmaceuticals Mfr
N.A.I.C.S.: 325411

Allergopharma (Beijing) Pharmaceutical Technology Co., Ltd. (1)
Room 19 2nd Floor Building 8 Number 1 Baohui Street, Shunyi District, Beijing, 101300, China
Tel.: (00) 1004750207
Herbal Product Mfr & Distr
N.A.I.C.S.: 325411

Allergopharma Espana S.L. (1)
C/ Amaltea 9 40 planta letra B, 28045, Madrid, Spain
Tel.: (34) 910761878
Web Site: https://allergopharma.es
Medicinal Product Mfr
N.A.I.C.S.: 325412

Allergopharma Vertriebsges, mbH (1)
Kleeblattgasse 4/13, 1010, Vienna, Austria
Tel.: (43) 161571540
Medicinal Product Mfr
N.A.I.C.S.: 325413

Biokirch GmbH (1)
Bei den Kampen 11, 21220, Seevetal, Germany
Tel.: (49) 41857010
Web Site: http://www.biokirch-gmbh.de
Pharmaceuticals Product Mfr
N.A.I.C.S.: 325412

Dermapharm AG (1)
Lil-Dagover-Ring 7, 82031, Grunwald, Germany
Tel.: (49) 89641860
Pharmaceuticals Mfr
N.A.I.C.S.: 325412

Subsidiary (Domestic):

Anton Hubner GmbH & Co. KG (2)
Schlossstrasse 11-17, Ehrenkirchen, 79238, Freiburg im Breisgau, Germany
Tel.: (49) 76339090
Web Site: https://huebner-vital.com
Pharmaceuticals Product Mfr
N.A.I.C.S.: 325412

Axicorp GmbH (2)
Marie-Curie-Strasse 11, 61381, Friedrichsdorf, Germany
Tel.: (49) 617249990
Web Site: https://www.axicorp.de
Emp.: 280
Pharmaceuticals Mfr
N.A.I.C.S.: 325412

Subsidiary (Non-US):

Dermapharm AG (2)
Bosch 104, 6331, Hunenberg, Switzerland
Tel.: (41) 417856340
Web Site: http://www.dermapharm.ch
Pharmaceuticals Mfr
N.A.I.C.S.: 325412

Subsidiary (Domestic):

Fitvia GmbH (2)
Sonnenberger Str 64, 65193, Wiesbaden, Germany
Tel.: (49) 61126248688
Web Site: http://www.fitvia.de
Pharmaceuticals Mfr
N.A.I.C.S.: 325412
Sebastian Merkhoffer *(Mng Dir)*

Hubner Naturarzneimittel GmbH (2)
Schlossstrasse 11-17, Ehrenkirchen, 79238, Freiburg im Breisgau, Germany
Tel.: (49) 89641860
Web Site: https://huebner.dermapharm.com
Pharmaceuticals Product Mfr
N.A.I.C.S.: 325412

Mibe GmbH Arzneimittel (2)
Munchener Strasse 15, Brehna, 06796, Bitterfeld, Germany
Tel.: (49) 349542470
Pharmaceuticals Mfr

N.A.I.C.S.: 325412

Subsidiary (Domestic):

Acis Arzneimittel GmbH (3)
Lil-Dagover-Ring 7, 82031, Grunwald, Germany
Tel.: (49) 8944232460
Pharmaceuticals Product Mfr
N.A.I.C.S.: 325412

Subsidiary (Non-US):

Mibe Pharma Italia Srl (2)
Via Ampere 56, Segrate, 20131, Milan, Italy
Tel.: (39) 0249652675
Web Site:
   https://www.mibepharmaitalia.com
Pharmaceuticals Product Mfr
N.A.I.C.S.: 325412

Mibe Pharma UK Ltd. (2)
Marco Polo House 3-5 Lansdowne Road, Croydon, CRO 2BX, United Kingdom
Tel.: (44) 2038707503
Web Site: http://www.mibepharmauk.com
Pharmaceuticals Product Mfr
N.A.I.C.S.: 325412

Mibe Pharmaceuticals d.o.o (2)
Zavrtnica 17, 10000, Zagreb, Croatia
Tel.: (385) 16061137
Pharmaceuticals Product Mfr
N.A.I.C.S.: 325412

Mibe Ukraine LLC (2)
Klovsky Descent 13, 01021, Kiev, Ukraine
Tel.: (380) 442543936
Web Site: http://www.dermapharm.com.ua
Pharmaceuticals Product Mfr
N.A.I.C.S.: 325412

Subsidiary (Domestic):

Strathmann GmbH & Co. KG (2)
Langenhorner Chaussee 602, 22419, Hamburg, Germany
Tel.: (49) 40559050
Web Site:
   https://strathmann.dermapharm.com
Emp.: 65
Pharmaceutical & Cosmetic Bottle Mfr
N.A.I.C.S.: 327213

Subsidiary (Non-US):

Sun-Farm Sp. z o.o. (2)
street Dolna 21, 05-092, Lomianki, Poland
Tel.: (48) 223506669
Web Site: https://www.sunfarm.pl
Emp.: 50
Pharmaceuticals Product Mfr
N.A.I.C.S.: 325412

Subsidiary (Domestic):

Trommsdorff GmbH & Co. KG (2)
Trommsdorffstr 2-6, 52477, Alsdorf, Germany
Tel.: (49) 240455301
Web Site:
   https://trommsdorff.dermapharm.com
Emp.: 230
Pharmaceuticals Product Mfr
N.A.I.C.S.: 325412

Digital Hub mibe GmbH (1)
Schafflerstr 4, 80333, Munich, Germany
Tel.: (49) 8964186259
Web Site: https://www.gesund-pharma.de
Natural Cosmetic & Medical Product Distr
N.A.I.C.S.: 456120

Euromed S.A. (1)
Carrer Rec de Dalt 21-23 Mollet del Valles, 08100, Barcelona, Spain
Tel.: (34) 935440110
Web Site: https://www.euromedgroup.com
Botanical Extracts & Botanical Active Ingredients Mfr
N.A.I.C.S.: 325411

DERRIMON TRADING CO., LTD.
235 Marcus Garvey Dr 11, Kingston, Jamaica
Tel.: (876) 9013344
Web Site: https://www.derrimon.com
Year Founded: 1998

DTL—(JAM)
Rev.: $121,598,204
Assets: $108,001,080
Liabilities: $63,412,851
Net Worth: $44,588,229
Earnings: $1,180,655
Emp.: 700
Fiscal Year-end: 12/31/23
Logistic Services
N.A.I.C.S.: 541614
Derrick Cottrell *(Chm)*

Subsidiaries:

Caribbean Flavours & Fragrances Limited (1)
226 Spanish Town Road, Kingston, Jamaica
Tel.: (876) 9235111
Web Site:
   https://www.caribbeanflavoursjm.com
Fragrance Whslr
N.A.I.C.S.: 456120
Howard S. Mitchell *(Chm)*

DERWENT LONDON PLC
25 Savile Row, London, W1S 2ER, United Kingdom
Tel.: (44) 2076593000
Web Site:
   https://www.derwentlondon.com
DLN—(LSE)
Rev.: $314,062,106
Assets: $6,954,556,930
Liabilities: $1,810,022,722
Net Worth: $5,144,534,209
Earnings: ($354,077,253)
Emp.: 184
Fiscal Year-end: 12/31/22
Commercial Real Estate Investment & Development Services
N.A.I.C.S.: 531390
John D. Burns *(Co-Founder & Chm)*

Subsidiaries:

Caledonian Properties Limited (1)
2 The Cross Court, Bishopbriggs, Glasgow, G64 2RD, United Kingdom
Tel.: (44) 141 761 1200
Web Site:
   http://www.caledonianproperty.co.uk
Sales Range: $50-74.9 Million
Emp.: 3
Real Estate Mortgage Consulting Services
N.A.I.C.S.: 531390

Caledonian Property Investments Limited (1)
2 The Cross Ct Bishopbriggs, Glasgow, G64 2RD, United Kingdom
Tel.: (44) 1417611200
Web Site: http://www.derwentlondon.com
Emp.: 5
Property Investment Services
N.A.I.C.S.: 523999
Alan Ewing *(Controller-Fin)*

The New River Company Limited (1)
25 Savile Row, London, W1S 2ER, United Kingdom
Tel.: (44) 2076593000
Web Site: http://www.derwentlondon.com
Emp.: 100
Property Development Services
N.A.I.C.S.: 531190

DERZHAVA PJSCB
Bolshoi Savvinsky Lane 2 Building 9, Moscow, 119435, Russia
Tel.: (7) 4953800480
Web Site: http://www.derzhava.ru
DERZP—(RUS)
Sales Range: Less than $1 Million
Investment Banking Services
N.A.I.C.S.: 523150

DES EAUX DE DOUAI SA
ZI Dorignies 676 rue du Maurice Caullery, 59500, Douai, France
Tel.: (33) 327943727
Water Distr
N.A.I.C.S.: 221310

DESA DERI SANAYI VE TICARET A.S.
Halkali St No 208, Sefakoy, 34295, Istanbul, Turkiye
Tel.: (90) 2124731800
Web Site: https://www.desa.com.tr
Year Founded: 1972
DESA—(IST)
Rev.: $72,568,242
Assets: $68,513,265
Liabilities: $37,858,220
Net Worth: $30,655,045
Earnings: $15,346,846
Emp.: 1,092
Fiscal Year-end: 12/31/22
Leather Product Distr
N.A.I.C.S.: 458320
Melih Celet *(Chm)*

DESAILLY SA
Min 6 Rue De Strasbourg, 94150, Rungis, Val De Marne, France
Tel.: (33) 146872445
Rev.: $30,700,000
Emp.: 48
N.A.I.C.S.: 424430
Freddy Taieb *(Dir-Fin)*

DESANE GROUP HOLDINGS LTD
Suite 4 Jones Bay Wharf 26-32 Pirrama Road, Pyrmont, 2009, NSW, Australia
Tel.: (61) 295559922
Web Site:
   https://www.desane.com.au
DGH—(ASX)
Rev.: $1,500,401
Assets: $67,875,935
Liabilities: $23,551,683
Net Worth: $44,324,252
Earnings: $1,097,089
Emp.: 7
Fiscal Year-end: 06/30/24
Investment Services
N.A.I.C.S.: 541611
John Blair Sheehan *(Chm)*

Subsidiaries:

Desane Properties Pty. Ltd. (1)
PO Box 331, Leichhardt, 2040, NSW, Australia
Tel.: (61) 295690344
Web Site: http://www.desane.com.au
Real Estate Manangement Services
N.A.I.C.S.: 531390

DESARROLLADORA HOMEX, S.A. DE C.V.
Blvd Alfonso Zaragoza Maytorena #2204, Fracc Bonanza, 80020, Culiacan, Sinaloa, Mexico
Tel.: (52) 6677585800   MX
Web Site: http://www.homex.com.mx
Year Founded: 1989
Sales Range: $1-4.9 Billion
Emp.: 9,975
Low & Middle-Income Housing Developer Services
N.A.I.C.S.: 236115
Eustaquio Tomas De Nicolas Gutierrez *(Chm)*

Subsidiaries:

Administradora Picsa, S.A. de C.V. (1)
Heroe De Nacataz No 3419, Nuevo Laredo, 88040, Tamaulipas, Mexico
Tel.: (52) 8677154249
Administrative Management Consulting Services
N.A.I.C.S.: 541611

Aerohomex, S.A. de C.V. (1)
Andador Javier Mina 891-B, Col Centro Sinaloa, Culiacan, 80200, Mexico   **(100%)**
Tel.: (52) 6677585800

Desarrolladora Homex, S.A. de C.V.—(Continued)

Sales Range: $25-49.9 Million
Emp.: 50
Air Transportation
N.A.I.C.S.: 481219

Altos Mandos de Negocios, S.A. de C.V. (1)
Bulevar Alfonso Zaragoza No 2204 Norte, Culiacan, 80020, Mexico (100%)
Tel.: (52) 6677585800
Sales Range: $150-199.9 Million
Emp.: 800
Management Consulting Services
N.A.I.C.S.: 541618

Casas Beta Del Centro, S De R L De C V (1)
Blvd Alfonso Zaragoza Maytorena No 2204, Culiacan, Mexico (100%)
Tel.: (52) 6677585800
Web Site: http://www.homex.mx
Sales Range: $200-249.9 Million
Emp.: 800
New Single-Family Housing Construction
N.A.I.C.S.: 236115
Gerardo Denicalos (CEO)

Subsidiary (Domestic):

Super Abastos Centrales y Comerciales, S.A. de C.V. (2)
Quinana Roo No 3 Int 303 Roma Sur Cuauhtemoc, Mexico, 06760, Mexico
Tel.: (52) 6677585800
Real Estate Development Services
N.A.I.C.S.: 531390

Casas Beta Del Noroeste, S.A. de C.V. (1)
Blvd Alfonso Zaragoza Maytorena No 2204, Culiacan, Mexico (100%)
Tel.: (52) 6677585800
New Single-Family Housing Construction
N.A.I.C.S.: 236115

Casas Beta Del Norte, S.A. de C.V. (1)
Blvd Alfonso Zaragoza Maytorena No 2204, Culiacan, Mexico (100%)
Tel.: (52) 6677585800
New Single-Family Housing Construction
N.A.I.C.S.: 236115

Desarrolladora De Casas Del Noroeste, S.A. de C.V. (1)
Alfonso Zaragoza Maytorena 2204 Bonanza, Culiacan, Mexico (100%)
Tel.: (52) 6677585800
Sales Range: $75-99.9 Million
Emp.: 500
Engineering Services
N.A.I.C.S.: 541330

HXMTD, S.A. de C.V. (1)
435319 La Joya No Sn, San Jose del Cabo, 23429, Mexico
Tel.: (52) 624 1636500
Sales Range: $25-49.9 Million
Emp.: 50
Commercial Building Construction Services
N.A.I.C.S.: 236220

Homex Atizapan, S.A. de C.V. (1)
Blvd Alfonso Zaragoza Maytorena No 2204, Culiacan, 80020, Sinaloa, Mexico
Tel.: (52) 6677585800
Sales Range: $150-199.9 Million
Emp.: 1,000
Construction Engineering Services
N.A.I.C.S.: 541330
Gerardo de Nicolas Gutierrez (Gen Mgr)

Homex Central Marcaria, S.A. de C.V. (1)
Alfonso Zaragoza Maytorena 2204 Bonanza, Culiacan, 80020, Sinaloa, Mexico
Tel.: (52) 6 677585800
Sales Range: $350-399.9 Million
Emp.: 2,000
Intellectual Property Management Services
N.A.I.C.S.: 541618

Homex Infraestructura Obras, S.A. de C.V. (1)
Boulevard Alfonzo Zaragoza Maytorena 2204 Bonanza, 80020, Culiacan, Sinaloa, Mexico

Tel.: (52) 667 7585800
Construction Engineering Services
N.A.I.C.S.: 541330

Homex Infraestructura, S.A. de C.V. (1)
Alfonso Zaragoza Maytorena 2204, Culiacan, 25050, Sinaloa, Mexico
Tel.: (52) 667 7585800
Construction Engineering Services
N.A.I.C.S.: 541330

DESARROLLOS ESPECIALES DE SISTEMAS DE ANCLAJE, S.A.
CL Guitard 43, 08840, Barcelona, Spain
Tel.: (34) 936305300
Web Site: https://www.desa.es
Year Founded: 1956
DESA—(MAD)
Sales Range: Less than $1 Million
Anchors & Fastening Product Mfr
N.A.I.C.S.: 332722

DESBROW THOMPSON CHAFFE
1-2 Faulkners Alley Cowcross St., London, EC1M 6DD, United Kingdom
Tel.: (44) 2072535040
Web Site: http://www.d-t-c.co.uk
Year Founded: 1989
Sales Range: $10-24.9 Million
Emp.: 7
Business-To-Business, Consumer Marketing
N.A.I.C.S.: 541810
John Chaffe (Owner)

DESCOURS & CABAUD SA
10 rue General Plessier, PO Box 2437, 69219, Lyon, Cedex 2, France
Tel.: (33) 472408585
Web Site: http://www.descours-cabaud.com
Year Founded: 1782
Sales Range: $1-4.9 Billion
Emp.: 13,500
Holding Company; Iron & Steel Products Mfr & Whslr
N.A.I.C.S.: 551112
Alain Morvand (Chm-Exec Bd)

Subsidiaries:

Carrel SA (1)
Route de Lausanne 2, PO Box 292, 1401, Yverdon-les-Bains, Switzerland
Tel.: (41) 24 424 24 74
Web Site: http://www.carrel.ch
Building Hardware Product Distr
N.A.I.C.S.: 423710

DELUX s.r.o. (1)
1 maja 939, 952 01, Vrable, Slovakia
Tel.: (421) 37 77 68 711
Web Site: http://www.delux.sk
Apparel & Accessory Distr
N.A.I.C.S.: 424350

DESCOURS & CABAUD ILE-DE-F (1)
31 quai du Rancy, 94380, Bonneuil-sur-Marne, France
Tel.: (33) 1 43 99 69 00
Web Site: http://www.dc-idf.com
Industrial Equipment Distr
N.A.I.C.S.: 423830

DESCOURS & CABAUD NORMANDIE (1)
Avenue Eugene Varlin - Z I du Grand Launay, 76120, Le Grand-Quevilly, France
Tel.: (33) 2 35 18 24 00
Web Site: http://www.dc-normandie.com
Building Hardware Product Distr
N.A.I.C.S.: 423710

DESCOURS & CABAUD PACA (1)
Z I Toulon Est - 520 Avenue J L Lambot, 83000, Toulon, France
Tel.: (33) 4 94 14 88 14
Web Site: http://www.dc-paca.com

Building Hardware Product Distr
N.A.I.C.S.: 423710

DESCOURS & CABAUD RHONE ALPES AUVERGNE (1)
176 avenue de Pressense, 69200, Venissieux, France
Tel.: (33) 4 72 78 23 00
Web Site: http://www.dc-raa.com
Building Hardware Product Distr
N.A.I.C.S.: 423710

DESCOURS & CABAUD SAVOIE (1)
3 et 8 rue des Garennes, 74960, Cran-Gevrier, France
Tel.: (33) 4 50 57 40 46
Web Site: http://www.dc-savoie.fr
Industrial Equipment Distr
N.A.I.C.S.: 423830

Dillon Supply Company (1)
440 Civic Blvd, Raleigh, NC 27610-2967
Tel.: (919) 838-4200
Web Site: http://www.dillonsupply.com
Sales Range: $150-199.9 Million
Emp.: 370
Industrial Supplies, Steel, Safety Equipment & Materials Handling Equipment Mfr & Distr
N.A.I.C.S.: 423830

Ferramenta 2000 Spa (1)
via R Lombardi 9, Levata di Curtatone, 46010, Mantua, Italy
Tel.: (39) 0376 47 88 71
Web Site: http://www.ferramenta2000.it
Building Hardware Product Distr
N.A.I.C.S.: 423710

Hahn Systems, LLC (1)
8416 Zionsville Rd, Indianapolis, IN 46268
Tel.: (317) 243-3796
Web Site: http://www.hahnsystems.com
Pneumatic Stapling & Nailing Equipment, Carton Closing Equipment, Strapping Glues & Adhesives Distr
N.A.I.C.S.: 423840
Scott Brown (Pres)

IMES DEXIS (1)
Noorderlaan 31a, 2030, Antwerp, Belgium
Tel.: (32) 3 645 91 88
Web Site: http://www.imes.be
Emp.: 280
Power Tool Distr
N.A.I.C.S.: 423710

LAMAN BV (1)
Industrieterrein Kraaiven nr 3777 Laurent Janssensstraat 101, 5048 AR, Tilburg, Netherlands
Tel.: (31) 13 465 30 00
Web Site: http://www.laman.nl
Emp.: 350
Power Tool Distr
N.A.I.C.S.: 423710

Metalco SA (1)
Ronda de Ponent 6 y 8, El Prat de Llobregat, 08820, Barcelona, Spain
Tel.: (34) 93 378 95 50
Web Site: http://www.metalco.es
Industrial Tools Distr
N.A.I.C.S.: 423840

Multijoint SA (1)
Route du Nant-d'Avril 101, 1217, Meyrin, Switzerland
Tel.: (41) 22 782 51 44
Web Site: http://www.multijoint.ch
Valve Distr
N.A.I.C.S.: 423720

SLS-TECHNACO s.r.o (1)
Sasinkova 37, 010 01, Zilina, Slovakia
Tel.: (421) 41 50 70 814
Web Site: http://www.slstechnaco.sk
Industrial Tools Distr
N.A.I.C.S.: 423840

TKD GmbH (1)
Georg-Schaeffler-Strasse 6, 42499, Huckeswagen, Germany
Tel.: (49) 2192937230
Web Site: https://tkd-gmbh.com
Emp.: 6
Bearing Distr
N.A.I.C.S.: 423840
Carlos Dantas (Gen Mgr)

DESENIO GROUP AB

Desenio Group AB publ, PO Box 11025, 100 61, Stockholm, Sweden
Tel.: (46) 8120587000
Web Site: https://www.deseniogroup.com
Year Founded: 2008
DSNO—(OMX)
Rev.: $90,589,789
Assets: $125,244,692
Liabilities: $129,571,871
Net Worth: ($4,327,180)
Earnings: ($26,618,712)
Emp.: 129
Fiscal Year-end: 12/31/23
Online Shopping Services
N.A.I.C.S.: 425120
Alexander Hars (Chm)

Subsidiaries:

Poster Store Sverige AB (1)
Box 11025, 100 61, Stockholm, Sweden
Tel.: (46) 812058700
Web Site: https://posterstore.se
Painting Equipment Mfr & Distr
N.A.I.C.S.: 325510

DESERT CONTROL AS
Grenseveien 21 FOMO Works, 4313, Sandnes, Norway
Tel.: (47) 95777777 NO
Web Site: https://desertcontrol.com
Year Founded: 2017
DSRT—(OSL)
Rev.: $128,210
Assets: $12,332,718
Liabilities: $410,770
Net Worth: $11,921,947
Earnings: ($5,483,466)
Emp.: 20
Fiscal Year-end: 12/31/23
Software Development Services
N.A.I.C.S.: 541511
Bernt Arne Breistein (COO)

DESERT GOLD VENTURES INC.
Suite 210 - 9648-128th Street, Surrey, V3T 2X9, BC, Canada
Tel.: (604) 357-4726
Web Site: https://www.desertgold.ca
Year Founded: 2003
DAUGF—(OTCQB)
Assets: $1,513,956
Liabilities: $476,937
Net Worth: $1,037,019
Earnings: ($4,183,238)
Fiscal Year-end: 12/31/21
Mineral Exploration Services
N.A.I.C.S.: 213114
Sonny Janda (Chm)

Subsidiaries:

Ashanti Gold Corp. (1)
2300 1177 West Hastings Street, Vancouver, V6E 2K3, BC, Canada
Tel.: (604) 638-3847
Web Site: http://ashantigoldcorp.com
Assets: $1,356,634
Liabilities: $281,963
Net Worth: $1,074,672
Earnings: ($3,704,060)
Fiscal Year-end: 08/31/2018
Gold Exploration Services
N.A.I.C.S.: 212220
Timothy McCutcheon (CEO)

DESERT METALS LIMITED
Level 2 Suite 9 389 Oxford Street Mt, Hawthorn, 6016, WA, Australia
Tel.: (61) 893839997 AU
Web Site: https://www.desertmetals.com.au
Year Founded: 2017
DM1—(ASX)
Rev.: $112,977
Assets: $6,184,136
Liabilities: $184,196
Net Worth: $5,999,941

Earnings: ($460,569)
Fiscal Year-end: 06/30/23
Metal Exploration Services
N.A.I.C.S.: 213114
Mark Stewart *(Chm)*

DESERT MOUNTAIN ENERGY CORP.
2500 Park Place 666 Burrard Street,
Vancouver, V6C 2X8, BC, Canada
Tel.: (604) 617-5448   Ca
Web Site:
  https://www.desertmountain.com
Year Founded: 2008
DMEHF—(OTCQX)
Assets: $1,729,570
Liabilities: $91,755
Net Worth: $1,637,815
Earnings: ($259,526)
Fiscal Year-end: 09/30/19
Mineral Exploration Services
N.A.I.C.S.: 213114
Robert Rohlfing *(Chm, Pres & CEO)*

DESERTOAK LTD
Unit 7 Briar Close Business Park,
Evesham, WR11 4JT, Worcs, United
Kingdom
Tel.: (44) 1386765451
Web Site: http://www.desertoak.co.uk
Year Founded: 1986
Rev.: $12,236,543
Emp.: 30
Refurbishment Services
N.A.I.C.S.: 238390
Jum Ditchfield *(Founder & Chm)*

DESH GARMENTS LIMITED
Awal Center 6th Floor34 Kemal Atat-
urk AvenueBanani C/A, Dhaka, 1213,
Bangladesh
Tel.: (880) 2222276019
Web Site:
  https://www.deshgroup.com
Year Founded: 1977
DSHGARME—(DHA)
Rev.: $2,159,220
Assets: $3,434,233
Liabilities: $1,712,026
Net Worth: $1,722,207
Earnings: $34,853
Emp.: 752
Fiscal Year-end: 06/30/21
Garments Mfr
N.A.I.C.S.: 314999
Rokeya Quader *(Chm)*

Subsidiaries:

Tutelar Oil Services Co. (Pvt)
Ltd.   (1)
Awal Centre 7th Floor 34 Kemal Ataturk
Avenue, Banani, Dhaka, 1213, Bangladesh
Tel.: (880) 29820994
Air Horse Compressor Mfr
N.A.I.C.S.: 333414

**DESH RAKSHAK AUSHDHA-
LAYA LIMITED**
Bhagwant Kuti Kankhal, Haridwar,
249408, Uttarakhand, India
Tel.: (91) 9084712065
Web Site:
  https://www.deshrakshak.in
Year Founded: 1901
531521—(BOM)
Rev.: $902,680
Assets: $1,988,992
Liabilities: $787,552
Net Worth: $1,201,440
Earnings: $57,354
Fiscal Year-end: 03/31/21
Pharmaceutical Product Mfr & Distr
N.A.I.C.S.: 325412
Tosh Kumar Jain *(Chm & Mng Dir)*

**DESHBANDHU POLYMER LIM-
ITED**
Mostafa Center House - 59 Road -
27 Block - K Banani, Dhaka, 1213,
Bangladesh
Tel.: (880) 241081489
Web Site: https://www.dbg.com.bd
Year Founded: 2006
DESHBANDHU—(CHT)
Rev.: $9,983,946
Assets: $22,984,956
Liabilities: $12,237,219
Net Worth: $10,747,737
Earnings: $328,015
Emp.: 15,000
Fiscal Year-end: 06/30/23
Woven Bag Mfr
N.A.I.C.S.: 339999
Golam Rahman *(Mng Dir)*

DESIGN CAPITAL LIMITED
130 Joo Seng Road 07-05, Singa-
pore, 368357, Singapore
Tel.: (65) 63832222   Ky
Web Site:
  https://www.designcapital.sg
Year Founded: 1981
1545—(HKG)
Rev.: $67,792,168
Assets: $65,831,250
Liabilities: $23,000,076
Net Worth: $42,831,175
Earnings: $2,940,241
Emp.: 123
Fiscal Year-end: 12/31/23
Furniture Product Retailer
N.A.I.C.S.: 423210
Terence Eu Jin Goon *(Chm & CEO)*

DESIGN MILK CO. LIMITED
Level 5 126 Phillip Street, Sydney,
2000, NSW, Australia
Tel.: (61) 1300266517
Web Site: http://www.ahalife.com
DMC—(ASX)
Rev.: $1,497,610
Assets: $387,402
Liabilities: $213,690
Net Worth: $173,712
Earnings: ($2,688,886)
Fiscal Year-end: 06/30/22
Online Shopping Services
N.A.I.C.S.: 561422

DESIGN STUDIO GROUP LTD.
8 Sungei Kadut Crescent, Singapore,
728682, Singapore
Tel.: (65) 63670133
Web Site: http://www.ds-group.com
Rev.: $122,472,390
Assets: $116,962,475
Liabilities: $69,204,510
Net Worth: $47,757,965
Earnings: ($19,297,137)
Fiscal Year-end: 12/31/18
Furniture Mfr & Distr
N.A.I.C.S.: 337127
Steven James Salo *(CEO)*

Subsidiaries:

DDS Contracts & Interior Solutions
(Thailand) Co., Ltd.   (1)
Euro Creations Building (B!) 119 Sukhumvit
55, North Klong Ton Wattana, Bangkok,
10110, Thailand
Tel.: (66) 2 712 7080
Furniture Sales
N.A.I.C.S.: 449110

DDS Contracts & Interior Solutions
Pte Ltd   (1)
62 Sungei Kadut Loop #05-01 International
Furniture Centre, Singapore, 728682, Sin-
gapore
Tel.: (65) 6362 6366
Furniture Sales
N.A.I.C.S.: 449110

DDS Contracts & Interior Solutions
Sdn Bhd   (1)
18th Floor West Block Wisma Selangor
Dredging, 142C Jalan Ampang, 50450,
Kuala Lumpur, Malaysia
Tel.: (60) 3 2164 6686
Furniture Sales
N.A.I.C.S.: 449110

DS Furniture Manufacturer Sdn
Bhd   (1)
PLO 44 Kawasan Penndustrian Senai, Se-
nai Johor Bahru, 81400, Johor, Malaysia
Tel.: (60) 7 598 6363
Furniture Mfr
N.A.I.C.S.: 337121

DS Project Management Sdn
Bhd   (1)
No 158 Jalan Maarof Taman Bandaraya,
59100, Kuala Lumpur, Malaysia
Tel.: (60) 3 2164 6686
Furniture Sales
N.A.I.C.S.: 449110

Design Studio (Huizhou) Home Fur-
nishing Co., Ltd.   (1)
1 North Road Technology Park, Boluo
County Shiwan Town, Huizhou, 516127,
Guangdon, China
Tel.: (86) 752 636 0333
Web Site: http://www.designstudio.com.cn
Furniture Mfr
N.A.I.C.S.: 337121

**DESIGN YOUR HOME HOLD-
ING AB**
Gamla Brogatan 32 2 tr, 111 20,
Stockholm, Sweden
Tel.: (46) 851971210
Web Site: http://www.dyh-ab.se
MLDYH—(EUR)
Sales Range: $1-9.9 Million
Online Furniture Distribution Services
N.A.I.C.S.: 561422
Connie D'Orville *(CEO & Member-
Exec Bd)*

DESIGNCAPITAL PLC
Woodbine Cottage The Long Road,
Rowledge, Farnham, GU10 4DL,
United Kingdom
Tel.: (44) 2075548555   UK
Sales Range: $10-24.9 Million
Investment Services
N.A.I.C.S.: 523999
Frederic J. Bobo *(Chm & CEO)*

DESIGNONE JAPAN, INC.
Nishi-Shinjuku Prime Square 8thfloor
7-5-25 Nishi-Shinjuku, Tokyo, 160-
0023, Japan
Tel.: (81) 364217438
Web Site: https://www.designone.jp
6048—(TKS)
Rev.: $14,082,080
Assets: $20,594,420
Liabilities: $2,823,880
Net Worth: $17,770,540
Earnings: ($1,928,200)
Emp.: 165
Fiscal Year-end: 08/31/24
Local Information Marketing Services
N.A.I.C.S.: 541613
Yasuo Takahata *(Founder & CEO)*

**DESLAURIER CUSTOM CABI-
NETS INC.**
550 Hall Avenue East, Renfrew, K7V
2S9, ON, Canada
Tel.: (613) 432-5431
Web Site: http://www.deslaurier.ca
Year Founded: 1979
Emp.: 180
Cabinetry Mfr
N.A.I.C.S.: 337110
Denis Staples *(Co-Owner & Pres)*

DESMAZIERES SA

2 rue du Petit Quinquin, 59816,
Lesquin, Cedex, France
Tel.: (33) 3 20 87 70 05
Web Site: http://www.chaussures-
  desmazieres.fr
Sales Range: $125-149.9 Million
Emp.: 750
Shoe Retailer, Mail Order & Internet
Sales
N.A.I.C.S.: 458210
Guy Serge Desmazieres *(CEO)*

**DESON DEVELOPMENT IN-
TERNATIONAL HOLDINGS
LTD**
11th Floor Nanyang Plaza 57 Hung
To Road, Kwun Tong, Kowloon,
China (Hong Kong)
Tel.: (852) 25701118
Web Site: https://www.deson.com
0262—(HKG)
Rev.: $14,187,155
Assets: $318,559,318
Liabilities: $102,891,344
Net Worth: $215,667,974
Earnings: ($3,996,703)
Emp.: 173
Fiscal Year-end: 03/31/22
Real Estate Industry
N.A.I.C.S.: 237210
Angus Wing Wai Lam *(Sec &
Controller-Fin)*

Subsidiaries:

Allied Health Elements Company
Limited   (1)
11th Floor Nanyang Plaza 57 Hung To
Road, Kwun Tong, Kowloon, China (Hong
Kong)
Tel.: (852) 36140871
Personal Care Product Distr
N.A.I.C.S.: 456120

Deson Innovative Limited   (1)
11th Floor Nanyang Plaza 57 Hung To
Road, Kwun Tong, Kowloon, China (Hong
Kong)
Tel.: (852) 25701118
Security System Component Mfr & Distr
N.A.I.C.S.: 334290

Medical Technologies Limited   (1)
11/F Nanyang Plaza 57 Hung To Rd, Kwun
Tong, Kowloon, China (Hong Kong)
Tel.: (852) 21577057
Diagnostic Imaging Medical Equipment Distr
N.A.I.C.S.: 423450

Smart City Development Holdings
Limited   (1)
11th Floor Nanyang Plaza 57 Hung To
Road, Kwun Tong, Kowloon, China (Hong
Kong)
Tel.: (852) 2 111 2988
Web Site: http://www.smartcity-d.com
Rev.: $41,906,118
Assets: $38,669,236
Liabilities: $21,853,984
Net Worth: $16,815,252
Earnings: $1,943,084
Emp.: 92
Fiscal Year-end: 03/31/2022
Building Construction, Electrical & Mechani-
cal Engineering
N.A.I.C.S.: 236210
May Ngan Mei Li *(Mgr-Admin)*

**DESOTO RESOURCES LIM-
ITED**
Level 2 10 Outram Street, West
Perth, 6055, WA, Australia
Tel.: (61) 861497516   AU
Web Site:
  https://www.desotoresources.com
Year Founded: 2022
DES—(ASX)
Rev.: $183,113
Assets: $6,378,558
Liabilities: $341,575
Net Worth: $6,036,983
Earnings: ($1,131,359)

DeSoto Resources Limited—(Continued)

Fiscal Year-end: 06/30/24
Exploration & Mining Services
N.A.I.C.S.: 213115
Paul Roberts *(Exec Chm)*

DESPEC BILGISAYAR PAZAR-LAMA VE TICARET A.S.
Ayazaga Mahallesi Mimar Sinan
Sokak No 21 Seba Office Boulevard
D, Blok Kat 1 Bolum No 9 Sariyer,
34485, Istanbul, Turkiye
Tel.: (90) 2123312424
Web Site: https://www.despec.com.tr
Year Founded: 1998
DESPC—(IST)
Rev.: $137,152,817
Assets: $43,555,512
Liabilities: $35,886,083
Net Worth: $7,669,429
Earnings: ($2,691,165)
Fiscal Year-end: 12/31/23
Computer Peripheral Whslr
N.A.I.C.S.: 423430
Nevres Erol Bilecik *(Chm)*

DESPEC GROUP B.V.
Smidsstraat 2, 8601 WB, Sneek,
Netherlands
Tel.: (31) 515438200
Web Site: http://www.despec.com
Sales Range: $900-999.9 Million
Emp.: 650
IT Consumer Products Distr
N.A.I.C.S.: 423430

Subsidiaries:

DESPEC AFRICA EPZ LTD   (1)
Mabibo External Mandela Road, PO Box
54215, Dar es Salaam, Tanzania
Tel.: (255) 779 888255
Computer Hardware & Printer Distr
N.A.I.C.S.: 423430
Shahid Riyaz *(Product Mgr-East Africa Region)*

DESPEC EUROPE B.V.   (1)
Rietveldenkade 15, 5222 AJ, Den Bosch,
Netherlands
Tel.: (31) 736 2422 00
Computer Hardware & Printer Distr
N.A.I.C.S.: 423430

DESPEC IBERIA SL.   (1)
Pol Principe Felipe Avenida de Elche 157
Nave 12, Alicante, Spain
Tel.: (34) 965 105396
Computer Hardware & Printer Distr
N.A.I.C.S.: 423430
Miguel Angel Garcia Martinez *(Gen Mgr)*

DESPEC JORDAN FZE   (1)
Office No 104 82 Gardens Street, PO Box
1852, 119747, Amman, Jordan
Tel.: (962) 656 26440
Computer Hardware & Printer Distr
N.A.I.C.S.: 423430

DESPEC KENYA LTD   (1)
1st Floor Almont Park Church Road, West-lands, Nairobi, Kenya
Tel.: (254) 204 442241
Computer Hardware & Printer Distr
N.A.I.C.S.: 423430

DESPEC LEBANON SAL   (1)
2nd Floor Plaza Centre Jal El Dib Square,
Beirut, Lebanon
Tel.: (961) 471 7762
Web Site: http://www.despec.com
Emp.: 4
Computer Hardware & Printer Distr
N.A.I.C.S.: 423430
Bachir Sleit *(Gen Mgr)*

DESPEC TANZANIA LTD   (1)
Plot No 212 Magore Maweni Street, PO
Box 25097, Upanga, Dar es Salaam, Tanzania
Tel.: (255) 222 151349
Computer Hardware & Printer Distr
N.A.I.C.S.: 423430
Roshin Chacko *(Country Mgr)*

DESPEC TURKEY A.S.   (1)
Cendere Yolu No 23 Kagrithane, 34418,
Istanbul, Turkiye
Tel.: (90) 212 3312424
Computer Hardware & Printer Distr
N.A.I.C.S.: 423430

DESPEC UGANDA LTD   (1)
49-51 Bukoto Street, PO Box 5623, Kam-pala, Uganda
Tel.: (256) 312 202605
Computer Hardware & Printer Distr
N.A.I.C.S.: 423430

Despec Denmark A/S   (1)
Vassingerodvei 25, 3540, Lynge, Denmark
Tel.: (45) 45764300
Web Site: http://www.despec.dk
Sales Range: $50-74.9 Million
Emp.: 60
IT Consumer Products Distr
N.A.I.C.S.: 423430
Michael Voll *(Mng Dir)*

Despec Doo   (1)
Strahinica Bana 1, 11000, Belgrade, Serbia
Tel.: (381) 113284979
Web Site: http://www.despec-yu.com
IT Consumer Products Distr
N.A.I.C.S.: 423430

Despec Mera Ltd.   (1)
Jebel Ali Free Zone, PO Box 61050, Jebel
Ali Free Zone, Dubai, 61050, United Arab
Emirates
Tel.: (971) 48811191
Web Site: http://www.despecmera.com
Sales Range: $25-49.9 Million
Emp.: 40
IT Consumer Products Distr
N.A.I.C.S.: 423430
Riyaz Jamal *(Chm)*

Despec Supplies BVBA   (1)
Dok-Noord 4/C103, 9000, Gentbrugge, Bel-gium
Tel.: (32) 92442030
Web Site: http://www.despec-benelux.com
Sales Range: $50-74.9 Million
Emp.: 60
IT Consumer Products Distr
N.A.I.C.S.: 423430
Carsten Preavf *(CEO)*

Despec Supplies Utibu A Islandi
AS   (1)
Dalvegur 16A, IS-200, Kopavogur, Iceland
Tel.: (354) 5445533
Web Site: http://www.despec.is
Sales Range: $50-74.9 Million
Emp.: 4
IT Consumer Products Distr
N.A.I.C.S.: 423430

Despec Sweden AB   (1)
Pyramidbacken 6, PO Box 5049, 141 75,
Kungens Kurva, Sweden
Tel.: (46) 84495900
Web Site: http://www.despec.se
Sales Range: $25-49.9 Million
Emp.: 40
IT Consumer Products Distr
N.A.I.C.S.: 423430
Mats Lindmark *(Acct Mgr)*

DESPEGAR.COM, CORP.
Juana Manso 999 Ciudad Autonoma
de, C1107CBR, Buenos Aires, Argen-tina
Tel.: (54) 1148943500   VG
Web Site: https://www.despegar.com
Year Founded: 1999
DESP—(NYSE)
Rev.: $537,972,000
Assets: $804,192,000
Liabilities: $931,342,000
Net Worth: ($127,150,000)
Earnings: ($68,521,000)
Emp.: 4,543
Fiscal Year-end: 12/31/22
Online Travel Agency Services
N.A.I.C.S.: 561599
Damian Scokin *(CEO)*

Subsidiaries:

Despegar.com USA, Inc.   (1)

2665 S Bayshore Dr, Miami, FL 33133
Tel.: (305) 856-4409
Web Site: http://www.despegar.com
Telephone Communication, Except Radio
N.A.I.C.S.: 517810

DESPRED PLC
84 Veslets street, 1202, Sofia, Bul-garia
Tel.: (359) 2 931 39 50
Web Site: http://www.despred.com
Year Founded: 1947
Transportation Arrangement Services
N.A.I.C.S.: 488510
Vasla Stefanova Tzvetkova *(Dir-IR)*

DESTAMPES EMBALLAGES
BP 27, Etagnac, 16150, Limoges,
France
Tel.: (33) 545890203
Web Site: http://www.destampes-emballages.fr
Sales Range: $10-24.9 Million
Emp.: 123
Designer, Mfr & Recycler of Wood
Packaging
N.A.I.C.S.: 321920
Nathalie Mandoux *(Dir-Admin)*

DESTEK FAKTORING A.S.
Ferko Signature Buyukdere Caddesi
No 175 K 26, Sisli, 34394, Istanbul,
Turkiye
Tel.: (90) 2123252550
Web Site:
http://www.destekfaktoring.com
Year Founded: 1996
Financial Consulting Services
N.A.I.C.S.: 541611

**DESTICON TRANSPORTATION
SERVICES INC**
678 2397 King George Highway, Sur-rey, V4A 9N3, BC, Canada
Tel.: (604) 244-7244
Web Site: http://www.desticon.com
Rev.: $27,387,659
Emp.: 76
Logistic Services
N.A.I.C.S.: 488510
Jade Stevenson *(Pres)*

DESTILACIJA A.D.
79 Svetog Save Street, Teslic, 74270,
Bosnia & Herzegovina
Tel.: (387) 53431300
Web Site: https://www.destilacija.net
Year Founded: 1896
DEST—(BANJ)
Sales Range: $1-9.9 Million
Emp.: 326
Basic Organic Chemical Mfr
N.A.I.C.S.: 325199
Vojin Peuraca *(Chm-Mgmt Bd)*

DESTINATION AUTO VEN-TURES INC
1600 Marine Drive, North Vancouver,
V7P 1T9, BC, Canada
Tel.: (604) 980-8501
Web Site:
http://www.destinationchrysler.ca
Year Founded: 1984
Rev.: $51,558,355
Emp.: 100
New & Used Car Dealers
N.A.I.C.S.: 441110
Stephen Dobish *(Sr Mgr-Sls)*

DESTINATION ITALIA SPA
Galleria Sala dei Longobardi 2,
20121, Milan, Italy
Tel.: (39) 0648902040
Web Site:
https://destinationitaliagroup.com
DIT—(ITA)
Travel Agency

N.A.I.C.S.: 561510
Julius Valiant *(Chm)*

DESTINATION MAZDA VAN-COUVER
1595 Boundary Road, Vancouver,
V5K 5C4, BC, Canada
Tel.: (604) 294-4299
Web Site: http://www.newmazda.ca
Year Founded: 1986
Rev.: $12,954,798
Emp.: 628
New & Used Car Dealers
N.A.I.C.S.: 441110
Nash Sharei *(Mgr-Sls)*

DESTINI BERHAD
No 10 Jalan Jurunilai U1/20, Hicom
Glenmarie Industrial Park, 40150,
Shah Alam, 40150, Selangor Darul
Ehsan, Malaysia
Tel.: (60) 355670333
Web Site:
https://www.destinigroup.com
DESTINI—(KLS)
Rev.: $39,401,075
Assets: $59,377,988
Liabilities: $33,414,032
Net Worth: $25,963,956
Earnings: ($6,948,193)
Emp.: 466
Fiscal Year-end: 12/31/22
Aviation Parts Mfr
N.A.I.C.S.: 336413
Rozabil Abdul Rahman *(Pres & CEO-Grp)*

Subsidiaries:

AMS Marine Pte. Ltd.   (1)
42A Penjuru Road 06-00 Mencast Central
Lobby 1, Singapore, 609164, Singapore
Tel.: (65) 6 264 8222
Web Site: https://www.amsmarinegroup.com
Marine Engineering Services
N.A.I.C.S.: 541330
J. Rizwan *(Gen Sls Mgr)*

Destini Marine Safety Solutions
Ltd.   (1)
Montrose Port Authority South Quay, Fer-ryden, Montrose, DD10 9SL, Angus, United
Kingdom
Tel.: (44) 3304450001
Web Site: http://www.destinimss.com
Lifeboat Mfr
N.A.I.C.S.: 336612

Destini Prima Sdn. Bhd.   (1)
No 10 Jalan Jurunilai U1/20 HICOM Glen-marie, Industrial Park, 40150, Shah Alam,
Selangor, Malaysia
Tel.: (60) 355670333
Safety Equipment Maintenance Services
N.A.I.C.S.: 811310

Destini Shipbuilding & Engineering
Sdn. Bhd.   (1)
No 23 NKS Industrial Area Jalan Pelabuhan
Utara, 42000, Port Klang, Selangor, Malay-sia
Tel.: (60) 331655080
Ship Repair Services
N.A.I.C.S.: 488390

Safeair Technical Sdn. Bhd.   (1)
B-06 Contact Pier Ground Floor Main Ter-minal Building, Kuala Lumpur International
Airport, 64000, Sepang, Selangor, Malaysia
Tel.: (60) 387760590
Pre Flight Services
N.A.I.C.S.: 488190

System Enhancement Resources &
Technologies Sdn. Bhd.   (1)
No 1 Jalan Apollo U5/194 Bandar Pinggiran
Subang, 40150, Shah Alam, Selangor, Ma-laysia
Tel.: (60) 378471501
Web Site: https://www.destinigroup.com
Vehicle Mfr
N.A.I.C.S.: 336110

Techno Fibre (S) Pte. Ltd.   (1)
24 Jurong Port Road 02-01, Singapore,

619097, Singapore
Tel.: (65) 62661412
Lifeboat Mfr
N.A.I.C.S.: 336612

Techno Fibre Australia Pty. Ltd.   **(1)**
Unit 2/125 Barrington Street, Bibra Lake,
6163, WA, Australia
Tel.: (61) 894942622
Lifeboat Mfr
N.A.I.C.S.: 336612

Techno Fibre Middle East Marine
Services FZE   **(1)**
WS 106 Dubai Maritime City, Dubai, United
Arab Emirates
Tel.: (971) 45849333
Lifeboat Mfr
N.A.I.C.S.: 336612

Vanguarde Pte. Ltd.   **(1)**
24 Jurong Port Road 02-01, Singapore,
619097, Singapore
Tel.: (65) 62661412
Web Site:
   https://www.vanguardlifeboat.com
Lifeboat Mfr
N.A.I.C.S.: 336612

DESTINY LOGISTICS & INFRA LIMITED

375 Dakshindari Road, Parganas
North, Kolkata, 700048, India
Tel.: (91) 9836000343
Web Site: https://www.destinyinfra.in
Year Founded: 2011
DESTINY—(NSE)
Rev.: $474,379,089
Assets: $365,564,986
Liabilities: $137,762,359
Net Worth: $227,802,627
Earnings: $17,714,065
Emp.: 8
Fiscal Year-end: 03/31/22
Logistics Consulting Servies
N.A.I.C.S.: 541614

DESTINY MEDIA TECHNOLO-GIES, INC.

428 - 1575 West Georgia Street,
Vancouver, V6G 2V3, BC, Canada
Tel.: (604) 609-7736   CO
Web Site: https://investors.dsny.com
DSNY—(OTCQB)
Rev.: $51,201
Assets: $3,688,352
Liabilities: $522,934
Net Worth: $3,165,418
Earnings: $111,758
Emp.: 30
Fiscal Year-end: 08/31/24
Digital Content Distribution Solutions
Including Audio & Video Streaming
Solutions
N.A.I.C.S.: 513210
Frederick Vandenberg *(Pres, CEO & Sec)*

DESTINY PHARMA PLC

Sussex Innovation Centre Science
Park Square, Brighton, BN1 9SB,
United Kingdom
Tel.: (44) 1273704440   UK
Web Site:
   https://www.destinypharma.com
Year Founded: 1996
DEST—(AIM)
Rev.: $191,857
Assets: $10,922,603
Liabilities: $1,452,610
Net Worth: $9,469,993
Earnings: ($8,076,132)
Emp.: 24
Fiscal Year-end: 12/31/22
Pharmaceutical Preparation Manufac-
turing
N.A.I.C.S.: 325412
William Love *(Founder & Chief Scien-tific Officer)*

DESTINY SOLUTIONS, INC.

40 Holly Street Suite 701, Toronto,
M4S 3C3, ON, Canada
Tel.: (416) 480-0500
Web Site:
   http://www.destinysolutions.com
Year Founded: 1995
Software Publisher
N.A.I.C.S.: 513210
Peter DeVries *(President & CEO)*

DESUN REAL ESTATE IN-VESTMENT SERVICES GROUP CO., LTD.

Room 1803 Block A Desun Interna-
tional No 1480, North Section of
Tianfu Avenue High-tech Industrial
Development Zone, Chengdu, China
Tel.: (86) 2880983333   Ky
Web Site: https://www.desunhui.com
Year Founded: 2010
2270—(HKG)
Rev.: $47,067,041
Assets: $117,036,581
Liabilities: $73,754,292
Net Worth: $43,282,288
Earnings: $5,539,018
Emp.: 957
Fiscal Year-end: 12/31/23
Investment Management Service
N.A.I.C.S.: 523999
Zhicheng Zhang *(Chm)*

DESWELL INDUSTRIES, INC.

10B Edificio Associacao Industrial De
Macau, 32 Rua do Comandante Mata
e Oliveira, Macau, China (Macau)
Tel.: (853) 28322096   HK
Web Site: http://www.deswell.com
Year Founded: 1987
DSWL—(NASDAQ)
Rev.: $77,337,000
Assets: $110,379,000
Liabilities: $20,730,000
Net Worth: $89,649,000
Earnings: $2,059,000
Emp.: 941
Fiscal Year-end: 03/31/23
Injection-Molded Plastic Parts &
Components, Electronic Products &
Sub-Assemblies, Metallic Molds &
Accessory Parts Mfr
N.A.I.C.S.: 326199
Chin Pang Li *(Exec Dir-Manufacturing-Administration-Plastic Ops)*

Subsidiaries:

Dongguan Jetcrown Technology
Limited   **(1)**
Huangang Industrial Estate Houjie Town,
Dongguan, 523946, Guangdong, China
Tel.: (86) 769 83086666
Liquid Crystal Display Monitor Mfr
N.A.I.C.S.: 334419

Dongguan Kwan Hong Electronics
Co. Ltd.   **(1)**
Xiaobian 2nd Industrial Zone, Dongguan,
523840, Guangdong, China
Tel.: (86) 76988619858
Web Site: http://www.deswell.com
Vending Machine Mfr
N.A.I.C.S.: 333310

Jetcrown Industrial (Dongguan)
Limited   **(1)**
Huangang Industrial Estate Houjie Town,
Dongguan, 523946, China
Tel.: (86) 76989138233
Web Site: https://www.jetcrown.com.cn
Sales Range: $450-499.9 Million
Emp.: 200
Injection Molding Plastic Products Mfr
N.A.I.C.S.: 326199
Weiye Gan *(Gen Mgr)*

Jetcrown Industrial (Macao Commercial Offshore) Limited   **(1)**
17B Edificio Comercial Rodrigues 599

Avenida Da Praia Grande, Macau, China
(Macau)
Tel.: (853) 2 832 2096
Plastics Product Mfr
N.A.I.C.S.: 326199

Shenzhen Kwan Wing Trading Com-
pany Limited   **(1)**
Room 901 JiaDe Building Red Star Alliance,
Commercial and Residential District Song-
gang Town Bao An District, Shenzhen,
Guangdong, China
Plastics Product Mfr
N.A.I.C.S.: 326199

DET DANSKE FILMINSTITUT

55 Gothersgade, 1123, Copenhagen,
Denmark
Tel.: (45) 33743400
Web Site: http://www.dfi.dk
Sales Range: $50-74.9 Million
Emp.: 150
Film Promoter
N.A.I.C.S.: 512199
Dorthe Tauber Lassen *(Head-Admin)*

DET DANSKE HEDESELSKAB

Klostermarken 12, 8800, Viborg, Den-
mark
Tel.: (45) 87 28 11 33   DK
Web Site:
   http://www.hedeselskabet.dk
Year Founded: 1866
Environmental Services
N.A.I.C.S.: 813312
Christian Bogh *(Dir-Comm)*

Subsidiaries:

Dalgasgroup A/S   **(1)**
Klostermarken 12, Viborg, 8800, Denmark
Tel.: (45) 87281133
Web Site: http://www.dalgasgroup.com
Sales Range: $250-299.9 Million
Emp.: 1,100
Holding Company
N.A.I.C.S.: 551112
Ove Kloch *(CEO & Mng Dir)*

Subsidiary (Domestic):

HedeDanmark a/s   **(2)**
Klostermarken 12, 8800, Viborg, Denmark
Tel.: (45) 87281000
Web Site: http://www.hededanmark.com
Sales Range: $200-249.9 Million
Emp.: 1,000
Landscape & Forest Consulting & Manage-
ment Services
N.A.I.C.S.: 541320
Lars H. Petersen *(CEO)*

Subsidiary (Non-US):

Heidegesellaschaft G.m.b.H.   **(3)**
Technologiepark 24, 22946, Trittau, Ger-
many
Tel.: (49) 415 484 480
Web Site: http://www.hd2412.de
Wood Product Distr
N.A.I.C.S.: 423310
Mario Stabenow *(Reg Mgr-Round timber-Brandenburg & Sachsen)*

Subsidiary (Domestic):

Skaelskor Anlaegsgartnere A/S   **(3)**
Kirkebjergvej 7, 4180, Soro, Denmark
Tel.: (45) 58 16 47 00
Web Site: http://www.skag.dk
Construction Engineering Services
N.A.I.C.S.: 541330

Subsidiary (Non-US):

Hedeselskabet Sp. z.o.o.   **(2)**
ul Grzybowska 2 lok 80 budynek B, 00-131,
Warsaw, Poland
Tel.: (45) 22 33 93 610
Web Site: http://www.hedeselskabet.pl
Eletric Power Generation Services
N.A.I.C.S.: 221117

Subsidiary (Domestic):

Silva Estate A/S   **(2)**
Kokholm 3, 6000, Kolding, Denmark
Tel.: (45) 76 33 34 84

Web Site: http://www.silvaestate.dk
Real Estate Consulting Service
N.A.I.C.S.: 531390

DETACH AB

Valtstigen 4, PO Box 165, SE 645 41,
Strangnas, Sweden
Tel.: (46) 15222830
Web Site: http://www.detach.se
Sales Range: $1-9.9 Million
Emp.: 25
Medical Office Products & Systems
N.A.I.C.S.: 621112

DETAI NEW ENERGY GROUP LIMITED

Suite 2702-27/F China Resources
Building 26 Harbour Road, Wan Chai,
Hong Kong, China (Hong Kong)
Tel.: (852) 31000600
Web Site: http://www.detai-
   group.com
0559—(HKG)
Rev.: $5,294,887
Assets: $92,717,015
Liabilities: $14,094,290
Net Worth: $78,622,726
Earnings: ($17,520,385)
Emp.: 27
Fiscal Year-end: 06/30/22
Holding Company; Alcoholic Bever-
age Distr
N.A.I.C.S.: 551112
Hin Shek Wong *(Chm)*

Subsidiaries:

Emission Particle Solution Sweden
AB   **(1)**
Norra Hamngatan 18, 411 06, Gothenburg,
Sweden
Tel.: (46) 31 701 0600
Web Site: https://www.eps.se
Fuel Additive Mfr & Distr
N.A.I.C.S.: 325199
Lars Olausson *(CTO)*

DETECTION TECHNOLOGY OYJ

Elektroniikkatie 17, FI-90590, Oulu,
Finland
Tel.: (358) 207669700   FI
Web Site: https://www.deetee.com
DETEC—(HEL)
Rev.: $106,389,240
Assets: $98,627,573
Liabilities: $20,105,982
Net Worth: $78,521,591
Earnings: $5,520,867
Emp.: 469
Fiscal Year-end: 12/31/22
Diagnostic Imaging Equipment Mfr
N.A.I.C.S.: 339112
Hannu Martola *(Pres & CEO)*

Subsidiaries:

Beijing DT Electronic Technology Co.,
Ltd.   **(1)**
4F Building A Lizeyuan, Chaoyang District,
Beijing, 100102, China
Tel.: (86) 1064399970
Diagnostic Imaging Equipment Mfr
N.A.I.C.S.: 339112

DT Electronic Manufacturing (Beijing)
Co., Ltd.   **(1)**
2F Building 9 Han's Enterprise Bay 8 Liang-
shuihe 2nd Street, Economical and Techno-
logical Development Zone, Beijing, 100176,
China
Tel.: (86) 1067832601
Diagnostic Imaging Equipment Mfr
N.A.I.C.S.: 339112
Mika Matto *(Dir-Dev)*

DT Electronic Technology (Wuxi) Co.,
Ltd.   **(1)**
No 30 Yanxin East Road Huishan Economic
Development Area, Wuxi, 214000, China
Tel.: (86) 51083560010
X-Ray Imaging Product Mfr & Distr

Detection Technology Oyj—(Continued)

N.A.I.C.S.: 334517

DTF (H.K.) Ltd. (1)
Flat J 13/F Century Industrial Centre 33-35,
Au Pui Wan Street Fo Tan NT, Sha Tin,
China (Hong Kong)
Tel.: (852) 26629927
Diagnostic Imaging Equipment Mfr
N.A.I.C.S.: 339112

Detection Technology S.A.S. (1)
235 Rue de Corporat, 38430, Moirans,
France
Tel.: (33) 667614819
X-Ray Detector Mfr
N.A.I.C.S.: 334517

Detection Technology, Inc. (1)
6 Fortune Dr, Billerica, MA 01821
Tel.: (978) 362-8921
Diagnostic Imaging Equipment Mfr
N.A.I.C.S.: 339112

DETERRA ROYALTIES LIMITED

Level 16 140 St George's Terrace,
Perth, 6000, WA, Australia
Tel.: (61) 862778880   **AU**
Web Site:
https://www.deterraroyalties.com
Year Founded: 2020
DRR—(ASX)
Rev.: $149,484,254
Assets: $73,986,438
Liabilities: $13,910,804
Net Worth: $60,075,634
Earnings: $99,405,360
Emp.: 8
Fiscal Year-end: 06/30/23
Investment Management Service
N.A.I.C.S.: 523999
Brendan Ryan (CFO)

Subsidiaries:

Trident Royalties Plc (1)
6th Floor 60 Gracechurch Street, London,
EC3V 0HR, United Kingdom
Tel.: (44) 2084344688
Web Site: https://www.tridentroyalties.com
Rev.: $7,850,000
Assets: $150,007,000
Liabilities: $45,137,000
Net Worth: $104,870,000
Earnings: ($3,684,000)
Emp.: 4
Fiscal Year-end: 12/31/2022
Vehicle Investment Management Services
N.A.I.C.S.: 525990
Adam Davidson (CEO)

DETROIT CHILE S.A.

Baron de Juras Reales N 5250, PO
Box 10114, Conchali, Santiago, Chile
Tel.: (56) 24408500
Web Site: http://www.detroit.cl
Year Founded: 1949
Engine Mfr & Logistics Support Services
N.A.I.C.S.: 333618

DETRON ICT SOLUTIONS BV

Traverse 1, PO Box 721, 3905 NL,
Veenendaal, Netherlands
Tel.: (31) 88 44 60 000   **NI**
Web Site: http://www.detron.nl
IT & Telecom Services
N.A.I.C.S.: 541990
George Banks (CEO)

DETSKY MIR GROUP

Tel.: (7) 4957810808
Web Site: http://corp.detmir.ru
Year Founded: 1997
DSKY—(MOEX)
Rev.: $1,928,907,000
Assets: $1,309,419,000
Liabilities: $1,344,951,000
Net Worth: ($35,532,000)
Earnings: $91,111,500
Emp.: 15,000

Fiscal Year-end: 12/31/20
Clothing Retailer
N.A.I.C.S.: 424350
Maria Davydova (Chm & Gen Dir)

DEUFOL SE

Johannes-Gutenberg-Str 3-5, 65719,
Hofheim, Germany
Tel.: (49) 6122 5000
Web Site: http://www.deufol.com
Year Founded: 1998
Sales Range: $300-349.9 Million
Emp.: 2,561
Packaging & Logistics Services
N.A.I.C.S.: 561910
Detlef W. Hubner (Chm & Mng Dir)

Subsidiaries:

Aircon Airfreight Container Mainte-
nance GmbH (1)
Dieselstr 5, 64546, Morfelden, 64546, (56.7%)
Hesse, Germany
Tel.: (49) 610524455
Sales Range: $25-49.9 Million
Emp.: 16
Air Freight Services
N.A.I.C.S.: 481212
Heiko Wedmann (Mng Dir)

Deufol (Suzhou) Packaging Co.,
Ltd. (1)
No 2010 20th floor Golden River Tower,
Suzhou, 215011, China
Tel.: (86) 51253985068
Packaging & Logistic Services
N.A.I.C.S.: 488510

Deufol Austria Supply Chain Solu-
tions GmbH (1)
Linzer Strasse 55, 3100, Saint Polten, Austria
Tel.: (43) 27648298
Packaging & Logistic Services
N.A.I.C.S.: 488510

Deufol Belgie N.V. (1)
Industriepark 16 2, 3300, Tienen, Belgium
Tel.: (32) 16801011
Web Site: http://www.deufol.be
Sales Range: $100-124.9 Million
Emp.: 300
Packaging & Warehousing Services
N.A.I.C.S.: 493110
Ronald Schrooten (Mgr)

Subsidiary (Domestic):

AT+S N.V. (2)
Centrum Zuid 1611, 3530, Houthalen, Limburg, Belgium
Tel.: (32) 11606400
Sales Range: $25-49.9 Million
Emp.: 20
Transportation Services
N.A.I.C.S.: 484220

Arcus Installation N.V. (2)
Centrum-Zuid 1611, Houthalen, 3530, Limburg, Belgium
Tel.: (32) 11606399
Sales Range: $25-49.9 Million
Emp.: 3
Logistic Services
N.A.I.C.S.: 541614
Ronald Schrooten (Mng Dir)

Subsidiary (Domestic):

Deufol Waremme S.A. (2)
Rue du Parc Industriel 29, 4300, Waremme,
Liege, Belgium
Tel.: (32) 19339730
Sales Range: $25-49.9 Million
Emp.: 6
Logistic Services
N.A.I.C.S.: 541614

Deufol CZ Production s. r. o. (1)
Logisticka 170/2, Hradiste, 350 02, Cheb,
Czech Republic
Tel.: (420) 720949431
Packaging & Logistic Services
N.A.I.C.S.: 488510

Deufol Ceska republika a.s. (1)
Videnska 188/190, 619 00, Brno, Czech
Republic
Tel.: (420) 606714121
Web Site: http://www.deufol.cz

Packaging & Logistic Services
N.A.I.C.S.: 488510

Deufol Italia S.p.A. (1)
via Magellano 22, 21054, Fagnano Olona,
Italy
Tel.: (39) 0331613721
Packaging Material Mfr & Related Services
N.A.I.C.S.: 322220

Deufol Lier NV (1)
Paaiestraat 17, 2500, Lier, Belgium
Tel.: (32) 34882192
Web Site: http://www.deufol.be
Packaging & Logistic Services
N.A.I.C.S.: 488510

Deufol Packaging Tienen N.V. (1)
Industriepark 16, Box 3, 3300, Tienen,
Flemish Brabant, Belgium
Tel.: (32) 16801011
Sales Range: $50-74.9 Million
Emp.: 150
Packaging & Warehousing Services
N.A.I.C.S.: 493110

Deufol Port of Antwerp NV (1)
Churchilldok Zuid Wilmarsstraat kaai 414,
2030, Antwerp, Belgium
Tel.: (32) 35408686
Packaging & Logistic Services
N.A.I.C.S.: 488510

Deufol Slovensko s.r.o. (1)
Bedzianska cesta 667, 956 31, Krusovce,
Slovakia
Tel.: (421) 385328403
Web Site: http://www.logis.sk
Sales Range: $25-49.9 Million
Emp.: 25
Logistics & Packaging Services
N.A.I.C.S.: 541614
Peter Petras (Mng Dir)

Deufol Sunman Inc. (1)
924 S Meridian St, Sunman, IN 47041-8498
Tel.: (812) 623-1140
Web Site: http://www.deufol.com
Sales Range: $50-74.9 Million
Emp.: 500
Automated Packaging & Crating Services
N.A.I.C.S.: 561910
Lisa Nichols (Mgr-HR)

Deufol Tailleur GmbH (1)
Essener Strasse 2-24, 46047, Oberhausen,
Nordrhein-Westfalen, Germany
Tel.: (49) 2088596100
Sales Range: $25-49.9 Million
Emp.: 10
Packaging Services
N.A.I.C.S.: 561910

Subsidiary (Domestic):

DTG Verpackungslogistik GmbH (2)
Ringstrasse 71-73, 70736, Fellbach, Germany
Tel.: (49) 7113426680
Web Site: http://www.dtg-
verpackungslogistik.com
Sales Range: $25-49.9 Million
Emp.: 33
Logistics & Packaging Services
N.A.I.C.S.: 541614
Herr Ziegler (Mgr)

Deufol Berlin GmbH (2)
Piesporter Strasse 50-52, 13088, Berlin,
Germany
Tel.: (49) 3092403590
Web Site: http://www.deufol.de
Sales Range: $10-24.9 Million
Emp.: 50
Packaging Services
N.A.I.C.S.: 561910

Deufol Bochum GmbH (2)
Arnoldschacht 11, 44894, Bochum, 44894,
Nordrhein-Westfalen, Germany
Tel.: (49) 23423960
Web Site: http://www.deufol.com
Packaging Services
N.A.I.C.S.: 561910

Deufol Frankfurt GmbH (2)
Cargo City Sud Gebaude 638 E, Frankfurt
am Main, 60549, Hesse, Germany
Tel.: (49) 696380940

Sales Range: $25-49.9 Million
Emp.: 10
Packaging Services
N.A.I.C.S.: 561910
Stefen Tjaden (Mng Dir)

Deufol Hamburg GmbH (2)
Ellerholzdamm 16-20, 20457, Hamburg,
Germany
Tel.: (49) 403197510
Web Site: http://www.deufol.com
Sales Range: $25-49.9 Million
Emp.: 5
Packaging Services
N.A.I.C.S.: 561910
Thomas Vachta (Gen mgr)

Deufol Munchen GmbH (2)
Lichtlocherberg 40, 06333, Hettstedt,
Saxony-Anhalt, Germany
Tel.: (49) 3476893020
Web Site: http://www.ias-hettstedt.de
Packaging Services
N.A.I.C.S.: 561910

Deufol Nord GmbH (2)
Vohrumer Str 40, Peine, 31228, Germany
Tel.: (49) 51712960
Web Site: http://www.deufol.com
Sales Range: $25-49.9 Million
Packaging Services
N.A.I.C.S.: 561910

Deufol Nurnberg GmbH (2)
Rotterdamer Strasse 130, 90451, Nuremberg, Bavaria, Germany
Tel.: (49) 9119686890
Web Site: http://www.deufol.de
Sales Range: $10-24.9 Million
Packaging Services
N.A.I.C.S.: 561910
Jurgen Schmid (Mgr)

Deufol Remscheid GmbH (2)
Essener Strasse 2-24, 46047, Oberhausen,
Germany
Tel.: (49) 2088596200
Sales Range: $25-49.9 Million
Emp.: 60
Packaging & Freight Transportation Services
N.A.I.C.S.: 481212

Deufol Sud GmbH (2)
Neugablonzer Str 1, 93073, Neutraubling,
Germany
Tel.: (49) 9401 607655
Packaging Services
N.A.I.C.S.: 561910
Jurgen Schmid (Mgr)

Deufol West GmbH (2)
Essener Strasse 2-24, 46047, Oberhausen,
Nordrhein-Westfalen, Germany
Tel.: (49) 20885 96100
Packaging Services
N.A.I.C.S.: 561910

Horst Lange GmbH (2)
Schlossstrasse 112, 22041, Hamburg, Germany
Tel.: (49) 404191940
Packaging Services
N.A.I.C.S.: 561910

IAD Industrieanlagen-Dienst
GmbH (2)
Lemgostr 21, 80935, Munich, Bavaria, Germany
Tel.: (49) 89 3515081
Sales Range: $25-49.9 Million
Packaging Wooden Boxes Mfr & Distr
N.A.I.C.S.: 321920

Subsidiary (Non-US):

Logis Industriedienstleistung
GmbH (2)
Jahnstrasse 45, 3430, Tulln, Austria
Tel.: (43) 2272 8173520
Web Site: http://www.logis-group.eu
Sales Range: $25-49.9 Million
Logistics & Packaging Services
N.A.I.C.S.: 541614

Logis prumyslove obaly a.s. (2)
Za Mostem 303 8, 664 91, Ivancice, Czech
Republic
Tel.: (420) 546 451 101
Web Site: http://www.deufol.com

Sales Range: $25-49.9 Million
Logistics & Packaging Services
N.A.I.C.S.: 541614

Subsidiary (Domestic):

Walpa Gesellschaft fur Ubersee- und
Spezialverpackung mbH **(2)**
Daimlerstrasse 38a, 69190, Walldorf, Germany
Tel.: (49) 622782600
Web Site: http://www.walpa.de
Sales Range: $10-24.9 Million
Packaging Services
N.A.I.C.S.: 561910

Deufol Technics NV **(1)**
Centrum Zuid 1611, 3530, Houthalen, Belgium
Tel.: (32) 11606400
Packaging & Logistic Services
N.A.I.C.S.: 488510

DEUTA-WERKE GMBH
Paffrather Str 140, 51465, Bergisch
Gladbach, Germany
Tel.: (49) 2202958100
Web Site: http://www.deuta.de
Year Founded: 1905
Sales Range: $25-49.9 Million
Emp.: 143
Automotive Products Mfr
N.A.I.C.S.: 336110
Rudolf Ganz *(Mng Dir)*

Subsidiaries:

DEUTA AMERICA CORP. **(1)**
510 Research Rd, Richmond, VA 23236
Tel.: (804) 464-1860
Web Site: http://www.deuta-america.com
Electronic Components Distr
N.A.I.C.S.: 423690

DEUTRUCK GMBH
Ahrwald Strasse 7, Garlstorf, 21376,
Germany
Tel.: (49) 41726647
Web Site: http://www.deutruck.com
Rev.: $16,222,256
Emp.: 20
Forklift Truck Mfr
N.A.I.C.S.: 333924
Georg Grochutek *(Mng Dir)*

DEUTSCH MOTORS INC.
Dong-il-ro 111, Seongdong-gu, Seoul,
Korea (South)
Tel.: (82) 222436165
Web Site:
  https://www.deutschmotors.com
Year Founded: 2000
067990—(KRS)
Rev.: $1,501,079,563
Assets: $974,480,959
Liabilities: $671,281,322
Net Worth: $303,199,636
Earnings: $29,575,544
Emp.: 1,144
Fiscal Year-end: 12/31/22
Automobile Dealers
N.A.I.C.S.: 441110
Bumjoo Sohn *(Asst Mgr)*

**DEUTSCHE APOTHEKER-
UND ARZTEBANK EG**
Richard-Oskar-Mattern-Strasse 6,
40547, Dusseldorf, Germany
Tel.: (49) 21159980   De
Web Site: http://www.apobank.de
Year Founded: 1902
Rev.: $932,184,152
Assets: $55,548,959,020
Liabilities: $53,457,022,552
Net Worth: $2,091,936,468
Earnings: $71,813,837
Emp.: 2,448
Fiscal Year-end: 12/31/19
Financial & Banking Services
N.A.I.C.S.: 522110

Ulrich Sommer *(Chm-Mgmt Bd & CEO)*

Subsidiaries:

Apo Asset Management GmbH **(1)**
Richard-Oskar-Mattern-Str 6, 40547, Dusseldorf, Germany
Tel.: (49) 2118632310
Web Site: http://www.apoasset.de
Sales Range: $50-74.9 Million
Emp.: 20
Direct Property & Casualty Insurance Carrier Services
N.A.I.C.S.: 524126

Apo Immobilien-KAG **(1)**
Richard-Oskar-Mattern-Strasse 8, 40547, Dusseldorf, Germany
Tel.: (49) 2115374200
Web Site: http://www.aik-invest.de
Sales Range: $25-49.9 Million
Emp.: 50
Real Estate Agents & Brokers Offices
N.A.I.C.S.: 531210
Stephan Hinsche *(Mng Dir)*

ApoFinanz GmbH **(1)**
Richard-Oskar-Mattern-Strasse 6, 40547, Dusseldorf, Germany
Tel.: (49) 21159988703
Web Site: http://www.apofinanz.de
Financial Transactions Processing Reserve & Clearinghouse Activities
N.A.I.C.S.: 522320

DGN Service GmbH **(1)**
Niederkasseler Lohweg 185, 40547, Dusseldorf, Germany
Tel.: (49) 211770080
Web Site: http://www.dgn.de
Sales Range: $50-74.9 Million
Emp.: 35
International Trade Financing
N.A.I.C.S.: 522299
Armin Flender *(Mng Dir & Editor)*

medisign GmbH **(1)**
Richard-Oskar-Mattern-Strasse 6, 40547, Dusseldorf, Germany
Tel.: (49) 2115382230
Web Site: http://www.medisign.de
Digital Security Services
N.A.I.C.S.: 541519
Peter Gabriel *(Mng Dir)*

DEUTSCHE BAHN AG
Europaplatz 1, 10785, Berlin, Germany
Tel.: (49) 302970   De
Web Site:
  https://www.deutschebahn.com
Year Founded: 1994
Rev.: $49,885,197,049
Assets: $85,519,373,011
Liabilities: $72,133,789,612
Net Worth: $13,385,583,400
Earnings: ($2,243,073,187)
Emp.: 304,451
Fiscal Year-end: 12/31/23
Holding Company; Passenger & Freight Transportation & Logistics Services
N.A.I.C.S.: 551112
Richard Lutz *(CEO & Member-Mgmt Bd)*

Subsidiaries:

AMEROPA-REISEN GmbH **(1)**
Hewlett-Packard-Strasse 4, 61352, Bad Homburg, Germany
Tel.: (49) 61721090
Web Site: http://www.ameropa.de
Railway Freight Transportation Services
N.A.I.C.S.: 482111

ARRIVA Liorbus, a. s. **(1)**
Bystricka cesta 62, 03431, Ruzomberok, Slovakia
Tel.: (421) 915733733
Passenger Transport Services
N.A.I.C.S.: 485999

ARRIVA Slovakia a.s. **(1)**
Sturova 72, 949 44, Nitra, Slovakia
Tel.: (421) 915733733

Passenger Transport Services
N.A.I.C.S.: 485999
Peter Nagy *(Fin Dir)*

ASIMEX Anterist + Schneider Import - Export SAS **(1)**
Zone Industrielle de la Heid Rue Robert Schuman, Stiring-Wendel, 57350, France
Tel.: (33) 387874187
Logistics Consulting Servies
N.A.I.C.S.: 541614

Anterist + Schneider Zeebrugge B.V. **(1)**
Koggenstraat 3 Bus 3, 8380, Zeebrugge, Belgium
Tel.: (32) 50548571
Logistics Consulting Servies
N.A.I.C.S.: 541614

Arriva City s.r.o. **(1)**
U Stavoservisu 692 1b, Malesice, 10800, Prague, Czech Republic
Tel.: (420) 605231100
Bus Transportation Services
N.A.I.C.S.: 485210

Arriva Galicia S.L. **(1)**
Fifth Avenue 64 Parc E 16, Poligono Industrial Pocomaco, 15190, A Coruna, Spain
Tel.: (34) 981330046
Web Site: http://www.arriva.gal
Emp.: 300
Bus Transportation Services
N.A.I.C.S.: 485210

Arriva Madrid Movilidad S.L. **(1)**
C/Fraguas 27 Pol Ind Urtinsa, Alcorcon, 28923, Madrid, Spain
Tel.: (34) 912260418
Web Site: http://www.arrivamadrid.es
Bus Transportation Services
N.A.I.C.S.: 485210

Arriva Rail London Limited **(1)**
Overground House 125 Finchley Road Swiss Cottage, London, NW3 6HY, United Kingdom
Tel.: (44) 2030319200
Web Site: http://www.arrivaraillondon.co.uk
Emp.: 1,500
Passenger Transport Services
N.A.I.C.S.: 485999
Matt Pocock *(Dir-Performance)*

Arriva Stredni Cechy s.r.o. **(1)**
Pod Hajem 97, 267 01, Kraluv Dvur, Czech Republic
Tel.: (420) 311563749
Passenger Transport Services
N.A.I.C.S.: 485999

Arriva Trnava, a. s. **(1)**
Nitrianska 5, 917 02, Trnava, Slovakia
Tel.: (421) 915733733
Passenger Transport Services
N.A.I.C.S.: 485999

Autocares Mallorca, s.l. **(1)**
C/ Eivissa 15, Alcudia, 7400, Spain
Tel.: (34) 971545696
Transportation Services
N.A.I.C.S.: 488490

Autokraft GmbH **(1)**
Hamburger Chaussee 10, 24114, Kiel, Germany
Tel.: (49) 431666222
Transportation Services
N.A.I.C.S.: 485113

Autoprometno Poduzece d.d. **(1)**
Industrijska 14, Pozega, Croatia
Tel.: (385) 34273103
Passenger Transport Services
N.A.I.C.S.: 485999

Autotrans d.d. **(1)**
Sluzba podrske prometa i prodaje pp288, 51000, Rijeka, Croatia
Tel.: (385) 72660660
Passenger Transport Services
N.A.I.C.S.: 485999
Elizabeth Michelle Benison *(Chm)*

BBH BahnBus Hochstift GmbH **(1)**
Bahnhofstrasse 17, 33102, Paderborn, Germany
Tel.: (49) 525120130
Transportation Services
N.A.I.C.S.: 485113

BVO Busverkehr Ostwestfalen GmbH **(1)**
Wilhelm-Bertelsmann-Strasse 13a, 33602, Bielefeld, Germany
Tel.: (49) 521520700
Web Site: http://www.ostwestfalen-lippe-bus.de
Emp.: 10
Transportation Services
N.A.I.C.S.: 485113

BVR Busverkehr Rheinland GmbH **(1)**
Graf-Adolf-Strasse 67-69, 40210, Dusseldorf, Germany
Tel.: (49) 211169900
Web Site: http://www.rheinlandbus.de
Transportation Services
N.A.I.C.S.: 485113

Bayern Express&P. Kuhn Berlin GmbH **(1)**
Mannheimer Strasse 33/34, Wilmersdorf, 10713, Berlin, Germany
Tel.: (49) 30860960
Web Site: http://www.bex.de
Transportation Services
N.A.I.C.S.: 485113
Volkswirt Jorg Schaube *(Mng Dir)*

Bergamo Trasporti Est S.c.a.r.l. **(1)**
Piazza Marconi 4, 24125, Bergamo, Italy
Tel.: (39) 035289000
Web Site: http://www.bergamotrasporti.it
Transportation Services
N.A.I.C.S.: 488490

Bischof Gesellschaft mbH. **(1)**
Freudenauer Hafenstrasse 16, 1020, Vienna, Austria
Tel.: (43) 57686211900
Freight Forwarding Services
N.A.I.C.S.: 488510

Botniatag AB **(1)**
Storgatan 115, Umea, 90333, Sweden
Tel.: (46) 84492544
Transportation Services
N.A.I.C.S.: 488490

Busverkehr Markisch-Oderland GmbH **(1)**
Ernst-Thalmann-Strasse 71, 15344, Brandenburg, Germany
Tel.: (49) 3341478310
Web Site: http://www.busmol.de
Transportation Services
N.A.I.C.S.: 485113

Busverkehr Oder-Spree GmbH **(1)**
James-Watt-Strasse 4, 15517, Furstenwalde, Germany
Tel.: (49) 336155610
Web Site: http://www.bos-fw.de
Transportation Services
N.A.I.C.S.: 485113

Classic Coaches (Continental) Limited **(1)**
Fell Bank Chester Le Street, Birtley, DH3 2SP, United Kingdom
Tel.: (44) 1914104107
Web Site: http://www.jhminibreaks.co.uk
Travel & Ticketing Services
N.A.I.C.S.: 561510

DB Bahn Italia S.r.l. **(1)**
Interno Stazione P Nuova P zza XXV Aprile, Verona, 37122, Italy
Tel.: (39) 0267479578
Travel & Ticketing Services
N.A.I.C.S.: 561510

DB BahnPark GmbH **(1)**
Tauentzienstrasse 9-12, 10789, Berlin, Germany
Tel.: (49) 3031986170
Web Site: http://www.dbbahnpark.de
Parking Garage Operator
N.A.I.C.S.: 812930

DB Barnsdale AG **(1)**
Bellevuestr 3, 10785, Berlin, Germany
Tel.: (49) 3029754024
Web Site: http://www.dbbarnsdale.com
Parking Garage Operator
N.A.I.C.S.: 812930

DB Busverkehr Hessen GmbH **(1)**
Neustadt 26, 35390, Giessen, Germany

Deutsche Bahn AG—(Continued)

Tel.: (49) 641701100
Web Site: http://Www.busverkehrhessen.de
Travel & Ticketing Services
N.A.I.C.S.: 561510

DB Cargo Belgium BV   **(1)**
Noorderlaan 111 bus 17, 2030, Antwerp,
Belgium
Tel.: (32) 35450249
Web Site: http://www.wisselvanspoor.be
Railroad Cargo Handling Services
N.A.I.C.S.: 488210
Dimitri Goovaerts *(Mgr-IT)*

DB Cargo Bulgaria EOOD   **(1)**
2 Teophan Raynov Str, Karlovo, Plovdiv,
4300, Bulgaria
Tel.: (359) 72862529
Web Site: http://www.bg.dbcargo.com
Rail Freight Services
N.A.I.C.S.: 488210
Ivan Sinev *(Sls Mgr)*

DB Cargo Eurasia GmbH   **(1)**
Bellevuestrasse 3, 10785, Berlin, Germany
Tel.: (49) 3029754804
Web Site: http://eurasia.dbcargo.com
Rail Cargo Shipping Services
N.A.I.C.S.: 488210
Dmitrij Hasenkampf *(Dir-Sls & Bus Dev)*

DB Cargo Hungaria Kft.   **(1)**
Eszperantou 19, 9024, Gyor, Hungary
Tel.: (36) 96542176
Web Site: http://www.hu.dbcargo.com
Railroad Switching Services
N.A.I.C.S.: 488210
Jan Busch *(CEO)*

DB Cargo Italia S.r.l.   **(1)**
Via G Spadolini 12, 20026, Novate Mila-
nese, MI, Italy
Tel.: (39) 0285113863
Web Site: http://www.it.dbcargo.com
Rail Cargo Services
N.A.I.C.S.: 488210
Marianna Foti *(Head-HR)*

DB Cargo Italia Services S.r.l.   **(1)**
Via G Spadolini 12, 20026, Novate Mila-
nese, MI, Italy
Tel.: (39) 0267100748
Rail Cargo Services
N.A.I.C.S.: 488210
Pieralberto Vecchi *(Mng Dir)*

DB Cargo Logistics GmbH   **(1)**
Langer Kornweg 34 h i, 65451, Kelster-
bach, Germany
Tel.: (49) 61075090
Web Site: http://www.dbcargo.com
Rail Transport Logistics Services
N.A.I.C.S.: 488510
Arthur Meurer *(CFO)*

DB Cargo Nederland N.V.   **(1)**
Moreelsepark 1, 3511 EP, Utrecht, Nether-
lands
Tel.: (31) 302358347
Web Site: http://www.nl.dbcargo.com
Emp.: 700
Rail Transport Logistics Services
N.A.I.C.S.: 488510
Jan Jansen *(Head-Sls-Intl)*

DB Cargo Schweiz GmbH   **(1)**
Sagereistrasse 21, 8152, Glattbrugg, Swit-
zerland
Tel.: (41) 448075900
Web Site: http://www.ch.dbcargo.com
Freight Forwarding Services
N.A.I.C.S.: 488510
Martin Brunner *(Chm)*

DB Cargo Spedkol Sp. z o.o.   **(1)**
Szkolna 15 Street, 47-225, Kedzierzyn-
Kozle, Poland
Tel.: (48) 774886581
Freight Forwarding Services
N.A.I.C.S.: 488510

DB Dialog GmbH   **(1)**
Salzufer 6, 10587, Berlin, Germany
Tel.: (49) 30755453444
Web Site: http://www.dbdialog.de
Travel & Ticketing Services
N.A.I.C.S.: 561510

DB Dienstleistungen GmbH   **(1)**

Kothener Strasse 2-3, 10963, Berlin, Ger-
many
Tel.: (49) 3029746006
Building Maintenance & Renovation Ser-
vices
N.A.I.C.S.: 236118

**DB Engineering & Consulting USA
Inc.**   **(1)**
770 L St Ste 1240, Sacramento, CA 95814
Tel.: (916) 890-7206
Engineeering Services
N.A.I.C.S.: 541330
Mark Evans *(Pres & CEO)*

DB Fahrwegdienste GmbH   **(1)**
Elisabeth-Ebonlocke-Platz 1Â , 10115, Ber-
lin, Germany
Railway Maintenance Services
N.A.I.C.S.: 488210

**DB Fahrzeuginstandhaltung
GmbH**   **(1)**
Weilburger Strasse 22, 60326, Frankfurt,
Germany
Tel.: (49) 69 265 46525
Web Site: http://www.db-fzi.com
Emp.: 120
Automobile Maintenance Services
N.A.I.C.S.: 811111
Uwe Fresenborg *(Chm & Mng Dir)*

**DB Fernverkehr
Aktiengesellschaft**   **(1)**
Stephensonstrasse 1, 60326, Frankfurt,
Germany
Tel.: (49) 1806996633
Automobile Maintenance Services
N.A.I.C.S.: 811111

DB FuhrparkService GmbH   **(1)**
Mainzer Landstrasse 169Â , 60327, Frank-
furt, Germany
Tel.: (49) 6926540500
Automobile Maintenance Services
N.A.I.C.S.: 811111

DB Gastronomie GmbH   **(1)**
Weilburger Str 28, 60326, Frankfurt, Ger-
many
Catering Services
N.A.I.C.S.: 722320

**DB Kommunikationstechnik
GmbH**   **(1)**
Alfred-Herrhausen-Allee 1, 65760, Es-
chborn, Germany
Tel.: (49) 6926550050
Communication Equipment Technology Ser-
vices
N.A.I.C.S.: 541512
Schlicke Peter *(Mgr-Sls)*

**DB Mobility Services Austria
GmbH**   **(1)**
Bosendorferstrasse 2/1, 1010, Vienna, Aus-
tria
Tel.: (43) 12675066
Communication Equipment Technology Ser-
vices
N.A.I.C.S.: 541512

DB Netz AG   **(1)**
Theodor-Heuss-Allee 7, 60486, Frankfurt,
Germany   **(100%)**
Tel.: (49) 1806996633
Web Site: http://www.fahrweg.dbnetze.com
Railway Infrastructure Support Services
N.A.I.C.S.: 488210
Pascal Guinomet *(Officer-Compliance)*

DB ProjektBau GmbH   **(1)**
Euref-Campus 14Â Torgauer Strasse 12-
15, 10829, Berlin, Germany
Tel.: (49) 1806673040
Web Site:
  http://www.dbprojektbau.dbnetze.com
Mechanical Engineering Services
N.A.I.C.S.: 541330

DB Regio Bus Mitte GmbH   **(1)**
Erthalstrasse 1, 55118, Mainz, Germany
Tel.: (49) 62168597855
Bus Transportation Services
N.A.I.C.S.: 485999
Kai Jakupka *(Mgr-HR)*

**DB Schenker Rail Deutschland
AG**   **(1)**

Rheinstrasse 2, D-55116, Mainz,
Germany   **(92%)**
Tel.: (49) 6131159
Web Site: http://rail.dbschenker.de
Sales Range: $5-14.9 Billion
Emp.: 29,242
Rail Freight Carrier & Logistics
N.A.I.C.S.: 482111
Alexander Hedderich *(CEO & Head-Bus
Segment Germany & Central Reg)*

Subsidiary (Non-US):

Autologistic Poland Sp. z o. o.   **(2)**
Ul Turynska 100, 43-100, Tychy, Poland
Tel.: (48) 322161686
Web Site: http://www.alp.com.pl
Logistics Consulting Servies
N.A.I.C.S.: 541614

Axiom Rail Components Limited   **(2)**
Whieldon Road, Stoke-on-Trent, ST4 4HP,
United Kingdom
Tel.: (44) 7801905799
Web Site: http://www.axiomrail.com
Railway Freight Transportation Services
N.A.I.C.S.: 482111
Derek Parker *(Acct Mgr)*

DB Cargo Russija OOO   **(2)**
Proektiruemiy proezd Nr 4062 6 bldg 16
office 11-3, 115432, Moscow, Russia
Tel.: (7) 4952803905
Web Site: http://www.ru.dbcargo.com
Railway Freight Transportation Services
N.A.I.C.S.: 482111
Uwe Leuschner *(Head-Sls-Intl)*

Subsidiary (Domestic):

DB Intermodal Services GmbH   **(2)**
Rheinstrasse 2, 55116, Mainz, Germany
Tel.: (49) 6131153500
Ship Repair Services
N.A.I.C.S.: 336611
Rainer Godde *(Mng Dir)*

DB Schenker BTT GmbH   **(2)**
Rheinstr 2 a, 55116, Mainz, Germany
Tel.: (49) 61311573000
Logistics Consulting Servies
N.A.I.C.S.: 541614

DB Schenker Nieten GmbH   **(2)**
Kerschensteinerstr 1, 83395, Freilassing,
Germany
Tel.: (49) 865401040
Logistics Consulting Servies
N.A.I.C.S.: 541614

Subsidiary (Non-US):

DB Schenker Rail (UK) Limited   **(2)**
Lakeside Business Park Carolina Way,
Doncaster, DN4 5PN, United Kingdom
Tel.: (44) 8701405000
Web Site:
  http://www.railwaydbschenker.com
Sales Range: $1-4.9 Billion
Emp.: 500
Holding Company; Railroad Freight Trans-
portation Services
N.A.I.C.S.: 551112
Geoff Spencer *(CEO)*

Subsidiary (Domestic):

Axiom Rail Limited   **(3)**
Lakeside Business Park Carolina Way,
Doncaster, DN4 5PN, United
Kingdom   **(100%)**
Tel.: (44) 870 140 5330
Web Site: http://www.axiomrail.com
Railway Rolling Stock Maintenance & Sup-
port Services
N.A.I.C.S.: 488210

Subsidiary (Domestic):

Axiom Rail (Stoke) Limited   **(4)**
Whieldon Rd, Stoke-on-Trent, ST4 4HP,
United Kingdom   **(100%)**
Tel.: (44) 1782844075
Web Site: http://www.axiomrail.com
Sales Range: $50-74.9 Million
Emp.: 200
Railroad Rolling Stock Rental & Manage-
ment
N.A.I.C.S.: 532411

Subsidiary (Domestic):

**DB Schenker Rail Automotive
GmbH**   **(2)**
Langer Kornweg 34, 65451, Kelsterbach,
Germany
Tel.: (49) 61075090
Logistics Consulting Servies
N.A.I.C.S.: 541614
Jens Noldner *(Chm-Mgmt Bd & CEO)*

Subsidiary (Non-US):

**DB Schenker Rail Bulgaria
EOOD**   **(2)**
Industrial Zone, 2070, Sofia, Bulgaria
Tel.: (359) 72862247
Logistics Consulting Servies
N.A.I.C.S.: 541614
Matthias Reichel *(CEO)*

**DB Schenker Rail Danmark Services
A/S**   **(2)**
Spotorno Alle 12, 2630, Taastrup, Denmark
Tel.: (45) 88300900
Logistics Consulting Servies
N.A.I.C.S.: 541614
Niels Malling Hansen *(Acct Mgr)*

DB Schenker Rail Hungaria Kft.   **(2)**
Iroda Hutohaz u 23, 9027, Gyor, Hungary
Tel.: (36) 96542176
Logistics Consulting Servies
N.A.I.C.S.: 541614
Nandor Nemeth *(CEO)*

**DB Schenker Rail Information Ser-
vices Limited**   **(2)**
Lakeside Business Park Carolina Way,
Doncaster, DN4 5PN, United Kingdom
Tel.: (44) 1302575000
Logistics Consulting Servies
N.A.I.C.S.: 541614

DB Schenker Rail Italia S.r.l.   **(2)**
Via Umberto Giordano, I-15100, Alessan-
dria, Italy   **(100%)**
Tel.: (39) 0131218788
Web Site: http://www.rail.dbschenker.it
Freight Rail Carrier
N.A.I.C.S.: 482111
Olaf Muller *(CFO)*

Subsidiary (Domestic):

NORDCARGO S.R.L.   **(3)**
Via Spadolini 12, Novate Milanese, Milan,
20026, Italy   **(60%)**
Tel.: (39) 0285113800
Web Site: http://www.rail.dbschenker.it
Sales Range: $125-149.9 Million
Emp.: 300
Rail Freight Carrier Services
N.A.I.C.S.: 482111
Emanuele Vender *(CEO)*

Subsidiary (Non-US):

**DB Schenker Rail Nederland N.
V.**   **(2)**
Jelle RebbersÂ Moreelsepark 1, 3511 EPÂ ,
Utrecht, Netherlands
Tel.: (31) 302358347
Emp.: 650
Railway Freight Transportation Services
N.A.I.C.S.: 482111
Nigel Smith *(CEO)*

DB Schenker Rail Polska S.A.   **(2)**
ul Wolnosci 337, 41-800Â , Zabrze, Poland
Tel.: (48) 322714441
Emp.: 3,402
Railway Freight Transportation Services
N.A.I.C.S.: 482111
Marek Staszek *(CEO)*

**DB Schenker Rail Romania
S.R.L.**   **(2)**
Bucharest officeÂ Delea Noua 3 Street 3-4
Floor, 30925, Bucharest, Romania
Rail Freight Transportation Services
N.A.I.C.S.: 482111
Eduard Iancu *(CEO)*

**DB Schenker Rail Schweiz
GmbH**   **(2)**
Saagereistrasse 21, 8152, Opfikon, Switzer-
land
Rail Freight Transportation Services
N.A.I.C.S.: 482111

Martin Brunner *(Chm-Mgmt Bd)*

DB Schenker Rail Spedkol Sp. z o.o. **(2)**
ul Szkolna 15, 47-225, Kedzierzyn-Kozle, Poland
Tel.: (48) 774886058
Railway Freight Transportation Services
N.A.I.C.S.: 482111
Krzysztof Chmielewski *(Dir-Comml)*

DBPORT SZCZECIN Sp. z o.o. **(2)**
Bytomska 14 street, Szczecin, 70-603Â, Poland
Tel.: (48) 914308660
Web Site:
http://www.portszczecin.deutschebahn.com
Cargo Shipping Services
N.A.I.C.S.: 488510
Pawel Wac *(Pres, CEO & Member-Mgmt Bd)*

Subsidiary (Domestic):

DCH Dusseldorfer Container-Hafen GmbH **(2)**
Wesermunderstrasse 17, 40221, Dusseldorf, Germany
Tel.: (49) 2 11 9 01 49 0
Web Site: http://www.dch.container-terminal.de
Cargo Transportation Services
N.A.I.C.S.: 488490
Klaus Furchtenicht *(Head-Ops)*

Deutsche TRANSFESA GmbH **(2)**
Allensteinerstrasse 20, 77694, Kehl, Germany
Tel.: (49) 78517990
Logistics Consulting Servies
N.A.I.C.S.: 541614

Subsidiary (Non-US):

Doker-Port Sp. z o.o. **(2)**
Ul Bytomska7, 70-603, Szczecin, Poland
Tel.: (48) 500155315
Web Site: http://www.doker-port.szczecin.pl
Cargo Shipping Services
N.A.I.C.S.: 488510

Euro Cargo Rail SAS **(2)**
11 rue de Cambrai Batiment 028, 75945, Paris, Cedex 19, France
Rail Freight Transportation Services
N.A.I.C.S.: 482111

Infra Silesia S.A. **(2)**
ul Klokocinska 51, 44-251, Rybnik, Poland
Tel.: (48) 327394810
Web Site: http://www.infrasilesia.pl
Construction Management Services
N.A.I.C.S.: 236220

Subsidiary (Domestic):

KombiTerminal Burghausen GmbH **(2)**
Terminalstrasse 1, 84489, Burghausen, Germany
Tel.: (49) 86778760000
Web Site: http://www.kt-burghausen.de
Railway Freight Transportation Services
N.A.I.C.S.: 482111

Subsidiary (Non-US):

Logistica Sanmival S.L. **(2)**
Ctra Madrid-Irun km 245, 9007, Burgos, Spain
Tel.: (34) 947474453
Web Site: http://www.sanmival.com
Logistics Consulting Servies
N.A.I.C.S.: 541614

MDL Distribucion y Logistica S.A. **(2)**
C/Mario Roso de Luna 31 Nave 3, 28022, Madrid, Spain
Tel.: (34) 913120250
Transportation Services
N.A.I.C.S.: 488490

Subsidiary (Domestic):

Mitteldeutsche Eisenbahn GmbH **(2)**
Postfach 1461, PO Box 1461, 06204, Merseburg, Germany
Tel.: (49) 3461492249
Web Site: http://www.meg-bahn.de
Railway Freight Transportation Services

N.A.I.C.S.: 482111

RBH Logistics GmbH **(2)**
Talstrasse 7, 45966, Gladbeck, Germany
Tel.: (49) 2043501320
Web Site: http://www.rbh-logistics.com
Sales Range: $150-199.9 Million
Emp.: 800
Logistic Services
N.A.I.C.S.: 541614

Subsidiary (Non-US):

Rail Service Center Rotterdam B. V. **(2)**
Albert Plesmanweg 200, 3088 GD, Rotterdam, Netherlands
Tel.: (31) 104913600
Web Site: http://www.rscrotterdam.nl
Transportation Services
N.A.I.C.S.: 541614

Transervi S.A. **(2)**
C/ Mario Roso de Luna 31, 28022, Madrid, Spain
Tel.: (34) 902114011
Web Site: http://www.transervi.es
Industrial Management Services
N.A.I.C.S.: 541611

Transfesa Portugal Lda. **(2)**
Campo Grande 30 5 D, 1700-093, Lisbon, Portugal
Tel.: (351) 218824850
Railway Freight Transportation Services
N.A.I.C.S.: 482111

Transfesa Rail S.A. **(2)**
Calle Musgo 1, 28023, Madrid, Spain
Tel.: (34) 913879900
Web Site: http://www.transfesa.com
Logistics Consulting Servies
N.A.I.C.S.: 541614
Antonio Esparza Sanz *(Dir-Safety)*

Transfesa UK Ltd **(2)**
Rainham House Manor Way, Rainham, RM13 8RE, Essex, United Kingdom
Tel.: (44) 1708529200
Railway Freight Transportation Services
N.A.I.C.S.: 482111

DB Services GmbH **(1)**
Elisabeth-Schwarzhaupt-Platz 1, 10115, Berlin, Germany
Tel.: (49) 3029753400
Web Site: http://www.dbservices.de
Engineeering Services
N.A.I.C.S.: 541330

DB Sicherheit GmbH **(1)**
Kothener Strasse 4, 10963, Berlin, Germany
Rail Transportation Support Services
N.A.I.C.S.: 488210

DB Station&Service Aktiengesellschaft **(1)**
Europaplatz 1, 10557, Berlin, Germany
Tel.: (49) 3029765050
Property Protection & Security Services
N.A.I.C.S.: 561612
Andreas Hamprecht *(Gen Mgr)*

DB Systel GmbH **(1)**
jurgen-Ponto-Platz 1, 60329, Frankfurt, Germany
Tel.: (49) 6926550000
Web Site: http://www.dbsystel.de
Emp.: 2,400
Logistics Consulting Servies
N.A.I.C.S.: 541614
Christa Koenen *(Chm & Mng Dir)*

DB Systemtechnik GmbH **(1)**
Pionierstrasse 10, 32423, Minden, Germany
Tel.: (49) 5713935437
Web Site: http://www.db-systemtechnik.de
Emp.: 780
Engineeering Services
N.A.I.C.S.: 541330
Hans Peter Lang *(Member-Mgmt Bd)*

DB ZugBus Regionalverkehr Alb-Bodensee GmbH **(1)**
Karlstr 31-33, 89073, Ulm, Germany
Tel.: (49) 73115500
Web Site: http://www.zugbus-rab.de
Transportation Services
N.A.I.C.S.: 485113

DB broadband GmbH **(1)**
Rotfeder-Ring 9, 60327, Frankfurt am Main, Germany
Tel.: (49) 6926528667
Web Site:
http://www.broadband.dbnetze.com
Internet Services
N.A.I.C.S.: 517121
Xenia Knochenhauer *(Owner)*

DVA - Deutsche Verkehrs-Assekuranz-Vermittlungs GmbH **(1)**
Marienbader Platz 1, 61348, Bad Homburg, Germany
Tel.: (49) 617248680
Web Site: http://www.dva-assekuranz.de
Sales Range: $10-24.9 Million
Emp.: 120
Insurance Agency Services
N.A.I.C.S.: 524210
Christian Heidersdorf *(Mng Dir & Member-Mgmt Bd)*

Deutsche Bahn Cargo Romania S.R.L. **(1)**
Delea Noua no 3 Street Floors 1, 030925, Bucharest, Romania
Tel.: (40) 213312207
Web Site: http://www.ro.dbcargo.com
Freight Forwarding Services
N.A.I.C.S.: 488510
Eduard Iancu *(CEO)*

Deutsche Bahn Connect GmbH **(1)**
Mainzer Landstrasse 169Â, 60327, Frankfurt am Main, Germany
Tel.: (49) 6926540500
Web Site:
http://www.deutschebahnconnect.com
Emp.: 600
Rail Transportation Services
N.A.I.C.S.: 488210
Jurgen Gudd *(Chm)*

Deutsche Bahn Engineering&Consulting India Private Limited **(1)**
82 Lavelle Road 3nd Floor Brigade Hulkul, Bengaluru, 560001, India
Tel.: (91) 8046553700
Engineeering Services
N.A.I.C.S.: 541330
Milind Nirmal *(CEO)*

Deutsche Bahn Finance B. V. **(1)**
De Entree 99 - 197, Amsterdam Zuid-Oos, Amsterdam, Â 1101 HE, Netherlands
Tel.: (31) 205554609
Finance & Banking Services
N.A.I.C.S.: 522110

Deutsche Bahn France Voyages&Tourisme SAS **(1)**
20 rue Laffitte, 75009, Paris, France
Tel.: (33) 144589540
Travel & Ticketing Services
N.A.I.C.S.: 561510

Deutsche Bahn Iberica Holding, S.L. **(1)**
Z I Zona Franca C/ 4 Numero 57-61 Sector C, Barcelona, 8040, Spain
Tel.: (34) 933782898
Financial Consulting Services
N.A.I.C.S.: 523940

Deutsche Bahn International Operations GmbH **(1)**
Torgauer Strasse 12-15, 10829, Berlin, Germany
Tel.: (49) 3029764947
Web Site: http://io.deutschebahn.com
Emp.: 300,000
Rail Freight Services
N.A.I.C.S.: 488210
Michael Hetzer *(COO)*

Deutsche Bahn Stiftung gGmbH **(1)**
Bellevuestrasse 3, 10785, Berlin, Germany
Tel.: (49) 3029754901
Web Site:
http://www.deutschebahnstiftung.de
Trust Management Services
N.A.I.C.S.: 523940

Deutsche Umschlaggesellschaft Schiene-Strasse (DUSS) mbH **(1)**
Am Kummerling 24-26, 55294, Bodenheim, Germany

Tel.: (49) 613581910
Web Site: http://www.dbnetze.com
Emp.: 30
Logistics Consulting Servies
N.A.I.C.S.: 541614
Andreas Schulz *(CEO)*

EMPRESA DE BLAS Y COMPANIA S.A. **(1)**
Poligono Industrial Urtinsa C/ Las Fraguas 27, Alcorcon, Madrid, Spain
Tel.: (34) 902103320
Transportation Services
N.A.I.C.S.: 485999

ESFERA BUS S.L. **(1)**
Av de Gumersindo Llorente 54, 28022, Madrid, Spain
Tel.: (34) 917476143
Transportation Services
N.A.I.C.S.: 485999

EVAG Emder Verkehrs und Automotive Gesellschaft mbH **(1)**
Schweckendieckplatz 1, POB 1452, 26721, Emden, Germany
Tel.: (49) 49218950
Web Site: http://www.evag.com
Logistics Consulting Servies
N.A.I.C.S.: 541614
Karsten Dirks *(Mng Dir)*

Engelberg Transportes Internacionales C.A. **(1)**
Calle Suapure diagonal con CANTV, 1050, Caracas, Venezuela
Tel.: (58) 2127532233
Transportation Services
N.A.I.C.S.: 485999

Flight Delay Services Limited **(1)**
Regus Buliding Room 110 Manchester Park 30 aviator way, Manchester, M22 5TG, United Kingdom
Tel.: (44) 1614939444
Web Site:
http://www.flightdelayservices.co.uk
Online Travel Ticketing Services
N.A.I.C.S.: 561599
Gemma Johnson *(Mgr-Bus)*

Friedrich Muller Omnibusunternehmen GmbH **(1)**
Schmollerstrasse 13, 74523, Schwabisch Hall, Germany
Tel.: (49) 791930090
Web Site: http://www.fmobus.de
Transportation Services
N.A.I.C.S.: 541614

Grand Central Railway Company Limited **(1)**
Cannon House 18 The Priory Queensway, Birmingham, B4 6BS, United Kingdom
Tel.: (44) 3001232350
Web Site: http://www.grandcentralrail.com
Travel & Ticketing Services
N.A.I.C.S.: 561510
Richard McClean *(Mng Dir)*

Great North Eastern Railway Company Ltd **(1)**
88 The Mount, York, YO24 1AR, United Kingdom
Tel.: (44) 1904628904
Web Site: http://www.gner.scot
Transportation Services
N.A.I.C.S.: 488999

HANGARTNER Terminal S.r.l. **(1)**
Via Sommacampagna 26/28, 37137, Verona, Italy
Rail Terminal Management Services
N.A.I.C.S.: 488210

Haller Busbetrieb GmbH **(1)**
Kupferweg 4, 29664, Walsrode, Germany
Tel.: (49) 5161481450
Web Site: http://www.haller-walsrode.de
Transportation Services
N.A.I.C.S.: 485113

Hanekamp Busreisen GmbH **(1)**
Daimlerstrasse 13, 49661, Cloppenburg, Germany
Tel.: (49) 447194970
Web Site: http://www.hanekamp-reisen.de
Transportation Services
N.A.I.C.S.: 485113

Deutsche Bahn AG—(Continued)

INTERTEC Polska Sp.zo.o. (1)
Stara Wies ul 22, Nadarzyn, 05-830,
Grodzisk Wielkopolski, Poland
Car Accessory Distr
N.A.I.C.S.: 423120

**Immobilien-Vermietungsgesellschaft
Schumacher&Co Objekt Bahnhofe
Deutschland KG** (1)
Konigsallee 106, 40215, Dusseldorf,
Nordrhein-Westfalen, Germany
Tel.: (49) 1805996633
Commercial Real Estate Consulting Ser-
vices
N.A.I.C.S.: 531210

**Inter-Union Technohandel Gesell-
schaft m.b.H.** (1)
Percostrasse 14, 1220, Vienna, Austria
Tel.: (43) 1250350
Emp.: 15
Mechanical Equipment Distr
N.A.I.C.S.: 423840

Joyau S.A. (1)
ZI Nord, 85607, Montaigu, Cedex, France
Freight Transportation Services
N.A.I.C.S.: 484110
Cyrille Bonjean (Mng Dir)

KD SERVIS a.s. (1)
Zeleznicaru 885 Krocehlavy, 272 80,
Kladno, Czech Republic
Tel.: (420) 312825111
Web Site: http://www.kdserviskladno.eu
Bus Transportation Services
N.A.I.C.S.: 485999

KOB GmbH (1)
Hans-Bordlein-Str 2, 97723, Oberthulba,
Germany
Tel.: (49) 973681080
Web Site: http://www.kob-bus.de
Transportation Services
N.A.I.C.S.: 485113

Karpeles Flight Services GmbH (1)
CargoCity Sud Gebaude 529, Flughafen,
60549, Frankfurt, Germany
Tel.: (49) 6924450380
Logistics Consulting Services
N.A.I.C.S.: 541614

Kiinteisto Oy Tir-Trans
Joentaustankatu 11, 33330, Tampere, Fin-
land
Tel.: (358) 1052000
Transportation Services
N.A.I.C.S.: 488490

Lecco Trasporti S.c.a.r.l. (1)
Via Della Pergola 2, 23900, Lecco, Italy
Tel.: (39) 0341363148
Transportation Services
N.A.I.C.S.: 488490

**London and North Western Railway
Company Limited** (1)
Crewe Carriage Shed Off Weston Road,
Crewe, CW1 6NE, Cheshire, United King-
dom
Tel.: (44) 1270508000
Web Site: http://www.arrivatc.com
Railway Freight Transportation Services
N.A.I.C.S.: 482111
Sean Forster (Mng Dir)

**MegaHub Lehrte Betreibergesell-
schaft mbH** (1)
Georgstrasse 54, 30159, Hannover, Ger-
many
Tel.: (49) 511368880
Transportation Services
N.A.I.C.S.: 488490

Mobimeo GmbH (1)
Hallesches Ufer 60, 10963, Berlin, Germany
Tel.: (49) 30403646620
Web Site: http://www.mobimeo.com
Information Technology Services
N.A.I.C.S.: 513210
Darryl Feldman (Chief Product Officer)

**NSH Nahverkehr Schleswig-Holstein
GmbH** (1)
Hamburger Chaussee 10, 24114, Kiel, Ger-
many
Tel.: (49) 4316667516

Web Site: http://www.n-sh.de
Rail Transportation Services
N.A.I.C.S.: 488210

**NVO Nahverkehr Ostwestfalen
GmbH** (1)
Bahnhofstr 1 5, 48143, Munster, Germany
Tel.: (49) 25128740
Transportation Services
N.A.I.C.S.: 488490

**ORN Omnibusverkehr Rhein-Nahe
GmbH** (1)
Erthalstrasse 1, 55118, Mainz, Germany
Tel.: (49) 613163930
Web Site: http://www.orn-online.de
Transportation Services
N.A.I.C.S.: 485113

Omnibusverkehr Franken GmbH (1)
Sandstrasse 38-40, 90443, Nuremberg,
Germany
Tel.: (49) 911430570
Web Site: http://www.ovf.de
Transportation Services
N.A.I.C.S.: 485113

**Panturist dionicko drustvo za prijevoz
putnika i turizam d.d.** (1)
Sv L B Mandica 33, 31000, Osijek, Croatia
Tel.: (385) 31226226
Web Site: http://www.panturist.hr
Tour Operator
N.A.I.C.S.: 561520

**RBO Regionalbus Ostbayern
GmbH** (1)
Von-Donle-Str 7, 93055, Regensburg, Ger-
many
Tel.: (49) 94160000
Web Site: http://www.ostbayernbus.de
Transportation Services
N.A.I.C.S.: 541614

**RIVIERA TRASPORTI LINEA
S.P.A.** (1)
Via Nazionale 365, 18100, Imperia, Italy
Tel.: (39) 0183276339
Transportation Services
N.A.I.C.S.: 541614

**RMV Rhein-Mosel Verkehrsgesell-
schaft mbH** (1)
Neversstr 5, 56068, Koblenz, Germany
Tel.: (49) 261100010
Web Site: http://www.rhein-mosel-bus.de
Transportation Services
N.A.I.C.S.: 541614

**RVE Regionalverkehr Euregio Maas-
Rhein GmbH** (1)
Neukollner Str 1, 52068, Aachen, Germany
Tel.: (49) 241912890
Logistics Consulting Services
N.A.I.C.S.: 541614

**RVN Regionalverkehr Niederrhein
GmbH** (1)
Franz-Etzel-Platz 19, 46483, Wesel,
Nordrhein-Westfalen, Germany
Tel.: (49) 2813007490
Logistics Consulting Services
N.A.I.C.S.: 541614

**RVS Regionalbusverkehr Sudwest
GmbH** (1)
Gartenstr 76, 76135, Karlsruhe, Germany
Tel.: (49) 72184060
Logistics Consulting Services
N.A.I.C.S.: 541614

**Railway Approvals Germany
GmbH** (1)
Pionierstrasse 10, 32423, Minden, Germany
Tel.: (49) 5713932020
Web Site: http://www.railwayapprovals.com
Railway System Inspection Services
N.A.I.C.S.: 488210

Railway Approvals Ltd (1)
Derwent House rtc Business Park London
Road, Derby, DE24 8UP, United Kingdom
Tel.: (44) 1332483800
Web Site: http://www.railwayapprovals.co.uk
Business Certification Services
N.A.I.C.S.: 561110

**Regio Verkehrsverbund Lorrach
GmbH** (1)
Luisenstrasse 16, 79539, Lorrach, Germany

Tel.: (49) 7621415460
Web Site: http://www.rvl-online.de
Transportation Services
N.A.I.C.S.: 541614

Regional Bus Stuttgart GmbH (1)
Seyfferstr 34, 70197, Stuttgart, Germany
Tel.: (49) 711666070
Web Site: http://www.bahn.de
Transportation Consulting Services
N.A.I.C.S.: 541614

**Regionalbus Braunschweig
GmbH** (1)
Sachsenfeld 4, 20097, Hamburg, Germany
Tel.: (49) 53148283090
Web Site: http://www.rbb-bus.de
Transportation Services
N.A.I.C.S.: 541614

Regionalverkehr Allgau GmbH (1)
Poststrasse 4, 87561, Oberstdorf, Germany
Tel.: (49) 832296770
Web Site: http://www.oberstdorf.de
Transportation Services
N.A.I.C.S.: 541614

**Regionalverkehr Kurhessen
GmbH** (1)
Bruder-Grimm-Strasse 32, 63450, Hanau,
Germany
Tel.: (49) 6181933030
Web Site: http://www.rmv.de
Transportation Services
N.A.I.C.S.: 541614

**Regionalverkehre Start Deutschland
GmbH** (1)
Hahnstrasse 40, 60528, Frankfurt am Main,
Germany
Tel.: (49) 69999993640
Web Site: http://www.startgmbh.com
Bus Transportation Services
N.A.I.C.S.: 485999

Rengaslinja Oy (1)
Nosturikatu 18, Nokia, 37150, Finland
Tel.: (358) 400625455
Apparel Distr
N.A.I.C.S.: 458110

**Rhein-Westerwald Nahverkehr
GmbH** (1)
Neversstr 8, 56068, Koblenz, Germany
Tel.: (49) 26129683468
Web Site: http://www.rhein-mosel-bus.de
Transportation Services
N.A.I.C.S.: 541614

Rheinpfalzbus GmbH (1)
Pasadenaallee 7, 67059, Ludwigshafen,
Germany
Tel.: (49) 62168597855
Web Site: http://www.vrn.de
Transportation Services
N.A.I.C.S.: 541614

S-Bahn Berlin GmbH (1)
Fahrgastmarketing Elisabeth-Schwarzhaupt-
Platz 1, 10115, Berlin, Germany
Tel.: (49) 3029743333
Web Site: http://www.s-bahn-berlin.de
Transportation Services
N.A.I.C.S.: 541614
Manfred Rudhart (Chm)

S-Bahn Hamburg GmbH (1)
Hammerbrookstrasse 44, 20097, Hamburg,
Germany
Tel.: (49) 4039184385
Web Site: http://www.s-bahn-hamburg.de
Transportation Services
N.A.I.C.S.: 541614

**S.I.A. Societa Italiana Autoservizi
S.P.A.** (1)
Via Cassala 3/A, 25126, Brescia, Italy
Tel.: (39) 03044061
Logistics Consulting Services
N.A.I.C.S.: 541614

SAB Piemonte S.r.l. (1)
Piazza Guglielmo Marconi 4, 24122, Ber-
gamo, Italy
Tel.: (39) 035215857
Logistics Consulting Services
N.A.I.C.S.: 541614

SAIA TRASPORTI S.P.A. (1)
Via Cassala 3, 25126, Brescia, Italy
Tel.: (39) 0302989911

Web Site: http://www.arriva.it
Transportation Services
N.A.I.C.S.: 541614

**SAVDA Autoservizi Valle d'Aosta
S.p.A.** (1)
Strada Pont Suaz 6, 11100, Aosta, AO, Italy
Tel.: (39) 0165367011
Web Site: http://www.savda.it
Bus Transportation Services
N.A.I.C.S.: 485510

SBG SudbadenBus GmbH (1)
Bismarckallee 1Am Busbahnhof, 79098,
Freiburg, Germany
Tel.: (49) 7613680388
Web Site: http://www.suedbadenbus.de
Transportation Services
N.A.I.C.S.: 541614

SW Zoll-Beratung GmbH (1)
Dr-Georg-Schafer-Str 17, 93437, Furth im
Wald, Germany
Tel.: (49) 997350677
Web Site: http://www.swzoll.de
Logistics Consulting Services
N.A.I.C.S.: 541614

Saar-Pfalz-Bus GmbH (1)
Regionalbereich Westpfalz Bahnhofsstrasse
67, 66869, Kusel, Germany
Tel.: (49) 681416230
Web Site: http://www.saarpfalzbus.de
Transportation Services
N.A.I.C.S.: 541614

Saar-Pfalz-Mobil GmbH (1)
Saarpfalz-Park 18, 66450, Bexbach, Ger-
many
Tel.: (49) 6826930820
Logistics Consulting Services
N.A.I.C.S.: 541614
Marion Heber (Mng Dir)

Sadem - Societa Per Azioni (1)
Via della Repubblica 14, 10095, Grugliasco,
TO, Italy
Tel.: (39) 0113000611
Web Site: http://www.sadem.it
Bus Transportation Services
N.A.I.C.S.: 485999
Giuseppe Proto (Mng Dir)

Schenker AG (1)
Kruppstrasse 4, 45128, Essen,
Germany (100%)
Tel.: (49) 20187814990
Web Site: http://www.dbschenker.com
Freight Forwarding, Fairs in Foreign Coun-
tries, Travel Agencies & Railroad Traffic to
the Far East
N.A.I.C.S.: 488510
Jochen Thewes (Chm-Mgmt Bd)

Subsidiary (Non-US):

AS Schenker (2)
Kaabli 13, 10112, Tallinn, Estonia
Tel.: (372) 6060600
Logistics Consulting Services
N.A.I.C.S.: 541614

**DB Schenker (Cambodia)
Limited.** (2)
No 86 8th Floor Street 388 Sangkat Toul
Svay Prey II, Chamkamorn, Phnom Penh,
Cambodia
Tel.: (855) 23210572
Logistics Consulting Services
N.A.I.C.S.: 541614
Juergen Braunbach (Mng Dir)

DB Schenker FLLC (2)
500m vostochnee d Bogatyrevo AHZ Up-
ravdelami Presidenta RB Office 325,
223021, Minsk, Belarus
Logistics Management Services
N.A.I.C.S.: 541614

**DB Schenker Global Services Europe
S.R.L.** (2)
196C Calea Rahovei, 50908, Bucharest,
Romania
Tel.: (40) 212340000
Corporate Secretarial & Accounting Ser-
vices
N.A.I.C.S.: 541219

DP Schenker (2)
3 Kompressorna str v Bilogorodka, Kiev,
8140, Ukraine

Tel.: (380) 445001100
Logistics Consulting Servies
N.A.I.C.S.: 541614

Oy Schenker East AB (2)
Metsalantie 2, 620, Helsinki, Finland
Tel.: (358) 1052000
Logistics Consulting Servies
N.A.I.C.S.: 541614

PT. Schenker Petrolog Utama (2)
Simatupang, Jakarta, 12560, Indonesia
Tel.: (62) 2178843788
Logistics Consulting Servies
N.A.I.C.S.: 541614
Asok Kumar *(Pres)*

SCHENKER DOOEL (2)
Ul 36 bd p fah 3 Industrial Zone Ilinden,
1041, Skopje, North Macedonia
Tel.: (389) 23107655
Web Site: http://www.dbschenker.com
Logistics Consulting Servies
N.A.I.C.S.: 541614

SCHENKER EOOD (2)
Evropa 1A Blvd, 2227, Bozhurishte, Bul-
garia
Tel.: (359) 29429100
Web Site: http://www.dbschenker.com
Logistics Consulting Servies
N.A.I.C.S.: 541614

**SCHENKER INDIA PRIVATE
LIMITED** (2)
DLF Building No 8-C 12th Floor DLF Cyber
City Phase II, Gurgaon, India
Tel.: (91) 1244645000
Web Site: http://www.dbschenker.com
Logistics Consulting Servies
N.A.I.C.S.: 541614
Mayur Gandhi *(CFO)*

**SCHENKER LUXEMBURG
GMBH** (2)
9 Rue Nicolas Brosius, 3372, Leudelange,
Luxembourg
Tel.: (352) 3720051
Web Site: http://www.logistics.dbschenker.lu
Logistics Consulting Servies
N.A.I.C.S.: 541614
Axel Quadt *(Mng Dir)*

SCHENKER N.V. (2)
Oceanfreight activities Noorderlaan 147
11efloor, 2030, Antwerp, Belgium
Tel.: (32) 35436211
Web Site:
http://www.logistics.dbschenker.be
Logistics Consulting Servies
N.A.I.C.S.: 541614

SCHENKER d.o.o. (2)
Halilovici 9, 71000, Sarajevo, Bosnia & Her-
zegovina
Tel.: (387) 33777551
Web Site: http://www.dbschenker.com
Logistics Consulting Servies
N.A.I.C.S.: 541614

SCHENKER s.r.o. (2)
Kopcianska 94, 851 01, Bratislava, Slovakia
Tel.: (421) 268293369
Web Site: http://www.dbschenker.com
Logistics Consulting Servies
N.A.I.C.S.: 541614

SCHENKER spol. s r.o. (2)
K Vypichu 1087 Rudna u Prahy, Rudna,
252 19, Czech Republic
Tel.: (420) 311711111
Logistics Consulting Servies
N.A.I.C.S.: 541614
Tomas Holomoucky *(Gen Mgr)*

SIA Schenker (2)
Katlakalna str 11c, Riga, 1073, Latvia
Tel.: (371) 67800087
Web Site: http://www.dbschenker.com
Logistics Consulting Servies
N.A.I.C.S.: 541614

Schenker & Co AG (2)
Stella-Klein-Low Weg 11, 1020, Vienna,
Austria **(100%)**
Tel.: (43) 57686210900
Web Site: http://www.dbschenker.com
Sales Range: $50-74.9 Million
Freight Forwarding, Fairs in Foreign Coun-
tries, Travel Agencies & Railroad Traffic to
the Far East

N.A.I.C.S.: 488510
Xavier Garijo *(Member-Mgmt Bd-Contract
Logistics)*

Schenker (L.L.C) (2)
Airport Road, PO Box 62532, Deira, Dubai,
United Arab Emirates
Tel.: (971) 42956111
Web Site: http://www.dbschenker.ae
Logistics Consulting Servies
N.A.I.C.S.: 541614
Farook Al Zeer *(Mng Dir)*

Schenker (NZ) Ltd. (2)
33 Richard Pearse Drive, Airport Oaks Man-
gere, Auckland, New Zealand
Tel.: (64) 92552800
Web Site: http://www.dbschenker.com.au
Emp.: 110
Logistics Consulting Servies
N.A.I.C.S.: 541614
Reon Edwards *(Dir)*

Schenker (Thai) Ltd. (2)
3388/54-61 63 66-67 Sirinrat Building 16-
19/F Rama IV Road, Klongtoey, Bangkok,
10110, Thailand
Tel.: (66) 22696500
Logistics Consulting Servies
N.A.I.C.S.: 541614

Schenker A/S (2)
Helseholmen 31-39, Hvidovre, Denmark
Tel.: (45) 36869500
Logistics Consulting Servies
N.A.I.C.S.: 541614
Kent Cyril Larsen *(Dir-Sls)*

Schenker AB (2)
Lilla Bommen 3, 412 97, Gothenburg,
Sweden **(100%)**
Tel.: (46) 317038000
Web Site: http://www.schenker.se
Road Haulage, Freight Forwarding, General
Warehousing & Storage, Air & Railway
Transport & Logistics Services
N.A.I.C.S.: 484122

Subsidiary (Domestic):

Schenker Consulting AB (3)
Lilla Bommen 3, Gothenburg, 412 97, Swe-
den
Tel.: (46) 317038000
Web Site:
http://www.consulting.dbschenker.se
Logistics Consulting Servies
N.A.I.C.S.: 541614
Linda Borgenstam *(CEO)*

Schenker Logistics AB (3)
Marieholmsgatan 42, Gothenburg, 415 02,
Sweden
Tel.: (46) 317038000
Logistics Consulting Servies
N.A.I.C.S.: 541614

Subsidiary (Non-US):

Schenker AS (2)
Ostre Akervei 17, Oslo, 581, Norway
Tel.: (47) 7500
Logistics Consulting Servies
N.A.I.C.S.: 541614

Subsidiary (Domestic):

Schenker Argentina S.A. (2)
Tucuman 117 Piso 6, Capital Federal, Bue-
nos Aires, C1049AAC, Argentina
Tel.: (54) 11 4310 1200
Web Site: http://www.dbschenker.com.ar
Freight Shipping Services
N.A.I.C.S.: 488510
Esteban Marino *(Gen Mgr)*

Schenker Australia Pty. Ltd. (2)
72-80 Bourke Road, Alexandria, 2015,
NSW, Australia
Tel.: (61) 293330333
Web Site: http://www.dbschenker.com.au
Logistics Consulting Servies
N.A.I.C.S.: 541614

Schenker B.V. (2)
Emma Goldmanweg 1, 5032 MN, Tilburg,
Netherlands
Tel.: (31) 134625111
Web Site: http://www.dbschenker.nl
Logistics Consulting Servies
N.A.I.C.S.: 541614
Leon Janssen *(Gen Mgr)*

**Schenker BITCC Logistics (Beijing)
Co. Ltd.** (2)
No 9 Wangjing Zhonghuan Nanlu, Chaoy-
ang, Beijing, 100102, China
Tel.: (86) 1064721166
Web Site: http://www.bitcc.cn
Logistics Consulting Servies
N.A.I.C.S.: 541614

Schenker Chile S.A. (2)
General del Canto 421 Piso 3, Providencia,
Santiago, Chile
Tel.: (56) 224281300
Web Site: http://www.dbschenker.com.au
Emp.: 100
Logistics Consulting Servies
N.A.I.C.S.: 541614
Jorn Baetke *(Mng Dir & Member-Mgmt Bd)*

Schenker China Ltd. (2)
8/F Raffles City Office Tower 268 Xi Zang
Zhong Road, Shanghai, 200001, China
Tel.: (86) 2161708888
Web Site: http://www.dbschenker.com
Transportation Services
N.A.I.C.S.: 541614

Subsidiary (Domestic):

**Schenker Logistics (Guangzhou)
Company Ltd.** (3)
23/F No 410-412 Dongfeng Middle Rd,
Yuexiu, Guangzhou, 510030, Guangdong,
China
Tel.: (86) 2083486635
Logistics Consulting Servies
N.A.I.C.S.: 541614

**Schenker Logistics (Shanghai) Co.,
Ltd.** (3)
Ostre Aker vei 1, Shanghai, 200131, China
Tel.: (86) 2150574788
Logistics Consulting Servies
N.A.I.C.S.: 541614

**Schenker Logistics (Suzhou) Com-
pany Ltd.** (3)
Rm 2006 No 8 Suhua Rd Industry, Suzhou,
215021, China
Tel.: (86) 51262957618
Logistics Consulting Servies
N.A.I.C.S.: 541614
Wayn Xie *(Gen Mgr)*

**Schenker Logistics (Xiamen) Co.
Ltd.** (3)
No 5 Xiangxing No1 Rd Xiangyu F, Xiamen,
361006, China
Tel.: (86) 5925658133
Logistics Consulting Servies
N.A.I.C.S.: 541614

Subsidiary (Non-US):

Schenker Customs Agency B.V. (2)
Nieuwesluisweg 250, Botlek, Rotterdam,
3197 KV, Zuid-Holland, Netherlands
Tel.: (31) 104940494
Web Site: http://www.dbschenker.nl
Logistics Consulting Servies
N.A.I.C.S.: 541614

Subsidiary (Domestic):

Schenker Deutschland AG (2)
Lyoner Strasse 15, 60528, Frankfurt am
Main, Germany
Tel.: (49) 69 24744 0
Web Site: http://www.dbschenker.com
Freight Logistics Services
N.A.I.C.S.: 488510
Julia Kahle *(Head-HR Mktg & Recruiting)*

Subsidiary (Non-US):

Schenker Egypt Ltd. (2)
Cairo International Airport Building CT2, PO
Box 11861, New Cargo Village, Cairo,
11361, Egypt
Tel.: (20) 222690961
Web Site: http://www.dbschenker.com
Logistics Consulting Servies
N.A.I.C.S.: 541614

**Schenker High Tech Logistics
B.V.** (2)
Schrijnwerkerstraat 2, Ridderkerk, 2984 BC,
Zuid-Holland, Netherlands
Tel.: (31) 180446600
Logistics Consulting Servies

N.A.I.C.S.: 541614

**Schenker International HK
Limited** (2)
Fl 35 Skyline Twr 39 Wang Kwong Road,
Kowloon Bay, Kowloon, China (Hong Kong)
Tel.: (852) 23799280
Web Site: http://www.schenker.com
Sales Range: $75-99.9 Million
Emp.: 300
Freight Transportation Services
N.A.I.C.S.: 488510
Anup Nair *(Dir-Projects-Schenker India Pvt.
Ltd.)*

Schenker Italiana S.p.A. (2)
Via Fratelli Bandiera 29, Peschiera Borro-
meo, 20068, Milan, Italy
Tel.: (39) 02516661
Web Site: http://www.dbschenker.com
Logistics Consulting Servies
N.A.I.C.S.: 541614

Schenker Khimji's LLC (2)
PO Box 206, 105, Muscat, Oman
Tel.: (968) 24616400
Logistics Consulting Servies
N.A.I.C.S.: 541614

Schenker Korea Ltd. (2)
Airport Logistics Park G3 block 97-49,
Seoul, Korea (South)
Tel.: (82) 327440300
Logistics Consulting Servies
N.A.I.C.S.: 541614

**Schenker Logistics (Malaysia) Sdn
Bhd.** (2)
Lot No 1 & 3 Persiaran Pasak Bumi Bukit
Jelutong Industrial Park, Seksyen U8 Darul
Ehsan, 40150, Shah Alam, Selangor, Ma-
laysia
Tel.: (60) 379497888
Web Site: http://www.dbschenker.com.my
Logistics Consulting Servies
N.A.I.C.S.: 541614

**Schenker Logistics Vietnam Co.
Ltd.** (2)
Ground 4th 5th 6th Floors South Building
60 Truong Son St Ward 2, Tan Binh District,
Ho Chi Minh City, Vietnam
Tel.: (84) 2862971860
Web Site: http://www.dbschenker.com
Logistics Consulting Servies
N.A.I.C.S.: 541614

Subsidiary (Domestic):

**Schenker-Gemadept Logistics Viet-
nam Company Limited** (3)
Song Than 1 Industrial Park Lot J 2 St 8, Di
An Ward, Di An, Binh Duong, Vietnam
Tel.: (84) 6503772772
Logistics Consulting Servies
N.A.I.C.S.: 541614
Thorsten Kipp *(Gen Mgr)*

Subsidiary (Non-US):

Schenker Ltd. (2)
Schenker House Cargo Village 1st Freight
Lane JKIA, PO Box 46757, 100, Nairobi,
Kenya
Tel.: (254) 706787787
Web Site: http://www.gbakenya.com
Logistics Consulting Servies
N.A.I.C.S.: 541614
Darren Brown *(Mng Dir)*

Schenker Middle East FZE (2)
West Wing Building 2 Office G 02 Dubai
Airport Free Zone, PO Box 293682, Dubai,
United Arab Emirates
Tel.: (971) 42149100
Logistics Consulting Servies
N.A.I.C.S.: 541614

Subsidiary (Domestic):

Schenker Logistics L.L.C. (3)
Hamdam Street Mezzanine 2 Block B Al
Saman Towers, PO Box 44256, Abu Dhabi,
United Arab Emirates
Tel.: (971) 26277333
Logistics Consulting Servies
N.A.I.C.S.: 541614
Farooq Alzeer *(Gen Mgr)*

Subsidiary (Non-US):

Schenker Namibia (Pty) Ltd. (2)

Deutsche Bahn AG—(Continued)

Plenarg Industrial Park Unit 3 Gold Street
Prosperita, PO Box 80502, Windhoek, Namibia
Tel.: (264) 61376550
Web Site: http://www.dbschenker.co.za
Logistics Consulting Servies
N.A.I.C.S.: 541614

Schenker OY (2)
Tikkurilantie 147, PO Box 293682, 1530, Vantaa, Finland
Tel.: (358) 1052000
Web Site: http://www.logistics.dbschenker.fi
Emp.: 1,470
Logistics Consulting Servies
N.A.I.C.S.: 541614
Goran Aberg (CEO & Head-Cluster)

Schenker Panama S.A. (2)
Edificio Plaza Real oficina 406 Avenida Marina Norte, Costa del Este, Panama, Panama
Tel.: (507) 2755400
Web Site: http://www.dbschenker.com.pa
Logistics Consulting Servies
N.A.I.C.S.: 541614

Schenker Peru S.R.L. (2)
Calle Dean Valdivia 148 Of 801, San Isidro, Lima, Peru
Tel.: (51) 17128500
Web Site: http://www.dbschenker.pe
Logistics Consulting Servies
N.A.I.C.S.: 541614

Schenker Philippines, Inc. (2)
44th Floor PBCom Tower 6795 Ayala Avenue, cor VA Rufino Street, Makati, 1200, Philippines
Tel.: (63) 28196033
Web Site: http://www.schenker.com.ph
Freight Transportation Services
N.A.I.C.S.: 488510

Schenker SA (2)
37 route principale du port, 92637, Gennevilliers, Cedex, France
Tel.: (33) 141854646
Logistics Consulting Servies
N.A.I.C.S.: 541614

Subsidiary (Domestic):

SCHENKER FRANCE SAS (3)
ZI Nord, 85607, Montaigu, Cedex, France
Tel.: (33) 251452000
Web Site: http://www.schenker.fr
Logistics Consulting Servies
N.A.I.C.S.: 541614

Subsidiary (Non-US):

Schenker Saudi Arabia LLC
Riyadh Avenue Mall Avenue 2 3rd Floor, PO Box 51615, Riyadh, 11553, Saudi Arabia
Tel.: (966) 112176035
Web Site: http://www.dbschenker.com
Logistics Consulting Servies
N.A.I.C.S.: 541614

Schenker Singapore (Pte) Ltd. (2)
17 Changi South Street 2, Singapore, 486129, Singapore
Tel.: (65) 459788
Web Site: http://www.dbschenker.com
Sales Range: $150-199.9 Million
Emp.: 1,000
Freight Transportation Services
N.A.I.C.S.: 488510

Schenker South Africa (Pty) Ltd. (2)
PO Box 379, Isando, Kempton Park, 1600, South Africa
Tel.: (27) 119718400
Web Site: http://www.dbschenker.com
Logistics Consulting Servies
N.A.I.C.S.: 541614

Schenker Switzerland AG (2)
Rautistrasse 77, 8048, Zurich, Switzerland
Tel.: (41) 585895600
Logistics Consulting Servies
N.A.I.C.S.: 541614
Jorg Eggenberger (CEO)

Schenker d.o.o (2)
Franje Lucica 32, Jankomir, 10090, Zagreb, Croatia

Tel.: (385) 12480900
Web Site: http://www.dbschenker.com
Logistics Consulting Servies
N.A.I.C.S.: 541614

Schenker d.o.o. (2)
Treca Logisticka 1, 22304, Sremska Mitrovica, Serbia
Tel.: (381) 114141870
Web Site: http://www.dbschenker.com
Logistics Consulting Servies
N.A.I.C.S.: 541614
Jelena Kojic (Dir-Ops)

Schenker do Brasil Transportes Internacionais Ltda.
Rua Geraldo Flausino Gomes 78 12th Fl, Sao Paulo, 04575 060, SP, Brazil
Tel.: (55) 11 3318 9200
Web Site: http://www.dbschenker.com.br
Emp.: 300
Shipping & Transportation Services
N.A.I.C.S.: 488510
Roberto Moreno (CEO)

Subsidiary (US):

Schenker, Inc. (2)
150 Albany Ave, Freeport, NY 11520-4702
Tel.: (516) 377-3000
Web Site: http://www.dbschenkerusa.com
Insurance, Logistics & Foreign Freight Forwarding
N.A.I.C.S.: 488510
Randy Creel (Head-Vertical Market-Automotive-Americas)

Subsidiary (Domestic):

Schenker (BAX) Holding Corp. (3)
120 White Plains Rd, Tarrytown, NY 10591
Tel.: (914) 366-7200
Transportation Services
N.A.I.C.S.: 541614

Subsidiary (Non-US):

Schenker of Canada Limited (3)
(10%)
Tel.: (905) 676-0676
Web Site: http://www.schenker.ca
Sales Range: $25-49.9 Million
Emp.: 120
Freight Transportation Arrangement
N.A.I.C.S.: 488510

Subsidiary (Domestic):

USA Truck, Inc. (3)
3200 Industrial Park Rd, Van Buren, AR 72956-6110
Tel.: (479) 471-2500
Web Site: http://www.usa-truck.com
Rev.: $710,387,000
Assets: $364,035,000
Liabilities: $252,610,000
Net Worth: $111,425,000
Earnings: $24,768,000
Emp.: 2,100
Fiscal Year-end: 12/31/2021
Freight Transportation Services
N.A.I.C.S.: 484121
Zachary B. King (CFO & Sr VP)

Subsidiary (Domestic):

Davis Transfer Logistics Inc. (4)
520 Busha Rd, Carnesville, GA 30521
Tel.: (479) 471-3547
Logistic Services
N.A.I.C.S.: 541614

International Freight Services, Inc. (4)
712 N Central Ave Ste A, Wood Dale, IL 60191
Tel.: (630) 274-6000
Web Site: https://www.ifscargo.com
Logistic Services
N.A.I.C.S.: 541614
Bob Roubitchek (Pres)

Subsidiary (Non-US):

Schenker-Arkas Nakliyat Ve Tic. A.S. (2)
Zincirlikuyu Kore Sehitleri Cad No 15A, Istanbul, 34394, Turkiye
Tel.: (90) 2123360036
Logistics Consulting Servies
N.A.I.C.S.: 541614

Togan Moler (Product Mgr-Ocean & Projects)

Schenker-BTL Ltd. (2)
Schenker House Scylla Road LHR Portal, Hounslow, TW6 3FE, United Kingdom
Tel.: (44) 2088314500
Logistics Consulting Servies
N.A.I.C.S.: 541614

Schenker-Seino Co. Ltd. (2)
2-2-24 Higashi, Shinagawa-ku, Tokyo, 140-0002, Japan
Tel.: (81) 357697300
Web Site: http://www.dbschenker-seino.jp
Logistics Consulting Servies
N.A.I.C.S.: 541614
Herbert Wilhelm (Pres & CEO)

UAB Schenker (2)
Sausiai LT, 21401, Vilnius, Lithuania
Tel.: (370) 52602525
Logistics Consulting Servies
N.A.I.C.S.: 541614
Andrius Lomakinas (Mgr-Sls)

ZAO Schenker (2)
Bldg 4 47 Varshavscoye shosse, Moscow, 115230, Russia
Tel.: (7) 4957772585
Emp.: 10
Logistics Consulting Servies
N.A.I.C.S.: 541614

Schenker Americas, Inc. (1)
800 NW 62nd Ave Ste 600, Miami, FL 33126
Tel.: (786) 388-4247
Web Site:
    http://www.dbschenkeramericas.com
Logistic Services
N.A.I.C.S.: 327910
Daphne Robboy (Sr Mgr-Mktg & Comm)

Schenker International (HK) Ltd. (1)
35/F Skyline Tower 39 Wang Kwong Road, Kowloon Bay, China (Hong Kong)
Tel.: (852) 25859688
Air & Ocean Freight Logistics Services
N.A.I.C.S.: 488510
Jovi Liu (Ops Mgr)

Schenker Jinbei Logistics (Shenyang) Co. Ltd. (1)
Room 1906 Tower C President Building 69 Heping Street, Heping District, Shenyang, 110003, Liaoning, China
Tel.: (86) 2488076868
Air & Ocean Freight Logistics Services
N.A.I.C.S.: 488510

Schenker Kazakhstan TOO (1)
KenDala Center Dostyk Avenue 38 Office 26, Almaty, Kazakhstan
Tel.: (7) 7771763344
Air & Ocean Freight Logistics Services
N.A.I.C.S.: 488510

Schenker Logistics (Bangladesh) Limited (1)
206/A Level 4 Tejgaon I/A Area, Dhaka, 1208, Bangladesh
Tel.: (880) 29889790
Air & Ocean Freight Logistics Services
N.A.I.C.S.: 488510

Schenker Logistics (Jiaxing) Co., Ltd. (1)
Room 1106 Building 2 Modern Square 1560 Changsheng South Road, Jiaxing, 314001, Zhejiang, China
Tel.: (86) 57383388001
Air & Ocean Freight Logistics Services
N.A.I.C.S.: 488510

Schenker Logistics (Kunshan) Co., Ltd. (1)
2188 Huan Qing North Road, Kunshan, 215300, Jiangsu, China
Tel.: (86) 51262957738
Air & Ocean Freight Logistics Services
N.A.I.C.S.: 488510

Schenker Logistics Romania S.A. (1)
196C Calea Rahovei, District 5, 050908, Bucharest, Romania
Tel.: (40) 212340000
Air & Ocean Freight Logistics Services
N.A.I.C.S.: 488510

Albin Budinsky (CEO)

Schenker Myanmar Co., Ltd. (1)
Sule Square Units 07-09 9th Floor Sule Pagoda Road, Kyautada Township, Yangon, Myanmar
Tel.: (95) 19255157
Air & Ocean Freight Logistics Services
N.A.I.C.S.: 488510
Sandar Hlaing (Head-HR & Admin)

Schenker Philippines, Inc. (1)
Schenker Compound Km 19 West Service Road, Sucat, Paranaque, 1700, Philippines
Tel.: (63) 29829999
Air & Ocean Freight Logistics Services
N.A.I.C.S.: 488510
Siew-Wei Ong (CEO)

Schenker Schweiz AG (1)
Rautistrasse 75, 8048, Zurich, Switzerland
Tel.: (41) 585895600
Emp.: 36
Air & Ocean Freight Logistics Services
N.A.I.C.S.: 488510
Hans-Peter Trachsler (CEO)

Schenker, Inc. (1)
1305 Executive Blvd, Chesapeake, VA 23320
Tel.: (602) 458-6200
Air & Ocean Freight Logistics Services
N.A.I.C.S.: 488510
Donna Hanson (CFO)

Sky Partners OU (1)
Valukoja 22, 11415, Tallinn, Estonia
Tel.: (372) 6051125
Web Site: http://www.skypartners.ee
Logistics Consulting Servies
N.A.I.C.S.: 541614

Sudwest Mobil GmbH (1)
Europaplatz 13, 55543, Bad Kreuznach, Germany
Tel.: (49) 61314948146
Logistics Consulting Servies
N.A.I.C.S.: 541614

TEGRO AG (1)
Ringstrasse 3, 8603, Schwerzenbach, Switzerland
Tel.: (41) 448068888
Web Site: http://www.tegro.ch
Logistics Consulting Servies
N.A.I.C.S.: 541614

TFG Transfracht GmbH (1)
Rheinstrasse 2, 55116, Mainz, Germany
Tel.: (49) 61311563050
Web Site: http://www.transfracht.com
Emp.: 200
Freight Forwarding Services
N.A.I.C.S.: 488510
Bernd Pahnke (Mng Dir)

TRANSA Spedition GmbH (1)
Sprendlinger Landstr 175, 63069, Offenbach, Germany
Tel.: (49) 69840070
Web Site: http://www.transa.dbschenker.de
Logistics Consulting Servies
N.A.I.C.S.: 541614
Christian Jeck (Chm & Mng Dir)

TUF-TRANSPORTES URBANOS DE FAMALICAO, LDA (1)
Estacao Central de Camionagem, 4760-012, Vila Nova de Famalicao, Portugal
Tel.: (351) 252309886
Web Site: http://www.tuf.pt
Transportation Distr
N.A.I.C.S.: 485113

The Chiltern Railway Company Limited (1)
Banbury ICC Merton Street, Banbury, OX16 4RN, Oxfordshire, United Kingdom
Tel.: (44) 3456 005 165
Web Site: http://www.chilternrailways.co.uk
Railway Freight Transportation Services
N.A.I.C.S.: 482111
John Elvin (Chm)

Transfesa Logistics, S.A. (1)
Calle Musgo 1, 28023, Madrid, Spain
Tel.: (34) 913879900
Web Site: http://www.transfesa.com
Transport Logistic Services
N.A.I.C.S.: 488510

Samuel Nevado Serrano *(Dir-Logistics & Rail FV Div)*

Transportes Sul do Tejo S.A. **(1)**
Rua Marcos de Portugal, Laranjeiro, 2810-260, Almada, Portugal
Tel.: (351) 211126200
Web Site: http://www.tsuldotejo.pt
Transportation Services
N.A.I.C.S.: 485113
Carlos Guerreiro *(Mgr-Depot)*

UBB Usedomer Baderbahn GmbH **(1)**
Am Bahnhof 1 Seebad, 17424, Berlin, Germany
Tel.: (49) 38378271
Web Site: http://www.ubb-online.com
Transportation Services
N.A.I.C.S.: 485113

UCPLUS A/S **(1)**
Mileparken 12 A, 2740, Skovlunde, Denmark
Tel.: (45) 44870100
Web Site: https://www.ucplus.dk
Emp.: 200
Training Services
N.A.I.C.S.: 611692

VT-ARRIVA Szemelyszallito es Szolgaltato Kft. **(1)**
Berenyi ut 72 - 100, Szekesfehervar, 8000, Hungary
Tel.: (36) 22330575
Web Site: http://www.vt-arriva.hu
Bus Transportation Services
N.A.I.C.S.: 485999
Szabo Istvan *(Mgr-CEE Category)*

VVW Verkehrsverbund Warnow GmbH **(1)**
Stampfmullerstr 40, 18057, Rostock, Germany
Tel.: (49) 3814923696
Web Site: http://www.verkehrsverbund-warnow.de
Transportation Services
N.A.I.C.S.: 485113

Verkehrsgesellschaft Start NRW mbH **(1)**
Schifferstrasse 166, 47059, Duisburg, Germany
Tel.: (49) 203295190
Web Site: http://www.start-nrw.de
Bus Transportation Services
N.A.I.C.S.: 485999

Verkehrsgesellschaft Start Unterelbe mbH **(1)**
Am Bahnhof 1, 27472, Cuxhaven, Germany
Tel.: (49) 47212049724
Web Site: http://www.start-unterelbe.de
Rail Transportation Services
N.A.I.C.S.: 488210

Verkehrsgesellschaft mbH Untermain -VU **(1)**
Ludwigstrasse 8, 63739, Aschaffenburg, Germany
Tel.: (49) 602133920
Web Site: http://www.untermainbus.de
Emp.: 63
Transportation Services
N.A.I.C.S.: 488490

Verkehrsverbund Rottweil GmbH **(1)**
Lehrstrasse 50, 78628, Rottweil, Germany
Tel.: (49) 74117575714
Web Site: http://www.vvr-info.de
Railway Freight Transportation Services
N.A.I.C.S.: 482111

WB Westfalen Bus GmbH **(1)**
Bahnhofstrasse 1 - 5, 48143, Munster, Germany
Tel.: (49) 1806607085
Transportation Services
N.A.I.C.S.: 485113

White Rose Bus Company Limited **(1)**
Friedrich-Rauers-Strasse 9, 28195, Bremen, Germany
Tel.: (49) 421308970
Transportation Services
N.A.I.C.S.: 485113

XC Trains Limited **(1)**

Admiral Way Doxford International Business, Sunderland, SR3 3XP, United Kingdom
Tel.: (44) 8448110125
Railway Freight Transportation Services
N.A.I.C.S.: 482111

Zentral-Omnibusbahnhof Berlin GmbH **(1)**
Masurenallee 4-6, 14057, Berlin, Germany
Tel.: (49) 303010380
Railway Freight Transportation Services
N.A.I.C.S.: 482111

Zeta Automotive Limited **(1)**
Telford Road, Bicester, OX26 4LB, Oxfordshire, United Kingdom
Tel.: (44) 1869326710
Web Site: http://www.zetaautomotive.com
Automotive Electronic Component Mfr & Distr
N.A.I.C.S.: 336320
Neil O'Leary *(Gen Mgr)*

ioki GmbH **(1)**
An der Welle 3, 60322, Frankfurt am Main, Germany
Tel.: (49) 69154487980
Web Site: http://www.ioki.com
Rail Transportation Services
N.A.I.C.S.: 488210
Michael Barillere-Scholz *(CEO)*

vgf Verkehrs-Gemeinschaft Landkreis Freudenstadt GmbH **(1)**
Heiligenbronner Str 2, 72178, Waldachtal, Germany
Tel.: (49) 7443247340
Web Site: http://www.vgf-info.de
Travel Operator
N.A.I.C.S.: 561510

DEUTSCHE BALATON AG
Ziegelhauser Landstrasse 3, 69120, Heidelberg, Germany
Tel.: (49) 6221649240
Web Site: https://www.deutsche-balaton.de
Year Founded: 1991
BBH—(DEU)
Sales Range: $125-149.9 Million
Financial Investment Services
N.A.I.C.S.: 523940
Rolf Birkert *(Member-Mgmt Bd)*

DEUTSCHE BANK AKTIENG-ESELLSCHAFT
Taunusanlage 12, 60325, Frankfurt am Main, Germany
Tel.: (49) 6991000   De
Web Site: https://www.db.com
Year Founded: 1870
DB—(NYSE)
Rev.: $47,058,441,684
Assets: $1,998,414,855,138
Liabilities: $1,895,682,508,525
Net Worth: $102,732,346,613
Earnings: $3,697,513,643
Emp.: 82,969
Fiscal Year-end: 12/31/21
Financial Investment Services
N.A.I.C.S.: 522110
James Von Moltke *(CFO & Member-Mgmt Bd)*

Subsidiaries:

ADD ONE GmbH & Co. KG **(1)**
Elsa-Brandstrom-Str 10-12, Cologne, 50668, Nordrhein-Westfalen, Germany
Tel.: (49) 221 14501
Business Management Consulting Services
N.A.I.C.S.: 541611

Agena S.A. **(1)**
Chemin du Grand-Pre 1C, 1510, Moudon, Switzerland
Tel.: (41) 219052656
Web Site: http://www.agena-energies.ch
Solar Renewable Energy Services
N.A.I.C.S.: 221118

AheadCom Beteiligungs-GmbH **(1)**
Taunusanlage 12, Frankfurt am Main, 60325, Germany

Tel.: (49) 69 910 00
Financial Management Consulting Services
N.A.I.C.S.: 541611

Alfred Herrhausen Gesellschaft - Das internationale Forum der Deutschen Bank - mbH **(1)** **(56.5%)**
Tel.: (49) 3034074206
Web Site: http://www.alfred-herrhausen-gesellschaft.de
Emp.: 8
Commercial Banking Services
N.A.I.C.S.: 522110

Apex Fleet Inc. **(1)**
2036 Washington St, Hanover, MA 02339
Tel.: (617) 217-6100
Investment Management Service
N.A.I.C.S.: 523940

Aqueduct Capital S.a r.l. **(1)**
2 Boulevard Konrad Andenauer 1115, 1115, Luxembourg, Luxembourg
Tel.: (352) 42122 1
Investment Management Service
N.A.I.C.S.: 523940
Pawan Chaturvedi *(Head-Investments)*

B.T. Vordertaunus (Luxembourg), S.a r.l. **(1)**
67 Haaptstrooss, 9806, Hosingen, Luxembourg
Tel.: (352) 92 341 6
Investment Management Service
N.A.I.C.S.: 523940

B.T.I. Investments INC. **(1)**
Winchester House 1 Great Winchester Street, London, EC2N 2DB, United Kingdom
Tel.: (44) 2075456000
Investment Management Service
N.A.I.C.S.: 523940

BAL Servicing Corporation **(1)**
1011 Centre Rd Ste 200, Wilmington, DE 19805
Tel.: (302) 636-3301
Financial Management Services
N.A.I.C.S.: 523999

BHW - Gesellschaft fur Wohnung-swirtschaft mbH **(1)**
Lubahnstrasse 2, 31789, Hameln, Niedersachsen, Germany
Tel.: (49) 5151 180
Investment Management Service
N.A.I.C.S.: 523940

BHW - Gesellschaft fur Wohnung-swirtschaft mbH & Co. Immobilienver-waltungs KG **(1)**
Lubahnstr 2, Hameln, 31789, Niedersachsen, Germany
Tel.: (49) 515 1180
Investment Management Service
N.A.I.C.S.: 523940

BT Globenet Nominees Limited **(1)**
1 Appold St, London, EC2A 2AA, United Kingdom
Tel.: (44) 2075458000
Financial Management Services
N.A.I.C.S.: 523999

BT Muritz GmbH **(1)**
Alfred-Herrhausen-Allee 16-24, 65760, Eschborn, Hessen, Germany
Tel.: (49) 69 910 33974
Financial Management Services
N.A.I.C.S.: 523999

BT Sable, L.L.C. **(1)**
2711 Centerville Rd Ste 400, Wilmington, DE 19808
Tel.: (302) 636-3301
Investment Management Service
N.A.I.C.S.: 523940

Bankers International Corporation **(1)**
1011 Center Rd Ste 200, Wilmington, DE 19805-1266
Tel.: (302) 636-3363
Investment Management Service
N.A.I.C.S.: 523940

Bankers International Corporation (Brasil) Ltda. **(1)**

Av Brg Faria Lima 3900, Sao Paulo, 04538-133, Brazil
Tel.: (55) 11 2113 5000
Commercial Banking Services
N.A.I.C.S.: 522110

Barkly Investments Ltd. **(1)**
St Paul's Gate New Street, JE4 8ZB, Saint Helier, Jersey
Tel.: (44) 1534 889 900
Investment Management Service
N.A.I.C.S.: 523940

Bebek Varlik Yonetym A.S. **(1)**
Eski Buyukdere Cad Tekfen Tower No 209 Kat 17-18-3 Podium, 34394, Istanbul, Turkiye
Tel.: (90) 212 317 01 00
Real Estate Development Services
N.A.I.C.S.: 531390

Benefit Trust GmbH **(1)**
Stosswitzer Strasse 5, Lutzen, 06686, Sachsen-Anhalt, Germany
Tel.: (49) 34444901061
Investment Management Service
N.A.I.C.S.: 523940

Berliner Bank AG & Co. KG **(1)**
Hardenberg Suite 32, 60486, Berlin, Germany
Tel.: (49) 3031090
Web Site: http://www.berliner-bank.de
Sales Range: $700-749.9 Million
Emp.: 1,100
International Banking
N.A.I.C.S.: 522110

Beta DB Lindsell Limited S.C.S. **(1)**
Boulevard Konrad Adenauer 2, Luxembourg, Luxembourg
Tel.: (352) 42122 1
Investment Management Service
N.A.I.C.S.: 523940

Bfl-Beteiligungsgesellschaft fur Industriewerte mbH **(1)**
Bockenheimer Landstr 10, 60323, Frankfurt am Main, Germany
Tel.: (49) 69 718 0
Investment Management Service
N.A.I.C.S.: 523940

Biomass Holdings S.a r.l. **(1)**
Boulevard Konrad Adenauer 2, Luxembourg, Luxembourg
Tel.: (352) 42122 1
Investment Management Service
N.A.I.C.S.: 523940
Boris Liedtke *(CEO)*

Bluewater Creek Management Co. **(1)**
1011 Centre Rd Ste 200, Wilmington, DE 19805
Tel.: (302) 636-3301
Financial Management Services
N.A.I.C.S.: 523999

Bolsena Holding GmbH & Co. KG **(1)**
Grosse Gallusstrasse 10-14, 60311, Frankfurt am Main, Germany
Tel.: (49) 69 910 00
Investment Management Service
N.A.I.C.S.: 523999

Bonsai Investment AG **(1)**
Oberstadtstrasse 4, 8500, Frauenfeld, Switzerland
Tel.: (41) 52 730 18 80
Fund Management Services
N.A.I.C.S.: 523940

Britannia Limited **(1)**
Regis House 45 King William Street, London, EC4R 9AN, United Kingdom
Tel.: (44) 2074073588
Financial Management Services
N.A.I.C.S.: 523999

Cape Acquisition Corp. **(1)**
10951 Bonita Beach Rd SE, Bonita Springs, FL 34135-8502
Tel.: (239) 495-8200
Web Site: http://www.freyandson.com
Emp.: 25
Financial Management Services
N.A.I.C.S.: 523999

Career Blazers Learning Center of Los Angeles, Inc. **(1)**

Deutsche Bank Aktiengesellschaft—(Continued)

3500 Wilshire Blvd 2nd Fl, Los Angeles, CA
90010
Tel.: (213) 620-8200
Training Center Operating Services
N.A.I.C.S.: 611430

**Cinda - DB NPL Securitization Trust
2003-1** (1)
60 Wall St Lbby 1, New York, NY 10005-
2880
Tel.: (212) 250-2500
Business Management Consulting Services
N.A.I.C.S.: 541611

City Leasing Limited (1)
23 Great Winchester Street, London, EC2P
2AX, United Kingdom
Tel.: (44) 2075458000
Financial Lending Services
N.A.I.C.S.: 523999

Subsidiary (Domestic):

City Leasing (Donside) Limited (2)
23 Great Winchester Street, London, EC2P
2AX, United Kingdom
Tel.: (44) 2075458000
Financial Lending Services
N.A.I.C.S.: 523999

City Leasing (Wearside) Limited (2)
23 Great Winchester Street, London, EC2P
2AX, United Kingdom
Tel.: (44) 2075458000
Financial Lending Services
N.A.I.C.S.: 523999

D.B. International Delaware, Inc. (1)
1011 Centre Rd, Wilmington, DE 19805
Tel.: (302) 636-3290
Financial Management Services
N.A.I.C.S.: 523999

DB Advisors SICAV (1)
No 2 Blvd Konrad Adenauer, Luxembourg,
1115, Luxembourg
Tel.: (352) 273321
Emp.: 15
Financial Advisory Services
N.A.I.C.S.: 523940
Leif Bjurstrom *(Gen Mgr)*

DB Akela, S.a.r.l. (1)
2 boulevard Konrad Adenauer, Luxem-
bourg, 1115, Luxembourg
Tel.: (352) 42122 1
Commercial Banking Services
N.A.I.C.S.: 522110

**DB Alex. Brown Holdings
Incorporated** (1)
1011 Centre Rd Ste 200, Wilmington, DE
19805
Tel.: (302) 636-3290
Investment Management Service
N.A.I.C.S.: 523940

DB Alternative Strategies Limited (1)
Boundary Hall Cricket Sq 171 Elgin Ave,
PO Box 1984, KY1-1104, Georgetown,
Grand Cayman, Cayman Islands
Tel.: (345) 949 8244
Financial Management Services
N.A.I.C.S.: 523999

**DB Aotearoa Investments
Limited** (1)
Elizabethan Square, Georgetown, Grand
Cayman, Cayman Islands
Tel.: (345) 949 8244
Investment Management Service
N.A.I.C.S.: 523940

DB Bagheera, S.a r.l. (1)
2 boulevard Konrad Adenauer, Luxem-
bourg, 1115, Luxembourg
Tel.: (352) 42122 1
Financial Management Services
N.A.I.C.S.: 523999

**DB Bluebell Investments (Cayman)
Partnership** (1)
171 Elgin Avenue, Georgetown, Grand Cay-
man, Cayman Islands
Tel.: (345) 949 8244
Commercial Banking Services
N.A.I.C.S.: 522110

**DB Capital Markets (Deutschland)
GmbH** (1)

Taunusanlage 12, 60325, Frankfurt, Ger-
many
Regional Management Headquarters
Securities Brokerage Services
N.A.I.C.S.: 523150

**DB Capital Markets Asset Manage-
ment Holding GmbH** (1)
Taunusanlage 12, Frankfurt am Main,
60325, Hessen, Germany
Tel.: (49) 6991000
Investment Management Service
N.A.I.C.S.: 523940

DB Chestnut Holdings Limited (1)
171 Elgin Avenue, KY1-1104, Georgetown,
Grand Cayman, Cayman Islands
Tel.: (345) 949 8244
Investment Management Service
N.A.I.C.S.: 523940

DB Commodities Canada Ltd. (1)
199 Bay St Suite 4700, Toronto, M5L 1E9,
ON, Canada
Tel.: (416) 682-8422
Financial Management Services
N.A.I.C.S.: 523999

DB Concerto Limited (1)
171 Elgin Avenue, KY1-1104, Georgetown,
Grand Cayman, Cayman Islands
Tel.: (345) 949 8244
Web Site: http://www.db.com
Emp.: 45
Investment Management Service
N.A.I.C.S.: 523940

DB Consorzio S. Cons. a r. l. (1)
Piazza Del Calendario 3, Milan, 20126, Italy
Tel.: (39) 024 0241
Financial Management Services
N.A.I.C.S.: 523999

DB Crest Limited (1)
St Paul's Gate New Street, JE4 8ZB, Saint
Helier, Jersey
Tel.: (44) 1534889900
Financial Management Services
N.A.I.C.S.: 523999

**DB Delaware Holdings (Europe)
Limited** (1)
1209 Orange St, Wilmington, DE 19801
Tel.: (302) 636-3301
Investment Management Service
N.A.I.C.S.: 523940

DB Depositor Inc. (1)
1011 Centre Rd Ste 200, Wilmington, DE
19805-1266
Tel.: (302) 636-3301
Commercial Banking Services
N.A.I.C.S.: 522110

DB Equity S.a r.l. (1)
6 Avenue Pasteur, 2310, Luxembourg, Lux-
embourg
Tel.: (352) 26 20 27 80
Commercial Banking Services
N.A.I.C.S.: 522110

DB Global Technology SRL (1)
Business Center Upground 6A Dimitrie
Pompeiu Blvd, 2nd District 1st Floor,
020337, Bucharest, Romania
Tel.: (40) 312224000
N.A.I.C.S.: 523150

DB Global Technology, Inc. (1)
3000 Centre Green Way, Cary, NC 27513-
5775
Tel.: (919) 481-7900
Web Site: http://www.db.com
Emp.: 650
Commercial Banking Services
N.A.I.C.S.: 522110

DB Group Services (UK) Limited (1)
Winchester House 1 Great Winchester
Street, London, EC2N2DB, United Kingdom
Tel.: (44) 2075 45 80 00
Web Site: http://www.db.com
Sales Range: $350-399.9 Million
Emp.: 1,000
Commercial Banking Services
N.A.I.C.S.: 522110

DB HR Solutions GmbH (1)
Alfred-Herrhausen-Allee 16-24, 65760, Es-
chborn, Hessen, Germany
Tel.: (49) 6991000

Business Management Consulting Services
N.A.I.C.S.: 541611

DB Holdings (New York), Inc. (1)
60 Wall St, New York, NY 10005
Tel.: (212) 250-2500
Investment Management Service
N.A.I.C.S.: 523940

DB IROC Leasing Corp. (1)
60 Wall St Lbby 1, New York, NY 10005-
2880
Tel.: (212) 250-2500
Web Site: http://www.db.com
Securities Brokerage Services
N.A.I.C.S.: 523150

**DB Industrial Holdings Beteiligungs
GmbH & Co. KG** (1)
Taunusanlage 12, 60325, Frankfurt am
Main, Germany
Tel.: (49) 6991000
Investment Management Service
N.A.I.C.S.: 523940

DB Industrial Holdings GmbH (1)
Taunusanlage 12, Frankfurt am Main,
60262, Germany
Tel.: (49) 6991000
Investment Management Service
N.A.I.C.S.: 523940

DB International (Asia) Limited (1)
One Raffles Quay South Tower Level 17,
Singapore, 048583, Singapore
Tel.: (65) 64238001
Financial Banking Services
N.A.I.C.S.: 522110

**DB Investment Management,
Inc.** (1)
652 Marsten Green Ct, Ambler, PA 19002
Tel.: (215) 646-6762
Business Management Consulting Services
N.A.I.C.S.: 541611

**DB Investment Resources (US)
Corporation** (1)
60 Wall St, New York, NY 10005
Tel.: (212) 250-2500
Investment Management Service
N.A.I.C.S.: 523940

**DB Investment Resources Holdings
Corp.** (1)
60 Wall St Lbby 1, New York, NY 10005-
2880
Tel.: (212) 250-2500
Investment Management Service
N.A.I.C.S.: 523999

DB Investment Services GmbH (1)
Wilhelm-Fay-Strasse 31-37, 65936, Frank-
furt am Main, Germany (51%)
Tel.: (49) 69120120
Sales Range: $150-199.9 Million
Emp.: 700
Business Processing Services for Securities
N.A.I.C.S.: 541519
Thomas Beemelmann *(CEO)*

DB Io LP (1)
60 Wall St Lbby 1, New York, NY 10005-
2880
Tel.: (212) 250-2500
Securities Brokerage Services
N.A.I.C.S.: 523150

DB Maia LLC (1)
60 Wall St Lbby 1, New York, NY 10005-
2880
Tel.: (212) 250-2500
Business Management Consulting Services
N.A.I.C.S.: 541611

DB Management Partners, L.P. (1)
60 Wall St Frnt 1, New York, NY 10005-
2836
Tel.: (212) 250-2500
Web Site: http://www.db.com
Securities Brokerage Services
N.A.I.C.S.: 523150

DB Management Support GmbH (1)
Theodor-Heuss-Allee 72, 60486, Frankfurt
am Main, Germany
Tel.: (49) 6991034050
Web Site: https://www.db-
managementsupport.com
Business Management Consulting Services
N.A.I.C.S.: 541611

Gerhard Spennemann *(Gen Mgr)*

DB Overseas Holdings Limited (1)
1 Great Winchester Street, London, EC2N
2DB, United Kingdom
Tel.: (44) 2075458000
Investment Management Service
N.A.I.C.S.: 523940

**DB Partnership Management II,
LLC** (1)
60 Wall St Lbby 1, New York, NY 10005-
2880
Tel.: (212) 250-2500
Business Management Consulting Services
N.A.I.C.S.: 541611

**DB Partnership Management
Ltd.** (1)
1011 Centre Rd, Wilmington, DE 19805-
1267
Tel.: (302) 636-3290
Commercial Banking Services
N.A.I.C.S.: 522110
Donna Mitchell *(Gen Mgr)*

DB Perry Investments Limited (1)
60 Wall St Lbby 1, New York, NY 10005
Tel.: (212) 250-2500
Business Management Consulting Services
N.A.I.C.S.: 541611

DB Petri LLC (1)
60 Wall St Lbby 1, New York, NY 10005-
2880
Tel.: (212) 250-2500
Administrative Management & General
Management Consulting Services
N.A.I.C.S.: 541611

DB Platinum Advisors S.A. (1)
Boulevard Konrad Adenauer 2, Luxem-
bourg, 1115, Luxembourg
Tel.: (352) 42122 1
Emp.: 8
Investment Management Service
N.A.I.C.S.: 523940
Barbara Schots *(Gen Mgr)*

DB Print GmbH (1)
Friedrich-Kahl-Str 10, Frankfurt, 60489,
Germany
Tel.: (49) 6991086523
Commercial Printing Services
N.A.I.C.S.: 323111

DB Private Clients Corp. (1)
345 Park Ave, New York, NY 10154
Tel.: (212) 454-3600
Financial Management Services
N.A.I.C.S.: 523999

DB Private Wealth Mortgage Ltd. (1)
60 Wall St, New York, NY 10005
Tel.: (212) 250-8174
Mortgage Loan Brokerage Services
N.A.I.C.S.: 522310

DB Service Centre Limited (1)
Block D Abbey Ct Irish Life Centre Abbey
Street, Dublin, Ireland
Tel.: (353) 18051000
Credit Intermediation Services
N.A.I.C.S.: 522299

DB Services Americas, Inc. (1)
60 Wall St, New York, NY 10005
Tel.: (212) 250-2500
Financial Management Services
N.A.I.C.S.: 523999

DB Strategic Advisors, Inc. (1)
Unit 17E Petron MegaPlaza Sen Gil Puyat
Avenue, Makati, 1200, Philippines
Tel.: (63) 28565984
Commercial Banking Services
N.A.I.C.S.: 522110

**DB Trust Company Limited
Japan** (1)
Sanno Park Tower Nagatacho 2-11-1,
Chiyoda-ku, Tokyo, Japan
Tel.: (81) 351567704
Trust Management Services
N.A.I.C.S.: 523991

DB Trustee Services Limited (1)
23 Great Winchester Street, London, EC2P
2AX, United Kingdom
Tel.: (44) 2075458000
Trust Management Services

N.A.I.C.S.: 523991

DB Trustees (Hong Kong)
Limited (1)
Level 60 International Commerce Centre 1
Austin Road West, Kowloon, Hong Kong,
China (Hong Kong)
Tel.: (852) 22038888
Trust Management Services
N.A.I.C.S.: 523991

DB UK Bank Limited (1)
6 Bishopsgate 1 Great Winchester St, Lon-
don, EC2N 4DA, United Kingdom
Tel.: (44) 1715458000
Commercial Banking Services
N.A.I.C.S.: 522110

DB VersicherungsManager
GmbH (1)
Theodor-Heuss-Allee 72, 60486, Frankfurt
am Main, Germany
Tel.: (49) 6925510691
Web Site: https://www.db-
   versicherungsmanager.de
N.A.I.C.S.: 523940
Bjorn Renker (Exec Dir)

DB Vita S.A. (1)
2 Boulevard Konrad Adenauer, 1115, Lux-
embourg, Luxembourg
Tel.: (352) 264229300
Web Site: https://www.db-vita.de
General Insurance Services
N.A.I.C.S.: 524210

DBAH Capital, LLC (1)
60 Wall St, New York, NY 10005
Tel.: (212) 250-2500
Web Site: http://www.db.com
Investment Management Service
N.A.I.C.S.: 523940

DBC Continuance Inc. (1)
199 Bay Street Suite 4700 Commerce
Court West, Box 263, Toronto, M5L 1E9,
ON, Canada
Tel.: (416) 682-8000
Commercial Banking Services
N.A.I.C.S.: 522110

DBD Pilgrim America Corp. (1)
1011 Centre Rd, Wilmington, DE 19805
Tel.: (302) 636-3290
Investment Management Service
N.A.I.C.S.: 523999

DBG Vermogensverwaltungsgesell-
schaft mbH (1)
Taunusanlage 10-12, 60329, Frankfurt am
Main, Hessen, Germany
Tel.: (49) 6991000
Investment Management Service
N.A.I.C.S.: 523940

DBOI Global Services (UK)
Limited (1)
1 Great Winchester Street, London, EC2N
2DB, United Kingdom
Tel.: (44) 2075458000
Business Management Consulting Services
N.A.I.C.S.: 541611

DBOI Global Services Private
Limited (1)
6th Floor Nirlon Knowledge Park Block B4
Western Express Highway, Goregaon,
Mumbai, 400 063, India
Tel.: (91) 2267113000
Financial Management Services
N.A.I.C.S.: 523999

Subsidiary (Non-US):

Deutsche Asset Management (Asia)
Limited (2)
One Raffles Quay South Tower Level 15,
Singapore, 048583, Singapore (100%)
Tel.: (65) 65387011
Sales Range: $75-99.9 Million
Emp.: 150
Securities Dealer
N.A.I.C.S.: 523150

Deutsche Bank AG-Singapore (2)
One Raffles Quay South Tower Level 17,
Singapore, 048583, Singapore (100%)
Tel.: (65) 64238001
Web Site: https://country.db.com

Sales Range: $400-449.9 Million
Emp.: 900
Corporate & Investment Banking Services
N.A.I.C.S.: 523150
Kamran Khan (Head-ESG-Asia Pacific)

DBUSBZ2, LLC (1)
1011 Centre Rd Ste 200, Wilmington, DE
19805
Tel.: (302) 636-3290
Financial Management Services
N.A.I.C.S.: 523999

DBX Advisors LLC (1)
345 Park Ave, New York, NY 10154
Tel.: (212) 250-5883
Web Site: http://www.dbx.com
Financial Management Services
N.A.I.C.S.: 523999

DEBEKO Immobilien GmbH & Co
Grundbesitz OHG (1)
Alfred-Herrhausen-Allee 16-24, 65760, Es-
chborn, Germany
Tel.: (49) 6971704841
Real Estate Advisory Services
N.A.I.C.S.: 531390

DEUKONA
Versicherungs-Vermittlungs-GmbH (1)
Taunusanlage 12, 60325, Frankfurt, Ger-
many
Tel.: (49) 69 91008
Web Site: http://www.deutschebank.de
Investment Management Service
N.A.I.C.S.: 523940

DEUTSCHE BANK A.S. (1)
Eski Buyukdere Caddesi Tekfen Tower No
209 K 17-18 4 Levent, Istanbul, 34394,
Turkiye
Tel.: (90) 2123170100
Commercial Banking Services
N.A.I.C.S.: 522110

DFC Residual Corp. (1)
101 Convention Ctr Dr, Las Vegas, NV
89109-2001
Tel.: (702) 380-4928
Investment Banking Services
N.A.I.C.S.: 523150

DI Deutsche Immobilien Treuhandge-
sellschaft mbH (1)
Mainzer Landstr 178-190, 60327, Frankfurt,
Hessen, Germany
Tel.: (49) 697170400
Real Estate Development Services
N.A.I.C.S.: 531390

DISCA Beteiligungsgesellschaft
mbH (1)
Konigsallee 106, 40215, Dusseldorf,
Nordrhein-Westfalen, Germany
Tel.: (49) 21199460
Investment Management Service
N.A.I.C.S.: 523940

DWS Alternatives Global Limited (1)
1 Appold Street, London, EC2A 2UU,
United Kingdom
Tel.: (44) 2075456853
Investment Management Service
N.A.I.C.S.: 523940

Subsidiary (Non-US):

Hansea NV (2)
Groenendaallaan 387, 2030, Antwerp, Bel-
gium
Tel.: (32) 3544 3370
Web Site: http://www.hansea.be
Sales Range: $150-199.9 Million
Emp.: 1,100
Passenger Transport Services Operator
N.A.I.C.S.: 485999
Luc Jullet (Mng Dir)

DWS Asset Management (Korea)
Company Limited (1)
11F Centropolis Tower A 26 Ujeongguk-Ro,
Jongno-ku, Seoul, 03161, Korea (South)
Tel.: (82) 27247400
N.A.I.C.S.: 523940

DWS CH AG (1)
Primetower Hardstrasse 201, 8021, Zurich,
Switzerland
Tel.: (41) 442247700
Investment Management Service
N.A.I.C.S.: 523940

Stefano Recchione (CFO)

DWS Distributors, Inc. (1)
222 S Riverside Plz, Chicago, IL 60606-
5808
Tel.: (212) 250-2500
N.A.I.C.S.: 523940

DWS Far Eastern Investments
Limited (1)
7F 207 Tun Hua South Road Section 2,
Taipei, 10602, Taiwan
Tel.: (886) 223777717
Commercial Banking Services
N.A.I.C.S.: 522110

DWS Finanz-Service GmbH (1)
Mainzer Landstrasse 11-17, 60329, Frank-
furt am Main, Germany
Tel.: (49) 69719092371
Web Site: https://www.dws.de
Financial Management Services
N.A.I.C.S.: 523999

DWS Grundbesitz GmbH (1)
Mainzer Landstr 11-17, 60329, Frankfurt am
Main, Germany
Tel.: (49) 6991012371
Web Site: http://realestate.dws.com
Investment Management Service
N.A.I.C.S.: 523940
Clemens Heinrich Grunewald (Head-Closed
End Fund Mgmt)

DWS Holding & Service GmbH (1)
Mainzer Landstr 178-190, 60327, Frankfurt,
Hessen, Germany
Tel.: (49) 69719090
Investment Management Service
N.A.I.C.S.: 523940

DWS Investment S.A. (1)
2 Boulevard Konrad Adenauer, 1115, Lux-
embourg, Luxembourg
Tel.: (352) 421011
Web Site: https://funds.dws.com
N.A.I.C.S.: 523940

DWS Investments Australia
Limited (1)
Level 16 126 Phillip Street, Sydney, 2000,
NSW, Australia
Tel.: (61) 282581234
Investment Management Service
N.A.I.C.S.: 523940
Lidia Tomova (Head-Coverage)

DWS Investments Distributors,
Inc. (1)
222 S Riverside Plz, Chicago, IL 60606-
5808
Tel.: (212) 454-6778
Web Site: http://www.dws-investments.com
Sales Range: $200-249.9 Million
Emp.: 500
Investment Management Service
N.A.I.C.S.: 523150

Subsidiary (Non-US):

DWS (Austria) Investmentgesellschaft
mbH (2)
Flaischmarkt 1, 1010, Indiana, Austria
Tel.: (43) 1531810
Sales Range: $50-74.9 Million
Emp.: 100
Investment Management Service
N.A.I.C.S.: 523150
Rainer Polster (Gen Mgr)

DWS Investment GmbH (2)
Mainzer Landstrasse 11-17, 60329, Frank-
furt am Main, Germany
Tel.: (49) 6991012371
Web Site: https://www.dws.com
Investment Management Service
N.A.I.C.S.: 523150

DWS Investment S.A.
Luxembourg (2)
2 Boulevard Konrad Adenauer, 1115, Lux-
embourg, Luxembourg (100%)
Tel.: (352) 421011
Web Site: https://funds.dws.com
Sales Range: $75-99.9 Million
Emp.: 130
Investment Banking Services
N.A.I.C.S.: 523910

DWS Investments S.G.I.I.C. (2)

Paseo de la Castellana 18, 28046, Madrid,
Spain
Tel.: (34) 913351179
Web Site: http://www.dws.com
Sales Range: $25-49.9 Million
Emp.: 40
Investment Management Service
N.A.I.C.S.: 523150

DWS Polska TFI S.A. (2)
Budynek FOCUS 10 pitro, Armii Ludowej
26, 00 609, Warsaw, Poland
Tel.: (48) 22 5 79 97 00
Investment Management Service
N.A.I.C.S.: 523150

DWS Investments Hong Kong
Limited (1)
Level 60 International Commerce Centre 1
Austin Road West, Kowloon, China (Hong
Kong)
Tel.: (852) 22038888
Investment Advisory Services
N.A.I.C.S.: 523940

DWS Investments Service
Company (1)
210 W 10th St, Kansas City, MO 64105-
1614
Tel.: (800) 621-1148
Investment Management Service
N.A.I.C.S.: 523940

DWS Investments Shanghai
Limited (1)
39A/F 2IFC No 8 Century Avenue, Pudong,
Shanghai, 200120, China
Tel.: (86) 2120802800
N.A.I.C.S.: 541219

Deutsche Access Investments
Limited (1)
Deutsche Bank Place Level 16 Cnr Hunter
and Phillip Street, Sydney, 2000, NSW,
Australia
Tel.: (61) 1300551346
Web Site: http://www.dbaccess.db.com
Investment Management Service
N.A.I.C.S.: 523940

Deutsche Asia Pacific Holdings Pte
Ltd. (1)
One Raffles Quay South Tower Level 17,
Singapore, 048583, Singapore (100%)
Tel.: (65) 64238001
Sales Range: $250-299.9 Million
Emp.: 900
Financial Holding Company
N.A.I.C.S.: 551111

Deutsche Asset & Wealth
Management (1)
345 Park Ave, New York, NY
10154-0004 (80%)
Tel.: (212) 250-2500
Web Site: http://www.db.com
Sales Range: $300-349.9 Million
Emp.: 2,300
Investment Counseling Firm
N.A.I.C.S.: 561110

Subsidiary (Domestic):

RREEF Management LLC (2)
875 N Michigan Ave 41st Fl, Chicago, IL
60611
Tel.: (312) 266-9300
Financial Management & Investment Services
N.A.I.C.S.: 523999

Subsidiary (Non-US):

RREEF China REIT Management
Limited (3)
Level 52 International Commerce Centre 1
Austin Road West, Kowloon, China (Hong
Kong)
Tel.: (852) 2203 7872
Web Site: http://www.rreef.com
Investment Management Service
N.A.I.C.S.: 523940

Branch (Domestic):

RREEF Management LLC (3)
280 Park Ave 23rd Fl, New York, NY 10017
Tel.: (212) 454-3900
Financial Management & Investment Services

Deutsche Bank Aktiengesellschaft—(Continued)

N.A.I.C.S.: 523999

Holding (Domestic):

Winridge Apartments (3)
2075 S Paris Way, Aurora, CO 80014-1173
Tel.: (303) 337-9102
Web Site: http://www.srgliving.com
Sales Range: $50-74.9 Million
Emp.: 4
Apartment Building Operator
N.A.I.C.S.: 531110

Affiliate (Domestic):

**RREEF North American Infrastructure
Onshore Fund A, L.P.** (2)
60 Wall St, New York, NY 10005
Tel.: (212) 454-6619
Fund Management Services
N.A.I.C.S.: 523940

RREEF Property Trust, Inc. (2)
875 3rd Ave 26th Fl, New York, NY 10022
Tel.: (212) 454-4500
Web Site:
https://www.rreefpropertytrust.com
Rev.: $42,486,000
Assets: $1,625,489,000
Liabilities: $1,446,938,000
Net Worth: $178,551,000
Earnings: ($14,923,000)
Fiscal Year-end: 12/31/2022
Real Estate Investment Services
N.A.I.C.S.: 523999
Anne-Marie Vandenberg (Pres & CEO)

**Deutsche Asset Management (Japan)
Limited** (1)
Sanno Park Tower 2 11 1 Nagatacho,
Chiyoda-ku, Tokyo, 100 6173,
Japan (100%)
Tel.: (81) 351565000
Web Site: http://www.db.co.jp
Securities Dealer
N.A.I.C.S.: 523150

**Deutsche Asset Management (Korea)
Company Limited** (1)
33 Seorin-Dong, Jongno-Gu, Seoul, 110-
752, Korea (South)
Tel.: (82) 2 724 7400
Investment Management Service
N.A.I.C.S.: 523940
Christopher Kimm (Mng Dir & Head-Real
Estate)

**Deutsche Asset Management Canada
Limited** (1)
199 Bay Street Suite 4700 Commerce
Court West, Box 263, M5L 1E9, Toronto,
ON, Canada
Tel.: (416) 682-8000
Investment Management Service
N.A.I.C.S.: 523940

**Deutsche Asset Management
GmbH** (1)
Mainzer Landstrasse 178 190, 60327,
Frankfurt, Germany (100%)
Tel.: (49) 180310111011
Web Site: http://www.deam-global.com
Investment Banking
N.A.I.C.S.: 523150
David Bianco (Head-Equities-US)

Subsidiary (Domestic):

**DB Real Estate Investment
GmbH** (2)
Mergenthalerallee 73 75, 65760, Eschborn,
Germany
Tel.: (49) 697170400
Web Site: http://www.rreef.com
Sales Range: $75-99.9 Million
Emp.: 200
Real Estate Investment Trust
N.A.I.C.S.: 525990

**Deutsche Asset Management
Schweiz** (1)
Prime Tower Hardstrasse 201, 8005, Zurich,
Switzerland (100%)
Tel.: (41) 581110111
Sales Range: $1-9.9 Million
Emp.: 70
Asset Management
N.A.I.C.S.: 531390

Phillip Hensler (COO)

**Deutsche Asset Management
Switzerland** (1)
Hardstrasse 201, Hardstrasse 201 8005,
Zurich, 8005, Switzerland (100%)
Tel.: (41) 442247272
Web Site: http://www.dws.ch
Sales Range: $50-74.9 Million
Emp.: 60
Asset Management
N.A.I.C.S.: 531390

Deutsche Australia Limited (1)
Level 16 Deutsche Bank Place Corner of
Hunter and Phillip Streets, Sydney, 2000,
NSW, Australia
Tel.: (61) 2 8258 1234
Web Site: http://www.australia.db.com
Commercial Banking Services
N.A.I.C.S.: 522110

Deutsche Bank (1)
Tel.: (213) 620-8200
Web Site: http://www.db.com
Sales Range: $50-74.9 Million
Emp.: 100
National Consumer Cooperative Bank
N.A.I.C.S.: 522110
Amy H. Rice (Executives)

Deutsche Bank (Chile) S.A. (1)
Ave El Bosque Sur 130 Piso 5, Las Con-
des, Santiago, 7550-0288, Chile
Tel.: (56) 23377700
Web Site: http://www.db.com
Sales Range: $75-99.9 Million
Emp.: 52
Asset Management & Investment Banking
Services
N.A.I.C.S.: 523150

Deutsche Bank (China) Co., Ltd. (1)
28/F Deutsche Bank Tower China Central
Place No 81 Jianguo Avenue, Chaoyang
District, Beijing, 100025, China (100%)
Tel.: (86) 1059698888
Asset Management, Corporate & Invest-
ment Banking Services
N.A.I.C.S.: 523150

**Deutsche Bank (Malaysia)
Berhad** (1)
Tel.: (60) 320536788
Sales Range: $100-124.9 Million
Emp.: 250
Corporate & Institutional Banking Services
N.A.I.C.S.: 522299
Yusof Annuar Yaacob (Exec Dir)

Deutsche Bank (Malta) Ltd (1)
Forni Complex 1E, Level 2, Pinto Wharf,
Valletta Waterfront, Floriana, FRN 1913,
Malta
Tel.: (356) 2137 3666
Web Site: http://www.db.com
Emp.: 10
Commercial Banking Services
N.A.I.C.S.: 522110

**Deutsche Bank (Mauritius)
Limited** (1)
4th Floor Barkly Wharf East, PO Box 615,
Le Caudan Waterfront, Port Louis, Mauritius
Tel.: (230) 202 7878
Web Site: http://www.db.com
Sales Range: $100-124.9 Million
Emp.: 200
Commercial Banking Services
N.A.I.C.S.: 522110

Deutsche Bank (Peru) S.A. (1)
Miguel Dasso 104 - 8th Floor, San Isidro,
Lima, Peru
Tel.: (51) 1 219 6800
Web Site: http://www.db.com
Sales Range: $50-74.9 Million
Emp.: 28
Commercial Banking Services
N.A.I.C.S.: 522110

Deutsche Bank (Schweiz) AG (1)
(100%)
Sales Range: $100-124.9 Million
Emp.: 200
Web Site: http://www.db.com
International Banking
N.A.I.C.S.: 522299

Deutsche Bank (Suisse) S.A. (1)
Place des Bergues 3, 1211, Geneva,
Switzerland (100%)

Tel.: (41) 227390111
Web Site: http://www.db.com
Sales Range: $350-399.9 Million
Emp.: 600
International Banking
N.A.I.C.S.: 522299

Deutsche Bank (Svizzera) S.A. (1)
Via Francesco Soave 5, 6901, Lugano,
Switzerland (100%)
Tel.: (41) 919103838
Web Site: http://www.pwm.db.com
Rev.: $7,008,500
Emp.: 26
International Banking
N.A.I.C.S.: 522299
Marco Piano (Mng Dir)

**Deutsche Bank (Uruguay)
S.A.I.F.E.** (1)
World Trade Ctr Av Luis, Alberto De Herrera
Piso 19, Montevideo, 1248,
Uruguay (100%)
Tel.: (598) 26222950
Web Site: http://www.db.com
International Banking
N.A.I.C.S.: 522299

Deutsche Bank AG (1)
Level 60 International Commerce Centre 1
Austin Road West Kowloon, Kowloon,
China (Hong Kong) (100%)
Tel.: (852) 22038888
Web Site: https://www.db.com
Rev.: $65,516,061,385
Assets: $1,448,648,857,693
Liabilities: $1,366,059,167,870
Net Worth: $82,589,689,823
Earnings: $5,400,154,543
Emp.: 90,130
Fiscal Year-end: 12/31/2023
Branch of Foriegn Bank
N.A.I.C.S.: 522299

Deutsche Bank AG (1)
1 Great Winchester Street, London, EC2N
2DB, United Kingdom
Tel.: (44) 207 54 58000
Web Site: http://www.db.com
Investment Management Service
N.A.I.C.S.: 523940

Deutsche Bank AG (Bombay) (1)
Hazarimal Somani Marg Fort, Mumbai, 400
001, India (100%)
Tel.: (91) 2222074720
Web Site: http://www.db.com
International Banking
N.A.I.C.S.: 522299

Deutsche Bank AG (Istanbul) (1)
Esentepe Mah Buyukdere Cad Ferko Sig-
nature No 175 / 149, Sisli, Istanbul,
Turkiye (100%)
Tel.: (90) 2123170100
Sales Range: $50-74.9 Million
Emp.: 4
Representative Office
N.A.I.C.S.: 523150

Deutsche Bank AG (Macau) (1)
99 Avenida Almeida Ribeiro 7/F, Nam Wah
Commercial Edificio, Macau, China (Macau)
Tel.: (853) 3356200
Web Site: http://www.db.com
International Banking
N.A.I.C.S.: 522299

Deutsche Bank AG (Manila) (1)
Ayala Tower 1 Ayala Triangle, Makati, 1226,
Manila, Philippines (100%)
Tel.: (63) 28946900
Web Site: http://www.db.com
Sales Range: $50-74.9 Million
Emp.: 100
International Banking
N.A.I.C.S.: 522299

Deutsche Bank AG (New Delhi) (1)
Tolstoy House 15-17 Tolstoy Marg, New
Delhi, 110 001, India
Tel.: (91) 113721154
Web Site: http://www.db.com
International Banking
N.A.I.C.S.: 522299

Deutsche Bank AG (New York) (1)
Tel.: (212) 250-2500
Web Site: http://www.db.com
Sales Range: $1-4.9 Billion
Emp.: 5,000
Commercial Banking

N.A.I.C.S.: 522110

Subsidiary (Domestic):

**Sharps Pixley Brokers
Incorporated** (2)
200 Park Ave Fl 25, New York, NY 10166-
2599
Tel.: (212) 351-5780
Future Commission Merchant
N.A.I.C.S.: 523160

Deutsche Bank AG (Prague) (1)
(100%)
Tel.: (420) 221191111
Web Site: http://www.db.com
Sales Range: $50-74.9 Million
Emp.: 75
Full Banking Services
N.A.I.C.S.: 522299

Deutsche Bank AG (Seoul) (1)
(100%)
Tel.: (82) 27244500
Web Site: http://www.db.com
Sales Range: $200-249.9 Million
Emp.: 300
International Banking
N.A.I.C.S.: 522299

Deutsche Bank AG (Taipei) (1)
(100%)
Tel.: (886) 221924666
Web Site: http://www.db.com
Sales Range: $100-124.9 Million
Emp.: 130
International Banking
N.A.I.C.S.: 522299

Deutsche Bank AG (Tehran) (1)
Valiasr Ave No 1409 Sayeh Twr, 14th Floor
Apt No 5, Tehran, Iran
Tel.: (98) 122046575
Web Site: http://www.db.com
Representative Office
N.A.I.C.S.: 522299

Deutsche Bank AG (Tokyo) (1)
Sanno Park Tower 2 11 1, Tokyo, 100 6170,
Japan (100%)
Tel.: (81) 351564000
Web Site: http://www.db.com
Sales Range: $50-74.9 Million
Emp.: 100
International Banking
N.A.I.C.S.: 522299

**Deutsche Bank AG - UK Representa-
tive Office** (1)
1 Great Winchester Street, London, EC2N
2DB, United Kingdom
Tel.: (44) 207 54 58000
Web Site: http://www.db.com
Private Wealth Management Services
N.A.I.C.S.: 523999
James Cox (COO)

Deutsche Bank AG Canada (1)
199 Bay Street Suite 4700 Commerce
Court West, Toronto, M5L 1E9, ON,
Canada (100%)
Tel.: (416) 682-8000
Web Site: http://www.db.com
Sales Range: $125-149.9 Million
Emp.: 100
Security Brokers & Dealers
N.A.I.C.S.: 523150

**Deutsche Bank AG
Johannesburg** (1)
(100%)
Web Site: http://www.db.com
Sales Range: $100-124.9 Million
Emp.: 187
Representative Office; International Banking
N.A.I.C.S.: 522299
Muneer Ismail (Chief Country Officer)

Deutsche Bank AG-Amsterdam (1)
(100%)
Tel.: (31) 205554911
Web Site: http://www.db.com
Sales Range: $100-124.9 Million
Emp.: 210
International Banking
N.A.I.C.S.: 522299

Deutsche Bank AG-Bangkok (1)
Athenee Tower Level 27-29, 63 Wireless
Road, Lumpini Pathumwan, Bangkok,
10330, Thailand (100%)

Tel.: (66) 2646515000
Web Site: http://www.db.com
Sales Range: $150-199.9 Million
Emp.: 143
Asset Management, Corporate & Investment Banking Services
N.A.I.C.S.: 523150

Deutsche Bank AG-Berlin (1)
Otto Suhr Allee 6 16, 10585, Berlin,
Germany (100%)
Tel.: (49) 3034070
Web Site: http://www.db.de
Sales Range: $50-74.9 Million
Emp.: 100
International Banking Services
N.A.I.C.S.: 523150

Deutsche Bank AG-Cairo (1)
6 Boulos Hanna St 1st Fl, Doki, Giza,
123111, Egypt (100%)
Tel.: (20) 233336358
Web Site: http://www.db.com
Sales Range: $100-124.9 Million
Emp.: 10
Asset Management, Corporate & Investment Banking Services
N.A.I.C.S.: 523150

Deutsche Bank AG-Colombo (1)
86 Galle Road, PO Box 314, Colombo, 3,
Sri Lanka (100%)
Tel.: (94) 112447 062
Web Site: http://www.db.com
Sales Range: $100-124.9 Million
Emp.: 60
Asset Management, Corporate & Investment Banking Services
N.A.I.C.S.: 523150

Deutsche Bank AG-Jakarta (1)
Deutsche Bank Building No 80 Jalan Imam
Bonjol, Jakarta, 10310, Indonesia
Tel.: (62) 2131931092
Web Site: http://www.db.com
Sales Range: $300-349.9 Million
Emp.: 300
Asset Management, Corporate & Investment Banking Services
N.A.I.C.S.: 523150

Deutsche Bank AG-Karachi (1)
Unitowers Unicentre I I, PO Box 4925, Karachi, Pakistan (100%)
Tel.: (92) 21111555777
Web Site: http://www.db.com
Sales Range: $100-124.9 Million
Emp.: 55
Asset Management, Corporate & Investment Banking Services
N.A.I.C.S.: 523150

Deutsche Bank AG-Lahore (1)
307 Upper Mall, Lahore, 42000,
Pakistan (100%)
Tel.: (92) 42111555777
Web Site: http://www.db.com
Sales Range: $100-124.9 Million
Emp.: 21
Asset Management, Corporate & Investment Banking Services
N.A.I.C.S.: 523150

Deutsche Bank AG-London (1)
1 Great Winchester St, London, EC2N 2DB,
United Kingdom (100%)
Tel.: (44) 2075458000
Web Site: http://www.deutsche-bank.com
Sales Range: $1-4.9 Billion
Emp.: 7,000
International Investment Banking
N.A.I.C.S.: 522299

Subsidiary (Domestic):

Deutsche Asset Management (UK)
Ltd. (2)
1 Appold St, London, EC2A 2HE, United
Kingdom (100%)
Tel.: (44) 2075456000
Web Site: http://www.deam.co.uk
Asset Management
N.A.I.C.S.: 531390
Neel Mehta *(CFO-Private Equity Bus-Global)*

Subsidiary (Non-US):

Deutsche Asset Management Italy
S.p.A. (3)

Via Melchiorre Gioia 8, 20126, Milan, Italy
Tel.: (39) 0262994212
Private Equity Fund
N.A.I.C.S.: 551112

Subsidiary (Non-US):

Deutsche Bank Group Services
Ltd. (2)
(100%)
Web Site: http://www.db.com
Sales Range: $300-349.9 Million
Emp.: 1,000
Commercial Banking
N.A.I.C.S.: 522110

Deutsche Bank AG-Manama (1)
Manama Ctr 6th Floor Entrance 1 Government Road, PO Box 20619, Manama,
Bahrain (100%)
Tel.: (973) 17218222
Web Site: http://www.db.com
Sales Range: $100-124.9 Million
Emp.: 16
Asset Management, Corporate & Investment Banking Services
N.A.I.C.S.: 523150

Deutsche Bank AG-Paris (1)
23-25 avenue Franklin Roosevelt, 75008,
Paris, France (100%)
Tel.: (33) 144956400
Web Site: https://country.db.com
Sales Range: $250-299.9 Million
Emp.: 350
Corporate & Investment Banking Services
N.A.I.C.S.: 523150

Deutsche Bank AG-Surabaya (1)
Wisma Dharmala Lt 7 Suite 6, Jalan Panglima, Sudirman 101-103, Surabaya,
60271, Indonesia (100%)
Tel.: (62) 315311822
Web Site: http://www.db.com
Sales Range: $100-124.9 Million
Emp.: 15
Asset Management, Corporate & Investment Banking Services
N.A.I.C.S.: 523150

Deutsche Bank AG-Vienna (1)
Fleischmarkt 1, 1010, Vienna, 1010,
Austria (100%)
Tel.: (43) 1531810
Web Site: http://www.db.com
Sales Range: $25-49.9 Million
Emp.: 50
International Banking
N.A.I.C.S.: 523150

Deutsche Bank Americas Finance
LLC (1)
60 Wall St Lbby 1, New York, NY 10005-2880
Tel.: (212) 250-2500
Web Site: http://www.deutschebank.com
Financial Management Services
N.A.I.C.S.: 523999

Deutsche Bank Australia (1)
Level 16 Deutsche Bank Place, Corner of
Hunter and Phillip Streets, Sydney, 2000,
NSW, Australia
Tel.: (61) 282581234
Web Site: https://country.db.com
Sales Range: $25-49.9 Billion
Emp.: 800
Corporate & Investment Banking
N.A.I.C.S.: 523150

Branch (Domestic):

Deutsche Bank AG-Melbourne (2)
Level 23 333 Collins St, Melbourne, 3000,
VIC, Australia (100%)
Tel.: (61) 392704141
Web Site: http://www.deutschebank.com.au
Sales Range: $50-74.9 Million
Emp.: 50
Corporate & Investment Banking Services
N.A.I.C.S.: 523150

Deutsche Bank Capital
Corporation (1)
60 Wall St, New York, NY
10005-2836 (100%)
Tel.: (212) 250-2500
Web Site: http://www.db.com
Investment Banking
N.A.I.C.S.: 522291

Deutsche Bank Capital Markets
S.r.l. (1)
Piazza Del Calendario 3, Milan, 20126, Italy
Tel.: (39) 024 0241
Investment Management Service
N.A.I.C.S.: 523940

Deutsche Bank Corretora de Valores
S.A. (1)
Rua Alexandre Dumas 2200, Sao Paulo,
04717-004, Brazil
Tel.: (55) 1151895492
Securities Brokerage Services
N.A.I.C.S.: 523150

Deutsche Bank Europe GmbH (1)
Taunusanlage 12, 60325, Frankfurt am
Main, Germany
Tel.: (49) 6991000
Commercial Banking Services
N.A.I.C.S.: 522110
Cathal Deasy *(Head-Mergers & Acq-EMEA)*

Deutsche Bank Factoring S.p.A. (1)
Piazza del Calendario 3, 20126, Milan, Italy
Tel.: (39) 0240241
Emp.: 1,600
Factoring
N.A.I.C.S.: 522299

Deutsche Bank Finance N.V. (1)
Pietermaai 17, PO Box 4905, Willemstad,
Curacao
Tel.: (599) 94612369
International Financing Company
N.A.I.C.S.: 522299

Deutsche Bank Government Securities, Inc. (1)
60 Wall St, New York, NY 10005-2858
Tel.: (212) 250-2500
Web Site: http://www.db.com
Government Bond Trading
N.A.I.C.S.: 523150

Deutsche Bank Holdings, Inc. (1)
1011 Centre Rd Ste 200, Wilmington, DE
19805-1266
Tel.: (302) 636-3299
Investment Management Service
N.A.I.C.S.: 523940

Deutsche Bank Insurance Agency of
Delaware, Inc. (1)
1011 Centre Rd Ste 200, Wilmington, DE
19805
Tel.: (302) 636-3300
General Insurance Services
N.A.I.C.S.: 524210

Deutsche Bank International (1)
1 Biscayne Tower Ste 1820 2 S Biscayne
Blvd, Miami, FL 33131-1806 (100%)
Tel.: (305) 577-6600
Web Site: http://www.db.com
Sales Range: $10-24.9 Million
Emp.: 30
Foreign Trade & International Banks
N.A.I.C.S.: 522299

Deutsche Bank International
Limited (1)
St Paul's Gate New Street, PO Box 727,
Saint Helier, JE4 8ZB, Jersey
Tel.: (44) 1534889900
Web Site: https://www.db-ci.com
Financial Banking Services
N.A.I.C.S.: 522110

Deutsche Bank International Trust
Co. (Cayman) Limited (1)
PO Box 1984, Georgetown, Grand Cayman, Cayman Islands
Tel.: (345) 9498244
Commercial Trust Services
N.A.I.C.S.: 523991

Deutsche Bank International Trust
Co. (Jersey) Limited (1)
Dumaresq Street, Saint Helier, JE2 3WP,
Jersey
Tel.: (44) 20 7545 8000
Trust Management Services
N.A.I.C.S.: 523991

Deutsche Bank International Trust
Co. Limited (1)
Lefebvre Court Lefebvre Street, PO Box
523, Saint Peter Port, GY1 6EJ, Guernsey
Tel.: (44) 1481 702000

Trust Management Services
N.A.I.C.S.: 523991

Deutsche Bank Investments (Guernsey) Limited (1)
Lefebvre Court Lefebvre Street, PO Box
523, Saint Peter Port, GY1 6EJ, Guernsey
Tel.: (44) 1481 702000
Investment Banking Services
N.A.I.C.S.: 523150

Deutsche Bank Ltd. (1)
5 Lesnaya Street, Municipal District Tverskoy, 125047, Moscow, Russia (100%)
Tel.: (7) 4957975000
Web Site: http://country.db.com
Sales Range: $100-124.9 Million
Emp.: 150
Provider of Corporate Banking Services
N.A.I.C.S.: 522299

Deutsche Bank Luxembourg
S.A. (1)
2 Boulevard Konrad Adenauer, 1115, Luxembourg, Luxembourg (100%)
Tel.: (352) 421221
Sales Range: $1-4.9 Billion
Emp.: 359
Asset Management, Corporate & Investment Banking Services
N.A.I.C.S.: 523150

Deutsche Bank Mexico S.A. De
C.V. (1)
House Address Blvd Manuel Avila Camacho
No 40 Colonia, Lomas de Chapultepec,
Mexico, 11000, Mexico (100%)
Tel.: (52) 5552018000
Web Site: http://www.db.com
Sales Range: Less than $1 Million
Emp.: 100
Representative Office; International Banking
N.A.I.C.S.: 522299
Jorge Arce *(Chief Country Officer)*

Subsidiary (Domestic):

BRIMCO, S. de R.L. de C.V. (2)
Tampico No 42 Int 3, Mexico, 06700,
Mexico
Tel.: (52) 5513278730
Financial Management Services
N.A.I.C.S.: 523999

DB Servicios Mexico, S.A. de
C.V. (2)
Bvd Manuel Avila Camacho No 40 Lomas
de Chapultepec Piso 17, Miguel Hidalgo,
Mexico, 11000, Mexico
Tel.: (52) 5552018000
Commercial Banking Services
N.A.I.C.S.: 522110

Deutsche Securities, S.A. de
C.V. (2)
Pedregal 24 1902 - C Colonia Molino del
Rey, 11040, Mexico, Mexico
Tel.: (52) 5552018000
Securities Brokerage Services
N.A.I.C.S.: 523150

Deutsche Bank Mutui S.p.A. (1)
Piazza Del Calendario 3, 20126, Milan, Italy
Tel.: (39) 0240241
N.A.I.C.S.: 523940

Deutsche Bank Nederland N.V. (1)
Tel.: (31) 205554911
Commercial Banking Services
N.A.I.C.S.: 522110

Deutsche Bank Nominees (Jersey)
Limited (1)
St Paul's Gate New Street, Saint Helier,
JE2 3WP, Jersey
Tel.: (44) 1534889336
Commercial Banking Services
N.A.I.C.S.: 522110

Deutsche Bank Polska S.A. (1)
al Armii Ludowej 26, 00-609, Warsaw,
Poland (100%)
Tel.: (48) 225799000
Web Site: http://www.db-polska.pl
Sales Range: $125-149.9 Million
Emp.: 200
Corporate & Investment Banking Services
N.A.I.C.S.: 523150
Tomasz Kowalski *(Pres & Member-Mgmt Bd)*

Deutsche Bank Aktiengesellschaft—(Continued)

Deutsche Bank Privat und Ge-
schaftskunden AG **(1)**
Kohlmarkt 7 15, 23552, Lubeck,
Germany **(100%)**
Tel.: (49) 4511492179
Sales Range: $75-99.9 Million
Emp.: 60
Banking Services
N.A.I.C.S.: 522110

Deutsche Bank Private Wealth
Management **(1)**
Tel.: (44) 2075458000
Web Site: http://www.secure.deutsche-
bank.de
Wealth Management Services
N.A.I.C.S.: 523999

Deutsche Bank RT **(1)**
Hold Utca 27, H 1054, Budapest,
Hungary **(100%)**
Web Site: http://www.db.com
Sales Range: $50-74.9 Million
Emp.: 70
Provider of Corporate & Real Estate Bank-
ing Services
N.A.I.C.S.: 522299

Deutsche Bank Real Estate (Japan)
Y.K. **(1)**
2-11-1 Nagatacho, Chiyoda-Ku, Tokyo, 100-
6171, Japan
Tel.: (81) 351566513
Web Site: http://www.db.com
Sales Range: $300-349.9 Million
Emp.: 800
Real Estate Development Services
N.A.I.C.S.: 531390

Deutsche Bank Realty Advisors,
Inc. **(1)**
1168 Wantagh Ave, Wantagh, NY 11793
Tel.: (516) 826-1111
Real Estate Advisory Services
N.A.I.C.S.: 531390

Deutsche Bank Representative Office
Nigeria Limited **(1)**
4 Adeyemi Lawson Road, Ikoyi, Lagos,
Nigeria
Tel.: (234) 12772500
Financial Banking Services
N.A.I.C.S.: 522110

Deutsche Bank S.A.-Banco
Alemao **(1)**
Av Brigadeiro Faria Lima 3900, 13 14 15
Andar, Sao Paulo, CEP 04538-132,
Brazil **(100%)**
Web Site: http://www.db.com
Sales Range: $50-74.9 Million
Emp.: 100
Global Corporate & Institutional Banking
Services
N.A.I.C.S.: 522299

Deutsche Bank S.A.E. **(1)**
Avenida Diagonal 446, 8006, Barcelona,
Spain **(100%)**
Tel.: (34) 934042102
Web Site: http://www.db.com
Head Office & Main Branch; International
Banking
N.A.I.C.S.: 522299

Deutsche Bank S.A.E. **(1)**
Paseo de La Castellana 18, 28046, Madrid,
Spain **(100%)**
Tel.: (34) 900828032
Sales Range: $200-249.9 Million
Emp.: 300
Head Branch & Main Branch; International
Banking
N.A.I.C.S.: 523150

Deutsche Bank S.p.A. **(1)**
Piazza del Calendario 3, 20126, Milan,
Italy **(100%)**
Tel.: (39) 0240241
Sales Range: $100-124.9 Million
Emp.: 200
International Banking
N.A.I.C.S.: 522299
Flavio Valeri *(Chm-Mgmt Bd, CEO & Chief
Country Officer)*

Deutsche Bank Saar AG **(1)**

Kaiserstrasse 29 31, Saarbrucken, 66111,
Germany **(100%)**
Tel.: (49) 68130020
Web Site: http://www.db.com
Sales Range: $200-249.9 Million
Emp.: 400
International Banking Services
N.A.I.C.S.: 523150

Deutsche Bank Sao Paulo **(1)**
Av Brigadeiro Faria Lima, 3 900 13 ba 15
Andares, Sao Paulo, 04538132,
Brazil **(100%)**
Tel.: (55) 1121135000
Sales Range: $200-249.9 Million
Emp.: 400
International Banking
N.A.I.C.S.: 522299

Deutsche Bank Securities Inc. **(1)**
60 Wall St, New York, NY 10005
Tel.: (212) 250-2500
Web Site: http://www.db.com
Sales Range: $350-399.9 Million
Emp.: 800
Financial Services
N.A.I.C.S.: 523999
Richard Grellier *(Mng Dir)*

Division (Domestic):

Deutsche Bank Alex. Brown
Incorporated **(2)**
1 S St 28th Fl, Baltimore, MD 21202
Tel.: (410) 727-1700
Private Client Financial Services
N.A.I.C.S.: 523999
John McCauley *(Mng Dir-Houston)*

Deutsche Bank Securities
Limited **(1)**
199 Bay Street Suite 4700 Commerce
Court West, Box 263, Toronto, M5L 1E9,
ON, Canada
Tel.: (416) 682-8000
Investment Banking Services
N.A.I.C.S.: 523150

Deutsche Bank Services (Jersey)
Limited **(1)**
St Paul's Gate New Street, Saint Helier,
JE48ZB, Jersey
Tel.: (44) 1534 889 900
Web Site: http://www.db-ci.com
Emp.: 100
Commercial Banking Services
N.A.I.C.S.: 522110

Deutsche Bank Trust Company
Delaware **(1)**
1011 Centre Rd, Wilmington, DE 19805
Tel.: (302) 636-3369
Commercial Banking Services
N.A.I.C.S.: 522110

Deutsche Bank Trust Company New
Jersey Ltd. **(1)**
100 Plaza One, Jersey City, NJ 07311
Tel.: (212) 602-1764
Trust Management Services
N.A.I.C.S.: 523991

Deutsche Bank Trust Company, Na-
tional Association **(1)**
280 Park Ave, New York, NY 10017
Tel.: (212) 454-3600
Trust Management Services
N.A.I.C.S.: 523991

Deutsche Bank Trust
Corporation **(1)**
60 Wall St 40th Fl, New York, NY 10005-
2836
Tel.: (212) 250-2500
Trust Management Services
N.A.I.C.S.: 523991

Deutsche Bank Trustee Services
(Guernsey) Limited **(1)**
Lefebvre Court Lefebvre Street, PO Box
523, Saint Peter Port, GY1 6EJ, Guernsey
Tel.: (44) 1481 702000
Commercial Banking Services
N.A.I.C.S.: 522110

Deutsche Capital Markets Australia
Limited **(1)**
L 16 Deutsche Bank Pl Corner Of Hunter St
& Phillip St, Sydney, 2000, NSW, Australia
Tel.: (61) 282581234

Securities Brokerage Services
N.A.I.C.S.: 523150

Deutsche Climate Change Fixed In-
come QP Trust **(1)**
11 Northeastern Blvd, Salem, NH 03079
Tel.: (212) 250-7228
Fund Management Services
N.A.I.C.S.: 523940

Deutsche Colombia S.A. **(1)**
Cl 67 7 35 Of 1204, Bogota, Colombia
Tel.: (57) 1 3192900
Investment Management Service
N.A.I.C.S.: 523940

Deutsche Custody N.V. **(1)**
Herengracht 450, Amsterdam, 1017 CA,
Netherlands
Tel.: (31) 205554351
Commercial Banking Services
N.A.I.C.S.: 522110

Deutsche Equities India Private
Limited **(1)**
The Capital Level 14 C-70 G Block Bandra
Kurla Complex, Mumbai, 400 051, India
Tel.: (91) 2271804444
N.A.I.C.S.: 523940

Deutsche Fiduciary Services (Suisse)
SA **(1)**
Place des Bergues 3, 1201, Geneva, Swit-
zerland
Tel.: (41) 22 739 0664
Web Site: http://www.db.com
Commercial Trust Services
N.A.I.C.S.: 523991

Deutsche Futures Singapore Pte
Ltd **(1)**
One Raffles Quay South Tower Level 17,
Singapore, 048583, Singapore
Tel.: (65) 64238001
Investment Management Service
N.A.I.C.S.: 523940

Deutsche Group Services Pty
Limited **(1)**
L 16 Deutsche Bank Pl Corner Of Hunter St
And 126 Phillip St, Sydney, 2000, NSW,
Australia
Tel.: (61) 282581234
Financial Management Services
N.A.I.C.S.: 523999

Deutsche Grundbesitz Beteili-
gungsgesellschaft mbH **(1)**
Mergenthalerallee 73-76, 65760, Eschborn,
Germany
Tel.: (49) 697170402
Investment Management Service
N.A.I.C.S.: 523940

Deutsche Grundbesitz-
Anlagegesellschaft mit beschrankter
Haftung **(1)**
Mergenthalerallee 73-75, 65760, Eschborn,
Hessen, Germany
Tel.: (49) 6971704831
Investment Management Service
N.A.I.C.S.: 523940

Deutsche Holdings (Malta) Ltd. **(1)**
Forni Complex Valletta Waterfront, Floriana,
FRN 1913, Malta
Tel.: (356) 21373666
Investment Management Service
N.A.I.C.S.: 523999

Deutsche Immobilien Leasing
GmbH **(1)**
Herzogstrasse 15, 40217, Dusseldorf, Ger-
many
Tel.: (49) 21199460
Web Site: https://www.dil.de
Real Estate Services
N.A.I.C.S.: 531390

Deutsche International Corporate
Services (Ireland) Ltd. **(1)**
5 Harbourmaster Place International Finan-
cial Services Centre 3rd Fl, Dublin, 1, Ire-
land
Tel.: (353) 16806000
Sales Range: $50-74.9 Million
Emp.: 40
Banking & Securities
N.A.I.C.S.: 523150
Mike Hughes *(VP)*

Deutsche International Corporate
Services Limited **(1)**
St Paul's Gate New Street, PO Box 727,
Saint Helier, JE4 8ZB, Jersey
Tel.: (44) 1534889900
Financial Management Services
N.A.I.C.S.: 523999

Deutsche International Finance (Ire-
land) Limited **(1)**
5 Harbourmaster Place, Dublin, Ireland
Tel.: (353) 1 6806000
Sales Range: $25-49.9 Million
Emp.: 65
Business Management Consulting Services
N.A.I.C.S.: 541618
Michael Whelan *(Gen Mgr)*

Deutsche International Trust Corpora-
tion (CI) Limited **(1)**
St Pauls Gate New Street, PO Box 727,
JE4 8ZB, Saint Helier, Jersey **(100%)**
Tel.: (44) 534889900
Web Site: http://www.deutsche-bank.com
Banking, Investment Management & Com-
pany Management
N.A.I.C.S.: 522299

Deutsche Inversiones Limitada **(1)**
Avenida El Bosque Sur 130 Piso 5, Las
Condes, Santiago, Chile
Tel.: (56) 2 3377710
Investment Management Service
N.A.I.C.S.: 523940

Deutsche Investments India Private
Limited **(1)**
Nirlon Knowledge Park Block B1 Western
Express Highway, Goregaon, Mumbai, 400
063, India
Tel.: (91) 2271806145
Investment Management Service
N.A.I.C.S.: 523940

Deutsche Investor Services Private
Limited **(1)**
Nirlon Knowledge Park Block 4th Floor B1
Western Express Highway, Goregaon E,
Mumbai, 400 063, India
Tel.: (91) 22 71806145
Web Site: http://www.displ.co.in
Investment Management Service
N.A.I.C.S.: 523940

Deutsche Managed Investments
Limited **(1)**
Deutsche Bank Place Level 16 Cnr Hunter
and Phillip Streets, Sydney, 2000, NSW,
Australia
Tel.: (61) 2 8258 2515
Web Site: http://www.dbaccess.db.com
Investment Management Service
N.A.I.C.S.: 523940

Deutsche Nederland N.V. **(1)**
The Entrance 195, 1101 HE, Amsterdam,
Netherlands
Tel.: (31) 205554911
N.A.I.C.S.: 523940
Boudewijn Dornseiffen *(CFO)*

Deutsche New Zealand Limited **(1)**
Level 36-48 Shortland Street Vero Centre,
Auckland, 1010, New Zealand
Tel.: (64) 93511000
Commercial Banking Services
N.A.I.C.S.: 522110

Deutsche Nominees Limited **(1)**
23 Great Winchester Street, London, EC
2P2AX, United Kingdom
Tel.: (44) 2075458000
Commercial Banking Services
N.A.I.C.S.: 522110

Deutsche Oppenheim Family Office
AG **(1)**
Keferloh 1a, Grasbrunn, 85630, Germany
Tel.: (49) 89 45 69 16 0
Web Site: http://www.deutsche-
oppenheim.de
Emp.: 40
Asset Management Services
N.A.I.C.S.: 523940
Jorn Matthias Hauser *(Member-Exec Bd)*

Deutsche Securities (India) Private
Limited **(1)**
ECE House 28 K G Marg, Goregaon, New
Delhi, 110 001, India

Tel.: (91) 2266703066
Securities Brokerage Services
N.A.I.C.S.: 523150

Deutsche Securities (Proprietary)
Limited (1)
3 Exchange Square 87 Maude Street,
Sandton, 2196, South Africa
Tel.: (27) 117757000
Sales Range: $200-249.9 Million
Emp.: 300
Securities Brokerage Services
N.A.I.C.S.: 523150
Sharlene Rajah (Chief Compliance Officer)

Deutsche Securities Asia Limited (1)
Level 52, International Commerce, 1st Aus-
tin Road West, Center, China (Hong Kong)
Tel.: (852) 2203 8888
Web Site: http://www.dp.com
Securities Brokerage Services
N.A.I.C.S.: 523150

Deutsche Securities Corredores de
Bolsa Ltda. (1)
Avda el Bosque Sur 130 P 5, Santiago,
Chile
Tel.: (56) 2 337 7700
Securities Brokerage Services
N.A.I.C.S.: 523150

Deutsche Securities Inc. (1)
Sanno Park Tower 2-11-1 Nagatacho,
Chiyoda-ku, Tokyo, 100-6171,
Japan (100%)
Tel.: (81) 351566000
Investment Company
N.A.I.C.S.: 523150

Deutsche Securities Israel Ltd. (1)
46 Rothschild Blvd, Tel Aviv, 66883, Israel
Tel.: (972) 37102000
Web Site: http://www.db.com
Emp.: 20
Securities Brokerage Services
N.A.I.C.S.: 523150

Deutsche Securities Korea Co (1)
11F Centropolis Tower A 26 Ujeongguk-ro,
Jongno-ku, Seoul, 03161, Korea (South)
Tel.: (82) 23168888
Securities Brokerage Services
N.A.I.C.S.: 523150

Deutsche Securities Menkul Degerler
A.S. (1)
Esentepe Quarter Buyukdere Street Tekfen
Tower No 209 K 18, Sisli, 34394, Istanbul,
Turkiye
Tel.: (90) 2123190319
Financial Banking Services
N.A.I.C.S.: 522110
Albert Krespin (CEO & Gen Mgr)

Deutsche StiftungsTrust GmbH (1)
Taunusanlage 12, 60325, Frankfurt am
Main, Germany
Tel.: (49) 69 910 47800
Web Site: http://www.dstt.de
Trust Management Services
N.A.I.C.S.: 523991

Deutsche Trustee Company
Limited (1)
Winchester House 1 Great Winchester
Street, London, EC2N 2DB, United King-
dom
Tel.: (44) 2075458000
Trust Management Services
N.A.I.C.S.: 523991

Deutsche Trustee Services (India)
Private Limited (1)
14th Floor The Capital C-70 G Block Ban-
dra Kurla Complex, Mumbai, 400 051, India
Tel.: (91) 2222071050
Trust Management Services
N.A.I.C.S.: 523991

Deutsches Institut fur Altersvorsorge
GmbH (1)
Franzosische Strasse 12, 10117, Berlin,
Germany
Tel.: (49) 3020188581
Web Site: https://www.dia-vorsorge.de
Pension & Retirement Services
N.A.I.C.S.: 525110

EC EUROPA IMMOBILIEN FONDS
NR. 3 GmbH & CO. KG (1)

Bleichenbrucke 9, 20354, Hamburg, Ger-
many
Tel.: (49) 40376690
Investment Management Service
N.A.I.C.S.: 523999

ECT Holdings Corp. (1)
1011 Centre Rd, Wilmington, DE 19805
Tel.: (302) 636-3290
Investment Management Service
N.A.I.C.S.: 523940

Elizabethan Holdings Limited (1)
235 Broadway Newmarket, Auckland, New
Zealand
Tel.: (64) 95290071
Investment Management Service
N.A.I.C.S.: 523940

Enterprise Fleet Management Ex-
change, Inc. (1)
600 Corporate Park Dr, Saint Louis, MO
63105-4204
Tel.: (314) 512-5000
Web Site: http://www.enterprise.com
Financial Management Services
N.A.I.C.S.: 523999

Erste Frankfurter Hoist GmbH (1)
Steinweg 3-5, 60313, Frankfurt, Germany
Tel.: (49) 6929925385
Financial Management Services
N.A.I.C.S.: 523999

Frankfurter Vermogens-Treuhand Ge-
sellschaft mit beschrankter
Haftung (1)
Bockenheimer Landstr 10, 60323, Frankfurt,
Germany
Tel.: (49) 69 7180
Investment Management Service
N.A.I.C.S.: 523999

Funfte SAB Treuhand und Verwaltung
GmbH & Co. Suhl Rimbachzentrum
KG (1)
Kaiser-Friedrich Promenade 61a, 61348,
Bad Homburg, Hessen, Germany
Tel.: (49) 3641537310
Financial Management Services
N.A.I.C.S.: 523999
Inge Burow (Gen Mgr)

KEBA Gesellschaft fur interne Ser-
vices mbH (1)
Theodor-Heuss-Allee 72, 60486, Frankfurt
am Main, Germany
Tel.: (49) 6991000
Investment Management Service
N.A.I.C.S.: 523940

Kingfisher Canada Holdings LLC (1)
2711 Centerville Rd Ste 400, Wilmington,
DE 19808
Tel.: (302) 636-5401
Investment Management Service
N.A.I.C.S.: 523940

Klockner Industriebeteiligungsgesell-
schaft mbH (1)
Taunusanlage 12, Frankfurt am Main,
60325, Germany
Tel.: (49) 6991000
Investment Management Service
N.A.I.C.S.: 523940

Konsul Inkasso GmbH (1)
Lindenallee 29, 45127, Essen, Germany
Tel.: (49) 20124646059
Banking Services
N.A.I.C.S.: 522110

London Industrial Leasing
Limited (1)
23 Great Winchester Street, London, EC2P
2AX, United Kingdom
Tel.: (44) 2075458000
Financial Lending Services
N.A.I.C.S.: 523999

Luxembourg Family Office S.A. (1)
534 Rue de Neudorf, 2220, Luxembourg,
Luxembourg
Tel.: (352) 4576761
Emp.: 40
Commercial Banking Services
N.A.I.C.S.: 522110
Fteies Roland (Mng Dir)

MPP Beteiligungsgesellschaft
mbH (1)

Junghofstr 5-9, Frankfurt am Main, 60311,
Germany
Tel.: (49) 699100
Investment Management Service
N.A.I.C.S.: 523940

Mira GmbH & Co. KG (1)
Genslerweg 7, Buxtehude, 21614, Germany
Tel.: (49) 41 61 59 33 10
Web Site: http://www.mira-anlagen.de
Investment Advisory Service
N.A.I.C.S.: 523940

Nevada Property 1 LLC (1)
3708 Las Vegas Blvd S, Las Vegas, NV
89109
Tel.: (702) 698-7000
Sales Range: $700-749.9 Million
Emp.: 4,577
Casino Hotel & Resort Management Ser-
vices
N.A.I.C.S.: 721120

New Prestitempo S.p.A. (1)
Piazza del Calendario 1, 20126, Milan, Italy
Tel.: (39) 0240242417
Commercial Banking Services
N.A.I.C.S.: 522110

Newport Harbor Corporation (1)
Bowens Wharf, Newport, RI 02840
Tel.: (401) 841-8884
Web Site:
    https://www.newportrestaurantgroup.com
Home Management Services
N.A.I.C.S.: 721110

Norisbank GmbH (1)
Rathenauplatz 12 18, 90489, Nuremberg,
Germany
Tel.: (49) 91153900
Web Site: http://www.norisbank.de
Sales Range: $700-749.9 Million
Emp.: 1,073
Banking
N.A.I.C.S.: 522299

Numis Corporation Limited (1)
10 Paternoster Square, London, EC4M 7LT,
United Kingdom
Tel.: (44) 2072601000
Web Site: http://www.numiscorp.com
Rev.: $304,532,523
Assets: $999,227,611
Liabilities: $745,705,986
Net Worth: $253,521,625
Earnings: $78,540,029
Emp.: 319
Fiscal Year-end: 09/30/2021
Investment Banking & Securities Dealing
Services
N.A.I.C.S.: 523150
Alex Ham (Co-CEO)

Subsidiary (US):

Numis Securities Inc (2)
575 Fifth Ave 25th Fl, New York, NY 10017
Tel.: (212) 277-7300
Web Site: http://www.numiscorp.com
Investment Banking Services
N.A.I.C.S.: 523150

OPB Verwaltungs- und Treuhand
GmbH (1)
Unter Sachsenhausen 4, Cologne, 50667,
Germany
Tel.: (49) 22114501
Financial Management Services
N.A.I.C.S.: 523999

PADUS Grundstucks-
Vermietungsgesellschaft mbH (1)
Konigsallee 106, Dusseldorf, 40215, Ger-
many
Tel.: (49) 21199460
Administrative Management Services
N.A.I.C.S.: 561110

PB Factoring GmbH (1)
Bundeskanzlerplatz 6, 53113, Bonn, Ger-
many
Tel.: (49) 22892028001
Web Site: https://www.pb-factoring.de
Financial Services
N.A.I.C.S.: 541611
Dinko Mehmedagic (Mng Dir)

PS plus Portfolio Software + Consult-
ing GmbH (1)

Carl Zeiss Str 10/4, 63322, Rodermark,
Germany
Tel.: (49) 6074910635
Web Site: https://www.psplus.de
Emp.: 35
Software Development Services
N.A.I.C.S.: 541511
Peter Dobler (Mng Dir)

Postbank Immobilien GmbH (1)
Lubahnstrasse 2, 31789, Hameln, Germany
Tel.: (49) 22855001197
Web Site:
    https://www.immobilien.postbank.de
Real Estate Services
N.A.I.C.S.: 531390

Postbank Leasing GmbH (1)
Bundeskanzlerplatz 6, 53113, Bonn, Ger-
many
Tel.: (49) 22892023423
Financial Services
N.A.I.C.S.: 541611

Primelux Insurance S.A. (1)
2 Boulevard Konrad Adenauer, Luxem-
bourg, 1115, Luxembourg
Tel.: (352) 42 12 25 50
General Insurance Services
N.A.I.C.S.: 524298
Marleen van Malderen (Mng Dir)

Pt Deutsche Securities Indonesia (1)
Gedung Deutsche Bank Lantai 6 - Jl Imam
Bonjol No 80, Jakarta, 10310, Indonesia
Tel.: (62) 2129644545
Securities Brokerage Services
N.A.I.C.S.: 523150

Public Joint Stock Company Deut-
sche Bank DBU (1)
Tel.: (380) 444959200
Web Site: http://www.db.com
Commercial Banking Services
N.A.I.C.S.: 522110

RREEF Investment GmbH (1)
Mainzer Landstrasse 11-17, 60329, Frank-
furt am Main, Germany
Tel.: (49) 91012371
Investment Management Service
N.A.I.C.S.: 523940
Georg Allendorf (Mgr)

RREEF Management GmbH (1)
Mainzer Landstrasse 178-190, 60327,
Frankfurt am Main, Germany
Tel.: (49) 697170400
Web Site: http://www.rreef.com
Real Estate Management Services
N.A.I.C.S.: 531390
Georg Allendorf (Mng Dir)

RREEF Spezial Invest GmbH (1)
Mainzer Landstrasse 11-17, 60329, Frank-
furt am Main, Germany
Tel.: (49) 22841080
Web Site: https://realassets.dws.com
Investment Management Service
N.A.I.C.S.: 523999
Georg Allendorf (Mng Dir)

SAMOS Vermogensverwaltungs
GmbH (1)
Unter Sachsenhausen 4, Cologne, 50667,
Germany
Tel.: (49) 221 14501
Administrative Management Services
N.A.I.C.S.: 561110

SCUDO Grundstucks-
Vermietungsgesellschaft mbH & Co.
Objekt Kleine Alexanderstrasse
KG (1)
Konigsallee 106, 40215, Dusseldorf, Ger-
many
Tel.: (49) 211 99460
Real Estate Management Services
N.A.I.C.S.: 531390

SEDO Grundstucks-
Vermietungsgesellschaft mbH (1)
Konigsallee 106, Dusseldorf, 40215, Ger-
many
Tel.: (49) 21199460
Real Estate Management Services
N.A.I.C.S.: 531390

SIMA Private Equity 1 Beteiligungs
GmbH (1)

Deutsche Bank Aktiengesellschaft—(Continued)

Kapstadtring 8, 22297, Hamburg, Germany
Tel.: (49) 2219370850
Financial Management Services
N.A.I.C.S.: 523999

SIMA Private Equity 1 GmbH & Co. KG (1)
Kapstadtring 8, 22297, Hamburg, Germany
Tel.: (49) 40300570
Financial Management Services
N.A.I.C.S.: 523999

STUPA Heizwerk Frankfurt (Oder) Nord Beteiligungsgesellschaft mbH (1)
Berliner Str 1, 12529, Schonefeld, Germany
Tel.: (49) 33555330
Commercial Banking Services
N.A.I.C.S.: 522110

Sal. Oppenheim jr. & Cie. AG & Co. KGaA (1)
Oppenheimstrasse 11, 50668, Cologne, Germany
Tel.: (49) 221577720
Web Site: https://deutsche-oppenheim.de
Sales Range: $200-249.9 Million
Emp.: 350
Asset Management & Investment Banking Services
N.A.I.C.S.: 523150

Subsidiary (Domestic):

Collineo Asset Management GmbH (2)
Phoenixseestrasse 22a, 44263, Dortmund, Germany
Tel.: (49) 23110821
Web Site: https://collineo-group.com
Sales Range: $50-74.9 Million
Emp.: 100
Financial Management Services
N.A.I.C.S.: 525990

Subsidiary (Non-US):

Deutsche Bank Osterreich AG (2)
Web Site: http://www.db.com
Commericial Banking
N.A.I.C.S.: 522110

Subsidiary (Domestic):

Frankfurt Family Office GmbH (2)
Bockenheimer Landstr 10, 60323, Frankfurt, Germany
Tel.: (49) 697180
Web Site: http://www.bhf-bank.com
Investment Banking & Securities Dealing
N.A.I.C.S.: 523150
Jurgen Unger (Mng Dir)

Frankfurter Beteiligungs-Treuhand GmbH (2)
Bockenheimer Landstr 10, 60323, Frankfurt, Germany
Tel.: (49) 697180
Web Site: http://www.bhs-bank.com
Personal Care Services
N.A.I.C.S.: 812199

Subsidiary (Non-US):

Hauck & Aufhauser Asset Management Services S.a r.l. (1)
1c rue Gabriel Lippmann, 5365, Munsbach, Luxembourg
Tel.: (352) 4513141
Web Site: http://www.hauck-aufhaeuser.com
Asset Management & Investment Banking Services
N.A.I.C.S.: 523150

Subsidiary (Domestic):

OPPENHEIM Capital Advisory GmbH (2)
Unter Sachsenhausen 4, Cologne, 50667, Germany
Tel.: (49) 22114501
Investment Advisory Services
N.A.I.C.S.: 523940

OPPENHEIM PRIVATE EQUITY Verwaltungsgesellschaft mbH (2)
Unter Sachsenhausen 4, Cologne, 50667, Germany

Tel.: (49) 2212582010
Administrative Management Services
N.A.I.C.S.: 561110

Subsidiary (Non-US):

Oppenheim Asset Management GmbH (2)
Seilergasse 3, 1010, Vienna, Austria
Tel.: (43) 1 51866 2510
Web Site: http://www.oppenheim.at
Asset Management Services
N.A.I.C.S.: 523940

Subsidiary (Domestic):

Oppenheim Kapitalanlagegesellschaft mbH (2)
Unter Sachsenhausen 4, 50667, Cologne, Germany
Tel.: (49) 22114503
Web Site: http://www.oppenheim.de
Sales Range: $350-399.9 Million
Investment Fund Services
N.A.I.C.S.: 525910

Subsidiary (Non-US):

Oppenheim Landert Family Office AG (2)
Alte Landstrasse 102, PO Box 377, 8702, Zollikon, Switzerland
Tel.: (41) 443963300
Web Site: https://www.landert.ch
Asset Management & Investment Banking Services
N.A.I.C.S.: 523150

Subsidiary (Domestic):

Oppenheim Vermogenstreuhand GmbH (2)
Oppenheimstrasse 11, 50667, Cologne, Germany
Tel.: (49) 2211452400
Web Site: http://www.oppenheim.de
Sales Range: $25-49.9 Million
Emp.: 50
Trusts Estates & Agency Accounts
N.A.I.C.S.: 525920

Oppenheim Verwaltung von Immobilienvermogen GmbH (2)
Unter Sachsenhausen 4, 50667, Cologne, 50667, Germany
Tel.: (49) 22114501
Web Site: http://www.oppenheim.de
Real Estate Agents & Brokers Offices
N.A.I.C.S.: 531210

Subsidiary (Non-US):

Sal Oppenheim France (2)
4 Place Verdome, 75001, Paris, France
Tel.: (33) 144508888
Fund & Portfolio Management Services for Institutional & Private Investors
N.A.I.C.S.: 523940

Sal. Oppenheim jr. & Cie. (Switzerland) Ltd. (2)
Prime Tower Hardstrasse 201, 8022, Zurich, Switzerland
Tel.: (41) 442142214
Web Site: http://www.oppenheim.ch
Sales Range: $75-99.9 Million
Emp.: 150
Investment Banking & Securities Dealing
N.A.I.C.S.: 523150

Stoneridge Apartments, Inc. (1)
930 N Maple Grove Rd, Boise, ID 83704
Tel.: (208) 375-3800
Web Site: http://www.stoneridgeboise.com
Emp.: 4
Residential & Commercial Building Leasing Services
N.A.I.C.S.: 531120

Suddeutsche Vermogensverwaltung Gesellschaft mit beschrankter Haftung (1)
Taunusanlage 12, Frankfurt am Main, 60325, Germany
Tel.: (49) 6991034838
Wealth Management Services
N.A.I.C.S.: 541611

TAKIR Grundstucks-Vermietungsgesellschaft mbH (1)

Konigsallee 106, Dusseldorf, 40215, Germany
Tel.: (49) 21199460
Real Estate Management Services
N.A.I.C.S.: 531390

TERGO Grundstucks-Vermietungsgesellschaft mbH (1)
Konigsallee 106, Dusseldorf, 40215, Germany
Tel.: (49) 211 99460
Real Estate Management Services
N.A.I.C.S.: 531390

TERRUS Grundstucks-Vermietungsgesellschaft mbH (1)
Konigsallee 106, Dusseldorf, 40215, Germany
Tel.: (49) 211 99460
Real Estate Management Services
N.A.I.C.S.: 531390

TERRUS Grundstucks-Vermietungsgesellschaft mbH & Co. Objekt Bernbach KG (1)
Konigsallee 106, Dusseldorf, 40215, Germany
Tel.: (49) 211 99460
Real Estate Management Services
N.A.I.C.S.: 531390

TQI Exchange, LLC (1)
2711 Centerville Rd Ste 400, Wilmington, DE 19808
Tel.: (302) 636-5401
Investment Management Service
N.A.I.C.S.: 523940

TRIPLA Grundstucks-Vermietungsgesellschaft mbH (1)
Konigsallee 106, Dusseldorf, 40215, Germany
Tel.: (49) 21199460
Real Estate Prorperty Leasing Services
N.A.I.C.S.: 531190

Tagus - Sociedade de Titularizacao de Creditos, S.A. (1)
Rua Castilho 20, Lisbon, 1250-069, Portugal
Tel.: (351) 213111200
Commercial Banking Services
N.A.I.C.S.: 522110

Telefon-Servicegesellschaft der Deutschen Bank mbH (1)
Tel.: (49) 6991000
Web Site: http://www.dbdirektjobs.de
Telecommunication Servicesb
N.A.I.C.S.: 517810

Thai Asset Enforcement and Recovery Asset Management Company Limited (1)
999 9 Ramai Road, 10330, Bangkok, Thailand
Tel.: (66) 23818188
Asset Management Services
N.A.I.C.S.: 523940

Treuinvest Service GmbH (1)
Mainzer Landstr 178-190, Frankfurt am Main, 60327, Germany
Tel.: (49) 6991000
Financial Planning Services
N.A.I.C.S.: 523940

VOB-ZVD Processing GmbH (1)
Eckenheimer Landstrasse 242, 60320, Frankfurt, Germany
Tel.: (49) 69 95 90 92 0
Web Site: http://www.voeb-zvd.de
Commercial Banking Services
N.A.I.C.S.: 522110

Vertriebsgesellschaft mbH der Deutschen Bank Privat- und Geschaftskunden (1)
Hardenbergstr 32, Berlin, 10623, Germany
Tel.: (49) 3031088551
Investment Banking Services
N.A.I.C.S.: 523150
Bernd Schulte (Mng Dir)

Whispering Woods LLC (1)
120 Garden Dr Ofc A, Martinsburg, WV 25404-7530
Tel.: (301) 365-9314
Residential Building Leasing Services
N.A.I.C.S.: 531110

World Trading (Delaware) Inc. (1)
1011 Centre Rd Ste 200, Wilmington, DE 19805
Tel.: (302) 636-3290
Investment Advisory Services
N.A.I.C.S.: 523940

ZAO Deutsche Securities (1)
82 Sadovnicheskaya Street Building 2, 115035, Moscow, Russia
Tel.: (7) 495 797 5000
Web Site: http://www.deutsche-bank.ru
Securities Brokerage Services
N.A.I.C.S.: 523150

ZAO UFG Invest (1)
Petrovka Ul 5, 107031, Moscow, Russia
Tel.: (7) 495 721 1212
Investment Management Service
N.A.I.C.S.: 523940

ZARAT Beteiligungsgesellschaft mbH & Co. Objekt Leben II KG (1)
Konigsallee 106, Dusseldorf, 40215, Germany
Tel.: (49) 21199460
General Insurance Services
N.A.I.C.S.: 524210

db home lending holdings llc (1)
60 Wall St, New York, NY 10005
Tel.: (212) 250-0382
Investment Management Service
N.A.I.C.S.: 523940

DEUTSCHE BETEILIGUNGS AG

Untermainanlage 1, 60313, Frankfurt am Main, Germany
Tel.: (49) 699578701   De
Web Site: https://www.dbag.com
Year Founded: 1965
DBAN—(DUS)
Rev.: $167,747,680
Assets: $764,374,056
Liabilities: $41,970,645
Net Worth: $722,403,410
Earnings: $114,159,292
Emp.: 84
Fiscal Year-end: 09/30/23
Investment Services
N.A.I.C.S.: 523999
Susanne Zeidler (CFO & Member-Mgmt Bd)

Subsidiaries:

DBG Beteiligungsgesellschaft mbH (1)
Borsenstrase 1, 60313, Frankfurt am Main, Germany
Tel.: (49) 699578701
Web Site: http://www.deutsche-beteiligungs.de
Emp.: 5
Investment Management Service
N.A.I.C.S.: 523999

DBG New Fund Management GmbH & Co. KG (1)
Borsenstr 1, Frankfurt am Main, 60313, Hessen, Germany
Tel.: (49) 699578703
Investment Management Service
N.A.I.C.S.: 523999
Torsten Trader (Mng Dir)

Deutsche Beteiligungsgesellschaft mbH (1)
Nibelungenplatz 3, 60318, Frankfurt am Main, Germany
Tel.: (49) 6995507680
Web Site: http://www.deutschebeteiligungsgesell.de
Investment Management Service
N.A.I.C.S.: 523940

FRIMO Group GmbH (1)
Hansaring 1, 49504, Lotte, Germany
Tel.: (49) 54048860
Web Site: https://www.frimo.com
System Solutions Mfr
N.A.I.C.S.: 513210
Christof Bonsch (CEO)

Subsidiary (US):

FRIMO Inc. (2)

50685 Century Ct, Wixom, MI 48393
Tel.: (248) 668-3160
System Developer & Solutions
N.A.I.C.S.: 811114

**Infiana Germany GmbH & Co.
KG** (1)
Zweibruckenstrasse 15 25, 91301, Forch-
heim, Germany (100%)
Tel.: (49) 9191810
Web Site: http://www.infiana.com
Emp.: 800
Plastics Films Mfr
N.A.I.C.S.: 326112
Peter K. Wahsner (CEO)

Subsidiary (Non-US):

Infiana (Thailand) Limited (2)
1/28 Moo 2 Samutsakorn Industrial Estate
Rama 2 Road, Ta-Sai Muang, Samut Sak-
hon, 74000, Thailand
Tel.: (66) 3440 3300
Plastics Films Mfr
N.A.I.C.S.: 326112

Subsidiary (US):

Infiana USA, Inc. (2)
Malvern Operations 2400 Continental Blvd,
Malvern, PA 19355
Tel.: (484) 527-2000
Web Site: http://www.infiana.com
Plastics Films Mfr
N.A.I.C.S.: 326112
Robert Shumoski (Gen Mgr)

Karl Eugen Fischer GmbH (1)
Karl-Eugen-Fischer-Strasse 6 8, 96224,
Burgkunstadt, Germany
Tel.: (49) 9572390
Web Site: https://www.kefischer.de
Metalworking Machines Mfr
N.A.I.C.S.: 333519
Wolfgang Krause (Mng Dir)

Subsidiary (US):

K.E. Fischer L.L.C. (2)
2512 SW 38th St, Lawton, OK 73505
Tel.: (580) 353-2862
Industrial Equipment Distr
N.A.I.C.S.: 423830

duagon AG (1)
Riedstrasse 12, 8953, Dietikon, Switzerland
Tel.: (41) 44743 73 00
Web Site: http://www.duagon.com
Computer Software & Hardware Solutions
Developer & Designer
N.A.I.C.S.: 334118
Kalina Scott (CFO)

Subsidiary (Non-US):

MEN Mikro Elektronik GmbH (2)
Neuwieder Strasse 1-7, 90411, Nuremberg,
Germany
Tel.: (49) 911 99 33 5 0
Web Site: http://www.men.de
Computer Boards & Components Mfr
N.A.I.C.S.: 334118

DEUTSCHE BIOTECH INNOVA-
TIV AG
Neuendorfstrasse 15a, 16761, Hen-
nigsdorf Berlin, 16761, Germany
Tel.: (49) 33022077824
Web Site: https://www.dbi-ag.de
DBI—(DUS)
Sales Range: Less than $1 Million
Biotechnology Research & Develop-
ment Services
N.A.I.C.S.: 541714
Bernd Wegener (Chm-Mgmt Bd &
CEO)

DEUTSCHE BORSE AG
Mergenthalerallee 61, 65760, Es-
chborn, Germany
Tel.: (49) 692110   De
Web Site: https://www.deutsche-
boerse.com
Year Founded: 1993
DB1—(DEU)
Rev.: $6,620,440,319
Assets: $256,558,277,574

Liabilities: $245,657,996,978
Net Worth: $10,900,280,596
Earnings: $1,939,132,312
Emp.: 13,522
Fiscal Year-end: 12/31/23
Investment Management Service
N.A.I.C.S.: 523999
Thomas Book (Member-Exec Bd)

Subsidiaries:

360 Treasury Systems AG (1)
Gruneburgweg 16-18 / Westend Carree,
60322, Frankfurt am Main, Germany
Tel.: (49) 699002890
Web Site: https://www.360t.com
Commodity Trading Advisory Services
N.A.I.C.S.: 523150
Carlo Koelzer (CEO & Head-FX-Deutsche
Borse Grp)

Subsidiary (US):

360 Trading Networks Inc (2)
521 5th Ave 38th Fl, New York, NY 10175
Tel.: (212) 776-2900
Web Site: http://www.360t.com
Commodity Trading Advisory Services
N.A.I.C.S.: 523150
Matt O'Hara (CEO)

Subsidiary (Non-US):

360 Trading Networks LLC (2)
Dubai International Financial Centre Liberty
House Level 8 App 810C, PO Box 482036,
Dubai, United Arab Emirates
Tel.: (971) 44587440
Web Site: http://www.360t.com
Commodity Trading Advisory Services
N.A.I.C.S.: 523150

360T Asia Pacific Pte. Ltd. (2)
9 Raffles Place 56-01 Republic Plaza Tower
1, Singapore, 048619, Singapore
Tel.: (65) 65971770
Web Site: http://www.360t.com
Commodity Trading Advisory Services
N.A.I.C.S.: 523150

**ThreeSixty Trading Networks (India)
Pvt Ltd** (2)
Level 8 Vibgyor Towers G Block C-62 Ban-
dra Kurla Complex, Mumbai, 400 051, India
Tel.: (91) 22 4090 7165
Web Site: http://www.360t.com
Commodity Trading Advisory Services
N.A.I.C.S.: 523150

Axioma (CH) GmbH (1)
Rue Du Rhone 69 2nd Floor, 1207, Ge-
neva, Switzerland
Tel.: (41) 227008300
N.A.I.C.S.: 523210

Axioma Argentina S.A.U (1)
WeWork Espacios De Oficinas & Coworking
Corrientes Av Corrientes 800, C1008, Bue-
nos Aires, Argentina
Tel.: (54) 1159830320
N.A.I.C.S.: 523210

Axioma Germany GmbH (1)
Mainzer Landstrasse 41, 60329, Frankfurt
am Main, Germany
Tel.: (49) 6956608997
N.A.I.C.S.: 523210

Axioma Japan G.K (1)
Tekko Building 4F 1-8-2 Marunouchi,
Chiyoda-ku, Tokyo, 100-0005, Japan
Tel.: (81) 368707766
N.A.I.C.S.: 523210

Axioma S.A.S.U (1)
Regus office 19 Bd Malesherbes, 75008,
Paris, France
Tel.: (33) 155273838
N.A.I.C.S.: 523210

Centana Growth Partners, LLC (1)
292 Madison Ave 20th Fl, New York, NY
10017
Tel.: (212) 256-8450
Web Site: https://www.centanagrowth.com
Crypto Currency & Related Services
N.A.I.C.S.: 523160

Clearstream Australia Limited (1)

Level 3 1 Bligh Street, Sydney, 2000, NSW,
Australia
Tel.: (61) 282972000
Financial Transaction Services
N.A.I.C.S.: 522320

Clearstream Banking Japan, Ltd. (1)
Marunouchi Kitaguchi Building Floor 27
1-6-5 Marunouchi, Chiyoda-ku, Tokyo, 100-
0005, Japan
Tel.: (81) 345786600
Financial Services
N.A.I.C.S.: 523999

Clearstream Fund Centre AG (1)
Hardstrasse 201, 8005, Zurich, Switzerland
Tel.: (41) 432100500
Financial Transaction Services
N.A.I.C.S.: 522320

**Clearstream Global Securities Ser-
vices Limited** (1)
Navigation Square Albert Quay East, Cork,
Ireland
Tel.: (353) 214324700
Financial Services
N.A.I.C.S.: 523999
Paula Breen (Head-Unit)

Clearstream Holding AG (1)
Clearstream Banking AG, 60485, Frankfurt,
Germany
Tel.: (49) 69 2 110
Emp.: 2,000
Investment Management Service
N.A.I.C.S.: 523999
Yves Baguet (Member-Exec Bd)

Clearstream International S.A. (1)
42 Ave JF Kennedy, 1855, Luxembourg,
Luxembourg (100%)
Tel.: (352) 2430
Web Site: http://www.clearstream.com
Sales Range: $350-399.9 Million
Emp.: 1,000
Settlement & Custody Services
N.A.I.C.S.: 523210

Subsidiary (Non-US):

Clearstream Banking AG (2)
Neue Borsenstrasse 1, Frankfurt, 60487,
Germany (100%)
Tel.: (49) 692110
Web Site: http://www.clearstream.com
Banking Services
N.A.I.C.S.: 523150

Subsidiary (Domestic):

Clearstream Banking S.A. (2)
42 Ave JF Kennedy, 1855, Luxembourg,
Luxembourg (100%)
Tel.: (352) 2430
Web Site: http://www.clearstream.com
Sales Range: $600-649.9 Million
Emp.: 1,100
Banking Services
N.A.I.C.S.: 523150

Subsidiary (Non-US):

**Clearstream Operations Prague
s.r.o** (2)
Futurama Business Park Sokolovska 136 B,
186 00, Prague, Czech Republic
Tel.: (420) 296429111
Data Processing Services
N.A.I.C.S.: 518210

Subsidiary (Domestic):

Clearstream Services S.A. (2)
42 Avenue JF Kennedy, 1855, Luxembourg,
Luxembourg
Tel.: (352) 243 0
Sales Range: $150-199.9 Million
Emp.: 100
Information Technology Consulting Services
N.A.I.C.S.: 541512
Jeffrey Tessler (CEO)

**Crypto Finance (Asset Management)
AG** (1)
Hardstrasse 201, 8005, Zurich, Switzerland
Tel.: (41) 5458811
Crypto Currency & Related Services
N.A.I.C.S.: 523160

Crypto Finance AG (1)
Hardstrasse 201, 8005, Zurich, Switzerland

Tel.: (41) 5524505
Web Site: https://www.crypto-finance.com
Crypto Currency & Related Services
N.A.I.C.S.: 523160

**Deutsche Boerse Market Data + Ser-
vices Singapore Pte. Ltd.** (1)
9 Raffles Place 56-01 Republic Plaza, Singapore, 048619, Singapore
Tel.: (65) 65973018
N.A.I.C.S.: 523210

Deutsche Boerse Systems Inc. (1)
Willis Tower 233 S Wacker Dr Ste 2455,
Chicago, IL 60606
Tel.: (312) 544-1300
N.A.I.C.S.: 523210

**Deutsche Borse IT-Holding
GmbH** (1)
Neue Borsenstr 1, 60485, Frankfurt am
Main, 60485, Germany (100%)
Tel.: (49) 692110
Web Site: http://www.deutscheborse.com
Sales Range: $1-4.9 Billion
Emp.: 3,000
Holding Company; IT Services
N.A.I.C.S.: 551112

**Deutsche Borse Photography Foun-
dation gGmbH** (1)
Borsenplatz 4, 60313, Frankfurt am Main,
Germany
Tel.: (49) 6921114060
Web Site:
http://www.deutscheboersephotography.org
Photography Exhibition Services
N.A.I.C.S.: 541921

Deutsche Borse Services s.r.o (1)
Futurama Business Park Sokolovska 136 B,
186 00, Prague, Czech Republic
Tel.: (420) 296429111
Sales Range: $200-249.9 Million
Emp.: 40
Financial Management Services
N.A.I.C.S.: 523999
Mats Andersson (Gen Mgr)

Discovery Data Holdings Inc. (1)
12 Christopher Way Ste 300, Eatontown,
NJ 07724
Tel.: (732) 933-1899
Web Site: https://discoverydata.com
Wealth Management Services
N.A.I.C.S.: 523940

Eurex Clearing AG (1)
Mergenthalerallee 61, 65760, Eschborn,
Germany
Tel.: (49) 692110
Web Site: http://www.eurex.com
Financial Services
N.A.I.C.S.: 523999
Jeffrey Tessler (Chm)

Eurex Global Derivatives AG (1)
Theilerstrasse 1a, 6300, Zug, Switzerland
Tel.: (41) 434307101
N.A.I.C.S.: 523210

Eurex Repo GmbH (1)
Mergenthalerallee 61, 65760, Eschborn,
Germany
Tel.: (49) 6921114040
Financial Services
N.A.I.C.S.: 523999
Frank Gast (Mng Dir & Head-Funding)

Eurex Zurich AG (1)
Lowenstrasse 3, CH-8021, Zurich,
Switzerland (100%)
Tel.: (41) 434307260
Web Site: http://www.eurexchange.com
Sales Range: $50-74.9 Million
Emp.: 40
Futures & Options Exchange; Owned 50%
by Deutsche Borse AG & 50% by SWX
Swiss Exchange
N.A.I.C.S.: 523210
Thomas Book (CEO)

Subsidiary (Non-US):

Eurex Frankfurt AG (2)
Mergenthalerallee 61, 65760, Eschborn,
Germany
Tel.: (49) 692110170
Web Site: http://www.eurexchange.com
Futures & Options Exchange
N.A.I.C.S.: 523210

Deutsche Borse AG—(Continued)

Michael Peters *(CEO)*

Subsidiary (US):

U.S. Exchange Holdings, Inc. (3)
141 W Jackson Blvd Lbby 14, Chicago, IL
60604-3136
Tel.: (312) 544-1100
Holding Company
N.A.I.C.S.: 551112

Subsidiary (US):

Nodal Exchange, LLC (2)
1921 Gallows Rd 3rd Fl, Tysons Corner, VA
22182 **(100%)**
Tel.: (703) 962-9800
Web Site: https://www.nodalexchange.com
Law firm
N.A.I.C.S.: 541199
Paul Cusenza *(Chm & CEO)*

European Energy Exchange AG (1)
Augustusplatz 9, 04109, Leipzig, Germany
Tel.: (49) 34121560
Web Site: https://www.eex.com
Energy Trading Services
N.A.I.C.S.: 523160
Peter Reitz *(CEO)*

Subsidiary (Non-US):

EEX Asia Pte. Limited (2)
103 Penang Road 11-07 Visioncrest Com-
mercial, Singapore, 238467, Singapore
Tel.: (65) 62069828
Web Site: https://www.eexasia.com
Energy Trading Services
N.A.I.C.S.: 523160
Ray Ang Zhi Rui *(CEO)*

Subsidiary (Domestic):

**European Commodity Clearing
AG (2)**
Augustusplatz 9, 04109, Leipzig, Germany
Tel.: (49) 341246800
Web Site: https://www.ecc.de
Energy Trading Services
N.A.I.C.S.: 523160
Peter Reitz *(CEO)*

Subsidiary (Non-US):

**European Commodity Clearing Lux-
embourg S.a r.l (3)**
The Square 42 Avenue JF Kennedy, 1855,
Luxembourg, Luxembourg
Tel.: (352) 24336120
Energy Trading Services
N.A.I.C.S.: 523160
Hugo Neuman *(Mng Dir)*

Subsidiary (Non-US):

Grexel Systems Oy (2)
Lautatarhankatu 6, 00580, Helsinki, Finland
Tel.: (358) 942413160
Web Site: http://www.grexel.com
Renewable Energy Services
N.A.I.C.S.: 221118
Marko Lehtovaara *(CEO)*

Indexium AG (1)
Selnaustrasse 30, 8021, Zurich,
Switzerland **(100%)**
Tel.: (41) 58 399 4920
Stock Market Index Information Services
N.A.I.C.S.: 519290

**Institutional Shareholder Services
Germany AG (1)**
Goethestrasse 28, 80336, Munich, Ger-
many
Tel.: (49) 89462248186
Investment Management Service
N.A.I.C.S.: 523940

**Institutional Shareholder Services
Inc. (1)**
702 King Farm Blvd Ste 400, Rockville, MD
20850 **(81%)**
Tel.: (646) 680-6350
Web Site: http://www.issgovernance.com
Emp.: 1,100
Corporate Governance Solutions
N.A.I.C.S.: 523940
Gary Retelny *(Pres & CEO)*

Subsidiary (Domestic):

ISS Corporate Services, Inc. (2)
702 King Farm Blvd Ste 400, Rockville, MD
20850-4045
Tel.: (301) 556-0570
Web Site:
   http://www.isscorporateservices.com
Financial Advisory Services
N.A.I.C.S.: 523940
Mark Brockway *(Mng Dir & Head-Corp So-
lutions)*

**Institutional Shareholder Services UK
Limited (1)**
4th & 5th Floor West Building 1 London
Bridge, London, SE1 9BG, United Kingdom
Tel.: (44) 2031925799
Investment Management Service
N.A.I.C.S.: 523940

LuxCSD S.A. (1)
42 Avenue JF Kennedy, 1855, Luxembourg,
Luxembourg
Tel.: (352) 24332820
Web Site: https://www.luxcsd.com
Trust & Fiduciary & Custody Services
N.A.I.C.S.: 523991

Nodal Clear, LLC (1)
1921 Gallows Rd 3rd Fl, Tysons Corner, VA
22182
Tel.: (703) 962-9800
Renewable Energy Services
N.A.I.C.S.: 221118
Paul Cusenza *(Chm & CEO)*

Nodal Exchange Holdings, LLC (1)
1921 Gallows Rd 3rd Fl, Tysons Corner, VA
22182
Tel.: (703) 962-9800
N.A.I.C.S.: 523210

Qontigo GmbH (1)
Mergenthalerallee 61, 65760, Eschborn,
Germany
Tel.: (49) 6196 771925
Web Site: http://www.qontigo.com
Holding Company
N.A.I.C.S.: 551112
Holger Wohlenberg *(Chief Strategy Officer)*

Qontigo Index GmbH (1)
Mergenthalerallee 61, 65760, Eschborn,
Germany
Tel.: (49) 434307272
Financial Services
N.A.I.C.S.: 523999
Holger Wohlenberg *(Chief Bus Officer)*

Quantitative Brokers LLC (1)
285 Madison Ave Ste 1700, New York, NY
10017
Tel.: (646) 293-1800
Web Site: https://quantitativebrokers.com
Financial Brokerage Services
N.A.I.C.S.: 523999

Quantitative Brokers UK Limited (1)
Office 5 03 5th Floor 18 King William
Street, London, EC4N 7BP, United King-
dom
Tel.: (44) 2037145831
Financial Brokerage Services
N.A.I.C.S.: 523999

STOXX Ltd. (1)
Selnaustrasse 30, CH 8021, Zurich,
Switzerland **(100%)**
Tel.: (41) 58 399 5300
Web Site: http://www.stoxx.com
Sales Range: $100-124.9 Million
Emp.: 70
Stock Market Index Services
N.A.I.C.S.: 519290
Holger Wohlenberg *(Chm)*

SimCorp A/S (1)
Weidekampsgade 16, 2300, Copenhagen,
Denmark
Tel.: (45) 35448800
Web Site: http://www.simcorp.com
Rev.: $609,543,578
Assets: $646,437,451
Liabilities: $249,584,509
Net Worth: $396,852,942
Earnings: $135,096,574
Emp.: 1,871
Fiscal Year-end: 12/31/2021
Investment Management Solution Services
N.A.I.C.S.: 523940

Georg Hetrodt *(Chief Product Officer)*

Subsidiary (US):

Axioma, Inc. (2)
17 State St Ste 2700, New York, NY 10004
Tel.: (212) 991-4500
Web Site: https://qontigo.com
Custom Computer Programming Services
N.A.I.C.S.: 541511

Subsidiary (Non-US):

SimCorp Asia Pty. Ltd. (2)
Level 15 68 Pitt Street, Sydney, 2000,
NSW, Australia
Tel.: (61) 2 9241 4222
Sales Range: $25-49.9 Million
Emp.: 26
Information Technology Consulting Services
N.A.I.C.S.: 541512
Oliver Johnson *(Mng Dir)*

SimCorp Benelux SA/NV (2)
Avenue Louise 143, 1050, Brussels, Bel-
gium
Tel.: (32) 2 213 30 00
Sales Range: $25-49.9 Million
Emp.: 40
Investment Management Software Develop-
ment Services
N.A.I.C.S.: 541511
Steve Audiens *(Mgr-Sls)*

SimCorp Canada Inc. (2)
Ste 1600 401 Bay St, Toronto, M5H 2Y4,
ON, Canada
Tel.: (647) 591-9200
Web Site: http://www.simcorp.com
Emp.: 22
Investment Management Software Develop-
ment Services
N.A.I.C.S.: 541511

**SimCorp Development Centre UK
Limited (2)**
Whitegates Business Center, Alexander
Lane, Shenfield, CM15 8QF, Essex, United
Kingdom
Tel.: (44) 1277 312300
Web Site: http://www.simcorp.com
Sales Range: $25-49.9 Million
Emp.: 30
Software Development Services
N.A.I.C.S.: 541511

SimCorp France S.A.S. (2)
29-31 rue Saint Augustin, 75002, Paris,
France
Tel.: (33) 1 5535 5454
Sales Range: $25-49.9 Million
Emp.: 20
Business Software Consulting Services
N.A.I.C.S.: 541512
Thomas Van Cauwelaert *(Head-Sls & Mktg)*

SimCorp GmbH (2)
Justus-von-Liebig-Strasse 1, 61352, Bad
Homburg, Germany
Tel.: (49) 6172 9240 0
Business Software Consulting Services
N.A.I.C.S.: 541512
Jochen Muller *(Co-Mng Dir)*

SimCorp Hong Kong Ltd. (2)
Suite 2122 21st Floor The Center 99
Queen's Road, Central, Hong Kong, China
(Hong Kong)
Tel.: (852) 3478 3699
Web Site: http://www.simcorp.com
Software Development Services
N.A.I.C.S.: 541511

SimCorp Italiana S.r.l. (2)
Via Monferrato 1, 20144, Milan, Italy
Tel.: (39) 02 485 5871
Software Development Services
N.A.I.C.S.: 541511
Carmelo Lauro *(Sls Mgr)*

SimCorp Japan KK (2)
Level 27 Tokyo Sankei Building 1-7-2
Otemachi, Chiyoda-ku, Tokyo, 100-0004,
Japan
Tel.: (81) 33 242 3263
Software Development Services
N.A.I.C.S.: 541511
Oliver Johnson *(Mng Dir)*

SimCorp Ltd. (2)
2nd Floor 100 Wood Street, London, EC2V

7AN, United Kingdom
Tel.: (44) 20 7260 1900
Emp.: 80
Software Development Services
N.A.I.C.S.: 541511
Daniel Peppett *(Dir-Customer Svcs)*

SimCorp Luxembourg S.A. (2)
Rue Eugene Ruppert 20, 2453, Luxem-
bourg, Luxembourg
Tel.: (352) 2 649 3565
Asset Management Services
N.A.I.C.S.: 523940
Hans Otto Engkilde *(Sr VP)*

SimCorp Norge AS (2)
Biskop Gunnerusgate 14A, PO Box 13, 51,
Oslo, Norway
Tel.: (47) 2310 4100
Web Site: http://www.simcorp.com
Emp.: 1,800
Electronic Data Processing Services
N.A.I.C.S.: 518210

SimCorp Osterreich GmbH (2)
Wollzeile 16, 1010, Vienna, Austria
Tel.: (43) 1 5120099
Emp.: 7
Software Development Services
N.A.I.C.S.: 541511
Ralf Schmuecker *(Gen Mgr)*

SimCorp Schweiz AG (2)
Sihlquai 253, 8005, Zurich, Switzerland
Tel.: (41) 44 360 59 00
Sales Range: $25-49.9 Million
Emp.: 30
Custom Computer Programming Services
N.A.I.C.S.: 541511
Frank Hausgen *(Mgr-Sls)*

SimCorp Singapore Pte. Ltd (2)
58-03/04 Republic Plaza 9 Raffles Place,
Singapore, 048619, Singapore
Tel.: (65) 6823 1517
Investment Management Software Develop-
ment Services
N.A.I.C.S.: 541511
Oliver Johnson *(Mng Dir-Asia Pacific)*

SimCorp Sp z o.o. (2)
Pulawska 182 4th Floor, 02-670, Warsaw,
Poland
Tel.: (48) 22 375 9710
Software Development Services
N.A.I.C.S.: 541511
Fred Bouteiller *(Sr VP)*

SimCorp Sverige AB (2)
Jakobsbergsgatan 22, Stockholm, 111 44,
Sweden
Tel.: (46) 8 528 01500
Web Site: http://www.simcorp.com
Emp.: 20
Information Technology Consulting Services
N.A.I.C.S.: 541512

Subsidiary (US):

SimCorp USA Inc (2)
1 State St Plz 1 State St 29th Fl, New York,
NY 10004
Tel.: (212) 994-9400
Web Site: http://www.simcorp.com
Sales Range: $25-49.9 Million
Investment Management Software Services
N.A.I.C.S.: 541511
James Corrigan *(Exec VP & Mng Dir-North
America)*

Subsidiary (Non-US):

SimCorp Ukraine LLC (2)
Stusa 35-37 2nd Floor, 03142, Kiev,
Ukraine
Tel.: (380) 444 958 600
Sales Range: $25-49.9 Million
Emp.: 130
Investment Management Software Develop-
ment Services
N.A.I.C.S.: 541511

Tradegate Exchange GmbH (1)
Kurfurstendamm 119, 10711, Berlin, Ger-
many
Tel.: (49) 30 89 021 145
Web Site: http://www.tradegate.de
Emp.: 6
Stock Exchange Operating Services
N.A.I.C.S.: 523210
Thorsten Commichau *(Member-Exec Bd)*

Subsidiary (Domestic):

Boerse Berlin AG (2)
Fasanenstrasse 85, 10623, Berlin, Germany
Tel.: (49) 303110910
Web Site: http://www.boerse-berlin.de
Stock Exchange Operations
N.A.I.C.S.: 523210
Joerg Walter (Co-CEO-Exchange Svcs)

DEUTSCHE BUNDESBANK

Wilhelm-Epstein-Strasse 14, 60431, Frankfurt am Main, Germany
Tel.: (49) 69 9566 0   De
Web Site: http://www.bundesbank.de
Year Founded: 1957
Rev.: $8,404,549,300
Net Worth: $6,552,300,860
Earnings: $6,523,184,500
Emp.: 10,193
Fiscal Year-end: 12/31/19
Banking Services
N.A.I.C.S.: 522110
Jens Weidmann (Pres & Member-Exec Bd)

Subsidiaries:

Deutsche Bundesbank Hauptverwaltung Berlin (1)
Leibnizstr 10, 10625, Berlin, Germany
Tel.: (49) 3034752712
Banking Services
N.A.I.C.S.: 522110
Claus Tigges (Pres)

Deutsche Bundesbank Hauptverwaltung Dusseldorf (1)
Berliner Allee 14, 40212, Dusseldorf, Germany
Tel.: (49) 2118740
Web Site: http://www.bundesbank.de
Sales Range: $350-399.9 Million
Emp.: 800
Banking Services
N.A.I.C.S.: 522110

Deutsche Bundesbank Hauptverwaltung Frankfurt (1)
Taunusanlage 5, 60329, Frankfurt, Germany
Tel.: (49) 6923880
Web Site:
    http://www.deutschebundesbank.de
Banking Services
N.A.I.C.S.: 522110

Deutsche Bundesbank Hauptverwaltung Hamburg (1)
Willy-Brandt-Strasse 73, 20459, Hamburg, Germany
Tel.: (49) 4037070
Web Site: http://www.bundesbank.de
Sales Range: $200-249.9 Million
Emp.: 500
Banking Services
N.A.I.C.S.: 522110

Deutsche Bundesbank Hauptverwaltung Hannover (1)
Georgsplatz 5, 30159, Hannover, Germany
Tel.: (49) 51130330
Web Site: http://www.bundesbank.de
Sales Range: $200-249.9 Million
Emp.: 500
Banking Services
N.A.I.C.S.: 522110
Stephan Von Stenglin (Pres-Bremen, Lower Saxony & Saxony-Anhalt)

Deutsche Bundesbank Hauptverwaltung Leipzig (1)
Karl-Liebknecht-Strasse 141a, 04275, Leipzig, Germany
Tel.: (49) 3418600
Web Site: http://www.bundesbank.de
Sales Range: $100-124.9 Million
Emp.: 200
Banking Services
N.A.I.C.S.: 522110
Christopher Poppe (Pres)

Deutsche Bundesbank Hauptverwaltung Mainz (1)
Hegelstrasse 65, 55122, Mainz, Germany
Tel.: (49) 6131377

Web Site: http://www.bundesbank.de
Emp.: 500
Banking Services
N.A.I.C.S.: 522110

DEUTSCHE EFFECTEN- UND WECHSEL-BETEILIGUNGSGESELLSCHAFT AG.

Semmelweisstrasse 4, 07743, Jena, Germany
Tel.: (49) 36413100030
Web Site: https://dewb.de
EFF—(MUN)
Assets: $35,224,492
Liabilities: $18,820,984
Net Worth: $16,403,508
Earnings: ($1,788,269)
Emp.: 2
Fiscal Year-end: 12/31/23
Bank Independent Investment Company
N.A.I.C.S.: 523940
Bertram Kohler (CEO)

Subsidiaries:

DEWB-IT Beteiligungsgesellschaft mbH (1)
Leutragraben 1, 07743, Jena, Thuringia, Germany
Tel.: (49) 3641 5733600
Investment Management Service
N.A.I.C.S.: 523999

DEUTSCHE EIGENHEIM UNION AG

Ringbahnstrasse 16/18/20, 12099, Berlin, Germany
Tel.: (49) 3023321360
Web Site: https://www.deutsche-eigenheim-union.de
Year Founded: 2007
JZ6—(DEU)
Rev.: $15,663,981
Assets: $32,244,177
Liabilities: $8,875,152
Net Worth: $23,369,025
Earnings: $17,010,708
Emp.: 17
Fiscal Year-end: 12/31/23
Real Estate Development Services
N.A.I.C.S.: 531190
Christiane Bohm (CFO)

DEUTSCHE EUROSHOP AG

Heegbarg 36, 22391, Hamburg, Germany
Tel.: (49) 404135790
Web Site: https://www.deutsche-euroshop.de
DEQ—(MUN)
Rev.: $301,687,671
Assets: $4,923,480,974
Liabilities: $2,583,640,851
Net Worth: $2,339,840,123
Earnings: ($42,256,144)
Emp.: 6
Fiscal Year-end: 12/31/23
Shopping Malls & Shopping Centers Investment Services
N.A.I.C.S.: 236220
Patrick Kiss (Head-IR & PR)

Subsidiaries:

A10 Center Wildau GmbH (1)
Chausseestrasse 1, 15745, Wildau, Germany
Tel.: (49) 337556230
Web Site: https://www.a10center.de
Shopping Mall Operator
N.A.I.C.S.: 561439

Allee-Center Hamm KG (1)
Richard-Matthaei-Platz 1, 59065, Hamm, Germany
Tel.: (49) 2381498110
Web Site: https://www.allee-center-hamm.de

Sales Range: $50-74.9 Million
Emp.: 14
Shopping Mall Management Services
N.A.I.C.S.: 531120
Monika Block (Mgr)

Altmarkt-Galerie Dresden GmbH & Co. KG (1)
Center Management Webergasse 1, 01067, Dresden, Germany
Tel.: (49) 351482040
Web Site: https://www.altmarkt-galerie-dresden.de
Shopping Mall Operator
N.A.I.C.S.: 561439

City-Arkaden Wuppertal KG (1)
Alte Freiheit 9, 42103, Wuppertal, Germany
Tel.: (49) 202946460
Web Site: http://www.city-arkaden-wuppertal.com
Shopping Mall Management Services
N.A.I.C.S.: 445110

City-Galerie Wolfsburg KG (1)
Porschestrasse 45, 38440, Wolfsburg, Germany
Tel.: (49) 53616000
Web Site: http://www.city-galerie-wolfsburg.de
Shopping Mall Management Services
N.A.I.C.S.: 531120

Deutsche EuroShop Management GmbH (1)
Oderfelder Str 23, 20149, Hamburg, Germany
Tel.: (49) 404135790
Web Site: http://www.des.ag
Sales Range: $50-74.9 Million
Asset Management Services
N.A.I.C.S.: 531390
Claus Matthias Boge (Mng Dir)

Forum Wetzlar KG (1)
Am Forum 1, 35576, Wetzlar, Germany
Tel.: (49) 6441381970
Web Site: https://www.forum-wetzlar.de
Sales Range: $200-249.9 Million
Shopping Mall Management Services
N.A.I.C.S.: 445110

Main-Taunus-Zentrum KG (1)
Center-Management, 65843, Sulzbach, Germany
Tel.: (49) 693009010
Web Site: https://www.main-taunus-zentrum.de
Shopping Mall Operator
N.A.I.C.S.: 561439

Objekt City-Point Kassel GmbH & Co. KG (1)
Konigsplatz 61, 34117, Kassel, Germany
Tel.: (49) 561701300
Web Site: https://www.city-point-kassel.de
Shopping Mall Operator
N.A.I.C.S.: 561439

Olympia Brno s.r.o. (1)
U Dalnice 777, Modrice, 664 42, Brno, Czech Republic
Tel.: (420) 547423677
Web Site: https://www.olympia-centrum.cz
Shopping Mall Operator
N.A.I.C.S.: 561439

Stadt-Galerie Hameln KG (1)
Pferdemarkt 1, 31785, Hameln, Germany
Tel.: (49) 5151822270
Web Site: https://www.stadt-galerie-hameln.de
Sales Range: $50-74.9 Million
Emp.: 12
Shopping Mall Management Services
N.A.I.C.S.: 531120
Susanne Schubert (Gen Mgr)

Stadt-Galerie Passau KG (1)
Bahnhofstrasse 1, 94032, Passau, Germany
Tel.: (49) 8518517970
Web Site: https://www.stadtgalerie-passau.de
Emp.: 12
Shopping Mall Management Services
N.A.I.C.S.: 531120
Olaf Kindt (Gen Mgr)

DEUTSCHE GRUNDSTUECK-

SAUKTIONEN AG

Kurfuerstendamm 65, 10707, Berlin, Germany
Tel.: (49) 308846880
Web Site: https://www.dga-ag.de
Year Founded: 1984
DGR—(DEU)
Rev.: $6,529,247
Assets: $10,306,497
Liabilities: $852,579
Net Worth: $9,453,918
Earnings: $1,402,979
Emp.: 33
Fiscal Year-end: 12/31/22
Real Estate Auction Services
N.A.I.C.S.: 531210
Michael Plettner (Chm-Exec Bd)

Subsidiaries:

Deutsche Internet Immobilien Auktionen GmbH (1)
Kurfurstendamm 65, 10707, Berlin, Germany
Tel.: (49) 3088468880
Web Site: https://www.diia.de
Real Estate Services
N.A.I.C.S.: 531390
Thomas Engel (Mng Dir)

Norddeutsche Grundstucksauktionen AG (1)
Ernst-Barlach-Strasse 4, 18055, Rostock, Germany
Tel.: (49) 381444330
Web Site: https://www.ndga.de
Real Estate Services
N.A.I.C.S.: 531390
Michael Siegmund (Chm)

Plettner & Brecht Immobilien GmbH (1)
Kirschenallee 20, 14050, Berlin, Germany
Tel.: (49) 303067340
Web Site: https://www.plettner-brecht.de
Real Estate Services
N.A.I.C.S.: 531390
Hagen Wehrmeister (Mng Dir)

Sachsische Grundstucksauktionen AG (1)
Hohe Strasse 12, 01069, Dresden, Germany
Tel.: (49) 3514370800
Web Site: https://www.sga-ag.de
Real Estate Services
N.A.I.C.S.: 531390

Westdeutsche Grundstucksauktionen AG (1)
Apostelnstrasse 9, 50667, Cologne, Germany
Tel.: (49) 2212772660
Web Site: https://www.wdga-ag.de
Real Estate Services
N.A.I.C.S.: 531390

DEUTSCHE HYPOTHEKEN-BANK (ACTIEN-GESELLSCHAFT)

Osterstrasse 31, 30159, Hannover, Germany
Tel.: (49) 51130450
Web Site: http://www.deutsche-hypo.de
Year Founded: 1872
Sales Range: $50-74.9 Million
Emp.: 200
Mortgage Bank; Owned 25% BHF-Bank, 25% M.M. Warburg & Co. Kommanditgesellschaft Auf Aktien, 25% Sal. Oppenheimer Jr & Cie KGaA
N.A.I.C.S.: 522310
Andreas Rehfus (Mng Dir)

DEUTSCHE INDUSTRIE REIT-AG

August-Bebel-Str 68, 14482, Potsdam, Germany
Tel.: (49) 331740076529

Deutsche Industrie REIT-AG—(Continued)

Web Site: http://www.deutsche-industrie-reit.de
Year Founded: 2014
JB7—(DEU)
Rev.: $147,950,720
Assets: $879,234,007
Liabilities: $415,941,879
Net Worth: $463,292,128
Earnings: $62,419,771
Emp.: 6
Fiscal Year-end: 09/30/20
Real Estate Investment Trust Services
N.A.I.C.S.: 531190
Rolf Elgeti *(CEO & Member-Mgmt Bd)*

DEUTSCHE INVEST CAPITAL PARTNERS GMBH
Prinzregentenstrasse 56, 80538, Munich, Germany
Tel.: (49) 89 954 296 150   De
Web Site: http://www.dicapital.com
Year Founded: 2006
Investment Services
N.A.I.C.S.: 523999
Alexander von Mellenthin *(Mng Partner)*

Subsidiaries:

Deutsche Invest Mittelstand GmbH   **(1)**
Taunustor 1, 60310, Frankfurt am Main, Germany
Tel.: (49) 69 247 504 816
Web Site: http://www.dimittelstand.com
Investment Services
N.A.I.C.S.: 523999
Jens Biermann *(Mng Partner)*

Subsidiary (Domestic):

Babcock & Wilcox Loibl GmbH   **(2)**
Arberstrasse 40, 94315, Straubing, Germany
Tel.: (49) 942192560
Power & Heating Equipment Whslr
N.A.I.C.S.: 423720

Sundwiger Messingwerk GmbH & Co. KG   **(1)**
Honnetalstrasse 110, 58675, Hemer, Germany
Tel.: (49) 2372 661 0
Metal Products Mfr
N.A.I.C.S.: 331420
Sebastian Piel *(Head-Grp Controlling)*

DEUTSCHE KONSUM REIT-AG
Marlene-Dietrich-Allee 12b, 14482, Potsdam, Germany
Tel.: (49) 331740076555
Web Site: https://www.deutsche-konsum.de
Year Founded: 2009
DKG—(BER)
Rev.: $86,037,341
Assets: $1,111,783,078
Liabilities: $770,320,203
Net Worth: $341,462,875
Earnings: ($195,329,160)
Emp.: 20
Fiscal Year-end: 09/30/23
Real Estate Investment Trust Services
N.A.I.C.S.: 531190
Rolf Elgeti *(CEO & Member-Mgmt Bd)*

DEUTSCHE LAND PLC
15-19 Athol Street, Douglas, IM1 1LB, Isle of Man
Tel.: (44) 7711670320
Sales Range: $50-74.9 Million
Property Management Services
N.A.I.C.S.: 531312
David Maxwell *(CEO)*

DEUTSCHE LUFTHANSA AG
Lufthansa Aviation Center Airportring, 60546, Frankfurt am Main, Germany
Tel.: (49) 696960   De
Web Site: https://www.lufthansagroup.com
Year Founded: 1926
DLAKF—(OTCQX)
Rev.: $39,123,523,573
Assets: $50,028,700,747
Liabilities: $39,366,375,985
Net Worth: $10,662,324,761
Earnings: $1,846,782,206
Emp.: 110,264
Fiscal Year-end: 12/31/23
Holding Company; Airline Operations & Support Services
N.A.I.C.S.: 551112
Detlef Kayser *(COO & Member-Exec Bd)*

Subsidiaries:

ACS Aircontainer Services Gesellschaft m.b.H   **(1)**
Berggasse 16, 2401, Fischamend Dorf, Austria
Tel.: (43) 2232 77878
Sales Range: $25-49.9 Million
Emp.: 50
Air Container Repair & Maintenance Services
N.A.I.C.S.: 811310

AS InPro GmbH   **(1)**
Industriehof 5, Oldenburg, 26133, Germany
Tel.: (49) 441944180
Web Site: http://www.lufthansa-industry-solutions.de
Emp.: 80
Information Technology Consulting Services
N.A.I.C.S.: 541512
Annika Schulte *(Sec)*

AUA Beteiligungen Gesellschaft m.b.H.   **(1)**
Office Park 2, Wien-Flughafen, Vienna, 1300, Austria
Tel.: (43) 517661000
Web Site: http://www.austrian.com
Emp.: 50
Investment Management Service
N.A.I.C.S.: 523999
Jaan Albrecht *(CEO)*

Air Dolomiti S.p.A.   **(1)**
Via Paolo Bembo 70, Frazione di Dossobuono, 37062, Verona, Italy   **(100%)**
Tel.: (39) 045 860 5211
Web Site: https://www.airdolomiti.it
Sales Range: $50-74.9 Million
Emp.: 250
Regional Passenger Air Transportation Services
N.A.I.C.S.: 481111
Joerg Eberhart *(Pres & CEO)*

Airport Services Dresden GmbH   **(1)**
Wilhelmine-Reichard-Ring 1, 01109, Dresden, Germany
Tel.: (49) 351 881 4010
Web Site: https://www.handling-drs.com
Sales Range: $50-74.9 Million
Emp.: 14
Airport Baggage Handling Services
N.A.I.C.S.: 488119
Stephan J. Weinmann *(Mng Dir)*

Airport Services Friedrichshafen GmbH   **(1)**
Am Flughafen 64, 88046, Friedrichshafen, Germany
Tel.: (49) 7541284383
Web Site: http://www.airport-services-friedrichshafen.com
Airline Passenger Services
N.A.I.C.S.: 481211

Airport Services Leipzig GmbH   **(1)**
Terminalring 13, Flughafen Leipzig, 04435, Halle, Germany
Tel.: (49) 341 224 1602
Web Site: https://handling-lej.de
Sales Range: $50-74.9 Million
Emp.: 100
Airport Handling Services
N.A.I.C.S.: 488190

Stephan J. Weinmann *(Mng Dir)*

Albatraos Versicherungsdienste GmbH   **(1)**
Venloer Str 151 - 153, 50672, Cologne, Germany
Tel.: (49) 221 829 2002
Web Site: https://www.albatros.de
Sales Range: $100-124.9 Million
Insurance Management Services
N.A.I.C.S.: 524298
Lorenz Hanelt *(Mng Dir)*

Albatros Service Center GmbH   **(1)**
Gebaude 1335 A, Hahn-Flughafen, 55483, Kirchberg, Germany
Tel.: (49) 696969977
Web Site: http://www.albatros.de
Airport Call Center Services
N.A.I.C.S.: 561421

Austrian Airlines AG   **(1)**
Office Park 2, Postfach 100, A-1300, Vienna, Austria   **(95.4%)**
Tel.: (43) 517661000
Web Site: https://www.austrian.com
Sales Range: $1-4.9 Billion
Oil Transportation Services
N.A.I.C.S.: 481111
Alexis von Hoensbroech *(CEO, CFO & Member-Mgmt Bd)*

Subsidiary (Non-US):

Austrian Airlines Technik-Bratislava, s.r.o.   **(2)**
Letisko M R Stefanika Hangar C, 820 01, Bratislava, Slovakia
Tel.: (421) 911 487 038
Sales Range: $25-49.9 Million
Emp.: 16
Aircraft Maintenance Services
N.A.I.C.S.: 811198
Konstantin Essler *(Mng Dir, Mgr-Accountable & Dir-Technical)*

Subsidiary (Domestic):

Austrian myHoliday   **(2)**
Office Park 2 Flughafen Wien, PO Box 100, 1300, Vienna, Austria   **(100%)**
Tel.: (43) 5176676700
Web Site: http://myholiday.austrian.com
Sales Range: $25-49.9 Million
Passenger Airline Services
N.A.I.C.S.: 481111

SCA - Schedule Coordination Austria GmbH   **(2)**
Office Park I Top B 08/04, Vienna Airport, 1300, Vienna, Austria   **(54%)**
Tel.: (43) 170 072 3600
Web Site: https://www.slots-austria.com
Sales Range: $25-49.9 Million
Emp.: 7
Commercial Air Transportation Coordination & Scheduling Services
N.A.I.C.S.: 926120
Wolfgang Gallistl *(Mng Dir)*

Tyrolean Airways Tiroler Luftfahrt GmbH   **(2)**
Fürstenweg 176, A-6026, Innsbruck, Austria   **(100%)**
Tel.: (43) 517663000
Web Site: http://www.tyrolean.at
Passenger Airline Services
N.A.I.C.S.: 481111

Avionic Design GmbH   **(1)**
Wragekamp 10, 22397, Hamburg, Germany
Tel.: (49) 40881870
Web Site: https://www.avionic-design.de
Aircraft Mfr
N.A.I.C.S.: 336411

DLH Fuel Company mbH   **(1)**
Weg Beim Jager 193, Hamburg, 22335, Germany
Tel.: (49) 4050700
Airline Transportation Services
N.A.I.C.S.: 488190

Delvag Versicherungs-AG   **(1)**
Venloer Str 151-153, 50672, Cologne, Germany
Tel.: (49) 2218292001
Web Site: https://www.delvag.de
Transport Insurance Services
N.A.I.C.S.: 485991

Stephan J. Weinmann *(Mng Dir)*

Eurowings GmbH   **(1)**
Terminal-Ring 1 Zentralgebaude Ost Flughafen, 40474, Dusseldorf, Germany
Tel.: (49) 22159988222
Web Site: https://www.eurowings.com
Emp.: 9,000
Airline Reservation Services
N.A.I.C.S.: 561599
Jens Ritter *(COO)*

Evertaste Oy   **(1)**
Tikkurilantie 140 A, 01530, Vantaa, Finland
Tel.: (358) 503931932
Web Site: http://www.godeli.fi
Bakery Products Mfr
N.A.I.C.C.: 011011

GOAL German Operating Aircraft Leasing GmbH   **(1)**
Toelzer Strasse 15, 82031, Grunwald, Germany   **(40%)**
Tel.: (49) 8 964 1430
Web Site: https://www.goal-leasing.com
Aircraft Leasing Services
N.A.I.C.S.: 532411
Christian Schloemann *(Mng Dir & Head-Fin)*

GOAL Verwaltungsgesellschaft mbH & Co. Projekt Nr. 5 KG i.L.   **(1)**
Tolzer Strasse 15, 82031, Grunwald, Germany
Tel.: (49) 8964143149
Engineeering Services
N.A.I.C.S.: 541330

Germanwings GmbH   **(1)**
Germanwings-Strasse 1, 51147, Cologne, Germany
Tel.: (49) 23192450
Web Site: http://www.germanwings.com
Airline Operator
N.A.I.C.S.: 481111
Thomas Winkelmann *(Chm-Mgmt Bd)*

Global Load Control (Pty) Ltd.   **(1)**
13th Floor Picbel Parkade 58 Strand Street, Cape Town, 8001, South Africa
Tel.: (27) 21 415 3672
Web Site: https://www.globalloadcontrol.com
Emp.: 230
Remote Aviation Services
N.A.I.C.S.: 481219
Simone Brueckner *(Ops Mgr)*

Global Logistics System Europe Company for Cargo Information Services GmbH   **(1)**
Lyoner St 36, 60528, Frankfurt am Main, Germany   **(42.86%)**
Tel.: (49) 69669060
Web Site: http://www.traxon.com
Sales Range: $25-49.9 Million
Emp.: 30
Support Activities for Air Transportation
N.A.I.C.S.: 488190
Felix Keck *(Mng Dir)*

Handling Counts GmbH   **(1)**
CargoCity Sud Geb 568 B, 60549, Frankfurt am Main, Germany
Tel.: (49) 6969693625
Web Site: http://www.handling-counts.com
Air Freight Handling Services
N.A.I.C.S.: 481112

LH Cargo Holding GmbH   **(1)**
Langer Kornweg 34i, Kelsterbach, 65451, Germany
Tel.: (49) 6107 777666
Investment Management Service
N.A.I.C.S.: 523999

LSG Lufthansa Service Holding AG   **(1)**
Dornhofstr 38, 63263, Neu-Isenburg, Germany   **(100%)**
Tel.: (49) 6 102 2400
Web Site: https://www.lsg-group.com
Sales Range: $1-4.9 Billion
Holding Company; Airline Catering & Airport Contract Food Services
N.A.I.C.S.: 551112
Erdmann F. Rauer *(Chm-Exec Bd)*

Subsidiary (Non-US):

AIRO Catering Services - Ukraine   **(2)**
Airport Boryspil-7, Kiev, 08307, Ukraine
Tel.: (380) 44 230 00 23

Emp.: 79
Airline Catering Services
N.A.I.C.S.: 722320
Zeki Kocak *(Gen Mgr)*

AIRO Catering Services Eesti OU (2)
Kesk-Sojamae 26, Tallinn, 11415, Estonia
Tel.: (372) 6058230
Sales Range: $10-24.9 Million
Emp.: 50
Inflight Catering Services
N.A.I.C.S.: 722320
Andris Balicklis *(Mgr)*

Airo Catering Services Latvija SIA (2)
International Airport Riga, Marupe, 1053, Latvia
Tel.: (371) 67207201
Web Site: http://www.lsgskychefs.com
Sales Range: $25-49.9 Million
Emp.: 13
Airline Catering Services
N.A.I.C.S.: 722320
Andris Balickis *(Gen Mgr)*

Caterair Servicos de Bordo e Hotelaria S.A. (2)
Estrada do Galeao s/n, Cacuia, Rio de Janeiro, 21941-570, Brazil
Tel.: (55) 21 2468 6000
Sales Range: $25-49.9 Million
Emp.: 100
Food Processing Machinery Mfr
N.A.I.C.S.: 423830
Simone Okazawa *(Mgr)*

Comisariato de Baja California, S.A. de C.V (2)
Aeropuerto s/n intb Tijuana, Tijuana, 22300, Baja California, Mexico
Tel.: (52) 6646235427
Emp.: 250
Catering Services
N.A.I.C.S.: 722320
Jesus Galvan *(Mgr-Ops)*

Finnair Catering Oy
Teknikontie 1, PO Box 41, 01053, Vantaa, Finland
Tel.: (358) 9818 5025
Web Site: http://www.finnairgroup.com
Catering Services
N.A.I.C.S.: 722320

Inflight Catering Services Limited (2)
PO Box 76070, Dar es Salaam, Tanzania
Tel.: (255) 22 284 3541
Web Site: http://www.lsgskychefs.com
Emp.: 19
Flight Catering Services
N.A.I.C.S.: 722320
Thomas Cheah *(Gen Mgr)*

LSG Catering China Ltd (2)
No 6 Catering Road West Hong Kong International Airport, Chek Lap Kok, Hong Kong, China (Hong Kong)
Tel.: (852) 2767 5318
Web Site:
http://www.gcateringhk.lsgskychefs.com
General Catering Services
N.A.I.C.S.: 722320
Yau Sam *(Gen Mgr)*

LSG Lufthansa Service Asia Ltd. (2)
Suite 1704 Island Place Tower, 510 Kings Road, North Point, China (Hong Kong) (100%)
Tel.: (852) 29636388
Web Site: http://www.lsg-skychefs.com
Sales Range: $25-49.9 Million
Emp.: 30
Air Transportation Svcs
N.A.I.C.S.: 481111

Subsidiary (Domestic):

LSG Holding Asia Ltd. (3)
1704-1706 Island Place Tower, 510 Kings Road, North Point, China (Hong Kong) (100%)
Tel.: (852) 29636388
Web Site: http://www.lsg-skychefs.com
Sales Range: $10-24.9 Million
Emp.: 20
Air Transportation Catering Svcs
N.A.I.C.S.: 722320

Holding (Domestic):

LSG Lufthansa Service Hong Kong Ltd. (4)
No 6 Catering Road West Hong Kong International Airport, Chek Lap Kok, Hong Kong, China (Hong Kong) (47.9%)
Tel.: (852) 2769 8211
Airline Catering, Cleaning, Laundry & Food Service Contractor
N.A.I.C.S.: 722320
Eddy Yung *(Gen Mgr)*

Subsidiary (Non-US):

LSG Sky Chefs (India) Pvt. Ltd. (3)
Begaluru International Airport, Devanahalli, Bengaluru, 560 300, India (100%)
Tel.: (91) 8022018701
Web Site: http://www.lsgskychefs.com
Sales Range: $25-49.9 Million
Emp.: 500
Airline Catering & Food Service Contractor
N.A.I.C.S.: 722320
David Tuck *(Dir-Ops-India)*

LSG Sky Chefs (Thailand) Ltd. (3)
999 Moo 1 Nong Prue, Bang Phli, 10540, Samut Prakan, Thailand
Tel.: (66) 21311900
Web Site: http://www.lsgskychefs.com
Holding Company; Airline Catering & Laundry Services
N.A.I.C.S.: 551112

Subsidiary (Domestic):

LSG Catering (Thailand) Ltd. (4)
999 Moo 1 Nong Prue, Bang Phli, Samut Prakan, 10540, Thailand (100%)
Tel.: (66) 2 131 1900
Web Site: http://www.lsgskychefs.com
Sales Range: $10-24.9 Million
Emp.: 50
Airline Catering Services
N.A.I.C.S.: 722320
North More *(Gen Mgr)*

Holding (Domestic):

Siam Flight Services Ltd. (4)
Bangkok International Airport, Vipavadee-Rangsit Road, 10210, Bangkok, Donmuang, Thailand (66.67%)
Tel.: (66) 2 996 8890
Web Site: http://www.siamflight.com
Airline Food Service Contractor
N.A.I.C.S.: 722310

Subsidiary (Non-US):

LSG Lufthansa Service Cape Town (Pty) Ltd (2)
Madrid Street Airport Industry 2, Cape Town, 8001, South Africa
Tel.: (27) 213864093
Web Site: http://www.lsgskycheff.com
Emp.: 7
Airline Catering Services
N.A.I.C.S.: 722320
Karin Zimmermann *(Gen Mgr)*

Subsidiary (Domestic):

LSG Lufthansa Service Catering- und Dienstleistungsgesellschaft mbH (2)
Dornhofstr 40, Neu-Isenburg, 63263, Germany
Tel.: (49) 61022400
Web Site: http://www.lufthansa.com
Sales Range: $10-24.9 Million
Emp.: 10
Airline Catering Services
N.A.I.C.S.: 722320
Gert Schnicke *(Gen Mgr)*

LSG Lufthansa Service Europa/Afrika GmbH (2)
Dornhofstrasse 38, Neu-Isenburg, 63263, Germany (100%)
Tel.: (49) 61022400
Web Site: http://www.lsgskychefs.com
Holding Company; Airline Catering & Food Service Contractor
N.A.I.C.S.: 551112

Subsidiary (Non-US):

LSG Sky Chefs South Africa (Pty) Ltd. (3)

Corner Jones & Springbok Road, PO Box 26840, East Rand, Johannesburg, 1462, Boksburg, South Africa (100%)
Tel.: (27) 112810000
Web Site: http://www.lsgskychefs.com
Emp.: 500
Airline Catering, Food Service Contractor & Laundry Services
N.A.I.C.S.: 722320
Paul Elliot *(Mng Dir)*

Starfood Finland Oy (3)
Tikkurilantie 140 A, 01530, Vantaa, Finland (100%)
Tel.: (358) 9 818 2500
Web Site: http://www.finncatering.fi
Sales Range: $25-49.9 Million
Emp.: 200
Convenience Foods, Bakery & Takeaway Products Mfr
N.A.I.C.S.: 311999
Henriikka Siltanen *(Acct Dir)*

Subsidiary (Non-US):

LSG Sky Chefs Belgium N.V. (2)
Gebouw 53 Luchthaven, Zaventem, 1930, Belgium
Tel.: (32) 27237240
Catering Services
N.A.I.C.S.: 722320

Subsidiary (Domestic):

LSG Sky Chefs Deutschland GmbH (2)
Dornhofstrasse 38, Neu-Isenburg, 63263, Germany (100%)
Tel.: (49) 61022400
Web Site: http://www.lsgskychefs.com
Sales Range: $250-299.9 Million
Emp.: 1,400
Airline Catering & Food Service Contractor
N.A.I.C.S.: 722320

Subsidiary (Domestic):

LSG Sky Chefs Lounge GmbH (3)
Dornhofstr 38, Neu-Isenburg, 63263, Germany
Tel.: (49) 61022400
Airline Catering Services
N.A.I.C.S.: 722320

LSG-Food & Nonfood Handel GmbH (3)
Dornhofstrasse 38, 63263, Neu-Isenburg, Germany (100%)
Tel.: (49) 6102240801
Web Site: http://www.ringeltaube.de
Sales Range: $25-49.9 Million
Emp.: 28
Airport Gift Shops & Duty Free Shopping
N.A.I.C.S.: 459420
Katja Stahlhacke *(Mng Dir)*

LSG-Sky Food GmbH (3)
Otto-Lilienthal-Strasse 6-8, Alzey, 55232, Germany (100%)
Tel.: (49) 67319090
Web Site: http://www.lsgskychefs.com
Sales Range: $75-99.9 Million
Emp.: 400
Commercial Airline Frozen Meals Mfr
N.A.I.C.S.: 311412
Alexander Thies *(Mng Dir)*

Spiriant Gmbh (3)
Dornhofstr 40, 63263, Neu-Isenburg, Germany (100%)
Tel.: (49) 6102240609
Web Site: http://www.spiriant.com
Airline In-Flight Equipment & Logistics Services
N.A.I.C.S.: 541614
Thomas Berti *(Mng Dir)*

Subsidiary (Non-US):

LSG Sky Chefs Havacilik Hizmetleri A.S. (2)
Ataturk Hava Limani Ozel Hangarlar Bolgesi, Istanbul, Turkiye
Tel.: (90) 2125929800
Web Site: http://www.lsgskychefs.com
Catering Services
N.A.I.C.S.: 722320
Mehmet Senle Sekercioglu *(Gen Mgr)*

LSG Sky Chefs Korea Co Ltd. (2)

2840 Wunseo-Dong, Jung-Gu, Incheon, 400340, Korea (South)
Tel.: (82) 327445222
Web Site: http://www.lsgskychefs.com
Emp.: 150
Flight Catering Services
N.A.I.C.S.: 722320
Tareth Lytett *(Gen Mgr)*

LSG Sky Chefs New Zealand Limited (2)
1 Laurence Stevens Drive Auckland International Airport, Auckland, 2022, New Zealand
Tel.: (64) 9 255 0700
Web Site: http://www.lsgskychefs.com
Emp.: 60
Catering Services
N.A.I.C.S.: 722320

LSG Sky Chefs Norge AS (2)
Roald Amundsensvei, PO Box 16, 2061, Gardermoen, Norway (100%)
Tel.: (47) 64815800
Web Site: http://www.lsgskychefs.com
Sales Range: $10-24.9 Million
Emp.: 40
Airline Catering & Food Service Contractor
N.A.I.C.S.: 722320
Fredrik Karl Heinrici *(Mng Dir)*

Subsidiary (US):

LSG Sky Chefs North America Solutions, Inc. (2)
6191 N State Hwy 161, Irving, TX 75038-2246 (100%)
Tel.: (972) 793-9000
Web Site: http://www.lsgskychefs.com
Holding Company; Regional Managing Office; Airline Catering & Food Service Contractor
N.A.I.C.S.: 551112
Dennis Sadlowski *(Reg COO)*

Subsidiary (Non-US):

CLS Catering Services Ltd. (3)
3560 Jericho Rd, Vancouver International Airport, Richmond, V7B 1C2, BC, Canada (70%)
Tel.: (604) 273-4438
Web Site: http://www.clscatering.com
Sales Range: $1-9.9 Million
Emp.: 200
Airline Catering Services
N.A.I.C.S.: 722320

Subsidiary (Domestic):

LSG Sky Chefs USA, Inc. (3)
6191 N State Hwy 161, Irving, TX 75038-2246 (100%)
Tel.: (972) 793-9000
Web Site: http://www.lsgskychefs.com
Airline Catering & Food Service Contractor
N.A.I.C.S.: 722320

Subsidiary (Domestic):

LSG Sky Chefs Supply Chain Solutions, Inc. (4)
6191 N State Hwy 161 100, Irving, TX 75038-2246
Tel.: (972) 793-9000
Catering Services
N.A.I.C.S.: 722320

Subsidiary (Non-US):

LSG Sky Chefs Schweiz AG (2)
Hofwisenstrasse 48, CH-8153, Rumlang, Switzerland (100%)
Tel.: (41) 44 818 7571
Web Site: http://www.lsgskychefs.com
Airline Catering & Food Service Contractor
N.A.I.C.S.: 722320

LSG Sky Chefs Solutions Asia Limited (2)
Rm 2703-6a 27/F Exchange Twr 33 Wang Chiu Rd, Kowloon Bay, Kowloon, China (Hong Kong)
Tel.: (852) 29636388
Web Site: http://www.lsgskychefs.com
Sales Range: $100-124.9 Million
Emp.: 800
Airline Catering Services
N.A.I.C.S.: 722320

Deutsche Lufthansa AG—(Continued)

LSG Sky Chefs Sverige AB (2)
Skogsvagen 2, PO Box 188, 190 46, Stockholm, Sweden (100%)
Tel.: (46) 8 5220 6000
Airline Catering & Food Service Contractor
N.A.I.C.S.: 722320
Henrik Lindh (Mng Dir)

Subsidiary (Domestic):

LSG Sky Chefs Building AB (3)
Arlanda Flygplats, 190 60, Stockholm, Sweden (100%)
Tel.: (46) 87970900
Lessors of Other Real Estate Property
N.A.I.C.S.: 531190

Subsidiary (Non-US):

LSG Sky Chefs de Venezuela C.A.
Aeropuerto Intl Simon Bolivar Sector Tiyuca Alcabala Cojedes Catia, La Mar Edo Vargas Apdo 165, Caracas, Vargas, Venezuela (99.9%)
Tel.: (58) 2123552861
Web Site: http://www.lsgskychefs.com
Airline Catering & Food Service Contractor
N.A.I.C.S.: 722320

LSG/Sky Chefs Europe Holdings Ltd. (2)
Faraday Road, Crawley, RH10 9JX, W Sussex, United Kingdom (100%)
Tel.: (44) 1293 404 810
Web Site: http://www.lsgskychefs.com
Holding Company; Airline Catering & Food Service Contractor
N.A.I.C.S.: 551112

Affiliate (Domestic):

LSG Sky Chefs/GCC Ltd. (3)
27 Central Way, Feltham, TW14 0UU, Mddx, United Kingdom (50%)
Tel.: (44) 2088448000
Web Site: http://www.lsgskychefs.com
Sales Range: $25-49.9 Million
Emp.: 500
Airline Catering Services
N.A.I.C.S.: 722320

Subsidiary (Domestic):

LZ-Catering GmbH (2)
Sportallee 54b, 22335, Hamburg, Germany
Tel.: (49) 40 5070 5373
Web Site: http://www.lz-catering.de
Restaurant Operating Services
N.A.I.C.S.: 722511

Subsidiary (US):

SCIS Air Security Corporation (2)
1521 N Cooper St Ste 300, Arlington, TX 76011
Tel.: (817) 792-4500
Web Site: http://www.scisairsecurity.com
Sales Range: $25-49.9 Million
Emp.: 53
Airline Security Consulting Services
N.A.I.C.S.: 488119

Subsidiary (Non-US):

ServCater Internacional Ltda (2)
Rodovia Helio Smidt - Setor 1 - Base A, Guarulhos, 07190-100, Brazil
Tel.: (55) 1121492300
Processed Food Mfr
N.A.I.C.S.: 311999

Sky Chefs De Mexico, S.A. de C.V. (2)
Francisco Sarabia No 15 Penos De Los Banos Venustiano Carranza, Mexico, 15520, Mexico
Tel.: (52) 5557850360
Catering Services
N.A.I.C.S.: 722320

Sky Chefs de Panama, S.A. (2)
Aeropuerto Internacional De Tocumen, Panama, Panama
Tel.: (507) 2384010
Web Site: http://www.lsgskychefs.com
Catering Services
N.A.I.C.S.: 722320
Rolando Kourany (Office Mgr)

UAB Airo Catering Services Lietuva (2)
Rodunios Kelias 2, Vilnius, 2189, Lithuania
Tel.: (370) 5 230 62 42
Web Site: http://www.airo.lt
Emp.: 4
Inflight Catering Services
N.A.I.C.S.: 722320
Zileinas Karaleicius (Gen Mgr)

Joint Venture (Non-US):

ZAO Aeromar
Sheremetyevskoe highway ow 31, 141425, Moscow, Khimki, Russia
Tel.: (7) 1952319475
Web Site: http://www.aeromar.ru
Sales Range: $200-249.9 Million
Emp.: 2,500
Airline Catering Services; Owned 51% by Aeroflot Russian Airlines & 49% by Deutsche Lufthansa AG
N.A.I.C.S.: 722320

Lufthansa AG (1)
Lh Basis, Frankfurt, 60546, Germany (100%)
Tel.: (49) 696960
Web Site: http://www.lufthansa.com
Sales Range: $50-74.9 Million
Emp.: 250
Non-Scheduled Cargo Airline; Domestic & International Flights
N.A.I.C.S.: 481111

Unit (US):

Lufthansa German Airlines
1640 Hempstead Tpke, East Meadow, NY 11554
Tel.: (516) 296-9671
Web Site: http://www.lufthansa.com
Sales Range: $25-49.9 Million
Emp.: 100
Passenger Air Transportation Services
N.A.I.C.S.: 481111
Nils Haupt (Dir-Corp Comm)

Subsidiary (Non-US):

Delvag Luftfahrtversicherungs-AG (3)
Von-Gablenz-Strasse 2-6, 50679, Cologne, Germany
Tel.: (49) 221 8292 001
Web Site: http://www.delvag.de
Sales Range: $75-99.9 Million
Insurance Management Services
N.A.I.C.S.: 524298
Roland Kern (Exec VP)

Lufthansa AirPlus Servicekarten GmbH (1)
Dornhofstrasse 10, 63263, Neu-Isenburg, Germany
Tel.: (49) 6 102 2040
Web Site: https://www.airplus.com
Travel Payment Data Management Services
N.A.I.C.S.: 518210
Andreas Hagenbring (Mng Dir)

Subsidiary (Non-US):

AirPlus Air Travel Card Vertriebsgesellschaft mbH (2)
Rainergasse 1, 1041, Vienna, Austria
Tel.: (43) 1 50 135 0
Sales Range: $25-49.9 Million
Emp.: 80
Tour Operating Services
N.A.I.C.S.: 561520
Wolfgang Schneider (Gen Mgr)

AirPlus Holding GmbH (2)
Rainergasse 1, Vienna, 1041, Austria
Tel.: (43) 150135
Sales Range: $50-74.9 Million
Emp.: 75
Investment Management Service
N.A.I.C.S.: 523999
Hanno Kirsch (Gen Mgr)

AirPlus International Limited (2)
Building 4 Chiswick Park 566 Chiswick High Road, London, W4 5YE, United Kingdom
Tel.: (44) 20 8994 4725
Web Site: http://www.airplus.com
Sales Range: $25-49.9 Million
Travel Payment Management Services
N.A.I.C.S.: 522320

AirPlus International S.r.l. (2)
Via Della Salute 14/2, Bologna, Italy
Tel.: (39) 051 64 15.416
Travel Management Services
N.A.I.C.S.: 561510

Subsidiary (US):

AirPlus International, Inc. (2)
225 Reinekers Ln Ste 500, Alexandria, VA 22314
Tel.: (703) 373-0940
Web Site: http://www.airplus.com
Sales Range: $50-74.9 Million
Travel Payment Processing Services
N.A.I.C.S.: 522320
Andreas Hagenbring (CFO)

Lufthansa Aviation Training Austria GmbH (1)
Austrian Airlines Base, 1300, Vienna, Austria
Tel.: (43) 5176676613
Flight Operating Services
N.A.I.C.S.: 611512

Lufthansa Aviation Training GmbH (1)
Suedallee 15 FOC 4th floor, 85356, Munich, Germany
Tel.: (49) 89 977 5060
Web Site: https://www.lufthansa-aviation-training.com
Aviation Training Services
N.A.I.C.S.: 611512
Ola Hansson (Gen Mgr)

Subsidiary (Domestic):

Aviation Quality Services GmbH (2)
Main Airport Center Unterschweinstiege 10, 60549, Frankfurt am Main, Germany
Tel.: (49) 69 696 81739
Web Site: http://www.aviation-quality-services.com
Aviation Management Consulting Services
N.A.I.C.S.: 541618
Patrick Lutz (CEO & Mng Dir)

Lufthansa Aviation Training Berlin GmbH (2)
Schutzenstrasse 10, 12526, Berlin, Germany
Tel.: (49) 3088755700
Flight Operating Services
N.A.I.C.S.: 611512
Stefan Wendrich (Mng Dir)

Lufthansa Aviation Training Crew Academy GmbH (2)
Lilienthalstrasse 6, 12529, Schonefeld, Germany
Tel.: (49) 3062640916
Web Site: http://www.crewacademy.de
Safety & Emergency Training Services
N.A.I.C.S.: 611699
Andrea Resch (Mng Dir)

Lufthansa Aviation Training Germany GmbH (2)
Airportring Gate 24 Building 391 and 392, 60549, Frankfurt am Main, Germany
Tel.: (49) 6969672444
Flight Operating Services
N.A.I.C.S.: 611512

Subsidiary (Non-US):

Lufthansa Flight Training Vienna GmbH (2)
Austrian Airlines Basis Vienna Airport, 1300, Vienna, Austria
Tel.: (43) 1 7007 361 06
Web Site: http://www.lufthansa-flight-training.com
Sales Range: $10-24.9 Million
Emp.: 13
Flight Training Services
N.A.I.C.S.: 611512

Subsidiary (Domestic):

Pilot Training Network GmbH (2)
Airportring Gate 24 Bldg 392, Frankfurt am Main, 60549, Germany
Tel.: (49) 69 696 96290
Web Site: http://www.pilottraining-network.de

Sales Range: $10-24.9 Million
Emp.: 38
Flight Training Services
N.A.I.C.S.: 611512
Holger Hoffmann (Co-Mng Dir)

Lufthansa Aviation Training Operations Germany GmbH (1)
Schutzenstrasse 10, 12526, Berlin, Germany
Tel.: (49) 3088755700
Flight Operating Services
N.A.I.C.S.: 611512

Lufthansa Aviation Training USA Inc. (1)
1658 S Litchfield Rd, Goodyear, AZ 85338
Tel.: (623) 932-1600
Web Site: http://www.lufthansa-aviation-training-usa.com
Flight Operating Services
N.A.I.C.S.: 611512

Lufthansa Cargo AG (1)
Frankfurt Airport Gate 21 Building 322, 60546, Frankfurt am Main, Germany
Tel.: (49) 696960
Web Site: https://www.lufthansa-cargo.com
Emp.: 4,210
Freight Air Transportation Services
N.A.I.C.S.: 481112
Jurgen Jennerke (Vice Chm-Supervisory Bd)

Subsidiary (Domestic):

Jettainer GmbH (2)
Am Prime Parc 17, 65479, Raunheim, Germany
Tel.: (49) 61 421 7700
Web Site: https://www.jettainer.com
Sales Range: $10-24.9 Million
Unit Load Device Management Consulting Services
N.A.I.C.S.: 541690
Ingeborg Manz Maier (CFO & Member-Mgmt Bd)

Subsidiary (US):

Lufthansa Cargo (2)
Bldg 23, Jamaica, NY 11430
Tel.: (718) 289-7259
Sales Range: $25-49.9 Million
Emp.: 100
Freight Air Transportation Services
N.A.I.C.S.: 481112
Karl Ulrich Garnadt (Chm-Supervisory Bd & CEO)

Lufthansa Cargo (2)
05721 W Imperial Hwy, Los Angeles, CA 90045
Tel.: (310) 242-2590
Web Site: http://www.lufthansa-cargo.com
Sales Range: $25-49.9 Million
Freight Air Transportation Services
N.A.I.C.S.: 481112
Dorothea von Boxberg (Chm-Exec Bd, CEO & CFO)

Subsidiary (Non-US):

Lufthansa Cargo India (Priv) Ltd. (2)
2nd Floor 55 J L Nehru Road, Kolkata, 700 071, West Bengal, India
Tel.: (91) 3322821812
Air Cargo Handling Services
N.A.I.C.S.: 488119

Subsidiary (Domestic):

Lufthansa Leasing GmbH & Co. Echo-Zulu oHG (2)
Tolzer Str 15, Grunwald, 82031, Germany
Tel.: (49) 89 641430
Aircraft Leasing Services
N.A.I.C.S.: 532411

Lufthansa City Center International GmbH (1)
Lyoner Strasse 36, 60528, Frankfurt am Main, Germany
Tel.: (49) 6966075300
Web Site: http://www.lufthansa-city-center.com
Travel Management Services
N.A.I.C.S.: 561510

Lufthansa CityLine GmbH (1)
Waldstreet 247, Cologne Airport, 51147,

Cologne, Germany **(100%)**
Tel.: (49) 2203 596 0
Web Site: http://www.lufthansacityline.com
Sales Range: $650-699.9 Million
Emp.: 2,301
Regional Passenger Air Transportation Services
N.A.I.C.S.: 481111
Jorg Eberhart *(Member-Exec Bd)*

Lufthansa Commercial Holding GmbH **(1)**
Von Gablenz St 26, 50679, Cologne, Germany **(100%)**
Tel.: (49) 2218262242
Holding Company
N.A.I.C.S.: 551112

Subsidiary (Non-US):

Airline Accounting Center Sp. z o.o **(2)**
Al Pokoju 78, 31-564, Krakow, Poland
Tel.: (48) 12 6460 801
Web Site: http://www.airline-accounting-center.com
Sales Range: $50-74.9 Million
Emp.: 200
Airline Accounting & Administrative Services
N.A.I.C.S.: 488119

Airline Accounting Center de Mexico S.A. de C.V. **(2)**
Avenida Ejercito Nacional 418 Piso 11, 11570, Mexico, Mexico
Tel.: (52) 55 52 54 83 00
Web Site: http://www.airline-accounting-center.com
Sales Range: $25-49.9 Million
Emp.: 170
Airline Accounting Services
N.A.I.C.S.: 541219

Global Tele Sales (PTY) Ltd. **(2)**
9th Floor Picbel Parkade, Cape Town, 8001, South Africa
Tel.: (27) 214153526
Web Site: http://www.lh-intouch.com
Customer Care Services
N.A.I.C.S.: 561421
Will Schnabel *(Mng Dir)*

Global Tele Sales Brno s.r.o. **(2)**
Spielberk Office Centre Holandska 1, 639 00, Brno, Czech Republic
Tel.: (420) 515 503 100
Web Site: http://www.globaltelesales.cz
Sales Range: $25-49.9 Million
Flight Reservation Services
N.A.I.C.S.: 561599
Roman Tesar *(Mgr-Site Ops-Brno)*

Global Tele Sales Pty Limited **(2)**
Level 2 600 Collins Street, Melbourne, 3000, VIC, Australia
Tel.: (61) 386236051
Web Site: http://www.globaltelesales.com.au
Sales Range: $25-49.9 Million
Emp.: 100
Airline Call Center Services
N.A.I.C.S.: 561421

Global Telesales of Canada, Inc. **(2)**
1900 Fisher Drive, Peterborough, K9J 6X6, ON, Canada
Tel.: (705) 872-3021
Web Site: http://www.globaltelesales.ca
Sales Range: $25-49.9 Million
Emp.: 23
Flight Reservation Services
N.A.I.C.S.: 561599

Subsidiary (Domestic):

LRS Lufthansa Revenue Services GmbH **(2)**
Schutzenwall 1, Norderstedt, 22844, Germany
Tel.: (49) 40 5070 7303
Web Site: http://www.revenue-accounting.com
Sales Range: $150-199.9 Million
Emp.: 450
Revenue Accounting Services
N.A.I.C.S.: 522320
Reinhard Schafer *(Mng Dir)*

Lufthansa Consulting GmbH **(1)**
Von-Gablenz-Str 2-6, 50679, Cologne, Germany

Tel.: (49) 221 826 8109
Web Site: http://www.lhconsulting.com
Sales Range: $25-49.9 Million
Emp.: 90
Aviation Management Consulting Services
N.A.I.C.S.: 541690
Andreas Jahnke *(Mng Dir)*

Lufthansa Global Tele Sales GmbH **(1)**
Rudower Chaussee 12, 12489, Berlin, Germany
Tel.: (49) 30 50 57 01 00
Airline Travel Information Services
N.A.I.C.S.: 519290

Lufthansa Industry Solutions GmbH & Co. KG. **(1)**
Schutzenwall 1, 22844, Norderstedt, Germany
Tel.: (49) 4050 703 0000
Web Site: https://www.lufthansa-industry-solutions.com
Travel Management Services
N.A.I.C.S.: 561510
Bernd Appel *(Chm & Mng Dir)*

Lufthansa Innovation Hub GmbH **(1)**
Rosenthaler Str 32, 10178, Berlin, Germany
Tel.: (49) 305 524 2831
Web Site: http://www.lh-innovationhub.de
Research & Development Services
N.A.I.C.S.: 541713
Gleb Tritus *(Mng Dir)*

Lufthansa Leasing GmbH **(1)**
Tolzer Strasse 15, 82031, Grunwald, Germany **(49%)**
Tel.: (49) 8964143203
Emp.: 10
Aircraft Leasing Services
N.A.I.C.S.: 532411
Jochen Horger *(Mng Dir)*

Lufthansa Malta Pension Holding Ltd. **(1)**
Ana Capri Court Spinola Road, San Giljan, STJ 3012, Malta
Tel.: (356) 2010 7411
Web Site: http://www.lmp.com.mt
Investment Management Service
N.A.I.C.S.: 523999

Lufthansa Process Management GmbH **(1)**
Dornhofstrasse 34, 63263, Neu-Isenburg, Germany
Tel.: (49) 696 969 0885
Web Site: https://www.lpm-services.com
Emp.: 60
Revenue Management Services
N.A.I.C.S.: 561110
Harald Heichele *(Mng Dir)*

Lufthansa Seeheim GmbH **(1)**
Lufthansaring 1, 64342, Seeheim-Jugenheim, Germany
Tel.: (49) 6969 613 1000
Web Site: https://www.lh-seeheim.de
Hotel Services
N.A.I.C.S.: 721110
Fabian Balduf *(Mgr-Convention Sls)*

Lufthansa Services (Thailand) Ltd. **(1)**
Suvarnabhumi International Airport Room A4-091a 4th Floor 999 Moo 1, Bangna-Trad Rachathewa, Bang Phli, 10540, Samutprakarn, Thailand
Tel.: (66) 2 134 2210
Web Site: http://www.lst-thailand.com
Airport Ground Handling Services
N.A.I.C.S.: 488119

Lufthansa Shenzhen Management Company Limited **(1)**
Logistics Building Shenzhen Airport, Shenzhen, 518128, China
Tel.: (86) 75527771469
Sales Range: $25-49.9 Million
Emp.: 100
Air Cargo Handling Services
N.A.I.C.S.: 481112

Lufthansa Systems AG **(1)**
Am Messeplatz 1, 65479, Raunheim, Germany **(100%)**
Tel.: (49) 6969690000
Web Site: http://www.lhsystems.de

Sales Range: $800-899.9 Million
Information Technology Consulting & Support Services
N.A.I.C.S.: 541519

Subsidiary (Domestic):

Cargo Future Communications (CFC) GmbH **(2)**
Gebaude 1335, Hahn-Flughafen, 55483, Buchenbeuren, Germany
Tel.: (49) 65 43 983 103
Web Site: http://www.cfc-callcenter.de
Airline Call Center Services
N.A.I.C.S.: 561421
Christian Rothkirch *(Mng Dir)*

Lufthansa Systems AS GmbH **(2)**
Schutzenwall 1, Norderstedt, 22844, Germany
Tel.: (49) 4050707086
Web Site: http://www.lhsystems.com
Emp.: 1,000
Information Technology Consulting Services
N.A.I.C.S.: 541512
Bernd Appel *(Gen Mgr)*

Subsidiary (US):

Lufthansa Systems Americas, Inc. **(2)**
800 Brickell Ave Ste 1500, Miami, FL 33131
Tel.: (305) 423-6879
Web Site: http://www.lhsystems.com
Airline Software Development Services
N.A.I.C.S.: 541511

Subsidiary (Non-US):

Lufthansa Systems Asia Pacific Pte. Ltd. **(2)**
390 Orchard Road 07-03/04 Palais Renaissance Orchard, Singapore, 238871, Singapore
Tel.: (65) 65141330
Information Technology Consulting Services
N.A.I.C.S.: 541512
Olivier Krueger *(CEO)*

Subsidiary (Domestic):

Lufthansa Systems Berlin GmbH **(2)**
Salzufer 8, 10585, Berlin, Germany
Tel.: (49) 30 34 00 72 00
Web Site: http://www.lhsystems.com
Emp.: 200
Data Processing Services
N.A.I.C.S.: 518210

Lufthansa Systems Business Solutions GmbH **(2)**
Am Prime-Parc 1, Raunheim, 65479, Germany
Tel.: (49) 6969690000
Web Site: http://www.lufthansasystems.com
Information Technology Consulting Services
N.A.I.C.S.: 541512
Stefan Auerbach *(Dir)*

Subsidiary (Non-US):

Lufthansa Systems FlightNav AG **(2)**
Stelzenstrasse 6, Opfikon, 8152, Zurich, Switzerland
Tel.: (41) 448286511
Aviation Information Technology Consulting Services
N.A.I.C.S.: 541512

Lufthansa Systems Hungaria Kft **(2)**
Infopark Building E Neumann Janos u 1/E, 1117, Budapest, Hungary
Tel.: (36) 1 8824 900
Sales Range: $75-99.9 Million
Emp.: 50
Information Technology Consulting Services
N.A.I.C.S.: 541512

Subsidiary (Domestic):

Lufthansa Systems IS Consulting GmbH **(2)**
Schutzenwall 1, Norderstedt, 22844, Germany
Tel.: (49) 40 507060666
Web Site: http://www.ibmduetchland.de
Information Technology Consulting Services
N.A.I.C.S.: 541512
Pardo Buerlum *(Gen Mgr)*

Lufthansa Systems Network GmbH **(2)**
Schutzenwall 1, Norderstedt, Germany
Tel.: (49) 40507060666
Emp.: 5
Information Technology Consulting Services
N.A.I.C.S.: 541512

Lufthansa Systems Network Services GmbH **(2)**
Schutzenwall 1, Norderstedt, 22844, Germany
Tel.: (49) 40507060666
Information Technology Consulting Services
N.A.I.C.S.: 541512
Pardo Werum *(Gen Mgr)*

Lufthansa Systems Passenger Services GmbH **(2)**
Am Weiher 24, 65451, Kelsterbach, Hesse, Germany
Tel.: (49) 69 69690000
Airline Ticket Management Services
N.A.I.C.S.: 561599

Subsidiary (Non-US):

Lufthansa Systems Poland Sp. z o.o. **(2)**
Ul Dlugie Ogrody 8, 80-765, Gdansk, Poland
Tel.: (48) 58 3265 400
Information Technology Consulting Services
N.A.I.C.S.: 541512

Subsidiary (US):

Maptext, Inc. **(2)**
1060 State Rd Ste 101, Princeton, NJ 08540
Tel.: (732) 940-7100
Web Site: http://www.maptext.com
Emp.: 12
Software Development Services
N.A.I.C.S.: 541511
Jarek Malecki *(CEO)*

Lufthansa Technical Training GmbH **(1)**
Unterschweinstiege 12, 60549, Frankfurt am Main, Germany
Tel.: (49) 6969633840
Web Site: http://www.ltt.aero
Sales Range: $50-74.9 Million
Aviation Technology Training Services
N.A.I.C.S.: 611512
Rubin Siddique *(CEO & Chief Comml Officer)*

Lufthansa Technik AG **(1)**
Weg Beim Jaeger 193, 22335, Hamburg, Germany **(100%)**
Tel.: (49) 4050700
Web Site: http://www.lufthansa-technik.com
Sales Range: $5-14.9 Billion
Emp.: 20,300
Aircraft Maintenance, Repair & Overhaul Services
N.A.I.C.S.: 488190
Thomas Stuger *(Member-Mgmt Bd)*

Joint Venture (Non-US):

Aircraft Maintenance & Engineering Corp. **(2)**
Beijing Capital International Airport, Beijing, 100621, China
Tel.: (86) 10645611224
Web Site: http://www.ameco.com.cn
Sales Range: $800-899.9 Million
Aircraft Maintenance, Repair & Overhaul Services; Owned 60% by China National Aviation Holding Company & 40% by Deutsche Lufthansa AG
N.A.I.C.S.: 488190
Sun Wei *(Reg Dir)*

Subsidiary (US):

BizJet International Sales & Support, Inc. **(2)**
3515 N Sheridan Rd, Tulsa, OK 74115
Tel.: (918) 832-7733
Web Site: http://www.bizjet.com
Sales Range: $75-99.9 Million
Emp.: 230
Aircraft Engine Repair & Maintenance Services
N.A.I.C.S.: 811114

Deutsche Lufthansa AG—(Continued)

Jennifer Hoffman *(Dir-Engine Sls & Mktg)*

Subsidiary (Domestic):

Hamburger Gesellschaft fur Flughafenanlagen mbH (2)
Sportallee 54b, 22335, Hamburg, Germany
Tel.: (49) 4050703081
Emp.: 4
Aircraft Equipment Leasing Services
N.A.I.C.S.: 532411
Ralf Aljes *(Mng Dir)*

Subsidiary (US):

Hawker Pacific Aerospace (2)
11240 Sherman Way, Sun Valley, CA
91352-4942 **(72.7%)**
Tel.: (818) 765-6201
Web Site: http://www.hawker.com
Sales Range: $150-199.9 Million
Emp.: 350
Aircraft Repair & Overhaul Services & Parts
N.A.I.C.S.: 488519
Martin Martinez *(Mgr-Machining Production)*

Subsidiary (Domestic):

Lufthansa Engineering and Operational Services GmbH (2)
Lufthansa Basis, 60546, Frankfurt am Main, Germany
Tel.: (49) 696968222
Web Site: https://www.lufthansa-leos.com
Sales Range: $100-124.9 Million
Airport Ground Handling Services
N.A.I.C.S.: 488119

Lufthansa Technik AERO Alzey GmbH (2)
Rudolf-Diesel-Strasse 10, 55232, Alzey, Germany
Tel.: (49) 6 731 4970
Web Site: https://www.lhaero.com
Aircraft Repair & Maintenance Services
N.A.I.C.S.: 811198
Mark Johnson *(CEO)*

Subsidiary (Non-US):

Lufthansa Technik Airmotive Ireland Holdings Ltd. (2)
Naas Rd, Rathcoole, Dublin, Ireland
Tel.: (353) 1 4011111
Investment Management Service
N.A.I.C.S.: 523999

Lufthansa Technik Airmotive Ireland Leasing Ltd (2)
Naas Rd, Rathcoole, Dublin, Ireland
Tel.: (353) 14011111
Sales Range: $150-199.9 Million
Emp.: 480
Automobile Leasing Services
N.A.I.C.S.: 522220

Lufthansa Technik Airmotive Ireland Ltd. (2)
Naas Road, Rathcoole, Dublin, Ireland
Tel.: (353) 1 401 1111
Web Site:
  http://www.lufthansatechnikairmotive.com
Sales Range: $75-99.9 Million
Emp.: 480
Aircraft Repair & Maintenance Services
N.A.I.C.S.: 811198

Lufthansa Technik Brussels N.V. (2)
Vliegveld 117 D, Melsbroek, 1820, Steenokkerzeel, Belgium
Tel.: (32) 2 752 8660
Sales Range: $25-49.9 Million
Emp.: 85
Aircraft Repair & Maintenance Services
N.A.I.C.S.: 811198
Christoph Plaha *(Gen Mgr)*

Subsidiary (US):

Lufthansa Technik Component Services LLC
11240 Sherman Way, Sun Valley, CA 91352
Tel.: (818) 765-6201
Sales Range: $25-49.9 Million
Emp.: 70
Aircraft Component Repair & Maintenance Services
N.A.I.C.S.: 811198

Subsidiary (Domestic):

Lufthansa Technik Immobilien- und Verwaltungsgesellschaft mbH (2)
Sportallee 54b, Hamburg, 22335, Germany
Tel.: (49) 4050700
Property Management Services
N.A.I.C.S.: 531311
August-Wilhelm Henningsen *(Mng Dir)*

Subsidiary (US):

Lufthansa Technik Logistik of America LLC (2)
Cargo Bldg 23 N Door 3738, Jamaica, NY 11430
Tel.: (718) 289-7272
Sales Range: $25-49.9 Million
Emp.: 14
Freight Transportation Services
N.A.I.C.S.: 488510
Stephen Fondell *(Mng Dir)*

Subsidiary (Domestic):

Lufthansa Technik Maintenance International GmbH (2)
Frankfurt International Airport South, Frankfurt, 60549, Germany
Tel.: (49) 69 696 69660
Aircraft Repair & Maintenance Services
N.A.I.C.S.: 811198

Lufthansa Technik Objekt- und Verwaltungsgesellschaft mbH (2)
Sportallee 54b, Hamburg, 22335, Germany
Tel.: (49) 40 50700
Web Site: http://www.Lufthansa.com
Property Management Services
N.A.I.C.S.: 531312

Subsidiary (Non-US):

Lufthansa Technik Services India Private Limited (2)
Menzies Aviation Bobba Cargo Ter New Bangalore International Airport, Devanahalli, 560 300, Bengaluru, India
Tel.: (91) 22 3953 7405
Aircraft Repair & Maintenance Services
N.A.I.C.S.: 811198

Lufthansa Technik Switzerland GmbH (2)
C/O Kilian Wunder Steinenschanze 6, 4002, Basel, Switzerland
Tel.: (41) 61 568 3000
Web Site: http://www.lht-switzerland.com
Aircraft Repair & Maintenance Services
N.A.I.C.S.: 811198

Lufthansa Technik Turbine Shannon Limited (2)
World Aviation Park, Shannon, Co Clare, Ireland
Tel.: (353) 6 136 0512
Web Site: https://www.ltts.ie
Sales Range: $25-49.9 Million
Emp.: 200
Aircraft Engine Component Repair Services
N.A.I.C.S.: 811121
Brendan Roche *(Mgr-Quality)*

Shannon Aerospace Ltd. (2)
Shannon Airport, Shannon, Co Clare, Ireland **(100%)**
Tel.: (353) 61370000
Web Site:
  http://www.shannonaerospace.com
Sales Range: $200-249.9 Million
Emp.: 700
Aircraft Maintenance, Repair & Overhaul Services
N.A.I.C.S.: 488190

Lufthansa Technik Logistik Services GmbH (1)
Weg beim Jaeger 193, 22335, Hamburg, Germany
Tel.: (49) 405 0700
Web Site: https://www.ltls.aero
Emp.: 1,700
Logistics Transportation Services
N.A.I.C.S.: 488510
Andreas Tielmann *(Mng Dir)*

Lufthansa Technik Philippines Inc. (1)
MacroAsia Special Economic Zone Villamor

Air Base, Pasay, 1309, Philippines
Tel.: (63) 28 855 9122
Web Site: https://www.lht-philippines.com
Emp.: 3,000
Aircraft Maintenance & Overhaul Services
N.A.I.C.S.: 488190
Elmar Lutter *(Pres & CEO)*

Lufthansa Technik Puerto Rico LLC (1)
PO Box 797, San Antonio, PR 00690-0797
Tel.: (787) 230-7700
Web Site: http://www.lht-puertorico.com
Emp.: 400
Aircraft Maintenance & Overhaul Services
N.A.I.C.S.: 488190
Pat Foley *(Founder & Head-Bus Dev-Aircraft Maintenance Svcs-Americas)*

Lufthansa Training & Conference Center GmbH (1)
Lufthansaring 1, 64342, Seeheim-Jugenheim, Germany
Tel.: (49) 6969 613 1000
Web Site: https://www.lh-seeheim.de
Sales Range: $50-74.9 Million
Emp.: 27
Conference Hotel Operating Services
N.A.I.C.S.: 721110
Robert Barte *(Dir-Ops, Food & Beverage)*

Lufthansa WorldShop GmbH (1)
MAC Main Airport Center Unterschweinstiege 8, 60549, Frankfurt, Germany
Tel.: (49) 69478689180
Web Site: http://www.worldshop.eu
Consumer Products Whslr
N.A.I.C.S.: 423620

Miles & More International GmbH (1)
MAC Main Airport Center Unterschweinstiege 8, 60539, Frankfurt am Main, Germany
Tel.: (49) 69719168159
Web Site: http://www.miles-and-more.com
Advertising Agency Services
N.A.I.C.S.: 541810
Sebastian Riddle *(Mng Dir)*

Passage Services Holding GmbH (1)
Terminalstrasse Sud 1, Munich, 85325, Germany
Tel.: (49) 8997572001
Web Site: http://www.lufthansa.com
Investment Management Service
N.A.I.C.S.: 523999
Udo Janurek *(VP)*

Reservation Data Maintenance India Private Ltd. (1)
E-9 Connaught House Connaught Place, New Delhi, 110 001, India
Tel.: (91) 1123412313
Web Site: http://www.rdm.co.in
Emp.: 700
Outsourcing Services
N.A.I.C.S.: 541219

Retail In Motion Mexico S. de R.L. de C.V. (1)
Francisco Sarabia Penon De Los Banos, Venustiano Carranza, 15700, Mexico, Mexico
Tel.: (52) 5551336200
Web Site: https://www.rimmexico.com
Individual & Family Services
N.A.I.C.S.: 624190

Retail in Motion Limited (1)
Hangar 57 Blackthorn Road, Sandyford Business Park, Dublin, Ireland
Tel.: (353) 14451212
Web Site: https://www.retailinmotion.com
Emp.: 165
Aircraft Product Distr
N.A.I.C.S.: 423860

Star Risk Services Inc. (1)
536 Silicon Dr Ste 103, Southlake, TX 76092
Tel.: (817) 552-6207
Web Site: http://www.starrisk.com
Sales Range: $50-74.9 Million
Emp.: 4
General Insurance Services
N.A.I.C.S.: 524210
Martin Schmaz *(Mng Dir)*

Swiss International Air Lines AG (1)
Malzgasse 15, CH-4052, Basel, Switzerland
Tel.: (41) 435479919
Web Site: https://www.swiss.com
Sales Range: $1-4.9 Billion
Emp.: 6,026
Passenger Air Transportation Services
N.A.I.C.S.: 481111
Harry Hohmeister *(?)*

Subsidiary (Domestic):

Edelweiss Air AG (2)
Airport Kloten, 8058, Zurich, Switzerland
Tel.: (41) 84 833 3593
Wob Site: http://www.flyedelweiss.com
Sales Range: $400-449.9 Million
Emp.: 1,026
Airline
N.A.I.C.S.: 481111
Markus Gander *(Chief Product Officer & Member-Mgmt Bd)*

Swiss Aviation Software AG (2)
Lachenstrasse 18, 4123, Allschwil, Switzerland
Tel.: (41) 61 582 3032
Web Site: https://www.swiss-as.com
Sales Range: $25-49.9 Million
Emp.: 230
Aviation Maintenance Software Development Services
N.A.I.C.S.: 541511
Ronald Schauffele Scherer *(CEO)*

Swiss European Air Lines AG (2)
Zurich Airport, 8058, Zurich, Switzerland
Tel.: (41) 445640000
Web Site: http://www.swiss.com
Sales Range: $50-74.9 Million
Emp.: 233
Airline Transportation Services
N.A.I.C.S.: 488190

Subsidiary (Non-US):

Swiss WorldCargo (India) Private Limited (2)
501 Solitaire Corporate Park 167 Guru Hargovindji Marg, Andheri East, Mumbai, 400 093, India
Tel.: (91) 22 6177 4687
Sales Range: $25-49.9 Million
Emp.: 8
General Airfreight Cargo Handling Services
N.A.I.C.S.: 488119
Shankar Iyer *(Reg Mgr)*

Swiss Private Aviation AG (1)
Obstgartenstrasse 25, Kloten, 8302, Zurich, Switzerland
Tel.: (41) 43 255 50 70
Web Site: http://www.swiss-private-aviation.com
Aircraft Management & Flight Chartering Services
N.A.I.C.S.: 488119

TATS - Travel Agency Technologies & Services GmbH (1)
Hahnstrasse 70, Frankfurt am Main, 660528, Germany
Tel.: (49) 6966377150
Sales Range: $25-49.9 Million
Emp.: 50
Travel Agency Data Processing Services
N.A.I.C.S.: 518210
Rainer Burghardt *(Gen Mgr)*

TRAINICO Training und Ausbildung Cooperation in Berlin Brandenburg GmbH (1)
Schutzenstrasse 10, 12526, Berlin, Germany
Tel.: (49) 30 8875 5050
Staffing Agency & Technical Training Services
N.A.I.C.S.: 561311

TRAVIAUSTRIA Datenservice fur Reise und Touristik Gesellschaft m.b.H. & Co NFG. KG (1)
Dresdner Strasse 81 - 85, 1200, Vienna, Austria
Tel.: (43) 1 33733 0
Web Site: http://www.travi.com
Sales Range: $25-49.9 Million
Emp.: 65
Travel Agencies

N.A.I.C.S.: 561510
Rudolf Mertl *(Mng Dir)*

Time Matters GmbH **(1)**
Gutenbergstr 6, 63263, Neu-Isenburg, Germany
Tel.: (49) 61023 673 8800
Web Site: https://www.time-matters.com
Emp.: 330
Logistics Transportation Services
N.A.I.C.S.: 488510
Alexander Kohnen *(CEO)*

TraviAustria GmbH **(1)**
Dresdner Str 81-85, 1200, Vienna, Austria
Tel.: (43) 1 33733 0
Web Site: http://www.traviaustria.com
Sales Range: $50-74.9 Million
Emp.: 50
Travel Services
N.A.I.C.S.: 721199
Rudolf Mertl *(Mng Dir)*

XEOS Sp. z o.o. **(1)**
Swiete ul Innowacji 2, 55-300, Sroda Slaska, Poland
Tel.: (48) 71 716 5858
Web Site: https://www.xeos.aero
Emp.: 600
Aircraft Mfr
N.A.I.C.S.: 336411
Sebastian Froehlich *(Head-Engrg)*

Yilu Travel Services GmbH **(1)**
Gormannstr 14, 10119, Berlin, Germany
Tel.: (49) 1759702590
Web Site: http://www.yiluhub.com
Travel Management Services
N.A.I.C.S.: 561510
Sascha Erwin Gunther *(Mng Dir)*

ZeroG GmbH **(1)**
Am Messeplatz 1, 65479, Raunheim, Germany
Tel.: (49) 696 966 6666
Web Site: https://www.zerog.aero
Travel Management Services
N.A.I.C.S.: 561510
Peter Ahnert *(Mng Dir)*

DEUTSCHE MESSE AG
Messegelande, 30521, Hannover, Germany
Tel.: (49) 511 89 0
Web Site: http://www.messe.de
Year Founded: 1947
Sales Range: $350-399.9 Million
Emp.: 930
Trade Shows, Events & Conventions
N.A.I.C.S.: 561920
Andreas Gruchow *(Member-Mgmt Bd)*

Subsidiaries:

Deutsche Messe Interactive GmbH **(1)**
Lister Strasse 15, 30163, Hannover, Germany
Tel.: (49) 511 330 60 111
Web Site: http://www.messe-interactive.de
Trade Fair Management Services
N.A.I.C.S.: 561920
Eric Berger *(CEO)*

HANNOVER FAIRS DO BRASIL S/C LTDA **(1)**
Herr Constantino Baumle Av 7 de Setembro 5890, 80240-001, Curitiba, Brazil
Tel.: (55) 41 30 27 67 07
Web Site: http://www.hf-brazil.com
Trade Fair Management Services
N.A.I.C.S.: 561920

HANNOVERMASSANS SVERIGEKONTOR AB **(1)**
Herr Nils Fickler Frau Helga Sandstrom, Enhagsslingan 3, 1874, Taby, Sweden
Tel.: (46) 8 6 11 44 06
Web Site: http://www.hf-sweden.com
Trade Fair Management Services
N.A.I.C.S.: 561920

Hannover Consultancy B.V. **(1)**
Westeinde 18b, 2969 BL, Oud-Alblas, Netherlands
Tel.: (31) 184 69 30 50

Web Site:
http://www.hannoverconsultancy.nl
Trade Fair Management Services
N.A.I.C.S.: 561920
Victor Koppelaar *(Mng Dir)*

Hannover Fairs Australia Pty. Ltd. **(1)**
Level 11 60 Pitt Street, Sydney, 2000, NSW, Australia
Tel.: (61) 2 9280 3400
Web Site: http://www.cebit.com.au
Trade Fair Management Services
N.A.I.C.S.: 561920
Ana Moreno *(Dir-Ops)*

Hannover Fairs Turkey Fuarcilik A.S. **(1)**
Buyukdere Cad Sarli is Merkezi No 103 B Blok Kat 2-5-6, Mecidiyekoy, 34394, Istanbul, Turkiye
Tel.: (90) 2123346900
Web Site: http://www.hmist.com.tr
Trade Fair Management Services
N.A.I.C.S.: 561920
Alexander Kuhnel *(Gen Mgr)*

Hannover Fairs USA Inc. **(1)**
2 Research Way, Princeton, NJ 08540
Tel.: (609) 987-1202
Web Site: http://www.hfusa.com
Trade Show & Event Management & Marketing
N.A.I.C.S.: 561920
Larry Turner *(Pres & CEO)*

Hannover Milano Fairs China Ltd. **(1)**
Room 1106 Golden Gate Commercial Building 136-138 Austin Road, Tsim Sha Tsui, Kowloon, China (Hong Kong)
Tel.: (852) 35292053
Web Site: http://www.hmf-china.com
Trade Fair Management Services
N.A.I.C.S.: 561920
Fiona Song *(Sr Project Mgr)*

Hannover Milano Fairs India Pvt. Ltd. **(1)**
B-102 Business Square Off Solitaire Corporate Park, 1st floor Chakala Andheri, Mumbai, 400093, India
Tel.: (91) 22 66875500
Web Site: http://www.hmf-india.com
Emp.: 65
Trade Fair Management Services
N.A.I.C.S.: 561920
Mehul Lanvers Shah *(Mng Dir)*

Hannover Milano Fairs Shanghai Ltd. **(1)**
Rm 301 B&Q Pudong Office Tower 393 Yinxiao Rd, Pudong, Shanghai, 201204, China
Tel.: (86) 21 5045 6700
Trade Fair Management Services
N.A.I.C.S.: 561920
Sarah Shui *(Project Mgr)*

OOO Deutsche Messe RUS **(1)**
Bolshoy Patriarshiy Per 6 bld 1, Moscow, 123001, Russia
Tel.: (7) 495 6694646
Web Site: http://www.messe-russia.ru
Emp.: 10
Trade Fair Management Services
N.A.I.C.S.: 561920
Marina Ivkina *(Dir-Show)*

event it AG **(1)**
Pelikanplatz 7-9, 30177, Hannover, Germany
Tel.: (49) 511 866 846 0
Web Site: http://www.eventit.de
Emp.: 80
Trade Fair Management Services
N.A.I.C.S.: 561920

spring Messe Management GmbH **(1)**
Guterhallenstrasse 18a, 68159, Mannheim, Germany
Tel.: (49) 621 70019 0
Web Site: http://www.messe.org
Emp.: 60
Trade Fair Management Services
N.A.I.C.S.: 561920
Ralf Hocke *(Founder, CEO & Mng Dir)*

DEUTSCHE MITTELSTANDSHOLDING GMBH

Guiollettstr. 19, D-60325, Frankfurt am Main, Germany
Tel.: (49) 69 94597814
Web Site:
http://www.deutschemittelstand.de
Privater Equity Firm
N.A.I.C.S.: 523999
Holger Buetzler *(Mng Dir)*

Subsidiaries:

Pluradent AG & Co. KG **(1)**
Kaiserleistr 3, 63067, Offenbach, Germany
Tel.: (49) 69829830
Web Site: http://www.pluradent.de
Sales Range: $350-399.9 Million
Emp.: 1,200
Dental Equipment
N.A.I.C.S.: 423450

DEUTSCHE NICKEL GMBH
Rosenweg 15, 58239, Schwerte, Germany
Tel.: (49) 23041080 RI
Web Site: http://www.deutsche-nickel.de
Emp.: 100
Provider of Metals Services
N.A.I.C.S.: 332812
Christoph Arntz *(Co-Mng Dir)*

Subsidiaries:

Deutsche Nickel America Inc. **(1)**
70 Industrial Rd, Cumberland, RI 02864-1905
Tel.: (508) 342-5395
Providers of Nickel Services
N.A.I.C.S.: 423510

DEUTSCHE POST AG
Charles-de-Gaulle-Str 20, 53113, Bonn, Germany
Tel.: (49) 2281820 De
Web Site: https://group.dhl.com
DHL—(DEU)
Rev.: $93,327,078,057
Assets: $73,754,277,524
Liabilities: $48,486,587,930
Net Worth: $25,267,689,594
Earnings: $4,343,746,551
Emp.: 551,233
Fiscal Year-end: 12/31/23
Express Delivery & Logistics Services
N.A.I.C.S.: 492110
Melanie Kreis *(Member-Mgmt Bd-Fin)*

Subsidiaries:

ABIS GmbH **(1)**
Lyoner Str 20, 60528, Frankfurt, Germany
Tel.: (49) 697920090
Web Site: http://www.abis-online.net
Online Information Updating Services
N.A.I.C.S.: 519290

AEI Drawback Services Inc. **(1)**
22210 Highland Knolls Dr, Katy, TX 77450-5868
Tel.: (281) 578-9605
Logistics Consulting Servies
N.A.I.C.S.: 541614

AGENCIA DE ADUANAS DHL GLOBAL FORWARDING (COLOMBIA) S.A. **(1)**
Popa Cl 30 18 A-226 P-2, Cartagena, Colombia
Tel.: (57) 56723920
Logistics Consulting Servies
N.A.I.C.S.: 541614

Adcloud Gmbh **(1)**
Venloer Strasse 25-27, 50672, Cologne, Germany
Tel.: (49) 2212920950
Web Site: http://www.adcloud.com
Sales Range: $25-49.9 Million
Emp.: 45
Advertising Agencies
N.A.I.C.S.: 541810
Alexander Beyer *(Country Mgr-Switzerland)*

Adcloud Operations Spain S.L. **(1)**
Paseo De Las Castellana 140 Floor 18,

28046, Madrid, Spain
Tel.: (34) 638 262 462
Web Site: http://www.adcloud.com
Sales Range: $25-49.9 Million
Emp.: 6
Online Advertising Services
N.A.I.C.S.: 541890
Henrik Varga *(Country Mgr)*

Aero Express del Ecuador (TransAm) Ltda. **(1)**
Av de Las Americas ave, Guayaquil, 090513, Ecuador
Tel.: (593) 42282510
Sales Range: $25-49.9 Million
Emp.: 39
Air Cargo Handling Services
N.A.I.C.S.: 488119
Jimmy Rendon *(Gen Mgr)*

Aero Express del Ecuador TransAm Cia Ltd. **(1)**
Avenida El Dorado No 106-81 Bodega DHL Aeropuerto el Dorado, Nuevo Terminal de Carga, Bogota, Colombia
Tel.: (57) 1 7457666
Air Freight Transportation Services
N.A.I.C.S.: 481112

Aerocar B.V. **(1)**
Freight Terminal 207 / Schillingweg 60, Nieuw-Vennep, 524, Netherlands
Tel.: (31) 252 361 300
Web Site: http://www.aerocar.nl
Air & Marine Cargo Handling Services
N.A.I.C.S.: 488119
Guy Hachey *(Mng Dir)*

Agencia de Aduanas dhl Express Colombia Ltda. **(1)**
Carrera 106 No 15-25 - Manzana 9 - Bodega 12 Zona Franca de Bogota, Bogota, Colombia
Tel.: (57) 14227800
Logistics Consulting Servies
N.A.I.C.S.: 541614

Agheera GmbH **(1)**
Junkersring 57, 53844, Troisdorf, Germany
Tel.: (49) 2241252840
Web Site: https://www.agheera.com
Sales Range: $25-49.9 Million
Emp.: 30
Logistics Consulting Servies
N.A.I.C.S.: 541614
Raphael Wischnewsky *(Mng Dir)*

Air Express International USA, Inc. **(1)**
1 Slater Dr Ste 8, Elizabeth, NJ 07206-2138
Tel.: (908) 289-6006
Logistics Consulting Servies
N.A.I.C.S.: 541614

Albert Scheid GmbH **(1)**
Marktstrasse 10, 50968, Cologne, Germany
Tel.: (49) 2213763771
Web Site: http://www.spedition-scheid.com
Container Logistics Services
N.A.I.C.S.: 541614

Asia-Pacific Information Services Sdn. Bhd. **(1)**
No 3509-3511 Jalan Teknokrat 5, Cyberjaya, 63000, Malaysia
Tel.: (60) 383158000
Web Site: http://www.dhl.com
Sales Range: $150-199.9 Million
Emp.: 100
Business Process Outsourcing Services
N.A.I.C.S.: 561499

Bieffe Container Logistic S.r.l. **(1)**
Via Delle Colline 100 Collesalvetti, 57122, Livorno, Italy
Tel.: (39) 0586210076
Web Site: https://www.bieffelogistic.it
Shipping & Logistical Support Services
N.A.I.C.S.: 541614

Blue Dart Aviation Ltd. **(1)**
Bluedart Aviation Terminal Gate Number 6, Old International Airport Meenambakkam, Chennai, 600 027, India
Tel.: (91) 4422568200
Web Site: https://www.bluedartaviation.com
Emp.: 1,249
Logistics Consulting Servies
N.A.I.C.S.: 541614
Tushar Jani *(Chm)*

Deutsche Post AG—(Continued)

CSG GmbH (1)
Godesberger Allee 157, 53175, Bonn, Germany
Tel.: (49) 228 5289 0
Web Site: http://www.csg-gmbh.com
Property & Facility Management Services
N.A.I.C.S.: 561210
Georg Behrens *(Mng Dir)*

Circuit Logistics Inc. (1)
8 Burford Rd, Hamilton, L8E 5B1, ON, Canada
Tel.: (905) 561-5848
Warehousing & Storage Services
N.A.I.C.S.: 493190

Concorde Air Logistics Ltd. (1)
17 Adarsh Industrial Estate Sahar Road Chakala, Andheri East, Mumbai, 400099, India
Tel.: (91) 228366270
Air Cargo Handling Services
N.A.I.C.S.: 488119

DANMAR LINES AG (1)
Peter Merian-Strasse 88, Basel, 4002, Switzerland
Tel.: (41) 612747474
Web Site: http://www.dhl.com
Sales Range: $25-49.9 Million
Emp.: 3
Electronic Data Processing Services
N.A.I.C.S.: 518210

DHL (BVI) Ltd. (1)
Fish Bay, PO Box 3255, Tortola, Virgin Islands (British)
Tel.: (284) 4944659
Web Site: http://www.dhl.vg
Sales Range: $25-49.9 Million
Emp.: 15
Logistics Consulting Servies
N.A.I.C.S.: 541614

DHL (Bahamas) Limited (1)
31 Shirley St, Nassau, Bahamas
Tel.: (242) 3024075
N.A.I.C.S.: 541614

DHL (Bolivia) SRL (1)
Av Mcal Santa Cruz 1282 Edf Seguros, La Paz, Bolivia
Tel.: (591) 22116161
Web Site: http://www.dhl.com.bo
Sales Range: $25-49.9 Million
Emp.: 130
Logistics Consulting Servies
N.A.I.C.S.: 541614

DHL (Tanzania) Ltd. (1)
Tel.: (255) 222194901
Courier Service
N.A.I.C.S.: 492110

DHL 2-Mann-Handling GmbH (1)
Strasschensweg 10, 53113, Bonn, Germany
Tel.: (49) 2281820
Logistic Services
N.A.I.C.S.: 541614

DHL Aviation (France) SAS (1)
Zone Industrielle Paris Nord Ii 241 Rue De La Belle Etoile, Roissy-en-France, 95700, France
Tel.: (33) 155307103
Air Freight Transportation Services
N.A.I.C.S.: 481112

DHL Aviation (Nigeria) Ltd. (1)
Cargo Terminal MM International Airport, Lagos, Nigeria
Tel.: (234) 12700719
Air Freight Transportation Services
N.A.I.C.S.: 481112

DHL Bwlog GmbH (1)
Regioparkring 26, Monchengladbach, 41199, Nordrhein-Westfalen, Germany
Tel.: (49) 2281820
Logistics Consulting Servies
N.A.I.C.S.: 541614

DHL Corporate Services SC Mexico (1)
Autopista Mexico-Queretaro Km 34 5 Nave 1, Cuautitlan, 54740, Mexico
Tel.: (52) 5530032600
Administrative Management Services
N.A.I.C.S.: 541611

DHL Elancourt SARL (1)
65 avenue Georges Politzer Z A de Trappes Elancourt, 78190, Trappes, France
Tel.: (33) 820 20 25 25
Logistics Consulting Servies
N.A.I.C.S.: 541614

DHL Exel Slovakia, s.r.o. (1)
Dialnicna 2/4149, Senec, 90301, Slovakia
Tel.: (421) 232161111
Logistics Consulting Servies
N.A.I.C.S.: 541614

DHL Exel Supply Chain Portugal, S.A. (1)
Quinta Da Verdelha Corpo B Fraccao 5, Alverca do Ribatejo, 2619-501, Vila Franca De Xira, Portugal
Tel.: (351) 263659000
Logistics Consulting Servies
N.A.I.C.S.: 541614

DHL Express (Canada) Ltd. (1)
18 Parkshore Drive, Brampton, L6T 5M1, ON, Canada
Tel.: (905) 861-3672
N.A.I.C.S.: 541614
Geoff Walsh *(CEO)*

DHL Express (Ecuador) S.A. (1)
Eloy Alfaro 113A De Los Juncos, Pasaje, Ecuador
Tel.: (593) 1800345345
N.A.I.C.S.: 541614

DHL Express (Finland) Oy (1)
Tullimiehentie 10, 01530, Vantaa, Finland
Tel.: (358) 3045345
N.A.I.C.S.: 541614

DHL Express (Malaysia) Sdn. Bhd. (1)
12th Floor Menara Symphony No 5 Jalan Semangat Seksyen 13, 46200, Petaling Jaya, Selangor, Malaysia
Tel.: (60) 379642800
N.A.I.C.S.: 541614
Julian Neo *(Mng Dir)*

DHL Express (Papua New Guinea) Ltd. (1)
Morea Tobo Rd Kittyhawke St 6 Mile, NCD, 121, Port Moresby, Papua New Guinea
Tel.: (675) 1802345
N.A.I.C.S.: 541614
Cameron Taylor *(Country Mgr)*

DHL Express (Rwanda) Limited (1)
Avenue De La Jeunesse, PO Box 359, Kigali, Rwanda
Tel.: (250) 788167200
N.A.I.C.S.: 541614
Fred Gashumba *(Country Mgr)*

DHL Express Colombia Ltda. (1)
Carrera 85D N 46a 38, Bogota, Colombia
Tel.: (57) 15920400
N.A.I.C.S.: 541614

DHL Express Estonia AS (1)
Valukoja 32/2, 11415, Tallinn, Estonia
Tel.: (372) 6808555
Web Site: https://dhlexpress.ee
N.A.I.C.S.: 541614
Kristina Laaneots *(Country Mgr)*

DHL Express Laos Sole Company Limited (1)
795 Unit 3 P3 Road, Phonsavang Village Chanthabuly Dist, Vientiane, Laos
Tel.: (856) 21418100
N.A.I.C.S.: 541614

DHL Express Latvia SIA (1)
Maza Gramzdas Iela 9A Lidosta, Marupe County, Riga, 1053, Latvia
Tel.: (371) 66010000
Web Site: https://dhlexpresslatvia.lv
N.A.I.C.S.: 541614
Artis Deksenieks *(Mng Dir)*

DHL Express Macedonia d.o.o.e.l. (1)
Ul 32 Br 5 Nas Ilinden, 1041, Skopje, North Macedonia
Tel.: (389) 22581581
N.A.I.C.S.: 541614
Radoslav Nanovic *(Country Mgr)*

DHL Express Spain S.L. (1)

Edificio Servicios Generales Centro De Carga Aerea, Barajas Avenida Central s/n, 28042, Madrid, Madrid, Spain
Tel.: (34) 913098452
N.A.I.C.S.: 541614
Raul Cuadrado *(Dir-Customer Service)*

DHL Express, Unipessoal, Lda. (1)
Avenida Presidente Nicolau Lobato Fatuhada, Dili, East Timor
Tel.: (670) 8001333333
N.A.I.C.S.: 541614
Ahmad Mohamad *(Mng Dir)*

DHL Food Logistics Egypt Ltd. (1)
11 Sharkat Misr Street Sultan Hussein Azarita, Alexandria, Egypt
Tel.: (20) 34836290
N.A.I.C.S.: 541614

DHL FoodLogistics GmbH (1)
Welserstrasse 5, 51149, Cologne, Germany
Tel.: (49) 22032994100
N.A.I.C.S.: 541614

DHL Freight (France) SAS (1)
ZI De Trepillot 7 Rue Albert Thomas, 25000, Besancon, France
Tel.: (33) 806009950
N.A.I.C.S.: 541614

DHL Freight CZ s.r.o. (1)
Nadrazni 2967/93 Moravska Ostrava, 702 00, Ostrava, Czech Republic
Tel.: (420) 239018222
N.A.I.C.S.: 541614

DHL Freight Denmark A/S (1)
Banemarksvej 48, 2605, Brondby, Denmark
Tel.: (45) 43310900
N.A.I.C.S.: 541614

DHL Freight Germany Holding GmbH (1)
Godesberger Allee 102-104, Bonn, 53175, Germany
Tel.: (49) 228377880
Freight Forwarding Services
N.A.I.C.S.: 488510

DHL Freight Portugal, Unipessoal Lda. (1)
Parque Logistico Do Passil Lote 93-A, 2890-191, Alcochete, Portugal
Tel.: (351) 707100210
N.A.I.C.S.: 541614

DHL Freight Romania S.R.L. (1)
15A Orhideelor Street Orhideea Building 1st Floor, 060071, Bucharest, Romania
Tel.: (40) 373788704
N.A.I.C.S.: 541614

DHL Freight Slovakia, s.r.o. (1)
Galvaniho 17/B, 820 01, Bratislava, Slovakia
Tel.: (421) 248285111
N.A.I.C.S.: 541614

DHL Freight Tasimacilik ve Lojistik Hizmetleri A.S. (1)
Merkez Mahallesi Basin Ekspres Yolu Street No 9 Floor 10 No 81-82, Capital Tower Kucukcekmece, 34307, Istanbul, Türkiye
Tel.: (90) 2126925700
N.A.I.C.S.: 541614

DHL Freight d.o.o. (1)
Industrijska 20, 10431, Sveta Nedelja, Croatia
Tel.: (385) 72707777
N.A.I.C.S.: 541614
Ivan Posavec *(Mng Dir)*

DHL Global Event Logistics GmbH (1)
Welserstrasse 10d, 51149, Cologne, Germany
Tel.: (49) 2203368000
Web Site: https://www.event-logistics.dhl
N.A.I.C.S.: 541614
Frederik Reifegerste *(Mng Dir)*

DHL Global Forwarding (Argentina) S.A. (1)
Emp.: 150
Freight Forwarding Services
N.A.I.C.S.: 488510
Rodrigo Jalil *(Gen Mgr)*

DHL Global Forwarding (Cameroon) PLC (1)

22 Rue Pierre Loti, BP 625, Douala, Cameroon
Tel.: (237) 33423872
Freight Forwarding Services
N.A.I.C.S.: 488510
Lubabalo Mtya *(CEO-Southern Africa)*

DHL Global Forwarding (Mauritius) Ltd. (1)
Old airport Road Plaine Magnien, Port Louis, Mauritius
Tel.: (230) 2601144
Logistic Services
N.A.I.C.S.: 541614

DHL Global Forwarding (Thailand) Limited (1)
209 K Tower A 12th-12Ath Floor Sukhumvit 21 Road Asoke Klongtoey-Nua, Watthana, Bangkok, 10110, Thailand
Tel.: (66) 27918000
Freight Forwarding Services
N.A.I.C.S.: 488510

DHL Global Forwarding Bahrain WLL (1)
Bahrain Financial Harbour BLD 1459 Floor 15th RD 4626 BLK 346, 343, Manama, Bahrain
Tel.: (973) 17728151
Logistic Services
N.A.I.C.S.: 541614

DHL Global Forwarding Customs, LLC (1)
Leningradskaya street 39 Bldg 5 Khimki Business Park 10th floor, Moscow, 141400, Russia
Tel.: (7) 4959332200
Logistic Services
N.A.I.C.S.: 541614

DHL Global Forwarding Management GmbH (1)
Tel.: (49) 22818264800
Freight Traffic Consulting Services
N.A.I.C.S.: 541614
Ashutosh Dixit *(Sr Dir-Mktg & Sls-India)*

DHL Global Forwarding Nigeria Limited (1)
Oregun Business Park 2 Billingsway, Oregun, Lagos, Nigeria
Tel.: (234) 8025011806
Freight Forwarding Services
N.A.I.C.S.: 488510
Agnaldo Laice *(Mgr-Kenya)*

DHL Global Forwarding Portugal, Unipessoal, Lda. (1)
Aeroporto de Lisboa Edificio 124 2o Piso-Gab 1A, 1700-008, Lisbon, Portugal
Tel.: (351) 218438946
Logistic Services
N.A.I.C.S.: 541614

DHL Global Forwarding Zimbabwe Ltd. (1)
168 Herbert Chitepo Avenue, Harare, Zimbabwe
Tel.: (263) 8677345343
Logistic Services
N.A.I.C.S.: 541614

DHL Global Forwarding d.o.o. Belgrade (1)
Milutina Milankovica 9d, 11070, Belgrade, Serbia
Tel.: (381) 112288122
Logistic Services
N.A.I.C.S.: 541614

DHL Global Mail UK (1)
Ocean House The Ring, Bracknell, RG12 1AN, Berkshire, United Kingdom
Tel.: (44) 1344302000
Web Site: http://www.dhl.com
Investment Management Service
N.A.I.C.S.: 523940

DHL Global Management GmbH (1)
Kurt-Schumacher-Str 28, 53113, Bonn, Nordrhein-Westfalen, Germany
Tel.: (49) 2281820
Financial Investment Management Services
N.A.I.C.S.: 523999

DHL Global Match (Belgium) N.V. (1)
Bedrijvenzone Machelen Cargo 830, 1830,

Machelen, Belgium
Tel.: (32) 27520211
Logistic Services
N.A.I.C.S.: 541614

DHL Group Services NV/SA   **(1)**
Gebouw 3 Luchthaven, Zaventem, 1930,
Vlaams Brabant, Belgium
Tel.: (32) 27181211
Logistics Consulting Servies
N.A.I.C.S.: 541614

DHL International (Thailand) Ltd. **(1)**
Grand Amarin Tower Floor 22 1550 New
Petchburi Road, Makasan Khet Ra-
chatevee, Bangkok, 10400, Thailand
Tel.: (66) 2 658 8000
Courier Service
N.A.I.C.S.: 492110

DHL International Antilles SARL **(1)**
Z.I Acajou-Californie, Lamentin, 97232,
Martinique
Tel.: (596) 596504141
Web Site: http://www.dhl-mq.com
Logistic Supply Chain Management Ser-
vices
N.A.I.C.S.: 541614

**DHL International Botswana (Pty)
Ltd.**   **(1)**
Broadhurst Industrial Western By-pass, PO
Box 1077, Gaborone, 9999, Botswana
Tel.: (267) 3912000
Web Site: http://www.dhl.com
Emp.: 44
Courier Service
N.A.I.C.S.: 492110

DHL International GmbH   **(1)**
Charles-de-Gaulle-Strasse 20, 53113, Bonn,
Germany
Tel.: (49) 2281820
Web Site: https://developer.dhl.com
Courier Service
N.A.I.C.S.: 492110
Frank Appel *(CEO)*

**DHL International Mauritanie
SARL**   **(1)**
Avenue Mamadou Konate ILot A 639, PO
Box 1996, Nouakchott, Mauritania
Tel.: (222) 254706
Courier Service
N.A.I.C.S.: 492110

DHL International Reunion SARL **(1)**
Za St Exupery Zone Aeropor, Sainte-Marie,
97438, Reunion
Tel.: (262) 262295776
Courier Service
N.A.I.C.S.: 492110

DHL International S.A./N.V.   **(1)**
Industriepark Diegem Hoek Woluwelaan
151, 1831, Diegem, Belgium   **(100%)**
Tel.: (32) 27155050
Web Site: http://www.dhl.be
Sales Range: $25-49.9 Billion
Emp.: 1,500
Express & Global Mail Deliveries & Logis-
tics Services
N.A.I.C.S.: 492110

Subsidiary (Non-US):

DHL (Costa Rica) S.A.   **(2)**
600 Metros Noreste De La Interseccion
Real Cariari, Heredia, Costa Rica
Tel.: (506) 22090000
Sales Range: $50-74.9 Million
Emp.: 21
Freight Forwarding Services
N.A.I.C.S.: 488510

DHL (Ghana) Limited   **(2)**
Logistics Consulting Servies
N.A.I.C.S.: 541614

DHL (Israel) Ltd.   **(2)**
Ben Gurion Airport Maman Building Suite
807, Lod, 71100, Israel
Tel.: (972) 39722233
Web Site: http://www.dhl.co.il
Logistics Consulting Servies
N.A.I.C.S.: 541614

DHL (Jamaica) Ltd   **(2)**
19 Haining Road Kgn 5, Kingston, Jamaica
Tel.: (876) 9200010
Web Site: http://www.dhl.com.jm

Logistics Consulting Servies
N.A.I.C.S.: 541614

DHL (Latvia) SIA   **(2)**
International Airport Riga, 1053, Riga, Lat-
via
Tel.: (371) 7802555
Web Site: http://www.dhl.lv
Sales Range: $25-49.9 Million
Emp.: 53
Express Mail Services
N.A.I.C.S.: 492110

DHL (Mauritius) Ltd.   **(2)**
Cnr Mgr Gonin/Sir Virgil Naz Street, Port
Louis, Mauritius
Tel.: (230) 2087711
Sales Range: $25-49.9 Million
Emp.: 150
Express Mail Services
N.A.I.C.S.: 492110

DHL (Namibia) (Pty) Ltd.   **(2)**
14 Ongoporo Street Prosperita, Windhoek,
9000, Namibia
Tel.: (264) 612040800
Web Site: https://www.dhl.com
Parcel & Courier Services
N.A.I.C.S.: 492210

DHL (Paraguay) S.R.L.   **(2)**
Gral Santos 1170 c/ Concoria, Asuncion,
7000, Paraguay
Tel.: (595) 21 21 62000
Web Site: http://www.dhl.com.py
Sales Range: $25-49.9 Million
Emp.: 10
Logistics Consulting Servies
N.A.I.C.S.: 541614

DHL (Uruguay) S.R.L.   **(2)**
Tel.: (598) 26041331
Sales Range: $25-49.9 Million
Emp.: 135
Logistics Consulting Servies
N.A.I.C.S.: 541614

DHL Air Limited   **(2)**
EMA Cargo West East Midlands Airport,
Derby, Castle Donington, DE74 2TR, United
Kingdom
Tel.: (44) 1332857815
Air Freight Services
N.A.I.C.S.: 481112

DHL AirWays GmbH   **(2)**
Flughafen, 51147, Cologne, Germany
Tel.: (49) 22034790
Air Freight Transportation Services
N.A.I.C.S.: 481112

**DHL Asia Pacific Shared Services
Sdn. Bhd.**   **(2)**
Level 11 Menara Axis No 2 Jalan 51A/223,
Petaling Jaya, 46100, Selangor, Malaysia
Tel.: (60) 379484848
Web Site: http://www.dhl.com
Courier Service
N.A.I.C.S.: 492110

DHL Automotive GmbH   **(2)**
Rungedamm 32, Hamburg, 21035, Ger-
many
Tel.: (49) 4073450
Automotive Parts Logistics Services
N.A.I.C.S.: 541614

DHL Aviation (Netherlands) B.V. **(2)**
Anchoragelaan 32, 1118 LD, Schiphol,
Netherlands
Tel.: (31) 20 6582300
Logistics Distribution Services
N.A.I.C.S.: 541614

DHL Aviation (UK) Limited   **(2)**
Building 559 Shoreham Road West London
Heathrow Airport, London, TW6 3SJ, United
Kingdom
Tel.: (44) 2082834000
Web Site: http://www.dhl.co.uk
Emp.: 40
Parcel & Courier Services
N.A.I.C.S.: 492210

Subsidiary (Domestic):

DHL Aviation NV / SA   **(2)**
Gebouw Drie Brussel Nationale Luchthaven
Bldg 3, 1930, Zaventem, Belgium
Tel.: (32) 27181211
Web Site: http://www.dhl.com

Emp.: 1,200
Air Freight Transportation Services
N.A.I.C.S.: 481112

Subsidiary (Non-US):

DHL Customs Brokerage Ltd.   **(2)**
3950 Malden Road Suite 6, Windsor, N9C
2G4, ON, Canada
Tel.: (519) 972-1994
Web Site: http://www.dhl.com
Sales Range: $25-49.9 Million
Emp.: 15
Customs Brokerage Services
N.A.I.C.S.: 488510

DHL Danzas Air & Ocean   **(2)**
Peter Merian Str 88, Basel, 4002,
Switzerland   **(100%)**
Tel.: (41) 612747474
Web Site: http://www.dhl.com
Sales Range: $25-49.9 Million
Emp.: 100
Freight Forwarding & Transportation Ser-
vices
N.A.I.C.S.: 488510

Subsidiary (Non-US):

**DHL Danzas Air & Ocean (Canada)
Inc.**   **(3)**
100 World Dr, Mississauga, L5T 3A2, ON,
Canada
Tel.: (905) 405-9300
Web Site: http://www.ca.danzas.com
Sales Range: $50-74.9 Million
Freight Forwarding & Transportation Ser-
vices
N.A.I.C.S.: 488510

Subsidiary (US):

**DHL Danzas Air & Ocean North
America**   **(3)**
1200 S Pine Is Rd Fl 6, Plantation, FL
33324
Tel.: (954) 888-7000
Freight Forwarding & Transportation Ser-
vices
N.A.I.C.S.: 492110

Subsidiary (Non-US):

DHL Finland   **(3)**
Katriinatie 14-16, 1530, Vantaa, Finland
Tel.: (358) 205333
Web Site: http://www.dhl.fi
Sales Range: $50-74.9 Million
Freight Forwarding & Transportation Ser-
vices
N.A.I.C.S.: 488510

Danzas AEI S.A. de C.V.   **(3)**
Fundidora Monterrey 97, 15520, Mexico,
Mexico
Tel.: (52) 5551331700
Web Site: http://www.dhl.com
Marine Cargo Handler; Freight Forwarding
& Transportation Services
N.A.I.C.S.: 488320

Danzas Ecuador S.A.   **(3)**
Eloy Alfaro y de los Juncos, Lote 113-A,
Quito, Ecuador
Tel.: (593) 22485100
Web Site: http://www.dhl.com.ec
Sales Range: $25-49.9 Million
Emp.: 30
Freight Forwarding & Transportation Ser-
vices
N.A.I.C.S.: 488510

Danzas S.A.   **(3)**
15 rue de Nancy, 75010, Paris, France
Tel.: (33) 144526666
Web Site: http://www.dhl.de
Sales Range: $25-49.9 Million
Emp.: 100
Freight Forwarding & Transportation Ser-
vices
N.A.I.C.S.: 488510

Subsidiary (Non-US):

DHL Egypt W.L.L.   **(2)**
El Mona Towers, 16 Lebanon Street, Mo-
handessin, Cairo, Egypt
Tel.: (20) 23029801
Web Site: http://www.dhl.com
Express Mail Services
N.A.I.C.S.: 492110

DHL Ekspres (Slovenija), d.o.o. **(2)**
Spruha 19, Trzin, 1236, Slovenia
Tel.: (386) 1588800
Web Site: http://www.dhl.com
Emp.: 4
Freight Forwarding Services
N.A.I.C.S.: 488510

Subsidiary (Domestic):

DHL Employee Benefit Fund ofp. **(2)**
De Kleetlaan 1, 1831, Machelen, Belgium
Tel.: (32) 2 713 40 00
Web Site: http://www.dhlebf.be
Pension Fund Services
N.A.I.C.S.: 525110
Gilbert McArthy *(Mgr)*

Subsidiary (Non-US):

**DHL Exel Supply Chain (Spain),
S.L.U.**   **(2)**
Centro de Transportes de Coslada Calle
Rumania 1, 28820, Coslada, Madrid, Spain
Tel.: (34) 916707595
Logistics Consulting Servies
N.A.I.C.S.: 541614

**DHL Exel Supply Chain (Sweden)
AB**   **(2)**
Bjornstigen 85, Stockholm, 170 87, Sweden
Tel.: (46) 8 543 450 00
Web Site: http://www.dhl.se
Emp.: 250
Logistics Consulting Servies
N.A.I.C.S.: 541614

**DHL Exel Supply Chain Euskal-Log,
S.L.U.**   **(2)**
Poligono Industrial Agurain 7 - Par, Salvati-
erra, 1200, Alava, Spain
Tel.: (34) 945301900
Logistics Consulting Servies
N.A.I.C.S.: 541614

**DHL Exel Supply Chain Hungary
Limited**   **(2)**
Zoldmezo street 1, 2225, Ullo, Hungary
Tel.: (36) 29 523 100
Logistics Consulting Servies
N.A.I.C.S.: 541614

**DHL Exel Supply Chain Phils.,
Inc.**   **(2)**
Km 17 West Service Road South Super
Highway Bicutan, Paranaque, 1704, Philip-
pines
Tel.: (63) 2 8584600
Web Site: http://www.dhl.com.ph
Logistics Consulting Servies
N.A.I.C.S.: 541614

**DHL Exel Supply Chain Trade (Po-
land) Sp.Z.O.O.**   **(2)**
Bokserska 66, Warsaw, 02690, Poland
Tel.: (48) 224557655
Web Site: http://www.dhl.com
Logistics Consulting Servies
N.A.I.C.S.: 541614

Division (Non-US):

DHL Express Germany GmbH   **(2)**
Tel.: (49) 18053453001
Web Site: http://www.dhl.de
Express Parcel Services
N.A.I.C.S.: 492110
Markus Reckling *(CEO)*

Subsidiary (Non-US):

DHL Express (Argentina) S.A.   **(3)**
Web Site: http://www.dhl.com.ar
Emp.: 40
Logistics Consulting Servies
N.A.I.C.S.: 541614

DHL Express (Australia) Pty Ltd. **(3)**
Sydney Airport Cte, Level 5 15 Bourke Rd,
Mascot, 2020, NSW, Australia
Tel.: (61) 293178300
Web Site: http://www.dhl.com.au
Express Mail Services
N.A.I.C.S.: 492110

DHL Express (Austria) GmbH   **(3)**
Viaduktstrasse 20, 2353, Guntramsdorf,
Austria
Web Site: http://www.dhl.at
Logistics Consulting Servies

Deutsche Post AG—(Continued)

N.A.I.C.S.: 541614

DHL Express (Brazil) Ltda. (3)
Logistics Consulting Servies
N.A.I.C.S.: 541614

DHL Express (Brunei) Sdn. Bhd. (3)
Unit 2-8 Ground Floor Wisma LCY Gadong
Simpang 92, Jalan Gadong, BE3719, Bandar Seri Begawan, Brunei Darussalam
Tel.: (673) 244499123
Web Site: http://www.dhl.com.bn
Air Freight Transportation Services
N.A.I.C.S.: 481112

DHL Express (Cambodia) Ltd. (3)
DHL Building Plot 174-175 Russian Boulevard, Phnom Penh, Cambodia
Tel.: (855) 523970999
Web Site: http://www.dhl.com.kh
Logistics Consulting Servies
N.A.I.C.S.: 541614

DHL Express (Chile) Ltda. (3)
San Francisco 301, Santiago, Chile
Tel.: (56) 22802000
Web Site: http://www.dhl.cl
Logistics Consulting Servies
N.A.I.C.S.: 541614

**DHL Express (Czech Republic)
s.r.o.** (3)
Nadrazne, Ostrava, 702 00, Czech Republic
Tel.: (420) 596279211
Web Site: http://www.dhl.cz
Express Mail Services
N.A.I.C.S.: 492110

**DHL Express (El Salvador) S.A.de
C.V.** (3)
Tel.: (503) 22396500
Logistics Consulting Servies
N.A.I.C.S.: 541614

DHL Express (Fiji) Ltd. (3)
Grantham Rd Raiwaqa, Box 13036, Suva, Fiji
Tel.: (679) 3372766
Web Site: http://www.dhl.com
Emp.: 5
Logistics Consulting Servies
N.A.I.C.S.: 541614

DHL Express (France) SAS (3)
241 Rue de la Belle Etoile ZI Paris Nord 2,
95700, Roissy-en-France, France
Tel.: (33) 149387070
Emp.: 200
Logistics Consulting Servies
N.A.I.C.S.: 541614
Michel Ikavi (Gen Mgr)

DHL Express (Hellas) S.A. (3)
44 Alimou Ave & Rwma 17, Alimos, 17455,
Athens, Greece
Tel.: (30) 210 9890000
Emp.: 20
Logistics Consulting Servies
N.A.I.C.S.: 541614
Panagiotis Ziakris (Mgr-Import & Export)

DHL Express (Hong Kong) Ltd (3)
Level 20 348 Kwun Tong Road, Kwun Tong,
Kowloon, China (Hong Kong) **(100%)**
Tel.: (852) 24002988
Web Site: http://www.dhl.com.hk
Freight Forwarding & Transportation Services
N.A.I.C.S.: 492110

DHL Express (Iceland) EHF (3)
Tel.: (354) 5351100
Web Site: http://www.dhl.is
Logistics Consulting Servies
N.A.I.C.S.: 541614

DHL Express (India) Pvt. Ltd. (3)
DHL Express Silver Utopia 8th FlCardinal
Gracias Road Chakala Andheri, Mumbai,
400099, India
Tel.: (91) 2267412615
Web Site: http://www.dhl.co.in
Logistics Consulting Servies
N.A.I.C.S.: 541614

DHL Express (Ireland) Ltd. (3)
Unit 3 Elm Rd Dublin Airport Logistics Pk,
St Margaret's Rd, Swords, Co Dublin, Ireland
Tel.: (353) 18700700
Web Site: http://www.dhl.ie
Emp.: 350
Express Mail Services
N.A.I.C.S.: 492110

DHL Express (Luxembourg) S.A. (3)
11A rue Edmond Reuter, 5326, Contern,
Luxembourg
Tel.: (352) 350909
Web Site: http://www.dhl.lu
Air Freight Services
N.A.I.C.S.: 481112

DHL Express (Macau) Ltd. (3)
Avenipapo Conselheiro Ferreira de Almeita
106-122, Macau, China (Macau)
Tel.: (853) 28372828
Web Site: http://www.dhl.com
Logistics Consulting Servies
N.A.I.C.S.: 541614

DHL Express (Netherlands) B.V. (3)
Web Site: http://www.dhl.nl
Emp.: 180
Logistics Consulting Servies
N.A.I.C.S.: 541614

DHL Express (Norway) AS (3)
Gneisveien 3, 2020, Skedsmokorset, Norway
Emp.: 70
Logistics Consulting Servies
N.A.I.C.S.: 541614

DHL Express (Philippines) Corp. (3)
DHL House 2306 Chino Roces Avenue
Kayamanan C, Makati, 1231, Philippines
Tel.: (63) 28117000
Air Freight Services
N.A.I.C.S.: 481112

DHL Express (Poland) Sp.zo.o. (3)
Osmanska 2 Str, 02-823, Warsaw, Poland
Tel.: (48) 225650000
Web Site: http://www.dhl.com.pl
Express Mail Services
N.A.I.C.S.: 492110

DHL Express (Schweiz) AG (3)
Pumpwerkstrasse 51, 8105, Regensdorf,
Switzerland
Tel.: (41) 848 711 711
Emp.: 20
Freight Forwarding Services
N.A.I.C.S.: 488510
Chris Hillis (CEO)

**DHL Express (Singapore) Pte
Ltd.** (3)
DHL Air Express Centre No 1 Tai Seng Dr,
535215, Singapore, Singapore
Tel.: (65) 68806060
Web Site: http://www.dhl.com.sg
Emp.: 1,100
Express Mail Services
N.A.I.C.S.: 492110

**DHL Express (Slovakia), spol. s r.
o.** (3)
Letisko M R Stefanika, 820 01, Bratislava,
Slovakia
Emp.: 20
Logistics Consulting Servies
N.A.I.C.S.: 541614

DHL Express (Sweden) AB (3)
Bjornstigen 85, PO Box 23260, Stockholm,
17072, Sweden
Tel.: (46) 854345000
Web Site: http://www.dhl.com
Express Mail Services
N.A.I.C.S.: 492110

DHL Express (Taiwan) Corp. (3)
1st Floor No 82 Section 2 Jianguo North
Road, Zhongshan District, Taipei, 10416,
Taiwan
Tel.: (886) 225036858
Web Site: http://www.dhl.com.tw
Express Mail Services
N.A.I.C.S.: 492110

DHL Express (Thailand) Limited (3)
319 Chamchuri Square Building 22 and 23
Phayathai Road, Sathorn, Bangkok, 10330,
Thailand
Tel.: (66) 23455000
Web Site: http://www.dhl.com
Courier Delivery Services
N.A.I.C.S.: 492110

Subsidiary (US):

DHL Express (USA), Inc. (3)
1210 S Pine Island Rd 4th Fl, Plantation,
FL 33324
Tel.: (954) 888-7000
Web Site: http://www.dhl-usa.com
Parcel & Courier Delivery Services
N.A.I.C.S.: 492210
Greg Hewitt (CEO)

Subsidiary (Non-US):

DHL Express (uk) Limited (3)
Orbital Park 178-188 Great South West
Road, Hounslow, TW4 6JS, United Kingdom
Tel.: (44) 844 248 0844
Web Site: http://www.dhl.co.uk
Air & Ocean Freight Transportation Services
N.A.I.C.S.: 481112

DHL Express A/S (3)
Jydekrogen 14, Vallensbaek, 2625, Denmark
Tel.: (45) 70345345
Web Site: http://www.dhl.dk
Express Mail Services
N.A.I.C.S.: 492110
Ken Allen (CEO-DHL ECommerce Solutions
Div)

**DHL Express Aduanas Peru
S.A.C.** (3)
Calle Uno Mz A Lt 6 Bocanegra, Lima, Peru
Tel.: (51) 15172500
Customs Consulting Services
N.A.I.C.S.: 541614

**DHL Express Aduanas Venezuela
C.A.** (3)
Edificio DHL La California Sur, Caracas,
1060, Venezuela
Tel.: (58) 2126206000
Logistics Consulting Servies
N.A.I.C.S.: 541614

**DHL Express Barcelona Spain
S.L.** (3)
Poligono Industrial Les Minetes 2 - 3 Par,
Santa Perpetua de Mogoda, 8130, Barcelona, Spain
Tel.: (34) 935656564
Logistics Consulting Servies
N.A.I.C.S.: 541614
Juan Sabanes (Gen Mgr)

DHL Express Bulgaria EOOD (3)
Tel.: (359) 70017700
Web Site: http://www.dhl.bg
Emp.: 30
Logistics Consulting Servies
N.A.I.C.S.: 541614

DHL Express Cyprus (3)
64 Bethleem Stovlos, 2033, Nicosia, 2033,
Cyprus
Tel.: (357) 22799000
Web Site: http://www.dhl.com.cy
Express Mail Services
N.A.I.C.S.: 492110

**DHL Express Hungary Forwarding
and Services LLC** (3)
Feherakac U 3, Budapest, 1097, Hungary
Tel.: (36) 13823200
Postal Service
N.A.I.C.S.: 491110

DHL Express Hungary Ltd. (3)
Feheakas 3, 1097, Budapest, Hungary
Tel.: (36) 13823222
Web Site: http://www.dhl.hu
Express Mail Services
N.A.I.C.S.: 492110

DHL Express Iberia S.L. (3)
Paseo Mikeletegi 65, San Sebastian,
20009, Spain
Tel.: (34) 943 37 66 00
Courier & Parcel Services
N.A.I.C.S.: 492210

**DHL Express International (Thailand)
Ltd.** (3)
319 Chamchuri Square Building 22nd-23rd
Floor, Bangkok, 10120, Thailand
Tel.: (66) 23455000
Web Site: http://www.dhl.com.th
Express Mail Services

N.A.I.C.S.: 492110

DHL Express Lda (3)
Rua do Barreiro 300, Crestins, 4470- 573,
Maia, Portugal
Tel.: (351) 229 43 05 00
Web Site: http://www.dhl.pt
Logistics Consulting Servies
N.A.I.C.S.: 541614

DHL Express Maroc S.A. (3)
Tel.: (212) 522972020
Logistics Consulting Servies
N.A.I.C.S.: 541614
Feyclalel Haggami (Office Mgr)

**DI IL Express Mexico, S.A. de
C.V.** (3)
Av Fuerza Aerea Mexicana 540 Col Federal, Deleg Venustiano Carranza, 15700,
Mexico, DF, Mexico
Tel.: (52) 5553457000
Web Site: http://www.dhl.com.mx
Express Mail Services
N.A.I.C.S.: 492110

**DHL Express Navarra Spain,
S.L.** (3)
Poligono Ciudad Del Transporte CI Alemania Nave 5c, Navarra, 31119, Spain
Tel.: (34) 948368245
Logistics Consulting Servies
N.A.I.C.S.: 541614

DHL Express Nepal Pvt. Ltd. (3)
KUK Building Sinamangal Chowk Near
Tribhuvan International Airport, GPO Box
21841, Kathmandu, Nepal
Web Site: http://www.dhl.com
Emp.: 55
Logistics Consulting Servies
N.A.I.C.S.: 541614

DHL Express Peru S.A.C. (3)
Calle Uno Mz A Lote 6 Fundo Bocanegra
Etapa I, Lima, Peru
Tel.: (51) 1 517 2500
Logistics Consulting Servies
N.A.I.C.S.: 541614

DHL Express Portugal, Lda. (3)
Ave D Joao II 51 4th Fl, 1990-085, Lisbon,
Portugal
Tel.: (351) 707505606
Web Site: http://www.dhl.com
Logistics Consulting Servies
N.A.I.C.S.: 541614

DHL Express S.r.l. (3)
Viale Milanofiori, Palazzo U3 Strada 5,
20089, Rozzano, MI, Italy
Tel.: (39) 024677871
Web Site: http://www.dhl.it
Express Mail Services
N.A.I.C.S.: 492110

**DHL Express Services (France)
SAS** (3)
53 Avenue Jean Jaures, 95952, Le Bourget,
France
Tel.: (33) 149387070
Web Site: http://www.dhl.fr
Logistics Consulting Servies
N.A.I.C.S.: 541614
Michel Akavi (Mng Dir)

**DHL Express Valencia Spain
S.L.** (3)
Parque Cientifico y Tecnologico de
Gipuzkoa, San Sebastian, 20009, Guipuzcoa, Spain
Tel.: (34) 961368484
Web Site: http://www.dhl.es
Courier Delivery Services
N.A.I.C.S.: 492110

Subsidiary (Non-US):

DHL Finance Services B.V. (2)
P de Coubertinweg 5, 6225 XT, Maastricht,
Netherlands
Tel.: (31) 433564000
Emp.: 400
Financial Management Services
N.A.I.C.S.: 523999

DHL Fletes Aereos, C.A. (2)
Avenida Chicago con Calle Milan, Edificio
DHL, Urb la California Sur, Caracas, Venezuela
Tel.: (58) 212 205 6340

Web Site: http://www.dhl.com.ve
Sales Range: $75-99.9 Million
Emp.: 450
Express Mail Services
N.A.I.C.S.: 492110

DHL Food Services GmbH **(2)**
Marktstr 10, 50968, Cologne, Germany
Tel.: (49) 2 213 76 90 31
Logistics Consulting Servies
N.A.I.C.S.: 541614
Andreas Lenz *(Gen Mgr)*

Subsidiary (Domestic):

DHL Freight (Belgium) NV **(2)**
Eppegemsesteenweg 31-33, Grimbergen,
1850, Belgium
Tel.: (32) 22551124
Web Site: http://www.dhl.be
Sales Range: $100-124.9 Million
Emp.: 490
Freight Transportation Services
N.A.I.C.S.: 488510

Subsidiary (Non-US):

DHL Freight (Netherlands) B.V. **(2)**
Web Site: http://www.dhl.nl
Freight Transportation Services
N.A.I.C.S.: 488510

DHL Freight (Sweden) AB **(2)**
Bjornstigen 85, 170 87, Stockholm, Sweden
Tel.: (46) 771345345
Freight Forwarding Services
N.A.I.C.S.: 488510
Peter A. Hesslin *(CEO)*

DHL Freight Estonia AS **(2)**
Betooni 6, 11415, Tallinn, Estonia
Tel.: (372) 6 808 400
Web Site: http://www.dhl.ee
Logistics Consulting Servies
N.A.I.C.S.: 541614

DHL Freight Finland OY **(2)**
Katriinatie 14-16, 01530, Vantaa, Finland
Tel.: (358) 205333
Air & Road Transportation Services
N.A.I.C.S.: 488190

DHL Freight GmbH **(2)**
Godesberger Allee 102-104, Bonn, 53175,
Germany
Tel.: (49) 228377880
Web Site: http://www.dhl.de
Freight Forwarding Services
N.A.I.C.S.: 488510
Bernhard Wirth *(Chm)*

**DHL Freight Hungary Forwarding and
Logistics Ltd.** **(2)**
Tel.: (36) 29556000
Web Site: http://www.dhl.com
Sales Range: $25-49.9 Million
Emp.: 7
Freight Transportation & Logistics Consult-
ing Services
N.A.I.C.S.: 488510

**DHL Freight Services (Netherlands)
B.V.** **(2)**
De Riemsdijk 1, 4004 LC, Tiel, Netherlands
Tel.: (31) 344609300
Freight Transportation Services
N.A.I.C.S.: 488510
Linda Truijen *(Mgr-Bus Support)*

DHL Freight Spain, S.L. **(2)**
Centro de Transportes de Coslada C/ Ru-
mania 4, 28821, Coslada, Madrid, Spain
Tel.: (34) 91 660 43 00
Freight Transportation Services
N.A.I.C.S.: 488510

DHL GBS (UK) Limited **(2)**
Solstice House 251 Midsummer Boulevard,
Milton Keynes, MK9 1EQ, Bucks, United
Kingdom
Tel.: (44) 1908 244180
Web Site: http://www.dhl.com
Logistics Consulting Servies
N.A.I.C.S.: 541614

**DHL Global Forwarding & Co.
LLC** **(2)**
Al Khuwair, PO Box 730, 133, Muscat,
Oman
Tel.: (968) 244 70300

Sales Range: $50-74.9 Million
Emp.: 15
Freight Forwarding Services
N.A.I.C.S.: 488510

**DHL Global Forwarding (Australia)
Pty Ltd.** **(2)**
96 - 106 Link Road Melbourne Airport, Mel-
bourne, 3045, VIC, Australia
Tel.: (61) 3 9344 8888
Web Site: http://www.dhl.com
Sales Range: $100-124.9 Million
Emp.: 30
Freight Forwarding Services
N.A.I.C.S.: 488510

**DHL Global Forwarding (Austria)
GmbH** **(2)**
Freudenauer Hafenstrasse 20-22, 1020,
Vienna, Austria
Tel.: (43) 50 345
Air & Ocean Freight Services
N.A.I.C.S.: 481112
Andrew Wingfield *(Gen Mgr)*

Subsidiary (Domestic):

**DHL Global Forwarding (Belgium)
NV** **(2)**
Building 830, 1931, Brussels, Belgium
Tel.: (32) 27520211
Sales Range: $200-249.9 Million
Emp.: 560
Freight Forwarding Services
N.A.I.C.S.: 488510
David Bellon *(Dir-Air Freight)*

Subsidiary (Non-US):

**DHL Global Forwarding (CZ) s. r.
o.** **(2)**
Web Site: http://www.dhlgf.cz
Sales Range: $25-49.9 Million
Emp.: 5
Freight Forwarding Services
N.A.I.C.S.: 488510
Kamil Kuzba *(Gen Mgr)*

**DHL Global Forwarding (Canada)
Inc.** **(2)**
6200 Edwards Boulevard, Mississauga, L5T
2V7, ON, Canada
Tel.: (289) 562-6500
Sales Range: $100-124.9 Million
Emp.: 260
Freight Forwarding Services
N.A.I.C.S.: 488510

**DHL Global Forwarding (Chile)
S.A.** **(2)**
Av del Vale 890 Ciudad Encesarial Hue-
churaba, Santiago, Chile
Tel.: (56) 2 4737100
Web Site: http://www.dhl.cl
Freight Forwarding Services
N.A.I.C.S.: 488510

**DHL Global Forwarding (Colombia)
Ltda.** **(2)**
Av Cl 26 No 85 B 09, Bogota, Colombia
Tel.: (57) 1 4292900
Web Site: http://www.dhl.com.co
Freight Forwarding Services
N.A.I.C.S.: 488510

**DHL Global Forwarding (Denmark) A
/ S** **(2)**
Kirstinehoej 42, 2770, Kastrup, Denmark
Tel.: (45) 3690 5500
Sales Range: $50-74.9 Million
Emp.: 15
Freight Forwarding Services
N.A.I.C.S.: 488510
Christoffer Kronborg Hagen *(Mgr-HR)*

**DHL Global Forwarding (Ecuador)
S.A.** **(2)**
Centro de Convenciones Guayaquil Centro
Empresarial Oficina 3 Av De, las Americas
No 406, Guayaquil, Ecuador
Tel.: (593) 4 2597666
Web Site: http://www.dhl.com.ec
Emp.: 16
Freight Forwarding Services
N.A.I.C.S.: 488510

**DHL Global Forwarding (Finland)
OY** **(2)**
Katriinantie 14-16, 01530, Vantaa, Finland

Tel.: (358) 20 533 11
Sales Range: $100-124.9 Million
Emp.: 50
Freight Forwarding Services
N.A.I.C.S.: 488510
Ben Angelvirta *(Dir-Mktg & Sls)*

**DHL Global Forwarding (Gabon)
SA** **(2)**
PO Box 736, Libreville, Gabon
Tel.: (241) 1442972
Sales Range: $25-49.9 Million
Emp.: 18
Freight Forwarding Services
N.A.I.C.S.: 488510

**DHL Global Forwarding (Guatemala)
S.A.** **(2)**
46 Calle 24-30 Zona 12, Guatemala, Gua-
temala
Web Site: http://www.dhl.com.gt
Emp.: 20
Freight Forwarding Services
N.A.I.C.S.: 488510

**DHL Global Forwarding (Hong Kong)
Limited** **(2)**
Tel.: (852) 22186888
Sales Range: $200-249.9 Million
Emp.: 60
Freight Forwarding Services
N.A.I.C.S.: 488510

**DHL Global Forwarding (Ireland)
Limited** **(2)**
Cedar Drive Dublin Airport Logistics Park St
Margaret s, Dublin, Ireland
Tel.: (353) 1 816 1000
Freight Forwarding Services
N.A.I.C.S.: 488510
Dermot Walsh *(Dir-Customer Svc)*

**DHL Global Forwarding (Italy) S. p.
A.** **(2)**
Via delle Industrie 1, 20060, Pozzuolo Mar-
tesana, Milan, Italy
Tel.: (39) 02 95252 1
Freight Forwarding Services
N.A.I.C.S.: 488510

**DHL Global Forwarding (Kuwait)
Company WLL** **(2)**
Ardiya, PO Box 2358, Kuwait, 13024, Ku-
wait
Tel.: (965) 1800345
Web Site: http://www.dhl.com.kw
Freight Forwarding Services
N.A.I.C.S.: 488510

**DHL Global Forwarding (Luxem-
bourg) S.A.** **(2)**
Tel.: (352) 346409450
Web Site: http://www.dhl.lu
Sales Range: $25-49.9 Million
Emp.: 15
Freight Forwarding Services
N.A.I.C.S.: 488510

**DHL Global Forwarding (Mexico) S.A.
de C.V.** **(2)**
Insurgentes Sur 859 Piso 9, Col Napoles
Ampliacion, 03810, Mexico, Mexico
Tel.: (52) 5551331700
Emp.: 300
Freight Forwarding Services
N.A.I.C.S.: 488510

**DHL Global Forwarding (Netherlands)
B.V.** **(2)**
Prestwickweg 1 Schiphol Zuid Oost, 1118
LC, Amsterdam, Netherlands
Tel.: (31) 203169000
Sales Range: $200-249.9 Million
Emp.: 60
Air & Ocean Freight Services
N.A.I.C.S.: 481112

**DHL Global Forwarding (New Zea-
land) Limited** **(2)**
Tel.: (64) 39404044
Web Site: http://www.dhl.com
Emp.: 12
Freight Forwarding Services
N.A.I.C.S.: 488510

**DHL Global Forwarding (Nicaragua)
S.A.** **(2)**
Tel.: (505) 22558700
Web Site: http://www.dhl.com

Emp.: 99
Freight Forwarding Services
N.A.I.C.S.: 488510

**DHL Global Forwarding (Philippines)
Inc.** **(2)**
Tel.: (63) 288837900
Web Site: http://www.dhl.com.ph
Sales Range: $100-124.9 Million
Emp.: 480
Freight Forwarding Services
N.A.I.C.S.: 488510

**DHL Global Forwarding (Senegal)
S.A.** **(2)**
KM 3 5 Boulevard du Centenaire de la
Commune de Dakar, BP 16840, Dakar,
Senegal
Tel.: (221) 33 859 09 00
Freight Forwarding Services
N.A.I.C.S.: 488510

**DHL Global Forwarding (Uganda)
Limited** **(2)**
Plot M248 Ntinda Industrial Area Kyambogo
Off Jinja, PO Box 72085, Kampala, Uganda
Tel.: (256) 312265722
Freight Forwarding Services
N.A.I.C.S.: 488510
Stephen Wanyama *(Controller-Fin)*

**DHL Global Forwarding (sweden)
AB** **(2)**
Molndalsvagen 30B, 412 63, Gothenburg,
Sweden
Tel.: (46) 771400400
Web Site: http://www.dhl.se
Freight Forwarding Services
N.A.I.C.S.: 488510

**DHL Global Forwarding (uk)
Limited** **(2)**
Danzas House Kestrel Way Dawley Park,
Hayes, UB3 1HJ, United Kingdom
Web Site: http://www.dhl.com
Sales Range: $100-124.9 Million
Emp.: 30
Freight Forwarding Services
N.A.I.C.S.: 488510

**DHL Global Forwarding Aduanas
Peru S.A.** **(2)**
Freight Forwarding Services
N.A.I.C.S.: 488510

**DHL Global Forwarding Egypt
S.A.E.** **(2)**
Tel.: (20) 226969800
Sales Range: $25-49.9 Million
Emp.: 10
Freight Forwarding Services
N.A.I.C.S.: 488510

DHL Global Forwarding GmbH **(2)**
Tel.: (49) 6913016
Emp.: 400
Freight Forwarding Services
N.A.I.C.S.: 488510

**DHL Global Forwarding Hellas
S.A.** **(2)**
Agiou Dimitriou 41, 185 46, Piraeus,
Greece
Web Site: http://www.dhl.gr
Sales Range: $25-49.9 Million
Emp.: 95
Freight Forwarding Services
N.A.I.C.S.: 488510

**DHL Global Forwarding Hungary
Kft.** **(2)**
Budapest BUD Nemzetkozi Repuloter DHL
epulet 264, 2220, Vecses, Hungary
Tel.: (36) 29 556 000
Web Site: http://www.dhl.hu
Freight Forwarding Services
N.A.I.C.S.: 488510

**DHL Global Forwarding Lanka (Pri-
vate) Limited** **(2)**
Tel.: (94) 117321321
Web Site: http://www.dhl.com
Emp.: 135
Freight Forwarding Services
N.A.I.C.S.: 488510

**DHL Global Forwarding Lebanon
S.A.L.** **(2)**
490 Harbour Drive Saifi, PO Box 175772,
Beirut, Lebanon

Deutsche Post AG—(Continued)

Tel.: (961) 1 564789
Emp.: 44
Freight Forwarding Services
N.A.I.C.S.: 488510
Rita Mansour (Country Mgr)

DHL Global Forwarding Management (Asia Pacific) Pte. Ltd. (2)
Freight Forwarding Services
N.A.I.C.S.: 488510

DHL Global Forwarding Pakistan (Private) Limited (2)
187/1/E PECHS Block II Shahrah-e-Quaideen, Karachi, 75400, Pakistan
Web Site: http://www.dhl.com.pk
Sales Range: $50-74.9 Million
Emp.: 200
Freight Forwarding Services
N.A.I.C.S.: 488510

DHL Global Forwarding Peru S.A. (2)
Tel.: (51) 14401936
Web Site: http://www.dhl.com.pe
Freight Forwarding Services
N.A.I.C.S.: 488510

DHL Global Forwarding Portugal, Lda. (2)
Aeroporto De Lisboa Edificio 124 2 Gab 1A, 1700-008, Lisbon, Portugal
Tel.: (351) 21 8438930
Web Site: http://www.dhl.pt
Sales Range: $25-49.9 Million
Emp.: 1
Freight Forwarding Services
N.A.I.C.S.: 488510

DHL Global Forwarding Sp. Z.O.O. (2)
Tel.: (48) 227037500
Web Site: http://www.dhlgf.pl
Sales Range: $25-49.9 Million
Emp.: 50
Freight Forwarding Services
N.A.I.C.S.: 488510

DHL Global Forwarding Tasimacilik A.S. (2)
Tel.: (90) 2126925050
Sales Range: $100-124.9 Million
Emp.: 30
Freight Forwarding Services
N.A.I.C.S.: 488510

DHL Global Forwarding Venezuela, C.A. (2)
Av San Francisco Cruce Con Palmarito Edif Parmalat - Piso 6, Estado Miranda Municipio Sucre, Caracas, Venezuela
Tel.: (58) 212205 02 00
Web Site: http://www.dhl.com.ve
Freight Transportation Services
N.A.I.C.S.: 488510

Subsidiary (US):

DHL Global Mail (2)
2700 S Commerce Pkwy Ste 400, Weston, FL 33331
Tel.: (954) 903-6300
Web Site: http://www.globalmail.com
Sales Range: $100-124.9 Million
Emp.: 100
Global Mail Delivery Network
N.A.I.C.S.: 491110
Lee Spratt (CEO)

Subsidiary (Non-US):

DHL Global Mail (Japan) k. k. (2)
1-37-8 Higashi-Shinagawa, Tokyo, 140-0002, Japan
Tel.: (81) 34332 4668
Sales Range: $25-49.9 Million
Emp.: 5
Courier Delivery Services
N.A.I.C.S.: 492110
Ciichiro Yamashita (Mng Dir)

DHL Global Mail (Singapore) Pte. Ltd. (2)
80 Alps Ave 03-07, Singapore, 498792, Singapore
Tel.: (65) 6883 0771
Sales Range: $25-49.9 Million
Emp.: 10
Courier Delivery Services

N.A.I.C.S.: 492110
Nitin Tatiwala (Gen Mgr)

DHL Holding (France) SAS (2)
53 Avenue Jean Jaures, 95700, Le Bourget, France
Tel.: (33) 149387070
Web Site: http://www.dhl.com
Sales Range: $50-74.9 Million
Emp.: 450
Investment Management Service
N.A.I.C.S.: 523940

Subsidiary (US):

DHL Holdings (USA), Inc. (2)
1200 S Pine Island Rd Ste 600, Plantation, FL 33324
Tel.: (954) 888-7000
Web Site: http://www.dhl-usa.com
Sales Range: $1-4.9 Billion
Express Delivery & Logistics Services
N.A.I.C.S.: 492110

Subsidiary (Non-US):

DHL Dominicana S.A. (3)
Ave Sarasota 26, Santo Domingo, Dominican Republic
Tel.: (809) 5347888
Web Site: https://www.dhl.com
Sales Range: $25-49.9 Million
Emp.: 60
Express Mail Services
N.A.I.C.S.: 492110

DHL de El Salvador S.A. de C.V. (3)
47 Av Norte 104, San Salvador, CA, El Salvador
Tel.: (503) 22607722
Web Site: http://www.dhl.com.sv
Sales Range: $25-49.9 Million
Emp.: 150
Express Mail Services
N.A.I.C.S.: 492110

DHL, S.A. (3)
Ave Hincapie 25-10 Zona 13, Guatemala, Guatemala
Tel.: (502) 23791111
Web Site: http://www.dhl.com.gt
Sales Range: $25-49.9 Million
Emp.: 144
Express Mail Services
N.A.I.C.S.: 541614

Subsidiary (Non-US):

DHL Home Delivery GmbH (2)
Rungedamm 37 B, 21035, Hamburg, Germany
Tel.: (49) 4073459010
Web Site: http://www.dhl.com
Sales Range: $10-24.9 Million
Emp.: 2
Courier Delivery Services
N.A.I.C.S.: 492210

DHL Hradflutningar EHF (2)
Skutuvogi 1 D, 104, Reykjavik, Iceland
Tel.: (354) 5351100
Web Site: http://www.dhl.is
Sales Range: $25-49.9 Million
Emp.: 60
Express Mail Services
N.A.I.C.S.: 492110

DHL Hub Leipzig GmbH (2)
Hermann-Kohl-Str 1, Flughafen, 4435, Leipzig, Germany
Tel.: (49) 34144990
Freight Transportation Services
N.A.I.C.S.: 488510

DHL ISC (Hong Kong) Limited (2)
21/F Tower 5 China Hong Kong City 33 Canton Road, Tsim Sha Tsui, Kowloon, China (Hong Kong)
Tel.: (852) 29763668
Logistics Consulting Servies
N.A.I.C.S.: 541614

DHL Information Services (Europe) S.R.O. (2)
V Parku 2308/10, Prague, 14800, Czech Republic
Tel.: (420) 288800000
Web Site: http://www.dhl.com
Sales Range: $350-399.9 Million
Emp.: 130

Software Development & Data Processing Services
N.A.I.C.S.: 541511

DHL International (Algerie) S.A.R.L (2)
7 Ave Blaise Pascal, 16000, Algiers, Algeria
Tel.: (213) 21230101
Web Site: http://www.dhl.com
Express Mail Services
N.A.I.C.S.: 492110

DHL International (Beograde) d.o.o. (2)
Omladinskih Brigada 86, 11070, Belgrade, Serbia
Tel.: (381) 0113105500
Web Site: http://www.dhl.com
Express Mail Services
N.A.I.C.S.: 492110

DHL International (Brunei) Sdn Bhd (2)
Unit 05 & 06 Ground Fl Bgh Pg Hj Mohd Daud Jalan Gadong, Bandar Seri Begawan, BE3919, Brunei Darussalam
Tel.: (673) 244 4991 2
Emp.: 45
Logistics Consulting Servies
N.A.I.C.S.: 541614
Kamarul Azman (Branch Mgr)

DHL International (Congo) SPRL (2)
180 Avenue du Marche, Gombe, Congo, Democratic Republic of
Tel.: (243) 817888810
Web Site: http://www.dhl.com
Courier Delivery Services
N.A.I.C.S.: 492210

DHL International (Gambia) Ltd. (2)
59 Mamadi Maniyang Highway Kanifing Industrial Estate, Banjul, Gambia
Tel.: (220) 4396658
Web Site: http://www.dhl.com
Emp.: 13
Freight Transportation Services
N.A.I.C.S.: 483111

DHL International (Nigeria) Ltd. (2)
DHL House Isolo Expressway, New Airport Road Junction, Isolo, Lagos, Nigeria
Tel.: (234) 14527086
Web Site: http://www.dhl.com.ng
Sales Range: $125-149.9 Million
Emp.: 700
Express Mail Services
N.A.I.C.S.: 492110

DHL International (Pty) Ltd. (2)
Old Mutual Business Park South, Gewel Street, 1600, Isando, South Africa
Tel.: (27) 0119213812
Web Site: http://www.dhl.com
Sales Range: $125-149.9 Million
Emp.: 700
Express Mail Services
N.A.I.C.S.: 492110

DHL International (UK) Ltd. (2)
Orbital Park, 178-188 Great South West Road, Hounslow, TW4 6JS, Mddx, United Kingdom
Tel.: (44) 8703661217
Web Site: http://www.dhl.co.uk
Sales Range: $1-4.9 Billion
Express Mail Services
N.A.I.C.S.: 492110

DHL International (Uganda) Ltd. (2)
4 Upper Kololo Terrace andLugogo Bypass, Jinja, Uganda
Tel.: (256) 312210006
Web Site: http://www.dhl.co.ug
Emp.: 3
Logistics Consulting & Courier Distribution Services
N.A.I.C.S.: 541614

DHL International B.S.C. (C) (2)
Block 224 Bulding 342 Bahrain Regional Distribution Centre, PO Box 5741, Muharraq, Bahrain
Tel.: (973) 17335005
Web Site: http://www.dhl.com.bh
Logistics Consulting & Courier Distribution Services
N.A.I.C.S.: 541614

DHL International B.V. (2)

Terminalweg 36, PB 2717, 3821 AJ, Amersfoort, Netherlands
Tel.: (31) 33257 77 77
Web Site: http://www.dhl.nl
Courier Delivery Services
N.A.I.C.S.: 492110

DHL International Cameroon SARL (2)
244 Boulevard De La Liberte, BP 3582, 3582, Douala, Cameroon
Tel.: (237) 33423636
Sales Range: $25-49.9 Million
Emp.: 80
Logistics Consulting Servies
N.A.I.C.S.: 541614
Ousmanou Koudtou (Country Mgr)

DHL International Cote D'Ivoire SARL (2)
Immeuble Le Massai 1er Etage Lot 86 Boulevard VGE Marcory, BP 2069, Abidjan, Cote d'Ivoire
Tel.: (225) 21219998
Web Site: http://www.dhl.ci
Logistics Consulting Servies
N.A.I.C.S.: 541614
Eliane Koidou (Area Mgr-Customer Svc-DHL Express)

DHL International Express (France) SAS (2)
241 Rue de la Belle Etoile, 95957, Roissy-en-France, France
Tel.: (33) 149387235
Sales Range: $25-49.9 Million
Emp.: 20
Logistics Consulting & Courier Distribution Services
N.A.I.C.S.: 541614
Florence Noblot (Head-Global Comml Project)

DHL International Hellas S.A. (2)
44 Alimou avenue & 17 Roma Strs, Athens, 17455, Greece
Tel.: (30) 2109890800
Web Site: http://www.dhl.gr
Sales Range: $75-99.9 Million
Emp.: 450
Express Mail Services
N.A.I.C.S.: 492110

DHL International Kazakhstan, TOO (2)
1/1 Dzhandosov Str, Almaty, 50008, Kazakhstan
Tel.: (7) 7272588588
Web Site: http://www.dhl.kz
Sales Range: $75-99.9 Million
Emp.: 30
Logistics Consulting Servies
N.A.I.C.S.: 541614

DHL International Ltd. (2)
MIA Cargo Village, Luqa, LQA 3290, Malta
Tel.: (356) 21800148
Web Site: http://www.dhl.com.mt
Logistics Consulting & Courier Distribution Services
N.A.I.C.S.: 541614

DHL International Ltd. (2)
06 Thang Long Street Ward 4 ; Tan Binh Dist, Ho Chi Minh City, Vietnam
Tel.: (84) 8 3844 6203
Web Site: http://www.dhl.com.vn
Sales Range: $125-149.9 Million
Emp.: 670
Express Mail Services
N.A.I.C.S.: 492110

DHL International Madagascar SA (2)
Lot II J 181 F Bis Ivandry, Antananarivo, 101, Madagascar
Tel.: (261) 202242839
Logistics Consulting Servies
N.A.I.C.S.: 541614
Andry Ramarijaona (Project Mgr)

DHL International Malawi Ltd. (2)
Masauko Chipembere Highway Kristwick, PO Box 1762, Blantyre, Malawi
Tel.: (265) 1870688
Web Site: http://www.dhl.co.mw
Sales Range: $25-49.9 Million
Emp.: 20
Logistics Consulting & Courier Distribution Services

N.A.I.C.S.: 541614

DHL International Romania SRL   (2)
Emanoil Porumbaru Str 85-87, Sector 1,
11424, Bucharest, Romania
Tel.: (40) 21 2221469
Web Site: http://www.dhl.ro
Express Mail Services
N.A.I.C.S.: 492110

DHL International S.R.L.   (2)
Calle 1 Manzana A Lote 6 Fundo Bocanegra Callao 1, Lima, Peru
Tel.: (51) 1 575 4433
Web Site: http://www.dhl.com.pe
Sales Range: $75-99.9 Million
Emp.: 400
Express Mail Services
N.A.I.C.S.: 492110

DHL International Senegal SARL   (2)
Rue Leon Gontran Damas X Rue F Fann
Residence, BP 3554, Dakar, Senegal
Tel.: (221) 338691111
Emp.: 100
Parcel & Courier Services
N.A.I.C.S.: 492210
Abdoulaye Thiam *(Country Mgr)*

DHL International d.o.o.   (2)
Turinina 3, 10020, Zagreb, Croatia
Tel.: (385) 016651111
Web Site: http://www.dhl.hr
Sales Range: $25-49.9 Million
Emp.: 200
Express Mail Services
N.A.I.C.S.: 492110

**DHL International-Sarajevo
D.O.O.**   (2)
Dzemala Bijedica 166a, 71000, Sarajevo,
Bosnia & Herzegovina
Tel.: (387) 33774000
Sales Range: $25-49.9 Million
Emp.: 5
Logistic Consulting & Courier Services
N.A.I.C.S.: 541614
Djenan Dzumhur *(Mgr-Comml)*

DHL Intl (Bulgaria) E.O.O.D.   (2)
10 Prodan Tarakchiev str, 1528, Sofia, Bulgaria
Tel.: (359) 293094
Web Site: http://www.dhl.bg
Sales Range: $75-99.9 Million
Emp.: 300
Express Mail Services
N.A.I.C.S.: 492110

DHL Intl (Slovakia) spol. s r.o.   (2)
Letisko MR Stefanika 65, 82001, Bratislava,
Slovakia
Tel.: (421) 800100300
Web Site: http://www.dhl.sk
Sales Range: $25-49.9 Million
Emp.: 175
Express Mail Services
N.A.I.C.S.: 492110

DHL Japan, Inc.   (2)
Web Site: http://www.dhl.co.jp
Sales Range: $25-49.9 Million
Emp.: 138
Express Mail Services
N.A.I.C.S.: 492110

DHL Keells (Private) Limited   (2)
148 Vauxhall Street, Colombo, 200, Sri
Lanka
Tel.: (94) 112304304
Web Site: http://www.dhl.com
Emp.: 25
Parcel & Courier Services
N.A.I.C.S.: 492210

DHL Korea Ltd.   (2)
Ilyang Bldg 164-6 Yeomri-dong Mapo-ku,
Seoul, 121874, Korea (South)
Tel.: (82) 27108213
Web Site: http://www.dhl.co.kr
Sales Range: $250-299.9 Million
Emp.: 1,200
Express Mail Services
N.A.I.C.S.: 492110

DHL Kuwait Co. Ltd   (2)
1 Arabian Gulf Strreet, 80017, Kuwait, Kuwait
Tel.: (965) 22434752
Web Site: http://www.dhl.com

Sales Range: $25-49.9 Million
Emp.: 200
Express Mail Services
N.A.I.C.S.: 492110

DHL Lao Limited   (2)
031 Nongno St Ban Wattaynoy Thong, PO
Box 7083, Vientiane, Lao People's Democratic Republic
Tel.: (856) 21 214 868
Web Site: http://www.fastforward.dhl.com
Logistics Consulting Servies
N.A.I.C.S.: 541614

DHL Lesotho (Proprietary) Ltd.   (2)
Options Bldg Pioneer Rd, Maseru, 100,
Lesotho
Tel.: (266) 22311082
Web Site: http://www.dhl.com
Emp.: 15
Real Estate Manangement Services
N.A.I.C.S.: 531390

DHL Logistica D.O.O.   (2)
Vojkovo Nabrezje 30/A, 6000, Koper, Slovenia
Tel.: (386) 5 600 9943
Web Site: http://www.dhl.com
Sales Range: $25-49.9 Million
Emp.: 18
Logistics Consulting Servies
N.A.I.C.S.: 541614

DHL Logistics (Cambodia) Ltd.   (2)
Regency Complex A 1st Fl No 8A/298 Mao
Tse Toung Blvd St 245 Sangkat, Tomnoubteouk Khan Chamkamon, Phnom Penh,
Cambodia
Tel.: (855) 523885968
Freight Forwarding Services
N.A.I.C.S.: 488510

DHL Logistics (Schweiz) AG   (2)
Tel.: (41) 613159259
Web Site: http://external.dhl.ch
Freight Forwarding Services
N.A.I.C.S.: 488510

**DHL Logistics (Slovakia), spol. s r.
o.**   (2)
Letisko M R Stefanika, 821 04, Bratislava,
Slovakia
Tel.: (421) 243426651
Logistics Consulting Servies
N.A.I.C.S.: 541614

DHL Logistics (Ukraine) Ltd.   (2)
11 Polskiy Spusk, Odessa, 65026, Ukraine
Tel.: (380) 487341134
Web Site: http://www.dhl.com.ua
Sales Range: $25-49.9 Million
Emp.: 9
Logistics Consulting Servies
N.A.I.C.S.: 541614

DHL Logistics OOO   (2)
Leningradskoye Highway 39 Bldg 5 Khimki
Business Park 10th Floor, 141400, Khimki,
Russia
Tel.: (7) 4959332200
Web Site: http://www.dhl.com
Sales Range: $25-49.9 Million
Emp.: 13
Logistics Consulting Servies
N.A.I.C.S.: 541614

DHL Logistics Tanzania Limited   (2)
Capri Point Station Road, PO Box 1904,
Mwanza, Tanzania
Tel.: (255) 282500800
Web Site: http://www.dhl.com
Logistics Consulting Servies
N.A.I.C.S.: 541614

DHL Lojistik Hizmetleri A.S.   (2)
Kocadag Plaza Kat 3 9 Cubuklu Mahallesi
Orhan Veli Kanik Caddesi, 34810, Istanbul,
Turkiye
Tel.: (90) 2165370707
Logistics Consulting Servies
N.A.I.C.S.: 541614

DHL Management (Schweiz) AG   (2)
Peter Merian-Strasse 88, Postfach 4002,
4052, Basel, Switzerland
Tel.: (41) 612747474
Web Site: http://www.dhl.com
Sales Range: $25-49.9 Million
Emp.: 3
Real Estate Investment Services
N.A.I.C.S.: 525990

DHL Mozambique Lda.   (2)
Cnr Ave 24 de Julho & Av Da Tanzania Nbr
147, Maputo, Mozambique
Tel.: (258) 21 225 300
Web Site: http://www.dhl.co.mz
Emp.: 8
Logistics Consulting & Courier Distribution
Services
N.A.I.C.S.: 541614

DHL Pakistan (Private) Limited   (2)
Survey Number 137 Jinnah International
Airport, Karachi, 75100, Pakistan
Tel.: (92) 111345111
Web Site: https://www.dhl.com
Sales Range: $200-249.9 Million
Emp.: 60
Air Freight Transportation Services
N.A.I.C.S.: 481112

DHL Panama S.A.   (2)
Ave Centenario Costa del Este DHL
Panama Building, Panama, Panama
Tel.: (507) 2713400
Web Site: https://www.dhl.com
Parcel & Courier Services
N.A.I.C.S.: 492210

**DHL Pensions Investment Fund
Limited**   (2)
The Marton Center, Bedford, MK40 2UB,
United Kingdom
Tel.: (44) 1234 273727
Sales Range: $75-99.9 Million
Emp.: 20
Pension Fund Services
N.A.I.C.S.: 525110
Robert Sharratt *(Gen Mgr)*

DHL Pipelife Logistik GmbH   (2)
IZ NO Sudstrasse 14 Objekt 24, 2355, Wiener Neudorf, Austria
Tel.: (43) 2732855020
Web Site: http://www.dhl.com
Emp.: 4
Logistics Consulting Servies
N.A.I.C.S.: 541614

DHL Quality Cargo AS   (2)
Sven Of Tetalsveiem 10, 0901, Oslo, Norway
Tel.: (47) 23243600
Web Site: http://www.dhl.no
Emp.: 15
Cargo Handling Services
N.A.I.C.S.: 488320

DHL Rail AB   (2)
Algatan 27, Box 57, Trelleborg, 231 42,
Sweden
Tel.: (46) 410740600
Web Site: http://www.dhl.com
Sales Range: $25-49.9 Million
Emp.: 14
Logistics Consulting Servies
N.A.I.C.S.: 541614

DHL Sainghin SARL   (2)
Rue Des Hauts De Sainghin Centre De
Gros N 3, 59262, Sainghin-en-Melantois,
France
Tel.: (33) 320904610
Logistics Consulting Servies
N.A.I.C.S.: 541614

DHL Services Limited   (2)
45 St Peters Street, Bedford, MK40 2PN,
Bedfordshire, United Kingdom
Tel.: (44) 1234273727
Logistics Consulting Servies
N.A.I.C.S.: 541614

DHL Services Logistiques SAS   (2)
Quais Atlantique Port Ouest Dunkerque
Route Ameriques, Loon-Plage, 59279,
France
Tel.: (33) 328660666
Logistics Consulting Servies
N.A.I.C.S.: 541614

Subsidiary (Domestic):

DHL Solutions (Belgium) NV   (2)
Zandvoortstraat 3, Mechelen, 2800, Belgium
Tel.: (32) 15299111
Sales Range: $25-49.9 Million
Emp.: 150
Logistics Consulting Servies
N.A.I.C.S.: 541614

Subsidiary (US):

DHL Solutions (USA), Inc.   (2)
1 Carr 869 Bldg C, Catano, PR 00962-5880
Tel.: (787) 788-3888
Logistics Consulting Servies
N.A.I.C.S.: 541614

Subsidiary (Non-US):

DHL Solutions Fashion GmbH   (2)
Hafenstr 70, Essen, 45356, Germany
Tel.: (49) 201 80601
Emp.: 500
Transportation Services
N.A.I.C.S.: 488999
Mr. Lippe *(Mgr)*

DHL Solutions GmbH   (2)
Hammerbrookstr 94, 21035, Hamburg, Germany
Tel.: (49) 4073450
Sales Range: $25-49.9 Million
Emp.: 80
Logistics Consulting Servies
N.A.I.C.S.: 541614
Michael Rolle *(Co-Mng Dir)*

DHL Solutions Grossgut GmbH   (2)
Keine Strasse Angegeben, 56477,
Rennerod, Germany
Tel.: (49) 26 64 50 83 00
Logistics Consulting Servies
N.A.I.C.S.: 541614

DHL Solutions Retail GmbH   (2)
Giesserstrasse 5, 59425, Unna, Nordrhein-Westfalen, Germany
Tel.: (49) 2303 6780
Web Site: http://www.dhl.com
Freight Transportation Services
N.A.I.C.S.: 488510

**DHL Supply Chain (Australia) Pty
Limited**   (2)
Rhodes Corporate Park L 3 Building A 1
Homebush Bay Dr, Rhodes, Sydney, 2138,
NSW, Australia
Tel.: (61) 287597000
Web Site: http://www.dhl.com.au
Emp.: 14
Freight Forwarding Services
N.A.I.C.S.: 488510

Subsidiary (Domestic):

DHL Supply Chain (Belgium) NV   (2)
Zandvoortstraat 3, 2800, Mechelen, Belgium
Tel.: (32) 15299111
Web Site: http://www.dhl.com
Sales Range: $25-49.9 Million
Emp.: 100
Freight Transportation Services
N.A.I.C.S.: 488510

Subsidiary (Non-US):

DHL Supply Chain (Chile) S.A.   (2)
Panamericana Norte 19001 - Km 19,
Colina, Santiago, Chile
Tel.: (56) 25805700
Web Site: http://www.dhl.cl
Emp.: 1,300
Freight Forwarding Services
N.A.I.C.S.: 488510

DHL Supply Chain (Finland) Oy   (2)
Katriinantie 14-16, 1530, Vantaa, Finland
Tel.: (358) 205333
Sales Range: $75-99.9 Million
Emp.: 33
Logistics Consulting Servies
N.A.I.C.S.: 541614
Otso Forsblom *(Mng Dir)*

**DHL Supply Chain (Ireland)
Limited**   (2)
Oak Road Western Business Park, Dublin,
12, Ireland
Tel.: (353) 14050800
Web Site: http://www.dhl.ie
Sales Range: $50-74.9 Million
Emp.: 20
Freight Forwarding Services
N.A.I.C.S.: 488510

DHL Supply Chain (Korea) Ltd.   (2)
4 5F Yonsei Building 84-11 Namdaemunro
5ga, Jung-gu, Seoul, 100-753, Korea
(South)

Deutsche Post AG—(Continued)

Tel.: (82) 262201500
Web Site: http://www.dhl.co.kr
Logistics & Freight Forwarding Services
N.A.I.C.S.: 541614

DHL Supply Chain (New Zealand) Limited (2)
7-9 Burgess Road Mt Wellington, Auckland, 1051, New Zealand
Tel.: (64) 95741450
Web Site: http://www.dhl.com
Sales Range: $25-49.9 Million
Emp.: 75
Logistics Consulting Servies
N.A.I.C.S.: 541614

DHL Supply Chain (Norway) AS (2)
Ulvenveien 111, 665, Oslo, Norway
Tel.: (47) 66929648
Sales Range: $50-74.9 Million
Emp.: 20
Freight Forwarding Services
N.A.I.C.S.: 488510

DHL Supply Chain (Poland) Sp. z o.o. (2)
66 Bokserska, 02-690, Warsaw, Poland
Tel.: (48) 224557655
Sales Range: $150-199.9 Million
Emp.: 100
Logistics Consulting Servies
N.A.I.C.S.: 541614
Szymon Siodmiaki (Project Mgr)

DHL Supply Chain K. K. (2)
Gotenyama Trust Tower 8F 4-7-35 Kita-Shinagawa, Shinagawa-ku, Tokyo, 140-0001, Japan
Tel.: (81) 357929001
Web Site: http://www.dhl.co.jp
Freight Forwarding Services
N.A.I.C.S.: 488510

DHL Supply Chain Singapore Pte. Ltd. (2)
600 North Bridge Road 23-01 Parkview Square, 188778, Singapore
Tel.: (65) 63728200
Sales Range: $100-124.9 Million
Emp.: 50
Freight Forwarding Services
N.A.I.C.S.: 488510
Steven Kok Wha Sim (Sr Mgr-Logistics)

DHL Swaziland (Proprietary) Ltd. (2)
Karlyn Centre Cooper Lane, Mbabane, 8100, Eswatini
Tel.: (268) 24045829
Real Estate Manangement Services
N.A.I.C.S.: 531390
Wayne Van Rensburg (Gen Mgr)

DHL Trade Fairs and Events (uk) Limited (2)
Unit 17 21 2nd Exhibition Avenue N E C, Birmingham, B40 1PJ, United Kingdom
Tel.: (44) 1217824626
Web Site: https://www.dhl-exh.com
Sales Range: $25-49.9 Million
Emp.: 6
Event Management & Logistics Services
N.A.I.C.S.: 541618

DHL Verwaltungs GmbH (2)
Charles de Gaulle Strasse 20, 53113, Bonn, Germany
Tel.: (49) 806345300
Web Site: http://www.deutschepost.de
Sales Range: $1-4.9 Billion
Holding Company
N.A.I.C.S.: 551112

DHL Voigt International GmbH (2)
Herbert-voigt Strasse 1, 24539, Neumunster, Germany
Tel.: (49) 4321 8730
Web Site: http://www.voigt-logistik.de
Logistics Consulting Servies
N.A.I.C.S.: 541614
Janina Pries (Sec)

DHL Wahl International GmbH (2)
Gildemeisterstrasse 150, 33689, Bielefeld, Germany
Tel.: (49) 52057550
Logistics Consulting Servies
N.A.I.C.S.: 541614

DHL Worldwide Express (Bangladesh) Private Limited (2)

Courier Delivery Services
N.A.I.C.S.: 492110

DHL Worldwide Express (PH) Corp. (2)
DHL House 2306 Chino Roces Avenue Pasong Tamo Extension Kayamanan C, Makati, 1231, Philippines
Tel.: (63) 288117113
Web Site: http://www.dhl.com.ph
Sales Range: $125-149.9 Million
Emp.: 900
Express Mail Services
N.A.I.C.S.: 492110

DHL Worldwide Express (PNG) Ltd. (2)
PO Box 1775, Port Moresby, Papua New Guinea
Tel.: (675) 325 9866
Web Site: http://www.fastforward.dhl.com
Courier Service
N.A.I.C.S.: 492110

DHL Worldwide Express Cambodia Ltd (2)
353 St 110 Sangkat Sras Chark, Khan Daun Penh, Phnom Penh, 12201, Cambodia
Tel.: (855) 23 427 726
Web Site: http://www.dhl.com
Emp.: 5
Logistics Consulting Services
N.A.I.C.S.: 541614
Prayag Chitrakar (Country Mgr)

DHL Worldwide Express Cargo LLC (2)
Sh Zayed Rd Khalid Al Attar Tower, PO Box 6252, Dubai, 6252, United Arab Emirates
Tel.: (971) 48004004
Web Site: http://www.dhl.com
Courier Delivery Services
N.A.I.C.S.: 492110

DHL Worldwide Express Kenya Ltd. (2)
Corner Lusaka Road and Witu Road, PO Box 67577, 00200, Nairobi, Kenya
Tel.: (254) 711017120
Web Site: https://www.dhl.com
Sales Range: $25-49.9 Million
Emp.: 132
Express Mail Services
N.A.I.C.S.: 492110

DHL Worldwide Express Tasimacilik ve Ticaret A.S. (2)
Courier Service
N.A.I.C.S.: 492110

DHL Yemen Ltd. (2)
100 Haddah St, PO Box 19600, Sana'a, Yemen
Tel.: (967) 1441096
Web Site: http://www.ye.dhl.com
Express Mail Services
N.A.I.C.S.: 492110

DHL-Transportadores Rapidos Internacionais Lda. (2)
Rua Palmira 35A, 1170, Lisbon, Portugal
Tel.: (351) 218146422
Web Site: http://www.dhl.pt
Express Mail Services
N.A.I.C.S.: 492110

DHL-VNPT Express Ltd. (2)
Tel.: (84) 838446203
Emp.: 50
Logistics Consulting Servies
N.A.I.C.S.: 541614
Chao Nguyen (Mgr-HR)

Dongguan DHL Supply Chain Co., Ltd. (2)
Industrial Park Metro Avenue 4 First Floor, Southern District, Dongguan, 523808, China
Tel.: (86) 13798943525
Freight Forwarding Services
N.A.I.C.S.: 488510

LLC DHL Express (2)
st 8 March no 14, Moscow, 127 083, Russia
Tel.: (7) 4959561000
Web Site: https://www.logistics.dhl.ru
Parcel & Courier Services
N.A.I.C.S.: 492210

LLC DHL International Kazakhstan (2)
1/1 Dzhandosova str, 50009, Almaty, Kazakhstan
Tel.: (7) 3272588588
Web Site: http://www.dhl.kz
Sales Range: $25-49.9 Million
Emp.: 80
Express Mail Services
N.A.I.C.S.: 492110

Myanmar DHL Limited (2)
No 220 Inseen Road, Hlaing Township, 11061, Yangon, Myanmar
Tel.: (95) 12305405
Web Site: http://www.dhl.com
Sales Range: $25-49.9 Million
Emp.: 58
Express Mail Services
N.A.I.C.S.: 492110

P.T. Birotika Semesta/DHL (2)
Siemens Business Park Building F Jalan MT Haryono Kav 58-60, 12780, Jakarta, Indonesia
Tel.: (62) 2179173333
Web Site: http://www.dhl.co.id
Sales Range: $75-99.9 Million
Emp.: 350
Express Mail Services
N.A.I.C.S.: 492110

PT DHL Global Forwarding Indonesia (2)
Lot 8 Block A Soewarna Business Park Soekarna Hatta Intl Airport, Jakarta, 19110, Indonesia
Tel.: (62) 2155913161
Freight Forwarding Services
N.A.I.C.S.: 488510

Tradeteam Limited (2)
Edison Road Hams Hall, National Distribution Park, Coleshill, B46 1TT, United Kingdom (100%)
Tel.: (44) 1215043111
Web Site: http://www.tradeteam.com
Sales Range: $300-349.9 Million
Beverage Transportation & Logistics Services
N.A.I.C.S.: 541614

UAB DHL Lietuva (2)
Tel.: (370) 52360700
Sales Range: $25-49.9 Million
Emp.: 10
Logistics Consulting Servies
N.A.I.C.S.: 541614

ZAO DHL International Russia (2)
8th Marta St 14, Moscow, 127092, Russia
Tel.: (7) 4959561000
Web Site: http://www.dhl.ru
Sales Range: $1-9.9 Million
Emp.: 495
Express Mail Services
N.A.I.C.S.: 492110

DHL Logistics Ghana Ltd. (1)
18 Kwame Nkruma Avenue Ridge, Accra, Ghana
Tel.: (233) 247935760
Logistics Consulting Servies
N.A.I.C.S.: 541614

DHL Logistik Service GmbH (1)
IZ NO SUD Strasse 14 Objekt 24, 2355, Wiener Neudorf, Austria
Tel.: (43) 22366030
Logistics Consulting Servies.
N.A.I.C.S.: 541614

DHL Metropolitan Logistics sc Mexico S.A. de C.V. (1)
Autopista Mexico-Queretaro Km 34 5 Nave 1, Cuautitlan, 54740, Mexico
Tel.: (52) 5530032600
Logistics Consulting Servies
N.A.I.C.S.: 541614

DHL Network Operations (usa), Inc. (1)
1210 S Pine Island Rd 1st Fl Legal Dept, Plantation, FL 33324
Logistics Consulting Servies
N.A.I.C.S.: 541614

DHL Paket GmbH (1)
Strasschensweg 10, 53113, Bonn, Germany
Tel.: (49) 2281820

Web Site: https://www.dhl.de
N.A.I.C.S.: 541614

DHL Parcel Portugal, Unipessoal Lda. (1)
Av Alvaro Cunhal n 6, 2660-341, Loures, Portugal
Tel.: (351) 210608217
Express Delivery Services
N.A.I.C.S.: 541219

DHL SC Transport SASU (1)
ZA Trappes Elancourt 2-4 Avenue Enrico Fermi, 78190, Trappes, France
Tel.: (33) 1 30 16 20 23
Logistics Consulting Servies
N.A.I.C.S.: 541614

DHL Sandouville SARL (1)
266 Avenue Du President Wilson, Saint Denis, 93200, France
Tel.: (33) 1 46 88 89 02
Logistics Consulting Servies
N.A.I.C.S.: 541614

DHL Stock Express SAS (1)
Logistics Consulting Servies
N.A.I.C.S.: 541614

DHL Supply Chain (Denmark) A/S (1)
Moenten 7, 6000, Kolding, Denmark
Tel.: (45) 76343666
Logistics Consulting Servies
N.A.I.C.S.: 541614

DHL Supply Chain (South Africa) (Pty) Ltd. (1)
110 South Coast Road, Congella, 4000, South Africa
Tel.: (27) 312047600
Logistics Consulting Servies
N.A.I.C.S.: 541614

DHL Supply Chain (Vietnam) Limited (1)
364 Cong Hoa Street 11F eTown 2 Building, Tan Binh, Ho Chi Minh City, Vietnam
Tel.: (84) 838123888
Logistics Consulting Servies
N.A.I.C.S.: 541614

DHL Supply Chain Inc. (1)
570 Polaris Pkwy, Westerville, OH 43082
Tel.: (614) 865-8500
Web Site: http://www.dhl.com
Logistics Consulting Servies
N.A.I.C.S.: 541614
Scott Sureddin (CEO-North America)

DHL Supply Chain Management GmbH (1)
Tel.: (49) 2281820
Logistics Consulting Servies
N.A.I.C.S.: 541614
Paul Graham (COO)

DHL Trade Fairs & Events GmbH (1)
Welserstrasse 10d, 51149, Cologne, Germany
Tel.: (49) 2203368000
Web Site: http://www.dhl-tfe.com
Exhibition & Event Logistic Services
N.A.I.C.S.: 541614

DHL Worldwide Express Logistics NV /SA (1)
De Kleetlaan 1, 1831, Diegem, Belgium
Tel.: (32) 27134000
Logistics Consulting Servies
N.A.I.C.S.: 541614

DHL Worldwide Express, Inc (1)
50 California St, San Francisco, CA 94111
Tel.: (415) 677-6800
Logistics Consulting Servies
N.A.I.C.S.: 541614

DHL eCommerce (Malaysia) Sdn. Bhd. (1)
3 Jalan PPU 1 Taman Perindustrian Puchong Utama, 47100, Puchong, Selangor, Malaysia
Tel.: (60) 327792300
N.A.I.C.S.: 541614

DHL eCommerce (Singapore) Pte. Ltd. (1)
150 Beach Road 11-01 Gateway West, Sin-

gapore, 189720, Singapore
Tel.: (65) 68798000
N.A.I.C.S.: 541614

DHL global forwarding cote d'ivoire SA (1)
Immeuble Le Massai 1er etage lot 86 Boulevard VGE Marcory 01, BP 2069, Abidjan, 01, Cote d'Ivoire
Tel.: (225) 21 21 28 80
Freight Forwarding Services
N.A.I.C.S.: 488510

DHL of Curacao N.V. (1)
Courier Service
N.A.I.C.S.: 492110

DPWN Holdings (USA), Inc. (1)
1200 S Pine Island Rd Ste 600, Plantation, FL 33324
Tel.: (954) 888-7000
Logistics Consulting Servies
N.A.I.C.S.: 541614

Danzas Abu Dhabi LLC (1)
Mezzanine Fl Mafco Bldg Muroor E Rd, Abu Dhabi, United Arab Emirates
Tel.: (971) 2 4452788
Freight Forwarding Services
N.A.I.C.S.: 488510

Danzas Bahrain WLL (1)
PO Box 56, Manama, Bahrain
Tel.: (973) 17728151
Web Site: http://www.dhl.com.bh
Freight Forwarding Services
N.A.I.C.S.: 488510

Danzas Deutschland Holding GmbH (1)
Obenhauptstrasse 9, 22335, Hamburg, Germany
Tel.: (49) 405002330
Emp.: 7
Investment Management Service
N.A.I.C.S.: 523999

Danzas Fashion NV (1)
Square de l'Atomium, 1020, Brussels, Belgium
Tel.: (32) 2 478 17 77
Logistics Consulting Servies
N.A.I.C.S.: 541614

Danzas Fashion Service Centers B.V. (1)
Industrieweg 55, 5145 PD, Waalwijk, Netherlands
Tel.: (31) 416565520
Sales Range: $25-49.9 Million
Emp.: 2
Air Freight Transportation Services
N.A.I.C.S.: 488510

Danzas Grundstucksverwaltung Gross-Gerau GmbH (1)
Andreas-Meyer-Strasse 45, 22113, Hamburg, Germany
Tel.: (49) 4038605114
Real Estate Manangement Services
N.A.I.C.S.: 531390

Danzas Holding AG (1)
Peter Merian-Strasse 88, Basel, 4002, Switzerland
Tel.: (41) 612747474
Investment Management Service
N.A.I.C.S.: 523940

Danzas Kiev Ltd. (1)
3 Hrinchenka Building Office 3A, Kiev, 3680, Ukraine
Tel.: (380) 442466046
Sales Range: $50-74.9 Million
Emp.: 7
Air & Marine Cargo Handling Services
N.A.I.C.S.: 488119
Aleksandra Matvienko (Gen Mgr)

Deutsche Post Adress GmbH (1)
Am Anger 33, Gutersloh, 33332, Germany
Tel.: (49) 524153930
Web Site: http://www.deutschepost.de
Emp.: 120
Address Correction Services
N.A.I.C.S.: 541614
Philip Rurup (Gen Mgr)

Deutsche Post Beteiligungen Holding GmbH (1)

Straesschensweg 10, Bonn, 53113, Germany
Tel.: (49) 22818264800
Investment Management Service
N.A.I.C.S.: 523940

Deutsche Post Com GmbH (1)
Tulpenfeld 9, Bonn, 53113, Germany
Tel.: (49) 22890860
Web Site: http://www.dpcom.de
Sales Range: $25-49.9 Million
Emp.: 90
Electronic Transaction Services
N.A.I.C.S.: 561499
Rudiger Haase (Mng Dir)

Deutsche Post Customer Service Center GmbH (1)
Heinestrasse 3-7, Monheim, 40789, Nordrhein-Westfalen, Germany
Tel.: (49) 21733900
Business Support Services
N.A.I.C.S.: 561499

Deutsche Post DHL Beteiligungen GmbH (1)
Charles-de-Gaulle-Str 20, Bonn, 53113, Germany
Tel.: (49) 2281820
Financial Management Services
N.A.I.C.S.: 523999
Frank Appel (Chm)

Deutsche Post DHL Corporate Real Estate Management GmbH (1)
Godesberger Allee 157, Bonn, 53175, Germany
Tel.: (49) 228 5289 0
Sales Range: $75-99.9 Million
Emp.: 120
Real Estate Manangement Services
N.A.I.C.S.: 531390
Dennis Boeing (Mgr)

Deutsche Post DHL Inhouse Consulting GmbH (1)
Tulpenfeld 1, Bonn, 53113, Nordrhein-Westfalen, Germany
Tel.: (49) 22824350
Information Technology Consulting Services
N.A.I.C.S.: 541512

Deutsche Post DHL Research and Innovation GmbH (1)
Tulpenfeld Haus 2, 53113, Bonn, Germany
Tel.: (49) 2282435700
Emp.: 28
Marketing Research Service
N.A.I.C.S.: 541910
Doris Sibum (VP)

Deutsche Post Direkt GmbH (1)
Junkersring 57, 53844, Troisdorf, Germany
Tel.: (49) 22818915990
Web Site: https://www.deutschepost.de
Sales Range: $75-99.9 Million
Emp.: 100
Address & Document Management Services
N.A.I.C.S.: 561499

Deutsche Post Global Mail (Australia) Pty Ltd. (1)
1/55 Kent Rd, Mascot, 2020, Australia
Tel.: (61) 1800688280
Air Freight Transportation Services
N.A.I.C.S.: 481112

Deutsche Post Global Mail (France) SAS (1)
143 Bis Avenue De Verdun, 92130, Issy-les-Moulineaux, France
Tel.: (33) 141083170
Web Site: http://www.dhlglobalmail.fr
Sales Range: $25-49.9 Million
Emp.: 2
Air Freight Transportation Services
N.A.I.C.S.: 481112
Marcel Bassant (Gen Mgr)

Deutsche Post Global Mail GmbH (1)
Charles-de-Gaulle-Strasse 20, 53113, Bonn, Germany
Tel.: (49) 2281820
Web Site: http://www.dhl.com
Mail Delivery Services
N.A.I.C.S.: 492110

Subsidiary (Non-US):

Deutsche Post Global Mail (Switzerland) AG (2)

Peter-Merian-Strasse 88, 4002, Basel, Switzerland
Web Site: http://www.dhl-globalmail.ch
Mail Services
N.A.I.C.S.: 492110

Deutsche Post Global Mail (UK) Ltd. (2)
4-8 Queensway, Croydon, CRO4BD, United Kingdom
Tel.: (44) 8081007678
Web Site: http://www.dhlglobalmail.co.uk
Mail Services
N.A.I.C.S.: 492110

Deutsche Post Global Mail B.V. (2)
Reactorweg 25, 3542 AD, Utrecht, 3542 AD, Netherlands
Tel.: (31) 306008494
Web Site: http://www.deutschepost.com
Sales Range: $25-49.9 Million
Emp.: 20
Mail Services
N.A.I.C.S.: 492110
Roel Menheere (Mgr)

Subsidiary (US):

Deutsche Post Global Mail Ltd. (2)
22560 Glenn Dr, Sterling, VA 20164
Web Site: http://www.globalmail.com
Express Mail Services
N.A.I.C.S.: 492110

Genesis Logistics Inc. (2)
800 N Thomas Dr, Bensenville, IL 60106
Tel.: (630) 766-5855
Web Site: https://www.genesislogistics.com
Emp.: 100
Logistics & Transportation Services
N.A.I.C.S.: 327910

Plant (Domestic):

Genesis Logistics Inc. - Charlestown Facility (3)
97 Industrial Way, Charlestown, IN 47111
Tel.: (651) 287-0215
Logistics & Transportation Services
N.A.I.C.S.: 541614

Genesis Logistics Inc. - Dayton Facility (3)
200 Herrod Blvd, Dayton, NJ 08810
Tel.: (609) 409-1810
Logistics & Transportation Services
N.A.I.C.S.: 541614

Genesis Logistics Inc. - Eagan Facility (3)
3140 Neil Armstrong Rd Ste124, Eagan, MN 55121
Tel.: (651) 287-0215
Logistics & Transportation Services
N.A.I.C.S.: 541614

Genesis Logistics Inc. - Forest Park Facility (3)
5158-H Kennedy Rd, Forest Park, GA 30279
Tel.: (404) 669-9009
Logistics & Transportation Services
N.A.I.C.S.: 541614

Subsidiary (Non-US):

Global Mail (Austria) Ges. m.b.H. (2)
Clemens-Holzmeister-Strasse 4, 1100, Vienna, Austria
Tel.: (43) 017064616
Web Site: http://www.duetschepost.com
Sales Range: $10-24.9 Million
Emp.: 151
Express Mail Services
N.A.I.C.S.: 492110

Deutsche Post Grundstucks- Vermietungsgesellschaft beta mbH (1)
Charles-de-Gaulle-Strasse 20, 53113, Bonn, Nordrhein-Westfalen, Germany
Tel.: (49) 22852890
Real Estate Manangement Services
N.A.I.C.S.: 531390

Deutsche Post IT BRIEF GmbH (1)
Hullerser Str 20, 37574, Einbeck, 37574, Germany
Tel.: (49) 5561 314 131
Information Technology Consulting Services
N.A.I.C.S.: 541512

Dietmrl Mueller (CEO)

Deutsche Post IT Services GmbH (1)
Tel.: (49) 61519573535
Information Technology Consulting Services
N.A.I.C.S.: 541512

Deutsche Post Immobilien GmbH (1)
Charles-de-Gaulle-Str 20, 53113, Bonn, Germany
Tel.: (49) 22818259550
Emp.: 7,000
Real Estate Manangement Services
N.A.I.C.S.: 531390
Frank Atteln (CEO)

Deutsche Post Investments GmbH (1)
Charles-De-Gaulle-Str 20, 53113, Bonn, Germany
Tel.: (49) 2281820
Financial Investment Services
N.A.I.C.S.: 523999

Deutsche Post Pensions-Treuhand GmbH & Co. KG (1)
Charles-de-Gaulle-Str 20, 53113, Bonn, Germany
Tel.: (49) 2289200
Pension Fund Services
N.A.I.C.S.: 525110

Deutsche Post Pensionsfonds AG (1)
Charles-de-Gaulle-Str 20, 53113, Bonn, Germany
Tel.: (49) 2281820
Pension Fund Services
N.A.I.C.S.: 525110

Deutsche Post Reinsurance S.A. (1)
Rue De Merl 74, Luxembourg, 2146, Luxembourg
Tel.: (352) 496951
Sales Range: $50-74.9 Million
Emp.: 35
Insurance Management Services
N.A.I.C.S.: 524298
Claude Weber (Mng Dir)

Deutsche Post Shop Hannover GmbH (1)
Davenstedter Str 80, Hannover, 30453, Germany
Tel.: (49) 5119239930
Postal Delivery Services
N.A.I.C.S.: 491110

Deutsche Post Zahlungsdienste GmbH (1)
fritzschreffer str 729, 53113, Bonn, Germany
Tel.: (49) 228 18254280
Web Site: http://www.dpzahlungsdienste.de
Sales Range: $25-49.9 Million
Emp.: 3
Postal Delivery Services
N.A.I.C.S.: 491110
Mathias Adamak (Gen Mgr)

Subsidiary (Domestic):

BHW Bausparkasse AG (2)
Lubahnstrasse 2, 31789, Hameln, Germany
Tel.: (49) 5151183555
Web Site: http://www.bhw.de
Home-Savings Bank Services
N.A.I.C.S.: 522180
Timo Heider (Executives, Supervisory Bd of Dirs)

Subsidiary (Domestic):

BHW Immobilien GmbH (3)
Lubahnstrasse 2, 31789, Hameln, Germany
Tel.: (49) 5151180
Web Site: http://www.bhw.de
Real Estate Services
N.A.I.C.S.: 531210

Deutsche Post gemeinnutzige Gesellschaft fur sichere und vertrauliche Kommunikation im Internet mbH (1)
Charles-de-Gaulle-Strasse 20, 53113, Bonn, Germany
Tel.: (49) 228 182 9944
Software Development Services
N.A.I.C.S.: 541511

Deutsche Post AG—(Continued)

Frank Appel *(Gen Mgr)*

Deutsche Postbank AG (1)
Friedrich-Ebert-Allee 114-126, 53113, Bonn,
Germany (50%)
Tel.: (49) 2289200
Web Site: http://www.postbank.de
Rev.: $4,258,392,300
Assets: $174,102,961,700
Liabilities: $165,580,187,800
Net Worth: $8,522,773,900
Earnings: $299,465,000
Emp.: 17,441
Fiscal Year-end: 12/31/2017
Private & Commercial Banking Services
N.A.I.C.S.: 522110
Lars Stoy *(Member-Mgmt Bd)*

DigiHaul Limited (1)
1&2 Carters Row The Melon Ground Hatfield Park, Hatfield, AL9 5NB, Hertfordshire,
United Kingdom
Tel.: (44) 2045265580
Web Site: https://digihaul.com
Software Development Services
N.A.I.C.S.: 541511

Dimalsa Logistics Inc. (1)
Km 1/5 Bo Palmas Rr 869, Catano, PR
00962
Tel.: (787) 788-3935
Web Site: http://www.dhl.com
Sales Range: $25-49.9 Million
Emp.: 16
Logistics Consulting Servies
N.A.I.C.S.: 541614
Ewar Rivera *(Pres)*

**EV Logistics Ltd. - Ambient
Facility** (1)
5111 - 272nd Street, Langley, V4W 3Z2,
BC, Canada
Tel.: (604) 857-6750
Grocery Distr
N.A.I.C.S.: 492210

**EV Logistics Ltd. - Perishables
Facility** (1)
5016 - 272nd Street, Langley, V4W 1S3,
BC, Canada
Tel.: (604) 857-6750
Grocery Distr
N.A.I.C.S.: 492210

Eurodifarm S.r.l. (1)
Strada Provinciale 159 Km 1 400, 26831,
Casalmaiocco, Lodi, Italy
Tel.: (39) 029810991
Web Site: https://www.eurodifarm.com
Pharmaceutical & Diagnostic Products Distr
N.A.I.C.S.: 424210

Exel Automocion S.A. de C.V. (1)
Autopista Mexico Puebla Km 117 Nave 4a,
Cuautlancingo, 72710, Puebla, Mexico
Tel.: (52) 2223034400
Freight Trucking Services
N.A.I.C.S.: 484122

Exel Canada Ltd. (1)
90 Matheson Blvd W, Etobicoke, L5R 3R3,
ON, Canada
Tel.: (905) 366-7700
Sales Range: $25-49.9 Million
Emp.: 7
Logistics Consulting Servies
N.A.I.C.S.: 541614
Ross Weber *(Dir-Ops)*

Exel Distribution (Thailand) Ltd. (1)
76/1 Moo 6 Talingchan-Bangbuathong Rd
Bangrakpatana, Bang Bua Thong, Nonthaburi, 11110, Thailand
Tel.: (66) 2925 3291
Logistics Consulting Servies
N.A.I.C.S.: 541614

**Exel Global Logistics do Brasil
S.A.** (1)
Av Djalma Batista 735 sl 214, Manaus,
Amapa, Brazil
Tel.: (55) 92 3236 7760
Logistics Consulting Servies
N.A.I.C.S.: 541614

**Exel Group Holdings (Nederland)
B.V.** (1)
Huygensweg 10, Postbus 100, 5466AN,
Veghel, Netherlands

Tel.: (31) 413347911
Logistics Consulting Servies
N.A.I.C.S.: 541614

Exel International Holdings (Netherlands 1) B.V. (1)
Huygensweg 10, 5466AN, Veghel, Netherlands
Tel.: (31) 413347911
Logistics Consulting Servies
N.A.I.C.S.: 541614

Exel International Holdings (Netherlands 2) B.V. (1)
Huygensweg 10, Postbus 100, 5466 AN,
Veghel, Netherlands
Tel.: (31) 413347911
Logistics Consulting Servies
N.A.I.C.S.: 541614

Exel Investments Inc. (1)
1105 N Market St Ste 1300, Wilmington, DE
19801
Tel.: (302) 427-3547
Financial Investment Services
N.A.I.C.S.: 523999

**Exel Supply Chain Services (South
Africa) (Pty) Ltd.** (1)
107 Andre Greyvenstein St Isando, 1600,
Kempton Park, Gauteng, South Africa
Tel.: (27) 11 9237767
Logistics Consulting Servies
N.A.I.C.S.: 541614

**Exel Supply Chain Services de
Mexico, S.A. de C.V.** (1)
Autopista Mexico-Queretaro Km 34 5 Nave
1, Cuautitlan Izcalli, 54740, Mexico
Tel.: (52) 5530032600
Logistics Consulting Servies
N.A.I.C.S.: 541614

Exel Supply Chain Solutions Ltd. (1)
Unit D 1 & 2 Airport Business Pk Swords
Rd, Dublin, Ireland
Tel.: (353) 1844 55 45
Freight Forwarding Services
N.A.I.C.S.: 488510

**F.C. (Flying Cargo) International
Transportation Ltd.** (1)
4 Ha Melacha st North Industrial Zone, Lod,
71520, Israel
Tel.: (972) 8 9144444
Web Site: http://www.flying-cargo.com
Air Freight Transportation Services
N.A.I.C.S.: 481112

FACT Denmark A / S (1)
Kirstinehoj 17, Kastrup, 2770, Arhus, Denmark
Tel.: (45) 32464600
Logistics Consulting Servies
N.A.I.C.S.: 541614

Gerlach & Co Internationale Expediteurs B.V. (1)
Van Heemskerckweg 6, 5928 LL, Venlo,
Netherlands
Tel.: (31) 773246500
Web Site: http://www.gerlachcs.com
Emp.: 50
Customs Consulting Services
N.A.I.C.S.: 541614

Gerlach & Co. nv (1)
Schouwkensstraat 7 Haven 200, 2030, Antwerp, Belgium
Tel.: (32) 3 545 0220
Web Site: http://www.gerlachcs.be
Sales Range: $25-49.9 Million
Emp.: 20
Customs Consulting Services
N.A.I.C.S.: 541614

Gerlach AG (1)
St Jakobs-Strasse 222, 4002, Basel, Switzerland
Tel.: (41) 613159696
Web Site: http://www.gerlachcs.ch
Customs Consulting Services
N.A.I.C.S.: 541614

**Gerlach Customs Services
EOOD** (1)
Web Site: http://www.gerlachcs.bg
Sales Range: $25-49.9 Million
Emp.: 5
Customs Consulting Services

N.A.I.C.S.: 541614

**Gerlach Customs Services UK
Limited** (1)
3rd Floor Charlton House Dour Street, Dover, CT16 1AT, Kent, United Kingdom
Tel.: (44) 1304200940
N.A.I.C.S.: 541614

**Gerlach European Customs Services,
spol. s.r.o.** (1)
Logistics Consulting Servies
N.A.I.C.S.: 541614

**Gerlach European Services
S.R.L.** (1)
Timisoara Blvd No 90, 063127, Bucharest,
Romania
Tel.: (40) 757018009
N.A.I.C.S.: 541614

Gerlach Spol s.r.o. (1)
K Vypichu 1086, 252 19, Rudna, Czech
Republic
Web Site: http://www.gerlachcs.cz
Sales Range: $25-49.9 Million
Emp.: 12
Customs Consulting Services
N.A.I.C.S.: 541614

Gerlach Sweden AB (1)
Boplatsgatan 4, 213 76, Malmo, Sweden
Tel.: (46) 771181100
N.A.I.C.S.: 541614

Gerlach Zolldienste GmbH (1)
Keniastrasse 12, 47269, Duisburg, Germany
Tel.: (49) 2033485990
Web Site: http://www.gerlachcs.de
Sales Range: $25-49.9 Million
Emp.: 6
Customs Consulting Services
N.A.I.C.S.: 541614

Giorgio Gori International Freight Forwards (Pty) Ltd. (1)
Blaauklip Office Park 1 Weber Valley Rd,
Stellenbosch, 7600, Westerncape, South
Africa
Tel.: (27) 218801680
Web Site: http://www.ggori.com
Emp.: 10
Freight Forwarding Services
N.A.I.C.S.: 488510

Giorgio Gori S.r.l. (1)
Via Lepori 9, 57017, Livorno, Italy
Tel.: (39) 0586967001
Web Site: http://www.ggori.com
Alcoholic Beverage Transportation Service
N.A.I.C.S.: 488999

Subsidiary (Non-US):

Giorgio Gori (France) sas (2)
9 Rue de Guerlande Zone Verte, 71880,
Chatenoy-le-Royal, France
Tel.: (3) 3 85 97 20 60
Alcoholic Beverage Transportation Service
N.A.I.C.S.: 488999

Gori Argentina S.A. (2)
Ruta Panamericana 2650 Office B/D Palmares Open Mall - Bureau, 5501, Godoy
Cruz, Mendoza, Argentina
Tel.: (54) 2614429000
Alcoholic Beverage Transportation Service
N.A.I.C.S.: 488999

Gori Australia Pty Ltd. (2)
3C / 34 MacMahon Street, Hurstville, 2220,
NSW, Australia
Tel.: (61) 295700000
Web Site: http://www2.ggori.com
Alcoholic Beverage Transportation Service
N.A.I.C.S.: 488999

Gori Iberia S.L. (2)
Passeig del Ferrocarril 335 2 Planta, 8860,
Castelldefels, Barcelona, Spain
Tel.: (34) 936 342 636
Alcoholic Beverage Transportation Service
N.A.I.C.S.: 488999
Simone Giusti *(Mng Dir)*

Gori Iberia Transitarios, Limitada (2)
AV Dr Antunes Guimaraes Nr 505 6 Floor,
Leca Da Palmeira, Matosinhos, 4450-621,
Portugal
Tel.: (351) 229982080

Web Site: http://www.ggori.com
Emp.: 8
Alcoholic Beverage Transportation Service
N.A.I.C.S.: 488999

Giorgio Gori USA, Inc. (1)
80 River St, Hoboken, NJ 07030
Tel.: (201) 653-6800
Web Site: http://www.ggori.com
Emp.: 50
Logistics Consulting Servies
N.A.I.C.S.: 541614

Global Mail, Inc. (1)
72 Van Reipen Ave, Jersey City, NJ 07306-2806
Tel.: (201) 222-8800
Parcel & Courier Services
N.A.I.C.S.: 492210

**Gravis-Computervertriebsgesellschaft
mbH** (1)
Ernst-Reuter-Platz 8, 10587, Berlin, Germany
Tel.: (49) 3039022222
Web Site: https://www.gravis.de
Mobile Accessory Retailer
N.A.I.C.S.: 449210

Higgs International Limited (1)
Q E D Distribution Park Purfleet By Pass,
Purfleet, RM19 1NA, Essex, United Kingdom
Tel.: (44) 1708 892 800
Web Site: http://www.higgs.co.uk
Sales Range: $25-49.9 Million
Emp.: 9
Logistics Consulting Servies
N.A.I.C.S.: 541614

Higgs International Publishing Logistics Ltd (1)
Unit D Q E D Distribution Park, Purfleet,
RM19 1NA, United Kingdom
Tel.: (44) 1708 892 800
Web Site: http://www.higgs.co.uk
Sales Range: $25-49.9 Million
Emp.: 9
Newspaper & Book Publishing Services
N.A.I.C.S.: 513110

**Hillebrand Gori Hong Kong
Limited** (1)
Unit 2607-08 26/F Tower 2 Ever Gain Plaza
88 Container Port Road, New Territories,
Kwai Chung, China (Hong Kong)
Tel.: (852) 38905180
N.A.I.C.S.: 312111

Hillebrand Gori Japan K.K. (1)
NMF Surugadai Building 6F 2-5-12, Kanda
Surugadai Chiyoda-Ku, Tokyo, 101-0062,
Japan
Tel.: (81) 356510455
N.A.I.C.S.: 312111

Hillebrand Gori Korea Ltd. (1)
4F 15 Namdaemun-Ro, Jung-gu, Seoul,
4526, Korea (South)
Tel.: (82) 25217356
N.A.I.C.S.: 312111

Hillebrand Kenya Limited (1)
Mombasa Road Liberty Plaza, PO Box
27751, 00506, Nairobi, Kenya
Tel.: (254) 777581120
Logistic Services
N.A.I.C.S.: 722410

Hull Blyth & Co Ltd (1)
10 Coldbath Square, London, EC1R 5HL,
United Kingdom
Tel.: (44) 7709 483429
Web Site: http://www.hull-blyth.com
Emp.: 5
Marine Shipping Services
N.A.I.C.S.: 483111

Subsidiary (Non-US):

Hull Blyth Ghana Ltd (2)
Seatec House Akosombo Road, PO Box
214, Tema, Ghana
Tel.: (233) 303 300894
Freight Transportation Services
N.A.I.C.S.: 488510

Hull Blyth Nigeria Ltd. (2)
34 Wharf Rd, Apapa, 23401, Logas, Nigeria
Tel.: (234) 1 764 4914
Web Site: http://www.hull-blyth.com

Logistics Consulting Servies
N.A.I.C.S.: 541614

Hull Blyth South Africa Pty Ltd (2)
18 Musgrave Road, Durban, 4001, South
Africa
Tel.: (27) 312029621
Web Site: http://www.hull-blyth.com
Sales Range: $25-49.9 Million
Emp.: 4
Ocean Freight Transportation Services
N.A.I.C.S.: 488510

**Hyperion Inmobilaria S.A. de
C.V.** (1)
Carr Mexico-Queretaro Km 34 5 Nave 1,
Rancho San Isidro, 54740, Cuautitlan
Izcalli, Mexico
Tel.: (52) 55 3003 2600
Real Estate Manangement Services
N.A.I.C.S.: 531390

ITG Global Logistics B.V. (1)
Van Weerden Poelmanweg 10, 3088 EB,
Rotterdam, Netherlands
Tel.: (31) 10 8511 600
Sales Range: $25-49.9 Million
Emp.: 7
Logistics Consulting Servies
N.A.I.C.S.: 541614
Reinier Velding (Dir-Logistics)

ITG International Transports, Inc. (1)
6 Kimball Ln, Lynnfield, MA 01940
Tel.: (617) 455-6020
Web Site: http://www.itg.de
Sales Range: $25-49.9 Million
Emp.: 9
Logistics Consulting Servies
N.A.I.C.S.: 541614
Guido Voss (VP & Branch Mgr)

**ITG Internationale Spedition
GmbH** (1)
Objekt 262 Stiege 7 Zimmer A02 067,
1300, Vienna, Austria
Tel.: (43) 1 7007 32946
Emp.: 3
Air & Sea Freight Transportation Services
N.A.I.C.S.: 481112
Tamara Grill (Office Mgr)

J.F. Hillebrand Benelux B.V. (1)
Wilhelminaplein 1-40, 3072, Rotterdam,
Netherlands
Tel.: (31) 104035566
Logistic Services
N.A.I.C.S.: 722410

J.F. Hillebrand Sverige AB (1)
Armaturvagen 4, 136 50, Jordbro, Sweden
Tel.: (46) 850066600
Logistic Services
N.A.I.C.S.: 722410

JF Hillebrand Group AG (1)
Carl Zeiss Strasse 6, PO Box 100254,
55129, Mainz, Germany
Tel.: (49) 61315030
Web Site: http://www.jfhillebrand.com
Sales Range: $10-24.9 Million
Emp.: 8
Freight Transportation Services
N.A.I.C.S.: 488510

Subsidiary (Non-US):

J.F. Hillebrand Scotland Limited (2)
Tel.: (44) 1413413900
Freight Transportation Services
N.A.I.C.S.: 488510
Graeme Strachan (Branch Mgr)

JF Hillebrand (Thailand) Limited (2)
2/32 Todsapol land 4 building 7th floor Soi
Bangna-Trad 25, Bangna Road Bangna,
Bangkok, 10260, Thailand
Tel.: (66) 27695691
Freight Transportation Services
N.A.I.C.S.: 488510
Pattarapon Munkongsupaleark (Country
Mgr)

JF Hillebrand Argentina SA (2)
Tel.: (54) 2614057000
Freight Transportation Services
N.A.I.C.S.: 488510

JF Hillebrand Canada Inc. (2)
2210 - 6900 Graybar Road, Richmond,
V6W 0A5, BC, Canada

Tel.: (604) 214-7600
Web Site: http://www.jfhillebrand.com
Emp.: 19
Freight Transportation Services
N.A.I.C.S.: 488510
Myla Marrinier (Coord-Import Dispatch)

**JF Hillebrand Central Europe
GmbH** (2)
Wickenburggasse 26 Top 4, 1080, Vienna,
Austria
Tel.: (43) 15233737
Freight Transportation Services
N.A.I.C.S.: 488510

JF Hillebrand Chile Ltda (2)
Encomenderos 260 of 42-43 Las Condes,
Santiago, Chile
Tel.: (56) 22 810 4600
Freight Transportation Services
N.A.I.C.S.: 488510
Ricardo Esteban Pantoja Pasmino (Mgr-Fin
& Admin)

JF Hillebrand China Co. Ltd (2)
Unit 1204-1205 CITIC - Shenhong Plaza No
1350 North Si Chuan Road, Shanghai,
China
Tel.: (86) 21 6070 3200
Freight Transportation Services
N.A.I.C.S.: 488510
Grace Qiao (Mgr-Sls)

Subsidiary (Domestic):

**JF Hillebrand Deutschland
GmbH** (2)
Carl-Zeiss-Strasse 6, Mainz-Hechtsheim,
55129, Mainz, Germany
Tel.: (49) 6131 50 30
Freight Transportation Services
N.A.I.C.S.: 488510

Subsidiary (Non-US):

JF Hillebrand Finland Oy (2)
Seilorinkatu 1 A Door A21 Vuosaari Port,
00980, Helsinki, Finland
Tel.: (358) 95657830
Web Site: http://www.jfhillebrand.com
Emp.: 6
Freight Transportation Services
N.A.I.C.S.: 488510
Susanne Holm (Mgr-Fin)

JF Hillebrand France SAS (2)
ZI Beaune Vignoles 11 rue Gaston Chevro-
let BP 49, 21202, Beaune, France
Tel.: (33) 380 24 43 00
Freight Transportation Services
N.A.I.C.S.: 488510
Elodie Robet (Mgr-Bus Dev)

**JF Hillebrand Group Management
Services** (2)
A-206 Great Eastern Summit Sector 15
CBD Belapur, Navi Mumbai, 400614, India
Tel.: (91) 22 2756 0935
Freight Transportation Services
N.A.I.C.S.: 488510

JF Hillebrand Ireland Ltd (2)
Unit 27 3rd Floor The Hyde Building The
Park, Carrickmines, Dublin, Ireland
Tel.: (353) 1 284 3073
Freight Transportation Services
N.A.I.C.S.: 488510

JF Hillebrand Italia SPA (2)
Via Volturno 10/12, PO Box 1095 Osman-
noro, 50019, Sesto Fiorentino, Italy
Tel.: (39) 055 34151 1
Freight Transportation Services
N.A.I.C.S.: 488510
Elisabetta Ceccherini (Branch Mgr-Ops)

JF Hillebrand Japan KK (2)
Ningyo-cho First Building 3F 3-3-6 Nihon-
bashi Ningyo-cho, Chuo-ku, Tokyo, 103-
0013, Japan
Tel.: (81) 3 5651 0455
Emp.: 40
Freight Transportation Services
N.A.I.C.S.: 488510
Kazuyuki Kido (Branch Mgr)

JF Hillebrand Korea Ltd. (2)
3F Hyunwoo Bldg 1439-14 Seocho-dong,
Seocho-gu, Seoul, 06722, Korea (South)
Tel.: (82) 2 521 7356
Freight Transportation Services

N.A.I.C.S.: 488510
JF Hillebrand Malaysia Sdn Bhd (2)
Freight Transportation Services
N.A.I.C.S.: 488510
Trina Chee (Mgr-Sls)

JF Hillebrand Mexico SA de CV (2)
Tel.: (52) 5552824499
Freight Transportation Services
N.A.I.C.S.: 488510
Jose Roberto Munoz Espinosa (Mgr-Fin &
Admin)

JF Hillebrand Middle East LLC (2)
Office 1205 Latifa Tower Sheikh Zayed
Road, PO Box 191061, Dubai, United Arab
Emirates
Tel.: (971) 4 343 00 54
Freight Transportation Services
N.A.I.C.S.: 488510

JF Hillebrand Netherlands (2)
Maaskade 119, PO Box 9230, 3007 AE,
Rotterdam, Netherlands
Tel.: (31) 10 403 55 66
Web Site: http://www.jfhillebrand.com
Freight Transportation Services
N.A.I.C.S.: 488510
Hans Schipper (Mng Dir)

JF Hillebrand Philippines Inc (2)
Unit 501 A & Unit 501 B 5/F A Place Bldg
Coral Way Drive, Central Business Park 1,
Mall of Asia Complex, Pasay, 1300, Philip-
pines
Tel.: (63) 2828 2425
Web Site: http://www.jfhillebrand.com
Emp.: 14
Freight Transportation Services
N.A.I.C.S.: 488510
Jacqueline Edora (Mgr-Fin)

**JF Hillebrand Portugal-transitarios
Lda** (2)
Av D Afonso Henriques 1136 E, 4450-011,
Matosinhos, Portugal
Tel.: (351) 229 397 470
Freight Transportation Services
N.A.I.C.S.: 488510
Maria Lafuente (Country Mgr)

JF Hillebrand Russia (OOO) (2)
Stremyanny Pereulok 38 4th floor, 115054,
Moscow, Russia
Tel.: (7) 4955424290
Freight Transportation Services
N.A.I.C.S.: 488510
Mikhail Gavrikov (Mgr-Sls)

JF Hillebrand Scandinavia A/S (2)
Smakkedalen 4, 2820, Gentofte, Denmark
Tel.: (45) 45 28 88 88
Freight Transportation Services
N.A.I.C.S.: 488510
Charlotte Damm Morch (Mgr-Ops)

JF Hillebrand Singapore Pte Ltd (2)
1 Harbourfront Place 03-08 Harbourfront
Tower One, Singapore, 098633, Singapore
Tel.: (65) 65015201
Freight Transportation Services
N.A.I.C.S.: 488510
Jane Wong (Mgr-Fin,Admin & HR)

**JF Hillebrand South Africa (Pty)
Ltd** (2)
Bosman's Crossing Distillery Road, PO Box
684, Stellenbosch, 7599, South Africa
Tel.: (27) 21 8092000
Freight Transportation Services
N.A.I.C.S.: 488510
Marliese Martin (Mng Dir)

JF Hillebrand Spain SA (2)
Avda Catedral 6-8 2nd floor, 08002, Barce-
lona, Spain
Tel.: (34) 93 268 28 98
Freight Transportation Services
N.A.I.C.S.: 488510
Patricio Bravo Poduje (Mgr-Claims)

JF Hillebrand Sweden AB (2)
Tradskolevagen 17, Johanneshov, 121 62,
Stockholm, Sweden
Tel.: (46) 8 500 092 46
Freight Transportation Services
N.A.I.C.S.: 488510
Frank Hansen (Country Mgr)

JF Hillebrand UK Limited (2)

Dissegna House Weston Avenue, West
Thurrock, RM20 3ZP, Essex, United King-
dom
Tel.: (44) 1708 689 000
Freight Transportation Services
N.A.I.C.S.: 488510
Daniel Morris (Dir-Ops)

Subsidiary (US):

JF Hillebrand USA Inc (2)
1600 Saint Georges Ave, Rahway, NJ
07065
Tel.: (732) 388-0101
Freight Transportation Services
N.A.I.C.S.: 488510
Colin Edgar (Mgr-Ops)

Subsidiary (Non-US):

JF Hillebrand Uruguay (2)
Guatemala Street, 11800, Montevideo, Uru-
guay
Tel.: (598) 2 924 45 25
Freight Transportation Services
N.A.I.C.S.: 488510

JF Hillebrand Vietnam Co., Ltd (2)
Level 8 A&B Tower 76A Le Lai Street, Ben
Thanh Ward District 1, Ho Chi Minh City,
Vietnam
Tel.: (84) 838272200
Freight Transportation Services
N.A.I.C.S.: 488510
Trent McLachlan (Country Mgr)

Jf Hillebrand Brasil Ltda (2)
Edificio Esplanada Park Rua Jeronimo da
Veiga 164 cj 141/142 Jardim, Paulista,
04536-900, Brazil
Tel.: (55) 11 3702 2050
Freight Transportation Services
N.A.I.C.S.: 488510
Roberta Fiorotti (Mgr-Ops Logistics)

PT. JF Hillebrand Indonesia (2)
Menara 165 21st Floor unit A JL T B Si-
matupang Kav 1, Cilandak Timur Jakarta
Selatan, Jakarta, 12560, Indonesia
Tel.: (62) 21 2940 7100
Freight Transportation Services
N.A.I.C.S.: 488510
Edlan Utama (Branch Mgr)

Subsidiary (US):

Satellite Logistics Group, Inc. (2)
12621 Featherwood Ste 390, Houston, TX
77034-4902
Tel.: (281) 902-5500
Web Site: http://www.slg.com
Logistics Consulting Servies
N.A.I.C.S.: 541614
Andreas M. Bornefeld (VP-Ops)

JF Hillebrand Limited (1)
Unit 27 3rd Floor The Hyde Building The
Park Carrickmines, Dublin, D18 YY89, Ire-
land
Tel.: (353) 12843073
Logistic Services
N.A.I.C.S.: 722410

Joint Retail Logistics Limited (1)
Hyde Park Indstl Est, Newtownabbey, BT36
4PP, United Kingdom
Tel.: (44) 28 9083 3671
Sales Range: $50-74.9 Million
Emp.: 130
Freight Trucking Services
N.A.I.C.S.: 484122
Una Doherty (Gen Mgr)

LLC Williams Lea (1)
2 Paveletskaya Sq Bl 2, 115 054, Moscow,
Russia
Tel.: (7) 495 258 55 58
Business Process Outsourcing Services
N.A.I.C.S.: 561499

Matrix Logistics Services Ltd. (1)
6941 Kennedy Road, Mississauga, L5T
2R6, ON, Canada
Tel.: (905) 795-2200
Logistics Consulting Servies
N.A.I.C.S.: 541614

Mitradiopharma S.r.l. (1)
Via Artigianato 12, Carugate, 20061, Milan,
Italy
Tel.: (39) 02921591

Deutsche Post AG—(Continued)

Web Site: http://www.mitradiopharma.it
Logistics & Transportation Services
N.A.I.C.S.: 541614

Monta Breda B.V. (1)
Zoete Inval 4, 4815 HK, Breda, Netherlands
Tel.: (31) 763031470
Logistics & Warehousing Services
N.A.I.C.S.: 541614

Monta Den Bosch B.V. (1)
De Vutter 1, 5221 BD, Den Bosch, Netherlands
Tel.: (31) 732200490
Logistics & Warehousing Services
N.A.I.C.S.: 541614

Monta Enschede B.V. (1)
Ir Hanlostraat 15, 7547 RD, Enschede, Netherlands
Tel.: (31) 534305515
Logistics & Warehousing Services
N.A.I.C.S.: 541614

Monta Gorinchem Edisonweg B.V. (1)
Edisonweg 11, 4207 HE, Gorinchem, Netherlands
Tel.: (31) 183745910
N.A.I.C.S.: 541511

Monta Gorinchem Papland B.V. (1)
Papland 16, 4206 CL, Gorinchem, Netherlands
Tel.: (31) 184208700
Logistics & Warehousing Services
N.A.I.C.S.: 541614

Monta Gorinchem Weide B.V. (1)
Weide 30, 4206, Gorinchem, Netherlands
Tel.: (31) 183610450
Logistic Services
N.A.I.C.S.: 541614

Monta Krefeld GmbH (1)
Markische Strasse 10, 47809, Krefeld, Germany
Tel.: (49) 21519645070
Logistics & Warehousing Services
N.A.I.C.S.: 541614

Monta Lelystad B.V. (1)
Zuiveringweg 21, 8243 PZ, Lelystad, Netherlands
Tel.: (31) 320796000
Logistics & Warehousing Services
N.A.I.C.S.: 541614

Monta Molenaarsgraaf B.V. (1)
Polderweg-Oost 19, 2973 AN, Molenaarsgraaf, Netherlands
Tel.: (31) 850208690
Logistics & Warehousing Services
N.A.I.C.S.: 541614

Monta Nieuwveen B.V. (1)
Schoterhoek 2, 2441 LD, Nieuw-Vennep, Netherlands
Tel.: (31) 172536096
Logistics & Warehousing Services
N.A.I.C.S.: 541614

Monta Oosterhout B.V. (1)
Krombraak 4, 4906 CR, Oosterhout, Netherlands
Tel.: (31) 162748120
Logistics & Warehousing Services
N.A.I.C.S.: 541614

Monta Oud Gastel B.V. (1)
Watermolen 6, 4751 VK, Oud Gastel, Netherlands
Tel.: (31) 165760005
Logistics & Warehousing Services
N.A.I.C.S.: 541614

Monta Platform B.V. (1)
Polderweg-Oost 19, 2973 AN, Molenaarsgraaf, Netherlands
Tel.: (31) 850208692
Logistics & Warehousing Services
N.A.I.C.S.: 541614

Monta Services B.V. (1)
Papland 16, 4206 CL, Gorinchem, Netherlands
Tel.: (31) 184208700
Logistics & Warehousing Services
N.A.I.C.S.: 541614

Monta TWI B.V. (1)
Schoterhoek 16, 2441, Nieuw-Vennep, Netherlands
Tel.: (31) 172536000
Web Site: https://www.twi.nl
Logistic Services
N.A.I.C.S.: 541614

Monta Waspik B.V. (1)
Hooiweg 11, 5165 NL, Waspik, Netherlands
Tel.: (31) 416684800
Logistics & Warehousing Services
N.A.I.C.S.: 541614

New Transport Applications, S.A. de C.V (1)
Via Gustavo Baz 109-Interior 13 San Pedro Barrientos, 54010, Tlalnepantla, Mexico
Tel.: (52) 15553907056
Web Site: https://www.ntapharma.com
Freight Transportation Services
N.A.I.C.S.: 561910

Ocean Group Investments Limited (1)
Ocean House The Ring, Bracknell, RG12 1AN, Berkshire, United Kingdom
Tel.: (44) 1344 302000
Web Site: http://www.dhl.com
Emp.: 30
Financial Investment Services
N.A.I.C.S.: 523999

PPL CZ s. r. o. (1)
U Vozovny 658/8, Malesice, Prague, 108 00, Czech Republic
Tel.: (420) 844 775 775
Web Site: http://www.ppl.cz
Parcel & Courier Services
N.A.I.C.S.: 492210

PT DANZAS SARANA PERKASA (1)
Soekarno-Hatta Int I Airport Wisma Soewarna, 19110, Jakarta, Indonesia
Tel.: (62) 2155912930
Freight Forwarding Services
N.A.I.C.S.: 488510

Pharma Logistics NV (1)
Gustave Demeurslaan 71, 1654, Huizingen, Belgium
Tel.: (32) 23631570
Web Site: http://www.pharma-logistics.com
Healthcare Logistics Services
N.A.I.C.S.: 541614

Presse-Service Gull GmbH (1)
Gaiserwaldstrasse 14, Saint Gallen, 9015, Switzerland
Tel.: (41) 713 14 0606
Web Site: http://www.guell-presseservice.de
Sales Range: $25-49.9 Million
Emp.: 50
Magazine Publishing Services
N.A.I.C.S.: 513120

RISER ID Services GmbH (1)
Tel.: (49) 30236076999
Web Site: http://www.riserid.eu
Data Processing Services
N.A.I.C.S.: 518210
Arne Bassler (Mng Dir)

Radix Group International, Inc. (1)
Freight Forwarding Services
N.A.I.C.S.: 488510

Rio Lopes Transportes Ltd. (1)
Rua Francisco De Sousa e Melo 1590 Cordovil, Rio de Janeiro, 21010-410, Brazil
Tel.: (55) 2121024700
Web Site: https://riolopes.com.br
N.A.I.C.S.: 541614

SNAS Lebanon SARL (1)
Airport Road DHL Building 1 Floor Aster Libanpost Building, PO Box 166-439, Beirut, Lebanon
Tel.: (961) 1629700
Logistics Consulting Servies
N.A.I.C.S.: 541614
John Chedid (Gen Mgr)

SW Post Beheer B.V. (1)
Reactorweg 25, 3542 AD, Utrecht, Netherlands
Tel.: (31) 302149500
Financial Investment Management Services
N.A.I.C.S.: 523999

Saloodo GmbH (1)
Siegburger Str 191-193, 50679, Cologne, Germany
Web Site: http://www.saloodo.com
Transport & Logistic Services
N.A.I.C.S.: 541614
Elaine Li-Suan Tan (Co-Mng Dir)

Saturn Integrated Logistics Inc. (1)
100 Disco Rd, Etobicoke, M9W 1M1, ON, Canada
Tel.: (416) 798-0258
Logistics Consulting Services
N.A.I.C.S.: 541614

Scherbauer Spedition GmbH (1)
Oberheisinger Strasse 7, 93073, Neutraubling, Germany
Tel.: (49) 940152260
Web Site: http://www.scherbauer.de
Emp.: 250
Freight Forwarding Services
N.A.I.C.S.: 488510

Selektvracht B.V. (1)
Atoomweg 30, 3542 AB, Utrecht, Netherlands (100%)
Tel.: (31) 302477999
Web Site: http://www.selektvracht.nl
Sales Range: $25-49.9 Million
Emp.: 150
Mail Delivering Services
N.A.I.C.S.: 541860

Siegfried Vogele Institut (SVI) - Internationale Gesellschaft fur Dialogmarketing mbH (1)
Olmuhlweg 12, 61462, Konigstein, Germany
Tel.: (49) 6174 20170
Web Site: http://www.sv-institut.de
Emp.: 20
Educational Consulting Services
N.A.I.C.S.: 611710
Frank Appel (Mgr)

Sky Courier, Inc. (1)
21240 Ridgetop Cir, Sterling, VA 20166
Tel.: (703) 433-2800
Sales Range: $25-49.9 Million
Emp.: 200
Air Express Services
N.A.I.C.S.: 492110
Debra Gruen (Controller)

Smoke and Mirrors Productions Limited (1)
1-5 Piland Street, London, W1F 8PR, United Kingdom
Tel.: (44) 20 74681000
Web Site: http://www.smoke-mirrors.co.uk
Sales Range: $25-49.9 Million
Emp.: 7
Video Production Services
N.A.I.C.S.: 512110

Unit (Non-US):

Smoke and Mirrors Productions Limited - Shanghai Unit (2)
201-202 Red Town Building D 570 Huai Hai Xi Road, Chang Ning District, Shanghai, 200052, China
Tel.: (86) 2152580928
Sales Range: $25-49.9 Million
Emp.: 1
Video Production Services
N.A.I.C.S.: 512110
Nic George (Gen Mgr)

Standard Forwarding Co. Inc. (1)
2925 Morton Dr, East Moline, IL 61244
Tel.: (309) 755-4504
Web Site: http://www.standardforwarding.com
Sales Range: $25-49.9 Million
Emp.: 245
Freight Transportation Services
N.A.I.C.S.: 484121
Terry Olsen (Dir-Bus Process & Mgmt)

Standard Forwarding LLC (1)
2925 Morton Dr, East Moline, IL 61244
Web Site: https://standardforwarding.com
N.A.I.C.S.: 541614
John Mugnaini (CEO)

StarBroker AG (1)
Peter Merian-Strasse 88, 4002, Basel, Switzerland

Tel.: (41) 612747474
Web Site: http://www.dhl.com
Sales Range: $25-49.9 Million
Emp.: 2
Transportation Services
N.A.I.C.S.: 488999

StreetScooter GmbH (1)
Julicher Strasse 209 b, 52070, Aachen, Germany
Tel.: (49) 2419900230
Web Site: https://www.streetscooter.com
Electric Vehicle Mfr
N.A.I.C.S.: 335312

T & B Whitwood Holdings Limited (1)
Ocean House The Ring, Bracknell, RG12 1AN, Berkshire, United Kingdom
Tel.: (44) 1344 302000
Investment Management Service
N.A.I.C.S.: 523999

TCL Supply Chain (Canada) Inc. (1)
26875 96 Avenue, Acheson, T7X 5A6, AB, Canada
Tel.: (780) 948-7400
Web Site: https://www.tclsupplychain.com
Logistics & Distribution Services
N.A.I.C.S.: 541614
Raeleen Routhier (Mgr-HR)

TEDI Translogic Express Dedicated Inc. (1)
420 Ambassdor Dr 2nd Fl, Mississauga, L5T 2R5, ON, Canada
Tel.: (905) 451-3033
Freight Trucking Services
N.A.I.C.S.: 484121

TSO Holdings A Limited (1)
St Crispins House, Norwich, NR3 1PD, United Kingdom
Tel.: (44) 1603 622211
Books Publishing Services
N.A.I.C.S.: 513130

TSO Holdings B Limited (1)
St Crispins, Norwich, NR3 1PD, United Kingdom
Tel.: (44) 1603 622211
Books Publishing Services
N.A.I.C.S.: 513130

Tag Pac Limited (1)
Aldgate Tower 2 Leman Street, London, E1 8FA, United Kingdom
Tel.: (44) 20 7251 4571
Web Site: http://www.tag-pac.com
Graphic Design Services
N.A.I.C.S.: 541430

The Stationery Office Enterprises Limited (1)
Mandela Way, London, SE1 5SS, United Kingdom
Tel.: (44) 20 7394 4200
Web Site: http://www.tso.co.uk
Sales Range: $50-74.9 Million
Emp.: 150
Online Book Publishing Services
N.A.I.C.S.: 513130

TheNetherlands622009 b. v. (1)
Reactorweg 25, 3542 AD, Utrecht, Netherlands
Tel.: (31) 30 2149500
Logistics Consulting Servies
N.A.I.C.S.: 541614

Tracker Logistics Inc. (1)
3905 81 Ave, Leduc, T9E 8S6, AB, Canada
Tel.: (780) 980-8900
Emp.: 17
Logistics Consulting Servies
N.A.I.C.S.: 541614

Trailar Limited (1)
Unit 4 Whitney Court Hamilton Street, Oldham, OL4 1DB, United Kingdom
Tel.: (44) 3031231113
Web Site: https://www.trailar.co.uk
N.A.I.C.S.: 221114

Transcare Supply Chain Management Inc. (1)
7491 Jane St Unit 3, Concord, L4K 2M7, ON, Canada
Tel.: (905) 660-4477
Logistics Warehousing & Storage Services
N.A.I.C.S.: 493110

UK Mail Group Limited (1)
120 Buckingham Avenue, Slough, SL1 4LZ,
Berks, United Kingdom
Tel.: (44) 2476937770
Web Site: http://www.ukmail.com
Sales Range: $650-699.9 Million
Holding Company; Overnight & Express
Delivery Postal Services
N.A.I.C.S.: 551112
Steven Glew (Fin Dir)

Subsidiary (Domestic):

UK Mail Ltd (2)
120 Buckingham Avenue, Slough, SL1 4LZ,
Berks, United Kingdom
Tel.: (44) 2476937770
Web Site: http://www.ukmail.com
Business Mail Collection & Delivery Services
N.A.I.C.S.: 492210
Richard Gould (Sr Dir-Client)

USC Distribution Services LLC (1)
3015 Ana St, Rancho Dominguez, CA
90221
Tel.: (310) 609-1153
Web Site: http://www.uscds.com
Logistics Distribution Services
N.A.I.C.S.: 541614

Van Gend & Loos - Euro Express NV (1)
Essenestraat 26, Ternat, 1740, Belgium
Tel.: (32) 2 5834209
Freight Forwarding Services
N.A.I.C.S.: 488510

Venture Logistics S.A. de C.V. (1)
Av De Los Tejocotes S/N, Cuautitlan Izcalli,
54769, Mexico
Tel.: (52) 5519402000
Logistics Consulting Servies
N.A.I.C.S.: 541614

Veron Grauer AG (1)
PO Box 1047, Geneva 5 Airport, 1211, Geneva, Switzerland
Tel.: (41) 227095193
Web Site: http://www.verongrauer.ch
Freight Transportation Services
N.A.I.C.S.: 488510

Vetsch AG, Internationale Transporte (1)
Heldaustrasse 66, 9471, Buchs, Switzerland
Tel.: (41) 81 354 25 00
Web Site: http://www.vetsch.net
Freight Forwarding Services
N.A.I.C.S.: 488510

VignoblExport S.A.S. (1)
69B Rue Du Colombier, 45000, Orleans,
France
Tel.: (33) 980802020
Web Site: https://www.vignoblexport.com
N.A.I.C.S.: 424820
Marjolaine Leteurtre (Co-Founder)

Zenith Logistics Inc. (1)
1 Boudreau Rd, Saint Albert, T8N 5A6, AB,
Canada
Tel.: (780) 458-2898
Logistics Warehousing & Storage Services
N.A.I.C.S.: 493110

audio.digital NRW GmbH (1)
Erna-Scheffler-Strasse 1, 51103, Cologne,
Germany
Tel.: (49) 22171015012
Web Site: https://audio.digital
Radio Broadcasting Services
N.A.I.C.S.: 516110

interServ Gesellschaft fur Personalund Beraterdienstleistungen mbH (1)
Charles-de-Gaulle-Str 20, 53113, Bonn,
Nordrhein-Westfalen, Germany
Tel.: (49) 2281820
Logistics Consulting Services
N.A.I.C.S.: 541614

it4logistics AG (1)
Am Luftschiffhafen 1, 14471, Potsdam, Germany
Tel.: (49) 331 2002 0
Web Site: http://www.it4logistics.de
Logistics Consulting Servies

N.A.I.C.S.: 541614

DEUTSCHE ROHSTOFF AG

Q7 24, 68161, Mannheim, Germany
Tel.: (49) 6214908170   De
DR0—(MUN)
Rev.: $217,076,035
Assets: $545,057,890
Liabilities: $345,952,858
Net Worth: $199,105,032
Earnings: $71,950,247
Emp.: 44
Fiscal Year-end: 12/31/23
Metal Mining Services
N.A.I.C.S.: 212290
Thomas Gultschlag (CEO)

Subsidiaries:

Ceritech AG (1)
Q7 24, 68161, Mannheim, Germany
Tel.: (49) 6214908170
Web Site: https://www.ceritech.com
Metal Mining Services
N.A.I.C.S.: 213114
Jorg Reichert (CEO)

DEUTSCHE RUCKVERSICH-ERUNG AG

Hansaallee 177 Entrance B/Heerdter
Lohweg, 40549, Dusseldorf, Germany
Tel.: (49) 211455401
Web Site:
    http://www.deutscherueck.de
Year Founded: 1951
Rev.: $1,696,512,312
Assets: $2,626,417,297
Liabilities: $2,305,204,042
Net Worth: $321,213,254
Earnings: $54,070,815
Emp.: 125
Fiscal Year-end: 12/31/18
Insurance Services
N.A.I.C.S.: 524210

Subsidiaries:

Deutsche Ruckversicherung Switzerland Ltd. (1)
Schweizergasse 21, 8001, Zurich, Switzerland
Tel.: (41) 442157666
Web Site: http://www.drswiss.ch
Insurance Services
N.A.I.C.S.: 524130

DEUTSCHE STEINZEUG CRE-MER & BREUER AG

Servaisstrasse, 53347, Bonn, Germany
Tel.: (49) 2283910
Web Site: http://www.deutsche-steinzeug.de
Sales Range: $200-249.9 Million
Emp.: 1,676
Ceramic Products Mfr
N.A.I.C.S.: 327110
Dieter Schafer (Member-Mgmt Bd)

Subsidiaries:

Deutsche Steinzeug America Inc. (1)
367 Curie Dr, Alpharetta, GA 30005
Tel.: (770) 442-5500
Web Site: http://www.deutsche-steinzeugusa.com
Sales Range: $25-49.9 Million
Emp.: 10
Ceramic Products Mfr
N.A.I.C.S.: 327120
Chris McMahan (Project Mgr)

Deutsche Steinzeug Italia s.r.l. (1)
Strada Statale 467 nr 134, Veggia, 42010,
Casalgrande, Reggio Emilia, Italy
Tel.: (39) 0536990288
Web Site: http://www.deutsche-steinzeug.it
Ceramic Products Sales
N.A.I.C.S.: 327120

Jasba Mosaik GmbH (1)

Im Petersborn 2, 56244, Otzingen, Germany
Tel.: (49) 26026820
Web Site: http://www.jasba.de
Sales Range: $50-74.9 Million
Emp.: 200
Ceramic Products Mfr
N.A.I.C.S.: 327120
Alexandra Schmidt (Mng Dir)

Meissen Keramik Vertriebs GmbH & Co. KG (1)
Wulffshof Wandweg 3, 44149, Dortmund,
Germany
Tel.: (49) 231187500
Web Site: http://www.meissen-keramik.de
Ceramic Products Mfr
N.A.I.C.S.: 327120

Subsidiary (Non-US):

Archi-Ro Kft. (2)
Radnoti Miklos utca 3 / A fszt / 5, 9025,
Gyor, Hungary
Tel.: (36) 96517017
Web Site: http://www.buchtal.hu
Emp.: 4
Ceramic Products Mfr
N.A.I.C.S.: 327120
Fekete Roland (Mng Dir)

Staloton Klinker Vertriebs GmbH (1)
Buchtal, Schwarzenfeld, 92521, Bavaria,
Germany
Tel.: (49) 943539100
Bricks Whslr
N.A.I.C.S.: 423320

DEUTSCHE TELEKOM AG

Friedrich-Ebert-Allee 140, 53113,
Bonn, Germany
Tel.: (49) 2281810   De
Web Site: https://www.telekom.com
Year Founded: 1995
DTE—(DEU)
Rev.: $124,051,011,760
Assets: $325,381,656,080
Liabilities: $236,272,844,080
Net Worth: $89,108,812,000
Earnings: $5,107,021,920
Emp.: 223,539
Fiscal Year-end: 12/31/20
Telecommunication Servicesb
N.A.I.C.S.: 517111
Thorsten Langheim (Member-Mgmt Bd)

Subsidiaries:

Asiacom Philippines, Inc. (1)
, Makati, Manila, Philippines (49.88%)
Provider of Digital Wireless Communications
N.A.I.C.S.: 517112

Subsidiary (Domestic):

Bayan Telecommunications Holdings Corp. (2)
234 Roosevelt Ave, San Francisco Del
Monte, Quezon City, Philippines
Tel.: (63) 24493000
Web Site: http://www.bayantel.com.ph
Communications Services Provider
N.A.I.C.S.: 517112
Oscar M. Lopez (Chm)

Subsidiary (Domestic):

Bayan Telecommunications, Inc. (3)
5 Fl Benpres Bldg Exchange Rd, PH 1605,
Pasig, Philippines
Tel.: (63) 24493000
Web Site: http://www.bayantel.com.ph
Communications Services Provider
N.A.I.C.S.: 517111
Oscar M. Lopez (Chm)

Atrada Trading Network AG (1)
Hugo-Junkers-Strasse 9, D-90461, Nuremberg, Germany
Tel.: (49) 9115205100
Web Site: http://www.atrada.net
Sales Range: $25-49.9 Million
Emp.: 30
Ecommerce Services
N.A.I.C.S.: 517810

DeTeMedien, Deutsche Telekom Medien GmbH (1)
Wiesenhuttenstr 18, 60329, Frankfurt,
Germany (100%)
Tel.: (49) 6926820
Web Site: https://www.dtme.de
Sales Range: $50-74.9 Million
Emp.: 120
Publicity Production & Execution
N.A.I.C.S.: 513120

Deutsche Telecom AG (1)
Ul Metschnikow 3, 01023, Kiev,
Ukraine (100%)
Tel.: (380) 442302669
Web Site: http://www.telekom.com
Provider of Digital Wireless Communications
N.A.I.C.S.: 517112

Deutsche Telekom France (1)
30 Rue Galilee, 75116, Paris,
France (100%)
Tel.: (33) 144430000
Web Site: http://www.telekom.com
Sales Range: $25-49.9 Million
Emp.: 20
Provider of Digital Wireless Communications
N.A.I.C.S.: 517112

Deutsche Telekom SA/NV (1)
Leonardo Da Vincilaan 19, 1030, Diegem,
Belgium
Tel.: (32) 23009111
Web Site: http://www.telekom.com
Sales Range: $25-49.9 Million
Emp.: 10
Provider of Digital Wireless Communications
N.A.I.C.S.: 517112

GTS Hungary Telecommunication Kft. (1)
Ipartelep u 13-15, 2040, Budaors, Hungary
Tel.: (36) 18144000
Web Site: http://www.gts.hu
Sales Range: $50-74.9 Million
Emp.: 200
Telecommunication Servicesb
N.A.I.C.S.: 517810
Peter Kollar (Mng Dir)

GTS Telecom Romania (1)
92-96 Izvor Street 2nd Floor Sector 5,
050564, Bucharest, Romania
Tel.: (40) 312200200
Web Site: http://www.gts.ro
Sales Range: $50-74.9 Million
Emp.: 150
Telecommunication Servicesb
N.A.I.C.S.: 517810

Hrvatski Telekom d.d. (1)
Radnicka cesta 21, 10000, Zagreb,
Croatia (51%)
Tel.: (385) 14911000
Web Site: https://www.t.ht.hr
Rev.: $1,147,295,507
Assets: $2,275,633,072
Liabilities: $408,438,017
Net Worth: $1,867,195,055
Earnings: $147,493,101
Emp.: 4,917
Fiscal Year-end: 12/31/2023
All Other Telecommunications
N.A.I.C.S.: 517810
Ivan Misetic (Deputy Chm-Supervisory Bd)

Isla Communications Co., Inc. (1)
12/F Trafalgar Plaza H.V. dela Costa,
Makati, Manila, Philippines (10.42%)
Tel.: (63) 6328140332
N.A.I.C.S.: 238210

MagyarCom Holding GmbH (1)
Krisztina Krt 55, Budapest, 1013,
Hungary (100%)
Tel.: (36) 228 181 0
Holding Company
N.A.I.C.S.: 551112

Subsidiary (Domestic):

Magyar Telekom Telecommunications plc (2)
1097 Budapest Konyves Kalman krt 36,
HU-1097, Budapest, Hungary (59.21%)
Tel.: (36) 14580000

Deutsche Telekom AG—(Continued)

Web Site: https://www.telekom.com
Rev.: $2,046,116,957
Assets: $3,991,058,314
Liabilities: $1,977,532,062
Net Worth: $2,013,526,252
Earnings: $183,804,670
Emp.: 6,711
Fiscal Year-end: 12/31/2022
Telecommunication Servicesb
N.A.I.C.S.: 517112
Robert Hauber *(Chm)*

**PT Satelit Palapa Indonesia
Satelindo** **(1)**
J Daan Mogot Km 11, Jakarta, 11710, Jakarta Barat, Indonesia **(25%)**
Tel.: (62) 215451745
Web Site: http://www.satelindo.co.id
Sales Range: Less than $1 Million
Emp.: 50
Telecommunications & Satellite Svcs
N.A.I.C.S.: 517410

Slovak Telekom A.S. **(1)**
Bajkalska 28, 81762, Bratislava, Slovakia
Tel.: (421) 903903903
Web Site: https://www.telekom.sk
Telecommunication Servicesb
N.A.I.C.S.: 517810

**T-Mobile International AG & Co.
KG** **(1)**
Landgrabenweg 151, 53227, Bonn,
Germany **(100%)**
Tel.: (49) 2289360
Web Site: http://www.tmobile.de
Sales Range: $25-49.9 Billion
Emp.: 44,592
Telecommunication Servicesb
N.A.I.C.S.: 517112

Subsidiary (Non-US):

T-Mobile Austria GmbH **(2)**
Rennweg 97 99, 1030, Vienna,
Austria **(100%)**
Tel.: (43) 1795850
Web Site: http://www.t-mobile.at
Sales Range: $400-449.9 Million
Emp.: 2,000
Wireless Telecommunication Services
N.A.I.C.S.: 517112
Andreas Bierwirth *(CEO)*

Subsidiary (Domestic):

UPC Austria GmbH **(3)**
Wolfganggasse 58-60, 1120, Vienna, Austria
Tel.: (43) 96060600
Web Site: http://www.upc.at
Emp.: 1,000
Cable & Other Subscription Programming
N.A.I.C.S.: 516210
Thomas Hintze *(Gen Mgr)*

Subsidiary (Domestic):

UPC Austria Services GmbH **(4)**
Wolfganggasse 58-60, 1120, Vienna, Austria
Tel.: (43) 96060600
Web Site: http://www.upc.at
Sales Range: $150-199.9 Million
Emp.: 400
Television & Internet Communication Services
N.A.I.C.S.: 516120

UPC Telekabel Wien GmbH **(4)**
Wolfganggasse 58-60, PO Box 47, A-1120, Vienna, Austria
Tel.: (43) 1960 60600
Web Site: http://www.upc.at
Sales Range: $200-249.9 Million
Television & Internet Communication Services
N.A.I.C.S.: 517111

Subsidiary (Domestic):

UPC Telekabel Klagenfurt GmbH **(5)**
VillacherStrasse 161, A-9020, Klagenfurt, Austria
Tel.: (43) 46391515
Web Site: http://www.upc.at
Sales Range: $200-249.9 Million
Television & Internet Communication Services

**UPC Telekabel-Fernsehnetz Wiener
Neustadt/Neunkirchen Betriebsgesell-
schaft mbH** **(5)**
Bahngasse 8, 2700, Vienna, Neustadt, Austria
Tel.: (43) 262299299
Web Site: http://www.upc.at
Sales Range: $200-249.9 Million
Television & Internet Communication Services
N.A.I.C.S.: 517810

Subsidiary (Non-US):

T-Mobile Czech Republic a.s. **(2)**
Tomickova 2144/1, 148 00, Prague, 4, Czech Republic
Tel.: (420) 603601111
Web Site: https://www.t-mobile.cz
Telecommunication Servicesb
N.A.I.C.S.: 517112

T-Mobile Netherlands BV **(2)**
Binckhoearlaan 117, 2516 BA, Hague,
Netherlands **(75%)**
Tel.: (31) 884477777
Web Site: http://www.t-mobile.nl
Sales Range: $100-124.9 Million
Emp.: 500
Provider of Digital Wireless Communications
N.A.I.C.S.: 517112
Soren Abildgaard *(CEO)*

Subsidiary (Domestic):

Tele2 Netherlands B.V. **(3)**
Wisselwerking 58, Diemen, 1112 XS, Netherlands
Tel.: (31) 20754 4444
Web Site: http://www.tele2.nl
Fixed & Mobile Telecommunications, Data & Internet Services
N.A.I.C.S.: 517111
Jon James *(CEO)*

Subsidiary (Domestic):

BBned NV **(4)**
Wisselwerking 58, 1112 XS, Diemen, Netherlands
Tel.: (31) 23 5659999
Web Site: http://www.bbned.nl
Sales Range: $50-74.9 Million
Emp.: 200
Broadband Internet Services
N.A.I.C.S.: 517810

Affiliate (US):

T-Mobile US, Inc. **(2)**
12920 SE 38th St, Bellevue, WA
98006-1350 **(43%)**
Tel.: (425) 378-4000
Web Site: https://www.t-mobile.com
Rev.: $78,558,000,000
Assets: $207,682,000,000
Liabilities: $142,967,000,000
Net Worth: $64,715,000,000
Earnings: $8,317,000,000
Emp.: 67,000
Fiscal Year-end: 12/31/2023
Holding Company; Wireless Telecommunications Services
N.A.I.C.S.: 551112
Timotheus Hottges *(Chm)*

Subsidiary (Domestic):

T-Mobile USA, Inc. **(3)**
12920 SE 38th St, Bellevue, WA 98006-1350
Tel.: (425) 378-4000
Web Site: http://www.t-mobile.com
Wireless Telecommunication Services
N.A.I.C.S.: 517112
Mike Sievert *(Pres & CEO)*

Subsidiary (Domestic):

Sprint Corporation **(4)**
6200 Sprint Pkwy, Overland Park, KS 66251
Tel.: (703) 433-4000
Web Site: https://www.sprint.com
Rev.: $33,600,000,000
Assets: $84,601,000,000
Liabilities: $58,474,000,000
Net Worth: $26,127,000,000

Earnings: ($1,943,000,000)
Emp.: 28,500
Fiscal Year-end: 03/31/2019
Holding Company; Wireless, Long Distance & Local Telecommunication Services
N.A.I.C.S.: 551112
Robert Hackl *(Sr VP-Handset Leasing & Insurance)*

Subsidiary (Domestic):

Sprint Communications, Inc. **(5)**
6200 Sprint Pkwy, Overland Park, KS 66251
Tel.: (703) 433-4000
Web Site: http://www.sprint.com
Wireless & Wireline Communications Products & Services
N.A.I.C.S.: 517810

Subsidiary (Domestic):

Telekom Deutschland GmbH **(4)**
Landgrabenweg 151, 53227, Bonn, Germany
Tel.: (49) 2281810
Web Site: https://www.telekom.de
Wireless Telecommunication Services
N.A.I.C.S.: 517112
Michael Hagspihl *(Mng Dir-Private Customers)*

T-Systems International GmbH **(1)**
Hahnstrasse 43, 60528, Frankfurt,
Germany **(100%)**
Tel.: (49) 69665310
Web Site: http://www.t-systems.com
Sales Range: $800-899.9 Million **(1)**
Emp.: 4,000
Digital Wireless Communications
N.A.I.C.S.: 517112
Christoph Ahrendt *(Member-Mgmt Bd & Dir-Fin & Controlling)*

Subsidiary (Non-US):

T-Systems Austria Ges.m.b.H **(2)**
Rennweg 97-99, 1030, Vienna, Austria
Tel.: (43) 570570
Web Site: http://www.t-systems.com
Sales Range: $150-199.9 Million
Emp.: 647
Telecommunication Servicesb
N.A.I.C.S.: 517810
Peter Lenz *(Mng Dir)*

T-Systems Belgium S.A. **(2)**
't Hofveld 8, 1702, Groot-Bijgaarden, Belgium
Tel.: (32) 23009111
Web Site: http://www.t-systems.be
Sales Range: $25-49.9 Million
Emp.: 75
Communication Technology Solutions
N.A.I.C.S.: 517810
Daniela Theisinger *(Mng Dir)*

Subsidiary (Domestic):

T-Systems Business Services **(2)**
Mainzer Landstrasse 50, 60325, Frankfurt, Germany
Tel.: (49) 69665310
Web Site: http://www.t-systems.com
Sales Range: $150-199.9 Million
Emp.: 1,000
Digital Wireless Communication Services
N.A.I.C.S.: 517112

Subsidiary (Domestic):

gedas AG **(3)**
Dernburgstrasse 44 50 54, 14057, Berlin, Germany
Tel.: (49) 30303920
Web Site: http://www.t-systems.de
Sales Range: $750-799.9 Million
Information Technology Service Provider
N.A.I.C.S.: 541512

Subsidiary (Non-US):

T-Systems **(4)**
18 Place des Nympheas, BP 55341, Immeuble Le Tropical, 95941, Villepinte, Roissy Ch De Gaulle, France
Tel.: (33) 149908600
Web Site: http://www.t-systems.fr
Sales Range: $50-74.9 Million
Emp.: 500
Information Technology Services

N.A.I.C.S.: 541512
Werner Rolf *(Pres)*

gedas Argentina, S.A. **(4)**
Delcasse Y Av Henry Ford, PO Box B1610BKK, Gral Pacheco, Buenos Aires, B1610, Argentina
Tel.: (54) 43179555
Sales Range: $50-74.9 Million
Emp.: 260
Information Technology Service Provider
N.A.I.C.S.: 541512

gedas Mexico, S.A. de C.V. **(4)**
Km 117 Autopista Mexico Puebla Parque Indus, Finsa Nave 1, CP 72710, Puebla, Mexico
Tel.: (52) 2222234000
Web Site: http://www.gedas.com.mx
Sales Range: $125-149.9 Million
Emp.: 613
Information Technology Service Provider
N.A.I.C.S.: 541512

gedas United Kingdom Ltd. **(4)**
Futura House, Bradbourne Drive, Tilbrook, Milton Keynes, MK7 8AZ, Buckinghamshire, United Kingdom
Tel.: (44) 364656
Web Site: http://www.gedas.co.uk
Sales Range: $50-74.9 Million
Emp.: 309
Information Technology Services
N.A.I.C.S.: 541512

Subsidiary (Non-US):

T-Systems China Ltd. **(2)**
50/F Ste 5008, Central Plz 18 Harbour Rd, Wanchai, China (Hong Kong)
Tel.: (852) 25935300
Web Site: http://www.t-systems.cn
Sales Range: $25-49.9 Million
Emp.: 30
Communication Technology Solutions
N.A.I.C.S.: 517810

T-Systems Danmark AS **(2)**
Lautrupvang 8, 2750, Ballerup, Denmark
Tel.: (45) 70122626
Web Site: http://www.t-systems.dk
Sales Range: $50-74.9 Million
Emp.: 150
Communication Technology Solutions
N.A.I.C.S.: 517810
Jesper Kryhlmand *(Mng Dir)*

T-Systems Hungary Kft. **(2)**
Krisztina Krt 55, 1013, Budapest, Hungary
Tel.: (36) 14587000
Web Site: http://www.t-systems.com
Sales Range: $50-74.9 Million
Emp.: 200
Communication Technology Solutions
N.A.I.C.S.: 517810

T-Systems Italia S.p.A. **(2)**
Strada 2 Palazzo D3, 20090, Assago, MI, Italy
Tel.: (39) 0289241
Web Site: http://www.t-systems.it
Communication Technology Solutions
N.A.I.C.S.: 517810

T-Systems Japan K.K. **(2)**
Nishikicho MK Building 3F 3-23 Kanda Nishiki-cho, Chiyoda-ku, Tokyo, 101-0054, Japan
Tel.: (81) 345881240
Web Site: http://www.t-systems.jp
Communication Technology Solutions
N.A.I.C.S.: 517810

T-Systems Ltd. **(2)**
21st Floor Euston Tower 286 Euston Road, London, NW1 3DP, United Kingdom
Tel.: (44) 2071213900
Web Site: http://www.t-systems.co.uk
Emp.: 700
Communication Technology Solutions
N.A.I.C.S.: 517810

T-Systems Luxemburg S.A. **(2)**
117 Route d'Arlon, 8009, Strassen, Luxembourg
Tel.: (352) 26119121
Web Site: http://www.t-systems.lu
Sales Range: $25-49.9 Million
Emp.: 8
Communication Technology Solutions
N.A.I.C.S.: 517810

Ralf Beyer *(Mng Dir)*

T-Systems Nederland B.V.　　(2)
Lage Biezenweg 3, 4131 LV, Vianen, Netherlands
Tel.: (31) 347327327
Web Site: http://www.t-systems.nl
Sales Range: $50-74,9 Million
Emp.: 250
Communication Technology Services
N.A.I.C.S.: 517810
Wouter Knoester *(Dir-ICT Ops)*

Subsidiary (US):

T-Systems North America Inc.　　(2)
1901 Butterfield Rd Ste 700, Downers Grove, IL 60515
Tel.: (630) 493-6100
Web Site: http://www.t-systemsus.com
Sales Range: $100-124.9 Million
Emp.: 350
Communication Technology Solutions
N.A.I.C.S.: 517810
Arrie Redelinghuys *(VP-ICT Ops & Member-Mgmt Bd)*

Subsidiary (Non-US):

T-Systems Polska Sp. z o.o.　　(2)
Ul Sw Antoniego 7, 50-073, Wroclaw, Poland
Tel.: (48) 713751100
Web Site: http://www.t-systems.pl
Sales Range: $25-49.9 Million
Emp.: 100
Communication Technology Solutions
N.A.I.C.S.: 517810

T-Systems Singapore Pte. Ltd.　　(2)
8 Shenton Way 10-01, Singapore, 068811, Singapore
Tel.: (65) 63170700
Web Site: http://www.t-systems.com.sg
Sales Range: $50-74.9 Million
Emp.: 190
Communication Technology Solutions
N.A.I.C.S.: 517810
Arkadiusz Czopor *(Mng Dir)*

T-Systems South Africa (Pty) Ltd.　　(2)
173 Oxfort Road, Halfway House, Johannesburg, 2196, South Africa
Tel.: (27) 112547400
Web Site: http://www.t-systems.com
Sales Range: $100-124.9 Million
Emp.: 300
Communication Technology Solutions
N.A.I.C.S.: 517810
Dineo Molefe *(Mng Dir)*

T-Systems Switzerland Ltd.　　(2)
Industriestrasse 21, 3052, Zollikofen, Switzerland
Tel.: (41) 848112211
Web Site: https://www.t-systems.com
Sales Range: $150-199.9 Million
Emp.: 600
Communication Technology Solutions
N.A.I.C.S.: 517810
Stefan Zuger *(Chief Digital Officer & Member-Exec Bd)*

Subsidiary (Domestic):

T-Systems debis Systemhaus　　(2)
Dachauer Str 651, 80995, Munich, Germany　　**(100%)**
Tel.: (49) 8910110
Web Site: http://www.t-systems.telekom.de
Sales Range: $75-99.9 Million
Emp.: 5
Software Services
N.A.I.C.S.: 334610

Subsidiary (Non-US):

T-Systems do Brasil Ltda.　　(2)
Rua Olimpiadas 205 3rd Floor, Sao Paulo, 04551-000, SP, Brazil
Tel.: (55) 1121842386
Web Site: http://www.t-systems.com
Sales Range: $350-399.9 Million
Emp.: 2,300
Communication Technology Solutions
N.A.I.C.S.: 517810

Subsidiary (Domestic):

rola Security Solutions GmbH　　(2)

Essener Strasse 5, 46047, Oberhausen, Germany
Tel.: (49) 208 30 66 16 0
Web Site: http://www.rola.com
Emp.: 60
Information Technology Security Solutions
N.A.I.C.S.: 513210

T-Venture Holding GmbH　　(1)
Gotenstrasse 156, 53175, Bonn, Germany
Tel.: (49) 228308480
Web Site: http://www.t-venture.de
Sales Range: $50-74.9 Million
Emp.: 25
Venture Capital Services
N.A.I.C.S.: 523999

Subsidiary (US):

T-Venture of America, Inc.　　(2)
Metro Tower Ctr 950 Tower Ln Ste 1600, Foster City, CA 94404
Tel.: (650) 358-2011
Web Site: http://www.t-venture.de
Venture Capital Services
N.A.I.C.S.: 523999

congster GmbH　　(1)
Weinsbergstrasse 70, 50823, Cologne, Germany
Tel.: (49) 22179700700
Web Site: http://www.congster.de
Internet Services
N.A.I.C.S.: 541519

DEUTSCHE TRANSPORT-COMPAGNIE ERICH BOGDAN GMBH & CO. KG
Donaustr 126, 90451, Nuremberg, Germany
Tel.: (49) 91199620
Web Site: http://www.dtc.de
Year Founded: 1946
Sales Range: $25-49.9 Million
Emp.: 270
Logistic Services
N.A.I.C.S.: 481212
Manfred Heuer *(Co-Mng Dir)*

DEUTSCHE WERTPAPIERSERVICE BANK AG
Wildunger Strasse 14, 60487, Frankfurt, Germany
Tel.: (49) 6950990
Web Site: http://www.dwpbank.de
Banking Services
N.A.I.C.S.:

DEUTSCHE WOHNEN SE
Mecklenburgische Strabe 57, 14197, Berlin, Germany
Tel.: (49) 30897860　　　　De
Web Site: https://www.deutsche-wohnen.com
Year Founded: 1998
DWNI—(MUN)
Rev.: $1,450,264,406
Assets: $30,009,809,820
Liabilities: $14,984,924,863
Net Worth: $15,024,884,957
Earnings: ($2,977,799,712)
Emp.: 796
Fiscal Year-end: 12/31/23
Holding Company; Property Management
N.A.I.C.S.: 551112
Andreas Kretschmer *(Deputy Chm-Supervisory Bd)*

Subsidiaries:

Communication Concept Gesellschaft fur Kommunikationstechnik mbH　　(1)
Wilhelm-Sammet-Str 37, 04157, Leipzig, Germany
Tel.: (49) 341234050
Web Site: https://www.ccgmbh.de
Communication Service
N.A.I.C.S.: 517810

Deutsche Wohnen Management GmbH　　(1)
Mecklenburgische Strasse 57, 14197, Ber-

lin, Germany
Tel.: (49) 30897860
Web Site: http://www.deutsche-wohnen.com
Sales Range: $100-124.9 Million
Emp.: 226
Residential Properties Management & Development
N.A.I.C.S.: 531311
Kathrin Wolff *(Mng Dir)*

FACILITA Berlin GmbH　　(1)
Tino-Schwierzina-Str 32, 13089, Berlin, Germany
Tel.: (49) 3020613490
Web Site: http://www.facilita-berlin.de
Residential Property Services
N.A.I.C.S.: 531311

GSW Immobilien AG　　(1)
Charlottenstrasse 4, 10969, Berlin, Germany　　**(94%)**
Tel.: (49) 30 68 99 99 0
Web Site: http://www.gsw.ag
Emp.: 545
Apartments & Other Residential Housing Management & Leasing Services
N.A.I.C.S.: 531311
Andreas Segal *(Vice Chm-Supervisory Bd)*

GSW Pegasus GmbH　　(1)
Potsdamer Str 98, 10785, Berlin, Germany
Tel.: (49) 3025700380
Web Site: https://www.pegasusgmbh.de
Information Technology Services
N.A.I.C.S.: 541519

KATHARINENHOF Seniorehwohn- und Pflegeanlage Betriebs-GmbH　　(1)
Markrafenstrasse 19, 10969, Berlin, Germany
Tel.: (49) 30 847 151 902
Web Site: http://www.katharinenhof.net
Nursing & Residential Care Homes Management
N.A.I.C.S.: 623110
Nikolaus Hensel *(Chm)*

Pflegen & Wohnen Hamburg GmbH　　(1)
Finkenau 11, 22081, Hamburg, Germany
Tel.: (49) 20223066
Web Site: https://www.pflegenundwohnen.de
Nursing Home Care Services
N.A.I.C.S.: 621610

SYNVIA media GmbH　　(1)
Erzbergerstrasse 1, 39104, Magdeburg, Germany
Tel.: (49) 39150860600
Web Site: https://www.synvia.de
Communication Service
N.A.I.C.S.: 517810

Tele AG　　(1)
Wilhelm-Sammet-Str 37, D-04157, Leipzig, Germany
Tel.: (49) 3415238010
Web Site: https://www.tele-ag.de
Communication Service
N.A.I.C.S.: 517810

Wohn- und Pflegewelt Lahnblick GmbH　　(1)
Lahnstrasse 70, 56130, Bad Ems, Germany
Tel.: (49) 2603 509 0
Web Site: http://www.lahnblick-bad-ems.de
Elder Care Services
N.A.I.C.S.: 621610

DEUTSCHER SPARKASSEN-UND GIROVERBAND E.V.
Charlottenstrasse 47, 10117, Berlin, Germany
Tel.: (49) 30 2 02 250　　　　De
Web Site: http://www.dsgv.de
Year Founded: 1924
Sales Range: $75-99.9 Billion
Banking Services
N.A.I.C.S.: 813910
Karl-Peter Schackmann-Fallis *(Mng Dir)*

Subsidiaries:

Landesbank Berlin Holding AG　　(1)
Alexanderplatz 2, 10178, Berlin, Germany

Tel.: (49) 30245500
Web Site: http://www.lbb.de
Sales Range: $1-4.9 Billion
Bank Holding Company
N.A.I.C.S.: 551111
Barbel Wulff *(Deputy Chm-Supervisory Bd)*

Subsidiary (Domestic):

Berlin Hyp AG　　(2)
Budapester Strasse 1, 10787, Berlin, Germany　　**(100%)**
Tel.: (49) 30259990
Web Site: http://www.berlinhyp.de
Rev.: $471,259,520
Assets: $30,259,910,460
Liabilities: $29,211,829,951
Net Worth: $1,048,080,510
Earnings: $68,319,468
Emp.: 606
Fiscal Year-end: 12/31/2019
Real Estate Financing, Credit & Brokerage Services
N.A.I.C.S.: 522299
Jana Pabst *(Deputy Chm-Supervisory Bd)*

Representative Office (Non-US):

Berlin Hyp AG - Warsaw Office　　(3)
Mokotowska Square Mokotowska 49, 00 542, Warsaw, Poland
Tel.: (48) 22 376 5121
Web Site: http://www.berlinhyp.de
Emp.: 3
Real Estate Financing & Credit Services
N.A.I.C.S.: 522299

Subsidiary (Domestic):

Berlin Hyp Immobilien GmbH　　(3)
Budapester Strasse 1, 10787, Berlin, Germany
Tel.: (49) 30 2599 9908
Web Site: http://www.berlinhyp-immobilien.de
Real Estate Agency
N.A.I.C.S.: 531210
Gaby Hartmann *(Mng Dir)*

Subsidiary (Domestic):

Landesbank Berlin AG　　(2)
Alexanderplatz 2, 10178, Berlin, Germany
Tel.: (49) 30 245 500
Web Site: http://www.lbb.de
Sales Range: $1-4.9 Billion
Emp.: 5,000
Commercial & Investment Banking
N.A.I.C.S.: 522110
Johannes Evers *(Chm-Mgmt Bd)*

Subsidiary (Domestic):

BankenService GmbH　　(3)
Brunnenstrasse 111, 13355, Berlin, Germany
Tel.: (49) 3024557301
Web Site: http://www.bankenservice.de
Sales Range: $350-399.9 Million
Emp.: 800
Banking
N.A.I.C.S.: 522110

DEUTZ AG
Ottostrasse 1, 51149, Cologne, Germany
Tel.: (49) 2218220　　　　De
Web Site: https://www.deutz.com
Year Founded: 1864
DEZ—(MUN)
Rev.: $2,277,504,584
Assets: $1,755,374,074
Liabilities: $934,977,890
Net Worth: $820,396,184
Earnings: $90,406,953
Emp.: 4,972
Fiscal Year-end: 12/31/23
Diesel Engine Mfr
N.A.I.C.S.: 336310
Michael Wellenzohn *(Member-Mgmt Bd-Sls, Svc & Mktg)*

Subsidiaries:

Ausma Motorenrevisie B.V.　　(1)
Exportweg 2, Roden, 9301 ZV, Groningen, Netherlands
Tel.: (31) 505016028

DEUTZ AG—(Continued)

Web Site: https://www.ausma-motorenrevisie.nl
Engine Motor Parts Mfr
N.A.I.C.S.: 336320

DEUTZ Beteiligung GmbH (1)
Ottostr 1, Nordrhein-Westfalen, 51149, Cologne, Germany
Tel.: (49) 221 8220
Web Site: http://www.deutz.com
Sales Range: $800-899.9 Million
Automotive Engine Mfr
N.A.I.C.S.: 333618

DEUTZ CS s.r.o. (1)
Brnenska 1066, 66442, Modrice, Czech Republic
Tel.: (420) 545214651
Web Site: https://www.deutz.cz
Diesel Engine & Parts Whslr
N.A.I.C.S.: 423830

DEUTZ Corporation (1)
3883 Steve Reynolds Blvd, Norcross, GA 30093-3051
Tel.: (770) 564-7100
Sales Range: $125-149.9 Million
Emp.: 100
Air Cooled Diesel Engines & Spare Parts Distr
N.A.I.C.S.: 423830
Greg Tremaine (Mgr-Bus-Northwest & Mountains)

DEUTZ DITER S.A. (1)
Ctra Badajoz - Granada Km 74 6, Zafra, 06300, Badajoz, Spain
Tel.: (34) 92 456 5100
Web Site: https://www.deutz.es
Components Machining & Assembling Services
N.A.I.C.S.: 561990
Alejandro Castilla de la Hoya (Dir-Engrg)

DEUTZ FRANCE S.A. (1)
115 Rue du Fosse Blanc, 92230, Gennevilliers, France
Tel.: (33) 14 613 8787
Web Site: https://www.deutz.fr
Sales Range: $25-49.9 Million
Emp.: 40
Diesel Engines Maintenance & Sales
N.A.I.C.S.: 811198

DEUTZ Netherlands B.V. (1)
Malachiet 300, 3316 LD, Dordrecht, Netherlands
Tel.: (31) 180333111
Web Site: https://www.deutz.nl
Engine Motor Parts Mfr
N.A.I.C.S.: 336320

DEUTZ SICHERHEIT Gesellschaft fur Industrieservice mbH (1)
Wiersbergstrasse 43, Cologne, 51149, Nordrhein-Westfalen, Germany
Tel.: (49) 2218226744
Web Site: http://www.deutz-sicherheit.com
Emp.: 2,000
Safety Consulting Services
N.A.I.C.S.: 541690
Jens Sebald (Mng Dir)

DEUTZ UK Ltd. (1)
Unit 3 Willow Park Burdock Close, Cannock, WS11 7FQ, Staffordshire, United Kingdom
Tel.: (44) 154 343 8900
Web Site: https://www.deutzuk.com
Sales Range: $25-49.9 Million
Emp.: 30
Diesel Engine Mfr
N.A.I.C.S.: 333618

Deutz Asia-Pacific (Pte) Ltd. (1)
16-D TUAS Avenue 1 JTC SPACE TUAS 01-60, Singapore, 639536, Singapore
Tel.: (65) 6 672 7800
Web Site: https://www.deutz.com.sg
Diesel Engine Sales & Services
N.A.I.C.S.: 423860

Deutz Australia (Pty) Ltd. (1)
136-140 South Park Drive, Dandenong South, 3175, VIC, Australia
Tel.: (61) 39 549 8400
Web Site: https://www.deutz.com.au
Motor Engine Mfr
N.A.I.C.S.: 336310

Deutz Austria GmbH (1)
7 Haidequerstrasse 5, 1110, Vienna, Austria
Tel.: (43) 174916710
Web Site: https://www.deutz.co.at
Engine Motor Parts Mfr
N.A.I.C.S.: 336320

Deutz Belgium N.V. (1)
Zwarte weg 1, 2030, Antwerp, Belgium
Tel.: (32) 35460260
Web Site: https://www.deutz.be
Engine Motor Parts Mfr
N.A.I.C.S.: 336320

Deutz Benelux B.V. (1)
Malachiet 300, 3316 LD, Dordrecht, Netherlands
Tel.: (31) 180333111
Web Site: https://www.deutz.nl
Industrial Machinery Mfr
N.A.I.C.S.: 332911

Deutz Do Brasil Ltda. (1)
Rua Carlos Ayres 542 - Shed 03 - Independencia, Sao Bernardo do Campo, 09860-065, SP, Brazil
Tel.: (55) 113 611 0911
Web Site: https://www.deutz.com.br
Diesel Engine Mfr
N.A.I.C.S.: 333618

Deutz Italy S.r.l. (1)
via Garcia Lorca 25, 23871, Lomagna, LC, Italy
Tel.: (39) 039 591 4600
Web Site: https://www.deutz.it
Emp.: 64
Motor Engine Mfr
N.A.I.C.S.: 336310
Matteo Bonfanti (Ops Mgr)

Subsidiary (Non-US):

Deutz Romania S.r.l. (2)
Str Brailei 332-1, Galati, 800396, Romania
Tel.: (40) 236406250
Motor Engine Mfr
N.A.I.C.S.: 336310

Subsidiary (Domestic):

Service Center Milan S.r.l. (2)
Via Della Liberazione 38, Peschiera Borromeo, 20068, Milan, Italy
Tel.: (39) 0255300000
Web Site: http://www.csdmilano.it
Diesel Engine Mfr
N.A.I.C.S.: 333618

Deutz Spain S.A. (1)
Ctra Badajoz-Granada Km 74 6, Zafra, 06300, Badajoz, Spain
Tel.: (34) 92 456 5100
Web Site: https://www.deutz.es
Emp.: 500
Motor Engine Mfr
N.A.I.C.S.: 336310

Diesel Motor Nordic AB (1)
Saldovagen 6-8, 175 62, Jarfalla, Sweden
Tel.: (46) 856470700
Web Site: http://www.dieselmotornordic.se
Diesel Engine Distr
N.A.I.C.S.: 423830

Subsidiary (Non-US):

Diesel Motor Nordic A/S (2)
Norddigesvej 6, 8240, Risskov, Denmark
Tel.: (45) 43269000
Diesel Engine Distr
N.A.I.C.S.: 423830
Jens Anker Hog (Mgr-Site)

Futavis GmbH (1)
Nerscheider Weg 170, 52076, Aachen, Germany
Tel.: (49) 24193851804
Web Site: https://www.futavis.de
Emp.: 70
Battery Component Mfr
N.A.I.C.S.: 335910

Motor Center Austria GmbH (1)
Europastrasse 5, A-4600, Wels, Austria
Tel.: (43) 7242471610
Web Site: https://www.mca.at
Engine Motor Parts Mfr
N.A.I.C.S.: 336320

Nouvelle Societe MAGIDEUTZ S.A. (1)

Rue Sergent Khalich Mohamed 6, BP 13024, 20300, Casablanca, Morocco
Tel.: (212) 522303023
Web Site: http://www.deutz.ma
Sales Range: $25-49.9 Million
Emp.: 48
Diesel Engine Sales & Maintenance Services
N.A.I.C.S.: 423830
Ahmed Hamdi (Mgr-Sls)

Unterstutzungsgesellschaft mbH der Deutz Aktiengesellschaft (1)
Wiersbergstrasse 01, Cologne, 51149, Nordrhein-Westfalen, Germany
Tel.: (49) 2218226744
Industrial Fire Safety & Maintenance Services
N.A.I.C.S.: 561990

DEV HARI EXPORTS INDIA LTD.
9 Siddharth Shopping Centre, Jamnagar, 361 008, Gujarat, India
Tel.: (91) 2882661942
Web Site:
http://www.devhariexports.com
Year Founded: 1994
539197—(BOM)
Rev.: $155,859
Assets: $1,436,666
Liabilities: $446,894
Net Worth: $989,772
Earnings: $658
Fiscal Year-end: 03/31/20
Steel Trading Services
N.A.I.C.S.: 523160
Sanjay S. Bhayani (CFO)

DEV INFORMATION TECHNOLOGY PVT. LTD.
14 Aaryans Corporate Park Near Shilaj Railway Crossing, Thaltej Shilaj Road, Ahmedabad, 380059, Gujarat, India
Tel.: (91) 9879107870   In
Web Site: https://www.devitpl.com
Year Founded: 1997
DEVIT—(NSE)
Rev.: $11,680,132
Assets: $8,595,970
Liabilities: $3,944,205
Net Worth: $4,651,765
Earnings: $111,550
Emp.: 929
Fiscal Year-end: 03/31/21
IT Services
N.A.I.C.S.: 519290
Jaimin Shah (Co-CEO & Co-Mng Dir)

Subsidiaries:

DRS Technologies Canada Ltd. (1)
115 Emily St, Carleton Place, K7C 4J5, ON, Canada
Tel.: (613) 253-3020
Web Site: http://www.drs.com
Sales Range: $100-124.9 Million
Emp.: 355
Provider of Flight Safety System for Military & Commercial Aircraft Services
N.A.I.C.S.: 334511

Dev Info-Tech North America Limited (1)
2425 Matheson Blvd E 8th Floor, Mississauga, L4W 5K4, ON, Canada
Tel.: (905) 361-2861
Software Development Services
N.A.I.C.S.: 541511

DEV LABTECH VENTURE LTD.
GF/22-23 Pattani Plaza Dairy Road Near Nilambaug Circle, Bhavnagar, 364002, Gujarat, India
Tel.: (91) 9324485010
Web Site:
https://www.devlabtechventure.com
Year Founded: 1993
543848—(BOM)
Jewelry Product Mfr

N.A.I.C.S.: 339910
Jay Jerambhai Donda (CFO)

DEVA BIKAS BANK LIMITED
125 Bina Marg, PO Box 25092, Lal Durbar, Kathmandu, Nepal
Tel.: (977) 14242272   NP
Web Site:
http://www.devabank.com.np
Year Founded: 2015
Sales Range: Less than $1 Million
Banking & Lending Services
N.A.I.C.S.: 522180
Cubarna Lal Dajracharya (Chm)

DEVCO PARTNERS OY
Kasarmikatu 27 B 15, Helsinki, 00130, Finland
Tel.: (358) 10 2354820
Web Site: http://www.devco.fi
Year Founded: 2014
Private Investment Firm
N.A.I.C.S.: 523999
Otto Kukkonen (Partner)

Subsidiaries:

Bluefors Oy (1)
Arinatie 10, 00370, Helsinki, Finland
Tel.: (358) 956174800
Web Site: https://bluefors.com
Emp.: 270
Cryogen-free Dilution Refrigeration Systems Research & Development
N.A.I.C.S.: 333415
Rob Blaauwgeers (CEO)

Subsidiary (US):

Cryomech, Inc. (2)
113 Falso Dr, Syracuse, NY 13211
Tel.: (315) 455-2555
Web Site: http://www.cryomech.com
Air-Conditioning & Warm Air Heating Equipment & Commercial & Industrial Refrigeration Equipment Mfr
N.A.I.C.S.: 333415
Brent Zerkle (Dir-Prototyping)

Oy Medix Biochemica Ab (1)
Klovinpellontie 3, FI 02180, Espoo, Finland
Tel.: (358) 9 547 680
Web Site: http://www.medixbiochemica.com
Pharmaceutical Development & Mfr
N.A.I.C.S.: 325412
Mariella Paroma (VP-HR)

Subsidiary (US):

Biostride, Inc. (2)
1201 Douglas Ave, Redwood City, CA 94063
Tel.: (650) 367-4954
Web Site: http://www.biostrideinc.com
Pharmaceutical Preparation Mfr
N.A.I.C.S.: 325412
Todd Corneillie (Pres)

Lee Biosolutions, Inc. (2)
10850 Metro Ct, Maryland Heights, MO 63043
Tel.: (314) 968-1091
Web Site: http://www.leebio.com
Pharmaceutical Preparation Mfr
N.A.I.C.S.: 325412
J. Burton Lee (Chm & CEO)

ViroStat, LLC (2)
PO Box 8522, Portland, ME 04104-8522
Tel.: (207) 856-6620
Web Site: http://www.virostat-inc.com
Research & Development in the Physical, Engineering & Life Sciences
N.A.I.C.S.: 541715
Doug McAllister (Pres)

Vexve Oy (1)
Pajakatu 11, 38200, Sastamala, Finland
Tel.: (358) 107340800
Web Site: http://www.vexve.com
Valve, Meter & Control Mfr
N.A.I.C.S.: 332912
Johanna Perkola (Coord-Cust Svc-HVAC/R products)

DEVELCON

155 Champagne Dr Ste 7, Toronto, ON, Canada
Tel.: (416) 385-1390
Web Site: http://www.develcon.com
Year Founded: 1974
Rev.: $18,713,958
Emp.: 130
Wireless Products Supplier
N.A.I.C.S.: 517112
Geoffrey Bennett *(Pres)*

DEVELIA S.A.

ul Powstancow Slaskich Street 2-4, 53-333, Wroclaw, Poland
Tel.: (48) 717165571
Web Site: https://www.develia.pl
Year Founded: 2006
DVL—(WAR)
Rev.: $268,280,912
Assets: $740,826,006
Liabilities: $380,346,933
Net Worth: $360,479,074
Earnings: $58,240,215
Emp.: 177
Fiscal Year-end: 12/31/22
Real Estate Development Services
N.A.I.C.S.: 531390
Pawel Malyska *(Vice Chm-Supervisory Bd)*

Subsidiaries:

Arkady Wroclawskie S.A. **(1)**
ul Powstancow Slaskich 2-4, 53-333, Wroclaw, Poland
Tel.: (48) 514907867
Web Site: http://www.arkadywroclawskie.pl
Commercial Space Rental Services
N.A.I.C.S.: 531120

DEVELICA DEUTSCHLAND LIMITED

1st Floor Royal Chambers Saint Julian's Avenue, PO Box 650, Saint Peter Port, GY1 3JX, Guernsey
Tel.: (44) 1481715601
Web Site:
http://www.develicadeutsch.com
Sales Range: $100-124.9 Million
Investment Services
N.A.I.C.S.: 523940
Derek Butler *(Chm)*

DEVELOP GLOBAL LTD.

234 Railway Parade, West Leederville, 6007, WA, Australia
Tel.: (61) 863897400
Web Site: https://develop.com.au
DVP—(ASX)
Rev.: $98,310,596
Assets: $314,657,498
Liabilities: $81,322,551
Net Worth: $233,334,947
Earnings: ($7,985,246)
Emp.: 17
Fiscal Year-end: 06/30/24
Mineral Exploration & Mining Services
N.A.I.C.S.: 212220
Trevor Hart *(CFO & Sec)*

DEVELOP NORTH PLC

Eagle House Asama Court, Newcastle upon Tyne, NE4 7YD, United Kingdom
Tel.: (44) 1912220099 **UK**
Web Site:
https://www.tocpropertybacked.com
Year Founded: 2017
DVNO—(LSE)
Rev.: $2,230,734
Assets: $30,846,041
Liabilities: $183,292
Net Worth: $30,662,748
Earnings: $1,261,322
Fiscal Year-end: 11/30/21
Property Investment Services
N.A.I.C.S.: 531311

John Newlands *(Chm)*

DEVELOPMENT ADVANCE SOLUTION CO., LTD.

26-2 Dongnonggong-gil Dong-myeon, Hwasun, Jeollanam-do, Korea (South)
Tel.: (82) 613702114
Web Site: https://www.dasco.kr
Year Founded: 1996
058730—(KRS)
Rev.: $290,295,276
Assets: $265,472,252
Liabilities: $155,617,972
Net Worth: $109,854,281
Earnings: $1,714,198
Emp.: 239
Fiscal Year-end: 12/31/22
Steel Frameworks Mfr
N.A.I.C.S.: 339999
Sang-Won Han *(Chm & CEO)*

DEVELOPMENT BANK OF JAPAN, INC.

Otemachi Financial City South Tower 9-6 Otemachi 1-chome, Chiyoda-ku, Tokyo, 100-8178, Japan
Tel.: (81) 3 3270 3211 **JP**
Web Site: http://www.dbj.jp
Year Founded: 1951
Rev.: $2,728,926,360
Assets: $154,740,994,800
Liabilities: $124,876,100,040
Net Worth: $29,864,894,760
Earnings: $832,940,160
Emp.: 1,186
Fiscal Year-end: 03/31/19
International Banking Services
N.A.I.C.S.: 522299
Hajime Watanabe *(Pres & CEO)*

Subsidiaries:

AdvanIDe Pte. Ltd. **(1)**
7 Temasek Boulevard # 06-01 Suntec Tower One, 038987, Singapore, Singapore
Tel.: (65) 3157 0271
Web Site: http://www.advanide.de
Sales Range: $25-49.9 Million
Emp.: 15
Semiconductor Distr
N.A.I.C.S.: 423690
Holger Roessner *(Mng Dir)*

Subsidiary (Non-US):

AdvanIDe GmbH **(2)**
Am Klingenweg 6a, Walluf, Germany
Tel.: (49) 6123 791 400
Web Site: http://www.advanide.de
Semiconductor Device Distr
N.A.I.C.S.: 423690

Subsidiary (US):

AdvanIDe Inc. **(2)**
19 Sylvester Rd, Natick, MA 01760
Tel.: (617) 710-1974
Web Site: http://www.advanide.com
Semiconductor Distr
N.A.I.C.S.: 423690
Ken Hutchins *(Regl Dir-Sls)*

C&A Tool Engineering, Inc. **(1)**
4100 N US 33, Churubusco, IN 46723 **(49%)**
Tel.: (260) 693-2167
Web Site: https://www.catool.com
Emp.: 650
Diamond Dies & Metalworking
N.A.I.C.S.: 333514
Jeff Herron *(Mgr-Ops)*

DBJ Americas Inc. **(1)**
1251 Avenue of the Americas Ste 2330, New York, NY 10020
Tel.: (212) 221-0708
Loan & Financial Services
N.A.I.C.S.: 522291
Yukio Iseki *(VP)*

DBJ Asset Management Co., Ltd. **(1)**
Otemachi Financial City Grand Cube 1-9-2

Otemachi, Chiyoda-ku, Tokyo, 100-0004, Japan
Tel.: (81) 332415300
Web Site: http://www.dbj-am.jp
Emp.: 94
Financial Investment Services
N.A.I.C.S.: 523999
Takeshi Kiriyama *(Chm)*

DBJ Europe Limited **(1)**
8 Finsbury Circus, London, EC2M 7EA, United Kingdom
Tel.: (44) 20 7507 6070
Web Site: http://www.dbj.jp
Emp.: 20
Commercial Banking Services
N.A.I.C.S.: 522110
Takeshi Kiriyama *(CEO)*

DBJ Investment Consulting (Beijing) Co., Ltd. **(1)**
Beijing Fortune Bldg Suite 814-815 5 Dong San Huan Bei Lu, Chaoyang, Beijing, 100004, China
Tel.: (86) 1065909770
Loan & Financial Services
N.A.I.C.S.: 522291
Takuya Watanabe *(Mgr)*

DBJ Securities Co., Ltd. **(1)**
Otemachi Financial City Grand Cube 15F 1-9-2, Chiyoda-ku, Tokyo, 100-0004, Japan
Tel.: (81) 332755301
Web Site: http://www.dbj-sec.jp
Emp.: 17
Financial Investment Services
N.A.I.C.S.: 523999
Kato Hiroyuki *(Pres & CEO)*

DBJ Singapore Limited **(1)**
Capita Green 138 Market Street Unit 15-02, Singapore, 48946, Singapore
Tel.: (65) 6221 1779
Commercial Banking Services
N.A.I.C.S.: 522110
Brian Ng *(VP-Investment Banking)*

Dexerials Corporation **(1)**
Gate City Osaki East Tower 8th Floor 1-11-2 Osaki, Shinagawa-ku, Tokyo, 141-0032, Japan
Tel.: (81) 354353941
Web Site: https://www.dexerials.jp
Rev.: $695,358,780
Assets: $912,285,760
Liabilities: $350,746,430
Net Worth: $561,539,330
Earnings: $141,335,020
Emp.: 4,349
Fiscal Year-end: 03/31/2024
Chemical & Recording Media Components Mfr & Distr
N.A.I.C.S.: 325998
Hisashi Ando *(Mng Exec Officer)*

Subsidiary (Non-US):

Dexerials (Shenzhen) Corporation **(2)**
2F Excellence Logistics Center Building No 18 Shihua Road, Futian Free Trade Zone, Shenzhen, 518038, Guangdong, China
Tel.: (86) 755 8373 8880
Web Site: http://www.dexerials.jp
Mfr of Anisotropic Conductive Film (ACF)
N.A.I.C.S.: 334610

Dexerials (Suzhou) Co., Ltd. **(2)**
No169 JinFeng Road, New District, Suzhou, 215011, Jiangsu, China
Tel.: (86) 512 6825 2005
Web Site: http://www.dexerials.jp
Mfr of Anisotropic Conductive Film (ACF) , Touch Panels & Thermal Conductive Sheets
N.A.I.C.S.: 334610

Subsidiary (US):

Dexerials America Corporation **(2)**
215 Satellite Blvd NE Ste 400, Suwanee, GA 30024
Tel.: (770) 945-3845
Web Site: http://www.dexerials.com
Emp.: 15
UV Curing Resins Mfr
N.A.I.C.S.: 325998
Breck Barnes *(Mgr-IT & Compliance)*

Subsidiary (Non-US):

Dexerials Europe B.V. **(2)**

Singaporestraat 9-11, 1175 RA, Lijnden, Netherlands
Tel.: (31) 20 4499 700
Web Site: http://www.dexerials.jp
UV Curing Resins Mfr
N.A.I.C.S.: 325998

Dexerials Hong Kong Limited **(2)**
Suites 1201-2 12F Tower 3 China Hong Kong City 33 Canton Road, Tsim Sha Tsui, Kowloon, China (Hong Kong)
Tel.: (852) 2156 0505
Web Site: http://www.dexerials.jp
Sales of Electronic Parts, Adhesive Materials, Optical Materials
N.A.I.C.S.: 423690

Dexerials Korea Corporation **(2)**
10F Serveone Gangnam Building 2621 Nambusunhwan-ro, Gangnam, Seoul, 06267, Korea (South)
Tel.: (82) 264679400
Web Site: http://www.dexerials.jp
Emp.: 30
Sales of Electronic Parts, Adhesive Materials, Optical Materials
N.A.I.C.S.: 423690
Eric Joung *(Pres)*

Dexerials Singapore Pte. Ltd. **(2)**
9 Jurong Town Hall Road Ste 02 17/18, Singapore, 609431, Singapore
Tel.: (65) 6933 1968
Web Site: http://www.dexerials.jp
Emp.: 10
Sales of Electronic Parts, Adhesive Materials, Optical Materials
N.A.I.C.S.: 423690
Lee How Choon *(Mng Dir)*

Dexerials Taiwan Corporation **(2)**
3F No 167 Sec 2 Nanjing E Road, Zhongshan District, Taipei, 104, Taiwan
Tel.: (886) 2 2515 2585
Emp.: 25
Sales of Electronic Parts, Adhesive Materials, Optical Materials
N.A.I.C.S.: 423690

Grohe AG **(1)**
Feldmuhleplatz 15, Dusseldorf, 40545, Germany
Tel.: (49) 21191303000
Web Site: http://www.grohe.com
Sales Range: $1-4.9 Billion
Faucets, Shower Heads & Fittings Mfr & Exporter
N.A.I.C.S.: 332913
Thomas Fuhr *(Exec Dir-Ops)*

Subsidiary (Domestic):

AQERO Vertriebs GmbH **(2)**
Parkstr 1 5 1335, 14974, Ludwigsfelde, Germany
Tel.: (49) 33788180
Web Site: http://www.grohe.de
Mfr of Faucets, Shower Heads & Fittings
N.A.I.C.S.: 332913

Dal-Georg Rost & Sohne Sanitararmaturen Gmbh
Zur Porta 8 12, Porta Westfalica, 32457, Germany
Web Site: http://www.grohe.de
Sales Range: $25-49.9 Million
Emp.: 100
Shower Heads & Fittings Mfr
N.A.I.C.S.: 332913
Jorguwe Ramaker *(Gen Mgr)*

GROHEDAL Sanitarsysteme GmbH & Co. KG **(2)**
Zur Porta 8 12, 32457, Porta Westfalica, Germany
Tel.: (49) 57179510
Web Site: http://www.grohe.com
Sales Range: $25-49.9 Million
Emp.: 300
Faucets, Shower Heads & Fittings Mfr
N.A.I.C.S.: 332913

Subsidiary (Non-US):

Grohe A/S **(2)**
Sluseholmen 8c 2th, 2450, Copenhagen, Denmark
Tel.: (45) 44656800
Web Site: http://www.grohe.dk

Development Bank of Japan, Inc.—(Continued)

Sales Range: $10-24.9 Million
Emp.: 50
Faucets, Shower Heads & Fittings Mfr
N.A.I.C.S.: 332913

Grohe AS (2)
Engebrets Vei 3, 0275, Oslo, Norway
Tel.: (47) 22072070
Web Site: http://www.grohe.no
Sales Range: Less than $1 Million
Emp.: 8
Faucets, Shower Heads & Fittings Mfr
N.A.I.C.S.: 332913

Subsidiary (US):

Grohe America, Inc. (2)
200 N Gary Ave Ste G, Roselle, IL 60172
Tel.: (630) 582-7711
Web Site: http://www.grohe.la
Sales Range: $25-49.9 Million
Emp.: 100
Distr of Faucets & Shower Heads
N.A.I.C.S.: 332913

Subsidiary (Domestic):

Grohe Deutschland Vertriebs GmbH (2)
Zur Porta 9, 32457, Porta Westfalica, Germany
Tel.: (49) 5713989333
Web Site: http://www.grohe.de
Sales Range: $25-49.9 Million
Emp.: 125
Faucets, Shower Heads & Fittings Mfr
N.A.I.C.S.: 332913

Subsidiary (Non-US):

Grohe Espana, S.A. (2)
Avenida de Sarria 106 8 Planta Edificio, Sarria Forum, 08017, Barcelona, Spain
Tel.: (34) 933368850
Web Site: http://www.grohe.es
Sales Range: $10-24.9 Million
Emp.: 40
Mfr Faucets, Shower Heads & Fittings
N.A.I.C.S.: 332913
Miguel Rubio (Mng Dir)

Grohe GmbH (2)
Wienerbergstrasse 11/A7, 1100, Vienna, Austria
Tel.: (43) 1 680 60
Web Site: http://www.grohe.at
Sales Range: $10-24.9 Million
Emp.: 45
Plumbing Fixture Mfr
N.A.I.C.S.: 332913
Robert H. Friedl (Mng Dir)

Grohe Japan Ltd. (2)
A-PLACE Aoyama 6F 2-11-3 Kita-Aoyama, Minato-ku, Tokyo, 107-0061, Japan
Tel.: (81) 357757500
Web Site: http://www.grohe.co.jp
Sales Range: Less than $1 Million
Emp.: 40
Faucets, Shower Heads & Fittings Mfr
N.A.I.C.S.: 332913

Grohe Limited (2)
World Business Centre 2 Newall Road London Heathrow Airport, Hounslow, TW6 2SF, Middlesex, United Kingdom
Tel.: (44) 2082832840
Web Site: http://www.grohe.co.uk
Faucets, Shower Heads & Fittings Mfr
N.A.I.C.S.: 332913
Paul Bailey (Sr Mgr-Product)

Grohe N.V. S.A. (2)
Leuvensesteenweg 369, 1932, Zaventem, Belgium
Tel.: (32) 28993077
Web Site: http://www.grohe.be
Sales Range: $10-24.9 Million
Emp.: 34
Faucets, Shower Heads & Fittings Mfr
N.A.I.C.S.: 332913
Jean Pierre Boogaerts (Dir-Fin)

Grohe Nederland B.V. (2)
Metaalstraat 2, 2718 SW, Zoetermeer, Netherlands
Tel.: (31) 793680133
Web Site: http://www.grohe.nl

Sales Range: $75-99.9 Million
Emp.: 75
Mfr of Faucets, Shower Heads & Fittings
N.A.I.C.S.: 332913
Loprop Maageun (Mng Dir)

Grohe Pacific Pte. Ltd. (2)
180 Clemenceau Avenue 06-02 Haw Par Centre, Singapore, 239922, Singapore
Tel.: (65) 63113611
Web Site: http://www.grohe.sg
Sales Range: $10-24.9 Million
Emp.: 25
Faucets, Shower Heads & Fittings Mfr
N.A.I.C.S.: 332913

Grohe Polska Sp. zo.o. (2)
ul Pulawska 182, 02-670, Warsaw, Poland
Tel.: (48) 225432640
Web Site: http://www.grohe.pl
Sales Range: $10-24.9 Million
Emp.: 10
Plumbing Fixture Mfr
N.A.I.C.S.: 332913

Grohe S.a.r.l. (2)
60 Bld de la Mission Marchand, La Defense, 92418, Courbevoie, France
Tel.: (33) 149972900
Web Site: http://www.grohe.fr
Sales Range: $25-49.9 Million
Emp.: 150
Faucets, Shower Heads & Fittings Mfr
N.A.I.C.S.: 332913

Grohe S.p.A. (2)
Via Crocefisso 19, 20122, Milan, Italy
Tel.: (39) 02959401
Web Site: http://www.grohe.it
Sales Range: $10-24.9 Million
Emp.: 50
Faucets, Shower Heads & Fittings Mfr
N.A.I.C.S.: 332913

Subsidiary (Domestic):

Grohe Water Technology AG & Co. Kg (2)
Industriepark Edelburg, 58675, Hemer, Germany
Tel.: (49) 2372930
Faucets, Shower Heads & Fittings Mfr
N.A.I.C.S.: 332913

H.D. Eichelberg & Co. GmbH (2)
Werler Str 3, 58706, Menden, Germany
Tel.: (49) 2372930
Web Site: http://www.eichelberg-armaturen.de
Faucets, Shower Heads & Fittings Mfr
N.A.I.C.S.: 332913

Japan Economic Research Institute Inc.
Otemachi Financial City Grand Cube 15F 1-9-2 Otemachi, Chiyoda-ku, Tokyo, 100-0004, Japan
Tel.: (81) 36214 4600
Web Site: http://www.jeri.co.jp
Emp.: 139
Commercial Banking Services
N.A.I.C.S.: 522110
Hiroshi Takahashi (Pres)

Kinugawa Rubber Industrial Co., Ltd. (1)
330 Naganuma-Cho, Inage-ku, Chiba, 263-0005, Japan (100%)
Tel.: (81) 432593164
Web Site: http://www.kinugawa-rubber.co.jp
Rubber & Plastic Automotive Parts Mfr
N.A.I.C.S.: 326291
Hiromi Takaoka (Pres)

Subsidiary (Domestic):

Kinugawa Brake Parts Co., Ltd. (2)
8-1 Matuyama-cho, Moka, 321-4346, Tochigi, Japan
Tel.: (81) 285 82 6118
Web Site: http://www.kinugawa-rubber.co.jp
Brake Components Mfr
N.A.I.C.S.: 336340

Kinugawa Koriyama Co., Ltd. (2)
2-16 Machiikedai, Koriyama, 963-0215, Fukushima, Japan
Tel.: (81) 249593411
Web Site: http://www.kinugawa-rubber.co.jp
Gasket Packing & Sealing Device Mfr

N.A.I.C.S.: 339991

Kinugawa Oita Co., Ltd. (2)
370 Inumarusakuragi, Nakatsu, Oita, 8790105, Japan
Tel.: (81) 979326531
Web Site: http://www.kinugawa-rubber.co.jp
Gasket Packing & Sealing Device Mfr
N.A.I.C.S.: 339991

Value Management Institute, Inc. (1)
Otemachi Financial City Grand Cube 15F 9-2 Otemachi 1-chome, Chiyoda-ku, Tokyo, 100-0004, Japan
Tel.: (81) 352057900
Web Site: http://www.vmi.co.jp
Financial Investment Services
N.A.I.C.S.: 523999
Takayuki Yamamoto (Pres)

DEVELOPMENT CAPITAL BANK JSC
5 Bld 15 Nizhny Susalny Side-Street, 105064, Moscow, Russia
Tel.: (7) 4959379150
Web Site: http://www.dcapital.ru
Sales Range: Less than $1 Million
Commercial Banking Services
N.A.I.C.S.: 522110

DEVELOPMENT FINANCE COMPANY OF UGANDA LTD.
Plot 26 Kyadondo Road, PO Box 2767, Kampala, Uganda
Tel.: (256) 414351000 UG
Web Site: http://www.dfcugroup.com
Year Founded: 1964
DFCU—(UGAN)
Rev.: $94,487,339
Assets: $835,450,652
Liabilities: $665,078,162
Net Worth: $170,372,490
Earnings: $7,597,589
Emp.: 1,237
Fiscal Year-end: 12/31/23
Commericial Banking
N.A.I.C.S.: 522110
Jimmy D. Mugerwa (Chm)

Subsidiaries:

dfcu Bank Limited (1)
Plot 26 5th Floor Kyadondo Road, PO Box 70, Nakasero, Kampala, Uganda
Tel.: (256) 776760760
Web Site: https://www.dfcugroup.com
Banking Services
N.A.I.C.S.: 522110
Kate K. Kiiza (CFO)

DEVELOPMENT INVESTMENT CONSTRUCTION HOI AN JSC
25 Hung Vuong Cam Pho, Hoi An, Quang Nam, Vietnam
Tel.: (84) 2353863531
Web Site: https://www.dichoian.vn
Year Founded: 1979
DIH—(HNX)
Rev.: $17,577,800
Assets: $91,990,700
Liabilities: $82,400,500
Net Worth: $9,590,200
Earnings: $604,200
Fiscal Year-end: 12/31/22
Investment Management Service
N.A.I.C.S.: 523999
Tran Dinh Loi (Chm)

DEVELOPMENT INVESTMENT CONSTRUCTION JSC
15 Thi Sach Street Thang Tam Ward, Vung Tau, Tinh Ba Ria, Vietnam
Tel.: (84) 2543859248
Web Site: https://www.dic.vn
Year Founded: 1990
DIG—(HOSE)
Rev.: $42,810,952
Assets: $693,297,406
Liabilities: $368,082,821
Net Worth: $325,214,585

Earnings: $4,598,876
Emp.: 1,789
Fiscal Year-end: 12/31/23
Real Estate Development, Investment & Construction Services
N.A.I.C.S.: 236220

Subsidiaries:

DIC No. 4 Joint Stock Company (1)
No 4 - Street 6 - Chi Linh Urban, Vung Tau, Vietnam
Tel.: (84) 643613518
Web Site: http://www.dic4.vn
Rev.: $12,836,003
Assets: $13,959,136
Liabilities: $8,183,572
Net Worth: $5,775,563
Earnings: $552,504
Emp.: 500
Fiscal Year-end: 12/31/2018
Construction Engineering Services
N.A.I.C.S.: 237990

Sports TOTO Vietnam Joint Stock Company (1)
Room 002 Van Phuc Building No 2 Nui Truc Kim Ma, Ba Dinh, Hanoi, Vietnam
Tel.: (84) 942933468
Web Site: https://www.sporttotovietnam.com
Management Consulting Services
N.A.I.C.S.: 541611

DEVELOPMENT WORKS FOOD CO
Prince Mamduh Bin Abdulaziz St As Sulimaniyah, Riyadh, 12241, Saudi Arabia
Tel.: (966) 1886880
Rev.: $36,866,092
Assets: $37,672,213
Liabilities: $27,393,978
Net Worth: $10,278,234
Earnings: $2,211,438
Emp.: 187
Fiscal Year-end: 12/31/19
Catering Services
N.A.I.C.S.: 722320
Mohammed Iqbal (CFO)

DEVELOPPEMENT ACTIVITES CHIMIQUES DISTRIBUTION SA
125 rue du Royans Zone d activites Mathias, BP 9, 26320, Saint-Marcel-les-Valence, France
Tel.: (33) 4 75 58 80 10
Web Site: http://www.dacd.com
Chemical Products Mfr
N.A.I.C.S.: 325199

DEVERNOIS SA
13 boulevard des Etines, PB 9, 42120, Le Coteau, Cedex, France
Tel.: (33) 477442100
Web Site: https://www.devernois.com
ALDEV—(EUR)
Women Apparel Mfr & Distr
N.A.I.C.S.: 315250
Severine Brun (CEO)

DEVERSIFY HEALTH AB
Skeppsbron 34, 111 30, Stockholm, Sweden
Tel.: (46) 703862497
Web Site: https://www.euroafricadigital.com
Year Founded: 2014
DEV—(OMX)
Rev.: $1,852,403
Assets: $1,571,465
Liabilities: $1,543,669
Net Worth: $27,796
Earnings: ($2,100,582)
Emp.: 9
Fiscal Year-end: 12/31/23
Software Development Services
N.A.I.C.S.: 541511
Lotta Tjulin Thornqvist (CEO)

DEVEX RESOURCES LIMITED

Level 3 1292 Hay Street, West Perth, 6005, WA, Australia
Tel.: (61) 861869490
Web Site:
https://www.devexresources.com.au
DEV—(ASX)
Rev.: $5,141
Assets: $17,569,468
Liabilities: $2,289,455
Net Worth: $15,280,013
Earnings: ($7,201,999)
Emp.: 8
Fiscal Year-end: 06/30/24
Mineral Exploration Services
N.A.I.C.S.: 213115
Timothy Rupert Barr Goyder *(Chm)*

DEVINE IMPEX LIMITED
The Groove C-157 Ist Floor Industrial Focal Point Phase VII, Mohali, 160059, Punjab, India
Tel.: (91) 1725099522   In
Web Site: https://www.devineimp.in
Year Founded: 1995
531585—(BOM)
Rev.: $286,814
Assets: $1,856,741
Liabilities: $6,661
Net Worth: $1,850,080
Earnings: $3,726
Fiscal Year-end: 03/31/21
Financial Investment Services
N.A.I.C.S.: 523999
Rohit Jain *(CFO)*

DEVIR FAKTORING A.S.
Maslak Mah Meydan Sok Kapi No 20 Veko Giz Plaza K 7 No 23-24, Sariyer, 34398, Istanbul, Turkiye
Tel.: (90) 2122975020
Web Site:
http://www.devirfaktoring.com
DEVIR—(IST)
Financial Investment Services
N.A.I.C.S.: 523999
Adnan Turkmen *(Gen Mgr)*

DEVITT & FORAND CONTRACTORS INC.
5716 Burbank Cres SE, Calgary, T2H 1Z6, AB, Canada
Tel.: (403) 255-8565
Web Site: https://www.devitt-forand.com
Year Founded: 1964
Rev.: $29,605,010
Emp.: 45
General Contract Services
N.A.I.C.S.: 238290

DEVJO INDUSTRIES, INC.
375 Steelcase Road East, Markham, L3R 1G3, ON, Canada
Tel.: (905) 477-7689   Ca
Web Site: http://www.devjo.com
Year Founded: 1986
Sales Range: $10-24.9 Million
Emp.: 50
Holding Company Mechanical Engineered & Specialty Chemical Product Mfr
N.A.I.C.S.: 325998
Joseph A. Devine *(CEO)*

Subsidiaries:

Elasto Valve Rubber Products Inc.   (1)
1691 Pioneer Rd, Sudbury, T3G 1B2, ON, Canada   **(100%)**
Tel.: (705) 523-2026
Web Site: http://www.evrproducts.com
Distr of A Full Range of Elastomeric Piping Products
N.A.I.C.S.: 326122
Andy Frescura *(Mgr-Ops & Pur)*

Sluyter Company Ltd.   (1)
375 Steelcase Road East, Markham, L3R

1G3, ON, Canada   **(50%)**
Tel.: (905) 475-6011
Web Site: http://www.sluyter.com
Proprietary Specialty Chemicals & Adhesive Type Products Related to the Plumbing & Heating, Automotive Care, Shoe Care, Furniture & Upholstery & Janitorial Chemical Field Mfr
N.A.I.C.S.: 325520
Sol Buck *(Pres)*

DEVK SERVICE GMBH
Riehler Strasse 190, 50735, Cologne, Germany
Tel.: (49) 2217570
Web Site: http://www.devk.de
Sales Range: $450-499.9 Million
Emp.: 1,500
Insurance Services
N.A.I.C.S.: 524210
Reinhard Schmalstieg *(Mng Dir)*

Subsidiaries:

DVA - Deutsche Verkehrs-Assekuranz-Vermittlungs GmbH   (1)
Marienbader Platz 1, 61348, Bad Homburg, Germany
Tel.: (49) 617248680
Web Site: http://www.dva-assekuranz.de
Sales Range: $10-24.9 Million
Emp.: 120
Insurance Agency Services
N.A.I.C.S.: 524210
Christian Heidersdorf *(Mng Dir & Member-Mgmt Bd)*

DEVKI GROUP OF COMPANIES
Opposite the RuiruStation Kamiti Road, 00621, Nairobi, Kenya
Tel.: (254) 756020000
Web Site: https://devkigroupke.com
KNOS—(OTC)
Emp.: 100
Holding Company
N.A.I.C.S.: 551112

Subsidiaries:

National Cement Holdings Limited   (1)
Off Mombasa Road Opposite Lukenya Hill, 00600, Nairobi, Kenya
Tel.: (254) 756020000
Web Site: https://nccke.com
Cement Mfr
N.A.I.C.S.: 327310

DEVKI LEASING & FINANCE PRIVATE LIMITED
Velocity Multiplex Plot No 18A Scheme 94C Ring Road, Indore, 452 010, India
Tel.: (91) 7314735510   In
Web Site:
http://www.devkileasing.com
Year Founded: 1993
530765—(BOM)
Rev.: $30,635
Assets: $41,082
Liabilities: $614
Net Worth: $40,467
Earnings: ($43,027)
Emp.: 5
Fiscal Year-end: 03/31/22
Financial Services
N.A.I.C.S.: 523999
Sudhir Bindal *(Mng Dir)*

DEVLIN ELECTRONICS LIMITED
Unit A1 Davy Close, Basingstoke, RG22 6PW, Hampshire, United Kingdom
Tel.: (44) 1256467367
Web Site: http://www.devlin.co.uk
Sales Range: $1-9.9 Million
Emp.: 40
Keyboard & Accessory Designer Mfr
N.A.I.C.S.: 334118

DEVONIAN HEALTH GROUP, INC.
360 rue des Entrepreneurs, Montmagny, G5V 4T1, QC, Canada
Tel.: (514) 248-7509
Web Site:
https://www.groupedevonian.com
GSD—(TSXV)
Rev.: $4,543,807
Assets: $13,122,400
Liabilities: $5,411,195
Net Worth: $7,711,205
Earnings: ($2,279,968)
Fiscal Year-end: 07/31/19
Pharmaceuticals Product Mfr
N.A.I.C.S.: 325412
Andre P. Boulet *(Chief Scientific Officer)*

DEVONSHIRE CAPITAL LTD.
CDF Trading Lake Rajada Office Complex 195/13 Ratchadapisek Road, Klong Toey, Bangkok, 10110, Thailand
Tel.: (66) 26619576
Web Site:
http://www.devonshirecapital.com
Privater Equity Firm
N.A.I.C.S.: 523999
Philip Newson *(Exec Chm & Partner)*

DEVONSHIRE INDUSTRIES LIMITED
9 Watlington Road, Devonshire, DV 06, Bermuda
Tel.: (441) 2364662   BM
DEVON.BH—(BERM)
Rev.: $2,621,079
Assets: $2,612,074
Liabilities: $168,856
Net Worth: $2,443,218
Earnings: $140,711
Fiscal Year-end: 03/31/22
Consumable Products Supplier & Mfr
N.A.I.C.S.: 812990
Richard A. Moulder *(Gen Mgr)*

Subsidiaries:

Bermuda Paint Company Limited   (1)
9 Watlington Road, Devonshire, Bermuda
Tel.: (441) 2364662
Web Site: http://www.bermudapaint.bm
Emp.: 10
Paints & Coatings Mfr
N.A.I.C.S.: 325510
Richard Moulder *(Gen Mgr)*

DEVOTEAM SA
73 rue Anatole France, 92300, Levallois-Perret, France
Tel.: (33) 141494848
Web Site: http://www.devoteam.com
Year Founded: 1995
DVT—(EUR)
Rev.: $933,918,077
Assets: $836,327,040
Liabilities: $552,372,690
Net Worth: $283,954,349
Earnings: $56,989,108
Emp.: 7,623
Fiscal Year-end: 12/31/20
Information Technology Consulting
N.A.I.C.S.: 611710
Godefroy de Bentzmann *(Co-Pres, Co-Founder & Co-Member-Exec Bd)*

Subsidiaries:

Alegri International Austria GmbH   (1)
Walfischgasse 11 7, 1010, Wiener Neustadt, Austria
Tel.: (43) 130009340
Information Technology Services
N.A.I.C.S.: 513210

Alegri International Service GmbH   (1)

Innsbrucker Ring 15, 81673, Munich, Germany
Tel.: (49) 896661070
Emp.: 240
Information Technology Services
N.A.I.C.S.: 513210
Gregor Emhart *(Mng Dir & CFO)*

Avalon Solutions Inc.   (1)
18 E 48th St 14th Fl, New York, NY 10017
Tel.: (917) 338-6825
Web Site: https://www.avalonsolution.com
Software Development Services
N.A.I.C.S.: 541511

Axance SA   (1)
43 Boulevard Barbes, 75018, Paris, France
Tel.: (33) 140282440
Web Site: http://www.axance.fr
Management Consulting Services
N.A.I.C.S.: 541611
Victor Lutreau *(Bus Mgr)*

Be Team S.r.l.   (1)
Via Pavia 9/A1, 10098, Rivoli, TO, Italy
Tel.: (39) 011 444 0911
Web Site: https://www.be-team.eu
Information Technology Services
N.A.I.C.S.: 513210
Giorgio Igor Giuliano *(Sr Acct Mgr)*

Bold International SA   (1)
Torre Fernao de Magalhaes Avenida D Joao II 43 9th Floor, 1990-084, Lisbon, Portugal
Tel.: (351) 217959541
Web Site: http://www.boldint.com
Emp.: 750
Information Technology Services
N.A.I.C.S.: 513210
Joao Malpica *(Partner)*

DaVinci Consulting AS   (1)
Hoffsveien 21-23, Oslo, Norway
Tel.: (47) 23253300
Web Site: http://www.davinci.no
Sales Range: $25-49.9 Million
Emp.: 100
Other Management Consulting Services
N.A.I.C.S.: 541618

Devoteam A/S   (1)
Lyngbyvej 2, 2100, Copenhagen, Denmark
Tel.: (45) 2 045 0700
Web Site: https://dk.devoteam.com
Information Technology Services
N.A.I.C.S.: 513210
Jane Eis Larsen *(Bus Dir)*

Devoteam Belgium SA/NV   (1)
Belgicastraat 17, 1930, Zaventem, Belgium
Tel.: (32) 2 474 0500
Web Site: https://belgium.devoteam.com
Sales Range: $25-49.9 Million
Emp.: 70
Other Computer Related Services
N.A.I.C.S.: 541519

Devoteam Consulting GmbH   (1)
Palais der Schonen Kunste Lowengasse 47, 1030, Vienna, Austria
Tel.: (43) 1 715 0000
Web Site: http://at.devoteam.com
Sales Range: $25-49.9 Million
Emp.: 23
Information Technology Consulting Services
N.A.I.C.S.: 541512

Devoteam Davinci AS   (1)
Hoffsveien 21-23, 275, Oslo, Norway
Tel.: (47) 23253300
Web Site: http://www.davinci.no
Information Technology Consulting Services
N.A.I.C.S.: 541512
Alex Kielland *(Mgr-Knowledge)*

Devoteam Genesis AG   (1)
Europaallee 41, 8004, Zurich, Switzerland
Tel.: (41) 435082404
Web Site: http://www.devoteam.ch
Emp.: 20
Information Technology Consulting Services
N.A.I.C.S.: 541512

Devoteam GmbH   (1)
Gutenbergstrasse 10, 64331, Weiterstadt, Germany
Tel.: (49) 6 151 8680
Web Site: https://de.devoteam.com

Devoteam SA—(Continued)

Sales Range: $50-74.9 Million
Emp.: 400
Telecommunications Information Technology
Consulting, Software Development, Sys-
tems Integration & Products
N.A.I.C.S.: 334290

Devoteam Guidance S.A. (1)
7 rue des Trois Cantons, 8399, Windhof,
Luxembourg
Tel.: (352) 3137361
Web Site: http://lu.devoteam.com
Sales Range: $25-49.9 Million
Emp.: 70
Computer Software Consulting Services
N.A.I.C.S.: 541512

**Devoteam Information Technology &
Consultancy AS** (1)
Acibadem Mah Cecen Sok Akasya Kent
Etabi A-1 Blok Kat 22 No 112, Uskudar,
34660, Istanbul, Turkiye
Tel.: (90) 8502159305
Web Site: http://www.tr.devoteam.com
Information Technology Services
N.A.I.C.S.: 513210

Devoteam Integra (1)
Acibadem Mah Cecen Sok Akasya Kent
Etabi, A-1 Blok Kat 22 No 112 Uskudar,
34660, Istanbul, Turkiye
Tel.: (90) 8502159305
Web Site: http://tr.devoteam.com
Information Technology Consulting Services
N.A.I.C.S.: 541512

Devoteam Italia S.r.l. (1)
Via Eustachi 7, 20129, Milan, Italy (20%)
Tel.: (39) 024 549 1078
Web Site: https://it.devoteam.com
Sales Range: $25-49.9 Million
Emp.: 41
Other Management Consulting Services
N.A.I.C.S.: 541618

**Devoteam Management Consulting
NV**
Belgicastraat 17, 1930, Zaventem, Belgium
Tel.: (32) 2 474 0500
Web Site: https://belgium-management-
consulting.devoteam.com
Emp.: 30
Management Consulting Services
N.A.I.C.S.: 541611
Marnix De Troyer (CEO)

Devoteam Mexico, S.a. de C.V. (1)
Darwin 74 Anzures, Delegacion Miguel Hi-
dalgo, 11590, Mexico, Hidalgo, Mexico
Tel.: (52) 442 230 2954
Web Site: https://mx.devoteam.com
Information Technology Services
N.A.I.C.S.: 513210
Guillermo Vargas (Sls Dir)

Devoteam Middle East (1)
Bldg 17 Office 369 Dubai Internet City, PO
Box 500612, Dubai, United Arab Emirates
Tel.: (971) 4 3912943
Web Site: http://www.devoteam.com
Sales Range: $25-49.9 Million
Emp.: 150
Information Technology Consulting Services
N.A.I.C.S.: 541512

Devoteam Morocco (1)
7 Rue Al Mariniyinne, Hassan, 10020, Ra-
bat, Morocco
Tel.: (212) 53 770 5964
Web Site: https://africa.devoteam.com
Information Technology Services
N.A.I.C.S.: 541512

Devoteam NV (1)
Belgicastraat 17, 1930, Zaventem, Belgium
Tel.: (32) 2 474 0500
Web Site: https://belgium.devoteam.com
Information Technology Services
N.A.I.C.S.: 513210
Benny Moonen (Gen Mgr)

Devoteam Nederland BV (1)
Pr Catharina-Amaliastraat 5, 2496 XD,
Hague, Netherlands
Tel.: (31) 70 301 1720
Web Site: https://nl.devoteam.com
Sales Range: $25-49.9 Million
Emp.: 150
Information Technology Consulting Services

N.A.I.C.S.: 541512

Devoteam Netherlands BV (1)
Pr Catharina Amaliastraat 5, 2496 XD,
Hague, Netherlands
Tel.: (31) 703011720
Information Technology Services
N.A.I.C.S.: 513210
Guido Dijkhuizen (Mktg Mgr)

Devoteam OSIconsult GmbH (1)
Palais der Schonen Kunste, Lowengasse
47, Vienna, 1030, Austria
Tel.: (43) 171500000
Web Site: http://www.devoteam.at
Sales Range: $25-49.9 Million
Emp.: 18
Other Management Consulting Services
N.A.I.C.S.: 541618

Devoteam Polska Sp. z o.o. (1)
Spektrum Tower ul Twarda 18, 00-105,
Warsaw, Poland
Tel.: (48) 4318400
Web Site: http://pl.devoteam.com
Sales Range: $25-49.9 Million
Emp.: 200
Educational Support Services
N.A.I.C.S.: 611710

Devoteam Quaint AB (1)
Barnhusgatan 20, 111 23, Stockholm, Swe-
den
Tel.: (46) 8 212125
Web Site: http://www.devoteam.se
Sales Range: $25-49.9 Million
Emp.: 40
Information Technology Consulting Services
N.A.I.C.S.: 541511

Devoteam SA (1)
7 rue des Trois Cantons, 8399, Windhof,
Luxembourg
Tel.: (352) 313 7361
Web Site: https://lu.devoteam.com
Information Technology Services
N.A.I.C.S.: 513210

Devoteam Secura (1)
Levent, Sisli, 34381, Istanbul, Turkiye
Tel.: (90) 2123739393
Web Site: http://www.devoteam.com
Emp.: 55
Information Technology Consulting Services
N.A.I.C.S.: 541512

Devoteam Spain (1)
C/Cronos 63, 28037, Madrid, Spain
Tel.: (34) 91 376 8820
Web Site: https://es.devoteam.com
Emp.: 850
Information Technology Consulting Services
N.A.I.C.S.: 541512

**Devoteam Technology Consulting
SARL** (1)
52 Avenue Charles Nicolle Cite El Mah-
rajene, 1082, Tunis, Tunisia
Tel.: (216) 71842117
Web Site: http://www.tn.devoteam.com
Information Technology Services
N.A.I.C.S.: 513210

Devoteam Telecom AS (1)
Televeien 1, N-4898, Grimstad,
Norway (100%)
Tel.: (47) 37800000
Web Site: http://www.devoteam.no
Sales Range: $50-74.9 Million
Emp.: 100
Telecommunications & Data Communica-
tions Accessories & Equipment Mfr
N.A.I.C.S.: 423430

Devoteam Teligent (1)
27 bld Vyatskaya Str, Moscow, Russia
Tel.: (7) 495 514 05 78
Web Site: http://www.teligent.ru
Information Technology Consulting Services
N.A.I.C.S.: 541512

Devoteam UK Ltd. (1)
34-37 Liverpool Street, London, EC2M 7PP,
United Kingdom
Tel.: (44) 20 7288 2800
Web Site: http://uk.devoteam.com
Information Technology Consulting Services
N.A.I.C.S.: 541512

Devoteam s.r.o. (1)

Ovocny trh 1096/8, 110 00, Prague, Czech
Republic
Tel.: (420) 237836015
Web Site: http://cz.devoteam.com
Sales Range: $25-49.9 Million
Emp.: 12
Information Technology Consulting Services
N.A.I.C.S.: 541512
Sylvain Bernolle (Mng Dir)

Fornebu Consulting AS (1)
Kronprinsens gate 17, 0251, Oslo, Norway
Tel.: (47) 23253300
Web Site: http://www.no.devoteam.com
Software Development Services
N.A.I.C.S.: 541511
Bjorn Husby (Project Mgr)

Jayway ApS (1)
Sjaeleboderne 2 4 sal tv, 1122, Copenha-
gen, Denmark
Tel.: (45) 53516000
Software Development Services
N.A.I.C.S.: 541511
Philip Kron (CEO-Grp)

Jayway Halmstad AB (1)
Storgatan 18, 302 43, Halmstad, Sweden
Tel.: (46) 352606500
Software Development Services
N.A.I.C.S.: 541511
Philip Kron (CEO-Grp)

Jayway Inc. (1)
100 S Murphy Ave Ste 200, Sunnyvale, CA
94086
Tel.: (415) 231-8301
Software Development Services
N.A.I.C.S.: 541511
Philip Kron (CEO)

Jayway Malmo AB (1)
Hans Michelsensgatan 10, 211 20, Malmo,
Sweden
Tel.: (46) 406023100
Software Development Services
N.A.I.C.S.: 541511
Philip Kron (CEO-Grp)

Jayway Stockholm AB (1)
Klara Ostra Kyrkogata 2B, 111 52, Stock-
holm, Sweden
Tel.: (46) 87508820
Software Development Services
N.A.I.C.S.: 541511
Philip Kron (CEO-Grp)

MY G SAS (1)
36 rue de clery, 75002, Paris, France
Tel.: (33) 14 274 5732
Web Site: https://www.my-g.fr
Information Technology Services
N.A.I.C.S.: 513210

Oredev AB (1)
Hans Michelsensgatan 10 3rd Floor, 211
20, Malmo, Sweden
Tel.: (46) 702456294
Web Site: http://www.oredev.org
Software Development Services
N.A.I.C.S.: 541511
Emily Holweck (Mng Dir)

**Q-Partners Consulting & Manage-
ment GmbH** (1)
Gutenbergstrasse 10, 64331, Weiterstadt,
Germany
Tel.: (49) 61516291443
Web Site: http://www.qpcm.eu
Management Consulting Services
N.A.I.C.S.: 541611
Achim Zimmermann (Exec VP-Ops & Dir-
SAP)

**DEVOTED CONSTRUCTION
LTD**
M-55 Third Floor Greater Kailash-II,
New Delhi, 110048, India
Tel.: (91) 1141611740 BM
Web Site:
https://www.devotedconstruct.com
Year Founded: 2016
542002—(BOM)
Real Estate Construction Services
N.A.I.C.S.: 236220
Narsimha Kavadi (Chm)

**DEVOTION ENERGY GROUP
LIMITED**

47 Hill Street 06 04 SCCCI Building,
Singapore, 179365, Singapore
Tel.: (65) 62200100
Web Site:
http://www.devotionenergy.com
Year Founded: 1993
Sales Range: $75-99.9 Million
Emp.: 440
Holding Company; Industrial Boilers
Mfr, Sales & Maintenance
N.A.I.C.S.: 551112
Shengbin Geng (Gen Mgr-
Guangzhou Devotion Thermal Facility
Co Ltd)

Subsidiaries:

**Guangzhou Devotion Domestic Boil-
ers Manufacturing Co. Ltd.** (1)
Devotion Industry Park East Section of
GETDD, Hongming Road, Guangzhou,
510760, China (100%)
Tel.: (86) 2082268411
Web Site: http://www.squirrelboilers.com
Sales Range: $100-124.9 Million
Emp.: 300
Heating Equipment Mfr
N.A.I.C.S.: 333414

**Guangzhou Devotion Thermal Facility
Co., Ltd.** (1)
Cang Road on the 3rd United Radisson In-
dustrial Park, Luogang District, Guangzhou,
510760, Guandong, China
Tel.: (86) 2082268372
Web Site: http://www.devotionboiler.com
Central Heating Equipment Mfr
N.A.I.C.S.: 333414
Shengbin Geng (Gen Mgr)

DEVPORT AB
Theres Svenssons Gata 10, 417 55,
Gothenburg, Sweden
Tel.: (46) 31505900
Web Site: https://www.devport.se
DEVP.B—(OMX)
Rev.: $49,650,789
Assets: $22,750,048
Liabilities: $17,400,121
Net Worth: $5,349,926
Earnings: $1,712,577
Emp.: 490
Fiscal Year-end: 12/31/19
Software Development Services
N.A.I.C.S.: 541511
Nils Malmros (CEO)

DEVSISTERS CO., LTD.
327 Dosan-daero Gangnam-gu,
Seoul, 06019, Korea (South)
Tel.: (82) 221480750
Web Site: https://www.devsisters.com
Year Founded: 2007
194480—(KRS)
Rev.: $25,784,859
Assets: $230,420,636
Liabilities: $91,410,511
Net Worth: $139,010,124
Earnings: ($5,133,618)
Emp.: 395
Fiscal Year-end: 12/31/22
Mobile Gaming Software
N.A.I.C.S.: 513210
Ji-Hoon Lee (Co-Founder)

**DEVYANI INTERNATIONAL
LIMITED**
Plot No 18 Sector 35 Near Hero
Honda Chowk, Gurgaon, 122001,
Haryana, India
Tel.: (91) 1244786000
Web Site: https://www.dil-rjcorp.com
Year Founded: 1997
DEVYANI—(NSE)
Rev.: $363,324,501
Assets: $358,315,089
Liabilities: $242,711,828
Net Worth: $115,603,261
Earnings: $31,474,612
Emp.: 15,685

Fiscal Year-end: 03/31/23
Restaurant Operators
N.A.I.C.S.: 722511
Virag Joshi *(Pres & CEO)*

DEVYSER DIAGNOSTICS AB

Instrumentvagen 19, 12653, Hagersten, Sweden
Tel.: (46) 856215850
Web Site: https://www.devyser.com
Year Founded: 2004
DVYSR—(OMX)
Rev.: $15,856,960
Assets: $47,776,935
Liabilities: $11,707,737
Net Worth: $36,069,197
Earnings: ($5,020,278)
Emp.: 113
Fiscal Year-end: 12/31/23
Biotechnology Research & Development Services
N.A.I.C.S.: 541714
Abina Berlin *(CFO)*

Subsidiaries:

Devyser AB   (1)
Instrumentvagen 19, SE-126 53, Hagersten, Sweden
Tel.: (46) 856215850
Diagnostic Device Distr
N.A.I.C.S.: 423450

Devyser France S.A.S.   (1)
29 rue du Pont, 92200, Neuilly-sur-Seine, France
Tel.: (33) 615357394
Diagnostic Device Distr
N.A.I.C.S.: 423450

Devyser GmbH   (1)
Raiffeisenstr 6, 35510, Butzbach, Germany
Tel.: (49) 66317938803
Laboratory Testing Services
N.A.I.C.S.: 621511

Devyser Iberia S.L.   (1)
Paseo de la Castellana 81 planta 11, 28046, Madrid, Spain
Tel.: (34) 654797283
Diagnostic Device Distr
N.A.I.C.S.: 423450

Devyser S.R.L.   (1)
Square de Meeus 37 4th Floor, 1000, Brussels, Belgium
Tel.: (32) 27917534
Diagnostic Device Distr
N.A.I.C.S.: 423450

DEWAN FAROOQUE MOTORS LIMITED

Dewan Centre 3-A Lalazar Beach Luxury Hotel Road, Karachi, 75350, Pakistan
Tel.: (92) 2135205244
Web Site:
   https://www.yousufdewan.com
Year Founded: 1998
Rev.: $13,240
Assets: $24,590,796
Liabilities: $41,482,687
Net Worth: ($16,891,891)
Earnings: ($1,754,103)
Emp.: 107
Fiscal Year-end: 06/30/19
Automobile Parts Mfr & Whslr
N.A.I.C.S.: 336110
Dewan Muhammad Yousuf Farooqui *(Co-Chm)*

Subsidiaries:

Dewan Automative Engineering Ltd.   (1)
Dewan Centre 3-A Lalazar Beach Luxury Hotel Road, Karachi, 75350, Pakistan
Tel.: (92) 21352052445
Automotive Part Whslr
N.A.I.C.S.: 423110
Haroon Iqbal *(Chm)*

Dewan Mushtaq Textile Mills Limited   (1)

Dewan Centre 3-A Lalazar Beach Luxury Hotel Road, Karachi, 75350, Pakistan
Tel.: (92) 21352052445
Textile Mfr
N.A.I.C.S.: 313310
Muhammad Anwar *(Chm)*

Dewan Sugar Mills Limited   (1)
Dewan Centre 3-A Lalazar Beach Luxury Hotel Road, Karachi, 75350, Pakistan
Tel.: (92) 21352052445
Sugar Mfr
N.A.I.C.S.: 311314
Muhammad Baqar Jafferi *(CEO)*

DEWAN KHALID TEXTILE MILLS LIMITED

Finance & Trade Centre 7th Floor Block-A, Sharea Faisal, Karachi, Pakistan
Tel.: (92) 21111364111
Textile Mill Operator
N.A.I.C.S.: 314999

DEWAN SALMAN FIBRE LIMITED

Dewan Centre 3-A Lalazar Beach Luxury Hotel Road, Karachi, 75350, Pakistan
Tel.: (92) 21352052445
Web Site:
   https://www.yousufdewan.com
Assets: $65,518,103
Liabilities: $150,469,034
Net Worth: ($84,950,931)
Earnings: ($12,276,328)
Emp.: 57
Fiscal Year-end: 06/30/19
Polyester Staple Fiber Mfr
N.A.I.C.S.: 325220
Zafar Asim *(CEO)*

DEWAN TEXTILE MILL LIMITED

Dewan Centre 3A Lalazar Beach Luxury Hotel Road, Karachi, 75350, Pakistan
Tel.: (92) 2135205244
Web Site:
   https://www.yousufdewan.com
Rev.: $951,152
Assets: $16,472,537
Liabilities: $36,537,127
Net Worth: ($20,064,590)
Earnings: ($6,276,553)
Emp.: 69
Fiscal Year-end: 06/30/19
Textile Mill
N.A.I.C.S.: 313210
Ishtiaq Ahmed *(CEO)*

DEWAVRIN GROUPE

29 Avenue De La Marne, 59290, Wasquehal, Cedex, France
Tel.: (33) 320692828
Web Site: http://www.dewavrin.com
Sales Range: $50-74.9 Million
Emp.: 200
Holding Company; Wood Trade & Topmaking
N.A.I.C.S.: 551111
Dimitri Dewavrin *(CEO)*

Subsidiaries:

British Mohair Spinners Limited   (1)
Lowr Holme Mills, Baildon, Shipley, BD1 7EU, W Yorkshire, United Kingdom
Tel.: (44) 274583111
Web Site: http://www.dewavrin.com
Sales Range: $25-49.9 Million
Emp.: 2
Yarn, Worsted Spinners, Synthetic Yarn Processors & Textile Machinery Accessories Mfr
N.A.I.C.S.: 313210

DEWBERRY REDPOINT LTD

Riverbridge House Anchor Boulevard,

Crossways Business Park, Dartford, DA2 6SL, Kent, United Kingdom
Tel.: (44) 845 000 2500
Web Site:
   http://www.dewberryredpoint.co.uk
Sales Range: $25-49.9 Million
Emp.: 25
Food Service Magazine Publisher
N.A.I.C.S.: 513199
Andrew Archer *(Mng Dir)*

DEWHURST GROUP PLC

Unit 9 Hampton Business Park Hampton Road West, Feltham, TW13 6DB, United Kingdom
Tel.: (44) 2087448200   UK
Web Site:
   https://www.dewhurst.co.uk
Year Founded: 1919
DWHT—(LSE)
Rev.: $75,516,386
Assets: $91,809,026
Liabilities: $35,626,573
Net Worth: $56,182,454
Earnings: $6,354,130
Emp.: 300
Fiscal Year-end: 09/30/20
Push Buttons & Keypads Mfr
N.A.I.C.S.: 335999
Richard M. Dewhurst *(Chm)*

Subsidiaries:

A&A Electrical Distributors Ltd.   (1)
234-262 Maybank Road South Woodford, London, E18 1ET, United Kingdom
Tel.: (44) 2085597000
Web Site: https://www.aa-electrical.com
Electrical Product Mfr & Distr
N.A.I.C.S.: 335999

Australian Lift Components Pty. Ltd.   (1)
5 Saggart Field Road, Minto, 2566, NSW, Australia
Tel.: (61) 296030200
Web Site: http://www.alc.au.com
Sales Range: $25-49.9 Million
Emp.: 30
Elevator Products Mfr
N.A.I.C.S.: 335999
Bradley Newell *(Gen Mgr)*

Dewhurst (Hong Kong) Ltd   (1)
Ste 19 7 F Block A Hoi Luen Industrial Ctr 55 Hoi Yuen Rd, Hong Kong, China (Hong Kong)
Tel.: (852) 35231563
Electrical Component Mfr
N.A.I.C.S.: 335999

Dewhurst (Hungary) Kft   (1)
HRSZ 3518/8, Soskut, 2038, Hungary
Tel.: (36) 23560551
Electrical Component Mfr
N.A.I.C.S.: 335999

Dewhurst Ltd.   (1)
Unit 9 Hampton Business Park Hampton Road West, Feltham, TW13 6DB, United Kingdom
Tel.: (44) 2087448200
Web Site: https://www.dewhurst.co.uk
Emp.: 300
Computer Aided Design Equipment Mfr & Distr
N.A.I.C.S.: 334118

Dewhurst UK Manufacturing Ltd   (1)
Unit 9 Hampton Business Park Hampton Road West, Feltham, TW13 6DB, Mddx, United Kingdom
Tel.: (44) 2087448200
Web Site: https://www.dewhurst.co.uk
Sales Range: $25-49.9 Million
Emp.: 10
Electrical Component Mfr
N.A.I.C.S.: 335999

Dual Engraving Pty. Ltd.   (1)
104 Howe Street Osborne Park, Perth, 6017, WA, Australia
Tel.: (61) 894433677
Web Site:
   https://www.dualengraving.com.au
Lift Car Interior Parts Mfr

N.A.I.C.S.: 327110

Dupar Controls Inc.   (1)
150 Goddard Crescent, Cambridge, N3E 0A9, ON, Canada
Web Site: http://www.dupar.com
Sales Range: $25-49.9 Million
Emp.: 50
Elevator Push Button Mfr & Distr
N.A.I.C.S.: 334419

Elevator Research Manufacturing Corp.   (1)
1417 Elwood St, Los Angeles, CA 90021
Tel.: (213) 746-1914
Web Site: https://www.elevatorresearch.com
Elevator Fixture & Accessory Mfr
N.A.I.C.S.: 333921

Lift Material Australia Pty Ltd   (1)
Unit 2 73 Beauchamp Road, Matraville, 2036, NSW, Australia
Tel.: (61) 293104288
Sales Range: $50-74.9 Million
Emp.: 6
Lift Materials Distr
N.A.I.C.S.: 423830
Tony Pegg *(Mng Dir & Mgr-Escalator Div)*

Lift Materials Australia   (1)
Unit 2 73 Beauchamp Road, Matraville, 2036, NSW, Australia
Tel.: (61) 293104288
Sales Range: $25-49.9 Million
Emp.: 6
Elevator Products Mfr & Sales
N.A.I.C.S.: 335999

LiftStore Ltd.   (1)
Inverness Road, Hounslow, TW3 3LT, Mddx, United Kingdom
Tel.: (44) 2085381770
Web Site: http://www.liftstore.com
Sales Range: $25-49.9 Million
Emp.: 30
Development & Marketing of Elevator Products
N.A.I.C.S.: 335999
Eamonn Reid *(Dir-Sls)*

P&R Liftcars Pty. Ltd.   (1)
7 Kiama Street, Miranda, 2228, NSW, Australia
Tel.: (61) 295224777
Web Site: https://www.prlift.com.au
Lift Car & Fixture Mfr
N.A.I.C.S.: 327110

The Fixture Company   (1)
8770 W Bryn Mawr Ave Ste 1300, Chicago, IL 60631-3557
Tel.: (847) 214-3100
Web Site: http://www.thefixtureco.com
Emp.: 1
Standard, Modified & Custom Signal Fixtures Mfr
N.A.I.C.S.: 335999

Traffic Management Products Ltd.   (1)
Unit 6 Britannia Park Trident Drive, Wednesbury, WS10 7XB, United Kingdom
Tel.: (44) 2087448201
Web Site: https://www.tmp.solutions
Emp.: 300
Traffic Bollard Mfr
N.A.I.C.S.: 339950

DEWILDT CAR SALES LIMITED

1600 Main Street East, Hamilton, L8K 1E7, ON, Canada
Tel.: (905) 312-0090
Web Site:
   http://www.dewildtchrysler.com
Year Founded: 1960
Rev.: $21,678,274
Emp.: 47
New Car Dealers
N.A.I.C.S.: 441110
Richard Dewildt *(Pres)*

DEXELANCE S.P.A.

Corso Venezia 29, 20121, Milan, Italy
Tel.: (39) 0283975225
Web Site:
   https://www.dexelance.com

DEXELANCE S.P.A.

Dexelance S.p.A.—(Continued)

Year Founded: 2015
DEX—(ITA)
Rev.: $247,594,760
Assets: $336,992,209
Liabilities: $264,796,262
Net Worth: $72,195,947
Earnings: ($7,285,920)
Emp.: 555
Fiscal Year-end: 12/31/22
Holding Company
N.A.I.C.S.: 551112
Alberto Bortolin (CFO)

Subsidiaries:

Axo Light S.R.L.   (1)
via Treviso 56, Scorze, 30037, Venezia, Italy
Tel.: (39) 0415845193
Web Site: https://www.iubenda.com
Interior Design Services
N.A.I.C.S.: 541410

Borman Lighting S.R.L.   (1)
Via Lisbona 21, Pontassieve, 50065, Florence, Italy
Tel.: (39) 0558316743
Web Site: https://www.bormanlighting.com
LED Light Mfr
N.A.I.C.S.: 335131

Cenacchi Int.l S.R.L.   (1)
Via della Liberta 31, Ozzano dell'Emilia, 40064, Bologna, Italy
Tel.: (39) 051797923
Web Site:
  https://www.cenacchiinternational.it
Interior Design Services
N.A.I.C.S.: 541410

Cubo Design S.R.L.   (1)
Loc Case Sciarroni, Grasciano, 64024, Teramo, TE, Italy
Tel.: (39) 085871131
Web Site: https://www.miton.it
Kitchen Design Services
N.A.I.C.S.: 541410

Davide Groppi S.R.L.   (1)
Via Belizzi 22 - 20/A, 29122, Piacenza, Italy
Tel.: (39) 0390523571590
Web Site: https://www.davidegroppi.com
Light Design Services
N.A.I.C.S.: 541490

Flexalighting North America Ltd.   (1)
Unit 22 - 15531 24th Ave, Surrey, V4A 2J4, BC, Canada
Tel.: (604) 385-4311
Web Site: https://www.flexalighting-na.com
LED Light Mfr
N.A.I.C.S.: 335131

Flexalighting S.R.L.   (1)
Via Lisbona 21, Pontassieve, 50065, Florence, Italy
Tel.: (39) 0558323021
Web Site: https://www.flexalighting.net
Light Design Services
N.A.I.C.S.: 541490

Gamma Arredamenti Int.l Inc.   (1)
108 S Walnut Cir Ste B, Greensboro, NC 27409
Tel.: (336) 886-8060
Steel & Wooden Mfr
N.A.I.C.S.: 321991

Gamma Arredamenti Int.l S.p.A.   (1)
Via Pitagora 3, 47121, Forli, FC, Italy
Tel.: (39) 0543708311
Web Site: https://www.gammarr.com
Steel & Wooden Mfr
N.A.I.C.S.: 321991

Gervasoni S.p.A.   (1)
Viale del Lavoro 88, 33050, Pavia di Udine, UD, Italy
Tel.: (39) 0432656611
Web Site: https://www.gervasoni1882.com
Steel & Wooden Mfr
N.A.I.C.S.: 321991

Meridiani S.R.L.   (1)
Via Birago 16, 20826, Misinto, MB, Italy
Tel.: (39) 029669161
Web Site: https://www.meridiani.it
Emp.: 75

Steel & Wooden Mfr
N.A.I.C.S.: 321991

Modar S.p.A.   (1)
Via Raffaello Sanzio 18, 20825, Barlassina, MB, Italy
Tel.: (39) 03621338200
Web Site: https://modar.it
Interior Design Services
N.A.I.C.S.: 541410

Saba Italia S.R.L.   (1)
Via Dell'industria 17, San Martino di Lupari, 35018, Padua, Italy
Tel.: (39) 0499462227
Web Site: https://sabaitalia.com
Steel & Wooden Mfr
N.A.I.C.S.: 337121

Turri S.R.L.   (1)
Via U Foscolo 6, 22060, Carugo, CO, Italy
Tel.: (39) 031760111
Web Site: https://turri.it
Steel & Wooden Mfr
N.A.I.C.S.: 337121

Turri UK Ltd.   (1)
Chelsea Harbour Design Centre Chelsea Harbour, London, SW10 0XE, United Kingdom
Tel.: (44) 7716637700
Steel & Wooden Mfr
N.A.I.C.S.: 321991

Turri USA Corp.   (1)
1680 Michigan Ave Ste 700, Miami Beach, FL 33139
Tel.: (366) 619-3797
Steel & Wooden Mfr
N.A.I.C.S.: 321991

DEXIA SA

Bastion Tower - Place du Champ de Mars 5, 1050, Brussels, Belgium
Tel.: (32) 22135700   BE
Web Site: http://www.dexia.com
Year Founded: 1996
DEXB—(EUR)
Rev.: $3,435,387,280
Assets: $140,543,818,480
Liabilities: $132,330,577,600
Net Worth: $8,213,240,880
Earnings: ($759,052,320)
Emp.: 538
Fiscal Year-end: 12/31/20
Bank Holding Company
N.A.I.C.S.: 551111
Veronique Hugues (CFO, CFO & Member/Member-Mgmt Bd)

Subsidiaries:

Ausbil Investment Management   (1)
Grosvenor Place Level 27 225 George Street, Sydney, 2000, NSW, Australia
Tel.: (61) 292590200
Web Site: http://www.ausbil.com.au
Equities Trading Services
N.A.I.C.S.: 523150
Paul Xiradis (Chm, Chief Investment Officer & Co-Head-Equities)

Centrabail SA   (1)
Blvd Pacheco 44, 1000, Brussels, Belgium   **(100%)**
Tel.: (32) 222211111
Sales Range: $50-74.9 Million
Emp.: 50
Banking Services
N.A.I.C.S.: 522320

Corona Direct   (1)
De Kleetlaan 7A, 1831, Diegem, Belgium   **(100%)**
Tel.: (32) 2 244 23 23
Web Site: http://www.coronadirect.be
Sales Range: $1-9.9 Million
Emp.: 200
Insurance Services
N.A.I.C.S.: 524113

Dexia Bank Denmark A/S   (1)
Gronningen 17, 1270, Copenhagen, Denmark
Tel.: (45) 33 46 11 00
Web Site: http://www.dexia.jobs
Commercial Banking Services
N.A.I.C.S.: 522110

Dexia Bank Nederland N.V.   (1)
Parnassusweg 819, 1082 LZ, Amsterdam, Netherlands   **(100%)**
Tel.: (31) 882036500
Web Site: http://www.dexia.nl
Sales Range: $200-249.9 Million
Emp.: 300
Short-Term Business Credit
N.A.I.C.S.: 522299

Dexia Crediop S.p.A.   (1)
Via Antonio Salandra 18, 00187, Rome, Italy   **(70%)**
Tel.: (39) 0647711
Web Site: http://www.dexia-crediop.it
Sales Range: $700-740.0 Million
Banking Services
N.A.I.C.S.: 522110
Claude Edgar L. G. Piret (Vice Chm)

Subsidiary (Non-US):

Crediop Overseas Bank Ltd.   (2)
West Bay Road, PO Box 707, Georgetown, Cayman Islands
Tel.: (345) 9474777
Provider of Financial Services
N.A.I.C.S.: 523999

Dexia Credit Local   (1)
800 Square Victoria Suite 1620, CP 201, Montreal, H4Z 1 E3, QC, Canada
Tel.: (514) 868-1200
Web Site: http://www.dexia.jobs
Sales Range: $50-74.9 Million
Emp.: 3
Credit Management Services
N.A.I.C.S.: 522299

Dexia Credit Local   (1)
445 Park Ave Fl 8, New York, NY 10022
Tel.: (212) 515-7000
Web Site: http://www.dexia.com
Sales Range: $100-124.9 Million
Emp.: 110
Credit Management Services
N.A.I.C.S.: 522299

Subsidiary (Domestic):

Dexia Real Estate Capital Markets   (2)
1180 NW Maple St Ste 202, Issaquah, WA 98027-8106
Tel.: (425) 313-4600
Web Site: http://www.dexia-cmbs.com
Sales Range: $50-74.9 Million
Emp.: 17
Securities Mortgages
N.A.I.C.S.: 523910

Dexia Credit Local SA   (1)
Tour CBX 1 Passerelle des Reflets La Defense 2 - TSA 12203, La Defense, 92919, Paris, France
Tel.: (33) 158587777
Credit Card Management Services
N.A.I.C.S.: 522299

Subsidiary (Domestic):

Dexia CLF Banque S.A   (2)
1 Passerelle des Reflets Tour Dexia La Defense 2 TSA 72200, La Defense, 92919, Paris, France
Tel.: (33) 1 58 58 88 02
Web Site: http://www.dexia.jobs
Commercial Banking Services
N.A.I.C.S.: 522110

Subsidiary (US):

Dexia Delaware LLC   (2)
445 Park Ave Fl 8, New York, NY 10022
Tel.: (212) 515-7000
Financial Management Services
N.A.I.C.S.: 523999

Subsidiary (Non-US):

Dexia Kommunalkredit Bank AG   (2)
Fischhof 3, Vienna, 1010, Austria
Tel.: (43) 174 040 35 40
Web Site: http://www.dexia.com
Commercial Banking Services
N.A.I.C.S.: 522110

Subsidiary (Non-US):

Dexia Kommunalkredit Bulgaria EOOD   (3)
19 Kamigradska, 1000, Sofia, Bulgaria
Tel.: (359) 897 886 761
Financial Management Services
N.A.I.C.S.: 523999

Subsidiary (Non-US):

Dexia Sabadell Banco Local SA   (2)
Paseo de las Doce Estrellas 4 Campo de las Naciones, Madrid, 28043, Spain
Tel.: (34) 917213310
Web Site: http://www.dexiasabadell.es
Sales Range: $25-49.9 Million
Emp.: 50
Financial Management Services
N.A.I.C.S.: 523999
Patrick Giacobbi (Mng Dir)

Municipal Bank Ltd.   (2)
Ha'tichon Tower 19 Haarbaa St, Tel Aviv, Israel   **(65.3%)**
Tel.: (972) 3 7647600
Commercial Banking Services
N.A.I.C.S.: 522110
Olivier Gutman (CEO & Gen Mgr)

Dexia Epargne Pension SA   (1)
65 Rue de la Victoire, 75009, Paris, France
Tel.: (33) 1 55 50 15 15
Web Site: http://www.dexia.jobs
Insurance Management Services
N.A.I.C.S.: 524298

Dexia Finance SA   (1)
1 Passerelle des Reflets Tour Dexia La Defense 2 TSA 92202, La Defense, Paris, 92919, France
Tel.: (33) 1 58 58 77 77
Web Site: http://www.dexia.com
Financial Management Services
N.A.I.C.S.: 523999

Dexia Ingenierie Sociale SA   (1)
13 Rue Croquechataigne, PB 30064, La Chapelle-Saint-Mesmin, 45380, France
Tel.: (33) 2 36 56 00 00
Web Site: http://www.dexia-is.com
Financial Management Services
N.A.I.C.S.: 523999

Dexia Societe de Credit SA   (1)
Rue des Clarisses 38, 4000, Liege, Belgium
Tel.: (32) 4 232 45 45
Web Site: http://www.dexia-societedecredit.be
Sales Range: $50-74.9 Million
Emp.: 90
Credit Management Services
N.A.I.C.S.: 522299

Fonds Mercator   (1)
Zuidstraat 2, 1000, Brussels, Belgium   **(100%)**
Tel.: (32) 25482535
Web Site: http://www.mercatorfonds.be
Sales Range: $1-9.9 Million
Emp.: 4
Book Publishing & Printing
N.A.I.C.S.: 513130

REKORD Versicherungvermittlungs- und Betreuungsgesellschaft fur Selbstandige mbH & Co. KG   (1)
Grafenberger Allee 277 287, D 40237, Dusseldorf, Germany   **(100%)**
Tel.: (49) 211914801
Web Site: http://www.rekord.ag
Sales Range: $50-74.9 Million
Emp.: 60
Insurance Agents, Brokers & Service
N.A.I.C.S.: 524298

DEXIN CHINA HOLDINGS CO., LTD.

565 Zhongshan North Road, Hangzhou, 310014, China
Tel.: (86) 57185801700
Web Site:
  http://www.dothinkgroup.com
2019—(HKG)
Rev.: $3,109,225,532
Assets: $15,450,793,114
Liabilities: $12,625,634,970
Net Worth: $2,825,158,144
Earnings: $22,679,374
Emp.: 1,561
Fiscal Year-end: 12/31/22

Residential Property Management
Services
N.A.I.C.S.: 531311
Zhang Ce *(VP)*

DEXIN SERVICES GROUP LIMITED
Room 488 Building 2 No 2008-2010
Jinchang Road Liangzhu Street,
Hangzhou, Zhejiang, China
Tel.: (86) 57188173911   Ky
Web Site: https://www.dexinfuwu.com
Year Founded: 2020
2215—(HKG)
Rev.: $132,307,820
Assets: $197,254,237
Liabilities: $92,159,947
Net Worth: $105,094,290
Earnings: $8,653,218
Emp.: 2,942
Fiscal Year-end: 12/31/23
Property Management Services
N.A.I.C.S.: 531311
Betty Shuk Yi So *(Sec)*

DEXTECH MEDICAL AB
Dag Hammarskjolds Vag 34A, 752
37, Uppsala, Sweden
Tel.: (46) 707104788
Web Site:
    https://www.dextechmedical.com
Year Founded: 2004
Pharmaceuticals Product Mfr
N.A.I.C.S.: 325412
Svante Wadman *(Chm)*

DEXTER STUDIOS CO., LTD
DDMC 18/19F 75 Maebongsan-ro,
Mapo-gu, Seoul, 03926, Korea
(South)
Tel.: (82) 263917000
Web Site:
    https://www.dexterstudios.com
Year Founded: 2011
206560—(KRS)
Rev.: $50,549,695
Assets: $70,497,905
Liabilities: $26,295,043
Net Worth: $44,202,862
Earnings: ($5,040,400)
Emp.: 317
Fiscal Year-end: 12/31/22
Motion Picture & Video Production
Services
N.A.I.C.S.: 512110
Hyeri Park *(Assoc Dir)*

DEXTERRA GROUP INC.
5915 Airport Road Suite 425, Mississauga, L4V 1T1, ON, Canada
Tel.: (416) 483-5152   AB
Web Site: http://www.dexterra.com
Year Founded: 2006
DXT—(TSX)
Rev.: $373,785,118
Assets: $401,718,772
Liabilities: $166,271,267
Net Worth: $235,447,505
Earnings: $50,440,632
Emp.: 2,262
Fiscal Year-end: 12/31/20
Logistic Services
N.A.I.C.S.: 541614
William H. Anderson *(Exec VP-Quality, Health, Safety & Environment)*

Subsidiaries:

NRB Inc.   **(1)**
115 South Service Road, PO Box 129,
Grimsby, L3M 4G3, ON, Canada
Tel.: (905) 945-9622
Web Site: http://www.nrb-inc.com
Rev.: $14,812,509
Emp.: 150
Prefabricated Modular Buildings Mfr
N.A.I.C.S.: 332311

Robert George McNeil *(Co-Founder)*

Subsidiary (US):

NRB (USA), Inc.   **(2)**
191 Quality Cir, New Holland, PA 17557
Tel.: (717) 354-7770
Construction Engineering Services
N.A.I.C.S.: 541330
Robert McNeil *(Pres)*

Swamp Mats Inc   **(1)**
505 3 St Sw Ste 1600, Calgary, AB,
Canada
Tel.: (403) 265-8757
Web Site: http://www.swampmats.ca
Sales Range: $25-49.9 Million
Emp.: 4
Matting Solutions Provider
N.A.I.C.S.: 337910

DEXTERS LONDON LIMITED
66 Grosvenor Street, Mayfair, London, W1K 3JL, United Kingdom
Tel.: (44) 2075909590
Web Site: https://www.dexters.co.uk
Emp.: 525
Real Estate
N.A.I.C.S.: 531190
Jeff Doble *(Founder & CEO)*

DEXTON BUSINESS SOLUTIONS
Rivium 1e straat 35, 2909 LE,
Capelle aan den IJssel, Netherlands
Tel.: (31) 102885020
Web Site: http://www.dexton.nl
Sales Range: $1-9.9 Million
Emp.: 22
Customer Relationship Management
Software
N.A.I.C.S.: 334610
Jos Halkus *(Owner, CEO & Mng Dir)*

DEXUS
Tel.: (61) 290171100
Web Site: http://www.dexus.com
Year Founded: 1984
DXS—(ASX)
Rev.: $1,457,216,761
Assets: $13,501,876,799
Liabilities: $4,223,086,042
Net Worth: $9,278,790,757
Earnings: $753,164,770
Emp.: 552
Fiscal Year-end: 06/30/20
Real Estate Development Services
N.A.I.C.S.: 531390
Melanie Bourke *(COO)*

Subsidiaries:

APN Property Group Limited   **(1)**
Level 30 101 Collins Street, Melbourne,
3000, VIC, Australia
Tel.: (61) 386561000
Web Site: http://www.apngroup.com.au
Rev.: $18,694,695
Assets: $105,502,982
Liabilities: $16,113,946
Net Worth: $89,389,036
Earnings: $10,164,235
Fiscal Year-end: 06/30/2019
Real Estate Investment Services
N.A.I.C.S.: 531390
Michael Doble *(Chief Investment Officer-Real Estate Securities)*

Subsidiary (Domestic):

Dexus Asset Management
Limited   **(2)**
Level 30 101 Collins Street, Melbourne,
3000, VIC, Australia
Tel.: (61) 1800996456
Web Site: http://www.apngroup.com.au
Sales Range: $50-74.9 Million
Emp.: 34
Investment Fund Management Services
N.A.I.C.S.: 523940
Howard Benchley *(Exec Dir)*

Affiliate (Domestic):

Dexus Convenience Retail REIT   **(3)**

101 Collins Street Level 30, Melbourne,
3000, VIC, Australia   **(2.13%)**
Tel.: (61) 386561000
Web Site: http://www.apngroup.com
Rev.: $38,233,173
Assets: $503,377,402
Liabilities: $175,575,587
Net Worth: $327,801,815
Earnings: $2,274,973
Emp.: 330
Fiscal Year-end: 06/30/2024
Real Estate Investment Trust
N.A.I.C.S.: 525990
Chris Brockett *(Mgr-Fund)*

Dexus Industria REIT   **(3)**
Level 30 101 Collins Street, Melbourne,
3000, VIC, Australia
Tel.: (61) 386561000
Web Site: http://apngroup.com.au
Rev.: $616,920,403
Assets: $10,565,170,897
Liabilities: $3,777,777,762
Net Worth: $6,787,393,135
Earnings: ($1,057,558,756)
Emp.: 972
Fiscal Year-end: 06/30/2024
Real Estate Investment Trust
N.A.I.C.S.: 525990
Geoff Brunsdon *(Chm)*

DEXUS Holdings Pty Limited   **(1)**
264 George Street, Sydney, 2000, NSW,
Australia
Tel.: (61) 1800819675
Web Site: https://www.dexus.com
Real Estate Development Services
N.A.I.C.S.: 531390

DEXXON GROUPE SA
79 Avenue Louis Roche, 92230,
Gennevilliers, Cedex, France
Tel.: (33) 141322121   FR
Web Site: http://www.plus.dexxon.eu
Year Founded: 1975
Sales Range: $700-749.9 Million
Emp.: 550
IT & Office Products Distr
N.A.I.C.S.: 449210

Subsidiaries:

Dexxon GmbH   **(1)**
Peter Sander Strasse 13, Mainz-Kastel,
55252, Germany
Tel.: (49) 61345670
Web Site: http://www.emtec-international.com
Sales Range: $750-799.9 Million
Emp.: 35
Audio & Video Magnetic Recording Media;
Data Storage Media
N.A.I.C.S.: 334310

Subsidiary (Non-US):

Dexxon Belgium S.A.   **(2)**
Pegasuslaan 5, 1831, Diegem, Belgium
Tel.: (32) 2 333 7333
Web Site: http://www.dexxon.eu
Sales Range: $25-49.9 Million
Emp.: 15
Audio & Video Magnetic Recording Media
N.A.I.C.S.: 334610

Dexxon Italia Spa   **(2)**
Piazza Don Mapelli 75, 20099, Sesto San
Giovanni, MI, Italy
Tel.: (39) 02 2430 3067
Web Site: http://www.emtec-international.com
Sales Range: $25-49.9 Million
Digital Audio & Video Magnetic Recording
Media
N.A.I.C.S.: 334610

Subsidiary (Domestic):

EMTEC International Holding
GmbH   **(2)**
Kaiser Wilhelm Strasse 52, 67059, Ludwigshafen, Germany
Tel.: (49) 62159200
Web Site: http://www.emtec-group.com
Sales Range: $50-74.9 Million
Emp.: 160
Holding Company
N.A.I.C.S.: 551112

Subsidiary (Non-US):

EMTEC Magnetics (Schweiz)
GmbH   **(2)**
Appital, Postfach 99, CH-8820, Wadenswil,
Switzerland
Tel.: (41) 17819511
Web Site: http://www.emtec-group.ch
Sales Range: $25-49.9 Million
Emp.: 8
Audio & Video Magnetic Recording Media
N.A.I.C.S.: 334610

EMTEC Magnetics Iberica S.A.   **(2)**
Paseo De La Castellana 143, E 28046, Madrid, Spain
Tel.: (34) 912108080
Web Site: http://www.emtec.es
Sales Range: $25-49.9 Million
Audio & Video Magnetic Recording Media
N.A.I.C.S.: 334610

EMTEC Magnetics Polska Sp.
z.o.o.   **(2)**
Ul Wschodnia 5a, PL 05 090, Warsaw, Poland
Tel.: (48) 227115100
Web Site: http://www.emtec-group.com
Sales Range: $25-49.9 Million
Emp.: 14
Audio & Video Magnetic Recording Media
N.A.I.C.S.: 334610

Digital Storage Incorporated   **(1)**
7611 Green Meadows Dr, Lewis Center,
OH 43035-9445
Tel.: (740) 548-7179
Web Site: http://www.digitalstorage.com
Sales Range: $25-49.9 Million
Emp.: 30
Computer Media, Hardware & Supplies
Distr
N.A.I.C.S.: 424120
Dave Burke *(Exec VP-Fin)*

DEYAAR DEVELOPMENT PJSC
Deyaar Head Office Building, PO Box
30833, Al Barsha, Dubai, United Arab
Emirates
Tel.: (971) 43957700
Web Site: https://www.deyaar.ae
Year Founded: 2002
DEYAAR—(DFM)
Rev.: $341,507,302
Assets: $1,787,428,962
Liabilities: $442,883,909
Net Worth: $1,344,545,053
Earnings: $119,994,012
Emp.: 2,075
Fiscal Year-end: 12/31/23
Real Estate Services
N.A.I.C.S.: 531390
Saeed Mohammed Al Qatami *(CEO)*

Subsidiaries:

Deyaar Facilities Management
LLC   **(1)**
Office No 102 First Floor 51 Tower Al Abraj
St Business Bay, Dubai, United Arab Emirates
Tel.: (971) 45530325
Web Site: https://www.deyaarfm.com
Property Maintenance Services
N.A.I.C.S.: 561790
Mohamad Abou Laban *(CEO)*

DEYUN HOLDING LTD.
No 97 Longjiangnan Road, Longxia
Village Songxia Town Changle District, Fuzhou, Fujian, China
Tel.: (86) 59128769145   Ky
Web Site: https://www.ds-lace.com
Year Founded: 2002
1440—(HKG)
Rev.: $43,940,103
Assets: $68,145,630
Liabilities: $24,408,922
Net Worth: $43,736,708
Earnings: ($1,397,181)
Emp.: 527
Fiscal Year-end: 12/31/23
Holding Company

Deyun Holding Ltd.—(Continued)

N.A.I.C.S.: 551112
Jing Xu (Sec)

DEZHAN HEALTH CO., LTD.

No 235 Yin Chuan Road, Urumqi, 830054, Xinjiang, China
Tel.: (86) 9914311866
Year Founded: 1980
000813—(SSE)
Rev.: $80,148,744
Assets: $796,685,760
Liabilities: $54,810,756
Net Worth: $741,875,004
Earnings: ($6,586,164)
Fiscal Year-end: 12/31/22
Chemical & Pharmaceutical Mfr
N.A.I.C.S.: 325412

DF DEUTSCHE FORFAIT AG

Nordliche Munchner Strasse 9 c, 82031, Grunwald, Germany
Tel.: (49) 89215519000
Web Site: https://www.dfag.de
Year Founded: 2003
DFTK—(MUN)
Rev.: $32,608,320
Assets: $54,729,875
Liabilities: $22,938,419
Net Worth: $31,791,456
Earnings: $1,832,424
Emp.: 16
Fiscal Year-end: 12/31/23
Financial & Foreign Trade Services
N.A.I.C.S.: 541611
Ludolf-Georg von Wartenberg (Chm-Supervisory Bd)

Subsidiaries:

DF Deutsche Forfait AG Pakistan (PVT.) LTD. **(1)**
Ste No 307 3rd Fl.Siddiq Trade Ctr 72 Main Blvd, Gulberg, Lahore, 54660, Punjab, Pakistan
Tel.: (92) 42111332433
Web Site: http://www.dfag.de
Sales Range: $75-99.9 Million
Emp.: 10
Forfaiting Business Services
N.A.I.C.S.: 522299

DF Deutsche Forfait Americas Inc. **(1)**
9045 SW 64th Ct, Miami, FL 33156-1824
Tel.: (305) 377-2688
Forfaiting & Financial Services
N.A.I.C.S.: 522299

DF Deutsche Forfait s.r.o **(1)**
Panska 894 4, Prague, 11000, Czech Republic
Tel.: (420) 221014620
Sales Range: $75-99.9 Million
Emp.: 2
Forfaiting Business Services
N.A.I.C.S.: 522299
Dalibor Hanka (Mgr)

Deutsche Forfait GmbH **(1)**
Gustav-Heinemann-Ufer 56, 50968, Cologne, Germany
Tel.: (49) 221973760
Foreign Trade Financing Services
N.A.I.C.S.: 522220

DFCC BANK PLC

73/5 Galle Rd, 3, Colombo, 3, Sri Lanka
Tel.: (94) 112442442
Web Site: https://www.dfcc.lk
Year Founded: 1955
DFCC.N0000—(COL)
Rev.: $244,732,665
Assets: $1,895,818,994
Liabilities: $1,714,996,778
Net Worth: $180,822,216
Earnings: $10,125,865
Emp.: 1,736
Fiscal Year-end: 12/31/22
Banking Services

Chinthika Amarasekara (CFO & Sr VP)

Subsidiaries:

DFCC Consulting (Pvt) Limited **(1)**
No 73 5 Galle Road, 03, Colombo, Sri Lanka
Tel.: (94) 112442442
Web Site: https://www.dfcc.lk
Business Consulting Services
N.A.I.C.S.: 541611

DFCC Vardhana Bank Limited **(1)**
73 W A D Ramanayake, Mawatha, Colombo, 00200, Sri Lanka
Tel.: (94) 112371371
Web Site: http://www.dfcc.lk
Emp.: 1,700
Commercial Banking Services
N.A.I.C.S.: 522110
Hemanatha Samaranayaka (Head-Customer Rels)

Lanka Industrial Estates Limited **(1)**
Pattiwila Road, Sapugaskanda, Makola, Sri Lanka
Tel.: (94) 11 240 0318
Web Site: http://www.lindel.biz
Sales Range: $50-74.9 Million
Industrial Estate Operation Services
N.A.I.C.S.: 531390
A N Fonseka (Chm)

Synapsys Limited **(1)**
540 Nawala Road, 10107, Rajagirya, Sri Lanka
Tel.: (94) 112880770
Web Site: https://synapsys.lk
Information Technology & Enabled Services
N.A.I.C.S.: 541512

DFCITY GROUP BERHAD

Lot 197 Jalan Sungai Putat, Batu Berendam, 75350, Melaka, Malaysia
Tel.: (60) 63172028
Web Site:
https://www.hockheng.com.my
Year Founded: 1988
DFCITY—(KLS)
Rev.: $4,661,048
Assets: $19,237,688
Liabilities: $7,053,964
Net Worth: $12,183,725
Earnings: $73,539
Fiscal Year-end: 12/31/22
Dimension Stone Products Mfr & Distr
N.A.I.C.S.: 327991
Kim Hock Low (Mng Dir)

Subsidiaries:

Hock Heng Granite Sdn. Bhd **(1)**
Lot 197 Jalan Sungai Putat, Batu Berendam, 75350, Melaka, Malaysia
Tel.: (60) 63172028
Dimension Stone Mining Services
N.A.I.C.S.: 212311
Yong Seng Low (Gen Mgr)

Hock Heng Marketing (KL) Sdn Bhd **(1)**
23 Jalan Rajawali 2 Bandar Puchong Jaya, 47100, Puchong, Selangor, Malaysia
Tel.: (60) 3 8075 7793
Granites & Marbles Distr
N.A.I.C.S.: 423320

Hock Heng Marketing (KL) Sdn. Bhd. **(1)**
Lot 13 Jalan TUDM Seksyen U6 Kg Baru Subang, 40150, Shah Alam, Selangor Darul Ehsan, Malaysia
Tel.: (60) 378456793
Web Site: http://www.hockheng.com.my
Dimension Stones Mfr & Sales
N.A.I.C.S.: 327991

Hock Heng Marketing (Southern Region) Sdn Bhd **(1)**
Lot 197 Jalan Sungai Putat, 75350, Batu Berendam, Johor Darul Takzim, Malaysia
Tel.: (60) 63172028
Emp.: 10
Granites & Marbles Distr

N.A.I.C.S.: 423320

Hock Heng Stone **(1)**
Lot 197-1 Batu 5 1/2 Jalan Sungai Putat, 75350, Batu Berendam, Melaka, Malaysia
Tel.: (60) 63172028
Granites Whslr
N.A.I.C.S.: 423320

Hock Heng Stone (East Coast) Sdn Bhd **(1)**
10 Jalan Indus Semambu 9/3 Cocopalm Indus Park, 25300, Kuantan, Pahang Darul Makmur, Malaysia
Tel.: (60) 95602212
Dimension Stone Mfr
N.A.I.C.S.: 327991
Tom Wang (Gen Mgr)

DFDS A/S

Marmorvej 18, DK 2100, Copenhagen, Denmark
Tel.: (45) 33423342
Web Site: https://www.dfds.com
Year Founded: 1866
DFDS—(CSE)
Rev.: $3,888,382,457
Assets: $4,931,776,418
Liabilities: $3,031,210,661
Net Worth: $1,900,565,757
Earnings: $292,138,733
Emp.: 11,500
Fiscal Year-end: 12/31/22
Freight & Passenger Transportation Services
N.A.I.C.S.: 483111
Claus V. Hemmingsen (Chm)

Subsidiaries:

AB DFDS Seaways **(1)**
Sauliu Str 19, 92233, Klaipeda, Lithuania
Tel.: (370) 46395000
Web Site: http://www.dfdsseaways.lt
Freight Transportation Services
N.A.I.C.S.: 483111
Martynas Jonkus (Gen Mgr-Legal Dept)

DFDS (Deutschland) GmbH **(1)**
Hogerdamm 41, 20097, Hamburg, Germany
Tel.: (49) 40389030
Web Site: http://www.dfdsseaways.de
Deep Sea Passenger Transportation Services
N.A.I.C.S.: 483112

DFDS Denizcilik ve Tasimacilik A.S. **(1)**
Nidakule Atasehir Guney, Barbaros Mahallesi Mor Sumbul Sokak No 7/3 Floor 2-8-9 Atasehir, 34746, Istanbul, Turkiye
Tel.: (90) 2165851500
Web Site: https://www.dfds.com.tr
Logistics Transportation Services
N.A.I.C.S.: 488510

DFDS Koletransport A/S **(1)**
Majsmarken 1, 9500, Hobro, Denmark
Tel.: (45) 97536211
Freight Forwarding & Logistics Management Services
N.A.I.C.S.: 541614

DFDS Logistics (Ireland) Ltd. **(1)**
Blanchardstown Corporate Park Block 10 1 Floor 1, Dublin, Ireland
Tel.: (353) 18129400
Web Site: http://www.dfds.com
Emp.: 32
Freight Forwarding & Logistics Consulting Services
N.A.I.C.S.: 488510
Andrew Scott (Dir-Comml)

DFDS Logistics AB **(1)**
Sydatlanten 10, 41834, Gothenburg, Sweden
Tel.: (46) 31 58 60 00
Web Site: http://www.dfds.com
Emp.: 60
Freight Forwarding & Logistics Consulting Services
N.A.I.C.S.: 488510
Orjan Braten (Mgr-Sls)

DFDS Logistics AS **(1)**
Tel.: (47) 22122000
Web Site: http://www.dfds.com

Freight Forwarding & Logistics Consulting Services
N.A.I.C.S.: 488510

DFDS Logistics BV **(1)**
Burgemeester van Lierplein 57, 3134 ZB, Vlaardingen, Netherlands
Tel.: (31) 104451700
Web Site: http://www.dfds.com
Emp.: 100
Freight Forwarding & Logistics Consulting Services
N.A.I.C.S.: 488510
Ruud van der Wilt (Mgr-Sls)

DFDS Logistics GmbH **(1)**
Blohmstrasse 31, 21079, Hamburg, Germany
Tel.: (49) 40 4192789 21
Freight Forwarding & Logistics Consulting Services
N.A.I.C.S.: 488510
Sven Ohlsen (Mng Dir)

DFDS Logistics Intermodal A/S **(1)**
Centerhavn 23, 7000, Fredericia, Denmark
Tel.: (45) 76 20 67 00
Web Site: http://www.dfds.com
Freight Forwarding & Logistics Consulting Services
N.A.I.C.S.: 488510
Kennet Andresen (Mgr-Intermodal)

DFDS Logistics Limited **(1)**
Web Site: http://www.dfdslogistics.com
Emp.: 100
Logistic Services
N.A.I.C.S.: 541614

DFDS Logistics NV **(1)**
Fritiof Nilsson Piratenstraat Haven 3880 A, 9042, Gent, Belgium
Tel.: (32) 9 255 94 94
Web Site: http://www.dfds.com
Emp.: 30
Freight Forwarding & Logistics Consulting Services
N.A.I.C.S.: 488510

DFDS Logistics Nijmegen B.V. **(1)**
Bedrijfsweg 8, 6541 DC, Nijmegen, Netherlands
Tel.: (31) 243712255
Freight Forwarding Services
N.A.I.C.S.: 488510

DFDS Logistics OU **(1)**
Lootsa 8a A-torn, 11415, Tallinn, Estonia
Tel.: (372) 6661677
Freight Forwarding & Logistics Management Services
N.A.I.C.S.: 541614

DFDS Logistics OY **(1)**
Tel.: (358) 52234160
Freight & Logistics Management Services
N.A.I.C.S.: 488510
Kimmo Salmi (Mng Dir-Sls)

DFDS Logistics Polska Sp. z o.o. **(1)**
Ul Jana Pawla II nr 38, 89-200, Szubin, Poland
Tel.: (48) 523911700
Freight Transportation Services
N.A.I.C.S.: 561910

DFDS Logistics S.p.A. **(1)**
Via Vela 12, 21054, Fagnano Olona, Varese, Italy
Tel.: (39) 0331 388 310
Freight & Logistics Management Services
N.A.I.C.S.: 488510
Roberto Barbagallo (Gen Mgr)

DFDS Logistics SARL **(1)**
Tel.: (33) 321320876
Logistics Consulting Servies
N.A.I.C.S.: 541614
Geert Liefhooghe (Mng Dir)

DFDS Logistics Services NV **(1)**
Dampoortstraat 265, Bus 2, Sint-Kruis, 8310, Brugge, Belgium
Tel.: (32) 50 55 68 00
Web Site: http://www.dfdslogistics.com
Emp.: 25
Logistics Consulting Servies
N.A.I.C.S.: 541614
Geert Liefhooghe (Gen Mgr)

DFDS Logistics Wijchen B.V. **(1)**
Bijsterhuizen 4020, 6604 LW, Wijchen, Netherlands
Tel.: (31) 243718900
Web Site: https://www.dfdswijchen.com
Logistics Transportation Services
N.A.I.C.S.: 488510

DFDS Logistics Winterswijk B.V. **(1)**
Misterweg 165, 7102 EN, Winterswijk, Netherlands
Tel.: (31) 543543333
Freight Forwarding Services
N.A.I.C.S.: 488510

DFDS Polska Sp. Z.o.o. **(1)**
Ul Roosevelta 18, 60-829, Poznan, Poland
Tel.: (48) 616 589 000
Web Site: http://www.dfds.com
Freight & Logistics Management Services
N.A.I.C.S.: 488510

DFDS SIA **(1)**
Juras Str 28, Liepaja, 3401, Latvia
Tel.: (371) 63420220
Freight Transport Services
N.A.I.C.S.: 561910

DFDS Seaways AB **(1)**
Sydatlanten 6, 418 34, Gothenburg, Sweden
Tel.: (46) 31650800
Deep Sea Freight & Passenger Transportation Services
N.A.I.C.S.: 483111
Niclas Bohlin (Sr Mgr-Sls)

DFDS Seaways AS **(1)**
Akershusstranda 53 Skur 44, 0150, Oslo, Norway
Tel.: (47) 21621375
Web Site: http://www.dfdsseaways.no
Emp.: 5
Deep Sea Freight Transportation Services
N.A.I.C.S.: 483111

DFDS Seaways Baltic GmbH **(1)**
Ostuferhafen 15, 24149, Kiel, Germany
Tel.: (49) 431209760
Web Site: http://www.dfds.com
Emp.: 27
Deep Sea Freight & Passenger Transportation Services
N.A.I.C.S.: 483111

DFDS Seaways GmbH **(1)**
Leuchtturmweg 5, 27472, Cuxhaven, Germany
Tel.: (49) 4721 7960 0
Web Site: http://www.dfds.com
Deep Sea Freight & Passenger Transportation Services
N.A.I.C.S.: 483111

DFDS Seaways Hispania S.L **(1)**
Street La Safor No 10 Office 5, 46015, Valencia, Spain
Tel.: (34) 963673171
Freight Forwarding Services
N.A.I.C.S.: 488510

DFDS Seaways Holding AB **(1)**
Sydatlanten 21, Box 8888, 40272, Vastra Gotaland, Sweden
Tel.: (46) 703099838
Holding Company
N.A.I.C.S.: 551112

DFDS Seaways IJmuiden BV **(1)**
Sluisplein 33, 1975 AG, IJmuiden, Netherlands
Tel.: (31) 255546666
Web Site: http://www.dfds.com
Deep Sea Freight & Passenger Transportation Services
N.A.I.C.S.: 483111
Teun Leene (Gen Dir)

DFDS Seaways Ltd. **(1)**
14-th Line VO d 7 office 6.2 1, 199034, Saint Petersburg, Russia
Tel.: (7) 812 334 5715
Web Site: http://www.dfdsseaways.ru
Deep Sea Freight Transportation Services
N.A.I.C.S.: 483111

DFDS Seaways NV **(1)**
Mercatordok Multimodal Terminal Philips Landsbergjuslaan 11, Havennummer, Gent, 9000, Belgium
Tel.: (32) 9 269 12 69

Emp.: 14
Marine Shipping Services
N.A.I.C.S.: 488510

DFDS Seaways Newcastle Ltd. **(1)**
Nordic House Western Access Road, Immingham, DN40 2LZ, Lincolnshire, United Kingdom
Tel.: (44) 1469575231
Web Site: http://www.dfdsseaways.co.uk
Deep Sea Freight & Passenger Transportation Services
N.A.I.C.S.: 483111

DFDS Seaways OU **(1)**
Lootsa 12b 6th Floor, 11.415, Tallinn, Estonia
Tel.: (372) 6661677
Web Site: http://www.dfds.com
Emp.: 15
Deep Sea Freight & Passenger Transportation Services
N.A.I.C.S.: 483111
Peter Ogisaar (Gen Mgr)

DFDS Seaways S.A.S. **(1)**
Terminal Car Ferry 7 Quai Gaston Lalitte, 76200, Dieppe, France
Tel.: (33) 232145239
Web Site: http://www.dfdsseaways.fr
Deep Sea Freight & Passenger Transportation Services
N.A.I.C.S.: 483111

DFDS Seaways SIA **(1)**
Unijas str 47, 1039, Riga, Latvia
Tel.: (371) 67840777
Web Site: http://www.dfdsseaways.lv
Deep Sea Freight & Passenger Transportation Services
N.A.I.C.S.: 483111
Zigmunds Jankovskis (CEO)

DFDS Seaways Terminals BV **(1)**
Vulcaanweg 20, 3134 KL, Vlaardingen, Netherlands
Tel.: (31) 102084991
Web Site: http://www.dfds.com
Emp.: 200
Deep Sea Freight & Passenger Transportation Services
N.A.I.C.S.: 483111
Jacob Andersen (Dir-Route)

DFDS Stevedoring A/S **(1)**
Dagvej 1, Ribe, Esbjerg, 6700, Denmark
Tel.: (45) 79177000
Freight & Logistics Management Services
N.A.I.C.S.: 488510

Euro Asia cold Chain Logistic Co., Ltd. **(1)**
Room 312 Jingyuan business hotel Jingxi road, Baiyun district, Guangzhou, China
Tel.: (86) 18620456655
Web Site: https://euro-asia-logistics.com
Logistic Services
N.A.I.C.S.: 541614

Gothenburg RO/RO Terminal AB **(1)**
Ytterhamnsvagen 1, 41834, Gothenburg, Sweden
Tel.: (46) 31650700
Freight Forwarding Services
N.A.I.C.S.: 488510

HSF Beteiligungs GmbH **(1)**
Auf Der Leuchtenburg 4, 49434, Neuenkirchen, Germany
Tel.: (49) 549391390
Freight Forwarding Services
N.A.I.C.S.: 488510

ICT Holding A/S **(1)**
Transportbuen 6, 7400, Herning, Denmark
Tel.: (45) 70266288
Freight Forwarding & Logistics Management Services
N.A.I.C.S.: 541614

ICT Logistics GmbH **(1)**
Gutenbergring 69D 3OG, DE-22848, Norderstedt, Germany
Tel.: (49) 4087408372
Freight Forwarding & Logistics Management Services
N.A.I.C.S.: 541614

ICT Logistics UAB **(1)**
Sauliu Str 19, 92233, Klaipeda, Lithuania
Tel.: (370) 46395000

Freight Transport Services
N.A.I.C.S.: 561910

Karlshamn Express AB **(1)**
Munkahusveagen, Box 194, 374 23, Karlshamn, Sweden
Tel.: (46) 45437800
Web Site: http://www.karlshamnsexpress.se
Container Transport & Logistics Services
N.A.I.C.S.: 484110
Per-Christian Persson (Mgr-Logistics & Transport)

LLC DFDS **(1)**
JCS ICT DK Mykilsko-Slobidska St 1a Office 308, UA-02002, Kiev, Ukraine
Tel.: (380) 445864944
Freight Forwarding & Logistics Management Services
N.A.I.C.S.: 541614

Lucey Transport Logistics Ltd. **(1)**
Greenogue Business Park, Rathcoole, Dublin, Ireland
Tel.: (353) 14018670
Transportation Logistics Services
N.A.I.C.S.: 541614

Moss Container Terminal AS **(1)**
Strandgaten 10, 1531, Moss, Norway
Tel.: (47) 22 12 21 40
Marine Terminal Services
N.A.I.C.S.: 488310
Steinar Heia (Dir-Terminal)

N&K Spedition Spain S.L. **(1)**
Plaza Adolfo Ventas 7, 43870, Tarragona, Spain
Tel.: (34) 977425240
Freight Forwarding Services
N.A.I.C.S.: 488510

Norfolkline B.V. **(1)**
Kranenburgweg 180, NL 2583 ER, Hague, Netherlands **(100%)**
Tel.: (31) 703527400
Web Site: http://www.norfolkline.com
Sales Range: $450-499.9 Million
Emp.: 1,500
Channel Ferry Services
N.A.I.C.S.: 483112

U.N. Ro-Ro Isletmeleri A.S. **(1)**
Salacak Iskele Arkasi.Sok Kiz Kulesi Villalari A-1 Villa No 15, Salacak Uskudar, 34660, Istanbul, Turkiye
Tel.: (90) 2163100506
Web Site: http://www.dfds.com.tr
Marine Cargo Transportation Services
N.A.I.C.S.: 483111
John L. Pfeffer (Chm)

UAB Krantas Travel **(1)**
Teatro g 5, 91247, Klaipeda, Lithuania
Tel.: (370) 846395111
Web Site: http://www.krantas.lt
Emp.: 27
Travel Tour Operator
N.A.I.C.S.: 561520

primeRail GmbH **(1)**
Sieglarer Strasse 6, 53840, Troisdorf, Germany
Tel.: (49) 22412674300
Web Site: https://www.primerail.eu
Freight Forwarding Services
N.A.I.C.S.: 488510

DFI INC.
10F No 97 Sec 1 Xintai 5th Rd, Xizhi Dist, New Taipei City, 22175, Taiwan
Tel.: (886) 226972986
Web Site: https://www.dfi.com
Year Founded: 1981
2397—(TAI)
Rev.: $300,342,446
Assets: $297,642,325
Liabilities: $134,691,221
Net Worth: $162,951,104
Earnings: $11,999,673
Emp.: 205
Fiscal Year-end: 12/31/23
Computer Motherboard & Embedded Board Mfr
N.A.I.C.S.: 334118
Peter Chen (Chm)

Subsidiaries:

DFI America, LLC **(1)**

960 Riverside Pkwy Ste 10, West Sacramento, CA 95605
Tel.: (916) 378-4166
Automation Machinery Mfr
N.A.I.C.S.: 333998

DFI Co.,LTD. **(1)**
542 1 Daman Ri Jinrye Myun, Kimhae, 621 881, Gyeongsangnam-do, Korea (South)
Tel.: (82) 553461882
Web Site: http://www.cybow.com
Sales Range: $25-49.9 Million
Emp.: 60
Medical Device Mfr & Distr
N.A.I.C.S.: 334510

Diamond Flower Information (NL) B.V. **(1)**
Klompenmakerstraat 89, Hoogvliet, 3194 DD, Rotterdam, Netherlands
Tel.: (31) 103134100
Sales Range: $50-74.9 Million
Emp.: 6
Computer Mother Boards Distr
N.A.I.C.S.: 423430

ITOX, LLC **(1)**
15 Corporate Pl S Ste 201, Piscataway, NJ 08854
Tel.: (732) 390-2815
Web Site: http://www.dfi-itox.com
Sales Range: $25-49.9 Million
Emp.: 10
Computer Peripheral Equipment Distr
N.A.I.C.S.: 423430
Nancie Frank (Mgr-Sls)

DFJ TAMIR FISHMAN VENTURES
Habarzel St 38, Tel Aviv, 69710, Israel
Tel.: (972) 3 6849333
Web Site:
http://www.tamirfishman.co.in
Sales Range: Less than $1 Million
Investment Management Service
N.A.I.C.S.: 523999
Shai Saul (Mng Gen Partner)

DFL HOLDINGS PTY LTD
Upper Ground Level Queen Adelaide Building, 90-112 Queen Street, Brisbane, 4000, QLD, Australia
Tel.: (61) 7 3229 2999
Holding Company
N.A.I.C.S.: 551112
Lina Wood (Founder)

Subsidiaries:

Premier Fasteners Pty Limited **(1)**
1 & 3 Ladbroke Street, Milperra, 2214, NSW, Australia
Tel.: (61) 297721888
Web Site:
http://www.Premierfasteners.com.au
Sales Range: $1-9.9 Million
Emp.: 25
Fasteners Mfr & Sales
N.A.I.C.S.: 339993
Ivan James Mikkelsen (Gen Mgr)

DFL INFRASTRUCTURE FINANCE LIMITED
No 14 Ramakrishna Street T Nagar, Chennai, 600 017, India
Tel.: (91) 4428141778
Web Site: http://www.dflfinance.com
Rev.: $46,230
Assets: $4,976,456
Liabilities: $21,396,413
Net Worth: ($16,419,957)
Earnings: ($1,765,606)
Fiscal Year-end: 03/31/16
Commercial Vehicle Finance Services
N.A.I.C.S.: 522291

DFM FOODS LIMITED
8377 Roshanara Road, Delhi, 110007, India
Tel.: (91) 1123826445
Web Site: http://www.dfmfoods.com
Year Founded: 1983

DFM Foods Limited—(Continued)

519588—(NSE)
Rev.: $72,478,770
Assets: $55,189,680
Liabilities: $30,883,125
Net Worth: $24,306,555
Earnings: $3,917,550
Emp.: 582
Fiscal Year-end: 03/31/21
Corn Chips Mfr & Whlsr
N.A.I.C.S.: 311919
Mohit Jain *(Chm & Mng Dir)*

DFNN, INC.
14/F PSE Tower L2-L5 5th Avenue
corner 28th Street, Bonifacio Global
City, Taguig, Philippines
Tel.: (63) 28183366
Web Site: https://www.dfnn.com
DFNN—(PHI)
Rev.: $17,717,608
Assets: $34,561,079
Liabilities: $31,565,025
Net Worth: $2,996,054
Earnings: ($2,914,122)
Emp.: 124
Fiscal Year-end: 12/31/23
Information Technology Services
N.A.I.C.S.: 541511
Antonio A. Lopa *(Co-Chm)*

Subsidiaries:

DCG, Inc. **(1)**
PO Box 550, Mount Pleasant, MI 48804-0550
Tel.: (989) 773-1201
Web Site: https://www.dcgtech.com
Software Development Services
N.A.I.C.S.: 513210

Inter-Active Entertainment Solutions
Technologies, Inc. **(1)**
14/F PSE Tower L2 - L5 5th Ave corner
28th Street, Bonifacio Global City, Taguig,
1634, Manila, Philippines
Tel.: (63) 288183366
Web Site: https://www.instawin.com.ph
Gaming Developer Services
N.A.I.C.S.: 513210

DFP HOLDINGS LIMITED
1/F No 22 Lane 50 Section 3 Nangang Road, Nangang District, Taipei,
115607, Taiwan
Tel.: (886) 287722001   **NV**
Year Founded: 2021
DFPH—(OTCIQ)
Rev.: $1,483,227
Assets: $2,282,249
Liabilities: $439,310
Net Worth: $1,842,939
Earnings: ($334,397)
Fiscal Year-end: 09/30/24
Holding Company
N.A.I.C.S.: 551112

DFR GOLD INC.
Suite 303 - 595 Howe Street, Box 4,
Vancouver, V6C 2T5, BC, Canada
Tel.: (604) 283-7185   **BC**
Web Site:
http://www.diamondfields.com
Year Founded: 1996
I13—(DEU)
Assets: $337,772
Liabilities: $2,397,175
Net Worth: ($2,059,403)
Earnings: ($4,214,394)
Fiscal Year-end: 12/31/23
Diamond Mining & Exploration
N.A.I.C.S.: 212319
Sybrand Van Der Spuy *(Pres & CEO)*

Subsidiaries:

Diamond Fields Namibia (Pty)
Ltd. **(1)**
76 Plato St, Academia, Namibia **(100%)**
Tel.: (264) 61372180

Sales Range: $50-74.9 Million
Diamond Mining
N.A.I.C.S.: 212319

DFS FURNITURE LTD.
1 Rockingham Way Redhouse Interchange Adwick Le Street, Doncaster,
DN6 7NA, United Kingdom
Tel.: (44) 1302330365
Web Site: http://www.dfs.co.uk
Year Founded: 1969
Sales Range: $100-124.9 Million
Emp.: 600
Upholstered Furniture Mfr & Retailer
N.A.I.C.S.: 337121
Paul Walker *(Grp Sec)*

Subsidiaries:

Coin Furniture Limited **(1)**
Renny Park Road, Newport Pagnell, MK16
9FB, Buckinghamshire, United Kingdom
Tel.: (44) 3456759090
Web Site: http://www.dwell.co.uk
Furniture Whlsr
N.A.I.C.S.: 423210
Vivienne Livingstone *(Mgr-Customer Care)*

DFV DEUTSCHE FAMILIEN-VERSICHERUNG AG
Reuterweg 47, 60323, Frankfurt am
Main, Germany
Tel.: (49) 699586969
Web Site: https://www.deutsche-familienversicherung.de
Year Founded: 2007
DFV—(DEU)
Rev.: $128,930,499
Assets: $327,575,005
Liabilities: $215,181,308
Net Worth: $112,393,697
Earnings: $4,486,294
Emp.: 172
Fiscal Year-end: 12/31/23
Health Insurance Services
N.A.I.C.S.: 524114

DG INNOVATE PLC
Unit 2 De Clare Court, Pontygwindy
Industrial Estate, Caerphilly, CF83
3HU, United Kingdom
Tel.: (44) 2920849009   **UK**
Web Site: https://www.dgiplc.com
Year Founded: 2000
DGI—(LSE)
Sales Range: Less than $1 Million
Emp.: 4
Investment Management Service
N.A.I.C.S.: 523940
Nicholas Tulloch *(Chm)*

DGA S.A.
Ul Towarowa 35, 61-896, Poznan,
Poland
Tel.: (48) 618595900
Web Site: https://www.dga.pl
Year Founded: 1990
DGA—(WAR)
Rev.: $2,491,870
Assets: $7,087,144
Liabilities: $2,736,026
Net Worth: $4,351,118
Earnings: $166,413
Fiscal Year-end: 12/31/23
Investment Management Service
N.A.I.C.S.: 523940
Andrzej Glowacki *(Chm-Mgmt Bd & Pres)*

DGB ASIA BERHAD
Lot 13 5 Level 13 Menara Lien Hoe
No 8 Persiaran Tropicana, Tropicana
Golf & Country Resort, 47410, Petaling Jaya, Selangor Darul Ehsan, Malaysia
Tel.: (60) 76226986   **MY**
Web Site: https://www.dgbasia.com
Year Founded: 1993

DGB—(KLS)
Rev.: $8,456,410
Assets: $64,311,534
Liabilities: $33,725,110
Net Worth: $30,586,423
Earnings: ($6,073,045)
Fiscal Year-end: 12/31/22
Engineeering Services
N.A.I.C.S.: 541330
Khai Shyuan Kua *(Exec Dir)*

Subsidiaries:

DSC Systems (M) Sdn. Bhd. **(1)**
Blk B-2-1 Ioi Boulevard Jalan Kenari 5 Bandar Puchong Jaya, 47170, Puchong, Selangor, Malaysia
Tel.: (60) 380790133
Scanning Equipment Whslr
N.A.I.C.S.: 423430

Digital Scanning Corporation Pte
Ltd **(1)**
11 Sims Drive 03-04A Scn Centre, Singapore, Singapore
Tel.: (65) 6665 7500
Software Development Services
N.A.I.C.S.: 541511

DGB FINANCIAL GROUP CO., LTD.
9th floor Daegu Bank Second Main
Branch 111 Oksanro, Buk-gu, Daegu,
Korea (South)
Tel.: (82) 537407900   **KS**
Web Site: https://www.dgbfg.co.kr
Year Founded: 2011
139130—(KRS)
Rev.: $2,989,335,233
Assets: $69,296,040,687
Liabilities: $64,632,090,063
Net Worth: $4,663,950,624
Earnings: $287,872,074
Emp.: 143
Fiscal Year-end: 12/31/23
Bank Holding Company
N.A.I.C.S.: 551111
Kim Tae-oh *(CEO)*

Subsidiaries:

DGB Asset Management Co.,
Ltd. **(1)**
14F Kyobo Securities Building 97 Uisadang-daero, Yeongdeungpo-gu, Seoul, Korea
(South)
Tel.: (82) 27074200
Web Site: http://www.dgbam.com
Investment Services
N.A.I.C.S.: 523940
Park Jung-Hong *(CEO)*

DGB Capital Ltd. **(1)**
18FL 39 Eonju-ro 30-gil, Gangnam-gu,
Seoul, Korea (South)
Tel.: (82) 2 2193 7700
Web Site: http://www.dgbfncapital.co.kr
Financial Management Services
N.A.I.C.S.: 523999
Park Chang-ho *(CEO)*

DGB Credit Information Co., Ltd. **(1)**
183 Dalseo-ro Bisan-dong, Seo-gu, Daegu,
Korea (South)
Tel.: (82) 535737700
Claim Collection Services
N.A.I.C.S.: 561440
Hyo-Taek Lim *(CEO)*

Daegu Credit Information Co.
Ltd. **(1)**
527-4 Bisan-dong Seo-gu, 703-040, Daegu,
Korea (South)
Tel.: (82) 535737700
Web Site: http://www.daegucredit.co.kr
Commericial Banking
N.A.I.C.S.: 522110

Hi Investment & Securities Co.,
Ltd. **(1)**
25-15 Yeouido-dong, Yeongdeungpo-gu,
Seoul, Korea (South)
Tel.: (82) 261113200
Web Site: http://www.hi-ib.com
Financial Investment Services
N.A.I.C.S.: 523999

Kim Kyung Kyu *(CEO)*

Korea Lease Financing Co., Ltd. **(1)**
15th Fl Seorin Bldg 88 Seorin-dong,
Jongno-gu, Seoul, Korea (South)
Tel.: (82) 23984114
Financial Lending Services
N.A.I.C.S.: 522220

Korea Non-Bank Lease Financing
Co. Ltd **(1)**
Seolin Bldg 15th Floor, Seolin-dong 88
Jongro-gu, Seoul, Korea (South)
Tel.: (82) 23984113
Financial Investment Activities
N.A.I.C.S.: 523999

The Daegu Bank, Ltd. **(1)**
2310 Dalgubeol-daero Suseong-gu, Daegu,
706-712, Korea (South)
Tel.: (82) 53 740 7900
Web Site: http://www.dgb.co.kr
Sales Range: $1-4.9 Billion
Emp.: 2,793
Banking Services
N.A.I.C.S.: 522110

U-Payment Ltd. **(1)**
2503 Dalgubeol-daero, Suseong-gu, Daegu,
Korea (South)
Tel.: (82) 80 427 2342
Software Development Services
N.A.I.C.S.: 541511
Lee Chun-ki *(CEO)*

DGB GROUP N.V.
Siriusdreef 60, 2132 WT, Hoofddorp,
Netherlands
Tel.: (31) 108080126
DGB—(EUR)
Sales Range: Less than $1 Million
Holding Company
N.A.I.C.S.: 551112
Selwyn A. M. Duijvestijn *(CEO & Member-Exec Bd)*

DGENX CO., LTD.
No 38 Gongdan 1-daero 27 Beon-gil,
Siheung, Gyeonggi-do, Korea (South)
Tel.: (82) 315055200
Web Site: https://www.dgenx.com
Year Founded: 2006
113810—(KRS)
Rev.: $49,818,120
Assets: $42,585,972
Liabilities: $30,091,794
Net Worth: $12,494,178
Earnings: ($1,610,764)
Emp.: 147
Fiscal Year-end: 12/31/22
Automobile Exhaust Systems Mfr
N.A.I.C.S.: 336390
Seok Woo Lee *(CEO)*

Subsidiaries:

Dgenx Co., Ltd. - Gunsan Plant **(1)**
43-20 Gobong-ri Sungsan-myun, Jeonbuk,
Gunsan, Korea (South)
Tel.: (82) 63 453 3001
Web Site: http://www.dgenx.com
Automobile Parts Mfr
N.A.I.C.S.: 336390

DGL GROUP LIMITED
Level 4 91 William Street, Melbourne,
2150, NSW, Australia
Tel.: (61) 6493099254
Web Site: https://www.dglgroup.com
Year Founded: 1999
DGL—(ASX)
Rev.: $311,254,673
Assets: $404,573,316
Liabilities: $176,068,375
Net Worth: $228,504,940
Earnings: $9,567,308
Emp.: 800
Fiscal Year-end: 06/30/24
Specialty Chemical Formulation &
Manufacturing, Warehousing & Distribution, Waste Management & Environmental Solutions
N.A.I.C.S.: 325199

Ben Halsey *(CFO)*

DGP CO.,LTD.
23 Greentech-ro, Yeonggwang-eup, Seoul, Jeollanam-do, Korea (South)
Tel.: (82) 25625310
Web Site:
   https://www.daehangreenpower.com
Year Founded: 1997
060900—(KRS)
Rev.: $25,722,541
Assets: $54,127,664
Liabilities: $28,935,632
Net Worth: $25,192,032
Earnings: ($13,632,541)
Emp.: 55
Fiscal Year-end: 12/31/22
Biofuel Product Mfr & Distr
N.A.I.C.S.: 324199
Oh Kyung-won *(CEO)*

DGR GLOBAL LIMITED
9C London Offices 30 Florence St, Brisbane, 4005, QLD, Australia
Tel.: (61) 733030680   **AU**
Web Site:
   https://www.dgrglobal.com.au
DGR—(ASX)
Rev.: $655,702
Assets: $31,600,533
Liabilities: $11,496,165
Net Worth: $20,104,368
Earnings: ($33,675,743)
Emp.: 50
Fiscal Year-end: 06/30/24
Mineral Exploration Services
N.A.I.C.S.: 212220
Nicholas Mather *(Founder & Mng Dir)*

Subsidiaries:

Clara Resources Australia Ltd   **(1)**
              (53.4%)
Tel.: (61) 733038703
Web Site:
   https://www.clararesources.com.au
Rev.: $13,026
Assets: $6,517,084
Liabilities: $1,439,863
Net Worth: $5,077,221
Earnings: ($3,540,382)
Fiscal Year-end: 06/30/2024
Nickel Mining Services
N.A.I.C.S.: 212230
Peter Williams *(CEO)*

Eastern Exploration Pty Ltd   **(1)**
14 Harris Place, Kalgoorlie, 6430, WA, Australia
Tel.: (61) 890913730
Gold Exploration Services
N.A.I.C.S.: 212220

DGS DRUCKGUSS SYSTEME AG
Industriestrasse 10, Saint Gallen, 9015, Switzerland
Tel.: (41) 713138888
Web Site: http://www.dgs-druckguss.com
Sales Range: $125-149.9 Million
Emp.: 500
Industry Castings (Ferrous Metals)
N.A.I.C.S.: 331511
Andreas Muller *(CEO)*

Subsidiaries:

DGS (China) Co Ltd.   **(1)**
Plot 1-17 Zhujiang Industrial Park, Nansha District, Guangzhou, 511462, Guangdong, China
Tel.: (86) 208 4982488
Web Site: http://www.dgs-druckguss.com
Emp.: 250
Die Cast Distr
N.A.I.C.S.: 331511
Tobias Song *(Gen Mgr)*

DGS Druckguss Systeme s.r.o   **(1)**
Volgogradska 89, 460 10, Liberec, Czech Republic

Tel.: (420) 482429710
Sales Range: $100-124.9 Million
Emp.: 300
Steel Foundry
N.A.I.C.S.: 331513

DGTL HOLDINGS INC.
510-580 Hornby Street, Vancouver, V6C 3B6, BC, Canada
Web Site: https://www.dgtlinc.com
Year Founded: 2018
DGTHD—(OTCIQ)
Rev.: $3,110,966
Assets: $4,828,467
Liabilities: $2,401,220
Net Worth: $2,427,247
Earnings: ($5,266,566)
Fiscal Year-end: 05/31/21
Software Development Services
N.A.I.C.S.: 541511
Michael Racic *(Pres, CEO & Sec)*

Subsidiaries:

Engagement Labs Inc.   **(1)**
200 Front Street West Suite 2300, Toronto, M5V 3K2, ON, Canada
Tel.: (514) 317-6448
Web Site: http://www.engagementlabs.com
Rev.: $3,124,855
Assets: $3,901,283
Liabilities: $1,131,694
Net Worth: $2,769,590
Earnings: ($4,048,186)
Emp.: 23
Fiscal Year-end: 12/31/2019
Software Development Services
N.A.I.C.S.: 541511
Gilbert Boyer *(CFO)*

Subsidiary (Domestic):

Edu-Performance Canada Inc.   **(2)**
3185 Montee St-Hubert Ste 201, Saint-Hubert, J3Y 4J4, QC, Canada
Tel.: (450) 466-7275
Web Site: http://www.eduperformance.com
Educational Support Services
N.A.I.C.S.: 611710
Andre Goli *(CEO)*

Subsidiary (Non-US):

EDU-PERFORMANCE MEXICO   **(3)**
San Francisco 715, Mexico, Mexico
Tel.: (52) 55 5687 8811
Educational Support Services
N.A.I.C.S.: 611710

Edu-Performance Europe   **(3)**
28 Rue du chemin vert, 75011, Paris, France
Tel.: (33) 7 81 49 08 03
Educational Support Services
N.A.I.C.S.: 611710

Subsidiary (US):

Keller Fay Group   **(2)**
65 Church St, New Brunswick, NJ 08901
Tel.: (732) 846-6800
Web Site: http://www.kellerfay.com
Emp.: 5
Administrative Management & General Management Consulting Service
N.A.I.C.S.: 541611
Edward B. Keller *(CEO)*

Subsidiary (Domestic):

M Thirty Communications Inc.   **(2)**
103 Richmond St E Ste 400, Toronto, M5C 1N9, ON, Canada
Tel.: (416) 204-0082
Web Site: http://www.mthirty.com
Media Production Services
N.A.I.C.S.: 512120
Ed King *(Co-Founder)*

DH HOLDINGS CO., LTD.
Donghee Bldg 705-32 Yeoksam-dong, Gangnam-gu, Seoul, Korea (South)
Tel.: (82) 2 2016 2000   **KR**
Web Site: http://www.donghee.co.kr
Year Founded: 1972

Holding Company; Motor Vehicle Suspension, Fuel Tank, Pedal, Roof System & Body Mfr
N.A.I.C.S.: 551112
Dong-ho Lee *(CEO)*

Subsidiaries:

DONGHEE Czech s.r.o.   **(1)**
Prumyslova 2060, 737 01, Cesky Tesin, Czech Republic
Tel.: (420) 552 530 111
Web Site: http://www.donghee.cz
Motor Vehicle Parts Mfr
N.A.I.C.S.: 336110
Daniel Kula *(Mgr-Production)*

DONGHEE RUS LLC   **(1)**
Gorskoye highway 165 build 1 lit A, Levashovo, Saint Petersburg, 194361, Russia
Tel.: (82) 7070936328
Motor Vehicle Parts Mfr
N.A.I.C.S.: 336211

DONGHEE Slovakia s.r.o.   **(1)**
SNP 768/150, 013 24, Strecno, Slovakia
Tel.: (421) 41 507 9600
Web Site: http://www.donghee.sk
Motor Vehicle Parts Mfr
N.A.I.C.S.: 336211

Webasto Donghee Co., Ltd.   **(1)**
13-21 Sujan Ri Sinchang Myung, Chung-Nam, 336 884, Asan, Korea (South)
Tel.: (82) 415385200
Web Site: http://www.webasto.com
Motor Vehicle Sunroof Mfr
N.A.I.C.S.: 336390

DH PRIVATE EQUITY PARTNERS LLP
45 Pall Mall, London, SW1Y 5JG, United Kingdom
Tel.: (44) 2076639300   **UK**
Web Site:
   http://www.doughtyhanson.com
Year Founded: 1985
Sales Range: $1-4.9 Billion
Private Equity Firm
N.A.I.C.S.: 523999
Richard P. Hanson *(CEO & Head-Private Equity)*

Subsidiaries:

Harman Technology, Ltd.   **(1)**
Town Lane, Mobberley, Knutsford, WA16 7JL, Cheshire, United Kingdom   **(100%)**
Tel.: (44) 156550000
Web Site: http://www.ilford.com
Sales Range: $150-199.9 Million
Mfr of Copying Machines
N.A.I.C.S.: 423420

DHABRIYA POLYWOOD LIMITED
B-9D 1 Malviya Industrial Area, Jaipur, 302017, Rajasthan, India
Tel.: (91) 1414057171
Web Site: https://www.polywood.org
Year Founded: 1992
538715—(BOM)
Rev.: $14,600,363
Assets: $16,029,755
Liabilities: $8,514,391
Net Worth: $7,515,364
Earnings: $610,529
Emp.: 312
Fiscal Year-end: 03/31/21
PVC Products Mfr
N.A.I.C.S.: 326199
Digvijay Dhabriya *(Founder, Chm & Mng Dir)*

Subsidiaries:

Dynasty Modular Furnitures Private Limited   **(1)**
F-13 Malviya Industrial Area, Jaipur, 302017, Rajasthan, India
Tel.: (91) 9929600056
Web Site:
   https://www.dynastyfurnitures.com
Modular Kitchen Product Mfr

N.A.I.C.S.: 337110

Polywood Profiles Private Limited   **(1)**
SF No 51/1 Siruvani Main Road, Theetipalayam Village, Coimbatore, 641010, India
Tel.: (91) 4222607006
Polywood Mfr
N.A.I.C.S.: 332321

DHAKA BANK PLC
71 Purana Paltan Lane, Dhaka, Bangladesh
Tel.: (880) 258314424
Web Site:
   https://www.dhakabankltd.com
DHAKABANK—(CHT)
Rev.: $124,451,876
Assets: $3,171,513,875
Liabilities: $2,975,308,443
Net Worth: $196,205,431
Earnings: $15,259,906
Emp.: 2,070
Fiscal Year-end: 12/31/22
Banking Services
N.A.I.C.S.: 523150
Abdullah Al Ahsan *(Vice Chm)*

Subsidiaries:

Dhaka Bank Securities Limited   **(1)**
115-120 Adamjee Court 1st Floor Motijheel C/A, Dhaka, 1000, Bangladesh
Tel.: (880) 47115063
Web Site: https://dhakabanksecurities.com
Financial Investment Services
N.A.I.C.S.: 523999
Reshadur Rahman *(Chm)*

DHAKA ELECTRIC SUPPLY COMPANY LIMITED
22/B Faruque Sarani Nikunja-2, Dhaka, 1229, Bangladesh
Tel.: (880) 290011011
Web Site: https://desco.gov.bd
DESCO—(CHT)
Rev.: $38,990,710
Assets: $795,438,281
Liabilities: $759,461,446
Net Worth: $35,976,835
Earnings: ($50,105,581)
Emp.: 1,931
Fiscal Year-end: 06/30/23
Electric Power Distribution Services
N.A.I.C.S.: 221122
A. K. M. Mostafa Kamal *(Exec Dir-Procurement)*

DHAKA INSURANCE LIMITED
Dhaka Insurance Bhaban 71Purana Paltan Line, Dhaka, 1000, Bangladesh
Tel.: (880) 58316146
Web Site:
   https://www.dhakainsurancebd.com
Year Founded: 2000
DHAKAINS—(CHT)
Rev.: $1,773,523
Assets: $23,280,073
Liabilities: $10,592,213
Net Worth: $12,687,860
Earnings: $1,508,496
Emp.: 264
Fiscal Year-end: 12/31/23
Insurance Services
N.A.I.C.S.: 524298
Fazlur Rahman *(Founder & Co-Chm)*

DHAKA STOCK EXCHANGE LTD.
Stock Exchange Building 9 F Motijheel C A, Dhaka, 1000, Bangladesh
Tel.: (880) 029564601
Web Site: http://www.dsebd.org
Sales Range: $1-4.9 Billion
Emp.: 300
Stock Exchange Services
N.A.I.C.S.: 523210

Shaikh Mohammadullah (Sec & Gen Mgr)

DHAMECHA GROUP, INC.
First Way, Wembley, HA9 0TU, United Kingdom
Tel.: (44) 20 8903 8181
Web Site: http://www.dhamecha.com
Year Founded: 1976
Sales Range: $800-899.9 Million
Emp.: 432
Grocery Store Operator
N.A.I.C.S.: 445110
Rupen Dhamecha (Owner)

DHAMPUR BIO ORGANICS LIMITED
Second Floor Plot No 201 Okhla Industrial Estate Phase-III, New Delhi, 110020, India
Tel.: (91) 1169055200
Web Site: https://www.dhampur.com
Year Founded: 2020
DBOL—(NSE)
Rev.: $211,382,535
Assets: $273,073,710
Liabilities: $153,301,785
Net Worth: $119,771,925
Earnings: $13,907,985
Emp.: 1,655
Fiscal Year-end: 03/31/22
Refined Sugar Mfr
N.A.I.C.S.: 311314

DHAMPUR SUGAR MILLS LIMITED
6th Floor Max House Okhla Industrial Estate Phase -III, New Delhi, 110020, India
Tel.: (91) 1141259400
Web Site: https://www.dhampur.com
Year Founded: 1933
DHAMPURSUG—(NSE)
Rev.: $579,984,405
Assets: $473,765,565
Liabilities: $260,817,375
Net Worth: $212,948,190
Earnings: $31,254,405
Emp.: 2,806
Fiscal Year-end: 03/31/21
Sugar Mfr
N.A.I.C.S.: 311314
V. K. Goel (Chm)

DHAMPURE SPECIALTY SUGARS LTD
24 School Lane Opp WTC, New Delhi, 110 001, India
Tel.: (91) 1123711223
Web Site:
https://www.dhampurgreen.com
531923—(BOM)
Rev.: $2,428,578
Assets: $5,019,048
Liabilities: $1,720,424
Net Worth: $3,298,624
Earnings: $221,813
Emp.: 36
Fiscal Year-end: 03/31/21
Sugar Mfr
N.A.I.C.S.: 311313

DHANADA CORPORATION LIMITED
Dhanada Flat No D/2 Jaiprakash Apartment Near Garve Hyundai, Vadgaon BK, Pune, Maharashtra, India
Tel.: (91) 9822037104
Web Site:
https://www.dhanadacorp.com
Year Founded: 1986
531198—(BOM)
Rev.: $411,691
Assets: $5,142,602

Liabilities: $4,453,238
Net Worth: $689,364
Earnings: ($806,811)
Emp.: 42
Fiscal Year-end: 03/31/21
Home Management Services
N.A.I.C.S.: 721110
Ramesh R. Havele (Chm & Mng Dir)

Subsidiaries:

Dhanada Education Pvt. Ltd.   (1)
Dhanada House Near Mhatre Bridge Opp Gharkul Lawns, Maharshi Karvenagar, Pune, 411 052, India
Tel.: (91) 20 65209990
Web Site: http://www.dhanadaedu.com
Educational Support Services
N.A.I.C.S.: 611710
Ramesh Havele (Founder & Chm)

Dhanada Engineering Pvt. Ltd.   (1)
J 276 MIDC Bhosari, Pune, 411 026, India
Tel.: (91) 20 4123 2206
Web Site: http://www.dhanadaengg.com
Sheet Metal Mfr
N.A.I.C.S.: 332322
Amey Kale (Engr-Product Dev)

DHANALAXMI ROTO SPINNERS LTD.
The Laxmi 82686B6DK 82686BMK 4th Floor, Road No 12 Banjara Hills Near Indian Bank, Hyderabad, 500034, Telangana, India
Tel.: (91) 8374310011
Web Site: https://www.dhanroto.com
521216—(BOM)
Rev.: $10,408,707
Assets: $5,280,527
Liabilities: $2,172,188
Net Worth: $3,108,339
Earnings: $553,095
Emp.: 5
Fiscal Year-end: 03/31/21
Wood Pulp Mfr
N.A.I.C.S.: 321920
Rajkumar Inani (Mng Dir)

DHANASHREE ELECTRONICS LIMITED
Rashmi Building Salt Lake Electronic Complex Block Ep Plot No Xi, Sector-V, Kolkata, 700091, India
Tel.: (91) 3340224022
Web Site:
https://www.rashmilighting.com
Year Founded: 1989
542679—(BOM)
Rev.: $5,804,445
Assets: $12,029,505
Liabilities: $7,952,297
Net Worth: $4,077,208
Earnings: $227,545
Fiscal Year-end: 03/31/21
Electric Bulb & Part Mfr
N.A.I.C.S.: 335139
Mandan Gopal Maheshwari (Chm)

DHANI SERVICES LTD.
5th Floor Plot No 108 IT ParkUdyog Vihar Phase 1 Industrial Complex, Dundahera, Gurgaon, 122016, Haryana, India
Tel.: (91) 1246555555
Web Site: https://www.dhani.com
Year Founded: 1995
532960—(BOM)
Rev.: $186,111,881
Assets: $1,382,603,531
Liabilities: $616,503,165
Net Worth: $766,100,367
Earnings: ($31,363,469)
Emp.: 11
Fiscal Year-end: 03/31/21
Customer Lending Services
N.A.I.C.S.: 522291
Sameer Gehlaut (Founder, Chm & CEO)

Subsidiaries:

Dhani Healthcare Limited   (1)
3rd Floor Office No 301-a Vedanta Building CTS No 779 Makwana Road, Andheri East, Mumbai, 400059, Maharashtra, India
Tel.: (91) 794 255 5205
Web Site: https://www.dhanihealthcare.com
Pharmaceutical Products Distr
N.A.I.C.S.: 424210
Ruchi Gupta (CEO)

Dhani Loans & Services Limited   (1)
M-62 and 63 First Floor Connaught Place, New Delhi, 110001, India
Tel.: (91) 113 025 2900
Web Site:
  https://www.dhaniloansandservices.com
Financial Services
N.A.I.C.S.: 522310
Pinank Jayant Shah (CEO)

DHANLAXMI BANK LTD.
Dhanalakshmi Buildings Naickanal, Thrissur, 680 001, Kerala, India
Tel.: (91) 4872999711
Web Site: https://www.dhanbank.com
Year Founded: 1927
532180—(BOM)
Rev.: $146,358,808
Assets: $1,787,673,165
Liabilities: $1,669,723,706
Net Worth: $117,949,459
Earnings: $5,076,176
Emp.: 1,656
Fiscal Year-end: 03/31/21
Commercial Banking Services
N.A.I.C.S.: 522110
Sajeev Krishnan (Chm)

DHANLAXMI COTEX LTD.
285 Princess Street CJ House 1st Fl, Mumbai, 400002, Maharashtra, India
Tel.: (91) 2249764268
Web Site: https://www.dcl.net.in
Year Founded: 1987
512485—(BOM)
Rev.: $3,035,549
Assets: $6,009,652
Liabilities: $89,575
Net Worth: $5,920,077
Earnings: $28,404
Emp.: 14
Fiscal Year-end: 03/31/23
Financial Investment Services
N.A.I.C.S.: 523999
Mahesh Sohanlal Jhawar (Chm)

DHANLAXMI FABRICS LTD.
Manpada Road, Dombivli E, Thane, 421 204, Maharashtra, India
Tel.: (91) 2512870589
Web Site: https://www.dfl.net.in
Year Founded: 1994
521151—(BOM)
Rev.: $6,494,397
Assets: $9,720,670
Liabilities: $2,389,378
Net Worth: $7,331,292
Earnings: $102,935
Emp.: 83
Fiscal Year-end: 03/31/21
Textile Fabric Mfr & Distr
N.A.I.C.S.: 313310
Vinod Sohanlal Jhawar (Chm & Mng Dir)

DHANLEELA INVESTMENTS & TRADING COMPANY LIMITED
13 N G Park Building No 02 Rawalpada, Dahisar East, Mumbai, 400068, Maharashtra, India
Tel.: (91) 9029222523
Web Site:
  http://www.dhanleelainvest.com
Year Founded: 1980
Rev.: $37,671
Assets: $3,537,348
Liabilities: $1,408,289

Net Worth: $2,129,059
Earnings: $4,372
Fiscal Year-end: 03/31/18
Investment Management Service
N.A.I.C.S.: 523999
Vipul Dangi (Chm & Mng Dir)

DHANUKA AGRITECH LIMITED
Global Gateway Towers Near Guru Dronacharya Metro Station MG Road, Gurgaon, 122002, Haryana, India
Tel.: (91) 1244345000
Web Site: https://www.dhanuka.com
507717—(DOM)
Rev.: $193,989,896
Assets: $154,384,913
Liabilities: $45,705,018
Net Worth: $108,679,894
Earnings: $28,741,413
Emp.: 941
Fiscal Year-end: 03/31/21
Agro-Chemicals, Fertilizers & Seeds
N.A.I.C.S.: 325320
Ram Gopal Agarwal (Chm)

DHANUKA REALTY LTD.
5th Floor Solitaire Building Plot C-212 and 213 Gautam Marg, Vaishali Nagar Hanuman Nagar, Jaipur, 302020, India
Tel.: (91) 1414014792
Web Site:
  https://www.dhanukarealty.in
Year Founded: 2008
DRL—(NSE)
Rev.: $445,538
Assets: $2,656,995
Liabilities: $1,701,022
Net Worth: $955,974
Earnings: ($100,164)
Emp.: 5
Fiscal Year-end: 03/31/23
Real Estate Development Services
N.A.I.C.S.: 531390
Girish Chandra Dhanuka (Chm)

DHANVANTRI JEEVAN REKHA LTD.
No 1 Saket, Meerut, 250001, Uttar Pradesh, India
Tel.: (91) 1212648151
Web Site: https://www.djrl.org.in
Year Founded: 1993
531043—(BOM)
Rev.: $1,360,533
Assets: $1,748,231
Liabilities: $514,943
Net Worth: $1,233,288
Earnings: ($194,286)
Fiscal Year-end: 03/31/21
Health Care Srvices
N.A.I.C.S.: 621610
Varinder Singh Phull (Mng Dir)

DHANVARSHA FINVEST LIMITED
2nd Floor Building No 4 D J House, Old Nagardas Road Andheri East, Mumbai, 400069, Maharashtra, India
Tel.: (91) 9222244349
Web Site: https://trucapfinance.com
Year Founded: 1994
540268—(BOM)
Rev.: $4,103,750
Assets: $25,455,612
Liabilities: $11,817,392
Net Worth: $13,638,220
Earnings: $177,587
Emp.: 97
Fiscal Year-end: 03/31/21
Financial Lending Services
N.A.I.C.S.: 522310
Nimir Kishore Mehta (Chm)

DHARANI FINANCE LIMITED
PGP House 59 Sterling Road, Nun-

gambakkam, Chennai, 600 034, India
Tel.: (91) 4428311313
Web Site: https://dharanifinance.com
Year Founded: 1990
511451—(BOM)
Rev.: $75,648
Assets: $1,233,250
Liabilities: $157,207
Net Worth: $1,076,043
Earnings: $1,379
Emp.: 2
Fiscal Year-end: 03/31/21
Financial Management Services
N.A.I.C.S.: 523999
N. Sivabalan *(CFO)*

DHARANI SUGARS & CHEMICALS LIMITED

PGP House New No 59 Sterling Road, Nungambakkam, Chennai, 600 034, India
Tel.: (91) 4428311313
Web Site:
https://www.dharanisugars.in
Year Founded: 1987
507442—(BOM)
Rev.: $5,038,911
Assets: $77,481,113
Liabilities: $94,775,786
Net Worth: ($17,294,673)
Earnings: ($5,192,214)
Emp.: 777
Fiscal Year-end: 03/31/21
Sugar Mfr
N.A.I.C.S.: 311314
Palani G. Periasamy *(Chm)*

Subsidiaries:

DHARANI SUGARS & CHEMICALS
LIMITED - Unit - I   (1)
Dharani Nagar, Vasudevanallur, Tirunelveli, 627 760, India
Tel.: (91) 4636 241370
Cane Sugar Mfr
N.A.I.C.S.: 311314
Rama Lingam *(Mng Dir)*

DHARANI SUGARS & CHEMICALS
LIMITED - Unit - II   (1)
Karaipoondi Village Chethpet Road, Polur, 606 803, India
Tel.: (91) 4181 223161
Cane Sugar Mfr
N.A.I.C.S.: 311314

DHARANI SUGARS & CHEMICALS
LIMITED - Unit - III   (1)
Kalayanallur Village Pallagacherry Post, Sankarapuram, 606 206, India
Tel.: (91) 9363228200
Cane Sugar Mfr
N.A.I.C.S.: 311314

DHARMAJ CROP GUARD LIMITED

Office No 901 to 903 & 911 B-square 2 Iscon Ambli Road, Ahmedabad, 380058, Gujarat, India
Tel.: (91) 7929603735
Web Site:
https://www.dharmajcrop.com
Year Founded: 2015
543687—(BOM)
Rev.: $54,093,312
Assets: $29,967,893
Liabilities: $18,376,586
Net Worth: $11,591,307
Earnings: $1,343,297
Fiscal Year-end: 03/31/22
Chemical Product Mfr & Distr
N.A.I.C.S.: 325199

DHARNI CAPITAL SERVICES LIMITED

226 Brigade Metropolis Arcade Whitefield Main Road, Garudacharpalya, Bengaluru, 560048, Karnataka, India
Tel.: (91) 9945164270   In

Web Site:
https://www.dharnicapital.com
543753—(BOM)
Rev.: $2,005,731
Assets: $334,753
Liabilities: $25,253
Net Worth: $309,500
Earnings: $131,832
Fiscal Year-end: 03/31/22
Investment Management Service
N.A.I.C.S.: 523999
Hemant Dharnidharka *(Mng Dir)*

DHATRE UDYOG LIMITED

ERGO Tower Plot No Al-4 Block EP & GP Unit No 1406 14th Floor Sector, Kolkata, 700091, West Bengal, India
Tel.: (91) 8100719986
Web Site: https://dhatre.com
540080—(BOM)
Rev.: $13,195,264
Assets: $7,603,801
Liabilities: $285,019
Net Worth: $7,318,782
Earnings: $801,259
Emp.: 8
Fiscal Year-end: 03/31/23
Steel Product Mfr & Distr
N.A.I.C.S.: 331221

DHAUTOWARE CO LTD

5F Sj Techno Ville 278 beotkkot-ro, Geumcheon-gu, Seoul, 08511, Korea (South)
Tel.: (82) 221023000
Web Site: https://dhautoware.co.kr
Year Founded: 1979
025440—(KRS)
Rev.: $292,848,265
Assets: $111,176,292
Liabilities: $63,565,633
Net Worth: $47,610,658
Earnings: ($3,450,728)
Emp.: 405
Fiscal Year-end: 12/31/22
Electronic Products Mfr
N.A.I.C.S.: 334419
Won-Gi Yang *(CEO)*

DHC SOFTWARE CO., LTD.

1501 15F Building No 3 Zijin Digital Park, Haidian District, Beijing, 100190, China
Tel.: (86) 1062662218
Web Site: http://www.dhcc.com.cn
Year Founded: 2002
002065—(SSE)
Rev.: $1,661,399,532
Assets: $3,120,533,208
Liabilities: $1,509,153,984
Net Worth: $1,611,379,224
Earnings: $56,283,552
Fiscal Year-end: 12/31/22
Software Development Services
N.A.I.C.S.: 513210
Xiangdong Xue *(Chm)*

DHENU BUILDCON INFRA LIMITED

Office No 4 Building No 4 Vahatuk Nagar Amboli, Andheri West, Mumbai, 400 058, Maharashtra, India
Tel.: (91) 2222072311   In
Web Site:
https://www.dhenubuildconinfra.com
Year Founded: 1909
501945—(BOM)
Rev.: $74,829
Assets: $470,865
Liabilities: $6,289
Net Worth: $464,577
Earnings: ($134,867)
Emp.: 2
Fiscal Year-end: 03/31/21
Investment Management Service
N.A.I.C.S.: 523150

Shivhari Jalan *(Sec)*

DHH SPA

Via Caldera 21, Green Building ala 2, 20153, Milan, Italy
Tel.: (39) 0287365100
Web Site:
https://www.dhh.international
Year Founded: 2015
DHH—(ITA)
Rev.: $31,911,687
Assets: $57,692,445
Liabilities: $31,656,329
Net Worth: $26,036,117
Earnings: $935,928
Emp.: 180
Fiscal Year-end: 12/31/22
Software Development Services
N.A.I.C.S.: 541511
Matija Jekovec *(COO)*

Subsidiaries:

Connesi S.p.a.   (1)
Viale IV Novembre 12, 06034, Foligno, pg, Italy
Tel.: (39) 0742514000
Web Site: https://www.connesi.it
Emp.: 35
Wireless Telecommunication Services
N.A.I.C.S.: 517111

Evolink Ad   (1)
16V Barzaritsa Str, Ovcha Kupel, 1618, Sofia, Bulgaria
Tel.: (359) 29691555
Web Site: https://www.evolink.com
Information Technology Services
N.A.I.C.S.: 541511

System Bee d.o.o.   (1)
Marianijeva 11, 52100, Pula, Croatia
Tel.: (385) 52492060
Web Site: https://www.sysbee.net
Web Hosting Services
N.A.I.C.S.: 518210

WEBTASY d.o.o.   (1)
Under the hill 55, 1000, Ljubljana, Slovenia
Tel.: (386) 17777877
Web Site: https://www.webtasy.com
Web Hosting Services
N.A.I.C.S.: 518210

mCloud d.o.o.   (1)
Kralja Milutina 55, Novi Beograd, Serbia
Tel.: (381) 114118855
Web Site: https://www.mcloud.rs
Information Technology Services
N.A.I.C.S.: 541511

DHOFAR BEVERAGE AND FOOD STUFF COMPANY S.A.O.G

Al Rubat Street, PO Box 390, Saada, 211, Salalah, 211, Oman
Tel.: (968) 23225705
Web Site:
https://www.dhofarbeverages.com
Year Founded: 1978
DBCI—(MUS)
Rev.: $10,765,883
Assets: $14,213,545
Liabilities: $4,661,243
Net Worth: $9,552,302
Earnings: ($397,458)
Emp.: 193
Fiscal Year-end: 12/31/19
Soft Drink & Beverage Mfr
N.A.I.C.S.: 312111
Mohammed Aufait Abdullah Al Shanfari *(Chm)*

DHOFAR CATTLE FEED COMPANY SAOG

Feed Mill Division Raysut, PO Box 298, 211, Salalah, 211, Oman
Tel.: (968) 23219074
Web Site:
https://www.dhofarcattlefeed.com
Year Founded: 1983

DFIN—(MUS)
Rev.: $147,307,722
Assets: $237,380,191
Liabilities: $129,364,399
Net Worth: $108,015,792
Earnings: ($1,070,158)
Emp.: 701
Fiscal Year-end: 12/31/23
Cattle Feed Mfr
N.A.I.C.S.: 311119
Salim Ahmed Sabah Al Kathiri *(Gen Mgr-Operation)*

DHOFAR FISHERIES & FOOD INDUSTRIES COMPANY S.A.O.G.

Raysut Industrial Area, 211, Salalah, Oman
Tel.: (968) 23219140
Web Site:
https://www.dhofarfisheries.com
Year Founded: 2001
DFII—(MUS)
Rev.: $22,661,958
Assets: $41,514,699
Liabilities: $47,796,412
Net Worth: ($6,281,713)
Earnings: ($3,175,088)
Emp.: 100
Fiscal Year-end: 12/31/20
Fish Product Distr
N.A.I.C.S.: 424460
Hamid Ali Al-Nahdi *(Gen Mgr)*

DHOFAR INSURANCE COMPANY S.A.O.G

PO Box 1002, 112, Ruwi, Oman
Tel.: (968) 24705305   OM
Web Site:
https://www.dhofarinsurance.com
Year Founded: 1989
DICS—(MUS)
Rev.: $139,605,578
Assets: $350,787,597
Liabilities: $280,681,504
Net Worth: $70,106,093
Earnings: $6,619,583
Emp.: 377
Fiscal Year-end: 12/31/21
Insurance Management Services
N.A.I.C.S.: 524298
Tahir Ayub *(Deputy Gen Mgr-Reinsurance)*

DHOFAR INTERNATIONAL DEVELOPMENT & INVESTMENT HOLDING COMPANY S.A.O.G

DIDIC Building 23rd July Stree, PO Box 2163, 211, Salalah, 211, Oman
Tel.: (968) 23295400
Web Site: https://www.didic.com
Year Founded: 1987
DIDI—(MUS)
Rev.: $18,172,201
Assets: $581,516,345
Liabilities: $268,520,947
Net Worth: $312,995,398
Earnings: $10,065,587
Emp.: 35
Fiscal Year-end: 12/31/21
Banking & Invetsment Management Services
N.A.I.C.S.: 522110
Khalid Mustahail Ahmed Al Mashani *(Chm)*

DHOFAR POULTRY COMPANY SAOG

Al Safwah Dairy Beverages, PO Box 1220, 211, Salalah, Oman
Tel.: (968) 23292804
Web Site:
https://www.dhofarchicken.com
Year Founded: 1993
DPCI—(MUS)
Rev.: $23,405,581

Dhofar Poultry Company SAOG—(Continued)

Assets: $31,733,484
Liabilities: $28,340,578
Net Worth: $3,392,906
Earnings: ($3,590,809)
Emp.: 60
Fiscal Year-end: 12/31/21
Poultry Processing Services
N.A.I.C.S.: 311615
Salim Taman Musallam Al Mashani (CEO)

DHOFAR TOURISM COMPANY SAOG
Mirbat Resort Mirbat, PO Box 2808, Salalah, 211, Oman
Tel.: (968) 23275500
Web Site: http://www.dhofartourism.net
Year Founded: 1993
DTCS—(MUS)
Rev.: $994,346
Assets: $151,182,833
Liabilities: $18,176,458
Net Worth: $133,006,375
Earnings: $569,463
Emp.: 144
Fiscal Year-end: 12/31/20
Tourism Management Services
N.A.I.C.S.: 561520
Ahmed Yusuf Alawi Al Ibrahim (Chm)

DHOFAR UNIVERSITY
Sultanate of Oman, PO Box 2509, Salalah, 211, Oman
Tel.: (968) 23237081
Web Site: http://www.du.edu.om
DHUS—(MUS)
Sales Range: Less than $1 Million
Education Services
N.A.I.C.S.: 611710
Mustahil Ahmed Al Mashani (Chm)

DHOLLANDIA FRANCE
30 Rue de pueplliers, 92000, Nanterre, France
Tel.: (33) 156052000
Web Site: http://www.dhollandia.be
Year Founded: 1968
Rev.: $40,800,000
Emp.: 45
Hydraulic Lifts & Tail Lifts Mfr
N.A.I.C.S.: 423120
Marc Gamblin (Mng Dir)

DHOOT INDUSTRIAL FINANCE LIMITED
504 Raheja Centre 214 Nariman Point, Mumbai, 400 021, India
Tel.: (91) 2222845050
Web Site: https://www.dhootfinance.com
526971—(BOM)
Rev.: $6,758,643
Assets: $35,300,702
Liabilities: $10,531,853
Net Worth: $24,768,850
Earnings: $4,536,123
Emp.: 9
Fiscal Year-end: 03/31/21
Trading & Distribution Services
N.A.I.C.S.: 561499
Rajgopal Ramdayal Dhoot (Chm)

Subsidiaries:

Dhoot Industrial Finance Limited - SAMPOORNA TRADERS Division **(1)**
504 Raheja Centre 214 Nariman Point, Mumbai, 400 021, India
Tel.: (91) 22 2284 5050
Sales Range: $50-74.9 Million
Emp.: 15
Financial Management Services
N.A.I.C.S.: 523999

DHOUSE PATTANA PUBLIC COMPANY LIMITED
99 Mahasarakham-Wapipathum Road, Talad Muang, Amphur Muang, 44000, Maha Sarakham, Thailand
Tel.: (66) 43722999 **TH**
Web Site: https://www.dhousepattana.com
Year Founded: 2010
DHOUSE—(THA)
Rev.: $4,344,936
Assets: $24,054,202
Liabilities: $10,628,475
Net Worth: $13,125,727
Earnings: ($594,365)
Emp.: 65
Fiscal Year-end: 12/31/23
Real Estate Development Services
N.A.I.C.S.: 531390
Chaiyut Lerdrungporn (VP)

DHP INDIA LIMITED.
7B Shreelekha 7th Floor 42A Park Street, Kolkata, 700 016, India
Tel.: (91) 3322295735
Web Site: https://www.dilindia.co.in
531306—(BOM)
Rev.: $17,700,298
Assets: $22,061,703
Liabilities: $1,590,437
Net Worth: $20,471,266
Earnings: $4,860,420
Emp.: 229
Fiscal Year-end: 03/31/22
Industrial Machinery
N.A.I.C.S.: 333248
Asheesh Dabriwal (CEO & Mng Dir)

DHRUV CONSULTANCY SERVICES LIMITED
501 Pujit Plaza Palm Beach Road Sector-11 Near Cbd Station, Opp K-Star Hotel Cbd Belapur, Navi Mumbai, 400614, Maharashtra, India
Tel.: (91) 9619497305
Web Site: https://www.dhruvconsultancy.in
Year Founded: 2003
541302—(BOM)
Building Construction Services
N.A.I.C.S.: 236220
Raja Mukherjee (CFO)

DHRUV ESTATES LIMITED
B/709 Sagar Tech Plaza Sakinaka Junction Andheri Kurla Road, Andheri E, Mumbai, 400 072, India
Tel.: (91) 222 850 0081
Web Site: http://www.dhruvestates.com
Year Founded: 1983
507886—(BOM)
Rev.: $901
Assets: $205,637
Liabilities: $4,068
Net Worth: $201,570
Earnings: ($3,672)
Fiscal Year-end: 03/31/21
Real Estate Development Services
N.A.I.C.S.: 531390
Sanjay Kanungo (Mng Dir)

DHRUV WELLNESS LIMITED
207 Royal Appartment Kasam Baug, Malad East, Mumbai, 400097, Maharashtra, India
Tel.: (91) 28711486 **In**
Web Site: http://www.dhruvwellness.com
Year Founded: 2015
540695—(BOM)
Assets: $844,161
Liabilities: $2,791,486
Net Worth: ($1,947,325)
Earnings: ($703,404)
Emp.: 14

Fiscal Year-end: 03/31/21
Pharmaceutical Products Distr
N.A.I.C.S.: 424210
Pravinkumar Narayanbhai Prajapati (Chm & Mng Dir)

DHRUVA CAPITAL SERVICES LIMITED
003-A Circle View Apartments 169 Fatehpura Near Sukhadia Circle, Udaipur, 313 001, India
Tel.: (91) 2942425555
Web Site: https://www.dhruvacapital.com
531237—(BOM)
Rev.: $30,359
Assets: $668,253
Liabilities: $46,779
Net Worth: $621,474
Earnings: $4,598
Fiscal Year-end: 03/31/21
Financial Services
N.A.I.C.S.: 523999
Kailash Karnawat (Mng Dir)

DHSTEEL
13 Sanmakgongdanbuk 4-gil, Yangsan, Gyeongsangnam-do, Korea (South)
Tel.: (82) 553884001
Web Site: https://www.dhstl.co.kr
Year Founded: 1988
021040—(KRS)
Rev.: $235,350,548
Assets: $167,177,845
Liabilities: $126,722,454
Net Worth: $40,455,391
Earnings: ($3,235,951)
Emp.: 242
Fiscal Year-end: 12/31/22
Automotive Products Mfr
N.A.I.C.S.: 336110
Gun-Wook Kang (CEO)

Subsidiaries:

DSP Co., Ltd. **(1)**
725-4 Hakjang-dong, Sasang-gu, Busan, Korea (South)
Tel.: (82) 51 323 3511
Sales Range: $150-199.9 Million
Emp.: 300
Steel Product Distr
N.A.I.C.S.: 423510

Daeho Co., Ltd **(1)**
24 Jeongmunsongsan-ro 241beon-gil, Yanggam-myeon, Hwaseong, Gyeonggi, Korea (South)
Tel.: (82) 313524083
Real Estate Leasing Services & Steel Products Distr
N.A.I.C.S.: 531190

Daeho P&C Co., Ltd. - Busan Factory **(1)**
725-4 Hakjang-dong, Sasang-gu, Busan, Korea (South)
Tel.: (82) 51 323 3511
Web Site: http://www.daehopnc.co.kr
Industrial Pipe Mfr
N.A.I.C.S.: 332996

Hwaseung Savings Bank **(1)**
1287-11 Yeonsan 5 dong, Yeonjae-gu, Busan, Korea (South)
Tel.: (82) 51 867 7701
Web Site: http://www.daehopnc.co.kr
Investment Banking Services
N.A.I.C.S.: 523150

Mijuland Co., Ltd. **(1)**
San 27-7 Harim-li Daeshin-meon, Yeoju-gun, Harim, Gyeonggi, Korea (South)
Tel.: (82) 881 0714
Landscape Architectural Services
N.A.I.C.S.: 541320

Posco Mvwpc S.A. De C.V. **(1)**
Carretera Celaya-Villagran KM 11 7 Col El Pintor Villagran, 38260, Celaya, Guanajuato, Mexico
Tel.: (52) 1411 160 4000
Web Site: https://www.poscomvwpc.com

Cold Heading Quality Wire Product Mfr & Distr
N.A.I.C.S.: 332618

DHT HOLDINGS, INC.
Clarendon House 2 Church Street, Hamilton, HM 11, Bermuda
Tel.: (441) 2951422 **MH**
Web Site: https://www.dhtankers.com
DHT—(NYSE)
Rev.: $454,146,000
Assets: $1,508,474,000
Liabilities: $434,988,000
Net Worth: $1,073,486,000
Earnings: $61,520,000
Emp.: 1,252
Fiscal Year-end: 12/31/22
Bulk Shipping Services
N.A.I.C.S.: 483111
Svenn Magne Edvardsen (Dir-Technical)

Subsidiaries:

DHT Management AS **(1)**
Haakon VIIs GT 1 7th floor, POB 2039, Vika, 0161, Oslo, 0125, Norway
Tel.: (47) 23115080
Crude Oil Distr
N.A.I.C.S.: 424710

DHT Management S.A.M. **(1)**
One Monte-Carlo-G Place du Casino, 98000, Monaco, Monaco
Tel.: (377) 92000710
Crude Oil Distr
N.A.I.C.S.: 424710

DHT Ship Management (Singapore) Pte. Ltd. **(1)**
20 Science Park Road 02-24 Teletech Park, Singapore, 117674, Singapore
Tel.: (65) 65004190
Crude Oil Distr
N.A.I.C.S.: 424710

DHUNSERI INVESTMENTS LIMITED
Dhunseri House 4A Woodburn Park, Kolkata, 700 020, India
Tel.: (91) 3322801950 **In**
Web Site: https://www.dhunseriinvestment.com
Year Founded: 1997
533336—(BOM)
Sales Range: $25-49.9 Million
Emp.: 4
Financial Investment Services
N.A.I.C.S.: 523999
Chandra Kumar Dhanuka (Chm)

DHUNSERI TEA & INDUSTRIES LTD.
Dhunseri House 4A Woodburn Park, Kolkata, 700 020, India
Tel.: (91) 3322801950
Web Site: https://www.dhunseritea.com
DTIL—(NSE)
Rev.: $55,245,836
Assets: $142,348,056
Liabilities: $40,180,345
Net Worth: $102,167,711
Earnings: $12,863,078
Emp.: 6,726
Fiscal Year-end: 03/31/22
Resin & Tea Producer; Information Technology Infrastructure Development Services
N.A.I.C.S.: 311920
Mrigank Dhanuka (Exec Dir)

DHX MEDIA LTD.
5657 Spring Garden Road Suite 505, Halifax, B3J 3R4, NS, Canada
Tel.: (902) 423-0260
Web Site: http://www.dhxmedia.com
DHXM—(NASDAQ)
Rev.: $322,360,206
Assets: $966,754,446

Liabilities: $600,285,572
Net Worth: $366,468,875
Earnings: ($74,392,057)
Emp.: 443
Fiscal Year-end: 06/30/19
Family Television Programming Services
N.A.I.C.S.: 512191
Josh Scherba *(Pres)*

Subsidiaries:

DHX Media Ltd. - Toronto **(1)**
Queen's Quay Terminal 207 Queen's Quay West Suite 550, Toronto, M5J 1A7, ON, Canada
Tel.: (416) 363-8034
Web Site: http://www.dhxmedia.com
Sales Range: $25-49.9 Million
Emp.: 50
Television Programming Services
N.A.I.C.S.: 512110
Deirdre Brennan *(Exec VP-Content Partnerships)*

DHX Media Ltd. - Vancouver **(1)**
6th Floor 190 Alexander Street, Vancouver, V6A 1B5, BC, Canada
Tel.: (604) 684-2363
Web Site: http://www.dhxmedia.com
Sales Range: $50-74.9 Million
Emp.: 150
Animation Production Services
N.A.I.C.S.: 512110
Amir Nasrabadi *(Exec VP & Gen Mgr)*

The Family Channel, Inc. **(1)**
181 Bay St Ste 100, PO Box 787, Toronto, M5J 2T3, ON, Canada
Tel.: (416) 956-2010
Web Site: http://www.family.ca
Sales Range: $50-74.9 Million
Emp.: 150
National Pay Television Service
N.A.I.C.S.: 516210
Eric Ellenbogen *(CEO)*

DHYAANI TILE & MARBLEZ LIMITED
420 Times Square Arcade Nr Baghban Party Plot, Thaltej, Ahmedabad, 380058, Gujarat, India
Web Site: https://www.dhyaaniinc.com
Year Founded: 2014
543516—(NSE)
Household Product Distr
N.A.I.C.S.: 423620
Chintan Nayan Bhai Rajyaguru *(Mng Dir & Chm)*

DI CORP.
No 58-6 Nonhyeon-dong, Gangnam-gu, Seoul, Korea (South)
Tel.: (82) 25465501
Web Site: https://www.di.co.kr
Year Founded: 1955
003160—(KRS)
Rev.: $177,180,351
Assets: $210,607,326
Liabilities: $85,295,452
Net Worth: $125,311,874
Earnings: $11,198,211
Emp.: 192
Fiscal Year-end: 12/31/22
Semiconductor Product Mfr
N.A.I.C.S.: 334413
Joe Yun Hyung *(CEO)*

Subsidiaries:

DI Corp. - The DongTan Plant **(1)**
20-7 Seoku-dong 32 Samsung 1-ro 3-gil, Hwaseong, Gyeonggi, Korea (South)
Tel.: (82) 31 8052 7100
Semiconductor Product Mfr
N.A.I.C.S.: 334413

DI. ENVIRO CORPORATION **(1)**
Water Treatment Equipment Mfr
N.A.I.C.S.: 333310

Dong-il SHIMADZU Corp. **(1)**

9F Eonju-ro, Gangnam-gu, Seoul, 06108, Korea (South)
Tel.: (82) 2 540 5541
Web Site: http://www.shimadzu.co.kr
Measuring Instruments Mfr
N.A.I.C.S.: 334513
Jaejoon Lee *(Pres)*

DI DONG IL CORPORATION
Jung-Hun Bldg 516 Teheran-ro, Gangnam-gu, Seoul, Korea (South)
Tel.: (82) 222223071
Web Site: https://www.dong-il.com
Year Founded: 1955
001530—(KRS)
Rev.: $700,825,438
Assets: $767,216,692
Liabilities: $292,293,517
Net Worth: $474,923,175
Earnings: $41,290,238
Emp.: 236
Fiscal Year-end: 12/31/22
Textile Product Mfr & Distr
N.A.I.C.S.: 314999
Yin Hwan Kim *(CEO & Mng Dir)*

DI-NIKKO ENGINEERING CO., LTD.
6971 Nemuro, Nikko, 321-2342, Tochigi, Japan
Tel.: (81) 288263930
Web Site: https://www.dne.co.jp
Year Founded: 1979
6635—(TKS)
Rev.: $277,942,180
Assets: $207,006,730
Liabilities: $157,823,400
Net Worth: $49,183,330
Earnings: $2,474,410
Emp.: 177
Fiscal Year-end: 12/31/23
Electronic Equipment Engineering Services
N.A.I.C.S.: 541330
Yukio Yamaguchi *(Chm & CEO)*

Subsidiaries:

Bon Artisan Co., Ltd. **(1)**
697-1 Nemuro, Nikko, 321-2342, Tochigi, Japan
Tel.: (81) 28 826 4739
Web Site: https://www.bon-artisan.jp
Human Resource Consulting Services
N.A.I.C.S.: 541612

Di-Nikko Engineering Co., Ltd. - Todoroku Factory **(1)**
1195-6 Todoroku, Nikko, 321-2404, Tochigi, Japan
Tel.: (81) 288310800
Electric Equipment Mfr
N.A.I.C.S.: 334511

NC Network Factory, Co., Ltd. **(1)**
UM Building 8th Floor 1-14-5 Higashi-Ueno, Taito Ward, Tokyo, 110-0015, Japan
Tel.: (81) 36 284 3080
Web Site: https://corporate.nc-net.com
Network Related Product Mfr & Distr
N.A.I.C.S.: 334111
Yasuo Uchihara *(Pres)*

NC Network, Inc. **(1)**
21171 S Western Ave Ste 2814, Torrance, CA 90501
Tel.: (310) 755-2516
Web Site: https://www.ncnetwork-us.com
Electric Equipment Mfr
N.A.I.C.S.: 335311

TROIS (THAILAND) CO., LTD. **(1)**
150/66 Moo9 Tambol Nongkham Amphur, Si Racha, 20110, Chonburi, Thailand
Tel.: (66) 38347091
Electronic Equipment Distr
N.A.I.C.S.: 423690

TROIS ELECTRONICS (WUXI) CO., LTD. **(1)**
Plot 8 Wuxi Boustead Industrial Park Lot 117 Xin Mei Road, Wuxi New District, Wuxi, Jiangsu, China
Tel.: (86) 51085342688

Electronic Equipment Distr
N.A.I.C.S.: 423690

Tochigi Electronics Industry Co., Ltd. **(1)**
444-1 Hinokuchimachi, Tochigi, 328-0024, Japan
Tel.: (81) 28 224 4131
Web Site: https://www.tochiden.co.jp
Emp.: 70
Electric Equipment Mfr
N.A.I.C.S.: 335311

Trois Engineering Pretec Hong Kong Ltd. **(1)**
Room 2301-06 23/F Technology Park 18 On Lai Street N T, Hong Kong, New Territories, China (Hong Kong)
Tel.: (852) 26492270
Electronic Equipment Distr
N.A.I.C.S.: 423690

Trois Takaya Electronics (Thailand) Co., Ltd. **(1)**
Pington Industrial Complex Phase II, 20110, Si Racha, Chonburi, Thailand
Tel.: (66) 3 834 7161
Electric Device Mfr
N.A.I.C.S.: 334419

Trois Vietnam Co., Ltd. **(1)**
Room 1201 Ruby Plaza Building 44 Le Ngoc Han Street, Pham Dinh Ho Ward Hai Ba Trung District, Hanoi, Vietnam
Tel.: (84) 778301347
Electrical Products Mfr
N.A.I.C.S.: 335999

Wuxi Rongzhi Electronics Co., Ltd. **(1)**
No 26 Xinyi Road Zone B, High-tech Industrial Development Zone, Wuxi, Jiangsu, China
Tel.: (86) 75527311870
Electrical Products Mfr
N.A.I.C.S.: 335999

DIA DENTAL AESTHETICS INTERNATIONAL INC.
Lindenmattstrasse 13, 5616, Meisterschwanden, Switzerland
Tel.: (41) 56 664 53 93
Web Site: http://www.dental-aesthetics.net
Dental Products
N.A.I.C.S.: 339114
Drew Reid *(Mng Dir)*

DIABLO RESOURCES LIMITED
Level 2 10 Outram Street, West Perth, 6005, WA, Australia
Tel.: (61) 863837837 **AU**
Web Site:
https://www.diabloresources.com.au
Year Founded: 2021
DBO—(ASX)
Rev.: $608
Assets: $10,464,775
Liabilities: $49,330
Net Worth: $10,415,444
Earnings: ($617,758)
Fiscal Year-end: 06/30/22
Exploration & Mining Services
N.A.I.C.S.: 213115
Shaun Menezes *(Sec)*

DIAC SALAF S.A.
32 Boulevard de la Resistance, Casablanca, Morocco
Tel.: (212) 522303681
DIS—(CAS)
Sales Range: Less than $1 Million
Consumer Lending Services
N.A.I.C.S.: 522291
Abdelkrim Bencherki *(Chm & Mng Dir)*

DIACEUTICS PLC
First Floor Dataworks - King's Hall Building, Dataworks At Kings Hall Health & Wellbeing Park, Belfast, BT9 6GW, United Kingdom **UK**

Web Site: https://www.diaceutics.com
Year Founded: 2005
DXRX—(AIM)
Rev.: $24,620,045
Assets: $60,913,911
Liabilities: $7,248,170
Net Worth: $53,665,741
Earnings: $913,911
Emp.: 142
Fiscal Year-end: 12/31/22
Pharmaceutical Product Mfr & Distr
N.A.I.C.S.: 325412
Ryan Keeling *(CEO)*

DIADORA INVICTA
Montello 80 Caerano San Marco, Treviso, 31031, Italy
Tel.: (39) 04236581 **IT**
Web Site: http://www.diadora.com
Sales Range: $300-349.9 Million
Emp.: 400
Mfr of Footwear
N.A.I.C.S.: 316210
Mauricio Dangelo *(Gen Mgr)*

Subsidiaries:

Diadora America, Inc. **(1)**
6102 S 225th St 21929 67th Ave, Kent, WA 98032-1874
Tel.: (253) 520-8868
Web Site: http://www.diadorasoccer.com
Sales Range: $300-349.9 Million
Athletic Footwear & Apparel Distr & Mfr
N.A.I.C.S.: 424340
Linda Walker *(COO)*

DIADROM HOLDING AB
Foersta Langgatan 19, 413 27, Gothenburg, Sweden
Tel.: (46) 317741100 **SE**
Web Site: https://diadrom.se
Year Founded: 1999
DIAH—(OMX)
Rev.: $6,628,453
Assets: $3,179,821
Liabilities: $1,335,619
Net Worth: $1,844,203
Earnings: $938,492
Emp.: 68
Fiscal Year-end: 12/31/22
Software Development Services
N.A.I.C.S.: 541511
Martin Solevid *(Mgr-Bus & Consulting)*

DIAGEO PLC
16 Great Marlborough Street, London, W1F 7HS, United Kingdom
Tel.: (44) 2079479100 **UK**
Web Site: https://www.diageo.com
Year Founded: 1997
DEO—(NYSE)
Rev.: $27,891,000,000
Assets: $45,474,000,000
Liabilities: $33,404,000,000
Net Worth: $12,070,000,000
Earnings: $4,166,000,000
Emp.: 30,367
Fiscal Year-end: 06/30/24
Holding Company; Alcoholic Beverages Mfr
N.A.I.C.S.: 551112
Debra A. Crew *(CEO)*

Subsidiaries:

Belsazar GmbH **(1)**
Reeperbahn 1, 20359, Hamburg, Germany
Tel.: (49) 40402364860
Web Site: https://www.belsazar.com
N.A.I.C.S.: 312130
Olena Neznal *(Mng Dir)*

Bundaberg Distilling Company Pty. Limited **(1)**
Hills Street, Bundaberg East, Bundaberg, 4670, QLD, Australia
Tel.: (61) 743483443
Web Site:
https://www.bundabergrum.com.au

Diageo plc—(Continued)

Rum Distr
N.A.I.C.S.: 424820

Diageo Brands BV **(1)**
Molenwerf 10-12, 1014BG, Amsterdam,
Netherlands
Tel.: (31) 205814242
Web Site: http://www.diageo.com
Sales Range: $50-74.9 Million
Emp.: 100
Wholesale Grocery Services
N.A.I.C.S.: 424410
Edward P. Demery (CEO)

Diageo Canada, Inc. **(1)**
401 The W Mall Ste 800, Toronto, M9C
5P8, ON, Canada
Tel.: (416) 626-2000
Web Site: http://www.diageo.com
Sales Range: $150-199.9 Million
Emp.: 1,400
Distilled Spirits & Wines, Fruit Juices &
Juice Beverages Mfr & Marketer
N.A.I.C.S.: 312130

Branch (Domestic):

Diageo Canada Inc. **(2)**
9523 41 Ave NW, Edmonton, T6E 5X7, AB,
Canada **(100%)**
Tel.: (780) 451-5566
Web Site: http://www.diageo.com
Sales Range: $25-49.9 Million
Emp.: 15
Distilled & Blended Liquors
N.A.I.C.S.: 312140

Diageo Canada Inc. **(2)**
5 A Unit 1080 Waverly st, Winnipeg, R3T
4J6, MB, Canada **(100%)**
Tel.: (204) 453-7447
Web Site: http://www.diageo.com
Sales Range: $25-49.9 Million
Emp.: 6
Distilled & Blended Liquors
N.A.I.C.S.: 312140

Diageo Capital BV **(1)**
Molenwerf 10-12, Amsterdam, 1014 BG,
Netherlands
Tel.: (31) 207745000
Web Site: http://www.diageo.com
Emp.: 250
Financial Management Services
N.A.I.C.S.: 523999

Diageo Capital Plc **(1)**
Edinburg Park 5 Lochside Way, Edinburgh,
EH129DT, United Kingdom
Tel.: (44) 1315192090
Web Site: http://www.diageo.com
Sales Range: $75-99.9 Million
Emp.: 200
Holding Company
N.A.I.C.S.: 551112
Ian Scott (CEO)

Diageo Colombia S.A. **(1)**
100 street No13 21 Office 502, Bogota,
Colombia
Tel.: (57) 16405606
Web Site: http://www.diageocolombia.co
Rum Distr
N.A.I.C.S.: 424820

Diageo Great Britain Limited **(1)**
8 Henrietta Place, W1G0NB, London,
United Kingdom
Tel.: (44) 2079275200
Sales Range: $1-4.9 Billion
Emp.: 1,483
Production, Marketing & Distribution of Pre-
mium Drinks
N.A.I.C.S.: 424810

Diageo Holdings Ltd. **(1)**
8 Henrietta Pl, London, W1G 0NB, United
Kingdom **(100%)**
Tel.: (44) 2079275200
Web Site: http://www.diageo.com
Sales Range: $50-74.9 Million
Emp.: 250
Holding Company
N.A.I.C.S.: 445320

Subsidiary (Non-US):

Croft Jerez SA **(2)**
Rancho Croft, PO Box 414, 11407, Jerez

de la Frontera, Cadiz, Spain
Tel.: (34) 956306600
Sales Range: $25-49.9 Million
Emp.: 100
Produces & Markets Premium Sherries
N.A.I.C.S.: 312130

Diageo Ireland **(2)**
Saint James Gate, Dublin, Ireland **(100%)**
Tel.: (353) 14536700
Web Site: http://www.diageo.ie
Brewing, Marketing & Distribution of Beer
N.A.I.C.S.: 312130
John Kennedy (Pres-Europe, Turkey & In-
dia)

Unit (Domestic):

Diageo Northern Ireland **(2)**
Gilbey House 58 Boucher Rd, Belfast, BT12
6HR, United Kingdom **(100%)**
Tel.: (44) 2890682021
Web Site: http://www.diageo.com
Sales Range: $25-49.9 Million
Emp.: 50
Brewer & Distiller
N.A.I.C.S.: 312120

Diageo UK **(2)**
16 Great Marlborough Street, London, W1F
7HS, United Kingdom **(100%)**
Tel.: (44) 2079479100
Web Site: https://www.diageo.com
Mfr & Distributor of Alcoholic Beverages
N.A.I.C.S.: 312130

Subsidiary (Non-US):

Guinness Nigeria Plc **(2)**
24 Oba Akran Avenue, Ikeja, 21071, Lagos,
Nigeria **(58.02%)**
Tel.: (234) 12709100
Web Site: http://www.guinness-nigeria.com
Rev.: $491,232,883
Assets: $517,582,776
Liabilities: $396,777,673
Net Worth: $120,805,103
Earnings: ($38,897,776)
Emp.: 791
Fiscal Year-end: 06/30/2023
Alcoholic Beverage Distr
N.A.I.C.S.: 445320
Babatunde Abayomi Savage (Chm)

International Distillers South Asia **(2)**
50 Raffles Place, 230 Orchard Road, Singapore, 0923, Singapore
Tel.: (65) 6534 5315
Manufacturing, Marketing & Sales Organizations
N.A.I.C.S.: 445320

Unit (Domestic):

Justerini & Brooks Ltd. **(2)**
61 St James's Street, London, SW1A 1LZ,
United Kingdom **(100%)**
Tel.: (44) 2074846430
Web Site: https://www.justerinis.com
Sales Range: $25-49.9 Million
Emp.: 100
Distills, Blends & Markets Scotch Whiskies;
Marketer of Wines & Gin
N.A.I.C.S.: 312130
Chadwick Delaney (Mng Dir)

Subsidiary (Non-US):

W & A Gilbey SA **(2)**
PO Box 137 16 Stellentia Avenue, Stellen-
bosch, 7600, Cape Province, South Africa
Tel.: (27) 21 808 6911
Produces, Imports, Markets & Distributes
Alcoholic & Non-Alcoholic Beverages in
South Africa
N.A.I.C.S.: 312130

Diageo India Private Limited **(1)**
UB Tower 24 Vittal Mallya Road, Bengaluru,
560 001, Karnataka, India
Tel.: (91) 8022210705
Web Site: https://www.diageoindia.com
N.A.I.C.S.: 312130
Rashmi Singh (Mgr-Reg Customer Mktg)

Diageo Investment Corporation **(1)**
801 Main Ave, Norwalk, CT 06851-1127
Tel.: (203) 229-2100
Investment Management Service
N.A.I.C.S.: 523999
Tracy Allery (Mgr-Global Category)

Diageo Japan K.K **(1)**
43F Midtown Tower 9-7-1 Akasaka, Minato-
ku, Tokyo, 107-6243, Japan
Tel.: (81) 334708287
Emp.: 60
Liquor Distr
N.A.I.C.S.: 424820

Diageo Korea Company Limited **(1)**
Hongdae Wework 5F 147 Yanghwa-Ro,
Mapo-gu, Seoul, Korea (South)
Tel.: (82) 221881900
N.A.I.C.S.: 312130

Diageo North America, Inc. **(1)**
801 Main Ave. Norwalk, CT 06851 **(100%)**
Tel.: (203) 229-2100
Web Site: http://www.diageo.com
Sales Range: $1-4.9 Billion
Emp.: 1,000
Spirits & Wines Producer, Importer & Mar-
keter
N.A.I.C.S.: 424820
Debra A. Crew (Pres)

Unit (Domestic):

Chalone Vineyard **(2)**
32020 Stonewall Canyon Rd, Soledad, CA
93960
Tel.: (203) 229-2100
Web Site: http://www.chalonevineyard.com
Vineyard & Winery
N.A.I.C.S.: 312130

Branch (Domestic):

Diageo North America **(2)**
5301 Blue Lagoon Dr, Miami, FL 33126-
2097
Tel.: (305) 269-4500
Web Site: http://www.whfreeman.com
Sales Range: $25-49.9 Million
Emp.: 180
Spirits & Wines Marketing & Distr
N.A.I.C.S.: 561110

Diageo North America **(2)**
24440 W 143rd St, Plainfield, IL 60544-
8555
Tel.: (815) 267-4400
Sales Range: $25-49.9 Million
Emp.: 90
Alcoholic Beverages
N.A.I.C.S.: 312140
Sandie Demierre (Mgr-Procurement)

Diageo North America **(2)**
5080 Spectrum Dr Ste 1200, Addison, TX
75001-4648
Tel.: (972) 716-7700
Web Site: http://www.diageo.com
Sales Range: $25-49.9 Million
Emp.: 100
Mfr & Supplier of Alcoholic Beverages
N.A.I.C.S.: 424820

Diageo North America Inc. **(2)**
333 W Wacker Dr Ste 1050, Chicago, IL
60606
Tel.: (312) 279-3400
Web Site: http://www.diageo.com
Sales Range: $25-49.9 Million
Emp.: 50
Beverage Producer
N.A.I.C.S.: 424820

Diageo North America Inc. **(2)**
530 5th Ave, New York, NY 10036
Tel.: (646) 223-2000
Web Site: http://www.diageo.com
Emp.: 200
Spirits & Wines Producer, Importer & Mar-
keter
N.A.I.C.S.: 424810

Subsidiary (Domestic):

George A. Dickel & Co. **(2)**
1950 Cascade Hollow Rd, Tullahoma, TN
37388
Tel.: (931) 408-2410
Web Site: https://www.georgedickel.com
Sales Range: $10-24.9 Million
Emp.: 26
Distilling, Bottling & Warehousing Alcoholic
Beverages
N.A.I.C.S.: 312140
John R. Lunn (Pres)

Diageo Scotland Limited **(1)**

5 Lochside Way, Edinburgh Park, Edin-
burgh, United Kingdom
Tel.: (44) 2079275480
Web Site: http://www.diageo.com
Sales Range: $1-4.9 Billion
Emp.: 2,585
Production, Marketing & Distribution of Pre-
mium Drinks
N.A.I.C.S.: 424820
Roger Hugh Myddelton (CEO)

Diageo USVI Inc. **(1)**
1 Estate Annaberg & Shannon Grove, King-
shill, VI 00850-9703
Tel.: (340) 713-5600
Web Site: https://www.diageousvi.com
N.A.I.C.S.: 312130

East African Breweries Limited **(1)**
Corporate Centre, PO Box 30161, Ruaraka,
00100, Nairobi, Kenya **(65%)**
Tel.: (254) 208644000
Web Site: https://www.eabl.com
Rev.: $833,328,872
Assets: $1,007,700,160
Liabilities: $766,448,617
Net Worth: $241,251,543
Earnings: $93,653,420
Emp.: 2,000
Fiscal Year-end: 06/30/2023
Beer Brewery
N.A.I.C.S.: 445320
Martin Oduor-Otieno (Chm-Grp)

Subsidiary (Domestic):

Central Glass Industries Ltd **(2)**
PO Box 49835, Nairobi, Kenya
Tel.: (254) 803681
Glass Mfr
N.A.I.C.S.: 327213
James Karegi (Mng Dir)

Subsidiary (Non-US):

Uganda Breweries Ltd **(2)**
Plot 3 - 17, PO Box 7130, Port Bell, Kam-
pala, Luzira, Uganda
Tel.: (256) 312210011
Web Site:
https://www.ugandabreweries.com
Beer & Spirits
N.A.I.C.S.: 312120

Guinness Ghana Breweries PLC **(1)**
Plot 1 Block L Industrial Area Kaasi, PO
Box 1536, Kumasi, Ghana **(72.42%)**
Tel.: (233) 5126301
Web Site: https://www.guinness.com
Rev.: $187,765,164
Assets: $150,158,782
Liabilities: $86,943,284
Net Worth: $63,215,498
Earnings: $12,160,305
Emp.: 548
Fiscal Year-end: 06/30/2021
Beer & Malt Liquor Mfr & Sales
N.A.I.C.S.: 312120
Felix E. Addo (Chm)

Guinness Storehouse Limited **(1)**
St James's Gate, Dublin, 8, Ireland
Tel.: (353) 14084800
Web Site: https://www.guinness-
storehouse.com
Travel & Tourism Services
N.A.I.C.S.: 561510

**Mey Alkollu Ickiler Sanayi ve Ticaret
A.S** **(1)**
Buyukdere Cad Bahar Sok No 13 River
Plaza Kat 25, Sisli, 34394, Istanbul, Turkiye
Tel.: (90) 2123734400
N.A.I.C.S.: 312130

Mey Icki Sanayi ve Ticaret A.S. **(1)**
Buyukdere Cad Bahar Sok No13 River
Plaza Kat25-29, Sisli, 34394, Istanbul, Tur-
kiye
Tel.: (90) 2123734400
Web Site: https://www.meydiageo.com
Sales Range: $350-399.9 Million
Emp.: 200
Wine & Spirit Mfr & Distr
N.A.I.C.S.: 312140

R&A Bailey & Co. **(1)**
Nangor House Nangor Rd, Dublin, 12,
Ireland **(100%)**
Tel.: (353) 014051300
Web Site: http://www.bailey.com

Sales Range: $50-74.9 Million
Emp.: 200
Mfr & Marketing of Original Irish Cream
N.A.I.C.S.: 445298
John Miller *(Mng Dir)*

Serengeti Breweries Limited **(1)**
Plot 117/2 Access Road Nelson Mandela
Expressway, PO Box 41080, Chang Ombe
Industrial Area, Dar es Salaam, Tanzania
Tel.: (255) 784104100
Web Site:
  https://www.serengetibreweries.co.tz
N.A.I.C.S.: 312130
Obinna Anyalebechi *(Mng Dir)*

Seychelles Breweries Limited **(1)**
O Brien House, PO Box 273, Le Rocher
Mahe, Victoria, Seychelles
Tel.: (248) 4382600
Web Site:
  https://seybrew.diageoplatform.com
N.A.I.C.S.: 424820
Yvonne Mwangi *(Mng Dir)*

Sichuan Swellfun Co., Ltd. **(1)**
No 9 Quanxing Road, Jinniu District,
Chengdu, 610036, Sichuan,
China **(63.14%)**
Tel.: (86) 2886252847
Web Site: http://www.swellfun.com
Rev.: $656,052,317
Assets: $989,463,412
Net Worth: $485,566,436
Earnings: $170,703,978
Fiscal Year-end: 12/31/2022
Alcohol Product Mfr & Distr
N.A.I.C.S.: 312130
Xiangfu Fan *(Chm & Gen Mgr)*

Stirrings LLC **(1)**
175 Greenwich St 3 World Trade Ctr, New
York, NY 10007
Web Site: https://stirrings.com
N.A.I.C.S.: 424820

The Gleneagles Hotel **(1)**
Auchterarder, Perth, PH3 1NF, Perthshire,
United Kingdom **(100%)**
Tel.: (44) 1764290027
Web Site: https://www.gleneagles.com
Sales Range: $125-149.9 Million
Emp.: 800
Hotel
N.A.I.C.S.: 721199
Karen McIntosh *(Sr Partner-Corp Comm)*

United Spirits Ltd. **(1)**
UB Tower 24 Vittal Mallya Road, Bengaluru,
560 001, India **(54.78%)**
Tel.: (91) 3344263000
Web Site: https://www.diageoindia.com
Rev.: $3,748,030,650
Assets: $1,165,300,500
Liabilities: $611,260,650
Net Worth: $554,039,850
Earnings: $49,426,650
Emp.: 3,261
Fiscal Year-end: 03/31/2021
Liquor Distiller & Distr
N.A.I.C.S.: 312140
Kedar Ulman *(Chief Supply Chain Officer)*

Subsidiary (Domestic):

Balaji Distilleries Ltd. **(2)**
Bye-Pass Road Poonamallee, Chennai,
600056, Tamil Nadu, India
Tel.: (91) 4426272436
Distilled Beverages Producer
N.A.I.C.S.: 312140
R. Raghuram *(Mng Dir)*

Pioneer Distilleries Limited **(2)**
UB Tower Level-10 No 24 Vittal Mallya
Road, Bengaluru, 560 001, India **(54.7%)**
Tel.: (91) 80 3964 2207
Web Site: http://www.pioneerdistilleries.com
Rev.: $23,260,965
Assets: $54,680,535
Liabilities: $92,607,060
Net Worth: ($37,926,525)
Earnings: ($11,816,805)
Emp.: 152
Fiscal Year-end: 03/31/2021
Alcohol & Alcoholic Beverages Mfr
N.A.I.C.S.: 312140
Sanjoy Sarkar *(CFO)*

**Royal Challengers Sports Private
Limited** **(2)**

UB Towers 24 Vittal Mallya Road, Benga-
luru, 560 001, Karnataka, India
Tel.: (91) 8039856616
Web Site: https://www.royalchallengers.com
Cricket Team Franchise Owner
N.A.I.C.S.: 711211
Anand Kripalu *(Chm)*

Zepf Technologies UK Limited **(1)**
45/47 Napier Road Wardpark North, Cum-
bernauld, G68 0EF, United Kingdom
Tel.: (44) 1236455554
Web Site: https://www.zepf.co.uk
Machinery Equipment Mfr
N.A.I.C.S.: 333248

DIAGNOS INC.
7005 Taschereau Blvd suite 265, Bro-
ssard, J4Z 1A7, QC, Canada
Tel.: (450) 678-8882   Ca
Web Site: https://www.diagnos.com
Year Founded: 1998
4D4A—(DEU)
Rev.: $125,698
Assets: $490,350
Liabilities: $2,744,799
Net Worth: ($2,254,449)
Earnings: ($2,305,224)
Emp.: 15
Fiscal Year-end: 03/31/24
Data Extraction & Analytical Services
N.A.I.C.S.: 518210
Andre Larente *(Pres & CEO)*

Subsidiaries:

Diagnos Poland sp. Z o.o. **(1)**
Ul Laczyny 4, 02-820, Warsaw, Poland
Tel.: (48) 223310503
Web Site: http://www.diagnos.pl
Medical Equipment Distr
N.A.I.C.S.: 423450

DIAGNOSTIC AND THERA-
PEUTIC CENTER OF ATHENS-
HYGEIA S.A.
4 Erythrou Stavrou Str & Kifisias Av,
Marousi, 15123, Athens, Greece
Tel.: (30) 2106867000
Web Site: http://www.hygeia.gr
Rev.: $243,612,960
Assets: $459,215,848
Liabilities: $330,095,021
Net Worth: $129,120,827
Earnings: $813,003
Emp.: 3,213
Fiscal Year-end: 12/31/16
Medical Devices
N.A.I.C.S.: 622110
George Politis *(Vice Chm)*

Subsidiaries:

ALPHA LAB A.E. **(1)**
11 Anastasiou Str, 115 24, Athens, Greece
Tel.: (30) 2106984174
Web Site: http://www.alphalab.gr
Sales Range: $25-49.9 Million
Emp.: 20
Molecular Biology Research & Development
Services
N.A.I.C.S.: 541715

**CHRYSSAFILIOTISSA PUBLIC
LTD** **(1)**
9 Stygos Street, CY-3117, Limassol, Cyprus
Tel.: (357) 25200000
Hospital Management Services
N.A.I.C.S.: 622110

LETO S.A. **(1)**
7-13 Mousson, 11524, Athens, Greece
Tel.: (30) 2106902000
Web Site: http://www.leto.gr
Sales Range: $25-49.9 Million
Emp.: 250
Health Care Srvices
N.A.I.C.S.: 621491
L. Papadopoulos *(CEO)*

**LIMASSOL MEDICAL CENTRE
'ACHILLION' LTD** **(1)**
9 Stygos Street, CY-3117, Limassol, Cyprus
Tel.: (357) 25200000
Health Care Srvices

N.A.I.C.S.: 621491

MITERA S.A. **(1)**
Kifissias Avenue & 6 Erythrou Stavrou Str,
Maroussi, 15123, Athens, Greece
Tel.: (30) 2106869000
Web Site: https://www.mitera.gr
Health Care Srvices
N.A.I.C.S.: 621491
Alexios Komninos *(Mng Dir)*

Y-PHARMA S.A. **(1)**
13th Klm Athens-Lamia National Road,
Metamorfosi, Athens, 14451, Greece
Tel.: (30) 2108991626
Sales Range: $10-24.9 Million
Emp.: 19
Health Care Srvices
N.A.I.C.S.: 621999

DIAGNOSTIC MEDICAL SYS-
TEMS S.A.
9 Av du canal philippe lamour, Mau-
guio, 30660, Gallargues-le-Montueux,
France
Tel.: (33) 466290907
Web Site: https://www.dms.com
Year Founded: 1993
DGM—(EUR)
Sales Range: $25-49.9 Million
Emp.: 130
Medical Imaging Equipment Designer,
Mfr & Marketer
N.A.I.C.S.: 339112
Jean-Paul Ansel *(CEO)*

Subsidiaries:

Apelem SAS **(1)**
Parc Scientifique Georges Besse, 175 allee
Von Neumann, 30035, Nimes, France
Tel.: (33) 466290907
Web Site: http://www.dms.com
Sales Range: $10-24.9 Million
Emp.: 50
Medical Diagnostic Services
N.A.I.C.S.: 621512

Hybrigenics S.A. **(1)**
3-5 impasse Reille, 75014, Paris,
France **(80%)**
Tel.: (33) 175662054
Web Site: https://www.hybrigenics.com
Sales Range: Less than $1 Million
Biotechnology & Pharmaceuticals Mfr
N.A.I.C.S.: 325412

Unit (Domestic):

Hybrigenics Pharma **(2)**
3-5 Impasse Reille, Paris, 7540, France
Tel.: (33) 158103823
Web Site: http://www.hybrigenics.com
Emp.: 50
Pharmaceutical Research & Development
Services
N.A.I.C.S.: 541715
Remi Delansorne *(CEO)*

Hybrigenics Services **(2)**
3-5 Impasse Reille, 75014, Paris, France
Tel.: (33) 158103829
Web Site: http://www.hybrigenics.com
Emp.: 40
Financial & Administrative Management
Services
N.A.I.C.S.: 541611
Etienne Formstecher *(CEO)*

DIAGNOSTICA STAGO S.A.S.
3 Allee Theresa, CS 10009, 92665,
Asnieres-sur-Seine, Cedex, France
Tel.: (33) 146882020   FR
Web Site: http://www.stago.com
Year Founded: 1945
Hemostasis Instrumentation & Re-
agent Kit Mfr
N.A.I.C.S.: 334516
Lionel Viret *(Pres)*

Subsidiaries:

Diagnostica Stago, Inc. **(1)**
5 Century Dr, Parsippany, NJ 07054
Tel.: (973) 631-1200
Web Site: http://www.stago-us.com

Sales Range: $50-74.9 Million
Emp.: 200
Hemostasis Instrumentation & Reagent Kit
Mfr
N.A.I.C.S.: 334516
Stephane Zamia *(CEO)*

HemoSonics, LLC **(1)**
400 Preston Ave Ste 250, Charlottesville,
VA 22903
Tel.: (919) 504-1030
Web Site: http://www.hemosonics.com
Ambulatory Health Care Services
N.A.I.C.S.: 621999
Francesco Viola *(Founder & Chief Scientific
Officer)*

DIAGNOSTICOS DA AMERICA
S.A.
Avenida Jurua 434, Alphaville, Ba-
rueri, 06455-010, SP, Brazil
Tel.: (55) 26303000   BR
Web Site: http://www.dasa.com.br
Year Founded: 1966
DASA3—(BRAZ)
Rev.: $2,937,091,182
Assets: $5,401,998,955
Liabilities: $3,890,650,376
Net Worth: $1,511,348,579
Earnings: ($232,822,256)
Emp.: 19,272
Fiscal Year-end: 12/31/23
Medical Diagnostic Services
N.A.I.C.S.: 621511
Emerson Leandro Gasparetto *(Chief
Medical Officer)*

Subsidiaries:

Previlab Analises Clinicas Ltda **(1)**
Av Dr Joao Teodoro 603 Vila Rezende, Pi-
racicaba, Sao Paulo, Brazil
Tel.: (55) 19 3413 2612
Diagnostic Imaging Services
N.A.I.C.S.: 621512

DIAGONAL BIO AB
The Spark, Medicon Village, 223 81,
Lund, Sweden
Tel.: (46) 735262759
Web Site:
  https://www.diagonalbio.com
Year Founded: 2020
DIABIO—(OMX)
Rev.: $1,985
Assets: $2,830,226
Liabilities: $720,710
Net Worth: $2,109,516
Earnings: ($1,159,489)
Emp.: 4
Fiscal Year-end: 12/31/23
Biotechnology Research & Develop-
ment Services
N.A.I.C.S.: 541714
Andreas Nyberg *(Founder)*

DIAL A.D.
Vojvode Misica Bb, 74270, Teslic,
Bosnia & Herzegovina
Tel.: (387) 53431772
Year Founded: 2001
DIAL-R-A—(BANJ)
Rev.: $8,008
Assets: $560,050
Liabilities: $76,218
Net Worth: $483,832
Earnings: $60
Fiscal Year-end: 12/31/12
Hardware Tool Mfr
N.A.I.C.S.: 333991
Borislav Zelenbabiae *(Chm-Mgmt Bd)*

DIAL ONE WOLFEDALE ELEC-
TRIC LTD.
20 Floral Pkwy, Concord, L4K 4R1,
ON, Canada
Tel.: (905) 564-8999
Web Site:
  http://www.dialonewolfedale.com
Rev.: $16,337,906

Dial One Wolfedale Electric Ltd.—(Continued)

Emp.: 120
Electrical Products Distr
N.A.I.C.S.: 423620
Steven Muzzo *(Pres)*

DIALCOM24 SP. Z O.O.

ul Kanclerska 15, 60 327, Poznan, Poland
Tel.: (48) 48618475264
Web Site: http://www.przelewy24.pl
Electronic Payment Services
N.A.I.C.S.: 522320
Michal Bzowy *(VP & COO)*

Subsidiaries:

Infinite Sp.z.o.o   **(1)**
Ceramiczna St 8, Lublin, 20209, Poland   **(100%)**
Tel.: (48) 817451750
Web Site: http://www.infinite.pl
Sales Range: $25-49.9 Million
Emp.: 150
Computer System Design Services
N.A.I.C.S.: 541512
Jacek Dudzik *(Chm-Mgmt Bd)*

DIALES

190 Aztec West Park Avenue, Almondsbury, Bristol, BS32 4TP, United Kingdom
Tel.: (44) 1454275010
Web Site: https://www.diales.com
DRV—(AIM)
Rev.: $66,218,720
Assets: $42,648,701
Liabilities: $13,772,712
Net Worth: $28,875,989
Earnings: $1,512,500
Emp.: 318
Fiscal Year-end: 09/30/21
Construction Consulting Services
N.A.I.C.S.: 541690
Thomas Ferns *(Sec)*

Subsidiaries:

Driver Consult (Oman) LLC   **(1)**
18th November Street Alghubra Villa No 4247 House No 2847, Muscat, 121, Oman
Tel.: (968) 24613361
Web Site: http://www.driverconsult.com
Sales Range: $25-49.9 Million
Emp.: 70
Construction & Engineering Consulting Services
N.A.I.C.S.: 541330

Driver Consult Limited   **(1)**
Driver House Fourth St Crispin Way, Haslingden, Rossendale, BB4 4PW, Lancashire, United Kingdom
Tel.: (44) 1706223999
Web Site: http://www.driverconsult.com
Sales Range: $25-49.9 Million
Emp.: 50
Construction Consulting Services
N.A.I.C.S.: 541330

Driver Project Services (UAE) LLC   **(1)**
Ofc 105 Al Mansoori Plz Sheikh Hamdan St, Abu Dhabi, United Arab Emirates
Tel.: (971) 26780466
Sales Range: $25-49.9 Million
Emp.: 30
Construction Engineering Services
N.A.I.C.S.: 237990

Driver Trett (Canada) Ltd.   **(1)**
200 Granville Street 15th Floor, Vancouver, V6C 2R6, BC, Canada
Tel.: (604) 692-1151
Dispute Resolution Services
N.A.I.C.S.: 541990

Driver Trett (Hong Kong) Ltd.   **(1)**
Unit E 14/F Neich Tower 128 Gloucester Road, Wanchai, China (Hong Kong)
Tel.: (852) 3 460 7900
Dispute Resolution Services
N.A.I.C.S.: 541990

Driver Trett (Singapore) Pte. Ltd.   **(1)**

---

18 Cross Street 09-04 Cross Street Exchange, Singapore, 048423, Singapore
Tel.: (65) 6 226 4317
Dispute Resolution Services
N.A.I.C.S.: 541990

North Gate Executive Search Limited   **(1)**
3rd Floor 110 Cannon Street, London, EC4N 6EU, United Kingdom
Tel.: (44) 2072800190
Web Site: http://www.north-gate.co.uk
Sales Range: $25-49.9 Million
Emp.: 70
Construction & Engineering Executives Recruitment Services
N.A.I.C.S.: 561311

Trett Ltd.   **(1)**
Driver House 4 St Crispin Way, Rossendale, Haslingden, BB4 4PW, United Kingdom
Tel.: (44) 170 622 3999
Dispute Resolution Services
N.A.I.C.S.: 541990

DIALIGHT PLC

Leaf C Level 36 Tower 42 25 Old Broad Street, London, EC2N 1HQ, United Kingdom
Tel.: (44) 2030583540   **UK**
Web Site: http://www.dialight.com
Year Founded: 1990
DIA—(LSE)
Rev.: $189,432,816
Assets: $160,024,899
Liabilities: $76,766,121
Net Worth: $83,258,778
Earnings: ($41,374,775)
Fiscal Year-end: 12/31/23
Mfr of Light Emitting Diode (LED) Indicators, Traffic Signals, Beacons & Vehicle Lighting
N.A.I.C.S.: 334419
Fariyal Khanbabi *(CEO)*

Subsidiaries:

Dialight Asia Pte. Ltd.   **(1)**
33 Ubi Avenue 3 07-72 Vertex Tower A, Singapore, 408863, Singapore
Tel.: (65) 6 578 7157
Lighting Product Distr
N.A.I.C.S.: 423610

Dialight BTI A/S   **(1)**
Ejby Industrivej 91B, 2600, Glostrup, Denmark
Tel.: (45) 8 877 4545
Web Site: http://www.dialightbti.com
Sales Range: $25-49.9 Million
Emp.: 20
Navigational Lights Mfr & Distr
N.A.I.C.S.: 423610
Jesper Engesgaard *(CEO)*

Dialight Corporation   **(1)**
1501 Route 34 S, Farmingdale, NJ 07727   **(100%)**
Tel.: (732) 919-3119
Web Site: http://www.dialight.com
Sales Range: $25-49.9 Million
Emp.: 100
Mfr of LED Products
N.A.I.C.S.: 334419

Dialight Europe Limited   **(1)**
Exning Road, Newmarket, CB8 0AX, Suffolk, United Kingdom
Tel.: (44) 1638666541
Lighting Fixture Distr
N.A.I.C.S.: 423610

DIALOG FINANCE PLC

Tel.: (94) 114317317
Web Site:
   https://www.dialogfinance.lk
CALF.N0000—(COL)
Rev.: $3,376,653
Assets: $18,388,370
Liabilities: $10,218,955
Net Worth: $8,169,415
Earnings: $138,204
Emp.: 97
Fiscal Year-end: 12/31/23
Financial Consulting Services

N.A.I.C.S.: 541611
Hans Wijayasuriya *(Chm)*

DIALOG GROUP BERHAD

DIALOG TOWER No 15 Jalan PJU 7/5 Mutiara Damansara, 47810, Petaling Jaya, Selangor Darul Ehsan, Malaysia
Tel.: (60) 377171111
Web Site: https://www.dialogasia.com
DIALOG—(KLS)
Rev.: $635,245,291
Assets: $1,970,716,614
Liabilities: $666,945,820
Net Worth: $1,303,770,794
Earnings: $110,184,762
Emp.: 2,744
Fiscal Year-end: 06/30/23
Oil, Gas & Petrochemical Products Services
N.A.I.C.S.: 324110
Rokmanhili Zakaria *(Mgr-Indonesia)*

Subsidiaries:

Cendana Sutera Sdn. Bhd.   **(1)**
Projet Jalan Klang banting, 41200, Kelang, Selangor, Malaysia
Tel.: (60) 333234928
Petroleum Retailer
N.A.I.C.S.: 424710

DIV Services Sdn. Bhd.   **(1)**
Dialog Tower Level 3 No 15 Jalan PJU 7/5, Mutiara Damansara, 47810, Petaling Jaya, Selangor Darul Ehsan, Malaysia
Tel.: (60) 377201800
Web Site: https://www.whalet.com.my
Financial Services
N.A.I.C.S.: 523999

Dialog E & C Sdn. Bhd.   **(1)**
15 Jalan PJU 7/5 Mutiara Demensara, Petaling Jaya, 47810, Selangor, Malaysia
Tel.: (60) 379551199
Sales Range: $75-99.9 Million
Emp.: 300
Construction Engineering Services
N.A.I.C.S.: 541330
Jamal Kamaludin *(CEO)*

Dialog ESECO Sdn. Bhd.   **(1)**
No 15 Jalan PJU 7/5 Mutiara Damansara, 47810, Petaling Jaya, Selangor, Malaysia
Tel.: (60) 377171111
Web Site: https://www.dialogeseco.com
Recycling Services
N.A.I.C.S.: 562920

Dialog International (L) Ltd.   **(1)**
No 10 Tuas Avenue 16, Singapore, Singapore
Tel.: (65) 63363377
Petrochemical Product Distr
N.A.I.C.S.: 424690
Steven Teow Yee *(Mgr-Mktg)*

Dialog Services Pty. Ltd.   **(1)**
7 Burgay Court, Osborne Park, Perth, 6017, WA, Australia
Tel.: (61) 892449899
Catalyst Handling Services
N.A.I.C.S.: 541690
Andy Copland *(Gen Mgr)*

Dialog Services, Inc.   **(1)**
1311 C Ave A, South Houston, TX 77587
Tel.: (832) 668-5726
Web Site: http://www.dialogasia.com
Sales Range: $25-49.9 Million
Emp.: 54
Catalyst Handling Services
N.A.I.C.S.: 488320

Dialog Technivac Ltd.   **(1)**
Unit 4 Raven Close Bridgend Industrial Estate, Bridgend, CF31 3RF, Mid Glamorgan, United Kingdom
Tel.: (44) 1656645856
Web Site: http://www.technivac.co.uk
Sales Range: $25-49.9 Million
Emp.: 25
Research & Development of Purpose Designed Catalyst Handling Equipment & Eliminating Dust Emissions
N.A.I.C.S.: 333413
David Morgan *(Gen Mgr)*

Fineline Services Limited   **(1)**
215 Connett Rd E, Bell Block, New Plymouth, 4373, New Zealand
Tel.: (64) 67551691
Web Site: http://www.finelineservices.co.nz
Fabricated Metal Products Mfr
N.A.I.C.S.: 332996

Overseas Technical Engineering and Construction Pte. Ltd.   **(1)**
10 Tuas Ave 16, Singapore, 638931, Singapore
Tel.: (65) 67786300
Web Site: http://www.otec.com.sg
Sales Range: $25-49.9 Million
Emp.: 100
Construction Engineering Services
N.A.I.C.S.: 541330

Pan Orient Energy Corp.   **(1)**
505 3rd Street SW Suite 1505, Calgary, T2P 3E6, AB, Canada
Tel.: (403) 294-1770
Web Site: http://www.panorient.ca
Rev.: $3,742,024
Assets: $112,227,037
Liabilities: $8,613,541
Net Worth: $103,613,496
Earnings: ($19,228,185)
Emp.: 160
Fiscal Year-end: 12/31/2019
Oil & Gas Exploration
N.A.I.C.S.: 211120
Jeff Chisholm *(CEO & Dir)*

DIAMANT ART CORP.

100 Warden Ave Unit 5-7, Markham, L3R 8B5, ON, Canada
Tel.: (905) 477-0252
Marketing Consulting Services
N.A.I.C.S.: 541613
Michel Van Herreweghe *(Chm)*

DIAMANT INFRASTRUCTURE LIMITED

Plot No 3 Hindustan Colony Wardha Road, Nagpur, 440 010, Maharashtra, India
Tel.: (91) 7126610222   **In**
Web Site:
   https://www.diamantinfra.com
Year Founded: 1980
508860—(BOM)
Rev.: $19,793
Assets: $4,209,930
Liabilities: $1,982,684
Net Worth: $2,227,246
Earnings: ($81,625)
Fiscal Year-end: 03/31/20
Construction & Engineering Services
N.A.I.C.S.: 237990
Naresh Satyanarayan Saboo *(Mng Dir & CFO)*

DIAMCOR MINING INC.

630-1620 Dickson Avenue, Kelowna, V1Y 9Y2, BC, Canada
Tel.: (250) 862-3212
Web Site:
   https://www.diamcormining.com
DMIFF—(OTCQB)
Rev.: $5,379,236
Assets: $5,983,434
Liabilities: $7,774,957
Net Worth: ($1,791,523)
Earnings: ($568,682)
Fiscal Year-end: 03/31/23
Diamond Mining Services
N.A.I.C.S.: 212311
Dean H. Taylor *(Chm, Pres & CEO)*

DIAMINES AND CHEMICALS LIMITED

Plot No 13 PCC Area P O Petrochemicals, Vadodara, 391346, India
Tel.: (91) 2653534200
Web Site: https://www.dacl.co.in
Year Founded: 1976
DIAMINESQ—(NSE)
Rev.: $12,779,781
Assets: $19,504,816

Liabilities: $1,745,936
Net Worth: $17,758,881
Earnings: $1,904,899
Emp.: 151
Fiscal Year-end: 03/31/24
Ethylene Amines Mfr
N.A.I.C.S.: 325199
Amit M. Mehta (Chm)

DIAMOND AGENCY, INC.

Sanyo Akasaka Building 3-5-2 Akasaka, Minato-ku, Tokyo, 107-0052, Japan
Tel.: (81) 335683421   JP
Web Site: http://www.diamond-ag.co.jp
Year Founded: 1962
Sales Range: $1-4.9 Billion
Emp.: 50
N.A.I.C.S.: 541810
Masao Ono (Dir-Fin)

DIAMOND AIRCRAFT INDUSTRIES GMBH

NA Ottostrasse 5, 2700, Wiener Neustadt, Austria
Tel.: (43) 262226700
Web Site: http://www.diamond-air.at
Sales Range: $75-99.9 Million
Emp.: 500
Aircraft Mfr
N.A.I.C.S.: 336411
Bin Chen (Chm)

Subsidiaries:

Austro Engine GmbH   (1)
Rudolf Diesel-Strasse 11, 2700, Wiener Neustadt, Austria
Tel.: (43) 2622 23000
Web Site: http://www.austroengine.at
Emp.: 80
Aircraft Engine Mfr & Distr
N.A.I.C.S.: 336412
Jurgen Heinrich (Gen Mgr)

Diamond Airborne Sensing
GmbH   (1)
Ferdinand Graf von Zeppelin Strasse 1, 2700, Wiener Neustadt, Austria
Tel.: (43) 2622 26700
Web Site: http://www.diamond-sensing.com
Aircraft Mfr
N.A.I.C.S.: 336411
Christian Dries (CEO)

Diamond Simulation GmbH   (1)
Am Flugplatz / Diamond Terminal, 63329, Egelsbach, Germany
Tel.: (49) 6103 3785 2174
Web Site: http://www.diamond-air.com
Aircraft Training Services
N.A.I.C.S.: 611512
Kristen Dries (Gen Mgr)

DIAMOND BUILDING PRODUCTS PUBLIC COMPANY LIMITED

69-70 Moo 1 Mitraphap Km 115 Thambon Talingchan Amphur Muang, Saraburi, 18000, Thailand
Tel.: (66) 36224171
Web Site: https://www.dbp.co.th
Year Founded: 1985
DRT—(THA)
Rev.: $164,843,465
Assets: $110,249,223
Liabilities: $34,930,430
Net Worth: $75,318,793
Earnings: $18,610,043
Emp.: 1,059
Fiscal Year-end: 12/31/23
Roofing Tiles, Siding Boards & Other Roofing Equipment Mfr & Distr
N.A.I.C.S.: 327120
Prakit Pradipasen (Chm)

Subsidiaries:

Diamond Materials Co., Ltd.   (1)
Number 263 Moo 10, Tambon Maefaek Am-

phur Sansai, Chiang Mai, 50290, Thailand
Tel.: (66) 362241718
Roofing Product Mfr & Distr
N.A.I.C.S.: 324122

DIAMOND COMPANY OF ARMENIA

1 Sovkhozyan Street, 375082, Yerevan, Armenia
Tel.: (374) 1589993
Web Site: http://www.dca.nt.am
Sales Range: $125-149.9 Million
Emp.: 1,000
Diamonds & Other Jewelry Mfr
N.A.I.C.S.: 339910

DIAMOND ELECTRIC HOLDINGS CO., LTD.

1-15-27 Tsukamoto, Yodogawa-ku, Osaka, 532-0026, Japan
Tel.: (81) 663028211
Web Site: https://www.diaelec-hd.co.jp
Year Founded: 2018
6699—(TKS)
Rev.: $616,937,740
Assets: $542,231,520
Liabilities: $474,280,720
Net Worth: $67,950,800
Earnings: ($12,539,170)
Emp.: 3,751
Fiscal Year-end: 03/31/24
Holding Company
N.A.I.C.S.: 551112
Yuuri Ono (Chm, Pres & CEO)

DIAMOND ELECTRIC MFG. CO., LTD.

1-15-27 Tsukamoto, Yodogawa-ku, Osaka, 532-0026, Japan
Tel.: (81) 6 63028141
Web Site: http://www.diaelec.co.jp
Year Founded: 1937
Rev.: $515,004,480
Assets: $308,873,040
Liabilities: $243,249,840
Net Worth: $65,623,200
Earnings: $9,048,720
Emp.: 2,203
Fiscal Year-end: 03/31/18
Automobile & Electronic Equipment Mfr & Whslr
N.A.I.C.S.: 336320
Yuuri Ono (Pres & CEO)

Subsidiaries:

Tabuchi Electric Co., Ltd.   (1)
Nissay Shin-osaka Bldg 3-4-30 Miyahara, Yodogawa-ku, Osaka, 532-0003, Japan   (68.89%)
Tel.: (81) 648073500
Web Site: http://www.zbr.co.jp
Rev.: $234,582,960
Assets: $201,531,600
Liabilities: $190,191,840
Net Worth: $11,339,760
Earnings: ($78,410,400)
Emp.: 3,364
Fiscal Year-end: 03/31/2018
Transformers & Power Supplies for Electronic & Electrical Equipment
N.A.I.C.S.: 334416
Yuuri Ono (Pres)

Subsidiary (Non-US):

Korea Transformer Co. Ltd.   (2)
237-18 Kuro-dong, Kuro-ku, Seoul, 152848, Korea (South)
Tel.: (82) 28568951
Web Site: http://www.kortrans.co.kr
Sales Range: $25-49.9 Million
Emp.: 20
Mfr of Transformers
N.A.I.C.S.: 334416
Kim Dong Kg (Gen Mgr)

Subsidiary (US):

Tabuchi Electric Company of
America   (2)

65 Germantown Ct Ste 107, Cordova, TN 38018-4259
Tel.: (901) 757-2300
Web Site: http://www.zbr.co.jp
Sales Range: $25-49.9 Million
Emp.: 3
Sales of Transformers & Accounting & Administration of Transformers
N.A.I.C.S.: 334416

Subsidiary (Non-US):

Tabuchi Electric U.K. Ltd.   (2)
Tabuchi House Teeside Industrial Estate Thornaby, Stockton-on-Tees, TS17 9LS, United Kingdom   (100%)
Tel.: (44) 1642750750
Mfr of Transformers
N.A.I.C.S.: 334416

DIAMOND ESTATES WINES & SPIRITS, INC.

1067 Niagara Stone Rd, Niagara-on-the-Lake, L0S 1J0, ON, Canada
Tel.: (905) 685-5673
Web Site: https://www.lakeviewwineco.com
DWS—(TSXV)
Rev.: $21,057,317
Assets: $38,851,527
Liabilities: $23,414,915
Net Worth: $15,436,612
Earnings: ($7,869,136)
Fiscal Year-end: 03/31/24
Wine & Spirits Mfr & Distr
N.A.I.C.S.: 312140
J. Murray Souter (Pres & CEO)

Subsidiaries:

Backyard Vineyards Corp.   (1)
3033 232 Street, Langley, V2Z 3A8, BC, Canada
Tel.: (604) 539-9463
Web Site: https://www.backyardvineyards.ca
Alcoholic Beverage Product Distr
N.A.I.C.S.: 424820

Kirkwood Diamond Canada   (1)
1155 North Service Road West Suite 5, Oakville, L6M 3E3, ON, Canada   (100%)
Tel.: (905) 849-4346
Web Site: http://www.kirkwooddiamond.com
Emp.: 35
Wines, Spirits & Beers Distr
N.A.I.C.S.: 424820
Russell Sandham (Dir-Mktg-Wines)

DIAMOND INDUSTRIES LIMITED

23-Km Multan Road Mohlanwal, Lahore, Pakistan
Tel.: (92) 938270697
Web Site: http://www.diamondfoam.com
DIIL—(PSX)
Rev.: $129,247
Assets: $2,771,704
Liabilities: $1,478,052
Net Worth: $1,293,653
Earnings: ($203,006)
Emp.: 7
Fiscal Year-end: 06/30/19
Chemical Products Mfr
N.A.I.C.S.: 325998

DIAMOND INFOSYSTEMS LTD

ESSEN Info-Park 5/9-10 BIDC, Gorwa, Baroda, 390016, Gujarat, India
Tel.: (91) 265 2283969   In
Web Site: http://www.diinsy.com
Year Founded: 1993
Rev.: $43,639,155
Assets: $13,390,905
Liabilities: $7,755,060
Net Worth: $5,635,846
Earnings: $34,931
Fiscal Year-end: 03/31/16
Information Technology Consulting Services
N.A.I.C.S.: 541512

Amit Suresh Bhatnagar (Vice Chm)

DIAMOND INTERNATIONAL TRUCKS LTD.

17020-118 Avenue, Edmonton, T5S 1S4, AB, Canada
Tel.: (780) 454-1541
Web Site: http://www.dit.ca
Year Founded: 1989
Sales Range: $25-49.9 Million
Truck Distr
N.A.I.C.S.: 441227
Don MacAdam (Pres)

Subsidiaries:

Diamond International Trucks (GP) Ltd.   (1)
9916-108 Street, Grande Prairie, T8V 4E2, AB, Canada
Tel.: (780) 532-3541
Web Site: http://www.dit.ca
Sales Range: $25-49.9 Million
Emp.: 30
Truck Dealers
N.A.I.C.S.: 441227

DIAMOND KEY INTERNATIONAL PTY. LTD

110 Henderson Rd Rowville, Victoria, 3178, Australia
Tel.: (61) 397308888
Web Site: https://www.diamondkey.com
Year Founded: 1998
Emp.: 103
Oil, Gas & Chemical & Lubes Industries. Dist.
N.A.I.C.S.: 221210
Lily Chen (CEO)

Subsidiaries:

Cool Sorption A/S   (1)
Smedeland 6, Glostrup, 2600, Copenhagen, Denmark
Tel.: (45) 43454745
Web Site: http://www.coolsorption.com
Vapor Recovery Installation Services
N.A.I.C.S.: 213112
Tine Hoj Andersen (CEO)

DIAMOND POWER INFRASTRUCTURE LTD.

Vadadala PHASE - II Savli, PO Box 3008, Vadodara, 391520, Gujarat, India
Tel.: (91) 2667251516
Web Site: https://www.dicabs.com
522163—(BOM)
Power Transmission Equipment Mfr
N.A.I.C.S.: 333613
Amit Bhatnagar (Co-Mng Dir)

DIAMOND SA

Via Dei Patrizi 5, Losone, 6616, Locarno, Switzerland
Tel.: (41) 583074545
Web Site: https://www.diamond-fo.com
Year Founded: 1958
MW8—(DEU)
Emp.: 200
Jewelry Retailer
N.A.I.C.S.: 423940

Subsidiaries:

Diamond USA Inc.   (1)
85 Rangeway Rd Bldg 3, North Billerica, MA 01862
Tel.: (978) 256-6544
Web Site: https://www.diausa.com
Emp.: 300
Fiber Optic Product Mfr
N.A.I.C.S.: 335921

DIAMOND TRUST BANK KENYA LIMITED

DTB Centre Mombasa Road, PO Box 61711, 00200, Nairobi, Kenya

Diamond Trust Bank Kenya Limited—(Continued)

Tel.: (254) 719031888
Web Site: https://dtbk.dtbafrica.com
Year Founded: 1945
DTK—(NAI)
Rev.: $282,917,198
Assets: $3,867,991,709
Liabilities: $3,246,333,108
Net Worth: $621,658,601
Earnings: $32,110,497
Emp.: 2,223
Fiscal Year-end: 12/31/20
Personal Banking Services
N.A.I.C.S.: 522201
Alkarim Jiwa *(Dir-Fin)*

Subsidiaries:

Diamond Trust Bank Burundi
S.A. (1)
14 Chaussee Prince Louis Rwagasore, Bujumbura, Burundi
Tel.: (257) 22259988
Web Site: https://dtbb.co.bi
Commercial Banking Services
N.A.I.C.S.: 522110

Diamond Trust Bank Uganda
Limited (1)
Diamond Trust Building Plot 17/19 Kampala Road, PO Box 7155, Kampala, Uganda
Tel.: (256) 414387000
Banking Services
N.A.I.C.S.: 522110

DIAN DIAGNOSTICS GROUP CO., LTD.

5th Floor Building 2 No 329 Jinpeng Street, Sandun Town Xihu District, Hangzhou, 310030, Zhejiang, China
Tel.: (86) 57158085608 CN
Web Site: https://www.dazd.cn
Year Founded: 2001
300244—(CHIN)
Rev.: $2,847,658,788
Assets: $2,956,258,188
Liabilities: $1,622,177,388
Net Worth: $1,334,080,800
Earnings: $201,360,276
Emp.: 10,000
Fiscal Year-end: 12/31/22
Medical Diagnostic Services
N.A.I.C.S.: 621512
Haibin Chen *(Chm & Gen Mgr)*

DIANA DOLLS FASHIONS INC

555 Barton St, Stoney Creek, L8E
5S1, ON, Canada
Tel.: (905) 643-9118
Web Site: http://www.kushies.com
Year Founded: 1953
Sales Range: $25-49.9 Million
Baby Products & Accessories Mfr
N.A.I.C.S.: 315250
Sam Perez *(Pres & CEO)*

DIANA SHIPPING INC.

Pendelis 16, Palaio Faliro, 17564,
Athens, Greece
Tel.: (30) 2109470100 MH
Web Site:
https://www.dianashippinginc.com
DSX—(NYSE)
Rev.: $262,098,000
Assets: $1,166,410,000
Liabilities: $677,389,000
Net Worth: $489,021,000
Earnings: $44,075,000
Emp.: 1,018
Fiscal Year-end: 12/31/23
Cargo Transport Services
N.A.I.C.S.: 483111
Simeon P. Palios *(Chm)*

DIANA TEA COMPANY LIMITED

Sir RNM House 4th Floor 3/B Lal Bazar Street, Kolkata, 700 001, India

Tel.: (91) 3322488672
Web Site: https://www.dianatea.in
Year Founded: 1911
530959—(BOM)
Rev.: $9,862,466
Assets: $13,471,567
Liabilities: $4,655,360
Net Worth: $8,816,207
Earnings: $644,580
Emp.: 3,628
Fiscal Year-end: 03/31/21
Tea & Coffee Mfr
N.A.I.C.S.: 311920
Sandeep Singhania *(Mng Dir)*

DIANGUANG EXPLOSION-PROOF TECHNOLOGY CO., LTD.

No 180 Weiwu Road Yueqing Economic Development Zone, Wenzhou, 325600, Zhejiang, China
Tel.: (86) 57761666333
Web Site: http://www.dianguang.com
Year Founded: 1965
002730—(SSE)
Rev.: $88,124,868
Assets: $311,811,552
Liabilities: $97,721,208
Net Worth: $214,090,344
Earnings: $6,817,824
Emp.: 140
Fiscal Year-end: 12/31/22
Explosion-Proof Electrical Products
N.A.I.C.S.: 335999
Sui Biao Shi *(Chm)*

DIANOMI PLC

Thomas House 84 Ecclestone Square, London, SW1V 1PX, United Kingdom UK
Web Site: https://www.dianomi.com
Year Founded: 2002
DNM—(LSE)
Rev.: $44,599,247
Assets: $25,363,765
Liabilities: $10,726,668
Net Worth: $14,637,097
Earnings: $602,273
Emp.: 46
Fiscal Year-end: 12/31/22
Digital Marketing Services
N.A.I.C.S.: 541810
Charlotte Stranner *(CFO)*

Subsidiaries:

Dianomi Inc. (1)
12 E 49th St 15th Fl, New York, NY 10017
Tel.: (917) 281-2649
Advertising Services
N.A.I.C.S.: 541810

DIASFIN SA

Sos Pantelimon nr 1A sector 2, Bucharest, Romania
Tel.: (40) 212521450
Web Site: https://www.diasfin.ro
Year Founded: 1991
DIAS—(BUC)
Rev.: $153,223
Assets: $2,686,642
Liabilities: $49,558
Net Worth: $2,637,084
Earnings: $9,046
Emp.: 5
Fiscal Year-end: 12/31/23
Metal Plating Services
N.A.I.C.S.: 332812

DIASORIN S.P.A.

Via Crescentin, 13040, Saluggia, Vercelli, Italy
Tel.: (39) 01614871
Web Site: https://int.diasorin.com
DIA—(ITA)
Rev.: $1,082,454,053
Assets: $1,530,934,835
Liabilities: $356,345,586

Net Worth: $1,174,589,249
Earnings: $304,967,079
Emp.: 2,000
Fiscal Year-end: 12/31/20
Bioengineering Products
N.A.I.C.S.: 325413
Gustavo Denegri *(Chm)*

Subsidiaries:

Biofin Holding International BV (1)
Rokin 55, 1012 KK, Amsterdam,
Netherlands (100%)
Tel.: (31) 205214713
Sales Range: $150-199.9 Million
Emp.: 638
Bioengineering
N.A.I.C.S.: 541330

Subsidiary (US):

DiaSorin Inc. (2)
1951 Northwestern Ave, Stillwater, MN 55082-7536
Tel.: (651) 439-9710
Web Site: https://us.diasorin.com
Sales Range: $50-74.9 Million
Emp.: 160
In-Vitro Diagnostics Mfr
N.A.I.C.S.: 325413

Holding (Non-US):

DiaSorin AB (3)
Solna Torg 19 floor 5, Solna, 171 45, Sundbyberg, Sweden (100%)
Tel.: (46) 855520300
Sales Range: $50-74.9 Million
Emp.: 9
Diagnostic Products Mfr
N.A.I.C.S.: 325412

DiaSorin Deutschland GmbH (3)
Von-Hevesy-Strasse 3, 63128, Dietzenbach, Germany
Tel.: (49) 60744010
Web Site: http://www.diasorin.de
Sales Range: $25-49.9 Million
Emp.: 100
In-Vitro Diagnostics Mfr
N.A.I.C.S.: 325413

DiaSorin Ltd. (3)
(100%)
Tel.: (44) 1322317949
Sales Range: $25-49.9 Million
Emp.: 19
Mfr & Marketing of Diagnostic Products
N.A.I.C.S.: 325412

DiaSorin Australia (Pty) Ltd, (1)
Building B Suite 1 Level 4 11 Talavera Road, Macquarie Park, 2113, NSW, Australia
Tel.: (61) 293384888
Biotechnology Research & Development Services
N.A.I.C.S.: 541714

DiaSorin Canada Inc. (1)
5975 Whittle Road Suite 210, Mississauga, L4Z 3N1, ON, Canada
Tel.: (905) 677-1600
Biotechnology Research & Development Services
N.A.I.C.S.: 541714

DiaSorin Czech s.r.o. (1)
K Hajum 2B, 155 00, Prague, 5, Czech Republic
Tel.: (420) 235311904
Biotechnology Research & Development Services
N.A.I.C.S.: 541714

DiaSorin Iberia S.A. (1)
Tel.: (34) 916623321
Biotechnology Research & Development Services
N.A.I.C.S.: 541714

DiaSorin Ltda (1)
Av Ermano Marchetti 1435 B, Sao Paulo, 05038-001, SP, Brazil
Tel.: (55) 113618600
Biotechnology Research & Development Services
N.A.I.C.S.: 541714

DiaSorin Mexico S.A de C.V. (1)

Blvd Manuel Avila Camacho 118 Piso 3 of 301, Lomas de Chapultepec Miguel Hidalgo, 11000, Mexico, Mexico
Tel.: (52) 5555364891
Biotechnology Research & Development Services
N.A.I.C.S.: 541714

DiaSorin Molecular LLC (1)
11331 Valley View St, Cypress, CA 90630
Tel.: (562) 240-6500
Web Site: https://molecular.diasorin.com
Diagnostic Product Mfr & Distr
N.A.I.C.S.: 334510

DiaSorin Poland Sp. z o.o. (1)
ul Jutrzenki 137a, 02-231, Warsaw, Poland
Tel.: (48) 222236260
Biotechnology Research & Development Services
N.A.I.C.S.: 541714

DiaSorin S.A. (1)
11 Rue George Besse Batiment Galilee, 92182, Antony, Cedex, France
Tel.: (33) 155590400
Biotechnology Research & Development Services
N.A.I.C.S.: 541714

DiaSorin S.A./N.V. (1)
Boulevard Paepsem/Paepsemlaan 11, 1070, Brussels, Belgium
Tel.: (32) 23402929
Biotechnology Research & Development Services
N.A.I.C.S.: 541714

Diasorin Italia S.p.a. (1)
Via Crescentino, 13040, Saluggia, VC, Italy
Tel.: (39) 0161487093
Diagnostic Services
N.A.I.C.S.: 621512

Focus Diagnostics, Inc. (1)
1131 Valley View St, Cypress, CA 90630-4717
Web Site: http://www.focusdx.com
Testing Laboratory Services
N.A.I.C.S.: 621511

Luminex Corporation (1)
12212 Technology Blvd, Austin, TX 78727
Tel.: (512) 219-8020
Web Site: http://www.luminexcorp.com
Rev.: $417,396,000
Assets: $825,463,000
Liabilities: $307,752,000
Net Worth: $517,711,000
Earnings: $15,170,000
Emp.: 1,325
Fiscal Year-end: 12/31/2020
Molecular Diagnostics, Life Science Research & Multiplexing
N.A.I.C.S.: 541714
Nachum Shamir *(CEO & Chm,Pres)*

Subsidiary (Non-US):

Luminex (Australia) Pty. Ltd (2)
Unit 15 Pacific Place 10 Old Chatswood Road, Daisy Hill, Logan, 4127, QLD, Australia
Tel.: (61) 732730273
Web Site: http://www.luminex.com
Emp.: 9
Biological Testing Products Mfr
N.A.I.C.S.: 541380

Luminex BV (2)
Het Zuiderkruis 1, 5215 MV, Den Bosch, Netherlands
Tel.: (31) 738001900
Web Site: http://www.luminexcorp.com
Mfr of Computer Hardware
N.A.I.C.S.: 334118

Luminex Molecular Diagnostics (2)
439 University Ave Ste 900, Toronto, M5G 1Y8, ON, Canada
Tel.: (416) 593-4323
Web Site: http://www.tmbioscience.com
Sales Range: $1-9.9 Million
Emp.: 150
Resources for Genetic Testing Market
N.A.I.C.S.: 325412

DIATREME RESOURCES LIMITED

Unit 8 55-61 Holdsworth Street, PO

Box 382, Coorparoo, 4151, QLD, Australia
Tel.: (61) 733972222
Web Site:
https://www.diatreme.com.au
DRX—(ASX)
Rev.: $5,602,507
Assets: $36,940,905
Liabilities: $1,727,470
Net Worth: $35,213,435
Earnings: $3,323,565
Emp.: 90
Fiscal Year-end: 12/31/22
Mineral Mining Services
N.A.I.C.S.: 213115
Neil John McIntyre *(CEO)*

Subsidiaries:

Lost Sands Pty Ltd **(1)**
Level 2 87 Wickham Terr, Spring Hill, 4000, QLD, Australia
Tel.: (61) 738325666
Web Site: http://www.diatreme.com.au
Sales Range: $50-74.9 Million
Mineral Exploration Services
N.A.I.C.S.: 212290

Metallica Minerals Limited **(1)**
Tel.: (61) 732493000
Web Site:
https://www.metallicaminerals.com.au
Rev.: $212,692
Assets: $6,757,644
Liabilities: $301,472
Net Worth: $6,456,172
Earnings: ($2,340,704)
Emp.: 6
Fiscal Year-end: 06/30/2021
Mineral Exploration Services
N.A.I.C.S.: 212290
Nicholas Villa *(Gen Mgr)*

Regional Exploration Management Pty Ltd **(1)**
Level 1 47 McKenzie St, Ceduna, 5690, SA, Australia
Tel.: (61) 886253567
Mineral Exploration Services
N.A.I.C.S.: 213115

DIC - DONG TIEN JOINT STOCK COMPANY
Plot 17 Street 25B Nhon Trach II Industrial Zone, Dong Nai, Vietnam
Tel.: (84) 613521752
Web Site: http://www.dicdongtien.vn
DID—(HNX)
Rev.: $35,272,700
Assets: $38,769,300
Liabilities: $20,452,800
Net Worth: $18,316,500
Earnings: $47,300
Fiscal Year-end: 12/31/22
Readymix Concrete Mfr
N.A.I.C.S.: 327320

DIC ASSET AG
Neue Mainzer Strasse 20, MainTor, 60311, Frankfurt am Main, Germany
Tel.: (49) 6994548580
Web Site: https://branicks.com
BRNK—(MUN)
Rev.: $237,872,946
Assets: $5,349,541,678
Liabilities: $4,196,284,534
Net Worth: $1,153,257,144
Earnings: ($72,811,265)
Emp.: 305
Fiscal Year-end: 12/31/23
Commercial Real Estate Investment & Management Services
N.A.I.C.S.: 531390
Gerhard Schmidt *(Chm-Supervisory Bd)*

Subsidiaries:

BK Immobilien Verwaltung GmbH **(1)**
Bahnhofstr 17, 66740, Saarlouis, Germany
Tel.: (49) 68318935404

Web Site:
https://www.bkimmobilienverwaltung.de
Real Estate Manangement Services
N.A.I.C.S.: 531210

DIC Onsite GmbH **(1)**
New Mainzer Strasse 20, MainTor, 60311, Frankfurt am Main, Germany
Tel.: (49) 6921937890
Web Site: http://www.dic-onsite.de
Real Estate Services
N.A.I.C.S.: 531390

DIC CORPORATION
DIC Building 7-20 Nihonbashi 3-chome, Chuo-ku, Tokyo, 103-8233, Japan
Tel.: (81) 367333000   **JP**
Web Site: https://www.dic-global.com
Year Founded: 1908
4631—(TKS)
Rev.: $7,364,638,240
Assets: $8,826,263,010
Liabilities: $5,995,459,980
Net Worth: $2,830,803,030
Earnings: ($282,586,130)
Emp.: 22,255
Fiscal Year-end: 12/31/23
Specialty Chemicals & Printing Inks Mfr & Sales
N.A.I.C.S.: 325910
Masayuki Saito *(Exec VP)*

Subsidiaries:

Cast Film Japan Co., Ltd. **(1)**
2100-28 Kamiyoshiba, Satte, 340-0121, Saitama, Japan
Tel.: (81) 480481670
Web Site: https://castfilm.co.jp
Emp.: 189
Cast Polyolefin Film Mfr
N.A.I.C.S.: 326113

Changzhou Huari New Material Co., Ltd. **(1)**
No 2 Donggang Road 3, Xinbei District, Changzhou, 213127, Jiangsu, China
Tel.: (86) 5198 521 2688
Web Site: https://www.czdic.com.cn
Polyester Resin Mfr
N.A.I.C.S.: 325211

Chia Lung Chemical Industrial Corp. **(1)**
10th Floor Chang An Building No 18 Chang An East Road, Section 1, Taipei, Taiwan **(100%)**
Tel.: (886) 225677071
Web Site: http://www.dic.co.jp
Sales Range: $25-49.9 Million
Emp.: 87
Mfr & Sales of Plastic Colorants, Compounds & Printing Inks
N.A.I.C.S.: 325211

Coates Brothers (South Africa) (Pty). Ltd. **(1)**
7 18 Ave Maitland, PO Box 1057, Cape Town, 7405, South Africa **(100%)**
Tel.: (27) 215905100
Web Site: http://www.sunchemical.com
Sales Range: $50-74.9 Million
Emp.: 180
Sales of Chemicals
N.A.I.C.S.: 325998

DC Katsuya Co., Ltd. **(1)**
Nagoya DIC Building 9F 3-7-15 Nishiki, Naka-ku, Nagoya, 460-0003, Aichi, Japan
Tel.: (81) 52 971 7117
Web Site: https://www.dc-katsuya.com
Printing Technology Equipment Distr
N.A.I.C.S.: 423830

DIC (China) Co., Ltd. **(1)**
12th Fl Metro Plaza No 555 Lou Shan Guan Road, Shanghai, 200051, China
Tel.: (86) 216 228 9922
Web Site: http://www.dic.com.cn
Emp.: 58
Printing Ink Mfr & Distr
N.A.I.C.S.: 325910

Subsidiary (Domestic):

Lianyungang DIC Color Co., Ltd. **(2)**

Chemical Industry Park, Dui Gou Gang Town Guan Nan, 222523, Lianyungang, Jiangsu, China
Tel.: (86) 518 8361 8888
Organic Pigment Mfr & Distr
N.A.I.C.S.: 424950

DIC (Guangzhou) Co., Ltd. **(1)**
Tel.: (86) 2083849737
Emp.: 27
Printing Ink Distr
N.A.I.C.S.: 423840

DIC (Malaysia) Sdn. Bhd. **(1)**
(95%)
Tel.: (60) 351910033
Web Site: http://www.dic.com.my
Sales Range: $75-99.9 Million
Emp.: 200
Sales of Printing Inks, Synthetic Resins & Chemicals
N.A.I.C.S.: 423840

DIC (Shanghai) Co., Ltd. **(1)**
12th Fl Metro Plaza No 555 Lou Shan Guan Road, Shanghai, 200051, China
Tel.: (86) 216 228 9911
Web Site: http://www.dic.com.cn
Printing Ink Distr
N.A.I.C.S.: 423840

DIC (Taiwan) Ltd. **(1)**
Room 801 8th Fl Chang An Bldg No 18 Chang An East Road Section 1, Taipei, 104406, Taiwan **(100%)**
Tel.: (886) 225518621
Sales Range: $25-49.9 Million
Emp.: 20
Sales of Printing Inks & Resins
N.A.I.C.S.: 423840

DIC (Vietnam) Co., Ltd. **(1)**
31 VSIP Street 6, Vietnam-Singapore Industrial Park, Thuan An, Binh Duong, Vietnam
Tel.: (84) 274 376 7357
Web Site: https://www.dic-global.com
Emp.: 3
Printing Ink & Resin Mfr & Distr
N.A.I.C.S.: 325910

DIC Alkylphenol Singapore Pte., Ltd. **(1)**
78 Shenton Way 27-02/03, Singapore, 079120, Singapore
Tel.: (65) 6 224 0600
Web Site: http://www.dic-global.com
Sales Range: $25-49.9 Million
Emp.: 27
Alkyl Phenol Mfr
N.A.I.C.S.: 325199

DIC Asia Pacific Pte Ltd. **(1)**
78 Shenton Way, Singapore, 079120, Singapore **(100%)**
Tel.: (65) 62240600
Web Site: http://www.dic.com.jp
Sales Range: $25-49.9 Million
Emp.: 85
Administration of Graphic Arts Materials Operations in Asia & Oceania; Investment in Related Subsidiaries; Sales, Export & Import of Related Products
N.A.I.C.S.: 325910

DIC Australia Pty Ltd. **(1)**
323 Chisholm Road, Auburn, Sydney, 2144, NSW, Australia
Tel.: (61) 29 752 1200
Web Site: http://www.dic.com.au
Emp.: 19
Printing Ink Mfr & Distr
N.A.I.C.S.: 325910
Phillip Roy *(Mgr-Ops)*

DIC Berlin GmbH R & D Laboratory **(1)**
Otisstra 39, D 13403, Berlin, Germany **(100%)**
Tel.: (49) 304357900
Web Site: http://www.dic-berlin.de
Sales Range: $25-49.9 Million
Emp.: 25
Research of Polymers
N.A.I.C.S.: 325211

DIC Color Coatings, Inc. **(1)**
373 Koujibukuro, Konan, 520-3233, Shiga, Japan
Tel.: (81) 748727390

Coating Material Mfr & Whslr
N.A.I.C.S.: 324122

DIC Color Design, Inc. **(1)**
DIC Building 7-20 Nihonbashi 3-chome, Chuo-ku, Tokyo, 103-8233, Japan
Tel.: (81) 36 733 5530
Web Site: https://www.dic-global.com
Sales Range: $25-49.9 Million
Emp.: 53
Graphic Design Services
N.A.I.C.S.: 541430

DIC Colorants Taiwan Co., Ltd. **(1)**
No 15 Ching Chien 6th Road, Kuan Yin Industrial Park Kuan Yin District, Taoyuan, 328, Taiwan
Tel.: (886) 3 483 3311
Web Site: http://www.dic-global.com
Plastic Colorant & Compounds Mfr & Distr
N.A.I.C.S.: 325130

DIC Compounds (Malaysia) Sdn. Bhd. **(1)**
Plot 481 Lorong Perusahaan Baru 2 Kawasan Perindustrian, 13600, Perai, Penang, Malaysia **(100%)**
Tel.: (60) 43902311
Web Site: http://www.dcm-dic.com.my
Sales Range: $50-74.9 Million
Emp.: 150
Plastic Colorants Mfr
N.A.I.C.S.: 325130

DIC Covestro Polymer Ltd. **(1)**
Hamamatsucho Place 1-7-6 Shibakoen, Minato-ku, Tokyo, 105-0011, Japan
Tel.: (81) 364039107
Web Site: https://www.dic-covestro.com
Thermoplastic Polyurethane Mfr & Whslr
N.A.I.C.S.: 325211

DIC Decor, Inc. **(1)**
DIC Building 7-20 Nihonbashi 3-chome, Chuo-ku, Tokyo, 103-8233, Japan
Tel.: (81) 36 733 5895
Web Site: http://www.dic-decor.co.jp
Emp.: 160
Poly Vinyl Chloride Sheet Mfr & Distr
N.A.I.C.S.: 325211
Koji Miura *(CEO)*

DIC EP Corp. **(1)**
11-5 Kitasode, Sodegaura, 299-0125, Chiba, Japan
Tel.: (81) 438630070
Web Site: https://www.dic-ep.co.jp
Emp.: 131
Polymer Resin Mfr
N.A.I.C.S.: 325211

DIC Epoxy (Malaysia) Sdn. Bhd. **(1)**
Plot 408 Jalan Pekeliling, 81700, Pasir Gudang, Johor, Malaysia
Tel.: (60) 72551558
Sales Range: $50-74.9 Million
Emp.: 60
Epoxy Resin Mfr & Distr
N.A.I.C.S.: 325211
Y. K. Tay *(Mgr-Gen Affairs)*

DIC Estate Co., Ltd. **(1)**
DIC Building 7-20 Nihonbashi 3-chome, Chuo-Ku, Tokyo, 103-8233, Japan
Tel.: (81) 367335520
Real Estate Lending Services
N.A.I.C.S.: 531190

DIC Europe GmbH **(1)**
Immermannstr 65D, 40210, Dusseldorf, Germany **(100%)**
Tel.: (49) 2111643170
Web Site: http://www.dic.europe.com.eu
Sales Range: $25-49.9 Million
Emp.: 25
Mfr of Inks
N.A.I.C.S.: 325910
Yasuhisa Nakano *(Gen Mgr)*

Division (Non-US):

DIC Europe - UK **(2)**
Wexham Springs Framewood Road, Slough, SL3 6PJ, United Kingdom **(100%)**
Tel.: (44) 2031390077
Web Site: http://www.dic-global.com
Sales Range: $50-74.9 Million
Emp.: 2
Pigments & Raw Materials for Printing Inks Distr
N.A.I.C.S.: 424950

DIC Corporation—(Continued)

DIC Filtec, Inc. (1)
2100-28 Kamiyoshiba, Satte, 340-0121,
Saitama, Japan
Tel.: (81) 480 48 1670
Plastic Film Mfr & Distr
N.A.I.C.S.: 326113

**DIC Fine Chemicals Private
Limited** (1)
Plot Z3 Dahej Special Economic Zone
Dahej Tal Vagra, Bharuch, 392 130, Guja-
rát, India
Tel.: (91) 9099940176
Printing Ink Mfr
N.A.I.C.S.: 325910
Ram karke (Mgr-HR)

DIC Graphics (Dongguan) Ltd. (1)
No 36 Li Sha Avenue, Shatin Town, Dong-
guan, 523989, Guangdong, China
Tel.: (86) 2032223200
Printing Ink Mfr
N.A.I.C.S.: 325910

DIC Graphics (Guangzhou) Ltd. (1)
No 77 Xi Zhuang Er Road Yonghe Sub-
zone, Guangzhou Economic Technological
Development District, Guangzhou, 511356,
China
Tel.: (86) 203 222 3200
Web Site: http://www.dicgz.com
Printing Ink Mfr & Distr
N.A.I.C.S.: 325910

DIC Graphics (Hong Kong) Ltd. (1)
18 Dai Fu Street Tai Po Industrial Estate,
Tai Po, China (Hong Kong) (100%)
Tel.: (852) 26650280
Web Site: http://www.dic.co.jp
Sales Range: $25-49.9 Million
Emp.: 30
Mfr & Sales of Printing Ink
N.A.I.C.S.: 325910

**DIC Graphics (Shenyang) Co.,
Ltd.** (1)
No 116 Building G25 Northeast City Dia-
mond Road, Xincheng District, Tieling,
112000, Liaoning, China
Tel.: (86) 2486606418
Printing Ink Mfr & Distr
N.A.I.C.S.: 325910

**DIC Graphics (Thailand) Co.,
Ltd.** (1)
159/34 Serm-Mit Tower 20th Floor Soi
Asoke Sukhumvit21 Road, Kwang North
Klongtoey Khet Wattana, Bangkok, 10110,
Thailand
Tel.: (66) 22 606 6307
Web Site: https://www.dic.co.th
Printing Ink Mfr
N.A.I.C.S.: 325910
Thasita Deepatarakul (Sls Mgr)

DIC Graphics Chia Lung Corp. (1)
No 12 Dinghu 1st Street Dahuali, Guishan
District, Taoyuan, 33378, Taiwan
Tel.: (886) 33283301
Web Site: https://www.dicgchialung.com.tw
Sales Range: $50-74.9 Million
Emp.: 90
Printing Ink Mfr
N.A.I.C.S.: 325910
Kaoru Ino (Pres)

DIC Graphics Corporation (1)
DIC Building 7-20 Nihonbashi 3-chome,
Chuo-ku, Tokyo, 103-8233, Japan
Tel.: (81) 36 733 5001
Web Site: https://www.dic-graphics.co.jp
Emp.: 720
Printing Ink Mfr & Distr
N.A.I.C.S.: 325910

Plant (Domestic):

**DIC Graphics Corporation - Chiba
Plant** (2)
12 Yawatakaigandori, Ichihara, 290-8585,
Chiba, Japan
Tel.: (81) 43 641 4121
Web Site: https://www.dic-graphics.co.jp
Printing Ink Mfr
N.A.I.C.S.: 325910

**DIC Graphics Corporation - Gunma
Plant** (2)

Ooazasyowa-1banchi, Chiyoda-machi Oura-
gun, Gunma, 370-0723, Japan
Tel.: (81) 27 686 5811
Web Site: http://www.dic-graphics.co
Printing Ink Mfr
N.A.I.C.S.: 325910

**DIC Graphics Corporation - Hokuriku
Plant** (2)
64-2 Minatomachi-So, Hakusan, 929-0296,
Ishikawa, Japan
Tel.: (81) 76 278 2332
Printing Ink Mfr
N.A.I.C.S.: 325910

**DIC Graphics Corporation - Kansai
Plant** (2)
1-33-1 Kasugakita-cho, Hirakata, 573-0137,
Oosaka, Japan
Tel.: (81) 72 859 1171
Web Site: http://www.dic-graphics.co.jp
Printing Ink Mfr
N.A.I.C.S.: 325910

**DIC Graphics Corporation - Kashima
Plant** (2)
18 Higashifukashiba, Kamisu, 314-0193,
Ibaraki, Japan
Tel.: (81) 299 93 8141
Printing Ink Mfr
N.A.I.C.S.: 325910

**DIC Graphics Corporation - Komaki
Plant** (2)
151-1 Aza Nagare Oaza Shimosue, Ko-
maki, 485-0825, Aichi, Japan
Tel.: (81) 56 875 2751
Web Site: http://www.dic-graphics.co.jp
Printing Ink Mfr & Distr
N.A.I.C.S.: 325910

**DIC Graphics Corporation - Tokyo
Plant** (2)
35-58 Sakashita 3-chome, Itabashi-ku, To-
kyo, 174-8520, Japan
Tel.: (81) 3 3966 2111
Emp.: 480
Printing Ink Mfr
N.A.I.C.S.: 325910
Toshiyuki Kai (Gen Mgr)

DIC Graphics Taiyuan Co., Ltd. (1)
No 230 Donggang Rd, Taiyuan, 030012,
Shanxi, China
Tel.: (86) 3514292184
Sales Range: $150-199.9 Million
Emp.: 300
Printing Ink Mfr & Distr
N.A.I.C.S.: 325910
Zuhua Ma (Mgr)

DIC Imaging Products USA Inc. (1)
7300 S 10th St, Oak Creek, WI 53154-1906
Tel.: (414) 764-5100
Web Site: http://www.dic.co.jp
Emp.: 48
Plastic Materials & Resins
N.A.I.C.S.: 325211

DIC Interior Co., Ltd. (1)
270-8 Odate Komagata Hiratamura,
Ishikawa, 963-8113, Fukushima, Japan
Tel.: (81) 24 7542990
Interior Housing Design Material Mfr
N.A.I.C.S.: 337212

**DIC International (Thailand) Co.,
Ltd.** (1)
59/34 SERMMIT TOWER 20th Floor, Bang-
kok, 10110, Thailand (50%)
Tel.: (66) 22606630
Web Site: http://www.dic.co.th
Sales Range: $75-99.9 Million
Emp.: 200
Sales of Printing Inks & Resins
N.A.I.C.S.: 423840

DIC International (USA), LLC (1)
35 Waterview Blvd, Parsippany, NJ 07054
Tel.: (973) 404-6600
Sales Range: $50-74.9 Million
Emp.: 15
Retailer of Ink & Chemicals
N.A.I.C.S.: 424690
Richard Stanley (Dir-Comml)

**DIC International Australia Pty.
Ltd.** (1)
323 Chisholm Road, Auburn, 2144, NSW,
Australia (100%)

Tel.: (61) 297521200
Emp.: 100
Sales of Printing Inks
N.A.I.C.S.: 423840
Richard Kemp (Dir)

DIC KOREA Corp. (1)
11th floor HSBC Building 37 Chilpae-ro,
Jung-gu, Seoul, 100-773, Korea
(South) (100%)
Tel.: (82) 23176200
Web Site: https://www.dickorea.co.kr
Sales Range: $25-49.9 Million
Emp.: 13
Sales of Inks, Printing Supplies, Synthetic
Resins, Chemicals & Neo-Graphic Arts
N.A.I.C.S.: 325910

DIC Kako, Inc. (1)
185-342 Tokura, Tomisato, Chiba, 286-
0212, Japan
Tel.: (81) 476927611
Web Site: http://www.dic-kako.co.jp
Fiber-Reinforced Plastic Molding Com-
pounds & Molded Product Mfr & Distr
N.A.I.C.S.: 326199

DIC Kitanihon Polymer Co., Ltd. (1)
56 Shin-Oyoke Miya Zao-machi, Katta-gun,
Miyagi, 989-0701, Japan
Tel.: (81) 224322226
Sales Range: $25-49.9 Million
Emp.: 6
Synthetic Resin Mfr
N.A.I.C.S.: 325211

DIC Kyushu Polymer Co., Ltd. (1)
2680-1 Tajiri, Nakatsu, 879-0123, Oita, Ja-
pan
Tel.: (81) 979325370
Synthetic Resin Mfr
N.A.I.C.S.: 325211

DIC Lanka (Private) Ltd. (1)
147 Katuwana Industrial Estate, 10200,
Homagama, Sri Lanka
Tel.: (94) 11 285 5513
Web Site: http://www.dic-global.com
Emp.: 80
Printing Ink Mfr & Distr
N.A.I.C.S.: 325910

DIC Lifetec Co., Ltd. (1)
DIC Building 7-20 Nihonbashi 3-chome,
Chuo-ku, Tokyo, 103-8233, Japan
Tel.: (81) 36 733 5534
Web Site: https://www.dic-global.com
Emp.: 20
Nutritional Food Supplement Mfr & Distr.
N.A.I.C.S.: 311999
Takahiro Takemi (Pres)

**DIC Machinery & Printer's Supplies,
Inc.** (1)
3-35-58 Sakashita, Itabashi-Ku, Tokyo, 174-
0043, Japan
Tel.: (81) 353925387
Printing Ink Distr
N.A.I.C.S.: 423840

DIC Material Inc. (1)
DIC Building 7-20 Nihonbashi 3-chome,
Chuo-ku, Tokyo, 103-8233, Japan
Tel.: (81) 367335090
Polyester Resin Mfr & Whslr
N.A.I.C.S.: 325211

DIC Molding, Inc. (1)
4429-14 Shiku Komuro Ina-Machi, Kita
Adachi-Gun, Saitama, 362-0806, Japan
Tel.: (81) 487230611
Injection Molded Plastic Products Mfr
N.A.I.C.S.: 326199

DIC New Zealand Ltd. (1)
313 Church Street, PO Box 12-748, Pen-
rose, Auckland, 1642, New Zealand
Tel.: (64) 96362930
Web Site: https://dicanz.com
Printing Ink Mfr
N.A.I.C.S.: 325910

DIC Pakistan Ltd. (1)
Shahrah-e-Roomi PO Amer-sidhu, Lahore,
54760, Pakistan
Tel.: (92) 423582217880
Web Site: https://www.dic.com.pk
Emp.: 200
Printing Ink Mfr
N.A.I.C.S.: 325910
Syeda Henna Babar Ali (Chm)

DIC Performance Resins GmbH (1)
Breitenleer Strasse 97-99, 1220, Vienna,
Austria
Tel.: (43) 120 1100
Web Site: https://www.dic.co.at
Emp.: 6
Synthetic Resin Mfr
N.A.I.C.S.: 325211
Otto Stift (Mng Dir)

DIC Philippines, Inc. (1)
No 26 1st Avenue Bo Bagumbayan,
Tanyag, Taguig, 1631, Metro Manila, Philip-
pines
Tel.: (63) 28388888
Sales Range: $50-74.9 Million
Emp.: 50
Printing Ink Mfr & Distr
N.A.I.C.S.: 325910
Jet Labao (Mgr-Sls)

DIC Plastics, Inc. (1)
20th floor of Sonic City Building 1-7-5
Sakuragicho, Omiya-ku, Saitama, 330-
8669, Japan
Tel.: (81) 48 658 8855
Web Site: https://www.dic-plas.co.jp
Emp.: 230
Injection Molded Plastic Product Mfr & Distr
N.A.I.C.S.: 326199

DIC South Asia Private Limited (1)
903 B Wing Kanakia Wallstreet Building
Chakala Andheri Kurla Road, Andheri East,
Mumbai, 400093, India
Tel.: (91) 2249388000
Chemical Products Distr
N.A.I.C.S.: 424610

**DIC Synthetic Resins (Zhongshan)
Co., Ltd.** (1)
No 15 Shiyong Road, Torch Development
Zone, Zhongshan, 528437, Guangdong,
China
Tel.: (86) 76023381491
Synthetic Resin Mfr
N.A.I.C.S.: 325211

DIC Trading (HK) Ltd. (1)
Rm 1304 13th / Fl East Ocean Center 98
Granville Rd, Tsim Sha Tsui East, Kowloon,
China (Hong Kong)
Tel.: (852) 2 723 6111
Web Site: http://www.dic-global.com
Emp.: 40
Printing Ink Distr
N.A.I.C.S.: 423840

**DIC Zhangjiagang Chemicals Co.,
Ltd.** (1)
511 Changjiang East Road, Jiangsu Yang-
tze River International Chemical Industrial
Park, Zhangjiagang, 215635, Jiangsu,
China
Tel.: (86) 5125 893 7609
Web Site: https://www.dic-global.com
Sales Range: $25-49.9 Million
Emp.: 100
Plastic Materials & Synthetic Resin Mfr
N.A.I.C.S.: 325211

**Dainippon Ink & Chemicals (Philip-
pines), Inc.** (1)
No 26 1st Avenue Bo Bagumbayan Tanyag
Taguig, Manila, Philippines (99%)
Tel.: (63) 28388888
Web Site: http://www.dic.co.jp
Sales Range: $25-49.9 Million
Emp.: 59
Mfr & Sales of Printing Inks
N.A.I.C.S.: 325910

**Dainippon Ink & Chemicals (Singa-
pore) Pte., Ltd.** (1)
19 International Rd, Jurong, 619623, Singa-
pore, Singapore (100%)
Tel.: (65) 62610644
Web Site: http://www.dic.com.sg
Sales Range: $25-49.9 Million
Emp.: 80
Mfr of Printing Inks; Sales of Printing Sup-
plies, Pigment Preparations & Chemicals
N.A.I.C.S.: 325910

Dainippon Ink & Chemicals, Inc. (1)
Beijing Fortune Bldg Rm 902 5 Dong San
Huan Bei Lu, Chaoyang District, Beijing,
100004, China (100%)
Tel.: (86) 1065908461
Web Site: http://www.dic.co.jp

Representative Office; Printing Ink & Resins
N.A.I.C.S.: 325910

Deqing DIC Synthetic Resins, Ltd. (1)
245 Chaoyang Road West, Deqing County, Zhaoqing, 526600, Guangdong, China
Tel.: (86) 758 777 1878
Web Site: http://www.dic.co.at
Sales Range: $50-74.9 Million
Emp.: 106
Synthetic Resin Mfr
N.A.I.C.S.: 325211

Earthrise Nutritional LLC (1)
2151 Michelson Dr Ste 262, Irvine, CA 92612
Tel.: (949) 623-0980
Web Site: https://www.earthrise.com
Sales Range: $25-49.9 Million
Emp.: 54
Spirulina Nutritional Product Mfr
N.A.I.C.S.: 325411

Fuji Label Co., Ltd. (1)
1-331-8 Hayashi, Tokorozawa, 359-1167, Saitama, Japan
Tel.: (81) 42 938 7670
Web Site: https://www.fuji-label.co.jp
Labelling Machinery Mfr
N.A.I.C.S.: 333993

Guangzhou Lidye Resin Co., Ltd. (1)
No 16 Qinlong Street Liye Road, Dongchong Town Panyu, Guangzhou, 511453, China
Tel.: (86) 2084909670
Synthetic Resin Mfr
N.A.I.C.S.: 325211

Hainan DIC Microalgae Co., Ltd. (1)
Room 2309 Tianying Square Fuli Capital No 22 Guoxing Avenue, Qiongshan District, Haikou, 571199, Hainan, China
Tel.: (86) 89866768881
Human Supplement Mfr & Whslr
N.A.I.C.S.: 325411

Ideal Chemi Plast Private Limited (1)
Plot A2 Kulgaon MIDC, Badlapur, Mumbai, 421 503, Maharashtra, India
Tel.: (91) 2512690469
Synthetic Resin Mfr & Whslr
N.A.I.C.S.: 325211

Innovation DIC Chimitroniques Inc. (1)
725 rue Trotter, Saint-Jean-sur-Richelieu, J3B8J8, QC, Canada
Tel.: (450) 348-0901
Web Site: http://www.pcas.com
Chemical Products Mfr
N.A.I.C.S.: 325998

Japan Formalin Company, Inc. (1)
DIC Building 7-20 Nihonbashi 3-chome, Chuo-ku, Tokyo, 103-8233, Japan
Tel.: (81) 367333046
Organic Chemical Mfr & Whslr
N.A.I.C.S.: 325199

Kangnam Chemical Co., Ltd. (1)
9th Fl 12 Seoun ro 1 gil, Seocho-gu, 1355 21, Seoul, Korea (South) (50%)
Tel.: (82) 234158000
Web Site: http://kangnamchem.com
Sales Range: $125-149.9 Million
Emp.: 270
Synthetic Resins Mfr & Distr
N.A.I.C.S.: 325211

Lidye Chemical Co., Ltd. (1)
10th Fl The Lidye Commercial Bldg 22 Nanking West Road, Taipei, 103614, Taiwan
Tel.: (886) 225553271
Web Site: http://www.lidyechemical.com.tw
Synthetic Resins Mfr & Distr
N.A.I.C.S.: 325211

Nantong DIC Color Co., Ltd. (1)
No 11 Zhong Yang Road, Nantong Economic Technological Development Area, Nantong, 226009, Jiangsu, China
Tel.: (86) 5138 592 8600
Web Site: http://www.dic.com
Emp.: 300
Organic Pigment & Printing Ink Mfr
N.A.I.C.S.: 325130

Nihon Packaging Material Co., Ltd. (1)
2100-30 Kamiyoshiba, Satte, 340-0121, Saitama, Japan
Tel.: (81) 480480681
Packaging Paper Materials Mfr
N.A.I.C.S.: 322220

P.T. Pardic Jaya Chemicals (1)
Jl Gatot Subroto Km 1 Kel, Cibodas, Tangerang, 15138, Banten, Indonesia (93.7%)
Tel.: (62) 21 552 3752
Web Site: https://www.pardic.co.id
Sales Range: $125-149.9 Million
Emp.: 300
Mfr & Sales of Synthetic Resins
N.A.I.C.S.: 325211

PT DIC Astra Chemicals (1)
Jl Pulobuaran Raya Blok III DD 5 10 Kawasan Industri, Pulogadung, Jakarta, 13930, Indonesia (75%)
Tel.: (62) 214603255
Web Site: http://www.dac.co.id
Sales Range: $50-74.9 Million
Emp.: 220
Colorant Mfr
N.A.I.C.S.: 325130

PT DIC Graphics (1)
JIEPJI Rawagelam III Blok II L Kav 8 9, Jakarta Industrial Estate Pulogadung, Jakarta, 13930, Indonesia (98.5%)
Tel.: (62) 214613525
Web Site: http://www.dic.co.id
Sales Range: $50-74.9 Million
Emp.: 100
Mfr & Sales of Printing Inks
N.A.I.C.S.: 325910

PT. DIC Trading Indonesia (1)
Jl Rawagelam III Blok II L Kav 8-9, Jakarta Timur, Jakarta, 13930, Indonesia
Tel.: (62) 214613525
Web Site: https://dic.co.id
Ink Mfr & Distr
N.A.I.C.S.: 325910

Qingdao DIC Finechemicals Co., Ltd. (1)
Huite Industrial City No 177 Zhuzhou Road, Qingdao, 266101, Shandong, China
Tel.: (86) 5328 870 1763
Web Site: https://www.qdic.com
Emp.: 100
Printing Ink Mfr & Distr
N.A.I.C.S.: 325910
Qiang Gong (Co-Chm)

Qingdao DIC Liquid Crystal Co., Ltd. (1)
A Area Hit Industrial City 177 Zhuzhou Road, Qingdao, 266101, Shandong, China
Tel.: (86) 53266729020
Construction Material Component Mfr
N.A.I.C.S.: 327999

SUNDIC Inc. (1)
3rd Floor Moritani Bldg 83 1-4-22 Yaesu, Chuo-ku, Tokyo, 103-0028, Japan
Tel.: (81) 352058667
Web Site: https://www.sundic.co.jp
Emp.: 117
Plastic Sheet Mfr & Whslr
N.A.I.C.S.: 326112
Naoya Furuyashiki (Mng Dir)

Samling Housing Products Sdn. Bhd. (1)
Lot 818 Block 1 Kuala Baram Industrial Estate CDT No 83, 98009, Miri, Sarawak, Malaysia
Tel.: (60) 85604668
Home Product Mfr
N.A.I.C.S.: 321991

Shanghai DIC Ink Co., Inc. (1)
No 3888 Humin Road, Minhang District, Shanghai, 201108, China (65%)
Tel.: (86) 2164890888
Web Site: http://www.shdic.com.cn
Mfr & Sales of Printing Inks
N.A.I.C.S.: 325910

Shanghai DIC Pressure-Sensitive Adhesive Materials Co., Ltd. (1)
B No 559 Fu Te Rd N Waigaoqiao F T Z, Pudong, Shanghai, 200131, China
Tel.: (86) 2158682011

Adhesive Material Whslr
N.A.I.C.S.: 424690

Shanghai Long Feng Food Additives Co., Ltd. (1)
Sheshan Town, Song Jiang County, Shanghai, 201602, China (35%)
Tel.: (86) 2157652271
Web Site: http://www.dic.co.jp
Mfr of Food Additives
N.A.I.C.S.: 424690

Shenzhen DIC Chemicals Co., Ltd. (1)
No 300 Huilong Rd Center City, Longgang Dist, Shenzhen, 518172, China
Tel.: (86) 75528941170
Printing Ink Mfr & Distr
N.A.I.C.S.: 325910

Shenzhen-DIC Co., Ltd. (1)
1035 Nanshan Road, Shenzhen, 518052, China (90%)
Tel.: (86) 75526432333
Web Site: http://www.dicsz.com
Sales Range: $50-74.9 Million
Emp.: 200
Mfr & Sales of Printing Inks
N.A.I.C.S.: 325910
Connie Want (Mgr-Fin)

Siam Chemical Industry Co., Ltd. (1)
159/34 SERM-MIT Tower 20th Floor Soi Asoke Sukhumvit 21 Road, Kwang North Klongtoey Khet Wattana, Bangkok, 10110, Thailand (50%)
Tel.: (66) 22607400
Web Site: https://www.siamchem.com
Sales Range: $125-149.9 Million
Emp.: 340
Mfr & Sales of Synthetic Resins
N.A.I.C.S.: 325211

Sun Chemical Corporation (1)
35 Waterview Blvd, Parsippany, NJ 07054-1285
Tel.: (973) 404-6000
Web Site: http://www.sunchemical.com
Sales Range: $1-4.9 Billion
Emp.: 200
Mfr of Printing Inks & Organic Pigments & Dispersions
N.A.I.C.S.: 325910
Rudi Lenz (Vice Chm)

Subsidiary (Non-US):

Benda-Lutz Werke GmbH (2)
Ferdinand-Lutz-Strasse 8, 3134, Nussdorf ob der Traisen, Austria
Tel.: (43) 278362020
Web Site: http://www.benda-lutz.com
Sales Range: $50-74.9 Million
Emp.: 113
Metal Powders & Pigments Mfr
N.A.I.C.S.: 325510
Dieter Lutz (Mng Dir)

Subsidiary (US):

Benda-Lutz Corporation (3)
10500 Toebben Dr, Independence, KY 41051
Tel.: (859) 746-0392
Web Site: http://www.benda-lutz.com
Sales Range: $1-9.9 Million
Emp.: 34
Metal Powders & Pigments Mfr
N.A.I.C.S.: 325510
William Pofahl (Mgr-Sls & Mktg)

Affiliate (Non-US):

Benda-Lutz-Alpoco Sp.z o.o. (3)
ul Pilsudskiego 23, 32 050, Skawina, Poland
Tel.: (48) 122761110
Sales Range: $75-99.9 Million
Emp.: 66
Metal Powders & Pigments Mfr
N.A.I.C.S.: 325510
Janusz Jedrusik (Gen Mgr)

Subsidiary (Non-US):

Coates Brothers (Caribbean) Ltd. (2)
12 Label Blvd, Trincity, Trinidad & Tobago
Tel.: (868) 640 9835
Sales Range: $25-49.9 Million
Emp.: 11
Printing Ink Mfr

N.A.I.C.S.: 325910
Suzetta Ali (Gen Mgr)

Coates Brothers (Zambia) Ltd. (2)
Ulengo Road No 3291, Ndola, 230025, Zambia
Tel.: (260) 212650945
Sales Range: $25-49.9 Million
Emp.: 18
Printing Ink Mfr
N.A.I.C.S.: 325910
Edson Kalunga (Chm)

Division (Domestic):

Coates Electrographics Inc. (2)
Country Club Rd, Dallas, PA 18612
Tel.: (570) 675-1131
Sales Range: $25-49.9 Million
Emp.: 55
Chemical Preparations
N.A.I.C.S.: 325910

Subsidiary (Non-US):

Coates Screen Inks GmbH (2)
Wiederholdplatz 1, 90451, Nuremberg, Germany
Tel.: (49) 9 116 4220
Web Site: https://www.coates.de
Emp.: 10
Printing Ink & Coating Mfr
N.A.I.C.S.: 325910
Edwin Tafelmeier (Mgr-Laboratory)

IMS Concepts S.A./N.V. (2)
Avenue Fleming 2, Wavre, 1300, Brabant Wallon, Belgium
Tel.: (32) 87340153
Printing Ink Mfr
N.A.I.C.S.: 325910

Division (Domestic):

KVK USA Inc. (2)
19 A Home News Row, New Brunswick, NJ 08901-3601
Tel.: (732) 846-2355
Rev.: $1,200,000
Emp.: 10
Inorganic Pigments
N.A.I.C.S.: 325130

Subsidiary (Non-US):

Parker Williams Design Ltd. (2)
3rd Floor Voysey House Barley Mow Passage, London, W4 4PH, United Kingdom
Tel.: (44) 20 8995 6411
Web Site: http://www.parkerwilliams.co.uk
Sales Range: $25-49.9 Million
Emp.: 18
Packaging Design Services
N.A.I.C.S.: 541490
Jo Saker (Exec Creative Dir)

SUN Chemical Ltd. (2)
Wexham Springs, Framewood Road, Slough, SL3 6PJ, United Kingdom (100%)
Tel.: (44) 2031390000
Web Site: http://www.sunchemical.com
Sales Range: $25-49.9 Million
Emp.: 50
Mfr of Printing Inks & Coatings
N.A.I.C.S.: 325910

Sun Branding Solutions Ltd. (2)
Albion Mills, Greengates, Bradford, BD10 9TQ, West Yorkshire, United Kingdom
Tel.: (44) 127 420 0700
Web Site: https://www.sun-strategy.com
Emp.: 100
Brand Design Consulting Services
N.A.I.C.S.: 541613
Paul Bean (Mng Dir)

Sun Chemical A/S (2)
Kobenhavnsvej 112, 4600, Koge, Denmark
Tel.: (45) 56 67 75 85
Web Site: http://www.sunchemical.com
Emp.: 14
Printing Ink & Organic Pigment Mfr
N.A.I.C.S.: 325910
Nobuhisa Hosokawa (Dir-Fin)

Sun Chemical A/S (2)
Stlfjaera 1, PO Box 164, NO-0975, Oslo, Norway (100%)
Tel.: (47) 22975100
Web Site: http://www.suneurope.com

DIC Corporation—(Continued)

Sales Range: $25-49.9 Million
Emp.: 13
Mfr of Printing Inks
N.A.I.C.S.: 325910
Lars Doresyus (Controller)

Sun Chemical AB (2)
Malaxgatan 1, PO Box 16, Kista, 164 74,
Sweden (100%)
Tel.: (46) 87950700
Web Site: http://www.sunchemical.com
Sales Range: $25-49.9 Million
Emp.: 30
Mfr of Printing Inks
N.A.I.C.S.: 325910

Sun Chemical AG (2)
Perfektastrasse 82, A 1230, Vienna,
Austria (100%)
Tel.: (43) 018697606
Web Site: http://www.sunchemical.com
Sales Range: $1-9.9 Million
Emp.: 150
Mfr & Sales of Printing Inks
N.A.I.C.S.: 325910

Sun Chemical AG (2)
Grindlenstrasse 3, 8954, Geroldswil,
Switzerland (100%)
Tel.: (41) 447495050
Web Site: http://www.suneurope.com
Sales Range: $50-74.9 Million
Emp.: 150
Printing Ink Mfr
N.A.I.C.S.: 325910

Sun Chemical Albania SHPK (2)
Rr Kavajes Ish Kombinati Misto Mame, Ti-
rana, Albania
Tel.: (355) 42255464
Printing Ink & Organic Pigment Mfr
N.A.I.C.S.: 325910

Sun Chemical B.V. (2)
Leeuwenveldseweg 3t, Weesp, 1382 LV,
North Holland, Netherlands
Tel.: (31) 294492100
Sales Range: $25-49.9 Million
Emp.: 12
Printing Ink Mfr
N.A.I.C.S.: 325910

Sun Chemical Chile S.A. (2)
Vicuna MacKenna 4815, Santiago, 10018,
Chile (100%)
Tel.: (56) 25102000
Web Site: http://www.sunchemicals.com
Sales Range: $50-74.9 Million
Emp.: 150
Mfr of Printing Inks
N.A.I.C.S.: 325910

Division (Domestic):

**Sun Chemical Corporation of
Michigan** (2)
4925 Evanston Ave, Muskegon, MI 49442-
4827
Tel.: (231) 788-2371
Web Site: http://www.sunchemical.com
Sales Range: $125-149.9 Million
Pigment Mfr for Printing Ink
N.A.I.C.S.: 325130

**Sun Chemical Corporation, Pigments
Division** (2)
5020 Spring Grove Ave, Cincinnati, OH
45232-1926
Tel.: (513) 681-5950
Web Site: http://www.sunpigments.com
Sales Range: $1-4.9 Billion
Emp.: 300
Mfr of Pigments for Printing Inks, Paints &
Plastics
N.A.I.C.S.: 325130

Subsidiary (Non-US):

**Sun Chemical Druckfarben
GmbH** (2)
Rolandsweg 22 24, Osterode am Hartz,
37520, Germany (100%)
Tel.: (49) 552286060
Web Site: http://www.suneurope.com
Sales Range: $50-74.9 Million
Emp.: 125
Mfr of Printing Inks
N.A.I.C.S.: 325910
Sontag Karl (Mng Dir)

Sun Chemical ECP S.A./N.V. (2)
Ave Fleming 2, B 1300, Wavre,
Belgium (100%)
Tel.: (32) 010231500
Web Site: http://www.sunchemical.com
Sales Range: $25-49.9 Million
Emp.: 70
Mfr of Printing Inks
N.A.I.C.S.: 325910

**Sun Chemical Group Cooperatief
U.A.** (2)
Leeuwenveldseweg 3-t, 1382 LV, Weesp,
Netherlands
Tel.: (31) 294492100
Printing Ink & Organic Pigment Mfr
N.A.I.C.S.: 325910

Sun Chemical Group S.p.A. (2)
Via Achille Grandi 3/6, Settala, 20090, Mi-
lan, Italy
Tel.: (39) 02957901
Web Site: http://www.sunchemical.com
Emp.: 30
Printing Ink & Organic Pigment Mfr
N.A.I.C.S.: 325910

Branch (Domestic):

Sun Chemical S.p.A. (3)
Via Delle Due Case 2, 50127, Florence,
Italy (100%)
Tel.: (39) 05542591
Web Site: http://www.sunchemical.com
Mfr of Printing Inks
N.A.I.C.S.: 325910

Division (Domestic):

Sun Chemical Ink (2)
135 W Lake St, Northlake, IL 60164
Tel.: (708) 562-0550
Sales Range: $800-899.9 Million
General Printing Inks Mfr
N.A.I.C.S.: 325910
Corey Soeldner (Dir-Pur & Supply Chain-N
America)

Subsidiary (Non-US):

Sun Chemical Inks A/S (2)
Meterbuen 3, Skovlunde, 2740, Denmark
Tel.: (45) 44949122
Sales Range: $25-49.9 Million
Emp.: 30
Printing Ink Mfr.
N.A.I.C.S.: 325910

Sun Chemical Inks Ltd. (2)
Glenside Words Mill, Palmerstown, Ireland
Tel.: (353) 16206868
Web Site: http://www.sunchemical.com
Printing Ink Mfr
N.A.I.C.S.: 325910
Mark Sedgwick (Mgr)

Sun Chemical Inks S.A. (2)
Zavaleta 699, Buenos Aires, 1437, Argen-
tina
Tel.: (54) 1149091000
Web Site: http://www.sunchemical.com
Printing Ink Mfr
N.A.I.C.S.: 325910

Sun Chemical Lasfelde GmbH (2)
Rolandsweg 26, Osterode am Hartz, 37520,
Germany
Tel.: (49) 5522507240
Web Site: http://www.sunchemical.com
Emp.: 33
Printing Ink & Pigment Mfr
N.A.I.C.S.: 325910
Niels G. Johansen (Mng Dir)

Sun Chemical Limited (2)
10 W Dr, Brampton, L6T 4Y4, ON,
Canada (100%)
Tel.: (905) 796-2222
Web Site: http://www.sunchemical.com
Sales Range: $50-74.9 Million
Emp.: 250
Mfr of Printing Inks
N.A.I.C.S.: 325910

Sun Chemical Ltd. (2)
Wexham Springs Framewood Rd, Slough,
SL3 6PJ, United Kingdom (100%)
Tel.: (44) 203 139 0000
Web Site: http://www.sunchemical.com

Sales Range: $1-9.9 Million
Emp.: 8
Mfr of Printing Inks
N.A.I.C.S.: 325910

Subsidiary (Non-US):

Hartmann Druckfarben GmbH (3)
Borsigallee 13, PO Box 600349, Frankfurt
am Main, 60388, Germany (100%)
Tel.: (49) 6940000
Web Site: http://www.sunchemical.com
Mfr of Printing Inks
N.A.I.C.S.: 325910

Hartmann-Sun Chemical EOOD (3)
Tzarigradsko Chaussee 117 A, 1184, Sofia,
Bulgaria (100%)
Tel.: (359) 29753218
Web Site: http://www.suneurope.com
Mfr of Printing Inks & Coatings
N.A.I.C.S.: 325910
Iota Konstantinova (Mgr-Sls)

Subsidiary (Non-US):

**Sun Chemical Matbaa Murekkepleri
Ve Gerecleri Sanayii Ve Ticaret
A.S.** (2)
10037 Sokak No 4 AOSB, Cigli, Izmir,
35620, Turkiye
Tel.: (90) 232 376 8890
Web Site: http://www.sunchemical.com
Sales Range: $25-49.9 Million
Emp.: 150
Printing Ink Mfr
N.A.I.C.S.: 325910

Sun Chemical Moscow (2)
35 Volnaya St, 105187, Moscow,
Russia (98.1%)
Tel.: (7) 4959331303
Web Site: http://www.sunchemical.com
Sales Range: $25-49.9 Million
Emp.: 80
Mfr & Sales of Printing Inks & Coatings
N.A.I.C.S.: 325910

Sun Chemical N.V./S.A. (2)
Donkerstraat 63, Ternat, 1740, Vlaams Bra-
bant, Belgium
Tel.: (32) 25833511
Emp.: 94
Printing Ink & Organic Pigment Mfr
N.A.I.C.S.: 325910
Paul Nys (Mgr)

**Sun Chemical Nyomdafestek
Kereskedelmi Es Gyarto KFT** (2)
Telek Utca 7-9, Budapest, 1152, Hungary
Tel.: (36) 13061410
Web Site: http://www.sunchemical.com
Emp.: 13
Printing Ink & Coating Mfr
N.A.I.C.S.: 325910
Levay Zoltan (Mng Dir)

**Sun Chemical Osterode Druckfarben
GmbH** (2)
Rolandsweg 22-24, Osterode am Hartz,
37520, Germany
Tel.: (49) 552286060
Web Site: http://www.suneurope.com
Printing Ink Mfr
N.A.I.C.S.: 325910
Dirk Lambrecht (Gen Mgr)

Sun Chemical Oy (2)
Pieni Teollisuuskatu 2, Espoo, 2920, Uusi-
maa, Finland
Tel.: (358) 207 509 700
Web Site: http://www.sunchemical.com
Sales Range: $25-49.9 Million
Emp.: 7
Printing Ink & Paint Mfr
N.A.I.C.S.: 325910
Tapani Arila (Mgr-Fin)

Sun Chemical Pigments S.L. (2)
Calle Occitania 75, Badalona, 8911, Barce-
lona, Spain
Tel.: (34) 933893600
Web Site: http://www.sunchemical.com
Emp.: 35
Printing Ink Mfr
N.A.I.C.S.: 325910
Melissa Pavetich (Gen Mgr)

**Sun Chemical Portugal Tintas Grafi-
cas Unipessoal, Ltda.** (2)

Rua Caminho do Senhor 380, 4410-083,
Serzedo, Portugal (100%)
Tel.: (351) 227300100
Web Site: http://www.sunchemical.com
Sales Range: $25-49.9 Million
Emp.: 31
Mfr of Printing Inks
N.A.I.C.S.: 325910

Sun Chemical Printing Ink d.o.o. (2)
64 Vitezova Karadordeve Zvezde, Belgrade,
11000, Serbia
Tel.: (381) 113343350
Sales Range: $25-49.9 Million
Emp.: 4
Printing Ink & Organic Pigment Mfr
N.A.I.C.S.: 325910

Sun Chemical S.A. (2)
Ctra De La Cantera S N, 48950, Asua,
Vizcaya, Spain (100%)
Tel.: (34) 944022747
Web Site: http://www.suneurope.com
Sales Range: $25-49.9 Million
Emp.: 95
Mfr of Printing Inks
N.A.I.C.S.: 325910

Sun Chemical S.A. de C.V. (2)
Alce Blanco No 20, PO Box 7186, 53370,
Naucalpan, Mexico (100%)
Tel.: (52) 5553732000
Web Site: http://www.chemical.com.mx
Sales Range: $100-124.9 Million
Mfr of Printing Inks
N.A.I.C.S.: 325910

Sun Chemical S.A.S. (2)
89/91 Avenue du Marechal Joffre Cedex,
Nanterre, 92000, France
Tel.: (33) 3 44 90 60 00
Printing Ink & Organic Pigment Mfr
N.A.I.C.S.: 325910

Sun Chemical Sp. zo.o. (2)
Wal Miedzeszynski 646, 03-994, Warsaw,
Poland (100%)
Tel.: (48) 226713361
Web Site: http://www.suneurope.com
Mfr of Printing Inks & Coatings
N.A.I.C.S.: 325910

Sun Chemical ZAO (2)
Aeroportovskaya Street 14 Bykovo, Mos-
cow, 140150, Russia
Tel.: (7) 495 933 13 03
Web Site: http://www.sunchemical.com
Sales Range: $25-49.9 Million
Emp.: 50
Printing Ink & Organic Pigment Mfr
N.A.I.C.S.: 325910
Robert Fitzka (Gen Mgr)

**Sun Chemical de Centro America,
S.A. de C.V.** (2)
Boulevard Del Ejercito National Km 4 1/2,
PO Box 2108, San Salvador, El
Salvador (50%)
Tel.: (503) 22776999
Web Site: http://www.sunchemical.com
Sales Range: $25-49.9 Million
Emp.: 99
Mfr of Printing Inks
N.A.I.C.S.: 325910

Sun Chemical de Panama, S.A. (2)
Trasistmita Des Nacones Ave 85, PO Box
0819-09350, El Dorado, Panama, 0819-
09350, Panama (100%)
Tel.: (507) 2315438
Web Site: http://www.tintas.com
Sales Range: $1-9.9 Million
Emp.: 25
Printing Ink Mfr
N.A.I.C.S.: 325910

Sun Chemical do Brasil Ltda. (2)
Avenida Amancio Gaiolli 770 Agua Chata,
Guarulhos, 07222-000, Sao Paulo, Brazil
Tel.: (55) 1124622500
Printing Ink Mfr
N.A.I.C.S.: 325910

Sun Chemical s.r.l. (2)
Nr Ap Camera 10 19 Somesului Rm201,
Sibiu, 550003, Romania
Tel.: (40) 369436928
Web Site: http://www.sunchemical.com
Sales Range: $25-49.9 Million
Emp.: 2
Printing Ink & Organic Pigment Mfr

N.A.I.C.S.: 325910
Geza Kovacs (Gen Mgr)

Sun Chemical s.r.o. (2)
Udolni 527/27, Brno, 602 00, Czech
Republic (100%)
Tel.: (420) 542422731
Web Site: http://www.sunchemical.com
Sales Range: $25-49.9 Million
Emp.: 17
Mfr of Printing Inks & Coatings
N.A.I.C.S.: 325910

Sun Chemical s.r.o. (2)
UI SNP 264/3, SK-05921, Svit,
Slovakia (100%)
Tel.: (421) 52 77 152 425
Web Site: http://www.suneurope.com
Mfr of Printing Inks & Coatings
N.A.I.C.S.: 325910

Sun Chemical, Inc. S.A. (2)
Zabaleta 699, C1437EYM, San Martin, Bue-
nos Aires, Argentina (100%)
Tel.: (54) 49114200
Sales Range: $25-49.9 Million
Emp.: 90
Mfr of Printing Inks
N.A.I.C.S.: 325910

Sun Chemical, Inc. S.A. (2)
Zavaleta 699, 1437, Buenos Aires,
Argentina (100%)
Tel.: (54) 49091000
Web Site: http://www.tintas.com
Sales Range: $25-49.9 Million
Emp.: 70
Printing Ink Mfr
N.A.I.C.S.: 325910

Sun Chemical, d.o.o. (2)
Kovinska 4a, Zagreb, 10000, Croatia
Tel.: (385) 12406609
Web Site: http://www.sunchemical.com
Sales Range: $25-49.9 Million
Emp.: 2
Organic Pigment & Printing Ink Mfr
N.A.I.C.S.: 325130
Igor Belosic (Gen Mgr)

Sun Chemicals (2)
Cray Ave, Saint Mary Cray, BR5 3PP, Kent,
United Kingdom (100%)
Tel.: (44) 1689894000
Web Site: http://www.coates.com
Sales Range: $25-49.9 Million
Emp.: 100
Mfr of Printing Inks
N.A.I.C.S.: 325910

Sun Chemicals S.A.-Pigments
International (2)
Parc Industrielle de la Noire Epine, Ave
Fleming 2, Wavre, 1300, Belgium (100%)
Tel.: (32) 10231500
Web Site: http://www.sunchemical.com
Sales Range: $25-49.9 Million
Emp.: 70
Sales of Printing Inks
N.A.I.C.S.: 423840

Division (Domestic):

US Ink Corporation (2)
631 Central Ave, Carlstadt, NJ
07072-1609 (100%)
Tel.: (201) 935-8666
Web Site: http://www.usink.com
Sales Range: $25-49.9 Million
Emp.: 60
Mfr of Inks
N.A.I.C.S.: 325910
John Corcoran (VP-Sls)

Division (Domestic):

US Ink Corporation, Eastern
Region (3)
343 Murray Hill Pkwy, East Rutherford, NJ
07073-2110
Tel.: (201) 933-7100
Web Site: http://www.usink.com
Sales Range: $25-49.9 Million
Emp.: 15
Mfr of Printing Inks
N.A.I.C.S.: 325910

US Ink Corporation, Midwest
Region (3)
600 Redna Ter, Cincinnati, OH 45215-1108

Tel.: (513) 771-4030
Web Site: http://www.sunchemical.com
Sales Range: $25-49.9 Million
Emp.: 14
Mfr of Printing Inks
N.A.I.C.S.: 325910
Steven Cornwell (Plant Mgr)

US Ink Corporation, Southern
Region (3)
5200 Shawland Rd, Jacksonville, FL 32254-
1651
Tel.: (904) 786-1474
Web Site: http://www.usink.com
Sales Range: $25-49.9 Million
Emp.: 40
Mfr of Printing Inks
N.A.I.C.S.: 325910

US Ink Corporation, Southwest
Region (3)
12010 Corp Dr, Dallas, TX 75228-8102
Web Site: http://www.usink.com
Sales Range: $25-49.9 Million
Emp.: 50
Ink Mfr
N.A.I.C.S.: 325910

US Ink Corporation, Western
Region (3)
14465 Griffith St, San Leandro, CA 94577
Tel.: (510) 357-5200
Web Site: http://www.usink.com
Sales Range: $25-49.9 Million
Emp.: 35
Mfr of Printing Inks
N.A.I.C.S.: 325910

Sun Chemical Trading (Shanghai)
Co., Ltd. (1)
12th Fl Metro Plaza No 555 Lou Shan
Guan Road, Shanghai, 200051, China
Tel.: (86) 2162289922
Printing Ink Mfr & Whslr
N.A.I.C.S.: 325910

Suqian Lintong New Materials Co.,
Ltd. (1)
No 36 Yangzi Road, Suyu District, Suqian,
223809, Jiangsu, China
Tel.: (86) 52784829362
Pigment & Dyestuff Mfr & Whslr
N.A.I.C.S.: 325130

Suzhou Lintong Chemical Science
Corp. (1)
No 56 Yinshan Bridge, Suzhou, 215124,
China
Tel.: (86) 51265252072
Chemical Mfr & Distr
N.A.I.C.S.: 325199

TOA-DIC Zhangjiagang Chemical
Co., Ltd. (1)
66 Jiangsu Yangtze River International
Chemical Industrial Park, Zhangjiagang,
215633, Jiangsu, China
Tel.: (86) 5125 872 7220
Web Site: http://www.tdz.cn
Chemical Mfr & Whslr
N.A.I.C.S.: 325199
Chandler Yuan (Mgr-Bus Dev)

Techno Science, Inc. (1)
12-12 Mizuho 3-chome, Utsunomiya, 321-
0921, Tochigi, Japan
Tel.: (81) 286570020
Disposable Filter Mfr & Whslr
N.A.I.C.S.: 333413

Tien Lee Hong Co., Ltd. (1)
Ste 222 China Chen Golden Pl Mody Rd,
Kowloon, China (Hong Kong) (100%)
Tel.: (852) 23953217
Web Site: http://www.dic.co.jp
Sales Range: Less than $1 Million
Emp.: 20
Sales of Synthetic Resins, Printing Inks,
Supplies & Chemicals
N.A.I.C.S.: 423840

Topic Co., Ltd. (1)
14-28 Kami-Aoki 1-chome, Kawaguchi, 333-
0844, Saitama, Japan
Tel.: (81) 48 241 2211
Web Site: http://www.topic-dic.com
Emp.: 89
Precise Photomask Product Mfr & Distr
N.A.I.C.S.: 325992

YD Plastics Co., Ltd. (1)
54-15 Kyoei, Kitahiroshima, 061-1112, Hok-
kaido, Japan
Tel.: (81) 113732331
Pet Bottle Mfr & Whslr
N.A.I.C.S.: 326199

Zhongshan DIC Colour Co., Ltd. (1)
No 1 Zhenxing North Road No 2 Industrial
Zone, Zhanzhou Town, Zhongshan, 528467,
Guangdong, China
Tel.: (86) 760 8665 5822
Web Site: http://www.zsdic.com.cn
Plastic & Leather Colorant Mfr & Distr
N.A.I.C.S.: 325510

DIC INDIA LTD

Fusion Square 5A & B 5th Floor Sec-
tor 126, District Gautam Budh Nagar,
Noida, 201303, Uttar Pradesh, India
Tel.: (91) 1206361414
Web Site: https://www.dic.co.in
13217—(KOL)
Rev.: $102,969,512
Assets: $83,408,571
Liabilities: $30,728,457
Net Worth: $52,680,114
Earnings: $1,691,030
Emp.: 492
Fiscal Year-end: 12/31/21
Industrial Coating Mfr
N.A.I.C.S.: 325510
Dipak Kumar Banerjee (Chm)

Subsidiaries:

Guangdong DIC TOD Resins Co.,
Ltd. (1)
Huacai Chemical Coating Area Wengcheng
Industrial Transfer Park, Wengyuan County,
Shaoguan, China
Tel.: (86) 7512616820
Web Site: https://www.en.todchem.com
Coating Resin Mfr & Distr
N.A.I.C.S.: 325211

Suqian Lintong New Material Co.,
Ltd. (1)
No 36 Yangzi Road, Suyu District, Suqian,
223809, China
Tel.: (86) 52784829362
Pigment Mfr
N.A.I.C.S.: 325130

DIC INVESTMENT AND TRAD-
ING JOINT STOCK COMPANY

6th Floor 29 Nguyen Khac Nhu, Co
Giang Ward District 1, Ho Chi Minh
City, Vietnam
Tel.: (84) 839310504
Web Site: https://www.dic-intraco.vn
Year Founded: 2005
Cement Clinker Mfr
N.A.I.C.S.: 327310
Thanh Nguyen (Mgr-Wood)

Subsidiaries:

DIC Da Lat Investment & Trading
Joint Stock Company (1)
Phu Hoi Industrial Zone, Duc Trong District,
Phu Hoi, Lam Dong, Vietnam
Tel.: (84) 633679292
Emp.: 50
Roof Tile Mfr & Distr
N.A.I.C.S.: 327120
Nguyen Manh Chien (Pres)

DIC Da Nang Investment & Trading
Joint Stock Company (1)
Street 10, Hoa Khanh Industrial Zone, Da
Nang, Vietnam
Tel.: (84) 5113736896
Emp.: 120
Roof Tile Mfr & Distr
N.A.I.C.S.: 327120
Duong Dinh Thai (Gen Dir)

DICE SPORT & CASUAL
WEAR S.A.E.

5 6 Petrol St from Gessr El Suez St,
Industrial Area Heliopolis, Cairo,
Egypt

Tel.: (20) 21820120
Web Site:
http://www.ir.dicefactory.net
Year Founded: 1989
DSCW.CA—(EGX)
Sales Range: Less than $1 Million
Sport Product Mfr & Distr
N.A.I.C.S.: 339920
Nagy Samir Toma (Vice Chm, CEO &
Mng Dir)

DICHTUNGSPARTNER HAM-
BURG GMBH

Ferdinand-Harten-Strasse 15, 22949,
Ammersbek, Germany
Tel.: (49) 40 66 86 13 0
Web Site: http://www.dph.de
Year Founded: 1986
Seal & Gasket Mfr
N.A.I.C.S.: 339991
Holger Krause (Mng Dir)

Subsidiaries:

dph (south Africa) Industrial, Mining &
Automotive Supplies (pty) Ltd (1)
33 Montague Drive Montague Gardens,
Cape Town, South Africa
Tel.: (27) 215525808
Web Site: http://www.dph.co.za
Oil Seal Mfr
N.A.I.C.S.: 339991
Jason Grove (Mgr-Quality Assurance)

dph Asia Ltd (1)
C3305 Jixiang Qipei City 788 Sanyuanli
Dadao, Baiyun, Guangzhou, Guangdong,
China
Tel.: (86) 2086337734
Steel Mfrs
N.A.I.C.S.: 332999

dph Turkey (1)
Ikitelli Dolapdere San Sit 16 Ada No 1, Is-
tanbul, Turkiye
Tel.: (90) 2126710444
Web Site: http://www.dph.com.tr
Steel Mfrs
N.A.I.C.S.: 332999

DICKER DATA LIMITED

238 Captain Cook Drive, Kurnell,
2231, NSW, Australia
Tel.: (61) 1800688586
Web Site:
https://www.dickerdata.com.au
Year Founded: 1978
D0D—(DEU)
Rev.: $2,072,502,781
Assets: $712,161,632
Liabilities: $558,516,830
Net Worth: $153,644,802
Earnings: $48,766,177
Fiscal Year-end: 12/31/22
Computer Hardware Distr
N.A.I.C.S.: 423430
David Dicker (CEO, Co-Founder &
Chm)

Subsidiaries:

Dicker Data Financial Services Pty
Ltd (1)
238 Captain Cook Drive, Kurnell, 2231,
NSW, Australia
Tel.: (61) 295898409
Web Site: http://www.dickerdata.com.au
Hardware & Software Distr
N.A.I.C.S.: 423430
David Dicker (Chm & CEO)

Dicker Data New Zealand Ltd. (1)
68 Plunket Ave, Papatoetoe, Auckland,
2104, New Zealand
Tel.: (64) 800337253
Web Site: https://www.dickerdata.co.nz
Hardware & Software Distr
N.A.I.C.S.: 423430
David Vickery (Country Mgr)

Express Data Holdings Pty Ltd (1)
14 A Baker Street, Botany, 2019, NSW,
Australia (100%)
Tel.: (61) 283365100

Dicker Data Limited—(Continued)

Web Site: http://www.expressdata.com.au
Sales Range: $25-49.9 Million
Emp.: 380
Business-to-Business Systems Integrator
N.A.I.C.S.: 541512
David Gage (CEO)

DICKSON CONCEPTS (INTERNATIONAL) LIMITED

4th Floor East Ocean Centre 98
Granville Road Tsimshatsui East,
Kowloon, China (Hong Kong)
Tel.: (852) 23113888   RM
Web Site:
  https://www.dickson.com.hk
DCOHF—(OTCIQ)
Rev.: $271,675,088
Assets: $713,995,410
Liabilities: $281,885,925
Net Worth: $432,109,485
Earnings: $32,211,218
Emp.: 732
Fiscal Year-end: 03/31/23
Jewelry Products Sales
N.A.I.C.S.: 458310
Dickson Poon (Chm)

Subsidiaries:

Ambrose China Limited   (1)
98 Granville Road Tsimshatsui East, Kowloon, China (Hong Kong)
Tel.: (852) 2268 8864
Watch Distr
N.A.I.C.S.: 423940

Bertolucci SA   (1)
Route des Jeunes 5C, Case Postale 1113,
1211, Geneva, Switzerland
Tel.: (41) 22 756 9500
Web Site: https://www.bertolucci-watches.com
Watch Distr
N.A.I.C.S.: 423940

China Tone Limited   (1)
4/F E Ocean Ctr 98 Granville Rd, Tsim Sha
Tsui, Kowloon, China (Hong Kong)
Tel.: (852) 23113888
Sales Range: $75-99.9 Million
Emp.: 200
Fashion Products Distr
N.A.I.C.S.: 424990

Dickson (Shanghai) Company
Limited   (1)
Room F 6/F No 1358 Yan'an West Rd,
Changning, Shanghai, 200052, China
Tel.: (86) 2162820366
Watch Distr
N.A.I.C.S.: 423940

Dickson Concepts (Retail)
Limited   (1)
12B Des Voeux Road G/F The Landmark,
Central, China (Hong Kong)
Tel.: (852) 25214245
Emp.: 13
Watch Distr
N.A.I.C.S.: 423940

Dickson Concepts Limited   (1)
4th Floor East Ocean Centre 98 Granville
Road, Tsimshatsui East, Kowloon, China
(Hong Kong)
Tel.: (852) 2311 3888
Investment Management Service
N.A.I.C.S.: 523999

Dickson Express Company
Limited   (1)
4/F E Ocean Ctr 98 Granville Rd, Tsim Sha
Tsui E, Kowloon, China (Hong Kong)
Tel.: (852) 23113888
Fashion Apparel Distr
N.A.I.C.S.: 424310

Dickson Interior Design Limited   (1)
4/F E Ocean Ctr 98 Granville Rd, Tsim Sha
Tsui E, Kowloon, 852, China (Hong Kong)
Tel.: (852) 23113888
Interior Design Services
N.A.I.C.S.: 541410

Dickson Investments (H.K.)
Limited   (1)

4/F E Ocean Ctr 98 Granville Rd, Tsim Sha
Tsui, Kowloon, China (Hong Kong)
Tel.: (852) 23113888
Investment Management Service
N.A.I.C.S.: 523999

Hong Kong Seibu Enterprise Company Limited   (1)
Rm A 21/F Manulife Twr 169 Electric Rd,
North Point, China (Hong Kong)
Tel.: (852) 28773627
Fashion Apparels Retailer
N.A.I.C.S.: 424310

Leading Way Apparel Shanghai
Limited   (1)
Rm 201c International Commercial Trading
Mansion No 118, Shanghai, 200131, China
Tel.: (86) 2150462328
Cosmetics Goods Distr
N.A.I.C.S.: 456120

Raglan Resources Limited   (1)
Offshore Incorporations Centre, Road Town,
Virgin Islands (British)
Tel.: (284) 494 8184
Investment Management Service
N.A.I.C.S.: 523999

The Dickson Shop Sdn. Bhd.   (1)
7K Jalan 1/57D Off Jalan Segambut,
51200, Kuala Lumpur, Malaysia
Tel.: (60) 3 62580122
Fashion Product Retailer
N.A.I.C.S.: 456120

The Dickson Trading (Taiwan) Co.,
Ltd.   (1)
11F-12F No 156 Jiankang Road, Songshan
District, Taipei, 105, Taiwan
Tel.: (886) 2 3766 3388
Emp.: 200
Watch Distr
N.A.I.C.S.: 423940

Tommy Hilfiger Asia-Pacific
Limited   (1)
No 156 Jiankang Road 11-12th Floor, Song-
shan District, Taipei, 10586, Taiwan
Tel.: (886) 2 2546 7316
Apparel & Accessories Retailer
N.A.I.C.S.: 458110

Tommy Hilfiger Marketing
Limited   (1)
Rm 804 8/F Skyway House S Block 3
Sham Mong Rd, Tai Kok Tsui, Kowloon,
China (Hong Kong)
Tel.: (852) 23011288
Fashion Apparels Retailer
N.A.I.C.S.: 424310

Top Creation Limited   (1)
Unit 4 8/F Skyway House South Block No 3
Sham Mong Road, Tai Kok Tsui, Kowloon,
China (Hong Kong)
Tel.: (852) 23011288
Fashion Product Whslr
N.A.I.C.S.: 456120

DIDI GLOBAL INC.

RongKe RongZhi zhichuangzhongxin
Building 1 Yard 6 North Ring Road,
Tangjialing Haidian District, Beijing,
100000, China
Tel.: (86) 1083043181   Ky
Web Site: https://www.didiglobal.com
Year Founded: 2013
DIDIY—(OTCIQ)
Rev.: $26,632,093,197
Assets: $23,440,844,264
Liabilities: $4,221,147,696
Net Worth: $19,219,696,568
Earnings: ($7,559,942,762)
Emp.: 24,396
Fiscal Year-end: 12/31/21
Software Development Services
N.A.I.C.S.: 541511
Will Wei Cheng (Co-Founder, Chm & CEO)

DIDIM E&F

39-24 46 gil Nonhyeon-ro, Namdong-
gu, Incheon, Korea (South)
Tel.: (82) 328196870
Web Site: https://didimglobal.com

Year Founded: 2015
217620—(KRS)
Rev.: $46,682,606
Assets: $55,141,374
Liabilities: $47,124,805
Net Worth: $8,016,569
Earnings: ($6,734,126)
Emp.: 485
Fiscal Year-end: 12/31/22
Financial Investment Management
Services
N.A.I.C.S.: 523940

DIE SCHWEIZERISCHE POST AG

Wankdorfallee 4, 3030, Bern, Swit-
zerland
Tel.: (41) 848 888 780
Web Site: http://www.post.ch
Year Founded: 1849
Rev.: $7,811,133,420
Assets: $126,142,035,240
Liabilities: $119,304,881,400
Net Worth: $6,837,153,840
Earnings: $411,326,100
Emp.: 58,180
Fiscal Year-end: 12/31/18
Postal Services; Goods & Logistics
N.A.I.C.S.: 491110
Philippe Milliet (Vice Chm)

Subsidiaries:

Asendia Management SAS   (1)
9 rue du Colonel Pierre Avia, 75757, Paris,
Cedex, France
Tel.: (33) 810 821 821
Web Site: http://www.asendia.com
Emp.: 1,500
International Postal Services
N.A.I.C.S.: 491110
Marc Pontet (CEO)

Subsidiary (US):

Asendia USA   (2)
701 C Ashland Ave Bldg 24 Ste 3, Folcroft,
PA 19032
Tel.: (610) 461-3661
Web Site: http://www.asendiausa.com
International Postal Services
N.A.I.C.S.: 491110
Michael J. Hastings (Chm)

Asmiq AG   (1)
Geerenweg 2, 8048, Zurich, Switzerland
Tel.: (41) 44 305 8160
Web Site: https://www.asmiq.ch
Media Services
N.A.I.C.S.: 541840

BPS Speditions-Service AG   (1)
Wanistrasse 5, Pfungen, 8422, Zurich, Swit-
zerland
Tel.: (41) 52 305 0404
Web Site: https://www.bps-spedition.ch
Logistics Consulting Servies
N.A.I.C.S.: 541614

BPS Speditions-Service Basel
AG   (1)
Talstrasse 45, Arlesheim, 4144, Basel, Swit-
zerland
Tel.: (41) 61 465 3000
Logistics Consulting Servies
N.A.I.C.S.: 541614

Bachle Logistics GmbH   (1)
Auf Herdenen 24, 78052, Villingen-
Schwenningen, Germany
Tel.: (49) 77 218 4530
Web Site: https://www.baechle-logistics.de
Logistics Consulting Servies
N.A.I.C.S.: 541614

Bluesped France Sarl   (1)
Technoparc Rue Pierre Dreyfus, BP 94,
90100, Delle, France
Tel.: (33) 38 436 6381
Logistics Consulting Servies
N.A.I.C.S.: 541614

Bluesped Logistics Sarl   (1)
Chemin des Pommerats 5, Boncourt, 2926,
Porrentruy, Switzerland
Tel.: (41) 32 495 1616

Web Site: https://www.bluesped.ch
Logistics Consulting Servies
N.A.I.C.S.: 541614

Botec Boncourt S.A.   (1)
Plateforme douaniere, Boncourt, 2926, Por-
rentruy, Switzerland
Tel.: (41) 32 475 5252
Web Site: https://www.botecsa.ch
Logistics Consulting Servies
N.A.I.C.S.: 541614

Botec Sarl   (1)
8 Rue Pierre Dreyfus, 90100, Delle, France
Tel.: (33) 38 456 2215
Logistics Consulting Servies
N.A.I.C.S.: 541614

CF Card Factory GmbH   (1)
In the valley 10, 37235, Hessisch Lich-
tenau, Germany
Tel.: (49) 56 02 91 74 0
Web Site: http://www.cardfactory-gmbh.de
Smartcard Mfr
N.A.I.C.S.: 322299

Caporin Voyages SARL   (1)
1 Boulevard Etivalliere, 42000, Saint Eti-
enne, France
Tel.: (33) 9 61 40 72 19
Bus Transportation Services
N.A.I.C.S.: 487110

CarPostal Agde SAS   (1)
1 B Quai Du Commandant Reveille, 34300,
Agde, France
Tel.: (33) 800350310
Bus Transportation Services
N.A.I.C.S.: 487110

CarPostal Dole SAS   (1)
39 rue Macedonio Melloni, 39100, Dole,
France
Tel.: (33) 3 84 72 98 36
Bus Transportation Services
N.A.I.C.S.: 487110

CarPostal Macon SAS   (1)
9029 Rue Lavoisier, 71000, Macon, France
Tel.: (33) 3 85 21 98 70
Bus Transportation Services
N.A.I.C.S.: 487110

CarPostal Mediterranee SAS   (1)
9061 Route De Guiraudette, 34300, Agde,
France   (100%)
Tel.: (33) 4 67 01 22 24
Bus Transportation Services
N.A.I.C.S.: 487110

Destinas AG   (1)
Internationale Spedition Hauptstrasse 137E,
Tagerwilen, 8274, Kreuzlingen, Switzerland
Tel.: (41) 71 677 4177
Web Site: https://www.destinas.ch
Logistics Consulting Servies
N.A.I.C.S.: 541614
Gerhard Reinig (Mng Dir)

Direct Mail Company AG   (1)
Reinacherstrasse 131, 4018, Basel, Swit-
zerland
Tel.: (41) 61 337 87 87
Web Site: http://www.dm-company.ch
Sales Range: $25-49.9 Million
Emp.: 50
Information Processing Services
N.A.I.C.S.: 518210
Martin Keller (COO)

Subsidiary (Domestic):

DMB Direct Mail Biel-Bienne AG   (2)
Johann-Renfer-Strasse 62, 2504, Biel, Swit-
zerland
Tel.: (41) 32 343 30 30
Direct Marketing Services
N.A.I.C.S.: 541613
Ralph Hugelshofer (Gen Mgr)

Direct Mail Logistik AG   (2)
Reinacherstrasse 131, 4018, Basel, Swit-
zerland
Tel.: (41) 61 337 83 50
Web Site: http://www.dm-logistics.ch
Logistics Consulting Servies
N.A.I.C.S.: 541614

EDS Media AG   (1)
Bergstrasse 58 Postfach 731, 8706, Meilen,
Switzerland
Tel.: (41) 44 925 2000

Web Site: https://www.edsmedia.ch
Logistics Consulting Servies
N.A.I.C.S.: 541614
Carsten Vossmeyer *(CEO)*

Epsilon SA **(1)**
Route Des Jeunes 95, Case Postale 1169,
1211, Geneva, Switzerland
Tel.: (41) 22 343 01 00
Web Site: http://www.epsilon-sa.ch
Letter, Parcel & Express Delivery Services
N.A.I.C.S.: 492110

FMC Insights Limited **(1)**
Briarslea House Kilgobbin Road, Dublin,
Ireland
Tel.: (353) 1 294 4584
Letter, Parcel & Express Delivery Services
N.A.I.C.S.: 492110

IN-Media AG **(1)**
Reinacherstrasse 131, 4018, Basel, Switzerland
Tel.: (41) 613389891
Web Site: http://www.in-media.ch
Magazine Publisher
N.A.I.C.S.: 513120
Patrick Flad *(Mng Dir)*

Iemoli Trasporti S.r.l. **(1)**
Viale Alessandro Volta 40, 22071, Cadorago, CO, Italy
Tel.: (39) 03 190 4506
Logistics Consulting Servies
N.A.I.C.S.: 541614

Iemoli Trasporti SA **(1)**
Via Motta 6, 6828, Balerna, Switzerland
Tel.: (41) 91 683 6787
Web Site: https://www.iemolitrasporti.com
Warehouse Services
N.A.I.C.S.: 493110

InTraLog Hermes AG **(1)**
Durrenhubelstrasse 7, 4133, Prattein, Switzerland
Tel.: (41) 61 467 1503
Web Site: https://www.intralog.ch
Warehouse Services
N.A.I.C.S.: 493110
Beat Eugster *(CEO)*

InTraLog Overseas AG **(1)**
Steinackerstrasse 34, 8302, Kloten, Switzerland
Tel.: (41) 43 501 3600
Warehouse Services
N.A.I.C.S.: 493110

InfraPost AG **(1)**
Viktoriastrasse 72, 3030, Bern, Switzerland
Tel.: (41) 58 338 94 04
Rev.: $155,422,080
Emp.: 1,711
Facility Management Services
N.A.I.C.S.: 561210

Livesystems AG **(1)**
Waldeggstrasse 37, 3097, Liebefeld, Switzerland
Tel.: (41) 84 000 0008
Web Site: https://www.livesystems.ch
Media Services
N.A.I.C.S.: 541840
Nicola Molinara *(Chief Client Officer)*

Mobility Solutions AG **(1)**
Stockackerstrasse 50, 3030, Bern, Switzerland
Tel.: (41) 58 338 55 00
Web Site: http://www.mobilitysolutions.ch
Sales Range: $50-74.9 Million
Emp.: 100
Fleet Management Services
N.A.I.C.S.: 532112

Mobility Solutions Management AG **(1)**
Stockackerstrasse 50, Bern, 3030, Switzerland
Tel.: (41) 31 338 55 00
Web Site: http://www.post.ch
Emp.: 100
Fleet Management Services
N.A.I.C.S.: 532112
Rahel Bonny *(Gen Mgr)*

OSA Logistik GmbH **(1)**
Andreas-Meyer-Strasse 45, 22113, Hamburg, Germany
Tel.: (49) 402 714 4670

Pharmaceuticals Product Mfr
N.A.I.C.S.: 325412

Ost-West Cargo Baltic UAB **(1)**
Barklainiu 2, LT-36227, Panevezys, Lithuania
Tel.: (370) 4 543 6494
Logistic Services
N.A.I.C.S.: 541614
Virginijus Pilipavicius *(Mng Dir)*

Ost-West Cargo Europe GmbH **(1)**
Zahn-Nopper-Strasse 1, Zuffenhausen,
70435, Stuttgart, Germany
Tel.: (49) 711 782 3970
Web Site: https://www.ost-west-cargo.de
Logistics Consulting Servies
N.A.I.C.S.: 541614
Sebastian Schmid *(Mng Dir)*

Ost-West Cargo Transport UAB **(1)**
Barklainiu 2, LT-36227, Panevezys, Lithuania
Tel.: (370) 4 559 8003
Logistics Consulting Servies
N.A.I.C.S.: 541614

Otto Schmidt AG **(1)**
St Jakobs-Strasse 200, 4052, Basel, Switzerland
Tel.: (41) 61 690 9090
Web Site: https://www.otto-schmidt.ch
Warehouse Services
N.A.I.C.S.: 493110

Post CH Network Ltd. **(1)**
Wankdorfallee 4, 3030, Bern, Switzerland
Tel.: (41) 84 888 8888
Web Site: https://www.post.ch
Logistics Consulting Servies
N.A.I.C.S.: 541614
Christian Levrat *(Chm)*

Post Company Cars AG **(1)**
Stockackerstrasse 50, 3030, Bern, Switzerland
Tel.: (41) 58 338 3442
Web Site:
https://www.postcompanycars.post.ch
Car Lending Services
N.A.I.C.S.: 532112
Nigel Storny *(Mng Dir)*

Post Immobilien Management und Services AG **(1)**
Wankdorfallee 4, 3030, Bern, Switzerland
Tel.: (41) 84 888 8780
Web Site: https://www.immobilien.post.ch
Logistics Consulting Servies
N.A.I.C.S.: 541614
Silvio Gloor *(Head)*

PostAuto Liechtenstein Anstalt **(1)**
Wuhrstrasse 25, PO Box 575, 9490, Vaduz,
Liechtenstein
Tel.: (423) 388 29 89
Web Site: http://www.postauto.ch
Rev.: $17,269,120
Emp.: 95
Bus Transportation Services
N.A.I.C.S.: 485113

PostFinance AG **(1)**
Mingerstrasse 20, 3030, Bern, Switzerland
Tel.: (41) 84 888 89 00
Web Site: http://www.postfinance.ch
Sales Range: $1-4.9 Billion
Emp.: 3,473
Payment Transaction Services
N.A.I.C.S.: 522320
Kurt Fuchs *(Head-Fin)*

PostLogistics AG **(1)**
Lagerstrasse 12, Dintikon, 5606, Switzerland
Tel.: (41) 58 448 64 00
Logistics Consulting Servies
N.A.I.C.S.: 541614

PostMail AG **(1)**
Viktoriastrasse 21, Bern, 3030, Switzerland
Tel.: (41) 31 338 11 11
Information Processing Services
N.A.I.C.S.: 518210

Presto Presse-Vertriebs AG **(1)**
Zentweg 5, Bern, 3006, Switzerland
Tel.: (41) 58 448 07 07
Newspaper Publishers
N.A.I.C.S.: 513110

PubliBike SA **(1)**
Route des Arsenaux 15, Fribourg, 1700,
Switzerland **(100%)**
Tel.: (41) 21 533 10 10.
Web Site: http://www.publibike.ch
Emp.: 40
Bicycle Sharing & Rental Services
N.A.I.C.S.: 532284
Bruno Rohner *(CEO)*

Relatra AG **(1)**
Hauptstrasse 137E, Tagerwilen, 8274,
Kreuzlingen, Switzerland
Tel.: (41) 71 677 4141
Web Site: https://www.relatra.ch
Logistics Consulting Servies
N.A.I.C.S.: 541614
Gerhard Reinig *(Mng Dir)*

SecurePost AG **(1)**
Viktoriastrasse 21, 3030, Berne, Switzerland
Tel.: (41) 313380777
Web Site: http://www.post.ch
Emp.: 440
Cash Handling Services
N.A.I.C.S.: 522320

Societè d'Affretement et de Transit S.A.T. SAS **(1)**
6 Rue Robert Schuman, 68870, Bartenheim, France
Tel.: (33) 3 89 69 14 00
Bus Transportation Services
N.A.I.C.S.: 487110

Steriplus AG **(1)**
Benknerstrasse 48, 8722, Kaltbrunn, Switzerland
Tel.: (41) 55 283 2020
Web Site: https://www.steriplus.ch
Surgical Instrument Logistics Services
N.A.I.C.S.: 488510

Swiss Post International Holding AG **(1)**
Viktoriastrasse 21, Bern, 3030, Switzerland
Tel.: (41) 84 888 88 88
Logistics Consulting Servies
N.A.I.C.S.: 541614

Swiss Post International Management AG **(1)**
Viktoriastrasse 21, Bern, 3030, Switzerland
Tel.: (41) 313381111
Information Processing Services
N.A.I.C.S.: 518210
Davide Boeri *(Product Mgr)*

Swiss Post Solutions AG **(1)**
Pfingstweidstrasse 60B, 8080, Zurich, Switzerland
Tel.: (41) 9519168100
Web Site:
http://www.swisspostsolutions.com
Information Processing Services
N.A.I.C.S.: 518210
Art Tatge *(COO-North America)*

Swiss Post Solutions GmbH **(1)**
Linzer Strasse 221/4 2, 1140, Vienna, Austria
Tel.: (43) 18904052
Web Site:
http://www.swisspostsolutions.com
Sales Range: $25-49.9 Million
Emp.: 32
Information Processing Services
N.A.I.C.S.: 518210

Swiss Post Solutions GmbH **(1)**
Am Borstig 5, 96052, Bamberg, Germany
Tel.: (49) 9519168200
Web Site:
http://www.swisspostsolutions.com
Sales Range: $100-124.9 Million
Emp.: 300
Information Processing Services
N.A.I.C.S.: 518210
Michael Auerbach *(CEO)*

Swiss Post Solutions GmbH, Prien **(1)**
Systemformstr 5, Prien am Chiemsee,
83209, Germany
Tel.: (49) 8051 602 0
Information Processing Services
N.A.I.C.S.: 518210
Thomas Hatn *(Gen Mgr)*

Swiss Post Solutions GmbH, Pulsnitz **(1)**
Geothestr 6, 01896, Pulsnitz, Germany
Tel.: (49) 35955 7150
Information Processing Services
N.A.I.C.S.: 518210

Swiss Post Solutions Holding Pte. Ltd. **(1)**
5 Shenton Way 10-01 UIC Building, Singapore, 068808, Singapore
Tel.: (65) 6 904 0028
Logistics Consulting Servies
N.A.I.C.S.: 541614

Swiss Post Solutions Inc. **(1)**
10 E 40th St 9thÂ Fl, New York, NY 10016
Tel.: (212) 204-0777
Web Site:
http://www.swisspostsolutions.com
Rev.: $7,500,000
Emp.: 147
Information Processing Services
N.A.I.C.S.: 518210
Dan Moscatiello *(CEO-North America)*

Subsidiary (Non-US):

GHP Far East Co. Ltd. **(2)**
8th Floor Saigon ICT Tower Quang Trung
Software City, District 12, Ho Chi Minh City,
Vietnam
Tel.: (84) 8 3715 5359
Web Site: http://www.ghp-fareast.com.vn
Emp.: 1,200
Software Development Services
N.A.I.C.S.: 541511
Frank Schellenberg *(CEO)*

Swiss Post Solutions Ltd **(1)**
Richmond Place 15 Petersham Road, Richmond upon Thames, London, TW10 6TP,
Surrey, United Kingdom
Tel.: (44) 845 301 3708
Web Site:
http://www.swisspostsolutions.com
Information Processing Services
N.A.I.C.S.: 518210
Gary Harrold *(CEO)*

Swiss Post Solutions S.p.A. **(1)**
Via Luigi Galvani 24, 20124, Milan, Milano,
Italy
Tel.: (39) 02 4549 1102
Web Site: http://www.swisspostsolutions.it
Emp.: 200
Information Processing Services
N.A.I.C.S.: 518210
Anna Fornara *(Gen Dir)*

Swiss Post Solutions SAS **(1)**
60-62 rue de Wattignies, 75012, Paris,
France
Tel.: (33) 1 44 74 35 15
Web Site:
http://www.swisspostsolutions.com
Information Processing Services
N.A.I.C.S.: 518210
Alexander Valkenberg *(CEO-South West
Europe)*

Swiss Post Solutions Singapore **(1)**
10 Anson Road27-15 International Plaza,
Singapore, 079903, Singapore
Tel.: (65) 67045451
Web Site:
http://www.swisspostsolutions.com
Sales Range: $25-49.9 Million
Emp.: 3
Information Processing Services
N.A.I.C.S.: 518210

Swiss Post Solutions s.r.o **(1)**
Puchovska 16, PO Box 70, Bratislava,
83005, Slovakia
Tel.: (421) 2492774
Web Site: http://www.swiss-point.eu
Sales Range: $50-74.9 Million
Emp.: 200
Information Processing Services
N.A.I.C.S.: 518210

SwissSign AG **(1)**
Sagereistrasse 25, CH-8152, Glattbrugg,
Switzerland
Tel.: (41) 848776655
Web Site: http://swisssign.com
Software Development Services
N.A.I.C.S.: 541511

Die Schweizerische Post AG—(Continued)

SwissSign Group AG (1)
Sagereistrasse 25, 8152, Glattbrugg, Switzerland
Tel.: (41) 84 877 6655
Web Site: https://www.swisssign-group.com
Information Technology Services
N.A.I.C.S.: 519290
Markus Naef (CEO)

DIEFFENBACHER HOLDING GMBH & CO. KG
Heilbronner Strasse 20, 75031, Eppingen, Germany
Tel.: (49) 7262 65 0
Web Site:
 http://www.dieffenbacher.de
Year Founded: 1873
Sales Range: $500-549.9 Million
Emp.: 1,780
Hydraulic Press Production Systems Engineer & Supplier
N.A.I.C.S.: 333517
Wolf-Gerd Dieffenbacher (Chm-Mgmt Bd)

Subsidiaries:

B. Maier Zerkleinerungstechnik GmbH (1)
Schweriner Strasse 1, 33605, Bielefeld, Germany
Tel.: (49) 521 584943 20
Web Site: http://www.dieffenbacher-maier.de
Engineering, Chipping Technology, Conveying & Cleaning Technology
N.A.I.C.S.: 541330
Alexander Hoffmann (Mng Dir)

Dieffenbacher Asia Pacific Sdn. Bhd. (1)
Unit 11-02 11th Floor Menara Multi-Purpose Capital Square, No 8 Jalan Munshi Abdullah, Kuala Lumpur, 50100, Malaysia
Tel.: (60) 3 7490 0183
Web Site: http://www.dieffenbacher.de
Emp.: 20
Industrial Machinery Sales & Service
N.A.I.C.S.: 423830
Beekoon Lee (Office Mgr)

Dieffenbacher Australasia Pty, Ltd. (1)
3 Lauren Court, PO Box 279, Lilydale, 3140, VIC, Australia
Tel.: (61) 3 9735 2537
Industrial Machinery Sales & Service
N.A.I.C.S.: 423830
Alan McKinna (Mgr)

Dieffenbacher CZ hydraulicke lisy, s.r.o (1)
Ripska 15, 627 00, Brno, Czech Republic (98%)
Tel.: (420) 548423111
Web Site: http://www.dieffenbacher.cz
Sales Range: $25-49.9 Million
Emp.: 100
Hydraulic Presses Mfr
N.A.I.C.S.: 333248
Miroslav Jopek (Mng Dir)

Dieffenbacher Customer Support, LLC (1)
795 Branch Dr, Alpharetta, GA 30004
Tel.: (770) 663-4383
Web Site: http://www.dieffenbacher.com
Services & Spare Parts for Wood Panel Manufacturing Machinery
N.A.I.C.S.: 423830
Marc Keller (CFO & Sec)

Dieffenbacher India Pvt. Ltd. (1)
Unit 105 First Floor Prestige Towers, 99 Residency Road, Bengaluru, 560 025, India
Tel.: (91) 80 4151 0060
Industrial Machinery Sales & Service
N.A.I.C.S.: 423830

Dieffenbacher Machinery (Changzhou) Co., Ltd. (1)
No 18 environmental protection 1st road The National, Xin Bei District, Changzhou, 213034, Jiangsu, China
Tel.: (86) 519 586 6378
Food Processing Equipment Distr

N.A.I.C.S.: 423830

Dieffenbacher Machinery Services (Beijing) Co., Ltd. (1)
Scitech Tower Unit 1305, 22 Jianguomen Wai Dajie, Beijing, 100004, China
Tel.: (86) 10 6522 0935
Web Site: http://www.dieffenbacher.de
Emp.: 18
Industrial Machinery Sales & Service
N.A.I.C.S.: 423830
Shouhua Liu (Mgr-Sls & Svc)

Dieffenbacher Maschinenfabrik GmbH (1)
Gewerbestrasse 29, 75059, Zaisenhausen, Germany
Tel.: (49) 7258 609 0
Web Site: http://www.dieffenbacher-zaisenhausen.de
Emp.: 90
Industrial Machinery Mfr
N.A.I.C.S.: 333248
Ralf Hagner (Head-Sls)

Dieffenbacher North America, Inc. (1)
9495 Twin Oaks Drive, Windsor, N8N 5B8, ON, Canada (100%)
Tel.: (519) 979-6937
Web Site: http://www.dieffenbacher.ca
Sales Range: $25-49.9 Million
Emp.: 65
Press & Forming Machinery Mfr
N.A.I.C.S.: 333248

Dieffenbacher Panelboard Oy (1)
Wipaktie 1, 15560, Nastola, Finland
Tel.: (358) 10 572 9000
Web Site: http://www.dieffenbacher.com
Emp.: 60
Supplies Production Lines, Single Machines & After-Market Services to Fiberboard & Particleboard Industries
N.A.I.C.S.: 423830
Sirkau Karva (Controller)

Dieffenbacher Schenck Panel GmbH (1)
Werner Von Siemens Strasse 2, D 64319, Pfungstadt, Baden Wurttemberg, Germany (100%)
Tel.: (49) 61578030
Web Site: http://www.dieffenbacher.com
Emp.: 30
Metal Tools
N.A.I.C.S.: 333517

Dieffenbacher System-Automation GmbH (1)
Jakob-Dieffenbacher-Strasse 4, 75031, Eppingen, Germany (100%)
Tel.: (49) 7262650
Web Site: http://www.dieffenbacher.com
Sales Range: $25-49.9 Million
Emp.: 40
Metal Tools
N.A.I.C.S.: 333517

Dieffenbacher USA, Inc. (1)
2000 McFarland 400 Blvd, Alpharetta, GA 30004 (100%)
Tel.: (770) 226-6394
Web Site: http://www.dieffenbacher.com
Sales Range: $50-74.9 Million
Emp.: 50
Industrial Machinery & Equipment Sales
N.A.I.C.S.: 423830
Marc Keller (CFO & Sec)

Dieffenbacher do Brasil Construcao de Maquinas e Instalacoes Ltda. (1)
Cyro Correia Pereira Street 667 Block 02-C, Neighborhood Cidade Industrial de Curitiba, Curitiba, 81 170 230, Parana, Brazil (100%)
Tel.: (55) 41 3268 4205
Industrial Machinery Sales & Service
N.A.I.C.S.: 423830

INSERCO Brasil Servicos Industriais Ltda. (1)
Rua Cyro Correia Pereira 667 Predio 1-C, 81170-230, Curitiba, Brazil
Tel.: (55) 41 3044 1462
Food Processing Equipment Distr
N.A.I.C.S.: 423830

Karle und Jung GmbH (1)

Heinrich-Hertz-Strasse 3, 76470, Oetigheim, Germany (100%)
Tel.: (49) 7222 40 655 0
Web Site: http://www.karle-jung.de
Sales Range: $25-49.9 Million
Emp.: 35
Tool & Mechanical Engineering
N.A.I.C.S.: 333517
Mathias Jung (Gen Mgr)

Maertiens Robotec GmbH (1)
Zum Haug 10, 76646, Bruchsal, Germany
Tel.: (49) 7251 9573 0
Web Site: http://www.maertiens.de
Mfr of Industrial Machinery for Automotive Industry
N.A.I.C.S.: 333248
Steffen Maertiens (CEO)

OOO Dieffenbacher Moscow (1)
Barklay Street 6 Building 9, 121087, Moscow, Russia
Tel.: (7) 4952152257
Industrial Machinery Sales & Service
N.A.I.C.S.: 423830

Shanghai Wood Based Panel Machinery Co., Ltd. (1)
No 299 Hejing Road, Anting, Shanghai, 201805, China
Tel.: (86) 21 5957 7480
Web Site: http://www.shbanji.com
Supplier of Industrial Machinery for Wood Panel Production Plants
N.A.I.C.S.: 423830
Jinxing Wang (Mng Dir)

Sunds MDF Technologies AB (1)
Universitetsallen 32, 85171, Sundsvall, Sweden
Tel.: (46) 60 524 200
Web Site: http://www.sunds-mdf.com
Emp.: 12
Engineering & Supply of Front-End Systems for Fiberboard Plants
N.A.I.C.S.: 333248
Kenth Eklund (Mng Dir)

DIEGEM-KENNEDY
Place de lAlbertine 2, 1000, Brussels, Belgium
DIEG—(EUR)
Real Estate Investment Services
N.A.I.C.S.: 531190

DIEHL STIFTUNG & CO. KG
Stephanstrasse 49, 90478, Nuremberg, Germany
Tel.: (49) 9119470
Web Site: http://www.diehl.com
Sales Range: $1-4.9 Billion
Emp.: 16,000
Holding Company
N.A.I.C.S.: 551112
Thomas Diehl (Pres & CEO)

Subsidiaries:

Apparatebau Gauting Gesellschaft mit beschrankter Haftung (1)
Friedrichshafener Str 5, 82205, Gilching, Germany
Tel.: (49) 8105 210 0
Web Site: http://www.aoa-gauting.de
Emp.: 200
Commercial Building Services
N.A.I.C.S.: 236220
Dieter Faust (Mng Dir)

DIEHL Gas Metering GmbH (1)
Industriestrasse 13, 91522, Ansbach, Germany
Tel.: (49) 981 1806 300
Emp.: 50
Measuring Equipment Whslr
N.A.I.C.S.: 423830

DIEHL POWER ELECTRONIC SAS (1)
Siaugues St Romain, 43300, Siaugues-Sainte-Marie, France
Tel.: (33) 471740930
Metal Products Mfr
N.A.I.C.S.: 331420
Yves Garmy (Mgr-Ops)

DST Defence Service Tracks GmbH (1)
Industriegelande, 66629, Sankt Wendel, Germany
Tel.: (49) 2191 976 0
Web Site: http://www.defence-st.com
Explosives Mfr
N.A.I.C.S.: 325920

Diehl & Eagle-Picher Gesellschaft mit beschrankter Haftung (1)
Fischbachstr 20, Pegnitz, 90552, Rothenbach, Germany
Tel.: (49) 911 957 2100
Metal Products Mfr
N.A.I.C.S.: 331420
Andreas Leikauf (CFO)

Diehl AKO Stiftung & Co. KG (1)
Pfannerstrasse 75, PO Box 1163, 88239, Wangen, Germany (100%)
Tel.: (49) 7522730
Web Site: http://www.diehlako.com
Sales Range: $50-74.9 Million
Emp.: 250
Electromechanical & Electronic Controls for Washing Machines, Dryers & Dishwashers; Radiant Heating Systems
N.A.I.C.S.: 334513

Diehl Aerospace GmbH (1)
Alte Nussdorfer Strasse 23, D 88662, Uberlingen, Germany
Tel.: (49) 75518902
Web Site: http://www.diehl-aerospace.de
Sales Range: $125-149.9 Million
Emp.: 425
Development of Missiles, Flight Training Systems & Munitions
N.A.I.C.S.: 336414

Subsidiary (Domestic):

Diehl Aerospace GmbH (2)
An der Sanelmuhle 13, 60439, Frankfurt, Germany
Tel.: (49) 6958050
Web Site: http://www.diehl-aerospace.de
Sales Range: $100-124.9 Million
Emp.: 400
Development of Missiles, Flight Training Systems & Munitions
N.A.I.C.S.: 336414
Gerardo Walle (Pres & Mng Dir)

Diehl Aerospace, Inc. (1)
12001 Highway 280, Starrett, AL 35147
Tel.: (205) 678-7101
Aircraft Components Mfr
N.A.I.C.S.: 332510
Robert Hottel (VP-Ops)

Diehl Aerosystems-Holding GmbH (1)
Stephanstr 49, 90478, Nuremberg, Germany
Tel.: (49) 911 947 0
Aircraft Components Mfr
N.A.I.C.S.: 332510

Diehl Aircabin GmbH (1)
Am Flugplatz, 88471, Laupheim, Germany
Tel.: (49) 7392 703 0
Metal Products Mfr
N.A.I.C.S.: 331420
Robert Dolp (VP-Quality)

Diehl Aircabin Hungary Kft. (1)
Ipari Park utca 9, 4300, Nyirbator, Hungary
Tel.: (36) 42510720
Aircraft Cabin Mfr
N.A.I.C.S.: 332510
Attila Krasznai (Head-Quality & Supply Chain)

Diehl Auge Decoupage SAS (1)
12 Bd J F Kennedy, 25000, Besancon, Cedex, France
Tel.: (33) 3381402200
Metal Products Mfr
N.A.I.C.S.: 331420
Eric Devaux (Mng Dir-Bus Dev)

Diehl Aviation Gilching GmbH (1)
Friedrichshafener Str 5, 82205, Gilching, Germany
Tel.: (49) 405287220
Automotive Electronic Component Mfr
N.A.I.C.S.: 336320
Albert Beer (Mng Dir)

Diehl Comfort Modules GmbH **(1)**
Hein-Sass-Weg 41, 21129, Hamburg, Germany
Tel.: (49) 40 74314 0
Metal Products Mfr
N.A.I.C.S.: 331420
Florian Knecht *(Engr-Mfg)*

Diehl Connectivity Solutions GmbH **(1)**
Stephanstrasse 49, 90478, Nuremberg, Germany
Tel.: (49) 91197479853
Automotive Electronic Component Mfr
N.A.I.C.S.: 336320
Horst Leonberger *(Mng Dir)*

Diehl Controls (Nanjing) Co. Ltd. **(1)**
139 Jiangjun Avenue Jiangning Development Zone, 211100, Nanjing, China
Tel.: (86) 2552105790
Electronic Control Equipment Mfr
N.A.I.C.S.: 334513
Maggie Han *(Dir-HR)*

Diehl Controls Mexico S.A. de C.V. **(1)**
Ave El Tepeyac 1730 Parque Industrial El Tepeyac, El Marques, 76250, Queretaro, Mexico
Tel.: (52) 4422781350
Electronic Control Equipment Mfr
N.A.I.C.S.: 334513
Jaime Colin Rodriguez *(Engr-Test Dev)*

Diehl Controls North America Inc. **(1)**
1842 Centre Point Cir Ste 110, Naperville, IL 60563
Tel.: (630) 946-1500
Electronic Control Equipment Mfr
N.A.I.C.S.: 334513
Craig Mitchell Sr. *(Acct Mgr)*

Diehl Controls Polska Sp. z o.o. **(1)**
ul Pulaskiego 6, 46-100, Namyslow, Poland
Tel.: (48) 774037300
Electronic Control Equipment Mfr
N.A.I.C.S.: 334513
Wojciech Paruzel *(Dir-Ops)*

Diehl Defence GmbH & Co. KG **(1)**
Alte Nussdorfer Strasse 13, 88662, Uberlingen, Germany
Tel.: (49) 75518901
Emp.: 2,700
Arm Mfr
N.A.I.C.S.: 332994
Helmut Rauch *(CEO)*

Diehl Metal Applications GmbH **(1)**
Am Stichkanal 6 - 8, 14167, Berlin, Germany
Tel.: (49) 30 84784 438
Metal Electroplating Services
N.A.I.C.S.: 332813
Matthias Mockel *(Head-Specific Projects)*

Diehl Metal India Private Limited **(1)**
S No 225 Hissa Nr 1/8 Hinjewadi, Mulshi, 411057, Pune, India
Tel.: (91) 2066742603
Metal Products Mfr
N.A.I.C.S.: 331523
Pravin Badadare *(Head-Mfg)*

Diehl Metall (Shenzhen) Co. Ltd. **(1)**
Block 25 Shatoujiao Free Trade Zone, 518081, Shenzhen, China
Tel.: (86) 755252614540
Metal Products Mfr
N.A.I.C.S.: 331420

Diehl Metall Stiftung & Co. KG **(1)**
Heinrich-Diehl-Strasse 9, 90552, Rothenbach, Germany **(100%)**
Tel.: (49) 91157040
Web Site: http://www.diehlmetall.com
Sales Range: $400-449.9 Million
Emp.: 1,200
Mfr of Rods, Tubes & Brass Forged Parts
N.A.I.C.S.: 331210
Werner Reino *(CEO)*

Diehl Metering (Jinan) Co. Ltd. **(1)**
Wuzhou Building 1100 Shunfeng Road High-Tech Development Zone, 250101, Jinan, China
Tel.: (86) 53158820999
Emp.: 120

Measuring Equipment Whslr
N.A.I.C.S.: 423830
Yongkai Yuan *(Engr-Software)*

Diehl Metering AB **(1)**
Stalgatan 1 3 tr, 195 72, Rosersberg, Sweden
Tel.: (46) 8800400
Metering Device Mfr
N.A.I.C.S.: 334514
Steven Silverang *(Head-Technical Customer Svcs)*

Diehl Metering ApS **(1)**
Glentevej 1, 6705, Esbjerg, Denmark
Tel.: (45) 76134300
Measuring Equipment Whslr
N.A.I.C.S.: 423830
Henrich Munk Svendsen *(Mgr-Svc)*

Diehl Metering FZE **(1)**
Jebel Ali Freezone, PO Box 261507, Dubai, United Arab Emirates
Tel.: (971) 48849237
Measuring Equipment Whslr
N.A.I.C.S.: 423830
Ali Badran *(Mgr-Technical)*

Diehl Metering GesmbH **(1)**
Hainburger Strasse 33, 1031, Vienna, Austria
Tel.: (43) 1716700
Emp.: 48
Measuring Equipment Whslr
N.A.I.C.S.: 423830

Diehl Metering LLC **(1)**
1813 N Mill Street Ste C, Naperville, IL 60563
Tel.: (331) 204-6540
Metering Device Mfr
N.A.I.C.S.: 334514
Peter Zisterer *(Pres & CEO)*

Diehl Metering Limited **(1)**
22c Salmon Fields Business Village, Royton, Oldham, OL2 6HT, United Kingdom
Tel.: (44) 1616209593
Measuring Equipment Whslr
N.A.I.C.S.: 423830

Diehl Metering S.A.S. **(1)**
67 Rue du Rhone, BP 10160, 68304, Saint Louis, Cedex, France
Tel.: (33) 389695400
Emp.: 290
Measuring Equipment Whslr
N.A.I.C.S.: 423830
Sebastien Dubail *(Head-Embedded Software Dev)*

Diehl Metering S.L. **(1)**
C/Diego de Leon 47, 28006, Madrid, Spain
Tel.: (34) 918306626
Metering Device Mfr
N.A.I.C.S.: 334514

Diehl Metering S.R.L. **(1)**
Via Pelizza da Volpedo 20, Cinisello Balsamo, 20092, Milan, Italy
Tel.: (39) 0266012417
Measuring Equipment Whslr
N.A.I.C.S.: 423830
Rochi Dommarco *(Country Mgr)*

Diehl Metering Sp. z o.o. **(1)**
ul Cieszynska 1 A, 43-440, Bazanowice, Poland
Tel.: (48) 338510439
Emp.: 180
Measuring Equipment Whslr
N.A.I.C.S.: 423830
Piotr Spyrka *(Product Mgr-Thermal Energy)*

Diehl Metering Systems GmbH **(1)**
Donaustrasse 120, 90451, Nuremberg, Germany
Tel.: (49) 911 6424 0
Measuring Equipment Whslr
N.A.I.C.S.: 423830
Achim Schmidt *(Engr-System)*

Diehl Remscheid GmbH & Co **(1)**
Vieringhausen 118, 42857, Remscheid, Germany **(100%)**
Tel.: (49) 21919760
Web Site: http://www.diehlremscheid.de
Sales Range: $75-99.9 Million
Emp.: 400
Production of Tracks for Tanks & Armored Vehicles

N.A.I.C.S.: 336992

Diehl Retrofit Missile Systeme GmbH **(1)**
Alte Nussdorfer Strasse 19, 88662, Uberlingen, Germany
Tel.: (49) 7551894284
Automotive Electronic Product Mfr
N.A.I.C.S.: 336320

Diehl Service Modules GmbH **(1)**
Vierenkamp 1, 22453, Hamburg, Germany
Tel.: (49) 40 528722 0
Emp.: 200
Aircraft Components Mfr
N.A.I.C.S.: 332510
Urs Borgward *(Sr Mgr-Contract)*

Diehl SynchroTec Manufacturing (Wuxi) Co., Ltd. **(1)**
B28-a Wuxi Hi-Tec Industrial Development Zone No 59 XiMei Road, Mei Cun Town, 214112, Wuxi, Jiangsu, China
Tel.: (86) 51088156401
Metal Products Mfr
N.A.I.C.S.: 331523
Kevin Huang *(Mgr-Maintenance)*

Diehl Ventures GmbH **(1)**
Stephanstr 49, 90478, Nuremberg, Germany
Tel.: (49) 9119472002
Business Management Services
N.A.I.C.S.: 541611
Alexander Schmidt *(Mgr-Investment)*

Diehl Werkzeugbau Seebach GmbH **(1)**
Neue Strasse 67, 99846, Seebach, Germany
Tel.: (49) 36929 6402 0
Machine Tools Mfr
N.A.I.C.S.: 333517

Diehl do Brasil Metalurgica Limitada **(1)**
Rua Lagrange 171 Villa Socorro, 04761-050, Sao Paulo, Brazil
Tel.: (55) 1121640102
Metal Products Mfr
N.A.I.C.S.: 331523
Martin Braunholz *(Dir-Comml)*

DynITEC GmbH **(1)**
Kaiserstrasse 3, 53840, Troisdorf, Germany
Tel.: (49) 22 41 2 08 42 00
Emp.: 60
Explosives Mfr
N.A.I.C.S.: 325920

Franconia Industries, Inc. **(1)**
145 Center St, Meriden, CT 06450
Tel.: (203) 639-5220
Metal Products Mfr
N.A.I.C.S.: 331523

JUNGHANS Microtec GmbH **(1)**
Unterbergenweg 10, Seedorf, 78655, Dunningen, Germany
Tel.: (49) 7402 181 0
Explosives Mfr
N.A.I.C.S.: 325920
Sven Stollenwerk *(Product Mgr)*

Junghans T2M SAS **(1)**
Route d'Ardon, 45240, La Ferte-Saint-Aubin, France
Tel.: (33) 238516422
Explosives Mfr
N.A.I.C.S.: 325920
Didier Creusot *(Mgr-Sls & Mktg)*

Magyar Optikai Muvek Vizmeresztechnikai Zartkoruen Mukodo Reszvenytarsasag **(1)**
Ipari ut 16, 4700, Mateszalka, Hungary
Tel.: (36) 44502100
Emp.: 163
Measuring Equipment Whslr
N.A.I.C.S.: 423830
Regis Metens *(CEO & Chm)*

SMH Suddeutsche Metallhandelsgesellschaft mit beschrankter Haftung **(1)**
Heinrich-Diehl-Strasse 9, 90552, Rothenbach, Germany
Tel.: (49) 911 5704 0
Metal Recycling Services
N.A.I.C.S.: 423930

Zehdenick Innovative Metall- und Kunststofftechnik GmbH **(1)**
Liebenwalder Ausbau 13, 16792, Brandenburg, Germany
Tel.: (49) 3307 4664 0
Metal Product Mfr331420
N.A.I.C.S.: 331420
Andreas Kaltenbach *(Plant Mgr)*

DIEN QUANG LAMP JSC
125 Ham Nghi, Quan 1, Ho Chi Minh City, Vietnam
Tel.: (84) 838290135
Web Site: https://dienquang.com
Year Founded: 1973
DQC—(HOSE)
Rev.: $35,391,542
Assets: $59,495,231
Liabilities: $22,392,818
Net Worth: $37,102,413
Earnings: ($1,376,657)
Emp.: 793
Fiscal Year-end: 12/31/23
Glass Products Mfr
N.A.I.C.S.: 327215
Ho Quynh Hung *(Chm & CEO)*

DIERIG HOLDING AG
Tel.: (49) 8215210395
Web Site: https://www.dierig.de
DIE—(MUN)
Rev.: $55,182,461
Assets: $130,113,157
Liabilities: $74,908,618
Net Worth: $55,204,539
Earnings: $2,682,404
Emp.: 137
Fiscal Year-end: 12/31/23
Textile Product Mfr & Distr
N.A.I.C.S.: 313310
Benjamin Dierig *(Member-Mgmt Bd)*

Subsidiaries:

Adam Kaeppel GmbH **(1)**
Spicherer Strasse 48, 86157, Augsburg, Germany
Tel.: (49) 821325870
Web Site: http://www.kaeppel.de
Bed Linen Distr
N.A.I.C.S.: 423220

Bimatex GmbH **(1)**
Kirchbergstr 23, 86157, Augsburg, Germany
Tel.: (49) 8215210600
Web Site: http://www.bimatex.de
Textile Clothing Mfr
N.A.I.C.S.: 313310
Gerhard Sigl *(Mng Dir)*

Christian Dierig GmbH **(1)**
Kirchbergstrasse 23, 86157, Augsburg, Germany
Tel.: (49) 8215210610
Web Site: https://www.christian-dierig.de
Cloth & Fabric Mfr
N.A.I.C.S.: 313310
Christian Dierig *(Mng Dir)*

Dierig AG **(1)**
Gallusstrasse 17, St Gallen, 9500, Wil, Switzerland
Tel.: (41) 719133850
Web Site: http://www.dierig.ch
Bed Linen Distr
N.A.I.C.S.: 423220

Dierig Textilwerke GmbH **(1)**
Kirchbergstrasse 23, 86157, Augsburg, Germany
Tel.: (49) 8215210630
Web Site: http://www.immobilien-dierig.de
Real Estate Development Services
N.A.I.C.S.: 531390

Fleuresse GmbH **(1)**
Kirchbergstrasse 23, 86157, Augsburg, Germany
Tel.: (49) 8215210620
Web Site: http://www.fleuresse.de
Bed Linen Distr
N.A.I.C.S.: 423220

DIESEL & MOTOR ENGINEERING PLC

Diesel & Motor Engineering PLC—(Continued)

No 65 Jetawana Road, PO Box 339, 14, Colombo, 14, Sri Lanka
Tel.: (94) 112449797
Web Site:
   https://www.dimolanka.com
DIMO—(COL)
Rev.: $117,503,415
Assets: $131,694,641
Liabilities: $80,585,720
Net Worth: $51,108,921
Earnings: $2,323,971
Emp.: 1,617
Fiscal Year end: 00/01/20
Agricultural Machinery Sales & Services
N.A.I.C.S.: 423820
Asoka Ranjith Pandithage *(Chm & Mng Dir)*

Subsidiaries:

Dimo (Pvt) Ltd. **(1)**
Tel.: (94) 112449797
Web Site: http://www.dimolanka.com
Sales Range: $200-249.9 Million
Emp.: 1,500
Automotive Components Mfr
N.A.I.C.S.: 333618

DIESEL SPA

Via dell Industria 4-6, Breganze, 36042, Vicenza, Italy
Tel.: (39) 0242409555   IT
Web Site: http://www.diesel.com
Year Founded: 1978
Sales Range: $1-4.9 Billion
Emp.: 330
Casual Clothing & Accessory Mfr
N.A.I.C.S.: 458110
Eraldo Poletto *(CEO-North America)*

DIESSE SRL

Via Cavicchione di Sopra 88-90, Calcinato, 25010, Italy
Tel.: (39) 0309964552
Web Site: http://www.diessesrl.com
Year Founded: 1971
Polystyrene Packaging Products Mfr
N.A.I.C.S.: 326112
Vincenzo Di Massa *(Head-R&D)*

DIETHELM KELLER HOLDING LIMITED

Muhlebachstrasse 20, Zurich, 8032, Switzerland
Tel.: (41) 442653300   CH
Web Site:
   http://www.diethelmkeller.com
Year Founded: 1865
Sales Range: $5-14.9 Billion
Emp.: 24,000
Holding Company; International Trade, Proprietary Brand Management & Travel Services
N.A.I.C.S.: 551112
Andreas W. Keller *(Chm)*

Subsidiaries:

DK Industrial Solutions, LLC **(1)**
137 Peach St, Walpole, MA 02081
Tel.: (617) 839-7713
Web Site: http://www.dk-industrial.com
Industrial Machinery Mfr & Distr
N.A.I.C.S.: 333131

DKB Household Switzerland AG **(1)**
Eggbuhlstrasse 28, 8052, Zurich, Switzerland
Tel.: (41) 798208844
Web Site: http://www.dkbrands.com
Emp.: 264
Household Appliance Mfr & Distr
N.A.I.C.S.: 332215
Christof Gassner *(Mng Dir)*

DKSH (Cambodia) Ltd. **(1)**
No 797 Corner Preah Monivong Boulevard and Street 484, Phnom Penh, Cambodia
Tel.: (855) 23212838

General Marketing Services
N.A.I.C.S.: 541613
Yang Navuth *(Dir-HR)*

DKSH (France) S.A. **(1)**
1475 Quai du Rhone, Miribel, France
Tel.: (33) 478557855
General Marketing Services
N.A.I.C.S.: 541613

DKSH Corporate Shared Services Center Sdn. Bhd. **(1)**
Lot L4-E-3A Enterprise 4 Technology Park Malaysia, Bukit Jalil, Kuala Lumpur, Malaysia
Tel.: (60) 389922888
Information Technology Consulting Services
N.A.I.C.S.: 541512
Mandy Chen *(Mgr-Branding & Comm)*

DKSH GmbH **(1)**
Baumwall 3, 22159, Hamburg, Germany
Tel.: (49) 403747340
General Marketing Services
N.A.I.C.S.: 541613
Thomas Sul *(Head-Bus Unit)*

DKSH Great Britain Ltd. **(1)**
Wellington House 60-68 Wimbledon Hill Road, London, SW19 7PA, United Kingdom
Tel.: (44) 2088795500
General Marketing Services
N.A.I.C.S.: 541613
Daniel Hollister *(Mgr-Comm)*

DKSH Guam, Inc. **(1)**
1807 Army Dr, Dededo, GU 96929
Tel.: (671) 646-8850
Web Site: http://www.dksh.fm
General Marketing Services
N.A.I.C.S.: 541613
Angel Mendoza *(Pres & Gen Mgr)*

DKSH Holding Limited **(1)**
Wiesenstrasse 8, PO Box 888, 8034, Zurich, Switzerland
Tel.: (41) 443867272
Web Site: http://www.dksh.com
Rev.: $9,771,596,640
Assets: $5,074,493,840
Liabilities: $3,498,031,680
Net Worth: $1,576,462,160
Earnings: $179,200,320
Emp.: 31,077
Fiscal Year-end: 12/31/2022
Holding Company; Commercial Sourcing, Marketing, Logistics & Distribution Support Services
N.A.I.C.S.: 551112
Joerg W. Wolle *(Chm)*

Subsidiary (Non-US):

Auric Pacific Marketing Pte Ltd **(2)**
2 Enterprise Road, 629814, Singapore, Singapore **(100%)**
Tel.: (65) 68679100
Sales Range: $25-49.9 Million
Emp.: 200
Food Service Contractors
N.A.I.C.S.: 722310
Yao Che Wan *(CEO)*

DKSH (Thailand) Limited **(2)**
2535 Sukhumvit Road Bangchack, Prakhanong, Bangkok, 10260, Thailand
Tel.: (66) 26954000
Web Site: http://www.dksh.co.th
Sales Range: $600-649.9 Million
Emp.: 2,000
Commercial Sourcing, Marketing, Logistics & Distribution Support Services
N.A.I.C.S.: 425120
Peter Hornby *(Gen Mgr-Consumer Goods & Fashion Apparel)*

DKSH Australia Pty. Ltd. **(2)**
14-17 Dansu Ct, Hallam, 3803, VIC, Australia
Tel.: (61) 395546666
Web Site: http://www.dksh.com
Sales Range: $25-49.9 Million
Emp.: 130
Commercial Sourcing, Marketing, Logistics & Distribution Support Services
N.A.I.C.S.: 425120

DKSH Holdings (Malaysia) Berhad **(2)**
B-11-01 The Ascent Paradigm, No 1 Jalan SS7/26A Kelana Jaya, 47301, Petaling

Jaya, Selangor Darul Ehsan, Malaysia
Tel.: (60) 378828888
Web Site: https://www.dksh.com
Rev.: $12,615,262,812
Assets: $6,055,770,078
Liabilities: $3,919,478,670
Net Worth: $2,136,291,408
Earnings: $260,581,347
Emp.: 31,453
Fiscal Year-end: 12/31/2021
Holding Company; Commercial Sourcing, Marketing, Logistics & Distribution Support Services
N.A.I.C.S.: 551112
Andre' P'o-Lieng P'o-Lieng Chai *(Co-Sec)*

Subsidiary (Domestic):

Auric Pacific (M) Sdn Bhd **(3)**
Lot 35 Jalan Delima 1-3, Subang Hi-Tech Industrial Park, 40000, Shah Alam, Selangor, Malaysia **(100%)**
Tel.: (60) 356213968
Dairy Products, except Dried or Canned Whslr
N.A.I.C.S.: 424430

DKSH Malaysia Sdn. Bhd. **(3)**
74 Jalan University, PO Box 77, Petaling Jaya, 46700, Selangor Darul Ehsan, Malaysia **(100%)**
Tel.: (60) 379660288
Web Site: http://www.dksh.com
Sales Range: $1-4.9 Billion
Commercial Sourcing, Marketing, Logistics & Distribution Support Services
N.A.I.C.S.: 425120
Teng Hai Lian *(Exec Dir-Consumer Goods)*

Subsidiary (Non-US):

DKSH Japan K.K. **(2)**
3-4-19 Mita Minato-ku Dksh Mita Building, Minato-ku, Tokyo, 108-8360, Japan
Tel.: (81) 354414511
Web Site: http://www.dksh.jp
Sales Range: $350-399.9 Million
Emp.: 300
Commercial Sourcing, Marketing, Logistics & Distribution Support Services
N.A.I.C.S.: 425120

DKSH Korea Ltd. **(2)**
4-7 Floor Sunghwan Building 156 DoGok-Ro, GangNam-gu, Seoul, 135-858, Korea (South)
Tel.: (82) 221929500
Web Site: http://www.dksh.com
Sales Range: $25-49.9 Million
Emp.: 400
Commercial Sourcing, Marketing, Logistics & Distribution Support Services
N.A.I.C.S.: 425120
Matthew Beebar *(Country Mgr)*

Subsidiary (Domestic):

DKSH Management Ltd. **(2)**
Wiesenstrasse 8, 8034, Zurich, Switzerland **(100%)**
Tel.: (41) 443867272
Web Site: http://www.dksh.com
Corporate Legislative Services
N.A.I.C.S.: 921140

Subsidiary (Non-US):

DKSH Netherlands B.V. **(2)**
Vogelaarsweg 23, NL-3313 LL, Dordrecht, Netherlands
Tel.: (31) 786220622
Web Site: http://www.dksh.com
Sales Range: $75-99.9 Million
Emp.: 200
Commercial Sourcing, Marketing, Logistics & Distribution Support Services
N.A.I.C.S.: 425120

Subsidiary (Domestic):

DKSH Switzerland Ltd. **(2)**
Wiesenstrasse 8, Zurich, 8034, Switzerland
Tel.: (41) 443867272
Web Site: http://www.dksh.com
Sales Range: $50-74.9 Million
Emp.: 100
Commercial Sourcing, Marketing, Logistics & Distribution Support Services
N.A.I.C.S.: 425120
Robert Koller *(Sr Dir-Global Regulatory Affairs & Performance Materials)*

Subsidiary (Non-US):

DKSH Taiwan Ltd. **(2)**
10F Hannover High-Tech Square No 22 Lane 407, Ti Ding Boulevard Section 2, Neihu Technology Park, Taipei, 114, Taiwan
Tel.: (886) 287526666
Web Site: http://www.dksh.com
Sales Range: $250-299.9 Million
Emp.: 550
Commercial Sourcing, Marketing, Logistics & Distribution Support Services
N.A.I.C.S.: 425120
Teresa Chen *(Gen Mgr-Healthcare Div)*

Edward Keller (Philippines) Inc. **(2)**
101 Prosperity Avenue corner Unity Avenue Carmelray Industrial Park I; Canlubang, Calamba, Philippines
Tel.: (63) 2 864 1600
Web Site: http://www.dksh.com.ph
Emp.: 250
General Marketing Services
N.A.I.C.S.: 541613
Bernadette Tang *(VP)*

DKSH Holdings (Asia) Sdn. Bhd. **(1)**
74 Jalan Universiti, Petaling Jaya, 46200, Malaysia
Tel.: (60) 379660288
Asset Management Services
N.A.I.C.S.: 531390

DKSH Hong Kong Ltd. **(1)**
23rd Floor Tower A Southmark 11 Yip Hing Street Wong Chuk Hang, Hong Kong, China (Hong Kong)
Tel.: (852) 28950888
General Marketing Services
N.A.I.C.S.: 541613
Victor Hew *(Mng Dir)*

DKSH India Pvt. Ltd. **(1)**
Fantree Building Plot No 369 Sarla Software Park Marol Maroshi Road, Andheri East, Mumbai, India
Tel.: (91) 2261577000
Healthcare Product Distr
N.A.I.C.S.: 424210
Atul Nagarkar *(Mng Dir & Country Mgr)*

DKSH Logistics Ltd. **(1)**
57 Choji1-Li Dewal-Myun, Icheon, Korea (South)
Tel.: (82) 7075805000
General Marketing Services
N.A.I.C.S.: 541613

DKSH Luxury and Lifestyle Europe GmbH **(1)**
Stuttgarter Strasse 8, 75179, Pforzheim, Germany
Tel.: (49) 72319140
Watch Whslr
N.A.I.C.S.: 423940
Ditmar Coblenzer *(Mgr-Supply Chain)*

DKSH Management Pte Ltd. **(1)**
238A Thomson Road 25-01/03 Novena Square Office Tower A, Singapore, 307684, Singapore
Tel.: (65) 65789830
General Marketing Services
N.A.I.C.S.: 541613

DKSH New Zealand Ltd. **(1)**
279 Railway Road, Milson, 4470, Palmerston North, New Zealand
Tel.: (64) 63565323
Web Site: http://www.dksh.co.nz
General Marketing Services
N.A.I.C.S.: 541613

DKSH Pharmaceutical (Shanghai) Ltd. **(1)**
Rm 1603 Block A Shen Fang Plaza No 3006 Renminnan Road, Luohu, Shenzhen, China
Tel.: (86) 75525188877
Web Site: http://www.dksh.com.cn
Pharmaceutical Products Distr
N.A.I.C.S.: 424210

DKSH Philippines Inc. **(1)**
2nd Floor The Athenaeum Bldg 160 L P Leviste Street, Salcedo, Makati, Philippines
Tel.: (63) 25534821
General Marketing Services
N.A.I.C.S.: 541613
Patrocinia Cortez *(Pres)*

DKSH Shanghai Ltd. (1)
3rd Floor Tomson Commercial Building 710
Dong Fang Road, Pudong, 200122, Shanghai, China
Tel.: (86) 2158300518
Food Products Distr
N.A.I.C.S.: 424490
Sally Xia *(Mgr-HR Bus Partnering)*

DKSH Singapore Pte Ltd. (1)
24 Penjuru Rd, Singapore, 609128, Singapore
Tel.: (65) 64711466
General Marketing Services
N.A.I.C.S.: 541613

DKSH Technology Sdn. Bhd. (1)
No 14 Jalan Bersatu 13/4, 46200, Petaling Jaya, Malaysia
Tel.: (60) 379548888
Healthcare Product Distr
N.A.I.C.S.: 424210
Nick Grantham *(Mng Dir)*

DKSH Vietnam Co. Ltd. (1)
2nd Floor Etown 2 Building 364 Cong Hoa Street, Tan Binh, Ho Chi Minh City, Vietnam
Tel.: (84) 838125848
General Marketing Services
N.A.I.C.S.: 541613

Diethelm & Co. Ltd. (1)
Ban Phonsinouan Unit 18 New Road, Vientiane, Lao People's Democratic Republic
Tel.: (856) 21453100
General Marketing Services
N.A.I.C.S.: 541613

Diethelm Keller Brands AG (1)
DKB Household Eggbuhlstrasse 28, 8052, Zurich, Switzerland
Tel.: (41) 44 306 16 16
Web Site: http://www.dkbrands.com
Household Cooking Appliance Mfr & Distr
N.A.I.C.S.: 332215
Andreas W. Keller *(Chm)*

Diethelm Keller Logistics Ltd. (1)
2533 Sukhumvit Rd Bangchak, Phra Khanong, Bangkok, 10260, Thailand
Tel.: (66) 23015700
Logistics Consulting Servies
N.A.I.C.S.: 541614

Medinova AG (1)
Eggbuhlstrasse 14, POB 8050, Zurich, Switzerland
Tel.: (41) 443061322
Web Site: http://www.medinova.ch
Pharmaceutical Products Distr
N.A.I.C.S.: 424210
Frank Buennig *(Mng Dir)*

PT DKSH Indonesia (1)
Wisma Jaksa Tiga Jalan Jaksa No 3, Kebon Sirih, Jakarta, 10340, Indonesia
Tel.: (62) 2131924289
General Marketing Services
N.A.I.C.S.: 541613
Yunni Damayanti *(Dir-HR)*

Queloz SA (1)
Bel-Air 14, 2350, Saignelegier, Switzerland
Tel.: (41) 329524646
Web Site: http://www.quelozsa.ch
Watch Mfr
N.A.I.C.S.: 339910

STA Travel (Holdings) Pte Ltd (1)
70 Stamford Road B 1/46, Singapore, 178901, Singapore
Tel.: (65) 67377188
Web Site: http://www.statravel.sg
Sales Range: $125-149.9 Million
Emp.: 30
Holding Company; Travel Services
N.A.I.C.S.: 551112
Christine Sutton *(Sr VP-US)*

Co-Headquarters (Non-US):

STA Travel Ltd. (2)
Priory House, 6 Wrights Lane, London, W8 6TA, United Kingdom
Tel.: (44) 2073616100
Web Site: http://www.statravelgroup.com
Sales Range: $25-49.9 Million
Travel Agencies & Services
N.A.I.C.S.: 561510
Reinhard Kotzaurek *(Mng Dir-CEU)*

Subsidiary (Non-US):

STA Travel Pty Ltd (3)
Level 3 6 Riverside Quay, Abbotsford, Southbank, 3067, VIC, Australia
Tel.: (61) 384176911
Web Site: http://www.statravel.com.au
Sales Range: $25-49.9 Million
Emp.: 70
Travel Services
N.A.I.C.S.: 561510
Basil Symin *(Dir-Mktg)*

Subsidiary (US):

STA Travel, Inc (3)
750 State Hwy 121 Ste 250, Lewisville, TX 75067
Tel.: (972) 538-8843
Web Site: http://www.statravel.com
Sales Range: $25-49.9 Million
Emp.: 70
Travel Agency Services
N.A.I.C.S.: 561510
Jane Armstrong *(Controller)*

The United Drug (1996) Co. Ltd. (1)
208 Romklao Road Minburi, Bangkok, 10510, Thailand
Tel.: (66) 254382102
Web Site: http://www.united-drug.co.th
Pharmaceuticals Product Mfr
N.A.I.C.S.: 325412
Suebphong Wattanasin *(Mng Dir)*

Zeus Quimica S.A.U. (1)
Santalo 152 154 bajos, 08021, Barcelona, Spain
Tel.: (34) 932402222
Web Site: http://www.zeusquimica.com
Chemical Products Distr
N.A.I.C.S.: 424690
Ramon J. Vinas *(Country Mgr)*

DIETSMANN N.V.
Wilhelminasingel 19, 4818 AC, Breda, Netherlands
Tel.: (31) 76 530 19 88   Nl
Web Site: http://www.dietsmann.com
Year Founded: 1977
Operations & Maintenance Services for Oil, Gas, LNG & Power Plants
N.A.I.C.S.: 213112
Peter R. G. Kutemann *(Founder, Chm & Pres)*

Subsidiaries:

Dietsmann AD (1)
10 Dimitar Manov Str Administrative Bldg, 1408, Sofia, Bulgaria   (97.5%)
Tel.: (359) 2 8133577
Web Site:
    http://www.dietsmannenergoremont.bg
Engineering Services
N.A.I.C.S.: 541330

Subsidiary (Domestic):

Energoremont Bobov Dol EAD (2)
2635 village of Golemo village, Kyustendil, Bulgaria
Tel.: (359) 701 501 01
Web Site: http://www.erbobovdol.com
Electric Machinery Repair Services
N.A.I.C.S.: 811114

Energoremont Kozloduy EOOD (2)
3321 Kozlodui, PO Box 7, Kozloduy, 3321, Bulgaria
Tel.: (359) 9738 02 42
Web Site: http://www.energoremont-kozlodui.com
Industrial Supplies Whslr
N.A.I.C.S.: 423840

Energoremont Radnevo EOOD (2)
12 Tacho Daskalov Str, Radnevo, 6260, Bulgaria
Tel.: (359) 417 82 666
Web Site: http://www.energoremont-radnevo.bg
Industrial Equipment Mfr & Repair Services
N.A.I.C.S.: 332999

Energoremont Ruse AD (2)
East Industrial Zone, 7009, Ruse, Bulgaria
Tel.: (359) 82 844 651

Web Site: http://www.energoremont-ruse.com
Industrial Equipment Repair Services
N.A.I.C.S.: 811310
Alexander Videnov *(Mgr)*

DIETSWELL S.A.
Immeuble Le Naiade Parc Ariane 3 1 rue Alfred KASTLER, 78280, Guyancourt, France
Tel.: (33) 1 39 30 02 60
Web Site: http://www.dietswell.com
Year Founded: 2000
ALDIE—(EUR)
Sales Range: $25-49.9 Million
Engineering & Drilling Services
N.A.I.C.S.: 237990
Jean-Claude Bourdon *(Founder & CEO)*

Subsidiaries:

FACT-O-RIG (1)
Parc Ariane 3 Immeuble Le Naiade 1 rue Alfred Kastler, 78284, Guyancourt, France
Tel.: (33) 139 302 160
Web Site: http://www.factorig.com
Drilling Rig Inspection & Auditing Services
N.A.I.C.S.: 213112
Nicolas Chevalier *(Mgr)*

DIETZEL GMBH
1 Haidequerstrasse 3-5, 1111, Vienna, Austria
Tel.: (43) 1760760
Web Site: http://www.dietzel.at
Year Founded: 1938
Sales Range: $50-74.9 Million
Emp.: 210
Plastics & Metal Products Mfr
N.A.I.C.S.: 326199
Michael Pocksteiner *(Owner & Co-Mng Dir)*

Subsidiaries:

Dietzel Univolt Deutschland GmbH (1)
Benno Strauss-Strasse 13, 90763, Furth, Germany
Tel.: (49) 911994270
Web Site: http://www.univolt.de
Industrial Equipment Distr
N.A.I.C.S.: 423830

UNIVOLT (UK) Ltd. (1)
Unit 4 Quadrant Park Black Fan Road, Welwyn Garden City, AL7 1FS, United Kingdom
Tel.: (44) 1707379820
Industrial Equipment Distr
N.A.I.C.S.: 423830

Univolt (HK) Limited (1)
Unit 1006 Yan Hing Centre 9-13 Wong Chuk Yeung Street Fo Tan, Shatin, Hong Kong, China (Hong Kong)
Tel.: (852) 26919184
Industrial Equipment Distr
N.A.I.C.S.: 423830

Univolt Canada Ltd. (1)
11 Hoover Drive, Thornhill, L3T 5M6, ON, Canada
Tel.: (905) 731-9155
Industrial Equipment Distr
N.A.I.C.S.: 423830

Univolt Hungaria Kft. (1)
Kozponti ut 65, 1211, Budapest, Hungary
Tel.: (36) 12764056
Industrial Equipment Distr
N.A.I.C.S.: 423830
ward Schmidt *(Mgr-Replacement Parts)*

Univolt Remat s.r.o. (1)
Senkvicka cesta 16, 90201, Pezinok, Slovakia
Tel.: (421) 336902450
Industrial Equipment Mfr
N.A.I.C.S.: 332919

DIEVINI HOPP BIOTECH HOLDING GMBH & CO. KG

Johann-Jakob-Astor-Str 57, 69190, Walldorf, Germany
Tel.: (49) 62278608462   De
Web Site: http://www.dievini.com
Year Founded: 2005
Life & Health Science Investment Services
N.A.I.C.S.: 523940
Friedrich von Bohlen und Halbach *(Co-Founder & Mng Dir)*

Subsidiaries:

LTS Lohmann Therapie-Systeme AG (1)
Lohmannstrasse 2, 56626, Andernach, Germany
Tel.: (49) 26 32 99 0
Web Site: http://www.ltslohmann.de
Sales Range: $350-399.9 Million
Emp.: 1,228
Transdermal Therapeutic Systems & Oral Thin Films Mfr
N.A.I.C.S.: 325412
Peter Schwarz *(CTO, Chief Quality Officer & Member-Exec Bd)*

Subsidiary (US):

LTS Lohmann Therapy Systems Corp. (2)
21 Henderson Dr, West Caldwell, NJ 07006
Tel.: (973) 396-5345
Web Site: http://www.ltslohmann.com
Emp.: 300
Pharmaceutical Preparations
N.A.I.C.S.: 325412
Ken Glade *(Dir-Engrg)*

Tapemark, Inc. (2)
1685 Marthaler Ln, Saint Paul, MN 55118-4002
Tel.: (651) 455-1611
Web Site: http://www.tapemark.com
Emp.: 175
Custom Coating, Fabricating & Printing of Adhesive Based Material Components, Products & Packaging
N.A.I.C.S.: 323111
Dave O'Brien *(VP & Controller)*

DIF MANAGEMENT HOLDING B.V.
WTC Schiphol Airport Tower D 10th Floor Schiphol Boulevard 269, 1118 BH, Schiphol, Netherlands
Tel.: (31) 20 717 3151   Nl
Web Site: http://www.dif.eu
Holding Company; Investment Fund Management
N.A.I.C.S.: 551112
Wim Blaasse *(Mng Partner)*

Subsidiaries:

American Roads, LLC (1)
100 E Jefferson Ave, Detroit, MI 48226
Tel.: (313) 567-4422
Web Site: http://www.americanroads.com
Transportation Infrastructure Owner, Operator & Developer
N.A.I.C.S.: 488490
Neal Belitsky *(CEO)*

Bernhard, LLC (1)
1 Galleria Blvd Ste 825, Metairie, LA 70001
Tel.: (504) 833-8291
Web Site: https://www.bernhard.com
Engineering & Construction Services
N.A.I.C.S.: 541330
Ed Tinsley *(CEO)*

Subsidiary (Domestic):

Etc Group Inc (2)
1997 S 1100 E, Salt Lake City, UT 84106
Tel.: (801) 278-1927
Web Site: http://www.etcgrp.com
Rev.: $1,200,000
Emp.: 12
Engineering Services
N.A.I.C.S.: 541330
Mark E. Case *(Principal)*

DIF Management B.V. (1)
WTC Schiphol Airport Tower D 10th Floor

DIF Management Holding B.V.—(Continued)

Schiphol Boulevard 269, 1118 BH, Schiphol, Netherlands
Tel.: (31) 20 717 3151
Web Site: http://www.dif.eu
Investment Fund Management
N.A.I.C.S.: 523940
Wim Blaasse (Mng Partner)

Hospital de Majadahonda, S.A. **(1)**
C/ Joaquin Rodrigo 2, 28222, Majada-honda, Madrid, Spain
Tel.: (34) 916799300
General Medical Services
N.A.I.C.S.: 622110

Thyssengas GmbH **(1)**
Emil-Moog-Platz 13, 44137, Dortmund, Germany **(50%)**
Tel.: (49) 231912910
Web Site: http://www.thyssengas.com
Natural Gas Logistics & Transmission
N.A.I.C.S.: 486210
Thomas Gossmann (Chm-Exec Bd)

DIFC INVESTMENTS LLC
The Gate Level 15, PO Box 74777, Dubai, United Arab Emirates
Tel.: (971) 43622222
Web Site: http://www.difc.ae
Investment Holding Company
N.A.I.C.S.: 523999

Subsidiaries:

D-Clear LLC **(1)**
Level 15 Business Centre The Gate, PO Box 74777, Dubai, United Arab Emirates
Tel.: (971) 4 3622222
Investment Services
N.A.I.C.S.: 523999

Holding (Non-US):

SmartStream Technologies Ltd. **(2)**
St Helens, 1 Undershaft, London, EC3A 8EE, United Kingdom
Tel.: (44) 20 7898 0600
Web Site: http://www.smartstream-stp.com
Sales Range: $75-99.9 Million
Software Publisher
N.A.I.C.S.: 513210
Philippe Chambadal (Pres)

Villa Moda Lifestyle Company K.S.O.C. **(1)**
Commercial Free Zone Shuwaikh Port, PO Box 12112, Shamiya, Kuwait, 71652, Kuwait **(70%)**
Tel.: (965) 24827004
Web Site: http://www.villa-moda.com
Sales Range: $25-49.9 Million
Clothing Store Owner & Operator
N.A.I.C.S.: 458110

DIFFER GROUP HOLDING CO., LTD.
33rd Floor Tower 11 166 Tapu East Road, Xiamen, China
Tel.: (86) 5928396999
Web Site: http://www.dingfeng-cn.com
6878—(HKG)
Sales Range: $1-9.9 Million
Emp.: 100
Diversified Financial Holding Company
N.A.I.C.S.: 551112
Mingxian Hong (Chm)

DIFFERENCE CAPITAL FINANCIAL INC.
1201-2 St Clair Avenue West, Toronto, M4V 1L5, ON, Canada
Tel.: (416) 649-5085   Ca
Web Site:
http://www.differencecapital.com
Year Founded: 2012
DCF—(TSX)
Sales Range: $1-9.9 Million
Investment & Financial Services
N.A.I.C.S.: 523999
Henry Knies (Co-Founder & CEO)

Subsidiaries:

Mogo Finance Technology, Inc. **(1)**
2100-401 West Georgia Street, Vancouver, V6B 5A1, BC, Canada
Tel.: (604) 659-4380
Web Site: http://www.mogo.ca
Sales Range: $25-49.9 Million
Financial Credit Services
N.A.I.C.S.: 522210

DIFFUSION AUTOMOBILE CLERMONTAISE
24 Route De Montpellier, 34800, Clermont, France
Tel.: (33) 467960342
Sales Range: $10-24.9 Million
Emp.: 49
New & Used Car Dealers
N.A.I.C.S.: 441110
Patrice Ravaut (Personnel Dir)

DIFGEN PHARMACEUTICALS PVT. LTD.
5-35/189-A 100 Ft Road Prashanthi Nagar IE, Kukatpally, Hyderabad, 500072, India
Tel.: (91) 4069756975
Web Site: https://difgen.com
Emp.: 100
Pharmaceuticals Product Mfr
N.A.I.C.S.: 325412
Santhanakrishnan Srinivasan (Co-CEO & Founder)

Subsidiaries:

Aveva Drug Delivery Systems, Inc **(1)**
3250 Commerce Pkwy, Miramar, FL 33025
Tel.: (954) 430-3340
Development & Advancement of Transdermal Drug Delivery Systems
N.A.I.C.S.: 325520

DIGATRADE FINANCIAL CORP.
1500 West Georgia Street Suite 1300, Vancouver, V6G 2Z6, BC, Canada
Tel.: (604) 200-0071   BC
Web Site:
https://www.digatradefinancial.com
Year Founded: 2000
DIGAF—(OTCIQ)
Rev.: $10,414
Assets: $237,710
Liabilities: $665,459
Net Worth: ($427,750)
Earnings: ($341,753)
Emp.: 1
Fiscal Year-end: 12/31/21
Investment Services
N.A.I.C.S.: 523999
Bradley J. Moynes (Chm, Pres, CEO & CFO-Interim)

DIGGI MULTITRADE LIMITED
D-106 Crystal Plaza Opposite Infiniti Mall Link Road Andheri West, Mumbai, 400 053, Maharashtra, India
Tel.: (91) 2226744365
Web Site: https://diggimultitrade.co.in
Year Founded: 2010
540811—(BOM)
Rev.: $40,169
Assets: $1,557,257
Liabilities: $105,283
Net Worth: $1,451,974
Earnings: $6,758
Emp.: 8
Fiscal Year-end: 03/31/21
Real Estate Manangement Services
N.A.I.C.S.: 531110
Anilkumar Pannalal Patni (Mng Dir)

DIGI COMMUNICATIONS N.V

75 Dr Staicovici Street Forum 2000 building Phase I fourth floor, 5th district, Bucharest, Romania
Tel.: (40) 314006505
Web Site: https://www.digi-communications.ro
DIGI—(BUC)
Rev.: $1,611,017,699
Assets: $3,074,391,323
Liabilities: $2,409,886,682
Net Worth: $664,504,641
Earnings: $397,092,597
Emp.: 20,059
Fiscal Year-end: 12/31/22
Telecommunication Servicesb
N.A.I.C.S.: 517112
Zoltan Teszari (Pres)

Subsidiaries:

RCS & RDS S.A. **(1)**
Str Dr Staicovici No 75 Forum 2000 Building Phase I Floor 2 Sector 5, Bucharest, Romania
Tel.: (40) 314004401
Web Site: https://www.digi.ro
Telecommunication Servicesb
N.A.I.C.S.: 517810

DIGIA PLC
Atomitie 2 A, FI-00370, Helsinki, Finland
Tel.: (358) 103133000   UK
Web Site: https://www.digia.com
Year Founded: 1997
DIGIA—(HEL)
Rev.: $192,077,084
Assets: $175,687,450
Liabilities: $92,078,696
Net Worth: $83,608,753
Earnings: $14,458,841
Emp.: 1,339
Fiscal Year-end: 12/31/21
Holding Company; Internet Software Technology Services
N.A.I.C.S.: 551112
Robert Ingman (Chm)

Subsidiaries:

Digia Finland Oy **(1)**
Valimotie 21, Helsinki, 00380, Finland
Tel.: (358) 103133000
Information Technology Consulting Services
N.A.I.C.S.: 541512

Digia Sweden AB **(1)**
Upplandsgatan 14 1 tr, 111 23, Stockholm, Sweden
Tel.: (46) 857236400
Web Site: http://www.digia.com
Computer Software Development Services
N.A.I.C.S.: 541511

Productivity Leap Oy **(1)**
Lansikatu 15, 80100, Joensuu, Finland
Tel.: (358) 408369962
Web Site: https://www.productivityleap.com
Software Development Services
N.A.I.C.S.: 541511

DIGIASIA CORP
1 Raffles Place Suite 28-02, Singapore, 048616, Singapore
Tel.: (646) 314-3555   Ky
Year Founded: 2021
FAAS—(NASDAQ)
Assets: $27,621,119
Liabilities: $14,517,389
Net Worth: ($14,412,530)
Earnings: ($63,563)
Emp.: 2
Fiscal Year-end: 12/31/23
Software Publr
N.A.I.C.S.: 513210
Prashant Gokarn (Co-CEO)

DIGICANN VENTURES INC
Ste 1890 1075 W Georgia St, Vancouver, V6C 2T7, BC, Canada
Tel.: (604) 678-2531   Ca

Web Site: https://digicann.io
Year Founded: 2004
DCNN—(CNSX)
Rev.: $497,463
Assets: $808,699
Liabilities: $14,798,835
Net Worth: ($13,990,136)
Earnings: ($30,977,866)
Fiscal Year-end: 12/31/22
Investment Services
N.A.I.C.S.: 523999
Nick Kuzyk (Interim CEO)

DIGICAP CO., LTD.
D&C CAMPUS 11 Magokjungang 8-ro 7-gil, Gangseo-gu, Seoul, Korea (South)
Tel.: (82) 234772101
Web Site: https://www.digicaps.com
Year Founded: 2000
197140—(KRS)
Rev.: $19,783,226
Assets: $41,156,510
Liabilities: $6,163,420
Net Worth: $34,993,090
Earnings: $607,719
Emp.: 94
Fiscal Year-end: 12/31/22
Digital Content Security & Copy Protection Software & Solutions
N.A.I.C.S.: 513210
Pete Han (CEO)

DIGICEL GROUP LTD.
5th Floor Washington House, PO Box 896, 16 Church Street, Hamilton, HM11, Bermuda
Tel.: (441) 5005600   BM
Web Site:
http://www.digicelgroup.com
Year Founded: 2001
Wireless Telecommunication Services
N.A.I.C.S.: 517112
Denis O'Brien (Chm)

Subsidiaries:

Digicel (BVI) Limited **(1)**
5th Floor Jayla Place Wickham's Cay, PO Box 4168, Road Town, Tortola, VG1110, Virgin Islands (British)
Tel.: (284) 300 0001
Web Site: http://www.digicelbvi.com
Wireless Telecommunication Services
N.A.I.C.S.: 517112
Conor Looney (CEO)

Digicel (Barbados) Limited **(1)**
2nd Floor Williams Tower Williams Industries Complex, Warrens, Saint Michael, Barbados
Tel.: (246) 467 7000
Web Site: http://www.digicelbarbados.com
Wireless Telecommunication Services
N.A.I.C.S.: 517112
Dwight Grannum (Mgr-Core Network)

Digicel (Bermuda) Limited **(1)**
Washington Mall Phase II 22 Church Street, Hamilton, HM 11, Bermuda
Tel.: (441) 500 5000
Web Site: http://www.digicelbermuda.com
Wireless Telecommunication Services
N.A.I.C.S.: 517112
Alistair Beak (CEO-Cayman, Turks & Caicos)

Digicel (PNG) Limited **(1)**
Kennedy Road Gordons, PO Box 1618, Port Moresby, Papua New Guinea
Tel.: (675) 7222 2222
Web Site: http://www.digicelpng.com
Wireless Telecommunication Services
N.A.I.C.S.: 517112
Michael Townsley (Dir-Sls & Distr)

Digicel (St. Lucia) Limited **(1)**
PO Box GM 791, Rodney Bay, Gros Islet, Saint Lucia
Tel.: (758) 728 3400
Web Site: http://www.digicelstlucia.com
Wireless Telecommunication Services
N.A.I.C.S.: 517112
Holly Hughes (Mgr-Saint Lucia)

Digicel (Tonga) Limited (1)
Fatafehi Road Opposite Talamahu Market,
PO Box 875, Nuku'alofa, Tonga
Tel.: (676) 8761000
Web Site: http://www.digiceltonga.com
Wireless Telecommunication Services
N.A.I.C.S.: 517112
Justin Kaitapu *(CTO)*

Digicel (Trinidad & Tobago) Limited (1)
Ansa Centre 11C Maraval Road, Port of
Spain, Trinidad & Tobago
Tel.: (868) 399 9998
Web Site: http://www.digiceltt.com
Wireless Telecommunication Services
N.A.I.C.S.: 517112
Garvin Medera *(COO)*

Digicel Aruba (1)
Marisol Building L G Smith Blvd 60, PO Box
662, Oranjestad, Aruba
Tel.: (297) 522 2222
Web Site: http://www.digicelaruba.com
Wireless Telecommunication Services
N.A.I.C.S.: 517112
Bob Sprengers *(Gen Mgr)*

Digicel Bonaire (1)
Kaya Grandi 26, Kralendijk, Netherlands
Tel.: (31) 7174400
Web Site: http://www.digicelbonaire.com
Wireless Telecommunication Services
N.A.I.C.S.: 517112
Sander Gielen *(CEO)*

Digicel Cayman Ltd. (1)
Cayman Technology Centre 115 Printer
Way, PO Box 700, Grand Cayman, George-
town, KY1-1107, Cayman Islands
Tel.: (345) 6233445
Web Site: http://www.digicelcayman.com
Wireless Telecommunication Services
N.A.I.C.S.: 517112

Digicel Curacao (1)
Biesheuvel 24-25, Willemstad, Curacao
Tel.: (599) 9 736 1056
Web Site: http://www.digicelcuracao.com
Wireless Telecommunication Services
N.A.I.C.S.: 517112
Remko van der Veldt *(Dir-Comml)*

Digicel Dominica Ltd. (1)
PO Box 2236, Roseau, Dominica
Tel.: (767) 616 1500
Web Site: http://www.digiceldominica.com
Wireless Telecommunication Services
N.A.I.C.S.: 517112
Nathalie Walsh *(Mgr-Sls & Mktg)*

Digicel El Salvador (1)
Alameda Dr Manuel Enrique Araujo y calle
Nueva No1 Edif Palic 5o Nivel, Col Es-
calon, San Salvador, El Salvador
Tel.: (503) 2285 5100
Web Site: http://www.digicel.com.sv
Wireless Telecommunication Services
N.A.I.C.S.: 517112
Jose Antonio Rodriguez *(CEO)*

Digicel Fiji Ltd (1)
Ground Floor Kadavu House, PO Box
13811, Victoria Parade, Suva, Fiji
Tel.: (679) 331 0200
Web Site: http://www.digicelfiji.com
Wireless Telecommunication Services
N.A.I.C.S.: 517112
Farid Mohammed *(CFO)*

Digicel Grenada Ltd. (1)
Pointe Salines, Saint George's, Grenada
Tel.: (473) 439 4505
Web Site: http://www.digicelgrenada.com
Wireless Telecommunication Services
N.A.I.C.S.: 517112
Ciaran Burke *(CEO)*

Digicel Guyana Ltd. (1)
Fort & Barrack Streets, Kingston, George-
town, Guyana
Tel.: (592) 669 2677
Web Site: http://www.digicelguyana.com
Wireless Telecommunication Services
N.A.I.C.S.: 517112
Gregory Dean *(CEO)*

Digicel Haiti Ltd. (1)
151 Angle Ave Jean Paul II & Impasse Du-
verger, PO Box 15516, Angle rues
Clerveaux et Darguin, Port-au-Prince, Haiti

Tel.: (509) 37 11 34 44
Web Site: http://www.digicelhaiti.com
Wireless Telecommunication Services
N.A.I.C.S.: 517112
Brendan Hunt *(CFO)*

Digicel Jamaica Ltd. (1)
14 Ocean Boulevard, Kingston, Jamaica
Tel.: (876) 619 5000
Wireless Telecommunication Services
N.A.I.C.S.: 517112
Krishna Phillipps *(CTO)*

Digicel Panama Ltd. (1)
Via Transistmica Edificio Digicel, Panama,
Panama
Tel.: (507) 306 0688
Web Site: http://www.digicelpanama.com
Wireless Telecommunication Services
N.A.I.C.S.: 517112

Digicel Samoa Limited (1)
SNPF Plaza Building, Savalalo, Apia, Sa-
moa (Western)
Tel.: (685) 84 28003
Web Site: http://www.digicelsamoa.com
Wireless Telecommunication Services
N.A.I.C.S.: 517112
Abdallah Nassar *(CTO)*

Digicel St. Vincent Limited (1)
Tel.: (784) 453 3000
Web Site: http://www.digicelsvg.com
Wireless Telecommunication Services
N.A.I.C.S.: 517112
Fanta Williams *(Mgr-Admin Sls)*

Digicel Turks & Caicos Ltd. (1)
Unit 207 Graceway House, Providenciales,
Turks & Caicos Islands
Tel.: (649) 331 3444
Web Site: http://www.digiceltci.com
Wireless Telecommunication Services
N.A.I.C.S.: 517112
E. Jay Saunders *(CEO)*

Digicel Vanuatu Ltd. (1)
Digicel House, PMB 9103, Port-Vila, Vanu-
atu
Tel.: (678) 555 6001
Web Site: http://www.digicelvanuatu.com
Wireless Telecommunication Services
N.A.I.C.S.: 517112
Yaser Maher *(CEO)*

The Bermuda Telephone Company Limited (1)
46 Cedar Avenue, Hamilton, HM 11, Ber-
muda
Tel.: (441) 2951001
Web Site: http://www.btc.bm
Communication Service
N.A.I.C.S.: 517810
Robin Seale *(CEO)*

DIGICONTENT LIMITED

Hindustan Times House Second
Floor 18-20 Kasturba Gandhi Marg,
New Delhi, 110001, India
Tel.: (91) 1166561355
Web Site:
https://www.digicontent.co.in
Year Founded: 2017
542685—(BOM)
Media Representative Services
N.A.I.C.S.: 541840
Priyavrat Bhartia *(Chm)*

DIGIHOST TECHNOLOGY, INC.

110 Yonge St Ste 1601, Toronto,
M5C 1T4, ON, Canada
Tel.: (647) 259-1790   **Ca**
DGHI—(NASDAQ)
Rev.: $26,112,908
Assets: $42,147,347
Liabilities: $12,900,608
Net Worth: $29,246,739
Earnings: ($21,885,410)
Emp.: 13
Fiscal Year-end: 12/31/23
Software Development Services
N.A.I.C.S.: 541511

DIGILIFE TECHNOLOGIES LIMITED

1 North Bridge Road 19-04/05 High
Street Centre, Singapore, 179094,
Singapore
Tel.: (65) 60187657   **SG**
Web Site: https://digilifelimited.com
Year Founded: 1993
BAI—(SES)
Rev.: $129,456,261
Assets: $29,179,508
Liabilities: $6,770,637
Net Worth: $22,408,872
Earnings: $400,410
Emp.: 2,135
Fiscal Year-end: 12/31/22
Mobile Communications Services
N.A.I.C.S.: 517112
Maneesh Tripathi *(CEO)*

Subsidiaries:

Alpha One Limited (1)
A2 9 2/F Hang Fung Industrial Building
Phase II 2G Hok Yuen Street, Hung Hom,
Kowloon, China (Hong Kong)
Tel.: (852) 283 66191
Mobile Phone Distr
N.A.I.C.S.: 423690

Autonomous Electric Mobility Pvt. Ltd. (1)
3rd floor C5/85 New Kondli, Delhi, 110096,
India
Tel.: (91) 1204141579
Electronic Equipment Mfr & Distr
N.A.I.C.S.: 335314

Bharat IT Services Limited (1)
C-10 Sector 65, Noida, 201 301, UP,
India   **(100%)**
Tel.: (91) 1204141560
Web Site: http://www.bharatitservices.com
Emp.: 600
Information Technology Consulting Services
N.A.I.C.S.: 541512
Arun Seth *(CEO)*

CSL Communication (Shenzhen) Co Ltd (1)
Block A Unit 1201-A10 29 Terra 4th Road,
Futian District, Shenzhen, 518042, Guang-
dong, China
Tel.: (86) 75533330890
Mobile Phone Distr
N.A.I.C.S.: 423690

CSL Mobile Care (M) Sdn. Bhd. (1)
Wisma Paradise No 63 Jalan Ampang,
50450, Kuala Lumpur, Malaysia
Tel.: (60) 320708055
Mobile Phone Repair & Maintenance Ser-
vices
N.A.I.C.S.: 811210

Cavu Corp Pte. Ltd. (1)
Smart Innovation Centre 152 Ubi Avenue 4
04-00, 408826, Singapore, Singapore
Tel.: (65) 64411213
Computer Hardware Services
N.A.I.C.S.: 541512
Ai Wah Lim *(Asst VP)*

Subsidiary (Domestic):

Delteq Pte. Ltd. (2)
Smart Innovation Centre 152 Ubi Avenue 4
04-00, Singapore, 408826, Singapore
Tel.: (65) 64411213
Mobile Communications Services
N.A.I.C.S.: 517112

Peremex Pte. Ltd. (2)
1 North Bridge Road 19-04/05 High Street
Centre, Singapore, 179094, Singapore
Tel.: (65) 67473020
Computer Hardware & Peripheral Equip-
ment Distr
N.A.I.C.S.: 423430

Centia Technologies Sdn Bhd (1)
Menara Merais Suite 11 02 11th Floor Jalan
19/3, Petaling Jaya, 46300, Malaysia
Tel.: (60) 3 6201808
Computer Hardware & Peripheral Equip-
ment Rental & Distr
N.A.I.C.S.: 532420

Delteq Systems (M) Sdn Bhd (1)
5 Floor Delteq Technopies 2A Jalan

51A/243, Petaling Jaya, 46100, Selangor, Malaysia
Tel.: (60) 3 7877 0877
Web Site: http://www.delteq.com.my
Emp.: 18
Information Technology Consulting Services
N.A.I.C.S.: 541512
Tan Kok *(VP)*

Dot Mobile Sdn Bhd (1)
Plaza Alam Sentral Lot A3-04 3rd Floor
Jalan Institusi, Shah Alam, 40000, Selan-
gor, Malaysia
Tel.: (60) 19 332 0921
Mobile Phone Distr
N.A.I.C.S.: 423690

Homestead Shop (M) Sdn Bhd (1)
Anggunpuri Condominium Jln Dutamas
Raya, Segambut, 51200, Kuala Lumpur,
Malaysia
Tel.: (60) 3 6257 3796
Mobile Phone Distr
N.A.I.C.S.: 423690

MJKI India Pvt. Ltd. (1)
326/6 Ansal Chambers II Bhikaji Cama
Place, South Delhi, New Delhi, 110066,
India
Tel.: (91) 1171211262
Real Estate Management Services
N.A.I.C.S.: 531210

MediaRing.com (Shanghai) Limited (1)
Tel.: (86) 2138685901
Web Site: http://www.mediaring.com
Voice, Data & Computing Services
N.A.I.C.S.: 518210

Mellon Technology Pte Ltd (1)
152 Ubi Avenue 4 #04-00 Smart Innovation
Centre, Singapore, 408826, Singapore
Tel.: (65) 6441 1213
Mobile Phone Distr
N.A.I.C.S.: 423690
Siow Lee Ping *(Gen Mgr-Sls)*

Mobile Service International Co. Ltd. (1)
Block A Unit 1201-A10 29 Terra 4th Road,
Futian District, Shenzhen, 518042, Guang-
dong, China
Tel.: (86) 75533330898
Mobile Communications Services
N.A.I.C.S.: 517112

Modi Aircrete Private Limited (1)
3rd floor C5/85 New Kondli, Delhi, 110096,
India
Tel.: (91) 1204141579
Electronic Equipment Mfr & Distr
N.A.I.C.S.: 335314

Modi Indonesia 2020 Pte. Ltd. (1)
Rukan Grand Aries Niaga Blok G1 No 1S
Jln Taman Aries RT 012 RW 008, Kel Mer-
uya Utara Kec Kembangan Kota Adminis-
trasi, Jakarta Barat, 11620, Indonesia
Tel.: (62) 215602111
Real Estate Manangement Services
N.A.I.C.S.: 531210

Newtel Corporation Company Limited (1)
Mobile Phone & Accessory Mfr & Whslr
N.A.I.C.S.: 334220
Naveen Bajaj *(Head-Bus)*

P.T. Metrotech Jaya Komunika Indonesia (1)
Rukan Grand Aries Niaga Blok G1 No 1S
Jln Taman Aries RT 012 RW 008, Kel Mer-
uya Utara Kec Kembangan Kota Adminis-
trasi, Jakarta Barat, 11620, Indonesia
Tel.: (62) 215602111
Real Estate Manangement Services
N.A.I.C.S.: 531210

PT Selular Global Net (1)
Blue Dot Center Blok E-I Jl Gelong Baru
Utara No 5-8, Tomang, Jakarta, 11440, In-
donesia
Tel.: (62) 21 5602 111
Mobile Phone Distr
N.A.I.C.S.: 423690

Peremex Computer Systems Pvt Ltd (1)
415 3rd Floor Oxford Towers 139 Airport

Digilife Technologies Limited—(Continued)

Road, Bengaluru, 560 017, India
Tel.: (91) 80 41151656
Computer Hardware & Peripheral Equipment Rental & Distr
N.A.I.C.S.: 532420

Real & Virtual Technologies Sdn Bhd (1)
No 12-A Jalan TPJ 4, Taman Perindustrian Jaya, Subang Jaya, 47200, Selangor, Malaysia
Tel.: (60) 3 78474512
Mobile Communications Services
N.A.I.C.S.: 517112

SEV Projects Pte Limited (1)
1 North Bridge Road 19-04/05 High Street Centre, Singapore, 179094, Singapore
Tel.: (65) 67473020
Real Estate Manamgement Services
N.A.I.C.S.: 531210

Singapore Electric Vehicles Pte. Ltd. (1)
152 Ubi Avenue 4 Level 2 Smart Innovation Centre, Singapore, 408826, Singapore
Tel.: (65) 63036836
Computer Hardware & Peripheral Equipment Distr
N.A.I.C.S.: 423430

Spice CSL International Sdn. Bhd. (1)
No 63 Jalan Ampang Wisma Paradise Ground Floor, 50450, Kuala Lumpur, Malaysia
Tel.: (60) 3 2078 1222
Web Site: http://www.s-csl.my
Mobile Phone & Accessory Mfr & Whslr
N.A.I.C.S.: 334220

T.H.C. International Co., Ltd. (1)
972 Business Thailand Building 1st Floor Soi Saengiam-imklongsamsen, Rama IX Road Bangkapi Sub-district Huaykwang District Metropolis, Bangkok, 10310, Thailand
Tel.: (66) 294135846
Mobile Communications Services
N.A.I.C.S.: 517112

DIGIMAX GLOBAL INC.
Suite 500 33 Bloor Street East, Toronto, M4W 3H1, ON, Canada
Tel.: (647) 341-8033
Web Site: http://www.digicrypts.com
DBKSF—(OTCIQ)
Rev.: $2,031,000
Assets: $3,158,000
Liabilities: $3,837,000
Net Worth: ($679,000)
Earnings: ($7,898,000)
Fiscal Year-end: 12/31/23
Data Processing Services
N.A.I.C.S.: 518210
Chris Carl *(CEO)*

DIGISPICE TECHNOLOGIES LTD.
S Global Knowledge Park 19A & 19B Sector-125, Noida, 201 301, Uttar Pradesh, India
Tel.: (91) 1205029101
Web Site: https://www.digispice.com
DIGISPICE—(NSE)
Rev.: $100,550,473
Assets: $72,528,224
Liabilities: $39,592,371
Net Worth: $32,935,853
Earnings: $762,858
Emp.: 208
Fiscal Year-end: 03/31/21
Mobile Telecommunications Services
N.A.I.C.S.: 517112
Dilip Kumar Modi *(Chm)*

Subsidiaries:

WSFx Global Pay Limited (1)
Unit 622 6th Floor The Summit Business Bay Omkar, MV Road Opp PVR Cinema Chakala Andheri East, Mumbai, 400 093, India

Tel.: (91) 8976707222
Web Site: https://www.wsfx.in
Rev.: $3,120,881
Assets: $6,353,925
Liabilities: $2,298,496
Net Worth: $4,055,429
Earnings: ($701,255)
Emp.: 175
Fiscal Year-end: 03/31/2021
Financial Services
N.A.I.C.S.: 522390
Roshan Dalal *(Head-Bus-Wholesale Bank Notes)*

DIGISTAR CORPORATION BERHAD
B5/5/5 4th Floor One Ampang Business Avenue, Jalan Ampang Utama Selangor, 68000, Ampang, Malaysia
Tel.: (60) 342534319 MY
Web Site:
https://www.digistar.com.my
Year Founded: 1982
DIGISTA—(KLS)
Rev.: $4,087,869
Assets: $83,572,677
Liabilities: $68,370,224
Net Worth: $15,202,453
Earnings: ($2,054,008)
Fiscal Year-end: 09/30/21
Computer Security System Design Services
N.A.I.C.S.: 541512
Wah Cheong Lee *(Mng Dir-Grp)*

Subsidiaries:

Digistar Holdings Sdn. Bhd. (1)
B5/5/5 5th Floor One Ampang Business Avenue Jalan Ampang Utama, 68000, Ampang, Selangor, Malaysia
Tel.: (60) 342534319
Web Site: https://www.digistar.com.my
Information Technology Services
N.A.I.C.S.: 541511

Subsidiary (Domestic):

Protecs A & A CMS Sdn. Bhd. (2)
B5/5/5 One Ampang Business Avenue Jalan Ampang Utama 1/2, 68000, Ampang, Selangor, Malaysia
Tel.: (60) 342510227
Web Site: http://www.aacms.com
Industrial Security Services
N.A.I.C.S.: 561612

Full Image Sdn. Bhd. (1)
B5/5/5 4th Floor One Ampang Business Avenue Jalan Ampang Utama, 68000, Ampang, Selangor, Malaysia
Tel.: (60) 109868911
Web Site: https://www.panther911.com
Industrial Security Services
N.A.I.C.S.: 561612

DIGITAL 9 INFRASTRUCTURE PLC
26 New Street, Saint Helier, JE2 3RA, Jersey JE
Web Site:
https://www.d9infrastructure.com
Year Founded: 2021
DGI9—(LSE)
Rev.: $138,663,944
Assets: $1,293,077,593
Liabilities: $3,759,527
Net Worth: $1,289,318,066
Earnings: $125,003,923
Fiscal Year-end: 12/31/22
Investment Management Service
N.A.I.C.S.: 523999
Phil Jordan *(Chm)*

Subsidiaries:

Giggle Broadband Limited (1)
2nd Floor 124 St Vincent Street, Glasgow, G2 5HF, United Kingdom
Tel.: (44) 1416742156
Web Site: https://www.giggle.co.uk
Fibre Broadband Services
N.A.I.C.S.: 541618

Sea Fibre Networks Limited (1)
26 Upper Fitzwilliam Street, Dublin, 2, Ireland
Tel.: (353) 16624399
Web Site: https://seafibrenetworks.com
Network Bandwidth Infrastructure Services
N.A.I.C.S.: 532490

DIGITAL ARTS INC.
Otemachi First Square West Tower 14F 1-5-1 Otemachi, Chiyoda-ku, Tokyo, 100-0004, Japan
Tel.: (81) 352201110
Web Site: https://www.daj.jp
Year Founded: 1995
2326—(TKS)
Rev.: $76,094,320
Assets: $148,843,980
Liabilities: $43,097,200
Net Worth: $105,746,780
Earnings: $28,931,970
Emp.: 257
Fiscal Year-end: 03/31/24
Internet Security Software & Appliances
N.A.I.C.S.: 513210
Toshio Dogu *(Pres, Pres & CEO)*

Subsidiaries:

Digital Arts America, Inc. (1)
4675 Stevens Creek Blvd Ste 130, Santa Clara, CA 95051
Tel.: (408) 441-0655
IT Consulting Services
N.A.I.C.S.: 541618

Digital Arts Asia Pacific Pte. Ltd. (1)
8 Temasek Boulevard 35-02A Suntec Tower Three, Singapore, 038988, Singapore
Tel.: (65) 65497879
IT Consulting Services
N.A.I.C.S.: 541618

Digital Arts Consulting Inc. (1)
14F Otemachi First Square West Tower 1-5-1 Otemachi, Chiyoda-ku, Tokyo, Japan
Tel.: (81) 362063421
Web Site: https://con.daj.jp
Emp.: 125
IT Consulting Services
N.A.I.C.S.: 541618

DIGITAL BARRIERS PLC
Cargo Works 1-2 Hatfields, London, SE1 9PG, United Kingdom
Tel.: (44) 203 553 5888
Web Site:
http://www.digitalbarriers.com
Sales Range: $25-49.9 Million
Security Products Mfr
N.A.I.C.S.: 561621
Zak Doffman *(Founder & CEO)*

Subsidiaries:

Brimtek, Inc. (1)
21660 red Rum Dr, Ashburn, VA 20147
Tel.: (571) 918-4921
Web Site: http://www.brimtek.com
Sales Range: $10-24.9 Million
Emp.: 23
Specialist Technical Surveillance & Tactical Solutions to Government Departments in Security Functions
N.A.I.C.S.: 921190
Dave Tilton *(CEO)*

Stryker Communications Limited (1)
1A Howard Road, Surbiton, KT6 8SA, United Kingdom
Tel.: (44) 1483237200
Integrated Security Services
N.A.I.C.S.: 561621

DIGITAL BROS SPA
Via Tortona 37, 20144, Milan, Italy
Tel.: (39) 02413031 IT
Web Site:
https://www.digitalbros.com
DIB—(ITA)
Rev.: $162,420,001
Assets: $277,964,223
Liabilities: $109,304,762

Net Worth: $168,659,460
Earnings: $35,196,445
Emp.: 379
Fiscal Year-end: 06/30/22
Video Games Distr
N.A.I.C.S.: 532282
Abramo Galante *(Chm & Co-CEO)*

Subsidiaries:

505 Games S.r.l (1)
Via Tortona 37, Milan, 20144, Italy
Tel.: (39) 02413031
Web Site: http://www.505games.com
Sales Range: $50-74.9 Million
Emp.: 6
Video Games Distr
N.A.I.C.S.: 423430
Neil Ralley *(Pres)*

Subsidiary (Non-US):

505 Games GmbH (2)
Brunnfeld 2-6, 93133, Burglengenfeld, Germany
Tel.: (49) 9471 308879 1
Video Games Distr
N.A.I.C.S.: 423430

505 Games Ltd (2)
402-420 Silbury Court Silbury Boulevard, Milton Keynes, MK9 2AF, United Kingdom
Tel.: (44) 1908607772
Web Site: http://www.505games.co.uk
Sales Range: $25-49.9 Million
Video Game Publisher
N.A.I.C.S.: 513210
Tim Woodley *(Head-Global Brand)*

D3Publisher of America, Inc. (1)
11500 W Olympic Blvd Ste 460, Los Angeles, CA 90064
Tel.: (310) 268-0820
Web Site: http://www.d3publisher.us
Sales Range: $25-49.9 Million
Emp.: 16
Video Game Publisher & Distr
N.A.I.C.S.: 513210
Yoji Takenaka *(Pres & CEO)*

Digital Bros France S.a.r.l. (1)
2 Chemin de la Chauderaie, Francheville, 69340, France
Tel.: (33) 456384520
Web Site: http://www.digital-bros.fr
Sales Range: $50-74.9 Million
Emp.: 8
Video Games Distr
N.A.I.C.S.: 423430

Digital Bros Iberia S.L. (1)
c/ Londres 38 Oficina 105, Las Rozas, Madrid, 28230, Spain
Tel.: (34) 916409518
Web Site: http://www.digital-bros.net
Video Game Publisher
N.A.I.C.S.: 513210

Game Service S.r.l. (1)
Via Leonardo Da Vinci Snc, Marostica, 36063, Italy
Tel.: (39) 042477777
Web Site: http://www.games-servicesrl.it
Sales Range: $25-49.9 Million
Emp.: 15
Video Games Distr
N.A.I.C.S.: 423430

DIGITAL CHINA GROUP CO., LTD.
No 9 Digital Technology Plaza Shangdi 9th Street, Haidian District, Beijing, 100085, China
Tel.: (86) 1082705588 CN
Web Site: https://en.digitalchina.com
Year Founded: 2000
000034—(SSE)
Rev.: $16,269,554,808
Assets: $5,646,332,016
Liabilities: $4,492,246,824
Net Worth: $1,154,085,192
Earnings: $141,019,164
Emp.: 1,800
Fiscal Year-end: 12/31/22
Real Estate Manamgement Services
N.A.I.C.S.: 551112

Wei Guo *(Chm)*

Subsidiaries:

Digital China (China) Limited **(1)**
No 9 Digital Technology Plaza Shangdi 9th
Street, PO Box 8608, Haidian District, Bei-
jing, 100085, China
Tel.: (86) 1082705588
Information Technology Products Distr
N.A.I.C.S.: 423430

Subsidiary (Domestic):

Guangzhou Digital China Limited **(2)**
Building A7 Headquarters Economic Zone
No 247 Science Avenue, Science City
Huangpu District, Guangzhou, 510530,
Guangdong, China
Tel.: (86) 2038118888
Information Technology Products Mfr & Distr
N.A.I.C.S.: 334111

Shanghai Digital China Limited **(2)**
Digital China Technology Park No111
Fuquan Road, Changning District, Shang-
hai, 200335, China
Tel.: (86) 212 201 9999
Web Site: https://www.digitalchina.com
Information Technology Products Mfr & Distr
N.A.I.C.S.: 334111

DIGITAL CHINA HOLDINGS LIMITED

31/F Fortis Tower 77-79 Gloucester
Road Wanchai, Hong Kong, China
(Hong Kong)
Tel.: (852) 34168000　　**BM**
Web Site:
　https://www.digitalchina.com
Year Founded: 1984
DCHIF—(OTCIQ)
Rev.: $2,457,629,320
Assets: $3,429,297,879
Liabilities: $1,724,536,165
Net Worth: $1,704,761,714
Earnings: $64,590,164
Emp.: 15,166
Fiscal Year-end: 12/31/22
Holding Company; Information Tech-
nology Solutions & Services
N.A.I.C.S.: 551112
Wei Guo *(Chm & CEO)*

Subsidiaries:

Digital China Limited **(1)**
F31 Fortis Tower 77-79 Gloucester Road,
979 King's Road, Wanchai, China (Hong
Kong)
Tel.: (852) 3 416 8000
Web Site: http://www.digitalchina.com.hk
Information Technology Services
N.A.I.C.S.: 541512

Subsidiary (Non-US):

Beijing Digital China Limited **(2)**
Digital China Building 16 Suzhou Street,
Haidian District, Beijing, 100080, China
Tel.: (86) 10 62694338
Information Technology Management Ser-
vices
N.A.I.C.S.: 561110

Changsha Digital China Company
Limited **(2)**
Room 1601-1603 Hunan Cultural Building
139 North Shaoshan Road, Changsha,
410001, Hunan, China
Tel.: (86) 73184161486
Information Technology Products Distr
N.A.I.C.S.: 423430

Chengdu Digital China Limited **(2)**
40 Wuqing South Road Wuhou District,
Chengdu, 610045, Sichuan, China
Tel.: (86) 28 2885003399
Information Technology Management Ser-
vices
N.A.I.C.S.: 541519

Subsidiary (Domestic):

Digital China (HK) Limited **(2)**
Room 2008 20 F Devon House Taikoo

Place 979 Kings Road, Quarry Bay, China
(Hong Kong)
Tel.: (852) 34168000
Web Site: http://www.digitalchina.com.hk
Emp.: 100
Computer Peripheral Distr
N.A.I.C.S.: 423430

Subsidiary (Non-US):

Digital China (Hefei) Company
Limited **(2)**
14 F Jincheng Building 436 Changjiang
Middle Road, Hefei, 230061, Anhui, China
Tel.: (86) 5512834200
Information Technology Products Distr
N.A.I.C.S.: 423430

Digital China (Shenzhen) Limited **(2)**
11D Block 1 Financial Services Technical
Innovation Base, No 8 Kefa Road Nanshan
District, Shenzhen, 518057, Guangdong,
China
Tel.: (86) 7558 296 6699
Web Site: http://www.digitalchina.com
Emp.: 300
Information Technology Products Mfr & Distr
N.A.I.C.S.: 334111
Quing Ping *(Gen Mgr)*

Digital China (Zhengzhou)
Limited **(2)**
18 F Block D Building 2 Jincheng Interna-
tional Plaza 68 Jingsan Road, Zhengzhou,
Henan, China
Tel.: (86) 371 69508188
Information Technology Products Distr
N.A.I.C.S.: 423430

Digital China Macao Commercial Off-
shore Limited **(2)**
Room C-D F13 Centro Comercial Chong
Fok Avenida De Marciano Baptista, No 26-
54-B, Macau, China (Macau)
Tel.: (853) 2 871 7039
Web Site: http://www.digitalchinahk.com
Information Technology Consulting Services
N.A.I.C.S.: 541512
Steven Siao *(Gen Mgr)*

Subsidiary (Domestic):

Digital China Technology Limited **(2)**
Suite 2008 Devon House Taikoo Place 979
Kings Road, Quarry Bay, China (Hong
Kong)
Tel.: (852) 34168000
Computer Peripheral Equipment Mfr
N.A.I.C.S.: 334118

Subsidiary (Non-US):

Fuzhou Digital China Company
Limited **(2)**
8/F Chuangye Center Building 318 Wushan
West Road, Gulou District, Fuzhou, 350002,
Fujian, China
Tel.: (86) 591 83306330
Information Technology Production Distr
N.A.I.C.S.: 423430

Hangzhou Digital China Limited **(2)**
2201 Block A Wanfu Center No 228 Binkang Road, Binjiang District, Hangzhou,
310051, Zhejiang, China
Tel.: (86) 5718 736 2221
Web Site: http://www.digitalchina.com.hk
Computer System Network Integration Services
N.A.I.C.S.: 541512

Nanjing Digital China Limited **(2)**
10/f Huijie Mansion No 268 Zhongshan
Road, Xuanwu Dist, Nanjing, 210008, Ji-
angsu, China
Tel.: (86) 2583351122
Computer Network System Integration Ser-
vices
N.A.I.C.S.: 541512

Navimentum Information System
Limited **(2)**
22/F Block B Zhong Shang Plaza 9 Zhong-
nan Road, Wuchang District, Wuhan,
430071, Hubei, China
Tel.: (86) 27 87312266
Information Technology Consulting Services
N.A.I.C.S.: 541512

Shenyang Digital China Limited **(2)**

6F Chengda Technology Building 63 South
Sanhao Street, Heping District, Shenyang,
110004, Liaoning, China
Tel.: (86) 24 23582588
Computer Network System Integration Ser-
vices
N.A.I.C.S.: 541512

Yunke China Information Technology
Limited **(2)**
Digital Technology Plaza NO 9 Shangdi 9th
Street, Box 8608, Haidian District, Beijing,
100085, China
Tel.: (86) 108 270 7033
Web Site: https://www.dcnglobal.com
Networking Products Mfr & Distr
N.A.I.C.S.: 334210

Wai On Service Limited **(1)**
Suite 2008 20/F Devon House Taikoo Place
979 Kings Road, Hong Kong, China (Hong
Kong)
Tel.: (852) 34228403
Web Site: http://www.waiongroup.com
Oil & Gas Operation Support Services
N.A.I.C.S.: 213112
Raymond Wei *(Mng Dir)*

DIGITAL CHINA INFORMATION SERVICE GROUP CO., LTD.

DCITS Building No E 18 A-Park No
10 Xibeiwang Dong Rd, Haidian Dis-
trict, Beijing, 100193, China
Tel.: (86) 1062693001
Web Site: https://www.dcits.com
Year Founded: 1984
000555—(SSE)
Rev.: $1,684,696,104
Assets: $1,746,549,324
Liabilities: $885,335,724
Net Worth: $861,213,600
Earnings: $28,994,004
Emp.: 14,000
Fiscal Year-end: 12/31/22
Software Development Services
N.A.I.C.S.: 513210
Liu Weigang *(Sec)*

DIGITAL CHOSUN INC.

135 Sejong-daero, Jung-gu, Seoul,
04519, Korea (South)
Tel.: (82) 237012280
Web Site: https://www.chosun.com
Year Founded: 1995
033130—(KRS)
Rev.: $26,626,233
Assets: $69,762,260
Liabilities: $6,766,510
Net Worth: $62,995,750
Earnings: $2,108,332
Emp.: 159
Fiscal Year-end: 12/31/22
Online Information Services
N.A.I.C.S.: 519290
Dae Yong Lee *(Gen Mgr)*

DIGITAL DAESUNG CO., LTD.

181 Bangbae-ro Bangbae-dong Dan-
woo Building 6-8th floor, Seocho-gu,
Seoul, Korea (South)
Tel.: (82) 221048600
Web Site:
　https://www.digitaldaesung.co.kr
Year Founded: 2000
068930—(KRS)
Rev.: $161,697,087
Assets: $188,186,584
Liabilities: $61,518,300
Net Worth: $126,668,283
Earnings: $16,302,887
Emp.: 456
Fiscal Year-end: 12/31/22
Learning Services
N.A.I.C.S.: 611710

DIGITAL DOMAIN HOLDINGS LIMITED

Suite 1201 12/F Li Po Chun Chambers 189 Des Voeux Road, Central,
China (Hong Kong)

Tel.: (852) 31508050　　**BM**
Web Site: http://www.ddhl.com
0547—(HKG)
Rev.: $122,228,003
Assets: $131,287,133
Liabilities: $93,927,210
Net Worth: $37,359,923
Earnings: ($27,446,288)
Emp.: 1,138
Fiscal Year-end: 12/31/22
Investment Holding Company; Media
Operations, Property Investment
N.A.I.C.S.: 551112
Daniel Seah *(Chm & CEO)*

Subsidiaries:

Digital Domain Productions 3.0 (BC),
Ltd. **(1)**
1618 W 8th Avenue, Vancouver, V6J 1V4,
BC, Canada
Tel.: (778) 783-6000
Rev.: $19,343,425
Visual Effect Production Services
N.A.I.C.S.: 512110

IM360 Entertainment Inc. **(1)**
12641 Beatrice St, Los Angeles, CA 90066
Tel.: (888) 833-7964
Interactive Media Development Services
N.A.I.C.S.: 512110

Immersive Media Company **(1)**
1700 Main St Ste 248, Washougal, WA
98671
Tel.: (360) 718-5255
Interactive Media Development Services
N.A.I.C.S.: 512110

Immersive Ventures Inc. **(1)**
Suite 200 532 Leon Avenue, Kelowna, V1Y
6J6, BC, Canada
Tel.: (250) 448-7158
Rev.: $609,134
Interactive Media Development Services
N.A.I.C.S.: 512110

DIGITAL GARAGE, INC.

DG Bldg 3-5-7 Ebisu Minami,
Shibuya-ku, Tokyo, 150-0022, Japan
Tel.: (81) 363671111
Web Site: https://www.garage.co.jp
Year Founded: 1995
4819—(TKS)
Rev.: $250,208,330
Assets: $1,529,758,910
Liabilities: $920,726,730
Net Worth: $609,032,180
Earnings: $38,377,660
Emp.: 909
Fiscal Year-end: 03/31/24
Information Technology Services
N.A.I.C.S.: 541519
Kaoru Hayashi *(Co-Founder, Pres,
CEO-Grp & Exec Officer)*

Subsidiaries:

Academy du Vin Co., Ltd. **(1)**
Cosmos Aoyama Garden Floor 5-53-67,
Jingumae Shibuya-ku, Tokyo, 150-0001,
Japan
Tel.: (81) 33 486 7769
Web Site: https://www.adv.gr.jp
Wine Whslr
N.A.I.C.S.: 424820

CGM Marketing Inc. **(1)**
1-6-3 Higashi-Gotanda, Shinagawa-ku, To-
kyo, 141-0022, Japan
Tel.: (81) 362771944
Web Site: https://cgmj.co.jp
Sales Range: $75-99.9 Million
Emp.: 270
Marketing Consulting Services
N.A.I.C.S.: 541613

DG Communications, Inc. **(1)**
Digital Gate Bldg 11th Floor 3-5-7 Ebisu
Minami, Shibuya-ku, Tokyo, 150-0022, Ja-
pan
Tel.: (81) 5017413455
Web Site: https://www.dg-c.co.jp
N.A.I.C.S.: 541810

Branch (Domestic):

Sogei Inc.-Sapporo Branch **(2)**

Digital Garage, Inc.—(Continued)

3F Sapporo Fukokuseimei Building 1-2-3
Kita yonjo higashi, Chou-Ku, Sapporo, 060-
0034, Japan
Tel.: (81) 11 221 6881
Web Site: http://www.sogei.co.jp
Advetising Agency
N.A.I.C.S.: 541810

Sogei Inc.-Sendai Branch (2)
14F Sendai kowa Building 2-4-1 Ichibancho,
Aoba-Ku, Sendai, 980-0811, Japan
Tel.: (81) 22 208 6211
Web Site: http://www.sogei.co.jp
Advetising Agency
N.A.I.C.S.: 541810

DG Financial Technology, Inc. (1)
Digital Gate Bldg 10F Reception / 9F 3-5-7
Ebisu Minami, Shibuya-ku, Tokyo, 150-
0022, Japan
Tel.: (81) 36 367 1500
Web Site: https://www.dgft.jp
Payment Information Processing Services
N.A.I.C.S.: 522320

DG Mobile, Inc. (1)
3-5-7 Ebisuminami Daikanyamadg Building,
Shibuya-ku, Tokyo, 150-0022, Japan
Tel.: (81) 363671300
Web Site: http://www.dgmobile.co.jp
Mobile Software Development Services
N.A.I.C.S.: 541511

Naviplus Co., Ltd. (1)
Digital Gate Bldg 11th Floor 3-5-7 Ebisu
Minami, Shibuya-ku, Tokyo, 150-0022, Ja-
pan
Tel.: (81) 36 367 1458
Web Site: https://corporate.naviplus.co.jp
Marketing Services
N.A.I.C.S.: 541613

VeriTrans Inc. (1)
10F Digital Gate Building 3-5-7 Ebisu Mi-
nami, Shibuya-ku, Tokyo, 150-0022,
Japan **(41.6%)**
Tel.: (81) 363671500
Web Site: https://www.dgft.jp
Electronic Payment Settlements for
E-Commerce Businesses
N.A.I.C.S.: 541519
Yoshitaka Kitao (CEO)

Wheel, Inc. (1)
3-5-7 Ebisu Minami, Shibuya-ku, Tokyo,
150-0022, Japan
Tel.: (81) 354657747
Web Site: https://
Smartphones Content Distr
N.A.I.C.S.: 541519
Kaoru Hayashi (Pres & CEO)

DIGITAL GRAPHICS INCORPO-RATION
52 Cheongdam-Ro, Yangju, 11459,
Gyeonggi, Korea (South)
Tel.: (82) 318208900
Web Site: https://www.dgi-net.com
Year Founded: 1985
043360—(KRS)
Rev.: $12,331,712
Assets: $36,513,020
Liabilities: $2,237,324
Net Worth: $34,275,695
Earnings: $527,407
Emp.: 66
Fiscal Year-end: 12/31/22
Inkjet Plotter Mfr
N.A.I.C.S.: 334118
Bryan Choi (CEO)

DIGITAL HEARTS HOLDINGS CO., LTD.
Tokyo Opera City Bldg 41F 3-20-2
Nishi-Shinjuku, Shinjuku-ku, Tokyo,
163-1441, Japan
Tel.: (81) 333730082 JP
Web Site: https://www.digitalhearts-
hd.com
Year Founded: 2013
3676—(TKS)
Rev.: $256,401,900
Assets: $139,490,830
Liabilities: $80,979,110

Net Worth: $58,511,720
Earnings: $1,163,360
Emp.: 1,811
Fiscal Year-end: 03/31/24
Holding Company; Computer Soft-
ware & Applications Testing & Debug-
ging Services
N.A.I.C.S.: 551112
Eiichi Miyazawa (Chm)

Subsidiaries:

Agest, Inc. (1)
Tokyo Opera City Building 41st Floor 3-20-2
Nishi-Shinjuku, Shinjuku ku, Tokyo, 163
1441, Japan
Tel.: (81) 35 333 1246
Web Site: https://agest.co.jp
Computer Related Services
N.A.I.C.S.: 541519

**DIGITAL Hearts (Thailand) Co.,
Ltd.** (1)
54 BB Building 14th Floor Room 1401
Sukhumvit 21 Road, Klongtoey-Nua Wat-
tana, Bangkok, 10110, Thailand
Tel.: (66) 2 664 2298
Web Site: http://www.digitalhearts.co.jp
Emp.: 60
Software Debugging Services
N.A.I.C.S.: 541519
Kengo Honjo (Pres)

DIGITAL Hearts Korea Co., Ltd. (1)
S-808 64 Yanghwa-ro, Mapo-gu, Seoul, Ko-
rea (South)
Tel.: (82) 7043491938
Software Debugging Services
N.A.I.C.S.: 541519
Teppei Komiya (Pres)

DIGITAL Hearts USA Inc. (1)
3625 Del Amo Blvd Ste 130, Torrance, CA
90503
Tel.: (424) 247-2800
Web Site: http://www.digitalheartsusa.com
Software Debugging Services
N.A.I.C.S.: 541519
John Yamamoto (Pres & CEO)

Digital Hearts Co., Ltd. (1)
Tokyo Opera City Bldg 41F 3-20-2 Nishi-
Shinjuku, Shinjuku-ku, Tokyo, 163-1441,
Japan
Tel.: (81) 333792053
Web Site: https://www.digitalhearts.com
Emp.: 8,477
Computer Software & Applications Debug-
ging Services
N.A.I.C.S.: 541519

FLAME Hearts Co., Ltd. (1)
Daiwa Azabu Terrace Bldg B1F 3-20-1 Mi-
nami Azabu, Minato-ku, Tokyo, 106-0047,
Japan
Tel.: (81) 36 866 7281
Information Technology Services
N.A.I.C.S.: 541519
Toshiya Tsukushi (Pres)

Logigear Japan Corporation (1)
Hatsudai Center Bldg 1-51-1, Hatsudai
Shibuya, Tokyo, 151-0061, Japan
Tel.: (81) 34 500 8702
Web Site: https://www.logigear.com
Software Development Services
N.A.I.C.S.: 541511
Hung Q. Nguyen (CEO & Chm)

NetWork21 Co., Ltd. (1)
Newchiyoda Bldg 3F 1-8-4 Kandasakuma-
cho, Chiyoda-ku, Tokyo, 101-0025,
Japan **(66.4%)**
Tel.: (81) 3 3526 5151
Web Site: http://www.nt21.jp
System Development Services
N.A.I.C.S.: 541512
Hiroshi Tsunoda (Pres)

Orgosoft Co., Ltd. (1)
Floor 3 9-30 Gwanak-daero 434beon-gil,
Dongan-gu, Anyang, Gyeonggi, Korea
(South)
Tel.: (82) 704 849 1090
Web Site: http://orgosoft.com
Software Quality Control Services
N.A.I.C.S.: 541511

Premium Agency Inc. (1)

Azabu Green Terrace Bldg 3F 3-20-1 Mi-
nami Azabu, Minato-ku, Tokyo, 106-0047,
Japan **(58.5%)**
Tel.: (81) 3 6866 7281
Web Site: http://www.premiumagency.com
Emp.: 150
Video & Audio Production Services
N.A.I.C.S.: 512110
Masaharu Ohtsubo (Pres)

DIGITAL HOLDINGS, INC.
Tokyu Bancho Bldg 6 Yonbancho,
Chiyoda-ku, Tokyo, 102-0081, Japan
Tel.: (81) 357453611
Web Site: https://www.digital-
holdings.co.jp
Year Founded: 1994
2389—(TKS)
Rev.: $115,311,760
Assets: $356,506,470
Liabilities: $116,212,190
Net Worth: $240,294,280
Earnings: $1,680,330
Emp.: 1,031
Fiscal Year-end: 12/31/23
Holding Company
N.A.I.C.S.: 551112
Daisuke Kanazawa (COO & Exec
Officer)

Subsidiaries:

Growth Gear Co. Ltd (1)
3 Chome-4 Kanda Surugadai Chiyoda-Ku,
Tokyo, 101-0062, Japan
Tel.: (81) 357453859
Web Site: http://www.growth-gear.co.jp
Human Resource Consulting Services
N.A.I.C.S.: 541612

Heartlass Inc. (1)
Tokyu bancho building 7F 6 Yonbancho,
Chiyoda-ku, Tokyo, 102-0081, Japan
Tel.: (81) 357453660
Web Site: http://www.heartlass.co.jp
Emp.: 64
Advertising Management Services
N.A.I.C.S.: 541810
Fumiari Mizokawa (CEO)

Shuttlerock Japan, Inc. (1)
6F Kudanminami 3-2-5, Chiyoda-ku, Tokyo,
Japan
Tel.: (81) 30 6304 2864
Web Site: http://www.shuttlerock.co.jp
Digital Marketing Services
N.A.I.C.S.: 541613
Jonathan Glassey (Engr-Support)

**SkillUp Video Technologies
Corporation** (1)
9-8 Sakuragaokacho Shibuya-ku, Tokyo,
150-0031, Japan
Tel.: (81) 357848064
Web Site: http://www.suvt.co.jp
Digital Advertising Services
N.A.I.C.S.: 541810

DIGITAL HOLLYWOOD INTER-ACTIVE LIMITED
2nd Floor No 368 Jiang Nan Da Dao
South, Haizhu District, Guangzhou,
China
Tel.: (86) 26200862 Ky
Web Site:
http://www.gamehollywood.com
Year Founded: 2010
2022—(HKG)
Rev.: $11,142,371
Assets: $44,297,414
Liabilities: $9,998,674
Net Worth: $34,298,740
Earnings: ($5,863,468)
Emp.: 153
Fiscal Year-end: 12/31/22
Software Publishing Services
N.A.I.C.S.: 513210
Yuanfeng Lu (Co-Founder, Chm &
CEO)

DIGITAL INFORMATION TECH-NOLOGIES CORPORATION

Forecast Sakurabashi Bld 5F 4-5-4
Hacchobori, Chuo-ku, Tokyo, 104-
0032, Japan
Tel.: (81) 363116520
Web Site: https://www.ditgroup.jp
3916—(TKS)
Rev.: $123,703,360
Assets: $63,549,740
Liabilities: $19,648,980
Net Worth: $43,900,760
Earnings: $10,486,920
Emp.: 1,499
Fiscal Year-end: 06/30/24
Computer Software
N.A.I.C.S.: 513210
Norikazu Ichikawa (Chm)

DIGITAL LEARNING MARKET-PLACE PLC
Livingston House, 2 Queens Road,
Teddington, TW11 0LB, Mddx, United
Kingdom
Tel.: (44) 8450583960
Sales Range: $1-9.9 Million
Emp.: 23
Software Publishing & E-Learning
N.A.I.C.S.: 513210
Bruce H. Leith (Dir-Sls)

Subsidiaries:

Zenosis Limited (1)
Livingston House 2 Queens Rd, Teddington,
TW110LB, Middlesex, United Kingdom
Tel.: (44) 845 058 3960
Web Site: http://www.zenosis.com
Online Educational Support Services
N.A.I.C.S.: 611710

DIGITAL MEDIA PROFESSION-ALS INC.
Nakano Central Park South 16F
4-10-2 Nakano, Nakano-ku, Tokyo,
164-0001, Japan
Tel.: (81) 364540450
Web Site: https://www.dmprof.com
Year Founded: 2002
3652—(TKS)
Rev.: $19,935,760
Assets: $25,904,590
Liabilities: $3,053,820
Net Worth: $22,850,770
Earnings: $2,187,910
Emp.: 44
Fiscal Year-end: 03/31/24
Graphics Processor, 3D Graphics
Software & Consulting Services
N.A.I.C.S.: 334118
Tatsuo Yamamoto (Pres & CEO)

DIGITAL MULTIMEDIA TECH-NOLOGY CO., LTD.
14F Doosan Bldg 726 Eonju-ro,
Gangnam-gu, Seoul, 06057, Korea
(South)
Tel.: (82) 234004600
Web Site: http://www.dmt.kr
Year Founded: 2007
134580—(KRS)
Rev.: $17,345,846
Assets: $45,151,675
Liabilities: $16,464,664
Net Worth: $28,687,011
Earnings: ($2,246,813)
Emp.: 34
Fiscal Year-end: 12/31/22
Wireless Technology Products Mfr
N.A.I.C.S.: 334220
Kwoun Young Chul (CEO)

DIGITAL ONE CONSULTING SP. Z O.O.
Dowborczykow 25, 90-019, Lodz,
Poland
Tel.: (48) 42 677 1477
Web Site: http://www.digitalone.pl
Sales Range: $100-124.9 Million
Emp.: 45

Advertising Agencies
N.A.I.C.S.: 541810
Olgierd Cygan *(CEO & Mng Partner)*

DIGITAL ONLINE MEDIA GMBH

Bismarckstr 60, 50672, Cologne, Germany
Tel.: (49) 221951680
Web Site: http://www.dom.de
Year Founded: 1995
Emp.: 25
E Commerce & Online Marketing Solution Services
N.A.I.C.S.: 541910
Markus Schulte *(Mng Dir)*

DIGITAL PAYMENTS PLC

1 Garrick House Carrington Street, Mayfair, London, W1J 7AF, United Kingdom
Tel.: (44) 2074930387
Web Site:
   http://www.digitalpaymentsplc.com
Investment Firm
N.A.I.C.S.: 523999
David Carr *(CEO)*

Subsidiaries:

Muscato Group, Inc.   **(1)**
2301 Maitland Ctr Pkwy Ste 240, Maitland, FL 32751
Tel.: (407) 551-1300
Web Site: http://www.muscato.com
Sales Range: Less than $1 Million
Holding Company
N.A.I.C.S.: 551112
Joseph W. Adams *(CEO)*

Subsidiary (Domestic):

M2 Systems Corporation   **(2)**
500 Winderley Pl Ste 226, Maitland, FL 32751
Tel.: (407) 551-1300
Web Site: http://www.m2-corp.com
Custom Computer Programming Services
N.A.I.C.S.: 513210
Joseph W. Adams *(CEO)*

DIGITAL PLUS INC.

Onest Motoyoyogi Square 30-13 Motoyoyogi-cho, Shibuya-ku, Tokyo, 151-0062, Japan
Tel.: (81) 354650690
Web Site: https://digital-plus.co.jp
Year Founded: 2005
3691—(TKS)
Rev.: $2,933,040
Assets: $12,564,640
Liabilities: $4,433,440
Net Worth: $8,131,200
Earnings: $319,440
Emp.: 130
Fiscal Year-end: 09/30/21
Advertising Media Services
N.A.I.C.S.: 541890

DIGITAL UNITED, INC.

220 Gangqien Road Neihu District, Taipei, 114, Taiwan
Tel.: (886) 2 449 5000
Web Site:
   http://www.digitalunited.com
Year Founded: 1998
Sales Range: $50-74.9 Million
Emp.: 540
Dial-up & Broadband Internet Services
N.A.I.C.S.: 517810
Jyh Jong Fu *(Sr VP-Bus Dev)*

DIGITAL VALUE S.P.A.

Via Della Maglianella 65/E, 00166, Rome, Italy
Tel.: (39) 0666411156
Web Site: http://www.digitalvalue.it
Year Founded: 2018

DGV—(ITA)
Rev.: $935,413,401
Assets: $805,546,970
Liabilities: $597,557,126
Net Worth: $207,989,844
Earnings: $42,588,586
Emp.: 400
Fiscal Year-end: 12/31/23
Software Development Services
N.A.I.C.S.: 541511
Massimo Rossi *(Chm, Pres & CEO)*

Subsidiaries:

ITD Solutions S.p.A.   **(1)**
Via Galileo Galilei 7, 20124, Milan, Italy
Tel.: (39) 0262610400
Web Site: https://www.itdsolutions.it
Information Technology Services
N.A.I.C.S.: 541511

Italware S.r.l.   **(1)**
Sede Legale Via della Maglianella 65/E, 00166, Rome, RM, Italy
Tel.: (39) 0666411156
Web Site: https://www.italware.it
Information Technology Services
N.A.I.C.S.: 541511

DIGITAL VIRGO GROUP SAS

88 rue Paul Bert, 69003, Lyon, France
Tel.: (33) 4 3748 2300   FR
Web Site: http://www.digitalvirgo.com
Year Founded: 2016
Sales Range: $250-299.9 Million
Emp.: 700
Holding Company; Digital Content Licensor & Marketer
N.A.I.C.S.: 551112
Eric Peyre *(Co-Founder & Chm)*

Subsidiaries:

Digital Virgo SAS   **(1)**
88 rue Paul Bert, 69446, Lyon, Cedex 03, France
Tel.: (33) 437482300
Web Site: http://www.digitalvirgo.com
Mobile Phone & Internet Multimedia Services
N.A.I.C.S.: 513210
Laurent Radix *(Sec)*

Subsidiary (Non-US):

Digital Virgo Espana   **(2)**
Calle de Juan Ignacio Luca de Tena 1, Madrid, 28027, Spain
Tel.: (34) 902 01 02 01
Web Site: http://www.jetmultimedia.es
Mobile Telecommunications Services
N.A.I.C.S.: 517112

Digital Virgo S.A.   **(2)**
ul Inflancka 4, 00-189, Warsaw, Poland
Tel.: (48) 223121000
Web Site: http://www.digitalvirgo.pl
Mobile Phone Multimedia Services
N.A.I.C.S.: 513210
Artur Witan *(Chm)*

Jet Multimedia Tunisie SA   **(2)**
Rue du lac Turkane Residence Babel App B9, Les berges du lac de Tunis, 1053, Tunis, Tunisia
Tel.: (216) 71964973
Web Site: http://www.jetmultimedia.com.tn
Mobile Telecommunications Services
N.A.I.C.S.: 517112

DIGITAL WORKFORCE SERVICES PLC

Mechelininkatu 1a, 00180, Helsinki, Finland
Web Site:
   https://www.digitalworkforce.com
Year Founded: 2015
DWF—(HEL)
Rev.: $26,894,021
Assets: $25,285,992
Liabilities: $9,367,580
Net Worth: $15,918,411
Earnings: ($755,450)
Emp.: 186

Fiscal Year-end: 12/31/23
Information Technology Services
N.A.I.C.S.: 541512
Heini Kautonen *(CFO)*

Subsidiaries:

Digital Workforce Sp. z o.o.   **(1)**
Al Pilsudskiego 3, 90-368, Lodz, Poland
Tel.: (48) 514519375
Robotic Process Automation Services
N.A.I.C.S.: 518210

DIGITAL360 S.P.A.

Via Copernico 38, 20125, Milan, Italy
Tel.: (39) 0292852779
Web Site: http://www.digital360.it
DIG—(ITA)
Rev.: $27,866,817
Assets: $25,541,215
Liabilities: $16,417,744
Net Worth: $9,123,470
Earnings: ($496,088)
Emp.: 192
Fiscal Year-end: 12/31/19
Media Advertising Services
N.A.I.C.S.: 541840
Andrea Rangone *(Chm)*

DIGITALBOX PLC

Digitalbox 2nd & 3rd Floors Northgate House, Bath, BA1 1RG, United Kingdom
Tel.: (44) 1225430091   UK
Web Site: https://www.digitalbox.com
Year Founded: 2010
DBOX—(LSE)
Rev.: $3,551,878
Assets: $10,243,157
Liabilities: $830,045
Net Worth: $9,413,113
Earnings: ($8,500,318)
Emp.: 32
Fiscal Year-end: 12/31/23
Holding Company
N.A.I.C.S.: 551112
James Carter *(CEO)*

DIGITALIST GROUP OYJ

siltasaarenkatu 18-20 C, PO Box 486, 530, Helsinki, Finland
Tel.: (358) 4242231   FI
Web Site: https://www.digitalist.global
DIGIGR—(HEL)
Rev.: $20,033,456
Assets: $13,180,445
Liabilities: $46,392,186
Net Worth: ($33,211,742)
Earnings: ($6,952,299)
Emp.: 150
Fiscal Year-end: 12/31/22
Software Development, Consulting, Maintenance & Project Management Solutions
N.A.I.C.S.: 541519
Ville Tolvanen *(Co-CEO)*

Subsidiaries:

Chengdu Ixonos Technology Co., Ltd.   **(1)**
6F A7 Building 765 Tianfu Avenue Hightech Zone, Chengdu, 610041, Sichuan, China
Tel.: (86) 2865590999
Sales Range: $25-49.9 Million
Emp.: 70
Computer Software Publishing Services
N.A.I.C.S.: 513210
Lieven Hauspie *(Gen Mgr)*

Digitalist Canada Ltd.   **(1)**
1100-1200 W 73 Ave, Vancouver, V6P 6G5, BC, Canada
Tel.: (604) 248-2644
Web Site: https://www.digitalistgroup.ca
Information Technology Services
N.A.I.C.S.: 541511
Marty Banting *(Dir-Technology)*

Grow AB   **(1)**
A house Ostermalmsgatan 26A, 114 26,

Stockholm, Sweden
Tel.: (46) 709632700
Web Site: https://www.grow.eu
Management Consulting Services
N.A.I.C.S.: 541611
Isabelle Dahlborga Lidstrom *(Dir-Creative & Head)*

Ixonos Denmark ApS   **(1)**
Vesterbrogade 149 5th Floor, 1620, Copenhagen, Denmark
Tel.: (45) 29666850
Telecommunication Software Development Services
N.A.I.C.S.: 541511

Ixonos Finland MTSW Ltd.   **(1)**
Hitsaajankatu 24, 00810, Helsinki, Finland
Tel.: (358) 4242231
Web Site: http://www.ixonos.com
Medical Software Development Services
N.A.I.C.S.: 541511
Sami Paihonen *(Gen Mgr)*

Ixonos Germany GmbH   **(1)**
Rosenstr 2, 10178, Ulm, Germany
Tel.: (49) 15162917899
Web Site: http://www.ixonos.com
Communication Software Development for Various Industries
N.A.I.C.S.: 541511
Timo Salminen *(Head-Automotive)*

Ixonos Technology Consulting Ltd   **(1)**
Hermiankatu 8 C, PO Box 57, 33721, Tampere, Finland
Tel.: (358) 95404010
Management Consulting Services
N.A.I.C.S.: 541618

Ixonos Testhouse Ltd.   **(1)**
Hitsaajankatu 24, 00810, Helsinki, Finland
Tel.: (358) 4242231
Telecommunication Software Development Services
N.A.I.C.S.: 541511

Ixonos USA Ltd.   **(1)**
400 Tradecenter Ste 4950, Woburn, MA 01801
Tel.: (781) 938-0289
Sales Range: $25-49.9 Million
Emp.: 11
Business Software Development Services
N.A.I.C.S.: 541511

DIGITALX LIMITED

Suite 2 Level 4 66 Kings Park Road, West Perth, 6005, WA, Australia
Tel.: (61) 893221587
Web Site: https://www.digitalx.com
DCC—(ASX)
Rev.: $2,173,791
Assets: $39,138,511
Liabilities: $14,413,436
Net Worth: $24,725,075
Earnings: ($3,200,388)
Fiscal Year-end: 06/30/24
Digital Currency Solutions
N.A.I.C.S.: 513210
Leigh Travers *(Exec Dir)*

DIGITECH SA

ZAC Saumaty Seon, BP 173 21, avenue Fernand Sardou, 13322, Marseille, Cedex, France
Tel.: (33) 495069400
Web Site: http://www.digitech.fr
Year Founded: 1992
Software Publishing Services
N.A.I.C.S.: 513210
Joel Couderc *(Founder)*

DIGITECH SYSTEMS CO., LTD.

Seonyu Industry Complex 701-3 Hyangyang-ri Paju-eup, Hwasun, Gyeonggi-do, Korea (South)
Tel.: (82) 319503000   KR
Web Site:
   http://www.digitechsys.co.kr
Year Founded: 2000
Sales Range: $200-249.9 Million
Emp.: 180

Digitech Systems Co., Ltd.—(Continued)

Touch Screen Solution Developer &
Mfr
N.A.I.C.S.: 334118
Tommy Hwan Yong Lee *(CEO)*

DIGITEST ELEKTRONIK SERVICE GMBH

Im Justus 1, Postfach 1471, 76829,
Landau, Rhineland-Palatinate, Germany
Tel.: (49) 63419354321
Web Site: http://www.digitest.de
Year Founded: 1991
Sales Range: $10-24.9 Million
Emp.: 50
Computer Equipment Repair & Maintenance Services
N.A.I.C.S.: 811210
William Ngu *(VP-LCD & LCD TV Repair)*

DIGITOUCH S.P.A.

Viale Vittorio Veneto 22, Entrance on
Via Zarotto 2A, 20124, Milan, Italy
Tel.: (39) 0289295100
Web Site:
　　https://www.gruppodigitouch.it
DGT—(ITA)
Sales Range: $10-24.9 Million
Emp.: 120
Digital Marketing Services
N.A.I.C.S.: 541890
Simone Ranucci Brandimarte *(Chm)*

DIGITREE GROUP S.A.

ul Raciborska 35A, 44-200, Rybnik,
Poland
Tel.: (48) 324210180
Web Site: https://www.digitree.pl
Year Founded: 2005
DTR—(WAR)
Rev.: $22,750,508
Assets: $10,105,691
Liabilities: $4,991,870
Net Worth: $5,113,821
Earnings: ($207,571)
Fiscal Year-end: 12/31/23
Digital Marketing Services
N.A.I.C.S.: 541613
Rafal Zakrzewski *(CEO & Member-Mgmt Bd)*

Subsidiaries:

Fast White Cat S.A.　　　　　　**(1)**
ul Olawska 27/29, 50-123, Wroclaw, Poland
Tel.: (48) 713822648
Web Site: http://www.fastwhitecat.com
Ecommerce Services
N.A.I.C.S.: 513210
Joe Crowley *(Product Dir-Design)*

Salelifter sp. z o.o.　　　　　　**(1)**
ul Raciborska 35a, 44-200, Rybnik, Poland
Tel.: (48) 530407176
Web Site: http://www.salelifter.com
Online Marketing Services
N.A.I.C.S.: 541613

Sales Intelligence sp. z o.o.　　**(1)**
ul Jodlowa 1/3, 81-526, Gdynia, Poland
Tel.: (48) 585858900
Web Site: http://www.salesintelligence.pl
Ecommerce Services
N.A.I.C.S.: 541618

DIGITRONIC GMBH

Carl-Spitzweg-Strasse 33, D-50127,
Bergheim, Germany
Tel.: (49) 22717910
Web Site: http://www.digitronic-gmbh.de
Year Founded: 1977
Rev.: $12,438,419
Emp.: 106
Electronic Components Mfr
N.A.I.C.S.: 334419
Rolf Kratz *(CTO)*

DIGIWEB LTD.

IDA Business & Technology Park,
County Louth, Dundalk, A91 KR80,
Dublin, Ireland
Tel.: (353) 1 256 9200　　　　　IE
Web Site: http://www.digiweb.ie
Year Founded: 1997
Sales Range: $50-74.9 Million
Emp.: 150
Telecommunication Servicesb
N.A.I.C.S.: 517810
Colm Piercy *(Founder & Chm)*

Subsidiaries:

Viatel Holding (Europe) Limited　**(1)**
Inbucon House, Wick Road, Egham, TW20
0HR, Surrey, United Kingdom
Tel.: (44) 1784494200
Web Site: http://www.viatel.com
Sales Range: $25-49.9 Million
Emp.: 142
Holding Company; Telecommunications
Services
N.A.I.C.S.: 551112
Tony Frewer *(Sr VP-Svc, Ops & Engrg)*

Subsidiary (Domestic):

Viatel Infrastructure (UK) Limited　**(2)**
Inbucon House, Wick Road, Egham, TW20
0HR, Surrey, United Kingdom
Tel.: (44) 1784 494 360
Web Site: http://www.vtlwavenet.com
Internet Service Provider
N.A.I.C.S.: 517111

Subsidiary (Non-US):

Viatel Infrastructure France SA　　**(2)**
35 Rue des Jeuneurs, 75002, Paris, France
Tel.: (33) 1 55 34 11 60
Sales Range: $25-49.9 Million
Emp.: 10
Telecommunication Servicesb
N.A.I.C.S.: 517810

Viatel Infrastructure Nederland
B.V.　　　　　　　　　　　　**(2)**
Hoornseweg 8, 1687 ND, Wognum, Netherlands
Tel.: (31) 6 51619176
Emp.: 50
Telecommunication Servicesb
N.A.I.C.S.: 517810
Colm Piercy *(CEO)*

Viatel Infrastructure Switzerland
AG　　　　　　　　　　　　　**(2)**
Badenerstrasse 569, 8048, Zurich, Switzerland
Tel.: (41) 56401 34 18
Telecommunication Servicesb
N.A.I.C.S.: 517810
Colm Piercy *(CEO)*

DIGIWIN SOFTWARE CO., LTD.

22F Building 1 Greenland Central
Plaza Lane 1377 Jiangchang Road,
Jingan District, Shanghai, 200072,
China
Tel.: (86) 2151791699
Web Site: http://www.digiwin.com.cn
Year Founded: 2001
300378—(CHIN)
Rev.: $280,126,080
Assets: $398,995,740
Liabilities: $128,006,892
Net Worth: $270,988,848
Earnings: $18,756,036
Emp.: 3,772
Fiscal Year-end: 12/31/22
Software Publisher
N.A.I.C.S.: 513210
Ye Zizhen *(Chm & Gen Mgr)*

Subsidiaries:

Digiwin Software (Vietnam) Co.,
Ltd.　　　　　　　　　　　　**(1)**
Floor 12A Golden King Building 15 Nguyen
Luong Bang, Tan Phu Ward District 7, Ho
Chi Minh City, Vietnam
Tel.: (84) 2873070788
Web Site: https://www.digiwin.com.vn

Enterprise Application Development Services
N.A.I.C.S.: 541511

DIGNITANA AB

Traktorgranden 3, 226 60, Lund,
Sweden
Tel.: (46) 46163090
Web Site: https://www.dignitana.com
Year Founded: 2001
DIGN—(OMX)
Rev.: $8,060,543
Assets: $4,198,863
Liabilities: $3,518,878
Net Worth: $679,985
Earnings: ($1,625,971)
Emp.: 28
Fiscal Year-end: 12/31/23
Electronic Products Mfr
N.A.I.C.S.: 334419

Subsidiaries:

Dignitana Inc.　　　　　　　　**(1)**
10925 Estate Ln W-185, Dallas, TX 75238
Tel.: (469) 917-5555
Medical Equipment Mfr
N.A.I.C.S.: 339112

DIGNITY PLC

4 King Edwards Court King Edward
Square, Sutton Coldfield, B73 6AP,
West Midlands, United Kingdom
Tel.: (44) 1213541557
Web Site:
　　http://www.dignityfunerals.co.uk
DTY—(LSE)
Rev.: $407,851,553
Assets: $2,009,972,229
Liabilities: $2,542,918,455
Net Worth: ($532,946,226)
Earnings: ($347,387,023)
Emp.: 3,500
Fiscal Year-end: 12/31/22
Funeral Services, Cremations & Prearranged Funeral Plans
N.A.I.C.S.: 812210
Mike McCollum *(CEO)*

Subsidiaries:

Advance Planning Limited　　　**(1)**
4 King Edwards Ct King Edwards Sq, Sutton Coldfield, B73 6AP, West Midlands,
United Kingdom
Tel.: (44) 1213215592
Emp.: 350
General Insurance Services
N.A.I.C.S.: 524128
Steve Wallis *(Dir-Comml)*

Dignity Caring Funeral Services　**(1)**
4 King Edwards Court, King Edwards
Square, Sutton Coldfield, B73 6AP, W Midlands, United Kingdom
Tel.: (44) 121 354 1557
Web Site:
　　http://www.dignityfuneralplans.co.uk
Emp.: 200
Funeral Services
N.A.I.C.S.: 812210
Steve Wallis *(Gen Mgr)*

Dignity Crematoria Limited　　　**(1)**
Westhampnett Rd, Chichester, PO19 7UH,
West Sussex, United Kingdom
Tel.: (44) 1243 536 267
Crematories
N.A.I.C.S.: 812220

Dignity Funerals Limited　　　　**(1)**
Harrowby Rd, Grantham, NG31 9DT, Lincolnshire, United Kingdom
Tel.: (44) 1476590905
Web Site: http://www.dignityfunerals.co.uk
Sales Range: $25-49.9 Million
Emp.: 10
Funeral Services
N.A.I.C.S.: 812210

Dignity Services Ltd.　　　　　**(1)**
Leisure Commerce Square Block A2 Unit
126 Level 1 Jalan PJS 8/9, Bandar Sunway, 46150, Petaling Jaya, Selangor, Malaysia

Tel.: (60) 37 865 3151
Web Site:
　　https://www.dignityandservices.org
Educational Support Services
N.A.I.C.S.: 611710

Pitcher and Le Quesne Limited　**(1)**
59 Kensington Pl, Saint Helier, JE2 4UQ,
Jersey
Tel.: (44) 1534733330
Web Site: http://www.dignityuk.co.uk
Sales Range: $25-49.9 Million
Emp.: 10
Funeral Services
N.A.I.C.S.: 812210

DIGUANG INTERNATIONAL DEVELOPMENT COMPANY LTD.

23 rd Floor Building A Galaxy Century
Building, Futian District, Shenzhen,
518026, China
Tel.: (86) 75526553152　　　　NV
DGNG—(OTCIQ)
Sales Range: Less than $1 Million
Electronic Components Mfr
N.A.I.C.S.: 334419
Song Yi *(Chm, Pres & CEO)*

DIHAG HOLDING GMBH

Altendorfer Strasse 44, Essen,
D-45127, Germany
Tel.: (49) 201872450
Web Site: http://www.dihag.com
Rev.: $240,996,243
Emp.: 2,000
Producer of Cast Components for
Energy Generating Systems, Engineering, Mining & Ship Building
N.A.I.C.S.: 336330
Viktor Babushchak *(CEO)*

Subsidiaries:

Eisenwerk Arnstadt GMBH　　　**(1)**
Bierweg 4, 99310, Arnstadt, Germany
Tel.: (49) 3628596101
Web Site: http://www.ewa-guss.de
Iron Casting Mfr
N.A.I.C.S.: 333517
Hartwig Haurand *(Mng Dir)*

Euro Metall Kft.　　　　　　　**(1)**
Elem utca 5-7, 1045, Budapest, Hungary
Tel.: (36) 13700078
Web Site: http://www.eurometall.hu
Iron Casting Mfr
N.A.I.C.S.: 333517
Laszlo Retter *(Mng Dir)*

Lintorfer Eisengiesserei GmbH　**(1)**
Rehhecke 83 87, 40885, Ratingen, Germany
Tel.: (49) 210238060
Web Site: http://www.lintorfereg.de
Machine Tools Mfr
N.A.I.C.S.: 333517
Olaf Lock *(Mng Dir)*

Mecklenburger Metallguss
GmbH　　　　　　　　　　　**(1)**
Teterower Strasse 1, 17192, Waren, Germany
Tel.: (49) 39917360
Web Site: http://www.mmg-propeller.de
Propeller Mfr
N.A.I.C.S.: 332999
Manfred Urban *(CEO)*

Meuselwitz Guss Eisengiesserei
GmbH　　　　　　　　　　　**(1)**
Industriepark Nord, 04610, Meuselwitz, Germany
Tel.: (49) 3448820
Web Site: http://www.meuselwitz-guss.de
Die Casting Machine Mfr
N.A.I.C.S.: 333517

Odlewnia Zeliwa Bydgoszcz Sp. z
o.o.　　　　　　　　　　　　**(1)**
Ul Zygmunta Augusta 11, 85-082, Bydgoszcz, Poland
Tel.: (48) 523259011
Web Site: http://www.odlewnia.com.pl
Iron Brake Shoe Mfr
N.A.I.C.S.: 331511

Robert Zuchlinski *(Dir-Technical)*

SHB Stahl- und Hartgusswerk Boesdorf GmbH (1)
Werkstrasse 7, 04249, Leipzig, Germany
Tel.: (49) 34142790
Web Site: http://www.shb-guss.de
Die Casting Mfr
N.A.I.C.S.: 333517
Angela Kluge *(Sec)*

Schmiedeberger Giesserei GmbH (1)
Altenberger Strasse 59a, 01744, Dippoldiswalde, Germany
Tel.: (49) 350522130
Web Site: http://www.schmie-guss.de
Machine Tools Mfr
N.A.I.C.S.: 333517

Spezialguss Wetzlar GmbH (1)
Sophienstrasse 52-54, 35576, Wetzlar, Germany
Tel.: (49) 6441492307
Web Site: http://www.spezialguss.com
Die Casting Mfr
N.A.I.C.S.: 333517

Walzengiesserei Coswig GmbH (1)
Grenzstrasse 1, 01640, Coswig, Germany
Tel.: (49) 3523950
Web Site: http://www.walze-coswig.de
Die Casting Machine Mfr
N.A.I.C.S.: 333517
Wilfried Pfaffe *(CEO)*

DIJAMANT A.D
Temisvarski drum 14, 23101, Zrenjanin, Serbia
Tel.: (381) 23551001
Web Site: http://www.dijamant.rs
Year Founded: 1938
DJMN—(BEL)
Sales Range: Less than $1 Million
Vegetable Oil Mfr
N.A.I.C.S.: 311225

DIJET INDUSTRIAL CO., LTD
2-1-18 Kami-Higashi, Hirano-ku, Osaka, 547-0002, Japan
Tel.: (81) 667916781
Web Site: https://www.dijet-tool.com
Year Founded: 1938
6138—(TKS)
Rev.: $55,153,840
Assets: $108,846,870
Liabilities: $57,262,430
Net Worth: $51,584,440
Earnings: ($859,300)
Fiscal Year-end: 03/31/24
Carbide Tool Mfr
N.A.I.C.S.: 333517
Ayumu Ikezumi *(Pres)*

Subsidiaries:

DIJET GmbH (1)
Immermannstrasse 9, 40210, Dusseldorf, Germany
Tel.: (49) 2115 008 8820
Web Site: https://dijet.de
Carbide Tool Mfr
N.A.I.C.S.: 333515
Satoru Kimura *(Mng Dir)*

DIJET Industrial Co., Ltd - Mie Plant (1)
758-14 Iseji, Iga, 518-0205, Mie, Japan
Tel.: (81) 595522800
Cutting Tool Mfr
N.A.I.C.S.: 333515

DIJET Industrial Co., Ltd - Tondabayashi Plant (1)
2-1-23 Nakano-cho-Higashi, Tondabayashi, 584-0022, Osaka, Japan
Tel.: (81) 721232700
Cutting Tool Mfr
N.A.I.C.S.: 333515

Dijet Incorporated (1)
45807 Helm St, Plymouth, MI 48170
Tel.: (734) 454-9100
Web Site: https://www.dijetusa.com
Cutting Tool Distr
N.A.I.C.S.: 423830

DIKSATTRANSWORLD LIMITED
New No 24 & Old No 32 1st Floor South Mada Street Mylapore, Chennai, 600 004, India
Tel.: (91) 4424640347
Web Site:
 https://www.diksattransworldltd.com
540151—(BOM)
Rev.: $4,526,736
Assets: $5,111,270
Liabilities: $2,262,105
Net Worth: $2,849,165
Earnings: $108,040
Emp.: 16
Fiscal Year-end: 03/31/22
Television Broadcasting Services
N.A.I.C.S.: 516120
T. Dhevanathan Yadav *(Chm & Mng Dir)*

DIKSHA GREENS LTD.
11 Sambhu Chatterjee Street Suit No 7 2nd Floor, Kolkata, 700007, India
Tel.: (91) 3322198219
Web Site:
 https://www.dikshagreens.co.in
Year Founded: 2004
542155—(BOM)
Rev.: $110,503
Assets: $3,898,556
Liabilities: $4,376,535
Net Worth: ($477,979)
Earnings: ($3,096,773)
Emp.: 7
Fiscal Year-end: 03/31/21
Wood Product Distr
N.A.I.C.S.: 423310
Rajesh Pirogiwal *(Mng Dir)*

DILAWRI GROUP OF COMPANIES
87 Front St E,, Toronto, M5E 1B8, ON, Canada
Tel.: (306) 525-2333
Web Site: https://www.dilawri.ca
Year Founded: 1985
Car Dealer
N.A.I.C.S.: 441110

Subsidiaries:

MCL Motor Cars (1992) Inc. (1)
1730 Burrard St, Vancouver, V6J 3G7, BC, Canada
Tel.: (604) 738-5577
Web Site: https://www.jlrvancouver.ca
New & Used Car Dealers
N.A.I.C.S.: 441110
James Graff *(Gen Mgr)*

DILIGENT INDUSTRIES LIMITED
Dwaraka Thirumala Road Denduluru Village and Mandal, West Godavari, Hyderabad, 534432, Andhra Pradesh, India
Tel.: (91) 8829256077
Web Site:
 https://www.diligentindustries.com
Year Founded: 1995
531153—(BOM)
Rev.: $9,825,417
Assets: $6,020,752
Liabilities: $4,331,242
Net Worth: $1,689,511
Earnings: $65,582
Emp.: 13
Fiscal Year-end: 03/31/21
Edible Oil Mfr
N.A.I.C.S.: 311225
Bhanu Prakash Vankineni *(Mng Dir)*

DILIGENT MEDIA CORPORATION LIMITED
A Wing Marathon Futurex 14th Floor

N M Joshi Marg Lower Parel, Mumbai, 400013, Maharashtra, India
Tel.: (91) 2271055001
Web Site: http://www.dnaindia.com
Year Founded: 2005
540789—(BOM)
Rev.: $443,297
Assets: $27,979,320
Liabilities: $107,000,180
Net Worth: ($79,020,860)
Earnings: ($6,226,721)
Emp.: 2
Fiscal Year-end: 03/12/21
Newspaper Publisher Services
N.A.I.C.S.: 513110
Rajendra Bathula *(CFO)*

DILIP BUILDCON LIMITED
Plot No 5 Inside Govind Narayan Singh Gate Chuna Bhatti Kolar Road, Bhopal, 462 016, Madhya Pradesh, India
Tel.: (91) 7554029999
Web Site:
 https://www.dilipbuildcon.com
Year Founded: 1988
540047—(BOM)
Rev.: $1,393,732,649
Assets: $2,507,199,786
Liabilities: $1,992,249,427
Net Worth: $514,950,359
Earnings: $59,588,543
Emp.: 34,262
Fiscal Year-end: 03/31/21
Construction Engineering Services
N.A.I.C.S.: 541330
Dilip Suryavanshi *(Chm & Mng Dir)*

DILLI INCORPORATED
30 Gangbyeon-ro 702beon-gil, Dongducheon, 11303, Gyeonggi-do, Korea (South)
Tel.: (82) 318605500
Web Site: https://www.dilli.co.kr
Year Founded: 1975
131180—(KRS)
Rev.: $28,515,942
Assets: $53,789,496
Liabilities: $9,009,827
Net Worth: $44,779,669
Earnings: $2,008,628
Emp.: 78
Fiscal Year-end: 12/31/22
Printers, Printing Ink & Drawing Instruments Mfr
N.A.I.C.S.: 333248
Keun Soo Choi *(Pres)*

DILLISTONE GROUP PLC
Unit 9 Crockford Lane Chineham Business Park, Basingstoke, RG24 8WD, Hampshire, United Kingdom
Tel.: (44) 2077496100
Web Site:
 https://www.ikirupeople.com
DSG—(LSE)
Rev.: $7,122,852
Assets: $8,696,372
Liabilities: $4,600,891
Net Worth: $4,095,481
Earnings: $3,819
Emp.: 70
Fiscal Year-end: 12/31/23
Software Publisher
N.A.I.C.S.: 513210
Jason S. Starr *(CEO)*

Subsidiaries:

Dillistone Solutions Limited (1)
50-52 Paul St 3rd Fl, London, EC2A 4LB, United Kingdom
Tel.: (44) 2077496100
Computer Software Support Services
N.A.I.C.S.: 541511

Dillistone Systems (Australia) Pty Ltd (1)
Level 12 56 Berry Street, North Sydney,

2060, New South Wales, Australia
Tel.: (61) 294550400
Computer Software Support Services
N.A.I.C.S.: 541511

Dillistone Systems (US) Inc. (1)
50 Harrison St Ste 201, Hoboken, NJ 07030
Tel.: (201) 653-0013
Web Site: http://www.dillistonegroup.com
Sales Range: $25-49.9 Million
Emp.: 6
Computer Software Support Services
N.A.I.C.S.: 541511

DILMAH CEYLON TEA SERVICES PLC
111 Negombo Road, Peliyagoda, Colombo, Sri Lanka
Tel.: (94) 114822000
Web Site: https://www.dilmahtea.com
Year Founded: 1988
CTEA.N0000—(COL)
Rev.: $74,275,187
Assets: $93,275,920
Liabilities: $17,765,481
Net Worth: $75,510,439
Earnings: $16,758,277
Emp.: 643
Fiscal Year-end: 03/31/23
Coffee & Tea Mfr
N.A.I.C.S.: 311920
Merrill J. Fernando *(Founder & Chm)*

DIMA LTDA.
Av Sanchez Lima 2626, La Paz, 11373, Bolivia
Tel.: (591) 2 2435253
Web Site: http://www.dima.com.bo
Year Founded: 1981
Sales Range: $10-24.9 Million
Emp.: 60
Information Technology Services
Computer & Computer Peripheral Equipment Whslr
N.A.I.C.S.: 423410
Ricardo Zamora *(Reg Mgr)*

DIMARK LTD
Unit D1 Stonehill Business Park, Harbet Road, London, N18 3Qp, United Kingdom
Tel.: (44) 8700 61 66 61
Web Site:
 http://www.gardenfoods.co.uk
Sales Range: $1-9.9 Million
Emp.: 20
Polish & Eastern European Food & Drink Distr
N.A.I.C.S.: 424490
Ali Caktu *(Mng Dir)*

DIMCO PLC
47 Kennedy Av, 1076, Nicosia, Cyprus
Tel.: (357) 22 446565 CY
Web Site: http://www.dimco.eu
Year Founded: 1966
Emp.: 110
Lighting Product Mfr
N.A.I.C.S.: 335132
Michalakis Demetriou *(Chm)*

DIMED S.A. DISTRIBUIDORA DE MEDICAMENTOS
Av Industrial Belgraff 865 Predio 100, 92990000, Porto Alegre, 92990000, RS, Brazil
Tel.: (55) 5132189500
Web Site: https://www.dimed.com.br
Year Founded: 1968
PNVL3—(BRAZ)
Rev.: $797,450,328
Assets: $550,127,799
Liabilities: $340,368,236
Net Worth: $209,759,563
Earnings: $16,607,676
Emp.: 4,494

Dimed S.A. Distribuidora de
Medicamentos—(Continued)

Fiscal Year-end: 12/31/23
Drugs Whslr
N.A.I.C.S.: 424210
Roberto Coimbra Santos *(Dir-IR)*

DIMENSIONS JORDAN & EMIRATES COMMERCIAL INVESTMENTS CORPORATION

AbuAlanda, PO Box 566, Amman,
11592, Jordan
Tel.: (962) 64738476　　　　JO
Web Site: http://www.dimensions-
　inv.com
Year Founded: 2007
JEDI—(AMM)
Rev.: $12,415
Assets: $6,924,238
Liabilities: $226,488
Net Worth: $6,697,749
Earnings: ($830,653)
Emp.: 7
Fiscal Year-end: 12/31/20
Investment Management Service
N.A.I.C.S.: 523999

DIMENSIONS TRAINING SOLUTIONS LTD.

Dearing House, 1 Young S, Sheffield,
S1 4UP, United Kingdom
Tel.: (44) 7919 200723
Web Site:
　http://www.dimensionstraining.co.uk
Training & Apprenticeship Services
N.A.I.C.S.: 611519
Wayne Janse Van Rensburg *(CEO)*

Subsidiaries:

learndirect Limited　　　　　(1)
1st Floor Wilson House, Lorne Park Road,
Bournemouth, BH1 1JN, United Kingdom
Tel.: (44) 01202 006 464
Web Site: http://www.learndirect.com
Online Learning Products & Services
N.A.I.C.S.: 611699
Wayne Janse van Rensburg *(CEO)*

DIMERCO DATA SYSTEM CORP.

8th FL No 151 Xing ai Rd, Neihu
Dist, Taipei, Taiwan
Tel.: (886) 281705168
Web Site: https://www.ddsc.com.tw
Year Founded: 1981
5403—(TPE)
Rev.: $77,631,179
Assets: $163,566,019
Liabilities: $89,740,112
Net Worth: $73,825,908
Earnings: $16,590,220
Emp.: 382
Fiscal Year-end: 12/31/22
Software Development Services
N.A.I.C.S.: 541511
Chuang Si-Wei *(Chm)*

DIMERCO EXPRESS CORPORATION

11/12 F No 160 Min-Chuan E Rd Sec
6, Taipei, 11490, Taiwan
Tel.: (886) 227963660
Web Site: https://www.dimerco.com
Year Founded: 1971
5609—(TPE)
Rev.: $720,843,820
Assets: $290,448,565
Liabilities: $96,217,924
Net Worth: $194,230,641
Earnings: $33,243,990
Emp.: 1,900
Fiscal Year-end: 12/31/23
Freight Transportation Services
N.A.I.C.S.: 488510
Paul Chien *(Founder & Chm)*

Subsidiaries:

Dimerco Express (Taiwan)
Corporation　　　　　　　　(1)
1F No 719 Gongyuan Rd, North Dist,
T'ainan, 704, Taiwan　　　　(100%)
Tel.: (886) 62812381
Web Site: http://www.dimerco.com
Arrangement of Freight Transportation
N.A.I.C.S.: 488510

Dimerco Express (Taiwan)
Corporation　　　　　　　　(1)
Rm 506 5F No 306 Sec 1 Wen Hsing Rd,
Taichung, 408, Taiwan　　　　(100%)
Tel.: (000) 420190721
Web Site: http://www.dimerco.com
Sales Range: $450-499.9 Million
Emp.: 1,947
Arrangement of Freight Transportation
N.A.I.C.S.: 488510

Dimerco Express (Taiwan)
Corporation　　　　　　　　(1)
6F-3 NO 110 Sec 4 Sanduo Road, Lingya
Dist, Kaohsiung, 802, Taiwan　(100%)
Tel.: (886) 73350078
Web Site: http://www.dimerco.com
Sales Range: $25-49.9 Million
Emp.: 15
Arrangement of Freight Transportation
N.A.I.C.S.: 488510

Dimerco Express (Taiwan)
Corporation　　　　　　　　(1)
7F-1 No 38 Tai-Yuen St, Chupei, Hsin-chu,
302, Taiwan　　　　　　　(100%)
Tel.: (886) 35600608
Web Site: http://www.dimerco.com
Sales Range: $25-49.9 Million
Emp.: 10
Arrangement of Freight Transportation
N.A.I.C.S.: 488510

Dimerco Express USA Corp.　(1)
133-33 Brookville Blvd Ste 208 1 Cross Is-
land Plz, Rosedale, NY 11422　(100%)
Tel.: (516) 708-4500
Web Site: http://www.dimerco.com
Sales Range: $25-49.9 Million
Emp.: 7
Freight Transportation Arrangement
N.A.I.C.S.: 488510
Herbert Liou *(Pres)*

Diversified Freight System
Corporation　　　　　　　　(1)
11F-1 No 160 Sec 6 Minquan E Rd, Neihu
Dist, Taipei, 11490, Taiwan　(100%)
Tel.: (886) 227916455
Web Site: http://www.dimerco.com
Sales Range: $25-49.9 Million
Emp.: 24
Arrangement of Freight Transportation
N.A.I.C.S.: 488510

Diversified Freight System Philippines
Corporation　　　　　　　　(1)
3rd Floor DPC Place 2322 Chino Roces
Avenue, Makati, 1232, Philippines
Tel.: (63) 288452346
Logistic Services
N.A.I.C.S.: 541614

Diversified International Logistics Pte.
Ltd.　　　　　　　　　　　(1)
80 Marine Parade Road 10-02 Parkway Pa-
rade, Singapore, 449269, Singapore
Tel.: (65) 65422233
Logistic Services
N.A.I.C.S.: 541614

DIMERIX LIMITED

425 Smith Street, Fitzroy, 3065, VIC,
Australia
Tel.: (61) 1300813321　　　　AU
Web Site: https://www.dimerix.com
DXB—(ASX)
Rev.: $5,721,275
Assets: $21,419,971
Liabilities: $9,276,869
Net Worth: $12,143,102
Earnings: ($11,401,631)
Emp.: 12
Fiscal Year-end: 06/30/24
Biotechnology Research & Develop-
ment Services

N.A.I.C.S.: 541714
Nina Webster *(CEO & Mng Dir)*

DIMET (SIAM) PUBLIC COMPANY LIMITED

602 Moo 2 Bangpoo Industrial Estate
Soi 1 Muang, Soi 1Muang, Samut
Prakan, 10280, Samutprakran, Thai-
land
Tel.: (66) 23232800
Web Site: http://www.dimetsiam.com
Year Founded: 1982
DIMET—(THA)
Rev.: $2,978,105
Assets: $12,487,449
Liabilities: $1,944,769
Net Worth: $10,542,680
Earnings: ($2,648,296)
Fiscal Year-end: 12/31/23
Coating Product Mfr
N.A.I.C.S.: 325510
Teng-Shih Huang *(Chm)*

DIMKO MITREV JSC

St Dimko Najdov No 94, 1400, Veles,
North Macedonia
Tel.: (389) 43232144
Web Site:
　　https://www.dimkomitrev.com.mk
DIMI—(MAC)
Rev.: $5,058,870
Assets: $6,725,584
Liabilities: $4,236,302
Net Worth: $2,489,282
Earnings: $3,298
Fiscal Year-end: 12/31/23
Fur Product Mfr
N.A.I.C.S.: 315250

DIMMI LIFE HOLDINGS LIMITED

Unit 1 17th Floor Office Tower 1 The
Harbourfront 18 Tak Fung Street,
Kowloon, China (Hong Kong)
Tel.: (852) 39110500　　　　Ky
Web Site: http://www.milestone.hk
Year Founded: 2001
1667—(HKG)
Rev.: $15,544,799
Assets: $40,438,841
Liabilities: $36,374,553
Net Worth: $4,064,289
Earnings: ($7,802,645)
Emp.: 57
Fiscal Year-end: 03/31/22
Construction Management Services
N.A.I.C.S.: 236220
Lingling Hou *(Exec Dir)*

Subsidiaries:

Speedy Engineering & Trading Com-
pany Limited　　　　　　　(1)
Unit B 15/F 9 Po Lun Street, Lai Chi Kok,
Kowloon, China (Hong Kong)
Tel.: (852) 35687721
Web Site: https://www.speedyltd.com
Construction Engineering Services
N.A.I.C.S.: 541330

DIMNICAR A.D.

Deligradska 26, Belgrade, Serbia
Tel.: (381) 112646355
Web Site: https://www.dimnicar.com
Year Founded: 1948
DMNR—(BEL)
Rev.: $3,751,503
Assets: $2,523,261
Liabilities: $1,484,179
Net Worth: $1,039,082
Earnings: $21,326
Emp.: 48
Fiscal Year-end: 12/31/23
Building Cleaning Services
N.A.I.C.S.: 561790
Slobodan Mihajilovic *(Exec Dir)*

DIMOS

648 rue du Tertre, BP 80029, 44151,
Ancenis, Cedex, France
Tel.: (33) 240832501
Web Site: http://www.dimos.fr
Rev.: $20,400,000
Emp.: 62
Professional Equipment
N.A.I.C.S.: 423490
Michel Goubaud *(Chm)*

DIN TEXTILE MILLS LTD.

35-A/1 Lalazar Area Opp Beach
Luxury Hotel, PO Box 4696, Karachi,
74000, Pakistan
Tel.: (92) 2135610001
Web Site: https://dingroup.com
Year Founded: 1987
DINT—(KAR)
Rev.: $83,004,260
Assets: $75,655,485
Liabilities: $60,124,744
Net Worth: $15,530,741
Earnings: $2,602,378
Emp.: 2,632
Fiscal Year-end: 06/30/19
Knitting & Weaving Yarn Mfr
N.A.I.C.S.: 313110
Mohammad Tanveer *(CEO)*

Subsidiaries:

Din Leather(Pvt) Ltd.　　　　(1)
Din House 35-A/1 Lalazar Area Opp Beach
Luxury Hotel, PO Box No 4696, Karachi,
74000, Pakistan
Tel.: (92) 21 561 0001
Web Site: http://www.dingroup.com
Sales Range: $50-74.9 Million
Emp.: 600
Leather Mfr
N.A.I.C.S.: 315250

DINA IRON & STEEL LIMITED

Abdul Rehmanpur Road Didargunj,
Patna, 800009, Bihar, India
Tel.: (91) 9334463311
Web Site: http://www.dinairon.com
Year Founded: 1993
Sales Range: $25-49.9 Million
Iron & Steel Product Mfr
N.A.I.C.S.: 331110
Sanjay Kumar Bhartiya *(Mng Dir)*

DINAMIK ISI MAKINA YALITIM MALZEMELERI SANAYI VE TICARET A.S.

Ibni Melek Mah 3 Yol No 20, Tire Or-
ganize Sanayi Bolgesi Tire, 35900,
Izmir, Turkiye
Tel.: (90) 2324491250
Web Site: https://www.dinamik-
　izmir.com
Year Founded: 1991
DNISI—(IST)
Investment Brokerage Services
N.A.I.C.S.: 524210
Metin Akdas *(Chm)*

DINARA A.D.

Save Maskovica 3, 11040, Belgrade,
Serbia
Tel.: (381) 112462241
Web Site: https://www.dinara.rs
Year Founded: 1952
DINR—(BEL)
Rev.: $533,769
Assets: $575,853
Liabilities: $150,929
Net Worth: $424,925
Earnings: $22,671
Emp.: 6
Fiscal Year-end: 12/31/22
Motor Vehicle Parts & Accessories
Retailer
N.A.I.C.S.: 441330
Biljana Sunkic *(Exec Dir)*

DINARA GRADNJA A.D.

Crnotravska br 11, 11000, Belgrade, Serbia
Tel.: (381) 113971039
Web Site:
　https://www.dinaragradnja.rs
Year Founded: 2005
DNGR—(BEL)
Rev.: $85,551
Assets: $398,080
Liabilities: $10,086
Net Worth: $387,993
Earnings: ($28,099)
Emp.: 3
Fiscal Year-end: 12/31/22
Motor Vehicle Parts Whslr
N.A.I.C.S.: 423120
Savo Corovic *(Dir)*

DINARA SERVIS AD
Save Maskovica 3-5, 11000, Belgrade, Serbia
Tel.: (381) 11 2491 891
Web Site:
　http://www.dinaraservisad.rs
Year Founded: 2005
DNSR—(BEL)
Sales Range: Less than $1 Million
Motor Vehicle Repair & Maintenance Services
N.A.I.C.S.: 811114
Radovan Milosevic *(Dir)*

DINE S.A.B. DE C.V.
Paseo de los Tamarindos 400-B piso 28, Bosques de las Lomas, 05120, Mexico, Mexico
Tel.: (52) 5552618282
Web Site: https://www.dine.com.mx
Year Founded: 1978
DINE—(MEX)
Rev.: $81,846,578
Assets: $519,457,031
Liabilities: $350,504,802
Net Worth: $168,952,230
Earnings: ($6,353,406)
Emp.: 252
Fiscal Year-end: 12/31/23
Construction & Property Development Services
N.A.I.C.S.: 236117
Eduardo Philibert Garza *(Dir-Fin)*

DINEEN CONSTRUCTION CORPORATION
70 Disco Road Suite 300, Toronto, M9W 1L9, ON, Canada
Tel.: (416) 675-7676
Web Site: http://www.dineen.com
Year Founded: 1927
Rev.: $18,258,440
Emp.: 75
General Building Construction Services
N.A.I.C.S.: 236220
William E. Love *(Pres & COO)*

DINEOUT SA LTD.
145-157 St. John St, London, EC1V 4PY, United Kingdom
Tel.: (44) 2032952050
Sales Range: $10-24.9 Million
Emp.: 3
Franchise Restaurant Owner & Operator
N.A.I.C.S.: 722511
Michael D. Pruitt *(Pres & CEO)*

DING HE MINING HOLDINGS LIMITED
Flat B 21/F Neich Tower 128 Gloucester Road, Wanchai, China (Hong Kong)
Tel.: (852) 2598 1668　　　　HK
Web Site:
　http://www.dinghemining.com.hk
Rev.: $26,064,895

Assets: $19,216,774
Liabilities: $26,404,768
Net Worth: ($7,187,994)
Earnings: $6,502,509
Emp.: 80
Fiscal Year-end: 12/31/16
Magnesium Mining & Exploration Services
N.A.I.C.S.: 212290
Wai Kwan Leung *(CEO)*

DINGDANG HEALTH TECHNOLOGY GROUP LIMITED
Building 1 Yard 50 Dengshikou Street, Dongcheng District, Beijing, China　　　　　　　　　　　　Ky
Web Site: https://www.ddjkjt.com
Year Founded: 2014
9886—(HKG)
Rev.: $663,257,581
Assets: $505,206,145
Liabilities: $168,267,326
Net Worth: $336,938,819
Earnings: ($435,464,953)
Emp.: 2,565
Fiscal Year-end: 12/31/22
Health Care Srvices
N.A.I.C.S.: 621610
Ning Xu *(VP)*

DINGDONG (CAYMAN) LTD.
No 6 Building 500 Lane Shengxia Road, Shanghai, 201210, China
Tel.: (86) 2168585011　　　Ky
Year Founded: 2018
DDL—(NYSE)
Rev.: $2,765,177,642
Assets: $1,065,927,669
Liabilities: $1,012,962,727
Net Worth: $52,964,942
Earnings: ($12,638,320)
Emp.: 3,015
Fiscal Year-end: 12/31/23
Online Shopping Services
N.A.I.C.S.: 423690
Changlin Liang *(Founder & CEO)*

DINGLI CORPORATION LTD.
Unit B6 7/F Shui Ki Ind Bldg 18 Wong Chuk Hang Road, Hong Kong, China (Hong Kong)
Tel.: (852) 30129893
Web Site: http://www.dingli.com
300050—(CHIN)
Rev.: $65,705,796
Assets: $148,648,500
Liabilities: $52,313,040
Net Worth: $96,335,460
Earnings: ($52,859,196)
Emp.: 2,100
Fiscal Year-end: 12/31/22
Wireless Communication Network Optimization Testing Systems & Software Mfr
N.A.I.C.S.: 334290
Yun Wang *(Chm & Gen Mgr)*

DINGLONG CULTURE CO., LTD.
Yuting Road Chenghua Industrial Area, Chenghai District, Shantou, 510000, Guangdong, China
Tel.: (86) 2032615774
Web Site: http://www.huawei-stock.com
Year Founded: 1997
002502—(SSE)
Rev.: $50,261,796
Assets: $327,515,292
Liabilities: $83,028,348
Net Worth: $244,486,944
Earnings: ($33,905,196)
Fiscal Year-end: 12/31/22
TV & Animation Production; Mobile Online Games Developer
N.A.I.C.S.: 516120

Xueqin Long *(Chm & Pres)*

DINGWALL FORD SALES
Highway 17 East, Kenora, P9N3X3, ON, Canada
Tel.: (807) 468-6443
Rev.: $29,039,613
Emp.: 60
New & Used Car Dealers
N.A.I.C.S.: 441110
Bill Dingwall *(Pres)*

DINGYI GROUP INVESTMENT LIMITED
Units 2708 27/F Convention Plaza-Office Tower 1 Harbour Road, Wanchai, China (Hong Kong)
Tel.: (852) 2 845 5188　　　BM
Web Site: http://www.dingyi.hk
Year Founded: 1970
0508—(HKG)
Rev.: $19,989,836
Assets: $569,599,154
Liabilities: $379,405,891
Net Worth: $190,193,263
Earnings: ($13,069,027)
Emp.: 91
Fiscal Year-end: 03/31/22
Holding Company; Restaurant & Food Kiosk Owner & Operator
N.A.I.C.S.: 551112
Kwong Yuk Li *(Chm)*

DINO ENERGY CORPORATION
Suite 2806 505 - 6th Street SW, Calgary, T2P 1X5, AB, Canada
Tel.: (403) 237-8330　　　NV
Web Site:
　http://dinoenergycorporation.com
DINO—(OTCBB)
Investment Services
N.A.I.C.S.: 523999
Eric David Lawson *(Pres, CEO & CFO)*

DINO POLSKA SA
Ostrowska 122, 63-700, Krotoszyn, Poland
Tel.: (48) 627255400
Web Site: https://www.grupadino.pl
Year Founded: 1999
DNP—(WAR)
Rev.: $4,974,531,980
Assets: $2,261,734,161
Liabilities: $1,205,666,482
Net Worth: $1,056,067,678
Earnings: $284,401,095
Emp.: 37,383
Fiscal Year-end: 12/31/22
Food Products Distr
N.A.I.C.S.: 445110
Michal Krauze *(CFO)*

Subsidiaries:

Agro-Rydzyna sp, z o.o.　　　(1)
UL KOLEJOWA 7K, Kloda, 64-130, Rydzyna, Poland
Tel.: (48) 691400497
Web Site: https://www.agrorydzyna.pl
Meat Production Services
N.A.I.C.S.: 311615

DIO CORPORATION
66 Centum seoro, Haeundae-gu, Busan, 612-020, Korea (South)
Tel.: (82) 517457777
Web Site:
　https://www.dioimplant.com
Year Founded: 1988
039840—(KRS)
Rev.: $100,711,968
Assets: $253,354,179
Liabilities: $125,071,883
Net Worth: $128,282,296
Earnings: ($15,422,616)
Emp.: 437
Fiscal Year-end: 12/31/22

Medical Instrument Mfr & Whslr
N.A.I.C.S.: 339114
Jin-Cheol Kim *(Chm)*

Subsidiaries:

DIO Implant Australia Pty Ltd.　(1)
Tel.: (61) 292791422
Web Site: http://www.dioimplant.com.au
Medical Instrument Mfr & Distr
N.A.I.C.S.: 339114

DIOK ONE AG
Kleingedankstrasse 11a, 50677, Cologne, Germany
Tel.: (49) 22129199333
Web Site: https://www.diok-one.de
CVK—(DUS)
Sales Range: Less than $1 Million
Real Estate Services
N.A.I.C.S.: 531390
Daniel L. Grosch *(Member-Mgmt Bd)*

DIOKI D.D.
Zitnjak Bb, 10000, Zagreb, Croatia
Tel.: (385) 12483000
Web Site: http://www.dioki.hr
Year Founded: 1995
Sales Range: $150-199.9 Million
Emp.: 540
Organic Petrochemicals
N.A.I.C.S.: 325110
Zdenko Belosevic *(Pres)*

DION GLOBAL SOLUTIONS LIMITED
C-25 MIQB First Floor Gautam buddha nagar, Sector 125, Noida, 201 301, Uttar Pradesh, India
Tel.: (91) 1204345518　　　In
Web Site:
　https://www.dionglobal.com
Year Founded: 1994
Software Publr
N.A.I.C.S.: 513210
Michel Borst *(CEO)*

Subsidiaries:

Dion Global Solutions (Asia Pacific) Pty Ltd.　　　　　　　　(1)
Level 1 55 Southbank Boulevard, Southbank, 3006, VIC, Australia
Tel.: (61) 3 9674 9900
Web Site: http://www.dionglobal.com
Sales Range: $25-49.9 Million
Emp.: 30
Software Development Services
N.A.I.C.S.: 541511
Rudi Pecker *(Mng Dir)*

Dion Global Solutions (NZ) Ltd.　(1)
Level 7 220 Queen Street, Auckland, 1010, New Zealand
Tel.: (64) 9 309 3988
Software Development Services
N.A.I.C.S.: 541519

DIONIC INDUSTRIAL & TRADING S.A
95 Aristotelous Str, 13674, Acharnes, Greece
Tel.: (30) 210 2419600
Web Site:
　http://www.dionicgroup.com
Year Founded: 1995
DION—(ATH)
Sales Range: $75-99.9 Million
Emp.: 300
Consumer Products Distr
N.A.I.C.S.: 424350
Thomas Roumpas *(Chm)*

Subsidiaries:

Atcom Internet & Multimedia Ltd.　(1)
24 Averof Street, Nea Ionia, 14232, Athens, Greece
Tel.: (30) 2102419599
Web Site: http://www.atcom.gr
Web Application Development Services
N.A.I.C.S.: 541511

Dionic Industrial & Trading S.A.—(Continued)

Grigoris Papadopoulos (Dir-Creative)

Atcom SA (1)
Aristotelous 95, 13674, Acharnes, Greece
Tel.: (30) 210 241 9599
Internet Marketing Services
N.A.I.C.S.: 541613

Dionic Trading LTD (1)
Boumpoulinas 11, 1060, Nicosia, Cyprus
Tel.: (357) 22458500
Consumer Electronics Distr
N.A.I.C.S.: 423620

MARM LIGHTING LTD (1)
Kallipoleos & Ifigeneias 1 AMARAL 30 5th
floor, Office 501, 1055, Nicosia, Cyprus
Tel.: (357) 2275 2008
Electrical Products Distr
N.A.I.C.S.: 423610

DIORK A.D.
Sumadijska 12, Kragujevac, Serbia
Tel.: (381) 34 335 964
Year Founded: 1990
DIOR—(BEL)
Sales Range: Less than $1 Million
Footwear Mfr
N.A.I.C.S.: 316210
Ljubinko Jankovic (Exec Dir)

DIOS EXPLORATION INC.
CP 114 succ NDG, Montreal, H4A
3P4, QC, Canada
Tel.: (514) 923-9123
Web Site: https://www.diosexplo.com
DOS—(TSXV)
Sales Range: Less than $1 Million
Mineral Exploration Services
N.A.I.C.S.: 213114
Marie-Jose Girard (Pres & CEO)

DIOS FASTIGHETER AB
Tel.: (46) 770332200
Web Site: http://www.dios.se
DIOS—(OMX)
Rev.: $248,575,460
Assets: $3,148,291,594
Liabilities: $2,059,483,427
Net Worth: $1,088,808,167
Earnings: ($84,380,648)
Emp.: 142
Fiscal Year-end: 12/31/23
Real Estate Development Services
N.A.I.C.S.: 531390
Knut Rost (CEO)

DIP CORPORATION
Roppongi Grand Tower 31F 3-2-1
Roppongi, Minato-ku, Tokyo, 106-
6231, Japan
Tel.: (81) 351141177
Web Site: https://www.dip-net.co.jp
Year Founded: 1997
2379—(TKS)
Rev.: $381,314,380
Assets: $359,973,480
Liabilities: $78,443,760
Net Worth: $281,529,720
Earnings: $64,164,500
Emp.: 2,964
Fiscal Year-end: 02/29/24
Online Job Portal
N.A.I.C.S.: 513140
Hideki Tomita (Pres & CEO)

DIPHARMA FRANCIS S.R.L.
Via Bissone 5, Barazate, 2021, Milan,
Italy
Tel.: (39) 02 38228 1
Web Site: http://www.dipharma.it
Pharmaceutical Ingredient Mfr
N.A.I.C.S.: 325412
Marc-Olivier Geinoz (Chm)

Subsidiaries:

Kalexsyn, Inc. (1)

4502 Campus Dr Ste 800, Kalamazoo, MI
49008
Tel.: (269) 488-8488
Web Site: http://www.kalexsyn.com
Medicinal & Botanical Mfr
N.A.I.C.S.: 325411
Brian Eklov (CEO)

DIPL. ING. K. DIETZEL GMBH
Windmuhlenstrasse 6, 04626, Beer-
walde, Germany
Tel.: (49) 366021400
Web Site: http://www.dietzel-
hydraulik.de
Rev.: $12,690,480
Emp.: 300
Pipe Fitting Equipment Mfr
N.A.I.C.S.: 332996
Bertram Wossner (Co-Mng Dir)

DIPLOMA GROUP LIMITED
First Floor 140 Abernethy Road, Bel-
mont, 6104, WA, Australia
Tel.: (61) 89 475 3500   AU
Web Site: http://www.diploma.com.au
Year Founded: 1976
DGX—(ASX)
Sales Range: $50-74.9 Million
Emp.: 92
Construction & Property Development
N.A.I.C.S.: 212321
Simon Oaten (CFO)

Subsidiaries:

Diploma Properties Pty. Ltd. (1)
PO Box 91, Belmont, 6984, Western Aus-
tralia, Australia
Tel.: (61) 892213674
Web Site:
http://www.diplomaproperties.com.au
Sales Range: $50-74.9 Million
Luxury Apartments Construction Services
N.A.I.C.S.: 236116

DIPLOMA PLC
12 Charterhouse Square, London,
EC1M 6AX, United Kingdom
Tel.: (44) 207 549 5700   UK
Web Site: http://www.diplomaplc.com
DPLM—(LSE)
Rev.: $1,069,068,728
Assets: $1,335,181,848
Liabilities: $600,655,328
Net Worth: $734,526,520
Earnings: $94,633,084
Emp.: 2,498
Fiscal Year-end: 09/30/21
Hydraulic Seal & Cylinder Compo-
nents; Consumable Laboratory Items
& Instrumentation; Wiring, Connec-
tors & Heat-Shrink Fit Components
N.A.I.C.S.: 333995
John Nicholas (Chm)

Subsidiaries:

A1-CBISS Limited (1)
5 Valiant Way Lairdside Technology Park,
Tranmere, Wirral, CH41 9HS, United King-
dom
Tel.: (44) 1513210275
Web Site: http://www.a1-cbiss.com
Gas Monitoring Product Mfr
N.A.I.C.S.: 334513
Kevin Priest (Mktg Mgr)

Abacus dx Pty Limited (1)
34 Corporate Drive, Meadowbrook, Cannon
Hill, 4170, QLD, Australia
Tel.: (61) 730347900
Web Site: http://www.abacusdx.com
Clinical Diagnostic Product Whslr
N.A.I.C.S.: 423450

All Seals, Inc. (1)
20762 Linear Ln, Lake Forest, CA 92630
Tel.: (714) 556-4931
Web Site: https://www.allsealsinc.com
Sales Range: $25-49.9 Million
Emp.: 25
Design, Engineering & Distribution of Seals,
Packings & Gaskets

N.A.I.C.S.: 423840

**Big Green Surgical Company Pty
Limited** (1)
Level 3 369 Royal Parade, Parkville, 3052,
VIC, Australia
Tel.: (61) 1300244473
Web Site: https://www.biggreen.com.au
Sales Range: $50-74.9 Million
Emp.: 4
Surgical Equipment Supplies & Distr
N.A.I.C.S.: 423450
Tristan Duggan (Mng Dir)

Cablecraft Limited (1)
Cablecraft House Circle Business Centre
Blackburn Road, Houghton Regis, Dun-
stable, LU5 5DD, United Kingdom
Tel.: (44) 1727849869
Web Site: http://www.cablecraft.co.uk
Electrical Product Mfr & Distr
N.A.I.C.S.: 335999

**Cabletec Interconnect Components
Systems Limited** (1)
Sunnyside Road, Weston-super-Mare,
BS23 3PZ, North Somerset, United King-
dom
Tel.: (44) 1934424900
Sales Range: $25-49.9 Million
Emp.: 70
Metal Braid & Cables Mfr
N.A.I.C.S.: 332999
Alan Malone (Gen Mgr)

Carsen Medical Inc. (1)
14-151 Amber Street, Markham, L3R 3B3,
ON, Canada
Tel.: (866) 677-4121
Web Site: http://www.carsenmedical.com
Sales Range: $25-49.9 Million
Emp.: 25
Medical Device Mfr
N.A.I.C.S.: 334510
Michael McGrath (Gen Mgr)

DMR Seals Limited (1)
Units 22-26 Julian Road, Roman Ridge In-
dustrial Estate, Sheffield, S9 1FZ, United
Kingdom
Tel.: (44) 1142432777
Web Site: http://dmrseals.co.uk
Sealing Product Mfr & Distr
N.A.I.C.S.: 339991

FPE Limited (1)
Barrington Way, Yarm Road Industrial Es-
tate, Darlington, DL1 4WF, Durham, United
Kingdom   (100%)
Tel.: (44) 1325282732
Sales Range: $25-49.9 Million
Emp.: 50
Seals, Seal Kits, Cylinder Parts & Sealants
Supplier
N.A.I.C.S.: 423830

FS Cables limited (1)
Alban Point Alban Park Hatfield Road, Saint
Albans, AL4 0JX, Hertfordshire, United
Kingdom
Tel.: (44) 1727840841
Web Site: https://www.fscables.com
Cable & Wire Distr
N.A.I.C.S.: 423610
Mark Taylor (Mng Dir)

Filcon Electronic GmbH (1)
Rotwandweg 5, 82024, Taufkirchen, Ger-
many
Tel.: (49) 896141690
Web Site: https://www.filcon.de
Emp.: 16
Connector Mfr
N.A.I.C.S.: 334417
Oliver Schulz (Gen Mgr)

Gremtek SAS (1)
58 Rue du Fosse Blanc, 92230, Gennevil-
liers, France
Tel.: (33) 141473570
Web Site: https://www.gremtek.com
Industrial Products Mfr
N.A.I.C.S.: 333242

HA Wainwright (Group) Limited (1)
1 Lower South Street, Godalming, GU7
1BZ, Surrey, United Kingdom
Web Site: http://www.hawco.co.uk
Sales Range: $50-74.9 Million
Emp.: 70
Electronic Components Distr

N.A.I.C.S.: 423830
Chris Hodges (Dir-Sls)

HKX Inc. (1)
16761 146th St SE Ste 115, Monroe, WA
98272   (100%)
Tel.: (360) 805-8600
Sales Range: $25-49.9 Million
Emp.: 50
Supplier of Auxiliary Hydraulic Kits for Exca-
vators
N.A.I.C.S.: 423830

Hercules Europe BV (1)
Elftweg 38, 4941 VP, Raamsdonksveer,
Netherlands
Tel.: (31) 162521422
Web Site: http://www.herculeseu.com
Sales Range: $50-74.9 Million
Emp.: 9
Bearing Product Distr
N.A.I.C.S.: 423830

Hercules Sealing Products Inc. (1)
420 Park Place Blvd Ste 100, Clearwater,
FL 33759   (100%)
Tel.: (727) 796-1300
Web Site: https://www.herculesus.com
Sales Range: $75-99.9 Million
Emp.: 150
Hydraulic & Pneumatic Seals, Seal Kits &
Cylinders Distr
N.A.I.C.S.: 423830

Hitek Limited (1)
Foundry Lane, Horsham, RH13 5PY, West
Sussex, United Kingdom
Tel.: (44) 1403 243
Web Site: http://www.hitek.co.uk
Sales Range: $50-74.9 Million
Emp.: 10
Instruments Distr & Maintenance Services
N.A.I.C.S.: 423830

IS Rayfast Limited (1)
2 Lydiard Fields, Great Western Way, Swin-
don, SN5 8UB, Wiltshire, United
Kingdom   (100%)
Tel.: (44) 1793616700
Web Site: https://www.is-rayfast.com
Emp.: 80
Electrical Apparatus & Equipment, Wiring,
Interconnect & Fastener Products Distr
N.A.I.C.S.: 423610

J. Royal Co. Inc. (1)
2441 Salem Park Dr, Winston Salem, NC
27127
Tel.: (336) 794-0400
Web Site: http://www.jroyal.com
Sales Range: $10-24.9 Million
Emp.: 25
O-Rings, Industrial Seals & Gaskets Sup-
plier
N.A.I.C.S.: 423840

Branch (Domestic):

J Royal Co. Inc.-Barrington (2)
40 Bay Spring Ave, Barrington, RI 02806
Tel.: (401) 246-0600
Web Site: http://www.jroyal.com
Sales Range: $1-9.9 Million
Emp.: 11
O-Rings, Industrial Seals & Gaskets Sup-
plier
N.A.I.C.S.: 423840

Kentek Oy (1)
Nuolikuja 8, 01740, Vantaa, Finland
Tel.: (358) 98494200
Web Site: http://www.kentek.fi
Industrial Equipment Distr
N.A.I.C.S.: 423840
Jari Puukko (Acct Mgr)

Kubo Tech AG (1)
Im Langhag 5, 8307, Effretikon, Switzerland
Tel.: (41) 523541818
Web Site: http://www.kubo.ch
Sealing Products Mfr
N.A.I.C.S.: 339991
Mark Van Den Bosch (Sls Dir)

Kubo Tech GmbH (1)
Gewerbeallee 12a, 4221, Steyregg, Austria
Tel.: (43) 7327819370
Sealing Products Mfr
N.A.I.C.S.: 339991
Dirk Steiner (Mng Dir)

M Seals A/S (1)
Bybjergvej 13, 3060, Espergaerde, Denmark
Tel.: (45) 49130205
Emp.: 28
Seal Products Mfr
N.A.I.C.S.: 339991

M Seals AB (1)
Industrivagen 17, 302 41, Halmstad, Sweden
Tel.: (46) 35158940
Bearing Product Distr
N.A.I.C.S.: 423840

M Seals UK Limited (1)
Quartz Close, Enderby, LE19 4SG, Leicestershire, United Kingdom
Tel.: (44) 1162754720
Web Site: http://www.m-seals.co.uk
Sealing Product Mfr & Distr
N.A.I.C.S.: 339991

Peerless Aerospace Fastener Corp. (1)
141 Executive Blvd, Farmingdale, NY 11735
Tel.: (631) 420-8200
Sales Range: $1-9.9 Million
Emp.: 33
Aircraft Part Mfr
N.A.I.C.S.: 336413
Gerald Tuttle (Exec VP)

PumpNSeal Australia Pty Limited (1)
5 Innovation Cct, Wangara, 6065, WA, Australia
Tel.: (61) 893028444
Web Site: https://www.pumpnseal.com.au
Pump Product Mfr
N.A.I.C.S.: 333914
Gavin Taylor (Mng Dir-Fluid Sealing Div)

SIA Kentek Latvija (1)
Kengaraga iela 10A, Riga, 1063, Latvia
Tel.: (371) 67796060
Web Site: http://www.kentek-filter.com
Industrial Filter Mfr & Distr
N.A.I.C.S.: 333413

Somagen Diagnostics Inc. (1)
9220 25 Avenue NW, Edmonton, T6N 1E1, AB, Canada
Tel.: (780) 702-9500
Web Site: https://www.somagen.com
Diagnostic Products Mfr
N.A.I.C.S.: 325413
Elena LoCastro (Pres)

Sommer GmbH (1)
Kraichgaustr 5, 73765, Neuhausen, Germany (100%)
Tel.: (49) 7158981270
Web Site: https://www.sommer-global.com
Sales Range: $25-49.9 Million
Emp.: 28
Heatshrink Products, Wire & Wire Associated Accessories Distr
N.A.I.C.S.: 423610

Techno-Path (Distribution) Limited (1)
Unit 1A - 1D Fort Henry Business Park, Ballina, Tipperary, V94 W967, Ireland
Tel.: (353) 61335844
Web Site: https://www.techno-path.com
Clinical Diagnostic Product Whslr
N.A.I.C.S.: 423450

Tennessee Industrial Electronics, LLC (1)
44810 Vic Wertz Dr., Clinton Township, MI 48036
Web Site: https://www.tieindustrial.com
Metals Mfr
N.A.I.C.S.: 332439
Tony Wisniewski (Pres & CEO)

Subsidiary (Domestic):

The Parker Group, Inc. (2)
44810 Vic Wertz Dr, Clinton Township, MI 48036
Tel.: (586) 469-0606
Web Site: https://www.parkergroupinc.com
Electrical Repair
N.A.I.C.S.: 811210

TotalSeal Group Australia Pty Limited (1)

72 Platinum Street, Crestmead, 4132, QLD, Australia
Tel.: (61) 734898000
Web Site: http://totalsealau.com
Sealing Product Mfr & Distr
N.A.I.C.S.: 339991

UAB Kentek Lietuva (1)
Biciuliu str 29, Bukiskis Avizieniu sen, 14182, Vilnius, Lithuania
Tel.: (370) 52403932
Web Site: https://www.kentek.lt
Industrial Filter Mfr
N.A.I.C.S.: 333413

VSP Technologies, Inc. (1)
8140 Quality Dr, Prince George, VA 23875
Web Site: https://www.vsptechnologies.com
Fluid Sealing Product Mfr & Distr
N.A.I.C.S.: 339991
Tyler Ragsdale (Pres)

Windy City Wire Cable & Technology Products LLC (1)
386 Internationale Dr Ste H, Bolingbrook, IL 60440
Tel.: (630) 633-4500
Web Site: https://www.smartwire.com
Rev.: $67,000,000
Emp.: 118
Electrical Apparatus & Equipment, Wiring Supplies & Related Equipment Merchant Whslr
N.A.I.C.S.: 423610
Richard Galgano (Founder & CEO)

a1-envirosciences GmbH (1)
Eichsfelder Str 1, 40595, Dusseldorf, Germany
Tel.: (49) 2117584830
Web Site: https://a1-envirosciences.com
Sales Range: $25-49.9 Million
Emp.: 2
Environmental Consulting Services
N.A.I.C.S.: 541620
Olaf Wolf-Kunz (Mng Dir)

a1-envirosciences Limited (1)
910 Birchwood Boulevard, Birchwood, Warrington, WA3 7QN, Northumberland, United Kingdom
Tel.: (44) 8458738181
Web Site: https://a1-envirosciences.co.uk
Sales Range: $25-49.9 Million
Emp.: 9
Environmental Consulting Services
N.A.I.C.S.: 541620

DIPLOMAT HOLDINGS LTD.
4 Hermon St, Airport City, 701000, Israel
Tel.: (972) 39766666
Web Site: https://www.diplomat-global.com
Year Founded: 1968
DIPL—(TAE)
Rev.: $914,501,925
Assets: $501,857,003
Liabilities: $275,388,265
Net Worth: $226,468,738
Earnings: $21,780,814
Emp.: 2,652
Fiscal Year-end: 09/30/23
Holding Company
N.A.I.C.S.: 551112
Noam Weiman (CEO)

Subsidiaries:

Diplomat Georgia, LLC (1)
Orkhevi Industrial zone, Isani-Samgori district, 0109, Tbilisi, Georgia
Tel.: (995) 5322919293
Personal Care Product Distr
N.A.I.C.S.: 424210
Tamar Kovziridze (CEO)

Diplomat New Zealand Limited (1)
Level 4 1-7 The Strand, PO Box 303233, Takapuna North Harbour, Auckland, 0751, New Zealand
Tel.: (64) 94776400
Personal Care Product Distr
N.A.I.C.S.: 424210
Barry Guerin (Gen Mgr)

DIPNA PHARMACHEM LIMITED

A/211 Siddhi Vinayak Towers Kataria Arcade Behind DCP Office, Off S G Highway Makarba, Ahmedabad, 380051, Gujarat, India
Tel.: (91) 9898066121
Web Site: https://www.dipnapharmachem.com
Year Founded: 2011
543594—(BOM)
Rev.: $4,233,615
Assets: $3,384,303
Liabilities: $3,306,270
Net Worth: $78,034
Earnings: $3,307
Fiscal Year-end: 03/31/21
Pharmaceutical Product Mfr & Distr
N.A.I.C.S.: 325412

DIPULA INCOME FUND LIMITED
12th Floor Firestation Rosebank 16 Baker Street, Johannesburg, 2196, South Africa
Tel.: (27) 113252112
Web Site: https://www.dipula.co.za
Year Founded: 2005
DIB—(JSE)
Rev.: $73,672,145
Assets: $533,818,481
Liabilities: $203,777,818
Net Worth: $330,040,664
Earnings: $35,829,065
Emp.: 85
Fiscal Year-end: 08/31/23
Investment Management Service
N.A.I.C.S.: 525990
Izak Petersen (CEO)

DIRECIONAL ENGENHARIA S.A.
Rua dos Otoni 177 10 andar, Belo Horizonte, 30150-270, MG, Brazil
Tel.: (55) 3134315509
Web Site: http://www.ri.direcional.com.br
Year Founded: 1981
DIRR3—(BRAZ)
Rev.: $431,272,510
Assets: $1,303,142,487
Liabilities: $1,005,029,415
Net Worth: $298,113,072
Earnings: $41,746,021
Fiscal Year-end: 12/31/22
Real Estate Development & Construction Services
N.A.I.C.S.: 531390
Ricardo Valadares Gontijo (Chm)

Subsidiaries:

Santa Ines Empreendimentos Imobiliarios Ltda. (1)
Av Candido Garcia de Lima 776 - Nova Lima, Campo Grande, 79017-120, Brazil
Tel.: (55) 67991250909
Web Site: https://santainesempreendimentos.com.br
Real Estate Services
N.A.I.C.S.: 531311

DIRECT ENERGIE SA
2 Bis ue Louis Armand, Paris, 75015, France
Tel.: (33) 1 70 60 74 00
Gas & Electricity Distr
N.A.I.C.S.: 213112

DIRECT HEALTHCARE LTD
Unit 8 Demuth Way, Oldbury, B69 4LT, United Kingdom
Tel.: (44) 121 541 1800
Web Site: http://www.chemistdirect.co.uk
Year Founded: 2007
Sales Range: $1-9.9 Million
Online Pharmaceutical Retailer
N.A.I.C.S.: 424210
Mitesh Soma (CEO)

DIRECT IT CANADA INC.
675 Cochrane Dr East Tower 6th Floor, Markham, L3R 0B8, ON, Canada
Tel.: (905) 530-2373
Web Site: http://www.directitcanada.com
Year Founded: 2001
Sales Range: Less than $1 Million
Emp.: 6
Infrastucture Assets, Planning & Development Management Software
N.A.I.C.S.: 541511
George Lykoudis (Pres, CEO & VP-Tech-Customer Svcs)

DIRECT LINE INSURANCE GROUP PLC
Churchill Court Westmoreland Road, Bromley, BR1 1DP, Kent, United Kingdom
Tel.: (44) 2083133030 UK
Web Site: https://www.directlinegroup.com
Year Founded: 1985
DLG—(OTCIQ)
Rev.: $3,996,213,078
Assets: $10,546,074,224
Liabilities: $7,667,381,974
Net Worth: $2,878,692,249
Earnings: ($49,861,146)
Emp.: 9,387
Fiscal Year-end: 12/31/22
Insurance Holding Company
N.A.I.C.S.: 551112
Humphrey Tomlinson (Gen Counsel)

Subsidiaries:

Churchill Insurance Company Limited (1)
Churchill Ct Westmoreland Rd, Bromley, BR1 1DP, Kent, United Kingdom (100%)
Tel.: (44) 8001116768
Web Site: https://www.churchill.com
Sales Range: $1-4.9 Billion
Emp.: 3,200
Automobile & Homeowners Insurance
N.A.I.C.S.: 524126

DLG Legal Services Limited (1)
The Wharf Neville Street, Leeds, LS1 4AZ, United Kingdom
Tel.: (44) 344 892 8000
Web Site: https://www.dlglegalservices.com
Fire Insurance Services
N.A.I.C.S.: 524124

Direct Line Group Limited (1)
Churchill Court Westmoreland Road, Bromley, BR1 1DP, Kent, United Kingdom
Tel.: (44) 1132920667
Direct Health & Medical Insurance Services
N.A.I.C.S.: 551112

Direct Line Insurance plc (1)
Direct Line House 3 Edridge Rd, Croydon, CR9 1AG, Surrey, United Kingdom (100%)
Tel.: (44) 2086863313
Web Site: http://www.directline.com
Sales Range: $200-249.9 Million
Emp.: 500
Insurance
N.A.I.C.S.: 524128

Subsidiary (Domestic):

Green Flag Limited (2)
The Wharf Neville Street, Leeds, LS1 4AZ, United Kingdom
Tel.: (44) 141 349 0516
Web Site: https://www.greenflag.com
Breakdown & Roadside Assistance Insurance
N.A.I.C.S.: 524298

Farmweb Limited (1)
Avening House Falcon Close Green Farm Business Park, Quedgeley, Gloucester, GL2 4LY, United Kingdom
Tel.: (44) 145 236 1645
Web Site: https://farmweb.co.uk
Fire Insurance Services
N.A.I.C.S.: 524210

Direct Line Insurance Group plc—(Continued)

National Insurance and Guarantee Corporation Limited (1)
Crown House 145 City Road, London, EC1V 1LP, United Kingdom
Tel.: (44) 2076566000
Web Site: http://www.nig-uk.com
Sales Range: $200-249.9 Million
Emp.: 400
Vehicle, Home & Business Insurance Products
N.A.I.C.S.: 524128

DIRECT MARKETING MIX, INC.
12th floor JRE Umeda Square Bldg 1-12-17 Umeda, Kita-Ku, Osaka, 530-0001, Japan
Tel.: (81) 668091615
Web Site: https://www.dmix.co.jp
Year Founded: 2017
7354—(TKS)
Rev.: $190,373,590
Assets: $185,580,750
Liabilities: $92,808,100
Net Worth: $92,772,650
Earnings: $2,197,900
Emp.: 1,014
Fiscal Year-end: 12/31/23
Marketing Consulting Services
N.A.I.C.S.: 541613
Yuki Kobayashi (Chm, Pres & CEO)

DIRECT NICKEL LIMITED
Level 6 2 Bulletin Place, Sydney, 2000, NSW, Australia
Tel.: (61) 2 8014 7780　　　　AU
Web Site: http://www.directnickel.com
Year Founded: 2005
Sales Range: Less than $1 Million
Nickel Extraction Services
N.A.I.C.S.: 212230
Russell Debney (Mng Dir)

Subsidiaries:

PT Direct Nickel Pte (1)
Alamanda Tower 23rd Floor Jl TB Simatupang Kav 23-24, Cilandak Barat, Jakarta, 12430, Indonesia
Tel.: (62) 21 2966 0023
Nickel Extraction Services
N.A.I.C.S.: 212230

DIRECT RESPONSE MEDIA GROUP INC.
240 Wyecroft Rd, Oakville, L6K 2G7, ON, Canada
Tel.: (905) 465-1233
Web Site: http://drmg.com
Direct Mail Marketing Services
N.A.I.C.S.: 541860
Jason Bradbury (Founder & CEO)

Subsidiaries:

Valassis Canada Inc. (1)
47 Jutland Road, Toronto, M8Z 2G6, ON, Canada
Tel.: (416) 259-3600
Sales Range: $10-24.9 Million
Emp.: 30
Direct Mail Marketing Services
N.A.I.C.S.: 541860
Stacey Allen (VP & Gen Mgr)

DIRECT SOURCE SPECIAL PRODUCTS, INC.
2695 Dollard St, La Salle, H8N 2J8, QC, Canada
Tel.: (514) 363-8882
Web Site: http://www.dsspinc.com
Sales Range: $10-24.9 Million
Emp.: 15
Compact Disc & DVD Direct Marketing
N.A.I.C.S.: 449210
Bill Shannon (Pres)

DIRECT WINES LIMITED
New Aquitaine House Exeter Way,

Theale, Reading, RG7 4PL, Berkshire, United Kingdom
Tel.: (44) 8704448383
Web Site: http://www.laithwaites.co.uk
Year Founded: 1969
Rev.: $492,500,000
Earnings: $13,100,000
Emp.: 891
Wine & Alcoholic Beverages Distr
N.A.I.C.S.: 424820
Tony Laithwaite (Founder)

Subsidiaries:

Virgin Wines Ltd. (1)
St James Mill, Whitefriars, Norwich, NR3 1TN, United Kingdom
Tel.: (44) 8455438864
Web Site: http://www.virginwines.com
Online Wine Distr
N.A.I.C.S.: 424820

DIRECT WONEN N V
Nieuwe Duinweg 24, Hague, 2587 AD, Netherlands
Tel.: (31) 707115000
Web Site: http://www.directwonen.nl
Sales Range: $25-49.9 Million
Emp.: 303
Housing & Financial Services
N.A.I.C.S.: 522291
Jan-Peter Duijvestijn (CFO)

DIRECTA PLUS PLC
7th Floor50 Broadway, London, SW1H 0DB, United Kingdom
Tel.: (44) 2072682453　　　　UK
Web Site: http://www.directa-plus.com
Year Founded: 2005
DCTA—(AIM)
Rev.: $7,804,091
Assets: $21,494,627
Liabilities: $8,556,585
Net Worth: $12,938,042
Earnings: ($5,498,061)
Emp.: 26
Fiscal Year-end: 12/31/20
Graphene Product Mfr & Distr
N.A.I.C.S.: 335991
Giulio Cesareo (Founder & CEO)

Subsidiaries:

Setcar S.A. (1)
Str Gradinii Public nr 6, 810022, Braila, Romania (50.99%)
Tel.: (40) 239614852
Waste Management Services
N.A.I.C.S.: 562998

DIRECTA SIM S.P.A.
Via Bruno Buozzi 5, 10121, Turin, Italy
Tel.: (39) 0110884141
Web Site: https://www.directa.it
Year Founded: 1995
D—(EUR)
Investment Management Service
N.A.I.C.S.: 523999
Massimo Segre (Chm)

DIRECTEL HOLDINGS LIMITED
Rooms 01 02 14 & 15 37/F Hong Kong Plaza 188 Connaught Road West, Hong Kong, China (Hong Kong)
Tel.: (852) 28599388　　　　Ky
Web Site: http://www.directel.hk
8337—(HKG)
Rev.: $19,376,940
Assets: $6,201,728
Liabilities: $969,893
Net Worth: $5,231,835
Earnings: ($1,570,928)
Emp.: 20
Fiscal Year-end: 12/31/22

Mobile Virtual Network Operator
N.A.I.C.S.: 517112
Kin Shing Li (Chm)

DIRECTI GROUP
Directiplex Old Nagardas Road, Adheri East, Mumbai, 400069, Maharashtra, India
Tel.: (91) 2261966300
Web Site: http://www.directi.com
Year Founded: 1998
Sales Range: $350-399.9 Million
Emp.: 1,000
Internet Solutions
N.A.I.C.S.: 518210
Bhavin Turakhia (Co-Founder & CEO)

Subsidiaries:

Direct Information FZC (1)
F/19 RAK FTZ, 16113, Ras al Khaimah, United Arab Emirates
Tel.: (971) 72046060
Application Software Development Services
N.A.I.C.S.: 541511

DIREKTNA BANKA A.D.
Kralja Petra I 26, 34000, Kragujevac, Serbia
Tel.: (381) 34335617　　　　SI
Web Site: http://www.direktnabanka.rs
Year Founded: 1955
Sales Range: $1-9.9 Million
Emp.: 400
Commericial Banking
N.A.I.C.S.: 522110
Ljubinka Lovcevic (Chm)

DIRHAM CONSTRUCTION LTD
PO Box 351, Grande Prairie, T8V 3A5, AB, Canada
Tel.: (780) 532-4094
Web Site: http://www.dirhamhomes.com
Year Founded: 1976
Rev.: $34,271,882
Emp.: 41
Home Building Contractors
N.A.I.C.S.: 236116
Henry Peter Hamm (Pres)

DIRITEKS DIRILIS TEKSTIL SANAYI VE TICARET A.S.
Suleyman Demirel Organize Sanayi Bolgesi 114 Cad No 4, Isparta, Turkiye
Tel.: (90) 8503360621
Web Site: https://www.diriteks.com
Year Founded: 1996
DIRIT—(IST)
Rev.: $657,005
Assets: $8,847,909
Liabilities: $837,174
Net Worth: $8,010,734
Earnings: $1,670,923
Fiscal Year-end: 12/31/23
Apparels Mfr
N.A.I.C.S.: 315990
Mehmet Bedir (Gen Mgr)

DIRTT ENVIRONMENTAL SOLUTIONS LTD.
7303 30th Street Southeast, Calgary, T2C 1N6, AB, Canada
Tel.: (403) 723-5000　　　　AB
Web Site: https://www.dirtt.com
Year Founded: 2012
DRTT—(NASDAQ)
Rev.: $181,931,000
Assets: $124,317,000
Liabilities: $117,216,000
Net Worth: $7,101,000
Earnings: ($14,584,000)
Emp.: 874
Fiscal Year-end: 12/31/23

Environmental Software; Interior Construction Services
N.A.I.C.S.: 513210
Benjamin Urban (CEO)

Subsidiaries:

Ice Edge Business Solutions Ltd. (1)
4021 S 700 E Ste 600, Salt Lake City, UT 84107
Tel.: (801) 747-0373
Web Site: https://www.ice-edge.com
Application Software Development Services
N.A.I.C.S.: 541511

DIRUI INDUSTRIAL CO., LTD.
3333 Yiju Road New and High Tech Development Zone, Changchun, 130103, Jilin, China
Tel.: (86) 43185083742
Web Site: https://www.dirui.com.cn
Year Founded: 1992
300396—(CHIN)
Rev.: $171,289,404
Assets: $410,706,504
Liabilities: $141,162,372
Net Worth: $269,544,132
Earnings: $36,745,488
Emp.: 1,700
Fiscal Year-end: 12/31/22
Medical Testing Instruments Mfr
N.A.I.C.S.: 334510
Wang Xuemin (Gen Mgr)

DIS-CHEM PHARMACIES LTD.
Tel.: (27) 115892200　　　　ZA
Web Site: http://www.dischem.co.za
Year Founded: 1978
DCP—(JSE)
Rev.: $2,074,643,069
Assets: $960,345,096
Liabilities: $729,348,474
Net Worth: $230,996,622
Earnings: $60,731,796
Emp.: 20,000
Fiscal Year-end: 02/28/22
Pharmacy Product Retailer
N.A.I.C.S.: 456110
Laurence Michael Nestadt (Bd of Dirs & Chm)

Subsidiaries:

CJ Marketing Proprietary Limited (1)
6A Schoeman Street, Polokwane, Limpopo, South Africa
Tel.: (27) 152955951
Web Site: http://www.cjmarketing.co.za
Marketing Services
N.A.I.C.S.: 541613

CJ Pharmaceutical Enterprises Limited (1)
12 4th Street, Delmas, Mpumalanga, 2210, South Africa
Tel.: (27) 136651011
Web Site: http://www.cjdsa.com
Clinical Services
N.A.I.C.S.: 622110
Darren Brooks (Sls Mgr)

Culemborg Pharmacy Proprietary Limited (1)
Shop 01 St George Mall The Heriat Second Street, Cape Town, South Africa
Tel.: (27) 215410049
Clinical Services
N.A.I.C.S.: 622110

Dis-Chem Airport Junction Proprietary Limited (1)
Shop 301 upper level Airport Junction Shopping Centre, Cnr A1 And Airport Road, Gaborone, Botswana
Tel.: (267) 3713835
Clinical Services
N.A.I.C.S.: 622110

Dis-Chem Ballito Junction Proprietary Limited (1)
Ballito Junction Shopping Centre Leonora Drive, Ballito, 4420, KwaZulu-Natal, South Africa
Tel.: (27) 329468580

Clinical Services
N.A.I.C.S.: 622110

Dis-Chem Ballito Lifestyle Proprietary Limited (1)
Cnr 398/445 Main Road, Ballito, 4420, KwaZulu-Natal, South Africa
Tel.: (27) 329468540
Web Site:
http://www.ballitolifestylecentre.co.za
Clinical Services
N.A.I.C.S.: 622110

Dis-Chem Ferndale Proprietary Limited (1)
Shop 47 Ferndale on Republic 186 President Ridge Ext 7, Randburg, 2194, South Africa
Tel.: (27) 105410150
Clinical Services
N.A.I.C.S.: 622110

Dis-Chem Festival Mall Proprietary Limited (1)
Corner CR Swart Drive and Kelvin Street, Kempton Park, 1619, South Africa
Tel.: (27) 113947549
Web Site: http://www.festivalmall.co.za
Clinical Services
N.A.I.C.S.: 622110
Daphne Smith *(Gen Mgr)*

Dis-Chem Flamewood Value Centre Proprietary Limited (1)
Shop 23 Flamwood Walk Shopping Center 1 Brother Patrick Road, Flamwood, Klerksdorp, 2571, South Africa
Tel.: (27) 184877300
Clinical Services
N.A.I.C.S.: 622110

Dis-Chem Glen Fair Proprietary Limited (1)
Glenfair Shopping Centre Cnr Lynnwood and Daventry Road, Lynnwood Manor, Pretoria, 0081, South Africa
Tel.: (27) 124728720
Clinical Services
N.A.I.C.S.: 622110

Dis-Chem Goodwood Proprietary Limited (1)
Shop 74 N1 City Value Centre Solly Smeidt Street, Goodwood, Cape Town, 59412, South Africa
Tel.: (27) 215410004
Clinical Services
N.A.I.C.S.: 622110

Dis-Chem Jubilee Proprietary Limited (1)
Cnr Jubilee and Harry Gwala Road, Hamanskraal, 0400, South Africa
Tel.: (27) 127271241
Web Site: http://www.jubileemall.co.za
Clinical Services
N.A.I.C.S.: 622110
Stephina Lebepe *(Gen Mgr)*

Dis-Chem Krugersdorp Proprietary Limited (1)
President Square Shopping Centre Cnr Pretoria And Market St, Krugersdorp, 1739, South Africa
Tel.: (27) 119515800
Clinical Services
N.A.I.C.S.: 622110

Dis-Chem Mams Mall Proprietary Limited (1)
Shop 77 Mams Mall Cnr Tsamaya Avenue and Solomon Mahlangu, Mamelodi East, Pretoria, 0122, South Africa
Tel.: (27) 125740092
Clinical Services
N.A.I.C.S.: 622110

Dis-Chem Maponya Proprietary Limited (1)
2127 Maponya Mall Chris Hani Rd, Soweto, Johannesburg, 1809, South Africa
Tel.: (27) 119384448
Web Site: http://www.maponyamall.co.za
Clinical Services
N.A.I.C.S.: 622110
Johannes Morobe *(Mgr-Center)*

Dis-Chem Mega Mall Proprietary Limited (1)

Shop 103-107 Mega City Shopping Centre Cnr Sekama and Dr James Drive, Unit 1 Mmabatho, Mafikeng, South Africa
Tel.: (27) 181080095
Clinical Services
N.A.I.C.S.: 622110

Dis-Chem Swakopmund Proprietary Limited (1)
Platz Am Meer Shopping Centre Erf 71 Hollam's Bird Island, Vineta North, 9000, Swakopmund, Namibia
Tel.: (264) 833300400
Clinical Services
N.A.I.C.S.: 622110

Dis-Chem TLC De Wiekus Proprietary Limited (1)
Shop 8-11 Green Line Supermarket 98 Elgin Road, Birchleigh, Kempton Park, 1619, South Africa
Tel.: (27) 119728114
Clinical Services
N.A.I.C.S.: 622110

Dis-Chem The Galleria Amanzimtoti Proprietary Limited (1)
Cnr Moss Kolnik and Arbour Road, Amanzimtoti, Durban, 4126, South Africa
Tel.: (27) 319042233
Web Site: http://www.galleria.co.za
Clinical Services
N.A.I.C.S.: 622110
Kurt Hoggan *(Gen Mgr)*

Dis-Chem Three Rivers Proprietary Limited (1)
Riverwalk Shopping Centre 7 Nile Drive, Three Rivers, Vereeniging, 1929, South Africa
Tel.: (27) 164547500
Clinical Services
N.A.I.C.S.: 622110

Dis-Chem Walvis Bay Proprietary Limited (1)
Dunes Mall 18 de Weg, 9000, Walvis Bay, Namibia
Tel.: (264) 64284300
Clinical Services
N.A.I.C.S.: 622110

Dis-Chem Wernhill Proprietary Limited (1)
Corner Fidel Castro and Mandume Ndemufayo Street, PO Box 16, Windhoek, Namibia
Tel.: (264) 61374545
Web Site: http://www.wernhil.com
Clinical Services
N.A.I.C.S.: 622110
Johan Westhuizen *(Gen Mgr)*

Dis-Chem Worcester Proprietary Limited (1)
Mountain Mill Shopping Centre 13 Mountain Mill Drive, Worcester, 6850, South Africa
Tel.: (27) 233465340
Clinical Services
N.A.I.C.S.: 622110

Quenets Proprietary Limited (1)
Shop 4/5 at Q-Square 72 High Street, Worcester, 6850, South Africa
Tel.: (27) 233477188
Web Site: https://www.quenets.com
Gun Cleaning Product Mfr
N.A.I.C.S.: 325612

Rynfield Terrace Proprietary Limited (1)
Rynfield Terrace 20 Tjello Street, Benoni, 1514, South Africa
Tel.: (27) 100039991
Clinical Services
N.A.I.C.S.: 622110

TLC Medipark Proprietary Limited (1)
98 Elgin Rd Shop 8-11 Green Line Supermarket, Birchleigh, Kempton Park, 1619, South Africa
Tel.: (27) 119728114
Web Site: http://www.thelocalchoice.co.za
Clinical Services
N.A.I.C.S.: 622110

The Local Choice Proprietary Limited (1)
Cnr 4th Street and 2nd Ave, Delmas, 2210,

Mpumalanga, South Africa
Tel.: (27) 136651698
Clinical Services
N.A.I.C.S.: 622110
Christopher Williams *(CEO)*

The Pharmacy Development Academy Proprietary Limited (1)
No 7 Fourth street, Delmas, 2210, South Africa
Tel.: (27) 130100091
Web Site: https://www.pdacademy.co.za
Pharmacy Development Services
N.A.I.C.S.: 611699
Christine Venter *(Mng Dir)*

DISA LIMITED

438A Alexandra Road 08-12 Alexandra Technopark Block A Lobby 3, Singapore, 119967, Singapore
Tel.: (65) 63816888
532—(CAT)
Rev.: $8,340,126
Assets: $2,579,474
Liabilities: $893,664
Net Worth: $1,685,810
Earnings: ($1,819,933)
Emp.: 2,000
Fiscal Year-end: 06/30/23
Anti-Theft Protection Technology Mfr & Distr
N.A.I.C.S.: 423430
Eddie Weng Wah Chng *(CEO & Mng Dir)*

Subsidiaries:

Disa Digital Safety Pte. Ltd. (1)
120 Lower Delta Rd 03-15 Cendex Centre, Singapore, 169208, Singapore
Tel.: (65) 62554905
Web Site: http://www.digital-safety.sg
Digital Security Systems Retailer
N.A.I.C.S.: 459999
Eddie Weng Wah Chng *(Chm)*

Equation Energy Pte. Ltd. (1)
Blk 1001, Jalan Bukit Merah, #06-11, Singapore, Singapore
Tel.: (65) 62707500
Web Site: http://www.equcorp.com
Energy Consulting Services
N.A.I.C.S.: 541690

Equation Recycling Pte. Ltd. (1)
6B Jalan Papan, Singapore, 639401, Singapore
Tel.: (65) 68982220
Web Site: http://www.equrecycling.com.sg
Emp.: 6
Electronic Waste Recycling Services
N.A.I.C.S.: 561990
David Tan *(Gen Mgr)*

Equation Resources Pte. Ltd. (1)
Redhill Industrial Estate 1001 Jalan Bukit Merah 06-11, Singapore, 159455, Singapore
Tel.: (65) 62707080
Web Site: http://www.eqsummit.sg
Construction Materials Whslr
N.A.I.C.S.: 423320

M3 Electronic GmbH (1)
Lyoner Street 44-48, 60528, Frankfurt am Main, Hesse, Germany
Tel.: (49) 69 2713 86 0
Web Site: http://www.m3-electronic.com
Electronic Equipment Mfr & Whslr
N.A.I.C.S.: 334310
Matthias Claus *(Mng Dir)*

DISASTER PREPAREDNESS SYSTEMS, INC.

3531 Commercial Street, Vancouver, V5N 4E8, BC, Canada
Tel.: (604) 785-0184   NV
Year Founded: 2004
Emp.: 5
Homeland Security, Disaster Response & Emergency Preparedness Equipment & Technologies Designer & Marketer
N.A.I.C.S.: 561621

Mark J. Henrickson *(Chm, Pres, CEO & CTO)*

DISBROWE CHEVROLET BUICK GMC CADILLAC
116 Edward St, Saint Thomas, N5P 4E6, ON, Canada
Tel.: (519) 631-7960
Web Site: http://www.disbrowe.com
Year Founded: 1923
Rev.: $25,424,880
Emp.: 55
New & Used Car Dealers
N.A.I.C.S.: 441110
Gary Tebbutt *(Mgr-Parts)*

DISCO CORPORATION
13-11 Omori Kita 2-Chome, Ota-ku, Tokyo, 143 8580, Japan
Tel.: (81) 345901111   JP
Web Site: https://www.disco.co.jp
Year Founded: 1937
6146—(TKS)
Rev.: $2,032,071,358
Assets: $3,673,987,446
Liabilities: $987,763,462
Net Worth: $2,686,223,984
Earnings: $556,399,075
Emp.: 4,790
Fiscal Year-end: 03/31/24
Machine Tools Mfr
N.A.I.C.S.: 333517
Takao Tamura *(CFO, Chief Privacy Officer & Gen Mgr-Corp Support Div)*

Subsidiaries:

Aurotech Corporation (1)
Paseo 4B Paseo De Sta Rosa, Greenfield City, Santa Rosa, 4026, Laguna, Philippines
Tel.: (63) 495012436
Web Site: https://www.aurotech.com
Industrial Machinery & Equipment Whslr
N.A.I.C.S.: 423830

DISCO HI-TEC (VIETNAM) CO., LTD. (1)
Room 502 5th Floor LANT Building No 56-58-60 Hai Ba Trung Street, Ben Nghe Ward District 1, Ho Chi Minh City, Vietnam
Tel.: (84) 2838223832
Sales Range: $25-49.9 Million
Emp.: 3
Cutting Tool Repair & Maintenance Services
N.A.I.C.S.: 811310
Mikoto Oyimi *(Mng Dir)*

DISCO HI-TEC CHINA CO., LTD. (1)
Building 115 No 166 Meiyue Rd, Pudong New District, Shanghai, 200131, China
Tel.: (86) 2150278018
Web Site: http://www.disco.co.jp
Cutting Tool Sales & Maintenance Services
N.A.I.C.S.: 423830

DSD, Ltd. (1)
2 15 Minami Shinagawa 2 Chome, Shinagawa Ku, Tokyo, 1400004, Japan   **(86%)**
Tel.: (81) 334509919
Sales Range: $25-49.9 Million
Emp.: 10
Designs, Develops & Manufactures Communication Networks & Control Boards for Application & Semiconductor Control Systems
N.A.I.C.S.: 334418

Dhk Solution Corporation (1)
8F DHK Solution Bldg 28 Pangyo-ro 255beon-gil, Bundang-gu, Seongnam, 13486, Gyeonggi, Korea (South)
Tel.: (82) 3180388111
Industrial Machinery & Equipment Whslr
N.A.I.C.S.: 423830

Disco Corporation - Chino Plant (1)
480 Toyohira, Chino, 391-0297, Nagano, Japan
Tel.: (81) 266712111
Web Site: http://www.disco.co.jp
Emp.: 160
Cutting Tool Mfr
N.A.I.C.S.: 333515

Disco Corporation—(Continued)

Disco Corporation - Kure Plant (1)
1-23 Hiro Bunka-cho, Kure, 737-0198, Hiroshima, Japan
Tel.: (81) 823722211
Web Site: http://www.disco.co.jp
Cutting Tool Mfr
N.A.I.C.S.: 333515

Disco Corporation - Kuwabata Plant (1)
4010-1 Gohara-cho, Kure, 737-0161, Hiroshima, Japan
Tel.: (81) 823771010
Web Site: http://www.discoeurope.com
Cutting Tool Mfr
N.A.I.C.S.: 333515

Disco Hi-Tec (Singapore) Pte. Ltd. (1)
80 Ubi Avenue 4 06-01, Singapore, 408831, Singapore **(100%)**
Tel.: (65) 67473737
Web Site: http://www.discosin.com.sg
Sales Range: $50-74.9 Million
Emp.: 87
Marketer of Industrial Diamond Tools
N.A.I.C.S.: 423830

Subsidiary (Non-US):

Disco Hi-Tec (Malaysia) Sdn. Bhd. (2)
L10-1 2 Volt Business Suites Tower 5 Icon City No 1B, Jalan SS8/39, 47300, Petaling Jaya, Selangor Darul Ehsan, Malaysia
Tel.: (60) 378658062
Web Site: http://www.disco.co.jp
Disco-Produced Equipment Mfr & Marketer
N.A.I.C.S.: 334413

Disco Hi-Tec (Thailand) Co., Ltd. (2)
123 Suntowers bldg B 32nd Floor Room no 3204 Vibhavadi-Rangsit Rd, Chomphon Chatuchak, Bangkok, 10900, Thailand **(100%)**
Tel.: (66) 26176934
Web Site: http://www.discosin.com.sg
Sales Range: $1-9.9 Million
Emp.: 18
Marketer of Disco-Produced Equipment
N.A.I.C.S.: 334413

Disco Hi-Tec America, Inc. (1)
5921 Optical Ct, San Jose, CA 95138 **(100%)**
Tel.: (408) 987-3776
Web Site: http://www.discousa.com
Sales Range: $25-49.9 Million
Emp.: 40
Marketer of Disco-Produced Equipment
N.A.I.C.S.: 423830
Shinji Ueno (Exec VP)

Disco Hi-Tec Czech s.r.o. (1)
Vaclavske Namesti 808/66, Nove Mesto, 110 00, Prague, Czech Republic
Tel.: (420) 89909030
Precision Cutting & Grinding & Polishing Machine Mfr & Distr
N.A.I.C.S.: 333517

Disco Hi-Tec Europe GmbH (1)
Liebigstrasse 8, b Munchen, 85551, Kirchheim, Germany **(100%)**
Tel.: (49) 89909030
Web Site: https://www.dicing-grinding.com
Sales Range: $50-74.9 Million
Emp.: 70
Marketer of Industrial Diamond Tools
N.A.I.C.S.: 423830

Subsidiary (Non-US):

Disco Hi-Tec France Sarl (2)
Rousset Industrial Zone 460 Avenue Victoire, 13106, Rousset, Cedex, France **(100%)**
Tel.: (33) 89909030
Web Site: http://www.discoeurope.com
Sales Range: $1-9.9 Million
Emp.: 4
Marketer of Industrial Diamond Tools
N.A.I.C.S.: 423830

Disco Hi-Tec UK Ltd. (2)
Unit 34 Basepoint Business Centre, Crawley, RH11 7XX, West Sussex, United Kingdom **(100%)**

Tel.: (44) 1293817730
Web Site: http://www.discoeurope.com
Sales Range: $25-49.9 Million
Emp.: 4
Marketer of Industrial Diamond Tools
N.A.I.C.S.: 423830

Disco Hi-Tec Korea Corporation (1)
3F DHK Solution Bldg 28 Pangyo-ro 255beon-gil, Bundang-gu, Seongnam, 13486, Gyeonggi, Korea (South)
Tel.: (82) 3180388250
Industrial Machinery & Equipment Whslr
N.A.I.C.S.: 423830

Disco Hi-Tec Morocco Sarl (1)
219 Boulevard Zerktouni Residence El Bardai 1er etage-Appt No1, 20100, Casablanca, Morocco
Tel.: (212) 61369404
Industrial Machinery Mfr
N.A.I.C.S.: 333248

Disco Hi-Tec Philippines, Inc. (1)
Unit 3B Unioil Center Center Bldg Commerce Ave cor, Acacia Ave Madrigal Business Park 1, Muntinlupa, 1780, Philippines
Tel.: (63) 284784426
Industrial Machinery & Equipment Whslr
N.A.I.C.S.: 423830

Disco Hi-Tec Taiwan Co., Ltd. (1)
1F 9F No 188 Baoqiao Rd, Xindian, New Taipei City, 231238, Taiwan
Tel.: (886) 229138877
Web Site: http://www.disco.co.jp
Sales Support & Maintenance of Dicing/Cutting Saws, Grinders, Blades/Wheels, Related Machines & Applications Support
N.A.I.C.S.: 423830

Disco Technology (Shanghai) Co., Ltd. (1)
1F Bldg 5 No 690 Bi-Bo Rd, Zhang Jiang High Tech Pk, Shanghai, 201203, China **(100%)**
Tel.: (86) 2150278018
Web Site: http://www.disco.co.jp
Sales Range: $25-49.9 Million
Emp.: 50
Marketer of Disco-Produced Equipment
N.A.I.C.S.: 334413

Disco-Sea Europe S.R.L. (1)
Via Augera, Cadelbosco Sopra, 42023, Reggio nell'Emilia, Italy **(25%)**
Tel.: (39) 0522915251
Web Site: http://www.sedia.com
Marketer of Industrial Diamond Tools
N.A.I.C.S.: 333514

Ikar-Impulse Ltd. (1)
pr Vernadskogo 78, 119454, Moscow, Russia
Tel.: (7) 4954334777
Industrial Machinery & Equipment Whslr
N.A.I.C.S.: 423830

New Tronics Co., Ltd. (1)
Flat F 11th Floor Valiant Ind Bldg 2-12 Au Pui Wan Street, Fotan, Shatin, China (Hong Kong)
Tel.: (852) 26871431
Web Site: https://www.ntc-hk.com
Industrial Machinery & Equipment Whslr
N.A.I.C.S.: 423830

Picotech Ltd. (1)
17 Hamefalsim St, POB 3265, Petach Tikva, 4951447, Israel
Tel.: (972) 36356650
Web Site: https://www.picotech.co.il
Industrial Machinery & Equipment Whslr
N.A.I.C.S.: 423830

DISCOVER WELLNESS SOLUTIONS INC.
500 707 5th Street SW, Calgary, T2P 0Y3, AB, Canada
Tel.: (403) 984-6446
Web Site:
http://www.discoverwellness.ca
WLNS—(CNSX)
Assets: $11,821,189
Liabilities: $1,582,440
Net Worth: $10,238,749
Earnings: ($2,590,173)

Fiscal Year-end: 12/31/20
Medical Cannabis Product Retailer
N.A.I.C.S.: 459999
Sunny Dabas (Mgr-Quality Assurance)

DISCOVERIE GROUP PLC
2 Chancellor Court Occam Road Surrey Research Park, Guildford, GU2 7AH, United Kingdom
Tel.: (44) 1483544500 **UK**
Web Site:
https://www.discoverieplc.com
Year Founded: 1900
DSCV—(LSE)
Rev.: $557,444,020
Assets: $727,322,260
Liabilities: $350,311,780
Net Worth: $377,010,480
Earnings: $26,450,340
Emp.: 4,863
Fiscal Year-end: 03/31/23
Electronic Components & Equipment Distr
N.A.I.C.S.: 449210
Nicholas J. Jefferies (CEO)

Subsidiaries:

ATM Parts Company Ltd. (1)
Units 11-12 Admiralty Way, Camberley, GU15 3DT, Surrey, United Kingdom **(100%)**
Tel.: (44) 1276607200
Web Site: http://www.acal-atmparts.com
Distribution of ATM Parts
N.A.I.C.S.: 423420

Acal Australia Pty. Ltd. (1)
PO Box 2406, Caulfield Junction, Melbourne, 3150, VIC, Australia **(100%)**
Tel.: (61) 3 9523 1895
Distr of Electronic Components & Equipment
N.A.I.C.S.: 423690

Acal BFi UK Ltd. (1)
3 The Business Centre Molly Millars Lane, Wokingham, RG41 2EY, United Kingdom **(100%)**
Tel.: (44) 1189 788 878
Web Site: http://www.acalbfi.com
Sales Range: $50-74.9 Million
Emp.: 100
Electronics, Photonics & Imaging Products Distr
N.A.I.C.S.: 423690

Unit (Domestic):

Acal BFi UK Ltd (2)
Challenge House Sherwood Drive Bletchley, Milton Keynes, MK3 6DP, United Kingdom
Tel.: (44) 1189788878
Web Site: http://www.acalbfi.com
Sales Range: $25-49.9 Million
Emp.: 50
Electronics, Photonics & Imaging Products Distr
N.A.I.C.S.: 423690

Acal Controls Ltd. (1)
Redfields Park Church Crookham, Fleet, GU52 0RD, Hampshire, United Kingdom **(100%)**
Tel.: (44) 252858062
Distr of Electronic Controls for Refrigeration & Air Conditioning
N.A.I.C.S.: 423740

Acal Europe Holding BV (1)
Eindhoven Airport Beatrix De Rijkweg 12, 5657 EG, Eindhoven, Netherlands **(100%)**
Tel.: (31) 402507400
Web Site: http://www.acel.nl
Sales Range: $75-99.9 Million
Emp.: 125
Holding Company
N.A.I.C.S.: 551112
Simon Gibbins (Grp Fin Dir-Tech Bus)

Subsidiary (Non-US):

Acal BFi Belgium nv/sa (2)
Lozenberg 4, 1932, Zaventem, Belgium **(100%)**

Tel.: (32) 27205983
Web Site: http://www.acalbfi.com
Sales Range: $25-49.9 Million
Emp.: 25
Electronic Components & Equipment Distr
N.A.I.C.S.: 423690

Acal BFi Denmark (2)
Jernbanegade 23b, 4000, Roskilde, Denmark
Tel.: (45) 70 26 22 25
Web Site: http://www.acalbfi.com
Electric Component Whslr
N.A.I.C.S.: 423690

Acal BFi France SAS (2)
4 Allee du Cantal, ZI La Petite Montagne Sud CE1834, 91018, Lisses, Cedex, France
Tel.: (33) 160795900
Web Site: http://www.acalbfi.com
Electronic Product Whslr
N.A.I.C.S.: 423690

Acal BFi Germany GmbH (2)
Oppelner Strasse 5, 82194, Grobenzell, Germany **(100%)**
Tel.: (49) 8142 6520 0
Web Site: http://www.acalbfi.com
Emp.: 60
Electronics, Photonics & Imaging Products Distr
N.A.I.C.S.: 423690

Unit (Domestic):

Acal BFi Germany GmbH (3)
Assar-Gabrielsson-Strasse 1, 63128, Dietzenbach, Germany
Tel.: (49) 607440980
Web Site: http://www.acalbfi.com
Sales Range: $50-74.9 Million
Emp.: 70
Electronics, Photonics & Imaging Products Distr
N.A.I.C.S.: 423690
Hans Schmidt (Mng Dir)

Subsidiary (Non-US):

Acal BFi Germany GmbH (2)
Assar Gabrielsson Strasse 1, 63128, Dietzenbach, Germany
Tel.: (49) 6074 4098 0
Web Site: http://www.acalbfi.com
Sales Range: $25-49.9 Million
Emp.: 5
Electronic Components Distr
N.A.I.C.S.: 423690
Joerg Duebener (Mng Dir)

Acal BFi Iberia SLU (2)
C Anabel Segura 7 Planta Acceso, Alcobendas, 28108, Madrid, Spain
Tel.: (34) 914531160
Web Site: http://www.bfioptilas.es
Sales Range: $25-49.9 Million
Emp.: 50
Electronics, Photonics & Imaging Products Distr
N.A.I.C.S.: 423690
Oscar Romero (Mng Dir)

Acal BFi Italy S.r.l. (2)
Via Cascina Venina 20, 20057, Assago, MI, Italy **(100%)**
Tel.: (39) 02 53 58 31
Web Site: http://www.acalbfi.com
Distr of Electronic Components & Equipment
N.A.I.C.S.: 423690

Unit (Domestic):

Acal BFi Italy Sr (3)
Via Brembo 27, 20139, Milan, Italy
Tel.: (39) 0002535831
Web Site: http://www.bfioptilas.it
Sales Range: $25-49.9 Million
Emp.: 15
Electronics, Photonics & Imaging Products Distr
N.A.I.C.S.: 423690

Subsidiary (Domestic):

Acal BFi Netherlands BV (2)
Luchthavenweg 53, 5657 EA, Eindhoven, Netherlands **(100%)**
Tel.: (31) 402507400
Web Site: http://www.acalbfi.com
Distr of Logistics Equipment

N.A.I.C.S.: 423690

Unit (Domestic):

Acal BFi Netherlands BV　　　　　　**(3)**
Christiaan Huygensweg 17, 2408 AJ, Al-
phen aan den Rijn, Netherlands
Tel.: (31) 172446060
Web Site: http://www.bfioptilas.nl
Sales Range: $25-49.9 Million
Emp.: 20
Electronics, Photonics & Imaging Products
Distr
N.A.I.C.S.: 423690

Subsidiary (Non-US):

EAF France SA　　　　　　　　　　**(3)**
36 Rue Luzene Dueuis, Fontenay Sous
Bois, F94043, Creteil, Cedex,
France　　　　　　　　　　　　　**(100%)**
Tel.: (33) 145147337
Web Site: http://www.acalplc.co.uk
Sales Range: $25-49.9 Million
Emp.: 50
Distr of Logistics Equipment
N.A.I.C.S.: 423690

Subsidiary (Non-US):

Acal BFi Nordic AB　　　　　　　　**(2)**
PO Box 3002, 750 03, Uppsala, Sweden
Tel.: (46) 18565830
Web Site: http://www.acalbfi.com
Sales Range: $25-49.9 Million
Emp.: 18
Electronics, Photonics & Imaging Products
Distr
N.A.I.C.S.: 423690

Unit (Domestic):

Acal BFi Nordic AB　　　　　　　　**(3)**
Rissneleden 138, 174 57, Sundbyberg,
Sweden　　　　　　　　　　　　**(100%)**
Tel.: (46) 854656500
Web Site: http://www.acalbfi.com
Sales Range: $25-49.9 Million
Emp.: 8
Electronics, Photonics & Imaging Products
Distr
N.A.I.C.S.: 423690

Subsidiary (Domestic):

Acal Nederland BV　　　　　　　　**(2)**
53, 5657 EG, Eindhoven,
Netherlands　　　　　　　　　　**(100%)**
Tel.: (31) 402507400
Web Site: http://www.acal.nl
Sales Range: $25-49.9 Million
Emp.: 40
Distr of Electronic Components & Equip-
ment
N.A.I.C.S.: 423690
Peater Gan Rovels (Mng Dir)

Subsidiary (Non-US):

CompoTron GmbH　　　　　　　　**(2)**
Sandstrasse 26, 80335, Munich, Germany
Tel.: (49) 89 53 88 66 0
Web Site: http://www.compotron.de
Communication Fiber Wire Mfr
N.A.I.C.S.: 335929

Acal Management Services Ltd.　**(1)**
2 Chancellor Court Occam Rd Surrey Re-
search Park, Guildford, GU2 7AH, United
Kingdom　　　　　　　　　　　**(100%)**
Tel.: (44) 1483 544 500
Web Site: http://www.acalplc.co.uk
Sales Range: $25-49.9 Million
Emp.: 20
Management Services
N.A.I.C.S.: 541611
Nick Jefferies (CEO)

Coil-Tran LLC　　　　　　　　　　**(1)**
160 S Illinois St, Hobart, IN 46342
Tel.: (219) 947-1555
Web Site: http://www.hobart-electronics.com
Transformer Mfr
N.A.I.C.S.: 335311

Computer Parts International Ltd.　**(1)**
Head Office Parts House, Glaisdale Pkwy,
Nottingham, NG8 4GP, United
Kingdom　　　　　　　　　　　**(100%)**
Tel.: (44) 159196000

Sales Range: $10-24.9 Million
Emp.: 100
Distr of IT Parts & Equipment
N.A.I.C.S.: 449210

Contour Electronics Asia Limited　**(1)**
Unit 601 6/F Shing Yip industrial Building
19-21 Shing Yip Street, Kwun Tong, Kow-
loon, China (Hong Kong)
Tel.: (852) 27901623
Electrical & Electronic Equipment Mfr
N.A.I.C.S.: 336320

Contour Electronics Limited　　　**(1)**
Unit 9 Bartley Point Osborn Way, Hook,
RG27 9GX, Hampshire, United Kingdom
Tel.: (44) 1256761111
Web Site:
　http://www.contourelectronics.com
Electric Equipment Mfr
N.A.I.C.S.: 336320

Cursor Controls Limited　　　　　**(1)**
Conroi House Brunel Drive, Newark, NG24
2EG, Nottinghamshire, United Kingdom
Tel.: (44) 1636615600
Web Site: http://www.cursorcontrols.com
Trackball Mfr & Distr
N.A.I.C.S.: 334118

Flux A/S　　　　　　　　　　　　**(1)**
Industrivangen 5, 4550, Asnaes, Denmark
Tel.: (45) 59650089
Web Site: http://www.flux-int.com
Electrical Component Mfr
N.A.I.C.S.: 334416

Flux International Ltd.　　　　　　**(1)**
Blk C 5 41/27 Bangna-Trad KM 16 5,
Bangchalong, Bang Phli, Thailand
Tel.: (66) 23370201
Electrical Component Mfr
N.A.I.C.S.: 334416

Foshan Noratel Electric Co., Ltd.　**(1)**
22-2 Xingye Road Zone C Shishan Science
And, Technology Industrial Park Nanhai Dis-
trict, Foshan, 528225, Guangdong, China
Tel.: (86) 75781166369
Transformer & Wound Component Mfr
N.A.I.C.S.: 334416

Foss Fiberoptisk Systemsalg AS　**(1)**
Dansrudveien 45, 3036, Drammen, Norway
Tel.: (47) 32210800
Web Site: http://www.fossfiberoptikk.no
Emp.: 130
Electrical Component Mfr & Distr
N.A.I.C.S.: 334416

Foss Fibre Optics s.r.o　　　　　**(1)**
Odborarska 52, 831 02, Bratislava, Slovakia
Tel.: (421) 248205200
Web Site: http://www.fossfibreoptics.com
Emp.: 130
Electrical Component Mfr & Distr
N.A.I.C.S.: 334416

Heason Technology Limited　　　**(1)**
Motion Solutions Centre Unit 11 Spring
Copse Business Park, Slinfold, Horsham,
RH13 0SZ, West Sussex, United Kingdom
Tel.: (44) 1403792300
Web Site: http://www.heason.com
Servo Motor Electric Actuator Mfr
N.A.I.C.S.: 335312
Richard Causley (Mgr-Bus Dev)

Hectronic AB　　　　　　　　　　**(1)**
Akaregatan 2, 754 54, Uppsala, Sweden
Tel.: (46) 18660700
Web Site: http://www.hectronic.se
Embedded Computer Mfr
N.A.I.C.S.: 334111
Stefan Lof (Mng Dir)

Herga Technology Limited　　　　**(1)**
Northern Way, Bury Saint Edmunds, IP32
6NN, Suffolk, United Kingdom
Tel.: (44) 1284701422
Web Site: http://www.herga.com
Emp.: 85
Sensor & Transducer System Mfr & Distr
N.A.I.C.S.: 334519
Graham Pattison (Mng Dir)

Ixthus Instrumentation Limited　　**(1)**
The Stables Williams' Barn Tiffield Road,
Towcester, NN12 6HP, Northamptonshire,
United Kingdom
Tel.: (44) 1327353437

Web Site: http://www.ixthus.co.uk
Sensor & Transducer System Mfr & Distr
N.A.I.C.S.: 334519
Graham Pattison (Mng Dir)

MTC Micro Tech Components
GmbH　　　　　　　　　　　　**(1)**
Hausener Strasse 9, 89407, Dillingen, Ger-
many
Tel.: (49) 907179450
Web Site: http://www.mtc.de
Electronic Equipment Mfr & Distr
N.A.I.C.S.: 336320

Myrra Power Sp Zoo　　　　　　**(1)**
Chlodna 29, 00-867, Warsaw, Poland
Tel.: (48) 257576496
Emp.: 100
Electrical Component Mfr
N.A.I.C.S.: 334416

Myrra SAS　　　　　　　　　　　**(1)**
2 Bd de la Haye ZI Gustave Eiffel, Marne la
Valle, 77607, Bussy-Saint-Georges, Cedex,
France
Tel.: (33) 160375555
Electrical Component Mfr
N.A.I.C.S.: 334416

NSI bvba　　　　　　　　　　　　**(1)**
Kapittelstraat 18, 3740, Bilzen, Belgium
Tel.: (32) 89519000
Web Site: http://www.nsi-be.com
Emp.: 14
Keyboard & Trackball Mfr
N.A.I.C.S.: 334111

Noratel AS　　　　　　　　　　　**(1)**
Elektroveien 7, 3300, Hokksund, Norway
Tel.: (47) 32251500
Transformer & Wound Component Mfr
N.A.I.C.S.: 334416

Noratel Denmark A/S　　　　　　**(1)**
Naverland 15, 2600, Glostrup, Denmark
Tel.: (45) 43280000
Transformer & Wound Component Mfr
N.A.I.C.S.: 334416

Noratel Finland OY　　　　　　　**(1)**
Kiertokatu 5, PO Box 11, 24280, Salo, Fin-
land
Tel.: (358) 27772800
Transformer & Wound Component Mfr
N.A.I.C.S.: 334416

Noratel Germany AG　　　　　　**(1)**
Thalenhorststrasse 15a, 28307, Bremen,
Germany
Tel.: (49) 85524077740
Transformer & Wound Component Mfr
N.A.I.C.S.: 334416

Noratel India Power Components Pvt
Ltd　　　　　　　　　　　　　　**(1)**
Nila Technopark Campus, Trivandrum, 695
581, Kerala, India
Tel.: (91) 4714028275
Transformer & Wound Component Mfr
N.A.I.C.S.: 334416

Noratel International Pvt Ltd　　　**(1)**
Phase 2 KEPZ, PO Box 15, Katunayake,
Sri Lanka
Tel.: (94) 112252300
Transformer & Wound Component Mfr
N.A.I.C.S.: 334416

Noratel North America Inc.　　　　**(1)**
13663 Providence Rd Ste 345, Weddington,
NC 28104
Tel.: (704) 819-1882
Transformer & Wound Component Mfr
N.A.I.C.S.: 334416

Noratel Power Engineering Inc.　　**(1)**
1117 E Janis St, Carson, CA 90746
Tel.: (310) 763-1524
Transformer & Wound Component Mfr
N.A.I.C.S.: 334416

Noratel SP Z.o.o　　　　　　　　**(1)**
ul Szczecinska 1K, Dobra, 72-003, Szc-
zecinek, Poland
Tel.: (48) 914250674
Transformer & Wound Component Mfr
N.A.I.C.S.: 334416

Noratel Sweden AB　　　　　　　**(1)**
Lars Lindahlsvag 2, PO Box 108, 695 22,
Laxa, Sweden

Tel.: (46) 584444400
Transformer & Wound Component Mfr
N.A.I.C.S.: 334416

Noratel UK Ltd.　　　　　　　　　**(1)**
Unit 7 George House Princes court Beam
Heath Way, Nantwich, CW5 6GD, Cheshire,
United Kingdom
Tel.: (44) 1270611368
Transformer & Wound Component Mfr
N.A.I.C.S.: 334416

Phoenix America, Inc.　　　　　　**(1)**
4717 Clubview Dr, Fort Wayne, IN 46804
Tel.: (260) 432-9664
Web Site: http://www.phoenixamerica.com
Sales Range: $1-9.9 Million
Emp.: 27
Magnetic & Optical Recording Media Mfr
N.A.I.C.S.: 334610

Plitron Manufacturing
Incorporated　　　　　　　　　　**(1)**
8-601 Magnetic Drive, Toronto, M3J 3J2,
ON, Canada
Tel.: (416) 667-9914
Transformer & Wound Component Mfr
N.A.I.C.S.: 334416

Positek Limited　　　　　　　　　**(1)**
L6 The Link, Andoversford Industrial Estate,
Cheltenham, GL54 4LB, Gloucestershire,
United Kingdom
Tel.: (44) 1242820027
Web Site: http://www.positek.com
Displacement Transducer Mfr
N.A.I.C.S.: 334519
Mark Spreadbury (Comml Dir)

RSG Electronic Components
GmbH　　　　　　　　　　　　**(1)**
Assar-Gabrielsson-Strasse 1, 63128, Di-
etzenbach, Germany
Tel.: (49) 607440980
Web Site: http://www.rsg-electronic.de
Electrical Component Distr
N.A.I.C.S.: 423690
Elmar Holzmann (Mng Dir)

Santon Circuit Breaker Services
B.V.　　　　　　　　　　　　　　**(1)**
Hekendorpstraat 69, 3079 DX, Rotterdam,
Netherlands
Tel.: (31) 102832614
Web Site: http://www.santoncbs.com
Electrical & Electronic Mfr
N.A.I.C.S.: 335999
Henny Vogelenzang (Sls Mgr-Intl)

Santon GmbH　　　　　　　　　　**(1)**
Oberstrasse 1, Postfach 5217, Altes
Rathaus Hinsbeck, 41334, Nettetal, Ger-
many
Tel.: (49) 1801184088
Electro-Mechanical Switchgear Mfr
N.A.I.C.S.: 335999

Santon Holland B.V.　　　　　　　**(1)**
Hekendorpstraat 69, 3079 DX, Rotterdam,
Netherlands
Tel.: (31) 102832600
Electronic Components Mfr
N.A.I.C.S.: 334419

Santon International B.V.　　　　　**(1)**
Hekendorpstraat 69, 3079 DX, Rotterdam,
Netherlands
Tel.: (31) 102832600
Web Site: http://www.santonswitchgear.com
Electro-Mechanical Switchgear Mfr
N.A.I.C.S.: 335999
Harold Curtice Sander (Co-Founder)

Santon Switchgear Limited　　　　**(1)**
Unit 1 Phoenix Park Telford Street, New-
port, NP19 0LW, United Kingdom
Tel.: (44) 1633252371
Electro-Mechanical Switchgear Mfr
N.A.I.C.S.: 335999

Stortech Electronics Ltd.　　　　　**(1)**
Unit 2 Spire Green Centre Pinnacles West,
Harlow, CM19 5TQ, Essex, United
Kingdom　　　　　　　　　　　**(100%)**
Tel.: (44) 1279451100
Web Site: http://www.stortech.co.uk
Sales Range: $25-49.9 Million
Emp.: 22
Distr of Electronic Components & Equip-
ment

discoverIE Group plc—(Continued)

N.A.I.C.S.: 423690

Townsend Coates Ltd. (1)
Lunsford Rd, Leicester, LE5 0HH, United
Kingdom (100%)
Tel.: (44) 1162744444
Sales Range: $50-74.9 Million
Emp.: 100
Distr of Electrical Parts & Equipment
N.A.I.C.S.: 423690

Variohm Holdings Limited (1)
Williams Barn Tiffield Road, Towcester,
NN12 6HP, Northamptonshire, United King-
dom
Tel.: (44) 1327351004
Web Site: http://www.variohm.com
Sensor & Transducer System Mfr & Distr
N.A.I.C.S.: 334519

Variohm-Eurosensor Limited (1)
Williams' Barn Tiffield Road, Towcester,
NN12 6HP, Northamptonshire, United King-
dom
Tel.: (44) 1327351004
Web Site: http://www.variohm.com
Electrical & Electronic Mfr
N.A.I.C.S.: 335999
Graham Pattison (Mng Dir)

Vertec Scientific Ltd. (1)
Unit 44 Easter Park Benyon Road,
Silchester, Reading, RG27 2PQ, United
Kingdom (100%)
Tel.: (44) 1189702100
Web Site: http://www.vertec.co.uk
Sales & Service of Medical & Scientific
Equipment
N.A.I.C.S.: 423450

**Zhongshan Myrra Electronic Co.,
Ltd.** (1)
39 Industrial Road Xiaolan Industrial Zone,
Xiaolan Town, Zhongshan, 528415, Guang-
dong, China
Tel.: (86) 76022286600
Electrical Component Mfr
N.A.I.C.S.: 334416

DISCOVERY ALASKA LIMITED
18 Sangiorgio Court, Osborne Park,
6017, WA, Australia
Year Founded: 2003
DAF—(ASX)
Rev.: $5,455
Assets: $461,553
Liabilities: $36,605
Net Worth: $424,948
Earnings: ($1,056,436)
Fiscal Year-end: 06/30/24
Graphite Exploration Services
N.A.I.C.S.: 212390
Alan Thomas (Sec)

DISCOVERY CAPITAL CORPO-
RATION
Suite 880 1500 West Georgia Street,
Vancouver, V6G 2Z6, BC, Canada
Tel.: (604) 683-3000   BC
Web Site:
http://www.discoverycapital.com
Year Founded: 1986
Sales Range: $10-24.9 Million
Emp.: 5
Venture Capital Financing Services
N.A.I.C.S.: 523160
Harry A. Jaako (Chm & Co-CEO)

DISCOVERY COMPUTERS &
WIRELESS INC.
200 3301 Douglas St, Victoria, V8Z
3L2, BC, Canada
Tel.: (250) 382-0499
Web Site:
http://www.discoverycomputers.com
Year Founded: 1997
Sales Range: $1-9.9 Million
Emp.: 25
Western Canada Computer & Wire-
less Store Operators & Franchises
N.A.I.C.S.: 449210

DISCOVERY FOODS LTD.
Nimbus House Maidstone Rd, Kings-
ton, Milton Keynes, MK10 0BD,
Bucks, United Kingdom
Tel.: (44) 1908933000
Web Site:
http://www.discoveryfoods.co.uk
Sales Range: $50-74.9 Million
Emp.: 32
Food Products Mfr
N.A.I.C.S.: 311999

DISCOVERY FORD BURLING-
TON LTD.
850 Brant Street, Burlington, L7R
2J5, ON, Canada
Tel.: (905) 632-8696
Web Site:
http://discoveryford.autotrader.ca
Year Founded: 1961
Rev.: $51,558,355
Emp.: 75
New & Used Car Dealers
N.A.I.C.S.: 441110
Rob Leggat (Mng Partner)

DISCOVERY HARBOUR RE-
SOURCES CORP.
250-750 Pender St, Vancouver, V6C
2T7, BC, Canada
Tel.: (604) 681-3170   BC
Web Site:
https://www.discoveryharbour.com
Year Founded: 2009
DHR—(OTCIQ)
Rev.: $142
Assets: $2,322,730
Liabilities: $212,321
Net Worth: $2,110,409
Earnings: ($274,914)
Fiscal Year-end: 09/30/21
Investment Services
N.A.I.C.S.: 523999
Rodney Stevens (CFO-Interim & VP)

DISCOVERY HONDA
6466 Bell McKinnon Road, Duncan,
V9L 6C1, BC, Canada
Tel.: (250) 748-5814
Web Site:
http://www.discoveryhonda.com
Year Founded: 1974
New & Used Car Dealers
N.A.I.C.S.: 441110
Jason Alderborg (Mgr-Sls)

DISCOVERY LIMITED
1 Discovery Place, PO Box 786722,
Sandton, 2146, South Africa
Tel.: (27) 115292888   ZA
Web Site:
https://www.discovery.co.za
DSY—(JSE)
Rev.: $3,816,445,050
Assets: $16,831,931,620
Liabilities: $13,664,763,250
Net Worth: $3,167,168,370
Earnings: $219,700,600
Emp.: 11,811
Fiscal Year-end: 06/30/21
Holding Company; Insurance Ser-
vices
N.A.I.C.S.: 551112
Barry Swartzberg (CEO-Vitality Grp)

Subsidiaries:

Discovery Health (Proprietary)
Limited (1)
155 West St, Johannesburg, Sandton,
21496, Gauteng, South Africa
Tel.: (27) 115292888
Sales Range: $1-4.9 Billion
Emp.: 10,000
Health Insurance Services
N.A.I.C.S.: 524114

Global Access Health Network
SARL (1)
1 Croisement des Avenues Tchad et Bas-
Congo, Gombe, Kinshasa, Congo, Demo-
cratic Republic of
Tel.: (243) 995205260
Health Care Provider Services
N.A.I.C.S.: 621999
Sylvain Mbiye Saluseke (Gen Mgr)

Prudential Health Holdings
Limited (1)
Laurence Pountney Hill, London, EC4R
0HH, United Kingdom (75%)
Tel.: (44) 1202 447 208
Holding Company, Health Insurance
N.A.I.C.S.: 551112

Holding (Domestic):

Prudential Health Insurance Ltd (2)
Laurence Pountney Hill, London, EC4R
0HH, United Kingdom
Tel.: (44) 1202447208
Web Site: http://www.pruhealth.co.uk
Health Insurance
N.A.I.C.S.: 524114
Neville S. Koopowitz (CEO)

The Vitality Group Inc (1)
120 S Riverside Ste 400, Chicago, IL
60606-5075
Tel.: (312) 224-7100
Web Site: https://www.vitalitygroup.com
Health Insurance Services
N.A.I.C.S.: 524114
Maia Surmava (CEO)

Vitality Corporate Services
Limited (1)
3 More London Riverside, London, SE1
2AQ, United Kingdom
Tel.: (44) 2071338600
Web Site: https://www.vitality.co.uk
Insurance Claims Services
N.A.I.C.S.: 524291

DISCOVERY METALS CORP.
701 - 55 University Ave, Toronto, ON,
Canada
Tel.: (416) 613-9410
Web Site: http://dsvmetals.com
Metal Mining
N.A.I.C.S.: 212290
Murray John (Chm)

Subsidiaries:

Levon Resources Ltd. (1)
Suite 500 666 Burrard Street, Vancouver,
V6C 2X8, BC, Canada
Tel.: (778) 379-0040
Web Site: http://www.levon.com
Rev.: $26,605
Assets: $46,150,940
Liabilities: $143,080
Net Worth: $46,007,860
Earnings: ($4,624,871)
Emp.: 6
Fiscal Year-end: 03/31/2018
Metal Exploration Services
N.A.I.C.S.: 212390
JoAnne Odette (CFO)

DISCOVERY ONE INVEST-
MENT CORP.
5761 Seaview Place West, Vancou-
ver, V7W 1R7, BC, Canada
Tel.: (604) 921-6041
DOIT.P—(TSXV)
Rev.: $25,563
Assets: $795,378
Liabilities: $18,824
Net Worth: $776,554
Earnings: ($92,577)
Fiscal Year-end: 04/30/21
Asset Management Services
N.A.I.C.S.: 523940

DISCOVERY RIDGE RE-
SOURCES, INC.
Suite 1250 639 5th Avenue South-
west, Calgary, T2P 0M9, AB,
Canada   NV
Year Founded: 2008

Oil & Gas Exploration Services
N.A.I.C.S.: 211120
Will Wagner (Pres, CFO & Chief
Acctg Officer)

DISCOVERY WORLD CORPO-
RATION
Station 1 Balabag, Aklan, Malay,
1231, Philippines
Tel.: (63) 288138857
Web Site:
https://www.discovery.com.ph
Year Founded: 1993
DWC—(PHI)
Rev.: $16,451,169
Assets: $223,224,255
Liabilities: $122,238,769
Net Worth: $100,985,486
Earnings: ($870,453)
Fiscal Year-end: 12/31/23
Leisure Management Services
N.A.I.C.S.: 721120
Leslie Ann T. Yapkianwee (Treas)

Subsidiaries:

Discovery Fleet Corporation (1)
4th Floor JTKC Centre 2155 Chino Roces
Ave former Pasong Tamo, Makati, 1231,
Metro Manila, Philippines
Tel.: (63) 285195674
Web Site: https://discoveryfleet.com
Cloud Data Migration Services
N.A.I.C.S.: 518210

DISCOVERY-CORP ENTER-
PRISES INC.
Suite 1108 - 193 Aquarius Mews,
Vancouver, V6Z 2Z2, BC, Canada
Tel.: (778) 371-9936   Ca
Web Site: https://www.discovery-
corp.com
Year Founded: 1986
DCY—(TSXV)
Rev.: $32
Assets: $74,567
Liabilities: $9,452
Net Worth: $65,115
Earnings: ($99,486)
Fiscal Year-end: 07/31/21
Mineral Exploration Services
N.A.I.C.S.: 213114
Alex Pannu (Pres & CEO)

DISCOVEX RESOURCES LIM-
ITED
68A Hay Street, Subiaco, 6008, WA,
Australia
Tel.: (61) 893809440
Web Site:
http://www.syndicatedmetals.com.au
DCX—(ASX)
Rev.: $105,748
Assets: $6,232,702
Liabilities: $377,942
Net Worth: $5,854,760
Earnings: ($626,841)
Emp.: 9
Fiscal Year-end: 06/30/22
Mineral Exploration Services
N.A.I.C.S.: 213115
Paul Bridson (Sec)

DISCRETIX TECHNOLOGIES
LTD.
Grand Netter Industrial Zone Delta
Bldg, POB 3641, Kfar Netter, 40593,
Israel
Tel.: (972) 732558800
Web Site: http://www.discretix.com
Embedded Security Platform Mfr
N.A.I.C.S.: 334413
Gal Salomon (Founder & CEO)

Subsidiaries:

Commtone Solution Co. Ltd (1)
Room 4107 580 Nanjing Road W, Shang-
hai, China
Tel.: (86) 2129264120

Web Site: http://www.discretix.com
Embedded Security Platform Mfr
N.A.I.C.S.: 334413

Discretix Technologies K.K. (1)
Tukiji Akashicho Duplex Rs 702 6-23-702
Akashi-cho, Chuo-ku, Tokyo, 104-0044,
Japan
Tel.: (81) 351482053
Web Site: http://www.discretix.com
Embedded Security Platform Mfr
N.A.I.C.S.: 334413

Discretix Technologies Ltd. (1)
2F No 45 Lane 76 Reiguang Road, Neihu
District, Taipei, 114, Taiwan
Tel.: (886) 287929423
Web Site: http://www.discretix.com
Embedded Security Platform Mfr
N.A.I.C.S.: 334413

Discretix, Inc. (1)
1521 California Cir 2nd Fl, Milpitas, CA
95035
Tel.: (408) 969-9991
Web Site: http://www.discretix.com
Sales Range: $1-9.9 Million
Emp.: 61
Designs & Licenses Processors for Mobile
Devices & Flash Memory Data Security
N.A.I.C.S.: 334118
David Voschina (VP-R&D)

**DISENOS Y PROYECTOS TEC-
NICOS SA**
Avenida de la Buhaira 28 1a Planta
Oficina 3, Seville, Spain
Tel.: (34) 954 680 909
Web Site:
http://www.grupoditecsa.com
Year Founded: 1993
Emp.: 900
Engineering, Manufacturing, Installa-
tion, Operation & Maintenance of In-
dustrial Projects
N.A.I.C.S.: 541330
Gonzalo Madariaga (Pres)

DISH TV INDIA LTD
Office No 803 8th Floor DLH Park S
V Road, Goregaon, Mumbai, 400
062, Maharashtra, India
Tel.: (91) 2249734054   In
Web Site: https://www.dishtv.in
Year Founded: 1988
532839—(BOM)
Rev.: $445,667,040
Assets: $1,267,369,740
Liabilities: $908,647,740
Net Worth: $358,722,000
Earnings: ($162,415,890)
Emp.: 388
Fiscal Year-end: 03/31/21
Entertainment Services
N.A.I.C.S.: 516120
Ranjit Singh (Compliance Officer, Sec
& Sr VP-Legal)

DISHA RESOURCES LIMITED
3 Rajesh Apartment B/h Ajanta
Comm Estate Off Ashram Road,
Ahmedabad, 380 014, Gujarat, India
Tel.: (91) 7927540790
Web Site:
https://disharesourcesltd.com
Year Founded: 1995
531553—(BOM)
Rev.: $542,773
Assets: $1,959,983
Liabilities: $332,953
Net Worth: $1,627,030
Earnings: $59,865
Emp.: 1
Fiscal Year-end: 03/31/21
Securities Dealing Services
N.A.I.C.S.: 523150
Krishn Awtar J. Kabra (Mng Dir &
Compliance Officer)

**DISHMAN CARBOGEN AMCIS
LIMITED**

Dishman Corporate House, Iscon-
Bopal Road Ambli, Ahmedabad, 380
058, India
Tel.: (91) 2717420124   In
Web Site: https://imdcal.com
540701—(BOM)
Rev.: $266,240,520
Assets: $1,136,307,900
Liabilities: $358,418,970
Net Worth: $777,888,930
Earnings: ($22,540,245)
Emp.: 2,200
Fiscal Year-end: 03/31/21
Drug Development Services
N.A.I.C.S.: 325412
Mark C. Griffiths (CEO)

Subsidiaries:

Carbogen Amcis AG (1)
Hauptstrasse 171, 4416, Bubendorf, Swit-
zerland
Tel.: (41) 589090000
Web Site: https://www.carbogen-amcis.com
Sales Range: $50-74.9 Million
Emp.: 600
Specialty Chemical Products
N.A.I.C.S.: 325998
Mark C. Griffiths (CEO)

Subsidiary (Non-US):

Carbogen Amcis Ltd. (U.K.) (2)
303 Clayton Lane, Manchester, M11 4SX,
United Kingdom
Tel.: (44) 161 223 33 44
Web Site: http://www.carbogen-amcis.com
Sales Range: $25-49.9 Million
Emp.: 30
Pharmaceuticals Product Mfr
N.A.I.C.S.: 325412
Stephan Fritschi (Mng Dir)

**Carbogen Amcis Real Estate
Sas** (1)
10 Rue des Boules, 63200, Riom, France
Tel.: (33) 473337240
Pharmaceutical Mfr & Distr
N.A.I.C.S.: 325412

Dishman Europe Limited (1)
85 New Cavendish Street, London,
W1W6XD, Greater London, United Kingdom
Tel.: (44) 2073230608
Web Site: http://www.dishman-europe.com
Sales Range: $25-49.9 Million
Emp.: 7
Pharmaceutical Preparation Mfr
N.A.I.C.S.: 325412

**Dishman International Trade (Shang-
hai) Co., Ltd.** (1)
Room 1101 Times Building, 655# Hubing
Road Wuxi, 214071, Nanjing, China
Tel.: (86) 51085840486
Web Site: http://www.dishmangroup.com
Sales Range: $25-49.9 Million
Emp.: 10
Pharmaceutical Preparation Mfr
N.A.I.C.S.: 325412

Dishman Japan Ltd. (1)
1-1-8 Hirakawa-cho Chiyoda-ku, 3-19
Hayabusa-cho Chiyoda-ku, Tokyo, 102-
0093, Japan
Tel.: (81) 332217571
Web Site: http://www.dishman-japan.com
Sales Range: $25-49.9 Million
Emp.: 7
Pharmaceutical Preparation Mfr
N.A.I.C.S.: 325412

Dishman Netherlands B.V. (1)
Nieuweweg 2a 3901 BE Veenendaal, PO
Box 70, 3900 AB, Veenendaal, Utrecht,
Netherlands
Tel.: (31) 318 545 754
Web Site: http://www.dishman-
netherlands.com
Sales Range: $50-74.9 Million
Emp.: 75
Pharmaceutical Products Mfr & Sales
N.A.I.C.S.: 424210
P. Alberti (Mgr-HR)

Dishman Pharma Solutions AG. (1)
Hauptstrasse 171, Bubendorf, 4416, Basel-
Landschaft, Switzerland

Tel.: (41) 619355353
Pharmaceutical Products Distr
N.A.I.C.S.: 424210

**Dishman Pharmaceuticals & Chemi-
cals (Shanghai) Co. Ltd.** (1)
No 69 Shungong Road Shanghai Chemical
Industry Park, Shanghai, 201507, China
Tel.: (86) 21 6712 1166
Web Site: http://www.dishmangroup.com
Pharmaceutical Products Distr
N.A.I.C.S.: 424210

Dishman Switzerland Ltd. (1)
1 Av De Longueville, 2013, Colombier,
Vaud, Switzerland
Tel.: (41) 328416870
Pharmaceuticals Product Mfr
N.A.I.C.S.: 325412

Dishman USA Inc. (1)
476 Union Ave Ste 2, Middlesex, NJ 08846
Tel.: (732) 560-4300
Web Site: http://www.dishmangroup.com
Pharmaceutical Product Mfr
N.A.I.C.S.: 325412

DISKUS WERKE AG
Gutleutstr 175, D-60327, Frankfurt
am Main, Germany
Tel.: (49) 69 2400 0868
Web Site: http://www.diskus-werke-
ag.dvs-gruppe.com
Sales Range: $150-199.9 Million
Emp.: 982
Industrial Machinery Mfr
N.A.I.C.S.: 333248
Bernd Rothenberger (Chief Sls Offi-
cer & Member-Mgmt Bd)

DISMO
Rue De Poitiers, 79700, Mauleon,
Deux-Sevres, France
Tel.: (33) 549814301
Sales Range: $25-49.9 Million
Emp.: 66
Supermarket
N.A.I.C.S.: 445110
Franck Couprie (Pres)

DISPLAY ART PLC
23 Tefkrou Anthia Street, Idalion In-
dustrial Zone, 2540, Nicosia, Cyprus
Tel.: (357) 22485420
Web Site:
https://www.displayartgroup.com
Year Founded: 1982
DISP—(CYP)
Sales Range: Less than $1 Million
Digital Printing Services
N.A.I.C.S.: 323111

DISPLAY TECH CO., LTD.
86-9 6-ro 3rd Industrial Complex,
Seobuk-gu, Cheonan, 31085,
Chungcheongnam-do, Korea (South)
Tel.: (82) 317767500
Web Site: https://www.dtccorp.co.kr
Year Founded: 1998
066670—(KRS)
Rev.: $52,973,750
Assets: $133,316,781
Liabilities: $11,883,674
Net Worth: $121,433,107
Earnings: $5,241,222
Emp.: 19
Fiscal Year-end: 12/31/22
LCD Module Mfr
N.A.I.C.S.: 334419
Yoon-min Park (CEO)

**DISRUPTIVE CAPITAL ACQUI-
SITION COMPANY LIMITED**
First Floor 10 Lefebvre Street, Saint
Peter Port, GY1 2PE, Guernsey   GG
Tel.: (44) 2072231100
Web Site:
https://www.disruptivecapitalac.com
Year Founded: 2021

DCACS—(EUR)
Rev.: $4,825,530
Assets: $175,588,479
Liabilities: $183,285,391
Net Worth: ($7,696,912)
Earnings: ($4,233,368)
Fiscal Year-end: 12/31/22
Investment Management Service
N.A.I.C.S.: 523999
Edi Truell (CEO)

DISTIL PLC
73 Watling Street, London, EC4M
9BJ, United Kingdom
Tel.: (44) 2034050475
Web Site: https://www.distil.uk.com
DIS—(AIM)
Rev.: $1,639,176
Assets: $9,693,491
Liabilities: $1,246,767
Net Worth: $8,446,724
Earnings: ($928,866)
Emp.: 5
Fiscal Year-end: 03/31/23
Alcoholic Beverage Mfr & Distr
N.A.I.C.S.: 312140
Don Goulding (Chm)

**DISTILLERIE MERLET ET FILS
SARL**
Lieu Dit Chevessac, 17610, Poitiers,
France
Tel.: (33) 546914781
Web Site: http://www.merlet.fr
Rev.: $23,700,000
Emp.: 44
Wines, Brandy & Brandy Spirits
N.A.I.C.S.: 312130
Emmanuel Rottaro (Mgr-DP)

**DISTILLERIES COMPANY OF
SRI LANKA PLC**
110 Norris Cannal Road, 10, Co-
lombo, 10, Sri Lanka
Tel.: (94) 115507000
Web Site: https://www.dcslgroup.com
Year Founded: 1913
DIST—(COL)
Rev.: $493,856,499
Assets: $122,742,652
Liabilities: $74,430,263
Net Worth: $48,312,388
Earnings: $38,666,590
Emp.: 953
Fiscal Year-end: 03/31/21
Liquor Distillation
N.A.I.C.S.: 312140
Nimal Nagahawatte (Head-Fin)

**DISTINCT INFRASTRUCTURE
GROUP INC.**
77 Belfield Rd Suite 102, Toronto,
M9W 1G6, ON, Canada
Tel.: (416) 675-6485   AB
Web Site: http://www.diginc.ca
Year Founded: 2012
DSTFF—(OTCIQ)
Sales Range: $50-74.9 Million
Emp.: 385
Turnkey Solutions for the Telecommu-
nications & Cable Industries
N.A.I.C.S.: 517810
Joe Lanni (Co-CEO)

**DISTINCTIVE DESIGNS FURNI-
TURE, INC.**
600 Clayson Road, North York, M9M
2H2, ON, Canada
Tel.: (416) 740-7773
Web Site:
http://www.distinctivedesigns.com
Sales Range: $10-24.9 Million
Emp.: 80
Furniture Mfr
N.A.I.C.S.: 337121
Alan Kornblum (Pres)

Distinctive Designs Furniture, Inc.—(Continued)

DISTIT AB
Glasfibergatan 8, 125 45, Alvsjo,
Sweden
Tel.: (46) 855576200
Web Site: https://distit.se
Year Founded: 1991
DIST—(OMX)
Rev.: $240,289,041
Assets: $157,098,635
Liabilities: $103,760,338
Net Worth: $53,338,297
Earnings: ($1,546,077)
Emp.: 260
Fiscal Year-end: 12/31/22
IT Products Distr
N.A.I.C.S.: 423430
Stefan Charette (Chm)

Subsidiaries:

Alcadon AB   **(1)**
Segelbatsvagen 7, 112 64, Stockholm,
Sweden
Tel.: (46) 86573600
Web Site: https://www.alcadon.se
Emp.: 35
Computer Peripheral Mfr & Distr
N.A.I.C.S.: 334118
Pierre Fors (Mgr)

Subsidiary (Non-US):

Alcadon A/S   **(2)**
Alfaset 1 Industrivei 4, 0668, Oslo, Norway
Tel.: (47) 2 317 7880
Web Site: https://www.alcadon.no
Computer Peripheral Mfr & Distr
N.A.I.C.S.: 334118
Peirre Thors (Gen Mgr)

Aurdel Sweden AB   **(1)**
Glasfibergatan 8, 125 45, Alvsjo, Sweden
Tel.: (46) 855576200
Computer Parts Distr
N.A.I.C.S.: 423430

Aurora Group Danmark A/S   **(1)**
Lautruphoj 5-7, 2750, Ballerup, Denmark
Tel.: (45) 38869171
Web Site: https://aurdel.com
Computer Peripheral Mfr & Distr
N.A.I.C.S.: 334118
Kenneth Jensen (Mgr-Sls)

Subsidiary (Non-US):

Aurora Group Finland Oy   **(2)**
Hameenkatu 13b, 33100, Tampere, Finland
Tel.: (358) 207120390
Web Site: https://aurdel.com
Computer Peripheral Mfr & Distr
N.A.I.C.S.: 334118
Iikka Buss (Country Mgr)

Aurora Group Norge AS   **(2)**
Kjopmannsgata 34, 7500, Stjordal, Norway
Tel.: (47) 73829440
Web Site: https://www.auroragroup.no
Computer Peripheral Mfr & Distr
N.A.I.C.S.: 334118
Pal Johannessen (Country Mgr)

Aurora Group Sverige AB   **(2)**
Glasfibergatan 8, 125 45, Alvsjo, Sweden
Tel.: (46) 855576200
Web Site: https://aurdel.com
Computer Peripheral Mfr & Distr
N.A.I.C.S.: 334118
Per Nilsson (Country Mgr)

Electric Fuel Infrastructure Sweden 2
AB   **(1)**
Kommendorsgatan 28, 114 48, Stockholm,
Sweden
Tel.: (46) 108885346
Web Site: https://www.efuel.se
Emp.: 21
Electric Car Charger Mfr & Distr
N.A.I.C.S.: 336320

LiteNordic AB   **(1)**
Uggledalsvagen 23, 427 40, Billdal, Sweden
Tel.: (46) 104100800
Web Site: https://www.litenordic.com
Dynamic Lighting Retailer
N.A.I.C.S.: 335131

LydRommet AS   **(1)**
Waldemar Thranes gate 86 b, 0175, Oslo,
Norway
Tel.: (47) 23232800
Web Site: https://www.lydrommet.no
Audio & Video Product Distr
N.A.I.C.S.: 423690

Septon Electronic AB   **(1)**
Uggledalsvagen 23, 427 40, Billdal, Sweden
Tel.: (46) 31939270
Web Site: https://www.septon.se
Audio & Video Product Distr
N.A.I.C.S.: 423690
Peter Backius (COO)

SweDeltaco AB   **(1)**
Glasfibergatan 8, 125 45, Alvsjo, Sweden
Tel.: (46) 85 557 6200
Web Site: https://www.deltaco.se
Sales Range: $25-49.9 Million
Emp.: 65
Computer Products & Accessories
N.A.I.C.S.: 541519
Ali Motazedi (Mng Dir)

Subsidiary (Non-US):

DanDeltaco A/S   **(2)**
Lautruphoj 5-7, 2750, Ballerup, Denmark
Tel.: (45) 38869171
Web Site: https://www.deltaco.dk
Computer Peripheral Mfr & Distr
N.A.I.C.S.: 334118

FinDeltaco OY   **(2)**
Hameenkatu 13b, 33100, Tampere, Finland
Tel.: (358) 207120390
Web Site: https://www.deltaco.fi
Computer Peripheral Mfr & Distr
N.A.I.C.S.: 334118

NorDeltaco A/S   **(2)**
Gjellebekkstubben 10 2 etasje, 3420, Lier-
skogen, Norway
Tel.: (47) 22830906
Web Site: https://www.deltaco.no
Computer Peripheral Mfr & Distr
N.A.I.C.S.: 334118
Lasse Lovik (Mgr-Sls)

Winther Wireless AB   **(1)**
Sagvagen 38E, 184 40, Akersberga, Swe-
den
Tel.: (46) 855119644
Web Site: https://wintherbredband.se
Emp.: 14
Wireless Broadband Services
N.A.I.C.S.: 517112

DISTOKEN ACQUISITION CORPORATION
Unit 1006 Block C Jinshangjun Park
No 2 Xiaoba Road, Panlong District,
Kunming, Yunnan, China
Tel.: (86) 87168227160   Ky
Year Founded: 2020
DIST—(NASDAQ)
Assets: $680,816
Liabilities: $664,816
Net Worth: $16,000
Earnings: ($2,155)
Emp.: 4
Fiscal Year-end: 12/31/22
Investment Services
N.A.I.C.S.: 523999
Jian Zhang (Chm & CEO)

DISTRIBUIDORA DE GAS DEL CENTRO S.A.
Av Juan B Justo 4301, Cordoba,
5000, Argentina
Tel.: (54) 8105550427
Web Site: http://www.ecogas.com.ar
Sales Range: $250-299.9 Million
Emp.: 600
Natural Gas Distribution Services
N.A.I.C.S.: 221210
Enrique J. Flaiban (CEO)

DISTRIBUTEL COMMUNICA-TIONS LIMITED
300 177 Nepean St, Ottawa, K2P
0B4, ON, Canada

Tel.: (613) 237-7055
Web Site: http://www.distributel.ca
Year Founded: 1988
Wired Telecommunication & Internet
Services
N.A.I.C.S.: 517111
Matt Stein (CEO)

Subsidiaries:

Primus Telecommunications Canada
Inc.   **(1)**
5343 Dundas Street West Suite 400, Etobi-
coke, M9B 6K5, ON, Canada
Tel.: (416) 236-3636
Web Site: http://www.primus.ca
Digital Telecommunications Services
N.A.I.C.S.: 517121

ThinkTel Communications Ltd.   **(1)**
1506-10250 101 St NW, Edmonton, T5J
3P4, AB, Canada
Web Site: http://www.thinktel.ca
Emp.: 300
Wired Telecommunication Services
N.A.I.C.S.: 517810
Dave Damer (Pres & CEO)

DISTRIBUTION AND WARE-HOUSING NETWORK LIMITED
Cnr Barlow Road & Cavaleros Drive
Jupiter Ext 3, Germiston, South Africa
Tel.: (27) 113230450
Web Site: http://www.dawnltd.co.za
Sales Range: $200-249.9 Million
Emp.: 4,150
Hardware, Sanitary Ware Mfr & Whslr
N.A.I.C.S.: 332999

Subsidiaries:

Africa Swiss Trading (Mauritius)
Limited   **(1)**
3rd Fl Aisha Bldg 25 27 Louis Pasteur St,
Port Louis, Mauritius
Tel.: (230) 217 3643
Building Materials Whslr
N.A.I.C.S.: 423390

Africa Swiss Trading (Proprietary)
Limited   **(1)**
C/O Barlow & Caveleros Dr Jupiter Ext 3,
Germiston, Johannesburg, 1401, Gauteng,
South Africa
Tel.: (27) 113230000
Web Site: http://www.africaswisstrading.com
Emp.: 3,500
Kitchen & Bathroom Accessories Supplier
N.A.I.C.S.: 423220
Derek Tod (Mng Dir)

Africa Swiss Trading (Zambia)
Limited   **(1)**
Plot 7305 Kambala Rd Indus Area, Lusaka,
Zambia
Tel.: (260) 211287230
Sales Range: $50-74.9 Million
Emp.: 12
Kitchen & Bathroom Accessories Distr
N.A.I.C.S.: 423220

Cobra Watertech (Proprietary)
Limited   **(1)**
18 Ealing Crescent, Bryanston, Johannes-
burg, 2194, Gauteng, South Africa
Tel.: (27) 118757400
Web Site: http://www.cobra.co.za
Sales Range: $25-49.9 Million
Emp.: 20
Taps Mfr
N.A.I.C.S.: 335931
Ken Kearns (Gen Mgr)

DPI Holdings (Proprietary)
Limited   **(1)**
1 Setchell Rd, Roodekop, Germiston, 1401,
Gauteng, South Africa
Tel.: (27) 113455600
Web Site: http://www.dpiplastics.co.za
Sales Range: $50-74.9 Million
Emp.: 240
Polyvinyl Chloride Pipes Mfr & Distr
N.A.I.C.S.: 326122
Renier Snyman (Mgr-Tech)

DPI Plastics (Proprietary) Limited   **(1)**

Setchell Rd, Roodekop, 1401, Gauteng,
South Africa
Tel.: (27) 113455600
Web Site: http://www.dpiplastics.co.za
Sales Range: $50-74.9 Million
Emp.: 250
Polyvinyl Chloride Pipes Mfr
N.A.I.C.S.: 326122
Juan Muller (Mng Dir)

Dawn Kitchen Fittings (Proprietary)
Limited   **(1)**
6 Barlinka Rd Saxenburg Park, Cape Town,
7581, Gauteng, South Africa
Tel.: (27) 219051225
Web Site: http://www.roco.co.za
Sales Range: $25-49.9 Million
Emp.: 50
Kitchen Fittings Whslr
N.A.I.C.S.: 449129
Christophe Pichon (Mgr-Bus Dev)

Isca (Proprietary) Limited   **(1)**
20 Wright Street Factoria, Kew, Kru-
gersdorp, 1790, South Africa
Tel.: (27) 118829100
Web Site: http://www.isca.co.za
Sales Range: $50-74.9 Million
Emp.: 200
Brass Taps & Mixers Mfr
N.A.I.C.S.: 335931
Brett Solomon (Mng Dir)

Vaal Sanitaryware (Proprietary)
Limited   **(1)**
Corner Morris & Lilly Rd, Meyerton, 1960,
Gauteng, South Africa
Tel.: (27) 163606000
Web Site: http://www.vaalsan.co.za
Sales Range: $125-149.9 Million
Emp.: 500
Sanitary Ware Mfr & Sales
N.A.I.C.S.: 332999
Robin Coen (Dir-Sls & Mktg-Inland)

DISTRIBUTION FINANCE CAPITAL HOLDINGS PLC
61-95 Oxford Street St James' Build-
ing, Manchester, M1 6EJ, United
Kingdom
Tel.: (44) 2039376406   UK
Web Site: https://www.dfcapital-
investors.com
Year Founded: 2016
DFCH—(LSE)
Rev.: $76,346,277
Assets: $880,888,610
Liabilities: $753,054,109
Net Worth: $127,834,501
Earnings: $4,016,550
Emp.: 133
Fiscal Year-end: 12/31/23
Holding Company Services
N.A.I.C.S.: 551112
Gavin Morris (CFO)

Subsidiaries:

DF Capital Bank Limited   **(1)**
St James Building 61-95 Oxford Street,
Manchester, M1 6EJ, United Kingdom
Tel.: (44) 2039376390
Web Site: https://www.dfcapital.bank
Renting Services
N.A.I.C.S.: 522110

DISTRIBUTION MARCEL DION INC.
1660 boul Industriel, Farnham, J2N
2X8, QC, Canada
Tel.: (450) 293-3909
Web Site: http://www.dmdion.com
Year Founded: 1948
Rev.: $20,124,345
Emp.: 70
Truck Transportation Services
N.A.I.C.S.: 484110
Sylvain Dion (Pres)

DISTRIBUTION TECHNOLOGY LTD.
Sovereign House Vastern Road,
Reading, RG1 8BT, United Kingdom

Tel.: (44) 118 903 5850
Web Site: http://www1.distribution-technology.com
Year Founded: 2003
Sales Range: $10-24.9 Million
Emp.: 71
Financial Planning Software & Solutions
N.A.I.C.S.: 513210
Ben Goss (Founder & CEO)

DISTRIBUTIONS JRV INC.
5 Rue Regnault, Sept-Iles, G4R 3R4, QC, Canada
Tel.: (418) 962-9457
Web Site: http://www.jrv.com
Year Founded: 1946
Rev.: $10,804,892
Emp.: 100
Industrial Equipment Distr
N.A.I.C.S.: 423840
Daniel Larouche (Pres)

Subsidiaries:

Distributions JRV Inc. - Lifting Division   (1)
5 rue Regnault, Sept-Iles, G4R 3R4, QC, Canada
Tel.: (418) 962-6249
Industrial Equipment Distr
N.A.I.C.S.: 423830

DISTRIBUTIVNI CENTAR A.D.
Neznahih Junaka br 69, 76300, Bijeljina, Bosnia & Herzegovina
Tel.: (387) 55210477
DSTC—(BANJ)
Sales Range: Less than $1 Million
Emp.: 2
Real Estate Prorperty Leasing Services
N.A.I.C.S.: 531190
Mirko Savic (Member-Mgmt Bd)

DISTRICT COPPER CORP.
142-1146 Pacific Blvd, Vancouver, V6Z 2X7, BC, Canada
Tel.: (604) 620-7737
Web Site:
https://www.districtcoppercorp.com
DCOP—(TSXV)
Assets: $1,430,920
Liabilities: $35,342
Net Worth: $1,395,578
Earnings: ($560,260)
Fiscal Year-end: 10/31/23
Mineral Properties Exploration Services
N.A.I.C.S.: 213114
Jevin Werbes (Pres & CEO)

DISTRICT MINES LTD.
Suite 1003 538 West 7th Street, Vancouver, V5Z 0A1, BC, Canada
Tel.: (604) 910-1804   AB
Year Founded: 1987
CA—(CNSX)
Rev.: $18,050
Assets: $448,369
Liabilities: $672,773
Net Worth: ($224,403)
Earnings: ($295,805)
Emp.: 2
Fiscal Year-end: 12/31/21
Investment Services
N.A.I.C.S.: 211120

DISWAY SA
8 Lotissement la Colline Sidi Maarouf, Casablanca, Morocco
Tel.: (212) 522509600
Web Site: https://www.disway.com
Year Founded: 1982
Sales Range: $150-199.9 Million
Emp.: 200
Computer Peripheral Equipment Whslr

N.A.I.C.S.: 423430
Najib Hakim Belmaachi (Chm-Mgmt Bd)

DIT GROUP LIMITED
Room 7707-7708 77th Floor International Commerce Centre, 1 Austin Road West, Kowloon, China (Hong Kong)
Tel.: (852) 25013388   BM
Web Site:
http://southeastgroup.todayir.com
0726—(HKG)
Лev.: $200,641,905
Assets: $852,965,565
Liabilities: $480,863,955
Net Worth: $372,101,610
Earnings: ($19,580,813)
Emp.: 631
Fiscal Year-end: 12/31/22
Property Development & Investment Management Services
N.A.I.C.S.: 531390
Weixing Liu (Chm)

DITAS DOGAN YEDEK PARCA IMALAT VE TEKNIK A.S.
Kustepe Mahallesi Mecidiyekoy Yolu Caddesi No 12 Trump Towers Kule 2, Kat 34 Sisli, 34387, Istanbul, Turkiye
Tel.: (90) 2162420001
Web Site: https://www.ditas.com
Year Founded: 1972
DITAS—(IST)
Rev.: $51,096,035
Assets: $40,162,012
Liabilities: $29,422,380
Net Worth: $10,739,633
Earnings: ($1,283,408)
Emp.: 340
Fiscal Year-end: 12/31/23
Motor Vehicle Suspension Parts Mfr
N.A.I.C.S.: 336330
Tolga Babali (Vice Chm)

DITEMSA, S.A. DE C.V.
Blvd Luis Echeverria 1280, Saltillo, Coahuila, Mexico
Tel.: (52) 8444386200
Web Site:
http://www.ditemsa.com.mx
Foundry Tool Mfr
N.A.I.C.S.: 333248
Marco Antonio Barraza (Dir Gen)

DIV GRUPA DOO
Bobovica 10/A, HR-10430, Samobor, Croatia
Tel.: (385) 1 3377 000
Web Site: http://www.divgroup.eu
Ship Building, Mechanical Engineering, Offshore & Steel Construction Services
N.A.I.C.S.: 336611
Tomislav Debeljak (Owner & CEO)

DIVA LABORATORIES LTD.
9F No 351 Sec 2 Zhongshan Rd, Zhonghe, New Taipei City, 235, Taiwan
Tel.: (886) 222268631
Web Site: https://www.diva.com.tw
4153—(TPE)
Rev.: $29,678,392
Assets: $39,139,480
Liabilities: $7,366,914
Net Worth: $31,772,567
Earnings: $1,552,731
Emp.: 32
Fiscal Year-end: 12/31/22
Digital Advertising Services
N.A.I.C.S.: 541850
Gene Chen (Chm)

Subsidiaries:

Suzhou Diva Lab. Inc.   (1)

Room201 No 205 TangZhuang Rd, Suzhou, Jiangsu, China
Tel.: (86) 51262888268
Medical Equipment Whslr
N.A.I.C.S.: 423450

DIVA TRADE A.D.
Pop Lukina 45, 14000, Valjevo, Serbia
Tel.: (381) 14 232 739
Year Founded: 2008
Sales Range: Less than $1 Million
Commodity Contracts Dealing Services
N.A.I.C.S.: 523160
Sasa Knezevic (Exec Dir)

DIVERGENT ENERGY SERVICES CORP.
2020 715-5th Ave SW, Calgary, T2P 2X6, AB, Canada
Tel.: (403) 543-0060   AB
Web Site:
https://www.divergentenergy.com
DVG—(TSXV)
Rev.: $12,506,000
Assets: $3,112,000
Liabilities: $5,038,000
Net Worth: ($1,926,000)
Earnings: $561,000
Fiscal Year-end: 12/31/22
Oil, Gas, Utilities, Communications & Transportation Support Services
N.A.I.C.S.: 213112
Kenneth Berg (Pres & CEO)

Subsidiaries:

Extreme Pump Solutions   (1)
210 Limestone Ave, Gillette, WY 82717
Tel.: (307) 682-0999
Emp.: 30
Electric Submersible Pumps Mfr
N.A.I.C.S.: 333914
Gary Kelly (Gen Mgr)

ILI Technologies (2002) USA Corp.   (1)
4900 Woodway Dr Ste 925, Houston, TX 77056
Tel.: (713) 960-0811
Web Site: http://www.ilitech.com
Oil, Gas, Utilities, Communications & Transportation Support Services
N.A.I.C.S.: 213112

DIVERSCO SUPPLY INC.
495 Conestoga Blvd, Cambridge, N1R 7P4, ON, Canada
Tel.: (519) 740-1210
Web Site:
https://www.diverscosupply.com
Year Founded: 1986
Rev.: $24,931,116
Emp.: 50
Propane Equipment Whslr
N.A.I.C.S.: 213112
Jon Huddle (Co-Founder)

DIVERSIFIED ROYALTY CORP.
Suite 330 - 609 Granville Street, PO Box 10033, Vancouver, V7Y 1A1, BC, Canada
Tel.: (604) 235-3146
Web Site:
https://www.diversifiedroyalty.com
BEW—(DEU)
Rev.: $42,258,025
Assets: $428,418,087
Liabilities: $249,149,579
Net Worth: $179,268,508
Earnings: $23,954,672
Fiscal Year-end: 12/31/23
Investment Services
N.A.I.C.S.: 523999
Sean Morrison (Pres & CEO)

DIVERSIFIED UNITED INVESTMENT LIMITED

Level 20 101 Collins Street, Melbourne, 3000, VIC, Australia
Tel.: (61) 396540499   AU
Web Site: https://dui.com.au
Year Founded: 1991
DUI—(ASX)
Rev.: $31,061,699
Assets: $893,135,680
Liabilities: $202,832,531
Net Worth: $690,303,149
Earnings: $24,060,497
Fiscal Year-end: 06/30/24
Investment Management Service
N.A.I.C.S.: 523999
Charles Barrington Goode (Chm)

DIVESTCO INC.
Suite 2500 715 - 5th Avenue SW, Calgary, T2P 2X6, AB, Canada
Tel.: (587) 952-8000   AB
Web Site: https://www.divestco.com
DSVTF—(OTCIQ)
Sales Range: $10-24.9 Million
Emp.: 500
Oil & Gas Industry Software Developer, Data Integration & Consulting Services
N.A.I.C.S.: 541519
Stephen Popadynetz (Pres & CEO)

Subsidiaries:

Divertco USA Inc.   (1)
1900 Grant St Ste 850, Denver, CO 80203
Tel.: (303) 571-1942
Software Developer for the Oil & Gas Industry; Data, Seismic Brokerage & Technical Services
N.A.I.C.S.: 541519

DIVI ARUBA BEACH RESORT
JE Irausquin Blvd 41, Oranjestad, Aruba
Tel.: (297) 5255200
Web Site: http://www.diviaruba.com
Sales Range: $75-99.9 Million
Emp.: 1,000
Resort & Hotel
N.A.I.C.S.: 721110
Alex Nieuwmeyer (Mng Dir)

DIVIDEND SWEDEN AB
Kungsgatan 29, 111 56, Stockholm, Sweden
Tel.: (46) 840020820
Web Site:
https://www.dividendsweden.se
Year Founded: 2013
Financial Investment Services
N.A.I.C.S.: 523999
Bo Linden (CEO)

DIVINUS FABRICS LIMITED
P 37/38 IInd Floor Gomti Complex Near Ahlcon Public School, Mayur Vihar Phase 1, New Delhi, 110091, India
Tel.: (91) 11 43583832
Web Site: http://www.divinusfabrics.in
Year Founded: 1984
Rev.: $27,621
Assets: $697,793
Liabilities: $4,020
Net Worth: $693,773
Earnings: $5,022
Fiscal Year-end: 03/31/19
Fabric Product Distr
N.A.I.C.S.: 424310
Gagan Anand (Mng Dir & CFO)

DIVIS LABORATORIES LIMITED
1-72/23P/DIVIS/303 Divi Towers, Cyber Hills Gachibowli, Hyderabad, 500 032, Telangana, India
Tel.: (91) 4023786300
Web Site: http://www.divislabs.com
Year Founded: 1990

Divis Laboratories Limited—(Continued)

DIVISLAB—(NSE)
Rev.: $959,862,540
Assets: $1,470,660,555
Liabilities: $201,946,290
Net Worth: $1,268,714,265
Earnings: $270,855,585
Emp.: 5,847
Fiscal Year-end: 03/31/21
Chemical Compound Mfr
N.A.I.C.S.: 325998
Murali K. Divi *(Founder, Chm & Mng Dir)*

Subsidiaries:

Divi's Laboratories Europe AG   **(1)**
Freie Strasse 32, 4001, Basel, Switzerland
Tel.: (41) 613616767
Carotenoid Mfr
N.A.I.C.S.: 311513

Divis Laboratories (USA) Inc.   **(1)**
25A Hanover Rd Ste 300, Florham Park, NJ 07932
Tel.: (973) 993-1060
Carotenoid Mfrs
N.A.I.C.S.: 311513

DIVISO GRUPO FINANCIERO S.A.
Dionisio Derteano 184 20th Floor, San Isidro, Lima, Peru
Tel.: (51) 5122460
Web Site: https://www.diviso.pe
Year Founded: 2004
DIVIC1—(LIM)
Rev.: $39,023,831
Assets: $233,275,578
Liabilities: $204,854,668
Net Worth: $28,420,911
Earnings: ($13,475,832)
Fiscal Year-end: 12/31/23
Financial Services
N.A.I.C.S.: 523999

DIVYASHAKTI LIMITED
Flat No 1-304 3rd Floor Divyashakti Complex, Ameerpet, Hyderabad, 500 016, Telangana, India
Tel.: (91) 4023730240
Web Site: https://www.divyashakti.com
Year Founded: 1993
526315—(BOM)
Rev.: $9,151,288
Assets: $18,080,299
Liabilities: $2,032,744
Net Worth: $16,047,554
Earnings: $975,948
Fiscal Year-end: 03/31/22
Polished Granite Mfr & Distr
N.A.I.C.S.: 327991
Satyanarayana D. N. *(Compliance Officer)*

DIWANG INDUSTRIAL HOLDINGS LIMITED
No 2 Jiangshan Road Meicheng Town, Jiande, Hangzhou, Zhejiang, China
Web Site: https://www.slkj.cn
Year Founded: 2003
1950—(HKG)
Rev.: $76,825,163
Assets: $68,389,573
Liabilities: $14,707,394
Net Worth: $53,682,179
Earnings: $6,069,874
Emp.: 200
Fiscal Year-end: 12/31/22
Holding Company
N.A.I.C.S.: 551112
Ming Kei Chan *(Sec)*

DIXIE GOLD INC.
1890 - 1075 West Georgia St, Vancouver, V6E 3C9, BC, Canada

Tel.: (604) 687-2038   **AB**
Web Site: https://www.dixiegold.ca
Year Founded: 2011
DG—(TSXV)
Rev.: $16,607
Assets: $1,693,573
Liabilities: $28,566
Net Worth: $1,665,008
Earnings: ($781,702)
Fiscal Year-end: 12/31/19
Investment Services
N.A.I.C.S.: 523999
Ryan E. S. K. Cheung *(CFO)*

DIXON NETWORKS CORPORATION
7782 Progress Way, Delta, V4G 1A4, BC, Canada
Tel.: (604) 940-8817
Web Site: http://www.dixonnetworks.com
Year Founded: 1966
Rev.: $49,732,511
Emp.: 300
Engineeering Services
N.A.I.C.S.: 541330
Steve V. Sanders *(Co-Chm)*

DIXON TECHNOLOGIES (INDIA) LIMITED
B 14 & 15 Noida Phase II, Noida, 201 305, Uttar Pradesh, India
Tel.: (91) 1204737200   In
Web Site: http://www.dixoninfo.com
Year Founded: 1993
DIXON—(NSE)
Rev.: $880,390,547
Assets: $388,431,252
Liabilities: $287,788,233
Net Worth: $100,643,020
Earnings: $21,811,499
Emp.: 1,934
Fiscal Year-end: 03/31/21
Consumer Electronic Product Mfr & Distr
N.A.I.C.S.: 335220
Sunil Vachani *(Chm)*

DIXON, R B HOLDINGS LTD.
600 Broad St, Regina, S4R 8H8, SK, Canada
Tel.: (306) 543-3345
Web Site: http://www.reginamazda.ca
Rev.: $10,397,709
Emp.: 19
New & Used Car Dealers
N.A.I.C.S.: 441110
Barry Dixon *(Pres & Gen Mgr)*

DIXY GROUP AO
1st Krasnogvardeisky Proezd 15, Mercury City Tower, 123100, Moscow, Russia
Tel.: (7) 4952233337
Web Site: http://www.dixy.ru
Financial Management Services
N.A.I.C.S.: 523999

DIZBI PRIVATE LIMITED
No 1637 Suprabha 7th Sector HSR Layout, Near BDA Park Bangalore Urban, Bengaluru, 560102, Karnataka, India
Tel.: (91) 9019597000   In
Web Site: https://www.dizbi.com
Information Technology Services
N.A.I.C.S.: 541512
Dakavarapu Suresh *(Co-Founder & COO)*

DIZON COPPER-SILVER MINES, INC.
7th Floor Peaksun Bldg 1505 Princeton Street Brgy Wack-Wack, Greenhills East Metro Manila, Mandaluyong, Philippines

Tel.: (63) 288562011   **PH**
Web Site: https://www.dizminings.com
Year Founded: 1966
DIZ—(PHI)
Assets: $1,223,738
Liabilities: $664,863
Net Worth: $558,876
Earnings: $11,147
Fiscal Year-end: 12/31/23
Investment Management Service
N.A.I.C.S.: 523910
Delfin S. Castro Jr. *(Chm, Pres & Exec Dir)*

DIZZ FINANCE PLC
Dizz Buildings Carob Street, Santa Vennera, SVR 1700, Malta
Tel.: (356) 21225589
Web Site: http://www.dizz.com.mt
Year Founded: 2000
DF26A—(MAL)
Rev.: $1,063,857
Assets: $19,572,662
Liabilities: $13,221,708
Net Worth: $6,350,954
Earnings: $135,153
Fiscal Year-end: 12/31/21
Fashion Apparels Retailer
N.A.I.C.S.: 458110
Diane Izzo *(CEO)*

DJ MEDIAPRINT & LOGISTICS LTD.
24 1st Floor Palkhinwala House Tara manzil, 1st Dhobi Talao Lane, Mumbai, 400 002, Maharashtra, India
Tel.: (91) 9323185444
Web Site: https://www.djcorp.in
Year Founded: 1999
543193—(BOM)
Rev.: $3,387,764
Assets: $2,935,465
Liabilities: $1,898,905
Net Worth: $1,036,560
Earnings: $172,594
Emp.: 48
Fiscal Year-end: 03/31/21
Express Delivery Services
N.A.I.C.S.: 492110
Dinesh Muddu Kotian *(Mng Dir)*

DJERRIWARRH INVESTMENTS LIMITED
Level 21 101 Collins Street, Melbourne, 3000, VIC, Australia
Tel.: (61) 396509911   **AU**
Web Site: https://www.djerri.com.au
DJW—(ASX)
Rev.: $24,552,617
Assets: $600,746,525
Liabilities: $21,048,344
Net Worth: $579,698,181
Earnings: $26,897,703
Fiscal Year-end: 06/30/24
Investment Management
N.A.I.C.S.: 523940
Geoffrey N. Driver *(Gen Mgr-Bus Dev & IR)*

DJURSLANDS BANK A/S
Torvet 5, 8500, Grena, 8500, Denmark
Tel.: (45) 86303055
Web Site: https://www.djurslandsbank.dk
DJUR—(CSE)
Rev.: $66,095,122
Assets: $1,757,767,939
Liabilities: $1,555,341,407
Net Worth: $202,426,531
Earnings: $18,801,638
Emp.: 219
Fiscal Year-end: 12/31/22
Banking Services
N.A.I.C.S.: 522110

Jesper Vernegaard *(Deputy Mng Dir)*

DK AZTEC CO., LTD.
459-19 Jimun-ro Wongok-myeon, Anseong, Korea (South)
Tel.: (82) 70 7731 4617
Web Site: http://www.dkaztec.com
Crystal Material Mfr
N.A.I.C.S.: 327999
Seonggyun Kim *(CEO)*

DK COMPANY A/S
La Cours Vej 6, 7430, Ikast, Denmark
Tel.: (45) 96600700
Web Site: http://www.dkcompany.dk
Year Founded: 2001
Sales Range: $450-499.9 Million
Fashion & Lifestyle Brands Distr & Whslr
N.A.I.C.S.: 458110
Jens Poulsen *(Founder, Co-Owner & CEO)*

Subsidiaries:

Saint Tropez af 1993 A/S   **(1)**
Nordre Strandvej nr 119H, 3150, Hellebaek, Denmark
Tel.: (45) 49762526
Web Site: http://gb.sainttropez.com
Apparel Mfr & Distr
N.A.I.C.S.: 315990

DK ELECTRONIC MATERIALS, INC.
No 8 Yongsheng Road, Qiting Subdistrict, Yixing, 214200, Jiangsu, China
Tel.: (86) 51087825727
Web Site: http://www.dkem.cn
Year Founded: 2010
300842—(SSE)
Rev.: $528,840,468
Assets: $471,068,676
Liabilities: $338,344,344
Net Worth: $132,724,332
Earnings: ($2,431,728)
Fiscal Year-end: 12/31/22
Electronic Product Mfr & Distr
N.A.I.C.S.: 334419
Weili Shi *(Chm & Gen Mgr)*

DK TECH
25 Pyeongcheon-ro 199-gil, Bupyeong-gu, Incheon, Korea (South)
Tel.: (82) 7043243293
Year Founded: 1996
290550—(KRS)
Rev.: $278,837,439
Assets: $153,437,576
Liabilities: $76,126,058
Net Worth: $77,311,518
Earnings: $15,063,522
Emp.: 2,215
Fiscal Year-end: 12/31/22
Electronic Components Mfr
N.A.I.C.S.: 334419
Lee Ji Yull *(Pres)*

DK&D CO., LTD.
345 Byeolmang-ro, Danwon-Gu, Ansan, 15604, Gyeonggi-do, Korea (South)
Tel.: (82) 314916633
Web Site: https://www.dknd.co.kr
Year Founded: 2001
263020—(KRS)
Rev.: $84,851,713
Assets: $85,357,797
Liabilities: $37,207,703
Net Worth: $48,150,094
Earnings: $5,411,516
Emp.: 82
Fiscal Year-end: 12/31/22
Synthetic Leather Mfr
N.A.I.C.S.: 316990
Min-Seok Choi *(CEO)*

Subsidiaries:

DK Vina Co., Ltd.   (1)
Lot D10 - D11, Viet Huong Industrial Park
2- An Tay Commune, Ben Cat, Binh Duong,
Vietnam
Tel.: (84) 2743581991
Non Woven Fabric Mfr & Distr
N.A.I.C.S.: 313230

DK-LOK CORPORATION
7 Golden root-ro 129beon-gi, Juchon-
myeon, Gimhae, 621-842,
Gyeongsangnam-do, Korea (South)
Tel.: (82) 553380114
Web Site: https://www.dklok.com
Year Founded: 1986
105740—(KRS)
Rev.: $84,322,602
Assets: $132,581,766
Liabilities: $46,116,228
Net Worth: $86,465,537
Earnings: $4,483,421
Emp.: 328
Fiscal Year-end: 12/31/22
Tube Fittings & Valves Mfr & Sales
N.A.I.C.S.: 332912
Eun-Sik Noh *(CEO)*

DK-SPEC INC.
1060 chemin Olivier, Saint-Nicolas,
G7A 2M8, QC, Canada
Tel.: (418) 831-3333
Web Site: http://www.dkspec.com
Rev.: $14,718,407
Emp.: 100
Hand & Edge Tool Mfr
N.A.I.C.S.: 332216
Clermont Levasseur *(Pres)*

DKK CO., LTD.
7th floor Shin Tokyo Building 3-3-1
Marunouchi, Chiyoda-ku, Tokyo, 100-
0005, Japan
Tel.: (81) 332161671
Web Site:
   https://www.denkikogyo.co.jp
6706—(TKS)
Rev.: $190,791,040
Assets: $365,116,570
Liabilities: $109,157,540
Net Worth: $255,959,030
Earnings: ($13,067,970)
Fiscal Year-end: 03/31/24
Communication Equipment Mfr
N.A.I.C.S.: 334290
Mikio Matsuzawa *(Pres)*

Subsidiaries:

DKK (THAILAND) Co., Ltd.   (1)
Tel.: (66) 23319860
Web Site: http://www.denkikogyo.co.jp
Induction Heating Equipment Mfr
N.A.I.C.S.: 333994

DKK Manufacturing (Thailand) Co.,
Ltd.   (1)
90 Moo 3, Banchang Sub-District U-Thai
District, Phra Nakhon Si Ayutthaya, 13210,
Thailand
Tel.: (66) 3 574 6830
Heating Coil Mfr
N.A.I.C.S.: 333414

DKK of America, Inc.   (1)
6345 S Inwood Dr, Columbus, IN 47201
Tel.: (812) 342-1700
Induction Heating Equipment Mfr
N.A.I.C.S.: 333994

Denki Kogyo (Changzhou) Heat
Treatment Equipment Co., Ltd.   (1)
No 7 Lvshu 2nd Road, Xuejia town Xinbei
District, Changzhou, Jiangsu, China
Tel.: (86) 5198 512 5233
Heating Coil Mfr
N.A.I.C.S.: 333414

Denki Kogyo Co., Ltd. - Atsugi
Plant   (1)
Nairiku Industrial Park 4052-1 Nakatsu,

Aiko-gun, Aikawa, 243-0303, Kanagawa,
Japan
Tel.: (81) 46 285 1411
Web Site: http://www.denkikogyo.co.jp
Induction Heating Equipment Mfr
N.A.I.C.S.: 333994

Denki Kogyo Co., Ltd. - Kanuma
Plant   (1)
Kanuma Industrial Park 13-4 Satsuki-cho,
Kanuma, 322-0014, Tochigi, Japan
Tel.: (81) 289 76 2275
Web Site: http://www.denkikogyo.co.jp
Telecommunication Antenna Mfr
N.A.I.C.S.: 334220

Denki Kogyo Co., Ltd. - Kawagoe
Plant   (1)
2-8-76 Yoshinodai, Kawagoe, 350-0833,
Saitama, Japan
Tel.: (81) 49 225 5100
Web Site: http://www.denkikogyo.co.jp
Sales Range: $25-49.9 Million
Emp.: 50
Telecommunication Steel Tower Mfr
N.A.I.C.S.: 332312

Denki Kogyo Co., Ltd. - Suzuka
Plant   (1)
1820-39 Mikkaichi-cho, Suzuka, 513-0803,
Mie, Japan
Tel.: (81) 593821829
Induction Heating Equipment Mfr
N.A.I.C.S.: 333994

Denko Co., Ltd.   (1)
2-8-76 Yoshinodai, Kawagoe, 350-0833,
Saitama, Japan
Tel.: (81) 492255100
Web Site: https://denko-dnk.co.jp
Emp.: 250
Steel Tower Mfr & Distr
N.A.I.C.S.: 332312

Denko Seisakusho Co., Ltd.   (1)
637-1 Moro, Kanuma, 322-0026, Tochigi,
Japan
Tel.: (81) 289762258
Web Site: https://www.denko-ss.co.jp
Emp.: 67
Antenna Peripheral Equipment Mfr
N.A.I.C.S.: 334220

Denko Techno Heat Co., Ltd.   (1)
15 Ogumi Hajodo-cho, Kariya, 448-0804,
Aichi, Japan
Tel.: (81) 56 621 0681
Heating Coil Mfr & Distr
N.A.I.C.S.: 333414

Denko Techno Heat Co., Ltd. - Ha-
mamatsu Plant   (1)
170 Tsumori-cho, Minami-ku, Hamamatsu,
430-0815, Shizuoka, Japan
Tel.: (81) 53 441 8451
Web Site: http://www.denkikogyo.co.jp
Induction Heating Equipment Mfr
N.A.I.C.S.: 333994

Fukoku Denko Co., Ltd.   (1)
1-15-8 Sanno, Hakata-ku, Fukuoka, 812-
0015, Japan
Tel.: (81) 924525311
Web Site: https://www.fukokud.co.jp
Telecommunication Equipment Distr
N.A.I.C.S.: 423690
Kenji Nakajima *(Pres & Dir)*

Koshuha Co., Ltd.   (1)
4052-1 Nakatsu, Aiko-gun, Aikawa, 243-
0303, Kanagawa, Japan
Tel.: (81) 46 286 8175
Web Site: http://www.koshuha-kogyo.jp
Sales Range: $50-74.9 Million
Emp.: 75
Induction Heating Equipment Mfr
N.A.I.C.S.: 333994
Masatomo Kitamura *(Chm & Mgr)*

DKK-TOA CORPORATION
1-29-10 Takadanobaba, Shinjuku-ku,
Tokyo, 169-8648, Japan
Tel.: (81) 332020211
Web Site: https://www.toadkk.co.jp
Year Founded: 1944
6848—(TKS)
Rev.: $115,304,840
Assets: $191,974,230

Liabilities: $44,115,140
Net Worth: $147,859,090
Earnings: $8,540,120
Emp.: 132
Fiscal Year-end: 03/31/24
Measuring Instrument Mfr & Whslr
N.A.I.C.S.: 334513
Yasuo Yamamori *(Chm)*

Subsidiaries:

Bionics Instrument Co., Ltd.   (1)
6-1254-2 Shimizu, Higashiyamato, 207-
0004, Tokyo, Japan
Tel.: (81) 425614856
Emp.: 55
Measuring & Controlling Device Mfr
N.A.I.C.S.: 334519
Kenji Muroi *(Pres)*

DKK-TOA Alice Corporation   (1)
613 Kitairiso, Sayama, 350 1315, Saitama,
Japan
Tel.: (81) 429597141
Measuring Instrument Distr
N.A.I.C.S.: 423830

DKK-TOA Analytica Corporation   (1)
214 2-Chome, Sakuragaoka
Higashiyamato-shi, Tokyo, 207-0022, Japan
Tel.: (81) 425672727
Measuring Equipment Distr
N.A.I.C.S.: 423830
Satoshi Aonuma *(Pres)*

DKK-TOA Iwate Corporation   (1)
9-9-3 Misazaki, Ayaori-cho Tono city, Iwate,
028-0534, Japan
Tel.: (81) 198625800
Measuring Equipment Distr
N.A.I.C.S.: 423830

DKLS INDUSTRIES BERHAD
16th Floor and Penthouse Ipoh Tower
Jalan Dato Seri Ahmad Said, 30450,
Ipoh, Perak Darul Ridzuan, Malaysia
Tel.: (60) 52532688
Web Site: https://www.dkls.com.my
Year Founded: 1995
DKLS—(KLS)
Rev.: $38,032,463
Assets: $108,412,194
Liabilities: $18,810,099
Net Worth: $89,602,095
Earnings: $2,391,148
Emp.: 231
Fiscal Year-end: 12/31/22
Construction & Property Management
Services
N.A.I.C.S.: 531311
Soo King Ding *(Exec Dir-Fin)*

Subsidiaries:

DKLS Construction Sdn Bhd   (1)
16th Floor & Penthouse Ipoh Tower Jalan
Dato Seri Ahmad Said, 30450, Ipoh, Perak,
Malaysia
Tel.: (60) 52532688
Sales Range: $25-49.9 Million
Emp.: 30
Property Development & Construction Ser-
vices
N.A.I.C.S.: 531390
Ding Poibor *(Mgr)*

DKLS Development Sdn. Bhd.   (1)
No 1 Bizhub DKLS Lot 55005 Jalan Raja
Omar, 32000, Sitiawan, Perak, Malaysia
Tel.: (60) 56925531
Web Site: https://dklsproperty.com
Property Construction Services
N.A.I.C.S.: 236116
Julia Koo *(Mgr)*

DKLS Energy Sdn. Bhd.   (1)
16th Floor & Penthouse Ipoh Tower Jalan
Dato Seri Ahmad Said, 30450, Ipoh, Perak,
Malaysia
Tel.: (60) 52532688
Web Site: http://www.dkls.com.my
Emp.: 200
Hydroelectric Power Generation Services
N.A.I.C.S.: 221111
Kong Aheoon *(Mgr-Contract)*

DKLS Equity Sdn Bhd   (1)

Wisma DKLS Tower 8 Avenue 5, Bangsar
South City, 59200, Kuala Lumpur, Malaysia
Tel.: (60) 52532688
Property Investment Services
N.A.I.C.S.: 531190

DKLS Marketing Sdn. Bhd.   (1)
No 1 BizHub DKLS Lot 55005 Jalan Raja
Omar, 32000, Sitiawan, Perak, Malaysia
Tel.: (60) 56914660
Building Materials Distr
N.A.I.C.S.: 423390

DKLS Precast System Sdn Bhd   (1)
16th Floor & Penthouse Ipoh Tower Jln
Dato Seri Ahmad Said, 30450, Ipoh, Perak,
Malaysia
Tel.: (60) 56833146
Sales Range: $75-99.9 Million
Emp.: 150
Precast Concrete Mfr & Distr
N.A.I.C.S.: 327390

DKLS Premierhome Sdn Bhd   (1)
GFR-01 Ground Floor Ipoh Tower Jalan
Dato' Seri Ahmad Said, 30450, Ipoh, Perak,
Malaysia
Tel.: (60) 52532876
Web Site: https://dklspremierhome.com.my
Property Development Services
N.A.I.C.S.: 531312

DKLS Quarry & Premix Sdn.
Bhd.   (1)
Jalan 5KM Sitiawan Lumut, 32200, Lumut,
Perak, Malaysia
Tel.: (60) 56914660
Sales Range: $50-74.9 Million
Emp.: 30
Sand Quarrying Services
N.A.I.C.S.: 212321
Lawrence Ling *(Mgr-Quarry)*

DKLS Signaturehomes Sdn.
Bhd.   (1)
C607 Level 6 Block C Kelana Square Jalan
SS7/26, 47301, Petaling Jaya, Selangor,
Malaysia
Tel.: (60) 327764847
Web Site:
   https://www.dklssignaturehomes.com.my
Property Rental Services
N.A.I.C.S.: 531110

DKS CO. LTD.
48-2 Higashikujo-Kamitonodacho,
Minami-ku, Kyoto, 601-8002, Japan
Tel.: (81) 752763030
Web Site: https://www.dks-web.co.jp
Year Founded: 1909
4461—(TKS)
Rev.: $417,209,980
Assets: $624,889,570
Liabilities: $351,916,400
Net Worth: $272,973,170
Earnings: $7,760,140
Emp.: 584
Fiscal Year-end: 03/31/24
Surfactant Mfr & Distr
N.A.I.C.S.: 325998
Sakamoto Takashi *(Chm & CEO)*

Subsidiaries:

DKS (Shanghai) International Trading
Co., Ltd.   (1)
Room 1104 New Town Center Building 83
Loushanguan Rd, Changning, Shanghai,
China
Tel.: (86) 2162368080
Web Site: http://www.dksshweb.isitestar.vip
Chemical Products Distr
N.A.I.C.S.: 424690

Dai-ichi Ceramo Co., Ltd.   (1)
432 Gokasho Hiyoshi-cho, Higashiomi, 529-
1403, Shiga, Japan
Tel.: (81) 748485377
Chemical Products Mfr
N.A.I.C.S.: 325998
Miura Hiroyuki *(Chm)*

Dai-ichi Kenkou Co., Ltd.   (1)
8th Floor Yaesuguchi Daiei Building 1-3-1
Kyobashi, Chuo-ku, Tokyo, 104-0031, Japan
Tel.: (81) 332750583

DKS Co. Ltd.—(Continued)

Chemical Product Mfr & Distr
N.A.I.C.S.: 325998

Elexcel Corporation (1)
13th Floor Laboratory Keihanna Plaza 1-7
Hikaridai, Soraku-gun Seikacho, Kyoto,
619-0237, Japan
Tel.: (81) 774 98 2673
Web Site: http://www.elexcel.co.jp
Lithium Battery Mfr
N.A.I.C.S.: 335910

Gembu Co., Ltd. (1)
5 Kisshoin Okawaramachi, Minami-ku,
Kyoto, 601-8391, Japan
Tel.: (81) 753235740
Detergent Distr
N.A.I.C.S.: 424690

Kyoto Elex Co., Ltd. (1)
1 Oogawaracho Kisshoin, Minami-ku,
Kyoto, 601-8391, Japan
Tel.: (81) 753262883
Chemical Product Mfr & Distr
N.A.I.C.S.: 325998
Hiroyuki Matsumura (Pres)

Yokkaichi Chemical Co., Ltd. (1)
2-1 Miyahigashi-cho, Yokkaichi, 510-0843,
Mie, Japan
Tel.: (81) 593451161
Chemical Products Mfr
N.A.I.C.S.: 325998

Subsidiary (Domestic):

**Yokkaichi Chemical Co., Ltd. -
Rokuromi Facility** (2)
710 Oaza Rokuromi, Yokkaichi, 510-0881,
Mie, Japan
Tel.: (81) 593461166
Chemical Products Mfr
N.A.I.C.S.: 325998

DL CONSTRUCTION CO., LTD.
1143-6 Guwol-Dong, Namdong-Gu,
Incheon, Korea (South)
Tel.: (82) 325183535
Web Site:
http://www.dlconstruction.co.kr
Year Founded: 1956
001880—(KRS)
Rev.: $1,505,175,630
Assets: $1,339,808,492
Liabilities: $573,808,798
Net Worth: $765,999,694
Earnings: $42,508,046
Emp.: 1,035
Fiscal Year-end: 12/31/22
Commercial Building Construction
Services
N.A.I.C.S.: 236220
Sang-Taek Lee (Exec Dir)

DL HOLDINGS GROUP LIM-
ITED
5/F AIA Financial Centre 112 King
Fuk Street San Po Kong, Kowloon,
China (Hong Kong)
Tel.: (852) 3 471 8000   Ky
Web Site:
http://www.seasonpacific.com
Year Founded: 2013
1709—(HKG)
Rev.: $39,863,204
Assets: $117,988,324
Liabilities: $50,124,079
Net Worth: $67,864,246
Earnings: $14,158,780
Emp.: 67
Fiscal Year-end: 03/31/22
Apparel Product Distr
N.A.I.C.S.: 424310
Ying Ying Chin (Sec)

DL SOFTWARE
50 rue de Monceau, 75008, Paris,
France
Tel.: (33) 158572294
Web Site: http://www.dlsoftware.fr
Software Producer

N.A.I.C.S.: 513210
Jean-Noel Drouin (CEO)

DLA PIPER BAZ NLD SPA
Av El Golf 150 Piso 10, CP 7550107,
Las Condes, Santiago, Chile
Tel.: (56) 2 2798 2600   CL
Web Site: http://www.dlapiper.cl
Law firm
N.A.I.C.S.: 541110
Matias Zegers (Partner-Corp Area)

DLA PIPER GLOBAL
3 Noble Street, London, EC2V 7EE,
United Kingdom
Tel.: (44) 20 7153 7127
Web Site: http://www.dlapiper.com
Legal & Advisory Services Organiza-
tion
N.A.I.C.S.: 813910
Roger Meltzer (Co-Chm-USA)

Subsidiaries:

DLA Piper International LLP (1)
3 Noble Street, London, EC2V 7EE, United
Kingdom
Tel.: (44) 20 7153 7127
Web Site: http://www.dlapiper.com
Emp.: 1,000
Holding Company; Legal & Advisory Ser-
vices
N.A.I.C.S.: 551112
Nigel Knowles (Chm)

Affiliate (Non-US):

DLA Piper Australia (2)
Level 22 No 1 Martin Place, Sydney, 2000,
NSW, Australia
Tel.: (61) 2 9286 8000
Web Site: http://www.dlapiper.com
Law firm
N.A.I.C.S.: 541110
Gitanjali Bajaj (Partner)

Branch (Domestic):

DLA Piper Australia - Melbourne (3)
Level 21 140 William Street, Melbourne,
3000, VIC, Australia
Tel.: (61) 3 9274 5000
Web Site: http://www.dlapiper.com
Emp.: 215
Law firm
N.A.I.C.S.: 541110
James Newnham (Partner)

Affiliate (Non-US):

**DLA Piper Denmark Law Firm
P/S** (2)
Raadhuspladsen 4, 1550, Copenhagen, V,
Denmark
Tel.: (45) 3334 0000
Web Site: http://www.dlapiper.com
Emp.: 300
Law firm
N.A.I.C.S.: 541110
Sebastian Ingversen (Partner & Head-Corp
Mergers & Acq)

DLA Piper Gallastegui y Lozano (2)
Paseo de los Tamarindos No 400 A Piso
31, Col Bosques de las Lomas, 05120,
Mexico, Mexico
Tel.: (52) 5552611800
Web Site: http://www.dlapiper.com
Legal & Advisory Services Organization
N.A.I.C.S.: 813910

Subsidiary (Domestic):

**Gonzalez Luna, Moreno y Armida,
S.C.** (3)
Av Paseo de la Reforma 925 Lomas de
Chapultepec, Mexico, 11000, Mexico
Tel.: (52) 55 11 00 38 80
Law firm
N.A.I.C.S.: 541110

Affiliate (Non-US):

DLA Piper Kuwait (2)
Suad Commercial Complex 9th Floor Block
A, Kuwait, Kuwait
Tel.: (965) 2247 2317
Web Site: http://www.dlapiper.com

Emp.: 11
Law firm
N.A.I.C.S.: 541110

DLA Piper Rus Ltd. (2)
Leontievsky Pereulok 25, 125009, Moscow,
Russia
Tel.: (7) 495 221 4400
Web Site: http://www.dlapiper.com
Law firm
N.A.I.C.S.: 541110
Sergey Koltchin (Partner)

Affiliate (Domestic):

DLA Piper UK LLP (2)
3 Noble Street, London, EC2V 7EE, United
Kingdom
Tel.: (44) 8700 111 111
Web Site: http://www.dlapiper.com
Emp.: 1,232
Law firm
N.A.I.C.S.: 541110

DLA Piper LLP (US) (1)
6225 Smith Ave, Baltimore, MD 21209-3626
Tel.: (410) 580-3000
Web Site: http://www.dlapiper.com
Emp.: 300
Law firm
N.A.I.C.S.: 541110
Roger Meltzer (Co-Chm)

Affiliate (Non-US):

DLA Piper (Canada) LLP (2)
666 Burrard Street 2800 Park Place, Van-
couver, V6C 2Z7, BC, Canada
Tel.: (604) 687-9444
Web Site: http://www.dlapiper.com
Emp.: 200
Law firm
N.A.I.C.S.: 541110
Chris Bennett (Partner)

Branch (Domestic):

**DLA Piper LLP (US) - Washington,
D.C.** (2)
500 8th St NW, Washington, DC 20004-
1404
Tel.: (202) 799-4000
Web Site: http://www.dlapiper.com
Law firm
N.A.I.C.S.: 541110
Matthew C. Bernstein (Partner)

Liner LLP (1)
1100 Glendon Ave, Los Angeles, CA 90024-
3518
Tel.: (310) 500-3500
Law firm
N.A.I.C.S.: 541110
Angela C. Agrusa (Partner)

DLALA BROKERAGE AND IN-
VESTMENTS HOLDING COM-
PANY Q.SC
386 Salwa Road, Doha, Qatar
Tel.: (974) 44285444
Web Site:
https://www.dlalaholding.com
Year Founded: 2005
DBIS—(QE)
Rev.: $9,737,890
Assets: $214,210,424
Liabilities: $156,905,428
Net Worth: $57,304,996
Earnings: $1,790,194
Fiscal Year-end: 12/31/20
Brokerage Services
N.A.I.C.S.: 524210
Suhaim Khalid Al-Thani (Chm)

Subsidiaries:

**Dlala Islamic Brokerage Company
(W.L.L)** (1)
PO Box 24571, Doha, Qatar
Tel.: (974) 44285444
Web Site: http://www.dlalaislamic.com
Securities Brokerage Services
N.A.I.C.S.: 523150

Dlala Real Estate S.P.C. (1)
Dlala Holding Building Salwa Road, PO Box
24571, Azizia, Doha, Qatar
Tel.: (974) 4 428 6660

Web Site: https://www.dlalarealestate.com
Real Estate Manangement Services
N.A.I.C.S.: 531390

DLC ASIA LTD.
Units 2601-3 Tai Tung Building 8
Fleming Road, Wanchai, China
(Hong Kong)
Tel.: (852) 2 811 8281   Ky
Web Site: http://www.derivaasia.com
8210—(HKG)
Rev.: $7,174,384
Assets: $12,242,137
Liabilities: $853,332
Net Worth: $11,388,805
Earnings: ($457,234)
Emp.: 29
Fiscal Year-end: 03/31/21
Securities Brokerage Services
N.A.I.C.S.: 523150
Lambert Ming Yeung Lau (Chm)

DLC HOLDINGS CORP.
1600-609 Granville Street, Vancou-
ver, V7Y 1C3, BC, Canada
Tel.: (604) 669-1322   BC
Rev.: $25,796
Assets: $13,047,215
Liabilities: $880,994
Net Worth: $12,166,221
Earnings: ($4,363,452)
Fiscal Year-end: 12/31/18
Investment Services
N.A.I.C.S.: 523999
Tamra Spink (CFO)

DLE INC.
7th Floor KDX Kojimachi Building
3-3-4 Kojimachi, Chiyoda-ku, Tokyo,
102-0083, Japan
Tel.: (81) 332213990
Web Site: http://www.dle.jp
3686—(TKS)
Rev.: $11,270,050
Assets: $23,895,150
Liabilities: $4,448,530
Net Worth: $19,446,620
Earnings: ($3,437,200)
Emp.: 132
Fiscal Year-end: 03/31/24
Movie & Video Production
N.A.I.C.S.: 512110

DLF AMBA
Ny Ostergade 9, 4000, Roskilde,
Denmark
Tel.: (45) 46 33 03 00
Web Site: http://www.dlf.com
Year Founded: 1988
Grass & Clover Seed Producer &
Whslr
N.A.I.C.S.: 111199
Stig Oddershede (Head-Comm)

Subsidiaries:

Pickseed West Inc. (1)
33149 Hwy 99 E, Tangent, OR 97389
Tel.: (541) 926-8886
Web Site: http://www.pickseed.com
Sales Range: $10-24.9 Million
Emp.: 45
Grass Seed Whslr
N.A.I.C.S.: 561730
Martin C. Pick (Sec & VP)

DLF LIMITED
DLF Gateway Tower R Block DLF
City Phase-III, Gurgaon, 122002,
Haryana, India
Tel.: (91) 1244568900   In
Web Site: https://www.dlf.in
Year Founded: 1946
DLF—(NSE)
Rev.: $726,266,524
Assets: $6,514,501,289
Liabilities: $1,961,320,010
Net Worth: $4,553,181,278
Earnings: $245,700,749

Emp.: 2,417
Fiscal Year-end: 03/31/23
Real Estate Services
N.A.I.C.S.: 531110
Subhash Setia *(Officer-Compliance & Sec)*

Subsidiaries:

Amancruises Company Limited **(1)**
PO Box 292, Muang Phuket, Phuket, 83000, Thailand
Tel.: (66) 76271162
Web Site: http://www.amanpuri.th.com
Sales Range: $200-249.9 Million
Emp.: 500
Boat & Yacht Rental Services
N.A.I.C.S.: 532284

Amanresorts International Private Limited **(1)**
1 Orchard Spring Ln No 05-01 Tourism Ct, Singapore, 247729, Singapore
Tel.: (65) 6883 2555
Web Site: http://www.aman.com
Resort Operation & Maintenance Services
N.A.I.C.S.: 541611

Amanresorts Limited **(1)**
12th Fl Friendship Comml Bldg 105 Hollywood Rd, Central, China (Hong Kong)
Tel.: (852) 28685005
Sales Range: $10-24.9 Million
Emp.: 10
Hotel & Motel Management Services
N.A.I.C.S.: 721110

DLF Akruti Info Parks (Pune) Limited **(1)**
Akruti Trade Ctr 6th Fl Rd No 7 Marol M I D C, Andheri E, Mumbai, 400093, Maharashtra, India
Tel.: (91) 2266772301
Special Economic Zone Development Services
N.A.I.C.S.: 236220

DLF Cyber City Developers Limited **(1)**
10th Floor Gateway Tower DLF City Phase-III, Near Naaz Cinema Complex, Gurgaon, 122 002, Haryana, India
Tel.: (91) 1244568900
Web Site: https://www.dlf.in
Property Development Services
N.A.I.C.S.: 531311

DLF Emporio Limited **(1)**
4 Nelson Mandela Marg, Vasant Kunj, Delhi, 110 070, India
Tel.: (91) 1146116666
Web Site: https://www.dlfemporio.com
Shopping Center Services
N.A.I.C.S.: 455219

DLF Estate Developers Limited **(1)**
Shopping Mall Arjun Marg, DLF City Phase I, Gurgaon, 122 002, Haryana, India
Tel.: (91) 1242350418
Real Estate Property Development Services
N.A.I.C.S.: 531390

DLF Financial Services Limited **(1)**
DLF Centre Sansad Marg, New Delhi, 110 001, India
Tel.: (91) 1123719300
Real Estate Investment Services
N.A.I.C.S.: 531110

DLF Golf Resort Limited **(1)**
Golf Course Road DLF5, Gurgaon, 122 009, Haryana, India
Tel.: (91) 1244525274
Web Site: http://www.dlfgolfresort.com
Sales Range: $125-149.9 Million
Emp.: 325
Golf Course Development & Management Services
N.A.I.C.S.: 237990

DLF Home Developers Limited **(1)**
2nd Floor Arjun Marg DLF Shopping Mall DLF City Phase-I, Sansad Marg, Gurgaon, 122002, India
Tel.: (91) 1142102030
Residential Property Development Services
N.A.I.C.S.: 236116
Devinder Singh *(Mng Dir)*

DLF Info City Developers (Chennai) Ltd. **(1)**

No 1 124 Shivaji Garden, Manapakkam Ramapuram, Chennai, 600089, Tamil Nadu, India
Tel.: (91) 4445497001
Property Development Services
N.A.I.C.S.: 531311

DLF International Holdings Pte Limited **(1)**
9 Temasek Blvd, Singapore, 038989, Singapore
Tel.: (65) 6305 2819
Sales Range: $50-74.9 Million
Emp.: 2
Property Management Services
N.A.I.C.S.: 531312

DLF Projects Limited **(1)**
3rd Floor DLF Shopping Mall Arjun Marg, DLF City Phase I, Gurgaon, 122002, Haryana, India
Tel.: (91) 1244769000
Sales Range: $1-4.9 Billion
Real Estate Manangement Services
N.A.I.C.S.: 531390

DLF Promenade Limited **(1)**
3 Nelson Mandela Road, Vasant Kunj Malls, New Delhi, 110 070, India
Tel.: (91) 1146104466
Web Site: https://www.dlfpromenade.com
Shopping Center Services
N.A.I.C.S.: 455219

DLF Recreational Foundation Limited **(1)**
DLF City Club Phase-IV Opposite Galleria Market, DLF City Phase IV, Gurgaon, 122002, Haryana, India
Tel.: (91) 1244129100
Web Site: http://www.thecityclub.in
Emp.: 250
Real Estate Manangement Services
N.A.I.C.S.: 531210

DLF Retail Developers Limited **(1)**
DLF Ctr Sansad Marg, New Delhi, 110 017, India
Tel.: (91) 1123719300
Sales Range: $50-74.9 Million
Emp.: 12
Property Development & Management Services
N.A.I.C.S.: 531312

DLF Universal Limited **(1)**
DLF Ctr Sansad Marg, New Delhi, 110001, India
Tel.: (91) 1123719300
Real Estate Development & Management Services
N.A.I.C.S.: 531311

DLF Utilities Limited **(1)**
3rd Floor Shopping Mall Arjun Marg, DLF City Phase-I, Gurgaon, 122002, Haryana, India
Tel.: (91) 1244778718
Project Construction Services
N.A.I.C.S.: 237110

P.T. Amanresorts Indonesia **(1)**
Jalan Nusa Dua Selatan, PO Box 33, Nusa Dua, Bali, 80361, Indonesia
Tel.: (62) 361772333
Web Site: http://www.amanresorts.com
Sales Range: $25-49.9 Million
Emp.: 175
Home Management Services
N.A.I.C.S.: 721110
Sean Flakelar *(Office Mgr)*

Shivajimarg Properties Limited **(1)**
1-E Jhandewalan Extn 3rd Fl D Wing, Near Naaz Cinema Complex, New Delhi, 110 055, India
Tel.: (91) 1143013248
Real Estate Development Services
N.A.I.C.S.: 531210

Silverlink Holdings Limited **(1)**
Stockbridge House Trinity Gardens, Newcastle upon Tyne, NE1 2HJ, Tyne And Wear, United Kingdom
Tel.: (44) 1912220607
Web Site: http://www.cloustongroup.com
Sales Range: $50-74.9 Million
Emp.: 9
Property Development Services
N.A.I.C.S.: 531312

David Clouston *(Mng Dir)*

DLF SEEDS A/S
Ny Oestergade 9, 4000, Roskilde, Denmark
Tel.: (45) 46 330 300　　　　**DK**
Web Site: http://www.dlf.com
Year Founded: 2005
Forage & Amenity Seeds & Other Crops Producer & Supplier
N.A.I.C.S.: 111998
Christian Hoegh-Andersen *(Chm)*

Subsidiaries:

PGG Wrightson Seeds Limited **(1)**
57 Waterloo Road, Hornby, Christchurch, 8142, New Zealand
Tel.: (64) 800 805505
Web Site:
　http://www.pggwrightsonseeds.com
Agro Products Mfr & Distr
N.A.I.C.S.: 111199
Paul Kenny *(Mgr-Natl Sls & Mktg)*

Subsidiary (Domestic):

Agricom Limited **(2)**
PO Box 3761, Christchurch, New Zealand
Tel.: (64) 33414580
Web Site: http://www.agricom.co.nz
Sales Range: $25-49.9 Million
Emp.: 12
Forage Seeds Distr
N.A.I.C.S.: 424910
Mark Brown *(Mgr-Sls & Mktg)*

DLG EXHIBITIONS & EVENTS CORP LTD.
16th Floor Greenbelt Bund Center 55 Huiguan Street, Huangpu District, Shanghai, 200437, China
Tel.: (86) 13916126899
Web Site: https://www.dlg-expo.com
Year Founded: 1983
600826—(SHG)
Rev.: $108,541,569
Assets: $808,793,463
Liabilities: $305,231,931
Net Worth: $503,561,532
Earnings: $16,076,937
Fiscal Year-end: 12/31/22
Consumer Goods Store Operator
N.A.I.C.S.: 445110
Chen Xiaohong *(Co-Chm)*

Subsidiaries:

Shanghai East Best Convention & Exhibition management Co., Ltd. **(1)**
1099 Guo Zhan Road, Shanghai, China
Tel.: (86) 2120893600
Web Site: http://www.shexpocenter.com
Furniture Leasing & Management Services
N.A.I.C.S.: 532420

Shanghai Industry & Commerce Exhibition Co., Ltd. **(1)**
15F Building T3 Greenland Bund Center No 55 Huiguan Street, Huangpu District, Shanghai, China
Tel.: (86) 2122068388
Product Design & Logistics Services
N.A.I.C.S.: 541614

Shanghai International Trade Promotion Co., Ltd. **(1)**
12th Floor Jincheng Building, No 511 Tianmu West Road, Shanghai, 200070, China
Tel.: (86) 2163539977
Human Resouce Services
N.A.I.C.S.: 541612

Shanghai Lansheng Real Estate Co., Ltd. **(1)**
34/F Lansheng Mansion No 8 Huaihai M Rd Luwan Dist, Shanghai, 200021, China
Tel.: (86) 2163862590
Web Site: http://www.ls-bldg.com.cn
Real Estate Manangement Services
N.A.I.C.S.: 531210

Shanghai Modern International Exhibition Co., Ltd. **(1)**

15th floor Greenbelt Bund Center 55 Huiguan Street, Huangpu District, Shanghai, 200011, China
Tel.: (86) 2163288899
Web Site: https://www.chinamie.com
Design & Construction Services
N.A.I.C.S.: 236220

DLOCAL LTD.
Dr Luis Bonavita 1294, 11300, Montevideo, 11300, Uruguay
Tel.: (598) 4243927437　　　**Ky**
Web Site: https://www.dlocal.com
Year Founded: 2021
DLO—(NASDAQ)
Rev.: $650,351,000
Assets: $1,084,453,000
Liabilities: $629,313,000
Net Worth: $455,140,000
Earnings: $149,086,000
Emp.: 901
Fiscal Year-end: 12/31/23
Digital Marketing Services
N.A.I.C.S.: 541870
Jacobo Singer *(Co-Pres & COO)*

DLP RESOURCES INC.
201 - 135 - 10th Ave S, Cranbrook, V1C 2N1, BC, Canada
Tel.: (250) 426-7808
Web Site:
　https://www.dlpresourcesinc.com
DLP—(OTCIQ)
Assets: $1,181,625
Liabilities: $137,807
Net Worth: $1,043,817
Earnings: ($1,940,194)
Fiscal Year-end: 04/30/21
Real Estate Development Services
N.A.I.C.S.: 531390
James Stypula *(CEO)*

DLS LAND UND SEE SPEDITIONSGESELLSCHAFT MBH
Jacobsrade 1, Siek, 22962, Hamburg, Germany
Tel.: (49) 410787700
Web Site: http://www.dls-logistics.de
Year Founded: 1986
Rev.: $81,961,441
Emp.: 200
Transport & Logistic Solution Services
N.A.I.C.S.: 488390
Bodo Engler *(CEO)*

Subsidiaries:

dls Trans Ltd. Sp. z o.o **(1)**
Ul Modlinska 3, 81-260, Gdynia, Poland
Tel.: (48) 58667333034
Oil Transportation Services
N.A.I.C.S.: 481112
Radoslaw Magiera *(Mgr-Sls)*

dls-Eurasia TOO **(1)**
Ul Gogolja 39A Office 403, Almaty, Kazakhstan
Tel.: (7) 7272448602
Oil Transportation Services
N.A.I.C.S.: 481112

dls-Russija, Ltd **(1)**
Gorbunova St 2 building 3 Business Center Grand Setun Plasa off A809, 121596, Moscow, Russia
Tel.: (7) 4952696290
Web Site: http://www.dls-logistics.ru
Oil Transportation Services
N.A.I.C.S.: 481112

DLSA AUTOMOBILES
29-31 Rue de Paris, 95310, Saint-Ouen-l'Aumone, France
Tel.: (33) 134485656
Web Site: http://www.dlsaauto.com
Rev.: $21,900,000
Emp.: 30
New & Used Car Dealers
N.A.I.C.S.: 441110
Michelle Lemonier *(Mgr-Fin)*

DLSA Automobiles—(Continued)

DLSI SA
avenue Jean Eric Bousch, PO Box 40163, 57603, Forbach, France
Tel.: (33) 387881280
Web Site:
https://www.groupedlsi.com
Year Founded: 1992
ALDLS—(EUR)
Employment Agency Services
N.A.I.C.S.: 561311
Jean-Marie Nantern *(CFO)*

DLT ASA
Grundingen 2, 0250, Oslo, Norway
Tel.: (47) 23082308
Web Site:
http://www.elementasa.com
Year Founded: 1996
ELE—(OSL)
Rev.: $156,000
Assets: $7,660,000
Liabilities: $788,000
Net Worth: $6,872,000
Earnings: ($14,048,000)
Fiscal Year-end: 12/31/19
Investment Management Service
N.A.I.C.S.: 523940
Thomas Christensen *(Chm)*

Subsidiaries:

Intex Resources Philippines, Inc. **(1)**
Unit 13E 13th Flr Strata 100 Bldg F Ortigas Jr Road, Ortigas Center, Pasig, 1605, Philippines
Tel.: (63) 2 687 4161
Web Site: http://www.intexresources.com.ph
Mineral Exploration Services
N.A.I.C.S.: 213114
Joselito R. Bacani *(Gen Mgr)*

DM HEALTHCARE MANAGE-MENT SERVICES LLC
702-703 Khalid Bin Al Walid Street, PO Box 8703, Dubai, United Arab Emirates
Tel.: (971) 4 3933033
Web Site:
http://asterdmhealthcare.com
Year Founded: 1987
Specialty Hospitals, Diagnostic Centers, Medical Clinics & Pharmacies Owner & Operator
N.A.I.C.S.: 622310
Azad Moopen *(Chm & Mng Dir)*

DM PLC
Green Heys Walford Road, Ross-on-Wye, HR9 5DB, Herefordshire, United Kingdom
Tel.: (44) 1989769292   UK
Web Site: http://www.dmplc.com
Sales Range: $25-49.9 Million
Emp.: 120
Holding Company; Directory Database Management & Home Gaming Direct Marketer
N.A.I.C.S.: 551112
Adrian John Williams *(Owner & Chm)*

Subsidiaries:

Data Locator Group Limited **(1)**
64 Clarendon Rd, Watford, WD17 1DA, Hertfordshire, United Kingdom
Tel.: (44) 1923281700
Web Site: http://www.dlg.co.uk
Sales Range: $25-49.9 Million
Emp.: 80
Consumer Data Collection & Analysis Services
N.A.I.C.S.: 541910
Graham Tomblin *(Grp Dir-Sls)*

McIntyre Dodd Marketing Ltd **(1)**
Green Heys Walford Road, Ross-on-Wye, HR9 5DB, Herefordshire, United Kingdom
Tel.: (44) 1989769797
Web Site: http://www.mcintyreanddodd.com

Home Gaming & Competition Operation Services
N.A.I.C.S.: 713290

PDV Ltd **(1)**
3rd Floor 64 Clarendon Road, Watford, WD17 1DA, Hertfordshire, United Kingdom
Tel.: (44) 1923478060
Web Site: http://www.pdvltd.com
Sales Range: $25-49.9 Million
Emp.: 20
Online Marketing Services
N.A.I.C.S.: 541613
Nigel Goldthorpe *(Mng Dir)*

Strike Lucky Games Ltd **(1)**
Green Heys Walford Road, Ross-on-Wye, HR9 5DB, Herefordshire, United Kingdom
Tel.: (44) 1989769292
Web Site: http://www.strikelucky.com
Casino Operation Services
N.A.I.C.S.: 713210

Subsidiary (Domestic):

Purely Creative Ltd **(2)**
1 Mannin Way Lancaster Business Park Caton Road, Lancaster, LA1 3SU, Lancashire, United Kingdom
Tel.: (44) 8700 500 755
Web Site: http://www.purelycreative.co.uk
Sales Range: $10-24.9 Million
Emp.: 35
Promotional Marketing Services
N.A.I.C.S.: 541613

DM SOLUTIONS CO., LTD
1-1-3 Crystal Park Building 2F, Tokyo, 180-0005, Japan
Tel.: (81) 422573915
Web Site: https://www.dm-s.co.jp
Year Founded: 2004
6549—(TKS)
Rev.: $120,348,270
Assets: $47,208,620
Liabilities: $27,973,520
Net Worth: $19,235,100
Earnings: $2,657,220
Fiscal Year-end: 03/31/24
Direct Mailing Service
N.A.I.C.S.: 541860
Takuji Hanaya *(Board of Directors, Pres & CEO)*

DM WENCESLAO & ASSOCI-ATES, INC.
15th Floor Aseana 3 Bldg Pres D Macapagal Boulevard cor Asean Ave, Metro Manila, Paranaque, Philippines
Tel.: (63) 88545711
Web Site: https://www.dmwai.com
Year Founded: 1960
DMW—(PHI)
Rev.: $71,691,629
Assets: $769,256,455
Liabilities: $265,393,550
Net Worth: $503,862,905
Earnings: $43,491,418
Emp.: 311
Fiscal Year-end: 12/31/21
Construction Services
N.A.I.C.S.: 236220
Paul Mar M. Quinto *(Chief Legal Officer)*

Subsidiaries:

Aseana Holdings, Inc. **(1)**
15th Floor Aseana 3 Building President Diosdado Macapagal Blvd, cor Asean Ave Aseana City, Paranaque, 1701, Philippines
Tel.: (63) 288545711
Web Site:
https://www.aseanaholdingsinc.com
Real Estate Lending Services
N.A.I.C.S.: 531110

DM-DROGERIE MARKT GMBH & CO. KG
Carl Metz Str 1, 76185, Karlsruhe, Germany
Tel.: (49) 72155920

Web Site: http://www.dm-drogeriemarkt.de
Year Founded: 1973
Sales Range: $1-4.9 Billion
Emp.: 21,000
Drug Store
N.A.I.C.S.: 456110
Marco Mescoli *(Dir-Fin Control & Quality Brands)*

DMA MEDIA LTD.
First Floor 10-11 Percy Street, London, W1T 1DN, United Kingdom
Tel.: (44) 20 7432 2800
Web Site: http://www.dma-media.com
Marketing Services
N.A.I.C.S.: 541613
Rob Beynon *(Founder & CEO)*

Subsidiaries:

Synaptic Digital, Inc. **(1)**
79 5 Ave, New York, NY 10003
Tel.: (212) 682-8300
Web Site: http://www.synapticdigital.com
Marketing Agency
N.A.I.C.S.: 541810
Laura Pair *(Sr VP-Bus Dev)*

DMB DR. DIETER MURMANN BETEILIGUNGSGESELL-SCHAFT MBH
Brauner Berg 15, 24159, Kiel, Germany
Tel.: (49) 431 39 40 122
Web Site: http://www.dmb-holding.com
Holding Company
N.A.I.C.S.: 551112
Dieter Murmann *(Mng Dir)*

Subsidiaries:

Anschutz GmbH **(1)**
Zeyestrasse 16-24, 24106, Kiel, Germany
Tel.: (49) 431301996440
Web Site: https://www.anschuetz.com
Integrated Bridge Systems & Nautical Equipment Mfr
N.A.I.C.S.: 334511

Subsidiary (Non-US):

Anschuetz Singapore Pte. Ltd. **(2)**
51 Bukit Batok Crescent 07-08 Unity Centre, Singapore, 658077, Singapore
Tel.: (65) 64730048
Web Site: https://www.anschuetz.com
Integrated Bridge Systems & Nautical Equipment Distr
N.A.I.C.S.: 334511
Ron Lee *(Mng Dir)*

Branch (Non-US):

Raytheon Anschuetz GmbH Shanghai **(2)**
Room 713 Tomson Commercial Building 710 Dong Fang Road, Pudong, Shanghai, 200122, China
Tel.: (86) 2168769906
Web Site: http://www.raytheon-anschuetz.com
Emp.: 6
Integrated Bridge Systems & Nautical Equipment Sales & Service
N.A.I.C.S.: 334511
Peter Zhu *(Gen Mgr)*

DBW Advanced Fiber Technologies GmbH **(1)**
Rodetal 40, 37120, Bovenden, Germany
Tel.: (49) 5594 801 0
Web Site: http://www.dbw.de
Emp.: 630
Fiber Mfr
N.A.I.C.S.: 314999

Subsidiary (Non-US):

DBW Hungary KFT **(2)**
Strand u 6, 8300, Tapolca, Hungary
Tel.: (36) 873 21578
Web Site: http://www.dbw.de
Fiber Mfr
N.A.I.C.S.: 314999

DBW Iberica Industria Automocion, S.A. **(2)**
Poligono Industrial Belcaire Parcela N 603, 12600, La Vall d'Uixo, Castellon, Spain
Tel.: (34) 964 697 840
Web Site: http://www.dbw.de
Fiber Mfr
N.A.I.C.S.: 314999

Subsidiary (Domestic):

DBW Metallverarbeitung GmbH **(2)**
Am Gewerbepark, 17373, Ueckermunde, Germany
Tel.: (49) 39771 5275 0
Web Site: http://www.dbw.do
Fiber Mfr
N.A.I.C.S.: 314999

DMC-NORTHERN PETROLIUM CHEMICALS JOINT STOCK COMPANY
Te Xuyen, Dinh Xuyen Gia Lam, Hanoi, Vietnam
Tel.: (84) 438271483
Rev.: $570,140
Assets: $984,935
Liabilities: $532,719
Net Worth: $452,217
Earnings: ($308,256)
Fiscal Year-end: 12/31/19
Petroleum Chemical Mfr
N.A.I.C.S.: 325110

DMCARD CARTOES DE CREDITO S.A.
Av Cassiano Ricardo 521 3 Andar Torre B, Sao Jose dos Campos, Sao Paulo, 12246-870, Brazil
Tel.: (55) 800702504
Web Site: http://www.dmcard.com.br
Year Founded: 2002
Financial Services
N.A.I.C.S.: 522320
Sandra Castello *(Mktg Dir)*

DMCI HOLDINGS, INC.
3rd Floor Dacon Building 2281Chino Roces Avenue, Makati, 1231, Philippines
Tel.: (63) 28883000   PH
Web Site:
https://www.dmciholdings.com
Year Founded: 1995
DMCHY—(OTCIQ)
Rev.: $2,218,274,133
Assets: $4,477,660,389
Liabilities: $1,996,173,548
Net Worth: $2,481,486,841
Earnings: $665,106,322
Emp.: 35,495
Fiscal Year-end: 12/31/23
Investment Holding Company
N.A.I.C.S.: 551112
Cesar A. Buenaventura *(Vice Chm)*

Subsidiaries:

D.M. Consunji, Inc. **(1)**
DMCI Plaza Building 2281 Chino Roces Avenue Extension, Makati, 1231, Philippines **(100%)**
Tel.: (63) 288883624
Web Site: https://web.dmcinet.com
Commercial, Institutional, Multi-Family Residential, Industrial & Infrastructure Engineering & Construction Services
N.A.I.C.S.: 541330
Isidro A. Consunji *(Chm)*

DMCI Mining Corporation **(1)**
3rd Floor DMCI Homes Corporate Center 1321 Apolinario St Bangkal, Makati, 1231, Philippines **(78%)**
Tel.: (63) 288237963
Holding Company; Metal Ore & Mineral Exploration & Mining
N.A.I.C.S.: 551112
Cesar Simbulen *(Pres)*

Subsidiary (Non-US):

ENK PLC **(2)**

6th Floor Kildare House 3 Dorset Rise, London, EC4Y 8EN, United Kingdom **(100%)**
Tel.: (44) 2072903130
Web Site: http://www.enk.co.uk
Sales Range: $100-124.9 Million
Emp.: 228
Nickel Mining Services
N.A.I.C.S.: 212230
Vincent Smith *(Mgr-Tech)*

Branch (Non-US):

ENK PLC Australian Regional Office **(3)**
Level 1 83 Havelock Street, West Perth, 6005, WA, Australia
Tel.: (61) 8 9226 1111
Mineral Exploration Services
N.A.I.C.S.: 212390

ENK PLC Philippines Regional Office **(3)**
4th Floor Pilgrim Building 111 Aguirre Street, Legaspi Village, Makati, 1229, Philippines
Tel.: (63) 2 8151656
Sales Range: $25-49.9 Million
Emp.: 10
Mineral Exploration Services
N.A.I.C.S.: 213115

Subsidiary (Non-US):

Sardes Nikel Madencilik A.S **(3)**
Akdeniz Caddesi No 14 Birsel Is Merkezi, Kat 5 D 502, Konak, 35210, Izmir, Turkiye
Tel.: (90) 2324550030
Sales Range: $25-49.9 Million
Emp.: 30
Mining & Exploration Services
N.A.I.C.S.: 212390

Subsidiary (Non-US):

Toledo Mining Corporation plc **(2)**
First Floor 10 Dover Street, London, W1S 4LQ, United Kingdom **(66.52%)**
Tel.: (44) 2072903100
Web Site: http://www.toledomining.com
Sales Range: Less than $1 Million
Emp.: 2
Nickel Mining Services
N.A.I.C.S.: 212230

DMCI Power Corporation **(1)**
3rd Floor East Wing DMCI Plaza Bldg 2281 Chino Roces Avenue, Formerly Pasong Tamo Extension, Makati, 1231, Philippines
Tel.: (63) 288883000
Web Site: https://www.dmcipower.com
Eletric Power Generation Services
N.A.I.C.S.: 221118
Isidro A. Consunji *(Chm & CEO)*

Sem-Calaca Power Corporation **(1)**
Brgy San Rafael Calaca, Batangas, 4212, Philippines
Tel.: (63) 28883323
Web Site: https://www.semcalacapower.ph
Eletric Power Generation Services
N.A.I.C.S.: 221118

Semirara Mining and Power Corporation **(1)**
2nd Floor DMCI Plaza 2281, Chino Roces Avenue Extension, Makati, 1231, Philippines **(56.32%)**
Tel.: (63) 28883055
Web Site: https://www.semiramining.com
Rev.: $1,389,553,394
Assets: $1,537,030,643
Liabilities: $410,769,415
Net Worth: $1,126,261,228
Earnings: $504,347,677
Fiscal Year-end: 12/31/2023
Coal Producer
N.A.I.C.S.: 212114
Isidro A. Consunji *(CEO & Chm)*

Subic Water & Sewerage Company Inc. **(1)**
Rizal Avenue, Sub Com Area Subic Bay Freeport Zone, Subic, 2222, Philippines **(40%)**
Tel.: (63) 472522965
Web Site: http://www.subicwater.com.ph
Water Treatment & Distribution Services
N.A.I.C.S.: 221310

Wire Rope Corporation of the Philippines **(1)**

Unit 618 Globe Telecom Plaza Tower 1 Pioneer Highlands Building, Corner Pioneer and Madison Streets, Mandaluyong, 1550, Philippines
Tel.: (63) 277462202
Web Site: https://www.wrcp.com.ph
Wire Rope Mfr & Distr
N.A.I.C.S.: 314994

DMDCONNECTS SERVICES INC.
2 Place du Commerce Suite 206, Verdun, H3E 1A1, QC, Canada
Tel.: (514) 769-5858   QC
Web Site:
   http://www.dmdconnects.com
Sales Range: $25-49.9 Million
Computer-Related Healthcare Services
N.A.I.C.S.: 541519
Roger Korman *(Chm & CEO)*

Subsidiaries:

Direct Medical Data Marketing Corp. **(1)**
10255 W Higgins Rd Ste 280, Rosemont, IL 60018
Tel.: (847) 813-1170
Web Site: http://www.dmdconnects.com
Emp.: 50
Digital Publishing & Marketing Communication Services
N.A.I.C.S.: 513199
Roger Korman *(Pres)*

DMED BIOPHARMACEUTICAL CO. LTD.
298 Xiangke Road 3/F 301-305, Pudong New District, Shanghai, 201210, China
Tel.: (86) 21 5090 0085
Web Site:
   http://www.dmedglobal.com
Year Founded: 2016
Full-service Clinical Contract Research Organization
N.A.I.C.S.: 541715
Lingshi Tan *(Chm & CEO)*

Subsidiaries:

Clinipace, Inc. **(1)**
3800 Paramount Pkwy Ste 100, Morrisville, NC 27560
Tel.: (919) 224-8800
Web Site: http://www.clinipace.com
Digital Clinical Research Organization
N.A.I.C.S.: 541715
Jeff L. Williams *(Co-Founder & Pres)*

DMG BLOCKCHAIN SOLUTIONS INC.
4193 104 Street, Delta, V4K 3N3, BC, Canada
Tel.: (516) 222-2560   BC
Web Site:
   https://www.dmgblockchain.com
Year Founded: 2011
DMGGF—(OTCQB)
Rev.: $7,993,727
Assets: $86,932,969
Liabilities: $4,547,365
Net Worth: $82,385,604
Earnings: ($7,472,656)
Emp.: 16
Fiscal Year-end: 09/30/21
Cryptocurrency & Blockchain Services
N.A.I.C.S.: 541519
Sheldon Bennett *(CEO & COO)*

DMG MORI CO., LTD.
2-3-23 Shiomi, Koto-ku, Tokyo, 135-0052, Aichi, Japan
Tel.: (81) 367585900   KR
Web Site: https://www.dmgmori.co.jp
Year Founded: 1948
6141—(TKS)
Rev.: $3,824,700,500

Assets: $5,429,564,540
Liabilities: $3,497,220,490
Net Worth: $1,932,344,050
Earnings: $240,662,960
Emp.: 13,484
Fiscal Year-end: 12/31/23
Machine Tools Mfr
N.A.I.C.S.: 333517
Masahiko Mori *(Pres)*

Subsidiaries:

DMG MORI (Thailand) Co., Ltd. **(1)**
700 146 Moo 1 Tambol Bankao, Amphur Panthong, Chon Buri, 20160, Thailand
Tel.: (66) 384687202
Machine Tools Mfr
N.A.I.C.S.: 333517

DMG MORI AKTIENGESELLSCHAFT **(1)**
Gildemeisterstrasse 60, 33689, Bielefeld, Germany **(52.5%)**
Tel.: (49) 5205740
Web Site: https://de.dmgmori-ag.com
Rev.: $2,758,096,466
Assets: $3,055,236,192
Liabilities: $1,551,809,407
Net Worth: $1,503,426,785
Earnings: $169,333,658
Emp.: 7,515
Fiscal Year-end: 12/31/2023
Cutting Machine Tools, Lathes, Electronic Controls, Programming Systems, Deep Hole Drilling Machines & Blow Moulding Systems Mfr
N.A.I.C.S.: 333517
Masahiko Mori *(Chm-Supervisory Bd)*

Subsidiary (Non-US):

DMG MORI Brasil **(2)**
Av Dos Imares 437, Sao Paulo, 04085-000, SP, Brazil
Tel.: (55) 1132547070
Web Site: http://br.dmgmori.com
Machine Tool Distr
N.A.I.C.S.: 423830

DMG MORI India Pvt. Ltd. **(2)**
3/1 3rd Main KIADB Peenya 1st Stage, Ward 1 HMT, Bengaluru, 560058, India **(100%)**
Tel.: (91) 80 40 89 65 00
Web Site: http://in.dmgmori.com
Sales Range: $25-49.9 Million
Emp.: 25
Machine Tool Distr
N.A.I.C.S.: 423830

Subsidiary (Domestic):

DMG Vertriebs und Service GmbH DECKEL MAHO GILDEMEISTER **(2)**
Gildemeisterstrasse 60, 33689, Bielefeld, Germany
Tel.: (49) 52 05 74 0
Sales Range: $50-74.9 Million
Emp.: 1,000
Cutting Machine Tool Sales & Repair Services
N.A.I.C.S.: 423830

Subsidiary (Domestic):

DMG MORI Academy GmbH **(3)**
Gildemeisterstrasse 60, 33689, Bielefeld, Germany **(100%)**
Tel.: (49) 520 5740
Web Site: http://de.dmgmori.com
Emp.: 45
CNC Machine Tools Training & Service Training
N.A.I.C.S.: 611519
Raimund Klinkner *(Chm-Supervisory Bd)*

DMG MORI Deutschland GmbH **(3)**
Riedwiesenstrasse 19, 71229, Leonberg, Germany **(100%)**
Tel.: (49) 715290900
Sales Range: $50-74.9 Million
Emp.: 116
Long Turning Automatic Machines & Multi-Spindle Automatic Lathes Mfr
N.A.I.C.S.: 333517
Sascha Mertins *(Mng Dir)*

Subsidiary (Domestic):

DMG MORI Berlin GmbH **(4)**

Rudower Chaussee 46, 12489, Berlin, Germany **(100%)**
Tel.: (49) 303519060
Web Site: http://de.dmgmori.com
Sales Range: $25-49.9 Million
Emp.: 5
Machine Tools Mfr, Sales & Service
N.A.I.C.S.: 333517
Holger Zunft *(Mng Dir)*

DMG MORI Bielefeld GmbH **(4)**
Gildemeisterstr 60, 33689, Bielefeld, Germany
Tel.: (49) 52 05 74 22 33
Web Site: http://de.dmgmori.com
Machine Tool Distr
N.A.I.C.S.: 423830

DMG MORI Frankfurt GmbH **(4)**
Steinmuhlstrasse 12 d, 61352, Bad Homburg, Germany
Tel.: (49) 617 249 5570
Web Site: http://de.dmgmori.com
Sales Range: $25-49.9 Million
Emp.: 50
Machine Tool Distr
N.A.I.C.S.: 423830
Frank Michel *(Mng Dir)*

DMG MORI Hamburg GmbH **(4)**
Wilhelm-Bergner-Strasse 11A, 21509, Glinde, Germany
Tel.: (49) 40 694 58 0
Web Site: http://de.dmgmori.com
Machine Tools Mfr, Sales & Service
N.A.I.C.S.: 333517
Holger Zunft *(Mng Dir)*

DMG MORI Hilden GmbH **(4)**
Im Hulsenfeld 23, 40721, Hilden, Germany **(100%)**
Tel.: (49) 210357010
Web Site: http://de.dmgmori.com
Sales Range: $25-49.9 Million
Emp.: 60
Machine Tool Distr
N.A.I.C.S.: 423830

DMG MORI Munchen GmbH **(4)**
Lausitzer Str 7, 82538, Geretsried, Germany **(100%)**
Tel.: (49) 817178175150
Web Site: http://de.dmgmori.com
Emp.: 100
Machine Tool Distr
N.A.I.C.S.: 423830

Subsidiary (Non-US):

DMG MORI Europe AG **(3)**
Sulzer-Allee 70, 8404, Winterthur, Switzerland
Tel.: (41) 58 611 50 00
Machine Tools Mfr
N.A.I.C.S.: 333517
Philippe Berton *(Dir-Svcs-EMEA)*

Subsidiary (Non-US):

DMG MORI Austria GmbH **(4)**
Oberes Ried 11, 6833, Klaus, Austria
Tel.: (43) 55 23 6 91 41 0
Web Site: http://at.dmgmori.com
Machine Tool Distr
N.A.I.C.S.: 423830

DMG MORI BeLux BVBA - SPRL **(4)**
Het Hofveld 8, 1702, Dilbeek, Belgium
Tel.: (32) 2 712 1090
Web Site: https://be.dmgmori.com
Cutting Machine Tool Distr
N.A.I.C.S.: 333517

DMG MORI Czech, s.r.o. **(4)**
Kastanova 8, 62000, Brno, Czech Republic
Tel.: (420) 545426311
Web Site: http://cz.dmgmori.com
Machine Tool Distr
N.A.I.C.S.: 423830

DMG MORI Denmark ApS **(4)**
Snaremosevej 188A, 7000, Fredericia, Denmark
Tel.: (45) 70 21 11 11
Web Site: http://dk.dmgmori.com
Machine Tool Distr
N.A.I.C.S.: 423830

DMG MORI France S.A.S. **(4)**
Parc du Moulin 1 rue du Noyer CDG, BP

DMG MORI Co., Ltd.—(Continued)

19236, 95705, Roissy-en-France, Cedex,
France
Tel.: (33) 13 994 6800
Web Site: https://fr.dgmori.com
Machine Tool Distr
N.A.I.C.S.: 423830
Philippe Berton (Dir Gen)

Branch (Domestic):

**DMG MORI France -
Haute-Savoie** **(5)**
Espace Scionzier - 520 avenue des Lacs,
74950, Scionzier, France **(100%)**
Tel.: (33) 45 096 4162
Web Site: https://fr.dmgmori.com
Sales Range: $25-49.9 Million
Emp.: 85
Machine Tool Distr
N.A.I.C.S.: 423830
Alexander Lae (Mng Dir)

DMG MORI France - Lyon **(5)**
Parc des Lumieres 1205 Rue Nicephore
Niepce, Rue Nicephore Niepce, 69800,
Saint Priest, France
Tel.: (33) 47 890 9595
Web Site: https://fr.dmgmori.com
Cutting Machine Tool Mfr
N.A.I.C.S.: 333517
Sylvain Badin (Mng Dir)

Subsidiary (Non-US):

DMG MORI Hungary Kft. **(4)**
Vegyesz u 17-25 B Epulet, 1116, Budapest,
Hungary
Tel.: (36) 1 430 1614
Emp.: 21
Machine Tool Distr
N.A.I.C.S.: 423830
Laszlo Bodi (Reg Sls Mgr)

DMG MORI Iberica S.L.U. **(4)**
Pol Ind Els Pinetons Avda Torre Mateu 2-8
Nave 1, 08291, Ripollet, Barcelona, Spain
Tel.: (34) 93 586 3086
Web Site: https://es.dmgmori.com
Machine Tool Distr
N.A.I.C.S.: 423830
Javier Plaza (Mgr-Fin)

**DMG MORI Istanbul Makine Ticaret
ve Servis Limited Sirketi** **(4)**
Ferhatpasa Mah Gazipasa Cad No 11,
Atasehir, 34888, Istanbul, Turkiye
Tel.: (90) 216 471 6636
Web Site: http://tr.dmgmori.com
Machine Cutting Tools Distr
N.A.I.C.S.: 423830
Fatih Girit (Gen Mgr)

DMG MORI Italia S.r.l. **(4)**
Via G Donizetti 138, 24030, Brembate di
Sopra, BG, Italy
Tel.: (39) 0356022801
Web Site: http://it.dmgmori.com
Sales Range: $25-49.9 Million
Emp.: 85
Machine Tool Distr
N.A.I.C.S.: 423830
Ugo Ghilardi (Gen Mgr)

DMG MORI Middle East FZE **(4)**
Jebel Ali Free Zone JAFZA Towers Lob 18
Office 2403, PO Box 262 607, Dubai,
United Arab Emirates
Tel.: (971) 4 88 65 740
Machine Cutting Tools Distr
N.A.I.C.S.: 423830
Ehtesham Karim (Dir-Sls)

DMG MORI Netherlands B.V. **(4)**
Wageningselaan 48, 3903 LA, Veenendaal,
Netherlands
Tel.: (31) 31 855 7611
Web Site: https://nl.dmgmori.com
Machine Tool Distr
N.A.I.C.S.: 423830
John Kooning (Mng Dir)

DMG MORI Polska Sp. z o.o. **(4)**
ul Fabryczna 7, 63 300, Pleszew, Poland
Tel.: (48) 62 7428 000
Web Site: http://pl.dmgmori.com
Machine Tool Distr
N.A.I.C.S.: 423830
Pawel Napierala (Reg Sls Mgr)

Subsidiary (Domestic):

DMG MORI Schweiz AG **(4)**
Sulzer-Allee 70, 8404, Winterthur, Switzer-
land
Tel.: (41) 58 611 50 00
Web Site: http://ch-de.dmgmori.com
Machine Tool Distr
N.A.I.C.S.: 333517
Silvio Lehmann (Gen Dir)

Subsidiary (Non-US):

DMG MORI UK Limited **(4)**
4030 Siskin Parkway East Middlemarch
Business Park, Coventry, CV3 4PE, United
Kingdom
Tel.: (44) 247 651 6120
Web Site: http://uk.dmgmori.com
Machine Tool Distr
N.A.I.C.S.: 423830
Stephen Peter Finn (Mng Dir)

Subsidiary (Domestic):

**DMG MORI Global Service Milling
GmbH** **(3)**
Deckel-Maho-Str 1, 87459, Pfronten, Ger-
many
Tel.: (49) 8363 890
Web Site: http://www.dmgmori.com
Engineeering Services
N.A.I.C.S.: 541330

**DMG MORI Global Service Turning
GmbH** **(3)**
Gildemeisterstr 60, Bielefeld, 33689, Ger-
many
Tel.: (49) 521 74 0
Engineeering Services
N.A.I.C.S.: 541330

**DMG MORI Used Machines
GmbH** **(3)**
Lausitzer Strasse 7, 82538, Geretsried,
Germany **(100%)**
Tel.: (49) 817 181 7826
Web Site: http://de.dmgmori.com
Sales Range: $25-49.9 Million
Emp.: 25
Machine Tool Distr
N.A.I.C.S.: 423830
Thomas Trump (Mng Dir)

Subsidiary (Non-US):

**antiquitas Verwaltungsgesellschaft
mbH** **(3)**
Oberes Ried 11, Klaus, 6833, Austria
Tel.: (43) 55 23 6 91 44 0
Emp.: 38
Investment Management Service
N.A.I.C.S.: 523999
Silvio B. Lehmann (Gen Mgr)

Subsidiary (Domestic):

DMG ecoline GmbH **(4)**
Oberes Ried 11, 6833, Klaus, Austria
Tel.: (43) 5523 90 601 600
Emp.: 10
Industrial Machinery Mfr
N.A.I.C.S.: 333248
Ralph Christnacht (Gen Mgr)

Subsidiary (Domestic):

**GILDEMEISTER Beteiligungen
AG** **(2)**
Gildemeisterstrasse 60, 33689, Bielefeld,
Germany
Tel.: (49) 5205740
Sales Range: $50-74.9 Million
Emp.: 1,000
Investment Management Service
N.A.I.C.S.: 523999

Subsidiary (Non-US):

**DECKEL MAHO GILDEMEISTER
(Shanghai) Machine Tools Co.,
Ltd.** **(3)**
No 178 Yin Du Xi Road Chen Chun Road,
Shanghai, 201612, China
Tel.: (86) 21 67 64 83 33
Machine Tools Mfr
N.A.I.C.S.: 333517

Subsidiary (Domestic):

DECKEL MAHO Pfronten GmbH **(3)**

Deckel Maho Strasse 1, 87459, Pfronten,
Germany
Tel.: (49) 83 63 89 0
Emp.: 1,800
Molding Machine Mfr
N.A.I.C.S.: 333248
Alfred Geissler (Mng Dir-Tech Mgmt)

Subsidiary (Domestic):

SAUER GmbH **(4)**
Gildemeisterstrasse 1, 55758, Stipshausen,
Germany
Tel.: (49) 6544 99199 0
Web Site: http://de.dmgmori.com
Emp.: 6
Ultrasonic Equipment Mfr
N.A.I.C.S.: 333248
Darryl Pahlke (Mng Dir)

Subsidiary (Domestic):

DECKEL MAHO Seebach GmbH **(3)**
Neue Strasse 61, 99846, Seebach, Ger-
many
Tel.: (49) 36929 81 0
Industrial Machinery Mfr
N.A.I.C.S.: 333248
Markus Rehm (Co-Mng Dir)

**DMG MORI Software Solutions
GmbH** **(3)**
DECKEL MAHO-Str 1, 87459, Pfronten,
Germany
Tel.: (49) 83 63 89 8460
Web Site: http://de.dmgmori.com
Machine Tool Distr
N.A.I.C.S.: 423830

DMG MORI Spare Parts GmbH **(3)**
Lausitzer Strasse 7, 82538, Geretsried,
Germany
Tel.: (49) 8171 817 203
Emp.: 167
Cutting Machine Tool Mfr & Distr
N.A.I.C.S.: 333515
Michael Neumann (Gen Mgr)

**GILDEMEISTER Drehmaschinen
GmbH** **(3)**
Gildemeisterstrasse 60, 33689, Bielefeld,
Germany
Tel.: (49) 520 5740
Web Site: http://de.dmgmori.com
Machine Tools Mfr
N.A.I.C.S.: 333517

Subsidiary (Non-US):

GILDEMEISTER Italiana S.p.A **(3)**
Via G Donizetti 138, IT-24030, Brembate di
Sopra, BG, Italy **(100%)**
Tel.: (39) 035 60 71 11
Web Site: http://it.dmgmori.com
Multi-Spindle Automatic Lathes Mfr
N.A.I.C.S.: 333517
Alessandro Spinelli (Mgr-Production)

GRAZIANO Tortona S.r.l. **(3)**
Via Wilmer Graziano 15, 15057, Tortona,
Alessandria, Italy
Tel.: (39) 0131 8181
Web Site: http://it.dmgmori.com
Emp.: 150
Machine Tool Distr
N.A.I.C.S.: 423830
Claudio Merlo (Gen Mgr)

DMG MORI Australia Pty. Ltd. **(1)**
Unit 6 / 6 Garden Road, Clayton, Mel-
bourne, 3168, VIC, Australia
Tel.: (61) 38 545 0900
Web Site: https://au.dmgmori.com
Cutting Machine Tool Mfr
N.A.I.C.S.: 333517

DMG MORI B.U.G. Co., Ltd. **(1)**
1-1-14 Shimonopporo Techno Park,
Atsubetsu-ku, Sapporo, 004-0015, Hok-
kaido, Japan
Tel.: (81) 11 807 6666
Web Site: https://www.bug.co.jp
Emp.: 147
Computer System Development & Software
Developer
N.A.I.C.S.: 513210
Akihiko Kawashima (Pres)

DMG MORI CASTECH Co., Ltd. **(1)**
1378 Otsu-cho, Izumo, 693-0011, Japan
Tel.: (81) 853213344

Web Site: https://dmgmori-castech.com
Emp.: 170
Casting Product Mfr
N.A.I.C.S.: 331523

DMG MORI Co., Ltd. - Plant 1 **(1)**
362 Idono-cho, Yamato-koriyama, 639-
1183, Nara, Japan
Tel.: (81) 743531121
Machine Tools Mfr
N.A.I.C.S.: 333517

DMG MORI Czech s.r.o. **(1)**
Bmianska 2, 911 05, Trencin, Slovakia
Tel.: (421) 326494824
Machine Tools Mfr
N.A.I.C.S.: 333517

DMG MORI Digital Co., Ltd. **(1)**
1-1-14 Shimonopporo Techno Park,
Atsubetsu-ku, Sapporo, 004-0015, Japan
Tel.: (81) 118076666
Web Site: https://www.dmgmori-digital.co.jp
Emp.: 183
Computer Hardware Mfr & Distr
N.A.I.C.S.: 334111

DMG MORI Finland Oy Ab **(1)**
Jasperintie 310, 33960, Pirkkala, Finland
Tel.: (358) 10 271 4450
Web Site: https://fi.dmgmori.com
Machine Tools Mfr
N.A.I.C.S.: 333517

**DMG MORI Global Marketing
GmbH** **(1)**
Antoniusstrasse 14, 73249, Wernau,
Baden-Wurttemberg, Germany
Tel.: (49) 71539340
Sales Range: $25-49.9 Million
Emp.: 100
Sale, Maintenance & Service of Machines &
Equipment
N.A.I.C.S.: 423830
Irene Bader (Mng Dir)

DMG MORI Greece Ltd. **(1)**
Ag Georgiou 5 - Patriarchiko Pylaias Cos-
mos Offices, PO 60233, 57001, Thessa-
loniki, Greece
Tel.: (30) 231 047 4486
Web Site: http://gr.dmgmori.com
Machine Tools Mfr
N.A.I.C.S.: 333517

DMG MORI Korea Co., Ltd. **(1)**
12 Iljik-ro 106beon-gil Manan-gu, Anyang,
13-901, Gyeonggi-do, Korea (South)
Tel.: (82) 314880500
Sales Range: $25-49.9 Million
Emp.: 60
Machine Tool Distr
N.A.I.C.S.: 423830

**DMG MORI Machine Tools Trading
Co., Ltd.** **(1)**
No 178 West YinDu Road, Songjiang Dis-
trict, Shanghai, 201612, China
Tel.: (86) 2167648876
Machine Tools Mfr
N.A.I.C.S.: 333517

DMG MORI Norway AS **(1)**
PO Box 64, 3106, Notteroy, Norway
Tel.: (47) 33222993
Web Site: http://no.dmgmori.com
Machine Tools Mfr
N.A.I.C.S.: 333517

DMG MORI Philippines Inc. **(1)**
Unit 2207 22nd Floor Philippine AXA Life
Centre Metro Manila, Senator Gil Puyat Av-
enue corner Tindalo Street, Makati, 1200,
Philippines
Tel.: (63) 288943318
Machine Tools Mfr
N.A.I.C.S.: 333517

DMG MORI Romania S.R.L. **(1)**
Autostrada Pitesti DN65B km 4 471,
110180, Bucharest, Romania
Tel.: (40) 248610408
Machine Tools Mfr
N.A.I.C.S.: 333517

DMG MORI SEIKI Canada Inc. **(1)**
395 Ambassador Drive, Mississauga, L5T
2J3, ON, Canada **(100%)**
Tel.: (905) 795-2891
Web Site: http://www.dmgcanada.com

Sales Range: $25-49.9 Million
Emp.: 30
Machine Tool Distr
N.A.I.C.S.: 423830

DMG MORI SEIKI Co., Ltd. - Nara Campus No. 1 Plant (1)
362 Idono-cho, Yamato-koriyama, 639-1183, Nara, Japan
Tel.: (81) 74 353 1121
Web Site: http://www.moriseiki.com
Lathes & Machining Centers Mfr
N.A.I.C.S.: 333517

DMG MORI SEIKI Co., Ltd. - Nara Campus No. 2 Plant (1)
106 Kitakoriyama-cho, Yamato-koriyama, 639-1160, Nara, Japan
Tel.: (81) 743531125
Web Site: http://www.moriseiki.co.jp
Sales Range: $1-4.9 Billion
Emp.: 4,000
Loaders & Pallet Pools Mfr
N.A.I.C.S.: 321920

DMG MORI SEIKI India Pvt. Ltd. (1)
502 5th Fl Plot No D9 Gopal Heights Netaji Subhash Pl, Pitampura, Delhi, 110 034, India
Tel.: (91) 1146469600
Sales Range: $25-49.9 Million
Emp.: 5
Machine Tool Distr
N.A.I.C.S.: 333515

DMG MORI Singapore Pte. Ltd. (1)
3 Tuas Link 1, Singapore, 638584, Singapore
Tel.: (65) 66606688
Web Site: http://en.dmgmori.com
Machine Tool Distr
N.A.I.C.S.: 423830

Subsidiary (Non-US):

DMG MORI (Malaysia) Sdn. Bhd. (2)
19 Jalan Pendidik U1/31 Seksyen U1, Hicom Glenmarie Industrial Park, Shah Alam, 40150, Selangor Darul Ehsan, Malaysia (100%)
Tel.: (60) 355695282
Emp.: 24
Machine Tools Mfr
N.A.I.C.S.: 333517
Au Chunwai *(Controller-Fin)*

DMG MORI SEIKI (Thailand) Co., Ltd. (2)
40 Moo 4 Rojana Indus Park 2 Rojana Rd, Tambol U-Thai Amphur U-Thai, 13210, Ayutthaya, Thailand
Tel.: (66) 3574672030
Web Site: http://www.dmtmoriseiki.com
Sales Range: $25-49.9 Million
Emp.: 42
Machine Tools Mfr
N.A.I.C.S.: 333517

DMG MORI Stuttgart GmbH (1)
Riedwiesenstr 19, 71229, Leonberg, Germany
Tel.: (49) 715290900
Machine Tools Mfr
N.A.I.C.S.: 333517

DMG MORI Sweden AB (1)
EA Rosengrens gata 5, 421 31, Vastra Frolunda, Sweden
Tel.: (46) 31 348 9800
Web Site: https://se.dmgmori.com
Emp.: 25
Machine Tools Mfr
N.A.I.C.S.: 333517

DMG MORI Taiwan Co. Ltd. (1)
No 12-3 Industrial 33 Road Industrial Park, Taichung, 40768, Taiwan
Tel.: (886) 42 355 6490
Web Site: http://tw.dmgmori.com
Emp.: 50
Machine Tool Distr
N.A.I.C.S.: 423830
Woody Wang *(Mng Dir)*

DMG MORI USA, Inc. (1)
2400 Huntington Blvd, Hoffman Estates, IL 60192
Tel.: (847) 593-5400
Web Site: http://us.dmgmori.com

Sales Range: $25-49.9 Million
Emp.: 100
Machine Tools Mfr & Distr
N.A.I.C.S.: 333517

Subsidiary (Domestic):

DMG America Inc. (2)
2400 Huntington Blvd, Hoffman Estates, IL 60192
Tel.: (847) 593-5400
Web Site: http://www.dmgmoriseikiusa.com
Holding Company; Regional Managing Office
N.A.I.C.S.: 551112
Heather Plummer *(Mgr-HR)*

DMG MORI Viet Nam Co., Ltd. (1)
235-237-239-241 Cong Hoa street, Ward 13 Tan Binh District, Ho Chi Minh City, Vietnam
Tel.: (84) 862816636
Machine Tools Mfr
N.A.I.C.S.: 333517

DMG Mori Sales & Service Co., Ltd. (1)
2-35-16 Meieki, Nakamura-ku, Nagoya, 450-0002, Aichi, Japan
Tel.: (81) 525871862
Machine Tools Mfr
N.A.I.C.S.: 333517

DMG Mori Used Machines Co., Ltd. (1)
98 Sanagucho, Iga, 518-0001, Mie, Japan
Tel.: (81) 595263060
Machine Tools Mfr
N.A.I.C.S.: 333517

MORI SEIKI (Shanghai) Co., Ltd. (1)
Rm 4301 4307 Maxdo Ctr No 8 Xing Yi Rd, Hong Qiao Dev Zone, Shanghai, 200336, China
Tel.: (86) 2152080270
Web Site: http://www.moriseiki.com
Sales Range: $25-49.9 Million
Emp.: 50
Machine Tools Mfr
N.A.I.C.S.: 333517

MORI SEIKI Brasil Ltda. (1)
Av dos Imares 437, Indianopolis, Sao Paulo, CEP 04085-000, SP, Brazil
Tel.: (55) 1155431762
Web Site: http://www.dmgmoriseikiusa.com
Sales Range: $25-49.9 Million
Emp.: 20
Machine Tools Mfr
N.A.I.C.S.: 333517

MORI SEIKI Espana S.A. (1)
Ave Corts Caparanes 9 Office 16 D, 08173, Sant Cugat del Valles, Barcelona, Spain
Tel.: (34) 935753646
Web Site: http://www.moriseiki.com
Sales Range: $25-49.9 Million
Emp.: 5
Machine Tools Mfr
N.A.I.C.S.: 333517

MORI SEIKI Hong Kong Ltd. (1)
Ste 08 23 F The Metropolis Ofc Tower 10 Metropolis Dr, Hung Hom, Kowloon, China (Hong Kong)
Tel.: (852) 27578910
Web Site: http://www.moriseiki.com
Machine Tools Mfr
N.A.I.C.S.: 333517

MORI SEIKI Israel Ltd. (1)
6 Meitav St, 6789805, Tel Aviv, Israel
Tel.: (972) 35626266
Machine Tools Mfr
N.A.I.C.S.: 333517

MORI SEIKI Techno GmbH (1)
Antoniusstrasse 14, 73249, Wernau, Baden-Wurttemberg, Germany
Tel.: (49) 7153934227
Web Site: http://www.mstechno.de
Machine Tools Mfr
N.A.I.C.S.: 333517

MORI SEIKI Techno Ltd. (1)
106 Kitakoriyama-cho, Yamato-koriyama, 639-1160, Nara, Japan
Tel.: (81) 743531203
Sales Range: $25-49.9 Million
Emp.: 50
Machine Tools Mfr

N.A.I.C.S.: 333517

MORI SEIKI Trading Ltd. (1)
2-35-16 Meieki, Nakamura-Ku, Nagoya, 450-0002, Aichi, Japan
Tel.: (81) 525871811
Web Site: http://www.moriseiki.com
Machine Tools Sales
N.A.I.C.S.: 423830

Magnescale Co., Ltd. (1)
45 Suzukawa, Isehara, 259-1146, Kanagawa, Japan
Tel.: (81) 46 392 1011
Web Site: https://www.magnescale.com
Measuring Equipment Mfr
N.A.I.C.S.: 334519
Toru Fujimori *(Pres)*

Subsidiary (US):

Magnescale Americas Inc. (2)
1 Technology Dr Ste F217, Irvine, CA 92618 (100%)
Tel.: (949) 727-4017
Web Site: http://www.magnescale.com
Sales of Measuring Equipment for Semiconductor Products
N.A.I.C.S.: 423830

Subsidiary (Non-US):

Magnescale Europe GmbH (2)
Antoniusstrasse 14, 73249, Wernau, Germany
Tel.: (49) 7153 934 291
Web Site: http://www.magnescale.com
Emp.: 25
Sales of Measuring Devices for Semiconductor Products
N.A.I.C.S.: 423830

Mahoroba Farm Co., Ltd. (1)
201 Mishiro, Iga, 519-1414, Japan
Tel.: (81) 595454267
Web Site: https://www.mahorobafarm.co.jp
Wine Mfr
N.A.I.C.S.: 312130

PT. DMG MORI SEIKI Indonesia (1)
Komplek Gading Bukit Indah Blok M 01 Jl Bukit Gading Raya, Jakarta, Jakarta, 14240, Indonesia
Tel.: (62) 214531199
Web Site: http://www.dmgmoriseiki.com
Sales Range: $25-49.9 Million
Emp.: 18
Machine Tools Sales & Service
N.A.I.C.S.: 333517

PT. DMG Mori Indonesia (1)
Jl Danau Sunter Selatan Blok O3 No 41-42, Kel Sunter Jaya Tg Priok, Jakarta Utara, 14360, Indonesia
Tel.: (62) 2129561991
Machine Tools Mfr
N.A.I.C.S.: 333517

Saki Corporation (1)
Dmg Mori Tokyo Digital Innovation Center 3-1-4 Edagawa, Koto-ku, Tokyo, 135-0051, Japan
Tel.: (81) 366327910
Web Site: https://www.sakicorp.com
Visual Inspection Equipment Mfr
N.A.I.C.S.: 334412

T Project Co., Ltd. (1)
3-1-4 Edagawa, Koto-ku, Tokyo, 135-0051, Japan
Tel.: (81) 366327939
Web Site: http://www.tprj.co.jp
Machine Tools Mfr
N.A.I.C.S.: 333517

Taiyo Koki Co., Ltd. (1)
221-35 Seiryo-machi, Nagaoka, 940-2045, Niigata, Japan (50.81%)
Tel.: (81) 258428808
Web Site: https://www.taiyokoki.com
Sales Range: $50-74.9 Million
Emp.: 200
Grinding Machine Tools Mfr
N.A.I.C.S.: 333517
Noboru Watanabe *(Pres)*

DMI UK LTD.
West Chirton Industrial Estate Gloucester Rd, West Chirton Industrial Es-

tate, North Shields, NE29 8RQ, Tyne & Wear, United Kingdom
Tel.: (44) 1912575577   UK
Web Site: http://www.dmiglobal.com
Sales Range: $10-24.9 Million
Emp.: 75
Metal Treatment & Coating Services
N.A.I.C.S.: 332812
Kevin Woodmansey *(Dir-Comml)*

Subsidiaries:

AMI Exchangers Ltd. (1)
Apex Workshops, Graythorp Industrial Estate, Hartlepool, TS25 2DF, United Kingdom
Tel.: (44) 1429 860187
Web Site: http://www.ami-exchangers.co.uk
Marine & Industrial Heat Exchangers Mfr
N.A.I.C.S.: 332410
Nick Welford *(Dir-Sls)*

Applied Cooling Technology LLC (1)
75 Mid Cape Ter Units 5 6 & 7, Cape Coral, FL 33991
Tel.: (239) 217-5080
Web Site: http://www.appliedcool.com
Emp.: 9
Air Conditioning System Mfr & Distr
N.A.I.C.S.: 333415
Ian Mansell *(Mgr-Sls)*

DMI Automotive Inc. (1)
1200 Durant Dr, Howell, MI 48843
Tel.: (517) 548-1414
Web Site: http://www.dmiautomotive.com
Sales Range: $25-49.9 Million
Emp.: 18
Die Chrome Plating
N.A.I.C.S.: 332813
Alan Gray *(Sec & Treas)*

DMI Dalian Ltd (1)
No 28 District ETDZ, Dalian, 116620, China
Tel.: (86) 411 87320309
Web Site: http://www.dmidalian.com
Emp.: 100
Marine Engineering Services
N.A.I.C.S.: 541330
Cage Chang *(Mgr-Mktg)*

DMI Diesel Offshore (S) Pte Ltd. (1)
No 19 Link Road, Singapore, 619035, Singapore
Tel.: (65) 6262 3422
Web Site: http://www.dmi.com.sg
Engine Parts Mfr & Distr
N.A.I.C.S.: 333618

DMI Guangzhou Ltd (1)
No 4 Cai Hui Street GETDZ Huang Pu New Port, Guangzhou, 510730, China
Tel.: (86) 20 8209 8223
Emp.: 80
Electroplating Material Mfr & Distr
N.A.I.C.S.: 332813
Weijie Ying *(Mng Dir)*

DMI Marine Inc. (1)
330 Wareham St, Middleboro, MA 02346
Tel.: (774) 213-9744
Web Site: http://www.dmimarine.com
Marine Engineering Services
N.A.I.C.S.: 541330

DMI Nantong Ltd (1)
No 1 Zhongyuan Road, Nantong, 226006, Jiangsu, China
Tel.: (86) 513 83508014
Web Site: http://www.dminantong.com
Engine Parts Mfr & Distr
N.A.I.C.S.: 333618

DMI Scandinavia AS. (1)
Elisenberg, PO Box 3070, 207, Oslo, Norway
Tel.: (47) 230 84890
Marine Equipment Distr
N.A.I.C.S.: 423860

DMI Wolfgang Drechsler GmbH (1)
Hohe-Schaar-Strasse 40-42, 21107, Hamburg, Germany
Tel.: (49) 40 284 110 0
Web Site: http://www.dmi-drechsler.de
Steel Construction & Machinery, Welding & Metal Spraying; Reconditioning of Engine Components
N.A.I.C.S.: 332710

DMI Young & Cunningham Ltd. (1)

DMI UK Ltd.—(Continued)

Gloucester Road, West Chirton Industrial
Estate, North Shields, NE29 8RQ, Tyne and
Wear, United Kingdom
Tel.: (44) 191 270 4690
Web Site: http://www.yandc.co.uk
Emp.: 20
Taps & Valves Mfr
N.A.I.C.S.: 332911
George Wood (Gen Mgr)

Diesel Marine International Dubai
L.L.C.   (1)
Road 120 28A Plot No 364-0376 B562
Near 3rd Interchange Sheikh Zayed, PO
Box 8807, Road Al Quoz Indus Area,
Dubai, 8807, United Arab Emirates
Tel.: (971) 4 339 2219
Web Site: http://www.dmidubai.co.uk
Marine Reconditioning Services
N.A.I.C.S.: 332812
Ram K. Shringi (Mgr)

Highland Electroplaters Ltd.   (1)
Howe Moss Drive, Kirkhill Industrial Estate,
Dyce, AB21 0GL, Aberdeen, United King-
dom
Tel.: (44) 1224 725581
Web Site: http://www.hiplaters.co.uk
Emp.: 18
Surface Coatings Mfr
N.A.I.C.S.: 325510
Norrie Jerrard (Mng Dir)

DMK DEUTSCHES MILCHKON-TOR GMBH
Industriestrasse 27, 27404, Zeven,
Germany
Tel.: (49) 4281 72 0   De
Web Site: http://www.dmk.de
Sales Range: $5-14.9 Billion
Emp.: 1,004
Dairy Products Mfr & Distr
N.A.I.C.S.: 311511
Volkmar Taucher (CFO)

Subsidiaries:

D.P. Supply B.V   (1)
Waanderweg 50, 7812 HZ, Emmen, Nether-
lands
Tel.: (31) 591.679 988
Web Site: http://www.dpsupply.nl
Emp.: 30
Dried Ingredient Mfr
N.A.I.C.S.: 311423

Subsidiary (Non-US):

DP Supply GmbH   (2)
Hauptstr 2, 49832, Beesten, Germany
Tel.: (49) 590593000
Emp.: 104
Food Products Mfr
N.A.I.C.S.: 311514

DMK Eis GmbH   (1)
Munsterstrasse 31, 48351, Everswinkel,
Germany   (100%)
Tel.: (49) 2582 77 0
Web Site: http://www.dmk-eis.de
Sales Range: $75-99.9 Million
Emp.: 270
Ice Cream Mfr
N.A.I.C.S.: 311520
Helga Gels (Head-Product Dev)

Plant (Domestic):

Rosen Eiskrem Sud GmbH -
Prenzlau   (2)
Brussower Allee 85, 17291, Prenzlau, Ger-
many
Tel.: (49) 3984 8504 02
Web Site: http://www.roseneis.de
Sales Range: $25-49.9 Million
Emp.: 200
Ice Cream Mfr
N.A.I.C.S.: 311520

Euro Cheese Vertriebs-GmbH   (1)
Heidbergtrift 1, 17087, Altentreptow, Ger-
many
Tel.: (49) 39612720
Emp.: 206
Cheese Mfr
N.A.I.C.S.: 311513

Fude + Serrahn GmbH & Co.
KG   (1)
Englische Planke 2, 20459, Hamburg, Ger-
many
Tel.: (49) 40 300 88 300
Web Site: http://www.fs-milchprodukte.de
Dairy Products Mfr
N.A.I.C.S.: 311514

Subsidiary (Domestic):

Molkerei Niesky GmbH   (2)
Muskauer Str 38, 02906, Niesky, Germany
Tel.: (49) 358825520
Web Site: http://www.molkerei-niesky.de
Cheese Mfr
N.A.I.C.S.: 311513
Andreas Serrahn (Mng Dir)

Humana GmbH   (1)
Bielefelder Strasse 66, 32051, Herford,
Germany
Tel.: (49) 5221 181 0
Web Site: http://www.humana.de
Fluid Milk Mfr
N.A.I.C.S.: 311511

Subsidiary (Non-US):

Humana Italia S.p.A.   (2)
Viale Liguria 22/A, 20143, Milan, Italy
Tel.: (39) 02 58 117 1
Web Site: http://www.humana.it
Food Products Mfr
N.A.I.C.S.: 311422
Fabrizio Conconi (CFO)

Subsidiary (Domestic):

HUMANA Pharma International
SpA   (3)
Via E Mattei snc, Casorate Primo, 27022,
Pavia, Italy
Tel.: (39) 0286877234
Web Site: http://www.hpinternational.it
Food Supplement & Cosmetics Mfr
N.A.I.C.S.: 311999
Andrea Fenili (Gen Mgr)

Milte Italia SpA   (3)
via Boscovich 55, 20124, Milan, Italy
Tel.: (39) 02917961
Web Site: http://www.milte.it
Food Products Mfr
N.A.I.C.S.: 311999
Gabriele di Filippo (Dir-Medical & Sls)

Subsidiary (Non-US):

Humana Spain S.L.   (2)
Avenida Bruselas 5, 28108, Alcobendas,
Spain
Tel.: (34) 915178970
Web Site: http://www.humana-baby.es
Baby Food Mfr
N.A.I.C.S.: 311422
David Manzano Garcia (Mgr-Unit)

Muritz Milch GmbH   (1)
Ernst-Alban-Strasse 11, 17192, Waren,
Germany
Tel.: (49) 39911540
Emp.: 85
Cheese Mfr
N.A.I.C.S.: 311513

NORLAC GmbH   (1)
Industriestrasse 27, D 27404, Zeven,
Germany   (100%)
Tel.: (49) 4281 72 2226
Web Site: http://www.norlac.de
Milk Substitute Products for Calf Rearing
N.A.I.C.S.: 311119
Gerhard Rudlof (Head-Sls)

TURM-Sahne GmbH   (1)
Westerender Weg 24a, 26125, Oldenburg,
Germany
Tel.: (49) 441932980
Web Site: http://www.turm-sahne.de
Food Products Mfr
N.A.I.C.S.: 311511

Zentralkaserei MV GmbH   (1)
Am Bahndamm 7, 17159, Dargun, Ger-
many
Tel.: (49) 39959510
Web Site: http://www.pommernmilch.de
Emp.: 98
Dairy Products Mfr
N.A.I.C.S.: 311513

indoc milk GmbH   (1)
Flughafenallee 17, 28199, Bremen, Ger-
many
Tel.: (49) 4212432440
Web Site: http://www.indocmilk.com
Dairy Products Mfr
N.A.I.C.S.: 311511

wheyco GmbH   (1)
Haubachstr 86, 22765, Hamburg, Germany
Tel.: (49) 4035964080
Web Site: http://www.wheyco.de
Food Products Mfr
N.A.I.C.S.: 311999
Alexander Bayer (Mng Dir)

DMK DRILLING FLUIDS LTD.
400 525 8th Avenue SW, Calgary,
T2P 1G1, AB, Canada
Tel.: (403) 232-8883
Web Site:
http://www.dmkdrillingfluids.com
Year Founded: 1985
Rev.: $33,318,656
Emp.: 40
Chemical Products Supplier
N.A.I.C.S.: 424690
Dennis Kostiuk (Owner & Pres)

DMOA CO., LTD
11F 726 Eonju-ro, Gangnam-gu,
Seoul, 6057, Korea (South)
Tel.: (82) 220469323
Web Site: http://www.pobis.co.kr
Year Founded: 1982
016670—(KRS)
Rev.: $28,171,679
Assets: $65,326,403
Liabilities: $25,072,614
Net Worth: $40,253,789
Earnings: ($14,470,427)
Emp.: 260
Fiscal Year-end: 12/31/22
Software Development Services &
Tobacco Product Distr
N.A.I.C.S.: 423430
Song Seyeol (CFO)

DMR HYDROENGINEERING & INFRASTRUCTURES LTD.
473 Sector-30, Faridabad, 121003,
Haryana, India
Tel.: (91) 1294360445
Web Site:
https://www.dmrengineering.net
Year Founded: 2009
543410—(BOM)
Rev.: $332,056
Assets: $460,077
Liabilities: $43,076
Net Worth: $417,001
Earnings: $82,975
Fiscal Year-end: 03/31/21
Engineeering Services
N.A.I.C.S.: 541330
S. C. Mittal (Co-Founder, Chm & Mng
Dir)

DMS CO., LTD.
U-Tower 120 Heungdeok Jungang-ro,
Yongin, Gyeonggi-do, Korea (South)
Tel.: (82) 3180311133
Web Site: https://www.dms21.co.kr
Year Founded: 1999
068790—(KRS)
Rev.: $243,175,713
Assets: $326,998,164
Liabilities: $73,712,419
Net Worth: $253,285,745
Earnings: $19,740,841
Emp.: 171
Fiscal Year-end: 12/31/22
Display Equipment Mfr
N.A.I.C.S.: 334417
Yong-seok Park (Chm, Pres & CEO)

DMS IMAGING SA

Avenue Louise 231, Ixelles, 1050,
Brussels, Belgium
Tel.: (32) 471563533
Web Site: http://www.asitbiotech.com
Year Founded: 1997
ASIT—(EUR)
Rev.: $5,697,805
Assets: $3,950,020
Liabilities: $6,068,734
Net Worth: ($2,118,714)
Earnings: $4,783,995
Fiscal Year-end: 12/31/21
Immunotherapy Drug Mfr & Distr
N.A.I.C.S.: 325412
Samuel Sancerni (CEO & Gen Mgr)

DMS INC.
10F Chiyoda Ogawamachi Crossta
111 Kanda Ogawamachi, Chiyoda-ku,
Tokyo, 101-0052, Japan
Tel.: (81) 332932961
Web Site: https://www.dmsjp.co.jp
Year Founded: 1961
9782—(TKS)
Rev.: $270,807,680
Assets: $188,914,880
Liabilities: $48,612,960
Net Worth: $140,301,920
Earnings: $10,086,560
Emp.: 312
Fiscal Year-end: 03/31/22
Sales Promotion Services
N.A.I.C.S.: 561990
Katsuhiko Yamamoto (Pres)

DMSS SOFTWARE LTDA.
Rua Arandu 281 7 Andar, Brooklin
Novo, Sao Paulo, Brazil
Tel.: (55) 1155053644   BR
Web Site: http://www.dmss.com.br
Year Founded: 1990
Sales Range: $10-24.9 Million
Emp.: 50
Predictive Analytics & Data Mining
Software Distr & Technical Consulting
Services
N.A.I.C.S.: 423430
Ricardo Ventura (CEO)

DMT DEMMINER MASCHINEN-BAU TECHNIK GMBH
Woldeforster Strasse 5, 17109, Dem-
min, Germany
Tel.: (49) 39984350
Web Site: http://www.dmt-demmin.de
Rev.: $11,283,492
Emp.: 130
Industrial Machinery Mfr
N.A.I.C.S.: 333248
Johann Erich Wilms (Mng Dir)

DMW CORPORATION
1-5-1 Omorikita Ota Ward, Tokyo,
143-8558, Japan
Tel.: (81) 332985115
Web Site: https://www.dmw.co.jp
Year Founded: 1910
6365—(TKS)
Rev.: $159,274,560
Assets: $244,464,240
Liabilities: $71,606,130
Net Worth: $172,858,110
Earnings: $11,567,500
Emp.: 1,086
Fiscal Year-end: 03/31/24
Pumps, Fans, Blowers, Ventilators,
Turbo-Compressors, Valves, Water
Treatment Systems, Electric Control
Panels & Other Machinery Mfr &
Sales
N.A.I.C.S.: 332312
Norio Hikosaka (Sr Mng Officer &
Mgr-Admin Div & Mgmt Strategy Of-
fice)

Subsidiaries:

DMW Corporation - Houston
Branch　　　　　　　　　　　**(1)**
4265 San Felipe St Ste 1100, Houston, TX
77027
Tel.: (713) 651-7876
Industrial Machinery & Equipment Whslr
N.A.I.C.S.: 423830

DMW Corporation - Mishima
Plant　　　　　　　　　　　　**(1)**
3-27 Miyoshi-Cho, Mishima, 411-8560, Shi-
zuoka, Japan
Tel.: (81) 559758221
Web Site: http://www.dmw.co.jp
Emp.: 500
Industrial Machinery Mfr
N.A.I.C.S.: 333248

DMW Corporation India Private
Limited　　　　　　　　　　　**(1)**
211 2F Great Eastern Galleria Sector 4 Off
Palm Beach Road, Nerul, Navi Mumbai,
400706, India
Tel.: (91) 2227710610
Industrial Machinery & Equipment Whslr
N.A.I.C.S.: 423830

DMW ELECTRICAL INSTRU-
MENTATION INC.
227 Confederation Street, Sarnia,
N7T 1Z9, ON, Canada
Tel.: (519) 336-3003
Web Site:
　　http://www.dmwelectrical.com
Year Founded: 1984
Rev.: $19,388,724
Emp.: 160
Electrical Contractor
N.A.I.C.S.: 238210
Carlo Maola *(Pres)*

DMX TECHNOLOGIES GROUP
LIMITED
4303 AIA Kowloon Tower 100 How
Ming Street, Kwun Tong, Kowloon,
China (Hong Kong)
Tel.: (852) 25202660
Web Site:
　　http://www.dmxtechnologies.com
5CH—(SES)
Sales Range: $350-399.9 Million
Software Solutions Services
N.A.I.C.S.: 541511
Iwao Oishi *(Vice Chm)*

DN AUTOMOTIVE CORPORA-
TION
103 Sanmakgongdanbuk 11-gil,
Yangsan, Gyeongsangnam-do, Korea
(South)
Tel.: (82) 553805800　　　　**KR**
Web Site:
　　http://www.dtrautomotive.com
Year Founded: 1971
007340—(KRS)
Sales Range: $800-899.9 Million
Automotive Products Mfr
N.A.I.C.S.: 326211
Sang Heon Kim *(CEO)*

Subsidiaries:

DN Automotive VMS Limited　**(1)**
Aintree Avenue, Trowbridge, BA14 0XB,
United Kingdom
Tel.: (44) 1225785660
Web Site: https://uk.dtrvms.com
Automotive Parts Designer, Mfr & Supplier
N.A.I.C.S.: 336390
Binay Azman *(Mgr-Logistics)*

Subsidiary (Non-US):

DN Automotive Germany GmbH　**(2)**
Am Flugplatz 50, 56743, Mendig, Germany
Tel.: (49) 26324603887
Web Site: http://www.dtrvms.com
Automotive Parts Research, Testing & Mfr
N.A.I.C.S.: 336390

Joint Venture (Non-US):

DTR VMS Italy S.r.l.　　　　　**(2)**
Sede Legale e Stabilimento Via S Antonio
59, 25050, Passirano, BS, Italy
Tel.: (39) 030 6855
Emp.: 1,900
Automobile Parts Mfr
N.A.I.C.S.: 336390
Luca Olivetti *(VP-Bus Dev)*

Dong Ah Tire & Rubber Co., Ltd. -
Bukjeong Plant　　　　　　　**(1)**
1077 Yangsan-daero, Yangsan,
Gyeongsangnam-do, Korea (South)
Tel.: (02) 550091000
Web Site: https://www.dongahtire.co.kr
Automobile Parts Mfr
N.A.I.C.S.: 336390

DN HOLDINGS CO.,LTD
300 Kanda Neribeicho, Chiyoda-ku,
Tokyo, 101-222, Japan
Tel.: (81) 366757002
Holding Company
N.A.I.C.S.: 551112
Arai Nobuhiro *(Pres)*

Subsidiaries:

Dia Consultants Co., Ltd.　　　**(1)**
4th floor Sanbancho UF Building 6-3 Sanb-
ancho, Chiyoda-ku, Tokyo, 102-0075, Japan
Tel.: (81) 332213205
Web Site: http://www.diaconsult.co.jp
Environmental Consulting Services
N.A.I.C.S.: 541620
Yasuhiko Noguchi *(Pres)*

Nippon Engineering Consultants Co.,
Ltd.　　　　　　　　　　　　**(1)**
4F Akihabara Station Bldg Sumitomo Fu-
dosan, 300 Kanda Neribeicho Chiyoda-ku,
Tokyo, 101-0022, Japan
Tel.: (81) 3 5298 2051
Web Site: http://www.ne-con.co.jp
Rev.: $142,486,620
Assets: $113,394,960
Liabilities: $62,541,180
Net Worth: $50,853,780
Earnings: $2,301,240
Emp.: 636
Fiscal Year-end: 06/30/2019
Construction Engineering Consulting Ser-
vices
N.A.I.C.S.: 541330
Akira Takaku *(Chm & CEO)*

Subsidiary (Domestic):

NE TECHNO CO., LTD.　　　**(2)**
2 Shintoshin 11-2, Chuo-ku, Saitama, 330-
6013, Saitama, Japan
Tel.: (81) 486006661
Web Site: http://www.ne-techno.co.jp
Emp.: 40
Civil Engineering Consulting Services
N.A.I.C.S.: 541330

Subsidiary (Non-US):

Nippon Engineering-Vietnam Co.,
Ltd.　　　　　　　　　　　　**(2)**
364 Cong Hoa, Tan Binh District E-Town
9F, Ho Chi Minh City, Vietnam
Tel.: (84) 8 3810 6300
Construction Engineering Consulting Ser-
vices
N.A.I.C.S.: 541330

DN TYRE & RUBBER PLC
Plot 23 Ikeja Industrial Estate, Ikeja,
Nigeria
Tel.: (234) 4900410
Vehicle Tire Mfr & Distr
N.A.I.C.S.: 314994
Mohammed Jimoh Yinusa *(CEO &
Mng Dir-Grp)*

DNA CHIP RESEARCH INC.
Suzue Baydium 1-15-1 Kaigan,
Minato-ku, Tokyo, 105-0022, Japan
Tel.: (81) 357771700
Web Site: https://www.dna-chip.co.jp
Year Founded: 1999
2397—(TKS)

Sales Range: Less than $1 Million
Deoxyribonucleic Acid Research Ser-
vices
N.A.I.C.S.: 541715
Ryo Matoba *(Pres)*

DNA HOLDINGS CORPORA-
TION
29th floor World Plaza 5th Ave,
Taguig, 2196, Manila, Philippines
Tel.: (63) 9176531818　　　　**PH**
Web Site: http://www.dnaholdings.ph
Year Founded: 1958
DNA　(PHI)
Sales Range: $1-9.9 Million
Medical Equipment Mfr & Distr
N.A.I.C.S.: 339113
Jose Miguel V. Vergara *(Dir-Medical)*

DNA INVESTMENT JOINT
STOCK CORPORATION
Le Chan Road Chau Son Industrial
Park, Chau Son Ward, Phu Ly, Ha
Nam, Vietnam
Tel.: (84) 2263840408
Web Site:
　　https://www.hangermetal.com
Year Founded: 2003
KSD—(HNX)
Sales Range: Less than $1 Million
Domestic Appliances Mfr & Distr
N.A.I.C.S.: 449210
Bui Viet Vuong *(CEO & Member-
Mgmt Bd)*

DNA LINK INC.
31 Magokjungang 8-ro 3-gil,
Gangseo-gu, Seoul, Korea (South)
Tel.: (82) 231531500
Web Site: https://www.dnalink.com
Year Founded: 2000
127120—(KRS)
Rev.: $13,024,486
Assets: $33,369,841
Liabilities: $11,977,991
Net Worth: $21,391,850
Earnings: ($6,195,604)
Emp.: 80
Fiscal Year-end: 12/31/22
Biotechnology Research & Develop-
ment
N.A.I.C.S.: 541714
Jeong Jinsik *(Head-Dept)*

Subsidiaries:

DNA Link USA, Inc.　　　　　**(1)**
4901 Morena Blvd Ste 703, San Diego, CA
92117
Biotechnology Research & Development
Services
N.A.I.C.S.: 541714

DNA TESTING CENTERS,
CORP.
2378 Parkhaven Blvd, Oakville, L6H
0E7, ON, Canada
Tel.: (905) 582-5299　　　　　**FL**
Web Site:
　　https://www.dnatestingcanada.com
Year Founded: 2014
Rev.: $31,886
Assets: $10,008
Liabilities: $119,541
Net Worth: ($109,533)
Earnings: ($161,287)
Emp.: 5
Fiscal Year-end: 12/31/16
DNA Diagnostic Testing Kits Distr
N.A.I.C.S.: 423450
Barjinder Sohal *(Pres & CEO)*

Subsidiaries:

DNA Testing Centres of Canada,
Ltd.　　　　　　　　　　　　**(1)**
2378 Parkhaven Boulevard, Oakville, L6H
0E7, ON, Canada
Tel.: (905) 582-5299

Web Site: http://www.dnatestingcanada.com
Rev.: $23,099
Assets: $443
Net Worth: $443
Earnings: $443
Emp.: 4
Fiscal Year-end: 12/31/2013
DNA Diagnostic Testing Kits Distr
N.A.I.C.S.: 423450
Barjinder Sohal *(Pres & CEO)*

DNAKE XIAMEN INTELLIGENT
TECHNOLOGY CO., LTD.
No 8 Haijing North 2nd Rd, Xiamen,
361000, Fujian, China
Tel.: (86) 5925705812
Web Site: https://www.dnake-
　　global.com
Year Founded: 2005
300884—(SSE)
Rev.: $118,264,536
Assets: $258,090,300
Liabilities: $69,884,100
Net Worth: $188,206,200
Earnings: $11,262,888
Emp.: 1,200
Fiscal Year-end: 12/31/22
Software Development Services
N.A.I.C.S.: 541511
Guodong Miao *(Chm & Gen Mgr)*

DNB BANK ASA
Dronning Eufemias gate 30, Bjorvika,
0191, Oslo, Norway
Tel.: (47) 91504800　　　　　**NO**
Web Site: https://www.dnb.no
DNB—(OSL)
Rev.: $6,950,027,711
Assets: $298,949,842,971
Liabilities: $275,016,903,750
Net Worth: $23,932,939,220
Earnings: $2,956,770,737
Emp.: 10,351
Fiscal Year-end: 12/31/22
Commercial & Investment Banking
N.A.I.C.S.: 522110
Olaug Svarva *(Chm)*

Subsidiaries:

DNB (UK) Limited　　　　　　**(1)**
8th Floor The Walbrook Building 25, Wal-
brook, London, EC4N 8AF, United Kingdom
Tel.: (44) 2076211111
Financial Management Services
N.A.I.C.S.: 523999

DNB Asia Ltd.　　　　　　　　**(1)**
8 Shenton Way 48-02 Temasek Tower, Sin-
gapore, 068811, Singapore
Tel.: (65) 62206144
Sales Range: $50-74.9 Million
Emp.: 100
Commercial Banking Services
N.A.I.C.S.: 522110

DNB Asset Management AS　　**(1)**
Dronning Eufemias gate 30, N-0191, Oslo,
Norway
Tel.: (47) 22474000
Financial Services
N.A.I.C.S.: 523999
Natasja Henriksen *(Head-Nordic Sls)*

DNB Auto Finance Oy　　　　**(1)**
Urho Kekkosenkatu 7B, 00100, Helsinki,
Finland
Tel.: (358) 102060700
Web Site: https://www.dnbautofinance.fi
Financial Services
N.A.I.C.S.: 523150

DNB Bank Polska S.A.　　　　**(1)**
ul Przyokopowa 31, 01-208, Warsaw, Po-
land
Tel.: (48) 225241000
Web Site: https://www.dnb.pl
Banking Services
N.A.I.C.S.: 522110
Artur Tomaszewski *(Co-Pres & CEO)*

DNB Boligkreditt AS　　　　　**(1)**
Torgallmenningen 2, 5020, Bergen, Norway
Tel.: (47) 55211000
Financial Services

DNB Bank ASA—(Continued)

N.A.I.C.S.: 522110

DNB Eiendom AS (1)
Dronning Eufemiasgate 30, Bjorvika, 0191,
Oslo, Norway
Tel.: (47) 91509999
Web Site: https://www.dnbeiendom.no
Sales Range: $1-4.9 Billion
Emp.: 4,000
Banking Services
N.A.I.C.S.: 522110

DNB Livsforsikring AS (1)
Solheimsgaten 7C, 5058, Bergen, Norway
Tel.: (47) 91504800
Life Insurance & Wealth Management Products & Services
N.A.I.C.S.: 524113

Subsidiary (Domestic):

DNB Naeringseiendom AS (2)
Solheimsgaten 7C, 5058, Bergen,
Norway (100%)
Tel.: (47) 46844100
Real Estate Manangement Services
N.A.I.C.S.: 531390

DNB Luxembourg S.A. (1)
13 rue Goethe, 1637, Luxembourg, Luxembourg
Tel.: (352) 4549451
Web Site: https://www.dnb.no
Sales Range: $50-74.9 Million
Emp.: 30
Commercial Banking Services
N.A.I.C.S.: 522110
Haakon Hansen (Exec VP-Wealth Mgmt & Insurance)

DNB Markets, Inc. (1)
30 Hudson Yards 81st fl, New York, NY
10001
Tel.: (212) 681-3800
Web Site: http://www.dnb.com
Sales Range: $50-74.9 Million
Emp.: 30
Securities Brokerage Services
N.A.I.C.S.: 523150

DNB Naeringsmegling AS (1)
Dronning Eufemias gt 30, 0191, Norway
Tel.: (47) 22948660
Web Site:
https://www.dnbnaringsmegling.no
Sales Range: $50-74.9 Million
Emp.: 45
Financial Services
N.A.I.C.S.: 522110

DNB Sweden AB (1)
Regeringsgatan 59, SE-105 88, Stockholm,
Sweden
Tel.: (46) 84734100
Web Site: https://www.dnb.se
Car Financial Services
N.A.I.C.S.: 522220

IOS Tubular Management AS (1)
Norsea Base Building No 42, 4056, Tananger, Norway
Tel.: (47) 4 804 0500
Web Site: https://www.iostubular.no
Down Hole Equipment Mfr
N.A.I.C.S.: 333132

Sbanken ASA (1)
PO Box 7077, 5020, Bergen, Norway
Tel.: (47) 55 26 00 00
Web Site: http://www.sbanken.no
Sales Range: Less than $1 Million
Online Retial Banking Services
N.A.I.C.S.: 522110

Svensk Fastighetsformedling AB (1)
Vasagatan 28, 111 20, Stockholm, Sweden
Tel.: (46) 850535800
Web Site: https://www.svenskfast.se
Emp.: 1,200
Real Estate Brokerage Services
N.A.I.C.S.: 531210
Liza Maria Karin Nyberg (Mng Dir)

Vipps AS (1)
Robert Levins gate 5, 0154, Oslo,
Norway (45%)
Tel.: (47) 22482800
Web Site: https://www.vipps.no

Financial Services
N.A.I.C.S.: 522320
Rune Garborg (CEO)

DNC MEDIA CO., LTD.
111 Digital-Ro 26-Gil, Guro-Gu,
Seoul, Korea (South)
Tel.: (82) 23332513
Web Site: http://www.dncmedia.co.kr
Year Founded: 2012
263720—(KRS)
Rev.: $45,436,204
Assets: $69,732,203
Liabilities: $13,016,281
Net Worth: $56,715,922
Earnings: $4,559,169
Emp.: 48
Fiscal Year-end: 12/31/22
Books Publishing Services
N.A.I.C.S.: 513130
Seo-Jin Lee (Gen Mgr)

DNF CO., LTD.
142 Daehwa-ro 132beon-gil,
Daedeok-gu, Daejeon, 34366, Korea
(South)
Tel.: (82) 429327939
Web Site:
https://www.dnfsolution.com
Year Founded: 2001
092070—(KRS)
Rev.: $103,682,022
Assets: $146,147,756
Liabilities: $25,139,552
Net Worth: $121,008,204
Earnings: $4,428,962
Emp.: 268
Fiscal Year-end: 12/31/22
Chemical Compounds & Catalysts
Mfr
N.A.I.C.S.: 325998
Myong-Woon Kim (CEO)

Subsidiaries:

**DNF Co Ltd - Electronic Material
Division** (1)
142 Daehwa-ro 132 Beon-gil Daedeok-gu,
Daejeon, 306-802, Korea (South)
Tel.: (82) 42 932 7939
Web Site: http://www.dnfsolution.com
Emp.: 150
Electronic Materials Mfr
N.A.I.C.S.: 333992

**DNF Co Ltd - Fine Chemical
Division** (1)
142 Daehwa-ro 132beon-gil, Daedeok-gu,
Daejeon, 34366, Korea (South)
Tel.: (82) 429327939
Web Site: http://www.dnfsolution.com
Chemical Materials Mfr
N.A.I.C.S.: 325199
Kim Myong-woon (CEO)

DNF Co., Ltd - DNF Ulsan Plant (1)
Daejeong-ro 10-19 Onsan-eup, Ulju-Gun,
Ulsan, 45009, Korea (South)
Tel.: (82) 522397939
Web Site: http://www.dnfsolution.com
Electronic Components Mfr
N.A.I.C.S.: 334419

DNI METALS INC.
129Pinewood Trail, Mississauga, L5G
2L2, ON, Canada
Tel.: (416) 720-0754 QC
Web Site: https://www.dnimetals.com
Year Founded: 1954
DMNKF—(OTCIQ)
Sales Range: Less than $1 Million
Mineral Exploration Services
N.A.I.C.S.: 213114

DNIPROAZOT JSC
S H Gorobtsya Street 1, Dnipropetrovsk, 51909, Ukraine
Tel.: (380) 569584980
Web Site: http://www.azot.com.ua
DNAZ—(UKR)
Sales Range: Less than $1 Million

Chemical Products Distr
N.A.I.C.S.: 424690
Sergey L. Sidorov (Gen Dir)

DNIPROVAGONMASH JSC
4 Ukrayinska Str, Dniprodzerzhinsk,
51925, Ukraine
Tel.: (380) 5692 3 30 46
Web Site: http://www.dvmash.biz
Freight Railway & Industrial Vehicle
Mfr
N.A.I.C.S.: 336110
A. I. Kobylyakov (Gen Dir)

Subsidiaries:

Dneprovagonmash Ltd. (2)
Radio Str 24 Building 1 Office 700, 105005,
Moscow, Russia
Tel.: (7) 4957953304
Industrial Vehicle Mfr
N.A.I.C.S.: 336120

DNO ASA
Dokkveien 1, 0250, Oslo, Norway
Tel.: (47) 23238480 NO
Web Site: https://www.dno.no
Year Founded: 1971
DTNOF—(OTCIQ)
Rev.: $667,500,000
Assets: $2,638,300,000
Liabilities: $1,403,500,000
Net Worth: $1,234,800,000
Earnings: $18,600,000
Emp.: 1,085
Fiscal Year-end: 12/31/23
Oil & Gas Exploration Services
N.A.I.C.S.: 211120
Haakon Sandborg (CFO)

Subsidiaries:

DNO Norge AS (1)
Badehusgata 37, 4014, Stavanger, Norway
Tel.: (47) 23238480
Synthetic Resin Mfr & Distr
N.A.I.C.S.: 325211

DNO Technical Services AS (1)
Office 1201 Boulevard Plaza 2 Downtown,
PO Box 25353, Dubai, United Arab Emirates
Tel.: (971) 44029300
Synthetic Resin Mfr & Distr
N.A.I.C.S.: 325211

DNO Yemen AS (1)
Street No 8 Off Damaskus Street, Sana'a,
Yemen
Tel.: (967) 1428230
Oil & Gas Exploration Services
N.A.I.C.S.: 211120

DNO NORTH SEA PLC
24 Carden Place, Aberdeen, AB10
1UQ, United Kingdom
Tel.: (44) 20 7839 9720 UK
Web Site: http://www.dno.no
Year Founded: 2002
Rev.: $277,304,981
Assets: $1,026,968,394
Liabilities: $715,553,424
Net Worth: $311,414,970
Earnings: $12,498,578
Emp.: 86
Fiscal Year-end: 12/31/18
Holding Company; Oil & Gas Exploration Services
N.A.I.C.S.: 551112
Bijan Mossavar-Rahmani (Chm)

Subsidiaries:

Faroe Petroleum (UK) Limited (1)
24 Carden Place, Aberdeen, AB10 1UQ,
United Kingdom
Tel.: (44) 1224650920
Web Site: http://www.fp.fo
Oil & Gas Exploration Services
N.A.I.C.S.: 213112
Julian Riddick (Sec & Dir-Comml)

Subsidiary (Non-US):

Faroe Petroleum Norge AS (2)
Haakon VIIs Gate 7, PO Box 309, Sentrum,
4002, Stavanger, Norway
Tel.: (47) 51 21 51 00
Web Site: http://www.faroe-petroleum.com
Emp.: 35
Oil & Gas Field Exploration Services
N.A.I.C.S.: 213112

Foroyar Kolvetni P/F (2)
Bryggjubakki 22, PO Box 1098, FO-110,
Torshavn, Faroe Islands
Tel.: (298) 298 350 460
Petroleum Exploration Services
N.A.I.C.S.: 211120

DNV GL GROUP AS
Veritasveien 1, 1322, Hovik, Norway
Tel.: (47) 67579900 NO
Web Site: http://www.dnvgl.com
Year Founded: 1864
Sales Range: $750-799.9 Million
Emp.: 3,000
Holding Company; Technical Support
Services
N.A.I.C.S.: 551112
Thomas Vogth-Eriksen (Dir-Certification Div-Bus Assurance)

Subsidiaries:

DNV Alesund (1)
Nedre Strandgate 29, N 6004, Alesund,
Norway (100%)
Tel.: (47) 70115110
Sales Range: $25-49.9 Million
Emp.: 35
N.A.I.C.S.: 483113

DNV Bergen (1)
Johan Berentsenvei 109 111, PO Box
7400, N 5020, Bergen, Norway (100%)
Tel.: (47) 55943600
Web Site: http://www.dnv.com
Sales Range: $1-9.9 Million
Emp.: 140
N.A.I.C.S.: 483113
Kore Samnaoy (Mng Dir)

DNV Business Assurance India Private Ltd (1)
ROMA No 10 G S T Road Near Kathipara
Flyover, Chennai, 600016, India
Tel.: (91) 2652322622
Business Support Services
N.A.I.C.S.: 561499

DNV Eiendom (1)
Veritasveien 25, 4007, Stavanger,
Norway (100%)
Tel.: (47) 51506000
Web Site: http://www.dnvgl.com
Sales Range: $50-74.9 Million
Emp.: 120
Transportation & Logistics Services
N.A.I.C.S.: 483113
Remi Eriksen (Grp CEO & Pres)

DNV Floro (1)
Kolkaia 1, N 6900, Floro, Norway
Tel.: (47) 57745590
Web Site: http://www.dnv.com
Sales Range: $25-49.9 Million
Emp.: 4
N.A.I.C.S.: 483113

DNV Forde (1)
Fordetunet AS, Hafstadvegen 23, N 6800,
Forde, Norway (100%)
Tel.: (47) 57745590
Sales Range: $25-49.9 Million
Emp.: 1
N.A.I.C.S.: 483113
Olav Golten (Gen Mgr)

DNV Fredrikstad (1)
KG Meldahls Vei 9, PO Box 304, 1610, Fredrikstad, Norway (100%)
Tel.: (47) 69355850
Web Site: http://www.dnv.com
Sales Range: $25-49.9 Million
Emp.: 5
N.A.I.C.S.: 483113

DNV GL SE (1)
Brooktorkai 18, Hamburg, 20457, Germany
Tel.: (49) 40361490

Web Site: http://www.dnvgl.com
Sales Range: $1-4.9 Billion
Maritime & Industrial Safety Services
N.A.I.C.S.: 488390
Bernhard Stander *(Mng Dir)*

Subsidiary (Non-US):

Cesky Lodni a Prumyslovy Registr, S.r.o. (2)
Sobeslavska 2063/46, Vinohrady, Prague, Czech Republic
Tel.: (420) 271000011
Web Site: http://www.clpr.cz
Sales Range: $25-49.9 Million
Emp.: 19
Navigational Services to Shipping
N.A.I.C.S.: 488330

DNV GL - Lithuania (2)
Minijos G 43, 91208, Klaipeda, Lithuania
Tel.: (370) 46310199
Web Site: http://www.dnvgl.lt
Emp.: 82
Navigational Services to Shipping
N.A.I.C.S.: 488330
Andrej Dutov *(Country Mgr)*

DNV GL Business Assurance Denmark A/S (2)
Tuborg Parkvej 8 2nd Floor, 2900, Hellerup, Denmark
Tel.: (45) 36390090
Sales Range: $25-49.9 Million
Emp.: 15
Navigational Services to Shipping
N.A.I.C.S.: 488330

DNV GL Cyprus Ltd. (2)
226 Makarios III Avenue Office No 22 2nd Floor, 3030, Limassol, Cyprus
Tel.: (357) 25361393
Web Site: http://www.dnvgl.com
Emp.: 3
Navigational Services to Shipping
N.A.I.C.S.: 488330
Evgenios Koumoudhis *(Area Mgr)*

Subsidiary (Domestic):

DNV GL SE - Hamburg (2)
Brooktorkai 18, 20457, Hamburg, Germany
Tel.: (49) 4036149302
Web Site: http://www.dnvgl.com
Navigational Services to Shipping
N.A.I.C.S.: 488330
Lutz Wittenberg *(Mng Dir)*

GL Garrad Hassan Deutschland GmbH (2)
Sommerdeich 14b, 25709, Kaiser-Wilhelm-Koog, Germany
Tel.: (49) 48569010
Web Site: http://www.dnvgl.com
Sales Range: $25-49.9 Million
Emp.: 50
Navigational Services to Shipping
N.A.I.C.S.: 488330
Koehne Volker *(Mng Dir)*

Subsidiary (Non-US):

GL Luxembourg GmbH (2)
26 place de la Gare, 1616, Luxembourg, Luxembourg
Tel.: (352) 480062
Sales Range: $25-49.9 Million
Emp.: 2
Navigational Services to Shipping
N.A.I.C.S.: 488330

GL Station Ningbo Co.,Ltd. (2)
Room 1301 Prime Center 21, 31 Hualou Lane Haishu District, 315000, Ningbo, China
Tel.: (86) 57427820606
Navigational Services to Shipping
N.A.I.C.S.: 488330

Germanischer Lloyd (Australia) Pty. Ltd. (2)
88 Pitt St, Suite 51 Level 10, 2000, Sydney, NSW, Australia
Tel.: (61) 292331119
Sales Range: $25-49.9 Million
Emp.: 12
Navigational Services to Shipping
N.A.I.C.S.: 488330

Germanischer Lloyd (Chile) Ltda. (2)

Libertad 1405 Oficina 1502, Edificio Torre Coraceros, Vina del Mar, Chile
Tel.: (56) 322688323
Sales Range: $25-49.9 Million
Emp.: 7
Navigational Services to Shipping
N.A.I.C.S.: 488330

Germanischer Lloyd (Kaohsiung) Taiwan Pte Ltd. (2)
Chenggong 2nd Road 6F-3 No 25, Cianjhen District, Kaohsiung, 802, Taiwan
Tel.: (886) 673387571
Web Site: http://www.dnvgl.com
Navigational Services to Shipping
N.A.I.C.S.: 488330

Germanischer Lloyd (Korea) Pty Ltd. (2)
19th Floor Hanjin Shipping Building, 79-9 Jungang-dong 4-ga Jung-gu, 600755, Busan, Korea (South)
Tel.: (82) 514401237
Sales Range: $50-74.9 Million
Emp.: 140
Navigational Services to Shipping
N.A.I.C.S.: 488330
Au-Hak Jung *(Mgr)*

Germanischer Lloyd (Malaysia) Sdn. Bhd. (2)
Level 18 Menara Prestige No 1 Jalan Pinang, 50450, Kuala Lumpur, Malaysia
Tel.: (60) 321601088
Emp.: 200
Navigational Services to Shipping
N.A.I.C.S.: 488330

Germanischer Lloyd (Thailand) Co., Ltd. (2)
16th Floor Richmond Office 75/57, Sukhumvit 26 Klongton Klongtoe, Bangkok, 10110, Thailand
Tel.: (66) 226184012
Web Site: http://www.gl-group.com
Sales Range: $25-49.9 Million
Emp.: 5
Navigational Services to Shipping
N.A.I.C.S.: 488330

Subsidiary (US):

Germanischer Lloyd (USA), Inc. (2)
303 S Broadway Ste 460, Tarrytown, NY 10591
Tel.: (914) 366-6606
Sales Range: $25-49.9 Million
Emp.: 7
Navigational Services to Shipping
N.A.I.C.S.: 488330

Subsidiary (Non-US):

Germanischer Lloyd - Lebanon S.A.R.L. (2)
Pyramide Center 2nd Fl Al Saide St, Amchit, Lebanon
Tel.: (961) 9622551
Web Site: http://www.dnvgl.com
Sales Range: $25-49.9 Million
Emp.: 2
Navigational Services to Shipping
N.A.I.C.S.: 488330
Andre Abdel Calyl *(Mgr)*

Germanischer Lloyd Argentina S.A.
Avenida Leandro N Alem 790 9 Piso, C1001AAP, Buenos Aires, Argentina
Tel.: (54) 1143112085
Web Site: http://www.gr.com
Sales Range: $25-49.9 Million
Emp.: 2
Navigational Services to Shipping
N.A.I.C.S.: 488330

Germanischer Lloyd Austria GmbH (2)
Markgraf-Rudiger-Str 6, Vienna, 1150, Austria
Tel.: (43) 19824303
Web Site: http://www.gl-group.com
Sales Range: $25-49.9 Million
Emp.: 3
Navigational Services to Shipping
N.A.I.C.S.: 488330
York Jahn *(Gen Mgr)*

Germanischer Lloyd Bangladesh Ltd. (2)

HBFC Building 4th Floor, 1-D Agrabad Commercial Area, 4100, Chittagong, Bangladesh
Tel.: (880) 31713759
Web Site: http://www.gl-group.com
Sales Range: $25-49.9 Million
Emp.: 12
Navigational Services to Shipping
N.A.I.C.S.: 488330

Germanischer Lloyd Belgium N.V. (2)
Atlantic House Noorderlaan 147, 2030, Antwerp, Belgium
Tel.: (32) 36460416
Web Site: http://www.glvgl.com
Sales Range: $25-49.9 Million
Emp.: 45
Navigational Services to Shipping
N.A.I.C.S.: 488330
Francis Paarvekooeer *(Country Mgr)*

Germanischer Lloyd Bulgaria Ltd. (2)
12 General Stolipin St, 9002, Varna, Bulgaria
Tel.: (359) 52699000
Web Site: http://www.Germanischer.com
Sales Range: $25-49.9 Million
Emp.: 12
Navigational Services to Shipping
N.A.I.C.S.: 488330
Stilian Proykov *(Mgr)*

Germanischer Lloyd Canada Ltd. (2)
300 St Sacrement Suite 530, H2Y1X4, Montreal, QC, Canada
Tel.: (514) 287-7102
Web Site: http://www.gl-group.com
Sales Range: $25-49.9 Million
Emp.: 4
Navigational Services to Shipping
N.A.I.C.S.: 488330

Subsidiary (Domestic):

Germanischer Lloyd Certification GmbH (2)
Brooktorkai 18, 20457, Hamburg, Germany
Tel.: (49) 4036149288
Web Site: http://www.gl-group.com
Sales Range: $200-249.9 Million
Emp.: 1,000
Navigational Services to Shipping
N.A.I.C.S.: 488330

Subsidiary (Non-US):

Germanischer Lloyd Certification Services, S.L. (2)
Pedro Teixeira 8, Planta 6 Oficina 32, 28020, Madrid, Spain
Tel.: (34) 914170018
Navigational Services to Shipping
N.A.I.C.S.: 488330

Germanischer Lloyd Colombia Ltda. (2)
Edificio Banco Popular Centro Oficina 503 Calle 32 No 26-13, Cartagena, Colombia
Tel.: (57) 56643256
Web Site: http://www.gl-group.com
Navigational Services to Shipping
N.A.I.C.S.: 488330
Rafailemisro Mesa Abad *(Gen Mgr)*

Germanischer Lloyd Colombo Pvt. Ltd. (2)
6th Floor Sampath Centre, 110 Sir James Peiris Mawatha, Colombo, Sri Lanka
Tel.: (94) 112300259
Sales Range: $25-49.9 Million
Emp.: 3
Navigational Services to Shipping
N.A.I.C.S.: 488330

Germanischer Lloyd Engineering Services East Asia (ESEA) (2)
Room 1201-1211 Shanghai Central Plaza, 381Huaihai M Road, 200020, Shanghai, China
Tel.: (86) 2161416735
Navigational Services to Shipping
N.A.I.C.S.: 488330

Germanischer Lloyd Espana, S.L. (2)
Pedro Teixeira 8, Planta 6 Oficina 32, 28020, Madrid, Spain

Tel.: (34) 914170049
Web Site: http://www.gl.group.com
Sales Range: $25-49.9 Million
Emp.: 6
Navigational Services to Shipping
N.A.I.C.S.: 488330

Germanischer Lloyd Estonia OU (2)
Regati Pst 1, Korpus 5VE Nr 220/221, 11911, Tallinn, Estonia
Tel.: (372) 6398602
Web Site: http://www.gl-group.com
Navigational Services to Shipping
N.A.I.C.S.: 488330

Germanischer Lloyd Finland Oy (2)
Puutarhakatu 12, 20100, Turku, Finland
Tel.: (358) 207598910
Web Site: http://www.gl-group.com
Sales Range: $25-49.9 Million
Emp.: 4
Navigational Services to Shipping
N.A.I.C.S.: 488330
Hannu Jokela *(Country Mgr)*

Germanischer Lloyd France SARL (2)
Technoparc du Griffon Batiment XI, 511 route de la Seds, 13127, Vitrolles, France
Tel.: (33) 442107133
Navigational Services to Shipping
N.A.I.C.S.: 488330

Germanischer Lloyd GLM Sdn. Bhd. (2)
Level 38 Menara AmBank Jalan Yap Kwan Seng, 50450, Kuala Lumpur, Malaysia
Tel.: (60) 321610088
Web Site: http://www.gl-group.com
Sales Range: $25-49.9 Million
Emp.: 100
Navigational Services to Shipping
N.A.I.C.S.: 488330

Germanischer Lloyd Hellas Survey E.P.E. (2)
Aitolikou 05, 18538, Piraeus, Greece
Tel.: (30) 2104290373
Web Site: http://www.gl-group.com
Sales Range: $25-49.9 Million
Emp.: 25
Navigational Services to Shipping
N.A.I.C.S.: 488330
George Teriakidis *(Mgr-Bus Dev)*

Germanischer Lloyd Hong Kong Ltd. (2)
Room 918 9th-Floor Star House, 3 Salisbury Road Tsim Sha Tsui, Kowloon, China (Hong Kong)
Tel.: (852) 23171980
Sales Range: $25-49.9 Million
Emp.: 10
Navigational Services to Shipping
N.A.I.C.S.: 488330
Kwok-Kee Yuen *(Office Mgr)*

Germanischer Lloyd Hungary Kft. (2)
Ov utca 105-b, 1141, Budapest, Hungary
Tel.: (36) 14221795
Navigational Services to Shipping
N.A.I.C.S.: 488330

Germanischer Lloyd Iceland Ltd. (2)
Tryggvagata 11, Hafnarhvoll, Reykjavik, Iceland
Tel.: (354) 5522851
Sales Range: $25-49.9 Million
Emp.: 1
Navigational Services to Shipping
N.A.I.C.S.: 488330
Hafsteinn Jonsson *(Country Mgr)*

Germanischer Lloyd Industrial Services Co.,Ltd. (2)
Room 3201 Central Plaza, 381 Huaihai M Road, 200020, Shanghai, China
Tel.: (86) 2153510866
Navigational Services to Shipping
N.A.I.C.S.: 488330

Germanischer Lloyd Industrial Services Egypt Ltd. (2)
9 Road 259, New Maadi, Cairo, Egypt
Tel.: (20) 227544285
Industrial Supplies Whslr
N.A.I.C.S.: 423840
Essa Bayoumi *(Mng Dir)*

DNV GL Group AS—(Continued)

Germanischer Lloyd Industrial Services Italia S.r.l. (2)
Via Gozzano 14, Cinisello Balsamo, 20092, Italy
Tel.: (39) 026124121
Web Site: http://www.gl-group.com
Sales Range: $25-49.9 Million
Emp.: 10
Navigational Services to Shipping
N.A.I.C.S.: 488330
Dario Buccellato *(Office Mgr)*

Germanischer Lloyd Industrial Services do Brasil Ltda. (2)
Ave Pompeia 2425, Sao Paulo, 05023-001, Brazil
Tel.: (55) 1138624781
Sales Range: $25-49.9 Million
Emp.: 25
Navigational Services to Shipping
N.A.I.C.S.: 488330

Germanischer Lloyd Industrie Services Russland (LCC) (2)
Kadashevskaya nab. 6/1/2 building 1, 119017, Moscow, Russia
Tel.: (7) 4956642192
Web Site: http://www.gl-nobledenton.com
Sales Range: $25-49.9 Million
Emp.: 35
Navigational Services to Shipping
N.A.I.C.S.: 488330

Germanischer Lloyd Ireland Ltd. (2)
Unit A3 First Fl, Nutgrove Office Pk Rathfarnh, Dublin, Ireland
Tel.: (353) 12986112
Marine Cargo Handling
N.A.I.C.S.: 488320

Germanischer Lloyd Israel Ltd. (2)
Julius Simon Road, PO Box 10630, 26118, Haifa, Israel
Tel.: (972) 48412639
Sales Range: $25-49.9 Million
Emp.: 1
Navigational Services to Shipping
N.A.I.C.S.: 488330

Germanischer Lloyd Malta Ltd. (2)
20 Flat 2 Parish Priest Street, Gudja, GDJ1080, Valletta, Malta
Tel.: (356) 21894921
Sales Range: $25-49.9 Million
Emp.: 3
Navigational Services to Shipping
N.A.I.C.S.: 488330
John Abdula *(Gen Mgr)*

Germanischer Lloyd Morocco S.A.R.L. (2)
Lotissement 33 La Coline II Residence les Alizes 1er Etage, Bureau 103 Sidi Maarouf, 20190, Casablanca, Morocco
Tel.: (212) 22582390
Navigational Services to Shipping
N.A.I.C.S.: 488330

Germanischer Lloyd Netherlands B.V. (2)
Jan van Galenstraat 56, Schiedam, 3115 JG, Netherlands
Tel.: (31) 102040404
Web Site: http://www.dnvgl.com
Emp.: 100
Navigational Services to Shipping
N.A.I.C.S.: 488330
Harald Seibicke *(Mgr)*

Germanischer Lloyd New Zealand Ltd. (2)
4B 4 Pacific Rise, Mt Wellington, Auckland, New Zealand
Tel.: (64) 95730018
Navigational Services to Shipping
N.A.I.C.S.: 488330

Germanischer Lloyd Norge AS (2)
Strandveien 50, 1366, Lysaker, Norway
Tel.: (47) 67102590
Web Site: http://www.gl-group.com
Navigational Services to Shipping
N.A.I.C.S.: 488330

Germanischer Lloyd Offshore & Industrial Services Korea Ltd. Co. (2)
20th Floor Kyopo Bldg 1 Jong-Ro, Jongno-Gu, Seoul, 110-714, Korea (South)

Tel.: (82) 28631421
Web Site: http://www.dnvgl.com
Sales Range: $25-49.9 Million
Emp.: 16
Navigational Services to Shipping
N.A.I.C.S.: 488330
Sangho Ha *(Gen Mgr)*

Germanischer Lloyd Peru S.A.C. (2)
Amador Merino Reyna 307 Of 603, San Isidro, Lima, 27, Peru
Tel.: (51) 12218124
Sales Range: $25-49.9 Million
Emp.: 5
Navigational Services to Shipping
N.A.I.C.S.: 488330
Ronny Cattarinich *(Gen Mgr)*

Germanischer Lloyd Philippines, Inc. (2)
Unit 2114 Cityland 10 Tower 2, Ayala Ave N Cor H V Dela Costa, Manila, Philippines
Tel.: (63) 28937720
Web Site: http://www.gl-group.com
Sales Range: $25-49.9 Million
Emp.: 8
Navigational Services to Shipping
N.A.I.C.S.: 488330

Germanischer Lloyd Polen Sp. z o.o. (2)
Poland Szczecin, 71 011, Szczecin, Poland
Tel.: (48) 914315302
Web Site: http://www.gl-group.com
Sales Range: $25-49.9 Million
Emp.: 35
Navigational Services to Shipping
N.A.I.C.S.: 488330

Germanischer Lloyd Portugal Inspeccao de Navios, Lda. (2)
Av Infante Santo 43-1 Dto, Lisbon, 1350-177, Portugal
Tel.: (351) 213139150
Sales Range: $25-49.9 Million
Emp.: 9
Navigational Services to Shipping
N.A.I.C.S.: 488330

Subsidiary (Domestic):

Germanischer Lloyd Pruflabor GmbH (2)
Tempowerkring 11, 21079, Hamburg, Germany
Tel.: (49) 4020003970
Sales Range: $25-49.9 Million
Emp.: 15
Navigational Services to Shipping
N.A.I.C.S.: 488330
Feyer Manfred *(Mng Dir)*

Subsidiary (Non-US):

Germanischer Lloyd Romania S.R.L. (2)
Marc Aureliu 8, 900744, Constanta, Romania
Tel.: (40) 241616202
Navigational Services to Shipping
N.A.I.C.S.: 488330
Siegmund Rainhard *(Country Mgr)*

Germanischer Lloyd Sankt Petersburg GmbH (2)
nab Kryukova kan 4-29, 190000, Saint Petersburg, Russia
Tel.: (7) 8123468277
Sales Range: $25-49.9 Million
Emp.: 11
Navigational Services to Shipping
N.A.I.C.S.: 488330

Germanischer Lloyd Shanghai Co.,Ltd. (2)
Room 3209-3220 Shanghai Central Plaza, 381 Huaihai Middle Road, 200020, Shanghai, China
Tel.: (86) 2161416789
Web Site: http://www.gl-group.com
Navigational Services to Shipping
N.A.I.C.S.: 488330

Germanischer Lloyd Singapore Pte. Ltd. (2)
83 Clemenceau Avenue, #13-05/06 UE Square, 239920, Singapore, Singapore
Tel.: (65) 68359610

Sales Range: $25-49.9 Million
Emp.: 30
Navigational Services to Shipping
N.A.I.C.S.: 488330

Germanischer Lloyd Slovenija d.o.o. (2)
Liminjanska Cesta 94 A, 6230, Portoroz, Slovenia
Tel.: (386) 56773505
Sales Range: $25-49.9 Million
Emp.: 2
Navigational Services to Shipping
N.A.I.C.S.: 488330

Germanischer Lloyd South Africa (Pty) Ltd. (2)
391 Smith Street, 13th Floor Metlife Building, 4001, Durban, South Africa
Tel.: (27) 313074904
Sales Range: $25-49.9 Million
Emp.: 12
Navigational Services to Shipping
N.A.I.C.S.: 488330

Germanischer Lloyd Split d.o.o. (2)
Osjecka 8, 21000, Split, Croatia
Tel.: (385) 21548149
Web Site: http://www.gl-group.com
Sales Range: $25-49.9 Million
Emp.: 8
Navigational Services to Shipping
N.A.I.C.S.: 488330
Ivo Siljic *(Gen Mgr)*

Germanischer Lloyd Teknik Hizmetler Ltd. Sti. (2)
Bayar CadSehit MFatih Ongul Sok, Bagdatlioglu Plaza No3 Kat 1 D, 34742, Istanbul, Turkiye
Tel.: (90) 2166586860
Web Site: http://www.gvt.com
Sales Range: $25-49.9 Million
Emp.: 15
Navigational Services to Shipping
N.A.I.C.S.: 488330
Akif Tuna *(Mgr-Distr)*

Germanischer Lloyd Ukraine (2)
11 Grecheskaya Street Office 26, 65026, Odessa, Ukraine
Tel.: (380) 487860636
Web Site: http://www.dnvgl.com
Sales Range: $25-49.9 Million
Emp.: 10
Navigational Services to Shipping
N.A.I.C.S.: 488330
Oleksiy Kozachemko *(Mgr)*

Germanischer Lloyd Universal Industrial Services Ltd. (2)
1st of September Street, International Energy Foundatio, Tripoli, Libya
Tel.: (218) 213336170
Navigational Services to Shipping
N.A.I.C.S.: 488330

Germanischer Lloyd de Panama, Ltd. (2)
Building 33 Office D Amelia Denis de Icaza St, Ancon Quarry Heights, Panama, Panama
Tel.: (507) 3141347
Web Site: http://www.gl-group.com
Sales Range: $25-49.9 Million
Emp.: 4
Navigational Services to Shipping
N.A.I.C.S.: 488330

Germanischer Lloyd do Brasil Ltda. (2)
Rua Sete de Setembro 55-24 andar, 20050-004, Rio de Janeiro, Brazil
Tel.: (55) 2125071458
Sales Range: $25-49.9 Million
Emp.: 11
Navigational Services to Shipping
N.A.I.C.S.: 488330

Germanischer Lloyd-Havana (2)
Edificio Bacardi, Office 1-B Habana Vieja, Havana, 10100, Cuba
Tel.: (53) 78606019
Emp.: 1
Navigational Services to Shipping
N.A.I.C.S.: 488330

Lloyd German Iran Kish; Ltd. (2)
2nd Floor Bldg No 11, 9th St Vozara Ave, 15137, Tehran, Iran

Tel.: (98) 2188557156
Sales Range: $25-49.9 Million
Emp.: 2
Navigational Services to Shipping
N.A.I.C.S.: 488330

Lloyd Germanico de Mexico, S. de R.L. de C.V. (2)
Bosques de Duraznos No 75-605, Col Bosques de las Lomas, 11700, Mexico, Mexico
Tel.: (52) 5552450165
Sales Range: $25-49.9 Million
Emp.: 100
Navigational Services to Shipping
N.A.I.C.S.: 400000

P.T. GL- Indonesia - Station Batam (2)
3rd Floor Dana Graha Building, Jl Imam Bonjol, 29432, Batam, Indonesia
Tel.: (62) 778450097
Web Site: http://www.gl-group.com
Sales Range: $25-49.9 Million
Emp.: 4
Navigational Services to Shipping
N.A.I.C.S.: 488330

P.T. Germanischer Lloyd Nusantara (2)
Wisma Barito Pacific Tower B 3rd Fl, Jl Letjend S Parman Kav 62-63, 11410, Jakarta, Indonesia
Tel.: (62) 2153679201
Web Site: http://www.gl-group.com
Navigational Services to Shipping
N.A.I.C.S.: 488330

Windtest Iberica S.L. (2)
C/ Valentin Beato 42 2 flr, 28037, Madrid, Spain
Tel.: (34) 913757577
Web Site: http://www.windtest.de
Sales Range: $25-49.9 Million
Emp.: 20
Navigational Services to Shipping
N.A.I.C.S.: 488330
Andres Ferreras *(Mng Dir)*

Subsidiary (Domestic): (1)

DNV Haugesund (1)
Flathaugqt 12, 5523, Haugesund, Norway (100%)
Tel.: (47) 52703640
Web Site: http://www.dnvgl.com
Sales Range: $25-49.9 Million
N.A.I.C.S.: 483113
Henrik Matsen *(Mgr)*

DNV Kristiansand S (1)
Kansgaarb Alle 53, Kristiansand, 4632, Norway (100%)
Tel.: (47) 38127800
Web Site: http://www.dnvgl.com
Sales Range: $25-49.9 Million
Emp.: 15
N.A.I.C.S.: 483113
Alf Haaland *(Mgr)*

DNV Kristiansund N (1)
Verksted 11, N 6517, Kristiansund, Norway (100%)
Tel.: (47) 71585000
Web Site: http://www.dnv.com
Sales Range: $25-49.9 Million
Emp.: 10
Freight Transportation
N.A.I.C.S.: 483113

DNV Porsgrunn (1)
Leif Weldingsvei 12, 3208, Sandefjord, Norway (100%)
Tel.: (47) 33485550
Web Site: http://www.dnv.com
N.A.I.C.S.: 483113
Nils Boe *(Gen Mgr)*

DNV Region Norge AS (1)
Nessevegen 2 B, N 9411, Harstad, Norway (100%)
Tel.: (47) 77016550
Web Site: http://www.dnv.in
Sales Range: $25-49.9 Million
Emp.: 10
N.A.I.C.S.: 483113

DNV Region Norge AS (1)
Professor Brochs gate 2, Trondheim, 7030, Norway
Tel.: (47) 73903500
Sales Range: $25-49.9 Million
Emp.: 40
N.A.I.C.S.: 483113

DNV Stord (1)
Torget 10 235, N-5402, Stord, Norway
Tel.: (47) 53402900
Web Site: http://dnv.com
Sales Range: $25-49.9 Million
Emp.: 7
N.A.I.C.S.: 483113

DNV Tromso (1)
Strandveien 106, 9006, Tromso,
Norway (100%)
Tel.: (47) 77016550
Web Site: http://www.dnv.com
Sales Range: $25-49.9 Million
Emp.: 1
Shipping Logistics
N.A.I.C.S.: 483113

DNV Ulsteinvik (1)
Sjogata 45, 6065, Ulsteinvik,
Norway (100%)
Tel.: (47) 70015200
Web Site: http://www.dnv.no
Sales Range: $25-49.9 Million
Emp.: 11
Transportation
N.A.I.C.S.: 483113

Det Norske Veritas Eiendom AS (1)
Veritasveien 1, Hovik, 1369,
Norway (100%)
Tel.: (47) 67579900
Web Site: http://www.dnv.no
Sales Range: $450-499.9 Million
Emp.: 2,000
Services to Shipping, Offshore & Land
Based Process Industry, Management &
Operation
N.A.I.C.S.: 483113
Hendric Madsen (Mng Dir)

Branch (Domestic):

Det Norske Veritas Eiendom AS -
Harstad (2)
Maries vei 20, Hovik, Oslo, 1363,
Norway (100%)
Tel.: (47) 4767579900
Web Site: http://www.dnv.com
Sales Range: $350-399.9 Million
Emp.: 1,500
Risk Management & Management System
Certification
N.A.I.C.S.: 541618
Elisabeth Terstad (CEO-Oil & Gas)

Det Norske Veritas Eiendom AS -
Trondheim (2)
Professor Brochs Gate 2, Trondheim, 7030,
Norway (100%)
Tel.: (47) 67579900
Web Site: http://www.dnvgl.com
Sales Range: $450-499.9 Million
Emp.: 200
N.A.I.C.S.: 483113

Det Norske Veritas Holding USA
Inc. (1)
1400 Rivallo Dr, Houston, TX 77449
Tel.: (281) 721-6600
Web Site: http://www.dnv.com
Sales Range: $100-124.9 Million
Emp.: 450
Business Services
N.A.I.C.S.: 541511

Subsidiary (Domestic):

DNV Certification (2)
3805 Crestwood Pkwy NW Ste 200, Duluth,
GA 30096-7145
Tel.: (770) 279-0001
Web Site: http://www.dnvtraining.com
Sales Range: $25-49.9 Million
Emp.: 16
N.A.I.C.S.: 483113

DNV GL (2)
1 Intl Blvd Ste 406, Mahwah, NJ 07495
Tel.: (201) 512-8900
Web Site: http://www.dnvgl.com
Sales Range: $25-49.9 Million
Emp.: 12
Freight Transportation
N.A.I.C.S.: 483113
Remi Eriksen (Pres & CEO)

Division (Domestic):

DNV Maritime North America New
Orleans (3)

3445 N Causeway Blvd 3525, Metairie, LA
70002
Tel.: (504) 835-7334
Web Site: http://www.dnv.com
Sales Range: $25-49.9 Million
Emp.: 7
N.A.I.C.S.: 483113
Captain Lall (Mgr)

Det Norske Veritas Certification (3)
3800 Kilroy Airport Way Ste 410, Long
Beach, CA 90806 (100%)
Tel.: (562) 426-0500
Web Site: http://www.dnvgl.com
Sales Range: $25-49.9 Million
Emp.: 7
Quality Systems Certification for Manufac-
turing Industries
N.A.I.C.S.: 541990
Henrik Madsen (CEO)

Maritime North America
Jacksonville (3)
496 Crosswinds Dr, Fernandina Beach, FL
32034-4545 (100%)
Tel.: (904) 277-1606
N.A.I.C.S.: 483113

Maritime North America Seattle (3)
1501 4th Ave Ste 900, Seattle, WA 98101
Tel.: (425) 861-7977
Web Site: http://www.dnvgl.com
Sales Range: $25-49.9 Million
Emp.: 3
Marine Investigation Services
N.A.I.C.S.: 512110

Subsidiary (Domestic):

DNV Inc. (2)
1400 Ravello Dri, Katy, TX 77449
Tel.: (281) 396-1000
Sales Range: $100-124.9 Million
Emp.: 300
Mfr of Industrial Machinery
N.A.I.C.S.: 541511

DNV Software USA (2)
1400 Ravello Dr, Katy, TX 77449 (100%)
Tel.: (281) 721-6600
Web Site: http://www.dnv.com
Software Development Services
N.A.I.C.S.: 541511

Det Norske Veritas Certification
Inc. (2)
1400 Ravello Dr, Katy, TX
77449-5164 (100%)
Tel.: (281) 396-1000
Web Site: http://www.dnvcert.com
Sales Range: $25-49.9 Million
Emp.: 215
Business Services
N.A.I.C.S.: 541990
Bjorn-Harald Bangstein (Head-Section &
Tech Advisory Maritime-North America)

Det Norske Veritas USA Inc. (2)
1400 Ravelo Dr, Katy, TX 77449 (100%)
Tel.: (281) 721-6600
Sales Range: $25-49.9 Million
Emp.: 200
Business Services
N.A.I.C.S.: 541511
Yehuda Dror (Mgr)

Det Norske Veritas-North & Central
America (2)
1 International Blvd Ste 1200, Mahwah, NJ
07495 (100%)
Tel.: (201) 512-8900
Web Site: http://www.wwww.dnv.com
Sales Range: $25-49.9 Million
Emp.: 30
Clearing & Forwarding Agents
N.A.I.C.S.: 813910
Blaine Collins (Mgr-Reg)

Det Norske Veritas Puerto Rico (1)
Cond Playa Serena Apt 605, Carolina, PR
00979
Tel.: (787) 399-5634
Web Site: http://www.dnv.com
Sales Range: $25-49.9 Million
Emp.: 1
Freight Transportation
N.A.I.C.S.: 483111

Det Norske Veritas Technology
Services (1)

Veritasveien 1, Hovik, 3012,
Norway (100%)
Tel.: (47) 67579900
Web Site: http://www.dnv.com
Sales Range: $450-499.9 Million
Emp.: 2,500
N.A.I.C.S.: 483113
Henrick O. Matson (CEO)

KEMA N.V. (1)
Utrechtseweg 310, Arnhem, 6812 AR, Neth-
erlands
Tel.: (31) 263569111
Web Site: http://www.dnvgl.com
Sales Range: $800-899.9 Million
Emp.: 600
Holding Company; Energy Industry Techni-
cal & Management Consulting, Inspection,
Certification & Operational Support Services
N.A.I.C.S.: 551112
P. X. H. M. Dautzenberg (Dir-Strategy,
Mergers & Acq)

Subsidiary (Domestic):

DNV GL (2)
Energy Business Park Arnhems Buiten,
Utrechtseweg 310, 6812 AR, Arnhem, Neth-
erlands
Tel.: (31) 263569111
Web Site: http://www.dnvgl.com
Energy Industry Technical & Management
Consulting, Inspection, Certification & Op-
erational Support Services
N.A.I.C.S.: 561990
Jacob P. Fontijne (COO)

KEMA USA Inc. (1)
4377 County Line Rd, Chalfont, PA 18914
Tel.: (215) 997-3815
Business Support Services
N.A.I.C.S.: 561499

Marine Cybernetics AS (1)
Marine Cybernetics AS Vestre Rosten 77,
7075, Tiller, Norway
Tel.: (47) 72884330
Web Site:
   http://www.marinecybernetics.com
Application Software Development Services
N.A.I.C.S.: 541511
Stein Eggan (CEO)

Mo i Rana (1)
PO Box 149, Mo i Rana, 7149,
Norway (100%)
Tel.: (47) 75160175
Sales Range: $25-49.9 Million
Emp.: 2
N.A.I.C.S.: 483113

NV KEMA (1)
Utrechtseweg 310, PO Box 9035, Arnhem,
6800 ET, Netherlands
Tel.: (31) 263562850
Business Support Services
N.A.I.C.S.: 561499

Subsidiary (US):

KEMA Inc. (2)
67 S Bedford St Ste 201 E, Burlington, MA
01803-5108 (100%)
Tel.: (781) 273-5700
Web Site: http://www.kema.com
Holding Company; Regional Managing Of-
fice
N.A.I.C.S.: 551112

Subsidiary (Domestic):

KEMA Services Inc. (3)
67 S Bedford St, Burlington, MA 01803
Tel.: (781) 273-5700
Web Site: http://www.kema.com
Sales Range: $400-449.9 Million
Emp.: 60
Energy Industry Technical & Management
Consulting, Inspection, Certification & Op-
erational Support Services
N.A.I.C.S.: 561990
Julie Blunden (Executives)

Branch (Domestic):

KEMA Services Inc. - Anaheim (4)
1440 S State College Blvd Unit 2 F, Anaheim, CA 92806
Tel.: (714) 939-9020
Web Site: http://www.kema.com

Sales Range: $25-49.9 Million
Emp.: 10
Energy Industry Technical & Management
Consulting, Inspection, Certification & Op-
erational Support Services
N.A.I.C.S.: 561990
Javier Chaves (Gen Mgr)

KEMA Services Inc. - Madison (4)
122 W Washington Ave Ste 1000, Madison,
WI 53703-2366
Tel.: (608) 259-9152
Web Site: http://www.kema.com
Sales Range: $25-49.9 Million
Emp.: 15
Energy Industry Technical & Management
Consulting, Inspection, Certification & Op-
erational Support Services
N.A.I.C.S.: 561990
Mimi Goldberg (Sr VP)

KEMA Services Inc. - Oakland (4)
155 Grand Ave Ste 500, Oakland, CA
94612
Tel.: (510) 891-0446
Web Site: http://www.kema.com
Sales Range: $10-24.9 Million
Emp.: 30
Energy Industry Technical & Management
Consulting, Inspection, Certification & Op-
erational Support Services
N.A.I.C.S.: 561990

Nixu Corporation (1)
Keilaranta 15 B, PL 39, FI-02151, Espoo,
Finland
Tel.: (358) 94781011
Web Site: http://www.nixu.com
Rev.: $65,430,801
Assets: $50,004,107
Liabilities: $32,800,149
Net Worth: $17,203,958
Earnings: ($2,253,820)
Emp.: 373
Fiscal Year-end: 12/31/2020
Information Security Consulting
N.A.I.C.S.: 561621
Kimmo Rasila (Chm)

DNXCORP SE
42 Rue de Hollerich, 2530, Luxem-
bourg, Luxembourg
Tel.: (352) 27002800
Web Site: https://www.dnxcorp.com
DNX—(EUR)
Sales Range: $10-24.9 Million
Website Development Services
N.A.I.C.S.: 541611
Patrice Macar (Chm)

DO & CO AKTIENGESELL-
SCHAFT
Stephansplatz 12, A-1010, Vienna,
Austria
Tel.: (43) 1740001001
Web Site: https://www.doco.com
Year Founded: 1981
DOCO—(IST)
Rev.: $1,963,576,513
Assets: $1,286,401,897
Liabilities: $934,027,626
Net Worth: $352,374,271
Earnings: $79,678,394
Emp.: 13,291
Fiscal Year-end: 03/31/24
Restaurant & Catering Services
N.A.I.C.S.: 722320
Attila Dogudan (Chm-Mgmt Bd)

Subsidiaries:

B & B Betriebsrestaurants GmbH (1)
Dampfmuhlgasse 5, 1110, Vienna, Austria
Tel.: (43) 1740001010
Catering Services
N.A.I.C.S.: 722320

DO & CO Airline Catering Austria
GmbH (1)
Dampfmuhlg 5, 1110, Vienna, Austria
Tel.: (43) 1740000
Web Site: http://www.doco.com
Catering Services
N.A.I.C.S.: 722320
Harald Hrastnig (Gen Mgr)

DO & CO Aktiengesellschaft—(Continued)

DO & CO Albertina GmbH (1)
Albertinaplatz 1, 1010, Vienna, Austria
Tel.: (43) 15329669
Catering Services
N.A.I.C.S.: 722511

DO & CO Berlin GmbH (1)
An der Spreeschanze 2, 13599, Berlin, Germany
Tel.: (49) 303377300
Sales Range: $10-24.9 Million
Emp.: 30
Catering Services
N.A.I.C.S.: 722320

DO & CO Catering & Logistics Austria GmbH (1)
Stephansplatz 12, Vienna, 1010, Austria
Tel.: (43) 1740000
Web Site: http://www.doco.com
Catering & Logistics Services
N.A.I.C.S.: 722320

DO & CO Catering-Consult & Beteiligungs GmbH (1)
Stephansplatz 12, 1010, Vienna, Austria
Tel.: (43) 1740001010
Web Site: http://www.doco.com
Catering Services
N.A.I.C.S.: 722320
Akila Togean *(Gen Mgr)*

Subsidiary (Domestic):

K.u.K. Hofzuckerbacker Ch. Demel (2)
Kohlmarkt 14, 1010, Vienna, Austria
Tel.: (43) 153517170
Baked Food Products Mfr
N.A.I.C.S.: 311999

Sky Gourmet - airline catering and logistics GmbH (2)
Postfach 22, Flughafen, 1300, Schwechat, Austria
Tel.: (43) 1700731300
Airline Catering Services
N.A.I.C.S.: 722320

DO & CO Chicago Catering, INC. (1)
2150 Frontage Rd, Des Plaines, IL 60018
Tel.: (718) 974-9430
Catering Services
N.A.I.C.S.: 722320

DO & CO Event & Airline Catering Ltd (1)
Unit 2 Girling Way Great South West Road, Feltham, TW14 0PH, Middlesex, United Kingdom
Tel.: (44) 2085870000
Web Site: http://www.doco.com
Emp.: 500
Catering Services
N.A.I.C.S.: 722320

DO & CO Event Austria GmbH (1)
Stephansplatz 12, 1010, Vienna, Austria
Tel.: (43) 174000191
Web Site: http://www.doco.com
Sales Range: $500-549.9 Million
Emp.: 3,000
Catering Services
N.A.I.C.S.: 722320

DO & CO Frankfurt GmbH (1)
Langer Kornweg 38, 65451, Kelsterbach, Germany
Tel.: (49) 610798570
Web Site: http://www.doco.com
Sales Range: $10-24.9 Million
Emp.: 100
Catering Services
N.A.I.C.S.: 722320

DO & CO Gastronomie GmbH (1)
Spiridon-Louis Ring 7, 80809, Munich, Germany
Tel.: (49) 89350948540
Catering Services
N.A.I.C.S.: 722320

DO & CO Hotel Munchen GmbH (1)
Filserbraugasse 1, 80333, Munich, Germany
Tel.: (49) 8969313780
Web Site: http://www.docohotel.com

Restaurant Services
N.A.I.C.S.: 722511

DO & CO International Catering Ltd (1)
Unit 2 Girling Way Great South West Road, Feltham, TW14 0PH, Middlesex, United Kingdom
Tel.: (44) 2085870000
Web Site: http://www.doco
Emp.: 400
Catering Services
N.A.I.C.S.: 722320

DO & CO Kyiv LLC (1)
Zaporizka str 6, 08300, Kiev, Kyiv, Ukraine
Tel.: (380) 445912800
Catering Services
N.A.I.C.S.: 722320

DO & CO Los Angeles, Inc. (1)
4000 Redondo Beach Ave Ste 101, Redondo Beach, CA 90278
Tel.: (424) 390-4200
Catering Services
N.A.I.C.S.: 722320

DO & CO Lounge GmbH (1)
Langer Kornweg 38, 65451, Kelsterbach, Germany
Tel.: (49) 610798570
Catering Services
N.A.I.C.S.: 722320

DO & CO Munchen GmbH (1)
Werner-Heisenberg-Allee 25, 80939, Munich, Germany
Tel.: (49) 89323764440
Sales Range: $10-24.9 Million
Emp.: 30
Catering Services
N.A.I.C.S.: 722320

DO & CO Museum Catering Ltd (1)
Great Russell St, London, WC1B 3DG, United Kingdom
Tel.: (44) 2077238000
Catering Services
N.A.I.C.S.: 722320

DO & CO New York Catering, Inc. (1)
149-32 132nd St, Jamaica, NY 11430
Tel.: (718) 529-4570
Web Site: http://www.doco.com
Sales Range: $25-49.9 Million
Emp.: 250
Catering Services
N.A.I.C.S.: 722320

DO & CO Party-Service & Catering GmbH (1)
Dampfmuhlgasse 5, 1110, Vienna, Austria
Tel.: (43) 1740001101
Sales Range: $100-124.9 Million
Emp.: 1,000
Party & Catering Services
N.A.I.C.S.: 722320

DO & CO Pastry GmbH (1)
Dampfmuhlgasse 5, 1110, Vienna, Austria
Tel.: (43) 1740001001
Catering Services
N.A.I.C.S.: 722320

DO & CO Poland Sp. z o.o. (1)
Ul Sekundowa 2, 02-178, Warsaw, Poland
Tel.: (48) 223908235
Web Site: https://www.doco.pl
Catering Services
N.A.I.C.S.: 722310

DO & CO Salzburg Restaurants & Betriebs GmbH (1)
Wilhelm-Spazier-Str 8, Salzburg, 5020, Austria
Tel.: (43) 66283990
Web Site: http://www.doco.com
Sales Range: $10-24.9 Million
Emp.: 40
Catering Services
N.A.I.C.S.: 722320

DO & CO Service GmbH (1)
Parkring 35, 85748, Garching, Germany
Tel.: (49) 893509480
Catering Services
N.A.I.C.S.: 722320

DO & CO im Haas Haus Restaurantbetriebs GmbH (1)

Stephansplatz 12, 1010, Vienna, Austria
Tel.: (43) 15353969
Web Site: http://www.docohotel.com
Catering Services
N.A.I.C.S.: 722320

DO & CO im Platinum Restaurantbetriebs GmbH (1)
Untere Donaustrasse 21, 1029, Vienna, Austria
Tel.: (43) 1211754513
Web Site: https://www.platinum-events.at
Restaurant Services
N.A.I.C.S.: 722511

FR Freiraum Gastronomie GmbH (1)
Parkring 35, 85748, Garching, Germany
Tel.: (49) 893509480
Web Site: http://www.freiraum.rest
Restaurant Services
N.A.I.C.S.: 722511

Henry-The Art of Living GmbH (1)
Stephansplatz 12, 1010, Vienna, Austria
Tel.: (43) 664807772100
Web Site: http://www.enjoyhenry.com
Restaurant Services
N.A.I.C.S.: 722511

Lasting Impressions Food Co., Ltd. (1)
Unit 3 Girling Way Great South West Road, Feltham, TW14 0PH, Middlesex, United Kingdom
Tel.: (44) 2088904071
Web Site: http://www.lifoodcompany.co.uk
Restaurant Services
N.A.I.C.S.: 722511

DO DAY DREAM PCL

No 32 Kaha Romklao Road, Saphansung, Bangkok, 10240, Thailand
Tel.: (66) 29173055
Web Site:
https://www.dodaydream.com
DDD—(THA)
Rev.: $48,691,286
Assets: $146,425,120
Liabilities: $12,312,691
Net Worth: $134,112,429
Earnings: ($668,395)
Emp.: 622
Fiscal Year-end: 12/31/23
Cosmetics Products Mfr
N.A.I.C.S.: 325620

Subsidiaries:

Alexi Training & Consulting Company Limited (1)
32 Keharomklao Road, Ratpattana Saphansung, Bangkok, 10240, Thailand
Tel.: (66) 29173055
Personnel Management Services
N.A.I.C.S.: 541612

Do Infinite Dream Company Limited (1)
No 32 Keharomklao Road Ratpattana, Saphansung, Bangkok, 10240, Thailand
Tel.: (66) 29173055
Cosmeceutical Product Distr
N.A.I.C.S.: 456120

Dream Dermatology Company Limited (1)
No 32 Keharomklao Road Ratpattana, Saphansung, Bangkok, 10240, Thailand
Tel.: (66) 29173178
Web Site: https://oxecureofficial.com
Skin Care Products Distr
N.A.I.C.S.: 456120
Waranya Chattrakoonphong *(Gen Mgr)*

Kuron Corporation Limited (1)
No 32 Keharomklao Road Ratpattana, Saphansung, Bangkok, 10240, Thailand
Tel.: (66) 29173055
Oral Care Product Distr
N.A.I.C.S.: 424210

Namu Life Plus Company Limited (1)
No 32 Keharomklao Road Ratpattana, Saphansung, Bangkok, 10240, Thailand
Tel.: (66) 29171888

Web Site: https://www.namulife.com
Skin Care Products Distr
N.A.I.C.S.: 456120

DO THANH TECHNOLOGY CORPORATION

59-65 Huynh Man Dat St, Dist 5, Ho Chi Minh City, Vietnam
Tel.: (84) 89236238
Web Site: https://dothanhtech.com
Year Founded: 1994
DTT—(HOSE)
Rev.: $7,051,215
Assets: $7,064,935
Liabilities: $1,695,916
Net Worth: $5,369,019
Earnings: $350,365
Emp.: 181
Fiscal Year-end: 12/31/23
Plastics Product Mfr
N.A.I.C.S.: 326199

DO-FLUORIDE NEW MATERIALS CO LTD

Jiaoke Road, Zhongzhan District, Jiaozuo, 454150, Henan, China
Tel.: (86) 3912956992
Web Site: http://www.dfdchem.com
Year Founded: 1999
002407—(SSE)
Rev.: $1,735,064,604
Assets: $2,560,550,616
Liabilities: $1,438,319,376
Net Worth: $1,122,231,240
Earnings: $273,504,816
Emp.: 1,000
Fiscal Year-end: 12/31/22
Fluoride Chemical Products Mfr
N.A.I.C.S.: 325998
Li Shijiang *(Chm)*

DOAN XA PORT JSC

15 Ngo Quyen Road Van My Ward, Ngo Quyen district, Haiphong, Vietnam
Tel.: (84) 2253765029
Web Site:
https://www.doanxaport.com.vn
DXP—(HNX)
Rev.: $10,782,600
Assets: $58,576,900
Liabilities: $2,257,600
Net Worth: $56,319,300
Earnings: $3,464,500
Fiscal Year-end: 12/31/22
Freight Forwarding Services
N.A.I.C.S.: 488510
Quang Van Hoang *(Chm-Mgmt Bd)*

DOBANK SPA

Piazzetta Monte 1, Verona, 37121, Italy
Tel.: (39) 0800443394
Web Site: http://www.dobank.com
Year Founded: 2015
Emp.: 1,270
Banking Services
N.A.I.C.S.: 522110

Subsidiaries:

Italfondiario S.p.A. (1)
Via M Carucci 131, 00143, Rome, Italy
Tel.: (39) 06 47971
Web Site: http://www.italfondiario.com
Emp.: 433
Financial & Investment Management Services
N.A.I.C.S.: 523940
Andrea Giovanelli *(CEO)*

DOBOJINVEST A.D.

Kralja Petra I 15, 74000, Doboj, Bosnia & Herzegovina
Tel.: (387) 53224122
Year Founded: 2001
DOIN-R-A—(BANJ)
Rev.: $253,018

Assets: $3,151,479
Liabilities: $839,140
Net Worth: $2,312,339
Earnings: ($139,329)
Emp.: 44
Fiscal Year-end: 12/31/12
Technical Consulting Services
N.A.I.C.S.: 541690
Dorde Stanisiae (Chm-Mgmt Bd)

DOBOJKA A.D.
Nikole Pasica 4, 74101, Doboj, Bosnia & Herzegovina
Tel.: (387) 53204351
DBJK—(BANJ)
Sales Range: Less than $1 Million
Emp.: 22
Bakery Products Mfr
N.A.I.C.S.: 311813
Slobodan Dukanovic (Chm-Mgmt Bd)

DOBRUDZHA HOLDING AD
Drava Sobolch St No 2 fl 4 apartment 16, 9002, Varna, Bulgaria
Tel.: (359) 878794945
Web Site: https://www.dobhold.com
DOBH—(BUL)
Sales Range: Less than $1 Million
Holding Company
N.A.I.C.S.: 551112

DOCCHECK AG
Vogelsanger Str 66, 50823, Cologne, Germany
Tel.: (49) 22192053100
Web Site: https://www.doccheck.ag
Year Founded: 1990
AJ91—(DEU)
Rev.: $58,957,697
Assets: $61,971,262
Liabilities: $20,763,795
Net Worth: $41,207,467
Earnings: $2,505,785
Emp.: 459
Fiscal Year-end: 12/31/23
Online Medical Information Services
N.A.I.C.S.: 541613
Joachim Pietzko (Chm-Supervisory Bd)

Subsidiaries:

DocCheck Medizinbedarf & Logistik GmbH **(1)**
Carl-Zeiss-Str 3, Weil im Schonbuch, 71093, Germany **(90%)**
Tel.: (49) 7157 56 56 50
Web Site: http://www.doccheckshop.de
Emp.: 20
Electronic Shopping & Logistics Consulting Services
N.A.I.C.S.: 541614
Helmut Rieger (Gen Mgr)

antwerpes ag **(1)**
Vogelsanger Strasse 66, 50823, Cologne, Germany
Tel.: (49) 221 92053 0
Web Site: http://www.antwerpes.de
Healthcare Marketing Services
N.A.I.C.S.: 541613
Frank Antwerpes (CEO)

DOCEBO, INC.
366 Adelaide Street West Suite 701, Toronto, M5V 1R7, ON, Canada Ca
Web Site: https://www.docebo.com
Year Founded: 2005
DCBO—(NASDAQ)
Rev.: $142,912,000
Assets: $283,669,000
Liabilities: $91,458,000
Net Worth: $192,211,000
Earnings: $7,018,000
Emp.: 880
Fiscal Year-end: 12/31/22
Software Development Services
N.A.I.C.S.: 541511
Claudio Erba (Founder & CEO)

Subsidiaries:
Docebo France S.A.S. **(1)**
109 Rue Montmartre, 75002, Paris, France
Tel.: (33) 143069027
Software Development Services
N.A.I.C.S.: 541511

Docebo NA Inc. **(1)**
600 N Thomas St Ste A, Athens, GA 30601
Learning Services
N.A.I.C.S.: 611710

Docebo S.p.A **(1)**
Viale Luigi Majno 26, 20129, Milan, Italy
Tel.: (39) 0392323286
Learning Services
N.A.I.C.S.: 611710
Claudio Erba (CEO)

Docebo UK Ltd. **(1)**
6th Floor 48 Gracechurch Street, London, EC3V 0EJ, United Kingdom
Tel.: (44) 2072838677
Learning Services
N.A.I.C.S.: 611710

DOCON TECHNOLOGIES PRIVATE LIMITED
Block 1 4th Floor Prestige Blue Chip Software Park Adugodi, Dairy Colony Landmark, Bengaluru, 560029, India
Tel.: (91) 80 6823 6823
Web Site: http://docon.co.in
CRM, Billing & Analytics Platform
N.A.I.C.S.: 518210

Subsidiaries:

Thyrocare Technologies Limited **(1)**
D-37/1 MIDC Turbhe Opp Sandoz, Navi, Mumbai, 400 703, India **(66.1%)**
Tel.: (91) 2230900000
Web Site: https://www.thyrocare.com
Rev.: $69,212,325
Assets: $74,501,700
Liabilities: $16,177,980
Net Worth: $58,323,720
Earnings: $15,444,975
Emp.: 1,582
Fiscal Year-end: 03/31/2021
Health Care Service Provider
N.A.I.C.S.: 621498
A. Velumani (Founder & Chm)

Subsidiary (Non-US):

Thyrocare Bangladesh Limited **(2)**
Confidence Centre 12th Floor Kha-9 Pragoti Sarani Shazadpur Gulshan, Dhaka, 1212, Bangladesh
Tel.: (880) 9666737373
Web Site: http://www.thyrocarebd.com
Laboratory Testing Services
N.A.I.C.S.: 621511

DOCPLANNER GROUP
Kolejowa 5/7, 01-217, Warsaw, Poland
Tel.: (48) 606962293
Web Site:
http://www.Docplanner.com
Emp.: 2,000
Web Based Search Services
N.A.I.C.S.: 519290
Mariusz Gralewski (Founder & CEO)

Subsidiaries:

jameda GmbH **(1)**
St Cajetan Str 41, 81669, Munich, Germany
Tel.: (49) 892000 185 80
Web Site: http://www.jameda.de
Online Publishing Services
N.A.I.C.S.: 513199
Florian Weiss (CEO)

DOCTOR ANYWHERE PTE LTD.
460 Alexandra Rd Ste40-01, mTower, Singapore , 119963, Singapore
Tel.: (65) 31584622
Web Site:
https://doctoranywhere.com
Year Founded: 2017
Hospital & Healthcare

N.A.I.C.S.: 621491
Lim Wai Mun (Founder, Chm & CEO)

Subsidiaries:

Asian Healthcare Specialists Limited **(1)**
38 Irrawaddy Road 09-42, Singapore, 329563, Singapore
Tel.: (65) 65817388
Web Site:
http://www.asianhealthcare.com.sg
Rev.: $21,298,459
Assets: $46,605,053
Liabilities: $8,362,048
Net Worth: $38,243,005
Earnings: $5,117,942
Emp.: 61
Fiscal Year-end: 09/30/2021
Healtcare Services
N.A.I.C.S.: 621491
David Hsien Ching Su (Co-Founder)

Subsidiary (Domestic):

The Orthopaedic Centre (Farrer) Pte. Ltd. **(2)**
1 Farrer Park Station Rd 14-05 to 20 Connexion, Singapore, 217562, Singapore
Tel.: (65) 64435263
Healtcare Services
N.A.I.C.S.: 621999

The Orthopaedic Centre (Gleneagles) Pte. Ltd. **(2)**
6 Napier Road 07-15 Gleneagles Medical Centre, Singapore, 258499, Singapore
Tel.: (65) 64753408
Healtcare Services
N.A.I.C.S.: 621999

The Orthopaedic Centre (Novena) Pte. Ltd. **(2)**
38 Irrawaddy Road 09-42 Mount Elizabeth Novena Specialist Centre, Singapore, 329563, Singapore
Tel.: (65) 63395063
Healtcare Services
N.A.I.C.S.: 621999

The Orthopaedic Centre (Orchard) Pte. Ltd. **(2)**
Mount Elizabeth Medical Centre 3 Mount Elizabeth 17-18, Singapore, 228510, Singapore
Tel.: (65) 62353689
Healtcare Services
N.A.I.C.S.: 621999

DOCTOR CARE ANYWHERE GROUP PLC
13-15 Bouverie Street 2nd Floor, London, EC4Y 8DP, United Kingdom
Tel.: (44) 3300884980
Web Site:
https://www.doctorcare.com
Year Founded: 2013
DOC—(ASX)
Rev.: $25,077,916
Assets: $12,784,117
Liabilities: $11,263,611
Net Worth: $1,520,506
Earnings: ($5,324,379)
Emp.: 604
Fiscal Year-end: 12/31/23
Health Care Srvices
N.A.I.C.S.: 621610
Ben Kent (CEO)

Subsidiaries:

Doctor Care Anywhere Limited **(1)**
13-15 Bouverie Street 2nd Floor, London, EC4Y 8DP, United Kingdom
Tel.: (44) 3300884980
Web Site: https://doctorcareanywhere.com
Digital Health Care Services
N.A.I.C.S.: 621999

DOCTORGLASSES CHAIN CO LTD
Unit 2201-02 Block A Kingkey 100 Tower No 5016 Shennan East Road,

Guiyuan Subdistrict Luohu District, Shenzhen, 518001, Guangdong, China
Tel.: (86) 75582095801
Web Site:
http://www.doctorglasses.com.cn
Year Founded: 1997
300622—(CHIN)
Rev.: $165,620,656
Assets: $158,002,023
Liabilities: $43,591,174
Net Worth: $114,410,849
Earnings: $18,037,927
Fiscal Year-end: 12/31/23
Optical Glass Distr
N.A.I.C.S.: 423460
Alexander Liu (Chm)

DOD BIOTECH PUBLIC COMPANY LIMITED
111 Village No 2, Tha Chin Subdistrict Mueang Samut Sakhon District, Samut Sakhon, 74000, Thailand
Tel.: (66) 34446333 TH
Web Site:
https://www.dodbiotech.com
Year Founded: 2011
DOD—(THA)
Rev.: $20,729,209
Assets: $42,551,362
Liabilities: $11,022,277
Net Worth: $31,529,086
Earnings: $607,907
Emp.: 398
Fiscal Year-end: 12/31/23
Food Product Mfr & Distr
N.A.I.C.S.: 311423
Dusit Chongsutthanamanee (Vice Chm)

DODLA DAIRY LIMITED
8-2-293/82/A 270/Q Road No 10-C Jubilee Hills, Hyderabad, 500033, Telangana, India
Tel.: (91) 4045467777
Web Site:
https://www.dodladairy.com
Year Founded: 1995
543306—(BOM)
Rev.: $266,226,051
Assets: $132,711,443
Liabilities: $42,898,538
Net Worth: $89,812,905
Earnings: $17,194,905
Emp.: 2,551
Fiscal Year-end: 03/31/21
Dairy Product Mfr & Distr
N.A.I.C.S.: 112120
Anjaneyulu Ganji (CFO)

DOEPKER INDUSTRIES LTD.
300 Doepker Ave, Annaheim, S0K 0G0, SK, Canada
Tel.: (306) 598-2171
Web Site: http://www.doepker.com
Year Founded: 1963
Rev.: $41,672,562
Emp.: 525
Trailers Equipment Mfr
N.A.I.C.S.: 333924
Bill Schuler (Chief Customer Officer)

DOF ASA
Alfabygget, 5392, Storebo, Norway
Tel.: (47) 56181000
Web Site: http://www.dof.no
Year Founded: 1981
DOF—(OSL)
Rev.: $712,639,800
Assets: $2,664,337,200
Liabilities: $2,272,476,150
Net Worth: $391,861,050
Earnings: $327,137,550)
Emp.: 3,500
Fiscal Year-end: 12/31/19
Offshore & Subsea Vessel Owner & Operator

DOF ASA—(Continued)

N.A.I.C.S.: 483111
Mons Svendal Aase *(CEO)*

Subsidiaries:

DOF Management Australia Pty
Ltd   **(1)**
5th Floor 181 St Georges Tce, Perth, 6000,
WA, Australia
Tel.: (61) 892788700
Freight Transportation Services
N.A.I.C.S.: 483111
Darren McCormick *(Gen Mgr)*

DOF Subsea AS   **(1)**
Thormohlensgate 53 C, 5006, Bergen,
Norway   **(64.94%)**
Tel.: (47) 55252200
Freight Transportation Services
N.A.I.C.S.: 483111
Mons S. Aase *(CEO)*

Subsidiary (Non-US):

DOF Subsea Australian Pty.   **(2)**
5th Floor 181 St Georges Tce, Perth, 6000,
WA, Australia
Tel.: (61) 892788700
Web Site: http://www.dofsubsea.com
Freight Transportation Services
N.A.I.C.S.: 483111

Subsidiary (US):

DOF Subsea US Inc.   **(2)**
5365 W Sam Houston Pkwy N Ste 400,
Houston, TX 77041
Tel.: (713) 896-2500
Freight Transportation Services
N.A.I.C.S.: 483111

DOF GROUP ASA
Alfabygget, 5392, Storebo, Norway
Tel.: (47) 56181000
Web Site: https://www.dof.com
Year Founded: 1981
DOFG—(OSL)
Rev.: $1,101,884,352
Assets: $2,518,935,895
Liabilities: $1,547,016,442
Net Worth: $971,919,453
Earnings: $386,569,370
Emp.: 4,108
Fiscal Year-end: 12/31/23
Transportation Services
N.A.I.C.S.: 488330
Hilde Dronen *(CFO)*

Subsidiaries:

DOF Management Argentina
S.A.   **(1)**
Tte Gral J D Peron 315 piso 1 Oficina 6-B
CABA, C1038AAG, Buenos Aires, Argentina
Tel.: (54) 1143424622
Vessel Operation & Offshore Services
N.A.I.C.S.: 561110

Maersk Supply Service A/S   **(1)**
Esplanaden 50, 1098, Copenhagen, Den-
mark
Tel.: (45) 73737000
Web Site:
    http://www.maersksupplyservice.com
Sales Range: $50-74.9 Million
Emp.: 200
Transportation of Equipment to Offshore
Platforms & Drilling Rigs
N.A.I.C.S.: 483211
Steen S. Karstensen *(CEO)*

DOGA
ZA Pariwest 8 Avenue Gutenberg,
78310, Maurepas, France
Tel.: (33) 130664141
Web Site:
    http://www.dogassembly.com
Rev.: $20,400,000
Emp.: 132
Industrial Machinery & Equipment
N.A.I.C.S.: 423830
Jerome Vandewiele *(Dir-Pur)*

Subsidiaries:

DOGA CZ s.r.o.   **(1)**
Hlizovska 358, 281 23, Kolin, Czech Re-
public
Tel.: (420) 326 533 646
Web Site: http://www.doga-cz.cz
Industrial Machinery & Equipment Distr
N.A.I.C.S.: 423830

Doga FZ   **(1)**
Zone Franche d'Exportation de Tanger Ilot
26-A2 3eme etg N 44, 90100, Tangiers,
Morocco
Tel.: (212) 5 39 39 53 37
Industrial Machinery & Equipment Distr
N.A.I.C.S.: 423830

Doga Industries   **(1)**
Angle rue des gaves / rue Boured, Roches
Noires, Casablanca, Morocco
Tel.: (212) 522 244 241
Industrial Machinery & Equipment Distr
N.A.I.C.S.: 423830

Sarl Global Service Industry   **(1)**
Cooperative Sid Ahmed DEBIH-BT A
Quartier Seghir, Bejaia, Algeria
Tel.: (213) 34 20 40 82
Industrial Machinery & Equipment Distr
N.A.I.C.S.: 423830

DOGAN BURDA DERGI YAYIN-
CILIK VE PAZARLAMA A.S.
Trump Towers, Sisli, 34387, Istanbul,
Turkiye
Tel.: (90) 2124780300
Web Site:
    https://www.doganburda.com
DOBUR—(IST)
Magazine Publishing Services
N.A.I.C.S.: 513120
Paul-Bernhard Kallen *(Chm)*

DOGNESS (INTERNATIONAL)
CORPORATION
Tongsha Industrial Estate East Dis-
trict, Dongguan, 523217, Guangdong,
China
Tel.: (86) 13829214680   VG
Web Site: http://www.dogness.com
Year Founded: 2016
DOGZ—(NASDAQ)
Rev.: $17,584,454
Assets: $97,871,328
Liabilities: $21,526,023
Net Worth: $76,345,305
Earnings: ($7,200,263)
Emp.: 259
Fiscal Year-end: 06/30/23
Pet Product Mfr & Distr
N.A.I.C.S.: 316990
Silong Chen *(Founder, Chm & CEO)*

DOGTAS KELEBEK MOBILYA
SANAYI VE TICARET A.S.
E-5 Maltepe Bridge Strawberry Street
No 5, Zumrutevler District, Istanbul,
Turkiye
Tel.: (90) 2164250002
Web Site:
    https://www.doganlarmobily.com
Year Founded: 1972
DGKLB—(IST)
Rev.: $297,092,042
Assets: $249,419,227
Liabilities: $175,054,597
Net Worth: $74,364,630
Earnings: $23,176,788
Emp.: 2,741
Fiscal Year-end: 12/31/23
Furniture Mfr
N.A.I.C.S.: 337121
Davut Dogan *(Chm)*

DOGUS GAYRIMENKUL
YATIRIM ORTAKLIGI A.S.
Dogus Center Maslak Ahi Evran Cad
No No 4/7, Maslak Mah, 34398, Is-
tanbul, Turkiye

Tel.: (90) 2123352850
Web Site:
    https://www.dogusgyo.com.tr
Year Founded: 1995
DGGYO—(IST)
Rev.: $18,575,916
Assets: $339,089,785
Liabilities: $104,978,767
Net Worth: $234,111,018
Earnings: $62,518,520
Fiscal Year-end: 12/31/23
Real Estate Investment Services
N.A.I.C.S.: 531390
Cagan Erkan *(Gen Mgr)*

DOGUS HOLDING AS
Buyukdere Cad No 249, Maslak Sa-
riyer, Istanbul, 34398, Turkiye
Tel.: (90) 2123353232
Web Site:
    http://www.dogusgrubu.com.tr
Year Founded: 1951
Rev.: $2,998,343,503
Assets: $6,785,673,582
Liabilities: $6,121,518,948
Net Worth: $664,154,633
Earnings: ($106,149,553)
Emp.: 20,363
Fiscal Year-end: 12/31/19
Holding Company
N.A.I.C.S.: 551112
Ferit F. Sahenk *(Chm & CEO)*

Subsidiaries:

Antur Turizm A.S.   **(1)**
Maslak Mah Buyukdere Cad No 249 Kat 5,
34398, Sariyer, Istanbul, Turkiye
Tel.: (90) 2123542200
Web Site: http://www.antur.com.tr
Travel Tour Operator Service
N.A.I.C.S.: 561520

Atasehir Restoran Isletmeleri Gida
Turizm Ticaret A.S.   **(1)**
No 6 Palladium Alis Veris Merk K 3 Halk
Cad, Anatolia, Istanbul, Turkiye
Tel.: (90) 2164731901
Restaurant Operators
N.A.I.C.S.: 722511

Ayson Geoteknik ve Deniz Insaat
A.S.   **(1)**
Mahallesi Cumhuriyet Caddesi No 2 A Blok
Kat 3, Kavacik Beykoz, 34810, Istanbul,
Turkiye
Tel.: (90) 2165381700
Web Site: http://www.ayson.com.tr
Construction Engineering Services
N.A.I.C.S.: 541330
Gonul Talu *(Chm)*

BMK Turizm Ve Otelcilik Hizmetleri
A.S.   **(1)**
Fulya Ortaklar Cd Pehlivan Sk No 1 Meric
Konak 11 A Blk D 20, Sisli, Istanbul, Turkiye
Tel.: (90) 2523112400
Hospitality Services
N.A.I.C.S.: 561110

Bal Turizm ve Gida Pazarlama
A.S.   **(1)**
Bjk Plaza A Bl K 13 Visnezade M, Levent,
Besiktas, Turkiye
Tel.: (90) 2122274404
Restaurant Operators
N.A.I.C.S.: 722511
Gurkan Yelckencl *(Gen Mgr)*

Buke Turizm ve Lokantacilik Ticaret
A.S.   **(1)**
5 Salhane Sokak, Istanbul, Turkiye
Tel.: (90) 2122682222
Restaurant Operators
N.A.I.C.S.: 722511

Cukurambar Lokantacilik Gida Turizm
A.S   **(1)**
Muhsin Yazicioglu Cad No 2 Hayat Sebla
Evleri B Blok Dk 6 Sogutozu Mah, Can-
kaya, Ankara, Turkiye
Tel.: (90) 3122843666
Restaurant Operators
N.A.I.C.S.: 722511

D Marine Investment Holding
B.V.   **(1)**
Keizersgracht 569 -575, Amsterdam, 1017
DR, Netherlands
Tel.: (31) 205539700
Holding Company
N.A.I.C.S.: 551112

D Otel Marmaris Turizm Isletmeciligi
Ticaret ve Sanayi A.S.   **(1)**
42-3 Buyukdere Caddesi, Mecidiyekoy Sisli,
Istanbul, Turkiye
Tel.: (90) 2123542222
Hospitality Services
N.A.I.C.S.: 561110

D-Auto Suisse SA   **(1)**
Route de Bussigny 38, Crissier, 1023, Swit-
zerland
Tel.: (41) 213499911
Automotive Spare Parts Distr
N.A.I.C.S.: 423120
Cagri Duman *(Mgr-Fin)*

Dogus Didim Marina Isletmeleri ve
Ticaret A.S.   **(1)**
3 Koy Camlik Mah, Didim, Aydin, Turkiye
Tel.: (90) 2568138081
Marine Support Services
N.A.I.C.S.: 488510
Ahmet Aricasoy *(Gen Mgr)*

Dogus Musteri Sistemleri A.S.   **(1)**
Uniq Istanbul Huzur Mah Ayazaga Cad No
4/B Kat 4, 34450, Sariyer, Istanbul, Turkiye
Tel.: (90) 2122904010
Web Site:
    http://www.dogusmusterisistemleri.com
Marketing Consulting Services
N.A.I.C.S.: 541810
Nilay Karagulmez Abamor *(Dir-People &*
Corp Culture)

Dogus Oto Pazarlama ve Ticaret
A.S.   **(1)**
Isci Bloklari Mah Mevlana Bulvari No 182/A,
Cankaya, Ankara, Turkiye
Tel.: (90) 3125838383
Web Site: http://www.dogusoto.com.tr
Automotive Spare Parts Distr
N.A.I.C.S.: 423120

Dogus Saglikli Yasam ve Danismanlik
Hizmetleri Ticaret A.S.   **(1)**
Ahmet Adnan Saygun Cad Turk Hava Yol-
lari Sitesi Sok No 3, Besiktas, Istanbul, Tur-
kiye
Tel.: (90) 2123813000
Healtcare Services
N.A.I.C.S.: 621999

Dogus Sigorta Aracilik Hizmetleri
A.S.   **(1)**
Perpa Tic Merkezi No 11454 Halil Rfat Pasa
Mh, Okmeydani Sisli, Istanbul, Turkiye
Tel.: (90) 2123205545
General Insurance Services
N.A.I.C.S.: 524210

Dogus Telekomunikasyon Hizmetleri
A.S.   **(1)**
Koca Sinan Mahmut Bey Caddesi 65,
Bahcelievler, 34188, Istanbul, Turkiye
Tel.: (90) 2123353232
Wireless Telecommunication Services
N.A.I.C.S.: 517112

Dogus Yayin Grubu A.S.   **(1)**
Ahi Evran Cad No 4, Maslak, 34398, Sa-
riyer, Istanbul, Turkiye
Tel.: (90) 2123350000
Web Site:
    http://www.dogusyayingrubu.com.tr
Advertising Agencies
N.A.I.C.S.: 541810

Doors Akademi Egitim ve Danisman-
lik Hizmetleri A.S.   **(1)**
Meliksah Sokak 9-1, Kartal, 34880, Istan-
bul, Turkiye
Tel.: (90) 2122222000
Automotive Spare Parts Distr
N.A.I.C.S.: 423120

Doors Uluslararasi Yonetim Danis-
manligi Ticaret A.S.   **(1)**
Levent Mh Buyukdere Cd N 168 K 1, Besiktas, Istanbul, Turkiye
Tel.: (90) 2122682222

Financial Investment Services
N.A.I.C.S.: 523999

Gunaydin Et Sanayi ve Ticaret
A.S.   (1)
Kasaplar Carsisi 10-a Altintepe Ma,
Maltepe, Istanbul, Turkiye
Tel.: (90) 2164891805
Restaurant Operators
N.A.I.C.S.: 722511

Havana Yayincilik Turizm ve Gida
Pazarlama Ticaret A.S.
Esentepe Mah Kardesler Sok No 42/1, Sisli,
Istanbul, Turkiye
Tel.: (90) 2122912165
Restaurant Operators
N.A.I.C.S.: 722511

Marina Borik d.o.o   (1)
Obala kneza Domagoja 1, 23000, Zadar,
Croatia
Tel.: (385) 23333036
Web Site: http://www.d-marin.com
Marine Support Services
N.A.I.C.S.: 488510

Marina Dalmacija d.o.o   (1)
Bibinje-Sukosan 1, 23206, Dalmatia, Croa-
tia
Tel.: (385) 23200300
Web Site: http://www.marinadalmacija.hr
Marine Support Services
N.A.I.C.S.: 488510

Teknik Muhendislik ve Musavirlik
A.S.   (1)
Cevizlidere Mh 1243 Sokak Taspnar Is
Merkezi No 2/11-12, Balgat Cankaya, 6520,
Ankara, Turkiye
Tel.: (90) 3124722335
Engineeering Services
N.A.I.C.S.: 541330

Toms Kitchen Ltd   (1)
27 Cale Street, Chelsea, London, SW3
3QP, United Kingdom
Tel.: (44) 2073490202
Web Site: http://www.tomskitchen.co.uk
Restaurant Operators
N.A.I.C.S.: 722511
Lauren Webster (Gen Mgr)

Villa Dubrovnik d.d.   (1)
Vlaha Bukovca 6, 20000, Dubrovnik, Croa-
tia
Tel.: (385) 20500300
Web Site: http://www.villa-dubrovnik.hr
Restaurant Operators
N.A.I.C.S.: 722511

DOGUS OTOMOTIV SERVIS VE TICARET A.S.

Sekerpinar Mah Anadolu Cad No 22
ve 45 Cayrova, PK 411420, Kocaeli,
Turkiye
Tel.: (90) 2626769090
Web Site:
   http://www.dogusotomotiv.com.tr
DOAS—(IST)
Rev.: $5,054,351,019
Assets: $2,298,390,075
Liabilities: $881,240,629
Net Worth: $1,417,149,446
Earnings: $669,268,134
Fiscal Year-end: 12/31/23
Automobile Spare Parts Sales
N.A.I.C.S.: 423110
Emir Ali Bilaloglu (Chm-Exec Bd &
CEO)

DOGUSAN BORU SANAYII VE TICARET A.S.

Erzincan Sivas Karayolu 14 Km Pk
74, Erzincan, Turkiye
Tel.: (90) 4462362401
Web Site:
   https://www.dogusanas.com.tr
DOGUB—(IST)
Concrete Pipe Mfr
N.A.I.C.S.: 327332
Hilal Ozturk (Chm)

DOHA BANK Q.S.C.

Corniche Street West Bay, PO Box
3818, Doha, Qatar
Tel.: (974) 44456000
Web Site: https://qa.dohabank.com
Year Founded: 1978
DHBK—(QE)
Rev.: $969,368,036
Assets: $27,548,608,383
Liabilities: $23,664,146,309
Net Worth: $3,884,462,073
Earnings: $191,764,340
Emp.: 1,094
Fiscal Year-end: 12/31/21
Banking Services
N.A.I.C.S.: 522110
Abdul Rehman Mohammad Jabor Al
Thani (Mng Dir)

Subsidiaries:

Doha Bank Assurance Company
W.L.L   (1)
4th Floor Doha Bank Tower Al Corniche St,
West Bay, Doha, Qatar
Tel.: (974) 40154000
Web Site: http://www.dbac.com.qa
Sales Range: $50-74.9 Million
Emp.: 50
General Insurance Services
N.A.I.C.S.: 524210
Abdul Rehman Mohammed Jabor Al Thani
(Chm)

DOHA INSURANCE GROUP QPSC

213 C Ring Road, Doha, Qatar
Tel.: (974) 44292777   QA
Web Site: https://www.dig.qa
Year Founded: 1999
DOHI—(QE)
Rev.: $376,675,915
Assets: $764,210,026
Liabilities: $431,588,877
Net Worth: $332,621,149
Earnings: $41,340,635
Fiscal Year-end: 12/31/23
Insurance & Reinsurance Services
N.A.I.C.S.: 524298
Nawaf Nasser Khaled Al-Thani (Chm)

Subsidiaries:

MENA RE Underwriters Ltd.   (1)
2nd Floor Gate Village 8 DIFC, Dubai,
United Arab Emirates
Tel.: (971) 45194888
Web Site: http://www.menare.ae
Reinsurance Services
N.A.I.C.S.: 524130
Selva Kumar M. (CEO)

DOHLE HANDELSGRUPPE HOLDING GMBH & CO. KG

Jean-Dohle-Strasse 1, 53721,
Siegburg, Germany
Tel.: (49) 22411220   De
Web Site: http://www.dohle-
   gruppe.com
Year Founded: 1928
Sales Range: $1-4.9 Billion
Emp.: 8,000
Supermarket Franchisor, Owner &
Operator, Grocery Whslr
N.A.I.C.S.: 551112

Subsidiaries:

HIT Handelsgruppe GmbH & Co.
KG   (1)
Alte Lohmarer Strasse 59, D-53721,
Siegburg, Germany
Tel.: (49) 22411220
Web Site: http://www.hit.de
Emp.: 300
Supermarket Franchisor & Operator
N.A.I.C.S.: 445110
Carl Bauerschmitz (Mng Dir)

Subsidiary (Domestic):

HIT Frische GmbH & Co. KG   (2)
Alte Lohmarer Strasse 59, 53721, Siegburg,
Germany

Tel.: (49) 2241 122 0
Sales Range: $150-199.9 Million
Emp.: 260
Supermarket Produce Management
N.A.I.C.S.: 425120

DOHLER GMBH

Riedstrasse 7-9, 64295, Darmstadt,
Germany
Tel.: (49) 6151 306 0   De
Web Site: http://www.doehler.com
Emp.: 4,000
Food & Beverage Ingredient Mfr &
Marketer
N.A.I.C.S.: 311999
Andreas Klein (Member-Exec Bd)

Subsidiaries:

Bureau de liaison Dohler France
S.A.R.L.   (1)
28 Micro-zone d'activite, Hydra, Algeria
Tel.: (213) 23531437
Natural Food Ingredient Mfr
N.A.I.C.S.: 311999

DOEHLER INDIA PVT. LTD.   (1)
Plot No 3 Survey No 285 Raisoni Industrial
Park, Hinjewadi, Pune, 411057, India
Tel.: (91) 20 6674 4646
Web Site: http://www.doehler.com
Emp.: 180
Chemical Products Distr
N.A.I.C.S.: 424690
Taney Srivastav (Mng Dir)

DOEHLER ITALIA S.R.L.   (1)
Via Primo Maggio 56, Vallecrosia, 18019,
Imperia, Italy
Tel.: (39) 0184 29 80 41
Web Site: http://www.doehler.com
Chemical Products Distr
N.A.I.C.S.: 424690

DOEHLER KAZAKHSTAN LLP   (1)
Office 8 Tole Bi Str 302, 050031, Almaty,
Kazakhstan
Tel.: (7) 727 238 16 03
Chemical Products Distr
N.A.I.C.S.: 424690

DOEHLER MEXICO S.A. DE
C.V.   (1)
Av Toluca 541 Int 2 Col Olivar de los Pa-
dres, 1780, Mexico, Mexico
Tel.: (52) 55 5681 7119
Chemical Products Distr
N.A.I.C.S.: 424690

DOEHLER NATURAL FOOD & BEV-
ERAGE INGREDIENTS (JINSHAN)
CO. LTD.   (1)
600 Jinbai Road, Jinshan Industrial Zone,
201506, Shanghai, China
Tel.: (86) 21 67225066
Chemical Products Distr
N.A.I.C.S.: 424690

DOEHLER NF & BI   (1)
Krasnopolyanskoye Shosse 4, Lobnya,
141734, Moscow, Russia
Tel.: (7) 495 223 86 26
Chemical Products Distr
N.A.I.C.S.: 424690

DOEHLER NORTH AMERICA   (1)
400 High Point Rd SE Ste 100, Cartersville,
GA 30120
Tel.: (770) 387-0451
Chemical Products Distr
N.A.I.C.S.: 424690

DOEHLER TASHKENT   (1)
Ljadowa Str 9a Khamsinskiy Bezirk,
100047, Tashkent, Uzbekistan
Tel.: (998) 71 289 4422
Chemical Products Distr
N.A.I.C.S.: 424690

DOEHLER UKRAINE LTD   (1)
Lenina Str 2, Troeschina Village, 02230,
Kiev, Ukraine
Tel.: (380) 445 34 3540
Chemical Products Distr
N.A.I.C.S.: 424690

DOHLER (UK) LIMITED   (1)
1a Opal Court Opal Drive, Fox Milne, Milton
Keynes, MK15 ODF, United Kingdom

Tel.: (44) 1908 550 333
Chemical Products Distr
N.A.I.C.S.: 424690

DOHLER AMERICA LATINA
LTDA.   (1)
Rua Miguel Guidotti 905 Chacara Baiana,
13485 342, Limeira, Sao Paulo, Brazil
Tel.: (55) 1921146000
Web Site: https://www.doehler.com
Emp.: 105
Chemical Products Distr
N.A.I.C.S.: 424690
Martin Tolksdorf (Mng Dir)

DOHLER COLOMBIA S.A.S   (1)
Oikos de Occidente Bodega E-79, Autopista
Bogota-Medellin Km 2 5 via Parcelas, Bo-
gota, Colombia
Tel.: (57) 1 898 5253
Chemical Products Distr
N.A.I.C.S.: 424690

DOHLER CZ S.R.O.   (1)
Nad Sutkou 1811/12, 182 00, Prague,
Czech Republic
Tel.: (420) 2 3536 1297
Chemical Products Distr
N.A.I.C.S.: 424690

DOHLER DINTER UKRAINE SKALA
LTD.   (1)
Kamyanets-Podilska Str 1A, v/s Skala- Po-
dilska, 48720, Ternopil, Ukraine
Tel.: (380) 3541 51687
Chemical Products Distr
N.A.I.C.S.: 424690

DOHLER EGYPT FOR THE PRO-
DUCTION OF NATURAL FOOD &
BEVERAGE INGREDIENTS
S.A.E.   (1)
Engineering Square - North Expansions, 6th
of October City, Egypt
Tel.: (20) 2 38642055
Chemical Products Distr
N.A.I.C.S.: 424690

DOHLER ESPANA NATURAL BEV-
ERAGE INGREDIENTS S.L.   (1)
Parque Empresarial Alvia C/Jose Echega-
ray No 8 Edificio 3 Pl 2 Of 11, Las Rozas,
28230, Madrid, Spain
Tel.: (34) 91 360 01 24
Chemical Products Distr
N.A.I.C.S.: 424690

DOHLER FOOD & BEVERAGE IN-
GREDIENTS RIZHAO CO. LTD.   (1)
Sanya Road No 1 Food Industry Park of
Economic Development Zone, Rizhao,
Shandong, China
Tel.: (86) 633 8369388
Chemical Products Distr
N.A.I.C.S.: 424690

DOHLER FOOD & BEVERAGE IN-
GREDIENTS SHANGHAI CO.
LTD.   (1)
No 739 Shen Nan Road, Minhang district,
Shanghai, 201108, China
Tel.: (86) 21 33231888
Chemical Products Distr
N.A.I.C.S.: 424690

DOHLER FRANCE S.A.R.L.   (1)
16 rue Francis de Pressense, Saint-Denis-
la-Plaine, 93210, Paris, France
Tel.: (33) 1 41627000
Chemical Products Distr
N.A.I.C.S.: 424690

DOHLER GIDA SAN. VE TIC. LTD.
STI.   (1)
Bahcelievler Eregli Road street No 16,
70100, Karaman, Turkiye
Tel.: (90) 338224 15 70
Chemical Products Distr
N.A.I.C.S.: 424690

DOHLER HOLLAND B.V.   (1)
Albusstraat 5, 4903 RG, Oosterhout, Neth-
erlands
Tel.: (31) 162479500
Chemical Products Distr
N.A.I.C.S.: 424690

DOHLER HUNGARIA KFT.   (1)
Vasut utca 42, 2144, Kerepes, Hungary
Tel.: (36) 28 561 110

Dohler GmbH—(Continued)

Chemical Products Distr
N.A.I.C.S.: 424690

DOHLER IRANIAN LIMITED (1)
Unit 5 12th floor No 2551 Kian Tower Val-
iasr ave, PO Box 1968643111, Tehran, Iran
Tel.: (98) 21 88656934
Chemical Products Distr
N.A.I.C.S.: 424690

DOHLER JAPAN K.K. (1)
Level 8 Omori Raruta Building 3-27-6, San-
nou, Ota, 143-0023, Tokyo, Japan
Tel.: (81) 3 5322 1323
Chemical Products Distr
N.A.I.C.S.: 424690

DOHLER MARMARA (1)
Kocyatagi Mevkii, Ovakoy PK 200 Merkez,
10010, Balikesir, Turkiye
Tel.: (90) 2662921360
Chemical Products Distr
N.A.I.C.S.: 424690

DOHLER MIDDLE EAST LTD. (1)
Plot no S10114, PO Box 262766, Jebel Ali
South Zone, Dubai, United Arab Emirates
Tel.: (971) 4 8036333
Chemical Products Distr
N.A.I.C.S.: 424690

**DOHLER NEUENKIRCHEN
GMBH** (1)
Dorfstrasse 17, Neuenkirchen, 21763, Cux-
haven, Germany
Tel.: (49) 4751 9220 0
Chemical Products Distr
N.A.I.C.S.: 424690

DOHLER NEUSS GMBH (1)
Kreitzweg 10, 41472, Neuss, Germany
Tel.: (49) 6151 306 1067
Chemical Products Distr
N.A.I.C.S.: 424690

DOHLER POLSKA SP. Z O.O. (1)
Kozietuly Nowe 66 J, 05-640, Mogielnica,
woj Mazowieckie, Poland
Tel.: (48) 48 368 98 00
Web Site: http://www.doehler.com
Emp.: 400
Chemical Products Distr
N.A.I.C.S.: 424690
Podoba Piotr (Pres)

DOHLER ROGGEL B.V. (1)
Kunneweg 9, Roggel, 6088 NV, Leudal,
Netherlands
Tel.: (31) 475 711 400
Chemical Products Distr
N.A.I.C.S.: 424690

DOHLER ROMANIA S.R.L. (1)
Strada Industriilor Nr 23, 077040, Chiajna,
Romania
Tel.: (40) 21 317 33 04
Chemical Products Distr
N.A.I.C.S.: 424690

DOHLER SCANDINAVIA A/S (1)
Torvet 11 2 tv, 4600, Koge, Denmark
Tel.: (45) 56 67 00 00
Chemical Products Distr
N.A.I.C.S.: 424690

DOHLER SCHWEIZ AG (1)
Route Andre-Piller 21 Zone Industrielle 3,
1762, Givisiez, Switzerland
Tel.: (41) 26 4663011
Chemical Products Distr
N.A.I.C.S.: 424690

DOHLER SOFIA EOOD (1)
8 Vsevolod Garshin Str, 1619, Sofia, Bul-
garia
Tel.: (359) 2818 8724
Web Site: http://www.doehler.com
Chemical Products Distr
N.A.I.C.S.: 424690
Lyudmila Marinova (Gen Mgr)

**DOHLER SOUTH AFRICA (PTY)
LTD.** (1)
5 De Vreugde Crescent, Dal Josaphat,
Paarl, 7646, South Africa
Tel.: (27) 21 872 4976
Chemical Products Distr
N.A.I.C.S.: 424690

DOHLER WEST AFRICA (1)

Maison Adouke Nr 7 Rue 366 Les Co-
cotiers, Cotonou, Benin
Tel.: (229) 21 30 50 89
Chemical Products Distr
N.A.I.C.S.: 424690

Dairy Fruit A/S (1)
Hestehaven 3, 5260, Odense, Denmark
Tel.: (45) 66131370
Web Site: http://www.dairy-fruit.dk
Sales Range: $25-49.9 Million
Emp.: 81
Food & Beverage Ingredients Mfr
N.A.I.C.S.: 311999
Soren Navne (Mgr-Dev)

Doehler Australia Pty Ltd (1)
96 Woolwich Road, Hunters Hill, 2110,
NSW, Australia
Tel.: (61) 298442107
Food & Beverage Distr
N.A.I.C.S.: 424490

Doehler Bukovina LLC (1)
44-D Kitsmanska str, Mamaivtsi vil, 59343,
Chernivtsi, Kitsmanskyy, Ukraine
Tel.: (380) 372584353
Food & Beverage Distr
N.A.I.C.S.: 424490

Doehler Georgia, Ltd (1)
118 Tsereteli Ave exhibition territory 2nd
pavilion, 0119, Tbilisi, Georgia
Tel.: (995) 32 235 69 07
Chemical Products Distr
N.A.I.C.S.: 424690

Doehler NZ Ltd. (1)
224 Waihi Road, Judea, 3110, Tauranga,
New Zealand
Tel.: (64) 211353325
Food & Beverage Distr
N.A.I.C.S.: 424490

**Doehler Natural Food & Beverage
Ingredients (Bangkok) Co., Ltd.** (1)
183 The Regent House Building 13th Floor
Rajdamri Road Kwaeng Lumpini, Khet Pa-
thumwan, Bangkok, 10330, Thailand
Tel.: (66) 22533503
Food & Beverage Distr
N.A.I.C.S.: 424490

Dohler Austria GmbH (1)
Floridsdorfer Hauptstrasse 1, 1210, Vienna,
Austria
Tel.: (43) 66488178891
Food & Beverage Distr
N.A.I.C.S.: 424490

Dohler East Africa Ltd. (1)
Daisy Drive Off United Nations Avenue Ca-
mellia Close House No 79, PO Box 63789-
00619, Runda Estate, Nairobi, Kenya
Tel.: (254) 707520138
Food & Beverage Distr
N.A.I.C.S.: 424490

Dohler Eisleben GmbH (1)
Alleebreite 14-15, Lutherstadt, 6295, Eisle-
ben, Germany
Tel.: (49) 347575110
Food & Beverage Distr
N.A.I.C.S.: 424490

Dohler GmbH (1)
Slavonska avenija 6A, 10 000, Zagreb,
Croatia
Tel.: (385) 16524026
Food & Beverage Distr
N.A.I.C.S.: 424490

Dohler-Milne Aseptics LLC (1)
804 Bennett Ave, Prosser, WA 99350
Tel.: (509) 786-2240
Web Site: http://www.doehler-milne.com
Fruit Juice Blending & Compounding;
Owned by Wyckoff Farms, Incorporated &
by Dohler GmbH
N.A.I.C.S.: 311411
David Wyckoff (Mng Partner)

JSC BVT Exim (1)
2nd Prilukskiy Pereulok 8, 220089, Minsk,
Belarus
Tel.: (375) 172566147
Food & Beverage Distr
N.A.I.C.S.: 424490

Narplast LLC (1)
3/3 Teyshebain str, Yerevan, Armenia

Tel.: (374) 10473447
Web Site: http://www.narplast.am
Plastics Product Mfr
N.A.I.C.S.: 326199

OOO Technology Polimery (1)
Pervomayskaya Str 86, 700126, Gafurov,
Tajikistan
Tel.: (992) 919120015
Food & Beverage Distr
N.A.I.C.S.: 424490

PT. DOEHLER INDONESIA (1)
Ruko Cordoba H 22 Bukit Golf, Mediterania
Pantai Indah Kapuk, Jakarta Utara, Indone-
sia
Tel.: (62) 21 5698 3472
Web Site: http://www.doehler.com
Emp.: 8
Chemical Products Distr
N.A.I.C.S.: 424690
Ricky Sutanto (Gen Dir)

DOHLER S.A.
Rua Arno Waldemar Dohler 145,
North Industrial Zone, Joinville,
89219-902, SC, Brazil
Tel.: (55) 8006438800   BR
Web Site: https://www.dohler.com.br
Year Founded: 1881
DOHL3—(BRAZ)
Sales Range: Less than $1 Million
Apparel Store Operator
N.A.I.C.S.: 315990
Cesar Pereira Dohler (Dir-Investor
Relations)

**DOHOD INVESTMENT COM-
PANY JSC**
6/2 A Canal Griboyedova Emb, Saint
Petersburg, 191186, Russia
Tel.: (7) 8126356860
Web Site: http://www.dohod.ru
Year Founded: 1993
Sales Range: Less than $1 Million
Investment Management Service
N.A.I.C.S.: 523940
Yakov G. Markov (CEO)

**DOHOME PUBLIC COMPANY
LIMITED**
60 Soi Ruam Mit Din Daeng Road,
Sam Sen Nai Sub-District Phaya Thai
District, Bangkok, 10400, Thailand
Tel.: (66) 20278787   TH
Web Site: https://www.dohome.co.th
Year Founded: 1983
DOHOME—(THA)
Rev.: $921,712,708
Assets: $992,023,196
Liabilities: $636,592,824
Net Worth: $355,430,372
Earnings: $17,085,687
Emp.: 7,636
Fiscal Year-end: 12/31/23
Home Furnishings Retailer
N.A.I.C.S.: 449129
Chatrchai Tuongratanaphan (Chm)

Subsidiaries:

**Dohome Energy Company
Limited** (1)
37 Srimongkol Road, Warinchamrab Sub-
district Warinchamrab District, Ubon
Ratchathani, Thailand
Tel.: (66) 45959888
Eletric Power Generation Services
N.A.I.C.S.: 221118

**Dohome Group Company
Limited** (1)
37-47 Srimongkol Road, Warinchamrab
Sub-district Warinchamrab District, Ubon
Ratchathani, 34190, Thailand
Tel.: (66) 45959888
Non-Residential Building Buying Services
N.A.I.C.S.: 531120

**DOHWA ENGINEERING CO.,
LTD.**

438 Samseong-ro, Gangnam-gu,
Seoul, 06178, Korea (South)
Tel.: (82) 263233000   KR
Web Site: http://www.dohwa.co.kr
Year Founded: 1957
002150—(KRS)
Rev.: $426,786,847
Assets: $449,135,512
Liabilities: $245,488,758
Net Worth: $203,646,754
Earnings: $15,397,225
Emp.: 2,300
Fiscal Year-end: 12/31/23
Engineering Consulting Services
N.A.I.C.S.: 237990
Jun-Sang Kwak (Pres & Co-CEO)

**DOKA WAWASAN TKH HOLD-
INGS BERHAD**
Wisma TKH Lot 6 Jalan Teknologi,
Taman Sains Selangor 1 Kota Da-
mansara, 47810, Petaling Jaya, Se-
langor Darul Ehsan, Malaysia
Tel.: (60) 362860888
Web Site:
   http://www.wawasantkh.com
Kaolin Mining Services
N.A.I.C.S.: 212323
Peir Chyun Wong (Co-Sec)

Subsidiaries:

**Associated Kaolin Industries Sdn.
Bhd.** (1)
Lot 6 Jalan Teknologi, Taman Sains Selan-
gor, 47810, Petaling Jaya, Selangor Darul
Ehsan, Malaysia
Tel.: (60) 362860888
Web Site: http://www.aki.com.my
Emp.: 15
Kaolin Mining & Processing Services
N.A.I.C.S.: 212323
Tan Boon Pun (CEO)

Greatpac Sdn. Bhd. (1)
Lot 6 Jalan Teknologi Taman Sains Selan-
gor 1, 47810, Petaling Jaya, Selangor Darul
Ehsan, Malaysia
Tel.: (60) 362860888
Web Site: http://www.great-pac.com
Disposable Food Packaging Products Mfr
N.A.I.C.S.: 322220

Subsidiary (Domestic):

Greatpac (S) Pte. Ltd. (2)
Lot 6 Jalan Teknologi taman Sains Selangor
1, 47810, Petaling Jaya, Selangor Darul
Ehsan, Malaysia
Tel.: (60) 3 6286 0888
Web Site: http://www.great-pac.com
Disposable Food & Packaging Products Mfr
N.A.I.C.S.: 322220

DOKIC NTK A.D.
Cara Dusana 1, Knjazevac, Serbia
Tel.: (381) 601485514
Year Founded: 2003
DJKC—(BEL)
Rev.: $329,517
Assets: $236,177
Liabilities: $91,536
Net Worth: $144,641
Earnings: $45,370
Fiscal Year-end: 12/31/23
Grocery Store Operator
N.A.I.C.S.: 445110
Miroljub Dokic (Gen Dir)

**DOKTAS METAL SANAYI VE
TICARTE A.S.**
Fatih Mahallesi Gol Yolu No 26,
Orhangazi, 16400, Bursa, Turkiye
Tel.: (90) 224 573 4263
Web Site: http://www.doktas.com
Year Founded: 1973
Aluminum Casting Mfr
N.A.I.C.S.: 331315
Andreas Hecker (Gen Mgr)

DOLAT INVESTMENTS LTD.

301-308 Bhagwati House Plot no
A-19 Veera Desai Road, Andheri
west, Mumbai, 400058, India
Tel.: (91) 7045820985
Web Site:
   https://www.dolatinvest.com
505526—(BOM)
Rev.: $38,951,430
Assets: $68,246,774
Liabilities: $18,566,039
Net Worth: $49,680,735
Earnings: $20,065,925
Emp.: 26
Fiscal Year end: 03/31/21
Securities Trading Services
N.A.I.C.S.: 523150
Sandeepkumar G. Bhanushali *(Compliance Officer & Sec)*

DOLCE & GABBANA S.R.L.
Via S Cecilia 7, 20122, Milan, Italy
Tel.: (39) 027742710
Web Site: http://www.dolcegabbana.it
Sales Range: $100-124.9 Million
Emp.: 900
Clothing Accessory Mfr & Distr
N.A.I.C.S.: 315990
Domenico Dolce *(Co-Founder)*

Subsidiaries:

Dolce & Gabbana Hong Kong
Ltd **(1)**
20/F One Peking 1 Peking Road, Kowloon,
China (Hong Kong)
Tel.: (852) 35111300
Fashion Apparel Distr
N.A.I.C.S.: 424310

Dolce & Gabbana Japan K.K. **(1)**
8/F Aoyama Palacio Tower 3-6-7 Kita
Aoyama, Minato, Tokyo, 107-0061, Japan
Tel.: (81) 364192288
Fashion Apparel Distr
N.A.I.C.S.: 424310

Dolce & Gabbana S.R.L. - Incisa in
Val d'Arno Facility **(1)**
Loc Santa Maria Maddalena 49, Incisa in
Val d Arno, 50064, Florence, Italy
Tel.: (39) 05583311
Fashion Apparel Distr
N.A.I.C.S.: 424310

Dolce & Gabbana S.R.L. - Lonate
Pozzolo Facility **(1)**
Via Papa Giovanni XXIII 114, Lonate Pozzolo, 21015, Varese, Italy
Tel.: (39) 0331663111
Fashion Apparel Distr
N.A.I.C.S.: 424310

Dolce & Gabbana Shanghai Co.,
Ltd. **(1)**
19/F Verdant Place No 128 Nanjing West
Road, Huangpu, Shanghai, 20003, China
Tel.: (86) 2123303800
Fashion Apparel Distr
N.A.I.C.S.: 424310

Dolce & Gabbana USA, Inc. **(1)**
660 Madison Ave 10th Fl, New York, NY
10065
Tel.: (212) 750-0055
Web Site: http://www.dolcegabbana.it
Sales Range: $50-74.9 Million
Emp.: 100
Mens & Womens Apparel Distr
N.A.I.C.S.: 424350

Dolce & Gabbana do Brasil Comercio, Importacao e Participacoes
Ltda. **(1)**
Rua do Rocio N 350- CJ 21, Vila Olimpia,
Sao Paulo, 04552-000, Brazil
Tel.: (55) 1130453744
Fashion Apparel Distr
N.A.I.C.S.: 424310

DOLE PLC
29 North Anne Street, Dublin, D07
PH36, Ireland
Tel.: (353) 18872600   IE
Web Site: https://www.doleplc.com
Year Founded: 2017

DOLE—(NYSE)
Rev.: $9,228,853,000
Assets: $4,591,842,000
Liabilities: $3,305,168,000
Net Worth: $1,286,674,000
Earnings: $86,496,000
Emp.: 37,422
Fiscal Year-end: 12/31/22
Holding Company; Fruit & Vegetable
Whslr
N.A.I.C.S.: 551112
Carl McCann *(Chm)*

Subsidiaries:

Ace Produce Ltd. **(1)**
Whitestown Road, Rush, Dublin, K56 E529,
Ireland
Tel.: (353) 18438002
Fruit & Vegetable Distr
N.A.I.C.S.: 424480

Alichampi Alicante S.L. **(1)**
Ctra Madrid km 4 Nave Multiservicio 11-12,
03006, Alicante, Spain
Tel.: (34) 965104977
Web Site: https://www.alichampi.com
Fruit & Vegetable Distr
N.A.I.C.S.: 424480

Aroherbs Spain S.L. **(1)**
Plataforma Baja Parcela B3 3, 28053, Madrid, Spain
Tel.: (34) 917796645
Fruit & Vegetable Distr
N.A.I.C.S.: 424480

Asf Holland B.V. **(1)**
Lage Brugweg 11a, 5759 PK, Helenaveen,
Netherlands
Tel.: (31) 493348948
Fruit & Vegetable Distr
N.A.I.C.S.: 424480

Avofun Europe S.L. **(1)**
Denario 5 P I Carretera De La Isla, 41700,
Dos Hermanas, Seville, Spain
Tel.: (34) 954931970
Web Site: https://avofun.es
Fruit Mfr & Distr
N.A.I.C.S.: 311421

Champi Canarias S.L. **(1)**
Pl Mayorazgo Sector 2 Puestos de venta
131 133 135 137, Almacen Naves 2 y 10
Islas Canarias, 38110, Santa Cruz de Tenerife, Spain
Tel.: (34) 922203672
Fruit & Vegetable Distr
N.A.I.C.S.: 424480

Chef Maestro Galicia S.L. **(1)**
Mercagalicia Poligono Industrial del Tambre
Puestos 45-46, Santiago de Compostela,
15890, La Coruna, Spain
Tel.: (34) 680341272
Fruit Mfr & Distr
N.A.I.C.S.: 311421

Chef Maestro Horeca S.L. **(1)**
Partida Salt Del Agua No 19, Benidorm,
03503, Alicante, Spain
Tel.: (34) 965860744
Web Site: https://www.chefmaestro.es
Fruit Mfr & Distr
N.A.I.C.S.: 311421

Del fraile frutas y verduras S.L. **(1)**
La Grela Industrial Estate Fruit Market Stall
No 5, 15008, A Coruna, Spain
Tel.: (34) 981295422
Web Site: https://www.frutasdelfraile.com
Fruit & Vegetable Distr
N.A.I.C.S.: 424480

Dole Exotics B.V. **(1)**
Spectrumlaan 29, 2665 NM, Bleiswijk, Netherlands
Tel.: (31) 880890800
Fruit & Vegetable Distr
N.A.I.C.S.: 424480

Dole Hellas Ltd. **(1)**
249 Mesogeion Avenue, 15451 N, Psychiko, Greece
Tel.: (30) 2103634233
Fruit & Vegetable Distr
N.A.I.C.S.: 424480

Dole Holding Company, LLC **(1)**

1 Dole Dr, Westlake Village, CA 91362-
7300
Tel.: (818) 865-8379
Web Site: http://www.dole.com
Holding Company
N.A.I.C.S.: 551112

Holding (Domestic):

Dole Food Company, Inc. **(2)**
1 Dole Dr, Westlake Village, CA 91362
Tel.: (818) 879-6600
Web Site: http://www.dole.com
Rev.: $4,507,262,000
Assets: $2,906,696,000
Liabilities: $2,429,498,000
Net Worth: $477,198,000
Earnings: ($23,658,000)
Emp.: 30,500
Fiscal Year-end: 12/31/2016
Fresh Vegetable & Fruit Mfr & Distr
N.A.I.C.S.: 311999
David Howard Murdock *(Owner & Chm)*

Subsidiary (Non-US):

AB Banan-Kompaniet **(3)**
Frihamnemen, PO Box 27294, 11556,
Stockholm, Sweden
Tel.: (46) 86679160
Web Site: http://www.banan-kompaniet.se
Sales Range: $25-49.9 Million
Emp.: 20
Fruit & Vegetable Distr
N.A.I.C.S.: 424480

Subsidiary (Domestic):

Bud Antle, Inc. **(3)**
2959 Monterey Salinas Hwy, Monterey, CA
93940
Tel.: (831) 641-4200
Fresh Produce Whslr
N.A.I.C.S.: 424480

Dole Berry Company **(3)**
480 W Beach, Watsonville, CA 95076
Tel.: (831) 724-1366
Berry Grower & Distr
N.A.I.C.S.: 111333
David J. Gladstone *(Chm)*

Dole Deciduous **(3)**
1718 Sainsbury Ct, Bakersfield, CA 93311
Tel.: (661) 664-2701
Sales Range: $350-399.9 Million
Emp.: 5,000
Processed Foods; Nut Confections & Gifts;
Grapes
N.A.I.C.S.: 115114

Subsidiary (Non-US):

Dole Europe SAS **(3)**
36 rue de Chateaudun, 75009, Paris,
France
Tel.: (33) 144173060
Sales Range: $10-24.9 Million
Emp.: 50
Fresh Fruit & Packaged Foods Marketer
N.A.I.C.S.: 111331

Unit (Domestic):

Dole Food Co., Inc. - Hawaii **(3)**
1116 Whitmore Ave, Honolulu, HI 96786
Tel.: (808) 847-3234
Web Site: http://www.dole.com
Sales Range: $25-49.9 Million
Emp.: 250
Grow & Market Fresh Pineapple, Coffee,
Papaya & Other Crops
N.A.I.C.S.: 311421
Dan Nellis *(VP & Gen Mgr)*

Subsidiary (Non-US):

Dole Foods of Canada Ltd. **(3)**
1200 Boul Chomedey Ste 915, Laval, H7V
3Z3, QC, Canada
Tel.: (450) 681-4888
Web Site: http://www.dole.com
Sales Range: $25-49.9 Million
Emp.: 3
Whslr of Fresh Fruits & Vegetables
N.A.I.C.S.: 445230

Subsidiary (Domestic):

Dole Fresh Fruit Company **(3)**
1 Hausel Rd, Wilmington, DE 19801

Tel.: (302) 652-2215
Web Site: http://www.dole.com
Sales Range: $25-49.9 Million
Emp.: 5
Fresh Produce Distr
N.A.I.C.S.: 424480
Sean Clancy *(Mgr-Terminal)*

Subsidiary (Non-US):

Dole Fresh Fruit Europe OHG **(3)**
Stadtdeich 7, 20097, Hamburg,
Germany **(100%)**
Tel.: (49) 40329060
Web Site: http://www.dole.de
Sales Range: $25-49.9 Million
Emp.: 130
Fresh Produce Import & Distr
N.A.I.C.S.: 424480
Johan Linden *(Mng Dir)*

Subsidiary (Domestic):

Dole Fresh Vegetables, Inc. **(3)**
639 S Sanborn Rd, Salinas, CA 93901
Tel.: (831) 754-3519
Web Site: http://www.dole.com
Vegetable Production
N.A.I.C.S.: 115114
Roger D. Billingsley *(Sr VP-Tech & Product Dev)*

Subsidiary (Non-US):

Dole South Africa (Pty), Ltd. **(3)**
D Urban Square 26 Bella Rosa Street,
Rosenpark, Bellville, 7530, South Africa
Tel.: (27) 219833600
Web Site: http://www.dolesa.co.za
Emp.: 83
Fresh Fruit Export, Import & Distr
N.A.I.C.S.: 424480
Gerald Gant *(Mng Dir)*

Subsidiary (Domestic):

Oceanview Produce Company **(3)**
3000 E Hueneme Rd, Oxnard, CA 93033-
8112
Tel.: (805) 488-6401
Sales Range: $10-24.9 Million
Emp.: 50
Celery Farm
N.A.I.C.S.: 111219
Oscar Gutierrez *(Controller)*

Subsidiary (Non-US):

Paul Kempowski GmbH & Co.
KG **(3)**
Reepschlagerstr 3D, 23556, Lubeck, Germany
Tel.: (49) 451899070
Web Site: http://www.kempowski-luebeck.de
Sales Range: $25-49.9 Million
Emp.: 100
Fresh Produce Whslr
N.A.I.C.S.: 424480

Subsidiary (Domestic):

Royal Packing Company **(3)**
639 S Sanborn Rd, Salinas, CA 93901
Tel.: (831) 424-0975
Sales Range: $10-24.9 Million
Emp.: 8
Producer, Grower & Shipper of Field Crops
N.A.I.C.S.: 111219

Subsidiary (Non-US):

Saba Trading AB **(3)**
PO Box 15013, Helsingborg, 25015, Sweden
Tel.: (46) 42249500
Web Site: http://www.saba.se
Sales Range: $10-24.9 Million
Emp.: 50
Fresh Vegetables, Fruit & Flowers Importer
& Distr
N.A.I.C.S.: 111331
Mignus Malmgran *(Mgr)*

Dole Nordic A/S **(1)**
Sleipnersvej 3, DK-4600, Koge, Denmark
Tel.: (45) 36156322
Fruit & Vegetable Distr
N.A.I.C.S.: 424480

Dole Nordic AB **(1)**
Langebergavagen 190, 256 69, Helsing-

Dole plc—(Continued)

borg, Sweden
Tel.: (46) 424502300
Fruit Mfr & Distr
N.A.I.C.S.: 311421

Dole Tropical Products Latin America, Ltd. (1)
Edf Las Terrazas B Piso 6 Guachipelin, Escazu, San Jose, Costa Rica
Tel.: (506) 22872301
Fruit & Vegetable Distr
N.A.I.C.S.: 424480

Exportadora y Servicios El Parque S.p.A. (1)
Americo Vespucio Norte 2700 Office 501, Vitacura, Santiago, Chile
Tel.: (56) 222077681
Web Site:
https://www.exportadoraelparque.cl
Fruit Mfr & Distr
N.A.I.C.S.: 311411

Four Seasons Harvest Ltd. (1)
Conquest House Wood Street, Kingston, KT11TG, United Kingdom
Tel.: (44) 2083396359
Web Site: https://fourseasonsharvest.co.uk
Fruit & Vegetable Distr
N.A.I.C.S.: 424480

Frankort & Koning B.V. (1)
Venrayseweg 152, 5928 RH, Venlo, Netherlands
Tel.: (31) 773897272
Web Site: https://frankort.nl
Fruit & Vegetable Distr
N.A.I.C.S.: 424480

Frankort & Koning Polska Sp. z o.o. (1)
Zamoyskiego 53/1, 30-519, Krakow, Poland
Tel.: (48) 122942555
Fruit & Vegetable Distr
N.A.I.C.S.: 424480

Fruitpartner B.V. (1)
Honderdland 96, zuid-holland, 2676 LS, Maasdijk, Netherlands
Tel.: (31) 174272400
Web Site: https://fruitpartner.eu
Fruit & Vegetable Whslr
N.A.I.C.S.: 424480

Frutas Faustino S.L. (1)
Avenida Alcalde Cantos Ropero 0 Jerez de la Frontera, 11408, Cadiz, Spain
Tel.: (34) 956143224
Fruit & Vegetable Distr
N.A.I.C.S.: 424480

Frutas Iru S.A. (1)
Mercabilbao Puestos 326 - 330, Basauri, 48970, Bilbao, Spain
Tel.: (34) 944485200
Fruit & Vegetable Distr
N.A.I.C.S.: 424480

Gambles Ontario Produce Inc. (1)
302 Dwight Avenue, Toronto, M8V 2W7, ON, Canada
Tel.: (416) 259-6397
Fruit & Vegetable Distr
N.A.I.C.S.: 424480

Hortim SK, s.r.o. (1)
Dialnicna cesta 18, 903 01, Senec, Slovakia
Tel.: (421) 244872872
Fruit & Vegetable Distr
N.A.I.C.S.: 424480

MEDITTS Mediterranean Healthy Snacks S.L. (1)
Calle La Fragua 25, San Vicente del Raspeig, 03690, Alicante, Spain
Tel.: (34) 965437276
Web Site: https://meditts.com
Dry Fruits Mfr & Distr
N.A.I.C.S.: 311520

Manu Fruta Sur S.L. (1)
Mercamalaga Avda Jose Ortega y Gasset 553 Modulos 215-216, Mercado Frutas y Verduras, 29196, Malaga, Spain
Tel.: (34) 951281349
Fruit Mfr & Distr
N.A.I.C.S.: 311421

Nowaste Logistics AB (1)

Landskronavagen 5B, 252 32, Helsingborg, Sweden
Tel.: (46) 424502300
Web Site: https://nowastelogistics.com
Fruit & Vegetable Distr
N.A.I.C.S.: 424480

Total Produce plc (1)
29 North Anne Street, Dublin, D07 PH36, Ireland
Tel.: (353) 18872600
Web Site: http://www.totalproduce.com
Rev.: $6,913,114,153
Assets: $1,770,891,731
Liabilities: $1,155,117,672
Net Worth: $615,774,059
Earnings: $74,139,211
Emp.: 6,005
Fiscal Year-end: 12/31/2019
Holding Company; Fresh Produce Distr
N.A.I.C.S.: 551112
Rory P. Byrne (CEO)

Subsidiary (Non-US):

ARC Eurobanan, S.L. (1)
Mercamadrid Plataforma Baja Parcela B3 3, 28053, Madrid, Spain
Tel.: (34) 917796600
Web Site: http://www.madrideurobanan.com
Sales Range: $50-74.9 Million
Emp.: 120
Distr of Fresh Produce
N.A.I.C.S.: 445230
Angel Rey (Mng Dir)

Subsidiary (Domestic):

Allegro Limited (2)
Jamestown House Jamestown Business Park Finglas, Dublin, Ireland
Tel.: (353) 18580600
Web Site: http://www.allegro.ie
Consumer Goods Distr
N.A.I.C.S.: 424990
Brendan Coakley (Chm)

Subsidiary (Non-US):

Anaco & Greeve International B.V. (2)
ABC Westland 666, 2685 DH, Poeldijk, Netherlands (50%)
Tel.: (31) 174638666
Web Site: http://www.anacogreeve.nl
Sales Range: $100-124.9 Million
Emp.: 40
Produce Distr
N.A.I.C.S.: 424480

Brdr. Lembcke A/S (2)
Gronttorvet 348, 2500, Valby, Denmark (100%)
Tel.: (45) 36156322
Web Site: http://www.lembcke.dk
Sales Range: $75-99.9 Million
Emp.: 250
Fresh Produce Distr
N.A.I.C.S.: 424480

Everfresh AB (2)
Langebergavagen 190, 256 69, Helsingborg, Sweden
Tel.: (46) 424502300
Web Site: http://www.everfreshgroup.com
Fresh Fruits & Vegetables Distr
N.A.I.C.S.: 424480

Haluco B.V. (2)
Klappolder 224, Holland, 2665 MR, Bleiswijk, Netherlands
Tel.: (31) 105243600
Web Site: http://www.haluco.nl
Sales Range: $50-74.9 Million
Emp.: 180
Fruits & Vegetables Mfr & Distr
N.A.I.C.S.: 311411

Nedalpac B.V. (2)
Fresh Park Venlo Venrayseweg 198 Venlo 3840, 5928 RH, Venlo, Netherlands
Tel.: (31) 105243600
Web Site: http://www.nedalpac.nl
Sales Range: $25-49.9 Million
Emp.: 30
Fruits & Vegetables Distr
N.A.I.C.S.: 424480

Nordic Fruit Holding AB (2)
Langebergavagen 190, Helsingborg, 256 69, Skane, Sweden

Tel.: (46) 424502300
Fruit & Vegetable Distr
N.A.I.C.S.: 424480

Peviani S.p.A. (2)
Viale Lombardia 7 9, Pavia, 27010, Italy (50%)
Tel.: (39) 0382678511
Web Site: http://www.peviani.it
Sales Range: $25-49.9 Million
Emp.: 40
Fresh Produce Distr
N.A.I.C.S.: 424480

TPH (UK) Limited (2)
Total Produce Enterprise Way Pinchbeck, Spalding, PE11 3YR, Lincolnshire, United Kingdom
Tel.: (44) 7810548297
Print Knitting Machinery Distr
N.A.I.C.S.: 423830

Total Produce Holdings B.V. (2)
Port City I Waalhaven Zuidzijde 21, 3089 JH, Rotterdam, Netherlands
Tel.: (31) 102448400
Web Site: http://www.totalproduce.nl
Sales Range: $25-49.9 Million
Emp.: 50
Fruits & Vegetables Distr
N.A.I.C.S.: 424480

Subsidiary (Domestic):

Total Produce Ireland Limited (2)
Charles McCann Building, The Ramparts, Dundalk, A91X05D, Ireland
Tel.: (353) 429335451
Web Site: http://www.totalproduce.com
Sales Range: $25-49.9 Million
Emp.: 35
Fresh Produce Distr
N.A.I.C.S.: 424480

Subsidiary (Non-US):

Total Produce Nordic A/S (2)
Gronttorvet 348, Valby, 2500, Denmark
Tel.: (45) 36156322
Sales Range: $75-99.9 Million
Emp.: 160
Fresh Fruits & Vegetables Distr
N.A.I.C.S.: 424480

Subsidiary (Domestic):

Uniplumo (Ireland) Limited (2)
Rathbeale Rd, Swords, Dublin, Ireland (90%)
Tel.: (353) 18404395
Web Site: http://www.uniplumo.com
Sales Range: $25-49.9 Million
Emp.: 40
Cultivation & Distr of Houseplants
N.A.I.C.S.: 444240
Tom Summerville (Mng Dir)

Unitrade Holland B.V. (1)
ABC Westland 664, 2685 DH, Poeldijk, Netherlands
Tel.: (31) 174623750
Fruit & Vegetable Distr
N.A.I.C.S.: 424480

DOLFIN GROUP LTD.
50 Berkeley Street, London, W1J 8HA, United Kingdom
Tel.: (44) 20 3883 1800 BM
Web Site: http://www.dolfin.com
Holding Company
N.A.I.C.S.: 551112
Denis Nagy (CEO)

Subsidiaries:

Dolfin Financial (UK) Ltd. (1)
50 Berkeley Street, London, W1J 8HA, United Kingdom
Tel.: (44) 20 3883 1800
Web Site: http://www.dolfin.com
Wealth Management Services
N.A.I.C.S.: 523999
Denis Nagy (CEO)

Falcon Private Wealth Ltd. (1)
9th Floor 10 Exchange Square Broadgate, London, EC2A 2BR, United Kingdom (100%)
Tel.: (44) 20 7811 5100
Web Site: http://www.falconpw.com

Wealth Management Services
N.A.I.C.S.: 523940
Nick McCall (CEO)

DOLFIN RUBBERS LTD.
26-A BRS Nagar Opp Ramesh Eye Hospital Inside State Bank Street, Opp Verka Milk Plant, Ludhiana, 141002, Punjab, India
Tel.: (91) 1615031030
Web Site:
https://www.dolfintyres.com
Year Founded: 1995
542013—(BOM)
Rev.: $11,281,126
Assets: $5,501,164
Liabilities: $2,812,895
Net Worth: $2,688,269
Earnings: $387,368
Emp.: 403
Fiscal Year-end: 03/31/21
Rubber Products Mfr
N.A.I.C.S.: 326299
Ankita Sahu (Compliance Officer & Sec)

DOLKAM SUJA A.S.
Rajec, Suja, 015 01, Zilina, Slovakia
Tel.: (421) 415422310
Web Site: https://www.dolkam.sk
Year Founded: 1992
Sand & Gravel Quarrying Services
N.A.I.C.S.: 212321

DOLLAR INDUSTRIES LIMITED
Om Tower 15th Floor 32 J L Nehru Road, Kolkata, 700 071, West Bengal, India
Tel.: (91) 2288406466
Web Site: https://www.dollarglobal.in
Year Founded: 1972
541403—(BOM)
Rev.: $142,019,651
Assets: $114,284,475
Liabilities: $41,017,568
Net Worth: $73,266,907
Earnings: $11,645,757
Emp.: 1,515
Fiscal Year-end: 03/31/21
Clothing Product Mfr & Distr
N.A.I.C.S.: 315120
Gopalakrishnan Sarankapani (Exec Dir)

DOLLAR SWEETS COMPANY PTY LTD
22 Purton Road, Pakenham, 3810, Vic, Australia
Tel.: (61) 0359413866
Web Site:
http://www.dollarsweets.com.au
Year Founded: 1947
Sales Range: $25-49.9 Million
Emp.: 35
Chocolate & Sugar Confectionery Mfr
N.A.I.C.S.: 311352
Neil Higgins (CEO)

DOLLARAMA INC.
5805 Royalmount Ave, Town of Mount Royal, Montreal, H4P 0A1, QC, Canada
Tel.: (514) 737-1006 Ca
Web Site: https://www.dollarama.com
Year Founded: 1992
DR3—(MUN)
Rev.: $4,430,553,332
Assets: $3,974,657,183
Liabilities: $3,687,069,731
Net Worth: $287,587,452
Earnings: $763,018,555
Emp.: 25,840
Fiscal Year-end: 01/31/24
Department Store Retailer
N.A.I.C.S.: 455110
Neil Rossy (Pres & CEO)

DOLLY VARDEN SILVER CORPORATION

Suite 3123 - 595 Burrard Street, Vancouver, V7X 1J1, BC, Canada
Tel.: (604) 762-6388　　　　BC
Web Site:
　https://www.dollyvardensilver.com
Year Founded: 2012
DOLLF—(OTCQB)
Rev.: $57,608
Assets: $15,796,827
Liabilities: $268,849
Net Worth: $15,527,979
Earnings: ($6,417,559)
Emp.: 5
Fiscal Year-end: 12/31/21
Silver & Gold Mining
N.A.I.C.S.: 212220
Darren P. Devine *(Chm)*

DOLNOSLASKIE CENTRUM HURTU ROLNO-SPOZYWCZEGO SA

UI Gieldowa 12, 52-438, Wroclaw, Poland
Tel.: (48) 713340920
Web Site: http://www.dchrs.com.pl
Sales Range: $25-49.9 Million
Emp.: 25
Farm Product Warehousing & Storage Services
N.A.I.C.S.: 493130
Bartosz Horodyski *(Chm-Mgmt Bd)*

DOLOMATRIX PHILIPPINES INC.

102 E Rodriguez Jr Ave, Ugong, Pasig, Philippines
Tel.: (63) 26719086　　　　PH
Web Site:
　http://www.dolomatrix.com.ph
Year Founded: 2001
Toxic & Hazard Waste Treatment Services
N.A.I.C.S.: 562211

DOLOMITE CORPORATION BERHAD

19 Dolomite Park Avenue Jalan Batu Caves, 68100, Batu Caves, Selangor, Malaysia
Tel.: (60) 3619560000
Web Site:
　http://www.dolomite.com.my
DOLMITE—(KLS)
Rev.: $588,803
Assets: $89,498,228
Liabilities: $81,480,713
Net Worth: $8,017,515
Earnings: ($7,274,025)
Emp.: 29
Fiscal Year-end: 12/31/21
Construction & Property Development Services
N.A.I.C.S.: 236115
Choong Keong Lew *(Mng Dir)*

Subsidiaries:

Dolomite Berhad　　　　　　(1)
19 Dolomite Park Avenue Jalan, Batu Caves, 68100, Selangor, Malaysia
Tel.: (60) 361860000
Web Site: http://www.dolomite.com.my
Sales Range: $25-49.9 Million
Emp.: 50
Building Construction Products Mfr
N.A.I.C.S.: 327331
Lew Choong Keong *(Mng Dir)*

Subsidiary (Domestic):

Dolomite Industries Company Sdn. Bhd.　　　　　　　　(2)
11 3/4 Miles Sungai Serai, Hulu Langat, Selangor, Malaysia
Tel.: (60) 390211600
Residential Property Development Services
N.A.I.C.S.: 531390

Baldesh Singh *(Asst Gen Mgr)*

Subsidiary (Domestic):

Dolomite Properties Sdn. Bhd.　　(3)
19 Dolomite Pk Ave Jalan Batu Caves, 68100, Batu Caves, Selangor, Malaysia
Tel.: (60) 361861000
Web Site: http://www.dolomite.com.my
Emp.: 100
Residential Property Development Services
N.A.I.C.S.: 531390
Mary Eechai Hoo *(Office Mgr)*

Subsidiary (Domestic):

Dolomite Readymixed Concrete Sdn. Bhd.　　　　　　(2)
11 3/4 Mile Sg Serai, 43100, Hulu Langat, Selangor, Malaysia
Tel.: (60) 390211621
Web Site: https://www.dolomite.com.my
Sales Range: $25-49.9 Million
Readymix Concrete Mfr
N.A.I.C.S.: 327320
Choong Keong Lew *(Mng Dir)*

DOLOVO U RESTRUKTURIRANJU A.D.

Kralja Petra I 1, Dolovo, Serbia
Tel.: (381) 13 2634 306
Year Founded: 1989
Sales Range: $1-9.9 Million
Emp.: 35
Perennial Plant Farming Services
N.A.I.C.S.: 111421

DOLPHIN DELIVERY LTD.

4201 Lozells Avenue, Burnaby, V5A 2Z4, BC, Canada
Tel.: (604) 421-7059
Web Site:
　http://www.dolphindelivery.ca
Year Founded: 1968
Rev.: $44,412,050
Emp.: 500
Logistics & Transportation Services Provider
N.A.I.C.S.: 484110
William Morris Peter *(Pres)*

DOLPHIN HOTELS PLC

Hemas House No 75 Braybrooke Place, 02, Colombo, 02, Sri Lanka
Tel.: (94) 114731731　　　　LK
STAF.N0000—(COL)
Rev.: $1,860,557
Assets: $17,146,745
Liabilities: $5,953,720
Net Worth: $11,193,026
Earnings: ($176,758)
Emp.: 295
Fiscal Year-end: 03/31/21
Hotel & Restaurant Operator
N.A.I.C.S.: 721110

DOLPHIN INTERCONNECT SOLUTIONS AS

Nils Hansens vei 13, Skullerud, 0694, Oslo, Norway
Tel.: (47) 24076210　　　　NO
Web Site: http://www.dolphinics.com
Year Founded: 1992
Develop Market High Speed High Bandwidth Interconnect Product Mfr
N.A.I.C.S.: 541511

Subsidiaries:

Dolphin Interconnect Solutions NA Inc.　　　　　　　　(1)
7 Boomhower Rd, Woodsville, NH 03785
Tel.: (603) 747-4100
Web Site: http://www.dolphinics.com
Interconnect Software & Hardware Products
N.A.I.C.S.: 423430
Laraine King *(Office Mgr)*

DOLPHIN MEDICAL SERVICES LTD.

417 Sanali Heavens Ameerpet, Hyderabad, 500073, Andhra Pradesh, India
Tel.: (91) 4065889357
Web Site:
　https://www.dolphinmedical.com
Year Founded: 1994
526504—(BOM)
Rev.: $822,410
Assets: $1,682,768
Liabilities: $250,960
Net Worth: $1,431,808
Earnings: ($42,620)
Fiscal Year-end: 03/31/21
Healtcare Services
N.A.I.C.S.: 621610
Turlapati Seshu Kumar *(Chm)*

DOLPHIN OFFSHORE ENTERPRISES (INDIA) LTD

701/702 Lakhani Centrium Plot No 27 Sector 15 CBD Belapur East, Navi Mumbai, 400 614, India
Tel.: (91) 2249063600　　　　In
Web Site:
　http://www.dolphinoffshore.com
Year Founded: 1979
DOLPHINOFF—(NSE)
Sales Range: $25-49.9 Million
Oil & Gas Offshore Services
N.A.I.C.S.: 213112
Kirpal Singh *(Chm)*

DOM DEVELOPMENT S.A.

PI Pilsudskiego 3 Metropolitan Building, 00-078, Warsaw, Poland
Tel.: (48) 223516633
Web Site: https://www.domd.pl
Year Founded: 1996
DOM—(WAR)
Rev.: $607,774,707
Assets: $1,032,999,045
Liabilities: $677,958,850
Net Worth: $355,040,195
Earnings: $103,074,160
Emp.: 532
Fiscal Year-end: 12/31/22
Real Estate & Property Development Services
N.A.I.C.S.: 531311
Markham Dumas *(Vice Chm-Supervisory Bd)*

Subsidiaries:

Dom Construction Sp. z o.o.　　(1)
PL PILSUDSKIEGO 3, 00-078, Warsaw, Poland
Tel.: (48) 223516104
Web Site: https://www.domc.pl
Residential Construction Services
N.A.I.C.S.: 531311
Grzegorz Gad *(Mgr-Site)*

Dom Development Wroclaw Sp. z o.o.　　　　　　　　　(1)
ul Kazimierza Wielkiego 1, 50-077, Wroclaw, Poland
Tel.: (48) 717477474
Web Site: http://www.wroclaw.domd.pl
Residential Developing Services
N.A.I.C.S.: 531311
Grzegorz Kielpsz *(Chm-Supervisory Bd)*

Euro Styl S.A　　　　　　　(1)
ul Leszczynowa 6, 80-175, Gdansk, Poland
Tel.: (48) 587795858
Web Site: https://www.eurostyl.com.pl
Residential Construction Services
N.A.I.C.S.: 531311
Aleksandra Wozniak *(Project Mgr)*

DOM VILLE SERVICES

N 12 14 12 Rue De La Verrerie, Nantes, 44204, Loire Atlantique, France
Tel.: (33) 240699480
Web Site: http://www.apparteiqu.com
Rev.: $21,400,000
Emp.: 51
Hotels & Motels

N.A.I.C.S.: 721110
Claude Jendron *(Dir)*

DOM.RF JSC

Vozdvizhenka 10 block B, 125009, Moscow, Russia
Tel.: (7) 4957754740
Web Site: http://xn--d1aqf.xn--p1ai
Emp.: 100
Mortgage Lending Services
N.A.I.C.S.: 522310
Vitaly Mutko *(Gen Dir)*

DOMACOM LIMITED

Level 5 607 Bourke Street, Melbourne, 3000, VIC, Australia
Tel.: (61) 1300365930
Web Site:
　https://www.domacom.com.au
Year Founded: 2015
Rev.: $250,351
Assets: $2,395,722
Liabilities: $2,768,355
Net Worth: ($372,633)
Earnings: ($4,043,002)
Fiscal Year-end: 06/30/19
Investment Fund Services
N.A.I.C.S.: 525910
Arthur Naoumidis *(Co-Founder & CEO)*

DOME GOLD MINES LIMITED

Level 46 680 George Street, Sydney, 2000, NSW, Australia
Tel.: (61) 282035620
Web Site:
　https://www.domegoldmines.com.au
Year Founded: 2011
DME—(ASX)
Rev.: $755
Assets: $24,393,154
Liabilities: $1,075,560
Net Worth: $23,317,594
Earnings: ($1,461,395)
Fiscal Year-end: 06/30/24
Gold, Silver & Copper Mining
N.A.I.C.S.: 212220
Marcelo Mora *(Sec)*

DOMES PHARMA SA

ZAC de Champ Lamet 3 rue Andre Citroen, 63430, Pont-du-Chateau, France
Tel.: (33) 473300230
Web Site:
　https://www.domespharma.com
Year Founded: 1947
Animal Health & Pharmaceutical Products Mfr
N.A.I.C.S.: 325412
Anne Moulin *(Pres-US)*

Subsidiaries:

SentrX Animal Care, Inc.　　　(1)
615 Arapeen Dr Ste 110, Salt Lake City, UT 84108
Tel.: (801) 583-2050
Web Site: http://www.sentrxanimalcare.com
Veterinary Care Services
N.A.I.C.S.: 541940
Sarah K. Atzet *(COO)*

DOMESCO MEDICAL JOINT STOCK CORPORATION

No 346 Nguyen Hue Street My Phu Ward, Cao Lanh, Dong Thap, Vietnam
Tel.: (84) 2773852278
Web Site: https://www.domesco.com
Year Founded: 1989
DMC—(HOSE)
Rev.: $159,272,700
Assets: $183,797,700
Liabilities: $37,846,700
Net Worth: $145,951,000
Earnings: $20,007,600
Emp.: 1,300

Domesco Medical Joint Stock
Corporation—(Continued)

Fiscal Year-end: 12/31/22
Pharmaceutical Products Mfr & Whslr
N.A.I.C.S.: 325412
Nguyen Phi Thuc *(Chm-Supervisory Bd)*

DOMETIC GROUP AB

Hemvarnsgatan 15, 171 54, Solna,
Sweden
Tel.: (46) 850102500   **SE**
Web Site: https://www.dometic.com
Year Founded: 2010
DOM—(OMX)
Rev.: $1,982,966,510
Assets: $3,931,102,770
Liabilities: $2,070,310,060
Net Worth: $1,860,792,710
Earnings: $142,000,250
Emp.: 7,257
Fiscal Year-end: 12/31/19
Holding Company; RV, Boat, Mobile
Home & Specialty Vehicle Appliances
& Air Conditioning Products & Acces-
sories Mfr & Whslr
N.A.I.C.S.: 551112
Anna Smieszek *(Gen Counsel)*

Subsidiaries:

Cadac Europe B.V.   **(1)**
Ratio 26, 6921 RW, Duiven, Netherlands
Tel.: (31) 263197740
Kitchen Tools & Accessory Distr
N.A.I.C.S.: 423620

CDI Electronics LLC   **(1)**
353 James Record Rd SW, Huntsville, AL
35824
Tel.: (256) 772-3829
Web Site: https://www.cdielectronics.com
Electronic Equipment Mfr & Distr
N.A.I.C.S.: 335314

Condaria 87 S.r.l.   **(1)**
Via Vesuvio 18, 20054, Nova Milanese, MB,
Italy
Tel.: (39) 036244182
Air-Conditioning & Air Heating Equipment
Mfr
N.A.I.C.S.: 333415

Dometic (Pty) Ltd.   **(1)**
South & Sub-Saharan Africa Aramex Build-
ing 2 Avalon Road, PO Box 2562, West
Lake Ext 11 Modderforntein, 2008,
Bedfordview, South Africa
Tel.: (27) 873530380
Air-Conditioning & Air Heating Equipment
Mfr
N.A.I.C.S.: 333415

Dometic (Shenzhen) Trading Co.
Ltd.   **(1)**
Building D No 39 Fangkeng Road Pinghu
Community Pinghu Street, Longgang Dis-
trict, Shenzhen, 518111, China
Tel.: (86) 75582932566
Air-Conditioning & Air Heating Equipment
Mfr
N.A.I.C.S.: 333415

Dometic Asia Co. Ltd.   **(1)**
Suites 2207-2210 22/F Tower 1 The Gate-
way 25 Canton Road, Tsim Sha Tsui, Kow-
loon, China (Hong Kong)
Tel.: (852) 24565199
Air-Conditioning & Air Heating Equipment
Mfr
N.A.I.C.S.: 333415
Chris Tai *(Mgr-HR)*

Dometic Austria GmbH   **(1)**
Neudorferstrasse 108, 2353, Guntramsdorf,
Austria
Tel.: (43) 2236908070
Air-Conditioning & Air Heating Equipment
Mfr
N.A.I.C.S.: 333415

Dometic Benelux B.V.   **(1)**
Ecustraat 3, 4879 NP, Etten-Leur, Nether-
lands
Tel.: (31) 765029000

Air-Conditioning & Air Heating Equipment
Mfr
N.A.I.C.S.: 333415

Dometic Denmark A/S   **(1)**
Nordensvej 15 Taulov, 7000, Fredericia,
Denmark
Tel.: (45) 75585966
Air-Conditioning & Air Heating Equipment
Mfr
N.A.I.C.S.: 333415

Dometic Deutschland GmbH   **(1)**
Industriegebiet Sud Hollefeldstrasse 63,
48282, Emsdetten, Germany
Tel.: (49) 25728790
Air-Conditioning & Air Heating Equipment
Mfr
N.A.I.C.S.: 333415

Dometic Finland Oy   **(1)**
Valimotie 15, 00380, Helsinki, Finland
Tel.: (358) 207413220
Air-Conditioning & Air Heating Equipment
Mfr
N.A.I.C.S.: 333415

Dometic Germany GmbH   **(1)**
Hollefeldstrasse 63, Industrial area south,
48282, Emsdetten, Germany
Tel.: (49) 25728790
Domestic Product Mfr & Retailer
N.A.I.C.S.: 335220

Dometic Germany MPS GmbH   **(1)**
Carsten Isenberg Dieselstr 27, 48485,
Neuenkirchen, Germany
Tel.: (49) 2572879399
Web Site: https://www.buettner-elektronik.de
Electrical Equipment Mfr & Distr
N.A.I.C.S.: 334515

Dometic International AB   **(1)**
Hemvarnsgatan 15, 171 54, Solna, Sweden
Tel.: (46) 850102500
Web Site: http://www.dometic.com
Sales Range: $150-199.9 Million
Emp.: 6,000
Holding Company; RV, Boat, Mobile Home
& Specialty Vehicle Appliances & Air Condi-
tioning Products & Accessories Mfr & Whslr
N.A.I.C.S.: 551112
Paul Hickinbotham *(Product Mgr-Marine-
EMEA)*

Subsidiary (Non-US):

Dometic GmbH   **(2)**
In der Steinwiese 16, 57074, Siegen, Ger-
many
Tel.: (49) 2716920
Web Site: http://www.dometic.de
Sales Range: $150-199.9 Million
Emp.: 500
RV, Boat, Mobile Home & Specialty Vehicle
Appliances & Air Conditioning Products &
Accessories Mfr & Whslr
N.A.I.C.S.: 335220

Dometic Italy S.r.l.   **(1)**
Via Virgilio 3, 47122, Forli, FC, Italy
Tel.: (39) 0543754901
Air-Conditioning & Air Heating Equipment
Mfr
N.A.I.C.S.: 333415

Dometic KK   **(1)**
Maekawa-Shibaura Bldg 2 2-13-9 Shibaura,
Minato-ku, Tokyo, 108-0023, Japan
Tel.: (81) 354453333
Air-Conditioning & Air Heating Equipment
Mfr
N.A.I.C.S.: 333415

Dometic Korea Co., Ltd.   **(1)**
2F Seonyu building 12 Yangpyeong-ro 22-
gil, Yeongdeungpo-gu, 07206, Seoul, Korea
(South)
Tel.: (82) 220886877
Air-Conditioning & Air Heating Equipment
Mfr
N.A.I.C.S.: 333415

Dometic Middle East FZCO   **(1)**
PO Box 17860, Jebel Ali, Dubai, United
Arab Emirates
Tel.: (971) 48833858
Air-Conditioning & Air Heating Equipment
Mfr
N.A.I.C.S.: 333415

Dometic Mx, S DE RL DE CV   **(1)**
Latin America and Caribbean Circuito Medi-
cos No 6 Local 1, Colonia Ciudad Satelite,
53100, Naucalpan, Estado de Mexico,
Mexico
Tel.: (52) 5553744108
Air-Conditioning & Air Heating Equipment
Mfr
N.A.I.C.S.: 333415

Dometic New Zealand Ltd.   **(1)**
PO Box 12011, Penrose, 1642, Auckland,
New Zealand
Tel.: (64) 96221490
Air-Conditioning & Air Heating Equipment
Mfr
N.A.I.C.S.: 333415

Dometic Norway AS   **(1)**
Elveveien 30B, 3262, Larvik, Norway
Tel.: (47) 33428450
Air-Conditioning & Air Heating Equipment
Mfr
N.A.I.C.S.: 333415

Dometic Poland Spolka z ogranic-
zona odpowiedzialnoscia   **(1)**
Ul Pulawska 435 A, 02-801, Warsaw, Po-
land
Tel.: (48) 224143200
Air-Conditioning & Air Heating Equipment
Mfr
N.A.I.C.S.: 333415

Dometic Pte. Ltd.   **(1)**
18 Boon Lay Way 06-141 Trade Hub 21,
Singapore, 609966, Singapore
Tel.: (65) 67953177
Air-Conditioning & Air Heating Equipment
Mfr
N.A.I.C.S.: 333415

Dometic RUS Limited Liability
Company   **(1)**
Komsomolskaya Sqare 6 Bld 1 Office 660
664 667, 107140, Moscow, Russia
Tel.: (7) 4957807939
Air-Conditioning & Air Heating Equipment
Mfr
N.A.I.C.S.: 333415

Dometic S.A.S   **(1)**
Z A du Pre de la Dame Jeanne B P 5,
60128, Plailly, France
Tel.: (33) 344633500
Air-Conditioning & Air Heating Equipment
Mfr
N.A.I.C.S.: 333415

Dometic Scandinavia AB   **(1)**
Gustaf Melins Gata 7, 421 31, Vastra Frol-
unda, Sweden
Tel.: (46) 317341100
Web Site: http://www.dometic.com
RV, Boat, Mobile Home & Specialty Vehicle
Appliances & Air Conditioning Products &
Accessories Mfr & Whslr
N.A.I.C.S.: 423620

Subsidiary (Domestic):

Dometic Seitz AB   **(2)**
Ostra Ringvagen, 522 35, Tidaholm, Swe-
den
Tel.: (46) 5021 7870
Mobile Air Conditioners & Refrigerators Mfr
N.A.I.C.S.: 333415

Dometic Slovakia s.r.o.   **(1)**
Nadrazna 34/A, Ivanka pri Dunaji, 900 28,
Bratislava, Slovakia
Tel.: (421) 245529680
Air-Conditioning & Air Heating Equipment
Mfr
N.A.I.C.S.: 333415
Juraj Holubek *(Mgr-Technical Sls & Aftersls)*

Dometic Spain SL   **(1)**
Avda Sierra del Guadarrama 16, Villanueva
de la Canada, 28691, Madrid, Spain
Tel.: (34) 918336089
Air-Conditioning & Air Heating Equipment,
Mfr
N.A.I.C.S.: 333415

Dometic Switzerland AG   **(1)**
Riedackerstrasse 7 A, 8153, Rumlang, Swit-
zerland
Tel.: (41) 448187171
Air-Conditioning & Air Heating Equipment
Mfr
N.A.I.C.S.: 333415

N.A.I.C.S.: 333415

Dometic UK Awnings Ltd.   **(1)**
Little Braxted Hall Little Braxted, Witham,
CM8 3EU, Essex, United Kingdom
Tel.: (44) 1376500111
Domestic Product Mfr & Retailer
N.A.I.C.S.: 335220

Dometic UK Blind Systems Ltd.   **(1)**
Atlantic House 1-3 Ellis Square, Selsey,
Chichester, PO20 0AY, West Sussex,
United Kingdom
Tel.: (44) 1243606909
Domestic Product Mfr & Retailer
N.A.I.C.S.: 335220

Front Runner GmbH   **(1)**
Zu den Mergelbruchen 4, 30559, Hannover,
Germany
Tel.: (49) 511474046400
Roof Rack Accessories Mfr & Distr
N.A.I.C.S.: 332313

Igloo Products Corporation   **(1)**
777 Igloo Rd, Katy, TX 77494
Tel.: (713) 584-6800
Web Site: http://www.igloocoolers.com
Sales Range: $200-249.9 Million
Emp.: 850
Seat Top Beverage Coolers & Ice Chests,
Industrial Plastic & Metal Water Coolers &
Heavy-Duty Utility Containers Mfr
N.A.I.C.S.: 326140
Brandon Davis *(Sr VP-Sls)*

Subsidiary (Domestic):

Cool Gear International LLC   **(2)**
10 Cordage Park Cir, Plymouth, MA 02360
Tel.: (508) 830-3440
Web Site: http://www.shop.coolgearinc.com
Sales Range: $1-9.9 Million
Food & Beverage Storage Product Mfr
N.A.I.C.S.: 326199
Donna J. Roth *(Co-Founder)*

SMEV S.r.l.   **(1)**
Via Apollonio 11, 36061, Bassano del
Grappa, VI, Italy
Tel.: (39) 0424500006
Air-Conditioning & Air Heating Equipment
Mfr
N.A.I.C.S.: 333415

SNJ Enterprises, Inc.   **(1)**
63255 Jamison St, Bend, OR 97703
Tel.: (541) 728-0924
Web Site: https://www.zampsolar.com
Solar Module Designer & Mfr
N.A.I.C.S.: 334413
Steven E. Nelson *(Pres & CEO)*

Sierra International LLC   **(1)**
1 Sierra Pl, Litchfield, IL 62056
Tel.: (877) 633-8396
Web Site: http://www.seastarsolutions.com
Marine Engine & Drive Parts Mfr
N.A.I.C.S.: 336310
Bill Longacre *(VP-Aftermarket Sls)*

Subsidiary (Domestic):

Inca Products Acquisition Corp.   **(2)**
801 N Spring St, Sparta, TN 38583
Rotationally-Molded Plastic Products Mfr
N.A.I.C.S.: 326199

Moeller Marine Products, Inc.   **(2)**
801 N Spring St, Sparta, TN 38583
Tel.: (931) 738-8090
Web Site: http://www.moellermarine.com
Plastics Product Mfr
N.A.I.C.S.: 326199
Kerry Pharris *(Mgr-Engrg)*

Unit (Domestic):

SeaStar Solutions - Prime Line Indus-
trial Controls   **(2)**
640 N Lewis Rd, Limerick, PA 19468-1228
Tel.: (610) 495-7013
Web Site: http://www.primelinecontrols.com
Mechanical Steering & Engine Control Sys-
tems Mfr
N.A.I.C.S.: 336330

WAECO Germany WSE GmbH   **(1)**
Hollefeldstrasse 63, 48282, Emsdetten,
Germany
Tel.: (49) 25728790

Web Site: https://www.waeco.com
Automotive Spare Parts Mfr & Distr
N.A.I.C.S.: 336390

WAECO Sweden WSE AB   **(1)**
Gustaf Melins gata 7, 421 31, Vastra Frol-
unda, Sweden
Tel.: (46) 317341100
Automotive Air Conditioner Distr
N.A.I.C.S.: 423730

DOMEXPORT INC.
8255 boul Henri Bourassa Bureau
260, Quebec, G1G 4C8, QC, Canada
Tel.: (418) 627-0160
Web Site: http://www.domexport.com
Year Founded: 1992
Rev.: $16,816,000
Emp.: 7
Lumber Product Whslr
N.A.I.C.S.: 423310
Pierre-Luc Bouchard *(Dir-Admin)*

DOMIKI KRITIS S.A.
14 Koroneou str Crete, 71202, Irak-
lion, Greece
Tel.: (30) 2810288287
Web Site: https://www.domik.gr
Year Founded: 1985
DOMIK—(ATH)
Sales Range: $10-24.9 Million
Emp.: 23
Civil Engineering Construction Ser-
vices
N.A.I.C.S.: 237990
Konstantinos Kritzas *(Mgr-Technical-
Port & Building Works)*

Subsidiaries:

DOMIKI AKINITON S.A.   **(1)**
Sorvolou 2, 11636, Athens, Greece
Tel.: (30) 2109245398
Construction Engineering Services
N.A.I.C.S.: 541330
George Synatsakis *(Chm & CEO)*

DOMINANT ENTERPRISE BERHAD
No 2 Jalan Gemilang 1 Taman Perin-
dustrian Maju Jaya, 81300, Johor
Bahru, Johor, Malaysia
Tel.: (60) 75588318
Web Site:
  https://www.dominant.com.my
DOMINAN—(KLS)
Rev.: $185,543,577
Assets: $136,082,055
Liabilities: $58,676,305
Net Worth: $77,405,750
Earnings: $3,491,713
Fiscal Year-end: 03/31/24
Laminated Wood Products Mfr &
Distr
N.A.I.C.S.: 321215
May Li Yong *(Co-Sec)*

Subsidiaries:

Akati Impex Pte. Ltd.   **(1)**
110 Tuas South Avenue 3 04-06 The Index,
Singapore, 637369, Singapore
Tel.: (65) 68630100
Wood Product Distr
N.A.I.C.S.: 423310

Akati Wood (Vietnam) Co., Ltd.   **(1)**
No 3 VSIP II Street 6, Viet Nam- Singapore
II Industrial Park, Thu Dau Mot, Binh
Duong, Vietnam
Tel.: (84) 2743628058
Wood Product Mfr & Distr
N.A.I.C.S.: 321999

Bripanel Industries Sdn. Bhd.   **(1)**
PTD 2805 Jalan Raja, Kawasan Perindus-
trian Bukit Pasir Muar, 84300, Johor, Malay-
sia
Tel.: (60) 69858599
Wood Products Mfr
N.A.I.C.S.: 321999

Favor Woodpanel (Thailand) Co.,
Ltd.   **(1)**
15 Bangkhuntein-Chaytalay Road, Samae
Dam Bangkhuntein, Bangkok, 10150, Thai-
land
Tel.: (66) 28941545
Wood Product Distr
N.A.I.C.S.: 423310

Green Panel Pty. Ltd.   **(1)**
68-72 York Street, South Melbourne, 3205,
VIC, Australia
Tel.: (61) 396740317
Wood Product Distr
N.A.I.C.S.: 423310

Jurihan Sdn. Bhd.   **(1)**
Wood Product Mfr & Distr
N.A.I.C.S.: 321999

Kim Guan Impex Sdn. Bhd.   **(1)**
No 5 Lot 1439 2246 Jalan Perbadanan,
Pending Industrial Estate, 93450, Kuching,
Malaysia
Tel.: (60) 82488102
Wood Product Distr
N.A.I.C.S.: 423310

Premier Woodprofile Sdn. Bhd.   **(1)**
No 7 Jalan Tembaga, Desa Perindustrian
Kulai Kelapa Sawit Kulai, 81030, Johor,
Malaysia
Tel.: (60) 7 652 2031
Web Site: https://www.dominant.com.my
Wood Products Mfr
N.A.I.C.S.: 321999

DOMINION HOLDING CORPO-RATION
165 The Queensway Suite 302, To-
ronto, M8Y 1H8, ON, Canada
Tel.: (416) 259-6328   **ON**
Web Site:
  http://www.dominioncitrus.com
Year Founded: 2016
Holding Company
N.A.I.C.S.: 551112

Subsidiaries:

Dominion Citrus Limited   **(1)**
165 The Queensway Suite 302, Toronto,
M8Y 1H8, ON, Canada
Tel.: (416) 259-6328
Web Site: http://www.dominioncitrus.com
Fruit & Vegetable Distr
N.A.I.C.S.: 424480
Paul Scarafile *(Pres, CEO & CFO-Acting)*

Division (Domestic)

Country Fresh Packaging   **(2)**
77 Akron Road, Toronto, M8W 1T3, ON,
Canada
Tel.: (416) 252-5801
Web Site: http://www.dominioncitrus.com
Fresh Fruits & Vegetables Packaging Ser-
vices
N.A.I.C.S.: 115114

Dominion Citrus Wholesale   **(2)**
165 The Queensway Suite 302, Toronto,
M8Y 1H8, ON, Canada
Tel.: (416) 259-6328
Web Site: http://www.dominioncitrus.com
Fresh Fruits & Vegetables Distr
N.A.I.C.S.: 424480

Subsidiary (Domestic):

Dominion Farm Produce Limited   **(2)**
215 Dissette St, Bradford, L3Z 2B3, ON,
Canada
Tel.: (416) 798-7741
Web Site: http://www.dominionfarms.ca
Fruits & Vegetables Whslr
N.A.I.C.S.: 445230
Tony Tomizza *(Gen Mgr-Sls)*

Les Aliments Dominion Citrus   **(2)**
1767 Rte de l'Aeroport, L'Ancienne-Lorett,
G2G 2P5, QC, Canada
Tel.: (418) 877-9908
Web Site: http://www.dominioncitrus.com
Fresh Fruit Distr
N.A.I.C.S.: 445298

Meschino Banana Company   **(2)**
1613 St Clair Ave W, Toronto, M6E 1C9,

ON, Canada
Tel.: (416) 654-7133
Web Site: http://www.dominioncitrus.com
Fresh Foods Whslr
N.A.I.C.S.: 424480

DOMINION LENDING CEN-TRES INC.
Suite 400 2207 4th Street SW, Cal-
gary, T2S 1X1, AB, Canada
Tel.: (403) 455-9660
Web Site: http://advantagecapital.ca
DLCG—(TSXV)
Rev.: $61,656,180
Assets: $198,640,449
Liabilities: $172,182,957
Net Worth: $26,457,492
Earnings: ($3,084,530)
Emp.: 138
Fiscal Year-end: 12/31/21
Investment Services
N.A.I.C.S.: 523999
Gary Mauris *(Chm)*

DOMINION MINERALS LIM-ITED
Level 21 10 Eagle Street, Brisbane,
4000, QLD, Australia
Tel.: (61) 733343900   **AU**
Web Site: https://dominion-
  minerals.com
1TT0—(DEU)
Rev.: $22,575
Assets: $3,925,579
Liabilities: $37,929
Net Worth: $3,887,650
Earnings: ($582,647)
Fiscal Year-end: 12/31/22
Biomedical Technology Research &
Development Services
N.A.I.C.S.: 541714
Stephen Kelly *(Sec)*

DOMINION MOTORS
882 Copper Crescent, Thunder Bay,
P7B 6C9, ON, Canada
Tel.: (807) 343-2277
Web Site:
  http://www.dominionmotors.com
Year Founded: 1911
New & Used Car Dealers
N.A.I.C.S.: 441110

DOMINION NICKEL ALLOYS LTD.
834 Appleby Line, Burlington, L7L
2Y7, ON, Canada
Tel.: (905) 639-9939
Web Site: http://www.domnickel.com
Year Founded: 1969
Rev.: $99,302,431
Emp.: 25
Stainless Steel & Nickel Alloys Distr
N.A.I.C.S.: 423930

DOMINION SURE SEAL LTD.
6175 Danville Road, Mississauga,
L5T 2H7, ON, Canada
Tel.: (905) 670-5411
Web Site:
  https://www.dominionsureseal.com
Year Founded: 1972
Adhesives & Other Plastic Products
Mfr
N.A.I.C.S.: 325520
Larry Cook *(VP-Sls & Mktg DSS)*

DOMINION WAREHOUSING & DISTRIBUTION SERVICES LTD.
1920 Albion Road, Toronto, M9W
5T2, ON, Canada
Tel.: (416) 744-2438
Web Site:
  http://www.godominion.com
Rev.: $13,006,965
Emp.: 102

Warehousing & Storage Services
N.A.I.C.S.: 493110
D. Robert Dineen *(Pres & Gen Mgr)*

DOMINIQUE DUTSCHER SAS
30 rue de l'Industrie, PO Box 62,
67172, Brumath, Cedex, France
Tel.: (33) 388593390   **FR**
Web Site: http://www.dutscher.com
Sales Range: $25-49.9 Million
Emp.: 100
Laboratory Equipment & Supplies
Distr
N.A.I.C.S.: 423450

Subsidiaries:

Biosigma S.r.l.   **(1)**
Via Valetta 6, Cantarana, 30010, Cona, VE,
Italy
Tel.: (39) 0426302224
Web Site: http://www.biosigma.com
Sales Range: $1-9.9 Million
Disposable Analytical Laboratory Supplies
Mfr & Whslr
N.A.I.C.S.: 334516

DD Biolab S.L.   **(1)**
Baldiri i Reixac 4 - 8 Torre I, 08028, Barce-
lona, Spain
Tel.: (34) 902 333 310
Web Site: http://www.ddbiolab.com
Laboratory Equipment Distr
N.A.I.C.S.: 423450

Dutscher Scientific Ltd   **(1)**
Suite 216 - Jubilee House - 3, Brentwood,
CM13 3FR, Essex, United Kingdom
Tel.: (44) 1277 725 996
Web Site: http://www.dutscher-
  scientific.co.uk
Laboratory Equipment Distr
N.A.I.C.S.: 423450

MC2   **(1)**
19 rue Patrick-Depailler - La Pardieu,
63063, Clermont-Ferrand, Cedex, France
Tel.: (33) 4 73 28 99 99
Web Site: http://www.mc2lab.fr
Laboratory Equipment Distr
N.A.I.C.S.: 423450

MUF - Pro s.r.o.   **(1)**
Jinonicka 80, Prague, 158 00, Czech Re-
public
Tel.: (420) 257 290 436
Web Site: http://www.muf-pro.cz
Laboratory Equipment Distr
N.A.I.C.S.: 423450

Milian SA   **(1)**
Chemin des coquelicots 16 Tour B-2eme
etage, Vernier, 1214, Geneva, Switzerland
Tel.: (41) 22 884 16 00
Web Site: http://www.milian.com
Laboratory Equipment Distr
N.A.I.C.S.: 423450
Mickael Rumiano *(Gen Dir)*

Subsidiary (US):

Milian USA   **(2)**
1000 B Taylor Sta Rd, Gahanna, OH 43230
Tel.: (614) 416-1600
Laboratory Equipment Distr
N.A.I.C.S.: 423450

STIRILAB s.r.o.   **(1)**
Textilna 23, 034 01, Ruzomberok, Slovakia
Tel.: (421) 44 432 27 20
Web Site: http://www.stirilab.com
Laboratory Equipment Distr
N.A.I.C.S.: 423450
Martina Spirkova *(Mgr-Sls)*

DOMINIQUE PRUDENT SAS
Bois De Chize, Branges, 71500,
Chanlon-sur-Saone, Saone Et Loire,
France
Tel.: (33) 385764411
Web Site:
  http://www.transportsprudent.fr
Rev.: $23,500,000
Emp.: 600
Local Trucking & Freight Transporta-
tion Services
N.A.I.C.S.: 484110

Jacky Bourlionne *(Dir)*

DOMINO'S PIZZA ENTERPRISES LTD.

Level 1 KSD1 485 Kingsford Smith Drive, Hamilton, 4007, QLD, Australia
Tel.: (61) 736333333   AU
Web Site:
   https://www.dominos.com.au
Year Founded: 1987
DMP—(ASX)
Rev.: $1,587,005,202
Assets: $1,731,296,067
Liabilities: $1,324,279,508
Net Worth: $407,016,558
Earnings: $61,663,328
Emp.: 300
Fiscal Year-end: 06/30/24
Franchise Restaurant Operator
N.A.I.C.S.: 722513
David Klages *(Mgr-Grp HR)*

Subsidiaries:

Construction, Supply & Service Pty Ltd   (1)
West 1A / 605 Zillmere Road, Aspley, Brisbane, 4034, QLD, Australia
Tel.: (61) 1300720622
Web Site:
   https://www.constructionsupply.com.au
Construction Equipment Distr
N.A.I.C.S.: 423810

DPFC S.A.R.L.   (1)
40 rue de Fontenoy, 02290, Vincennes, France
Tel.: (33) 437920101
Fastfood Restaurant Operators
N.A.I.C.S.: 722513

Domino's Pizza Deutschland GmbH   (1)
Am Sandtorkai 75-77, 20457, Hamburg, Germany
Tel.: (49) 404502330
Web Site: https://www.dominos.de
Pizza Mfr
N.A.I.C.S.: 311412

Domino's Pizza Nederland B.V.   (1)
Franklinweg 33, Postbus 112, 4200 AC, Gorinchem, Netherlands
Tel.: (31) 183696300
Web Site: https://www.dominos.nl
Sales Range: $10-24.9 Million
Emp.: 70
Pizza Stores Operator
N.A.I.C.S.: 722513

Domino's Pizza Netherlands B.V.   (1)
Defense Dock 4, 3433 KL, Nieuwegein, Netherlands
Tel.: (31) 886290100
Web Site: https://www.dominos.nl
Pizza Mfr
N.A.I.C.S.: 311412

Domino's Pizza New Zealand Limited   (1)
5/205 Queen Street, PO Box 27213, Mt Roskill, Auckland, 1010, New Zealand
Tel.: (64) 93771580
Web Site: https://www.dominos.co.nz
Sales Range: $25-49.9 Million
Emp.: 6
Pizza Mfr
N.A.I.C.S.: 311991

Dominos Pizza Belgium S.P.R.L.   (1)
Uitbreidingstraat 512, 2600, Berchem, Belgium
Tel.: (32) 32401150
Web Site: http://www.dominos.be
Sales Range: $25-49.9 Million
Emp.: 168
Pizza Mfr
N.A.I.C.S.: 311991

Fra-Ma-Pizz S.A.S.   (1)
Espace Performance Alphasis Bat H2, 35769, Saint-Gregoire, France
Tel.: (33) 223461615
Web Site: http://www.pizzasprint-commandes.com

Pizza Mfr & Distr
N.A.I.C.S.: 311412

IPG Marketing Solutions Pty Ltd   (1)
25 Strathwyn Street, Brendale, 4500, QLD, Australia
Tel.: (61) 738176200
Web Site: http://www.ipgmarketing.com.au
Commercial Printing Services
N.A.I.C.S.: 323111

Impressu Print Group Pty. Ltd.   (1)
25 Strathwyn Street, Brendale, QLD, Australia
Tel.: (61) 738176200
Web Site: https://www.impressu.com.au
Printing Services
N.A.I.C.S.: 518210

Ride Sports ANZ Pty Ltd   (1)
Building East 6/605 Zillmere Road, Aspley, Brisbane, 4034, QLD, Australia
Tel.: (61) 1300720622
Web Site: https://www.ridesports.com.au
Bicycle Retailer
N.A.I.C.S.: 459110

DOMINO'S PIZZA GROUP PLC

1 Thornbury West Ashland, Milton Keynes, MK6 4BB, Buckinghamshire, United Kingdom
Tel.: (44) 1908580000   UK
Web Site:
   http://corporate.dominos.co.uk
Year Founded: 1985
DOM—(LSE)
Rev.: $761,409,376
Assets: $708,729,840
Liabilities: $788,292,232
Net Worth: ($79,562,392)
Earnings: $106,309,476
Emp.: 2,247
Fiscal Year-end: 12/26/21
Holding Company; Pizzeria Restaurants Owner, Operator & Franchisor
N.A.I.C.S.: 551112
Simon Wallis *(Mng Dir-Intl)*

Subsidiaries:

Domino's Pizza Germany GmbH   (1)
Am Sandtorkai 75-77, 20457, Hamburg, Germany
Tel.: (49) 40 450 2330
Web Site: https://www.dominos.de
Online Food Services
N.A.I.C.S.: 722310

Domino's Pizza Group Limited   (1)
1 Thornbury West Ashland, Milton Keynes, MK6 4BB, United Kingdom
Tel.: (44) 1909000000
Web Site: http://www.dominos.co.uk
Sales Range: $25-49.9 Million
Emp.: 250
Pizzeria Restaurants Operator & Franchisor
N.A.I.C.S.: 722513

Subsidiary (Domestic):

DP Realty Limited   (2)
1 Thornbury West Ashland, Milton Keynes, MK6 4BB, United Kingdom
Tel.: (44) 1908 580 000
Commercial Property Investment & Management Services
N.A.I.C.S.: 531312

Domino's Pizza (Isle of Man) Limited   (2)
Dominos Pizza Halfords Retail Park Wellington Road, Aberdeen, AB11 8HX T, United Kingdom
Tel.: (44) 1908 580 000
Holding Company; Pizzeria Restaurants Operator & Franchisor
N.A.I.C.S.: 551112

DOMO CHEMICAL GMBH

Am Haupttor Bau 3101, Leuna, 06237, Sachsen-Anhalt, Germany
Tel.: (49) 3461432200
Web Site:
   http://www.domochemicals.com
Year Founded: 2004
Material Engineering Services

N.A.I.C.S.: 325998
Yves Bonte *(Chm & CEO)*

DOMO NV

Nederzwijnaarde 2, 9052, Zwijnaarde, Belgium
Tel.: (32) 9 241 45 06
Web Site:
   http://www.domoinvestments.com
Holding Company & Investment Firm
N.A.I.C.S.: 551112
Gregory De Clerck *(Mng Dir)*

Subsidiaries:

Domo Caproleuna GmbH   (1)
Am Haupttor Bau 3101, 06237, Leuna, Germany
Tel.: (49) 3461 43 2200
Sales Range: $1-4.9 Billion
Emp.: 850
Plastics Materials & Resins Mfr
N.A.I.C.S.: 325211
Alex Segers *(CEO)*

Subsidiary (US):

Technical Polymers, LLC   (2)
4917 Golden Pkwy Ste 300, Buford, GA 30518
Tel.: (770) 237-2311
Web Site: http://www.techpolymers.com
Sales Range: $25-49.9 Million
Emp.: 50
Plastic Polymers & Resin Compounds Mfr
N.A.I.C.S.: 325211
Brian Hall *(Mgr-Standards & Sys)*

DOMTECH, INC.

40 E Davis St, Trenton, K8V 6S4, ON, Canada
Tel.: (613) 394-4884
Web Site: http://www.domtech.net
Sales Range: $1-9.9 Million
Emp.: 150
Electrical Wire & Cable
N.A.I.C.S.: 332618

DOMUS FIN S.A.

Via Bagutta 20, 20121, Milan, Italy
Tel.: (39) 02 4547 5531   LU
Web Site: http://www.gruppozunino.it
Holding Company; Real Estate Investment Services
N.A.I.C.S.: 551112
Luigi Zunino *(Founder)*

Subsidiaries:

Risanamento S.p.A.   (1)
Via Bonfadini 148, 20138, Milan, Italy
Tel.: (39) 024547551
Web Site: https://www.risanamentospa.com
Sales Range: $75-99.9 Million
Holding Company; Real Estate Investment, Management & Brokerage Services
N.A.I.C.S.: 551111
Claudio Calabi *(CEO)*

Subsidiary (Domestic):

Tradital S.p.A.   (2)
Via Bonfadini 148, Milan, 20138, Italy   (100%)
Tel.: (39) 024547551
Web Site: http://www.risanamentospa.com
Real Estate Agents & Brokers Offices
N.A.I.C.S.: 531210

DON AGRO INTERNATIONAL LIMITED

10 Collyer Quay 10-01, Singapore, 049315, Singapore
Tel.: (65) 65312266   SG
Web Site:
   https://www.donagroint.com
Year Founded: 2018
GRQ—(CAT)
Rev.: $23,463,607
Assets: $59,959,858
Liabilities: $16,538,665
Net Worth: $43,421,192
Earnings: ($3,247,747)

Emp.: 656
Fiscal Year-end: 12/31/23
E Commerce Site Operator
N.A.I.C.S.: 111150
Marat Devlet-Kildeyev *(CEO)*

DON DOCKSTEADER MOTORS LTD

8530 Cambie Street, Vancouver, V6P-6N6, BC, Canada
Tel.: (604) 325-1000
Web Site:
   http://www.dondocksteader.com
Year Founded: 1940
Rev.: $52,601,695
Emp.: 105
New & Used Car Dealers
N.A.I.C.S.: 441110
Paul Docksteader *(Pres)*

DON FOLK CHEVROLET KELOWNA

2350 Highway 97 N, Kelowna, V1X 4H8, BC, Canada
Tel.: (250) 860-6000
Web Site:
   http://www.donfolkchev.com
Year Founded: 1975
Sales Range: $25-49.9 Million
Emp.: 62
New & Used Car Dealers
N.A.I.C.S.: 441110
Jason Jones *(Controller)*

DON VALLEY VOLKSWAGEN LTD.

1695 Eglinton Ave E, Toronto, M4A 1J6, ON, Canada
Tel.: (416) 751-3131
Web Site: http://www.donvalley-vw.ca
Year Founded: 1966
Rev.: $23,735,971
Emp.: 50
New & Used Car Dealers
N.A.I.C.S.: 441110
Michael Martan *(Pres & CEO)*

DON WHEATON CHEVROLET BUICK GMC LTD.

10727-82 Avenue, Edmonton, T6E 2B1, AB, Canada
Tel.: (780) 439-0071
Web Site:
   http://www.donwheaton.com
Year Founded: 1963
New & Used Car Dealers
N.A.I.C.S.: 441110
Nick Seredych *(Mgr-New Vehicle Sls)*

DON'S PHOTO SHOP LTD.

1839 Main Street, Winnipeg, R2V 2A4, MB, Canada
Tel.: (204) 942-7887
Web Site: http://www.donsphoto.com
Year Founded: 1979
Camera & Accessories Supplier
N.A.I.C.S.: 449210
Mike Godfrey *(Pres)*

DON-BUR (BODIES & TRAILERS) LTD

Mossfield Road Adderley Green, Stoke-on-Trent, ST3 5BW, Staffordshire, United Kingdom
Tel.: (44) 1782599666
Web Site: http://www.donbur.co.uk
Sales Range: $50-74.9 Million
Emp.: 374
Vehicle Trailer Mfr
N.A.I.C.S.: 336211
Chris Griffiths *(Mgr-Svc)*

DONACO INTERNATIONAL LIMITED

Level 18 420 George Street, Sydney, 2000, NSW, Australia

Tel.: (61) 291062149
Web Site:
  https://www.donacointernational.com
DNA—(ASX)
Rev.: $29,135,923
Assets: $134,117,918
Liabilities: $31,819,058
Net Worth: $102,298,860
Earnings: $25,564,105
Fiscal Year-end: 06/30/24
Casino & Gaming Software
N.A.I.C.S.: 721120
Leo Chan *(Exec Dir)*

DONAGHYS LIMITED
16 Sheffield Crescent, PO Box 20-
449, Harewood, Christchurch, 8543,
New Zealand
Tel.: (64) 39834100
Web Site: http://www.donaghys.com
Year Founded: 1895
High End Yatching Braids & Marine
Cordage Mfr
N.A.I.C.S.: 314994
Jeremy Silva *(Mng Dir)*

Subsidiaries:

Donaghys Australia Pty Ltd   **(1)**
PO Box 4205, Sydney, 2560, NSW, Austra-
lia
Tel.: (61) 393840153
Industrial Machinery Mfr
N.A.I.C.S.: 333248
Bill Fretwell *(Gen Mgr)*

Donaghys Limited - Dunedin
Factory   **(1)**
63 Bradshaw Street, Dunedin, New Zealand
Tel.: (64) 34551189
Dairy Products Mfr
N.A.I.C.S.: 112120

DONALD WARD LIMITED
Griffon Rd Quarry Hill Industrial Es-
tate, Ilkeston, DE7 4RF, Derbyshire,
United Kingdom
Tel.: (44) 1159305899
Web Site:
  http://www.wardrecycling.com
Year Founded: 1944
Emp.: 400
Recyclable Metals Whslr
N.A.I.C.S.: 423930
David Ward *(Owner & Mng Dir)*

DONBASENERGO PJSC
34 A Predslavinskaya St, 03150,
Kiev, Ukraine
Tel.: (380) 442909707
Web Site: http://www.de.com.ua
Year Founded: 1930
DOEN—(UKR)
Sales Range: Less than $1 Million
Eletric Power Generation Services
N.A.I.C.S.: 221111
Eduard Bondarenko *(Chm)*

**DONE & DUSTED GROUP LIM-
ITED**
4th Floor 93 Newman Street, London,
W1T 3EZ, United Kingdom
Tel.: (44) 207 479 4343   UK
Web Site:
  http://www.doneandusted.com
Year Founded: 1998
Events Staging & Television Produc-
tion Services
N.A.I.C.S.: 711320
Simon Pizey *(CEO)*

Subsidiaries:

Done & Dusted Productions, Inc. **(1)**
The India Bldg 146 W 29th St 4th Fl, New
York, NY 10001
Tel.: (212) 366-6904
Web Site: http://www.doneandusted.com
Events Staging & Television Production
Services

N.A.I.C.S.: 711320

Done+Dusted Inc   **(1)**
1727 Berkeley St, Santa Monica, CA 90404
Tel.: (310) 829-6400
Emp.: 100
Media Production Services
N.A.I.C.S.: 512110
Ian Stewart *(Pres)*

DONEAR INDUSTRIES LTD
Donear House Plot No A-50 Road No
1 MIDC, Andheri East, Mumbai, 400
093, India
Tel.: (91) 2268348100
Web Site: https://www.donear.com
Year Founded: 1987
512519—(BOM)
Rev.: $100,212,493
Assets: $62,387,699
Liabilities: $41,877,885
Net Worth: $20,509,814
Earnings: $4,345,063
Emp.: 2,478
Fiscal Year-end: 03/31/23
Textile Products Mfr
N.A.I.C.S.: 314999
Rajendra V. Agarwal *(Mng Dir)*

**DONEGAL INVESTMENT
GROUP PLC**
Ballyraine, Letterkenny, Co Donegal,
Ireland
Tel.: (353) 749121766   IE
Web Site:
  http://www.donegaligroup.com
Year Founded: 1898
Rev.: $50,650,148
Assets: $53,930,218
Liabilities: $15,450,708
Net Worth: $38,479,509
Earnings: $5,033,771
Emp.: 224
Fiscal Year-end: 08/31/19
Holding Company; Milk & Agricultural
Production
N.A.I.C.S.: 551112
Geoffrey Vance *(Chm)*

Subsidiaries:

An Grianan Grain Company
Limited   **(1)**
Ballyraine, Letterkenny, Donegal, Ireland
Tel.: (353) 74 91 21766
Web Site: http://www.donegalcreameries.ir
Sales Range: $25-49.9 Million
Emp.: 40
Agriculture Product Distr
N.A.I.C.S.: 424910

Donegal Potatoes Limited   **(1)**
Colehill, Newtowncunningham, Donegal,
Ireland
Tel.: (353) 749156155
Sales Range: $50-74.9 Million
Emp.: 4
Potato Whslr
N.A.I.C.S.: 424480

IPM Holland B.V.   **(1)**
Marssumerdyk 1, 9033 WD, Deinum, Fries-
land, Netherlands
Tel.: (353) 582991672
Sales Range: $25-49.9 Million
Emp.: 4
Seed Production & Sales
N.A.I.C.S.: 111199
Eric Apeldoorn *(Gen Mgr)*

IPM Perth Limited   **(1)**
E Den Brae, Letham, Forfar, DD8 2PJ, An-
gus, United Kingdom
Tel.: (44) 1307818121
Potato Whslr
N.A.I.C.S.: 424480

IPM Potato Group Limited   **(1)**
Unit 602 Q House 76 Furze Road Sandy-
ford Industrial Estate, Dublin, 18, Ireland
Tel.: (353) 1 2135410
Web Site: http://www.ipmpotatogroup.com
Emp.: 8
Potato Seed Production & Sales

N.A.I.C.S.: 111211
Marcel de Sousa *(Gen Mgr)*

Maybrook Dairy Limited   **(1)**
14A Dromore Road, Omagh, BT78 1QZ, Co
Tyrone, United Kingdom
Tel.: (44) 2882244184
Dairy Products
N.A.I.C.S.: 112120

Milburn Dairy Limited   **(1)**
Milburn, Castlefinn, Donegal, Ulster, Ireland
Tel.: (353) 74 9146631
Dairy Products Mfr
N.A.I.C.S.: 311514

The Different Dairy Company
Limited   **(1)**
Crossroads Killygordon, Lifford, Donegal,
Ulster, Ireland
Tel.: (353) 749149678
Web Site: http://www.nomadic-dairy.com
Emp.: 40
Dairy Products Mfr
N.A.I.C.S.: 311514
Alan Cunningham *(Gen Mgr)*

Zopitar Limited   **(1)**
Ballyraine, Letterkenny, Donegal, Ireland
Tel.: (353) 749 12 20 11
Dairy Product Whslr
N.A.I.C.S.: 424430

DONETSKKOKS PJSC
1 Zarichna str, Donetsk, 83086,
Ukraine
Tel.: (380) 62 387 30 70
Web Site:
  http://www.donetskcoke.com
Chemical Products Mfr
N.A.I.C.S.: 325998

DONG A ELTEK CO., LTD.
1428-2 Gwanyang-dong, Dongan-gu,
Anyang, Gyeonggi-do, Korea (South)
Tel.: (82) 313451500
Year Founded: 1999
088130—(KRS)
Rev.: $163,964,441
Assets: $234,976,729
Liabilities: $72,854,293
Net Worth: $162,122,436
Earnings: $1,144,930
Emp.: 143
Fiscal Year-end: 12/31/22
LCD Testing Device Mfr
N.A.I.C.S.: 334515
Jae-Peoung Kim *(Pres)*

DONG A PAINT JSC
1387 Ben Binh Dong Ward 15 District
8, Thanh Xuan District, Ho Chi Minh
City, Vietnam
Tel.: (84) 2838552689
Web Site: https://adongpaint.com
Year Founded: 1974
HDA—(HNX)
Rev.: $24,349,200
Assets: $48,652,400
Liabilities: $16,092,900
Net Worth: $32,559,500
Earnings: $114,900
Fiscal Year-end: 12/31/22
Paints Mfr
N.A.I.C.S.: 325510
Tam Mai *(Chm-Mgmt Bd)*

DONG A PLASTIC GROUP JSC
9 Floor Thap Tay Building 28 Floor
Thang Long Village, Cau Giay, Ha-
noi, Vietnam
Tel.: (84) 437342888
Web Site: https://www.dag.com.vn
Year Founded: 2001
DAG—(HOSE)
Rev.: $50,078,353
Assets: $59,422,018
Liabilities: $56,118,479
Net Worth: $3,303,540
Earnings: ($24,998,100)
Emp.: 150

Fiscal Year-end: 12/31/23
Plastic Door & Window Mfr
N.A.I.C.S.: 326199

**DONG BANG TRANSPORT
LOGISTICS CO., LTD.**
3F 16 Tongil-ro 2-gil, Jung-gu, Seoul,
100-770, Korea (South)
Tel.: (82) 221908100
Web Site:
  https://www.dongbang.co.kr
Year Founded: 1965
004140—(KRS)
Rov.: $581,795,027
Assets: $435,629,098
Liabilities: $335,704,170
Net Worth: $99,924,928
Earnings: $626,948
Emp.: 735
Fiscal Year-end: 12/31/22
Freight Transportation Services
N.A.I.C.S.: 488510
Chang-Ki Park *(CEO)*

**DONG DO MARINE JOINT
STOCK COMPANY**
19th Floor Office of International
Peace 106 Hoang Quoc Viet Street,
Cau Giay District, Hanoi, Vietnam
Tel.: (84) 4 3755 6140
Web Site:
  http://www.dongdomarine.com.vn
Year Founded: 1985
Emp.: 147
Maritime Transport Services
N.A.I.C.S.: 488320
Duy Luan Nguyen *(Gen Dir)*

Subsidiaries:

Dongdo Ship Repair Co. ltd   **(1)**
Thon Trung Street Phuc Le Village, Thuy
Nguyen Town, Haiphong, Vietnam
Tel.: (84) 313672151
Ship Repair & Maintenance Services
N.A.I.C.S.: 336611

**DONG HAI JOINT STOCK
COMPANY**
Block AIII - Giao Long Industrial Park
An Phuoc Commune, Chau Thanh
District, Ben Tre, Vietnam
Tel.: (84) 2753822288
DHC—(HOSE)
Rev.: $393,472,700
Assets: $288,248,300
Liabilities: $113,112,700
Net Worth: $175,135,600
Earnings: $37,945,900
Emp.: 550
Fiscal Year-end: 12/31/22
Paper Products Mfr
N.A.I.C.S.: 322120
Le Ba Phuong *(Exec Dir)*

**DONG IL STEEL MFG CO.,
LTD.**
446-2 Yangbyeon-ri, Miyang-myeon,
Anseong, Gyeonggi, Korea (South)
Tel.: (82) 316771234
Web Site: https://www.dongil-
  steel.com
Year Founded: 1959
002690—(KRS)
Rev.: $150,913,091
Assets: $137,836,588
Liabilities: $16,895,666
Net Worth: $120,940,921
Earnings: $2,565,729
Emp.: 136
Fiscal Year-end: 12/31/22
Steel Products Mfr
N.A.I.C.S.: 331110
Park Sungjun *(Dir)*

**DONG NAI PAINT CORPORA-
TION**

Dong Nai Paint Corporation—(Continued)

Road 7 Bien Hoa 1 Industrial Zone,
Bien Hoa, Dong Nai, Vietnam
Tel.: (84) 2513836112
Web Site:
https://www.dongnaipaint.com.vn
Year Founded: 1987
SDN—(HNX)
Rev.: $4,770,090
Assets: $2,894,709
Liabilities: $958,494
Net Worth: $1,936,215
Earnings: $521,124
Fiscal Year-end: 12/31/21
Paint Product Mfr
N.A.I.C.S.: 325510

DONG NAI PORT
1B-D3 Binh Duong Neighbourhood,
Long Binh Tan Ward, Bien Hoa, Dong
Nai, Vietnam
Tel.: (84) 613832225
Web Site: http://www.dongnai-
port.com
Sales Range: $25-49.9 Million
Emp.: 250
Port Operation Services
N.A.I.C.S.: 488310
Sam Van Do (Deputy Gen Dir)

Subsidiaries:

Dong Nai Maritime Services Joint
Stock Company   (1)
Go Dau B Port Go Dau Industrial Zone,
Phuoc Thai, Bien Hoa, Dong Nai, Vietnam
Tel.: (84) 613543857
Marine Shipping Services
N.A.I.C.S.: 488510

DONG NAI ROOFSHEET & CONSTRUCTION MATERIAL JOINT STOCK COMPANY
Duong so 4 KCN Bien Hoa I, Dong
Nai, Vietnam
Tel.: (84) 61 3 836130
Web Site: http://www.donac.net
Sales Range: $10-24.9 Million
Roofsheet & Construction Material
Mfr
N.A.I.C.S.: 327120
Nguyen Cong Ly (Exec Dir)

DONG PHU RUBBER JOINT STOCK COMPANY
Thuan Phu, Dong Phu Dist, Ho Chi
Minh City, Binh Phuoc, Vietnam
Tel.: (84) 2713819786
Web Site: https://www.doruco.com.vn
DPR—(HOSE)
Rev.: $42,894,226
Assets: $175,440,188
Liabilities: $49,601,463
Net Worth: $125,838,726
Earnings: $10,469,126
Fiscal Year-end: 12/31/23
Rubber Products Mfr
N.A.I.C.S.: 326299
Thanh Hai Nguyen (Dir Gen)

DONG SUH COMPANIES INC.
Dongsuh Building 324 Dokmak-ro,
Mapo-gu, Seoul, Korea (South)
Tel.: (82) 27015050   KR
Web Site: http://www.dongsuh.com
Year Founded: 1975
Sales Range: $200-249.9 Million
Emp.: 250
Packaged Material & Food Distr
N.A.I.C.S.: 493120
Jong Won Kim (Pres)

DONG SUNG PHARMACEUTI-CAL COMPANY LTD.
683 Dobong-ro, Dobong-gu, 01340,
Seoul, 01340, Korea (South)
Tel.: (82) 269113600

Web Site: https://dongsung-
pharm.com
Year Founded: 1957
002210—(KRS)
Rev.: $71,582,725
Assets: $82,607,481
Liabilities: $49,772,776
Net Worth: $32,834,705
Earnings: ($1,627,321)
Emp.: 338
Fiscal Year-end: 12/31/22
Pharmaceutical Product Mfr & Distr
N.A.I.C.S.: 325412
Yang Gu Lee (CEO)

Subsidiaries:

Dong Sung Pharmaceutical Company
Ltd. - Asan Factory   (1)
31411 45 Gwandaean-gil, Dunpo-myeon,
Asan, Chungnam, Korea (South)
Tel.: (82) 414205400
Pharmaceuticals Product Mfr
N.A.I.C.S.: 325412

DONG WHA PHARM CO., LTD.
6-8F FastFive Tower 24
Namdaemun-ro 9-gil, Jung-gu, Seoul,
04522, Korea (South)
Tel.: (82) 220219300   KR
Web Site: https://www.dong-
wha.co.kr
Year Founded: 1897
000020—(KRS)
Rev.: $261,106,993
Assets: $353,691,664
Liabilities: $63,249,281
Net Worth: $290,442,383
Earnings: $16,560,459
Emp.: 797
Fiscal Year-end: 12/31/22
Pharmaceutical Product Mfr & Sup-
plier
N.A.I.C.S.: 325412
Doh Joon Yoon (Chm)

Subsidiaries:

Dong Wha G&P Corporation   (1)
305 Okepmgpmgeop-gil, Uiwang-si, 16072,
Ansan, Gyeonggi-Do, Korea (South)
Tel.: (82) 314292176
Web Site: http://www.dong-wha.co.kr
Glass Container Mfr
N.A.I.C.S.: 327213

Medyssey Co Ltd   (1)
129 Hanbang expo-ro, Jecheon, 27116,
Chungcheongbuk-do, Korea
(South)   (59.95%)
Tel.: (82) 437161014
Web Site: https://www.medyssey.co.kr
Surgical Instrument Mfr & Distr
N.A.I.C.S.: 339112

Subsidiary (US):

Medyssey USA, Inc.   (2)
1550 E Higgins Rd Ste 123, Elk Grove Vil-
lage, IL 60077
Tel.: (847) 427-0200
Web Site: http://www.medyssey.com
Orthopaedic Implant Distr
N.A.I.C.S.: 423450

DONG WON FISHERIES CO., LTD.
38 Dongmak-ro 8-gil, Mapo-gu,
Seoul, Korea (South)
Tel.: (82) 25288000
Web Site:
https://www.dongwonfish.co.kr
Year Founded: 1970
030720—(KRS)
Rev.: $135,788,791
Assets: $93,412,625
Liabilities: $45,418,918
Net Worth: $47,993,708
Earnings: $4,652,616
Emp.: 206
Fiscal Year-end: 12/31/22
Deep Sea Fishing Services

N.A.I.C.S.: 114111
Wang Jr Ki Yong (Co-CEO)

Subsidiaries:

YK Food Service Co., Ltd.   (1)
6th floor Dongju Building 8 Teheran- ro 8-
gil, Gangnam-gu, Seoul, Korea (South)
Tel.: (82) 15220147
Web Site: https://www.hottomotto.co.kr
Food Service
N.A.I.C.S.: 722310

You Wang Co., Ltd.   (1)
10 Eulsukdo-daero 677beon-gil, Saha-gu,
Busan, Korea (South)
Tel.: (82) 512026622
Web Site: https://www.youwang.co.kr
Seafood Product Mfr
N.A.I.C.S.: 311710

DONG YANG S.TEC CO., LTD.
20 Jungang-ro 164beon-gil, Jung-gu,
Daejeon, Korea (South)
Tel.: (82) 422216900
Web Site: https://www.dystec.co.kr
Year Founded: 1981
060380—(KRS)
Rev.: $178,295,958
Assets: $110,061,650
Liabilities: $48,497,610
Net Worth: $61,564,040
Earnings: $3,810,890
Emp.: 137
Fiscal Year-end: 12/31/22
Rolled Steel Products Mfr
N.A.I.C.S.: 331221
Nam-Wook Cho (CEO)

DONG YANG STEEL PIPE CO., LTD.
515 Pungse-ro Pungse-myeon,
Dongnam-gu, Cheonan, Chun-
gcheong nam-do, Korea (South)
Tel.: (82) 415785511
Web Site: https://www.dysp.co.kr
Year Founded: 1973
008970—(KRS)
Rev.: $204,153,678
Assets: $139,972,945
Liabilities: $72,508,706
Net Worth: $67,464,239
Earnings: $3,045,928
Emp.: 166
Fiscal Year-end: 12/31/22
Steel Pole Mfr
N.A.I.C.S.: 331210

Subsidiaries:

Dong Yang Steel Pipe Co., Ltd. -
Chungju Factory   (1)
403 Chungjuhosu-ro, Chungju,
Chungcheongbuk-do, Korea (South)
Tel.: (82) 438533131
Wall Pipe Mfr
N.A.I.C.S.: 331210

DONG YI RI SHENG HOME DECORATION GROUP COM-PANY LIMITED
West Side Fangyi Road, Changgou
Town Fangshan District, Beijing,
100015, China
Tel.: (86) 1058637710
Web Site: http://www.dyrs.com.cn
Year Founded: 1996
002713—(SSE)
Rev.: $354,372,408
Assets: $453,477,960
Liabilities: $412,999,236
Net Worth: $40,478,724
Earnings: ($105,451,632)
Emp.: 3,700
Fiscal Year-end: 12/31/21
Architecture Decoration Engineering
& Interior Design Services
N.A.I.C.S.: 337212
Hui Chen (Chm, Fin Dir & Gen Mgr)

DONG-A HWASUNG CO., LTD.
154-9 Yuha-ro, Gimhae, Gyungnam,
Korea (South)
Tel.: (82) 553131800
Web Site: https://www.dacm.com
Year Founded: 1974
041930—(KRS)
Rev.: $268,173,183
Assets: $212,261,031
Liabilities: $103,364,668
Net Worth: $108,896,363
Earnings: $11,790,988
Emp.: 317
Fiscal Year end: 12/31/22
Rubber Products Mfr
N.A.I.C.S.: 326299
Kyung-sik Lim (Chm & CEO)

Subsidiaries:

D.A RUS, LLC   (1)
LLC House no 9 Solntseva Ruza, Ruza,
143100, Moscow, Russia
Tel.: (7) 4957851391
Rubber Products Mfr
N.A.I.C.S.: 326299

DONG-A HWA SUNG TECHNOLO-
GY(WUXI) CO., LTD.   (1)
AQU - 45 Jingjiyuan Nanzhan, Huangtu
Zhen, Wuxi, 214 445, Jiangsu, China
Tel.: (86) 51082124986
Rubber Products Mfr
N.A.I.C.S.: 326299

DONG-A INDIA AUTOMOTIVE PVT.
LTD.   (1)
New 55 Thandalam Village NH4 Madras-
Bangalore High Way, Sriperumbudur,
Kanchipuram, 602 105, India
Tel.: (91) 4427156354
Rubber Products Mfr
N.A.I.C.S.: 326299
Vijay Kanna (Mgr-Bus Dev)

DONG-A POLAND Sp.z o.o   (1)
ul Wroclawska 73, Sroda Slaska, 55-300,
Wroclaw, Poland
Tel.: (48) 511417663
Rubber Products Mfr
N.A.I.C.S.: 326299

DONGA HWASUNG MEXICO, S.A.
DE C.V.   (1)
Av De La Construction Lote 10 Santa Rosa
Manzana M - 3, Amolacion Parque Indus-
trial Queretaro 1A, 76220, Queretaro,
Mexico
Tel.: (52) 4423851690
Rubber Products Mfr
N.A.I.C.S.: 326299

DONG-A SOCIO HOLDINGS CO., LTD.
64 Cheonhodaero, Dongdaemun-gu,
Seoul, Korea (South)
Tel.: (82) 29208114
Web Site: https://www.donga.co.kr
Year Founded: 1932
000640—(KRS)
Rev.: $778,398,309
Assets: $1,328,023,736
Liabilities: $562,050,910
Net Worth: $765,972,826
Earnings: $6,009,595
Emp.: 90
Fiscal Year-end: 12/31/22
Pharmaceutical Products Mfr & Sales
N.A.I.C.S.: 325412
Jae-Hun Jung (CEO)

Subsidiaries:

DA INFORMATION CO., LTD.   (1)
7th floor Dongjin Hall 3 Cheonho- daero,
Dongdaemun-gu, Seoul, Gyeonggi-do, Ko-
rea (South)
Tel.: (82) 7086363800
Web Site: https://www.dainform.co.kr
Pharmaceutical Information Technology
Consulting Services
N.A.I.C.S.: 541512

DONG-A AMERICA CORP   (1)

17215 Studebaker Rd Ste 335, Cerritos, CA 90703
Tel.: (562) 860-3153
Web Site: http://en.donga.co.kr
Sales Range: $50-74.9 Million
Emp.: 1
Healthcare Product Distr
N.A.I.C.S.: 424210

Dong-A ST Co., Ltd.   **(1)**
64 Cheonhodaero, Dongdaemun-gu, Seoul, Korea (South)
Tel.: (82) 29208111
Web Site: https://www.donga-st.com
Rev.: $487,346,188
Assets: $887,075,024
Liabilities: $358,659,885
Net Worth: $529,315,139
Earnings: $9,795,582
Emp.: 1,653
Fiscal Year-end: 12/31/2022
Pharmaceutical Product Mfr & Distr
N.A.I.C.S.: 325412
Eom Dae-Sik *(CEO)*

KOREA SHINTO CO., LTD.   **(1)**
434-5 Moknae-dong, Danwon-gu, Ansan, Gyeonggi-do, Korea (South)
Tel.: (82) 31 491 8121
Web Site: http://en.donga.co.kr
Industrial Machinery Mfr
N.A.I.C.S.: 333248

SOOSEOK CO., LTD.   **(1)**
313 Bakdal - ro, Manan-gu, Anyang, Gyeonggi-do, Korea (South)
Tel.: (82) 314496151
Glass Container Mfr
N.A.I.C.S.: 327213

ST Pharm Co., Ltd.   **(1)**
7F I Park Tower Bldg Yeongdongdae-ro 520, Gangnam-gu, Seoul, 06170, Korea (South)   **(33%)**
Tel.: (82) 25276300
Web Site: https://www.stpharm.co.kr
Sales Range: $50-74.9 Million
Emp.: 20
Pharmaceutical Ingredient Mfr
N.A.I.C.S.: 325412

Yongma Logis Co., Ltd.   **(1)**
249-9 Yongdu-dong Dongdaemun-gu, Seoul, Korea (South)
Tel.: (82) 2 3290 6400
Web Site: http://www.yongmalogis.co.kr
Emp.: 400
Warehousing & Logistics Services
N.A.I.C.S.: 493110
Yong-Rok Kim *(Mng Partner-Transportation Consultation)*

DONG-EE-JIAO CO., LTD.
No 78 E-Jiao Street, Dong-E County, Liaocheng, 252201, Shandong, China
Tel.: (86) 6353260887
Web Site:
https://www.dongeejiao.com
Year Founded: 1952
000423—(SSE)
Rev.: $567,471,528
Assets: $1,773,445,752
Liabilities: $320,194,836
Net Worth: $1,453,250,916
Earnings: $109,512,000
Fiscal Year-end: 12/31/22
Pharmaceuticals Product Mfr
N.A.I.C.S.: 325412
Cheng Jie *(Pres & Sec-Party)*

DONGAH GEOLOGICAL ENGI-NEERING CO., LTD.
347 Geumsaem-ro, Geumjeong-gu, Busan, 46235, Korea (South)
Tel.: (82) 515805500
Web Site: https://www.dage.co.kr
Year Founded: 1971
028100—(KRS)
Rev.: $204,238,892
Assets: $285,539,799
Liabilities: $115,542,592
Net Worth: $169,997,207
Earnings: ($17,510,482)
Emp.: 293
Fiscal Year-end: 12/31/22

Construction Engineering Services
N.A.I.C.S.: 541330
Jung-Woo Lee *(Founder, Chm & CEO)*

Subsidiaries:

Dong-Ah Geological Engineering Company Limited   **(1)**
1st Floor A1 House 43-45 Alley 130 Doc Ngu, Ba Dinh District, Hanoi, Vietnam
Tel.: (84) 437263620
Construction Services
N.A.I.C.S.: 236220

DongAh Geological Engineering Co., Ltd. - EUMSEONG PLANT   **(1)**
669 Gagok-ro Munchon-ri Gamgok-myeon, Eumseong, Chungcheongbuk-do, Korea (South)
Tel.: (82) 438820283
Geological Surveying Equipment Mfr
N.A.I.C.S.: 333248

Dongah Geological Engineering India Private Ltd.   **(1)**
329 3rd Floor Tower-B Spazedge Sector-47 Gurgaon-Sohna Road, Gurgaon, 122 018, Haryana, India
Tel.: (91) 1244816748
Sales Range: $25-49.9 Million
Emp.: 6
Geological Engineering Services
N.A.I.C.S.: 541330
Deepak Gupta *(Mgr)*

DONGBANG AGRO CORP.
Dongbang Building 2028 Nambusunhwan-ro, Gwanak-gu, Seoul, 8804, Korea (South)
Tel.: (82) 16447337
Web Site:
https://www.dongbangagro.co.kr
Year Founded: 1971
007590—(KRS)
Rev.: $112,536,425
Assets: $166,076,999
Liabilities: $50,395,597
Net Worth: $115,681,401
Emp.: 238
Fiscal Year-end: 12/31/22
Agricultural Product Mfr
N.A.I.C.S.: 325320
Tae-Geun Yeom *(Chm & CEO)*

DONGBANG SHIP MACHIN-ERY CO., LTD.
No 414-2 Jukgok-Dong, Jinhae-gu, Changwon, Gyeongsangnam-do, Korea (South)
Tel.: (82) 555450882
Web Site:
http://www.dongbangsm.co.kr
Year Founded: 1994
099410—(KRS)
Rev.: $19,067,495
Assets: $33,989,778
Liabilities: $10,752,186
Net Worth: $23,237,592
Earnings: $981,982
Emp.: 43
Fiscal Year-end: 12/31/22
Ship Equipment Mfr
N.A.I.C.S.: 339999
Kim Seong Uk *(CEO)*

DONGBU GROUP
Dongbu Financial Center 891-10 Daechi-dong, Gangnam-gu, Seoul, 135-523, Korea (South)
Tel.: (82) 2 1588 0100
Web Site: http://www.dongbu.com
Year Founded: 1969
Sales Range: $25-49.9 Billion
Emp.: 37,000
Holding Company
N.A.I.C.S.: 551112
Jun-ki Kim *(Founder, Chm & CEO)*

Subsidiaries:

Agriculture Technology Research Institute   **(1)**
175-1 Botong-ri Jeongnam-myun, Hwasung-gun, Suwon, Korea (South)
Tel.: (82) 31 354 6810
Agricultural Research Services
N.A.I.C.S.: 541715

Breeding Research Institute   **(1)**
481-3 Deogbong-ri, Yangseong-myun An-sung City, Suwon, Korea (South)
Tel.: (82) 3167469115
Web Site: http://www.dongbuchem.com
Sales Range: $25-49.9 Million
Emp.: 50
Breeding Research Services
N.A.I.C.S.: 541715

DB Insurance Co., Ltd.   **(1)**
432 Teheran-Ro Deachi-Dong, Gangnam-gu, Seoul, 06194, Korea (South)
Tel.: (82) 230113163
Rev.: $14,696,069,552
Assets: $44,564,841,672
Liabilities: $36,916,913,831
Net Worth: $7,647,927,841
Earnings: $1,290,447,976
Emp.: 4,697
Fiscal Year-end: 12/31/2023
Insurance Services
N.A.I.C.S.: 524113
Jong Pyo Jeong *(Pres & CEO)*

Subsidiary (Domestic):

Dongbu Life Insurance Co., Ltd.   **(2)**
7F Dongbu Financial Center 891-10 Deachi-dong, Kangnam-gu, Seoul, 135-523, Korea (South)   **(39.49%)**
Tel.: (82) 2 1588 4028
Web Site: http://www.dongbulife.com
Sales Range: $550-599.9 Million
Emp.: 300
Life Insurance Products & Services
N.A.I.C.S.: 524113

Daewoo Electronics Corporation   **(1)**
1-dong-dong 1-2 Eastern Daewoo Electronics, Jung-gu, Seoul, 121709, Korea (South)
Tel.: (82) 23607114
Web Site: http://www.dwe.co.kr
Sales Range: $1-4.9 Billion
Emp.: 8,600
Television Sets, Microwave Ovens, Refrigerators, Air Conditioners, Vacuum Cleaners, Personal Computers & Peripherals Mfr, Distr & Sales
N.A.I.C.S.: 333415

Subsidiary (Non-US):

Daewoo Electronics (M) Sdn. Bhd.   **(2)**
Lot 8 Sungai Petani Industrial Estate, Sungai Petani, 81000, Kedah Darul Aman, Malaysia
Tel.: (60) 44416216
Web Site: http://www.dongbudaewoo.com
Sales Range: $25-49.9 Million
Emp.: 30
Electronic Products Mfr & Sales
N.A.I.C.S.: 334310
Yoo Youngjae *(Mng Dir)*

Daewoo Electronics (Panama) S.A.   **(2)**
Via Espana y Calle Elvira Mendez Torre Bank Boston Piso 19, Apartado 0816-01094 Zona 5, Panama, Panama
Tel.: (507) 3052000
Web Site: http://www.decpanama.com
Electronic Products Mfr & Sales
N.A.I.C.S.: 334310
Tae Hee Lim *(Pres)*

Subsidiary (US):

Daewoo Electronics America, Inc.   **(2)**
120 Chubb Ave, Lyndhurst, NJ 07071
Tel.: (201) 460-2000
Web Site: http://www.e-daewoo.com
Electronic Products Mfr & Sales
N.A.I.C.S.: 334310

Subsidiary (Non-US):

Daewoo Electronics Europe GmbH   **(2)**

Otto-Hahn-Strasse 21, D-35510, Butzbach, Germany
Tel.: (49) 603396910
Web Site: http://www.daewoo-electronics.com
Sales Range: $50-74.9 Million
Emp.: 60
Electronic Products Mfr & Sales
N.A.I.C.S.: 334310

Subsidiary (Non-US):

DAEWOO Electronics Deme Fze.   **(3)**
Akademika Kapitsy Street 34/121, 117647, Moscow, Russia
Tel.: (7) 0957452018
Web Site: http://www.dwec.ru
Electronic Products Distr & Sales
N.A.I.C.S.: 423690

Daewoo Electronics Manufacturing Poland Sp. z o.o.   **(3)**
Ul Bokserska 66, 02-690, Warsaw, Poland
Tel.: (48) 224550900
Web Site: http://www.d-e.pl
Electronic Products Mfr, Distr & Sales
N.A.I.C.S.: 423690

Daewoo Electronics S.A.   **(3)**
Paris Nord II 277 rue de la Belle Etoile, BP 50068, 95947, Roissy-en-France, CDG, France
Tel.: (33) 141599200
Web Site: http://www.daewoo.fr
Electronic Products Distr & Sales
N.A.I.C.S.: 423690

Daewoo Electronics Sales UK Ltd.   **(3)**
640 Wharfedale Road, Winnersh Triangle, Wokingham, RG41 5TP, Berks, United Kingdom
Tel.: (44) 1189252500
Web Site: http://www.daewoo-electronics.co.uk
Sales Range: $50-74.9 Million
Emp.: 20
Electronic Products Distr & Sales
N.A.I.C.S.: 423690
S. Chae *(Mng Dir)*

Subsidiary (Non-US):

Daewoo Electronics Middle East FZE Ltd.   **(2)**
Jabal Ali Free Zone Between 8 & 12, PO Box 61163, Dubai, United Arab Emirates
Tel.: (971) 48838349
Web Site: http://www.dwe.co.kr
Sales Range: $25-49.9 Million
Emp.: 22
Electronic Product Distr
N.A.I.C.S.: 423690
Kw Lee *(Gen Mgr)*

Daewoo Electronics Sales U.K. Limited   **(2)**
640 Wharfedale Road Winnersh Triangle, Wokingham, RG41 5TP, Berkshire, United Kingdom
Tel.: (44) 118 9252 500
Web Site:
http://www.daewooelectronics.co.uk
Emp.: 22
Electronic Products Mfr
N.A.I.C.S.: 334310
C. S. Park *(Mng Dir)*

Dongbu Daewoo Electronics Japan Co., Ltd.   **(2)**
7F Akihabara Shinkou Daiichi Seimei B/L, 1-2 Ueno 3-chome Taito-ku, Tokyo, 110-0005, Japan
Tel.: (81) 3 3836 2764
Web Site:
http://www.dongbudaewooelec.com
Electronic Product Distr
N.A.I.C.S.: 423690
Jingyun Choi *(Vice Chm & CEO)*

Dongbu Asset Management Co., Ltd.   **(1)**
Dongbu Securities Building 36-5 Youido-dong, Youngdungpo-gu, Seoul, Korea (South)
Tel.: (82) 27873700
Web Site: http://www.dongbuam.co.kr
Rev.: $1,069,000,000

Dongbu Group—(Continued)

Emp.: 47
Investment Management Service
N.A.I.C.S.: 523999

Dongbu Capital Co., Ltd. (1)
6F Dongbu Da-dong Bldg 103 Da-dong,
Chung-gu, Seoul 100-180, Korea (South)
Tel.: (82) 2 2264 7000
Web Site: http://www.dongbucapital.co.kr
Sales Range: $10-24.9 Million
Commercial Capital Funding Services
N.A.I.C.S.: 522390

Dongbu Corporation (1)
Dongbu Financial Center Building, 890-10
Daechi-dong Gangnam-gu, Seoul, 135-523,
Korea (South)
Tel.: (82) 234842114
Web Site: http://www.dongbu.co.kr
Sales Range: $1-4.9 Billion
Emp.: 1,700
Construction & Engineering Services
N.A.I.C.S.: 541330

Division (Domestic):

Dongbu Corp - Construction (2)
Dongbu Financial Center Building 890-10
Daechi-dong, Gangnam-gu, Seoul (South)
Tel.: (82) 234842114
Web Site: http://dbcon.dongbu.co.kr
Business Support Services
N.A.I.C.S.: 561499

Dongbu Corp - Logistics (2)
Dongbu Financial Center Building 890-10
Daechi-dong, Gangnam-gu, Seoul (South)
Tel.: (82) 234842624
Web Site: http://www.dongbulogis.co.kr
Business Support Services
N.A.I.C.S.: 541614

Dongbu Engineering Co., Ltd . (1)
4 Jung Gu Inheyun Pong 2nd Ga, 73/1
Pung Jeon Bldg 5th Fl, Seoul, 140709, Ko-
rea (South)
Tel.: (82) 221226700
Web Site: http://www.dbeng.co.kr
Sales Range: $75-99.9 Million
Emp.: 500
Engineering Contractor & Consulting Ser-
vices
N.A.I.C.S.: 541330

Dongbu Fine Chemical Co., Ltd. (1)
Dongbu Financial Center Building, 890-10
Daechi-dong Gangnam-gu, Seoul, 135-523,
Korea (South)
Tel.: (82) 234841600
Web Site:
http://www.dongbufinechemical.com
Sales Range: $150-199.9 Million
Emp.: 300
Pesticide Raw Materials, Adhesives, Pesti-
cides, Information & Communications Mate-
rial Mfr
N.A.I.C.S.: 325998

Dongbu HiTek Co., Ltd. (1)
Dongbu Financial Center Building 891-10 Daechi-
dong, Gangnam-gu, Seoul, 135523, Korea
(South)
Tel.: (82) 234842863
Web Site: http://www.dongbuhitek.com
Sales Range: $250-299.9 Million
Emp.: 1,800
Semiconductor Material Mfr
N.A.I.C.S.: 334413

Plant (Domestic):

Dongbu HiTek Fabrication 1 (2)
90 Soodo-ro Wonmi-gu, Bucheon, Gyeo-
nggi, Korea (South) (100%)
Tel.: (82) 32 680 4116
Web Site: http://www.dongbuhitek.com
Wafer Fabrication & Chip Mfr
N.A.I.C.S.: 541512

Dongbu HiTek Fabrication 2 (2)
Sangwooan-gil Gamgok-myeon, Eumseong,
Chungcheongbuk, Korea (South) (100%)
Tel.: (82) 43 879 5175
Web Site: http://www.dongbuhitek.co.kr
Wafer Fabrication, Flash Memory & Chip
Mfr
N.A.I.C.S.: 334419

Dongbu Inc. (1)
24F Dongbu Financial Center 891-10,
Daechi-Dong Gangnam-gu, Seoul, Korea
(South)
Tel.: (82) 2 3011 5537
Information Technology Consulting Services
N.A.I.C.S.: 541512
Chang Hwan Kim *(Sr Mgr)*

Dongbu Metal Co., Ltd. (1)
Dongbu Financial Center 432 Teheran-ro,
Gangnam-gu, Seoul, Korea (South)
Tel.: (82) 2 3484 1800
Web Site: http://www.dongbumetal.co.kr
Steel & Metal Product Distr
N.A.I.C.S.: 423510
Jeremy Choi *(Mgr-Sls)*

Dongbu Organic Foods (1)
5F Dongbu Financial Center 891-10
Daechi-Dong, Gangnam-gu, Seoul, Korea
(South)
Tel.: (82) 2 3484 1500
Organic Food Services
N.A.I.C.S.: 325311

Dongbu Savings Bank Co., Ltd. (1)
Dongbu Da-dong Bldg, 103 Da-dong,
Seoul, Korea (South)
Tel.: (82) 237051700
Sales Range: $25-49.9 Million
Emp.: 103
Banking Services
N.A.I.C.S.: 522110

Dongbu Solar Co., Ltd. (1)
92BL1112 Lot Gojan-dong, Namdong-gu,
Incheon, 135523, Korea (South)
Tel.: (82) 3 2720 1000
Engineeering Services
N.A.I.C.S.: 541330

Dongbu Steel Co.,Ltd. (1)
891-10 Daechi-dong, Gangnam-gu, Seoul,
Korea (South)
Tel.: (82) 234508114
Web Site: http://www.edongbusteel.com
Sales Range: $1-4.9 Billion
Emp.: 2,000
Steel Products Mfg
N.A.I.C.S.: 331110

Dongbu Technology Institute (1)
103-2 Munji-dong, Yuseong-gu, Daejeon,
Korea (South)
Tel.: (82) 428668019
Web Site: http://www.dongbuchem.com
Sales Range: $25-49.9 Million
Emp.: 100
Business Support Services
N.A.I.C.S.: 561499

Hyulim ROBOT Co., Ltd. (1)
27 4 Sandan 6 Gil, Jiksan-eup, Cheonan,
Chungcheongnam-do, Korea (South)
Tel.: (82) 415901700
Web Site: http://www.dstrobot.com
Rev.: $42,548,836
Assets: $87,809,384
Liabilities: $25,719,950
Net Worth: $62,089,433
Earnings: ($9,157,320)
Emp.: 98
Fiscal Year-end: 12/31/2022
Robot Mfr
N.A.I.C.S.: 333248
Yeong Seok Son *(CEO)*

**DONGBUKA NO 12 SHIP IN-
VESTMENT CO., LTD.**
40 Munhyeongeumyung-ro, Nam-gu,
Busan, Korea (South)
Tel.: (82) 25901400
83370—(KRS)
Rev.: $453,782
Assets: $6,975,173
Liabilities: $153,989
Net Worth: $6,821,185
Earnings: $409,100
Fiscal Year-end: 12/31/19
Investment Management Service
N.A.I.C.S.: 525990
Sung-Mu Cheon *(CEO)*

**DONGBUKA NO.13 SHIP IN-
VESTMENT CO., LTD.**

40 Munhyeongeumyung-ro, Nam-gu,
Busan, Korea (South)
Tel.: (82) 25901400
Investment Management Service
N.A.I.C.S.: 525990
Sung-Mu Cheon *(CEO)*

**DONGFANG ELECTRIC COR-
PORATION LIMITED**
18 Xixin Avenue, High-tech Zone
West Park, Chengdu, 611731, Sich-
uan, China
Tel.: (86) 2887898609
Web Site:
https://www.dongfang.com.cn
600875—(SHG)
Rev.: $7,771,580,870
Assets: $16,183,214,494
Liabilities: $10,760,282,536
Net Worth: $5,422,931,959
Earnings: $400,792,944
Emp.: 17,463
Fiscal Year-end: 12/31/22
Electric Power Generating Equipment
Mfr
N.A.I.C.S.: 333611
Lei Zou *(Chm)*

Subsidiaries:

Dongfang Electric (Wuhan) Nuclear (1)
Equipement Co., Ltd.
No 8 Yangguang Ave Miaoshan Econom,
Wuhan, 430223, China
Tel.: (86) 2751827448
Power Equipment Mfr
N.A.I.C.S.: 333611

**DONGFANG ELECTRONICS
CO., LTD.**
2 JiChang Road, Yantai, 264001,
Shandong, China
Tel.: (86) 5355520916
Web Site: https://www.dongfang-
china.com
Year Founded: 1957
000682—(SSE)
Rev.: $766,619,100
Assets: $1,342,746,288
Liabilities: $702,200,772
Net Worth: $640,545,516
Earnings: $61,555,572
Emp.: 8,300
Fiscal Year-end: 12/31/22
Automatic Controlling System Mfr
N.A.I.C.S.: 334512
Fang Zhengji *(Chm)*

**DONGFENG ELECTRONIC
TECHNOLOGY CO., LTD.**
22F No 2000 Zhongshan North Road,
Shanghai, 200063, China
Tel.: (86) 2162033003
Web Site: http://www.detc.com.cn
Year Founded: 1997
600081—(SHG)
Rev.: $961,785,560
Assets: $1,251,766,007
Liabilities: $675,316,432
Net Worth: $576,449,574
Earnings: $15,265,299
Emp.: 14,000
Fiscal Year-end: 12/31/22
Automobile Parts Mfr & Distr
N.A.I.C.S.: 336390
Cai Shilong *(Chm)*

**DONGFENG MOTOR CORPO-
RATION**
1 Dongfeng Road, Wuhan, 430056,
Hubei, China
Tel.: (86) 2784285555
Web Site: https://www.dongfeng-
global.com
Year Founded: 1969
Sales Range: $5-14.9 Billion
Emp.: 121,000

Automobile Mfr
N.A.I.C.S.: 336110
Yanfeng Zhu *(CEO)*

Subsidiaries:

Dongfeng Automobile Co,, Ltd. (1)
Block 3 Jinfeng Road Dongfeng Moto Av-
enue Hi-tech Zone, Xiangyang, 430056,
Hubei, China
Tel.: (86) 2784287988
Web Site: http://www.dfac.com
Rev.: $1,711,474,919
Assets: $2,483,125,197
Liabilities: $1,292,301,523
Net Worth: $1,100,823,674
Earnings: $40,025,794
Fiscal Year-end: 12/31/2022
Light Duty Commercial Vehicles Mfr &
Sales
N.A.I.C.S.: 336110
Zhou Xianpeng *(Chm)*

Dongfeng Electric Vehicle Co., (1)
Ltd.
No 108 Dongfeng Ave Wuhan Economic
and Technological Development Zone, Wu-
han, 430056, Hubei, China
Tel.: (86) 27 84289808
Web Site: http://www.dfev.com.cn
Automobile Mfr & Distr
N.A.I.C.S.: 336110

Dongfeng Motor Group Co. Ltd. (1)
No 1 Dongfeng Avenue Wuhan Economic
and Technological Development Zone, Spe-
cial No 1 Dongfeng Road, Wuhan, 430056,
Hubei, China (66.86%)
Tel.: (86) 2784285002
Web Site: https://www.dfmg.com.cn
Rev.: $13,750,969,207
Assets: $45,785,057,599
Liabilities: $23,685,893,886
Net Worth: $22,099,163,713
Earnings: ($943,315,241)
Emp.: 112,706
Fiscal Year-end: 12/31/2023
Commercial Vehicles, Passenger Cars &
Automotive Components Mfr
N.A.I.C.S.: 336110
Qing Yang *(Chm & VP)*

Joint Venture (Domestic):

Dongfeng Cummins Engine Co., (2)
Ltd.
Automobile Industry Development Zone,
Xiangcheng, 441004, China
Tel.: (86) 7103320888
Web Site: http://www.dfac.com
Sales Range: $500-549.9 Million
Emp.: 2,400
Engine Mfr
N.A.I.C.S.: 333618

Subsidiary (Domestic):

Dongfeng Iseki Agricultural Machinery (2)
(Hubei) Co., Ltd.
No 8 Xinguang Road, Hi-Tech Development
Zone, Xiangfan, 441000, China (75%)
Tel.: (86) 710 338 7579
Rice Transplanters Mfr
N.A.I.C.S.: 333111

Affiliate (Domestic):

Dongfeng Peugeot Citroen Automo- (2)
bile Company Ltd.
Wuhan Economic & Technological Develop-
ment Zone, 165 Shenlong Avenue, Wuhan,
China
Tel.: (86) 27 6885 2945
Web Site: http://www.dpca.com.cn
Automobile Mfr; Owned 50% by Dongfeng
Motor Group Co. Ltd. & 50% by PSA Peu-
geot Citroen S.A.
N.A.I.C.S.: 336110

**DONGFENG SCI-TECH GROUP
CO., LTD.**
Xiabancheng Town, Chengde,
067400, Hebei, China
Tel.: (86) 314 3115049
Sales Range: $10-24.9 Million
Emp.: 139

Chemical Product Mfr; Real Estate
Services
N.A.I.C.S.: 325998

DONGGUAN AOHAI TECH-
NOLOGY CO., LTD.

No 2 Yinyuan Street, Jiaoyitang District Tangxia Town, Dongguan,
523723, Guangdong, China
Tel.: (86) 76986975555
Web Site: https://www.aohai.com
Year Founded: 2012
002993—(SSE)
Rev.: $627,145,740
Assets: $990,562,716
Liabilities: $341,393,832
Net Worth: $649,168,884
Earnings: $61,450,272
Emp.: 7,000
Fiscal Year-end: 12/31/22
Electronic Product Mfr & Distr
N.A.I.C.S.: 334419
Hao Liu *(Chm & Gen Mgr)*

DONGGUAN CHITWING TECH-
NOLOGY CO LTD

No 166 Xinmin Road, Changan Town,
Dongguan, 523857, Guangdong,
China
Tel.: (86) 75525865177
Web Site: http://www.chitwing.com
Year Founded: 2007
002855—(SSE)
Rev.: $378,785,160
Assets: $365,726,556
Liabilities: $221,104,728
Net Worth: $144,621,828
Earnings: ($17,631,432)
Emp.: 5,000
Fiscal Year-end: 12/31/22
Precision Structural Parts Mfr & Distr
N.A.I.C.S.: 331110
Zhang Shouzhi *(Chm & Pres)*

DONGGUAN DEVELOPMENT
(HOLDINGS) CO., LTD.

38F Rail Transit Building, Nancheng
Subdistrict, Dongguan, 523073,
Guangdong, China
Tel.: (86) 76988999292
Web Site: http://www.dgholdings.cn
Year Founded: 1988
000828—(SSE)
Rev.: $576,198,792
Assets: $3,716,279,892
Liabilities: $1,669,795,452
Net Worth: $2,046,484,440
Earnings: $116,380,368
Fiscal Year-end: 12/31/22
Holding Company
N.A.I.C.S.: 551112
Wang Chong'en *(Chm)*

DONGGUAN DINGTONG PRE-
CISION METAL CO., LTD.

No 7 Yinzhu Road Zhouwu Community, Dongcheng, Dongguan, 523118,
Guangdong, China
Tel.: (86) 76985377166
Web Site: http://www.dingtong.net.cn
Year Founded: 2003
688668—(SHG)
Rev.: $117,812,195
Assets: $283,179,626
Liabilities: $40,124,060
Net Worth: $243,055,566
Earnings: $23,652,753
Fiscal Year-end: 12/31/22
Electronic Product Mfr & Distr
N.A.I.C.S.: 334419
Chenghai Wang *(Chm & Gen Mgr)*

DONGGUAN EONTEC CO.,
LTD.

Yinquan Industrial District, Qingxi,
Dongguan, 523662, Guangdong,
China
Tel.: (86) 76987737777
Web Site: https://www.e-ande.com
Year Founded: 1993
300328—(CHIN)
Rev.: $226,884,996
Assets: $392,378,688
Liabilities: $218,553,660
Net Worth: $173,825,028
Earnings: $457,704
Fiscal Year-end: 12/31/22
Aluminum & Magnesium Alloy Die
Castings
N.A.I.C.S.: 331523
Liu Shoujun *(Chm)*

DONGGUAN GOLDEN SUN
ABRASIVES CO., LTD.

No 1 Dahuan Road, Dalingshan,
Dongguan, 523821, Guangdong,
China
Tel.: (86) 76938823020
Web Site:
 https://www.chinagoldensun.cn
Year Founded: 2004
300606—(CHIN)
Rev.: $79,600,011
Assets: $155,760,705
Liabilities: $56,401,777
Net Worth: $99,358,928
Earnings: $7,371,202
Fiscal Year-end: 12/31/23
Abrasive Product Mfr & Distr
N.A.I.C.S.: 327910
Ding Fulin *(CFO)*

DONGGUAN KINGSUN OPTO-
ELECTRONIC CO., LTD.

Hengjiangxia Administration Zone,
Changping Town, Dongguan, 523565,
Guangdong, China
Tel.: (86) 76983395678
Web Site:
 https://www.kingsunlights.com
002638—(SSE)
Rev.: $79,636,284
Assets: $420,832,152
Liabilities: $33,665,112
Net Worth: $387,167,040
Earnings: $6,098,976
Emp.: 3,000
Fiscal Year-end: 12/31/22
LED Street Lighting Mfr
N.A.I.C.S.: 335132

DONGGUAN LIESHENG ELEC-
TRONIC TECHNOLOGY CO.,
LTD.

Hongtu Road, Dongguan, 523000,
Guangdong, China
Tel.: (86) 15622993430   CN
Year Founded: 2015
Consumer Electronics Mfr
N.A.I.C.S.: 423690
Hao Ma *(Chm)*

DONGGUAN MENTECH OPTI-
CAL & MAGNETIC CO., LTD.

Building 1 No 157 Dongyuan Avenue,
Shipai Town, Dongguan, 523330,
Guangdong, China
Tel.: (86) 76986921000
Web Site: https://www.mentech.com
Year Founded: 2008
002902—(SSE)
Rev.: $326,205,360
Assets: $405,993,276
Liabilities: $249,944,292
Net Worth: $156,048,984
Earnings: $9,670,752
Fiscal Year-end: 12/31/22
Electronic Component Mfr & Distr
N.A.I.C.S.: 334419
Li Jingzhou *(Gen Mgr)*

Subsidiaries:

Dongguan Mentech Optical & Magnetic Co., Ltd. - Morgan Hill
Branch   (1)
16995 Del Monte Ave Apt 125, Morgan Hill,
CA 95037
Tel.: (408) 612-4549
Electronic Components Mfr
N.A.I.C.S.: 334419

DONGGUAN RURAL COM-
MERCIAL BANK CO., LTD.

No 2 Hongfu East Road, Dongcheng
District, Dongguan, 523123, Guangdong, China
Tel.: (86) 769961122   CN
Web Site: https://www.drcbank.com
Year Founded: 1952
9889—(HKG)
Rev.: $3,195,967,130
Assets: $98,146,542,977
Liabilities: $90,186,787,633
Net Worth: $7,959,755,344
Earnings: $740,171,688
Emp.: 7,924
Fiscal Year-end: 12/31/23
Commercial Banking Services
N.A.I.C.S.: 522110
Yaoqiu Wang *(Chm)*

DONGGUAN TARRY ELEC-
TRONICS CO., LTD.

48 Hongjin Road, Hongmei Town,
Dongguan, 523000, Guangdong,
China
Tel.: (86) 76981833815
Web Site: https://www.dgtarry.com
Year Founded: 2003
300976—(SSE)
Rev.: $206,292,528
Assets: $498,519,684
Liabilities: $52,026,624
Net Worth: $446,493,060
Earnings: $28,130,544
Fiscal Year-end: 12/31/22
Electronic Product Mfr & Distr
N.A.I.C.S.: 334419
Qingping Li *(Chm & Gen Mgr)*

DONGGUAN WINNERWAY IN-
DUSTRY ZONE LTD.

6th Floor Hongyuan Building No 1
Hongyuan Road, Nancheng District,
Dongguan, 523087, Guangdong,
China
Tel.: (86) 76922412655
Web Site:
 https://www.winnerway.com.cn
Year Founded: 1992
000573—(SSE)
Rev.: $133,012,152
Assets: $359,512,452
Liabilities: $128,583,936
Net Worth: $230,928,516
Earnings: $5,833,620
Fiscal Year-end: 12/31/22
Real Estate Development Services
N.A.I.C.S.: 531190
Mingxuan Zhou *(Chm & Gen Mgr)*

DONGGUAN YIHEDA AUTO-
MATION CO., LTD.

No 33 Taoyuan 2nd Road, Cunwei
Village Hengli Town, Dongguan,
523000, Guangdong, China
Tel.: (86) 76982886777
Web Site: https://www.yiheda.com
Year Founded: 2010
301029—(CHIN)
Rev.: $405,844,337
Assets: $513,933,520
Liabilities: $81,122,465
Net Worth: $432,811,055
Earnings: $76,835,479
Fiscal Year-end: 12/31/23
Electrical Component Mfr & Distr

N.A.I.C.S.: 335210

DONGGUAN YUTONG OPTI-
CAL TECHNOLOGY CO., LTD.

No 99 East Jinghai Road, Changan
Town, Dongguan, 523863, Guangdong, China
Tel.: (86) 76989266655
Web Site: https://www.ytotglobal.com
Year Founded: 2011
300790—(SSE)
Rev.: $259,202,268
Assets: $600,225,444
Liabilities: $333,562,320
Net Worth: $266,663,124
Earnings: $20,240,064
Emp.: 2,400
Fiscal Year-end: 12/31/22
Optical Instrument Mfr & Distr
N.A.I.C.S.: 333310
Pinguang Zhang *(Chm)*

Subsidiaries:

Shangrao Yutong Optical Technology
Co., Ltd.   (1)
8 Chaoyang Avenue, Chaoyang Industrial
Park Xinzhou District, Shangrao, Jiangxi,
China
Tel.: (86) 7935209999
Optical Lens Mfr
N.A.I.C.S.: 333310

DONGHUA TESTING TECH-
NOLOGY CO., LTD.

No 208 Xingang Avenue, Jingjiang,
214500, Jiangsu, China
Tel.: (86) 52384854399
Web Site: https://www.dhtest.com
Year Founded: 1993
300354—(CHIN)
Rev.: $51,538,032
Assets: $97,200,324
Liabilities: $12,989,808
Net Worth: $84,210,516
Earnings: $17,097,912
Emp.: 380
Fiscal Year-end: 12/31/22
Structural Mechanical Performance
Testing Equipment Mfr
N.A.I.C.S.: 334515
Shigang Liu *(Chm)*

DONGIL METAL CO., LTD.

6 Kumho-Lo, Yeongcheon, 700-802,
Gyungsangbuk-Do, Korea (South)
Tel.: (82) 543335501
Web Site:
 http://www.dongilmetal.co.kr
Year Founded: 1966
109860—(KRS)
Rev.: $85,473,800
Assets: $135,896,871
Liabilities: $18,092,865
Net Worth: $117,804,007
Earnings: $10,676,799
Emp.: 57
Fiscal Year-end: 12/31/22
Steel Casting Mfr
N.A.I.C.S.: 331513
Kilbong Oh *(CEO)*

Subsidiaries:

Dongil Industries Co., Ltd.   (1)
140-30 aJangheung-dong, Namgu, Pohang,
Kyungbuk, Korea (South)
Tel.: (82) 54 285 7251
Web Site: http://www.dongil.co.kr
Steel Casting Mfr
N.A.I.C.S.: 331513
Oh Soon Tsck *(Pres)*

Dongil Metal Co., Ltd. - Ogye
Factory   (1)
6 - 2 Ogyegongdan - gil Geumho - eup,
Yeongcheon, 38882, Gyeongsangbuk - do,
Korea (South)
Tel.: (82) 543335506
Steel Casting Mfr
N.A.I.C.S.: 331513

Dongil Metal Co., Ltd.—(Continued)

PT. DONGIL METAL INDONESIA (1)
Block C-8 No 14 15 16, Cibarusa, Bekasi, 17550, Jawa Barat, Indonesia
Tel.: (62) 218972202
Steel Casting Mfr
N.A.I.C.S.: 331513

DONGIL STEEL CO., LTD.
46 Gaya-daero, Sasang-gu, Busan, 617843, Korea (South)
Tel.: (82) 513165341
Web Site:
　https://www.dongilsteel.com
Year Founded: 1967
023790—(KRS)
Rev.: $24,713,658
Assets: $73,651,467
Liabilities: $45,508,992
Net Worth: $28,142,476
Earnings: ($11,991,763)
Emp.: 39
Fiscal Year-end: 12/31/22
Steel Products Mfr
N.A.I.C.S.: 331110
In-Hwa Jang (CEO)

DONGIL TECHNOLOGY LTD.
28 Namyang-ro 930beon-gil
Namyang-eup, Hwaseong, Gyeonggi-do, Korea (South)
Tel.: (82) 312995479
Web Site:
　https://www.dongiltech.co.kr
Year Founded: 1986
032960—(KRS)
Rev.: $20,478,434
Assets: $50,949,899
Liabilities: $3,273,396
Net Worth: $47,676,504
Earnings: $856,291
Emp.: 132
Fiscal Year-end: 12/31/22
Sensor Mfr
N.A.I.C.S.: 334513
Dong-Jun Sohn (CEO)

**DONGJIANG ENVIRONMEN-
TAL COMPANY LIMITED**
1st Floor 3rd Floor North Side Dongji-ang Environmental Building 9, No 9
Langshan Rd North Area Hightech
Industrial Park Nanshan District, Shenzhen, China
Tel.: (86) 75586676186
Web Site:
　http://www.dongjiang.com.cn
Year Founded: 1999
002672—(SSE)
Rev.: $544,537,750
Assets: $1,643,517,065
Liabilities: $972,899,834
Net Worth: $670,617,230
Earnings: ($79,844,638)
Emp.: 4,958
Fiscal Year-end: 12/31/22
Waste Treatment, Recycling, Facility
Construction & Management
N.A.I.C.S.: 562211
Wang Jianying (CFO)

Subsidiaries:

Beijing Novel Environmental Protec-
tion Co Limited (1)
8/F Tower A Xue Yan Building Tsinghua Uni-
versity, Haidian District, Beijing, 100084, China
Tel.: (86) 1062770877
Web Site: http://www.e-e.com.cn
Environmental Consulting Services
N.A.I.C.S.: 541620

Huizhou Dongjiang Environment
Technology Co. Limited (1)
No 39 Lianfa Avenue Zhongkai Hi-Tech De-
velopment Zone, Tongqiao Industrial Park

Tongqiao Town, Huizhou, Guangdong, China
Tel.: (86) 7523796392
Environmental Consulting Services
N.A.I.C.S.: 541620

Qingdao Dongjiang Environmental
Recycled Power Limited (1)
1812 Unit 1 Building 3 Huanyukangting
Shangdong Road No 118, Qingdao, Shan-dong, China
Tel.: (86) 53280862027
Eletric Power Generation Services
N.A.I.C.S.: 221118

Qingyuan Dongjiang Environmental
Technologies Company Limited (1)
No 13 Taiji Industrial Park, Longtang Town
Qingcheng District, Qingyuan, China
Tel.: (86) 7636861628
Waste Treatment & Disposal Services
N.A.I.C.S.: 562211

Shaoguan Green Recycling Resource
Development Co Limited (1)
Jiangjuntun, Tielong Town Wengyuan
County, Shaoguan, 512629, Guangdong, China
Tel.: (86) 7512663228
Waste Treatment & Disposal Services
N.A.I.C.S.: 562211

DONGJIN SEMICHEM CO., LTD.
KGIT 23rd Floor 402 World Cup Buk-Ro, Mapo-gu, Seoul, Korea (South)
Tel.: (82) 263556100
Web Site: https://www.dongjin.com
Year Founded: 1967
005290—(KRS)
Rev.: $1,117,683,758
Assets: $1,054,090,808
Liabilities: $516,586,900
Net Worth: $537,503,908
Earnings: $119,801,808
Emp.: 1,007
Fiscal Year-end: 12/31/22
Semiconductor Mfr
N.A.I.C.S.: 334413
Chun Hyuk Lee (Vice Chm & Co-CEO)

Subsidiaries:

BEIJING DONGJIN SEMICHEM Co.,
Ltd. (1)
No 10 Xingyejie BDA, Beijing, 100176, China
Tel.: (86) 1067856305
Electronic Components Distr
N.A.I.C.S.: 423690

Chengdu Dongjin Semichem Co.,
Ltd. (1)
1188 HE-zuo-Rd West District Hi-Tech
Zone, Chengdu, 611731, Sichuan, China
Tel.: (86) 2887958650
Electronic Components Distr
N.A.I.C.S.: 423690

DONGJIN SEMICHEM (XI'AN) SEMI-
CONDUCTOR MATERIALS CO.,
Ltd. (1)
No 1170 Bao Ba Road, High Tech Compre-
hensive Bonded Zone, Xi'an, Shaanxi, China
Tel.: (86) 2989521060
Electronic Components Distr
N.A.I.C.S.: 423690

DONGJIN SEMICHEM ORDOS CITY
TECHNOLOGY Co., Ltd. (1)
NO 37Kexue-Rd ordos Equipmeng Manu-
facturing Base, Dongsheng District Inner
Mongolia, Ordos, China
Tel.: (86) 1004773115266
Electronic Components Distr
N.A.I.C.S.: 423690

DONGJIN SEMICHEM TECHNOL-
OGY (QIDONG) Co., Ltd. (1)
Shanghai Road 368 Binjiang Fine Chemical
Industry Park, Economic Development Area,
Qidong, 226221, Jiangsu, China
Tel.: (86) 51383201882
Electronic Components Distr

N.A.I.C.S.: 423690

Dongjin Semichem Co., Ltd. - Balan
Plant (1)
35 Jageundollae-gil Yanggam-myeon,
Hwaseong, Gyeonggi-do, Korea (South)
Tel.: (82) 313536430
Electronic Components Distr
N.A.I.C.S.: 423690

Dongjin Semichem Co., Ltd. - In-
cheon Plant (1)
644 Baekbeom-ro, Seo-gu, Incheon, Korea
(South)
Tel.: (82) 325785091
Electronic Components Distr
N.A.I.C.S.: 423690

Dongjin Semichem Co., Ltd. - Shiwha
Plant (1)
16 Somanggongwon-ro, Siheung,
Gyeonggi-do, Korea (South)
Tel.: (82) 313190011
Electronic Components Distr
N.A.I.C.S.: 423690

HEFEI DONGJIN SEMICHEM Co.,
Ltd. (1)
The North West Cape of Wulishan Road
and Life Road Crossing Point, Xinzhan De-
velopment Test District, Hefei, Anhui, China
Tel.: (86) 5515190912
Electronic Components Distr
N.A.I.C.S.: 423690

PT. Dongjin Indonesia (1)
Kawasan Industri PT Krakatau Industrial
Estate Cilegon, Jalan Raya Anyer Km 123
Ds Gunung Sugih Kec Ciwandan, Cilegon,
Banten, Indonesia
Tel.: (62) 254601245
Electronic Components Distr
N.A.I.C.S.: 423690

Shinam Oil Co., Ltd. (1)
82-8 Yongsan-ro, Sinam-myeon, Yesan,
Chungcheongnam, Korea (South)
Tel.: (82) 413315140
Concrete Ready Mix Distr
N.A.I.C.S.: 423320

Taiwan Dongjin Semichem Co.,
Ltd. (1)
No 21 Hsiengong North 1st Road,
Changbin Ind Complex, Chang-Hua, Taiwan
Tel.: (886) 47580475
Semiconductor & Related Device Mfr
N.A.I.C.S.: 334413

**DONGKOO BIO & PHARMA
CO., LTD.**
14th Floor Building B Beobwonro
114, Songpa-Gu, Seoul, Korea (South)
Tel.: (82) 2268454218
Web Site: https://www.dongkoo.com
Year Founded: 1970
006620—(KRS)
Rev.: $149,555,616
Assets: $131,969,270
Liabilities: $53,654,151
Net Worth: $78,315,118
Earnings: $5,072,886
Emp.: 370
Fiscal Year-end: 12/31/22
Pharmaceutical Preparation Mfr
N.A.I.C.S.: 325412
Yong-Jun Cho (CEO)

**DONGKOOK PHARMACEUTI-
CAL CO., LTD.**
715 Yeongdong-daero, Gangnam-gu,
Seoul, Korea (South)
Tel.: (82) 221919800
Web Site: https://www.dkpharm.co.kr
Year Founded: 1968
086450—(KRS)
Rev.: $507,483,627
Assets: $589,309,174
Liabilities: $181,982,776
Net Worth: $407,326,398
Earnings: $41,998,441
Emp.: 1,132
Fiscal Year-end: 12/31/22

Pharmaceutical Mfr & Whslr
N.A.I.C.S.: 325412
Heung Ju Oh (CEO)

Subsidiaries:

Dong Kook Lifescience Co., Ltd. (1)
4F Teheran-ro 114-gil 16, Gangnam-gu,
Seoul, Korea (South)
Tel.: (82) 220512713
Web Site: http://www.dkls.co.kr
Pharmaceuticals Product Mfr
N.A.I.C.S.: 325412
Ki-Ho Cheong (CEO)

**DONGKUK INDUSTRIES CO.,
LTD.**
46 Dadaong-gil, Chung gu, Seoul,
Korea (South)
Tel.: (82) 23167500
Web Site: https://www.dkis.co.kr
Year Founded: 1976
005160—(KRS)
Rev.: $660,026,153
Assets: $670,954,205
Liabilities: $245,662,744
Net Worth: $425,291,461
Earnings: $4,955,914
Emp.: 360
Fiscal Year-end: 12/31/22
Cold-Rolled Steel Products Mfr
N.A.I.C.S.: 331221
An Sang Cheol (CEO)

Subsidiaries:

Dongkuk Industries Co., Ltd. - Po-
hang Factory (1)
57 Goedong-ro, Nam-gu, Pohang,
Gyeongsangbuk-do, Korea (South)
Tel.: (82) 542710114
Steel Mfrs
N.A.I.C.S.: 332999

Dongkuk Industries Co., Ltd. - Si-
heung Factory (1)
233 Huimanggongwon ro, Siheung,
Gyeonggi-do, Korea (South)
Tel.: (82) 314326521
Steel Mfrs
N.A.I.C.S.: 332999

**DONGKUK REFRACTORIES &
STEEL CO., LTD.**
5F 6F 10 Oncheonjang-ro 107beon-
gil, Dongnae-gu, Busan, 47709, Ko-
rea (South)
Tel.: (82) 515505050
Web Site: https://www.dkref.co.kr
Year Founded: 1974
075970—(KRS)
Rev.: $90,645,397
Assets: $100,716,468
Liabilities: $37,476,093
Net Worth: $63,240,375
Earnings: $3,017,754
Emp.: 71
Fiscal Year-end: 12/31/22
Refractory & Steel Mfr
N.A.I.C.S.: 212323
Lee Kang Hak (CEO)

DONGKUK S&C CO., LTD.
62 Daesong-ro, Nam-gu, Pohang,
Gyeongsangbuk-do, Korea (South)
Tel.: (82) 542854500
Web Site:
　https://www.dongkuksnc.co.kr
Year Founded: 2001
100130—(KRS)
Rev.: $365,968,599
Assets: $385,818,259
Liabilities: $171,034,288
Net Worth: $214,783,971
Earnings: ($6,011,569)
Emp.: 112
Fiscal Year-end: 12/31/22
Steel Structures Mfr
N.A.I.C.S.: 339999
Yang Seung Joo (CEO)

Subsidiaries:

Dongkuk S&C Co., Ltd. - DK Wind
Power Plant   (1)
547-3 Jangheung-Dong, Nam-Gu, Pohang,
Gyeong Puk, Korea (South)
Tel.: (82) 54 271 0520
Web Site: http://www.dongkuksnc.co.kr
Emp.: 9
Eletric Power Generation Services
N.A.I.C.S.: 221118

Hallyeo Energy Resource   (1)
Manheung-dong 855, Yeosu, Jeollanam-do,
Korea (South)
Tel.: (82) 61 654 3945
Eletric Power Generation Services
N.A.I.C.S.: 221118

Shinan Wind Power Generation
Co   (1)
Gurim-ri 175 Bigum-myun, Gurim, Jeol-
lanam, Korea (South)
Tel.: (82) 61 275 4777
Web Site: http://www.dongkuksnc.co.kr
Wind Power Generation Services
N.A.I.C.S.: 221115

DONGKUK STEEL MILL CO., LTD.

Ferrum Tower 19 Euljio 5-gil, Jung-
gu, Seoul, Korea (South)
Tel.: (82) 23171114   KR
Web Site:
https://www.dongkuksteel.com
Year Founded: 1954
001230—(KRS)
Rev.: $6,528,033,859
Assets: $4,948,107,060
Liabilities: $2,427,276,216
Net Worth: $2,520,830,844
Earnings: $316,803,531
Emp.: 2,570
Fiscal Year-end: 12/31/22
Steel Producer
N.A.I.C.S.: 331110
Sae Wook Chang (Vice Chm & Co-
CEO)

Subsidiaries:

Branson Machinery LLC   (1)
2100 Cedartown Hwy SW, Rome, GA
30161-9565
Tel.: (706) 290-2500
Web Site: http://www.bransontractor.com
Sales Range: $25-49.9 Million
Emp.: 20
Industrial Machinery Distr
N.A.I.C.S.: 423830

DK UIL (Tianjin) Electronics Co.,
Ltd   (1)
No 18 Xin Yuan Dao Xiqing Economic De-
velopment area, Tianjin, 300400, China
Tel.: (86) 2283968735
Web Site: http://www.dkuil.com
Keypad Mfr
N.A.I.C.S.: 334111
Sang Ju Kim (Pres & CEO)

DK UNC Co., Ltd.   (1)
9th floor Ferrum Tower 19 Eulji-ro 5-gil,
Jung-gu, Seoul, 152-848, Korea (South)
Tel.: (82) 221010900
Web Site: https://www.dongkuksystems.com
Sales Range: $75-99.9 Million
Emp.: 500
Information Technology Consulting Services
N.A.I.C.S.: 541512

Dongkuk Corporation   (1)
7Floor PMO Nihonbashi kayaba-cho 3-11-
10, Chuo-ku, Tokyo, 103-0025, Japan
Tel.: (81) 356235723
Structured Steel Products Mfr
N.A.I.C.S.: 331110
Janjhoe Koo (Pres)

Dongkuk International, Inc.   (1)
19750 Magellan Dr, Torrance, CA
90502   (100%)
Tel.: (310) 523-9595
Web Site: http://www.dongkuk.com
Sales Range: $25-49.9 Million
Emp.: 12
Steel Products Mfr

N.A.I.C.S.: 331110
Jaipoong Kim (Pres)

Dongkuk Steel China Co., Ltd.   (1)
Xiagang Zone Jiangyin Riverside Economy
Development Area, Jiangyin, 214442, Ji-
angsu, China
Tel.: (86) 51086032308
Steel Products Mfr
N.A.I.C.S.: 331110

Dongkuk Steel India Private
Limited   (1)
B-3/2 Ecotech-1 Extension, Noida, 201 308,
Uttar Pradesh, India
Tel.: (91) 1204818156
Steel Products Mfr
N.A.I.C.S.: 331110

Dongkuk Steel Mexico, S.A. de
C.V.   (1)
Av Internacional 303, Parque Industrial Hui-
nala, 66645, Apodaca, Nuevo Leon, Mexico
Tel.: (52) 8181452122
Steel Products Mfr
N.A.I.C.S.: 331110

Dongkuk Steel Mill Co., Ltd. - Busan
Works   (1)
588-1 Gamman-Dong, Nam-Gu, Busan,
604-836, Korea (South)
Tel.: (82) 23171114
Steel Products Mfr
N.A.I.C.S.: 331110

Dongkuk Steel Mill Co., Ltd. - Dangjin
Works   (1)
25 Godaegongdan 1-gil, Songak-eup, Dan-
gjin, 343-823, Chungcheongnam-do, Korea
(South)
Tel.: (82) 413514984
Steel Products Mfr
N.A.I.C.S.: 331110

Dongkuk Steel Mill Co., Ltd. - In-
cheon Works   (1)
15 Jungbong-daero, Dong-gu, Incheon,
401-712, Korea (South)
Tel.: (82) 328306216
Web Site: http://www.dongkuk.com
Sales Range: $100-124.9 Million
Emp.: 500
Steel Products Mfr
N.A.I.C.S.: 331110

Dongkuk Steel Mill Co., Ltd. - Pohang
Works   (1)
195 Cheolgangsandan-ro Daesong-myeon,
Nam-gu, Pohang, 790-841,
Gyeongsangbuk-do, Korea (South)
Tel.: (82) 542786111
Sales Range: $200-249.9 Million
Emp.: 1,000
Steel Products Mfr
N.A.I.C.S.: 331110

Dongkuk Steel Thailand Ltd.   (1)
No 217/9 Moo 6 Bowin, Pinthong Industrial
Estate Project 3 Sriracha, Chon Buri,
20230, Thailand
Tel.: (66) 38110570
Steel Products Mfr
N.A.I.C.S.: 331110

Intergis Co., Ltd.   (1)
13th floor of Marine Center 52 Chungjang
road, Jung-gu, Busan, 48936, Korea
(South)
Tel.: (82) 516043333
Web Site: https://www.intergis.co.kr
Rev.: $552,227,477
Assets: $332,239,271
Liabilities: $137,079,747
Net Worth: $195,159,524
Earnings: $23,633,752
Fiscal Year-end: 12/31/2022
Transportation Related Services
N.A.I.C.S.: 488999
Dong-ho Park (CEO)

DONGLAI COATING TECH-NOLOGY SHANGHAI CO., LTD.

No 1221 Xinhe Road, Jiading District,
Shanghai, 201807, China
Tel.: (86) 2139538590
Web Site: https://www.onwings.com
Year Founded: 2005

688129—(SHG)
Rev.: $55,267,926
Assets: $174,251,690
Liabilities: $55,735,276
Net Worth: $118,516,414
Earnings: $3,019,892
Fiscal Year-end: 12/31/22
Coating Product Mfr
N.A.I.C.S.: 325510
Zhongmin Zhu (Chm & Gen Mgr)

DONGNAI PLASTIC JSC

Road 9 Bien Hoa 1 Industrial Park,
Dong Nai, Vietnam
Tel.: (84) 61836269
Web Site: https://dnpcorp.vn
Year Founded: 1975
DNP—(HNX)
Rev.: $320,110,497
Assets: $662,361,894
Liabilities: $470,431,761
Net Worth: $191,930,133
Earnings: $5,270,905
Emp.: 3,671
Fiscal Year-end: 12/31/23
Plastics Product Mfr
N.A.I.C.S.: 326122
Tran Huu Chuyen (Vice Chm)

Subsidiaries:

Binh Hiep Joint Stock Company   (1)
No A6-A7 Kenh Bau Residential Area, Phan
Thiet, Binh Thuan, Vietnam
Tel.: (84) 623833287
Plastic Pipe Mfr & Distr
N.A.I.C.S.: 326122

Tay Ninh Water Supply Sewerage
Joint Stock Company   (1)
489 April 30 Street, Ward 1, Tay Ninh, Viet-
nam
Tel.: (84) 2763822240
Web Site:
https://capthoatnuoctayninh.com.vn
Water Supply & Sewerage Services
N.A.I.C.S.: 237110

DONGNAM CHEMICAL CO., LTD.

80-61 Tancheonsaneopdanji-gil,
Tancheon-myeon, Gongju,
Chungcheongnam-do, Korea (South)
Tel.: (82) 314727616
Web Site:
https://www.dongnamchem.com
Year Founded: 1965
023450—(KRS)
Rev.: $143,551,132
Assets: $68,350,004
Liabilities: $31,218,087
Net Worth: $37,131,917
Earnings: $7,883,959
Emp.: 172
Fiscal Year-end: 12/31/22
Agricultural Chemical Mfr
N.A.I.C.S.: 325998

DONGNAN ELECTRONICS CO., LTD.

No 218 Weixi Road, Economic Devel-
opment Zone, Yueqing, 325600, Zhe-
jiang, China
Tel.: (86) 61527114
Web Site: https://www.switch-
china.com
Year Founded: 1987
301359—(CHIN)
Rev.: $36,593,169
Assets: $127,939,507
Liabilities: $7,697,338
Net Worth: $120,242,169
Earnings: $5,501,648
Fiscal Year-end: 12/31/23
Electronic Component Mfr & Distr
N.A.I.C.S.: 334419
Wenkui Qiu (Chm)

DONGPENG HOLDINGS COM-PANY LIMITED

No 8 jiangwan Third Road,
Chancheng District, Foshan, 528031,
Guangdong, China
Tel.: (86) 75782701155
Web Site: http://www.dongpeng.com
Year Founded: 1972
Holding Company
N.A.I.C.S.: 551112
Xinming He (Chm)

DONGRUI FOOD GROUP CO., LTD.

Butterfly Ridge Industrial Park, Xian-
tang Town Dongyuan County,
Heyuan, 517500, Guangdong, China
Tel.: (86) 7628729999
Web Site:
https://www.gdruichang.com
Year Founded: 2002
001201—(SSE)
Rev.: $170,835,912
Assets: $662,146,056
Liabilities: $226,076,292
Net Worth: $436,069,764
Earnings: $6,024,564
Fiscal Year-end: 12/31/22
Veal Product Mfr
N.A.I.C.S.: 311612
Jiankang Yuan (Chm & Gen Mgr)

DONGSHENG PHARMACEUTI-CAL INTERNATIONAL CO., LTD.

China Bing'qi Plaza Floor 17 No 69,
Zi Zhu Yuan Road, Haidian District,
Beijing, China
Tel.: (86) 10 8858 0708   DE
Year Founded: 2008
Sales Range: $10-24.9 Million
Emp.: 69
Pharmaceuticals Mfr
N.A.I.C.S.: 325412
Xiaodong Zhu (Chm, Pres & CEO)

DONGSHIN ENGINEERING & CONSTRUCTION CO., LTD.

217 Seodongmun-ro, Andong, Gyeo-
ngsangbuk, Korea (South)
Tel.: (82) 537567701
Web Site: https://dongshin.info
025950—(KRS)
Rev.: $37,336,192
Assets: $84,086,717
Liabilities: $17,598,024
Net Worth: $66,488,693
Earnings: $4,504,637
Fiscal Year-end: 12/31/22
Construction Engineering Services
N.A.I.C.S.: 541330

DONGSUNG CHEMICAL CO., LTD.

99 Sinsan-Ro, Saha-gu, Busan, Ko-
rea (South)
Tel.: (82) 512004500
Web Site: https://www.dschem.co.kr
Year Founded: 1959
102260—(KRS)
Rev.: $874,474,816
Assets: $689,925,516
Liabilities: $314,857,528
Net Worth: $375,067,987
Earnings: $35,920,906
Emp.: 616
Fiscal Year-end: 12/31/22
Plastic Adhesive Mfr
N.A.I.C.S.: 325211
Dongsung Chemical (CEO)

Subsidiaries:

Dong Sung America Inc.   (1)
472 Shinpyong-dong, Saha, Busan, Korea
(South)
Tel.: (82) 51 200 4777

Dongsung Chemical Co., Ltd.—(Continued)

Real Estate Lending Services
N.A.I.C.S.: 531390
Ui Ho Sin (CEO)

Dongsung Biopol Co., Ltd.　　(1)
226-8 Beakto-ri Hyangname-up, Hwaseong,
Gyeonggi, Korea (South)
Tel.: (82) 31 354 3521
Pharmaceuticals Product Mfr
N.A.I.C.S.: 325412
Jin Seok Choi (CEO)

Dongsung Biorane Co., Ltd.　　(1)
411 Gumgangtechvalley 133-1 Sandaewon
1-dong, Jungwon gu, Seongnam, Gyeonggi,
Korea (South)
Tel.: (82) 31 777 5345
Pharmaceutical Products Distr
N.A.I.C.S.: 456110
Jin Seok Choi (CEO)

Dongsung Chemical Co., Ltd. -
SINPYEONG FACTORY　　(1)
19 Hasinbeonyeong-ro, Saha, Busan, Ko-
rea (South)
Tel.: (82) 51 604 1101
Chemical Products Mfr
N.A.I.C.S.: 325998

Dongsung Chemical Co., Ltd. - Sihwa
Factory　　(1)
1239-2 Jeongwang-dong, Siheung, Gyeo-
nggi, Korea (South)
Tel.: (82) 31 497 4162
Resin Mfr & Whslr
N.A.I.C.S.: 325211

Dongsung Chemical Co., Ltd. - Yeo-
cheon Factory　　(1)
345 Boche-ri Miyang-my son, Anseong,
Gyeonggi, Korea (South)
Tel.: (82) 31 677 7000
Chemical Products Mfr
N.A.I.C.S.: 325998
Jae in Lee (Co-CEO)

Dongsung Ecore Co., Ltd.　　(1)
8F Keongil Tower 677-25 Yeoksam-dong,
Gangnam-gu, Seoul, Korea (South)
Tel.: (82) 2 2136 4300
Chemical Products Mfr
N.A.I.C.S.: 325998
Chung Ryeol Park (CEO)

Dongsung Holdings Co., Ltd.　　(1)
8F Keongil Tower 677-25 Yeoksam-dong,
Gangnam-gu, Seoul, Korea (South)
Tel.: (82) 2 2136 4358
Web Site:
　http://www.dongsungholdings.com
Holding Company
N.A.I.C.S.: 551112
Jin Seok Choi (CEO)

Genewel Co., Ltd.　　(1)
37 62-gil Sagimakgol-ro 5/6th fl Star Tower,
Jungwon-gu Sangdaewon-dong, Seong-
nam, Gyeonggi, Korea (South)
Tel.: (82) 3180185500
Web Site: https://www.genewel.com
Surgical Appliance Mfr
N.A.I.C.S.: 339113
Sang-Deok Han (CEO)

Guangzhou Dongsung Chemical Co.,
LTD.　　(1)
No19 Jungong Road East Section,
Guangzhou Economical and Technological
Development District, Guangzhou, 510730,
China
Tel.: (86) 2082266428
Emp.: 90
Resin Mfr & Whslr
N.A.I.C.S.: 325211
Seok Han Bae (CEO)

P.T. Dongsung Jakarta　　(1)
Jalan Raya Pajajaran Nomor 121 Desa
Gandasari Kecamatan Jatiuwung,
Tangerang, 15137, Banten, Indonesia
Tel.: (62) 5910304
Web Site: https://www.dongsungjakarta.com
Emp.: 69
Resin Mfr & Whslr
N.A.I.C.S.: 325211

**DONGSUNG FINETEC CO.,
LTD.**

120 Hyeopdonghanji-gil, Miyang-
myeon, Anseong, Gyeonggi-do, Ko-
rea (South)
Tel.: (82) 316777000
Web Site: https://www.dsfinetec.co.kr
Year Founded: 1985
033500—(KRS)
Rev.: $332,994,241
Assets: $263,856,008
Liabilities: $149,867,803
Net Worth: $113,988,205
Earnings: $6,459,495
Emp.: 455
Fiscal Year-end: 12/31/22
Inorganic Chemical Product Mfr
N.A.I.C.S.: 325180
Yong-Seok Choe (CEO)

Subsidiaries:

Dongsung Finetec International,
Inc.　　(1)
11777 Katy Freeway Ste 138, South Hous-
ton, TX 77079
Tel.: (832) 617-8360
Web Site: http://www.dsfinetecintl.com
Pipe Insulation Product Mfr
N.A.I.C.S.: 327999
Harry Park (CEO)

**DONGSUNG NSC COMPANY
LTD.**

472 Shinpyung Dongo, Saha Ku, Pu-
san, 604-030, Korea (South)
Tel.: (82) 512004800
Web Site:
　http://www.dongsungnsc.com
Sales Range: $25-49.9 Million
Emp.: 100
Adhesive Mfr
N.A.I.C.S.: 325520
Jae Cho (Pres & CEO)

Subsidiaries:

Dongsung NSC Vietnam Company
Ltd.　　(1)
No 7 9A St Bien Hoa II Industrial Zones,
Bien Hoa, Dong Nai, Vietnam
Tel.: (84) 61835461
Sales Range: $25-49.9 Million
Emp.: 68
Adhesive Mfr
N.A.I.C.S.: 325520

**DONGWHA HOLDINGS CO.,
LTD.**

53-2 Yeouinaru-ro, Yeongdeungpo-
gu, Seoul, Korea (South)
Tel.: (82) 221220589
Web Site: http://www.dongwha.co.kr
Year Founded: 1948
025900—(KRS)
Rev.: $844,018,391
Assets: $1,415,965,015
Liabilities: $824,341,801
Net Worth: $591,623,214
Earnings: $33,213,153
Emp.: 769
Fiscal Year-end: 12/31/22
Investment Management Service
N.A.I.C.S.: 523999
Myung-Ho Seung (Chm)

Subsidiaries:

Daesung Wood Ind. Co., Ltd.　　(1)
164 Wolmi-ro, Jung-gu, Incheon, Korea
(South)
Tel.: (82) 32 770 9300
Wood Panel Mfr
N.A.I.C.S.: 321211

Dongwha Dubai　　(1)
1409 X3 Towers Jumeirah Bay Cluster X
Jumeirah Lakes Towers, Dubai, United Arab
Emirates
Tel.: (971) 1 4 453 7284
Wood Panel Mfr
N.A.I.C.S.: 321211

Dongwha Hong Kong International
Co Ltd　　(1)

Roomm 2001 20/F Jubilee Centre 46
Gloucester Rd, Wanchai, China (Hong
Kong)
Tel.: (852) 2542 2093
Wood Panel Mfr
N.A.I.C.S.: 321211

Subsidiary (Non-US):

Dongwha Australia Holdings Pty
Ltd.　　(2)
1 Sandy Lane, Bombala, 2632, NSW, Aus-
tralia
Tel.: (61) 264595555
Web Site: https://www.dongwha.com
Holding Company
N.A.I.C.S.: 551112

Dongwha India Private Limited　　(1)
Penta Building Pmc Xvi/325 1St Floor Opp
Jacobite Church, Perumbavoor, Cochin,
India
Tel.: (91) 9447343997
Wood Panel Mfr
N.A.I.C.S.: 321211
Libin Babu Kakkanattu (Branch Mgr)

Dongwha Malaysia Holdings Sdn.
Bhd.　　(1)
Suite 39-04A Level 39 Menara Citibank 165
Jalan Ampang, 50450, Kuala Lumpur, Ma-
laysia
Tel.: (60) 3 2161 0216
Web Site: http://www.dongwha.com.my
Wood Panel Mfr
N.A.I.C.S.: 321211
Man Sik Kim (CEO & Gen Dir)

Plant (Domestic):

Dongwha Malaysia Holdings Sdn.
Bhd. - Kulim Plant　　(2)
Lot 833 Mukim Padang Meha, Padang Se-
rai, 09400, Kulim, Kedah Darul Aman, Ma-
laysia
Tel.: (60) 44022100
Web Site: https://www.dongwha.com
Wood Panel Mfr
N.A.I.C.S.: 321211

Dongwha Malaysia Holdings Sdn.
Bhd. - Merbok Plant　　(2)
Lot 2998 Jalan Raya, 08400, Merbok, Ke-
dah Darul Aman, Malaysia
Tel.: (60) 44573070
Wood Panel Mfr
N.A.I.C.S.: 321211

Dongwha Malaysia Holdings Sdn.
Bhd. - Nilai Plant　　(2)
Lot 3726 3728 Nilai Industrial Estate, Mu-
kim Setul Nilai, 71800, Seremban, Negeri
Sembilan, Malaysia
Tel.: (60) 67993000
Wood Panel Mfr
N.A.I.C.S.: 321211
Myung Sik Kim (CEO)

Dongwha Shenzhen　　(1)
Rm A10 Floor 17 Block C Tianan Int l Bldg
Renmin South Rd, Shenzhen, China
Tel.: (86) 755 8225 0917
Wood Panel Mfr
N.A.I.C.S.: 321211

**DONGWON DEVELOPMENT
CO., LTD.**

9th floor Dongwon Building 754
Suyeong-ro, Suyeong-gu, Busan, Ko-
rea (South)
Tel.: (82) 516453113
Web Site:
　https://www.dongwonapt.co.kr
Year Founded: 1978
013120—(KRS)
Rev.: $461,649,320
Assets: $1,099,874,799
Liabilities: $313,098,332
Net Worth: $786,776,468
Earnings: $62,978,830
Emp.: 293
Fiscal Year-end: 12/31/22
Real Estate Related Services
N.A.I.C.S.: 531390
Bok Man Jang (CEO)

**DONGWON ENTERPRISE CO.,
LTD.**

Dongwon Industries Bldg 68
Mabang-ro 275 Yangjae-dong,
Seocho-gu, Seoul, Korea (South)
Tel.: (82) 7051019539　　KR
Web Site: http://www.dongwon.com
Year Founded: 1969
Holding Company
N.A.I.C.S.: 551112
Jae-cheol Kim (Chm)

Subsidiaries:

Dongbu Express Co., Ltd.　　(1)
140-821 Centreville Asterium D Dong 251,
Hangang-daero Yongsan-gu, Seoul, Korea
(South)
Tel.: (82) 2 6363 2600
Web Site: http://www.dongbuexpress.com
Cargo & Transportation Logistics Services
N.A.I.C.S.: 541614

Dongwon F&B Co., Ltd.　　(1)
68 Mabang-ro, Seocho-gu, Seoul, 06775,
Korea (South)　　(45%)
Tel.: (82) 805893223
Web Site: https://www.dongwonfnb.com
Rev.: $3,086,084,015
Assets: $1,589,002,192
Liabilities: $911,123,534
Net Worth: $677,878,658
Earnings: $69,659,385
Emp.: 3,191
Fiscal Year-end: 12/31/2022
Processed Foods Mfr & Distr
N.A.I.C.S.: 424460
Sung-yong Kim (CEO)

Subsidiary (Non-US):

DONGWON F&B (SHANGHAI) CO.,
LTD.　　(2)
Room 2406 Block A Far east International
Plaza, 319 Xianxia Road Changning,
Shanghai, 200051, China
Tel.: (86) 21 6278 0931
Frozen Seafood Distr
N.A.I.C.S.: 424460

DONGWON JAPAN Co., Ltd.　　(2)
10F Yotsuya Orchid Building 23-3, Daikyo-
cho Shinjuku-ku, Tokyo, 160-0015, Japan
Tel.: (81) 3 5363 5376
Frozen Seafood Distr
N.A.I.C.S.: 424460

Plant (Domestic):

Dongwon F&B Co., Ltd - Gangjin
Factory　　(2)
1405 Haegang-ro, Gangjin-eup, Seoul, 527
805, Jeollanam-do, Korea (South)
Tel.: (82) 61 432 9191
Seafood Product Distr
N.A.I.C.S.: 424460

Dongwon F&B Co., Ltd Jeongeup
Factory　　(2)
271-9 Usan-ri Jeongu-myeon, Jeongeup,
527 805, jeollabuk-do, Korea (South)
Tel.: (82) 63 536 7600
Frozen Seafood Distr
N.A.I.C.S.: 424460

Dongwon F&B Co., Ltd Suwon
Factory　　(2)
Cheoncheon-ro 210beon-gil, Jangan-gu,
Suwon, 440 310, Gyeonggi- do, Korea
(South)
Tel.: (82) 70 7860 2091
Frozen Seafood Distr
N.A.I.C.S.: 424460

Subsidiary (Domestic):

Dongwon Farms　　(2)
49 Ojung ro, Bucheon, 14643, Gyeonggi-
do, Korea (South)
Tel.: (82) 326803114
Web Site: http://www.dongwon.com
Livestock Feed Mfr
N.A.I.C.S.: 311119

Dongwon Home Food Co., Ltd.　　(2)
68 Mabang-ro Seocho-gu, Seoul, Korea
(South)
Tel.: (82) 2 589 6200

Web Site: http://www.dwhf.co.kr
Rev.: $558,000
Emp.: 1,639
Catering Services
N.A.I.C.S.: 722320
Shin Young Su *(CEO)*

Samjo Celltech Ltd.   **(2)**
289-7 Sinbong-Li Youngin-Myun, Asan, 336
822, Chungcheongnam-Do, Korea (South)
Tel.: (82) 2 598 7375
Food Products Mfr
N.A.I.C.S.: 311942

Subsidiary (US):

StarKist Co.   **(2)**
225 North Shore Dr Ste 400, Pittsburgh, PA
15212
Tel.: (412) 323-7400
Web Site: http://www.starkist.com
Sales Range: $550-599.9 Million
Producer, Distr & Marketer of Shelf-Stable
Seafood Products
N.A.I.C.S.: 311710
Frank Pogue *(VP-Innovation, Mktg, & Corp Affairs)*

Dongwon Industries Co., Ltd.   **(1)**
Dongwon Industries Building 7th floor
Mabang-ro 68 Yangjae-dong, Seocho-Gu,
Seoul, 137-717, Korea (South)
Tel.: (82) 25893333
Web Site: https://www.dwml.co.kr
Rev.: $6,923,140,168
Assets: $5,415,924,705
Liabilities: $3,185,124,051
Net Worth: $2,230,800,655
Earnings: $227,450,229
Emp.: 673
Fiscal Year-end: 12/31/2022
Catching, Processing, Transporting & Distributing of Marine Products, Including
Mackerel & Tuna
N.A.I.C.S.: 114119
Myoung-woo Lee *(Pres & CEO)*

Dongwon OLEV Corp.   **(1)**
103-6 Munji-dong Yuseong-gu, Daejeon,
Korea (South)
Tel.: (82) 2 589 4230
Web Site: http://www.dongwonolev.com
Electric Vehicle Mfr
N.A.I.C.S.: 333612

Dongwon Systems Corp.   **(1)**
68 Mabang-ro, Seocho-gu, Seoul, Korea
(South)
Tel.: (82) 25894700
Web Site:
    https://www.dongwonsystems.com
Rev.: $1,102,178,579
Assets: $1,113,430,876
Liabilities: $553,804,975
Net Worth: $559,625,902
Earnings: $55,480,639
Emp.: 1,686
Fiscal Year-end: 12/31/2022
Flexible Packing Material & Aluminum Foil
Mfr
N.A.I.C.S.: 326112
Jeom-Keun Cho *(CEO)*

Dongwon Wineplus Co. Ltd.   **(1)**
4th Fl Dongwon Industries Co Bldg 275,
Yangjae 2-dong Seocho-gu, Seoul, Korea
(South)
Tel.: (82) 2 589 3354
Web Site: http://www.dongwonwine.co.kr
Wine Mfr
N.A.I.C.S.: 312130

Societe de Conserverie en Afrique
S.A.   **(1)**
Nouveau Quai de Peche Mole 10, Dakar,
Senegal
Tel.: (221) 33 823 1235
Emp.: 400
Packaged Sea Food Mfr
N.A.I.C.S.: 311710
Jong-Koo Lee *(CEO)*

DONGWON METAL CO., LTD.
69 1-gil Buk-ri Jilyang-eup, Gyeong-
san, Gyongbuk, Korea (South)
Tel.: (82) 538592311
Web Site: http://www.dwmic.co.kr
Year Founded: 1971

018500—(KRS)
Rev.: $409,366,582
Assets: $370,779,316
Liabilities: $302,599,311
Net Worth: $68,180,005
Earnings: $13,807,731
Emp.: 538
Fiscal Year-end: 03/31/23
Automotive Parts Mfr & Sales
N.A.I.C.S.: 336110
Eun-Woo Lee *(CEO)*

Subsidiaries:

DAK Co., Ltd   **(1)**
644-7 Jang bang-ri Hal lim-myun, Kimhae,
Gyeong Nam, Korea (South)
Tel.: (82) 55 343 9883
Automotive Exterior Parts Mfr
N.A.I.C.S.: 336390

Dongwon Autopart Technology Ala-
bama L.L.C   **(1)**
12970 Montgomery Hwy, Luverne, AL
36049
Tel.: (334) 537-5000
Web Site: http://www.dwautoal.com
Automobile Parts Mfr
N.A.I.C.S.: 336390

Dongwon Metal Co., Ltd. - ASAN
PLANT   **(1)**
12-6 So dong-ri Eum bong-myun, 336864,
Asan, Chung Nam, Korea (South)
Tel.: (82) 41 530 3100
Sales Range: $100-124.9 Million
Emp.: 50
Automotive Exterior Parts Mfr
N.A.I.C.S.: 336390
Eun-Woo Lee *(CEO)*

Dongwon Metal Co., Ltd. - KYUNG-
SAN PLANT   **(1)**
330-1 Yang gi-ri Jil yang-eup, Gyeongsan,
712835, Gyong buk, Korea (South)
Tel.: (82) 53 859 2311
Web Site: http://www.dwmic.com
Sales Range: $100-124.9 Million
Emp.: 500
Automotive Exterior Parts Mfr
N.A.I.C.S.: 336390
Jung-Deok Seo *(Mng Dir)*

DONGWOO FARM TO TABLE CO., LTD.
1095 Donggunsan-ro, Seosu-myeon,
Gunsan, 54051, Jeollabuk-do, Korea
(South)
Tel.: (82) 634502000
Web Site:
    https://www.dongwoofarmtable.com
Year Founded: 1993
088910—(KRS)
Rev.: $258,362,012
Assets: $220,264,629
Liabilities: $71,651,723
Net Worth: $148,612,906
Earnings: $12,399,422
Emp.: 550
Fiscal Year-end: 12/31/22
Veal Product Mfr
N.A.I.C.S.: 112320
Kim Tae-Ho *(CEO)*

DONGWOON ANATECH CO., LTD.
13th Floor Pyeonghwa Building 22
Banpo-daero, Seocho-gu, Seoul, Ko-
rea (South)
Tel.: (82) 234658765
Web Site:
    https://www.dwanatech.com
Year Founded: 2006
094170—(KRS)
Rev.: $38,455,979
Assets: $48,355,851
Liabilities: $32,129,075
Net Worth: $16,226,776
Earnings: ($6,450,609)
Emp.: 124
Fiscal Year-end: 12/31/22
Semiconductor Devices Mfr

N.A.I.C.S.: 334413
Byung Bae Lim *(Dir)*

DONGWU CEMENT INTERNA-TIONAL LIMITED
Unit 8505B-06A Level 85 Interna-
tional Commerce Centre, 1 Austin
Road West, Kowloon, China (Hong
Kong)
Tel.: (852) 25200978   Ky
Web Site:
    http://www.dongwucement.com
Year Founded: 2011
0695—(HKG)
Rev.: $47,473,095
Assets: $131,916,983
Liabilities: $57,931,665
Net Worth: $73,985,318
Earnings: ($5,491,808)
Emp.: 218
Fiscal Year-end: 12/31/22
Investment Management Service
N.A.I.C.S.: 523940
Yingxia Xie *(Chm)*

Subsidiaries:

Suzhou Dongwu Cement Co.,
Ltd.   **(1)**
East Taipu River Bridge Southeast, Lili
Town, Wujiang, 215212, Jiangsu Province,
China
Tel.: (86) 51263622088
Investment Management Service
N.A.I.C.S.: 523940

DONGXING INTERNATIONAL INC.
Room 1001 International Finance
Building 633 Keji er Street, Songbei
District, Harbin, 150028, Heilongjiang,
China
Tel.: (86) 13946000887   DE
Rev.: $76,562
Assets: $114,364
Liabilities: $606,206
Net Worth: ($491,842)
Earnings: ($64,788)
Emp.: 7
Fiscal Year-end: 12/31/19
Investment Services
N.A.I.C.S.: 523999
Zhao Cheng *(Founder, Chm, CEO,
CFO & Chief Acctg Officer)*

DONGXING SECURITIES CO., LTD.
12F and 15F Xinsheng Building No 5
Financial Avenue, Xicheng District,
Beijing, 100033, China
Tel.: (86) 1066555171
Web Site: https://www.dxzq.net
Year Founded: 2008
601198—(SHG)
Rev.: $481,458,795
Assets: $14,286,176,981
Liabilities: $10,623,330,366
Net Worth: $3,662,846,614
Earnings: $72,614,543
Emp.: 50,000
Fiscal Year-end: 12/31/22
Security Brokerage & Investment
Management Services
N.A.I.C.S.: 523150
Li Juan *(Chm)*

DONGXU OPTOELECTRONIC TECHNOLOGY CO., LTD.
Lin 5 Courtyard No 23A Fuxing Road,
Haidian District, Beijing, 100036,
China
Tel.: (86) 1068297016
000413—(SSE)
Rev.: $827,320,872
Assets: $8,226,764,606
Liabilities: $4,908,779,605
Net Worth: $3,317,985,001

Earnings: ($231,076,076)
Fiscal Year-end: 12/31/22
Electronic Products Mfr
N.A.I.C.S.: 334413
Lipeng Wang *(Gen Mgr)*

DONGYANG E&P INC.
76 Jinwisandan-ro Jinwi-myeon,
Pyeongtaek, Gyeonggi, Korea
(South)
Web Site: http://www.dyenp.com
Year Founded: 1987
079960—(KRS)
Rev.: $429,375,266
Assets: $296,158,479
Liabilities: $82,424,884
Net Worth: $213,733,595
Earnings: $17,608,037
Emp.: 374
Fiscal Year-end: 12/31/22
Power Supply Unit Mfr
N.A.I.C.S.: 335999
Jae Man Kim *(CEO)*

DONGYANG ENGINEERING & CONSTRUCTION CORP.
Lexus NT bldg 1009 Daechi-dong,
Gangnam-gu, Seoul, 135-080, Korea
(South)
Tel.: (82) 234208000
Web Site:
    http://www.dongyangex.co.kr
Year Founded: 1968
Sales Range: $150-199.9 Million
Emp.: 290
Construction Services
N.A.I.C.S.: 236220
Kil-jae Lee *(CEO)*

Subsidiaries:

Dong Yang Energy Co., Ltd.   **(1)**
F7 Ilbeonga Shopping Mall, Manan-gu, 674-
26, Anyang, Gyeonggi-do, Korea (South)
Tel.: (82) 314639000
Solar Photovoltaic Device Mfr
N.A.I.C.S.: 334413

Dongyang Paragon Co., Ltd.   **(1)**
225-5 Nonhyeon-dong, Gangnam-gu,
Seoul, Korea (South)
Tel.: (82) 234960300
Web Site: http://www.dyparagon.co.kr
Real Estate Consulting Service
N.A.I.C.S.: 531210

DONGYANG EXPRESS CORP.
67 Heungan-daero, Dongan-gu, Any-
ang, 14119, Gyeonggi, Korea (South)
Tel.: (82) 25353111
Web Site:
    https://www.dyexpress.co.kr
Year Founded: 2005
084670—(KRS)
Rev.: $80,097,054
Assets: $126,937,253
Liabilities: $69,226,294
Net Worth: $57,710,959
Earnings: ($9,802,695)
Emp.: 643
Fiscal Year-end: 12/31/22
Express Bus Transportation Services
N.A.I.C.S.: 485210
Jae Cheol Lee *(Mng Dir)*

DONGYANG PISTON CO., LTD.
16 Haebong-ro 255 begon-gil,
Danwog-gu, Ansan, 425-839,
Gyeonggi-do, Korea (South)
Tel.: (82) 314899000
Web Site: https://www.dypiston.co.kr
Year Founded: 1977
092780—(KRS)
Rev.: $305,176,336
Assets: $287,062,048
Liabilities: $191,551,204
Net Worth: $95,510,845
Earnings: $2,206,395
Emp.: 540

Dongyang Piston Co., Ltd.—(Continued)

Fiscal Year-end: 12/31/22
Automobile Parts Distr
N.A.I.C.S.: 423120
Sun Gyum Hong *(Chm & CEO)*

Subsidiaries:

Dongyang Piston USA Inc.   **(1)**
42001 Koopernick Rd, Canton, MI 48187
Tel.: (734) 667-7051
Product Distribution Services
N.A.I.C.S.: 541614

Dongyang Tech Co., Ltd.   **(1)**
102 Mangsung 1 gil Gyeongju-si, Naenam-myeun, Seoul, 780-853, Gyeongsangbuk-do, Korea (South)
Tel.: (82) 547610983
Automotive Piston Mfr
N.A.I.C.S.: 336310

Oriens Co., Ltd.   **(1)**
1055-51 Anhyun-ro Gyeongju-si, Angang-eup, Seoul, 780-803, Gyeongsangbuk-do, Korea (South)
Tel.: (82) 547603000
Emp.: 124
Gasoline Piston Mfr
N.A.I.C.S.: 336310

Wendeng Dongyang Piston Co., Ltd.   **(1)**
8 Moonchang Road EDA, Wendeng, Shandong, China
Tel.: (86) 6318083798
Emp.: 98
Automotive Piston Mfr
N.A.I.C.S.: 336310

DONGYUE GROUP LIMITED
Zibo Dongyue Economic Development Zone, 151 Gloucester Road, Wanchai, China (Hong Kong)
Tel.: (852) 5338510072   **Ky**
Web Site:
    https://www.dongyuechem.com
Year Founded: 2006
DNGYF—(OTCIQ)
Rev.: $2,773,037,771
Assets: $3,412,293,559
Liabilities: $851,721,311
Net Worth: $2,560,572,247
Earnings: $578,217,352
Emp.: 7,065
Fiscal Year-end: 12/31/22
Chemical Products Mfr
N.A.I.C.S.: 325998
Jianhong Zhang *(Chm & CEO)*

Subsidiaries:

Shandong Dongyue Chemical Co., Ltd.   **(1)**
Dongyue international fluorine silicon material industry zone, Zibo, Shandong, China
Tel.: (86) 533 8220867
Fluoride Product Mfr
N.A.I.C.S.: 325180

Shandong Dongyue Polymer Material Co., Ltd   **(1)**
8th floor Industrial & Commerical Bank Building Xinghuan street, Zibo, 256400, China
Tel.: (86) 53 3822 2259
Sales Range: $25-49.9 Million
Emp.: 100
Fluorpolymer Product Mfr
N.A.I.C.S.: 325998

Shandong Huaxia Shenzhou New Co., Ltd.   **(1)**
Tangshan Town, Huantai County, Zibo, 256401, Shandong, China
Tel.: (86) 5338521777
Web Site: https://www.huaxiashenzhou.com
Fluoropolymer & Fluorinated Fine Chemical Mfr
N.A.I.C.S.: 325199

Shandong Huaxia Shenzhou New Materials Co., Ltd.   **(1)**
Tangshan town, Huantai County, Zibo, 256401, Shandong, China
Tel.: (86) 5338521169

Web Site: https://www.huaxiashenzhou.com
Polymer Mfr & Distr
N.A.I.C.S.: 325211

DONGZHU ECOLOGICAL ENVIRONMENT PROTECTION CO., LTD.
No 90 Xihu Middle Road, Xishan District, Wuxi, 214101, Jiangsu, China
Tel.: (86) 51088227528
Web Site: https://www.jsdzjg.com
Year Founded: 2001
603359—(SHG)
Rev.: $174,001,953
Assets: $1,296,579,146
Liabilities: $775,701,267
Net Worth: $520,877,879
Earnings: $4,883,842
Fiscal Year-end: 12/31/22
Landscape Management Services
N.A.I.C.S.: 541320
Xi Huiming *(Chm)*

DONKEYREPUBLIC HOLDING A/S
Skelbaekgade 4, 1717, Copenhagen, Denmark
Tel.: (45) 89887227   **DK**
Web Site: https://www.donkey.bike
Year Founded: 2014
DONKEY—(CSE)
Rev.: $16,609,512
Assets: $24,806,471
Liabilities: $16,537,165
Net Worth: $8,269,306
Earnings: ($3,339,555)
Emp.: 137
Fiscal Year-end: 12/31/23
Holding Company
N.A.I.C.S.: 551112
Caroline Soeborg Ahlefeldt *(Chm)*

DONMAR CAR SALES LTD
17990 102 Ave Nw, Edmonton, T5S 1M9, AB, Canada
Tel.: (780) 454-0422
Web Site:
    http://www.sundancemazda.com
Year Founded: 1975
Rev.: $16,550,000
Emp.: 25
New & Used Car Dealers
N.A.I.C.S.: 441110
Jerry Karpiuk *(Dir-Fin)*

DONPON
338020 No 58 Sec 2 Changxing Rd Luzhu Dist, West District, Taoyuan, Taiwan
Tel.: (886) 33249666
Web Site: http://www.donpon.com
Year Founded: 1995
3290—(TPE)
Rev.: $56,119,595
Assets: $97,160,460
Liabilities: $48,329,644
Net Worth: $48,830,816
Earnings: $3,644,374
Fiscal Year-end: 12/31/22
Electronic Product Distr
N.A.I.C.S.: 449210
Chien-Chang Tei *(Chm)*

DONSKOY FACTORY OF RADIOCOMPONENTS OJSC
Privokzalnaya 10 Mkr Tsentraln Donskoy Regio, 301760, Tula, Russia
Tel.: (7) 4874655747
Web Site: http://www.alund.ru
DZRDP—(MOEX)
Sales Range: Less than $1 Million
Building Material Mfr & Distr
N.A.I.C.S.: 327120
Aleksey Pankov *(Chm-Mgmt Bd & Gen Dir)*

DONT NOD ENTERTAINMENT SA
11 rue de Cambrai Parc du Pont de Flandre, Le Beauvaisis, 75019, Paris, France
Web Site: https://www.dontnod-bourse.com
Year Founded: 2008
ALDNE—(EUR)
Software Development Services
N.A.I.C.S.: 541511
Oskar Guilbert *(Chm)*

DONWAY FORD SALES LTD.
1975 Eglinton Avenue East, Scarborough, M1L 2N1, ON, Canada
Tel.: (416) 751-2200
Web Site:
    http://www.donwayford.com
Rev.: $44,086,090
Emp.: 90
New & Used Car Dealers
N.A.I.C.S.: 441110
Kim Williams *(Dir-Sls)*

DOODEH SANATI PARS COMPANY
No 12 Sepidar Alley Africa Street Haghani Blvd, Tehran, Iran
Tel.: (98) 21 88783062
Web Site: http://www.dsp.co.ir
Year Founded: 1994
Emp.: 187
Carbon Black Mfr
N.A.I.C.S.: 325180

DOOK MEDIA GROUP LIMITED.
Ground Floor Building 3 No 6441 Tingfeng Road, Fengjing Town Jinshan District, Shanghai, 201107, China
Tel.: (86) 2133608311
Web Site: https://www.dookbook.com
Year Founded: 2009
301025—(CHIN)
Rev.: $72,136,116
Assets: $113,552,712
Liabilities: $21,423,636
Net Worth: $92,129,076
Earnings: $8,749,728
Fiscal Year-end: 12/31/22
Digital Marketing Services
N.A.I.C.S.: 541810
Hua Nan *(Chm & Gen Mgr)*

DOOSAN CORPORATION
Doosan Tower 275 Jangchungdan-ro, Jung-gu, Seoul, Korea (South)
Tel.: (82) 233980114   **KR**
Web Site: https://www.doosan.com
Year Founded: 1896
000150—(KRS)
Rev.: $39,367,505
Assets: $338,778,023
Liabilities: $13,073,933
Net Worth: $325,704,091
Earnings: ($11,782,090)
Emp.: 195
Fiscal Year-end: 12/31/23
Holding Company
N.A.I.C.S.: 551112
Geewon Park *(Vice Chm-Doosan Grp)*

Subsidiaries:

Bobcat Bensheim GmbH   **(1)**
Berliner Ring 89, 64625, Bensheim, Germany
Tel.: (49) 625184820
Web Site: https://bobcat.de
N.A.I.C.S.: 423810

Bobcat Equipment Ltd.   **(1)**
1185 Matheson Blvd East, Mississauga, L4W 1B6, ON, Canada
Tel.: (905) 206-0022
Machinery Distr

N.A.I.C.S.: 423830

CJSC Doosan International Russia   **(1)**
Naryshkinskaya Alley 5/1 office 14-16, 125167, Moscow, Russia
Tel.: (7) 4957488008
Machinery Distr
N.A.I.C.S.: 423830

Clark Equipment Co.   **(1)**
3901 Morrison Ave, Bismarck, ND 58504-6875
Tel.: (701) 222-5000
Industrial Machinery Mfr & Distr
N.A.I.C.S.: 333248

DBC Co., Ltd.   **(1)**
4F No 959 Zhongzheng Rd, Zhonghe Dist, New Taipei City, 235, Taiwan
Tel.: (886) 282281168
Web Site: https://www.dbc.com.tw
N.A.I.C.S.: 325998

Doosan ATS America, LLC   **(1)**
11360 N Jog Rd Palm Beach, Winter Garden, FL 33418
Tel.: (561) 572-9031
Construction & Engineering Services
N.A.I.C.S.: 541330

Doosan Advertising Company   **(1)**
19th Fl Tower B Gateway No 18 Xiaguangli N Rd E Third Ring, Chaoyang Dist, Beijing, 100027, China
Tel.: (86) 1084547185
Advertising Services
N.A.I.C.S.: 541810
Gong Young Jin *(Gen Mgr)*

Doosan Babcock Energy Germany GmbH   **(1)**
OT Hohenthurm Droyssiger Weg 56, 06188, Landsberg, Germany
Tel.: (49) 3460233200
Web Site: http://www.doosanbabcock.de
Power Plant Installation Services
N.A.I.C.S.: 237130

Doosan Bears Inc.   **(1)**
Jamsil Baseball Stadium 25 Olympic-ro, Songpa-gu, Seoul, Korea (South)
Tel.: (82) 222401777
Web Site: https://www.doosanbears.com
Sports Services
N.A.I.C.S.: 611620

Doosan Bobcat Chile S.A.   **(1)**
Avenida Americo Vespucio 1151-Mega Centro, Quilicura, Santiago, Chile
Tel.: (56) 229643050
Web Site: http://www.doosanbobcat.cl
Heavy Equipment Distr
N.A.I.C.S.: 423810

Doosan Bobcat China Co., Ltd.   **(1)**
NO 68 Suhong East Road SIP, Jiangsu, China
Tel.: (86) 51287777777
N.A.I.C.S.: 333120

Doosan Bobcat EMEA s.r.o.   **(1)**
U Kodetky 1810, 263 12, Dobris, Czech Republic
Tel.: (420) 318532444
Web Site: https://www.bobcatdobris.cz
Emp.: 1,000
Construction Machinery Mfr
N.A.I.C.S.: 333120

Doosan Bobcat Global Collaboration Center, Inc.   **(1)**
5th St Towers 150 S 5th St, Minneapolis, MN 55402
Tel.: (320) 693-4967
N.A.I.C.S.: 333120

Doosan Bobcat Inc   **(1)**
Bundang, Jung-gu, Seoul, Gyeonggi-do, Korea (South)
Tel.: (82) 233980993
Web Site: https://www.doosanbobcat.com
Rev.: $3,868,699,952
Assets: $5,790,496,048
Liabilities: $2,353,748,530
Net Worth: $3,436,747,518
Earnings: $233,445,601
Emp.: 75
Fiscal Year-end: 12/31/2019
Construction Equipment Mfr & Distr
N.A.I.C.S.: 333120

Scott Park *(Pres & CEO)*

Doosan Bobcat Korea Co., Ltd. (1)
155 Jeongjail-Ro, Bundang-gu, Seongnam,
Gyeonggi do, Korea (South)
Tel.: (82) 3151793300
N.A.I.C.S.: 333120

Doosan Bobcat Singapore Pte.
Ltd. (1)
3A International Business Park 08-02 ICON
IBP, Singapore, 609935, Singapore
Tel.: (65) 6490200
Industrial Machinery Mfr
N.A.I.C.S.: 333248

Doosan China Financial Leasing
Corp. (1)
20/F Tower B Gateway No 18 Xiaguangli
North Road East Third Ring, Chaoyang Dis-
trict, Beijing, 100027, China
Tel.: (86) 10 8454 7200
Web Site: http://www.doosan.com
Financial Lending Services
N.A.I.C.S.: 522220

Doosan Corporation - Iksan
factory (1)
889 Palbong-dong, Iksan, Jeonbuk, Korea
(South)
Tel.: (82) 63 830 8320
Electronic Products Mfr
N.A.I.C.S.: 334419

Doosan Corporation - Jeungpyeong
Factory (1)
661 Yonggang-ri, Jeungpyeong, 101-534,
Chungbuk, Korea (South)
Tel.: (82) 43 820 8220
Web Site: http://www.doosan.com
Emp.: 400
Photovoltaic Device Mfr
N.A.I.C.S.: 334413
Sungwoo Jo *(Gen Mgr)*

Doosan Digital Innovation America
LLC (1)
400 Perimeter Center Ter Ste 750, Atlanta,
GA 30346
Tel.: (770) 353-3800
Industrial Machinery Mfr
N.A.I.C.S.: 333248

Doosan Electro-Materials (Changshu)
Co., Ltd. (1)
No 168 Hualian Road Tonggang Industrial
Park, Changshu Economic Development
Zone, Changshu, China
Tel.: (86) 51282359980
N.A.I.C.S.: 333120

Doosan Electro-Materials (Shenzhen)
Limited (1)
4B 209-210 International Commerce & Ex-
hibition Center No 1001, Hong Hua Road
Fu Tien Trade Zone, Shenzhen, China
Tel.: (86) 75582788231
N.A.I.C.S.: 333120

Doosan Electro-Materials America,
LLC (1)
2570 N 1st St Ste 23, San Jose, CA 95131
Tel.: (408) 273-4531
Machinery Distr
N.A.I.C.S.: 423830

Doosan Electro-Materials Singapore
Pte Co., Ltd. (1)
No 3International 03-14 Nordic European
Centre, Singapore, 609927, Singapore
Tel.: (65) 6862 6327
Sales Range: $50-74.9 Million
Emp.: 8
Electric Component Whslr
N.A.I.C.S.: 423690

Doosan Electro-Materials Singapore
Pte Ltd (1)
No 10 Toh Guan Road 04-01B TT Interna-
tional Tradepark, Singapore, 608838, Sin-
gapore
Tel.: (65) 68626327
Civil Engineering Construction Services
N.A.I.C.S.: 237990

Doosan Electro-Materials Vietnam
Co., Ltd. (1)
Workshop No 3 & workshop No 4 Lot NQ
Dai An, Industrial Zone Km 51 Highway 5

Tu Minh Ward, Hai Duong, Hai Duong, Viet-
nam
Tel.: (84) 2203833656
N.A.I.C.S.: 333120

Doosan Enerbility (1)
22 Doosan volvo-ro, Seongsan-gu,
Changwon, 51711, Gyeongsangnam, Korea
(South) **(100%)**
Tel.: (82) 552786114
Rev.: $13,632,080,000
Assets: $19,053,930,000
Liabilities: $10,688,790,000
Net Worth: $8,365,140,000
Earnings: $401,216,900
Emp.: 5,000
Fiscal Year-end: 12/31/2023
Power Plant Mfr
N.A.I.C.S.: 237120
Geewon Park *(Chm & CEO)*

Subsidiary (Domestic):

Doosan Mecatec Co., Ltd. (2)
64 Sinchon-dong, Changwon,
Gyeongsangnam-do, Korea (South)
Tel.: (82) 552795555
Web Site: http://www.doosanmecatec.com
Sales Range: $150-199.9 Million
Emp.: 1,000
Industrial Equipment Mfr
N.A.I.C.S.: 811310
Ho Seon Shin *(CEO)*

Subsidiary (Non-US):

Doosan Vina Haiphong Co., Ltd. (2)
Km 92 No 5 Highway, So Dau Ward Hong
Bang District, Haiphong, Vietnam
Web Site:
http://www.doosanvinahaiphong.com
Sales Range: $10-24.9 Million
Emp.: 1,000
Specialists in Oversized & Overweighted
Steel Structures, Boilers, Pressure Vessels,
Storage Tanks, Steel Fabrication & Piping
Works
N.A.I.C.S.: 332410

Subsidiary (US):

HFControls (2)
1624 W Crosby Ste 124, Carrollton, TX
75006
Tel.: (469) 568-6500
Web Site: http://www.hfcontrols.com
Sales Range: $25-49.9 Million
Emp.: 70
Mfr of High-Quality Control Systems for
Power Plants & Industrial Plants
N.A.I.C.S.: 332911

Doosan GridTech LLC (1)
71 Columbia St Ste 300, Seattle, WA 98104
Software System Services
N.A.I.C.S.: 541511

Doosan H2 Innovation Co., Ltd. (1)
260 Changnyong-Daero, Yeongtong-gu, Suwon, Gyeonggi do, Korea (South)
Tel.: (82) 3180667730
N.A.I.C.S.: 333120

Doosan Heavy Industries America
LLC (1)
400 Kelby St Parker Plz 10th Fl, Fort Lee,
NJ 07024
Tel.: (201) 944-4554
Machinery Whslr
N.A.I.C.S.: 423830

Doosan Heavy Industries Japan
Corp. (1)
Room 410 Sanno Park Tower 2-11-1, Naga-
tacho Chiyoda-ku, Tokyo, 100-6104, Japan
Tel.: (81) 355105460
Machinery Whslr
N.A.I.C.S.: 423830

Doosan Heavy Industries Vietnam
Co., Ltd. (1)
Dung Quat Economic Zone, Binh Son,
Quang Ngai, Binh Thuan, Vietnam
Tel.: (84) 2553618900
Web Site: https://www.doosan-vina.com
Engine & Turbine Mfr
N.A.I.C.S.: 333611
Jeong Young Chil *(CEO & Gen Dir)*

Doosan Industrial Development Co.,
Ltd. (1)

105-7 Nonhyeon-dong Gangnam-gu, Seoul,
Korea (South)
Tel.: (82) 25103114
Web Site: http://www.hdkid.com
Sales Range: $250-299.9 Million
Emp.: 890
Construction Services
N.A.I.C.S.: 236210

Doosan Industrial Vehicle America
Corp. (1)
2475 Mill Center Pkwy Ste 400, Buford, GA
30518
Tel.: (678) 745-2200
Web Site: http://www.doosanlift.com
Sales Range: $1-9.9 Million
Forklift Mfr
N.A.I.C.S.: 333924
Eddie Marshall *(Coord-Parts Mktg)*

Doosan Industrial Vehicle Europe
N.V. (1)
Europark-Noord 36A, 9100, Saint-Niklaas,
Belgium
Tel.: (32) 37600987
Web Site: http://doosan-iv.eu
Forklift Mfr
N.A.I.C.S.: 333924

Doosan Industrial Vehicle U.K.,
Ltd. (1)
12 Kilvey Road, Brackmills Industrial Estate,
Northampton, NN4 7BQ, United Kingdom
Tel.: (44) 1604825600
Web Site: http://doosanflt.com
Forklift Mfr
N.A.I.C.S.: 333924

Doosan Infracore (China) Investment
Co., Ltd. (1)
19th Fl Tower B Gateway No 18 Xiaguangli
North Road East Third Ring, Chaoyang Dis-
trict, Beijing, 100027, China
Tel.: (86) 1084547000
Industrial Machinery Mfr
N.A.I.C.S.: 333248

Doosan Infracore China Co., Ltd. (1)
No 28 Wuzhishan Road, ECO and Tech
Development Zone, Yantai, Shandong,
China
Tel.: (86) 5356382000
Industrial Machinery Mfr & Distr
N.A.I.C.S.: 333248

Doosan Infracore North America
LLC (1)
2905 Shawnee Industrial Way, Suwanee,
GA 30024
Tel.: (678) 714-6000
Web Site: http://na.doosanequipment.com
Heavy Equipment Distr
N.A.I.C.S.: 423810

Doosan International Australia Pty
Ltd (1)
11A Columbia Way, Baulkham Hills, 2153,
NSW, Australia
Tel.: (61) 288482701
Machinery Distr
N.A.I.C.S.: 423830

Doosan International South Africa Pty
Ltd (1)
Unit 1 Dakota Business Park 15 Dakota
Crescent Airport Park, Germiston, 1401,
South Africa
Tel.: (27) 118647574
Web Site: http://www.doosansa.co.za
Machinery & Equipment Mfr
N.A.I.C.S.: 333248

Doosan International UK Ltd. (1)
Unit 6 3- Nantgarw Park Treforest Ind Es-
tate, Cardiff, CF15 7QU, United Kingdom
Tel.: (44) 1443845650
Machinery Distr
N.A.I.C.S.: 423830

Doosan Logistics Europe GmbH (1)
Am Stieg 17 OT Freiwalde, Bersteland,
15910, Brandenburg, Germany
Tel.: (49) 354742080
N.A.I.C.S.: 333120

Doosan Logistics Solution Co.,
Ltd. (1)
7F 10 Suji-ro 112beon-gil, Suji-gu, Yongin,
16858, Gyeonggi-do, Korea (South)
Tel.: (82) 312701800

Web Site: https://www.doosanlogistics.com
Emp.: 300
Software Development Services
N.A.I.C.S.: 541511
Kim Hwan Sung *(CEO)*

Doosan Magazine (1)
Doosan Bldg 726 Eonju-ro, Gangnam-gu,
Seoul, Korea (South)
Tel.: (82) 25104500
Sales Range: $25-49.9 Million
Emp.: 180
Magazine Advertising Services
N.A.I.C.S.: 541840
Jaechur Seung *(VP)*

Doosan Mobility Innovation (Shen-
zhen) Co. Ltd. (1)
B403 Building G4 TCL International E City
Shuguang Community, Xili Street Nanshan
District, Shenzhen, China
Tel.: (86) 75585272687
N.A.I.C.S.: 333120

Doosan Mobility Innovation Inc. (1)
Suji-ro 112beon-gil 10, Suji-gu, Yongin,
16858, Gyeonggi-do, Korea (South)
Tel.: (82) 312701703
Web Site: https://www.doosanmobility.com
Software Development Services
N.A.I.C.S.: 541511

Doosan Power Systems Arabia Com-
pany Limited (1)
8th Floor Al Olaya Tower Prince Sultan
Road, PO Box 7937, Al Mohammadiah,
Jeddah, 23617, Saudi Arabia
Tel.: (966) 126155550
Industrial Machinery Mfr
N.A.I.C.S.: 333248

Doosan Power Systems Co.,
Ltd. (1)
Doosan House Crawley Business Quarter
Manor Royal, Crawley, RH10 9AD, West
Sussex, United Kingdom
Tel.: (44) 1293 612888
Web Site:
http://www.doosanpowersystems.com
Power Plant Construction & Maintenance
Services
N.A.I.C.S.: 237130
Myong Dong Ryu *(CEO)*

Subsidiary (Non-US):

AE&E Lentjes Praha s.r.o. (2)
Tel.: (420) 241095150
Power Boiler & Heat Exchanger Mfr
N.A.I.C.S.: 332410

Doosan Lentjes GmbH (2)
Daniel-Goldbach-Str 19, 40880, Ratingen,
Germany
Tel.: (49) 2102 166 0
Web Site:
http://www.doosanpowersystems.com
Sales Range: $25-49.9 Million
Emp.: 50
Power Generation Plant Construction & En-
gineering Services
N.A.I.C.S.: 237990
Thomas Wehrheim *(COO)*

Doosan Power Systems India Private
Ltd. (1)
16th Floor DLF Square Jacaranda Marg
Near NH-8 DLF Phase-II, Gurgaon, 122
002, Haryana, India
Tel.: (91) 1244398200
Construction & Engineering Services
N.A.I.C.S.: 541330

Doosan Robotics Inc. (1)
79 Saneop-ro 156beon-gil, Gwonseon-gu,
Suwon, Gyeonggi-do, Korea (South)
Tel.: (82) 3180145500
Software Development Services
N.A.I.C.S.: 541511

Doosan Skoda Power s.r.o (1)
Tylova 1/57, 301 28, Plzen, Czech Republic
Tel.: (420) 378185961
Industrial Machinery Mfr
N.A.I.C.S.: 333248

Doosan Tower Corporation (1)
Doosan Tower 18-12 Euljiro 6-ga, Jung-gu,
Seoul, 100-730, Korea (South)
Tel.: (82) 233982386

Doosan Corporation—(Continued)

Web Site: http://www.doosan.com
Sales Range: $200-249.9 Million
Emp.: 1,000
Apparel Designing Services
N.A.I.C.S.: 315250

Doosan Turbomachinery Services Inc. (1)
12000 N P St, La Porte, TX 77571
Tel.: (713) 364-7500
Industrial Machinery Mfr
N.A.I.C.S.: 333248

HFC Controls. Corp. (1)
1631 W Crosby Rd Suite 104, Carrollton, TX 75006
Tel.: (469) 568-6500
Web Site: http://www.hfcontrols.com
Electronic Components Mfr
N.A.I.C.S.: 334419

Hanjung Power Co., Ltd. (1)
PO Box 2803, Boroko, Port Moresby, Papua New Guinea
Tel.: (675) 320 0529
Electric Power Distribution Services
N.A.I.C.S.: 221122

Oricom Inc. (1)
726 Eonju-ro, Gangnam-gu, Seoul, Korea (South)
Tel.: (82) 25104100
Web Site: https://www.oricom.com
Rev.: $145,798,640
Assets: $164,481,937
Liabilities: $82,749,274
Net Worth: $81,732,663
Earnings: $9,423,504
Emp.: 299
Fiscal Year-end: 12/31/2022
Media Advertising & Integrated Marketing Communications Services
N.A.I.C.S.: 541810
Ho-Tae Kim (Gen Mgr)

Rushlift Ltd. (1)
12 Kilvey Road, Brackmills Industrial Estate, Northampton, NN4 7BQ, United Kingdom
Tel.: (44) 8007315035
Web Site: https://www.rushlift.co.uk
N.A.I.C.S.: 811310

Skoda Power Private Ltd. (1)
Plot No 448A Enkay Square Ground Floor Vanijya Nikunj, Udyog Vihar- Phase 5, Gurgaon, 122016, Haryana, India
Tel.: (91) 1244559500
N.A.I.C.S.: 221112

DOOSAN TESNA INC
72 Road 16 Sandanro, Pyeongtaek, 17746, Gyeonggi-do, Korea (South)
Tel.: (82) 316468500
Web Site: https://www.doosan-tesna.com
Year Founded: 2002
131970—(KRS)
Rev.: $212,962,104
Assets: $588,301,835
Liabilities: $350,659,140
Net Worth: $237,642,695
Earnings: $40,139,437
Emp.: 574
Fiscal Year-end: 12/31/22
Semiconductor Testing Services
N.A.I.C.S.: 541380
Kim Do-Won (CEO)

Subsidiaries:

Tesna Inc. - Anseong Factory (1)
116 Guansangil Wongokmyeon, Anseong, Kyungki, Korea (South)
Tel.: (82) 316468500
Semiconductor Product Mfr
N.A.I.C.S.: 334413

DOOVLE LIMITED
1 Clive Place, Esher, KT10 9LH, Surrey, United Kingdom
Tel.: (44) 1372464753
Web Site: http://www.doovle.com
Sales Range: $1-9.9 Million
Web Applications
N.A.I.C.S.: 513210

Stephen M. Anderson (CEO)

DOPLA S.P.A.
Via Nuova Trevigiana 126, Casale sul Sile, 31032, Treviso, Italy
Tel.: (39) 04223885   IT
Web Site: http://www.dopla.it
Year Founded: 1964
Sales Range: $200-249.9 Million
Emp.: 450
Plastic Cup, Plate & Cutlery Mfr
N.A.I.C.S.: 326199
Carlo Levada (Gen Mgr)

Subsidiaries:

F. Bender Limited (1)
Gresford Industrial Park Chester Road, Wrexham, LL12 8LX, United Kingdom
Tel.: (44) 1978 855 661
Web Site: http://www.benders.co.uk
Sanitary Food & Beverage Containers & Service Products Mfr
N.A.I.C.S.: 322219
Andrew Cunliffe (Mng Dir)

DOPPELMAYR GROUP
Konrad Doppelmayr Str 1, PO Box 20, Wolfurt, 6922, Austria
Tel.: (43) 5574604
Web Site:
   http://www.doppelmayr.com
Year Founded: 1892
Sales Range: $550-599.9 Million
Emp.: 2,100
Holding Company
N.A.I.C.S.: 551112

Subsidiaries:

ALEX - Mechkov OOD (1)
ul Yuri Venelin 36, 1142, Sofia, Bulgaria
Tel.: (359) 298 73955
Ropeway Engineering Services
N.A.I.C.S.: 541330

Briton Engineering Developments Ltd. (1)
Lee Mills Scholes Holmfirth, Huddersfield, HD9 1RT, United Kingdom
Tel.: (44) 148 4689933
Web Site: http://www.snowflex.com
Emp.: 10
Ropeway Engineering Services
N.A.I.C.S.: 541330
Richard Platt (Mgr-Workshop)

CWA Constructions SA (1)
Bornfeldstrasse 6, 4601, Olten, Switzerland
Tel.: (41) 622056000
Web Site: https://www.cwa.ch
Railroad Equipment Mfr & Distr
N.A.I.C.S.: 336510
Christoph Grob (Head-Sales-Marketing)

Doan Viet Co. Ltd (1)
No 45 Alley 97 Van Cao Str, Ba Dinh District, Hanoi, Vietnam
Tel.: (84) 438 464610
Ropeway Engineering Services
N.A.I.C.S.: 541330

Doppelmayr A/S (1)
Svetsrvaegen 1, PO Box 316, 686626, Sunne, Scandinavia, Sweden
Tel.: (46) 65688570
Sales Range: $25-49.9 Million
Emp.: 8
Support Activities for Transportation
N.A.I.C.S.: 488999

Doppelmayr Andorra S.A. (1)
Aveinjuda Joan Marti 114 Edifici Prat del Rector, Despatx 2 Encamp, Andorra La Vella, 200, Andorra
Tel.: (376) 732732
Sales Range: $25-49.9 Million
Emp.: 23
Holding Company
N.A.I.C.S.: 551112
Gulien Croses (Mng Dir)

Doppelmayr Australia Pty. Ltd. (1)
57 Lee Ave, PO Box 515, Jindabyne, 2627, NSW, Australia
Tel.: (61) 264562385
Web Site: http://www.doppelmayr.com

Sales Range: $50-74.9 Million
Emp.: 8
Industrial Machinery & Equipment Whslr
N.A.I.C.S.: 423830
Bruce Tyner (Gen Mgr)

Doppelmayr Brasil Sistemas de Transporte Ltda. (1)
Av Paulista 2421-11 and ar-Sala 04, Bela Vista, Sao Paulo, 01310-300, Brazil
Tel.: (55) 1131923865
Ropeway & Cable Car Mfr & Distr
N.A.I.C.S.: 336999

Doppelmayr Cable Car GmbH (1)
Konrad-Doppelmayr-Strasse 1, Postfach 6, 6922, Wolfurt, Austria
Tel.: (43) 55746041230
Ropeway & Cable Car Mfr & Distr
N.A.I.C.S.: 336999

Doppelmayr Canada Ltd. (1)
800 St Nicolas Street, Saint-Jerome, J7Y 4C8, QC, Canada
Tel.: (450) 432-1128
Web Site: http://www.doppelmayr.com
Emp.: 80
Ropeway Engineering Services
N.A.I.C.S.: 541330
Andre Lamoureux (Gen Mgr)

Doppelmayr Chile Holding SpA (1)
Bucarest 150 piso 6 of 601, Providencia, Santiago, 7510018, Chile
Tel.: (56) 993196582
Ropeway & Cable Car Mfr & Distr
N.A.I.C.S.: 336999

Doppelmayr Colombia S.A.S. (1)
Carrera 7 A No 123-25 Piso 5 Edificio MPH 123, 110111, Bogota, Colombia
Tel.: (57) 15804829
Ropeway & Cable Car Mfr & Distr
N.A.I.C.S.: 336999

Doppelmayr Finn Oy (1)
Mekaanikonkatu 21A, 00880, Helsinki, Finland
Tel.: (358) 96844300
Web Site: http://www.doppelmayr.com
Sales Range: $50-74.9 Million
Emp.: 5
Industrial Machinery & Equipment Whslr
N.A.I.C.S.: 423830

Doppelmayr France S.A. (1)
837/903 Rue de l'Isle Pole industriel de Frejus, PO Box 50080, 73500, Modane, France
Tel.: (33) 479050371
Web Site: http://www.doppelmayr.com
Sales Range: $25-49.9 Million
Emp.: 45
Overhead Traveling Crane Hoist & Monorail System Mfr
N.A.I.C.S.: 333923
Bernard Teiller (Chm)

Doppelmayr Holding AG (1)
Rickenbacherstrasse 8-10, Wolfurt, 6922, Austria
Tel.: (43) 55746040
Web Site: http://www.doppelmayr.com
Sales Range: $250-299.9 Million
Emp.: 1,000
Holding Company
N.A.I.C.S.: 551112
Michael Doppelmayr (Mng Dir)

Doppelmayr India Private Limited (1)
B-505 5th Floor Pioneer Urban Square Sector 62 Golf Course Ext Road, Gurgaon, 122098, India
Tel.: (91) 1244216313
Ropeway & Cable Car Mfr & Distr
N.A.I.C.S.: 336999

Doppelmayr Italia Srl (1)
Zona Industriale 14, Lana, 39011, Bolzano, Italy
Tel.: (39) 0473262100
Web Site: http://www.doppelmayr.com
Sales Range: $25-49.9 Million
Emp.: 100
Heavy & Civil Engineering Construction
N.A.I.C.S.: 237990

Doppelmayr Lifts (NZ) Ltd. (1)
16 Queen St, PO Box 11, 7673, Coalgate, New Zealand
Tel.: (64) 33182725

Web Site: http://www.doppelmayr.co.nz
Sales Range: $50-74.9 Million
Emp.: 3
Industrial Machinery & Equipment Whslr
N.A.I.C.S.: 423830

Doppelmayr Mexico S.A. de C.V. (1)
Av Paseo de las Palmas 239 Piso 3, Col Lomas de Chapultepec, 11000, Mexico, Mexico
Tel.: (52) 5562741092
Ropeway & Cable Car Mfr & Distr
N.A.I.C.S.: 336999

Doppelmayr New Zealand Ltd. (1)
39 Islington Ave, Islington, Christchurch, 8042, New Zealand
Tel.: (64) 33182725
Web Site: https://www.doppelmayr.nz
Ropeway Engineering Services
N.A.I.C.S.: 484210
Garreth Hayman (Gen Mgr)

Doppelmayr Panama Corp. (1)
PH Soleo 2nd Floor Suite 218, Blvd Martin Torrijos Panama Pacifico Howard, Panama, Panama Oeste, Panama
Tel.: (507) 2098097
Ropeway & Cable Car Mfr & Distr
N.A.I.C.S.: 336999

Doppelmayr Peru S.A.C. (1)
Av Juan de Aliaga 425 Int 05 Ofc 403 Magdalena del Mar, Lima, Peru
Tel.: (51) 14800685
Ropeway & Cable Car Mfr & Distr
N.A.I.C.S.: 336999

Doppelmayr Polska Sp z o.o. (1)
Al Army 220, 43-316, Bielsko-Biala, Poland
Tel.: (48) 338 138328
Web Site: http://www.doppelmayr-polska.pl
Emp.: 5
Ropeway Engineering Services
N.A.I.C.S.: 541330
Bogeam Tarko (Mgr)

Doppelmayr Portugal Unipessola, Lda. (1)
Rua Novas dos Mercadores 33-A, 1990-239, Lisbon, Portugal
Tel.: (351) 967886520
Ropeway & Cable Car Mfr & Distr
N.A.I.C.S.: 336999

Doppelmayr Scandinavia AB (1)
Svetsarevagen 1, 68633, Sunne, Sweden
Tel.: (46) 565688570
Web Site: http://www.doppelmayr.com
Sales Range: $25-49.9 Million
Emp.: 7
Fiber Optic Cable Mfr
N.A.I.C.S.: 335921

Doppelmayr Seilbahnen GmbH (1)
Rickenbacherstrasse 8-10, PO Box 20, Stetten, 6922, Wolfurt, Austria
Tel.: (43) 226272508
Web Site: http://www.doppelmayr.com
Sales Range: $400-449.9 Million
Conveyor & Conveying Equipment Mfr
N.A.I.C.S.: 333922
Michael Doppelmayr (Mng Dir)

Doppelmayr Skidalyftur hf. (1)
PO Box 333, Akureyri, Iceland
Tel.: (354) 4621720
Web Site: http://www.doppelmayr.com
Sales Range: $50-74.9 Million
Emp.: 1
Industrial Machinery & Equipment Whslr
N.A.I.C.S.: 423830

Doppelmayr Skioalyftur ehf (1)
Kaupangi v/Myrarveg, 600, Akureyri, Iceland
Tel.: (354) 4604440
Ropeway & Cable Car Mfr & Distr
N.A.I.C.S.: 336999

Doppelmayr South Caucasus (1)
Green Building Marjanishwili Str 6, 0102, Tbilisi, Georgia
Tel.: (995) 322252505
Ropeway & Cable Car Mfr & Distr
N.A.I.C.S.: 336999

Doppelmayr Transport Technology GmbH (1)
Konrad-Doppelmayr-Str 1, 6922, Wolfurt, Austria

Tel.: (43) 55746041800
Web Site: https://www.doppelmayr-mts.com
Ropeway Engineering Services
N.A.I.C.S.: 484210
Hermann Fruhstuck *(Mng Dir)*

Doppelmayr Turkey Asansor Teleferik ve Kablolu Tasima Sistemleri Ins. Taah. Ltd. Sti (1)
Ahmet Mithat Efendi sk 52/4 Cankaya, 06550, Ankara, Turkiye
Tel.: (90) 312 4390290
Ropeway Engineering Services
N.A.I.C.S.: 541330

Doppelmayr Turkey Asansor Teleferik ve Kablolu Tasiyici Sistemler Ins. Taah. Ltd. Sti. (1)
Ahmet Mithat Efendi sk 52/4, Cankaya, 06550, Ankara, Turkiye
Tel.: (90) 3124390290
Ropeway & Cable Car Mfr & Distr
N.A.I.C.S.: 336999

Doppelmayr USA, Inc (1)
12441 W 49th Ave Ste 1, Wheat Ridge, CO 80033
Tel.: (303) 277-9476
Web Site: http://www.doppelmayrusa.com
Sales Range: $25-49.9 Million
Emp.: 100
Transportation Equipment Mfr
N.A.I.C.S.: 336999
Mark Bee *(Pres)*

Doppelmayr Vietnam Co. Ltd. (1)
Room 1003 10th Floor Zen Plaza Building 54-56 Nguyen Trai Street, Ben Thanh Ward District 1, Ho Chi Minh City, Vietnam
Tel.: (84) 2839255360
Ropeway & Cable Car Mfr & Distr
N.A.I.C.S.: 336999

Doppelmayr do Brasil Sistemas de Transporte Ltda. (1)
Praia de Botafogo 501 - 1 Andar Torre Pao de Acucar, 22250-040, Rio de Janeiro, Brazil
Tel.: (55) 212 5866338
Ropeway Engineering Services
N.A.I.C.S.: 541330

Doppelmayr lanove drahy, spol. s r. o. (1)
Drazni 7, 62700, Brno, Czech Republic
Tel.: (420) 531022266
Web Site: http://www.doppelmayr.cz
Sales Range: $50-74.9 Million
Holding Company
N.A.I.C.S.: 551112
Norbert Beneder *(Sec)*

Frey AG (1)
Erlenwaldlistrasse 11, 6370, Oberdorf, Switzerland
Tel.: (41) 6202161
Web Site: https://www.freyag-stans.ch
Ropeway Installation Control Product Mfr
N.A.I.C.S.: 335314

GB Impex (Pvt.) Limited (1)
313 Service Road East F-11/4, 44000, Islamabad, Pakistan
Tel.: (92) 518311733
Ropeway & Cable Car Mfr & Distr.
N.A.I.C.S.: 336999

Garaventa AG (1)
Birkenstr 47, 6343, Rotkreuz, Switzerland
Tel.: (41) 418 591111
Ropeway Engineering Services
N.A.I.C.S.: 541330

Garaventa Algerie Sarl (1)
26 Lot Ben Achour, 16002, Cheraga, Algeria
Tel.: (213) 213 71675
Ropeway Engineering Services
N.A.I.C.S.: 541330

Garaventa SA (1)
Rte des Trembles 14, 1950, Sion, Switzerland
Tel.: (41) 273276900
Ropeway & Cable Car Mfr & Distr
N.A.I.C.S.: 336999

Ing. Tomas Fried (1)
Pribinova 3026/38, 010 01, Zilina, Slovakia
Tel.: (421) 905 653141

Ropeway Engineering Services
N.A.I.C.S.: 541330

Input Projektentwicklungs GmbH (1)
Birkenstrasse 2, Hallwang, 5300, Salzburg, Austria
Tel.: (43) 6626686223
Web Site: https://www.input-projekt.com
Business Consulting Services
N.A.I.C.S.: 541611

Inversiones Doppelmayr de Venezuela C.A. (1)
Av Francisco de Miranda Torre E CC Centro Lido Nivel Piso 7 OFC 73-E, El Rosal, Caracas, 1060, Venezuela
Tel.: (58) 2129536444
Ropeway & Cable Car Mfr & Distr
N.A.I.C.S.: 336999

LTW Intralogistics GmbH (1)
Achstrasse 53, 6922, Wolfurt, Austria
Tel.: (43) 557468290
Ropeway & Cable Car Mfr & Distr
N.A.I.C.S.: 336999

N. Argyropoulos & SIA E.E. (1)
Mitropoleos 43 I32 Marousi, 15124, Athens, Greece
Tel.: (30) 210 8027030
Ropeway Engineering Services
N.A.I.C.S.: 541330
Nikolaos Argyropoulos *(Mgr)*

Nepal Ropeway Systems (P) Ltd (1)
PO Box 4416, Naxal Nagpokhari, Kathmandu, Nepal
Tel.: (977) 144 34718
Ropeway Engineering Services
N.A.I.C.S.: 541330

Nippon Cable Co. Ltd. (1)
3-1-4 Akanehama, Narashino, 275-0024, Chiba, Japan
Tel.: (81) 474 517 111
Web Site: http://www.nipponcable.com
Cable Mfr
N.A.I.C.S.: 332618
Masayoshi Ohkubo *(Pres & CEO)*

OOO Doppelmayr Russia (1)
Gastello Str 23A Adler District Krasnodar Krai, 354340, Sochi, Russia
Tel.: (7) 84993220502
Ropeway Engineering Services
N.A.I.C.S.: 541330

PT Hans R. Jost (1)
Jl H Marzuki 9 RT 12 RW 02, Menteng Dalam Pancoran-Tebet, South Jakarta, 12870, Indonesia
Tel.: (62) 218352400
Ropeway & Cable Car Mfr & Distr
N.A.I.C.S.: 336999

Pilet Intersistemas S.R.L (1)
Av de los Constituyentes 4621, 1431, Buenos Aires, Argentina
Tel.: (54) 114 5231010
Ropeway Engineering Services
N.A.I.C.S.: 541330

Promociones Munich, C.A. (1)
Apartado Postal 65191, Postal 65191, Caracas, 1065-A, Venezuela
Tel.: (58) 212 9536444
Web Site:
　http://www.promocionesmunich.com
Ropeway Engineering Services
N.A.I.C.S.: 541330

Sanhe Doppelmayr Transport Systems Co., Ltd. (1)
Yanchang Road No 235, Yanjiao Economic and Technological Development Zone, Sanhe, 065201, Hebei, China
Tel.: (86) 3163393030
Web Site: http://www.doppelmayr.com
Sales Range: $25-49.9 Million
Emp.: 70
Activities for Transportation Distr
N.A.I.C.S.: 488999

Shin Chang International Inc. (1)
Kang Nam, PO Box 102, 135-601, Seoul, Korea (South)
Tel.: (82) 251 15522
Ropeway Engineering Services
N.A.I.C.S.: 541330

Special Methods & Engineering Techniques Sdn Bhd (1)

Level 19 Penas Tower Midlands Park 488A, Jalan Burma, 10350, Penang, Malaysia
Tel.: (60) 42287118
Ropeway & Cable Car Mfr & Distr
N.A.I.C.S.: 336999

TOC International (1)
Aleea Otelarilor Nr 5/6, 331008, Hunedoara, Romania
Tel.: (40) 254 742288
Ropeway Engineering Services
N.A.I.C.S.: 541330

TOC Jit International Serv S.R.L. (1)
Aleea Otelarilor Nr 5/6, 331008, Hunedoara, Romania
Tel.: (40) 254748687
Ropeway & Cable Car Mfr & Distr
N.A.I.C.S.: 336999

Tehnounion 1 d.o.o. (1)
Ljubljanska 43, 1230, Domzale, Slovenia
Tel.: (386) 15135072
Web Site: http://www.tehnounion.eu
Emp.: 3
Ropeway Engineering Services
N.A.I.C.S.: 541330
Caba Gara *(Gen Mgr)*

Telefericos Doppelmayr Bolivia S.A. (1)
Av 20 de Octubre No 2665 Esquina campos Edif Torre Azul Piso 11, La Paz, Bolivia
Tel.: (591) 224 31918
Ropeway Engineering Services
N.A.I.C.S.: 541330

Transportes por Cable S.A. (1)
C/ Monte Perdido Parcela 8D Poligono Industrial Valdeconsejo, 50410, Cuarte de Huerva, Zaragoza, Spain
Tel.: (34) 976 274382
Web Site: http://www.doppelmayr.com
Emp.: 16
Ropeway Engineering Services
N.A.I.C.S.: 541330
Javier Geleria *(Mgr)*

DOR ALON ENERGY IN ISRAEL (1988) LTD
France building Europark, PO Box 1, Yakum, 60972, Israel
Tel.: (972) 99618555
Web Site: https://www.doralon.co.il
Year Founded: 1988
DRAL—(TAE)
Rev.: $2,056,802,289
Assets: $1,621,805,196
Liabilities: $1,250,483,196
Net Worth: $371,322,000
Earnings: $18,316,342
Fiscal Year-end: 12/31/23
Petroleum Bulk Stations & Terminals
N.A.I.C.S.: 424710
Amit Zeev *(CEO)*

DORA CONSTRUCTION LIMITED
60 Dorey Avenue Suite 101, Dartmouth, B3B 0B1, NS, Canada
Tel.: (902) 468-2941
Web Site:
　https://www.doraconstruction.com
Year Founded: 2003
Rev.: $15,642,363
Emp.: 55
Construction Services
N.A.I.C.S.: 236220
Jamie Miles *(CFO)*

DORAL GROUP RENEWABLE ENERGY RSRCS LTD.
6 Hilzon, Ramat Gan, 5252270, Israel
Tel.: (972) 747876888
Web Site: https://www.doral-energy.com
Year Founded: 2007
DORL—(TAE)
Rev.: $21,330,459
Assets: $1,226,992,029
Liabilities: $681,274,605
Net Worth: $545,717,423
Earnings: ($15,762,432)

Fiscal Year-end: 09/30/23
Electric Power Generation Services
N.A.I.C.S.: 221118
Dori Davidovitz *(Owner & Chm)*

DORAL INTERNATIONAL INC.
1991 3e Avenue, Grand-Mere, G9T 2W6, QC, Canada
Tel.: (819) 538-0781
Web Site: http://www.doralboat.com
Year Founded: 1972
Rev.: $29,076,000
Emp.: 252
Boat Distr
N.A.I.C.S.: 441222
Denis Poliseno *(Pres)*

DORCHESTER GROUP OF COMPANIES
12 Hay Hill Mayfair, London, W1J 8NR, United Kingdom
Tel.: (44) 1869238200
Web Site:
　http://www.dorchestergrp.com
Year Founded: 1996
Sales Range: $250-299.9 Million
Emp.: 650
Hotel Holding Company
N.A.I.C.S.: 551112
Gary Silver *(Head-Acq)*

Subsidiaries:

The Beverly Hills Hotel (1)
9641 Sunset Blvd, Beverly Hills, CA 90210-2938
Tel.: (310) 276-2251
Web Site:
　http://www.dorchestercollection.com
Emp.: 640
Hotel Services
N.A.I.C.S.: 721110
Kayal Moore *(Asst Dir-Room Reservations)*

DORE COPPER MINING CORPORATION
130 King St W Suite 1800, Toronto, M5X 1E3, ON, Canada
Tel.: (416) 792-2229
Web Site:
　https://www.dorecopper.com
Year Founded: 2017
DRCMF—(OTCQX)
Rev.: $24,732
Assets: $9,066,437
Liabilities: $1,102,266
Net Worth: $7,964,171
Earnings: ($7,118,347)
Fiscal Year-end: 12/31/20
Mineral Exploration Services
N.A.I.C.S.: 213115
Gavin Nelson *(CFO)*

DOREEN POWER GENERATIONS & SYSTEMS LIMITED
192/A Eastern Road 3rd Floor Lane-01 New DOHS Mohakhali, Dhaka, Bangladesh
Tel.: (880) 222260744
Web Site: https://doreenpower.coms
DOREENPWR—(DHA)
Rev.: $168,106,273
Assets: $245,241,324
Liabilities: $161,375,206
Net Worth: $83,866,118
Earnings: $5,917,383
Emp.: 605
Fiscal Year-end: 06/30/23
Electric Power Distribution Services
N.A.I.C.S.: 221122
Anjabeen Alam Siddique *(Chm)*

DOREL INDUSTRIES, INC.
1255 Greene Avenue Suite 300, Westmount, H3Z 2A4, QC, Canada
Tel.: (514) 934-3034
Web Site: https://www.dorel.com
Year Founded: 1962

Dorel Industries, Inc.—(Continued)

DIIBF—(OTCIQ)
Rev.: $1,388,748,000
Assets: $1,000,927,000
Liabilities: $776,225,000
Net Worth: $224,702,000
Earnings: ($62,350,000)
Emp.: 3,900
Fiscal Year-end: 12/30/23
Mfr of Consumer Products; Ready-to-
Assemble Furniture, Juvenile Furni-
ture & Home Furnishings
N.A.I.C.S.: 339999
Martin Schwartz *(Pres & CEO)*

Subsidiaries:

AMPA 2P SAS (1)
Zone Industrielle 9 Boulevard Du Poitou,
Cholet, 49300, Maine Et Loire, France
Tel.: (33) 241492323
Web Site: http://www.dorel.com
Emp.: 400
Juvenile Products Distr
N.A.I.C.S.: 424350

AMPA Developpement SAS (1)
Zone Industrielle 9 Boulevard Du Poitou,
Cholet, France
Tel.: (33) 2 41 49 23 23
Clothing Products Distr
N.A.I.C.S.: 424350

Ameriwood Industries, Inc. (1)
410 E S 1st St, Wright City, MO
63390 **(100%)**
Tel.: (636) 745-3351
Web Site: http://www.ameriwood.com
Sales Range: $25-49.9 Million
Mfr of Wood Furniture & Plastic Products
N.A.I.C.S.: 337122

BeBe & Co. SAS (1)
Rue De La Vendee, La Seguiniere, 49280,
Maine Et Loire, France
Tel.: (33) 241752900
Juvenile Products Distr
N.A.I.C.S.: 424350

Cannondale Bicycle Corporation (1)
172 Friendship Rd, Bedford, PA 15522-
6600
Tel.: (814) 623-9073
Web Site: http://www.cannondale.com
Sales Range: $200-249.9 Million
Aluminum Bicycles, Cycling Accessories &
Apparel
N.A.I.C.S.: 336991

Subsidiary (Non-US):

Cannondale Japan KK (2)
1-4-19 Minamihorie Nishi-Ku Namba
Sumiso Bldg 9f, Osaka, Japan
Tel.: (81) 6 6110 9390
Web Site: http://www.cannondale.co.jp
Bicycle Mfr
N.A.I.C.S.: 336991

**Cycling Sports Group Australia Pty
Ltd** (1)
Unit 8 31-41 Bridge Road, Stanmore, 2048,
NSW, Australia
Tel.: (61) 2 8595 4444
Sales Range: $25-49.9 Million
Emp.: 25
Cycling & Push Bikes Mfr
N.A.I.C.S.: 339920

**Cycling Sports Group Europe
B.V** (1)
Hanzepoort 27, Oldenzaal, 7575 DB, Neth-
erlands
Tel.: (31) 541589898
Sales Range: $25-49.9 Million
Emp.: 90
Sport & Athletic Goods Mfr
N.A.I.C.S.: 339920
Jos Hofste *(Gen Mgr)*

Cycling Sports Group Inc. (1)
172 Friendship Village Rd, Bedford, PA
15522-6600
Tel.: (814) 623-9073
Web Site:
http://www.cyclingsportsgroup.com
Bicycle & Sporting Products Mfr
N.A.I.C.S.: 336991

Russell Merry *(Sr VP & Gen Mgr-North
America & UK)*

Dorel (UK) Ltd. (1)
Building 4 Imperial Place, Borehamwood,
WD6 1JN, Hertfordshire, United
Kingdom **(100%)**
Tel.: (44) 1284413141
Web Site: http://www.dorel.co.uk
Sales Range: $25-49.9 Million
Emp.: 30
Designs, Manufactures & Markets Infant
Nursery Products
N.A.I.C.S.: 449110

Dorel Belgium SA (1)
Atomiumsquare 1, BP 177, Brussels, 1020,
Belgium
Tel.: (32) 2 257 44 70
Child Care Accessories Mfr
N.A.I.C.S.: 339930

**Dorel Consulting (Shanghai) Co.,
Ltd.** (1)
Rm 205 No 3203 Hongmei Rd, Shanghai,
201103, China
Tel.: (86) 2164468999
Sales Range: $50-74.9 Million
Emp.: 1
Juvenile Products Whslr
N.A.I.C.S.: 424350
Wendy Zhang *(Gen Mgr)*

Dorel Germany GmbH (1)
Augustinusstrasse 11 b, 50226, Frechen,
Germany
Tel.: (49) 2234 96 430
Sales Range: $25-49.9 Million
Emp.: 20
Sport & Athletic Goods Mfr
N.A.I.C.S.: 339920
Michael Neumann *(Gen Mgr)*

Dorel Hispania SA (1)
Calle Pare Rodes 26 4 Ed Llac Center
Torre A, Sabadell, 8208, Barcelona, Spain
Tel.: (34) 937247100
Child Care Products Mfr & Sales
N.A.I.C.S.: 339930

Dorel Home Furnishings, Inc. (1)
410 E First St S, Wright City, MO 63390
Tel.: (636) 745-3351
Furniture Mfr & Distr
N.A.I.C.S.: 337126
Norman Braunstein *(Pres-Grp)*

Subsidiary (Non-US):

Alphason Designs Limited (2)
244 Swan Lane Hindley Green, Wigan,
WN2 4EY, United Kingdom
Tel.: (44) 1942 524 100
Web Site: http://www.alphasondesigns.com
Television & Home Entertainment Stands &
Wall Mounting Systems Mfr & Distr
N.A.I.C.S.: 337126

Dorel Home Products (1)
12345 Albert-Hudon Blvd Suite 100, Mon-
treal, H1G 3K9, QC, Canada **(100%)**
Tel.: (514) 323-1247
Web Site: http://www.dorel.com
Sales Range: $50-74.9 Million
Emp.: 125
N.A.I.C.S.: 449110
Ira Goldstein *(Pres)*

Dorel Italia SpA (1)
Via Giuseppe Verdi 14, Telgate, 24060, Ber-
gamo, Italy
Tel.: (39) 0354421035
Children Care Products Mfr & Distr
N.A.I.C.S.: 339930

Dorel Juvenile Group, Inc. (1)
2525 State St, Columbus, IN
47201-7443 **(100%)**
Tel.: (812) 372-0141
Web Site: https://www.doreljuvenile.com
Sales Range: $550-599.9 Million
Emp.: 1,100
Step Stools, Bars, Counter Stools, Carts,
Baby Products & Baby Furniture Mfr
N.A.I.C.S.: 326199
Raul Sepulveda *(Pres & CEO-Europe)*

Subsidiary (Non-US):

Dorel France S.A. (2)

Z I - 9 Bd du Poitou, 49300, Cholet, Cedex,
France
Tel.: (33) 241492323
Web Site: http://www.bebeconfort.com
Sales Range: $75-99.9 Million
Juvenile Products Mfr
N.A.I.C.S.: 337122

Dorel Netherlands (1)
Korendijk 5, 5704 RD, Helmond,
Netherlands **(100%)**
Tel.: (31) 492578111
Web Site: http://www.dorel.eu
Sales Range: $50-74.9 Million
Emp.: 250
N.A.I.C.S.: 449110

Dorel Suisse SARL (1)
Rue de Geneve 77bis, 1004, Lausanne,
Switzerland
Tel.: (41) 21 622 00 50
Sales Range: $25-49.9 Million
Emp.: 4
Bicycle Mfr & Whslr
N.A.I.C.S.: 336991

IBD Bikes UK Limited (1)
Vantage Way The Fulcrum, Poole, BH12
4NU, Dorset, United Kingdom
Tel.: (44) 1202 732288
Web Site:
http://www.cyclingsportsgroup.co.uk
Sales Range: $25-49.9 Million
Emp.: 42
Sporting Goods Whslr
N.A.I.C.S.: 423910
Jon Watson *(Mgr-Territory)*

Maxi Miliaan B.V (1)
Korendijk 5, Helmond, 5704 RD, Noord-
Brabant, Netherlands
Tel.: (31) 492578111
Web Site: http://www.doreleurope.com
Sales Range: $50-74.9 Million
Emp.: 240
Sporting & Athletic Goods Mfr & Distr
N.A.I.C.S.: 339920

Pacific Cycle Inc. (1)
4902 Hammersley Rd, Madison, WI 53711-
2614
Tel.: (608) 268-2468
Web Site: http://www.pacific-cycle.com
Sales Range: $400-449.9 Million
Emp.: 100
Mfr & Distr of Bicycles & Accessories
N.A.I.C.S.: 423910
Bob Kmoch *(CFO)*

Branch (Domestic):

Pacific Cycle Inc. (2)
4730 E Radio Tower Ln, Olney, IL 62450-
4743
Tel.: (618) 393-2991
Web Site: http://www.pacific-cycle.com
Sales Range: $50-74.9 Million
Mfr & Sales of Bicycles & Accessories
N.A.I.C.S.: 336991

Ridgewood (1)
3305 Loyalist Street, Cornwall, K6H 6W6,
ON, Canada
Web Site: http://www.mjbridgewood.co.uk
N.A.I.C.S.: 449110

**SUGOI Performance Apparel Limited
Partnership** (1)
4084 McConnell Ct, Burnaby, V5A 3N7, BC,
Canada
Tel.: (604) 875-0887
Web Site: http://www.sugoi.com
Sales Range: $50-74.9 Million
Emp.: 25
Sportswear & Athletic Clothing Mfr
N.A.I.C.S.: 339920

DORF-KETAL CHEMICALS IN-
DIA PVT. LTD.
Dorf Ketal Tower DMonte Street,
Mumbai, 400064, Orlem, India
Tel.: (91) 22 42974777
Web Site: http://www.dorfketal.com
Year Founded: 1992
Specialty Chemicals Mfr
N.A.I.C.S.: 325199
Sudhir Menon *(Chm & Mng Dir)*

Subsidiaries:

Flow-Chem Technologies, LLC (1)
PO Box 62066, Lafayette, LA 70596-2066
Tel.: (337) 873-0171
Web Site: http://www.flowchem.net
Mining
N.A.I.C.S.: 213114
Horace Darby *(Plant Mgr)*

DORFIN INC.
5757 Boul Thimens, Saint Laurent,
H4R 2H6, QC, Canada
Tel.: (514) 335-0333
Web Site: http://www.dorfin.com
Year Founded: 1954
Rev.: $23,245,298
Emp.: 90
Consumer Products Supplier
N.A.I.C.S.: 532289

DORI MEDIA GROUP LTD.
2 Raoul Wallenberg St, 6971901, Tel
Aviv, Israel
Tel.: (972) 36478185
Web Site: http://www.dorimedia.com
Sales Range: $25-49.9 Million
Television Broadcasting Distr & Mer-
chandiser; Owned 38% by Mapal
Eden Telenobles Ltd.
N.A.I.C.S.: 516120
Leora Nir *(VP-Content)*

Subsidiaries:

Dori Media Contenidos S.A. (1)
A M de Justo 1960 1 103, Buenos Aires,
Argentina **(100%)**
Tel.: (54) 1151997970
Motion Picture & Video Production
N.A.I.C.S.: 512110

**Dori Media Distribution Argentina
S.A.** (1)
Costa Rica 4941, Buenos Aires,
C1414BSO, Argentina **(100%)**
Tel.: (54) 1148333800
Sales Range: $25-49.9 Million
Emp.: 12
Motion Picture & Video Production
N.A.I.C.S.: 512110

Dori Media Distribution GmbH (1)
Seefeldstrasse 113, 8008, Zurich,
Switzerland **(100%)**
Tel.: (41) 438177050
Management Consulting Services
N.A.I.C.S.: 541618

Dori Media International GmbH (1)
Seefeldstrasse 113, Zurich, 8008,
Switzerland **(100%)**
Tel.: (41) 438177050
Web Site: http://www.dorimedia.com
Broadcasting Producer & Distr
N.A.I.C.S.: 516120

Subsidiary (US):

Dori Media America Inc. (2)
9800 NW 41st St, Miami, FL 33178-2968
Tel.: (786) 662-3051
Music Compact Discs Distr
N.A.I.C.S.: 423990

Dori Media Ot Ltd. (1)
2 Raoul Wallenberg Street, Tel Aviv, 69719,
Israel
Tel.: (972) 37684141
Web Site: http://www.dorimedia.com
Emp.: 15
Video Dubbing Services
N.A.I.C.S.: 512191
Ofir Moran *(CEO)*

Dori Media Spike Ltd. (1)
3 Habarzel, Tel Aviv, 69710, Israel
Tel.: (972) 36498282
Web Site: http://www.dorimediaspike.com
Emp.: 50
Television Broadcasting Services
N.A.I.C.S.: 516120

DORIC NIMROD AIR ONE LIM-
ITED
Ground Floor Dorey Court Admiral

Park, Saint Peter Port, GY1 2HT,
Guernsey
Tel.: (44) 1481 702400 **GY**
Web Site: http://www.dnairone.com
Year Founded: 2010
DNA—(LSE)
Rev.: $20,111,927
Assets: $60,124,842
Liabilities: $22,542,709
Net Worth: $37,582,134
Earnings: ($406,376)
Fiscal Year-end: 03/31/21
Aircraft Investment Services
N.A.I.C.S.: 523999
Charles Edmund Wilkinson *(Chm)*

DORIC NIMROD AIR THREE LIMITED

Ground Floor Dorey Court Admiral
Park, PO Box 156, Saint Peter Port,
GY1 2HT, Guernsey
Tel.: (44) 1481702400 **GY**
Web Site: https://www.dnairthree.com
Year Founded: 2012
DNA3—(LSE)
Rev.: $94,461,639
Assets: $229,769,570
Liabilities: $104,568,780
Net Worth: $125,200,790
Earnings: $58,189,116
Fiscal Year-end: 03/31/24
Financial Lending Services
N.A.I.C.S.: 523910

DORIC NIMROD AIR TWO LIMITED

Ground Floor Dorey Court Admiral
Park, Saint Peter Port, GY1 2HT,
Guernsey
Tel.: (44) 1481702400 **GY**
Web Site: https://www.dnairtwo.com
Year Founded: 2011
DNA2—(LSE)
Rev.: $167,606,875
Assets: $392,142,911
Liabilities: $141,258,125
Net Worth: $250,884,785
Earnings: $80,086,086
Emp.: 450
Fiscal Year-end: 03/31/23
Aircraft Investment Services
N.A.I.C.S.: 523999
Geoffrey Alan Hall *(Chm)*

DORIEMUS PLC

The Broadgate Tower 20 Primrose
Street, London, EC2A 2EW, United
Kingdom
Tel.: (44) 2072839033 **UK**
Web Site:
https://www.doriemus.co.uk
DOR—(ASX)
Assets: $2,904,626
Liabilities: $42,140
Net Worth: $2,862,486
Earnings: ($2,259,494)
Fiscal Year-end: 12/31/21
Oil & Gas Investment Services
N.A.I.C.S.: 523999
Greg Lee *(Exec Dir-Technical)*

DORIGHT CO., LTD.

No 668 Binzhou Road, Jiaozhou,
Qingdao, 266300, China
Tel.: (86) 53282298811
Web Site: https://www.doright.biz
Year Founded: 2004
300950—(SSE)
Rev.: $45,423,612
Assets: $127,589,904
Liabilities: $38,953,980
Net Worth: $88,635,924
Earnings: $9,204,624
Fiscal Year-end: 12/31/22
Industrial Equipment Mfr & Distr
N.A.I.C.S.: 333248

Zhenwen Wei *(Chm & Pres)*

DORMAC PTY. LTD.

1 Belfast Road, Bayhead, Durban,
South Africa
Tel.: (27) 312741500
Web Site: http://www.dormac.net
Sales Range: $75-99.9 Million
Emp.: 200
Commercial Ship Construction & Repair Services
N.A.I.C.S.: 336611
Craig Samuel *(Dir-Fin)*

DORMAKABA HOLDING AG

Hofwisenstrasse 24, 8153, Rumlang,
Switzerland **CH**
Web Site: http://www.dormakaba.com
Year Founded: 1862
DOKA—(SWX)
Rev.: $3,158,314,856
Assets: $2,157,982,262
Liabilities: $1,787,028,825
Net Worth: $370,953,437
Earnings: $98,115,299
Emp.: 15,519
Fiscal Year-end: 06/30/23
Holding Company; Door, Access Control & Asset Protection Systems Mfr
N.A.I.C.S.: 551112
Andreas Haberli *(CTO)*

Subsidiaries:

ATM-Turautomatik GmbH **(1)**
Lassnitzthal 1b, 8200, Gleisdorf, Austria
Tel.: (43) 313338099
Web Site: https://www.tuerautomatik.at
Automatic Sliding Door Installation Services
N.A.I.C.S.: 238290

Alvarado Manufacturing Co. Inc. **(1)**
12660 Colony St, Chino, CA 91710
Tel.: (909) 591-8431
Web Site: https://www.alvaradomfg.com
Sales Range: $10-24.9 Million
Emp.: 70
Turnstiles, Equipped With Counting Mechanisms
N.A.I.C.S.: 334519

Atimo Personeelstechniek B.V. **(1)**
Computerweg 1, 3542 DP, Utrecht, Netherlands
Tel.: (31) 850402123
Web Site: https://www.atimo.nl
Information Technology Services
N.A.I.C.S.: 541511

Best Doors Australia Pty. Ltd. **(1)**
8 Oasis Crt, Clontarf, QLD, Australia
Tel.: (61) 732601154
Web Site: https://www.bestdoors.com.au
Food Retailer
N.A.I.C.S.: 445110

Corporacion Cerrajera Alba, S.A. de
C.V. **(1)**
Prolongacion Avenida Independencia No
14, CP 54900, Los Reyes, Mexico **(100%)**
Tel.: (52) 5553667200
Web Site: http://www.kaba-mexico.com
Security System Services
N.A.I.C.S.: 561621

DORMA Hueppe Pty. Ltd. **(1)**
14 Yulong Close, Moorebank, 2170, NSW,
Australia
Tel.: (61) 296458336
Web Site: https://dorma-hueppe.com.au
Operable Partition Mfr
N.A.I.C.S.: 337215

DORMA Huppe Asia Sdn. Bhd. **(1)**
PLO 217 Jalan Siber 10 Kawasan Perindustrian Senai IV, 81400, Senai, Johor,
Malaysia
Tel.: (60) 75985730
Web Site: https://www.dorma-hueppe.com.my
Operable Partition Mfr
N.A.I.C.S.: 337215

E Plus Building Products Pty.
Ltd. **(1)**

12-13 Dansu Court, Hallam, 3803, VIC,
Australia
Tel.: (61) 387950634
Web Site: https://e-core.com.au
Metal Door Mfr & Distr
N.A.I.C.S.: 332321

Fermatic Fresnais S.A.S. **(1)**
La Chere, Les Touches Loire-Atlantique,
44390, Nantes, France
Tel.: (33) 251123300
Web Site:
https://www.laporteautomatique.com
Door Retailer & Installation Services
N.A.I.C.S.: 238350

Fermetures Groom S.A.S. **(1)**
2-6 Place du General Gaulle, 92160,
Antony, France
Tel.: (33) 158430402
Web Site: https://www.groom.fr
Door Closer System Equipment Mfr
N.A.I.C.S.: 332510

Judlin Fermetures S.A.R.L. **(1)**
25 Rue des Malmaisons, 75013, Paris,
France
Tel.: (33) 14 585 4848
Web Site: https://judlinfermetures.com
Automatic Door Repair Services
N.A.I.C.S.: 238290

KIWS Property LLC **(1)**
306 N Spokane St Unit I, Post Falls, ID
83854-7016
Tel.: (208) 292-2198
Web Site: https://www.kwiproperties.com
Real Estate Services
N.A.I.C.S.: 531390

Kaba Access Control **(1)**
2941 Indiana Ave, Winston Salem, NC
27105
Tel.: (800) 849-8324
Web Site: http://www.kaba-adsamericas.com
Electronic & Pushbutton Locks Mfr
N.A.I.C.S.: 332510
Jason Patterson *(Sls Mgr)*

Kaba Gallenschutz GmbH **(1)**
Nikolaus Otto Strasse 1, 77815, Buhl,
Germany **(100%)**
Tel.: (49) 72232860
Web Site: http://www.kaba-gallenschuetz.de
Security Systems
N.A.I.C.S.: 561621

Kaba GmbH **(1)**
Albertistrasse 3, 78056, Villingen-Schwenningen, Germany
Tel.: (49) 77206030
Web Site: http://www.kaba.com
Security Systems
N.A.I.C.S.: 561621

Kaba Ilco Corp. **(1)**
400 Jeffreys Rd, Rocky Mount, NC
27804 **(100%)**
Tel.: (252) 446-3321
Web Site: https://www.ilco.us
Access Control Systems Mfr
N.A.I.C.S.: 332510
Karen Blount *(Mgr-Creative Svcs)*

Subsidiary (Non-US):

Kaba Ilco Inc. **(2)**
7301 Decarie Blvd, Montreal, H4P 2G7,
QC, Canada **(100%)**
Tel.: (877) 468-3555
Web Site: http://www.kaba-adsamericas.com
Hotel Locks Mfr
N.A.I.C.S.: 561621
Eddy Rosenberg *(Mgr)*

Kaba Immobilien GmbH **(1)**
Albertistr 3, 78056, Villingen-Schwenningen,
Germany **(100%)**
Tel.: (49) 77206030
Security Systems
N.A.I.C.S.: 561621

Kaba Mas LLC **(1)**
1051 Newtown Pike Ste 150, Lexington, KY
40511 **(100%)**
Tel.: (859) 629-2510
Web Site: https://www.kabamas.com
Security System Services
N.A.I.C.S.: 332510

Kaba New Zealand Limited **(1)**
Building P 61-69 Patiki Road, Avondale,
1026, Auckland, New Zealand **(100%)**
Tel.: (64) 800436762
Web Site: http://www.kaba.co.nz
Security System Services
N.A.I.C.S.: 561621

Kaba S.A.S. **(1)**
3 rue Descartes, 78320, Saint Denis,
France
Tel.: (33) 130 13 0404
Web Site: http://www.kaba.fr
Security Systems
N.A.I.C.S.: 561621

Kaba Workforce Solutions, LLC **(1)**
3015 N Commerce Pkwy, Miramar, FL
33025
Tel.: (954) 416-1720
Web Site: http://www.kaba-benzing-usa.com
Workforce Management Software Development Services
N.A.I.C.S.: 541511
Steve Slovin *(Dir-Technical Svcs)*

Kaba do Brasil Ltda. **(1)**
Rua Guilherme Asbahr Neto 510, CEP
04646-001, Sao Paulo, Brazil **(100%)**
Tel.: (55) 1155454510
Web Site: http://www.kabadobrasil.com.br
Security System Services
N.A.I.C.S.: 561621

Kaba srl **(1)**
Piazza Della Liberta' 23, 40013, Gaeta, Italy
Tel.: (39) 0514178311
Web Site: http://www.kaba.it
Security Systems
N.A.I.C.S.: 561621

Mesker Door, LLC **(1)**
3440 Stanwood Blvd, Huntsville, AL 35811
Tel.: (256) 851-6670
Web Site: http://www.meskeropeningsgroup.com
Metal Window & Door Mfr
N.A.I.C.S.: 332321
Mike Earrey *(CFO)*

Plant (Domestic):

Mesker Southeast **(2)**
710 S Powerline Rd Ste E, Deerfield
Beach, FL 33442
Tel.: (954) 312-4652
Web Site: https://meskeropeningsgroup.com
Door Mfr
N.A.I.C.S.: 332321

Minda Silca Engineering Pvt.
Ltd. **(1)**
37 Toy City, Noida, Uttar Pradesh, India
Tel.: (91) 1202397224
Web Site: https://www.mindasilca.in
Automotive Security System Services
N.A.I.C.S.: 561621

Saflok **(1)**
31750 Sherman Ave, Madison Heights, MI
48071
Tel.: (248) 837-3700
Web Site: http://www.kaba.com
Electronic Security Products
N.A.I.C.S.: 335999

Silca S.p.A. **(1)**
Via Podgora 20 Z I, 31029, Vittorio Veneto,
TV, Italy **(97%)**
Tel.: (39) 04389136
Web Site: https://www.silca.it
Security System Services
N.A.I.C.S.: 561621

Subsidiary (Non-US):

Silca GmbH **(2)**
Siemensstrasse 33, 42551, Velbert, Germany
Tel.: (49) 20512710
Web Site: https://www.silca.de
Security System Services
N.A.I.C.S.: 561621
Stefano Aurelio Zocca *(Mng Dir)*

Silca Key Systems S.A. **(2)**
C/Santander 73/A, 08020, Barcelona, Spain
Tel.: (34) 934981400
Web Site: https://www.silca.es
Security System Services
N.A.I.C.S.: 561621

dormakaba Holding AG—(Continued)

Silca Ltd. (2)
Unit 6 Lloyds Court Manor Royal, Crawley,
RH10 9QU, United Kingdom
Tel.: (44) 1293531134
Web Site: http://www.silca.biz
Security System Services
N.A.I.C.S.: 561621

Silca S.A.S. (2)
12 rue de Rouen ZI Limay, 78440, Porche-
ville, France
Tel.: (33) 130983500
Web Site: https://www.silca.fr
Security System Services
N.A.I.C.S.: 561621

Silca South America S.A. (1)
Km 1 5 Via Briceno-Zipaquira Parque Ind
Trafalgar Bodega 3, Cundinamarca, Tocan-
cipa, Colombia
Tel.: (57) 17366480
Web Site: https://www.flexon-silca.co
Lock Key Product Mfr
N.A.I.C.S.: 332510

Skyfold Inc. (1)
325 Lee Avenue, Montreal, H9X 3S3, QC,
Canada
Tel.: (514) 457-4767
Web Site: https://skyfold.com
Operable Partition Mfr
N.A.I.C.S.: 337215

**Solus Security Systems Private
Limited** (1)
202 Shivam Chembers Next to Sahara SV
Road, Goregaon West, Mumbai, India
Tel.: (91) 8043336666
Web Site: https://www.solus.co.in
Security Services
N.A.I.C.S.: 561621

TLHM Co. Ltd. (1)
No 62 Zhongxiao 1st Street, Hou-Hu-Li,
Chiayi, 600, Taiwan
Tel.: (886) 52770688
Web Site: https://www.tlhmco.com
Commercial Lock Product Mfr & Distr
N.A.I.C.S.: 332510

**Transquest Tag & Tracing Solutions
B.V.** (1)
Computerweg 1, 3542 DP, Utrecht, Nether-
lands
Tel.: (31) 850402120
Web Site: https://transquest.nl
Security System Services
N.A.I.C.S.: 561621

Wah Yuet Hong Kong Limited (1)
Room 2302-2303 23/F Technology Plaza
651 King's Road, North Point, China (Hong
Kong)
Tel.: (852) 27395592
Web Site: https://www.wahyuet.com
Lock Key Product Mfr
N.A.I.C.S.: 332510

**Wah Yuet Industrial Company
Limited** (1)
Rm 1501 15/F Tower 5 China Hongkong
City, 33 Canton Road, Kowloon, China
(Hong Kong)
Tel.: (852) 2739 5592
Web Site: http://www.kaba.hk
Locking System Hardware Mfr
N.A.I.C.S.: 332510

dormakaba (Thailand) Ltd. (1)
762/2 Room No A258 Rama 3 Road,
Bangpongpang Yannawa, Bangkok, 10120,
Thailand
Tel.: (66) 20592612
Door Hardware Mfr & Distr
N.A.I.C.S.: 332510

**dormakaba Access Indonesia,
PT** (1)
Jl Ciputat Raya No 335 RT 002 RW 007,
Kebayoran Lama Utara Kebayoran Lama
Kota Adm, Jakarta Selatan, 12240, Jakarta,
Indonesia
Tel.: (62) 2129303762
Door Hardware Mfr & Distr
N.A.I.C.S.: 332510
Jeffrey Budiyanto (Specification Mgr)

dormakaba Australia Pty. Ltd. (1)

12 - 13 Dansu Ct, Hallam, 3803, VIC,
Australia (100%)
Tel.: (61) 800675411
Web Site: https://www.dormakaba.com
Security System Distr
N.A.I.C.S.: 444140

dormakaba Austria GmbH (1)
Ulrich-Bremi-Strasse 2, 3130, Herzogen-
burg, Austria (100%)
Tel.: (43) 27828080
Web Site: https://www.dormakaba.com
Emp.: 570
Provider of Security Systems
N.A.I.C.S.: 561621

dormakaba Belgium N.V. (1)
Monnikenwerve 17-19, 8000, Brugge,
Belgium (100%)
Tel.: (32) 50451570
Web Site: https://www.dormakaba.be
Emp.: 105
Security Systems
N.A.I.C.S.: 561621

**dormakaba Brasil Solucoes de
Acesso Ltda.** (1)
Av Piracema 1400 - Tambore, Barueri, Sao
Paulo, 06460-933, Brazil
Tel.: (55) 1146899200
Web Site: https://www.dormakaba.com
Emp.: 250
Automated Door Installation Services
N.A.I.C.S.: 238290

dormakaba Deutschl & GmbH (1)
Dorma Platz 1, 58256, Ennepetal, Germany
Tel.: (49) 2 333 7930
Web Site: https://www.dormakaba.de
Automatic Sliding Door Installation Services
N.A.I.C.S.: 238290

dormakaba EAD GmbH (1)
Frankenstr 8-12, 24579, Heiligenhaus, Ger-
many
Tel.: (49) 20565960
Web Site: https://www.kaba-mauer.com
Security Lock System & Hardware Distr
N.A.I.C.S.: 423710

**dormakaba Holding Australia Pty.
Ltd.** (1)
12 - 13 Dansu Ct, Hallam, VIC, Australia
Tel.: (61) 1800675411
Web Site: https://www.dormakaba.com
Security Services
N.A.I.C.S.: 561621

**dormakaba Holding GmbH & Co.
KGaA** (1)
Dorma Platz 1, 58256, Ennepetal,
Germany (52.5%)
Tel.: (49) 23337930
Web Site: http://www.dormakaba.com
Door Hardware, Door Security Systems,
Automatic & Revolving Doors, Glass Fit-
tings, Decorative & Structural Glass Sys-
tems, Partitions & Movable Door Mfr
N.A.I.C.S.: 332510

Subsidiary (Non-US):

**DORMA DOOR SYSTEMS
d.o.o.** (2)
Vidska 8, 11 050, Belgrade, Serbia
Tel.: (381) 11 2852 414
Web Site: http://www.dorma.rs
Glass Window & Door Mfr
N.A.I.C.S.: 327211

DORMA Door Controls Limited (2)
Room 701 651 Kings Road, North Point,
Hong Kong, China (Hong Kong)
Tel.: (852) 2503 4632
Web Site: http://www.dorma.com
Automated Door Installation Services
N.A.I.C.S.: 238290

DORMA Door Controls Pty Ltd (2)
12 - 13 Dansu Ct, Hallam, 3803, VIC, Aus-
tralia
Tel.: (61) 800675411
Web Site: https://www.dormakaba.com
Glass Door Distr
N.A.I.C.S.: 332510

DORMA Gulf Door Controls FZE (2)
Plot No S 20135 Road no SW 301 G Jebel
Ali Free Zone South, PO Box 17268, Dubai,
United Arab Emirates

Tel.: (971) 4 8020 400
Web Site: http://www.dorma.com
Glass Door Distr
N.A.I.C.S.: 327211
Ben Shaw (Reg Mgr)

DORMA Huppe Austria GmbH (2)
Hollabererstrasse 4 b, 4020, Linz, Austria
Tel.: (43) 732600451
Web Site: https://www.dorma-hueppe.at
Glass Door Distr
N.A.I.C.S.: 327211
Martin Ecker (Mng Dir)

Subsidiary (Domestic):

**DORMA Huppe Raumtrennsysteme
GmbH + Co. KG** (2)
Industriestrasse 5, 26655, Westerstede,
Germany (100%)
Tel.: (49) 44096660
Web Site: https://www.dorma-hueppe.com
Glass Window & Door Mfr
N.A.I.C.S.: 327211

Subsidiary (Non-US):

DORMA India Private Limited (2)
14 Pattullous Road, Chennai, 600 002, In-
dia
Tel.: (91) 44 2855 9192
Web Site: http://www.dorma.com
Glass Window & Door Mfr & Distr
N.A.I.C.S.: 327211
V. R. Ramesh (Mng Dir)

DORMA Italiana S.r.l. (2)
Via Tolmezzo 15 Edificio A, 20132, Milan,
Italy
Tel.: (39) 02 494842
Web Site: http://www.dorma.com
Glass Window & Door Mfr & Distr
N.A.I.C.S.: 327211

DORMA Romania S.R.L. (2)
Splaiul Unirii 243-245 Sector 3, Bucharest,
Romania
Tel.: (40) 213210882
Web Site: http://www.dorma.com
Glass Window & Door Mfr
N.A.I.C.S.: 327211

DORMA Ukraine LLC (2)
Mikhail Donets Street 6 Office 307, 3061,
Kiev, Ukraine (99%)
Tel.: (380) 445938973
Web Site: http://www.dorma.com
Glass Window & Door Mfr
N.A.I.C.S.: 327211
Oleksandr Balakin (Country Mgr)

Subsidiary (Domestic):

DORMA-Glas GmbH (2)
Max-Planck-Strasse 33 - 45, 32107, Bad
Salzuflen, Germany
Tel.: (49) 52229240
Web Site: https://www.dormakaba.com
Buliding Supplies Including Doors, Locks,
Handles & Other Related Products Mfr
N.A.I.C.S.: 332510

Subsidiary (Non-US):

**Kaba Access Systems (Shanghai)
Co., Ltd.** (2)
Rooms 1705-1707 Unicom International
Tower No 547 West Tianmu Road, Shang-
hai, 200070, China
Tel.: (86) 21 6317 0077
Web Site: http://www.kaba.cn
Security System Software Development
Services
N.A.I.C.S.: 541511

dormakaba Austria GmbH (2)
Ulrich-Bremi-Strasse 2, 3130, Herzogen-
burg, Austria (100%)
Tel.: (43) 27828080
Web Site: https://www.dormakaba.com
Glass Window & Door Distr
N.A.I.C.S.: 423310
Elmar Knittl (Mng Dir)

dormakaba Bulgaria EOOD (2)
Druzhba 2 15 Heidelberg St, 1582, Sofia,
Bulgaria
Tel.: (359) 29714904
Web Site: http://www.dorma.com
Emp.: 90
Glass Window & Door Mfr

N.A.I.C.S.: 332510
Boris Goshev (Mgr-Sls)

dormakaba Cesko s.r.o (2)
Radlicka 714/113a, 158 00, Prague, 5,
Czech Republic
Tel.: (420) 2671321789
Web Site: https://www.dormakaba.com
Emp.: 30
Glass Window & Door Mfr
N.A.I.C.S.: 332510
Martin Stanko (Mgr-Product Sls)

dormakaba Danmark A/S (2)
Roholmsvej 10A 1, 2620, Albertslund, Den-
mark
Tel.: (45) 44543000
Web Site: https://www.dormakaba.com
Glass Window & Door Mfr
N.A.I.C.S.: 321911

Subsidiary (Domestic):

dormakaba Deutschland GmbH (2)
Dorma Platz 1, 58256, Ennepetal, Germany
Tel.: (49) 23337930
Web Site: https://www.dormakaba.com
Door Technology, Glass Fiitings Security &
Access Solutions
N.A.I.C.S.: 561621

Subsidiary (Non-US):

dormakaba Espana S.A.U. (2)
C/ Maria Tubau 4, 28050, Madrid, Spain
Tel.: (34) 917362460
Web Site: https://www.dormakaba.com
Emp.: 191
Door Distr
N.A.I.C.S.: 423710

dormakaba Eurasia LLC (2)
ul Akademika Pilyugina 22, Moscow,
117393, Russia
Tel.: (7) 4959662050
Web Site: https://www.dormakaba.com
Glass Window & Door Mfr
N.A.I.C.S.: 332510
Michael Lagunov (Product Mgr)

dormakaba France S.A.S (2)
2-4 Rue des Sarrazins, 94046, Creteil, Ce-
dex, France
Tel.: (33) 141942400
Web Site: https://www.dormakaba.com
Security Systems Products & Services Pro-
vider
N.A.I.C.S.: 561621

dormakaba Hrvatska d.o.o. (2)
Kovinska 4A, 10090, Zagreb, Croatia
Tel.: (385) 13497597
Web Site: https://www.dormakaba.com
Glass Window & Door Mfr
N.A.I.C.S.: 321911

dormakaba Ireland Ltd. (2)
Block B Maynooth Business Campus, May-
nooth, W23 W5X7, Kildare, Ireland
Tel.: (353) 12958280
Web Site: https://www.dormakaba.com
Glass Window & Door Distr
N.A.I.C.S.: 423710
Shane Christie (Dir-Fin & IT)

**dormakaba Kapi Ve Guvenlik Sistem-
leri Sanayi Ve Ticaret A.S.** (2)
Ayazaga mah Kemerburgaz cad No 59,
34396, Istanbul, Türkiye (100%)
Tel.: (90) 2123320000
Web Site: http://www.dormakaba.com
Glass Window & Door Distr
N.A.I.C.S.: 327211

dormakaba Magyarorszag Zrt. (2)
Oradna utca 3/b, 1044, Budapest, Hungary
Tel.: (36) 13501011
Web Site: https://www.dormakaba.com
Emp.: 48
Glass Window & Door Mfr
N.A.I.C.S.: 332510

dormakaba Malaysia Sdn. Bhd. (2)
No 3 Jalan TP 6 Taman Perindustrian UEP,
47600, Subang Jaya, Selangor Darul Eh-
san, Malaysia
Tel.: (60) 380818009
Glass Window & Door Mfr
N.A.I.C.S.: 321911

dormakaba Middle East LLC (2)

Shk Zayed Road South, PO Box 121732, Dubai, United Arab Emirates
Tel.: (971) 438801419
Web Site: http://www.dorma.com
Glass Window & Door Mfr
N.A.I.C.S.: 327211
Ashish Aundhkar *(Mgr-Country Sls)*

dormakaba Norge AS (2)
Tel.: (47) 6866
Web Site: https://www.dormakaba.com
Glass Window & Door Mfr
N.A.I.C.S.: 332510
Anders Peter Larsson *(CEO & Mng Dir)*

dormakaba Portugal S.A.U. (2)
Alameda dos Oceanos 23A, 1990-196, Lisbon, Portugal
Tel.: (351) 215960021
Web Site: https://www.dormakaba.com
Door Lock Distr
N.A.I.C.S.: 423710

dormakaba Singapore Pte Ltd (2)
12 Tukang Innovation Dr 04-01, Singapore, 618303, Singapore
Tel.: (65) 62687633
Web Site: https://www.dormakaba.com
Emp.: 200
Glass Window & Door Mfr
N.A.I.C.S.: 321911
Thomas Tng *(Project Mgr-Sales-Product)*

dormakaba Slovensko s.r.o. (2)
Prievozska 1318/14, 821 09, Bratislava, Slovakia (100%)
Tel.: (421) 250221283
Web Site: https://www.dormakaba.com
Glass Window & Door Mfr
N.A.I.C.S.: 327211

dormakaba South Africa Pty Ltd. (2)
2 Gravel Drive Kya Sands Business Park, Johannesburg, 2169, South Africa
Tel.: (27) 115101500
Web Site: https://www.dormakaba.com
Glass Window & Door Mfr
N.A.I.C.S.: 321911

dormakaba UK Limited - Hitchin Office (2)
Wilbury Way, Hitchin, SG4 0AB, Hertfordshire, United Kingdom
Tel.: (44) 1462477600
Web Site: https://www.dormakaba.com
Glass Window & Door Distr
N.A.I.C.S.: 423710
Shane Christie *(Reg Dir-Fin)*

Subsidiary (US):

dormakaba USA Inc. (2)
1 Dorma Dr Drawer AC, Reamstown, PA 17567
Tel.: (717) 336-3881
Web Site: https://www.dormakaba.com
Revolving Doors, Automatic Doors & Door Hardware Mfr
N.A.I.C.S.: 332510

Subsidiary (Domestic):

Modernfold, Inc. (3)
215 W New Rd, Greenfield, IN 46140 (100%)
Tel.: (800) 869-9685
Web Site: http://www.modernfold.com
Operable Wall Systems & Space Division Solutions for Interior Environments; Operable Partitions, Moveable Glass Walls & Accordion Doors Designer, Mfr & Servicer
N.A.I.C.S.: 337214
Michael Beeler *(Mgr-Design Engrg)*

Subsidiary (Domestic):

Modernfold of Nevada, LLC (4)
6380 S Valley View Blvd, Las Vegas, NV 89118 (100%)
Tel.: (800) 869-9685
Glass Door Distr
N.A.I.C.S.: 327211
Bryan Welch *(Mgr)*

dormakaba Italia Srl (1)
Via Tolmezzo 15, 20132, Milan, MI, Italy
Tel.: (39) 02494842
Web Site: https://www.dormakaba.it
Emp.: 77
Door Hardware Mfr & Distr
N.A.I.C.S.: 332510

dormakaba Japan Co., Ltd. (1)
1-3-11 Fukuura, Kanazawa-ku, Yokohama, 236-0004, Japan
Tel.: (81) 453678769
Web Site: https://www.dormakaba.com
Security Systems
N.A.I.C.S.: 561621

dormakaba Kenya Limited (1)
Watermark Business Park Corner Langata and Ndege Rd, Karen, Nairobi, Kenya
Tel.: (254) 700894406
Door Hardware Mfr & Distr
N.A.I.C.S.: 332510

dormakaba Korea Inc. (1)
3rd floor Yoonchun building Teheran-ro 86 gil 14, Gangnam-gu, Seoul, 06179, Korea (South)
Tel.: (82) 69564382
Web Site: https://www.dormakaba.com
Automatic Door Repair Services
N.A.I.C.S.: 238290

dormakaba Luxembourg S.A. (1)
50 Duchscherstrooss, 6868, Wecker, Luxembourg
Tel.: (352) 26710870
Web Site: https://www.dormakaba.com
Door Partition Mfr
N.A.I.C.S.: 337215

dormakaba Maroc SARL (1)
320 Boulevard Zerktouni 4eme etage, 20040, Casablanca, Morocco
Tel.: (212) 522272293
Web Site: https://www.dormakaba.com
Door Hardware Mfr
N.A.I.C.S.: 332510

dormakaba Nederland B.V. (1)
Dlawagen 45, 6669 CB, Dodewaard, Netherlands (100%)
Tel.: (31) 883523323
Web Site: https://www.dormakaba.com
Security Systems
N.A.I.C.S.: 561621

Subsidiary (Domestic):

H. Cillekens & B.V. (2)
Metaalweg 4, 6045 JB, Roermond, Netherlands (100%)
Tel.: (31) 475325147
Web Site: https://www.hcillekens.nl
Locking System Hardware Distr
N.A.I.C.S.: 423710

dormakaba Philippines Inc. (1)
R1&R2 2F 58th Jupiter Building 58th Jupiter Street Bel Air, Legaspi Village, Makati, 1209, Philippines
Tel.: (63) 288934077
Door Hardware Mfr & Distr
N.A.I.C.S.: 332510

dormakaba Polska Sp. z o.o. (1)
st Warszawska 72, 05-520, Konstancin-Jeziorna, Poland (100%)
Tel.: (48) 227365900
Web Site: https://www.dormakaba.com
Emp.: 120
Locking System Hardware Mfr
N.A.I.C.S.: 332510

dormakaba Portugal, Unipessoal Lda. (1)
Alameda dos Oceanos 23A Loja 1, 1990-196, Lisbon, Portugal
Tel.: (351) 215960021
Web Site: https://www.dormakaba.com
Automatic Door Repair Services
N.A.I.C.S.: 238290

dormakaba Production Malaysia Sdn. Bhd. (1)
No 3 Jalan TP 6 Taman Perindustrian UEP, 47600, Subang Jaya, Selangor, Malaysia
Tel.: (60) 380818009
Door Hardware Mfr & Distr
N.A.I.C.S.: 332510

dormakaba Romania S.R.L. (1)
Tel.: (40) 213214061
Web Site: https://www.dormakaba.com
Emp.: 30
Automatic Door Repair Services
N.A.I.C.S.: 238290

dormakaba Schweiz AG (1)

Muhlebuhlstrasse 23, CH 8620, Wetzikon, Switzerland (100%)
Tel.: (41) 848858687
Web Site: https://www.dormakaba.com
Door & Access Control Systems Mfr
N.A.I.C.S.: 332510

Subsidiary (Non-US):

Kaba Jaya Security Sdn. Bhd. (2)
No 16 Jalan Pelukis U1/46B Temasya Industrial Park, 40150, Shah Alam, Selangor, Darul Ehsan, Malaysia (70%)
Tel.: (60) 355698188
Web Site: http://www.kaba.com
Door Locking Hardware Distr
N.A.I.C.S.: 423710

Subsidiary (Domestic):

Legic Identsystems AG (2)
Binzackerstrasse 41, 8620, Wetzikon, Switzerland
Tel.: (41) 449336464
Web Site: https://www.legic.com
Contactless Identification Solutions
N.A.I.C.S.: 513210
Marcel Pluss *(VP-Innovation & Tech)*

Subsidiary (Non-US):

dormakaba Gulf FZE (2)
Plot No S 20135 Road No SW 301 Jebel Ali, PO Box 17268, Dubai, United Arab Emirates
Tel.: (971) 48020400
Web Site: http://www.dormakaba.com
Security Lock & Hardware Distr
N.A.I.C.S.: 423710

dormakaba Suomi Oy (1)
Mannerheimintie 113, 00280, Helsinki, Suomi, Finland
Tel.: (358) 102188100
Web Site: https://www.dormakaba.com
Door Hardware Mfr
N.A.I.C.S.: 332510

dormakaba Sverige AB (1)
F O Petersons gata 28, 421 31, Vastra Frolunda, Sweden (100%)
Tel.: (46) 313552000
Web Site: https://www.dormakaba.com
Provider of Security Systems
N.A.I.C.S.: 561621

dormakaba UK Holding Limited (1)
Wilbury Way, Hitchin, United Kingdom
Tel.: (44) 1462477600
Web Site: https://www.dormakaba.com
Security Services
N.A.I.C.S.: 561621

dormakaba UK Limited - Tiverton Office (1)
Lower Moor Way, Tiverton, EX16 6SS, Devon, United Kingdom
Tel.: (44) 8700005625
Web Site: http://www.dormakaba.com
Security System Services
N.A.I.C.S.: 561621
Steve Bewick *(Sr VP)*

dormakaba Zrt. (1)
3/b Oradna utca, 1044, Budapest, Hungary
Tel.: (36) 13501011
Security System Services
N.A.I.C.S.: 561621

DORNACOM SA
Str M Eminescu Nr 28, Vatra Dornei, Suceava, Romania
Tel.: (40) 230 371 052
Sales Range: Less than $1 Million
Emp.: 4
Real Estate Management Services
N.A.I.C.S.: 531390

DORNBIRNER SPARKASSE BANK AG
Bahnhofstrasse 2, Dornbirn, 6850, Austria
Tel.: (43) 5010074000
Web Site: http://www.sparkasse.at
Year Founded: 1867
Sales Range: $1-4.9 Billion
Emp.: 350

International Banking
N.A.I.C.S.: 522110
Hubert Singer *(CEO)*

DORNOD AUTO ZAM JOINT STOCK COMPANY
3th khoroo Barmash center door 213, 1st bag Kha-Uul distict, Choibalsan, Dornod, Mongolia
Tel.: (976) 88067746
DAZ—(MONG)
Rev.: $362,701
Assets: $140,320
Liabilities: $21,729
Net Worth: $118,591
Earnings: $737
Fiscal Year-end: 12/31/20
Petroleum & Coal Product Mfr
N.A.I.C.S.: 324199

DORO AB
Jorgen Kocksgatan 1b, 211 20, Lund, Sweden
Tel.: (46) 462805000
Web Site: https://www.doro.com
DORO—(OMX)
Rev.: $85,185,497
Assets: $84,651,625
Liabilities: $40,162,222
Net Worth: $44,489,402
Earnings: $3,830,772
Emp.: 108
Fiscal Year-end: 12/31/22
Design-Driven Products Designer, Developer & Seller
N.A.I.C.S.: 423620
Henri Osterlund *(Vice Chm)*

Subsidiaries:

Doro A/S, Norway (1)
Krakeroyveien 2, Krakeroy, 1671, Fredrikstad, Norway
Tel.: (47) 69358600
Web Site: http://www.doro.com
Sales Range: $25-49.9 Million
Emp.: 5
Telecommunications Equipment Mfr
N.A.I.C.S.: 334220

Doro Hong Kong Ltd (1)
Shop 347 3/F 138 Sha Tin Rural Committe Road, Home Square, Sha Tin, NT, China (Hong Kong)
Tel.: (852) 25777107
Sales Range: $25-49.9 Million
Emp.: 6
Mobile Communication Equipment Mfr
N.A.I.C.S.: 334220
Calle Krokstade *(Gen Mgr)*

Doro SAS (1)
BP 446 Ville, 78180, Saint-Quentin-en-Yvelines, France
Tel.: (33) 130071700
Web Site: http://www.doro.com
Sales Range: $25-49.9 Million
Emp.: 20
Mobile Communication Equipment Mfr
N.A.I.C.S.: 334220

IVS Industrievertretung Schweiger GmbH (1)
In Frauental 14, 92224, Amberg, Germany
Tel.: (49) 962167710
Web Site: https://www.ivsgmbh.de
Mobile Phone & Accessory Distr
N.A.I.C.S.: 423690

DORSAVI LTD
Unit 3 11 13 Milgate Street, Melbourne, 3167, VIC, Australia
Tel.: (61) 1800367728   AU
Web Site: https://www.dorsavi.com
DVL—(ASX)
Rev.: $870,885
Assets: $1,458,376
Liabilities: $775,049
Net Worth: $683,327
Earnings: ($833,054)
Fiscal Year-end: 06/30/24
Medicinal Product Mfr

dorsaVi Ltd—(Continued)

N.A.I.C.S.: 339112
Andrew James Ronchi (CEO)

DORSEL BAZ LTD.

2 Hamada St, PO Box 142, Yok-
neam, 20692, Israel
Tel.: (972) 49596777
Web Site: http://dorsel.co.il
DRSL—(TAE)
Rev.: $20,416,192
Assets: $318,100,971
Liabilities: $198,257,687
Net Worth: $119,843,284
Earnings: $26,174,557
Fiscal Year-end: 12/31/22
Real Estate Manangement Services
N.A.I.C.S.: 531210
Isaac Zinger (Chm)

DORTMUNDER GUSSAS-PHALT GMBH & CO. KG

Teinenkamp 43, 59494, Soest, Ger-
many
Tel.: (49) 2921 8907 0   De
Web Site: http://www.dga.de
Sales Range: $25-49.9 Million
Emp.: 200
Paving Asphalt Mfr
N.A.I.C.S.: 324121
K. H. Kolb (Bus Mgr)

Subsidiaries:

Interasphalt Sp. z o.o.   (1)
ul Przemyslowa 3, 64-600, Oborniki, Poland
Tel.: (48) 616462938
Web Site: http://www.interasphalt.pl
Road Construction Services
N.A.I.C.S.: 237310

Isoliererzeugnisse Grossrohrsdorf
GmbH   (1)
Radeberger Str 115, 01900, Grossrohrsdorf,
Germany
Tel.: (49) 359523420
Web Site: http://www.iso-sachsen.de
Textile Products Mfr
N.A.I.C.S.: 313310

Proxan Dichtstoffe GmbH   (1)
Liebigstrasse 7, Gera, D-07973, Germany
Tel.: (49) 3661442980
Web Site: http://www.proxan.de
Sales Range: $25-49.9 Million
Emp.: 10
Polysulphide Sealing Materials Mfr
N.A.I.C.S.: 325998
Gritt Volland (Founder & Mng Dir)

TEWE Bauchemiegesellschaft
mbH   (1)
Eichendamm 1, 15306, Vierlinden, Ger-
many
Tel.: (49) 334688310
Web Site: http://www.tewe-bc.de
Road Construction Services
N.A.I.C.S.: 237310

Wm. Hilgers GmbH & Co. KG   (1)
Kappeler Strasse 128, 40599, Dusseldorf,
Germany
Tel.: (49) 211998933
Web Site: http://www.wm-hilgers.de
Building Construction Material Mfr & Distr
N.A.I.C.S.: 327991
Mario Kowsky (Mgr-Bus)

fischer Austria GmbH   (1)
Wiener Strasse 95, 2514, Traiskirchen, Aus-
tria
Tel.: (43) 2252537300
Building Hardware Distr
N.A.I.C.S.: 423710

DORUK FAKTORING A.S.

Kustepe Mh Mecidiyekoy Yolu Cd N
12 Trump Towers Kule 2 Kat 24, Sisli,
Istanbul, 34387, Turkiye
Tel.: (90) 2126770175
Web Site:
http://www.dorukfaktoring.com.tr
DFKTR—(IST)

Financial Investment Services
N.A.I.C.S.: 523999
Caglar Gogus (Chm)

DOSEOLOGY SCIENCES INC.

406-460 Doyle Avenue, Kelowna,
V1Y 0C2, BC, Canada
Tel.: (236) 349-0064   BC
Web Site: https://www.doseology.com
Year Founded: 2019
DOSEF—(OTCQB)
Rev.: $11,972
Assets: $2,886,502
Liabilities: $650,146
Net Worth: $2,236,356
Earnings: ($1,446,733)
Fiscal Year-end: 06/30/22
Health Care Srvices
N.A.I.C.S.: 621610

DOSHISHA CO., LTD.

1-5-5 Higashi-Shinsaibashi, Chuo-ku,
Osaka, 542-8525, Japan
Tel.: (81) 661215888
Web Site: https://www.doshisha.co.jp
Year Founded: 1974
7483—(TKS)
Rev.: $699,496,640
Assets: $678,853,610
Liabilities: $121,736,370
Net Worth: $557,117,240
Earnings: $38,232,240
Emp.: 649
Fiscal Year-end: 03/31/24
Household Product Whslr
N.A.I.C.S.: 423620
Masaharu Nomura (Chm)

Subsidiaries:

Hong Kong Victoria Well Industrial
Limited   (1)
Flat C 17/F Thomson Commercial Building
8 Thomson Road, Wanchai, China (Hong
Kong)
Tel.: (852) 2815 8077
Household Product Distr
N.A.I.C.S.: 423620

Karinpia Co., Ltd.   (1)
5F Higashi-Shinsaibashi Bldg 1-5-9 Higashi-
Shinsaibashi, Chuo-ku, Osaka, 542-0083,
Japan
Tel.: (81) 662443996
Web Site: https://www.karinpia-hp.com
Emp.: 57
Household Product Distr
N.A.I.C.S.: 423620

DOSJAN TEMIR JOLY JSC

N P 7a 25 Syganak St, Esil district,
Nur-Sultan, 010000, Kazakhstan
Tel.: (7) 172792972
Web Site: http://www.dtz.kz
DTJL—(KAZ)
Rev.: $17,090
Assets: $18,559
Liabilities: $41,777
Net Worth: ($23,218)
Earnings: $2,895
Fiscal Year-end: 12/31/22
Railway Track Construction Services
N.A.I.C.S.: 237990
Bayzhanov Nurlan (Chm-Mgmt Bd)

DOST STEELS LIMITED

4th Floor Ibrahim Trade Centre
1-Aibak Block Barkat Market, New
Garden Town, Lahore, 54700, Paki-
stan
Tel.: (92) 423594137577
Web Site: https://www.doststeels.com
Year Founded: 2004
DSL—(KAR)
Rev.: $4,110,404
Assets: $19,983,385
Liabilities: $14,293,041
Net Worth: $5,690,344
Earnings: ($2,249,559)
Emp.: 131

Fiscal Year-end: 06/30/19
Quenched Steel Bars Mfr
N.A.I.C.S.: 331110
Naim Anwar (Chm)

DOT RESOURCES LTD.

Suite 3 4015 1st Street SE, Calgary,
T2G 4X7, AB, Canada
Tel.: (403) 264-2647   AB
Web Site:
http://www.dotresourcesltd.com
Year Founded: 2007
Metal Mining Services
N.A.I.C.S.: 212290
John J. Komarnicki (Chm, Pres &
CEO)

DOTDIGITAL GROUP PLC

No 1 London Bridge, London, SE1
9BG, United Kingdom
Tel.: (44) 2039533072
Web Site:
https://www.dotdigitalgroup.com
DOTD—(AIM)
Rev.: $87,387,023
Assets: $126,449,129
Liabilities: $25,073,214
Net Worth: $101,375,915
Earnings: $15,898,763
Emp.: 384
Fiscal Year-end: 06/30/23
Web, Online & Email Marketing Ser-
vices
N.A.I.C.S.: 541890
Milan Patel (CEO)

Subsidiaries:

Dotdigital EMEA Limited   (1)
No 1 London Bridge, London, SE1 9BG,
United Kingdom
Tel.: (44) 2039533072
Web Site: https://dotdigital.com
Emp.: 350
Digital Marketing Services
N.A.I.C.S.: 541613

Dotdigital Poland Sp. z o.o   (1)
Al Jana Pawla II 22, 00-133, Warsaw, Po-
land
Tel.: (48) 223079490
Digital Marketing Services
N.A.I.C.S.: 541613

Netcallidus Limited   (1)
Hall Farm Wellingborough Road Sywell
Aerodrome Business Park, Sywell,
Northampton, NN6 0BN, United Kingdom
Tel.: (44) 1604 781.044
Web Site: http://www.netcallidus.com
Sales Range: $25-49.9 Million
Emp.: 10
Search Engine Optimization Services
N.A.I.C.S.: 519290

dotMailer Limited   (1)
20th Floor No 1 Croydon 12-16 Addiscombe
Road, Croydon, CR0 0XT, United Kingdom
Tel.: (44) 20 8662 2762
Web Site: http://www.dotmailer.co.uk
Sales Range: $50-74.9 Million
Emp.: 150
Email Marketing Services
N.A.I.C.S.: 518210

DOTSTAY S.P.A.

Via Benigno Crespi 57, Lombardy,
20159, Milan, Italy
Web Site:
https://www.investors.dotstay.it
Year Founded: 2013
DOT—(EUR)
Real Estate Investment Services
N.A.I.C.S.: 531190
Simone Brugnara (Chm)

DOTTIKON ES HOLDING AG

Hembrunnstrasse 17, 5605, Dottikon,
Switzerland
Tel.: (41) 566168201
Web Site: https://www.dottikon.com
Year Founded: 1913

DESN—(SWX)
Rev.: $247,892,021
Assets: $868,327,035
Liabilities: $125,638,487
Net Worth: $742,688,548
Earnings: $59,245,168
Emp.: 639
Fiscal Year-end: 03/31/21
Fine Chemical Mfr for Pharmaceutical
& Chemical Industries
N.A.I.C.S.: 325998
Markus Blocher (Chm, CEO & Mng
Dir)

Subsidiaries:

Dottikon ES America, Inc.   (1)
3559 N Cumberland Ave Ste 106, Chicago,
IL 60634
Tel.: (773) 887-5582
Pharmaceutical Ingredient Mfr
N.A.I.C.S.: 325412

Dottikon Exclusive Synthesis AG   (1)
Hembrunnstrasse 17, 5605, Dottikon,
Switzerland   (100%)
Tel.: (41) 566168111
Sales Range: $75-99.9 Million
Research & Development in the Physical
Engineering & Life Sciences
N.A.I.C.S.: 541715
Markus Blocher (Mng Dir)

SYSTAG, System Technik AG   (1)
Bahnhofstrasse 76, 8803, Ruschlikon, Swit-
zerland
Tel.: (41) 44 704 5454
Web Site: https://www.systag.ch
Industrial Automation Services
N.A.I.C.S.: 541330
Markus Blocher (Pres)

DOUBLE A (1991) PUBLIC COMPANY LIMITED

187/3 Moo 1 Bangna-Trad km 42
Road, Bangwua District, Bang Pa-
kong, 24180, Chachoengsao, Thai-
land
Tel.: (66) 26591234
Web Site:
http://www.doubleapaper.com
Year Founded: 1989
Sales Range: $100-124.9 Million
Emp.: 3,000
Pulp & Paper Mfr
N.A.I.C.S.: 322110
Kitti Dumnernchanvanit (Co-Chm)

Subsidiaries:

A.A. Pulp Mill 2 Company
Limited   (1)
Tha Toom Mills 1 Mu 2, Si Maha Phot,
25140, Prachin Buri, Thailand
Tel.: (66) 3 720 8800
Web Site: http://www.doublepaper.com
Paper & Pulp Mfr
N.A.I.C.S.: 322120

Double A Alizay   (1)
ZI du Clos Pre, BP 1, 27460, Alizay, France
Tel.: (33) 2 35 02 72 72
Paper & Pulp Mfr
N.A.I.C.S.: 322120
Christine Jamain (Mgr-Channel Dev)

Double A International Business (Bei-
jing) Co., Ltd.   (1)
Room 501 Huateng Mansion A302 3rd Jin-
song Quarter, Chaoyang District, Beijing,
100021, China
Tel.: (86) 10 8591 0942
Web Site: http://www.doublea.com.cn
Paper & Pulp Mfr
N.A.I.C.S.: 322120
Larry Lee (Sr Mgr-Mktg)

Double A International Business
(Guangzhou) Co., Ltd.   (1)
2601 Riverside Business Center No 298
Yan Jiang Road, Guangzhou, China
Tel.: (86) 20 2226 8822
Web Site: http://www.doublea.com.cn
Paper & Pulp Mfr
N.A.I.C.S.: 322120
Sam Huang (Reg Gen Mgr)

Double A International Business (Shanghai) Co., Ltd   **(1)**
Floor 30 Guangming building No 02 East Jinling Road, Shanghai, China
Tel.: (86) 21 6329 7325
Web Site: http://www.doublea.com.cn
Paper & Pulp Mfr
N.A.I.C.S.: 322120
Julian Zhou *(Reg Gen Mgr)*

Double A International Business Korea Ltd   **(1)**
6th Fl Kangnam-Building Shisa-Dong Kangnam-Gu, Shinsa-dong Kangnam-gu, 135-722, Seoul, Korea (South)
Tel.: (82) 25155960
Web Site: http://www.double-a.co.kr
Emp.: 35
Paper Mills
N.A.I.C.S.: 322120
Ch Lee *(Mgr-Channel Dev)*

Double A International Hong Kong Limited   **(1)**
9/F The Cameron No 33 Cameron Road, Tsim Sha Tsui, Kowloon, China (Hong Kong)
Tel.: (852) 2549 2579
Web Site: http://www.doublea.com.hk
Paper & Pulp Mfr
N.A.I.C.S.: 322120
Danny Law *(Gen Mgr)*

Double A International Network (Australia) Pty Ltd   **(1)**
Unit 80 Level 8 18-20 Orion Road, Lane Cove, 2066, NSW, Australia
Tel.: (61) 2 9424 3400
Web Site: http://www.doublea.com.au
Paper & Pulp Mfr
N.A.I.C.S.: 322120
David Cross *(Gen Mgr)*

Double A International Network (M) Sdn Bhd   **(1)**
T1-7-1 7th Fl Tower 1 Jaya 33 Hyperoffice Lot 33, Jalan Semangat Seksyen 14, 46100, Petaling Jaya, Selangor, Malaysia
Tel.: (60) 379609988
Web Site: http://www.doubleapaper.com.my
Sales Range: $25-49.9 Million
Emp.: 35
Paper Mills
N.A.I.C.S.: 322120
Tan Lin Seng *(Gen Mgr)*

Double A International Network (Philippines) Inc.   **(1)**
Unit 1508 Antel Global Corporate Center 3 Dona Julia Vargas Ave Ortiga, Pasig, 1605, Philippines
Tel.: (63) 2 706 2347
Web Site: http://www.doubleapaper.com
Paper & Pulp Mfr
N.A.I.C.S.: 322120

Double A International Network B.V.   **(1)**
Boompjes 55, 3011XB, Rotterdam, Netherlands
Tel.: (31) 102229096
Web Site: http://www.doubleapaper.eu
Sales Range: $25-49.9 Million
Emp.: 6
Pulp Mill
N.A.I.C.S.: 322110

Double A International Network Co. (Private) Limited   **(1)**
Suite 907 9th Floor Horizon Tower Block - 3 Clifton, Karachi, Pakistan
Tel.: (92) 21 35820223
Web Site: http://www.doubleapaper.com
Emp.: 6
Paper & Pulp Mfr
N.A.I.C.S.: 322120
Mohammed Harshad *(Gen Mgr)*

Double A International Network Co., Ltd   **(1)**
12 Aljunied Road No 02-01 KH Plaza, Singapore, 389838, Singapore
Tel.: (65) 67442288
Web Site: http://www.doublea.com.sg
Sales Range: $25-49.9 Million
Emp.: 10
Paper Mills
N.A.I.C.S.: 322120
Michael Lim *(Gen Mgr)*

Double A Pulp and Paper Company Limited   **(1)**
Suite 7 4th Floor Mahtab Centre 177 Shahid Nazrul Islam Sarani Bijoy N, Dhaka, 1000, Bangladesh
Tel.: (880) 2 9334451
Web Site: http://www.doubleapaper.com.bd
Paper & Pulp Mfr
N.A.I.C.S.: 322120
Nadim Adnan Shams *(Country Mgr)*

Double A Serbia. Double A International Network Company Limited   **(1)**
Milovana Jankovica 9g, Belgrade, Serbia
Tel.: (381) 600 453 551
Web Site: http://www.doubleapaper.com
Paper & Pulp Mfr
N.A.I.C.S.: 322120

DOUBLE BOND CHEMICAL IND. CO., LTD.
4F No 959 Zhongzheng Rd, Zhonghe Dist, New Taipei City, 235, Taiwan
Tel.: (886) 282281168
Web Site: https://www.dbc.com.tw
Year Founded: 1994
4764—(TAI)
Rev.: $72,830,371
Assets: $148,564,042
Liabilities: $77,560,055
Net Worth: $71,003,987
Earnings: $2,781,320
Fiscal Year-end: 12/31/23
Chemical Products Mfr
N.A.I.C.S.: 325998
Tsay Maw-Der *(Chm)*

DOUBLE MEDICAL TECHNOLOGY INC.
No 18 Shanbianhong East Road, Haicang District, Xiamen, 361026, China
Tel.: (86) 5926087101
Web Site: https://www.doublemedicalgp.com
Year Founded: 2004
002901—(SSE)
Rev.: $201,347,640
Assets: $552,844,656
Liabilities: $116,655,552
Net Worth: $436,189,104
Earnings: $12,947,688
Fiscal Year-end: 12/31/22
Medical Equipment Mfr & Distr
N.A.I.C.S.: 339113
Lin Zhixiong *(Chm)*

Subsidiaries:

Shenzhen World Surgery Medical Device Technology Co.,Ltd.   **(1)**
3/F No 32 Longping Road West, Dong Pingxing Innovative Tech Park Longgang District, Shenzhen, China
Tel.: (86) 75589452169
Web Site: https://www.szswq.com
Medical Device Distr
N.A.I.C.S.: 423450

Surgaid Medical (Xiamen) Co., Ltd.   **(1)**
Web Site: http://www.surgaid-medical.com
Healtcare Services
N.A.I.C.S.: 621999

DOUBLE STANDARD INC.
4F Hulic Aoyama Gaien Higashidori Building 2-2-3 Minamiaoyama, Minato-ku, Tokyo, 107-0062, Japan
Tel.: (81) 363845411
Web Site: https://www.double-std.com
Year Founded: 2012
3925—(TKS)
Rev.: $47,241,670
Assets: $43,520,240
Liabilities: $6,715,760
Net Worth: $36,804,480
Earnings: $10,932,940
Fiscal Year-end: 03/31/24
Business Planning
N.A.I.C.S.: 561499

Yasuhiro Shimizu *(Chm, Pres & CEO)*

DOUBLE STAR DRILLING (1998) LTD
312 Hayes Crescent, Acheson, T7X 5A4, AB, Canada
Tel.: (780) 484-4276
Web Site:
http://www.doublestardrilling.ca
Year Founded: 1986
Rev.: $14,486,726
Emp.: 70
Drilling Contractor
N.A.I.C.S.: 213111
Ian Hunt *(Owner & VP)*

DOUBLEDRAGON CORPORATION
10th floor Tower 1 DoubleDragon Plza DD Meridian Park corner, Macapagal Avenue and EDSA Extension Bay Area, Pasay, Philippines
Tel.: (63) 288567111
Web Site:
https://www.doubledragon.com.ph
Year Founded: 2011
DD—(PHI)
Rev.: $446,725,281
Assets: $3,272,365,174
Liabilities: $1,564,892,566
Net Worth: $1,707,472,608
Earnings: $287,575,325
Emp.: 593
Fiscal Year-end: 12/31/23
Commercial & Residential Property Developer
N.A.I.C.S.: 237210
Tony Tan Caktiong *(Co-Chm)*

Subsidiaries:

DD HappyHomes Residential Centers Inc.   **(1)**
Brgy Onate De Leon St, Mandurriao, Iloilo, 5000, Philippines
Tel.: (63) 9175078111
Web Site:
http://www.ddhappyhomes.com.ph
Residential Housing Services
N.A.I.C.S.: 624229

Hotel 101 Management Corporation   **(1)**
EDSA Extension Mall of Asia Complex, Pasay, 1300, Philippines
Tel.: (63) 285531111
Web Site:
http://www.hotel101manila.com.ph
Hotel Services
N.A.I.C.S.: 721110
Sonny Salmasan *(Mgr-IT)*

DOUBLEUGAMES CO., LTD.
16F GFC 152 Teheran ro, Gangnam gu, Seoul, 06236, Korea (South)
Tel.: (82) 25017216
Web Site:
https://www.doubleugames.com
Year Founded: 2012
192080—(KRS)
Rev.: $473,439,969
Assets: $947,732,887
Liabilities: $175,902,916
Net Worth: $771,829,971
Earnings: $(169,556,159)
Emp.: 319
Fiscal Year-end: 12/31/22
Online Games Publishing Services
N.A.I.C.S.: 513210
Ga Rham Kim *(CEO)*

Subsidiaries:

Double Down Interactive LLC   **(1)**
605 5th Ave S Ste 300, Seattle, WA 98104-3887   **(100%)**
Tel.: (206) 402-4964
Web Site:
https://www.doubledowninteractive.com
Online Software Game Publishing Services

N.A.I.C.S.: 513210

DoubleDown Interactive Co., Ltd.   **(1)**
13F Gangnam Finance Center 152 Teheran-ro Gangnam-gu, Seoul, 06236, Korea (South)
Tel.: (82) 25017216
Web Site:
http://www.doubledowninteractive.com
Rev.: $308,864,000
Assets: $803,344,000
Liabilities: $75,454,000
Net Worth: $727,890,000
Earnings: $100,928,000
Emp.: 240
Fiscal Year-end: 12/31/2023
Digital Game Development Services
N.A.I.C.S.: 513210
In Keuk Kim *(CEO)*

DOUBLEVIEW GOLD CORP.
822 470 Granville St, Vancouver, V6C 1V5, BC, Canada
Tel.: (604) 678-9587   BC
Web Site: https://www.doubleview.ca
Year Founded: 2008
DBLVF—(OTCQB)
Rev.: $475,922
Assets: $15,230,677
Liabilities: $342,971
Net Worth: $14,887,705
Earnings: $(1,226,911)
Fiscal Year-end: 02/29/24
Investment Services
N.A.I.C.S.: 523999
Farshad Shirvani *(Pres & CEO)*

DOUCETTE REALTY LTD.
1272 5th Avenue, Prince George, V2L 3L2, BC, Canada
Tel.: (250) 562-2121
Web Site:
http://www.doucetterealty.com
Year Founded: 1984
Rev.: $51,668,486
Emp.: 20
Real Estate Brokerage Services
N.A.I.C.S.: 531210
Sid Doucette *(Founder)*

DOUG MARSHALL CHEVROLET CORVETTE CADILLAC
11044 100 Street, Grande Prairie, T8V 2N1, AB, Canada
Tel.: (780) 532-9333
Web Site:
http://www.dougmarshallgm.com
Year Founded: 2001
New & Used Car Dealers
N.A.I.C.S.: 441110
Rolly Marie *(Gen Mgr-Sls)*

DOUGLAS LAKE CATTLE CO.
General Delivery, Douglas Lake, V0E 1SO, BC, Canada
Tel.: (250) 350-3344
Web Site:
http://www.douglaslake.com
Year Founded: 2004
Sales Range: $10-24.9 Million
Emp.: 110
Beef Cattle
N.A.I.C.S.: 112111

DOUJA PROMOTION GROUPE ADDOHA SA
Km 7 Route de Rabat Ain Sebaa, Casablanca, Morocco
Tel.: (212) 522679975
Web Site:
http://www.groupeaddoha.com
Year Founded: 1988
ADH—(CAS)
Sales Range: $350-399.9 Million
Emp.: 500
Real Estate Support Services
N.A.I.C.S.: 531390
Rachid Iben Khayat *(Deputy Mng Dir-Low & Mid Range Real Estate)*

Douja Promotion Groupe Addoha SA—(Continued)

DOUMOB
5F Bldg C11 Phase 2 Dongyi Intl Media Ind Park, Beijing, 100020, China
Tel.: (86) 1056272546
1917—(HKG)
Rev.: $7,199,572
Assets: $10,668,856
Liabilities: $1,593,119
Net Worth: $9,075,737
Earnings: ($7,621,193)
Emp.: 71
Fiscal Year-end: 12/31/22
Advertising & Marketing Services
N.A.I.C.S.: 541810
Bin Yang (Founder, Chm & CEO)

DOUSHEN BEIJING EDUCATION & TECHNOLOGY INC.
Doushen Education Group Phase I Zhongguancun Software Park, Haidian District, Beijing, 100193, China
Tel.: (86) 1083058000
Web Site: https://www.lanxum.com
Year Founded: 1999
300010—(SSE)
Rev.: $142,277,148
Assets: $334,525,464
Liabilities: $433,913,220
Net Worth: ($99,387,756)
Earnings: ($96,444,972)
Fiscal Year-end: 12/31/22
Information Management Services
N.A.I.C.S.: 519290
Dou Xin (Chm)

DOUTOR-NICHIRES HOLDINGS CO., LTD.
10-11 Sarugakucho, Shibuya-ku, Tokyo, Japan
Tel.: (81) 354599178   JP
Web Site: https://www.dnh.co.jp
Year Founded: 2007
3087—(TKS)
Rev.: $997,031,250
Assets: $906,016,920
Liabilities: $200,746,260
Net Worth: $705,270,660
Earnings: $38,931,190
Emp.: 1,365
Fiscal Year-end: 02/29/24
Holding Company; Coffee & Tea Mfr; Restaurant Operator
N.A.I.C.S.: 551112
Masanori Hoshino (Pres & Co-CEO)

Subsidiaries:

Doutor Coffee Co., Ltd.   (1)
1-10-1 Jinnan, Shibuya-ku, Tokyo, 150-8412, Japan
Tel.: (81) 354599036
Web Site: https://www.doutor.co.jp
Sales Range: $600-649.9 Million
Emp.: 921
Coffee Distr, Restaurant & Coffee Shop Management, Marketing & Consulting Services
N.A.I.C.S.: 311920

Nippon Restaurant System, Inc.   (1)
10-11 Sarugaku-cho, Shibuya-ku, Tokyo, 150-8567, Japan
Tel.: (81) 6701 3014
Web Site: http://www.n-rs.co.jp
Emp.: 1,195
Multi-Type Restaurants Operator; Processed Food, Sauces, Confectionaries & Cooking Ingredients Mfr & Whslr
N.A.I.C.S.: 722513
Minoru Yamauchi (Pres & CEO)

DOUYU INTERNATIONAL HOLDINGS LIMITED
20/F Building A New Development International Center, No 473 Guanshan Avenue Hongshan District, Wuhan, 430073, Hubei, China
Tel.: (86) 2787750710   Ky

Web Site: https://ir.douyu.com
Year Founded: 2014
DOYU—(NASDAQ)
Rev.: $1,089,053,198
Assets: $1,247,951,588
Liabilities: $242,808,167
Net Worth: $1,005,143,420
Earnings: ($11,555,467)
Emp.: 1,973
Fiscal Year-end: 12/31/22
Holding Company
N.A.I.C.S.: 551112
Shaojie Chen (Co-Founder, Chm & CEO)

DOUZONE BIZON CO., LTD.
130 Beodeul 1-gi Namsan-myeon, Chuncheon, Gangwon-do, Korea (South)
Tel.: (82) 262333000   KR
Web Site: http://entest.douzone.biz
Year Founded: 1977
012510—(KRS)
Rev.: $273,851,933
Assets: $684,181,361
Liabilities: $339,244,398
Net Worth: $344,936,963
Earnings: $26,589,296
Emp.: 1,802
Fiscal Year-end: 12/31/23
Computer Software Development Services
N.A.I.C.S.: 541511
Yong Wu Kim (CEO)

DOVERIE UNITED HOLDING AD
Dianabad residential quarter 5 Lachezar Stanchev Street, Office Building A Floor 7 Sopharma Business Towers Izgrev district, 1756, Sofia, Bulgaria
Tel.: (359) 29845611
Web Site: https://www.doverie.bg
Year Founded: 1996
5DOV—(BUL)
Rev.: $11,718,422
Assets: $1,204,920,175
Liabilities: $1,001,788,831
Net Worth: $203,131,344
Earnings: $102,957,900
Fiscal Year-end: 12/31/19
Investment Management Service
N.A.I.C.S.: 523940
Radosvet Krumov Radev (Chm-Supervisory Bd)

Subsidiaries:

Insurance Company Medico 21 AD   (1)
92 Maria Luiza Blvd Fl 2, Sofia, Bulgaria
Tel.: (359) 29310421
Web Site: http://www.medico-21.net
Insurance Services
N.A.I.C.S.: 524210

Moldindconbank S.A.   (1)
Str Armeneasca 38, Chisinau, Moldova
Tel.: (373) 22576782
Web Site: https://www.micb.md
Banking Services
N.A.I.C.S.: 522110

DOVRE GROUP PLC
Ahventie 4 B, FI-02170, Espoo, Finland
Tel.: (358) 204362000
Web Site:
    https://www.dovregroup.com
DOV1V—(HEL)
Rev.: $219,049,212
Assets: $89,034,103
Liabilities: $51,985,754
Net Worth: $37,048,349
Earnings: $6,271,314
Emp.: 681
Fiscal Year-end: 12/31/22

Project Management & Software Services
N.A.I.C.S.: 541511
Arve Jensen (CEO)

Subsidiaries:

Dovre Canada Ltd.   (1)
5 Hill O'Chips, Saint John's, A16 0A8, NL, Canada
Tel.: (709) 754-2145
Management Consulting Services
N.A.I.C.S.: 541611
Faustina Cornick (Ops Mgr)

Dovre Group Energy AS   (1)
Bjergsted Terrasse 1, 4007, Stavanger, Norway
Tel.: (47) 40005900
Management Consulting Services
N.A.I.C.S.: 541611

Dovre Group Inc.   (1)
13501 Katy Fwy Ste 1655, Houston, TX 77079
Tel.: (281) 914-4910
Project Management Services
N.A.I.C.S.: 561110

ProCountor International Oy   (1)
Keilaranta 8, FIN 02150, Espoo, Finland   (80%)
Tel.: (358) 20 7879 838
Web Site: http://www.procountor.com
Sales Range: Less than $1 Million
Emp.: 9
Financial Management Solutions Software
N.A.I.C.S.: 541511
Mikko Siivola (Mng Dir)

Proha Oy   (1)
Ahventie 4 B, 02170, Espoo, Finland
Tel.: (358) 204362000
Web Site: https://proha.com
Consulting Services
N.A.I.C.S.: 541618

Safran Software Solutions AS   (1)
Lokkeveien 99, NO-4008, Stavanger, Norway
Tel.: (47) 5187 4560
Web Site: http://www.safranna.com
Software Products & Services
N.A.I.C.S.: 513210

Suvic Oy   (1)
Elektroniikkatie 4, 90590, Oulu, Finland
Tel.: (358) 207418840
Web Site: https://www.suvic.fi
Construction Services
N.A.I.C.S.: 236210

DOW MOTORS (OTTAWA) LIMITED
845 Carling Avenue, Ottawa, K1S 2E7, ON, Canada
Tel.: (613) 237-2777
Web Site: http://www.dowhonda.com
Year Founded: 1972
Rev.: $34,281,000
Emp.: 50
New & Used Car Dealers
N.A.I.C.S.: 441110

DOW HOLDINGS CO., LTD.
22F Akihabara UDX 14-1 Sotokanda 4-Chome, Chiyoda-ku, Tokyo, 101-0021, Japan
Tel.: (81) 368471100   JP
Web Site: https://hd.dowa.co.jp
Year Founded: 1884
5714—(TKS)
Rev.: $4,740,652,340
Assets: $4,182,609,700
Liabilities: $1,612,707,800
Net Worth: $2,569,901,900
Earnings: $184,108,330
Emp.: 11,417
Fiscal Year-end: 03/31/24
Holding Company; Nonferrous Metal Smelting & Refining; Environmental & Recycling Services; Electrical & Electronic Materials Producer; Metal Production & Fabrication Services; Heat Treating

N.A.I.C.S.: 551112
Masao Yamada (Chm)

Subsidiaries:

Act-B Recycling Co., Ltd.   (1)
278-6 Shiohama-cho, Minamata, 867-0067, Kumamoto, Japan
Tel.: (81) 966623300
Web Site: https://www.act-b.co.jp
Emp.: 119
Product Recycling Services to Major Appliance Manufacturers
N.A.I.C.S.: 423930
Kazuyuki Toyama (CEO)

Akita Engineering Co., Ltd.   (1)
123-1 Maeda, Hanaoka-machi, Odate, 017-0005, Akita, Japan
Tel.: (81) 186461653
Construction Machinery Maintenance Services
N.A.I.C.S.: 811310

Akita Recycle & Finepack Co., Ltd.   (1)
76-1 Otarube Kosakakouzan, Kosaka-machi Kazuno-gun, Akita, 017-0202, Japan
Tel.: (81) 186293467
Plastics Material & Resin Mfr
N.A.I.C.S.: 325211

Akita Zinc Co., Ltd.   (1)
217-9 Furumichi-shimokawabata, Iijima, Akita, 011-0911, Japan   (86%)
Tel.: (81) 188461121
Web Site: http://www.dowa.co.jp
Industrial Process Furnace & Oven Mfr
N.A.I.C.S.: 333994

Akita Zinc Solutions Co., Ltd.   (1)
1 Sunada, Iijima, Akita, 011-0911, Japan   (84%)
Tel.: (81) 188456069
Emp.: 70
Primary Smelting & Refining of Nonferrous Metal
N.A.I.C.S.: 331410
Takashi Ujihara (Pres)

CEMM Co., Ltd.   (1)
19-1 Ukishimacho, Miizuho-ku, Nagoya, 467-0854, Aichi, Japan   (100%)
Tel.: (81) 526930181
Power Boiler & Heat Exchanger Mfr
N.A.I.C.S.: 332410

DOWA HD Europe GmbH   (1)
Aeussere-Cramer-Klett-Str 19, 90489, Nuremberg, Germany
Tel.: (49) 91156989320
Sales Range: $25-49.9 Million
Emp.: 4
Marketing Consulting Services
N.A.I.C.S.: 541613

Dowa Eco-System Co., Ltd.   (1)
(100%)
Tel.: (81) 368471230
Web Site: http://www.dowa-eco.co.jp
Sales Range: $350-399.9 Million
Emp.: 100
Environmental & Industrial Waste Management & Recycling
N.A.I.C.S.: 562998
Minoru Tobita (Pres)

Subsidiary (Domestic):

Auto Recycle Akita Co., Ltd.   (2)
96 Sugisawa Kosaka Mine Kosaka-machi, Kazuno-gun, Akita, 017-0202, Japan
Tel.: (81) 186307313
Web Site: http://www.dowa.co.jp
Automobile Mfr
N.A.I.C.S.: 336110

Subsidiary (Non-US):

Bangpoo Environmental Complex Ltd.   (2)
965 Moo 2 Soi 3B Bangpoo Industrial Estate Sukhumvit Rd Bangpoo Mai, Muang Samutprakarn, Samut Prakan, 10280, Thailand
Web Site: http://wms-thailand.com
Emp.: 100
Waste Management Services
N.A.I.C.S.: 562998
Naota Famoto (Pres)

Subsidiary (Domestic):

Biodiesel Okayama Co., Ltd. (2)
1-3-1 Kaigan-dori, Minami-ku, Okayama, 702-8506, Japan
Tel.: (81) 862616050
Emp.: 5
Biodiesel Fuel Mfr
N.A.I.C.S.: 324199

Subsidiary (Non-US):

Dowa Environmental Engineering (Suzhou) Co., Ltd. (2)
No 28 Sanlian Street, Suzhou, 215129, Jiangsu, China
Tel.: (86) 512 8518 7700
Groundwater Remediation Services
N.A.I.C.S.: 562910

Subsidiary (Domestic):

Dowa-Tsuun Co., Ltd. (2)
69-1 Nakada Sakurakawa, Mizusawa-ku, Oshu, 023-0003, Iwate, Japan
Tel.: (81) 197 25 5353
Web Site: http://www.dowa.co.jp
Transportation & Warehousing Services
N.A.I.C.S.: 488999

Subsidiary (Non-US):

Eastern Seaboard Environmental Complex Co., Ltd. (2)
88 Moo 8 Tambon Bowin Amphur, Sriracha, Chon Buri, 20230, Thailand
Tel.: (66) 38346364
Web Site: https://wms-thailand.com
Liquid Waste Treatment Services
N.A.I.C.S.: 562212

Subsidiary (Domestic):

Eco-System Akita Co., Ltd. (2)
42 Tsutsumisawa, Hanaoka-machi, Odate, 017-0005, Akita, Japan
Tel.: (81) 186461436
Industrial Waste Management Services
N.A.I.C.S.: 562998

Green Fill Kosaka Co., Ltd. (2)
60-1 Otarube Kosakakouzan, Kosaka-machi Kazuno, Akita, 017-0202, Japan
Tel.: (81) 186292924
Industrial Waste Disposal Services
N.A.I.C.S.: 562211

Subsidiary (Non-US):

JIANGXI DOWA ENVIRONMENTAL MANAGEMENT CO., LTD. (2)
10F-2 No 41 Nanking W Rd, Taipei, 10352, Taiwan
Tel.: (886) 2 2558 0577
Groundwater Recycling Services
N.A.I.C.S.: 562920

Subsidiary (Domestic):

Kowa Seiko Co., Ltd. (2)
46-93 Nakahara, Tobata-ku, Kitakyushu, 804-0002, Fukuoka, Japan
Tel.: (81) 93 872 5155
Web Site: http://www.kowa-seiko.co.jp
Industrial Waste Recovery Services
N.A.I.C.S.: 562998

Meltec Co., Ltd. (2)
2333-29 Atago, Yana, Oyama, 323-0158, Tochigi, Japan
Tel.: (81) 285491080
Web Site: http://www.dowa.co.jp
Incinerated Ash Recycling Services
N.A.I.C.S.: 562111

Okayama Koyu Co., Ltd. (2)
1048-1 Hinotani Kichigahara, Misaki-cho Kume, Okayama, 708-1523, Japan
Tel.: (81) 869642775
Web Site: http://www.dowa.co.jp
Cargo Handling Services
N.A.I.C.S.: 488320

Subsidiary (Non-US):

P.T. Prasadha Pamunah Limbah Industri (2)
Jl Raya Narogong Desa Nambo, PO Box 18, Kecamatan Klapanunggal, Bogor, 16820, Indonesia
Tel.: (62) 21 867 4042

Web Site: http://www.ppli.co.id
Waste Management Services
N.A.I.C.S.: 562998

Waste Management Siam Ltd. (2)
25th Floor Central City Tower 1 Building 589/142 Debaratana Road, Kwang North Bangna Khet Bangna, Bangkok, 10260, Thailand
Tel.: (66) 27456926
Web Site: https://wms-thailand.com
Waste Management Services
N.A.I.C.S.: 562998

Dowa Electronic Materials Co., Ltd. (1)
22F Akihabara UDX 4-14-1 Sotokanda, Chiyoda-ku, Tokyo, 101-0021, Japan (100%)
Tel.: (81) 368471250
Web Site: https://www.dowa-electronics.co.jp
Sales Range: $450-499.9 Million
Emp.: 1,000
Electronic & Magnetic Materials Supplier
N.A.I.C.S.: 334413

Dowa Electronics Materials Okayama Co., Ltd. (1)
1-3-1 Kaigan-dori, Minami-ku, Okayama, 702-8506, Japan (100%)
Tel.: (81) 862621121
Web Site: https://www.dowa.okayama.jp
Sales Range: $50-74.9 Million
Emp.: 170
Powder Metallurgy Part Mfr
N.A.I.C.S.: 332117

Subsidiary (Domestic):

Dowa IP Creation Co., Ltd. (2)
7 Chikkosakae-cho, Minami-ku, Okayama, 702-8053, Japan (70%)
Tel.: (81) 862622228
Web Site: https://www.dowa-ip.co.jp
Sales Range: $25-49.9 Million
Emp.: 130
Powder Metallurgy Part Mfr
N.A.I.C.S.: 332117

Dowa Environmental Management Co., Ltd. (1)
No 28 Sanlian Street, New District, Suzhou, 215129, Jiangsu, China
Tel.: (86) 51285188100
Web Site: http://www.dowa.co.jp
Sales Range: $25-49.9 Million
Emp.: 50
Recyclable Material Merchant Whslr
N.A.I.C.S.: 423930

Dowa F-Tec (Singapore) Pte. Ltd. (1)
No 13 Benoi Crescent, Jurong, 629976, Singapore, Singapore (100%)
Tel.: (65) 62617366
Web Site: http://www.dowa.co.jp
Sales Range: $25-49.9 Million
Emp.: 9
Powder Metallurgy Part Mfr
N.A.I.C.S.: 332117

Dowa F-Tec Co., Ltd. (1)
1045 Kichigahara Misaki-cho, Kume, Okayama, 708-1523, Japan
Tel.: (81) 868621144
Web Site: http://www.dowa.co.jp
Sales Range: $25-49.9 Million
Emp.: 47
Ferrite Powder Mfr
N.A.I.C.S.: 325998
Masayasu Senda (Pres)

Dowa Gallium Wax Sales Co., Ltd. (1)
6-5 Shimomachi, Nenoshiroishi Izumi-ku, Sendai, 981-3221, Aoba, Japan
Tel.: (81) 223482261
Web Site: https://www.galliumwax.co.jp
Durable Goods Merchant Whslr
N.A.I.C.S.: 423990

Dowa Hightech Co., Ltd. (1)
1718 Nitte, Honjo, 367-0002, Saitama, Japan (100%)
Tel.: (81) 495216111
Web Site: http://www.dowa-hightech.co.jp
Chemical Product & Preparation Mfr
N.A.I.C.S.: 325998

Dowa International Corporation (1)
420 Lexington Ave Graybar Bldg 23F Ste 2300, New York, NY 10170
Tel.: (212) 697-3217
Web Site: http://www.dowa.com
Sales Range: $25-49.9 Million
Emp.: 20
Marketing Consulting Services
N.A.I.C.S.: 541613

Dowa Kohsan Co., Ltd. (1)
31-10 Chikkou-sakaemachi, Minami-ku, Okayama, 702-8609, Japan
Tel.: (81) 862621141
Web Site: http://www.dowa.co.jp
Business Support Services
N.A.I.C.S.: 561499

Dowa Management Services Co., Ltd. (1)
22F Akihabara UDX 4-14-1, Sotokanda Chiyoda-ku, Tokyo, 101-0021, Japan
Tel.: (81) 368471151
Web Site: http://www.dowa.co.jp
Business Support Services
N.A.I.C.S.: 561499

Dowa Metal Co., Ltd. (1)
767 Matsunokishima, Iwata, 438-0125, Shizuoka, Japan (100%)
Tel.: (81) 539623131
Web Site: http://www.dowa.co.jp
Sales Range: $50-74.9 Million
Emp.: 300
Copper Rolling Drawing & Extruding
N.A.I.C.S.: 331420

Dowa Metals & Mining (Thailand) Co., Ltd. (1)
7/395 Moo6 Mabyangporn, Pluakdaeng, Rayong, 21140, Thailand
Tel.: (66) 33010714
Zinc Product Distr
N.A.I.C.S.: 423520

Dowa Metals & Mining America, Inc. (1)
109 Connecticut Dr, Burlington, NJ 08016
Tel.: (609) 900-3692
Spent Catalyst Collecting Distr
N.A.I.C.S.: 423930

Dowa Metals & Mining Co., Ltd. (1)
22F Akihabara UDX 14-1 Sotokanda 4-Chome, Chiyoda-ku, Tokyo, 101-0021, Japan (100%)
Tel.: (81) 368471201
Web Site: https://www.dowa.co.jp
Sales Range: $25-49.9 Million
Emp.: 30
Non-Ferrous Metal Smelting & Recycling
N.A.I.C.S.: 331410
Nobuo Yanazaki (Pres)

Subsidiary (Domestic):

Acids Co., Ltd. (2)
Shinbashi M-SQUARE 4 1-10-6, Shinbashi Minato-ku, Tokyo, 105-0004, Japan
Tel.: (81) 362814765
Specialty Chemicals Distr
N.A.I.C.S.: 424690

Akita Rare Metals Co., Ltd (2)
217-9 Furumichi-shimokawabata, Iijima, Akita, 011-0911, Japan
Tel.: (81) 188461794
Electronic Components Mfr
N.A.I.C.S.: 334419

Akita Zinc Recycling Co., Ltd. (2)
217-9 Furumichi-shimokawabata, Iijima, Akita, 011-0911, Japan
Tel.: (81) 188467918
Web Site: http://www.dowa.co.jp
Industrial Chemicals Mfr
N.A.I.C.S.: 325998

Kosaka Smelting & Refining Co., Ltd (2)
60-1 Otarube Kosaka-machi, Kazuno-gun, Akita, 017-0202, Japan
Tel.: (81) 186292700
Web Site: https://dowa-kosaka.co.jp
Emp.: 320
Copper & Lead Smelting Services
N.A.I.C.S.: 331410

Dowa Metaltech (Thailand) Co., Ltd. (1)

177/1 Moo7 T Huasamrong A Plaengyao, Gateway City Industrial Estate, Chachoengsao, 24190, Thailand
Tel.: (66) 3857 5715
Web Site: http://www.dowa.co.jp
Copper Strip Mfr & Distr
N.A.I.C.S.: 331420

Dowa Metaltech Co., Ltd. (1)
22F Akihabara UDX Bldg 4-14-1 Sotokanda, Chiyoda-ku, Tokyo, 101-0021, Japan (100%)
Tel.: (81) 368471252
Web Site: https://www.dowa.co.jp
Sales Range: $600-649.9 Million
Emp.: 1,000
High-Value-Added Metal Alloy Plating & Processing
N.A.I.C.S.: 331420

Subsidiary (Non-US):

Dowa Advanced Materials (Shanghai) Co., Ltd. (2)
No 7 Studio 8 Rongxiang Road, Shanghai Songjiang Comprehensive Bonded Zone, Shanghai, 201613, China
Tel.: (86) 2157748118
Copper Strip Mfr & Distr
N.A.I.C.S.: 331420

Subsidiary (Domestic):

Dowa Metanix Co., Ltd. (2)
2630 Shingai, Iwata, 438-0025, Shizuoka, Japan (90%)
Tel.: (81) 538327138
Web Site: http://www.metanix.co.jp
Sales Range: $100-124.9 Million
Emp.: 219
Nickel- & Copper-Based Alloys & Electronic Parts Mfr
N.A.I.C.S.: 331420
Masahiro Furo (Sr Mng Dir)

New Nippon Brass Co., Ltd. (2)
5844-3 Kamakazu, Asahi, 289-2505, Chiba, Japan
Tel.: (81) 479620444
Web Site: http://www.dowa.co.jp
Forged Brass Mfr & Distr
N.A.I.C.S.: 331420

Dowa New Materials (Shanghai) Co., Ltd. (1)
D-906 Hongqiao Int'l Technology Plaza No 999 Jinzhong Road, Shanghai, 200335, China
Tel.: (86) 2162752121
Copper Strip Product Distr
N.A.I.C.S.: 423510

Dowa Power Device Co., Ltd. (1)
Shiojiri-inter Rinkan Industrial Zone 9637-3, Manaitahara Kataoka, Shiojiri, 399-0711, Nagano, Japan (100%)
Tel.: (81) 263530770
Web Site: http://www.dowa.co.jp
Sales Range: $25-49.9 Million
Emp.: 50
Bare Printed Circuit Board Mfr
N.A.I.C.S.: 334412

Dowa Precision (Thailand) Co., Ltd. (1)
177/1 Moo7 T Huasamrong, Gateway City Industrial Estate A Plaengyao, Chachoengsao, 24190, Thailand
Tel.: (66) 38575402
Copper Strip Product Distr
N.A.I.C.S.: 423510

Dowa Precision Co., Ltd. (1)
No 3 Aly 31 Ln 236 Heping Rd, Yangmei Dist, Taoyuan, 326, Taiwan
Tel.: (886) 34758400
Copper Strip Product Distr
N.A.I.C.S.: 423510

Dowa Semiconductor Akita Co., Ltd. (1)
1 Sunada, Iijima, Akita, 011-0911, Japan (100%)
Tel.: (81) 188468000
Emp.: 360
Semiconductor & Related Device Mfr
N.A.I.C.S.: 334413
Ryoichi Nakamura (Pres)

Dowa THT America, Inc. (1)

Dowa Holdings Co., Ltd.—(Continued)

**2130 S Woodland Cir, Bowling Green, OH
43402** **(100%)**
Tel.: (419) 354-4144
Sales Range: $25-49.9 Million
Emp.: 100
Plumbing Heating & Air-Conditioning Contractors
N.A.I.C.S.: 238220
Elijah Rittenhouse (VP)

**Dowa Techno Engineering Co.,
Ltd.** **(1)**
31-10 Chikkou-sakaemachi, Minami-ku,
Okayama, 702-8609, Japan **(100%)**
Tel.: (81) 862629208
Commercial & Service Industry Machinery
Mfr
N.A.I.C.S.: 333310

Dowa Techno-Research Co., Ltd. **(1)**
60-1 Otarube Kosakakouzan, Kosaka-machi
Kazuno, Akita, 017-0202, Japan
Tel.: (81) 186292781
Environmental Engineering Services
N.A.I.C.S.: 541330

Dowa Technology Co., Ltd. **(1)**
22F Akihabara UDX 4-14-1, Sotokanda
Chiyoda-ku, Tokyo, 101-0021,
Japan **(100%)**
Tel.: (81) 368471105
Web Site: http://www.dowa.co.jp
Business Support Services
N.A.I.C.S.: 561499

Dowa Tecno-Reseach Co., Ltd. **(1)**
60-1 Otarube Kosakakouzan, Kosaka-machi, Kazuno, 017-0202, Akita, Japan
Tel.: (81) 186292781
Web Site: http://www.dowa.co.jp
Sales Range: $25-49.9 Million
Emp.: 100
Environmental Consulting Services
N.A.I.C.S.: 541620

Dowa Thermotech Co., Ltd. **(1)**
19-1 Ukishimacho, Mizuho-ku, Nagoya,
467-0854, Aichi, Japan
Tel.: (81) 526930800
Web Site: https://www.dowa.co.jp
Metal Heat Treatment Operations
N.A.I.C.S.: 332811
Ryuji Tsuji (Pres)

Subsidiary (Non-US):

**Dowa Thermotech (Thailand) Co.,
Ltd.** **(2)**
300/33 Moo 1 Tambol Tasit; Amphur Pluak-daeng, Rayong, 21140, Thailand
Tel.: (66) 38959008
Web Site: http://www.dowa-tht.co.th
Emp.: 50
Metal Heat Treatment & Maintenance Services
N.A.I.C.S.: 332811

**Dowa Thermotech Mexico S.A. de
C.V.** **(1)**
Avenida Europa 203 del Parque Industrial
Desarrollo Logistik II, Super Carretea San
Luis-Villade Arriaga Laguna de San Vicente,
79526, San Luis Potosi, Mexico
Tel.: (52) 4448117742
Heat Treatment Metal Product Mfr
N.A.I.C.S.: 332811

E & E Solutions Inc. **(1)**
Akihabara UDX Building 4-14-1 Sotokanda,
Chiyoda-Ku, Tokyo, 101-0021, Japan
Tel.: (81) 363280080
Web Site: http://www.eesol.co.jp
Sales Range: $25-49.9 Million
Emp.: 50
Surveying & Mapping Services
N.A.I.C.S.: 541370

Eco-Recycle Co., Ltd. **(1)**
30-2 Doyashiki Hanaoka-machi, Odate,
017-0005, Akita, Japan **(59%)**
Tel.: (81) 186471001
Web Site: http://www.dowa.co.jp
Sales Range: $25-49.9 Million
Emp.: 100
Consumer Electronics Repair & Maintenance
N.A.I.C.S.: 811210

Eco-System Chiba Co., Ltd. **(1)**

**1-30-2 Taku Nagaura, Sodegaura, 299-
0265, Chiba, Japan** **(100%)**
Tel.: (81) 438624097
Web Site: https://www.dowa-eco.co.jp
Emp.: 80
Waste Management Services
N.A.I.C.S.: 562998

Eco-System Hanaoka Co., Ltd. **(1)**
42 Tsutsumisawa Hanaoka-machi, Odate,
017-0005, Akita, Japan **(100%)**
Tel.: (81) 186462311
Waste Management Services
N.A.I.C.S.: 562998

Eco-System Japan Co., Ltd. **(1)**
22F Akihabara UDX 4-14-1, Sotokanda
Chiyoda-ku, Tokyo, 101-0021,
Japan **(90%)**
Tel.: (81) 368477010
Web Site: http://www.dowa.co.jp
Sales Range: $25-49.9 Million
Emp.: 100
Waste Collection
N.A.I.C.S.: 562112

Eco-System Kosaka Co., Ltd. **(1)**
60-1 Otarube Kosakakouzan, Kosaka-machi, Kazuno, 017-0202, Akita,
Japan **(100%)**
Tel.: (81) 186292962
Web Site: http://www.dowa.co.jp
Sales Range: $25-49.9 Million
Emp.: 24
Hazardous Waste Collection
N.A.I.C.S.: 562112

Eco-System Okayama Co., Ltd. **(1)**
1-3-1 Kaigan-dori, Minami-ku, Okayama,
702-8506, Japan **(100%)**
Tel.: (81) 862629020
Sales Range: $50-74.9 Million
Emp.: 30
Nonferrous Metal Rolling Drawing & Extruding
N.A.I.C.S.: 331491
Kentaro Yamauchi (Pres)

Eco-System Recycling Co., Ltd. **(1)**
1718-3 Nitte, Honjo, 367-0002, Saitama,
Japan
Tel.: (81) 495211982
Web Site: https://www.dowa-erc.co.jp
Recyclable Material Whslr
N.A.I.C.S.: 423930

Eco-System Sanyo Co., Ltd. **(1)**
1125 Kichigahara, Misaki-cho Kume,
Okayama, 708-1523, Japan **(100%)**
Tel.: (81) 868621346
Web Site: http://www.dowa.co.jp
Sales Range: $50-74.9 Million
Emp.: 100
Metal Ore Mining
N.A.I.C.S.: 212290

Geotechnos Co., Ltd. **(1)**
(100%)
Tel.: (81) 336264580
Web Site: http://www.geotechnos.co.jp
Sales Range: $25-49.9 Million
Emp.: 50
Water Well Drilling Contractor
N.A.I.C.S.: 237110

**Golden Dowa Eco-System Myanmar
Company Limited** **(1)**
Lot No E1 Thilawa SEZ Zone A, Yangon,
Myanmar
Tel.: (95) 12309051
Web Site: http://www.golden-dowa.com
Emp.: 40
Industrial Waste Management Services
N.A.I.C.S.: 562998
Hideki Yomo (Mng Dir)

Hightemp Furnaces Ltd. **(1)**
1C 2nd Phase, PO Box 5809, Peenya Industrial Area, Bengaluru, 560058, Karnataka, India
Tel.: (91) 8028395917
Web Site: http://www.hightemp-furnaces.com
Sales Range: $25-49.9 Million
Emp.: 100
Industrial Process Furnace & Oven Mfr
N.A.I.C.S.: 333994
M. Gopal (Mng Dir)

Hoei Shoji Co., Ltd. **(1)**

**1598-1 Kotehashi-cho, Hanamigawa-ku,
Chiba, 262-0013, Japan**
Tel.: (81) 432862601
Aluminium Products Mfr & Distr
N.A.I.C.S.: 331315

**Kunshan Dowa Thermo Furnace Co.,
Ltd.** **(1)**
No 298 Jiguang South Road, Shipu Qiandeng, Kunshan, Jiangsu, China
Tel.: (86) 51282625600
Web Site: http://www.dowafurnace.com
Emp.: 100
Heat Treatment Equipment Mfr & Distr
N.A.I.C.S.: 333414
Tamura Akio (Chm)

Meltec Iwaki Co., Ltd. **(1)**
1-75 Yoshinosawa Yotsukura-machi, Iwaki,
979-0201, Fukushima, Japan
Tel.: (81) 246849507
Metal Recovery Services
N.A.I.C.S.: 562920

Minera Tizapa, S.A. de C.V. **(1)**
Calzada Manuel Gomez Morin 44, Col
Torreon Residencial, 27268, Torreon, Coahuila, Mexico
Tel.: (52) 8717293442
Copper Ore & Nickel Ore Mining
N.A.I.C.S.: 212230

**Modern Asia Environmental Holdings
Pte. Ltd.** **(1)**
23 Tuas Avenue 11, Singapore, 639086,
Singapore
Tel.: (65) 68623130
Web Site: https://www.dowa-maeh.com.sg
Industrial Waste Management Services
N.A.I.C.S.: 562998

Nippon PGM America Inc. **(1)**
500 Richards Run, Burlington, NJ 08016
Tel.: (609) 747-9994
Sales Range: $50-74.9 Million
Emp.: 10
Crushed & Broken Stone Mining & Quarrying
N.A.I.C.S.: 212319

Nippon PGM Co., Ltd. **(1)**
76-1 Otarube, Kosaka Kazuno, Akita, 017-
0202, Japan **(60%)**
Tel.: (81) 186292744
Sales Range: $25-49.9 Million
Emp.: 30
Primary Smelting & Refining Nonferrous
Metal
N.A.I.C.S.: 331410
Ogino Masahika (Gen Mgr)

Nippon PGM Co., Ltd. **(1)**
22F Akihabara UDX Bldg 4-14-1 Sotokanda, Chiyoda-Ku, Tokyo, 101-0021, Japan
Tel.: (81) 368471205
Web Site:
https://www.nipponpgm.dowa.co.jp
Emp.: 300
Collection & Smelting of Spent Automobile
& Petrochemical Catalyst for Recovery of
Platinum Group Metals
N.A.I.C.S.: 331410
Masao Yamada (Mng Dir)

Subsidiary (US):

Nippon PGM America Inc. **(2)**
500 Richards Run, Burlington, NJ 08016
Tel.: (609) 747-9994
Web Site: http://www.dowa.co.jp
Catalyst Smelting
N.A.I.C.S.: 332999

Nippon PGM Europe s.r.o. **(1)**
Heyrovskeho 488, 46312, Liberec, Czech
Republic
Tel.: (420) 488100271
Metal Recycling Services
N.A.I.C.S.: 423930

PT. Dowa Thermotech Furnaces **(1)**
Jl Maligi VI Lot G-4, Kawasan Industri KIIC,
Karawang, 41361, West Java, Indonesia
Tel.: (62) 2189114346
Heat Treatment Equipment Distr
N.A.I.C.S.: 423720

PT. Dowa Thermotech Indonesia **(1)**
Jln Maligi VI Lot G-4 Sukaluyu, Kawasan
Industri KIIC Telukjambe Timur, Karawang,

41361, Jawa Barat, Indonesia
Tel.: (62) 2189114346
Heat Treatment Equipment Mfr & Distr
N.A.I.C.S.: 333994

Showa Kaihatsu Kogyo Co., Ltd. **(1)**
31-10 Chikkou-Sakaemachi, Okayama,
702-8609, Japan **(100%)**
Tel.: (81) 862629200
Web Site: http://www.dowa.co.jp
Crushed & Broken Stone Mining & Quarrying
N.A.I.C.S.: 212319

**Soso Smart Eco-Company Co.,
Ltd.** **(1)**
123 Choujahara Ottozawa, Okuma-machi,
Futaba, 979-1301, Fukushima, Japan
Tel.: (81) 240235940
Non-Combustible Waste Recovery Services
N.A.I.C.S.: 562111

**Technochem Environmental Complex
Pte. Ltd.** **(1)**
23 Tuas Avenue 11, Singapore, 639086,
Singapore
Tel.: (65) 68623130
Web Site: https://wms-technochem.com
Waste Treatment Services
N.A.I.C.S.: 562211

Tonetsu Kosan Co., Ltd. **(1)**
2-102 Sunosaki-cho, Handa, 475-0021,
Aichi, Japan
Tel.: (81) 569892301
Web Site: http://www.dowa.co.jp
Business Associations
N.A.I.C.S.: 813910

Yowa Engineering Co., Ltd. **(1)**
7-2 Chikkou-sakaemachi, Minami-ku,
Okayama, 702-8053, Japan
Tel.: (81) 862649034
Web Site: http://www.yowa.co.jp
Construction Equipment Mfr
N.A.I.C.S.: 333120

Yowa Kouei Co., Ltd. **(1)**
7-2 Chikkou-Sakaemachi, Okayama, 702-
8609, Japan **(100%)**
Tel.: (81) 862649034
Web Site: http://www.dowa.co.jp
Heavy & Civil Engineering Construction
N.A.I.C.S.: 237990
Yuko Saito (Gen Mgr)

Zinc Excel Co., Ltd. **(1)**
22F Akihabara UDX 4-14-1, Sotokanda
Chiyoda-ku, Tokyo, 101-0021,
Japan **(85%)**
Tel.: (81) 368471270
Web Site: http://zinc-excel.co.jp
Sales Range: $25-49.9 Million
Emp.: 40
Metal Service Centers & Offices
N.A.I.C.S.: 423510

DOWLAIS GROUP PLC
2nd Floor Nova North 11 Bressenden
Place, London, SW1E 5BY, United
Kingdom
Tel.: (44) 2045513383   **UK**
Web Site: https://www.dowlais.com
Year Founded: 2023
DWL—(LSE)
Automotive Parts & Accessories Retailers
N.A.I.C.S.: 441330
Helen Redfern (Chief People Officer)

DOWN2EARTH CAPITAL NV
Hessenstraatje 20, 2000, Antwerp,
Belgium
Tel.: (32) 3 689 45 01   **BE**
Web Site: http://d2e.be
Investment Services
N.A.I.C.S.: 523999
Alain Keppens (Co-Founder & Partner)

Subsidiaries:

Down2Earth Partners NV **(1)**
Hessenstraatje 20, 2000, Antwerp, Belgium
Tel.: (32) (3) 689.45
Investment Services
N.A.I.C.S.: 523999

Subsidiary (Domestic):

Grandeco Wallfashion Group - Belgium NV **(2)**
Wakkensesteenweg 49-Industriepark Zuid, 8700, Tielt, Belgium
Tel.: (32) 51424 711
Web Site: http://www.grandecogroup.com
Wall Covering Mfr
N.A.I.C.S.: 327120
Patrick Molemans (CEO)

DOWNER EDI LIMITED

Triniti Business Campus 39 Delhi Road, North Ryde, 2113, NSW, Australia
Tel.: (61) 298138915   AU
Web Site:
    https://www.downergroup.com
Year Founded: 1933
DOW—(ASX)
Rev.: $7,379,006,380
Assets: $4,506,009,597
Liabilities: $2,997,329,048
Net Worth: $1,508,680,549
Earnings: $54,821,047
Emp.: 33,000
Fiscal Year-end: 06/30/24
Infrastructure, Engineering & Mining Services
N.A.I.C.S.: 236210
David Cattell (Head-Strategy-Grp)

Subsidiaries:

CPG Environmental Engineering Co. Ltd **(1)**
A4-A6 19F Phase III International Science Park No 1355, Jinji Hu Ave Suzhou Industrial Park, Suzhou, 215021, China
Tel.: (86) 51262528618
Web Site: http://www.cpgenv.com
Environmental Engineering Services
N.A.I.C.S.: 541330
Wen Chai Koa (Gen Mgr)

CPG New Zealand **(1)**
1st Fl John Wickliffe House, 265-269 Princess St, Dunedin, 9054, New Zealand **(100%)**
Tel.: (64) 3 64777133
Engineering & Consulting Services
N.A.I.C.S.: 541330

CPG Resources - Mineral Technologies (Proprietary) Ltd **(1)**
14 Dockside Bay, Richards Bay, 3900, Kwazulu-Natal, South Africa
Tel.: (27) 357973230
Sales Range: $50-74.9 Million
Emp.: 21
Mineral Mining Services
N.A.I.C.S.: 212390
Steven MacDonald (Gen Mgr)

CPG Resources - Mineral Technologies Pty Ltd **(1)**
Carrara, Carrara, Gold Coast, 4211, QLD, Australia
Tel.: (61) 755691300
Web Site:
    https://www.mineraltechnologies.com
Sales Range: $100-124.9 Million
Emp.: 200
Mineral Processing Services
N.A.I.C.S.: 213115
Andrew Foster (Gen Mgr)

CPG Resources - QCC Pty Ltd **(1)**
6 16 Galleghan Road, Newcastle, 2323, NSW, Australia
Tel.: (61) 249379900
Web Site: http://www.qccresources.com
Mineral Mining Services
N.A.I.C.S.: 212390

CPG Signature Pte. Ltd. **(1)**
1 Gateway Drive, Westgate Tower 25-01, Singapore, 608531, Singapore **(100%)**
Tel.: (65) 63574839
Web Site: http://www.cpgcorp.com.sg
Sales Range: $700-749.9 Million
Emp.: 3,000
Professional Organizations
N.A.I.C.S.: 813920

CPG Traffic Pty Ltd **(1)**

46 Wadhurst Dr, Boronia, 3155, VIC, Australia
Tel.: (61) 388053400
Engineeering Services
N.A.I.C.S.: 541330

Cendrill Supply Pty Limited **(1)**
51 Fulciun Street, Richlands, 4077, QLD, Australia **(100%)**
Tel.: (61) 737184444
Industrial Machinery & Equipment Merchant Whslr
N.A.I.C.S.: 423830

Chan Lian Construction Pte Ltd **(1)**
11 Lorong 3 Toa Payoh 03-18 Jackson Square, Singapore, 319579, Singapore
Tel.: (65) 65170757
Civil Engineering Construction Services
N.A.I.C.S.: 237990

Construction Professionals Pte Ltd **(1)**
1 North Coast Avenue 04-11 1 North Coast, Singapore, 737663, Singapore
Tel.: (65) 63574829
Construction Engineering Services
N.A.I.C.S.: 541330

Downer Australia Pty Ltd **(1)**
Triniti Business Campus 39 Delhi Road, North Ryde, 2113, NSW, Australia
Tel.: (61) 294689700
Web Site: http://www.downergroup.com
Civil Engineering Construction Services
N.A.I.C.S.: 237990

Downer Construction (Fiji) Limited **(1)**
Lot 1 Royal Palm Street, Lautoka, Fiji **(100%)**
Tel.: (679) 6652106
Engineeering Services
N.A.I.C.S.: 541330

Downer EDI (USA) Pty Ltd **(1)**
Triniti Business Campus 39 Delhi Rd, North Ryde, 2113, NSW, Australia
Tel.: (61) 294689700
Web Site: http://www.downergroup.com
Emp.: 650
Construction Engineering Services
N.A.I.C.S.: 541330

Downer EDI Engineering (S) Pte Ltd **(1)**
11 Lorong 3 Toa Payoh 01-41 Block D Jackson Square, Singapore, 319579, Singapore
Tel.: (65) 65170757
Sales Range: $25-49.9 Million
Emp.: 6
Engineeering Services
N.A.I.C.S.: 541330

Downer EDI Engineering - Projects Pty Ltd **(1)**
39 Delhi Rd, North Ryde, 2113, NSW, Australia
Tel.: (61) 294689700
Engineeering Services
N.A.I.C.S.: 541330

Downer EDI Engineering Group Pty Limited **(1)**
Level 7 76 Berry Street, Sydney, 2060, NSW, Australia **(100%)**
Tel.: (61) 299662400
Engineeering Services
N.A.I.C.S.: 541330

Division (Domestic):

Downer EDI Engineering - Contracting / Power Systems **(2)**
Building B 480 Victoria Road, Gladesville, 2111, NSW, Australia **(100%)**
Tel.: (61) 298798400
Web Site: http://www.downergroup.com
Sales Range: $25-49.9 Million
Emp.: 200
Telecommunications Contracting Services
N.A.I.C.S.: 517810
John Maclellan (Mgr)

Downer EDI Engineering Holdings Pty Ltd **(1)**
39 Delhi Rd, North Ryde, 2113, NSW, Australia
Tel.: (61) 294689700

Web Site: http://www.downergroup.com
Sales Range: $25-49.9 Million
Emp.: 200
Electronic Engineering Services
N.A.I.C.S.: 541330

Downer EDI Engineering Transmission Pty Ltd **(1)**
Triniti Business Campus 39 Delhi Rd, North Ryde, 2113, NSW, Australia
Tel.: (61) 294689700
Web Site: http://www.downergroup.com
Power Plant Construction Engineering Services
N.A.I.C.S.: 237130

Downer EDI Group (NZ) Ltd **(1)**
Airport Retail Centre Auckland Airport, PO Box 201220, 2150, Manukau, New Zealand **(100%)**
Tel.: (64) 92569810
Web Site: http://www.downeredi.co.nz
Sales Range: $700-749.9 Million
Emp.: 5,000
Engineering Services
N.A.I.C.S.: 541330

Downer EDI Group Insurance Pte. Ltd. **(1)**
18 Cross Street 04-00 Marsh & Mclennan Centre, Singapore, 048423, Singapore
Tel.: (65) 62208141
Sales Range: $50-74.9 Million
Emp.: 18
Insurance Management Services
N.A.I.C.S.: 524298

Downer EDI Mining - Minerals Exploration Pty Ltd **(1)**
L 7 104 Melbourne St, Brisbane, 4101, QLD, Australia
Tel.: (61) 730266666
Web Site: http://www.downergroup.com
Emp.: 400
Oil & Gas Well Drilling Services
N.A.I.C.S.: 213111

Downer EDI Mining Holding Pty Ltd. **(1)**
104 Melbourne St, Brisbane, 4101, QLD, Australia **(100%)**
Tel.: (61) 755691300
Web Site: http://www.downergroup.com
Holding Company
N.A.I.C.S.: 551112
David Overal (CEO)

Subsidiary (Domestic):

Downer EDI Mining Pty Ltd. **(2)**
104 Melbourne Street, Brisbane, 4101, QLD, Australia **(100%)**
Tel.: (61) 730266666
Web Site: http://www.downeredimining.com
Emp.: 250
Engineering Services
N.A.I.C.S.: 541330
David Overall (CEO)

Downer EDI Rail Pty Ltd **(1)**
2b Factory St, Granville, 2142, NSW, Australia
Tel.: (61) 296378288
Web Site: http://www.downergroup.com
Sales Range: $125-149.9 Million
Emp.: 300
Rail Rolling Stock Operating Services
N.A.I.C.S.: 488210

Downer EDI Services Pty Ltd **(1)**
Triniti Business Campus 39 Delhi Road, North Ryde, 2113, NSW, Australia
Tel.: (61) 2 9468 9700
Engineeering Services
N.A.I.C.S.: 541330

Subsidiary (Domestic):

Spotless Group Holdings Limited **(2)**
549 St Kilda Road, Melbourne, 3004, VIC, Australia
Tel.: (61) 392697600
Web Site: http://www.spotless.com
Facility Management Services
N.A.I.C.S.: 561210
Peter Tompkins (Dir)

Subsidiary (Domestic):

A.E. Smith & Son Proprietary Limited **(3)**

549 St Kilda Road, Melbourne, 3004, VIC, Australia
Tel.: (61) 1300313313
Web Site: http://www.aesmith.com.au
Emp.: 700
Heating, Ventilation, Air Conditioning & Building Management Services
N.A.I.C.S.: 238220

Subsidiary (Domestic):

A.E. Smith Service Pty Ltd **(4)**
T1 Trinity Business Campus 39 Delhi Road, North Ryde, 2113, NSW, Australia
Tel.: (61) 1300313313
Air Conditioning Installation & Mechanical Services
N.A.I.C.S.: 238220

Subsidiary (Domestic):

Cleanevent International Pty Ltd **(3)**
549 St Kilda Rd, Melbourne, 3004, VIC, Australia
Tel.: (61) 392697600
Waste Management Services
N.A.I.C.S.: 562998

Spotless Defence Services Pty. Ltd. **(3)**
549 St Kilda Rd, Melbourne, 3004, VIC, Australia
Tel.: (61) 392697600
Construction Engineering Services
N.A.I.C.S.: 541330

Spotless Facility Services Pty Ltd **(3)**
549 St Kilda Rd, Melbourne, 3004, VIC, Australia
Tel.: (61) 392697600
Facilities Management Services
N.A.I.C.S.: 561210

Spotless Group Limited **(3)**
549 St Kilda Rd, Melbourne, 3004, VIC, Australia
Tel.: (61) 392697600
Painting & Building Support Services
N.A.I.C.S.: 238320

Subsidiary (Non-US):

Spotless Services (NZ) Ltd. **(3)**
Level 3 Millennium Building B 600 Great South Rd, Ellerslie, Ellerslie, Auckland, New Zealand
Tel.: (64) 9 251 0138
Web Site: http://www.spotless.co.nz
Food Catering Services
N.A.I.C.S.: 722320

Subsidiary (Domestic):

Spotless Services Australia Limited **(3)**
549 St Kilda Rd, Melbourne, 3004, VIC, Australia
Tel.: (61) 392697600
Facility Management Services
N.A.I.C.S.: 561499

Subsidiary (Domestic):

Berkeleys Franchise Services Pty. Ltd. **(4)**
549 St Kilda Rd, Melbourne, 3004, VIC, Australia
Tel.: (61) 392697600
Commercial Cleaning Services
N.A.I.C.S.: 561720

Subsidiary (Domestic):

Utility Services Group Limited **(3)**
549 St Kilda Road, Melbourne, 3004, VIC, Australia
Tel.: (61) 392697600
Engineering Consulting Services
N.A.I.C.S.: 541330

Subsidiary (Domestic):

Skilltech Consulting Services Pty Ltd **(4)**
10 - 16 South Street, Rydalmere, 2116, NSW, Australia
Tel.: (61) 1300377170
Web Site: https://www.skilltech.com.au
Technical Metering Services
N.A.I.C.S.: 561990

Downer EDI Limited—(Continued)

Downer EDI Works Pty Ltd. (1)
37 Syrimi Rd, Burma, Berrimah, 0828, NT,
Australia (100%)
Tel.: (61) 889443600
Web Site: http://www.downer.com.au
Sales Range: $25-49.9 Million
Emp.: 40
Highway Street & Bridge Construction
N.A.I.C.S.: 237310

**Downer Engineering Power Pty
Limited** (1)
Triniti Business Campus, 39 Delhi Road,
North Ryde, 2113, NSW, Australia (100%)
Tel.: (61) 294689700
Web Site: http://www.downergroup.com
Engineeering Services
N.A.I.C.S.: 541330

**Downer Group Finance Pty
Limited** (1)
L 3 190 George St, Sydney, NSW,
Australia (100%)
Tel.: (61) 292519899
Web Site: http://www.downeredi.com
Holding Company
N.A.I.C.S.: 551112

Downer Holdings Pty Ltd (1)
Triniti Business Campus 39 Delhi Road,
North Ryde, 2113, NSW, Australia (1)
Tel.: (61) 294689700
Web Site: http://www.downergroup.com
Investment Management Service
N.A.I.C.S.: 523999

Downer MBL Pty Limited (1)
Level 1 650 Lorimer Street, Locked Bag
1200, 3207, Melbourne, VIC,
Australia (100%)
Tel.: (61) 395931157
Engineeering Services
N.A.I.C.S.: 541330

Downer New Zealand Limited (1)
130 Kerrs Road Wiri, North Island, Auck-
land, New Zealand
Tel.: (64) 92510340
Infrastrcuture Management Services
N.A.I.C.S.: 561110

Downer Pipetech Pty. Limited (1)
Unit 1/ Building D Seven Hills Business
Park 22 Powers Road, Seven Hills, 2147,
NSW, Australia
Tel.: (61) 286032000
Web Site: http://www.itspipetech.com.au
Innovative Pipeline Rehabilitation Services
N.A.I.C.S.: 624310

Downer Pte Ltd (1)
11 Lor 3 Toa Payoh 03-16, Singapore,
319570, Singapore
Tel.: (65) 65170757
Infrastrcuture Management Services
N.A.I.C.S.: 561499

EDI Rail (Maryborough) Pty Ltd. (1)
2 Allena St Maryborough, Maryborough,
Queensland, 3111, VIC, Australia (100%)
Tel.: (61) 741208100
Web Site: www.downergroup.com
Sales Range: $100-124.9 Million
Emp.: 3
Mining Machinery & Equipment Mfr
N.A.I.C.S.: 333131
David Hill (Mgr-Facility)

**Emoleum Roads Group Pty
Limited** (1)
L 11 468 St Kilda Rd, Melbourne, VIC,
Australia (100%)
Tel.: (61) 398640868
Financial Investment Activities
N.A.I.C.S.: 523999

**Envar Engineers And Contractors Pty.
Ltd.** (1)
47 Furnace Road, Welshpool, 6106, WA,
Australia
Tel.: (61) 893505377
Engineering & Construction Management
Services
N.A.I.C.S.: 541330

Fowlers Asphalting Pty. Limited (1)
100 Contour Road, Trafalgar, 3824, VIC,
Australia

Tel.: (61) 356332918
Web Site:
https://www.fowlersasphalting.com.au
Asphalt & Pavement Construction Services
N.A.I.C.S.: 541330

Gippsland Asphalt Pty. Ltd. (1)
171 Bosworth Road, Bairnsdale, 3824, VIC,
Australia
Tel.: (61) 457001077
Web Site:
https://www.rivieraconcrete.com.au
Pavement Construction Services
N.A.I.C.S.: 541330

Green Vision Recycling Limited (1)
39-59 Miami Parade Pikes Point, One-
hunga, Auckland, 1061, New Zealand
Tel.: (64) 8000047336
Web Site: https://greenvisionrecycling.co.nz
Construction Aggregate Product Recycling
Services
N.A.I.C.S.: 562920

Mineral Technologies Pty. Ltd. (1)
11 Elysium Rd, Carrara, Gold Coast, 4211,
QLD, Australia
Tel.: (61) 755691300
Web Site:
http://www.mineraltechnologies.com
Mineral Mining Services
N.A.I.C.S.: 212210

Subsidiary (US):

Mineral Technologies, Inc. (2)
24 Cathedral Pl Ste 208, Saint Augustine,
FL 32084
Tel.: (904) 342-8354
Web Site:
http://www.mineraltechnologies.com
Emp.: 4
Mineral Mining Services
N.A.I.C.S.: 212210
William Weldon (Sec & Dir)

Otracom Pty Ltd. (1)
Level 1 130 Fauntleroy Avenue, Redcliffe,
6134, WA, Australia
Tel.: (61) 894737500
Web Site: http://www.otraco.com
Sales Range: $25-49.9 Million
Emp.: 25
Custom Computer Programming Services
N.A.I.C.S.: 541511
Bernd Thansen (Mng Dir)

PT Otraco Indonesia (1)
PO Box 120, 6100, Burswood, WA,
Australia (100%)
Tel.: (61) 894737500
Web Site: http://www.otraco.com.au
Sales Range: $25-49.9 Million
Emp.: 180
Engineeering Services
N.A.I.C.S.: 541330
Alistair Swanson (Gen Mgr)

Peridian Asia Pte Ltd. (1)
5 Purvis St #02-01, Talib Court, 188584,
Singapore, Singapore (100%)
Tel.: (65) 62277998
Sales Range: $25-49.9 Million
Emp.: 50
Geophysical Surveying & Mapping Services
N.A.I.C.S.: 541360
Dennis M. Taylor (Mng Dir)

Roche Contractors Pty Ltd (1)
L 7 104 Melbourne St, Brisbane, 4101,
QLD, Australia
Tel.: (61) 730266666
Construction Engineering Services
N.A.I.C.S.: 541330

Roche Mining (MT) India Pvt Ltd. (1)
406 F Vrindavan Apartments, Vyttila Junc-
tion, 682019, Cochin, Vyttila, India (100%)
Tel.: (91) 4842389097
Web Site: http://www.rochemt.com.br
Sales Range: $25-49.9 Million
Emp.: 5
Engineeering Services
N.A.I.C.S.: 541330

Rpq Asphalt Pty. Ltd. (1)
206-258 Swanbank Road, Swanbank, 4306,
QLD, Australia
Tel.: (61) 732944555
Web Site: https://www.rpq.com.au
Road Construction & Maintenance Services

N.A.I.C.S.: 237310

Rpq Mackay Pty. Ltd. (1)
1-3 Graeme Heggie St, Mackay Harbour,
4740, QLD, Australia
Tel.: (61) 749555235
Road Maintenance Services
N.A.I.C.S.: 237310

Rpq North Coast Pty. Ltd. (1)
68-70 Link Crescent, Coolum Beach, 4573,
QLD, Australia
Tel.: (61) 7329944555
Road Construction & Maintenance Services
N.A.I.C.S.: 237310

Rpq Pty. Ltd. (1)
206-258 Swanbank Road, Swanbank, 4306,
QLD, Australia
Tel.: (61) 732944555
Web Site: https://www.rpq.com.au
Emp.: 300
Road Maintenance Services
N.A.I.C.S.: 237310

Sillars (B. & C.E.) Ltd (1)
Silicon House Graythorp Industrial Estate,
Cleveland, Hartlepool, TS25 2DF, United
Kingdom
Tel.: (44) 1429268125
Road Construction Engineering Services
N.A.I.C.S.: 237310

Sillars Holdings Limited (1)
Silicon House Graythorp Industrial Estate,
Cleveland, Hartlepool, TS25 2DF, United
Kingdom
Tel.: (44) 1429 268125
Investment Management Service
N.A.I.C.S.: 523999

**Snowden Mining Industry Consultants
Limited** (1)
1090 Pender St, W Suite 600, Vancouver,
V6E 2N7, BC, Canada (100%)
Tel.: (604) 683-7645
Web Site: http://www.snowdengroup.com
Sales Range: $25-49.9 Million
Emp.: 10
Engineeering Services
N.A.I.C.S.: 541330
David Lawrence (Mng Dir)

**Snowden Mining Industry Consultants
Pty Ltd.** (1)
Level 6 130 Stirling Street, Perth, 6004,
WA, Australia (100%)
Tel.: (61) 892139213
Web Site: http://www.snowdengroup.com
Sales Range: $25-49.9 Million
Emp.: 60
Management Consulting Services
N.A.I.C.S.: 541618
David Cormick (CEO)

Snowden Technologies Pty Ltd. (1)
Level 6 130 Stirling Street, Perth, 6000,
WA, Australia (100%)
Tel.: (61) 892139213
Web Site: http://www.snowdengroup.com
Sales Range: $25-49.9 Million
Emp.: 110
Business Service Centers 561439
N.A.I.C.S.: 561439
Craig Morley (CEO)

TSE Wall Arlidge Limited (1)
Level 1 Manthels Building 19-23 Taranaki
Street, PO Box 6643, Wellington, 6141,
New Zealand
Tel.: (64) 43850096
Sales Range: $25-49.9 Million
Emp.: 37
Property Management Services
N.A.I.C.S.: 531312

Underground Service Locators (1)
Level 13 Kordoidii Suite 109 Willis Street,
Wellington, 9016, New Zealand
Tel.: (64) 800425622
Web Site:
https://www.undergroundlocators.co.nz
Sales Range: $25-49.9 Million
Emp.: 50
Underground Engineering Services
N.A.I.C.S.: 541330
Steve Worthington (Mgr-Ops)

Vec Civil Engineering Pty. Ltd. (1)
10b Industrial Drive, Ulverstone, 7315, TAS,
Australia

Tel.: (61) 364256530
Web Site: https://www.vec.com.au
Civil Engineering & Construction Services
N.A.I.C.S.: 541330

Waste Solutions Limited (1)
Unit 4 Westpoint Trade Centre Link Road,
Ballincollig, Ireland (100%)
Tel.: (353) 578576595
Web Site: https://www.wastesolutions.ie
Waste Management Services
N.A.I.C.S.: 562998

Works Finance (NZ) Limited (1)
130 Kerrs Road, Wiri, Auckland, 2104, New
Zealand
Tel.: (64) 92569810
Web Site: http://www.downergroup.com
Property Management Services
N.A.I.C.S.: 531311

DOWNEY FORD SALES
35 Consumers Drive, Saint John, E2J
3S9, NB, Canada
Tel.: (506) 632-6000
Web Site: http://www.downeys.ca
New & Used Car Dealers
N.A.I.C.S.: 441110
Jim Mason (Mgr-Sls)

DOWNING LLP
St Magnus House 3 Lower Thames
Street, London, EC3R 6HD, United
Kingdom
Tel.: (44) 2074167780
Web Site: http://www.downing.co.uk
Investment Services
N.A.I.C.S.: 525910
Nick Lewis (Chm)

DOWNING ONE VCT PLC
1 Old Hall Street 5th Floor, Liverpool,
L3 9HF, United Kingdom
Tel.: (44) 1517072666
Web Site: https://www.downing.com
Year Founded: 1999
DDV1—(LSE)
Rev.: $1,809,841
Assets: $138,346,237
Liabilities: $737,242
Net Worth: $137,608,995
Earnings: ($836,356)
Fiscal Year-end: 03/31/21
Investment Management Service
N.A.I.C.S.: 525990
George Downing (Founder)

DOWNING RENEWABLES &
INFRASTRUCTURE TRUST
PLC
Central Square 29 Wellington Street,
Leeds, LS1 4DL, United Kingdom
Tel.: (44) 2074167780
Web Site: https://www.doretrust.com
Year Founded: 1986
DORE—(LSE)
Rev.: $44,831,464
Assets: $274,141,010
Liabilities: $2,312,232
Net Worth: $271,828,778
Earnings: $41,221,551
Emp.: 200
Fiscal Year-end: 12/31/22
Asset Management Services
N.A.I.C.S.: 523999
Hugh Little (Chm)

DOWNING STRATEGIC
MICRO-CAP INVESTMENT
TRUST PLC
St Magnus House 3 Lower Thames
Street, London, EC3R 6HD, United
Kingdom
Tel.: (44) 2074167780   UK
Web Site:
https://www.downingstrategic.co.uk
Year Founded: 2017
DSM—(LSE)
Rev.: $4,365,070

Assets: $58,787,918
Liabilities: $325,853
Net Worth: $58,462,065
Earnings: $3,285,682
Fiscal Year-end: 02/28/22
Investment Trust Management Services
N.A.I.C.S.: 523940
Judith MacKenzie *(Mgr-Investment)*

DOWNING TWO VCT PLC
St Magnus House 3 Lower Thames Street, London, EC3R 6HD, United Kingdom
Tel.: (44) 2074167780   UK
Web Site: http://www.downing.co.uk
Year Founded: 2005
Rev.: $2,057,081
Assets: $42,268,518
Liabilities: $568,521
Net Worth: $41,699,997
Earnings: ($4,573,548)
Fiscal Year-end: 12/31/18
Investment Management Service
N.A.I.C.S.: 523940
Hugh Gillespie *(Chm)*

DOWNS CONSTRUCTION LTD.
870 Devonshire Road, Victoria, V9A 4T6, BC, Canada
Tel.: (250) 384-1390
Web Site: https://www.downsconstruction.com
Year Founded: 1981
Construction Services
N.A.I.C.S.: 236220
Susan Downs *(Office Mgr)*

DOWNSVIEW CHRYSLER PLYMOUTH (1964) LTD.
199 Rimrock Road, Toronto, M3J 3C6, ON, Canada
Tel.: (416) 635-1660
Web Site: http://www.downsviewchrysler.com
Year Founded: 1964
Sales Range: $25-49.9 Million
Emp.: 100
Car Dealer
N.A.I.C.S.: 441110
Carlos Baptista *(VP)*

DOWNSVIEW DRYWALL CONTRACTING
160 Bass Pro Mills Dr, Concord, L4K 0A7, ON, Canada
Tel.: (905) 660-0048
Web Site: http://www.downsviewdrywall.com
Year Founded: 1977
Rev.: $10,838,170
Emp.: 100
Drywall & Insulation Contractors
N.A.I.C.S.: 238310
Sam Sgotto *(Pres)*

DOWNSVIEW HEATING & AIR CONDITIONING
4299 Queen St E Unit 2, Brampton, L6T 5V4, ON, Canada
Tel.: (905) 794-1489
Web Site: http://www.downsview.ca
Rev.: $12,433,128
Emp.: 90
Plumbing Contractor
N.A.I.C.S.: 238220
Frank Quattrociocch *(Owner)*

DOWNTOWN PONTIAC BUICK (1983) LIMITED
449 Queen Street West, Saint Marys, N4X1B7, ON, Canada
Tel.: (519) 284-3310
Web Site: http://www.downtownpontiac.ca

Year Founded: 1983
Rev.: $11,561,746
Emp.: 26
New & Used Car Dealers
N.A.I.C.S.: 441110
Chris West *(Pres)*

DOWWAY HOLDINGS LTD.
No 6112 DRC No 1 Compound Xindong Road, Chaoyang District, Beijing, 100600, China
Tel.: (86) 1085325952   Ky
Web Site: http://www.dowway-exh.com
Year Founded: 2002
8403—(HKG)
Rev.: $24,869,333
Assets: $19,244,768
Liabilities: $16,139,542
Net Worth: $3,105,227
Earnings: ($5,190,167)
Emp.: 63
Fiscal Year-end: 12/31/22
Exhibition & Event Management Services
N.A.I.C.S.: 531120
Xiaodi Huang *(Chm & CEO)*

Subsidiaries:

Beijing Dowway Cultural Development Company Limited   (1)
No 6-2-151 DRC No 1 Compound Xindong Road, Chaoyang District, Beijing, 100600, China
Tel.: (86) 1085326005
Event Management Services
N.A.I.C.S.: 561920

DOXA AB
Axel Johanssons gata 4-6, SE-754 50, Uppsala, Sweden
Tel.: (46) 184782000
Web Site: https://www.doxa.se
Year Founded: 1987
DOXA—(OMX)
Rev.: $982,786
Assets: $347,826,956
Liabilities: $27,875,395
Net Worth: $319,951,561
Earnings: $28,977,307
Emp.: 800
Fiscal Year-end: 12/31/23
Dental Bioceramic Products Mfr
N.A.I.C.S.: 339114
Henrik Nedoh *(CEO-IR)*

DOXEE S.P.A
Viale Virgilio 48/B, 41123, Modena, Italy
Tel.: (39) 05988680
Web Site: https://www.doxee.com
Year Founded: 2001
Emp.: 100
Software Development Services
N.A.I.C.S.: 541511
Sergio Muratori Casali *(Co-Founder & CEO)*

Subsidiaries:

Doxee Czech s.r.o.   (1)
Vaclavske namesti 795/40, 110 00, Prague, Czech Republic
Tel.: (420) 602663661
Information Technology Services
N.A.I.C.S.: 513210

Littlesea S.r.l.   (1)
Via Palermo 8, 20121, Milan, Italy
Tel.: (39) 0283649269
Web Site: http://www.littleseavideo.com
Information Technology Services
N.A.I.C.S.: 513210
Francesco Piccolomini Bandini *(Founder & CEO)*

DOYEN INTERNATIONAL HOLDINGS LIMITED
Room 2206 Harbour Centre 25 Har-

bour Road, Wanchai, China (Hong Kong)
Tel.: (852) 25960668
Web Site: https://www.doyenintl.com
0668—(HKG)
Rev.: $13,657,800
Assets: $128,077,703
Liabilities: $8,157,195
Net Worth: $119,920,508
Earnings: ($2,358,623)
Emp.: 30
Fiscal Year-end: 12/31/22
Investment Services
N.A.I.C.S.: 523999
Siu Yu Lo *(Chm)*

DOYLE HOTELS (HOLDINGS) LIMITED
156 Pembroke Rd, Ballsbridge, Dublin, 4, Ireland
Tel.: (353) 16070070   IE
Web Site: http://www.doylecollection.com
Year Founded: 1964
Sales Range: $350-399.9 Million
Emp.: 1,400
Hotel Owner & Operator
N.A.I.C.S.: 721110
Bernadette C. Gallagher *(Chm)*

DOZA DERD A.D.
Salas 291, 24300, Backa Topola, Serbia
Tel.: (381) 24 711650
Web Site: http://www.doza-djerdj.rs
Year Founded: 1946
DOZA—(BEL)
Sales Range: $1-9.9 Million
Emp.: 111
Pig Farming Services
N.A.I.C.S.: 112210
Milan Catic *(Mng Dir)*

DP AIRCRAFT I LIMITED
East Wing Trafalgar Court Les Banques, Saint Peter Port, GY1 3PP, Guernsey
Tel.: (44) 1481749700   GY
Web Site: https://www.dpaircraft.com
Year Founded: 2008
DPA—(LSE)
Rev.: $8,714,249
Assets: $150,864,020
Liabilities: $108,633,586
Net Worth: $42,230,434
Earnings: ($2,505,687)
Fiscal Year-end: 12/31/23
Aircraft Leasing Services
N.A.I.C.S.: 532411

DP DATA SYSTEMS LIMITED
15 Carnarvon Street, Manchester, M3 1HJ, United Kingdom
Tel.: (44) 161 832 6969
Web Site: http://www.dpdata.co.uk
Sales Range: $100-124.9 Million
Emp.: 100
Computer Products Distr
N.A.I.C.S.: 423430
Philip Hodari *(Mng Dir)*

DP IRAN CO.
No 164 Ostad Nejatollahi Ave, PO Box 11365-3479, Tehran, 15987 51314, Iran
Tel.: (98) 21 8890 3251
Web Site: http://www.dpi.ir
Year Founded: 1957
Computer Hardware Whslr
N.A.I.C.S.: 423430

DP POLAND PLC
1 Chamberlain Square CS, Surrey, Birmingham, B3 3AX, United Kingdom
Tel.: (44) 2033936954

Web Site: https://www.dppoland.com
DPP—(AIM)
Rev.: $42,988,605
Assets: $47,975,235
Liabilities: $25,162,005
Net Worth: $22,813,230
Earnings: ($5,251,620)
Fiscal Year-end: 12/31/22
Pizza Chain Franchiser
N.A.I.C.S.: 722513
Patrick Michael Bodenham *(Sec)*

Subsidiaries:

DP Pizza Limited   (1)
Unit 1B Toughers Business Park, Co Kildare, Naas, Leinster, Ireland
Tel.: (353) 45437666
Pizza Stores Management Services
N.A.I.C.S.: 722511
Colin Halpern *(Mng Dir)*

DPC DASH LTD.
Level 8 Block A 33 Caobao Road, Xuhui District, Shanghai, China
Tel.: (86) 2153685888   VG
Web Site: https://www.dpcdash.com
Year Founded: 2008
1405—(HKG)
Pizza Distr
N.A.I.C.S.: 424420
Aileen Yi Wang *(CEO)*

DPE DEUTSCHE PRIVATE EQUITY GMBH
Ludwigstrasse 7, 80539, Munich, Germany
Tel.: (49) 89 2000 38 0   De
Web Site: http://www.dpe.de
Year Founded: 2007
Emp.: 7,437
Privater Equity Firm
N.A.I.C.S.: 523999
Volker Hichert *(Co-Founder & Partner)*

Subsidiaries:

AWK Group AG   (1)
Leutschenbachstrasse 45, 8050, Zurich, Switzerland
Tel.: (41) 584119500
Web Site: http://www.awk.ch
Consulting Management Services
N.A.I.C.S.: 541618
Thomas Vogt *(Mgr)*

Air Alliance GmbH   (1)
Flughafen Siegerland Werfthalle G1, 57299, Burbach, Germany
Tel.: (49) 273644280
Web Site: http://www.air-alliance.de
Emp.: 130
Integrated Aviation Services
N.A.I.C.S.: 488119
Dagmar Imhof *(Officer-Data Protection)*

BE-terna GmbH   (1)
Bornaer Strasse 19, 04288, Leipzig, Germany
Tel.: (49) 342976480
Web Site: http://www.be-terna.com
Information Technology Services
N.A.I.C.S.: 541519
Christian Kranebitter *(Mng Dir)*

Calvias GmbH   (1)
An den Kaiserthermen 5, 54290, Trier, Germany
Tel.: (49) 65197023250
Web Site: http://www.calvias.de
Holding Company Services
N.A.I.C.S.: 551112

DPE Deutsche Private Equity Management III GmbH   (1)
Ludwigstrasse 7, 80539, Munich, Germany
Tel.: (49) 89 2000 38 0
Investment Services
N.A.I.C.S.: 523999

Engelmann Sensor GmbH   (1)
Rudolf-Diesel-Strasse 24-28, 69168, Wiesloch, Germany
Tel.: (49) 6222 9800 0

DPE Deutsche Private Equity
GmbH—(Continued)

Web Site: http://www.engelmann.de
Heat Meter Mfr & Distr
N.A.I.C.S.: 334519
Jens Bickel (Mgr-Intl Sls)

Euro-Druckservice GmbH (1)
Medienstr 5b, 94036, Passau, Germany
Tel.: (49) 8518516000
Web Site: http://www.edsgroup.de
Printing Services
N.A.I.C.S.: 561439
Daniel Adam (Mng Dir & COO)

Massenberg GmbH (1)
Cathostrasse 3a, 45356, Essen, Germany
Tel.: (49) 201861080
Web Site: http://www.massenberg.de
Construction Services
N.A.I.C.S.: 236220

VTU-Engineering GmbH (1)
Parkring 18, Raaba, 8074, Grambach, Austria
Tel.: (43) 3164009200
Industrial Equipment Mfr
N.A.I.C.S.: 333248
Robert Wutti (Mng Dir)

valantic GmbH (1)
Ainmillerstrasse 22, 80801, Munich, Germany
Tel.: (49) 89200085910
Web Site: http://www.valantic.com
Sales Range: $100-124.9 Million
Emp.: 800
Digital Solutions & Consulting Services
N.A.I.C.S.: 541690
Andrea Hefti (Mgr-Mktg & Comm)

Subsidiary (Domestic):

**Dion Transaction Solutions
GmbH** (2)
Ainmillerstrasse 22, 80801, Munich, Germany
Tel.: (49) 89200085910
Equity Brokerage Software Designer & Developer
N.A.I.C.S.: 513210
Jurgen Dahmen (Mng Dir)

DPECO CO., LTD.
60-44 Ucheonsaneopdanji-ro,
Hoengseong-gun, Ucheon-myeon,
15845, Gangwon-do, Korea (South)
Tel.: (82) 333404800
Web Site: https://www.dpeco.com
Year Founded: 1998
Automobile Parts Mfr
N.A.I.C.S.: 336390
Song Sing-Guen (CEO)

DPG BV
Geijstraat 3-9, 5753 RP, Deurne,
Netherlands
Tel.: (31) 85 782 14 80
Web Site: http://www.dpgbv.nl
Emp.: 500
Paints Mfr
N.A.I.C.S.: 325510
Tjark Bos (Mng Dir)

DPG MEDIA GROUP NV
Brusselsesteenweg 347, 1730, Asse,
Belgium
Tel.: (32) 2 454 2211
Web Site: http://www.persgroep.be
Year Founded: 1955
Sales Range: $1-4.9 Billion
Emp.: 5,000
Media Holding Company
N.A.I.C.S.: 551112
Christian Van Thillo (CEO)

Subsidiaries:

DPG Media BV (1)
Jacob Bontiusplaats 9, Gebouw INIT, 1018
LL, Amsterdam, Netherlands (58.5%)
Tel.: (31) 205629111
Web Site: https://www.dpgmediagroup.com
Media Holding Company; Regional Managing Office

N.A.I.C.S.: 551112
Frits Campagne (CEO)

Subsidiary (Domestic):

De Persgroep Printing B.V. (2)
Wibautstraat 150, 1091 GR, Amsterdam,
Netherlands
Tel.: (31) 20 562 3408
Newspaper Publishers
N.A.I.C.S.: 513110

Het Parool B.V. (2)
Jacob Bontiusplaats 9, 1018 LL, Amsterdam, Netherlands
Tel.: (31) 205629111
Web Site: http://www.persgroep.nl
Newspaper Publishers
N.A.I.C.S.: 513110

Independer.nl N.V. (2)
Celebeslaan 2, 1217 GV, Hilversum, Netherlands
Tel.: (31) 35 626 5544
Web Site: http://www.independer.nl
Financial Comparison & Insight Services
N.A.I.C.S.: 519290

Subsidiary (Domestic):

Independer Services B.V. (3)
Celebeslaan 2, 1217 GV, Hilversum, Netherlands
Tel.: (31) 356265799
Web Site: http://www.independerservices.nl
General Insurance Services
N.A.I.C.S.: 524210

Subsidiary (Domestic):

Qmusic Nederland B.V. (2)
De Kauwgomballenfabriek Paul van Vlissingenstraat 10D, 1096 BK, Amsterdam, Netherlands
Tel.: (31) 207970500
Web Site: http://qmusic.nl
Radio Broadcasting Stations
N.A.I.C.S.: 516110
Jelle Klerx (Mgr-PR)

Sanoma Media B.V. (2)
Jachthavenweg 124, 1081 KJ, Amsterdam,
North Holland, Netherlands
Tel.: (31) 20 851 21 00
Web Site: http://www.sanomamedia.com
Sales Range: $25-49.9 Million
Emp.: 35
Magazine Publishing Services
N.A.I.C.S.: 513199
Marc Duijndam (CEO-Belgium & Netherlands)

Subsidiary (Domestic):

Aldipress B.V. (3)
19 Savannah, Utrecht, 3542, Netherlands
Tel.: (31) 306660611
Web Site: http://www.aldipress.nl
Magazine Distr
N.A.I.C.S.: 424920

Subsidiary (Non-US):

Sanoma Budapest Zrt (3)
Montevideo Utca 9, PO Box 1872, Budapest, 1037, Hungary
Tel.: (36) 1 437 1100
Web Site: http://www.sanomabp.hu
Sales Range: $100-124.9 Million
Magazine Publishing Services
N.A.I.C.S.: 513199
Szabo Gyoergy (CEO)

Subsidiary (Domestic):

Nemzeti Tankonyvkiado Zrt (4)
Szobranc utca 6-8, 1143, Budapest, Hungary
Tel.: (36) 14601893
Web Site: http://www.ntk.hu
School Books Publishing Services
N.A.I.C.S.: 513130

Perfekt Zrt (4)
Szep utca 2, 1053, Budapest, Hungary
Tel.: (36) 15771910
Web Site: http://www.perfekt.hu
Sales Range: $10-24.9 Million
Emp.: 100
Education & Training Services
N.A.I.C.S.: 611710

Vavro Marta (Asst Dir-Education)

Subsidiary (Domestic):

**Sanoma Digital The Netherlands
B.V.** (3)
Maassluisstraat 2, 1062 GD, Amsterdam,
Netherlands
Tel.: (31) 208404500
Newspaper Publishers
N.A.I.C.S.: 513110

Subsidiary (Non-US):

Sanoma Entertainment Ltd. (3)
Toolonlahdenkatu 2, 00089, Helsinki, Finland
Tel.: (358) 107071111
Web Site:
   http://www.sanomaentertainment.com
Sales Range: $75-99.9 Million
Electronic Entertainment Services
N.A.I.C.S.: 561990

Subsidiary (Domestic):

Sanoma Television Oy (4)
Tehtaankatu 27-29 D, PO Box 350, 00151,
Helsinki, Finland
Tel.: (358) 945451
Sales Range: $50-74.9 Million
Emp.: 220
Television Broadcasting Services
N.A.I.C.S.: 516120

Subsidiary (Domestic):

**Sanoma Magazines International
B.V.** (3)
Jachthavenweg 124, 1081 KJ, Amsterdam,
Netherlands
Tel.: (31) 20 851 2150
Web Site:
   http://www.sanomamagazines-int.com
Rev.: $304,255,420
Emp.: 9
Magazine Publisher
N.A.I.C.S.: 513120

Subsidiary (Non-US):

Sanoma Magazines Belgium NV (4)
Telecomlaan 5-7, 1831, Diegem, Flemish
Brabant, Belgium
Tel.: (32) 27762211
Web Site: http://www.sanoma-magazines.be
Magazine Publishing Services
N.A.I.C.S.: 513199

**Sanoma Magazines Finland
Corporation** (4)
Lapinmaentie 1, 00350, Helsinki, Finland
Tel.: (358) 91201
Web Site: http://www.sanomamagazines.fi
Rev.: $271,183,086
Magazine Publisher
N.A.I.C.S.: 513120

Subsidiary (Domestic):

Suomen Rakennuslehti Oy (5)
Haemeentie 33, 00500, Helsinki, Finland
Tel.: (358) 207418600
Web Site: http://www.rakennuslehti.fi
Real Estate Magazine Pubishers
N.A.I.C.S.: 513120

Subsidiary (Non-US):

Sanoma Media Ukraine (3)
Vorovskogo St 33 3rd Fl, 01601, Kiev,
Ukraine
Tel.: (380) 442386048
Web Site: http://www.sanomamedia.com.ua
Sales Range: $50-74.9 Million
Emp.: 144
Magazine Publisher
N.A.I.C.S.: 513120

Subsidiary (Non-US):

Uitgeverij Van In N.V. (3)
Nijverheidsstraat 92/5, 2160, Wommelgem,
Antwerp, Belgium
Tel.: (32) 472403955
Web Site: https://www.vanin.be
Sales Range: $50-74.9 Million
Emp.: 120
Educational Books Publishing Services
N.A.I.C.S.: 513130

Subsidiary (Domestic):

Tweakers.net B.V. (2)

Mt Lincolnweg 40, 1033 SN, Amsterdam,
Netherlands
Tel.: (31) 20 204 2100
Web Site: http://www.tweakers.net
Online News Publisher
N.A.I.C.S.: 513110
Wilbert de Vries (Editor-in-Chief)

De Persgroep Publishing NV (1)
Brusselsesteenweg 347, 1730, Asse,
Belgium (100%)
Tel.: (32) 2 454 2211
Web Site: http://www.persgroep.be
Newspaper, Magazine & New Media Publisher
N.A.I.C.S.: 513110
Rudy Bartels (Co-CEO)

Subsidiary (Domestic):

Eco Print Center NV (2)
Brandstraat 30, 9160, Lokeren, Belgium
Tel.: (32) 9 353 4800
Web Site: http://www.epc-nv.be
Newspaper & Magazine Publisher
N.A.I.C.S.: 513110
Wim Maes (Dir-Technical)

Mecom Group plc (1)
Audley House 13 Palace Street, London,
SW1E 5HX, United Kingdom
Tel.: (44) 2079257200
Web Site: http://www.mecom.co.uk
Sales Range: $1-4.9 Billion
Regional Publishing Services
N.A.I.C.S.: 513110
Lisbeth Knudsen (CEO-Denmark)

Subsidiary (Non-US):

Berlingske Media A/S (2)
Pilestraede 34, 1147, Copenhagen, Denmark
Tel.: (45) 3375 7575
Web Site: http://www.berlingskemedia.dk
Rev.: $642,123,762
Emp.: 2,500
Newspaper Publisher Services
N.A.I.C.S.: 513110
Lisbeth Knudsen (CEO)

Joint Venture (Domestic):

Infomedia A/S (3)
Pilestrde 58.3, 1112, Copenhagen, Denmark
Tel.: (45) 33471450
Web Site: http://www.infomedia.dk
Sales Range: $50-74.9 Million
Emp.: 120
Media Intelligence Products & Services
N.A.I.C.S.: 513199
Tim Wolff Jacobse (Pres & CEO)

Subsidiary (Non-US):

Koninklijke Wegener N.V. (2)
Laan van Westenenk 6, 7336 AZ, Apeldoorn, Netherlands (99.7%)
Tel.: (31) 555388888
Web Site: http://www.wegener.nl
Sales Range: $600-649.9 Million
Emp.: 2,865
Newspaper & Magazine Publisher & Internet Portal Services
N.A.I.C.S.: 513110
Fieneke van den Brink (Member-Mgmt Bd &
Chief Admin Officer)

Subsidiary (Domestic):

AD NieuwsMedia BV (3)
Marten Meesweg 35, 3068AV, Rotterdam,
Netherlands
Tel.: (31) 104066216
Web Site: http://www.ad.nl
Sales Range: $150-199.9 Million
Emp.: 850
Newspaper Publishers
N.A.I.C.S.: 513110
Bernard Vanderheijden (Mng Dir)

Subsidiary (Non-US):

Actigroup (3)
Allee De La Recherche 65, 1070, Brussels,
Belgium (100%)
Tel.: (32) 25559770
Web Site: http://www.acti-group.com

Sales Range: $25-49.9 Million
Emp.: 10
Commercial Printing Mfr
N.A.I.C.S.: 323111
Michel Bruyr *(Owner & Gen Mgr)*

Subsidiary (Domestic):

Brabants Dagblad BV   **(3)**
Emmaplein 25, PO Box 235, 5201VZ, 's-
Hertogenbosch, Netherlands   **(100%)**
Tel.: (31) 736157157
Web Site: http://www.brabantsdagblad.nl
Sales Range: $25-49.9 Million
Emp.: 150
Engineering Services
N.A.I.C.S.: 541330
Marco Paans *(Mng Dir)*

Subsidiary (Non-US):

D-Trix NV   **(3)**
Researchdreef 65, Brussels,
Belgium   **(100%)**
Tel.: (32) 23063030
Public Relations Agencies
N.A.I.C.S.: 541820
Philip Corne *(Mng Dir)*

Subsidiary (Domestic):

Eindhovens Dagblad B.V.   **(3)**
Wal 2, 5611GG, Eindhoven,
Netherlands   **(100%)**
Tel.: (31) 402336120
Web Site: http://www.ed.nl
Sales Range: $100-124.9 Million
Emp.: 300
Newspaper Publishers
N.A.I.C.S.: 513110
Henk van Weert *(Editor)*

Imatra BV   **(3)**
Laan van Westenenk 4, 7336AZ, Apel-
doorn, Netherlands   **(100%)**
Tel.: (31) 5553 88888
Security System Services
N.A.I.C.S.: 561621

Koninklijke Wegener B.V.   **(3)**
Laan Van Westenenk 4, Apeldoorn, Nether-
lands
Tel.: (31) 555388888
Web Site: http://www.wegener.nl
Holding Company
N.A.I.C.S.: 551112
Frits Campagne *(Gen Mgr)*

Mensenlinq BV   **(3)**
Lubeckweg 2, 9723 HE, Groningen,
Netherlands   **(65%)**
Tel.: (31) 38 4559491
Web Site: http://www.mensenlinq.nl
Information Services
N.A.I.C.S.: 519290

Rondo B.V.   **(3)**
Overweg 17, Obdam, Netherlands   **(100%)**
Tel.: (31) 226450196
Web Site: http://www.rondoafvalbeheer.nl
Sales Range: $25-49.9 Million
Emp.: 10
Industrial Machinery & Equipment Merchant
Whslr
N.A.I.C.S.: 423830

Subsidiary (Non-US):

STM Packaging Group Ltd.   **(3)**
21-23 Concorde Road, Norwich, NR6 6BJ,
United Kingdom   **(100%)**
Tel.: (44) 1603 404217
Web Site: http://www.stmpackaging.com
Sales Range: $25-49.9 Million
Emp.: 25
Polythene Envelopes & Poly Bags Mfr
N.A.I.C.S.: 322230
Esther Evans *(Mng Dir)*

Subsidiary (Domestic):

Stadsnieuws BV   **(3)**
Hart van Brabantlaan 2, 5038 JL, Tilburg,
Netherlands   **(100%)**
Tel.: (31) 134627200
Web Site: http://www.stadsnieuws.no
Sales Range: $25-49.9 Million
Emp.: 10
Newspaper Publishers
N.A.I.C.S.: 513110
Mark Van Wijk *(Mgr)*

Twentsche Courant Tubantia BV   **(3)**
Postbus 28, Enschede, 7500 AA,
Netherlands   **(100%)**
Tel.: (31) 534842842
Web Site: http://www.tctubantia.nl
Sales Range: $150-199.9 Million
Emp.: 250
Publisher
N.A.I.C.S.: 513199
Martha Riemsma *(Mng Dir)*

Uitgeverij BN/de Stem B.V.   **(3)**
Spinveld 55, 4815HV, Breda,
Netherlands   **(100%)**
Tel.: (31) 765312311
Web Site: http://www.bndesdem.no
Sales Range: $100-124.9 Million
Emp.: 400
Publisher
N.A.I.C.S.: 513199
A. Verrsp *(Mng Dir)*

Wegener Bedrijfsvastgoed BV   **(3)**
Laan van Westenenk 4, PO Box 26, 7300
HB, Apeldoorn, Netherlands   **(100%)**
Tel.: (31) 555388888
Web Site: http://www.wegener.nl
Sales Range: $25-49.9 Million
Emp.: 5
Publisher
N.A.I.C.S.: 513199

Wegener Grafische Groep BV   **(3)**
Laan van Westenenk 8, 7336AZ, Apel-
doorn, Netherlands   **(100%)**
Tel.: (31) 555388450
Web Site: http://www.wegener.nl
Sales Range: $200-249.9 Million
Emp.: 750
Commercial Printing
N.A.I.C.S.: 323111
Koninklijke Wegener *(CEO)*

**Wegener Huis-aan-Huiskranten
BV**   **(3)**
Prins Hendrikkade 16 A, Rotterdam, 3071
KB, Netherlands   **(100%)**
Tel.: (31) 104699911
Web Site: http://www.wegenermedia.nl
Emp.: 100
Newspaper Publishers
N.A.I.C.S.: 513110
Bas Stitkalorem *(Gen Mgr)*

Wegener Ict Media BV   **(3)**
Laan Van Westenenk 4, Apeldoorn, 7336
AZ, Netherlands   **(100%)**
Tel.: (31) 555388888
Web Site: http://www.wegener.nl
Sales Range: $75-99.9 Million
Emp.: 300
Management Consulting Services
N.A.I.C.S.: 541618
S. Duinhoven *(CEO)*

Wegener Koninklijke B.V.   **(3)**
Laan Van Westenenk 4, Apeldoorn, Nether-
lands
Tel.: (31) 555388888
Holding Company
N.A.I.C.S.: 551112

Wegener Nederland BV   **(3)**
Laan van Westenenk 4, 7336 AZ, Apel-
doorn, Netherlands
Tel.: (31) 555388674
Web Site: http://www.wegener.nl
Sales Range: $25-49.9 Million
Emp.: 50
Publisher
N.A.I.C.S.: 513199
Truls Velgaard *(CEO)*

Wegener NieuwsDruk   **(3)**
Laan van Westenenk 8, 7336 AZ, Apel-
doorn, Netherlands   **(100%)**
Tel.: (31) 6 22 93 1050
Web Site: http://www.wegenernieuwsdruk.nl
Magazine & Newspaper Publisher
N.A.I.C.S.: 513110
Robert Hoogsteden *(Dir-Comml)*

Wegener Post BV   **(3)**
Laan van Westenenk 4, 7336AZ, Apel-
doorn, Netherlands   **(95.1%)**
Tel.: (31) 555388988
Web Site: http://www.wegener.nl
Sales Range: $200-249.9 Million
Emp.: 1,000
Specialized Freight Trucking, Local

N.A.I.C.S.: 484220
Truls Velgaard *(Mng Dir)*

Wegener Regio Partners BV   **(3)**
Laan van Westenenk 4, 7336 AZ, Apel-
doorn, Netherlands   **(100%)**
Tel.: (31) 555388888
Web Site: http://www.wegener.nl
Sales Range: $25-49.9 Million
Emp.: 8
Religious Organizations
N.A.I.C.S.: 813110
Truls Velgaard *(CEO)*

Wegener Transport BV   **(3)**
Laan van Westenenk 4, 7336 AZ, Apel-
doorn, Netherlands   **(100%)**
Tel.: (31) 555388888
Web Site: http://www.wegener.nl
Couriers
N.A.I.C.S.: 492110

Subsidiary (Domestic):

Mecom Finance Limited   **(2)**
1st Floor Parnell House 25 Wilton Road,
Westminster, London, SW1V 1LW, United
Kingdom
Tel.: (44) 20 7925 7200
Web Site: http://www.mecom.com
Sales Range: $50-74.9 Million
Emp.: 2
Financial Management Services
N.A.I.C.S.: 523999
Henry Davies *(Dir-Fin)*

DPI HOLDINGS BERHAD
K69 Jalan Perindustrian 6 Tanjong
Agas Industrial Estate, Ledang Muar,
84000, Johor, Malaysia
Tel.: (60) 69522854   **MY**
Web Site:
   https://www.dpiaerosol.com
Year Founded: 1980
DPIH—(KLS)
Rev.: $10,931,406
Assets: $19,658,568
Liabilities: $1,662,051
Net Worth: $17,996,517
Earnings: $608,641
Emp.: 160
Fiscal Year-end: 05/31/23
Holding Company
N.A.I.C.S.: 551112
Choy Mui Seng *(Chm & Mng Dir)*

Subsidiaries:

DPI Alliance Pte. Ltd.   **(1)**
4 Wan Lee Road, Singapore, 627936, Sin-
gapore
Tel.: (65) 62654200
Industrial Wood Coating Mfr & Distr
N.A.I.C.S.: 325510

DPI Chemicals Sdn. Bhd.   **(1)**
Lot 2 Jalan Kecapi 33/2, Elite Industrial
Park, 40400, Shah Alam, Selangor, Malay-
sia
Tel.: (60) 351318218
Industrial Wood Coating Mfr & Distr
N.A.I.C.S.: 325510

DPI Plastics Sdn. Bhd.   **(1)**
PTK21 Jalan Perindustrian Tanjong Agas
Industrial Estate, Ledang, 84000, Muar, Jo-
hor, Malaysia
Tel.: (60) 69594777
Wood Coating Mfr
N.A.I.C.S.: 324122

DPNK CO., LTD
334 Dongil-Road Gwangjin-gu, Seoul,
Korea (South)
Tel.: (82) 24617067
Web Site: http://www.dpnk.co.kr
Year Founded: 2007
Apparel Product Mfr & Distr
N.A.I.C.S.: 315250
Chang-Se Lee *(CEO)*

**DPS BRISTOL (HOLDINGS)
LTD.**
Serbert Road, Portishead, Bristol,
BS20 7GF, United Kingdom

Tel.: (44) 1275741071   **UK**
Web Site: http://www.dps-global.com
Holding Company; Engineering Ser-
vices for Upstream Oil & Gas & Envi-
ronmental Technology Industries
N.A.I.C.S.: 551112
David Parkinson *(Vice Chm & CTO)*

DPS RESOURCES BERHAD
Lot 76 Kawasan Perindustrian Bukit
Rambai, 75250, Melaka, Malaysia
Tel.: (60) 3513111   **MY**
Web Site: https://www.dps.com.my
DPS—(KLS)
Rev.: $11,536,054
Assets: $47,439,249
Liabilities: $13,495,017
Net Worth: $33,944,232
Earnings: $653,894
Emp.: 600
Fiscal Year-end: 03/31/23
Holding Company
N.A.I.C.S.: 551112
Emily Mei Chet Sow *(Exec Dir)*

Subsidiaries:

**Shantawood Manufacturing Sdn.
Bhd.**   **(1)**
No 76 77 Kawasan Perindustrian Bukit
Rambai, Bukit Rambai, 75250, Melaka,
Malaysia
Tel.: (60) 63513111
Web Site: https://www.shantawood.com.my
Sales Range: $50-74.9 Million
Emp.: 600
Furniture Mfr & Whslr
N.A.I.C.S.: 423210

Shantawood Sdn Bhd   **(1)**
No 76 & 77, Kawasan Perindustrian Bukit
Rambai, 75250, Melaka, Malaysia
Tel.: (60) 63513111
Web Site: https://shantawood.com.my
Furniture Product Mfr
N.A.I.C.S.: 321999

**DPV DRUCK UND PA-
PIERVEREDELUNG GMBH**
Parkstrasse 14b, 86462, Langweid,
Foret, Germany
Tel.: (49) 821249950
Web Site: http://www.dpv.net
Rev.: $13,352,415
Emp.: 50
Printing & Paper Finishing, Prepress,
Cold Foil Finishing & Rotogravure
N.A.I.C.S.: 322299
Thomas Mayr *(Mgr-Internal Svcs)*

DR CORPORATION LIMITED
Unit 306 Podium Building Luohu In-
vestment Holding Building No 112,
Qingshuihe 1st Road Qingshuihe
Community Qingshuihe Subdistrict
Luohu, Shenzhen, 518019, Guang-
dong, China
Tel.: (86) 75586664586
Year Founded: 2010
301177—(CHIN)
Rev.: $516,892,428
Assets: $1,237,731,300
Liabilities: $282,583,080
Net Worth: $955,148,220
Earnings: $102,385,296
Fiscal Year-end: 12/31/22
Jewelry Product Mfr & Distr
N.A.I.C.S.: 339910
Guotao Zhang *(Chm)*

DR LALCHANDANI LABS LTD.
M-20 GK-1 Greater Kailash-1, New
Delhi, 110048, India
Tel.: (91) 1149057058
Web Site:
   https://www.lalchandanipathlab.com
541299—(BOM)
Rev.: $1,334,968
Assets: $2,074,205
Liabilities: $770,357

Dr Lalchandani Labs Ltd.—(Continued)

Net Worth: $1,303,848
Earnings: $138,048
Fiscal Year-end: 03/31/21
Health Care Srvices
N.A.I.C.S.: 621999
Mohit Lalchandani *(CEO)*

DR. ABIDI PHARMACEUTI-CALS PJSC

No 72 Abidi Blvd Lashgari Highway,
Tehran, 13897 76363, Iran
Tel.: (98) 9844522451
Year Founded: 1946
ABDI1—(THE)
Sales Range: Less than $1 Million
Pharmaceuticals Product Mfr
N.A.I.C.S.: 325412

DR. AGARWAL'S EYE HOSPITAL LIMITED

1st&3rd Floor Buhari Towers No 4
Moores Road Off Greams Road,
Near Asan Memorial School, Chennai, 600006, Tamil Nadu, India
Tel.: (91) 9594924026
Web Site: https://www.dragarwal.com
Year Founded: 1957
526783—(BOM)
Rev.: $19,193,988
Assets: $21,189,182
Liabilities: $13,727,709
Net Worth: $7,461,472
Earnings: ($196,369)
Emp.: 730
Fiscal Year-end: 03/31/21
Eye Care Service
N.A.I.C.S.: 621999
Amar Agarwal *(Co-Founder)*

DR. AICHHORN GMBH

Werk-VI-Strasse 52, 8605, Kapfenberg, Austria
Tel.: (43) 3862 303 0   AT
Web Site: http://www.aichhorn-group.at
Investment Holding Company
N.A.I.C.S.: 551112
Harald J. Aichhorn *(Owner & CEO)*

Subsidiaries:

BFT GmbH   **(1)**
Industriepark 24, 8682, Hönigsberg, Austria
Tel.: (43) 3862 303 300
Web Site: http://www.bft-pumps.at
Waterjet Cutting Technologies Mfr
N.A.I.C.S.: 333515
Franz H. Trieb *(Pres & CEO)*

BHDT GmbH   **(1)**
Werk-VI-Strasse 52, 8605, Kapfenberg, Austria
Tel.: (43) 3862 303 0
Web Site: http://www.bhdt.at
Chemical Industry High Pressure Equipment & Components Mfr & Whslr
N.A.I.C.S.: 333248
Harald J. Aichhorn *(Pres & CEO)*

G. Volkl GmbH   **(1)**
Depotstrasse 125, 8712, Niklasdorf, Austria
Tel.: (43) 3842 812 340
Web Site: http://www.voelkl.co.at
Custom Sheet Metal & Structural Metal Fabrication Services
N.A.I.C.S.: 332999
Jorg Sussenbacher *(CEO)*

GIG Karasek GmbH   **(1)**
Neusiedlerstrasse 15-19, 2640, Gloggnitz, Austria
Tel.: (43) 2662 42780
Web Site: http://www.gigkarasek.at
Industrial Thermal Separation Equipment Mfr
N.A.I.C.S.: 333994
Peter Mandl *(CEO & Mng Dir)*

Hitzinger GmbH   **(1)**
Helmholtzstrasse 56, Linz, 4021, Austria   **(100%)**

Tel.: (43) 7323816810
Web Site: http://www.hitzinger.at
Generators & Electric Goods Mfr
N.A.I.C.S.: 423610
DI Werner Kordasch *(Mng Dir)*

Subsidiary (Non-US):

Hitzinger UK Limited   **(2)**
50 Churchill Square, Kings Hill, West Malling, ME19 4YU, Kent, United Kingdom
Tel.: (44) 1732 529 641
Web Site: http://www.hitzinger.net
Rotary Diesel UPS, Airport Ground Power, Stand-by Generators, Frequency Converters & Alternators Mfr
N.A.I.C.S.: 335999
Paul Williams *(Mgr)*

DR. AUGUST OETKER KG

Lutterstrasse 14, 33617, Bielefeld, Germany
Tel.: (49) 5211550   De
Web Site: http://www.oetker-group.com
Year Founded: 1891
Diversified Holding Company Services
N.A.I.C.S.: 551112
Albert Christmann *(Gen Partner)*

Subsidiaries:

Atlantic Forfaitierungs AG   **(1)**
Othmarstrasse 8, CH-8008, Zurich, Switzerland
Tel.: (41) 44 254 53 00
Web Site: http://www.atlanticforfaiting.com
Emp.: 10
Trade Financing Services
N.A.I.C.S.: 522299
Martin Fankhauser *(CEO)*

Bankhaus Lampe KG   **(1)**
Jagerhofstr 10, 40479, Dusseldorf, Germany
Tel.: (49) 2114952444
Web Site: http://www.bankhaus-lampe.de
Emp.: 612
Banking Services
N.A.I.C.S.: 522110
Klemens Breuer *(Gen Partner)*

Subsidiary (Domestic):

Lampe Equity Management GmbH   **(2)**
Speersort 10, D-20095, Hamburg, Germany
Tel.: (49) 40 688788 0
Web Site: http://www.lampe-equity.de
Emp.: 30
Investment Services
N.A.I.C.S.: 523999

Subsidiary (Domestic):

Lampe Privatinvest Management GmbH   **(3)**
Brandstwiete 36, 20457, Hamburg, Germany
Tel.: (49) 40882158330
Web Site: http://www.lampe-pm.de
Privater Equity Firm
N.A.I.C.S.: 523999

Chemische Fabrik Budenheim KG   **(1)**
Rheinstrasse 27, 55257, Budenheim, Germany
Tel.: (49) 6139 89 0
Web Site: http://www.budenheim.com
Phosphate Mfr
N.A.I.C.S.: 325998
Harald Schaub *(Mng Dir)*

Subsidiary (US):

Budenheim USA, Inc.   **(2)**
2219 Westbrooke Dr, Columbus, OH 43228
Tel.: (614) 345-2400
Web Site: http://www.budenheim.com
Phosphate Mfr
N.A.I.C.S.: 325998
Douglas Lim *(VP-Sls & Mktg)*

Dr. Oetker Verlag KG   **(1)**
Am Bach 11, 33602, Bielefeld, Germany
Tel.: (49) 521 5206 0
Web Site: http://www.oetker-verlag.de

Publishing
N.A.I.C.S.: 513120
Annelore Strullkotter *(Mng Dir)*

FrischeParadies KG   **(1)**
Larchenstrasse 80, 65933, Frankfurt am Main, Germany
Tel.: (49) 69 351026 0
Web Site: http://www.frischeparadies.eu
Gourmet Food Product Distr
N.A.I.C.S.: 424490
Dietmar Mukusch *(Mng Dir)*

Henkell & Co. Sektkellerei KG   **(1)**
Biebricher Allee 142, 65187, Wiesbaden, Germany
Tel.: (49) 611 630
Web Site: http://www.henkell-sektkellerei.com
Sales Range: $900-999.9 Million
Emp.: 2,030
Wine & Spirits Distr
N.A.I.C.S.: 424820
Andreas Brokemper *(CEO)*

Subsidiary (Non-US):

Freixenet S.A.   **(2)**
Placa Joan Sala 2, Sant Sadurni d Anoia, 08770, Barcelona, Spain   **(50.76%)**
Tel.: (34) 938917030
Web Site: http://www.freixenet.es
Wine Mfr & Dist
N.A.I.C.S.: 312130
Pedro Bonet Ferrer *(CEO)*

Subsidiary (US):

Freixenet U.S.A.   **(3)**
23555 Hwy 121, Sonoma, CA 95476-9285   **(100%)**
Tel.: (707) 996-4981
Web Site: http://www.freixenetusa.com
Sales Range: $50-74.9 Million
Emp.: 100
Wines, Sparkling Wines & Champagnes
N.A.I.C.S.: 424820
Geraldine Flatt *(VP-HR & Retail Ops)*

Subsidiary (Domestic):

Freixenet Sonoma Caves, Inc.   **(4)**
23555 Hwy 121, Sonoma, CA 95476   **(100%)**
Tel.: (707) 996-4981
Web Site: http://www.freixenetusa.com
Sales Range: $25-49.9 Million
Emp.: 75
Winery
N.A.I.C.S.: 312130

Martin Braun-Gruppe   **(1)**
Tillystrasse 17, 30459, Hannover, Germany
Tel.: (49) 511 41 07 0
Web Site: http://www.martinbraungruppe.de
Emp.: 14,000
Baking Ingredient Mfr
N.A.I.C.S.: 311999
Detlev Kruge *(Chm-Mgmt Bd)*

Oetker Daten- und Informationsverarbeitung KG   **(1)**
Bechterdisser Str 10, 33719, Bielefeld, Germany
Tel.: (49) 521 26050 101
Web Site: http://www.oediv.de
Data Center Services
N.A.I.C.S.: 541513
Martin Stratmann *(CEO)*

Oetker Hotel Management Company GmbH   **(1)**
Schillerstrasse 7, 76530, Baden-Baden, Germany
Tel.: (49) 1 53 43 41 47
Web Site: http://www.oetkerhotels.com
Luxury Hotel Operator
N.A.I.C.S.: 721110
Jean-Pierre Soutric *(Sr VP)*

Radeberger Gruppe AG   **(1)**
Darmstadter Landstrasse 185, 60598, Frankfurt am Main, Germany
Tel.: (49) 6960650
Web Site: http://www.radeberger-gruppe.de
Sales Range: $1-4.9 Billion
Emp.: 700
Brewery Mfr
N.A.I.C.S.: 312120

Roland Transport KG   **(1)**

Artur-Ladebeck-Strasse 100 Gebaude 36, 33647, Bielefeld, Germany
Tel.: (49) 521 155 2970
Web Site: http://www.roland-transport.de
Logistic Services
N.A.I.C.S.: 541614
Joachim Haupt *(Mng Partner)*

DR. BABOR GMBH & CO. KG

Neuenhofstrasse 180, Aachen, 52078, Germany
Tel.: (49) 241 5296 0   De
Web Site: http://www.babor.de
Year Founded: 1955
Sales Range: $25-49.9 Million
Emp.: 270
Natural Skin Care & Cosmetics
N.A.I.C.S.: 325620
Michael Schummert *(Mng Dir)*

Subsidiaries:

Babor Cosmetics America Corp.   **(1)**
430 S Congress Ave Ste 2, West Palm Beach, FL 33409
Tel.: (888) 222-6791
Web Site: http://www.babor.com
Sales Range: $25-49.9 Million
Emp.: 25
Natural Cosmetics & Skin Care Systems
N.A.I.C.S.: 325620
Brian Brazeau *(CEO-North America)*

DR. BOCK INDUSTRIES AG

Welle 23, 31749, Auetal-Rolfshagen, Germany
Tel.: (49) 5753 9274 0
Web Site: http://www.drbockindustries.com
Year Founded: 1984
DBI—(VIE)
Sales Range: Less than $1 Million
Clothing Mfr
N.A.I.C.S.: 315250
Ema Alexa *(Head-Key Acct Mgmt)*

Subsidiaries:

Ready Garment Technology Italia Srl.   **(1)**
Via Alessandro Volta 21, 35010, Limena, PD, Italy
Tel.: (39) 049769697
Textile Products Mfr
N.A.I.C.S.: 314999

Ready Garment Technology Romania SRL   **(1)**
Str Ciucului No 149/A Jud, Covasna, Sfantu Gheorghe, 520036, Romania
Tel.: (40) 267316161
Emp.: 200
Textile Products Mfr
N.A.I.C.S.: 314999
Csongor Fazakas *(Mgr-Sls Treatments)*

Ready Garment Technology Ukraine Ltd.   **(1)**
148 Zhytomyrska Street, Novohrad-Volynskyi, Zhytomyr, 11701, Ukraine
Tel.: (380) 414138217
Trousers Mfr
N.A.I.C.S.: 315250

DR. FALK PHARMA GMBH

Leinenweberstr 5, 79041, Freiburg, Germany
Tel.: (49) 76115140
Web Site: http://www.drfalkpharma.de
Year Founded: 1960
Sales Range: $200-249.9 Million
Emp.: 89
Drugs Whslr
N.A.I.C.S.: 424210
Ursula Falk *(Mng Dir)*

Subsidiaries:

Dr Falk Pharma UK Ltd   **(1)**
Unit K Bourne End Business Park Cores End Rd, Bourne End, SL8 5AS, United Kingdom
Tel.: (44) 1628536600

Web Site: http://www.drfalk.co.uk
Drugs Whslr
N.A.I.C.S.: 424210

Dr. Falk Pharma Benelux B.V. (1)
Claudius Prinsenlaan 136A, 4818 CP,
Breda, Netherlands
Tel.: (31) 765244200
Web Site: http://www.drfalkpharma-
benelux.eu
Drugs Whslr
N.A.I.C.S.: 424210

Dr. Falk Pharma Espana S.L. (1)
Edificio America II Nucleo 4 1a Planta I
C/Procion 7, 28023, Madrid, Spain
Tel.: (34) 913729508
Web Site: http://www.drfalkpharma.de
Drugs Whslr
N.A.I.C.S.: 424210

Dr. Falk Pharma LLC (1)
Butyrskiy Val Ulitsa 68/70 bl 4 5, 127055,
Moscow, Russia
Tel.: (7) 4959339904
Drugs Whslr
N.A.I.C.S.: 424210

DR. FOODS, INC.
5-21 Toyosawacho, Minato-ku, Hana-
maki, 025-0089, Japan
Tel.: (81) 9060024978   NV
Year Founded: 2021
DRFS—(OTCQB)
Rev.: $15,922
Assets: $21,606
Liabilities: $50,019
Net Worth: ($28,413)
Earnings: ($761,837)
Emp.: 1
Fiscal Year-end: 03/31/24
Information Technology Services
N.A.I.C.S.: 541512
Koichi Ishizuka *(Pres, Sec & Dir)*

**DR. FRITZ FAULHABER GMBH
& CO. KG**
Daimlerstrasse 23/25, Schonaich,
71101, Germany
Tel.: (49) 7031 638 0
Web Site: http://www.faulhaber.com
Sales Range: $250-299.9 Million
Emp.: 1,900
Electric Motor Mfr
N.A.I.C.S.: 334419

Subsidiaries:

FAULHABER Benelux B.V. (1)
High Tech Campus 9, 5656 AE, Eindhoven,
Netherlands
Tel.: (31) 408515540
Electrical Equipment Distr
N.A.I.C.S.: 423830

**FAULHABER Drive System Technol-
ogy (Taicang) Co., Ltd.** (1)
Eastern Block Incubator Building No 6 Bei-
jing Road West, Taicang, 215400, Jiangsu,
China
Tel.: (86) 51253372626
Electrical Equipment Distr
N.A.I.C.S.: 423830

FAULHABER France SAS (1)
Parc d'activites du Pas du Lac 2 Rue Mi-
chael Faraday, 78180, Montigny-le-
Bretonneux, France
Tel.: (33) 130804500
Electrical Equipment Distr
N.A.I.C.S.: 423830

FAULHABER Singapore Pte Ltd (1)
Blk 67 Ubi Road 1 06-07 Oxley Bizhub, Sin-
gapore, 408730, Singapore
Tel.: (65) 65628270
Electrical Equipment Distr
N.A.I.C.S.: 423830
Vester Tan *(Mgr-Sls)*

MicroMo Electronics, Inc. (1)
14881 Evergreen Ave, Clearwater, FL
33762
Tel.: (727) 572-0131
Web Site: http://www.micromo.com

Sales Range: $50-74.9 Million
Emp.: 65
Motor & Generator Mfr
N.A.I.C.S.: 335999
Fritz Faulhaber *(Owner)*

**DR. HABEEBULLAH LIFE SCI-
ENCES LIMITED**
6-3-354/13/B2 Suryateja Apartments
Hindinagar Punjagutta, Rajendra Na-
gar Mandal, Hyderabad, 500082, Te-
langana, India
Tel.: (91) 4029703333
Web Site: https://www.drhlsl.com
539267—(BOM)
Rev.: $21,936
Assets: $3,910,733
Liabilities: $1,842,379
Net Worth: $2,068,354
Earnings: ($106,016)
Emp.: 3
Fiscal Year-end: 03/31/21
Paper & Related Product Trading
Services
N.A.I.C.S.: 523160
K. Krishnam Raju *(Chm)*

**DR. HELMUT ROTHEN-
BERGER HOLDING GMBH**
Spessarstrasse 2-4, 65779,
Kelkheim, Germany
Tel.: (49) 61958002001   De
Web Site: http://www.rothenberger-
holding.de
Sales Range: $700-749.9 Million
Emp.: 3,000
Holding Services
N.A.I.C.S.: 551112
Helmut Rothenberger *(Mng Dir)*

Subsidiaries:

Autania AG (1)
Spessartstrasse 2-4 Taunus, 65779,
Kelkheim, Germany
Tel.: (49) 6195976611
Web Site: http://www.autania.de
Management & Investment Holding Ser-
vices
N.A.I.C.S.: 551112
Ingo Muller *(CEO)*

Rothenberger AG (1)
Spesserstrasse 2-4, 65779, Kelkheim, Ger-
many
Tel.: (49) 6195 800 1
Web Site: http://www.rothenberger.com
Holding Company; Heating, Ventilation, Re-
frigeration & Plumbing Tools & Machinery
Mfr & Distr
N.A.I.C.S.: 551112
Helmut Rothenberger *(CEO)*

Subsidiary (Non-US):

Rothenberger Australia Pty. Ltd. (2)
Unit 6 13 Hoyle Avenue, Castle Hill, 2154,
NSW, Australia   **(100%)**
Tel.: (61) 298997577
Web Site: http://www.rothenberger.com.au
Sales Range: $50-74.9 Million
Emp.: 25
Distribution & Sales of Tools
N.A.I.C.S.: 423830

Rothenberger Benelux bvba (2)
Antwerpsesteenweg 59, Aartselaar, 2630,
Belgium   **(100%)**
Tel.: (32) 38772277
Web Site: http://www.rothenberger.be
Sales Range: $25-49.9 Million
Emp.: 12
Distribution & Sales of Industrial Tools
N.A.I.C.S.: 423830

Rothenberger Bulgaria GmbH (2)
Boul Sitniakovo 79, Sofia, 1111,
Bulgaria   **(100%)**
Tel.: (359) 29461459
Web Site: http://www.rothenberger.bg
Sales Range: $50-74.9 Million
Emp.: 6
Sales & Distribution of Pipe Tools
N.A.I.C.S.: 423990
Gyula Horvath *(Mng Dir)*

Rothenberger France S.A. (2)
24 Rue des Drapiers, PO Box 45033, F
57071, Metz, Cedex 3, France   **(100%)**
Tel.: (33) 387749292
Sales Range: $25-49.9 Million
Emp.: 8
Distribution & Sales of Tools
N.A.I.C.S.: 423830
Bruno Petry *(Mng Dir)*

Rothenberger Hellas S.A. (2)
Agias Kyriakis 45, Paleo Faliro, 17564, Ath-
ens, Greece   **(100%)**
Tel.: (30) 210 94 02 049
Web Site: http://www.ruthenberger.com
Sales Range: $50-74.0 Million
Emp.: 5
Distribution & Sales of Industrial Tools &
Equipment
N.A.I.C.S.: 423830

Rothenberger Hungary Kft. (2)
Gubacsi ut 26, 1097, Budapest,
Hungary   **(100%)**
Tel.: (36) 13475040
Web Site: http://www.rothenberger.hu
Sales Range: $25-49.9 Million
Emp.: 15
Distribution & Sales of Industrial Tools
N.A.I.C.S.: 423830
Gyula Horvath *(Mng Dir)*

Rothenberger Italiana s.r.l. (2)
Via G Reiss Romoli 17-19, Settimo Mila-
nese, I 20019, Italy   **(100%)**
Tel.: (39) 02 33 50 601
Web Site: http://www.rothenberger.it
Sales Range: $25-49.9 Million
Emp.: 35
Marketing & Distribution of Pipe Tools
N.A.I.C.S.: 423830
Vjollca Hoxha *(Mgr-Mktg)*

**Rothenberger Naradi a Stroje,
s.r.o.** (2)
Prumyslova 1306/7, 102 00, Prague, 10,
Czech Republic   **(100%)**
Tel.: (420) 271730183
Web Site: http://www.rothenberger.cz
Sales Range: $50-74.9 Million
Emp.: 7
Sales & Distribution of Pipe Tools
N.A.I.C.S.: 423990
Gyula Horvath *(Mng Dir)*

Rothenberger Nederland bv (2)
Postbus 45, Rijen, 5120 AA,
Netherlands   **(100%)**
Tel.: (31) 161 29 35 79
Emp.: 6
Distribution & Marketing of Industrial Tools
& Equipment
N.A.I.C.S.: 423830
Dynaka Kap *(Gen Mgr)*

**Rothenberger Pipe Tool (Shanghai)
Co., Ltd.** (2)
D-4 No 195 Qianpu Road, East New Area
of Songjiang, Shanghai, 201611,
China   **(100%)**
Tel.: (86) 21 6760 2077
Web Site: http://www.rothenberger.cn
Sales Range: $50-74.9 Million
Emp.: 10
Cutting Tools Distr & Sales
N.A.I.C.S.: 423830

Rothenberger Polska Sp. z.o.o. (2)
ul Annopol 4A Budynek C, 03 236, Warsaw,
Poland   **(100%)**
Tel.: (48) 22 213 5900
Web Site: http://www.rothenberger.pl
Sales Range: $25-49.9 Million
Emp.: 50
Sales & Distribution of Pipe Tools
N.A.I.C.S.: 423830
Miroslaw Honek *(VP)*

Rothenberger S.A. (2)
Carretera De Durango Elorrio Km 2, 48220,
Abadiano, Biscay, Spain   **(100%)**
Tel.: (34) 946210100
Web Site: http://www.rothenberger.es
Sales Range: $75-99.9 Million
Emp.: 200
Distribution & Sales of Industrial Tools &
Equipment
N.A.I.C.S.: 423830
Eoseema Ciopiuiaca *(Mng Dir)*

Rothenberger Scandinavia A/S (2)
Smedevaenget 8, 9560, Hadsund,
Denmark   **(100%)**
Tel.: (45) 98157566
Web Site: http://www.rothenberger.dk
Sales Range: $50-74.9 Million
Emp.: 8
Marketing of Industrial Torches & Soldering
Equipment
N.A.I.C.S.: 423830

Rothenberger Schweiz AG (2)
Herostrasse 9, 8048, Zurich,
Switzerland   **(100%)**
Tel.: (41) 44 435 30 30
Sales Range: $50-74.9 Million
Emp.: 6
Distribution & Sales of Tools
N.A.I.C.S.: 423830

Rothenberger Sweden AB (2)
Hemvarnsgatan 22, PO Box 1366, 171 54,
Solna, Sweden
Tel.: (46) 8 546 023 00
Web Site:
http://www.rothenbergersweden.se
Sales & Distribution of Tools
N.A.I.C.S.: 423830
Anders Dahl *(Mng Dir)*

Rothenberger UK Limited (2)
2 Kingsthorne Park, Henson Way, Ketter-
ing, NN16 8PX, Northants, United
Kingdom   **(100%)**
Tel.: (44) 1536310300
Web Site: http://www.rothenberger.co.uk
Sales Range: $25-49.9 Million
Emp.: 35
Marketing & Distribution of Pipe Tools
N.A.I.C.S.: 423830
Guy Hadwin *(Mgr-Mktg)*

Subsidiary (US):

Rothenberger USA LLC (2)
4455 Boeing Dr, Rockford, IL
61109-2988   **(100%)**
Tel.: (815) 397-7617
Web Site: http://www.rothenberger-usa.com
Sales Range: $25-49.9 Million
Emp.: 25
Plumbing Tools Mfr
N.A.I.C.S.: 333515

Division (Domestic):

**Rothenberger USA - West Coast
Operations** (3)
955 Monterey Pass Rd, Monterey Park, CA
91754   **(100%)**
Tel.: (323) 268-1381
Web Site: http://www.rothenberger-usa.com
Sales Range: $25-49.9 Million
Emp.: 15
Mfr & Sales of Pipe Threading Machines
N.A.I.C.S.: 333517

Subsidiary (Non-US):

**Rothenberger Werkzeug und Maschi-
nen GmbH** (2)
Gewerbeparkstrasse 9, 5081, Anif,
Austria   **(100%)**
Tel.: (43) 6246 72091 45
Web Site: http://www.rothenberger.at
Sales Range: $25-49.9 Million
Emp.: 30
Distribution & Sales of Tools
N.A.I.C.S.: 423990

Subsidiary (Domestic):

Rothenberger Werkzeuge GmbH (2)
Industriestrasse 7, D 65779, Kelkheim, Ger-
many
Tel.: (49) 6195 800 0
Web Site: http://www.rothenberger.com
Sales Range: $500-549.9 Million
Emp.: 1,600
Holding Company; Tools & Welding Equip-
ment Mfr & Whslr
N.A.I.C.S.: 551112

Subsidiary (Domestic):

**RUKO GmbH
Prazisionswerkzeuge** (3)
Robert Bosch Strasse 7-9, 71088, Holzger-
lingen, Baden Wuerttemburg,
Germany   **(70%)**

Dr. Helmut Rothenberger Holding GmbH—(Continued)

Tel.: (49) 703168000
Web Site: http://www.ruko.de
Sales Range: $25-49.9 Million
Emp.: 60
Precision & Metal Cutting Tool Mfr
N.A.I.C.S.: 332216

Rothenberger Werkzeuge Produktion GmbH (3)
Lilienthalstrasse 71-87, 37235, Hessisch Lichtenau, Germany (100%)
Tel.: (49) 560293940
Web Site: http://www.rothenberger.com
Emp.: 30
High Pressure & Mechanical Drain Cleaning Machinery Mfr
N.A.I.C.S.: 333310
Marco Paerette (Plant Mgr)

Subsidiary (Non-US):

Rothenberger do Brasil Ltda. (2)
Rua Marinho de Carvalho 72, Diadema, 09921-005, SP, Brazil
Tel.: (55) 11 4044 4748
Web Site: http://www.rothenberger.com.br
Distribution & Sales of Tools
N.A.I.C.S.: 423830

Rothenberger-Tools SA (Pty) Ltd. (2)
165 Vanderbijl Street, Meadowdale, Germiston, 1610, South Africa (100%)
Tel.: (27) 11 3 72 96 33
Web Site: http://www.rothenberger.co.za
Sales Range: $50-74.9 Million
Emp.: 9
Distribution & Sale of Tools
N.A.I.C.S.: 423990
Steven van Zyl (Mng Dir & Sls Dir)

Virax S.A. (2)
39 Quai de Marne, PO Box 197, Epernay, 15206, France
Tel.: (33) 326595678
Web Site: http://www.virax.fr
Sales Range: $25-49.9 Million
Emp.: 200
Construction Tools Mfr
N.A.I.C.S.: 333991
Michel Moulin (Pres & CEO)

nexMart GmbH & Co. KG (1)
Gropiusplatz 10, 70563, Stuttgart, Germany
Tel.: (49) 71199783300
Web Site: http://www.nexmart.com
Emp.: 100
Business Support Services
N.A.I.C.S.: 561499
Bjorn Bode (Head-Sls-Central Europe)

DR. HONLE AG
UV Technology Nicolaus Otto Str 2, D-82205, Gilching, Germany
Tel.: (49) 89856080
Web Site: https://www.hoenle.de
Year Founded: 1976
HNL—(DEU)
Rev.: $114,765,810
Assets: $190,110,080
Liabilities: $86,361,968
Net Worth: $103,748,111
Earnings: ($11,793,654)
Emp.: 594
Fiscal Year-end: 09/30/23
UV Adhesives, Lamps, Measuring Instrumentation, Dryers, Offset Printing Products & Inkjet Printing Products Mfr & Distr
N.A.I.C.S.: 333248
Norbert Haimerl (CFO, Member-Mgmt Bd-Fin & HR & Mng Dir-IT, HR & IR)

Subsidiaries:

Aladin GmbH (1)
Am Eckfeld 10, 83543, Rott am Inn, Germany
Tel.: (49) 8039 908670
Web Site: http://www.aladin-uv.de
UV Lamp Mfr
N.A.I.C.S.: 335139

Eleco Produits S.A.S. (1)
125 av Louis Roche, ZA des Basses Noels,

92238, Gennevilliers, Cedex, France
Tel.: (33) 147924180
Web Site: http://www.eleco-produits.fr
Sales Range: $25-49.9 Million
Emp.: 30
Glues & Adhesives Mfr
N.A.I.C.S.: 424690

Eltosch Grafix Asia (1)
6/F Luk Kwok Centre 72 Gloucester Road, Wanchai, China (Hong Kong)
Tel.: (852) 90997462
Ultraviolet Lamp Mfr
N.A.I.C.S.: 335139

Eltosch-Grafix GmbH (1)
Fahltskamp 64, 25421, Pinneberg, Germany
Tel.: (49) 41015150700
Web Site: https://www.eltosch-grafix.com
Emp.: 25
UV Lamps Designer & Mfr
N.A.I.C.S.: 335139

Subsidiary (US):

Eltosch Grafix America Inc. (2)
1888 E Fabyan Pkwy - Ste 7, Batavia, IL 60510
Tel.: (630) 482-2266
Light Emitting Diode Mfr
N.A.I.C.S.: 334413

GRAFIX GmbH (1)
Kupferstr 40-46, 70565, Stuttgart, Germany
Tel.: (49) 711 786900
Web Site: http://www.grafix-online.de
Printing Equipment Mfr
N.A.I.C.S.: 333248

Hoenle UV Technology (Shanghai) Trading Ltd. (1)
Room 821 No 800 Shangcheng Road, Cimic Building Pudong, Shanghai, 200120, China
Tel.: (86) 2164 730200
Web Site: http://www.hoenle.cn
UV Lamps Sales
N.A.I.C.S.: 335139

Honle UV France S.a.r.l. (1)
38 rue Delandine, 69002, Lyon, France
Tel.: (33) 472549902
Sales Range: $25-49.9 Million
Emp.: 3
UV Lamps Designer & Mfr
N.A.I.C.S.: 335139

Mitronic GmbH (1)
Lochhamer Schlag 1, 82166, Grafelfing, Germany
Tel.: (49) 89 85608 270
Web Site: http://www.mitronic.com
Lighting Product Mfr
N.A.I.C.S.: 335139

Panacol-Elosol GmbH (1)
Stierstadter Strasse 4, Taunus, 61449, Steinbach, Germany
Tel.: (49) 617162020
Web Site: https://www.panacol.de
Emp.: 15
Adhesive Product Mfr
N.A.I.C.S.: 325520

Subsidiary (Non-US):

Panacol-Korea Co., Ltd. (2)
707 Kranz Techno 388 Dunchon-daero, Jungwon-gu, Seongnam, 13403, Gyeonggi-do, Korea (South)
Tel.: (82) 317491701
Web Site: https://www.panacol-korea.com
Adhesive Product Distr
N.A.I.C.S.: 424690

PrintConcept UV-Systeme GmbH (1)
Philipp-Jakob-Manz-Str 18, 72664, Kohlberg, Germany
Tel.: (49) 7025 912770
Web Site: http://www.printconcept-uv.de
Sales Range: $25-49.9 Million
Emp.: 15
UV Lamps Designer & Mfr
N.A.I.C.S.: 335139
Juergen Welle (Founder & CEO)

Raesch Quarz (Germany) GmbH (1)
In den Folgen 3, Ilmenau OT, 98704, Ilmenau, Germany
Tel.: (49) 367746960

Web Site: https://www.raesch.net
Lighting Equipment Mfr
N.A.I.C.S.: 335139

Raesch Quarz (Malta) Ltd. (1)
Oxford Centre F5 Technopark, Mosta, MST 3000, Malta
Tel.: (356) 21 419615
Web Site: http://www.raesch.net
Emp.: 50
UV Lighting Products Mfr
N.A.I.C.S.: 335139
Marisa Xuereb (Mgr)

Sterilsystems GmbH (1)
Markt 384, Mauterndorf, 5570, Salzburg, Austria
Tel.: (43) 647220007
Web Site: https://sterilsystems.com
UV Control Equipment Distr
N.A.I.C.S.: 423830

UV-Technik International Ltd. (1)
Innovation Centre and Business Base Office E04 110, Butterfield Great Marlings, Luton, LU2 8DL, Bedfordshire, United Kingdom
Tel.: (44) 1582522345
Web Site: https://www.uv-technik.co.uk
Electronic Equipment Mfr & Distr
N.A.I.C.S.: 335999

UV-Technik Speziallampen GmbH (1)
(51%)
Tel.: (49) 367855200
Emp.: 50
UV Lighting Products Mfr
N.A.I.C.S.: 335139

DR. ING. GOSSLING MASCHINENFABRIK GMBH
Kapellenweg 40, 46514, Schermbeck, Germany
Tel.: (49) 285391440
Web Site: http://www.dr-goessling.de
Rev.: $13,480,350
Emp.: 79
Conveying Equipment Mfr
N.A.I.C.S.: 333922
Manfred Gossling (Owner)

Subsidiaries:

Goessling USA, Inc. (1)
748 Mountain View Dr, Piney Flats, TN 37686
Tel.: (423) 915-0472
Web Site: http://www.goesslingusa.com
Emp.: 15
Industrial Machinery & Equipment Mfr
N.A.I.C.S.: 333922
Bill Gregory (Mgr-Sls)

DR. ING. K. BUSCH GMBH
Schauinslandstrasse 1, Maulburg, 79689, Germany
Tel.: (49) 76226810
Web Site:
http://www.buschvacuum.com
Year Founded: 1963
Vacuum Pumps, Blowers & Compressor Mfr
N.A.I.C.S.: 333912
Karl Busch (Chm)

Subsidiaries:

Ateliers Busch S.A. (1)
Zone Industrielle, Chevenez, 2906, Switzerland
Tel.: (41) 324760200
Web Site: http://www.busch.ch
Sales Range: $50-74.9 Million
Emp.: 200
Vacuum Pumps, Blowers & Compressor Mfr
N.A.I.C.S.: 333912

BNM Stenstrup A/S (1)
Tvaervej 23, 5771, Svendborg, Denmark
Tel.: (45) 62261405
Web Site: http://www.busch.com
Sales Range: $25-49.9 Million
Emp.: 20
Vacuum Pumps, Blowers & Compressor Mfr
N.A.I.C.S.: 333912

Busch (UK) Ltd. (1)
Hortonwood 30, Telford, TF1 7YB, Shropshire, United Kingdom
Tel.: (44) 1952677432
Web Site: http://www.busch.co.uk
Sales Range: $25-49.9 Million
Emp.: 60
Vacuum Pumps, Blowers & Compressor Mfr
N.A.I.C.S.: 333912
Ian Graves (Mng Dir)

Busch AG (1)
Waldweg 22, 4312, Magden, Switzerland
Tel.: (41) 618459090
Web Site: http://www.buschag.ch
Sales Range: $25-49.9 Million
Emp.: 20
Vacuum Pumps, Blowers & Compressor Mfr
N.A.I.C.S.: 333912
Christian Muser (Mng Dir)

Busch Argentina S.R.L. (1)
Amenabar 1444 Piso 10 C, C 1426AJZ, Buenos Aires, Argentina
Tel.: (54) 11 4781 4143
Web Site: http://www.busch-vacuum.com.ar
Vacuum Pumps, Blowers & Compressor Mfr
N.A.I.C.S.: 333912

Busch Australia Pty. Ltd. (1)
30 Lakeside Dr, Broadmeadows, 3047, Vic, Australia
Tel.: (61) 393550600
Web Site: http://www.busch.com.au
Sales Range: $25-49.9 Million
Emp.: 40
Vacuum Pumps, Blowers & Compressor Mfr
N.A.I.C.S.: 333912
K. Porslit (Mng Dir)

Busch Austria GmbH (1)
Businesspark 1, 2100, Korneuburg, Austria
Tel.: (43) 2262756650
Web Site: http://www.buschvacuum.com
Vacuum Pumps, Blowers & Compressor Mfr
N.A.I.C.S.: 333912
Karl Bluamer (Gen Mgr)

Busch B.V. (1)
Pompmolenlaan 2, 3447 GK, Woerden, Netherlands
Tel.: (31) 348462300
Web Site: http://www.buschvacuum.com
Emp.: 80
Vacuum Pumps, Blowers & Compressor Mfr
N.A.I.C.S.: 333912
Arjan Stolk (Mng Dir)

Busch Chile S. A. (1)
Calle El Roble N 375-G, Santiago, Chile
Tel.: (56) 23765136
Web Site: http://www.busch.cl
Vacuum Pumps, Blowers & Compressor Mfr
N.A.I.C.S.: 333912

Busch Clean Air S.A. (1)
Chemin des Grandes-Vies 54, 2900, Porrentruy, Switzerland
Tel.: (41) 32 46589 60
Web Site: http://www.buschcleanair.com
Air Compressor Mfr
N.A.I.C.S.: 333912
Oliver Wudtke (Dir-Sls & Pur)

Busch Colombia SAS (1)
Calle 24 No 95 - 12 Bodega 17 Parque Ind Portos, Bogota, Colombia
Tel.: (57) 1 309 9212
Web Site: http://www.buschvacuum.com
Blower Distr
N.A.I.C.S.: 423830
Andres Monsegny (Country Mgr)

Busch France S.A.S. (1)
16 Rue du Bois Chaland, 91029, Lisses, France
Tel.: (33) 169898989
Web Site: http://www.busch.fr
Sales Range: $25-49.9 Million
Emp.: 66
Vacuum Pumps, Blowers & Compressor Mfr
N.A.I.C.S.: 333912
Eric Lebreton (Mgr)

Busch GVT Ltd. (1)
Westmere Dr, CW1 6ZT, Crewe, Chesire, United Kingdom - England (100%)
Tel.: (44) 1260274721
Web Site: http://www.busch-gvt.co.uk
Rev.: $7,432,000
Emp.: 65

Liquid Ring Vacuum Pumps Mfr
N.A.I.C.S.: 333914

Busch Ireland Ltd. (1)
A10-11 Howth Junction Business Centre,
Kilbarrack, Dublin, Ireland
Tel.: (353) 18321330
Web Site: http://www.busch.ie
Sales Range: $25-49.9 Million
Emp.: 10
Vacuum Pumps, Blowers & Compressor Mfr
N.A.I.C.S.: 333912
Ian Graves *(Mng Dir)*

Busch Israel Ltd. (1)
1 Move Sivan Street, Kiryat Gat, 8202271,
Israel
Tel.: (972) 86810485
Web Site: http://www.buschvacuum.com
Sales Range: $25-49.9 Million
Emp.: 9
Vacuum Pumps Blowers & Compressor Mfr
N.A.I.C.S.: 333912

Busch Italia S.r.l. (1)
Via Ettore Majorana 16, 20054, Nova Mila-
nese, Italy
Tel.: (39) 036237091
Web Site: http://www.busch.it
Sales Range: $25-49.9 Million
Emp.: 25
Vacuum Pumps, Blowers & Compressor Mfr
N.A.I.C.S.: 333912

Busch Korea Ltd. (1)
248-2 Ichi-ri Majang-Myun Icheon-si, 467-
813, Icheon, Kyunggi-Do, Korea (South)
Tel.: (82) 313218114
Web Site: http://www.buschkorea.co.kr
Vacuum Pumps, Blowers & Compressor Mfr
N.A.I.C.S.: 333912

Busch LLC (1)
516 Viking Dr, Virginia Beach, VA 23452
Tel.: (757) 463-7800
Web Site: http://www.buschusa.com
Sales Range: $50-74.9 Million
Emp.: 95
Pumps & Pumping Equipment Mfr
N.A.I.C.S.: 423830
Ing K. Busch *(Owner)*

Branch (Domestic):

Busch LLC - Morgan Hill (2)
18430 Sutter Blvd, Morgan Hill, CA 95037
Tel.: (408) 782-0800
Web Site: http://www.buschusa.com
Vacuum Pump & System Sales
N.A.I.C.S.: 423830

Subsidiary (Domestic):

Busch Manufacturing LLC (2)
516-A Viking Drive, Virginia Beach, VA
23452
Tel.: (757) 463-8412
Vacuum Pumps, Blowers & Compressor Mfr
N.A.I.C.S.: 333912
Gary Tedder *(Supvr-Quality Assurance)*

Busch Malaysia Sdn Bhd (1)
No 1 Jalan Sungai Jerluh 32 /196 Seksyen
32, 40460, Shah Alam, Malaysia
Tel.: (60) 355259500
Web Site: http://www.buschvacuum.com
Sales Range: $25-49.9 Million
Emp.: 10
Vacuum Pumps, Blowers & Compressor Mfr
N.A.I.C.S.: 333912
Jimmy Teo *(Mng Dir)*

Busch Manufacturing Korea Ltd. (1)
189-51 Soicheon-ro, Majang-myun, Icheon,
467-813, Kyunggi-do, Korea (South)
Tel.: (82) 31 6452700
Web Site: http://www.buschkorea.co.kr
Vacuum Pump Mfr
N.A.I.C.S.: 333912
Kyung-nam Kang *(Mgr-Acctg)*

Busch N.V. (1)
Kruinstraat 7, Lokeren, 9160, Belgium
Tel.: (32) 93484722
Web Site: http://www.busch.be
Sales Range: $25-49.9 Million
Emp.: 22
Vacuum Pumps, Blowers & Compressor Mfr
N.A.I.C.S.: 333912
Dirk Strypsteen *(Gen Mgr)*

Busch New Zealand Ltd. (1)
Unit D 41 Arrenway Drive Albany, Auckland,
0632, New Zealand
Tel.: (64) 9414 7782
Web Site: http://www.buschvacuum.com
Vacuum Pumps, Blowers & Compressor Mfr
N.A.I.C.S.: 333912
Mike Winter *(Mgr)*

Busch Peru SRL (1)
Jr San Patricio Nro 326 Urb Santa Anita
Villa Marina, Chorrillos, Lima, Peru
Tel.: (51) 1 234 6836
Web Site: http://www.buschvacuum.com
Blower Distr
N.A.I.C.S.: 420000

Busch Polska Sp. z o.o. (1)
Ul Dedala 7, 87-853, Nowa Wies, Poland
Tel.: (48) 542315400
Web Site: http://www.buschvacuum.com
Vacuum Pump Blower & Compressor Mfr
N.A.I.C.S.: 333912

Busch Taiwan Corporation (1)
1F No 69 Sec 3 Beishen Road, Taipei,
22244, Taiwan
Tel.: (886) 226620775
Web Site: http://www.busch.com.tw
Sales Range: $25-49.9 Million
Emp.: 25
Vacuum Pumps, Blowers & Compressor Mfr
N.A.I.C.S.: 333912
Plackett Hwang *(Pres)*

**Busch Vacuum (Shanghai) Co.
Ltd.** (1)
No 5 Lane 195 Xipu Road, Songjiang In-
dustrial Estate, Shanghai, 201611, China
Tel.: (86) 2167600800
Web Site: http://www.busch-china.com
Sales Range: $25-49.9 Million
Emp.: 50
Vacuum Pumps, Blowers & Compressor Mfr
N.A.I.C.S.: 333912

**Busch Vacuum (Thailand) Co.
Ltd.** (1)
888/30 Moo 19 Soi Yingcharoen, Bangplee-
Tamru Road, Bangkok, 10540, Thailand
Tel.: (66) 23825428
Web Site: http://www.busch.co.th
Vacuum Pumps, Blowers & Compressor Mfr
N.A.I.C.S.: 333912

Busch Vacuum FZE (1)
A-3/71 & 73 Sharjah Airport International
Free zone, Sharjah, United Arab Emirates
Tel.: (971) 65528654
Web Site: http://www.buschvacuum.com
Blower Distr
N.A.I.C.S.: 423830
Jens Carsten Claus *(Mng Dir)*

Busch Vacuum India Pvt Ltd. (1)
J Block Plot number 5-7 Bhosari Midc,
Pune, 411026, India
Tel.: (91) 2064102886
Web Site: http://www.buschindia.com
Vacuum Pumps, Blowers & Compressor Mfr
N.A.I.C.S.: 333912

Busch Vacuum Kft. (1)
Gare No 3, 2310, Szigetszentmiklos, Hun-
gary
Tel.: (36) 24887308
Web Site: http://www.busch-vacuum.hu
Sales Range: $25-49.9 Million
Emp.: 8
Vacuum Pumps, Blowers & Compressor Mfr
N.A.I.C.S.: 333912
Totok Sandor *(Gen Mgr)*

**Busch Vacuum Mexico S de R.L. de
C.V** (1)
Tlaquepaque 4865 Los Altos, Monterrey,
64370, Mexico
Tel.: (52) 8183111385
Web Site: http://www.busch.com.mx
Sales Range: $25-49.9 Million
Emp.: 15
Vacuum Pumps, Blowers & Compressor Mfr
N.A.I.C.S.: 333912
Louis Gomez *(Mng Dir)*

Busch Vacuum Russia OOO (1)
Kotlyakovskaya Str 6/9, 115201, Moscow,
Russia
Tel.: (7) 4956486726
Web Site: http://www.busch.de

Vacuum Pumps, Blowers & Compressor Mfr
N.A.I.C.S.: 333912

**Busch Vacuum Singapore Pte.
Ltd.** (1)
77 A Joo Koon Circle, Singapore, 629098,
Singapore
Tel.: (65) 64880866
Web Site: http://www.busch.com.sg
Sales Range: $25-49.9 Million
Emp.: 8
Vacuum Pumps, Blowers & Compressor Mfr
N.A.I.C.S.: 333912
Sophia Lee *(Mng Dir)*

**Busch Vacuum South Africa (Pty)
Ltd.** (1)
87 Mimetes Road, Johannesburg, 2094,
South Africa
Tel.: (27) 118560650
Web Site: http://www.busch.co.za
Sales Range: $25-49.9 Million
Emp.: 10
Vacuum Pumps, Blowers & Compressor Mfr
N.A.I.C.S.: 333912

Busch Vacuum Technics Inc. (1)
1740 Lionel Bertrand, Boisbriand, J7H 1N7,
QC, Canada
Tel.: (450) 435-6899
Web Site: http://www.busch.ca
Emp.: 50
Vacuum Pumps, Blowers & Compressor Mfr
N.A.I.C.S.: 333912
Paul Wieser *(Founder & Pres)*

Busch Vakuum s.r.o. (1)
Prazakova 10, 61900, Herspice, Czech
Republic
Tel.: (420) 543424855
Web Site: http://www.buschpumps.cz
Vacuum Pumps, Blowers & Compressor Mfr
N.A.I.C.S.: 333912

Busch Vakuumteknik AB (1)
Brata Industriomrade, 43533, Molnlycke,
Sweden
Tel.: (46) 313380080
Web Site: http://www.busch.se
Sales Range: $25-49.9 Million
Emp.: 17
Vacuum Pumps, Blowers & Compressor Mfr
N.A.I.C.S.: 333912
Magnus Johansson *(Mng Dir)*

Busch Vakuumteknik AS (1)
Holterkollveien 3, 1448, Drobak, Norway
Tel.: (47) 64989850
Web Site: http://www.buschvacuum.com
Emp.: 20
Vacuum Pumps, Blowers & Compressor Mfr
N.A.I.C.S.: 333912
Oyvind Hansen Billing *(Gen Mgr)*

Busch Vakuumteknik Oy (1)
Sinikellontie 4, 01300, Vantaa, Finland
Tel.: (358) 97746060
Web Site: http://www.busch.fi
Vacuum Pumps, Blowers & Compressor Mfr
N.A.I.C.S.: 333912

Busch do Brasil Ltda. (1)
Rod. Edgard Maximo Zambotto Km 64,
13240-00, Sao Paulo, Brazil
Tel.: (55) 1140161400
Web Site: http://www.buschdobrasil.com.br
Sales Range: $25-49.9 Million
Emp.: 40
Vacuum Pumps, Blowers & Compressor Mfr
N.A.I.C.S.: 333912

Busch Iberica S.A (1)
Travessa da Barrosinha N 84 Frac B Marco
da Raposa, Z I EN 1 Norte Raso de Tra-
vasso, 3750-753, Agueda, Portugal
Tel.: (351) 234648070
Web Site: http://www.busch.pt
Sales Range: $25-49.9 Million
Emp.: 3
Vacuum Pumps Blower & Compressor Mfr
N.A.I.C.S.: 333912

Composites Busch S.A. (1)
Chemin des Grandes-Vies 54, 2900, Por-
rentruy, Switzerland
Tel.: (41) 324657030
Web Site: http://compositesbusch.ch
Sales Range: $25-49.9 Million
Emp.: 50
Vacuum Pumps, Blowers & Compressor Mfr

N.A.I.C.S.: 333912
Mugerris Ahmed *(Mng Dir)*

Nippon Busch K.K. (1)
1-23-33 Megumigaoka, Hiratsuka, 259-
1220, Kanagawa, Japan
Tel.: (81) 463504000
Web Site: http://www.busch.co.jp
Sales Range: $25-49.9 Million
Emp.: 70
Vacuum Pumps, Blowers & Compressor Mfr
N.A.I.C.S.: 333912
Yoichiro Sasave *(Pres)*

Pfeiffer Vacuum Benelux B.V. (1)
Newtonweg 11, 4104 BK, Culemborg, Neth-
erlands
Tel.: (31) 345478400
Pump Equipment Mfr
N.A.I.C.S.: 333914

**Pfeiffer Vacuum Taiwan Corporation
Ltd.** (1)
No 169-9 Sec 1 Kang-Leh Road Hsin-Feng,
Song-Lin Village Hsin-Feng, 30444, Hsin-
chu, Taiwan
Tel.: (886) 35599230
Pump Equipment Mfr
N.A.I.C.S.: 333914

Pfeiffer Vacuum Technology AG (1)
Berliner Strasse 43, 35614, Asslar,
Germany   **(50.02%)**
Tel.: (49) 64418020
Web Site: https://www.pfeiffer-vacuum.de
Rev.: $1,055,575,687
Assets: $1,063,490,435
Liabilities: $445,433,622
Net Worth: $618,056,813
Earnings: $85,053,184
Emp.: 4,003
Fiscal Year-end: 12/31/2023
Vacuum Pumps & Equipment Developer &
Mfr
N.A.I.C.S.: 333914
Goetz Timmerbeil *(Deputy Chm-Supervisory
Bd)*

Subsidiary (US):

Advanced Test Concepts, LLC (2)
4037 Guion Ln, Indianapolis, IN 46268
Tel.: (317) 328-8492
Web Site: http://www.atcinc.net
Leak Testing Products Mfr & Services
N.A.I.C.S.: 333998
Hemi Sagi *(Founder)*

Subsidiary (Domestic):

Dreebit GmbH (2)
Zur Wetterwarte 50 Haus 301, 01109, Dres-
den, Germany
Tel.: (49) 35121270010
Web Site: http://www.dreebit.com
Emp.: 50
Vacuum Pump & Leak Detector Device Mfr
N.A.I.C.S.: 335210
Lars Grossmann *(Mng Dir)*

Subsidiary (Non-US):

**Nor-Cal Products Asia Pacific Pte.
Ltd.** (2)
Serangoon Garden, PO Box 428, Singa-
pore, 915531, Singapore
Tel.: (65) 66341228
Vacuum Pump & Leak Detector Device Mfr
N.A.I.C.S.: 334519

Nor-Cal Products Korea Co., Ltd. (2)
Gadong 2nd Floor 531-8, Gajang-ro, Osan,
18103, Gyeonggi, Korea (South)
Tel.: (82) 3180031341
Vacuum Pump & Leak Detector Device Mfr
N.A.I.C.S.: 334519

Division (US):

Nor-Cal Products, Inc. (2)
1967 S Oregon St, Yreka, CA 96097
Tel.: (530) 842-4457
Web Site: http://www.n-c.com
Stainless Steel Vacuum Mfr
N.A.I.C.S.: 332919
Tom Deany *(CEO)*

Subsidiary (Non-US):

Pfeiffer Vacuum Benelux B. V. (2)

Dr. Ing. K. Busch GmbH—(Continued)

Newtonweg 11, 4104 BK, Culemborg, Netherlands
Tel.: (31) 345478400
Vacuum Pump & Leak Detector Device Mfr
N.A.I.C.S.: 334519

Subsidiary (Domestic):

Pfeiffer Vacuum GmbH   **(2)**
Berliner Strasse 43, 35614, Asslar, Germany
Tel.: (49) 64418020
Sales Range: $200-249.9 Million
Emp.: 800
Mfr of Individual Components & Vacuum Systems
N.A.I.C.S.: 335210

Subsidiary (Non-US):

Pfeiffer Vacuum (Schweiz) AG   **(3)**
Forrlibuckstrasse 30, 8005, Zurich, Switzerland
Web Site: http://www.pfeiffer-vacuum.ch
Sales Range: $25-49.9 Million
Emp.: 12
Sales & Service of Vacuum Components & Systems
N.A.I.C.S.: 423830

Pfeiffer Vacuum (Shanghai) Co., Ltd.   **(3)**
Unit B 5th Floor Building 3 YouYou Park 428 Yanggao South Road, Pudong, Shanghai, 200127, China
Tel.: (86) 2133933940
Web Site: http://www.pfeiffer-vacuum.de
Emp.: 100
Sales & Service of Vacuum Components & Systems
N.A.I.C.S.: 423830

Pfeiffer Vacuum Austria GmbH   **(3)**
Diefenbachgasse 35, 1150, Vienna, Austria
Tel.: (43) 18941704
Web Site: http://www.pfeiffer-vacuum.com
Sales Range: $25-49.9 Million
Emp.: 19
Sales & Service of Vacuum Components & Systems
N.A.I.C.S.: 423830

Pfeiffer Vacuum Brasil Ltda   **(3)**
Avenue Pedro Bueno 1783 Parque Jabaquara, Sao Paulo, 04342-011, Brazil
Tel.: (55) 11 3130 7999
Sales Range: $25-49.9 Million
Emp.: 7
Vaccum Pump Mfr
N.A.I.C.S.: 333248

Subsidiary (Domestic):

Pfeiffer Vacuum Components & Solutions GmbH   **(3)**
Anna-Vandenhoeck-Ring 44, 37081, Gottingen, Germany
Tel.: (49) 551999630
Pump Equipment Mfr
N.A.I.C.S.: 333914

Branch (Domestic):

Pfeiffer Vacuum GmbH   **(3)**
Berliner Strasse 43, 35614, Asslar, Germany   **(100%)**
Tel.: (49) 64418020
Web Site: http://www.pfeiffer-vacuum.com
Sales Range: $25-49.9 Million
Emp.: 25
Pumping Systems Mfr
N.A.I.C.S.: 333914
Daniel Salzer (Member-Exec Bd)

Subsidiary (US):

Pfeiffer Vacuum Inc.   **(3)**
24 Trafalgar Sq, Nashua, NH 03063
Tel.: (603) 578-6500
Web Site: http://www.pfeiffer-vacuum.com
Sales Range: $50-74.9 Million
Emp.: 125
Sales & Service of Vacuum Components & Systems
N.A.I.C.S.: 423830
Robert Campbell (Pres)

Subsidiary (Non-US):

Pfeiffer Vacuum India Ltd.   **(3)**
25/5 Nicholson Road, Tarbund, Secunderabad, 500 009, India
Tel.: (91) 4027750014
Web Site: http://www.pfeiffer-vacuum.com
Sales Range: $25-49.9 Million
Emp.: 27
Sales & Service of Vacuum Components & Systems
N.A.I.C.S.: 423830

Pfeiffer Vacuum Italia S.p.A.   **(3)**
Via Luigi Einaudi 21, 20037, Paderno Dugnano, Milan, Italy
Tel.: (39) 02 93 99 051
Web Site: http://www.pfeiffer-vacuum.it
Sales Range: $25-49.9 Million
Emp.: 28
Sales & Service of Vacuum Components & Systems
N.A.I.C.S.: 423830

Pfeiffer Vacuum Korea Ltd.   **(3)**
7F Hyundai Green Food 30 Munin-ro, Suji-gu, Yongin, Gyeonggi-do, Korea (South)
Tel.: (82) 312660741
Web Site: http://www.pfeiffer-vacuum.co.kr
Sales Range: $25-49.9 Million
Emp.: 16
Sales & Service of Vacuum Components & Systems
N.A.I.C.S.: 423830
Sam Oh (Mng Dir)

Pfeiffer Vacuum Ltd.   **(3)**
16 Plover Close, Interchange Park, Newport Pagnell, MK16 9PS, United Kingdom
Tel.: (44) 1908500600
Web Site: http://www.pfeiffer-vacuum.co.uk
Sales & Service of Vacuum Components & Equipment
N.A.I.C.S.: 423830

Pfeiffer Vacuum Scandinavia AB   **(3)**
Johanneslundsvagen 3, 194 61, Upplands Vasby, Sweden
Tel.: (46) 6035786500
Web Site: http://www.pfeiffer-vacuum.se
Sales Range: $25-49.9 Million
Emp.: 13
Sales & Service of Vacuum Components & Systems
N.A.I.C.S.: 423830

Subsidiary (Non-US):

Pfeiffer Vacuum SAS   **(2)**
Avenue de Brogny, PO Box 2069-98, 74009, Annecy, Cedex, France
Tel.: (33) 450657777
Pump Equipment Mfr
N.A.I.C.S.: 333914

Subsidiary (Non-US):

Pfeiffer Vacuum Romania S.r.l.   **(3)**
Parc Industrial Nervia Str Constructorilor Nr 38, Apahida, Cluj-Napoca, Romania
Tel.: (40) 372649614
Pump Equipment Mfr
N.A.I.C.S.: 333914

Subsidiary (Non-US):

Pfeiffer Vacuum Singapore Pte. Ltd.   **(2)**
49 Jalan Pemimpin 01-01/04, Aps Industrial Building, Singapore, 577203, Singapore
Tel.: (65) 62540828
Vacuum Pump & Leak Detector Device Mfr
N.A.I.C.S.: 334519
Eguzkine Calzada (Mgr-QA)

Pfeiffer Vacuum Taiwan Corporation Ltd.   **(2)**
No 169-9 Sec 1 Kang-Leh Rd Hsin Feng Hsiang, Song-Lin Village, 30444, Hsinchu, Taiwan
Tel.: (886) 35599230
Vacuum Pump & Leak Detector Device Mfr
N.A.I.C.S.: 334519
Neil Chen (Gen Mgr)

Subsidiary (Domestic):

Trinos Vakuum-Systeme GmbH   **(2)**
Anna-vandenhoeck-ring 44, 37081, Gottingen, Germany
Tel.: (49) 551999630

Web Site: http://www.trinos.de
Sales Range: $50-74.9 Million
Emp.: 150
Vacuum Component Mfr
N.A.I.C.S.: 335999
Peter Spreitz (Co-Mng Dir)

Subsidiary (Non-US):

adixen Vacuum Products SAS   **(2)**
98 Avenue Brogny, 74009, Annecy, France   **(100%)**
Tel.: (33) 4 50 65 77 77
Web Site: http://www.adixen.com
Sales Range: $200-249.9 Million
Emp.: 600
Mfr of Pumping Equipment
N.A.I.C.S.: 333914

adixen Vacuum Technology Korea Ltd.   **(2)**
11F Starplaza 92-7 Bansong-Dong, Hwaseong, 445160, Gyeonggi-Do, Korea (South)   **(100%)**
Tel.: (82) 31 8014 7202
Web Site: http://www.pfeiffer-vacuum.com
Vacuum Pumps Sales & Service
N.A.I.C.S.: 423830

Vakutek   **(1)**
Emlak Kredi Ishani No. 179, 34672 Uskudar, Istanbul, Turkiye
Tel.: (90) 2163100573
Web Site: http://www.vakutek.com.tr
Vacuum Pumps, Blowers & Compressor Mfr
N.A.I.C.S.: 333912

DR. KURT WOLFF GMBH & CO. KG
Johanneswerkstrasse 34-36, Bielefeld, 33611, Germany
Tel.: (49) 521880800
Web Site: http://www.alpecin.de
Rev.: $73,067,500
Emp.: 246
Haircare Product Mfr
N.A.I.C.S.: 339999
Eduard R. Dorrenberg (Mng Dir)

DR. LAL PATHLABS LTD.
Block E Sector 18 rohini, Medicity Sector 38, New Delhi, 110085, Haryana, India
Tel.: (91) 1243016500
Web Site:
  https://www.lalpathlabs.com
LALPATHLAB—(NSE)
Rev.: $222,849,764
Assets: $226,771,545
Liabilities: $52,595,498
Net Worth: $174,176,048
Earnings: $40,469,384
Emp.: 3,996
Fiscal Year-end: 03/31/21
Health Care Providers
N.A.I.C.S.: 621999
Om Prakash Manchanda (Mng Dir)

Subsidiaries:

Dr. Lal Path Labs Bangladesh Private Limited   **(1)**
Haque Tower 1St Floor 44/9 West Panthapath, Dhaka, 1205, Bangladesh
Tel.: (880) 29102353
Pharmaceuticals Product Mfr
N.A.I.C.S.: 325412

Dr. Lal PathLabs Nepal Private Limited   **(1)**
Chappal Karkhana Chandol-4, Maharajgunj, Kathmandu, Nepal
Tel.: (977) 14416719
Pharmaceuticals Product Mfr
N.A.I.C.S.: 325412

Paliwal Diagnostics Private Limited   **(1)**
117/H-1/02 Opp J K Temple Gate, Pandu Nagar, Kanpur, 208005, India
Tel.: (91) 5123262052
Medical Testing Equipment Mfr
N.A.I.C.S.: 339112

DR. MACH GMBH & CO. KG

Flossmannstrasse 28, Ebersberg, 85560, Germany
Tel.: (49) 809220930
Web Site: http://www.dr-mach.de
Year Founded: 1947
Rev.: $16,711,431
Emp.: 60
Medical Applications Lighting Systems Mfr
N.A.I.C.S.: 335139
Walter Mach (Founder)

DR. O.K. WACK CHEMIE GMBH
Bunsenstrasse 6, Ingolstadt, 85053, Germany
Tel.: (49) 8416350
Web Site: http://www.wackchem.com
Rev.: $17,916,883
Emp.: 180
Automobile Care Products Mfr
N.A.I.C.S.: 325180
Stefan Wind (Mng Dir-Consumer Products)

DR. PAUL LOHMANN GMBH KG
Hasttstrasse 2, 31860, Emmerthal, Germany
Tel.: (49) 5155630
Web Site: http://www.lohmann-chemikalien.de
Year Founded: 1886
Sales Range: $75-99.9 Million
Emp.: 320
Inorganic & Organic Mineral Compounds
N.A.I.C.S.: 327999
Juergen Lohmann (Owner)

DR. PENG TELECOM & MEDIA GROUP CO., LTD.
Room 1201 Building No 1 No 169 Binhai Road, Jimo District, Qingdao, 610041, Shandong, China
Tel.: (86) 1052206808   CN
Web Site: http://www.drpeng.com.cn
Year Founded: 1985
600804—(SHG)
Rev.: $520,169,954
Assets: $1,035,234,612
Liabilities: $906,790,487
Net Worth: $128,444,126
Earnings: ($63,636,188)
Emp.: 40,000
Fiscal Year-end: 12/31/22
Holding Company; Telecommunications & Internet Services
N.A.I.C.S.: 551112
Xueping Yang (Chm)

Subsidiaries:

Great Wall Broadband Network Service Co., Ltd.   **(1)**
68 ZijinBuilding Floor 17th Wanquan Road, Haidian District, Beijing, 100086, China   **(50%)**
Tel.: (86) 1082659931
Computer Storage Technology Mfr
N.A.I.C.S.: 334112

DR. REDDY'S LABORATORIES LIMITED
8-2-337 Road No 3 Banjara Hills, Hyderabad, 500 034, Telangana, India
Tel.: (91) 4049002900   In
Web Site: https://www.drreddys.com
Year Founded: 1984
RDY—(NYSE)
Rev.: $3,347,089,503
Assets: $4,646,220,251
Liabilities: $1,282,513,039
Net Worth: $3,363,707,212
Earnings: $667,633,835
Emp.: 23,550
Fiscal Year-end: 03/31/24

Generic & Branded Pharmaceutical
Mfr
N.A.I.C.S.: 325412
K. Satish Reddy *(Co-Chm)*

Subsidiaries:

Aurigene Discovery Technologies
Limited **(1)**
39-40 KIADB Industrial Area Phase II Elec-
tronic City Hosur Road, Bengaluru, 560100,
Karnataka, India
Tel.: (91) 8071025444
Web Site: http://www.aurigene.com
Sales Range: $75-99.9 Million
Emp.: 400
Drug Discovery Services
N.A.I.C.S.: 541715
Murali Ramachandra *(CEO)*

Subsidiary (Non-US):

Aurigene Discovery Technologies
(Malaysia) SDN BHD **(2)**
Level-2 Research Management and Innova-
tion Complex, University of Malaya, 50603,
Kuala Lumpur, Malaysia
Tel.: (60) 379607601
Pharmaceuticals Product Mfr
N.A.I.C.S.: 325412

Dr. Reddy's Laboratories **(1)**
Abbey House 18 / 24 Stoke Rd, SL25AG,
Slough, United Kingdom **(100%)**
Tel.: (44) 753495500
Web Site: http://www.drreddys.com
Sales Range: $25-49.9 Million
Emp.: 30
Mfr of Chemicals
N.A.I.C.S.: 325998

Dr. Reddy's Laboratories (Australia)
Pty. Limited **(1)**
Suite 3 03 Level 3/390 St Kilda Road, Mel-
bourne, 3004, VIC, Australia
Tel.: (61) 383941888
Web Site: https://www.drreddys.au
Emp.: 108
Pharmaceutical Products Distr
N.A.I.C.S.: 424210

Dr. Reddy's Laboratories (EU)
Limited **(1)**
Steanard Lane, Mirfield, WF14 8HZ, West
Yorkshire, United Kingdom
Tel.: (44) 1482860228
Sales Range: $50-74.9 Million
Emp.: 65
Pharmaceutical Products Distr
N.A.I.C.S.: 424210

Dr. Reddy's Laboratories (Proprietary)
Limited **(1)**
South Wing The Place 1 Sandton Drive,
Sandton, 2196, South Africa
Tel.: (27) 117830104
Web Site: http://www.drreddys.com
Sales Range: $50-74.9 Million
Emp.: 93
Pharmaceutical Products Distr
N.A.I.C.S.: 424210

Dr. Reddy's Laboratories LLC **(1)**
str Kyivsky shlach 121-A p Velyka Oleksan-
drivka, Boryspil district Kyiv region, 08320,
Kiev, Ukraine
Tel.: (380) 444923173
Web Site: https://www.drreddys.ua
Emp.: 230
Pharmaceutical Products Distr
N.A.I.C.S.: 424210

Dr. Reddy's Laboratories New York,
Inc **(1)**
1974 Route 145, Middleburgh, NY 12122-
5315
Tel.: (518) 827-7702
Pharmaceutical Products Research Ser-
vices
N.A.I.C.S.: 541715

Dr. Reddy's Laboratories Romania
SRL **(1)**
Nicolae Caramfil st No71-73 5th floor, Bu-
charest, 014142, Romania
Tel.: (40) 212240032
Web Site: https://www.drreddys.ro
Sales Range: $25-49.9 Million
Emp.: 100
Pharmaceutical Products Distr

N.A.I.C.S.: 424210

Dr. Reddy's Laboratories, Inc. **(1)**
107 College Rd E, Princeton, NJ 08540
Tel.: (609) 375-9900
Sales Range: $50-74.9 Million
Emp.: 70
Pharmaceutical Services
N.A.I.C.S.: 424210

Subsidiary (Domestic):

Dr. Reddy's Laboratories Louisiana
LLC **(2)**
8800 Line Ave, Shreveport, LA 71106
Tel.: (318) 861-8070
Pharmaceutical Products Distr
N.A.I.C.S.: 424210

Promius Pharma LLC **(2)**
200 Somerset Corporate Blvd, Bridgewater,
NJ 08807
Tel.: (908) 429-4500
Web Site: http://www.promiuspharma.com
Dermatology Products Research Services
N.A.I.C.S.: 541715
Sagar Munjal *(Chief Medical Officer & VP)*

Dr. Reddy's New Zealand Ltd. **(1)**
Level 6 AMI Building 63 Albert Street, Auck-
land, 1142, New Zealand
Tel.: (64) 93567000
Web Site: http://www.drreddys.com
Pharmaceutical Products Distr
N.A.I.C.S.: 424210

Eurobridge Consulting BV **(1)**
Prins Bernhardplein 200, 1097 JB, Amster-
dam, Netherlands
Tel.: (31) 205214777
Pharmaceutical Products Research Ser-
vices
N.A.I.C.S.: 541715

Industrias Quimicas Falcon de
Mexico, S.A. de CV **(1)**
Carretera Federal Cuernavaca-Cuautla Km
4 5 Civac, 62578, Cuernavaca, Morelos,
Mexico
Tel.: (52) 7773293450
Sales Range: $50-74.9 Million
Emp.: 200
Pharmaceuticals Product Mfr
N.A.I.C.S.: 325412
Alberto Flores *(Gen Mgr)*

Reddy Holding GmbH **(1)**
Kobelweg 95, 86156, Augsburg, Germany
Tel.: (49) 821748810
Emp.: 80
Pharmaceutical Products Distr
N.A.I.C.S.: 424210
Clemens Johannes Troche *(Mng Dir)*

Subsidiary (Domestic):

beta Institut for Sozialmedizinische
Forschung and Entwicklung
GmbH **(2)**
Steinerne Furt 78, 86156, Augsburg, Ger-
many
Tel.: (49) 821 450540
Web Site: http://www.beta-institut.de
Emp.: 3
Laboratory Testing Services
N.A.I.C.S.: 541380
Anna Yankers *(Mgr-Operational)*

betapharm Arzneimittel GmbH **(2)**
Kobelweg 95, 86156, Augsburg, Germany
Tel.: (49) 821748810
Emp.: 80
Pharmaceuticals Product Mfr
N.A.I.C.S.: 325412

Reddy Pharma Iberia SA **(1)**
Avenida Josep Tarradellas 38, 08029, Bar-
celona, Spain
Tel.: (34) 933554916
Web Site: https://www.drreddys.es
Sales Range: $50-74.9 Million
Emp.: 1
Pharmaceutical Products Distr
N.A.I.C.S.: 424210

DR. SCHUMACHER GMBH
Am Roggenfeld 3, Melsungen, 34323,
Germany
Tel.: (49) 566494960

Web Site: http://www.schumacher-
online.com
Rev.: $51,036,310
Emp.: 92
Health Care Products Mfr
N.A.I.C.S.: 325412
Beatrix Witteler *(Acct Mgr-Export)*

**DR. SULAIMAN AL HABIB
MEDICAL SERVICES GROUP
COMPANY**
King Fahad Road Olaya, Riyadh,
11643, Saudi Arabia
Tel.: (966) 115259999
Web Site: https://hmg.com
4013—(SAU)
Rev.: $2,535,245,639
Assets: $4,212,249,451
Liabilities: $2,408,158,845
Net Worth: $1,804,090,606
Earnings: $560,317,445
Fiscal Year-end: 12/31/23
Hospitals & Health Care Services
N.A.I.C.S.: 621999
Faisal Abdullah Ali Al-Nassar *(Grp
CEO & CFO)*

**DR. THEISS NATURWAREN
GMBH**
Michelinstr 10, PO Box 1559, 66424,
Homburg, Germany
Tel.: (49) 68417090 De
Web Site: http://www.naturwaren-
theiss.de
Year Founded: 1978
Sales Range: $10-24.9 Million
Emp.: 1,000
Healthcare & Beauty Product Mfr &
Distr
N.A.I.C.S.: 325620
Peter Theiss *(Mng Dir)*

Subsidiaries:

Dr. Theiss Naturwaren Sarl **(1)**
11 rue du Chene, BP 90114, Nordhouse,
67152, Erstein, France
Tel.: (33) 388598969
Web Site: http://www.naturwaren.fr
Cosmetics & Healthcare Products Distr
N.A.I.C.S.: 456120

Naturprodukt KFT **(1)**
Depo Pf 8, 2046, Torokbalint, Hungary
Tel.: (36) 23336333
Web Site: http://www.naturprodukt.hu
Natural Skin Care Products & Vitamin
Supplements Mfr & Retailer
N.A.I.C.S.: 456199

Naturwaren Italia s.r.l. **(1)**
Quartiere Girasole snc, Lacchiarella, 20084,
MI, Italy
Tel.: (39) 02 90090083
Web Site: http://www.naturwaren.it
Healthcare & Beauty Products Distr
N.A.I.C.S.: 424210

**DR. THOMAS + PARTNER
GMBH & CO. KG**
Am Sandfeld 9, Karlsruhe, 76149,
Germany
Tel.: (49) 72178340
Web Site: http://www.tup.com
Rev.: $12,408,238
Emp.: 80
Employee Training Services
N.A.I.C.S.: 611430
Frank Thomas *(Founder)*

**DR. WILLMAR SCHWABE
GMBH & CO. KG**
Willmar-Schwabe-Strasse 4,
Karlsruhe, 76227, Germany
Tel.: (49) 72140050
Web Site: http://www.schwabe.de
Sales Range: $800-899.9 Million
Emp.: 3,200
Phytomedicines Mfr
N.A.I.C.S.: 325411

Dirk Reischig *(CEO)*

Subsidiaries:

Austroplant Arzneimittel GmbH **(1)**
Richard Sträuss-Strasse 13, 1230, Vienna,
Austria
Tel.: (43) 1 6162644 0
Web Site: http://www.austroplant.at
Pharmaceutical Products Distr
N.A.I.C.S.: 424210

DHU Iberica, S.A. **(1)**
Poligono Industrial Francoli Parcela 3 naves
1 y 2, 43006, Tarragona, Spain
Tel.: (34) 977 55 05 42
Web Site: http://www.dhu.es
Pharmaceutical Products Distr
N.A.I.C.S.: 424210

Deutsche Homoopathie-Union DHU
Arzneimittel GmbH & Co. KG **(1)**
Ottostr 24, 76227, Karlsruhe, Germany
Tel.: (49) 721 4093 01
Web Site: http://www.dhu.de
Pharmaceutical Products Distr
N.A.I.C.S.: 424210

Dr. Willmar Schwabe India Pvt.
Ltd. **(1)**
A-36 Sector 60, Noida, 201 304, Uttar
Pradesh, India
Tel.: (91) 120 4016500
Web Site: http://www.schwabeindia.com
Pharmaceutical Product Mfr & Distr
N.A.I.C.S.: 325412

Nature's Way Holding Co. **(1)**
825 Challenger Dr, Green Bay, WI 54311
Tel.: (920) 469-1313
Web Site: http://www.naturesway.com
Sales Range: $75-99.9 Million
Emp.: 200
Holding Company; Nutritional Supplement
Mfr
N.A.I.C.S.: 551112
Rory Mahony *(COO)*

Subsidiary (Domestic):

Enzymatic Therapy Inc. **(2)**
825 Challenger Dr, Green Bay, WI 54311
Tel.: (920) 469-1313
Web Site: http://www.enzy.com
Sales Range: $50-74.9 Million
Natural & Synthetic Vitamins Mfr
N.A.I.C.S.: 325411
Randy J. Rose *(CEO)*

Nature's Way Products, Inc. **(1)**
3051 W Maple Loop Dr Ste 125, Lehi, UT
84043
Tel.: (920) 469-1313
Web Site: http://www.naturesway.com
Pharmaceutical Products Distr
N.A.I.C.S.: 424210
Tom Murdock *(Founder)*

SCHWABE PHARMA AG **(1)**
Erlistrasse 2, PO Box 473, 6403,
Kussnacht, Switzerland
Tel.: (41) 41 854 18 60
Web Site: http://www.schwabepharma.ch
Pharmaceutical Products Distr
N.A.I.C.S.: 424210

Schwabe Czech Republic s.r.o. **(1)**
Cestmirova 1, 140 00, Prague, Czech Re-
public
Tel.: (420) 241 740 447
Web Site: http://www.schwabe.cz
Pharmaceutical Products Distr
N.A.I.C.S.: 424210

Schwabe Hungary Kft **(1)**
Fehervari 50 52, Budapest, 1117, Hungary
Tel.: (36) 1 431 89 34
Web Site: http://www.schwabe.hu
Pharmaceutical Products Distr
N.A.I.C.S.: 424210

Schwabe North America, Inc. **(1)**
2696 Nootka St, Vancouver, V5M 3M5, BC,
Canada
Tel.: (604) 421-0777
Web Site: http://www.natureswaycanada.ca
Pharmaceutical Products Distr
N.A.I.C.S.: 424210

Schwabe Pharma (UK) Ltd. **(1)**
Alexander House Mere Park Dedmere

Dr. Willmar Schwabe GmbH & Co. KG—(Continued)

Road, Marlow, SL7 1FX, Bucks, United
Kingdom
Tel.: (44) 1628 401980
Web Site: http://www.schwabepharma.co.uk
Pharmaceutical Products Distr
N.A.I.C.S.: 424210

Schwabe Pharma Asia Pacific Pte.
Ltd.   (1)
101 Thomson Road 25-01/02 United
Square, Singapore, 307591, Singapore
Tel.: (65) 6423 9420
Web Site: http://www.schwabepharma-
apac.com
Pharmaceutical Products Distr
N.A.I.C.S.: 424210

Schwabe Slovakia s.r.o.   (1)
Grosslingova 58, 811 09, Bratislava, Slova-
kia
Tel.: (421) 2 52 924 583
Web Site: http://www.schwabe.sk
Pharmaceutical Products Distr
N.A.I.C.S.: 424210

VSM BELGIUM bvba   (1)
Prins Boudewijnlaan 24/C, 2550, Kontich,
Belgium
Tel.: (32) 3 450 81 60
Web Site: http://www.vsm.be
Pharmaceutical Products Distr
N.A.I.C.S.: 424210

VSM Geneesmiddelen bv   (1)
Berenkoog 35, 1822 BH, Alkmaar, Nether-
lands
Tel.: (31) 72 566 11 22
Web Site: http://www.vsm.nl
Pharmaceutical Products Distr
N.A.I.C.S.: 424210

W. Spitzner Arzneimittelfabrik
GmbH   (1)
Bunsenstrasse 6 - 10, 76275, Ettlingen,
Germany
Tel.: (49) 72 43 10 62 65
Web Site: http://www.spitzner.de
Pharmaceutical Products Distr
N.A.I.C.S.: 424210

DR.WU SKINCARE CO., LTD.
13F No 70 Section 3 Nanjing East
Road, Taipei, 100, Taiwan
Tel.: (886) 800083999
Web Site: https://www.drwu.com
Year Founded: 2003
6523—(TPE)
Rev.: $28,977,613
Assets: $55,755,714
Liabilities: $7,948,566
Net Worth: $47,807,148
Earnings: $10,630,053
Fiscal Year-end: 12/31/22
Cosmetic Product Mfr & Distr
N.A.I.C.S.: 325620
Eric Wu (Chm & Gen Mgr)

DRA CONSULTANTS LIMITED
58 Ingole Nagar Opp Airport Behind
Hotel Pride Wardha Road, Nagpur,
440 005, India
Tel.: (91) 7123027575
Web Site: https://www.dra.net.in
540144—(BOM)
Rev.: $2,156,401
Assets: $4,234,114
Liabilities: $908,607
Net Worth: $3,325,507
Earnings: $220,405
Emp.: 123
Fiscal Year-end: 03/31/21
Engineering Consulting Services
N.A.I.C.S.: 541620
Dinesh Chhaganlal Rathi (Chm &
Mng Dir)

**DRA GROUP HOLDINGS PRO-
PRIETARY LIMITED**
No 3 Inyanga Close, Sunninghill, Jo-
hannesburg, 2157, South Africa
Tel.: (27) 11 202 8600   ZA

Web Site: http://www.draglobal.com
Sales Range: $1-9.9 Million
Emp.: 3,300
Engineeering Services
N.A.I.C.S.: 541330
Anerew Naute (Chm)

Subsidiaries:

DRA Taggart, LLC   (1)
4000 Town Ctr Blvd, Canonsburg, PA 15317
Tel.: (724) 754-9800
Coal Processing Plant & Material Handling
Systems Engineering & Construction Ser-
vices Contractor
N.A.I.C.O.: 200210
Daniel S. Placha (COO-North America)

Subsidiary (Domestic):

DRA Taggart Site Services, LLC   (2)
4000 Town Center Blvd, Canonsburg, PA
15317
Tel.: (724) 754-9800
Construction Site Preparation Contractor
N.A.I.C.S.: 238910
Daniel S. Placha (COO-North America)

Minopex   (1)
Ground Floor Building 7 Pinewood Office
Park 33 Riley Road, Woodmead, 2196,
South Africa
Tel.: (27) 117857000
Web Site: http://www.minopex.com
Gold & Silver Exploration Services
N.A.I.C.S.: 213115
Dave Spottiswoode (Mng Dir)

**DRAEGERWERK AG & CO.
KGAA**
Moislinger Allee 53-55, 23558,
Lubeck, Germany
Tel.: (49) 4518820
Web Site: https://www.draeger.com
Year Founded: 1889
DRW3—(DEU)
Rev.: $3,723,905,445
Assets: $3,415,980,908
Liabilities: $1,863,078,670
Net Worth: $1,552,902,239
Earnings: $121,900,364
Emp.: 16,273
Fiscal Year-end: 12/31/23
Safety & Gas Detection Products Mfr
& Sales
N.A.I.C.S.: 213112
Siegfrid Kasang (Vice Chm-
Supervisory Bd)

Subsidiaries:

AEC SAS   (1)
High Technology Park 2 1 Alle Socrate,
92182, Antony, Cedex, France
Tel.: (33) 146114140
Web Site: https://www.medibio.com
Biomedical Maintenance Services
N.A.I.C.S.: 811210

Beijing Fortune Draeger Safety
Equipment Co., Ltd.   (1)
Beijing Tianzhu Airport Industrial Zone A22
Yu An Rd B Area, Honshayu Shunyi
County, Beijing, 100300, China
Tel.: (86) 1080498000
Web Site: http://www.draeger.cn
Sales Range: $25-49.9 Million
Emp.: 50
Mfr of Toxic Gas Monitoring Instrumentation
& Respiratory Protection Equipment
N.A.I.C.S.: 334513
Joerg Daehn (Gen Mgr)

Draeger Arabia Co. Ltd.   (1)
PO Box 365642, Riyadh, 11393, Saudi Ara-
bia
Tel.: (966) 118288200
Medical Equipment Mfr
N.A.I.C.S.: 339112
Shady Mokhtar (Mgr-IT Project)

Draeger Australia Pty. Ltd.   (1)
8 Acacia Place, Notting Hill, 3168, VIC,
Australia
Tel.: (61) 1800372437
Medical Equipment Mfr
N.A.I.C.S.: 339112

Anne Pattinson (Head-Mktg)

Draeger Canada Ltd.   (1)
7555 Danbro Cres, Mississauga, L5N 6P9,
ON, Canada   (100%)
Tel.: (905) 821-8988
Web Site: http://www.draeger.ca
Sales Range: $25-49.9 Million
Emp.: 20
Distr of Toxic Gas Monitoring Instrumenta-
tion & Respiratory Protection Equipment
N.A.I.C.S.: 334513

Draeger Colombia SA   (1)
Calle 100 13-21 Of 503-Edificio Megatower,
110221, Bogota, Colombia
Tel.: (57) 6017945050
Emp.: 100
Medical Equipment Whslr
N.A.I.C.S.: 423450
Ramon Lago (Product Mgr)

Draeger Croatia d.o.o.   (1)
Avenija Veceslava Holjevca 40, Zagreb, 100
10, Croatia   (100%)
Tel.: (385) 16599444
Web Site: http://www.draeger.com
Sales Range: Less than $1 Million
Emp.: 25
Distr of Toxic Gas Monitoring Instrumenta-
tion & Respiratory Protection Equipment
N.A.I.C.S.: 334513

Draeger Hellas A.E.   (1)
150 El Venizelou Str, 142 31, Nea Ionia,
Greece
Tel.: (30) 2102821809
Emp.: 30
Medical Industrial Technology Services
N.A.I.C.S.: 541511
George Kotzampasakis (Engr-Sls)

Draeger Hong Kong Limited   (1)
Room 1701-02 17/F APEC Plaza 49 Hoi
Yuen Road, Kwun Tong, Kowloon, 999077,
China (Hong Kong)
Tel.: (852) 28773077
Medical Equipment Whslr
N.A.I.C.S.: 423450

Draeger India Private Limited   (1)
10th Floor Commerz II International Busi-
ness Park, Oberoi Garden City Off Western
Express Highway Goregaon East, Mumbai,
400 063, Maharashtra, India
Tel.: (91) 2261335600
Medical Equipment Whslr
N.A.I.C.S.: 423450

Draeger Ireland Ltd.   (1)
Unit 2 4075 Kingswood Road, Citywest
Business Campus, Dublin, Ireland
Tel.: (353) 14286400
Medical Device Mfr
N.A.I.C.S.: 339112

Draeger Italia S.p.A.   (1)
Via Galvani 7, 20094, Corsico, MI, Italy
Tel.: (39) 02458721
Medical Device Mfr
N.A.I.C.S.: 339112
Anna Maria Sicari (Mgr-HR)

Draeger Korea Ltd.   (1)
S-21 8th Floor 10 Chungmin-ro Munjeong-
dong, Garden Five Tool 8th Floor Songpa-
gu, Seoul, 05840, Korea (South)
Tel.: (82) 27086400
Medical Equipment Mfr
N.A.I.C.S.: 339112
Waqas Ahmed (Mng Dir)

Draeger Malaysia Sdn. Bhd.   (1)
No 6 Jalan 15/22 Taman Perindustrian
Tiong Nam Seksyen 15, 40200, Shah Alam,
Selangor Darul Ehsan, Malaysia
Tel.: (60) 355262000
Emp.: 57
Medical Equipment Mfr
N.A.I.C.S.: 339112
Mohd Asyraf Adnan (Acct Mgr)

Draeger Maroc SARLAU   (1)
Premises 6 7 Promoffice Building Lotisse-
ment Mandarona N 1, Sidi Maarouf Ain
Chock, 20000, Casablanca, Morocco
Tel.: (212) 529064158
Medical Equipment Mfr
N.A.I.C.S.: 339112

Draeger Medical (Thailand) Ltd.   (1)

111 True Digital Park West Unicorn Building
9th Floor Sukhumvit Road, Bangchak Phra
Khanong, Bangkok, 10260, Thailand
Tel.: (66) 209521003
Medical Equipment Mfr
N.A.I.C.S.: 339112
Wassana Chalermlap (Product Mgr)

Draeger Medical Bulgaria EOOD   (1)
Tel.: (359) 29634403
Medical Device Mfr
N.A.I.C.S.: 339113

Draeger Medical Hispania S.A.   (1)
c/ Xaudaro 5, 28034, Madrid,
Spain   (100%)
Tel.: (34) 917283400
Web Site: http://www.draeger.es
Sales Range: $50-74.9 Million
Emp.: 140
Distr of Toxic Gas Monitoring Instrumenta-
tion & Respiratory Protection Equipment
N.A.I.C.S.: 334513

Draeger Medical Italiana S.p.A.   (1)
Via Galvani 7, 20094, Corsico,
Italy   (100%)
Tel.: (39) 02458721
Web Site: http://www.draeger.com
Distr of Toxic Gas Monitoring Instrumenta-
tion & Respiratory Protection Equipment
N.A.I.C.S.: 334513

Draeger Medical South Africa (Pty)
Ltd   (1)
Corner Beatty Old Pretoria Road 2 Rua
Cana Street Waterfall Commercial, Block A
Leslie Road, Johannesburg, 2055, South
Africa   (100%)
Tel.: (27) 115572300
Web Site: http://www.draeger.com
Sales Range: $25-49.9 Million
Emp.: 52
Distr of Toxic Gas Monitoring Instrumenta-
tion & Respiratory Protection Equipment
N.A.I.C.S.: 334513

Draeger Medical Taiwan Ltd.   (1)
8th Floor No 653 Bannan Road, Zhonghe
District, New Taipei City, 235030, Taiwan
Tel.: (886) 222236388
Medical Equipment Mfr
N.A.I.C.S.: 339112

Draeger Medical UK Ltd.   (1)
The Willows Mark Road, Hemel Hemp-
stead, HP2 7BW, Herts, United Kingdom
Tel.: (44) 1442213542
Medical Device Mfr
N.A.I.C.S.: 339112
Michael Norris (Mng Dir)

Draeger Medikal Ticaret ve Servis
Anonim Sirketi   (1)
Esentepe Mah Milangaz Cad No 75, Monu-
mento Plaza Kat 12 Kartal, 34870, Istanbul,
Turkiye
Tel.: (90) 2164690555
Medical Equipment Mfr
N.A.I.C.S.: 339112

Draeger Myanmar Limited   (1)
No 36/C Kant Kaw Myaing Street, 8 Ward
Yankin Township, 11041, Yangon, Myanmar
Tel.: (95) 9758936759
Medical Equipment Mfr
N.A.I.C.S.: 339112

Draeger New Zealand Limited   (1)
Unit 4 24 Bishop Dunn Place, East Tamaki,
2013, Auckland, New Zealand
Tel.: (64) 800372437
Medical Equipment Mfr
N.A.I.C.S.: 339112
Melissa Parris (Acct Mgr)

Draeger OOO   (1)
Tel.: (7) 4957751520
Web Site: http://www.draeger.com
Medical Tehnology Mfr
N.A.I.C.S.: 339113
Sergey Balluseck (Mktg Mgr)

Draeger Panama Comercial, S. de
R.L.   (1)
Calle 50 Plaza Credicorp Bank Building
Floor 31, Panama, Panama
Tel.: (507) 3779100
Medical Equipment Whslr
N.A.I.C.S.: 423450

Draeger Panama S. de R.L. (1)
Business Park Tower V 10th Floor Avenida
De la Rotonda, Costa del Este, Panama,
Panama
Tel.: (507) 3779101
Medical Equipment Whslr
N.A.I.C.S.: 423450
Monika Zwilling (Mgr-Customer Support)

Draeger Peru S.A.C. (1)
Av San Borja Sur 573-575, 41, Lima, Peru
Tel.: (51) 16269595
Emp.: 50
Medical Equipment Whslr
N.A.I.C.S.: 423450
Jose L. Grande A (Acct Mgr)

Draeger Philippines Corporation (1)
2504-C West Tower Tektite Towers Ex-
change Road, Ortigas Center Metro Manila,
Pasig, 1605, Philippines
Tel.: (63) 284703825
Medical Equipment Mfr
N.A.I.C.S.: 339112

Draeger Safety (Schweiz) AG (1)
Rue du Grand Pre 4, 1007, Lausanne,
Switzerland (100%)
Tel.: (41) 216473700
Web Site: http://www.draeger.com
Sales Range: $25-49.9 Million
Emp.: 35
Distr of Toxic Gas Monitoring Instrumenta-
tion & Respiratory Protection Equipment
N.A.I.C.S.: 334513

Draeger Safety (Thailand) Ltd. (1)
Safety Equipment Whslr
N.A.I.C.S.: 423830
Aaron Ng (Mng Dir)

Draeger Safety Austria GmbH (1)
Wallackgasse 8, Vienna, 1230,
Austria (100%)
Tel.: (43) 1 6093602 0
Web Site: http://www.draeger.com
Sales Range: $25-49.9 Million
Emp.: 31
Distr of Toxic Gas Monitoring Instrumenta-
tion & Respiratory Protection Equipment
N.A.I.C.S.: 334513

Draeger Safety Bulgaria EOOD (1)
2 James Boucher Blvd, 1164, Sofia, Bul-
garia
Tel.: (359) 29634366
Medical Device Whslr
N.A.I.C.S.: 423450
Georgi Popov (Engr-Service)

Draeger Safety Canada Ltd. (1)
2425 Skymark Ave Unit 1, Mississauga,
L4W 4Y6, ON, Canada
Safety Equipment Whslr
N.A.I.C.S.: 423830
Jonathan Wong (Reg Sls Mgr)

**Draeger Safety Equipment (China)
Co., Ltd.** (1)
No 22 Yu'an Road Area B, Tianzhu Airport
Industrial Zone Shunyi, Beijing, 101300,
China
Tel.: (86) 1080498000
Medical Equipment Whslr
N.A.I.C.S.: 423450
Michael Zhong (Mgr-Engineered Solution
Dept)

Draeger Safety India Pvt. Ltd. (1)
9th Floor Commerz II International Business
Park, Oberoi Garden City Off Western Ex-
press Highway Goregaon, Mumbai, 400
063, Maharashtra, India
Tel.: (91) 2261335600
Medical Equipment Whslr
N.A.I.C.S.: 423450

**Draeger Safety Korunma Teknolojileri
Anonim Sirketi** (1)
Mustafa Kemal Mahallesi 2139 Sokak No 2,
Ekim Plaza Kat 3 D 14-15 Cankaya, An-
kara, Turkiye
Tel.: (90) 3124910666
Medical Equipment Mfr
N.A.I.C.S.: 339112

Draeger Safety Ltd. (1)
Ullswater Close Riverside Business Park,
Blyth, NE24 4RG, United Kingdom (100%)
Tel.: (44) 1670352891

Web Site: http://www.draeger.com
Sales Range: $100-124.9 Million
Emp.: 400
Mfr of Toxic Gas Monitoring Instrumentation
& Respiratory Protection Equipment
N.A.I.C.S.: 334513

Draeger Safety Nederland B V (1)
Postbus 310 Edisonstraat 53, Zoetermeer,
NL 2700 AH, Netherlands (100%)
Tel.: (31) 793444666
Web Site: http://www.draegersafety.com
Sales Range: $25-49.9 Million
Emp.: 100
Mfr of Toxic Gas Monitoring Instrumentation
& Respiratory Protection Equipment
N.A.I.C.S.: 334513
Robert Den Brave (Mng Dir)

Draeger Safety Norge A/S (1)
Nils Hansenvej 2, 0667, Oslo,
Norway (100%)
Tel.: (47) 23069500
Web Site: http://www.draeger.com
Sales Range: $25-49.9 Million
Emp.: 25
Toxic Gas Monitoring Instrumentation & Re-
spiratory Protection Equipment
N.A.I.C.S.: 334513

Draeger Safety Pacific Ltd. (1)
8 Acacia Place, Notting Hill, 3168, VIC,
Australia (100%)
Tel.: (61) 1800372437
Web Site: http://www.draeger.com
Sales Range: $25-49.9 Million
Emp.: 60
Mfr of Toxic Gas Monitoring Instrumentation
& Respiratory Protection Equipment
N.A.I.C.S.: 334513

Draeger Safety S.A. (1)
3C Rue De La Federation, PO Box 141,
Strasbourg, 67025, France (100%)
Tel.: (33) 388407676
Web Site: http://www.draeger.com
Sales Range: $25-49.9 Million
Emp.: 70
Distr of Toxic Gas Monitoring Instrumenta-
tion & Respiratory Protection Equipment
N.A.I.C.S.: 334513

Draeger Safety S.A. de C.V. (1)
Av Santa Fe 170 5-4-14, Col Lomas de
Santa Fe Mexico, 01210, Mexico, Mexico
Tel.: (52) 5552614000
Security Services
N.A.I.C.S.: 561621
Felipe Matus Norero (Mktg Dir)

Draeger Safety Sweden AB (1)
Ogardesvagen 19 D, 433 30, Partille,
Sweden (100%)
Tel.: (46) 313409090
Web Site: http://www.draegersafety.se
Sales Range: $25-49.9 Million
Emp.: 40
Distr of Toxic Gas Monitoring Instrumenta-
tion & Respiratory Protection Equipment
N.A.I.C.S.: 334513

Draeger Safety UK Ltd. (1)
Ullswater Close Blyth Riverside, Business
Park, Blyth, NE24 4RG, United Kingdom
Tel.: (44) 1670352891
Medical Device Mfr
N.A.I.C.S.: 339112
Vicky Judson (Dir-HR)

Draeger Singapore Pte Ltd. (1)
61 Science Park Road The Galen 04-01,
Singapore, 117525, Singapore
Tel.: (65) 68729288
Medical Equipment Mfr
N.A.I.C.S.: 339112
Aaron Ng (Country Mgr)

Draeger Tehnika d.o.o. (1)
Danijelova 12-16, Vozdovac, 11010, Bel-
grade, Serbia
Tel.: (381) 113911222
Medical Device Mfr
N.A.I.C.S.: 339112
Milos Lalic (Acct Mgr)

Draeger Vietnam Co., Ltd. (1)
41-43 Nguyen Co Thach, An Loi Dong
Ward District 2, Ho Chi Minh City, Vietnam
Tel.: (84) 2862583687
Medical Equipment Mfr
N.A.I.C.S.: 339112

Nguyen Binh (Mgr-Bus Dev)

Draeger, Inc. (1)
3135 Quarry Rd, Telford, PA 18969
Tel.: (215) 723-9824
Web Site: http://www.draeger-medical.com
Surgical & Medical Instrument Mfr
N.A.I.C.S.: 339112
Ruben Derderian (Pres)

Drager Argentina SA (1)
Colectora Panamericana Este 1717,
B1607BLF, San Isidro, Buenos Aires, Ar-
gentina
Tel.: (54) 1148368300
Medical Equipment Mfr
N.A.I.C.S.: 339112
Licurgo Coppo (Acct Mgr-Reg)

Drager Austria GmbH (1)
Perfectastrasse 67, 1230, Vienna, Austria
Tel.: (43) 1609040
Medical Tehnology Mfr
N.A.I.C.S.: 339113

Drager Chile Ltda. (1)
Av E Frei Montalva, El Cortijo Conchali,
6001-68, Santiago, Chile
Tel.: (56) 6000060001
Medical Equipment Whslr
N.A.I.C.S.: 423450
Fernando Catron (Country Mgr)

Drager Danmark A/S (1)
Lyskaer 9, 2730, Herlev, Denmark
Tel.: (45) 44500000
Medical Device Mfr
N.A.I.C.S.: 339113
Peter Sonne (Acct Mgr)

Drager France SAS (1)
25 rue Georges Besse, High Technology
Park, 92160, Antony, France
Tel.: (33) 146115600
Medical Device Mfr
N.A.I.C.S.: 339113
Yves Le Gouguec (Pres & Mng Dir)

**Drager Gebaude und Service
GmbH** (1)
Moislinger Allee 53-55, 23558, Lubeck, Ger-
many
Tel.: (49) 4518824600
Medical Device Mfr
N.A.I.C.S.: 339112

Drager Hispania S.A.U. (1)
Xaudaro n o 5, 28034, Madrid, Spain
Tel.: (34) 900116424
Safety Technology Equipment Mfr & Distr
N.A.I.C.S.: 325998

Drager Ireland Ltd. (1)
4075 Kingswood Rd Citywest Business
Campus, Unit 2, Dublin, D24 YY36, Ireland
Tel.: (353) 14286400
Medical & Safety Equipment Distr
N.A.I.C.S.: 423450

Drager MSI GmbH (1)
Rohrstrasse 32, 58093, Hagen, Germany
Tel.: (49) 233195840
Web Site: https://draeger-msi.de
Measuring & Controlling Device Mfr
N.A.I.C.S.: 334519
Jorg Koppel (Mng Dir)

Drager Medical ANSY GmbH (1)
Alt-Moabit 101 B, 10559, Berlin, Germany
Tel.: (49) 8008828820
Medical Device Mfr
N.A.I.C.S.: 339112
Michael Reddehase (Mgr-Pur)

Drager Medical Belgium NV (1)
Heide 10, 1780, Wemmel, Belgium
Medical Device Mfr
N.A.I.C.S.: 339113

Drager Medical Croatia d.o.o. (1)
Avenija Veceslava Holjevca 40, 10010, Za-
greb, Croatia
Tel.: (385) 16599444
Medical Device Mfr
N.A.I.C.S.: 339112
Danijel Horvat (Engr-Sls)

**Drager Medical Deutschland
GmbH** (1)
Sudwestpark 63, 90449, Nuremberg, Ger-
many

Tel.: (49) 8008828820
Medical Device Mfr
N.A.I.C.S.: 339112

**Drager Medical Equipment (Shang-
hai) Co., Ltd.** (1)
No 229 Hubo Road, Shanghai International
Medical Park Pudong New Area, Shanghai,
201321, China
Tel.: (86) 2131086000
Medical Equipment Whslr
N.A.I.C.S.: 423450

Drager Medical Hispania SA (1)
C / Pintor Nicolas Massieu n 14 Portal 7
Local 13, Lomo Los Frailes, 35018, Las
Palmas, Spain
Tel.: (34) 900116424
Medical Device Mfr
N.A.I.C.S.: 339112

Drager Medical Hungary Kft. (1)
Szent Laszlo ut 95, 1135, Budapest, Hun-
gary
Tel.: (36) 12885000
Medical Equipment Mfr
N.A.I.C.S.: 339112
Tamas Tibor Takacs (Acct Mgr)

Drager Medical Romania SRL (1)
Str Daniel Danielopolu Nr 42A, Sector 1,
014134, Bucharest, Romania
Tel.: (40) 212331060
Medical Tehnology Mfr
N.A.I.C.S.: 339113
Dumitru Stroe (Engr-Service)

Drager Nederland B.V. (1)
Huygensstraat 3-5, 2721 LT, Zoetermeer,
Netherlands
Tel.: (31) 793444666
Medical Device Mfr
N.A.I.C.S.: 339112
Robert Den Brave (Mng Dir)

Drager Norge AS (1)
Innspurten 9, Etterstad, 0663, Oslo, Norway
Tel.: (47) 23653800
Medical Device Mfr
N.A.I.C.S.: 339112
Hans Ingebrigtsen (Mng Dir)

Drager Portugal, Lda. (1)
Rua Nossa Sr da Conceicao no 3 R/c,
2790-111, Carnaxide, Portugal
Tel.: (351) 211554586
Medical Tehnology Mfr
N.A.I.C.S.: 339113
Hector Rocha (Engr-Tech & Sls)

Drager Romania SRL (1)
AFI Park Floreasca Calea Floreasca No
169, Floor 3 Sector 1, 014459, Bucharest,
Romania
Tel.: (40) 212509168
Web Site: https://www.draeger.com
Medical & Safety Equipment Distr
N.A.I.C.S.: 423450

Drager Safety AG & Co. KGaA (1)
Revalstrasse 1, 23560, Lubeck, Germany
Tel.: (49) 8008828830
Measuring & Controlling Device Mfr
N.A.I.C.S.: 334513
Christian Hagendorf (Product Mgr-Global)

Drager Safety Belgium N.V. (1)
Heide 10, 1780, Wemmel, Belgium
Tel.: (32) 24626211
Medical & Safety Equipment Distr
N.A.I.C.S.: 423450

Drager Safety Danmark A/S (1)
Generatorvej 6B, 2730, Herlev,
Denmark (100%)
Tel.: (45) 44500000
Web Site: http://www.draeger.com
Sales Range: $25-49.9 Million
Emp.: 20
Distr of Toxic Gas Monitoring Instrumenta-
tion & Respiratory Protection Equipment
N.A.I.C.S.: 334513

Drager Safety Hispania SA (1)
c/ Garrotxa 10-12 / Edificio Oceano I,
Parque Mas Blau, 08820, El Prat de Llobre-
gat, Spain
Tel.: (34) 900116424
Medical Device Mfr
N.A.I.C.S.: 339112

Draegerwerk AG & Co. KGaA—(Continued)

Drager Safety Hungaria Kft. (1)
Szent Laszlo ut 95, 1135, Budapest, Hungary
Tel.: (36) 14522020
Medical Equipment Mfr
N.A.I.C.S.: 339112
Ferenc Beregszaszi (Acct Mgr)

Drager Safety Romania SRL (1)
Str Daniel Danielopolu Nr 42A, Sector 1, 014134, Bucharest, Romania
Tel.: (40) 212509168
Medical Tehnology Mfr
N.A.I.C.S.: 339112
Lucia Capota (Mgr-HH)

Drager Safety d.o.o. (1)
Avenija Veceslava Holjevac 40, 10010, Zagreb, Croatia
Tel.: (385) 16501777
Medical Device Mfr
N.A.I.C.S.: 339112

Drager Schweiz AG (1)
Waldeggstrasse 30, 3097, Liebefeld, Switzerland
Tel.: (41) 587487474
Medical Tehnology Mfr
N.A.I.C.S.: 339113
Claus Schramm (Mgr-Bus Dev)

Drager Slovenija d.o.o. (1)
Nadgoriska cesta 19, Crnuce, 1231, Ljubljana, Slovenia
Tel.: (386) 15612263
Medical Device Mfr
N.A.I.C.S.: 339112
Marko Zigon (Mng Dir)

Drager Slovensko s.r.o. (1)
Radlinskeho 40a, 921 01, Piestany, Slovakia
Tel.: (421) 337940061
Medical Device Mfr
N.A.I.C.S.: 339112
Nina Bresticova (Mgr-Fin, Controlling & Acctg)

Drager South Africa (Pty) Ltd. (1)
Beatty Street Ext 9, Waterfall Commercial District Buccleuch, Sandton, South Africa
Tel.: (27) 110594200
Medical Equipment Mfr
N.A.I.C.S.: 339112
Pauline Moonsamy (Country Mgr-HR)

Drager Suomi Oy (1)
Juurakkotie 3, 01510, Vantaa, Finland
Tel.: (358) 207119600
Web Site: https://www.draeger.com
Medical Device Whslr
N.A.I.C.S.: 423450
Raine Mero (Mgr-Pur & Logistics)

Drager Sverige AB (1)
Borgarfjordsgatan 13 B, 16440, Kista, Sweden
Tel.: (46) 103444000
Medical Tehnology Mfr
N.A.I.C.S.: 339113
Mats Insulander (Mgr-Svc Team & Project Solution)

Drager TGM GmbH (1)
Moislinger Allee 53-55, 23558, Lubeck, Germany
Tel.: (49) 4518820
Medical Device Mfr
N.A.I.C.S.: 339112

Drager do Brasil Ltda. (1)
Alameda Pucurui 61/51, Tambore, Barueri, 06460-100, Sao Paulo, Brazil
Tel.: (55) 1146894900
Emp.: 230
Medical Equipment Mfr
N.A.I.C.S.: 339112

GasSecure AS (1)
Innspurten 9, 0663, Oslo, Norway
Tel.: (47) 40100102
Web Site: https://www.gassecure.com
Oil & Gas Operation Services
N.A.I.C.S.: 213112
Jorgen Svare (Head-Ops)

N.V. Draeger Safety Belgium S.A. (1)

Heide 10, 1780, Wemmel, 1780, Belgium (100%)
Tel.: (32) 24626211
Web Site: http://www.draeger.com
Sales Range: $25-49.9 Million
Emp.: 100
Toxic Gas Monitoring Instrumentation & Respiratory Protection Equipment
N.A.I.C.S.: 334513

PT Draeger Medical Indonesia (1)
32nd Floor Alamanda Tower Jl TB Simatupang Kav 23-24, 12430, Jakarta, Indonesia
Tel.: (62) 2180669030
Medical Equipment Mfr
N.A.I.C.S.: 339112
Binsar Ferdinand (Mgr-Channel)

PT Draegerindo Jaya (1)
Alamanda Tower 32nd Floor Jl TB Simatupang kav 23-24, Cilandak, Jakarta, 12430, Indonesia
Tel.: (62) 2180669030
Medical Equipment Mfr
N.A.I.C.S.: 339112
Santi Rahmiyati (Mgr-HR)

QuaDigi UAB (1)
Ukmerges g 322, 12106, Vilnius, Lithuania
Tel.: (370) 52330974
Web Site: https://quadigi.com
Information Technology Services
N.A.I.C.S.: 541511

Stimit Ag (1)
Aarbergstr 46, 2503, Biel, Switzerland
Tel.: (41) 325139300
Web Site: https://www.stimit.com
Health Care Srvices
N.A.I.C.S.: 621610

bentekk GmbH (1)
Kasernenstrasse 12 TUHH Campus Building F Room 1 06, 21073, Hamburg, Germany
Tel.: (49) 4057136357
Web Site: http://www.bentekk.com
Medical Device Mfr
N.A.I.C.S.: 339112
Matthias Schmittmann (Founder & Mng Dir)

DRAEXLMAIER GRUPPE

Landshuter Str 100, 84137, Vilsbiburg, Germany
Tel.: (49) 8741470
Web Site:
    http://www.draexlmaier.com
Year Founded: 1958
Sales Range: $1-4.9 Billion
Emp.: 34,000
Electronic Components Mfr
N.A.I.C.S.: 334419
Fritz Draxlmaier (Partner-Personally Liable)

Subsidiaries:

D&A Electrical Systems Sdn. Bhd. (1)
Lot 2755 Persiaran Kilan Jelapang Light, Industrial Estate, 30100, Perak, Ipoh, Malaysia
Tel.: (60) 55280913
Electronic Components Mfr
N.A.I.C.S.: 334419

D&B Interiors (Pty) Ltd. (1)
30 Helium Street Stand 452, Automotive Supplier Park, Rosslyn, 0200, Gauteng, South Africa
Tel.: (27) 125411900
Sales Range: $25-49.9 Million.
Emp.: 51
Specialized Design Services
N.A.I.C.S.: 541490
Peter Merrington (Mgr-Fin)

DAU Draxlmaier Automotive UK Ltd. (1)
111 Hollymoor Way Great Park, Birmingham, B315HE, Rubery, United Kingdom (100%)
Tel.: (44) 1212566262
Web Site: http://www.draexlmaier.de
Sales Range: $25-49.9 Million
Emp.: 70
Automotive Transmission Repair
N.A.I.C.S.: 811114

Ralph Meser (Gen Mgr)

DCM Draexlmaier Components Automotive de Mexico S.A. DE C.V. (1)
Avenida Central 180 Park Logistico, 78395, San Luis Potosi, Mexico
Tel.: (52) 4441372700
Web Site: http://www.draexlmaier.de
Electronic Components Mfr
N.A.I.C.S.: 334419

DEE Draxlmaier Elektrik-und Elektroniksysteme GmbH (1)
Carl-von-Ossietzky-Str 3, 83043, Bad Aibling, Germany
Tel.: (49) 8061 495190
Automobile Component Distr
N.A.I.C.S.: 423120

DFE Draxlmaier Fahrzeugelektrik GmbH (1)
Wankel Strasse 4, 26723, Emden, Germany (100%)
Tel.: (49) 4921966200
Web Site: http://www.draexlmaier.de
Sales Range: $25-49.9 Million
Emp.: 40
Electronic Components Mfr
N.A.I.C.S.: 334419

DFS Draxlmaier Fahrzeugsysteme GmbH (1)
Pascal-Strasse 4, 85057, Ingolstadt, Germany
Tel.: (49) 8419515950
Web Site: http://www.draexlmaier.de
Motor Vehicle Parts Mfr
N.A.I.C.S.: 336390

DIS Draxlmaier Industrial Solutions GmbH (1)
Landshuter Str 100, Vilsbiburg, 84137, Germany
Tel.: (49) 8741 470
Web Site: http://www.draexlmaier.de
Emp.: 17,000
Automobile Component Distr
N.A.I.C.S.: 423120

DKS Draxlmaier Kunststoffsysteme GmbH (1)
Im Finigen 2, 28832, Achim, Germany (100%)
Tel.: (49) 42025190
Web Site: http://www.draexlmaier.de
Sales Range: $125-149.9 Million
Emp.: 260
Rubber & Plastics Hoses & Belting Mfr
N.A.I.C.S.: 326220

DRE Draxlmaier Elektrotek S.r.o. (1)
Kvasiny 145, 51702, Mlada Boleslav, Czech Republic
Tel.: (420) 494539911
Engine Equipment Mfr
N.A.I.C.S.: 333618

DRM Sisteme Electrice SRL (1)
Strada Vulturului 34, 440268, Satu-Mare, Romania (100%)
Tel.: (40) 361403100
Web Site: http://www.draexlmaier.de
Sales Range: $800-899.9 Million
Emp.: 7,000
Electronic Components Mfr
N.A.I.C.S.: 334419
Kotthoff Mark (Dir-Comml)

DSE Draxlmaier Systemy Elektryczne Sp. Z o.o. (1)
Ul Spoldzielcza 45, Jelenia Gora, 58500, Legnica, Poland
Tel.: (48) 757538824
Web Site: http://www.draexlmaier.de
Sales Range: $200-249.9 Million
Emp.: 600
Electronic Components Mfr
N.A.I.C.S.: 334419

DSV Draxlmaier Systemverkabelungen GmbH (1)
Dieselstrasse 14, 84056, Rottenburg an der Laaber, Germany (100%)
Tel.: (49) 87812080
Web Site: http://www.draexlmaier.de
Sales Range: $25-49.9 Million
Emp.: 24
Electronic Components Mfr

N.A.I.C.S.: 334419
Irngard Daffner (Office Mgr)

DTR Draxlmaier Sisteme Tehnice Romania S.R.L. (1)
Str Gradinarilor Nr 29, Codlea, 505100, Brasov, Romania
Tel.: (40) 268507200
Web Site: http://www.draexlmaier.de
Sales Range: $200-249.9 Million
Emp.: 700
Electronic Components Mfr
N.A.I.C.S.: 334419
Suranyi Marius (Pres)

DVS Draxlmaier Verdrahtungssysteme GmbH (1)
Otto-Lilienthal-Str 26, 71034, Boblingen, Germany (100%)
Tel.: (49) 703128600
Web Site: http://www.draexlmaier.de
Electronic Components Mfr
N.A.I.C.S.: 334419

Draexlmaier (Shenyang) Automotive Components Co., Ltd. (1)
Wen Guan Street No 6, Dadong District, 110045, Shenyang, China
Tel.: (86) 2484553888
Sales Range: $25-49.9 Million
Emp.: 25
Motor Vehicle Parts Mfr
N.A.I.C.S.: 336390

Draexlmaier Automotive Systems (Thailand) Co., Ltd. (1)
7-18 Moo 6 Amata City Industrial Estate, Tambol Mabyangporn Amphur Plua, Rayong, 1140, Thailand
Tel.: (66) 38956340
Web Site: http://www.draexlmaier.com
Sales Range: $25-49.9 Million
Emp.: 200
Motor Vehicle Parts Mfr
N.A.I.C.S.: 336390
Kiattisak Promsiri (Mng Dir)

Draexlmaier Automotive of America, LLC (1)
PO Box 1345, Duncan, SC 29334-1345
Tel.: (864) 433-8910
Web Site: http://www.draexlmaier-automotive.com
Sales Range: $125-149.9 Million
Emp.: 350
Mfr of Motor Vehicle Parts & Accessories
N.A.I.C.S.: 336390

EKB Elektro und Kunststofftechnik GmbH (1)
Industriezeile 1-3, Braunau, 5280, Austria
Tel.: (43) 77228830
Sales Range: $125-149.9 Million
Emp.: 450
Rubber & Plastics Hoses & Belting Mfr
N.A.I.C.S.: 326220
Gunter Sauerlachner (Gen Mgr)

Eldra Kunststofftechnik GmbH (1)
Wiesenweg 10, Landau, 94405, Hessen, Germany
Tel.: (49) 99516980
Web Site: http://www.draexlmaier.de
Sales Range: $125-149.9 Million
Emp.: 350
Plastics Product Mfr
N.A.I.C.S.: 326199
Edmund Eggensberger (Plant Mgr)

Holzindustrie Bruchsal GmbH (1)
Ernst Blickle Strasse 21 25, D 76646, Bruchsal, Germany (100%)
Tel.: (49) 72517220
Web Site: http://www.hibautomotive.com
Sales Range: $200-249.9 Million
Emp.: 600
Mfr & Assembly Company
N.A.I.C.S.: 336110

Lisa Draxlmaier Autopart Romania SRL (1)
Str N Balcescu Nr 186, Pitesti, 110101, Arges, Romania (100%)
Tel.: (40) 248201342
Sales Range: $800-899.9 Million
Emp.: 5,000
Automobile Mfr
N.A.I.C.S.: 336110

Lisa Draxlmaier GmbH (1)

Landshuter Strasse 100, 84137, Vilsbiburg,
Germany **(100%)**
Tel.: (49) 8741470
Web Site: http://www.draexlmaier.de
Sales Range: $400-449.9 Million
Emp.: 2,400
Electronic Components Mfr
N.A.I.C.S.: 334419

DRAFT INC.
MA5-6-19 Minamiaoyama, Minato,
Tokyo, 107-0062, Japan
Tel.: (81) 354121001
Web Site: https://www.draft.co.jp
Year Founded: 2008
5070—(TKS)
Rev.: $75,877,180
Assets: $52,926,850
Liabilities: $28,289,100
Net Worth: $24,637,750
Earnings: $3,658,440
Emp.: 206
Fiscal Year-end: 12/31/23
Construction Services
N.A.I.C.S.: 236210

**DRAGANFLY INVESTMENTS
LIMITED**
Forum 4 Grenville Street, PO Box
264, Saint Helier, JE4 8TQ, Jersey
Tel.: (44) 1534 753400   JE
Web Site:
   http://www.draganflyinvestment.com
Year Founded: 2005
Investment Management Service
N.A.I.C.S.: 523999
Dennis Vernon Edmonds *(Fin Dir)*

DRAGANFLY, INC.
2108 St George Avenue, Saskatoon,
S7M0K7, SK, Canada
Web Site: https://www.draganfly.com
DPRO—(NASDAQ)
Rev.: $5,949,286
Assets: $11,451,432
Liabilities: $2,814,371
Net Worth: $8,637,060
Earnings: ($21,633,456)
Emp.: 55
Fiscal Year-end: 12/31/22
Aircraft Mfr
N.A.I.C.S.: 336411
Cameron Chell *(Pres & CEO)*

**DRAGISA BRASOVAN TRUD-
BENIK A.D.**
Gospodara Vucica 223, Belgrade,
Serbia
Tel.: (381) 11 2415 155
Year Founded: 1998
Sales Range: Less than $1 Million
Engineering & Technical Consulting
Services
N.A.I.C.S.: 541690

DRAGO ENTERTAINMENT SA
ul Malborska 130, 30-624, Krakow,
Poland
Tel.: (48) 123462857
Web Site: https://www.drago-
   entertainment.com
Year Founded: 1998
65M—(DEU)
Software Development Services
N.A.I.C.S.: 541511
Joanna Tynor *(CEO)*

**DRAGON CROWN GROUP
HOLDINGS LIMITED**
Suite 1803 Convention Plaza Office
Tower 1 Harbour Road, Wanchai,
China (Hong Kong)
Tel.: (852) 25003888   Ky
Web Site:
   http://www.dragoncrown.com
935—(HKG)
Rev.: $30,716,329

Assets: $184,972,798
Liabilities: $31,238,956
Net Worth: $153,733,842
Earnings: $11,832,883
Emp.: 339
Fiscal Year-end: 12/31/20
Terminal Chemical Storage Services
N.A.I.C.S.: 424710
Wai Man Ng *(Founder, Chm & CEO)*

Subsidiaries:

Nanjing Dragon Crown Liquid Chemi-
cal Terminal Company Limited   **(1)**
No 101 Hao-Jia-Ba Xinli Village County of
Yudai, Nanjing Chemical Industry Park
Liuhe District, Nanjing, Jiangsu, China
Tel.: (86) 2557625695
Terminal Storage Services
N.A.I.C.S.: 424710
Qing Long Zou *(Gen Mgr)*

Ningbo Ningxiang Liquid Chemicals
Terminal Co., Ltd.   **(1)**
No 338 Hou Da Jie No 14 Dan Shui Jing
Tou Zhao Bao Shan Street, Zhen Yuan
Street Zhenhai, Ningbo, China
Tel.: (86) 57427695880
Terminal Storage Services
N.A.I.C.S.: 424710
Xiao Chu Xiang *(Gen Mgr)*

**DRAGON JADE INTERNA-
TIONAL LIMITED**
Unit 2 23/F New World Tower I 18
Queens Road, Central, China (Hong
Kong)
Tel.: (852) 3588 1780   VG
Web Site: http://www.dragonjade.com
Rev.: $923,158
Assets: $2,740,892
Liabilities: $1,338,725
Net Worth: $1,402,167
Earnings: ($5,468,758)
Emp.: 8
Fiscal Year-end: 03/31/19
Business Consulting Services
N.A.I.C.S.: 541611
Lok Bun Law *(Chm & Pres)*

**DRAGON KING GROUP HOLD-
INGS LIMITED**
Office A 20th Floor TG Place 10
Shing Yip Street, Kwun Tong, Kow-
loon, China (Hong Kong)
Tel.: (852) 29550668   Ky
Web Site:
   http://www.dragonkinggroup.com
Year Founded: 2004
Rev.: $51,661,911
Assets: $32,990,070
Liabilities: $30,653,393
Net Worth: $2,336,677
Earnings: ($4,555,088)
Emp.: 590
Fiscal Year-end: 12/31/19
Restaurant Management Services
N.A.I.C.S.: 722511
Angel Ching Nung Lee *(Chm)*

**DRAGON LEGEND ENTER-
TAINMENT (CANADA) INC.**
3467 Commercial Street, Vancouver,
V5N 4E8, BC, Canada
Tel.: (604) 668-5972   BC
Year Founded: 1990
Investment Services
N.A.I.C.S.: 523999
Simon Tam *(Pres)*

DRAGON MINING
Unit B1 431 Roberts Road, Subiaco,
6008, WA, Australia
Tel.: (61) 8 6311 8000
Web Site:
   http://www.dragonmining.com
Rev.: $32,210,822
Assets: $39,296,891
Liabilities: $14,821,505

Net Worth: $24,475,386
Earnings: ($455,026)
Emp.: 5
Fiscal Year-end: 12/31/17
Gold Mining
N.A.I.C.S.: 212220
Arthur George Dew *(Chm)*

Subsidiaries:

Dragon Mining (Sweden) AB   **(1)**
Pautrask 100, 923 98, Storuman, Lapland,
Sweden
Tel.: (46) 95115451
Gold Bullion Mining Services
N.A.I.C.S.: 212220

Polar Mining Oy   **(1)**
Kummunkuja 38, Vammala, 38200, Sasta-
mala, Finland
Tel.: (358) 403007800
Web Site: http://www.dragonmining.fi
Sales Range: $50-74.9 Million
Gold Mining & Exploration Services
N.A.I.C.S.: 212220

**DRAGON MOUNTAIN GOLD
LIMITED**
182 Claisebrook Road, Perth, 6000,
WA, Australia
Tel.: (61) 894260666
Web Site:
   https://www.dragonmountain.com.au
Rev.: $46,905
Assets: $2,049,665
Liabilities: $392,766
Net Worth: $1,656,899
Earnings: ($512,393)
Fiscal Year-end: 06/30/18
Gold Exploration Services
N.A.I.C.S.: 212220
Robert C. Gardner *(Chm)*

**DRAGON RISE GROUP HOLD-
INGS LIMITED**
Office K 12F Kings Wing Plaza 2 No
1 On Kwan Street, Shek Mun, Sha
Tin, New Territories, China (Hong
Kong)
Tel.: (852) 2 164 6888   Ky
Web Site: http://www.kitkee.com.hk
Year Founded: 1993
6829—(HKG)
Rev.: $119,034,094
Assets: $38,965,761
Liabilities: $6,988,007
Net Worth: $31,977,753
Earnings: ($2,593,788)
Emp.: 335
Fiscal Year-end: 03/31/21
Construction Work Services
N.A.I.C.S.: 238910
Yuk Kit Yip *(Founder, Chm & CEO)*

**DRAGON SWEATER & SPIN-
NING LIMITED**
25/2 D I T Road Malibagh Chow-
dhury Para, Dhaka, 1219, Bangla-
desh
Tel.: (880) 29331404
Web Site: https://www.dsslbd.com
DSSL—(CHT)
Rev.: $9,621,444
Assets: $38,740,676
Liabilities: $3,494,614
Net Worth: $35,246,062
Earnings: $1,028,299
Emp.: 1,779
Fiscal Year-end: 06/30/23
Sweater Mfr
N.A.I.C.S.: 315250
Mostafa Quamrus Sobhan *(Chm)*

**DRAGON UKRAINIAN PROP-
ERTIES & DEVELOPMENT
PLC**
2nd floor St Mary s Court 20 Hill

Street, Douglas, IM1 1EU, Isle of
Man
Tel.: (44) 1624 693062
Web Site: http://www.dragon-
   upd.com
Year Founded: 2007
DUPD—(LSE)
Sales Range: Less than $1 Million
Property Development Services
N.A.I.C.S.: 531390

Subsidiaries:

Bi Dolyna Development LLC   **(1)**
Bud 36d Vul Saksaganskogo, 1033, Kiev,
Ukraine
Tel.: (380) 444907120
Real Estate Property Development Services
N.A.I.C.S.: 531390

EF Nova Oselya LLC   **(1)**
Bud 36 D Vul Saksaganskogo, 1033, Kiev,
Ukraine
Tel.: (380) 444907120
Real Estate Development Services
N.A.I.C.S.: 531390

J Komfort Neruhomist LLC   **(1)**
Bud 36-D Vul Saksaganskogo, Kiev,
Ukraine
Tel.: (380) 444907120
Real Estate Manangement Services
N.A.I.C.S.: 531390

Korona Development LLC   **(1)**
Bud 36-D Vul Saksaganskogo, 01033, Kiev,
Ukraine
Tel.: (380) 444907120
Web Site: http://www.dragonhabitor.com
Emp.: 200
Real Estate Property Development Services
N.A.I.C.S.: 531390

Mountcrest LTD   **(1)**
3285 Hillcrest Rd, Medford, OR 97504
Tel.: (541) 608-3898
General Freight Trucking Services
N.A.I.C.S.: 484110

Rivnobud LLC   **(1)**
Bud 36 Lit D Vul Saksaganskogo, Kiev,
Ukraine
Tel.: (380) 444907120
Residential Property Management Services
N.A.I.C.S.: 531311

DRAGONFLY CAPITAL CORP.
120 Adelaide Street West Suite 1410,
Toronto, M5H 1T1, ON, Canada
Tel.: (647) 891-1721   BC
Year Founded: 2010
R96—(DEU)
Rev.: $110,475
Assets: $10,531,892
Liabilities: $86,257
Net Worth: $10,445,635
Earnings: ($4,594,680)
Emp.: 10
Fiscal Year-end: 12/31/23
Investment Services
N.A.I.C.S.: 523999
Anthony Kent Deuters *(CEO)*

DRAGONFLY GF CO., LTD.
80 Seochojungang-ro 22-gil, Seocho-
gu, Seoul, 6632, Korea (South)
Tel.: (82) 25229393
Web Site:
   https://www.dragonflygame.com
Year Founded: 1995
030350—(KRS)
Rev.: $5,443,248
Assets: $50,639,022
Liabilities: $7,681,861
Net Worth: $42,957,161
Earnings: ($11,067,521)
Emp.: 62
Fiscal Year-end: 12/31/22
Online Game Software Development
Services
N.A.I.C.S.: 513210
Chul-Wu Park *(CEO)*

Dragonfly GF Co., Ltd.—(Continued)

DRAGONTAIL SYSTEMS LIMITED
L2 707 Collins Street, Docklands, Melbourne, 3008, VIC, Australia
Tel.: (61) 390216862 **AU**
Web Site: http://www.dragontail.com
DTS—(ASX)
Rev.: $1,274,126
Assets: $1,428,911
Liabilities: $3,949,326
Net Worth: ($2,520,415)
Earnings: ($7,697,087)
Fiscal Year-end: 12/31/19
Software Development Services
N.A.I.C.S.: 541511
Ido Levanon (Mng Dir)

Subsidiaries:

Dragontail Systems Limited **(1)**
BSR1 Tower Ben Gurion 2, Ramat Gan, Israel
Tel.: (972) 37943362
Web Site: http://www.dragontail.co.il
Food Delivery Services
N.A.I.C.S.: 492210

Subsidiary (US):

DragonTail Systems USA Inc. **(2)**
306 E 78th St Ste 1B, New York, NY 10075
Tel.: (613) 818-1815
Food Delivery Services
N.A.I.C.S.: 492210

DRAHTWERK FRIEDR. LOTTERS GMBH & CO. KG
Hellestrasse 40, 58675, Hemer, Germany
Tel.: (49) 237286090
Web Site: http://www.loetters-draht.de
Year Founded: 1912
Rev.: $32,415,900
Emp.: 120
Silo Mfr
N.A.I.C.S.: 331420
Jurgen Beckmann (Mgr-Sls-Europe, Africa & GUS)

Subsidiaries:

Lotters & Miruna Arames Ltd. **(1)**
295 Jardim da Gloria, Cotia, 6711280, Sao Paulo, Brazil
Tel.: (55) 1146120844
Pipe Distr
N.A.I.C.S.: 423510

Lotters Polska Sp. z o.o. **(1)**
UL Krosnienska 10, 60-162, Poznan, Poland
Tel.: (48) 618685042
Pipe Distr
N.A.I.C.S.: 423510

DRAKE & MORGAN LIMITED
Suite 199 3rd Floor Temple Chambers Temple Avenue, London, EC4Y 0HP, United Kingdom
Tel.: (44) 207 583 3446
Web Site: http://www.drake-morgan.co.uk
Year Founded: 2008
Sales Range: $25-49.9 Million
Emp.: 400
Bar & Restaurant Operator
N.A.I.C.S.: 722410
Jillian MacLean (Founder)

Subsidiaries:

Corney & Barrow Limited **(1)**
1 Thomas More Street, London, E1W 1YZ, United Kingdom
Tel.: (44) 20 7265 2400
Web Site: http://www.corneyandbarrow.com
Wine Whslr
N.A.I.C.S.: 424820
Adam Brett-Smith (Mng Dir)

DRAKE & SCULL INTERNATIONAL PJSC
Office 205 Street 4, PO Box 65794, Al Quoz, Dubai, United Arab Emirates
Tel.: (971) 45283444
Web Site: https://www.drakescull.com
Year Founded: 1966
Rev.: $185,509,482
Assets: $172,118,655
Liabilities: $1,257,663,825
Net Worth: ($1,085,545,170)
Earnings: $71,368,290
Emp.: 15,000
Fiscal Year-end: 12/31/19
Mechanical, Electrical, Plumbing, Infrastructure, Water, Power & Civil Contracting Services
N.A.I.C.S.: 238210
Ahmed Saeed Al-Hamiri (Vice Chm)

Subsidiaries:

Drake & Scull International L.L.C **(1)**
Airport Road Opposite Abu Dhabi Chamber of comm, PO Box 44325, Abu Dhabi, 44325, United Arab Emirates
Tel.: (971) 26226005
Sales Range: $800-899.9 Million
Emp.: 5,000
Electrical & Mechanical Engineering Services
N.A.I.C.S.: 335999

Gulf Technical Construction Company L.L.C **(1)**
Electra St, PO Box 66123, Abu Dhabi, United Arab Emirates
Tel.: (971) 48112300
Web Site: http://www.gulftcc.com
Sales Range: $25-49.9 Million
Emp.: 80
Civil Engineering Services
N.A.I.C.S.: 541330

Passavant Energy & Environment GmbH **(1)**
Hahnstrasse 31-35, 60528, Frankfurt, Germany
Tel.: (49) 69 947 4150
Web Site: https://www.passavant-ee.com
Waste Treatment Services
N.A.I.C.S.: 221310
Mokhtar Haddad (CEO)

Passavant-Roediger GmbH **(1)**
Hahnstrase 31-35, 60528, Frankfurt, Germany **(100%)**
Tel.: (49) 69 94 74 15 0
Web Site: http://www.passavant-roediger.de
Sales Range: $75-99.9 Million
Emp.: 125
Water & Sewage Plant Construction & Engineering Services
N.A.I.C.S.: 237110

DRAKE NEW ZEALAND LTD.
Level 3 79 Queen Street Auckland Central, Auckland, 1010, New Zealand
Tel.: (64) 9 379 5610
Web Site: http://www.nz.drakeintl.com
Staffing Solutions
N.A.I.C.S.: 561311
Gay Barton (Gen Mgr)

Subsidiaries:

BOSS Group Ltd. **(1)**
86 Ford Road, PO Box 1010, Napier, 4140, New Zealand
Tel.: (64) 6 834 3071
Staffing Solutions
N.A.I.C.S.: 561311

Drake Australia Pty Ltd **(1)**
Level 40 55 collins Street, Melbourne, 3000, VIC, Australia
Tel.: (61) 392450245
Web Site: http://www.au.drakeintl.com
Employee Recruitment Services
N.A.I.C.S.: 561311
Ron Urwin (Chm)

DRAKE RESOURCES LIMITED

283 Rokeby Road, Subiaco, 6008, WA, Australia
Tel.: (61) 8 6141 3500
Web Site: http://www.drakeresources.com.au
Sales Range: Less than $1 Million
Emp.: 4
Mining Services
N.A.I.C.S.: 213114
Jay Stephenson (Sec)

DRAKKAR & ASSOCIES INC.
780 Brewster Ave Suite 03-200, Montreal, H1C 2K1, QC, Canada
Tel.: (514) 733-6655
Web Site: http://www.drakkarcorpo.ca
Rev.: $32,500,000
Emp.: 2,500
Employment & Consulting Agencies
N.A.I.C.S.: 561311

Subsidiaries:

Drakkar MAK Inc. **(1)**
108 Montagnais Blvd, Uashat, G4R 5P9, QC, Canada
Tel.: (418) 962-6075
Employee Placement Services
N.A.I.C.S.: 561311

DRALON GMBH
Alte Heerstrasse 2 Chempark, Dormagen, 41540, Germany
Tel.: (49) 213377863630
Web Site: http://www.dralon.com
Year Founded: 1954
Acrylic Fiber Mfr
N.A.I.C.S.: 325220
Stefan Braun (CEO & Mng Dir)

Subsidiaries:

Dolan GmbH **(1)**
Regensburger Str 109, 93309, Kelheim, Germany
Tel.: (49) 9441990
Web Site: http://www.dolan-gmbh.de
Outdoor & Industrial Acrylic Fiber Mfr
N.A.I.C.S.: 325220
Sylvia Ebel (Mgr-Sls Dept)

DRANCO CONSTRUCTION LIMITED
1919 Albion Road, Etobicoke, M9W 6J9, ON, Canada
Tel.: (416) 675-2682
Web Site: http://www.dranco.com
Year Founded: 1956
Rev.: $24,143,647
Emp.: 200
Sewer & Water Main Construction Services
N.A.I.C.S.: 237110
Realdo Di Donato (Pres)

DRAW DISTANCE S.A.
Cystersow 20A, 31-553, Krakow, Poland
Tel.: (48) 123461141
Web Site: https://www.drawdistance.dev
Year Founded: 2009
IF4—(STU)
Sales Range: Less than $1 Million
Software Development Services
N.A.I.C.S.: 541511
Michal Mielcarek (CEO)

DRAX GROUP PLC
Drax Power Station, Selby, YO8 8PH, N Yorkshire, United Kingdom
Tel.: (44) 1757618381 **UK**
Web Site: https://www.drax.com
Year Founded: 2006
DRXGY—(OTCIQ)
Rev.: $6,908,079,360
Assets: $7,907,904,368
Liabilities: $6,133,635,872
Net Worth: $1,774,268,496
Earnings: $107,531,424

Emp.: 3,122
Fiscal Year-end: 12/31/21
Power Plant Operator
N.A.I.C.S.: 221112
Mark Strafford (Head-Investor Relations)

Subsidiaries:

Abergelli Power Limited **(1)**
Drax Power Station, Selby, YO8 8PH, North Yorkshire, United Kingdom
Tel.: (44) 1757618381
Web Site: http://www.abergellipower.co.uk
Power Generation Services
N.A.I.C.S.: 221118

Amite BioEnergy LLC **(1)**
850 New Burton Rd Ste 201, Dover, DE 19904
Tel.: (617) 588-2902
Biomass Fuel Generation Services
N.A.I.C.S.: 221112

Drax Biomass International Inc. **(1)**
1 Burlington Woods Dr, Burlington, MA 01803
Tel.: (617) 588-2900
Web Site: http://www.draxbiomass.com
Holding Company
N.A.I.C.S.: 551112

Drax Power Limited **(1)**
Drax Power Station, PO Box 3, Selby, YO8 8PH, North Yorkshire, United Kingdom
Tel.: (44) 1757618381
Web Site: https://www.drax.com
Power Plant Operating Services
N.A.I.C.S.: 221112
Dorothy Carrington Thompson (Exec Dir)

Haven Power Limited **(1)**
Ransomes Europark, Ipswich, IP3 9SJ, United Kingdom
Tel.: (44) 473852932
Web Site: http://www.havenpower.com
Emp.: 350
Power Generation Services
N.A.I.C.S.: 221118
Paul Sheffield (COO)

Millbrook Power Limited **(1)**
Drax Power Station, Selby, YO8 8PH, North Yorkshire, United Kingdom
Tel.: (44) 1757618381
Web Site: http://www.millbrookpower.co.uk
Power Generation Services
N.A.I.C.S.: 221118

Pinnacle Renewable Energy, Inc. **(1)**
350 - 3600 Lysander Lane, Richmond, V7B 1C3, BC, Canada
Tel.: (604) 270-9613
Web Site: http://www.pinnaclepellet.com
Rev.: $289,113,794
Assets: $482,033,094
Liabilities: $322,314,497
Net Worth: $159,718,597
Earnings: ($7,632,504)
Fiscal Year-end: 12/27/2019
Industrial Wood Pellet Mfr & Distr
N.A.I.C.S.: 321999

DRAYTEK CORPORATION
No 26 Fu Shin Rd Hsin-Chu Industrial Park, Hsin-chu, 30352, Taiwan
Tel.: (886) 35972727
Web Site: http://www.draytek.com
6216—(TAI)
Rev.: $25,353,510
Assets: $61,217,990
Liabilities: $5,629,877
Net Worth: $55,588,114
Earnings: $4,021,322
Fiscal Year-end: 12/31/23
Communication Equipment Mfr
N.A.I.C.S.: 334210
Calvin Ma (Founder & Chm)

Subsidiaries:

DrayTek GmbH **(1)**
Zeppelinstr 3, 12529, Schonefeld, Germany
Tel.: (49) 30780009432
Web Site: http://www.draytek.de
Networking Components Distr
N.A.I.C.S.: 423690

DRAYTON VALLEY FORD SALES LTD
5214 Power Centre Blvd, PO Box 6389, Drayton Valley, T7A 1R8, AB, Canada
Tel.: (780) 542-4438
Web Site:
https://www.draytonvalleyford.com
Rev.: $20,952,086
Emp.: 44
New & Used Car Dealers
N.A.I.C.S.: 441110
Darren Gagnon *(CEO)*

DRB HOLDING CO., LTD.
28 Gongdandong-ro 55 beon-gil, Geumjeong-gu, Busan, Korea (South)
Tel.: (82) 515209000
Web Site: http://www.drbworld.com
Year Founded: 1945
004840—(KRS)
Rev.: $507,611,351
Assets: $724,997,925
Liabilities: $357,015,344
Net Worth: $367,982,581
Earnings: $1,177,115
Emp.: 81
Fiscal Year-end: 12/31/22
Holding Company
N.A.I.C.S.: 551112
Lee Sangil *(Dir)*

Subsidiaries:

DRB Industrial Co., Ltd. **(1)**
28 Gongdandong-ro 55beon-gil, Geumjeong-gu, Busan, Korea (South)
Tel.: (82) 515209114
Web Site: http://www.drbworld.com
Rev.: $299,467,365
Assets: $292,402,184
Liabilities: $125,193,287
Net Worth: $167,208,897
Earnings: $5,978,137
Emp.: 574
Fiscal Year-end: 12/31/2022
Industrial Rubber Product Mfr
N.A.I.C.S.: 326220
Yun Hwan Lee *(CEO)*

Dongil Rubber Belt America, Inc. **(1)**
16811 Knott Ave, La Mirada, CA 90638
Tel.: (714) 739-2922
Rubber Belt Mfr & Distr
N.A.I.C.S.: 326220

Dongil Rubber Belt Japan Co., Ltd. **(1)**
7F CR Hakata Bldg 1-8-6 Hakataeki-minami, Hakata-ku, Fukuoka, 812-0016, Japan
Tel.: (81) 92481730
Rubber Belt Mfr & Distr
N.A.I.C.S.: 326220

Dongil Rubber Belt Slovakia, s.r.o. **(1)**
Robotnicka 2198, 017 01, Povazska Bystrica, Slovakia
Tel.: (421) 424450400
Rubber Belt Mfr & Distr
N.A.I.C.S.: 326220

Dongil Rubber Belt Vietnam Co., Ltd. **(1)**
F-1-CN & F-7-CN, My Phuoc 2 Industrial Park, Ben Cat, Binh Duong, Vietnam
Tel.: (84) 2743556070
Rubber Belt Mfr & Distr
N.A.I.C.S.: 326220

PT. Dongil Rubber Belt Indonesia **(1)**
Wisma Korindo Lt 5 Jl MT Haryono Kav 62, Pancoran, Jakarta, 12780, Indonesia
Tel.: (62) 217976232
Rubber Belt Mfr & Distr
N.A.I.C.S.: 326220

Shanghai Dongil Rubber Belt Co., Ltd. **(1)**
Room 806 Laiyin Hongjing Center Block A Wuzhong Rd, Minhang District, Shanghai, 201101, China
Tel.: (86) 2154225691

Rubber Belt Mfr & Distr
N.A.I.C.S.: 326220

DRB-HICOM BERHAD
Level 5 Wisma DRB-HICOM No 2 Jalan Usahawan U1/8 Section U1, 40150, Shah Alam, Selangor Darul Ehsan, Malaysia
Tel.: (60) 320528000　　　　**MY**
Web Site: https://www.drb-hicom.com
1619—(KLS)
Rev.: $3,282,966,349
Assets: $10,897,182,646
Liabilities: $8,846,727,407
Net Worth: $2,050,455,238
Earnings: $61,613,333
Emp.: 45,000
Fiscal Year-end: 12/31/22
Real Estate, Infrastructure & Defense Services & Automotive Mfr & Distr
N.A.I.C.S.: 336110
Amalanathan Thomas *(Dir-Fin Svcs)*

Subsidiaries:

Bank Muamalat Malaysia Berhad **(1)**
Menara Bumiputra 21 Jalan Melaka, 50100, Kuala Lumpur, Malaysia
Tel.: (60) 326005500
Web Site: http://www.muamalat.com.my
Commercial Banking Services
N.A.I.C.S.: 522110
Tajuddin Atan *(Chm)*

CTRM Aero Composites Sdn. Bhd. **(1)**
Composites Technology City, Batu Berendam, 75350, Melaka, Malaysia
Tel.: (60) 63171007
Aerospace Parts & Component Mfr
N.A.I.C.S.: 336413
Nor Azham Baharin *(COO)*

CTRM Composites Engineering Sdn. Bhd. **(1)**
Composites Technology City, Batu Berendam, 75350, Melaka, Malaysia
Tel.: (60) 63174105
Aerospace Parts & Component Mfr
N.A.I.C.S.: 336413

CTRM Testing Laboratory Sdn. Bhd. **(1)**
CTRM Complex, Batu Berendam, 75350, Melaka, Malaysia
Tel.: (60) 63171007
Web Site: http://www.ctrmtl.com
Laboratory Testing Services
N.A.I.C.S.: 541380
Mohd Azizi *(Head-Technical Testing)*

DEFTECH Systems Integration Sdn. Bhd. **(1)**
No 30 Jalan 15/22 Seksyen 15, Taman Perindustrian Tiong Nam, 40200, Shah Alam, Selangor, Malaysia
Tel.: (60) 355238900
Web Site: http://www.csysint.com
Electronic Device Repair Services
N.A.I.C.S.: 811210

DEFTECH Unmanned Systems Sdn. Bhd. **(1)**
Lot-26 Jalan Pengapit 15/19 Section 15, 40200, Shah Alam, Selangor, Malaysia
Tel.: (60) 355228877
Web Site: http://www.deftechust.com
UAV Inspection & Monitoring Services
N.A.I.C.S.: 811198
Pahlawan Zulkifli Mansor *(COO)*

DRB-HICOM Commercial Vehicles Sdn. Bhd. **(1)**
Lot 17498 and 17521, Kawasan Perindustrian Selayang Baru, 68100, Batu Caves, Selangor, Malaysia
Tel.: (60) 361202334
Web Site: http://www.tatamotors.com.my
Automobile Mfr & Distr
N.A.I.C.S.: 336110
Suresh Rangarajan *(Head-Corp Comm)*

DRB-HICOM EZ-Drive Sdn. Bhd. **(1)**
Level 2 EON Head Office Complex No 2 Persiaran Kerjaya Section U1, Glemarie Industrial Park, 40150, Shah Alam, Selangor, Malaysia

Tel.: (60) 378037555
Web Site: http://www.avis.com.my
Car Rental & Leasing Services
N.A.I.C.S.: 532111

Glenmarie Properties Sdn. Bhd. **(1)**
Level 1 Wisma DRB-HICOM No 2 Jalan Usahawan U1/8 Seksyen U1, 40150, Shah Alam, Selangor, Malaysia
Tel.: (60) 320528500
Web Site:
　http://www.glenmarieproperties.com
Property Development Services
N.A.I.C.S.: 531390

HICOM Diecastings Sdn. Bhd. **(1)**
Lot 16 Jalan Sementa 27/91 Section 27, 40000, Shah Alam, Selangor, Malaysia
Tel.: (60) 351018000
Web Site: http://www.hdsb.com.my
Aluminum Die Casting Product Mfr & Distr
N.A.I.C.S.: 331523
Faisal Albar *(Chm)*

HICOM Holdings Bhd **(1)**
2 Jalan Usahawan Wisma DRB-HICOM, Shah Alam, 40150, Selangor, Malaysia
Tel.: (60) 320528156
Web Site: http://www.drb-hicom.com
Sales Range: $1-4.9 Billion
Emp.: 200
Holding Company
N.A.I.C.S.: 551112
Mohd Khamil Jamil *(Chm)*

Holding (Domestic):

Auto Prominence (M) Sdn Bhd **(2)**
Wisma Keringat 2, Lorong Batu Caves 2, Batu Caves, 68100, Selangor, Malaysia
Tel.: (60) 36189 4414
Automobile Dealers
N.A.I.C.S.: 423110

Automotive Corporation (Malaysia) Sdn Bhd **(2)**
Lot 3 Jalan Perusahaan Dua Kawasan Perindustrian Batu Caves, 68100, Batu Caves, Selangor, Malaysia
Tel.: (60) 36 188 1133
Web Site: https://www.acm.com.my
Emp.: 60
Motor Vehicles Mfr
N.A.I.C.S.: 336110
Chin Tanhee *(COO)*

Composites Technology Research Malaysia Sdn. Bhd. **(2)**
Level 2 EON Complex Persiaran Kerjaya Seksyen U1, 40150, Shah Alam, Selangor, Malaysia
Tel.: (60) 37 880 0256
Web Site: https://www.ctrm.com.my
Emp.: 3,000
Aerospace & Commercial Composite Components Mfr
N.A.I.C.S.: 326199
Shamsuddin Mohamed Yusof *(CEO)*

DRB-HICOM Auto Solutions Sdn Bhd **(2)**
No 2 Jalan Usahawan U1/8 Seksyen U1, Shah Alam, 40150, Selangor, Malaysia
Tel.: (60) 320528218
Web Site: http://www.drb-hicom.com.my
Sales Range: $25-49.9 Million
Emp.: 68
Motor Vehicle Business Support Services
N.A.I.C.S.: 561499
Inham Helmi *(COO)*

Edaran Otomobil Nasional Berhad **(2)**
EON Head Office Complex, 2 Persiaran Kerjaya Seksy, Shah Alam, 40150, Selangor Darul Ehsan, Malaysia
Tel.: (60) 377112211
Sales Range: $600-649.9 Million
Emp.: 90
Motor Vehicle Distr
N.A.I.C.S.: 441227
Marzuki Bin Mohd Noor *(Chm)*

Subsidiary (Domestic):

Euromobil Sdn Bhd **(3)**
Audi Centre Glenmarie 4S Centre 27 Jalan Pelukis U1 /46, Temasya Industrial Park, 40150, Shah Alam, Selangor, Malaysia
Tel.: (60) 376887688

Web Site: https://euromobil.my
Sales Range: $25-49.9 Million
Emp.: 52
Used Car Dealers
N.A.I.C.S.: 441120
Godfrey Fernandez *(Head-After Sls)*

Holding (Domestic):

Euro Truck & Bus (Malaysia) Sdn Bhd **(2)**
KM 6 Jalan Ipoh, Gurun, 08300, Malaysia
Tel.: (60) 44667000
Motor Vehicle Mfr & Distr
N.A.I.C.S.: 336110

HICOM Automotive Manufacturers (Malaysia) Sdn Bhd **(2)**
DRB-Hicom Pekan Automotive Complex, PO Box 7, Peramu Jaya Industrial Area, 26607, Pekan, Pahang Darul Makmur, Malaysia
Tel.: (60) 9 424 4000
Web Site: https://www.hicom-automotive.com.my
Sales Range: $350-399.9 Million
Emp.: 1,500
Motor Vehicle Assembly Facilities & Testing Equipment Services
N.A.I.C.S.: 336110
Shamsuddin Mohammad Yousuf *(CEO)*

Isuzu Service Center Sdn. Bhd. **(1)**
Lot 730 Jalan Sg Rasa Section 17, 40000, Shah Alam, Selangor, Malaysia
Tel.: (60) 355130518
Automotive Vehicle Parts Mfr
N.A.I.C.S.: 336390

Konsortium Logistik Berhad **(1)**
Lot 22202 Jalan Gambus 33/4, Off Jalan Bukit Kemuning Bt 8 5, 40350, Shah Alam, Malaysia **(61.6%)**
Tel.: (60) 351219988
Web Site: http://www.klb.my
Sales Range: $75-99.9 Million
Freight Transportation Logistics Services
N.A.I.C.S.: 541611
Mohd Khamil Jamil *(Chm)*

Subsidiary (Domestic):

Aman Freight (Malaysia) Sdn. Bhd. **(2)**
Lot 6 Jalan Sltn Mhmd 3 Kawasan Perindustrian Selat Klang Utara, Bdr Sltn Sulaiman Darul Ehsan, 42000, Port Klang, Selangor, Malaysia
Tel.: (60) 331769822
Freight Transportation Arrangement Services
N.A.I.C.S.: 488510

Asia Pacific Freight System Sdn. Bhd. **(2)**
Lot D 20 Malaysia Airline Freight Forwarders Complex, KLIA Free Comml Zone, 64000, Sepang, Selangor, Malaysia
Tel.: (60) 387873099
Sales Range: $25-49.9 Million
Emp.: 9
Freight Transportation Arrangement Services
N.A.I.C.S.: 488510

Cougar Logistics (Malaysia) Sdn. Bhd. **(2)**
Locked Bag No 246 Lot 16 Lebuh Sultan Muhamed 1, Kaw Perusahaan Bdr, 42000, Port Klang, Selangor, Malaysia
Tel.: (60) 331761995
Sales Range: $25-49.9 Million
Emp.: 25
Freight Transportation Arrangement Services
N.A.I.C.S.: 488510

Malaysian Shipping Agencies Sdn. Bhd. **(2)**
12th Floor Unit No 13/006 Casa Mila Tower Bukit Idaman Batu Caves, Puchong, 68100, Selangor, Malaysia
Tel.: (60) 63346548
Web Site: http://www.klb.my
Freight Transportation Arrangement Services
N.A.I.C.S.: 488510
Chiang Cheng Guan *(Gen Mgr-Logistics Distr & Warehousing)*

DRB-HICOM Berhad—(Continued)

Westport Distripark (M) Sdn. Bhd. (2)
Pulau Indah, PO Box 286, Port Klang, 42009, Selangor, Malaysia
Tel.: (60) 331011818
Sales Range: $10-24.9 Million
Emp.: 31
Private Warehousing Services
N.A.I.C.S.: 493190

Motosikal Dan Enjin Nasional Sdn. Bhd. (1)
Kawasan Perindustrian Gurun, 08300, Gurun, Kedah, Malaysia
Tel.: (60) 44668000
Web Site: http://www.modenas.my
Motorcycle Parts Mfr
N.A.I.C.S.: 336991

Muamalat Invest Sdn. Bhd. (1)
4th Floor Menara Bumiputra Jalan Melaka, 50100, Kuala Lumpur, Malaysia
Tel.: (60) 326158400
Fund Management Services
N.A.I.C.S.: 523920
Mohd Faruk Abdul Karim (CEO, Head-Investment & Exec Dir)

PHN Industry Sdn. Bhd. (1)
Lot PT 75-77 Jalan 26/6 Seksyen 26 Peti Surat 7306, Kawasan Perindustrian HICOM, 40710, Shah Alam, Selangor, Malaysia
Tel.: (60) 351914636
Web Site: http://www.phn.com.my
Emp.: 2,000
Automotive Component Mfr & Distr
N.A.I.C.S.: 336390

POS Aviation Sdn. Bhd. (1)
Tingkat 8 Ibu Pejabat Pos Kompleks Dayabumi, 50670, Kuala Lumpur, Malaysia
Tel.: (60) 322672040
Web Site: http://www.posaviation.com.my
Aviation Ground Services
N.A.I.C.S.: 488119
Mohamad Asif Abd Talib (CEO)

POS Digicert Sdn. Bhd. (1)
8-3A-02 Star Central Lingkaran Cyberpoint Timur, 63000, Cyberjaya, Selangor Darul Ehsan, Malaysia
Tel.: (60) 388006000
Web Site: https://www.posdigicert.com.my
Electronic Identity & Security Services
N.A.I.C.S.: 541990
Md Najib Md Noor (CEO)

PROTON Holdings Berhad (1)
HICOM Industrial Estate Batu Tiga, 40000, Shah Alam, Selangor Darul Ehsan, Malaysia (50.1%)
Tel.: (60) 351911055
Web Site: http://www.proton.com
Sales Range: $1-4.9 Billion
Emp.: 12,000
Holding Company; Automotive Engineering, Assembly & Trading
N.A.I.C.S.: 551112
Andreas Prinz (COO-Comml)

Subsidiary (Domestic):

PROTON Edar Sdn. Bhd. (2)
Centre of Excellence Complex KM 33 8 Westbound Shah Alam Expressway, 47600, Subang Jaya, Selangor Darul Ehsan, Malaysia
Tel.: (60) 380269999
Web Site: http://www.proton-edar.com.my
New Car Dealers
N.A.I.C.S.: 441110
Abdul Rashid Musa (CEO)

Subsidiary (Non-US):

PT Proton Edar Indonesia (2)
Jalan Raya Pekayon Jaya No 27B Pekayon Jakasetia-Bekasi, Selatan, Bekasi, 17147, Jawa Barat, Indonesia
Tel.: (62) 217392268
Web Site: http://www.proton-edar.co.id
New Car Dealers
N.A.I.C.S.: 441110

Subsidiary (Domestic):

Perusahaan Otomobil Nasional Sdn. Bhd. (2)

HICOM Industrial Estate, Batu Tiga, 40000, Shah Alam, Selangor, Malaysia
Tel.: (60) 351911055
Web Site: http://www.protonr.com
Sales Range: $1-4.9 Billion
Emp.: 7,000
Motor Vehicles Mfr
N.A.I.C.S.: 336320
Zainal Abidin Ahmad (Pres & CEO)

Subsidiary (Non-US):

Proton Cars (UK) Ltd (2)
1-3 Crowley Wy, Avonmouth, BS11 9YR, Bristol, United Kingdom
Tel.: (44) 80078010777
Web Site: http://www.proton.co.uk
Automotive Distr
N.A.I.C.S.: 441110

Proton Cars Australia Pty Limited (2)
Unit 1/25-33 Alfred Road, Chipping Norton, 2170, NSW, Australia
Tel.: (61) 28 707 2707
Web Site: https://www.proton.com.au
Sales Range: $25-49.9 Million
Emp.: 18
New Car Dealers
N.A.I.C.S.: 441110

Proton Motors (Thailand) Limited (2)
4 Soi 2 Seri 7 Srinakarintara Road, Suan Luang, Bangkok, 10250, Thailand
Tel.: (66) 25611020
Motor Vehicle Distr
N.A.I.C.S.: 423110

Subsidiary (Domestic):

Proton Parts Centre Sdn Bhd (2)
No 1 Jalan Arkitek U1/22 Seksyen U1, PO Box 7400, Hicom Glenmarie Industrial Park, 40150, Shah Alam, Selangor, Malaysia
Tel.: (60) 378095555
Web Site: http://www.protonparts.com.my
Motor Vehicle Supplies & New Parts Whslr
N.A.I.C.S.: 423120

Subsidiary (Non-US):

Proton Singapore Pte Ltd (2)
2 Kung Chong Road, Singapore, 159140, Singapore
Tel.: (65) 68970500
Web Site: http://www.proton.com.sg
Sales Range: $25-49.9 Million
Emp.: 25
New Car Dealers
N.A.I.C.S.: 441110

Subsidiary (Domestic):

Proton Tanjung Malim Sdn. Bhd. (2)
Mukim Hulu Bernam Timur Daerah Batang Padang, Behrang Stesen, 35950, Tanjung Malim, Perak, Malaysia
Tel.: (60) 54578888
New Car Dealers
N.A.I.C.S.: 441110
Sukri Hamidi (Gen Mgr)

PUSPAKOM Sdn. Bhd. (1)
Level 3 Wisma DRB-HICOM No 2 Jalan Usahawan U1/8 Seksyen U1, 40150, Shah Alam, Selangor, Malaysia
Tel.: (60) 320527424
Web Site: http://www.puspakom.com.my
Vehicle Inspection Services
N.A.I.C.S.: 811198
Mohammed Shukor Ismail (CEO)

Pos Logistics Berhad (1)
Lot 22202 Jalan Gambus 33/4 Off Jalan Bukit Kemuning Bt 8 5, 40350, Shah Alam, Selangor, Malaysia
Tel.: (60) 351219988
Web Site: http://www.poslogistics.com.my
Emp.: 1,600
Air Freight Services
N.A.I.C.S.: 488510
Akhma Ismail (CEO)

Proton City Development Corporation Sdn. Bhd. (1)
No 1 Jalan Kempas 3A Warisan Avenue Parcel 19, Proton city, 35900, Tanjung Malim, Perak Darul Ridzuan, Malaysia
Tel.: (60) 54595858
Web Site: http://www.proton-city.com
Real Estate Development Services
N.A.I.C.S.: 531390

DRDGOLD LIMITED
Constantia Office Park Cnr 14th Avenue Hendrik Potgieter Road, Cycad House Building 17 Ground Floor Weltevred Park, Johannesburg, 1709, South Africa
Tel.: (27) 114702600   ZA
Web Site: https://www.drdgold.com
Year Founded: 1895
DRD—(NYSE)
Rev.: $346,574,902
Assets: $524,908,481
Liabilities: $142,246,955
Net Worth: $382,661,527
Earnings: $73,800,675
Emp.: 2,956
Fiscal Year-end: 06/30/24
Gold Mining & Refining
N.A.I.C.S.: 212220
Adriaan Jacobus Davel (CFO)

DREADNOUGHT RESOURCES LTD.
Unit 1 4 Burgay Court, Osborne Park, 6017, WA, Australia
Tel.: (61) 894738345   AU
Web Site: https://www.dreadnought.com.au
Year Founded: 2006
DRE—(ASX)
Rev.: $162,118
Assets: $35,657,083
Liabilities: $909,801
Net Worth: $34,747,282
Earnings: ($4,219,673)
Emp.: 18
Fiscal Year-end: 06/30/24
Gold Exploration Services
N.A.I.C.S.: 212220
Kaitlin Louise Smith (Sec)

DREAM IMPACT TRUST
30 Adelaide Street East Suite 301, Toronto, M5C 3H1, ON, Canada
Tel.: (416) 365-3535
Web Site: https://www.dream.ca
Year Founded: 2014
DDHRF—(OTCIQ)
Rev.: $25,009,492
Assets: $507,319,532
Liabilities: $84,984,552
Net Worth: $422,334,980
Earnings: $12,781,673
Fiscal Year-end: 12/31/20
Asset Management Services
N.A.I.C.S.: 523940
Amar Bhalla (Chm)

DREAM INCUBATOR INC.
Tokyo Club Building 4F 3-2-6 Kasumigaseki, Chiyoda-ku, Tokyo, 100-0013, Japan
Tel.: (81) 355323200
Web Site: https://www.dreamincubator.co.jp
Year Founded: 2000
4310—(TKS)
Rev.: $35,548,580
Assets: $115,370,940
Liabilities: $14,846,060
Net Worth: $100,524,880
Earnings: ($12,208,670)
Emp.: 227
Fiscal Year-end: 03/31/24
Investment, Incubation & Consulting Services
N.A.I.C.S.: 523999
Koichi Hori (Founder)

Subsidiaries:

DI Asia Inc. (1)
3 Chome-2-6 Kasumigaseki, Chiyoda, Tokyo, 100-0013, Japan
Tel.: (81) 344056431
Web Site: http://www.dreamincubator.asia
Digital Marketing Services
N.A.I.C.S.: 541910

Hideyuki Kato (Pres & CEO)

Dream Incubator (Vietnam) Joint Stock Company (1)
L7-11 7th Floor Vincom Center 72 Le Thanh Ton St, Dist 1, Ho Chi Minh City, 70000, Vietnam
Tel.: (84) 283 827 8450
Strategic Consulting Services
N.A.I.C.S.: 541613
Nguyen Doan Duc Anh (Mng Dir)

Ipet Insurance Co., Ltd. (1)
MFPR Roppongi Azabudai Building 1-8-7 Roppongi, Minato-ku, Tokyo, 106-0032, Japan
Tel.: (81) 355748610
Web Site: http://www.ipet-ins.com
Emp.: 378
Insurance Services
N.A.I.C.S.: 524128
Tetsuhei Yamamura (Pres)

DREAM INTERNATIONAL LTD
6/F Tower 1 South Seas Centre 75 Mody Road, Tsim Sha Tsui, Kowloon, China (Hong Kong)
Tel.: (852) 23756811
Web Site: https://www.dream-i.com.hk
1126—(HKG)
Rev.: $797,241,435
Assets: $559,045,043
Liabilities: $150,345,450
Net Worth: $408,699,593
Earnings: $87,604,740
Emp.: 28,924
Fiscal Year-end: 12/31/22
Toy Producer
N.A.I.C.S.: 339930
Kyoo Yoon Choi (Founder, Chm & CEO)

Subsidiaries:

C & H Mekong Company Limited (1)
Uyen Hung, Tan Uyen Town, Binh Dong, Vietnam
Tel.: (84) 2743641386
Web Site: https://www.cnhvina.com
Tarpaulin Mfr
N.A.I.C.S.: 314910

C & H Tarps Co., Ltd. (1)
Thai Hoa Ward, Tan Uyen, Binh Duong, Vietnam
Tel.: (84) 2743658805
Tarpaulin Mfr
N.A.I.C.S.: 314910

C & H Vina Joint Stock Company (1)
Uyen Hung Ward, Tan Uyen, Binh Duong, Vietnam
Tel.: (84) 2743641386
Tarpaulin Mfr
N.A.I.C.S.: 314910

C&H Toys (Suzhou) Co , Ltd (1)
Cross Liutai Road, Banmao Road Ban Qiao District, Suzhou, Jiangsu, China
Tel.: (86) 51253586555
Doll & Stuffed Toy Mfr
N.A.I.C.S.: 339930

Dream Inko Co., Ltd. (1)
35 Teheran-ro 87-gil, Seoul, 135-879, Korea (South)
Tel.: (82) 7070135406
Toy & Game Mfr
N.A.I.C.S.: 339930

Dream International USA, Inc (1)
7001 Village Dr Ste 280, Buena Park, CA 90621
Tel.: (714) 521-6007
Web Site: https://dream-i.com.hk
Sales Range: $25-49.9 Million
Emp.: 15
Doll & Stuffed Toy Mfg
N.A.I.C.S.: 339930

Dream VINA Co., Ltd. (1)
Uyen Hung Ward, Tan Uyen, Binh Doung, Vietnam
Tel.: (84) 274 364 1380
Web Site: http://www.dream-i.com.hk
Toy & Hobby Goods & Supplies Whslr

N.A.I.C.S.: 423920

J & Y International Company
Limited   (1)
Room 1604 16th Floor Fortress Twr, North
Point, China (Hong Kong)
Tel.: (852) 25129541
Sales Range: $25-49.9 Million
Emp.: 50
Industrial Machinery & Equipment Merchant
Whslr
N.A.I.C.S.: 423830

DREAM T ENTERTAINMENT CO., LTD.

89 9th Floor Seongsu-Dong 2-Ga Mg
Building Seongsu Iro, Seongdong-gu,
Seoul, 135-820, Korea (South)
Tel.: (82) 2 3452 2525
Web Site:
http://www.dreamteaent.co.kr
Music Content Planning & Artist Man-
agement Services
N.A.I.C.S.: 713990
U-Sik Lee (CEO)

Subsidiaries:

YMC Co., Ltd.   (1)
154-25 Asanvalleyjungang-ro, Dunpo-
Myeon, Asan, 31409, Chungcheongnam-do,
Korea (South)
Tel.: (82) 415385200
Web Site: https://www.ymc-inc.com
Rev.: $180,537,500
Assets: $108,978,679
Liabilities: $20,369,318
Net Worth: $88,609,361
Earnings: $15,710,302
Emp.: 754
Fiscal Year-end: 12/31/2022
Flat Panel Display Processing Equipment
Mfr
N.A.I.C.S.: 334419
Youn-Yong Lee (CEO)

DREAM UNLIMITED CORP.

State Street Financial Centre Suite
301 30 Adelaide Street East, Toronto,
M5C 3H1, ON, Canada
Tel.: (416) 365-3535   ON
Web Site: https://www.dream.ca
Year Founded: 2013
DRM—(TSX)
Rev.: $271,938,520
Assets: $2,225,096,110
Liabilities: $1,124,731,675
Net Worth: $1,100,364,435
Earnings: $124,881,615
Emp.: 208
Fiscal Year-end: 12/31/20
Real Estate Investment & Asset Man-
agement Services
N.A.I.C.S.: 523940
Michael J. Cooper (Pres & Chief Re-
sponsible Officer)

Subsidiaries:

Dream Industrial Real Estate Invest-
ment Trust   (1)
30 Adelaide Street East Suite 301, Toronto,
M5C 3H1, ON, Canada
Tel.: (416) 365-3535
Web Site: www.dream.ca
Rev.: $330,441,267
Assets: $5,933,989,701
Liabilities: $2,479,393,478
Net Worth: $3,454,596,223
Earnings: $78,758,261
Emp.: 138
Fiscal Year-end: 12/31/2023
Real Estate Investment Trust
N.A.I.C.S.: 525990
Vincenza Sera (Chm)

Joint Venture (Domestic):

Summit Industrial Income REIT   (2)
75 Summerlea Road Unit B, Brampton, L6T
4V2, ON, Canada
Tel.: (905) 791-1181
Web Site: http://www.summitiireit.com

Sales Range: $50-74.9 Million
Real Estate Investment Services
N.A.I.C.S.: 523999
Paul Dykeman (CEO)

Dream Office Real Estate Investment
Trust   (1)
State Street Financial Centre Suite 301 30
Adelaide Street East, Toronto, M5C 3H1,
ON, Canada
Tel.: (416) 365-3535
Web Site: http://www.dream.ca
Rev.: $161,607,314
Assets: $2,259,913,046
Liabilities: $1,087,272,980
Net Worth: $1,172,640,067
Earnings: $138,679,469
Emp.: 500
Fiscal Year-end: 12/31/2020
Real Estate Investment Trust
N.A.I.C.S.: 525990
Michael J. Cooper (Chm & CEO)

DREAM VISION CO., LTD.

3-2-1 Ishibashi, Osaka, Ikeda, 563-
0032, Japan
Tel.: (81) 727619293
Web Site: https://www.dreamv.co.jp
Year Founded: 1998
3185—(TKS)
Rev.: $30,776,160
Assets: $17,549,550
Liabilities: $15,685,530
Net Worth: $1,864,020
Earnings: ($2,326,720)
Emp.: 2,765
Fiscal Year-end: 03/31/24
Electronic Shopping
N.A.I.C.S.: 458110
Toru Shiota (Pres & CEO)

DREAMEAST GROUP LIMITED

2901 Tower 2 Times Square 1 Mathe-
son Street Causeway Bay, Hong
Kong, China (Hong Kong)
Tel.: (852) 36282555   BM
Web Site: http://www.skyocean.com
0593—(HKG)
Rev.: $3,197,190
Assets: $992,326,253
Liabilities: $1,099,055,738
Net Worth: ($106,729,485)
Earnings: ($116,116,673)
Emp.: 72
Fiscal Year-end: 12/31/22
Holding Company; Elderly Continuing
Care & Assisted Living Facilities Op-
erator
N.A.I.C.S.: 551112
Lei Yang (Exec Dir)

Subsidiaries:

Senior Care Elderly Limited   (1)
9th Floor Allied Kajima Building 138 Glouc-
ester Road, Central District, Chai Wan,
China (Hong Kong)   (100%)
Tel.: (852) 23222033
Web Site: https://www.seniorcare.com.hk
Sales Range: $25-49.9 Million
Emp.: 30
Elder Care Services
N.A.I.C.S.: 624120

Senior Care Nursing Home
Limited   (1)
6th Floor 303-307 Des Voeux Road Central,
Sheung Wan, China (Hong Kong)   (100%)
Tel.: (852) 23222033
Web Site: http://www.seniorcare.com.hk
Elderly Nursing Homes Operator
N.A.I.C.S.: 623312

DREAMFOLKS SERVICES LTD.

501 Tower-2 Fifth Floor Worldmark
Sector-65, Gurgaon, 122018, Hary-
ana, India
Tel.: (91) 18001234109
Web Site:
https://www.dreamfolks.com
Year Founded: 2008

DREAMFOLKS—(NSE)
Rev.: $38,764,226
Assets: $23,024,684
Liabilities: $11,808,752
Net Worth: $11,215,932
Earnings: $2,217,716
Fiscal Year-end: 03/31/22
Airport Support Services
N.A.I.C.S.: 488119

DREAMSCAPE NETWORKS LIMITED

Suite 4.07 247 Coward Street, Mas-
cot, 2020, NSW, Australia
Tel.: (61) 894220894
Web Site:
http://www.dreamscapenetwork.com
Assets: $187,527
Liabilities: $190,399
Net Worth: ($2,872)
Earnings: ($10,119)
Network Integration Services
N.A.I.C.S.: 541512
Mark Evans (CEO & Mng Dir)

Subsidiaries:

Crazy Domains FZ-LLC   (1)
I Mate Building 11 Sheikh Zayed Road
Dubai Internet City, PO Box 502318, Dubai,
United Arab Emirates
Tel.: (971) 43116784
Web Site: http://www.crazydomains.in
Web Hosting Services
N.A.I.C.S.: 518210
Mark Evans (CEO)

IT Works Internet Pte. Ltd.   (1)
61 Ubi Ave 1 05-08, Singapore, 408941,
Singapore
Tel.: (65) 67201800
Web Site: http://www.iwi.com.sg
Web Hosting Services
N.A.I.C.S.: 518210

Net Logistics Pty Ltd.   (1)
47 Bourke Rd, Alexandria, 2015, NSW,
Australia
Tel.: (61) 2 9043 3968
Web Site: http://www.netlogistics.com.au
Web Hosting Services
N.A.I.C.S.: 518210

Subsidiary (Domestic):

Enetica Pty Ltd   (2)
Level 2 Suite 202 4-8 Inglewood Pl, PO
Box 7829, Baulkham Hills, 2153, NSW,
Australia
Tel.: (61) 288941010
Web Site: http://www.enetica.com.au
Web Hosting Services
N.A.I.C.S.: 518210

Vodien Internet Solutions Pte Ltd   (1)
61 Ubi Ave 1 05-07, Singapore, 408941,
Singapore
Tel.: (65) 62886264
Web Site: http://www.vodien.com
Web Hosting Services
N.A.I.C.S.: 518210
Alvin Poh (CEO)

DREAMTECH CO., LTD.

Uspace2 670 Daewangpangyo-ro,
Bundang-gu, Seongnam, 13494,
Gyeonggi-do, Korea (South)
Tel.: (82) 415894600   KR
Web Site:
https://www.idreamtech.co.kr
Year Founded: 1998
192650—(KRS)
Rev.: $1,049,749,589
Assets: $633,048,890
Liabilities: $248,279,721
Net Worth: $384,769,169
Earnings: $65,216,073
Emp.: 461
Fiscal Year-end: 12/31/22
Electronic Components Mfr
N.A.I.C.S.: 334419
Seonghyun An (CEO)

DREAMUS COMPANY

18-gil 5 Bangbaero, Seocho-Gu,
Seoul, 06664, Korea (South)
Tel.: (82) 262456700
Web Site: https://www.iriver.com
Year Founded: 1999
060570—(KRS)
Rev.: $210,443,583
Assets: $208,507,001
Liabilities: $79,816,997
Net Worth: $128,690,004
Earnings: $20,916,231
Emp.: 336
Fiscal Year-end: 12/31/22
MP-3 Player Mfr
N.A.I.C.S.: 334310
Dong-Hoon Kim (CEO)

Subsidiaries:

Iriver Inc   (1)
39 Peters Canyon Rd, Irvine, CA 92606
Tel.: (949) 336-4540
Web Site: http://www.iriver.com
Emp.: 50
Multimedia Device Mfr
N.A.I.C.S.: 334419
Owen Kwon (Gen Mgr)

DREAMWORLD LIMITED

Dreamworld Towers 65 Strachen
Road Opp Arts Council, Behind Sindh
Assembly, Karachi, Pakistan
Tel.: (92) 21 8692000
Web Site: http://www.dreamworld.pk
Hotel Operator
N.A.I.C.S.: 721110

DRECOM CO., LTD.

1-8-1 Shimomeguro Meguro Gajoen
Arco Tower 17F, Meguro-ku, Tokyo,
153-0064, Japan
Tel.: (81) 366825700
Web Site: https://www.drecom.co.jp
Year Founded: 2001
3793—(TKS)
Rev.: $64,639,190
Assets: $93,518,280
Liabilities: $56,052,800
Net Worth: $37,465,480
Earnings: $687,440
Emp.: 369
Fiscal Year-end: 03/31/24
Internet Content Development Ser-
vices
N.A.I.C.S.: 541511
Yuki Naito (Founder, Chm, Pres &
CEO)

DREDGING CORPORATION OF INDIA LTD

Dredge House HB Colony Main
Road, Seethammadhara, Visakhapat-
nam, 530 022, India
Tel.: (91) 8912523250
Web Site: https://www.dredge-
india.com
Year Founded: 1976
DREDGECORP—(NSE)
Rev.: $104,685,153
Assets: $312,481,260
Liabilities: $121,092,549
Net Worth: $191,388,711
Earnings: ($23,534,552)
Emp.: 325
Fiscal Year-end: 03/31/21
Dredging Services
N.A.I.C.S.: 237990
K. Aswini Sreekanth (Compliance Of-
ficer & Sec)

DREES & SOMMER SE

Obere Waldplatze 13, 70569, Stutt-
gart, Germany
Tel.: (49) 711 1317 0
Web Site: http://www.dreso.com
Year Founded: 1970
Rev.: $350,432,724

Drees & Sommer SE—(Continued)

Assets: $189,371,074
Liabilities: $126,367,079
Net Worth: $63,003,995
Earnings: $35,469,189
Emp.: 3,280
Fiscal Year-end: 12/31/18
Construction Project Management &
Engineering Services
N.A.I.C.S.: 236220
Bernhard Unseld *(Partner)*

Subsidiaries:

Drees & Sommer Belgium
S.P.R.L **(1)**
Boulevard Brand Whitlock 87, 1200, Brussels, Belgium
Tel.: (32) 2 73770 30
Web Site: http://www.dreso.com
Emp.: 5
Construction Engineering Services
N.A.I.C.S.: 541330
Christopher Matthies *(Mng Dir)*

Drees & Sommer Berlin GmbH **(1)**
Bundesallee 39 - 40 a, 10717, Berlin, Germany
Tel.: (49) 30 254394 0
Construction Engineering Services
N.A.I.C.S.: 541330

Drees & Sommer Cologne
GmbH **(1)**
Habsburgerring 2 Westgate Office Building, 50674, Cologne, Germany
Tel.: (49) 221130505260
Real Estate Consulting Service
N.A.I.C.S.: 531390

Drees & Sommer Dresden
GmbH **(1)**
Freiberger Strasse 39, 01067, Dresden, Germany
Tel.: (49) 3518732390
Real Estate Consulting Service
N.A.I.C.S.: 531390

Drees & Sommer Espana S.L. **(1)**
Ronda de Sant Pere 17 2, 08010, Barcelona, Spain
Tel.: (34) 93 451 0839
Construction Engineering Services
N.A.I.C.S.: 541330

Drees & Sommer France SARL **(1)**
3 rue de Liege, 75009, Paris, France
Tel.: (33) 142936320
Construction Engineering Services
N.A.I.C.S.: 541330

Drees & Sommer Hamburg
GmbH **(1)**
Ludwig-Erhard-Strasse 1, 20459, Hamburg, Germany
Tel.: (49) 405149440
Real Estate Consulting Service
N.A.I.C.S.: 531390
Gesa Rohwedder *(Head-Hospitality)*

Drees & Sommer Italia Engineering
S.r.l. **(1)**
Corso Garibaldi 86, 20121, Milan, Italy
Tel.: (39) 02 29062666
Web Site: http://www.dreso.com
Construction Engineering Services
N.A.I.C.S.: 541330
Ambra Francisci *(Project Mgr)*

Drees & Sommer Leipzig GmbH **(1)**
Bruhl 65, 04109, Leipzig, Germany
Tel.: (49) 341919300
Real Estate Consulting Service
N.A.I.C.S.: 531390

Drees & Sommer Luxembourg
SARL **(1)**
6c rue Gabriel Lippmann, 5365, Munsbach, Luxembourg
Tel.: (352) 261205 5550
Construction Engineering Services
N.A.I.C.S.: 541330

Drees & Sommer Netherlands
B.V. **(1)**
Butterbur Street 20-22, Nieuw Vennep, 2153 EX, Amsterdam, Netherlands
Tel.: (31) 887762670

Real Estate Consulting Service
N.A.I.C.S.: 531390

Drees & Sommer Nordic A/S **(1)**
Wildersgade 10B 2 floor, 1408, Copenhagen, Denmark
Tel.: (45) 45 26 90 00
Construction Engineering Services
N.A.I.C.S.: 541330

Drees & Sommer Polska
Sp.z.O.O. **(1)**
ul Chmielna 132/134, 00-805, Warsaw, Poland
Tel.: (48) 22 487 78 29
Construction Engineering Services
N.A.I.C.S.: 541330

Drees & Sommer Project Management & Consulting (Beijing) Co.,
Ltd. **(1)**
No 1Gongti North Road Room No 072 7th Floor Unit 1 Sanlitun DRC, Chaoyang District, 100600, Beijing, China
Tel.: (86) 10 65900 265
Construction Engineering Services
N.A.I.C.S.: 541330

Drees & Sommer Projektmanagement und bautechnische Beratung
GmbH **(1)**
Lothringerstrasse 16 top 9, 1030, Vienna, Austria
Tel.: (43) 1 5335660 0
Construction Engineering Services
N.A.I.C.S.: 541330

Drees & Sommer Romania
S.R.L **(1)**
Str Lt Av Serban Petrescu Nr 15 Et 2, 011891, Bucharest, Romania
Tel.: (40) 31 6908 001
Web Site: http://www.dreso.com
Emp.: 15
Construction Engineering Services
N.A.I.C.S.: 541330
Anton Marius Stroe *(Dir-Technical)*

Drees & Sommer Russia & CIS **(1)**
Truda Square 2 lit A, 190000, Saint Petersburg, Russia
Tel.: (7) 812 309 9323
Web Site: http://www.dreso.ru
Construction Engineering Services
N.A.I.C.S.: 541330

Drees & Sommer Schweiz
GmbH **(1)**
St Alban-Vorstadt 80, 4052, Basel, Switzerland
Tel.: (41) 617857200
Web Site: http://www.dreso.ch
Construction Engineering Services
N.A.I.C.S.: 541330

Drees & Sommer Turkiye Ltd. **(1)**
Sirket Inonu Cad 29/3 Gumussuyu, 34 427, Istanbul, Turkiye
Tel.: (90) 212 29284 00
Web Site: http://www.dreso.com
Emp.: 4
Construction Engineering Services
N.A.I.C.S.: 541330
Sasha Ampel *(Gen Mgr)*

Drees & Sommer UK Ltd. **(1)**
Ground Floor 13 New North Street, London, WC1N 3PJ, United Kingdom
Tel.: (44) 2038580221
Real Estate Consulting Service
N.A.I.C.S.: 531390
Marco Abdallah *(Head-Engrg-UK)*

Drees & Sommer Ukraine **(1)**
Pereulok Muzejny 10 Office 803/804, 01001, Kiev, Ukraine
Tel.: (380) 442535677
Construction Engineering Services
N.A.I.C.S.: 541330

Drees & Sommer Ulm GmbH **(1)**
Hampgasse 9, 89073, Ulm, Germany
Tel.: (49) 7311758990
Real Estate Consulting Service
N.A.I.C.S.: 531390

DREFA MEDIA HOLDING GMBH

Eilenburger Strasse 4, 04317, Leipzig, Germany
Tel.: (49) 3 41 3500 5959
Web Site: http://www.drefa.de
Emp.: 600
Holding Company Services
N.A.I.C.S.: 551112
Heinz Spremberg *(Mng Dir)*

Subsidiaries:

DREFA Immobilien Management
GmbH **(1)**
Altenburger Strasse 13, 04275, Leipzig, Germany
Tel.: (49) 34135002501
Web Site: http://www.media-city-leipzig.de
Administrative Management & General Management Consulting Services
N.A.I.C.S.: 541611
Ulrike von Radowitz *(Mng Dir)*

DREWEX S.A.

ul Kalwaryjska 69, 30-504, Krakow, Poland
Tel.: (48) 603 553 392
Web Site: http://www.drewex.com
DRE—(WAR)
Sales Range: $1-9.9 Million
Furniture & Clothes Mfr
N.A.I.C.S.: 424350
Pawel Paluchowski *(Chm)*

DRGEM CORP.

7F E-B/D Gwangmyeong Techno-Park 60 Haan-ro, Gwangmyeong, 14322, Gyeonggi-do, Korea (South)
Tel.: (82) 28698566
Web Site: https://www.drgem.co.kr
Year Founded: 2003
263690—(KRS)
Rev.: $84,496,569
Assets: $97,182,786
Liabilities: $40,706,108
Net Worth: $56,476,677
Earnings: $11,039,273
Emp.: 236
Fiscal Year-end: 12/31/22
Medical Device Mfr & Distr
N.A.I.C.S.: 339112
Dae-Hee Park *(Mng Dir)*

DRH HOLDINGS JOINT STOCK COMPANY

67 Ham Nghi Nguyen Thai Binh Ward, District 1, 700000, Ho Chi Minh City, 700000, Vietnam
Tel.: (84) 2838223771
Web Site: https://drh.vn
Year Founded: 2006
DRH—(HOSE)
Rev.: $362,478
Assets: $162,261,380
Liabilities: $99,648,833
Net Worth: $62,612,546
Earnings: ($3,912,723)
Fiscal Year-end: 12/31/23
Real Estate Development Services
N.A.I.C.S.: 531390
Dat Tan Phan *(Chm & Gen Dir)*

DRINA OSIGURANJE A.D.

Ulica 9 Januar broj 4, 75446, Milici, Bosnia & Herzegovina
Tel.: (387) 56741610
Web Site: https://www.drina-osiguranje.com
Year Founded: 1996
DROS-R-A—(BANJ)
Sales Range: Less than $1 Million
Insurance Services
N.A.I.C.S.: 524210
Rajko Dukic *(Chm)*

DRINA TRANS A.D.

Karakaj 40B, 75400, Zvornik, Bosnia & Herzegovina
Tel.: (387) 56260077

Web Site: http://www.drinatrans.com
DRTR-R-A—(BANJ)
Sales Range: Less than $1 Million
Bus Rental Services
N.A.I.C.S.: 485510

DRIVE MOTOR RETAIL LIMITED

Freemens Common Road, Leicester, LE2 7SL, United Kingdom
Tel.: (44) 3300198767
Web Site: http://www.drivevauxhall.co.uk
Sales Range: $350-399.9 Million
Emp.: 700
Car Distr
N.A.I.C.S.: 441110
Simon Reeves *(Gen Mgr)*

Subsidiaries:

DRIVE Kawasaki Bristol **(1)**
64-66 Avon Street, Bristol, BS2 0PX, United Kingdom **(100%)**
Tel.: (44) 1179772272
Sales Range: $25-49.9 Million
Emp.: 15
Vehicle Motor Retailing
N.A.I.C.S.: 441110

DRIVE Vauxhall Aldershot **(1)**
Bakers Corner, 1 Lower Farnham Road, Aldershot, GU12 4DZ, Hants, United Kingdom **(100%)**
Tel.: (44) 1252369200
Sales Range: $50-74.9 Million
Emp.: 100
N.A.I.C.S.: 488210
Bruce Smith *(Gen Mgr)*

DRIVE Vauxhall Bristol **(1)**
65-71 Avon St, Bristol, BS2 0PZ, United Kingdom **(100%)**
Tel.: (44) 8445583189
Web Site: http://www.drivevauxhall.co.uk
Vehicle Sales, Servicing, Rentals, Parts, Accessories & Bodyshop
N.A.I.C.S.: 423120
Dave Andrews *(Gen Mgr)*

DRIVE Vauxhall Bury St.
Edmunds **(1)**
Cotton Lane, Bury Saint Edmunds, IP33 1XP, Suffolk, United Kingdom **(100%)**
Tel.: (44) 1284603999
Web Site: http://www.drivevauxhall.co.uk
Sales Range: $25-49.9 Million
Emp.: 70
New Car Retailer
N.A.I.C.S.: 441110
Steve Bessex *(Co-Mng Dir)*

DRIVE Vauxhall Clevedon **(1)**
654 Old Church Rd, Clevedon, BS21 6NW, United Kingdom
Tel.: (44) 275872201
N.A.I.C.S.: 488210

DRIVE Vauxhall Haverhill **(1)**
Duddery Hill, Haverhill, CB9 8DS, Sunnolk, United Kingdom **(100%)**
Tel.: (44) 01440703606
Web Site: http://www.drivevauxhall.co.uk
Sales Range: $50-74.9 Million
Emp.: 14
N.A.I.C.S.: 488210
Sarah Ferrari *(Gen Mgr)*

DROEGE GROUP AG

Poststrasse 5-6, 40213, Dusseldorf, Germany
Tel.: (49) 211867310 De
Web Site: http://www.droege-group.com
Management Consulting Services
N.A.I.C.S.: 541611
Walter P.J. Droege *(Exec Mng Dir)*

Subsidiaries:

ALSO Holding AG **(1)**
Meierhofstrasse 5, CH-6032, Emmen, Switzerland **(51.3%)**
Tel.: (41) 412661800
Web Site: https://www.also.com
Rev.: $12,468,029,355

Assets: $3,403,320,742
Liabilities: $2,280,492,122
Net Worth: $1,122,828,621
Earnings: $164,095,618
Emp.: 4,204
Fiscal Year-end: 12/31/2022
Holding Company; Distribution & Logistics Services
N.A.I.C.S.: 551112
Walter P. J. Droege *(Vice Chm)*

Subsidiary (Non-US):

ALSO A/S   **(2)**
Markaervej 2, 2630, Taastrup, Denmark
Tel.: (45) 4355 8888
Web Site: http://www.also.dk
Emp.: 150
Electronics Distr
N.A.I.C.S.: 423430
Ole Eklund *(Mng Dir)*

ALSO AS   **(2)**
Ostre Kullerod 2, NO-3241, Sandefjord, Norway
Tel.: (47) 33 44 95 99
Web Site: http://www.also.no
Computer Equipment Distr
N.A.I.C.S.: 423430

ALSO Austria GmbH   **(2)**
Industriestrasse 14, AT-2301, Gross-Enzersdorf, Austria
Tel.: (43) 2249 7003 0
Web Site: http://www.also.at
Emp.: 40
Computer Equipment Distr
N.A.I.C.S.: 423430

ALSO Cloud Oy   **(2)**
Pieni Roobertinkatu 11 A, 00130, Helsinki, Finland
Tel.: (358) 20 757 9780
Web Site: http://www.nervogrid.eu
Software Development Services
N.A.I.C.S.: 541511
Aleksi Partanen *(Co-Founder)*

Subsidiary (Non-US):

Nervogrid Netherlands   **(3)**
Herengracht 282, 1016 BX, Amsterdam, Netherlands
Tel.: (31) 20 893 2650
Software Development Services
N.A.I.C.S.: 541511

Subsidiary (Non-US):

ALSO Deutschland GmbH   **(2)**
Lange Wende 43, D-59494, Soest, Germany
Tel.: (49) 2921990
Web Site: http://www.also.de
Computer Equipment Distr
N.A.I.C.S.: 423430
Reiner Schwitzki *(Mng Dir)*

ALSO Digital B.V   **(2)**
Beurtvaartweg 2, 6541 BW, Nijmegen, Netherlands
Tel.: (31) 24 645 2544
Web Site: http://www.alsodigital.com
Software Distr
N.A.I.C.S.: 423430
Jeff Schrik *(Sr Mgr-Ops)*

ALSO Eesti OU   **(2)**
Kalmistu tee 26F Tallinna Jinn Harju maa-kond, EE-11216, Tallinn, Estonia
Tel.: (372) 6504900
Web Site: http://www.also.ee
Emp.: 40
Computer Equipment Distr
N.A.I.C.S.: 423430
Termo Naiste *(Gen Mgr)*

ALSO Finland OY   **(2)**
Kalevantie 2 Building D 6th Floor, Tampere, FI-33100, Finland
Tel.: (358) 3 2136100
Web Site: http://www.also.fi
Computer Equipment Distr
N.A.I.C.S.: 423430
Olavi Malmi *(Mgr-Sls)*

ALSO France S.A.S.   **(2)**
10 avenue des Louvresses, FR-92230, Gennevilliers, France
Tel.: (33) 825 74 24 24
Web Site: http://www.alsofrance.fr

Computer Equipment Distr
N.A.I.C.S.: 423430

ALSO Hungary Kft.   **(2)**
Kethly Anna ter 1, 1077, Budapest, Hungary   **(100%)**
Tel.: (36) 1 501 5319
Web Site: http://www.also.com
Consumer Electronics Whslr
N.A.I.C.S.: 423620
Poros Gabor *(Mng Dir & Country Mgr)*

ALSO MPS GmbH   **(2)**
Ernst-Heinkel-Strasse 4, 94315, Straubing, Germany
Tel.: (49) 9421 933000
Electronic Equipment Distr
N.A.I.C.S.: 423690

ALSO Nederland B.V.   **(2)**
Archimedesbaan 26, NL-3439 ME, Nieuwegein, Netherlands
Tel.: (31) 340284700
Web Site: http://www.also.nl
Computer Equipment Distr
N.A.I.C.S.: 423430

ALSO Nordic Holding Oy   **(2)**
Hatanpaan valtatie 48, Tampere, 33900, Finland
Tel.: (358) 3213 6100
Electronic Equipment Distr
N.A.I.C.S.: 423690

ALSO Polska Sp. z o.o.   **(2)**
ul Daniszewska 14, 03-230, Warsaw, Poland   **(100%)**
Tel.: (48) 22 676 0900
Web Site: http://www.also.com
Information Technology Products Distr & Services
N.A.I.C.S.: 423430

Subsidiary (Domestic):

ALSO Schweiz AG   **(2)**
Meierhofstrasse 5, 6032, Emmen, Switzer-land
Tel.: (41) 41 266 11 11
Web Site: http://www.also.ch
Computer Hardware Distr
N.A.I.C.S.: 423430
Tom Brunner *(Chief Customer Officer)*

Subsidiary (Non-US):

ALSO Slovakia s.r.o.   **(2)**
Palisady 33, 811 06, Bratislava, Slovakia   **(100%)**
Tel.: (421) 232 144 592
Web Site: http://www.also.com
Consumer Electronics Whslr
N.A.I.C.S.: 423620
Radoslav Kuris *(Key Acct Mgr)*

ALSO Sweden AB   **(2)**
Finlandsgatan 14, 164 74, Kista, Sweden
Tel.: (46) 8 633 90 00
Web Site: http://www.also.com
Logstics & Digital Services
N.A.I.C.S.: 488510

ALSO Technology SRL   **(2)**
Strada Halelor 7, A9-B9 sector 5, Bucha-rest, 050121, Romania   **(100%)**
Tel.: (40) 372 030 999
Web Site: http://www.also.com
Consumer Electronics Whslr
N.A.I.C.S.: 423620

Alpha International B.V.   **(2)**
Wijchenseweg 20, 6537 TL, Nijmegen, Netherlands
Tel.: (31) 24 357 9999
Web Site: http://www.alpha-international.eu
Computer Hardware Distr
N.A.I.C.S.: 423430

Beamer & more GmbH   **(2)**
Vogelsangstrasse 54a, 70197, Stuttgart, Germany
Tel.: (49) 711 993398 60
Web Site: http://www.beamerandmore.de
Electronic Equipment Distr
N.A.I.C.S.: 423690

Fulfilment Plus GmbH   **(2)**
Vor Der Hecke 2, Staufenberg, 34355, Ger-many
Tel.: (49) 55433036070

Business Management & Consulting Ser-vices
N.A.I.C.S.: 541611

LAFI Logiciels Application Formation Information S.A.S   **(2)**
69 R St Denis, 93400, Saint-Ouen, France
Tel.: (33) 8 92 68 52 34
Software Distr
N.A.I.C.S.: 423430

MEDIUM GmbH   **(2)**
Willstaetterstrasse 7, 40549, Dusseldorf, Germany   **(80%)**
Tel.: (49) 21152760
Web Site: http://www.medium.de
Sales Range: $50-74.9 Million
Emp.: 50
Presentation Equipments Distr
N.A.I.C.S.: 423690
Reinold Imdahl *(Co-Founder & Mng Dir-Mktg & Sls)*

Subsidiary (Domestic):

NRS Printing Solutions AG   **(2)**
Moosweg 38A, 3645, Thun, Switzerland
Tel.: (41) 33 334 55 00
Web Site: http://www.nrs.ch
Emp.: 40
Electronic Equipment Distr
N.A.I.C.S.: 423690
Daniel Eberhardt *(Mgr)*

Subsidiary (Non-US):

Pestinger GmbH   **(2)**
Wartburgstr 12, 65929, Frankfurt am Main, Germany
Tel.: (49) 69 33 005 0
Web Site: http://www.pestinger.de
Electronic Equipment Distr
N.A.I.C.S.: 423690

Subsidiary (Domestic):

Quatec AG   **(2)**
Bellevueweg 14, 6300, Zug, Switzerland
Tel.: (41) 41 710 10 60
Computer Hardware Distr
N.A.I.C.S.: 423430

Subsidiary (Non-US):

SEAMCOM GmbH & Co. KG   **(2)**
Leyer Strasse 24, 49076, Osnabruck, Ger-many
Tel.: (49) 541 77064 577
Web Site: http://www.seamcom.de
Electronic Equipment Distr
N.A.I.C.S.: 423690

SIA ALSO Latvia   **(2)**
Liliju iela 29, LV-2167, Marupes, Latvia
Tel.: (871) 67018300
Web Site: http://www.lv.also.com
Computer Equipment Distr
N.A.I.C.S.: 423430

UAB ALSO Lietuva   **(2)**
Verslo Street 6, Kumpiu, LT-54311, Kaunas, Lithuania   **(100%)**
Tel.: (370) 37 757550
Web Site: http://www.also.lt
Computer Equipment Distr
N.A.I.C.S.: 423430

Subsidiary (Domestic):

UAB ABC Data Lietuva   **(3)**
4 Jogailos Str, 01116, Vilnius, Lithuania   **(100%)**
Tel.: (370) 5 259 60 60
Web Site: http://www.abcdata.lt
Consumer Electronics Distr
N.A.I.C.S.: 423620
Raimundas Bycius *(Mng Dir)*

Subsidiary (Non-US):

druckerfachmann.de GmbH   **(2)**
Wegedornstrasse 36, 12524, Berlin, Ger-many
Tel.: (49) 30 505654 4
Web Site: http://www.druckerfachmann.de
Printer Distr
N.A.I.C.S.: 334118
Yvonne Daube *(Mgr-Mktg)*

Weltbild Retail GmbH & Co. KG.   **(1)**
Steinerne Furt 68-72, 86167, Augsburg, Germany

Tel.: (49) 821 70 04 0
Web Site: http://www.weltbild.de
Book Distr
N.A.I.C.S.: 424920

Subsidiary (Domestic):

Verlagsgruppe Weltbild GmbH   **(2)**
Steinerne Furt, 86167, Augsburg, Germany
Tel.: (49) 821 70 04 0
Web Site: http://www.weltbild.com
Sales Range: $1-4.9 Billion
Emp.: 6,500
Books, Music, DVDs, Software, Electronic Devices & Games Online Retailer
N.A.I.C.S.: 449210

DROGOBYCH TRUCK CRANE PLANT PJSC
Gaidamatska str 22, Drogobych, Lviv, 82100, Ukraine
Tel.: (380) 324417337
Web Site: http://www.dak.com.ua
Lifting Machinery Mfr
N.A.I.C.S.: 333998
Myhailo Yakymiv *(Dir-Technical)*

DROMEAS S.A
Industrial Area of Serres, 62121, Serres, Greece
Tel.: (30) 2321099220
Web Site: https://www.dromeas.com
Year Founded: 1979
DROME—(ATH)
Assets: $69,801,044
Liabilities: $39,597,963
Net Worth: $30,203,081
Earnings: $1,125,524
Emp.: 325
Fiscal Year-end: 12/31/21
Office Furniture Mfr & Marketing
N.A.I.C.S.: 337214
Athanasios Konstantinou Papapanag-iotou *(Chm & CEO)*

DRON & DICKSON LTD.
Cumberland Place Whapload Road Lowestoft, Lowestoft, NR32 1UQ, Suffolk, United Kingdom
Tel.: (44) 1502539991
Web Site:
    http://www.drondickson.com
Year Founded: 1927
Electrical Equipment Distr
N.A.I.C.S.: 423610
Jason Collatin *(Mgr-Bus Dev)*

Subsidiaries:

Totus Energy Trading LLC   **(1)**
Warehouse 3 & 4 Block C Plot 21 Sector M15, Mussafah, Abu Dhabi, United Arab Emirates
Tel.: (971) 25517002
Web Site: http://www.totusenergy.com
Electrical Engineering Services
N.A.I.C.S.: 541330
Nishad P. A. Majeed *(Mgr-Sls)*

DRONE DELIVERY CANADA CORP.
6221 Highway 7 Unit 6, Vaughan, L4H 0K8, ON, Canada
Tel.: (647) 476-2662   **BC**
Web Site:
    https://www.dronedelivery.com
Year Founded: 2011
TAKOF—(OTCQX)
Assets: $13,551,560
Liabilities: $1,659,764
Net Worth: $11,891,796
Earnings: ($11,935,604)
Fiscal Year-end: 12/31/19
Investment Services
N.A.I.C.S.: 523999
Greg Colacitti *(Dir-Field Ops)*

Subsidiaries:

Volatus Aerospace Corp.   **(1)**
2450 Derry Road East, Mississauga, L5S

Drone Delivery Canada Corp.—(Continued)

1B2, ON, Canada
Tel.: (905) 676-0092
Web Site: http://www.partnerjet.com
Rev.: $23,289,367
Assets: $26,292,421
Liabilities: $15,185,725
Net Worth: $11,106,696
Earnings: ($5,476,073)
Emp.: 136
Fiscal Year-end: 11/30/2022
Aircraft Sales & Maintenance Services
N.A.I.C.S.: 423860
Ian A. McDougall (Vice Chm)

DRONE VOLT SA
14 rue de la Perdrix Lot 201, 93420,
Villepinte, France
Tel.: (33) 180894444   **FR**
Web Site: https://www.dronevolt.com
Year Founded: 2011
ALDRV—(EUR)
Sales Range: $1-9.9 Million
Remote Controlled Drone Mfr
N.A.I.C.S.: 334310

DRONEACHARYA AERIAL INNOVATIONS LIMITED
A-202 2nd Floor Galore Tech IT Park
LMD Chowk, Bavdhan, Pune,
411021, Maharashtra, India
Tel.: (91) 9890003590
Web Site:
   https://www.droneacharya.com
Year Founded: 2017
543713—(BOM)
Rev.: $489,680
Assets: $2,111,000
Liabilities: $134,794
Net Worth: $1,976,206
Earnings: $55,487
Fiscal Year-end: 03/31/22
Information Technology Services
N.A.I.C.S.: 541512

DRONESHIELD LIMITED
Level 5 126 Phillip St, Sydney, 2000,
NSW, Australia
Tel.: (61) 299957280   **AU**
Web Site:
   https://www.droneshield.com
Year Founded: 2014
DRSHF—(OTCIQ)
Rev.: $11,273,148
Assets: $16,828,228
Liabilities: $4,144,226
Net Worth: $12,684,001
Earnings: ($633,753)
Emp.: 80
Fiscal Year-end: 12/31/22
Other Measuring & Controlling Device
Manufacturing
N.A.I.C.S.: 334519
Oleg Vornik (CEO & Mng Dir)

DROP S.A.
ul Syta 114z/1, 02-987, Warsaw, Poland
Tel.: (48) 22 885 14 21
Web Site: http://www.drop-sa.pl
Year Founded: 2000
Waste Material Recycling Services
N.A.I.C.S.: 562211

DROPSUITE LIMITED
Level 30 35 Collins Street, Melbourne, 3000, VIC, Australia
Tel.: (61) 68132090   **AU**
Web Site: https://dropsuite.com
DSE—(ASX)
Rev.: $21,354,812
Assets: $21,222,669
Liabilities: $2,569,307
Net Worth: $18,653,361
Earnings: $1,078,946
Emp.: 100
Fiscal Year-end: 12/31/23

Data Protection Services
N.A.I.C.S.: 541519
Kobe Li (Sec)

Subsidiaries:

Dropmysite Pte. Ltd.   (1)
70A Neil Road, Singapore, 088837, Singapore
Tel.: (65) 6 779 5131
Web Site: https://www.dropmysite.com
Information Technology Services
N.A.I.C.S.: 541512

DROZAPOL-PROFIL S.A.
Ul Torunska 298a, 85-880, Bydgoszcz, Poland
Tel.: (48) 523260900
Web Site: https://www.drozapol.pl
Year Founded: 1993
DPL—(WAR)
Rev.: $15,305,386
Assets: $21,857,469
Liabilities: $3,619,665
Net Worth: $18,237,805
Earnings: ($1,874,746)
Fiscal Year-end: 12/31/23
Steel Product Distr
N.A.I.C.S.: 423510

DRS DATA & RESEARCH SERVICES PLC
1 Danbury Court Linford Wood, Milton Keynes, MK14 6LR, Bucks,
United Kingdom
Tel.: (44) 1908666088
Web Site: http://www.drs.co.uk
Sales Range: $10-24.9 Million
Emp.: 140
Optical Mark Reading & Image Scanning Machinery Mfr & Marketer &
Data Capture Services
N.A.I.C.S.: 333248
Gary Brighton (Dir-Sls & Mktg-DRS Data Services Limited)

Subsidiaries:

DRS Data Services Limited   (1)
1 Danbury Court Linford Wood, Milton
Keynes, MK14 6LR, Bucks, United Kingdom
Tel.: (44) 1908666088
Web Site: http://www.drs.co.uk
Emp.: 250
Automated Data Capture Services
N.A.I.C.S.: 334610
Malcolm Brighton (Mng Dir)

DRS DILIP ROADLINES LTD.
306 Kabra Complex 61 MG Road,
Secunderabad, 500 003, India
Tel.: (91) 4027711504
Web Site: https://www.drsindia.in
Year Founded: 2009
DRSDILIP—(NSE)
Rev.: $20,009,765
Assets: $9,980,987
Liabilities: $3,509,560
Net Worth: $6,471,427
Earnings: $298,675
Emp.: 198
Fiscal Year-end: 03/31/21
Transporting Good & Relocation Services
N.A.I.C.S.: 484210
Anjani Kumar Agarwal (CEO & Mng Dir)

DRTECH CORPORATION
Dolma-ro 173, Bundang-gu, Seongnam, 13606, Gyeonggi-do, Korea
(South)
Tel.: (82) 317797400
Web Site: https://www.drtech.co.kr
Year Founded: 2000
214680—(KRS)
Rev.: $68,631,930
Assets: $92,636,560
Liabilities: $46,740,522
Net Worth: $45,896,038

Earnings: $4,563,322
Emp.: 267
Fiscal Year-end: 12/31/22
Medical Equipment Mfr & Distr
N.A.I.C.S.: 334510
Kilsoo Lee (CFO)

Subsidiaries:

DRTECH Corporation - DRTECH Korea Factory   (1)
29 Dunchon-daero 541 Beon-gil, Jungwon-gu, Seongnam, 462-807, Gyeonggi-do, Korea (South)
Tel.: (82) 317306800
X-Ray Detector Mfr
N.A.I.C.S.: 334517

DRTECH Europe GmbH   (1)
Am Kronberger Hang 2, 65824, Schwalbach am Taunus, Germany
Tel.: (49) 61969502906
X-Ray Detector Distr
N.A.I.C.S.: 423450

DRTECH North America Inc.   (1)
1047 Serpentine Ln Ste 100, Pleasanton,
CA 94566
Tel.: (925) 223-8729
X-Ray Detector Distr
N.A.I.C.S.: 423450

DRTECH Shanghai Co, Ltd   (1)
No. 908 9F No 3998 Hongxin Road Minhang
District, Shanghai, China
Tel.: (86) 2160905153
X-Ray Detector Distr
N.A.I.C.S.: 423450

DRU VERWARMING B.V.
Ratio 8, 6921 RW, Duiven, Netherlands
Tel.: (31) 263195319   **NI**
Web Site: http://www.drufire.nl
Sales Range: $10-24.9 Million
Emp.: 60
Gas & Electrical Fireplace Mfr
N.A.I.C.S.: 333414
Sander Teunissen (Mgr-Sls)

Subsidiaries:

DRU Belgium   (1)
Kontichsesteenweg 60, 2630, Aartselaar,
Belgium
Tel.: (32) 3 450 7000
Web Site: http://www.drufire.be
Heating Equipment Mfr
N.A.I.C.S.: 333414

Drugasar Ltd.   (1)
Deans Rd, Swinton, M27 0JH, Manchester,
United Kingdom   (100%)
Tel.: (44) 617938700
Web Site: http://www.drufire.co.uk
N.A.I.C.S.: 326199

DRUCKFARBEN HELLAS S.A.
Megaridos Avenue Kalistiri Site,
19300, Aspropyrgos, Greece
Tel.: (30) 2105519300
Web Site: http://www.druckfarben.gr
DROUK—(ATH)
Sales Range: $100-124.9 Million
Emp.: 325
Printing Ink Producer
N.A.I.C.S.: 325910
George Karavasilis (Chm & Mng Dir)

Subsidiaries:

Druckfarben Romania S.R.L.   (1)
St Atomistilor Nr 17 23, Magurele, 077125,
Romania
Tel.: (40) 214057100
Web Site: http://www.druckfarben.ro
Sales Range: $50-74.9 Million
Emp.: 180
Ink Chemicals Trading Services
N.A.I.C.S.: 325998

DRUMMOND VENTURES CORP.
400 Burrard Street Suite 1400, Vancouver, V6C 3A6, BC, Canada

Tel.: (604) 691-6425
DVX.P—(TSXV)
Rev.: $15,957
Assets: $291,800
Liabilities: $11,320
Net Worth: $280,479
Earnings: ($16,895)
Fiscal Year-end: 06/30/21
Investment Management Service
N.A.I.C.S.: 525990

DRUMZ PLC
2 Upper Tachbrook Street, London,
SW1V 1SH, United Kingdom
Tel.: (44) 2035820566
Web Site: http://www.drumzplc.com
ENGI—(AIM)
Rev.: $16,293
Assets: $2,142,482
Liabilities: $81,463
Net Worth: $2,061,019
Earnings: ($1,027,794)
Emp.: 4
Fiscal Year-end: 12/31/20
Investment Services
N.A.I.C.S.: 523999
Nishith Malde (Exec Dir & Sec)

DRURY COMMUNICATIONS LIMITED
1 Richview Office Park, Clonskeagh,
Dublin, 14, Ireland
Tel.: (353) 1 260 5000   **IE**
Web Site: http://www.drury.ie
Year Founded: 1989
Emp.: 15
Public Relations Services
N.A.I.C.S.: 541820
Billy Murphy (Chm)

DRUSTVENI STANDARD CAJAVEC A.D.
Jovana Ducica 25, 78000, Banja
Luka, Bosnia & Herzegovina
Tel.: (387) 51 214 961
Sales Range: Less than $1 Million
Emp.: 5
Real Estate Prorperty Leasing Services
N.A.I.C.S.: 531190

DRUZHBA AD
4 Tutrakan Str, 7200, Razgrad, Bulgaria
Tel.: (359) 898787242
Web Site: http://www.drouzhba.bg
Year Founded: 1964
DRR—(BUL)
Sales Range: Less than $1 Million
Piston Products Mfr
N.A.I.C.S.: 336310
Ivan Angelov Todorov (Chm)

DRVNA INDUSTRIJA SPACVA D.D
Duga Ulica 181, 32100, Vinkovci,
Croatia
Tel.: (385) 32303066
Web Site: http://www.spacva.eu
SPVA—(ZAG)
Rev.: $36,783,105
Assets: $51,912,091
Liabilities: $16,480,577
Net Worth: $35,431,514
Earnings: $386,683
Fiscal Year-end: 12/31/19
Wood Products Mfr
N.A.I.C.S.: 333243
Josip Faletar (Chm)

DRY CELL & STORAGE BATTERY JSC
No 321 Tran Hung Dao Street, Co
Giang Ward Dist 1, Ho Chi Minh City,
Vietnam
Tel.: (84) 2839203062

Year Founded: 1976
PAC—(HNX)
Primary Battery Product Mfr
N.A.I.C.S.: 335910
Tran Thanh Van *(Gen Dir)*

DRYERTECH INDUSTRIES LTD.
5614C Burbank Road SE, Calgary,
T2H 1Z4, AB, Canada
Tel.: (403) 800-3109   NV
Year Founded: 2010
Compressed Air Dryer Mfr & Distr
N.A.I.C.S.: 333912
Walter Romanchuk *(Pres)*

DRYLOCK TECHNOLOGIES NV
Spinnerijstraat 12, 9240, Zele, Bel-
gium
Tel.: (32) 52559560
Web Site: http://www.drylock.eu
Disposable Diaper Mfr
N.A.I.C.S.: 322291

Subsidiaries:

Presto Absorbent Products, Inc.   **(1)**
3925 N Hastings Way, Eau Claire, WI
54703   **(100%)**
Tel.: (877) 202-4652
Disposable Adult Incontinence Products Mfr
N.A.I.C.S.: 322291
Ryan Johnson *(Mgr-Customer Svc)*

DRYSHIPS INC.
109 Kifisias Avenue and Sina Street,
Marousi, 151 24, Athens, Greece
Tel.: (30) 216 200 6600   MH
Web Site: http://www.dryships.com
Year Founded: 2004
Rev.: $186,135,000
Assets: $1,011,305,000
Liabilities: $373,576,000
Net Worth: $637,729,000
Earnings: $21,780,000
Emp.: 3
Fiscal Year-end: 12/31/18
Holding Company; Deep Sea Freight
Transportation Services
N.A.I.C.S.: 551112
Dimitris Dreliozis *(VP-Fin)*

Subsidiaries:

Ocean Rig   **(1)**
16140 Waverly, Houston, TX 77032
Tel.: (713) 260-9667
Oil Drilling Services
N.A.I.C.S.: 213111

Ocean Rig 1 AS   **(1)**
Svanholmen 6, Stavanger, Norway
Tel.: (47) 51969000
Web Site: http://www.ocean-rig.com
Sales Range: $50-74.9 Million
Emp.: 70
Oil Rig Construction Services
N.A.I.C.S.: 213112

Ocean Rig AS   **(1)**
Vestre Svanholmen 6, N 4313, Sandnes,
Norway
Tel.: (47) 51969000
Web Site: http://www.ocean-rig.com
Sales Range: $50-74.9 Million
Emp.: 45
Oil Rig Construction Services
N.A.I.C.S.: 213112

Ocean Rig ASA   **(1)**
Forus, PO Box 409, Stavanger, Norway
Tel.: (47) 51 96 90 00
Web Site: http://www.ocean-rig.com
Offshore Petroleum Extraction Services
N.A.I.C.S.: 211120
Jan Rune Steinsland *(CFO)*

Ocean Rig Norway AS   **(1)**
Vestre Svanholmen 6 Forus, 4313,
Sandnes, Norway
Tel.: (47) 51969000
Web Site: http://www.ocean-rig.com

Sales Range: $50-74.9 Million
Emp.: 60
Oil Rig Construction Services
N.A.I.C.S.: 213112
Jan Rune Steinsland *(CEO & CFO)*

Ocean Rig UK Ltd.   **(1)**
Johnstone House Rose Street, Aberdeen,
AB10 1UD, United Kingdom
Tel.: (44) 1224 367940
Web Site: http://www.ocean-rig.com
Oil Rig Construction Services
N.A.I.C.S.: 213112

OceanFreight Inc.   **(1)**
80 Kifissias Ave. Athens, 15125, Greece
Tel.: (30) 2106140283
Web Site: http://www.oceanfreightinc.com
Sales Range: $75-99.9 Million
Holding Company; Deep Sea Freight Trans-
portation Services
N.A.I.C.S.: 551112

Subsidiary (Domestic):

Oceanship Owners Limited   **(2)**
80 Kifissias Avenue, Athens, 151 25,
Greece
Tel.: (30) 2106140283
Shipping Transportation Services
N.A.I.C.S.: 488320

Oceanventure Owners Limited   **(2)**
80 Kifissias Avenue, Athens, 15125, Greece
Tel.: (30) 2106140283
Shipping Transportation Services
N.A.I.C.S.: 488320

DS SMITH PLC
7th Floor 350 Euston Road Regent's
Place, London, NW1 3AX, United
Kingdom
Tel.: (44) 2077561800   UK
Web Site: http://www.dssmith.com
Year Founded: 1940
SMDS—(LSE)
Rev.: $10,203,083,100
Assets: $11,737,082,700
Liabilities: $6,664,707,000
Net Worth: $5,072,375,700
Earnings: $608,139,000
Fiscal Year-end: 04/30/23
Packaging & Paper Products Mfr
N.A.I.C.S.: 322299
Gareth Davis *(Chm)*

Subsidiaries:

Bertako S.L.U.   **(1)**
Poligono Industrial Areta n 1 parcela 348
calle Altzutzate n 46, Huarte, 31620, Na-
varra, Spain
Tel.: (34) 948335030
Corrugated Packaging Box Mfr
N.A.I.C.S.: 322211

Bilokalnik-IPA d.d.   **(1)**
Dravska ulica 19, Koprivnica, Croatia
Tel.: (385) 48647555
Web Site: https://www.bilokalnik.hr
Corrugated Packaging Paper Mfr
N.A.I.C.S.: 322211

Bretschneider Verpackungen
GmbH   **(1)**
Bretschneiderstrasse 5, 08309, Eibenstock,
Germany
Tel.: (49) 377525060
Web Site: https://www.bretschneider-
verpackung.de
Corrugated Packaging Paper Mfr
N.A.I.C.S.: 322211

Carton Plastico s.a.   **(1)**
C/ Portugal 6-7 Pol Ind Fagober, 28802,
Alcala de Henares, Madrid, Spain
Tel.: (34) 918821014
Sales Range: $25-49.9 Million
Emp.: 4
Plastics Product Mfr
N.A.I.C.S.: 326199

DS Smith Ambalaj A.S.   **(1)**
Selimpasa Mahallesi 5007 Sk No 4, Selim-
pasa, 34590, Istanbul, Turkiye
Tel.: (90) 2127235656
Web Site: https://www.dssmith.com.tr
Paper Product & Recycling Services

N.A.I.C.S.: 562920
DS Smith Belisce Croatia d.o.o.   **(1)**
Vijenac S H Gutmanna 30, 31551, Belisce,
Croatia
Tel.: (385) 31516202
Corrugated Paper Mfr
N.A.I.C.S.: 322211

DS Smith Bulgaria S.A.   **(1)**
Trakia Mill Glavinitsa Quarter, 4400,
Pazardzhik, Bulgaria
Tel.: (359) 34401202
Web Site: https://www.dssmith.com
Corrugated Packaging Paper Mfr
N.A.I.C.S.: 322211

DS Smith Hamburg Display
GmbH   **(1)**
Wilhelm-Bergner-Strasse 11e, 21509,
Glinde, Germany
Tel.: (49) 4072733250
Corrugated Packaging Paper Mfr
N.A.I.C.S.: 322211

DS Smith Inos Papir Servis
d.o.o.   **(1)**
Milorada Jovanovica 14, 11147, Belgrade,
Serbia
Tel.: (381) 116542066
Web Site: https://www.dssmith.com
Paper Product & Recycling Services
N.A.I.C.S.: 562920

DS Smith Kaysersberg S.A.S.   **(1)**
BP 1, 68320, Kunheim, France
Tel.: (33) 389722454
Web Site: http://www.dssmith-
kaysersberg.com
Sales Range: $300-349.9 Million
Emp.: 1,000
Corrugated Packaging, Paper & Plastic
Products Mfr
N.A.I.C.S.: 322211
Thibaut Laumonier *(Pres)*

Subsidiary (Non-US):

DS SMITH CORREX   **(2)**
Madleaze Industrial Estate Bristol Road,
Gloucester, GL1 5SG, United Kingdom
Tel.: (44) 1452316510
Web Site: http://www.dssmithcorrex.com
Sales Range: $25-49.9 Million
Emp.: 70
Plastic Sheets Mfr
N.A.I.C.S.: 326199
Iain Hannan *(Dir-Site)*

Subsidiary (Domestic):

DS SMITH DUCAPLAST   **(2)**
Zone d'Entreprises de la Kruysstraete,
59470, Wormhout, France
Tel.: (33) 3 28 65 98 90
Sales Range: $25-49.9 Million
Emp.: 40
Injection Molded Plastic Products Mfr
N.A.I.C.S.: 326199

DS SMITH RIVATEX   **(2)**
PEA de Tournebride 14 rue de la Guillaud-
erie, 44118, La Chevroliere, France
Tel.: (33) 2 51 70 91 12
Web Site: http://www.kaysersberg-
plastics.com
Injection Molded Plastic Products Mfr
N.A.I.C.S.: 326199

Subsidiary (Non-US):

DS Smith Polska S.A.   **(2)**
ul Malikow 150, 25-639, Kielce, Poland
Tel.: (48) 413673900
Web Site: https://www.dssmith.com
Sales Range: $250-299.9 Million
Emp.: 550
Mfr of Corrugated Board & Packaging
N.A.I.C.S.: 322211
Krzysztof Sadowski *(Mng Dir)*

DS Smith Slovakia s.r.o.   **(2)**
Novozamocka Cesta 3397, 947 03, Hur-
banovo, Slovakia
Tel.: (421) 35 77 10 894
Injection Molded Plastic Products Mfr
N.A.I.C.S.: 326199

DS Smith Packaging Ales SAS   **(1)**
Impasse St Alban - ZI de Croupillac, 30100,
Ales, France

Tel.: (33) 474597000
Corrugated Packaging Paper Mfr
N.A.I.C.S.: 322211

DS Smith Packaging Arenshausen
Mivepa GmbH   **(1)**
Miwepa 80, 37318, Arenshausen, Germany
Tel.: (49) 36081650
Web Site: https://mivepa-arenshausen.de
Corrugated Packaging Paper Mfr
N.A.I.C.S.: 322211

DS Smith Packaging Arnstadt
GmbH   **(1)**
Bierweg 11, 99310, Arnstadt, Germany
Tel.: (49) 36287430
Corrugated Packaging Paper Mfr
N.A.I.C.S.: 322211

DS Smith Packaging Austria
GmbH   **(1)**
Heidestrasse 15, Margarethen am Moos,
2433, Enzersdorf an der Fischa, Austria
Tel.: (43) 2230711110
Corrugated Packaging Paper Mfr
N.A.I.C.S.: 322211

DS Smith Packaging BH d.o.o.   **(1)**
Igmanska bb, Vogosca, 71320, Sarajevo,
Bosnia & Herzegovina
Tel.: (387) 33424995
Web Site: https://www.dssmith.com
Corrugated Packaging Paper Mfr
N.A.I.C.S.: 322211

DS Smith Packaging Baltic Holding
Oy   **(1)**
PL 426, PB 426, 33101, Tampere, Finland
Tel.: (358) 102452111
Corrugated Packaging Paper Mfr
N.A.I.C.S.: 322211

DS Smith Packaging Belgium
N.V.   **(1)**
New Orleansstr 100, 9000, Gent, Belgium
Tel.: (32) 92551313
Web Site: https://www.dssmith.com
Corrugated Packaging Paper Mfr
N.A.I.C.S.: 322211

DS Smith Packaging Czech Republic
s.r.o.   **(1)**
Teplicka 109, Martineves, 405 02, Jilove,
Czech Republic
Tel.: (420) 412595267
Corrugated Packaging Box Mfr
N.A.I.C.S.: 322211

DS Smith Packaging DPF SAS   **(1)**
Espace 3 Fontaines, 38140, Rives, France
Tel.: (33) 476918440
Corrugated Packaging Paper Mfr
N.A.I.C.S.: 322211

DS Smith Packaging Durtal SAS   **(1)**
ZA La Fontaine RN 23, 49430, Durtal,
France
Tel.: (33) 241213232
Corrugated Packaging Paper Mfr
N.A.I.C.S.: 322211

DS Smith Packaging Estonia AS   **(1)**
Pae 24, 11415, Tallinn, Estonia
Tel.: (372) 6138505
Web Site: https://www.dssmith.com
Corrugated Packaging Paper Mfr
N.A.I.C.S.: 322211

DS Smith Packaging Fegersheim
SAS   **(1)**
146 Rue de Lyon, 67640, Fegersheim,
France
Tel.: (33) 388645100
Corrugated Packaging Paper Mfr
N.A.I.C.S.: 322211

DS Smith Packaging Fuzesabony
Kft.   **(1)**
Patak ut 1, 3390, Fuzesabony, Hungary
Tel.: (36) 36543300
Corrugated Packaging Paper Mfr
N.A.I.C.S.: 322211

DS Smith Packaging Galicia S.A.   **(1)**
Poligono Industrial O Pousadoiro 4 Parcela
1, Vilagarcia de Arousa, 36617, Pontevedra,
Spain
Tel.: (34) 986344223
Corrugated Packaging Box Mfr
N.A.I.C.S.: 322211

DS Smith Plc—(Continued)

DS Smith Packaging Ghimbav SRL (1)
Str Fagarasului Nr 46, Ghimbav, 507075, Brasov, Romania
Tel.: (40) 26825855
Web Site: http://www.dssmith.com
Paperboard Container Mfr
N.A.I.C.S.: 322219
Remus Craciun *(Gen Mgr)*

DS Smith Packaging Kaypac SAS (1)
Zone Industrielle Voiveselles Croisette, 88800, Vittel, France
Tel.: (33) 329052002
Corrugated Packaging Paper Mfr
N.A.I.C.S.: 322211

DS Smith Packaging Larousse SAS (1)
Rue de la Deviniere, BP 7/5, 45510, Tigy, France
Tel.: (33) 238580004
Corrugated Packaging Paper Mfr
N.A.I.C.S.: 322211

DS Smith Packaging Ltd. (1)
Beech House Whitebrook Park 68 Lower Cookham Road, Maidenhead, SL6 8XY, Berkshire, United Kingdom
Tel.: (44) 1753754380
Web Site: http://www.dssmith-packaging.com
Sales Range: $25-49.9 Million
Emp.: 60
Packaging Mfr
N.A.I.C.S.: 322220
Gareth Jenkins *(Mng Dir)*

Subsidiary (Domestic):

Creo Retail Marketing Holdings Limited (2)
7 Lloyds Wharf Mill Street, London, SE1 2BD, United Kingdom
Tel.: (44) 20 7064 9820
Web Site: http://www.creo-pos.com
Holding Company; Display & Point-of-Sale Advertising Services
N.A.I.C.S.: 551112
Sarah Bell *(Client Dir)*

Subsidiary (Domestic):

Creo Retail Marketing Ltd (3)
7 Lloyds Wharf Mill Street, London, SE1 2BD, United Kingdom
Tel.: (44) 20 7064 9820
Web Site: http://www.creo-pos.com
Display & Point-of-Sale Advertising Services
N.A.I.C.S.: 541850
Richard Saysell *(Mng Dir)*

Subsidiary (Domestic):

DS Smith Corrugated Packaging Ltd (2)
Dodwells Road, Hinckley, LE10 3BX, Leicestershire, United Kingdom
Tel.: (44) 1455251400
Web Site: http://www.dssmithpackagingeurope.com
Sales Range: $50-74.9 Million
Packaging Paper Products Mfr
N.A.I.C.S.: 322220

Subsidiary (Non-US):

DS Smith Packaging Ceska Republica S.R.O. (2)
Teplicka 109 Martinine, Jilove u Decina, 405. 02, Jilove, Czech Republic
Tel.: (420) 412595267
Web Site: http://www.dssmithpackagingeurope.com
Sales Range: $25-49.9 Million
Emp.: 10
Packaging Material Distr
N.A.I.C.S.: 423840

DS Smith Packaging Denmark A/S (2)
Astrupvej 30, 8500, Grena, Denmark
Tel.: (45) 72149100
Web Site: https://www.dssmith.com
Corrugated & Solid Board Mfr
N.A.I.C.S.: 322211
Thomas Jacobsen *(Mng Dir)*

DS Smith Packaging Deutschland Stiftung & Co. KG (2)
Rollnerstrasse 14, 90408, Nuremberg, Germany
Tel.: (49) 9111801800
Sales Range: $25-49.9 Million
Emp.: 3
Containerboard Distr & Sales
N.A.I.C.S.: 424130

Plant (Domestic):

DS Smith Packaging Mannheim (3)
Essener Strasse 60, 68219, Mannheim, Germany (100%)
Tel.: (49) 6 218 9040
Web Site: https://www.dssmith.com
Sales Range: $25-49.9 Million
Containerboard Mfr
N.A.I.C.S.: 322219

DS Smith Witzenhausen Mill (3)
Witzenhausen Mill Kasseler Landstrasse 23, 37213, Witzenhausen, Germany
Tel.: (49) 55425020
Web Site: http://www.dssmith.com
Recycled Paper & Paper Products Mfr
N.A.I.C.S.: 322299
Mark Ketterle *(Gen Mgr)*

Subsidiary (Non-US):

DS Smith Packaging Finland Oy (2)
Tehdaskartanonkatu 10, PB 426, FI-33101, Tampere, Finland
Tel.: (358) 102452111
Web Site: http://www.dssmithpackagingeurope.com
Mfr of Corrugated Paper & Paperboard for Containers
N.A.I.C.S.: 322219

Affiliate (Non-US):

DS Smith Packaging France (2)
1 Terrasse Bellini, 92800, Puteaux, France
Tel.: (33) 155614411
Web Site: http://www.dssmithpackagingeurope.com
Sales Range: $25-49.9 Million
Emp.: 30
Containerboard Mfr
N.A.I.C.S.: 322219

DS Smith Packaging Italia SpA (2)
Via Torri Bianche 24, 20871, Vimercate, Italy (100%)
Tel.: (39) 03963541
Web Site: https://www.dssmith.com
Corrugated Packaging Box Mfr
N.A.I.C.S.: 322219

Plant (Domestic):

DS Smith Packaging Italia (3)
Via del Frizzone, 55016, Porcari, Lucca, Italy (100%)
Tel.: (39) 05832961
Web Site: http://www.dssmith.com
Sales Range: $25-49.9 Million
Emp.: 176
Containerboard Mfr
N.A.I.C.S.: 322219

Affiliate (Non-US):

DS Smith Packaging Nederland BV (2)
Coldenhovenseweg 130, 6961 EH, Eerbeek, Netherlands
Tel.: (31) 313 67 79 11
Sales Range: $50-74.9 Million
Emp.: 20
Packaging Paper Products Mfr
N.A.I.C.S.: 322220
E. Meyer *(Gen Mgr)*

DS Smith Packaging Poland Sp. z o.o. (2)
ul Pulawska 435A, PL 02-801, Warsaw, Poland (100%)
Tel.: (48) 225468050
Web Site: http://www.dssmithpackagingeurope.com
Packaging Mfr & Distr
N.A.I.C.S.: 322220

DS Smith Packaging Sweden AB (2)
Wellvagen 2, 331 92, Varnamo, Sweden (100%)

Tel.: (46) 37042000
Web Site: https://www.dssmith.com
Sales Range: $50-74.9 Million
Emp.: 600
Containerboard Mfr
N.A.I.C.S.: 322219

DS Smith Packaging Switzerland AG (2)
Werk Oftringen Industriestrasse, CH-4665, Oftringen, Switzerland (100%)
Tel.: (41) 627882323
Web Site: http://www.dssmithpackagingeurope.com
Sales Range: $125-149.9 Million
Containerboard Mfr
N.A.I.C.S.: 322219

DS Smith Paper Deutschland GmbH (2)
Aschaffenburg Mill Weichertstrasse 7, D-63741, Aschaffenburg, Germany (100%)
Tel.: (49) 60214000
Web Site: http://www.dssmithpackagingeurope.com
Containerboard Mfr
N.A.I.C.S.: 322219

DS Smith Verpackung + Display Vertriebsgesellschaft mbH (2)
Bellingerstrasse 5-9, 36043, Fulda, Germany
Tel.: (49) 6 618 8118
Web Site: https://www.dssmith.com
Packaging Paper Products Mfr
N.A.I.C.S.: 322220
Richard Oegl *(Mng Dir)*

Joint Venture (Non-US):

Selkasan Kagit ve Paketleme Malzemeleri Imalati San. ve Tic. A.S. (2)
Manisa OIZ 2nd Section Kecilikoy OSB Neighborhood, Mustafa Kemal Bulvari No 8 Yunusemre, 45030, Manisa, Turkiye (49%)
Tel.: (90) 236 213 0273
Web Site: https://www.selkasan.com
Sales Range: $25-49.9 Million
Paperboard Mfr
N.A.I.C.S.: 322299

Subsidiary (Domestic):

The Less Packaging Company Ltd. (2)
Thremhall Park, Start Hill, Bishop's Stortford, CM22 7WE, Herts, United Kingdom (100%)
Tel.: (44) 1279874659
Web Site: http://www.morefromlessglobal.com
Packaging Consulting Services
N.A.I.C.S.: 541618
Greg Lawson *(Grp Mng Dir)*

DS Smith Packaging Lucena, S.L. (1)
Carretera Nacional 331 Km 66 28, 14900, Lucena, Cordoba, Spain
Tel.: (34) 957786900
Corrugated Packaging Box Mfr
N.A.I.C.S.: 322211

DS Smith Packaging Mehun-CIM SASU (1)
ZI Route de Marmagne, BP 47, 18500, Mehun-sur-Yevre, France
Tel.: (33) 248235323
Corrugated Packaging Paper Mfr
N.A.I.C.S.: 322211

DS Smith Packaging Pakkausjaloste Oy (1)
Virranniementie 3, 70420, Kuopio, Finland
Tel.: (358) 102452350
Corrugated Packaging Box Mfr
N.A.I.C.S.: 322211

DS Smith Packaging Portugal, S.A. (1)
Rua Mestra Cecilia do Simao 378, Gondesende, 3885-593, Esmoriz, Portugal
Tel.: (351) 227470010
Web Site: https://www.dssmith.com
Corrugated Packaging Paper Mfr
N.A.I.C.S.: 322211

DS Smith Packaging Romania S.R.L. (1)

Tel.: (40) 256308981
Web Site: https://www.dssmith.com
Corrugated Packaging Paper Mfr
N.A.I.C.S.: 322211

DS Smith Packaging Slovakia s.r.o. (1)
Namestie Banikov 8, 048 01, Roznava, Slovakia
Tel.: (421) 587774600
Web Site: https://www.dssmith.com
Corrugated Packaging Paper Mfr
N.A.I.C.S.: 322211

DS Smith Packaging Sud Est SASU (1)
ZI du Pre de la Barre, 38440, Saint Jean Brevelay, France
Tel.: (33) 474597000
Corrugated Packaging Paper Mfr
N.A.I.C.S.: 322211

DS Smith Packaging Systems SAS (1)
12 Rue Gay Lussac, 21300, Chenove, France
Tel.: (33) 380540020
Corrugated Packaging Paper Mfr
N.A.I.C.S.: 322211

DS Smith Packaging Velin SASU (1)
ZI de la Plaine, Eloyes, 88214, Remiremont, France
Tel.: (33) 329324354
Corrugated Packaging Paper Mfr
N.A.I.C.S.: 322211

DS Smith Packaging-Holly Springs, LLC (1)
301 Thomas Mill Rd, Holly Springs, NC 27540
Tel.: (919) 567-0800
Corrugated Packaging Paper Mfr
N.A.I.C.S.: 322211

DS Smith Paper Coullons SAS (1)
Route de la Barbe Grise, 45720, Coullons, France
Tel.: (33) 238295270
Corrugated Board Mfr
N.A.I.C.S.: 322211

DS Smith Paper Italia Srl (1)
Via del Frizzone, Porcari, 55016, Lucca, Italy
Tel.: (39) 05832961
Containerboard Mfr
N.A.I.C.S.: 322211

DS Smith Paper Kaysersberg SAS (1)
77 route de Lapoutroie, 68240, Kaysersberg, France
Tel.: (33) 389783230
Corrugated Board Mfr & Distr
N.A.I.C.S.: 322211

DS Smith Paper Limited (1)
Kemsley Paper Mill, Sittingbourne, ME10 2TD, Kent, United Kingdom
Tel.: (44) 1795518900
Sales Range: $125-149.9 Million
Emp.: 400
Recycling Paper Mfr
N.A.I.C.S.: 322299

Plant (Domestic):

DS Smith Paper Ltd - Higher Kings Paper Mill (2)
Higher Kings Paper Mill, Cullompton, EX15 1QJ, Devon, United Kingdom
Tel.: (44) 1884 836300
Web Site: http://www.dssmithpaper.com
Sales Range: $50-74.9 Million
Emp.: 110
Paper Mfr
N.A.I.C.S.: 322299

DS Smith Paper Ltd - Hollins Paper Mill (2)
Hollins Road, Darwen, BB3 0BE, Lancashire, United Kingdom
Tel.: (44) 1254702728
Sales Range: $50-74.9 Million
Emp.: 120
Paper Mfr
N.A.I.C.S.: 322299

DS Smith Paper Ltd - Wansbrough Paper Mill (2)

Wansbrough Paper Mill, Watchet, TA23
0AY, Somerset, United Kingdom
Tel.: (44) 1984631456
Web Site: http://www.dssmithpaper.com
Sales Range: $50-74.9 Million
Emp.: 150
Paper Mfr
N.A.I.C.S.: 322299

Subsidiary (Domestic):

**St. Regis Paper Company
Limited** (2)
Level 3 1 Paddington Square, London, W2
1DL, Kent, United Kingdom
Tel.: (44) 1795510900
Web Site: http://www.stregis.co.uk
Sales Range: $125-149.9 Million
Waste Paper Processing Services
N.A.I.C.S.: 322299
Nick Britton (Dir-Sls & Mktg)

DS Smith Paper Rouen SAS (1)
Rue Desire Granet, 76808, Saint-Etienne-
du-Rouvray, France
Tel.: (33) 235645252
Corrugated Paper Mfr
N.A.I.C.S.: 322211

DS Smith Paper Viana, S.A. (1)
Estrada 23 de Fevereiro n 372, Deocriste,
4905-261, Viana do Castelo, Portugal
Tel.: (351) 258739600
Corrugated Paper Mfr
N.A.I.C.S.: 322211

DS Smith Paper Zarnesti. S.R.L. (1)
Strada 13 Decembrie no 18, Zarnesti,
505800, Brasov, Romania
Tel.: (40) 268223139
Corrugated Board Mfr
N.A.I.C.S.: 322211

**DS Smith Plc - KARTOTEX
Plant** (1)
Via Sicilia 111, Perignano, Lari, 56030, Italy
Tel.: (39) 058761921
Corrugated Board & Boxes Mfr
N.A.I.C.S.: 322211

**DS Smith Recycling Benelux
B.V.** (1)
Coldenhovenseweg 130, Postbus 193,
6961 EH, Eerbeek, Netherlands
Tel.: (31) 313670100
Web Site: https://www.dssmith.com
Paper Product & Recycling Services
N.A.I.C.S.: 562920

DS Smith Recycling Group (1)
Ty Gwyrdd 11 Beddau Way, Caerphilly,
CF83 2AX, United Kingdom
Tel.: (44) 2920102048
Web Site: http://www.dssmithrecycling.com
Emp.: 700
Waste Paper Collection & Processing Ser-
vices
N.A.I.C.S.: 322299
Mathew Prosser (Mng Dir)

Subsidiary (Non-US):

**DS Smith Recycling Deutschland
GmbH** (2)
Kufsteiner Strasse 27, 83064, Raubling,
Germany
Tel.: (49) 803587750
Web Site: https://www.dssmith.com
Sales Range: $25-49.9 Million
Emp.: 21
Paper Materials Recycling Services
N.A.I.C.S.: 562920
Herr Achim Wiese (CEO & Mng Dir)

Subsidiary (Domestic):

DS Smith Recycling UK Limited (2)
Level 3 1 Paddington Square, London, W2
1DL, Kent, United Kingdom
Tel.: (44) 622883000
Web Site: http://www.dssmithrecycling.com
Sales Range: $25-49.9 Million
Emp.: 100
Paper Recycling
N.A.I.C.S.: 423930

Subsidiary (Non-US):

Italmaceri S.r.l. (2)
Via Sacco E Vanzetti 13, 50145, Florence,
FI, Italy

Tel.: (39) 05 531 7772
Web Site: https://www.italmaceri.com
Sales Range: $25-49.9 Million
Emp.: 32
Wastepaper Collection & Processing
N.A.I.C.S.: 423930

DS Smith Recycling Italia Srl (1)
Strada Lanzo 237, 10148, Turin, Italy
Tel.: (39) 0112282912
Web Site: https://www.dssmith.com
Paper Product & Recycling Services
N.A.I.C.S.: 562920

DS Smith Recycling Spain S.A. (1)
Avenida de El Norte de Castilla 20 Poligono
de Argales, 47008, Valladolid, Spain
Tel.: (34) 983391622
Web Site: https://www.dssmith.com
Paper Product & Recycling Services
N.A.I.C.S.: 562920

DS Smith Slovenija d.o.o. (1)
Cesta Prvih Borcev 51, Brestanica, 8280,
Krsko, Slovenia
Tel.: (386) 74801500
Web Site: https://www.dssmith.com
Corrugated Packaging Paper Mfr
N.A.I.C.S.: 322211

DS Smith Triss s.r.o. (1)
Zirovnicka 3124, 106 00, Prague, Czech
Republic
Tel.: (420) 267182714
Corrugated Packaging Box Mfr
N.A.I.C.S.: 322211

**DS Smith Unijapapir Croatia
d.o.o.** (1)
Lastovska 5, 10000, Zagreb, Croatia
Tel.: (385) 16184729
Web Site: http://www.dssmith.com
Paper Product & Recycling Services
N.A.I.C.S.: 562920

Delta Packaging Services GmbH (1)
Siemensstrasse 8, D-50259, Pulheim, Ger-
many
Tel.: (49) 223894910
Web Site: https://www.deltapackaging.de
Corrugated Packaging Paper Mfr
N.A.I.C.S.: 322211
Reinhard Mitzkus (Co-CEO)

Ducaplast S.A.S (1)
La Kruys Straete Zone D Entreprises,
59470, Wormhout, France
Tel.: (33) 328659890
Plastics Foam Packaging Whslr
N.A.I.C.S.: 423840

Duropack GmbH (1)
Brunnerstrasse 75, 1230, Vienna, Austria
Tel.: (43) 1 86 300 0
Web Site: http://www.duropack.at
Sales Range: $300-349.9 Million
Emp.: 2,682
Packaging, Corrugated Board & Paper Mfr
N.A.I.C.S.: 322211

Subsidiary (Non-US):

DS Smith AD (2)
U I 1632 No 1, 1000, Skopje, North Mace-
donia
Tel.: (389) 2551081
Web Site: https://www.dssmith.com
Rev.: $8,204,701,960
Assets: $11,710,335,000
Liabilities: $7,160,615,280
Net Worth: $4,549,719,720
Earnings: $715,518,440
Emp.: 30,000
Fiscal Year-end: 04/30/2020
Online Advertising Services
N.A.I.C.S.: 541850
Geoff Drabble (Chm)

Duropack Krusevac A. D. (2)
Balkanska 72, 37000, Krusevac, Serbia
Tel.: (381) 37428556
Web Site: http://www.duropack.rs
Paper Products Mfr
N.A.I.C.S.: 322211

Duropack Starpack Kft. (2)
Duropack st 1, 3390, Fuzesabony, Hungary
Tel.: (36) 36543300
Web Site: http://www.duropack.hu
Paper Product Distr
N.A.I.C.S.: 424130

Duropack Stemi Ltd. (2)
Western Industrial Zone, 7200, Razgrad,
Bulgaria
Tel.: (359) 84660812
Paper Products Mfr
N.A.I.C.S.: 322211
Todor Karaboychev (Mgr-Sls)

Duropack Trakia Papir S.A. (2)
Glavinitsa Quarter, 4400, Pazardzhik, Bul-
garia
Tel.: (359) 34401202
Paper Products Mfr
N.A.I.C.S.: 322211
Atanas Kaludov (Exec Dir)

Duropack Turpak Obaly a.s. (2)
Robotnicka 1, 036 80, Martin, Slovakia
Tel.: (421) 434240111
Web Site: http://www.duropack.sk
Corrugated Board & Paper Mfr
N.A.I.C.S.: 322211

Duropack d.o.o. (2)
Trzaska cesta 1, 1370, Logatec, Slovenia
Tel.: (386) 17598200
Web Site: http://www.duropack.si
Paper Product Distr
N.A.I.C.S.: 424130
Alenka Cernelic (Mgr-Fin)

**Industria Cartonera Asturiana,
S.A.** (1)
Pol Ind San Claudio Nave 13, San Claudio,
33191, Oviedo, Spain
Tel.: (34) 985780005
Web Site:
    https://www.cartonerasturiana.com
Corrugated Fiber Board Mfr
N.A.I.C.S.: 322211

Mivepa GmbH (1)
Miwepa 80, 37318, Arenshausen, Germany
Tel.: (49) 36081650
Web Site: https://mivepa-arenshausen.de
Packaging Services
N.A.I.C.S.: 561910

**Nova DS Smith Embalagem,
S.A.** (1)
Rua do Monte Grande 3, Guilhabreu, 4485-
255, Vila do Conde, Portugal
Tel.: (351) 229871300
Corrugated Packaging Paper Mfr
N.A.I.C.S.: 322211

SIA DS Smith Packaging Latvia (1)
Hospitalu Iela 23-102, Riga, LV-1013, Latvia
Tel.: (371) 67860066
Web Site: https://www.dssmith.com
Corrugated Packaging Paper Mfr
N.A.I.C.S.: 322211

Tecnicarton France S.A.S. (1)
27 Rue du Tennis, Baume Les Dames,
25110, Besancon, France
Tel.: (33) 381605230
Corrugated Packaging Paper Mfr
N.A.I.C.S.: 322211

**Tecnicarton Portugal Unipessoal
Lda** (1)
Apartado 201 Raso de Paredes, Agueda,
3754-909, Aveiro, Portugal
Tel.: (351) 234690130
Corrugated Packaging Paper Mfr
N.A.I.C.S.: 322211

Toscana Ondulati SpA (1)
Via del Fanuccio 126, Frazione Capannori,
55010, Marlia, LU, Italy
Tel.: (39) 0583440911
Web Site: https://www.toscanaondulati.it
Corrugated Board & Boxes Mfr
N.A.I.C.S.: 322211

**UAB DS Smith Packaging
Lithuania** (1)
Savanoriu pr 183, LT-02300, Vilnius, Lithu-
ania
Tel.: (370) 52361700
Web Site: https://www.dssmith.com
Corrugated Packaging Paper Mfr
N.A.I.C.S.: 322211

DS SPEDITION GMBH
Leopoldstr 230, 80807, Munich, Ger-
many
Tel.: (49) 89350350   De

Web Site: http://www.ds-spedition.de
Year Founded: 1983
Sales Range: $25-49.9 Million
Freight Transport Logistics Services
N.A.I.C.S.: 541614
Janusch Swoboda (Co-CEO)

DSC INVESTMENT INC.
3F, 10 Ttukseom-ro 1-gil, Seongdong-
gu, Seoul, 06248, Korea (South)
Tel.: (82) 234533190
Web Site:
    https://www.dscinvestment.com
Year Founded. 2012
Emp.: 12
Venture Capital Investment Services
N.A.I.C.S.: 523910
Ara Koh (Gen Mgr)

DSEC CO., LTD.
67 Chungjang-daero13 beon-gil,
Jung-gu, Busan, Korea (South)
Tel.: (82) 516602114
Web Site: http://www.idsec.co.kr
Year Founded: 1993
Ship Building Services
N.A.I.C.S.: 336611
Shin Joon Sup (CEO)

DSG GLOBAL INC.
207-15272 Croydon Drive, Surrey,
V3Z 0Z5, BC, Canada
Tel.: (604) 575-3848   NV
Web Site: https://dsgtglobal.com
Year Founded: 2007
DSGT—(OTCQB)
Rev.: $3,833,853
Assets: $2,244,296
Liabilities: $11,799,933
Net Worth: ($9,555,637)
Earnings: ($7,547,391)
Emp.: 40
Fiscal Year-end: 12/31/22
Investment Services
N.A.I.C.S.: 523999
Clint Singer (Sr Engr-Software-
Vantage Tag Systems)

DSG INTERNATIONAL LIM-
ITED
1503 Millennium Trade Centre 56
Kwai Cheong Road, Kwai Chung,
China (Hong Kong)
Tel.: (852) 81998328   HK
Web Site: http://www.dsgil.com
Year Founded: 1973
Sales Range: $900-999.9 Million
Emp.: 40,012
Baby Diaper & Adult Incontinence
&Feminine Napkin & Training Pants
Product Mfr
N.A.I.C.S.: 322291
Brandon S. L. Wang (Chm)

Subsidiaries:

DSG (Malaysia) Sdn. Bhd. (1)
542 Jalan Subeng 2 Penaga Industrial
Park, 47500, Subang Jaya, Selangor,
Malaysia   (100%)
Tel.: (60) 380231833
Web Site: http://www.dsg.com.my
Sales Range: $50-74.9 Million
Emp.: 200
N.A.I.C.S.: 322291

**DSG International (Thailand) Public
Company Limited** (1)
11 Floor, Regent House Building 183
Rajdamri Road, Lumpini Pathumwan, Bang-
kok, 10330, Thailand
Tel.: (66) 26518061
Web Site: http://th.dsgap.com
Sales Range: $10-24.9 Million
Emp.: 450
Baby & Adult Diaper Mfr
N.A.I.C.S.: 322291
Heng Fai Chan (CEO)

DSG International Limited—(Continued)

Subsidiary (Non-US):

PT DSG Surya Mas Indonesia   **(2)**
Menara Duta 7th Floor Wing D Jalan HR
Rasuna Said Kav, Jakarta, 12910, Indonesia
Tel.: (62) 215256316
Web Site: http://in.dsgap.com
Diapers Mfr
N.A.I.C.S.: 322291

**Disposable Soft Goods (Malaysia)
Sdn. Bhd.**   **(1)**
542 Jalan Subeng 2 Penaga Indus Pk,
47500, Subang Jaya, Selangor, Malaysia
Tel.: (60) 380231833
Web Site: http://www.dsg.com.my
Sales Range: $50-74.9 Million
Emp.: 200
N.A.I.C.S.: 322291

**Disposable Soft Goods (S) Pte.
Ltd.**   **(1)**
3 Bukit Batok St 22, Singapore, 659582,
Singapore   **(100%)**
Tel.: (65) 68619155
Web Site: http://www.fitti.com
Sales Range: $25-49.9 Million
Emp.: 20
N.A.I.C.S.: 322291

Disposable Soft Goods Limited   **(1)**
Room 1503 Millennium Trade Centre, 56
Kwai Cheong Road, Kwai Chung, NT,
China (Hong Kong)   **(100%)**
Tel.: (852) 24276951
Web Site: http://www.dsgil.com
Sales Range: $25-49.9 Million
Emp.: 30
N.A.I.C.S.: 322291

DSK CO., LTD.
21 Ansantekom 1-gil, Sangnok-Gu,
Ansan, 426220, Gyeonggi, Korea
(South)
Tel.: (82) 314199100
Web Site: https://www.dsk.co.kr
Year Founded: 1995
109740—(KRS)
Rev.: $36,993,935
Assets: $148,666,628
Liabilities: $35,875,249
Net Worth: $112,791,379
Earnings: ($7,377,507)
Emp.: 126
Fiscal Year-end: 12/31/22
Flat Panel Displays Mfr
N.A.I.C.S.: 334118
Tae-Gu Kim *(Co-CEO)*

Subsidiaries:

Protox Co., Ltd.   **(1)**
96 Jeyakgongdan 4-gil Sangsin-ri,
Hyangnam-eup, Hwaseong, Gyeonggi-do,
Korea (South)
Tel.: (82) 7040188200
Web Site: https://www.iprotox.co.kr
Biological Product Mfr
N.A.I.C.S.: 325414
Dong-Bum Lee *(CEO)*

DSM-FIRMENICH AG
Wurmisweg 576, 4303, Kaiseraugst,
Switzerland
Tel.: (41) 618158888   CH
Web Site: https://www.dsm-
firmenich.com
Year Founded: 1902
DSFIR—(EUR)
Rev.: $11,710,954,000
Assets: $37,765,540,000
Liabilities: $12,342,400,000
Net Worth: $25,423,140,000
Earnings: ($700,872,000)
Emp.: 26,643
Fiscal Year-end: 12/31/23
Beauty Product Mfr
N.A.I.C.S.: 325620
Thomas Leysen *(Chm)*

DSNL CO LTD

4F Fortis Building 17 Seongnam-
daero 779 beon-gil, Bundang-gu,
Seongnam, 13567, Gyeonggi-do, Ko-
rea (South)
Tel.: (82) 317091407
Web Site: http://www.fortis.co.kr
Year Founded: 2006
141020—(KRS)
Rev.: $30,520,522
Assets: $13,311,492
Liabilities: $12,342,185
Net Worth: $969,307
Earnings: ($10,141,415)
Emp.: 45
Fiscal Year-end: 12/31/22
Digital Set Top Boxes Mfr
N.A.I.C.S.: 334220
Barry V. Perry *(Pres & CEO)*

DSNR MEDIA GROUP
8 Hapnina Street, 43215, Ra'anana,
Israel
Tel.: (972) 9 7626161
Web Site: http://www.dsnrmg.com
Year Founded: 2001
Sales Range: $10-24.9 Million
Emp.: 25
Online & Mobile Advertising Solutions
N.A.I.C.S.: 541890
Shauli Elimelech *(CEO)*

DSPACE GMBH
Rathenaustrasse 26, Paderborn,
33102, Germany
Tel.: (49) 525116380
Web Site: http://www.dspace.com
Year Founded: 1988
Rev.: $124,146,000
Emp.: 1,700
Digital Signal Processing & Control
Engineering Services
N.A.I.C.S.: 541330
Martin Goetzeler *(CEO)*

Subsidiaries:

dSPACE Inc.   **(1)**
50131 Pontiac Trl, Wixom, MI 48393-2020
Tel.: (248) 295-4700
Web Site: http://www.dspaceinc.com
Automotive Testing Services
N.A.I.C.S.: 811198
Peter Waeltermann *(Pres)*

dSPACE Japan K.K.   **(1)**
10F Gotenyama Trust Tower 4-7-35 Kitashi-
nagawa, Shinagawa-ku, Tokyo, 140-0001,
Japan
Tel.: (81) 357985460
Web Site: http://www.dspace.jp
Automotive Testing Services
N.A.I.C.S.: 811198
Takashi Miyano *(Pres)*

dSPACE Ltd.   **(1)**
Unit B7 Beech House Melbourn Science
Park, Melbourn, SG8 6HB, Hertfordshire,
United Kingdom
Tel.: (44) 1763269020
Web Site: http://www.dspace.co.uk
Automotive Testing Services
N.A.I.C.S.: 811198
Carene Kamel *(Engr-Sls Applications)*

**dSPACE Mechatronic Control Tech-
nology (Shanghai) Co., Ltd.**   **(1)**
Unit 1101-1105 11F/L Middle Xizang Rd 18
Harbour Ring Plaza, 200001, Shanghai,
China
Tel.: (86) 2163917666
Web Site: http://www.dspace.asia
Automotive Testing Services
N.A.I.C.S.: 811198
Zhou Zhiguo *(Engr-Field Application)*

dSPACE SARL   **(1)**
7 Parc Burospace Route de Gisy, 91573,
Bievres, Cedex, France
Tel.: (33) 169355060
Web Site: http://www.dspace.fr
Automotive Testing Services
N.A.I.C.S.: 811198

DSR CORP.
7 Noksansaneopjung-ro 192beon-gil,
Gangseo-gu, Busan, 46753, Korea
(South)
Tel.: (82) 519790500
Web Site: https://www.dsrcorp.com
Year Founded: 1965
155660—(KRS)
Rev.: $188,993,256
Assets: $214,473,271
Liabilities: $72,169,387
Net Worth: $142,303,884
Earnings: $14,752,721
Emp.: 168
Fiscal Year-end: 12/31/22
Fishing Nets & Ropes Mfr
N.A.I.C.S.: 314994
Choi Minhwan *(Mng Dir)*

Subsidiaries:

**DSR Corp. - Gwangyang Stainless
Steel Factory**   **(1)**
75 Chonamgongdan-gil, Gwangyang,
Jeollanam-do, Korea (South)
Tel.: (82) 61 762 8351
Web Site: http://www.dsr.com
Wire Ropes Mfr
N.A.I.C.S.: 332618

DSR International Corp   **(1)**
290 Broadhollow Rd Ste 240E, Melville, NY
11747
Tel.: (631) 427-2600
Wire Rope Distr
N.A.I.C.S.: 423840

DSR Qingdao Limited   **(1)**
Chengyang-Qu Liuting Jiedao Shuangyu-
anlu Xice, Qingdao, Shandong-Sheng,
China
Tel.: (86) 53287716901
Wire Ropes Mfr
N.A.I.C.S.: 332618

DSR TAIKO BERHAD
DSR Village Lot 118 Kg Sang Lee,
PT 1950, Raub, 27620, Pahang, Ma-
laysia
Tel.: (60) 386832285
Web Site: https://www.dsrfruits.com
Year Founded: 2017
DSR—(KLS)
Rev.: $3,877,804
Assets: $19,280,125
Liabilities: $5,795,237
Net Worth: $13,484,888
Earnings: $677,265
Fiscal Year-end: 06/30/24
Fruit Product Distr
N.A.I.C.S.: 424490
Carol Tong *(CMO)*

DSR WIRE CORPORATION
291 Seonpueng-ri, Seo-myeon, Sun-
cheon, Jeonnam, Korea (South)
Tel.: (82) 617520121
Web Site: http://www.dsr.com
Year Founded: 1965
069730—(KRS)
Rev.: $200,714,053
Assets: $198,958,386
Liabilities: $58,524,094
Net Worth: $140,434,292
Earnings: $22,186,585
Emp.: 162
Fiscal Year-end: 12/31/22
Wire Ropes Mfr
N.A.I.C.S.: 332618
Ok Ju You *(Exec Dir)*

Subsidiaries:

DSR Trading Corp   **(1)**
Astro Shinosaka Bldg Room No 805 5-7-18
Nishinakajima, Yodogawa-ku, Osaka, 532-
0011, Japan
Tel.: (81) 668852750
Wire Rope Distr
N.A.I.C.S.: 423510

**DSR Wire Corporation - Suncheon
Factory 1**   **(1)**
15 Sandan 1-gil Seo-myeon, Suncheon,
Jeollanam-do, Korea (South)
Tel.: (82) 61 729 3500
Wire Ropes Mfr
N.A.I.C.S.: 332618

**DSR Wire Corporation - Suncheon
Factory 2**   **(1)**
38 Sandan 4-gil, Seo-myeon, Suncheon,
Jeollanam-do, Korea (South)
Tel.: (82) 61 751 7121
Wire Ropes Mfr
N.A.I.C.S.: 332618

**DSR Wire Corporation - Yulchon
Factory**   **(1)**
80-21 Yulchonsandan 1-ro Haeryong-
myeon, Suncheon, Jeollanam-do, Korea
(South)
Tel.: (82) 61 729 3700
Wire Ropes Mfr
N.A.I.C.S.: 332618

DSS SUSTAINABLE SOLU-
TIONS SWITZERLAND SA
Chemin Jean-Baptiste Vandelle 3A,
1290, Versoix, Switzerland
Tel.: (41) 335880097
Web Site:
https://www.consultdss.com
Year Founded: 1968
Business Consulting & Services
N.A.I.C.S.: 541618
Alistair R. Cox *(Chm)*

Subsidiaries:

**ADS System Safety Consulting,
LLC**   **(1)**
13 N St, Brookeville, MD 20833
Tel.: (240) 882-1126
Web Site: http://www.adssafety.com
Engineeering Services
N.A.I.C.S.: 541330
Kahlil M. Allen *(CEO & Partner)*

DST CO., LTD.
853 Yulsaeng ri Daegot-Myeo,
Gimpo, Gyeonggi, Korea (South)
Tel.: (82) 319976181
Web Site: http://www.korid.co.kr
Year Founded: 1995
033430—(KRS)
Rev.: $21,284,851
Assets: $26,491,333
Liabilities: $19,768,041
Net Worth: $6,723,291
Earnings: $1,446,624
Emp.: 65
Fiscal Year-end: 12/31/22
Mining Services
N.A.I.C.S.: 212290

DSV A/S
Hovedgaden 630, PO Box 210, 2640,
Hedehusene, Denmark
Tel.: (45) 43203040   DK
Web Site: https://www.dsv.com
Year Founded: 1976
DSV—(CSE)
Rev.: $19,136,895,240
Assets: $15,887,987,500
Liabilities: $8,080,671,710
Net Worth: $7,807,315,790
Earnings: $702,868,060
Emp.: 56,621
Fiscal Year-end: 12/31/20
Freight Transportation & Logistic Ser-
vices
N.A.I.C.S.: 541614
Jens H. Lund *(COO-Grp & Member-
Exec Bd)*

Subsidiaries:

Agility Logistics SARL   **(1)**
24 Rue des Oasis-Hydra, 16000, Algiers,
Algeria
Tel.: (213) 21563483
Transport & Logistics Services

N.A.I.C.S.: 541614

Campbell Freight Agencies Limited (1)
World Cargo Centre 605 Antrim Road, Newtown Abbey, Belfast, BT36 4RF, United Kingdom
Tel.: (44) 2890849000
Web Site: http://www.dsv.com
Sales Range: $25-49.9 Million
Emp.: 50
Air & Sea Freight Transportation Services
N.A.I.C.S.: 481112

Collico Verpackungslogistik und Service GmbH (1)
To Eisenhammer 11, 46049, Oberhausen, Germany
Tel.: (49) 2086960280
Web Site: http://www.collico.de
Sales Range: $25-49.9 Million
Emp.: 35
Packaging & Logistics Services
N.A.I.C.S.: 561910
Peter Kohler *(Mng Dir)*

DSV AIR & SEA S.A. (1)
Juncal 1437 - Office 207, 11000, Montevideo, Uruguay
Tel.: (598) 29165352
Web Site: https://www.uy.dsv.com
Logistics Consulting Servies
N.A.I.C.S.: 541614

DSV AIR & SEA W.L.L. (1)
Bldg No737 Road 1510 Block 115, PO Box 1654, 1654, Al-Hidd, Bahrain
Tel.: (973) 17715530
Air & Sea Freight Transportation Services
N.A.I.C.S.: 541614

DSV Air & Sea (1)
Bairro de Muntanhane Estrada Circular Q2 Bloco F Nr 102, Marracuene-Sede, 1100, Maputo, Mozambique
Tel.: (258) 21427141
Web Site: http://www.mz.dsv.com
Air & Sea Freight Services
N.A.I.C.S.: 541614
John Philipp Buechler *(Mng Dir)*

DSV Air & Sea (Hungary) Ltd. (1)
Vasut U 11, Budaors, 2040, Hungary
Tel.: (36) 213780378
Web Site: https://www.hu.dsv.com
Sales Range: $50-74.9 Million
Emp.: 100
Air & Sea Freight Transportation Services
N.A.I.C.S.: 481112

DSV Air & Sea (PR) Inc. (1)
Lot 3-4C A St Sabana Gardens, Carolina, PR 00983
Tel.: (787) 474-0636
Transport & Logistics Services
N.A.I.C.S.: 541614

DSV Air & Sea (PTY) Limited (1)
Plot 43 Commerce Park, 9267, Gaborone, Botswana
Tel.: (267) 3913586
Freight Forwarding Services
N.A.I.C.S.: 488510

DSV Air & Sea A/S (1)
Hovedgaden 630, PO Box 210, 2640, Hedehusene, Hovedstaden, Denmark
Tel.: (45) 43203040
Emp.: 800
Air & Sea Freight Transportation Services
N.A.I.C.S.: 481112

DSV Air & Sea AB (1)
Industrigatan 11-13, 195 60, Arlandastad, Sweden
Tel.: (46) 859492030
Web Site: https://www.dsv.com
Air & Sea Freight Transportation Services
N.A.I.C.S.: 481112

DSV Air & Sea AG (1)
Schuppisstrasse 3, 9016, Saint Gallen, Switzerland
Tel.: (41) 712824545
Air & Sea Freight Transportation Services
N.A.I.C.S.: 541614

DSV Air & Sea AS (1)
Leiraveien 13 B, 2000, Lillestrom, Norway
Tel.: (47) 91509870
Web Site: https://www.dsv.com

Air & Sea Freight Transportation Services
N.A.I.C.S.: 481112

DSV Air & Sea AS (1)
Ruzgarlibahce Mh Cumhuriyet Cd No 10, Kavacik/Beykoz, 34810, Istanbul, Turkiye
Tel.: (90) 4444378
Sales Range: $25-49.9 Million
Emp.: 35
Air & Sea Freight Transportation Services
N.A.I.C.S.: 481112

DSV Air & Sea Co. Ltd. (1)
38F 1 Grand Gateway No 1 Hongqiao Road, Shanghai, China
Tel.: (86) 2154069800
Web Site: https://www.dsv.com
Sales Range: $250-299.9 Million
Emp.: 635
Air & Sea Freight Transportation Services
N.A.I.C.S.: 481112

Branch (Domestic):

DSV Air & Sea Co., Ltd. (2)
No 20 Jiuxianqiao Rd 2307-2308 23F One Indigo, Chaoyang District, Beijing, 100016, China
Tel.: (86) 1085407288
Web Site: http://www.cn.dsv.com
Emp.: 3,000
Air & Sea Freight Transportation Services
N.A.I.C.S.: 488510

DSV Air & Sea Co. Ltd. (1)
30 Phan Thuc Duyen St 5th Floor SCSC Building, Tan Binh Dist, 700000, Ho Chi Minh City, Vietnam
Tel.: (84) 2839487800
Web Site: https://www.dsv.com
Sales Range: $25-49.9 Million
Emp.: 70
Air & Sea Freight Transportation Services
N.A.I.C.S.: 481112

DSV Air & Sea Co., Ltd (1)
10F No 333 Ruiguang Road, Neihu District, Taipei, 114063, Taiwan
Tel.: (886) 227999000
Web Site: https://www.dsv.com
Freight Forwarding Services
N.A.I.C.S.: 488510

DSV Air & Sea Co., Ltd. (1)
Osaka Sangyo Bldg 2F 1-10-2, Shinmachi Nishi-ku, Osaka, 550-0013, Japan
Tel.: (81) 645604910
Web Site: https://www.jp.dsv.com
Sales Range: $25-49.9 Million
Emp.: 25
Air & Sea Freight Transportation Services
N.A.I.C.S.: 481112

DSV Air & Sea Dominicana, S.R.L. (1)
Av 27 de Febrero 325 Torre Profesional Km Evaristo Morales, National District, 10147, Santo Domingo, Dominican Republic
Tel.: (809) 8097328436
Transport & Logistics Services
N.A.I.C.S.: 541614

DSV Air & Sea GmbH (1)
Isarstrasse 5, 65451, Kelsterbach, Germany
Tel.: (49) 614292020
Web Site: http://www.dsv.com
Sales Range: $50-74.9 Million
Emp.: 90
Freight Forwarding
N.A.I.C.S.: 488510

DSV Air & Sea Inc. (1)
100 Walnut Ave Ste 405, Clark, NJ 07066
Tel.: (732) 850-8000
Web Site: http://www.dsv.com
Sales Range: $125-149.9 Million
Emp.: 440
Air & Sea Freight Services
N.A.I.C.S.: 481212
Carsten Trolle *(CEO)*

DSV Air & Sea Inc. (1)
2A Johanne St Bgy Sto Nino, Paranaque, 1704, Metro Manila, Philippines
Tel.: (63) 283969800
Web Site: https://www.dsv.com
Air & Sea Freight Services
N.A.I.C.S.: 481212

DSV Air & Sea Inc. (1)

2200 Yukon Court, Milton, L9E 1N5, ON, Canada
Tel.: (905) 203-2020
Air & Sea Freight Services
N.A.I.C.S.: 488510

DSV Air & Sea International Private Limited (1)
A203 B201 B204 B301 The Qube C T S No 1489/A M V Road Marol, Andheri East, Mumbai, 400059, Maharashtra, India
Tel.: (91) 2271999000
Transport & Logistics Services
N.A.I.C.S.: 541614

DSV Air & Sea JSC (1)
Derbenevskaya nab 7 bldg 9, 115114, Moscow, Russia
Tel.: (7) 4957218979
Transport & Logistics Services
N.A.I.C.S.: 541614

DSV Air & Sea LLC (1)
Dubai Intl Airport Rd WHSE 1406 Building B, PO Box 126110, Dubai Cargo Village, Dubai, United Arab Emirates
Tel.: (971) 44408636
Web Site: https://www.dsv.com
Sales Range: $50-74.9 Million
Emp.: 80
Air & Sea Freight Transportation Services
N.A.I.C.S.: 481112

DSV Air & Sea Limited (1)
19 Landing Drive Auckland International Airport, Auckland, 2022, New Zealand
Tel.: (64) 92551100
Sales Range: $25-49.9 Million
Emp.: 120
Freight Forwarding Services
N.A.I.C.S.: 488510

DSV Air & Sea Limited (1)
Alameda Dr Carlos D'Assumpcao 258 Praca Kin Heng Long 10/F T, Macau, China (Macau)
Tel.: (853) 28700482
Web Site: https://www.dsv.com
Freight Forwarding Services
N.A.I.C.S.: 488510

DSV Air & Sea Limited (1)
Plot 9466 Kafue Road, Makeni, Lusaka, Zambia
Tel.: (260) 211455400
Freight Forwarding Services
N.A.I.C.S.: 488510

DSV Air & Sea Limited (1)
Gateway House Stonehouse Lane, Purfleet, RM19 1NX, Essex, United Kingdom
Tel.: (44) 1708892000
Web Site: https://www.dsv.com
Sales Range: $25-49.9 Million
Emp.: 35
Air & Sea Freight Transportation Services
N.A.I.C.S.: 481112

DSV Air & Sea Limited (1)
Unit 609 Harbour Point BP Little Island, Cork, T45 D230, Ireland
Tel.: (353) 214520950
Sales Range: $50-74.9 Million
Emp.: 430
Air & Sea Freight Transportation Services
N.A.I.C.S.: 481112
Martin Slott *(Mng Dir)*

DSV Air & Sea Ltd (1)
Tel.: (880) 9604800800
Web Site: https://www.dsv.com
Emp.: 45
Freight Forwarding Services
N.A.I.C.S.: 488510

DSV Air & Sea Ltd. (1)
27/13 Phatthana Chonnabot 4 Rd, Khlong Song Ton Nun Lat Krabang, Bangkok, 10520, Thailand
Tel.: (66) 28378789
Web Site: https://www.dsv.com
Sales Range: $75-99.9 Million
Emp.: 189
Air & Sea Freight Transportation Services
N.A.I.C.S.: 481112

DSV Air & Sea Ltd. (1)
16th Floor Hanssem Bldg 179 Seongam-ro, Mapo-gu, Seoul, 03929, Korea (South)
Tel.: (82) 23231313
Web Site: https://www.dsv.com

Sales Range: $50-74.9 Million
Emp.: 60
Air & Sea Freight Transportation Services
N.A.I.C.S.: 481112

DSV Air & Sea Ltd. (1)
221 Sule Road Unit 1409/10 Sule Square, 11181, Yangon, Myanmar
Tel.: (95) 101376918
Freight Forwarding Services
N.A.I.C.S.: 488510

DSV Air & Sea Ltd. (1)
44 Hama'ayan Street, 7178566, Modi'in-Maccabim-Re'ut, Israel
Tel.: (972) 89146111
Freight Forwarding Services
N.A.I.C.S.: 488510

DSV Air & Sea Ltd. (1)
ATL Logistics Centre B 1/F 11/F 13/F, Kwai Tsing, Kwai Chung, NT, China (Hong Kong)
Tel.: (852) 22325300
Web Site: https://www.dsv.com
Sales Range: $75-99.9 Million
Emp.: 100
Air & Sea Freight Transportation Services
N.A.I.C.S.: 481112

DSV Air & Sea NV (1)
Straatsburgdok-Zuidkaai 6, 2030, Antwerp, Belgium
Tel.: (32) 36110600
Sales Range: $25-49.9 Million
Emp.: 40
Air & Sea Freight Transportation Services
N.A.I.C.S.: 481112
Gernbaptista Vanelslander *(Mgr-Sls)*

DSV Air & Sea OOD (1)
Tel.: (359) 29267800
Sales Range: $25-49.9 Million
Emp.: 12
Road Transport & Logistics Services
N.A.I.C.S.: 484110

DSV Air & Sea Oy (1)
Trukkikuja 3, PO Box 142, Uusimaa, 1360, Vantaa, Finland
Tel.: (358) 207388344
Air & Sea Freight Transportation Services
N.A.I.C.S.: 481112
Daniel Wikman *(Mng Dir)*

DSV Air & Sea PA Inc. (1)
Tel.: (507) 2801111
Transport & Logistics Services
N.A.I.C.S.: 541614

DSV Air & Sea Pakistan (SMC-Private) Limited (1)
Citi View Block 3 Shaheed-e-Millat 4th Floor, Bahadur Yar Jung Co-o Housing, Karachi, 74880, Sindh, Pakistan
Tel.: (92) 2138893985
Freight Forwarding Services
N.A.I.C.S.: 488510

DSV Air & Sea Portugal, Lda (1)
Rua Campo do Martelo 319, Vilar do Pinheiro, 4485-959, Porto, Portugal
Tel.: (351) 229479200
Transport & Logistics Services
N.A.I.C.S.: 541614

DSV Air & Sea Pte. Ltd (1)
9 Pioneer View, Singapore, 627581, Singapore
Tel.: (65) 64778640
Web Site: http://www.dsv.com
Sales Range: $25-49.9 Million
Emp.: 70
Logistics & Freight Services
N.A.I.C.S.: 481212

DSV Air & Sea Pty. Ltd. (1)
59 Calarco Drive, Derrimut, 3030, NSW, Australia
Tel.: (61) 393306222
Web Site: http://www.dsv.com
Sales Range: $75-99.9 Million
Emp.: 135
Air & Sea Freight Transportation Services
N.A.I.C.S.: 481112
Paul Thomson *(Mng Dir)*

DSV Air & Sea Pvt. Ltd. (1)
A203 B201 B204 B301 The Qube C T S No 1489/A M V Road, Marol Andheri East, Mumbai, 400059, Maharashtra, India
Tel.: (91) 2271999000

DSV A/S—(Continued)

Sales Range: $50-74.9 Million
Emp.: 100
Air & Sea Freight Transportation Services
N.A.I.C.S.: 481112

DSV Air & Sea S.A. (1)
Calle Amador Marino Reyna 281 2 Floor Off
201, 15046, Lima, Peru
Tel.: (51) 16208080
Transport & Logistics Services
N.A.I.C.S.: 541614

DSV Air & Sea S.A. (1)
Hipolito Bouchard 547 Piso 3, Federal District, 1106, Buenos Aires, Argentina
Tel.: (54) 1143484500
Transport & Logistics Services
N.A.I.C.S.: 541614

DSV Air & Sea S.A. (1)
Luxair Cargo Center, 1360, Luxembourg,
Luxembourg
Tel.: (352) 26932040
Transport & Logistics Services
N.A.I.C.S.: 541614

DSV Air & Sea S.A. (1)
Sabana Business Center 9th Floor Boulevard Ernesto Rohrmoser, 10108, San Jose,
Costa Rica
Tel.: (506) 40331680
Transport & Logistics Services
N.A.I.C.S.: 541614

DSV Air & Sea S.A. De C.V. (1)
Av de los Insurgentes Sur 819 1st Floor
Colonia Ampliacion Napoles, 03840,
Mexico, Mexico
Tel.: (52) 5554889960
Web Site: https://www.dsv.com
Sales Range: $25-49.9 Million
Emp.: 30
Air & Sea Freight Transportation Services
N.A.I.C.S.: 481212

DSV Air & Sea S.A.S. (1)
Tel.: (57) 16057777
Transport & Logistics Services
N.A.I.C.S.: 541614

DSV Air & Sea S.A.U. (1)
C/ Pagesia 1-33 P I Moli de la Bastida,
08191, Rubi, Catalonia, Spain
Tel.: (34) 931807400
Air & Sea Freight Transportation Services
N.A.I.C.S.: 481112
Evan Mas (Gen Mgr)

DSV Air & Sea SAS (1)
rue des 2 Cedres, BP 12439, Ile-de-France,
95700, Roissy-en-France, France
Tel.: (33) 800005193
Sales Range: $50-74.9 Million
Emp.: 100
Air & Sea Freight Transportation Services
N.A.I.C.S.: 481112

DSV Air & Sea SRL (1)
Str Tipografilor 11 - 15 etaj 3, 013714, Bucharest, Romania
Tel.: (40) 751174119
Transport & Logistics Services
N.A.I.C.S.: 541614

DSV Air & Sea Sdn. Bhd. (1)
Level 5 Block A Dataran PHB Saujana Resort Section U2, 40150, Shah Alam, Selangor, Malaysia
Tel.: (60) 374553700
Web Site: https://www.dsv.com
Sales Range: $25-49.9 Million
Emp.: 104
Air & Sea Freight Services
N.A.I.C.S.: 481112

DSV Air & Sea Sp. z.o.o (1)
Wirazowa 35, 02-158, Warsaw, Masovian,
Poland
Tel.: (48) 221648252
Freight Forwarding Services
N.A.I.C.S.: 488510

DSV Air & Sea d.o.o. (1)
Dialnicna cesta 5 Hala D, Senec, 903 01,
Bratislava, Slovakia
Tel.: (421) 948621124
Air & Sea Freight Transportation Services
N.A.I.C.S.: 541614

DSV Air & Sea s.r.o (1)

Prazakova 51, 619 00, Brno, South Moravian, Czech Republic
Tel.: (420) 311332444
Web Site: https://www.dsv.com
Sales Range: $25-49.9 Million
Emp.: 19
Air & Sea Freight Transportation Services
N.A.I.C.S.: 481112

DSV Air Services S.A. (1)
Luxair Cargo Center, 1360, Luxembourg,
Luxembourg
Tel.: (352) 26932020
Transport & Logistics Services
N.A.I.C.S.: 541614

DSV Air and Sea for Logistics Services Company W.L.L. (1)
Salman Al Farisi Street Dammam SeaPort
Area, Dammam, 31518, Eastern, Saudi
Arabia
Tel.: (966) 118742900
Transport & Logistics Services
N.A.I.C.S.: 541614

DSV Commercials Ltd. (1)
Eastfield Road South, Killingholme, DN40
3DR, Lincs, United Kingdom
Tel.: (44) 1469553672
Emp.: 26
General Freight Trucking Services
N.A.I.C.S.: 484110
Chris Marshal (Gen Mgr)

DSV Hellas S.A. (1)
69 Possidonos Ave & Alimou Ave, Alimos,
174 55, Athens, Greece
Tel.: (30) 2109883049
Web Site: http://www.dsv.com
Sales Range: $25-49.9 Million
Emp.: 50
Freight Trucking & Logistics Management
Services
N.A.I.C.S.: 481112

DSV Hrvatska d.o.o. (1)
Slavonska Avenija 56, 10000, Zagreb,
Croatia
Tel.: (385) 994654430
Web Site: https://www.dsv.com
Freight Trucking & Logistics Management
Services
N.A.I.C.S.: 484110

DSV Hungaria Kft (1)
Balatoni u 2/a, 1112, Budapest, Hungary
Tel.: (36) 213780000
Web Site: https://www.dsv.com
Emp.: 150
Logistics & Freight Forwarding Services
N.A.I.C.S.: 541614
Tamas Pechy (Mng Dir)

DSV Insurance A/S (1)
Banemarksvej 58, 2605, Brondby, Denmark
Tel.: (45) 43203040
Fire Insurance Services
N.A.I.C.S.: 524298

DSV International Hava ve Deniz Tasimaciligi Ltd.Sirketi (1)
Ruzgarlibahce Mh Kavak Sk Nu 29, Kavacik Beykoz, Istanbul, 34810, Turkiye
Tel.: (90) 4444378
Transport & Logistics Services
N.A.I.C.S.: 541614

DSV Logistics Co., Ltd. (1)
Building 69 No 36 Yiwei Road Waigaoqiao
Free Trade Zone, Shanghai, 201131, China
Tel.: (86) 2150460662
Web Site: https://www.dsv.com
Emp.: 200
Freight Trucking & Logistics Management
Services
N.A.I.C.S.: 484110

DSV Logistics LLC (1)
9 Dziuby Ivana St, 03134, Kiev, Ukraine
Tel.: (380) 443905121
Transport & Logistics Services
N.A.I.C.S.: 541614

DSV Logistics SA (1)
Via Passeggiata 24, 6828, Balerna, Ticino,
Switzerland
Tel.: (41) 916950606
Web Site: https://www.dsv.com
Freight Trucking & Logistics Management
Services
N.A.I.C.S.: 484110

DSV Osterreich Spedition GmbH (1)
Flughafenstrasse 1, 4063, Horsching, Austria
Tel.: (43) 7221 602 0
Web Site: http://www.dsv.com.at
Emp.: 15
Road Transport & Logistics Services
N.A.I.C.S.: 484110
Roman Fuchsberger (Mgr-Security)

DSV Panalpina Marine Shipping W.L.L. (1)
250 D-ring Road Building No 123 Marzooq
Al-Shamlan Building 2/F, 24024, Doha, Qatar
Tel.: (074) 44009700
Freight Forwarding Services
N.A.I.C.S.: 488510

DSV ROAD DOOEL Skopje (1)
bul Kiril I Metodij br 56a, 1000, Skopje,
North Macedonia
Tel.: (389) 23243100
Transport & Logistics Services
N.A.I.C.S.: 541614

DSV Road & Solutions A.S. (1)
Fatih Mah Katip Celebi No 4 Orhanli-Tuzla,
No 29 A Blok Kat 6 No 212 Kagithane,
34956, Istanbul, Turkiye
Tel.: (90) 4444378
Sales Range: $25-49.9 Million
Emp.: 50
Freight Trucking & Logistics Services
N.A.I.C.S.: 484110

DSV Road A/S (1)
Park Alle 354, PO Box 318, 2605, Brondby,
Hovedstaden, Denmark
Tel.: (45) 43203040
Road Transport & Logistics Services
N.A.I.C.S.: 484110

DSV Road AB (1)
Bjurogatan 15, PO Box 50122, SE 211 24,
Malmo, Sweden
Tel.: (46) 406801000
Web Site: http://www.dsv.com
Sales Range: $50-74.9 Million
Emp.: 230
Transportation Services
N.A.I.C.S.: 488999

Branch (Domestic):

DSV Road AB (2)
Stenbrovagen 15, PO Box 611, SE 251 06,
Helsingborg, Sweden
Tel.: (46) 42179000
Web Site: http://www.dsv.se
Sales Range: $125-149.9 Million
Concrete Production Machinery Mfr
N.A.I.C.S.: 333120

DSV Road AS (1)
Asbieveien 15, 4848, Arendal, Norway
Tel.: (47) 37004500
Web Site: http://www.dsv.com
General Freight Trucking Services
N.A.I.C.S.: 484110

DSV Road B.V. (1)
Tel.: (31) 773892378
Transport & Logistics Services
N.A.I.C.S.: 541614

DSV Road EOOD (1)
16 Nedelcho Bonchev str Industrialna zona
Gara Iskur, 1592, Sofia, Bulgaria
Tel.: (359) 29267800
Sales Range: $50-74.9 Million
Emp.: 100
Road Transport & Logistics Services
N.A.I.C.S.: 484110

DSV Road GmbH (1)
Hanns-Martin-Schleyer-Strasse 18 A Haus
5, 47877, Willich, Nordrhein-Westfalen, Germany
Tel.: (49) 2154 9544 0
General Freight Trucking Services
N.A.I.C.S.: 484110

DSV Road Holding A/S (1)
Park Alle 354, 2605, Brondby, Denmark
Tel.: (45) 43203040
Emp.: 25
Road Transport Services
N.A.I.C.S.: 484110

DSV Road Limited (1)

B1 Rowan Tree Road Naas Enterprise
Park, Naas, W91 VE82, Kildare, Ireland
Tel.: (353) 45444777
Sales Range: $150-199.9 Million
Emp.: 430
Freight Trucking & Logistics Management
Services
N.A.I.C.S.: 484110
Robert Greene (Mng Dir)

DSV Road Ltd. (1)
Stonehouse Lane, Purfleet, RM19 1NX, Essex, United Kingdom
Tel.: (44) 1708892000
Web Site: https://www.dsv.com
Sales Range: $75-100.0 Million
Emp.: 250
Freight Trucking & Logistics Management
Services
N.A.I.C.S.: 484110

DSV Road NV (1)
Industriezone Puurs 533 Schoonmansveld
40, Puurs, 2870, Antwerp, Belgium
Tel.: (32) 38972500
Web Site: http://www.be.dsv.com
Emp.: 350
Road Transport & Logistics Services
N.A.I.C.S.: 484110

DSV Road OOO (1)
Bakalinskaya St 11 Offices 9 10, Kirovskiy
region Bashkortostan, 450022, Ufa, Russia
Tel.: (7) 4957218979
Transport & Logistics Services
N.A.I.C.S.: 541614

DSV Road Oy (1)
Telakkatie 4, 23500, Uusikaupunki, Southwest Finland, Finland
Tel.: (358) 207388388
Web Site: https://www.dsv.com
Sales Range: $150-199.9 Million
Emp.: 300
Freight Trucking & Customs Clearance Services
N.A.I.C.S.: 484110

DSV Road S.A. (1)
39 Zone Industrielle, L-8287, Kehlen,
Capellen, Luxembourg
Tel.: (352) 312828
Web Site: http://www.dsv.com
Emp.: 45
Food Transportation Services
N.A.I.C.S.: 484110

DSV Road S.A.U. (1)
Calle 7 Parcela 7 Pol Ind Pla de la Vallonga, 03006, Alicante, Spain
Tel.: (34) 965 99 39 50
Sales Range: $25-49.9 Million
Emp.: 12
Freight Trucking & Logistics Management
Services
N.A.I.C.S.: 484110

DSV Road S.R.L. (1)
Str 22 Decembrie Nr 28 Biroul 2, 430314,
Baia Mare, Romania
Tel.: (40) 744756323
Transport & Logistics Services
N.A.I.C.S.: 541614

DSV Road Sp. z.o.o (1)
ul Ozarowska 40/42, Duchnice, 05-850,
Ozarow Mazowiecki, Masovian, Poland
Tel.: (48) 227392300
Web Site: http://www.pl.dsv.com
Sales Range: $25-49.9 Million
Emp.: 90
General Freight Trucking Services
N.A.I.C.S.: 484110

DSV Road Transport, Inc. (1)
PO Box 16050, Missoula, MT 59808
Tel.: (406) 728-2600
Web Site:
   https://mytms.roadtransport.us.dsv.com
Road Transportation Distr
N.A.I.C.S.: 484121

DSV Road a.s. (1)
Uprapi 224 Dobroviz, Prague, 25261,
Czech Republic
Tel.: (420) 311332444
Web Site: https://www.dsv.com
Sales Range: $50-74.9 Million
Emp.: 100
Road Transport & Logistics Services
N.A.I.C.S.: 484110

DSV Road d.o.o. (1)
Prva Industrijska bb, Krnjesevci, 22314,
Sremska Mitrovica, Serbia
Tel.: (381) 222150448
Transport & Logistics Services
N.A.I.C.S.: 541614

DSV Road, Inc. (1)
3525 Excel Dr, Medford, OR 97504
Tel.: (541) 773-3993
Web Site: https://mytms.us.dsv.com
Transportation Services
N.A.I.C.S.: 488999

DSV Road, Inc. (1)
8205 Parkhill Drive, Milton, L9T 5G8, ON,
Canada
Tel.: (905) 203-2020
Road Freight Services
N.A.I.C.S.: 484110

DSV S.A. (1)
Parc d'activites du Melantois Rue des Se-
quoias, BP 207, 59812, Lesquin, Nord,
France
Tel.: (33) 3 20 60 72 81
Web Site: http://www.dsv.com
Sales Range: $50-74.9 Million
Emp.: 93
Freight Trucking & Logistics Management
Services
N.A.I.C.S.: 484110

DSV S.p.A (1)
Via Dante Alighieri 134 Limito di Pioltello
Lombardy, 20096, Pioltello, Italy
Tel.: (39) 02921341
Transport & Logistics Services
N.A.I.C.S.: 541614

DSV SGPS, Lda. (1)
Rua Campo do Martelo 319, 4485-959,
Vilar do Pinheiro, Portugal
Tel.: (351) 229479200
Web Site: https://www.dsv.com
Sales Range: $75-99.9 Million
Emp.: 110
Freight Trucking & Logistics Management
Services
N.A.I.C.S.: 484110

DSV Sakhalin, OOO (1)
Zheleznodorozhnaya St 159, Sakhalin
Oblast, 693000, Yuzhno-Sakhalinsk, Russia
Tel.: (7) 4242466600
Transport & Logistics Services
N.A.I.C.S.: 541614

DSV Slovakia, s.r.o. (1)
Dialnicna cesta 5 Hala D, Senec, 903 01,
Bratislava, Slovakia
Tel.: (421) 915790531
Transport & Logistics Services
N.A.I.C.S.: 541614

DSV Solutions (Automotive) NV (1)
Eddastraat 21 Kennedy Industriepark, 9042,
Gent, Oost-Vlaanderen, Belgium
Tel.: (32) 92500811
Web Site: http://www.dsv.com
Sales Range: $250-299.9 Million
Emp.: 600
Road Transport & Logistics Services
N.A.I.C.S.: 484110

DSV Solutions (Dordrecht) B.V. (1)
Donker Duyvisweg 70, 3316 BL, Dordrecht,
Netherlands
Tel.: (31) 786520200
Transport & Logistics Services
N.A.I.C.S.: 541614

DSV Solutions (Moerdijk) B.V. (1)
Tradeboulevard 4, 4761 RL, Moerdijk, Neth-
erlands
Tel.: (31) 168413000
Transport & Logistics Services
N.A.I.C.S.: 541614

DSV Solutions 2 BV (1)
Cacaoweg 20-86L, 1047 BM, Amsterdam,
Noord-Holland, Netherlands
Tel.: (31) 20 407 0600
Logistics & Warehousing Services
N.A.I.C.S.: 493110

DSV Solutions A/S (1)
Mossvej 27, 8700, Horsens, Midtjylland,
Denmark
Tel.: (45) 43203040

Sales Range: $250-299.9 Million
Emp.: 1,000
Road Transport & Logistics Services
N.A.I.C.S.: 484110
Jens Bjorn (CEO)

DSV Solutions AB (1)
Nettovagen 4, 175 89, Jarfalla, Stockholm,
Sweden
Tel.: (46) 8 580 883 00
Freight Trucking & Logistics Management
Services
N.A.I.C.S.: 484110

DSV Solutions AS (1)
Gneisveien 16, Skedsmokorset, 2020, Nor-
way
Tel.: (47) 40403600
Web Site: https://www.dsv.com
Sales Range: $25-49.9 Million
Emp.: 100
Logistics & Warehousing Services
N.A.I.C.S.: 541614

DSV Solutions B.V. (1)
Tradeboulevard 4, 4761 RL, Moerdijk, Neth-
erlands
Tel.: (31) 168 41 30 00
Web Site: http://www.dsv.com
Emp.: 150
Logistics & Warehousing Services
N.A.I.C.S.: 541614

DSV Solutions Brasil Servicos de Lo-
gistica Ltda. (1)
Av J R Marinho 85 12 Andar Conj 121-122,
Cidade Moncoes, Sao Paulo, 04576-010,
Brazil
Tel.: (55) 1121655500
Transport & Logistics Services
N.A.I.C.S.: 541614

DSV Solutions GmbH (1)
Pfingstweidstr 1, Baden-Wurttemberg,
68199, Mannheim, Germany
Tel.: (49) 621803960
Logistics Consulting Servies
N.A.I.C.S.: 541614

DSV Solutions Group GmbH (1)
Schlachte 15/18, 28195, Bremen, Germany
Tel.: (49) 42117680
Web Site: https://www.de.dsv.com
Sales Range: $75-99.9 Million
Emp.: 180
Freight Trucking & Logistics Management
Services
N.A.I.C.S.: 484110

DSV Solutions Inc. (1)
2200 Yukon Court, Milton, L9E 1N5, ON,
Canada
Tel.: (905) 203-2020
Logistic Services
N.A.I.C.S.: 541614

DSV Solutions Lda. (1)
Quinta da Torre 9001A Quinta do Anjo,
2950-635, Palmela, Setubal, Portugal
Tel.: (351) 212110300
Web Site: https://www.dsv.com
Sales Range: $25-49.9 Million
Emp.: 26
Logistics & Freight Forwarding Services
N.A.I.C.S.: 488510

DSV Solutions Ltd. (1)
Unit 3 4 Stratus Park Brudenell Dr, Brink-
low, Milton Keynes, MK10 0DE, Bucking-
hamshire, United Kingdom
Tel.: (44) 1604925004
Sales Range: $25-49.9 Million
Emp.: 100
Logistics & Warehousing Services
N.A.I.C.S.: 493110

DSV Solutions NV (1)
Eddastraat 21 Kennedy Industriepark, 9042,
Gent, East Flanders, Belgium
Tel.: (32) 92500811
Sales Range: $150-199.9 Million
Emp.: 300
Road Transport & Logistics Services
N.A.I.C.S.: 484110
Albert-Derk Bruin (Mgr)

DSV Solutions Nederland B.V. (1)
Europalaan 18, Limburg, 6199 AB, Maas-
tricht, Netherlands
Tel.: (31) 433088670
Transport & Logistics Services

N.A.I.C.S.: 541614

DSV Solutions OOO (1)
Moskovskaya obl Istrinsky r-n, 143550,
Luchinskoye, Russia
Tel.: (7) 495 514 1115
General Freight Trucking Services
N.A.I.C.S.: 484110

DSV Solutions Oy (1)
Trukkikuja 3, PO Box 142, 01360, Vantaa,
Uusimaa, Finland
Tel.: (358) 207388322
Web Site: http://www.dsv.fi
Sales Range: $50-74.9 Million
Emp.: 150
Logistics & Warehousing Services
N.A.I.C.S.: 541614

DSV Solutions Pte. Ltd. (1)
No 09-11/18 163 Kallang Way, Singapore,
349256, Singapore
Tel.: (65) 64778640
Air & Sea Freight Transportation Services
N.A.I.C.S.: 541614

DSV Solutions Puurs NV (1)
Schoonmansveld 34, Puurs-Sint-Amands,
2870, Puurs, Antwerp, Belgium
Tel.: (32) 38603500
Web Site: http://www.dsv.com
Emp.: 80
Road Transport & Logistics Services
N.A.I.C.S.: 484110

DSV Solutions S.A.E. (1)
Pieces No 36 39A 39B 40 Industrial Zone
A7, 44629, 10th of Ramadan City, Egypt
Tel.: (20) 226736830
Transport & Logistics Services
N.A.I.C.S.: 541614

DSV Solutions S.A.S. (1)
33 Rue de Reckem, BP 147, Hauts-de-
France, 59960, Neuville-en-Ferrain, France
Tel.: (33) 320769330
Web Site: https://www.fr.dsv.com
Sales Range: $50-74.9 Million
Emp.: 130
Logistics & Warehousing Services
N.A.I.C.S.: 493110

DSV Solutions S.A.U. (1)
C/ Pagesia 1-33 P l Moli de la Bastida,
08191, Rubi, Catalonia, Spain
Tel.: (34) 931807400
Web Site: http://www.dsv.com
Logistics & Warehousing Services
N.A.I.C.S.: 541614

DSV Solutions SRL (1)
Strada Ion Ratiu fost DC 149 nr 9, 900565,
Bolintin-Vale, Romania
Tel.: (40) 751113522
Web Site: https://www.dsv.com
Sales Range: $100-124.9 Million
Emp.: 300
Logistics & Warehousing Services
N.A.I.C.S.: 541614

DSV Solutions Sp. z.o.o. (1)
ul Minska 63, 03-828, Warsaw, Masovian,
Poland
Tel.: (48) 221648380
Logistics & Warehousing Services
N.A.I.C.S.: 493110

DSV Solutions for Logistics Services
Company LLC (1)
Al Mishal Istanbul St As Sulay Eastern Ring
Road Wh-9, Riyadh, 14327, Saudi Arabia
Tel.: (966) 118742900
Air & Sea Freight Transportation Services
N.A.I.C.S.: 541614

DSV South Africa (Pty) Ltd. (1)
Meadowview Business Estate 1 Mead-
owview Ln Linbro Park, Sandton, 2065,
Gauteng, South Africa
Tel.: (27) 102480000
Freight Forwarding Services
N.A.I.C.S.: 488510
Keith Pienaar (CEO)

DSV Stuttgart GmbH & Co. KG (1)
Schlachte 15-18, 28195, Bremen, Germany
Tel.: (49) 42117680
Web Site: https://www.dsv.com
Freight Trucking & Logistics Management
Services
N.A.I.C.S.: 484110

DSV Transitarios Lda. (1)
Rua Campo do Martelo 319, 4485-959,
Vilar do Pinheiro, Portugal
Tel.: (351) 229479200
Web Site: https://www.dsv.com
Sales Range: $50-74.9 Million
Emp.: 57
Freight Trucking & Logistics Management
Services
N.A.I.C.S.: 484110

DSV Transport (US), Inc. (1)
100 Walnut Ave Ste 405, Clark, NJ 07066
Tel.: (732) 850-8000
Web Site: http://www.dsv.com
Sales Range: $25-49.9 Million
Emp.: 80
Provider of Freight Transportation Arrange-
ment Services
N.A.I.C.S.: 488510

DSV Transport AS (1)
Parnu mnt 535, Saku, 76404, Harju, Esto-
nia
Tel.: (372) 6599999
Web Site: http://www.dsv.com
Sales Range: $75-99.9 Million
Emp.: 150
Freight Trucking & Logistics Management
Services
N.A.I.C.S.: 484110
Jaanika Roosmann (Dir-Svc)

DSV Transport International S.A. (1)
355 Boulevard Mohamed V Espace Yousra,
Casablanca, Morocco
Tel.: (212) 522401666
Web Site: https://www.dsv.com
Sales Range: $25-49.9 Million
Emp.: 30
Freight Transport & Logistics Services
N.A.I.C.S.: 488510

DSV Transport Ltd. (1)
Lipkovsky line 12-503, 220138, Minsk, Be-
larus
Tel.: (375) 173770313
Web Site: http://www.dsv.com
Sales Range: $25-49.9 Million
Emp.: 50
Freight Trucking & Logistics Management
Services
N.A.I.C.S.: 484110

DSV Transport SIA (1)
31 Krustpils street, Riga, 1073, Latvia
Tel.: (371) 67100701
Web Site: http://www.dsv.com
Sales Range: $75-99.9 Million
Emp.: 153
Freight Trucking & Logistics Management
Services
N.A.I.C.S.: 484110

DSV Transport UAB (1)
Stasylu 21, Vilnius, 02241, Lithuania
Tel.: (370) 52686200
Web Site: http://www.dsv.com
Sales Range: $50-74.9 Million
Emp.: 80
Freight Trucking & Logistics Management
Services
N.A.I.C.S.: 484110
Kim Bartholdy (Mng Dir)

DSV Transport d.o.o. (1)
Polje 9a, 6310, Izola, Coastal-Karst, Slove-
nia
Tel.: (386) 56680517
Web Site: https://www.dsv.com
Sales Range: $75-99.9 Million
Emp.: 100
Freight Trucking & Logistics Management
Services
N.A.I.C.S.: 484110

DSV Ukraine (1)
9 Simyi Sosninyh St, Kievo-Svyatoshinskiy,
03134, Kiev, Ukraine
Tel.: (380) 443905121
Web Site: http://www.dsv.ua
Emp.: 120
Freight Trucking & Logistics Services
N.A.I.C.S.: 484110

DSV-UTI Egypt Ltd. (1)
Emoustafa Kamel Road Plot 3 Buliding E,
11865, Cairo, Egypt
Tel.: (20) 222460128
Freight Forwarding Services

DSV A/S—(Continued)
N.A.I.C.S.: 488510

G T Exhibitions Limited (1)
25-27 Blackwell Drive Springwood Ind Estate, Essex, Braintree, CM7 2PU, United Kingdom
Tel.: (44) 1376567567
Web Site: https://www.gtexhibitions.com
Exhibition Logistics & Transport Services
N.A.I.C.S.: 541614

International Freight Logistics (1)
23 Boulevard du 1er Novembre, PO Box 2261, Bujumbura, Bujumbura Mairie, Burundi
Tel.: (257) 22223160
Web Site: http://www.gof.dsv.com
Logistics Consulting Servies
N.A.I.C.S.: 541614

Logimar SRL (1)
Via Bolgare 1/A, 24060, Carobbio degli Angeli, Bergamo, Italy
Tel.: (39) 035951468
Web Site: http://www.logimar.it
Sales Range: $25-49.9 Million
Emp.: 12
Logistics & Freight Forwarding Services
N.A.I.C.S.: 488510

NTS European Distribution AB (1)
Stenbrovagen 15, 25107, Helsingborg, Skane, Sweden
Tel.: (46) 42179000
Web Site: http://www.dsv.com
Logistics & Warehousing Services
N.A.I.C.S.: 493110

OOO DSV Transport (1)
Datsky proezd 3 Dorozhnoie settl, Gurievsky district, 236005, Kaliningrad, Russia
Tel.: (7) 4012306215
Web Site: http://dsvrussia.ru
General Freight Trucking Services
N.A.I.C.S.: 484110

POP Gesellschaft fur Prozesslogistik mbH (1)
Am Mittelkai 9, 70327, Stuttgart, Baden-Wurttemberg, Germany
Tel.: (49) 7119189360
Freight Trucking & Logistics Management Services
N.A.I.C.S.: 484110

PT. DSV Transport Indonesia (1)
Jl By Pass Ngurah Rai No 99, Kedonganan, 80364, Denpasar, Bali, Indonesia
Tel.: (62) 2180629000
Transport & Logistics Services
N.A.I.C.S.: 541614

Panalpina Freight LLC (1)
18th November Street 48 Way, 130, Muscat, Oman
Tel.: (968) 24121104
Freight Forwarding Services
N.A.I.C.S.: 488510

Panalpina World Transport Holding Ltd. (1)
Viaduktstrasse 42, 4002, Basel, Switzerland
Tel.: (41) 612261111
Web Site: http://www.panalpina.com
Rev.: $5,666,838,235
Assets: $1,883,590,721
Liabilities: $1,254,407,256
Net Worth: $629,183,465
Earnings: $58,852,256
Emp.: 14,355
Fiscal Year-end: 12/31/2017
International Freight Forwarding & Logistics Services
N.A.I.C.S.: 488510
Christoph Hess (Chief Legal Officer, Sec & Member-Exec Bd)

Subsidiary (Non-US):

Bidvest Panalpina Logistics (2)
10-14 Skietlood Street, Isando, 1600, South Africa (100%)
Tel.: (27) 11 922 9600
Web Site: http://www.panalpina.com
Sales Range: $150-199.9 Million
Emp.: 500
Ocean Freight & Logistics Operations
N.A.I.C.S.: 488510

Grampian International Freight B.V. (2)
Waterland 2, Beverwijk, 1948, Netherlands
Tel.: (31) 251227242
Emp.: 8
Freight Forwarding Services
N.A.I.C.S.: 488510
Jim Greig (Mgr-Svc)

Grieg Triangle Logistics B.V. (2)
Wattweg 28, Spijkenisse, 3208, Netherlands
Tel.: (31) 181 618288
Freight Forwarding Services
N.A.I.C.S.: 488510

Subsidiary (US):

International Claims Handling Services Inc. (2)
Beacon Lakes Corporate Park Bldg 10 12430 NW 25 St Ste 100, Miami, FL 33182
Tel.: (305) 499-9800
Web Site: http://www.interchs.com
Logistics Consulting Servies
N.A.I.C.S.: 541614

Subsidiary (Non-US):

International Claims Handling Services Ltd. (2)
Top Floor ATL Logistics Center B Berth 3, Kwai Chung Container Terminal, Hong Kong, China (Hong Kong)
Tel.: (852) 27602600
Web Site: http://www.interchs.com
Logistics Consulting Servies
N.A.I.C.S.: 541614

P.T. Panalpina Nusajaya Transport (2)
Soewarna Business Park Block H Lot 11, Soekarno-Hatta, International Airport, Jakarta, 19110, Indonesia (100%)
Tel.: (62) 2155911308
Sales Range: $50-74.9 Million
Emp.: 60
N.A.I.C.S.: 488510

Panalpina (Ghana) Limited (2)
Rd C4 Terna Port Warehouse Commercial Area, PO Box B132, Community 2, Tema, Ghana (100%)
Tel.: (233) 22204899
Web Site: http://www.panalpina.com
Sales Range: $25-49.9 Million
Emp.: 30
N.A.I.C.S.: 488510

Panalpina A/S (2)
Kontinentalveien 31, 4056, Tananger, Norway
Tel.: (47) 51 600 820
Air Freight Transportation Services
N.A.I.C.S.: 481112

Panalpina AB (2)
Kanalvagen 18, Upplands Vasby, 19461, Sweden (100%)
Tel.: (46) 859125500
Web Site: http://www.panalpina.com
N.A.I.C.S.: 488510

Subsidiary (Domestic):

Panalpina AG (2)
Eichstrasse 50, 8152, Glattbrugg, Switzerland (100%)
Tel.: (41) 448294111
Web Site: http://www.panalpina.com
Sales Range: $25-49.9 Million
Emp.: 70
N.A.I.C.S.: 488510
Lucas Kuehner (Exec VP-Air Freight)

Subsidiary (Non-US):

Panalpina Asia-Pacific Services (Thailand) Ltd. (2)
Sirinrat Building 18th Floor 3388/65 Rama IV Road, Klongton Klongtoey, Bangkok, 10110, Thailand
Tel.: (66) 23486000
Air Freight Transportation Services
N.A.I.C.S.: 481112

Panalpina Asia-Pacific Services Ltd. (2)
1 Fl Center B ATL Logistics Center B, Kwai Chung, China (Hong Kong)
Tel.: (852) 34050800

Sales Range: $25-49.9 Million.
Emp.: 40
Freight Forwarding Services
N.A.I.C.S.: 488510
Stefan Karlen (CEO-Asia Pacific Reg)

Panalpina Bahrain W.L.L. (2)
Road 3618 AlAmal Tower 4th floor Building 892 Block 436, PO Box 11971, 11971, Manama, Bahrain (100%)
Tel.: (973) 17715530
Web Site: http://www.panalpina.com
Sales Range: $50-74.9 Million
Emp.: 20
N.A.I.C.S.: 488510

Panalpina Beverwijk B.V. (2)
Waterland 2, 1948 RK, Beverwijk, Netherlands
Tel.: (31) 251227242
Air Freight Transportation Services
N.A.I.C.S.: 481112
Harm van Dam (Mgr-Bus Unit)

Panalpina C.A. (2)
Edificio Panalpina Av Francisco de Miranda Piso 3 Los Ruices, Caracas, 1071, Venezuela
Tel.: (58) 2122026111
Air Freight Transportation Services
N.A.I.C.S.: 481112

Panalpina Central Asia Azerbaijan (2)
AGA Business Centre 12th Floor 55 Khojaly Avenue, Baku, 1025, Azerbaijan (100%)
Tel.: (994) 12 464 4270
Web Site: http://www.panalpina.com
Sales Range: $50-74.9 Million
Emp.: 70
Freight Transportation
N.A.I.C.S.: 488510

Panalpina Chile Transportes Mundiales Ltda. (2)
, Ojos del salado 710, Santiago, Chile (100%)
Tel.: (56) 23875100
Web Site: http://www.panalpina.com
Sales Range: $75-99.9 Million
Emp.: 200
N.A.I.C.S.: 488510

Panalpina China Limited (2)
30 Top Floor ATL Center B Berth 3, Kwai Chung Container Terminal, Hong Kong, China (Hong Kong) (100%)
Tel.: (852) 27602600
Sales Range: $150-199.9 Million
Emp.: 400
N.A.I.C.S.: 488510

Panalpina Czech Sro. (2)
Karlovarska Business Park Na Hurce 1077/4a, Ruzyne, 161 00, Prague, Czech Republic
Tel.: (420) 235031111
Air Freight Transportation Services
N.A.I.C.S.: 481112
Ive Vannuffelen (Country Mgr)

Panalpina Denmark (2)
Oliefabriksvej 45, Kastrup, 2770, Denmark
Tel.: (45) 32486600
Web Site: http://www.panalpina.com
Sales Range: $25-49.9 Million
Emp.: 15
Air Freight Transportation Services
N.A.I.C.S.: 481112

Panalpina Ecuador S.A. (2)
Av El Inca E 4181 y Amazonas, Quito, Ecuador
Tel.: (593) 23970100
Air Freight Transportation Services
N.A.I.C.S.: 481112

Panalpina Finland (2)
Tahkotie 1F, 01530, Vantaa, Finland (100%)
Tel.: (358) 987008600
Web Site: http://www.panalpina.com
Sales Range: $25-49.9 Million
Emp.: 15
N.A.I.C.S.: 488510

Panalpina Grieg AS (2)
Nordre Nostekaien 1, PO Box 973, Bergen, 5808, Norway
Tel.: (47) 55 21 23 00
Web Site: http://www.panalpina.no

Air Freight Services
N.A.I.C.S.: 481112

Panalpina Gulf LLC (2)
M4 DNATA Free Zone Logistics Ctr Bldg, Dubai Airport Free Zone (FLC), Dubai, United Arab Emirates (100%)
Tel.: (971) 42996235
Web Site: http://www.panalpina.com
Sales Range: $25-49.9 Million
Emp.: 100
Freight & Logistics Services
N.A.I.C.S.: 488510

Panalpina Hassi Messaoud (2)
CITE El Masdjid El ATIK No 15, PO Box 1225, 30500, Hassi Messaoud, Algeria
Tel.: (213) 29731833
Web Site: http://www.panalpina.com
Sales Range: $50-74.9 Million
Emp.: 3
N.A.I.C.S.: 488510

Panalpina IAF (Korea) Ltd. (2)
Panalpina IAF Bldg 35-22 Tongui-dong, Jongno-gu, Seoul, 110-040, Korea (South)
Tel.: (82) 23980114
Emp.: 150
Logistics Consulting Servies
N.A.I.C.S.: 541614
Seonghee Gong (Mgr-Tender)

Subsidiary (Domestic):

Panalpina Insurance Broker Ltd. (2)
Viaduktstrasse 42, 4051, Basel, Switzerland
Tel.: (41) 612261111
Insurance Brokerage Services
N.A.I.C.S.: 524210

Subsidiary (Non-US):

Panalpina Korea Ltd. (2)
23 Hyoja-ro Jongno-gu, Seoul, 110 040, Korea (South) (100%)
Tel.: (82) 23980114
Web Site: http://www.panalpina.com
Sales Range: $75-99.9 Million
Emp.: 158
Global Logistics & Freight Transportation
N.A.I.C.S.: 488510

Panalpina Logistics (Wuhan) Ltd. (2)
2/F Building A2 Optical Valley Software Park 1 Guanshan Blvd, Wuhan, 430073, China
Tel.: (86) 2768787000
Logistics Consulting Servies
N.A.I.C.S.: 541614

Subsidiary (Domestic):

Panalpina Ltd. (2)
Eichstrasse 50, 8152, Glattbrugg, Switzerland
Tel.: (41) 448294111
Logistics Consulting Servies
N.A.I.C.S.: 541614

Subsidiary (Non-US):

Panalpina Ltda. (2)
Avenida Santa Catrina 719, PO Box 18671, Vila Santa Catarina, 04378 300, Sao Paulo, SP, Brazil
Tel.: (55) 121655700
Web Site: http://www.panalpina.com
Sales Range: $25-49.9 Million
Emp.: 50
N.A.I.C.S.: 488510

Panalpina Luxembourg S.A. (2)
22 rue Gabriel Lippmann, PO Box 1707, Luxembourg, 5365, Luxembourg
Tel.: (352) 26932500
Web Site: http://www.panalpina.com
Sales Range: $125-149.9 Million
Emp.: 300
Transportation Services
N.A.I.C.S.: 481212

Panalpina Macau Empresa Transitaria Limitada (2)
12 F Macau Finance Ctr Unit D And E, Macau, China (Macau) (100%)
Tel.: (853) 700482
Sales Range: $25-49.9 Million
Emp.: 13
N.A.I.C.S.: 488510

Panalpina Magyarorszag Kft. (2)

Ulloi u 807/ B Airport City Logistics Park
Building C, 2220, Vecses, Hungary
Tel.: (36) 29 556 677
Web Site: http://www.panalpina.com
Sales Range: $25-49.9 Million
Emp.: 86
Freight Forwarding Services
N.A.I.C.S.: 488510

Subsidiary (Domestic):

Panalpina Management Ltd.   **(2)**
Viaduktstrasse 42, 4002, Basel, Switzerland
Tel.: (41) 612261111
Air Freight Services
N.A.I.C.C.: 401112

Subsidiary (Non-US):

Panalpina Polska Sp. z o.o.   **(2)**
ul Prosta 36, 53-508, Wroclaw, Poland
Tel.: (48) 713343710
Web Site: https://www.panalpina.com
Sales Range: $50-74.9 Million
Emp.: 100
Air Freight Services
N.A.I.C.S.: 481112
Jacek Strycharczyk (Country Mgr)

Panalpina Qatar W.L.L.   **(2)**
Gulf Automobile Car Showroom Bldg, PO
Box 24024, Airport Rd 1st Fl Ste 536,
Doha, 24024, Qatar   **(100%)**
Tel.: (974) 44669706
Web Site: http://www.panalpina.com
Sales Range: $25-49.9 Million
Emp.: 23
N.A.I.C.S.: 488510

Panalpina Romania S.R.L.   **(2)**
Sky Tower 18th Floor 246C Calea Floreas-
ca District 1, Bucharest, 14476, Romania
Tel.: (40) 31 403 93 00
Emp.: 30
Logistics Consulting Servies
N.A.I.C.S.: 541614
Adrian Pali (Country Mgr)

Panalpina S.A.   **(2)**
Diagonal 24 No 96-55, Bogota,
Colombia   **(100%)**
Tel.: (57) 14010500
Web Site: http://www.panalpina.com
Sales Range: $75-99.9 Million
Emp.: 250
N.A.I.C.S.: 488510

Panalpina S.A.   **(2)**
Los Andes No 2 Ojo De Aqua, Via Transist-
mica, Panama, Panama   **(100%)**
Tel.: (507) 2801111
Web Site: https://www.panalpina.com
Sales Range: $25-49.9 Million
Emp.: 100
Warehousing, Repacking & Document Han-
dling Services
N.A.I.C.S.: 493190

Panalpina Slovakia S.R.O.   **(2)**
Na pantoch 18, 831 06, Bratislava, Slovakia
Tel.: (421) 249 683 311
Sales Range: $25-49.9 Million
Emp.: 16
Freight Forwarding Services
N.A.I.C.S.: 488510
Debor Fodelmesi (Bus Mgr)

Panalpina Taiwan Ltd.   **(2)**
9 F Transworld Commercial Bldg, 2 Nan-
king East Rd Section 2, Taipei, 104,
Taiwan   **(100%)**
Tel.: (886) 225632160
Web Site: http://www.panalpina.com
Sales Range: $75-99.9 Million
Emp.: 130
N.A.I.C.S.: 488510

Panalpina Transport (Malaysia) Sdn.
Bhd.   **(2)**
Unit 501 Block F Phileo Damansara 1 9,
Jalan 16 11, 46350, Petaling Jaya,
Malaysia   **(100%)**
Tel.: (60) 379588610
Web Site: https://www.panalpina.com
Sales Range: $50-74.9 Million
Emp.: 70
N.A.I.C.S.: 488510

Panalpina Transport Mondiaux
SARL   **(2)**
Zone Portuaire Rue 1033, BP 3790,

Douala, 3790, Cameroon
Tel.: (237) 33438891
Web Site: http://www.panalpina.com
Sales Range: $25-49.9 Million
Emp.: 40
Air Freight Transportation Services
N.A.I.C.S.: 481112

Panalpina Transportes Mundiais
Lda.   **(2)**
Rua Professor Henrique De Barros No 4,
Edificio Sagres 6A, 2685 338, Lisbon,
Portugal   **(100%)**
Tel.: (351) 219498290
Sales Range: $25-49.9 Million
Emp.: 11
N.A.I.C.S.: 488510
Manuel Gallegos (Gen Mgr)

Panalpina Transportes Mundiais,
Navegacao & Transistos
S.A.R.L.   **(2)**
Rua C3 Tensai Business Center 1 Dt, PO
Box 3682, Luanda, Angola   **(100%)**
Tel.: (244) 226422000
Web Site: https://www.panalpina.com
Sales Range: $75-99.9 Million
Emp.: 150
N.A.I.C.S.: 488510

Panalpina Transportes Mundiales
C.A.   **(2)**
Edificio Panalpina Avenida Francisco De
Miranda, Piso 3 Los Ruices, Caracas, 1071,
Venezuela   **(100%)**
Tel.: (58) 2122026111
Web Site: http://www.panalpina.com.ve
Sales Range: $25-49.9 Million
Emp.: 40
N.A.I.C.S.: 488510

Panalpina Transportes Mundiales
S.A.   **(2)**
Centro de Carga Aerea Ave Central 34 -
Nave i y j, PO Box 6028, 28080, Madrid,
Spain   **(100%)**
Tel.: (34) 917481910
Web Site: http://www.panalpina.com
Sales Range: $25-49.9 Million
Emp.: 35
N.A.I.C.S.: 488510

Panalpina Transportes Mundiales
S.A.   **(2)**
713 Carlos Pellegrini 2nd Floor, C1009,
Buenos Aires, Argentina   **(100%)**
Tel.: (54) 11 4348 4500
Web Site: http://www.panalpina.com.ar
Sales Range: $50-74.9 Million
Emp.: 80
Freight & Logistics Services
N.A.I.C.S.: 488510

Panalpina Transportes Mundiales
S.A.   **(2)**
Avda El Inca E4-181 y Avda Amazonas,
Quito, Ecuador
Tel.: (593) 22413999
Freight Transportation
N.A.I.C.S.: 488510

Panalpina Transportes Mundiales
S.A.   **(2)**
Rocca De Vergallo 145 Magdalena Del Mar,
PO Box 4229, Lima, Peru   **(100%)**
Tel.: (51) 17147300
Web Site: http://www.panalpina.com
Rev.: $41,526,794
Emp.: 80
N.A.I.C.S.: 488510

Panalpina Transportes Mundiales
S.A.   **(2)**
Paseo Colon Calle 26 y 28 Ave 1, San
Jose, 8461007, Costa Rica
Tel.: (506) 2257 9191
Web Site: http://www.panalpina.com
Sales Range: $25-49.9 Million
Emp.: 26
Freight Forwarding Services
N.A.I.C.S.: 488510
Cristian Alvarez (Country Mgr)

Panalpina Transportes Mundiales
S.A. de C.V.   **(2)**
Calle Uno 129 Col Pantitlan Entre Ave
Norte E Iztacalco, CP 08100, Mexico, DF,
Mexico   **(100%)**
Tel.: (52) 5557169800

Web Site: http://www.panalpina.com.mx
Sales Range: $75-99.9 Million
Emp.: 200
N.A.I.C.S.: 488510

Panalpina Transporti Mondiali
S.p.A.   **(2)**
Via Luigi Zerbi 75 e 77, Localita Cantalupo,
20023, Milan, Italy   **(100%)**
Tel.: (39) 02932681
Web Site: http://www.panalpina.com
Sales Range: $75-99.9 Million
Emp.: 120
N.A.I.C.S.: 488510

Panalpina Transports Internationaux
S.A.   **(2)**
6 rue du Chapelier Zone de Fret No 4, PO
Box 14410, 95707, Roissy-en-France,
France   **(100%)**
Tel.: (33) 000148168500
Sales Range: $250-299.9 Million
Emp.: 550
N.A.I.C.S.: 488510
Christophe Mouterde (Gen Dir)

Panalpina Transports Mondiaux Cam-
eroon S.A.   **(2)**
Zone Portuaire Rue 1033, Douala,
Cameroon   **(100%)**
Tel.: (237) 33438891
Web Site: https://www.panalpina.com
Sales Range: $25-49.9 Million
Emp.: 35
Freight Transportation
N.A.I.C.S.: 488510

Panalpina Transports Mondiaux
Congo S.A.R.L.   **(2)**
3 avenue Lassy Zephirin, PO Box 1125,
Pointe Noire, Congo, Republic of
Tel.: (242) 2425301619
Web Site: http://www.panalpina.com
Sales Range: $50-74.9 Million
Emp.: 70
Freight Transportation
N.A.I.C.S.: 488510

Panalpina Transports Mondiaux Ga-
bon S.A.   **(2)**
Zone OPRAG, Port-Gentil, Gabon
Tel.: (241) 553092
Web Site: https://www.panalpina.com
Sales Range: $150-199.9 Million
Emp.: 500
N.A.I.C.S.: 488510

Panalpina Uruguay Transportes Mun-
diales S.A.   **(2)**
Rimcom 467 6th Fl A, 11000, Montevideo,
Uruguay   **(100%)**
Tel.: (598) 29151717
Sales Range: $50-74.9 Million
Emp.: 10
N.A.I.C.S.: 488510

Panalpina Welttransport
(Deutschland) GmbH   **(2)**
Kuthessenstrasse 12, Morfelden, 64546,
Germany   **(100%)**
Tel.: (49) 6105937777
Web Site: http://www.panalpina.com
Sales Range: $50-74.9 Million
Emp.: 60
N.A.I.C.S.: 488510
Volker Werner (Mgr-Bus Unit-Central)

Panalpina Welttransport GmbH   **(2)**
Theodore Hewss Allage 12, 67061, Mann-
heim, Germany   **(50%)**
Tel.: (49) 62158880
Web Site: http://www.panalpina.de
Sales Range: $25-49.9 Million
Emp.: 50
International Air Freight Forwarding
N.A.I.C.S.: 481112

Panalpina Welttransport GmbH   **(2)**
Schwieberdinger Strasse 25, 70435, Stutt-
gart, Germany   **(100%)**
Tel.: (49) 71198040
Sales Range: $75-99.9 Million
Emp.: 220
N.A.I.C.S.: 488510

Panalpina Welttransport GmbH   **(2)**
Naglwegstrasse 37, 20097, Hamburg,
Germany   **(100%)**
Tel.: (49) 40237710
Web Site: http://www.panalpina.com

Sales Range: $75-99.9 Million
Emp.: 200
N.A.I.C.S.: 488510

Panalpina Welttransport GmbH   **(2)**
Kurhessen Str 12, 64546, Morfelden,
Germany   **(100%)**
Tel.: (49) 61059370
Sales Range: $75-99.9 Million
Emp.: 200
N.A.I.C.S.: 488510
Christoph Schwab (Mgr-Tender Mgmt)

Panalpina Welttransport GmbH   **(2)**
Konsul Smidt Strasse 14, Bremen, 28217,
Germany   **(100%)**
Tel.: (49) 42130810
Web Site: http://www.panalpina.com
Sales Range: $75-99.9 Million
Emp.: 110
N.A.I.C.S.: 488510

Panalpina Welttransport GmbH   **(2)**
Reisholzer Werfstrasse 52, Dusseldorf,
40589, Germany   **(100%)**
Tel.: (49) 21197950
Web Site: http://www.panalpina.com
Sales Range: $75-99.9 Million
Emp.: 150
N.A.I.C.S.: 488510

Panalpina Welttransport GmbH   **(2)**
Am Europaplatz 5, 1231, Vienna,
Austria   **(100%)**
Tel.: (43) 01614420
Web Site: http://www.wwpanalpina.com
Sales Range: $75-99.9 Million
Emp.: 200
N.A.I.C.S.: 488510
Volker Bohringer (Mng Dir)

Panalpina World Transport (Dubai)
DWC-LLC   **(2)**
Dubai Logistics City Near Al Maktoum Inter-
national Airport, PO Box 52725, Jebel Ali,
Dubai, United Arab Emirates
Tel.: (971) 48701111
Web Site: http://www.panalpina.com
Sales Range: $25-49.9 Million
Emp.: 200
Air Freight Transportation Services
N.A.I.C.S.: 481112

Panalpina World Transport (India)
Pvt. Ltd.   **(2)**
Technopolis 2nd Floor, Sector 54, Near DLF
Golf Course, Gurgaon, 122002, Haryana,
India   **(100%)**
Tel.: (91) 1244375600
Web Site: http://www.panalpina.com
Sales Range: $50-74.9 Million
Emp.: 100
Freight Transportation Services
N.A.I.C.S.: 488510

Panalpina World Transport (Ireland)
Ltd.   **(2)**
Smithtown Industrial Est, Shannon,
Ireland   **(100%)**
Tel.: (353) 61718010
Sales Range: $25-49.9 Million
Emp.: 5
N.A.I.C.S.: 488510

Panalpina World Transport (Japan)
Ltd.   **(2)**
Hanwha Bldg 7F 4 10 1 Shiba, Minato Ku,
Tokyo, 108 0014, Japan   **(100%)**
Tel.: (81) 334517866
Web Site: http://www.panalpina.com
Sales Range: $25-49.9 Million
Emp.: 50
N.A.I.C.S.: 488510

Panalpina World Transport (PRC)
Ltd.   **(2)**
6/F AZIA Center 1233 Lujiazui Ring Road,
Pudong New Area, Shanghai, 200120,
China
Tel.: (86) 2161051500
Web Site: https://www.panalpina.com
Freight Forwarding Services
N.A.I.C.S.: 488510

Panalpina World Transport (Phils.)
Inc.   **(2)**
Zealcor Business Ctr 3rd 4th Fls Sta
Agueda Ave, Sto Nino 1700 Pascor Dr,
1700, Paranaque, Philippines   **(100%)**
Tel.: (63) 25809797

DSV A/S—(Continued)

Web Site: http://www.panalpina.com
Sales Range: $10-24.9 Million
Emp.: 75
N.A.I.C.S.: 488510

Panalpina World Transport (Saudi Arabia) Ltd. (2)
Energy Centre, Prince Sultan Street, Al Khobar, 31952, Saudi Arabia (100%)
Tel.: (966) 3 8811 280
Sales Range: $25-49.9 Million
Emp.: 32
Freight Transportation Services
N.A.I.C.S.: 488510

Panalpina World Transport (Singapore) Pte. Ltd. (2)
16 Whangi N Way, Singapore, 498772, Singapore (100%)
Tel.: (65) 62740188
Web Site: http://www.panalpina.com
Sales Range: $150-199.9 Million
Emp.: 300
N.A.I.C.S.: 488510

Panalpina World Transport (Thailand) Limited (2)
Sirinrat Bldg 14th Fl 3388 47-49 Rama IV Rd, Klongton Klongtoey, 10110, Bangkok, Thailand (100%)
Tel.: (66) 23486199
Sales Range: $75-99.9 Million
Emp.: 140
N.A.I.C.S.: 488510

Panalpina World Transport B.V. (2)
Rangoonwag 7, Amsterdam, 1118, Netherlands (100%)
Tel.: (31) 206552000
Web Site: http://www.panalpina.com
Sales Range: $10-24.9 Million
Emp.: 78
N.A.I.C.S.: 488510

Panalpina World Transport GmbH (2)
Rheinstrase 40, 90451, Nuremberg, Germany (100%)
Tel.: (49) 91143090
Web Site: http://www.pinalpina.com
Sales Range: $75-99.9 Million
Emp.: 200
N.A.I.C.S.: 488510

Panalpina World Transport LLP (2)
20 Tabachnozavodskaya str Swiss Center, 050050, Almaty, Kazakhstan
Tel.: (7) 7272507171
Web Site: http://www.panalpina.com
Air Freight Services
N.A.I.C.S.: 481112

Panalpina World Transport Ltd. (2)
Panalpina House Great S W Rd, Feltham, TW14 8NU, Middx, United Kingdom (100%)
Tel.: (44) 2085879000
Sales Range: $75-99.9 Million
Emp.: 150
N.A.I.C.S.: 488510
Chris Cooper (Mng Dir)

Panalpina World Transport Ltd. (2)
87 Bozhenko str, 3680, Kiev, Ukraine (100%)
Tel.: (380) 444943838
Web Site: https://www.panalpina.com
Sales Range: $25-49.9 Million
Emp.: 22
N.A.I.C.S.: 488510

Panalpina World Transport Ltd. (2)
285 Mguyen Van Choi Troei District Dua, Ho Chi Minh City, District 4, Vietnam (100%)
Tel.: (84) 89974780
Web Site: http://www.panalpina.com
Sales Range: $50-74.9 Million
Emp.: 5
Freight Transportation
N.A.I.C.S.: 488510

Panalpina World Transport N.V. (2)
Nooderlaan 133, 2030, Antwerp, Belgium (100%)
Tel.: (32) 35400800
Web Site: https://www.panalpina.com
Sales Range: $75-99.9 Million
Emp.: 250
N.A.I.C.S.: 488510

Gunther Mouws (Acct Mgr)

Panalpina World Transport N.V. (2)
Nooderlaan 133, 2030, Antwerp, Belgium (100%)
Tel.: (32) 35400810
Web Site: http://www.panalpina.com
Sales Range: $75-99.9 Million
Emp.: 150
N.A.I.C.S.: 488510

Panalpina World Transport Nakliyat Ltd. Sti.
Basin Ekspres Yolu Cemel Ulusoy Cad No 1 K 1, TR 80280, Istanbul, Turkiye (100%)
Tel.: (90) 2124110030
Sales Range: $25-49.9 Million
Emp.: 15
N.A.I.C.S.: 488510

Panalpina World Transport Nigeria Ltd. (2)
4 Creek Rd, PO Box 69, Apapa, Nigeria (69%)
Tel.: (234) 15803440
Web Site: http://www.panalpina.com
Sales Range: $150-199.9 Million
Emp.: 500
N.A.I.C.S.: 488510

Panalpina World Transport Pty. Ltd. (2)
Cnr Bourke Rd & Doody St, Alexandria, 2015, NSW, Australia (100%)
Tel.: (61) 296932600
Sales Range: $100-124.9 Million
Emp.: 130
N.A.I.C.S.: 488510
Mathew Mahony (Mng Dir)

Panalpina World Transport Pty. Ltd. (2)
4 Joseph Hammond Pl, Ivlangere, 1701, Auckland, New Zealand (100%)
Tel.: (64) 92756175
Sales Range: $25-49.9 Million
Emp.: 24
N.A.I.C.S.: 488510
Chris Imarkss (Mgr)

Panalpina World Transport ZAO (2)
Novospasskiy Dvor Derbenevskaya nab 7, block 9, 115114, Moscow, Russia (100%)
Tel.: (7) 0959612553
Web Site: http://www.panalpina.com
Sales Range: $50-74.9 Million
Emp.: 100
N.A.I.C.S.: 488510

Panalpina, Inc. (2)
6350 Cantay Rd, Mississauga, L5R 4E2, ON, Canada
Tel.: (905) 755-4500
Web Site: http://www.panalpina.com
Sales Range: $75-99.9 Million
Emp.: 200
N.A.I.C.S.: 488510

Subsidiary (US):

Panalpina, Inc. (2)
67 E Park Pl, Morristown, NJ 07960-7103
Tel.: (973) 683-9000
Web Site: http://www.panalpina.com
Sales Range: $50-74.9 Million
Emp.: 120
International Freight Forwarding Services
N.A.I.C.S.: 488510

Saima Avandero SpA (1)
Via Dante Alighieri 134, 20096, Pioltello, Milan, Italy
Tel.: (39) 02921341
Web Site: http://www.dsv.com
Air & Sea Freight Transportation Services
N.A.I.C.S.: 481112

Sandtorp Thermotransport AS (1)
Ramstadlokka 6, Mysen, 1850, Norway
Tel.: (47) 69 89 15 69
Web Site: http://www.sandtorp.no
Sales Range: $25-49.9 Million
Emp.: 30
General Freight Trucking Services
N.A.I.C.S.: 484110
Heyerdahl Jarle (Mng Dir)

Tacisa Transitaria S.L. (1)
C Copernicus n 3 1st A 3 Pol A Grela, La Coruna, 15008, Spain (100%)

Tel.: (34) 881241720
Web Site: https://www.tacisatransitaria.com
Freight Forwarding Services
N.A.I.C.S.: 488510

UTi Egypt/Jordan Ltd. (1)
Paris St-Sweifeyeh Alzaitoneh Complex, 11185, Amman, Jordan
Tel.: (962) 65885454
Freight Forwarding Services
N.A.I.C.S.: 488510

UTi Worldwide Inc. (1)
Commerce House Wickhams Cay 1 Road Town, Tortola, VG1 110, Virgin Islands (British) (100%)
Tel.: (284) 8521000
Supply Chain Management, Logistics & Freight Forwarding Services
N.A.I.C.S.: 488510

Subsidiary (Non-US):

UT Worldwide (India) Pvt. Ltd. (2)
2nd&3rd Floor Bldg No 6 Solitaire Corporate Park, Chakala Andheri East, Mumbai, 400 093, Maharashtra, India (100%)
Tel.: (91) 22 3911 9100
Web Site: http://www.in.dsv.com
Logistics Consulting Servies
N.A.I.C.S.: 541614

Subsidiary (US):

UTi Inventory Management Solutions Inc. (2)
1001 W Southern Ave Ste 106, Mesa, AZ 85210
Tel.: (480) 339-3800
Web Site: http://www.utiims.com
Inventory Management Services
N.A.I.C.S.: 541614
Avi Gilboa (Pres)

Subsidiary (Non-US):

UTi Pership (Pvt) Limited (2)
Level 03 Rainbow Business Center 135 Bauddhaloka Mawatha 04, Colombo, Sri Lanka
Tel.: (94) 1125979737
Web Site: http://www.gof.dsv.com
Supply Chain Management & Freight Forwarding Services
N.A.I.C.S.: 488510

Waagan Bil AS (1)
Blindheim Industrivei 4, 6020, Alesund, Norway
Tel.: (47) 70 19 70 09
Web Site: http://www.waagan.no
Sales Range: $50-74.9 Million
Emp.: 100
Freight Trucking & Logistics Management Services
N.A.I.C.S.: 484110

DSW CAPITAL PLC
7400 Daresbury Park, Daresbury, Warrington, WA4 4BS, Cheshire, United Kingdom
Tel.: (44) 1928378100　　　UK
Web Site: https://dswcapital.com
Year Founded: 2002
DSW—(AIM)
Rev.: $3,640,047
Assets: $12,243,919
Liabilities: $1,402,525
Net Worth: $10,841,394
Earnings: ($453,478)
Emp.: 16
Fiscal Year-end: 03/31/22
Investment Management Service
N.A.I.C.S.: 523999
James Dow (CEO)

DSWISS, INC.
Unit 18-11 18-12 and 18-01 Tower A, Vertical Business Suite Avenue, 3 Bangsar South No 8 Jalan Kerinchi, 59200, Kuala Lumpur, Malaysia
Tel.: (60) 327704032
Web Site:
https://www.dswissbeauty.com
Year Founded: 2015

DQWS—(OTCIQ)
Rev.: $1,849,047
Assets: $381,924
Liabilities: $283,773
Net Worth: $98,151
Earnings: ($2,937)
Emp.: 12
Fiscal Year-end: 12/31/22
Beauty Product Distr
N.A.I.C.S.: 456120
Leong Ming Chia (Pres, Co-CEO, CFO, Treas & Sec)

DT CAPITAL LIMITED
Room 6703 67/F The Center 99 Queens Road, Central, China (Hong Kong)
Tel.: (852) 27786110　　　Ky
Web Site: http://www.dt-capitalhk.com
Year Founded: 2001
0356—(HKG)
Rev.: $233,808
Assets: $13,198,923
Liabilities: $128,082
Net Worth: $13,070,841
Earnings: ($3,072,457)
Emp.: 5
Fiscal Year-end: 12/31/22
Investment Management Service
N.A.I.C.S.: 523150
Alex King Yue Leung (Exec Dir)

DT CLOUD ACQUISITION CORP.
30 Orange Street, London, WC2H 7HF, United Kingdom
Tel.: (44) 7918725316　　　Ky
Year Founded: 2022
DYCQ—(NASDAQ)
Assets: $588,264
Liabilities: $731,861
Net Worth: ($143,597)
Earnings: ($87,271)
Fiscal Year-end: 12/31/23
Investment Management Service
N.A.I.C.S.: 523999

DT&C CO., LTD.
42 Yurim-ro 154beon-gil, Cheoin-Gu, Yongin, 17042, Gyeonggi-Do, Korea (South)
Tel.: (82) 313212664
Web Site: https://www.dtnc.co.kr
Year Founded: 2000
187220—(KRS)
Rev.: $84,780,354
Assets: $174,287,685
Liabilities: $74,215,909
Net Worth: $100,071,775
Earnings: $2,110,332
Emp.: 276
Fiscal Year-end: 12/31/22
Test Certification Services
N.A.I.C.S.: 541380
Charlie Park (CEO)

DTB-DEUTSCHE BIOGAS AG
Barsseler Str 65, 26169, Friesoythe, Germany
Tel.: (49) 44919395930　　　De
Web Site: http://www.deutsche-biogas.de
Biogas Plant Construction Services
N.A.I.C.S.: 236210
Claudia Lammers (CEO & Member-Mgmt Bd)

DTCOM - DIRECT TO COMPANY S/A
Av Dom Pedro II 1720 Itapira, 83420-000, Quatro Barras, 83420-000, PR, Brazil
Tel.: (55) 8009424109
Web Site: https://www.dtcom.com.br
Year Founded: 2000

DTCY4—(BRAZ)
Sales Range: $1-9.9 Million
Emp.: 54
Distance Education Services
N.A.I.C.S.: 611710
Cristiane De Fatima Fialla *(Dir-Investor Relations)*

DTI GROUP LTD
31 Affleck Road, Perth, 6105, WA, Australia
Tel.: (61) 894791195
Web Site: https://www.dti.com.au
Year Founded: 1995
DTI—(ASX)
Rev.: $5,141,213
Assets: $7,264,393
Liabilities: $4,657,591
Net Worth: $2,606,802
Earnings: ($1,658,233)
Fiscal Year-end: 06/30/24
Surveillance Systems & Solutions for the Global Mass Transit Industry
N.A.I.C.S.: 561621
Greg Purdy *(Chm)*

DTM SYSTEMS INC.
Unit 130 2323 Boundary Road, Vancouver, V5M 4V8, BC, Canada
Tel.: (604) 257-6700
Web Site: http://www.dtm.ca
Year Founded: 1986
Rev.: $22,442,341
Emp.: 38
Computer & Software Stores
N.A.I.C.S.: 449210
Paul J. Martin *(CEO)*

DTS CORPORATION
Empire Building 2-23-1 Hatchobori Reception 8th floor, Chuo-ku, Tokyo, 104-0032, Japan
Tel.: (81) 339485488
Web Site: https://www.dts.co.jp
9682—(TKS)
Rev.: $764,955,470
Assets: $561,070,020
Liabilities: $141,982,800
Net Worth: $419,087,220
Earnings: $48,206,730
Emp.: 165
Fiscal Year-end: 03/31/24
Computer Services
N.A.I.C.S.: 541512

Subsidiaries:

ASTERIKS Inc.   (1)
5-32-8 Shimbashi, Minato-ku, Tokyo, 105-0004, Japan
Tel.: (81) 334375151
Web Site: http://www.asteriks.co.jp
Software Business Consulting Services
N.A.I.C.S.: 541611

DTS (Shanghai)
CORPORATION   (1)
Room 703A Bldg 4 No 1 Lane 399 Xinlong Road, Minhang District, Shanghai, 201101, China
Tel.: (86) 2150813773
Web Site: http://www.dts-cn.com
Emp.: 17
System Integration Services
N.A.I.C.S.: 541512

DTS Insight Corporation   (1)
Shinjuku Midwest Bldg 4-30-3 Yoyogi, Shibuya-ku, Tokyo, 151-0053, Japan
Tel.: (81) 367569400
Web Site: https://www.dts-insight.co.jp
Emp.: 374
Embedded System Development Services
N.A.I.C.S.: 541511
Isao Asami *(Pres)*

DTS Software Vietnam Co., Ltd.   (1)
3rd floor LADECO building 266 Doi Can Lieu Giai, Ba Dinh, Hanoi, Vietnam
Tel.: (84) 2437620150
Web Site: https://dtsvn.com
Software Development Services

N.A.I.C.S.: 541511
DTS West Corporation   (1)
2-3-13 Azuchimachi Osaka International Building 22nd floor, Chuo-ku, Osaka, 541-0052, Japan
Tel.: (81) 662645488
Web Site: http://www.dtswest.co.jp
Emp.: 266
Computer Sales & Data Processing Services
N.A.I.C.S.: 518210
Masami Adachi *(Chm & Pres)*

Dalian SuperElectronics Co., Ltd.   (1)
125 Kono-gai High-tech Park 13F Cloud Calculation Center Building, Dalian, 116085, Liaoning, China
Tel.: (86) 41184509286
Web Site: http://www.dlse.com.cn
IT Services
N.A.I.C.S.: 541511

FAITEC CORPORATION   (1)
4th Floor 31st Kowa Building 3-19-1 Shiroganedai Minato-ku, Tokyo, Japan
Tel.: (81) 354201213
Web Site: http://www.faitec.co.jp
Insurance & Pension Property Management Services
N.A.I.C.S.: 524126

JAPAN SYSTEMS ENGINEERING
CORPORATION   (1)
25th floor Shinjuku Dai-ichi Life Building 2-7-1 Nishi-Shinjuku, Shinjuku-ku, Tokyo, 163-0725, Japan
Tel.: (81) 333436460
Web Site: https://www.jse.co.jp
Sales Range: $25-49.9 Million
Emp.: 483
Software Development Services
N.A.I.C.S.: 541511
Koichi Sato *(Pres)*

KYUSYU DTS CORPORATION   (1)
7F Taihaku Center Building 2-19-24 Hakata Ekimae, Hakata-ku, Fukuoka, 812-0011, Japan
Tel.: (81) 924017575
Web Site: https://www.q-dts.co.jp
Emp.: 143
System Integration Services
N.A.I.C.S.: 541512

Kyushu Dts Corporation   (1)
7th Floor Taihaku Center Building 2-19-24 Hakata Ekimae, Hakata-ku, Fukuoka, 812-0011, Japan
Tel.: (81) 924017575
Web Site: https://www.q-dts.co.jp
Emp.: 143
Software Development Services
N.A.I.C.S.: 541511

MIRUCA CORPORATION   (1)
6F Issei Shiba Park Building 2-29-14 Shiba, Minato-ku, Tokyo, 105-0014, Japan
Tel.: (81) 357303405
Web Site: https://www.miruca.jp
Sales Range: $10-24.9 Million
Emp.: 20
Education Consulting & Professional Training Services
N.A.I.C.S.: 611430

Nelito Systems Private Limited   (1)
205-208 Building No 2 Sector -1 Millennium Business Park, Mahape, Mumbai, 400 710, Maharashtra, India
Tel.: (91) 2267314444
Web Site: https://www.nelito.com
Emp.: 800
Financial Services
N.A.I.C.S.: 522320

Nelito Sytems Limited   (1)
205-208 Building No 2 Sector-1, Millennium Business Park Mahape, Navi Mumbai, 400 710, Maharashtra, India
Tel.: (91) 2267314444
Web Site: https://www.nelito.com
Software Development Services
N.A.I.C.S.: 541511
Sanjay Dube *(CEO)*

Yokogawa Digital Computer
Corporation   (1)
Shinjuku Midwest Bldg 4-30-3 Yoyogi, Shibuya-ku, Tokyo, 151-0053, Japan   (90%)

Tel.: (81) 3 6756 9400
Web Site: http://www.yokogawa-digital.com
Emp.: 153
Electronic Components Mfr
N.A.I.C.S.: 334419
Toyohiko Furuta *(Pres)*

DTXS SILK ROAD INVESTMENT HOLDINGS COMPANY LIMITED
Room 811-817 8/F Bank of America Tower, 12 Harcourt Road, Central, China (Hong Kong)
Tel.: (852) 28529500
Web Site: http://www.dtxs.com
0620—(HKG)
Rev.: $144,618,660
Assets: $454,036,043
Liabilities: $281,325,053
Net Worth: $172,710,990
Earnings: $23,768,423
Emp.: 107
Fiscal Year-end: 12/31/22
Investment Services
N.A.I.C.S.: 523999
Jianzhong Lu *(Chm)*

Subsidiaries:

M-Finance Limited   (1)
Unit 1801 Fortis Tower 77-79 Gloucester Road, Wanchai, China (Hong Kong)
Tel.: (852) 34262750
Software Development Services
N.A.I.C.S.: 513210

DU PAREIL AU MEME SA
3 rue Christophe Colomb, 91300, Massy, France
Tel.: (33) 2 54 29 17 49
Web Site: http://www.dpam.com
Sales Range: $250-299.9 Million
Emp.: 1,400
Children's Clothing & Shoes Retailer
N.A.I.C.S.: 458110

DUAL CO. LTD
12th Fl DooSan B/D 726 Eonju-ro, Gangnam-gu, Seoul, Korea (South)
Tel.: (82) 269227272
Web Site: https://www.idual.co.kr
Year Founded: 1971
016740—(KRS)
Rev.: $434,118,961
Assets: $354,485,380
Liabilities: $202,486,558
Net Worth: $151,998,821
Earnings: $5,761,195
Emp.: 548
Fiscal Year-end: 12/31/22
Automobile Parts Mfr & Distr
N.A.I.C.S.: 336110
Ian Hwe Cho *(CEO)*

Subsidiaries:

DUAL Co. Ltd - Dual Asan Plant   (1)
611 Seobunam-ro Sinchang-myeon, Ansan, Chungcheongnam-do, Korea (South)
Tel.: (82) 414231100
Automotive Fabric Mfr
N.A.I.C.S.: 336360

DUAL Co. Ltd - Dual Banwoul
Plant   (1)
417 Haean-ro, Danwon-gu, Ansan, Gyeonggi-do, Korea (South)
Tel.: (82) 4995507
Automotive Fabric Mfr
N.A.I.C.S.: 336360

DUAL Co. Ltd - Dual Ganghwa
Plant   (1)
5 Ganghwa-daero192beon-gil Ganghwa-eup, Ganghwa-gun, Incheon, Korea (South)
Tel.: (82) 329320155
Automotive Fabric Mfr
N.A.I.C.S.: 336360

DUAL Co. Ltd - Dual Ulsan Plant   (1)
21-2 Hyosan 2-gil, Buk-gu, Ulsan, Korea (South)
Tel.: (82) 522880001

Automotive Fabric Mfr
N.A.I.C.S.: 336360

Dual Automotive Technologies
(Shanghai) Co., Ltd.   (1)
21 Floor Zstar Plaza No 7 Pubei Road, Shanghai, China
Tel.: (86) 2160737858
Automotive Fabric Distr
N.A.I.C.S.: 424310

Dual Borgstena Textile Portugal Unipessoal, Lda.   (1)
EN 234 - km 87 7 Chao do Pisco Apartado 35, 3521-909, Nelas, Portugal
Tel.: (351) 232427660
Web Site: https://www.borgstena.com
Automobile Parts Distr
N.A.I.C.S.: 423120

Dual Moolsan Co., Ltd   (1)
230 Yunposun-ro Yeongin-myeon, Ansan, Chungcheongnam-do, Korea (South)
Tel.: (82) 415324860
Automotive Fabric Mfr
N.A.I.C.S.: 336360

Jiangyin Dual Automotive Textile Co., Ltd.   (1)
30 Panlogshan Road, Economy Development Zone, Jiangyin, Jiangsu, China
Tel.: (86) 51086196791
Automotive Parts Retailer
N.A.I.C.S.: 441330

Jiangyin Dual Tech Co., Ltd   (1)
30 Panlogshan Road Economy Development Zone, Jiangyin, Jiangsu, China
Tel.: (86) 51086196791
Automotive Fabric Distr
N.A.I.C.S.: 424310

Trimsol Brazil, Ltda.   (1)
Avenida Augusto Simonetti No 80 Caixa D Agua Tiete, Sao Paulo, 18530-000, Brazil
Tel.: (55) 1532858090
Automotive Fabric Distr
N.A.I.C.S.: 424310

Trimsol Czech Republic s.r.o.   (1)
Na Prikope 1175, 738 01, Frydek-Mistek, Czech Republic
Tel.: (420) 702019830
Automotive Fabric Distr
N.A.I.C.S.: 424310

Trimsol Czech S.R.O.   (1)
Na Prikope 1175, 738 01, Frydek-Mistek, Czech Republic
Tel.: (420) 702019829
Automotive Parts Retailer
N.A.I.C.S.: 441330

Trimsol Romania Srl   (1)
Drum Gladnei n 16 Faget, 305300, Timis, Romania
Tel.: (40) 256307184
Automotive Fabric Distr
N.A.I.C.S.: 424310

Trimsol Sp. z o.o.   (1)
ul Waly Dwernickiego 117/121 lok 314, 42-200, Czestochowa, Poland
Tel.: (48) 343903997
Web Site: https://www.trimsol.pl
Automotive Fabric Mfr & Distr
N.A.I.C.S.: 336360

Yantai Dual Car Interior Co., Ltd.   (1)
No 89 Huanhai Road, Yantai, Shandong, China
Tel.: (86) 5356858170
Automotive Fabric Distr
N.A.I.C.S.: 424310

DUALTAP CO., LTD.
4-7 Nihonbashi-hisamatuscho, Chuo-ku, Tokyo, 103-0005, Japan
Tel.: (81) 368490055
Web Site: https://www.dualtap.co.jp
Year Founded: 2006
3469—(TKS)
Rev.: $32,169,840
Assets: $37,295,120
Liabilities: $26,173,760
Net Worth: $11,121,360
Earnings: ($2,400,920)
Fiscal Year-end: 06/30/24

Dualtap Co., Ltd.—(Continued)

Real Estate Consulting Service
N.A.I.C.S.: 531210
Takahiro Usui (CEO)

DUBAI AEROSPACE ENTER-PRISE LTD

DIFC The Gate District Building 4
Level 3, PO Box 506592, Dubai,
United Arab Emirates
Tel.: (971) 44289600
Web Site:
http://www.dubaiaerospace.com
Year Founded: 2006
Sales Range: $10-24.9 Million
Emp.: 30
Aviation Manufacturing, Services &
Education
N.A.I.C.S.: 488119
Ahmed Saeed Al Maktoum (Chm)

Subsidiaries:

DAE Airports   **(1)**
DIFC The Gate District Building 4 Level 3,
Dubai, United Arab Emirates
Tel.: (971) 4 329 2420
Airport Operations
N.A.I.C.S.: 488119

DAE Capital Advisors LLC   **(1)**
800 Bellevue Way NE Ste 550, Bellevue,
WA 98004
Tel.: (425) 440-6000
Financial Advisory Services
N.A.I.C.S.: 523940

DAE Capital Holdings Cooperatief   **(1)**
U.A.
Schipholboulevard 127-A3 Suite 3 13, 1118
BG, Schiphol, Netherlands
Tel.: (31) 20 316 3362
Holding Company
N.A.I.C.S.: 551112

Jordan Aircraft Maintenance
Limited   **(1)**
Queen Alia International Airport, PO Box
39328, Amman, 11104, Jordan   **(80%)**
Tel.: (962) 6 445 1445
Web Site: http://www.joramco.com.jo
Aircraft Maintenance Services
N.A.I.C.S.: 488190
Amjad Korshlow (CFO)

DUBAI FINANCIAL SERVICES AUTHORITY

DIFSA Level 13 The Gate Bldg, PO
Box 75850, Dubai, United Arab Emir-ates
Tel.: (971) 43621500
Web Site: http://www.dfsa.ae
Sales Range: $25-49.9 Million
Emp.: 99
Financial Services
N.A.I.C.S.: 521110
Saeb Eigner (Chm)

DUBAI HOLDING LLC

Umm Suqeim Road, PO Box 66000,
Dubai, United Arab Emirates
Tel.: (971) 43622000
Web Site:
http://www.dubaiholding.com
Sales Range: $1-4.9 Billion
Emp.: 20,000
Holding Company
N.A.I.C.S.: 551112
Abdulla al-Habbai (Chm)

Subsidiaries:

Dubai Group   **(1)**
Emirates Towers Level 15, PO Box 213311,
Sheikh Zayed Rd, Dubai, 213311, United
Arab Emirates
Tel.: (971) 43300707
Web Site: http://www.dubaigroup.com
Holding Company; Investment Banking &
Insurance
N.A.I.C.S.: 551112
Soud Ba'alawy (Chm)

Subsidiary (Domestic):

Dubai Financial Group   **(2)**
Emirates Tower Level 15 Sheikh Zayed
Road, PO Box 213311, Dubai, United Arab
Emirates
Tel.: (971) 4 3300707
Web Site: http://dubaigroup.com
Banking, Brokerage & Asset Management
Services
N.A.I.C.S.: 522110
Ahmed Al-Qassim (Chief Investment Offi-cer)

Dubai Insurance Group   **(2)**
Emirates Towers Level 30, PO Box 213311,
Sheikh Zayed Road, Dubai, United Arab
Emirates
Tel.: (971) 43300707
Web Site: http://www.dubaigroup.com
Sales Range: $25-49.9 Million
Emp.: 21
Holding Company; Insurance
N.A.I.C.S.: 551112
Jon Cimino (Dir-Fin)

Dubai Investment Group   **(2)**
Emirates Towers Level 38, Sheikh Zayed
Road, Dubai, United Arab Emirates
Tel.: (971) 9143189727
Web Site: http://www.dubaigroup.org
Global Financial Investor
N.A.I.C.S.: 523999

Dubai International Capital, LLC   **(1)**
Gate Building Level 13 Dubai International
Financial Centre, PO Box 72888, Dubai,
United Arab Emirates   **(100%)**
Tel.: (971) 43621888
Privater Equity Firm
N.A.I.C.S.: 523999
David Smoot (CEO-Private Equity)

Holding (Non-US):

Doncasters Group Ltd.   **(2)**
Milleniem Court 1st Avenue Centrum 100,
Burton-on-Trent, DE14 2WH, Staffs, United
Kingdom
Tel.: (44) 1332864900
Web Site: http://www.doncasters.com
Sales Range: $1-4.9 Billion
Emp.: 40
Holding Company; Aerospace, Automotive
& Industrial Turbine Precision Components
& Assemblies Mfr
N.A.I.C.S.: 551112
Craig Gooding (Mng Dir-Fabrications &
Combustors Div)

Subsidiary (US):

Certified Alloy Products, Inc.   **(3)**
3245 Cherry Ave, Long Beach, CA 90801
Tel.: (562) 595-6621
Web Site: http://www.doncasters.com
Rev.: $25,000,000
Emp.: 135
High-Performance Vacuum-Refined Alloys
Mfr
N.A.I.C.S.: 331492

Subsidiary (Domestic):

Doncasters Trucast Ltd.   **(3)**
Marlborough Road, Ryde, PO33 1AD, Isle
of Wight, United Kingdom
Tel.: (44) 1983 567611
Web Site: http://www.doncasters.com
Automotive & Power Generation Hot-End
Turbocharger Wheels Mfr
N.A.I.C.S.: 333248

Subsidiary (US):

Integrated Energy Technologies,
Inc.   **(3)**
225 W Morgan Ave, Evansville, IN 47710-2515
Tel.: (812) 421-7810
Web Site: http://ietglobal.com
Sales Range: $25-49.9 Million
Emp.: 45
Aerospace Engine & Turbine Component
Mfr
N.A.I.C.S.: 336412
Marvin Miller (Gen Mgr)

Subsidiary (Domestic):

GCE Industries, Inc.   **(4)**

1891 Nirvana Ave, Chula Vista, CA 91911
Tel.: (619) 421-1151
Web Site: http://ietglobal.com
Aerospace Engine Turbine Component Mfr
N.A.I.C.S.: 336412

MECO, Inc.   **(4)**
2121 S Main St, Paris, IL 61944
Tel.: (217) 465-6500
Web Site: http://www.ietglobal.com
Sales Range: $25-49.9 Million
Aerospace Turbine Cooling Component Mfr
N.A.I.C.S.: 336412
Tim Garrett (Gen Mgr)

Spun Metals, Inc.   **(4)**
2121 S Main St, Paris, IL 61944-2965
Tel.: (812) 448-2651
Web Site: http://ietglobal.com
Specialty Spun Metal Component Mfr
N.A.I.C.S.: 332999

Subsidiary (US):

Nelson Stud Welding, Inc.   **(3)**
7900 W Rdg Rd, Elyria, OH 44036-2019
Tel.: (440) 329-0400
Web Site: http://www.nelsonstud.com
Sales Range: $125-149.9 Million
Emp.: 120
Industrial, Construction & Automotive Fas-tener Systems Mfr
N.A.I.C.S.: 339993
Ken Caratelli (Pres)

Subsidiary (Domestic):

Automatic Screw Machine Products
Company, Inc.   **(4)**
709 2nd Ave SE, Decatur, AL
35601-2517   **(100%)**
Tel.: (256) 353-1931
Web Site: http://www.automaticsmp.com
Sales Range: $50-74.9 Million
Emp.: 115
Specialized Machine Parts Mfr
N.A.I.C.S.: 332721
Mike Selby (Gen Mgr)

Subsidiary (Domestic):

Ross Catherall Aerospace
Limited   **(3)**
Forge Lane Killamarsh, Sheffield, S21 1BA,
Derbyshire, United Kingdom
Tel.: (44) 1142486404
High-Performance Vacuum-Refined Alloys
Mfr
N.A.I.C.S.: 331492

Subsidiary (Domestic):

Ross Ceramics Limited   **(4)**
Derby Road, Derby, DE5 8NX, United King-dom
Tel.: (44) 1773570800
Web Site: http://www.rossceramics.com
Ceramic Casting Cores Mfr
N.A.I.C.S.: 331529
William Hodges (Mng Dir)

Subsidiary (US):

Specialty Bar Products Company   **(3)**
200 Martha St PO Box 127, Blairsville, PA
15717
Tel.: (724) 459-7500
Web Site: http://www.specialty-bar.com
Sales Range: $25-49.9 Million
Emp.: 50
Specialty Steel Bar Machining Services &
Mfr
N.A.I.C.S.: 331210

The Ferry Cap & Set Screw
Company   **(3)**
13300 Bramley Ave, Lakewood, OH 44107
Tel.: (216) 771-2533
Web Site: http://www.ferrycap.com
Cold-Headed Industrial Fasteners Mfr
N.A.I.C.S.: 332722

Dubai Properties Group LLC   **(1)**
Vision Tower Levels 7 to 10 Al Khaleej Al
Tejari 1 Street Business Bay, PO Box
500272, Dubai, United Arab Emirates
Tel.: (971) 4 435 1111
Web Site:
http://www.dubaipropertiesgroup.ae
Property Management Services
N.A.I.C.S.: 531312

Krishna Subramanian (CFO)

Subsidiary (Domestic):

Dubai Properties   **(2)**
The Lagoons Sales Centre Ras Al Khor,
Dubai, United Arab Emirates
Tel.: (971) 4 202 9000
Web Site: http://www.dubai-properties.ae
Property Management Services
N.A.I.C.S.: 531312
Naaman Atallah (CEO)

Ejadah Asset Management Group
L.L.C   **(2)**
6th Floor Block B Office Park, Knowledge
Village, Dubai, United Arab Emirates
Tel.: (971) 44337199
Property Management Services
N.A.I.C.S.: 531311
Billy Dally (CEO)

Emirates International Telecommuni-
cations LLC   **(1)**
Dubai Studio City Commercial Office Block
B 5th Floor Office 510, PO Box 73000,
Dubai, United Arab Emirates
Tel.: (971) 4 365 4564
Web Site: http://www.eitl.ae
Investment Management Service
N.A.I.C.S.: 523940
Deepak Padmanabhan (CEO)

Jumeirah Group LLC   **(1)**
Academic City Road, PO Box 214159,
Dubai, United Arab Emirates
Tel.: (971) 4 3647777
Web Site: http://www.jumeirah.com
Hotel Operator
N.A.I.C.S.: 721110
Gerald Lawless (Pres)

Subsidiary (Domestic):

Jumeirah International LLC   **(2)**
Al Sufouh Road, PO Box 73137, Dubai,
United Arab Emirates
Tel.: (971) 4 366 5000
Hotel Operator
N.A.I.C.S.: 721110
Karen Terrado Urminita (Mgr-Bus Excel-lence)

TECOM Investments LLC   **(1)**
PO Box 66000, Dubai, United Arab
Emirates   **(100%)**
Tel.: (971) 43189292
Web Site: http://dubaiholding.com
Real Estate & Licensing Services
N.A.I.C.S.: 531390
Catherine Thomas (Exec Dir-Mktg &
Comm-Dubai Design District)

Tatweer Dubai LLC   **(1)**
31st/24th Floor Emirates Towers Sheikh
Zayed Road, PO Box 65999, Dubai, United
Arab Emirates   **(100%)**
Tel.: (971) 43302222
Real Estate Development/Leisure & Enter-tainment
N.A.I.C.S.: 531390

Joint Venture (Domestic):

Dubai Mercantile Exchange
Limited   **(2)**
Bldg 10 4th floor, PO Box 66500, Dubai,
United Arab Emirates   **(9%)**
Tel.: (971) 43655500
Web Site: http://www.dubaimerc.com
Sales Range: $650-699.9 Million
Emp.: 20
Commodities Exchange; Owned by New
York Mercantile Exchange, Inc., by Dubai
Holding LLC & by Oman Investment Fund
N.A.I.C.S.: 523210
Ahmad Sharaf (Chm)

DUBAI INSURANCE COMPANY (PSC)

Al Riqqa Road Deira, PO Box 3027,
Dubai, United Arab Emirates
Tel.: (971) 42693030   **AE**
Web Site: http://www.dubins.ae
Rev.: $129,674,447
Assets: $321,952,716
Liabilities: $192,681,670
Net Worth: $129,271,046

Earnings: $10,478,611
Fiscal Year-end: 12/31/17
Insurance Services
N.A.I.C.S.: 524113
Mohammed Tahsin *(COO)*

DUBAI INVESTMENTS PJSC

PO Box 28171, Dubai, United Arab
Emirates
Tel.: (971) 48122400
Web Site:
  https://www.dubaiinvestments.com
Year Founded: 1995
DIC—(DFM)
Rev.: $1,117,919,586
Assets: $5,836,908,435
Liabilities: $2,116,074,142
Net Worth: $3,720,834,293
Earnings: $285,646,105
Emp.: 2,017
Fiscal Year-end: 12/31/23
Investment Services
N.A.I.C.S.: 523150
Khalid Jassim Mohamed Kalban
(Vice Chm & CEO)

Subsidiaries:

Al Taif Investment Company LLC **(1)**
PO Box 8080, Fujairah, United Arab Emirates
Tel.: (971) 92225444
Web Site: https://www.altaifinvestment.com
Investment Management Service
N.A.I.C.S.: 523940

Dubai Cranes & Technical Services
Ltd. **(1)**
PO Box 113744, Dubai, United Arab
Emirates **(70%)**
Tel.: (971) 43452940
Specialist in Advanced Overhead Lifting
Solutions & Maintenance Services
N.A.I.C.S.: 333923

Dubai International Driving Center
(DIDC) **(1)**
PO Box 28171, Dubai, United Arab Emirates
Tel.: (971) 48122400
Web Site: http://www.dubaiinvestments.com
Driver Training Centers
N.A.I.C.S.: 611692

Dubai Investments Park Development
Company LLC **(1)**
Dubai Investments House 3rd Floor, PO
Box 111485, Dubai, United Arab
Emirates **(100%)**
Tel.: (971) 48851188
Web Site: https://www.dipark.com
Miscellaneous Financial Investment Activities
N.A.I.C.S.: 523999

Dubai Investments Real Estate
Company **(1)**
PO Box 22727, Dubai, United Arab
Emirates **(100%)**
Tel.: (971) 2328888
Web Site: http://www.di-realestate.com
Real Estate Investment Trust
N.A.I.C.S.: 525990
Obaid Mohammed Alsalami *(Gen Mgr)*

Emirates Building Systems Company
LLC **(1)**
DIP 1 Near police Post, Dubai, United Arab
Emirates **(51%)**
Tel.: (971) 48851122
Web Site: http://www.ebsl.com
Sales Range: $50-74.9 Million
Other Building Material Dealers
N.A.I.C.S.: 444180

Emirates District Cooling Company
LLC **(1)**
PO Box 9152, Dubai, United Arab
Emirates **(50%)**
Tel.: (971) 48852452
Web Site: http://www.emicool.net
Sales Range: $25-49.9 Million
Engineeering Services
N.A.I.C.S.: 541330
Abdulaziz Yagub Al Serkal *(Chm)*

Emirates Extruded Polystyrene
LLC **(1)**
Behind Al - Futtaim Exova, Dubai, United
Arab Emirates **(51%)**
Tel.: (971) 48850471
Web Site: http://www.dubaiinvestments.com
Sales Range: $25-49.9 Million
Emp.: 40
Other Building Material Dealers
N.A.I.C.S.: 444180
Abdul Aziz Yagub Al Serkal *(Chm)*

Emirates Extrusions Factory LLC **(1)**
PO Box 235561, Technopark, Dubai,
Arab Emirates **(100%)**
Tel.: (971) 48807768
Web Site:
  https://www.emiratesextrusions.com
Sales Range: $50-74.9 Million
Emp.: 200
Aluminum Extruded Product Mfr
N.A.I.C.S.: 331318
Khalfan Al Suwaidi *(Mng Dir)*

Emirates Float Glass LLC **(1)**
353MR2-ICAD-2, Abu Dhabi, United Arab
Emirates
Tel.: (971) 25994000
Web Site: https://www.efgme.com
Sales Range: $125-149.9 Million
Clear Molten Glass Mfr
N.A.I.C.S.: 327215

Emirates Glass LLC **(1)**
St 10 Al Quoz Industrial 4, PO Box 29769,
Dubai, United Arab Emirates **(100%)**
Tel.: (971) 47094700
Web Site: https://www.emiratesglass.com
Sales Range: $125-149.9 Million
Emp.: 250
Glass Product Mfr Made Purchased Glass
N.A.I.C.S.: 327215

Folcra Beach Industrial Company
LLC **(1)**
MW4, Abu Dhabi, 46536, United Arab
Emirates **(80%)**
Tel.: (971) 25510888
Web Site: http://www.dubaiinvestments.com
Sales Range: $25-49.9 Million
Mfr & Industrial Building Construction
N.A.I.C.S.: 236210
Marwan Naaman *(Mng Dir)*

Glass LLC **(1)**
PO Box 26769, Dubai, United Arab Emirates
Tel.: (971) 43471515
Holding Company
N.A.I.C.S.: 551112

Globalpharma Company LLC **(1)**
PO Box 72168, Dubai, United Arab
Emirates **(100%)**
Tel.: (971) 148090900
Web Site: https://cj4dx.com
Pharmaceuticals Product Mfr
N.A.I.C.S.: 325412

Gulf Dynamic Services LLC
(GDS) **(1)**
Industrial Area 17 Al Malaiah Street No 19
Bldg 99, PO Box 1298, Sharjah, United
Arab Emirates **(70%)**
Tel.: (971) 65344424
Web Site: https://www.gdsuae.com
Sales Range: $50-74.9 Million
Emp.: 300
Interior Design Services
N.A.I.C.S.: 541410

Gulf Metal Craft (GMC) **(1)**
PO Box 16893, Jebel Ali, Dubai, United
Arab Emirates **(10%)**
Tel.: (971) 48815151
Web Site: http://www.gulfmetalcraft.com
Sales Range: $10-24.9 Million
Architectural Stainless Steel Products Mfr
N.A.I.C.S.: 541310

International Rubber Co. LLC **(1)**
Plot No 598 1299 Dubai Invt Park 1, PO
Box 27140, Dubai, United Arab
Emirates **(51%)**
Tel.: (971) 48859880
Web Site: https://www.ircdxb.ae
Sales Range: $25-49.9 Million
Synthetic Rubber Mfr
N.A.I.C.S.: 325212

Lite Tech Industries LLC **(1)**
Ras Al Khor Industrial 2, PO Box 60305,
Dubai, United Arab Emirates
Tel.: (971) 43331387
Web Site: https://www.litetechind.com
Sales Range: $25-49.9 Million
Commercial Industrial & Institutional Electric
Lighting Fixture Mfr
N.A.I.C.S.: 335132

Lumi Glass Industries LLC **(1)**
PO Box 113744, Dubai, United Arab
Emirates **(67%)**
Tel.: (971) 43403919
Web Site:
  http://www.lumiglassindustries.com
Sales Range: $50-74.9 Million
Glass & Glazing Contractors
N.A.I.C.S.: 238150

M/S Gulf Dynamic Switchgear Co.
Ltd **(1)**
Industrial 1, PO Box 6155, Sharjah, 6155,
United Arab Emirates **(100%)**
Tel.: (971) 65338568
Web Site: http://www.gulfdynamic.com
Sales Range: $25-49.9 Million
Emp.: 100
Other Lighting Equipment Mfr
N.A.I.C.S.: 335139

MSharie LLC **(1)**
Dubai Investment House, PO Box 3045,
Dubai, United Arab Emirates **(100%)**
Tel.: (971) 48122600
Web Site: https://www.masharie.com
Miscellaneous Financial Investment Activities
N.A.I.C.S.: 523999

Subsidiary (Domestic):

Emirates Thermostone Factory
LLC **(2)**
PO Box 114197, Dubai, United Arab Emirates
Tel.: (971) 4 8854656
Concrete Products Mfr
N.A.I.C.S.: 327390
Abdul Nazir Mohammed Kunju *(Mgr-Fin)*

Labtech Interiors LLC **(2)**
Industrial Area 17 Maliha Road Bldg 99
Faisal Amiri Bldg, PO Box 4275, Sharjah,
United Arab Emirates
Tel.: (971) 6 5344480
Web Site: http://www.labtecllc.com
Emp.: 300
Laboratory & Hospital Furniture Mfr
N.A.I.C.S.: 339113

Subsidiary (Non-US):

Techno Rubber Company **(2)**
Madina Street 2nd Industrial City, PO Box
14052, Dammam, 31424, Saudi Arabia
Tel.: (966) 3 812 3333
Web Site: http://www.technorubber.com.sa
Rubber Products Mfr
N.A.I.C.S.: 325212

Subsidiary (Domestic):

White Aluminum Extrusion LLC **(2)**
ICAD1 Mussafa, Abu Dhabi, United Arab
Emirates
Tel.: (971) 25500947
Web Site: https://www.whiteextrusion.com
Aluminium Products Mfr
N.A.I.C.S.: 331318
Khalfan Al Suwaidi *(Mng Dir)*

National Insulated Blocks
Industries **(1)**
PO Box 62869, Dubai, United Arab Emirates
Tel.: (971) 48851112
Sales Range: $25-49.9 Million
Emp.: 37
Commercial & Institutional Building Construction
N.A.I.C.S.: 236220

Saudi American Glass Company **(1)**
PO Box 8418, Riyadh, 11482, Saudi
Arabia **(100%)**
Tel.: (966) 12651212
Web Site: https://www.saglass.com
Sales Range: $25-49.9 Million
Architectural Services
N.A.I.C.S.: 541310

Stromek Emirates Foundations
LLC **(1)**
227 Marion Street, PO Box 62124, Dubai,
United Arab Emirates **(51%)**
Tel.: (971) 43979505
Web Site: http://www.stromek.ae
Sales Range: $100-124.9 Million
Building Equipment & Other Machinery Installation Contractors
N.A.I.C.S.: 238220
Ahmed Al Adl *(Mng Dir & Gen Mgr)*

Syscom Emirates LLC **(1)**
PO Box 49700, Dubai, United Arab
Emirates **(100%)**
Tel.: (071) 43034788
Web Site: http://www.syscom.ae
Sales Range: $25-49.9 Million
Internal Communications Network Installations & Maintenance Services
N.A.I.C.S.: 517810

Technological Laboratory Furniture
Manufacturer (LABTEC) **(1)**
Po Box 4275 Indusrial 17, PO Box 4275,
Indusrial 17, Sharjah, United Arab
Emirates **(70%)**
Tel.: (971) 65344480
Web Site: https://www.labtecllc.com
Sales Range: $25-49.9 Million
Laboratory Apparatus & Furniture Mfr
N.A.I.C.S.: 337127

Techsource LLC **(1)**
Dubai Investments PJSC building 5th Floor
Dubai Investments Park 1, Dubai, United
Arab Emirates
Tel.: (971) 48122022
Web Site: https://www.techsource.ae
Information Technology Support Services
N.A.I.C.S.: 541512
Venkatesh Mahadevan *(CEO & Gen Mgr)*

Thermoset Technologies (Middle
East) LLC **(1)**
PO Box 118157, Dubai, United Arab
Emirates **(51%)**
Tel.: (971) 48852228
Web Site: https://www.thermosetme.ae
Sales Range: $25-49.9 Million
Emp.: 35
All Other Professional Scientific & Technical
Services
N.A.I.C.S.: 541990

United Sales Partners LLC **(1)**
PO Box 31671, Dubai, United Arab Emirates
Tel.: (971) 4 8326440
Dairy Products Distr
N.A.I.C.S.: 424430

DUBAI ISLAMIC BANK PSJ

3rd Floor DIB Head Office, PO Box
1080, Dubai, United Arab Emirates
Tel.: (971) 46092222
Web Site: https://www.dib.ae
Year Founded: 1975
DIB—(DFM)
Rev.: $5,484,942,951
Assets: $85,584,375,732
Liabilities: $72,667,638,809
Net Worth: $12,916,736,922
Earnings: $1,908,873,730
Emp.: 2,040
Fiscal Year-end: 12/31/23
Commercial Banking Services
N.A.I.C.S.: 522110
H. E. Mohammad Al Shaibani *(Chm)*

Subsidiaries:

Al Tanmyah Services L.L.C. **(1)**
13th Floor Office 1302 Le Solarium Tower
Dubai Silicon Oasis, Dubai, United Arab
Emirates
Tel.: (971) 45569181
Web Site: https://www.tanmyah.ae
Emp.: 7,500
Banking Services
N.A.I.C.S.: 522110
Mubarak Al Halyan *(CEO)*

DIB Bank Kenya Ltd. **(1)**
Junction of Bunyala Lower Hill Road Upper
Hill, PO Box 6450-00200, Nairobi, Kenya
Tel.: (254) 20709913111

Dubai Islamic Bank PSJ—(Continued)

Web Site: https://www.dibkenya.co.ke
Banking Services
N.A.I.C.S.: 522110

DIB Capital Limited (1)
DIFC Gate East Wing 3rd Floor, Dubai,
United Arab Emirates
Tel.: (971) 43634100
Web Site: http://www.dibcapital.com
Investment Banking Services
N.A.I.C.S.: 523150

**Dubai Islamic Bank Printing Press
LLC** (1)
Al Quoz Industrial 3 Inside Naseej Fabrics
Compound, Dubai, United Arab Emirates
Tel.: (971) 43884472
Web Site: https://www.dibpress.ae
Printing Product Mfr & Distr
N.A.I.C.S.: 333248

**Dubai Islamic Financial Services
L.L.C.** (1)
Khalid Bin Waleed Street DIB Branch Build-
ing Bur, Dubai, United Arab Emirates
Tel.: (971) 43217000
Web Site: http://www.difs.ae
Banking Services
N.A.I.C.S.: 522110
Taha Hussain Nauman (CEO)

**Naseej Fabric Manufacturing
L.L.C.** (1)
Al Bashar Area, PO Box 52881, Dubai,
United Arab Emirates (99%)
Tel.: (971) 43470808
Sales Range: $50-74.9 Million
Emp.: 190
Fabricated Metal Products Mfr
N.A.I.C.S.: 332999

Noor Islamic Bank PJSC (1)
Emaar Square Building 1 8th Floor Busi-
ness Bay, PO Box 8822, Dubai, United
Arab Emirates
Tel.: (971) 600500607
Web Site: http://www.noorbank.com
Sales Range: $200-249.9 Million
Emp.: 598
Banking Services
N.A.I.C.S.: 522110

Rhein Logistics GMBH (1)
Bulowstrasse 61, 46562, Voerde, Germany
Tel.: (49) 28141976835
Web Site: http://www.rhein-logistics.de
Logistic & Supply Services
N.A.I.C.S.: 488510

Safwa Islamic Bank (1)
Jabal Amman - Safwa Islamic Bank Building
- 1st Floor, PO Box 840762, Amman,
11181, Jordan
Tel.: (962) 64602100
Web Site: https://www.safwabank.com
Rev.: $172,295,325
Assets: $3,645,763,610
Liabilities: $3,403,375,997
Net Worth: $242,387,614
Earnings: $21,320,571
Emp.: 695
Fiscal Year-end: 12/31/2022
Banking Services
N.A.I.C.S.: 522110
Salem Mohammad Abu-Hammour (Chm)

Tamweel PJSC (1)
Business Avenue Building Port Saeed, PO
Box 111555, Deira, United Arab
Emirates (58.3%)
Tel.: (971) 42944400
Web Site: http://www.tamweel.ae
Sales Range: $150-199.9 Million
Emp.: 160
Real Estate Financial & Investment Ser-
vices
N.A.I.C.S.: 522292

**DUBAI ISLAMIC INSURANCE
& REINSURANCE COMPANY
P.S.C**
Gulf Towers B1 M Floor Oud Metha
Road-Bur Dubai, PO Box 157, Dubai,
United Arab Emirates
Tel.: (971) 43193111 AE
Web Site: https://www.aman.ae

Year Founded: 2002
Sales Range: $100-124.9 Million
Insurance Services
N.A.I.C.S.: 524298
Mohammed Omair Yousef Al Muhairi
(Vice Chm)

**DUBAI NATIONAL INSURANCE
& REINSURANCE PSC**
Dubai National Insurance Building 3rd
Floor Sheikh Zayed Road, PO Box
1806, Next to Mazaya Center, Dubai,
United Arab Emirates
Tel.: (971) 000580000
Web Site: https://www.dni.ae
DNIR—(DFM)
Rev.: $122,073,896
Assets: $266,228,767
Liabilities: $69,470,160
Net Worth: $196,758,607
Earnings: $12,829,449
Emp.: 141
Fiscal Year-end: 12/31/23
Insurance & Reinsurance Services
N.A.I.C.S.: 524113
Khalaf Ahmad Al Habtoor (Chm)

**DUBAI REFRESHMENTS
(P.S.C.)**
Dubai Investment Park 2 Street 49,
Dubai, United Arab Emirates
Tel.: (971) 48025000 AE
Web Site: https://www.pepsidrc.com
Year Founded: 1959
DRC—(DFM)
Rev.: $218,652,802
Assets: $430,293,515
Liabilities: $89,020,095
Net Worth: $341,273,420
Earnings: $98,501,145
Fiscal Year-end: 12/31/23
Soft Drinks Mfr & Distr
N.A.I.C.S.: 312111
Ahmad Eisa Al Serkal (Chm)

Subsidiaries:

Dubai Refreshments (P.S.C.) - Dubai
Main Production Facility (1)
Sheikh Zayed Rd 2nd Interchange beside
Al Yousuf Motors, Dubai, United Arab Emir-
ates
Tel.: (971) 72442516
Web Site: http://www.pepsidrc.com
Soft Drinks Mfr
N.A.I.C.S.: 312111

**DUBAI TOURISM & COM-
MERCE MARKETING**
PO Box 594, Dubai, United Arab
Emirates
Tel.: (971) 42230000
Web Site: http://www.dubaitourism.ae
Sales Range: $25-49.9 Million
Emp.: 250
Tourism & Commerce Promotor
N.A.I.C.S.: 813920
Mohammed bin Rashid Al Maktoum
(Chm)

**DUBAI WORLD CORPORA-
TION**
PO Box 17000, Dubai, United Arab
Emirates
Tel.: (971) 43903800
Web Site: http://www.dubaiworld.ae
Sales Range: $5-14.9 Billion
Emp.: 50,000
Investment Holding Company
N.A.I.C.S.: 551112
Ahmed Saeed Al Maktoum (Chm)

Subsidiaries:

DP World PLC (1)
5th Floor JAFZA 17 Jebel Ali Free Zone,
PO Box 17000, Dubai, United Arab
Emirates (100%)
Tel.: (971) 48811110

Web Site: http://www.dpworld.ae
Marine Terminal Operations & Logistics
Services
N.A.I.C.S.: 488310
Ahmed Sulayem (Chm & CEO)

Subsidiary (Non-US):

Chennai Container Terminal Private
Limited (2)
Chennai Port Trust Administrative Building
Ground Floor 1 Rajaji Salai, Chennai, 600
001, Tamil Nadu, India
Tel.: (91) 44 25909798
Web Site: http://www.dpworldchennai.com
Logistics Consulting Services
N.A.I.C.S.: 541614
Chandrasekaran Rajendran (Gen Mgr-HR,
IR & Admin)

Container Rail Road Services Private
Limited (2)
First Floor Property No 40 Okhla Industrial
Estate Phase III, New Delhi, 110020, India
Tel.: (91) 11 4653 5860
Web Site:
http://www.dpworldintermodal.com
Logistics Consulting Services
N.A.I.C.S.: 541614
Ramakrishna Nagabhirava (Gen Mgr)

DP World (2)
Al Slaimanyah Prince Abdulazzia Bin M.
Jawly Street, PO Box 57207, Riyadh,
11574, Saudi Arabia
Tel.: (966) 14623550
Web Site: http://webapps.dpworld.com
Sales Range: $300-349.9 Million
Emp.: 2,000
Logistics, Distribution & Transportation Ser-
vices
N.A.I.C.S.: 541614
Ahmed Al Amoudi (Gen Mgr)

DP World (Canada) Inc. (2)
Tel.: (604) 255-5151
Logistics Consulting Services
N.A.I.C.S.: 541614
Maksim Mihic (CEO)

Subsidiary (US):

DP World Americas Ro, Inc. (2)
5605 Carnegie Blvd Ste 420, Charlotte, NC
28209
Tel.: (704) 246-0343
Web Site: http://www.dpworld.com
Sales Range: $25-49.9 Million
Emp.: 10
Marine Terminal Development & Operation
N.A.I.C.S.: 488310

Subsidiary (Non-US):

DP World Antwerp N.V. (2)
Nieuwe Westweg-Haven 742, 2040, Ant-
werp, Belgium
Tel.: (32) 3 730 33 00
Web Site: http://www.dpworld.be
Logistics Consulting Services
N.A.I.C.S.: 541614
Dirk Van Aerde (Mgr-Terminal Ops)

DP World Callao S.R.L. (2)
Av Manco Capac, 113, Callao, Peru
Tel.: (51) 1 206 6500
Web Site: http://www.dpworldcallao.com.pe
Logistics Consulting Services
N.A.I.C.S.: 541614
Jose Miguel Ugarte Maggiolo (Dir-Fin)

DP World Cargo Services (Pty)
Limited (2)
277 Umbilo Rd, Durban, 4001, South Africa
Tel.: (27) 31 365 0700
Logistics Consulting Services
N.A.I.C.S.: 541614

Subsidiary (Domestic):

DP World FZE (2)
JAFZA 17 Jebel Ali Free Zone, PO Box
17000, Dubai, United Arab Emirates
Tel.: (971) 4811110
Web Site: http://www.dpworld.com
Logistics & Supply Chain Services
N.A.I.C.S.: 541614

DP World Fujairah FZE (2)
PO Box 17000, Dubai, United Arab Emirates

Tel.: (971) 4 881 5555
Logistics Consulting Servies
N.A.I.C.S.: 541614
Dirk Van Den Bosch (VP-Trade & Bus Dev)

Subsidiary (Non-US):

DP World Germersheim, GmbH and
Co. KG (2)
Worthstrasse 13, 76726, Germersheim,
Germany
Tel.: (49) 7274 708 0
Logistics Consulting Servies
N.A.I.C.S.: 541614

Subsidiary (Domestic):

DP World Limited (2)
Office 27 Level 3 Gate Village Building 4,
PO Box 17000, Dubai International Finan-
cial Centre, Dubai, United Arab Emirates
Tel.: (971) 48811110
Web Site: http://www.dpworld.com
Rev.: $8,532,563,000
Assets: $37,342,358,000
Liabilities: $21,941,849,000
Net Worth: $15,400,509,000
Earnings: $942,002,000
Emp.: 53,367
Fiscal Year-end: 12/31/2020
Marine Terminal Operations & Logistics
Services
N.A.I.C.S.: 488310
Nick Loader (COO)

Subsidiary (US):

Boston Wharf Company (3)
253 Summer St, Boston, MA 02210-1114
Tel.: (617) 426-6034
Web Site: http://www.bostonwharf.com
Sales Range: $50-74.9 Million
Emp.: 22
Lessors of Office Space
N.A.I.C.S.: 531120

Denver Technological Center (3)
5750 DTC Pkwy Ste 200, Greenwood Vil-
lage, CO 80111-3226
Tel.: (303) 773-1700
Web Site: http://www.dtcmeridian.com
Sales Range: $25-49.9 Million
Emp.: 40
Real Estate Operations
N.A.I.C.S.: 237210

Subsidiary (Non-US):

London Gateway Port Limited (3)
1 London Gateway, Stanford-le-Hope, SS17
9DY, Essex, United Kingdom
Tel.: (44) 1375 648 300
Web Site: http://www.londongateway.com
Emp.: 500
Logistics Consulting Servies
N.A.I.C.S.: 541614
James Leeson (Dir-Ops)

P&O Ferries Holdings Limited (3)
Channel House Channel View Road, Dover,
CT17 9TJ, United Kingdom
Tel.: (44) 1304863000
Web Site: http://www.poferries.com
Ferry Operator
N.A.I.C.S.: 483114
John Garner (Dir-Fleet & Ports)

Subsidiary (Domestic):

P&O Ferries Ltd. (4)
Channel House Channel View Rd, Dover,
CT17 9TJ, Kent, United Kingdom
Tel.: (44) 1304863875
Web Site: http://www.poferriesfreight.com
Ferry Operator
N.A.I.C.S.: 488510

P&O Ferrymasters Limited (4)
Wherstaid Park, Whestaird, Ipswich, IP9
2WJ, United Kingdom
Tel.: (44) 473585200
Web Site: http://www.poferrymasters.com
Sales Range: $25-49.9 Million
Emp.: 85
Cargo Handling Distr
N.A.I.C.S.: 488320
Bas Belder (Mng Dir)

Affiliate (Non-US):

Wysepower Limited (3)

Lincoln Road, High Wycombe, HP12 3RH,
Bucks, United Kingdom
Tel.: (44) 1494560900
Web Site: http://www.wysepower.com
Sales Range: $25-49.9 Million
Contractors Hire & Support Services
N.A.I.C.S.: 238990

Subsidiary (Non-US):

**DP World Maritime Cooperatieve
U.A.** **(2)**
Albert Plesmanweg 43/G, 3088 GB, Rotterdam, Netherlands
Tel.: (31) 10 4282257
Logistics Consulting Servies
N.A.I.C.S.: 541614
John Thompson *(Gen Mgr)*

DP World Private Limited **(2)**
Darabshaw House Level 1 Narottam Morarji
Road, Ballard Estate, Mumbai, 400 001,
India
Tel.: (91) 2222610570
Web Site: http://www.dpworld.com
Sales Range: $25-49.9 Million
Emp.: 21
Marine Terminal Operations & Logistics
Services
N.A.I.C.S.: 488310
Anil Singh *(Mng Dir-Indian Subcontinent &
Sr VP)*

Subsidiary (Non-US):

MacKinnon MacKenzie & Co. of Pakistan (Pvt.) Ltd. **(3)**
MacKinnons Bldg II Chundrigar Rd, PO Box
4679, Karachi, 74000, Pakistan
Tel.: (92) 2124130417
Web Site: http://www.mackpak.com
Shipping Agents
N.A.I.C.S.: 488510

Subsidiary (Non-US):

DP World Tarragona S.A. **(2)**
Contarsa Sociedad de Estiba SA Moll dAndalusia s-n, PO BOX 1400, 43080, Tarragona, Spain
Tel.: (34) 977 249 010
Logistics Consulting Servies
N.A.I.C.S.: 541614
Alfonso Gonzalez Sanchez *(Gen Mgr)*

**DP World Yarimca Liman Isletmeleri
Anonim Sirketi** **(2)**
Mimar Sinan Mah Mehmet Akif Ersoy Cad
Gul Sk Tunsan is Merkezi No 10, Yarmca,
41780, Korfez, Kocaeli, Turkiye
Tel.: (90) 262 528 6334
Web Site: http://www.dpworld.com.tr
Logistics Consulting Servies
N.A.I.C.S.: 541614

Subsidiary (Domestic):

Dubai Maritime City LLC **(2)**
PO Box 8988, Dubai, United Arab Emirates
Tel.: (971) 56 6800393
Web Site: http://www.dubaimaritimecity.com
Logistics Consulting Servies
N.A.I.C.S.: 541614
Khalid Meftah *(Dir-Maritime Bus Dev)*

Dubai Trade FZE **(2)**
Floor 10 Galleries Suite 4 Building Downtown Jebel Ali, PO Box 18666, Dubai,
United Arab Emirates
Tel.: (971) 4 4339333
Web Site: http://www.dubaitrade.ae
Logistics Consulting Servies
N.A.I.C.S.: 541614
Mahmood Al Bastaki *(CEO)*

Subsidiary (Non-US):

Fraser Surrey Docks LP **(2)**
11060 Elevator Road, Surrey, V3V 2R7,
BC, Canada
Tel.: (604) 581-2233
Web Site: http://www.fsd.bc.ca
Rev.: $13,853,300
Emp.: 70
Marine Cargo Handling
N.A.I.C.S.: 488320
Jeff Scott *(Pres & CEO)*

Imperial Logistics Limited **(2)**
Imperial Place 79 Boeing Road East, Bedfordview, 2007, South Africa

Tel.: (27) 113726500
Web Site: http://www.imperiallogistics.com
Rev.: $3,562,151,840
Assets: $2,069,347,670
Liabilities: $1,539,951,100
Net Worth: $529,396,570
Earnings: $76,895,210
Emp.: 24,982
Fiscal Year-end: 06/30/2021
Holding Company
N.A.I.C.S.: 551112
Phumzile Langeni *(Chm)*

Subsidiary (Domestic):

Alert Engine Parts (Pty) Limited **(3)**
279 Voortrekker Road, Goodwood, Cape
Town, 7459, South Africa
Tel.: (27) 21 590 8250
Web Site: https://www.alert.co.za
Emp.: 55
Automobile Engine Parts Distr
N.A.I.C.S.: 333618

**Associated Motor Holdings (Pty)
Limited** **(3)**
7 Corobrick Rd, Meadowdale, Johannesburg, 1400, South Africa
Tel.: (27) 113989100
Web Site: http://www.amhgroup.net
Sales Range: $50-74.9 Million
Emp.: 30
Commercial Vehicle Distr
N.A.I.C.S.: 423110
Manny De Canha *(Pres)*

Europcar South Africa **(3)**
16 Ernest Oppenheimer Avenue, Bruma,
2026, Johannesburg, South Africa **(100%)**
Tel.: (27) 114794000
Web Site: http://www.europcar.co.za
Sales Range: $650-699.9 Million
Emp.: 1,500
Car Rental Services
N.A.I.C.S.: 532111

Imperial Bank Limited **(3)**
PO Box 6093, Rivonia, 2128, South
Africa **(100%)**
Tel.: (27) 112753000
Web Site: http://www.imperialbank.co.za
Sales Range: $100-124.9 Million
Emp.: 217
Provider of Passenger & Commercial Vehicle Financing
N.A.I.C.S.: 525990
Naeem Shah *(Interim Mng Dir)*

Imperial Capital Limited **(3)**
79 Boeing Road, Bedfordview, 2007, South
Africa
Tel.: (27) 113726500
Web Site: http://www.imperial.co.za
Truck Rental Services
N.A.I.C.S.: 532120
Willem Reitsma *(Gen Mgr)*

Imperial Daihatsu (Pty) Limited **(3)**
Cnr Rietfontein Madeley Road, Boksburg,
1462, South Africa
Tel.: (27) 113837000
Web Site: http://www.daihatsu.co.za
Sales Range: $25-49.9 Million
Emp.: 25
Automobile Mfr
N.A.I.C.S.: 336110
Pedro Perreira *(Mng Dir)*

Subsidiary (Non-US):

Imperial Group (Pty) Limited **(3)**
Tel.: (27) 11 372 6500
Web Site: http://www.imperial.co.za
Sales Range: $25-49.9 Million
Emp.: 50
Automotive Repair & Maintenance Services
N.A.I.C.S.: 811198
Russell Munford *(Gen Mgr-Fin)*

Subsidiary (Domestic):

Imperial Logistics & Transport **(3)**
10 Refinery Rd Goldfield Logistics Park,
Germiston, 1400, South Africa
Tel.: (27) 118215500
Web Site: http://www.imperiallogistics.co.za
Sales Range: $25-49.9 Million
Emp.: 60
Local & Long Distance Transport, Warehousing & Related Services

N.A.I.C.S.: 541614

Subsidiary (Domestic):

Imperial Sasfin Logistics **(4)**
Building K Clearwater Office Park Corner,
PO Box 11288, Atlas and Park Roads Boksburg Aston Manor, 1630, Johannesburg,
South Africa **(70%)**
Tel.: (27) 115739000
Web Site: http://imperialsasfin.com
International Freight Forwarding Services
N.A.I.C.S.: 488510
Abhilash Kunjupilla *(Dir-Ops)*

Subsidiary (Non-US):

**Imperial Logistics International B.V. &
Co. KG** **(3)**
Kasteelstrasse 2, 49119, Duisburg,
Germany **(100%)**
Tel.: (49) 20331880
Web Site: http://www.imperial-
international.com
Freight Logistics Services
N.A.I.C.S.: 541614
Thomas Schulz *(Member-Mgmt Bd)*

Subsidiary (Domestic):

Imperial Mobility Deutschland Beteiligungs GmbH **(4)**
Kasteelstrasse 2, Duisburg, 47119, Germany
Tel.: (49) 203 80050
Web Site: http://www.imperial-
international.com
Sales Range: $50-74.9 Million
Emp.: 150
Marine Shipping Services
N.A.I.C.S.: 483111
Eurgen Burow *(Gen Mgr)*

Subsidiary (Non-US):

Imperial Mobility International BV **(5)**
Waalbandijk 121, Druten, 6651 KB, Netherlands
Tel.: (31) 487587631
Web Site: http://www.imperial-mobility.nl
Sales Range: $25-49.9 Million
Emp.: 2
Logistic Services
N.A.I.C.S.: 541614

**Imperial Shipping Rotterdam
B.V.** **(5)**
Waalhaven Oostzijde 77 Dockworks 4
Portno 2203 A, 3087 BM, Rotterdam, Netherlands
Tel.: (31) 102831420
Web Site: http://www.imperial-shipping-
rotterdam.com
Sales Range: $25-49.9 Million
Emp.: 15
Cargo Handling Services
N.A.I.C.S.: 488320
Hans Valk *(Gen Mgr)*

Rijnaarde B.V. **(5)**
Van Heemstraweg 64C, 6641 AG, Beuningen, Netherlands
Tel.: (31) 243435343
Web Site: http://www.rijnaarde.com
Sales Range: $25-49.9 Million
Emp.: 6
Marine Shipping Services
N.A.I.C.S.: 483111
Jose Daanen *(Gen Mgr)*

Wijgula B.V **(5)**
Waalbandijk 123, 6651 KB, Druten, Netherlands
Tel.: (31) 487 587600
Web Site: http://www.wijgula.nl
Marine Transportation Services
N.A.I.C.S.: 483111

Subsidiary (Domestic):

Imperial Select Alberton **(3)**
7 Voortrekker Road, 1449, Alberton, Gauteng, South Africa
Tel.: (27) 119073110
Web Site: http://www.imperialselect.co.za
Automotive Distr
N.A.I.C.S.: 423110
Mike Salt *(Mgr-Used Cars)*

Imperilog Limited **(3)**
Unit 7 Gallagher Place South cnr Richards

Drive and Suttie Road, Midrand, 1685,
South Africa
Tel.: (27) 113122233
Web Site: http://www.imperilog.co.za
Sales Range: $25-49.9 Million
Emp.: 200
Logistic Services
N.A.I.C.S.: 541614

Subsidiary (Non-US):

Imres B.V. **(3)**
Larserpoortweg 26, 8218 NK, Lelystad,
Netherlands
Tel.: (31) 320296969
Web Site: http://www.imres.nl
Medical Equipment Supplier
N.A.I.C.S.: 423450
Yeressago Derikx *(Acct Mgr)*

Subsidiary (Domestic):

Jurgens Ci (Pty) Limited **(3)**
Cor Main Second Street Ga Rankuwa Industrial Park North West, PO Box 911-
1056, Rosslyn, 0200, South Africa
Tel.: (27) 127977300
Web Site: http://www.jurgensci.co.za
Emp.: 200
Automobile Mfr
N.A.I.C.S.: 336110
Bradley Salters *(Mng Dir)*

Subsidiary (Non-US):

MDS Logistics Limited **(3)**
Plot 32 Kudirat Abiola Way, Oregun, Ikeja,
Nigeria
Tel.: (234) 8159890211
Web Site: http://www.mdslogistics.net
Logistic & Supply Chain Services
N.A.I.C.S.: 541614

Subsidiary (Domestic):

National Airways Corporation **(3)**
Hangar 104C Gate 15 Lanseria International Airport, Lanseria, 1748, Johannesburg, South Africa **(62%)**
Tel.: (27) 112675000
Web Site: http://www.nac.co.za
Sales Range: $50-74.9 Million
Emp.: 200
Provider of Aviation Services
N.A.I.C.S.: 488119
Martin Banner *(CEO)*

Subsidiary (Non-US):

Palletways Group Limited **(3)**
Fradley Distribution Park Wood End Lane,
Fradley, Lichfield, WS13 8NE, United Kingdom
Tel.: (44) 1543418000
Web Site: http://uk.palletways.com
Emp.: 115
Freight Transportation Services
N.A.I.C.S.: 488510
Rob Gittins *(Mng Dir)*

Subsidiary (Non-US):

India Gateway Terminal Pvt. Ltd **(2)**
Administration Building ICTT Vallarpadam
SEZ, Mulavukadu Village, Kochi, 682 502,
India
Tel.: (91) 484 4156100
Web Site: http://www.dpworld.com
Emp.: 300
Logistics Consulting Servies
N.A.I.C.S.: 541614
James Koshy *(Gen Mgr-IT)*

Integra Port Services N.V. **(2)**
Havenlaan Zuid 12, Paramaribo, Suriname
Tel.: (597) 402890
Web Site:
http://www.integraportservices.com
Logistics Consulting Servies
N.A.I.C.S.: 327910
Marvin Asin *(Mgr-Fin)*

**Nhava Sheva International Container
Terminal Private Limited** **(2)**
Operations Center Container Gate, Sheva,
400707, Mumbai, India
Tel.: (91) 22 27243500
Web Site: http://www.dpworldmumbai.com
Logistics Consulting Servies
N.A.I.C.S.: 541614
Ajay Singh *(CEO)*

Dubai World Corporation—(Continued)

Subsidiary (Domestic):

P&O Maritime FZE **(2)**
JAZFA 17 Building 6th Floor, PO Box
17000, Dubai, United Arab Emirates
Tel.: (971) 4447 8300
Web Site: http://www.pomaritime.com
Logistics Consulting Servies
N.A.I.C.S.: 541614
Radostin Popov (Dir-Grp Comml & Bus
Dev)

Subsidiary (Non-US):

P&O Maritime Services Pty Ltd **(2)**
Level 4 70 City Road, Southbank, 3006,
VIC, Australia
Tel.: (61) 3 9254 1600
Web Site: http://www.pomaritime.com
Emp.: 30
Logistics Consulting Servies
N.A.I.C.S.: 541614

Remolcadores de Puerto y Altura,
S.A. **(2)**
Muelle De Reus S/N Edif Fruport, Tarra-
gona, 43004, Spain
Tel.: (34) 977 25 25 65
Web Site: http://www.repasa.net
Logistics Consulting Servies
N.A.I.C.S.: 541614
Belen Maldonado (CFO)

Southampton Container Terminals
Limited **(2)**
Berths 204-207 Western Dock, Southamp-
ton, SO15 1DA, United Kingdom
Tel.: (44) 2380 701701
Web Site:
    http://www.dpworldsouthampton.com
Logistics Consulting Servies
N.A.I.C.S.: 541614

Terminales Rio de la Plata SA **(2)**
Av Ramon Castillo and Av Comodoro Py,
Puerto Nuevo, Buenos Aires, 1104, Argen-
tina
Tel.: (54) 1143199500
Web Site: http://www.trp.com.ar
Logistics Consulting Servies
N.A.I.C.S.: 541614
Ricardo Alvarez (Dir-Ops)

Subsidiary (Domestic):

World Security FZE **(2)**
PO Box 18668, Dubai, United Arab Emir-
ates
Tel.: (971) 4 345 1515
Web Site: http://www.worldsecurity.ae
Security Alarm Services
N.A.I.C.S.: 561612
Essa Turkeya (Dir-Port & Free Zone)

Drydocks World LLC **(1)**
PO Box 8988, Dubai, United Arab Emirates
Tel.: (971) 43450626
Web Site: http://www.drydocks.gov.ae
Sales Range: $1-4.9 Billion
Ship Building, Repairing & Offshore Engi-
neering Services
N.A.I.C.S.: 336611
Rado Antolovic (CEO)

Economic Zones World
Company **(1)**
Building 14 Sheikh Zayed Road Jebel Ali
Free Zone 2nd Floor, PO Box 16888,
Dubai, United Arab Emirates
Tel.: (971) 4 881 2222
Logistics Consulting Servies
N.A.I.C.S.: 541614
Salma Ali Saif Hareb (CEO)

Imperial Commercials Ltd **(1)**
Imperial House 14/15 High Street, High Wy-
combe, HP11 2BE, Buckinghamshire,
United Kingdom
Tel.: (44) 1494 520 908
Web Site:
    http://www.imperialcommercials.co.uk
Sales Range: $25-49.9 Million
Emp.: 6
Commercial Vehicle Dealer
N.A.I.C.S.: 441227
Matt Lawrenson (Mng Dir)

Istithmar PJSC **(1)**

6th Floor Bldg 4 The Galleries, Downtown
Jebel Ali, PO Box 17000, Dubai, United
Arab Emirates
Tel.: (971) 4 364 4239
Sales Range: $50-74.9 Million
Emp.: 50
Equity Investment Firm
N.A.I.C.S.: 523999

Holding (US):

Hotel Washington, Inc. **(2)**
515 15th St NW, Washington, DC 20004-
1099
Tel.: (202) 638-5900
Web Site: http://www.hotelwashington.com
Luxury Hotel
N.A.I.C.S.: 721110

Loehmann's Holdings Inc. **(2)**
2500 Halsey St, Bronx, NY 10461
Tel.: (718) 409-2000
Sales Range: $350-399.9 Million
Holding Company; Women's & Men's Dis-
count Branded Apparel & Accessories
Stores Owner & Operator
N.A.I.C.S.: 551112
Arthur E. Reiner (Chm)

Subsidiary (Domestic):

Loehmann's, Inc. **(3)**
2500 Halsey St, Bronx, NY 10461
Tel.: (718) 409-2000
Women's & Men's Discount Branded Ap-
parel & Accessories Stores Operator
N.A.I.C.S.: 458110

Subsidiary (Non-US):

P&O Estates Ltd. **(2)**
16 Palace St, London, SW1E 5JQ, United
Kingdom
Tel.: (44) 2079014200
Web Site: http://www.poestates.com
Sales Range: $25-49.9 Million
Emp.: 10
International Property Management
N.A.I.C.S.: 531390
Ian Pirnett (Mng Dir)

Subsidiary (Domestic):

P&O Developments Ltd. **(3)**
4 Carlton Gardens, Pall Mall, London,
SW1Y 5AB, United Kingdom
Tel.: (44) 2078395611
Web Site: http://www.podevelopments.com
Sales Range: $50-74.9 Million
Commercial Property Development
N.A.I.C.S.: 531312

Limitless PJSC **(1)**
Al Khail Road, PO Box 261919, Dubai,
United Arab Emirates
Tel.: (971) 4 435 8888
Web Site: http://www.limitless.com
Residential & Commercial Real Estate De-
veloper
N.A.I.C.S.: 237210
Mohammed Rashed Dhabeah (CEO)

Nakheel PVT JSC **(1)**
PO Box 17777, Dubai, United Arab Emir-
ates
Tel.: (971) 4 390 3333
Web Site: http://www.nakheel.com
Sales Range: $550-599.9 Million
Emp.: 1,500
Property Development Services
N.A.I.C.S.: 237990
Ali Rashid Ahmed Lootah (Chm)

DUBBER CORPORATION LIM-
ITED
Level 5 2 Russell Street, Melbourne,
3000, VIC, Australia
Tel.: (61) 386586111 AU
Web Site: https://www.dubber.net
DUB—(ASX)
Rev.: $25,814,108
Assets: $36,254,557
Liabilities: $24,578,353
Net Worth: $11,676,204
Earnings: ($27,192,893)
Emp.: 240
Fiscal Year-end: 06/30/24
Software Developer

N.A.I.C.S.: 513210
Ian Hobson (Sec)

DUBEK LTD.
9 Martin Gahel st, Kiryat Arie,
4951252, Petah Tiqwa, Israel
Tel.: (972) 39265050
Web Site: http://www.en.dubek.co.il
Year Founded: 1935
Sales Range: $25-49.9 Million
Emp.: 265
Tobacco Product Mfr
N.A.I.C.S.: 312230
David Shaohi (VP HR)

Subsidiaries:

Israel Tobacco Co. (M.T.) Ltd. **(1)**
9 Martin Gehl Street Fl 1, Petah Tiqwa,
49512, Israel
Tel.: (972) 39265050
Web Site: http://www.dubek.com
Sales Range: $100-124.9 Million
Cigarette Mfr
N.A.I.C.S.: 312230
Gehl Roy (Mgr)

Jerusalem Cigarette Co. Ltd. **(1)**
Old Jericho Rd, Jerusalem, 97913, Israel
Tel.: (972) 22799777
Web Site: http://www.JeruCig.com
Sales Range: $25-49.9 Million
Emp.: 200
Cigarette Mfr
N.A.I.C.S.: 312230
Mohammad Alami (Chm & Gen Mgr)

DUBICKI ROBNI MAGAZIN
A.D.
Svetosavska 10, 79240, Kozarska
Dubica, Bosnia & Herzegovina
Tel.: (387) 52 410 487
DBRM—(BANJ)
Sales Range: Less than $1 Million
Emp.: 14
Magazine Publisher
N.A.I.C.S.: 513120
Strahinja Sunjka (Chm-Mgmt Bd)

DUBRAC TP
36 rue du Marechal Lyantey, 93200,
Saint Denis, France
Tel.: (33) 149711090
Web Site: http://www.dubrac.com
Rev.: $23,800,000
Emp.: 200
Highway & Street Construction
N.A.I.C.S.: 237310
Serge Desnos (Mgr-Fin)

DUBREUIL AUTOMOBILES
4 Place Jean Jaures, 27400, Lou-
viers, France
Tel.: (33) 232400228
Web Site: http://www.dubreuil-
automobiles.fr
Automobile Sales & Maintenance
Services
N.A.I.C.S.: 441110

DUBUS INDUSTRIES
68 rue du General Patton, Malesher-
bes, 45330, Fontainebleau, France
Tel.: (33) 238327575
Web Site: http://www.dubus-
group.com
Rev.: $20,200,000
Emp.: 105
Woodworking Machinery
N.A.I.C.S.: 333243
Thierry Nouchet (Pres)

DUC GIANG CHEMICALS
GROUP JOINT STOCK COM-
PANY
18/44 Duc Giang Thuong Thanh
Ward, Long Bien District, Hanoi, Viet-
nam
Tel.: (84) 2438271620

Web Site:
    https://www.ducgiangchem.vn
Year Founded: 1963
DGC—(HOSE)
Rev.: $401,618,218
Assets: $640,079,327
Liabilities: $144,569,482
Net Worth: $495,509,846
Earnings: $133,556,433
Emp.: 2,528
Fiscal Year-end: 12/31/23
Chemicals & Detergents Mfr
N.A.I.C.S.: 325998
Huu Huyen Dao (Chm, Pres, CEO &
Member-Mgmt Bd)

DUC LONG GIA LAI GROUP
JSC
90 Le Duan, Phu Dong Ward, Pleiku,
Gia Lai, Vietnam
Tel.: (84) 593748367
Web Site:
    https://www.duclonggroup.com
Year Founded: 1995
DLG—(HOSE)
Rev.: $46,240,161
Assets: $208,140,299
Liabilities: $186,406,681
Net Worth: $21,733,618
Earnings: ($23,844,088)
Emp.: 5,750
Fiscal Year-end: 12/31/23
Home Management Services
N.A.I.C.S.: 721110
Minh Viet Pham (Deputy Gen Dir)

Subsidiaries:

DLG Hanbit Co., Ltd. **(1)**
7F 712 274 Samsung-ro, Suwon,
Gyeonggi-do, Korea (South)
Tel.: (82) 312112523
Web Site: https://www.dlghb.co.kr
Memory Module & Storage Product Mfr &
Distr
N.A.I.C.S.: 334413

Duroc Laser Coating AB **(1)**
Fabriksvagen 16, 972 54, Lulea, Sweden
Tel.: (46) 920432220
Web Site: https://duroclasercoating.com
Pain Bearing & Bushing Mfr & Distr
N.A.I.C.S.: 332991
Soren Isaksson (Mgr)

Herber Engineering AB **(1)**
Silkesvagen 5, 331 53, Varnamo, Sweden
Tel.: (46) 370699550
Web Site: https://herber.se
Machine Tools Mfr
N.A.I.C.S.: 333517
Andreas Nord (CEO)

IFG Asota GmbH **(1)**
Schachermayerstrasse 22, 4020, Linz, Aus-
tria
Tel.: (43) 73269850
Textile Mfr
N.A.I.C.S.: 313310

IFG Exelto NV **(1)**
Nederzwijnaarde 2, 9052, Gent, Belgium
Tel.: (32) 93961041
Textile Mfr
N.A.I.C.S.: 313310

Universal Power Nordic AB **(1)**
Borgmastaregatan 21, 59634, Skanninge,
Sweden
Tel.: (46) 142299100
Web Site: https://universalpower.se
Motor Mfr
N.A.I.C.S.: 335312
Kajsa Milden (CEO)

Viet Nam Renewable Energy Group
JSC **(1)**
Lot I3-06 Road N2 High-Tech Park, Tang
Nhon Phu A Ward Thu Duc City, Ho Chi
Minh City, Gia Lai, Vietnam
Tel.: (84) 2837367187
Web Site: https://www.a7group.vn
Rev.: $11,588,448
Assets: $100,000,887
Liabilities: $42,422,322

Net Worth: $57,578,566
Earnings: $2,907,484
Emp.: 35
Fiscal Year-end: 12/31/2023
Food Transportation Services
N.A.I.C.S.: 485999

DUC THANH WOOD PRO-CESSING JSC
2214 Phan Huy Ich Street Ward 14,
Go Vap District, Ho Chi Minh City,
Vietnam
Tel.: (84) 835894287
Web Sito: https://www.dtwoodvn.com
Year Founded: 1991
GDT—(HOSE)
Rev.: $16,119,005
Assets: $15,954,461
Liabilities: $5,133,087
Net Worth: $10,821,375
Earnings: $3,199,079
Emp.: 1,200
Fiscal Year-end: 12/31/20
Kitchenware Mfr
N.A.I.C.S.: 321999

DUCART INTERNATIONAL PA-PER, LTD.
Kfar Masaryk, 25208, Haifa, Israel
Tel.: (972) 49854517
Web Site: http://www.ducart.co.il
Sales Range: $50-74.9 Million
Emp.: 200
Paper Mfr
N.A.I.C.S.: 322120
Avshalom Ben David *(CEO)*

DUCATEX S.A.
Ana Ipatescu Street No 44, 077120,
Jilava, Ilfov, Romania
Tel.: (40) 21 457 00 16
Web Site: http://www.ducatex.ro
Sales Range: $1-9.9 Million
Emp.: 148
Rubber Products Mfr
N.A.I.C.S.: 326299

DUCATT NV
Balendijk 161, Lommel, 3920, Bel-gium
Tel.: (32) 11 559 300
Web Site: http://www.ducatt.com
Emp.: 120
Glass Mfr
N.A.I.C.S.: 327212
Danny Berrens *(CFO)*

Subsidiaries:

Centrosolar Glas GmbH & Co.
KG   **(1)**
Siemensstrasse 3, 90766, Furth, Germany
Tel.: (49) 911950980
Web Site: http://www.centrosolarglas.com
Sales Range: $100-124.9 Million
Solar Components Mfr
N.A.I.C.S.: 334413
Ralf Ballasch *(Mng Dir)*

DUCHEMBIO CO., LTD.
3 6 7F 81 Wausan-ro, Mapo-gu,
Seoul, 04041, Korea (South)
Tel.: (82) 23324868
Web Site:
    https://www.duchembio.com
Year Founded: 2002
Pharmaceutical Product Whslr
N.A.I.C.S.: 424210
Jong-Woo Kim *(CEO)*

DUCKYANG INDUSTRY CO., LTD.
366 Hyoam-ro, Buk-gu, Ulsan, Korea
(South)
Tel.: (82) 522191114   KR
Web Site: https://www.dyauto.kr
Year Founded: 1977

024900—(KRS)
Rev.: $1,182,734,129
Assets: $399,006,851
Liabilities: $331,170,483
Net Worth: $67,836,368
Earnings: $8,812,124
Emp.: 834
Fiscal Year-end: 12/31/22
Automotive Interior Products Mfr
N.A.I.C.S.: 336390
Youngchan Jeong *(VP)*

DUDIGITAL GLOBAL LIMITED
C-4 Rai House Commorcial Complox,
Safdarjung Development Area, New
Delhi, 110016, India
Tel.: (91) 1140450533
Web Site:
    https://www.dudigitalglobal.com
Year Founded: 2007
DUGLOBAL—(NSE)
Rev.: $1,339,092
Assets: $2,050,121
Liabilities: $1,051,146
Net Worth: $998,975
Earnings: $17,636
Emp.: 115
Fiscal Year-end: 03/31/22
Information Technology Services
N.A.I.C.S.: 541512

DUDLEY BUILDING SOCIETY
7 Harbour Buildings The Waterfront,
Brierley Hill, DY5 1LN, United King-dom
Tel.: (44) 1384 231414
Web Site:
    http://www.dudleybuilding.co.uk
Rev.: $16,188,888
Assets: $556,518,569
Liabilities: $526,397,110
Net Worth: $30,121,459
Earnings: $1,635,767
Emp.: 55
Fiscal Year-end: 03/31/19
Mortgage Lending Services
N.A.I.C.S.: 522310
David J. Milner *(Chm)*

DUEARITY AB
Duearity AB Hojdrodergatan 21, 212
39, Malmo, Sweden
Tel.: (46) 738145215
Web Site: https://www.duearity.com
Year Founded: 2020
DEAR—(OMX)
Rev.: $163,798
Assets: $1,502,968
Liabilities: $1,740,227
Net Worth: ($237,259)
Earnings: ($2,599,917)
Emp.: 1
Fiscal Year-end: 12/31/23
Health Care Srvices
N.A.I.C.S.: 621610
Frederick Westman *(CEO)*

DUESENBERG TECHNOLO-GIES INC.
820 1130 West Pender St, Vancou-ver, V6E 4A4, BC, Canada
Tel.: (604) 648-0510   BC
Web Site:
    https://www.duesenbergtech.com
Year Founded: 2010
DUSYF—(OTCQB)
Rev.: $41,577
Assets: $41,021
Liabilities: $1,002,960
Net Worth: ($961,939)
Earnings: ($1,707,842)
Emp.: 8
Fiscal Year-end: 12/31/21
Communication Technology Devel-oper
N.A.I.C.S.: 541519
Joe Hun Beng Lim *(Pres & CEO)*

DUET ACQUISITION CORP.
V03-11-02 Designer Office V03
Lingkaran SV Sunway Velocity,
55100, Kuala Lumpur, Malaysia
Tel.: (60) 7867537867   DE
Web Site: https://duet-corp.com
Year Founded: 2021
DUET—(NASDAQ)
Rev.: $1,048,411
Assets: $88,619,227
Liabilities: $90,858,078
Net Worth: ($2,238,851)
Earnings: ($469,563)
Emp.: 3
Fiscal Year-end: 12/31/22
Investment Services
N.A.I.C.S.: 523999
Yeoh Oon Lai *(Co-CEO)*

DUFAYLITE DEVELOPMENTS LIMITED
Cromwell Rd, Cambridge, Saint Ne-ots, PE19 1QW, Cambs, United King-dom
Tel.: (44) 1480215000
Web Site: http://www.dufaylite.com
Year Founded: 1955
Sales Range: $25-49.9 Million
Emp.: 75
Paper Honeycomb Materials for
Doors & Panels, Packaging & Fire
Protection Products
N.A.I.C.S.: 321219
Tony Moscrop *(CEO)*

DUFERCO S.A.
Via Bagutti 9, Lugano, 6900, Switzer-land
Tel.: (41) 918225600
Web Site: http://www.duferco.com
Year Founded: 1979
Sales Range: $75-99.9 Million
Emp.: 360
Trader of Steel Products, Tin Plate &
Special Steels; Producer, Transformer
& Distr of Steel Products
N.A.I.C.S.: 331110
Bruno Bolfo *(Founder & Chm)*

Subsidiaries:

Duferco Steel Inc.   **(1)**
Metro Park S 100 Matawan Rd Ste 400,
Matawan, NJ 07747-3916
Tel.: (732) 566-3130
Web Site: http://www.duferco.com
Emp.: 30
Steel Roll Products Whslr
N.A.I.C.S.: 423510
Mike Vignale *(Sr VP)*

Subsidiary (Domestic):

Kreher Steel Company, LLC   **(2)**
1550 25th Ave, Melrose Park, IL
60160-1801   **(100%)**
Tel.: (708) 345-8180
Web Site: http://www.kreher.com
Sales Range: $50-74.9 Million
Emp.: 110
Steel Distr & Marketer
N.A.I.C.S.: 423510
Joseph L. Druzak *(Pres & CEO)*

Branch (Domestic):

Kreher Steel Co. - Detroit   **(3)**
8585 PGA Dr Ste 200, Walled Lake, MI
48390
Tel.: (248) 669-9003
Web Site: http://www.kreher.com
Steel Distr & Marketer
N.A.I.C.S.: 423510

Subsidiary (Domestic):

Kreher Wire Processing, Inc.   **(3)**
34822 Goddard Rd, Romulus, MI 48174-3406
Tel.: (734) 941-9500
Web Site: http://www.krehersteel.com

Sales Range: $25-49.9 Million
Emp.: 20
Metal Products Mfr
N.A.I.C.S.: 423510
Fred Smith *(Gen Mgr)*

DUFOUR S.A.
Quartier Les Barrieres, 04110, Reil-lanne, Alpes De Haute Prove, France
Tel.: (33) 492734020
Web Site: http://www.groupedufour.fr
Rev.: $22,300,000
Emp.: 47
Meat Product Whslr
N.A.I.C.S.: 424470

DUFU TECHNOLOGY CORP. BERHAD
19 Hilir Sungai Keluang 2 Taman
Perindustrian Bayan Lepas Fasa IV,
11900, Bayan Lepas, Penang, Malay-sia
Tel.: (60) 46161300   MY
Web Site:
    https://www.dufutechnology.com
Year Founded: 1987
DUFU—(KLS)
Rev.: $64,344,738
Assets: $89,819,835
Liabilities: $17,714,578
Net Worth: $72,105,257
Earnings: $14,182,718
Emp.: 389
Fiscal Year-end: 12/31/22
Holding Company; Industrial Machine
& Computer Peripherals Mfr
N.A.I.C.S.: 551112
Hui-Ta Lee *(Chm)*

Subsidiaries:

Dufu Industries Services Pte Ltd   **(1)**
623 Aljunied Rd 05-01, Aljunied Industrial
Complex, Singapore, 389835, Singapore
Tel.: (65) 68460919
Web Site: http://www.dufu.com.my
Emp.: 10
Screw Machine Product Mfr
N.A.I.C.S.: 333517

DUG TECHNOLOGY LTD.
76 Kings Park Rd, West Perth, 6005,
WA, Australia
Tel.: (61) 892874100   AU
Web Site: https://www.dug.com
Year Founded: 2003
DUG—(ASX)
Rev.: $53,468,000
Assets: $47,069,000
Liabilities: $26,155,000
Net Worth: $20,914,000
Earnings: $4,941,000
Emp.: 250
Fiscal Year-end: 06/30/23
Software Development Services
N.A.I.C.S.: 541511
Jacqueline Barry *(Sec)*

Subsidiaries:

DownUnder GeoSolutions (America)
LLC   **(1)**
16200 Park Row Dr Ste 100, Houston, TX
77084
Tel.: (832) 582-3221
Information Technology Services
N.A.I.C.S.: 541512

DownUnder GeoSolutions (Asia) Sdn.
Bhd.   **(1)**
Ground floor Gtower 199 Jalan Tun Razak,
50400, Kuala Lumpur, Malaysia
Tel.: (60) 364195200
Information Technology Services
N.A.I.C.S.: 541512

DownUnder GeoSolutions (London)
Pty Ltd.   **(1)**
3rd Floor 192-198 Vauxhall Bridge Road,
London, SW1V 1DX, United Kingdom
Tel.: (44) 2072905380
Information Technology Services

DUG Technology Ltd.—(Continued)

N.A.I.C.S.: 541512

DUGA A.D.
Viline vode 6, 11000, Belgrade,
11000, Serbia
Tel.: (381) 113217444
Web Site: https://www.duga-ibl.com
Year Founded: 1999
DUGAM—(BEL)
Rev.: $15,962
Assets: $110,519
Liabilities: $4,106,345
Net Worth: ($0,995,020)
Earnings: ($15,285)
Fiscal Year-end: 12/31/22
Building Materials Whslr
N.A.I.C.S.: 444180
Bojan Mikec (Mng Dir)

DUGA HOLDING AD
Viline Vode 6, 11000, Belgrade, Ser-
bia
Tel.: (381) 113392359
Web Site: http://www.duga-ibl.com
Sales Range: $75-99.9 Million
Emp.: 370
Paints, Varnishes, Resins, Corrosion
Inhibitors & PET
N.A.I.C.S.: 325510
Branko Dunjic (Chm)

DUIBA GROUP LIMITED
Room 501 Shuyu Building 98 Wenyi
West Road, Xihu, Hangzhou, China
Tel.: (86) 57128258680   Ky
Web Site: http://www.duiba.cn
Year Founded: 2011
1753—(HKG)
Rev.: $226,970,921
Assets: $254,079,634
Liabilities: $70,493,857
Net Worth: $183,585,776
Earnings: ($6,443,939)
Emp.: 748
Fiscal Year-end: 12/31/22
Software Development Services
N.A.I.C.S.: 541511
Chen Xiaoliang (Founder & CEO)

DUISBURGER
VERSORGUNGS- UND
VERKEHRSGESELLSCHAFT
MBH
Bungertstrasse 27, 47053, Duisburg,
Germany
Tel.: (49) 2036040   De
Web Site: http://www.dvv.dvv.de
Year Founded: 1971
Sales Range: $1-4.9 Billion
Emp.: 116
Electric Power Generation & Distr
N.A.I.C.S.: 221122
Hermann Janning (Chm)

DUJODWALA PAPER CHEMI-
CALS LIMITED
907 Raheja Centre 214, Nariman
Point, Mumbai, 400 021, India
Tel.: (91) 2267522780
Web Site: http://www.dpcl.net
Year Founded: 1993
Sales Range: $25-49.9 Million
Resin & Paper Chemical Mfr & Whslr
N.A.I.C.S.: 325211
N. C. Mansukhani (Mgr-Mktg)

DUK SAN NEOLUX CO., LTD.
21-32 Ssukgol-gil Ipjang-myeon,
Seobuk-gu, Cheonan, Chungnam,
Korea (South)
Tel.: (82) 415905400
Web Site: https://www.dsnl.co.kr
213420—(KRS)
Rev.: $135,511,392
Assets: $277,299,581

Liabilities: $31,605,184
Net Worth: $245,694,398
Earnings: $29,852,512
Emp.: 245
Fiscal Year-end: 12/31/22
Electronic Components Mfr
N.A.I.C.S.: 334413
Junho Lee (Chm & CEO)

DUKA & BOSNA D.D.
Brace Cuskica 10, 76 000, Brcko,
Bosnia & Herzegovina
Tel.: (387) 49216096
Sales Range: Less than $1 Million
Emp.: 104
Furniture Mfr & Distr
N.A.I.C.S.: 321999

DUKE OFFSHORE LIMITED
403 Urvashi Off Sayani Road Prab-
hadevi, Mumbai, 400 025, India
Tel.: (91) 2224221225
Web Site:
https://www.dukeoffshore.com
Year Founded: 1985
531471—(BOM)
Rev.: $260,500
Assets: $1,595,161
Liabilities: $176,826
Net Worth: $1,418,335
Earnings: ($268,607)
Emp.: 6
Fiscal Year-end: 03/31/21
Offshore Engineering Services
N.A.I.C.S.: 213112
Avik George Duke (Chm & Mng Dir)

DUKE ROYALTY LIMITED
Fourth Floor Plaza House Admiral
Park, Saint Peter Port, GY1 2HU,
Guernsey
Tel.: (44) 1481231816   GY
Web Site: https://dukecapital.com
Year Founded: 2014
DUKE—(AIM)
Rev.: $32,298,662
Assets: $300,824,287
Liabilities: $92,188,841
Net Worth: $208,635,446
Earnings: $14,652,865
Fiscal Year-end: 03/31/24
Investment Management Service
N.A.I.C.S.: 523940
Nigel Birrell (Chm)

DUKE STREET CAPITAL LIM-
ITED
Nations House 103 Wigmore St, Lon-
don, W1U 1QS, United Kingdom
Tel.: (44) 2076638500   UK
Web Site: http://www.dukestreet.com
Year Founded: 1988
Sales Range: $1-4.9 Billion
Emp.: 600
Privater Equity Firm
N.A.I.C.S.: 523999
Peter Taylor (Mng Partner)

Subsidiaries:

Sandpiper CI Limited   (1)
1 L Avenue le Bas, Longueville, Saint Sav-
iour, JE4 8NB, Jersey
Tel.: (44) 1534508508
Web Site: http://www.sandpiperci.com
Holding Company; General Retail, Liquor &
Convenience Stores & Supermarket Fran-
chises Operator; Owned by Duke Street
Capital Limited & by Europa Capital Part-
ners Limited
N.A.I.C.S.: 551112
Tony O'Neill (CEO)

Subsidiary (Domestic):

Sandpiper CI Retail Limited   (2)
1 L'Avenue le Bas, Longueville, Saint Saviour, JE4 8NB, Jersey
Tel.: (44) 153 450 8508
Web Site: https://www.sandpiperci.com

Sales Range: $600-649.9 Million
Holding Company; General Retail, Liquor &
Convenience Stores & Supermarket Fran-
chises Operator
N.A.I.C.S.: 551112
Tony O'Neill (CEO)

Suir Engineering Ltd.   (1)
Unit 9A Cleaboy Business Park Old
Kilmeaden Road, Waterford, X91 PX92,
Ireland
Tel.: (353) 51359500
Web Site: http://suireng.ie
Engineering Services
N.A.I.C.S.: 541330
Micheal Kennedy (CEO)

DUKEMOUNT CAPITAL PLC
70 Jermyn Street St James's, Lon-
don, SW1Y 6NY, United Kingdom
Tel.: (44) 2079766381   UK
Web Site:
https://www.dukemountcapital.com
Year Founded: 2011
DKE—(LSE)
Rev.: $4,476,036
Assets: $815,953
Liabilities: $1,654,800
Net Worth: ($838,847)
Earnings: ($1,240,721)
Emp.: 2
Fiscal Year-end: 04/30/21
Real Estate Investment Trust Ser-
vices
N.A.I.C.S.: 531190
Geoffrey Dart (Chm)

DUKETON MINING LIMITED
Level 2 45 Richardson St, West
Perth, 6005, WA, Australia
Tel.: (61) 863151490
Web Site:
http://www.duketonmining.com.au
DKM—(ASX)
Rev.: $20,513
Assets: $14,345,519
Liabilities: $586,991
Net Worth: $13,758,527
Earnings: ($7,136,497)
Fiscal Year-end: 06/30/22
Metal Ore Mining
N.A.I.C.S.: 212290
Stuart Fogarty (Mng Dir)

DUKSAN HI-METAL CO., LTD.
66 Muryong 1-ro, Buk-gu, Ulsan, Ko-
rea (South)
Tel.: (82) 522839000
Web Site: https://www.dshm.co.kr
Year Founded: 1999
077360—(KRS)
Rev.: $131,550,853
Assets: $278,834,140
Liabilities: $45,571,097
Net Worth: $233,263,043
Earnings: $4,682,424
Emp.: 237
Fiscal Year-end: 12/31/22
Semiconductor Devices Mfr
N.A.I.C.S.: 334413
Junho Lee (Chm & CEO)

DUKSAN TECHOPIA CO., LTD.
39 Pungsesandan 2-ro, Pungse-
myeon Dongnam-gu, Cheonan,
Chungcheongnam-do, Korea (South)
Tel.: (82) 419039700
Web Site: https://www.dstp.co.kr
Year Founded: 2006
317330—(KRS)
Rev.: $103,392,503
Assets: $224,789,055
Liabilities: $65,641,065
Net Worth: $159,147,989
Earnings: $16,400,843
Emp.: 215
Fiscal Year-end: 12/31/21
Rubber Products Mfr
N.A.I.C.S.: 326299

Steven Hwang (VP)

DUKSHINEPC CO., LTD.
Dukshin building 322
Nambusunhwan-ro, Yangcheon-gu,
Seoul, Korea
Tel.: (82) 226002600
Web Site: http://www.duckshin.com
Year Founded: 1996
090410—(KRS)
Rev.: $154,633,490
Assets: $106,699,675
Liabilities: $37,005,547
Net Worth: $60,604,128
Earnings: $7,789,187
Emp.: 194
Fiscal Year-end: 12/31/22
Steel Construction Products Mfr
N.A.I.C.S.: 332312
Kim Myung Hwan (Pres)

DUKSUNG CO., LTD.
25 Sinwon-ro, Yeongtong-Gu, 16677,
Suwon, 16677, Gyeonggi-Do, Korea
(South)
Tel.: (82) 312040781
Web Site:
https://www.duksung21.com
Year Founded: 1966
004830—(KRS)
Rev.: $102,239,397
Assets: $96,007,199
Liabilities: $32,032,042
Net Worth: $63,975,157
Earnings: $1,929,188
Emp.: 180
Fiscal Year-end: 12/31/22
Artificial Leather Mfr
N.A.I.C.S.: 313320
Bonggeun Lee (CEO)

Subsidiaries:

Duksung Co., Ltd. - Incheon
Factory   (1)
616-9 Namchong-Dong, Namdong-Gu, In-
cheon, Korea (South)
Tel.: (82) 32 812 2335
Artificial Leather Mfr
N.A.I.C.S.: 313320

Duksung Co., Ltd. - Osan
Factory   (1)
279-1 Songsan-Ri, Yanggam-Myeon, Pyeo-
ngtaek, Gyeonggi-Do, Korea (South)
Tel.: (82) 31 354 5990 1
Artificial Leather Mfr
N.A.I.C.S.: 313320

Duksung Co., Ltd. - Pyeongtaek
Factory   (1)
1206-10 Wonjung-Ri, Poseung-Myeon,
Pyeongtaek, Gyeonggi-do, Korea (South)
Tel.: (82) 31 686 6191
Artificial Leather Mfr
N.A.I.C.S.: 313320

DULAMIA COTTON SPINNING
MILLS LTD.
Ancher Tower 108 Bir Uttam C R
Dutta Road, Dhaka, 1205, Bangla-
desh
Tel.: (880) 286195212   UK
Web Site:
https://www.dulamiabd.com
Year Founded: 1987
DULAMIACOT—(DHA)
Rev.: $2,881
Assets: $786,361
Liabilities: $3,488,264
Net Worth: ($2,701,903)
Earnings: ($75,208)
Emp.: 900
Fiscal Year-end: 06/30/23
Cotton Yarn Mfr
N.A.I.C.S.: 313110

DUMAS AUTOMOBILES
Route De Montelimar, 07200, Bourg-
les-Valence, Aubenas, France

Tel.: (33) 475898295
Rev.: $20,200,000
Emp.: 44
New & Used Car Dealers
N.A.I.C.S.: 441110
Francois Dumas *(Pres)*

DUMMEN ORANGE HOLDING B.V.
Coldenhovelaan 6, 2678 PS, De Lier, Netherlands
Tel.: (31) 174 530 100
Web Site:
http://www.dummenorange.com
Holding Company
N.A.I.C.S.: 551112
Tetsuya Obara *(CEO)*

Subsidiaries:

Grow-Tech LLC   (1)
165 Pleasant Ave Unit B, South Portland, ME 04106
Tel.: (207) 353-5005
Web Site: http://www.grow-tech.com
Sales Range: $1-9.9 Million
Emp.: 10
Rooting Substrates for Commercial Grower Product Mfr
N.A.I.C.S.: 316990
Edwin Dijkshoorn *(Mng Dir)*

DUNA ASZFALT ZTR
Tiszakecske Beke u 150, 6060, Budapest, Hungary
Tel.: (376) 540060
Web Site: https://www.dunaaszfalt.hu
Emp.: 100
Construction Engineering Services
N.A.I.C.S.: 237310

DUNA HOUSE HOLDING PUBLIC COMPANY LIMITED
Gellerthegy Utca 17, 1st District, 1016, Budapest, Hungary
Tel.: (36) 15552222
Web Site:
https://www.dunahouse.com
Year Founded: 2003
DUNAHOUSE—(BUD)
Rev.: $84,043,566
Assets: $112,826,477
Liabilities: $98,437,268
Net Worth: $14,389,209
Earnings: $8,056,865
Emp.: 217
Fiscal Year-end: 12/31/22
Holding Company
N.A.I.C.S.: 551112
Gay Dymschiz *(Co-Founder & Mng Dir)*

Subsidiaries:

Credipass Polska S.A.   (1)
Ul Woloska 22, 02-675, Warsaw, Poland
Tel.: (48) 221121929
Web Site: https://credipass.pl
Real Estate Brokerage Services
N.A.I.C.S.: 531210

Home Management Kft.   (1)
Kiraly Street 13 1/1/4, 1075, Budapest, Hungary
Tel.: (36) 12690353
Web Site: https://hmgt.hu
Property Management Services
N.A.I.C.S.: 531311

Impact Alapkezelo Zrt.   (1)
Gellerthegy Street 17, 1016, Budapest, Hungary
Tel.: (36) 15552238
Web Site: https://impactalapkezelo.hu
Asset Management Services
N.A.I.C.S.: 531390

Medioinsurance S.r.l.   (1)
Via Martiri di Cefalonia 5, 24121, Italy
Tel.: (39) 03541616
Web Site: https://medioinsurance.com

Financial Consultancy & Insurance Protection Services
N.A.I.C.S.: 524210

REIF 2000 Kft.   (1)
Margit Korut 26, 1027, Budapest, Hungary
Tel.: (36) 13163111
Web Site:
https://reifketezer.mystrikingly.com
Real Estate Brokerage Services
N.A.I.C.S.: 531210

Realizza S.r.l.   (1)
Via Martiri di Cefalonia 5, 24121, Bergamo, Italy
Tel.: (39) 03541616
Web Site: https://realizza.casa
Real Estate Brokerage Services
N.A.I.C.S.: 531210

DUNAPREF SA
Str Portului Nr 2, Giurgiu, Romania
Tel.: (40) 372 037 344
Web Site: http://www.dunapref.ro
Sales Range: $1-9.9 Million
Emp.: 165
Precast Concrete Products Mfr
N.A.I.C.S.: 327390

DUNAV A.D.
Bulevar revolucije 15, 25260, Grocka, Serbia
Tel.: (381) 118501052
Web Site:
http://www.dunavapatin.com
Year Founded: 1946
Sales Range: Less than $1 Million
Emp.: 43
Kitchen Furniture Mfr
N.A.I.C.S.: 337122
Petar Stojanovic *(Dir)*

DUNAV A.D. GROCKA
Bulevar Revolucije 15, Grocka, 11306, Belgrade, Serbia
Tel.: (381) 118501052
Web Site:
https://www.dunavgrocka.rs
DNVG—(BEL)
Rev.: $1,502,265
Assets: $5,092,094
Liabilities: $2,040,144
Net Worth: $3,051,950
Earnings: ($322,414)
Emp.: 41
Fiscal Year-end: 12/31/23
Texturised Yarn Mfr
N.A.I.C.S.: 313110

DUNAV OSIGURANJE AD BANJA LUKA
Veselina Maslese 28, 78000, Banja Luka, Republika Srpska, Bosnia & Herzegovina
Tel.: (387) 51246100
Web Site: https://www.dunav.ba
Year Founded: 1991
KDVO-R-A—(BANJ)
Sales Range: $10-24.9 Million
Emp.: 200
Insurance Services
N.A.I.C.S.: 524126
Maja Cukovic *(Exec Dir-Finance & Accounting)*

DUNAV RE A.D.
Kralja Aleksandra Boulevard 18 1st floor, 11000, Belgrade, Serbia
Tel.: (381) 112634755
Web Site: https://www.dunavre.rs
DNREM—(BEL)
Rev.: $40,566,455
Assets: $118,086,463
Liabilities: $87,994,776
Net Worth: $30,091,687
Earnings: $6,661,631
Fiscal Year-end: 12/31/23
Reinsurance Services
N.A.I.C.S.: 524130

Aca Aleksic *(Mgr-Web Design & Member-Exec Bd)*

DUNAVPREVOZ A.D.
Novosadski put 12, 21400, Backa Palanka, Serbia
Tel.: (381) 21 6042 775
Web Site: http://www.dunavprevoz.rs
Year Founded: 1951
Sales Range: $1-9.9 Million
Emp.: 163
Passenger Transportation Services
N.A.I.C.S.: 485999
Damjanic Milenko *(CEO)*

DUNBIA GROUP
Granville Industrial Estate, Dungannon, BT70 1NJ, Co Tyrone, United Kingdom
Tel.: (44) 2887 723350
Web Site: http://www.dunbia.com
Year Founded: 1976
Sales Range: $1-4.9 Billion
Emp.: 3,156
Meat Product Whslr
N.A.I.C.S.: 424470
Jim Dobson *(CEO)*

Subsidiaries:

H. R. Jasper & Son Ltd.   (1)
Botathan Abattoir South Petherwin, Truro, PI15 7JI, Cornwall, United Kingdom
Tel.: (44) 1566772843
Web Site: http://www.jasperslamb.co.uk
Lamb Meat Whslr
N.A.I.C.S.: 311611
Keith Jasper *(Mng Dir)*

DUNCAN ENGINEERING LIMITED
F-33 MIDC Ranjangaon Karegoan Tal-Shirur, Pune, 412 209, Maharashtra, India
Tel.: (91) 2138660066
Web Site:
https://www.duncanengg.com
504908—(BOM)
Rev.: $5,732,700
Assets: $5,743,838
Liabilities: $1,596,804
Net Worth: $4,147,034
Earnings: $1,090,321
Emp.: 161
Fiscal Year-end: 03/31/21
Automotive Products Mfr
N.A.I.C.S.: 336110
Jagdish Prasad Goenka *(Chm)*

Subsidiaries:

Schrader Duncan Limited - Pneumatics Business Unit   (1)
502 Ishan Arcade II Ghokhale Road Opp Hanuman, Mandir, Thane, 400 602, Maharashtra, India
Tel.: (91) 22 4124 8999
Web Site: http://www.schraderduncan.com
Sales Range: $25-49.9 Million
Emp.: 30
Pneumatic Product Mfr
N.A.I.C.S.: 333998
Shashank Gune *(Gen Mgr)*

DUNCAN FOX S.A.
Av El Bosque Norte 0440 8th Floor, Santiago, Chile
Tel.: (56) 228610700
Web Site: https://www.duncanfox.cl
DUNCANFOX—(SGO)
Sales Range: Less than $1 Million
Canned Frozen Fish Mfr
N.A.I.C.S.: 114119
Sergio Lecaros Menendez *(Chm)*

DUNCAN HAMILTON & CO LIMITED
PO Box 222, Hook, RG27 9YZ, England, United Kingdom
Tel.: (44) 1256765000

Web Site:
http://www.duncanhamilton.com
Rev.: $22,518,711
Emp.: 6
Used Car Dealers
N.A.I.C.S.: 441120
Adrian Hamilton *(Mng Dir)*

DUNDAS MINERALS LIMITED
Suite 13 100 Railway Road, Daglish, Subiaco, 6008, WA, Australia
Tel.: (61) 457024143   AU
Web Site:
https://www.dundasminerals.com
Year Founded: 2000
DUN—(ASX)
Rev.: $33,160
Assets: $4,991,239
Liabilities: $121,660
Net Worth: $4,869,579
Earnings: ($393,471)
Emp.: 1
Fiscal Year-end: 06/30/23
Mineral Exploration Services
N.A.I.C.S.: 212390
Shane Raymond Volk *(Mng Dir & Sec)*

DUNDEE CORPORATION
80 Richmond Street West Suite 2000, Toronto, M5H 2A4, ON, Canada
Tel.: (416) 350-3388   ON
Web Site:
https://www.dundeecorporation.com
DDEJF—(OTCIQ)
Rev.: $25,361,518
Assets: $422,007,987
Liabilities: $62,219,422
Net Worth: $359,788,564
Earnings: ($68,898,529)
Emp.: 30
Fiscal Year-end: 12/31/20
Holding Company; Wealth Management & Real Estate Investment Services
N.A.I.C.S.: 551112
Jonathan C. Goodman *(Pres & CEO)*

Subsidiaries:

AgriMarine Holdings Inc.   (1)
1401-1130 West Pender St, Vancouver, V6E 4A4, BC, Canada
Tel.: (604) 568-4672
Web Site: http://www.agrimarine.com
Holding Company; Finfish Farming & Related Technologies Development Services
N.A.I.C.S.: 551112

Subsidiary (Domestic):

AgriMarine Industries Inc.   (2)
Suite 240 - 1829 Beaufort Avenue, Comox, V9M 1R9, BC, Canada
Tel.: (250) 941-3099
Sales Range: $25-49.9 Million
Emp.: 10
Finfish Farming Services
N.A.I.C.S.: 112511

Dundee 360 Real Estate Corporation   (1)
2001 rue University Bureau 400, Montreal, H3G 1K4, QC, Canada
Tel.: (514) 987-6452
Web Site: http://www.360vox.com
Sales Range: $50-74.9 Million
Real Estate Development Services
N.A.I.C.S.: 531390
Robin Conners *(Pres & CEO)*

Dundee Energy Limited   (1)
Web Site: http://www.dundee-energy.com
Sales Range: Less than $1 Million
Crude Petroleum & Natural Gas Extraction
N.A.I.C.S.: 211120
Bruce Sherley *(Pres & CEO)*

Dundee Realty Management Corporation   (1)
30 Adelaide Street East Suite 301, Toronto, M5C 3H1, ON, Canada
Tel.: (416) 365-3535

Dundee Corporation—(Continued)

Web Site: http://www.dundeerealty.com
Emp.: 200
Real Estate Services
N.A.I.C.S.: 531390

Subsidiary (Domestic):

Bellanca Developments Ltd. (2)
5201 - 50th Ave Ste 804, Yellowknife, X1A
3S9, NT, Canada
Tel.: (867) 920-2324
Sales Range: $25-49.9 Million
Real Estate Property Management Services
N.A.I.C.S.: 531312
Darin Benoit (Gen Mgr)

**Dundee Realty Management (B.C.)
Corp.** (2)
Station Tower Ste 1620 13401-108th Ave,
Surrey, V3T 5T3, BC, Canada
Tel.: (604) 586-5117
Web Site: http://www.dundeerealty.com
Emp.: 9
Property Management Services
N.A.I.C.S.: 531312

**Dundee Realty Management (Sask)
Corp.** (2)
Princeton Tower 123 2nd Ave Ste 602, Sas-
katoon, S7K 7E6, SK, Canada
Tel.: (306) 665-6120
Sales Range: $50-74.9 Million
Emp.: 9
Property Management & Leasing Services
N.A.I.C.S.: 531110

Subsidiary (US):

Dundee Realty USA Inc. (2)
225 Main St G 3003, Edwards, CO 81632
Tel.: (970) 845-7838
Web Site: http://www.dundeerealty.com
Sales Range: $25-49.9 Million
Emp.: 3
Real Estate Services
N.A.I.C.S.: 237210

Dundee Resources Ltd. (1)
1 Adelaide St East 20th Floor, Toronto,
M5C 2V9, ON, Canada
Tel.: (416) 350-3327
Gold & Precious Metal Mining
N.A.I.C.S.: 212220
Carl Calandra (VP-Legal)

Eight Capital (1)
100 Adelaide Street West Suite 2900, To-
ronto, M5H 1S3, ON, Canada (100%)
Tel.: (416) 350-3305
Web Site: https://viiicapital.com
Full-service Investment Dealer
N.A.I.C.S.: 523150

World Wide Minerals Ltd. (1)
917-211 Queen's Quay Blvd West, Toronto,
M5J 2M6, ON, Canada
Tel.: (416) 703-9120
Web Site:
http://www.worldwideminerals.com
Sales Range: $50-74.9 Million
Emp.: 6
Producer of Mineral Resources
N.A.I.C.S.: 213115
Paul A. Carroll (Pres & CEO)

DUNDEE PRECIOUS METALS INC.

150 King Street West Suite 902, PO
Box 195, Toronto, M5H 1H9, ON,
Canada
Tel.: (416) 365-5191 Ca
Web Site:
https://www.dundeeprecious.com
DPM—(TSX)
Rev.: $609,558,000
Assets: $974,860,000
Liabilities: $169,576,000
Net Worth: $805,284,000
Earnings: $194,863,000
Emp.: 2,159
Fiscal Year-end: 12/31/20
Gold Mining Services
N.A.I.C.S.: 212220
Jonathan C. Goodman (Chm)

Subsidiaries:

Dundee Precious Metals - Sofia (1)
26 Bacho Kiro Street 3rd Floor, Sofia, 1000,
Bulgaria
Tel.: (359) 29301500
Web Site: https://www.dundeeprecious.com
Copper & Gold Mining Services
N.A.I.C.S.: 212220
Iliya Garkov (Mng Dir & VP)

**Dundee Precious Metals Krumovgrad
EAD** (1)
1 Hristo Botev St, Krumovgrad, Kardjhali,
6900, Bulgaria
Tel.: (359) 36416803
Web Site: http://www.dundeeprecious.com
Mineral Mining Services
N.A.I.C.S.: 212390

INV Metals Inc. (1)
55 University Avenue Suite 700, Toronto,
M5J 2H7, ON, Canada
Tel.: (416) 703-8416
Web Site: http://www.invmetals.com
Rev.: $36,382
Assets: $71,009,849
Liabilities: $1,497,423
Net Worth: $69,512,426
Earnings: ($2,293,487)
Emp.: 39
Fiscal Year-end: 12/31/2019
Mineral Resource Development & Explora-
tion Services
N.A.I.C.S.: 212220
Jorge Barreno (Gen Mgr-Ecuador)

DUNDEE SUSTAINABLE TECHNOLOGIES INC.

3700 rue du Lac-Noir, Thetford
Mines, G6H 1S9, QC, Canada
Tel.: (514) 866-6001 Ca
Web Site:
https://www.dundeetechnology.com
Year Founded: 1997
DNDDF—(OTCIQ)
Rev.: $2,854,702
Assets: $3,473,069
Liabilities: $14,722,004
Net Worth: ($11,248,935)
Earnings: ($2,788,599)
Fiscal Year-end: 12/31/22
Base Metal Extraction Technologies
Developer
N.A.I.C.S.: 333248
Brent Johnson (VP)

DUNE MERCANTILE LIMITED

A-212 Titanium City Center Near IOC
Petrol Pump 100 Feet Road, Satel-
lite, Ahmedabad, 380 015, India
Tel.: (91) 7940392260
Web Site:
http://www.dunemercantile.co.in
Rev.: $286,302
Assets: $814,241
Liabilities: $61,857
Net Worth: $752,384
Earnings: $4,800
Fiscal Year-end: 03/31/16
Textile Goods Trading Services
N.A.I.C.S.: 523160
Kamlesh Solanki (Mng Dir)

DUNEDIN ENTERPRISE INVESTMENT TRUST PLC

Saltire Court 20 Castle Terrace, Edin-
burgh, EH1 2EN, United Kingdom
Tel.: (44) 1312256699
Web Site:
https://www.dunedinenterprise.com
Year Founded: 1974
DNE—(LSE)
Rev.: $1,037,298
Assets: $104,806,480
Liabilities: $3,083,382
Net Worth: $101,723,098
Earnings: ($7,899,215)
Emp.: 180
Fiscal Year-end: 12/31/20
Investment Services

N.A.I.C.S.: 523999
Shaun Middleton (Mng Partner)

Subsidiaries:

Dunedin Capital Partners Limited (1)
Saltire Ct 20 Castle Ter, Edinburgh, EH1
2EN, United Kingdom (100%)
Tel.: (44) 131 225 6699
Web Site: http://www.dunedin.com
Sales Range: $50-74.9 Million
Emp.: 28
Privater Equity Firm
N.A.I.C.S.: 523999
Simon Miller (Chm)

DUNEDIN INCOME GROWTH INVESTMENT TRUST PLC

Financial Ombudsman Service Ex-
change Tower, London, E14 9SR,
United Kingdom
Tel.: (44) 8085000040
Web Site:
https://www.dunedinincome.co.uk
DIG—(LSE)
Rev.: $9,575,775
Assets: $594,553,245
Liabilities: $54,202,500
Net Worth: $540,350,745
Earnings: $3,420,780
Fiscal Year-end: 01/31/23
Investment Management Service
N.A.I.C.S.: 525990
Luke Mason (Head-Bus Dev)

DUNELM GROUP PLC

Watermead Business Park, Syston,
LE7 1AD, Leicestershire, United
Kingdom
Tel.: (44) 1162644400 UK
Web Site: https://www.dunelm.com
Year Founded: 1979
DNEMF—(OTCIQ)
Rev.: $2,035,061,840
Assets: $865,286,240
Liabilities: $694,538,740
Net Worth: $170,747,500
Earnings: $188,629,420
Emp.: 7,273
Fiscal Year-end: 07/01/23
Holding Company; Home Furnishings
Retailer
N.A.I.C.S.: 551112
Bill Adderley (Founder & Pres-Life)

Subsidiaries:

**Dunelm (Soft Furnishings)
Limited** (1)
Watermead Business Park, Syston, LE7
1AD, Leics, United Kingdom
Tel.: (44) 116 264 4400
Web Site: http://www.dunelm.com
Home Furnishings Retailer
N.A.I.C.S.: 449129
Nick Wilkinson (CEO)

DUNI

Hallenborgs gata 1a 6 van, 211 19,
Malmo, Sweden
Tel.: (46) 40106200
Web Site: https://www.dunigroup.com
Year Founded: 1970
DUNI—(OTCIQ)
Rev.: $766,176,279
Assets: $686,262,843
Liabilities: $290,964,327
Net Worth: $395,298,516
Earnings: $43,977,208
Emp.: 2,326
Fiscal Year-end: 12/31/23
Napkins, Table Covers, Paper Plates,
Cups & Other Food Service Dispos-
able Items
N.A.I.C.S.: 322291
Mats Lindroth (CFO)

Subsidiaries:

Duni & Co. KG (1)
Robert Bosch St 4, Bramsche, 49565, Nie-

dersachsen, Germany (100%)
Tel.: (49) 5461820
Sales Range: $200-249.9 Million
Emp.: 1,000
Mfr of Paper Napkins, Tablecloths, Plates,
Plastic Cups
N.A.I.C.S.: 322291

Duni (CZ) s.r.o. (1)
Milady Horakove 2725, 272 01, Kladno,
Czech Republic
Tel.: (420) 60 227 2632
Web Site: https://cz.dunigroup.com
Sales Range: $25-49.9 Million
Emp.: 10
Paper Cups Mfr
N.A.I.C.S.: 322299

Duni AG (1)
Lettenstrasse 11 C, PO Box 241, 6343,
Rotkreuz, Zug, Switzerland (100%)
Tel.: (41) 41 798 0171
Web Site: https://ch.dunigroup.com
Sales Range: $25-49.9 Million
Emp.: 21
Mfr of Disposable Paper Items
N.A.I.C.S.: 322291

Duni Benelux B.V. (1)
Tinstraat 15, 4823 AA, Breda, Netherlands
Tel.: (31) 76 543 2300
Web Site: http://www.duni.com
Table Setting Products Distr
N.A.I.C.S.: 423990

Subsidiary (Non-US):

Duni A/S (2)
AP Mollers Alle 13, 2791, Dragor, Denmark
Tel.: (45) 44848422
Table Setting Products Distr
N.A.I.C.S.: 423990

Duni OY (2)
Ayritie 8 A, 01510, Vantaa, Finland
Tel.: (358) 89 868 9810
Web Site: http://www.duni.com
Sales Range: $25-49.9 Million
Emp.: 17
Candle Mfr
N.A.I.C.S.: 339999

Duni Verwaltungs GmbH (2)
Robert-Bosch-Strasse 4, 49565, Bramsche,
Germany
Tel.: (49) 546 1820
Web Site: http://www.duni.com
Emp.: 2
Table Setting Products Distr
N.A.I.C.S.: 423990

Duni Benelux B.V. (1)
Tinstraat 15, 4823 AA, Breda, Netherlands
Tel.: (31) 76 543 2300
Web Site: http://www.duni.com
Table Setting Products Distr
N.A.I.C.S.: 423990

**Duni Beteiligungsgesellschaft
mbH** (1)
Robert-Bosch-Str 4, 49565, Bramsche, Ger-
many
Tel.: (49) 5461 820
Table Top & Servings Distr
N.A.I.C.S.: 423220

Duni EFF Sp. z o.o. (1)
ul Krolowej Jadwigi 43, 61-872, Poznan,
Poland
Tel.: (48) 61 656 0700
Web Site: https://pl.dunigroup.com
Sales Range: $25-49.9 Million
Emp.: 4
Table Top & Servings Distr
N.A.I.C.S.: 423220

Duni GmbH (1)
Moosstrasse 41, Salzburg, 5020,
Austria (100%)
Tel.: (43) 6628354960
Sales Range: $1-9.9 Million
Emp.: 11
Mfr of Disposable Paper Items
N.A.I.C.S.: 322291
Heinz Purtaller (Mng Dir)

Duni Iberica S.L. (1)
Puerto Tarraco Moll Lleida Edificio 1 Planta
2 Oficina C, ES 43004, Tarragona,
Spain (100%)
Tel.: (34) 900983314

Sales Range: $25-49.9 Million
Emp.: 31
Disposable Paper Items Mfr & Distr
N.A.I.C.S.: 322291

Duni Ltd. (1)
Chester Road, Preston Brook, Runcorn,
WA7 3FR, Cheshire, United
Kingdom (100%)
Tel.: (44) 1928712377
Web Site: https://uk.dunigroup.com
Sales Range: $25-49.9 Million
Emp.: 20
Mfr of Paper Tablecloths, Dining Items &
Handkerchiefs
N.A.I.C.S.: 322291

Duni Sales Poland Sp. z o.o. (1)
Ul Syrenia 4, 61-017, Poznan, Poland
Tel.: (48) 618735000
Sales Range: $25-49.9 Million
Emp.: 300
Table Setting Products Distr
N.A.I.C.S.: 423990
Robert Wolniakowski *(Mng Dir)*

Duni ZAO (1)
14 Shuhova st bld 9 office 301, Business
center Shuhova Plaza, 115162, Moscow,
Russia
Tel.: (7) 495 646 2971
Web Site: http://www.duni.com
Emp.: 2,300
Table Setting Products Distr
N.A.I.C.S.: 423990

Rexcell Tissue & Airlaid AB (1)
Bruksvaegen 6, Skapafors, Se 666 40,
Bengtsfors, Sweden
Tel.: (46) 53172800
Web Site: http://www.rexcell.se
Sales Range: $50-74.9 Million
Emp.: 200
Disposable Sanitary Paper Mfr
N.A.I.C.S.: 322291

DUNIEC BROS. LTD.
Freeman St, Rishon le Zion, 75277,
Israel
Tel.: (972) 98638790
Web Site: https://www.dunietz.co.il
Year Founded: 1968
DUNI—(TAE)
Rev.: $85,214,255
Assets: $538,173,496
Liabilities: $261,486,113
Net Worth: $276,687,383
Earnings: ($976,102)
Emp.: 123
Fiscal Year-end: 12/31/23
Other Activities Related to Real Estate
N.A.I.C.S.: 531390
Nissim Achiezra *(CEO)*

**DUNLOP SLAZENGER GROUP
LTD.**
Dunlop House Riverside Way, Camberley, GU15 3YL, Surrey, United
Kingdom
Tel.: (44) 1276 803399
Web Site: http://www.slazenger.com
Sports Equipment
N.A.I.C.S.: 339920

DUNNS (LONG SUTTON) LTD
Winters Lane, Long Sutton, Spalding,
PE12 9BE, Lincolnshire, United Kingdom
Tel.: (44) 1406 362141
Web Site: http://www.dunns-ls.co.uk
Year Founded: 1834
Sales Range: $10-24.9 Million
Emp.: 30
Agricultural Seed Processor & Whslr
N.A.I.C.S.: 311224
David Shepherd *(Mng Dir)*

**DUNSTAN THOMAS GROUP
LIMITED**
Building 3000 Lakeside North Har-

bour, Portsmouth, PO6 3EN, United
Kingdom
Tel.: (44) 23 9282 2254   UK
Web Site: http://www.dthomas.co.uk
Holding Company; Commercial & Industrial Software Publisher & Consulting Services
N.A.I.C.S.: 551112
Ihab El-Saie *(COO)*

Subsidiaries:

Digital Keystone Limited (1)
5th Floor Hamilton House 111 Marlowes,
Hemel Hempstead, HP1 1BB, United Kingdom
Tel.: (44) 14 4245 0328
Web Site: http://www.dthomas.co.uk
Wealth Management & Investment Platform
Software Publisher & Support Services
N.A.I.C.S.: 513210
Graeme Gets *(Founder & Grp CTO)*

Dunstan Thomas Consulting
Limited (1)
Rawlings Suite Gunwharf Quays, Portsmouth, PO1 3TT, Hants, United Kingdom
Tel.: (44) 23 9282 2254
Web Site: http://www.dthomas-software.co.uk
Technology Consulting, Training & Software
Development Services
N.A.I.C.S.: 541690
Natanje Holt *(Mng Dir)*

Dunstan Thomas Energy Limited (1)
Rawlings Suite Gunwharf Quays, Portsmouth, PO1 3TT, Hants, United Kingdom
Tel.: (44) 23 9282 2254
Web Site: http://www.dthomas.co.uk
Energy Industry Software & Consulting Services
N.A.I.C.S.: 513210

Dunstan Thomas Holdings
Limited (1)
Rawlings Suite Gunwharf Quays, Portsmouth, PO1 3TT, Hants, United Kingdom
Tel.: (44) 23 9282 2254
Web Site: http://www.dthomas.co.uk
Financial Industry Software & Services
N.A.I.C.S.: 513210

DUNXIN FINANCIAL HOLDINGS LTD
23rd Floor LianFa International Building No 128 Xu Dong Road, Wuchang
District, Wuhan, 430063, Hubei,
China
Tel.: (86) 2788517899   Ky
Web Site: http://www.dunxin.us
DXF—(NYSEAMEX)
Rev.: $1,553,223
Assets: $39,255,095
Liabilities: $46,337,921
Net Worth: ($7,082,826)
Earnings: ($54,802,143)
Emp.: 10
Fiscal Year-end: 12/31/23
Men's Business Casual Apparel Mfr
N.A.I.C.S.: 315250
Qizhi Wei *(Chm & CEO)*

DUNYA VARLIK YONETIM A.S.
Profilo Plaza B Block Floor 1, Mecidiyekoy, 34394, Istanbul, Turkiye
Tel.: (90) 212 355 8054
Web Site: http://www.dunyavarlik.com
Year Founded: 2008
DNYVA—(IST)
Rev.: $51,462,236
Assets: $189,177,496
Liabilities: $104,687,290
Net Worth: $84,490,207
Earnings: $8,478,412
Emp.: 440
Fiscal Year-end: 12/31/21
Financial Investment Services
N.A.I.C.S.: 523999
Isak Antika *(Chm)*

DUOBACK CO., LTD
27 Gajaeul-ro 32beongil, Seo-Gu,
Incheon, 22829, Korea (South)
Tel.: (82) 262042505
Web Site: https://www.duorest.com
Year Founded: 1987
073190—(KRS)
Rev.: $24,214,741
Assets: $20,813,284
Liabilities: $5,035,203
Net Worth: $15,778,081
Earnings: ($2,811,593)
Emp.: 116
Fiscal Year-end: 12/31/22
Office Furniture Mfr
N.A.I.C.S.: 337214
Kim Jong Hyun *(Mng Dir)*

**DUOLUN TECHNOLOGY CO.,
LTD.**
No 1555 Tianyin Avenue Jiangning
District, Nanjing, Jiangsu, China
Tel.: (86) 2552168888
Web Site: http://www.duoluntech.com
Year Founded: 2013
603528—(SHG)
Rev.: $103,873,087
Assets: $415,265,840
Liabilities: $171,168,126
Net Worth: $244,097,713
Earnings: $7,156,146
Fiscal Year-end: 12/31/22
Intelligent Traffic Management System Mfr & Distr
N.A.I.C.S.: 334290
Anqiang Zhang *(Chm & Pres)*

Subsidiaries:

Hunan Bynav Technology Co.,
Ltd. (1)
Building 12 Phase 1 Zhongdian Software
Park No 39 Jianshan Road, High-tech
Zone, Changsha, 410205, Hunan, China
Tel.: (86) 73188958117
Web Site: https://www.bynav.com
Automotive Parts Mfr & Distr
N.A.I.C.S.: 336211

**DUONG HIEU TRADING &
MINING JSC**
Group 5 Gia Sang Ward, Thai
Nguyen, Vietnam
Tel.: (84) 2083832410
Web Site: https://dhmjsc.vn
DHM—(HOSE)
Rev.: $112,565,074
Assets: $38,413,356
Liabilities: $23,891,550
Net Worth: $14,521,805
Earnings: $246,294
Fiscal Year-end: 12/31/23
Metal Ore Mining Services
N.A.I.C.S.: 212290

**DUOYUAN INVESTMENTS
LIMITED**
5/F Duoyuan Building 3 Jinyuan
Road Daxing District, Industrial Development Zone, Beijing, 102600,
China
Tel.: (86) 10 60212222   VG
Web Site: http://www.duoyuan.com
Investment Holding Company
N.A.I.C.S.: 551112
Wenhua Guo *(Chm & CEO)*

Subsidiaries:

DUOYUAN PRINTING, INC. (1)
3 Jinyuan Road Daxing Industrial Development Zone, Beijing, 102600,
China (70.25%)
Tel.: (86) 10 6021 2222
Web Site: http://www.duoyuan.com
Sales Range: $100-124.9 Million
Emp.: 1,339
Offset Printing Equipment Mfr & Supplier
N.A.I.C.S.: 333248

Duoyuan Global Water Inc. (1)
3 Jinyuan Road Daxing Industrial Development Zone, Beijing, 102600, China
Tel.: (86) 10 60212222
Sales Range: $100-124.9 Million
Emp.: 1,166
Water Treatment Equipment Supplier
N.A.I.C.S.: 221310

DUPLEX SA
Fagaras Mihai Eminescu str, 505200,
Fagaras, Brasov, Romania
Tel.: (40) 268211804
Web Site:
https://www.duplexfagaras.ro
DUPX—(BUC)
Rev.: $6,842,310
Assets: $17,824,864
Liabilities: $16,973,500
Net Worth: $851,363
Earnings: $8,769
Emp.: 1
Fiscal Year-end: 12/31/23
Building Construction Services
N.A.I.C.S.: 236116
Gheorghe Mateiu *(Pres & Gen Mgr)*

DUPLI PRINT SAS
2 rue Descartes Domont, Paris,
95330, Ile-de-France, France
Tel.: (33) 39355454
Web Site: http://www.dupliprint.fr
Commercial Printing & Publishing
Svcs
N.A.I.C.S.: 323111
Frederic Fabi *(Founder & CEO)*

DUPNITSA-TABAC AD
Dupnitsa street Yakhinsko shose 1,
2600, Kyustendil, Bulgaria
Tel.: (359) 70133961
Web Site:
https://www.dupnicatabak.com
DUBT—(BUL)
Sales Range: Less than $1 Million
Tobacco Product Distr
N.A.I.C.S.: 424940

DUPONT & LEOSK ENTERPRISES SDN BHD
Lot 2878 Mukim Gemencheh, Negeri
Sembilan, Malaysia
Tel.: (60) 3 3181 7735
Palm Oil Mill
N.A.I.C.S.: 311999

DUQUETTE CONSTRUCTION
2336 Chemin de la Petite Cote, Laval, H7L 5N1, QC, Canada
Tel.: (450) 622-8111
Web Site:
http://www.duquetteconstruction.com
Year Founded: 1964
Rev.: $12,115,163
Emp.: 1
Building Construction Services
N.A.I.C.S.: 236220
Donat Duquette *(Founder)*

DUR HOSPITALITY CO.
Diplomatic Quarter-Abdullah bin
Huthafa Al Sahmi Street, PO Box
5500, Riyadh, 11422, Saudi Arabia
Tel.: (966) 114816666
Web Site: http://www.dur.sa
Year Founded: 1976
4010—(SAU)
Rev.: $151,551,816
Assets: $911,376,152
Liabilities: $469,219,626
Net Worth: $442,156,525
Earnings: $10,705,442
Emp.: 1,600
Fiscal Year-end: 12/31/22
Hotel Operator
N.A.I.C.S.: 721110
Abdullah Mohammed Al-Issa *(Chm)*

Dura Undercushions Ltd.—(Continued)

DURA UNDERCUSHIONS LTD.
8525 Delmeade Rd, Montreal, H4T
1M1, QC, Canada
Tel.: (514) 737-6561
Web Site:
  http://www.duracushion.com
Year Founded: 1957
Sales Range: $10-24.9 Million
Emp.: 25
Carpet Cushion Underpadding Mfr
N.A.I.C.S.: 314110
Michael N. Wilson *(Pres)*

DURABUILT WINDOWS & DOORS
10920 178 Street, Edmonton, T5S
1R7, AB, Canada
Tel.: (780) 455-0440
Web Site:
  http://www.durabuiltwindows.com
Year Founded: 1989
Rev.: $89,500,000
Emp.: 450
Windows & Doors Mfr
N.A.I.C.S.: 321911
Harry Sunner *(Pres)*

DURAN DOGAN BASIM VE AMBALAJ SANAYI A.S.
Hadimkoy Neighborhood Mustafa
Inan Street No 41, Arnavutkoy,
34555, Istanbul, Turkiye
Tel.: (90) 2127714606
Web Site: https://www.ddpack.com.tr
Year Founded: 2005
DURDO—(IST)
Rev.: $38,352,164
Assets: $33,640,793
Liabilities: $18,925,036
Net Worth: $14,715,757
Earnings: $8,318,783
Emp.: 300
Fiscal Year-end: 12/31/22
Paper Packaging Product Mfr &
Whslr
N.A.I.C.S.: 322219
Dikran Mihran Acemyan *(VP)*

DURANCE GRANULATS
Route De La Durance, 13860,
Peyrolles-en-Provence, ne, France
Tel.: (33) 442670930
Web Site: http://www.durance-
granulats.fr
Sales Range: $25-49.9 Million
Emp.: 65
Construction Sand & Gravel Mining
N.A.I.C.S.: 212321
Philippe Joffre *(Dir-Comml)*

DURAND SA
16 Rue De La Tour De Varan, 42700,
Firminy, Loire, France
Tel.: (33) 477563566
Sales Range: $10-24.9 Million
Emp.: 70
New & Used Car Dealers
N.A.I.C.S.: 441110
Bernard Durand *(Pres)*

DURAND SERVICES
301 Rue Louis Neel Zi du Levatel, 38
140, Saint Etienne, Rives sur Fure,
France
Tel.: (33) 476914602
Web Site:
  http://www.durandservices.fr
Rev.: $23,700,000
Emp.: 120
Automotive Repair Shops
N.A.I.C.S.: 811114
Chantal Durand *(Gen Mgr)*

DURANGO RESOURCES INC.

248-515 West Pender Street, Van-
couver, V6B 6H5, BC, Canada
Tel.: (604) 428-2900   BC
Web Site:
  https://www.durangoresources.com
Year Founded: 2006
ATOXF—(OTCQB)
Assets: $1,163,441
Liabilities: $349,793
Net Worth: $813,647
Earnings: ($215,369)
Fiscal Year-end: 07/31/23
Metal Mining Services
N.A.I.C.S.: 212290
Marcy Kiesman *(Pres & CEO)*

DURATEC LIMITED
1 Whipple Street, Balcatta, 6021,
WA, Australia
Tel.: (61) 1300402409   AU
Year Founded: 2010
DUR—(ASX)
Rev.: $320,659,842
Assets: $138,509,487
Liabilities: $108,475,582
Net Worth: $30,033,905
Earnings: $12,519,398
Emp.: 1,173
Fiscal Year-end: 06/30/23
Engineeering Services
N.A.I.C.S.: 541330
Phil Harcourt *(Mng Dir)*

Subsidiaries:

MEnD Consulting Pty. Ltd.   (1)
299 Fitzgerald St, West Perth, 6005, WA,
Australia
Tel.: (61) 861665300
Web Site: https://www.mend.com.au
Engineering Material Design Services
N.A.I.C.S.: 541330

Wilson's Pipe Fabrication Pty.
Ltd.   (1)
25 Buckley Street, Cockburn, 6164, WA,
Australia
Tel.: (61) 894147651
Web Site:
  https://www.wilsonspipefab.com.au
Oil & Gas Industry Engineering Services
N.A.I.C.S.: 213112

DURDANS HOSPITAL
3 Alfred Place, 3, Colombo, Sri Lanka
Tel.: (94) 112140000
Web Site: https://www.durdans.com
Year Founded: 1945
CHL.N0000—(COL)
Rev.: $41,713,061
Assets: $68,110,912
Liabilities: $24,050,142
Net Worth: $44,060,770
Earnings: $5,902,681
Emp.: 1,984
Fiscal Year-end: 03/31/22
General Hospital Services
N.A.I.C.S.: 622110
Ajith Erandan Tudawe *(Chm)*

Subsidiaries:

Ceygen Biotech (Pvt) Ltd.   (1)
No 03 Alfred Place, Colombo, 00300, Sri
Lanka
Tel.: (94) 112372548
Web Site: https://www.ceygenbiotech.com
Biotechnology Research & Development
Services
N.A.I.C.S.: 541714

DURISOL RAALTE B.V.
Almelosestraat 83, 8100 AA, Raalte,
Netherlands
Tel.: (31) 572346400   NI
Web Site: http://www.durisol.nl
Year Founded: 1904
Sales Range: $10-24.9 Million
Emp.: 40

Sound Insulation Technology & Wood
Fibre Concrete Mfr
N.A.I.C.S.: 327390
John Dogger *(Dir-Fin)*

DURO DAKOVIC HOLDING D.D.
Dr Mile Budaka 1, 35000, Slavonski
Brod, Croatia
Tel.: (385) 35446256
Web Site: http://www.duro-
dakovic.com
Year Founded: 1921
Sales Range: $800-899.9 Million
Emp.: 4,200
Holding Company
N.A.I.C.S.: 551112
Darko Grbac *(Dir Gen & VP)*

Subsidiaries:

Duro Dakovic Elektromont d.d.   (1)
Dr Mile Budaka 1, 35 000, Slavonski Brod,
Croatia
Tel.: (385) 35 446 089
Web Site: http://www.dd-elektromont.com
Electricity Generation Services
N.A.I.C.S.: 221122

Duro Dakovic Energetika i infras-
truktura d.o.o.   (1)
Dr Mile Budaka 1, 35 000, Slavonski Brod,
Croatia
Tel.: (385) 35 218 010
Energy & Infrastructure Services
N.A.I.C.S.: 221122

Duro Dakovic Inzenjering d.d.   (1)
Dr Mile Budaka 1, 35000, Slavonski Brod,
Croatia
Tel.: (385) 35 448 324
Web Site: http://www.dd-inzenjering.com
Emp.: 15
Engineeering Services
N.A.I.C.S.: 541330

Duro Dakovic Proizvodnja opreme
d.o.o.   (1)
Dr Mile Budaka 1, 35 000, Slavonski Brod,
Croatia
Tel.: (385) 35 218 409
Web Site: http://www.duro-dakovic.com
Engineeering Services
N.A.I.C.S.: 541330

Duro Dakovic Slobodna zona
d.o.o.   (1)
Dr Mile Budaka 1, Slavonski Brod, 35 000,
Croatia
Tel.: (385) 35 218 621
Web Site: http://www.freezone-brod.hr
Emp.: 8
Engineeering Services
N.A.I.C.S.: 541330
Vjeran Milkovic *(Gen Mgr)*

Duro Dakovic Specijalna vozila
d.d.   (1)
Dr Mile Budaka 1, 35000, Slavonski Brod,
Croatia
Tel.: (385) 35 446 045
Web Site: http://www.ddsv.hr
Engineeering Services
N.A.I.C.S.: 541330

Duro Dakovic Strojna obrada
d.o.o.   (1)
Dr Mile Budaka 1, 35000, Slavonski Brod,
Croatia
Tel.: (385) 35 446 469
Web Site: http://www.strojna-obrada.hr
Emp.: 136
Engineeering Services
N.A.I.C.S.: 541330
Hrvoje Kekez *(Gen Mgr)*

DURO DAKOVIC TERMOEN-ERGETSKA POSTROJENJA D.O.O.
Dr Mile Budaka 1, 35 000, Slavonski
Brod, Croatia
Tel.: (385) 35 213 497   HR
Web Site: http://www.ddtep.hr
Year Founded: 1921
Thermal Power Generation

N.A.I.C.S.: 221118

DURO DE MEXICO, S.A. DE C.V.
Av Uno No 498 Parque Industrial
Cartagena, Tultitlan, 54918, Mexico,
DF, Mexico
Tel.: (52) 8004003876
Web Site:
  http://www.duromex.com.mx
Year Founded: 1968
Lamps & Lighting Products Mfr
N.A.I.C.S.: 335139

DURO FELGUERA, S.A.
Parque Cientifico Tecnologico, C/ Ada
Byron 90, 33203, Gijon, Asturias,
Spain
Tel.: (34) 985199000
Web Site:
  https://www.durofelguera.com
Year Founded: 1858
MDF—(MAD)
Rev.: $440,003,073
Assets: $539,501,514
Liabilities: $517,741,514
Net Worth: $21,760,000
Earnings: $5,534,348
Emp.: 1,546
Fiscal Year-end: 12/31/19
Construction Engineering Services
N.A.I.C.S.: 541330
Rosa Isabel Aza Conejo *(Chm)*

Subsidiaries:

DF DO BRASIL DESENVOLVI-
MIENTO DE PROJETOS LTDA   (1)
Rua da Quitanda n 52 11 andar, Rio de Ja-
neiro, 20011-030, Brazil
Tel.: (55) 21 2505 2600
Construction Engineering Services
N.A.I.C.S.: 541330

DF Mompresa, S.A.U.   (1)
Calle Ada Byron Pq Cientifico Y Tecnologico
90, Gijon, 33203, Asturias, Spain
Tel.: (34) 985 35 53 77
Turbine Fitting & Maintenance Services
N.A.I.C.S.: 811310

Duro Felguera Industrial Projects
Consulting Co., Ltd.   (1)
Suite 2001 West Gate Mall 1038 Nanjing Xi
Lu, 200041, Shanghai, China
Tel.: (86) 21 621 80301
Web Site: http://www.durofelguera.com
Construction Engineering Services
N.A.I.C.S.: 541330

Duro Felguera Oil & Gas S.A.   (1)
Parque Empresarial Las Rozas C/ Jacinto
Benavente 4, 28230, Las Rozas, Spain
Tel.: (34) 91 640 20 51
Industrial Pressure Vessel Mfr
N.A.I.C.S.: 332420

Duro Felguera Plantas Industriales,
S.A.U.   (1)
Edif Centro de Protectros e Ingenieria
C/Hornos Altos S/N Le Felguera, Asturias,
33203, Spain
Tel.: (34) 98 567 98 25
Waste Management Services
N.A.I.C.S.: 562920

Subsidiary (Non-US):

Felguera Gruas India Private
Limited   (2)
3rd Floor 10-50-24/A Sravya Manor,
Siripuram, Visakhapatnam, 530003, Andhra
Pradesh, India
Tel.: (91) 891 255 8343
Web Site: http://www.fgindia.com
Emp.: 100
Construction Engineering Services
N.A.I.C.S.: 541330
T. P. Chakrapani *(Head-Fin & Acct)*

Felguera Calderreria Pesada,
S.A.U.   (1)
Travesia del Mar s/n, 33212, Gijon, Spain
Tel.: (34) 98 532 26 00
Industrial Pressure Vessel Mfr

N.A.I.C.S.: 332420
Ana Bernardo *(Gen Mgr)*

Felguera Rail, S.A.U. (1)
Ablana s/nn, 33600, Mieres, Spain
Tel.: (34) 98 545 41 47
Railway Equipment Mfr
N.A.I.C.S.: 333248

Felguera-IHI S.A. (1)
Via de los Poblados 7, Las Rozas, 28232, Madrid, Spain
Tel.: (34) 916402051
Sales Range: $25-49.9 Million
Emp.: 200
Engineeering Services
N.A.I.C.S.: 541330
Pedro Floriano *(Mng Dir-Mining & Handling)*

PT Duro Felguera Indonesia (1)
Ariobimo Sentral Building 4th fl Jl HR Rasuna Said Kav X-2/5, Jakarta, 12950, Indonesia
Tel.: (62) 21 5270737
Construction Engineering Services
N.A.I.C.S.: 541330
Sad Adi Nugroho *(Project Mgr)*

Tecnicas de Entibacion, S.A.U. (1)
Poligono de Silvota parcela 10, 33192, Llanera, Spain
Tel.: (34) 98 526 04 64
Industrial Equipment Mfr
N.A.I.C.S.: 333310

Turbogeneradores del Peru, S.A.C. (1)
C/ Pablo Carriquiry Maure 222, San Isidro, Lima, Peru
Tel.: (51) 1 2421672
Industrial Equipment Maintenance Services
N.A.I.C.S.: 811310

DURO SALAJ A.D.

Nemanjina 28, Belgrade, Serbia
Tel.: (381) 113611644
Web Site:
    https://www.djurosalaj.co.rs
Year Founded: 1952
DJRS—(BEL)
Rev.: $585,583
Assets: $3,457,920
Liabilities: $1,072,270
Net Worth: $2,385,650
Earnings: $5,208
Emp.: 16
Fiscal Year-end: 12/31/22
Educational Support Services
N.A.I.C.S.: 611710
Ivan Kovacevic *(Exec Dir)*

DUROC AB

Linnegatan 18, 114 47, Stockholm, Sweden
Tel.: (46) 87891130
Web Site: https://www.duroc.com
DURC.B—(OMX)
Rev.: $327,170,380
Assets: $176,056,272
Liabilities: $74,358,182
Net Worth: $101,698,090
Earnings: ($22,300,898)
Emp.: 859
Fiscal Year-end: 06/30/23
Metallic Materials & Components Surface Refinement Using Laser Technology
N.A.I.C.S.: 331492
John Hager *(CEO)*

Subsidiaries:

AB Traction (1)
Birger Jarlsgatan 33 3 tr, Box 3314, S-103 66, Stockholm, Sweden
Tel.: (46) 850628900
Web Site: http://www.traction.se
Assets: $355,212,753
Liabilities: $702,464
Net Worth: $354,510,289
Earnings: ($35,385,466)
Emp.: 4
Fiscal Year-end: 12/31/2022
Company Development Management Services

N.A.I.C.S.: 541611
Bengt Stillstrom *(Founder & Chm)*

Subsidiary (Domestic):

Ankarsrum Assistent AB (2)
Bruksvagen 1, 590 90, Ankarsrum, Sweden
Tel.: (46) 490 533 00
Web Site: http://assistent.nu
Kitchen Appliances Mfr
N.A.I.C.S.: 332215
Hukanften Berg *(Mgr-Export)*

Ankarsrum Industries AB (2)
Bruksvagen 1, 590 370, Ankarsrum, Sweden
Tel.: (46) 49053320
Web Site: http://www.ankarsrum.com
Sales Range: $50-74.9 Million
Emp.: 90
Holding Company; Medium-Sized Electrical, Universal & DC Motors Mfr, Developer & Marketer; Die Casting Services
N.A.I.C.S.: 551112
Werner Fritz *(Product Mgr)*

Subsidiary (Domestic):

Ankarsrum Motors AB (3)
Bruksvagen 1, 593 70, Ankarsrum, Sweden
Tel.: (46) 49053300
Web Site: http://www.ankarsrum.com
Sales Range: $25-49.9 Million
Emp.: 80
Motor Mfr, Developer & Marketer
N.A.I.C.S.: 335312

Ankarsrum Universal Motors AB (3)
Bruksvagen 1, 593-70, Ankarsrum, Sweden
Tel.: (46) 49053300
Web Site: http://www.ankarsrum.com
Sales Range: $25-49.9 Million
Emp.: 80
Motor Mfr, Developer & Marketer
N.A.I.C.S.: 335312

Subsidiary (Domestic):

Gnosjoplast AB (2)
Spikgatan 1, Box 193, Gnosjo, 335 24, Sweden
Tel.: (46) 370331550
Web Site: http://www.blowtechgroup.com
Emp.: 50
Plastic & Rubber Materials Processor
N.A.I.C.S.: 325211
Claes Jansson *(CEO)*

Nilorngruppen AB (2)
Wieslanders vag 3, 504 31, Boras, Sweden (65%)
Tel.: (46) 337008888
Web Site: https://www.nilorn.com
Rev.: $97,686,219
Assets: $67,884,904
Liabilities: $33,915,167
Net Worth: $33,969,737
Earnings: $10,674,431
Emp.: 553
Fiscal Year-end: 12/31/2021
Holding Company; Branded Labels, Packaging & Accessories Products & Services
N.A.I.C.S.: 551112
Petter Stillstrom *(Chm)*

Affiliate (Non-US):

Calmon Abacus Textiles Pte. Ltd. (3)
A-370 Road No 27, Thane Wagle Industrial Area, Thane, 400 604, Maharashtra, India (49%)
Tel.: (91) 225383881
Textile Labeling Products Designer & Mfr
N.A.I.C.S.: 313220

Subsidiary (Domestic):

Nilorn AB (3)
Wieslanders vag 3, Box 499, 504 31, Boras, Sweden (100%)
Tel.: (46) 337008800
Web Site: http://www.nilorn.com
Sales Range: $25-49.9 Million
Emp.: 50
Lithographic, Flexographic & Textile Label Designer, Mfr & Distr
N.A.I.C.S.: 561910

Subsidiary (Non-US):

Nilorn Belgium NV (3)

Brusselsesteenweg 525, 9090, Melle, Belgium (100%)
Tel.: (32) 92104090
Web Site: http://www.nilorn.com
Lithographic, Flexographic & Textile Label Products & Services
N.A.I.C.S.: 561910

Nilorn Denmark A/S (3)
Kongensgade 31B, 5000, Odense, Denmark (100%)
Tel.: (45) 70231623
Web Site: http://www.nilorn.dk
Lithographic, Flexographic & Textile Label Mfr & Distr
N.A.I.C.S.: 561910

Unit (Domestic):

Nilorn Denmark - Forsaljning (4)
Kongensgade 31B, 5000, Odense, Denmark
Tel.: (45) 70231623
Web Site: http://www.nilorn.com
Sales Range: $25-49.9 Million
Emp.: 20
Lithographic, Flexographic & Textile Label Whslr
N.A.I.C.S.: 424310
Michael Seedorff *(Mng Dir)*

Subsidiary (Non-US):

Nilorn East Asia Ltd. (3)
Unit 1701 17/F Westley Square 48 Hoi Yuen Road, Kwun Tong, Kowloon, China (Hong Kong) (100%)
Tel.: (852) 23712218
Web Site: http://www.nilorn.com
Sales Range: $10-24.9 Million
Emp.: 70
Labeling Products Designer & Whslr
N.A.I.C.S.: 561910
Andrew Hoppe *(Mng Dir)*

Nilorn Etiket Sa. Ve Tic. Ltd. Sti. (3)
Baglar Manhallesi 49 Sokak No 50 K 3, Bagcilar, Istanbul, 34212, Turkiye (100%)
Tel.: (90) 2126577676
Web Site: http://www.nilorn.com
Sales Range: $25-49.9 Million
Emp.: 15
Lithographic, Flexographic & Textile Label Products Distr
N.A.I.C.S.: 561910
Bekir Gencoguz *(Mng Dir)*

Nilorn Germany GmbH (3)
Itterpark 7, Postfach 110 120, 40724, Hilden, Germany (100%)
Tel.: (49) 2103908160
Web Site: http://www.nilorn.com
Sales Range: $25-49.9 Million
Emp.: 25
Lithographic, Flexographic & Textile Label Products & Services
N.A.I.C.S.: 561910

Nilorn Portugal Lda. (3)
Rua Central de Barrosas 304, Paredes, 4585-902, Recarei, Portugal (100%)
Tel.: (351) 224119580
Web Site: http://www.nilorn.com
Emp.: 50
Lithographic, Flexographic & Textile Label Products Mfr
N.A.I.C.S.: 561910
Elizabeth Sampaio *(Gen Mgr)*

Nilorn UK Ltd. (3)
Station Works Greens Mill Court, Cononley, Keighley, BD20 8FE, North Yorkshire, United Kingdom (100%)
Tel.: (44) 1535673500
Web Site: https://www.nilorn.co.uk
Sales Range: $25-49.9 Million
Emp.: 37
Lithographic, Flexographic & Textile Labeling Products Mfr & Distr
N.A.I.C.S.: 561910
Chris Nicholl *(Mgr-Design)*

Subsidiary (Domestic):

Zitiz AB (2)
Sveavagen 63, Stockholm, 113 59, Sweden
Tel.: (46) 707218835
Internet Publishing Services
N.A.I.C.S.: 513199

Duroc Engineering i Goteborg AB (1)
Importgatan 19-21, SE-422 46, Hisings Backa, Sweden
Tel.: (46) 31525265
Web Site: http://www.duroc.se
Sales Range: $25-49.9 Million
Emp.: 10
Laser Refined Surface Products for Industry
N.A.I.C.S.: 333310

Duroc Engineering i Helsingborg AB (1)
Lagerhaggsgatan 7, SE-256 68, Helsingborg, Sweden
Tel.: (46) 42240420
Laser Refined Surface Products for Industry
N.A.I.C.S.: 333517

Duroc Engineering i Umea AB (1)
Industrivagen 8, SE-90130, Umea, Sweden
Tel.: (46) 90711700
Web Site: http://www.duroc.se
Sales Range: $25-49.9 Million
Emp.: 12
Laser Refined Surface Products for Industry
N.A.I.C.S.: 333310
Katharina Persson *(Mgr-Sls)*

Duroc Machine Tool AB (1)
Snedgatan 1, 342 50, Vislanda, Sweden
Tel.: (46) 86302300
Web Site: https://www.durocmachinetool.se
Sales Range: $25-49.9 Million
Emp.: 45
Machine Tools Mfr
N.A.I.C.S.: 333517

Duroc Machine Tool AS (1)
Anolitveien 7, 1400, Ski, Norway
Tel.: (47) 64914880
Sales Range: $50-74.9 Million
Emp.: 3
Machine Tool Distr
N.A.I.C.S.: 423830
Jan-Erik Stokkebek *(Gen Mgr)*

Duroc Machine Tool OU (1)
Viljandi mnt 75/1, Ossu village Kambja parish, 61713, Tartu, Estonia
Tel.: (372) 7366648
Sales Range: $50-74.9 Million
Emp.: 5
Machine Tool Distr
N.A.I.C.S.: 423830
Peeter Sekavin *(Country Mgr)*

Duroc Machine Tool SIA (1)
Sigulda highway 2 Bergi, Garkalnes parish, Riga, 1024, Latvia
Tel.: (371) 67355175
Web Site: https://www.durocmachinetool.lv
Machine Tools Mfr
N.A.I.C.S.: 333517

Duroc Rail AB (1)
Svartons Industrial Area, 971 88, Lulea, Sweden
Tel.: (46) 920233900
Web Site: https://rail.duroc.com
Sales Range: $25-49.9 Million
Emp.: 30
Railway Wheels Maintenance Services
N.A.I.C.S.: 488210

Subsidiary (Non-US):

B & V Delitzsch GmbH (2)
Karl-Marx-Strsse 39, 04509, Delitzsch, Germany
Tel.: (49) 3420253026
Web Site: http://www.sfw-delitzsch.de
Sales Range: $50-74.9 Million
Rail Services
N.A.I.C.S.: 488210

Duroc Tooling i Olofstrom AB (1)
Ingenjorsgatan 26, SE-293 24, Olofstrom, Sweden
Tel.: (46) 45448930
Web Site: http://www.duroc.se
Sales Range: $25-49.9 Million
Emp.: 7
Metalworking Machines Mfr
N.A.I.C.S.: 333517

Impact Coatings AB (1)
Westmansgatan 29, SE-582 16, Linkoping, Sweden
Tel.: (46) 013103780

Duroc AB—(Continued)

Web Site: http://www.impactcoatings.se
Thin Film Coating Development & Services
N.A.I.C.S.: 332812
Torsten Rosell *(Chm)*

International Fibres Group (Holdings) Limited   **(1)**
Old Mills Off Whitehall Grove, Drighlington, Bradford, BD11 1BY, West Yorkshire, United Kingdom
Tel.: (44) 1132859020
Web Site: http://www.fibresgroup.com
Sales Range: $125-149.9 Million
Emp.: 327
Holding Company; Specialty Coatings, Fibers & Umbrella Frames Mfr
N.A.I.C.S.: 551112

Subsidiary (Non-US):

Asota GmbH   **(2)**
Schachermayerstrasse 22, 4020, Linz, Austria   **(100%)**
Tel.: (43) 73269850
Web Site: http://www.asota.com
Noncellulosic Organic Fiber Mfr
N.A.I.C.S.: 325220

Subsidiary (Domestic):

IFG Drake Ltd.   **(2)**
Victoria Mills Victoria Ln, Golcar, Huddersfield, HD7 4JG, United Kingdom   **(100%)**
Tel.: (44) 1484460339
Web Site: http://fibresgroup.com
Noncellulosic Organic Fiber Mfr
N.A.I.C.S.: 325220

Micor AB   **(1)**
Industrigatan 10, 312 34, Laholm, Sweden
Tel.: (46) 43049200
Web Site: https://www.micor.se
Sales Range: $25-49.9 Million
Emp.: 35
Saw Blades Mfr
N.A.I.C.S.: 333243
Bjoern Bernsfelt *(Mng Dir & Mgr-Market)*

Plastibert & Cie NV   **(1)**
Molenstraat 207, 8710, Wielsbeke, Belgium
Tel.: (32) 56665275
Web Site: https://www.plastibert.be
Textile Products Mfr
N.A.I.C.S.: 314999

Swedish Saw Blades AB   **(1)**
Industrigatan 10, SE-312 34, Laholm, Sweden
Tel.: (46) 43049205
Web Site: http://www.swesaw.se
Industrial Saw Blades Mfr
N.A.I.C.S.: 332216

DURON ONTARIO LTD.
1860 Shawson Dr, Mississauga, L4W 1R7, ON, Canada
Tel.: (905) 670-1998
Web Site: http://www.duron.ca
Year Founded: 1959
Sales Range: $25-49.9 Million
Emp.: 70
Flooring, Roofing & Restoration Services
N.A.I.C.S.: 238330

DUROPACK LTD
B-4/160 Safdarjung Enclave, New Delhi, 110029, India
Tel.: (91) 9717345777
Web Site:
  https://www.duropackindia.com
Year Founded: 1988
526355—(BOM)
Rev.: $2,824,540
Assets: $1,929,387
Liabilities: $369,656
Net Worth: $1,559,731
Earnings: $142,247
Emp.: 30
Fiscal Year-end: 03/31/21
Holographic Product Mfr & Distr
N.A.I.C.S.: 322230
Vivek Jain *(Mng Dir)*

DUROPLY INDUSTRIES LTD.
4th Floor North Block 113 Park Street, Kolkata, 700 016, India
Tel.: (91) 3322652274
Web Site: https://www.duroply.in
516003—(BOM)
Rev.: $25,016,942
Assets: $28,464,345
Liabilities: $18,891,341
Net Worth: $9,573,004
Earnings: ($334,602)
Emp.: 525
Fiscal Year-end: 03/31/21
Plywood Mfr
N.A.I.C.S.: 321211
Sudeep Chitlangia *(Mng Dir)*

Subsidiaries:

Sarda Plywood Industries Ltd. - Rajkot Factory   **(1)**
Rajkot Gondal Highway PO Sapar, Rajkot, 360 024, Gujarat, India
Tel.: (91) 332 265 2274
Web Site: http://www.sardaplywood.com
Sales Range: $150-199.9 Million
Emp.: 400
Plywood Product Mfr & Whslr
N.A.I.C.S.: 321211
Shank Shssaria *(Gen Mgr)*

DUROS S.A.
Maragkopoulou Str 80, 26331, Patras, Greece
Tel.: (30) 2610224113
Web Site: https://www.dur.gr
Year Founded: 1971
DUR—(ATH)
Sales Range: Less than $1 Million
Emp.: 55
Textile Products Mfr
N.A.I.C.S.: 314999

DURR AG
Carl Benz Strasse 34, 74321, Bietigheim-Bissingen, Germany
Tel.: (49) 7142780   De
Web Site: https://www.durr.com
Year Founded: 1895
DUE—(MUN)
Rev.: $5,107,970,767
Assets: $5,691,531,643
Liabilities: $4,400,114,130
Net Worth: $1,291,417,513
Earnings: $123,611,363
Emp.: 20,597
Fiscal Year-end: 12/31/23
Holding Company; Industrial Machinery Mfr
N.A.I.C.S.: 551112
Richard Bauer *(Deputy Chm-Supervisory Bd)*

Subsidiaries:

Agramkow Asia Pacific Pte. Ltd.   **(1)**
2 Gambas Crescent Nordcom II 08-18, Singapore, 757044, Singapore
Tel.: (65) 62750060
Fluid Filling Equipment Mfr
N.A.I.C.S.: 333995

Agramkow Fluid Systems A/S   **(1)**
Augustenborg Landevej 19, 6400, Sonderborg, Denmark
Tel.: (45) 74123636
Fluid Filling Equipment Mfr
N.A.I.C.S.: 333995

Agramkow do Brasil Ltda.   **(1)**
Av Francisco de Paula Leite 3627, Jardim Panorama, Indaiatuba, 13346-615, Sao Paulo, Brazil
Tel.: (55) 1938160087
Web Site: https://www.agramkow.com.br
Fluid Filling Equipment Mfr
N.A.I.C.S.: 333995

BBS Automation (Kunshan) Co., Ltd.   **(1)**
Dongguang Road No 188 Economic & Technological Development Zone, Kunshan, 215300, Jiangsu, China

Tel.: (86) 51257794767
Flexible Automation Machinery Mfr
N.A.I.C.S.: 333248

BBS Automation (Suzhou) Co., Ltd.   **(1)**
No 7-1 Tingrong Street, Weiting District Suzhou Industrial Park, Suzhou, 215122, Jiangsu, China
Tel.: (86) 51287770968
Flexible Automation Machinery Mfr
N.A.I.C.S.: 333248

BBS Automation (Tianjin) Co., Ltd.   **(1)**
Block 5 Rongyin Industrial Park No 3667 Zhongbin Avenue, Binhai New Area Sino-Singapore Tianjin Eco-City, Tianjin, 300467, China
Tel.: (86) 2266351260
Flexible Automation Machinery Mfr
N.A.I.C.S.: 333248

BBS Automation Blaichach GmbH   **(1)**
Hans-Bockler-Strasse 7, 87527, Sonthofen, Germany
Tel.: (49) 8321609660
Flexible Automation Machinery Mfr
N.A.I.C.S.: 333248

BBS Automation Chicago Inc.   **(1)**
1580 Hecht Ct, Bartlett, IL 60103
Tel.: (630) 351-3000
Flexible Automation Machinery Mfr
N.A.I.C.S.: 333248

BBS Automation GmbH   **(1)**
Parkring 22, Garching, 85748, Munich, Germany
Tel.: (49) 89856073540
Web Site: http://www.bbsautomation.com
Emp.: 800
Industrial Equipment Mfr
N.A.I.C.S.: 333248
Falk Baurle *(Mng Dir)*

Subsidiary (Non-US):

ixmation (Asia) Sdn. Bhd.   **(2)**
Plot 313 Lorong Perindustrian, Penang Science Park, 14100, Bukit Minyak, Penang, Malaysia
Tel.: (60) 45047777
Web Site: http://www.ixmation.com
Assembly Automation Systems
N.A.I.C.S.: 333248

ixmation (Suzhou) Co., Ltd.   **(2)**
No 7-1 Tingrong Street Weiting District, Suzhou Industrial Park, Suzhou, 215122, Jiangsu, China
Tel.: (86) 51287770968
Web Site: http://www.ixmation.com
Assembly Automation Systems
N.A.I.C.S.: 333248

ixmation (Tianjin) Co., Ltd.   **(2)**
Binhai Innovation Park, No 4668 Xinbei Road, Tanggu, 300451, Tianjin, China
Tel.: (86) 2266351260
Web Site: http://www.ixmation.com
Assembly Automation Systems
N.A.I.C.S.: 333248

Subsidiary (US):

ixmation Inc.   **(2)**
31 Presidential Dr, Roselle, IL 60172-3914   **(100%)**
Tel.: (630) 351-3000
Web Site: http://www.ixmation.com
Sales Range: $50-74.9 Million
Emp.: 150
Assembly Automation Systems
N.A.I.C.S.: 333310
Jason Schwarz *(Sr Project Mgr)*

BBS Automation Guadalajara S de R.L. de C.V.   **(1)**
Carretera San Isidro Mazatepec No 765 Building 73, Santa Cruz De Las Flores, 45640, Tlajomulco de Zuniga, Jalisco, Mexico
Tel.: (52) 3346705743
Flexible Automation Machinery Mfr
N.A.I.C.S.: 333248

BBS Automation India Private Ltd.   **(1)**

Pcndta Sector No 10 Plot No 129D, Bhosari, Pune, 411014, MH, India
Tel.: (91) 9405641066
Flexible Automation Machinery Mfr
N.A.I.C.S.: 333248

BBS Automation Lipany s.r.o.   **(1)**
Zeleznicna 9, 08221, Velky Saris, Slovakia
Tel.: (421) 903483181
Flexible Automation Machinery Mfr
N.A.I.C.S.: 333248

BBS Automation Penang Sdn. Bhd.   **(1)**
Plot 313 Lorong Perindustrian Bukit Minyak 18 Science Park, 14100, Penang, Penang, Malaysia
Tel.: (60) 42023466
Flexible Automation Machinery Mfr
N.A.I.C.S.: 333248

BBS Winding S.R.L.   **(1)**
Loc Fosci 26/E, 53036, Poggibonsi, SI, Italy
Tel.: (39) 0577988043
Flexible Automation Machinery Mfr
N.A.I.C.S.: 333248

CPM S.p.A.   **(1)**
Via A Spinelli 4, 10092, Beinasco, Italy
Tel.: (39) 0113988411
Web Site: http://www.cpm-spa.com
Sales Range: $25-49.9 Million
Emp.: 95
Paint Finishing Systems
N.A.I.C.S.: 325510
Andreas Hohmann *(CEO)*

Carl Schenck Machines en Installaties B.V   **(1)**
Schiedamsedijk 81a, 3011 EM, Rotterdam, Netherlands
Tel.: (31) 104117540
Web Site: https://www.schenck-rotec.nl
Emp.: 9
Industrial Machinery Mfr
N.A.I.C.S.: 333248

Cogiscan Inc.   **(1)**
28-B Boulevard de l'Aeroport, Bromont, J2L 1S6, QC, Canada
Tel.: (450) 534-2644
Web Site: https://cogiscan.com
Printed Circuit Board Mfr
N.A.I.C.S.: 334412

DUALIS GmbH   **(1)**
Tiergartenstrasse 32, 01219, Dresden, Germany
Tel.: (49) 351477910
Web Site: http://www.dualis-it.de
Software Services
N.A.I.C.S.: 541511

DUALIS GmbH IT Solution   **(1)**
Breitscheidstrasse 36, 01237, Dresden, Germany
Tel.: (49) 351477910
Web Site: https://www.dualis-it.de
Hardware Product Mfr
N.A.I.C.S.: 332510

Duerr Cyplan Limited   **(1)**
Carl-Benz-Str 34, 74321, Bietigheim-Bissingen, Germany
Tel.: (49) 7142782914
Mechanical & Plant Engineering Services
N.A.I.C.S.: 541330
Sebastian Baumann *(CFO & Sr VP)*

Durr (Thailand) Co., Ltd.   **(1)**
631 Media Gallery Building 2nd Floor Nonsee Rd Chongnonsee, Yannawa, Bangkok, 10120, Thailand
Tel.: (66) 21081830
Automation Machinery Mfr
N.A.I.C.S.: 333248
John Hager *(CEO)*
Andrej Capek *(CEO)*

Durr AIS S.A. de C.V.   **(1)**
Calle Urbina No 6, Parque Industrial, Naucalpan de Juarez, 53370, Naucalpan, Mexico
Tel.: (52) 5553291188
Environmental Systems & Automation & Conveyor Systems
N.A.I.C.S.: 334512

Durr Africa (Pty.) Ltd.   **(1)**
Tel.: (27) 878209000
Automation Machinery Mfr
N.A.I.C.S.: 333248

Michael Broek *(Mng Dir)*

Durr Anlagenbau GmbH (1)
Durrweg 2, 2225, Zistersdorf, 2225,
Austria   (100%)
Tel.: (43) 25322546
Web Site: http://www.durr.com
Sales Range: $1-9.9 Million
Emp.: 80
Environmental Systems & Automation &
Conveyor Systems
N.A.I.C.S.: 334512

Durr Assembly Products GmbH (1)
Kollner Strasse 122 - 128, 66346, Puttlingen, Germany
Tel.: (49) 68986920
Web Site: http://www.durr-ap.de
Sales Range: $75-99.9 Million
Emp.: 300
Vehicle Assembly Testing & Repair Services
N.A.I.C.S.: 811198
Thomas Kolb *(Mng Dir)*

Durr Brasil Ltda. (1)
  (100%)
Tel.: (55) 1156324500
Web Site: http://www.durr.com.br
Sales Range: $50-74.9 Million
Emp.: 200
Environmental Systems & Automation &
Conveyor Systems
N.A.I.C.S.: 334512

Durr Ecoclean Inc (1)
31077 Durr Dr, Wixom, MI 48393
Tel.: (248) 560-2100
Web Site: http://www.durr-ecoclean.com
Emp.: 55
Industrial Cleaning Machinery Whslr
N.A.I.C.S.: 423830
Andreas Reger *(Pres)*

Durr Ecoclean S.A.S. (1)
Rue des Etats Unis B P No 1, 72540, Loue,
France
Tel.: (33) 243397800
Industrial Cleaning Technology Mfr
N.A.I.C.S.: 333248

Durr IT Service GmbH (1)
Carl-Benz-Str 34, 74321, Bietigheim-Bissingen, Germany
Tel.: (49) 7142783805
Web Site: http://www.durr-it-service.com
Information Technology Consulting Services
N.A.I.C.S.: 541512
Ursula Ziwey *(Gen Mgr)*

Durr Inc. (1)
40600 Plymouth Rd, Plymouth, MI 48170-4297
Tel.: (734) 459-6800
Web Site: http://www.durr.com
Sales Range: $100-124.9 Million
Emp.: 300
Automotive Components Mfr
N.A.I.C.S.: 336390

Subsidiary (Domestic):

**Babcock & Wilcox MEGTEC,
LLC** (2)
830 Prosper St, De Pere, WI 54115
Tel.: (920) 336-5715
Boilers & Heating Equipment Mfr
N.A.I.C.S.: 333414

Subsidiary (Domestic):

MEGTEC Systems, Inc. (3)
830 Prosper Rd, De Pere, WI 54115
Tel.: (920) 336-5715
Web Site: http://www.megtec.com
Sales Range: $250-299.9 Million
Emp.: 400
Industrial Machinery Mfr
N.A.I.C.S.: 333248

Subsidiary (Non-US):

MEGTEC Systems AB (4)
Olskroksgatan 30, Box 6106, 40060, Gothenburg, Sweden
Tel.: (46) 31657800
Industrial Equipment & Machinery Repair
Services
N.A.I.C.S.: 811310

MEGTEC Systems Australia, Inc. (4)
21 Aristoc Road 25, Glen Waverley, 3150,

VIC, Australia
Tel.: (61) 395747450
Industrial Equipment & Machinery Repair
Services
N.A.I.C.S.: 811310

MEGTEC Systems SAS (4)
32 rue des Malines, Z I des Malines, 91090,
Lisses, France
Tel.: (33) 169894793
Web Site: http://www.megtec.com
Sales Range: $25-49.9 Million
Emp.: 100
Printing Trades Machinery
N.A.I.C.S.: 333248

MEGTEC Systems Shanghai Ltd (4)
125 Lane 1190 Jiujing Road, Jiuting Town
Songjian District, Shanghai, 201615, China
Tel.: (86) 2167697878
Web Site: http://www.megtec.com
Sales Range: $25-49.9 Million
Emp.: 80
Printing Equipment, Dryers, Splicers &
Commercial Newspaper Printing Machinery
Mfr
N.A.I.C.S.: 333248

MEGTEC TurboSonic, Inc. (4)
550 Parkside Drive #A-14, Waterloo, N2L
5V4, ON, Canada
Tel.: (519) 885-5513
Air Pollution Control Technologies Designer
& Marketer
N.A.I.C.S.: 541330
Egbert Q. van Everdingen *(Mng Dir)*

Subsidiary (Domestic):

Durr Universal, Inc. (2)
1925 Hwy 51 - 138, Stoughton, WI 53589-1911
Tel.: (608) 873-4272
Web Site: https://www.durr-universal.com
Sales Range: $75-99.9 Million
Emp.: 460
Noise Control & Air Filtration Equipment Mfr
N.A.I.C.S.: 333413
Cary Bremigan *(COO)*

Subsidiary (Non-US):

Durr Universal Europe Ltd. (3)
Barleyfield, Hinckley, LE10 1YE, Leicestershire, United Kingdom
Tel.: (44) 1455894488
Web Site: http://www.universalaet.com
Power & Heating Equipment Whslr
N.A.I.C.S.: 423720

**Durr Universal S. de R.L. de
C.V.** (3)
Av Mantenimiento No 130 Zona Industrial,
78395, San Luis Potosi, Mexico
Tel.: (52) 4448704700
Power & Heating Equipment Whslr
N.A.I.C.S.: 423720

Universal Acoustic & Emission Technologies Pvt. Ltd. (3)
4 Anmol Pride Survey No 270/1/16 Baner
Road, Pune, 411 045, India
Tel.: (91) 2065294051
Power & Heating Equipment Whslr
N.A.I.C.S.: 423720

Durr India Private Ltd. (1)
471 Prestige Polygon Anna Salai, Nandanam, 600 035, Chennai, 600 035, India
Tel.: (91) 4443931600
Automation Machinery Mfr
N.A.I.C.S.: 333248
Michael Berger *(Mng Dir)*

Durr Japan K.K. (1)
2-14-6 Sakae-cho, Kohoku-ku, Funabashi,
273-0018, Chiba, Japan
Tel.: (81) 474044141
Sales Range: $50-74.9 Million
Emp.: 4
Industrial Machinery & Equipment Whslr
N.A.I.C.S.: 423830

Durr Korea Inc. (1)
Tel.: (82) 264801000
Automation Machinery Mfr
N.A.I.C.S.: 333248
Martin Rotermund *(CEO)*

Durr Ltd. (1)

Broxell Close, Warwick, CV34 5QF, United
Kingdom   (100%)
Tel.: (44) 1926418800
Sales Range: $25-49.9 Million
Emp.: 100
Environmental Systems & Automation &
Conveyor Systems
N.A.I.C.S.: 334512
Sally Curzonf *(Mgr-HR)*

Durr MEGTEC LLC (1)
830 Prosper St, De Pere, WI 54115
Tel.: (920) 336-5715
Automation Machinery Mfr
N.A.I.C.S.: 333248

**Durr Paintshop Systems Engineering
(Shanghai) Co. Ltd.** (1)
No 665 YingShun Road Qingpu Industrial
Park, Shanghai, 201799, China   (100%)
Tel.: (86) 2139791000
Web Site: http://www.durr.com
Sales Range: $125-149.9 Million
Emp.: 300
Mfr of Paints
N.A.I.C.S.: 325510
Michael Baitinger *(CEO)*

Durr Poland Sp. z o.o. (1)
ul Zolkiewskiego 125, 26-600, Radom, Poland
Tel.: (48) 483610100
Web Site: http://www.durr.pl
Sales Range: $50-74.9 Million
Emp.: 15
Conveyor System Mfr & Whslr
N.A.I.C.S.: 333922
Andreas Federmann *(Pres & Member-Mgmt
Bd)*

Durr Somac GmbH (1)
Zwickauer Str 30, 09366, Stollberg, Germany
Tel.: (49) 372965470
Web Site: https://www.somac-filling.com
Emp.: 15
Filling Equipment Mfr
N.A.I.C.S.: 333248

Durr South Africa (Pty.) Ltd (1)
Roshan Road Framesby, PO Box 1017,
Port Elizabeth, 6070, South Africa
Tel.: (27) 41 393 54 00
Sales Range: $25-49.9 Million
Emp.: 4
Automotive Paint & Assembly System Mfr
N.A.I.C.S.: 325510
Michael Broek *(Gen Mgr)*

Durr System Spain SA (1)
Calle Doctor Esquerdo No 136 7 Planta,
Madrid, 28007, Spain   (100%)
Tel.: (34) 915517663
Web Site: http://www.durr.com
Sales Range: $25-49.9 Million
Emp.: 16
Environmental Systems & Automation &
Conveyor Systems
N.A.I.C.S.: 333922

Durr Systems (1)
Krasnoproletarskaya str 16 Building 2,
127473, Moscow, Russia
Tel.: (7) 4957410051
Web Site: http://www.durr.com
Sales Range: $25-49.9 Million
Emp.: 20
Environmental Systems & Automation &
Conveyor Systems
N.A.I.C.S.: 333922
Michael Broese *(Gen Mgr)*

**Durr Systems (Malaysia) Sdn.
Bhd.** (1)
4 Jalan SS 13/4 Subang Jaya Industrial
Estate, 47500, Subang Jaya, Selangor,
Malaysia
Tel.: (60) 378868222
Automation Machinery Mfr
N.A.I.C.S.: 333248
Andrej Capek *(CEO)*

Durr Systems Canada Inc. (1)
611 Kumpf Drive Suite 100, Waterloo, N2V
1K8, ON, Canada
Tel.: (519) 885-5513
Air Pollution Control System & Aftermarket
Services
N.A.I.C.S.: 924110

**Durr Systems Czech Republic
A.S.** (1)

Podoli 1237, 584 01, Ledec nad Sazavou,
Czech Republic
Tel.: (420) 569726097
Spray Gun Vertical Piston Mfr & Distr
N.A.I.C.S.: 333912
Josef Vondracek *(Mng Dir)*

Durr Systems GmbH (1)
Carl-Benz-Strasse 34, 74321, Bietigheim-Bissingen, Germany   (100%)
Tel.: (49) 7142780
Web Site: http://www.durr.com
Sales Range: $400-449.9 Million
Emp.: 1,500
Environmental Systems & Automation &
Conveyor Systems
N.A.I.C.S.: 238210

Branch (Domestic):

Durr Systems GmbH (2)
Schutzenstrasse 142, 48607, Ochtrup,
Germany   (100%)
Tel.: (49) 2553 927 0
Web Site: http://www.durr.com
Sales Range: $25-49.9 Million
Emp.: 40
Environmental Systems & Automation &
Conveyor Systems
N.A.I.C.S.: 333922

**Durr Systems Makine Muhendislik
Proje Ithalat ve Ihracat Ltd** (1)
Sahil Mahallesi D-130 Karayolu Caddesi No
45/4, Basiskele, 41030, Kocaeli, Turkiye
Tel.: (90) 2623257310
Industrial Machinery Distr
N.A.I.C.S.: 423830

Durr Systems Maroc SARL AU (1)
Zone Franche D exportation Lot 40 A,
Tanger-Medina, 90000, Tangiers, Morocco
Tel.: (212) 539394393
Automation Machinery Mfr
N.A.I.C.S.: 333248
Luis Echeveste *(Pres & CEO)*

Durr Systems S.A.S. (1)
Immeuble Gaia - 9 Parc ArianeBoulevard
des Chenes, 78280, Guyancourt, France
Tel.: (33) 169894714
Web Site: https://www.durr.com
Automotive Paint Assembly & Maintenance
Services
N.A.I.C.S.: 811121
Eytan Benhamou *(VP)*

**Durr Systems Slovakia spol. s
r.o.** (1)
Tomasikova 50/B, 83104, Bratislava, Slovakia
Tel.: (421) 41 507 84 03
Automotive Paint Mfr
N.A.I.C.S.: 325510
Meinols Ostremwinter *(Gen Mgr)*

Durr Systems Spain (1)
C/ Zuatzu 8 Planta 2a Parque Empresarial
Zuatzu - Edificio Oria, Donostia, 20018, San
Sebastian, Spain   (100%)
Tel.: (34) 943317000
Web Site: http://www.durr-spain.com
Emp.: 70
Mechanical & Plant Engineering Services
N.A.I.C.S.: 333310

Durr Systems Wolfsburg GmbH (1)
Carl-Benz-Str 34, 74321, Bietigheim-Bissingen, Germany
Tel.: (49) 7142780
Web Site: http://www.durr.com
Emp.: 70
Paint & Coating Mfr
N.A.I.C.S.: 333248
Michael Leitl *(Gen Mgr)*

Durr Systems, Inc. (1)
26801 Northwestern Hwy, Southfield, MI
48033   (100%)
Tel.: (248) 450-2000
Sales Range: $25-49.9 Million
Emp.: 105
Paint Finishing Systems
N.A.I.C.S.: 333248
Mike Boss *(Pres & CEO)*

Division (Domestic):

Durr Systems Inc. - Plymouth (2)
26801 Northwestern Hwy, Southfield, MI
48033

Durr AG—(Continued)

Tel.: (248) 450-2000
Web Site: http://www.durr-northamerica.com
Sales Range: $50-74.9 Million
Emp.: 370
Paint Finishing Systems
N.A.I.C.S.: 333994

Durr Vietnam Company Limited (1)
Room LA-02 03A 2nd Floor Block A Lexington Residence Building No 67, Mai Chi Tho Street An Phu Ward District 2, 700000, Ho Chi Minh City, Vietnam
Tel.: (84) 2836202752
Automation Machinery Mfr
N.A.I.C.S.: 333248
Andrej Capek (Mng Dir)

Durr de Mexico S.A. de C.V. (1)
Avenida La Noria 168 Parque Industrial, 76220, Queretaro, Mexico (100%)
Tel.: (52) 4421925700
Sales Range: $10-24.9 Million
Emp.: 320
Environmental Systems & Automation & Conveyor Systems
N.A.I.C.S.: 334512

Durrpol Sp.z.o.o. (1)
ul Zolkiewskiego 125, 26-600, Radom, Poland (87.5%)
Tel.: (48) 48 361 0100
Web Site: http://www.durrpol.com.pl
Sales Range: $50-74.9 Million
Emp.: 220
Environmental Systems & Automation & Conveyor Systems
N.A.I.C.S.: 334512
Dirk Bethmann (Pres)

Evotech S.A.S. (1)
10 Rue Ampere, 69680, Chassieu, France
Tel.: (33) 478044226
Web Site: https://www.evotech-automation.fr
Electrical Engineering & Industrial Automation Services
N.A.I.C.S.: 541330

HOMAG Group AG (1)
Homagstrasse 3-5, 72296, Schopfloch, Germany (77.9%)
Tel.: (49) 7443130
Web Site: https://www.homag.com
Rev.: $7,429,045
Assets: $425,365,266
Liabilities: $308,123,233
Net Worth: $117,242,033
Earnings: $37,873,780
Emp.: 72
Fiscal Year-end: 12/31/2023
Woodworking Machinery Mfr
N.A.I.C.S.: 333243
Pekka Paasivaara (Chm-Mgmt Bd)

Subsidiary (Domestic):

Benz Gmbh Werkzeugsysteme (2)
Im Muhlegrun 12, 77716, Haslach im Kinzigtal, Germany (75%)
Tel.: (49) 7832 704 0
Web Site: http://www.benz-tools.de
Sales Range: $50-74.9 Million
Emp.: 210
Wood Cutting Machinery Mfr
N.A.I.C.S.: 333243

Subsidiary (US):

Benz Incorporated (2)
1095 6th Ct S E, Hickory, NC 28602
Tel.: (704) 529-5300
Web Site: http://www.benz-inc.com
Sales Range: $50-74.9 Million
Emp.: 170
Industrial Machinery Mfr
N.A.I.C.S.: 333248
Gunther Zimmer (Gen Mgr)

Subsidiary (Domestic):

Brandt Kantentechnik GmbH (2)
Weststrasse 2, Lemgo, 32657, Germany
Tel.: (49) 52619740
Web Site: http://www.brandt.de
Sales Range: $100-124.9 Million
Emp.: 270
Wood Work Machinery Mfr
N.A.I.C.S.: 333243
Meik Kohring (Mgr-Trng Svcs)

Friz Kaschiertechnik Gmbh (2)
Im Holderbusch 7, 74189, Weinsberg, Germany
Tel.: (49) 71345057500
Web Site: http://www.friz.de
Sales Range: $25-49.9 Million
Emp.: 5
Wood Work Machinery Mfr
N.A.I.C.S.: 333243

Subsidiary (Non-US):

HA Malaysia Sdn. Bhd (2)
2-4-2C 4th Floor Tower 2 Jalan Puteri 1/2, Bandar Puteri Puchong, Puchong, 47100, Selangor, Malaysia
Tel.: (60) 3 8063 9506
Web Site: http://www.homag-asia.com
Sales Range: $25-49.9 Million
Emp.: 6
Wood Work Machinery Mfr
N.A.I.C.S.: 333243

HOMAG U.K. Ltd. (2)
10c Sills Road, Willow Farm Business Park, Derby, DE74 2US, United Kingdom
Tel.: (44) 1332856500
Web Site: http://www.homag-uk.co.uk
Sales Range: $25-49.9 Million
Emp.: 44
Woodworking Machinery Distr
N.A.I.C.S.: 423440
Simon Brooks (Mng Dir)

Holzma Plattenaufteiltechnik S.A. (2)
Industrial Mas Dorca S/N, 08480, L'Ametlla del Valles, Spain
Tel.: (34) 938431700
Sales Range: $25-49.9 Million
Emp.: 40
Woodworking Machinery Mfr
N.A.I.C.S.: 333243

Holzma Tech Gmbh (2)
144 Tsar Ivan Asen Ii Street Asenovgrad, Plovdiv, Bulgaria
Tel.: (359) 33163297
Web Site: http://www.holzma.de
Sales Range: $25-49.9 Million
Emp.: 5
Wood Work Machinery Mfr
N.A.I.C.S.: 333243

Homag (Schweiz) AG (2)
Haldenstrasse 5, Hori, 8181, Bulach, Switzerland
Tel.: (41) 448725151
Web Site: http://www.homag-schweiz.ch
Sales Range: $100-124.9 Million
Emp.: 500
Woodworking Machinery Mfr
N.A.I.C.S.: 333243

Homag Asia (PTE) Ltd (2)
2 Gambas Crescent 08-17 Nordcom II, Singapore, 757044, Singapore
Tel.: (65) 63698183
Web Site: http://www.homag-asia.com
Sales Range: $25-49.9 Million
Emp.: 40
Wood Work Machinery Mfr
N.A.I.C.S.: 333243
Toan Ha (Mgr-Sls)

Homag Australia Pty Ltd (2)
6-8 Tasha Place, Marayong, Sydney, 2148, NSW, Australia
Tel.: (61) 288652700
Sales Range: $25-49.9 Million
Emp.: 40
Woodworking Machinery Mfr
N.A.I.C.S.: 333243
Ross Campbell (Mng Dir)

Homag Canada Inc (2)
5090 Edwards Blvd, Mississauga, L5T2W3, ON, Canada
Tel.: (905) 670-1700
Web Site: http://www.homag-canada.ca
Sales Range: $25-49.9 Million
Emp.: 23
Woodworking Machinery Mfr
N.A.I.C.S.: 333243

Homag Danmark A/S (2)
Hjaltevej 12 Skovby, 8464, Galten, Denmark
Tel.: (45) 86946001
Web Site: http://www.homag-danmark.dk
Sales Range: $25-49.9 Million
Emp.: 6
Wood Work Machinery Mfr

N.A.I.C.S.: 333243
Jan Weier (Mng Dir)

Subsidiary (Domestic):

Homag Finance Gmbh (2)
Homagstrasse 3-5, 72296, Freudenstadt, Germany
Tel.: (49) 7443132638
Web Site: http://www.homag.com
Emp.: 4
Woodworking Machinery Mfr
N.A.I.C.S.: 333243
Thorsten Kubatzki (Mng Dir)

Subsidiary (Non-US):

Homag France S.A (2)
1 Rue De Madrid, PO Box 90001, Strasbourg, 67013, Schiltigheim, 67013, France
Tel.: (33) 390220921
Web Site: http://www.homag.fr
Coating Machinery & Equipment Mfr & Distr
N.A.I.C.S.: 333998

Subsidiary (Domestic):

Homag Holzbearbeitungssysteme Gmbh (2)
Homagstrasse 3-5, Schopfloch, 72296, Karlsruhe, Germany
Tel.: (49) 7443130
Web Site: http://www.homag.com
Sales Range: $400-449.9 Million
Emp.: 150
Wood Cutting Machinery Mfr
N.A.I.C.S.: 333243

Subsidiary (Domestic):

Holzma Plattenaufteiltechnik Gmbh (3)
Holzmastr 3, 75365, Calw-Holzbronn, Germany
Tel.: (49) 7053 69 0
Web Site: http://www.holzma.de
Sales Range: $75-99.9 Million
Woodworking Machinery Mfr
N.A.I.C.S.: 333243

Schuler Consulting Gmbh (3)
Karl-Berner-Strasse 4, 72285, Pfalzgrafenweiler, Germany
Tel.: (49) 744583079100
Web Site: https://www.schuler-consulting.com
Sales Range: $25-49.9 Million
Emp.: 30
Woodworking Machinery Mfr
N.A.I.C.S.: 333243
Uwe Jonas (Mng Dir)

Subsidiary (Non-US):

Homag India Private Ltd (2)
Plot No 285 Rajdhani Industrial Park Road no 7 KIADB 4th Phase, Dabaspet Industrial Area Billenkote Village Bengaluru Rural, Bengaluru, 562111, Karnataka, India
Tel.: (91) 8069495656
Web Site: http://www.homag-india.com
Sales Range: $25-49.9 Million
Emp.: 40
Wood Work Machinery Mfr
N.A.I.C.S.: 333243
Govind Assudani (Mng Dir)

Homag Italia S.p.A (2)
Via Vivaldi 15, 20833, Giussano, Monza Brianza, Italy
Tel.: (39) 0328681
Web Site: http://www.homag-italia.it
Emp.: 5
Wood Work Machinery Mfr
N.A.I.C.S.: 333243

Homag Japan Co. Ltd (2)
12F Honmachi Sankei Building 4-3-9 Honmachi, Chuo-ku, Osaka, 541-0053, Higashi-Osaka, Japan
Tel.: (81) 5034595070
Web Site: http://www.homag-japan.com
Sales Range: $25-49.9 Million
Emp.: 20
Woodworking Machinery Mfr
N.A.I.C.S.: 333243

Homag Korea Co., Ltd (2)
D-1107 261 Doyak-ro, Dodang-Dong, 14523, Bucheon, 14523, Gyeonggi-Do, Korea (South)

Tel.: (82) 326707297
Web Site: http://www.homagkorea.com
Wood Furniture Mfr & Sls
N.A.I.C.S.: 321999

Homag Machinery (Shanghai) Co., Ltd. (2)
658 Fang Ta Road North, Songjiang County, Shanghai, 201613, China
Tel.: (86) 2137747088
Web Site: http://www.homag-group.com
Emp.: 286
Woodworking Machinery Mfr
N.A.I.C.S.: 333243
Antonio Kwan (OEO)

Homag Machinery Sroda Sp. z o.o (2)
ul Pradzynskiego 24, 63000, Sroda Wielkopolska, Poland
Tel.: (48) 616474500
Web Site: http://www.homag-group.com
Sales Range: $50-74.9 Million
Emp.: 200
Wood Work Machinery Mfr
N.A.I.C.S.: 333243

Homag Polska Sp.z o.o (2)
ul Pradzynskiego 24, 63-000, Sroda Wielkopolska, Poland
Tel.: (48) 616474500
Web Site: http://www.homag-polska.pl
Sales Range: $25-49.9 Million
Emp.: 50
Woodworking Machinery Mfr
N.A.I.C.S.: 333243

Homag South America Ltda (2)
Rua Tucanos 882 Centro, Taboao da Serra, 86700-070, Brazil
Tel.: (55) 4332757630
Web Site: http://www.homag.com.br
Sales Range: $25-49.9 Million
Emp.: 50
Wood Work Machinery Mfr
N.A.I.C.S.: 333243

Subsidiary (Domestic):

Homag Vertrieb & Service Gmbh (2)
Alemannenstr 11, 85095, Denkendorf, Germany
Tel.: (49) 8466 9040 0
Web Site: http://www.homag.com
Sales Range: $400-449.9 Million
Emp.: 1,500
Woodworking Machinery Mfr
N.A.I.C.S.: 333243

Homag Vertriebs-Beteiligungs Gmbh (2)
Homag strasse 3-5, 72296, Schopfloch, Germany
Tel.: (49) 7443130
Web Site: http://www.homag.de
Sales Range: $400-449.9 Million
Emp.: 1,500
Wood Work Machinery Mfr
N.A.I.C.S.: 333243

Homag eSolution Gmbh (2)
Homagstr 3-5, Schopfloch, Freudenstadt, 72296, Germany
Tel.: (49) 7443 13 0
Web Site: http://www.homag-esolution.com
Sales Range: $25-49.9 Million
Emp.: 30
Wood Work Machinery Mfr
N.A.I.C.S.: 333243
Winfried Dell (Mng Dir)

Schuler Business Solutions S.L. (2)
Karl-Berner-Strasse 4, Pfalzgrafenweiler, 72285, Freudenstadt, Germany
Tel.: (49) 7445 830 0
Business Software Development Services
N.A.I.C.S.: 541511

Subsidiary (US):

Stiles Machinery, Inc. (2)
3965 44th St SE, Grand Rapids, MI 49512-3941
Tel.: (616) 698-7500
Web Site: http://www.stilesmachinery.com
Sales Range: $50-74.9 Million
Emp.: 320
Mfr of Industrial Machinery & Equipment
N.A.I.C.S.: 423830

Subsidiary (Domestic):

**Weinmann Holzbausystemtechnik
Gmbh** **(2)**
Forchenstr 50, 72813, Saint Johann,
Germany **(100%)**
Tel.: (49) 712282940
Web Site: http://www.weinmann-partner.com
Sales Range: $50-74.9 Million
Emp.: 15
Wood Work Machinery Mfr
N.A.I.C.S.: 333243
Darko Zimbakov (Mng Dir)

Henry Filters (Europe) Ltd. **(1)**
Broxell Close, Warwick, CV34 5QF, United
Kingdom **(100%)**
Tel.: (44) 1926 418800
Web Site: http://www.durr.com
Sales Range: $25-49.9 Million
Emp.: 20
Environmental Systems & Automation &
Conveyor Systems
N.A.I.C.S.: 333922

Homag Asia (Thailand) Co., Ltd. **(1)**
631 Nonsee Rd Chongnonsee, Yannawa,
10120, Bangkok, Thailand
Tel.: (66) 26818693
Woodworking Machinery Mfr
N.A.I.C.S.: 333243

**Homag Austria Gesellschaft
m.b.H.** **(1)**
Gewerbegebiet Salzweg 2a, Oberhofen am
Irrsee, 4894, Vocklabruck, Austria
Tel.: (43) 6213202020
Automation Machinery Mfr
N.A.I.C.S.: 333248
Thorsten Kubatzki (Mng Dir)

Homag Automation GmbH **(1)**
Homagstrasse 1, 09638, Lichtenberg, Ger-
many
Tel.: (49) 37323160
Automation Machinery Mfr
N.A.I.C.S.: 333248
Christian Breyer (Mng Dir)

Homag Bohrsysteme GmbH **(1)**
Benzstrasse 10-16, 33442, Herzbrock-
Clarholz, Germany
Tel.: (49) 52454450
Automation Machinery Mfr
N.A.I.C.S.: 333248
Frederik Meyer (Mng Dir)

Homag Espana S.A. **(1)**
Carrer Samalus 2, L Ametlla del Valles,
08480, Barcelona, Spain
Tel.: (34) 937017100
Automation Machinery Mfr
N.A.I.C.S.: 333248

Homag GmbH **(1)**
Homagstrasse 3-5, 72296, Schopfloch, Ger-
many
Tel.: (49) 7443130
Automation Machinery Mfr
N.A.I.C.S.: 333248
Sergej Schwarz (Mng Dir)

Homag Kantentechnik GmbH **(1)**
Weststrasse 2, 32657, Lemgo, Germany
Tel.: (49) 52619740
Automation Machinery Mfr
N.A.I.C.S.: 333248
Sergej Schwarz (Mng Dir)

**Homag Plattenaufteiltechnik
GmbH** **(1)**
Holzmastr 3, 75365, Calw-Holzbronn, Ger-
many
Tel.: (49) 7053690
Automation Machinery Mfr
N.A.I.C.S.: 333248
Jens Held (Mng Dir)

**Homag Services Poland Sp. z
o.o.** **(1)**
Ignacego Pradzynskiego 24, 63-000, Sroda
Wielkopolska, Poland
Tel.: (48) 616474500
Automation Machinery Mfr
N.A.I.C.S.: 333248

**Homag Trading And Services Sdn.
Bhd.** **(1)**
Lot 4 Jalan SS 13/4, 47500, Subang Jaya,
Selangor, Malaysia

Tel.: (60) 356118323
Hardware Product Mfr & Distr
N.A.I.C.S.: 332510

**Homag Vietnam Company
Limited** **(1)**
Room LA-02 03 2nd Floor Lexington Resi-
dence Building 67 Mai Chi Tho, An Phu
ward Dist 2, 70000, Ho Chi Minh City, Viet-
nam
Tel.: (84) 909199735
Automation Machinery Mfr
N.A.I.C.S.: 333248

Ingecal S.A.S. **(1)**
10 Rue Ampere, 69680, Chassieu, France
Tel.: (33) 472970130
Web Site: https://ingecal.fr
Industrial Equipment Mfr & Distr
N.A.I.C.S.: 333248

Kallesoe Machinery A/S **(1)**
Bredgade 115, 6940, Lem, Denmark
Tel.: (45) 97341555
Web Site: https://kallesoemachinery.com
Wood Products Mfr
N.A.I.C.S.: 321999

LOXEO GmbH **(1)**
Carl-Benz-Str 34, 74321, Bietigheim-
Bissingen, Germany
Tel.: (49) 7142784800
Web Site: http://www.loxeo.com
Machine Component Analyse Services
N.A.I.C.S.: 541512
Markus Bottger (Mng Dir)

**Luft- und Thermotechnik Bayreuth
GmbH** **(1)**
Markgrafenstrasse 4, 95497, Goldkronach,
Germany
Tel.: (49) 92735000
Web Site: http://www.ltb.de
Sales Range: $10-24.9 Million
Emp.: 100
Air Pollution Control Systems Mfr, Installa-
tion & Maintenance Services
N.A.I.C.S.: 333413

Novalia S.A.S. **(1)**
2 Rue Bergognon, 42502, Le Chambon-
Feugerolles, France
Tel.: (33) 477404949
Web Site: https://novalia.pro
Hand Tool Equipment Mfr
N.A.I.C.S.: 333991

Olpidurr S.T.A **(1)**
Via G Pascoli 14, 20090, Novegro di Seg-
rate, Italy
Tel.: (39) 02702121
Web Site: http://www.olpidurr.it
Sales Range: $25-49.9 Million
Emp.: 60
Environmental Systems & Automation &
Conveyor Systems
N.A.I.C.S.: 333922

Olpidurr S.p.A. **(1)**
Via G Pascoli 14 - I, 20054, Novegro di
Segrate, MI, Italy **(49%)**
Tel.: (39) 02702121
Web Site: http://www.olpidurr.it
Sales Range: $25-49.9 Million
Emp.: 60
Paint Finishing Systems
N.A.I.C.S.: 325510
Patric Pedruzzi (Gen Mgr)

PT Durr Systems Indonesia **(1)**
Tel.: (62) 2189461980
Automation Machinery Mfr
N.A.I.C.S.: 333248

Schenck Corporation **(1)**
535 Acorn St, Deer Park, NY 11729
Tel.: (631) 242-4010
Assembly Plant Mfr
N.A.I.C.S.: 311111

Schenck Italia S.r.l. **(1)**
Via G Amendola 25, 20037, Paderno Dug-
nano, Milan, Italy
Tel.: (39) 0291002431
Web Site: https://www.schenck-rotec.it
Aircraft Equipment Mfr
N.A.I.C.S.: 336413
Remo Moreo (Mgr-Rotec Div)

Schenck Ltd **(1)**

Broxell Close, Warwick, CV34 5QF, United
Kingdom
Tel.: (44) 1926 474 090
Web Site: http://www.schenck.co.uk
Sales Range: $25-49.9 Million
Emp.: 20
Rotating & Oscillating Machinery Mfr
N.A.I.C.S.: 333248
Paul Kearns (Mng Dir)

Schenck Mexico, S.A. de C.V. **(1)**
Lago Onega 423 Col Granada, 11520,
Mexico, Mexico
Tel.: (52) 5552541083
Assembly Plant Mfr
N.A.I.C.S.: 311111
Juan-Pablo Fernandez (Mng Dir)

Schenck RoTec Corporation **(1)**
26801 Northwestern Hwy, Southfield, MI,
48033
Tel.: (248) 377-2100
Web Site: http://www.schenck-usa.com
Emp.: 30
Automotive Balancing & Diagnostic System
Mfr
N.A.I.C.S.: 336390

Schenck RoTec GmbH **(1)**
Landwehrstrasse 55, D-64293, Darmstadt,
Germany
Tel.: (49) 6151322311
Web Site: https://www.schenck-rotec.de
Emp.: 110
Diagnostic System Mfr
N.A.I.C.S.: 334510
Jorg Brunke (CEO & Mng Dir)

Subsidiary (Non-US):

Datatechnic S.A.S. **(2)**
5 Impasse Du Stade, 88390, Uxegney,
France
Tel.: (33) 329812680
Web Site: http://www.datatechnic.net
Emp.: 34
Balancing Machinery Mfr
N.A.I.C.S.: 333248

Schenck RoTec India Limited **(1)**
Plot No A-5 Sector 81 Phase - II, Noida,
201 305, Uttar Pradesh, India
Tel.: (91) 1202563174
Web Site: https://www.schenck-india.com
Automation Machinery Mfr
N.A.I.C.S.: 333248
Manish Khanna (Mng Dir)

**Schenck Shanghai Machinery Corpo-
ration Ltd** **(1)**
No 36 Lane 239 Nujiang Road N, 200333,
Shanghai, China
Tel.: (86) 2162659663
Web Site: http://www.schenck.cn
Industrial Machinery Mfr
N.A.I.C.S.: 333248
Lenny Fan (Mgr)

**Schenck Technologie und Indus-
triepark GmbH** **(1)**
Landwehrstrasse 55, 64293, Darmstadt,
Germany
Tel.: (49) 6151321200
Web Site: https://www.schenck-
technologiepark.de
Infrastrcuture Management Services
N.A.I.C.S.: 561499

Schenck Test Automation Ltd **(1)**
Broxell Close, Warwick, CV34 5QF, United
Kingdom
Tel.: (44) 1926 474 090
Oscillating Component Research & Devel-
opment
N.A.I.C.S.: 541715

Schenck Trebel Corporation **(1)**
535 Acorn St, Deer Park, NY 11729
Tel.: (631) 242-4010
Web Site: https://www.schenck-usa.com
Industrial Balancing System Mfr
N.A.I.C.S.: 333248

Schenck USA Corp. **(1)**
535 Acorn St, Deer Park, NY 11729
Tel.: (631) 242-4010
Web Site: https://www.schenck-usa.com
Automobile Parts Mfr
N.A.I.C.S.: 336390

Shinhang Durr Inc. **(1)**

604 1 Yoksam Dong, Kangnam Ku, Seoul,
135-080, Korea (South)
Tel.: (82) 25692244
Web Site: http://www.durr.co.kr
Sales Range: $25-49.9 Million
Emp.: 54
Turnkey Paint Shops to the Automotive
Industry
N.A.I.C.S.: 811121

Stimas Engineering S.r.l. **(1)**
Via per Ripalta Arpina 1, Castelleone,
26012, Cremona, Italy
Tel.: (39) 037494861
Web Site: http://www.stimaengineering.it
Automation Machinery Mfr
N.A.I.C.S.: 333248

Stimas S.r.l. **(1)**
Via Prato 23, Agliana, 51031, Pistoia, Italy
Tel.: (39) 0574718898
Web Site: https://www.stimasrl.com
Oven Mfr & Distr
N.A.I.C.S.: 333994

System TM A/S **(1)**
Skovdalsvej 35, 8300, Odder, Denmark
Tel.: (45) 86543355
Web Site: https://systemtm.com
Industrial Machinery Mfr & Distr
N.A.I.C.S.: 333248

Tapio GmbH **(1)**
Karl-Berner-Strasse 4, 72285, Pfalzgrafen-
weiler, Germany
Tel.: (49) 74458379949
Web Site: https://tapio.one
Machinery Tool & Material Mfr
N.A.I.C.S.: 333517

Teamtechnik Automation GmbH **(1)**
Heinrich-Hertz-Strasse 1, 71642, Ludwigs-
burg, Germany
Tel.: (49) 714484760
Automation Product Mfr
N.A.I.C.S.: 335314

**Teamtechnik Maschinen und Anlagen
GmbH** **(1)**
Planckstrasse 40, 71691, Freiberg, Ger-
many
Tel.: (49) 714170030
Web Site: https://www.teamtechnik.com
Automation Product Mfr
N.A.I.C.S.: 335314

Techno-Step GmbH **(1)**
Otto-Lilienthal-Strasse 36, 71034, Boblin-
gen, Germany
Tel.: (49) 7031714540
Web Site: https://www.techno-step.de
Information Technology Services
N.A.I.C.S.: 541511

Test Devices Inc. **(1)**
571 Main St, Hudson, MA 01749-3035
Tel.: (978) 562-6017
Web Site: http://www.info.testdevices.com
Quality & Testing Equipment Mfr
N.A.I.C.S.: 334513
David Woodford (Pres)

UCM AG **(1)**
Langenhagstr 25, 9424, Rheineck, Switzer-
land
Tel.: (41) 71 886 67 60
Web Site: http://www.ucm-ag.com
Emp.: 45
Precision Cleaning Machinery Mfr
N.A.I.C.S.: 333310

Verind S.p.A. **(1)**
Via Papa Giovanni XXIII 25/29, 20053,
Rodano, MI, Italy **(25%)**
Tel.: (39) 029595171
Web Site: https://www.verind.it
Sales Range: $25-49.9 Million
Emp.: 70
Provider of Turnkey Paint Shops to the Au-
tomotive Industry
N.A.I.C.S.: 811121

iTAC Software AG **(1)**
Aubachstr 24, 56410, Montabaur, Germany
Tel.: (49) 260210650
Web Site: https://www.itacsoftware.com
Computer Software Design & Development
Services
N.A.I.C.S.: 541511
Peter Bollinger (CEO)

Durr AG—(Continued)

DURWEST CONSTRUCTION MANAGEMENT
301 4400 Chatterton Way, Victoria, V8X 5J2, BC, Canada
Tel.: (250) 881-7878
Web Site: http://www.durwest.com
Year Founded: 1983
Rev.: $12,100,000
Emp.: 70
Project & Construction Management Services
N.A.I.C.S.: 236220
Devon Kray (VP)

DUSIT THANI FREEHOLD & LEASEHOLD REIT
No 319 Chamchuri Square Building 29th Floor Phayathai Road, Pathumwan, Bangkok, 10330, Thailand
Tel.: (66) 22009999
Web Site: https://www.dtcreit.com
Year Founded: 2017
DREIT—(THA)
Rev.: $15,019,291
Assets: $225,884,148
Liabilities: $62,580,657
Net Worth: $163,303,491
Earnings: $10,122,104
Fiscal Year-end: 12/31/23
Real Estate Investment Trust Services
N.A.I.C.S.: 525990
Chanin Donavanik (Chm)

DUSIT THANI PUBLIC COMPANY LIMITED
319 Chamchuri Square Building 29th Floor Phayathai Road, Pathumwan District, Bangkok, 10330, Thailand
Tel.: (66) 22009999
Web Site: https://www.dusit.com
Year Founded: 1949
DUSIT—(THA)
Rev.: $156,958,479
Assets: $815,094,421
Liabilities: $689,186,068
Net Worth: $125,908,353
Earnings: ($17,050,037)
Emp.: 2,719
Fiscal Year-end: 12/31/23
Hotels & Resorts Owner & Operator
N.A.I.C.S.: 721110
Sinee Thienprasiddhi (Exec Dir)

Subsidiaries:

Devarana Spa Co., Ltd.   (1)
319 Chamchuri Square Building 29th Floor Phayathai Road, Pathumwan, Bangkok, 10330, Thailand
Tel.: (66) 22009999
Web Site: http://www.devaranaspa.com
Spa Services
N.A.I.C.S.: 812199

Dusit Excellence Co., Ltd.   (1)
588/5 Petchaburi Road, Ratchathewi, Bangkok, 10400, Thailand
Tel.: (66) 20139999
Real Property Management Services
N.A.I.C.S.: 531311

Dusit Thani Philippines, Inc.   (1)
Mezzanine Level Dusit Thani Manila Ayala Center, 1223, Makati, Philippines
Tel.: (63) 22388888
Home Management Services
N.A.I.C.S.: 721110
Jojo Baniqued (Mgr-IT)

Elite Havens Ltd.   (1)
20F Euro Trade Centre 21-23 Des Voeux Road, Central, China (Hong Kong)
Tel.: (852) 81937366
Web Site: http://www.elitehavens.com
Resort Operator
N.A.I.C.S.: 721110

Epicure Catering Co., Ltd.   (1)
43 Thai CC Tower 30 th Floor South

Sathorn Rd, Bangkok, 10120, Thailand
Tel.: (66) 26755735
Web Site: https://www.epicure.co.th
Emp.: 400
Catering Services
N.A.I.C.S.: 722320
Trevor Allen (Mng Dir)

DUSK GROUP LIMITED
Building 1 Level 3 75 O'Riordan Street, Alexandria, 2015, NSW, Australia
Tel.: (61) 293083620
Web Site: https://www.dusk.com.au
Year Founded: 2014
DSK—(ASX)
Rev.: $89,732,673
Assets: $58,371,259
Liabilities: $34,415,466
Net Worth: $23,955,793
Earnings: $7,554,933
Fiscal Year-end: 07/02/23
Furnishing Product Distr
N.A.I.C.S.: 423220

Subsidiaries:

Dusk New Zealand Limited   (1)
John Thorman Level 5 79 Queen Street, Auckland, AKL 1010, New Zealand
Tel.: (64) 800387543
Web Site: https://www.duskcandles.co.nz
Home Decor & Home Fragrance Retailer
N.A.I.C.S.: 445110

DUSKIN CO., LTD.
1-33 Toyotsu-Cho Suita-shi, Osaka, 564-0051, Japan
Tel.: (81) 668215071
Web Site: https://www.duskin.co.jp
Year Founded: 1963
4665—(TKS)
Rev.: $1,181,749,020
Assets: $1,335,742,190
Liabilities: $314,807,860
Net Worth: $1,020,934,330
Earnings: $30,234,140
Emp.: 6,157
Fiscal Year-end: 03/31/24
Dust Control Product Rental, Cleaning/Maintenance Service & Cleaning Products
N.A.I.C.S.: 424690
Teruji Yamamura (Pres & CEO)

Subsidiaries:

Duskin Serve Kyusu Co., Ltd.   (1)
6-7-47 Goryo, Higashi, Kumamoto, 861-8035, Japan
Tel.: (81) 963809933
Cleaning Equipment Rental Services
N.A.I.C.S.: 532490

Duskin Serve Tohoku Co., Ltd.   (1)
2-23 Okaji, Miyagino-ku, Sendai, 983-0835, Japan
Tel.: (81) 222934613
Cleaning Equipment Rental Services
N.A.I.C.S.: 532490

Duskin Serve Tokai Hokuriku Co., Ltd.   (1)
1-7-8 Kanayamacho Sumitomoseimeikanayama Bldg 7f, Atsuta-ku, Nagoya, 456-0002, Japan
Tel.: (81) 526787782
Cleaning Equipment Rental Services
N.A.I.C.S.: 532490

Minister Donut Taiwan Co., Ltd.   (1)
3 Fl No 65 Tung Hsing Rd, Songshan District, Taipei, Taiwan
Tel.: (886) 227460000
Cleaning Equipment Rental Services
N.A.I.C.S.: 532490

DUSSMANN STIFTUNG & CO. KGAA
Friedrichstrasse 90, 10117, Berlin, Germany
Tel.: (49) 3020250

Web Site: http://www.dussmanngroup.com
Year Founded: 1963
Sales Range: $1-4.9 Billion
Emp.: 61,200
Holding Company; Facility Management, Food Service, Cleaning, Security & Safety Services
N.A.I.C.S.: 551112
Jorg Braesecke (Member-Exec Bd)

Subsidiaries:

Dresdner Kuhlanlagenbau GmbH (1)
Wordauer Strasse 1 3, 01060, Dresden, Germany
Tel.: (49) 35140810
Web Site: http://www.dka-dresden.de
Refrigerator Equipment Mfr
N.A.I.C.S.: 333415
Marco Engler (Mgr-IT Team)

Dussmann Gulf LLC   (1)
AL Najda St, PO Box 106921, Abu Dhabi, United Arab Emirates
Tel.: (971) 2 4433120
Facility Management Services
N.A.I.C.S.: 561210

Dussmann Kulturkindergarten gemeinnutzige GmbH   (1)
Schutzenstrasse 25, 10117, Berlin, Germany
Tel.: (49) 3020252121
Web Site: http://www.kulturkindergarten.de
Child Care Services
N.A.I.C.S.: 624410
Ute Meltzer (Mng Dir)

Dussmann Middle East GmbH   (1)
PO Box 28030, Abu Dhabi, United Arab Emirates
Tel.: (971) 2 6 44 41 51
Web Site: http://www.dussmann-service.ae
Facility Management Services
N.A.I.C.S.: 561210
Anas Al-Bataineh (Mgr-Ops)

Dussmann Property Management (Shanghai) Co. Ltd.   (1)
3388 Yongding Building Gonghexin Rd, 28 Xuanhua Rd, Shanghai, 200436, China   (100%)
Tel.: (86) 2152551535
Web Site: http://www.dussmann.com.cn
Sales Range: $50-74.9 Million
Emp.: 52
Property Management Services
N.A.I.C.S.: 531190

Dussmann Service Deutschland GmbH   (1)
Viehhofstr 43, 52066, Aachen, Germany
Tel.: (49) 241 55 94 69 77
Emp.: 60
Facility Management Services
N.A.I.C.S.: 561210

Dussmann Service S.r.l.   (1)
Via Papa Giovanni XXIII 4, 24042, Capriate San Gervasio, Bergamo, Italy
Tel.: (39) 02 9 15 18
Web Site: http://www.dussmann.it
Facility Management Services
N.A.I.C.S.: 561210
Pietro Auletta (Pres)

Kursana AG   (1)
Moosbruggstrasse 1, 9000, Saint Gallen, Switzerland   (100%)
Tel.: (41) 712288282
Web Site: http://www.kursana.ch
Sales Range: $1-9.9 Million
Emp.: 49
N.A.I.C.S.: 561621
Cornales Vanderluyt (Mng Dir)

P. Dussmann EOOD   (1)
Hristo Georgiew Str 4 2nd Fl, 15504, Sofia, Bulgaria   (100%)
Tel.: (359) 29438398
Web Site: http://www.dussmannbg.com
Sales Range: $25-49.9 Million
Emp.: 16
Provider of Networking Services
N.A.I.C.S.: 541512
Vassil Popov (Mgr)

P. Dussmann Eesti OU   (1)

Pirni Tn 12, 10617, Tallinn, Estonia (100%)
Tel.: (372) 6990140
Web Site: http://www.dussmann.ee
Sales Range: $10-24.9 Million
Emp.: 150
Security & Safety Services
N.A.I.C.S.: 561621

P. Dussmann Ges.m.b.H.   (1)
Gruberstrasse 2, A-4020, Linz, Austria
Tel.: (43) 7327819510
Web Site: http://www.dussmann.at
Sales Range: $25-49.9 Million
Emp.: 13
Security & Safety Services
N.A.I.C.S.: 561621

P. Dussmann Guvenlik, Temizlik, Bakim, Onarim, Hizmet Limited Sirketi   (1)
Sirket 1 Yildez Caddesi Emek Is Merkezi 37 5 Yildiz, 80690, Istanbul, Turkiye
Tel.: (90) 2123479380
Sales Range: $10-24.9 Million
Emp.: 26
Security & Safety Services
N.A.I.C.S.: 561621

P. Dussmann Hong Kong Ltd.   (1)
8/F Edward Wong Tower 910 Cheung Sha Wan Road, 910 Cheung Sha Wan Road, Kowloon, China (Hong Kong)   (100%)
Tel.: (852) 25040777
Web Site: http://www.dussmann.com.hk
Sales Range: $300-349.9 Million
Emp.: 1,200
Security & Safety Services
N.A.I.C.S.: 561621
Gordon Lau (Gen Mgr)

P. Dussmann Kft.   (1)
Rakoczi Ut 1-3, H-1088, Budapest, Hungary
Tel.: (36) 12661066
Web Site: http://www.dussmann.com
Networking Services
N.A.I.C.S.: 541512
Michael Mertens (Mng Dir-Intl)

P. Dussmann Romania S.R.L.   (1)
Chiscani 25 27 Sekto 1, Bucharest, 012241, Romania
Tel.: (40) 212017983
Web Site: http://www.dussmann.ro
Sales Range: $25-49.9 Million
Emp.: 12
Networking Services
N.A.I.C.S.: 541512
Simona Spatacean (Mng Dir)

P. Dussmann Sp.zo.o.   (1)
Ul Kurpinskiego 55A, Warsaw, 02-733, Poland   (99%)
Tel.: (48) 228272290
Web Site: http://www.dussmann.pl
Sales Range: $25-49.9 Million
Emp.: 15
Security & Safety Services
N.A.I.C.S.: 561621

P. Dussmann TNHH   (1)
384 Kha Van Can St, Hiep Binh Chanh Ward, Thu Duc District, Ho Chi Minh City, Vietnam
Tel.: (84) 838275600
Web Site: http://www.dussmann.com
Sales Range: $10-24.9 Million
Emp.: 37
Security & Safety Services
N.A.I.C.S.: 561621

P. Dussmann UAB   (1)
Ukmerges gatve 223, LT-07156, Vilnius, Lithuania
Tel.: (370) 52339425
Web Site: http://www.dussmann.lt
Sales Range: $150-199.9 Million
Emp.: 700
Security & Safety Services
N.A.I.C.S.: 561621
Aurelija Maldutyte (Gen Dir)

P. Dussmann spol. s.r.o.   (1)
Zitna 1578/52, Prague, Czech Republic   (100%)
Tel.: (420) 222874479
Web Site: http://www.dussmann.cz
Sales Range: $75-99.9 Million
Emp.: 300
Security & Safety Services
N.A.I.C.S.: 561621

Oldrich Kozak *(Gen Mgr)*

P. Dussmann spol. s.r.o.   **(1)**
Pri Starej Pracharni 14, 83104, Bratislava,
Slovakia   **(100%)**
Tel.: (421) 255576363
Web Site: http://www.dussmann.sk
Emp.: 300
Networking Services
N.A.I.C.S.: 541512

Pedus Food Services Inc.   **(1)**
PO Box 513617, Los Angeles, CA 90051-
3617
Tel.: (323) 720-1020
Sales Range: $25-49.9 Million
Emp.: 174
Food Preparation, Service & Management
N.A.I.C.S.: 722310

Pedus Service S.a.r.l.   **(1)**
1 Square Peter Dussmann, Contern, 5324,
Luxembourg   **(100%)**
Tel.: (352) 3420501
Web Site: http://www.dussmann.lu
Sales Range: $10-24.9 Million
Emp.: 3,500
Security & Safety Services
N.A.I.C.S.: 561621
Neu Jeanpaul *(Mgr)*

Peter Dussmann - Vostok   **(1)**
Ul Tschetinkina 49, Buro 402, 630099, No-
vosibirsk, Russia   **(100%)**
Tel.: (7) 3832036071
Security & Safety Services
N.A.I.C.S.: 561621

SIA P. Dussmann   **(1)**
Perses Iela 9 11, LV 1011, Riga,
Latvia   **(100%)**
Tel.: (371) 7289515
Sales Range: $75-99.9 Million
Emp.: 300
Security & Safety Services
N.A.I.C.S.: 561621

DUSTIN GROUP AB
Augustendalsvagen 7, PO Box 1194,
131 27, Nacka, Strand, Sweden
Tel.: (46) 855344000
Web Site:
      https://www.dustingroup.com
Year Founded: 1984
DUST—(OMX)
Rev.: $2,208,304,064
Assets: $1,511,056,787
Liabilities: $1,005,816,404
Net Worth: $505,240,383
Earnings: $16,287,804
Emp.: 2,124
Fiscal Year-end: 08/31/23
Online IT Products Reseller
N.A.I.C.S.: 423430
Johan Karlsson *(CFO & Exec VP-Bus
Support)*

Subsidiaries:

ComPromise Domino B.V.   **(1)**
Klompmakerstraat 3 A/B, 9403 VL, Assen,
Netherlands
Tel.: (31) 887306300
Web Site: http://www.compromise.nl
Information Technology Services
N.A.I.C.S.: 541519

Dustin A/S   **(1)**
Ahave Parkvej 27, 8260, Viby, Denmark
Tel.: (45) 78712323
Web Site: https://www.dustin.dk
Information Technology Services
N.A.I.C.S.: 541519

Dustin Finland Oy   **(1)**
Puolikkotie 8, 02230, Espoo, Finland
Tel.: (358) 306238501
Web Site: https://www.dustin.fi
Online Information Technology Product Dis-
tribution Services
N.A.I.C.S.: 541512

Dustin Norway AS   **(1)**
Tykkemyr 1, 1597, Moss, Norway
Tel.: (47) 21044000
Web Site: https://www.dustin.no
Online Information Technology Product Dis-
tribution Services

N.A.I.C.S.: 541511

Subsidiary (Domestic):

IKT Gruppen AS   **(2)**
Innspurten 15, 0663, Oslo, Norway
Tel.: (47) 81500100
Web Site: http://www.ikt.no
Communication Equipment Distr
N.A.I.C.S.: 423690
Fredrik Vetteren *(CEO)*

Purity IT AS   **(2)**
Innspurten 15, 0663, Oslo, Norway
Tel.: (47) 22714444
Web Site: http://www.purity.no
Emp.: 23
Cloud Services
N.A.I.C.S.: 518210
John Robert Strengen *(Ops Mgr)*

IT-Hantverkarna Sverige AB   **(1)**
Runstensgatan 5, 582 78, Linkoping, Swe-
den
Tel.: (46) 134657660
Web Site: http://www.it-hantverkarna.se
Cloud Services
N.A.I.C.S.: 518210

ITaito Oy   **(1)**
Rahtitie 3, 01530, Vantaa, Finland
Tel.: (358) 108418100
Web Site: http://www.itaito.fi
Emp.: 1,800
Information Technology Services
N.A.I.C.S.: 541519
Tomi Tapper *(Mng Dir)*

Inventio IT A/S   **(1)**
Vallensbaekvej 45 1 sal, 2605, Brondby,
Denmark
Tel.: (45) 70269899
Web Site: https://www.inventio.it
Information Technology Services
N.A.I.C.S.: 541519

Issys ICT B.V.   **(1)**
Robonsbosweg 5c, 1816 MK, Alkmaar,
Netherlands
Tel.: (31) 728501000
Web Site: https://www.issys-ict.nl
Information Technology Services
N.A.I.C.S.: 541519

JML-System AB   **(1)**
Kvartsgatan 13, 749 40, Enkoping, Sweden
Tel.: (46) 200816600
Web Site: http://www.jml.se
Industrial Equipment Distr
N.A.I.C.S.: 423830

NORISK IT Groep B.V.   **(1)**
Johan van Zwedenlaan 1, 9744 DX, Gron-
ingen, Netherlands
Tel.: (31) 886674700
Web Site: https://www.noriskit.nl
Information Technology Services
N.A.I.C.S.: 541519

Saldab IT AB   **(1)**
Stenbarsgatan 8, 212 31, Malmo, Sweden
Tel.: (46) 10 102 26 00
Web Site: http://www.saldabit.se
Emp.: 90
Information Technology Services
N.A.I.C.S.: 541512

Sincerus B.V.   **(1)**
Institutenweg 21, 7521 PH, Enschede,
Netherlands
Tel.: (31) 384529829
Web Site: http://www.sincerus.nl
Information Technology Services
N.A.I.C.S.: 541519

Switch IT Solutions B.V.   **(1)**
Institutenweg 21, 7521 PH, Enschede,
Netherlands
Tel.: (31) 888282000
Web Site: http://www.switch.nl
Information Technology Services
N.A.I.C.S.: 541519

Unilogic B.V.   **(1)**
Bergerweg 110, 6135 KD, Sittard, Nether-
lands
Tel.: (31) 464571830
Web Site: https://www.unilogic.nl
Information Technology Services
N.A.I.C.S.: 541519

Vincere Group B.V.   **(1)**

Institutenweg 21, 7521 PH, Enschede,
Netherlands
Tel.: (31) 888282090
Web Site: http://www.vincere-group.com
Information Technology Services
N.A.I.C.S.: 541519

Xcellent Automatisering B.V.   **(1)**
Maanlander 39, 3824 MN, Amersfoort,
Netherlands
Tel.: (31) 334616464
Web Site: http://www.xcellent.nl
Information Technology Services
N.A.I.C.S.: 541519

DUTALAND BERHAD
Level 23 Menara Olympia No 8 Jalan
Raja Chulan, 50200, Kuala Lumpur,
Malaysia
Tel.: (60) 320723993
Web Site:
      https://www.dutaland.com.my
DUTALND—(KLS)
Rev.: $39,746,032
Assets: $271,443,598
Liabilities: $7,481,058
Net Worth: $263,962,540
Earnings: $2,225,185
Emp.: 93
Fiscal Year-end: 06/30/23
Oil Palm Plantations & Property De-
velopment Services
N.A.I.C.S.: 531312
Wee Chun Yap *(Exec Dir)*

Subsidiaries:

Duta Plantations Sdn. Bhd.   **(1)**
Level 23 Menara Olympia No 8 Jalan Raja
Chulan, Kuala Lumpur, 50200, Malaysia
Tel.: (60) 320723993
Web Site: http://www.dutaland.com.my
Sales Range: $50-74.9 Million
Emp.: 100
Investment Holding Services
N.A.I.C.S.: 523940

Jiwa Realty Sdn. Bhd.   **(1)**
Level 24 Menara Olympia 8 Jalan Raja
Chulan B4-1, 50200, Kuala Lumpur, 50200,
Wilayah Persekutuan, Malaysia
Tel.: (60) 320706688
Sales Range: $25-49.9 Million
Emp.: 1
Residential Property Development Services
N.A.I.C.S.: 236116
Yap Yong Seong *(Mng Dir)*

KH Land Sdn. Bhd.   **(1)**
Ground Floor Block P 1-13 & 1-15 Plaza
Damas Jln Sri Hartamas 1, Sri Hartamas,
50480, Kuala Lumpur, Malaysia
Tel.: (60) 362018388
Web Site: http://www.kennyheights.com.my
Sales Range: $25-49.9 Million
Emp.: 15
Residential Property Development Services
N.A.I.C.S.: 236116

Oakland Holdings Sdn. Bhd.   **(1)**
Level 23 Menara Olympia 8 Jalan Raja
Chulan, 50200, Kuala Lumpur, Malaysia
Tel.: (60) 67202636
Web Site: https://oaklandsquare.my
Sales Range: $50-74.9 Million
Emp.: 100
Property Development Services
N.A.I.C.S.: 531390

Olympia Land Berhad   **(1)**
Level 23 Menara Olympia No 8 Jalan Raja
Chulan, Kuala Lumpur, 50200, Malaysia
Tel.: (60) 320706688
Sales Range: $50-74.9 Million
Emp.: 12
Residential Property Management Services
N.A.I.C.S.: 531311
Yong Seong Yap *(Mng Dir)*

**Pertama Land & Development Sdn.
Bhd.**   **(1)**
Level 24 Menara Olympia 8 Jalan Raja
Chulan, 50200, Kuala Lumpur,
Malaysia   **(100%)**
Tel.: (60) 320723993
Web Site: https://pertamaland.com
Emp.: 80

Land & Property Development
N.A.I.C.S.: 237210

**DUTCH OVEN GOLD GROUP
INC.**
PO Box 91983, West Vancouver,
V7V4S4, BC, Canada
Tel.: (604) 925-7659   DE
Year Founded: 2008
Investment Services
N.A.I.C.S.: 523999
Gerry J. de Klerk *(Pres, CEO & CFO)*

DUTCH-BANGLA BANK PLC
47 Motijheel Commercial Area,
Dhaka, 1000, Bangladesh
Tel.: (880) 247110465
Web Site:
      https://www.dutchbanglabank.com
DUTCHBANGL—(CHT)
Rev.: $224,762,085
Assets: $5,066,803,197
Liabilities: $4,686,991,510
Net Worth: $379,811,687
Earnings: $51,643,616
Emp.: 10,407
Fiscal Year-end: 12/31/22
Commercial Banking Services
N.A.I.C.S.: 522110
Abul Kashem Mohammad Shirin
(CEO & Mng Dir)

**DUTCHMASTER NURSERIES
LTD.**
3735 Sideline 16 North, Brougham,
L0H 1A0, ON, Canada
Tel.: (905) 683-8211
Web Site:
      http://www.dutchmasternurseries.com
Year Founded: 1971
Sales Range: $10-24.9 Million
Landscaping Trees & Plants Whslr
N.A.I.C.S.: 111421

DUTECH HOLDINGS LIMITED
11G International Shipping & Finance
Centre 720 Pudong Avenue, Shang-
hai, 200120, China
Tel.: (86) 21 5036 8072   SG
Year Founded: 2000
CZ4—(SES)
Rev.: $269,336,953
Assets: $236,545,874
Liabilities: $94,658,074
Net Worth: $141,887,800
Earnings: $11,320,498
Fiscal Year-end: 12/31/19
Holding Company
N.A.I.C.S.: 551112
Johnny Jiayan Liu *(Founder, Chm &
CEO)*

Subsidiaries:

Metric Group Ltd.   **(1)**
Metric House Westmead Industrial Estate,
Westlea, Swindon, SN5 7AD, Wiltshire,
United Kingdom
Tel.: (44) 1793647800
Web Site: http://www.metricgroup.co.uk
Parking Tickets Vending Machine Installa-
tion Services
N.A.I.C.S.: 238290
Peter Aylward *(Mng Dir)*

DUTEXDOR
15 avenue du Parc de l'Horloge,
59840, Perenchies, France
Tel.: (33) 320009999
Web Site: http://www.dutexdor.fr
Rev.: $24,100,000
Emp.: 40
Clothing: Womens, Childrens & In-
fants
N.A.I.C.S.: 424350
Jean-Marc Terrier *(Pres)*

DUTRON POLYMERS LIMITED

Dutron Polymers Limited—(Continued)

Dutron House Nr Mithakhali Under-
bridge, Navrangpura, Ahmedabad,
380 009, Gujarat, India
Tel.: (91) 7926561849
Web Site:
https://www.dutronindia.com
Year Founded: 1962
517437—(BOM)
Rev.: $12,943,046
Assets: $5,384,439
Liabilities: $2,521,184
Net Worth: $2,863,255
Earnings: $311,203
Fiscal Year-end: 03/31/21
Plastic Tank Mfr
N.A.I.C.S.: 326122
Sudip B. Patel (Chm)

DUVALTEX INC.

1035 ave Wilfrid-Pelletier Ste 310,
Quebec, G1W 0C4, QC, Canada
Tel.: (877) 684-8347
Web Site: http://www.duvaltex.com
Year Founded: 2015
Textile Mfr
N.A.I.C.S.: 314999
Billy Ford (VP-Sls-North America)

Subsidiaries:

True Textiles, Inc.   (1)
5300 Corporate Grove Dr SE Ste 250,
Grand Rapids, MI 49512-5514
Tel.: (800) 550-4314
Web Site: http://www.truetextiles.com
Fabric Mfr & Distr
N.A.I.C.S.: 314999
Billy Ford (Dir-Sls)

DUVAN A.D.

Tel.: (387) 55241212
Web Site: https://www.duvanbn.com
Year Founded: 1989
DUVN—(BANJ)
Sales Range: $1-9.9 Million
Emp.: 12
Crop Farming Services
N.A.I.C.S.: 111998
Pasaga Halilovic (Chm-Mgmt Bd &
Pres)

DUVAN A.D.

Zvornicki put bb, Ljubovija, Serbia
Tel.: (381) 15561901
Year Founded: 1989
DVLJ—(BEL)
Rev.: $882,470
Assets: $1,101,870
Liabilities: $8,338,558
Net Worth: ($7,236,688)
Earnings: $62,174
Fiscal Year-end: 12/31/22
Tobacco Fermentation Services
N.A.I.C.S.: 312230
Milan Zivkovic (Exec Dir)

DUVAN CACAK A.D.

Nikole Tesle 44, 32000, Cacak, Ser-
bia
Tel.: (381) 32 55 24 048
Web Site: http://www.duvan.co.rs
Year Founded: 2003
Sales Range: Less than $1 Million
Grocery Store Operator
N.A.I.C.S.: 445110

DUVAN PROMET A.D.

Save Tekelije 14, Zrenjanin, Serbia
Tel.: (381) 23 523 798
Year Founded: 2002
Sales Range: Less than $1 Million
Emp.: 1
Grocery Store Operator
N.A.I.C.S.: 445110

DUVANSKA INDUSTRIJA A.D.

Sime Pogacarevica 43, 17520, Bu-
janovac, Serbia
Tel.: (381) 17 651110
Web Site:
http://www.dibbujanovac.com
Year Founded: 1937
DIBB—(BEL)
Sales Range: $1-9.9 Million
Emp.: 142
Tobacco Product Mfr
N.A.I.C.S.: 312230
Bogoljub Tomic (Dir)

DUVAPLAST A.D.

Kakmuz bb, 74317, Petrovo, Bosnia
& Herzegovina
Tel.: (387) 53260120
Web Site: http://www.duvaplast.ba
DPLS-R-A—(BANJ)
Rev.: $407,489
Assets: $1,037,285
Liabilities: $925,204
Net Worth: $112,081
Earnings: ($116,011)
Emp.: 27
Fiscal Year-end: 12/31/12
Plastic Packaging Products Mfr
N.A.I.C.S.: 326199
Predrag Petrovic (Chm-Mgmt Bd)

DUXTON FARMS LIMITED

Duxton House 7 Pomona Road,
Stirling, 5152, SA, Australia
Tel.: (61) 881309500
Web Site:
https://www.duxtonfarms.com
DBF—(ASX)
Rev.: $16,076,389
Assets: $126,209,268
Liabilities: $46,175,881
Net Worth: $80,033,386
Earnings: $3,467,548
Fiscal Year-end: 06/30/24
Trust, Fiduciary & Custody Activities
N.A.I.C.S.: 523991
Ed Peter (Chm)

DUXTON WATER LIMITED

Duxton House 7 Pomona Road,
Stirling, 5152, SA, Australia
Tel.: (61) 881309500
Web Site:
https://www.duxtonwater.com.au
Year Founded: 2016
1DV—(DEU)
Rev.: $7,981,158
Assets: $184,691,540
Liabilities: $87,980,334
Net Worth: $96,711,206
Earnings: $6,680,673
Fiscal Year-end: 12/31/22
Portfolio Management & Investment
Advice
N.A.I.C.S.: 523940
Edouard Peter (Chm)

DUZHE PUBLISHING & MEDIA
CO., LTD.

No 520 South Binhe East Road,
Chengguan District, Lanzhou,
730030, Gansu, China
Tel.: (86) 9312130678
Web Site: http://www.duzhe.com
Year Founded: 2009
603999—(SHG)
Rev.: $181,322,009
Assets: $343,720,892
Liabilities: $78,153,548
Net Worth: $265,567,344
Earnings: $12,070,988
Emp.: 500
Fiscal Year-end: 12/31/22
Book & Journal Publisher
N.A.I.C.S.: 513130
Yongsheng Liu (Chm)

DVX, INC.

Mejiro Nakano Bldg 5F 2-17-22
Takada, Toshima-ku, Tokyo, 171-
0033, Japan
Tel.: (81) 359856123
Web Site: https://www.dvx.jp
Year Founded: 1986
3079—(TKS)
Sales Range: $125-149.9 Million
Emp.: 100
Medical Devices Mfr & Sls; Software
& Book Publisher
N.A.I.C.S.: 339112
Makoto Wakabayashi (Founder &
Chm)

DW MANAGEMENT SER-
VICES, LLC

1 Toronto Street Suite 401, Toronto,
M5C 2V6, ON, Canada
Tel.: (416) 583-2420
Web Site: http://www.dwhp.com
Holding Company
N.A.I.C.S.: 551112
Andrew Carragher (Co-founder &
Mng Partner)

Subsidiaries:

Champion Manufacturing, Inc.   (1)
2601 Industrial Pkwy, Elkhart, IN 46516
Tel.: (574) 295-6893
Web Site: http://www.championchair.com
Healthcare Seating Products Mfr
N.A.I.C.S.: 337127
Doug Keeslar (Pres & CEO)

WillowWood Global LLC   (1)
15441 Scioto Darby Rd, Mount Sterling, OH
43143-9036
Tel.: (800) 848-4930
Web Site: https://willowwood.com
Surgical Appliance & Supplies Mfr
N.A.I.C.S.: 339113
Mahesh Mansukhani (CEO)

DWARF TECHNOLOGY HOLD-
INGS, INC.

10/Floor Weixing Building 252 Wen-
san Road, Hangzhou, 310012, Zheji-
ang, China
Tel.: (86) 571 28188199
Web Site: http://www.4006009090.cn
Year Founded: 2007
Sales Range: $1-9.9 Million
Emp.: 53
E-Commerce & IT Solutions
N.A.I.C.S.: 541519
Mianfu Zhang (Chm, Pres & CEO)

DWARIKESH SUGAR INDUS-
TRIES LTD

511 Maker Chambers V 221 Nariman
Point, Mumbai, 400 021, India
Tel.: (91) 2222832468
Web Site: https://www.dwarikesh.com
532610—(BOM)
Rev.: $251,971,138
Assets: $197,302,478
Liabilities: $118,281,113
Net Worth: $79,021,365
Earnings: $12,494,978
Emp.: 746
Fiscal Year-end: 03/31/21
Sugar Mfr & Distr
N.A.I.C.S.: 311314
G. R. Morarka (Founder & Chm)

DWC 3.0 S.P.A.

Via Trieste 10 San Donato Milanese,
Milan, 20097, Italy
Tel.: (39) 03457344543
Web Site: http://www.dwc3-0.com
Year Founded: 2012
Property Management Services
N.A.I.C.S.: 531312
Maurizio Berti (Chm & CEO)

DWITIYA TRADING LIMITED

27 Weston Street 5th Floor Room No
526, Kolkata, 700012, West Bengal,
India
Tel.: (91) 8231927952
Web Site:
http://www.dwitiyatrading.com
Year Founded: 1978
Rev.: $2,894
Assets: $827,325
Liabilities: $22,017
Net Worth: $805,308
Earnings: ($14,564)
Emp.: 5
Fiscal Year-end: 03/31/18
Security Brokerage Services
N.A.I.C.S.: 523150
Rabi Jalan (Mng Dir & Compliance
Officer)

DWS GROUP GMBH & CO.
KGAA

Mainzer Landstrasse 11-17, 60329,
Frankfurt am Main, Germany
Tel.: (49) 6991012371
Web Site: https://www.dws.com
Year Founded: 1956
DWS—(DEU)
Assets: $12,896,513,210
Liabilities: $4,296,262,040
Net Worth: $8,600,251,170
Earnings: $609,336,240
Emp.: 4,378
Fiscal Year-end: 12/31/23
Asset Management Services
N.A.I.C.S.: 531390
Anne-Marie Vandenberg (Portfolio
Mgr)

Subsidiaries:

DWS Investments Singapore
Limited   (1)
One Raffles Quay 17-10, Singapore,
048583, Singapore
Tel.: (65) 65385550
Web Site: http://funds.dws.com
Asset Management Services
N.A.I.C.S.: 523940

DWS LIMITED

Level 4 500 Collins St, Melbourne,
3000, VIC, Australia
Tel.: (61) 3 9650 9777
Web Site: http://www.dws.com.au
Rev.: $114,973,657
Assets: $101,364,944
Liabilities: $51,733,083
Net Worth: $49,631,861
Earnings: $7,241,760
Emp.: 800
Fiscal Year-end: 06/30/19
Information Technology Services
N.A.I.C.S.: 541512
Danny Wallis (Founder, CEO & Mng
Dir)

Subsidiaries:

Strategic Data Management Pty
Ltd   (1)
2nd floor 51-55 Johnston Street, Fitzroy,
3065, VIC, Australia
Tel.: (61) 393409000
Web Site: https://www.logicly.com.au
Software Development Services
N.A.I.C.S.: 518210
Adam Clarke (CTO)

Symplicit Pty Ltd   (1)
Level 7 160 Queen St, Melbourne, 3000,
VIC, Australia
Tel.: (61) 396700227
Web Site: https://www.symplicit.com.au
Graphic Design Services
N.A.I.C.S.: 541430
Gerard Murphy (Exec Gen Mgr)

Wallis Nominees (Computing) Pty.
Ltd.   (1)
Level 22 15 Collins St, Melbourne, 3000,
VIC, Australia
Tel.: (61) 396509777

Web Site: http://www.dws.com.au
Computer Repair & Maintenance Services
N.A.I.C.S.: 811210
Danny Wallis *(Mng Dir)*

DX & VX CO.

10F Elysia bldg 173 Digital-ro,
Geumchun-gu, Seoul, Korea (South)
Tel.: (82) 28908700
Web Site: https://www.dxvx.com
Year Founded: 2001
180400—(KRS)
Rev.: $24,685,419
Assets: $65,924,244
Liabilities: $39,577,260
Net Worth: $26,346,985
Earnings: ($743,841)
Emp.: 75
Fiscal Year-end: 12/31/22
Microarray Mfr
N.A.I.C.S.: 339112
Kim Jae-kwang *(Dir)*

DXB ENTERTAINMENTS PJSC

Sheikh Zayed Road opposite the
Palm Jebel Ali Exit 5, PO Box 33772,
Saih Shuaib, Dubai, United Arab
Emirates
Tel.: (971) 4 820 0820
Web Site:
http://www.dxbentertainments.com
Year Founded: 2012
DXBE—(DFM)
Rev.: $133,709,008
Assets: $2,624,895,987
Liabilities: $1,832,991,093
Net Worth: $791,904,893
Earnings: ($232,618,144)
Emp.: 263
Fiscal Year-end: 12/31/19
Theme Park & Resort Organiser
N.A.I.C.S.: 713110
Abdullah Habtoor *(Vice Chm)*

DXI CAPITAL CORP.

Suite 404-999 Canada Place, Van-
couver, V6C 3E1, BC, Canada
Tel.: (604) 638-5055　　　　BC
Web Site: http://www.dxienergy.com
Year Founded: 1969
DXI—(TSXV)
Assets: $21,143
Liabilities: $743,793
Net Worth: ($722,650)
Earnings: ($138,942)
Fiscal Year-end: 12/31/23
Oil & Gas Property Acquisition & Ex-
ploration Services
N.A.I.C.S.: 211120
Robert Lloyd Hodgkinson *(CEO)*

Subsidiaries:

Dejour Energy USA, Inc.　　(1)
1401 17th St Ste 850, Denver, CO 80202
Tel.: (303) 296-3535
Web Site: http://www.dejour.com
Sales Range: $50-74.9 Million
Emp.: 7
Oil & Gas Exploration Services
N.A.I.C.S.: 211120

DXN HOLDINGS BHD.

Block C 8 Suria boutique Offices
Jalan PJU 1 42, Datarama Prima,
47301, Petaling Jaya, Selangor, Ma-
laysia
Tel.: (60) 603 7809 3388
Web Site: http://www.dxn2uasia.com
Year Founded: 1993
Dietary Supplements, Food & Bever-
ages Mfr
N.A.I.C.S.: 311514
Siow Jin Lim *(Founder, Chm & CEO)*

Subsidiaries:

DXN (Singapore) Pte Ltd　　(1)
520 North Bridge Road 02-01 Wisma Alsag-
off, 188742, Singapore, Singapore

Tel.: (65) 62732668
Web Site: http://www.singapore.dxn2u.com
Sales Range: $25-49.9 Million
Emp.: 5
Health Foods Mfr & Distr
N.A.I.C.S.: 311999

DXN Comfort Tours Sdn. Bhd.　(1)
No 99 Lebuhraya Sultan Abdul Halim, Alor
Setar, Kedah, Malaysia
Tel.: (60) 47721199
Web Site: http://www.comfort.dxn2u.com
Sales Range: $25-49.9 Million
Emp.: 1
Touring & Travel Services
N.A.I.C.S.: 561520
Lim Yew Lin *(Exec Dir)*

DXN Herbal Manufacturing (India)
Private Limited　　　　　(1)
141/4 & 142/5 Whirlpool Road Thiruvandar
Koil, Mannadipet, Pondicherry, 605102,
India
Tel.: (91) 4132640618
Web Site: http://www.dxn2u.com
Medicine & Health Food Products Mfr
N.A.I.C.S.: 325412
Ramesh Subramaniam *(Mng Dir)*

DXN Industries (M) Sdn. Bhd.　(1)
213 Lebuhraya Sultan Abdul, Alor Setar,
05400, Kedah, Malaysia
Tel.: (60) 47723388
Web Site: http://www.dxn2u.com
Health Food Supplements Mfr
N.A.I.C.S.: 311999
Lim Boon Yee *(Mng Dir)*

DXN International (Australia) Pty.
Ltd.　　　　　　　　　(1)
Suite 504 Level 5 Office Tower Westfield
Shoppingtown, 159-175 Church Street, Par-
ramatta, 2150, NSW, Australia
Tel.: (61) 296892755
Web Site: http://www.dxnaus.com.au
Sales Range: $25-49.9 Million
Emp.: 7
Health Food Supplements Distr
N.A.I.C.S.: 456191
Frank Li *(Mgr)*

DXN International (Hong Kong)
Limited　　　　　　　　(1)
Room 921-923 9/F Hollywood Plaza 610
Nathan Road, Mongkok, Kowloon, China
(Hong Kong)
Tel.: (852) 23886583
Web Site: http://www.hk.dxn2u.com
Sales Range: $50-74.9 Million
Emp.: 4
Health Food Supplements Whslr
N.A.I.C.S.: 424490
Peggy Lam *(Mgr)*

DXN International Pakistan (Private)
Limited　　　　　　　　(1)
2nd Floor OPF Building Plot No 20-A/II
Block-06, PECHS Shahar-e-Faisal, Karachi,
Sindh, Pakistan
Tel.: (92) 21 4324475
Web Site: http://www.pakistan.dxn2u.com
Herbal Products & Food Supplements Distr
N.A.I.C.S.: 424490

DXN International Peru S.A.C.　(1)
Av Angamos Oeste 547, Miraflores, Lima,
Peru
Tel.: (51) 1 241 7148
Web Site: http://www.dxn2ulatam.com
Emp.: 18
Beverage Mixes Distr
N.A.I.C.S.: 424490

DXN Marketing Sdn. Bhd.　(1)
43 Jalan SS 22/23 Damansara Jaya,
47000, Petaling Jaya, Selangor, Malaysia
Tel.: (60) 377253388
Web Site: http://www.dxn2u.com
Sales Range: $25-49.9 Million
Emp.: 30
Health Food Supplements Whslr
N.A.I.C.S.: 424490
Lim Siow Jin *(Founder)*

DXN Pharmaceutical Sdn. Bhd.　(1)
Kg Padang Panjang Jalan Bukit Wang,
06000, Jitra, Kedah, Malaysia
Tel.: (60) 49161288
Health Food Supplements Mfr
N.A.I.C.S.: 311999

Daxen, Inc.　　　　　　(1)
565 Brea Canyon Rd Ste B, Walnut, CA
91789
Tel.: (909) 348-0188
Web Site:
http://www.international.dxn2u.com
Healthcare Product Distr
N.A.I.C.S.: 424210

Yiked-DXN Stargate Sdn. Bhd.　(1)
99 Lebuhraya Sultan Abdul Halim, Alor
Setar, 05400, Kedah, Malaysia
Tel.: (60) 47723399
Web Site: http://www.stargate.net.my
Sales Range: $25-49.9 Million
Emp.: 15
Housing Development Services
N.A.I.C.S.: 236117
Lim Boon Yee *(Mgr)*

DXN LIMITED

3 Dampier Road, Welshpool, Perth,
6106, WA, Australia
Tel.: (61) 1300328239　　　AU
Web Site: https://dxn.solutions
Year Founded: 2017
DXN—(ASX)
Rev.: $7,181,727
Assets: $9,455,169
Liabilities: $9,730,458
Net Worth: ($275,289)
Earnings: ($1,537,904)
Emp.: 33
Fiscal Year-end: 06/30/24
Data Management Technology Ser-
vices
N.A.I.C.S.: 518210
Shalini Lagrutta *(CEO)*

DXSTORM.COM INC.

824 Winston Churchill Blvd, Oakville,
L6J 7X2, ON, Canada
Tel.: (905) 842-8262　　　ON
Web Site: https://www.dxstorm.com
Year Founded: 1993
DXX—(TSXV)
Rev.: $114,544
Assets: $60,446
Liabilities: $401,130
Net Worth: ($340,685)
Earnings: ($156,339)
Fiscal Year-end: 06/30/21
E-Commerce Solutions
N.A.I.C.S.: 517810

Subsidiaries:

Medical Diagnostic Exchange
Corp　　　　　　　　　(1)
824 Winston Churchill Blvd, Oakville, L6J
7X2, ON, Canada
Tel.: (905) 707-5040
Medical Image Analysis Software Develop-
ment Services
N.A.I.C.S.: 513210

DY CORPORATION

36 362beongil Namdongseo ro,
Namdong-gu, Incheon, Korea (South)
Tel.: (82) 328104100　　　KR
Web Site: http://www.dy.co.kr
Year Founded: 1978
013570—(KRS)
Rev.: $839,724,559
Assets: $660,450,686
Liabilities: $273,588,113
Net Worth: $386,862,573
Earnings: ($3,312,223)
Emp.: 54
Fiscal Year-end: 12/31/22
Crane Mfr
N.A.I.C.S.: 333923
Byung-Ho Cho *(Chm)*

Subsidiaries:

DY Auto Corporation　　(1)
48-23 Dogo-myoen-ro, Ansan, 336-914,
Chungcheongnam-do, Korea (South)
Tel.: (82) 41 901 4500
Web Site: http://www.auto.dy.co.kr
Rev.: $353,600,000

Assets: $362,100,000
Liabilities: $187,170,000
Net Worth: $174,930,000
Earnings: $9,945,000
Emp.: 466
Fiscal Year-end: 12/31/2016
Automotive Component Mfr & Distr
N.A.I.C.S.: 336390
Jongheum Yun *(Gen Mgr-Pur)*

DY INNOVATE Corporation　(1)
118 13gil Seokam-ro, Iksan, Jeonrabuk-do,
Korea (South)
Tel.: (82) 638304400
Web Site: https://innovate.dy.co.kr
Power Supply Controller Mfr & Distr
N.A.I.C.S.: 335314

DY Iksan　　　　　　　(1)
833 Palbong-Dong, Iksan, Jollabukdo, Ko-
rea (South)
Tel.: (82) 63 830 4400
Emp.: 215
Crane Mfr
N.A.I.C.S.: 333923

DY Power Corporation　　(1)
Seongju-dong 812 Ungnam-ro, Seongsan-
gu, Changwon, Gyeongsangnam-do, Korea
(South)
Tel.: (82) 552780800
Web Site: http://www.power.dy.co.kr
Rev.: $321,387,348
Assets: $251,209,680
Liabilities: $66,846,634
Net Worth: $184,363,046
Earnings: $13,694,179
Emp.: 429
Fiscal Year-end: 12/31/2022
Excavator Mfr
N.A.I.C.S.: 333120

Dy America Inc.　　　　(1)
36199 Mound Rd, Sterling Heights, MI
48310
Tel.: (586) 580-3321
Automation Product Mfr & Distr
N.A.I.C.S.: 334512

HS Technology Co., Ltd.　(1)
79 156beongil Namdongdae-ro, Namdong-
gu, Incheon, Korea (South)
Tel.: (82) 328166101
Automation Product Mfr & Distr
N.A.I.C.S.: 334512

DY6 METALS LTD.

Level 8 99 St Georges Terrace,
Perth, 6000, WA, Australia
Tel.: (61) 894864036
Web Site:
https://www.dy6metals.com
Year Founded: 2022
DY6—(ASX)
Rev.: $66,144
Assets: $5,012,636
Liabilities: $173,383
Net Worth: $4,839,253
Earnings: ($1,025,738)
Fiscal Year-end: 06/30/24
Support Activities for Metal Mining
N.A.I.C.S.: 213114
John Kay *(Sec)*

DYACO INTERNATIONAL INC.

12F No 111 Song Jiang Road, Taipei,
10486, Taiwan
Tel.: (886) 225152288　　　TW
Web Site: https://www.dyaco.com
Year Founded: 1989
1598—(TAI)
Rev.: $254,634,576
Assets: $369,180,600
Liabilities: $213,136,360
Net Worth: $156,044,240
Earnings: ($3,609,405)
Emp.: 613
Fiscal Year-end: 12/31/23
Sporting Goods Mfr & Distr
N.A.I.C.S.: 339920
Ing-Gin Lin *(Chm)*

Subsidiaries:

CARDIO fitness GmbH & Co.
KG　　　　　　　　　　(1)

Dyaco International Inc.—(Continued)

Friedrich-Ebert-Str 75, 51429, Bergisch
Gladbach, Germany
Tel.: (49) 2204844320
Fitness Equipment Mfr & Retailer
N.A.I.C.S.: 339920

**Dyaco (Shanghai) Trading Co.,
Ltd.** (1)
Room 601 6th Floor Block A 125 Shijie
Road, Yangpu District, Shanghai, 200438,
China
Tel.: (86) 2165068300
Fitness & Sport Equipment Mfr & Distr
N.A.I.C.S.: 339920

Dyaco Canada Inc. (1)
5955 Don Murie Street, Niagara Falls, L2G
0A9, ON, Canada
Web Site: https://www.dyaco.ca
Exercise Equipment Mfr & Distr
N.A.I.C.S.: 339920

Dyaco Europe GmbH (1)
Friedrich Ebertstrasse 75, Bergisch Glad-
bach Technology Park, 51429, Bergisch
Gladbach, Germany
Tel.: (49) 2204844300
Fitness Equipment Mfr & Retailer
N.A.I.C.S.: 339920

Dyaco Germany GmbH (1)
Technologiepark Bergisch-Gladbach Haus
56 Friedrich-Ebert-Strae 75, 51429, Ber-
gisch Gladbach, Germany
Tel.: (49) 2204844340
Exercise Equipment Mfr
N.A.I.C.S.: 339920

**Dyaco International Inc. - Main
Factory** (1)
No 1 Gong 1st Road, Cyuan Sing Industrial
Park, Chang-Hua, 509, Taiwan
Tel.: (886) 47977888
Exercise Equipment Mfr
N.A.I.C.S.: 339920

Dyaco Japan Co., Ltd. (1)
Dai 2 Shirako Bldg 501 6-16-7 Nishi Kasai
Edogawa, Tokyo, 134-0088, Japan
Tel.: (81) 368084588
Exercise Equipment Distr
N.A.I.C.S.: 423910

Iuvo Industry Co., Ltd. (1)
No 460-1 Zhongsan Road Sec 1, Tachia
Dist, Taichung, Taiwan
Tel.: (886) 426804168
Web Site: https://www.iuvo.com.tw
Bicycle Mfr
N.A.I.C.S.: 336991

DYCENT BIOTECH (SHANG-
HAI) CO. LTD.
528 Rui Qing Road Building 8,
Shanghai, 201201, China
Tel.: (86) 21 50720072
Web Site:
http://dycentbio.lookchem.com
Year Founded: 2003
Biochemical Mfr
N.A.I.C.S.: 325199

Subsidiaries:

NuSep, Inc (1)
20271 Goldenrod Ln Ste 2041, Germantown, MD 20876
Web Site: http://www.nusep.com
Pharmaceutical Products Research & Development Services
N.A.I.C.S.: 541715

DYDO GROUP HOLDINGS,
INC.
2-2-7 Nakanoshima, Kita-ku, Osaka,
530-0005, Japan
Tel.: (81) 671660011 JP
Web Site: https://www.dydo-ghd.co.jp
Year Founded: 1975
2590—(TKS)
Rev.: $1,512,793,300
Assets: $1,258,921,670
Liabilities: $610,328,470
Net Worth: $648,593,200
Earnings: $31,359,070

Emp.: 5,182
Fiscal Year-end: 01/31/24
Holding Company
N.A.I.C.S.: 551112
Tomiya Takamatsu *(Pres)*

Subsidiaries:

DyDo DRINCO Inc. (1)
2-2-7 Nakanoshima, Kita-ku, Osaka, 530-
0005, Japan (100%)
Tel.: (81) 120559552
Web Site: https://www.dydo.co.jp
Emp.: 738
Soft Drinks Mfr
N.A.I.C.S.: 312111
Tatsumi Miyazaki *(Exec Officer)*

Subsidiary (Domestic):

**Daido Pharmaceutical
Corporation** (2)
214-1 Shinmura, Katsuragi, 639-2121,
Nara, Japan
Tel.: (81) 745625031
Web Site: https://www.daido-yakuhin.co.jp
Emp.: 270
Coffee Beverages Mfr
N.A.I.C.S.: 311920

**DyDo BEVERAGE SHIZUOKA,
INC.** (2)
2276 Yamashina Fukuroi-shi, Shizuoka,
437-0066, Japan (100%)
Tel.: (81) 538431066
Web Site: http://www.dydo-ghd.co.jp
Coffee Beverages Mfr
N.A.I.C.S.: 311920

**DyDo Drinco Turkey Icecek Satis ve
Pazarlama A.S.** (1)
Altunizade Mahallesi Ord Prof Fahrettin
Kerim Gokay Cad No 38/1, Uskudar,
34662, Istanbul, Türkiye
Tel.: (90) 850 221 1200
Web Site: https://www.dydodrinco.com.tr
Energy Drink Mfr & Distr
N.A.I.C.S.: 312111
Naoi Kagawa *(Pres & CEO)*

Michinoku, Ltd. (1)
3-84 Mizusawa Industrial Park, Oshu, 023-
0002, Japan
Tel.: (81) 197257760
Soft Drinks Mfr & Distr
N.A.I.C.S.: 312111

Tarami Corporation (1)
2178 Nakazato-machi, Nagasaki, 851-0198,
Japan
Tel.: (81) 95 839 1111
Web Site: https://www.tarami.co.jp
Food Mfr
N.A.I.C.S.: 311991

DYE & DURHAM LIMITED
1100-25 York Street, Toronto, M5J
2V5, ON, Canada
Web Site:
https://www.dyedurham.com
DND—(TSX)
Rev.: $163,453,495
Assets: $1,219,078,554
Liabilities: $631,651,204
Net Worth: $587,427,351
Earnings: ($31,955,356)
Emp.: 1,501
Fiscal Year-end: 06/30/21
Software Development Services
N.A.I.C.S.: 541511
Brian L. Derksen *(Chm)*

Subsidiaries:

Stanley Davis Group Limited (1)
1 George Yard Ground Floor, Langbourn,
London, EC3V 9DF, United Kingdom
Tel.: (44) 207 554 2222
Web Site: https://www.stanleydavis.co.uk
Law firm
N.A.I.C.S.: 541110

DYER HOLDINGS PTY. LTD.
1299 Boundary Rd, Wacol, 4076,
QLD, Australia
Tel.: (61) 7 3331 5200 AU

Year Founded: 1959
Sales Range: $75-99.9 Million
Emp.: 500
Holding Company
N.A.I.C.S.: 551112
Simon John Dyer *(CEO)*

Subsidiaries:

Madad Pty. Ltd. (1)
1299 Boundary Road, Wacol, 4076, QLD,
Australia
Tel.: (61) 7 3331 5200
Web Site: http://www.sealy.com.au
Emp.: 300
Mattress Mfr & Distr
N.A.I.C.S.: 337910
Simon John Dyer *(CEO)*

Joint Venture (Non-US):

Sealy Asia (Hong Kong) Ltd (2)
Room 1503 15/F Park Commercial Centre,
180 Tung Lo Wan Road, Causeway Bay,
China (Hong Kong) (50%)
Tel.: (852) 2578 8989
Web Site: http://www.sealy.com.hk
Mattresses & Box Springs Mfr
N.A.I.C.S.: 337910

Sealy Asia (Singapore) Pte., Ltd. (2)
SIS Bldg 4 Leng Kee Rd Suite 05-06/07,
Singapore, 68898, Singapore (50%)
Tel.: (65) 64756166
Web Site: http://www.sealy.com.sg
Mattresses & Bedding Products Distr
N.A.I.C.S.: 423210

DYFED STEELS LIMITED
Maescanner Road Dafen, Llanelli,
SA14 8NS, Dyfed, United Kingdom
Tel.: (44) 1554772255
Web Site:
http://www.dyfedsteel.co.uk
Rev.: $80,642,683
Emp.: 250
Steel Products Mfr
N.A.I.C.S.: 331210
David Thomas *(Owner & Mng Dir)*

DYMATIC CHEMICALS INC.
Chaogui South Road Science and
Technology Industrial Park, Shunde
New and High-tech Development
Zone, Foshan, 528305, Guangdong,
China
Tel.: (86) 75728399088
Web Site: https://www.dymatic.com
Year Founded: 1989
002054—(SSE)
Rev.: $459,745,416
Assets: $1,053,042,120
Liabilities: $613,473,588
Net Worth: $439,568,532
Earnings: $12,130,560
Emp.: 1,000
Fiscal Year-end: 12/31/22
Chemical Products Mfr
N.A.I.C.S.: 325180

DYMIN STEEL INC.
133 Van Kirk Dr, Brampton, L7A 1A4,
ON, Canada
Tel.: (905) 840-0808
Web Site: http://www.dymin-
steel.com
Year Founded: 1992
Rev.: $15,300,000
Emp.: 240
Structure Shaped Steel Distr
N.A.I.C.S.: 238120
Gary Crockford *(VP & Gen Mgr)*

DYMON ASIA CAPITAL (SIN-
GAPORE) PTE. LTD
1 Temasek Avenue #11-01 Millenia
Tower, Singapore, 039192, Singapore
Tel.: (65) 67051666
Web Site:
https://www.dymonasia.com
Year Founded: 2008

Investment Management
N.A.I.C.S.: 523999

Subsidiaries:

Penguin International Limited (1)
21 Tuas Road, Singapore, 638784, Singa-
pore
Tel.: (65) 68702700
Web Site: https://www.penguin.com.sg
Rev.: $138,159,509
Assets: $282,706,203
Liabilities: $122,588,806
Net Worth: $160,117,397
Earnings: $12,678,937
Emp.: 580
Fiscal Year-end: 12/31/2023
Ferry Operational Services
N.A.I.C.S.: 336611
Joanna May Fong Tung *(Dir-Admin & Fin)*

Subsidiary (Non-US):

**PT Kim Seah Shipyard
Indonesia** (2)
Kel Tg Riau No 61, Kawasan Industri Seku-
pang Sekupang, Batam, Indonesia
Tel.: (62) 778322199
Shipping Services
N.A.I.C.S.: 488510

Subsidiary (Domestic):

**Pelican Offshore Services Pte
Ltd** (2)
18 Tuas Basin Link, Singapore, 638784,
Singapore
Tel.: (65) 68652500
Web Site: http://www.penguin.com.sg
Emp.: 20
Vessel Chartering Services
N.A.I.C.S.: 483111
Chew Kia Hoe *(Gen Mgr)*

**Pelican Ship Management Servies
Pte Ltd** (2)
18 Tuas Basin Link, Singapore, 638784,
Singapore
Tel.: (65) 68702735
Shipping Services
N.A.I.C.S.: 488510

Subsidiary (Non-US):

**Penguin Marine Boats Services
L.L.C.** (2)
Port Rashid Berth 26, PO Box 119124,
Dubai, United Arab Emirates
Tel.: (971) 4 3454591
Ship Management & Operation Services
N.A.I.C.S.: 483113

Subsidiary (Domestic):

**Penguin Shipyard International Pte
Ltd** (2)
18 Tuas Basin Link, Singapore, 638784,
Singapore
Tel.: (65) 6 870 2709
Web Site: https://www.penguin.com.sg
Ship Building & Repair Services
N.A.I.C.S.: 336611

DYNAC SDN. BHD.
PLO 110 Jalan Nibong 3 Tanjung
Langsat Ind Estate, Pasir Gudang,
81707, Johor Darul Takzim, Malaysia
Tel.: (60) 7 259 9888 MY
Web Site: http://www.dynac.com.my
Year Founded: 1982
Emp.: 250
Oil, Gas & Chemical Industry Heat-
ing, Ventilation & Air Conditioning
Equipment Designer, Mfr, Whslr &
Installation Services
N.A.I.C.S.: 333415
Abdul Rahman Mohamed Shariff *(Co-
Owner)*

Subsidiaries:

Dynac UK Ltd. (1)
Charrington Park West Carr Lane, Kingston
upon Hull, HU7 0BW, United Kingdom
Tel.: (44) 1482 225 122
Web Site: http://www.dynac.co.uk
Emp.: 8

Oil, Gas & Chemical Industry Heating, Ventilation & Air Conditioning Equipment Whslr & Installation Services
N.A.I.C.S.: 423730
Paul Hart (Mng Dir)

Subsidiary (Domestic):

North Sea Ventilation Limited   (2)
Charrington Park West Carr Lane, Kingston upon Hull, HU7 0BW, United
Kingdom   (100%)
Tel.: (44) 1482 834 050
Web Site: http://www.nsv.co.uk
Oil, Gas & Chemical Industry Heating, Ventilation & Air Conditioning Equipment Designer, Mfr, Whslr & Installation Services
N.A.I.C.S.: 333415

DYNACERT INC.
101-501 Alliance Avenue, Toronto, M6N 2J1, ON, Canada
Tel.: (416) 766-9691
Web Site: https://www.dynacert.com
DYFSF—(OTCIQ)
Rev.: $330,075
Assets: $4,158,116
Liabilities: $4,112,795
Net Worth: $45,321
Earnings: ($6,374,751)
Emp.: 29
Fiscal Year-end: 12/31/23
Generator Mfr & Sales
N.A.I.C.S.: 335312
Murray James Payne (Pres & CEO)

Subsidiaries:

Dynacert GmbH   (1)
Industriehof 6, 77933, Lahr, Germany
Tel.: (49) 78215035867
Industrial Machinery & Equipment Distr
N.A.I.C.S.: 423830

DYNACOLOR CO., LTD.
No 116 Jou Tz Street, Neihu, Taipei, 114, Taiwan
Tel.: (886) 226598898
Web Site:
     http://www.dynacolor.com.tw
Year Founded: 1991
5489—(TPE)
Rev.: $54,588,938
Assets: $99,806,553
Liabilities: $26,295,188
Net Worth: $73,511,365
Earnings: $9,031,829
Fiscal Year-end: 12/31/22
Optical Component Mfr
N.A.I.C.S.: 333310
Warren Chen (Chm & CEO)

DYNACONS SYSTEMS & SOLUTIONS LTD.
78 Ratnajyot Inds Estate Irla Lane
Vile Parle West, Mumbai, 400056, India
Tel.: (91) 2266889900
Web Site: https://www.dynacons.com
532365—(BOM)
Rev.: $96,728,637
Assets: $48,272,274
Liabilities: $35,711,684
Net Worth: $12,560,590
Earnings: $4,011,019
Emp.: 1,009
Fiscal Year-end: 03/31/23
Information Technology Consulting Services
N.A.I.C.S.: 541512
Shirish M. Anjaria (Chm & Mng Dir)

DYNACOR GROUP INC.
625 Rene-Levesque Blvd West Suite 1200, Montreal, H3B 1R2, QC, Canada
Tel.: (514) 393-9000   QC
Web Site: https://www.dynacor.com
Year Founded: 2006

DNG—(TSX)
Rev.: $101,532,815
Assets: $76,296,157
Liabilities: $13,551,977
Net Worth: $62,744,180
Earnings: $4,334,589
Emp.: 390
Fiscal Year-end: 12/31/20
Gold Mining Services
N.A.I.C.S.: 212220
Jean Martineau (Pres & CEO)

Subsidiaries:

Minera Dynacor del Peru, S.A.C. (1)
Cal Luis Pasteur Nro 1297, Lynx, Lima, Peru
Tel.: (51) 12027630
Gold Mining Services
N.A.I.C.S.: 212220

DYNACTION SA
23 Rue Bossuet Zi de la Vigne aux Loups, PO Box 181, 91161, Longjumeau, Cedex, France
Tel.: (33) 169796062   FR
Web Site: http://www.dynaction.fr
Sales Range: $200-249.9 Million
Emp.: 930
Holding Company; Fine & Specialty Chemicals Mfr
N.A.I.C.S.: 551112
Christian Moretti (Chm)

DYNACURE SA
Bioparc III 850 Boulevard Sebastien Brant, F-67400, Illkirch-Graffenstaden, France
Tel.: (33) 374952500   FR
Year Founded: 2016
Assets: $74,313,433
Liabilities: $123,116,321
Net Worth: ($48,802,888)
Earnings: ($23,011,076)
Emp.: 22
Fiscal Year-end: 12/31/20
Biotechnology Research & Development Services
N.A.I.C.S.: 541714
Georges Gemayel (Chm)

DYNAFOND SA
ZI de la Porte Rouge, 27150, Etrepagny, France
Tel.: (33) 232550207
Web Site: https://www.dynafond.com
Year Founded: 1991
MLDYN—(EUR)
Sales Range: $1-9.9 Million
Aluminum Die-Casting Services
N.A.I.C.S.: 331523
Philippe Boulier (Chm & CEO)

DYNAGAS LNG PARTNERS LP
Poseidonos Avenue and Foivis 2 Street, Glyfada, 166 74, Athens, Greece
Tel.: (30) 2108917960   MH
Web Site:
     https://www.dynagaspartners.com
Year Founded: 2013
DLNG—(NYSE)
Rev.: $148,878,000
Assets: $908,913,000
Liabilities: $460,673,000
Net Worth: $448,240,000
Earnings: $35,872,000
Fiscal Year-end: 12/31/23
LNG Carrier Owner & Operator
N.A.I.C.S.: 488390
Michael Gregos (CFO)

Subsidiaries:

Lance Shipping S.A.   (1)
94 Poseidonos Ave & 2 Nikis Street, PO Box 70303, Athens, 166-75, Greece
Tel.: (30) 2108917700
Sea Transportation Services

N.A.I.C.S.: 488390

DYNAGREEN ENVIRONMENTAL PROTECTION GROUP CO., LTD.
2 F Jiuzhou Electronic Building 007 Keji South 12th Street, Nanshan District, Shenzhen, 518057, China
Tel.: (86) 75536807688   CN
Web Site:
     https://www.dynagreen.com.cn
Year Founded: 2000
601330 (SHG)
Rev.: $641,223,353
Assets: $3,183,912,604
Liabilities: $2,086,928,247
Net Worth: $1,096,984,358
Earnings: $104,565,329
Emp.: 3,389
Fiscal Year-end: 12/31/22
Waste Incinerator Plants
N.A.I.C.S.: 562213
Shengyong Hu (Bd of Dirs & CFO)

DYNAM JAPAN HOLDINGS, CO., LTD.
2-25-1-702 Nishinippori, Arakawa-ku, Tokyo, 116-0013, Japan
Tel.: (81) 356151222
Web Site: https://www.dyjh.co.jp
6889—(HKG)
Rev.: $861,334,414
Assets: $2,418,532,524
Liabilities: $1,549,765,010
Net Worth: $868,767,514
Earnings: $22,365,372
Emp.: 12,492
Fiscal Year-end: 03/31/24
Game Hall Management Consulting Services
N.A.I.C.S.: 541611
Makoto Sakamoto (Chm, Pres & CEO)

Subsidiaries:

Business Partners Co., Ltd.   (1)
5-15-7 Nishi-Suck-Nippori, Arakawa-ku, Tokyo, Japan
Tel.: (81) 3 5850 3590
Emp.: 21
Handmade Product Mfr & Distr
N.A.I.C.S.: 313230
Yuji Tago (Pres)

Cabin Plaza Co., Ltd.   (1)
6-5-8 Kanamachi, Katsushika-ku, Tokyo, 120-0000, Japan
Tel.: (81) 358500651
Web Site: https://www.cabinplaza.jp
Game Hall Management Services
N.A.I.C.S.: 713990

DYNAM Business Support Co., Ltd.   (1)
5-15-7 Nishi-Nippori, Arakawa-ku, Tokyo, 120-0000, Japan
Tel.: (81) 358503575
Web Site: https://www.dynam-business-support.jp
Business Support Services
N.A.I.C.S.: 561499

DYNAM Co., Ltd.   (1)
2-27-5 Nishi-Nippori, Arakawa-ku, Tokyo, 116-8580, Japan
Tel.: (81) 338078111
Web Site: https://www.dynam.jp
Emp.: 7,087
Game Hall Management Services
N.A.I.C.S.: 713990

Dynam Hong Kong Co., Limited   (1)
Unit 1 32/F Hong Kong Plaza 188 Connaught Road West, Admiralty, Hong Kong, China (Hong Kong)
Tel.: (852) 3769 0600
Web Site: http://www.dyjx.co.jp
Investment Management Service
N.A.I.C.S.: 523999
Kenneth Ng (Mgr-Investment)

Subsidiary (Non-US):

Beijing G.E.O. Coffee Co., Ltd.   (2)
202-01 12th Floor Building 3 No 29 Kechuang 13th-Street, Beijing Economic and Technological Development Zone, Beijing, China
Tel.: (86) 10 67892199
Web Site: http://www.geocoffee.com.cn
Coffee Mfr
N.A.I.C.S.: 311920

Erin International Co., Ltd.   (2)
Peace Avenue 20th khoroo, PO Box 268, Bayangol District, 16081, Ulaanbaatar, Mongolia
Tel.: (976) 95010888
Web Site: http://www.erin-group.mn
Freight Forwarding Services
N.A.I.C.S.: 488510

HUMAP Japan Co., Ltd.   (1)
5-15-7 Nishinippori Dynam Integrated Investment Building, Arakawa-ku, Tokyo, 116-0013, Japan
Tel.: (81) 338028141
Web Site: http://www.humap.jp
Emp.: 167
Food Restaurant Services
N.A.I.C.S.: 722511

Yume Corporation Co., Ltd.   (1)
195-1 Funahara-cho, Toyohashi, 440-0813, Aichi, Japan
Tel.: (81) 532571811
Web Site: http://www.yume-corp.co.jp
Emp.: 342
Logistic Services
N.A.I.C.S.: 488510

DYNAMATIC TECHNOLOGIES LIMITED
Dynamatic Park Peenya Industrial Area, Bengaluru, 560 058, India
Tel.: (91) 8028394933   In
Web Site:
     http://www.dynamatics.com
Sales Range: $200-249.9 Million
Emp.: 900
Hydraulic Gear Pump, Non-Ferrous Alloy Casting, Automotive Engine Parts & Aircraft Structural Components Mfr
N.A.I.C.S.: 333914
Udhyant Malhotra (CEO & Mng Dir)

Subsidiaries:

Dynamatic Limited UK   (1)
Cheney Manor Industrial Estates, Swindon, SN2 2PZ, Wilts, United Kingdom
Tel.: (44) 1793530101
Web Site: http://www.dynamatics.net
Sales Range: $10-24.9 Million
Emp.: 250
Open Circuit Gear Pump Mfr
N.A.I.C.S.: 333914
Ray Lawton (COO & Exec Dir)

Eisenwerk Erla GmbH   (1)
Giessereistrasse 1, 08340, Schwarzenberg, Saxony, Germany
Tel.: (49) 37741230
Web Site: http://www.eisenwerk-erla.de
Automobile Parts Distr
N.A.I.C.S.: 423120

JKM Ferrotech Limited   (1)
K-4 SIPCOT Phase II, Gummidipoondi, Tiruvallur, 601 201, Tamil Nadu, India
Tel.: (91) 4427921382
Automobile Parts Distr
N.A.I.C.S.: 423120
Narendran Lga (Engr-Quality)

DYNAMIC & PROTO CIRCUITS INC.
869 Barton St, Stoney Creek, L8E 5G6, ON, Canada
Tel.: (905) 643-9900
Web Site: http://www.dapc.com
Year Founded: 1974
Rev.: $12,000,000
Emp.: 120
Electric Circuit Boards Mfr
N.A.I.C.S.: 334412

Dynamic & Proto Circuits Inc.—(Continued)

Kieran Healy *(Pres)*

DYNAMIC ARCHISTRUC-TURES LIMITED

409 Swaika Centre 4A Pollock Street, Kolkata, 700 001, West Bengal, India
Tel.: (91) 3322342673 In
Web Site:
https://www.dynamicstructures.com
Year Founded: 1996
539681—(BOM)
Rev.: $747,821
Assets: $3,316,022
Liabilities: $7,059
Net Worth: $3,308,963
Earnings: $444,275
Emp.: 7
Fiscal Year-end: 03/31/21
Textile Material Mfr & Distr
N.A.I.C.S.: 313210
Danmal Porwal *(Chm & Mng Dir)*

DYNAMIC ARCHITECTURAL WINDOWS & DOORS INC.

30440 Progressive Way, Abbotsford, V2T 6W3, BC, Canada
Tel.: (604) 864-8200
Web Site:
http://www.dynamicwindows.com
Year Founded: 1991
Rev.: $10,924,369
Emp.: 200
Windows & Doors Distr
N.A.I.C.S.: 444180
John Mathews *(Pres)*

DYNAMIC CABLES LIMITED

F-260 Road Number 13 V K I Area, Jaipur, 302 013, Rajasthan, India
Tel.: (91) 1414042005
Web Site:
https://www.dynamiccables.co.in
540795—(BOM)
Rev.: $47,867,342
Assets: $40,507,576
Liabilities: $24,513,830
Net Worth: $15,993,746
Earnings: $1,343,843
Emp.: 764
Fiscal Year-end: 03/31/21
Electrical Equipment Mfr & Distr
N.A.I.C.S.: 335929
Ashish Mangal *(Mng Dir)*

DYNAMIC COLOURS LIMITED

21 Woodlands Close No 09-12 Primz Bizhub, Singapore, 737854, Singapore
Tel.: (65) 67523988
Web Site:
http://www.dynamiccolours.com
Rev.: $27,443,402
Assets: $44,583,487
Liabilities: $9,776,637
Net Worth: $34,806,850
Earnings: $2,874,527
Emp.: 135
Fiscal Year-end: 12/31/19
Color Pigments Mfr
N.A.I.C.S.: 325130
Seok Eng Goh *(Deputy Mng Dir & Dir-Technical)*

Subsidiaries:

Huiye (Vietnam) Plastic Co., Ltd. (1)
25 Dan Chu Street Vietnam Singapore Industrial Park II, Hoa Phu Ward, Thu Dau Mot, Binh Duong, Vietnam
Tel.: (84) 650 363 5388
Injection Molded Plastic Products Mfr
N.A.I.C.S.: 326121

S.L. Packaging Industries Pte Ltd (1)
SL Building 55A Yishun Industrial Park A, Singapore, 768729, Singapore

Tel.: (65) 67523988
Web Site: http://www.slpack.com
Sales Range: $25-49.9 Million
Emp.: 15
Polyethylene Bags Mfr.
N.A.I.C.S.: 326111

Suzhou Huiye Chemical & Light Industry Co., Ltd. (1)
No 96 South Yingchun Road Wuzhong District Economic Development Zone, Suzhou, 215128, Jiangsu, China
Tel.: (86) 512 6528 5023
Web Site: http://www.dynamiccolours.com
Resin Compounding, Injection Moulding, Polyethylene Packaging Mfr & Distr
N.A.I.C.S.: 325211

Suzhou Huiye Plastic Industry Co., Ltd. (1)
No 96 Yingchun Road, Wuzhong District, Suzhou, 215128, Jiangsu, China
Tel.: (86) 51265285023
Resin Compounding Services
N.A.I.C.S.: 325991

DYNAMIC DESIGN CO., LTD.

12 29beon-gil Cheomdanyeonsin-ro, Buk-gu, Gwangju, Korea (South)
Tel.: (82) 629446161
Web Site:
https://dynamicdesign.co.kr
Year Founded: 1981
145210—(KRS)
Rev.: $44,638,612
Assets: $75,049,069
Liabilities: $37,586,019
Net Worth: $37,463,050
Earnings: ($49,614,847)
Emp.: 340
Fiscal Year-end: 12/31/22
Tire Casting Molds
N.A.I.C.S.: 333511
Hwang Eung Yeon *(Exec Dir)*

DYNAMIC ELECTRONICS CO., LTD.

6F No 50 Minquan Rd, Luzhu Dist, Taoyuan, 33846, Taiwan
Tel.: (886) 33493300
Web Site:
http://www.dynamicpcb.com.tw
Year Founded: 1988
6251—(TAI)
Rev.: $449,039,273
Assets: $469,001,334
Liabilities: $286,482,203
Net Worth: $182,519,132
Earnings: $24,154,342
Emp.: 6,500
Fiscal Year-end: 12/31/20
Printed Circuit Boards & Other Electronic Components Mfr
N.A.I.C.S.: 334412

Subsidiaries:

Dynamic Electronics (Huangshi) Co., Ltd. (1)
No 88 Daqi Avenue Wangren Town, Economic and Technological Development Zone, Huangshi, 435000, Hubei, China
Tel.: (86) 7143501688
Printed Circuit Board Mfr
N.A.I.C.S.: 334412

Dynamic Electronics (Kunshan) Co., Ltd. (1)
No 1688 Jinshajiang North Rd, Kunshan, 215344, Jiangsu, China
Tel.: (86) 51257181688
Printed Circuit Board Mfr
N.A.I.C.S.: 334412

Dynamic PCB Electronics Co., Ltd. (1)
No 356 Shanying Rd Guishan Dist, Taoyuan, 33341, Taiwan
Tel.: (886) 33493300
Printed Circuit Board Mfr
N.A.I.C.S.: 334412

DYNAMIC GROUP HOLDINGS LIMITED

76 Hasler Road, Osborne Park, 6017, WA, Australia
Tel.: (61) 864042798 AU
Web Site:
https://dynamicgroupholdings.com
Year Founded: 2020
DDB—(ASX)
Rev.: $67,064,235
Assets: $69,053,601
Liabilities: $38,136,536
Net Worth: $30,917,065
Earnings: $1,295,229
Fiscal Year-end: 06/30/23
Holding Company
N.A.I.C.S.: 551112
Mark Davis *(Mng Dir)*

Subsidiaries:

Dynamic Drill & Blast Pty. Ltd. (1)
54 Achievement Way, Wangara, 6065, WA, Australia
Tel.: (61) 864042798
Web Site:
https://dynamicdrillandblast.com.au
Mining & Construction Services
N.A.I.C.S.: 532412

PDC Drilling Pty. Ltd. (1)
32 Poletti Road, Cockburn, 6164, WA, Australia
Tel.: (61) 894374633
Web Site: https://welldrill.com.au
Emp.: 50
Water Well Drilling Services
N.A.I.C.S.: 237110

DYNAMIC HOLDINGS LIMITED

17th Floor Eton Tower 8 Hysan Avenue, Causeway Bay, China (Hong Kong)
Tel.: (852) 28815221 BM
Web Site: http://www.dynamic-hk.com
0029—(HKG)
Rev.: $11,207,330
Assets: $346,370,244
Liabilities: $65,683,452
Net Worth: $280,686,792
Earnings: $3,957,622
Emp.: 50
Fiscal Year-end: 06/30/22
Construction Industry
N.A.I.C.S.: 551112
Polly Oi Yee Wong *(Sec)*

Subsidiaries:

Strong Way Investment Limited (1)
1702 Eton Tower 8 Hysan Ave, Causeway Bay, China (Hong Kong)
Tel.: (852) 28815221
Sales Range: $50-74.9 Million
Emp.: 10
Investment Management Service
N.A.I.C.S.: 523940

DYNAMIC INDUSTRIES LIMITED

Plot No 5501/2 Phase III Nr Trikampura Cross Roads GIDC, Vatva, Ahmedabad, 382 445, Gujarat, India
Tel.: (91) 6359905155
Web Site: https://www.dynaind.com
Year Founded: 1989
524818—(BOM)
Rev.: $4,870,839
Assets: $7,373,812
Liabilities: $1,197,023
Net Worth: $6,176,789
Earnings: $53,522
Emp.: 64
Fiscal Year-end: 03/31/21
Acid Dye Mfr
N.A.I.C.S.: 325130
Dipakkumar Navinchandra Choksi *(Vice Chm & Mng Dir)*

DYNAMIC METALS LIMITED

Level 1 33 Richardson Street, West Perth, 6005, WA, Australia
Tel.: (61) 865580637 AU
Web Site:
https://www.dynamicmetals.com.au
Year Founded: 2022
DYM—(ASX)
Rev.: $3,110,373
Assets: $8,610,541
Liabilities: $862,105
Net Worth: $7,748,435
Earnings: $1,930,371
Fiscal Year-end: 06/30/24
Support Activities for Metal Mining
N.A.I.C.S.: 213114
Karen Wellman *(CEO)*

DYNAMIC MICROSTEPPERS LIMITED

506 Mathura Arcade Above Axis Bank Near Garware Subhash Road, Vile Parle East, Mumbai, 400057, Maharashtra, India
Tel.: (91) 2226842631
Web Site:
https://www.dynamicsteppers.com
Year Founded: 1985
Clock Mfr
N.A.I.C.S.: 334519

DYNAMIC PORTFOLIO MANAGEMENT & SERVICES LIMITED

916 Pearl Omaxe Building Tower-2 Netaji Subhash Place Pitampura, Delhi, 110034, India
Tel.: (91) 1147012010 In
Web Site:
http://www.dynamicwealth.com
Year Founded: 1994
530779—(BOM)
Rev.: $125,010
Assets: $2,027,368
Liabilities: $329,668
Net Worth: $1,697,700
Earnings: $21,922
Emp.: 8
Fiscal Year-end: 03/31/21
Financial Services
N.A.I.C.S.: 523999
Mukesh Chauhan *(Exec Dir)*

DYNAMIC SERVICES & SECURITY LIMITED

Dynamic Services 139 Dakshindari Rd Sreebhumi, Patipukur, Kolkata, 700048, West Bengal, India
Tel.: (91) 40087463
Web Site: https://dssl.ind.in
Year Founded: 2001
DYNAMIC—(NSE)
Rev.: $984,207,900
Assets: $1,323,026,748
Liabilities: $701,389,966
Net Worth: $621,636,782
Earnings: $29,480,685
Emp.: 18
Fiscal Year-end: 03/31/22
Manpower Solution Services
N.A.I.C.S.: 561320

DYNAMIC SOURCE MANUFACTURING INC.

Unit 117 2765 48th Avenue NE, Calgary, T3J 5M9, AB, Canada
Tel.: (403) 516-1888
Web Site:
http://www.dynamicsourcemfg.com
Year Founded: 2000
Rev.: $23,660,619
Emp.: 125
Electronic Products Mfr
N.A.I.C.S.: 334419
Duane Macauley *(Pres & CEO)*

DYNAMIC SPECIALTY VE-HICLES LTD.
18550 96th Avenue, Surrey, V4N
3P9, BC, Canada
Tel.: (604) 882-9333
Web Site:
　http://www.dynamicspecialty.com
Year Founded: 1987
Rev.: $10,012,849
Emp.: 20
Automobile Mfrs & Distr
N.A.I.C.S.: 336110
Doug Fergusson (Mgr-Contract)

DYNAMIC SUPPLIES PTY. LTD.
66 - 72 Alexandra Place, Murarrie,
4172, QLD, Australia
Tel.: (61) 733449900
Web Site: http://www.ds.net.au
Year Founded: 1994
Emp.: 140
Computer Hardware Distr
N.A.I.C.S.: 423430
Scott McLennan (Mng Dir)

DYNAMIC SYSTEMS HOLD-INGS, INC.
780 Broadway, Orangeville, L9W
2Y9, ON, Canada
Fuel Efficiency Motor Mfr
N.A.I.C.S.: 335312
Allen Scott (Pres)

DYNAMIC TECHNOLOGIES GROUP INC.
717 Jarvis Avenue, Winnipeg, R2W
3B4, MB, Canada
Tel.: (407) 240-3490　　　　AB
Web Site:
　https://dynamictechgroup.com
DTG—(TSXV)
Rev.: $54,584,369
Assets: $54,429,478
Liabilities: $86,448,198
Net Worth: ($32,018,720)
Earnings: ($9,760,508)
Emp.: 340
Fiscal Year-end: 12/31/20
Holding Company; Fabricated Struc-tural Steel & Engineered Products Mfr
N.A.I.C.S.: 551112
Guy Nelson (Chm, Pres & CEO)

Subsidiaries:

Empire Iron Works Ltd.　　　(1)
21104 107th Avenue, Edmonton, T5S 1X2,
AB, Canada
Tel.: (780) 447-4650
Web Site: http://www.empireiron.com
Sales Range: $25-49.9 Million
Emp.: 100
Fabricated Structural Steel Products Mfr &
Construction Services
N.A.I.C.S.: 332312

Subsidiary (Domestic):

Empire Dynamic Structures Ltd.　(2)
1515 Kingsway Ave, Port Coquitlam, V3C
1S2, BC, Canada
Tel.: (604) 941-9481
Web Site: http://www.empireds.com
Sales Range: $10-24.9 Million
Movable Steel Structure Design & Fabrica-tion Services
N.A.I.C.S.: 332312

George Third & Son Partnership　(2)
6010 Trapp Avenue, Burnaby, V3N 2V4,
BC, Canada
Tel.: (604) 639-1708
Web Site: https://www.gthird.com
Emp.: 35
Structural & Architectural Steel Fabrication
N.A.I.C.S.: 238120

Parr Metal Fabricators Ltd　　(2)
717 Jarvis Ave, Winnipeg, R2W 3B4, MB,
Canada
Tel.: (204) 586-8121

Web Site: http://parrmetal.com
Sales Range: $25-49.9 Million
Emp.: 25
Pressure Vessel & Tank Mfr
N.A.I.C.S.: 332420

Ward Industrial Equipment Ltd　(2)
123 Victoria St, Welland, L3B 4L9, ON,
Canada
Tel.: (905) 732-7591
Web Site: http://www.ward.ca
Emp.: 20
Material Handling & Air Purification Equip-ment Mfr
N.A.I.C.S.: 333922

Petrofield Industries Inc　　(1)
Suite 611 7015 MacLeod Trl SW, Calgary,
T2H 2K6, AB, Canada
Tel.: (403) 204-6394
Web Site: http://www.petrofield.com
Sales Range: $25-49.9 Million
Emp.: 60
Oil Field Equipment Mfr
N.A.I.C.S.: 332420

DYNAMIC TECHNOLOGY SUP-PLIES COMPANY LTD.
Wasel 7097, Jeddah, 23343-3523,
Saudi Arabia
Tel.: (966) 126179573　　　　SA
Analytical Laboratory Instrument Mfr
N.A.I.C.S.: 334516

DYNAMIC TIRE CORP.
211 Hunters Valley Rd, Woodbridge,
L4H 3V9, ON, Canada
Tel.: (905) 595-5558
Web Site:
　http://www.dynamictire.com
Year Founded: 1997
Sales Range: $50-74.9 Million
Emp.: 50
Tire Mfr & Distr
N.A.I.C.S.: 326211
Robert Sherkin (Co-CEO)

DYNAMIX BALWAS GROUP OF COMPANIES
Dynamix House Yashodham General
AK Vaidya Marg, Goregaon E, Mum-bai, 400 063, India
Tel.: (91) 2240778600
Web Site: http://www.dbg.co.in
Sales Range: $50-74.9 Million
Emp.: 250
Holding Company
N.A.I.C.S.: 551112
Vinod K. Goenka (Chm)

Subsidiaries:

DB Realty Limited　　　　(1)
7th Floor Resham Bhavan Veer Nariman
Road Churchgate, Mumbai, 400020, India
Tel.: (91) 2249742706
Web Site: https://www.dbrealty.co.in
Rev.: $17,959,482
Assets: $1,002,570,360
Liabilities: $836,613,660
Net Worth: $165,956,700
Earnings: ($22,774,834)
Emp.: 5
Fiscal Year-end: 03/31/2021
Real Estate Services
N.A.I.C.S.: 531390
Vinod K. Goenka (Co-Founder, Chm & Mng
Dir)

DYNAMO AMUSEMENT, INC.
Awajicho MH Building 7Th floor 2-21,
Kanda-Awajicho Chiyoda-ku, Tokyo,
101-0063, Japan
Tel.: (81) 352565395
Web Site:
　https://dynamoamusement.jp
Sales Range: $25-49.9 Million
Emp.: 16
Computer Graphics & Animation
Planning & Production
N.A.I.C.S.: 512110

DYNAPAC CO., LTD.
7th and 8th floors Kagome Building
14-15 Nishiki 3-chome, Naka-Ku, Na-goya, 460-0003, Aichi, Japan
Tel.: (81) 529712651
Web Site: https://www.dynapac-gr.co.jp
Year Founded: 2005
3947—(TKS)
Rev.: $411,404,340
Assets: $517,754,340
Liabilities: $213,529,530
Net Worth: $304,224,810
Earnings: $11,386,540
Emp.: 2,143
Fiscal Year-end: 12/31/23
Packaging Material Mfr & Whslr
N.A.I.C.S.: 322220

Subsidiaries:

Crown Kamikogyo Co., Ltd.　(1)
1443-3 Nishi, Soka, 340-0035, Saitama,
Japan
Tel.: (81) 489251951
Corrugated Fiber Board Mfr
N.A.I.C.S.: 322211

Dynapac (HANOI) Co., Ltd.　(1)
Sai Dong B Industrial Zone Long Bien Dis-trict, Hanoi, Vietnam
Tel.: (84) 438751792
Corrugated Packaging Material Mfr
N.A.I.C.S.: 322211

Dynapac (HK) Ltd.　　　(1)
Corrugated Packaging Material Mfr
N.A.I.C.S.: 322211

Dynapac (Hai Phong) Co., Ltd.　(1)
No 126 Road No 6 VSIP Hai Phong Ip Dinh
Vu-Cat Hai EZ, Thuy Nguyen District, Hai-phong, Vietnam
Corrugated Packaging Material Mfr
N.A.I.C.S.: 322211

Dynapac (M) Sdn. Bhd.　　(1)
Lot 13 Lorong Bunga Tanjung 3/1
Senawang Industrial Park, 70400, Serem-ban, Negeri Sembilan, Malaysia
Tel.: (60) 66782075
Web Site: http://www.dynapac.co.jp
Emp.: 50
Corrugated Packaging Material Mfr
N.A.I.C.S.: 322211

Dynapac (SZ) Ltd.　　　(1)
Room B15 26/F Regalia Place 4018 Jiabin
Road, Luohu District, Shenzhen, 518001,
China
Tel.: (86) 75582310296
Emp.: 12
Corrugated Packaging Material Mfr
N.A.I.C.S.: 322211

Dynapac (Suzhou) Co., Ltd.　(1)
100 Jin Shan Rd New District, Suzhou,
China
Tel.: (86) 51268255621
Corrugated Packaging Material Mfr
N.A.I.C.S.: 322211

Dynapac Co., Ltd. - Fukushima
Plant　　　　　　　　(1)
1-1 Minami Nakakawahara Senoue-Town,
Fukushima, 960-0101, Fukushima, Japan
Tel.: (81) 245531121
Corrugated Packaging Material Mfr
N.A.I.C.S.: 322211

Dynapac Co., Ltd. - Kanie Plant　(1)
2-1 Imanishi Kanie-Town, Ama, 497-0037,
Aichi, Japan
Tel.: (81) 567953620
Corrugated Packaging Material Mfr
N.A.I.C.S.: 322211

Dynapac Co., Ltd. - Kawagoe
Plant　　　　　　　　(1)
1-3-3 Minamidai, Kawagoe, 350-1165, Sai-tama, Japan
Tel.: (81) 492431211
Corrugated Packaging Material Mfr
N.A.I.C.S.: 322211

Dynapac Co., Ltd. - Matsumoto
Plant　　　　　　　　(1)
1-1-53 Murai-Cho-Kita, Matsumoto, 399-

0035, Nagano, Japan
Tel.: (81) 263583211
Corrugated Packaging Material Mfr
N.A.I.C.S.: 322211

Dynapac Co., Ltd. - Miyoshi
Plant　　　　　　　　(1)
301 Kosaka Azabu-Town, Miyoshi, Aichi,
Japan
Tel.: (81) 561330521
Corrugated Packaging Material Mfr
N.A.I.C.S.: 322211

Dynapac Co., Ltd. - Shizuoka
Plant　　　　　　　　(1)
350 Asaoka, Fukuroi, 437-1122, Shizuoka,
Japan
Tel.: (81) 538232221
Corrugated Packaging Material Mfr
N.A.I.C.S.: 322211

Dynapac Co., Ltd. - Tsukuba
Plant　　　　　　　　(1)
1626 Kamioshima, Ibaraki-Ken, Tsukuba,
300-4351, Japan
Tel.: (81) 298661201
Web Site: http://www.dynapac-gr.co.jp
Emp.: 146
Corrugated Packaging Material Mfr
N.A.I.C.S.: 322211
Hiroatsu Aoki (Mgr)

Dynapac GF (Malaysia) Sdn.Bhd　(1)
No 10 Jalan TP4, Taman Perindustrian
Bukit Rambai Mukim Tanjung Minyak,
75250, Melaka, Malaysia
Tel.: (60) 63510888
Corrugated Fiber Board Mfr
N.A.I.C.S.: 322211

Kanbara Danboru Co., Ltd.　(1)
201 Kume Ikeda, Tokoname, 479-0002,
Aichi, Japan
Tel.: (81) 569440782
Corrugated Packaging Material Mfr
N.A.I.C.S.: 322211

Miyagi Dynapac Co., Ltd.　(1)
588-3 Ikazuchi Minamikata-Town, Tome,
987-0412, Miyagi, Japan
Tel.: (81) 220582301
Corrugated Packaging Material Mfr
N.A.I.C.S.: 322211

Plant (Domestic):

Miyagi Dynapac Co., Ltd. - Furukawa
plant　　　　　　　　(2)
221-1 Yogai Sanbongi Minamiyachi, Osaki,
989-6322, Miyagi, Japan
Tel.: (81) 229523851
Corrugated Packaging Material Mfr
N.A.I.C.S.: 322211

Numazu Dynapac Co., Ltd.　(1)
886-1 Ishiharada Ooka, Numazu, 410-0022,
Shizuoka, Japan
Tel.: (81) 559212757
Corrugated Packaging Material Mfr
N.A.I.C.S.: 322211

Ogura Shiki Co., Ltd.　　(1)
161-1 Marikoshinden, Suruga-ku, Shizuoka,
421-0111, Japan
Tel.: (81) 542571777
Corrugated Fiber Board Mfr
N.A.I.C.S.: 322211

Tajimi Dynapac Co., Ltd.　(1)
1-110 Koizumi-Town Tajimi, Gifu, 507-0073,
Japan
Tel.: (81) 572293225
Corrugated Packaging Material Mfr
N.A.I.C.S.: 322211

Toki Dynapac Co., Ltd.　　(1)
304-15 Oroshi-Town, Toki, 509-5202, Gifu,
Japan
Tel.: (81) 572 57 3111
Corrugated Packaging Material Mfr
N.A.I.C.S.: 322211

Plant (Domestic):

Toki Dynapac Co., Ltd. - Nakat-sugawa Plant　　　　　(2)
2081-15 Nasubigawa, Nakatsugawa, 509-9132, Gifu, Japan
Tel.: (81) 573682246
Corrugated Packaging Material Mfr
N.A.I.C.S.: 322211

Dynapac Co., Ltd.—(Continued)

Utsunomiya Dynapac Co., Ltd. (1)
3473-1 Ashinuma-town, Utsunomiya, 321-0404, Tochigi, Japan
Tel.: (81) 286741051
Corrugated Packaging Material Mfr
N.A.I.C.S.: 322211

DYNAPACK INTERNATIONAL TECHNOLOGY CORPORATION
13F No 188 Wenhe Rd, Guishan Dist, Taoyuan, 333, Taiwan
Tel.: (886) 33963399
Web Site:
  https://www.dynapack.com.tw
Year Founded: 1998
3211—(TPE)
Rev.: $596,317,637
Assets: $542,601,226
Liabilities: $274,830,504
Net Worth: $267,770,722
Earnings: $24,932,495
Emp.: 1,432
Fiscal Year-end: 12/31/22
Battery Pack Mfr & Distr
N.A.I.C.S.: 335910
Tsung-Ming Chung (Chm)

Subsidiaries:

Dynapack (Suchou) Co., Ltd. (1)
No 8 Hua-Gun Rd, Wujiang, Jiangsu, China
Tel.: (86) 51263408688
Battery Mfr & Distr
N.A.I.C.S.: 335910

DYNASTY CERAMIC PUBLIC COMPANY LIMITED
37/7 Suthisarn-Vinijchai Road Samsen-Nok Sub-district, Samsen-Nok Sub-district HuayKwang District, Bangkok, 10310, Thailand
Tel.: (66) 22769275
Web Site:
  https://www.dynastyceramic.com
Year Founded: 1989
DCC—(THA)
Rev.: $225,963,064
Assets: $293,675,026
Liabilities: $98,624,152
Net Worth: $195,050,873
Earnings: $34,527,659
Emp.: 2,921
Fiscal Year-end: 12/31/23
Ceramic Tiles Mfr & Distr
N.A.I.C.S.: 327120
Roongroj Saengsastra (Chm)

Subsidiaries:

Muangthong Ceramic Co., Ltd. (1)
37 7 Sutthisan Vinitchai Rd Samsennok, Huaykwanq, Bangkok, 10310, Thailand
Tel.: (66) 22769275
Web Site: http://www.dynastyceramic.com
Sales Range: $25-49.9 Million
Emp.: 100
Tiles & Ceramics Mfr
N.A.I.C.S.: 327120

Tile Top Industry Co., Ltd. (1)
48 5 Ratchada Rd, Samsennk Huaikhwang, Bangkok, 10310, Thailand
Tel.: (66) 22769276
Web Site: http://www.dynastyceramic.com
Sales Range: $25-49.9 Million
Emp.: 100
Tiles & Ceramics Mfr
N.A.I.C.S.: 327120

DYNASTY FINE WINES GROUP LIMITED
Units E&F 16F China Overseas Building 139 Hennessy Road, Wanchai, China (Hong Kong)
Tel.: (852) 29188000   Ky
Web Site: http://www.dynasty-wines.com
Year Founded: 1980
0828—(HKG)

Sales Range: $150-199.9 Million
Wineries
N.A.I.C.S.: 312130
Francois Heriard-Dubreuil (Vice Chm)

DYNASTY GOLD CORP.
1613 - 610 Granville Street, Vancouver, V6C 3T3, BC, Canada
Tel.: (604) 633-2100
Web Site:
  https://www.dynastygoldcorp.com
Year Founded: 1985
DGDCF—(OTCIQ)
Rev.: $5,735
Assets: $2,140,759
Liabilities: $262,511
Net Worth: $1,878,249
Earnings: ($150,292)
Fiscal Year-end: 12/31/22
Mineral Exploration Services
N.A.I.C.S.: 213114
Larry D. Kornze (VP-Exploration)

DYNASTY RESOURCES LIMITED
83 Brisbane Street, Perth, 6000, WA, Australia
Tel.: (61) 86 316 4414
Web Site:
  http://www.dynastyresources.com
DMA—(ASX)
Sales Range: Less than $1 Million
Iron Ore Mining
N.A.I.C.S.: 212210
Lewis Tay (Chm & Mng Dir)

DYNAVEST PTE. LTD.
8 Boon Lay Way 08-10 Tradehub 21, Singapore, 609964, Singapore
Tel.: (65) 68611881
Web Site:
  http://www.dynavest.com.sg
Year Founded: 1980
Sales Range: $10-24.9 Million
Emp.: 10
Electronic Equipment & Component Chemical & Raw Material Mfr
N.A.I.C.S.: 334419
Lawrence Kar Wah Yu (Pres)

Subsidiaries:

Avest Co., Ltd (1)
44 Lat Krabang Industrial Estate Soi Chalongkrung 31 Chalongkrung Rd, Lat Krabang, 10520, Bangkok, Thailand
Tel.: (66) 2 739 6277 8
Industrial Testing Equipment Distr
N.A.I.C.S.: 423830

Comacraft Sdn Bhd (1)
2033 Jalan Bukit Minyak Kawasan Industrial, Ringan Asas Jaya, Bukit Minyak, 14000, Malaysia
Tel.: (60) 45889933
Web Site: http://www.dynavest.com.sg
Electronic Components
N.A.I.C.S.: 334419

Dynavest (Thailand) Co, Ltd (1)
109/75 Sukaphiban 2 Road Soi Suansiam, Kannayao Buangkum, Bangkok, Thailand
Tel.: (66) 29196945
Electronic Components
N.A.I.C.S.: 334419

Dynavest Technologies (Suzhou) Co, Ltd (1)
445# Su Hong Middle Road, Suzhou Ind Park, Suzhou, China
Tel.: (86) 512625588516
Electronics Equipment & Components
N.A.I.C.S.: 334419

DYNAVISION LTD.
Apex Plaza 5th Floor No 3, Nungambakkam High Road, Chennai, 600 034, Tamil Nadu, India
Tel.: (91) 4428263651
Web Site: https://www.dynavision.in
Year Founded: 1973

517238—(BOM)
Rev.: $1,008,626
Assets: $3,135,501
Liabilities: $2,924,390
Net Worth: $211,111
Earnings: $624,528
Emp.: 7
Fiscal Year-end: 03/31/21
Electronic Components Mfr
N.A.I.C.S.: 334411
R. P. Agrawal (CFO)

DYNEA PAKISTAN LIMITED
Offioo No 406 Parsa Tower Plot No 31/1/A Block-6 Pechs, Shahrah-e-Faisal, Karachi, 75400, Pakistan
Tel.: (92) 2134520132   PK
Web Site: https://www.dynea.com.pk
Year Founded: 1982
DYNO—(LAH)
Rev.: $36,905,414
Assets: $16,949,627
Liabilities: $7,050,362
Net Worth: $9,899,265
Earnings: $1,629,153
Emp.: 221
Fiscal Year-end: 06/30/19
Resin Mfr; Owned by Dynea Oy & House of Habib
N.A.I.C.S.: 325211
Shabbir Abbas (CEO)

Subsidiaries:

Dynea Pakistan Limited - Gadoon Unit (1)
Gadoon Unit34-A 34-B 35 Road-3 Industrial Estate, Gadoon Amazai, Swabi, 44566, Khyber Pakhtunkhwa, Pakistan
Tel.: (92) 938270150
Formaldehyde Mfr
N.A.I.C.S.: 325199
Shabbir Abbas (CEO)

Dynea Pakistan Limited - Hub Unit (1)
A101 - A105 A132 - A136 Hub Industrial Trading Estate, Hub Chowki, Balochistan, Pakistan
Tel.: (92) 853363706
Formaldehyde Sales & Mfr
N.A.I.C.S.: 325199

DYNELYTICS AG
Pilatusstrasse 2, 8032, Zurich, Switzerland
Tel.: (41) 44 266 9030   CH
Web Site: http://www.dynelytics.com
Sales Range: $1-9.9 Million
Predictive Analytics & Data Mining Software Distr & Technical Consulting Services
N.A.I.C.S.: 423430
Gisela Boddenberg (Mng Partner)

DYNEMIC PRODUCTS LTD.
B-301 Satyamev Complex-1 Opp New Gujarat High Court, Sarkhej-Gandhinaga Road Sola, Ahmedabad, 380 060, Gujarat, India
Tel.: (91) 7927663071
Web Site: https://www.dynemic.com
Year Founded: 1990
532707—(BOM)
Rev.: $28,145,768
Assets: $47,930,146
Liabilities: $26,579,307
Net Worth: $21,350,839
Earnings: $3,889,445
Emp.: 199
Fiscal Year-end: 03/31/21
Organic Dye & Food Color Mfr
N.A.I.C.S.: 325130
Bhagwandas Kalidas Patel (Mng Dir)

DYNEX ENERGY SA
231 Val des Bons Malades, Kirchberg, 2121, Luxembourg, Luxembourg

Tel.: (352) 787909090
Web Site: https://www.dynex-energy.com
MLDYX—(EUR)
Sales Range: Less than $1 Million
Financial Investment Services
N.A.I.C.S.: 523940
Christian Kruppa (Chm)

DYNIC CORPORATION
Shin Onarimon Bldg 6-17-19 Shimbashi, Minato-ku, Tokyo, 105-0004, Japan
Tel.: (81) 354023143
Web Site: https://www.dynic.co.jp
Year Founded: 1919
3551—(TKS)
Rev.: $278,287,610
Assets: $396,414,920
Liabilities: $233,319,780
Net Worth: $163,095,140
Earnings: $5,605,280
Emp.: 38
Fiscal Year-end: 03/31/24
Printing Media Supplies Mfr & Whslr
N.A.I.C.S.: 325992
Yoshio Oishi (Pres)

Subsidiaries:

Dalian Dynic Office Products Co., Ltd. (1)
A7-3 Standard Factory Bldg Jin Ma Road, Dalian Economical Development Zone, Dalian, China
Tel.: (86) 41187614494
Ribbon Distr
N.A.I.C.S.: 424120

Dynic (HK) LTD. (1)
Room 1518 Austin Tower 22-26 Austin Avenue Tsimshatsui, Kowloon, China (Hong Kong)
Tel.: (852) 27245178
Bookbinding Material Mfr
N.A.I.C.S.: 323120

Dynic (UK) Ltd. (1)
Unit 7 Trident Park Ocean way, Cardiff, CF24 5EP, United Kingdom
Tel.: (44) 2920483973
Web Site: http://www.dynic.co.uk
Ribbon Mfr & Distr
N.A.I.C.S.: 339940

Dynic Corporation - Fuji Factory (1)
1-2 Nishimachi, Utogawa, Fuji, 417-0854, Shizuoka, Japan
Tel.: (81) 545523885
Nonwoven Fabric Product Mfr
N.A.I.C.S.: 313230

Dynic Corporation - Moka Factory (1)
16 Matsuyama-cho, Moka, 321-4346, Tochigi, Japan
Tel.: (81) 285824121
Nonwoven Fabric Product Mfr
N.A.I.C.S.: 313230

Dynic Corporation - Oji Factory (1)
5-4-44 Ukima, Kita-ku, Tokyo, 115-0051, Japan
Tel.: (81) 339660171
Nonwoven Fabric Product Mfr
N.A.I.C.S.: 313230

Dynic Corporation - Shiga Factory (1)
270 Oaza Taga Taga-cho, Inugami-gun, Shiga, 522-0341, Japan
Tel.: (81) 749481717
Nonwoven Fabric Product Mfr
N.A.I.C.S.: 313230

Dynic Factory Service Co., Ltd. (1)
500 Uchigashima, Fukaya, 366-0831, Saitama, Japan
Tel.: (81) 48 574 1935
Web Site: https://www.dynicfs.co.jp
Wooden Pallets Mfr
N.A.I.C.S.: 321920

Dynic International Trading (Shanghai) Co., Ltd. (1)
RM 516 Union Development Bldg No 728 Xin Hua Road, Shanghai, 200052, China

Tel.: (86) 2152581177
Non-Woven Fabric Product Distr
N.A.I.C.S.: 424310

Dynic Juno Co., Ltd. (1)
6-17-19 Shinbashi Shin-Onarimon Building
7F, Minato-ku, Tokyo, 105-0004, Japan
Tel.: (81) 35 402 1800
Web Site: https://www.dyjuno.co.jp
Emp.: 54
Nonwoven Fabric Mfr
N.A.I.C.S.: 313230

Dynic Singapore Pte. Ltd. (1)
2 Venture Drive 13-06 Vision Exchange,
Singapore, 608526, Singapore
Tel.: (65) 6 262 5355
Web Site: https://www.dynic.com.sg
Packaging & Labeling Services
N.A.I.C.S.: 561910

Dynic USA Corporation (1)
4750 NE Dawson Creek Dr, Hillsboro, OR
97124
Tel.: (503) 693-1070
Web Site: http://www.dynic.com
Ribbon Mfr
N.A.I.C.S.: 339940

Kunshan Staflex Textile Co., Ltd. (1)
Room A-8406 No 808 Hongqiao Road Jia-
hua Business Center, Shanghai, China
Tel.: (86) 2164481991
Textile Product Mfr & Distr
N.A.I.C.S.: 313310

Subsidiary (Domestic):

**Kunshan Staflex Textile Co., Ltd. -
Jiangsu Factory** (2)
No 2 Jinshajiang Nan Road Kaifa Qu, Kun-
shan, 215334, Jiangsu, China
Tel.: (86) 51257632028
Textile Products Mfr
N.A.I.C.S.: 313310

Nic Freight Co., Ltd. (1)
1-3-13 Higashi Tokorozawa, Tokorozawa,
359-0021, Saitama, Japan
Tel.: (81) 429442291
Web Site: https://www.nicf.co.jp
Emp.: 80
Railway Freight Transportation Services
N.A.I.C.S.: 482111

TPCNIC Co., Ltd. (1)
489 Rama 3 Rd Bang Khlo, Bangkholaem,
Bangkok, 10120, Thailand
Tel.: (66) 22940071
Web Site: https://www.tpcsplc.com
Non-Woven Filter Mfr
N.A.I.C.S.: 313230

Subsidiary (Domestic):

**TPCNIC Co., Ltd. - Chonburi
Factory** (2)
600/3 Moo 11 Sukapiban 8 Road Non-
gkham, Si Racha, 20230, Chonburi, Thai-
land
Tel.: (66) 38480004
Non-Woven Filter Mfr
N.A.I.C.S.: 313230

Taihei Sangyo Co., Ltd. (1)
5-16-13 Ukima, Kita-ku, Tokyo, 115-0051,
Japan
Tel.: (81) 339696150
Web Site: https://www.t-sangyo.co.jp
Emp.: 10
Paper Product Distr
N.A.I.C.S.: 424130

Yamato Shiko Co., Ltd. (1)
500 Uchigashima, Fukaya, 366-0831, Sai-
tama, Japan
Tel.: (81) 485723725
Web Site: http://www.yamatoshiko.co.jp
Freshness Agent Mfr
N.A.I.C.S.: 325199

**DYO BOYA FABRIKALARI
SANAYI VE TICARET AS**
Aosb Mahallesi 10003 Sok No 2/8,
Cigli, 35210, Izmir, Turkiye
Tel.: (90) 2323280880
Web Site: https://www.dyo.com.tr
DYOBY—(IST)
Rev.: $131,194,917

Assets: $156,893,698
Liabilities: $103,652,008
Net Worth: $53,241,691
Earnings: $8,804,423
Fiscal Year-end: 12/31/22
Construction Machinery Mfr
N.A.I.C.S.: 333120
Emin Feyhan Yasar *(Chm)*

DYPNF CO.,LTD
39 Magokjungang 8-ro 7-gil,
Gangseo-gu, Seoul, Korea (South)
Tel.: (82) 221068000
Web Site: https://dypnf.allonecare.kr
Year Founded: 1996
104460—(KRS)
Rev.: $86,758,904
Assets: $161,273,884
Liabilities: $79,301,325
Net Worth: $81,972,559
Earnings: ($8,591,417)
Emp.: 172
Fiscal Year-end: 12/31/22
General Purpose Machinery Mfr
N.A.I.C.S.: 333998

Subsidiaries:

**Dong Yang P&F Co., Ltd - Gimpo
Factory** (1)
3-27 Goyang-ri, Wolgot-myeon, Gimpo,
Gyeonggi-do, Korea (South)
Tel.: (82) 31 998 7371
General Purpose Machinery Mfr
N.A.I.C.S.: 333998

DYSON GROUP PLC
Totley Works Baslow Road, Sheffield,
S17 3BL, United Kingdom
Tel.: (44) 1142355300
Web Site: http://www.dyson-
group.com
Year Founded: 1810
Sales Range: $50-74.9 Million
Emp.: 83
Develops & Researches Performance
Materials (Metal Composites, Fibers)
& Thermal Products (Ceramics, Re-
fractories)
N.A.I.C.S.: 332999
Richard P. McQuinn *(Sec)*

Subsidiaries:

**P.T. Dyson Zedmark Indonesia
Limited** (1)
Jl Sulawesi II Kawasan Industri MM 2100 Bl
F-2-1, 17520, Bekasi, Indonesia
Tel.: (62) 218981269
Sales Range: $50-74.9 Million
Ceramic Wall & Floor Tile Mfr
N.A.I.C.S.: 327120

DYSON LTD.
Tetbury Hill, Malmesbury, SN16 0RP,
United Kingdom
Tel.: (44) 1666827200
Web Site: http://www.dyson.co.uk
Sales Range: $1-4.9 Billion
Emp.: 2,700
Vacuum Cleaner & Air Cooling De-
vice Mfr
N.A.I.C.S.: 335210
James Dyson *(Founder)*

Subsidiaries:

Dyson Inc. (1)
600 W Chicago Ave Ste 275, Chicago, IL
60654
Tel.: (866) 693-9766
Web Site: http://www.dyson.com
Vacuum Cleaner & Air Cooling Device Mfr
N.A.I.C.S.: 335210

DYTECNA LIMITED
Unit 2 Kites Croft, Fareham, PO14
0LW, United Kingdom
Tel.: (44) 1684 579000
Web Site: http://www.dytecna.co.uk
Year Founded: 1965

Sales Range: $50-74.9 Million
Engineeering Services
N.A.I.C.S.: 541330
John Fulford *(Pres & Mng Dir)*

Subsidiaries:

Dytecna Engineering Ltd (1)
Unit 2 Kite's Croft, Fareham, PO14 4LW,
Hampshire, United Kingdom
Tel.: (44) 1329 840 683
Engineeering Services
N.A.I.C.S.: 541330

**DZ BANK AG DEUTSCHE
ZENTRAL-
GENOSSENSCHAFTSBANK**
Platz der Republik, 60265, Frankfurt
am Main, Germany
Tel.: (49) 69744701 De
Web Site: http://www.dzbank.de
Year Founded: 1895
Rev.: $7,033,840,660
Assets: $626,426,166,940
Liabilities: $595,298,538,380
Net Worth: $31,127,628,560
Earnings: $2,097,497,780
Emp.: 24,295
Fiscal Year-end: 12/31/19
Banking Cooperative
N.A.I.C.S.: 551111
Wolfgang Kohler *(Mng Dir)*

Subsidiaries:

**ABO Grundstucksverwaltungsgesell-
schaft mbH** (1)
Hauptstr 131-137, 65760, Eschborn, Hes-
sen, Germany
Tel.: (49) 6196 9930
International Banking Services
N.A.I.C.S.: 522299

**AXICA Kongress- und Tagungszen-
trum Pariser Platz 3 GmbH** (1)
Pariser Platz 3, 10117, Berlin, Germany
Tel.: (49) 30 2000860
Web Site: http://www.axica.de
Convention Centre Services
N.A.I.C.S.: 561920
Marc-Alexander Mundstock *(Mng Dir)*

Assimoco Vita S.p.A. (1)
224 Via Cassanese, 20090, Segrate, Italy
Tel.: (39) 0498 888 511
International Banking Services
N.A.I.C.S.: 522299

**Aufbau und Handelsgesellschaft
mbH** (1)
Katharinenstrasse 20, 70182, Stuttgart,
Germany
Tel.: (49) 711227770
Home Rental Services
N.A.I.C.S.: 531110

**BIG-Immobilien Gesellschaft mit be-
schrankter Haftung** (1)
Hardenbergstr 12, 10623, Berlin, Germany
Tel.: (49) 30 319900
International Banking Services
N.A.I.C.S.: 522299

**Bausparkasse Schwabisch Hall Ak-
tiengesellschaft - Bausparkasse der
Volksbanken und
Raiffeisenbanken** (1)
Crailsheimer Str 52, 74523, Schwabisch
Hall, Germany
Tel.: (49) 791464444
Web Site: http://www.schwaebisch-hall.de
Money Transmission Services
N.A.I.C.S.: 522390
Alexander Lichtenberg *(Mng Dir & Member-
Mgmt Bd)*

CALYPSO GmbH (1)
Liebigstr 39, 74211, Leingarten, Germany
Tel.: (49) 713 159 4250
International Banking Services
N.A.I.C.S.: 522299

CHEMIE Pensionsfonds AG (1)
Raiffeisenplatz 1, 65189, Wiesbaden, Ger-
many
Tel.: (49) 800 533 1172

Web Site:
https://www.chemiepensionsfonds.de
Pension Fund Management Services
N.A.I.C.S.: 525110
Klaus-Peter Stiller *(Chm)*

Complina GmbH (1)
Raiffeisenplatz 1, 65189, Wiesbaden, Ger-
many
Tel.: (49) 61153376527
Web Site: http://www.geno-solar.de
Solar Photovoltaic Services
N.A.I.C.S.: 221114

**Condor Allgemeine
Versicherungs-Aktiengesellschaft** (1)
Admiralitatstrasse 67, 20459, Hamburg,
Germany
Tel.: (49) 61116750523
Life & Pension Insurance Services
N.A.I.C.S.: 525110

**Condor Lebensversicherungs-
Aktiengesellschaft** (1)
Admiralitatstrasse 67, 20459, Hamburg,
Germany
Tel.: (49) 4036139990
Life & Pension Insurance Services
N.A.I.C.S.: 525110

DVB Bank America N.V. (1)
Gaitoweg 35, Willemstad, Curacao
Tel.: (599) 94318700
Banking Financial Services
N.A.I.C.S.: 522110

**DVB Investment Management
N.V.** (1)
Schiphol Boulevard 255 Tower F 6th Floor,
Amsterdam, 1118 BH, Netherlands
Tel.: (31) 10 206 7900
Emp.: 60
International Banking Services
N.A.I.C.S.: 522299

DVB Transport (US) LLC (1)
609 5th Ave, New York, NY 10017-1021
Tel.: (212) 588-8864
Financial Management Services
N.A.I.C.S.: 522320

DZ BANK Ireland plc (1)
International House 3 Harbourmaster Pl
IFSC, Dublin, 1, Ireland **(100%)**
Tel.: (353) 16700715
Web Site: http://www.dzbank.ie
Sales Range: $50-74.9 Million
Emp.: 25
International Banking
N.A.I.C.S.: 522299
Mark Jacob *(Mng Dir)*

DZ BANK Polska (1)
Plac Pilsudskiego 3, Warsaw, 78, Poland
Tel.: (48) 225057000
Web Site: http://www.dzbank.pl
Sales Range: $100-124.9 Million
Emp.: 200
International Banking
N.A.I.C.S.: 522299

**DZ BANK Sao Paulo Representacao
Ltda.** (1)
R Sansao Alves Dos Santos 433 An 3
Parte, Sao Paulo, 04571-900, Brazil
Tel.: (55) 1224 859 000
Emp.: 2
International Banking Services
N.A.I.C.S.: 522299
Christian Koenigsfeld *(Gen Mgr)*

DZ Bank New York Branch (1)
100 Park Ave Fl 13, New York, NY
10017-1021 **(100%)**
Tel.: (212) 745-1400
Web Site: http://www.dzbank.de.com
Sales Range: $50-74.9 Million
Providers of International Banking Services
N.A.I.C.S.: 523150
Albert Yip *(Asst Treas)*

DZ CompliancePartner GmbH (1)
Wilhelm-Haas-Platz, 63263, Neu-Isenburg,
Germany
Tel.: (49) 6969783324
Web Site: http://www.dz-cp.de
Management Outsourcing Services
N.A.I.C.S.: 541611

DZ Financial Markets LLC (1)

DZ BANK AG Deutsche
Zentral-Genossenschaftsbank—(Continued)

100 Park Ave Fl 13, New York, NY 10017-
1021
Tel.: (212) 745-1400
Web Site: http://www.dzbank.de
Sales Range: $50-74.9 Million
Emp.: 50
International Banking
N.A.I.C.S.: 523150
Gerhard Summerer (Pres)

DZ HYP AG (1)
Rosenstrasse 2, 20095, Hamburg, Germany
Tel.: (49) 4033340
Web Site: http://www.dzhyp.de
Real Estate Banking Services
N.A.I.C.S.: 522292
Georg Reutter (CEO)

DZ Immobilien+Treuhand GmbH (1)
Sentmaringer Weg 21, 48151, Munster,
Germany
Tel.: (49) 251208400
Web Site: http://www.dz-immobilien-
treuhand.de
Real Estate Development Services
N.A.I.C.S.: 531390

DZ PRIVATBANK S.A. (1)
4 rue Thomas Edison, 1445, Strassen,
Luxembourg (89%)
Tel.: (352) 449031
Web Site: http://www.dz-privatbank.com
Rev.: $72,164,013
Assets: $20,936,677,299
Liabilities: $19,910,741,938
Net Worth: $1,025,935,361
Earnings: $35,858,467
Emp.: 955
Fiscal Year-end: 12/31/2020
International Banking
N.A.I.C.S.: 522110
Ralf Bringmann (Member-Exec Bd)

Subsidiary (Non-US):

DZ PRIVATBANK (Schweiz) AG (2)
Muensterhof 12, 8001, Zurich, Switzerland
Tel.: (41) 442149400
Web Site: http://www.dz-privatbank.com
Sales Range: $350-399.9 Million
Emp.: 200
International Banking
N.A.I.C.S.: 522299
Thomas Hirschbeck (Dir Gen)

DZ PRIVATBANK Singapore Ltd. (1)
50 Raffles Place 43-03 Singapore Land
Tower, Singapore, 48623, Singapore
Tel.: (65) 6513 8000
Investment Banking Services
N.A.I.C.S.: 523150
Richard Manger (Chm)

DZ Versicherungsvermittlung Gesellschaft mbH (1)
Am Platz der Republik, 60325, Frankfurt am
Main, Germany
Tel.: (49) 6974476311
Web Site: http://www.dgvv.de
Property Liability Insurance Services
N.A.I.C.S.: 524126

Dilax France SAS (1)
42 A avenue des Langories, 26000, Valence, France
Tel.: (33) 475257085
Sensor Product Mfr
N.A.I.C.S.: 334519
Bruno Valat (Gen Mgr)

Dilax Intelcom AG (1)
Rheinstr 8, 8280, Kreuzlingen, Switzerland
Tel.: (41) 716637575
Sensor Product Mfr
N.A.I.C.S.: 334519

Dilax Intelcom Iberica S.L.U. (1)
Jose Abascal 44 1, 28003, Madrid, Spain
Tel.: (34) 914416040
Sensor Product Mfr
N.A.I.C.S.: 334519
Jorge Caturla Werner (Gen Mgr)

Dilax Systems Inc. (1)
6 Desaulniers Suite 406, Saint-Lambert,
J4P 1L3, QC, Canada
Tel.: (450) 538-3898

Sensor Product Mfr
N.A.I.C.S.: 334519

Dilax Systems UK Ltd. (1)
Dalton House 60 Windsor Avenue, London,
SW19 2RR, United Kingdom
Tel.: (44) 1908607340
Sensor Product Mfr
N.A.I.C.S.: 334519

Evolit Consulting GmbH (1)
Marxergasse 1B/Top 6, 1030, Vienna, Austria
Tel.: (43) 15811454
Web Site: http://www.evolit.com
Software Development Services
N.A.I.C.S.: 513210
Paul Kleinrath (CEO)

FLORIN GmbH (1)
Daimlerstrasse 4, 47877, Willich, Germany
Tel.: (49) 21 54 91 38 0
Web Site: http://www.florin.de
Industrial Machinery & Equipment Mfr
N.A.I.C.S.: 333248

Fundamenta Erteklanc Ingatlankozvetito es Szolgaltato Kft. (1)
Alkotas utca 55-61, 1123, Budapest, Hungary
Tel.: (36) 616660000
Web Site: http://www.fundamentaingatlan.hu
Real Estate Rental Services
N.A.I.C.S.: 531110

Fundamenta-Lakaskasssza Lakastakarekpenztar Zrt. (1)
Alkotas u 55-61, Budapest, 1123, Hungary
Tel.: (36) 1 411 8181
Web Site: http://www.fundamenta.hu
Financial & Banking Services
N.A.I.C.S.: 522299

GENO Broker GmbH (1)
Niedenau 13-19, 60325, Frankfurt am Main,
Germany
Tel.: (49) 69210875181
Web Site: http://www.genobroker.de
Stock Brokerage Services
N.A.I.C.S.: 523150

**GENO-Haus Stuttgart GmbH & Co.
KG Verwaltungsgesellschaft** (1)
Heilbronner Strasse 41, 70191, Stuttgart,
Germany
Tel.: (49) 7112200950
Web Site: http://www.geno-haus.de
Home Management Services
N.A.I.C.S.: 721110

Gunther Kaltetechnik GmbH (1)
Boschstr 12, Pluderhausen, 73655, Schorndorf, Germany
Tel.: (49) 718183520
Web Site: http://www.kaelteguenther.de
Air Conditioning Repair Services
N.A.I.C.S.: 238220

**HANSEATICA Sechzehnte Grundbesitz Investitionsgesellschaft mbH &
Co. KG** (1)
Taunusstr 1, 65193, Wiesbaden, Germany
Tel.: (49) 611 5330
International Banking Services
N.A.I.C.S.: 522299

**HGI Immobilien GmbH & Co. GB I
KG** (1)
Bockenheimer Landstr 24, Frankfurt am
Main, 60323, Hessen, Germany
Tel.: (49) 6986003116
International Banking Services
N.A.I.C.S.: 522299

Hor Technologie GmbH (1)
Dr-von-Fromm-Str 5, Postfach 1754, 92637,
Weiden, Germany
Tel.: (49) 961 60 03 0
Web Site: http://www.hoer-technologie.de
Vehicle Gear & Aluminium Parts Mfr
N.A.I.C.S.: 336390

HumanProtect Consulting GmbH (1)
Worringer Strasse 25, 50668, Cologne,
Germany
Tel.: (49) 2 21 37 99 93 0
Web Site: http://www.humanprotect.de
Mental Health Care Services
N.A.I.C.S.: 621112

IPConcept (Luxemburg) S.A. (1)

---

4 rue Thomas Edison, 1445, Strassen, Luxembourg
Tel.: (352) 260248 1
Web Site: http://www.ipconcept.com
Fund Management Services
N.A.I.C.S.: 523999
Frank Muller (Chm)

IPConcept (Schweiz) AG (1)
Munsterhof 12, 8001, Zurich, Switzerland
Tel.: (41) 44224 3200
Web Site: http://www.ipconcept.com
Fund Management Services
N.A.I.C.S.: 523999

ITF Suisse AG (1)
Holbeinstrasse 30, PO Box 8034, 8006,
Zurich, 8006, Switzerland
Tel.: (41) 793332827
Web Site: http://www.itf-suisse.com
Transport Asset Management Services
N.A.I.C.S.: 523999

KRAVAG Umweltschutz und Sicherheitstechnik GmbH (1)
Heidenkampsweg 102, 20097, Hamburg,
Germany
Tel.: (49) 40236065877
Web Site: http://www.kussgmbh.de
Risk & Claim Management Services
N.A.I.C.S.: 524298

LITOS GmbH (1)
Roggenweg 8, 22926, Ahrensburg, Germany
Tel.: (49) 4102 67870
Web Site: http://www.litos.com
Locking Screw Mfr
N.A.I.C.S.: 339112

**MSU Management - Service - und
Unternehmensberatung GmbH** (1)
Fichtenstrasse 38, 76829, Landau, Germany
Tel.: (49) 63416200100
Web Site: http://www.msu-gmbh.de
General Insurance Services
N.A.I.C.S.: 524210

NTK Immobilien GmbH & Co. Management KG (1)
Rosenstrasse 2, 20095, Hamburg, Germany
Tel.: (49) 40 30 30 69 35
Web Site: http://www.ntk-immobilien.de
Financial Investment Management Services
N.A.I.C.S.: 523999

**PDZ Personaldienste & Zeitarbeit
GmbH** (1)
Landgraf-Philipps-Anlage 66, 64283, Darmstadt, Germany
Tel.: (49) 61 51 2 79 79 0
Web Site: http://www.pdz-online.de
Transfer Agency & Staffing Solution Services
N.A.I.C.S.: 561320

**Paul Ernst versicherungsvermittlungs
mbH** (1)
Preusserstr 1-9, 24105, Kiel, Germany
Tel.: (49) 431 57025 0
International Banking Services
N.A.I.C.S.: 522299

**Pension Consult-
Beratungsgesellschaft fur Altersvorsorge mbH** (1)
Abraham-Lincoln-Str 24, 65189, Wiesbaden, Germany
Tel.: (49) 611236190700
Web Site: http://www.pension-consult.de
Pension Fund Management Services
N.A.I.C.S.: 525110

Q, Inc. (1)
540 Main St, Winchester, MA 01890
Tel.: (508) 725-8336
Web Site: http://www.qincmarketing.com
Advertising & Marketing Agency Services
N.A.I.C.S.: 541810
Michael Quzor (Pres)

**R+V Allgemeine Versicherung
Aktiengesellschaft** (1)
Raiffeisenplatz 1, 65189, Wiesbaden, Germany
Tel.: (49) 6115330
Real Estate Rental Services
N.A.I.C.S.: 531110

Gunther Vornholt (Mgr-Credit Risk)

R+V Dienstleistungs GmbH (1)
Raiffeisenplatz 1, 65189, Wiesbaden, Germany
Tel.: (49) 6115332002
Catering & Conference Services
N.A.I.C.S.: 722320

R+V Direktversicherung AG (1)
Raiffeisenplatz 1, 65189, Wiesbaden, Germany
Tel.: (49) 6115337240
Web Site: http://www.rv24.de
Motor Vehicle Insurance Services
N.A.I.C.S.: 524126
Matthias Erker (Mgr-Portal)

R+V Luxembourg Lebensversicherung S.A. (1)
4 rue Thomas Edison, 1445, Strassen, Luxembourg
Tel.: (352) 4545654900
Web Site: http://www.ruv.lu
Life & Pension Insurance Services
N.A.I.C.S.: 525110

R+V Service Center GmbH (1)
Abraham-Lincoln-Strasse 11, 65189, Wiesbaden, Germany
Tel.: (49) 611 533 6200
Insurance Advisory Services
N.A.I.C.S.: 524298

RC II S.a.r.l. (1)
6 Rue Gabriel Lippmann, 5365, Munsbach,
Luxembourg
Tel.: (352) 26 78 61
International Banking Services
N.A.I.C.S.: 522299

RUV Agenturberatungs GmbH (1)
Kreuzberger Ring 66, 65205, Wiesbaden,
Germany
Tel.: (49) 6115336826
Web Site: http://www.ruv.de
General Insurance Services
N.A.I.C.S.: 524210

SECURON Hanse Versicherungsmakler GmbH (1)
Gotenstr 17, 20097, Hamburg, Germany
Tel.: (49) 40 46896360
Web Site: http://www.securon-hanse.de
General Insurance Services
N.A.I.C.S.: 524210
Marc Schumacher (Mng Dir)

**SECURON Versicherungsmakler
GmbH** (1)
Sendlinger Str 42a, 80331, Munich, Germany
Tel.: (49) 89 23 11 77 0
Web Site: http://www.securon.de
General Insurance Services
N.A.I.C.S.: 524210

**SHT Schwabisch Hall Training
GmbH** (1)
Crailsheimer Str 52, 74523, Schwabisch
Hall, Germany
Tel.: (49) 791462302
Web Site: http://www.shtraining.de
Educational Support Services
N.A.I.C.S.: 611710

**Schuster Versicherungsmakler
GmbH** (1)
Am Bach 1 b, 33602, Bielefeld, Germany
Tel.: (49) 521 5836 0
Web Site: http://www.schuster-bielefeld.de
Insurance & Risk Management Services
N.A.I.C.S.: 524298

**Schwabisch Hall Facility Management
GmbH** (1)
Crailsheimer Strasse 52, 74523, Schwabisch Hall, Germany
Tel.: (49) 791464710
Web Site: http://www.shfm.de
Facility Management Services
N.A.I.C.S.: 561210

Sprint Sanierung GmbH (1)
Dusseldorfer Strasse 334, 51061, Cologne,
Germany
Tel.: (49) 221 9668 0
Web Site: http://www.sprint.de
Building Renovation Services
N.A.I.C.S.: 236118

Janette Bohne *(CEO & Mng Dir)*

TOPAS GmbH **(1)**
Gasanstaltstrasse 47, 1237, Dresden, Germany
Tel.: (49) 351 2166 430
Web Site: http://www.topas-gmbh.de
Emp.: 89
Test System Mfr
N.A.I.C.S.: 334513
Andreas Rudolph *(Mng Dir)*

TeamBank AG **(1)**
Beuthener Str 25, 90471, Nuremberg,
Germany **(100%)**
Tel.: (49) 91153902000
Web Site: http://www.teambank.de
Commericial Banking
N.A.I.C.S.: 522110

**UIR verwaltungsgesellschaft
mbH** **(1)**
Valentinskamp 70 Emporio, Neustadt,
20355, Hamburg, Germany
Tel.: (49) 40 349190
Web Site: http://www.union-investement.de
International Banking Services
N.A.I.C.S.: 522299
Reinhard Kutscher *(Mng Dir)*

**UMB Unternehmens-
Managementberatungs GmbH** **(1)**
Kreuzberger Ring 66, 65205, Wiesbaden,
Germany
Tel.: (49) 611170763787
Real Estate Rental Services
N.A.I.C.S.: 531110

Union IT-Services GmbH **(1)**
Wiesenhuttenplatz 25, Frankfurt am Main,
60329, Germany
Tel.: (49) 69 2567 0
Information Technology Consulting Services
N.A.I.C.S.: 541512

Union Investment Austria GmbH **(1)**
Schottenring 16, 1010, Vienna, Austria
Tel.: (43) 1205505
Investment Management Service
N.A.I.C.S.: 523940
Andrea Bohm *(Acct Mgr)*

**Union Investment Financial Services
S.A.** **(1)**
308 route d Esch, 1471, Luxembourg, Luxembourg
Tel.: (352) 26401
Web Site: http://www.ufs.lu
Investment Financing Services
N.A.I.C.S.: 523940
Rainer Kobusch *(Chm)*

**Union Investment Institutional
GmbH** **(1)**
Weissfrauenstrasse 7, 60311, Frankfurt am
Main, Germany
Tel.: (49) 6925677652
Investment Management Service
N.A.I.C.S.: 523940
Alexander Schindler *(Chm)*

Union Investment Institutional Property GmbH **(1)**
Valentinskamp 70 Emporio, Postfach 30 11
99, 20355, Hamburg, Germany
Tel.: (49) 40349194152
Investment Management Service
N.A.I.C.S.: 523940
Christoph Holzmann *(COO)*

**Union Investment Real Estate Asia
Pacific Pte. Ltd.** **(1)**
50 Raffles Place 38-04 Singapore Land
Tower, Singapore, 048623, Singapore
Tel.: (65) 65080248
Investment Management Service
N.A.I.C.S.: 523940
Christopher Tay *(Sr Mgr-Investment)*

**Union Investment Real Estate Austria
AG** **(1)**
Schottenring 16, 1010, Vienna, Austria
Tel.: (43) 12055055172
Investment Management Service
N.A.I.C.S.: 523940
Barbara Lukanz *(Mgr-Investment)*

**Union Investment Real Estate France
S.A.S.** **(1)**
112 avenue Kleber, 75016, Paris, France

Tel.: (33) 156900690
Investment Management Service
N.A.I.C.S.: 523940
Tania Bontemps *(Pres)*

**Union Investment Service Bank
AG** **(1)**
Weissfrauenstrasse 7, 60311, Frankfurt am
Main, Germany
Tel.: (49) 69589980
Web Site: http://www.union-investment.de
Investment Fund Services
N.A.I.C.S.: 525910

VAUTID Austria GmbH **(1)**
Kiesstrasse 8, 4614, Marchtrenk, Austria
Tel.: (43) 7243520910
Web Site: http://www.vautid.at
Industrial Machinery & Equipment Mfr
N.A.I.C.S.: 333248
Helfried Mayer *(Mng Dir)*

VMB Vorsorgemanagement fur Banken GmbH **(1)**
Platanenweg 15, 51491, Overath, Germany
Tel.: (49) 2206 910091
Web Site: http://www.vmb-service.info
Pension Fund Management Services
N.A.I.C.S.: 525110

VR Consultingpartner GmbH **(1)**
Weissfrauenstrasse 7, 60311, Frankfurt am
Main, Germany
Tel.: (49) 1733476995
Web Site: http://www.vr-consultingpartner.de
Investment Management Service
N.A.I.C.S.: 523940
Harald Fuchs *(CEO)*

VR Equitypartner GmbH **(1)**
Platz der Republik, 60265, Frankfurt am
Main, Germany **(100%)**
Tel.: (49) 697104760
Web Site: http://www.vrep.de
Private Equity Financial Services
N.A.I.C.S.: 525990
Christian Futterlieb *(Mng Dir)*

Subsidiary (Domestic):

**Norafin Industries (Germany)
GmbH** **(2)**
Gewerbegebiet Nord 3, 09456, Mildenau,
Germany
Tel.: (49) 3733 5507 0
Web Site: http://www.norafin.com
Specialty Non-Woven & Composite Materials Mfr
N.A.I.C.S.: 339999
Andre Lang *(CEO)*

VR FACTOREM GmbH **(1)**
Hauptstrasse 131-137, 65760, Eschborn,
Germany
Tel.: (49) 61968020
Web Site: http://www.vr-factoring.de
Emp.: 80
Financial Services
N.A.I.C.S.: 523940
Christiane Addison *(Partner-HR)*

VR Kreditservice GmbH **(1)**
Uberseering 32, 22297, Hamburg, Germany
Tel.: (49) 4082 222 2000
Web Site: https://www.vrkreditservice.de
Software Development Services
N.A.I.C.S.: 541511

VR Payment GmbH **(1)**
Saonestrasse 3a, 60528, Frankfurt am
Main, Germany
Tel.: (49) 72112090
Web Site: http://www.vr-payment.de
Emp.: 300
Electronic Financial Payment Services
N.A.I.C.S.: 522320
Daniel Jagodzinski *(Head-Acct Mgmt & Sls)*

VR WERT Gesellschaft fur Immobilienbewertung mbH **(1)**
Rosenstrasse 2, 20095, Hamburg, Germany
Tel.: (49) 4033343528
Web Site: http://www.vrwert.de
Emp.: 65
Property Valuation Services
N.A.I.C.S.: 531320

Vautid India Private Limited **(1)**
103 Tiffany 1st Floor Ghodbunder Road,

Regus Suburbs Centre Hiranandani Estate,
Thane, 400607, India
Tel.: (91) 2268181607
Web Site: http://india.vautidgroup.com
Emp.: 450
Welding Consumable Mfr & Retailer
N.A.I.C.S.: 333992
Anand Sundaram *(Mng Dir)*

Vautid Latam S.A. **(1)**
Via a la Costa km 16 5, Guayaquil, Ecuador
Tel.: (593) 42046286
Welding Consumable Mfr & Retailer
N.A.I.C.S.: 333992

Vautid Middle East F.z.e **(1)**
Office E1-1109, Ajman, United Arab Emirates
Tel.: (971) 2268181607
Welding Consumable Mfr & Retailer
N.A.I.C.S.: 333992

Vautid North America, Inc. **(1)**
510 Fifth St, McDonald, PA 15057
Tel.: (412) 429-3288
Welding Consumable Mfr & Retailer
N.A.I.C.S.: 333992

Vautid-Belgium PGmbH **(1)**
Rovert 1 Industriezone, Eynatten, 4731,
Raeren, Belgium
Tel.: (32) 87 85 36 46
Web Site: http://www.vautid.be
Industrial Machinery & Equipment Mfr
N.A.I.C.S.: 333248

VisualVest GmbH **(1)**
Mainzer Landstrasse 50, 60325, Frankfurt
am Main, Germany
Tel.: (49) 69962355001
Web Site: http://www.visualvest.de
Financial Consulting Services
N.A.I.C.S.: 541611
Nina Albrecht *(Head-Mktg)*

**WBS Wohnwirtschaftliche
Baubetreuungs- und Servicegesellschaft mbH** **(1)**
Dostojewskistr 14, 65187, Wiesbaden, Germany
Tel.: (49) 61 1532400
International Banking Services
N.A.I.C.S.: 522299

ZPF Foundry4 GmbH **(1)**
Hajo-Ruter-Strasse 19, 65239, Hochheim,
Germany
Tel.: (49) 6146 90972 00
Web Site: http://www.zpf-foundry4.de
Emp.: 4
Non Ferrous Metal Mfr
N.A.I.C.S.: 333994
Walter Engel *(Office Mgr)*

attrax S.A. **(1)**
308 route d Esch, 1471, Luxembourg, Luxembourg
Tel.: (352) 26026 7010
Web Site: http://www.attrax.lu
Investment Brokerage Services
N.A.I.C.S.: 523150
Angela Meilen *(Acct Mgr)*

**carexpert Kfz-Sachverstandigen
GmbH** **(1)**
Am Klingenweg 4, 65396, Walluf, Germany
Tel.: (49) 61239777777
Web Site: http://www.carexpert.de
Car Insurance & Brokerage Services
N.A.I.C.S.: 524210

**compertis Beratungsgesellschaft fur
betriebliches Vorsorgemanagement
mbH** **(1)**
Kreuzberger Ring 17, 65205, Wiesbaden,
Germany
Tel.: (49) 6 11 23 61 0
Web Site: http://www.compertis.de
Pension Fund Management Services
N.A.I.C.S.: 525110

fragWILHELM GmbH **(1)**
Abraham-Lincoln-Strasse 34, 65189, Wiesbaden, Germany
Tel.: (49) 61117077677
Web Site: http://www.fragwilhelm.de
Life & Pension Insurance Services
N.A.I.C.S.: 525110

n3k Informatik GmbH **(1)**

Ferdinand-Braun-Str 2/1, 74074, Heilbronn,
Germany
Tel.: (49) 7131594950
Web Site: http://www.n3k.de
Network Management Services
N.A.I.C.S.: 611420
Daniel Brendle *(Project Mgr-IT)*

DZERZHYNSKY PJSC
Kirov Str 18B, Dniprodzerzhinsk,
51902, Ukraine
Tel.: (380) 5692 3 22 37
Web Site: http://www.dmkd.dp.ua
Iron & Steel Product Mfr
N.A.I.C.S.: 331110
Vyacheslav Mospan *(Chm & Gen
Mgr-Acting)*

DZETA CONSEIL SAS
21 rue des Pyramides, 75001, Paris,
France
Tel.: (33) 1 4316 7120 **FR**
Web Site:
http://www.dzetaconseil.com
Sales Range: $25-49.9 Million
Private Equity Services
N.A.I.C.S.: 523999
Claude Darmon *(Founder & Pres)*

**DZI AN MECHANOELECTRIC
JSC**
No C2-17 D Street Him Lam Phu
Dong residential area, An Binh ward,
Di An, Binh Duong, Vietnam
Tel.: (84) 866220122
Web Site: https://www.dzima.com
Year Founded: 2001
DZM—(HNX)
Sales Range: $1-9.9 Million
Generator Mfr & Whslr
N.A.I.C.S.: 335312
Dang Dinh Hung *(Chm, CEO & Gen
Mgr)*

E & S HOME OF COLOR, INC
ELC Schiffstraat 246, 7547 RD, Enschede, Netherlands
Tel.: (31) 534601010
Sales Range: $10-24.9 Million
Emp.: 70
Wallpaper & Fabrics
N.A.I.C.S.: 444120

E AUTOMOTIVE INC.
10 Lower Spadina Ave, Toronto, M5V
2Z2, ON, Canada
Tel.: (802) 734-4475
Web Site: https://e.inc
Year Founded: 2017
EINC—(TSX)
Automotive Technology Company
N.A.I.C.S.: 441110
Jason McClenahan *(Pres & CEO)*

Subsidiaries:

EBlock, Inc. **(1)**
212 Battery St, Ste 3, Burlington, VT 05401
Tel.: (833) 817-7247
Web Site: https://eblock.com
Online Vehicle Auction Services
N.A.I.C.S.: 441110

Subsidiary (Domestic):

**Louisiana's First Choice Auto Auction
LLC** **(2)**
18310 Woodscale Rd, Hammond, LA 70401
Tel.: (985) 345-3302
Web Site: http://www.lafcaa.com
Automobile & Other Motor Vehicle Merchant
Whslr
N.A.I.C.S.: 423110
John Poteet *(Owner)*

Houston Auto Auction, Inc. **(1)**
2000 Cavalcade St, Houston, TX 77009
Tel.: (713) 644-5566
Web Site:
http://www.houstonautoauction.com

E Automotive Inc.—(Continued)
Sales Range: $1-9.9 Million
Emp.: 60
Business Services Ret Used Automobiles
N.A.I.C.S.: 425120
Betty Bowers (VP)

E B TRANS SA
22 rue G Lippmann, 5365, Munsbach, Luxembourg
Tel.: (352) 270358   LU
Web Site: https://ebtrans.eu
Year Founded: 1996
Transportation & Logistics Services
N.A.I.C.S.: 484110

Subsidiaries:

Tratel S.a.s   (1)
Les Technodes, 78931, Guerville, Cedex, France
Tel.: (33) 134777800
Web Site: http://www.tratel.fr
Cement Transportation Services
N.A.I.C.S.: 484110

Subsidiary (Domestic):

Tratel Airvault   (2)
28 Rue De L.Aumonerie, 79600, Airvault, France
Tel.: (33) 549647125
Logistic Services
N.A.I.C.S.: 541614

Tratel Moult   (2)
ZI De La Gare, 14370, Moult, France
Tel.: (33) 2 31 38 38 38
Logistics Consulting Servies
N.A.I.C.S.: 541614

Tratel Pessac   (2)
162 Avenue de Haut Leveque, 33600, Pessac, France
Tel.: (33) 5 57 26 27 81
Logistics Consulting Servies
N.A.I.C.S.: 541614

E FACTOR EXPERIENCES LIMITED
SkyWaltz Haveli Suncity Project Road, Kukas, Jaipur, 302028, Rajasthan, India
Tel.: (91) 9999249984
Web Site:
  https://www.efactorexp.com
Year Founded: 2003
EFACTOR—(NSE)
Event Management Services
N.A.I.C.S.: 561920
Jai Thakore (COO)

E FOR L AIM PUBLIC COMPANY LIMITED
432 Ratchawithi Road, Bang Phlat District, Bangkok, 10700, Thailand
Tel.: (66) 28830871
Web Site: https://investor-th.eforl-aim.com
EFORL—(THA)
Rev.: $38,236,781
Assets: $39,944,161
Liabilities: $24,629,499
Net Worth: $15,314,662
Earnings: $392,019
Emp.: 412
Fiscal Year-end: 12/31/23
Advertising Display Designer
N.A.I.C.S.: 541850
Preecha Nuntnarumit (Chm, CEO & Mng Dir)

Subsidiaries:

Siam Snail Company Limited   (1)
942/119 Charn Issara Tower 1 4th Floor Rama 4 Road, Suriyawong Subdistrict Bangrak District, Bangkok, Thailand
Tel.: (66) 99 542 3965
Web Site: https://www.siamsnail.com
Skin Care Product Mfr
N.A.I.C.S.: 325620

E INK HOLDINGS, INC,
3 Li-Hsin Rd 1 Hsinchu Science Park, Hsin-chu, 300, Taiwan
Tel.: (886) 35643200
Web Site: https://www.eink.com
Year Founded: 1992
EINKH—(LUX)
Rev.: $886,875,110
Assets: $2,434,881,134
Liabilities: $814,538,084
Net Worth: $1,620,343,050
Earnings: $257,242,739
Emp.: 2,756
Fiscal Year-end: 12/31/23
LCD Screen Mfr; Electronic Paper Display Technology Developer & Mfr
N.A.I.C.S.: 334419
Johnson Lee (Interim Chm)

Subsidiaries:

E Ink Corporation   (1)
733 Concord Ave, Cambridge, MA 02138
Tel.: (617) 499-6000
Web Site: http://www.eink.com
Sales Range: $75-99.9 Million
Emp.: 127
Electronic Paper Display Technology Developer
N.A.I.C.S.: 334419
Giuseppe Forcucci (VP-Ops)

E INVESTMENT & DEVELOPMENT CO., LTD.
425 Gyeongchung-daero Gonjiam-eup, Gwangju, Gyeonggi-do, Korea (South)
Tel.: (82) 03180278855
Web Site: https://www.eid21.co.kr
Year Founded: 2002
093230—(KRS)
Rev.: $206,456,834
Assets: $434,285,291
Liabilities: $294,855,290
Net Worth: $139,430,002
Earnings: $(76,296,648)
Emp.: 27
Fiscal Year-end: 12/31/22
Telecommunication Equipment Mfr & Whslr
N.A.I.C.S.: 334419
Kang Tae Jin (Dir)

E KOCREF CR-REIT CO., LTD.
Golden Tower 511, Samseong-ro Gangnam-gu, Seoul, Korea (South)
Tel.: (82) 27870241
088260—(KRS)
Rev.: $16,819,529
Assets: $532,431,371
Liabilities: $349,239,716
Net Worth: $183,191,655
Earnings: $6,623,750
Fiscal Year-end: 06/30/23
Real Estate Manangement Services
N.A.I.C.S.: 531210
Soo-Kyung Jin (CEO)

E LIGHTING GROUP HOLDINGS LIMITED
10th Floor Tiffan Tower 199 Wanchai Road, Wanchai, China (Hong Kong)
Tel.: (852) 3 469 9700
Web Site: http://www.elighting.asia
8222—(HKG)
Rev.: $10,820,261
Assets: $7,010,063
Liabilities: $3,521,799
Net Worth: $3,488,264
Earnings: $308,907
Emp.: 50
Fiscal Year-end: 03/31/22
Home Lighting Products
N.A.I.C.S.: 423620
Chi Yan Lam (Co-Sec)

Subsidiaries:

Element Lighting Design Limited   (1)

G/F 48 Morrison Hill Road, Wanchai, China (Hong Kong)
Tel.: (852) 25737772
Household Appliance Distr
N.A.I.C.S.: 423620

Trendmall Gallery Limited   (1)
L5 - 9 MegaBox Enterprise Square Five 38 Wang Chiu Road, Kowloon Bay, China (Hong Kong)
Tel.: (852) 31019880
Web Site: http://www.trendmallgallery.com
Home Furnishing Product Distr
N.A.I.C.S.: 423220

E MEDIA HOLDINGS LIMITED
5 Summit Road Dunkeld West, Hyde Park, Johannesburg, 2196, South Africa
Tel.: (27) 115379300   ZA
Web Site:
  https://www.emediaholdings.co.za
EMH—(JSE)
Rev.: $165,034,010
Assets: $297,473,040
Liabilities: $81,487,394
Net Worth: $215,985,646
Earnings: $20,122,942
Fiscal Year-end: 03/31/23
Investment Holding Company
N.A.I.C.S.: 551112
Antonio Sergio Lee (Dir-Financial)

Subsidiaries:

Bibette (Pty) Ltd.   (1)
Induland Crescent, Nerissa Estate, Cape Town, South Africa   (100%)
Tel.: (27) 216918930
Womens & Girls Cut & Sew Blouse & Shirt Mfr
N.A.I.C.S.: 315250

Deneb Investments Limited   (1)
5th Floor Deneb House, Cnr Main and Browning Roads Observatory, Cape Town, 7925, South Africa
Tel.: (27) 214861400
Web Site: https://www.deneb.co.za
Rev.: $173,733,721
Assets: $190,924,175
Liabilities: $96,861,500
Net Worth: $94,062,675
Earnings: $7,436,126
Emp.: 2,394
Fiscal Year-end: 03/31/2023
Financial Investment Services
N.A.I.C.S.: 523999
Stuart Queen (CEO)

Subsidiary (Domestic):

Formex Industries (Proprietary) Limited   (2)
St Georges Road Aloes Industrial Park Markman, Port Elizabeth, 6211, Eastern Cape, South Africa
Tel.: (27) 414051500
Web Site: http://www.formex.co.za
Automotive Metal Formed Component Mfr
N.A.I.C.S.: 336390

Subsidiary (Domestic):

Formex Pressings (Proprietary) Limited   (3)
St Georges Road Aloes Industrial Park, Markman, Port Elizabeth, 6211, Eastern Cape, South Africa
Tel.: (27) 414051534
Web Site: http://www.formex.co.za
Pressed Components Mfr & Distr
N.A.I.C.S.: 811111

HCI Invest 3 Holdco Proprietary Limited   (1)
Suite 801 76 Regent Road, Sea Point, Cape Town, 8005, South Africa
Tel.: (27) 214817560
Web Site: https://www.hci.co.za
Investment Management Service
N.A.I.C.S.: 523150

Longkloof Ltd.   (1)
48-50 Esplande, Saint Helier, Y9 JE14HH, Jersey
Tel.: (44) 215 665 2006

Sales Range: $25-49.9 Million
Emp.: 10
Investment Holding Company
N.A.I.C.S.: 551112

Prima Toy & Leisure Group (Pty) Ltd.   (1)
36 Gunners Circle, Epping Industrial 1, Cape Town, 7764, South Africa   (100%)
Tel.: (27) 218182000
Web Site: http://www.primatoy.co.za
Sales Range: $25-49.9 Million
Emp.: 100
Games, Toys & Children's Vehicles Mfr
N.A.I.C.S.: 339930
Ian Morris (CEO)

eMedia Investments Proprietary Limited   (1)
4 Albury Road, Dunkeld West, Randburg, 2196, South Africa
Tel.: (27) 115379300
Web Site: https://emediaholdings.co.za
Content Creation Services
N.A.I.C.S.: 513199
John Copelyn (Chm)

E SPLIT CORP.
812 Memorial Drive NW, Calgary, T2N 3C8, AB, Canada
Tel.: (403) 269-2100
ENS—(TSX)
Rev.: $15,509,682
Assets: $64,164,405
Liabilities: $25,178,001
Net Worth: $38,986,404
Earnings: $13,373,022
Fiscal Year-end: 12/31/19
Portfolio Investment Services
N.A.I.C.S.: 523940
Dean C. Orrico (Mgr-Fund)

E& CORPORATION CO., LTD.
325 Teheran-ro Urban Bench bldg 12th floor, Gangnam-gu, Seoul, 06151, Korea (South)
Tel.: (82) 220177933
Web Site: http://www.braincontents.kr
Year Founded: 1998
066980—(KRS)
Rev.: $247,389,873
Assets: $231,157,851
Liabilities: $140,528,890
Net Worth: $90,628,961
Earnings: $(3,226,337)
Emp.: 31
Fiscal Year-end: 12/31/22
Electronic Components Mfr
N.A.I.C.S.: 334419
Jong Wuk Moon (CEO)

E&A LIMITED
Level 27 91 King William Street, Adelaide, 5000, SA, Australia
Tel.: (61) 88 212 2929
Web Site:
  http://www.ealimited.com.au
EAL—(ASX)
Sales Range: $100-124.9 Million
Emp.: 700
Holding Company
N.A.I.C.S.: 551112
Stephen Young (Mng Dir)

Subsidiaries:

Blucher (Australia) Pty. Ltd.   (1)
Corunna Avenue Melrose Park, Mitcham, 5039, SA, Australia
Tel.: (61) 883743426
Web Site: http://www.blucher.com.au
Sales Range: $50-74.9 Million
Emp.: 13
Stainless Steel Plumbing Equipment Mfr
N.A.I.C.S.: 532490
Adam Howkins (Mgr-Mktg)

E&A Contractors Pty. Ltd.   (1)
61-67 Plymouth Road, Wingfield, Adelaide, 5013, SA, Australia
Tel.: (61) 882448605
Web Site: http://www.eacontractors.com.au

Sales Range: $75-99.9 Million
Emp.: 460
Mining Engineering Services
N.A.I.C.S.: 541330

Equity & Advisory Ltd. (1)
Level 27 91 King William St, Adelaide,
5000, SA, Australia
Tel.: (61) 882122929
Web Site: http://www.ealtd.com.au
Sales Range: $50-74.9 Million
Emp.: 12
Corporate Advisory Services
N.A.I.C.S.: 523940
Mark Vartuli (Mng Dir)

Fabtech S.A. Pty. Ltd. (1)
53 S Terrace Wingfield, Adelaide, 5013, SA,
Australia
Tel.: (61) 883473111
Web Site: http://www.fabtech.com.au
Sales Range: $25-49.9 Million
Emp.: 70
Waste Water Management Services
N.A.I.C.S.: 562998
Graham Fairhead (Mng Dir)

Heavymech Pty. Ltd. (1)
717 Grand Junction Road Northfield, 5085,
Adelaide, SA, Australia
Tel.: (61) 882621420
Web Site: http://www.heavymech.com.au
Sales Range: $25-49.9 Million
Emp.: 25
Mining Equipment Services
N.A.I.C.S.: 811310
Vince Belperio (Gen Mgr)

**ICE Engineering & Construction Pty.
Ltd.** (1)
14 Beerwoth Av, Whyalla Playford, Whyalla,
4601, SA, Australia
Tel.: (61) 886442333
Sales Range: $25-49.9 Million
Emp.: 75
Construction Engineering Services
N.A.I.C.S.: 237990

**North West Mining & Civil Pty
Ltd** (1)
PO Box 93, Tom Price, 6751, WA, Australia
Tel.: (61) 891893606
Web Site: https://nwmcmining.com.au
Construction & Building Services
N.A.I.C.S.: 236220
Brian Lee (CEO)

Ottoway Engineering Pty. Ltd. (1)
61-67 Plymouth Rd, Wingfield, Adelaide,
5013, SA, Australia
Tel.: (61) 883410045
Web Site:
http://www.ottowayengineering.com.au
Sales Range: $100-124.9 Million
Emp.: 300
Steel Fabrication Services
N.A.I.C.S.: 331512
Brian Tidswell (CEO)

**Quarry & Mining Manufacture (QLD)
Pty. Ltd.** (1)
22 Duncan Ct, Ottoway, 5013, SA, Australia
Tel.: (61) 732056699
Web Site: http://www.quarrymining.com.au
Sales Range: $25-49.9 Million
Emp.: 20
Quarry & Mining Equipments Mfr
N.A.I.C.S.: 333131
Gary Lindholm (Gen Mgr)

**Quarry & Mining Manufacture Pty.
Ltd.** (1)
22 Duncan Court, Ottoway, Adelaide, 5013,
SA, Australia
Tel.: (61) 882684085
Web Site: http://www.quarrymining.com.au
Sales Range: $25-49.9 Million
Emp.: 25
Quarry & Mining Equipments Mfr
N.A.I.C.S.: 333131
Gary Lindholm (Mgr-Bus Dev)

E&H CO., LTD.
701 27 Seongsui-Ro 7-Gil,
Seongdong-Gu, Seoul, 04780, Korea
(South)
Tel.: (82) 23233385
Web Site: https://www.eandh.co.kr

Year Founded: 1973
341310—(KRS)
Filter Product Mfr & Distr
N.A.I.C.S.: 322299
Park Pal Jean (CEO)

**E&M BRUNNENBAU UND
BOHRTECHNIK GMBH**
Hofer Strasse 19, Hof, 95030, Ger-
many
Tel.: (49) 92 81 14450
Web Site: http://www.em-drilling.com
Year Founded: 1919
Sales Range: $1-9.9 Million
Emp.: 25
Drilling & Water Well Products & Ser-
vices
N.A.I.C.S.: 237110
Alexander Mohr (Mgr-Design)

**E&P FINANCIAL GROUP LIM-
ITED**
Level 32/1 O'Connell Street, Sydney,
2000, NSW, Australia
Tel.: (61) 1300069436   AU
Web Site: https://www.eap.com.au
EP1—(ASX)
Rev.: $100,480,769
Assets: $139,220,753
Liabilities: $64,911,191
Net Worth: $74,309,562
Earnings: ($18,482,238)
Emp.: 341
Fiscal Year-end: 06/30/24
Investment Advisory Services
N.A.I.C.S.: 523940
David Evans (Chm)

Subsidiaries:

Evans & Partners Pty. Limited (1)
Mayfair Building 171 Collins Street, Mel-
bourne, 3000, VIC, Australia
Tel.: (61) 1300372553
Web Site:
http://www.evansandpartners.com.au
Financial Investment Services
N.A.I.C.S.: 523999
Scott Favaloro (Mng Dir)

**Fort Street Real Estate Capital Pty.
Limited** (1)
Level 32 1 O'Connell Street, Sydney, 2000,
NSW, Australia
Tel.: (61) 1300454801
Web Site: http://www.fsrec.com.au
Real Estate Investment Services
N.A.I.C.S.: 531390
Warwick Keneally (Head-Fin)

**E&P GLOBAL HOLDINGS LIM-
ITED**
Units A & B 15/F Chinaweal Centre
414 - 424 Jaffe Road, Causeway
Bay, China (Hong Kong)
Tel.: (852) 25118999   Ky
Web Site:
http://enp.aconnect.com.hk
1142—(HKG)
Rev.: $160,336,457
Assets: $237,830,607
Liabilities: $494,879,106
Net Worth: ($257,048,498)
Earnings: $69,225,759
Emp.: 17
Fiscal Year-end: 03/31/21
Coal Mining Services
N.A.I.C.S.: 213113
Jonghak Im (Exec Dir)

E&R ENGINEERING CORP.
No 61 hengshan Rd, Yanchao Dis-
trict, Kaohsiung, Taiwan
Tel.: (886) 76156600
Web Site: https://en.enr.com.tw
Year Founded: 1994
8027—(TPE)
Rev.: $100,772,223
Assets: $148,159,647

Liabilities: $65,746,522
Net Worth: $82,413,126
Earnings: $12,198,199
Fiscal Year-end: 12/31/22
Electronic Packing Materials Mfr
N.A.I.C.S.: 339991
Ming-Ching Wang (Chm)

E'GRAND CO., LTD.
4th floor WORK VILLA MITOSHIRO
1-1 Kanda Mitoshiro-cho, Chiyoda-ku,
Tokyo, 101-0053, Japan
Tel.: (81) 332195050
Web Site: https://www.e-grand.co.jp
Year Founded: 1989
3294—(TKS)
Sales Range: $75-99.9 Million
Emp.: 60
Housing Restoration & Sales
N.A.I.C.S.: 236118
Hisashi Eguchi (Pres)

E-BOOK SYSTEMS PTE. LTD.
Blk 13 Lorong 8 Toa Payoh 06-02
Braddell Tech Park, Singapore,
319261, Singapore
Tel.: (65) 6258 6100
Web Site: http://www.flipviewer.com
Sales Range: $1-9.9 Million
Digital Publishing
N.A.I.C.S.: 513199
Khoon Wan Hong (CEO)

Subsidiaries:

E-Book Systems Europe (1)
Oppelner Str 30, 10997, Berlin, Germany
Tel.: (49) 30 44 033 223
Digital Publishing
N.A.I.C.S.: 513199

E-Book Systems Inc. (1)
5201 Great America Pkwy Ste 320, Santa
Clara, CA 95054
Tel.: (919) 656-8898
Digital Publishing
N.A.I.C.S.: 513199

E-Book Systems K. K. (1)
3004 2-Chome 16-1 Higashi-Gotanda, Shi-
nagawa, Tokyo, 141-0022, Japan
Tel.: (81) 3 5420 0379
Web Site: http://www.ebooksystems.co.jp
Books Publishing Services
N.A.I.C.S.: 513130

E-COMETRUE INC.
2-floor Park East Sapporo Bld 3 East
1 chome South 1jo, Chuo-ku, Sap-
poro, 060-0051, Hokkaido, Japan
Tel.: (81) 11 271 4761
Web Site: http://www.e-
cometrue.com
Year Founded: 2000
Rev.: $4,034,800
Assets: $2,833,530
Liabilities: $2,320,010
Net Worth: $513,520
Earnings: $27,510
Emp.: 26
Fiscal Year-end: 12/31/19
Software Service Provider
N.A.I.C.S.: 518210
Masami Ueda (Pres)

**E-COMMERCE CHINA DAN-
GDANG INC.**
21/F Jing An Center No 8 North Third
Ring Road East Chaoyang District,
Beijing, 100028, China
Tel.: (86) 400 10 66666 5   Ky
Web Site: http://www.dangdang.com
Year Founded: 1999
Business-to-Consumer Electronic
Shopping Services
N.A.I.C.S.: 459210

**E-COMMODITIES HOLDINGS
LIMITED**

Room 706 Tower B Tianrun Fortune
Center No 58 Dongzongbu Hutong,
Dongcheng District, Beijing, 100005,
China
Tel.: (86) 1085171200   VG
Web Site: http://www.e-comm.com
1733—(HKG)
Rev.: $4,387,817,385
Assets: $1,695,009,480
Liabilities: $777,153,555
Net Worth: $917,855,925
Earnings: $217,373,730
Emp.: 1,844
Fiscal Year-end: 12/31/22
Coal Production & Sales
N.A.I.C.S.: 324199
Hongchan Zhu (Sr VP)

E-CREDIBLE CO., LTD.
8F Samsung IT Valley 27 Digital-ro
33-gil, Guro-gu, Seoul, Korea (South)
Tel.: (82) 221019100
Web Site:
https://www.globalecredible.com
092130—(KRS)
Rev.: $36,148,760
Assets: $43,386,147
Liabilities: $7,913,648
Net Worth: $35,472,499
Earnings: $12,010,856
Emp.: 190
Fiscal Year-end: 12/31/22
Information Technology Service Pro-
vider
N.A.I.C.S.: 541512

E-ENERGY VENTURES INC.
3467 Commercial Street, Vancouver,
V5N 4E8, BC, Canada
Tel.: (604) 668-5931   BC
Year Founded: 1987
EEV—(TSXV)
Mineral Exploration Services
N.A.I.C.S.: 213114
Simon Tam (CEO)

E-FUTURE CO., LTD.
8F 113 Jungdae-ro, Songpa-gu,
Seoul, 05718, Korea (South)
Tel.: (82) 234000509
Web Site: https://www.efuture-elt.com
Year Founded: 2000
134060—(KRS)
Rev.: $8,517,160
Assets: $18,721,203
Liabilities: $2,110,337
Net Worth: $16,610,866
Earnings: $2,192,909
Emp.: 50
Fiscal Year-end: 12/31/22
Online Education Services
N.A.I.C.S.: 611710
Yoo Kyung Tae (Dir)

E-GLOBE S.P.A.
Lipuda zona industriale Via dell Arti-
gianato 80/82, Ciro Marina, 88811,
Calabria, KR, Italy
Tel.: (39) 096236106
Web Site: https://www.e-globe.it
Year Founded: 2008
EGB—(EUR)
Construction Engineering Services
N.A.I.C.S.: 541330

E-GUARDIAN, INC.
Toranomon Kotohira Tower 8F 1-2-8
Toranomon, Minato-ku, Tokyo, 105-
0001, Japan
Tel.: (81) 362058857
Web Site: https://www.e-
guardian.co.jp
Year Founded: 1998
6050—(TKS)
Rev.: $84,434,810
Assets: $64,604,080
Liabilities: $12,237,340

E-Guardian, Inc.—(Continued)

Net Worth: $52,366,740
Earnings: $8,713,610
Emp.: 2,378
Fiscal Year-end: 09/30/23
Online Monitoring Services
N.A.I.C.S.: 519290
Yasuhisa Takatani *(Pres)*

E-HOME HOUSEHOLD SER-VICE HOLDINGS LIMITED

18/F East Tower Building B Dongbai Center Yanqqiao Road, Gulou District, Fuzhou, 350001, China
Tel.: (86) 59187590668   Ky
Web Site: https://www.ej111.com
Year Founded: 2018
EJH—(NASDAQ)
Rev.: $50,685,314
Assets: $178,718,823
Liabilities: $15,561,047
Net Worth: $163,157,776
Earnings: ($19,468,052)
Emp.: 528
Fiscal Year-end: 06/30/24
Holding Company
N.A.I.C.S.: 551112
Wenshan Xie *(Founder, Chm & CEO)*

E-HOUSE (CHINA) ENTER-PRISE HOLDINGS LTD.

Qiushi Building No 383 Guangyan Road, Jing an, Shanghai, 200072, China
Tel.: (86) 2161330755
Web Site:
  http://www.ehousechina.com
Year Founded: 2004
2048—(HKG)
Rev.: $706,672,372
Assets: $821,473,801
Liabilities: $1,527,387,030
Net Worth: ($705,913,229)
Earnings: ($697,580,770)
Emp.: 6,146
Fiscal Year-end: 12/31/22
Real Estate Brokerage Services
N.A.I.C.S.: 531210
Ding Zuyu *(CEO)*

E-HOUSE (CHINA) HOLDINGS LIMITED

Qiushi Building 11/F 383 Guangyan Road, Jing an District, Shanghai, 200072, China
Tel.: (86) 2160868011   Ky
Web Site:
  http://www.ehousechina.com
Sales Range: $1-4.9 Billion
Emp.: 24,020
Holding Company; Real Estate Brokerage, Consulting & Investment Management Services
N.A.I.C.S.: 551112
Charles Guowei Chao *(Co-Chm)*

Subsidiaries:

CRIC Real Estate Database
Services   (1)
Qiushi Building 11F 383 Guangyan Road Zhabei District, Shanghai, 200072, China   (100%)
Tel.: (86) 2160868888
Web Site: http://www.cricchina.com
Sales Range: $1-4.9 Billion
Emp.: 3,712
Real Estate Information & Consulting Services
N.A.I.C.S.: 531390
Xin Zhou *(Chm & CEO)*

E-KANCELARIA GRUPA PRAWNO-FINANSOWA S.A.

Bema Plaza Building ul Gen Jozefa Bema 2, 50-265, Wroclaw, Poland
Tel.: (48) 713272800

Web Site: http://www.e-kancelaria.com
Year Founded: 2003
Emp.: 230
Debt Collection & Legal Services
N.A.I.C.S.: 561440
Mariusz Pawlowski *(Chm-Mgmt Bd)*

E-L FINANCIAL CORPORA-TION LIMITED

165 University Avenue Tenth Floor, Toronto, M5H 3B8, ON, Canada
Tel.: (416) 947-2578   Ca
Web Site: https://www.c lfinancial.ca
Year Founded: 1968
ELF—(TSX)
Rev.: $988,828,968
Assets: $19,216,656,378
Liabilities: $13,052,948,500
Net Worth: $6,163,707,878
Earnings: $816,937,140
Emp.: 13
Fiscal Year-end: 12/31/23
Holding Company; Insurance Services
N.A.I.C.S.: 551112
Richard B. Carty *(Gen Counsel & Sr VP-HR)*

Subsidiaries:

Empire Life Investments Inc.   (1)
165 University Avenue 9th Floor, Toronto, M5H 3B8, ON, Canada
Web Site:
  https://www.empirelifeinvestments.ca
Mutual Fund Investment Services
N.A.I.C.S.: 523940
Mark Sylvia *(Chm)*

The Empire Life Insurance
Company   (1)
259 King St E, Kingston, K7L 3A8, ON, Canada   (100%)
Tel.: (613) 548-1881
Web Site: https://www.empire.ca
Sales Range: $550-599.9 Million
Emp.: 625
Life Insurance & Financial Products
N.A.I.C.S.: 524113
Mark Sylvia *(Pres & CEO)*

E-LAND APPAREL LTD

16/2B Sri Vinayaka Indl Estate Singasandra Near Dakshin Honda Showroom, Hosur Road, Bengaluru, 560 068, Karnataka, India
Tel.: (91) 8042548800
Web Site:
  https://www.elandapparel.com
Year Founded: 1986
532820—(BOM)
Rev.: $16,994,591
Assets: $16,599,096
Liabilities: $72,751,756
Net Worth: ($56,152,660)
Earnings: ($7,234,445)
Emp.: 2,114
Fiscal Year-end: 03/31/21
Garments Mfr
N.A.I.C.S.: 315250
Jae Ho Song *(Mng Dir)*

E-LAND WORLD LTD.

19-8 Chanjeon-dong, Mapo-gu, Seoul, 121-751, Korea (South)
Tel.: (82) 2 323 0456
Web Site: http://www.eland.co.kr
Sales Range: $5-14.9 Billion
Holding Company
N.A.I.C.S.: 551112
SungKyung Park *(Pres)*

Subsidiaries:

E-Land Fashion China Holdings,
Limited   (1)
Room 1101 Parker House, 72 Queen's Road, Central, China (Hong Kong)
Tel.: (852) 25265024
Web Site: http://www.elandfashionchina.com

Sales Range: $200-249.9 Million
Emp.: 600
Women's Apparel & Accessories Retailer
N.A.I.C.S.: 458110
Hyun Jun Kim *(Exec Dir)*

Subsidiary (Non-US):

E-Land International Fashion (Shang-hai) Co., Ltd.   (2)
5/F Building 3 2005 Hongmei Road, Shanghai, China
Tel.: (86) 21 6113 5858
Women's Clothing Mfr
N.A.I.C.S.: 315250

K-Swiss Inc.   (1)
31248 Oak Crest Dr, Westlake Village, CA 91361
Tel.: (818) 706-5100
Web Site: http://www.kswiss.com
Rev.: $222,851,000
Assets: $176,723,000
Liabilities: $45,109,000
Net Worth: $131,614,000
Earnings: ($34,779,000)
Emp.: 542
Fiscal Year-end: 12/31/2012
Athletic Footwear Designer, Developer & Marketer
N.A.I.C.S.: 316210
Barney Waters *(Pres)*

Subsidiary (Non-US):

K S UK Limited   (2)
Tannery House, 4 Middle Leigh St, Somerset, BA16 0LA, United Kingdom
Tel.: (44) 1458449301
Web Site: http://www.k-swiss.co.uk
Sales Range: $75-99.9 Million
Emp.: 10
Athletic Footwear Designer, Developer & Marketer
N.A.I.C.S.: 316210

K-Swiss (Hong Kong) Ltd.   (2)
Unis 2001 Exchange Tower 33 Wang Chiu Road, Kowloon Bay, Hong Kong, China (Hong Kong)
Tel.: (852) 24852288
Web Site: http://www.k-swiss.com.hk
Emp.: 40
Athletic Footwear Designer & Marketer
N.A.I.C.S.: 316210
John Connolly *(Pres)*

K-Swiss Australia   (2)
43-53 Bridge Road, Stanmore, 2048, NSW, Australia
Tel.: (61) 295501187
Web Site: http://www.k-swiss.com.au
Sales Range: $75-99.9 Million
Athletic Footwear Designer, Developer & Marketer
N.A.I.C.S.: 316210

K-Swiss Canada   (2)
4800 East Gate Parkway Ste 6, Mississauga, L4W 3W6, ON, Canada
Tel.: (905) 625-4940
Sales Range: $50-74.9 Million
Emp.: 100
Athletic Footwear Designer, Developer & Marketer
N.A.I.C.S.: 316210
Tina Rizzo *(Country Mgr)*

Subsidiary (Domestic):

K-Swiss Direct, Inc   (2)
31248 Oak Crest Dr, Westlake Village, CA 91361
Tel.: (818) 706-5100
Sales Range: $150-199.9 Million
Athletic Footwear Designer, Developer & Marketer
N.A.I.C.S.: 327910

Subsidiary (Non-US):

K-Swiss Europe B.V.   (2)
Diakenhuisweg 45, 2033 AP, Haarlem, Netherlands
Tel.: (31) 235430543
Web Site: http://www.kswiss.nl
Athletic Footwear Designer, Developer & Marketer
N.A.I.C.S.: 316210

Subsidiary (Domestic):

K-Swiss Pacific Inc.   (2)
31248 Oak Crest Dr, Westlake Village, CA 91361-4692
Tel.: (818) 706-5100
Athletic Footwear Designer & Marketer
N.A.I.C.S.: 316210

Subsidiary (Non-US):

K-Swiss Retail Ltd.   (2)
4 Middle Leigh, Street, BA16 0LA, Somerset, United Kingdom
Tel.: (44) 1458445502
Sales Range: $25-49.9 Million
Emp.: 10
Athletic Footwear Designer & Marketer
N.A.I.C.S.: 316210

Subsidiary (Domestic):

K-Swiss Sales Corp.   (2)
31248 Oak Crest Dr, Westlake Village, CA 91361
Tel.: (818) 706-5100
Web Site: http://www.kswiss.com
Sales Range: $25-49.9 Million
Emp.: 50
Athletic Footwear Designer, Developer & Marketer
N.A.I.C.S.: 316210
Steven B. Nichols *(Pres)*

E-LEAD ELECTRONIC CO., LTD.

No 37 Gongdong 1st Rd, Changhua County, Shengang, 509004, Taiwan
Tel.: (886) 47977277   CN
Web Site: https://www.e-lead.com.tw
Year Founded: 1983
2497—(TAI)
Rev.: $123,165,992
Assets: $143,570,092
Liabilities: $72,046,958
Net Worth: $71,523,134
Earnings: $7,606,265
Emp.: 1,200
Fiscal Year-end: 12/31/23
Car Electronics Mfr
N.A.I.C.S.: 441330
Xixun Chen *(Chm)*

Subsidiaries:

E-LEAD Electronic Technology (Jiangsu) Co., Ltd.   (1)
No 167 Jinhu West Road, Wujiang District Economic and Technological Development Zone, Suzhou, Jiangsu, China
Tel.: (86) 51263404789
Web Site: https://www.e-lead.com.cn
Electronic Components Mfr
N.A.I.C.S.: 334310

E-Lead Electronic (Thailand) Co., Ltd.   (1)
888/4 Moo 7 Sukhumvit Rd Tambon Bangpoomai, Amphur Muang, Samut Prakan, 10280, Thailand
Tel.: (66) 23230558
Web Site: http://www.e-lead.com.tw
Automotive Electronic Product Mfr
N.A.I.C.S.: 336320

E-LEATHER LTD.

Kingsbridge Centre Sturrock Way, Peterborough, PE3 8TZ, United Kingdom
Tel.: (44) 1733 843939
Web Site:
  http://www.eleathergroup.com
Year Founded: 2006
Sales Range: $10-24.9 Million
Emp.: 102
Leather Product Mfr
N.A.I.C.S.: 316990
Chris McBean *(CEO)*

E-LIFE MALL CORPORATION

No 55 Wugong 6th Road, Wugu District, New Taipei City, Taiwan
Tel.: (886) 22989922
Web Site: https://ec.elifemall.com.tw

Year Founded: 1975
6281—(TAI)
Rev.: $66,789,624
Assets: $297,396,699
Liabilities: $204,028,214
Net Worth: $93,368,485
Earnings: $16,647,143
Emp.: 1,666
Fiscal Year-end: 12/31/23
Electronic Products Retailer
N.A.I.C.S.: 423690
Jeffrey Lin *(Chm & Gen Mgr)*

E-LITECOM CO., LTD.
520-1 Maetan-dong, Yeongtong-Ku,
Suwon, Korea (South)
Tel.: (82) 415293800
Web Site: http://www.e-litecom.com
Year Founded: 1984
041520—(KRS)
Rev.: $105,517,283
Assets: $178,612,354
Liabilities: $26,210,414
Net Worth: $152,401,940
Earnings: ($4,436,522)
Emp.: 63
Fiscal Year-end: 12/31/22
Electronic Components Mfr
N.A.I.C.S.: 334419
Cho Young Jun *(Deputy Gen Mgr)*

E-LOGIT CO., LTD.
3-11-11 Sotokanda, Chiyoda-Ku, To-
kyo, 101-0021, Japan
Tel.: (81) 335185460
Web Site: https://ec-bpo.e-logit.com
Year Founded: 2000
9327—(TKS)
Rev.: $86,729,810
Assets: $28,700,620
Liabilities: $35,746,880
Net Worth: ($7,046,260)
Earnings: ($16,300,260)
Emp.: 1,131
Fiscal Year-end: 03/31/24
Logistics Consulting Servies
N.A.I.C.S.: 541614
Ryoichi Kakui *(Founder, Chm & Pres)*

E-NET JAPAN CORP.
1-1-1 Manfukuji Aso-ku, Kawasaki,
215-0004, Japan
Tel.: (81) 449695223
Web Site: http://www.enet-japan.com
Rev.: $71,506,000
Earnings: $1,113,000
Electric Appliances & Computer Sales
N.A.I.C.S.: 449210

E-NOVIA S.P.A.
Via San Martino 12, 20122, Milan,
Italy
Tel.: (39) 0245902000
Web Site: https://www.e-novia.it
Year Founded: 2012
E9IA—(EUR)
Asset Management Services
N.A.I.C.S.: 523999
Vincent Costanzo Russi *(CEO)*

E-P:N MINKINREHU OY
Luhtalantie 245, 62420, Kortesjarvi,
Finland
Tel.: (358) 64880500
Web Site: http://www.ep-minkinrehu.fi
Sales Range: $10-24.9 Million
Emp.: 18
Fur-Bearing Animal Feed Mfr
N.A.I.C.S.: 311119
Jouko Huhtala *(Office Mgr)*

Subsidiaries:

Monas Feed Oy AB   **(1)**
Monasvagen 442, Hirvlax, FIN 66970, Uusi-
kaarlepyy, Finland
Tel.: (358) 67688100
Web Site: http://www.monasfeed.fi

Fur-Bearing Animal Feed Mfr
N.A.I.C.S.: 311119

E-PANGO SA
26 rue Vignon, 75009, Paris, France
Tel.: (33) 142333407
Web Site: https://www.e-pango.com
Year Founded: 2015
ALAGO—(EUR)
Electricity Distribution Services
N.A.I.C.S.: 237990
Philippe Girard *(CEO)*

E-PLEX LTD.
52-54 Riverside Sir Thomas Longley
Road Medway City Estate, Roches-
ter, ME2 4DP, Kent, United Kingdom
Tel.: (44) 1634711622   **UK**
Web Site: http://www.e-plex.co.uk
Sales Range: $25-49.9 Million
Emp.: 10
Data Transfer Modules & Logging
Systems Mfr
N.A.I.C.S.: 334519
Paul Holland *(Gen Mgr)*

E-PLUS LIMITED
Level 8 210 George Street, Sydney,
2000, NSW, Australia
Tel.: (61) 292909606   **AU**
Year Founded: 2004
8EP—(NSXA)
Rev.: $323,940
Assets: $213,627
Liabilities: $1,088,217
Net Worth: ($874,590)
Earnings: ($277,941)
Fiscal Year-end: 12/31/21
Event Management Services
N.A.I.C.S.: 561920
Keong Ngok Ching *(CEO)*

E-POWER RESOURCES INC.
400-3 Place Ville-Marie, Montreal,
H3B 2E3, QC, Canada
Tel.: (438) 701-3736   **QC**
Web Site: https://www.e-
powerresources.com
Year Founded: 2018
EPR—(CNSX)
Rev.: $3,739
Assets: $1,014,961
Liabilities: $92,082
Net Worth: $922,878
Earnings: ($589,044)
Fiscal Year-end: 09/30/22
Mineral Exploration Services
N.A.I.C.S.: 212390
Paul Haber *(CFO)*

E-SEIKATSU CO., LTD.
2-32 Minamiazabu 5-chome, Minato-
ku, Tokyo, 106-0047, Japan
Tel.: (81) 354237820
Web Site: https://www.e-seikatsu.info
Year Founded: 2000
3796—(TKS)
Rev.: $18,560,880
Assets: $16,789,400
Liabilities: $3,926,340
Net Worth: $12,863,060
Earnings: $965,060
Emp.: 126
Fiscal Year-end: 03/31/24
Internet Services
N.A.I.C.S.: 518210
Hiroyoshi Kitazawa *(COO & Exec
VP)*

E-STAR ALTERNATIVE PLC.
Szekacs Utca 29, 1122, Budapest,
Hungary
Tel.: (36) 12793550
Web Site: http://www.e-star.hu
Year Founded: 2000
Sales Range: $1-9.9 Million
Energy Consulting Services

N.A.I.C.S.: 541690

**E-STAR COMMERCIAL MAN-
AGEMENT COMPANY LIMITED**
32-33/F Tower A Galaxy World Inter-
section of Meiban Avenue, Yabao
Road, Shenzhen, 518000, China
Tel.: (86) 75523952280   **Ky**
Web Site: https://www.g-cre.com
Year Founded: 2004
6668—(HKG)
Rev.: $86,081,651
Assets: $328,153,911
Liabilities: $147,258,404
Net Worth: $180,895,507
Earnings: $22,810,211
Emp.: 826
Fiscal Year-end: 12/31/22
Property Management Services
N.A.I.C.S.: 531311
Benny Huang De-Lin *(Chm)*

E-STARCO CO., LTD.
Daehak Bldg 406-21 Mok1-dong,
Yangcheon-gu, Seoul, Korea (South)
Tel.: (82) 226437922
Web Site: http://www.e-starco.co.kr
Year Founded: 1980
015020—(KRS)
Rev.: $5,849,703
Assets: $61,199,974
Liabilities: $26,451,694
Net Worth: $34,748,280
Earnings: ($3,851,668)
Emp.: 54
Fiscal Year-end: 12/31/22
Real Estate Lending Services
N.A.I.C.S.: 531190
Seung Je Kim *(Board of Directors,
Chm & CEO)*

**E-STATION GREEN TECHNOL-
OGY GROUP CO., LIMITED**
1 Grange Road 12-01 Orchard Build-
ing, Singapore, 239693, Singapore
Tel.: (65) 62623845   **Ky**
Web Site: https://www.kgroup.com.hk
Year Founded: 2014
8475—(HKG)
Rev.: $4,398,666
Assets: $1,204,150
Liabilities: $7,431,641
Net Worth: ($6,227,492)
Earnings: ($1,780,660)
Emp.: 58
Fiscal Year-end: 08/31/23
Restaurant Operators
N.A.I.C.S.: 722511
Terence Weijie Lai *(Chm)*

Subsidiaries:

Gangnam Kitchen Pte. Ltd.   **(1)**
8A Admiralty Street 04-25, Singapore,
757437, Singapore
Tel.: (65) 87868988
Web Site:
    http://www.gangnamkitchen.oddle.me
Online Food Delivery Services
N.A.I.C.S.: 492210

E-SUPPORTLINK, LTD.
4F Mejiro Nakano Bldg 2-17-22
Takada, Toshima-Ku, Tokyo, 171-
0033, Japan
Tel.: (81) 359790666
Web Site: https://www.e-
supportlink.com
Year Founded: 1998
2493—(TKS)
Rev.: $32,351,670
Assets: $39,477,120
Liabilities: $15,342,760
Net Worth: $24,134,360
Earnings: $326,140
Emp.: 192
Fiscal Year-end: 11/30/23

Business Process Outsourcing Ser-
vices
N.A.I.C.S.: 541614
Shinsuke Horiuchi *(Pres)*

**E-TRANZACT INTERNATIONAL
PLC.**
4th & 5th Floor Fortune Towers 27/29
Adeyemo Alakija Street, Victoria Is-
land, Lagos, Nigeria
Tel.: (234) 17101060
Web Site: https://www.etranzact.com
Year Founded: 2003
ETRANZACT—(NIGL)
Rev.: $16,685,834
Assets: $13,091,958
Liabilities: $6,226,009
Net Worth: $6,865,949
Earnings: $869,712
Emp.: 290
Fiscal Year-end: 12/31/22
Software Development Services
N.A.I.C.S.: 513210
Wole Abegunde *(Chm)*

E-TRON CO., LTD
8 9F Line Bldg 823-30 Yeoksam-
dong, Kangnam-ku, Seoul, Korea
(South)
Tel.: (82) 25289377
Web Site: http://www.e-trons.co.kr
Year Founded: 1999
096040—(KRS)
Rev.: $54,889,322
Assets: $140,348,607
Liabilities: $82,167,703
Net Worth: $58,180,904
Earnings: ($23,472,073)
Emp.: 72
Fiscal Year-end: 12/31/22
Software Development Services
N.A.I.C.S.: 513210
Kim Tae Hyeong *(Dir)*

E-WORLD CO., LTD.
200 Duryu Park-ro, Dalseo-gu,
Daegu, Korea (South)
Tel.: (82) 536200001
Web Site: https://www.eworld.kr
Year Founded: 2005
084680—(KRS)
Rev.: $96,996,326
Assets: $331,117,746
Liabilities: $142,165,435
Net Worth: $188,952,311
Earnings: $4,320,514
Emp.: 421
Fiscal Year-end: 12/31/22
Amusement Park Services
N.A.I.C.S.: 713110
Park Wi Keun *(Dir)*

E. BON HOLDINGS LTD
16-18/F First Commercial Building 33
Leighton Road, Causeway Bay,
China (Hong Kong)
Tel.: (852) 31050599   **Ky**
Web Site: http://www.ebon.com.hk
0599—(HKG)
Rev.: $63,792,476
Assets: $90,572,852
Liabilities: $29,885,053
Net Worth: $60,687,799
Earnings: $1,534,088
Emp.: 147
Fiscal Year-end: 03/31/22
Hardware Whslr
N.A.I.C.S.: 423710
Terence Shiu Sun Lau *(Exec Dir)*

Subsidiaries:

Bonco Ironmongery Limited   **(1)**
16/F First Commercial Building 33 Leighton
Road, Causeway Bay, China (Hong Kong)
Tel.: (852) 28912188
Web Site: https://www.boncohardware.com
Hardware Sales

E. Bon Holdings Ltd—(Continued)

N.A.I.C.S.: 423710

Cypress Design Limited (1)
B/F 16 Queen's Road East, Hong Kong,
China (Hong Kong)
Tel.: (852) 2 528 8145
Web Site:
https://www.cypressdesign.com.hk
Interior Design Services
N.A.I.C.S.: 541410
Robert Shum (Founder & Principal)

**E. Bon Building Materials Company
Limited** (1)
Rm A1 18 Fl First Comml Bldg 33 Leighton
Rd, Causeway Bay, China (Hong Kong)
Tel.: (852) 28913389
Web Site: http://www.ebon.com.hk
Emp.: 300
Hardware Whslr
N.A.I.C.S.: 423710
Tony Tse (CEO)

H2O (Pro) Limited (1)
16 F First Comml Bldg 33 Leighton Rd,
Causeway Bay, China (Hong Kong)
Tel.: (852) 28919772
Web Site: http://www.h2opro.com.hk
Sales Range: $25-49.9 Million
Emp.: 50
Bathroom Hardware Fixtures Sales
N.A.I.C.S.: 423220
Tony Tse (Mgr)

Kitchen (Pro) Limited (1)
16 F First Comml Bldg 33 Leighton Rd,
Causeway Bay, China (Hong Kong)
Tel.: (852) 28913389
Web Site: http://www.kitchenpro.biz
Kitchen Fittings Whslr
N.A.I.C.S.: 423310

Massford (Hong Kong) Limited (1)
17 Fl First Comml Bldg 33 Leighton Rd,
Causeway Bay, China (Hong Kong)
Tel.: (852) 28916860
Sales Range: $50-74.9 Million
Emp.: 100
Hardware Whslr
N.A.I.C.S.: 423710

Right Century Limited (1)
Ground Fl Kai Kwong Comml Bldg 332-334
Lockhart Rd, Wanchai, China (Hong Kong)
Tel.: (852) 28341661
Web Site: http://www.ebon.com.hk
Sales Range: $50-74.9 Million
Emp.: 9
Bathroom Hardwares Sales
N.A.I.C.S.: 423220
Thomas Au (Mgr)

**Sunny Building And Decoration Mate-
rials Company Limited** (1)
Ground Fl 345 Lockhart Rd, Wanchai,
China (Hong Kong)
Tel.: (852) 28939118
Web Site: http://www.ebon.com.hk
Sales Range: $25-49.9 Million
Emp.: 5
Hardware Retailer
N.A.I.C.S.: 444140
Hercules Au (Sr Mgr)

Techpro Trading Limited (1)
16 F First Comml Bldg 33 Leighton Rd,
Causeway Bay, China (Hong Kong)
Tel.: (852) 28919984
Web Site: http://www.techprohk.com
Sales Range: $25-49.9 Million
Emp.: 30
Architectural Builders Hardware Whslr
N.A.I.C.S.: 423710

E. BOWMAN & SONS LTD
First Floor Cherryholt House Cherry-
holt Road, Stamford, PE9 2EP, Lin-
colnshire, United Kingdom
Tel.: (44) 1780751015
Web Site:
http://www.bowmanstamford.com
Year Founded: 1886
Rev.: $15,559,838
Emp.: 78
Modern & Historical Building Services
N.A.I.C.S.: 236220

**E. HAWLE ARMA-
TURENWERKE GMBH**
Wagrainer Strasse 13, 4840, Vock-
labruck, Austria
Tel.: (43) 767272576
Web Site: http://www.hawle.at
Year Founded: 1948
Rev.: $119,500,000
Emp.: 335
Valve Mfr
N.A.I.C.S.: 332911
Martin Kast (Gen Mgr)

E. OHMAN J:OR AB
Master Samuelsgatan 6, Stockholm,
Sweden
Tel.: (46) 8 407 58 00
Web Site: http://www.ohman.se
Privater Equity Firm
N.A.I.C.S.: 523999
Tom Dinkelspiel (Chm)

Subsidiaries:

Nordnet AB (1)
Gustavslundsvagen 141, Box 14077, Bro-
mma, 167 14, Sweden (60%)
Tel.: (46) 850633000
Web Site: http://www.nordnet.se
Sales Range: $125-149.9 Million
Banking Services
N.A.I.C.S.: 522110
Claes Dinkelspiel (Chm)

E. PAIRIS S.A.
Thesi Goritsa, 19300, Aspropyrgos,
Greece
Tel.: (30) 2105515555
Web Site: https://www.pairis.gr
Year Founded: 1974
PAIR—(ATH)
Sales Range: Less than $1 Million
Emp.: 135
Plastics Bottle Mfr
N.A.I.C.S.: 326160
Chris Kampolis (Vice Chm & Dir-
Technology)

**E. SCHNAPP & CO. WORKS
LTD.**
Shechterman St Old 22 AZA, Net-
anya, 42379, Israel
Tel.: (972) 98606111
Web Site: https://www.schnapp.co.il
Year Founded: 1951
SHNP—(TAE)
Rev.: $91,260,394
Assets: $125,639,175
Liabilities: $43,268,683
Net Worth: $82,370,492
Earnings: $11,292,906
Fiscal Year-end: 12/31/23
Battery Manufacturing
N.A.I.C.S.: 335910
Uriel Rosenshein (CEO)

**E. SUN FINANCIAL HOLDING
CO., LTD.**
14F No 117 1F No 115 Sec 3 MinSh-
eng E Road, Songshan District, Tai-
pei, 10546, Taiwan
Tel.: (886) 221751313   TW
Web Site: https://www.esunfhc.com
Year Founded: 2002
ESUNF—(LUX)
Rev.: $2,640,042,022
Assets: $113,763,483,726
Liabilities: $106,371,311,415
Net Worth: $7,392,172,310
Earnings: $679,978,958
Emp.: 9,109
Fiscal Year-end: 12/31/23
Holding Company
N.A.I.C.S.: 551112

James Deacon (Mng Dir)

Subsidiaries:

E.SUN Bank (China), Ltd. (1)
1F Building 7 One Excellence No 5109
Menghai Avenue, Qianhai Shenzhen-Hong
Kong Cooperation Zone, Shenzhen, China
Tel.: (86) 75588981313
N.A.I.C.S.: 522110

E.SUN Securities Co., Ltd. (1)
105-96 6th Floor No 158 Section 3 Minsh-
eng East Road, Songshan District, Taipei,
Taiwan
Tel.: (886) 25 580 5013
Web Site: https://www.esunsec.com.tw
Security Brokerage Services
N.A.I.C.S.: 523150
Yi-Hsin Tseng (Exec VP)

E.Sun Commercial Bank, Ltd. (1)
No 117 Sec 3 Minsheng E Rd, Songshan
District, Taipei, 10546, Taiwan (100%)
Tel.: (886) 22 175 1313
Web Site: https://www.esunbank.com.tw
Commercial Bank
N.A.I.C.S.: 522110

Subsidiary (Non-US):

Union Commercial Bank Plc. (2)
4th Floor UCB Building No 61 St 130,
Sangkat Phsa Chas Khan Daun Penh,
Phnom Penh, Cambodia (100%)
Tel.: (855) 23214159
Web Site: http://www.ucb.com.kh
Commercial Banking Services
N.A.I.C.S.: 522110

**E.Sun Securities Investment Trust
Co., Ltd.** (1)
8F No 117 Sec 3, Minsheng E Rd, Taipei,
Taiwan (100%)
Tel.: (886) 55561313
Web Site: http://www.esunfhc.com.tw
Investment Banking & Securities Dealing
N.A.I.C.S.: 523150

E.Sun Venture Capital Corp. (1)
6F No 115 Sec 3 Minsheng E Rd, Taipei,
Taiwan (100%)
Tel.: (886) 22 175 1313
Web Site: http://www.esunfhc.com.tw
Sales Range: $50-74.9 Million
Emp.: 10
Bank Holding Company
N.A.I.C.S.: 551111

**Union Commercial Bank Public Lim-
ited Corporation** (1)
No 441 Preah Monivong Blvd Sangkat Bo-
eng Proluet Khan, Prampir Meakkakra,
Phnom Penh, Cambodia
Tel.: (855) 23911313
Emp.: 500
Commercial Banking Services
N.A.I.C.S.: 522110

E.A TECHNIQUE (M) BHD
Setiawangsa Business Suites Unit
C-3A-3A No 2 Jalan Setiawangsa 11,
Taman Setiawangsa, 54200, Kuala
Lumpur, Malaysia
Tel.: (60) 342525422
Web Site:
https://www.eatechnique.com.my
Year Founded: 1993
EATECH—(KLS)
Rev.: $32,516,402
Assets: $112,308,995
Liabilities: $104,371,005
Net Worth: $7,937,989
Earnings: $4,241,905
Emp.: 457
Fiscal Year-end: 12/31/22
Logistics & Ship Management
N.A.I.C.S.: 488510
Ahamad Mohamad (Deputy Chm)

Subsidiaries:

**Johor Shipyard & Engineering Sdn
Bhd** (1)
Lot PT8436-A Mukim Hutan Melintang,
Daerah Hilir Perak, 36400, Perak, Malaysia
Tel.: (60) 56412514
Ship Building & Repair Services
N.A.I.C.S.: 541990

**E.A. GIBSON SHIPBROKERS
LIMITED**
Audrey House 16-20 Ely Place, PO
Box 278, London, EC1N 6SN, United
Kingdom
Tel.: (44) 2076671000   UK
Web Site: http://www.gibson.co.uk
Year Founded: 1893
Emp.: 180
Shipbroking Services
N.A.I.C.S.: 425120
Nigel Richardson (Mng Dir)

Subsidiaries:

Gibson (Asia) Ltd (1)
Room 1404 14/f Allied Kajima Building
No138 Gloucester Road, Wanchai, China
(Hong Kong)
Tel.: (852) 25118919
Web Site: http://www.gibsons.co.uk
Shipbroking Services
N.A.I.C.S.: 425120

Gibson Brokers Pte. Ltd (1)
8 Eu Tong Sen Street 12-89, Central, Sin-
gapore, 059818, Singapore
Tel.: (65) 65900220
Web Site: http://www.gibsons.co.uk
Shipbroking Services
N.A.I.C.S.: 425120

**E.A. JUFFALI & BROTHERS
COMPANY**
Juffali Building Medina Road, PO Box
1049, Jeddah, 21431, Saudi Arabia
Tel.: (966) 126672222
Web Site: http://www.juffali.com
Year Founded: 1946
Sales Range: $1-4.9 Billion
Emp.: 7,000
Trading Company; Automobiles;
Chemicals
N.A.I.C.S.: 551112
Ali Al Juffali (Owner)

Subsidiaries:

**Juffali Air Conditioning, Mechanical &
Electrical Company** (1)
Juffali Complex - Madinah Road Kilo- 14,
PO Box 1049, Jeddah, 21422, Saudi Arabia
Tel.: (966) 12 639 8808
Web Site: http://www.juffalijamed.com
Construction Engineering Services
N.A.I.C.S.: 541330
Nashwan Noury Al Assafi (Mgr-Admin)

Plant (Domestic):

**Juffali Air Conditioning, Mechanical &
Electrical Company - DUCTWORK
FACILITY** (2)
PO Box 5090, Jeddah, 21422, Saudi Arabia
Tel.: (966) 12 692 0304
Air Conditioner & Refrigerator Mfr
N.A.I.C.S.: 333415
Marwan Amin (Mgr-Factory)

**Juffali Air Conditioning, Mechanical &
Electrical Company - LOW VOLTAGE
PANEL BOARD FACILITY** (2)
PO Box 86, Jeddah, 11411, Saudi Arabia
Tel.: (966) 11 237 6125
Air Conditioner & Refrigerator Mfr
N.A.I.C.S.: 333415
Kadir Shaikh (Mgr-Factory)

Juffali Automotive Company (1)
PO Box 297, Jeddah, 21411, Saudi Arabia
Tel.: (966) 12 664 5678
Car Dealer Services
N.A.I.C.S.: 441110

Juffali Chemical Company (1)
Medinah Road, PO Box 5728, Jeddah,
21432, Saudi Arabia
Tel.: (966) 26633516
Chemical Distr
N.A.I.C.S.: 424690

Joint Venture (Domestic):

**Arabian Chemical Company (Latex)
Ltd.** (2)
Juffali Head Office Building 4th Floor Madi-

nah Rd, PO Box 5728, Jeddah, 21432,
Saudi Arabia
Tel.: (966) 26633516
Web Site: http://www.juffali.com
Styrene/Butadiene Latex (for the carpet,
paper & construction sectors) Mfr
N.A.I.C.S.: 424690

Arabian Chemical Company (Polystyrene) Limited　　(2)
Madinah Road, PO Box 5728, Jeddah,
21432, Saudi Arabia
Tel.: (966) 26633516
Web Site: http://www.eajb.com.sa
Chemical Distr
N.A.I.C.S.: 424690

Juffali Technical Equipment
Company　　(1)
PO Box 1049, Jeddah, 21431, Saudi Arabia
Tel.: (966) 12 667 2222
Web Site: http://www.juffali.com
Emp.: 200
Industrial Equipment Distr
N.A.I.C.S.: 423830
Husni Rifai (Gen Mgr)

Juffali Tyres Company　　(1)
PO Box 52440, Jeddah, 21563, Saudi Arabia
Tel.: (966) 12 667 2222
Vehicle Tire Distr
N.A.I.C.S.: 441340

Saudi Refrigerators Manufacturing
Co.Ltd.　　(1)
Jeddah Industrial City Phase 3, PO Box
3315, Jeddah, 21471, Saudi Arabia
Tel.: (966) 12 637 3202
Refrigerator Mfr
N.A.I.C.S.: 333415

E.B. CREASY & COMPANY PLC

No 98 Sri Sangaraja Mawatha, 10,
Colombo, 10, Sri Lanka
Tel.: (94) 112478806
Web Site: https://www.ebcreasy.com
EBCR—(COL)
Rev.: $77,701,904
Assets: $67,393,233
Liabilities: $44,732,329
Net Worth: $22,660,903
Earnings: $5,026,487
Emp.: 26,000
Fiscal Year-end: 03/31/23
Batteries & Spray Paint Mfr
N.A.I.C.S.: 238160
Rohan Chrisantha Anil Welikala
(Exec Dir)

Subsidiaries:

Darley Butler & Co. Ltd.　　(1)
No 98 Sri Sanagaraja Mawatha, Colombo,
Sri Lanka
Tel.: (94) 112421311
Web Site: http://www.darleybutler.com
Food Products Distr
N.A.I.C.S.: 424490
S. D. R. Arudprasagam (Co-Chm & Mng
Dir)

Lanka Special Steels Ltd　　(1)
53 A Ward Place, 07, Colombo, Sri Lanka
Tel.: (94) 114932416
Steel Products Mfr
N.A.I.C.S.: 331513
Samanmali Munasinghe (Head-Fin & Accts)

Lankem Tea & Rubber Plantations
(Pvt) Ltd.　　(1)
53 1/ 1 Sir Baron Jayathilake Mawatha, Colombo, Sri Lanka
Tel.: (94) 112381508
Web Site: https://www.lankemplantations.lk
Rubber Product Mfr & Distr
N.A.I.C.S.: 326299

Laxapana Batteries PLC.　　(1)
98 Sri Sangaraja Mawatha, 10, Colombo,
Sri Lanka
Tel.: (94) 114766000
Web Site: https://www.laxapana.com
Cell Battery Mfr
N.A.I.C.S.: 335910

E.BRICKS VENTURES

Rua Professor Atilio Innocenti 165,
Itaim Bibi, CEP 04538-000, Sao
Paulo, Brazil
Tel.: (55) 1130500755
Web Site:
　http://www.ebricksventures.com
Year Founded: 2013
Privater Equity Firm
N.A.I.C.S.: 523999
Pedro Sirotsky Melzer (Partner)

Subsidiaries:

Rock Content Servicos de Midia
Ltda.　　(1)
Rua Paraiba 330 -13 andar-Funcionarios,
Belo Horizonte, 30130-917, Brazil
Tel.: (55) 312555 3066
Content Marketing
N.A.I.C.S.: 541613
Matt Doyon (Chief RevenueOfficer)

Subsidiary (US):

CampusLogic, Inc.　　(2)
1340 S Spectrum Blvd Ste 200, Chandler,
AZ 85286
Tel.: (602) 643-1300
Web Site: http://www.campuslogic.com
Sales Range: $1-9.9 Million
Emp.: 50
Business Solution Software Developer
N.A.I.C.S.: 513210
Gregg Scoresby (Founder, Chm & CEO)

Subsidiary (Non-US):

Scribble Technologies Inc.　　(2)
49 Spadina Ave Ste 303, Toronto, M5V 2J1,
ON, Canada
Tel.: (416) 364-8118
Web Site: http://www.scribblelive.com
Content Performance Company; Infographics, Content & Digital Marketing & Communications, Media & Interactive Content
N.A.I.C.S.: 541810
Andre Beaulieu (General Counsel)

Subsidiary (US):

i-on interactive, Inc.　　(3)
1095 Broken Sound Pkwy NW Ste 200,
Boca Raton, FL 33487
Tel.: (416) 364-8118
Web Site: http://www.ioninteractive.com
Software Developer & Marketer & Other
Marketing & Services
N.A.I.C.S.: 513210
Parth Madhubhai (Mgr-Customer Success)

E.C. BIRCH PROPRIETARY LIMITED

104 Dougharty Road, Heidelberg
West, Melbourne, 3081, VIC, Australia
Tel.: (61) 3 9450 8900　　AU
Web Site:
　http://www.birchcreative.com.au
Year Founded: 1926
Knitting Products, Sewing Accesories
& Craft Supplies Whslr & Distr
N.A.I.C.S.: 313110

Subsidiaries:

J. Leutenegger Pty Ltd.　　(1)
68-72 Waterloo Rd, Sydney, 2113, NSW,
Australia　　(100%)
Tel.: (61) 2 9524 9200
Web Site: http://www.leutenegger.com.au
Fabric & Haberdashery Importer & Distr
N.A.I.C.S.: 423990

E.I. SIGNATURE INVESTMENTS LIMITED

Limassol Avenue 5 Eurosure Building
3rd Floor, Nicosia, Cyprus
Tel.: (357) 22023000
Investment Services
N.A.I.C.S.: 523940

E.ON SE

Brusseler Platz 1, 45131, Essen,
Germany
Tel.: (49) 20118400　　De
Web Site: https://www.eon.com
Year Founded: 2000
1EOAN—(ITA)
Rev.: $103,417,164,820
Assets: $125,295,868,220
Liabilities: $109,715,847,040
Net Worth: $15,580,021,180
Earnings: $570,700,790
Emp.: 71,629
Fiscal Year-end: 12/31/23
Energy Holding Company
N.A.I.C.S.: 551112
Marc Spieker (CFO & Member-Exec
Bd)

Subsidiaries:

ANCO Sp. z o.o.　　(1)
ul Grunwaldzka 219, 80-266, Gdansk, Poland
Tel.: (48) 58 557 31 18
Web Site: http://www.anco.com.pl
Sales Range: $50-74.9 Million
Emp.: 4
Safety Equipment Distr
N.A.I.C.S.: 423830

AWP GmbH　　(1)
Tegelweg 25, 33102, Paderborn, Germany
Tel.: (49) 52 51 5 03 62 57
Web Site: http://www.awp-gmbh.net
Sales Range: $75-99.9 Million
Emp.: 13
Sewage & Drinking Water Treatment Services
N.A.I.C.S.: 221320
Markus Schmitt (Mgr)

AggerEnergie GmbH　　(1)
Alexander-Fleming-Str 2, 51643, Gummersbach, Germany
Tel.: (49) 226130030
Web Site: https://www.aggerenergie.de
Electric Power & Natural Gas Distr
N.A.I.C.S.: 486210

Aircraft Klima-Warme- Kalte
-Rohrleitungsbau GmbH　　(1)
Drohnenberg 6, 38302, Wolfenbuttel, Germany
Tel.: (49) 53317079290
Web Site: https://www.aircraft-wf.de
Pipeline Construction Services
N.A.I.C.S.: 237120

Anacacho Wind Farm, LLC　　(1)
353 N Clark St Fl 30, Chicago, IL 60654-
4704
Tel.: (312) 245-3035
Eletric Power Generation Services
N.A.I.C.S.: 221118

Arena One GmbH　　(1)
Parkring 35, 85748, Garching, Germany
Tel.: (49) 89 350 948 0
Web Site: http://www.arena-one.com
Rev.: $87,211,740
Emp.: 454
Event Organizing & Catering Management
Services
N.A.I.C.S.: 711310
Barbara Bauer (Head-Events-Allianz Arena)

Aton Projects V.O.F.　　(1)
Nusterweg 80, 6136 KV, Sittard, Netherlands
Tel.: (31) 880239500
Web Site: https://www.aton-projects.com
Solar Panels Installation Services
N.A.I.C.S.: 238210

Avacon Wasser GmbH　　(1)
Halchtersche Strasse 33, 38304, Wolfenbuttel, Germany
Tel.: (49) 53319354990
Web Site: https://www.avacon-wasser.de
Waste Management Services
N.A.I.C.S.: 924110

BKW FMB Energie AG　　(1)
Viktoriaplatz 2, CH 3000, Bern,
Switzerland　　(20%)
Tel.: (41) 313305797
Web Site: http://www.bkw-fmb.ch
Sales Range: $1-4.9 Billion
Emp.: 400
Energy Services
N.A.I.C.S.: 221122

Bioenergie Merzig GmbH　　(1)
Brusseler Platz 1, 45131, Essen, Germany
Tel.: (49) 68699117614
Web Site: http://www.bioerdgas-merzig.de
Natural Gas Distr
N.A.I.C.S.: 221210

Bioerdgas Hallertau GmbH　　(1)
Kellerstrasse 1, 85283, Wolnzach, Germany
Tel.: (49) 8751846200
Web Site: http://www.bioerdgas-hallertau.de
Natural Gas Extraction & Production Services
N.A.I.C.S.: 211130

Biogas Ducherow GmbH　　(1)
Karl-Marx-Srasse 23, 17398, Ducherow,
Germany
Tel.: (49) 39726 25860
Natural Gas Distr
N.A.I.C.S.: 221210

Biomasseheizkraftwerk Emden
GmbH　　(1)
Zum Kraftwerk, Emden, 26725, Germany
Tel.: (49) 21 8921
Steam Heat Distribution Services
N.A.I.C.S.: 221330

CEC Energieconsulting GmbH　　(1)
Bahnhofstrasse 40, Kirchlengern, 32278,
Germany
Tel.: (49) 52 23 8 21 49 70
Web Site: http://www.cec-energie.de
Energy Consulting Services
N.A.I.C.S.: 541690
Michael Hoepping (Gen Mgr)

Cameleon B.V.　　(1)
Molenbeek 9, 5061 RK, Oisterwijk, Netherlands
Tel.: (31) 628262224
Web Site: http://www.cameleonpaint.com
Body Painting Services
N.A.I.C.S.: 238320

Celle-Uelzen Netz GmbH　　(1)
Sprengerstrasse 2, 29223, Celle, Germany
Tel.: (49) 5141160
Web Site: https://www.celle-uelzennetz.de
Electric Utility Services
N.A.I.C.S.: 926130

Celsium Serwis Sp. z o.o.　　(1)
ul 11 Listopada 7, 26 110, Skarzysko-
Kamienna, Poland
Tel.: (48) 412528980
Web Site: http://www.celsiumserwis.pl
Housing Community Services
N.A.I.C.S.: 624229

Celsium Sp. z o.o.　　(1)
ul 11 Listopada 7, 26 110, Skarzysko-
Kamienna, Poland
Tel.: (48) 412528980
Web Site: http://www.celsium.pl
Housing Community Services
N.A.I.C.S.: 624229

Champion Wind Farm, LLC　　(1)
53 N Clark St Fl 30, Chicago, IL 60654
Tel.: (312) 923-9463
Web Site: http://www.eon.com
Eletric Power Generation Services
N.A.I.C.S.: 221118
Steven Trenholm (Pres)

Clinton Wind, LLC　　(1)
353 N Clark St Ste 3000, Chicago, IL
60654
Tel.: (312) 923-9463
Web Site: http://www.clintonwind.com
Renewable Energy Services
N.A.I.C.S.: 221116
Lael Eason (Dir-Dev)

Cuculus GmbH　　(1)
Lindenstrasse 9-11, 98693, Ilmenau, Germany
Tel.: (49) 36776860000
Web Site: https://www.cuculus.com
Cloud Computing Services
N.A.I.C.S.: 541512
Kjartan V. Skaugvoll (CEO)

Debreceni Kombinalt Ciklusu Eromu
Kft.　　(1)
Mikepercsi ut 1, Debrecen, 4030, Hungary
Tel.: (36) 52512800
Eletric Power Generation Services
N.A.I.C.S.: 221118

E.ON SE—(Continued)

Delgaz Grid S.A. (1)
Bd Pandurilor nr 42 etaj 4, jud Mures,
540554, Targu Mures, Romania
Tel.: (40) 232200434
Web Site: https://www.delgaz.ro
Natural Gas Distr
N.A.I.C.S.: 221210

**Donau-Wasserkraft
Aktiengesellschaft** (1)
Blutenburgstr 20, Munich, 80636, Bavaria,
Germany
Tel.: (49) 89992220
Web Site: http://www.rmd.de
Sales Range: $125-149.9 Million
Emp.: 15
Eletric Power Generation Services
N.A.I.C.S.: 221118
Albrecht Schleich (Gen Mgr)

Dutchdelta Finance SARL (1)
Grand Rue 99, 1661, Luxembourg, Luxem-
bourg
Tel.: (352) 2686851
Financial Management Services
N.A.I.C.S.: 523999

**E WIE EINFACH Strom & Gas
GmbH** (1)
Salierring 47-53, 50677, Cologne, Germany
Tel.: (49) 22178965800
Web Site: http://www.e-wie-einfach.de
Electric Power & Gas Distribution Services
N.A.I.C.S.: 221122

E.ON Academy GmbH (1)
Ehrenhof 3, 40479, Dusseldorf, Germany
Tel.: (49) 21145797317
Web Site: http://www.academy.eon.com
Sales Range: $25-49.9 Million
Emp.: 30
Educational & Corporate Training Services
N.A.I.C.S.: 923110

E.ON Anlagenservice GmbH (1)
Zentrale Bergmannsgluecksstrasse 41-43,
45896, Gelsenkirchen, Germany
Tel.: (49) 2096015050
Web Site: http://www.eon-
anlagenservice.com
Process Plant Technology, Electrical Engi-
neering, Steam Generation, Mechanical En-
gineering, Instrumentation & Control
N.A.I.C.S.: 811310

E.ON Austria GmbH (1)
Niederhofstr 37, 1010, Vienna, Austria
Tel.: (43) 15322965
Sales Range: $75-99.9 Million
Emp.: 5
Electric Power Distribution Services
N.A.I.C.S.: 221122
Siegfried Lechner (Acct Mgr)

E.ON Avacon Vertrieb GmbH (1)
Schillerstrasse 3, Helmstedt, 38350, Nieder-
sachsen, Germany
Tel.: (49) 53511230
Electricity & Natural Gas Distribution Ser-
vices
N.A.I.C.S.: 221122

E.ON Avacon Warme GmbH (1)
Jacobistreet 3, 31157, Sarstedt, Germany
Tel.: (49) 5 066 830
Web Site: http://www.eon.de
Heating Equipment Distr
N.A.I.C.S.: 423730

**E.ON Bayern Warme 1.
Beteiligungs-GmbH** (1)
Lilienthalstr 7, 93049, Regensburg, Bayern,
Germany
Tel.: (49) 941 3839 0
Management Consulting Services
N.A.I.C.S.: 541618

E.ON Bayern Warme GmbH (1)
Lilienthalstrasse 7, 93049, Regensburg,
Germany
Tel.: (49) 9 41 2 01 00
Web Site: http://www.eon-bayern.com
Electricity & Natural Gas Distribution Ser-
vices
N.A.I.C.S.: 221122

E.ON Belgium N.V. (1)
Kunstlaan 40, 1040, Brussels, 1040, Belgium

Tel.: (32) 2 743 33 33
Web Site: http://www.eon.com
Sales Range: $75-99.9 Million
Emp.: 25
Electric Power & Gas Distribution Services
N.A.I.C.S.: 221122
Rob Oudshoorn (CEO)

E.ON Benelux CCS Project B.V. (1)
Capelseweg 400, Rotterdam, 3068 AX,
Netherlands
Tel.: (31) 102895097
Web Site: http://www.eon.nl
Electric Power Distribution Services
N.A.I.C.S.: 221122
F. Bruin (Gen Mgr)

**E.ON Beteiligungsverwaltungs
GmbH** (1)
E On-Platz 1, Dusseldorf, 40479,
Nordrhein-Westfalen, Germany
Tel.: (49) 21145790
Web Site: http://www.eon.com
Administrative Management Consulting Ser-
vices
N.A.I.C.S.: 541611

E.ON Bioerdgas GmbH (1)
Tel.: (49) 2011847831
Web Site: https://www.eon.com
Emp.: 10
Bio Gas Production & Distr
N.A.I.C.S.: 213112
Uwe Pauer (Mng Dir)

**E.ON Building Services
Academy** (1)
Unit 2 Bloomfield Pk Bloomfield Road, Tip-
ton, DY4 9AH, West Midlands, United King-
dom
Tel.: (44) 121 5226969
Industrial Training & Development Services
N.A.I.C.S.: 611430

**E.ON Climate & Renewables
GmbH** (1)
Brusseler Platz 1, 45131, Essen, Germany
Tel.: (49) 211 4579 0
Eletric Power Generation Services
N.A.I.C.S.: 221118
Mike Winkel (CEO)

Subsidiary (Non-US):

E.ON Renovables, S.L. (2)
Torre Picasso Pl 42 Pza Pablo Ruiz Pica-
sso s/n, Madrid, 28020, Spain
Tel.: (34) 9 1418 4400
Wind Electric Power Generation Services
N.A.I.C.S.: 221118

**E.ON Climate & Renewables North
America LLC** (1)
353 N Clark St Fl 30, Chicago, IL 60654
Tel.: (312) 923-9463
Web Site: http://www.eoncrna.com
Sales Range: $75-99.9 Million
Emp.: 75
Eletric Power Generation Services
N.A.I.C.S.: 221118
Steve Trenholm (CEO)

Subsidiary (Domestic):

EC&R Energy Marketing, LLC (2)
353 N Clark St Fl 30, Chicago, IL 60611
Tel.: (312) 923-9463
Management Consulting Services
N.A.I.C.S.: 541618

**E.ON Comercializadora de Ultimo
Recurso S.L.** (1)
Calle Medio 12, Santander, 39003, Spain
Tel.: (34) 942 24 60 00
Electric Power Distribution Services
N.A.I.C.S.: 221122

E.ON Danmark A/S (1)
Dirch Passers Alle 76, DK-2000, Frederiks-
berg, Denmark
Tel.: (45) 70270577
Web Site: https://www.eon.dk
Sales Range: $1-9.9 Million
Emp.: 60
Electric Power Distr
N.A.I.C.S.: 221122

Subsidiary (Domestic):

E.ON Varme Danmark ApS (2)
Dirch Passers Alle 76, DK-2000, Frederiks-

berg, Denmark
Tel.: (45) 44854100
Sales Range: $50-74.9 Million
Emp.: 5
Electric Power Distribution Services
N.A.I.C.S.: 221122

E.ON Direkt GmbH (1)
Brusseler Platz 1, 45131, Essen, Germany
Tel.: (49) 2 01 1 84 74 32
Web Site: http://www.eon.com
Sales Range: $75-99.9 Million
Emp.: 2
Electric Power Distribution Services
N.A.I.C.S.: 221122

E.ON Distribucija plina d.o.o. (1)
Ulica Mosna 15, 48000, Koprivnica, Croatia
Tel.: (385) 8005522
Web Site: https://www.eondistribucija.hr
Natural Gas Distr
N.A.I.C.S.: 486210

E.ON Drive GmbH (1)
Arnulfstrasse 203, 80634, Munich, Germany
Tel.: (49) 8001000380
Web Site: https://www.eon-drive.de
Eletric Power Generation Services
N.A.I.C.S.: 221118

E.ON Elektrarne s.r.o. (1)
SPP Kompresorova Stanica 3, 919 33, Tra-
kovice, Slovakia
Tel.: (421) 33 32 35 101
Web Site: http://www.elektraren-
malzenice.sk
Sales Range: $75-99.9 Million
Emp.: 35
Electric Power Generation & Distribution
Services
N.A.I.C.S.: 221118

E.ON Energiatermelo Kft. (1)
Szabo Kalman u 1, H- 4030, Debrecen,
Hungary (100%)
Tel.: (36) 52512800
Web Site: https://www.eon-hungaria.com
Electric Power Distribution Services
N.A.I.C.S.: 221122

E.ON Energie AG (1)
Brienner Strasse 40, 80333, Munich,
Germany (100%)
Tel.: (49) 89125401
Web Site: https://www.eon-energie.com
Sales Range: $550-599.9 Million
Emp.: 700
Production & Distribution of Electric Power;
Heating, Gas & Water Supply Services
N.A.I.C.S.: 221122
Johannes TysonTson (Mng Dir)

Subsidiary (Domestic):

Amrumbank-West GmbH (2)
Denisstr 2, Munich, 45131, Germany
Tel.: (49) 89 1254 01
Web Site: http://www.eon.com
Eletric Power Generation Services
N.A.I.C.S.: 221118

Joint Venture (Non-US):

Baltic Cable AB (2)
Nobelvaegen 66, 205 09, Malmo, Sweden
Tel.: (46) 40256130
Web Site: http://www.balticcable.com
Sales Range: $25-49.9 Million
Emp.: 3
Telecommunications Services; Owned
66.7% by Statkraft Energy Europe AS &
33.3% by E.ON Sverige AB
N.A.I.C.S.: 517111
Jan Brewitz (Mng Dir)

Subsidiary (Domestic):

BauMineral GmbH Herten (2)
Hiberniastrasse 12, 45699, Herten,
Germany (100%)
Tel.: (49) 23665090
Web Site: http://www.baumineral.de
Sales Range: $25-49.9 Million
Emp.: 100
Treatment & Marketing of Power Station
By-products
N.A.I.C.S.: 237130
Burkhard Jakobuss (CEO & Gen Mgr)

E.ON Avacon AG (2)

Schillerstrasse 3, Helmstedt, 38350,
Germany (67.2%)
Tel.: (49) 53511230
Web Site: http://www.eon-avacon.com
Sales Range: $200-249.9 Million
Emp.: 500
Electronic Services
N.A.I.C.S.: 221122

E.ON Bayern AG (2)
Henkel Strasse 1, 93049, Regensburg,
Germany (100%)
Tel.: (49) 8952080
Web Site: http://www.eon-bayern.com
Sales Range: $25-49.9 Million
Emp.: 260
Electronic Services
N.A.I.C.S.: 561990
Peter Deml (CEO)

Branch (Domestic):

Bayernwerk AG (3)
Lilienthalstrasse 7, 93049, Regensburg,
Germany
Tel.: (49) 94120100
Web Site: http://www.bayernwerk.de
Sales Range: $100-124.9 Million
Electronic Services
N.A.I.C.S.: 221122
Thomas Konig (Chm-Supervisory Bd)

Subsidiary (Domestic):

E.ON Bayern Vertrieb GmbH (2)
Luitpoldplatz 5, 95444, Bayreuth,
Germany (90.7%)
Tel.: (49) 9212850
Web Site: http://www.eon-netz.com
Energy Services
N.A.I.C.S.: 221122

Subsidiary (Non-US):

E.ON Ceska republika, s.r.o. (2)
F. A. Gerstnera 2151/6, Ceske Budejovice
7, 370 01, Ceske Budejovice, 7, Czech
Republic (100%)
Tel.: (420) 533039470
Electricity Production & Sales
N.A.I.C.S.: 221122

Subsidiary (Domestic):

E.ON Distribuce, a.s. (3)
Lannova 205/16, 370 49, Ceske Budejov-
ice, Czech Republic (100%)
Tel.: (420) 840111333
Web Site: http://www.eon-distribuce.cz
Electric Power Distr
N.A.I.C.S.: 221122

E.ON Energie, a.s. (3)
FA Gerstnera 2151/6, 37001, Ceske Bude-
jovice, 7, Czech Republic
Tel.: (420) 533039470
Electric Power Distr
N.A.I.C.S.: 221122
Claudia Viohl (CEO)

Subsidiary (Domestic):

E.ON Czech Holding AG (2)
Denisstr 2, Munich, 80335, Bayern, Ger-
many
Tel.: (49) 8912543156
Web Site: http://www.eon.cz
Sales Range: $50-74.9 Million
Emp.: 8
Investment Management Service
N.A.I.C.S.: 523999

**E.ON Energie 31. Beteiligungsgesell-
schaft mbH Munchen** (2)
Brienner Str 40, Munich, 80333, Germany
Tel.: (49) 89125401
Web Site: http://www.eonenergie.com
Financial Management Services
N.A.I.C.S.: 523999
Ingo Luge (Gen Mgr)

**E.ON Energie 39.
Beteiligungs-GmbH** (2)
Brienner Str 40, Munich, 80333, Bayern,
Germany
Tel.: (49) 89125401
Web Site: http://www.eon-energy.com
Energy Consulting Services
N.A.I.C.S.: 541690
Ingo Luge (CEO)

E.ON Energy Projects GmbH (2)
Denisstrasse 2, 80335, Munich, Germany
Tel.: (49) 89125409
Sales Range: $100-124.9 Million
Emp.: 60
Electricity, Heat Generation, Compressed
Air & Water & Renewable Energies Project
Developer, Financer & Plant Operator
N.A.I.C.S.: 221122

Subsidiary (Domestic):

**KGW-Kraftwerk Grenzach-Wyhlen
GmbH** (3)
Arnulfstr 56, Munich, 80335, Germany
Tel.: (49) 89125409
Web Site: https://www.eon.com
Eletric Power Generation Services
N.A.I.C.S.: 221118

Subsidiary (Domestic):

E.ON Energy Sales GmbH (2)
Brusseler Platz 1, 45131, Essen, Germany
Tel.: (49) 2011842756
Web Site: http://www.eon-energy-sales.com
Electric Power & Natural Gas Distribution
Services
N.A.I.C.S.: 221122

Subsidiary (Non-US):

E.ON Hungaria Zrt. (2)
Szechenyi Istvan ter 7-8, 1051, Budapest,
Hungary
Tel.: (36) 14722300
Web Site: http://www.eon-hungaria.com
Rev.: $1,498,077,056
Emp.: 600
Energy Services
N.A.I.C.S.: 221122
Konrad Kreuzer (Chm)

Subsidiary (Domestic):

**E.ON Del-dunantuli Aramszolgaltato
Zrt.** (3)
Rakoczi ut 73/b., 7626, Pecs,
Hungary (100%)
Tel.: (36) 72 501 000
Web Site: http://www.eon-hungaria.com
Sales Range: $75-99.9 Million
Emp.: 100
Electricity Distribution Services
N.A.I.C.S.: 221122

**E.ON Del-dunantuli Gazszolgaltato
Zrt.** (3)
Bzza tir 8/a, H-7626, Pecs,
Hungary (99.94%)
Tel.: (36) 40 220 220
Web Site: http://hungaria.com
Gas Supplies, System Operations, Network
Development & Maintenance
N.A.I.C.S.: 221210

E.ON Energiakereskedo Kft. (3)
Szechenyi rkp 8, H-1054, Budapest,
Hungary (100%)
Tel.: (36) 13542660
Web Site:
   http://www.eon-energiakereskedo.com
Rev.: $142,366,829
Energy Services
N.A.I.C.S.: 221122

**E.ON Eszak-Dunantuli Aramszolgal-
tato Zrt.** (3)
Kando Klmn u 13, 9027, Gyor,
Hungary (100%)
Tel.: (36) 96521000
Web Site: https://e-iroda.eon-
   eszakdunantul.com
Electric Power Distribution, Network Devel-
opment & Maintenance & System Opera-
tions
N.A.I.C.S.: 221122
Lajos Gelencser (Chm)

E.ON Szolgalato Kft. (3)
Kando Kando u 11-13, 9027, Gyor, Hungary
Tel.: (36) 696521637
Property & Vehicles Operator
N.A.I.C.S.: 561499

**E.ON Tiszantuli Aramszolgaltato
Rt.** (3)
Kossuth Ut 41, 4024, Debrecen,
Hungary (100%)
Tel.: (36) 52 512 400

Web Site: http://www.eon-hungaria.com
Sales Range: $250-299.9 Million
Electric Power Supplier
N.A.I.C.S.: 221122
Csaba Mezo (Chm)

**Energetikai es Tavkozlesi Haloza-
tepito es Szerelo Kft.** (3)
Kando Kalman utca 11-13, 9027, Gyor,
Hungary
Tel.: (36) 696521188
Web Site: http://www.eon.com
N.A.I.C.S.: 237130

KOGAZ Rt. (3)
Zrinyi Miklos utca 32, H-8800, Nagykanizsa,
Hungary (98.11%)
Tel.: (36) 93321300
Web Site: http://www.eon-hungaria.com
Pipeline Gas Supplier
N.A.I.C.S.: 221210

Subsidiary (Domestic):

E.ON IS Furstenwalde (2)
Langewahler Strasse 60, D-15517, Fursten-
walde, Germany (70%)
Tel.: (49) 180 12 13 14 0
Gas Services
N.A.I.C.S.: 213112

E.ON IS GmbH (2)
Humboldtstrasse 33, 30169, Hannover,
Germany (60%)
Tel.: (49) 51112178505
Web Site: http://www.eon-is.com
Sales Range: $400-449.9 Million
IT Services
N.A.I.C.S.: 541519

Subsidiary (Non-US):

E.ON IS Hungary Kft. (3)
Corvin ter 10, 1011, Budapest, Hungary
Tel.: (36) 014878200
Web Site: http://www.eon-is.hu
Sales Range: $75-99.9 Million
Emp.: 350
IT Services; Owned 51% by E.ON IS GmbH
& 49% by E.ON Hungaria Zrt.
N.A.I.C.S.: 541519
Josef Guggenhuber (Mng Dir)

Subsidiary (Domestic):

E.ON Kernkraft GmbH (2)
Tresckowstrasse 5, PO Box 4849, 30457,
Hannover, Germany (100%)
Tel.: (49) 05114390
Web Site: http://www.eon-kernkraft.com
Nuclear Fuels
N.A.I.C.S.: 325180

E.ON Kraftwerke GmbH (2)
Bergmannsgluckstrasse 41-43, 45896,
Gelsenkirchen, Germany (100%)
Tel.: (49) 20960102
Web Site: http://www.eon-kraftwerke.com
Sales Range: $150-199.9 Million
Emp.: 5,058
Energy Services
N.A.I.C.S.: 541690
Dirk Eckei (Head-Materials & Economics)

Subsidiary (Domestic):

E.ON Engineering GmbH (3)
Bergmannsgluckstrasse 41 43, 45896,
Gelsenkirchen, Germany (100%)
Tel.: (49) 020960105
Web Site: http://www.eon-engineering.com
Sales Range: $150-199.9 Million
Emp.: 500
Portfolio Management & Operation of
Power Station Units Scholven G & H at
Gelsenkirchen-Buer
N.A.I.C.S.: 523940

E.ON Fernwaerme GmbH (3)
Bergmannsgluckstrasse 41-43, 45896,
Gelsenkirchen, Germany (100%)
Tel.: (49) 2096015071
Web Site: http://www.eon-fernwaerme.com
Sales Range: $50-74.9 Million
Emp.: 130
Operation of a District Heating Line be-
tween the VKR Power Station Shamrock &
the VEW Power Station Bochum
N.A.I.C.S.: 237130
Volkhard Ape (Dir-Sls)

E.ON Kraftwerke GmbH (3)
Tresckowstrasse 5, 30457, Hannover,
Germany (100%)
Tel.: (49) 5114394774
Web Site: http://www.eon-kraftwerke.com
Conventional Power Plants, District Heating
Plants & Thermal Waste-Treatment Ser-
vices
N.A.I.C.S.: 221112

**Fernwarmeversorgung Herne
GmbH** (3)
Grenzweg 18, 4690, Herne,
Germany (50%)
Tel.: (49) 2349600
Web Site: http://www.stadtwerke-bochum.de
Sales Range: $50-74.9 Million
Emp.: 200
Construction & Operation of a District Heat-
ing Network in the Urban Area of Herne 1
N.A.I.C.S.: 236220

Kraftwerk Schkopau GmbH (3)
Glueckaufstr 56, 45896, Gelsenkirchen,
Germany (100%)
Tel.: (49) 2096016272
Construction, Acquisition & Operation of
Power Stations; Distribution of Electricity,
Steam & Heat
N.A.I.C.S.: 237110

**OEWA Wasser und Abwasser
GmbH** (3)
Walter Kohn Strasse 1A, D-04356, Leipzig,
Germany (50%)
Tel.: (49) 3415285430
Web Site: http://www.wa-gruppe.de
Financing, Planning, Construction & Opera-
tion of Water Supply & Waste Water Dis-
posal Plants
N.A.I.C.S.: 522299

**enertech Energie und Technik
GmbH** (3)
Wasastrasse 50, Radebeul, 1445,
Germany (50%)
Tel.: (49) 3518398610
Web Site: http://www.enertech-eut.de
Planning of Fossil-fired Thermal Power Sta-
tions, Hydroelectric Power Stations, Dis-
posal Plants & Natural Gas Pipelines &
Compressor Plants
N.A.I.C.S.: 423830

Subsidiary (Domestic):

E.ON Metering GmbH (2)
Carl-von-Linde-Strasse 38, 85716, Unter-
schleissheim, 85716, Germany
Tel.: (49) 89 12 54 04
Sales Range: $50-74.9 Million
Emp.: 30
Electric Power Distribution Services
N.A.I.C.S.: 221122
Robert Pfluegl (Mng Dir)

Subsidiary (Non-US):

E.ON Moldova-Furnizare (2)
Strasse Stefan Cel Mare nr 22, Bacau,
600359, Romania (51%)
Tel.: (40) 235 305 555
Web Site: http://www.eon-moldova.com
Electric Power Distr
N.A.I.C.S.: 221122

Subsidiary (Domestic):

E.ON Netz GmbH (2)
Regionalleitung Oberfranken, Luitpoldplatz
5, 95444, Bayreuth, Germany (100%)
Web Site: http://www.eon-netz.com
Energy Services Provider
N.A.I.C.S.: 221122

E.ON Portfolio Solution GmbH (2)
Holzstrasse 6, 40221, Dusseldorf, Germany
Tel.: (49) 211732752530
Web Site: https://www.eon-portfolio-
   solution.com
Emp.: 15
Portfolio Management Services
N.A.I.C.S.: 523940
Hakan Larsson (Member-Mgmt Bd)

Affiliate (Domestic):

E.ON Wasserkraft GmbH (2)
Luitpoldstr 27, Landshut, 84034,
Germany (100%)

Tel.: (49) 87169402
Web Site: http://www.eon-wasserkraft.com
Sales Range: $100-124.9 Million
Emp.: 120
Energy Services
N.A.I.C.S.: 221122
Christof Gattermann (Mng Dir-Comml)

E.ON Westfalen Weser AG (2)
Tegelweg 25, 33102, Paderborn,
Germany (62.8%)
Tel.: (49) 52515030
Web Site: http://www.eon-
   westfalenweser.com
Energy Services
N.A.I.C.S.: 221122

Subsidiary (Domestic):

**E.ON Westfalen Weser Vertrieb
GmbH** (3)
Rolandsweg 80, Paderborn, 33102,
Nordrhein-Westfalen, Germany
Tel.: (49) 52515030
Web Site: http://www.eon.de
Sales Range: $450-499.9 Million
Emp.: 1,000
Electric Power Distribution Services
N.A.I.C.S.: 221122

**Kraftverkehrsgesellschaft Paderborn
mbH** (3)
Barkhauser Strasse 6, 33106, Paderborn,
Germany
Tel.: (49) 5251 76545
Web Site: http://www.kvp-paderborn.de
Transportation Services
N.A.I.C.S.: 488999

Affiliate (Domestic):

**Elektrizitaetswerk
Minden-Ravensberg** (2)
Postfach 15 42, 32005, Herford,
Germany (25.1%)
Web Site: http://www.emr.de
Distribution of Electric Power
N.A.I.C.S.: 221122

**Energieobjektgesellschaft
mbH-EOG** (2)
Allee der Kosmonauten 29, 12681, Berlin,
Germany (20.9%)
Electric Distribution Services
N.A.I.C.S.: 221122

Subsidiary (Domestic):

Energiewerke Rostock AG (2)
Bleicherstrasse 1, 2500, Rostock,
Germany (100%)
Tel.: (49) 3813820
Electric Distribution Services
N.A.I.C.S.: 221122

Affiliate (Domestic):

**Gemeinschaftskernkraftwerk Grohnde
GmbH** (2)
PO Box 1230, 31860, Emmerthal,
Germany (100%)
Tel.: (49) 5155671
Web Site: https://www.eon.com
Sales Range: $200-249.9 Million
Emp.: 300
Production of Electric Power
N.A.I.C.S.: 335999

**Gemeinschaftskraftwerk Kiel
GmbH** (2)
Hasselfelde 40, 24149, Kiel,
Germany (50%)
Tel.: (49) 43120020
Web Site: http://www.gkk-kiel.de
Sales Range: $25-49.9 Million
Emp.: 120
Production of Electric Power
N.A.I.C.S.: 335999
Klaus Nieder Hoff (Gen Mgr)

Subsidiary (Domestic):

HanseWerk AG (2)
Schleswag-HeinGas-Platz 1, 25450, Quick-
born, Germany (73.8%)
Tel.: (49) 41069998032
Web Site: https://www.hansewerk.com
Sales Range: $100-124.9 Million
Electric Power & Gas Distribution
N.A.I.C.S.: 221122

E.ON SE—(Continued)

Matthias Boxberger *(CEO, CTO & Member-Exec Bd)*

Subsidiary (Domestic):

E.ON Hanse Vertrieb GmbH   **(3)**
Kuuhnehofe 1 - 5, Hamburg, 22761, Germany
Tel.: (49) 40 6 05 90 00 00
Web Site: http://www.eon.de
Eelectricity & Natural Gas Distribution Services
N.A.I.C.S.: 221122

E.ON Hanse Warme GmbH
Am Radeland 25, 21079, Hamburg, Germany
Tel.: (49) 40 23 78 27 325
Web Site: http://www.eon-hanse-waerme.com
Solar Thermal Heating & Storage Services
N.A.I.C.S.: 238220

Joint Venture (Domestic):

KKK GmbH & Co OHV   **(2)**
Elbuferstrasse 82, Geesthacht, 21502, Germany   **(50%)**
Tel.: (49) 4152150
Nuclear Electric Power Generation
N.A.I.C.S.: 221113
Torsten Fricke *(Plant Mgr)*

Affiliate (Domestic):

Kernkraftwerk Brokdorf GmbH   **(2)**
Osterende 999, 25576, Brokdorf, Germany   **(80%)**
Tel.: (49) 48297501616
Web Site: https://www.eon-kernkraft.com
Sales Range: $350-399.9 Million
Production of Electric Power
N.A.I.C.S.: 335999

Kernkraftwerk Unterweser GmbH   **(2)**
Dedesdorser Str 2, Postfach 4849, 26935, Stadland, Germany   **(100%)**
Tel.: (49) 4732801
Web Site: http://www.eon-kernkraft.com
Sales Range: $75-99.9 Million
Emp.: 300
Production of Electric Power
N.A.I.C.S.: 335999
Gerd Reinstrom *(Plant Mgr)*

LSW LandE-Stadtwerke Wolfsburg GmbH & Co. KG   **(2)**
Hesslinger Strasse 1-5, 38432, Wolfsburg, Germany   **(25%)**
Tel.: (49) 53611893600
Web Site: http://www.lsw.de
Sales Range: $400-449.9 Million
Emp.: 600
Electric Power & Gas Services
N.A.I.C.S.: 221122

Ueberlandwerk Leinetal GmbH   **(2)**
Am Eltwerk 1, 31028, Gronau, Germany   **(48%)**
Tel.: (49) 51825880
Web Site: http://www.uewl.de
Sales Range: $25-49.9 Million
Electric Power Distribution
N.A.I.C.S.: 221122

Joint Venture (Non-US):

Zapadoslovenska energetika, a.s,   **(2)**
Culenova 6, 816 47, Bratislava, Slovakia
Tel.: (421) 377763880
Web Site: http://www.zse.sk
Electric Power Distr; Owned 51% by National Property Fund of the Slovak Republic & 49% by E.ON Energie AG
N.A.I.C.S.: 221122
Eva Milucka *(Chm-Supervisory Bd)*

E.ON Energie Odnawialne Sp. z o.o.   **(1)**
Plac Rodla 8 Pok2003, 70-419, Szczecin, Poland
Tel.: (48) 913594281
Web Site: http://www.eon.pl
Sales Range: $75-99.9 Million
Emp.: 13
Electric Power Distribution Services
N.A.I.C.S.: 221122
Mathias Leistenschneider *(Gen Mgr)*

E.ON Energie Romania S.A.   **(1)**
Bd Pandurilor nr 42, RO-540554, Tirgu Mures, Mures, Romania
Tel.: (40) 265200366
Web Site: https://www.eon.ro
Electric Power & Natural Gas Distribution Services
N.A.I.C.S.: 221122

E.ON Energihandel Nordic AB   **(1)**
Carl Gustafs vag 1, 205 09, Malmo, Skane, Sweden
Tel.: (46) 40255000
Web Site: http://www.eon.se
Gas & Electric Power Distributing Services
N.A.I.C.S.: 221210
Jonas Abraham *(Gen Mgr)*

E.ON Energy Infrastructure Solutions d.o.o.   **(1)**
Capraska street 6, 10000, Zagreb, Croatia
Tel.: (385) 16447100
Solar Power Plant Construction Services
N.A.I.C.S.: 221114

E.ON Energy Trading Bulgarien EOOD   **(1)**
Varna Towers Tower G 258 Vladislav Varnenchik Blvd, Varna, 9009, Bulgaria
Tel.: (359) 52577000
Electric Power Distribution Services
N.A.I.C.S.: 221122

E.ON Energy Trading Holding GmbH   **(1)**
E On-Platz 1, Dusseldorf, 40479, Nordrhein-Westfalen, Germany
Tel.: (49) 211732750
Web Site: http://www.eon.com
Investment Management Service
N.A.I.C.S.: 523999

E.ON Energy Trading NL Staff Company B.V.   **(1)**
Capelseweg 400, Rotterdam, 3068 AX, Zuid-Holland, Netherlands
Tel.: (31) 102895711
Sales Range: $75-99.9 Million
Emp.: 9
Electric Power Distribution Services
N.A.I.C.S.: 221122

E.ON Eromuvek Termelo es Uzemelteto Kft   **(1)**
Roosevelt ter 7-8, 1051, Budapest, Hungary
Tel.: (36) 1 373 3529
Electric Power Distribution Services
N.A.I.C.S.: 221122

E.ON Europa, S.L.   **(1)**
Ribera Del Loira 60, Madrid, 28042, Spain
Tel.: (34) 915 66 88 00
Electricity Production & Distribution Services
N.A.I.C.S.: 221118

E.ON First Future Energy Holding B.V.   **(1)**
Capelseweg 400, Rotterdam, 3068 AX, Zuid-Holland, Netherlands
Tel.: (31) 102895711
Web Site: https://www.eon.com
Investment Management Service
N.A.I.C.S.: 523940

E.ON France Management S.A.S.   **(1)**
5 Rue Athenes, 75009, Paris, France
Tel.: (33) 144633998
Web Site: http://www.eon.de
Emp.: 15
Electric Power Generation & Distribution Services
N.A.I.C.S.: 221118

E.ON France S.A.S.   **(1)**
5 Rue d'Athenes, 75009, Paris, France
Tel.: (33) 1 44 63 39 98
Web Site: http://www.eon-france.com
Rev.: $2,625,601,930
Emp.: 885
Electric Power & Gas Distribution Services
N.A.I.C.S.: 221122
Luc Poyer *(Chm)*

E.ON Gaz Distributie S.A.   **(1)**
Piata Trandafirilor No 21, Tirgu Mures, 540049, Mures, Romania
Tel.: (40) 365 40 36 00
Web Site: http://www.eon-gaz-distributie.ro

Sales Range: $1-4.9 Billion
Emp.: 5,600
Natural Gas Distribution Services
N.A.I.C.S.: 221210
Virgil Metea *(Gen Dir)*

E.ON Gazdasagi Szolgalto Kft.   **(1)**
Kando Kalman Utca 11-13, Gyor, 9027, Hungary
Tel.: (36) 96521841
Sales Range: $200-249.9 Million
Emp.: 50
Financial Management Services
N.A.I.C.S.: 523999
Zsolt Temesvary *(Gen Mgr)*

E.ON Grid Solutions GmbH   **(1)**
Normannenweg 9, 20537, Hamburg, Germany
Tel.: (49) 402533453399
Web Site: https://www.eon-gridsolutions.com
Emp.: 1,150
Energy Data Management Services
N.A.I.C.S.: 541690

E.ON Gruga Geschaftsfuhrungsgesellschaft mbH   **(1)**
E On-Platz 1, 40479, Dusseldorf, Nordrhein-Westfalen, Germany
Tel.: (49) 21145790
Business Management Consulting Services
N.A.I.C.S.: 541611
Johannes Teyssen *(CEO)*

E.ON Gruga Objektgesellschaft mbH & Co. KG   **(1)**
E ON-Platz 1, 40479, Dusseldorf, Nordrhein-Westfalen, Germany
Tel.: (49) 21145790
Real Estate Manangement Services
N.A.I.C.S.: 531390

E.ON Halozati Szolgalato Kft.   **(1)**
Malomvolgyi Utca 2, Pecs, 7636, Hungary
Tel.: (36) 72501000
Water & Sewer Line Construction Services
N.A.I.C.S.: 237110

E.ON Human Resources International GmbH   **(1)**
Brienner Str 40, Munich, 80333, Germany
Tel.: (49) 89125401
Human Resource Consulting Services
N.A.I.C.S.: 541612

E.ON INTERNATIONAL FINANCE B.V.   **(1)**
Capelseweg 400, Rotterdam, 3068 AX, Netherlands
Tel.: (31) 102895640
Financial Management Services
N.A.I.C.S.: 523999
Eric Choy *(Gen Mgr)*

E.ON IT Bulgaria EOOD   **(1)**
Varna Towers 258 Vladislav Varnenchik, Varna, 9009, Bulgaria
Tel.: (359) 52577000
Information Technology Consulting Services
N.A.I.C.S.: 541512

E.ON IT Hungary Kft.   **(1)**
Szechenyi Istvan Ter 7-8, Budapest, 1051, Hungary
Tel.: (36) 14722300
Information Technology Consulting Services
N.A.I.C.S.: 541512

E.ON IT Netherlands B.V.   **(1)**
Capelseweg 400, Rotterdam, 3068 AX, Zuid-Holland, Netherlands
Tel.: (31) 102895711
Information Technology Consulting Services
N.A.I.C.S.: 541512

E.ON IT Sverige AB   **(1)**
Carl Gustavs vag 1, 205 09, Malmo, Sweden
Tel.: (46) 40 25 50 00
Information Technology Consulting Services
N.A.I.C.S.: 541618

E.ON IT UK Limited   **(1)**
Westwood Way, Coventry, CV4 8LG, United Kingdom
Tel.: (44) 24 7642 4000
Information Technology Consulting Services
N.A.I.C.S.: 541618

E.ON Iberia Holding GmbH   **(1)**

E On-Platz 1, Dusseldorf, 40479, Nordrhein-Westfalen, Germany
Tel.: (49) 21145790
Investment Management Service
N.A.I.C.S.: 523940

E.ON Inhouse Consulting GmbH   **(1)**
Grafinger Strasse 2, Munich, 81671, Germany
Tel.: (49) 89 418 601 185
Sales Range: $25-49.9 Million
Emp.: 100
Business Management Consulting Services
N.A.I.C.S.: 541611

E.ON Invest GmbH   **(1)**
Nordliche Munchner Strasse 14, 82031, Grunwald, 82031, Bavaria, Germany
Tel.: (49) 8964913672021
Investment Management Service
N.A.I.C.S.: 523999

E.ON Kainuu Oy   **(1)**
Ahontie 1 PL 5, 87101, Kajaani, Finland
Tel.: (358) 1022 6000
Web Site: http://www.eon.fi
Emp.: 40
Electricity Power Distribution & Transmission Services
N.A.I.C.S.: 221122
Markku Ryymin *(Gen Mgr)*

E.ON Kozep-dunantuli Gazhalozati Zrt.   **(1)**
Zrinyi Miklos Utca 32, Nagykanizsa, 8800, Hungary
Tel.: (36) 93503600
Oil & Gas Exploration Services
N.A.I.C.S.: 213112

E.ON Kundenservice GmbH   **(1)**
Steindamm 100, 20099, Hamburg, Germany
Tel.: (49) 402533450
Web Site: http://www.eon.
Sales Range: $500-549.9 Million
Emp.: 600
Electric Power Distr
N.A.I.C.S.: 221122
Hans-Gilbert Meyer *(Chm-Mgmt Bd)*

E.ON Mitte Warme GmbH   **(1)**
Monteverdistrasse 2, 34131, Kassel, Germany
Tel.: (49) 561 933 03
Web Site: http://www.eon-mitte-waerme.com
Electric Power Distribution Services
N.A.I.C.S.: 221122

E.ON MyEnergy Kft.   **(1)**
Vaci ut 17, 1134, Budapest, Hungary
Tel.: (36) 680200879
Eletric Power Generation Services
N.A.I.C.S.: 221118

E.ON NA Capital LLC   **(1)**
2751 Centerville Rd Ste 231, Wilmington, DE 19808
Tel.: (302) 996-9020
Financial Management Services
N.A.I.C.S.: 523999

E.ON New Build & Technology GmbH   **(1)**
Alexander-von-Humboldt-Strasse 1, 45896, Gelsenkirchen, 45896, Germany
Tel.: (49) 2 09 601 50 10
Engineering & Scientific Services
N.A.I.C.S.: 541330

Subsidiary (Domestic):

HGC Hamburg Gas Consult GmbH   **(2)**
Eiffestr 78, 20537, Hamburg, Germany
Tel.: (49) 40 23 53 30
Web Site: http://www.hgc-hamburg.de
Sales Range: $10-24.9 Million
Emp.: 50
Gas & Heat Supply Engineering Services
N.A.I.C.S.: 541330
Peter Uhl *(Mng Dir-Quality Mgmt & Supply Infrastructure)*

E.ON Produktion Danmark A/S   **(1)**
Norrelundvej 10, Herlev, 2730, Denmark
Tel.: (45) 44854100
Web Site: https://www.eon.dk
Sales Range: $50-74.9 Million
Emp.: 50
Eltric Power Generation Services

N.A.I.C.S.: 221118
Tore Harritshoj *(CEO)*

E.ON Produzione Centrale Livorno Ferraris S.p.A. **(1)**
SP 7 Km 430, 13046, Livorno Ferraris, Vercelli, Italy
Tel.: (39) 0161 1985201
Emp.: 30
Electric Power Production Services
N.A.I.C.S.: 221118
Alberto Barbieri *(Branch Mgr)*

E.ON Regenerabile Romania S.R.L **(1)**
146-150 Ciurchi Str, Iasi, 700359, Romania
Tel.: (40) 232405076
Sales Range: $75-99.9 Million
Emp.: 6
Eletric Power Generation Services
N.A.I.C.S.: 221118

E.ON Renovaveis Portugal, SGPS S.A. **(1)**
Avenida Dom Joao II Lote 1 06 2 3 7 B, 1990-095, Lisbon, Portugal
Tel.: (351) 211 554 944
Sales Range: $75-99.9 Million
Emp.: 4
Eletric Power Generation Services
N.A.I.C.S.: 221118

E.ON Risk Consulting GmbH **(1)**
Kennedydamm 17, Dusseldorf, 40476, Nordrhein-Westfalen, Germany
Tel.: (49) 21147970
Web Site: http://www.eon.com
Emp.: 300
Insurance Risk Management Services
N.A.I.C.S.: 524298
Johannesson Teyssen *(CEO)*

E.ON Romania S.R.L. **(1)**
Justitiei nr 12, 540069, Tirgu Mures, Romania **(99.92%)**
Tel.: (40) 365 40 35 46
Web Site: http://www.eon-romania.ro
Natural Gas & Electricity Distribution Services
N.A.I.C.S.: 221210
Patrick Lammers *(Pres)*

E.ON Ruhrgas AG **(1)**
Brueissilir Platz, 45131, Essen, Germany
Tel.: (49) 20118400
Web Site: http://www.eon-ruhrgas.com
Sales Range: $10-24.9 Million
Emp.: 11,520
Natural Gas Distr
N.A.I.C.S.: 221210
Klaus Schaefer *(Pres)*

Subsidiary (Non-US):

E.ON Ruhrgas Austria GmbH **(2)**
Kantgasse 1, Vienna, 1010, Austria
Tel.: (43) 15322963
Web Site: http://www.eon-ruhrgas-austria.at
Oil & Gas Exploration Services
N.A.I.C.S.: 213112

E.ON Ruhrgas BBL B.V. **(2)**
Capelseweg 400, Rotterdam, 3068 AX, Netherlands
Tel.: (31) 10 2 89 57 91
Natural Gas Distr
N.A.I.C.S.: 221210

E.ON Ruhrgas Dutch Holding B.V. **(2)**
Capelseweg 400, 3068 AX, Rotterdam, Zuid-Holland, Netherlands
Tel.: (31) 104780855
Investment Management Service
N.A.I.C.S.: 523940

Subsidiary (Domestic):

E.ON Ruhrgas E & P Agypten GmbH **(2)**
Brusseler Platz 1, 45138, Essen, Nordrhein-Westfalen, Germany
Tel.: (49) 201 18400
Web Site: http://www.eon.com
Eletric Power Generation Services
N.A.I.C.S.: 221118

E.ON Ruhrgas E & P GmbH **(2)**
Brusseler Platz 1, 45131, Essen, Germany
Tel.: (49) 2 01 1 84 44 43

Oil & Gas Exploration Services
N.A.I.C.S.: 213112

E.ON Ruhrgas GGH GmbH **(2)**
Brusseler Platz 1, Essen, 45131, Nordrhein-Westfalen, Germany
Tel.: (49) 20118400
Web Site: http://www.eon.com
Natural Gas Distribution Services
N.A.I.C.S.: 221210
Guy Creten *(CEO)*

E.ON Ruhrgas GPA GmbH **(2)**
Brusseler Platz 1, Essen, 45131, Nordrhein-Westfalen, Germany
Tel.: (49) 20118400
Oil & Gas Exploration Services
N.A.I.C.S.: 213112

E.ON Ruhrgas International AG **(2)**
Brusseler Platz 1, Essen, 45131, Germany **(100%)**
Tel.: (49) 20118400
Web Site: http://www.eon.com
Gas Production & Distr
N.A.I.C.S.: 221210
Ulrich Schoeler *(Chm & Mng Dir)*

E.ON Ruhrgas Personalagentur GmbH **(2)**
Brusseler Platz 1, Essen, 45131, Nordrhein-Westfalen, Germany
Tel.: (49) 20118400
Web Site: http://www.eon.com
Oil & Gas Exploration Services
N.A.I.C.S.: 213112

Subsidiary (Non-US):

E.ON Ruhrgas UK E&P Limited **(2)**
Davis Ho, London, SW1V 1JZ, United Kingdom
Tel.: (44) 20 3004 3700
Upstreaming Oil & Gas Services
N.A.I.C.S.: 213112

Subsidiary (Domestic):

E.ON E&P **(3)**
7th Floor Davis House 129 Wilton Road, London, SW1V 1JZ, United Kingdom
Tel.: (44) 2030043700
Web Site: http://www.eon.com
Natural Gas Exploration Service
N.A.I.C.S.: 211130

Subsidiary (Domestic):

Ferngas Nordbayern GmbH **(2)**
Further Strasse 13, 90429, Nuremberg, Bavaria, Germany **(53.1%)**
Tel.: (49) 911277700
Web Site: http://www.ferngas-nordbayern.de
Sales Range: $800-899.9 Million
Emp.: 35
Gas Supplier
N.A.I.C.S.: 221210

Gas-Union GmbH **(2)**
Riedbergplatz 1, 60438, Frankfurt am Main, Germany
Tel.: (49) 6930030
Web Site: http://www.gas-union.de
Emp.: 50
Gas Exploration
N.A.I.C.S.: 221210
Rainer Vogt *(Head-Tech Storage & Svcs)*

Harterei VTN Witten GmbH **(2)**
Rusbergstrasse 75, Herbede, 58456, Witten, Germany **(100%)**
Tel.: (49) 232493420
Web Site: http://www.ihi-vtn.com
Supplier of Heating Appliances.
N.A.I.C.S.: 423720

LOI Thermprocess Gmbh **(2)**
Am Lichtbogen 29, 45141, Essen, Germany **(100%)**
Tel.: (49) 20118911
Web Site: http://www.loi.tenova.com
Emp.: 120
N.A.I.C.S.: 221210
Hermann Stumpp *(Mng Dir)*

Lubmin-Brandov Gastransport GmbH **(2)**
Norbertstrasse 85, Essen, 45131, Nordrhein-Westfalen, Germany
Tel.: (49) 20143999992
Web Site: http://www.lbtg.de

Gas Transportation Services
N.A.I.C.S.: 486210
Oliver Giese *(Mng Dir)*

NGT Neue Gebaudetechnik GmbH **(2)**
Haengebank 13, 45307, Essen, Germany **(100%)**
Tel.: (49) 20185220
N.A.I.C.S.: 221210

PLE Pipeline Engineering GmbH **(2)**
Gurtelstrasse 29 A 30, 10247, Berlin, Germany **(85%)**
Tel.: (49) 30293855
Web Site: http://www.ple-engineering.com
Sales Range: $1-9.9 Million
Emp.: 100
Design, Install or Commission Plant & Equipment for the Transportation, Treatment, Storage or Distribution of Gases, Liquids or Solids
N.A.I.C.S.: 221210

E.ON Russia Holding GmbH **(1)**
E ON-Platz 1, Dusseldorf, 40479, Germany
Tel.: (49) 211 45790
Electric Power Generation & Distributing Services
N.A.I.C.S.: 221118

E.ON Service GmbH **(1)**
Brusseler Platz 1, Essen, 45131, Germany
Tel.: (49) 2 01 1 84 00
Web Site: http://www.eon-service.com
Human Resource Consulting Services
N.A.I.C.S.: 541612

E.ON Servisni, s.r.o. **(1)**
F A Gerstnera 2151/6, 370 01, Ceske Budejovice, Czech Republic
Tel.: (49) 387 861 111
Web Site: http://www.eon.cz
Electric Power & Gas Distribution Services
N.A.I.C.S.: 221122

E.ON Suomi Oy **(1)**
Itamerenkatu 1, 00180, Helsinki, Finland
Tel.: (358) 0102265500
Web Site: http://www.eonsuomi.fi
Sales Range: $75-99.9 Million
Emp.: 4
Energy Services
N.A.I.C.S.: 221122

E.ON Sverige AB **(1)**
Carlsgatan 22, 211 20, Malmo, Sweden
Tel.: (46) 40255000
Web Site: https://www.eon.se
Sales Range: $150-199.9 Million
Emp.: 5,000
Electric Power Distr
N.A.I.C.S.: 221122
Johan Mornstam *(CEO)*

Subsidiary (Domestic):

E.ON Biofor Sverige AB **(2)**
Nobelvagen 66, 212 15, Malmo, Sweden
Tel.: (46) 40255000
Web Site: http://www.eon.se
Emp.: 1,000
Gasoline Whslr
N.A.I.C.S.: 424720
Jonas Abrahamsonn *(Mgr)*

E.ON Elnat Stockholm AB **(2)**
Carl Gustafs vag 1, Malmo, 21742, Sweden
Tel.: (46) 40 255000
Web Site: http://www.eon.se
Electric Power Distribution Services
N.A.I.C.S.: 221122
Jonas Abrahamsson *(Pres)*

E.ON Elnat Sverige AB **(2)**
Nobelvagen 66, Malmo, 20509, Sweden
Tel.: (46) 40 25 50 00
Web Site: http://www.eon.se
Emp.: 100
Electric Power Distribution Services
N.A.I.C.S.: 221122
Johan Mornstam *(CEO)*

E.ON Fastigheter Sverige AB **(2)**
Carl Gustavs v 1, 217 42, Malmo, Sweden
Tel.: (46) 40255000
Real Estate Development Services
N.A.I.C.S.: 531390

E.ON Forsaljning Sverige AB **(2)**

Carl Gustafs Vag 4, 205 09, Malmo, Sweden
Tel.: (46) 40 25 50 00
Emp.: 30
Electric Power Distribution Services
N.A.I.C.S.: 221122
Siegfried Ruckriegel *(CEO)*

E.ON Gas Sverige AB **(2)**
Nobelvagen 66, 205 09, Malmo, Skane, Sweden
Tel.: (46) 40 25 50 00
Web Site: http://www.eon.se
Natural Gas Transmission Services
N.A.I.C.S.: 486210
Anna Grauers *(Head-Customer Rels)*

E.ON Gashandel Sverige AB **(2)**
Carl Gustafs vag 1, Malmo, 205 09, Skane, Sweden
Tel.: (46) 40255000
Natural Gas Distr
N.A.I.C.S.: 221210

E.ON Gasification Development AB **(2)**
Carl Gustafs Vag 1, Malmo, 205 09, Skane, Sweden
Tel.: (46) 40255000
Web Site: http://www.eon.se
Sales Range: $450-499.9 Million
Emp.: 150
Gas Storage Services
N.A.I.C.S.: 486210
Bjoern Fredriksson *(Project Mgr)*

E.ON Karnkraft Sverige AB **(2)**
Carl Gustafs vag 1, 205 09, Malmo, Skane, Sweden
Tel.: (46) 40 25 50 00
Eletric Power Generation Services
N.A.I.C.S.: 221118

E.ON Kundsupport Sverige AB **(2)**
Carl Gustafs Vag 4, 205 09, Malmo, Skane, Sweden
Tel.: (46) 40255000
Customer Support Management Services
N.A.I.C.S.: 541613

E.ON Trading Nordic AB **(2)**
Carl Gustafs vaeg 1, 20509, Malmo, Sweden
Tel.: (46) 40255000
Web Site: http://www.eon.se
Sales Range: $50-74.9 Million
Emp.: 1,000
Energy Trading Services
N.A.I.C.S.: 425120
Jonas Abrahamsson *(CEO)*

E.ON Varme Sverige AB **(2)**
Carl Gustafs Vag 1, 205 09, Malmo, Sweden
Tel.: (46) 40 25 50 00
Web Site: http://www.eon.se
Heating Equipment Distr
N.A.I.C.S.: 423730
Marc Hoffmann *(CEO)*

E.ON Varmekraft Sverige AB **(2)**
Turbingatan 10, 30245, Halmstad, Sweden
Tel.: (46) 706256548
Management Consulting Services
N.A.I.C.S.: 541618

E.ON Vind Sverige AB **(2)**
Carl Gustafs Vag 1, 205 09, Malmo, Sweden
Tel.: (46) 40255000
Emp.: 8
Wind Electric Power Generation Services
N.A.I.C.S.: 221118
Marten Larson *(Project Coord-Offshore)*

Karlshamn Kraft AB **(2)**
Munkahusvagen 181, Karlshamn, 374 21, Sweden
Tel.: (46) 454 850 00
Web Site: http://www.karlshamnkraft.se
Emp.: 10
Eletric Power Generation Services
N.A.I.C.S.: 221118
Karin Jarl-Mansson *(Mgr)*

Sakab Sellbergs AB **(2)**
O Dravsan, Rattvik, 795 90, Sweden
Tel.: (46) 24810433
Waste Management Services
N.A.I.C.S.: 562998

E.ON SE—(Continued)

E.ON Trend s.r.o. (1)
FA Gerstnera 2151/6, 370 49, Ceske Bude-
jovice, Czech Republic
Tel.: (420) 387 867 512
Electric Power Generation & Distribution
Services
N.A.I.C.S.: 221118

Subsidiary (Domestic):

Teplarna Otrokovice a.s. (2)
Objizdna 1777, 765 02, Otrokovice, Czech
Republic
Tel.: (420) 577 649 111
Web Site: http://www.tot.cz
Electric Power Generation & Distribution
Services
N.A.I.C.S.: 221118

E.ON UK plc (1)
Westwood Way Westwood Business Park,
Coventry, CV4 8LG, West Midlands, United
Kingdom (100%)
Tel.: (44) 8085015200
Web Site: https://www.eonenergy.com
Sales Range: $15-24.9 Billion
Emp.: 8,000
Electric Generation, Retail Energy Distribu-
tion & Support Services
N.A.I.C.S.: 221112

Subsidiary (Domestic):

Citigen (London) Limited (2)
47-53 Charterhouse Street, London, EC1M
6PB, United Kingdom
Tel.: (44) 2075537400
Web Site: https://www.eon-uk.com
Sales Range: $75-99.9 Million
Emp.: 21
Electric Power Generation & Distribution
Services
N.A.I.C.S.: 221118

E.ON Climate & Renewables UK Bio-
mass Limited (2)
Westwood Way Westwood Business Park,
Coventry, CV4 8LG, West Midlands, United
Kingdom
Tel.: (44) 24 7642 4000
Eletric Power Generation Services
N.A.I.C.S.: 221118

E.ON Climate & Renewables UK
London Array Limited (2)
Westwood Way Westwood Business Park,
Coventry, CV4 8LG, West Midlands, United
Kingdom
Tel.: (44) 24 7642 4000
Electric Power Distribution Services
N.A.I.C.S.: 221122

E.ON Climate & Renewables UK Off-
shore Wind Limited (2)
Westwood Way Westwood Business Park,
Coventry, CV4 8LG, West Midlands, United
Kingdom
Tel.: (44) 24 7642 4000
Eletric Power Generation Services
N.A.I.C.S.: 221118

E.ON Climate & Renewables UK
Robin Rigg West Limited (2)
Westwood Way Westwood Business Park,
Coventry, CV4 8LG, West Midlands, United
Kingdom
Tel.: (44) 24 7642 4000
Electric Power Distribution Services
N.A.I.C.S.: 221122

E.ON Climate & Renewables UK
Wind Limited (2)
Westwood Way Westwood Business Park,
Coventry, CV4 8LG, West Midlands, United
Kingdom
Tel.: (44) 24 7642 4000
Eletric Power Generation Services
N.A.I.C.S.: 221118

E.ON Energy (2)
HN House Straits Road Lower Gornal, Dud-
ley, DY3 2UY, United Kingdom
Tel.: (44) 1384 212 992
Plumbing & Heating Equipment Installation
Services
N.A.I.C.S.: 238220

Subsidiary (Domestic):

CHN Electrical Services Limited (3)

---

7 Zoar Street Lower Gornal, Dudley, DY3
2PA, United Kingdom
Tel.: (44) 1384217860
Electrical Contracting Services
N.A.I.C.S.: 238210

Subsidiary (Domestic):

E.ON Energy UK Limited (2)
Westwood Way, Coventry, CV4 8LG, West
Midlands, United Kingdom
Tel.: (44) 24 7642 4000
Electric Power Distribution Services
N.A.I.C.S.: 221122

E.ON UK CHP Limited (2)
Winnington Lane, Winnington, Northwich,
CW8 4GX, Cheshire, United Kingdom
Tel.: (44) 1606723700
Sales Range: $50-74.9 Million
Emp.: 30
Eletric Power Generation Services
N.A.I.C.S.: 221118
Neil Price (Mgr-Site)

E.ON UK Energy Services
Limited (2)
Westwood Way Westwood Business Park,
Coventry, CV4 8LG, West Midlands, United
Kingdom
Tel.: (44) 24 7642 4000
Electric Power Generation & Distributing
Services
N.A.I.C.S.: 221118

E.ON UK Energy Solutions
Limited (2)
Westwood Way Westwood Business Park,
Coventry, CV4 8LG, West Midlands, United
Kingdom
Tel.: (44) 24 7642 4000
Management Consulting Services
N.A.I.C.S.: 541618

E.ON UK Holding Company
Limited (2)
Westwood Way, Westwood Business Park,
Coventry, CV4 8LG, West Midlands, United
Kingdom
Tel.: (44) 2476424000
Investment Management Service
N.A.I.C.S.: 523999

E.ON UK Power Technology
Limited (2)
Ratcliffe-on-Soar, Nottingham, NG11 0EE,
United Kingdom
Tel.: (44) 115 936 2000
Emp.: 500
Eletric Power Generation Services
N.A.I.C.S.: 221118
Michael Frank (Gen Mgr)

E.ON UK Property Services
Limited (2)
241 High Street, Kingswinford, DY6 8BN,
West Midlands, United Kingdom
Tel.: (44) 1384 217860
Web Site: http://www.eon.com
Sales Range: $1-4.9 Billion
Emp.: 5,000
Property Management Services
N.A.I.C.S.: 531390
Adrian Harvey (Mng Dir)

E.ON UK Technical Services
Limited (2)
17 Camp Road Rutherglen, Glasgow, G73
1EW, Lanarkshire, United Kingdom
Tel.: (44) 141 613 1119
Central Heating Equipment Installation &
Maintenance Services
N.A.I.C.S.: 238220

Holford Gas Storage Limited (2)
Westwood Way Westwood Business Park,
Coventry, CV4 8LG, West Midlands, United
Kingdom
Tel.: (44) 24 7642 4000
Gas Storage & Transmission Services
N.A.I.C.S.: 493190

Lighting for Staffordshire Limited (2)
A B B Business Centre Oulton Road, Stone,
ST15 0RS, Staffordshire, United Kingdom
Tel.: (44) 9040498229
Street Light Maintaining Services
N.A.I.C.S.: 238210

Midlands Power (UK) Limited (2)

Whittington Hall, Worcester, WR5 2RA,
Worcestershire, United Kingdom
Tel.: (44) 800590866
Electric Power Generation Services
N.A.I.C.S.: 221118

Power Technology Limited (2)
First Avenue, Scunthorpe, DN15 8SE,
South Humberside, United Kingdom
Tel.: (44) 1724 282500
Electric Power Generation & Distributing
Services
N.A.I.C.S.: 221118

Statco Six Limited (2)
Wilford Road, Nottingham, NG2 1EB, Not-
tinghamshire, United Kingdom
Tel.: (44) 115 986 3471
Eletric Power Generation Services
N.A.I.C.S.: 221118

TXU Warm Front Limited (2)
Suffolk House Civic Drive, Ipswich, IP1
2AE, United Kingdom
Tel.: (44) 800 952 1555
Management Consulting Services
N.A.I.C.S.: 541618

E.ON Vertrieb Deutschland
GmbH (1)
Karlstrasse 68, 80335, Munich, Germany
Tel.: (49) 89 12 54 01
Electric Power Distribution Services
N.A.I.C.S.: 221122
Johannes Teyssen (Gen Mgr)

E.ON Westfalen Weser 2.
Vermogensverwaltungs-GmbH (1)
Bielefelder Str 3, 32051, Herford,
Nordrhein-Westfalen, Germany
Tel.: (49) 5221 1830
Business Management Consulting Services
N.A.I.C.S.: 541611
Michael Heidkamp (Gen Mgr)

E.ON Zwanzigste Verwaltungs
GmbH (1)
E On-Platz 1, Dusseldorf, 40479,
Nordrhein-Westfalen, Germany
Tel.: (49) 211 4579501
Management Consulting Services
N.A.I.C.S.: 541618

E.ON edis AG (1)
Langewahler Str 60, 15517, Furstenwalde,
Germany
Tel.: (49) 3361700
Web Site: https://www.e-dis.de
Power & Natural Gas Distribution Services
N.A.I.C.S.: 221122

Subsidiary (Domestic):

Netz-und Windservice (NWS)
GmbH (2)
Werkstrasse 708, 19061, Schwerin,
Germany (100%)
Tel.: (49) 385202855203
Web Site: http://www.netz-
wartungsservice.de
Wind Turbines Maintenance Services
N.A.I.C.S.: 926130

E.ON edis Contracting GmbH (1)
Langewahler Str 60, Furstenwalde, 15517,
Germany
Tel.: (49) 3361702022
Electric Power Distribution Services
N.A.I.C.S.: 221122

EAV Beteiligungs-GmbH (1)
Reutlinger Str 30, 76228, Karlsruhe, Baden-
Wurttemberg, Germany
Tel.: (49) 721 2010338
Management Consulting Services
N.A.I.C.S.: 541618

EBY Gewerbeobjekt GmbH (1)
Lilienthalstr 7, Regensburg, 93049, Bayern,
Germany
Tel.: (49) 941 201 0
Management Consulting Services
N.A.I.C.S.: 541618

EBY Port 3 GmbH (1)
Lilienthalstr 7, 93049, Regensburg, Ger-
many
Tel.: (49) 94138393350
Management Consulting Services
N.A.I.C.S.: 541618

EBY Port 5 GmbH (1)
Heinkelstrasse 1, 93049, Regensburg, Bay-
ern, Germany
Tel.: (49) 941 38393426
Management Consulting Services
N.A.I.C.S.: 541618

EC Serwis Sp. z o.o. (1)
ul Orlat Lwowskich 6, 76-200, Slupsk, Po-
land
Tel.: (48) 59 8474480
Web Site: http://www.engie-ecserwis.pl
Sales Range: $25-49.9 Million
Emp.: 1
Electrical Equipment Installation Services
N.A.I.C.C.: 200020
Izabela Drzal (Mng Dir)

EC&R NA Solar PV, LLC (1)
353 N Clark St, Chicago, IL 60654-4704
Tel.: (312) 245-3035
Electric Power Generation Services
N.A.I.C.S.: 221118

EC&R Panther Creek Wind Farm I&II,
LLC (1)
401 N Michigan Ave 1720, Chicago, IL
60611-4255
Tel.: (432) 398-5309
Wind Electric Power Generation Services
N.A.I.C.S.: 221118

EC&R Panther Creek Wind Farm III,
LLC (1)
353 N Clark St 30th Fl, Chicago, IL 60654
Tel.: (312) 923-9463
Emp.: 115
Eletric Power Generation Services
N.A.I.C.S.: 221118
Steven Trenholm (Pres)

EC&R Papalote Creek I, LLC (1)
401 N Michigan Ave Ste 1720, Chicago, IL
60611-4255
Tel.: (312) 923-9463
Eletric Power Generation Services
N.A.I.C.S.: 221118

EC&R Papalote Creek II, LLC (1)
812 San Antonio St Ste 201, Austin, TX
78701
Tel.: (512) 482-4045
Electric Power Generation & Distribution
Services
N.A.I.C.S.: 221118

EC&R QSE, LLC (1)
353 N Clark St Fl 30, Chicago, IL 60654
Tel.: (312) 923-9463
Emp.: 115
Eletric Power Generation Services
N.A.I.C.S.: 221118
Steve Trenholm (Pres)

EC&R Services, LLC (1)
353 N Clark St Fl 30, Chicago, IL 60654-
4704
Tel.: (312) 923-9463
Electric Power Generation Services
N.A.I.C.S.: 221118

ENERGETIKA SERVIS s.r.o. (1)
Krizikova 1690/1, Ceske Budejovice, 370
01, Czech Republic
Tel.: (420) 38 635 60 55
Web Site: http://www.energetika-servis.cz
Electric Power Generation & Distribution
Services
N.A.I.C.S.: 221118

ENERGO-PRO Grid AD (1)
Varna Towers Tower E 258 Vladislav Var-
nenchik Blvd, 9009, Varna, Bulgaria
Tel.: (359) 70016161
Web Site: http://www.energo-pro.bg
Electric Power Distribution Services
N.A.I.C.S.: 221122

EPS Polska Holding Sp. z o.o. (1)
Krolowej Marysienki 10, 02-954, Warsaw,
Poland
Tel.: (48) 228581450
Web Site: https://www.eonedes.com
Sales Range: $50-74.9 Million
Emp.: 10
Investment Management Service
N.A.I.C.S.: 523999
Monika Stypulkowska (Mng Dir)

Subsidiary (Domestic):

EPS Polska Sp. z o.o. (2)

ul Krolowej Marysienki 10, Warsaw, 02-954, Poland
Tel.: (48) 22 858 14 50
Electric Power Distribution Services
N.A.I.C.S.: 221122

ESN EnergieSystemeNord GmbH (1)
Lise-Meitner-Str 25-29, 24223, Schwentinental, Germany
Tel.: (49) 4307821100
Web Site: http://www.esn.de
Energy & Wastewater Services
N.A.I.C.S.: 924110

ESN Sicherheit und Zertifizierung GmbH (1)
Lise-Meitner-Str 25-29, 24223, Schwentinental, Germany
Tel.: (49) 4307821100
Web Site: http://www.esn-sicherheit-und-zertifizierung.de
Energy Utility Services
N.A.I.C.S.: 926130

EZH-SEON b.v. (1)
Capelseweg 400, 3068 AX, Rotterdam, Netherlands
Tel.: (31) 10 2895711
Management Consulting Services
N.A.I.C.S.: 541618

ElbEnergie GmbH (1)
An der Reitbahn 17, 21218, Seevetal, Germany
Tel.: (49) 41051579900
Web Site: https://www.elbenergie.com
Natural Gas Distr
N.A.I.C.S.: 221210

Energetika Malenovice, a.s. (1)
Trida 3 Kvetna, cp 1173, 763 02, Zlin, Czech Republic
Tel.: (420) 577 533 111
Web Site: http://www.energetikamalenovice.cz
Emp.: 2
Electric Power Distribution Services
N.A.I.C.S.: 221122
George Stedl (Chm)

Energie und Wasser Potsdam GmbH (1)
Steinstrasse 101, 14480, Potsdam, Germany
Tel.: (49) 3316613000
Energy Utility Services
N.A.I.C.S.: 926130

Energie und Wasser Wahlstedt/Bad Segeberg GmbH & Co. KG (1)
Am Wasserwerk 5, Bad Segeberg, 23795, Wahlstedt, Germany
Tel.: (49) 455189390000
Web Site: https://www.ew-segeberg.de
Energy Utility Services
N.A.I.C.S.: 926130

EnergieWonen B.V. (1)
Bonnetstraat 53, 6718 XN, Ede, Netherlands
Tel.: (31) 8798204
Web Site: https://www.energiewonen.nl
Solar Panel Distr
N.A.I.C.S.: 423720

Energienetze Bayern GmbH (1)
Frankenthaler Strasse 2, 81539, Munich, Germany
Tel.: (49) 8968003352
Web Site: https://www.energienetze-bayern.de
Emp.: 35
Natural Gas Distribution Services
N.A.I.C.S.: 221210
Michael Schneider (Mng Dir)

Energienetze Schaafheim GmbH (1)
Lilienthalstrasse 77, 93049, Regensburg, Germany
Tel.: (49) 87196560020
Web Site: http://www.energienetze-schaafheim.com
Natural Gas Distribution Services
N.A.I.C.S.: 221210

Energieversorgung Alzenau GmbH (1)
Muhlweg 1, 63755, Alzenau, Germany
Tel.: (49) 6023949444

Web Site: https://www.eva-alzenau.de
Natural Gas Distr
N.A.I.C.S.: 221210

Energos Deutschland GmbH (1)
Schoninger Str 2-3, Helmstedt, 38350, Niedersachsen, Germany
Tel.: (49) 5351182383
Electric Power Distribution Services
N.A.I.C.S.: 221122

Enerjisa Enerji A.S. (1)
Sabanci Center Kule 2 Kat 4, Levent, 34330, Istanbul, Turkiye (50%)
Tel.: (90) 2123858866
Web Site: http://www.enerjisa.com.tr
Holding Company; Electric Power Generation, Distr & Natural Gas Distr
N.A.I.C.S.: 551112
Yetik K. Mert (CEO)

Subsidiary (Domestic):

Enerjisa Baskent Elektrik Dagitim A.S. (2)
Sabanci Center Kule 2, Levent, 6520, Istanbul, Turkiye
Tel.: (90) 2123858828
Web Site: http://www.enerjisa.com.tr
Retail Electric Power Distr
N.A.I.C.S.: 221122

Enerjisa Electrik Enerjisi Toptan Satis A.S. (2)
Barbaros Mahallesi Begonya Sokak Nida Kule Atasehir Bati Sit No1/1, 34330, Istanbul, Turkiye
Tel.: (90) 2123858866
Web Site: http://www.enerjisa.com.tr
Electric Power Whslr & Natural Gas Distr
N.A.I.C.S.: 221122

Enerjisa Enerji Uretim A.S. (2)
Barbaros Mahallesi Begonya Sokak Nida Kule Atasehir Bati Sit No1/1, 34330, Istanbul, Turkiye
Tel.: (90) 212 385 88 66
Web Site: http://www.enerjisa.com.tr
Geothermal, Hydro & Wind Electric Power Generation Services
N.A.I.C.S.: 221118

Plant (Domestic):

Enerjisa Enerji Uretim A.S. - Canakkale Power Plant (3)
Mahmudiye Koyu, Ezine, 17600, Canakkale, Turkiye
Tel.: (90) 286 628 77 78
Web Site: http://www.enerjisauretim.com.tr
Geothermal & Wind Electric Power Generation Services
N.A.I.C.S.: 221116

Enerjisa Enerji Uretim A.S. - Kentsa Power Plant (3)
Sabanci Center Kule 2, Levent, 41220, Izmit, Turkiye
Tel.: (90) 2123858866
Web Site: http://www.enerjisauretim.com.tr
Emp.: 20
Geothermal Electric Power Generation Services
N.A.I.C.S.: 221116

Enerjisa Enerji Uretim A.S. - Mersin Power Plant (3)
Dagpazari Village Road 12 Km, Mut, Mersin, Turkiye
Tel.: (90) 3247910053
Web Site: http://www.enerjisauretim.com.tr
Geothermal Electric Power Generation Services
N.A.I.C.S.: 221116

Essent N.V. (1)
Willemsplein 4, 5211 AK, 's-Hertogenbosch, Netherlands
Tel.: (31) 9001550
Web Site: https://www.essent.nl
Sales Range: $5-14.9 Billion
Supplier of Electricity, Gas, Heat & Waste Management Services
N.A.I.C.S.: 221122
Resi Becker (CEO)

Subsidiary (Non-US):

Essent Belgium N.V. (2)
Veldkant 7, 2550, Kontich, Belgium

Tel.: (32) 78157979
Web Site: https://www.essent.be
Electricity & Gas Distribution Services
N.A.I.C.S.: 221210

Subsidiary (Domestic):

Essent Retail Energie B.V. (2)
MKB Ondernemersdesk, PO Box 1024, 5200 BA, s-Hertogenbosch, Netherlands
Tel.: (31) 9001466
Electricity & Gas Distribution Services
N.A.I.C.S.: 221210

FAMIS GmbH (1)
Preussenstrasse 19, 66111, Saarbrucken, Germany
Tel.: (49) 6816071000
Web Site: https://www.famis-gmbh.de
Emp.: 1,000
Technical & Engineering Services
N.A.I.C.S.: 541330

FEV Europe GmbH (1)
Neuenhofstrsse 181, 52078, Aachen, Germany
Tel.: (49) 24156890
Vehicle Design & Development Services
N.A.I.C.S.: 541490

FITAS Verwaltung GmbH & Co. REGIUM-Objekte KG (1)
Emil-Riedl-Weg 6, 82049, Pullach, Bavaria, Germany
Tel.: (49) 815793410
Web Site: http://www.eon.com
Administrative Management Services
N.A.I.C.S.: 541611

FITAS Verwaltung GmbH & Co. Vermietungs-KG (1)
Emil-Riedl-Weg 6, Pullach, 82049, Bayern, Germany
Tel.: (49) 8951200
Real Estate Development Services
N.A.I.C.S.: 531390

Forest Creek WF Holdco, LLC (1)
220 W Main St Ste 500, Louisville, KY 40202-5324
Tel.: (502) 627-2000
Eletric Power Generation Services
N.A.I.C.S.: 221118

GASAG AG (1)
Henriette-Herz-Platz 4, 10178, Berlin, Germany (36.85%)
Tel.: (49) 3078723050
Web Site: https://www.gasag.de
Rev.: $1,401,660,451
Assets: $2,365,415,326
Liabilities: $1,610,674,481
Net Worth: $754,740,846
Earnings: $36,177,077
Emp.: 1,708
Fiscal Year-end: 12/31/2019
Liquid Natural Gas Distr
N.A.I.C.S.: 211120

Subsidiary (Domestic):

BAS Kundenservice GmbH & Co. KG (2)
Euref-Campus 23-24, 10829, Berlin, Germany
Tel.: (49) 3078724444
Web Site: https://www.bas-kundenservice.de
Telephone Meter Reading, Billing & Collection Services
N.A.I.C.S.: 561990

DSE Direkt-Service-Energie GmbH (2)
Henriette-Herz-Platz 4, 10178, Berlin, Germany
Tel.: (49) 3078721540
Web Site: http://www.dse-vertrieb.de
Energy Consulting Services
N.A.I.C.S.: 541690

GASAG Contracting GmbH (2)
Im Teelbruch 55, 45219, Essen, Germany
Tel.: (49) 20 54 96 954 0
Web Site: http://www.gasag-contracting.de
Sales Range: $25-49.9 Million
Emp.: 20
Energy Solutions & Contracting Projects
N.A.I.C.S.: 221118
Frank Mattat (Mgr)

GASAG Solution Plus GmbH (2)
Euref-Campus 23-24, 10829, Berlin, Germany
Tel.: (49) 3078724444
Web Site: https://www.gasag-solution.de
Sales Range: $25-49.9 Million
Emp.: 20
Electricity Meter Reading Services
N.A.I.C.S.: 561990

NBB Netz gesellschaft Berlin-Brandenburg mbH (2)
An der Spandauer Brucke 10, 10178, Berlin, Germany
Tel.: (49) 30 81876 0
Web Site: http://www.nbb-netzgesellschaft.de
Gas Supply & Meter Reading Services
N.A.I.C.S.: 221210

SpreeGas Gesellschaft fur Gasversorgung und Energiedienstleistung mbH (2)
Nordparkstrasse 30, 03044, Cottbus, Germany
Tel.: (49) 35578220
Web Site: http://www.spreegas.de
Natural Gas Services
N.A.I.C.S.: 221210

Stadtwerke Forst GmbH (2)
Euloer Strasse 90, 03149, Forst, Germany
Tel.: (49) 35629500
Web Site: http://www.stadtwerke-forst.de
Electricity, Gas, Water & Heat Administration Services
N.A.I.C.S.: 926130

GGG Gesellschaft fur Grundstucks-und Gebaudenutzung mbH (1)
Huttropstrasse 60, 45138, Essen, Germany
Tel.: (49) 201 18400
Real Estate Development Services
N.A.I.C.S.: 531390

GHD E.ON Bayern AG & Co. KG (1)
Lilienthalstr 7, Regensburg, 93049, Bayern, Germany
Tel.: (49) 9412010
Emp.: 2,000
Eletric Power Generation Services
N.A.I.C.S.: 221118

GVG Rhein-Erft GmbH (1)
Max-Planck-Strasse 11, 50354, Hurth, Germany
Tel.: (49) 223379090
Web Site: https://www.gvg.de
Natural Gas Distr
N.A.I.C.S.: 486210

Gasversorgung im Landkreis Gifhorn GmbH (1)
Hinterm Hagen 13, 38442, Wolfsburg, Germany (95%)
Tel.: (49) 5362120
Web Site: https://www.glg-gmbh.de
Natural Gas Distribution Services
N.A.I.C.S.: 221210

Subsidiary (Domestic):

GLG Netz GmbH (2)
Hinterm Hagen 13, 38442, Wolfsburg, Germany
Tel.: (49) 5362 12 0
Web Site: http://www.glg-netz.de
Natural Gas Distribution Services
N.A.I.C.S.: 221210

Gelsenberg Verwaltungs GmbH (1)
E On-Platz 1, Dusseldorf, 40479, Nordrhein-Westfalen, Germany
Tel.: (49) 2093895421
Business Management Consulting Services
N.A.I.C.S.: 541611

Gemeinschaftskernkraftwerk Grohnde Management GmbH (1)
Kraftwerksgelande, Emmerthal, 31860, Niedersachsen, Germany
Tel.: (49) 5155671
Eletric Power Generation Services
N.A.I.C.S.: 221118

Gemeinschaftskernkraftwerk Isar 2 GmbH (1)
Dammstr 32, Essenbach, Landshut, 84051, Germany
Tel.: (49) 8702384420

E.ON SE—(Continued)

Electric Power Generation Services
N.A.I.C.S.: 221118

**Gemeinschaftskraftwerk Veltheim Ge-
sellschaft mit beschrankter
Haftung** (1)
Mollberger Strasse 387, 32457, Porta West-
falica, Germany
Tel.: (49) 5706 399 0
Web Site: http://www.gk-veltheim.de
Eletric Power Generation Services
N.A.I.C.S.: 221118

**Gesellschaft fur Energie und Klimas-
chutz Schleswig- Holstein GmbH** (1)
Boschstrasse 1, 24118, Kiel, Germany
Tel.: (49) 4 31 98 05 8 00
Web Site: http://www.eksh.org
Environmental Protection Science & Re-
search Services
N.A.I.C.S.: 541620

GreyLogix GmbH (1)
Conrad-Rontgen-Str 1, 24941, Flensburg,
Germany
Tel.: (49) 461 505487 0
Web Site: http://www.greylogix.com
Sales Range: $75-99.9 Million
Emp.: 30
Automation Technology Services
N.A.I.C.S.: 541512
Gerd Witzel (Co-Founder & Mng Dir)

HEUREKA-Gamma AG (1)
Husmatt 1, 5405, Baden-Dattwil, Switzer-
land
Tel.: (41) 56 484 70 60
Web Site: http://www.heureka-gamma.ch
Sales Range: $25-49.9 Million
Emp.: 4
Human Resource Consulting Services
N.A.I.C.S.: 541612
Dieter Bader (Gen Mgr)

**Hamburger Hof
Versicherungs-Aktiengesellschaft** (1)
Kennedydamm 17, Dusseldorf, 40476,
Nordrhein-Westfalen, Germany
Tel.: (49) 21147970
Web Site: http://www.eon.com
Insurance Management Services
N.A.I.C.S.: 524298
Klaus Greimel (Gen Mgr)

**Hermann Seippel-
Unterstutzungseinrichtung GmbH** (1)
Brusseler Platz 1, 45131, Essen, Germany
Tel.: (49) 201 18400
Web Site: http://www.eon.com
Management Consulting Services
N.A.I.C.S.: 541618

ILSE Bergbau-GmbH (1)
Georg-von-Boeselager-Str 25, D-53117,
Bonn, Germany (100%)
Tel.: (49) 22855201
Chemical Mineral Mining Company
N.A.I.C.S.: 212390

Inadale WF Holdco, LLC (1)
220 W Main St Ste 500, Louisville, KY
40202-5324
Tel.: (502) 627-2000
Eletric Power Generation Services
N.A.I.C.S.: 221118

Inadale Wind Farm, LLC (1)
353 N Clark St Fl 30, Chicago, IL 60654
Tel.: (312) 923-9463
Eletric Power Generation Services
N.A.I.C.S.: 221118

**Induboden GmbH & Co. Industriew-
erte OHG** (1)
E On-Platz 1, 40479, Dusseldorf,
Nordrhein-Westfalen, Germany
Tel.: (49) 211 45791
Eletric Power Generation Services
N.A.I.C.S.: 221118

**Informacni sluzby - energetika,
a.s.** (1)
U Plynarny 500, 141 00, Prague, Czech
Republic
Tel.: (420) 267175400
Web Site: http://www.ise.cz
Sales Range: $25-49.9 Million
Emp.: 45
Information Technology Consulting Services

N.A.I.C.S.: 541512

Innogy SE (1)
Opernplatz 1, 45128, Essen,
Germany (100%)
Tel.: (49) 2011202
Energy Research & Development Services
N.A.I.C.S.: 926110

Subsidiary (US):

Broadband TelCom Power, Inc. (2)
1719 S Grand Ave, Santa Ana, CA 92705
Tel.: (714) 259-4888
Web Site: http://www.btcpower.com
Electronic Components Mfr.
N.A.I.C.S.: 334419
Frank Meza (CEO)

**Kernkraftwerk Stade GmbH & Co.
oHG** (1)
Bassenflether Chaussee, Stade, 21683,
Niedersachsen, Germany
Tel.: (49) 4141770
Nuclear Electric Power Generation Services
N.A.I.C.S.: 221113

**Kernkraftwerke Isar Verwaltungs
GmbH** (1)
Dammstr 33, Bessenbach, 84051, Bayern,
Germany
Tel.: (49) 8702380
Nuclear Electric Power Generation Services
N.A.I.C.S.: 221113
Christian Reilein (Mng Dir)

KommEnergie GmbH (1)
Hauptplatz 4, 82223, Eichenau, Germany
Tel.: (49) 814122870
Web Site: http://www.kommenergie.de
Electric Power Distribution Services
N.A.I.C.S.: 221122

**Kurgan Grundstucks-
Verwaltungsgesellschaft mbH & Co.
oHG** (1)
Tolzer Str 15, 82031, Grunwald, Bayern,
Germany
Tel.: (49) 89 64143 0
Real Estate Management Services
N.A.I.C.S.: 531390

**LSW LandE-Stadtwerke Wolfsburg
Verwaltungs-GmbH** (1)
Hesslinger Str 1-5, Wolfsburg, 38440, Ger-
many
Tel.: (49) 5361189662
Business Management Consulting Services
N.A.I.C.S.: 541611

LandE GmbH (1)
Hinterm Hagen 13, 38442, Wolfsburg,
38442, Niedersachsen, Germany
Tel.: (49) 5362120
Web Site: https://www.lsw.de
Electric Power Generation & Distribution
Services
N.A.I.C.S.: 221118
Horst Finkendey (Mng Dir)

Landwehr Wassertechnik GmbH (1)
Schwarzer Weg 2A, 38170, Schoppenstedt,
Germany
Tel.: (49) 53 32 96 87 0
Web Site: http://www.landwehr-wt.de
Sales Range: $25-49.9 Million
Emp.: 80
Water Treatment Plant Construction Ser-
vices
N.A.I.C.S.: 237110
Andreas Walenczyk (Mng Dir)

MEGAL Verwaltungs-GmbH (1)
Kallenbergstr 7, Essen, 45141, Nordrhein-
Westfalen, Germany
Tel.: (49) 20128953780
Business Management Consulting Services
N.A.I.C.S.: 541611

MEON Verwaltungs GmbH (1)
Nordliche Munchner Str 14, Grunwald,
82031, Germany
Tel.: (49) 8964143398
Business Management Consulting Services
N.A.I.C.S.: 541611

METHA-Methanhandel GmbH (1)
Brusseler Platz 1, 45131, Essen, Nordrhein-
Westfalen, Germany
Tel.: (49) 201 1844205
Natural Gas Distribution Services

N.A.I.C.S.: 221210

**Mainkraftwerk Schweinfurt Gesell-
schaft mit beschrankter Haftung** (1)
Blutenburgstrasse 20, 80636, Munich, Ger-
many
Tel.: (49) 89992220
Web Site: http://www.rmd.de
Sales Range: $50-74.9 Million
Emp.: 35
Eletric Power Generation Services
N.A.I.C.S.: 221118
Albrecht Schleich (Mng Dir)

Mampaey Installatietechniek B.V. (1)
Wieldrechtseweg 30, 3316 BG, Dordrecht,
Netherlands
Tel.: (31) 786522433
Web Site: http://www.mampaey.nl
Heating & Ventilation System Installation
Services
N.A.I.C.S.: 238220

Munnsville Investco, LLC (1)
220 W Main St Ste 500, Louisville, KY
40202-5324
Tel.: (502) 627-2000
Eletric Power Generation Services
N.A.I.C.S.: 221118

NORD-direkt GmbH (1)
Bismarckstrasse 67 - 69, 24534, Neumun-
ster, Germany
Tel.: (49) 43 21 49 90 200
Web Site: http://www.norddirekt.de
Environmental Consulting Services
N.A.I.C.S.: 541620

Netz Veltheim GmbH (1)
Mollberger Strasse 387, 32457, Porta West-
falica, Germany
Tel.: (49) 5706 900 49 0
Web Site: http://www.netz-veltheim.de
Electric Power Distribution Services
N.A.I.C.S.: 221122

**Netzgesellschaft Herrenwald Verwal-
tung GmbH** (1)
Bahnhofstr 2, Stadtallendorf, 35260, Hes-
sen, Germany
Tel.: (49) 64287070
Eletric Power Generation Services
N.A.I.C.S.: 221118

NordNetz GmbH (1)
Schleswag-HeinGas-Platz 1, 25451, Quick-
born, Germany
Tel.: (49) 41069998033
Web Site: https://www.nordnetz.com
Power Meter Reading Services
N.A.I.C.S.: 334515

**Norddeutsche Gesellschaft zur
Ablagerung von Mineralstoffen
mbH** (1)
Am Kraftwerk 1, Buddenstedt, 38372, Helm-
stedt, Germany
Tel.: (49) 535294393893
Web Site: http://www.norgam.de
Waste Management & Disposal Services
N.A.I.C.S.: 562998
Hans-Ulrich Terschueren (Exec Dir)

**Nordzucker Bioerdgas
Verwaltung-GmbH** (1)
Kuchenstr 9, Braunschweig, 38100, Nieder-
sachsen, Germany
Tel.: (49) 5312411100
Oil & Gas Exploration Services
N.A.I.C.S.: 213112

**OAO Shaturskaya Upravlyayush-
chaya Kompaniya** (1)
4 Pr Konny, 140700, Shatura, Russia
Tel.: (7) 4964523317
Eletric Power Generation Services
N.A.I.C.S.: 221118

OKG AB (1)
Simpevarp, 572 83, Oskarshamn, Sweden
Tel.: (46) 4 91 78 60 00
Web Site: http://www.okg.se
Rev.: $444,390,000
Emp.: 700
Eletric Power Generation Services
N.A.I.C.S.: 221118

**Obere Donau Kraftwerke
Aktiengesellschaft** (1)
Kraftwerk Faimingen Romerstrasse 1,

Lauingen, 89415, Germany
Tel.: (49) 9072 2096
Eletric Power Generation Services
N.A.I.C.S.: 221118

**Oberland Stromnetz GmbH & Co.
KG** (1)
Viehmarktplatz 1, 82418, Murnau am
Staffelsee, Germany
Tel.: (49) 8841489290
Web Site:
https://www.regionalwerkoberland.de
Power Meter Reading Services
N.A.I.C.S.: 334515

Open Grid Service GmbH (1)
Ruhrallee 307-309, 45136, Essen, Germany
Tel.: (49) 20136420
Web Site: http://www.open-grid-service.com
Gas Transmission Services
N.A.I.C.S.: 486210
Jean-Michel Douret (Mng Dir)

PADES Personalservice GmbH (1)
Marsstr 42, 80335, Munich, Germany
Tel.: (49) 89 51566 251
Web Site: http://www.pades.eu
Human Resource Consulting Services
N.A.I.C.S.: 541612

PEG Infrastruktur AG (1)
Route de Chancy 50, Geneve, 1213, Petit-
Lancy, Switzerland
Tel.: (41) 225456900
Web Site: https://www.pegeng.ch
Building Renovation & Infrastructure Ser-
vices
N.A.I.C.S.: 236220

**Peissenberger Kraftwerksgesellschaft
mit beschrankter Haftung** (1)
Stadelbachstr 4a, 82380, Peissenberg, Ger-
many
Tel.: (49) 8803 496 0
Web Site: http://www.pkg-peissenberg.de
Eletric Power Generation Services
N.A.I.C.S.: 221118

Powergen Limited (1)
Westwood Way Westwood Business Park,
Coventry, CV4 8LG, United Kingdom
Tel.: (44) 24 7642 4000
Electric Power & Gas Distribution Services
N.A.I.C.S.: 221122

**Powergen Luxembourg Holdings
SARL** (1)
17 Boulevard prince Henri, 1724, Luxem-
bourg, Luxembourg
Tel.: (352) 2686851
Investment Management Service
N.A.I.C.S.: 523999
Paul De Haan (Mgr)

Powergen UK Limited (1)
PO Box 111, Immingham, DN40 3NG,
South Humberside, United Kingdom
Tel.: (44) 1469 541155
Eletric Power Generation Services
N.A.I.C.S.: 221118

Powergen US Holdings Limited (1)
Westwood Way Westwood Business Park,
Coventry, CV4 8LG, United Kingdom
Tel.: (44) 2476424000
Investment Management Service
N.A.I.C.S.: 523940

Powergen US Investments (1)
Westwood Way Westwood Business Park,
Coventry, CV4 8LG, West Midlands, United
Kingdom
Tel.: (44) 24 7642 4000
Investment Management Service
N.A.I.C.S.: 523940

Powergen US Securities Limited (1)
Westwood Way, Coventry, CV4 8LG, West
Midlands, United Kingdom
Tel.: (44) 24.7642 4000
Investment Management Service
N.A.I.C.S.: 523940

**Prazska plynarenska Distribuce,
a.s.** (1)
U Plynarny 500, 145 08, Prague, Czech
Republic
Tel.: (420) 267175222
Web Site: http://www.ppdistribuce.cz
Natural Gas Distribution Services
N.A.I.C.S.: 221210

Martin Slaby *(Chm)*

Prazska plynarenska Holding a.s. **(1)**
U Plynarny 500, Prague, 140 00, Czech Republic
Tel.: (420) 2 6717 1111
Investment Management Service
N.A.I.C.S.: 523999

Prazska plynarenska Servis distri-buce, a.s. **(1)**
U Plynarny 1450/2a, Michle, 140 00, Prague, Czech Republic
Tel.: (420) 267175222
Web Site: http://www.ppad.oz
Sales Range: $125-149.9 Million
Emp.: 140
Natural Gas Distribution Services
N.A.I.C.S.: 221210
Tomas Macalik *(Chm-Supervisory Bd)*

Prazska plynarenska Sprava majetku, s.r.o. **(1)**
U Plynarny 500, Michle, 145 08, Prague, Czech Republic
Tel.: (420) 267175480
Web Site: http://www.ppsm.cz
Sales Range: $50-74.9 Million
Emp.: 70
Asset Management Services
N.A.I.C.S.: 523940

PreussenElektra GmbH **(1)**
Tresckowstrasse 5, 30457, Hannover, Germany
Tel.: (49) 51143903
Web Site: https://www.preussenelektra.de
Emp.: 2,000
Nuclear Power Plant Construction Services
N.A.I.C.S.: 237130

Promec Sp. z o.o. **(1)**
ul Prusa 4, 26-110, Skarzysko-Kamienna, Poland
Tel.: (48) 41 25 28 994
Web Site: http://www.promec.pl
Real Estate Manangement Services
N.A.I.C.S.: 531390

Przedsiebiorstwo Energetyki Cieplnej w Barlinku Sp. z o.o. **(1)**
ul Przemyslowa 7, 74-320, Barlinek, Poland
Tel.: (48) 95 746 26 51
Eletric Power Generation Services
N.A.I.C.S.: 221118

Purena GmbH **(1)**
Halchtersche Strasse 33, 38304, Wolfenbut-tel, Germany
Tel.: (49) 5331 88263 0
Web Site: http://www.purena.de
Waste Treatment Services
N.A.I.C.S.: 221310

Pyron Wind Farm, LLC **(1)**
353 N Clark St Fl 30, Chicago, IL 60654-4704
Tel.: (325) 766-3083
Sales Range: $500-549.9 Million
Emp.: 650
Eletric Power Generation Services
N.A.I.C.S.: 221118
Steve Trenholm *(CEO)*

Q-Energie b.v. **(1)**
Beemdstraat 23, 5653 MA, Eindhoven, Netherlands
Tel.: (31) 407070700
Web Site: http://www.kemkens.nl
Emp.: 100
Eletric Power Generation Services
N.A.I.C.S.: 221118
Philip Faber *(Mgr)*

RDE Regionale Dienstleistungen En-ergie GmbH & Co. KG **(1)**
Benzstrasse 11, Veitshochheim, 97209, Wurzburg, Germany
Tel.: (49) 93173045500
Web Site: http://www.rde-dienstleistungen.de
Electric Power Distribution Services
N.A.I.C.S.: 221122

RDE Verwaltungs-GmbH **(1)**
Bismarckstr 9-11, 97080, Wurzburg, Bara-via, Germany
Tel.: (49) 9313002230
Management Consulting Services

N.A.I.C.S.: 541618

RMD-Consult GmbH Wasserbau und Energie **(1)**
Blutenburgstrasse 20, 80636, Munich, Germany
Tel.: (49) 89 99 222 402
Web Site: http://www.rmd-consult.de
Sales Range: $50-74.9 Million
Emp.: 50
Eletric Power Generation Services
N.A.I.C.S.: 221118
Christian Gohl *(Gen Mgr)*

Rappold, Hermann & Co. GmbH **(1)**
Zollhauootr 121, D 52353, Duren, Germany **(100%)**
Tel.: (49) 242184070
Equipment for Iron & Steel Mills, Power Plants & Ceramic Burners
N.A.I.C.S.: 333519

Rauschbergbahn Gesellschaft mit beschrankter Haftung **(1)**
Rathausstrasse 12, 83324, Ruhpolding, Germany
Tel.: (49) 8663 5945
Web Site: http://www.rauschbergbahn.com
Cable Car Operating Services
N.A.I.C.S.: 487990

Roscoe Wind Farm, LLC **(1)**
200 E Broadway, Roscoe, TX 79545
Tel.: (312) 923-9463
Web Site: http://www.eon.com
Emp.: 95
Eletric Power Generation Services
N.A.I.C.S.: 221118
Jeson Gircceo *(Gen Mgr)*

S.C. Salgaz S.A. **(1)**
Loc Str Ion Creanga Nr 18, Jud Bihor, Sa-lonta, 415500, Romania
Tel.: (40) 259373928
Web Site: http://www.salgaz.ro
Sales Range: $25-49.9 Million
Emp.: 25
Gaseous Fuels & Natural Gas Distribution Services
N.A.I.C.S.: 457210
Ghita Adrian *(Dir Gen)*

SEC Energia Sp. z o.o. **(1)**
Ul Dembowskiego 6, Szczecin, 71-533, Poland
Tel.: (48) 914250800
Eletric Power Generation Services
N.A.I.C.S.: 221118

SEE-Sul Energia Eolica, Lda **(1)**
Parque Eolico Espinhaco Cao-Aljezur, Aljezur, 8670-120, Portugal
Tel.: (351) 282688117
Eletric Power Generation Services
N.A.I.C.S.: 221118

SERVICE plus GmbH **(1)**
Bismarckstr 67, 24534, Neumunster, Germany
Tel.: (49) 4321 49 90 100
Web Site: http://www.service-plus-gmbh.de
Information Technology Consulting Services
N.A.I.C.S.: 541511

SKW Stickstoffwerke Piesteritz GmbH **(1)**
Moellensdorfer Strasse 13, 06886, Luther-stadt Wittenberg, Germany **(50%)**
Tel.: (49) 3491680
Web Site: http://www.skwp.de
Sales Range: $250-299.9 Million
Emp.: 65
Agricultural & Industrial Chemicals
N.A.I.C.S.: 325320
Rudiger Giesrick *(Chm)*

SVO Access GmbH **(1)**
Sprengerstrasse 2, 29223, Celle, Germany
Tel.: (49) 5141162716
Telecommunication Servicesb
N.A.I.C.S.: 517810

SVO Vertrieb GmbH **(1)**
Sprengerstrasse 2, 29223, Celle, Germany
Tel.: (49) 514121960
Web Site: https://www.svo.de
Sales Range: $250-299.9 Million
Emp.: 30
Electric Power Distribution Services
N.A.I.C.S.: 221122

Safekont GmbH **(1)**
Kurpfalzring 98A, 69123, Heidelberg, Germany
Tel.: (49) 622165175133
Web Site: http://www.safekont.de
Human Resouce Services
N.A.I.C.S.: 624190

Safetec Entsorgungs- und Sicherheit-stechnik GmbH **(1)**
Kurpfalzring 98a, Postfach 120651, 69123, Heidelberg, Germany
Tel.: (49) 62216517526
Web Site: http://www.safetec-strahlenschutz.de
Sales Range: $25-49.9 Million
Emp.: 80
Radiation Protection & Nuclear Engineering Services
N.A.I.C.S.: 541330

Sakab AB **(1)**
Norrtorp, Kumla, 692 85, Sweden
Tel.: (46) 19 30 51 00
Web Site: http://www.sakab.se
Emp.: 25
Waste Treatment & Disposal Services
N.A.I.C.S.: 562211
Johanna Telander *(Mgr-Intl Sls)*

Schleswig-Holstein Netz Verwaltungs-GmbH **(1)**
Schleswag-HeinGas-Platz 1, 25451, Quick-born, Schleswig-Holstein, Germany
Tel.: (49) 4106 6489090
Electric Power Distribution Services
N.A.I.C.S.: 221122

Settlers Trail Wind Farm, LLC **(1)**
353 N Clark St Fl 30, Chicago, IL 60654-4704
Tel.: (312) 245-3035
Eletric Power Generation Services
N.A.I.C.S.: 221118

Stony Creek WF Holdco, LLC **(1)**
353 N Clark St Fl 30, Chicago, IL 60654-4704
Tel.: (312) 245-3035
Eletric Power Generation Services
N.A.I.C.S.: 221118

Stony Creek Wind Farm, LLC **(1)**
353 N Clark St Fl 30, Chicago, IL 60654
Tel.: (312) 923-9463
Web Site: http://www.eon.com
Emp.: 100
Eletric Power Generation Services
N.A.I.C.S.: 221118

Strom Germering GmbH **(1)**
Barenweg 13, 82110, Germering, Germany
Tel.: (49) 89 50 05 99 44
Web Site: http://www.strom-germering.de
Electric Power Distribution Services
N.A.I.C.S.: 221122
Andreas Haas *(Chm)*

Stromversorgung Ahrensburg GmbH **(1)**
Kurt-Fischer-Str 52, 22926, Ahrensburg, Germany
Tel.: (49) 4102 99 49 010
Web Site: http://www.stromversorgung-ahrensburg.de
Electric Power Distribution Services
N.A.I.C.S.: 221122

Stromversorgung Ruhpolding Gesell-schaft mit beschrankter Haftung **(1)**
Rathausstrasse 12, 83324, Ruhpolding, Germany
Tel.: (49) 8663 88280
Web Site: http://www.strom-ruhpolding.de
Sales Range: $75-99.9 Million
Emp.: 13
Electric Power Distribution Services
N.A.I.C.S.: 221122
Stibler Rolf *(Mng Dir)*

Strotog GmbH **(1)**
Hauptstrasse 19, 84513, Toging am Inn, Germany
Tel.: (49) 86311845540
Web Site: https://www.strotoeg.de
Electric Power Distribution Services
N.A.I.C.S.: 221122

SudWasser GmbH **(1)**

Bauhofstrasse 5, 91052, Erlangen, Germany
Tel.: (49) 9131933070
Web Site: http://www.suedwasser.com
Water Supply & Irrigation Services
N.A.I.C.S.: 221310

Surschiste, S.A. **(1)**
Rue Auguste Mariette Zone industrielle La Croisette, 62300, Lens, France
Tel.: (33) 3 21 45 73 73
Web Site: http://www.surschiste.com
Emp.: 32
Eletric Power Generation Services
N.A.I.C.S.: 221118

Sydkraft EC Slupsk Sp. z o.o. **(1)**
ul Koszalinska 3D, 76-200, Slupsk, Poland
Tel.: (48) 59 84 86 300
Web Site: http://www.ecslupsk.pl
Sales Range: $100-124.9 Million
Emp.: 70
Electric Power & Natural Gas Distribution Services
N.A.I.C.S.: 221122

Sydkraft Polen AB **(1)**
Carl Gustafs Vag 1, Malmo, 217 42, Skane, Sweden
Tel.: (46) 40255000
Electric Power Distribution Services
N.A.I.C.S.: 221122

Sydkraft Term Sp. z o.o. **(1)**
ul Za Dworcem 3, 77-400, Zlotow, Poland
Tel.: (48) 67 263 35 44
Web Site: http://www.engie-term.pl
Heat Energy Generation & Distribution Services
N.A.I.C.S.: 221330

Sydkraft Zlotow Sp. z o.o. **(1)**
ul Za Dworcem 3, 77-400, Zlotow, Poland
Tel.: (48) 67 263 29 69
Web Site: http://www.engie-zlotow.pl
Electricity Production & Distribution Services
N.A.I.C.S.: 221118

Szczecinska Energetyka Cieplna Sp. z o.o. **(1)**
ul Zbozowa 4, 70-653, Szczecin, Poland
Tel.: (48) 914509999
Web Site: https://www.sec.com.pl
Electric Power Distribution Services
N.A.I.C.S.: 221122

Subsidiary (Domestic):

SEC Lobez Sp. z o.o. **(2)**
ul Magazynowa 16, 73-150, Lobez, Poland **(100%)**
Tel.: (48) 91 397 33 97
Web Site: http://www.sec.com.pl
Thermal Electric Power Generation Services
N.A.I.C.S.: 221118

TEN Thuringer Energienetze GmbH **(1)**
Schwerborner Strasse 30, 99087, Erfurt, Germany
Tel.: (49) 3641631888
Web Site: http://www.thueringer-energienetze.com
Electric Power Transmission Services
N.A.I.C.S.: 221121

Teplarna Kyjov, a.s. **(1)**
Havlickova 180/18, 697 01, Kyjov, Czech Republic
Tel.: (420) 518 698 712
Sales Range: $75-99.9 Million
Emp.: 20
Electric Power Generation & Distribution Services
N.A.I.C.S.: 221118

Terrakomp GmbH **(1)**
Am Kraftwerk 1, Buddenstedt, 38372, Helm-stedt, Germany
Tel.: (49) 535294393888
Web Site: http://www.terrakomp.helmstedterrevier.de
Emp.: 14
Organic Waste Recycling Services
N.A.I.C.S.: 562920
Sophie Dutordoir *(Gen Mgr)*

Thuringer Energie Netzservice GmbH **(1)**

E.ON SE—(Continued)

Schwerborner Str 30, 99087, Erfurt, Thuringen, Germany
Tel.: (49) 361 652 0
Electric Power Distribution Services
N.A.I.C.S.: 221122

Subsidiary (Domestic):

Iridium Services Deutschland GmbH **(2)**
Jaegerhofstrabe 19 - 20, 40479, Dusseldorf, Germany **(100%)**
Tel.: (49) 2114973176
Electronic Services
N.A.I.C.S.: 221122

VEBACOM GmbH **(1)**
Am Bonneshof 35, 40474, Dusseldorf, Germany **(55%)**
Web Site: http://www.vebacom.de
Sales Range: $200-249.9 Million
Emp.: 1,219
Electricity Distribution Services
N.A.I.C.S.: 221122

VIAG Telecom Beteiligungs GmbH **(1)**
, Munich, Munich, Germany **(100%)**
Web Site: http://www.viag.de
Telecommunication Servicesb
N.A.I.C.S.: 517111

VR Telecommunications GmbH & Co. **(1)**
, Norderfriedrichskoog, Husum, Germany **(51.2%)**
Telecommunications Company
N.A.I.C.S.: 517111

Venado Wind Farm, LLC **(1)**
353 N Clark St Fl 30, Chicago, IL 60654-4704
Tel.: (312) 245-3035
Eletric Power Generation Services
N.A.I.C.S.: 221118

Versorgungsbetriebe Helgoland GmbH **(1)**
Kurpromenade, 27498, Heligoland, Schleswig-Holstein, Germany
Tel.: (49) 4725 8180
Eletric Power Generation Services
N.A.I.C.S.: 221118

Veszprem-Kogeneracio Energiatermelo Zrt. **(1)**
Kando Kalman Utca 13, 9027, Gyor, Hungary
Tel.: (36) 96521118
Emp.: 8
Eletric Power Generation Services
N.A.I.C.S.: 221118

WBG GmbH **(1)**
Sudstrasse 22, 38350, Helmstedt, Germany
Tel.: (49) 5351 18 2226
Web Site: http://www.wbg-helmstedt.de
Property Management Services
N.A.I.C.S.: 531311

WEVG Salzgitter GmbH & Co. KG **(1)**
Albert-Schweitzer-Strasse 7-11, 38226, Salzgitter, Germany
Tel.: (49) 53414080
Web Site: https://www.wevg.com
Electric Power & Gas Distribution Services
N.A.I.C.S.: 221122
Rainer Krause (Mng Dir)

WEVG Verwaltungs GmbH **(1)**
Albert-Schweitzer-Str 7-11, Salzgitter, 38226, Germany
Tel.: (49) 5341 408 111
Web Site: http://www.wevg.com
Sales Range: $300-349.9 Million
Emp.: 30
Electric Power & Natural Gas Distribution Services
N.A.I.C.S.: 221122
Rainer Krause (Mng Dir)

Warmeversorgungsgesellschaft Konigs Wusterhausen mbH **(1)**
Schillerstr 7, 15711, Konigs Wusterhausen, Brandenburg, Germany
Tel.: (49) 3375 256110
Electric Power Distribution Services

N.A.I.C.S.: 221122

Weissmainkraftwerk Rohrenhof Aktiengesellschaft **(1)**
Luitpoldplatz 5, 95444, Bayreuth, Germany
Tel.: (49) 921 285 2863
Web Site: http://www.weissmainkraftwerk.de
Sales Range: $75-99.9 Million
Emp.: 7
Hydroelectric Power Generation Services
N.A.I.C.S.: 221118

Windpark Mutzschen OHG **(1)**
Am Kanal 2-3, Potsdam, 14467, Brandenburg, Germany
Tel.: (49) 3312342903
Eltric Power Generation Services
N.A.I.C.S.: 221118

Windpark Naundorf OHG **(1)**
Am Kanal 2-3, Potsdam, 14467, Brandenburg, Germany
Tel.: (49) 331 2340
Eltric Power Generation Services
N.A.I.C.S.: 221118

e.dialog GmbH **(1)**
Am Kanal 2-3, 14467, Potsdam, Germany
Tel.: (49) 3312342401
Web Site: http://www.edialog-netz.de
Sales Range: $150-199.9 Million
Emp.: 1,000
Marketing Consulting Services
N.A.I.C.S.: 541613

e.discom Telekommunikation GmbH **(1)**
Erich-Schlesinger-Str 37, Mecklenburg-Vorpommern, 18059, Rostock, Germany
Tel.: (49) 33190802000
Web Site: http://www.ediscom.de
Sales Range: $25-49.9 Million
Emp.: 18
Data Transfer & Telecommunication Services
N.A.I.C.S.: 517810
Andreas Wuensch (Mgr-IT)

e.disnatur Erneuerbare Energien GmbH **(1)**
Am Kanal 2-3, 14467, Potsdam, Germany
Tel.: (49) 3312342725
Web Site: https://www.edisnatur.de
Renewable Energy Services
N.A.I.C.S.: 221116
Rene Frixel (Mgr-Technical Ops)

e.distherm Energielosungen GmbH **(1)**
Mizarstrasse 3, 12529, Schonefeld, Germany
Tel.: (49) 30634119402
Web Site: https://www.edistherm.de
Electric Power Distribution Services
N.A.I.C.S.: 221122

e.distherm Warmedienstleistungen GmbH **(1)**
Am Kanal 2-3, 14467, Potsdam, Germany
Tel.: (49) 3 31 2 34 32 30
Electric Power Distr
N.A.I.C.S.: 221122

e.kundenservice Netz GmbH **(1)**
Steindamm 100, 20099, Hamburg, Germany
Tel.: (49) 402533453399
Web Site: http://www.eknetz.de
Emp.: 900
Business Services
N.A.I.C.S.: 519290

energielosung GmbH **(1)**
Prufeninger Strasse 15, 93049, Regensburg, Germany
Tel.: (49) 9412017700
Web Site: http://www.energieloesung.de
Mobile Charging Services
N.A.I.C.S.: 457120

snt Deutschland AG **(1)**
Querstrasse 8 10, 60322, Frankfurt am Main, Germany
Tel.: (49) 8007682433
Web Site: http://www.snt-ag.de
Telephone Marketing Services
N.A.I.C.S.: 541613
Joan Schlieker (CFO)

E.P. BARRUS LTD.

Glen Way Launton Road, Bicester, OX26 4UR, Oxfordshire, United Kingdom
Tel.: (44) 1869363636
Web Site: http://www.barrus.co.uk
Year Founded: 1917
Sales Range: $25-49.9 Million
Emp.: 186
Holding Company; Garden Machinery, Garden Tools, Marine & Industrial Engine Markets
N.A.I.C.S.: 551112
Robert D. Glen (Chm)

Subsidiaries:

E.P. Barrus Limited **(1)**
Glen Way Launton Road, Bicester, OX26 4UR, Oxfordshire, United Kingdom
Tel.: (44) 1869363636
Web Site: http://www.barrus.co.uk
Sales Range: $50-74.9 Million
Emp.: 150
Vehicles & Engine for Garden Marine & Road Use Distr
N.A.I.C.S.: 444230
Robert D. Glen (Chm)

E.R. CAPITAL HOLDING GMBH & CIE. KG

Hohe Bleichen 12, 20354, Hamburg, Germany
Tel.: (49) 40 3008 0   De
Web Site: http://www.er-capital.com
Emp.: 3,500
Holding Company
N.A.I.C.S.: 551112
Nicholas Teller (CEO & Chm-Mgmt Bd)

Subsidiaries:

Equitrust GmbH **(1)**
Hohe Bleichen 12, 20354, Hamburg, Germany
Tel.: (49) 4030082112
Web Site: http://www.equitrust.de
Private Equity Fund Management Services
N.A.I.C.S.: 523940

Nordcapital GmbH **(1)**
Hohe Bleichen 12, 20354, Hamburg, Germany
Tel.: (49) 40 3008 0
Web Site: http://www.nordcapital.com
Investment Holding Company
N.A.I.C.S.: 551112
Felix von Buchwaldt (CEO & Mng Dir)

E.R. PROBYN LTD.

Ste 350 601 6th St, New Westminster, V3L 3C1, BC, Canada
Tel.: (604) 526-8545
Web Site: http://www.probynlog.com
Sales Range: $10-24.9 Million
Logging, Wholesale Forest Products, Manufacturer of Cedar Fencing & Specialty Cedar Products
N.A.I.C.S.: 321920
Edward Probyn (Chm)

Subsidiaries:

AJ Forest Products Ltd. **(1)**
PO Box 3831, Garibaldi Highlands, Squamish, V0N 1T0, BC, Canada
Tel.: (604) 898-3712
Web Site: http://www.ajforest.com
Lumber Whslr
N.A.I.C.S.: 423310

E.R. Probyn Export Ltd. **(1)**
350 601 63, New Westminster, V3L 3C1, BC, Canada **(100%)**
Tel.: (604) 526-8546
Web Site: http://www.probynexport.com
Emp.: 8
Export Lumber
N.A.I.C.S.: 423310
Rod McCoy (Gen Mgr)

Probyn Log, Ltd. **(1)**
Ste 350 601 6th St, New Westminster, V3O 3C1, BC, Canada **(100%)**
Tel.: (604) 526-8545

Web Site: http://www.probynlog.com
Logging Sales
N.A.I.C.S.: 113310
Peter Sotraseher (Pres)

Raintree Lumber Specialties Ltd **(1)**
192nd Street 54th Ave, Surrey, V3S 8E5, BC, Canada
Tel.: (604) 574-0444
Web Site: http://www.raintree-lumber.com
Lumber Whslr
N.A.I.C.S.: 423310

Westcoast Moulding & Millwork Limited **(1)**
18810 96 Ave, Surrey, V4N 3R1, BC, Canada
Tel.: (604) 513-1138
Web Site: http://www.westcoastmoulding.com
Building Material Mfr & Distr
N.A.I.C.S.: 339999
Lance Bowerbank (Controller)

E.R.H.S.A.

Girardot 1368, C1427AKD, Buenos Aires, Argentina
Tel.: (54) 1145543232
Web Site: http://www.erhsa.com
Sales Range: $25-49.9 Million
Emp.: 40
Electronic & Mechanical Equipment Distr
N.A.I.C.S.: 423830
Ricardo Reich (Mgr)

E.S. FOX LIMITED

9127 Montrose Road, PO Box 1010, Niagara Falls, L2E 7J9, ON, Canada
Tel.: (905) 354-3700
Web Site: http://www.esfox.com
Year Founded: 1934
Rev.: $152,346,927
Emp.: 1,000
Engineering Services
N.A.I.C.S.: 541330
E. Spencer Fox (Pres)

E1 CORPORATION

20/21F LS Yongsan Tower 92 hangang-daero, Yongsan-gu, Seoul, 04386, Korea (South)
Tel.: (82) 234414114
Web Site: https://www.e1.co.kr
Year Founded: 1984
017940—(KRS)
Rev.: $6,128,918,978
Assets: $3,328,515,527
Liabilities: $2,170,072,702
Net Worth: $1,158,442,825
Earnings: $108,504,054
Emp.: 306
Fiscal Year-end: 12/31/22
Petroleum Whslr
N.A.I.C.S.: 424720
J. Y. Koo (Chm & CEO)

Subsidiaries:

E1 Container Terminal Corp. **(1)**
93 beongil 42, Incheon, 22342, Korea (South)
Tel.: (82) 328802222
Web Site: http://www.e1ct.co.kr
Construction Management Services
N.A.I.C.S.: 236220

M1-Energy LLC **(1)**
26th Khoroo Xiongnu Street Olympic Plaza 8th Floor Room 801, Bayanzurkh District, Ulaanbaatar, Mongolia
Tel.: (976) 77109616
Web Site: http://www.m1energy.mn
Construction Management Services
N.A.I.C.S.: 236220

E2E NETWORKS LIMITED

C/O Awfis A-24/9 Mohan Cooperative Industrial Estate, New Delhi, 110044, India
Tel.: (91) 1140844965

Web Site:
https://www.e2enetworks.com
Year Founded: 2009
E2E—(NSE)
Rev.: $4,949,218
Assets: $4,480,208
Liabilities: $1,258,749
Net Worth: $3,221,460
Earnings: ($154,352)
Emp.: 82
Fiscal Year-end: 03/12/21
Cloud Computing Services
N.A.I.C.S.: 541512
Tarun Dua *(Chm & Mng Dir)*

E2IP TECHNOLOGIES
750 Marcel-Laurin Blvd Suite 375,
Saint Laurent, H4M 2M4, QC,
Canada
Tel.: (514) 631-6662
Web Site: http://www.e2ip.com
Electrical & Electronic Mfr
N.A.I.C.S.: 335999
Eric Saint-Jacques *(CEO)*

Subsidiaries:

Serious Integrated, Inc. **(1)**
7211 E Southern Ave Ste 102, Mesa, AZ
85209
Tel.: (480) 646-8300
Web Site: http://www.seriousintegrated.com
Electrical Equipment & Component Mfr
N.A.I.C.S.: 335999
Gregg Lahti *(CTO & VP-Engrg)*

E2S CO., LTD.
29 Samsung-1ro 4-gil, Hwasung-si,
18449, Gyeonggi, Korea (South)
Tel.: (82) 24880586   KR
Web Site: http://www.e2s.co.kr
Year Founded: 1993
Nuclear Power & Thermal Power
Plants Control Systems Services
N.A.I.C.S.: 221118
Woo-sik Choi *(CEO)*

Subsidiaries:

Doosan HF Controls Corp. **(1)**
1624 W Crosby Rd Ste 124, Carrollton, TX
75006
Tel.: (469) 568-6500
Web Site: http://hfcontrols.com
Emp.: 8,000
Construction & Engineering Services
N.A.I.C.S.: 541330

E3 LITHIUM LTD.
400-725 Granville Street, Vancouver,
V7Y 1G5, BC, Canada
Tel.: (587) 324-2775
Web Site:
http://www.e3metalscorp.com
OW3—(DEU)
Rev.: $496,866
Assets: $46,807,370
Liabilities: $3,650,985
Net Worth: $43,156,384
Earnings: ($6,829,268)
Emp.: 28
Fiscal Year-end: 12/31/23
Mineral Exploration Services
N.A.I.C.S.: 213115
Chris Doornbos *(Pres & CEO)*

E4U A.S.
Hodoninska 1624, 69603, Dubnany,
Czech Republic
Tel.: (420) 222742940
Web Site: https://www.e4u.cz
Year Founded: 2006
EFORU—(PRA)
Rev.: $638,145
Assets: $4,509,793
Liabilities: $11,619
Net Worth: $4,498,174
Earnings: $601,441
Fiscal Year-end: 12/31/19
Eletric Power Generation Services

N.A.I.C.S.: 221118
Petr Neubauer *(Chm-Supervisory Bd)*

EA HOLDINGS BERHAD
Unit 25-5 Oval Damansara 685 Jalan
Damansara, 60000, Kuala Lumpur,
Malaysia
Tel.: (60) 377339762
Web Site: https://www.eah.com.my
Year Founded: 2009
EAH—(KLS)
Rev.: $18,449,671
Assets: $27,803,234
Liabilities: $3,487,423
Net Worth: $24,315,811
Earnings: ($3,585,092)
Emp.: 32
Fiscal Year-end: 03/31/23
Investment Holding, Management &
Consulting Services; Software &
Computer Related Solutions
N.A.I.C.S.: 551112
Mohammad Sobri Saad *(CEO)*

Subsidiaries:

DDSB (M) Sdn. Bhd. **(1)**
Unit 28-2 Oval Damansara 685 Jalan Da-
mansara, 60000, Kuala Lumpur, Malaysia
Tel.: (60) 377339764
Web Site: https://www.ddsb.com
Emp.: 40
IT Consulting Services
N.A.I.C.S.: 541618

EASS Sdn. Bhd. **(1)**
Unit 25-5 Level 25 Oval Damansara 685,
Jalan Damansara, 60000, Kuala Lumpur,
Malaysia
Tel.: (60) 377339763
Web Site: https://www.eass.com.my
Business Consulting Services
N.A.I.C.S.: 541618

Subsidiary (Domestic):

EA MSC Sdn. Bhd. **(2)**
91-1 Jalan BK5A/2, Bandar Kinrara, 47180,
Puchong, Selangor, Malaysia
Tel.: (60) 380809378
Web Site: https://www.eamsc.com
Hardware System Integration Services
N.A.I.C.S.: 541512

Murasaki Technology Sdn. Bhd. **(1)**
No 86A Jalan SS21/62 Damansara Utama,
Damansara Utama, 47400, Petaling Jaya,
Selangor, Malaysia
Tel.: (60) 377277388
Web Site: https://www.murasakitech.com.my
Software Development Services
N.A.I.C.S.: 541511

Sunland Volonte Agency Sdn.
Bhd. **(1)**
4 Jalan Sg Beting 2 Off Jalan Sg Putus,
Port Klang, Malaysia
Tel.: (60) 332920760
Web Site: https://www.sunland.com.my
Food & Beverage Product Distr
N.A.I.C.S.: 424490

EAAGADS LTD.
Kofinaf House Ngenda Road off
Ruiru-Githunguri Road, Ruiru Munici-
pality Kiambu County, Limuru, Kenya
Tel.: (254) 208011041   KE
Web Site: https://www.eaagads.co.ke
Year Founded: 1946
EGAD—(NAI)
Rev.: $1,448,663
Assets: $13,354,235
Liabilities: $2,436,928
Net Worth: $10,917,306
Earnings: $69,631
Emp.: 63
Fiscal Year-end: 03/31/24
Coffee Product Mfr
N.A.I.C.S.: 311920
Joseph Kimemia *(Chm)*

EAB GROUP OYJ

Kluuvikatu 3 3 krs, 00100, Helsinki,
Finland
Tel.: (358) 201558610
Web Site: http://www.eabgroup.fi
EAB—(HEL)
Rev.: $22,968,088
Assets: $40,286,272
Liabilities: $16,826,888
Net Worth: $23,459,384
Earnings: $368,472
Emp.: 93
Fiscal Year-end: 12/31/20
Investment Management Service
N.A.I.C.S.: 523940
Daniel Pasternack *(Pres, CEO &
Head-HR)*

EAC INVEST AS
EAC A/S 16 1 Indiakaj, DK 2100, Co-
penhagen, Denmark
Tel.: (45) 35254300   HK
Web Site: https://www.eac.dk
Year Founded: 1980
EAC—(CSE)
Rev.: $217,042
Assets: $6,077,180
Liabilities: $43,408
Net Worth: $6,033,772
Earnings: ($217,042)
Emp.: 1
Fiscal Year-end: 12/31/22
Holding Company; Food Products
Distr; Specialty Chemicals Marketer;
Moving & Storage Services
N.A.I.C.S.: 551112

Subsidiaries:

Briscoe Timber Limited **(1)**
16 18 Fatai Atere Way, PO Box 2104, Ma-
tori Industrial Scheme Lagos, Oshodi,
Nigeria **(80.5%)**
Tel.: (234) 14520564
N.A.I.C.S.: 425120

Domino Coding Ltd. **(1)**
Beijing Tianzhu Airport Industrial Zone, 12
Tianzhu West Street, 101312, Beijing,
China **(50%)**
Tel.: (86) 21 5050 9999
Web Site: http://www.domino.com.cn
Mfr & Supplier of Industrial Inks & Laser
Printing Equipment
N.A.I.C.S.: 325910

EAC (Philippines) Inc. **(1)**
3rd Fl IDC Bldg E Rodrigues Jr Ave, Bo
Ugong Norte Libis, Quezon City,
Philippines **(92.6%)**
Tel.: (63) 26381818
Develop & Market Nutritional Food Products
N.A.I.C.S.: 425120

EAC Chemicals Singapore Pte.
Ltd. **(1)**
47 Scotts Rd 06 00, Goldbell Towers, Sin-
gapore, 228233, Singapore **(100%)**
Tel.: (65) 62139095
Sales Range: $50-74.9 Million
Emp.: 50
N.A.I.C.S.: 425120

EAC Consumer Products Ltd.
ApS **(1)**
Indiakaj 20, Copenhagen, 2100,
Denmark **(100%)**
Tel.: (45) 35254300
Web Site: http://www.eastasiatic.com
Emp.: 10
N.A.I.C.S.: 425120
Niels Hendrick Jinsin *(CEO)*

Empacadora Ecuatoriano Danesa
(ECUADASA) S.A. **(1)**
Avenida Pedro J Menendez Gilbert, Apar-
tado 09-01-6368, Guayaquil,
Ecuador **(53.5%)**
Tel.: (593) 42288500
Web Site: http://www.eac.com
N.A.I.C.S.: 425120

Griffin Travel (HK) Ltd. **(1)**
Citicorp Centre 18 Whitfield Road, Cause-
way Bay, China (Hong Kong) **(25%)**
Tel.: (852) 28335083

Web Site: http://www.griffintravel.com
Sales Range: $50-74.9 Million
Emp.: 20
N.A.I.C.S.: 425120
Elveit Jfeung *(Gen Mgr)*

Heidelberg Hong Kong **(1)**
Unit 1605-1616 Metropolis Tower 10 Me-
tropolis Drive, Hunghom, Kowloon, China
(Hong Kong) **(100%)**
Tel.: (852) 28142300
Importer, Marketer & Distributor of Machin-
ery, Equipment & Consumer Products
N.A.I.C.S.: 423830

Interdean Auguste Daleiden Sarl **(1)**
Allee de la Poudrerie, 1899, Kockelscheuer,
Luxembourg
Tel.: (352) 484422
Web Site: http://www.interdean.com
Sales Range: $50-74.9 Million
Emp.: 6
Relocation Services
N.A.I.C.S.: 928120
Nicholas Sepulchre *(Gen Mgr)*

Interdean B.V. **(1)**
Albert Einsteinweg 12, Alphen aan den Rijn,
2408 AR, Netherlands
Tel.: (31) 172 447979
Web Site: http://www.interdean.com
Emp.: 12
Relocation Services
N.A.I.C.S.: 928120
Rene van Valen *(Gen Mgr)*

Interdean Bulgaria EOOD **(1)**
Kv Orlandovtzi Blvd First Bulgarian Army,
Sofia, 1225, Bulgaria
Tel.: (359) 2 9366203
Sales Range: $50-74.9 Million
Emp.: 5
Relocation Services
N.A.I.C.S.: 928120
Anton Vangelov *(Gen Mgr)*

Interdean Central Asia LLC **(1)**
103 Furmanova 8th Fl Office 836, 50000,
Almaty, Kazakhstan
Tel.: (7) 727 272 52 51
Sales Range: $25-49.9 Million
Emp.: 25
Relocation Services
N.A.I.C.S.: 928120

Interdean Eastern Europe
Ges.m.b.H **(1)**
Eitnergasse 5, 1230, Vienna, Austria
Tel.: (43) 18654706
Web Site: http://www.interdean.com
Emp.: 4
Relocation Services
N.A.I.C.S.: 928120
Peter Osel *(Gen Mgr)*

Interdean Holdings Limited **(1)**
Central Way Park Royal Brent, London,
NW10 7XW, United Kingdom
Tel.: (44) 2089632500
Investment Management Service
N.A.I.C.S.: 523940

Interdean Hungaria Nemzetkozi Kol-
tozteto Kft **(1)**
Szallito UTCA 6, 1211, Budapest, Hungary
Tel.: (36) 1888 6750
Sales Range: $50-74.9 Million
Emp.: 1
Relocation Services
N.A.I.C.S.: 928120
Anthony Heszberger *(Mgr)*

Interdean Int' Movers s.r.l. **(1)**
Via Zenale 82, 20024, Garbagnate Mila-
nese, Italy
Tel.: (39) 02 9955649
Web Site: http://www.interdean.com
Relocation Services
N.A.I.C.S.: 928120

Interdean International Relocation
SA **(1)**
Centro Empresarial Sintra Estoril I Ar-
mazem Q Estrada de Albarraque, Linho,
2710-297, Sintra, Portugal
Tel.: (351) 219 245 050
Emp.: 15
Relocation Services
N.A.I.C.S.: 928120
Tony Segundo *(Mgr)*

EAC Invest AS—(Continued)

Interdean International Relocation Ukraine LLC (1)
34 Chervonogvardiyska Str, 2094, Kiev, Ukraine
Tel.: (380) 442287370
Web Site: http://www.interdean.com
Sales Range: $25-49.9 Million
Emp.: 15
Relocation Services
N.A.I.C.S.: 928120
Marina Chornokozha (Gen Mgr)

Interdean Internationale Spedition Ges.m.b.H (1)
Eitnerg 5, 1230, Vienna, Austria
Tel.: (43) 1 8654706 0
Web Site: http://www.interdean.com
Emp.: 6
Relocation Services
N.A.I.C.S.: 928120

Interdean Limited (1)
Ismail Qutkashenli Str 99/16, AZ1073, Baku, Azerbaijan
Tel.: (994) 12 447 4346
Web Site: http://www.interdean.com
Sales Range: $50-74.9 Million
Emp.: 10
Relocation Services
N.A.I.C.S.: 928120

Interdean Relocation Services GmbH (1)
Haupstr 7, 14979, Grossbeeren, Germany
Tel.: (49) 33701 213
Web Site: http://www.interdean.com
Sales Range: $25-49.9 Million
Emp.: 15
Relocation Services
N.A.I.C.S.: 541614
Ralf Kessel (Mgr)

Interdean Relocation Services NV (1)
Jan-Baptist Vinkstraat 9, 3070, Kortenberg, Belgium
Tel.: (32) 2 757 9285
Sales Range: $25-49.9 Million
Emp.: 25
Relocation Services
N.A.I.C.S.: 928120
Joost Schramme (Mng Dir)

Interdean SA (1)
Im Langhag 9, Effretikon, Zurich, 8307, Switzerland
Tel.: (41) 52 355 36 36
Relocation Services
N.A.I.C.S.: 928120
Dave Norton (Branch Mgr)

Interdean Sp. Z.o.o (1)
Ul Geodetow 172, Piaseczno, 5500, Poland
Tel.: (48) 227017171
Relocation Services
N.A.I.C.S.: 928120

Interdean Srl (1)
Str Migdalului No 38 Sector 6, 60592, Bucharest, Romania
Tel.: (40) 21 220 11 68
Sales Range: $25-49.9 Million
Emp.: 5
Relocation Services
N.A.I.C.S.: 928120
Cristian Borcos (Gen Mgr)

Interdean, spol s.r.o (1)
6 Ruzyne U Silnice 949, 161 00, Prague, Czech Republic
Tel.: (420) 233313157
Sales Range: $25-49.9 Million
Emp.: 2
Relocation Services
N.A.I.C.S.: 928120
Michael Vincenec (Mgr)

PT Santa Fe Indonusa (1)
Building 208 Cilandak Commercial Estate Jl Raya Cilandak KKO, Jakarta, 12560, Indonesia
Tel.: (62) 21 789 2033
Relocation Services
N.A.I.C.S.: 541604
Jason Will (Mng Dir)

Plumrose Caracas C.A. (1)
Prolongacion Av Trieste Con Calle Miranda

Edf Plumrose Urb, Los Ruices Sur, Caracas, 1060, Venezuela
Tel.: (58) 212 2738711
Meat Product Distr
N.A.I.C.S.: 424470

Plumrose Latinoamericana C.A. (1)
Edificio Plumrose Urbanizacion Los Ruices Sur Ave Trieste Con, Calle Miranda Piso 2, Caracas, 1060, Venezuela (100%)
Tel.: (58) 2122738711
Web Site: http://www.eac.com
Sales Range: $50-74.9 Million
Emp.: 100
N.A.I.C.S.: 425120

Santa Fe Belgrade (1)
Zitna 28, Dobanovci, 11272, Belgrade, Serbia
Tel.: (381) 11 35 36 350
Sales Range: $50-74.9 Million
Emp.: 6
Relocation Services
N.A.I.C.S.: 928120
Vesna Dragic (Deputy Mgr)

Santa Fe India Private Limited (1)
1189/C 13th Main HAL II Stage, Indiranagar, Bengaluru, 560 008, India
Tel.: (91) 80 40522222
Web Site: http://www.santafe.in
Sales Range: $25-49.9 Million
Emp.: 45
Relocation Services
N.A.I.C.S.: 928120
Kim Becker (Mng Dir)

Santa Fe Moving and Relocation Services Phils., Inc. (1)
Warehouse 2 & 3 Southern Luzon Complex Purok 3 Barangay Batino, Manalac, Calamba, 4027, Laguna, Philippines
Tel.: (63) 2 838 1761
Web Site: http://www.santaferelo.com
Sales Range: $50-74.9 Million
Emp.: 10
Relocation & Immigration Services
N.A.I.C.S.: 928120
Vedit Kurangil (Mng Dir)

Santa Fe Relocation Services (1)
Agatova 22, 84103, Bratislava, Slovakia
Tel.: (421) 252632447
Web Site: http://www.santaferelo.com
Relocation Services
N.A.I.C.S.: 928120
Anthony Heszberger (Mng Dir & Reg Dir)

Santa Fe Relocation Services (1)
8th Fl Thien Son Bldg 5 Nguyen Gia Thieu St, Dist 3, Ho Chi Minh City, Vietnam
Tel.: (84) 8 3933 0065
Web Site: http://www.santaferelo.com
Sales Range: $25-49.9 Million
Emp.: 43
Relocation Services
N.A.I.C.S.: 928120
Khanh Nguyen (Mgr-Customer Svcs)

Santa Fe Relocation Services Japan K.K. (1)
AB Bldg 6th Floor 3-1-17 Roppongi, Minato-ku, Tokyo, 106-0032, Japan
Tel.: (81) 3 3589 6666
Web Site: http://www.santafejapan.co.jp
Relocation Services
N.A.I.C.S.: 928120
Scott Erickson (Gen Mgr)

Santa Fe Relocation Services Korea Co., Ltd. (1)
69 Ujeonguk Rojong, Jung-gu, Seoul, 110140, Korea (South)
Tel.: (82) 2 2234 3383
Emp.: 16
Relocation & Immigration Services
N.A.I.C.S.: 928120
Linda Choi (Mgr-Relocation)

Santa Fe Relocation Services LLC (1)
Warsan Building 501 Tecom, PO Box 125478, Dubai, United Arab Emirates
Tel.: (971) 4454 2724
Web Site: http://www.santaferelo.com
Sales Range: $25-49.9 Million
Emp.: 50
Relocation & Immigration Services
N.A.I.C.S.: 928120
Kim Creutzburg (Mng Dir)

Santa Fe Relocation Services Sdn. Bhd. (1)
No 4 Jalan Pengarah U1/29 Hicom-Glenmarie Industrial Park, Shah Alam, 40150, Selangor, Malaysia
Tel.: (60) 3 7805 4322
Web Site: http://www.santaferelo.com
Relocation & Immigration Services
N.A.I.C.S.: 928120
Eunice Look (Mgr-Visa & Immigration)

Santa Fe Relocation Services Taiwan Co., Ltd (1)
13F-4 No 141 Sec 1 Keelung Road, Xinyi District, Taipei, 11070, Taiwan
Tel.: (886) 2 2749 4420
Web Site: http://www.santaferelo.com
Relocation Services
N.A.I.C.S.: 928120
Jim Hill (Gen Mgr)

Santa Fe Transport International Limited (1)
18 Fl C C Wu Bldg, 302 308 Hennessy Rd, Wanchai, China (Hong Kong) (100%)
Tel.: (852) 25746204
Web Site: http://www.santaferelo.com
Sales Range: $100-124.9 Million
Emp.: 250
N.A.I.C.S.: 425120
Lars Lykke Iversen (CEO)

Subsidiary (Non-US):

Interdean International Ltd. (2)
Central Way Park Royal, NW10 7XW, London, United Kingdom - England
Tel.: (44) 2089614141
Web Site: http://www.interdean.com
Emp.: 160
Freight Forwarding Services
N.A.I.C.S.: 488510
Dale Collins (CEO)

Santa Fe (Thailand) ltd. (2)
207 Soi Saeng Uthai 50 Sukhumvit Rd, Kwang Prakanong Khet Klongtoey, 10110, Bangkok, Thailand (100%)
Tel.: (66) 27429890
Web Site: http://www.santaferelo.com
Sales Range: $25-49.9 Million
Emp.: 97
Relocation Services
N.A.I.C.S.: 493110

Subsidiary (Domestic):

Santa Fe International Projects Limited (2)
18 F C C Wu Bldg, 302 308 Hennessy Rd, Hong Kong, China (Hong Kong) (100%)
Tel.: (852) 25746204
Web Site: http://www.santaferelo.com
Sales Range: $75-99.9 Million
Emp.: 250
N.A.I.C.S.: 425120
Lance Allen (Mng Dir)

Subsidiary (Non-US):

Santa Fe Relocation Services Singapore Pvt. Ltd. (2)
54 Pandan Rd, Singapore, 609292, Singapore (100%)
Tel.: (65) 63988588
Web Site: http://www.santaferelo.com
Sales Range: $10-24.9 Million
Emp.: 159
N.A.I.C.S.: 425120
Bill Cain (Mng Dir)

Santa Fe Van Lines Co. Ltd. (2)
, Beijing, China (95%)
Industrial Machinery & Equipment
N.A.I.C.S.: 423830

Sino Santa Fe International Services Corporation (2)
2F Block J Eask Lk Villas, 35 Dongzhimenwai Main St, Beijing, 100027, China (50%)
Tel.: (86) 1084516666
Web Site: http://www.santaferelo.com
N.A.I.C.S.: 425120
Jemie Wong (Gen Mgr)

Wridgways Australia Limited (2)
26-40 Nina Link, Dandenong, 3175, VIC, Australia
Tel.: (61) 395547300

Web Site: http://www.wridgways.com.au
Sales Range: $100-124.9 Million
Removal & Storage Services
N.A.I.C.S.: 423840
Brian C. Clarke (Sec & Dir-Fin)

Subsidiary (Domestic):

Santa Fe Wridgways (3)
21 Oxenham Street, Dudley Park, Adelaide, 5008, SA, Australia
Tel.: (61) 882695566
Web Site: http://www.wridgways.com.au
Packing & Moving Services
N.A.I.C.S.: 484210

Subsidiary (Domestic):

Movedynamics (4)
14 Epic Place, Villawood, 2163, NSW, Australia
Tel.: (61) 296457744
Web Site: http://www.movedynamics.com.au
Sales Range: $25-49.9 Million
Emp.: 6
Removal Brokerage Services
N.A.I.C.S.: 484210
Charles Garnar (Mgr)

Division (Domestic):

Wridgways Australia Limited - Wridgways Move Solutions (3)
Ste 302 Level 3 697 Burke Rd, Camberwell, 3124, VIC, Australia
Tel.: (61) 398823400
Web Site: http://www.wridgwaysmovesolutions.com.au
Sales Range: $25-49.9 Million
Emp.: 10
Relocation Services
N.A.I.C.S.: 561499

Sino Santa Fe Real Estate (Beijing) Co. Ltd. (1)
Rm 1307 West Tower Guangzhou International Commercial Center No122, Tiyu Dong Rd, Guangzhou, 510620, China
Tel.: (86) 2038870630
Sales Range: $25-49.9 Million
Emp.: 4
Real Estate Manangement Services
N.A.I.C.S.: 531390

Southland Veneers Ltd. (1)
9 Matheson Rd Kennington, Invercargill, Southland, New Zealand (66.7%)
Tel.: (64) 32304820
Sales Range: $50-74.9 Million
Emp.: 25
N.A.I.C.S.: 425120

Thai Poly Acrylic Public Company Ltd. (1)
60-61 Moo 9 Phutthamonthon 4 Rd Krathumlom Sampran, Bangkok, 10600, Klongsan, Thailand (16.67%)
Tel.: (66) 28608765
Web Site: https://www.thaipolyacrylic.com
Sales Range: $200-249.9 Million
Emp.: 300
Mfr & Sales of Acrylic Sheets for Various Applications
N.A.I.C.S.: 326112

The East Asiatic 2010 (Thailand) Company Ltd. (1)
1168/98-100 Lumpini Tower 33rd Floor Rama IV Road Thungmahamek Sathorn, Bangkok, 10120, Thailand
Tel.: (66) 2 689 5999
Industrial Machinery Mfr
N.A.I.C.S.: 333248

EAF HOLDING GMBH
Borsigstrasse 8, 47574, Goch, Germany
Tel.: (49) 282393130
Web Site: http://www.eaf-gmbh.de
Emp.: 65
Holding Company
N.A.I.C.S.: 551112

Subsidiaries:

EAF Computer Service Supplies GmbH (1)
Borsigstrasse 8, 47574, Goch, Germany
Tel.: (49) 282393130

Web Site: http://www.eaf-gmbh.de
Sales Range: $25-49.9 Million
Emp.: 50
Information Technology & Supply Chain
Management Services for IT Hardware Industry
N.A.I.C.S.: 541519
Herbert Schiffer *(Mng Dir)*

EAG-BETEILIGUNGS AG
Fischhof 3/6, A-1010, Vienna, Austria
Tel.: (43) 1230603834   **AT**
Web Site: http://www.eag-bag.com
Sales Range: $1-9.9 Million
Investment Holding Company
N.A.I.C.S.: 551112

EAGERS AUTOMOTIVE LIMITED
5 Edmund Street, PO Box 199, Fortitude Valley, Brisbane, 4006, QLD,
Australia
Tel.: (61) 736087100
Web Site:
    https://www.apeagers.com.au
APE—(ASX)
Rev.: $6,710,497,241
Assets: $3,215,526,871
Liabilities: $2,326,359,921
Net Worth: $889,166,950
Earnings: $203,710,919
Emp.: 7,577
Fiscal Year-end: 12/31/23
Motor Vehicle Retailers
N.A.I.C.S.: 423110
Timothy Boyd Crommelin *(Chm)*

Subsidiaries:

A.P. Ford Pty Ltd   **(1)**
80 Mclachlan St, Fortitude Valley, 4006,
QLD, Australia
Tel.: (61) 732489455
Web Site: http://www.apeagers.com.au
Sales Range: $25-49.9 Million
Emp.: 15
Automotive Spare Parts Distr
N.A.I.C.S.: 423120

A.P. Motors (No.2) Pty Ltd   **(1)**
2 Hinkler Court Brendale, Brisbane, 4009,
QLD, Australia
Tel.: (61) 732602722
Emp.: 50
Motor Vehicle Spare Parts Distr
N.A.I.C.S.: 423120

A.P. Motors (No.3) Pty Ltd   **(1)**
55 southpimne, Brendale, 4500, QLD, Australia
Tel.: (61) 732054244
Automotive Spare Parts Distr
N.A.I.C.S.: 423120

Adtrans Group Ltd.   **(1)**
4 Greenhill Road, 1st Fl, Wayville, 5034,
SA, Australia
Tel.: (61) 883731991
Web Site: http://www.adtrans.com.au
Sales Range: $600-649.9 Million
Emp.: 837
Motor Vehicles & Trucks Retailer
N.A.I.C.S.: 441110

Subsidiary (Domestic):

Adtrans Australia Pty Ltd   **(2)**
198 Whitehall St, Footscray, 3011, VIC,
Australia
Tel.: (61) 396877244
Web Site:
    http://www.whitehorsetruckandbus.com.au
Sales Range: $10-24.9 Million
Emp.: 30
Truck Repair & Maintenance Services
N.A.I.C.S.: 811198

Adtrans Automotive Group Pty.
Ltd.   **(2)**
28-30 Tikalara St, 5010, Regents Park, SA,
Australia   **(100%)**
Tel.: (61) 883731991
Sales Range: $25-49.9 Million
Emp.: 100
Used Car Dealers
N.A.I.C.S.: 441120

Adtrans Corporate Pty. Ltd.   **(2)**
4 Greenhill Rd, Wayville, SA,
Australia   **(100%)**
Tel.: (61) 883731991
Web Site: http://www.adtrans.com.au
Sales Range: $25-49.9 Million
Emp.: 14
Used Car Dealers
N.A.I.C.S.: 441120

Adtrans Hino Pty Ltd   **(2)**
253 - 259 Coward Street, Mascot, 2020,
NSW, Australia
Tel.: (61) 95989444
Web Site: https://www.adtranshino.com.au
Emp.: 20
New & Used Truck Distr
N.A.I.C.S.: 423110

Adtrans Truck Centre Pty. Ltd.   **(2)**
Cnr Raymond and Boundary Rd, Laverton,
3026, VIC, Australia   **(100%)**
Tel.: (61) 393609922
Web Site: https://www.adtranstrucks.com.au
Sales Range: $200-249.9 Million
Automobile & Motor Vehicle Whslr
N.A.I.C.S.: 423110

Graham Cornes Motors Pty. Ltd.   **(2)**
46 Belair Road, Hawthorn, 5062, SA,
Australia   **(90%)**
Tel.: (61) 882721488
Web Site: http://www.cornestoyota.com.au
Sales Range: $25-49.9 Million
Emp.: 70
Used Car Dealers
N.A.I.C.S.: 441120

Stillwell Trucks Pty Ltd   **(2)**
20 Ashford Avenue, Milperra, 2214, NSW,
Australia
Tel.: (61) 29748500
Web Site: http://www.stillwelltrucks.com.au
Sales Range: $25-49.9 Million
Emp.: 100
Truck Retailer
N.A.I.C.S.: 441227

Whitehorse Trucks Pty Ltd   **(2)**
67 75 Princess Highway, VIC, Dandenong,
3175, SA, Australia
Tel.: (61) 397916533
Web Site:
    http://www.whitehorsetrucks.com.au
Sales Range: $25-49.9 Million
Emp.: 100
Truck Retailer
N.A.I.C.S.: 441227

Adtrans Trucks Pty Ltd   **(1)**
Cnr Raymond and Boundary Rd, Laverton
North, Melbourne, 3026, VIC, Australia
Tel.: (61) 393609922
Web Site: https://www.adtranstrucks.com.au
Sales Range: $25-49.9 Million
Emp.: 60
Truck Repair & Maintenance Services
N.A.I.C.S.: 811198

Austral Pty Ltd   **(1)**
80 Mclachlan St, Fortitude Valley, 4006,
QLD, Australia
Tel.: (61) 732489455
Web Site: http://www.apeagers.com.au
Emp.: 30
Motor Vehicle Spare Parts Distr
N.A.I.C.S.: 423120

Automotive Holdings Group
Limited   **(1)**
21 Old Aberdeen Place, West Perth, 6005,
WA, Australia
Tel.: (61) 894227676
Web Site: http://www.ahgir.com.au
Rev.: $5,052,933,626
Assets: $2,059,003,645
Liabilities: $1,452,942,233
Net Worth: $606,061,412
Earnings: $29,496,278
Emp.: 8,400
Fiscal Year-end: 06/30/2018
Automotive Retailer
N.A.I.C.S.: 441110
David Rowland *(Gen Counsel & Sec)*

Subsidiary (Domestic):

360 Finance Pty Ltd   **(2)**
64 Parramatta Rd, Underwood, 4119, QLD,
Australia   **(100%)**

Tel.: (61) 1300361360
Web Site: https://www.360finance.com.au
Automobile Financing Services
N.A.I.C.S.: 522220
Ruby Metla *(Specialist-Fin)*

AHG 1 Pty Ltd   **(2)**
43-63 Princes Hwy, Dandenong, 3175, VIC,
Australia
Tel.: (61) 392125555
New & Used Car Dealer
N.A.I.C.S.: 441110

AUT 6 Pty Ltd   **(2)**
101 Sterling Hwy, Nedlands, 6009, WA,
Australia
Tel.: (61) 892733131
Emp.: 40
New & Used Car Dealer
N.A.I.C.S.: 441110

Allpike Autos Pty Ltd   **(2)**
274 Scarborough Beach Rd, Osborne Park,
6017, WA, Australia
Tel.: (61) 8 6365 4057
Automobile Parts Distr
N.A.I.C.S.: 423120

Subsidiary (Non-US):

Auckland Auto Collection Limited   **(2)**
Quigg Partners Level 7 28 Brandon Street,
Wellington, New Zealand
Tel.: (64) 93769829
New Car Dealers
N.A.I.C.S.: 441110

Subsidiary (Domestic):

Big Rock 2005 Pty Ltd   **(2)**
445 Wanneroo Rd, Balcatta, 6021, WA,
Australia
Tel.: (61) 893440111
New & Used Car Dealer
N.A.I.C.S.: 441110

Big Rock Pty Ltd   **(2)**
Persival St, Lilyfield, Sydney, 2040, NSW,
Australia
Tel.: (61) 295526663
New & Used Car Dealer
N.A.I.C.S.: 441110

City Motors (1981) Pty Ltd   **(2)**
505 Newcastle Street, Wangara, 6065, WA,
Australia
Tel.: (61) 8 9309 9003
New & Used Car Dealer
N.A.I.C.S.: 441110

Falconet Pty Ltd   **(2)**
24-26 Kewdale Rd, Welshpool, 6106, WA,
Australia
Tel.: (61) 893512000
New & Used Car Dealer
N.A.I.C.S.: 441110

Geraldine Nominees Pty Ltd   **(2)**
268 Great Eastern Hwy, Belmont, 6104,
WA, Australia
Tel.: (61) 893331888
New & Used Car Dealer
N.A.I.C.S.: 441110

Giant Autos (1997) Pty Ltd   **(2)**
460 Scarborough Beach Rd, Osborne Park,
6017, WA, Australia
Tel.: (61) 894455666
New & Used Car Dealer
N.A.I.C.S.: 441110
Daniel Herring *(Gen Mgr)*

Grand Autos 2005 Pty Ltd   **(2)**
Corner Wanneroo Rd & Lancaster Rd,
Wangara, 6065, WA, Australia
Tel.: (61) 894039000
Emp.: 100
New & Used Car Dealer
N.A.I.C.S.: 441110

Highland Kackell Pty Ltd   **(2)**
52 Sunnyholt Rd, Blacktown, 2148, NSW,
Australia
Tel.: (61) 288844888
New & Used Car Dealer
N.A.I.C.S.: 441110

Janetto Holdings Pty Ltd   **(2)**
435 Scarborough Beach Rd, Osborne Park,
6017, WA, Australia
Tel.: (61) 892732333
Emp.: 500

New & Used Car Dealer
N.A.I.C.S.: 441110
Andy Diamantis *(Gen Mgr)*

MCM Autos Pty Ltd   **(2)**
511 Princes Hwy, Sutherland, 2232, NSW,
Australia
Tel.: (61) 295457344
New & Used Car Dealer
N.A.I.C.S.: 441110

Melborne City Autos (2012) Pty
Ltd   **(2)**
32-48 Johnson St, South Melbourne, 3205,
VIC, Australia
Tel.: (61) 386092240
New & Used Car Dealer
N.A.I.C.S.: 441110

Melville Autos Pty Ltd   **(2)**
174 Leach Hwy, Melville, 6156, WA, Australia
Tel.: (61) 893643346
New & Used Car Dealer
N.A.I.C.S.: 441110

Newcastle Commercial Vehicles Pty
Ltd   **(2)**
1 Kinta Dr, Newcastle, 2322, NSW, Australia
Tel.: (61) 249747800
Web Site: https://www.ncvtrucks.com.au
New & Used Car Dealer
N.A.I.C.S.: 441110

North City (1981) Pty Ltd   **(2)**
384 Scarborough Beach Road, Osborne
Park, 6017, WA, Australia
Tel.: (61) 892732222
Web Site:
    https://www.northcityholden.com.au
New & Used Car Dealer
N.A.I.C.S.: 441110
Joe Tarantolo *(Mgr-Used Car)*

Nuford Ford Pty Ltd   **(2)**
6 Automotive Dr, Wangara, 6065, WA, Australia
Tel.: (61) 893098888
Web Site: https://www.nuford.com.au
New & Used Car Dealer
N.A.I.C.S.: 441110

Rand Transport Pty Ltd   **(2)**
24 Ulm Place, Perth, 6105, WA, Australia
Tel.: (61) 8 9353 7099
Web Site: http://www.ahgrl.com.au
Logistics Consulting Servies
N.A.I.C.S.: 541614
David Cole *(Gen Mgr)*

Subsidiary (Domestic):

Butmac Pty Ltd   **(3)**
13 39 Pilbara St, Welshpool, 6106, WA,
Australia
Tel.: (61) 893514833
Emp.: 20
Logistics Consulting Servies
N.A.I.C.S.: 541614
Jeff Leisk *(Gen Mgr)*

Rand Transport (1986) Pty Ltd   **(3)**
1248 Lytton Rd, Hemmant, 4174, QLD,
Australia
Tel.: (61) 7 3907 8888
Web Site: http://www.rand.com.au
Logistics Consulting Servies
N.A.I.C.S.: 541614

Subsidiary (Domestic):

Southeast Automotive Group Pty
Ltd   **(2)**
1332 Logan Road, Mount Gravatt, 4122,
QLD, Australia
Tel.: (61) 732438888
Web Site:
    https://www.mtgravattmitsubishi.com.au
New & Used Car Dealer
N.A.I.C.S.: 441110
Bronte Houson *(Gen Mgr)*

Southside Autos (1981) Pty Ltd   **(2)**
1261-1273 Albany Hwy, Cannington, 6107,
WA, Australia
Tel.: (61) 893589555
New & Used Car Dealer
N.A.I.C.S.: 441110

Total Autos (1990) Pty Ltd   **(2)**

Eagers Automotive Limited—(Continued)

1251 Albany Highway, Cannington, 6107, WA, Australia
Tel.: (61) 893514444
Web Site: https://www.totalnissan.com.au
Emp.: 80
New & Used Car Dealer
N.A.I.C.S.: 441110
Stephen Hall (Gen Mgr)

Zupps Aspley Pty Ltd (2)
1448 1454 Gympie Road, Aspley, Brisbane, 4034, QLD, Australia
Tel.: (61) 732468000
Web Site: https://www.zupps.com.au
New & Used Car Dealer
N.A.I.C.S.: 441110
James Malone (Gen Mgr)

Zupps Mt Gravatt Pty Ltd (2)
143 Marshall Rd, Rocklea, 4106, QLD, Australia
Tel.: (61) 733207777
New & Used Car Dealer
N.A.I.C.S.: 441110

Bill Buckle Autos Pty Ltd (1)
790 Pittwater Road, Brookvale, 2100, NSW, Australia
Tel.: (61) 289229300
Web Site:
    https://www.northernbeachestoyota.com
Sales Range: $75-99.9 Million
Emp.: 14
Automotive Spare Parts Distr
N.A.I.C.S.: 423120

Bill Buckle Holdings Pty Ltd (1)
Cnr Pittwater & Harbord Rds, Brookvale, 2100, NSW, Australia
Tel.: (61) 299397766
Motor Vehicle Spare Parts Distr
N.A.I.C.S.: 423120

Carlin Auction Services (NSW) Pty. Ltd. (1)
169 Magowar Road, Girraween, 2145, NSW, Australia
Tel.: (61) 298965355
Car Retailer
N.A.I.C.S.: 441110

Carlin Auction Services (QLD) Pty. Ltd. (1)
1B 420 Nudgee Road, Hendra, 4011, QLD, Australia
Tel.: (61) 732602799
Car Retailer
N.A.I.C.S.: 441110

Carlins Automotive Auctioneers (WA) Pty. Ltd. (1)
2 Bannister Road, Canning Vale, 6155, WA, Australia
Tel.: (61) 894846600
Car Retailer
N.A.I.C.S.: 441110

City Automotive Group Pty Ltd (1)
Corner Breakfast Creek Rd Evelyn St, Newstead, 4006, QLD, Australia
Tel.: (61) 730007777
Web Site: http://www.city-automotive.com.au
Emp.: 25
Automotive Spare Parts Distr
N.A.I.C.S.: 423120
Shane Bright (Gen Mgr-Sls)

Eagers Nominees Pty Ltd (1)
80 Mclachlan St, Fortitude Valley, 4006, QLD, Australia
Tel.: (61) 732489400
Web Site: http://www.apeagers.com.au
Automobile Dealers
N.A.I.C.S.: 441110

Eagers Retail Pty Ltd (1)
143 Newmarket Rd, Windsor, 4030, QLD, Australia
Tel.: (61) 733641199
Web Site: http://www.eagers.com
Sales Range: $75-99.9 Million
Emp.: 50
Motor Vehicle Spare Parts Distr
N.A.I.C.S.: 423120
Akos Horvath (Gen Mgr)

IB Motors Pty. Ltd. (1)
3-9069 Shaughnessy St, Vancouver, V6P

6R9, BC, Canada
Tel.: (604) 218-7505
Web Site: https://www.ibmotors.ca
Vehicle Repair & Maintenance Services
N.A.I.C.S.: 811198

Northside Nissan (1986) Pty. Ltd. (1)
14 Berriman Drive, Wangara, 6065, WA, Australia
Tel.: (61) 894090000
Web Site:
    https://www.northsidenissan.com.au
Car Retailer
N.A.I.C.S.: 441110

Southern Automotive Group Pty. Ltd. (1)
79-83 Main South Road, Reynella, Adelaide, 5161, SA, Australia
Tel.: (61) 883222299
Web Site:
    https://www.southernautomotive.com.au
Car Retailer
N.A.I.C.S.: 441120

VMS Pty. Ltd. (1)
Unit 45 45 Green Street, Banksmeadow, 2019, NSW, Australia
Tel.: (61) 1800867000
Web Site: https://www.vms.com.au
Environmental Services
N.A.I.C.S.: 541620

Vehicle Storage & Engineering Pty. Ltd. (1)
43-63 Princes Hwy, Dandenong South, 3175, VIC, Australia
Tel.: (61) 392125580
Web Site: http://www.vsesolutions.com.au
Truck Warehousing Services
N.A.I.C.S.: 541614

EAGLE BAY RESOURCES CORP.
789 W Pender St Suite 1450, Vancouver, V6C 1H2, BC, Canada
Tel.: (604) 910-2607   **BC**
Web Site:
    https://www.eaglebayresources.com
Year Founded: 2018
EBR—(CNSX)
Mineral Exploration Services
N.A.I.C.S.: 213115
David Hodge (CEO)

EAGLE COPTERS LTD.
823 McTavish Road NE, Calgary, T2E 7G9, AB, Canada
Tel.: (403) 250-7370
Web Site:
    https://www.eaglecopters.com
Year Founded: 1975
Sales Range: $10-24.9 Million
Emp.: 175
Helicopters Leasing, Sales & Maintenance
N.A.I.C.S.: 488190
Jason Diniz (Pres, CEO, CFO, Principal & VP)

Subsidiaries:

Dart Holding Company Ltd. (1)
1270 Aberdeen Street, Hawkesbury, K6A 1K7, ON, Canada   **(50%)**
Tel.: (613) 632-3336
Web Site: http://www.dartaero.com
Emp.: 80
Holding Company
N.A.I.C.S.: 551112
Mike O'Reilly (Owner)

Subsidiary (Domestic):

Dart Helicopter Services Canada, Inc. (2)
1270 Aberdeen Street, Hawkesbury, K6A 1K7, ON, Canada
Tel.: (613) 632-3336
Emp.: 80
Markets & Sells Helicopters & Aftermarket Helicopter Accessories
N.A.I.C.S.: 488190
Bill Beckett (CEO)

Eagle Copters Australasia Pty. Ltd. (1)
67 Aviation Dr Coffs Harbour Airport, PO Box 4220, Coffs Harbour, 2450, NSW, Australia
Tel.: (61) 266903300
Web Site: http://www.eaglecopters.com.au
Aircraft Leasing Services
N.A.I.C.S.: 532411
Grant Boyter (Mng Dir)

Eagle Copters South America S.A. (1)
Aerodromo de Chicureo, Camino Guay Guay s/n, Colina, 9340000, Chile
Tel.: (56) 2 948 3200
Web Site: http://www.eaglecopters.cl
Helicopters Maintenance & Parts
N.A.I.C.S.: 488190

EAGLE ENERGY INC.
Suite 315 1615 10th Avenue SW, Calgary, T3C 0J7, AB, Canada
Tel.: (403) 531-1575   **AB**
Web Site:
    http://www.eagleenergy.com
EGRGF—(OTCIQ)
Sales Range: $25-49.9 Million
Oil & Gas Exploration Services
N.A.I.C.S.: 211120
Richard W. Clark (Chm)

EAGLE EYE SOLUTIONS GROUP PLC
31 Chertsey Street, Guildford, GU1 4HD, Surrey, United Kingdom
Tel.: (44) 8448243686   **UK**
Web Site: https://www.eagleeye.com
Year Founded: 2014
EYE—(AIM)
Rev.: $42,994,919
Assets: $31,382,340
Liabilities: $19,750,753
Net Worth: $11,631,587
Earnings: $752,177
Emp.: 162
Fiscal Year-end: 06/30/22
Holding Company; Digital Consumer Engagement Software Developer
N.A.I.C.S.: 551112
Steve Rothwell (Founder & CTO)

Subsidiaries:

Eagle Eye Solutions Ltd. (1)
3000 Cathedral Hill, Guildford, GU2 7YB, Surrey, United Kingdom
Tel.: (44) 1483 246 426
Web Site: http://www.eagleeye.com
Digital Consumer Engagement Software Developer
N.A.I.C.S.: 513210
Steve Rothwell (Founder)

Subsidiary (Domestic):

Eagle Eye Solutions (North) Ltd. (2)
2th Floor Digital World Centre 1 Lowry Plaza, The Quays, Salford, M50 3UB, Mancs, United Kingdom
Tel.: (44) 1618744222
Web Site: http://www.eagleeye.com
Emp.: 50
Digital Consumer Engagement Software Developer
N.A.I.C.S.: 513210
Michael Dougherty (Mgr-Sls & Mktg)

EAGLE FILTERS GROUP OYJ
Lonnrotinkatu 5, 120, Helsinki, Finland
Tel.: (358) 505810583
Web Site:
    https://eaglefiltersgroup.com
EAGLE—(HEL)
Rev.: $118,714
Assets: $19,091,302
Liabilities: $5,525,577
Net Worth: $13,565,724
Earnings: ($1,327,434)
Emp.: 4
Fiscal Year-end: 12/31/22

Clean Energy & Resource Efficiency Investment Services
N.A.I.C.S.: 523999
Timo Linnainmaa (Co-Founder, Mng Dir & CFO)

EAGLE FOOTBALL GROUP.
Groupama Stadium 10 Avenue Simone Veil, 70712, Lyon, France
Tel.: (33) 481075500
Web Site: http://www.olweb.fr
Year Founded: 1950
OLG—(EUR)
Rev.: $214,901,791
Assets: $800,283,833
Liabilities: $686,567,019
Net Worth: $113,716,814
Earnings: ($105,565,508)
Emp.: 644
Fiscal Year-end: 06/30/23
Sports Team Operator
N.A.I.C.S.: 711211
Jean-Michel Aulas (Pres)

EAGLE GRAPHITE INCORPORATED
82 Richmond Street East, Toronto, M5C 1P1, ON, Canada
Tel.: (877) 472-3483   **ON**
Web Site:
    http://www.eaglegraphite.com
APMFF—(OTCEM)
Assets: $370,722
Liabilities: $3,090,749
Net Worth: ($2,720,027)
Earnings: $118,678
Fiscal Year-end: 05/31/21
Metal Mining Services
N.A.I.C.S.: 212290
James T. Deith (Pres)

EAGLE HEALTH HOLDINGS LIMITED
Level 2 15-17 Queen Street, Melbourne, 3000, VIC, Australia
Tel.: (61) 385937378   **AU**
Web Site: http://www.auehh.com.au
Year Founded: 2001
Rev.: $78,066,971
Assets: $67,783,963
Liabilities: $14,571,322
Net Worth: $53,212,641
Earnings: $13,174,666
Fiscal Year-end: 12/31/18
Dietary Supplement Product Mfr & Distr
N.A.I.C.S.: 325412
Mingwang Zhang (Founder & Chm)

Subsidiaries:

Xiamen Eagle Don Pharmaceuticals Co., Ltd. (1)
No 220-228 Meihe 3rd Road, Xike Light Industrial Park Tongan, Xiamen, China
Tel.: (86) 5927231999
Web Site: http://www.eaglehealthltd.com
Pharmaceutical Preparation Mfr
N.A.I.C.S.: 325412

EAGLE INDUSTRY CO., LTD.
14F Shiba-Park Bldg -B 2-4-1 Shibakoen, Minato-ku, Tokyo, 105-8587, Japan
Tel.: (81) 334382291   **JP**
Web Site: https://www.ekkeagle.com
Year Founded: 1964
6486—(TKS)
Rev.: $1,104,147,620
Assets: $1,387,531,540
Liabilities: $556,846,230
Net Worth: $830,685,310
Earnings: $49,515,510
Fiscal Year-end: 03/31/24
Holding Company; Mechanical Seals, Valves, Marine Equipment, Bellows & Plant Devices Mfr
N.A.I.C.S.: 551112

Tetsuji Tsuru *(Chm & Pres)*

Subsidiaries:

Actuator Components GmbH & Co. KG (1)
Hohnerweg 2-4, 69465, Weinheim, Germany
Tel.: (49) 6201806694
Web Site: http://www.ekkeagle.com
Emp.: 125
Automotive Actuator Component Mfr & Distr
N.A.I.C.S.: 336390
Peter Lexa *(Mng Dir)*

EBI Asia Pacific Pte Ltd (1)
1 International Business Park 03-01A The Synergy, Singapore, 609917, Singapore
Tel.: (65) 6 565 6623
Web Site: https://www.eagleburgmann.sg
Sales Range: $25-49.9 Million
Emp.: 20
Holding Company
N.A.I.C.S.: 551112

EKK Eagle (Thailand) Co. Ltd. (1)
700/852 Moo 1, Panthong Subdistrict Panthong District, Chon Buri, 20160, Thailand
Tel.: (66) 381 851 6074
Web Site: http://www.ekk.co.jp
Sales Range: $25-49.9 Million
Emp.: 100
Metal Valve & Pipe Fitting Mfr
N.A.I.C.S.: 332919

EKK Eagle America Inc. (1)
31555 W 14 Mile Rd Ste 200, Farmington Hills, MI 48334
Tel.: (212) 967-5575
Construction Machinery Mfr
N.A.I.C.S.: 333120

EKK Eagle Industry Asia-Pacific Pte. Ltd. (1)
48 Toh Guan Road East 09-130 Enterprise Hub, 03-02 Ever Tech Building, Singapore, 608586, Singapore
Tel.: (65) 67791300
Web Site: http://www.ekk.co.jp
Sales Range: $50-74.9 Million
Emp.: 2
Industrial Supplies Whslr
N.A.I.C.S.: 423840

EKK Eagle Industry Mexico S.A. de C.V. (1)
Av Eje Central Lazaro Cardenas 209 Logistic, Villa de Reyes, 79526, San Luis Potosi, Mexico
Tel.: (52) 4448114828
Web Site: https://ekkeaglemx.com
Construction Machinery Mfr
N.A.I.C.S.: 333120

EKK Sales Europe B.V. (1)
Hopelerweg 250, 6468 XX, Kerkrade, Netherlands
Tel.: (31) 455469257
Construction Machinery Mfr
N.A.I.C.S.: 333120
Emile Spijkers *(Sls Mgr)*

EKK, Inc. (1)
2025 Gateway Pl Ste 360, San Jose, CA 95110
Tel.: (408) 578-9012
Automotive & Construction Machinery Distr
N.A.I.C.S.: 423810

Eagle Actuator Components GmbH & Co. KG (1)
Lise-Meitner-Strasse 19, 64646, Heppenheim, Germany
Tel.: (49) 6252980830
Electromagnetic Subassembly Mfr
N.A.I.C.S.: 334510

Eagle Engineering Aerospace Co., Ltd. (1)
13F Parale Mitsui Bldg 8 Higashidacho, Kawasaki-ku, Kawasaki, 210-0005, Kanagawa, Japan
Tel.: (81) 442009581
Web Site: http://www.eea.co.jp
Aerospace Equipment & Components Mfr & Whslr
N.A.I.C.S.: 336413

Subsidiary (US):

Aerospace Reserch & Trading, Inc. (2)

2025 Gateway Pl Ste 360, San Jose, CA 95110-1006
Tel.: (408) 573-9009
Web Site: http://www.eea.com.sg
Aerospace Research & Development Services
N.A.I.C.S.: 541715

Subsidiary (Non-US):

Eagle Engineering Aerospace Korea Co., Ltd. (2)
13 Gongdanseo3-gil Chilseo-myeon, Haman-gun, Changwon, 52001, Gyeongsannam, Korea (South)
Tel.: (82) 555877283
Sales Range: $25-49.9 Million
Emp.: 4
Aerospace Equipment & Components Whslr
N.A.I.C.S.: 423860

Eagle Engineering Aerospace Singapore Pte. Ltd. (2)
Ubi TechPark 07-78 Lobby D 10 Ubi Crescent, Singapore, 408564, Singapore
Tel.: (65) 64836162
Web Site: http://www.eea.com.sg
Sales Range: $25-49.9 Million
Emp.: 7
Aerospace Equipment & Components Whslr
N.A.I.C.S.: 423860

Eagle Engineering Aerospace Taiwan Co., Ltd. (2)
No 7 Lane 144, Chi Lin Rd, Taipei, Taiwan
Tel.: (886) 225629980
Web Site: http://www.eea.co.jp
Sales Range: $25-49.9 Million
Emp.: 1
Aerospace Equipment & Components Whslr
N.A.I.C.S.: 423860

Eagle Highcast Co., Ltd. (1)
36 Asari-cho, Gotsu, 695-0002, Shimane, Japan
Tel.: (81) 855551076
Industrial Machinery Mfr
N.A.I.C.S.: 333248

Eagle Holding Europe B.V. (1)
Hopelerweg 250, 6468 XX, Kerkrade, Netherlands
Tel.: (31) 45 546 9222
Web Site: http://www.ekk-europe.com
Sales Range: $50-74.9 Million
Emp.: 60
Investment Management Service
N.A.I.C.S.: 523999
Dennis van Well *(Dir)*

Eagle Industry (Wuxi) Co., Ltd. (1)
No 9 Lijiang Road, Wuxi, 214028, Jiangsu, China
Tel.: (86) 51085342955
Construction Machinery Mfr
N.A.I.C.S.: 333120

Eagle Industry Co., Ltd. - Okayama Factory (1)
1212 Abe Ochiaicho, Takahashi, 716-8511, Okayama, Japan
Tel.: (81) 866224061
Mechanical Seals Mfr
N.A.I.C.S.: 339991

Eagle Industry Co., Ltd. - Saitama Factory (1)
1500 Katayanagi, Sakado, 350-0285, Saitama, Japan
Tel.: (81) 492811111
Industrial Machinery Mfr
N.A.I.C.S.: 333248

Eagle Industry France S.A.S. (1)
5 Avenue de Lorraine, 57380, Faulquemont, 57380, France
Tel.: (33) 387297980
Emp.: 186
Industrial Machinery Mfr
N.A.I.C.S.: 333248

Eagle Industry Hokkaido Co., Ltd. (1)
83-19 Azatomino Oshamambe-cho, Yamakoshi-gun, Hokkaido, 049-3514, Japan
Tel.: (81) 137725890
Construction Machinery Mfr
N.A.I.C.S.: 333120

Eagle Industry Hungary Kft. (1)

Jaszberenyi ut 23, Maglod, 2234, Budapest, Hungary
Tel.: (36) 2 950 0600
Web Site: https://www.ekkeagle.hu
Public Work Services
N.A.I.C.S.: 237310

Eagle Industry Sales (Shanghai) Co., Ltd. (1)
Block A 14th Floor International Shipping Building 720 Pudong Avenue, Shanghai, China
Tel.: (86) 2150365066
Web Site: http://www.ekkchina-sh.com
Emp.: 40
Water Pump Mechanical Seal Mfr
N.A.I.C.S.: 333996

Eagle Industry Taiwan Corporation (1)
No 134 Hsi Lin Road, Yenchao, Kaohsiung, 824, Taiwan
Tel.: (886) 7 616 4401
Web Site: http://www.ekk.co.jp
Sales Range: $50-74.9 Million
Emp.: 200
Adhesive Mfr
N.A.I.C.S.: 325520
Isashi Shitsubo *(Gen Mgr)*

Eagle New Zealand Limited (1)
47 William Pickering Dr, PO Box 34285, Rosedale, Auckland, New Zealand
Tel.: (64) 94435772
Web Site: http://www.eagleseal.co.nz
Sales Range: $25-49.9 Million
Emp.: 40
Gasket Packing & Sealing Device Mfr
N.A.I.C.S.: 339991

Eagle Sealing Research & Development (Wuxi) Co., Ltd. (1)
No 9 Lijiang Road, Wuxi, 214028, Jiangsu, China
Tel.: (86) 51085342960
Construction Machinery Mfr
N.A.I.C.S.: 333120

EagleBurgmann Australasia Pty. Ltd. (1)
16 Stennett Road, Ingleburn, Sydney, 2565, NSW, Australia
Tel.: (61) 29 605 0600
Web Site:
   https://www.eagleburgmann.com.au
Emp.: 38
Mechanical Seals & Packing Mfr & Sales
N.A.I.C.S.: 339991

Branch (Domestic):

EagleBurgmann Australasia Pty. Ltd. - Melbourne (2)
19 Inglewood Drive, Thomastown, Melbourne, 3074, VIC, Australia
Tel.: (61) 39 464 6344
Web Site:
   https://www.eagleburgmann.com.au
Mechanical Seals Mfr
N.A.I.C.S.: 333991

EagleBurgmann India Pvt. Ltd. (1)
Gazebo House 52 Gulmohar Road Opp Cross Road No 7, JVPD Scheme Vile Parle W, Mumbai, 400 049, India
Tel.: (91) 226 702 1489
Web Site: https://www.eagleburgmann.co.in
Sales Range: $50-74.9 Million
Emp.: 20
Mechanical Seals & Packings Mfr & Sls
N.A.I.C.S.: 339991

Subsidiary (Domestic):

EagleBurgmann India Pvt. Ltd. (2)
Door No 10-50-18/17 Flat No 1/7 First Floor Siripuram Towers, Siripuram VIP Road, Visakhapatnam, 530 003, India
Tel.: (91) 8912755703
Mechanical Sealing Device Mfr
N.A.I.C.S.: 339991
Punkaj Dash *(VP)*

EagleBurgmann Japan Co., Ltd. (1)
514 Nakagawashin, Gosen, Niigata, 959-1693, Japan
Tel.: (81) 25 047 1111
Web Site: https://www.eagleburgmann.jp
Sales Range: $200-249.9 Million
Emp.: 800
Metal Valve & Pipe Fitting Mfr

N.A.I.C.S.: 332919
Takafumi Tsuchiya *(Pres)*

EagleBurgmann New Zealand, Ltd. (1)
47 William Pickering Drive, PO Box 300-858, North Shore City Albany, Auckland, 752, New Zealand
Tel.: (64) 94485001
Sales Range: $25-49.9 Million
Emp.: 45
Mechanical Seals Mfr
N.A.I.C.S.: 339991
John Hill *(Gen Mgr)*

Ekk Eagle Asia Pacific Pte. Ltd. (1)
48 Toh Guan Road East 09-130 Enterprise Hub, Singapore, 608586, Singapore
Tel.: (65) 67791300
Marine Services
N.A.I.C.S.: 488390

Ekk Eagle Products India Pvt. Ltd. (1)
Plot No 51, Ramtakdi Industrial Estate Hadapsar, Pune, 411013, India
Tel.: (91) 2026508398
Construction Machinery Mfr
N.A.I.C.S.: 333120

Hiroshima Eagle Co., Ltd. (1)
6 Shin-Ujigami Kitahiroshima-cho, Yamagata-gun, Hiroshima, 731-1514, Japan
Tel.: (81) 82 672 5900
Web Site: http://www.ekk.co.jp
Construction Machinery Mfr
N.A.I.C.S.: 333120

KEMEL Co., Ltd. - Kure Factory (1)
8-1 Showa-cho, Kure, 737-0027, Hiroshima, Japan
Tel.: (81) 823257121
Industrial Machinery Mfr
N.A.I.C.S.: 333248

KEMEL Co., Ltd. - Takasago Factory (1)
2-13-23 Shinhama Arai-cho, Takasago, 676-0008, Hyogo, Japan
Tel.: (81) 79 442 8300
Web Site: https://www.kemel.com
Emp.: 100
Industrial Machinery Mfr
N.A.I.C.S.: 333248

KEMEL Sales & Service (Shanghai) Co., Ltd. (1)
Rm2601 No 568 Hengfeng Road Henghui International Building, Jing'an District, Shanghai, 200070, China
Tel.: (86) 2150891887
Water Lubricated Stern Tube Seal Mfr
N.A.I.C.S.: 333996

Kemel Asia Pacific Pte. Ltd. (1)
26 Pandan Loop, Singapore, 128244, Singapore
Tel.: (65) 67791300
Web Site: http://www.kemel.com
Sales Range: $25-49.9 Million
Emp.: 20
SternTube Seal, SternTube Bearing & Intermediate Bearing Mfr
N.A.I.C.S.: 332912
Kaising Koh *(Gen Mgr)*

Kemel Co., Ltd. (1)
Shiba Park Bldg B-14F 2-4-1 Shibakoen, Minato-ku, Tokyo, 105-8587, Japan
Tel.: (81) 33 438 2291
Web Site: https://www.kemel.com
Sales Range: $50-74.9 Million
Emp.: 100
SternTube Seal, SternTube Bearing & Intermediate Bearing Mfr
N.A.I.C.S.: 332991

Kemel Europe Limited (1)
Unit No 9 Tower Road, Glover Industrial Estate, Washington, NE37 2SH, Tyne and Wear, United Kingdom
Tel.: (44) 191 416 0232
Web Site: http://www.kemel.com
Sales Range: $25-49.9 Million
Emp.: 6
SternTube Seal, SternTube Bearing & Intermediate Bearing Mfr
N.A.I.C.S.: 332991

NEK Co., Ltd. (1)

Eagle Industry Co., Ltd.—(Continued)

18 Gongdanseo3-gil Chilseo-myeon, Haman, 52001, Gyeongsangnam, Korea (South)
Tel.: (82) 55 567 1212
Web Site: https://www.nekkorea.com
Emp.: 222
Industrial Machinery Mfr
N.A.I.C.S.: 333248

Okayama Eagle Co., Ltd. (1)
4803-1 Ukan Ukan-cho, Takahashi, 716-1321, Okayama, Japan
Tel.: (81) 86 657 3150
Web Site: http://www.ekk.co.jp
Automobile Parts Mfr
N.A.I.C.S.: 336390

P.T. Eagle Industry Indonesia (1)
EJIP Industrial Park Plot 8G, Cikarang Selatan, Bekasi, 17550, Indonesia
Tel.: (62) 21 897 0178
Web Site: http://www.ekk.co.jp
Sales Range: $25-49.9 Million
Emp.: 123
Gasket Packing & Sealing Device Mfr
N.A.I.C.S.: 339991

P.T. EagleBurgmann Indonesia (1)
Kawasan East Jakarta Industrial Park EJIP Plot 7G-4, Cikarang Selatan, 17530, Bekasi, 17530, Jawa Barat, Indonesia
Tel.: (62) 218975728
Web Site: https://www.eagleburgmann.co.id
Sales Range: $50-74.9 Million
Emp.: 125
Mechanical Seals & Packings Mfr & Sls
N.A.I.C.S.: 339991

Shimane Eagle Co., Ltd. (1)
212-3 Tane Kakeya-cho, Unnan, 690-2706, Shimane, Japan
Tel.: (81) 85 462 1581
Web Site: https://www.ekkeagle.com
Emp.: 360
Automobile Parts Mfr
N.A.I.C.S.: 336390
Takase Kazuaki (Gen Mgr)

Valcom Co., Ltd. (1)
3-7-25 Minowa, Toyonaka, 560-0035, Osaka, Japan
Tel.: (81) 66 857 1811
Web Site: https://www.valcom.co.jp
Emp.: 89
Pressure Sensor Mfr & Distr
N.A.I.C.S.: 334513
Hidenori Murata (Mng Exec Officer & Sls Mgr)

EAGLE INSURANCE COMPANY LTD.
Eagle House 15 A5 Wall Street, Ebene, Mauritius
Tel.: (230) 4609200
Web Site: http://www.eagle.mu
Year Founded: 1973
Insurance Services
N.A.I.C.S.: 524210
John G. Pasqualetto (CEO)

EAGLE MOUNTAIN MINING LIMITED
Ground Floor 22 Stirling Highway, Nedlands, 6009, WA, Australia
Tel.: (61) 893896767   AU
Web Site: https://www.eaglemountain.com.au
Year Founded: 2017
EM2—(ASX)
Rev.: $38,625
Assets: $12,198,586
Liabilities: $10,063,625
Net Worth: $2,134,961
Earnings: ($4,303,669)
Emp.: 22
Fiscal Year-end: 06/30/24
Mineral Exploration Services
N.A.I.C.S.: 212220
Charles Bennett Bass (Mng Dir)

EAGLE NICE (INTERNATIONAL) HOLDINGS LTD.
9th Floor Tower B Regent Centre, 70 Ta Chuen Ping Street, Kwai Chung, New Territories, China (Hong Kong)
Tel.: (852) 2 610 1338
Web Site: http://www.eaglenice.com.hk
2368—(HKG)
Rev.: $419,039,898
Assets: $331,818,720
Liabilities: $131,761,325
Net Worth: $200,057,396
Earnings: $42,142,280
Emp.: 13,000
Fiscal Year-end: 03/31/21
Apparel & Accessories Mfr
N.A.I.C.S.: 315990
Christina Fang Mei Chen (Exec Dir)

Subsidiaries:

Eagle Nice Development Limited (1)
Well Fung Industrial Center, Kwai Chung, NT, China (Hong Kong)
Tel.: (852) 26101338
Sportswear Mfr & Sales
N.A.I.C.S.: 315210

Far East (EAG) Limited (1)
Rm 7-9 9 F Regent Ctr Block B 63 Wo Yi Hop Rd, Kwai Chung, New Territories, China (Hong Kong)
Tel.: (852) 26100378
Sportswear Mfr & Sales
N.A.I.C.S.: 315210

EAGLE NORTH HOLDINGS INC
2400 Eagle Street North, Cambridge, N3H 4R7, ON, Canada
Tel.: (519) 653-7030
Web Site: http://www.cambridgetoyota.com
Year Founded: 1979
Rev.: $24,100,000
Emp.: 45
New & Used Car Dealers
N.A.I.C.S.: 441110
Cameron Beaton (Principal)

EAGLE PLAINS RESOURCES LTD.
Suite 200 44 - 12th Ave South, Cranbrook, V1C 2R7, BC, Canada
Tel.: (250) 426-0749
Web Site: https://www.eagleplains.com
Year Founded: 1992
EPL—(TSXV)
Rev.: $7,752,932
Assets: $11,126,973
Liabilities: $689,405
Net Worth: $10,437,568
Earnings: $5,028,264
Fiscal Year-end: 12/31/23
Mineral Exploration Services
N.A.I.C.S.: 213114
Timothy Jay Termuende (Pres & CEO)

EAGLE RIVER CHRYSLER LTD.
3315 Caxton Street, PO Box 1558, Whitecourt, T7S 1P4, AB, Canada
Tel.: (780) 778-2844
Web Site: http://www.eagleriverchrysler.com
Year Founded: 1994
Rev.: $10,085,614
Emp.: 22
New & Used Car Dealers
N.A.I.C.S.: 441110
Dennis LaFreniere (Mgr-Svc)

EAGLE VET. TECH CO., LTD.
235-34 Chusa-ro, Sinam-Myeon, Yesan, 32417, Chungcheongnam-Do, Korea (South)
Tel.: (82) 413314100
Web Site: http://www.eaglevet.com

Year Founded: 1970
044960—(KRS)
Rev.: $33,394,945
Assets: $42,082,561
Liabilities: $9,136,628
Net Worth: $32,945,933
Earnings: $2,027,483
Emp.: 110
Fiscal Year-end: 12/31/22
Pharmaceuticals Product Mfr
N.A.I.C.S.: 325412

EAGLE VETRINARY TECHNOLOGY CO., LTD.
8F Eagle Town Bldg 20 6Gil Gwangnaru-ro, Sungdong-Ku, Seoul, Korea (South)
Tel.: (82) 24649065
Web Site: http://www.eaglevet.com
Year Founded: 1970
44960—(KRS)
Rev.: $32,317,217
Assets: $40,724,464
Liabilities: $8,841,769
Net Worth: $31,882,695
Earnings: $1,962,052
Emp.: 110
Fiscal Year-end: 12/31/22
Veterinary Medicine Mfr
N.A.I.C.S.: 325412
Sung-Ho Choi (Mgr-Personal Information)

EAGLE-I HOLDINGS PLC
Apollo House 41 Halton Station Road, Runcorn, WA7 3DN, Cheshire, United Kingdom
Tel.: (44) 1928795400
Web Site: http://www.eagle-i-telematics.com
Sales Range: $1-9.9 Million
Emp.: 5
Vehicle Tracking & Communication System Sales
N.A.I.C.S.: 423120

EAGLEMOSS PUBLICATIONS LTD
1st Floor Beaumont House Avonmore Road, Kensington Village, London, W14 8TS, United Kingdom
Tel.: (44) 1425462857   UK
Web Site: http://www.eaglemoss.com
Sales Range: $25-49.9 Million
Emp.: 85
Literature Publisher & Figurine Mfr
N.A.I.C.S.: 513130

Subsidiaries:

GE Fabbri Phoenix Sp. Z .o.o.
Ltd. (1)
Swojczycka 38, Wroclaw, Poland (67%)
Tel.: (48) 713447775
Sales Range: $25-49.9 Million
Newspaper Publishers
N.A.I.C.S.: 513110

EAGLERISE ELECTRIC & ELECTRONIC (CHINA) CO., LTD.
No 4 East Huanzhen Road Beijiao Shunde, Foshan, 528311, Guangdong, China
Tel.: (86) 75786250249   CN
Web Site: https://www.eaglerise.com
Year Founded: 1990
002922—(SSE)
Rev.: $396,081,036
Assets: $495,248,364
Liabilities: $247,921,128
Net Worth: $247,327,236
Earnings: $26,879,580
Emp.: 3,100
Fiscal Year-end: 12/31/22
Electronic Parts Mfr & Distr
N.A.I.C.S.: 334416

Subsidiaries:

Eaglerise Japan Co., Ltd. (1)
Tel.: (81) 368030441
Web Site: http://www.eaglerise.co.jp
Power Supply Component Mfr
N.A.I.C.S.: 334416

Eaglerise E&E (USA), Inc. (1)
13405 Benson Ave, Chino, CA 91710
Tel.: (909) 595-1880
Power Supply Component Distr
N.A.I.C.S.: 423690

Eaglerise E&E Inc. (1)
320 Constance Dr Unit 1, Warminster, PA 18974
Tel.: (267) 387-6022
Power Supply Component Distr
N.A.I.C.S.: 423690
Joey Qiao (Mgr-Sls)

Eaglerise Electric & Electronic (Jian) Co., Ltd. (1)
Industrial Park West, Jian County, Jian, Jiangxi, China
Tel.: (86) 7968466555
Web Site: http://www.eaglerise.cn
Power Supply Component Mfr
N.A.I.C.S.: 334416

Eaglerise-Magroots Technology Shenzhen Corporation Limited (1)
No 6099 Baoan Avenue Fuyong Street, Baoan District, Shenzhen, Guangdong, China
Tel.: (86) 75521013320
Web Site: http://www.magroots.cn
Power Supply Component Mfr
N.A.I.C.S.: 334416

Shanghai Eagleries Electric & Electronic Co., Ltd. (1)
Tel.: (86) 2155511466
Power Supply Component Mfr
N.A.I.C.S.: 334416

EAGON HOLDINGS CO., LTD.
91 Yeomjeon-ro, Nam-gu, Incheon, Korea (South)
Tel.: (82) 327600001
Web Site: http://www.eagon.com
Year Founded: 1988
039020—(KRS)
Rev.: $389,296,694
Assets: $540,875,953
Liabilities: $304,371,594
Net Worth: $236,504,360
Earnings: $1,599,854
Emp.: 52
Fiscal Year-end: 12/31/22
Window & Door Mfr
N.A.I.C.S.: 321911
Young-Ju Park (Chm)

Subsidiaries:

EAGON Energy Co., Ltd. (1)
132 Songnim-ro 307beon-gil, Nam-gu, Incheon, Korea (South)
Tel.: (82) 15221271
Wood Window & Door Mfr & Distr
N.A.I.C.S.: 321911

EAGON Green Tech Co., Ltd. (1)
49-38 Daemyeonghang-ro 205beon-gil, Daegot-myeon, Gimpo, Gyeonggi-do, Korea (South)
Tel.: (82) 319879151
Wood Window & Door Mfr & Distr
N.A.I.C.S.: 321911

EAGON Windows & Doors System Co., Ltd. (1)
91 Yeomjeon-ro, Nam-gu, Incheon, Korea (South)
Tel.: (82) 15221271
Wood Window & Door Mfr & Distr
N.A.I.C.S.: 321911

Eagon Lautaro S.A. (1)
Ruta 5 Sur KM644 Casills 220, Lautaro, Araucania, Chile
Tel.: (56) 45656800
Wood Window & Door Mfr & Distr
N.A.I.C.S.: 321911

Eagon Pacific Plantation Ltd. (1)

PO Box 529, Honiara, Solomon Islands
Tel.: (677) 30016
Wood Window & Door Mfr & Distr
N.A.I.C.S.: 321911

EAGON INDUSTRIAL CO., LTD.

91 Yeomjeon-ro, Michuhol-gu, Incheon, Korea (South)
Tel.: (82) 327600800
Web Site: http://www.eagon.com
Year Founded: 1972
008250—(KRS)
Rev.: $252,596,302
Assets: $339,648,258
Liabilities: $185,823,828
Net Worth: $153,824,430
Earnings: $4,107,836
Emp.: 214
Fiscal Year-end: 12/31/22
Plywood Products Mfr
N.A.I.C.S.: 321211
Young-Ju Park *(Chm)*

Subsidiaries:

Eagon USA Corp.   (1)
PO Box 22, Issaquah, WA 98027
Tel.: (425) 369-6629
Web Site: https://www.eagonusa.com
Plywood Mfr
N.A.I.C.S.: 321211

EAM GMBH & CO. KG

Monteverdistrasse 2, 34131, Kassel, Germany
Tel.: (49) 56193301
Web Site: http://www.eam.de
Sales Range: $800-899.9 Million
Emp.: 400
Gas Distribution Services
N.A.I.C.S.: 221210
Georg von Meibom *(Mng Dir)*

EAM SOLAR ASA

Cort Adelers gate 330254, 0250, Oslo, Norway
Tel.: (47) 91611009
Web Site: https://www.eamsolar.no
Year Founded: 2011
EA2—(DEU)
Rev.: $1,317,799
Assets: $11,503,560
Liabilities: $7,331,319
Net Worth: $4,172,242
Earnings: ($2,380,405)
Emp.: 16
Fiscal Year-end: 12/31/22
Solar Power Plants Owner & Operator
N.A.I.C.S.: 221118
Viktor E. Jakobsen *(CEO)*

EAO AG

Tannwaldstrasse 88, 4600, Olten, Switzerland
Tel.: (41) 622869111   CH
Web Site: http://www.eao.com
Year Founded: 1947
Sales Range: $125-149.9 Million
Emp.: 600
Industrial Electrical Equipment Mfr
N.A.I.C.S.: 335999
Kurt Loosli *(CEO)*

Subsidiaries:

EAO (Guangzhou) Limited   (1)
RM 3A03 3A/F Block A Guangzhou International Business Incubator Centre, Guangzhou, China
Tel.: (86) 20 32290390
Electric Equipment Mfr
N.A.I.C.S.: 335999

EAO Automotive GmbH & Co. KG   (1)
Richard-Wagner-Str 3, 08209, Auerbach, Vogtland, Germany
Tel.: (49) 3744 8264 0
Electrical Equipment Distr

N.A.I.C.S.: 423610

EAO Benelux B.V.   (1)
Kamerlingh Onnesweg 46, 3316 GL, Dordrecht, Netherlands   (100%)
Tel.: (31) 786531700
Web Site: http://www.eao.nl
Sales Range: $25-49.9 Million
Emp.: 16
Mfr of Electronic Controls & Regulators
N.A.I.C.S.: 336320
Dave Polman *(Mng Dir)*

EAO Corporation   (1)
1 Parrott Dr, Shelton, CT 06484
Tel.: (203) 951-4600
Electrical Equipment Distr
N.A.I.C.S.: 423610
Lance A. Scott *(Pres & CEO)*

EAO Far East Ltd.   (1)
Unit A1 1 F Block A Tin On Industrial Bldg, 777 Cheung Sha Wan Rd Lai Chi, Kowloon, China (Hong Kong)   (100%)
Tel.: (852) 27869141
Web Site: http://www.eao.com
Sales Range: $25-49.9 Million
Emp.: 70
Mfr of Electronic Controls & Regulators
N.A.I.C.S.: 335314

EAO France SAS   (1)
5 Rue Henri Francois, BP 3, FR-77831, Ozoir-la-Ferriere, France   (100%)
Tel.: (33) 164433737
Web Site: http://www.eao.com
Sales Range: $25-49.9 Million
Emp.: 9
Electronic Controls & Regulators Mfr
N.A.I.C.S.: 334416

EAO Japan Co. Ltd.   (1)
Net 1 Mita Bldg 3F 3 1 4 Mita, Minato-ku, Tokyo, 108-0073, Japan
Tel.: (81) 3 5444 5411
Web Site: http://www.eao.com
Emp.: 12
Electric Equipment Mfr
N.A.I.C.S.: 335999

EAO Limited   (1)
Highland House Albert Drive, RH15 9TN, Burgess Hill, Sussex, United Kingdom - England   (100%)
Tel.: (44) 01444245021
Web Site: http://www.eao.com
Sales Range: $25-49.9 Million
Emp.: 30
Mfr of Electronic Controls & Regulators
N.A.I.C.S.: 335314

EAO Lumitas GmbH   (1)
Langenberger Strasse 570, 45277, Essen, Germany   (100%)
Tel.: (49) 20185870
Web Site: http://www.eao.com
Sales Range: $25-49.9 Million
Emp.: 60
Mfr of Electronic Controls & Regulators
N.A.I.C.S.: 336320
Manfred Shveehorst *(Mng Dir)*

EAO Schweiz AG   (1)
Tannwaldstrasse 86, 4600, Olten, Switzerland
Tel.: (41) 62 286 95 00
Web Site: http://www.eao.com
Emp.: 10
Electrical Equipment Distr
N.A.I.C.S.: 423610
Leukas Moser *(Mgr-Sls)*

EAO Svenska AB   (1)
Grahundsvagen 80, Skarpnaeck, Stockholm, 12822, Sweden   (100%)
Tel.: (46) 86838660
Web Site: http://www.eao.se
Rev.: $3,299,151
Emp.: 8
Mfr of Electronic Controls & Regulators
N.A.I.C.S.: 336320

EAO Switch Corporation   (1)
98 Washington St, Milford, CT 06460-3670   (100%)
Tel.: (203) 877-4577
Web Site: http://www.eaoswitch.com
Sales Range: $25-49.9 Million
Emp.: 27
General Purpose Pushbutton Switches, Keypads, Indicators, Membranes & Custom Front Panels Mfr

N.A.I.C.S.: 423610
Micah Jenkins *(Mgr-Customer Svc)*

EAO Verkauf (Schweiz) AG   (1)
Altgraben 441, Harkingen, 4624, Switzerland   (100%)
Tel.: (41) 623889500
Web Site: http://www.eao.ch
Sales Range: $1-9.9 Million
Emp.: 10
Mfr of Electronic Controls & Regulators
N.A.I.C.S.: 336320

Switches Plus, Inc.   (1)
1 Parrott Dr Shelton, Milford, CT 06484-3670
Tel.: (203) 876-2697
Web Site: http://www.eaoswitch.com
Sales Range: $25-49.9 Million
Emp.: 40
Distr of Switches
N.A.I.C.S.: 423610
Kate Pikosky *(Controller)*

EARL SHILTON BUILDING SOCIETY

22 The Hollow Earl Shilton, Leicester, LE9 7NB, United Kingdom
Tel.: (44) 1455 844422
Web Site: http://www.esbs.co.uk
Rev.: $5,296,528
Assets: $174,375,012
Liabilities: $159,617,213
Net Worth: $14,757,799
Earnings: $592,639
Emp.: 18
Fiscal Year-end: 03/31/19
Mortgage Lending & Other Financial Services
N.A.I.C.S.: 522310
Neil D. Adams *(Deputy CEO & Dir-Fin)*

EARLY AGE CO., LTD.

ATT East 5F 2-11-7 Akasaka, Minato-ku, Tokyo, 107-0052, Japan
Tel.: (81) 355755590
Web Site: https://www.early-age.co.jp
Year Founded: 1986
3248—(TKS)
Rev.: $24,389,600
Assets: $95,629,920
Liabilities: $66,305,680
Net Worth: $29,324,240
Earnings: $2,311,340
Emp.: 17
Fiscal Year-end: 10/31/23
Real Estate Lending Services
N.A.I.C.S.: 531190

EARLY EQUITY PLC

59-60 Russell Square, London, WC1B 4HP, United Kingdom
Tel.: (44) 2032866388
Web Site: http://www.earlyequity.co.uk
EEQP—(AQSE)
Rev.: $64,376
Assets: $1,094,776
Liabilities: $332,826
Net Worth: $761,950
Earnings: ($677,410)
Fiscal Year-end: 08/31/20
Investment Services
N.A.I.C.S.: 523999
Gregory Collier *(Chm)*

EARLYPAY LTD.

Suite 1 Level 5 201 Miller St, North Sydney, 2060, NSW, Australia
Tel.: (61) 1300666177   AU
Web Site:
   https://www.earlypay.com.au
EPY—(ASX)
Rev.: $27,925,040
Assets: $240,535,612
Liabilities: $191,477,694
Net Worth: $49,057,918
Earnings: ($5,169,894)
Emp.: 44

Fiscal Year-end: 06/30/23
Employment Agencies
N.A.I.C.S.: 561311
Daniel Riley *(CEO & Mng Dir)*

Subsidiaries:

Cf Management Services Pty. Ltd.   (1)
90 Arthur Street, North Sydney, 2060, NSW, Australia
Tel.: (61) 284157064
Web Site:
   https://www.cfmanagementservices.com
Wealth Management Services
N.A.I.C.S.: 525910

Classic Finance Pty. Ltd.   (1)
300 Barangaroo Ave, Sydney, 2000, NSW, Australia
Tel.: (61) 1300219119
Web Site:
   https://www.classicfinance.com.au
Home Loan Financing Services
N.A.I.C.S.: 522310

EARLYWORKS CO., LTD.

MR Building 3F 5-7-11 Ueno, Taito-ku, Tokyo, 110-0005, Japan
Tel.: (81) 356140978   JP
Web Site: https://e-early.works
Year Founded: 2018
ELWS—(NASDAQ)
Rev.: $1,185,039
Assets: $3,802,879
Liabilities: $1,617,714
Net Worth: $2,185,165
Earnings: ($2,221,015)
Emp.: 15
Fiscal Year-end: 04/30/24
Information Technology Services
N.A.I.C.S.: 541512
Satoshi Kobayashi *(CEO)*

EARN-A-CAR, INC.

8 Jubilee Street Kempton Park CBD, Kempton Park, 1619, South Africa
Tel.: (27) 11 425 1666   NV
Web Site: http://www.earnacar.co.za
Year Founded: 2009
Rev.: $4,048,000
Assets: $6,921,000
Liabilities: $5,765,000
Net Worth: $1,156,000
Earnings: $257,000
Emp.: 38
Fiscal Year-end: 02/28/18
Car Rental Services
N.A.I.C.S.: 532111

EARNIX LTD.

4 Ariel Sharon St, Givatayim, 5320045, Israel
Tel.: (972) 37538292
Web Site: http://www.earnix.com
Year Founded: 2001
Software Development Services
N.A.I.C.S.: 541511
Robin Gilthorpe *(CEO)*

Subsidiaries:

Driveway Software Corp.   (1)
1730 S Amphlett Blvd UNIT 205, San Mateo, CA 94402
Tel.: (309) 807-2300
Web Site: http://www.drivewaysoftware.com
Software Publisher
N.A.I.C.S.: 513210
Igor Katsman *(Founder & CTO)*

EARTH & AEROSPACE MANUFACTURING IND. CO. LTD

670-1 Bangji-ri Sanam-myeon, Sacheon, Gyeongsangnam-do, Korea (South)
Tel.: (82) 558550071
Web Site:
   http://www.samcokorea.en.ec21.com
Year Founded: 2000

Earth & Aerospace Manufacturing Ind. Co.
Ltd—(Continued)

263540—(KRS)
Rev.: $25,890,948
Assets: $26,633,081
Liabilities: $20,471,827
Net Worth: $6,161,253
Earnings: $683,926
Emp.: 167
Fiscal Year-end: 12/31/22
Aircraft Door & Wing Component Assembly Mfr
N.A.I.C.S.: 336413
Jun-woo Hwang (Bus Mgr)

EARTH ALIVE CLEAN TECHNOLOGIES INC.
1050 Cote du Beaver Hall, Montreal,
H2Z 1S4, QC, Canada
Tel.: (438) 333-1680   Ca
Web Site:
   https://www.earthalivect.com
Year Founded: 2014
EAC—(TSXV)
Rev.: $2,174,662
Assets: $1,455,237
Liabilities: $287,808
Net Worth: $1,167,429
Earnings: ($1,107,345)
Emp.: 10
Fiscal Year-end: 12/31/20
Agricultural Chemicals & Fertilizer Mfr
N.A.I.C.S.: 325320
Robert Blain (Chm)

EARTH CORPORATION
12-1 Kanda-Tsukasamachi 2 Chome,
Chiyoda-ku, Tokyo, 101-0048, Japan
Tel.: (81) 352077451   JP
Web Site: https://corp.earth.jp
Year Founded: 1973
4985—(TKS)
Rev.: $1,122,658,960
Assets: $938,765,630
Liabilities: $428,285,630
Net Worth: $510,480,000
Earnings: $29,083,180
Emp.: 4,788
Fiscal Year-end: 12/31/23
Agrochemicals, Insecticides & Pet
Care Products Mfr
N.A.I.C.S.: 325320
Yoshinori Kawamura (Dir Gen-
Strategy-Intl & Mng Exec Officer)

Subsidiaries:

Bathclin Corporation   (1)
8F Kudan Center Building 4-1-7 Kudankita,
Chiyoda Ward, Tokyo, 102-0073, Japan
Tel.: (81) 335115811
Web Site: https://www.bathclin.co.jp
Emp.: 300
Non-Medical Cosmetic Product Mfr & Distr
N.A.I.C.S.: 325620
Shogo Sanmaido (Pres & CEO)

Earth (Thailand) Co., Ltd.   (1)
No 287 Liberty Square Building 12th Floor
Room No 1201 1202 Silom Road, Silom
Subdistrict Bang Rak District, Bangkok,
10500, Thailand
Tel.: (66) 26969770
Web Site: https://www.earth-th.com
Household Insect Care Product Mfr & Distr
N.A.I.C.S.: 325320

Earth Corporation   (1)
18th Floor A2 Block Viettel Tower 285 Cach
Mang Thang Tam Street, Ward 12 District
10, Ho Chi Minh City, Vietnam
Tel.: (84) 2862560710
Web Site: https://www.earth-vn.com
Household Insect Care Product Mfr & Distr
N.A.I.C.S.: 325320

Earth Environmental Service Co.,
Ltd.   (1)
1 1 2 Awaji Machi, Chuo Ku, Osaka,
5410047, Japan   **(65.1%)**
Tel.: (81) 662020640
Web Site: www.esco.ab.psiweb.com

Sales Range: $75-99.9 Million
Emp.: 340
Provider of Environmental Quality Assurance System Services
N.A.I.C.S.: 334512

Earth Home Products (Malaysia) Sdn.
Bhd.   (1)
A-8-02 Capital 1 Oasis Square No 2 Jalan
Pju 1A/7A Ara Damansara, 47301, Petaling
Jaya, Selangor, Malaysia
Tel.: (60) 377342118
Web Site: https://www.earth-my.com
Insecticides Mfr
N.A.I.C.S.: 325320

Earth Pet Co., Ltd.   (1)
4-11-1 Shinbashi A-PLACE Shimbashi 2F,
Minato-ku, Tokyo, 105-0004, Japan
Tel.: (81) 363612754
Pet Care Product Mfr & Distr
N.A.I.C.S.: 311111

Hakugen Earth Co., Ltd.   (1)
2-21-14 Higashiueno, Taito-ku, Tokyo, 110-
0015, Japan
Tel.: (81) 338352241
Emp.: 389
Miscellaneous Household Goods Mfr
N.A.I.C.S.: 339999

J.O. Pharma Co., Ltd.   (1)
127-1 Shimogoshi-cho, Izumo, 693-0032,
Shimane, Japan
Tel.: (81) 85 324 8760
Web Site: https://www.jo-pharma.co.jp
Emp.: 227
Prefilled Syringes Mfr
N.A.I.C.S.: 339112

Otsuka Medical Devices Co.,
Ltd.   (1)
The Second Building of Otsuka Pharmaceutical Kanda 2-2 Kanda, Tsukasamachi
Chiyoda-ku, Tokyo, 101-0048, Japan
Tel.: (81) 363617459
Web Site: http://www.omd.otsuka.com
Medical Device Mfr
N.A.I.C.S.: 339112
Noriko Tojo (Pres)

Otsuka Wellness Vending Co.,
Ltd.   (1)
2F JRE Kanda Ogawamachi Building 9-1
Kanda Mitoshirocho, Chiyoda-ku, Tokyo,
101-0053, Japan
Tel.: (81) 12 092 5405
Web Site: https://www.otsuka-wv.co.jp
Vending Machine Mfr
N.A.I.C.S.: 333310

Otsuka-MGC Chemical Company,
Inc.   (1)
Edobori 1-5-16 JMF-Bldg Higobashi 01,
Nishi-ku, Osaka, 550-0002, Japan
Tel.: (81) 66 445 1501
Web Site: https://www.moc-hh.co.jp
Inorganic Chemical Product Mfr & Distr
N.A.I.C.S.: 325180
Hiroyasu Hayashi (Pres)

EARTH INFINITY CO., LTD.
2-2-28 Dojimahama, Kita-Ku, Osaka,
530-0004, Japan
Tel.: (81) 647977522
Web Site: http://www.earth-
   infinity.co.jp
Year Founded: 2002
7692—(TKS)
Electronic Equipment Mfr & Distr
N.A.I.C.S.: 336320
Koichi Hamada (Founder, Pres &
CEO)

EARTH SIGNAL PROCESSING LTD.
Suite 1600 715 - 5th Avenue SW,
Calgary, T2P 2X6, AB, Canada
Tel.: (403) 264-8722
Web Site:
   https://www.earthsignal.com
Year Founded: 1993
Rev.: $10,000,000
Emp.: 200
Seismic Data Processing Services
N.A.I.C.S.: 518210

Steve P. Fuller Geoph (Pres)

EARTH STAHL & ALLOYS LTD.
5B Mohani Merlin Jayshree Vihar
PandraiTarai Mandi Gate, Raipur,
492001, Chhattisgarh, India
Tel.: (91) 8120009621   In
Web Site: https://www.earthstahl.com
Year Founded: 2009
543765—(BOM)
Rev.: $6,698,792
Assets: $4,961,461
Liabilities: $2,091,111
Net Worth: $2,070,350
Earnings: $1,022,481
Fiscal Year-end: 03/31/22
Automobile Parts Mfr & Distr
N.A.I.C.S.: 336110
Jain P. K. (Sec)

EARTH-PANDA ADVANCE MAGNETIC MATERIAL CO., LTD.
Lujiang High-tech Industrial Development Zone, Lujiang County, Hefei,
231500, Anhui, China
Tel.: (86) 55187033302
Web Site:
   http://www.earthpanda.com
Year Founded: 2003
688077—(SHG)
Rev.: $297,575,076
Assets: $396,780,396
Liabilities: $225,899,304
Net Worth: $170,881,093
Earnings: $21,035,823
Fiscal Year-end: 12/31/22
Magnetic Material Mfr
N.A.I.C.S.: 334610
Yongfei Xiong (Chm & Gen Mgr)

Subsidiaries:

Anhui Earth-Panda Advanced Magnetic Material Co., Ltd.   (1)
No 260 Haitang Road High-tech Zone, Hefei, Anhui, China
Tel.: (86) 55165306195
Permanent Magnet Material Mfr & Distr
N.A.I.C.S.: 327110

Earth-Panda (Baotou) Co., Ltd.   (1)
No 8-66 Rare Earth Application Industrial
Park Rare Earth Street, Rare Earth Development Zone, Baotou, China
Tel.: (86) 4722207125
Magnetic Material Research & Development
Services
N.A.I.C.S.: 541360

Earth-Panda (Suzhou) Co., Ltd.   (1)
Wangzhuang Industrial Park, Shanghu
Town, Changshu, Jiangsu, China
Tel.: (86) 51252438630
Permanent Magnet Material Mfr & Distr
N.A.I.C.S.: 327110

Earth-Panda (Suzhou) Magnet Co.,
Ltd.   (1)
Wangzhuang Industrial Park, Changshu,
Jiangsu, China
Tel.: (86) 51252438630
Magnetic Material Mfr
N.A.I.C.S.: 334111

Earth-Panda (Tianjin) Electrical Co.,
Ltd.   (1)
1-C-606 15 Rongyuan Road Huayuan Industrial Area, Tianjin Binhai New and High
Tech Zone, Tianjin, China
Tel.: (86) 2223722371
Magnetic Material Mfr
N.A.I.C.S.: 334111

Earth-Panda Co., Ltd.   (1)
Lujiang High-tech Industrial Development
Zone, Hefei, Anhui, China
Tel.: (86) 55187033333
Magnetic Material Research & Development
Services
N.A.I.C.S.: 541360

Earth-Panda Japan Co., Ltd.   (1)

6F 2-23-2YBG East Ikebukuro, Toshima-ku,
Tokyo, Japan
Tel.: (81) 339812201
Permanent Magnet Material Mfr & Distr
N.A.I.C.S.: 327110

Earth-Panda Magnetic Application
Tech Co., Ltd.   (1)
Econmic Development Zone, Lujiang
County, Hefei, Anhui, China
Tel.: (86) 55187033333
Magnetic Material Mfr
N.A.I.C.S.: 334111

REHT (Anhui) Permanent Magnet
Technology Co., Ltd.   (1)
Lujiang high tech Industrial Development
Zone, Hefei, Anhui, China
Tel.: (86) 55187533111
Permanent Magnet Material Mfr & Distr
N.A.I.C.S.: 327110

Shanghai Earth-Panda Permanent
Magnet Technology Co., Ltd.   (1)
Room 801 No 77 Zhenggao Road, Yangpu
District, Shanghai, China
Tel.: (86) 2165061378
Permanent Magnet Material Mfr & Distr
N.A.I.C.S.: 327110

EARTHLABS INC.
69 Yonge Street Suite 200, Toronto,
M5E 1K3, ON, Canada
Tel.: (647) 992-9837
Web Site: https://earthlabs.com
Year Founded: 2017
SPOT—(TSXV)
Rev.: $13,658,280
Assets: $18,561,288
Liabilities: $4,175,064
Net Worth: $14,386,224
Earnings: $8,108,629
Fiscal Year-end: 12/31/20
Mineral Exploration Services
N.A.I.C.S.: 213114
Denis Laviolette (Chm, Pres & CEO)

EARTHPORT PLC
140 Aldersgate Street, London, EC1A
4HY, United Kingdom
Tel.: (44) 2072209700   UK
Web Site: http://www.earthport.com
Year Founded: 1997
EPO—(LSE)
Rev.: $42,978,916
Assets: $60,679,370
Liabilities: $11,648,302
Net Worth: $49,031,068
Earnings: ($11,302,927)
Emp.: 200
Fiscal Year-end: 06/30/18
Holding Company; Foreign Exchange
Financial transaction Processing Services
N.A.I.C.S.: 551112
Michael R. Steinharter (Chief Comml
Officer-Global)

Subsidiaries:

Earthport Middle East Ltd.   (1)
Dubai Internet City Building 17 Office 167,
PO Box 500675, Dubai, United Arab Emirates
Tel.: (971) 4 434 7181
International Payment Solutions
N.A.I.C.S.: 561499

EARTHWISE MINERALS CORP.
Suite 1000 409 Granville Street, Vancouver, V6C 1T2, BC, Canada
Tel.: (604) 602-0001   BC
Web Site:
   https://earthwiseminerals.com
Year Founded: 2019
HWKRF—(OTCIQ)
Rev.: $41,087
Assets: $499,137
Liabilities: $633,461
Net Worth: ($134,325)
Earnings: ($1,620,290)

Fiscal Year-end: 03/31/23
Mineral Mining Services
N.A.I.C.S.: 213115
Patrick Morris (CEO)

EARTHWORKS INDUSTRIES INC.
Suite 615 - 800 West Pender Street,
Vancouver, V6C 2V6, BC, Canada
Tel.: (604) 669-3143   Ca
Web Site:
http://www.earthworksinc.com
Year Founded: 1993
EAATF—(OTCIQ)
Assets: $9,469,534
Liabilities: $7,605,280
Net Worth: $1,864,254
Earnings: ($1,440,319)
Fiscal Year-end: 11/30/22
Waste Management Services
N.A.I.C.S.: 562998
David B. Atkinson (CEO)

Subsidiaries:

Cortina Integrated Waste Management Inc.   (1)
1313 McDonald Ave, Santa Rosa, CA
95404
Waste Management Services
N.A.I.C.S.: 562998

EARUM PHARMACEUTICALS LIMITED
A-1106 Empire Business Hub Near
Auda Water Tank Science City Road,
Sola, Ahmedabad, 380060, Gujarat,
India
Tel.: (91) 7948402525
Web Site:
https://www.earumpharma.com
Year Founded: 2012
542724—(BOM)
Rev.: $6,827,151
Assets: $3,804,187
Liabilities: $1,824,776
Net Worth: $1,979,411
Earnings: $12,044
Emp.: 15
Fiscal Year-end: 03/31/21
Pharmaceuticals Distr
N.A.I.C.S.: 424210
Bhumishth Narendrabhai Patel (Chm
& Mng Dir)

EASE2PAY N.V.
Burgemeester Oudlaan 50 N building,
3062 PA, Rotterdam, Netherlands
Tel.: (31) 416631100   Nl
Web Site:
https://investor.ease2pay.com
EAS2P—(EUR)
Rev.: $2,972,734
Assets: $10,663,429
Liabilities: $3,089,745
Net Worth: $7,573,684
Earnings: ($1,511,204)
Emp.: 2
Fiscal Year-end: 12/31/23
Holding Company
N.A.I.C.S.: 551112
Marc E. T. Verstraeten (Chm, CEO,
CFO & Member-Mgmt Bd)

**EASON & CO PUBLIC COM-
PANY LTD.**
7/1-2 Ban Kao Rd Phan Thong, Phan
Thong District, Chon Buri, 20160,
Thailand
Tel.: (66) 38451833
Web Site: https://www.easonplc.com
Year Founded: 1965
EASON—(THA)
Rev.: $23,833,647
Assets: $38,731,497
Liabilities: $5,777,764
Net Worth: $32,953,732

Earnings: $3,805,833
Emp.: 193
Fiscal Year-end: 12/31/23
Paint Mfr & Distr
N.A.I.C.S.: 325510
Petcharat Eksangkul (Pres, Pres &
Mng Dir)

EASSON HOLDINGS LIMITED
Unit 1213 12 F Wing On Plaza No 62
Mody Road TST, Kowloon, China
(Hong Kong)
Tel.: (852) 24883088
Web Site:
https://www.eassonholdings.com
Year Founded: 2003
MLEAS—(EUR)
Mobile Value Added Services
N.A.I.C.S.: 517112

**EASSONS TRANSPORT LIM-
ITED**
1505 Harrington Rd, PO Box 159,
Kentville, B4N 3V7, NS, Canada
Tel.: (902) 679-1153
Web Site: https://www.eassons.com
Year Founded: 1945
Rev.: $21,013,557
Emp.: 146
Transportation Services
N.A.I.C.S.: 488999

Subsidiaries:

Choice Reefer Systems   (1)
Exit 538 Wallbridge-Loyalist Rd/401 R R 5,
Belleville, K8N 5B6, ON, Canada
Web Site: http://www.crstrucking.com
Sea Freight Transportation Services
N.A.I.C.S.: 483111
Stan Morrow (Pres)

**EAST & WEST ALUM CRAFT
LTD.**
7465 Conway Ave, Burnaby, V5E
2P7, BC, Canada
Tel.: (604) 438-6261
Web Site:
https://www.ewalumcraft.com
Year Founded: 1973
Rev.: $12,208,424
Emp.: 10
Architectural Metal Work Mfr
N.A.I.C.S.: 332323
G. Zen (Pres)

EAST 33 LIMITED
12 Point Road, Tuncurry, 2428, NSW,
Australia
Tel.: (61) 481585572   AU
Web Site: https://www.east33.sydney
Year Founded: 2019
E33—(ASX)
Rev.: $16,053,335
Assets: $31,665,254
Liabilities: $11,409,663
Net Worth: $20,255,591
Earnings: ($5,997,262)
Emp.: 130
Fiscal Year-end: 06/30/23
Seafood Product Distr
N.A.I.C.S.: 424460

Subsidiaries:

CMB Seafoods Pty. Ltd.   (1)
458 Bunnerong Road, Matraville, 2036,
NSW, Australia
Tel.: (61) 296941591
Web Site: https://www.cmb-
seafoods.business.site
Frozen Seafood Distr
N.A.I.C.S.: 424460

EAST AFRICA METALS INC.
777 Dunsmuir Street 17th Floor, Vancouver, V7Y 1K4, BC, Canada
Tel.: (604) 488-0822   Ca

Web Site:
https://www.eastafricametals.com
Year Founded: 2012
EAM—(OTCIQ)
Rev.: $15,068
Assets: $18,049,779
Liabilities: $1,828,184
Net Worth: $16,221,594
Earnings: ($1,242,843)
Fiscal Year-end: 12/31/19
Metal Ore Exploration
N.A.I.C.S.: 213114
Nick Watters (Dir-Bus Dev)

**EAST AFRICAN CABLES LIM-
ITED**
Addis Ababa Rd Industrial Area, PO
Box 18243, 00500, Nairobi, 00500,
Kenya
Tel.: (254) 722202125
Web Site: https://www.eacables.com
Year Founded: 1965
Rev.: $15,503,285
Assets: $61,368,297
Liabilities: $40,541,748
Net Worth: $20,826,549
Earnings: $6,170,906
Emp.: 100
Fiscal Year-end: 12/31/19
Copper & Aluminum Electrical Cables
& Conductors Mfr
N.A.I.C.S.: 335929
Joseph Kinyua (Mgr-Fin-Grp)

**EAST AFRICAN PORTLAND
CEMENT COMPANY LIMITED**
LR 337/113/1 Namanga Road off
Mombasa Road, PO Box 40101 -
00100, Nairobi, Kenya
Tel.: (254) 709 855 000
Web Site:
http://www.eastafricanportland.com
Sales Range: $50-74.9 Million
Emp.: 448
Cement Mfr
N.A.I.C.S.: 325520
William Lay (Chm)

**EAST ASIA HOLDINGS IN-
VESTMENT LIMITED**
Suite 501-2 5th Floor ICBC Tower 3
Garden Road, Central, China (Hong
Kong)
Tel.: (852) 21584075
Web Site:
https://www.eastasiaholdings.co.kr
Year Founded: 2009
900110—(KRS)
Rev.: $39,699,637
Assets: $212,838,845
Liabilities: $9,189,749
Net Worth: $203,649,095
Earnings: $2,149,357
Emp.: 774
Fiscal Year-end: 12/31/22
Holding Company; Sport Shoes &
Apparel Mfr & Marketer
N.A.I.C.S.: 551112
So-Young Jeong (CEO)

**EAST BALKAN PROPERTIES
PLC**
Dixcart House Sir William Place,
Saint Peter Port, GY1 4EZ, Guernsey
Tel.: (44) 1481 738723
Web Site: http://www.ebp-plc.com
Sales Range: $1-9.9 Million
Investment Services
N.A.I.C.S.: 523999
James Ede-Golightly (Chm)

EAST BUILDTECH LTD
D-3/2 Chokhani House Okhla Industrial Area Phase-II, New Delhi, 110
020, India
Tel.: (91) 1147105100

Web Site: https://www.ebl.co.in
Year Founded: 1984
507917—(BOM)
Rev.: $49,877
Assets: $961,670
Liabilities: $95,427
Net Worth: $866,243
Earnings: ($1,679)
Emp.: 1
Fiscal Year-end: 03/31/21
Real Estate Development Services
N.A.I.C.S.: 531390
Madhusudan Chokhani (Chm & Mng
Dir)

EAST BUY HOLDING LIMITED
18F New Oriental South Buildin 2,
Haidiandongsanjie, Beijing, 100080,
China
Tel.: (86) 1062609090
1797—(HKG)
Rev.: $624,425,260
Assets: $533,470,591
Liabilities: $145,260,578
Net Worth: $388,210,013
Earnings: $134,482,444
Emp.: 1,479
Fiscal Year-end: 05/31/23
Educational Support Services
N.A.I.C.S.: 611710
Dongxu Sun (CEO)

**EAST CHINA ENGINEERING
SCIENCE & TECHNOLOGY
CO., LTD.**
70 Wangjiang E Road, Hefei,
230024, Anhui, China
Tel.: (86) 13817524430
Web Site: https://www.chinaecec.com
Year Founded: 1963
002140—(SSE)
Rev.: $875,259,216
Assets: $1,649,414,988
Liabilities: $1,096,104,204
Net Worth: $553,310,784
Earnings: $40,523,652
Emp.: 1,800
Fiscal Year-end: 12/31/22
Engineeering Services
N.A.I.C.S.: 541330
Li Lixin (Chm)

Subsidiaries:

Anhui Donghua Environment & Mu-
nicipal Engineering Co., Ltd.   (1)
No 11 Tianhu Rd, Hefei, Anhui, China
Tel.: (86) 55162523577
Engineering Consulting Services
N.A.I.C.S.: 541330

Guizhou East China Engineering Co.,
Ltd.   (1)
99 Zuiyi Rd, Guiyang, China
Tel.: (86) 8515570071
Engineering Consulting Services
N.A.I.C.S.: 541330

**EAST COAST FURNITECH
PUBLIC COMPANY LIMITED**
37/9 Moo 10 Banbung-Klaeng Rd,
Thang Kwian Subdistrict Klaeng Dis-
trict, Rayong, 21110, Thailand
Tel.: (66) 38886372
Web Site:
https://www.eastcoast.co.th
Year Founded: 1992
ECF—(THA)
Rev.: $41,380,532
Assets: $117,758,161
Liabilities: $83,318,990
Net Worth: $34,439,171
Earnings: ($4,261,388)
Emp.: 349
Fiscal Year-end: 12/31/23
Wood Furniture Mfr & Distr
N.A.I.C.S.: 337122
Wanlop Suksawad (CEO)

East Coast Furnitech Public Company Limited—(Continued)

EAST DELTA FLOUR MILLS
Al Ahrar Rd, PO Box 284, Zagazig, Egypt
Tel.: (20) 2302759
Web Site:
http://www.eastdeltamills.com
Year Founded: 2010
EDFM.CA—(EGX)
Sales Range: Less than $1 Million
Flour Mill Operator
N.A.I.C.S.: 311211
Mohammed Mohammod Ali Ehaira *(Chm & Mng Dir)*

EAST ENERGY RESOURCES LIMITED
Level 2 22 Mount Street, Perth, 6000, WA, Australia
Tel.: (61) 8 6188 8181
Web Site:
http://www.eastenergy.com.au
Rev.: $103,196
Assets: $9,181,358
Liabilities: $1,004,142
Net Worth: $8,177,217
Earnings: ($1,340,048)
Fiscal Year-end: 06/30/19
Coal Exploration & Development Services
N.A.I.C.S.: 212115
Ranko Matic *(Co-Sec)*

EAST GROUP CO., LTD.
No 6 Northern Industry Road Songshan Lake, Science & Tech Industry Park, Dongguan, 523808, Guangdong, China
Tel.: (86) 76922898801
Web Site: https://www.eastups.com
Year Founded: 1989
300376—(SSE)
Rev.: $665,726,256
Assets: $1,976,311,116
Liabilities: $1,011,381,228
Net Worth: $964,929,888
Earnings: $51,556,284
Emp.: 1,600
Fiscal Year-end: 12/31/22
Power Supply Mfr
N.A.I.C.S.: 335311
He Jia *(Chm & Gen Mgr)*

EAST INDIA SECURITIES LIMITED
Da-14 Salt Lake City Sector-I, Kolkata, 700064, India
Tel.: (91) 3340205901
Web Site: http://www.eisec.com
Year Founded: 1995
541053—(BOM)
Rev.: $14,866,580
Assets: $92,588,865
Liabilities: $29,148,379
Net Worth: $63,440,486
Earnings: $9,803,809
Emp.: 41
Fiscal Year-end: 03/31/21
Financial Services
N.A.I.C.S.: 523999
Anupam Jain *(Sec & Compliance Officer)*

EAST JAPAN MARKETING & COMMUNICATIONS, INC.
JR Ebisu Building 1-5-5 Ebisu-Minami, Shibuya-ku, Tokyo, 150-8508, Japan
Tel.: (81) 3 5447 7800   JP
Web Site: http://www.jeki.co.jp
Year Founded: 1988
Sales Range: $900-999.9 Million
Emp.: 637
Advertising Services
N.A.I.C.S.: 541810

Shuji Kurimoto *(Mng Dir & Deputy Chief-Acct Svcs-Headquarters & JR Div)*

EAST JAPAN RAILWAY COMPANY
2-2-2 Yoyogi, Shibuya-ku, Tokyo, 151-8578, Japan
Tel.: (81) 353341151   JP
Web Site: https://www.jreast.co.jp
Year Founded: 1987
9020—(TKS)
Rev.: $18,046,079,980
Assets: $64,589,476,190
Liabilities: $46,483,152,670
Net Worth: $18,106,323,520
Earnings: $1,298,527,890
Emp.: 41,147
Fiscal Year-end: 03/31/24
Railways Transportation Services
N.A.I.C.S.: 551112
Kimitaka Mori *(Auditor)*

Subsidiaries:

East Japan Railway Company - New York Office   (1)
350 5th Ave Ste 4220, New York, NY 10118
Tel.: (212) 332-8686
Representative Office
N.A.I.C.S.: 551114

JR East Japan Information Systems Company   (1)
Shinjuku Garden Tower 7F 3-8-2 Okubo, Shinjuku-ku, Tokyo, 169-0072, Japan   (100%)
Tel.: (81) 332081555
Web Site: https://www.jeis.co.jp
Sales Range: $600-649.9 Million
Emp.: 1,690
Development & Operation of Information Processing Systems; Information Services; Consulting Services
N.A.I.C.S.: 519290
Akiyoshi Hosokawa *(Pres)*

JR East Net Station Co., Ltd.   (1)
Agrisquare Shinjuku 4th floor 5-27-11 Sendagaya, Shibuya-ku, Tokyo, 151-0051, Japan   (100%)
Tel.: (81) 362731126
Web Site: https://www.jrnets.com
Emp.: 107
Information Processing
N.A.I.C.S.: 519290
Washiya Atsuko *(Pres)*

JR East Retail Net Co., Ltd.   (1)
Tetsudo Kosei Kaikan 5-1 Kojimachi, Chiyoda-ku, Tokyo, Japan   (100%)
Tel.: (81) 352756713
Sales Range: $400-449.9 Million
Emp.: 2,000
Convenience Store & News Stand Operator
N.A.I.C.S.: 445131

Japan Transport Engineering Company   (1)
3-1 Okawa, Kanazawa-ku, Yokohama, 236-0043, Japan   (100%)
Tel.: (81) 457015155
Web Site: http://www.j-trec.co.jp
Emp.: 1,164
Railroad Rolling Stock Mfr
N.A.I.C.S.: 336510
Naoto Miyashita *(Pres)*

Nippon Hotel Co. Ltd.   (1)
1-6-1 Nishi-Ikebukuro, Toshima-ward, Tokyo, 171-8505, Japan   (100%)
Tel.: (81) 359541088
Web Site: http://www.nihonhotel.com
Holding Company; Hotel Network Operator
N.A.I.C.S.: 551112
Masayuki Satomi *(CEO)*

Subsidiary (Domestic):

Hotel Metropolitan Nagano Co., Ltd.   (2)
1346 Minamiishi Dou-cho, Nagano, 380-0824, Japan
Tel.: (81) 262917000
Web Site: https://nagano.metropolitan.jp
Hotel Operator

N.A.I.C.S.: 721110

Unit (Domestic):

Hotel Metropolitan Tokyo   (2)
1-6-1 Nishiikebukuro, Toshima-ku, Tokyo, 171-8505, Japan
Tel.: (81) 3 3980 1111
Web Site: http://ikebukuro.metropolitan.jp
Hotel Operator
N.A.I.C.S.: 721110

EAST MONEY INFORMATION CO., LTD.
Block 1 No. 2999 Bao an Highway, Jiading District, Shanghai, 201800, China
Tel.: (86) 2154660526
Web Site: http://www.eastmoney.com
300059—(CHIN)
Rev.: $1,534,315,366
Assets: $33,171,566,321
Liabilities: $23,207,723,195
Net Worth: $9,963,843,127
Earnings: $1,134,452,440
Fiscal Year-end: 12/31/23
Financial Investment Services
N.A.I.C.S.: 523999

EAST OCEAN OILS & GRAINS INDUSTRIES
Jingang, 215634, Zhangjiagang, China
Tel.: (86) 51258381018
Web Site: http://www.eogi.com.cn
Sales Range: $1-4.9 Billion
Emp.: 2,000
Oil & Grain Processing Services
N.A.I.C.S.: 311225
Dong Wei *(Gen Mgr)*

EAST PIPES INTEGRATED COMPANY FOR INDUSTRY
Street No 89 2nd Industrial City, PO Box 12943, Dammam, 31483, Saudi Arabia
Tel.: (966) 138616801
Web Site: https://www.eastpipes.com
Year Founded: 2010
1321—(SAU)
Rev.: $383,587,890
Assets: $263,249,363
Liabilities: $99,153,694
Net Worth: $164,095,669
Earnings: $26,642,004
Emp.: 480
Fiscal Year-end: 03/31/23
Steel Pipe Product Mfr
N.A.I.C.S.: 331210
Mohammed A. Al-Shaheen *(CEO)*

EAST STAR RESOURCES PLC
Eccleston Yards 25 Eccleston Place, London, SW1W 9NF, United Kingdom
Tel.: (44) 2039188792   UK
Web Site:
https://www.eaststarplc.com
Year Founded: 2020
EST—(LSE)
Assets: $5,348,059
Liabilities: $172,430
Net Worth: $5,175,629
Earnings: ($4,215,721)
Emp.: 7
Fiscal Year-end: 11/30/22
Gold Ore & Silver Ore Mining
N.A.I.C.S.: 212220
Alex Walker *(CEO)*

EAST WEST AGRO AB
Tikslo G 10 Kumpia, Kaunas, Lithuania
Tel.: (370) 37262318
Web Site: https://www.ewa.lt
Year Founded: 2006
EWA1L—(VSE)
Rev.: $38,834,793
Assets: $26,885,083

Liabilities: $15,608,494
Net Worth: $11,276,589
Earnings: $1,841,245
Fiscal Year-end: 12/31/23
Agricultural Machinery Distr
N.A.I.C.S.: 423820
Danas Sidlauskas *(Chm, Chm-Mgmt Bd & COO)*

EAST WEST HOLDINGS LIMITED
No 62 Adarsh Industrial Estate Sahar Chakala Road Andheri East, Mumbai, 400099, Maharashtra, India
Tel.: (91) 2242219000
Web Site: https://www.ewhl.in
Year Founded: 1981
540006—(BOM)
Rev.: $22,135,646
Assets: $20,006,510
Liabilities: $11,620,403
Net Worth: $8,386,107
Earnings: ($17,305)
Fiscal Year-end: 03/31/21
Logistic Services
N.A.I.C.S.: 541614
Mohammad Shafi *(Chm & Mng Dir)*

EAST WEST INSURANCE COMPANY LIMITED
B-401-404 4th Floor Lakson Square Building No-3, Sarwar Shaheed Road, Karachi, Pakistan
Tel.: (92) 2135630400   PK
Web Site: https://ewi.com.pk
Year Founded: 1983
EWIC—(KAR)
Rev.: $9,449,496
Assets: $23,442,946
Liabilities: $14,264,001
Net Worth: $9,178,945
Earnings: $1,183,968
Emp.: 129
Fiscal Year-end: 12/31/19
Property & Casualty Insurance Services
N.A.I.C.S.: 524126
Mahboob Ahmad *(Chm)*

EAST WEST LIFE ASSURANCE COMPANY LIMITED
Office No.1104 11th Floor Emerald Tower lot No. G-19, Block 5 KDA Improvement Scheme No 5 Clifton, Karachi, Pakistan
Tel.: (92) 21111225275
Web Site: http://askarilife.com
EWLA—(KAR)
Rev.: $1,944,629
Assets: $4,958,208
Liabilities: $3,128,945
Net Worth: $1,829,263
Earnings: ($1,692,947)
Fiscal Year-end: 12/31/19
Life & Health Insurance Services
N.A.I.C.S.: 524113
Maheen Yunus *(CEO & Mng Dir)*

EAST WEST PETROLEUM CORP.
1305-1090 West Georgia, Vancouver, V6E 3V7, BC, Canada
Tel.: (604) 685-9316
Web Site:
https://www.eastwestpetroleum.ca
Year Founded: 1987
EWPMF—(OTCIQ)
Rev.: $2,069,130
Assets: $4,452,552
Liabilities: $1,041,274
Net Worth: $3,411,277
Earnings: $652,103
Fiscal Year-end: 03/31/23
Oil & Gas Exploration Services
N.A.I.C.S.: 213112

Nick DeMare *(CFO, CFO, Sec & Sec)*

EAST-COURT FORD LINCOLN SALES

4700 Sheppard Avenue East, Toronto, M1S 3V6, ON, Canada
Tel.: (416) 292-1171
Web Site:
http://www.eastcourtfordlincoln.com
Sales Range: $25-49.9 Million
Emp.: 150
New & Used Car Dealers
N.A.I.C.S.: 441110

EASTBRIDGE GROUP

5 Rue Guillaume Kroll, L-1882, Luxembourg, Luxembourg
Tel.: (352) 26 49 58 40 95
Web Site:
http://www.eastbridgegroup.com
Year Founded: 1990
Holding Company; Investment Services
N.A.I.C.S.: 551112
Daniel Haimovic *(Mng Partner)*

Subsidiaries:

39 North Capital LLC   (1)
67 Wall St Ste 2502, New York, NY 10005
Tel.: (212) 482-1255
Web Site: http://www.39northcapital.com
Investment Services
N.A.I.C.S.: 523999
Timothy Lucey *(Mng Partner)*

Subsidiary (Domestic):

Eegees Inc.   (2)
3360 E Ajo Way, Tucson, AZ 85713
Tel.: (520) 294-3333
Web Site: http://www.eegees.com
Sales Range: $25-49.9 Million
Emp.: 450
Fast Food Restaurants & Stands
N.A.I.C.S.: 722513
Mark Reinhart *(Dir-Commissary)*

EASTBRIDGE INVESTMENTS PLC

3rd Floor 21 Blythswood Square, Glasgow, G2 4BL, United Kingdom
Tel.: (44) 1412434470
Web Site:
http://www.eastbridgeplc.com
Assets: $1,038,009
Liabilities: $158,051
Net Worth: $879,958
Earnings: ($615,116)
Emp.: 2
Real Estate Investment Services
N.A.I.C.S.: 525990
Greg Collier *(Chm)*

EASTCOAST STEEL LIMITED

A-123 Royal Den Apartments 16 Arul Theson Street, Palaniraja Udayar Nagar Lawspet, Pondicherry, 605008, India
Tel.: (91) 2240750100
Web Site:
https://www.eastcoaststeel.com
Year Founded: 1982
520081—(BOM)
Rev.: $5,801,071
Assets: $3,153,742
Net Worth: $2,587,769
Earnings: $4,808,437
Emp.: 4
Fiscal Year-end: 03/31/21
Steel Product Mfr & Distr
N.A.I.C.S.: 332999
P. K. R. K. Menon *(Officer-Compliance & Sec)*

EASTCOMPEACE TECHNOLOGY CO., LTD.

No 8 Ping Gong Zhong Road Nanping S and T Industry Community, Zhuhai, 519060, Guangdong, China
Tel.: (86) 7568695221
Web Site:
https://www.eastcompeace.com
Year Founded: 1998
002017—(SSE)
Rev.: $180,517,896
Assets: $404,502,228
Liabilities: $189,586,332
Net Worth: $214,915,896
Earnings: $12,881,700
Emp.: 2,000
Fiscal Year-end: 12/31/22
Smartcard Mfr
N.A.I.C.S.: 541519
Wan Qian *(Chm)*

Subsidiaries:

Eastcompeace (India) Co., Ltd.   (1)
A-8 D S I D C Complex F I E Patparganj Industrial Area, Delhi, 110092, India
Tel.: (91) 1143317774
Smartcard Mfr
N.A.I.C.S.: 326199
Hu Dan *(Pres & Gen Mgr-Intl Dept)*

Eastcompeace (Russia) Co., Ltd.   (1)
Yablonevaya Alleya 313 A Zelenograd, 124482, Moscow, Russia
Tel.: (7) 4997361431
Web Site: http://www.eastcompeace.com
Emp.: 50
Smartcard Mfr
N.A.I.C.S.: 326199
Chen Zongchao *(Chm & Gen Mgr-Investments Dev Dept & Pur Dept)*

Eastcompeace (Singapore) Co., Ltd.   (1)
No 7030 Ang Mo Kio Avenue 5 08-75/77/79 NorthStar AMK, Singapore, 569880, Singapore
Tel.: (65) 63923909
Smart Card Distr
N.A.I.C.S.: 424990
Hu Dan *(Pres & Gen Mgr-Intl Dept)*

Eastcompeace Smart Card (Bangladesh) Co., Ltd.   (1)
Smartcard Mfr
N.A.I.C.S.: 326199
Hu Dan *(Pres & Gen Mgr-Intl Dept)*

EASTCOMTRANS LLP

Al Farabi Avenue 77/7 Esentai Tower BC 11th Floor, Almaty, 050040, Kazakhstan
Tel.: (7) 727 3555 111
Web Site: http://www.ect.kz
Year Founded: 2002
ECTR—(KAZ)
Rev.: $107,799,977
Assets: $433,202,212
Liabilities: $208,904,144
Net Worth: $224,298,068
Earnings: $32,980,620
Emp.: 283
Fiscal Year-end: 12/31/19
Freight Transportation Services
N.A.I.C.S.: 488510

EASTERN & ORIENTAL BERHAD

Level 3A Annexe Menara Milenium No 8 Jalan Damanlela, Damansara Heights, 50490, Kuala Lumpur, Malaysia
Tel.: (60) 320956868
Web Site:
http://www.easternandoriental.com
E&O—(KLS)
Rev.: $75,419,438
Assets: $894,735,270
Liabilities: $469,922,310
Net Worth: $424,812,960
Earnings: ($17,133,187)
Fiscal Year-end: 03/31/21
Hotel & Property Management Services

Chai Lyn *(Dir-Corp Strategy)*

Subsidiaries:

Ambangan Puri Sdn. Bhd   (1)
Tel.: (60) 320956868
Web Site:
http://www.easternandoriental.com
Residential Real Estate Property Development Services
N.A.I.C.S.: 531311

Subsidiary (Non-US):

Seventy Damansara Sdn. Bhd.   (2)
Tel.: (60) 320953062
Residential Property Development Services
N.A.I.C.S.: 531311

E&O Customer Services Sdn. Bhd.   (1)
Pondok Jaga Idamansara Jalan Rosa 5 Bukit Damansara, 50490, Kuala Lumpur, Malaysia
Tel.: (60) 320952662
Web Site: http://www.eopro.com
Sales Range: $75-99.9 Million
Emp.: 150
Property Management Services
N.A.I.C.S.: 531311

E&O Property (Penang) Sdn. Bhd.   (1)
The Sales Gallery Seri Tanjung Pinang, Tanjung Tokong, 10470, George Town, Pulau Pinang, Malaysia
Tel.: (60) 48918000
Sales Range: $50-74.9 Million
Emp.: 100
Residential Property Development Services
N.A.I.C.S.: 531311
T. C. Kok Tuck Cheong *(Mng Dir)*

E&O Property Development Berhad   (1)
E O Gallery 211A Jalan Tun Razak, 50450, Kuala Lumpur, Malaysia
Tel.: (60) 321818881
Sales Range: $75-99.9 Million
Emp.: 150
Property Development Services
N.A.I.C.S.: 531390

Eastern & Oriental Hotel Sdn. Bhd.   (1)
10 Lebuh Farquhar, 10200, Penang, Malaysia
Tel.: (60) 42222000
Web Site: http://www.eohotels.com
Home Management Services
N.A.I.C.S.: 721110

Eminent Pedestal Sdn. Bhd   (1)
B-M-2 M Northpoint Offices Mdn Syed Putra Mid Valley City, 59200, Kuala Lumpur, Federal Territory, Malaysia
Tel.: (60) 322879220
Sales Range: $10-24.9 Million
Emp.: 6
Restaurant Operating Services
N.A.I.C.S.: 722511

Lone Pine Hotel (c) Sdn. Bhd.   (1)
97 Batu Ferringhi, 11100, Penang, Malaysia
Tel.: (60) 48868686
Web Site: http://www.lonepinehotel.com
Sales Range: $25-49.9 Million
Emp.: 190
Home Management Services
N.A.I.C.S.: 721110

EASTERN ASIA TECHNOLOGY LTD.

6 Shenton Way Suite 28-09 DBS Building Tower Two, Singapore, 06809, Singapore
Tel.: (65) 62500718
Web Site: http://www.eastech.com
Sales Range: $250-299.9 Million
Contract Mfr of Electronic Components & Equipment
N.A.I.C.S.: 334419
Jenq-Lin Liou *(Chm & CEO)*

Subsidiaries:

East Synergy Limited   (1)

Unit 1703-7 10 16 17F Hewlett Centre 54 Hoi Yuen Road, Kwun Tong, China (Hong Kong)
Tel.: (852) 23434225
Sales Range: $25-49.9 Million
Emp.: 20
Electronic Equipment Distr
N.A.I.C.S.: 423620
William Ho Hai Wai *(Mgr)*

Eastech Electronics (HK) Limited   (1)
Rm 1703-1707 17F Hewlett Center, 54 Hoi Yuen Road Kwun Tong, Kowloon, China (Hong Kong)   **(94.23%)**
Tel.: (852) 23431711
Web Site: http://www.eastech.com
Durable Goods Whslr
N.A.I.C.S.: 423990

Eastech Electronics (Taiwan) Inc.   (1)
8F-1 No 188 Baoqiao Road, Xindian District, New Taipei City, 23145, Taiwan
Tel.: (886) 2 2910 2626
Electronic Components Mfr
N.A.I.C.S.: 334419
Nancy Teng *(Asst VP)*

Eastern Asia Industries Sdn. Bhd   (1)
Plot 326 Jalan Pknk 3-3, Sungai Petani, Malaysia   **(100%)**
Tel.: (60) 44417789
Sales Range: $50-74.9 Million
Emp.: 200
Audio & Video Equipment Mfr
N.A.I.C.S.: 334310

Eastern Asia Technology (HK) Limited   (1)
Units 1703-1707 17th Floor Hewlett Centre, 54 Hoi Yuen Road Kwun Tong, Kowloon, China (Hong Kong)   **(100%)**
Tel.: (852) 27970268
Durable Goods Whslr
N.A.I.C.S.: 423990

EASTERN BANK PLC

100 Gulshan Avenue, Dhaka, 1212, Bangladesh
Tel.: (880) 9666777325
Web Site: https://www.ebl.com.bd
Year Founded: 1992
EBL—(CHT)
Rev.: $168,317,397
Assets: $4,194,731,794
Liabilities: $3,868,528,857
Net Worth: $326,202,937
Earnings: $46,707,896
Emp.: 2,202
Fiscal Year-end: 12/31/22
Commercial Banking Services
N.A.I.C.S.: 522110
Ali Reza Iftekhar *(CEO & Mng Dir)*

EASTERN BAY ENERGY TRUST

5 Richardson Street, Whakatane, 3120, New Zealand
Tel.: (64) 7 307 0893
Web Site: http://www.ebet.org.nz
Year Founded: 1994
Emp.: 3
Energy Asset Investment Trust
N.A.I.C.S.: 525990
Don Lewell *(Chm)*

Subsidiaries:

Horizon Energy Distribution Limited   (1)
Level 4 Commerce Plaza 52 Commerce Street, PO Box 281, Whakatane, 3158, New Zealand
Tel.: (64) 73062900
Web Site: http://www.horizonnetworks.nz
Electricity Distribution Network Operator
N.A.I.C.S.: 221122
Derek Caudwell *(Gen Mgr-Network)*

Subsidiary (Domestic):

Aquaheat New Zealand Limited   (2)
92-96 Main Road Tawa, Wellington, 5028, N Island, New Zealand
Tel.: (64) 42325179
Web Site: http://www.aquaheat.co.nz

Eastern Bay Energy Trust—(Continued)

Commercial & Industrial Heating, Ventilation, Air-Conditioning, Plumbing, Fire Protection, Roofing & Cladding Contractor
N.A.I.C.S.: 238990
Greg McCarthy *(Gen Mgr-Central Reg)*

Horizon Services Limited (2)
11 G Te Tahi Street, Whakatane, 3120, New
Zealand (100%)
Tel.: (64) 79228800
Web Site: http://www.horizonservices.co.nz
Emp.: 100
Electrical Contractor Services
N.A.I.C.S.: 238210
Ajay Anand *(CEO)*

EASTERN CARIBBEAN AMAL-
GAMATED BANK

1000 Airport Boulevard at Pavilion
Drive, PO Box 315, Coolidge, Antigua
& Barbuda
Tel.: (268) 2684805300
Web Site: http://www.ecabank.com
Banking Services
N.A.I.C.S.: 522110
Norris J. Antonio *(Sr Mgr-Credit Ad-
min)*

EASTERN CARIBBEAN CEN-
TRAL BANK

PO Box 89, Basseterre, Saint Kitts &
Nevis
Tel.: (869) 4652537
Web Site: http://www.eccb-
centralbank.org
Rev.: $30,901,105
Assets: $1,872,751,332
Liabilities: $1,793,644,404
Net Worth: $79,106,927
Earnings: $3,962,376
Emp.: 208
Fiscal Year-end: 03/31/18
Banking Services
N.A.I.C.S.: 522110
Karen Williams *(Dir-Res Department)*

EASTERN CARIBBEAN SECU-
RITIES EXCHANGE

Bird Rock, PO Box 94, Basseterre,
00265, Saint Kitts & Nevis
Tel.: (869) 4667192
Web Site: http://www.ecseonline.com
Sales Range: $1-9.9 Million
Emp.: 11
Stock Exchange Services
N.A.I.C.S.: 523210
Trevor E. Blake *(Gen Mgr)*

EASTERN COMMERCIAL
LEASING PUBLIC COMPANY
LIMITED

976/1 Soi Rama 9 Hospital Rim Kh-
long Samsen Road, Bangkapi Huayk-
wang, Bangkok, 10310, Thailand
Tel.: (66) 26415252
Web Site: https://www.ecl.co.th
Year Founded: 1982
ECL—(THA)
Rev.: $19,091,196
Assets: $145,440,654
Liabilities: $90,197,708
Net Worth: $55,242,946
Earnings: $3,158,696
Emp.: 224
Fiscal Year-end: 12/31/23
Automobile Finance Services
N.A.I.C.S.: 525990
Prapakorn Wiraphong *(Mng Dir)*

EASTERN COMMUNICATIONS
CO., LTD.

No 66 Dongxin Avenue, Binjiang Dis-
trict, Hangzhou, 310001, Zhejiang,
China
Tel.: (86) 57186676198
Web Site: http://www.eastcom.com

Year Founded: 1958
900941—(SHG)
Rev.: $453,457,855
Assets: $595,769,976
Liabilities: $118,301,082
Net Worth: $477,468,894
Earnings: $18,938,107
Emp.: 2,500
Fiscal Year-end: 12/31/22
Communication Software Develop-
ment Services
N.A.I.C.S.: 541511
Guo Duanduan *(Chm, Vice Chm &
Pres)*

Subsidiaries:

Eastcom Network Co., Ltd. (1)
3rd Floor Building R and d No 66 Eastcom
Road High-Tech Zone, Bingjiang District,
Hangzhou, 310053, China
Tel.: (86) 57186675388
Web Site: http://www.eastcomnetwork.com
Telecommunication Servicesb
N.A.I.C.S.: 517810

Hangzhou Eastcom City Co.Ltd. (1)
No 66 Eastcom Road, Binjiang District,
Hangzhou, 310053, China
Tel.: (86) 57186697160
Financial Electronic & Wireless Trunking
Communication Services
N.A.I.C.S.: 517112

EASTERN CONSTRUCTION
COMPANY LIMITED

505 Consumers Rd Ste 1100, To-
ronto, M2J 5G2, ON, Canada
Tel.: (416) 497-7110
Web Site:
http://www.easternconstruction.com
Year Founded: 1951
Sales Range: $25-49.9 Million
Emp.: 140
General Contracting Services
N.A.I.C.S.: 236220
Renato Tacconelli *(VP)*

EASTERN ENVIRONMENT SO-
LUTIONS, CORP.

Harbin Dongdazhi Street 165, Harbin,
150001, China
Tel.: (86) 451 53948666 NV
Web Site: http://www.useesc.com
Sales Range: $10-24.9 Million
Emp.: 56
Solid Waste Disposal
N.A.I.C.S.: 562212
Feng Yan *(Chm & CEO)*

Subsidiaries:

Harbin Yifeng Eco-environment Co.,
Ltd. (1)
No 165 Dongdazhi Street, Nangang Dist,
Harbin, 150001, China
Tel.: (86) 45153948666
Solid Waste Processing Services
N.A.I.C.S.: 562213
Feng Yan *(Gen Mgr)*

EASTERN GASES LIMITED

43 Palace Court 1 Kyd Street, Kol-
kata, 700016, West Bengal, India
Tel.: (91) 3322299897
Web Site: http://www.eastgas.in
Year Founded: 1995
Sales Range: $25-49.9 Million
Gas Distr
N.A.I.C.S.: 221210
Sushil Kumar Bhansali *(Chm & Mng
Dir)*

EASTERN GOLD JADE CO.,
LTD.

3F Eastern Gold Jade Jewery Man-
sion Section 2 Shuibei Indstl Prk, Bli
Nrth Rd Luohu District, Shenzhen,
Guangdong, China
Tel.: (86) 7552 526 6298

Web Site: http://www.goldjade.cn
600086—(SHG)
Rev.: $7,736,372
Assets: $1,520,886,963
Liabilities: $1,470,547,774
Net Worth: $50,339,189
Earnings: ($262,109,644)
Fiscal Year-end: 12/31/19
Jade & Gold Jewelry Whslr
N.A.I.C.S.: 423940
Wenfeng Zhang *(Chm & Pres)*

EASTERN HOLDING LIMITED

8F-1 No 188 Baoqlao Road, Xindlan
District, New Taipei City, 231028,
Taiwan
Tel.: (886) 289113535
Web Site: https://www.eastech.com
Year Founded: 1971
5225—(TAI)
Rev.: $347,968,200
Assets: $196,456,940
Liabilities: $103,384,476
Net Worth: $93,072,465
Earnings: $17,440,400
Emp.: 2,485
Fiscal Year-end: 12/31/23
Audio & Video Products Mfr
N.A.I.C.S.: 334310
Chin Chang Pai *(Co-Pres)*

Subsidiaries:

Eastech (Huizhou) Co., Ltd. (1)
Xinxu Hui Yang, Dong Fong District, Hu-
izhou, 516226, Guangdong, China
Tel.: (86) 752 333 9166
Speaker System Mfr & Distr
N.A.I.C.S.: 334310

Eastech (SG) Pte. Ltd., (1)
1 Pemimpin Drive 08-06 One Pemimpin,
Singapore, 576151, Singapore
Tel.: (65) 9 853 0520
Sound System Research & Development
Services
N.A.I.C.S.: 541715

Eastech Electronics (SG) Pte.
Ltd. (1)
1 Pemimpin Drive 08-06 One Pemimpin,
Singapore, 576151, Singapore
Tel.: (65) 98530520
Speaker Systems Mfr
N.A.I.C.S.: 334310

Eastech Innovations (TW) Inc. (1)
8F-1 No 188 Baoqiao Road, Xindian Dis-
trict, New Taipei City, 231028, Taiwan
Tel.: (886) 22 910 2626
Sound System Research & Development
Services
N.A.I.C.S.: 541715

Eastech Microacoustics (HK)
Limited (1)
Unit 906 9/F Nanyang Plaza 57 Hong To
Road, Kwun Tong, Kowloon, China (Hong
Kong)
Tel.: (852) 2 797 0268
Speaker System Distr
N.A.I.C.S.: 423620

Eastech Systems (Huiyang) Co.,
Ltd. (1)
8F-1 No 188 Baoqiao Road, Xindian Dis-
trict, New Taipei City, 231028, Taiwan
Tel.: (886) 22 910 2626
Speaker System Mfr & Distr
N.A.I.C.S.: 334310

Hymnario-EAW (Huiyang) Co.,
Ltd. (1)
Dong Fong District Xinxu Hui Yang, Hu-
izhou, 516226, Guangdong, China
Tel.: (86) 7523339166
Speaker System Mfr & Distr
N.A.I.C.S.: 334310

Scan-Speak A/S (1)
N C Madsensvej 1, 6920, Videbaek, Den-
mark
Tel.: (45) 60405200
Web Site: http://www.scan-speak.dk
Speaker System Mfr & Distr
N.A.I.C.S.: 334310

Shenzhen MaliMaliBox Trading Cor-
poration Limited (1)
8F International Science and Technology
Building, No 3007 Shennan Zhong Road
Futian District, Shenzhen, 518033, Guang-
dong, China
Tel.: (86) 75525153550
Speaker System Distr
N.A.I.C.S.: 423620

EASTERN HOLDINGS LTD.

1100 Lower Delta Road 02-01 EPL
Building, Singapore, 169206, Singa-
pore
Tel.: (65) 6379 2888 SG
Web Site: http://www.epl.com.sg
Year Founded: 1981
Sales Range: $10-24.9 Million
Holding Company; Property Develop-
ment; Publishing
N.A.I.C.S.: 551112
Kenneth Kay Soon Tan *(Chm & Mng
Dir)*

Subsidiaries:

Eastern Publishing Pte Ltd (1)
1100 Lower Delta Rd 04-01 EPL Building,
Singapore, 169206, Singapore
Tel.: (65) 63792888
Web Site: http://www.epl.com.sg
Emp.: 100
Magazines & Periodicals Publishing Ser-
vices
N.A.I.C.S.: 513120
Stephen Tay *(Chm)*

Eastern Trade Media Pte Ltd (1)
EPL Building 1100 Lower Delta Road 04-02,
Singapore, 169206, Singapore
Tel.: (65) 6379 2888
Sales Range: $25-49.9 Million
Magazine Publishing Services
N.A.I.C.S.: 513120
Lum Kum Kuen *(Mng Dir)*

Motherhood Pte Ltd (1)
12 Hoy Fatt Road Ste 03-01 Bryton House,
Singapore, 159506, Singapore
Tel.: (65) 6379 2888
Web Site: http://www.motherhood.com.sg
Emp.: 50
Child Care Magazine Publishing Services
N.A.I.C.S.: 513120
Berwick Shia *(Sr Mgr)*

EASTERN HOUSING LIMITED

59/B Kemal Ataturk Avenue Banani,
Dhaka, 1213, Bangladesh
Tel.: (880) 255033669
Web Site:
https://www.easternhousing.com
Year Founded: 1964
EHL—(CHT)
Rev.: $28,145,855
Assets: $219,328,994
Liabilities: $151,143,902
Net Worth: $68,185,092
Earnings: $6,276,229
Emp.: 565
Fiscal Year-end: 06/30/23
Real Estate Development Services
N.A.I.C.S.: 531390
Dhiraj Malakar *(Mng Dir)*

EASTERN INSURANCE COM-
PANY LIMITED

44 Dilkusha C/A 1st & 2nd Floor,
Dhaka, 1000, Bangladesh
Tel.: (880) 2223383033
Web Site:
https://www.easterninsurancebd.com
Year Founded: 1986
EASTERNINS—(CHT)
Rev.: $1,275,254
Assets: $26,402,730
Liabilities: $6,614,726
Net Worth: $19,788,004
Earnings: $1,031,850
Emp.: 235
Fiscal Year-end: 12/31/23

General Insurance Services
N.A.I.C.S.: 524210
Mujibur Rahman *(Chm)*

Subsidiaries:

Eic Securities Ltd. **(1)**
32 NIB House Agrabad, Chattogram, Bangladesh
Tel.: (880) 31727040
Share Trading Services
N.A.I.C.S.: 523210

EASTERN LOGICA INFOWAY LTD.
2 Saklat Place Chandani Chowk 1st Floor, Kolkata, 700072, West Bengal, India
Tel.: (91) 7003999192   In
Web Site:
https://www.easternlogica.com
Year Founded: 1995
543746—(BOM)
Rev.: $84,026,684
Assets: $17,285,964
Liabilities: $12,545,633
Net Worth: $4,740,331
Earnings: $342,752
Fiscal Year-end: 03/31/22
Electronic Product Mfr & Distr
N.A.I.C.S.: 334111
Gaurav Goel *(Chm)*

EASTERN LUBRICANTS BLENDERS LIMITED
Strand Road Sadarghat, Chittagong, 4000, Bangladesh
Tel.: (880) 316142357
Web Site: https://elbl.portal.gov.bd
Year Founded: 1963
EASTRNLUB—(DHA)
Rev.: $6,214,765,858
Assets: $8,202,550,994
Liabilities: $5,457,844,626
Net Worth: $2,744,706,368
Earnings: ($313,854,817)
Emp.: 99
Fiscal Year-end: 06/30/22
Lubricant Blending Services
N.A.I.C.S.: 311225
Shamsur Rahman *(Chm)*

EASTERN MEDIA INTERNATIONAL CORPORATION
8F No 368 Sec 1 Fuxing S Road, Da-an District, Taipei, 10656, Taiwan
Tel.: (886) 227557565
Web Site: https://www.emic.com.tw
2614—(TAI)
Rev.: $191,032,989
Assets: $574,506,404
Liabilities: $436,573,809
Net Worth: $137,932,596
Earnings: ($11,317,636)
Fiscal Year-end: 12/31/23
Warehousing Services
N.A.I.C.S.: 531130
Shang Wen Liao *(Chm & Pres)*

Subsidiaries:

Eastern Home Shopping & Leisure Co., Ltd. **(1)**
258 Ching Ping Rd, Zhonghe District, Taipei, 23581, Taiwan
Tel.: (886) 229437888
Web Site: http://www.etmall.com.tw
Sales Range: $50-74.9 Million
Emp.: 100
Virtual Shopping Services
N.A.I.C.S.: 425120

EASTERN MERCHANTS PLC
240 Torrington Avenue, 7, Colombo, 7, Sri Lanka
Tel.: (94) 112328406
Web Site:
https://www.easternmerchants.net
Year Founded: 1945

EMER—(COL)
Rev.: $9,026,407
Assets: $8,571,436
Liabilities: $1,756,693
Net Worth: $6,814,743
Earnings: $249,925
Emp.: 224
Fiscal Year-end: 03/31/23
Natural Rubber Mfr
N.A.I.C.S.: 326299
J. B. L. De Silva *(Chm)*

EASTERN METALS LIMITED
Level 8 210 George Street, Sydney, 2000, NSW, Australia
Tel.: (61) 292909600
Web Site:
https://easternmetals.com.au
Year Founded: 2021
EMS—(ASX)
Rev.: $6,820
Assets: $2,220,192
Liabilities: $86,408
Net Worth: $2,133,784
Earnings: ($1,620,829)
Fiscal Year-end: 06/30/23
Metal Exploration Services
N.A.I.C.S.: 213114
Robert H. Duffin *(Chm)*

EASTERN PIONEER DRIVING SCHOOL CO., LTD.
No 19 Jinxing West Road, Daxing District, Beijing, 102600, China
Tel.: (86) 1053223377
Web Site: http://www.dfss.com.cn
Year Founded: 2005
603377—(SHG)
Rev.: $140,424,795
Assets: $712,596,592
Liabilities: $380,089,476
Net Worth: $332,507,116
Earnings: ($6,062,949)
Emp.: 4,000
Fiscal Year-end: 12/31/22
Driving School Operator
N.A.I.C.S.: 611692
Wenhui Yan *(Vice Chm & Pres)*

EASTERN PLATINUM LIMITED
1080-1188 West Georgia Street, Vancouver, V6E 4A2, BC, Canada
Tel.: (604) 800-8200   BC
Web Site: https://www.eastplats.com
Year Founded: 2005
ELR—(TSX)
Rev.: $106,944,000
Assets: $160,770,000
Liabilities: $73,105,000
Net Worth: $87,665,000
Earnings: $13,749,000
Emp.: 560
Fiscal Year-end: 12/31/23
Platinum Exploration Services
N.A.I.C.S.: 212290
George Dorin *(Chm)*

Subsidiaries:

SA Victiria International Technology Pty. Ltd. **(1)**
Victoria International Unit 1 174 Teakwood Road Jacobs, Durban, South Africa
Tel.: (27) 314591869
Web Site:
http://www.victoriainternational.co.za
Cement Mfr & Distr
N.A.I.C.S.: 327310

EASTERN POLYMER GROUP PUBLIC COMPANY LIMITED
770 Theparak Road Theparak Sub-District, Mueang District, Samut Prakan, 10270, Thailand
Tel.: (66) 23836599
Web Site: https://www.epg.co.th
Year Founded: 1978

EPG—(THA)
Rev.: $362,172,334
Assets: $544,527,943
Liabilities: $201,083,968
Net Worth: $343,443,975
Earnings: $33,295,426
Emp.: 3,522
Fiscal Year-end: 03/31/24
Polymer & Plastic Products Mfr
N.A.I.C.S.: 325998
Pawat Vitoorapakorn *(CEO)*

Subsidiaries:

4 Way Suspension Products Pty. Ltd. **(1)**
14 Darling St, Marsden Park, 2765, NSW, Australia
Tel.: (61) 296728899
Web Site: https://www.toughdog.com.au
Steering Damper Spare Parts Mfr & Distr
N.A.I.C.S.: 336390

APS Co., Ltd. **(1)**
770 Moo 6 Theparak Road, Theparak, Mueang Samut Sakhon, 10270, Thailand
Tel.: (66) 23836599
Web Site: https://apscompany.co.th
Rubber Insulation Mfr
N.A.I.C.S.: 326220

Aeroflex USA Inc. **(1)**
232 Industrial Park Rd, Sweetwater, TN 37874
Web Site: https://aeroflexusa.com
Rubber Insulation Mfr
N.A.I.C.S.: 326220

Aeroklas (Shanghai) Co., Ltd. **(1)**
251 Minyi road, Songjiang industry Park, Shanghai, 201612, China
Tel.: (86) 2157686198
Automotive Accessories Mfr
N.A.I.C.S.: 336390

Aeroklas Asia Pacific Group Pty. Ltd. **(1)**
17 Johnstone Rd, Brendale, 4500, QLD, Australia
Tel.: (61) 300237655
Web Site:
https://aeroklasasiapacificgroup.com
Automotive Component Mfr & Distr
N.A.I.C.S.: 336390

Aeroklas Co., Ltd **(1)**
62 Soi Bangna-Trad 25 Bangna-Trad Rd, Bangna, Bangkok, 10260, Thailand
Tel.: (66) 274430209
Emp.: 950
Rubber & Plastic Products Mfr
N.A.I.C.S.: 326199

Subsidiary (Non-US):

Aeroklas Australia Pty Ltd. **(2)**
1831-1833 Sydney Rd, Campbellfield, 3061, VIC, Australia
Tel.: (61) 300 237 655
Web Site: http://www.aeroklas.com.au
Automotive Accessories Mfr & Distr.
N.A.I.C.S.: 326199

Subsidiary (Domestic):

Flexiglass Challenge Pty Ltd **(3)**
10 Fellowes Court, Tullamarine, 3043, VIC, Australia
Tel.: (61) 383367400
Web Site: https://www.flexiglass.com.au
Canopies Trays, Ute Lids, Racks & Storage Sales
N.A.I.C.S.: 332322

Aeroklas Malaysia Sdn. Bhd. **(1)**
No 13-5 Jalan USJ 9/5Q Subang Business Center, 47620, Subang Jaya, Selangor, Malaysia
Tel.: (60) 380235145
Web Site: https://www.aeroklass.com
Aircraft Parts Distr
N.A.I.C.S.: 423860

EPG Innovation Center Co., Ltd. **(1)**
111/1 Moo 2 Makhamku, Nikompattana, Rayong, 21180, Thailand
Tel.: (66) 38893599611
Web Site: https://eic.co.th
Plastics Product Mfr

N.A.I.C.S.: 326199

Eastern Polypack Co., Ltd. **(1)**
50 Soi Bangna-Trad 25 Bangna-Trad Rd, Bangna, Bangkok, 10260, Thailand
Tel.: (66) 2744313948
Web Site: https://www.eppcup.com
Plastic Product Mfr & Distr
N.A.I.C.S.: 326199

TJM Products Pty. Ltd. **(1)**
17 Johnstone Road, Brendale, 4500, QLD, Australia
Tel.: (61) 738659999
Polymer & Plastic Product Mfr & Distr
N.A.I.C.S.: 325211

EASTERN POWER GROUP PUBLIC COMPANY LIMITED
No 51/29 51/61 Vibhavadi Rangsit Soi 66 Siam Samakkhi, Talat Bang Khen Subdistrict Laksi, Bangkok, 10210, Thailand
Tel.: (66) 25510541
Web Site: https://www.epco.co.th
Year Founded: 1990
EP—(THA)
Rev.: $92,070,342
Assets: $279,287,007
Liabilities: $117,299,372
Net Worth: $161,987,634
Earnings: $52,149,543
Emp.: 300
Fiscal Year-end: 12/31/20
Commercial Printing Services
N.A.I.C.S.: 323111
Yuth Chinsupakul *(Chm & Chm-Exec Bd)*

EASTERN PROVINCE CEMENT COMPANY
King Fahd Rd, PO Box 4536, Dammam, 31412, Saudi Arabia
Tel.: (966) 138812222
Web Site: http://www.epcco.com.sa
Year Founded: 1983
3080—(SAU)
Rev.: $209,091
Assets: $760,259
Liabilities: $131,083
Net Worth: $629,176
Earnings: $38,208
Emp.: 902
Fiscal Year-end: 12/31/22
Cement Mfr
N.A.I.C.S.: 327310
Ibrahim Salem Al-Rowais *(Vice Chm)*

EASTERN REFRIGERATION SUPPLY CO.
49 Riviera Drive, Markham, L3R 5J6, ON, Canada
Tel.: (905) 475-0075
Web Site: http://www.easternref.ca
Year Founded: 1963
Rev.: $22,744,800
Emp.: 42
Refrigeration Equipment & Supplies Merchant Whslr
N.A.I.C.S.: 423740
George Merkel *(Founder, Co-Owner & Pres)*

EASTERN RESOURCES LIMITED
Level 1 80 Chandos Street, Saint Leonards, 2065, NSW, Australia
Tel.: (61) 299067551
Web Site:
https://www.easterniron.com.au
EFE—(ASX)
Rev.: $123,001
Assets: $8,291,360
Liabilities: $121,814
Net Worth: $8,169,547
Earnings: ($563,551)
Emp.: 2
Fiscal Year-end: 06/30/24

Eastern Resources Limited—(Continued)

Iron Ore Exploration
N.A.I.C.S.: 212210

**EASTERN SECURITY & PRO-
TECTION SERVICES, INC.**
68 Harbin Road, Shenyang, 110002,
Liaoning, China
Tel.: (86) 24 2250 1035   DE
Year Founded: 2005
Sales Range: $10-24.9 Million
Emp.: 148
Security & Safety Systems Mfr
N.A.I.C.S.: 561621
Rui Tan *(Pres & CEO)*

**EASTERN SILK INDUSTRIES
LIMITED**
19 R N Mukherjee Road, Kolkata,
700 001, West Bengal, India
Tel.: (91) 3322430817
Web Site:
    https://www.easternsilk.com
590022—(BOM)
Rev.: $10,180,607
Assets: $22,466,112
Liabilities: $26,406,744
Net Worth: ($3,940,632)
Earnings: ($937,073)
Emp.: 20,000
Fiscal Year-end: 03/31/22
Silk Yarn Mfr
N.A.I.C.S.: 313110
Sundeep Shah *(Chm & Mng Dir)*

**EASTERN STAR REAL ES-
TATE PUBLIC COMPANY LIM-
ITED**
5 th Floor Ploenchit Tower No 898
Ploenchit Road, Lumpini Pathumwan,
Bangkok, 10330, Thailand
Tel.: (66) 919490000
Web Site: https://www.estarpcl.com
Year Founded: 1980
ESTAR—(THA)
Rev.: $38,428,746
Assets: $200,489,439
Liabilities: $55,077,585
Net Worth: $145,411,854
Earnings: $952,090
Emp.: 151
Fiscal Year-end: 12/31/23
Real Estate Development Services
N.A.I.C.S.: 531390
Pongpinit Tejagupta *(Vice Chm)*

EASTERN STEEL SDN BHD
No 47 3Ath Floor Jalan 1/116B Ku-
chai Entrepreneurs Park Off, Jalan
Kuchai Lama, 58200, Kuala Lumpur,
Malaysia
Tel.: (60) 379830782
Steel Products Whslr
N.A.I.C.S.: 423510
Tee Choon Hock *(Dir-Projects)*

**EASTERN TECHNICAL ENGI-
NEERING PUBLIC CO., LTD.**
88 Soi Yothin Pattana Klongchan,
Bangkapi, Bangkok, 10240, Thailand
Tel.: (66) 21582000
Web Site: https://www.eastern-
groups.com
Year Founded: 1997
ETE—(THA)
Rev.: $46,919,449
Assets: $71,430,032
Liabilities: $43,351,816
Net Worth: $28,078,217
Earnings: $1,364,268
Fiscal Year-end: 12/31/23
Engineeering Services
N.A.I.C.S.: 541330
Pongsak Semson *(Chm)*

EASTERN TREADS LIMITED
3A 3rd Floor Eastern Corporate Of-
fice 34/137 E NH Bypass, Edappally
PO, Kochi, 682024, Kerala, India
Tel.: (91) 9447186564
Web Site:
    https://www.easterntreads.com
Year Founded: 1993
531346—(BOM)
Rev.: $10,202,379
Assets: $7,450,716
Liabilities: $6,735,511
Net Worth: $715,205
Earnings: ($134,098)
Emp.: 190
Fiscal Year-end: 03/31/21
Tread Mfr
N.A.I.C.S.: 326211
M. E. Mohamed *(Mng Dir)*

**EASTERN WATER RE-
SOURCES DEVELOPMENT &
MANAGEMENT PUBLIC COM-
PANY LIMITED**
s 1 East Water Building 23-26 Floors
Soi Vibhavadi Rangsit 5, Vibhavadi
Rangsit Road Chomphon Subdistrict
Chatuchak District, Bangkok, 10900,
Thailand
Tel.: (66) 22721600
Web Site: https://www.eastwater.com
Year Founded: 1992
EASTW—(THA)
Rev.: $127,064,552
Assets: $848,804,979
Liabilities: $509,058,768
Net Worth: $339,746,212
Earnings: $9,403,158
Emp.: 223
Fiscal Year-end: 12/31/23
Integrated Water Resources Manage-
ment Services
N.A.I.C.S.: 221310
Sombat Yusamart *(CFO & Sr Exec
VP)*

Subsidiaries:

Egcom Tara Co. Ltd.   (1)
No 332 Village No 2, Pongsawai Subdistrict
Mueang Ratchaburi District, Bangkok,
70000, Ratchaburi, Thailand   **(90.07%)**
Tel.: (66) 32327085
Web Site: https://www.egcomtara.com
Drinking Water Distr
N.A.I.C.S.: 221310

Global Water Group, Inc.   (1)
8601 Sovereign Row, Dallas, TX 75247
Tel.: (214) 678-9866
Web Site: http://www.globalwater.com
Water Purification, Wastewater Processing
& Wastewater Effluent Recycling Equipment
Mfr
N.A.I.C.S.: 333248
Alan M. Weiss *(Chm, Pres & CEO)*

Nakornsawan Water Supply Company Limited   (1)
1 Soi Vibhavadi Rangsit 5 Vibhavadi Rangsit Road Floor 23-25, Chatuchak, Bangkok,
10900, Thailand
Tel.: (66) 56256690
Drinking Water Distr
N.A.I.C.S.: 221310

Universal Utilities Public Company
Limited   (1)
No 1 East Water Building 18th Floor Soi
Vibhavadi Rangsit 5, Chomphon Subdistrict
Chatuchak District, Bangkok, 10900, Thai-
land
Tel.: (66) 22721688
Web Site: https://www.uu.co.th
Water Supply Management Services
N.A.I.C.S.: 221310

EASTFIELD RESOURCES LTD.
Suite 110 - 325 Howe Street, Van-
couver, V6C 1Z7, BC, Canada
Tel.: (604) 681-7913   Ca

Web Site:
    https://www.eastfieldresources.com
ETF—(OTCIQ)
Rev.: $24,948
Assets: $2,956,874
Liabilities: $391,346
Net Worth: $2,565,528
Earnings: ($501,125)
Emp.: 3
Fiscal Year-end: 02/28/22
Mineral Exploration Processes; Base
& Precious Metal Exploration
N.A.I.C.S.: 213114
William Morton *(Pres & CEO)*

EASTGATE BIOTECH CORP.
488 Champagne Dr, North York, M3J
2T9, ON, Canada
Tel.: (647) 692-0652   NV
Web Site:
    https://www.eastgatebiotech.com
Year Founded: 1999
Pharmaceutical Mfr & Distr
N.A.I.C.S.: 325412
Rose C. Perri *(CEO)*

Subsidiaries:

EastGate Pharmaceuticals, Inc.   (1)
488 Champagne Dr, North York, Toronto,
M3J 2T9, ON, Canada
Tel.: (647) 692-0652
Web Site:
    http://eastgatepharmaceuticals.com
Pharmaceuticals Mfr
N.A.I.C.S.: 325412
Ann Gluskin *(Chm & CEO)*

**EASTLAND INSURANCE COM-
PANY LIMITED**
13 Dilkusha C/A, Dhaka, 1000, Ban-
gladesh
Tel.: (880) 29564600
Web Site:
    https://www.eastlandinsurance.com
Year Founded: 1986
EASTLAND—(CHT)
Rev.: $2,048,111
Assets: $24,706,394
Liabilities: $8,492,957
Net Worth: $16,213,437
Earnings: $1,247,986
Emp.: 319
Fiscal Year-end: 12/31/22
General Insurance Services
N.A.I.C.S.: 524210
Mahbubur Rahman *(Chm)*

EASTMAN STAPLES LIMITED
131 Lockwood Road, Huddersfield,
HD1 3QW, West Yorkshire, United
Kingdom
Tel.: (44) 1484888888
Web Site: http://www.eastman.co.uk
Year Founded: 1886
Clothing Supplies Distr
N.A.I.C.S.: 459130
Andrew Kyprianou *(CEO)*

EASTNINE AB
Kungsgatan 33, PO Box 7214, Sver-
ige, 10388, Stockholm, Sweden
Tel.: (46) 850597700   SE
Web Site:
    http://www.eastcapitalexplorer.com
Year Founded: 2007
ECEX—(OMX)
Sales Range: Less than $1 Million
Emp.: 3
Equity Funds Investment Services
N.A.I.C.S.: 525910
Lars O. Gronsteddt *(Chm)*

Subsidiaries:

Alojas Biroji SIA   (1)
Kr Valdemara Street 62, Riga, LV-1013,
Latvia
Tel.: (371) 26689295
Web Site: http://www.alojasbiroji.lv

Real Estate Services
N.A.I.C.S.: 531390

**EASTON PHARMACEUTICALS,
INC.**
650 Bay St, Toronto, M5G 1M8, ON,
Canada
Tel.: (416) 619-0291
Web Site:
    http://www.eastonpharmainc.com
Sales Range: Less than $1 Million
Emp.: 7
Pharmaceuticals Mfr
N.A.I.C.S.: 025412

**EASTONE CENTURY TECH-
NOLOGY CO., LTD.**
Room 1201 Building 1 No 16 Keyun
Road, Tianhe District, Guangzhou,
510665, Guangdong, China
Tel.: (86) 2066235506
Web Site: http://www.etonetech.com
Year Founded: 2001
300310—(CHIN)
Rev.: $363,860,640
Assets: $418,377,960
Liabilities: $166,413,312
Net Worth: $251,964,648
Earnings: $2,774,304
Emp.: 3,700
Fiscal Year-end: 12/31/22
Telecommunications Equipment Mfr
N.A.I.C.S.: 334220
Zhong Feipeng *(Chm & Gen Mgr)*

EASTPACK LIMITED
678 Eastbank Road, Edgecumbe, Te
Puke, 3193, Bay of Plenty, New Zea-
land
Tel.: (64) 73048227   NZ
Web Site: http://www.eastpack.co.nz
Year Founded: 1983
Emp.: 2,500
Fresh Fruit Packer & Distr
N.A.I.C.S.: 424480
Matt Hill *(Gen Mgr-Grower Svcs &
EKO)*

Subsidiaries:

EastPack Avocado Company
Limited   (1)
Washer Road, Te Puke, 3119, Bay of
Plenty, New Zealand
Tel.: (64) 75733400
Avocado Farming Services
N.A.I.C.S.: 111339

EASTPHARMA LTD.
Clarendon House 2 Church Street,
Hamilton, HM 11, Bermuda
Tel.: (441) 212 692 9326
Web Site:
    http://www.eastpharmaltd.com
Year Founded: 2006
Rev.: $233,923,255
Assets: $368,784,048
Liabilities: $178,477,608
Net Worth: $190,306,440
Earnings: $34,162,306
Fiscal Year-end: 12/31/18
Pharmaceutical Products Mfr & Distr
N.A.I.C.S.: 325412
Philipp Daniel Haas *(Chm & CEO)*

Subsidiaries:

Deva Holding A.S.   (1)
Halkali Merkez Mah Basin Ekspres Cad No
1 Sicil No 70061, Kucukcekmece, 34303,
Istanbul, Turkiye
Tel.: (90) 2126929292
Web Site: https://www.deva.com.tr
Rev.: $383,714,227
Assets: $760,091,195
Liabilities: $259,444,781
Net Worth: $500,646,415
Earnings: $114,651,124
Emp.: 2,908
Fiscal Year-end: 12/31/2023

Holding Company; Pharmaceuticals
N.A.I.C.S.: 551112
Mesut Cetin (Deputy Chm & CFO)

Subsidiary (Non-US):

Deva Holdings (NZ) Ltd. (2)
Level 1 92 Spey Street, PO Box 1705, In-
vercargill, 9840, New Zealand
Tel.: (64) 3 2189933
Pharmaceuticals Product Mfr
N.A.I.C.S.: 325412

EASTROC BEVERAGE GROUP CO., LTD.
1F Building 3 No 142 Zhuguang
North Road, Taoyuan Subdistrict
Nanshan, Shenzhen, 518057, Guang-
dong, China
Tel.: (86) 75526980181
Web Site: http://www.szeastroc.com
Year Founded: 1994
605499—(SHG)
Rev.: $1,194,156,714
Assets: $1,666,498,621
Liabilities: $955,472,165
Net Worth: $711,026,456
Earnings: $202,249,092
Fiscal Year-end: 12/31/22
Drink Product Mfr & Distr
N.A.I.C.S.: 312111
Muqin Lin (Chm & Pres)

EASTSIBERIAN PLC
9 Esplanade, Saint Helier, JE2 3QA,
AB, Jersey
Tel.: (44) 7733 363 016 JE
Year Founded: 2008
Petroleum & Natural Gas Exploration
Services
N.A.I.C.S.: 213112
Graeme G. Phipps (Chm, Pres &
CEO-Interim)

EASTSIDE DODGE CHRYSLER JEEP LTD.
815-36th Street North-East, Calgary,
T2A4W3, AB, Canada
Tel.: (403) 273-4313
Web Site:
http://www.eastsidedodge.com
Year Founded: 1976
Rev.: $55,370,821
Emp.: 134
New & Used Car Dealers
N.A.I.C.S.: 441110
Darryl Ortt (CFO, COO & Principal)

EASTWAY PLYMOUTH CHRYS-LER LTD
2851 Eglinton Avenue East, Toronto,
M1J2E2, ON, Canada
Tel.: (416) 264-2501
Web Site:
http://www.eastwaychrysler.com
Rev.: $15,328,800
Emp.: 40
New & Used Car Dealers
N.A.I.C.S.: 441110
Syed Rizvi (Mgr-Leasing)

EASTWEST BIOSCIENCE, INC.
260 Okanagan East Ave, Penticton,
V2A 3J7, BC, Canada
Web Site:
https://www.eastwestbioscience.com
Year Founded: 2016
EAST—(TSXV)
Rev.: $827,393
Assets: $2,911,899
Liabilities: $2,964,296
Net Worth: ($52,397)
Earnings: ($1,273,437)
Fiscal Year-end: 07/31/21
Biotechnology Research & Develop-
ment Services
N.A.I.C.S.: 541714
Ciska Asriel (Co-Founder)

Subsidiaries:

Orchard Vale Naturals Inc. (1)
260 Okanagan Ave East, Penticton, V2A
3J7, BC, Canada
Web Site:
https://www.orchardvalenaturals.com
Health Product Mfr
N.A.I.C.S.: 339112

EASTWOOD BIO-MEDICAL CANADA INC.
1130-4871 Shell Road, Richmond,
V6X 3Z6, BC, Canada
Tel.: (604) 247-2100 BC
Web Site: https://www.eleotin.ca
Year Founded: 2010
EBM—(TSXV)
Rev.: $1,016,779
Assets: $457,269
Liabilities: $687,414
Net Worth: ($230,145)
Earnings: ($117,247)
Fiscal Year-end: 10/31/22
Medical Products
N.A.I.C.S.: 325411
Yunji Kim (Pres & CEO)

EASUN CAPITAL MARKETS LIMITED
7 Chittaranjan Avenue 3Rd Floor,
Bowbazar, Kolkata, 700072, West
Bengal, India
Tel.: (91) 3340145400
Web Site:
https://www.easuncapital.com
Year Founded: 1982
542906—(BOM)
Rev.: $183,620
Assets: $2,618,520
Liabilities: $7,644
Net Worth: $2,610,876
Earnings: $115,602
Emp.: 3
Fiscal Year-end: 03/31/21
Investment Management Service
N.A.I.C.S.: 523940

EASUN REYROLLE LTD
6th Floor Temple Tower 672 Anna
Salai Nandanam, Chennai, 600035,
India
Tel.: (91) 4424346425
Web Site:
https://www.easunreyrolle.com
EASUNREYRL—(NSE)
Sales Range: $10-24.9 Million
Emp.: 367
Electric Power Generation & Distribu-
tion Services
N.A.I.C.S.: 221118
Raj H. Eswaran (Mng Dir)

Subsidiaries:

ERL Phase Power Technologies
Ltd. (1)
74 Scurfield Blvd, Winnipeg, R3Y 1G4, MB,
Canada
Tel.: (204) 477-0591
Web Site: http://www.erlphase.com
Electric Equipment Mfr
N.A.I.C.S.: 335999
Anderson Oliveira (Engr-Field Applications)

EASY CLICK WORLDWIDE NETWORK TECHNOLOGY CO., LTD.
Room 903 Building C3 Phase II Soft-
ware New Town R & D Base, No 156
Tiangu 8th Road High-tech Zone,
Xi'an, 710077, Shaanxi, China
Tel.: (86) 2985221569
Web Site:
https://www.eclicktech.com.cn
Year Founded: 2005
301171—(CHIN)
Rev.: $301,876,098
Assets: $657,918,294

Liabilities: $178,566,873
Net Worth: $479,351,421
Earnings: $30,569,155
Fiscal Year-end: 12/31/23
Digital Marketing Services
N.A.I.C.S.: 541810
Peter Zou (Founder)

EASY DATE HOLDINGS LTD
23 Manor Place, Edinburgh, EH3
7DX, United Kingdom
Tel.: (44) 1312264890
Year Founded: 2002
Rev.: $15,467,131
Emp.: 140
Online Dating Services
N.A.I.C.S.: 812990
Max Polyakov (COO)

EASY FINCORP LIMITED
Duncan House 4th Floor 31 Netaji
Subhas Road, Kolkata, 700 001,
West Bengal, India
Tel.: (91) 3366251000
Web Site:
https://www.easyfincorp.com
Year Founded: 1984
511074—(BOM)
Rev.: $14,988
Assets: $1,242,123
Liabilities: $872,003
Net Worth: $370,120
Earnings: ($3,044)
Emp.: 3
Fiscal Year-end: 03/31/21
Financial Services
N.A.I.C.S.: 523999
Giriraj Ratan Kothari (Compliance
Officer & Sec)

EASY HOLDINGS CO., LTD.
3rd floor 310 Gangnam-daero,
Gangnam-gu, Seoul, 06253, Korea
(South)
Tel.: (82) 25019988
Web Site:
https://www.easyholdings.co.kr
Year Founded: 1988
035810—(KRS)
Rev.: $2,308,865,776
Assets: $2,037,375,535
Liabilities: $1,256,658,876
Net Worth: $780,716,659
Earnings: $20,645,470
Emp.: 130
Fiscal Year-end: 12/31/22
Feed Additive Mfr
N.A.I.C.S.: 311119
Kim Duck-Young (Dir)

Subsidiaries:

EASY BIO Philippines, Inc. (1)
Unit 1708-E Philippine Stock Exchange
Center Exchange Road, Ortigas Center,
Pasig, 1605, Philippines
Tel.: (63) 286874583
Web Site: https://www.easybiophils.ph
Animal Food Distr
N.A.I.C.S.: 423820

EASY ONE FINANCIAL GROUP LTD.
Suite 3202 32/F Skyline Tower 39
Wang Kwong Road, Kowloon Bay,
Kowloon, China (Hong Kong)
Tel.: (852) 2312 8202
Web Site: http://www.easyonefg.com
Rev.: $14,560,795
Assets: $190,084,938
Liabilities: $50,335,693
Net Worth: $139,749,245
Earnings: $5,324,007
Emp.: 70
Fiscal Year-end: 03/31/20
Investment Holding Company
N.A.I.C.S.: 523999

Thomas Chun Hong Chan (Chm &
Mng Dir)

EASY SMART GROUP HOLD-INGS LIMITED
Unit A 10/F Ming Tak Centre 135-137
Tung Chau Street, Kowloon, China
(Hong Kong)
Tel.: (852) 29428918 Ky
Web Site:
https://www.easysmart.com.hk
Year Founded: 2021
2442—(HKG)
Holding Company
N.A.I.C.S.: 551112

EASY SOFTWARE AG
Am Hauptbahnhof 4, 45468, Mulheim
an der Ruhr, Germany
Tel.: (49) 20 845 0160 De
Web Site: http://www.easy-
software.com
ESY—(DEU)
Rev.: $60,479,766
Assets: $56,432,715
Liabilities: $24,971,347
Net Worth: $31,461,368
Earnings: ($3,536,103)
Emp.: 364
Fiscal Year-end: 12/31/20
Hardware & Software Development &
Distr
N.A.I.C.S.: 513210
Stefan Ten Doornkaat (Chm-
Supervisory Bd)

Subsidiaries:

CFT Consulting GmbH (1)
Edisonstrasse 22a, 86399, Bobingen,
Germany (60%)
Tel.: (49) 8234 9669 0
Web Site: http://www.cft.de
Sales Range: $10-24.9 Million
Document & Content Management Custom
Software Developer
N.A.I.C.S.: 541511

Easy Apiomat GmbH (1)
Reichsstrasse 2, 04109, Leipzig, Germany
Tel.: (49) 34126422235
Information Technology Services
N.A.I.C.S.: 513210
Fabian Benusch (Head-Customer Success
Mgmt)

Easy International Consulting
GmbH (1)
Essener Strasse 2-24, 46047, Oberhausen,
Germany
Tel.: (49) 208450160
Web Site: http://www.easy-international-
consulting.de
Software Consulting Services
N.A.I.C.S.: 541512

Easy Software (Asia Pacific) Pte.
Ltd. (1)
4 Battery Road Bank of China Building 25-
01, Singapore, 049908, Singapore
Tel.: (65) 16103508677
Information Technology Services
N.A.I.C.S.: 513210

Easy Software (UK) PLC (1)
Reflection House The Anderson Ctr Olding
Rd Bury St, Bury Saint Edmunds, IP33 3TA,
Suffolk, United Kingdom
Tel.: (44) 1284727870
Web Site: http://www.easysoftware.co.uk
Sales Range: $25-49.9 Million
Emp.: 10
Software Development Services
N.A.I.C.S.: 541511
Howard Frear (Dir-Sls & Mktg)

Easy Software Deutschland
GmbH (1)
Edisonstrasse 22a, 86399, Bobingen, Ger-
many
Tel.: (49) 208450160
Information Technology Services
N.A.I.C.S.: 513210

Easy Software AG—(Continued)

Subsidiary (Domestic):

friendWorks GmbH (2)
Theresienplatz 17, 94315, Straubing, Germany
Tel.: (49) 94217550400
Web Site: http://www.friendworks.de
Information Services
N.A.I.C.S.: 513210

Easy Software GmbH (1)
Sebastian-Kneipp-Strasse 12, 5020, Salzburg, Austria
Tel.: (43) 662461546
Web Site: http://www.easy-austria.at
Sales Range: $25-49.9 Million
Emp.: 5
Documentation Software Development Services
N.A.I.C.S.: 541511
Christian Maerzendorfer (Mng Dir)

Easy Software Inc. (1)
102 Pickering Way Ste 503, Exton, PA 19341
Tel.: (610) 240-9260
Software Development Services
N.A.I.C.S.: 541511
Michael W. Rennell (Pres)

Easy Software Turkiye Ltd. Stl. (1)
Altaycesme Mah Zuhal Sok No 22 Niyazibey Business Center K 5 D 10, Maltepe, Istanbul, Turkiye
Tel.: (90) 2165377450
Web Site: http://www.easysoftware.com.tr
Information Technology Services
N.A.I.C.S.: 513210
Yunus Emre Yildiz (Founder & Mgr-Bus Dev)

EASY TECHNOLOGIES INC.
702- 595 Howe Street, Vancouver, V6C2T5, BC, Canada
Tel.: (778) 370-1372   BC
Year Founded: 2009
EZM—(OTCBB)
Sales Range: Less than $1 Million
Medical Information Technology Services
N.A.I.C.S.: 541519
Peter Wilson (CEO)

Subsidiaries:

EasyMed Technologies, Inc. (1)
1250 West Hastings Street Suite 1100, Vancouver, V6E 2M4, BC, Canada
Tel.: (416) 662-3971
Medical Information Technology Services
N.A.I.C.S.: 541519

EasyMedMobile India Private Ltd. (1)
7B KG 360 IT Business Park Plot No 41 232/1, dr MGR Salai Perungudi, Chennai, 600-096, India
Tel.: (91) 44 435 93 486
Medical Information Technology Services
N.A.I.C.S.: 541519

EASY TRIP PLANNERS LIMITED
Building No 223 Patparganj Industrial Area, New Delhi, 110092, India
Tel.: (91) 1143131313
Web Site:
    https://www.easemytrip.com
Year Founded: 2008
543272—(BOM)
Rev.: $20,578,058
Assets: $54,283,866
Liabilities: $32,080,230
Net Worth: $22,203,636
Earnings: $8,327,865
Emp.: 374
Fiscal Year-end: 03/31/21
Travel Agency Services
N.A.I.C.S.: 561510
Nishant Pitti (CEO)

Subsidiaries:

EaseMyTrip Thai Co., Ltd. (1)

ITF - Silom Palace Building - 23rd Floor 160/537-538 Si Lom Rd, Suriya Wong Bang Rak, Bangkok, 10500, Thailand
Tel.: (66) 20239932
Web Site: https://www.easemytrip.co.th
Tour & Travel Services
N.A.I.C.S.: 561599

EaseMyTrip Tours LLC (1)
1103 Fortune Tower Cluster C Jumeirah Lake Towers, PO Box 119200, Dubai, United Arab Emirates
Tel.: (971) 43973194
Web Site: https://www.easemytrip.com
Travel Agency Services
N.A.I.C.S.: 561510

Nutana Aviation Capital IFSC Private Limited (1)
Unit No 204 Signature Building Second Floor Block 13B Zone-1 Gift Sez, Gift City, Gandhinagar, 382355, Gujarat, India
Tel.: (91) 9167381787
Web Site: https://nutana.aero
Asset Financing & Leasing Services
N.A.I.C.S.: 522220

Spree Hotels and Real Estate Private Limited (1)
No 3615/A 6th Cross 13th G Main HAL 2nd Stage, Bengaluru, 560008, India
Tel.: (91) 8880158158
Web Site: https://www.spreehotels.com
Home Management Services
N.A.I.C.S.: 721110

YoloBus Private Limited (1)
Supreme Work Coworking Eros City Square Cabin No 10 2nd Floor, Sector 49, Gurugram, 122001, Haryana, India
Tel.: (91) 8035240274
Web Site: https://www.yolobus.in
Bus Repair & Maintenance Services
N.A.I.C.S.: 541330

EASY VISIBLE SUPPLY CHAIN MANAGEMENT CO., LTD.
10F Jiutian Building No 688 QianWei West Road, Xishan District, Kunming, 650228, Yunnan, China
Tel.: (86) 871 6573 9748
600093—(SHG)
Rev.: $1,488,740,038
Assets: $1,492,389,500
Liabilities: $2,025,109,863
Net Worth: ($532,720,363)
Earnings: ($1,765,608,893)
Fiscal Year-end: 12/31/20
Business Services
N.A.I.C.S.: 561499
Tianhui Leng (Chm)

EASYACCESS FINANCIAL SERVICES LIMITED
Access House No 24 Judge Jambulingam Road, Mylapore, Chennai, 600 004, India
Tel.: (91) 4449229800
Web Site:
    http://www.easyaccess.co.in
Sales Range: $25-49.9 Million
Emp.: 15
Financial Management Consulting Services
N.A.I.C.S.: 541611
K. Muthukumaran (Mng Dir)

EASYCALL COMMUNICA-TIONS PHILIPPINES, INC.
Four/NEO Building 4th Avenue corner 30th Street Bonifacio Global City, Taguig, 1634, Philippines
Tel.: (63) 288308888
Web Site:
    https://www.easycall.com.ph
Year Founded: 1989
ECP—(PHI)
Rev.: $7,376,616
Assets: $10,751,032
Liabilities: $5,612,831
Net Worth: $5,138,201
Earnings: $226,521

Fiscal Year-end: 12/31/23
Internet Services
N.A.I.C.S.: 513140
Renato Vicente R. Martinez (Officer-IR & Exec VP)

EASYFILL AB
Industrigatan 10, Bracke, 843 31, Ostersund, Sweden
Tel.: (46) 693661300
Web Site: https://www.easyfill.se
Bottled Product Mfr
N.A.I.C.S.: 312112
Hakan Sjoelander (CEO)

EASYHOME NEW RETAIL GROUP CO., LTD.
No 9 Zhongnan Road, Wuchang District, Wuhan, 100007, Hubei, China
Tel.: (86) 2787362507
Web Site:
    http://www.zhongshang.com.cn
Year Founded: 1990
000785—(SSE)
Rev.: $1,822,473,432
Assets: $7,495,713,108
Liabilities: $4,578,275,520
Net Worth: $2,917,437,588
Earnings: $231,426,936
Fiscal Year-end: 12/31/22
Departmental Store Operator
N.A.I.C.S.: 455110
Linpeng Wang (Chm & CEO)

EASYHOTEL PLC
3rd Floor 52 Grosvenor Gardens, London, SW1W 0AU, United Kingdom
Tel.: (44) 2031503183   UK
Web Site: http://www.easyhotel.com
Year Founded: 2004
Rev.: $14,281,389
Assets: $182,061,420
Liabilities: $30,233,943
Net Worth: $151,827,477
Earnings: $820,427
Emp.: 54
Fiscal Year-end: 09/30/18
Hotel Operator
N.A.I.C.S.: 721110
Harm Meijer (Chm)

Subsidiaries:

easyHotel France SAS (1)
38 Rue Barberis, 06300, Nice, France
Tel.: (33) 492002121
Hotel Operator
N.A.I.C.S.: 721110

easyHotel Spain S.L.U. (1)
Avinguda de la Granvia 22, 08902, Barcelona, Spain
Tel.: (34) 931990711
Hotel Operator
N.A.I.C.S.: 721110

EASYIO ENGINEERING PTE LTD.
32-3 Jalan Puteri 2/4, Bandar Puteri, 47100, Puchong, Selangor, Malaysia
Tel.: (60) 3 8063 7571
Web Site: http://www.easyio.eu
Year Founded: 2005
Building Energy Management Systems Services
N.A.I.C.S.: 513210

Subsidiaries:

Hantong Metal Component (Penang) Sdn. Bhd. (1)
Lot 83 & 84 Jalan 1/8 PKNK Kawasan Perindustrian, 08000, Sungai Petani, Kedah, Malaysia
Tel.: (60) 44411333
Metal Stamping Mfr
N.A.I.C.S.: 332119

EASYJET PLC

Hangar 89 London Luton Airport, Luton, LU2 9PF, Bedfordshire, United Kingdom
Tel.: (44) 1582525252   UK
Web Site: http://www.easyjet.com
Year Founded: 2000
EZJ—(LSE)
Rev.: $10,402,254,970
Assets: $12,528,281,870
Liabilities: $8,980,235,780
Net Worth: $3,548,046,090
Earnings: $412,474,680
Fiscal Year-end: 09/30/23
Holding Company; Airline Operator
N.A.I.C.S.: 551112
Andrew Findlay (CFO & Member-Mgmt Bd)

Subsidiaries:

easyJet Airline Company Limited (1)
Hangar 89 London Luton Airport, Luton, LU2 9PF, Bedfordshire, United Kingdom   (100%)
Tel.: (44) 8712442366
Web Site: https://www.easyjet.com
Airline Operator
N.A.I.C.S.: 481111
Andrew Findlay (CFO)

EASYKNIT INTERNATIONAL HOLDINGS LTD.
Block A 7th Floor Hong Kong Spinners Building Phase 6, 481-483 Castle Peak Road Cheung Sha Wan, Kowloon, China (Hong Kong)
Tel.: (852) 27456338
Web Site: http://www.easyknit.com
1218—(HKG)
Rev.: $41,709,810
Assets: $632,467,102
Liabilities: $215,804,306
Net Worth: $416,662,796
Earnings: $2,828,402
Emp.: 27
Fiscal Year-end: 03/31/21
Cotton-Based Knit Garments Mfr
N.A.I.C.S.: 315250
Ricky Wing Chiu Tse (VP)

Subsidiaries:

Constance Capital Limited (1)
18/F No 168 Queen's Road, Central, China (Hong Kong)
Tel.: (852) 3 615 8398
Web Site: https://www.constancecap.com
Private Equity & Investment Services
N.A.I.C.S.: 523940

Easyknit Global Company Limited (1)
Block A 7 F Phase 6 Hong Kong Spinners Bldg, 481-483 Castle Peak Rd, Cheung Sha Wan, Kowloon, China (Hong Kong)
Tel.: (852) 29906822
Clothing Merchant Whslr
N.A.I.C.S.: 424350

Easyknit Properties Management Limited (1)
Block A 7 F Phase 6 Hong Kong Spinners Bldg 481-483 Castle Peak Rd, Cheung Sha Wan, Kowloon, China (Hong Kong)
Tel.: (852) 27456338
Web Site: http://www.easyknit.com
Property Management Services
N.A.I.C.S.: 531311
Sunny Chan (Mgr-Property)

Eminence Enterprise Limited (1)
Block A 7th Floor Hong Kong Spinners Building Phase 6, 481-483 Castle Peak Road Cheung Sha Wan, Kowloon, China (Hong Kong)
Tel.: (852) 27456338
Web Site:
    http://www.eminence-enterprise.com
Rev.: $10,360,376
Assets: $591,070,331
Liabilities: $213,304,933
Net Worth: $377,765,398
Earnings: ($26,477,115)
Emp.: 55
Fiscal Year-end: 03/31/2020

Holding Company; Garment Sourcing &
Exporting
N.A.I.C.S.: 551112
Jimmy Cheung Tim Kwong (Exec Dir)

Mary Mac Apparel Inc. (1)
1412 Broadway Ste 1705, New York, NY
10018
Tel.: (212) 840-9191
Apparel Retailer
N.A.I.C.S.: 458110

EASYWELL BIOMEDICALS, INC.
No 10 Yanfa 2nd Rd Hsinchu Science Park, Hsinchu, Taiwan
Tel.: (886) 36669596
Web Site:
https://www.easywellbio.com
1799—(TPE)
Rev.: $5,593,503
Assets: $36,680,549
Liabilities: $12,587,781
Net Worth: $24,092,768
Earnings: ($5,265,110)
Fiscal Year-end: 12/31/22
Pharmaceuticals Product Mfr
N.A.I.C.S.: 325412
Han-Fei Lin (Chm)

EAT & BEYOND GLOBAL HOLDINGS INC.
1570 505 Burrard Street, Vancouver,
V7X 1M5, BC, Canada
Tel.: (604) 416-4099   BC
Web Site:
https://www.eatandbeyond.com
Year Founded: 2019
EATBF—(OTCQB)
Holding Company
N.A.I.C.S.: 551112
Don Robinson (Chm)

EAT WELL INVESTMENT GROUP INC.
1305-1090 W Georgia Street, Vancouver, V6E 3V7, BC, Canada
Tel.: (604) 685-9316
Web Site:
https://www.eatwellgroup.com
Year Founded: 2007
EWG—(CNSX)
Rev.: $23,726,405
Assets: $61,907,881
Liabilities: $42,964,824
Net Worth: $18,943,057
Earnings: $9,167,195
Fiscal Year-end: 12/31/22
Investment Services
N.A.I.C.S.: 523999
Nick DeMare (CFO & Sec)

Subsidiaries:

Minera Cuoro S.A.S. (1)
Cl 7 S 42-70 Int 22, Antioquia, Colombia
Tel.: (57) 4 3131787
Mineral Mining Services
N.A.I.C.S.: 212390

EAT&HOLDINGS CO.,LTD
15th floor Shinagawa Seaside East
Tower 4-12-8 Higashishinagawa,
Shinagawa-ku, Tokyo, 140-0002, Japan
Tel.: (81) 357695050
Web Site: https://www.eat-and.jp
Year Founded: 1977
2882—(TKS)
Rev.: $254,686,980
Assets: $181,482,730
Liabilities: $109,327,800
Net Worth: $72,154,930
Earnings: ($751,540)
Emp.: 1,745
Fiscal Year-end: 02/29/24
Restaurant Owner & Operator; Frozen Food Mfr & Marketer
N.A.I.C.S.: 722511

Subsidiaries:

9-block Co., Ltd. (1)
6th floor of Nunogame Building 1-9-18 Utsubohonmachi, Nishi-ku, Osaka, 550-0004, Japan
Tel.: (81) 664482620
Web Site: http://www.9-block.jp
Ecommerce Services
N.A.I.C.S.: 339999

EATGOOD SWEDEN AB
Kallbacksrydsgatan 6, 507 42, Boras, Sweden
Tel.: (46) 33101180
Web Site: https://www.eatgood.se
Year Founded: 2010
Lightfry Oven Product Mfr
N.A.I.C.S.: 333994
Bettina Klinger (Mgr-Sls-Europe)

EATMORE SPROUTS AND GREENS LTD.
2604 Grieve Rd, Courtenay, V9J
1S7, BC, Canada
Tel.: (250) 338-4860
Web Site:
http://www.eatmoresprouts.com
Rev.: $21,368,354
Emp.: 35
Organic Farm Products Mfr
N.A.I.C.S.: 111199
Glenn Wakeling (Co-Owner)

EATON CORPORATION PLC
Eaton House 30 Pembroke Road,
Dublin, D04 Y0C2, Ireland
Tel.: (353) 16372900   IE
Web Site: https://www.eaton.com
Year Founded: 1911
ETN—(NYSE)
Rev.: $23,196,000,000
Assets: $38,432,000,000
Liabilities: $19,363,000,000
Net Worth: $19,069,000,000
Earnings: $3,218,000,000
Emp.: 94,000
Fiscal Year-end: 12/31/23
Electric Equipment Mfr
N.A.I.C.S.: 551112
Ernest W. Marshall Jr. (Chief HR Officer & Exec VP)

Subsidiaries:

Eaton Corporation (1)
1000 Eaton Blvd, Cleveland, OH 44122
Tel.: (216) 523-5000
Web Site: http://www.eaton.com
Emp.: 73,000
Holding Company; Electrical Power, Aerospace, Hydraulic & Motor Vehicle Systems Mfr
N.A.I.C.S.: 551112
Ernest W. Marshall Jr. (Chief HR Officer & Exec VP)

Subsidiary (Non-US):

Aeroquip Iberica S.L. (2)
Avda Complutense 109, 28805, Alcala de Henares, Spain
Tel.: (34) 918770555
Electrical Apparatus & Equipment Whslr
N.A.I.C.S.: 423610

Bussmann do Brasil Ltda. (2)
Rodovia Santos Dumont km 23, Caixa Postal 095, Itu, 13300-000, Sao Paulo, Brazil
Tel.: (55) 1140248400
Web Site: http://www.cooperindustries.com
Electrical Equipment Distr
N.A.I.C.S.: 423440

CTI-VIENNA Gesellschaft zur Prufung elektrotechnischer Industrieprodukte GmbH (2)
Einzingergasse 4, 1210, Vienna, Austria
Tel.: (43) 12716400
Web Site: http://www.cti-vienna.at
Testing Laboratory Services
N.A.I.C.S.: 621511

Jurgen Wolf (Dir & Mgr)

Centralion Industrial Inc. (2)
No 93 Shin Hu 3rd Rd, Neihu, Taipei, 114, Taiwan
Tel.: (886) 266006688
Web Site: http://www.centralion.com
Electrical Equipment Manufacturers
N.A.I.C.S.: 335999

Cobham Mission Systems Wimborne Limited (2)
Brook Road, Wimborne Minster, BH21 2BJ, Dorset, United Kingdom
Tel.: (44) 1202882121
Sales Range: $100-124.9 Million
Emp.: 500
Military Aircraft Refueling, Life Support & Weapons Carriage Systems Developer & Mfr
N.A.I.C.S.: 336413

Subsidiary (US):

Carleton Life Support Systems Inc. (3)
2734 Hickory Grove Rd, Davenport, IA 52804-1203
Tel.: (563) 383-6000
Web Site: http://www.cobham.com
Sales Range: $75-99.9 Million
Emp.: 700
Oxygen Systems for Aviation Applications
N.A.I.C.S.: 333248
Rob Baugous (Dir-Human Resources)

Carleton Technologies Inc. (3)
10 Cobham Dr, Orchard Park, NY
14127-4121   (100%)
Tel.: (716) 662-0006
Sales Range: $100-124.9 Million
Emp.: 300
Aerospace Systems Design & Mfr
N.A.I.C.S.: 336413

Subsidiary (Non-US):

Cooper (China) Co., Ltd. (2)
955 Shengli Road, East Area of Zhangjiang High-Tech Park, Shanghai, 201201, China
Tel.: (86) 2128993888
Web Site: http://www.cooperchina.com
Electric Equipment Mfr
N.A.I.C.S.: 334515

Cooper (Ningbo) Electric Co., Ltd. (2)
Hangzhou Bay New Area Binhai 2 439, Ningbo, 315336, Zhejiang, China
Tel.: (86) 57463716999
Web Site: http://www.coopernature.com
Electrical Equipment Distr
N.A.I.C.S.: 423440

Cooper Bussmann (U.K.) Limited (2)
Melton Road Burton on the Wolds, Leicester, LE12 5TH, United Kingdom
Tel.: (44) 1509882737
Electrical Equipment Whslr
N.A.I.C.S.: 423610

Cooper Capri S.A.S. (2)
30-40 Rue des Fontenils, Loir-et-Cher, 41600, France
Tel.: (33) 254834900
Web Site: http://www.cooper-safety.com
Electrical Component Mfr
N.A.I.C.S.: 335313

Cooper Controls Limited (2)
Tel.: (44) 1633 838 088
Web Site:
http://www.eatonlightingsystems.com
Sales Range: $25-49.9 Million
Emp.: 50
Electrical Apparatus & Equipment Whslr
N.A.I.C.S.: 423610

Division (Non-US):

Cooper Controls Ltd. - North America (3)
Tel.: (770) 486-4782
Web Site: http://www.coopercontrol.com
Sales Range: $25-49.9 Million
Emp.: 75
Lighting Controls Mfr & Whslr
N.A.I.C.S.: 423610

Subsidiary (Non-US):

Cooper Csa Srl (2)

Via Antonio Meucci 10, 20094, Corsico, Italy
Tel.: (39) 024587911
Web Site: http://www.coopercsa.it
Electrical Equipment Whslr
N.A.I.C.S.: 423610

Cooper Electrical Australia Pty. Limited (2)
59 Kirby Street Sydney, Rydalmere, 2116, NSW, Australia
Tel.: (61) 287872777
Web Site:
http://www.cooperelectrical.com.au
Electrical Equipment Whslr
N.A.I.C.S.: 423610

Subsidiary (Domestic):

Cooper Enterprises LLC (2)
89 Curtis Dr, Shelby, OH 44875
Tel.: (419) 347-5232
Web Site: https://cooperenterprises.com
N.A.I.C.S.: 321999
Jerry Truex (Mgr-Sales & Marketing)

Subsidiary (Non-US):

Cooper Industries Holdings GmbH (2)
Senator-Schwartz-Ring 26, Soest, 59494, Germany
Tel.: (49) 2921690
Electrical Equipment Whslr
N.A.I.C.S.: 423610

Cooper Industries Japan K.K. (2)
7th Floor Ichigo Nogizaka Building 8-11-37 Akasaka, Minato-ku, Tokyo, 107-0052, Japan
Tel.: (81) 364347890
Web Site: https://www.cooperindustries.jp
N.A.I.C.S.: 335311

Cooper Industries Russia LLC (2)
10/2 Letnikovskaya St, 115114, Moscow, Russia
Tel.: (7) 4955102427
Web Site: http://www.cooper-russia.ru
Electrical Equipment Whslr
N.A.I.C.S.: 423610

Subsidiary (Domestic):

Cooper Industries, LLC (2)
600 Travis St Ste 5600, Houston, TX
77002-1001
Tel.: (713) 209-8400
Web Site: http://www.cooperindustries.com
Holding Company; Corporate Office
N.A.I.C.S.: 551112

Subsidiary (Domestic):

Cooper B-Line, Inc. (3)
509 W Monroe St, Highland, IL 62249
Tel.: (618) 654-2184
Web Site: http://www.cooperbline.com
Engineered Industrial Subsystem Applications & Enclosure Products Mfr
N.A.I.C.S.: 335999

Cooper Crouse-Hinds, LLC (3)
1201 Wolf St, Syracuse, NY 13208
Tel.: (315) 477-7000
Web Site: http://www.crouse-hinds.com
Damage-Resistant Electrical Components Mfr & Distr
N.A.I.C.S.: 335999

Subsidiary (Non-US):

Cooper Crouse-Hinds GmbH (4)
Senator-Schwartz-Ring 26, 59494, Soest, Germany
Tel.: (49) 2921690
Web Site: http://www.coopercrouse-hinds.eu
Emp.: 100
Damage-Resistant Electrical Components Mfr & Distr
N.A.I.C.S.: 335999
Matthias Stelzer (Gen Mgr)

Unit (Domestic):

Cooper Crouse-Hinds ICI (4)
3413 N Sam Houston Pkwy W Ste 210, Houston, TX 77086
Tel.: (281) 571-8065
Web Site: http://www.cooperindustries.com
Emp.: 150

Eaton Corporation plc—(Continued)

Industrial Control Mfr
N.A.I.C.S.: 334513

Subsidiary (Non-US):

Cooper Crouse-Hinds Japan KK (4)
Unizo Nogizaka Bldg 7th Floor 8 11 37 Aka-saka, Minato-ku, Tokyo, 107-0052, Japan
Tel.: (81) 364303128
Web Site: http://www.mtl-inst.com
Emp.: 20
Process Control, Safety & Surge Protection Products Whslr
N.A.I.C.S.: 423830

Cooper Crouse-Hinds Pte. Ltd. (4)
2 Serangoon N Ave 5 06-01, Singapore, 554911, Singapore
Tel.: (65) 6566459888
Electrical Apparatus & Equipment Whslr
N.A.I.C.S.: 423610

Cooper Crouse-Hinds, S. de R.L. de C.V. (4)
Av Javierr Rojo Gomez No 1170, Col Guadalupe Del Moral Delg Ixtapalapa, Mexico, 9300, Mexico
Tel.: (52) 555 804 4000
Web Site: http://www.crouse-hindslatam.com
Sales Range: $300-349.9 Million
Emp.: 600
Electrical Apparatus & Equipment Whslr
N.A.I.C.S.: 423610

The MTL Instruments Group Ltd. (4)
Great Marlings, Butterfield, Luton, LU2 8DL, Beds, United Kingdom
Tel.: (44) 1582723633
Emp.: 800
Holding Company; Process Control, Safety & Surge Protection Products Mfr
N.A.I.C.S.: 551112

Subsidiary (US):

Cooper Crouse-Hinds MTL, Inc. (5)
4300 Fortune Pl Ste A, Melbourne, FL 32904
Tel.: (321) 725-8000
Web Site: http://www.mtl-inst.com
Electrical Equipment & Component Mfr
N.A.I.C.S.: 335999

Subsidiary (Non-US):

Cooper Electric (Shanghai) Co. Ltd. (5)
No 955 Shengli Road East Area of Zhangjiang High-Tech Park, Zhangjiang High-Tech Park, Shanghai, 201201, China
Tel.: (86) 2128993600
System Infrastructure & Protection Equipment Distr
N.A.I.C.S.: 423610

MTL Instruments BV (5)
Terheijdenseweg 465, Breda, 4825 BK, Netherlands
Tel.: (31) 76 750 5360
Web Site: http://www.mtl-inst.com
Electrical Apparatus & Equipment Whslr
N.A.I.C.S.: 423610

MTL Instruments GmbH (5)
Heinrich-Hertz-Strasse 12, 50170, Kerpen, Germany
Tel.: (49) 227398120
Web Site: http://www.mtl.de
Emp.: 1,500
Process Control, Safety & Surge Protection Products Mfr & Whslr
N.A.I.C.S.: 423830

Subsidiary (Domestic):

GECMA Components Electronic GmbH (6)
Heinrich-Hertz-Strasse 12, 50170, Kerpen, Germany
Tel.: (49) 2273 9812 0
Web Site: http://www.gecma.com
Emp.: 40
Industrial Remote Computer Terminal & Peripheral Equipment Developer, Mfr & Whslr
N.A.I.C.S.: 334118

Subsidiary (Non-US):

MTL Instruments Pty. Limited (5)

10 Kent Road, Mascot, 2020, NSW, Australia
Tel.: (61) 1300 308 374
Web Site: http://www.mtl-inst.com
Process Control, Safety & Surge Protection Products Whslr
N.A.I.C.S.: 423830

MTL Instruments Pvt. Limited (5)
No 36 Nehru Street Off Old Mahabalipuram Road, Sholinganallur, Chennai, 600 119, India
Tel.: (91) 444450150
Emp.: 200
Electrical Apparatus & Equipment Whslr
N.A.I.C.S.: 423610

MTL Instruments Sarl (5)
7 rue des Rosieristes, 69410, Champagne-au-Mont-d'Or, France
Tel.: (33) 437461653
Emp.: 8
Process Control, Safety & Surge Protection Products Whslr
N.A.I.C.S.: 423830

Subsidiary (Domestic):

Measurement Technology Limited (5)
Great Marlings, Butterfield, Luton, LU2 8DL, Bedfordshire, United Kingdom
Tel.: (44) 1582723633
Sales Range: $50-74.9 Million
Emp.: 320
Electrical Apparatus & Equipment Whslr
N.A.I.C.S.: 423610

Subsidiary (Domestic):

Cooper Finance USA, Inc. (3)
600 Travis St Ste 5600, Houston, TX 77002-2909
Tel.: (713) 209-8400
Web Site: http://www.cooperus.com
Institutional Electric Lighting Fixture Mfr
N.A.I.C.S.: 335132

Cooper Power Systems, LLC (3)
2300 Badger Dr, Waukesha, WI 53188
Tel.: (262) 896-2400
Web Site: http://www.cooperindustries.com
Electrical Apparatus & Equipment Whslr
N.A.I.C.S.: 423610

Subsidiary (Domestic):

Cooper Power Systems Transportation Company (4)
2300 Badger Dr, Waukesha, WI 53188-5931
Tel.: (262) 896-2373
Web Site: http://www.cooperpower.com
Emp.: 100
Power Systems Freight Transportation Services
N.A.I.C.S.: 484122

Subsidiary (Non-US):

Cooper Power Systems do Brasil Ltda. (4)
Rua Placido Vieira 79, Porto Feliz, Sao Paulo, 04754-080, Brazil (100%)
Tel.: (55) 1156430700
Web Site: http://www.cooperindustries.com
Emp.: 60
Electrical Apparatus & Equipment Whslr
N.A.I.C.S.: 423610

Plant (Domestic):

Cooper Power Systems, LLC - Fayetteville Plant (4)
3660 S School Ave, Fayetteville, AR 72701
Tel.: (479) 521-3700
Web Site: http://www.cooperpower.com
Electrical Tools & Connectors Mfr
N.A.I.C.S.: 335999

Cooper Power Systems, LLC - Minneapolis Plant (4)
505 Hwy 169 N 1200, Minneapolis, MN 55441
Tel.: (763) 595-7777
Web Site: http://www.cooperpower.com
Emp.: 150
Electrical Advanced Metering Infrastructure, Capacitor Control, Voltage Control & Visual Asset Monitoring Equipment Mfr & Whslr

N.A.I.C.S.: 335314

Cooper Power Systems, LLC - Nacogdoches Plant (4)
2315 SE Stallings Dr, Nacogdoches, TX 75961
Tel.: (936) 569-9422
Web Site: http://www.cooperpower.com
Emp.: 120
Electrical Transformer Mfr
N.A.I.C.S.: 334416

Cooper Power Systems, LLC - Olean Plant (4)
1648 Dugan Rd, Olean, NY 14760-9527
Tel.: (716) 375-7100
Web Site: http://www.cooperpowersystems.com
Emp.: 200
Surge Arresters & Current-Limiting Fuse Mfr
N.A.I.C.S.: 335999

Cooper Power Systems, LLC - Pewaukee Plant (4)
1045 Hickory St, Pewaukee, WI 53072-3792
Tel.: (262) 691-0070
Web Site: http://www.cooperpower.com
Electrical Power Components & Protective Equipment Mfr
N.A.I.C.S.: 335999

Cooper Power Systems, LLC - South Milwaukee Plant (4)
2800 9th Ave, South Milwaukee, WI 53172
Tel.: (414) 762-1200
Web Site: http://www.cooperpower.com
Emp.: 999
Switchgear Mfr
N.A.I.C.S.: 335313

Plant (Non-US):

Cooper Power Systems, LLC - Taoyuan Plant (4)
2-7 Nan-Yuan, Chung Li Industrial Zone, Taoyuan, 32041, Hsien, Taiwan
Tel.: (886) 34529101
Web Site: http://www.cooperindustries.com
Fuses & Molded Rubber Products Mfr
N.A.I.C.S.: 335999

Plant (Domestic):

Cooper Power Systems, LLC - Waukesha (East North Street) Plant (4)
1900 E N St, Waukesha, WI 53188
Tel.: (262) 547-1251
Web Site: http://www.cooperpower.com
Transformers & Switchgear Mfr & Distr
N.A.I.C.S.: 335311

Subsidiary (Non-US):

Electromanufacturas, S. de R.L. de C.V. (4)
Antiguo Camino A Tlajomulco De Zuniga Margen Derecho 60 Int 0, Colonia Colonia Santa Cruz De Las Flores Tlajomulco De Zuniga, Jalisco, 45640, Mexico (100%)
Tel.: (52) 33 3770 3670
Web Site: http://www.cooperpower.com
Emp.: 150
Electrical Apparatus & Equipment Whslr
N.A.I.C.S.: 423610

Subsidiary (Domestic):

Cooper Wiring Devices, Inc. (3)
203 Cooper Cir, Peachtree City, GA 30269
Tel.: (770) 631-2100
Web Site: http://www.cooperindustries.com
Electrical Apparatus & Equipment Whslr
N.A.I.C.S.: 423610

Subsidiary (Domestic):

Cooper Interconnect, Inc. (4)
23 Front St, Salem, NJ 08079
Tel.: (856) 935-7560
Web Site: http://www.cooperinterconnect.com
Electrical Connector & Cable Assemblies Mfr & Whslr
N.A.I.C.S.: 334417

Plant (Domestic):

Cooper Interconnect, Inc. - Camarillo (5)

750 W Ventura Blvd, Camarillo, CA 93010-8382
Tel.: (805) 484-0543
Web Site: http://www.eaton.com
Emp.: 125
Electrical Connector & Cable Assemblies Mfr & Whslr
N.A.I.C.S.: 334417

Cooper Interconnect, Inc. - La Grange (5)
4758 Washington St, La Grange, NC 28551
Tel.: (252) 566-3014
Web Site: http://www.cooperinterconnect.com
Emp.: 2,954
Electrical Connector & Cable Assemblies Mfr & Whslr
N.A.I.C.S.: 334417

Cooper Interconnect, Inc. - Moorpark (5)
5455 Endeavour Ct, Moorpark, CA 93021-1712
Tel.: (805) 553-9633
Web Site: http://www.cooperinterconnect.com
Emp.: 100
Electrical Connector & Cable Assemblies Mfr & Whslr
N.A.I.C.S.: 334417

Subsidiary (Non-US):

Cooper Korea Ltd. (2)
13FL Vision Tower 707-2 Yeoksam-dong, Gangnam-gu, Seoul, 135 080, Korea (South)
Tel.: (82) 25392216
Web Site: http://www.cooper-ls.com
Electrical Equipment Whslr
N.A.I.C.S.: 423610

Cooper Safety Ltd. (2)
Jephson Court, Tancred Close Royal, Leamington Spa, CV31 3RZ, Warwickshire, United Kingdom
Tel.: (44) 1926 439 200
Web Site: http://www.cooper-safety.com
Sales Range: $550-599.9 Million
Commercial & Industrial Emergency Lighting, Security Systems, Fire Detection & Alarm Systems Mfr & Whslr
N.A.I.C.S.: 339999

Subsidiary (Non-US):

CEAG Notlichtsysteme GmbH (3)
Senator-Schwartz-Ring 26, 59494, Soest, Germany
Tel.: (49) 2921690
Emergency Lighting & Battery Systems Mfr
N.A.I.C.S.: 335132

Subsidiary (Domestic):

Cooper Fulleon Limited (3)
Llantarnam Park, South Wales, Cwmbran, NP44 3AW, United Kingdom
Tel.: (44) 1633628566
Web Site: http://www.cooperfulleon.com
Sales Range: $25-49.9 Million
Emp.: 100
Fire Alarm & Emergency Alert Systems Mfr & Whslr
N.A.I.C.S.: 334290

Cooper Lighting & Safety Ltd. (3)
Wheatley Hall Road, Doncaster, DN2 4NB, South Yorkshire, United Kingdom (100%)
Tel.: (44) 1302 321 541
Web Site: http://www.cooper-ls.com
Emp.: 600
Commercial & Industrial Emergency Lighting & Safety Equipment Mfr & Whslr
N.A.I.C.S.: 335139

Subsidiary (US):

Cooper Notification, Inc. (3)
273 Branchport Ave, Long Branch, NJ 07740
Tel.: (800) 631-2148
Web Site: http://www.cooperindustries.com
Sales Range: $75-99.9 Million
Emp.: 300
Electrical Apparatus & Equipment Whslr
N.A.I.C.S.: 423610

Subsidiary (Non-US):

Cooper Pretronica Lda. (3)

Parque Industrial Serra das Minas Av Irene
Lisboa Lote 19, Armazem C Piso 2, 2635-
001, Rio de Mouro, Portugal   **(100%)**
Tel.: (351) 219198500
Web Site: http://www.cooperpretronica.pt
Emergency Lighting, Fire Detection & Secu-
rity Systems Whslr
N.A.I.C.S.: 423690

Cooper Safety B.V.   **(3)**
Ambacht 6, 5301 KW, Zaltbommel,
Netherlands   **(100%)**
Tel.: (31) 418570200
Web Site: http://www.coopersafety.nl
Electrical Apparatus & Equipment Whslr
N.A.I.C.S.: 423610

Cooper Securite S.A.S.   **(3)**
Rue Beethoven, PO Box 10184, 63200,
Riom, France
Tel.: (33) 820867867
Electrical Equipment & Component Mfr
N.A.I.C.S.: 335999

Subsidiary (Domestic):

**Redapt Engineering Company
Limited**   **(3)**
Unit 1 1 Kingsway South, Aldridge, Walsall,
WS9 8FS, United Kingdom
Tel.: (44) 1215267058
Web Site: http://www.redapt.co.uk
Sales Range: $10-24.9 Million
Electrical Adaptors, Reducers, Stopping
Plugs & Accessories Mfr & Whslr
N.A.I.C.S.: 335999

Subsidiary (Non-US):

**Cooper Shanghai Power Capacitor
Co., Ltd.**   **(2)**
No 955 Shengli Road, Heqing, Shanghai,
201201, China
Tel.: (86) 2128993993
Electrical Apparatus & Equipment Whslr
N.A.I.C.S.: 423610

Cooper Univel S.A.   **(2)**
Komvos Korinou, PO Box 48, 60100, Kat-
erini, Greece
Tel.: (30) 2351059910
Web Site: http://www.univel.gr
Electrical Equipment Whslr
N.A.I.C.S.: 423610

Cooper Xi'an Fusegear Co., Ltd.   **(2)**
No 86 Jinye Road High Tech Zone, Xi'an,
710077, China
Tel.: (86) 2988241869
Electrical Apparatus & Equipment Whslr
N.A.I.C.S.: 423610
Du Peng *(Mgr-Quality)*

**Cooper Yuhua (Changzhou) Electric
Equipment Manufacturing Co.,
Ltd.**   **(2)**
No 60 Hehuan Road, Zhonglou District,
Changzhou, 213023, Jiangsu, China
Tel.: (86) 51983976927
Electrical Equipment Distr
N.A.I.C.S.: 423440

CopperLogic, Ltd.   **(2)**
505 Rue Edouard, Granby, J2G 3Z5, QC,
Canada
Tel.: (450) 378-2244
Electronic Controls Mfr
N.A.I.C.S.: 335314

D.P. Eaton Electric   **(2)**
Bereznjakovskaja 29 6 Floor, 02098, Kiev,
Ukraine
Tel.: (380) 444960958
N.A.I.C.S.: 335311

Subsidiary (Domestic):

Durodyne Inc.   **(2)**
81 Spence St, Bay Shore, NY 11706
Tel.: (631) 249-9000
Web Site: https://www.durodyne.com
N.A.I.C.S.: 332999
Malcolm J. Sweet *(Gen Mgr-Integrated Fa-
cility Svcs)*

Group (Domestic):

Eaton Aerospace LLC   **(2)**
9650 Jeronimo Rd, Irvine, CA 92618
Tel.: (949) 452-9500
Electrical Apparatus & Equipment Whslr

N.A.I.C.S.: 423610

Unit (Domestic):

**Eaton Aerospace LLC - Conveyance
Systems Division, Jackson**   **(3)**
300 S E Ave, Jackson, MI 49203
Tel.: (517) 787-8121
Web Site: http://www.eaton.com
Sales Range: $50-74.9 Million
Emp.: 350
Aircraft Fuel Conveyance Hoses, Couplings,
Ducting & Seals Mfr
N.A.I.C.S.: 332912

**Eaton Aerospace LLC - Electrical
Sensing & Controls Division, Costa
Mesa**   **(3)**
3184 Pullman, Costa Mesa, CA 92626-3319
Tel.: (949) 642-2427
Sales Range: $50-74.9 Million
Emp.: 175
Aircraft Electrical Sensors & Controls Mfr
N.A.I.C.S.: 334511

**Eaton Aerospace LLC - Electrical
Sensing & Controls Division,
Glenolden**   **(3)**
24 E Glenolden Ave, Glenolden, PA 19036
Tel.: (610) 522-4000
Sales Range: $125-149.9 Million
Emp.: 190
Aircraft Electrical Sensors & Controls Mfr &
Distr
N.A.I.C.S.: 334511

**Eaton Aerospace LLC - Electrical
Sensing & Controls Division, Grand
Rapids**   **(3)**
3675 Patterson Ave SE, Grand Rapids, MI
49512
Tel.: (616) 949-1090
Aircraft Electrical Sensors & Controls Mfr
N.A.I.C.S.: 334511

**Eaton Aerospace LLC - Electrical
Sensing & Controls Division,
Sarasota**   **(3)**
2250 Whitfield Ave, Sarasota, FL 34243
Tel.: (941) 758-7726
Web Site: http://www.aerospace.eaton.com
Sales Range: $100-124.9 Million
Emp.: 340
Aircraft Electrical Sensors & Controls Mfr
N.A.I.C.S.: 334511

**Eaton Aerospace LLC - Fuel Systems
Division, Cleveland**   **(3)**
23555 Euclid Ave, Cleveland, OH 44117
Tel.: (216) 692-6000
Sales Range: $200-249.9 Million
Emp.: 736
Aerospace Fuel Systems Equipment Mfr
N.A.I.C.S.: 336413

**Eaton Aerospace LLC - Hydraulic
Systems Division, Jackson**   **(3)**
5353 Highland Dr, Jackson, MS 39206-
3449
Tel.: (601) 981-2811
Web Site: http://www.eaton.com
Sales Range: $25-49.9 Million
Emp.: 550
Aerospace Hydraulic Systems Mfr
N.A.I.C.S.: 333998

**Eaton Aerospace LLC - Hydraulic
Systems Division, Los Angeles**   **(3)**
4690 Colorado Blvd, Los Angeles, CA
90039
Tel.: (818) 409-0200
Web Site: http://www.eaton.com
Sales Range: $50-74.9 Million
Emp.: 340
Aerospace Hydraulic Systems Mfr
N.A.I.C.S.: 336413

Unit (Non-US):

**Eaton Germany GmbH - Aerospace
Group, Conveyance Systems**   **(3)**
Rudolf-Diesel-Strasse 8, 82205, Gilching,
Germany
Tel.: (49) 8105750
Sales Range: $25-49.9 Million
Emp.: 50
Aircraft Fuel Conveyance Systems Mfr
N.A.I.C.S.: 332912

Subsidiary (Non-US):

**Eaton Limited - Fuel & Motion Control
Systems Division**   **(3)**
Abbey Park Titchfield, Fareham, PO14
4QA, Hampshire, United Kingdom
Tel.: (44) 1329853000
Sales Range: $250-299.9 Million
Emp.: 1,000
Aircraft Fuel Systems Equipment, Fuel Con-
veyance Components & Hydraulic Equip-
ment Mfr
N.A.I.C.S.: 336413

Subsidiary (Non-US):

**Eaton Automotive Components
Spolka z o.o.**   **(2)**
Ul 30 Stycznia 55, 83 110, Tczew, Poland
Tel.: (48) 585329461
Motor Vehicle Parts Mfr
N.A.I.C.S.: 336390
Adam Garczewski *(Mgr-Advance Pur)*

Eaton Automotive G.m.b.H.   **(2)**
Bleicheroder Strasse 2, Nordhausen,
99734, Germany
Tel.: (49) 36319290
Automotive Components Mfr
N.A.I.C.S.: 336390

**Eaton Automotive Systems Spolka z
o.o.**   **(2)**
Ul Rudawka 83, 43 382, Bielsko-Biala, Po-
land
Tel.: (48) 334993507
Motor Vehicle Parts Mfr
N.A.I.C.S.: 336390

Eaton Controls (UK) Limited   **(2)**
Brue Way Walrow Industrial Estate, Somer-
set, TA9 4AW, United Kingdom
Tel.: (44) 1278772600
Electrical Equipment Whslr
N.A.I.C.S.: 423610

**Eaton Controls, S. de R.L. de
C.V.**   **(2)**
Avenida Chapultepec Parque Industrial Co-
lonial, 88750, Reynosa, Tamaulipas, Mexico
Tel.: (52) 8999300884
Electrical Apparatus & Equipment Whslr
N.A.I.C.S.: 423610

Unit (Domestic):

Eaton Corp. - Airflex   **(2)**
9919 Clinton Rd, Cleveland, OH 44144
Tel.: (216) 281-2211
Sales Range: $75-99.9 Million
Emp.: 100
Industrial Clutches, Brakes & Assemblies
Mfr
N.A.I.C.S.: 336340

Group (Domestic):

**Eaton Corp. - Electrical Sector,
Americas**   **(2)**
1000 Cherrington Pkwy, Moon Township,
PA 15108
Tel.: (412) 893-3300
Web Site: http://www.eaton.com
Sales Range: $200-249.9 Million
Emp.: 500
Electrical Power Distribution, Control &
Management Products Mfr & Distr.
N.A.I.C.S.: 335999

Subsidiary (Domestic):

Cooper Bussmann, LLC   **(3)**
114 Old State Rd, Ellisville, MO 63021-5942
Tel.: (636) 394-2877
Web Site: http://www.cooperbussmann.com
Circuit Protection Products Mfr & Distr
N.A.I.C.S.: 335313

Subsidiary (Non-US):

Bussmann, S. de R.L. de C.V.   **(4)**
Poniente 148 No 933 Col Industrial Vallejo,
Azcapotzalco, Mexico, 02300, DF,
Mexico   **(100%)**
Tel.: (52) 5555870211
Electrical Apparatus & Equipment Whslr
N.A.I.C.S.: 423610

Plant (Domestic):

**Eaton Corp. - Electrical Sector,
Columbus**   **(3)**

811 Greencrest Dr, Columbus, OH 43031
Tel.: (614) 882-3282
Web Site: http://www.eaton.com
Sales Range: $25-49.9 Million
Emp.: 50
Mfr of Color Graphics, Software, Terminals
& Industrial Workstations
N.A.I.C.S.: 334118

Unit (Domestic):

**Eaton Corp. - Electrical Sector,
Power Quality USA**   **(3)**
8609 6 Forks Rd, Raleigh, NC 27615-5276
Tel.: (919) 872-3020
Web Site: http://www.eaton.com
Sales Range: $100-124.9 Million
Emp.: 300
Electrical Monitoring & Power Management
Systems Mfr, Distr & Support Services
N.A.I.C.S.: 334515

Plant (Domestic):

**Eaton Corp. - Electrical Sector,
Watertown**   **(3)**
901 S 12th St, Watertown, WI 53094-7101
Tel.: (920) 261-4070
Sales Range: $50-74.9 Million
Emp.: 200
Counting Devices & Control Instruments Mfr
N.A.I.C.S.: 334513

Subsidiary (Non-US):

Eaton Electrical Canada   **(3)**
5050 Mainway, Burlington, L7L 5Z1, ON,
Canada
Tel.: (905) 333-6442
Web Site: https://www.eaton.com
Sales Range: $25-49.9 Million
Emp.: 112
Starters, Contactors, Overload Relays, Re-
sistors & Brake Rectifier Panels Mfr
N.A.I.C.S.: 335313

Subsidiary (Domestic):

Eaton Ontario Sales   **(4)**
1-2025 Meadowvale Blvd, Mississauga,
L5N 5N1, ON, Canada
Tel.: (905) 363-5668
Sales Range: $10-24.9 Million
Emp.: 35
Electrical Circuit Breaker, Relay & Control
Device Distr
N.A.I.C.S.: 423610

Eaton Power Quality Company   **(4)**
380 Carlingview Drive, Toronto, M9W 5X9,
ON, Canada
Tel.: (416) 798-0112
Web Site:
    http://www.powerquality.eaton.com
Sales Range: $25-49.9 Million
Emp.: 50
Electrical Monitoring & Power Management
Systems Mfr, Distr & Support Services
N.A.I.C.S.: 334515

Subsidiary (Non-US):

Eaton Electrical S.A.   **(3)**
De La Entrada Del Antiguo Colegio Saint
Claire 300 Metros Al Oeste, Moravia, San
Jose, 101565-1000, Costa Rica   **(97.53%)**
Tel.: (506) 2477600
Web Site: http://www.eaton.cr
Sales Range: $50-74.9 Million
Emp.: 200
Starters, Contactors & Overload Relays
N.A.I.C.S.: 335314

Eaton Power Quality S.A.   **(3)**
Lima 355 Planta Baja Edificio World Trade
Center, C1073AAF, Buenos Aires, Argen-
tina
Tel.: (54) 1141244000
Web Site: http://www.eaton.com
Sales Range: $100-124.9 Million
Emp.: 50
Electrical Monitoring & Power Management
Systems Distr & Support Services
N.A.I.C.S.: 423610

Eaton Power Solutions Ltda.   **(3)**
Av Ermano Marchetti 1435 Agua Branca,
05038-001, Sao Paulo, SP, Brazil
Tel.: (55) 1136168500
Web Site: http://powerquality.eaton.com

Eaton Corporation plc—(Continued)

Sales Range: $100-124.9 Million
Electrical Monitoring & Power Management
Systems Distr & Support Services
N.A.I.C.S.: 423610

Eaton Technologies, S. de R.L. de C.V. (3)
Av De las Granjas No 473-B Col Jardin Az-peitia, Azcapotzalco, Mexico, 2530, Mexico
Tel.: (52) 5553960651
Web Site: http://www.eaton.com
Sales Range: $50-74.9 Million
Emp.: 150
Electrical Apparatus & Equipment Whslr
N.A.I.C.S.: 423610

Branch (Domestic):

Eaton Electrical Mexico - Guadalajara Sales Office (4)
Calle Lerdo de Tejada No 2105 Esq Mar-sella, Col Americana, 44160, Guadalajara, Jal, Mexico
Tel.: (52) 33 3630 3185
Web Site: http://www.eaton.mx
Sales Range: $1-9.9 Million
Emp.: 5
Electrical Power Distribution & Control Products Distr
N.A.I.C.S.: 423610

Eaton Electrical Mexico - Monterrey Sales Office (4)
Calle Loma Redona 2712, Col Lomas de San Francisco, 64710, Monterrey, Mexico
Tel.: (52) 1811239154
Web Site: http://www.eaton.mx
Sales Range: $1-9.9 Million
Emp.: 10
Electrical Power Distribution & Control Products Distr
N.A.I.C.S.: 423610

Unit (Domestic):

Eaton Power Solutions - Mexico & Central America (4)
Montecito No 38 piso 26 ofic 13-22, Col Napoles, 03810, Mexico, DF, Mexico
Tel.: (52) 5585035450
Sales Range: $100-124.9 Million
Electrical Monitoring & Power Management Systems Distr & Support Services
N.A.I.C.S.: 423610

Unit (Domestic):

Eaton Corp. - Golf Grip (2)
16900 Aberdeen Rd, Laurinburg, NC 28352
Tel.: (910) 277-3770
Web Site: http://www.golfpride.com
Sales Range: $50-74.9 Million
Emp.: 100
Golf Club Grip Mfr
N.A.I.C.S.: 326299

Eaton Corp. - Industrial Controls (2)
4201 N 27th St, Milwaukee, WI 53216-1897
Tel.: (414) 449-6207
Web Site: http://www.eaton.com
Sales Range: $25-49.9 Million
Emp.: 50
Switch Mfr
N.A.I.C.S.: 335312

Group (Domestic):

Eaton Corp. - Vehicle Group (2)
13100 E Michigan Ave, Galesburg, MI 49053
Tel.: (269) 342-3462
Sales Range: $100-124.9 Million
Emp.: 500
Motor Vehicle Component Mfr
N.A.I.C.S.: 336390
Joao Faria (Pres)

Unit (Domestic):

Eaton Corp. - Engine Air Management (3)
19218 B Dr S, Marshall, MI 49068-9790
Tel.: (616) 781-1733
Web Site: http://www.eaton.com
Sales Range: $100-124.9 Million
Emp.: 260
Internal Combustion Engine Components, Precision Forged Gears

Eaton Corp. - Fluid Connectors (3)
19700 Hall Rd Ste B, Clinton Township, MI 48038
Tel.: (586) 228-5000
Web Site: http://www.eaton.com
Sales Range: $75-99.9 Million
Emp.: 200
Mfr of Air Conditioning, Power Steering & Transmission Cooling Hose & Tube Assemblies
N.A.I.C.S.: 326220

Eaton Corp. - Superchargers (3)
19218 B Dr S, Marshall, MI 49068-8600
Tel.: (706) 543-5250
Web Site: http://www.eaton.com
Sales Range: $100-124.9 Million
Emp.: 250
Supercharger Mfr
N.A.I.C.S.: 336340

Eaton Corp. - Transmissions (3)
744 S Battleground Ave, Kings Mountain, NC 28086-1728
Tel.: (704) 937-7411
Web Site: http://www.eaton.com
Sales Range: $125-149.9 Million
Emp.: 300
Heavy Duty Transmission Mfr
N.A.I.C.S.: 336350

Division (Domestic):

Eaton Corp. - Vehicle Group, Automotive Division (3)
1101 W Hanover St, Marshall, MI 49068-1756
Tel.: (269) 781-2811
Emp.: 500
Motor Vehicle Components Mfr & Distr
N.A.I.C.S.: 336390

Plant (Domestic):

Eaton Corp. - Vehicle Group, Belmond Plant (3)
700 Luicks Ln S, Belmond, IA 50421
Tel.: (641) 444-3535
Web Site: http://www.eatoncorporation.com
Sales Range: $100-124.9 Million
Emp.: 450
Eaton Automotive Engine Valves
N.A.I.C.S.: 336310

Eaton Corp. - Vehicle Group, Kearney Plant (3)
4200 Hwy 30 E, Kearney, NE 68847
Tel.: (308) 234-4142
Web Site: http://www.eaton.com
Sales Range: $125-149.9 Million
Emp.: 400
Precision Forged Gears
N.A.I.C.S.: 336310

Division (Domestic):

Eaton Corp. - Vehicle Group, Truck Division (3)
13100 E Michigan Ave, Galesburg, MI 49053
Tel.: (269) 342-3000
Web Site: http://www.eaton.com
Sales Range: $100-124.9 Million
Emp.: 500
Commercial Vehicle Drive Train & Safety Systems Mfr
N.A.I.C.S.: 336390

Subsidiary (Non-US):

Eaton Truck Components (Pty.) Limited (3)
3 Eaton Africa Place Aeroport Spartan Extension 2, PO Box 17122, 1619, Johannesburg, Norkem Park, South Africa
Tel.: (27) 0113927770
Web Site: http://www.roadranger.com
Sales Range: $25-49.9 Million
Emp.: 20
Truck Components Mgr & Distr
N.A.I.C.S.: 336390
Tom Kellett (Mgr-Sales)

Joint Venture (Domestic):

U.S. Engine Valve Corporation (3)
7039 S Hwy 11, Westminster, SC 29693
Tel.: (864) 647-2061

Web Site: https://www.usenginevalve.com
Sales Range: $75-99.9 Million
Emp.: 400
Engine Valve Mfr
N.A.I.C.S.: 336310

Subsidiary (Non-US):

Eaton Electric (South Africa) Pty Ltd. (3)
Cnr Esander and Osborn Road Private Bag X019, Wadeville, 1422, Gauteng, South Africa
Tel.: (27) 118247400
Industrial Electrical Equipment Whslr
N.A.I.C.S.: 423830
Jacobus de Lange (Acct Mgr)

Subsidiary (Domestic):

Eaton Electric Holdings LLC (2)
1000 Eaton Blvd, Cleveland, OH 44122
Tel.: (440) 523-5000
Emp.: 20
Holding Company
N.A.I.C.S.: 551112
Kevin Condon (Sr VP)

Subsidiary (Non-US):

Eaton Electric SIA (2)
Zemitana Street 2b, Riga, 1012, Latvia
Tel.: (371) 67844435
Electrical Equipment Mfr & Sales
N.A.I.C.S.: 335999

Eaton Electric SPRL (2)
Oude Vijversstraat 44/-46, 1190, Brussels, Belgium
Tel.: (32) 23322040
Web Site: http://www.eaton.com
Electrical Apparatus & Equipment Whslr
N.A.I.C.S.: 423610

Eaton Electrical Systems Limited (2)
Wheatley Hall Road, Doncaster, DN1 9LH, United Kingdom
Tel.: (44) 1302321541
Electrical Equipment Whslr
N.A.I.C.S.: 423610

Eaton Electrical, S.A. (2)
Avenida Libertador El Rosal Ed Lex Piso 1, Caracas, 1060, Venezuela
Tel.: (58) 2129531697
Web Site: http://www.Eaton.com
Emp.: 20
Electric Equipment Mfr
N.A.I.C.S.: 335999

Eaton Elektrik Ticaret Limited Sirketi (2)
Degirmen Sok Nida Kule Business Center No 18 Floor 17, 34742, Istanbul, Turkiye
Tel.: (90) 2164642020
Electrical Equipment Whslr
N.A.I.C.S.: 423610

Eaton Elektrotechnika s.r.o. (2)
Komarovska 2406, 193 00, Prague, 9, Czech Republic
Tel.: (420) 267990411
Web Site:
   http://www.eatonelektrotechnika.cz
Industrial Equipment Mfr
N.A.I.C.S.: 334513

Eaton Enterprises (Hungary) Kft. (2)
Nagyenyed utca 8-14, Budapest, 1123, Hungary
Tel.: (36) 14999100
Electrical Equipment Whslr
N.A.I.C.S.: 423610

Eaton FZE (2)
Techno Park Jebel Ali South, PO Box 261768, Dubai, United Arab Emirates
Tel.: (971) 48066100
Web Site: http://www.eaton.ae
Electrical Equipment Whslr
N.A.I.C.S.: 423610

Eaton Filtration (Shanghai) Co. Ltd. (2)
No 3 Lane 280 Linhong Road, Changning District, Shanghai, 200335, China
Tel.: (86) 2152000099
Web Site: http://www.eaton.com
Filtration Component Mfr
N.A.I.C.S.: 335999

Eaton Holding SE & Co. KG (2)
Hein Moeller Str 7 11, 53115, Bonn, Germany
Tel.: (49) 2286020
Web Site: http://www.eaton.de
Electrical Equipment Whslr
N.A.I.C.S.: 423610

Eaton Holec AB (2)
Hammarvagen 19, Arlov, 232 37, Sweden
Tel.: (46) 40438840
Web Site: http://www.eaton.se
Emp.: 11
Electric Equipment Mfr
N.A.I.C.S.: 335999

Group (Domestic):

Eaton Hydraulics LLC (2)
14615 Lone Oak Rd, Eden Prairie, MN 55344-2200
Sales Range: $75-99.9 Million
Emp.: 250
Electrical Apparatus & Equipment Whslr
N.A.I.C.S.: 423610

Division (Domestic):

Eaton Cylinder (3)
2425 W Michigan Ave, Jackson, MI 49202-3964   (100%)
Tel.: (517) 787-7220
Web Site: http://www.eaton.com
Sales Range: $75-99.9 Million
Emp.: 200
Hydraulic & Pneumatic Cylinder Mfr
N.A.I.C.S.: 333995

Eaton Filtration LLC (3)
70 Wood Ave 2nd Fl, Iselin, NJ 08830
Tel.: (732) 767-4200
Web Site: http://www.eaton.com
Sales Range: $100-124.9 Million
Industrial Filtration Systems & Separators Mfr
N.A.I.C.S.: 333998

Unit (Domestic):

Eaton Filtration LLC - Ronningen-Petter (4)
9151 Shaver Rd, Portage, MI 49024
Tel.: (269) 323-0157
Web Site: http://www.ronningen-petter.com
Sales Range: $25-49.9 Million
Emp.: 80
Filtration Equipment Mfr
N.A.I.C.S.: 333998

Plant (Domestic):

Eaton Hydraulics LLC - Berea (3)
1000 W Bagley Rd, Berea, OH 44017-2906
Tel.: (440) 826-1115
Sales Range: $25-49.9 Million
Emp.: 200
Quick Connective Fluid Line Coupling Mfr
N.A.I.C.S.: 332912

Subsidiary (Non-US):

Eaton Industries (Japan) Ltd. (3)
Unizo Nogizaka Bldg 2F 8-11-37 Akasaka, Minato-ku, Tokyo, 107-0052, Japan
Tel.: (81) 357862560
Sales Range: $25-49.9 Million
Emp.: 200
Electrical Apparatus & Equipment Whslr
N.A.I.C.S.: 423610

Unit (Non-US):

Eaton Ltd. - Hydraulic Systems (3)
Larchwood Avenue Bedhampton, Havant, PO9 3QL, Hampshire, United Kingdom   (100%)
Tel.: (44) 2392487260
Web Site: http://www.aerospace.eaton.com
Sales Range: $50-74.9 Million
Emp.: 135
Mfr of Valves
N.A.I.C.S.: 332912

Plant (Non-US):

Eaton Ltda. - Fluid Power Division, Guaratingueta Plant (3)
Rodovia Washington Luiz 2755 Km 181, Bairro Rio Comprido, CEP 12522-010, Guaratingueta, SP, Brazil
Tel.: (55) 12 3128 6000

Web Site: http://www.eaton.com.br
Fluid Power Hose, Hose Fittings & Adaptors
Mfr
N.A.I.C.S.: 332912

Subsidiary (Non-US):

Vickers Systems Ltd. **(3)**
Rm 18-30 19/f Corporation Park 11 On Lai
St Siu Lek Yuen, Sha Tin, China (Hong
Kong) **(100%)**
Tel.: (852) 26377803
Web Site: http://www.eaton.com
Sales Range: $1-9.9 Million
Emp.: 30
Electrical Apparatus & Equipment Whslr
N.A.I.C.S.: 423610

Vickers Systems SBPD **(3)**
No 2 8th Floor Jalan 51A/243, PO Box 418,
46100, Petaling Jaya, Selangor Darul Eh-
san, Malaysia **(100%)**
Tel.: (60) 378737090
Sales Range: $10-24.9 Million
Emp.: 10
Distr of Hydraulic Systems
N.A.I.C.S.: 336340
George Hendro *(Gen Mgr)*

Subsidiary (Non-US):

**Eaton Industrial Systems Private
Limited** **(2)**
145 off Mumbai-Pune Road, Pimpri, Pune,
411018, Maharashtra, India
Tel.: (91) 2138674500
Electrical Apparatus & Equipment Whslr
N.A.I.C.S.: 423610

Eaton Industries (Belgium) BVBA **(2)**
Industrialaan 3, Groot-Bijgaarden, B-1702,
Belgium
Tel.: (32) 27198800
Web Site: http://www.eaton.be
Electrical Equipment Whslr
N.A.I.C.S.: 423610

**Eaton Industries (Canada)
Company** **(2)**
1743 McDonald Street, Regina, S4N 6A9,
SK, Canada
Tel.: (306) 216-7770
Electric Equipment Mfr
N.A.I.C.S.: 334515

**Eaton Industries (Colombia)
S.A.S.** **(2)**
Avenida El Dorado 68 C 61 Of 829, Bogota,
615, Colombia
Tel.: (57) 14043333
Web Site: http://www.eaton.com.co
Kitchen Equipment Distr
N.A.I.C.S.: 423440

Eaton Industries (Egypt) Ltd. **(2)**
Building No 289 Off 90th Street Apartment
4B 4th Floor 5th District, New Cairo, Egypt
Tel.: (20) 20226135747
Electrical Equipment Distr
N.A.I.C.S.: 423440

Eaton Industries (France) S.A.S. **(2)**
Immeuble Axe Etoile 103/105 Rue des 3
Fontanots, Nanterre, 92022, France
Tel.: (33) 800336858
Web Site: http://www.eaton.fr
Kitchen Equipment Distr
N.A.I.C.S.: 423440

**Eaton Industries (Shanghai) Co.,
Ltd.** **(2)**
No 2 Bldg No 139 Fanghua Rd Hu, Shang-
hai, 201204, China
Tel.: (86) 21589170
Web Site: http://www.eaton.com.cn
Electrical Apparatus & Equipment Whslr
N.A.I.C.S.: 423610

Subsidiary (Domestic):

Eaton Electrical Ltd. **(3)**
No 3 Lane 280 Linhong Road, Changning
District, Shanghai, 200335, China
Tel.: (86) 21 5200 0099
Web Site: www.eatonelectrical.com.cn
Sales Range: $100-124.9 Million
Emp.: 300
Electrical Power Distribution, Control &
Management Products Mfr & Distr
N.A.I.C.S.: 335999

Subsidiary (Domestic):

**Zhenjiang Daqo Eaton Electrical Sys-
tems Company Limited** **(4)**
No 66 Taquan Road, Yangzhong, 212211,
Jiangsu, China
Tel.: (86) 511 88411360
Web Site: http://www.daqo.com
Sales Range: $100-124.9 Million
Switchgear Mfr
N.A.I.C.S.: 335313

Subsidiary (Non-US):

Eaton Industries Pty. Ltd. **(3)**
10 Kent Rd, Mascot, 2020, NSW,
Australia **(100%)**
Tel.: (61) 408233852
Sales Range: $50-74.9 Million
Emp.: 120
Electrical Apparatus & Equipment Whslr
N.A.I.C.S.: 423610

Eaton Technologies Limited **(3)**
 (100%)
Tel.: (86) 2152000099
Web Site: http://www.eaton.com.cn
Sales Range: $75-99.9 Million
Emp.: 500
Technological Services
N.A.I.C.S.: 541990

Subsidiary (Non-US):

Eaton Industries EOOD **(2)**
83 Gioeshevo Str Room 412 Floor 4, 1330,
Sofia, Bulgaria
Tel.: (359) 248913536
Web Site: http://www.moeller.net
Electrical Equipment Distr
N.A.I.C.S.: 423440

Eaton Industries II G.m.b.H. **(2)**
In Langhag 14, CH-8307, Effretikon, Swit-
zerland
Tel.: (41) 584581414
Web Site: http://www.eaton.ch
Electrical Equipment Whslr
N.A.I.C.S.: 423610

**Eaton Industries Manufacturing
GmbH** **(2)**
7 - Route de la Longeraie, 1110, Morges,
Switzerland
Tel.: (41) 218114600
Sales Range: $75-99.9 Million
Emp.: 150
Holding Company; Regional Managing Of-
fice
N.A.I.C.S.: 551112

Subsidiary (Non-US):

Eaton Electric ApS **(3)**
Niels Bohrs Vej 2, 7100, Vejle,
Denmark **(100%)**
Tel.: (45) 76405400
Sales Range: $25-49.9 Million
Emp.: 120
Electrical Apparatus & Equipment Whslr
N.A.I.C.S.: 423610

Eaton Electric Limited **(3)**
Reddings Lane, Tyseley, Birmingham, B11
3EZ, United Kingdom
Tel.: (44) 1216852100
Web Site: http://www.eaton.com
Electrical Apparatus & Equipment Whslr
N.A.I.C.S.: 423610

Eaton Electric Sales S.A.S. **(3)**
346 Rue de la Belle Etoile, PO Box 51060,
Charles De Gaulle, 95947, Roissy-en-
France, France
Tel.: (33) 141845050
Sales Range: $50-74.9 Million
Emp.: 100
Electrical Circuit Breaker, Relay & Control
Device Mfr
N.A.I.C.S.: 335999

Eaton Germany GmbH **(3)**
Dr Reckeweg Strasse 1, Baden-Baden,
76532, Germany **(100%)**
Tel.: (49) 72216820
Web Site: http://www.eaton.com
Electrical Apparatus & Equipment Whslr
N.A.I.C.S.: 423610

Subsidiary (Domestic):

**Eaton Holding Investments GmbH &
Co. KG** **(4)**

Hammfelddamm 6, Allerheiligen, 41460,
Neuss, Germany **(100%)**
Tel.: (49) 213140630
Sales Range: $10-24.9 Million
Emp.: 10
Switchgear Mfr
N.A.I.C.S.: 335313

Eaton Industries GmbH **(4)**
Hein-Moeller-Str 7-11, 53115, Bonn, Ger-
many
Tel.: (49) 2286020
Sales Range: $1-4.9 Billion
Emp.: 500
Electrical Apparatus & Equipment Whslr
N.A.I.C.S.: 423610

Subsidiary (Non-US):

Eaton GmbH **(5)**
Scheydgasse 42, Vienna, 1215, Austria
Tel.: (43) 1 277 45 0
Web Site: http://www.eaton.com
Sales Range: $450-499.9 Million
Commercial & Residential Lighting, Heating
& Air Conditioning Control Systems Mfr
N.A.I.C.S.: 334512

Moeller Electric NV/SA **(5)**
Industrialaan 1, 1702, Groot-Bijgaarden,
Belgium
Tel.: (32) 27198800
Web Site: http://www.benelux.moeller.net
Sales Range: $10-24.9 Million
Emp.: 40
Electrical Circuit Breaker, Relay & Control
Device Mfr
N.A.I.C.S.: 333992

Subsidiary (Non-US):

**Eaton Industries (Netherlands)
B.V.** **(3)**
Europalaan 210, 7559 SC, Hengelo, Neth-
erlands
Tel.: (31) 1742469111
Web Site: https://www.eaton.com
Electrical Component Mfr
N.A.I.C.S.: 333992

Division (Domestic):

**Eaton Industries (Netherlands) B.V.
Hydraulics Division** **(4)**
Hoppenkuil 6, 5626 DD, Eindhoven, Nether-
lands
Tel.: (31) 402629900
Web Site: http://www.eatonindustries.nl
Sales Range: $50-74.9 Million
Emp.: 100
Hydraulic Cylinder Mfr
N.A.I.C.S.: 333995
Erwin de Bresser *(Engr-Sls & Project)*

Subsidiary (Domestic):

Eaton Manufacturing GmbH **(3)**
Route de la Longeraie 7, Morges, 1110,
Switzerland
Tel.: (41) 218114600
Sales Range: $75-99.9 Million
Emp.: 150
Electrical, Hydraulic, Aerospace & Motor
Vehicle Products Mfr, Distr & Support Ser-
vices
N.A.I.C.S.: 423610
Yannis Tsavalas *(VP & Gen Mgr)*

Subsidiary (Non-US):

Eaton Power Quality Limited **(3)**
221 Dover Road, Slough, SL1 4RF, Berks,
United Kingdom
Tel.: (44) 1753608906
Web Site: http://www.eaton.uk.com
Sales Range: $50-74.9 Million
Emp.: 70
Electrical Apparatus & Equipment Whslr
N.A.I.C.S.: 423610

Subsidiary (Non-US):

Eaton Industries Private Limited **(2)**
Interim Building 145 Masulkar Colony, Off
Mumbai Pune Road, Pimpri, 411 018, Pune,
India
Tel.: (91) 2066338610
Electric Equipment Mfr
N.A.I.C.S.: 335999

**Eaton Industries, S. de R.L. de
C.V.** **(2)**
Brecha E 99 SN Parque Industrial Reynosa,
88670, Reynosa, Tamaulipas, Mexico
Tel.: (52) 8999540200
Electrical Apparatus & Equipment Whslr
N.A.I.C.S.: 423610

**Eaton International Industries Nigeria
Limited** **(2)**
81 Adeniyi Jones Avenue, Ikeja, Lagos,
Nigeria
Tel.: (234) 9079237080
Industrial Electrical Equipment Whslr
N.A.I.C.S.: 423830

Eaton Investments Co., Ltd. **(2)**
Building 3 Lane 280 Linhong Road Changn-
ing, Shanghai, 200335, China
Tel.: (86) 52000099
Motor Vehicle Parts Mfr
N.A.I.C.S.: 336350

Eaton MEDC Limited **(2)**
Unit B Sutton Parkway Oddicroft Lane, Sut-
ton in Ashfield, NG17 5FB, United Kingdom
Tel.: (44) 1623444400
Web Site: http://www.coopermedc.com
Electric Equipment Mfr
N.A.I.C.S.: 335999

**Eaton Phoenixtec MMPL
Co.,Ltd.** **(2)**
114 Xiwan Rd Sec 2, New Taipei City,
22179, Taiwan
Tel.: (886) 66142000
Electrical Apparatus & Equipment Whslr
N.A.I.C.S.: 423610

Eaton Power Quality AB **(2)**
Farogatan 33, 164 40, Kista, Sweden
Tel.: (46) 859894000
Web Site:
http://www.powerquality.eaton.com
Emp.: 55
Electrical Apparatus & Equipment Whslr
N.A.I.C.S.: 423610

Eaton Power Quality Oy **(2)**
Koskelontie 14, PL 54, 2920, Espoo, Fin-
land
Tel.: (358) 9452661
Web Site: http://www.eaton.com
Electric Equipment Mfr
N.A.I.C.S.: 335999

Eaton S.A. **(2)**
2 Rue Lavoisier, BP 54, 78310, Coignieres,
France
Tel.: (33) 130693000
N.A.I.C.S.: 561210

Eaton Technologies G.m.b.H. **(2)**
Auf Der Heide 2, Nettersheim, 53947, Eu-
skirchen, Germany
Tel.: (49) 24868090
N.A.I.C.S.: 561210

**FHF Bergbautechnik GmbH & Co.
KG** **(2)**
Gewerbeallee 15-19, Mullheim, 45478, Ger-
many
Tel.: (49) 20882680
Web Site: http://www.fhf-bt.com
Other Communications Equipment Mfr
N.A.I.C.S.: 334290

**FHF Funke+Huster Fernsig
GmbH** **(2)**
Gewerbeallee 15-19, 45478, Mulheim an
der Ruhr, Germany
Tel.: (49) 20882680
Web Site: https://www.fhf.de
N.A.I.C.S.: 334290

Gitiesse S.r.l. **(2)**
Ponte Polcevera 8/14, 16161, Genoa, Italy
Tel.: (39) 0107416800
Web Site: http://www.gitiesse.com
Communication Equipment Merchant Whslr
N.A.I.C.S.: 423690

Guangzhou Nittan Valve Co. Ltd. **(2)**
No 79 JunYe Road Northern Part Eastern
Section, Guangzhou Economic and Techno-
logical Development District, Guangzhou,
510000, GuangDong, China
Tel.: (86) 2082266139
Web Site: http://www.niv.co.jp
Motor Vehicle Parts Mfr

Eaton Corporation plc—(Continued)

N.A.I.C.S.: 336350

Hernis Scan Systems - Asia Pte Ltd. (2)
100G Pasir Panjang Road Stuite 07-08 Interlocal Centre, Singapore, 118523, Singapore
Tel.: (65) 68251668
Closed Circuit Television Services
N.A.I.C.S.: 517111

Hernis Scan Systems A/S (2)
Tangen Alle 41 4817 His, PO Box 791, Arendal, 4809, Norway
Tel.: (17) 37063700
Closed Circuit Television Services
N.A.I.C.S.: 517111

Subsidiary (Domestic):

Innovative Technology, Inc.
150 Industry Dr, Pittsburgh, PA 15275-1014
Tel.: (352) 799-0713
Web Site:
    http://www.innovativetechnology.com
Sales Range: $1-9.9 Million
Emp.: 6
Voltage Surge Supressors
N.A.I.C.S.: 335931

Subsidiary (Non-US):

Institute for International Product Safety GmbH (2)
Hein-Moeller-Strasse 7-11, 53115, Bonn, Germany
Tel.: (49) 2287487080
Web Site: https://www.i2ps.de
Emp.: 50
Electric Equipment Mfr
N.A.I.C.S.: 335999
Heribert Schorn (Mng Dir)

MTL Italia Srl (2)
Via San Bovio 3, 20090, Milan, Italy
Tel.: (39) 02959501
N.A.I.C.S.: 335999

Norex AS (2)
PO Box 254, 3371, Vikersund, Norway
Tel.: (47) 32788585
Web Site: http://www.norex-as.no
Electrical Equipment Whslr
N.A.I.C.S.: 423610

Ocean Technical Systems Limited (2)
Oceantech House Sta Approach Cheam, Cheam, SM2 7AU, United Kingdom
Tel.: (44) 87226910
Web Site: http://www.oceantechsys.com
Electrical Equipment Whslr
N.A.I.C.S.: 423610

Subsidiary (Domestic):

Power Distribution, Inc. (2)
4200 Oakleys Ct, Richmond, VA 23223
Tel.: (804) 737-9880
Web Site: http://www.pdicorp.com
Power Distribution Equipment Mfr
N.A.I.C.S.: 335999
Dave Mulholland (VP-Svcs-Global & Dir-PQ Svc Sls)

Subsidiary (Domestic):

Onyx Power Inc. (3)
4011 W Carriage Dr, Santa Ana, CA 92704
Tel.: (714) 513-1500
Web Site: http://www.pdicorp.com
Power Transformer Mfr
N.A.I.C.S.: 334416

Subsidiary (Domestic):

Royal Die & Stamping Co., Inc. (2)
125 Mercedes Dr, Carol Stream, IL 60188
Tel.: (630) 384-5500
Web Site: http://royalpowersolutions.com
High-precision, Critical Electrical Connectivity Components Mfr
N.A.I.C.S.: 335999
Nicholas Pribus (CFO)

Subsidiary (Non-US):

Santak Electronics (Shenzhen) Co., Ltd. (2)

8 Baoshi Road, Bao'an District, Shenzhen, 518101, China
Tel.: (86) 75527572666
Web Site: http://www.santak.com
Electric Equipment Mfr
N.A.I.C.S.: 334515

Sefelec GmbH (2)
Karl-Bold-Strasse 40, D-77855, Achern, Germany
Tel.: (49) 7841640770
Web Site: http://www.sefelec.fr
Electrical Equipment Whslr
N.A.I.C.S.: 423610

Sefelec SAS (2)
19 rue des Campanules, 77185, Lognes, France
Tel.: (33) 164118342
Web Site: http://www.sefelec.fr
Measuring Device Mfr
N.A.I.C.S.: 334519

Semelec SAS (2)
11 Av de l Atlantique, 91955, Les Ulis, Cedex, France
Tel.: (33) 169076458
Electrical Equipment & Component Mfr
N.A.I.C.S.: 335999

Subsidiary (Domestic):

Sure Power, Inc. (2)
10955 SW Avery St, Tualatin, OR 97062
Tel.: (503) 692-5360
Web Site: http://www.sure-power.com
Emp.: 100
Electrical Apparatus & Equipment Whslr
N.A.I.C.S.: 423610

Subsidiary (Non-US):

Ulusoy Elektrik Imalat Taahhut Ve Ticaret A.S. (2)
1st Organized Industrial Zone Oghuz Street No 6, Sincan, 6935, Ankara, Turkiye
Tel.: (90) 3122670712
Web Site: https://www.ulusoyelektrik.com.tr
Rev.: $70,013,747
Assets: $55,215,941
Liabilities: $44,229,777
Net Worth: $10,986,164
Earnings: $1,833,813
Emp.: 700
Fiscal Year-end: 12/31/2022
Electrical Equipment & Components Mfr
N.A.I.C.S.: 335999
Fernando Zaramella Ceccarelli (Chm)

Subsidiary (Domestic):

Viking Electronics, Inc. (2)
1531 Industrial St, Hudson, WI 54016
Tel.: (715) 386-8861
Web Site: http://www.vikingelectronics.com
Security Device & Control Mfr
N.A.I.C.S.: 334290

WPI-Boston Division, Inc. (2)
222 Williams St, Chelsea, MA 02150
Tel.: (617) 889-3700
Electric Equipment Mfr
N.A.I.C.S.: 334515

Wright Line LLC (2)
160 Gold Star Blvd, Worcester, MA 01606-2791
Tel.: (508) 852-4300
Emp.: 400
Electrical Apparatus & Equipment Whslr
N.A.I.C.S.: 423610

EATWARE INC.
23rd Floor Westin Center 26 Hung To Road, Kwun Tong, Kowloon, China (Hong Kong)
Tel.: (852) 2295 1818   NV
Sales Range: $1-9.9 Million
Flatware Mfr
N.A.I.C.S.: 332215
Jonathan W. L. So (Chm)

EAVS SA
12 avenue des coquelicots PA des petits carreaux, 94380, Bonneuil-sur-Marne, France
Tel.: (33) 145132860
Web Site: https://eavs-groupe.fr

Year Founded: 2012
MLEAV—(EUR)
Sales Range: $1-9.9 Million
Emp.: 40
Audiovisual & Surveillance Products
N.A.I.C.S.: 334310
Christophe Botteri (Chm & CEO)

EB MAWSON & SONS PTY LTD.
141 King George Street, PO Box 66, Cohuna, 3568, VIC, Australia
Tel.: (61) 3 5456 2409
Web Site:
    http://www.mawsons.com.au
Sales Range: $25-49.9 Million
Emp.: 200
Concrete Quarrying & Concrete Products Mfr
N.A.I.C.S.: 327390
John Mawson (Mng Dir)

EB TECH CO., LTD
170-9 Techno 2-ro Yuseong-gu, Daejeon, 34028, Korea (South)
Tel.: (82) 429307510
Web Site: http://www.eb-tech.com
Year Founded: 2000
Electron Accelerator Mfr
N.A.I.C.S.: 335999
Jin-Kyu Kim (CEO)

EBANG INTERNATIONAL HOLDINGS INC.
Building 7 No 5 Nangonghe Road Linping Street, Yuhang District, Hangzhou, 311100, Zhejiang, China
Tel.: (86) 57188176197   Ky
Web Site: https://www.ebang.com.cn
Year Founded: 2018
EBON—(NASDAQ)
Rev.: $32,328,119
Assets: $344,165,084
Liabilities: $22,377,203
Net Worth: $321,787,881
Earnings: ($43,888,242)
Emp.: 41
Fiscal Year-end: 12/31/22
Holding Company
N.A.I.C.S.: 551112
Dong Hu (Founder, Chm & CEO)

EBARA CORPORATION
11-1 Haneda Asahi-cho, Ota-ku, Tokyo, 144-8510, Japan
Tel.: (81) 337436111   JP
Web Site: https://www.ebara.co.jp
Year Founded: 1912
6361—(TKS)
Rev.: $5,383,635,520
Assets: $6,479,551,000
Liabilities: $3,490,605,520
Net Worth: $2,988,945,480
Earnings: $427,406,470
Emp.: 19,629
Fiscal Year-end: 12/31/23
Mfr of Fluid Machinery; Construction of Environment Protection Facilities; Manufacturing of Precision Machinery for Semiconductor Industry
N.A.I.C.S.: 333311
Yoshiaki Okiyama (Exec Officer)

Subsidiaries:

Advanced Design Technology Limited (1)
30 Millbank, Westminster, London, SW1P 4DU, United Kingdom   (50%)
Tel.: (44) 207 299 1170
Web Site: https://www.adtechnology.com
Sales Range: $1-9.9 Million
Emp.: 10
Sale of Inverse Design Technology Program & Related Consulting Services
N.A.I.C.S.: 541690
Richard Hunsley (Mgr-Engrg Svcs)

Benguet Ebara Real Estate Corp. (1)
Canlubang Industrial Estate, Cebuyao, Laguna, 4025, Philippines
Tel.: (63) 495491806
Web Site: http://www.ebaraphilippines.com
Sales Range: Less than $1 Million
Real Estate; Joint Venture of Benguet Corporation (60%) & Ebara Corporation (40%)
N.A.I.C.S.: 531210

E-Square Co., Ltd. (1)
22-2 Nakasode, Sodegaura, 299-0267, Chiba, Japan
Tel.: (81) 438643101
Web Site: http://www.ebara.co.jp
Electric Power Distribution Services
N.A.I.C.S.: 221122

EBARA DENSAN LTD. (1)
11-1 Haneda Asahimachi, Ota-ku, Tokyo, 144-0042, Japan
Tel.: (81) 337436622
Web Site: https://www.ebd.co.jp
Emp.: 184
Electronic Equipment Mfr & Distr
N.A.I.C.S.: 334419

EBARA EARNEST Co., Ltd. (1)
11-1 Haneda Asahimachi, Ota-ku, Tokyo, 144-0042, Japan
Tel.: (81) 362758000
Web Site: https://www.ee.ebara.com
Emp.: 66
Business Administration Services
N.A.I.C.S.: 561110

EBARA HAMADA BLOWER CO., LTD. (1)
2470 Takaoka-cho, Suzuka, 513-0014, Mieken, Japan
Tel.: (81) 593838700
Web Site: http://www.ehb.ebara.com
Sales Range: $50-74.9 Million
Emp.: 150
Industrial Fan & Blower Mfr
N.A.I.C.S.: 333413

EBARA Pumps RUS Limited Liability Company (1)
Building 7 Andropova 18 prospect, 115432, Moscow, Russia
Tel.: (7) 4996830133
Web Site: http://www.ebaraeurope.ru
Pump Product Distr
N.A.I.C.S.: 423830

EBARA SHOHNAN SPORTS CENTER INC. (1)
1-9-1 Inari, Fujisawa, 251-0862, Kanagawa, Japan
Tel.: (81) 466813411
Web Site: https://www.ebarassc.co.jp
Sales Range: $50-74.9 Million
Emp.: 6
Sports Club Operating Services
N.A.I.C.S.: 711211
Masaru Uchiyama (Pres)

ECE Co., Ltd. (1)
30-1 Nakasode, Sodegaura, 299-0267, Chiba, Japan
Tel.: (81) 438601557
Web Site: https://www.ece.ebara.com
Chemical Filter Mfr & Distr
N.A.I.C.S.: 333413

Ebara (Thailand) Limited (1)
125 ACME Building 3rd Floor Petchburi Road, Tungphayathai Rajthevee, Bangkok, 10400, Thailand   (33%)
Tel.: (66) 26120322
Web Site: http://www.ebara.co.th
Sales Range: $1-9.9 Million
Emp.: 40
Marketing, Engineering & Construction of Ebara Products
N.A.I.C.S.: 333310

Ebara Agency Co., Ltd. (1)
11-1 Hanedaasahicho, Ota-ku, Tokyo, 144-0042, Japan
Tel.: (81) 36 275 8100
Web Site: https://www.ea.ebara.com
Emp.: 106
Real Estate Management Services
N.A.I.C.S.: 531390
Akira Ito (Pres)

Ebara Bombas America Do Sul Ltda. (1)

Rue Joaquim Marques de Figueiredo 2-31, Distrito Industrial Domingos Biancardi, Bauru, 17034-290, Sao Paulo, Brazil
Tel.: (55) 1440090000
Web Site: http://www.ebara.com.br
Pump Product Distr
N.A.I.C.S.: 423830

Ebara Bombas Colombia S.A.S. (1)
Calle 98 70 - 91 Oficina 1016 Centro Empresarial Pontevedra, Bogota, Colombia
Tel.: (57) 18269865
Web Site: http://www.ebaracolombia.com
Pump Product Distr
N.A.I.C.S.: 423830

Ebara Densan (Kunshan) Mfg. Co., Ltd. (1)
No 521 Qingyang N Road, Zhoushi Town, Kunshan, 215314, Jiangsu, China
Tel.: (86) 512 5762 6121
Web Site: http://www.ebara.co.jp
Industrial Pump Mfr & Distr
N.A.I.C.S.: 423830

Ebara Densan (Qingdao) Technology Co., Ltd. (1)
No 216 Shuang Yuan Road, Chengyang, Qingdao, Shandong, China
Tel.: (86) 53289653369
Automatic Control Equipment Mfr
N.A.I.C.S.: 334512

Ebara Engineering Singapore Pte. Ltd. (1)
1 Tuas Link 2, Singapore, 638550, Singapore (100%)
Tel.: (65) 6 862 3536
Web Site: https://www.ebara.com.sg
Sales Range: $25-49.9 Million
Emp.: 98
Engineering & Construction; Maintenance Services for Precision Machines
N.A.I.C.S.: 333310
Yuta Nagano (Mng Dir)

Ebara Environmental Plant Co., Ltd. (1)
11-1 Haneda Asahi-cho, Ohta-ku, Tokyo, 144-0042, Japan
Tel.: (81) 362758600
Web Site: https://www.eep.ebara.com
Emp.: 2,139
Waste Treatment Services
N.A.I.C.S.: 562219

Ebara Espana Bombas S.A. (1)
Poligono Industrial la Estacion
C/Cormoranes 6-8, 28320, Pinto, Madrid, Spain (98%)
Tel.: (34) 91 692 3630
Web Site: https://www.ebara.es
Sales Range: $25-49.9 Million
Emp.: 15
Mfr & Sales of Industrial & Standard Pumps
N.A.I.C.S.: 333914

Ebara Fan & Blower Co., Ltd. (1)
2470 Takaoka-cho, Suzuka, 513-0014, Mie, Japan
Tel.: (81) 593838700
Web Site: https://www.efb.ebara.com
Fan Mfr
N.A.I.C.S.: 333413

Ebara Field Tech. Corporation (1)
4-2-1 Honfujisawa, Fujisawa, 251-8502, Kanagawa, Japan
Tel.: (81) 466839171
Web Site: http://www.eft.ebara.com
Emp.: 10
Semiconductor Device Repair Services & Distr
N.A.I.C.S.: 811210

Ebara Fluid Machinery Korea Co., Ltd. (1)
6th Floor Suam Building 747-13 Banpodong 367 Sapyeong-daero, Seocho-gu, Seoul, 06541, Korea (South)
Tel.: (82) 22 135 6111
Web Site: https://www.ebara.kr
Pump Product Mfr & Distr
N.A.I.C.S.: 333914

Ebara Great Pumps Co., Ltd. (1)
No 111 Fengdu 1st Road, Tangxia Town, Ruian, 325204, Zhejiang, China
Tel.: (86) 57765322260
Web Site: http://www.ebaragreat.com

Pump Product Distr
N.A.I.C.S.: 423830

Ebara Hai Duong Company Ltd. (1)
Nguyen Trai Road, Hai Duong, Vietnam (70%)
Tel.: (84) 3203850182
Sales Range: $50-74.9 Million
Emp.: 105
Mfr & Sales of Pumps
N.A.I.C.S.: 333914

Ebara Industrias Mecanicas e Comercio Ltda. (1)
Joaquim Marques De Figueiredo 2-31, Domingos Biancardi Industrial District, Bauru, 17034-290, Sao Paulo, Brazil (100%)
Tel.: (55) 144 009 0000
Web Site: https://www.ebara.com.br
Sales Range: $50-74.9 Million
Emp.: 152
Mfr & Sales of Pumps
N.A.I.C.S.: 333914

Ebara International Corp. (1)
350 Salomon Cir, Sparks, NV 89434-6635
Tel.: (775) 356-2796
Web Site: http://www.ebaracryo.com
Sales Range: $50-74.9 Million
Emp.: 140
Mfr & Marketing of Pumps
N.A.I.C.S.: 333914
Eric Wonhof (Engr-Design)

Ebara Machinery China Co., Ltd. (1)
Room No303 Beijing Fortune Plaza No 7 Dongsanhuan Zhonglu Road, Chaoyang, Beijing, 100020, China (100%)
Tel.: (86) 1065309996
Web Site: http://www.ebara.cn
Standard Pumps & Related Equipment Mfr, Sales & Service
N.A.I.C.S.: 333248

Ebara Machinery India Private Limited (1)
First Floor No 133 Velachery Road, Guindy, Chennai, 600032, India
Tel.: (91) 4422351926
Web Site: http://www.ebara.com
Pump Product Mfr & Distr
N.A.I.C.S.: 333914

Ebara Machinery Zibo Co., Ltd. (1)
No 517 Zunxian Road, New Hi-tech Industrial Development Zone, Zibo, 255086, Shandong, China
Tel.: (86) 533 391 9586
Web Site: https://www.ebarazb.com
Pump Product Mfr & Distr
N.A.I.C.S.: 333914

Ebara Material Co., Ltd. (1)
30-1 Nakasode, Sodegaura, 299-0267, Chiba, Japan
Tel.: (81) 438 60 1551
Web Site: http://www.ebara.co.jp
Cast Products Mfr
N.A.I.C.S.: 331315

Ebara Meister Co., Ltd. (1)
11-1 Haneda Asahi-cho, Ota-ku, Tokyo, 144-0042, Japan
Tel.: (81) 362759510
Emp.: 5
Temporary Staffing Services
N.A.I.C.S.: 561320
Ofamu Eguchi (Pres)

Ebara Pompy Polska Sp. z o.o. (1)
UL Dzialkowa 115A, 02-234, Warsaw, Poland
Tel.: (48) 223909920
Pump Product Distr
N.A.I.C.S.: 423830

Ebara Precision Machinery Europe GmbH (1)
Roden Bacher Chaussee 6, Hanau, 63457, Hessen, Germany (100%)
Tel.: (49) 618118760
Web Site: http://www.ebara-europe.com
Sales Range: $25-49.9 Million
Emp.: 130
Maintenance Services for Pumps & Precision Machines
N.A.I.C.S.: 811210
Reinhart Richter (Mng Dir)

Ebara Precision Machinery Korea Inc. (1)

902 U Space 1B 6660 Daewangpangyo ro, Budanggu Seongnamsi Gyeonggido, 463400, Seoul, Korea (South) (100%)
Tel.: (82) 25816901
Web Site: http://www.ebara.co.kr
Sales Range: $25-49.9 Million
Emp.: 25
Precision Machines Maintenance Services
N.A.I.C.S.: 333310
Kyung Suk Lee (Gen Mgr)

Ebara Precision Machinery Taiwan Incorporated (1)
Rm No 1402 No 96 Chung Shan, North Rd Sec 2, Taipei, 104, Taiwan (100%)
Tel.: (886) 225601166
Sales Range: $75-99.9 Million
Emp.: 183
Maintenace Services for Precision Machines
N.A.I.C.S.: 423830

Ebara Pump Industries P.J.S. (1)
No 1 4th Alley Eshghyar Niloofar St, Khorramshahr Ave, Tehran, Iran (44%)
Tel.: (98) 2188514828
Web Site: http://www.ebara.ir
Sales Range: $25-49.9 Million
Emp.: 35
Standard Pump Sales
N.A.I.C.S.: 423830

Ebara Pumps Australia Pty. Ltd. (1)
7 Holloway Drive, Bayswater, 3153, VIC, Australia (80%)
Tel.: (61) 397613033
Web Site: http://www.ebara.com.au
Sales Range: $10-24.9 Million
Emp.: 7
Sale of Standard Pumps
N.A.I.C.S.: 333914
Mark Barrett (Gen Mgr)

Ebara Pumps Europe S.p.A. (1)
Via Torri di Confine 2/1 int C, Gambellara, 36053, Vicenza, Italy (100%)
Tel.: (39) 044 470 6811
Web Site: https://www.ebaraeurope.com
Sales Range: $50-74.9 Million
Emp.: 140
Pump Mfr & Sales
N.A.I.C.S.: 333914

Ebara Pumps Malaysia Sdn. Bhd. (1)
6 Jalan TP3 UEP Subang Jaya Industrial Park, 47620, Subang Jaya, Selangor, Malaysia
Tel.: (60) 380236622
Web Site: http://www.ebara.com.my
Pump Equipment Mfr
N.A.I.C.S.: 333914

Ebara Pumps Mexico, S.A. de C.V. (1)
Av Central Numero 230 Interior 146, en la Congregacion de San Sebastian de los Lermas, 67188, Guadalupe, Nuevo Leon, Mexico
Tel.: (52) 8124744090
Pump Product Distr
N.A.I.C.S.: 423830

Ebara Pumps Middle East FZE (1)
Blue Shed Warehouse Area Warehouse No ZF -05, PO Box 61383, Jebel Ali Free Zone, Dubai, United Arab Emirates
Tel.: (971) 48838889
Web Site: http://ebarame.ae
Pump Product Mfr & Distr
N.A.I.C.S.: 333914

Ebara Pumps Philippines, Inc. (1)
Canlubang Industrial Estate Bo Pittland, Cabuyao, Laguna, Philippines
Tel.: (63) 495491806
Web Site: http://ebaraphilippines.com
Pump Equipment Distr
N.A.I.C.S.: 423830

Ebara Pumps Saudi Arabia LLC (1)
St 98 Dammam Second Industrial City, PO Box 9210, Dammam, 34333, Saudi Arabia
Tel.: (966) 138022014
Pump Product Distr
N.A.I.C.S.: 423830

Ebara Pumps South Africa (Pty) Ltd. (1)
26 Kyalami Boulevard Kyalami Park, PO

Box 30011, Midrand, Johannesburg, 1684, South Africa
Tel.: (27) 11 466 1844
Web Site: https://ebarapumpssouthafrica.co.za
Pump Product Distr
N.A.I.C.S.: 423830

Ebara Qingdao Co. Ltd. (1)
412 Beijing Fortune Bldg, 5 Dong Sanhuan Bei Lu, 100004, Beijing, China (100%)
Tel.: (86) 65908150
Sales Range: $25-49.9 Million
Emp.: 15
Mfr of Boilers
N.A.I.C.S.: 333310

Ebara Refrigeration Equipment & Systems (China) Co., Ltd. (1)
No 720 Yongda Road, Fushan High-tech Industrial Park, Yantai, 265500, Shandong, China
Tel.: (86) 535 698 8668
Web Site: https://www.ebara-ersc.com
Electrical Equipment Distr
N.A.I.C.S.: 423690

Ebara Refrigeration Equipment & Systems Co., Ltd. (1)
Web Site: http://www.ers.ebara.com
Sales Range: $200-249.9 Million
Emp.: 765
Heating Equipment Mfr & Distr
N.A.I.C.S.: 333414
Osamu Shono (Pres)

Ebara Technologies Inc. (1)
51 Main Ave, Sacramento, CA 95838-2014
Tel.: (916) 920-5451
Web Site: https://www.ebaratech.com
Sales Range: $25-49.9 Million
Emp.: 90
Sale & Manufacture of Precision Machines
N.A.I.C.S.: 333912
Ray Campbell (Gen Mgr)

Ebara Thermal Systems (Thailand) Co., Ltd. (1)
ACME Building 3rd Fl 125 Petchburi Road, Thungphayathai Rajthevee, Bangkok, 10400, Thailand
Tel.: (66) 26 120 3146
Web Site: https://www.ebara-thermalth.com
Chillers Product Distr
N.A.I.C.S.: 423740

Ebara Vietnam Pump Company Limited (1)
Lot XN01 Lai Cach Industrial Park, Cam Giang District, Hai Duong, Vietnam
Tel.: (84) 220 385 0182
Web Site: https://ebarapump.com.vn
Pump Product Mfr & Distr
N.A.I.C.S.: 333914
Kenichi Mori (Gen Dir)

Ebara Yoshikura Hydro-Tech Co., Ltd. (1)
1-5-3 Nihonbashi-muromachi, Chuo-ku, Tokyo, 103-0022, Japan
Tel.: (81) 3 3510 7400
Web Site: http://www.eyh.ebara.com
Industrial Pump Mfr & Distr
N.A.I.C.S.: 333914

Ebara-Benguet, Inc. (1)
Canlubang Industrial Estate, Cabugao, 4025, Laguna, Philippines (89.4%)
Tel.: (63) 495491806
Web Site: http://www.ebaraphilippines.com
Sales Range: $1-9.9 Million
Emp.: 100
Casting Mfr
N.A.I.C.S.: 331523

Ebara-Byron Jackson, Ltd. (1)
Gotanda Nagaoka Bldg 7-17-7 Nishi Gotanda, Shinagawa-ku, Tokyo, 141-0031, Japan
Tel.: (81) 357195888
Web Site: http://www.ebara.co.jp
Industrial Pump Sales & Maintenance Services
N.A.I.C.S.: 423830

Ebara-Densan Taiwan Manufacturing Co., Ltd. (1)
No 7-2 Nanyuan 2nd Rd, Zhongli Dist, Taoyuan, 320, Tao Yuen Hsien, Taiwan (100%)

Ebara Corporation—(Continued)

Tel.: (886) 3 451 5881
Web Site: https://www.ebara.com.tw
Sales Range: $25-49.9 Million
Emp.: 70
Pumps & Submersible Motors Mfr, Sales & Services
N.A.I.C.S.: 333914

Ebara-Elliott Service (Taiwan) Co., Ltd. (1)
1 Road 42 Industrial Zone, Taichung, 00407, Taiwan (51%)
Tel.: (886) 423594202
Web Site: http://www.elliott-turbo.com
Sales Range: $25-49.9 Million
Emp.: 35
Maintenance & Repair of Turbomachinery & Compressors
N.A.I.C.S.: 333310

Elliott Company (1)
901 N 4th St, Jeannette, PA 15644
Tel.: (724) 527-2811
Web Site: https://www.elliott-turbo.com
Sales Range: $125-149.9 Million
Emp.: 800
Plant Air & Gas Compressors, Steam Turbines & Other Related Power Generating Equipment Mfr
N.A.I.C.S.: 333611
William E. Cox (VP-Legal)

Holding (Non-US):

Elliott Turbomachinery Canada, Inc. (2)
955 Maple Avenue, Burlington, L7S 2J4, ON, Canada (100%)
Tel.: (905) 333-4101
Web Site: http://www.elliott-turbo.com
Sales Range: $25-49.9 Million
Emp.: 35
Mfr of Industrial Machinery
N.A.I.C.S.: 333248

Elliott Turbomachinery Ltd. (2)
Unit 11 Easter Park Benyon Road, Silchester, Reading, RG7 2PQ, United Kingdom (100%)
Tel.: (44) 1256354334
Web Site: http://www.elliott-turbo.com
Sales Range: $25-49.9 Million
Emp.: 50
Compressor & Turbine Services
N.A.I.C.S.: 333912

Elliott Turbomachinery S.A. (2)
Feldstrasse 2, Post Fach 249, 8853, Lachen, Switzerland (100%)
Tel.: (41) 554518000
Web Site: http://www.elliott-turbo.com
Sales Range: $25-49.9 Million
Emp.: 50
Machinery Products Sales
N.A.I.C.S.: 423860
Guito Vesti (Gen Mgr)

Elliott Ebara Singapore Pte. Ltd. (1)
1A International Business Park 07-01, Singapore, 609933, Singapore
Tel.: (65) 6563 6776
Emp.: 50
Fluid Machinery Sales & Maintenance Services
N.A.I.C.S.: 423830
Josheop Medina (Mng Dir)

Elliott Ebara Turbomachinery Corporation (1)
20-1 Nakasode, Sodegaura, 299-0296, Chiba, Japan
Tel.: (81) 43 860 6111
Web Site: http://www.eetc.global
Industrial Machinery Mfr & Distr
N.A.I.C.S.: 333248

Elliott Group Holdings, Inc. (1)
20-1 Nakasode, Sodegaura, 299-0296, Chiba-ken, Japan
Tel.: (81) 43 860 6111
Web Site: https://www.elliott-turbo.com
Administrative Services
N.A.I.C.S.: 561110

Hayward Gordon Ltd (1)
5 Brigden Gate, Halton Hills, L7G 0A3, ON, Canada
Tel.: (905) 693-8595

Web Site: http://www.haywardgordon.com
Emp.: 70
Pumps, Mixers & Strainers Mfr
N.A.I.C.S.: 333914
John Hayward (Exec Dir)

Subsidiary (US):

Scott Turbon Mixer, Inc. (2)
9351 Industrial Way, Adelanto, CA 92301
Tel.: (760) 246-3430
Web Site: http://www.scottmixer.com
Manufactures Stainless Steel Mixers & Mixing Systems
N.A.I.C.S.: 333248
Bill Scott (Gen Mgr)

Sharpe Mixers, Inc. (2)
1541 S 92nd Pl Ste A, Seattle, WA 98108
Tel.: (206) 767-5660
Web Site: http://www.sharpemixers.com
Sales Range: $1-9.9 Million
Emp.: 25
Mixer Parts Mfr
N.A.I.C.S.: 333914
Jay Dinnison (CEO)

Hyosung Ebara Co., Ltd. (1)
(28%)
Sales Range: $25-49.9 Million
Emp.: 40
Mfr & Sales of Pumps; Joint Venture of Ebara Corporation & Hyosung Corporation
N.A.I.C.S.: 333914

P.T. Ebara Indonesia (1)
Jl Raya Jakarta - Bogor KM 32, Curug Cimanggis, Depok, 16453, Jawa Barat, Indonesia (55%)
Tel.: (62) 2187 408 5253
Web Site: https://www.ebaraindonesia.com
Sales Range: $100-124.9 Million
Emp.: 500
Mfr & Sales of Pumps
N.A.I.C.S.: 333914
Nobuki Abay (Pres)

P.T. Ebara Indonesia (1)
JL Raya Jakarta Bogor Km 32, Curug Cimanggis Kota Depok, Bogor, 16453, Jawa Barat, Indonesia
Tel.: (62) 218740853
Web Site: http://www.ebaraindonesia.com
Water Pump Mfr & Distr
N.A.I.C.S.: 333996

PT. Ebara Turbomachinery Services Indonesia (1)
5th Floor Setiabudi Atrium 510 Jl HR Rasuna Said Kav 62, Jakarta, 12910, Indonesia
Tel.: (62) 2152902086
Web Site: http://www.ebaraturbo.co.id
Pump Product Mfr & Distr
N.A.I.C.S.: 333914

Qingdao Jiaonan Ebara Electric Power Co., Ltd. (1)
183 Changcheng Road, Jiaonan, Shandong, China (57.6%)
Tel.: (86) 532 6181937
Special Industry Services
N.A.I.C.S.: 333310

Shanghai Ebara Engineering and Services Co., Ltd. (1)
20th Floor N Gate Plaza 99 Tian Mu West Road, Shanghai, 200070, China (90%)
Tel.: (86) 2151017677
Sales Range: $25-49.9 Million
Emp.: 50
Engineering & Construction of Environmental Facilities
N.A.I.C.S.: 541330

Shanghai Ebara Precision Machinery Co., Ltd. (1)
Tech Park No 76 Lane 887, Zuchongzhi Road, Shanghai, 200122, China
Tel.: (86) 151317008
Maintenance Services for Precision Machines
N.A.I.C.S.: 811210

Sumoto S.r.l. (1)
Via Peripoli ReG 1 3, Montecchio Maggiore, 36075, Vicenza, Italy (100%)
Tel.: (39) 0444490515
Web Site: http://www.sumoto.com

Sales Range: $25-49.9 Million
Emp.: 50
Mfr, Producer & Marketer of Submersible Motors for Deep Well Pumps
N.A.I.C.S.: 333310
Sebastiano Damico (Gen Mgr)

Swing Corporation (1)
27F Shiodome Sumitomo Bldg 9-2 Higashishimbashi 1-chome, Minato-ku, Tokyo, 105-0021, Japan
Tel.: (81) 343460600
Web Site: https://www.swing-w.com
Emp.: 4,300
Industrial Chemical Mfr & Distr
N.A.I.C.S.: 325411

Yantai Ebara Air Conditioning Equipment Co., Ltd. (1)
No720 Yongda Road, New & High-Tech Zone Fushan, Yantai, Shandong, China (100%)
Tel.: (86) 5356357171
Web Site: http://www.ebara-ersc.com
Sales Range: $100-124.9 Million
Emp.: 264
Mfr & Sales of Refrigerating Machineries
N.A.I.C.S.: 334512

Yingkou Ebara Co., Ltd. (1)
Economic And Technique Development Zone, Yingkou, 115007, Liaoning, China (60%)
Tel.: (86) 4176252125
Mfr of Wooden Patterns & Procurement of Pump Darts
N.A.I.C.S.: 337126

EBARA FOODS INDUSTRY, INC.

Yokohama iMark Place 14th floor 4-4-5 Minatomirai, Nishi-ku, Yokohama, 220-0012, Kanagawa, Japan
Tel.: (81) 452260226
Web Site:
https://www.ebarafoods.com
Year Founded: 1958
2819—(TKS)
Rev.: $298,877,760
Assets: $316,929,670
Liabilities: $100,002,690
Net Worth: $216,926,980
Earnings: $11,911,220
Emp.: 507
Fiscal Year-end: 03/31/24
Frozen Food Product Mfr & Whslr
N.A.I.C.S.: 311421

Subsidiaries:

Ebara Foods (Shanghai) Co., Ltd. (1)
4th Floor Building 1 No 188 Zhongchen Road, Songjiang District, Shanghai, China
Tel.: (86) 2151105518
Emp.: 22
Food Product Mfr & Distr
N.A.I.C.S.: 311941

Ebara Foods Industry, Inc. - Gunma Factory (1)
1744-4 Naganuma-machi, Isesaki, Gunma, Japan
Tel.: (81) 270322226
Soup Mfr
N.A.I.C.S.: 311710

Ebara Foods Industry, Inc. - Tochigi Factory (1)
570-1 Hakonomori Hakonomori-shinden, Sakura, Tochigi, Japan
Tel.: (81) 286829891
Food Products Mfr
N.A.I.C.S.: 311941

Ebara Foods Industry, Inc. - Tsuyama Factory (1)
Tsuyama Central Industrial Park 468-1 Kanai, Tsuyama, Okayama, Japan
Tel.: (81) 868268121
Food Products Mfr
N.A.I.C.S.: 311941

EBARA JITSUGYO CO., LTD.

7-14-1 Ginza, Chuo-ku, Tokyo, 104-8174, Japan

Tel.: (81) 355652881
Web Site: https://www.ejk.co.jp
Year Founded: 1946
6328—(TKS)
Rev.: $257,225,200
Assets: $297,191,530
Liabilities: $148,103,010
Net Worth: $149,088,520
Earnings: $22,269,690
Emp.: 595
Fiscal Year-end: 12/31/23
Equipment Mfr
N.A.I.C.S.: 333413

Subsidiaries:

Ebajitsu Co., Ltd. (1)
4-18 Kitamine-cho, Ota-ku, Tokyo, 145-0073, Japan
Tel.: (81) 337204161
Web Site: https://www.ebajitsu.com
Air Conditioner Maintenance Services
N.A.I.C.S.: 811412

Ebara Jitsugyo Power Co., Ltd. (1)
3-5-1 Kazusakamatari, Kisarazu, 292-0818, Chiba, Japan
Tel.: (81) 438523710
Measuring Device Mfr & Distr
N.A.I.C.S.: 334519

EBASE CO., LTD.

2F commercial second building 5-4-9 Toyosaki, Kita-ku, Osaka, 531-0072, Japan
Tel.: (81) 664863955
Web Site: https://www.ebase.co.jp
Year Founded: 2001
3835—(TKS)
Rev.: $34,304,582
Assets: $51,595,625
Liabilities: $5,735,050
Net Worth: $45,860,575
Earnings: $7,558,637
Fiscal Year-end: 03/31/24
Software Development Services
N.A.I.C.S.: 541512
Takao Iwata (Pres & CEO)

EBC INC.

1095 Valet Street, L'Ancienne-Lorett, G2E 4M7, QC, Canada
Tel.: (418) 872-0600
Web Site: http://www.ebcinc.com
Year Founded: 1968
Sales Range: $250-299.9 Million
Emp.: 1,500
General Construction Contractor
N.A.I.C.S.: 236220
Marie-Claude Houle (Pres & CEO)

Subsidiaries:

Don Bourgeois & Fils Contracteur Inc (1)
3851 Chemin Sullivan, Val d'Or, J9P 0B9, QC, Canada
Tel.: (819) 824-5681
Web Site: http://www.donbourgeoisetfils.ca
Emp.: 5
Mining Support Services
N.A.I.C.S.: 213114
Donald Proulx (Pres)

EBCO INDUSTRIES LTD.

7851 Alderbridge Way, Richmond, V6X 2A4, BC, Canada
Tel.: (604) 278-5578
Web Site: https://www.ebco.com
Year Founded: 1956
Emp.: 200
Heavy Industrial Machinery Mfr
N.A.I.C.S.: 333248
Richard Eppich (Pres & CEO)

EBENISTERIE ST-URBAIN LTEE

226 rue Principale, Saint-Louis-de-Gonzague, J0S 1T0, QC, Canada
Tel.: (450) 373-4861
Web Site: http://www.ebsu.ca

Year Founded: 1981
Emp.: 150
Kitchen Cabinet Mfr
N.A.I.C.S.: 337110
Napoleon Boucher *(Pres)*

Subsidiaries:

Euro-Rite Cabinets Ltd.   (1)
19100 Airport Way, Pitt Meadows, V3Y 0E2,
BC, Canada
Tel.: (604) 464-5060
Web Site: http://www.eurorite.com
Rev.: $16,961,032
Emp.: 115
Kitchen Cabinets & Accessories Mfr
N.A.I.C.S.: 337110
Bill Longman *(Founder)*

EBEST SPECIAL PURPOSE ACQUISITION 3 COMPANY

119 Seochojungang-ro, Seocho-gu,
Seoul, 06644, Korea (South)
Tel.: (82) 237798832
Year Founded: 2015
Financial Investment Management
Services
N.A.I.C.S.: 523940
Jung-Hoon Lee *(CEO)*

EBIOX LIMITED

822 Fountain Court Birchwood Boule-
vard, Birchwood, Warrington, WA3
7QZ, Cheshire, United Kingdom
Tel.: (44) 1925 202205
Web Site: http://www.ebiox.co.uk
Sales Range: $25-49.9 Million
Emp.: 5
Disinfectants & Hygiene Products Mfr
N.A.I.C.S.: 325612
Wendy Bradford *(Mgr-Comml)*

EBIQUITY PLC

Chapter House 16 Brunswick Place,
London, N1 6DZ, United Kingdom
Tel.: (44) 2076509600
Web Site: https://www.ebiquity.com
EBQ—(AIM)
Rev.: $92,730,419
Assets: $121,107,149
Liabilities: $68,516,627
Net Worth: $52,590,522
Earnings: ($5,423,278)
Fiscal Year-end: 12/31/23
Analysis & Consultancy Services For
Advertisers
N.A.I.C.S.: 541910
Alan Newman *(CFO & COO)*

Subsidiaries:

China Media (Shanghai) Manage-
ment Consulting Company
Limited   (1)
Room F1 29F June Yao International Plaza
789 Zhaojiabang Road, Shanghai, 200032,
China
Tel.: (86) 2154038196
Marketing & Media Consultancy Services
N.A.I.C.S.: 541613

Digital Balance Australia Pty.
Limited   (1)
Suite 5 Level 1 63 Hay Street, Subiaco,
6008, WA, Australia
Tel.: (61) 892278073
Web Site: http://www.digitalbalance.com.au
Digital Analytics Consultancy Services
N.A.I.C.S.: 541613
Tim Elleston *(Mng Dir)*

Ebiquity Germany GmbH   (1)
Hermannstrasse 40, 20095, Hamburg, Ger-
many
Tel.: (49) 40399277100
Marketing & Media Consultancy Services
N.A.I.C.S.: 541613
Christian Zimmer *(Mng Dir-DACH)*

Ebiquity Italia S.r.l.   (1)
Via della Moscova 40, 20121, Milan, Italy
Tel.: (39) 0236728000
Marketing & Media Consultancy Services

N.A.I.C.S.: 541613

Ebiquity Italy Media Advisor S.r.l.   (1)
Via della Moscova 40, 20121, Milan, Italy
Tel.: (39) 023 672 8000
Media Investment Analysis Services
N.A.I.C.S.: 541840

Ebiquity Marsh Limited   (1)
11 Ely Place, Dublin, Ireland
Tel.: (353) 16760934
Web Site: https://www.ebiquitymarsh.ie
Media Auditing & Consultancy Services
N.A.I.C.S.: 541618

Ebiquity Pte. Limited   (1)
61 Robinson Road 18-02 Robinson Centre,
Singapore, 068893, Singapore
Tel.: (65) 90925116
Marketing & Media Consultancy Services
N.A.I.C.S.: 541613
Regina Lim *(Reg Dir)*

Ebiquity Russia OOO   (1)
Centre-T Business Centre Bld 1 2 Gamson-
ovsky Pereulok, Moscow, 115191, Russia
Tel.: (7) 4952520415
Marketing & Media Consultancy Services
N.A.I.C.S.: 541613

Ebiquity SAS   (1)
30 Rue d Orleans, 92200, Neuilly-sur-
Seine, France
Tel.: (33) 176219050
Marketing & Media Consultancy Services
N.A.I.C.S.: 541613

FirmDecisions ASJP Germany
GmbH   (1)
Hermannstrasse 40, 20095, Hamburg, Ger-
many
Tel.: (49) 40399277250
Web Site: http://www.firmdecisions.com
Global Marketing Compliance Services
N.A.I.C.S.: 541618
Angelika Scarperi *(Mng Dir)*

Media Management, LLC   (1)
1801 Royal Ln Ste 906, Dallas, TX 75229
Tel.: (972) 409-0900
Web Site: http://www.mmgt.com
Sales Range: $1-9.9 Million
Emp.: 10
Motion Picture & Video Production
N.A.I.C.S.: 512110
Robert Dungan *(Principal)*

Mediaadvantage Consulting
L.d.a   (1)
Rua A Gazeta de Oeiras Ed Horizonte N
2-2 A, 2780-171, Oeiras, Portugal
Tel.: (351) 210995441
Marketing & Media Consultancy Services
N.A.I.C.S.: 541613

EBN B.V.

Daalsesingel 1, 3511 SV, Utrecht,
Netherlands
Tel.: (31) 30 233 9001   NI
Web Site: http://www.ebn.nl
Year Founded: 1973
Rev.: $2,456,972,840
Assets: $7,309,326,220
Liabilities: $6,441,434,720
Net Worth: $867,891,500
Earnings: $286,684,160
Emp.: 118
Fiscal Year-end: 12/31/19
Exploration & Production Activities for
Oil & Natural Gas
N.A.I.C.S.: 211120
Berend Scheffers *(Dir-Tech & Strat-
egy)*

Subsidiaries:

K13 Extensie Beheer B.V.   (1)
Moreelsepark 48, 3511EP, Utrecht, Nether-
lands
Tel.: (31) 30 2339001
Oil & Natural Gas Exploration Services
N.A.I.C.S.: 213112

EBNER GMBH & CO. KG

Karl-Ebner-Str 8, Eiterfeld, 36132,
Fulda, Germany
Tel.: (49) 66728900

Web Site: http://ebner-co.de
Year Founded: 1965
Rev.: $31,753,788
Emp.: 120
Plant & Apparatus Construction Ser-
vices
N.A.I.C.S.: 333248
Stefan Ebner *(Mng Partner)*

EBOOK INITIATIVE JAPAN CO., LTD.

2-5-2 Nishikanda Chiyoda-ku, Tokyo,
101-0065, Japan
Tel.: (81) 3 62729244
Web Site: http://www.ebookjapan.jp
3658—(TKS)
Sales Range: Less than $1 Million
E-Book Retailer
N.A.I.C.S.: 423430
Masamine Takahashi *(Chm, Pres & CEO)*

EBOS GROUP LIMITED

108 Wrights Road Addington,
Christchurch, 8024, New Zealand
Tel.: (64) 33380999
Web Site:
   https://www.ebosgroup.com
EBO—(ASX)
Rev.: $7,979,005,673
Assets: $4,197,061,355
Liabilities: $2,695,229,184
Net Worth: $1,501,832,171
Earnings: $171,770,881
Emp.: 5,000
Fiscal Year-end: 06/30/23
Surgical & Medical Equipment Retail-
ers
N.A.I.C.S.: 423450
Elizabeth Coutts *(Chm)*

Subsidiaries:

Australian Biotechnologies Pty.
Ltd.   (1)
Allambie Grove Business Park Unit 5 25
Frenchs Forest Road East, Frenchs Forest,
2086, NSW, Australia
Tel.: (61) 299759500
Web Site: https://ausbiotech.com.au
Allograft Tissue Product Mfr & Distr
N.A.I.C.S.: 339112

Botany Bay Imports & Exports Pty
Ltd   (1)
24 Underwood Ave, Botany, 2019, VIC,
Australia
Tel.: (61) 246248950
Web Site:
   https://www.botanybayimports.com.au
Pet Product Distr
N.A.I.C.S.: 424990

Clinect Pty Ltd   (1)
Level 7 737 Bourke St, Docklands, 3008,
VIC, Australia
Tel.: (61) 399185555
Web Site: https://www.clinect.com.au
Pharmaceutical Product Whslr
N.A.I.C.S.: 424210
Merryn Wallace *(Gen Mgr)*

DoseAid Pty Ltd   (1)
Level 7 737 Bourke Street, Docklands,
3008, VIC, Australia
Tel.: (61) 1300306748
Web Site: https://www.doseaid.com.au
Pharmaceutical Product Whslr
N.A.I.C.S.: 424210
Jenelle Moloney *(Natl Sls Mgr-Comml)*

Ebos Group Pty Limited   (1)
Unit 2 109 Vanessa St, Kingsgrove, 2208,
NSW, Australia
Tel.: (61) 295028426
Web Site: http://www.ebosonline.com.au
Sales Range: $10-24.9 Million
Emp.: 100
Healtcare Services
N.A.I.C.S.: 621491
David Lewis *(Gen Mgr)*

Ebos Health & Science Pty
Limited   (1)

Ste 2 109 Vanessa St, Kingsgrove, 2208,
NSW, Australia
Tel.: (61) 295028410
Healtcare Services
N.A.I.C.S.: 621491

Endeavour CH Pty Ltd   (1)
Level 7 737 Bourke Street, Docklands,
3008, VIC, Australia
Tel.: (61) 399185555
Web Site:
   http://www.endeavourconsumer.com.au
Pharmaceuticals Product Mfr
N.A.I.C.S.: 325412

Health Support Limited   (1)
56 Carrington Road, Point Chevalier, Auck-
land, 1025, New Zealand
Tel.: (64) 98152600
Web Site: http://www.healthsupport.co.nz
Rev.: $71,058,000
Emp.: 110
Surgical & Medical Products Distr
N.A.I.C.S.: 423450
Greg Managh *(Gen Mgr)*

Intellipharm Pty Ltd   (1)
Level 3 / 33 Remora Rd, Hamilton, 4007,
QLD, Australia
Tel.: (61) 1300255160
Web Site: http://www.intellipharm.com.au
Medical Software Services
N.A.I.C.S.: 541511

LMT Surgical Pty Ltd   (1)
237-239 Milton Rd, Milton, 4064, QLD, Aus-
tralia
Tel.: (61) 1300880155
Web Site: https://www.lmtsurgical.com
Healtcare Services
N.A.I.C.S.: 621999

Lifehealthcare Distribution Pty
Ltd.   (1)
Level 8 15 Talavera Road, North Ryde,
2113, NSW, Australia
Tel.: (61) 1800060168
Web Site: https://www.lifehealthcare.com.au
Medical Device Distr
N.A.I.C.S.: 423450
Matt Muscio *(CEO & Mng Dir)*

Masterpet Australia Pty Ltd   (1)
Lot 2 31 Topham Road, Smeaton Grange,
Sydney, 2567, NSW, Australia
Tel.: (61) 1300651111
Web Site: https://www.masterpet.com.au
Pet Product Distr
N.A.I.C.S.: 424990
Julie Dillon *(CEO-Animal Care)*

National Surgical Pty Ltd   (1)
Unit 25/22-30 Northumberland Road, Car-
ingbah, 2229, NSW, Australia
Tel.; (61) 1800138138
Web Site:
   http://www.nationalsurgical.com.au
Emp.: 20
Medical Equipment Mfr
N.A.I.C.S.: 339112

Nexus Australasia Pty Ltd   (1)
U8 12 Cowcher Place, Belmont, 6104, WA,
Australia
Tel.: (61) 894773777
Web Site:
   http://www.nexuspackaging.com.au
Packaging Machinery Distr
N.A.I.C.S.: 423830

Ophthaswissmed Philippines Inc.   (1)
9F Petron Mega Plaza 358 Sen Gil Puyat
Avenue, Brgy Bel-Air, Makati, 1209, Philip-
pines
Tel.: (63) 253176888
Medical Device Distr
N.A.I.C.S.: 423450

Pharmacy Retailing NZ Limited   (1)
Sylvia Park, PO Box 62-027, Auckland,
1644, New Zealand
Tel.: (64) 99159500
Web Site: https://www.propharma.co.nz
Pharmaceutical Product Whslr
N.A.I.C.S.: 424210

Sentry Medical Pty. Ltd.   (1)
22 Peter Brock Drive, Eastern Creek, Sydney, 2766, NSW, Australia
Tel.: (61) 288843995
Web Site: https://www.sentrymedical.com.au

EBOS Group Limited—(Continued)

Medical Product Mfr & Distr
N.A.I.C.S.: 339112

Surgical And Medical Supplies Pty. Ltd. (1)
16 Kensington Road, Rose Park, 5067, SA, Australia
Tel.: (61) 883321666
Web Site: https://www.surmed.com.au
Medical Care Services
N.A.I.C.S.: 622110

Swissmed Pte. Ltd. (1)
5 Jalan Kilang Barat 9th Floor Petro Centre, Singapore, 159349, Singapore
Tel.: (65) 67371945
Web Site: https://swissmed.asia
Emp.: 40
Medical Device Distr
N.A.I.C.S.: 423450

Swissmed Sdn. Bhd. (1)
C-10-30 Kompleks Rimbun Scott Garden 289 Jalan Kelang Lama, 58100, Kuala Lumpur, Malaysia
Tel.: (60) 379714552
Medical Device Distr
N.A.I.C.S.: 423450

Symbion Pty Ltd (1)
Level 7 737 Bourke Street, Docklands, 3008, VIC, Australia
Tel.: (61) 399185555
Web Site: https://www.symbion.com.au
Healtcare Services
N.A.I.C.S.: 621999
Brett Barons (CEO)

Transmedic (Thailand) Co. Ltd. (1)
888/209 2nd Floor and 888/87-89 8th Floor Mahatun Plaza, Ploenchit Road Lumpini Pathumwan, Bangkok, 10330, Thailand
Tel.: (66) 22550405
Medical Device Distr
N.A.I.C.S.: 423450

Transmedic China Ltd. (1)
Unit 1601 16/F Yen Sheng Centre 64 Hoi Yuen Road, Kwun Tong, Kowloon, China (Hong Kong)
Tel.: (852) 21074668
Medical Device Distr
N.A.I.C.S.: 423450

Transmedic Company Ltd. (1)
No 506 Nguyen Dinh Chieu Street, Ward 4 District 3 3rd Floor Phuong Long Building, Ho Chi Minh City, Vietnam
Tel.: (84) 2838327939
Medical Device Distr
N.A.I.C.S.: 423450

Transmedic Philippines, Inc. (1)
9F Petron Mega Plaza 358 Sen Gil Puyat Avenue, Bel-Air, Makati, 1209, Philippines
Tel.: (63) 253176888
Medical Device Distr
N.A.I.C.S.: 423450

Transmedic Pte. Ltd. (1)
5 Jalan Kilang Barat 9th Floor Petro Centre, Singapore, 159349, Singapore (90%)
Tel.: (65) 67371945
Web Site: https://www.transmedicgroup.com
Emp.: 506
Medical Device Distr
N.A.I.C.S.: 423450

Ventura Health Pty Ltd (1)
Suite 1 Level 1 Building C 1 Homebush Bay Drive, Rhodes, 2138, NSW, Australia
Tel.: (61) 296377205
Web Site: https://www.venturahealth.com.au
Pharmaceutical Product Retailer
N.A.I.C.S.: 456110

Warner & Webster Pty Ltd (1)
PO Box 105, Huntingdale, 3166, VIC, Australia
Tel.: (61) 1300556917
Web Site: http://www.warnerwebster.com.au
Medical Equipment Distr
N.A.I.C.S.: 423450

EBRAHIM K. KANOO COMPANY B.S.C.

Building 510 Road 366 Block 302 Qassim Al-Mehzaa Road, PO Box

119, Manama, Bahrain
Tel.: (973) 17262262
Web Site: http://www.ekkanoo.com.bh
Year Founded: 1920
Sales Range: $75-99.9 Million
Emp.: 200
Automotive Distr
N.A.I.C.S.: 423110
Mohamed Ebrahim Kanoo (Chm)

Subsidiaries:

Ebrahim K. Kanoo Company B.S.C - Auto Paint Division (1)
44 Sh Mhd Ave Rd 331 Blk 302, Manama, Bahrain
Tel.: (973) 17252689
Automotive Painting Services
N.A.I.C.S.: 811121

Ebrahim K. Kanoo Company B.S.C - Kanoo IT Division (1)
Villa 280 Rd 2510 Gudaibiya 325, PO Box 119, Manama, Bahrain
Tel.: (973) 17711722
Web Site: http://www.kanooit.com
Sales Range: $25-49.9 Million
Emp.: 38
Information Technology Services
N.A.I.C.S.: 541511

Ebrahim K. Kanoo Company B.S.C - Kanoo Vehicle Leasing Division (1)
Building 246 Road 1109 Block 611, Al Hamriya, Sitra, Bahrain
Tel.: (973) 17784042
Web Site: http://www.ekkanoo.com
Sales Range: $50-74.9 Million
Emp.: 135
Cars & Commercial Vehicles Leasing Services
N.A.I.C.S.: 532112

Ebrahim K. Kanoo Company B.S.C - Oils & Lubricants Division (1)
Bldg 510 Qassim Al-Mehzaa Rd 225 Block 302, PO Box 119, Manama, Bahrain
Tel.: (973) 17241001
Oils & Lubricants Distr
N.A.I.C.S.: 811191

Ebrahim K. Kanoo Company B.S.C - Security 1 Division (1)
Building No 1489 D Road No 2630 Block 626 West Eker, PO Box 119, Manama, 119, Bahrain
Tel.: (973) 17738738
Web Site: http://www.security1.com.bh
Sales Range: $25-49.9 Million
Emp.: 25
Security Systems Mfr & Monitoring Services
N.A.I.C.S.: 334290
Bijan Majidi (Gen Mgr)

Ebrahim K. Kanoo Company B.S.C - Kanoo Automotive Equipment Division (1)
Bldg D3110 Rd 181 Blk 701, Tubli, Bahrain
Tel.: (973) 17484808
Web Site: http://www.ekkanoo.com
Automotive Equipment Distr
N.A.I.C.S.: 423120

Ebrahim K. Kanoo Company B.S.C - Tyre Division (1)
44 Sh Mhd Ave Rd 331 Blk302, Manama, Bahrain
Tel.: (973) 17252689
Tire Distr
N.A.I.C.S.: 423130

Kanoo Power Solutions (1)
Bldg-510 Qassim Al-Mehzaa Road Road No-225 Block-302, Manama, Bahrain
Tel.: (973) 17241320
Electronic Equipment Distr
N.A.I.C.S.: 423690

EBRAINS, INC.

2970-6 Ishikawa-Machi, Hachioji-city, Tokyo, 192-0032, Japan
Tel.: (81) 426467171
Web Site: https://www.ebrain.co.jp
Year Founded: 1973
6599—(TKS)
Rev.: $26,354,070

Assets: $37,505,140
Liabilities: $7,746,920
Net Worth: $29,758,220
Earnings: $2,194,520
Fiscal Year-end: 03/31/24
Electronic Equipment Mfr & Distr
N.A.I.C.S.: 336320
Masato Kamimura (Pres & CEO)

Subsidiaries:

Suzhou EBRAIN Electronics Co., Ltd. (1)
12-4 2F Chuangye Building No 625 Binhe Road, Suzhou New District, Suzhou, Jiangsu, China
Tel.: (86) 5126 808 7270
Dielectric Constant Mfr
N.A.I.C.S.: 333994

EBRO FOODS S.A.

Paseo de la Castellana 20, 28046, Madrid, Spain
Tel.: (34) 917245267
Web Site: https://www.ebrofoods.es
Year Founded: 2000
EBRPF—(OTCEM)
Rev.: $3,310,924,218
Assets: $4,155,823,316
Liabilities: $1,770,536,712
Net Worth: $2,385,286,605
Earnings: $220,063,332
Emp.: 5,093
Fiscal Year-end: 12/31/23
Food Production Services
N.A.I.C.S.: 311423
Antonio Hernandez Callejas (Chm)

Subsidiaries:

Arotz Foods, S.A. (1)
Ctra Sagunto-Burgos Km 399, Navaleno, 42149, Soria, Spain
Tel.: (34) 975374100
Web Site: http://www.arotz.com
Food Products Mfr
N.A.I.C.S.: 311999

Arrozeiras Mundiarroz, S.A. (1)
Apartado 104 Monte da Barca, PO Box 104, Coruche, 2101-901, Santarem, Portugal
Tel.: (351) 243618196
Web Site: https://www.cigala.pt
Food Products Mfr
N.A.I.C.S.: 311999

Bertagni 1882 SpA (1)
Viale Sant'Agostino 12/13, 36057, Arcugnano, VI, Italy
Tel.: (39) 0444289241
Web Site: http://www.bertagni1882.it
Food Products Mfr
N.A.I.C.S.: 311999

Boost Nutrition S.C./C.V. (1)
Metropoolstraat 19, 2900, Schoten, Belgium
Tel.: (32) 36419200
Web Site: http://www.boost.be
Nutrition Product Distr
N.A.I.C.S.: 456191

Ebro India Private Limited (1)
7 Institutional Area Vasant Kunj Phase II 4th Floor, New Delhi, 110070, India
Tel.: (91) 1161322600
Web Site: https://www.ebroindia.in
Food Products Mfr
N.A.I.C.S.: 311999

Ebro Tilda Private Limited (1)
7 Institutional Area Vasant Kunj, Phase II 4th Floor, New Delhi, 110070, India
Tel.: (91) 1161322600
Web Site: https://www.ebroindia.in
Food & Beverage Product Mfr
N.A.I.C.S.: 311999

EbroFrost Denmark A/S (1)
Odensevej 16, Orbaek, 5853, Nyborg, Denmark
Tel.: (45) 65331770
Food Products Mfr
N.A.I.C.S.: 311999

Ebrofrost Denmark A/S (1)

Ringvej 14, Orbaek, 5853, Nyborg, Denmark
Tel.: (45) 65331770
Web Site: https://www.danrice.dk
Emp.: 35
Rice & Pasta Producer
N.A.I.C.S.: 311212

Ebrofrost Germany GmbH (1)
Rappenwoerthstrasse 5, Offingen, 89362, Gunzberg, Germany
Tel.: (49) 8224968440
Web Site: http://www.ebrofrost.com
Emp.: 50
Food Products Mfr
N.A.I.C.S.: 311999

Ebrofrost UK Ltd. (1)
Hobbs Lane, Beckley, Rye, TN31 6TS, United Kingdom
Tel.: (44) 1797260570
Emp.: 16
Food Products Mfr
N.A.I.C.S.: 311999

Euryza Reis GmbH (1)
Eiffestrasse 585, 20537, Hamburg, Germany
Tel.: (49) 4 078 1060
Web Site: http://www.euryza.de
Rice Producer
N.A.I.C.S.: 311212

Geovita Funtional Ingredients, S.R.L. (1)
Via Case Sparse 20, Bruno, 14046, Asti, Italy
Tel.: (39) 0141721022
Web Site: https://geovitagroup.it
Cereals & Legumes Retailer
N.A.I.C.S.: 424490

Geovita S.R.L. (1)
Corso Barolo 47, 12051, Alba, CN, Italy
Tel.: (39) 0141764805
Food Products Mfr
N.A.I.C.S.: 311999

Herba Bangkok, S.L. (1)
8th Floor Mercury Tower 540 Ploenchit Road Lumpini, Pathunwam, Bangkok, 10330, Thailand
Tel.: (66) 263937724
Food Products Mfr
N.A.I.C.S.: 311999

Herba Egypt Ricemills, S.L. (1)
11 Aflaton St off Abo Bakr Al Sedik St, Heliopolis, 11361, Cairo, Egypt
Tel.: (20) 222910635
Food Products Mfr
N.A.I.C.S.: 311999

Herba Ingredients, B.V. (1)
Lassiestraat 1, 1531 MG, Wormer, Netherlands
Tel.: (31) 756471230
Web Site: http://www.herbaingredients.com
Food Products Mfr
N.A.I.C.S.: 311999

Herba Nutricion, S.L.U. (1)
Calle Real 43, San Juan de Aznalfarache, Seville, 41920, Spain
Tel.: (34) 954589200
Web Site: http://www.herba.es
Food Processing Services
N.A.I.C.S.: 311999

Herba Ricemills Rom S.r.l. (1)
18 Mircea Eliade Blv 2nd floor Entry A room A4, District 1, 012015, Bucharest, Romania
Tel.: (40) 213 193123
Rice Producer
N.A.I.C.S.: 311212

Herba Ricemills, S.L.U. (1)
Calle Real 43, San Juan De Aznalfarache, 41920, Seville, Spain
Tel.: (34) 954589200
Web Site: https://www.brillante.es
Rice Production Services
N.A.I.C.S.: 311212

Lassie B.V. (1)
Antwoordnummer 308, 1520 VB, Wormerveer, Netherlands
Tel.: (31) 756471200
Web Site: https://www.lassie.nl
Rice Producer
N.A.I.C.S.: 311212

Mundi Riso S.r.l. **(1)**
Via Camillo De Rossi 14, 13100, Vercelli,
Italy
Tel.: (39) 0161282828
Web Site: https://www.mundiriso.it
Rice Producer
N.A.I.C.S.: 311212

Mundiriz, S.A. **(1)**
148 Rue Allal Ben Abdellah, Larache, Mo-
rocco
Tel.: (212) 395 10 416
Rice Producer
N.A.I.C.S.: 311212

New World Pasta Company **(1)**
85 Shannon Rd, Harrisburg, PA 17112-2799
Tel.: (717) 526-2200
Web Site: http://www.newworldpasta.com
Emp.: 800
Pasta Products Mfr
N.A.I.C.S.: 311824

Plant (Domestic):

New World Pasta Company **(2)**
2704 S Maple Ave, Fresno, CA 93725
Tel.: (559) 485-8110
Web Site: http://www.newworldpasta.com
Sales Range: $1-9.9 Million
Emp.: 100
Mfr of Macaroni & Egg Noodle Products
N.A.I.C.S.: 311824
Don Capshew *(Mgr)*

Olivieri Foods Limited **(1)**
1631 Derwent Way, Apartado Aero No
4028, Delta, V3M 6K8, BC,
Canada   **(100%)**
Tel.: (604) 525-2278
Web Site: http://www.olivieri.ca
Sales Range: $100-124.9 Million
Emp.: 105
Fresh & Frozen Pasta & Sauce Products
Mfr
N.A.I.C.S.: 311999

Panzani, S.A.S. **(1)**
37 bis rue Saint Romain, CS 38481, 69372,
Lyon, Cedex, France
Tel.: (33) 970809115
Web Site: http://www.panzani.fr
Food Products Mfr
N.A.I.C.S.: 311999

Pastificio Lucio Garofalo S.p.A. **(1)**
Via dei Pastai 42, Gragnano, 80054,
Naples, Italy
Tel.: (39) 0818011002
Web Site: https://www.pasta-garofalo.com
Food Products Mfr
N.A.I.C.S.: 311999

Riceland Magyarorszag Kft **(1)**
Vaci ut 18, 1132, Budapest, Hungary
Tel.: (36) 13029292
Web Site: https://www.riceland.hu
Rice Producer
N.A.I.C.S.: 311212

Riviana Foods Canada
Corporation **(1)**
401 The West Mall Suite 1100, Etobicoke,
M9C 5J5, ON, Canada
Tel.: (416) 626-3500
Food Products Mfr
N.A.I.C.S.: 311999

Riviana Foods Inc. **(1)**
2777 Allen Pkwy Ste 1500, Houston, TX
77019-2141
Tel.: (713) 942-1816
Web Site: https://www.riviana.com
Sales Range: $350-399.9 Million
Emp.: 2,752
Branded & Private-Label Rice & Other Food
Products Mfr, Marketer & Distr
N.A.I.C.S.: 311212
Bastiaan G. de Zeeuw *(Pres & CEO)*

Unit (Domestic):

American Rice, Inc. **(2)**
10700 N Fwy Ste 800, Houston, TX 77037-
1158
Tel.: (281) 272-8800
Web Site: http://www.amrice.com
Sales Range: $100-124.9 Million
Emp.: 360
Rice Producer
N.A.I.C.S.: 311212

Plant (Domestic):

American Rice, Inc.-Freeport **(3)**
505 Port Rd, Freeport, TX 77541
Tel.: (979) 233-8248
Web Site: http://www.amrice.com
Sales Range: $25-49.9 Million
Emp.: 40
Rice Processor
N.A.I.C.S.: 311212
Noelia Castron *(Gen Mgr)*

Subsidiary (Non-US):

Boost Nutrition C.V. **(2)**
Oostkaai 16, PO Box 30, 2170, Merksem,
Belgium
Tel.: (32) 3 641 9200
Web Site: https://www.ebrofoods.es
Sales Range: $25-49.9 Million
Emp.: 120
Mfr of Rice Products
N.A.I.C.S.: 311212

Pozuelo, S.A. **(2)**
Calle 70 entre Av 39 y 43 300 mt norte del
Puente, PO Box 1750, Juan Pablo II La
Uruca, 1000, San Jose, Costa Rica
Tel.: (506) 800 425 5382
Web Site: https://pozuelo.com
Emp.: 1,400
Mfr of Cookies & Crackers
N.A.I.C.S.: 311821

Unit (Non-US):

Riviana International Inc. **(2)**
Tel.: (713) 529-3251
Web Site: https://www.riviana.com
Sales Range: $150-199.9 Million
Emp.: 600
Holding Company
N.A.I.C.S.: 311212

Subsidiary (Non-US):

S&B Herba Foods, Ltd. **(2)**
Central Court 1b Knoll Rise, Orpington,
BR6 0JA, Kent, United Kingdom **(100%)**
Tel.: (44) 1689878700
Web Site: https://www.sbhf.com
Sales Range: $75-99.9 Million
Emp.: 36
Food Service
N.A.I.C.S.: 311212

Santa Rita Harinas, S.L. **(1)**
Ctra Perales Km 52, Loranca de Tajuna,
19141, Guadalajara, Spain
Tel.: (34) 949294683
Web Site: https://www.santaritaharinas.com
Food Products Mfr
N.A.I.C.S.: 311999

Tilda Limited **(1)**
Coldharbour Lane, Rainham, RM13 9YQ,
United Kingdom
Tel.: (44) 1708717888
Web Site: https://www.tilda.com
Food Processing & Distr
N.A.I.C.S.: 311412

Subsidiary (Non-US):

Tilda India Private Limited **(2)**
42km Stone Delhi-Jaipur Highway National
Highway -8, Gurgaon, 122001, Haryana,
India
Tel.: (91) 1243040000
Web Site: http://www.tildariceland.com
Emp.: 30
Food Processing & Distr
N.A.I.C.S.: 311412
R. A. Sasabri *(Gen Mgr)*

EBROKER GROUP LTD.
Rm 603 China Insurance B 141
Group Des Voeux Road, Central,
China (Hong Kong)
Tel.: (852) 29289008
8036—(HKG)
Rev.: $4,919,460
Assets: $8,767,920
Liabilities: $986,850
Net Worth: $7,781,070
Earnings: $251,430
Emp.: 51
Fiscal Year-end: 12/31/22

Software Development Services
N.A.I.C.S.: 541511
Douglas Chan *(Chm)*

Subsidiaries:

eBroker Systems Limited **(1)**
Suites 1410-11 14th Floor North Tower
World Finance Centre, 19 Canton Road
Tsim Sha Tsui, Kowloon, China (Hong
Kong)
Tel.: (852) 29289008
Web Site: https://www.ebrokernet.com
Financial Software Solution Services
N.A.I.C.S.: 541519

EBULLION, INC.
Room 1805-06 Tower 6 33 Canton
Road, Tsim Sha Tsui, Hong Kong,
China (Hong Kong)
Tel.: (852) 31874300 DE
Web Site:
http://www.ebulliongroup.com
Year Founded: 2013
EBML—(OTCIQ)
Sales Range: $1-9.9 Million
Emp.: 18
Precious Metals Online Trading Ser-
vices
N.A.I.C.S.: 423940
Kee Yuen Choi *(Pres & CEO)*

EBUSCO HOLDING N.V.
Vuurijzer 23, 5753 SV, Deurne, Neth-
erlands
Tel.: (31) 881100200 NI
Web Site: https://www.ebusco.com
Year Founded: 2010
EBUS—(EUR)
Rev.: $113,080,914
Assets: $353,053,317
Liabilities: $156,235,788
Net Worth: $196,817,530
Earnings: ($132,626,118)
Emp.: 557
Fiscal Year-end: 12/31/23
Holding Company
N.A.I.C.S.: 551112
Bjorn Krook *(Interim CFO)*

EBX GROUP LTD.
Praia do Flamengo 154 10 Andar Fla-
mengo, Rio de Janeiro, Brazil
Tel.: (55) 21 2555 550
Web Site: http://www.ebx.com.br
Sales Range: $900-999.9 Million
Emp.: 3,500
Investment Holding Company
N.A.I.C.S.: 551112
Eike Fuhrken Batista *(Chm &
Founder)*

Subsidiaries:

AUX Mineracao de Ouro **(1)**
Praia do Flamengo 154 10 Andar Fla-
mengo, Rio de Janeiro, Brazil
Tel.: (55) 21 2555 5550
Gold Mining
N.A.I.C.S.: 212220

MMX Mineracao e Metalicos
S.A. **(1)**
Rua Lauro Muller 116 24 Block Room 2403
Parte, Botafogo, Rio de Janeiro, Brazil
Tel.: (55) 2132375200
Web Site: http://www.mmx.com.br
Emp.: 178
Iron Ore Mineral Mining Services
N.A.I.C.S.: 212210
Maria Carolina Catarina Silva e Gedeon
(Chm)

OSX Brasil SA **(1)**
Rua Lauro Muller 116 24 Andar Sala 2403-
parte, Rio de Janeiro, 20021-290,
Brazil **(78.93%)**
Tel.: (55) 2132375200
Web Site: http://www.osx.com.br
Rev.: $8,088,164
Assets: $423,114,878
Liabilities: $1,640,251,293
Net Worth: ($1,217,136,415)

Earnings: ($212,914,851)
Fiscal Year-end: 12/31/2023
Offshore Oil & Gas Industry Equipment &
Support Services
N.A.I.C.S.: 213112
Eduardo Meira Farina *(Vice Chm, CEO,
Co-CFO & Dir-IR)*

EC HEALTHCARE
Room 2108 21/F Office Tower Lang-
ham Place, Mong Kok, Kowloon,
China (Hong Kong)
Tel.: (852) 3 975 4798 Ky
Web Site:
http://www.echealthcare.com
Year Founded: 2005
2138—(HKG)
Rev.: $376,557,110
Assets: $626,921,220
Liabilities: $323,746,507
Net Worth: $303,174,713
Earnings: $34,889,477
Emp.: 2,674
Fiscal Year-end: 03/31/22
Health Care Srvices
N.A.I.C.S.: 621610
Chi Fai Tang *(Chm & Co-CEO)*

EC WORLD REIT
9 Raffles Place 45-02 Republic
Plaza, Singapore, 048619, Singapore
Tel.: (65) 62219018
Web Site: https://www.ecwreit.com
BWCU—(SES)
Rev.: $81,625,388
Assets: $761,402,711
Liabilities: $689,554,646
Net Worth: $71,848,065
Earnings: ($340,281,754)
Emp.: 11
Fiscal Year-end: 12/31/23
Trust Management Services
N.A.I.C.S.: 523940
Goh Toh Sim *(CEO)*

ECARD S.A.
ul Czackiego 7/9/11, 00-043, Warsaw,
Poland
Tel.: (48) 22 493 44 90
Web Site: http://www.ecard.pl
Year Founded: 2000
Electronic Card Issuing Services
N.A.I.C.S.: 522210

ECARGO HOLDINGS LIMITED
13103N ATL Logistics Centre B Berth
3, Kwai Chung Container Terminals,
Hong Kong, NT, China (Hong Kong)
Tel.: (852) 24818308
Web Site: https://www.ecargo.com
Year Founded: 2014
ECG—(ASX)
Rev.: $16,173,945
Assets: $10,769,187
Liabilities: $15,709,682
Net Worth: ($4,940,496)
Earnings: $3,618,535
Fiscal Year-end: 12/31/22
Holding Company; eCommerce Solu-
tions
N.A.I.C.S.: 551112
Lawrence Lun *(CEO)*

Subsidiaries:

Metcash Export Services Pty.
Ltd. **(1)**
137 Magnesium Drive, Crestmead, Logan,
4132, QLD, Australia
Tel.: (61) 738044074
Sales Range: $75-99.9 Million
Emp.: 250
Grocery Distr
N.A.I.C.S.: 424410

ECARX HOLDINGS, INC.
F3-F6 Building 1 Zhongteng Building
2121 Longteng Avenue, Xuhui District, Shanghai, 200232, China

ECARX Holdings, Inc.—(Continued)

Tel.: (86) 5718530694   Ky
Web Site:
  https://www.ecarxgroup.com
Year Founded: 2017
ECX—(NASDAQ)
Emp.: 2,000
Holding Company ; Software Development
N.A.I.C.S.: 551112

ECCLESIASTICAL INSURANCE OFFICE PLC

Benefact House 2000 Pioneer Avenue Gloucester Business Park,
Brockworth, Gloucester, GL3 4AW,
United Kingdom
Tel.: (44) 3457773322   UK
Web Site:
  https://www.ecclesiastical.com
ELLA—(LSE)
Rev.: $449,989,155
Assets: $2,278,082,895
Liabilities: $1,536,604,740
Net Worth: $741,478,155
Earnings: $843,150
Fiscal Year-end: 12/31/22
Insurance & Financial Advisory Services
N.A.I.C.S.: 524298
Mark C. J. Hews (CEO)

Subsidiaries:

Ansvar Insurance Limited   (1)
Level 5 1 Southbank Blvd, Southbank,
3006, VIC, Australia
Tel.: (61) 1300650540
Web Site: https://www.ansvar.com.au
Insurance Services
N.A.I.C.S.: 524210
Phil Gare (COO)

EdenTree Investment Management
Limited   (1)
24 Monument Street, London, EC3R 8AJ,
United Kingdom
Tel.: (44) 8000113821
Web Site: https://www.edentreeim.com
Investment Management Service
N.A.I.C.S.: 523940

SEIB Insurance Brokers Limited   (1)
North Road, South Ockendon, RM15 5BE,
Essex, United Kingdom
Tel.: (44) 1708850000
Web Site: https://www.seib.co.uk
Insurance Services
N.A.I.C.S.: 524298

South Essex Insurance Brokers
Limited   (1)
North Road, South Ockendon, RM15 5BE,
Essex, United Kingdom
Tel.: (44) 170 885 0000
Web Site: https://www.seib.co.uk
Insurance Services
N.A.I.C.S.: 524210

ECCO AUTO WORLD CORPORATION

Unit C 4/F 48 Cameron Road, China
Insurance Building Tsim Sha Tsui,
Kowloon, China (Hong Kong)
Tel.: (852) 8 134 5953   NV
Year Founded: 2016
Assets: $1,544
Liabilities: $90,388
Net Worth: ($88,844)
Earnings: ($37,488)
Emp.: 5
Fiscal Year-end: 03/31/22
Mobile Application Development Services
N.A.I.C.S.: 541511
Jason Chee Hon Wong (Pres, CEO, Treas & Sec)

ECCO SKO A/S

Industrivej 5, 6261, Bredebro, Denmark

Tel.: (45) 74911625
Web Site:
  http://www.global.ecco.com
Year Founded: 1963
Sales Range: $1-4.9 Billion
Emp.: 20,000
Shoe Mfr, Retailer & Distr
N.A.I.C.S.: 316210
Hanni Toosbuy Kasprzak (Chm-Supervisory Bd)

Subsidiaries:

ECCO (Thailand) Co., Ltd.   (1)
113 Moo 4 Saharattananakorn Industrial
Estate Tambon Banprakru, Amphur Nakornluang, Phra Nakhon Si Ayutthaya, 13260,
Thailand
Tel.: (66) 35716601
Footwear Mfr
N.A.I.C.S.: 316210
Bo Grabowski (Mng Dir)

ECCO (Xiamen) Co. Ltd.   (1)
ChengNan Industrial Zone, Tong'an, Xiamen, 361100, China
Tel.: (86) 59 2719 4600
Footwear Mfr
N.A.I.C.S.: 316210
Christopher Skouenborg (Dir-Fin & HR)

ECCO Baltic SIA   (1)
Suur-Sojamae 4 Lasnamae, Tallinn, Estonia
Tel.: (372) 6034703
Footwear Distr
N.A.I.C.S.: 424340
Kavry Tivas (Gen Mgr)

ECCO EMEA Sales SE   (1)
Hoogoorddreef 15, Amsterdam Zuidoost,
Amsterdam, 1101 BA, Netherlands
Tel.: (31) 204097100
Footwear Mfr
N.A.I.C.S.: 316210

ECCO Leather B.V.   (1)
Vierbundersweg 11, 5107 NL, Dongen,
Netherlands
Tel.: (31) 162 380 400
Web Site: http://www.eccoleather.com
Leather Product Mfr
N.A.I.C.S.: 316990
Anke Louwers (Head-Leather Design)

ECCO Shoe Production Pte. Ltd.   (1)
51 Cuppage Road 06-01, Singapore,
229469, Singapore
Tel.: (65) 6608 8030
Web Site: http://www.sg.ecco.com
Footwear Distr
N.A.I.C.S.: 424340
Shaw Klat Phua (Sr Mgr-Technical)

ECCO Shoes (NZ) Limited   (1)
39 Willis Street, Wellington, New Zealand
Tel.: (64) 44995580
Web Site: http://www.nz.ecco.com
Footwear Distr
N.A.I.C.S.: 424340

ECCO Shoes Canada, Inc.   (1)
10 Whitehall Drive, Markham, L3R 5Z7,
ON, Canada
Tel.: (905) 475-9444
Web Site: http://www.ca.shop.ecco.com
Footwear Distr
N.A.I.C.S.: 424340
Lisa Zahn (Mgr-Mktg)

ECCO Shoes Pacific Pty. Ltd.   (1)
PO Box 7045, Baulkham Hills, 2153, NSW,
Australia
Tel.: (61) 1300138099
Web Site: http://www.au.shop.ecco.com
Footwear Distr
N.A.I.C.S.: 424340

ECCO Tannery Holding (Singapore)
Pte. Ltd.   (1)
Ang Mo Kio Street, Ang Mo Kio, Singapore,
651056, Singapore
Tel.: (65) 6376 9909
Commodity Trading Services
N.A.I.C.S.: 523210

Ecco USA Inc.   (1)
16 Delta Dr, Londonderry, NH 03053-2328
Tel.: (603) 537-7300
Web Site: http://www.eccousa.com

Sales Range: $75-99.9 Million
Emp.: 200
Footwear Sales
N.A.I.C.S.: 424340
Christian Burnham (Coord-Ops)

Eccolet (Portugal) Fabrica de Sapatos, Lda.   (1)
RuaFrancisco Rocha Nr 134 Aptd 107,
4520-605, Sao Joao De Ver, Galicia, Portugal
Tel.: (351) 256314000
Emp.: 600
Footwear Mfr
N.A.I.C.S.: 316210
Gustavo Frederico Kramer (Mng Dir)

P.T. ECCO Indonesia   (1)
Jl Raya Bligo no19 Candi, Sidoarjo, 61271,
East Java, Indonesia
Tel.: (62) 318964555
Footwear Mfr
N.A.I.C.S.: 316210
Rita Desyanti (Sr Mgr-MRP & Pur)

ECE INDUSTRIES LIMITED

ECE House 28-A Kasturba Gandhi
Marg, New Delhi, 110 001, India
Tel.: (91) 1123314237
Web Site:
  http://www.eceindustriesltd.com
Rev.: $54,615,351
Assets: $68,843,944
Liabilities: $26,111,641
Net Worth: $42,732,304
Earnings: $8,757,386
Emp.: 499
Fiscal Year-end: 03/31/18
Power Transmission Equipment Mfr &
Distr
N.A.I.C.S.: 333613
Prakash Kumar Mohta (Mng Dir)

Subsidiaries:

ECE Industries Limited - Elevator
Division   (1)
A-20 Industrial Area Meerut Road, Ghaziabad, 201 001, Uttar Pradesh, India
Tel.: (91) 120 2712065
Sales Range: $100-124.9 Million
Emp.: 50
Elevator Mfr
N.A.I.C.S.: 333921
S. B. Khandelwal (Sr Mgr)

ECE Industries Limited - Meter
Division   (1)
Ashok Marg, Sanathnagar, Hyderabad, 500
018, Andhra Pradesh, India
Tel.: (91) 40 23814433
Sales Range: $25-49.9 Million
Emp.: 7
Electric Meter Mfr
N.A.I.C.S.: 334515
H. M. Mot (Gen Mgr)

ECE PROJEKTMANAGEMENT GMBH & CO KG

Heegbarg 30, 22391, Hamburg, Germany
Tel.: (49) 40 60 60 60   De
Web Site: http://www.ece.com
Year Founded: 1965
Emp.: 3,400
Developer & Builder of Transport
Complexes, Logistics & Shopping
Centers & Other Real Estate Investment Properties
N.A.I.C.S.: 531390
Andreas Mattner (Member-Mgmt Bd
& Mng Dir-Office, Traffic & Industries)

Subsidiaries:

Auxideico Gestion, S.A.   (1)
c/ Genova 27 - 6 Planta, 28004, Madrid,
Spain
Tel.: (34) 911420810
Web Site: http://www.auxideico.com
Building Leasing Services
N.A.I.C.S.: 531110
Rouven Semel (COO)

Deutsche Einkaufs-Center Management G.m.b.H   (1)
Poststr 33, 20354, Hamburg, Neustadt,
Germany
Tel.: (49) 403480930
Asset Management Services
N.A.I.C.S.: 531390

ECE Italia s.r.l.   (1)
Piazzale Principessa Clotilde 8, 20121, Milan, Italy
Tel.: (39) 0263471442
Real Estate Services
N.A.I.C.S.: 531210
Davide Rainone (Mgr-Technical)

ECE Projektmanagement Austria
GmbH   (1)
Europaplatz 3/Stiege 4/7 OG, 1150, Vienna,
Austria
Tel.: (43) 1359990
Building Leasing Services
N.A.I.C.S.: 531110

ECE Projektmanagement Budapest
Kft.   (1)
Ors vezer tere 25/C, Budapest, 1106, Hungary
Tel.: (36) 14348200
Building Leasing Services
N.A.I.C.S.: 531110
Tamas Turi (Head-Leasing)

ECE Projektmanagement Polska Sp.
z o.o.   (1)
ul Fabryczna 5a, 00-446, Warsaw, Poland
Tel.: (48) 223106000
Web Site: http://www.ece.com
Building Leasing Services
N.A.I.C.S.: 531110
Leszek Sikora (Mng Dir)

ECE Projektmanagement Praha
s.r.o.   (1)
Na Prikope 583/15, 110 00, Prague, Czech
Republic
Tel.: (420) 222111425
Building Management Services
N.A.I.C.S.: 531120

ECE Projektmanagement Slovakia
s.r.o.   (1)
Metodova 6, 821 08, Bratislava, Slovakia
Tel.: (421) 232115121
Real Estate Services
N.A.I.C.S.: 531210
Milan Sloboda (Mgr-Technical)

ECE Real Estate Partners
G.m.b.H.   (1)
Wandsbeker Str 3 -7, 22179, Hamburg,
Germany
Tel.: (49) 40606060
Real Estate Management Services
N.A.I.C.S.: 531390
Ruediger Cornehl (Mng Partner)

ECE Real Estate Partners S.a
r.l.   (1)
17 Rue Edmond Reuter, 5326, Contern,
Luxembourg
Tel.: (352) 267859291
Real Estate Management Services
N.A.I.C.S.: 531390

ECE Russland OOO   (1)
Ul Bryanskaya 5, 121059, Moscow, Russia
Tel.: (7) 49522993000
Building Leasing Services
N.A.I.C.S.: 531110
Stefan Zeiselmaier (Mng Dir)

ECE Turkiye Proje Yonetimi A.S.   (1)
Defterdar Yokusu No 3 Tophane, Karakoy,
34425, Istanbul, Turkiye
Tel.: (90) 2123777700
Building Leasing Services
N.A.I.C.S.: 531110
Andreas Hohlmann (Mng Dir)

PPMG Potsdamer Platz Management
GmbH   (1)
Linkstrasse 2, 10785, Berlin, Germany
Tel.: (49) 306883150
Web Site: http://www.ppmg.eu
Asset Management Services
N.A.I.C.S.: 531390

UAB "ECE Projektmanagement
Vilnius"   (1)

Ozo g 18, Vilnius, 8243, Lithuania
Tel.: (370) 52100150
Building Management Services
N.A.I.C.S.: 531120

ECHANNELING PLC
No 108 W A D Ramanayake Ma-
watha, 2, Colombo, Sri Lanka
Tel.: (94) 710225225
Web Site:
    https://www.echannelling.com
Year Founded: 2001
ECL.N0000—(COL)
Rov.: $737,167
Assets: $1,847,167
Liabilities: $511,071
Net Worth: $1,336,096
Earnings: $218,101
Emp.: 34
Fiscal Year-end: 12/31/22
Software Development Services
N.A.I.C.S.: 513210

ECHEVERRIA IZQUIERDO S.A.
Rosario Norte 532 8th floor, Las Con-
des, Santiago, Chile
Tel.: (56) 226314600
Web Site: https://www.ei.cl
EISA—(SGO)
Rev.: $645,619,472
Assets: $600,026,400
Liabilities: $434,844,169
Net Worth: $165,182,231
Earnings: $20,212,484
Emp.: 11,361
Fiscal Year-end: 12/31/23
Construction Engineering Services
N.A.I.C.S.: 541330
Fernando Echeverria Vial *(Chm)*

Subsidiaries:

Nexxo S.A.   **(1)**
Gulmue Industrial Park Site Number 3A
Camino Internacional S/N, Concon, Val-
paraiso, Chile
Tel.: (56) 322133200
Web Site:
    https://testnexxo.azurewebsites.net
Construction Services
N.A.I.C.S.: 236220
Dario Barros *(Chm)*

Subsidiary (Non-US):

Arnexx S.A.   **(2)**
Primitivo de la Reta 1010 4th Floor Depart-
ment A, 5500, Mendoza, Argentina
Tel.: (54) 2615279274
Web Site:
    http://www.arnexxsa.blogspot.com
Construction Services
N.A.I.C.S.: 236220

Pilotes Terratest Peru S.A.C.   **(1)**
Av Mariscal de La Mar 750 of 701 Urb, Mi-
raflores, Santa Cruz, Peru
Tel.: (51) 16193535
Web Site: https://www.terratest.com.pe
Construction Services
N.A.I.C.S.: 236220

Terrafoundations S.A.   **(1)**
Calacoto Calle 9 ed Vitruvio II of 6J, La
Paz, Bolivia
Tel.: (591) 75210946
Web Site: http://www.terratest.com.bo
Construction Services
N.A.I.C.S.: 236220

Subsidiary (Non-US):

Pilotes Terratest S.A.   **(2)**
Rosario Norte 532 Of 203, Las Condes,
Santiago, Chile
Tel.: (56) 233295100
Web Site: https://www.terratest.cl
Construction Services
N.A.I.C.S.: 236220

ECHMI S.A.
Zymbrakaki & 17 P Askitou, 691 00,
Komotini, Greece
Tel.: (30) 2531037795

Web Site: https://www.echmi.eu
Year Founded: 1995
Investment Consulting Services
N.A.I.C.S.: 523940

ECHO ENERGY PLC
85 Great Portland Street First Floor,
London, W1W 7LT, United Kingdom
Tel.: (44) 2071909930
Web Site:
    https://www.echoenergyplc.com
ECHO—(AIM)
Rev.: $11,124,487
Assets: $14,022,314
Liabilities: $47,831,791
Net Worth: ($33,809,477)
Earnings: ($11,770,112)
Emp.: 7
Fiscal Year-end: 12/31/21
Crude Petroleum Extraction Services
N.A.I.C.S.: 211120
Martin Hull *(CEO)*

ECHO INTERNATIONAL HOLD-
INGS GROUP LIMITED
Rm 3207A 32/F Cable TV Tower 9
Hoi Shing Rd, Tsuen Wan, New Terri-
tories, China (Hong Kong)
Tel.: (852) 2 412 0878   Ky
Web Site:
    http://www.echogroup.com.hk
Year Founded: 1989
8218—(HKG)
Rev.: $10,361,995
Assets: $9,673,758
Liabilities: $9,121,982
Net Worth: $551,776
Earnings: ($2,818,471)
Emp.: 158
Fiscal Year-end: 03/31/22
Electric Equipment Mfr
N.A.I.C.S.: 335999
Yan Yee Lo *(Chm & Gen Mgr-
Factory)*

Subsidiaries:

Echo Electronics Company
Limited   **(1)**
Rm 3207A 32/F Cable TV Tower 9 Hoi
Shing Road, Tsuen Wan, China (Hong
Kong)
Tel.: (852) 24120878
Web Site: http://www.echo.com.hk
Electrical Equipment & Component Mfr
N.A.I.C.S.: 335999
Andy Lo *(Chm)*

Yuk Cuisine Limited   **(1)**
Shop 4 G/F 117 Lockhart Road, Wanchai,
China (Hong Kong)
Tel.: (852) 28158698
Web Site: https://www.yukcuisine.com
Restaurant Services
N.A.I.C.S.: 722511

ECHO INVESTMENT S.A.
Al Solidarnosci 36, 25-323, Kielce,
Poland
Tel.: (48) 413333333
Web Site: https://www.echo.com.pl
ECH—(WAR)
Rev.: $399,718,749
Assets: $1,514,694,610
Liabilities: $999,428,097
Net Worth: $515,266,513
Earnings: $29,944,868
Fiscal Year-end: 12/31/23
Real Estate & Property Development
Services
N.A.I.C.S.: 531311
Tomasz Aleszczyk *(Head-IR)*

Subsidiaries:

Archicom SA   **(1)**
MidPoint71 ul Powstancow slaskich 9, 53-
332, Wroclaw, Poland   **(66%)**
Tel.: (48) 717858800
Web Site: https://www.archicom.pl
Rev.: $279,741,869

Assets: $618,250,761
Liabilities: $298,751,524
Net Worth: $319,499,237
Earnings: $62,292,937
Fiscal Year-end: 12/31/2023
Real Estate Manangement Services
N.A.I.C.S.: 531390

ECHO MARKETING CO., LTD.
9 10 15F Luther Bldg 42 Olympicro
35dagil, Gangnam-gu, Seoul, 06060,
Korea (South)
Tel.: (82) 221821100
Web Site:
    https://www.echomarketing.co.kr
230360—(KRS)
Rev.: $270,563,975
Assets: $237,520,187
Liabilities: $73,727,775
Net Worth: $163,792,413
Earnings: $34,642,263
Emp.: 261
Fiscal Year-end: 12/31/22
Advertising Agency Services
N.A.I.C.S.: 541810
Cheolwoong Kim *(CEO)*

ECHO TRADING CO., LTD.
12th floor Shin-Osaka 5th Doi Build-
ing 1-2-4 Miyahara, Nishinomiya,
663-8142, Hyogo, Japan
Tel.: (81) 798418317
Web Site: https://www.echotd.co.jp
Year Founded: 1971
7427—(TKS)
Rev.: $761,508,540
Assets: $237,678,070
Liabilities: $162,226,290
Net Worth: $75,451,780
Earnings: $8,600,170
Fiscal Year-end: 02/29/24
Pet Food Whslr
N.A.I.C.S.: 424490
Kazuhiko Takahashi *(Chm)*

ECHOIQ LIMITED
3/33 Atchison Street, St Leonards,
Sydney, NSW, Australia
Tel.: (61) 291593719
Web Site:
    https://www.houstonwehave.ai
EIQ—(ASX)
Rev.: $1,333,421
Assets: $5,512,521
Liabilities: $993,295
Net Worth: $4,519,225
Earnings: ($3,611,876)
Fiscal Year-end: 06/30/24
Gold & Silver Mining Services
N.A.I.C.S.: 212220

ECI PARTNERS LLP
Brettenham House South Entrance
Lancaster Place, London, WC2E
7EN, United Kingdom
Tel.: (44) 20 7606 1000   UK
Web Site: http://www.ecipartners.com
Year Founded: 1976
Privater Equity Firm
N.A.I.C.S.: 523999
Jeremy Lytle *(Partner-IR)*

Subsidiaries:

Callitech Limited   **(1)**
Western Gateway, Wrexham, LL13 7ZB,
United Kingdom
Tel.: (44) 844 364 6621
Web Site: http://www.moneypenny.com
Telephone Answering, Outsourced Switch-
board & Live Chat Services
N.A.I.C.S.: 561421
Ed Reeves *(Founder)*

Subsidiary (US):

Sunshine Answering Service,
Inc.   **(2)**
159 Madeira Ave, Coral Gables, FL 33134
Tel.: (305) 442-1144

Sales Range: $1-9.9 Million
Emp.: 65
Paging
N.A.I.C.S.: 517112
Renee Gross *(Treas)*

VoiceNation, LLC   **(2)**
4908 Golden Pkwy Ste 100, Buford, GA
30518
Tel.: (678) 318-1300
Web Site: http://www.voicenation.com
Wireless Telecommunications Carriers
N.A.I.C.S.: 517112
Jay Reeder *(Founder & Pres)*

Citation Ltd.   **(1)**
Kings Court Water Lane, Wilmslow, SK9
5AR, Chesire, United Kingdom
Tel.: (44) 345 234 0404
Web Site: http://www.citation.co.uk
Professional Advice & Compliance Services
N.A.I.C.S.: 561499
Dave Lambert *(Dir-Sls)*

The Appointment Group Limited   **(1)**
The Linen House 253 Kilburn Lane, Lon-
don, W10 4BQ, United Kingdom
Tel.: (44) 2089601600
Holding Company; Travel Services
N.A.I.C.S.: 551112

Subsidiary (Domestic):

The Appointment Group (UK)
Limited   **(2)**
The Linen House 253 Kilburn Lane, Lon-
don, W10 4BQ, United Kingdom
Tel.: (44) 2089601600
Web Site: https://www.tag-group.com
Travel Arrangement Services
N.A.I.C.S.: 561599
Gabrielle Carr *(COO)*

Subsidiary (US):

Atlantis Travel & Tours   **(3)**
3030 Saturn St Ste 200, Brea, CA 92821-
6271
Tel.: (626) 839-0550
Web Site: http://www.atlantistravel.net
Travel Agencies
N.A.I.C.S.: 561510

ECI TECHNOLOGY HOLDINGS
LIMITED
Flat D 3/F Block 2 Camel Paint Build-
ing 62 Hoi Yuen Road Kwun Tong,
Kowloon, China (Hong Kong)
Tel.: (852) 2 876 2990   Ky
Web Site: http://www.ecinfohk.com
8013—(HKG)
Rev.: $17,825,939
Assets: $10,668,968
Liabilities: $2,350,145
Net Worth: $8,318,823
Earnings: $1,124,190
Emp.: 378
Fiscal Year-end: 08/31/21
Security System Services
N.A.I.C.S.: 561621
Tai Wing Ng *(Chm, CEO & Officer-
Compliance)*

ECKELMANN AG
Berliner Strasse 161, Wiesbaden,
65205, Germany
Tel.: (49) 61171030
Web Site: http://www.eckelmann.de
Year Founded: 1970
Sales Range: $50-74.9 Million
Emp.: 365
Electronic Control System Mfr
N.A.I.C.S.: 334513
Hubertus G. Krossa *(Chm-
Supervisory Bd)*

Subsidiaries:

Eckelmann Automation Technology
(Shanghai) Co., Ltd.   **(1)**
7866 Humin Road Room 701, Minhang Dis-
trict, Shanghai, China
Tel.: (86) 21 54150366
Electronic Control System Distr
N.A.I.C.S.: 423690

Eckelmann AG—(Continued)

Bernd Pannicke *(Co-Mng Dir)*

Eckelmann Industrial Automation Technologies (Beijing) Co., Ltd. (1)
Jinghandasha 205-1 Shixingdongjie 8 Hao Yuan 1 Hao Lou, Shijingshanqu, 100041, Beijing, China
Tel.: (86) 10 52659602
Web Site: http://www.eckelmann.cn
Electronic Control System Distr
N.A.I.C.S.: 423690
Guo Lei *(Co-Mng Dir)*

Eckelmann s.r.o. (1)
Ruzova 17, 69153, Tvrdonice, Czech Republic
public
Tel.: (420) 519 323 755
Electronic Control System Distr
N.A.I.C.S.: 423690
Gerd Eckelmann *(Co-Mng Dir)*

FTI Engineering Network GmbH (1)
Schmiedestrasse 2, 15745, Wildau, Germany
Tel.: (49) 3375 5235 0
Web Site: http://www.ftigroup.net
Aviation Support Services
N.A.I.C.S.: 488190
Michael Weisel *(Co-Mng Dir)*

Ferrocontrol Steuerungssysteme GmbH & Co. KG (1)
Bodelschwinghstrasse 20, 32049, Herford, Germany
Tel.: (49) 5221 966 0
Web Site: http://www.ferrocontrol.de
Electronic Control System Mfr
N.A.I.C.S.: 334513
Andreas Pottharst *(Co-Mng Dir)*

Rex Automatisierungstechnik GmbH (1)
Fichtenweg 36, 99098, Erfurt, Germany
Tel.: (49) 36203 9591 0
Web Site: http://www.rex-at.de
Electronic Control System Mfr
N.A.I.C.S.: 334513
Matthias Rex *(Mng Dir)*

ECKERT & ZIEGLER STRAHLEN- UND MEDIZIN-TECHNIK AG
Robert-Rossle-Strasse 10, 13125, Berlin, Germany
Tel.: (49) 309410840   De
Web Site: https://www.ezag.com
Year Founded: 1997
EUZ—(DEU)
Rev.: $271,651,368
Assets: $484,996,323
Liabilities: $239,738,487
Net Worth: $245,257,837
Earnings: $29,031,781
Emp.: 1,035
Fiscal Year-end: 12/31/23
Holding Company; Radioisotopes Processor & Isotope Technologies Developer & Mfr
N.A.I.C.S.: 551112
Andreas Eckert *(Founder & Chm-Exec Bd)*

Subsidiaries:

Ambientis Radioprotecao LTDA (1)
Avenida Real 236 - Aldeia da Serra, Barueri, 06429-200, SP, Brazil
Tel.: (55) 1141531839
Web Site: https://ambientis.com.br
Pharmaceutical Products Distr
N.A.I.C.S.: 424210

Eckert & Ziegler Analytics, Inc. (1)
1380 Seaboard Industrial Blvd, Atlanta, GA 30318
Tel.: (404) 352-8677
Emp.: 43
Radioactive Isotopes Mfr
N.A.I.C.S.: 325180
Evgeny Taskaev *(Mgr-Production)*

Eckert & Ziegler BEBIG S.A. (1)
Zone Industrielle C, 7180, Seneffe, Belgium   (78.68%)
Tel.: (32) 64520811

Web Site: http://www.bebig.com
Rev.: $31,017,387
Assets: $72,595,107
Liabilities: $17,900,820
Net Worth: $54,694,288
Earnings: $1,591,956
Emp.: 130
Fiscal Year-end: 12/31/2017
Cancer Treatment Radiation Therapy Technologies Developer, Mfr & Marketer
N.A.I.C.S.: 339112
Andreas Eckert *(Chm)*

Subsidiary (Non-US):

Eckert & Ziegler BEBIG GmbH (2)
                                         (100%)
Tel.: (49) 30941084130
Web Site: http://www.ibt-bebig.eu
Sales Range: $75-99.9 Million
Cancer Treatment Radiation Therapy Technologies Developer & Mfr
N.A.I.C.S.: 334510

Eckert & Ziegler BEBIG Ltd. (2)
Imperial House 4th Floor 15 Kingsway, London, WC2B 6UN, United Kingdom
Tel.: (44) 1446 773 433
Cancer Treatment Radiation Therapy Technologies Developer & Mfr
N.A.I.C.S.: 339112

Eckert & Ziegler BEBIG SARL (2)
37 Rue des Mathurins, 75008, Paris, France
Tel.: (33) 155280030
Web Site: http://www.bebig.eu
Emp.: 4
Cancer Treatment Radiation Therapy Technologies Developer & Mfr
N.A.I.C.S.: 339112

Eckert & Ziegler BEBIG do Brasil Ltda. (2)
Avenida Dom Luis 500 Sala 1925, 60160 230, Fortaleza, Brazil
Tel.: (55) 85 3241 0899
Web Site: http://www.bebig.eu
Emp.: 1
Cancer Treatment Radiation Therapy Technologies Developer & Mfr
N.A.I.C.S.: 339112

Eckert & Ziegler Iberia S.L. (2)
c/ Lanzarote 15, 28703, San Sebastian de los Reyes, Spain
Tel.: (34) 916526248
Emp.: 5
Cancer Treatment Radiation Therapy Technologies Developer & Mfr
N.A.I.C.S.: 339112

Eckert & Ziegler Italia s.r.l. (2)
Via Fiuggi 2, 20159, Milan, Italy
Tel.: (39) 02 69900435
Cancer Treatment Radiation Therapy Technologies Developer & Mfr
N.A.I.C.S.: 339112

Subsidiary (US):

Mick Radio-Nuclear Instrument, Inc. (2)
521 Homestead Ave, Mount Vernon, NY 10550
Tel.: (914) 667-3999
Web Site: http://www.micknuclear.com
Sales Range: $1-9.9 Million
Emp.: 25
Brachytherapy Instrumentation & Accessories Mfr
N.A.I.C.S.: 339112
Bill Dowd *(CEO)*

Eckert & Ziegler Cesio s.r.o. (1)
Radiova 1, 102 27, Prague, Czech Republic
Tel.: (420) 267008235
Sales Range: $25-49.9 Million
Emp.: 25
Radioactive Isotopes Mfr
N.A.I.C.S.: 325412

Eckert & Ziegler Chemotrade GmbH (1)
Benrather Schlossallee 2a, 40597, Dusseldorf, Germany
Tel.: (49) 211626062
Web Site: https://www.chemotrade.de
Pharmaceutical Products Distr
N.A.I.C.S.: 424210

Eckert & Ziegler EURO-PET Berlin GmbH (1)
Max-Planck-Street 4, 12489, Berlin, 12489, Germany
Tel.: (49) 3063922491
Web Site: http://www.ezag.de
Sales Range: $25-49.9 Million
Emp.: 15
Radioactive Isotopes Mfr
N.A.I.C.S.: 325180

Eckert & Ziegler Eurotope GmbH (1)
Robert Rossle Street 10, 13125, Berlin, Germany
Tel.: (49) 309410840
Web Site: http://www.ezag.com
Pharmaceuticals Mfr
N.A.I.C.S.: 325180

Eckert & Ziegler Isotope Products, Inc. (1)
24937 Ave Tibbitts, Valencia, CA 91355   (100%)
Tel.: (661) 309-1010
Web Site: http://www.isotopeproducts.com
Emp.: 84
Radioactive Components, Nuclear Imaging Reference & Testing Apparatus Mfr
N.A.I.C.S.: 334516

Subsidiary (Non-US):

Eckert & Ziegler Isotope Products, GmbH (2)
Harxbutteler Strasse 3, 38110, Braunschweig, Germany
Tel.: (49) 53079320
Web Site: http://www.ezag.de
Emp.: 7
Radioactive Isotopes Mfr
N.A.I.C.S.: 325412

Eckert & Ziegler Nuclitec GmbH (1)
Tel.: (49) 53079320
Web Site: http://www.nuclitec.com
Sales Range: $25-49.9 Million
Emp.: 125
Radiation Detection Equipment, Medical Product & Radioactive Reference Device Distr
N.A.I.C.S.: 334519

Eckert & Ziegler Umweltdienste GmbH (1)
Gieselweg 1, 38110, Braunschweig, Germany
Tel.: (49) 5307932182
Medical Equipment Mfr
N.A.I.C.S.: 339112

Eckert & Ziegler f-con Europe GmbH (1)
Robert-Rossle-Str 10, 13125, Holzhausen an der Haide, Germany
Tel.: (49) 30941084197
Web Site: http://www.ezag.com
Sales Range: $25-49.9 Million
Emp.: 5
Medical Instrument Mfr
N.A.I.C.S.: 339112
Axel Schmidt *(Mng Dir)*

Subsidiary (Domestic):

Eckert & Ziegler f-con Deutschland GmbH (2)
Nicolaus August Otto St 7a D, 56357, Holzhausen an der Haide, Rhineland-Palatinate, Germany
Tel.: (49) 6772 96 81 0
Web Site: http://www.ezag.com
Sales Range: $25-49.9 Million
Medical Instrument Mfr
N.A.I.C.S.: 339112
Axel Schmidt *(Mng Dir)*

Kompetenzzentrum fur sichere Entsorgung GmbH (1)
Gieselweg 1 D, 38110, Braunschweig, Germany
Tel.: (49) 5307932481
Radioactive Isotopes Mfr
N.A.I.C.S.: 325412

Pentixapharm GmbH (1)
Bismarckstrasse 13, 97080, Wurzburg, Germany
Tel.: (49) 93199136076
Web Site: https://www.pentixapharm.com

Research & Development Services
N.A.I.C.S.: 541713

Tecnonuclear S.A. (1)
Arias 4149, Buenos Aires, Argentina
Tel.: (54) 47301070
Web Site: https://www.tecnonuclear.com
Drug Mfr & Distr
N.A.I.C.S.: 325412

ECKES AG
Ludwig-Eckes-Platz 1, 55268, Nieder-Olm, Germany
Tel.: (49) 6136 35 0   De
Web Site: http://www.eckes-granini.com
Year Founded: 1857
Sales Range: $1-4.9 Billion
Emp.: 1,747
Holding Company
N.A.I.C.S.: 551112
Sidney Coffeng *(Member-Exec Bd)*

Subsidiaries:

Eckes-Granini France SNC (1)
138 Rue Lavoisier Zone Industrielle Sud, 71040, Macon, France
Tel.: (33) 38 5204700
Web Site: http://www.eckes-granini.fr
Soft Drinks Mfr
N.A.I.C.S.: 312111

Eckes-Granini Group GmbH (1)
Ludwig-Eckes-Platz 1, 55268, Nieder-Olm, Germany
Tel.: (49) 6136 35 0
Web Site: http://www.eckes-granini.com
Sales Range: $1-4.9 Billion
Holding Company; Branded Fruit Juice & Fruit Beverage Mfr & Distr
N.A.I.C.S.: 551112
Thomas Hinderer *(Chm-Mgmt Bd)*

Subsidiary (Non-US):

Bramhults Juice AB (2)
Kallbackrydsgatan 23, Box 71, Bramhults, Vastra Gotaland, 50731, Sweden (100%)
Tel.: (46) 33 20 4500
Web Site: http://www.bramhults.se
Emp.: 60
Fruit Juice & Fruit Beverage Mfr & Distr
N.A.I.C.S.: 311411
Henrik Jorgensen *(Country Mgr)*

Eckes-Granini (Suisse) S.A. (2)
Route de la Gare 1, Seigneux, 1525, Henniez, Switzerland   (51%)
Tel.: (41) 26 66 86 868
Web Site: http://www.eckes-granini.ch
Emp.: 250
Fruit Juice & Fruit Beverage Mfr & Distr
N.A.I.C.S.: 311411
Ina Wantulla *(Mng Dir)*

Eckes-Granini Austria GmbH (2)
Pummerinfeld 1b, Saint Florian, 4490, Asten, Austria
Tel.: (43) 72 24 418 880
Web Site: http://www.eckes-granini.at
Emp.: 50
Fruit Juice & Fruit Beverage Mfr & Distr
N.A.I.C.S.: 311411
Manfred Grestenberger *(Sls Dir)*

Subsidiary (Domestic):

PAGO International GmbH (3)
Schroedingerstrasse 61, 9021, Klagenfurt, Austria
Tel.: (43) 463 33 444 0
Web Site: http://www.pago.cc
Sales Range: $100-124.9 Million
Emp.: 100
Fruit Juice Mfr & Distr
N.A.I.C.S.: 311411
Alle Ypma *(Mng Dir)*

Subsidiary (Domestic):

Eckes-Granini Deutschland GmbH (2)
Ludwig-Eckes-Platz 1, Nieder-Olm, 55268, Germany   (100%)
Tel.: (49) 6136 35 04
Web Site: http://www.eckes-granini.de

Sales Range: $100-124.9 Million
Emp.: 250
Fruit Juice & Fruit Beverage Mfr & Distr
N.A.I.C.S.: 311411
Heribert Gathof *(Mng Dir)*

Subsidiary (Non-US):

Eckes-Granini Finland Oy Ab **(2)**
PO Box 411, 20101, Turku,
Finland **(100%)**
Tel.: (358) 207 207 300
Web Site: http://www.eckes-granini.fi
Fruit Juice & Fruit Beverage Mfr & Distr
N.A.I.C.S.: 311411
Timo Laukkanen *(Mng Dir)*

Eckes-Granini Iberica S.A.U. **(2)**
Travessera de Gracia No 73-79 3rd andar,
08006, Barcelona, Spain **(100%)**
Tel.: (34) 93 238 4384
Web Site: http://www.granini.es
Emp.: 60
Fruit Juices Distr
N.A.I.C.S.: 424490
Javier Lorenzo Benavides *(Mng Dir)*

Sio-Eckes Kft. **(2)**
Majus 1 Utca 61, 8600, Siofok,
Hungary **(100%)**
Tel.: (36) 84501501
Web Site: http://www.sioeckes.hu
Fruit Juice & Fruit Beverage Mfr & Distr
N.A.I.C.S.: 311411

UAB Eckes-Granini Lietuva **(2)**
Laisves Av 125, 06118, Vilnius,
Lithuania **(100%)**
Tel.: (370) 5 279 4408
Web Site: http://www.eckes-granini.lt
Emp.: 10
Fruit Juice & Fruit Beverage Mfr & Distr
N.A.I.C.S.: 311411
Marius Gudauskas *(Mng Dir)*

Affiliate (Non-US):

Yildiz Granini Meyve Suyu Sanayi Ve
Ticaret A.S. **(2)**
Kisikli Mah Ferah Cad No 1, Camlica Usku-
dar, 34692, Istanbul, Turkiye **(50%)**
Tel.: (90) 216 524 1525
Web Site: http://www.ulker.com.tr
Fruit Juice & Fruit Beverage Distr
N.A.I.C.S.: 424490
Mehmet Yilmaz *(Mng Dir)*

Melitta Belgie n.v. **(1)**
Brandstraat 8 Industriezone E17/3006,
9160, Lokeren, Belgium
Tel.: (32) 9 331 52 30
Web Site: http://www.melitta.be
Emp.: 25
Coffee Product Mfr
N.A.I.C.S.: 311920
Wim Swyngedouw *(Gen Mgr)*

Pago Croatia d.o.o. **(1)**
Samoborska Cesta 348, 10000, Zagreb,
Croatia
Tel.: (385) 1 390 9555
Web Site: http://www.pago.hr
Food Products Distr
N.A.I.C.S.: 424490
Martina Matosevic *(Mgr-Sls & Mktg)*

S.C. United Romanian Breweries
Bereprod **(1)**
Biruintei Bld 89, Pantelimon, Ilfov, Romania
Tel.: (40) 21 2055 000
Web Site: http://www.granini.ro
Soft Drinks Mfr
N.A.I.C.S.: 312111

ECKOH PLC

Telford House Corner Hall, Hemel
Hempstead, HP3 9HN, Hertfordshire,
United Kingdom
Tel.: (44) 1442458300 UK
Web Site: https://www.eckoh.com
ECK—(AIM)
Rev.: $48,207,918
Assets: $75,224,519
Liabilities: $23,307,344
Net Worth: $51,917,174
Earnings: $5,758,227
Emp.: 191
Fiscal Year-end: 03/31/23

Hosted Speech Recognition Products
& Services
N.A.I.C.S.: 561499
Nik B. Philpot *(CEO)*

Subsidiaries:

Eckoh UK Limited **(1)**
Telford House Corner Hall, Hemel Hemp-
stead, HP3 9HN, Hertfordshire, United
Kingdom
Tel.: (44) 1442 458300
Web Site: http://www.eckoh.com
Emp.: 150
Telecommunication Servicesb
N.A.I.C.S.: 517810
Nik Philpot *(CEO)*

ECL ENVIROCLEAN VEN-
TURES LTD.

5730 Production Way, Langley, V3A
4N4, BC, Canada
Tel.: (604) 532-5311
Ceramic Coating Mfr
N.A.I.C.S.: 325510
Roland J. Langset *(Pres)*

Subsidiaries:

ECI Envirocoatings (Canada)
Inc. **(1)**
5730 Production Way, Langley, V3A 4N4,
BC, Canada
Tel.: (604) 532-5311
Web Site: http://www.envirocoatings.com
Waterproof Protective Coating Distr
N.A.I.C.S.: 424950

Envirocoat Technologies Inc. **(1)**
5730 Production Way, Langley, V3A 4N4,
BC, Canada
Tel.: (604) 532-5311
Paint & Coating Mfr
N.A.I.C.S.: 325510

ECLAT FOREVER MACHINERY
CO., LTD.

No 16 Lane 760 Jiadong Road, Bade
Dist, Taoyuan, 33466, Taiwan
Tel.: (886) 33646445
Web Site: https://www.efm.com.tw
Year Founded: 1994
3485—(TAI)
Electronic Components Mfr
N.A.I.C.S.: 334419
Chou Kun-Lin *(Chm & Pres)*

ECLAT TEXTILE CO., LTD.

No 738 Zhongyang Rd, Wuku Dist,
Taipei, 248, Taiwan
Tel.: (886) 222996000
Web Site: https://www.eclat.com.tw
1476—(TAI)
Rev.: $1,006,915,231
Assets: $1,040,999,830
Liabilities: $201,515,869
Net Worth: $839,483,961
Earnings: $169,281,756
Emp.: 16,068
Fiscal Year-end: 12/31/23
Yarn Dyeing Mills
N.A.I.C.S.: 313310
Cheng-Hai Hung *(Founder, Chm &
CEO)*

Subsidiaries:

Antaeus Fashions Inc. **(1)**
2411 N Loma Ave, South El Monte, CA
91733-1617
Tel.: (626) 452-0797
Zipper Jackets Mfr
N.A.I.C.S.: 315210
Michael Lin *(Gen Mgr)*

E-Top (Vietnam) Co., Ltd. **(1)**
Lot IX 1-4 My Xuan B1 Tien Hung Industrial
Zone, My Xuan Ward, Phu My, Ba Ria
Vung Tau, Vietnam
Tel.: (84) 2543924919
Fabric & Garment Mfr
N.A.I.C.S.: 315250

Eclat Enterprise Ltd. **(1)**

Strovolos Avenue 79A, 2018, Nicosia, Cy-
prus
Tel.: (357) 22516013
Web Site: https://www.eclatent.com
Laboratory Equipment Distr
N.A.I.C.S.: 423490
Petros Petrides *(Mgr-Sls)*

Eclat Fabrics (Vietnam) Co., Ltd. **(1)**
My Xuan A2 Industrial Zone, My Xuan
Ward, Phu My, Ba Ria Vung Tau, Vietnam
Tel.: (84) 2543932211
Fabric & Garment Mfr
N.A.I.C.S.: 315250

Eclat Textile (Cambodia) Co.,
Ltd. **(1)**
Phum Angtakeat Wat Angtakeat Sangkat
Kantouk, Khan Porsenchey, Phnom Penh,
Cambodia
Tel.: (855) 95777961
Sports Apparel Mfr
N.A.I.C.S.: 315120

Eclat Textile (Combodia) Co.,
Ltd. **(1)**
Phum Angtakeat Wat Angtakeat Sangkat
Kantouk Khan Porsenchey, Phnom Penh,
Cambodia
Tel.: (855) 95777961
Fabric & Garment Mfr
N.A.I.C.S.: 315250

Eclat Textile (Vietnam) Co., Ltd. **(1)**
Lot 1 Road 5A, Nhon Trach 2 Industrial
Zone, Ho Chi Minh City, Dong Nai, Vietnam
Tel.: (84) 6156075160
Fabric & Garment Mfr
N.A.I.C.S.: 315250

P.T. Eclat Textile International **(1)**
Kawasan Ekonomi Khusus Kendal JL
Saptarengga No 11 KEL Wonorejo, Kec
Kaliwungu, Kendal, Jawa, Indonesia
Tel.: (62) 2433001900
Sports Apparel Mfr
N.A.I.C.S.: 315120

Tai-Yuan Garments Co., Ltd. **(1)**
LOT Le11-Le12, Xuyen A Industrial Park My
Hanh Bac Commune, Duc Hoa, Long An,
Vietnam
Tel.: (84) 2723758599
Fabric & Garment Mfr
N.A.I.C.S.: 315250

ECLERX SERVICES LTD

Sonawala Building 1st Floor 29 Bank
Street, Fort, Mumbai, 400 023, Maha-
rashtra, India
Tel.: (91) 2266148301
Web Site: https://www.eclerx.com
532927—(BOM)
Rev.: $218,255,993
Assets: $274,111,656
Liabilities: $69,127,695
Net Worth: $204,983,961
Earnings: $38,605,067
Emp.: 11,900
Fiscal Year-end: 03/31/21
Data Solutions Technical Services
N.A.I.C.S.: 518210
Pradeep Kapoor *(Chm)*

Subsidiaries:

CLX Europe Media Solution
GmbH **(1)**
Barmbeker Str 8, 22303, Hamburg, Ger-
many
Tel.: (49) 40524704060
Advertising Services
N.A.I.C.S.: 541810

CLX Europe S.P.A. **(1)**
Via dell'Artigianato 8A, 37135, Verona, Italy
Tel.: (39) 0458294999
Web Site: http://www.clxeurope.com
Advertising Services
N.A.I.C.S.: 541810

eClerx Limited **(1)**
1 Dover Street 1st floor, London, W1S 4LA,
United Kingdom
Tel.: (44) 2075296000
Web Site: http://www.eclerx.com
Emp.: 27
Business Process Outsourcing Services

N.A.I.C.S.: 561499
Gary Primrose *(Principal)*

ECLIPSE METALS LTD.

Principal Place Of Business Level 3
1060 Hay St, West Perth, 6005, WA,
Australia
Tel.: (61) 894800420
Web Site:
https://www.eclipsemetals.com.au
EPM—(ASX)
Rev: $9,226
Assets: $7,600,224
Liabilities: $49,751
Net Worth: $7,550,473
Earnings: ($1,010,410)
Fiscal Year-end: 06/30/22
Mineral Exploration Services
N.A.I.C.S.: 212290
Carl Popal *(Chm)*

ECLIPSE RESIDENTIAL MORT-
GAGE INVESTMENT CORPO-
RATION

181 Bay Street Suite 2930, Toronto,
M5J 2T3, ON, Canada
Tel.: (614) 642-9050 ON
Web Site:
http://www.bromptongroup.com
Year Founded: 2013
Rev.: $2,355,012
Assets: $32,232,884
Liabilities: $7,856,478
Net Worth: $24,376,406
Earnings: $1,520,547
Fiscal Year-end: 12/31/17
Real Estate Investment Services
N.A.I.C.S.: 523999
Craig T. Kikuchi *(CFO-Brompton
Funds Limited)*

ECM EQUITY CAPITAL MAN-
AGEMENT GMBH

Taunusanlage 18, Frankfurt, 60325,
Germany
Tel.: (49) 69971020 De
Web Site: http://www.ecm-pe.de
Year Founded: 1995
Emp.: 10
Private Equity & Investment Manage-
ment Services
N.A.I.C.S.: 523999
Axel Eichmeyer *(Mng Partner & Mng
Dir)*

Subsidiaries:

Bergmann Automotive GmbH **(1)**
Giessereiweg 1, 30890, Barsinghausen,
Germany
Tel.: (49) 5105 522 0
Web Site: http://www.bergmann-auto.de
Cylinder Liner Mfr
N.A.I.C.S.: 332313

LEITNER Touristik GmbH **(1)**
Am Spitalwald 2, 90584, Allersberg, Ger-
many
Tel.: (49) 9176 98 60 0
Web Site: http://www.leitner-reisen.de
Travel Tour Operator
N.A.I.C.S.: 561520

MediFox GmbH **(1)**
Junkersstrasse 1, 31137, Hildesheim, Ger-
many
Tel.: (49) 51 21 28 29 1
Web Site: http://www.medifox.de
Software Development Services
N.A.I.C.S.: 541511

Subsidiary (Domestic):

BFS Abrechnungs GmbH **(2)**
Lavesstrasse 8 - 12, 31137, Hildesheim,
Germany
Tel.: (49) 5121 93 56 23
Web Site: http://www.bfs-abrechnung.de
Financial Consulting Services
N.A.I.C.S.: 541611

ECM Real Estate Investments A.G.—(Continued)

ECM REAL ESTATE INVESTMENTS A.G.
2 avenue Charles de Gaulle, 1653, Luxembourg, Luxembourg
Tel.: (352) 26976165
Web Site: http://www.ecm.cz
Year Founded: 1991
Sales Range: $10-24.9 Million
Real Estate Development Services
N.A.I.C.S.: 531390
Milan Janku (Founder, Chm & Pres)

ECM TECHNOLOGIES SAS
46 rue Vaujany TechniSud, 38029, Grenoble, Cedex 2, France
Tel.: (33) 4 7649 6560   FR
Web Site: http://www.ecm-furnaces.com
Year Founded: 1928
Emp.: 350
Industrial Heat Treatment Technologies Mfr & Whslr
N.A.I.C.S.: 333415
Laurent Pelissier (Pres & CEO)

Subsidiaries:

ECM (USA), Inc.   (1)
9505 72nd Ave Ste 400, Pleasant Prairie, WI 53158
Tel.: (262) 605-4810
Web Site: http://www.ecm-usa.com
Warm Air Heating Equipment Whslr
N.A.I.C.S.: 423730

ECM Greentech SASU   (1)
46 rue Vaujany TechniSud, 38100, Grenoble, France
Tel.: (33) 4 7649 6560
Web Site: http://www.ecm-greentech.fr
Photovoltaic Equipment Mfr
N.A.I.C.S.: 334413

Joint Venture (Non-US):

Astana Solar LLP   (2)
Turan Avenue, Nur-Sultan, 010000, Kazakhstan
Tel.: (7) 7172 551400
Web Site: http://astanasolar.kz
Solar Module Mfr
N.A.I.C.S.: 334413

Joint Venture (Non-US):

Kazakhstan Solar Silicon LLP   (2)
st Sogrinskaya 223/6, Ust-Kamenogorsk, Oskemen, East Kazakhstan, Kazakhstan
Tel.: (7) 23 220 4150
Web Site: https://www.kazsolarsilicon.kz
Photovoltaic Silicon Cells Mfr
N.A.I.C.S.: 334413
Baizhumin Daniyar Anuarbekovich (Gen Dir)

Joint Venture (Non-US):

MK KazSilicon LLP   (2)
Komarova St 1, Karatal District, Bastobe, 041011, Almaty Region, Kazakhstan
Tel.: (7) 283440373
Web Site: http://www.kazsilicon.kz
Metallurgical & Polycrystalline Silicon Mfr & Whslr
N.A.I.C.S.: 331110

ECMOHO LIMITED
3rd Floor 1000 Tianyaoqiao Road, Xuhui District, Shanghai, 200030, China
Tel.: (86) 216 417 2213   Ky
Web Site: http://www.ecmoho.com
Year Founded: 2011
MOHO—(NASDAQ)
Rev.: $130,746,560
Assets: $93,554,436
Liabilities: $64,667,810
Net Worth: $28,886,626
Earnings: ($55,655,198)
Emp.: 300
Fiscal Year-end: 12/31/21
Healthcare Product Distr
N.A.I.C.S.: 424210

Zoe Wang (Co-Founder, Chm & CEO)

ECN CAPITAL CORP.
161 Bay Street Suite 2800, Toronto, M5J 2S1, ON, Canada
Tel.: (416) 646-4710
Web Site: https://www.ecncapitalcorp.com
Year Founded: 2007
ECN—(TSX)
Rev.: $87,227,000
Assets: $1,724,138,000
Liabilities: $845,112,000
Net Worth: $879,026,000
Earnings: ($14,749,000)
Emp.: 570
Fiscal Year-end: 12/31/19
Financial Services
N.A.I.C.S.: 921130
Steven K. Hudson (CEO)

Subsidiaries:

Triad Financial Services, Inc.   (1)
13901 Sutton Park Dr S Ste 300, Jacksonville, FL 32224
Tel.: (904) 223-1111
Web Site: https://www.triadfs.com
Loan Brokerage Services
N.A.I.C.S.: 522310
Seth Deyo (CFO, Sr VP, Sec & Treas)

Subsidiary (Domestic):

CIS Financial Services, Inc.   (2)
851 N Military St, Hamilton, AL 35570-0898
Tel.: (205) 430-8250
Web Site: http://www.cishomeloans.com
Home & Land Home Financing
N.A.I.C.S.: 522310

Triad Financial Service, Inc.   (2)
19 Heritage Dr, Bourbonnais, IL 60914
Tel.: (888) 936-1179
Web Site: https://www.triadfs.com
Loan Brokerage Services
N.A.I.C.S.: 524210

ECO (ATLANTIC) OIL & GAS LTD.
7 Coulson Ave, Toronto, M4V 1Y3, ON, Canada
Tel.: (416) 722-0804   ON
Web Site: https://www.ecooilandgas.com
Year Founded: 2007
EOI—(DEU)
Rev.: $66,571
Assets: $55,617,651
Liabilities: $4,965,062
Net Worth: $50,652,589
Earnings: ($36,554,754)
Fiscal Year-end: 03/31/23
Oil & Gas Exploration Services
N.A.I.C.S.: 213112
Gil Holzman (Founder, Pres & CEO)

ECO ANIMAL HEALTH GROUP PLC
The Grange 100 The High Street, Southgate, London, N14 6BN, Surrey, United Kingdom
Tel.: (44) 2084478899
Web Site: https://www.ecoanimalhealthplc.com
EAH—(AIM)
Rev.: $105,939,200
Assets: $150,648,967
Liabilities: $31,993,735
Net Worth: $118,655,232
Earnings: $3,838,404
Emp.: 234
Fiscal Year-end: 03/31/23
Developer, Mfr & Distr of Animal Health Products
N.A.I.C.S.: 115210
Julia Trouse (Sec & Exec Dir)

Subsidiaries:

Eco Animal Health Limited   (1)
The Grange 100 The High Street, PO Box 47542, Southgate, London, N14 6BN, United Kingdom
Tel.: (44) 2084478899
Web Site: http://www.ecoanimalhealth.com
Emp.: 50
Animal Drugs Mfr
N.A.I.C.S.: 424210

Zhejiang Eco Biok Animal Health Products Limited   (1)
Room 1502 Woge Plaza 99 Wuning Road, Putuo District, Shanghai, 200063, Shandong, China
Tel.: (86) 2152376381
Web Site: http://www.eco-biok.net
Emp.: 100
Pharmaceuticals Product Mfr
N.A.I.C.S.: 325412
Dann Yu (Owner)

ECO FRIENDLY FOOD PROCESSING PARK LTD.
49 Gujrawala Town Part-2, New Delhi, 110 009, India
Tel.: (91) 1165554037
Web Site: http://www.ecofriendlyfood.in
534839—(BOM)
Rev.: $430,233
Assets: $9,044,212
Liabilities: $3,229,241
Net Worth: $5,814,971
Earnings: $306,181
Emp.: 1
Fiscal Year-end: 03/31/21
Wheat, Rice & Vegetables Mfr
N.A.I.C.S.: 111140
Brij Kishore Sabharwal (Exec Dir)

ECO ORO MINERALS CORP.
Suite 300-1055 W Hastings St, Vancouver, V6E 2E9, BC, Canada
Tel.: (604) 682-8212   BC
Year Founded: 1997
GQQ—(DEU)
Rev.: $34,720
Assets: $834,010
Liabilities: $11,659,156
Net Worth: ($10,825,146)
Earnings: ($4,373,199)
Fiscal Year-end: 12/31/22
Metal Exploration Services
N.A.I.C.S.: 213114
Courtenay Wolfe (Co-Chm)

ECO RECYCLING LIMITED.
422 The Summit Business Bay Andheri Kurla Road, Andheri Kurla Road Andheri East, Mumbai, 400093, India
Tel.: (91) 2240052951
Web Site: https://ecoreco.com
530643—(BOM)
Rev.: $3,706,875
Assets: $9,159,136
Liabilities: $2,389,482
Net Worth: $6,769,653
Earnings: $1,732,746
Emp.: 40
Fiscal Year-end: 03/31/22
Electronic Waste Recycling Services
N.A.I.C.S.: 562998
Brij Kishor Soni (Chm & Mng Dir)

ECO SECURITIZADORA DE DIREITOS CREDITORIOS DO AGRONEGOCIO S.A.
Av Pedroso De Morais 1553-3rd Floor, Sao Paulo, 05419-001, Brazil
Tel.: (55) 1138114959
Web Site: http://www.ecoagro.agr.br
Year Founded: 2009
Emp.: 100
Financial Investment Services
N.A.I.C.S.: 523940
Milton Scatolini Menten (CEO)

ECO SUPPLIES EUROPE AB
Stora Avagen 21, Askim, 436 34, Gothenburg, Sweden
Tel.: (46) 317232122
Web Site: http://www.ecosupplieseuropeab.com
Sales Range: $1-9.9 Million
Emp.: 100
Office Systems & Printers Distr
N.A.I.C.S.: 423420
Svante Kumlin (Founder, Chm & CEO)

Subsidiaries:

Direct Printer Service GmbH   (1)
Bockgasse 2b, Linz, A-4020, Upper Austria, Austria
Tel.: (43) 732749290
Web Site: http://www.directprinterservice.com
Recycled Toner & Ink Cartridges Mfr
N.A.I.C.S.: 325992
Fredrik Stael von Holstein (CEO)

European Office Systems B.V.   (1)
Vasteland 12A, 3011 BL, Rotterdam, Zuid-Holland, Netherlands
Tel.: (31) 107988000
Web Site: http://www.eosprint.com
Laser & Ink Cartridges Sales
N.A.I.C.S.: 424120

European Office Systems GmbH   (1)
Virchowstr 17-19, 22767, Hamburg, Germany
Tel.: (49) 4032024500
Web Site: http://www.eosprint.com
Laser & Ink Cartridges Sales
N.A.I.C.S.: 424120

European Office Systems S.A.R.L   (1)
31 rue de Paris, 06000, Nice, Alpes-Maritimes, France
Tel.: (33) 4 97 19 00 29
Web Site: http://www.eosprint.com
Laser & Ink Cartridges Sales
N.A.I.C.S.: 424120

ECO SYSTEMS LTD.
294 Kings Way, South Melbourne, 3205, VIC, Australia
Tel.: (61) 1300 289 697
Web Site: http://www.buymyplace.com.au
Year Founded: 2008
Online Real Estate Services
N.A.I.C.S.: 531390

Subsidiaries:

PT Killara Resources   (1)
12th Floor Ratu Plaza Office Tower, Jl Jendral Sudirman Kav 9, Jakarta, 10270, Indonesia
Tel.: (62) 21 7278 1933
Gold Ore Mining Services
N.A.I.C.S.: 212220
Ansar Bayanta (Dir-Ops)

ECO VOLT CO.,LTD.
433-31 Sandong-ro, Eumbong-myeon, Asan, Chungcheongnam-do, Korea (South)
Tel.: (82) 415392500   KR
Web Site: https://ecovoltdynamics.co.kr
Year Founded: 2004
097780—(KRS)
Rev.: $133,518,627
Assets: $231,064,309
Liabilities: $51,283,047
Net Worth: $179,781,262
Earnings: ($48,378,462)
Emp.: 36
Fiscal Year-end: 12/31/22
Mobile Phone Parts Mfr
N.A.I.C.S.: 334310
Kyoungsook Cho (CEO)

ECO WAVE POWER GLOBAL AB

52 Derech Menachem Begin St, Tel Aviv, 6713701, Israel
Tel.: (972) 35094017   II
Web Site:
  https://www.ecowavepower.com
Year Founded: 2011
WAVE—(NASDAQ)
Rev.: $306,000
Assets: $10,009,000
Liabilities: $2,208,000
Net Worth: $7,801,000
Earnings: ($1,866,000)
Emp.: 13
Fiscal Year end: 12/31/23
Eletric Power Generation Services
N.A.I.C.S.: 221118
Inna Braverman *(Co-Founder & CEO)*

ECO WORLD DEVELOPMENT GROUP BERHAD

Suite 60 Setia Avenue No 2 Jalan Setia Prima S U13/S, Setia Alam Seksyen U13, 40170, Shah Alam, Selangor Darul Ehsan, Malaysia
Tel.: (60) 333442552
Web Site: https://www.ecoworld.my
ECOWLD—(KLS)
Rev.: $484,732,698
Assets: $1,937,928,398
Liabilities: $898,849,810
Net Worth: $1,039,078,588
Earnings: $41,210,928
Emp.: 1,083
Fiscal Year-end: 10/31/23
Real Estate Development Services
N.A.I.C.S.: 531390
Siew Chuan Chua *(Co-Sec)*

Subsidiaries:

Eco Botanic Sdn. Bhd.   (1)
No 25 27 29 Jalan Eko Botani 3/5 Taman Eko Botani, 79100, Iskandar Puteri, Johor, Malaysia
Tel.: (60) 75715252
Web Site: https://ecoworld.my
Real Estate Development Services
N.A.I.C.S.: 531390

Eco Business Park 1 Sdn. Bhd.   (1)
2 and 6 Jalan Ekoperniagaan 1/5 Taman Ekoperniagaan, 81100, Johor Bahru, Johor, Malaysia
Tel.: (60) 72882525
Web Site: https://ecoworld.my
Real Estate Development Services
N.A.I.C.S.: 531390

Eco Business Park 2 Sdn. Bhd.   (1)
No 36 Jalan Ekoperniagaan 2 Taman Ekoperniagaan 2 Senai Airport City, 81400, Senai, Johor Darul Takzim, Malaysia
Tel.: (60) 72882255
Web Site: https://ecoworld.my
Real Estate Development Services
N.A.I.C.S.: 531390

Eco Horizon Sdn. Bhd.   (1)
Lot PT 21145 PT 5261 Mukim 13 Lebuhraya Bandar Cassia, Bandar Cassia, 14110, Penang, Malaysia
Tel.: (60) 42272255
Web Site: https://ecoworld.my
Real Estate Development Services
N.A.I.C.S.: 531390

Eco Majestic Development Sdn. Bhd.   (1)
No 1 Lingkaran Eco Majestic, 43500, Semenyih, Selangor, Malaysia
Tel.: (60) 387232255
Web Site: https://ecoworld.my
Real Estate Development Services
N.A.I.C.S.: 531390

Eco Meadows Sdn. Bhd.   (1)
PT 740 Jalan Paboi Mukim 14, Daerah Seberang Perai Selatan Simpang Ampat, 14100, Penang, Malaysia
Tel.: (60) 45102255
Web Site: https://ecoworld.my
Real Estate Development Services
N.A.I.C.S.: 531390

Eco Sanctuary Sdn. Bhd.   (1)

Lot 41296 Persiaran Eco Sanctuary, 42500, Teluk Panglima Garang, Selangor, Malaysia
Tel.: (60) 386882255
Web Site: https://ecoworld.my
Real Estate Development Services
N.A.I.C.S.: 531390

Eco Sky Sdn. Bhd.   (1)
1-29 Eco Sky No 972 Batu 6 1/2 Jalan Ipoh, 68100, Kuala Lumpur, Malaysia
Tel.: (60) 123367231
Web Site: https://ecoworld.my
Real Estate Development Services
N.A.I.C.S.: 531390

Eco Summer Sdn. Bhd.   (1)
Jalan Ekoflora 1 Taman Ekoflora, 81100, Johor Bahru, Johor Darul Takzim, Malaysia
Tel.: (60) 73642552
Web Site: https://ecoworld.my
Real Estate Development Services
N.A.I.C.S.: 531390

Eco Terraces Sdn. Bhd.   (1)
PT2509 Jalan Paya Terubong, Paya Terubong George Town, 11060, Penang, Malaysia
Tel.: (60) 124339255
Web Site: https://ecoworld.my
Real Estate Development Services
N.A.I.C.S.: 531390

Eco Tropics Development Sdn. Bhd.   (1)
No 1 Jalan Kota Masai Taman Kota Masai, 81700, Pasir Gudang, Johor Darul Takzim, Malaysia
Tel.: (60) 72522255
Web Site: https://ecoworld.my
Real Estate Development Services
N.A.I.C.S.: 531390

Eco World Development Management (BBCC) Sdn. Bhd.   (1)
No 2 Jalan Hang Tuah, 55100, Kuala Lumpur, Malaysia
Tel.: (60) 321172255
Web Site: https://bbcckl.com
Real Estate Development Services
N.A.I.C.S.: 531390

Focal Aims Land Sdn. Bhd.   (1)
Unit 2 1 Level 2 Building A Peremba Square Saujana Resort Seksyen U2, 40150, Shah Alam, Selangor Darul Ehsan, Malaysia
Tel.: (60) 376229983
Sales Range: $25-49.9 Million
Emp.: 6
Building Construction Services
N.A.I.C.S.: 236210

Focal Aims Sdn. Bhd.   (1)
No 1 Jalan Kota Masai Taman Kota Masai, 81700, Pasir Gudang, Johor Darul Takzim, Malaysia
Tel.: (60) 72522255
Web Site: https://ecoworld.my
Sales Range: $25-49.9 Million
Emp.: 50
Building Construction Services
N.A.I.C.S.: 236210

ECO WORLD INTERNATIONAL BERHAD

Suite 59 Setia Avenue No 2 Jalan Setia Prima S U13/S Setia Alam, Seksyen U13, 40170, Shah Alam, Selangor Darul Ehsan, Malaysia
Tel.: (60) 333612552   MY
Web Site:
  https://www.ecoworldnational.com
5283—(KLS)
Rev.: $22,811,929
Assets: $363,414,456
Liabilities: $3,040,488
Net Worth: $360,373,968
Earnings: ($18,499,782)
Emp.: 109
Fiscal Year-end: 10/31/23
Real Estate Development Services
N.A.I.C.S.: 531210
Kee Sin Liew *(Vice Chm)*

Subsidiaries:

Eco World International Marketing Sdn Bhd   (1)

No 2 Jalan Hang Tuah, 55100, Kuala Lumpur, Malaysia
Tel.: (60) 321162525
Marketing Management Services
N.A.I.C.S.: 541613

Eco World Sydney Development Pty. Ltd.   (1)
1701/99 Mount Street, North Sydney, 2060, NSW, Australia
Tel.: (61) 296892525
Property Development Services
N.A.I.C.S.: 531312
Yap Foo Leong *(CEO-Intl Bus-Australia)*

Eco World-Ballymore Embassy Gardens Company Limited   (1)
Phase 2 Embassy Gardens Nine Elms Lane, London, SW8 5BL, United Kingdom
Tel.: (44) 2039301363
Web Site: http://www.embassygardens.com
Residential Property Development Services
N.A.I.C.S.: 236116

Eco World-Ballymore London City Island Company Limited   (1)
Land at Middle Wharf Baldwins Upper Wharf and Crown Wharf, Orchard Place, London, E14, United Kingdom
Tel.: (44) 2037331004
Web Site: http://www.londoncityisland.com
Residential Property Development Services
N.A.I.C.S.: 236116

ECO'S CO., LTD

11601 Nakagamicho, Akishima, 196-0022, Tokyo, Japan
Tel.: (81) 425463711
Web Site: https://www.eco-s.co.jp
Year Founded: 1977
7520—(TKS)
Rev.: $921,976,510
Assets: $369,949,110
Liabilities: $204,936,450
Net Worth: $165,012,660
Earnings: $25,368,020
Emp.: 2,859
Fiscal Year-end: 02/29/24
Supermarket Store Operator
N.A.I.C.S.: 445110
Tomio Taira *(Founder & Chm)*

ECO-SHIFT POWER CORP.

1090 Fountain Street North, Cambridge, N3H 4R7, ON, Canada
Tel.: (519) 650-9506   DE
Web Site: http://www.eco-shiftpower.com
Year Founded: 2011
Sales Range: $1-9.9 Million
Emp.: 25
Electrical Lighting Product Mfr.
N.A.I.C.S.: 335139
Alistair Haughton *(Pres & CEO)*

ECO-TEK GROUP INC.

15-65 Woodstream Boulevard, Woodbridge, L4L 7X6, ON, Canada   NV
Web Site: http://www.eco-tekgroup.net
Year Founded: 2007
ETEK—(OTCIQ)
Sales Range: Less than $1 Million
Emp.: 2
Eco-Friendly Products for Automotive & Industrial Sectors
N.A.I.C.S.: 324191
Maurizio Cochi *(Treas & Sec)*

ECO-TEK HOLDINGS LIMITED

Unit 5 11/F Westlands Centre 20 Westlands Road, Quarry Bay, China (Hong Kong)
Tel.: (852) 23427998   Ky
Web Site: http://www.eco-tek.com.hk
8169—(HKG)
Rev.: $12,587,803
Assets: $22,189,461
Liabilities: $8,301,153
Net Worth: $13,888,308
Earnings: $564,803

Emp.: 79
Fiscal Year-end: 10/31/22
Environmental Product Mfr & Distr.
N.A.I.C.S.: 333998
Wai Lun Leung *(Officer-Compliance)*

ECOBANK TRANSNATIONAL INCORPORATED

2365 Boulevard du Mono, BP 3261, Lome, Togo
Tel.: (228) 22210303   TG
Web Site: https://www.ecobank.com
Year Founded: 1985
ETI—(NIGE)
Rev.: $1,473,554,000
Assets: $27,561,793,000
Liabilities: $25,397,487,000
Net Worth: $2,164,306,000
Earnings: $357,366,000
Emp.: 13,167
Fiscal Year-end: 12/31/21
Bank Holding Company
N.A.I.C.S.: 551111

Subsidiaries:

EBI SA   (1)
Les Collines de l'Arche 76 route de la Demi Lune, Immeuble Concorde F, 92057, Paris, Cedex, France
Tel.: (33) 170922100
Web Site: https://www.ecobank.com
Sales Range: $50-74.9 Million
Emp.: 40
Commercial Banking Services
N.A.I.C.S.: 522110

EDCC Bank Ltd.   (1)
1 Bhawani Main Road Opposite VUC Park East Entrance, Karungal Palayam, Erode, 638 003, India
Tel.: (91) 4242213401
Web Site: https://edccbank.com
Transaction Banking Services
N.A.I.C.S.: 522320

Ecobank Benin Limited   (1)
Rue du Gouverneur Bayol 01, BP 1280, RP, Cotonou, Benin
Tel.: (229) 21313069
Transaction Banking Services
N.A.I.C.S.: 522320

Ecobank Burkina Faso S.A.   (1)
49 Rue de l Hotel de Ville 01, BP 145, Ouagadougou, Burkina Faso
Tel.: (226) 25333333
Transaction Banking Services
N.A.I.C.S.: 522320

Ecobank Burundi S.A.   (1)
6 Rue de la Science, BP 270, Bujumbura, Burundi
Tel.: (257) 22208100
Transaction Banking Services
N.A.I.C.S.: 522320

Ecobank Cameroon S.A.   (1)
Boulevard de la Liberte, BP 582, Douala, Cameroon
Tel.: (237) 233500700
Transaction Banking Services
N.A.I.C.S.: 522320

Ecobank Cape Verde Ltd.   (1)
Avenida Cidade de Lisboa, CP 374 /C, Praia, Cape Verde
Tel.: (238) 2603660
Transaction Banking Services
N.A.I.C.S.: 522320

Ecobank Centrafrique   (1)
Place de la Republique, BP 910, Bangui, Central African Republic   (72%)
Tel.: (236) 21610042
Web Site: http://www.ecobank.com
Emp.: 171
Commercial Banking Services
N.A.I.C.S.: 522110

Ecobank Chad Ltd.   (1)
Avenue Charles de Gaulle, BP 87, N'djamena, Chad
Tel.: (235) 22524314
Banking Services
N.A.I.C.S.: 522110

Ecobank Transnational Incorporated—(Continued)

Ecobank Congo Brazzaville Limited (1)
Immeuble de l'ARC - 3e etage Avenue du Camp, BP 2485, Brazzaville, Congo, Republic of
Tel.: (242) 66210808
Banking Services
N.A.I.C.S.: 522110

Ecobank Congo RDC Limited (1)
47 Avenue Ngongo-Lutete, BP 7515, Gombe, Kinshasa, Congo, Republic of
Tel.: (242) 996016000
Banking Services
N.A.I.C.S.: 522110

Ecobank Cote d'Ivoire S.A. (1)
Tel.: (225) 2720319200
Web Site: https://www.ecobank.com
Sales Range: $75-99.9 Million
Emp.: 429
Commercial Banking Services
N.A.I.C.S.: 522110

Ecobank Development Corporation (1)
2 Avenue Sylvanus Olympio, PO Box 3261, Lome, Togo (100%)
Tel.: (228) 2213168
Web Site: http://www.ecobank.com
Investment Banking Services
N.A.I.C.S.: 523150

Subsidiary (Non-US):

EDC Investment Corporation (2)
Immeuble Ecobank Avenue Houdaille Place de la Republique, BP 4107, Abidjan, Cote d'Ivoire
Tel.: (225) 20211044
Web Site: http://www.ecobank.com
Sales Range: $50-74.9 Million
Emp.: 15
Investment Banking Services
N.A.I.C.S.: 523150

EDC Stockbrokers Limited (2)
Second Ridge Link North Ridge, Accra, Ghana
Tel.: (233) 21251723
Web Site: http://www.ecobank.com
Investment Banking Services
N.A.I.C.S.: 523150

Ecobank Gabon S.A. (1)
336 Avenue du Colonel Parant, BP 12111, Libreville, Gabon
Tel.: (241) 11762073
Emp.: 108
Transaction Banking Services
N.A.I.C.S.: 522320

Ecobank Gambia Limited (1)
42 Kairaba Avenue, PO Box 3466, Serrekunda, Gambia
Tel.: (220) 4399031
Transaction Banking Services
N.A.I.C.S.: 522320

Ecobank Ghana Limited (1)
19 Seventh Avenue Ridge West, Accra, Ghana (60.41%)
Tel.: (233) 302680437
Web Site: http://www.ecobank.com
Sales Range: $25-49.9 Million
Commercial Banking Services
N.A.I.C.S.: 522110
Alain Nkontchou (Chm)

Ecobank Guinea Bissau S.A. (1)
Avenue Amilcar Cabral, BP 126, Bissau, Guinea Bissau
Tel.: (245) 955604026
Transaction Banking Services
N.A.I.C.S.: 522320

Ecobank Guinea Equatoriale Ltd. (1)
Avenida de la Independencia APDO 268, Malabo, Equatorial Guinea
Tel.: (240) 333098271
Banking Services
N.A.I.C.S.: 522110

Ecobank Guinea Ltd. (1)
Immeuble Al Iman Avenue de la Republique, BP 5687, Conakry, Guinea
Tel.: (224) 627272715
Transaction Banking Services
N.A.I.C.S.: 522320

Ecobank Kenya Limited (1)
Fortis Office Park Muthangari Drive off Waiyaki Way Westlands, PO Box 49584, 00100, Nairobi, Kenya
Tel.: (254) 202883000
Commercial Banking Services
N.A.I.C.S.: 522110

Ecobank Liberia Limited (1)
11th Street Sinkor Tubman Boulevard, PO Box 4825, Monrovia, Liberia
Tel.: (231) 886514298
Transaction Banking Services
N.A.I.C.S.: 522320

Ecobank Malawi Limited (1)
Corner Victoria Avenue & Henderson Street, Chichiri, Blantyre, Malawi
Tel.: (265) 1822099
Web Site: https://www.ecobank.com
Sales Range: $1-9.9 Million
Emp.: 49
Commercial Banking Services
N.A.I.C.S.: 522110

Ecobank Micro Finance Sierra Leone S.L. (1)
3 Charlotte Street, PO Box 1007, Freetown, Sierra Leone
Tel.: (232) 88141015
Transaction Banking Services
N.A.I.C.S.: 522320

Ecobank Mozambique S.A. (1)
Av Vladimir Lenine N 210, CP 1106, Maputo, Mozambique
Tel.: (258) 21313344
Transaction Banking Services
N.A.I.C.S.: 522320

Ecobank Nigeria Plc (1)
Plot 21 Ahmadu Bello Way, PO Box 72688, Victoria Island, Lagos, Nigeria
Tel.: (234) 127103912
Web Site: https://www.ecobank.com
Emp.: 7,759
Commercial Banking Services
N.A.I.C.S.: 522110

Ecobank Rwanda PLC (1)
KN4 Avenue, PO Box 3268, Kigali, Rwanda
Tel.: (250) 788161000
Banking Services
N.A.I.C.S.: 522110

Ecobank Sao Tome S.A. (1)
Travessa de Pelourinho, CP 316, Sao Tome, Sao Tome & Principe
Tel.: (239) 2222141
Transaction Banking Services
N.A.I.C.S.: 522320

Ecobank Senegal Ltd. (1)
Km 5 Avenue Cheikh Anta Diop, BP 9095, CD, Dakar, Senegal
Tel.: (221) 338599999
Transaction Banking Services
N.A.I.C.S.: 522320

Ecobank Sierra Leone Limited (1)
3 Charlotte Street, PO Box 1007, Freetown, Sierra Leone
Tel.: (232) 88141015
Banking Services
N.A.I.C.S.: 522110

Ecobank Tanzania Limited (1)
Acacia Building Kinondoni Road, PO Box 20500, Dar es Salaam, Tanzania
Tel.: (255) 222923471
Banking Services
N.A.I.C.S.: 522110

Ecobank Tchad S.A. (1)
Avenue de Charles De Gaulle, BP 87, N'djamena, Chad
Tel.: (235) 2252 43 14
Web Site: http://www.ecobank.com
Sales Range: $10-24.9 Million
Commercial Banking Services
N.A.I.C.S.: 522110

Ecobank Togo S.A. (1)
20 Avenue Sylvanus Olympio, BP 3 302, Lome, Togo
Tel.: (228) 22217214
Web Site: https://www.ecobank.com
Emp.: 238
Commercial Banking Services
N.A.I.C.S.: 522110

Ecobank Uganda Limited (1)
Plot 8A Kafu Road, PO Box 7368, Kampala, Uganda
Tel.: (256) 417700100
Transaction Banking Services
N.A.I.C.S.: 522320

Ecobank Zambia Limited (1)
Plot No 22768 Thabo Mbeki Road, PO Box 30705, Lusaka, Zambia
Tel.: (260) 2112500567
Web Site: https://www.ecobank.com
Sales Range: $1-9.9 Million
Commercial Banking Services
N.A.I.C.S.: 522110

Ecobank Zimbabwe Limited (1)
Block A Sam Levy's Office Park 2 Piers Road BW1464, Borrowdale, Harare, Zimbabwe
Tel.: (263) 48516449
Banking Services
N.A.I.C.S.: 522110

Export Inspection Council Private Limited (1)
2nd Floor B-Plate Block-I Commercial Complex East Kidwai Nagar, New Delhi, 110023, India
Tel.: (91) 1120815386
Web Site: https://www.eicindia.gov.in
Transaction Banking Services
N.A.I.C.S.: 522320

Oceanic Capital Management LLC (1)
125 Half Mile Rd Ste 200, Red Bank, NJ 07701
Tel.: (732) 345-1533
Web Site: https://www.oceaniccap.com
Wealth Management Services
N.A.I.C.S.: 523940

Pan-African Savings & Loans Ghana Limited (1)
No 4 Nortei Ababio Street Roman Ridge, Accra, Ghana
Tel.: (233) 302782755
Web Site: https://www.panafricansl.com
Financial Banking Services
N.A.I.C.S.: 522320

eProcess International S.A. (1)
20 Avenue Sylvanus Olympio, BP 4385, Lome, Togo (100%)
Tel.: (228) 2222370
Web Site: http://www.ecobank.com
Technology Support & Shared Services
N.A.I.C.S.: 541990
Patrick Akinwuntan (Mng Dir)

ECOBIO HOLDINGS CO., LTD.
Totaleco B/D 1302-7 Seocho-dong, Seocho-Gu, Seoul, 06609, Korea (South)
Tel.: (82) 234832900
Web Site: https://www.ecobio.co.kr
Year Founded: 1989
038870—(KRS)
Rev.: $12,873,143
Assets: $73,495,137
Liabilities: $20,199,568
Net Worth: $53,295,569
Earnings: ($3,606,258)
Emp.: 142
Fiscal Year-end: 12/31/22
Renewable Energy Development Services
N.A.I.C.S.: 221118
Hyo-Soon Song (CEO)

ECOBOARD INDUSTRIES LTD
65/1A Ecohouse Akarshak Building Opp Nal Stop Karve Road, Pune, 411 004, Maharashtra, India
Tel.: (91) 2040111927
Web Site: https://ecoyou.in
Year Founded: 1986
523732—(BOM)
Rev.: $2,249,534
Assets: $9,884,634
Liabilities: $7,820,153
Net Worth: $2,064,481
Earnings: $1,536,485

Emp.: 56
Fiscal Year-end: 03/31/21
Wood Board Mfr
N.A.I.C.S.: 321219
G. R. K. Raju (Mng Dir)

ECOBUILT HOLDINGS BERHAD
D-G-11 & D-1-11 Medan Connaught No 1 Jalan 3/144A, 56000, Kuala Lumpur, Malaysia
Tel.: (60) 391082802   MY
Web Site: https://www.ecobuilt.com.my
Year Founded: 2004
ECOHLDS—(KLS)
Rev.: $34,721,132
Assets: $38,589,642
Liabilities: $21,280,674
Net Worth: $17,308,968
Earnings: ($6,581,205)
Emp.: 67
Fiscal Year-end: 05/31/23
Media Company; Digital Data Content Processing Services
N.A.I.C.S.: 518210
Joanne Toh Joo Ann (Co-Sec)

ECOCAB CO., LTD.
137-66 Bancheonbansongsaneop-ro, Eonyang-eup Ulju-gun, Ulsan, Korea (South)
Tel.: (82) 522641681
Web Site: https://www.ecocab.co.kr
Year Founded: 2004
128540—(KRS)
Rev.: $93,315,779
Assets: $117,945,024
Liabilities: $50,007,913
Net Worth: $67,937,111
Earnings: ($2,472,494)
Emp.: 257
Fiscal Year-end: 12/31/22
Automobile Cable Mfr
N.A.I.C.S.: 335929
Jun-Sung Won (Mng Dir)

ECOCASH HOLDINGS ZIMBABWE LIMITED
1906 Borrowdale Road, Harare, Zimbabwe
Tel.: (263) 242486121
Web Site:
https://www.cszlinvestor.com
EHZL.zw—(ZIM)
Rev.: $287,941
Assets: $2,596,790
Liabilities: $2,222,732
Net Worth: $374,058
Earnings: $88,168
Fiscal Year-end: 02/28/19
Digital Marketing Services
N.A.I.C.S.: 541613
Edmore Chibi (CEO)

Subsidiaries:

Econet Insurance (Private) Limited (1)
196 Borrowdale Road, Harare, Zimbabwe
Tel.: (263) 3772023000
Web Site: https://econet.hollardti.com
Short Term Insurance Services
N.A.I.C.S.: 524298

Econet Life (Private) Limited (1)
158 Harare Street Ambica House, PO Box 66974, Harare, Zimbabwe
Tel.: (263) 719753070
Web Site: https://www.ecosure.co.zw
Funeral Assurance Services
N.A.I.C.S.: 812210

Liquid Intelligent Technologies Ltd. (1)
Ebene Mews, 57 Cybercity 5th Floor Ebene, Plaines Wilhems, Mauritius
Tel.: (230) 4667620
Web Site: https://liquid.tech
Telecommunication Services

N.A.I.C.S.: 517122

Subsidiary (Non-US):

Telrad Networks Ltd. **(2)**
3 Park Avenue Road, London, N17 0HX,
United Kingdom
Tel.: (44) 8444835723
Web Site: https://telrad.com
Rev.: $181,115,000
Assets: $124,674,000
Liabilities: $98,000,000
Net Worth: $26,674,000
Earnings: $8,553,000
Emp.: 400
Fiscal Year-end: 12/31/2020
Telecommunication Servicesb
N.A.I.C.S.: 517112

Subsidiary (Non-US):

Telrad Chile S.A. **(3)**
Agustinas 2356, Santiago, Chile
Tel.: (56) 22 495 7795
Web Site: https://www.telrad.cl
Emp.: 150
Telecommunication Servicesb
N.A.I.C.S.: 517112
Uri Dotan *(CEO-Latin America)*

Maisha Health Fund (Private)
Limited **(1)**
1906 Borrowdale Road, Harare, Zimbabwe
Tel.: (263) 778775200
Web Site: https://maishahealthfund.co.zw
Medical Aid Services
N.A.I.C.S.: 524114

ECOENER, S.A.
R San Andres 143 4 15003 A, 15003,
La Coruna, Spain
Tel.: (34) 981217003
Web Site: https://www.ecoener.es
Year Founded: 1988
ENER—(VAL)
Rev.: $70,659,013
Assets: $640,495,640
Liabilities: $488,451,264
Net Worth: $152,044,376
Earnings: $13,257,534
Emp.: 164
Fiscal Year-end: 12/31/23
Electricity Distribution Services
N.A.I.C.S.: 237990
Fernando Rodriguez Alfonso *(Vice Chm)*

Subsidiaries:

Genersol, S.A. **(1)**
Calle 65G On 78G 34, Bogota, Colombia
Tel.: (57) 14850818
Eletric Power Generation Services
N.A.I.C.S.: 221118

ECOFIBRE LIMITED
Level 12 680 George Street, Sydney,
2000, NSW, Australia
Tel.: (61) 732657630 AU
Web Site: https://www.ecofibre.com
Year Founded: 2009
EOF—(ASX)
Rev.: $21,197,105
Assets: $77,416,705
Liabilities: $28,745,517
Net Worth: $48,671,187
Earnings: ($26,023,994)
Fiscal Year-end: 06/30/23
Biotechnology Research & Development Services
N.A.I.C.S.: 541714
Alastair Bor *(CTO)*

ECOFIN GLOBAL UTILITIES & INFRASTRUCTURE TRUST PLC
Burdett House 15 Buckingham Street,
London, WC2N 6DU, United Kingdom
Tel.: (44) 2074512929 UK
Web Site: https://ecofininvest.com
Year Founded: 2016
EGL—(LSE)
Rev.: $29,391,912

Assets: $294,077,628
Liabilities: $30,218,418
Net Worth: $263,859,210
Earnings: $20,934,378
Fiscal Year-end: 09/30/22
Investment Management Service
N.A.I.C.S.: 523940
David Simpson *(Chm)*

ECOFIN U.S. RENEWABLES INFRASTRUCTURE TRUST PLC
15 Buckingham Street, London,
WC2N 6DU, United Kingdom
Tel.: (44) 2045139260 UK
Web Site:
https://www.ecofininvest.com
Year Founded: 2020
RNEW—(AIM)
Rev.: $6,284,000
Assets: $118,454,000
Liabilities: $795,000
Net Worth: $117,659,000
Earnings: ($6,728,000)
Fiscal Year-end: 12/31/23
Investment Management Service
N.A.I.C.S.: 523999
Max McKerchar *(VP)*

ECOFIRST CONSOLIDATED BHD
A-19 Menara Allianz Sentral 203
Jalan Tun Sambanthan KL Sentral,
50470, Kuala Lumpur, Malaysia
Tel.: (60) 327251888
Web Site: https://www.ecofirst.my
ECOFIRS—(KLS)
Rev.: $6,658,624
Assets: $200,282,751
Liabilities: $72,668,995
Net Worth: $127,613,757
Earnings: $2,271,746
Emp.: 82
Fiscal Year-end: 05/31/23
Construction Services
N.A.I.C.S.: 236115
Kwing Hee Tiong *(CEO & Mng Dir)*

Subsidiaries:

EcoFirst Products Sdn Bhd **(1)**
Lot 63A Lower Ground Level South City
Plaza Persiaran Serdang Perdana, 43300,
Seri Kembangan, Selangor, Malaysia
Tel.: (60) 389452185
Web Site: http://www.ecofirstproducts.com
Sales Range: $25-49.9 Million
Emp.: 14
Personal Care Product Mfr
N.A.I.C.S.: 325620

Tashima Development Sdn Bhd **(1)**
No 6 Jalan Nagasari 20 Bandar Segamat
Baru, 85000, Segamat, Johor, Malaysia
Tel.: (60) 79436222
Property Development Services
N.A.I.C.S.: 531390

ECOGRAF LIMITED
Level 3 18 Richardson Street, West
Perth, 6005, WA, Australia
Tel.: (61) 864249000 AU
Web Site:
https://www.ecograf.com.au
ECGFF—(OTCQB)
Rev.: $532,502
Assets: $50,362,435
Liabilities: $1,772,197
Net Worth: $48,590,237
Earnings: ($5,750,256)
Emp.: 300
Fiscal Year-end: 06/30/22
Nickel Mining Services
N.A.I.C.S.: 212230
Dale Harris *(COO)*

ECOGREEN INTERNATIONAL GROUP LIMITED
Suite 5301 53/F Central Plaza 18

Harbour Road, Wanchai, China
(Hong Kong)
Tel.: (852) 25300609 Ky
Web Site: http://www.ecogreen.com
Year Founded: 1994
2341—(HKG)
Rev.: $384,560,317
Assets: $830,974,576
Liabilities: $423,850,103
Net Worth: $407,124,473
Earnings: $62,574,794
Emp.: 650
Fiscal Year-end: 12/31/20
Fine Chemicals Mfr
N.A.I.C.S.: 325998
Yirong Yang *(Founder, Chm & Pres)*

Subsidiaries:

EcoGreen Fine Chemicals B.V. **(1)**
Koperstraat 60A, 2718 RE, Zoetermeer,
Netherlands
Tel.: (31) 107142281
Chemical Product Mfr & Distr
N.A.I.C.S.: 325998

EcoGreen Fine Chemicals
Limited **(1)**
3706 5301/F Central Plz, Wanchai, China
(Hong Kong)
Tel.: (852) 25300609
Web Site: http://www.ecogreen.com
Sales Range: $25-49.9 Million
Emp.: 5
Natural Fine Chemical Products Research,
Development, Production & Distribution
N.A.I.C.S.: 325998

EcoGreen Manufacturing **(1)**
Suite 5301 53rd Floor Central Plaza 18
Harbour Road, Wanchai, China (Hong
Kong)
Tel.: (852) 25300609
Web Site: http://www.ecogreen.com
Sales Range: $50-74.9 Million
Emp.: 5
Holding Company
N.A.I.C.S.: 551112

Subsidiary (Non-US):

Shanghai Fine Chemicals Co.,
Ltd. **(2)**
No 8-9 Max-Mall Lane 1500 South Lianhua
Road, Shanghai, 201108, China
Tel.: (86) 213 358 1117
Web Site: https://www.sfcc-chem.com
Sales Range: $25-49.9 Million
Fine Chemical Products Research, Development & Marketing of Other Technological
Services
N.A.I.C.S.: 325998

Xiamen Doingcom Chemical Co.,
Ltd. **(2)**
No 30 Xinchang Road, Xinyang Haichang,
Xiamen, 361026, Fujian, China
Tel.: (86) 592 651 5068
Web Site: https://www.doingcom.com
Chemical Product Mfr & Distr
N.A.I.C.S.: 325998

Sino Bright International Trading
Limited **(1)**
8F East Block 2 Seg Scientific Industrial
Zone, North Huaqiang Road, Shenzhen,
China
Tel.: (86) 7553767533
Trading of Fine Chemicals
N.A.I.C.S.: 424690

Xiamen Doingcom Food Co.,
Ltd. **(1)**
8th Floor 120 Xinyuan Road, Haicang, Xiamen, China
Tel.: (86) 5923196572
Chemical Product Mfr & Distr
N.A.I.C.S.: 325998

ECOLOGY BUILDING SOCIETY
7 Belton Road, Silsden, Keighley,
BD20 0EE, W Yorkshire, United Kingdom
Tel.: (44) 1535 650 770
Web Site: http://www.ecology.co.uk

Year Founded: 1981
Rev.: $8,462,443
Assets: $259,746,641
Liabilities: $244,414,037
Net Worth: $15,332,604
Earnings: $1,407,347
Emp.: 31
Fiscal Year-end: 12/31/19
Mortgage Lending & Other Financial
Services
N.A.I.C.S.: 522310
Paul Ellis *(CEO)*

ECOLUMBER S.A.
Calle Bruc 144 pirncipal primera,
08037, Barcelona, Spain
Tel.: (34) 932003723
Web Site:
https://www.ecolumbergroup.com
Year Founded: 2004
ECO—(MAD)
Sales Range: Less than $1 Million
Investment Management Service
N.A.I.C.S.: 523940
Joaquin Espallargas Iberni *(Pres)*

ECOLUTIONS GMBH & CO. KGAA
Grueneburgweg 18, D-60322, Frankfurt am Main, Germany
Tel.: (49) 6991501080
Web Site: http://www.ecolutions.de
Emp.: 8
Climate Protection Investment &
Management Services
N.A.I.C.S.: 541620
Sascha Magsamen *(Deputy Chm)*

Subsidiaries:

Ecolutions Carbon India Pvt. Ltd. **(1)**
Mahendra Chambers 15 Opp Dukes Factory, 619/28 WT Patil Marg, 400 071, Mumbai, India
Tel.: (91) 2225201742
Web Site: http://www.ecolutions.in
Sales Range: $25-49.9 Million
Emp.: 30
Investment Management & Consulting Services
N.A.I.C.S.: 541618

Ecolutions New Energy Investment
Co., Ltd. **(1)**
1505 Block 15 China Cent Pl 89 Jianguo
Rd, Beijing, 100025, Choayang, China
Tel.: (86) 1052036828
Web Site: http://www.ecolutions.de
Sales Range: $25-49.9 Million
Emp.: 9
Investment Management Service
N.A.I.C.S.: 541618

ECOM AGROINDUSTRIAL CORPORATION LTD.
Av Etienne Guillemin 16, PO Box 64,
1009, Pully, Switzerland
Tel.: (41) 58 721 7210
Web Site:
http://www.ecomtrading.com
Sales Range: $1-4.9 Billion
Emp.: 60
Coffee, Cotton & Cocoa Processing
N.A.I.C.S.: 311920
Alain Poncele *(CEO-Coffee & Cocoa)*

Subsidiaries:

Agroindustrias Arriba del Ecuador,
Agroarriba S.A. **(1)**
Km 4-5 Via Duran, Guayas, Ecuador
Tel.: (593) 4 280 6831
Coffee, Cotton & Cocoa Processing
N.A.I.C.S.: 311920

Agroindustrias Unidas de Mexico S.A.
de C.V. (AMSA) **(1)**
Bosques de Alisos 45A 2 Piso, Bosques de
Las Lomas, 05120, Mexico, Mexico
Tel.: (52) 55 5257 6500
Coffee, Cotton & Cocoa Processing
N.A.I.C.S.: 311920

Ecom Agroindustrial Corporation Ltd.—(Continued)

Algodonera Guarani S.A. (1)
Ruta Mcal Estigarribia 1460 y 1 de Mayo,
2300, Asuncion, Paraguay
Tel.: (595) 21 525162
Coffee, Cotton & Cocoa Processing
N.A.I.C.S.: 311920

Atlantic (USA), Inc., USA (1)
17 State St 23rd Fl, New York, NY 10004
Tel.: (212) 248-7475
Coffee, Cotton & Cocoa Processing
N.A.I.C.S.: 311920

Atlantic Commodities Vietnam
LTD (1)
8th Floor Dai Minh Building, 77 Hoang Van
Thai District 7, Ho Chi Minh City, 73000,
Vietnam
Tel.: (84) 8 54 160 559
Web Site: http://www.ecomtrading.com
Emp.: 1
Coffee, Cotton & Cocoa Processing
N.A.I.C.S.: 311920

Cafes de Especialidad de Chiapas,
S.A.P.I. de C.V (1)
Av Puerto Chiapas Manzana 3, Recinto Fis-
calizado Estrategico, Mexico, CP 30830,
Chiapas, Mexico
Tel.: (52) 962 6201470
Web Site: http://english.cafesca.com
Coffee & Cocoa Mfr
N.A.I.C.S.: 311920

Cafetalera Amazonica SAC (1)
Av Fco Tudela y Varela 450, Lima, 27001,
Peru
Tel.: (51) 421 4201
Coffee, Cotton & Cocoa Processing
N.A.I.C.S.: 311920

Cafetalera del Pacifico S.A de
C.V (1)
Carretera a Santa Tecla Centro Financiero
SISA, Edificio 4 local 8, Santa Tecla, El
Salvador
Tel.: (503) 2510 6969
Coffee, Cotton & Cocoa Processing
N.A.I.C.S.: 311920

Cafinter S.A. (1)
Terracampus Corporate CenterSecond
Floor, Offices 211 & 212, Tres Rios, Costa
Rica
Tel.: (506) 2278 9600
Coffee, Cotton & Cocoa Processing
N.A.I.C.S.: 311920

Compania Agroindustrial del Peru
SAC (1)
Av Paz Soldan 170 4to Piso Oficina 401,
San Isidro, Lima, Peru
Tel.: (51) 14228380
Web Site: http://www.agropesa.com.pe
Tea & Coffee Distr
N.A.I.C.S.: 445298

Compania Colombiana Agroindustrial
S.A. (1)
Cra 9 No 80-45 Torre Eskalar Piso 7, Bo-
gota, Colombia
Tel.: (57) 742 82 06
Coffee, Cotton & Cocoa Processing
N.A.I.C.S.: 311920

Condesa Pty Ltd (1)
Unit 15 110-116 Bourke Rd, Alexandria,
2015, NSW, Australia
Tel.: (61) 2 9114 8170
Coffee, Cotton & Cocoa Processing
N.A.I.C.S.: 311920

Dhanya Agroindustrial Pvt. Ltd. (1)
Ecom House 489/11, Borewell Road White-
field, 560 066, Bengaluru, India
Tel.: (91) 80 28450108
Coffee, Cotton & Cocoa Processing
N.A.I.C.S.: 311920

Dhanya Agroindustrial Pvt. Ltd. (1)
489/11 Borewell Road Whitefield, Benga-
luru, 560 066, India
Tel.: (91) 8028450108
Cotton Distr
N.A.I.C.S.: 424590
Prakash Shettigar *(Acct Mgr)*

ECOM Agrotrade Limited (1)
10th Floor 55 Old Broad Street, London,

EC2M 1RX, United Kingdom
Tel.: (44) 2032142100
Tea & Coffee Distr
N.A.I.C.S.: 445298

EISA - Empresa Interagricola
S.A. (1)
Rua do Comercio 54, Santos, 11010-140,
Brazil
Tel.: (55) 13 3213 9300
Coffee, Cotton & Cocoa Processing
N.A.I.C.S.: 311920

Ecom Agroindustrial Asia Pte
Ltd. (1)
Road # 105 Gulshan 2, House 12/B 1st
Floor, 1212, Dhaka, Bangladesh
Tel.: (880) 2 8817100
Coffee, Cotton & Cocoa Processing
N.A.I.C.S.: 311920

Ecom Agroindustrial Asia Pte.
Ltd. (1)
79 Robinson Road, CPF Building, Singa-
pore, 068897, Singapore
Tel.: (65) 6318 9928
Web Site: http://www.ecomtrading.com
Emp.: 30
Coffee, Cotton & Cocoa Processing
N.A.I.C.S.: 311920
Andrew Faulkner *(Mng Dir)*

Ecom Agroindustrial Corp. Ltd (1)
Rue du textile, BP2138, Abidjan, Cote
d'Ivoire
Tel.: (225) 21 25 99 06
Coffee, Cotton & Cocoa Processing
N.A.I.C.S.: 311920

Ecom Japan Ltd (1)
Kinsan Bldg 6F, 4-1-21 Nihonbashi Muro-
machi Chuo-ku, Tokyo, 103-0022, Japan
Tel.: (81) 3 5205 3113
Coffee, Cotton & Cocoa Processing
N.A.I.C.S.: 311920

Ecom Trading (Shanghai) Co.
Ltd. (1)
Room 3504-3505 Tower 2 Grand Gateway
Building No 3, Hongqiao Road, Shanghai,
200030, China
Tel.: (86) 21 6113 2399
Coffee, Cotton & Cocoa Processing
N.A.I.C.S.: 311920

Ecom USA, Inc., USA (1)
13760 Noel Rd Ste 500, Dallas, TX 75240
Tel.: (214) 520-1717
Web Site: http://www.ecomtrading.com
Coffee, Cotton & Cocoa Processing
N.A.I.C.S.: 311920
Andrew Halle *(CEO)*

Exportadora Atlantic S.A (1)
Centro Ejecutivo San Marino #A-101, Ma-
nagua, Nicaragua
Tel.: (505) 227 81477
Coffee, Cotton & Cocoa Processing
N.A.I.C.S.: 311920

Kawacom Uganda Limited (1)
Plot M284 Ntinda Industrial Area, Kampala,
Uganda
Tel.: (256) 414 2226
Coffee, Cotton & Cocoa Processing
N.A.I.C.S.: 311920

Mawenzi Coffee Exporters Ltd. (1)
Plot 1524 Msasani Peninsula, Dar es Sa-
laam, Tanzania
Tel.: (255) 756 790 295
Coffee, Cotton & Cocoa Processing
N.A.I.C.S.: 311920

Monpi Coffee Exports Ltd. (1)
PO Box 1326, Goroka, 411, Papua New
Guinea
Tel.: (675) 5322752
Web Site: http://www.monpiexports.com
Coffee Distr
N.A.I.C.S.: 445298

OOO Agroprom Vostok (1)
Prospekt Mira 101 str 1, Moscow, 129085,
Russia
Tel.: (7) 9852177773
Tea & Coffee Distr
N.A.I.C.S.: 445298

PT Indo CafCo (Robustas) (1)
Kompleks Padi Mas jlTirtayasa, Bandar

Lampung, 35122, Indonesia
Tel.: (62) 721350737
Tea & Coffee Distr
N.A.I.C.S.: 445298

Sangana Commodities (K) Ltd. (1)
Old Mombasa Road, Kenbelt Industrial
Park, Nairobi, Kenya
Tel.: (254) 20 6006751
Coffee, Cotton & Cocoa Processing
N.A.I.C.S.: 311920

Shanghai Weisen Trading
Co.Ltd. (1)
No 6-7 Zhuwei Logistic Park, Kunming,
China
Tel.: (86) 871 6334 1035
Coffee, Cotton & Cocoa Processing
N.A.I.C.S.: 311920

Yara Commodities Ltd. (1)
Plot 40/42 Jimoh Odutola Street, Off Eric
Moore Rd, Lagos, Nigeria
Tel.: (234) 70 985 04614
Coffee, Cotton & Cocoa Processing
N.A.I.C.S.: 311920

Zamacom S.A. (1)
06 BP 2138 Entrepot Ciciv, Abidjan, Cote
d'Ivoire
Tel.: (225) 21 25 99 06
Coffee, Cotton & Cocoa Processing
N.A.I.C.S.: 311920

ECOMB AB
Tel.: (46) 855012550
Web Site: https://www.ecomb.se
Year Founded: 1992
Emp.: 5
Heating Equipment Mfr
N.A.I.C.S.: 333414
Ulf Hagstrom *(Mng Dir)*

ECOMEMBRANE S.P.A.
Via Pari Opportunita 7, Gadesco
Pieve Delmona, 26030, Cremona,
Italy
Tel.: (39) 0372463599
Web Site:
   https://www.ecomembrane.com
Year Founded: 2000
ECMB—(EUR)
Polyethylene Product Mfr
N.A.I.C.S.: 326113
Lorenzo Spedini *(Chm)*

Subsidiaries:

Ecomembrane LLC (1)
3912 E Progress St, North Little Rock, AR
72114
Tel.: (501) 801-0397
Web Site: https://www.ecomembrane.com
Polyethylene Product Mfr
N.A.I.C.S.: 326113

Subsidiary (Domestic):

Splash SuperPools Ltd. (2)
3912 E Progress St, Maumelle, AR 72114-
5239
Tel.: (501) 604-3535
Web Site: https://splashpools.com
Sporting & Athletic Goods Mfr
N.A.I.C.S.: 339920

ECOMIAM SA
Zone de Gourvily 161 Route de
Brest, 29337, Quimper, France
Tel.: (33) 153673677
Web Site: https://www.ecomiam-
   bourse.com
Year Founded: 2009
ALECO—(EUR)
Frozen Food Product Distr
N.A.I.C.S.: 424420
Daniel Sauvaget *(Chm)*

ECOMIC CO LTD
Asahi Life Sapporo Odori Building 1-1
Odori Nishi 8-chome, Chuo-ku, Sap-
poro, 060-0042, Hokkaido, Japan
Tel.: (81) 112061945   JP
Web Site: https://ecomic.jp

Year Founded: 1997
3802—(TKS)
Rev.: $14,251,160
Assets: $13,947,100
Liabilities: $1,923,510
Net Worth: $12,023,590
Earnings: $839,470
Emp.: 323
Fiscal Year-end: 03/31/24
Payroll Accounting Service
N.A.I.C.S.: 541214
Koji Kumagai *(Pres & CEO)*

Subsidiaries:

BiZright Technology, Inc. (1)
2-17-2 Sotokanda, Chiyoda-Ku, Tokyo, 101-
0021, Japan
Tel.: (81) 335262090
Web Site: http://www.bizright.co.jp
Rev.: $3,741,360
Assets: $4,264,050
Liabilities: $3,860,570
Net Worth: $403,480
Earnings: $9,170
Fiscal Year-end: 06/30/2020
Software Development Services
N.A.I.C.S.: 541511
Hiromi Tanaka *(Pres)*

ECOMOTT, INC.
7th Floor Caress Sapporo Building
2-5 Kita 1-jo Higashi 1-chome, Chuo-
Ku, Sapporo, 060-0031, Japan
Tel.: (81) 115582211
Web Site: https://www.ecomott.co.jp
Year Founded: 2007
3987—(TKS)
Rev.: $16,744,240
Assets: $16,072,480
Liabilities: $10,704,620
Net Worth: $5,367,860
Earnings: ($429,180)
Emp.: 261
Fiscal Year-end: 08/31/24
Application Development Services
N.A.I.C.S.: 541511

ECONACH HOLDINGS CO.,
LTD.
7-8-4 Minami-Aoyama, Minato-ku,
Tokyo, 107-0062, Japan
Tel.: (81) 364184391
Web Site: https://www.econach.co.jp
Year Founded: 1926
3521—(TKS)
Rev.: $12,506,120
Assets: $39,712,880
Liabilities: $8,460,800
Net Worth: $31,252,080
Earnings: $634,560
Fiscal Year-end: 03/31/24
Holding Company
N.A.I.C.S.: 551112
Hideo Okumura *(Pres)*

ECONERGY RENEWABLE EN-
ERGY LTD.
Menivim Tower 1 Hatahana Street,
Kfar Saba, Israel
Tel.: (972) 547680868
Web Site:
   https://www.econergytech.com
ECNR—(TAE)
Rev.: $1,186,057
Assets: $401,616,663
Liabilities: $253,917,548
Net Worth: $147,699,115
Earnings: ($14,551,047)
Fiscal Year-end: 09/30/23
Eletric Power Generation Services
N.A.I.C.S.: 221118
Eyal Podhorzer *(CEO)*

ECONET WIRELESS ZIMBA-
BWE LIMITED
No 2 Old Mutare Road Msasa, PO
Box BE 1298, Belvedere, Harare,
Zimbabwe

Tel.: (263) 2424861245   ZW
Web Site: http://www.econet.co.zw
ECO—(ZIM)
Rev.: $40,764,166,897
Assets: $33,549,043,935
Liabilities: $11,825,186,516
Net Worth: $21,723,857,419
Earnings: ($3,029,505,388)
Emp.: 1,108
Fiscal Year-end: 02/29/24
Cellular Network Operator
N.A.I.C.S.: 517112
Strive T. Masiyiwa *(Founder)*

Subsidiaries:

Econet Global Ltd.   **(1)**
Willow Wood Office Park 220 Third Street,
Broadacres, Johannesburg, South Africa
Tel.: (27) 119 965 500
Web Site: https://www.econetafrica.com
IT Services & IT Consulting
N.A.I.C.S.: 519290

Econet Wireless (Pvt) Ltd   **(1)**
Econet Park 2 Old Mutare Road, PO Box
BE 1298, Harare, Zimbabwe
Tel.: (263) 4486121
Telecommunication Servicesb
N.A.I.C.S.: 517112

ECONFRAME BERHAD

No 1 Jalan Sungai Rasau 27A Kaw
16 Kaw Perindustrian Sungai Rasa,
41300, Klang, Selangor, Malaysia
Tel.: (60) 333487268   MY
Web Site:
   https://www.econframe.com
EFRAME—(KLS)
Rev.: $16,065,367
Assets: $20,206,509
Liabilities: $2,125,551
Net Worth: $18,080,958
Earnings: $2,764,841
Fiscal Year-end: 08/31/23
Metal Window & Door Mfr
N.A.I.C.S.: 332321
Yong Wai Kin *(CFO)*

ECONO TRADE (INDIA) LIMITED

161A Abdul Hamid Street 5 th Floor
Room No 5E, Kolkata, 700001, West
Bengal, India
Tel.: (91) 7890518016
Web Site: https://www.econo.in
Year Founded: 1982
538708—(BOM)
Rev.: $292,334
Assets: $5,691,393
Liabilities: $445,022
Net Worth: $5,246,372
Earnings: $97,314
Emp.: 3
Fiscal Year-end: 03/31/21
Investment Management Service
N.A.I.C.S.: 523940
Navinchandra Amratlal Kothari *(CFO)*

ECONOCOM GROUP SA

11 square Leon Blum, 92800, Puteaux, France
Tel.: (33) 141673000
Web Site:
   https://www.econocom.com
ECONB—(EUR)
Rev.: $2,933,628,319
Assets: $2,700,086,337
Liabilities: $2,207,101,230
Net Worth: $492,985,107
Earnings: $68,853,874
Emp.: 8,750
Fiscal Year-end: 12/31/22
Network Services
N.A.I.C.S.: 541512
Jean-Louis Bouchard *(Founder)*

Subsidiaries:

ASP Serveur SAS   **(1)**

Datacenter ASP Serveur 785 voie Antiope,
13600, La Ciotat, France
Tel.: (33) 80 536 0888
Web Site: https://www.aspserveur.com
Information Technology Services
N.A.I.C.S.: 541511
Sébastien Enderle *(Pres)*

Aciernet SA   **(1)**
2 rue Edison, 91620, Nozay, France
Tel.: (33) 169806446
Web Site: http://www.aciernet.com
Information Technology Services
N.A.I.C.S.: 541511

Altabox S.A.   **(1)**
C/ Rafael Pillado Mourelle 6 Pol Ind Rio de
Janeiro, Algete, 28110, Madrid, Spain
Tel.: (34) 90 243 0046
Web Site: https://www.altabox.net
Digital Technology Services
N.A.I.C.S.: 541511
Rafeal Negro *(Mgr-Bus Dev)*

Alterway Group Sarl   **(1)**
227 Hill offices 1 rue Royale - Bat D,
92210, Saint-Cloud, France
Tel.: (33) 141163495
Web Site: http://www.alterway.fr
Consulting Services
N.A.I.C.S.: 541618

Aperleasing Srl   **(1)**
Via Santa Radegonda 11, Milan,
Italy   **(95%)**
Tel.: (39) 026596056
Machinery & Equipment Rental & Leasing
N.A.I.C.S.: 532420

Aragon-eRH, SAS   **(1)**
42-46 Rue Mederic, 92110, Clichy, France
Tel.: (33) 141673240
Web Site: http://www.aragon-erh.com
Human Resource & Consulting Services
N.A.I.C.S.: 541612
Akalai Nawfal *(Mgr-SIRH)*

Asystel Italia SpA   **(1)**
Via Varesina 162, 20156, Milan, Italy
Tel.: (39) 0238 0841
Web Site: https://www.asystelitalia.it
Emp.: 250
Computer Integrated System Services
N.A.I.C.S.: 541512
Giorgio Sala *(Mgr-Svc)*

Atlance France SAS   **(1)**
42-46 rue Mederic, 92582, Clichy,
France   **(100%)**
Tel.: (33) 147563700
Web Site: http://www.atlance.com
Sales Range: $25-49.9 Million
Emp.: 150
Management Consulting Services
N.A.I.C.S.: 541618

Atlance SA/NV   **(1)**
Horizon Park Leuvensesteenweg 510 bus
80, 1930, Zaventem, Belgium
Tel.: (32) 27908155
Financial Services
N.A.I.C.S.: 523940

Atlance SAS   **(1)**
40 Quai de Dion Bouton, 92800, Puteaux,
France
Tel.: (33) 141674555
Financial Services
N.A.I.C.S.: 523940

BDF SpA   **(1)**
Via Bernardino Verro 90, 20141, Milan, Italy
Tel.: (39) 025220061
Web Site: http://www.gruppobdf.com
Information Technology Services
N.A.I.C.S.: 541511
Daniele Piovesan *(Sls Mgr)*

Bizmatica SpA   **(1)**
Via Varesina 162, 20156, Milan, MI, Italy
Tel.: (39) 028 312 4001
Web Site: https://www.bizmatica.com
Emp.: 90
Customer Management Services
N.A.I.C.S.: 541618
Paolo Bonetto *(Dir-Ops & Organization)*

Caverin Solutions S.A.   **(1)**
C/Cardenal Marcelo Spinola 4, 28016, Madrid, Spain
Tel.: (34) 913751057

Web Site: http://www.ps.econocom.es
Audio Visual Equipment Mfr & Distr
N.A.I.C.S.: 334310

Cineolia SAS   **(1)**
9 Avenue Maistrasse, 92500, Rueil-
Malmaison, France
Tel.: (33) 81 126 0400
Web Site: https://www.cineolia.fr
Hospital Services
N.A.I.C.S.: 622310
Ludovic Jaquet *(Pres)*

EFS International BV   **(1)**
42-46 rue Mederic, 92110, Clichy,
France   **(100%)**
Tel.: (33) 141673100
Web Site: http://www.econocom.com
Sales Range: $50-74.9 Million
Emp.: 150
Store Retailers
N.A.I.C.S.: 459999

Econocom Austria GmbH   **(1)**
Franzosengraben 12, 1030, Vienna, Austria
Tel.: (43) 179 5200
Web Site: https://www.econocom.at
Information Technology Services
N.A.I.C.S.: 541511
Socha Reinhard *(Acct Mgr-Enterprise)*

Econocom Brasil S.A.   **(1)**
Av Sagitario 138 - 24 Andar The City Tower
2 Alpha Square Offices, Barueri, 06473-
073, Brazil
Tel.: (55) 114 195 9663
Web Site: https://www.econocom.com.br
Emp.: 200
Information Technology Services
N.A.I.C.S.: 541511
Rodrigo Bocchi *(CEO)*

Econocom Deutschland GmbH   **(1)**
Herriotstr 1, 60528, Frankfurt, Germany
Tel.: (49) 697140800
Web Site: https://www.econocom.de
Information Technology Services
N.A.I.C.S.: 541511
Christoph Blaser *(Mng Dir)*

Econocom Digital Finance
Limited   **(1)**
3rd Floor - Ifsc House 1, Dublin, Ireland
Tel.: (353) 16700355
Information Technology Services
N.A.I.C.S.: 541511
Ciaran Hynes *(Mgr)*

Econocom Finance SNC   **(1)**
Leuvensesteenweg 510 B80, 1930,
Zaventem, Belgium
Tel.: (32) 27908111
Web Site: https://www.econocom.be
Information Technology Services
N.A.I.C.S.: 541511
Eric Philippart *(CFO-Benelux)*

Econocom Financial Services Interna-
tional BV   **(1)**
Rond Het Fort 36-40, Nieuwegein, 3439
MK, Netherlands
Tel.: (31) 306358333
Web Site: https://www.econocom.com
Emp.: 35
Financial Management Services
N.A.I.C.S.: 523999

Econocom France SAS   **(1)**
42-46 Rue Mederic, 92582, Clichy,
France   **(100%)**
Tel.: (33) 147563700
Web Site: https://www.econocom.fr
Sales Range: $75-99.9 Million
Emp.: 150
Computer & Computer Peripheral Equip-
ment & Software Merchant Whslr
N.A.I.C.S.: 423430

Econocom International Italia
SpA   **(1)**
Via Varesina 162, 20156, Milan, Italy
Tel.: (39) 02336261
Web Site: https://www.econocom.it
Information Technology Services
N.A.I.C.S.: 541511
Guglielmo Nannini *(Mgr)*

Econocom Lease SA/NV   **(1)**
Leuvensesteenweg 510-80, 1930,
Zaventem, Belgium

Tel.: (32) 27908111
Information Technology Consulting Services
N.A.I.C.S.: 541512

Subsidiary (Non-US):

Econocom Luxembourg SA   **(2)**
2 rue d'Arlon, L-8399, Windhof, Luxem-
bourg
Tel.: (352) 395550226
Emp.: 15
Information Technology Consulting Services
N.A.I.C.S.: 541512

Econocom Location SAS   **(1)**
42-46 Rue Mederic, 92582, Clichy,
France   **(100%)**
Tel.: (33) 147563700
Web Site: http://www.econocom.fr
Sales Range: $75-99.9 Million
Emp.: 150
Machinery & Equipment Rental & Leasing
N.A.I.C.S.: 532420

Econocom Ltd.   **(1)**
33 Queen Street 4th floor, Richmond-upon-
Thames, London, EC4R 1AP, United King-
dom
Tel.: (44) 208 940 2199
Web Site: https://www.econocom.co.uk
Information Technology Services
N.A.I.C.S.: 541511
Mark Orchard *(Mgr-Strategic Acct Team-
UK)*

Econocom Managed Services
SAS   **(1)**
106 rue des Trois Fontanot, 92751, Nan-
terre, Cedex, France   **(100%)**
Tel.: (33) 169182000
Web Site: http://www.econocom.fr
Sales Range: $25-49.9 Million
Emp.: 150
Computer & Machine Repair & Maintenance
N.A.I.C.S.: 811210

Subsidiary (Non-US):

Econocom Maroc Sarl   **(2)**
Residence Boissy 322 Bd Zerktoun 1
etage, Mandarina Sidi Maarouf, 20000,
Casablanca, Morocco
Tel.: (212) 522789032
Information Technology Consulting Services
N.A.I.C.S.: 541512

Econocom Nederland BV   **(1)**
Computerweg 23, 3542 DR, Utrecht, Neth-
erlands
Tel.: (31) 306358333
Web Site: https://www.econocom.nl
IT Financial Management Services
N.A.I.C.S.: 541519

Econocom PSF SA   **(1)**
4 Rue d Arlon, 8399, Windhof, Luxembourg
Tel.: (352) 395550
Information Technology Consulting Services
N.A.I.C.S.: 541512

Econocom Polska SP z.o.o   **(1)**
Ul Twarda 18, 00-105, Warsaw, Poland
Tel.: (48) 503666303
Web Site: https://www.econocom.pl
Information Technology Services
N.A.I.C.S.: 541511

Econocom Products & Solutions Be-
lux SA/NV   **(1)**
Leuvensesteenweg 510/80, 1930,
Zaventem, Belgium
Tel.: (32) 27908111
Web Site: https://www.econocom.com
Sales Range: $150-199.9 Million
Emp.: 800
Information Technology Consulting Services
N.A.I.C.S.: 541512

Econocom Products & Solutions
S.L.   **(1)**
C Cardenal Marcelo Spinola 4, 28016, Ma-
drid, Spain
Tel.: (34) 913751057
Web Site: https://www.econocomps.es
Computer Equipment Whslr
N.A.I.C.S.: 423430

Econocom Products and Solutions
SAS   **(1)**
41-42 Quai De Dion Bouton, BP 62, 92800,
Puteaux, France   **(100%)**

Econocom Group SA—(Continued)

Tel.: (33) 169182000
Sales Range: $75-99.9 Million
Emp.: 150
Electronic Parts & Equipment Merchant Whslr
N.A.I.C.S.: 423690

Subsidiary (Domestic):

Econocom Telecom Services SAS (2)
42 Rue Mederic, Clichy, 92110, France
Tel.: (33) 147563700
Sales Range: $50-74.9 Million
Telecommunication Servicesb
N.A.I.C.S.: 517810

Econocom Public BV (1)
Computerweg 22, 3542 DR, Utrecht, Netherlands
Tel.: (31) 306358333
Web Site: https://www.econocom.nl
Information Technology Services
N.A.I.C.S.: 541511
Michel Karreman (Project Mgr)

Econocom Re SA Luxembourg (1)
Etage 2 2 rue d'Arlon, 8399, Windhof, Luxembourg
Tel.: (352) 395550226
Computer Equipment Whslr
N.A.I.C.S.: 423430

Econocom SA (1)
Calle Cardenal Marcelo Spinola 4, 28016, Madrid, Spain (100%)
Tel.: (34) 914119120
Web Site: https://www.econocom.es
Holding Company
N.A.I.C.S.: 551112

Econocom SAS (1)
42-46 Rue Mederic, 92582, Clichy, France (100%)
Tel.: (33) 147563700
Web Site: http://www.econocom.fr
Sales Range: $250-299.9 Million
Emp.: 800
Computer & Computer Peripheral Equipment & Software Merchant Whslr
N.A.I.C.S.: 423430

Subsidiary (Domestic):

Econocom Managed Services SA/NV (2)
1 Rue de la Terre Neuve, Les Ulis, 91940, France
Tel.: (33) 1 69 18 35 00
Information Technology Consulting Services
N.A.I.C.S.: 541512

Econocom Servicios SA (1)
Calle Cardenal Marcelo Spinola 4, 28016, Madrid, Spain
Tel.: (34) 91 411 9120
Web Site: http://ps.econocom.es
Information Technology Services
N.A.I.C.S.: 541511
Carlos Perez-Herce (Mng Dir)

Econocom Telecom BV (1)
Rond T Fort 38, 3439 MK, Nieuwegein, Netherlands
Tel.: (31) 306358333
Web Site: http://www.econocom-nederland.nl
Sales Range: $25-49.9 Million
Emp.: 45
Computer & Software Stores
N.A.I.C.S.: 449210

Energy Net GmbH (1)
Gutleutstrasse 169-171, 60327, Frankfurt am Main, Germany
Tel.: (49) 699 769 7090
Web Site: https://www.energy-net.de
Information Technology Services
N.A.I.C.S.: 541511

Exaprobe SAS (1)
13 Avenue Albert Einstein, 69100, Villeurbanne, France
Tel.: (33) 47 269 9969
Web Site: https://www.exaprobe.com
Computer Integrated System Services
N.A.I.C.S.: 541512

Filiales Asytel S.p.A. (1)

Via Varesina 162, 20141, Milan, Italy
Tel.: (39) 02380841
Web Site: https://www.asystel-bdf.it
Computer Equipment Whslr
N.A.I.C.S.: 423430

Gigigo Group S.L. (1)
Dr Zamenhof 36 bis 1 A, 28027, Madrid, Spain
Tel.: (34) 917431436
Web Site: http://www.gigigo.com
Marketing & Advertising Services
N.A.I.C.S.: 541810
Fernando Kanacri (Dir-Ops & Delivery)

Helis SAS (1)
6 rue Royale, 75008, Paris, France
Tel.: (33) 15 320 0512
Web Site: https://www.groupe-helis.com
Consulting Services
N.A.I.C.S.: 541618

Infeeny S.A.S. (1)
40 Quai de Dion-Bouton, 92800, Puteaux, France
Tel.: (33) 14 970 8133
Web Site: https://www.infeeny.com
Information Technology Services
N.A.I.C.S.: 541511
Long Le Xuan (CEO)

Lydis B.V. (1)
Jool-Hulstraat 16, 1327 HA, Almere, Netherlands
Tel.: (31) 362020120
Web Site: https://www.lydis.nl
Telecommunication Servicesb
N.A.I.C.S.: 517410

Osiatis SA (1)
1 rue du Petit Clamart, 78142, Velizy-Villacoublay, France (51.9%)
Tel.: (33) 1 41 28 30 00
Web Site: http://www.osiatis.com
Sales Range: $350-399.9 Million
Emp.: 4,000
Computer Applications for Infrastructure & Facilities Management
N.A.I.C.S.: 541512

Subsidiary (Non-US):

Osiatis Belgium NV (2)
Leuvensesteenweg 573/2, 1930, Zaventem, Belgium
Tel.: (32) 2 718 26 11
Web Site: http://www.osiatis.be
Sales Range: $25-49.9 Million
Emp.: 80
Information Technology Consulting Services
N.A.I.C.S.: 541512
Jan Van Dee Broek (Gen Mgr)

Osiatis Computer Services GmbH (2)
Franzosengraben 12, 1030, Vienna, Austria
Tel.: (43) 1795200
Web Site: http://www.osiatis.at
Emp.: 75
Information Technology Consulting Services
N.A.I.C.S.: 541512

Subsidiary (Domestic):

Osiatis Ingenierie S.A.S. (2)
75 Cours Albert Thomas, 69003, Lyon, France
Tel.: (33) 4 72 13 16 16
Web Site: http://www.osiatis.fr
Construction Engineering Services
N.A.I.C.S.: 541330

Syner Trade S.A. (1)
66 Avenue Charles de Gaulle, 92200, Neuilly-sur-Seine, France
Tel.: (33) 15 698 2929
Web Site: https://www.synertrade.com
Software Services
N.A.I.C.S.: 541511
Nicolas Delage (Mgr-Technical Solution)

Synopse SAS (1)
BP 95 1 rue de Terre Neuve, 91943, Les Ulis, France (100%)
Tel.: (33) 169353070
Web Site: http://www.synopse.fr
Sales Range: $25-49.9 Million
Emp.: 50
Computer System Design Services
N.A.I.C.S.: 541512

ECONOMEDIA
20 Ivan Vazov Str, 1000, Sofia, Bulgaria
Tel.: (359) 24615349
Web Site: http://www.economedia.bg
Year Founded: 1993
Emp.: 180
Holding Company; Business Media Publisher
N.A.I.C.S.: 551112

Subsidiaries:

ICT Media Ltd. (1)
16 Ivan Vaznov Str, 1000, Sofia, Bulgaria
Tel.: (359) 2 400 1105
Web Site: http://www.ictmedia.bg
Information & Communication Technologies Trade Magazine Publisher
N.A.I.C.S.: 513120
Nadia Krusteva (Editor-in-Chief-CIO Magazine)

ECONOMIC INSTITUTE AD BANJA LUKA
Ulica Kralja Alfonsa XIII br 18, 78000, Banja Luka, Bosnia & Herzegovina
Tel.: (387) 51 211 501
Web Site: http://www.ekinst.org
Year Founded: 1960
Emp.: 15
Consulting Services
N.A.I.C.S.: 541690
Milorad Dekanovic (Project Mgr)

ECONOMIC INVESTMENT TRUST LIMITED
165 University Avenue 10th Floor, Toronto, M5H 3B8, ON, Canada
Tel.: (416) 947-2578
Web Site: http://www.evt.ca
EVT—(TSX)
Rev.: $27,771,722
Assets: $775,907,547
Liabilities: $59,346,108
Net Worth: $716,561,439
Earnings: $23,546,628
Fiscal Year-end: 12/31/20
Investment Management Service
N.A.I.C.S.: 327910
Duncan N. R. Jackman (Chm & Pres)

ECONOMY WHEELS LTD
129 Angeline Street North, Lindsay, K9V 4M9, ON, Canada
Tel.: (705) 324-5566
Web Site: http://www.economywheels.com
Rev.: $13,650,357
Emp.: 40
New & Used Car Dealers
N.A.I.C.S.: 441110
Chris Pretty (Mgr-Sls)

ECONOS CO., LTD.
325 Kitago 4jo 13chome, Shiroishi-Ku, Sapporo, 003-0834, Japan
Tel.: (81) 118751996
Web Site: https://www.eco-nos.com
3136—(SAP)
Rev.: $36,459,920
Assets: $24,007,060
Liabilities: $22,558,200
Net Worth: $1,448,860
Earnings: ($1,384,670)
Fiscal Year-end: 03/31/20
Real Estate Manangement Services
N.A.I.C.S.: 531390
Katsuya Hasegawa (Pres)

ECONPILE HOLDINGS BERHAD
Level 8 Tower Block Plaza Dwitasik Jalan Sri Permaisuri, Bandar Sri Permaisuri, 56000, Kuala Lumpur, Malaysia
Tel.: (60) 391719999
Web Site: https://ir2.chartnexus.com

ECONBHD—(KLS)
Rev.: $79,573,122
Assets: $139,212,063
Liabilities: $57,467,302
Net Worth: $81,744,762
Earnings: ($3,318,307)
Emp.: 587
Fiscal Year-end: 06/30/23
Foundation & Engineering Contractor
N.A.I.C.S.: 238190
Cheng Eng The (Mng Dir-Grp)

ECOPACK LTD
19 Main Street City Villas Near High Court Road, Rawalpindi, Pakistan
Tel.: (92) 515974098
Web Site: https://www.ecopack.com.pk
ECOP—(PSX)
Rev.: $24,080,318
Assets: $10,707,187
Liabilities: $6,478,964
Net Worth: $4,228,222
Earnings: $144,415
Emp.: 219
Fiscal Year-end: 06/30/23
Pet Bottles & Preforms Mfr
N.A.I.C.S.: 312112
Hussian Jamil (CEO)

ECOPETROL S.A.
Cr 13 No 36 - 24, Bogota, Colombia
Tel.: (57) 12344000
Web Site: https://www.ecopetrol.com.co
Year Founded: 1951
EC—(NYSE)
Rev.: $41,356,127,200
Assets: $78,455,220,330
Liabilities: $48,942,289,924
Net Worth: $29,512,930,407
Earnings: $9,120,383,062
Emp.: 18,903
Fiscal Year-end: 12/31/22
Refined Petroleum Mfr
N.A.I.C.S.: 324110
Alberto Consuegra Granger (COO)

Subsidiaries:

Cenit transporte y logistica de hidrocarburos S.A.S. (1)
Calle 113 7-80 Piso 10, 110111, Bogota, Colombia
Tel.: (57) 1 319 8800
Web Site: https://www.cenit-transporte.com
Hydrocarbon Logistics & Transportation Services
N.A.I.C.S.: 486110

Ecopetrol Oleo e Gas do Brasil Ltda. (1)
Praia de Botafogo 300 - Sala 1 101, Rio de Janeiro, 22250-905, Brazil
Tel.: (55) 212 559 7750
Web Site: https://www.ecopetrol.com.br
Hydrocarbons Exploration Services
N.A.I.C.S.: 213112

Ecopetrol USA Inc. (1)
2800 Post Oak Blvd Ste 4600, Houston, TX 77056
Tel.: (713) 634-3800
Web Site: https://www.ecopetrol-usa.com
Hydrocarbons Exploration Services
N.A.I.C.S.: 213112

Equion Energia Limited (1)
Duo Level 6 280 Bishopsgate, London, EC2M 4RB, United Kingdom
Tel.: (44) 2045306792
Web Site: https://equion-energia.uk
N.A.I.C.S.: 213112

Equion Energia Ltd. (1)
(51%)
Tel.: (57) 16284000
Web Site: https://www.equion-energia.com
Sales Range: $200-249.9 Million
Emp.: 500
Petroleum Exploration & Production
N.A.I.C.S.: 211120

Esenttia Masterbatch Ltda. (1)
Zona Franca Industrial De Mamonal Bodegas 7 y 8 Br Mamonal, Cartagena, Colombia
Tel.: (57) 6056688700
N.A.I.C.S.: 336211

Esenttia S.A. (1)
Avenida Calle 26 No 57 - 41 Building T7-T8 Floor 11 Tower 7, Bogota, Colombia
Tel.: (57) 1 596 0210
Web Site: https://www.esenttia.co
Polypropylene Mfr
N.A.I.C.S.: 325211

Interconexion Electrica S.A. E.S.P. (1)
Calle 12 sur N 18 -168 Bloque 3 piso 2, 50022, Medellin, Colombia (51.4%)
Tel.: (57) 6043252270
Web Site: https://www.isa.co
Rev.: $3,656,803,280
Assets: $18,376,879,579
Liabilities: $11,573,295,529
Net Worth: $6,803,584,050
Earnings: $1,110,327,283
Fiscal Year-end: 12/31/2023
Electronic Services
N.A.I.C.S.: 221122
Sonia Margarita Abuchar Aleman (Chief Legal Officer)

Subsidiary (Non-US):

ISA Capital do Brasil S.A. (2)
Tel.: (55) 1131387673
Web Site: http://www.isacapital.com.br
Emp.: 5
Electricity Transmission Services
N.A.I.C.S.: 221121
Fernando Augusto Rojas Pinto (CEO & VP)

Subsidiary (Domestic):

CTEEP - Companhia de Transmissao de Energia Eletrica Paulista (3)
R Casa do Ator 1 155 - 10 andar Vila Olimpia, 04546 004, Sao Paulo, SP, Brazil (89.4%)
Tel.: (55) 113 138 7557
Web Site: http://www.cteep.com.br
Sales Range: Less than $1 Million
Emp.: 1,600
Electric Energy Generation & Transmission
N.A.I.C.S.: 221118
Fernando Augusto Rojas Pinto (Vice Chm)

Subsidiary (Non-US):

Interconexion Electrica ISA Peru S.A. (2)
Avenida Canaval And Moreyra 522 Piso 10, San Isidro, 27, Lima, Peru
Tel.: (51) 1 712 67 83
Web Site: http://www1.isa.com.co
Electricity Generation & Distribution Services
N.A.I.C.S.: 221122
Luis Alejandro Camargo Suan (Gen Mgr)

Intervial Chile SA (2)
Cerro El Plomo 5630 piso 10, Las Condes, Santiago, Chile
Web Site: http://www.intervialchile.cl
Operation of Highways
N.A.I.C.S.: 488490

Subsidiary (Domestic):

XM Compania de Expertos en Mercados SA ESP (2)
Calle 12 Sur 18 168 Bloque 2, Medellin, Colombia
Tel.: (57) 43172244
Web Site: http://www.xm.com.co
Sales Range: $75-99.9 Million
Emp.: 100
Electricity Generation & Distribution Services
N.A.I.C.S.: 221122
Pablo Hernan Corredor (Gen Mgr)

Internexa S.A. (1)
Calle 12 Sur 18 - 168 Bloque 5, Medellin, Colombia
Tel.: (57) 6043171111
Web Site: https://www.internexa.com
Telecommunication Operator
N.A.I.C.S.: 517410

Isa Bolivia S.A. (1)
Subestacion Urubo, Santa Cruz, Bolivia
Tel.: (591) 33701323
Web Site: https://www.isa.com.bo
N.A.I.C.S.: 221118
Guido Nule Amin (Pres)

Oleoducto Bicentenario de Colombia S.A.S. (1)
Carrera 11 A No 93-35 Torre Uno 93 Floor 3, Bogota, Colombia
Tel.: (57) 601 646 1300
Web Site: https://www.bicentenario.com.co
Crude Oil Pipeline Transportation Services
N.A.I.C.S.: 486110

Refineria de Cartagena S.A.S. (1)
Industrial Mamonal Km 10, Cartagena, Colombia
Tel.: (57) 5 670 0960
Web Site: https://www.reficar.com.co
Oil Refining Services
N.A.I.C.S.: 324110

ECOPLAST LTD.
Unit No 1309 & 1310 Thirteenth Floor Hubtown Solaris N S Phadke Road, Opp Telli Galli Near East-West Flyover Andheri East, Mumbai, 400 069, India
Tel.: (91) 2226833452
Web Site:
    https://www.ecoplastindia.com
526703—(BOM)
Rev.: $10,441,113
Assets: $7,017,397
Liabilities: $2,684,057
Net Worth: $4,333,340
Earnings: $27,709
Emp.: 143
Fiscal Year-end: 03/31/21
Polyethylene Film Mfr
N.A.I.C.S.: 326113
Jaymin B. Desai (Mng Dir)

ECOPLASTIC CORPORATION
48 Yurim-ro 13beon-gil, Gyeongju, Gyeongsangbuk-do, Korea (South)
Tel.: (82) 547703114
Web Site: https://www.eco-plastic.com
Year Founded: 1984
038110—(KRS)
Rev.: $1,397,105,313
Assets: $621,983,722
Liabilities: $501,945,704
Net Worth: $120,038,018
Earnings: $18,103,987
Emp.: 585
Fiscal Year-end: 12/31/22
Automotive Components Mfr
N.A.I.C.S.: 332510
Han Sang (Pres)

Subsidiaries:

AIA Co., Ltd. (1)
87 Seonggok-ro, Danwon-gu, Ansan, Gyeonggi-do, Korea (South)
Tel.: (82) 314917968
Web Site: https://www.aia21.co.kr
Emp.: 326
Automotive Rubber Product Mfr & Distr
N.A.I.C.S.: 326291
Choi Young Sik (CEO)

Plant (Domestic):

AIA Co., Ltd. - AIA II Plant (2)
100 Gangchon-ro Danwon-gu, Ansan, Gyeonggi-do, Korea (South)
Tel.: (82) 314916500
Automotive Plastic Product Mfr
N.A.I.C.S.: 336390

KOMOS Co.,Ltd. (1)
122-11 Myeopuri, Ujeong-eup, Hwaseong, Gyeonggi-do, Korea (South) (69.52%)
Tel.: (82) 313591100
Web Site: https://www.secokomos.com
Automobile Parts Mfr
N.A.I.C.S.: 336110

Seojin Industrial Co., Ltd. (1)

296 301 Gongdan 1-daero, Siheung, Gyeonggi-do, Korea (South)
Tel.: (82) 31 428 2700
Web Site: https://www.seojin.com
Motor Vehicle Parts Mfr
N.A.I.C.S.: 336390

ECOPPIA SCIENTIFIC LTD.
4 Habarzel St, Ramat HaHayal, Tel Aviv, 6971008, Israel
Tel.: (972) 98917000
Web Site: http://www.ecoppia.com
Year Founded: 2013
ECPA.M—(TAE)
Rev.: $3,024,000
Assets: $64,626,000
Liabilities: $3,200,000
Net Worth: $61,426,000
Earnings: ($13,632,000)
Fiscal Year-end: 09/30/23
Solar Panel Cleaning Services
N.A.I.C.S.: 561740
Eran Meller (Founder & Chm)

ECOPRO BM CO., LTD.
100 2-sandan-ro, Ochang-eup Cheongwon-gu, Cheongju, 28117, Chungcheongbuk-do, Korea (South)
Tel.: (82) 432407700
Web Site:
    https://www.ecoprobm.co.kr
Year Founded: 2016
247540—(KRS)
Rev.: $4,109,284,752
Assets: $2,587,985,613
Liabilities: $1,446,524,610
Net Worth: $1,141,461,003
Earnings: $209,125,254
Emp.: 1,314
Fiscal Year-end: 12/31/22
Battery Product Mfr
N.A.I.C.S.: 335910
Kwon Woo-Seok (CEO)

ECOPRO CO., LTD.
587-40 Gwahaksaneop 2-ro, Ochang-eup Cheongwon-gu, Cheongju, 28116, Chungcheong-buk-do, Korea (South)
Tel.: (82) 432407700
Web Site: https://www.ecopro.co.kr
Year Founded: 1998
086520—(KRS)
Rev.: $4,325,681,598
Assets: $4,100,215,257
Liabilities: $2,166,009,495
Net Worth: $1,934,205,761
Earnings: $169,193,796
Emp.: 141
Fiscal Year-end: 12/31/22
Battery Material Mfr
N.A.I.C.S.: 334419
Dong-chae Lee (CEO)

ECOPRO HN CO., LTD.
587-40 Gwahaksaneop 2-ro Songdae-ri 311-1 Ochang-eup, Cheongwon-gu, Cheongju, 28116, Chungcheongbuk-do, Korea (South)
Tel.: (82) 432407700
Web Site: https://www.ecoprohn.co.kr
Year Founded: 1998
383310—(KRS)
Rev.: $167,388,350
Assets: $141,196,666
Liabilities: $74,859,503
Net Worth: $66,337,162
Earnings: $24,822,341
Emp.: 319
Fiscal Year-end: 12/31/22
Energy Material Mfr
N.A.I.C.S.: 335929
Lee Ju Hyung (Dir)

ECORA RESOURCES PLC
1 Savile Row, London, W1S 3JR, United Kingdom

Tel.: (44) 2034357400
Web Site:
    http://www.anglopacificgroup.com
ECRAF—(OTCQX)
Rev.: $85,295,000
Assets: $520,459,000
Liabilities: $163,356,000
Net Worth: $357,103,000
Earnings: $37,476,000
Emp.: 12
Fiscal Year-end: 12/31/21
Coal Mining Services
N.A.I.C.S.: 212115
Kevin Flynn (CFO)

ECORUB AB
Hokmark 114, Lovanger, 932 93, Skelleftea, Sweden
Tel.: (46) 91324780
Web Site: https://www.ecorub.se
Year Founded: 2010
Organic Rubber Mfr
N.A.I.C.S.: 326291
Ake Paulsson (CEO)

ECOSAVE HOLDINGS LIMITED
Unit 6 / 20-22 Foundry Road, Seven Hills, 2147, NSW, Australia
Tel.: (61) 1300 557 764
Web Site:
    http://www.ecosave.com.au
Energy Efficiency Services
N.A.I.C.S.: 541620
Marcelo Javier Rouco (Chm & CEO)

ECOSCIENCE INTERNATIONAL BERHAD
PLO555 Jalan Keluli 8 Pasir Gudang Industrial Estate, 81700, Pasir Gudang, Johor, Malaysia
Tel.: (60) 72553126
Web Site:
    https://www.ecosciencegroup.com
Year Founded: 2003
EIB—(KLS)
Rev.: $33,862,157
Assets: $37,159,162
Liabilities: $20,522,853
Net Worth: $16,636,309
Earnings: ($2,137,243)
Emp.: 229
Fiscal Year-end: 12/31/23
Construction Engineering Services
N.A.I.C.S.: 541330
Choi Ong Wong (Co-Founder & Co-CEO)

ECOSECURITIES GROUP PLC
40 Dawson Street, Dublin, Ireland
Tel.: (353) 16139814
Web Site:
    http://www.ecosecurities.com
Year Founded: 1997
Developer & Retailer of Emission Reduction Offsets
N.A.I.C.S.: 541620
Adrian Fernando (COO)

Subsidiaries:

EcoSecurities, Ltd. (1)
215 Park Ave S Ste 1903, New York, NY 10003-1617
Tel.: (212) 356-0160
Web Site: http://www.ecosecurities.com
Sales Range: $25-49.9 Million
Emp.: 20
Developer & Retailer of Emission Reduction Offsets
N.A.I.C.S.: 541620

ECOSLOPS SA
5 rue de Chazelles, 75017, Paris, France
Tel.: (33) 183644743
Web Site: https://www.ecoslops.com
ALESA—(EUR)
Sales Range: $1-9.9 Million

Ecoslops SA—(Continued)

Recycled Marine Fuels Mfr
N.A.I.C.S.: 324199
Sophie Dufosse (CTO)

ECOSSE ENERGY CORP.
8 King Street East Suite 300, Toronto, M4C 1S9, ON, Canada
Tel.: (416) 899-3304   Ca
Web Site:
http://www.ecosseenergy.com
Investment Services; Oil & Gas Exploration Services
N.A.I.C.C.: 520000
Alan W. Morrison (Pres & CEO)

ECOSUNTEK S.P.A.
Via Madre Teresa di Calcutta, Gualdo Tadino, PG, Italy
Tel.: (39) 0759141817
Web Site:
https://www.ecosuntek.com
ECK—(ITA)
Sales Range: $50-74.9 Million
Solar Energy Power Systems, Wind Power Plants & Biomass Systems Construction & Generation
N.A.I.C.S.: 237130
Lorenzo Bargellini (CFO)

ECOSYNTHETIX, INC.
3365 Mainway, Burlington, L7M 1A6, ON, Canada
Tel.: (905) 335-5669   ON
Web Site: https://ecosynthetix.com
Year Founded: 1996
ECO—(TSX)
Rev.: $18,161,891
Assets: $50,981,701
Liabilities: $3,183,675
Net Worth: $47,798,026
Earnings: ($3,179,740)
Emp.: 26
Fiscal Year-end: 12/31/21
Chemicals Mfr
N.A.I.C.S.: 325998
Robert Haire (CFO)

Subsidiaries:

Ecosynthetix Ltd.   (1)
120 N Washington Sq, Lansing, MI 48933
Tel.: (517) 336-4601
Chemical Products Distr
N.A.I.C.S.: 424690

ECOTEC S.R.L.
Zona Industriale Localita San Pietro, Lametino Comparto 5, 88048, Lamezia, Catanzaro, Italy
Tel.: (39) 0968 209863
Web Site: http://www.ecotecweb.net
Industrial Engineering Services
N.A.I.C.S.: 541330
Rita Chaco (Head-Pur)

Subsidiaries:

Duratel S.p.A.   (1)
Via Antonio Meucci 32, 50041, Calenzano, Italy
Tel.: (39) 055883201
Web Site: http://www.duratel.it
Telephone Apparatus Mfr
N.A.I.C.S.: 334210
Massimo Castellani (CEO)

ECOTEL COMMUNICATION AG
Prinzenallee 11, 40549, Dusseldorf, Germany
Tel.: (49) 211550070   De
Web Site: https://www.ecotel.de
Year Founded: 1998
E4C—(DEU)
Rev.: $117,330,170
Assets: $52,243,719
Liabilities: $26,050,194
Net Worth: $26,193,525
Earnings: $13,216,260

Emp.: 215
Fiscal Year-end: 12/31/23
Holding Company; Voice, Data & Mobile Telecommunications Services
N.A.I.C.S.: 551112
Peter Zils (Chm-Mgmt Bd & CEO)

Subsidiaries:

Carrier-Services.de GmbH   (1)
Bruckenstrasse 5a, 10179, Berlin, Germany
Tel.: (49) 3051 636 1060
Web Site: https://www.carrier-services.de
Software Development Services
N.A.I.C.S.: 541511

Init.Voice GmbH   (1)
Wiesenburger Str 11, 14806, Belzig, Germany
Tel.: (49) 3384 163 6600
Web Site: https://www.init-voice.com
Software Development Services
N.A.I.C.S.: 541511

Sparcall GmbH   (1)
Wiesenburger Str 11, 14806, Belzig, Germany
Tel.: (49) 33841 896 8880
Web Site: https://www.sparcall.com
Telecommunication Servicesb
N.A.I.C.S.: 517810

easybell GmbH   (1)
Bruckenstr 5A, 10179, Berlin, Germany
Tel.: (49) 308 095 1001
Web Site: https://en.easybell.de
Telecommunication Servicesb
N.A.I.C.S.: 517810

ecotel private GmbH   (1)
Prinzenallee 9-11, 40549, Dusseldorf, Germany
Tel.: (49) 211550070
Sales Range: $50-74.9 Million
Telecommunication Servicesb
N.A.I.C.S.: 517810

i-cube GmbH   (1)
Prinzenallee 11, 40549, Dusseldorf, Nordrhein-Westfalen, Germany
Tel.: (49) 2115476180
Web Site: http://www.i-cube.de
Telecommunication Servicesb
N.A.I.C.S.: 517810

synergyPLUS GmbH   (1)
Grunauer Fenn 42, 14712, Rathenow, Brandenburg, Germany
Tel.: (49) 1805682682
Web Site: http://www.synergyplus.de
Telecommunications Consulting Services
N.A.I.C.S.: 517810

ECOTRICITY GROUP LTD.
Lion House Rowcroft, Russell House, Stroud, GL5 3BY, Gloucestershire, United Kingdom
Tel.: (44) 1453 756111
Web Site: http://www.ecotricity.co.uk
Year Founded: 1995
Electricity Supply Services
N.A.I.C.S.: 221122
Dale Vince (Founder)

Subsidiaries:

Britwind Ltd.   (1)
Unit 6 Weldon Road, Loughborough, LE11 5RN, Leicestershire, United Kingdom
Tel.: (44) 1453790210
Web Site: http://www.britwind.co.uk
Wind Turbine Mfr
N.A.I.C.S.: 333611

ECOURIER UK LTD.
Cityside House 40 Adler St, London, E1 1EE, United Kingdom
Tel.: (44) 8451451000
Web Site: http://www.ecourier.co.uk
Year Founded: 2004
Sales Range: $10-24.9 Million
Emp.: 58
Courier Service
N.A.I.C.S.: 492110
Peter Davies (Chm)

ECOVACS ROBOTICS CO., LTD.
No 108 Shihu West Road, Wuzhong District, Suzhou, 215104, Jiangsu, China
Tel.: (86) 51265875866
Web Site: http://www.ecovacs.cn
Year Founded: 1998
603486—(SHG)
Rev.: $2,151,596,697
Assets: $1,868,663,923
Liabilities: $965,819,856
Net Worth: $902,844,067
Earnings: $200,460,499
Emp.: 5,000
Fiscal Year-end: 12/31/22
Household Equipment Distr
N.A.I.C.S.: 449210
Qian Dongqi (Chm)

ECOVER BELGIUM NV
Steenovenstraat 1A, 2390, Malle, Belgium
Tel.: (32) 3309 2500   BE
Web Site: http://www.ecover.com
Year Founded: 1980
Sales Range: $200-249.9 Million
Emp.: 300
Dish & Laundry Detergent Mfr
N.A.I.C.S.: 325611
Steven Vandenouwenland (Mgr-Sls & Mktg-Intl)

Subsidiaries:

Method Products, Inc.   (1)
637 Commercial St Ste 300, San Francisco, CA 94111
Tel.: (415) 931-3947
Web Site: http://www.methodhome.com
Sales Range: $25-49.9 Million
Emp.: 90
Biodegradable Laundry Detergent Dish Soap Spray Cleaner & Scented Plug-Ins Mfr
N.A.I.C.S.: 325611
Eric Ryan (Co-Founder)

ECOWISE HOLDINGS LIMITED
1 Commonwealth Lane One Commonwealth 0728, Singapore, 149544, Singapore
Tel.: (65) 62500001   SG
Web Site:
https://www.ecowise.com.sg
Year Founded: 1979
5CT—(SES)
Rev.: $26,851,263
Assets: $42,739,607
Liabilities: $18,804,793
Net Worth: $23,934,814
Earnings: ($5,157,955)
Fiscal Year-end: 10/31/21
Holding Company; Waste Collection & Recycling Services
N.A.I.C.S.: 551112
Thiam Seng Lee (Chm & CEO)

Subsidiaries:

Bee Joo Environmental Pte. Ltd.   (1)
5 Sungei Kadut Street 6, Singapore, 728855, Singapore
Tel.: (65) 63653288
Waste Management Services
N.A.I.C.S.: 562211

Bee Joo Industries Pte. Ltd.   (1)
5 Sungei Kadut St 6, 728853, Singapore, Singapore
Tel.: (65) 91061877
Web Site: http://www.ecowise.com.sg
Emp.: 300
Waste Treatment Services
N.A.I.C.S.: 562112

Changyi Enersave Biomass to Energy Co., Ltd.   (1)
55 Hanxing Road Binhai Economic Development Area, Changyi, Weifang, Shandong, China
Tel.: (86) 5367857999

Resource Recovery Services
N.A.I.C.S.: 562920

Chongqing eco-CTIG Rubber Technology Co., Ltd.   (1)
Room 16-5 Block A Fortune Tower 2 Caifu Road, Yubei District, Chongqing, China
Tel.: (86) 2363809909
Resource Recovery Services
N.A.I.C.S.: 562920

Sun Rubber Industry Sdn. Bhd   (1)
No 53 & 54 Senawang Industrial Estate, 70450, Seremban, Negeri Sembilan, Malaysia
Tel.: (60) 6 675 9999
Web Site: https://srit.com.my
Sales Range: $125-149.9 Million
Emp.: 500
Rubber Products Mfr
N.A.I.C.S.: 326211

Sun Tyre Industries Sdn. Bhd   (1)
No 53 & 54 Senawang Industrial Estate, 70450, Seremban, Negeri Sembilan, Malaysia
Tel.: (60) 66759977
Web Site: http://www.suntex.com
Emp.: 500
Tire Retreading Services
N.A.I.C.S.: 326212

Sunrich Integrated Sdn. Bhd   (1)
No 53 & 54 Senawang Industrial Estate, 70450, Seremban, Negeri Sembilan, Malaysia
Tel.: (60) 66759988
Web Site: http://www.srit.com.my
Sales Range: $150-199.9 Million
Emp.: 400
Rubber Products Mfr & Distr
N.A.I.C.S.: 326211

Subsidiary (Domestic):

Gulf Rubber (Malaysia) Sdn Bhd   (2)
Lot2 Jalan Bakau Off Jalan Undan Mile 5 1/2 Off Jalan Tuaran, Inanam, 88450, Kota Kinabalu, Sabah, Malaysia
Tel.: (60) 88382701
Resource Recovery Services
N.A.I.C.S.: 562920

Sunrich Tyre & Auto Products Sdn Bhd   (2)
No 53 and 54 Senawang Industrial Estate, 70450, Seremban, Negeri Sembilan, Malaysia
Tel.: (60) 66759966
Web Site: http://www.sunrich.com.my
Resource Recovery Services
N.A.I.C.S.: 562920

Sunrich Marketing Sdn. Bhd   (1)
53 Senawang Industrial Estate, 70450, Seremban, 70450, Negeri Sembilan, Malaysia
Tel.: (60) 66771711
Web Site: http://www.suntex.com
Sales Range: $125-149.9 Million
Emp.: 500
Tire Retreading Services
N.A.I.C.S.: 326212

ecoWise Holdings Limited - Co-gen Biomass Power Plant   (1)
5 Sungei Kadut Street 6, Singapore, 728853, Singapore
Tel.: (65) 63653288
Resource Recovery Services
N.A.I.C.S.: 562920

ecoWise Marina Power Pte. Ltd.   (1)
18 Marina Gardens Drive, Singapore, 018953, Singapore
Tel.: (65) 63360527
Resource Recovery Services
N.A.I.C.S.: 562920

ecoWise Solutions Pte. Ltd.   (1)
No 5 Sungei Kadut St 6, Singapore, 728853, Singapore
Tel.: (65) 63653288
Web Site: http://www.ecoWise.com
Recycling & Environmental Management Services
N.A.I.C.S.: 562998

ECP EMERGING GROWTH LIMITED

Level 4 The Pavilion 388 George
Street, Sydney, 2000, NSW, Australia
Tel.: (61) 286516800   AU
Web Site: https://ecpam.com
ECP—(ASX)
Sales Range: Less than $1 Million
Investment & Portfolio Management
N.A.I.C.S.: 523150
Murray Howard D'Almeida *(Chm)*

ECR MINERALS PLC

Office T3 Hurlingham Studios,
Ranelagh Gardens, London, SW6
3PA, United Kingdom - England
Tel.: (44) 2079291010   UK
Web Site:
   https://www.ecrminerals.com
Year Founded: 2004
ECR—(AIM)
Rev.: $14,205
Assets: $6,521,717
Liabilities: $194,523
Net Worth: $6,327,194
Earnings: ($2,237,655)
Emp.: 8
Fiscal Year-end: 09/30/23
Mineral Mining Services
N.A.I.C.S.: 212390
Craig William Brown *(CEO)*

ECRC

1201 - 275 Slater St, Ottawa, K1P
5H9, ON, Canada
Tel.: (613) 230-7369
Web Site: http://www.ecrc.ca
Year Founded: 1995
Rev.: $10,116,528
Emp.: 170
Ship & Oil Handling Services
N.A.I.C.S.: 336611
Paul Pouliotte *(CFO)*

ECS BIZTECH LIMITED

THE FIRST B-02 ECS Corporate
House Besides ITC Narmada Hotel,
Vastrapu, Ahmedabad, 380 015, India
Tel.: (91) 8980005006
Web Site:
   https://www.ecsbiztech.com
Rev.: $3,035,105
Assets: $16,075,956
Liabilities: $14,907,304
Net Worth: $1,168,652
Earnings: $577,118
Fiscal Year-end: 03/31/17
Information Technology Services
N.A.I.C.S.: 518210
Vijay Mansinhbhai Mandora *(Chm & Mng Dir)*

ECS ELECTRICAL CABLE SUPPLY LTD.

3135 - 6900 Graybar Road, Rich-
mond, V6W 0A5, BC, Canada
Tel.: (604) 276-9913
Web Site: http://www.ecswire.com
Year Founded: 1984
Electrical & Electronic Wire & Cable
Distr
N.A.I.C.S.: 423620
Mohammad H. Mohseni *(Founder & Chm)*

ECS ENGINEERING & CONSTRUCTION LIMITED

51 Ritin Lane Unit 1, Concord, L4K
4E1, ON, Canada
Tel.: (905) 761-7009
Web Site:
   http://www.ecsengineering.com
Year Founded: 1992
Rev.: $26,076,800
Emp.: 50
Engineering & Construction Services
N.A.I.C.S.: 236220
Jason Chidiac *(Pres)*

ECS IT BERHAD

Lot 3 Jalan Teknologi 3/5 Taman
Sains, Selangor Kota Damansara,
Petaling Jaya, 48710, Malaysia
Tel.: (60) 362868222
Web Site: http://www.ecsm.com.my
Year Founded: 1985
Sales Range: $125-149.9 Million
Emp.: 281
Holding Company; Information &
Communications Technology Prod-
ucts
N.A.I.C.S.: 551112
Foo Sen Chin *(Chm)*

ECS LIMITED

M11 Business Avenue, Sheikh
Rashid Road Deira, Dubai, United
Arab Emirates
Tel.: (971) 50 3414048
Web Site: http://www.ecs-limited.com
Information Technology & Manage-
ment Consulting Services
N.A.I.C.S.: 541618
Arvind R. Arora *(CEO)*

Subsidiaries:

Parity Training Limited   (1)
3rd Floor, 120 Moorgate, London, EC2M
6SS, United Kingdom
Tel.: (44) 2085409393
Web Site: http://www.paritytraining.com
Sales Range: $25-49.9 Million
Emp.: 250
Computer Training
N.A.I.C.S.: 611420

ECS TELECOM CO., LTD.

IL-Hong Bldg 8 Banpo-daero 28-gil,
Seocho-gu, Seoul, Korea (South)
Tel.: (82) 234158300
Web Site: https://www.ecstel.co.kr
Year Founded: 1999
067010—(KRS)
Rev.: $76,467,237
Assets: $64,292,521
Liabilities: $21,891,466
Net Worth: $42,401,056
Earnings: $3,527,848
Emp.: 207
Fiscal Year-end: 03/31/23
Communication Equipment Mfr
N.A.I.C.S.: 334210
H. N. Hyon *(CEO)*

ECZACIBASI HOLDING A.S.

Kanyon Office Buyukdere Caddesi
185, Levent, 34394, Istanbul, Turkiye
Tel.: (90) 212 371 7000   TR
Web Site:
   http://www.eczacibasi.com.tr
Sales Range: $1-4.9 Billion
Emp.: 10,950
Holding Company
N.A.I.C.S.: 551112
Bulent Eczacibasi *(Chm)*

Subsidiaries:

Burgad AG   (1)
Bad Fredeburg Kirchplatz 10, 57392, Sch-
mallenberg, Germany
Tel.: (49) 2974 9617 0
Web Site: http://www.burgbad.de
Furniture Distr
N.A.I.C.S.: 423220
Jorg Loew *(Gen Mgr)*

E-Kart Electronic Card Systems
Co.   (1)
Gebze Organize Sanayi Bolgesi Kemal
Nehrozoglu Cad No 503, Gebze, 41480,
Kocaeli, Turkiye
Tel.: (90) 262 648 58 00
Web Site: http://www.ekart.com.tr
Smartcard Mfr
N.A.I.C.S.: 326199
Enver Irdem *(Gen Mgr)*

Eczacibasi Asset Management
Co.   (1)

Buyukdere Cad No 209 Tekfen Tower Kat
5-6, Levent, Istanbul, Turkiye
Tel.: (90) 212 319 56 56
Asset Management Services
N.A.I.C.S.: 523940

Eczacibasi Girisim Co.   (1)
Kavacik Ofis Ruzgarli Bahce Mahallesi Ka-
vak Sok No 20, Beykoz, Istanbul, Turkiye
Tel.: (90) 216 333 71 00
Web Site:
   http://www.eczacibasigirisim.com.tr
Pharmaceutical Products Distr
N.A.I.C.S.: 424210
Asli Bicer *(Mgr-Mktg)*

Eczacibasi Investment Holding
Co.   (1)
Buyukdere Cad No 185, Levent, 34394,
Istanbul, Turkiye
Tel.: (90) 212 371 72 21
Financial Investment Services
N.A.I.C.S.: 541611
Levent Ersalman *(Gen Mgr)*

Eczacibasi Occupational Health and
Safety Services   (1)
Ekinciler Caddesi Erturk Sok No 4 Onat
Plaza Kat 1 Daire No 4 Kavacik, Beykoz,
Istanbul, Turkiye
Tel.: (90) 216 547 24 00
Web Site: http://www.eczacibasiosgb.com
Pharmaceutical Products Distr
N.A.I.C.S.: 424210
Anil Sugetiren *(Gen Mgr)*

Eczacibasi Pharmaceutical & Indus-
trial Investment Co.   (1)
Buyukdere Cad Ali Kaya Sok No 5, Levent,
34394, Istanbul, Turkiye   **(50.62%)**
Tel.: (90) 212 350 80 00
Web Site: http://www.eczacibasi.com.tr
Financial Investment Services
N.A.I.C.S.: 523999
Bulent Eczacibasi *(Chm)*

Subsidiary (Non-US):

EHP Eczacibasi Health Care Prod-
ucts Joint Stock Co.   (2)
Arhangelski pereulok D 5 Str 4, 101000,
Moscow, Russia
Tel.: (7) 495 980 84 99
Pharmaceutical Products Distr
N.A.I.C.S.: 424210

Subsidiary (Domestic):

Eczacibasi Hijyen Urunleri Sanayi ve
Ticaret A.S.   (2)
Ataturk Caddesi Ekin Sokak No 5 Kirac,
Esenyurt, 34522, Istanbul, Turkiye
Tel.: (90) 212 866 87 00
Web Site: http://www.uni.com.tr
Pharmaceutical Products Distr
N.A.I.C.S.: 424210
Coskun Beduk *(Gen Mgr)*

Holding (Domestic):

Eczacibasi Monrol Nukleer Urunler
San. ve Tic. A.S.   (2)
Ruzgarlibahce Mahallesi Kavak Sokak No
20, Beykoz, 34805, Istanbul, Turkiye
Tel.: (90) 2165440544
Web Site: http://www.monrol.com.tr
Sales Range: $25-49.9 Million
Emp.: 200
Nuclear Medicine Development Services
N.A.I.C.S.: 541715
Erdal Karamercan *(Chm)*

Eczacibasi Yapi Gerecleri Sanayi ve
Ticaret A.S.   (1)
Buyukdere Cad Ali Kaya Sok No 5, Levent,
Istanbul, 34394, Turkiye
Tel.: (90) 212 350 8000
Building Materials Mfr
N.A.I.C.S.: 327120
Ali Akoz *(Dir-Fin Affairs)*

Eczacibasi-Baxter Hospital Supply
Co.   (1)
Cendere Yolu Pirnal Keceli Bahcesi,
Ayazaga, 34390, Istanbul, Turkiye
Tel.: (90) 212 329 62 00
Web Site: http://www.eczacibasi-
baxter.com.tr
Pharmaceutical Products Distr
N.A.I.C.S.: 424210

Elif Celik *(Gen Mgr)*

Eczacibasi-Lincoln Electric Askaynak
Co.   (1)
TOSB Taysad Organize Sanayi Bolgesi 2
Cadde No 5, Sekerpinar, 41420, Cayirova,
Kocaeli, Turkiye
Tel.: (90) 262 679 78 00
Web Site: http://www.askaynak.com.tr
Industrial Machinery Mfr
N.A.I.C.S.: 333992
Ahmet Sevuk *(Gen Mgr)*

Eis Eczacibasi Ilac, Sinai ve Finansal
Yatirimlar Sanayi ve Ticaret A.S.   (1)
Eczacibasi Holding A SKanyon Office
Buyukdere Street 185, 34394, Istanbul,
Turkiye
Tel.: (90) 2123717000
Web Site: https://www.eczacibasi.com
Rev.: $56,543,158
Assets: $717,575,234
Liabilities: $138,320,304
Net Worth: $579,254,930
Earnings: $129,040,787
Fiscal Year-end: 12/31/2022
Pharmaceuticals Product Mfr
N.A.I.C.S.: 325412
Ferit Bulent Eczacibasi *(Chm)*

Engers Keramik GmbH & Co.
KG   (1)
Brucknerstrasse 43, 56566, Neuwied, Ger-
many
Tel.: (49) 2622 7007 0
Web Site: http://www.engerskeramik.de
Household Furniture Mfr
N.A.I.C.S.: 337121
Ulrich Griesar *(Gen Mgr)*

Esan Eczacibasi Industrial Raw Mate-
rials Co.   (1)
Istanbul Deri Organize Sanayi Bolgesi Kazli
Cesme Caddesi No 5, Tuzla, 34956, Istan-
bul, Turkiye
Tel.: (90) 216 581 64 00
Web Site: http://www.esan.com.tr
Steel Products Mfr
N.A.I.C.S.: 331110
Serpil Demirel *(Gen Mgr)*

Estan Italia Minerals SRL   (1)
Via Regina Pacis 42, 41049, Sassuolo,
Modena, Italy
Tel.: (39) 0536 813305
Web Site: http://www.esanitalia.it
Ceramic Product Distr
N.A.I.C.S.: 444180
Serpil Demirel *(Gen Mgr)*

Ipek Kagit San. ve Tic. A.S.   (1)
Kavacik Ofis Ruzgarli Bahce Mahallesi, Ka-
vak Sokak No 20, 34805, Istanbul, Beykoz,
Turkiye   **(100%)**
Tel.: (90) 216 333 7700
Web Site: http://www.eczacibasi.com
Tissue Paper Products Mfr & Marketer
N.A.I.C.S.: 322120

Mol-Image Molecular Imaging
Co.   (1)
Barbaros Mah Sutcuyolu Cad No 72/A,
Atasehir, 34746, Istanbul, Turkiye
Tel.: (90) 216 544 0 544
Web Site: http://www.molimg.com
Pharmaceutical Products Distr
N.A.I.C.S.: 424210
Batuhan Ozenc *(Dir-Mktg & Sls)*

V&B Fliesen GmbH   (1)
Rotensteiner Weg, 66663, Merzig, Germany
Tel.: (49) 6864 81 3300
Web Site: http://www.villeroyboch-
group.com
Ceramic Tile Mfr
N.A.I.C.S.: 327120
Eckard Kern *(Gen Mgr)*

VitrA (UK) Ltd.   (1)
Park 34 Collet Way, Didcot, Ox11 7WB,
Oxon, United Kingdom
Tel.: (44) 1235 750 990
Web Site: http://www.uk.vitra.com.tr
Building Product Distr
N.A.I.C.S.: 444180
Darren Paxford *(Mgr-Natl Sls)*

VitrA Bad GmbH   (1)
Agrippinawerft 24, 50678, Cologne, Germany

Eczacibasi Holding A.S.—(Continued)

Tel.: (49) 2 21 27 73 68 0
Web Site: http://www.vitra-bad.de
Bathroom Fitting Mfr
N.A.I.C.S.: 332999
Claudio Conigliello *(Mgr-Mktg)*

VitrA USA Inc. (1)
305 Shawnee North Dr Ste 600, Suwanee, GA 30024
Tel.: (770) 904-6830
Web Site: http://www.vitra-usa.com
Bathroom Fitting Mfr
N.A.I.C.S.: 332999

iPek Kagit Kazakhstan LLP (1)
Kunayev Str 21 B Business Center SAT Office No 72, Almaty, Kazakhstan
Tel.: (7) 727 244 66 25
Paper Products Mfr
N.A.I.C.S.: 322291

ECZACIBASI YATIRIM HOLDING ORTAKLIGI A.S.

Kanyon Ofis Buyukdere Caddesi 185, Levent, 34394, Istanbul, Turkiye
Tel.: (90) 2123717000   TR
Web Site:
   https://www.eczacibasi.com.tr
Year Founded: 1942
ECZYT—(IST)
Sales Range: Less than $1 Million
Investment Holding Company
N.A.I.C.S.: 551112
Ferit Bulent Eczacibasi *(Chm)*

ED & TECH INTERNATIONAL LIMITED

104-106 Lumbini Enclave Opp NIMS Hospital, Punjagutta, Hyderabad, 500 082, Telangana, India
Tel.: (91) 4023242865
Web Site: https://edtechintl.com
Year Founded: 1983
VISUINTL—(NSE)
Rev.: $480,761
Assets: $983
Liabilities: $1,980,087
Net Worth: ($1,979,104)
Earnings: ($615)
Fiscal Year-end: 03/31/21
Educational Consulting Services
N.A.I.C.S.: 611710
Chavva Chandrasekhar Reddy *(Chm)*

Subsidiaries:

Visu Academy Limited (1)
G-03 6-1-57 to 61 Mount Nasir Buildings Beside Ravindra Bharathi Near, Saifabad, Hyderabad, 500 004, India
Tel.: (91) 40 23296805
Web Site: http://www.visuacademy.com
Educational Consulting Services
N.A.I.C.S.: 611710

ED INVEST S.A.

ul Grochowska 306/308, 03-840, Warsaw, Poland
Tel.: (48) 222551555
Web Site: https://www.edinvest.pl
EDI—(WAR)
Rev.: $34,418,191
Assets: $25,298,272
Liabilities: $7,523,628
Net Worth: $17,774,644
Earnings: $4,995,935
Emp.: 11
Fiscal Year-end: 12/31/23
Residential Housing & Commercial Buildings Construction & Investment Services
N.A.I.C.S.: 531390
Zofia Egierska *(Chm-Mgmt Bd)*

ED LEARN FORD LINCOLN LTD.

375 Ontario Street, Saint Catharines, L2R 5L3, ON, Canada
Tel.: (905) 684-8791

Web Site:
   http://www.edlearnford.com
Year Founded: 1978
New & Used Car Dealers
N.A.I.C.S.: 441110
Jake Bijakowski *(Asst Mgr-Svc)*

ED&F MAN HOLDINGS LIMITED

3 London Bridge Street, London, SE1 9SG, United Kingdom
Tel.: (44) 2070898000   UK
Web Site: http://www.edfman.com
Year Founded: 1703
Sales Range: $10-24.9 Million
Emp.: 7,000
Sugar, Molasses & Coffee Trader & Distr
N.A.I.C.S.: 424490
Laurie Foulds *(CFO & Grp COO)*

Subsidiaries:

Becafisa S.A. de C.V. (1)
Carr Veracruz-Jamapa Km 15 No 1499, Col Granjas de la Boticaria, Veracruz, Mexico
Tel.: (52) 229 923 17 70
Sugar, Molasses & Coffee Trader & Distr
N.A.I.C.S.: 424490

Beneficios Volcafe S.A. (1)
Apartado Postal 8-4090-1000, San Jose, Costa Rica
Tel.: (506) 2 261 66 66
Sugar, Molasses & Coffee Trader & Distr
N.A.I.C.S.: 424490

CHL Shipping B.V. (1)
Maastorenflat Schiedamsedijk 200, Rotterdam, 3011 EP, Netherlands
Tel.: (31) 10 4360 800
Sugar, Molasses & Coffee Trader & Distr
N.A.I.C.S.: 424490

COFI-COM Trading Pty Limited (1)
73 Ryedale Road, PO Box 231, West Ryde, 1685, NSW, Australia
Tel.: (61) 2 9809 62 66
Web Site: http://www.coficomtrading.com.au
Grocery Product Distr
N.A.I.C.S.: 424490

Cafe Capris S.A. (1)
Apartado Postal 3568-1000, San Jose, Costa Rica
Tel.: (506) 2 261 60 60
Sugar, Molasses & Coffee Trader & Distr
N.A.I.C.S.: 424490

Carcafe Ltda C.I. (1)
Calle 72 no 10-07 Of 1301, Bogota, 110311, Colombia
Tel.: (57) 1 313 7474
Agriculture Product Distr
N.A.I.C.S.: 424910

Carcafe S.A (1)
Edificio Seguros Colmena Ed, Liberty Seguro, Calle 72 No 10-07 Of 1301, Bogota, Colombia
Tel.: (57) 1 313 7474
Sugar, Molasses & Coffee Trader & Distr
N.A.I.C.S.: 424490

Commerciale Sucriere S.A. (1)
Building #32A Parc Industriel Shodecosa Route, Nationale #1, Port-au-Prince, Haiti
Tel.: (509) 221 2144
Sugar, Molasses & Coffee Trader & Distr
N.A.I.C.S.: 424490

Copag-Cia Capital De Armazens Gerais S.A. (1)
Rua Maria Nazareth do Prado 155/205, Bairro Industrial Reinaldo Foresti, Varginha, 37026-520, Minas Gerais, Brazil
Tel.: (55) 353 214 1788
Agriculture Product Distr
N.A.I.C.S.: 424910

E D & F Man (Shanghai) Co., Limited (1)
Room 2406 JingAn China Tower 1701 Beijing Road West, JingAn District, 200040, Shanghai, China
Tel.: (86) 21 6145 7100
Grocery Product Distr
N.A.I.C.S.: 424490

E D & F Man Asia Pte Limited (1)
8 Shenton Way AXA Tower 16-02, Singapore, 068811, Singapore
Tel.: (65) 6922 6700
Grocery Product Distr
N.A.I.C.S.: 424490

E D & F Man Asia Pte Limited & SvG Intermol (1)
Unit C402/A Monririn Building 60/1 Soi Phaholyothin 8 Sailom Phaholyot, Samsen-Nai Phaya thai, Bangkok, 10400, Thailand
Tel.: (66) 2 615 4381 4
Grocery Product Distr
N.A.I.C.S.: 424490

E D & F Man Brasil S.A. (1)
Ladeira De Nossa Senhora 163-6o Andar Gloria, Rio de Janeiro, 22211-100, Brazil
Tel.: (55) 21 3235 9500
Grocery Product Distr
N.A.I.C.S.: 424490

E D & F Man Capital Markets Inc. (1)
440 S LaSalle St 18th Fl, Chicago, IL 60605
Tel.: (312) 300-5000
Grocery Product Distr
N.A.I.C.S.: 424490

E D & F Man Comercio S.A. de C.V. (1)
Torre Forum Andres Bello 10, Piso 14-B Col. Chapultepec Polanco, 11560, Mexico, Mexico
Tel.: (52) 55 52 79 0700
Sugar, Molasses & Coffee Trader & Distr
N.A.I.C.S.: 424490

E D & F Man Commodities India Pvt Limited (1)
Unit No 307 Level 2 Prestige Meridian-II M G Road, Bengaluru, 560 001, India
Tel.: (91) 80 25 58 26 26
Grocery Product Distr
N.A.I.C.S.: 424490

E D & F Man Commodities Sp z oo (1)
Ul Grzybowska 4/125, Warsaw, 00-131, Poland
Tel.: (48) 22 826 8261
Sugar, Molasses & Coffee Trader & Distr
N.A.I.C.S.: 424490

E D & F Man Deutschland GmbH (1)
Am Sandtorkai 62, Hamburg, Germany
Tel.: (49) 40 3330 6660
Sugar, Molasses & Coffee Trader & Distr
N.A.I.C.S.: 424490

E D & F Man Espana, S.A. (1)
Calle de Sagasta, 27 - 2 Izda, Madrid, 28004, Spain
Tel.: (34) 91 448 5162
Sugar, Molasses & Coffee Trader & Distr
N.A.I.C.S.: 424490

E D & F Man Korea Limited (1)
Haengrim Bldg 4F Seocho Jungang Ro 22gil 8 Seocho Dong, Seocho, Seoul, Korea (South)
Tel.: (82) 2 581 8833
Grocery Product Distr
N.A.I.C.S.: 424490

E D & F Man Liquid Products Belgium N.V. (1)
Schuttershofstraat 9, Antwerp, 2000, Belgium
Tel.: (32) 3 448 0978
Sugar, Molasses & Coffee Trader & Distr
N.A.I.C.S.: 424490

E D & F Man Liquid Products Europe BV (1)
Maastorenflat Schiedamsedijk 200, Rotterdam, 3011 EP, Netherlands
Tel.: (31) 10 4360 800
Grocery Product Distr
N.A.I.C.S.: 424490

E D & F Man Liquid Products Inc (1)
6 Place Du Commerce Suite 202, Brossard, J4W 3J9, QC, Canada
Tel.: (450) 465-1715
Grocery Product Distr
N.A.I.C.S.: 424490

E D & F Man Liquid Products Ireland Limited (1)
10 Lower Main Street, Kildare, Ireland
Tel.: (353) 45481070
Sugar, Molasses & Coffee Trader & Distr
N.A.I.C.S.: 424490

E D & F Man Liquid Products Italia s.r.l. (1)
Via A Majani 2, Bologna, 40122, Italy
Tel.: (39) 051 277 011
Sugar, Molasses & Coffee Trader & Distr
N.A.I.C.S.: 424490

E D & F Man Malaysia Sdn. Bhd. (1)
Unit 6 01 6th Fl Bangunan KWSP No 3 Changkat Raja Chulan, Off Jalan Raja Chulan, Kuala Lumpur, 50200, Malaysia
Tel.: (60) 3 2058 0188
Grocery Product Distr
N.A.I.C.S.: 424490

E D & F Man Mozambique Ltda (1)
Bagged Sugar Transit Shed No 1, Port of Maputo, Maputo, Mozambique
Tel.: (258) 82 319 5480
Sugar, Molasses & Coffee Trader & Distr
N.A.I.C.S.: 424490

E D & F Man Nicaragua Limited (1)
Canal Dos 2CLago, Abajo 1C Al Lago, Managua, Nicaragua
Tel.: (505) 266 3816
Sugar, Molasses & Coffee Trader & Distr
N.A.I.C.S.: 424490

E D & F Man Peru S.A.C. (1)
Av del Pinar 152 Of 307, Chacarilla del Estanque, Lima, Peru
Tel.: (51) 1 628 5073
Sugar, Molasses & Coffee Trader & Distr
N.A.I.C.S.: 424490

E D & F Man Philippines Inc. (1)
37-C 37th Floor Rufino Pacific Tower Ayala Avenue, Makati, 6784, Manila, Philippines
Tel.: (63) 2 811 1000
Grocery Product Distr
N.A.I.C.S.: 424490

E D & F Man Portugal, Lda (1)
Av Antonio Serpa 23-7 Andar, Lisbon, 1050-026, Portugal
Tel.: (351) 21 780 1488
Grocery Product Distr
N.A.I.C.S.: 424490

E D & F Man Sucre SARL (1)
42 Avvenue Montaigne, Paris, 75008, France
Tel.: (33) 1 5367 5234
Sugar, Molasses & Coffee Trader & Distr
N.A.I.C.S.: 424490

E D & F Man Sugar Bulgaria (1)
24 Stefaan Karagzka Street, Sofia, 1000, Bulgaria
Tel.: (359) 2980 0854
Grocery Product Distr
N.A.I.C.S.: 424490

E D & F Man Sugar Inc (1)
2525 Ponce De Leon Blvd Ste 1200 Coral Gables, Miami, FL 33134
Tel.: (786) 279-7320
Grocery Product Distr
N.A.I.C.S.: 424490

E D & F Man Trgovina d.o.o. (1)
Dunajska 22, Ljubljana, 1000, Slovenia
Tel.: (386) 01 2320047
Sugar, Molasses & Coffee Trader & Distr
N.A.I.C.S.: 424490

E D & F Man Uruguay SA (1)
Luis Alberto de Herrera 1248 Piso 6 Of 601, Torre World Centre A1, Montevideo, 11300, Uruguay
Tel.: (598) 2 628 3020
Sugar, Molasses & Coffee Trader & Distr
N.A.I.C.S.: 424490

ED & F Man Gulf DMCC (1)
#35H AU Tower Jumeirah Lake Towers, Dubai, United Arab Emirates
Tel.: (971) 4 3614240
Web Site: http://www.edfman.com
Sugar, Molasses & Coffee Trader & Distr
N.A.I.C.S.: 424490

ED&F Man Capital Markets Hong Kong Limited (1)
5613 56/F The Center 99 Queen's Road, Central, China (Hong Kong)
Tel.: (852) 2 170 6600
Agriculture Product Distr
N.A.I.C.S.: 424910

ED&F Man Capital Markets Mena Limited (1)
Emirates Financial Towers Office S404 South Tower Dubai International, Finance Centre, Dubai, United Arab Emirates
Tel.: (971) 4 279 8915
Agriculture Product Distr
N.A.I.C.S.: 424910

ED&F Man Commodities Egypt Limited (1)
The Spot Mall Unit 7 2nd Floor In Front of AUC, New Cairo, Egypt
Tel.: (20) 22 573 4060
Agriculture Product Distr
N.A.I.C.S.: 424910

ED&F Man Ingredients s.r.o. (1)
Zvoleneves 86, Zvoleneves, 273 25, Kladno, Czech Republic
Tel.: (420) 31 258 3044
Web Site: https://www.maningredients.com
Sugar Mfr & Distr
N.A.I.C.S.: 311314

ED&F Man Liquid Products Czech Republic s.r.o. (1)
Masarykovo namesti 3/3, Decin, 40502, Czech Republic
Tel.: (420) 412 513 475
Web Site: http://www.edfman.com
Sugar, Molasses & Coffee Trader & Distr
N.A.I.C.S.: 424490

ED&F Man Liquid Products Nederland B.V. (1)
De Ruyterkade 6 6th Floor, 1013 AA, Amsterdam, Netherlands
Tel.: (31) 20 754 0111
Web Site: http://www.edfman.com
Emp.: 40
Sugar & Molasses Wholesale Trading Services
N.A.I.C.S.: 425120
Re Ariesanderspec (Head-Trading)

Subsidiary (US):

ED&F Man Liquid Products LLC (2)
365 Canal St Ste 2900, New Orleans, LA 70130
Tel.: (504) 525-9741
Web Site:
    http://www.manliquidproducts.com
Trader & Distributor of Molasses
N.A.I.C.S.: 493190
Georgette O'Connor (Asst Mgr-Marine Div)

ED&F Man Liquid Products UK (1)
Alexandra House Regent Road, Liverpool, L20 1ES, United Kingdom
Tel.: (44) 1519443900
Web Site: http://www.edfman.com
Emp.: 20
Grocery Product Distr
N.A.I.C.S.: 424490

ED&F Man Mocambique Limitada (1)
Bagged Sugar Transit Shed 1 Port of Maputo, Maputo, Mozambique
Tel.: (258) 82 319 5480
Agriculture Product Distr
N.A.I.C.S.: 424910

ED&F Man Terminals Ireland Limited (1)
South Bank Road, Ringsend, Dublin, D04 TC98, Ireland
Tel.: (353) 1 668 5894
Agriculture Product Distr
N.A.I.C.S.: 424910

ED&F Man Terminals UK Limited (1)
19 Sandhills Lane, Liverpool, L5 9XE, Merseyside, United Kingdom
Tel.: (44) 151 922 2848
Emp.: 12
Bulk Liquid Storage & Other Related Services
N.A.I.C.S.: 493190
Phil Holder (CEO)

ED&F Man Venezuela S.A. (1)
Edif Banco Del Orinoco-Piso 9 Av Fco de Miranda-Sector la Floresta, Caracas, 1060, Venezuela
Tel.: (58) 244 390 1270
Agriculture Product Distr
N.A.I.C.S.: 424910

Empresas De Narino Ltda. (1)
Calle 18 No 51A-20, San Juan de Pasto, Colombia
Tel.: (57) 27 23 31 26
Grocery Product Distr
N.A.I.C.S.: 424490

Empresas Iansa S.A. (1)
Rosario Norte 615 Piso 23, Las Condes, Santiago, Chile
Tel.: (56) 2 2571 5400
Web Site: http://www.iansa.cl
Rev.: $471,630,000
Assets: $599,874,000
Liabilities: $233,708,000
Net Worth: $366,166,000
Earnings: $51,000
Emp.: 2,412
Fiscal Year-end: 12/31/2016
Agricultural Services
N.A.I.C.S.: 926140
Joaquin Noguera Wilson (Chm)

Empresas de Nario Ltda (1)
Calle 18 No 51A-20, Narino, Bogota, Colombia
Tel.: (57) 27 23 31 26
Sugar, Molasses & Coffee Trader & Distr
N.A.I.C.S.: 424490

Gollucke & Rothfos GmbH (1)
Schlachte 3-5, 28195, Bremen, Germany
Tel.: (49) 42 133 9733
Web Site: https://www.golluecke.de
Coffee Distr
N.A.I.C.S.: 445298

Golluecke & Rothfos GmbH (1)
Schlachte 3/5, Bremen, 28195, Germany
Tel.: (49) 421 33 97 33
Sugar, Molasses & Coffee Trader & Distr
N.A.I.C.S.: 424490

Kilombero Sugar Distributors Limited (1)
4th Floor Sukari House, Corner of Ohio Street/Sokoine Drive, Dar es Salaam, Tanzania
Tel.: (255) 222 119 525 /6
Sugar, Molasses & Coffee Trader & Distr
N.A.I.C.S.: 424490

Kyagalanyi Coffee Limited (1)
140 East 45th Street, Bugolobi, Kampala, Uganda
Tel.: (256) 41 4 25 93 60
Sugar, Molasses & Coffee Trader & Distr
N.A.I.C.S.: 424490

LLC E D & F Man (1)
Office 520 1 Vasilisy Kozhinoy street, 121096, Moscow, Russia
Tel.: (7) 4959377744
Sugar, Molasses & Coffee Trader & Distr
N.A.I.C.S.: 424490

Marcellino Martins & E Johnston Exportadores Ltda (1)
Rua XV De Novembro 46-Terreo, Santos, 11010-150, Brazil
Tel.: (55) 13 32 11 66 11
Grocery Product Distr
N.A.I.C.S.: 424490

Maviga East Africa Limited (1)
PO Box 3703, Dar es Salaam, Tanzania
Tel.: (255) 22 284 3335
Agriculture Product Distr
N.A.I.C.S.: 424910

Maviga Ghana Limited (1)
AH/10 Community 9, PO Box TT 419, Tema, Ghana
Tel.: (233) 24 432 8842
Agriculture Product Distr
N.A.I.C.S.: 424910

Molinos de Honduras S.A. (1)
Ave New Orleans, San Pedro Sula, R8167, Honduras
Tel.: (504) 25 56 66 61
Sugar, Molasses & Coffee Trader & Distr
N.A.I.C.S.: 424490

Frank Reese (Gen Mgr)

Mshale Commodities Limited (Sugar) (1)
3rd Floor Cannon Towers Bandari Wing, Mombasa, Kenya
Tel.: (254) 20 271 50 51
Sugar, Molasses & Coffee Trader & Distr
N.A.I.C.S.: 424490

PT Volkopi Indonesia (1)
Jl Pelajar Timur Gg Sempurna No 15, Medan, 20228, Indonesia
Tel.: (62) 736 64 37
Grocery Product Distr
N.A.I.C.S.: 424490

PT. E D & F Man Indonesia (1)
Menara Rajawali 12th Floor Jl Dr Ide Anak Agung Gde Agung Lot 5 1 Mega, Kuningan, Jakarta, 12950, Indonesia
Tel.: (62) 21 576 1605
Grocery Product Distr
N.A.I.C.S.: 424490

Peter Schoenfeld S.A. (1)
Diagonal 6 13-27 Zona 10, Guatemala, 01010, Guatemala
Tel.: (502) 2 427 1200
Agriculture Product Distr
N.A.I.C.S.: 424910

Procesadora Del Sur S.A. (1)
Av Pedro Ruiz Gallo Lt 124 C 125A, Urb Fundo la Estrella, Lima, Peru
Tel.: (51) 1 356 44 54
Sugar, Molasses & Coffee Trader & Distr
N.A.I.C.S.: 424490

Taylor Winch (Coffee) Limited (1)
Denis Pritt Road, Opposite St. Georges High School, Nairobi, 00100, Kenya
Tel.: (254) 20 271 50 51
Sugar, Molasses & Coffee Trader & Distr
N.A.I.C.S.: 424490

Taylor Winch (Tanzania) Limited (1)
Moshi Industrial Area, Viwanda Street, Tanga, Tanzania
Tel.: (255) 27 27 51 221
Sugar, Molasses & Coffee Trader & Distr
N.A.I.C.S.: 424490

The Dakman Vietnam Company Limited (1)
Km7 National Road 26, Buon Ma Thuot, Dak Lak, Vietnam
Tel.: (84) 500 3823 201
Web Site: http://www.dakmancoffee.com
Grocery Product Distr
N.A.I.C.S.: 424490
Jonathan Clark (Gen Mgr)

Volcafe France (1)
27 Rue Chateaubriand, Paris, 75008, France
Tel.: (33) 1 42 99 05 48
Web Site: http://www.volcafe-france.fr
Emp.: 4
Coffee Mfr
N.A.I.C.S.: 311920
Fournier Arnaud (Gen Mgr)

Volcafe Iberia S.A. (1)
Calle Sagasta 27, Madrid, 28004, Spain
Tel.: (34) 91 448 51 62
Sugar, Molasses & Coffee Trader & Distr
N.A.I.C.S.: 424490

Volcafe LTDA (1)
Rua Frei Gaspar 22 2/3 andar, Santos, 11010-090, Brazil
Tel.: (55) 13 32 13 92 00
Web Site: http://www.volcafe.com
Grocery Product Distr
N.A.I.C.S.: 424490

Volcafe Limited (1)
Technoparkstrasse 7, Winterthur, 8406, Switzerland
Tel.: (41) 52 264 94 94
Sugar, Molasses & Coffee Trader & Distr
N.A.I.C.S.: 424490

Volcafe Speciality Coffee LLC (1)
169 C St, Petaluma, CA 94952
Tel.: (707) 769-2680
Web Site: http://www.volcafespecialty.com
Coffee Product Mfr
N.A.I.C.S.: 311920
Claire L'Esperance (Mgr-Ops)

Volcafe Specialty Coffee Corp. (1)
3 W Main St Ste 203, Irvington, NY 10533
Tel.: (914) 752-7706
Web Site: https://www.volcafespecialty.com
Coffee Product Distr
N.A.I.C.S.: 424490
Mauricio Jimenez (Gen Mgr)

Waelti-Schoenfeld S.A (1)
Diagonal 6 13-27, Zona 10, Guatemala, 01010, Guatemala
Tel.: (502) 2427 12 00
Sugar, Molasses & Coffee Trader & Distr
N.A.I.C.S.: 424490

Westway Feed Products LLC (1)
14015 Park Dr Ste 217, Tomball, TX 77377
Tel.: (281) 351-4420
Web Site: http://www.westwayfeed.com
Emp.: 30
Liquid Animal Feed Products Mfr & Distr
N.A.I.C.S.: 311119
Steven Boehmer (Pres)

Plant (Domestic):

Westway Feed Products LLC - Western Regional Office (2)
2030 W Washington St, Stockton, CA 95203-2932
Tel.: (209) 946-0914
Web Site: http://www.westwayfeed.com
Emp.: 20
Liquid Animal Feed Products Mfr & Distr
N.A.I.C.S.: 311119
Rick Watson (Mgr-Ops-Hereford-TX)

Yunnan Volcafe Company Limited (1)
The Crossway of Si Lan Road and Ban Shan Road, Simao District, Pu'er, 665000, Yunnan, China
Tel.: (86) 879 824 6679
Agriculture Product Distr
N.A.I.C.S.: 424910

volcafe usa llc (1)
80 Cottontail Ln 1st Fl, Somerset, NJ 08873
Tel.: (732) 469-9622
Grocery Product Distr
N.A.I.C.S.: 424490

ED'S EASY DINER GROUP LIMITED
Avenfield House 118-127 Park Lane, London, W1K 7AG, United Kingdom
Tel.: (44) 20 7629 6151   UK
Web Site:
    http://www.edseasydiner.com
Year Founded: 1987
Sales Range: $10-24.9 Million
Emp.: 20
Retro-American Diner-Style Restaurants Operator
N.A.I.C.S.: 722511
Andrew Guy (CEO)

EDAN INSTRUMENTS, INC.
No 15 Jinhui Road, Pingshan New District, Shenzhen, 518122, China
Tel.: (86) 75526898326
Web Site: https://www.edan.com.cn
Year Founded: 1995
300206—(CHIN)
Rev.: $244,634,364
Assets: $313,868,412
Liabilities: $53,943,084
Net Worth: $259,925,328
Earnings: $32,711,796
Emp.: 800
Fiscal Year-end: 12/31/22
Electronic Medical Device Mfr
N.A.I.C.S.: 334510

Subsidiaries:

Edan Diagnostics, Inc. (1)
9918 Via Pasar, San Diego, CA 92126
Tel.: (858) 750-3066
Web Site: https://www.edandiagnostics.com
Electromedical Equipment Mfr
N.A.I.C.S.: 334510

Edan Instruments GmbH (1)

Edan Instruments, Inc.—(Continued)

Robert-Bosch-Str 11b, 63225, Langen, Germany
Tel.: (49) 61032020781
Emp.: 3
Electromedical Equipment Distr
N.A.I.C.S.: 423450

Edan Medical (UK) Ltd.   (1)
Unit 8 Charter Gate Moulton Park,
Northampton, NN3 6QF, Northamptonshire,
United Kingdom
Tel.: (44) 160 464 8600
Web Site: https://www.edanuk.com
Emp.: 5
Electromedical Equipment Distr
N.A.I.C.S.: 423450
Jake Maxwell (Mgr-Sls-Natl)

Edan Medical India Private Ltd.   (1)
207 New Delhi House 27 Barakhambha
Road, New Delhi, 110 001, India
Tel.: (91) 1143072203
Electromedical Equipment Distr
N.A.I.C.S.: 423450

EDAP TMS S.A.
4 rue du Dauphine PA La Poudrette
Lamartine, 69120, Vaulx-en-Velin,
France
Tel.: (33) 472153150   FR
Web Site: https://www.edap-tms.com
Year Founded: 1979
EDAP—(NASDAQ)
Rev.: $65,209,368
Assets: $98,799,914
Liabilities: $37,368,875
Net Worth: $61,431,038
Earnings: ($22,855,601)
Emp.: 307
Fiscal Year-end: 12/31/23
Mfr of Urological Medical Devices
N.A.I.C.S.: 334510
Marc Oczachowski (Chm & CEO)

Subsidiaries:

EDAP GmbH   (1)
Hulm 42, 24937, Flensburg,
Germany   (100%)
Tel.: (49) 4618072590
Sales Range: $25-49.9 Million
Emp.: 9
Ultrasound Therapeutic Device Mfr
N.A.I.C.S.: 334519
Judith Johannsen (Gen Mgr)

EDAP Russia   (1)
24 Tchetchiorskiiproezd St Bl I Room 2,
117042, Moscow, Russia   (100%)
Tel.: (7) 9165224104
Web Site: http://www.edap-tms.com
Therapeutic Ultrasound Device Mfr
N.A.I.C.S.: 334510
Jean-Francois Bachelard (Dir-Bus Unit)

EDAP TMS France S.A.   (1)
Parc dactivites la Poudrette Lamartine, 4
rue du Dauphine, 69120, Vaulx-en-Velin,
France
Tel.: (33) 472153150
Sales Range: $25-49.9 Million
Emp.: 102
Developer & Marketer of Therapeutic Ultra-
sound Devices
N.A.I.C.S.: 334510
Marc Oczachowski (Pres & CEO)

EDAP TMS Korea   (1)
Suite 12 13 24 Floor 85 Gwangnaru-ro 56-
gil, Gwangjin-gu, Seoul, 05116, Korea
(South)   (100%)
Tel.: (82) 262171481
Sales Range: $25-49.9 Million
Emp.: 2
Mfr of Therapeutic Ultrasound Devices
N.A.I.C.S.: 334510
Jong-Hyeon Jeon (Gen Mgr)

EDAP Technomed (M) Sdn Bhd   (1)
16 1st Floor Jalan USJ 10/1B Taipan Tri-
angle, UEP Suban Jaya, 47620, Petaling
Jaya, Malaysia   (100%)
Tel.: (60) 356349335
Web Site: https://us.edap-tms.com
Marketer of Urological Medical Devices
N.A.I.C.S.: 339112

Herve de Soultrait (Gen Mgr)

EDAP Technomed Co. Ltd.   (1)
1F Shinkawa Sanko Building, 1-3-17
Shinkawa, Tokyo, 104-0033, Chuo-ku,
Japan   (100%)
Tel.: (81) 355406767
Web Site: https://www.edaptechnomed.co.jp
Emp.: 32
Sales & Regulator of Urological Medical
Devices
N.A.I.C.S.: 339112
Jean Francois Bashler (CEO)

EDAP Technomed Inc.   (1)
5321 Industrial Oaks Blvd Ste 110, Austin,
TX 78735
Tel.: (512) 832-7956
Medical Equipment Distr
N.A.I.C.S.: 423450
Marc Oczachowski (Pres)

EDAP Technomed Italia Srl   (1)
Via Leonida Rech 44th Fl, Rome, 00156,
Italy   (100%)
Tel.: (39) 0686897190
Marketer of Urological Medical Devices
N.A.I.C.S.: 339112

Edap Technomed Sdn Bhd   (1)
16 1st Floor Jalan USJ 10/1B Taipan
Triangle-UEP Suban Jaya, 47620, Petaling
Jaya, Malaysia
Tel.: (60) 356349335
Medical Equipment Mfr
N.A.I.C.S.: 339112
Herve de Soultrait (Gen Mgr)

Edap Tms GmbH   (1)
Holm 42, 24937, Flensburg, Germany
Tel.: (49) 4618072590
Medical Equipment Mfr
N.A.I.C.S.: 339112
Judith Johannsen (Gen Mgr)

EDB INVESTMENTS PTE. LTD.
250 North Bridge Road 28-00 Raffles
City Tower, Singapore, 179101, Sin-
gapore
Tel.: (65) 68326832
Web Site: http://www.edbi.com
Year Founded: 1991
Sales Range: $125-149.9 Million
Emp.: 500
Investment Holding Company
N.A.I.C.S.: 523999
Swee-Yeok Chu (Pres & CEO)

Subsidiaries:

S*BIO Pte. Ltd.   (1)
1 Science Park Road 05 09 The Capricorn,
Singapore Science Park II, Singapore, 117
528, Singapore
Tel.: (65) 68275000
Web Site: http://www.sbio.com
Biotechnology Research & Development
Services
N.A.I.C.S.: 541714
Jan-Anders Karlsson (CEO)

EDCON HOLDINGS LIMITED
Edgardale Press Avenue Crown
Mines, Johannesburg, 2092, South
Africa
Tel.: (27) 11 495 6000   ZA
Web Site: http://www.edcon.co.za
Year Founded: 1929
Holding Company; Clothing, Foot-
wear, Textiles, Cosmetics & Home
Furnishings Retailer
N.A.I.C.S.: 551112
Charles Vikisi (Gen Counsel & Sec)

Subsidiaries:

Edcon Limited   (1)
Edgardale Press Avenue Crown Mines, Jo-
hannesburg, 2092, South Africa
Tel.: (27) 114956000
Web Site: http://www.edcon.co.za
Clothing Footwear Textile Cosmetic & Home
Furnishing Distr
N.A.I.C.S.: 458110
Charles Vikisi (Gen Counsel & Sec)

EDDA WIND ASA
Spannavegen 152, 5501, Haugesund,
Norway
Tel.: (47) 52704545
Web Site: https://www.eddawind.com
Year Founded: 2015
EWIND—(OSL)
Rev.: $42,486,510
Assets: $628,381,179
Liabilities: $320,932,441
Net Worth: $307,448,737
Earnings: ($4,174,401)
Emp.: 20
Fiscal Year end: 12/31/23
Offshore Services
N.A.I.C.S.: 211130
Havard Framnes (Chm)

EDDING AG
Bookkoppel 7, 22926, Ahrensburg,
Germany
Tel.: (49) 41028080
Web Site: https://www.edding.com
Year Founded: 1960
EDD3—(MUN)
Rev.: $177,491,257
Assets: $139,716,826
Liabilities: $65,271,833
Net Worth: $74,444,993
Earnings: ($4,735,602)
Emp.: 757
Fiscal Year-end: 12/31/23
Visual Communication Product Mfr
N.A.I.C.S.: 541430
Per Ledermann (Chm-Mgmt Bd &
CEO)

Subsidiaries:

Edding Expressive Skin GmbH   (1)
Burchardstrasse 13-15, 20095, Hamburg,
Germany
Tel.: (49) 40228652880
Stationery Product Mfr & Distr
N.A.I.C.S.: 322230

Edding International GmbH   (1)
Bookkoppel 7, 22926, Ahrensburg, Ger-
many
Tel.: (49) 41028080
Stationery Product Distr
N.A.I.C.S.: 424120

Legamaster BVBA   (1)
Schalienhoevedreef 20j, 2800, Mechelen,
Belgium
Tel.: (32) 15280101
Quality Marker & Writing Instrument Mfr
N.A.I.C.S.: 339940
Bart Saenen (Sls Mgr)

Legamaster GmbH   (1)
Bahnhofstr 24, 22941, Bargteheide, Ger-
many
Tel.: (49) 453228830
Web Site: https://www.legamaster.de
Stationery Product Distr
N.A.I.C.S.: 424120

Legamaster International BV   (1)
Kwinkweerd 62, PO Box 111, 7241 CW,
Lochem, Netherlands
Tel.: (31) 573713000
Emp.: 600
Quality Marker & Writing Instrument Mfr
N.A.I.C.S.: 339940
Erik Bosman (Mgr-Logistics)

Prismade Labs GmbH   (1)
Gustav-Adolf-Strasse 3, 09116, Chemnitz,
Germany
Tel.: (49) 37191222709
Web Site: https://www.prismade.com
Mass Printing Services
N.A.I.C.S.: 519290

V.D. Ledermann & Co. GmbH   (1)
Baschutzer Strasse 7, 02625, Bautzen,
Germany
Tel.: (49) 35916820
Fibre Tip Pen Mfr
N.A.I.C.S.: 339940
Franziska Sill (Mgr-Engrg & Lean Mgmt)

edding Argentina SA   (1)

Sargento Cabral 3770 Panamerican Bureau
Edificio III Piso 5, Partido de Vicente Lopez,
B1605EFJ, Munro, Buenos Aires, Argentina
Tel.: (54) 1132200420
Felt Tip Pen & Permanent Marker Mfr &
Distr
N.A.I.C.S.: 339940
Leonardo Rosas (Gen Mgr-Fin & Admin)

edding BeNeLux BV   (1)
Kwinkweerd 62, Postbus 111, 7240 AC,
Lochem, Netherlands
Tel.: (31) 573713100
Felt Tip Pen & Permanent Marker Mfr &
Distr
N.A.I.C.S.: 339940

edding Colombia SAS   (1)
Carrera 49 No 78C Sur 94, Sabaneta, An-
tioquia, Colombia
Felt Tip Pen & Permanent Marker Mfr &
Distr
N.A.I.C.S.: 339940
William Garcia Gutierrez (Mng Dir)

edding France SAS   (1)
4 Avenue de l'Europe, 59223, Roncq,
France
Tel.: (33) 320051213
Felt Tip Pen & Permanent Marker Mfr &
Distr
N.A.I.C.S.: 339940

edding Hellas Ltd.   (1)
Paparigopoulou 61, Agia Paraskevi, 153 43,
Athens, Greece
Tel.: (30) 2106748041
Web Site: http://www.edding-hellas.gr
Felt Tip Pen & Permanent Marker Mfr
N.A.I.C.S.: 339940
George Margas (Dir-Admin & Fin)

edding Ofis ve Kirtasiye   (1)
Merkez Mahallesi Baglar Caddesi Tekfen
Ofispark No14 K 3 B1 Blok, Kagithane,
34406, Istanbul, Turkiye
Tel.: (90) 2122899911
Felt Tip Pen & Permanent Marker Mfr &
Distr
N.A.I.C.S.: 339940

edding UK Ltd.   (1)
Edding House Merlin Centre Acrewood
Way, Saint Albans, AL4 0JY, Hertfordshire,
United Kingdom
Tel.: (44) 1727846688
Felt Tip Pen & Permanent Marker Mfr &
Distr
N.A.I.C.S.: 339940
Barry Hall (Mng Dir)

edding Vertrieb GmbH   (1)
An der Feldmark 9b, 31515, Wunstorf, Ger-
many
Tel.: (49) 50311500
Felt Tip Pen & Permanent Marker Mfr &
Distr
N.A.I.C.S.: 339940

EDDY GROUP LIMITED
660 St Anne St, PO Box 146, Ba-
thurst, E2A 3Z1, NB, Canada
Tel.: (506) 546-6631
Web Site: http://www.eddygroup.com
Year Founded: 1800
Sales Range: $25-49.9 Million
Emp.: 112
Residential & Commercial Products
Distr
N.A.I.C.S.: 444180

EDDYFI NDT, INC.
3425 Pierre-Ardouin Street, Quebec,
G1P 0B3, QC, Canada
Tel.: (418) 780-1565
Web Site: http://www.eddyfi-ndt.com
Professional, Scientific & Technical
Services
N.A.I.C.S.: 541990

Subsidiaries:

Dynamic Risk Assessment Systems,
Inc.   (1)
1110 333 11 Avenue SW, Calgary, T2R
1L9, AB, Canada
Tel.: (403) 547-8638

Web Site: http://www.dynamicrisk.net
Rev.: $3,145,475
Emp.: 30
Business Management Services
N.A.I.C.S.: 541611
Trevor MacFarlane *(CEO)*

EDEKA ZENTRALE AG & CO. KG
New York Ring 6, 22297, Hamburg, Germany
Tel.: (49) 4063770   De
Web Site: http://www.edeka.de
Year Founded: 1907
Sales Range: $25-49.9 Billion
Emp.: 200,000
Groceries Whslr & Retailer
N.A.I.C.S.: 445110
Markus Mosa *(CFO & CIO)*

Subsidiaries:

Marktkauf Holding GmbH   **(1)**
Fuggerstrasse 11, D-33689, Bielefeld, Germany
Tel.: (49) 52059401
Web Site: http://www.marktkauf.de
Sales Range: $5-14.9 Billion
Emp.: 14,150
Infrastructure Inspection Camera & Remote Control System Design & Mfr
N.A.I.C.S.: 551112

Netto Marken-Discount AG & Co. KG   **(1)**
Industriepark Ponholz 1, 93142, Maxhutte-Haidhof, Germany   **(100%)**
Tel.: (49) 94713200
Web Site: http://www.netto-online.de
Sales Range: $200-249.9 Million
Emp.: 600
Grocery & Convenience Store Operator
N.A.I.C.S.: 445110
Manfred Karl *(Mng Dir)*

EDEL SE & CO. KGAA
Neumuhlen 17, 22763, Hamburg, Germany
Tel.: (49) 40890850   De
Web Site: https://www.edel.com
EDL—(MUN)
Rev.: $309,326,451
Assets: $212,561,207
Liabilities: $158,637,158
Net Worth: $53,924,049
Earnings: $13,412,020
Emp.: 1,060
Fiscal Year-end: 09/30/23
Music & Entertainment Product Production & Distribution
N.A.I.C.S.: 512230
Michael Haentjes *(Founder)*

Subsidiaries:

Edel Germany GmbH   **(1)**
Neumuhlen 17, 22763, Hamburg, Germany
Tel.: (49) 40890850
Web Site: http://www.edel.com
Sales Range: $75-99.9 Million
Emp.: 16
Commercial Books Mfr & Distr
N.A.I.C.S.: 323111
Michael Haentjes *(Gen Mgr)*

Subsidiary (Domestic):

Edel Media & Entertainment GmbH   **(2)**
Neumuehlen 17, Hamburg, 22763, Germany   **(100%)**
Tel.: (49) 40890850
Web Site: http://www.edel.com
Sales Range: $75-99.9 Million
Music Producer
N.A.I.C.S.: 711130

Subsidiary (Non-US):

Edel Records GmbH   **(2)**
   (100%)
Tel.: (49) 40890850
Web Site: http://www.edel.com

Sales Range: $25-49.9 Million
Music Distributor
N.A.I.C.S.: 512290

Division (Non-US):

Edel Musica Vertriebs GmbH   **(3)**
   (100%)
Tel.: (43) 557223494
Web Site: http://www.edel.at
Sales Range: $25-49.9 Million
Emp.: 50
Music Distributor
N.A.I.C.S.: 512290

Edel Records (Switzerland) AG   **(3)**
Tel.: (41) 522020222
Music Distributor
N.A.I.C.S.: 512290

Edel Records Finland Oy   **(3)**
   (100%)
Tel.: (358) 97288320
Web Site: http://www.edel.fi
Sales Range: $1-9.9 Million
Emp.: 14
Music Distributor
N.A.I.C.S.: 512290

Edel UK Records Ltd.   **(3)**
   (100%)
Tel.: (44) 2074824848
Web Site: http://www.edel.com
Sales Range: $25-49.9 Million
Emp.: 100
Music Distributor
N.A.I.C.S.: 512290

Edel Music S.A.   **(1)**
Gran via 39 7a, 28013, Madrid, Spain
Tel.: (34) 917013990
Web Site: http://www.edel.com
Music Distributor
N.A.I.C.S.: 512290

Edlp Marketing, Lda.   **(1)**
Rua Quirino Da Fonseca 6 3 Dto, Lisbon, 1000 252, Portugal   **(100%)**
Tel.: (351) 218438580
Sales Range: Less than $1 Million
Emp.: 2
Music Producer Advertiser
N.A.I.C.S.: 541910

Kontor New Media GmbH   **(1)**
Neumuhlen 17, 22763, Hamburg, Germany
Tel.: (49) 4064690510
Web Site: https://www.kontornewmedia.com
Sales Range: $25-49.9 Million
Emp.: 30
Marketing Consulting Services
N.A.I.C.S.: 541613

Kontor Records GmbH   **(1)**
Neumuhlen 17, 22763, Hamburg, Germany
Tel.: (49) 406469050
Web Site: http://www.kontorrecords.de
Sales Range: $25-49.9 Million
Emp.: 30
Music Publishers
N.A.I.C.S.: 512230

Optimal Media Production GmbH   **(1)**
Glienholzweg 7, Robel/Muritz, 17207, Berlin, Germany   **(100%)**
Tel.: (49) 3993156500
Web Site: https://www.optimal-media.com
Sales Range: $25-49.9 Million
Emp.: 35
Mfr & Distribution of CDs, DVDs, Cassettes & Vinyl Records
N.A.I.C.S.: 334310
Jorg Hahn *(Mng Dir)*

Phonag Records AG   **(1)**
Zuercherstrasse 77, 8401, Winterthur, Switzerland
Tel.: (41) 522020151
Web Site: http://www.edel.com
Music Distributor
N.A.I.C.S.: 512290

Playground Music Scandinavia AB   **(1)**
Jorgen Ankersgatan 13B, 211 45, Malmo, Sweden
Tel.: (46) 40288180
Web Site: https://www.playgroundmusic.com
Sales Range: $25-49.9 Million
Emp.: 30

Physical & Digital Music Media Production, Marketing & Distribution
N.A.I.C.S.: 512250

Branch (Non-US):

Playground Music Scandinavia AB - Copenhagen Branch   **(2)**
Gronnegade 3, DK-1107, Copenhagen, Denmark
Tel.: (45) 33186572
Web Site: http://www.playgroundmusic.com
Sales Range: $25-49.9 Million
Emp.: 7
Physical & Digital Music Media Production, Marketing & Distribution
N.A.I.C.S.: 512250
Soren Krogh Thompson *(Gen Mgr)*

Playground Music Scandinavia AB - Oslo Branch   **(2)**
Ulvenveien 90B, 581, Oslo, Norway
Tel.: (47) 22666560
Web Site: http://www.playgroundmusic.com
Sales Range: $25-49.9 Million
Emp.: 6
Physical & Digital Music Media Production, Marketing & Distribution
N.A.I.C.S.: 512250
Tom Pannula *(Gen Mgr)*

EDELMANN GMBH
Steinheimer Strasse 45, 89518, Heidenheim, Germany
Tel.: (49) 7321 340 0
Web Site: http://www.edelmann-group.com
Year Founded: 1913
Sales Range: $300-349.9 Million
Emp.: 3,000
Board Packaging, Leaflet & System Solution Services
N.A.I.C.S.: 561910
Jorg Weidenfeld *(Chief Transformation Officer)*

Subsidiaries:

Carl Edelmann GmbH & Co. KG   **(1)**
Steinheimer Strasse 45, 89518, Heidenheim, Germany
Tel.: (49) 73213400
Beauty Product Retailer
N.A.I.C.S.: 456120
Marcel Heinze *(Acct Mgr)*

Edelmann (Beijing) Co., Ltd.   **(1)**
Beijing Tianzhu Airport Industrial Zone B YuHua Road 30th, Shunyi District, Beijing, 101300, China
Tel.: (86) 1080483300
Beauty Product Retailer
N.A.I.C.S.: 456120
David Boyle *(Mng Dir)*

Edelmann (Beijing) Pharmaceutical Packaging & Printing, Ltd.   **(1)**
Beijing-Shunyi-Airport Industrial Zone C-Zone ZhaoFeng First 27th, Beijing, 101301, China
Tel.: (86) 10 60441102
Web Site: http://www.edelmann-group.com
Folding Cartons & Specialty Packaging Products Mfr
N.A.I.C.S.: 322212
Xiaoguang Li *(Plant Mgr)*

Edelmann Bitterfeld GmbH   **(1)**
Zorbiger Strasse, 06749, Bitterfeld, Germany
Tel.: (49) 34933340
Beauty Product Retailer
N.A.I.C.S.: 456120
Heiko Pils *(Mng Dir)*

Edelmann Brazil Embalagens Ltda.   **(1)**
Av das Industrias Cachoeirinha, 715 Distrito Industrial, Rio Grande, RS, Brazil
Tel.: (55) 5121081313
Beauty Product Retailer
N.A.I.C.S.: 456120
Luiz Fancisco Albrecht *(Mng Dir)*

Edelmann France   **(1)**
12 rue Lavoisier, 95300, Pontoise, France
Tel.: (33) 1 34415000
Web Site: http://www.edelmann-group.com

Folding Cartons & Specialty Packaging Products Mfr
N.A.I.C.S.: 322212
Dominique Lasquibar *(Dir-Sls Beauty Care-Global)*

Edelmann Hungary Packaging Zrt.   **(1)**
Fuvar utca 21, 8900, Zalaegerszeg, Hungary
Tel.: (36) 92 549200
Web Site: http://www.edelmann.de
Folding Cartons & Specialty Packaging Products Mfr
N.A.I.C.S.: 322212
Gyoergy Czirkl *(Mng Dir)*

Edelmann Leaflet Solutions GmbH   **(1)**
Heuriedweg 37, 88131, Lindau, Germany
Tel.: (49) 8382 9630 0
Web Site: http://www.edelmann.de
Offset Printing of Leaflets
N.A.I.C.S.: 323111
Sascha Haag *(Head-Sls-Internal)*

Edelmann Norderstedt GmbH   **(1)**
Oststrasse 130, 22844, Norderstedt, Germany
Tel.: (49) 40325949501
Beauty Product Retailer
N.A.I.C.S.: 456120
Sebastian Eschke *(Mng Dir)*

Edelmann Packaging India Private Limited   **(1)**
Village Surajpur Haripur Road, Solan District, Barotiwala, 174103, Himachal Pradesh, India   **(65%)**
Tel.: (91) 1792 304 343
Web Site: http://www.edelmann.de
Folding Cartons & Specialty Packaging Products Mfr
N.A.I.C.S.: 322212
Munish Aggarwal *(Plant Mgr)*

Edelmann Packaging Mexico S.A. de C.V.   **(1)**
Maiz No 53 Granjas Esmeralda, Iztapalapa, 09810, Mexico, D.F., Mexico
Tel.: (52) 55 55822511
Web Site: http://www.edelmann.de
Emp.: 190
Folding Cartons & Specialty Packaging Products Mfr
N.A.I.C.S.: 322212
Alejandro Galvez *(Plant Mgr)*

Edelmann Pharmadruck GmbH   **(1)**
Zeller Strasse 25, 73235, Weilheim, Germany
Tel.: (49) 7023 707 0
Web Site: http://www.edelmann.de
Folding Cartons Mfr
N.A.I.C.S.: 322212
Rainer Schwan *(Plant Mgr)*

Edelmann Poland Sp.z o.o.   **(1)**
3-go Maja Street 8 Hall C7, Millenium Logistic Parks, 05 800, Pruszkow, Poland
Tel.: (48) 22 5737700
Web Site: http://www.edelmann.de
Folding Cartons & Specialty Packaging Products Mfr
N.A.I.C.S.: 322212
Milosz Glaser *(Mng Dir)*

Edelmann USA, Inc.   **(1)**
3800 N Mission Rd, Ontario, CA 91761
Tel.: (323) 669-5700
Web Site: http://www.edelmannusa.com
Sales Range: $50-74.9 Million
Emp.: 120
Mfr of Folding Cartons & Specialty Packaging Products
N.A.I.C.S.: 322212
Rose Van Der Zanden *(Controller)*

Plant (Domestic):

Edelmann USA, Inc. - Pulaski   **(2)**
260 Bennett Dr, Pulaski, TN 38478
Tel.: (931) 424-2200
Web Site: http://www.edelmannusa.com
Emp.: 75
Mfr of Folding Cartons & Specialty Packaging Products
N.A.I.C.S.: 322212
Brian Johnson *(Head-Production)*

Edelmann GmbH—(Continued)

Edelmann Wuppertal GmbH (1)
Linderhauser Str 77-79, 42279, Wuppertal, Germany
Tel.: (49) 202526060
Beauty Product Retailer
N.A.I.C.S.: 456120

EDELWEISS FINANCIAL SERVICES LTD.

Edelweiss House Off CST Road Kalina, Mumbai, 400 098, Maharashtra, India
Tel.: (91) 224079519
Web Site:
https://www.edelweissfin.com
EDELWEISS—(NSE)
Rev.: $997,076,672
Assets: $5,895,131,970
Liabilities: $4,858,780,290
Net Worth: $1,036,351,680
Earnings: $28,948,101
Emp.: 69
Fiscal Year-end: 03/31/22
Financial Services
N.A.I.C.S.: 523940
Venkatchalam Ramaswamy (Vice Chm)

Subsidiaries:

ECL Finance Limited (1)
Edelweiss House Off CST Road, Kalina, Mumbai, 400 098, India
Tel.: (91) 2222864400
Web Site: http://www.edelweissfin.com
Sales Range: $50-74.9 Million
Emp.: 45
Financial Services
N.A.I.C.S.: 525990

Edelweiss Broking Limited (1)
Edelweiss House off CST Road, Kalina, Mumbai, 400 098, India
Tel.: (91) 2240094279
Web Site: http://www.edelweissfin.com
Sales Range: $50-74.9 Million
Emp.: 6
Securities Broking Services
N.A.I.C.S.: 523150
Jinesh Shah (Compliance Officer)

Edelweiss Capital (Singapore) Pte. Limited (1)
1 Raffles Place 28-03 One Raffles Place Tower 1, Singapore, 048616, Singapore
Tel.: (65) 66926123
Financial Services
N.A.I.C.S.: 523999

Edelweiss Financial Products and Solutions Limited (1)
New India Ctr Ground Fl 17 A Cooperage Rd Colaba, Mumbai, 400 039, Maharashtra, India
Tel.: (91) 2240885757
Web Site: http://www.edelweiss.in
Sales Range: $700-749.9 Million
Emp.: 3,000
Investment Management Service
N.A.I.C.S.: 541618

Edelweiss General Insurance Company Limited (1)
Edelweiss House Off C S T Road, Kalina, Mumbai, 400098, India
Tel.: (91) 2242312000
Web Site:
http://www.edelweissinsurance.com
General Insurance Services
N.A.I.C.S.: 524210
Rujan Panjwani (Chm)

Edelweiss Insurance Brokers Limited (1)
Unit No 1201 & 1202 12th Floor C-Wing Godrej Coliseum Everard Nagar, Sion E, Mumbai, 400 022, India
Tel.: (91) 2267133737
Web Site: http://www.eibl.co.in
Sales Range: $50-74.9 Million
Emp.: 20
Insurance Broking Services
N.A.I.C.S.: 524210

Edelweiss Multi Strategy Fund Advisors LLP (1)
Edelweiss House Off C S T Road, Kalina Santacruz East, Mumbai, 400 098, India
Tel.: (91) 2240094400
Web Site: http://www.edelweissmsf.com
Fund Services
N.A.I.C.S.: 523940
Nalin Moniz (Co-Founder)

Edelweiss Securities Limited (1)
Nariman Point 14th Fl Express Towers, Mumbai, 400021, Maharastra, India
Tel.: (91) 2222864400
Web Site: http://www.edelcap.com
Sales Range: $50-74.9 Million
Emp.: 80
Stock Brokerage Services
N.A.I.C.S.: 523150

Subsidiary (Domestic):

Edelweiss Custodial Services Limited (2)
Edelweiss House Off C S T Road, Kalina, Mumbai, 400098, India
Tel.: (91) 2222864400
Web Site:
http://www.edelweissassetservices.com
Asset Finance Services
N.A.I.C.S.: 921130

Subsidiary (US):

Edelweiss Financial Services Inc. (2)
205 E 42nd St 20th Fl, New York, NY 10017
Tel.: (646) 201-9320
Financial Services
N.A.I.C.S.: 523999

Edelweiss Tokio Life Insurance Company Limited (1)
4nd Floor Tower 3 Wing B Kohinoor City Mall Kirol Road, Kurla W, Mumbai, 400070, India
Tel.: (91) 18002121212
Web Site: http://www.edelweisstokio.in
General Insurance Services
N.A.I.C.S.: 524210
Sumit Rai (CEO & Mng Dir)

L&T Infrastructure Development Projects Limited (1)
L & T House Ballard Estate, PO Box 278, Mumbai, 400001, India
Tel.: (91) 2266965328
Sales Range: $50-74.9 Million
Emp.: 150
Infrastructure Projects & Development Services
N.A.I.C.S.: 237990

Sekura India Management Limited (1)
Plot 294/3 Edelweiss House Off CST Road, Kolivery Village MMRDA Area Kalina Santacruz - East, Mumbai, 400 098, Maharashtra, India
Tel.: (91) 2240094400
Web Site: https://sekura.in
Asset Management Services
N.A.I.C.S.: 523940

EDEN AUTOMOTIVE INVESTMENTS LIMITED

38-40 Portman Road, Reading, RG30 1JG, United Kingdom
Tel.: (44) 1256354290
Web Site:
http://www.edenmotorgroup.com
Car Dealership Operator
N.A.I.C.S.: 441110
Graeme J. Potts (CEO)

Subsidiaries:

Eden Bracknell (1)
Bilton Industrial Estate, Bracknell, RG12 8YT, Berkshire, United Kingdom
Tel.: (44) 8451254574
Web Site: http://www.edenvauxhall.co.uk
Sales Range: $50-74.9 Million
Emp.: 150
Car Dealership
N.A.I.C.S.: 441110
Graeme J. Potts (Mng Dir)

EDEN EMPIRE INC.

310 36 Water Street, Vancouver, V6B 0B7, BC, Canada
Tel.: (778) 898-5045
Web Site: http://rosehearty.ca
Year Founded: 2000
EDEN—(CNSX)
Rev.: $170,485
Assets: $3,456,107
Liabilities: $3,213,140
Net Worth: $242,967
Earnings: ($3,110,520)
Fiscal Year-end: 07/31/21
Investment Services
N.A.I.C.S.: 523999
Kolten Taekema (Pres)

EDEN INC. BERHAD

15th Floor Amcorp Tower Amcorp Trade Centre, No 18 Jalan Persiaran Barat, 46050, Petaling Jaya, Malaysia
Tel.: (60) 379577781
Web Site: https://www.edenzil.com
EDEN—(KLS)
Rev.: $14,742,585
Assets: $92,211,570
Liabilities: $35,138,813
Net Worth: $57,072,758
Earnings: $231,165
Emp.: 86
Fiscal Year-end: 06/30/22
Holding Company
N.A.I.C.S.: 551112
Abd Rahim Mohamad (Chm)

Subsidiaries:

Eden Catering Sdn. Bhd. (1)
No 45 - 47 Jalan SS26/15 Taman Mayang Jaya, 47301, Petaling Jaya, Selangor, Malaysia
Tel.: (60) 378038204
Web Site: https://www.edenfood.com.my
Food Catering Services
N.A.I.C.S.: 722320

Musteq Hydro Sdn. Bhd. (1)
Sg Kenerong Hydro Power Station 2 6 km off Jalan Meranto Kampung Stong, Kelantan, Malaysia
Tel.: (60) 97471000
Web Site: https://www.edenzil.com
Electric power distribution services
N.A.I.C.S.: 221122

Stratavest Sdn. Bhd. (1)
Libran Power Station Sungai Jipon Jalan Datuk Tay Off Jalan Fook Kim, Bt 8 Jalan Labuk, 90737, Sandakan, Sabah, Malaysia
Tel.: (60) 89631326
Electric power distribution services
N.A.I.C.S.: 221122

Time Era Sdn. Bhd. (1)
25 Jalan P4/6 Bandar Teknologi Kajang, 43500, Semenyih, Selangor, Malaysia
Tel.: (60) 387235329
Low-Voltage Switchgear & Electrical Component Mfr
N.A.I.C.S.: 335999

Underwater World Langkawi Sdn. Bhd. (1)
Pantai Cenang Mukim Kedawang Langkawi, 07000, Kedah, Malaysia
Tel.: (60) 49556100
Web Site:
https://www.underwaterworldlangkawi.com
Aquarium Services
N.A.I.C.S.: 712130

EDEN INNOVATIONS LTD.

Level 15 197 St Georges Terrace, Perth, 6000, WA, Australia
Tel.: (61) 892825889 **AU**
Web Site:
https://www.edeninnovations.com
Year Founded: 2004
EDE—(ASX)
Rev.: $1,346,581
Assets: $12,736,590
Liabilities: $10,080,388
Net Worth: $2,656,203

Earnings: ($5,040,786)
Fiscal Year-end: 06/30/24
Clean Technology Solutions
N.A.I.C.S.: 213112
Roger W. Marmaro (Pres-Sls-US)

Subsidiaries:

Hythane Company LLC (1)
12420 N Dumont Way, Littleton, CO 80125-9755
Tel.: (303) 468-1705
Web Site: http://www.hythane.com
Emp.: 20
Hythane Fuels Mfr
N.A.I.C.S.: 324110

EDEN INTERNATIONAL SA

Chemin du Tresi 9A, 1028, Preverenges, Switzerland
Tel.: (41) 58 404 20 00
Web Site:
http://www.edensprings.com
Sales Range: $350-399.9 Million
Emp.: 2,200
Office Water & Coffee Machine Services
N.A.I.C.S.: 561210
Raanan Zilberman (CEO)

Subsidiaries:

Chateaud'eau SA (1)
139 rue Rateau Parc des Damiers Bat C, 93120, La Courneuve, France
Tel.: (33) 811247893
Web Site: http://www.chateaudeau.com
Office Coffee & Water Services
N.A.I.C.S.: 561210

Eden Springs (Denmark) A/S (1)
Stanholmen 165, 2650, Hvidovre, Denmark
Tel.: (45) 80 30 40 40
Web Site: http://www.edensprings.dk
Office Coffee & Water Services
N.A.I.C.S.: 561210
Karsten Hjerl Ehrhardt (Mng Dir)

Eden Springs (Estonia) OU (1)
Vana -Narva mnt 5C, 74114, Maardu, Estonia
Tel.: (372) 800 81 81
Web Site: http://www.edensprings.ee
Office Coffee & Water Services
N.A.I.C.S.: 561210
Ivo Allsaar (Country Mgr)

Eden Springs (Nederland) BV (1)
Vareseweg 140, 3047 AV, Rotterdam, Netherlands
Tel.: (31) 900 9283
Web Site: http://www.edensprings.nl
Office Coffee & Water Services
N.A.I.C.S.: 561210
Rik Feijt (Mgr-Ops)

Eden Springs (Norway) A/S (1)
Professor Birkelands vei 27 B, 1081, Oslo, Norway
Tel.: (47) 800 80 333
Web Site: http://www.edensprings.no
Office Coffee & Water Services
N.A.I.C.S.: 561210
Unni Hagen (Mgr-HR)

Eden Springs (Poland) Sp. z o.o. (1)
Ul Pulaskiego 2, 05-510, Konstancin-Jeziorna, Poland
Tel.: (48) 801 222 444
Web Site: http://www.eden.pl
Office Coffee & Water Services
N.A.I.C.S.: 561210

Eden Springs (Sweden) AB (1)
Fosievagen 15, 21 431, Malmo, Sweden
Tel.: (46) 20 521 521
Web Site: http://www.edensprings.se
Office Coffee & Water Services
N.A.I.C.S.: 561210
Johan Steen (Project Mgr)

Eden Springs (Switzerland) SA (1)
Chemin de Tresi 6A, CH-1028, Preverenges, Switzerland
Tel.: (41) 848 888 897
Web Site: http://www.edensprings.ch
Office Coffee & Water Services
N.A.I.C.S.: 561210

Eden Springs (UK) Limited **(1)**
Unit B 3 Livingstone Blvd, Blantyre, G72
0BP, United Kingdom
Tel.: (44) 8442737443
Web Site: http://www.edensprings.co.uk
Facility Management Services
N.A.I.C.S.: 561210
Damien Higgins Sr. *(Mgr-Mktg)*

Eden Springs Espana S.A. **(1)**
Pol Ind Gran Via Sur C/Motores 344-356
Hospitalet de Llobregat, 098908, Barcelona,
Spain
Tel.: (34) 902 33 36 37
Web Site: http://www.aguaeden.es
Office Water & Coffee Machine Services
N.A.I.C.S.: 561210
Alicia Feoli *(Controller)*

Eden Springs Latvia SIA **(1)**
Rigas gatve 8-2, LV-2164, Adazi, Latvia
Tel.: (371) 8000 81 81
Web Site: http://www.edensprings.lv
Office Coffee & Water Services
N.A.I.C.S.: 561210
Naveen Singh *(Mng Dir)*

Eden Springs Oy Finland **(1)**
Jannekuja 1, 01740, Vantaa, Finland
Tel.: (358) 10 800 700
Web Site: http://www.edensprings.fi
Office Water & Coffee Machine Services
N.A.I.C.S.: 561210
Nelli Huikari *(Coord-Mktg)*

Eden Springs Portugal SA **(1)**
Rua Jose Pereira Lote Ae, 1685-635, Fa-
moes, Portugal
Tel.: (351) 707215215
Web Site: http://www.selda.pt
Facility Management Services
N.A.I.C.S.: 561210

Eden Water & Coffee Deutschland
GmbH **(1)**
Sperberweg 49, 41468, Neuss, Germany
Tel.: (49) 213152590
Web Site: http://www.edensprings.de
Facility Management Services
N.A.I.C.S.: 561210
Timo Bosse *(Mgr-Customer Svc)*

Kafevend Group Limited **(1)**
Unit D The Fleming Centre Fleming Way,
Crawley, RH10 9NN, West Sussex, United
Kingdom
Tel.: (44) 1293523222
Web Site:
    http://www.kafevendingmachines.co.uk
Sales Range: $25-49.9 Million
Emp.: 50
Vending Machines Distribution & Manage-
ment Services
N.A.I.C.S.: 445132

Mey Eden IL **(1)**
19 Lechi St, Bene Beraq, Israel
Tel.: (972) 800 800 400
Web Site: http://www.meyeden.co.il
Office Coffee & Water Services
N.A.I.C.S.: 561210
Ginat Zehavi *(Mgr-Mktg)*

UAB Eden Springs Lietuva **(1)**
Savanoriu pr 174A, Vilnius, Lithuania
Tel.: (370) 5 247 73 77
Web Site: http://www.edensprings.lt
Office Coffee & Water Services
N.A.I.C.S.: 561210

EDEN RESEARCH PLC
67C Innovation Drive, Milton Park,
Abingdon, OX14 4RQ, Oxfordshire,
United Kingdom
Tel.: (44) 1285359555
Web Site:
    https://www.edenresearch.com
EDEN—(LSE)
Rev.: $4,063,688
Assets: $21,126,313
Liabilities: $3,881,505
Net Worth: $17,244,808
Earnings: ($8,264,718)
Emp.: 19
Fiscal Year-end: 12/31/23
Pesticide Mfr
N.A.I.C.S.: 325320

Alexander John Abrey *(CFO & Sec)*

EDENRED S.A.
Communications Department Be Issy
building 14-16, boulevard Garibaldi,
92130, Issy-les-Moulineaux, France
Tel.: (33) 174317500   FR
Web Site: https://www.edenred.com
EDEN—(OTCIQ)
Rev.: $2,775,140,744
Assets: $14,676,012,807
Liabilities: $15,304,117,454
Net Worth: ($628,104,647)
Earnings: $339,993,377
Emp.: 12,000
Fiscal Year-end: 12/31/23
Voucher Management Services
N.A.I.C.S.: 561499
Philippe Dufour *(Exec VP-Regulatory
Affairs)*

Subsidiaries:

AS Chile Energy Group SA **(1)**
Av Tobalaba 4033 OF D Metro Bilbao, San-
tiago, Chile
Tel.: (56) 99 619 1885
Web Site: https://www.aschile.cl
Mineral Products Mfr
N.A.I.C.S.: 327999

Accentiv Bresil Mimetica **(1)**
Sergio Marcondes Cesar Rua Jesuino 49,
Vila Olimpia, 04544 050, Sao Paulo, Brazil
Tel.: (55) 11 30532222
Sales Range: $75-99.9 Million
Emp.: 30
Marketing Consulting Services
N.A.I.C.S.: 541613
Sergio Marcondes *(Gen Mgr)*

Accentiv Shanghai Company **(1)**
6F Cross Tower 318 Fuzhou Road, Shang-
hai, 200001, China
Tel.: (86) 21 2306 6000
Web Site: http://www.accentiv.cn
Marketing Consulting Services
N.A.I.C.S.: 541613

Accentiv' Kadeos S.A.S. **(1)**
166-180 Blvd Gabriel Peri, 92240, Malakoff,
France
Tel.: (33) 174317500
Web Site: http://www.ticket-kadeos.fr
Gift Card Retailer
N.A.I.C.S.: 459420

Accentiv' Servicos Tecnologica Da
informacao S/A **(1)**
Rua Ministro Jesuino Cardoso 49 Vila Olim-
pia, Sao Paulo, 04544-050, SP, Brazil
Tel.: (55) 1130471300
Web Site: http://www.accentiv.com.br
Telecommunication Servicesb
N.A.I.C.S.: 517810

Be FuelCards Ltd. **(1)**
Upper Floor Gibraltar House Bowcliffe
Road, Off Gibraltar Island Road Hunslet,
Leeds, LS10 1HB, United Kingdom
Tel.: (44) 113 272 7400
Web Site: https://www.befuelcards.co.uk
Fuel Card Distr
N.A.I.C.S.: 424720
Amy Bolland *(Head-Customer Svcs)*

Big Pass S.A. **(1)**
Avenida 4 N 6 N - 67 Office 704 Siglo XXI
Building, Cali, Colombia
Tel.: (57) 2 485 0012
Web Site: https://www.edenred.co
Consumer Services
N.A.I.C.S.: 621498

CSI Enterprises, Inc. **(1)**
3301 Bonita Beach Rd 300, Bonita Springs,
FL 34134
Tel.: (866) 998-0437
Web Site:
    http://www.corporatespending.com
Corporate Payment Solutions Provider
N.A.I.C.S.: 522390
David Disque *(Pres)*

Subsidiary (Domestic):

Image Processing Systems, Inc. **(2)**

150 Meadowlands Pkwy, Secaucus, NJ
07094
Tel.: (201) 553-0200
Web Site: http://www.imageserv.com
Sales Range: $1-9.9 Million
Emp.: 70
Internet Service Provider
N.A.I.C.S.: 517810
Gregory Bartels *(Pres & CEO)*

Cardtrend Systems Sdn. Bhd. **(1)**
7 14 Level 7 One Tech Park No 7 Tanjung,
Bandar Utama, 47800, Petaling Jaya, Se-
langor, Malaysia
Tel.: (60) 377288380
Web Site: http://www.cardtrend.com
Information Technology & Services
N.A.I.C.S.: 541511

Csi Entreprises Inc. **(1)**
3301 Bonita Beach Rd Ste 300, Bonita
Springs, FL 34134
Web Site:
    https://www.corporatespending.com
Banking Services
N.A.I.C.S.: 522110

Delicard AB **(1)**
Liljeholmsstranden 3, 105 40, Stockholm,
Sweden
Tel.: (46) 855611616
Web Site: http://www.delicard.se
Emp.: 6
Employee Benefit Services
N.A.I.C.S.: 561499
Tatsuto Soichi *(Gen Mgr)*

Delicard Group AB **(1)**
Augustendalsvagen 19, Nacka Strand,
Stockholm, Sweden
Tel.: (46) 855611600
Employee Benefit Services
N.A.I.C.S.: 561499

Diesel 24 Limited **(1)**
Gibraltar House Bowcliffe Road, Hunslet,
Leeds, LS10 1HB, United Kingdom
Tel.: (44) 113 202 5110
Web Site: https://www.diesel24.co.uk
Fuel Card Distr
N.A.I.C.S.: 424720

E-Lunch srl **(1)**
Via Giovanni Battista Trener 8, Trento,
38121, Italy
Tel.: (39) 0461421418
Web Site: http://www.e-lunch.it
Catering Management Services
N.A.I.C.S.: 722320

E.C.P. Limited **(1)**
Unit 1c The Hertfordshire Business Centre
Alexander Road, London Colney, AL2 1JG,
Herts, United Kingdom
Tel.: (44) 172 780 8340
Web Site: https://www.ecplimited.com
Professional Training & Coaching Services
N.A.I.C.S.: 611430
Nicole Williamson *(Dir-Ops)*

Edenred (India) PVT Ltd **(1)**
Kalpataru Prime Unit 3 and 4 Level 4 Road
No 16, Wagle Industrial Estate, Thane,
400604, India
Tel.: (91) 222 545 5550
Web Site: https://www.edenred.co.in
Sales Range: $75-99.9 Million
Emp.: 50
Employee Benefit Services
N.A.I.C.S.: 813930
Dinesh Hinduja *(Exec Dir)*

Edenred Argentina **(1)**
Alferez Hipolito Bouchard 4169/4191 7th
Floor, C1043AAQ, Munro,
Argentina **(83.99%)**
Tel.: (54) 114 909 1400
Web Site: https://www.edenred.com.ar
Employer Subsidized Voucher Schemes
N.A.I.C.S.: 561499

Edenred Austria GmbH **(1)**
Wagenseilgasse 14, 1120, Vienna, Austria
Tel.: (43) 1 815 0800
Web Site: https://www.edenred.at
Sales Range: $25-49.9 Million
Emp.: 15
Tax Free Consulting Services
N.A.I.C.S.: 541611
Ursula Wurzl *(Gen Mgr)*

Edenred Belgium sa **(1)**
Boulevard du Souverain 165, Boite 9, 1160,
Brussels, Belgium
Tel.: (32) 2 678 2811
Web Site: https://www.edenred.be
Emp.: 20
Employees Meal Voucher Organizing Ser-
vices
N.A.I.C.S.: 561499
Michael Verhulsdonk *(Gen Mgr)*

Edenred Bulgaria ad **(1)**
137 Tsarigradsko shose Blvd, 1784, Sofia,
Bulgaria
Tel.: (359) 2 974 0220
Web Site: https://www.edenred.bg
Emp.: 2
Social Security Services
N.A.I.C.S.: 923130
Herve Combal *(Gen Mgr)*

Edenred CZ s.ro **(1)**
Pernerova 691/42, 186 00, Prague, Czech
Republic
Tel.: (420) 23 466 2340
Web Site: https://www.edenred.cz
Emp.: 14
Social Security Services
N.A.I.C.S.: 923130
Fernando Alvarez *(Gen Mgr)*

Edenred Corporate Payment
SAS **(1)**
Immeuble Be Issy 14-16 boulevard Garib-
aldi, 92130, Issy-les-Moulineaux, France
Tel.: (33) 186672173
Web Site: https://www.edenred.com
Fuel Card Distr
N.A.I.C.S.: 424720

Edenred Deutschland GmbH **(1)**
Claudius-Keller-Strasse 3C, 81669, Munich,
Germany
Tel.: (49) 89 558 9150
Web Site: https://www.edenred.de
Commercial Support Services
N.A.I.C.S.: 561499

Edenred Employee Benefits UK
Ltd **(1)**
Crown House 72 Hammersmith Rd, Lon-
don, W14 8TH, United Kingdom
Tel.: (44) 2073485500
Employee Benefit Plan Services
N.A.I.C.S.: 525120

Edenred Espana S.A. **(1)**
C/ Juan Esplandiu 11-13 portal 13 pl, portal
13, 28007, Madrid, Spain **(100%)**
Tel.: (34) 91 125 4500
Web Site: https://www.edenred.es
Sales Range: $25-49.9 Million
Emp.: 130
Voucher Management Services
N.A.I.C.S.: 561499

Edenred Finland OY **(1)**
Tel.: (358) 97 594 2848
Web Site: https://www.edenred.fi
Financial Services
N.A.I.C.S.: 523999

Edenred Finland Oy **(1)**
Elimaenkatu 15, 510, Helsinki, Finland
Tel.: (358) 975942848
Web Site: https://www.delicard.fi
Sales Range: $25-49.9 Million
Emp.: 16
Gift Store Operating Services
N.A.I.C.S.: 459420

Edenred Hong-Kong Limited **(1)**
Rm 1025 10/F Hitec 1 Trademart Dr, Kow-
loon, China (Hong Kong)
Tel.: (852) 21318998
Restaurant Management Services
N.A.I.C.S.: 722511

Edenred Incentives & Motivation
Ltd **(1)**
Carlton House Sandpiper Way, Chester,
CH4 9QE, United Kingdom
Tel.: (44) 1244625400
Management Consulting Services
N.A.I.C.S.: 541611

Edenred Incentives & Rewards
Deutschland **(1)**
Friedrich-Bergius-Strasse 15-17, 65203,
Wiesbaden, Germany

Edenred S.A.—(Continued)

Tel.: (49) 611188870
Employee Motivation Services
N.A.I.C.S.: 561499

Edenred Italia Fin S.r.l　　　　　(1)
Via GB Pirelli n 18, Milan, Italy
Tel.: (39) 0226 9041
Web Site: https://www.edenreditaliafin.it
Financial Services
N.A.I.C.S.: 523999

Edenred Italia Srl　　　　　　　(1)
Via Giovanni Battista Pirelli 18, Milan,
20124, Italy
Tol.: (30) 02260041
Sales Range: $75-99.9 Million
Emp.: 300
Employee Benefit Services
N.A.I.C.S.: 541612

Edenred Japan Co., Ltd.　　　　(1)
1-21-1 Kanda Nishikicho Hulic Kandabashi
Building 10th floor, Chiyoda-ku, Tokyo, Japan
Tel.: (81) 33 233 8120
Web Site: https://www.edenred.jp
Financial Services
N.A.I.C.S.: 523999

Edenred Liban　　　　　　　　(1)
Electricity St, Bauchrieh Metn, Lebanon
Tel.: (961) 1900333
Web Site: http://www.edenred.com.lb
Emp.: 18
Restaurant Management Services
N.A.I.C.S.: 722511

Edenred MD S.R.L.　　　　　　(1)
Str Vasile Alecsandri 141 B, Chisinau Municipality, Chisinau, Moldova
Tel.: (373) 22858282
Web Site: http://www.edenred.md
Financial Services
N.A.I.C.S.: 523999

Edenred Magyarorszag Kft　　　(1)
Vaci ut 45 Atrium Park G recepcio, 1134,
Budapest, Hungary
Tel.: (36) 1 413 3333
Web Site: https://www.edenred.hu
Tax Preparation Services
N.A.I.C.S.: 485310

Edenred Maroc SAS　　　　　　(1)
Chronopost Maroc building 110 Boulevard
Mohamed Zerktouni, 20000, Casablanca,
Morocco
Tel.: (212) 52 246 6700
Web Site: https://www.edenred.ma
Sales Range: $10-24.9 Million
Emp.: 22
Restaurant Management Services
N.A.I.C.S.: 722511
Badre Ouaicha (Mng Dir)

Edenred Mexico　　　　　　　(49%)
Lago Rodollo 29 Colonia Grana, 11520,
Mexico, DF, Mexico
Tel.: (52) 5552628888
Voucher Management Services
N.A.I.C.S.: 561499

Edenred North America Inc.　　　(1)
320 Nevada St Ste 401, Newton, MA 02460
Web Site: http://www.edenredusa.com
Human Resource Consulting Services
N.A.I.C.S.: 541612

Edenred Peru SA　　　　　　　(1)
777 Antequera St Fl 2, San Isidro, Lima,
Peru
Tel.: (51) 14425555
Employee Benefit Services
N.A.I.C.S.: 561990

Edenred Polska Sp. z o.o　　　　(1)
Ul Inflancka 4b bud C, 00-189, Warsaw,
Poland
Tel.: (48) 22 481 3908
Web Site: https://www.edenred.pl
Restaurant Management Services
N.A.I.C.S.: 722511
Agnieszka Ekielska (Mgr-Customer Care)

Edenred Portugal Lda　　　　　(1)
Edificio Adamastor, Torre B Av D Joao II n
9-I Piso 6, 1990-077, Lisbon, Portugal
Tel.: (351) 21 891 7700

Web Site: https://www.edenred.pt
Employee Benefit Services
N.A.I.C.S.: 813930

Edenred Pte Limited　　　　　(1)
3 Irving Road 11-01 Tai Seng Centre, Singapore, 369522, Singapore
Tel.: (65) 6 939 6184
Web Site: https://www.edenred.com.sg
Marketing & Advertising Services
N.A.I.C.S.: 541890

Edenred Romania srl　　　　　(1)
Calea Serban Voda 133, sector 4, Bucharest, Romania
Tel.: (40) 21 301 3315
Web Site: https://www.edenred.ro
Financial Services
N.A.I.C.S.: 523999

Edenred SAL　　　　　　　　(1)
Hachem Building - Electricity street,
Bauchrieh Metn, Beirut, Lebanon
Tel.: (961) 1900333
Web Site: http://www.edenred.com.lb
Financial Services
N.A.I.C.S.: 523999

Edenred Shanghai (China)　　　(1)
6F Cross Tower 318 Fuzhou Road, Shanghai, 200001, China
Tel.: (86) 2123066000
Restaurant Management Services
N.A.I.C.S.: 722511

Edenred Singapore Pte. Ltd.　　(1)
150 Beach Road No 06-05/07 Gateway
West, Singapore, 189720, Singapore
Tel.: (65) 69396184
Web Site: https://www.edenred.com.sg
Financial Investment Services
N.A.I.C.S.: 523999

Edenred Slovakia, s.r.o　　　　(1)
City Business Center I Karadzicova 8, PO
Box 21, 820 15, Bratislava, Slovakia
Tel.: (421) 25 070 7888
Web Site: https://www.edenred.sk
Restaurant Management Services
N.A.I.C.S.: 722511

Edenred Suisse SA　　　　　　(1)
4 Chemin de l'Esparcette, 1023, Crissier,
Switzerland
Tel.: (41) 219668090
Web Site: http://www.ticket-restaurant.ch
Emp.: 5
Restaurant Operating Services
N.A.I.C.S.: 722511
Anne-Sophie Chapuis (Gen Mgr)

Edenred Sweden AB　　　　　(1)
Liljeholmsstranden 3, 117 43, Stockholm,
Sweden　　　　　　　　　　　(100%)
Tel.: (46) 8 681 8100
Web Site: https://www.edenred.se
Sales Range: $25-49.9 Million
Emp.: 80
Voucher Management Services
N.A.I.C.S.: 561499

Edenred Travel Limited　　　　(1)
No 47 Westminster Road, Hoole, Chester,
CH2 3AX, United Kingdom
Tel.: (44) 1244353541
Web Site: http://www.edenredtravel.co.uk
Travel Agency Services
N.A.I.C.S.: 561510

Edenred UK　　　　　　　　(1)
50 Vauxhall Bridge Road, London, SW1V
2RS, United Kingdom　　　　　(100%)
Tel.: (44) 303 123 1113
Web Site: https://www.edenred.co.uk
Sales Range: $10-24.9 Million
Emp.: 140
Voucher Management Services
N.A.I.C.S.: 561499

Edenred Vouchers Deutschland　(1)
Claudius-Keller-Strasse 3C, 81669, Munich,
Germany
Tel.: (49) 895589150
Employee Motivation Services
N.A.I.C.S.: 561499

Itemion GmbH & Co. KG　　　(1)
Mainparkstrasse 2, 63801, Kleinostheim,
Germany
Tel.: (49) 6027 509 4000
Web Site: https://www.itemion.com

Commercial Support Services
N.A.I.C.S.: 561499

Merits & Benefits NV　　　　　(1)
Welvaartstraat 22 bus 3, 2200, Herentals,
Belgium
Tel.: (32) 14254020
Web Site: http://www.meritsandbenefits.be
Commercial Support Services
N.A.I.C.S.: 561499

Nikosax A/S　　　　　　　　(1)
Lejrvejen 8, 6330, Padborg, Denmark
Tel.: (45) 7 467 3690
Web Site: https://www.nikosax.com
Emp.: 60
Tax Preparation Services
N.A.I.C.S.: 485310

ProwebCE SA　　　　　　　(1)
14 rue Chaptal, 92352, Levallois-Perret,
Cedex, France　　　　　　　　(98.5%)
Tel.: (33) 825 808 000
Web Site: http://www.prowebce.com
Employee Benefits Services
N.A.I.C.S.: 561499
Patrice Thiry (Chm & CEO)

RWA Consulting S.R.L.　　　　(1)
Via Copernico 38, 20125, Milan, MI, Italy
Tel.: (39) 0292850601
Web Site: http://www.rwaconsulting.net
Management Consulting Services
N.A.I.C.S.: 541618

Reward Gateway (UK) Ltd　　　(1)
265 Tottenham Court Road, London, W1T
7RQ, United Kingdom
Tel.: (44) 2072290349
Web Site: http://www.rewardgateway.com
Human Resource Technology Firm; Employee Engagement Solutions Services
N.A.I.C.S.: 513210
Doug Butler (CEO)

Subsidiary (US):

Brand Integrity, Inc.　　　　　(2)
126 E Ave, Rochester, NY, 14604
Tel.: (585) 442-5404
Administrative Management & General
Management Consulting Services
N.A.I.C.S.: 541611
Gregg Lederman (CEO)

**The Right Fuelcard Company
Limited**　　　　　　　　　　(1)
One The Embankment Neville Street,
Leeds, LS1 4DW, United Kingdom
Tel.: (44) 113 202 5110
Web Site: https://www.rightfuelcard.co.uk
Fuel Card Distr
N.A.I.C.S.: 424720

Ticket Service, s.r.o.　　　　　(1)
City Business Center I Karadzicova 8, PO
Box 21, 820 15, Bratislava, Slovakia
Tel.: (421) 25 070 7888
Web Site: https://www.edenred.sk
Commercial Support Services
N.A.I.C.S.: 561499

Ticket Servicos S.A.　　　　　(1)
Av. Paulista 2313, 2 3 Andares, Sao Paulo,
01311-934, Brazil
Tel.: (55) 1138898754
Web Site: http://www.ticket.com.br
Sales Range: $300-349.9 Million
Emp.: 1,200
Voucher Services
N.A.I.C.S.: 561499

UTA Bulgaria OOD　　　　　(1)
3 Prof Yakim Yakimov Blvd, 8010, Burgas,
Bulgaria
Tel.: (359) 5 659 8445
Web Site: https://web.uta.com
Logistic Services
N.A.I.C.S.: 541614

UTA Czech s.r.o.　　　　　　(1)
Pernerova 691/42, 186 00, Prague, Czech
Republic
Tel.: (420) 27 000 6300
Web Site: https://www.palivovakartauta.cz
Logistic Services
N.A.I.C.S.: 541614

UTA France S.A.R.L.　　　　　(1)
3 rue du Verdon, 67100, Strasbourg,
France

Tel.: (33) 39 040.2590
Web Site: https://web.uta.com
Logistic Services
N.A.I.C.S.: 541614

UTA Romania Services srl　　　(1)
Calea Serban Voda 133, Sector 4, 040205,
Bucharest, Romania
Tel.: (40) 21 306 5900
Web Site: https://web.uta.com
Logistic Services
N.A.I.C.S.: 541614

Wiredcommute, LLC.　　　　　(1)
320 Nevada St Ste 401 4th Fl, Newton, MA
02460
Tel.: (800) 531-2828
Web Site: http://www.wiredcommute.com
Sales Range: $25-49.9 Million
Emp.: 50
Software Consulting Services
N.A.I.C.S.: 541512
Dharmesh Parikh (CFO)

EDENSOFT HOLDINGS LIMITED

West 2nd Floor Block A Shenzhen
International Innovation Center, Shennan Road Futian, Shenzhen, China
Tel.: (86) 75588262588　　　　　Ky
Web Site:
　http://www.edensoft.com.cn
Year Founded: 2002
1147—(HKG)
Holding Company
N.A.I.C.S.: 551112
Xinyun Ding (Chm & CEO)

Subsidiaries:

Dongguan Edensoft Limited　　(1)
Room 1206 North Funming Building Jianshe Road, Nancheng District, Dongguan,
China
Tel.: (86) 76989938410
Software Development Services
N.A.I.C.S.: 541511

EDENVILLE ENERGY PLC

Aston House Cornwall Avenue, London, N3 1LF, United Kingdom
Tel.: (44) 20 8371 3000　　　　　UK
Web Site: http://www.edenville-energy.com
EDL—(LSE)
Sales Range: Less than $1 Million
Coal & Uranium Mining
N.A.I.C.S.: 213113
Alistair Muir (CEO)

EDESA BIOTECH, INC.

100 Spy Ct, Markham, L3R 5H6, ON,
Canada
Tel.: (289) 800-9600
Web Site:
　https://www.edesabiotech.com
Year Founded: 1999
EDSA—(NASDAQ)
Rev.: $153,498
Assets: $3,813,982
Liabilities: $1,832,827
Net Worth: $1,981,155
Earnings: ($6,170,045)
Emp.: 16
Fiscal Year-end: 09/30/24
Pharmaceuticals Product Mfr
N.A.I.C.S.: 325412
Stephen L. Lemieux (CFO)

EDF INVEST

22-30, avenue de Wagram, 75008,
Paris, France
Web Site: https://www.edfinvest.com
Year Founded: 2013
Financial Services
N.A.I.C.S.: 523999

EDGARS STORES LIMITED

Edgars Head Office Cnr Ninth Avenue, PO Box 894, Herbert Chitepo
Street, Bulawayo, Zimbabwe

Tel.: (263) 988162635　　ZW
Web Site: http://www.edgars.co.zw
Year Founded: 1946
EDGR—(ZIM)
Rev.: $99,150,419
Assets: $57,723,778
Liabilities: $34,037,142
Net Worth: $23,686,636
Earnings: $536,677
Emp.: 1,247
Fiscal Year-end: 01/08/23
Apparel Store Operator
N.A.I.C.S.: 458110
Vusumuzi Mpofu *(Dir-Chain)*

EDGE CENTRES PTY LTD
107 Bacon St, Grafton, 2460, NSW,
Australia
Tel.: (61) 1300334332
Web Site: https://edgecentres.com
It Consulting
N.A.I.C.S.: 513210
Jonath Eaves *(Founder & CEO)*

Subsidiaries:

Hyson International Corp.　　(1)
210 N Tucker Blvd Ste 700, Saint Louis,
MO 63101
Tel.: (314) 621-9991
Web Site: http://www.hyson.com
Sales Range: $1-9.9 Million
Emp.: 17
Custom Computer Programming Services
N.A.I.C.S.: 541511
Joshua Chen *(Pres)*

EDGE GLOBAL LIMITED
71-75 Shelton Street, Covent Garden,
London, WC2H 9JQ, United Kingdom
Tel.: (44) 2071071640　　UK
Web Site:
　https://edgeglobalevents.com
Year Founded: 2008
Sporting Events Hospitality Services
N.A.I.C.S.: 561499
Andrew David Christy *(Owner)*

EDGE GROUP LIMITED
1 Marylebone High Street, London,
W1U 4LZ, United Kingdom
Tel.: (44) 2073171300　　UK
Web Site: http://www.edge.uk.com
Sales Range: $50-74.9 Million
Emp.: 10
Holding Company; Asset Manage-
ment, Corporate Finance, Investment
Advisory & Consulting Services
N.A.I.C.S.: 551112
David Glick *(Founder & CEO)*

Subsidiaries:

Edge Investment Management
Limited　　(1)
1 Marylebone High Street, London, W1U
4LZ, United Kingdom
Tel.: (44) 20 7317 1300
Web Site: http://www.edge.uk.com
Investment Management Service
N.A.I.C.S.: 523940
David Fisher *(Mgr-Investment)*

Edge Performance VCT plc　　(1)
1 Marylebone High Street, London, W1U
4LZ, United Kingdom
Tel.: (44) 2073171300
Web Site: http://www.edge.co.uk
Emp.: 8
Equity Investment Firm
N.A.I.C.S.: 523999
Robin Miller *(Chm)*

Holding (Domestic):

Coolabi Limited　　(2)
9 Kingsway, London, WC2B 6XF, United
Kingdom
Tel.: (44) 2070040980
Web Site: http://www.coolabi.com
Sales Range: $1-9.9 Million
Emp.: 12

Family Entertainment Production & Rights
Management Services
N.A.I.C.S.: 512110
Tim Ricketts *(Dir-Fin)*

**EDGE TOTAL INTELLIGENCE
INC.**
2600-1066 West Hastings Street,
North Vancouver, V6E 3X1, BC,
Canada
Tel.: (778) 855-7384
UNFYF—(OTCQB)
Rev.: $3,815,552
Assets: $2,744,005
Liabilities: $6,186,658
Net Worth: ($3,442,353)
Earnings: ($1,207,887)
Fiscal Year-end: 12/31/23
Business Consulting Services
N.A.I.C.S.: 522299
Geremy Connor *(CFO)*

EDGEMONT GOLD CORP.
9th Floor-1021 West Hastings Street,
Vancouver, V6E 0C3, BC, Canada
Tel.: (778) 773-4786
Web Site:
　https://www.edgemontgold.com
EG80—(DEU)
Rev.: $7,037
Assets: $1,816,681
Liabilities: $16,494
Net Worth: $1,800,187
Earnings: ($395,872)
Fiscal Year-end: 10/31/22
Gold Exploration Services
N.A.I.C.S.: 212220
Stuart Rogers *(Pres & CEO)*

**EDGESTONE CAPITAL PART-
NERS INC.**
175 Bloor Street East Suite 801, To-
ronto, M4W 3R8, ON, Canada
Tel.: (416) 860-3740
Web Site: http://www.edgestone.com
Investment Management Service
N.A.I.C.S.: 523940
Samuel L. DuBoc *(Partner)*

Subsidiaries:

Specialty Commerce Corp.　　(1)
400 Manley St, West Bridgewater, MA
02379
Tel.: (508) 638-7000
Web Site: http://www.scdirect.com
Sales Range: $10-24.9 Million
Emp.: 300
Wigs, Hairpieces, Extensions & Specialty
Apparel Direct Marketer
N.A.I.C.S.: 456120
Peter Tulp *(CFO & COO)*

Subsidiary (Domestic):

Paula Young Catalog　　(2)
400 Manley St W, West Bridgewater, MA
02379-1100
Tel.: (508) 238-0199
Web Site: http://www.paulayoung.com
Hair & Wig Catalog & Mail Order
N.A.I.C.S.: 458110
Peter Tulp *(CFO)*

EDGEWARE AB
Master Samuelsgatan 42 12th Floor,
111 57, Stockholm, Sweden
Tel.: (46) 736126840
Web Site: http://www.edgeware.tv
Year Founded: 2004
Rev.: $25,803,513
Assets: $35,595,273
Liabilities: $9,101,886
Net Worth: $26,493,387
Earnings: ($734,382)
Emp.: 99
Fiscal Year-end: 12/31/18
Video Advertising Services
N.A.I.C.S.: 541840

Johan Bolin *(Chief Product & Tech
Officer)*
Subsidiaries:

Cavena Image Products AB　　(1)
Master Samuelsgatan 42 12th Floor, 111
57, Stockholm, Sweden
Tel.: (46) 736126840
Web Site: http://www.cavena.com
Post Production Services
N.A.I.C.S.: 512191

Edgeware Inc.　　(1)
263 Shuman Blvd Ste 145, Naperville, IL
60563
Television Broadcasting Services
N.A.I.C.S.: 516120

**EDGEWATER EXPLORATION
LTD.**
1560 200 Burrard Street, PO Box
49167, Vancouver, V6C 3L6, BC,
Canada
Tel.: (604) 628-1010　　BC
Web Site:
　https://www.edgewaterx.com
Year Founded: 2007
EDW.H—(OTCIQ)
Rev.: $5,427
Assets: $648,613
Liabilities: $1,624,324
Net Worth: ($975,711)
Earnings: ($155,470)
Fiscal Year-end: 12/31/21
Gold Mining Services
N.A.I.C.S.: 212220
Edward Charles Farrauto *(CFO)*

Subsidiaries:

Rio Narcea Gold Mines S.L　　(1)
Calle Serrano 85 Piso 6 Iz, Madrid, 28006,
Spain
Tel.: (34) 924518173
Precious Metal Mining Services
N.A.I.C.S.: 212220

**EDGEWATER WIRELESS SYS-
TEMS INC.**
11 Hines Road Suite 202, Ottawa,
K2K 2X1, ON, Canada
Tel.: (613) 271-3710　　BC
Web Site:
　https://www.edgewaterwireless.com
Year Founded: 1980
KPIFF—(OTCIQ)
Assets: $1,224,650
Liabilities: $1,830,491
Net Worth: ($605,841)
Earnings: ($605,052)
Fiscal Year-end: 04/30/21
Communication Equipment Mfr; WiFi
Mfr
N.A.I.C.S.: 334290
Duane Anderson *(Founder)*

EDIA CO., LTD.
7F Kobun Kosan Building 2-4-3 Hitot-
subashi, Chiyoda-ku, Tokyo, 101-
0003, Japan
Tel.: (81) 352105801
Web Site: https://www.edia.co.jp
Year Founded: 1999
3935—(TKS)
Rev.: $23,233,930
Assets: $17,023,090
Liabilities: $8,926,310
Net Worth: $8,096,780
Earnings: $1,063,500
Fiscal Year-end: 02/29/24
Mobile Application Development Ser-
vices
N.A.I.C.S.: 513210
Yoshinari Kashima *(Pres & CEO)*

EDICO HOLDINGS LIMITED
8/F Wheelock House 20 Pedder
Street, Central, China (Hong Kong)
Tel.: (852) 37556911　　Ky

Web Site:
　https://www.edicoholdings.com.hk
8450—(HKG)
Rev.: $7,420,477
Assets: $11,790,191
Liabilities: $3,030,127
Net Worth: $8,760,064
Earnings: ($223,006)
Emp.: 66
Fiscal Year-end: 09/30/21
Financial Printing Services
N.A.I.C.S.: 513199
Izabel Yuen Yu Lok *(COO)*

Subsidiaries:

EDICO Financial Press Services
Limited　　(1)
8/F Wheelock House 20 Pedder Street,
Central, China (Hong Kong)
Tel.: (852) 21102233
Financial Document Services
N.A.I.C.S.: 561410
Amy Donati *(CEO)*

**EDIFIER TECHNOLOGY CO.,
LTD.**
Room 2101 21st Floor The L Plaza,
367-375 Queens Road, Central,
China (Hong Kong)
Tel.: (852) 25226989
Web Site: http://www.edifier.com
002351—(SSE)
Rev.: $310,901,760
Assets: $401,032,944
Liabilities: $68,720,184
Net Worth: $332,312,760
Earnings: $34,615,620
Emp.: 2,780
Fiscal Year-end: 12/31/22
Multimedia Sound Boxes, Head-
phones & Automobile Audio Products
Mfr
N.A.I.C.S.: 334310

EDIL.GI SRL
Via Di Acqua Acetosa Anagnina 10,
Rome, Italy
Tel.: (39) 011 99 21 82
Web Site: http://www.edil-gi.com
New Single-Family Housing Con-
struction
N.A.I.C.S.: 236115

EDILE SAN FELICE S.P.A.
Via On le Davide Barba SC Nola,
Nola, 80035, Naples, Italy
Tel.: (39) 081213869
Web Site: https://www.edilsanfelice.it
Year Founded: 1979
ESF—(EUR)
Emp.: 230
Construction Engineering Services
N.A.I.C.S.: 237310
Carmelo Intrisano *(Pres)*

EDILIZIACROBATICA S.P.A.
Via Turati 29, 20121, Milan, Italy
Tel.: (39) 0103106912
Web Site:
　https://www.ediliziacrobatica.com
Year Founded: 1994
EDAC—(ITA)
Rev.: $145,113,583
Assets: $134,432,533
Liabilities: $96,527,466
Net Worth: $37,905,067
Earnings: $16,444,926
Emp.: 1,055
Fiscal Year-end: 12/31/22
Building Construction Services
N.A.I.C.S.: 236115

Subsidiaries:

EdiliziAcrobatica France SAS　　(1)
17 place Jean Payra, Rivesaltes, 66000,
Perpignan, France
Tel.: (33) 805692222

EdiliziAcrobatica S.p.A.—(Continued)

Web Site: http://www.ediliziacrobatica.fr
Building Construction Services
N.A.I.C.S.: 236220

EdiliziAcrobatica Iberica S.L. (1)
Girona 134, 08037, Barcelona, Spain
Tel.: (34) 900800963
Web Site: https://acrobatica.es
Construction Services
N.A.I.C.S.: 236220

**Spider Access Cladding Works &
Building Cleaning LLC** (1)
Street 55 Dubai Investment Park 1, Dubai,
United Arab Emirates
Tel.: (971) 42360356
Web Site: https://spider-access.com
Construction Services
N.A.I.C.S.: 237990

Vertico Xtreme LLC (1)
Office 8-13 Abdella Qasim Building Dubai
Investment Park 1, Dubai, United Arab
Emirates
Tel.: (971) 44256060
Web Site: https://www.vertico-x.com
Safety Equipment Provider
N.A.I.C.S.: 423490

EDIMAX TECHNOLOGY CO., LTD.
No 278 Xinhu 1st Rd, Neihu Dist, Taipei, Taiwan
Tel.: (886) 277396888
Web Site: https://www.edimax.com
3047—(TAI)
Rev.: $139,324,760
Assets: $210,252,257
Liabilities: $112,226,753
Net Worth: $98,025,504
Earnings: ($8,534,092)
Emp.: 100
Fiscal Year-end: 12/31/23
Routers & Switches Mfr
N.A.I.C.S.: 334210

Subsidiaries:

**Beijing Edimax Science & Technology
Co., Ltd.** (1)
17 1708 Ideal Plaza No 111 ZhiChun Road,
HaiDian District, Beijing, 100085, China
Tel.: (86) 1082665815
Networking Components Mfr
N.A.I.C.S.: 334210

Edimax Computer Company (1)
3444 De La Cruz Blvd, Santa Clara, CA
95054
Tel.: (408) 496-1105
Web Site: http://www.edimax.com
Networking Components Distr
N.A.I.C.S.: 423690

**Edimax Technology (SE Asia) Pte.
Ltd.** (1)
B1K 1003 Bukit Merah Central 07-53, Singapore, 159836, Singapore
Tel.: (65) 31062273
Web Site: http://www.edimax.com
Sales Range: $50-74.9 Million
Emp.: 8
Networking Components Distr
N.A.I.C.S.: 423690

Edimax Technology (UK) Ltd. (1)
Suite 358 Silbury Court Silbury Boulevard,
Milton Keynes, MK9 2AF, Bucks, United
Kingdom
Tel.: (44) 8451238307
Web Site: http://www.edimax.co.uk
Sales Range: $50-74.9 Million
Emp.: 10
Networking Components Distr
N.A.I.C.S.: 423430

**Edimax Technology Australia Pty.
Ltd.** (1)
Level 1 203 Blackburn Road, Oakleigh
South, Mount Waverley, 3149, VIC, Australia
Tel.: (61) 3 9543 1888
Web Site: http://www.edimax.com
Networking Components Distr
N.A.I.C.S.: 423690

Edimax Technology Europe B.V. (1)
Fijenhof 2, 5652 AE, Eindhoven, Netherlands
Tel.: (31) 402501200
Web Site: http://www.edimax.com
Sales Range: $25-49.9 Million
Emp.: 13
Networking Components Distr
N.A.I.C.S.: 423430

Edimax Technology MEA FZE (1)
Plot MO 0646 Jebel Ali Free Zone, PO Box
18372, Dubai, United Arab Emirates
Tel.: (971) 48041888
Web Site: http://www.edimax-de.eu
Sales Range: $50-74.9 Million
Emp.: 70
Networking Components Distr
N.A.I.C.S.: 423430

**Edimax Technology Poland Sp. Z
o.o.** (1)
Ul Woloska 7, 02-675, Warsaw, Poland
Tel.: (48) 226079480
Web Site: http://www.edimax.pl
Sales Range: $50-74.9 Million
Emp.: 10
Networking Components Distr
N.A.I.C.S.: 423430

EDINBURGH WORLDWIDE INVESTMENT TRUST PLC
Baillie Gifford Calton Square 1
Greenside Row, Edinburgh, EH1
3AN, United Kingdom
Tel.: (44) 1312752000
Web Site:
   http://www.bailliegifford.com
EWI—(LSE)
Rev.: $425,349,889
Assets: $1,344,644,925
Liabilities: $66,404,128
Net Worth: $1,278,240,797
Earnings: $414,987,133
Fiscal Year-end: 10/31/20
Investment Management Service
N.A.I.C.S.: 525990

EDINTSVO AD
Gotse Delchev no 62, Strumica,
North Macedonia
Tel.: (389) 34321402
Web Site: https://www.edinstvosr.com
Year Founded: 1966
EDIN—(MAC)
Rev.: $904,246
Assets: $3,587,583
Liabilities: $1,368,189
Net Worth: $2,219,393
Earnings: ($194,723)
Emp.: 270
Fiscal Year-end: 12/31/19
Apparel Product Mfr
N.A.I.C.S.: 315250
Popovski Dimitar *(Deputy Dir)*

EDION CORPORATION
2-333 Nakanoshima Mitsui Bussan
Building, Kita-ku, Osaka, Japan
Tel.: (81) 666408711
Web Site: https://www.edion.co.jp
Year Founded: 2002
2730—(TKS)
Rev.: $4,766,371,850
Assets: $2,853,497,340
Liabilities: $1,432,869,530
Net Worth: $1,420,627,810
Earnings: $59,628,810
Emp.: 15,947
Fiscal Year-end: 03/31/24
Electronics Retailer
N.A.I.C.S.: 449210
Masataka Kubo *(Chm & CEO)*

Subsidiaries:

3Q Co., Ltd. (1)
1-601 Shinbokita, Fukui, 910-0838, Japan
Tel.: (81) 776571800
Web Site: https://www.100mv.com
Emp.: 1,220

Consumer Electric Home Appliances Retailer
N.A.I.C.S.: 423620
Yoshinori Kobayashi *(Pres)*

E.R. JAPAN Corporation (1)
106-5 Minooki-cho, Fukuyama, Hiroshima,
Japan
Tel.: (81) 849578530
Web Site: https://www.erjp.co.jp
Electronic Product Recycling Services
N.A.I.C.S.: 562920

EDION EAST Corporation (1)
2-80-1 Enjaku-cho, Minato-ku, Nagoya,
455-0054, Aichi, Japan
Tel.: (81) 526596611
Consumer Electronics Retailer
N.A.I.C.S.: 423620

EDION X Ventures Corporation (1)
8-70-1 Kakuozan-dori Ikeshita ES Building
5F, Chikusa Ward, Nagoya, 464-0841,
Aichi, Japan
Tel.: (81) 527592611
Web Site: https://exv.co.jp
Software Development Services
N.A.I.C.S.: 541511

**EIDEN COMMUNICATIONS Co.,
Ltd.** (1)
4-22-25 Meieki, Nakamura-ku, Nagoya,
450-0002, Aichi, Japan
Tel.: (81) 524860840
Web Site: http://www.e-coms.ne.jp
Mobile Communication Carriers
N.A.I.C.S.: 517112

**Edion House System
Corporation** (1)
1-1-50 Shioe Edion JR Amagasaki Station
Store 5F, Amagasaki, 661-0976, Hyogo,
Japan
Tel.: (81) 120821045
Web Site: https://hs.edion.co.jp
Remodeling Services
N.A.I.C.S.: 236118

Forest Co., Ltd. (1)
2-1-1 Shimocho Omiya Prime East 3F,
Omiya-ku, Saitama, 330-0844, Japan
Tel.: (81) 486100100
Web Site: http://www.forest.co.jp
Merchandising Services
N.A.I.C.S.: 459410

Jtop Co., Ltd. (1)
4-5-44 Migata, Izumi, 594-0042, Osaka,
Japan
Tel.: (81) 725513860
Emp.: 20
Environmental Protection Equipment Mfr &
Distr
N.A.I.C.S.: 334512
Jiichi Nakaki *(Pres)*

NWORK Co., Ltd. (1)
8-70-1 Ikeshita ES building the fifth floor,
Chikusa-ku, Nagoya, 464-0841, Kakuozan-tori, Japan
Tel.: (81) 527592611
Web Site: http://www.nwork.co.jp
Emp.: 171
Enterprise Resource Planning Software Development Services
N.A.I.C.S.: 541511
Hideo Shimizu *(Pres)*

Youemiru Inc. (1)
5th floor Nakamozu Ekimae Building 5-6
Nakamozu-cho, Kita-ku, Sakai, 591-8023,
Osaka, Japan
Tel.: (81) 668296783
Web Site: https://done-school.com
Emp.: 51
Programming Development Services
N.A.I.C.S.: 541511

e-Logi Corporation (1)
1-5-17 Dojima Grand Building 4th Floor,
Kita-ku, Osaka, 530-0003, Japan
Tel.: (81) 664504564
Web Site: http://www.e-logi.co.jp
Logistic Services
N.A.I.C.S.: 541614

EDIP (EDITION-DIFFUSION-IMPRESSION-PUBLICITE)
11-13 Avenue de la Republique,

69200, Venissieux, France
Tel.: (33) 4 7209 2882   FR
Year Founded: 1949
EDGR—(PJT)
Rev.: $10,500,000
Emp.: 25
Fashion/Apparel, Full Service, Planning & Consultation, Retail
N.A.I.C.S.: 541810
Philippe Rivain *(Pres & Mng Dir)*

EDIP GAYRIMENKUL YATIRIM SANAYI VE TICARET A.S.
Mahmutbey Merkez Mah Tasocagi
Cad No 5, Bagcilar, Istanbul, Turkiye
Tel.: (90) 2124463858
Web Site: https://www.edip.com
Year Founded: 1971
EDIP—(IST)
Rev.: $12,902,276
Assets: $138,230,302
Liabilities: $49,855,445
Net Worth: $88,374,856
Earnings: $63,057,869
Fiscal Year-end: 12/31/23
Real Estate Investment Services
N.A.I.C.S.: 523999
Nuri Akin *(Chm)*

EDIPRESSE SA
Ave de la Gare 33, 1001, Lausanne,
Switzerland
Tel.: (41) 21 588 04 20   CH
Web Site: http://www.edipresse.com
Year Founded: 1907
Sales Range: $150-199.9 Million
Emp.: 3,500
Newspaper & Magazine Publishing
Services
N.A.I.C.S.: 513110
Pierre Lamuniere *(Chm & CEO)*

Subsidiaries:

Edipresse AS Romania SRL (1)
Strada Buzesti 50-52 Floor 1 Sect 1,
011015, Bucharest, Romania   (100%)
Tel.: (40) 213193559
Sales Range: $25-49.9 Million
Emp.: 100
Periodical Publishers
N.A.I.C.S.: 513120
Cristiana Simion *(Mng Dir)*

Edipresse Asia Ltd (1)
6th Fl Guardian House 32 Oi Kwan Rd,
Wanchai, China (Hong Kong)   (100%)
Tel.: (852) 25477117
Web Site: http://www.edipresseasia.com
Sales Range: $25-49.9 Million
Emp.: 90
Publisher
N.A.I.C.S.: 513199

Edipresse Polska SA (1)
Ul Wiejska 19, 00-480, Warsaw, Poland
Tel.: (48) 225842200
Web Site: http://www.edipresse.pl
Sales Range: $100-124.9 Million
Emp.: 320
Periodical Publishers
N.A.I.C.S.: 513120

Edipresse Ukraine LLC (1)
Dymytrova Street 5 Bldg 10A 3rd fl, 03150,
Kiev, Ukraine
Tel.: (380) 444907140
Web Site: http://www.edipresse.ua
Magazine Publisher
N.A.I.C.S.: 513120
Olga Artyushina *(Mgr-Mktg)*

Edipresse-Konliga ZAO (1)
Ul Bakuninskaya 71 Bldg 10 6th Floor,
105082, Moscow, Russia   (69.9%)
Tel.: (7) 04957751435
Web Site: http://www.konliga.ru
Sales Range: $50-74.9 Million
Emp.: 200
Publisher
N.A.I.C.S.: 513199

EDISON LITHIUM CORP.

Suite 820-1130 West Pender St, Van-
couver, V6E 4A4, BC, Canada
Tel.: (416) 526-3217   BC
Web Site: https://edisonlithium.com
Year Founded: 2009
EDDYF—(OTCQB)
Rev.: $36,522
Assets: $4,826,241
Liabilities: $36,176
Net Worth: $4,790,065
Earnings: ($315,272)
Fiscal Year-end: 09/30/19
Metal Mining Services
N.A.I.C.S.: 212200
Chris Hobbs *(CFO)*

EDISON OPTO CORP.

17F No 17 Qiaohe Rd, Zhonghe Dist,
New Taipei City, 235029, Taiwan
Tel.: (886) 282276996
Web Site: https://www.edison-
opto.com.tw
Year Founded: 2001
3591—(TAI)
Rev.: $65,112,035
Assets: $126,883,968
Liabilities: $29,944,536
Net Worth: $96,939,432
Earnings: $1,455,312
Emp.: 303
Fiscal Year-end: 12/31/23
LCD Products Mfr
N.A.I.C.S.: 334419
Jason Chien Jung Wu *(Chm)*

Subsidiaries:

Edison Opto (Dong Guan) Co.,
Ltd.   (1)
No 9 Xiju Rd, Xi-Cheng Industrial Park
Heng-li, Dongguan, 523460, Guangdong,
China
Tel.: (86) 76981011898
Light Emitting Diode Distr
N.A.I.C.S.: 423690

Edison Opto USA Corporation   (1)
1809 Excise Ave Ste 201, Ontario, CA
91761
Tel.: (909) 284-9710
Light Emitting Diode Distr
N.A.I.C.S.: 423690

Yangzhou Edison Opto
Corporation   (1)
No 101 Hua-Yang West Rd, Yangzhou,
225009, Jiangsu, China
Tel.: (86) 51487777101
Light Emitting Diode Distr
N.A.I.C.S.: 423690

EDISTON PROPERTY INVEST-
MENT COMPANY PLC

Level 13 Broadgate Tower 20 Prim-
rose Street, London, EC2A 2EW,
United Kingdom
Tel.: (44) 131 240 8887   UK
Web Site: http://www.epic-reit.com
Year Founded: 2014
EPIC—(LSE)
Rev.: $23,584,954
Assets: $411,410,884
Liabilities: $154,056,415
Net Worth: $257,354,468
Earnings: $23,230,589
Fiscal Year-end: 09/30/21
Real Estate Investment Services
N.A.I.C.S.: 531311
William Hill *(Chm)*

EDISUN POWER EUROPE AG

Universitaetstr 51, 8006, Zurich, Swit-
zerland
Tel.: (41) 442666120
Web Site:
https://www.edisunpower.com
ESUN—(SWX)
Rev.: $21,031,042
Assets: $437,090,909
Liabilities: $352,325,942

Net Worth: $84,764,967
Earnings: $11,335,920
Emp.: 70
Fiscal Year-end: 12/31/22
Solar Power Generato
N.A.I.C.S.: 221118
Rainer Isenrich *(Chm)*

Subsidiaries:

Edisun Power Switzerland Ltd.   (1)
Universitatstr 51, 8006, Zurich, Switzerland
Tel.: (41) 442666120
Solar Power Generation Services
N.A.I.C.S.: 221114

EDITA FOOD INDUSTRIES
SAE

6th of October city Industrial zone 3,
Cairo, Egypt
Tel.: (20) 35400888
EFID.CA—(EGX)
Rev.: $255,726,690
Assets: $163,300,336
Liabilities: $90,586,151
Net Worth: $72,714,185
Earnings: $34,027,510
Emp.: 7,000
Fiscal Year-end: 12/31/23
Food Products Distr
N.A.I.C.S.: 445298
Hani Nabih Aziz Berzi *(Chm)*

EDITION LTD.

78 Gilstead Road, Singapore,
309116, Singapore
Tel.: (65) 62581856
Web Site: https://www.edn.sg
5HG—(CAT)
Rev.: $410,513
Assets: $6,096,342
Liabilities: $5,452,549
Net Worth: $643,793
Earnings: ($4,201,318)
Emp.: 34
Fiscal Year-end: 12/31/23
Software Solutions Services
N.A.I.C.S.: 513210
Ong Boon Chuan *(CEO)*

Subsidiaries:

Oniontech Co. Limited   (1)
3F PDC Building C-Dong 242 Pangya-ro,
Bundang-gu, Seongnam, 13487, Gyeonggi-
do, Korea (South)
Tel.: (82) 221926900
Web Site: http://www.oniontech.com
Emp.: 25
Mobile Content Delivery Software Develop-
ment Services
N.A.I.C.S.: 541511

EDITIONS DU SIGNE SA

10 rue Thomas Edison, BP 94,
67450, Mundolsheim, France
Tel.: (33) 388789191
Web Site:
https://www.editionsdusigne.fr
MLEDS—(EUR)
Sales Range: Less than $1 Million
Books Publishing Services
N.A.I.C.S.: 513130
Christian Riehl *(Chm & CEO)*

EDITIONS GRANADA SA

5 rue des Longs Pres, 92100,
Boulogne-Billancourt, France
Tel.: (33) 1 41 22 38 00   FR
Web Site:
http://www.granadaeditions.com
Arabic Language Textbooks, CD-
ROMs & Other Educational Products
N.A.I.C.S.: 513130

EDITIONS LEFEBVRE SAR-
RUT SA

40-42 Rue de Villers, Levallois-
Perret, 92300, France

Tel.: (33) 141052200
Web Site: http://www.lefebvre-
sarrut.eu
Year Founded: 1990
Emp.: 2,500
Legal, Tax, Regulatory, Risk Manage-
ment & Business Information Pub-
lisher
N.A.I.C.S.: 513199
Olivier Campenon *(Chm-Mgmt Bd)*

Subsidiaries:

Dalloz Formation, SAS   (1)
45 rue Liancourt, 75014, Paris, France
Tel.: (33) 140641300
Web Site: http://www.dalloz-formation.fr
Professional Coaching Services
N.A.I.C.S.: 611430
Damien Berthe *(Mgr-Community)*

Elegia Formation, SAS   (1)
76 boulevard Pasteur, 75737, Paris, Cedex,
France
Tel.: (33) 181695151
Web Site: http://www.elegia.fr
Professional Coaching Services
N.A.I.C.S.: 611430

Francis Lefebvre Formation Sas   (1)
13-15 rue Viete, 75849, Paris, Cedex,
France
Tel.: (33) 144013900
Web Site: http://www.flf.fr
Professional Coaching Services
N.A.I.C.S.: 611430

Giuffre Francis Lefebvre SpA   (1)
Via Busto Arsizio 40, 20151, Milan, Italy
Tel.: (39) 02380891
Web Site: http://www.giuffre.it
Emp.: 200
Legal, Tax, Regulatory, Risk Management &
Business Information Publisher
N.A.I.C.S.: 513199
Natacha de Saint Vincent *(Head)*

Indicator - FL Memo Ltd.   (1)
Calgarth House 39-41 Bank Street, Ashford,
TN23 1DQ, Kent, United Kingdom
Tel.: (44) 1233653500
Web Site: http://www.indicator-flm.co.uk
Publishing Services
N.A.I.C.S.: 513130

Intersentia Ltd.   (1)
8 Wellington Mews Wellington Street, Cam-
bridge, CB1 1HW, United Kingdom
Tel.: (44) 1223736170
Web Site: http://www.intersentia.com
Publishing Services
N.A.I.C.S.: 513130
Ann-Christin Maak-Scherpe *(Gen Mgr)*

Sdu Uitgevers B.V.   (1)
Maanweg 174, 2516 AB, Hague, Nether-
lands
Tel.: (31) 703789911
Web Site: http://www.sdu.nl
Publishing Services
N.A.I.C.S.: 513130
Dorien De Geus *(Mgr-Content House)*

EDITIONS PRIVAT SA

10 Rue des Arts, PO Box 38028,
31080, Toulouse, Cedex 6, France
Tel.: (33) 5 61 33 7700   FR
Web Site: http://www.editions-
privat.com
Year Founded: 1839
Book Publishers
N.A.I.C.S.: 513130
Philippe Terrancle *(Dir)*

EDIZIONE S.R.L.

Piazza del Duomo 19, 31100, Tre-
viso, Italy
Tel.: (39) 04225995   IT
Web Site: http://www.edizione.it
Year Founded: 1981
Rev.: $222,236,768,243
Liabilities: $24,480,593,416
Earnings: $196,666,643,937
Emp.: 67,000
Fiscal Year-end: 12/31/18
Investment Holding Company

N.A.I.C.S.: 551112
Gianni Mion *(Chm)*

Subsidiaries:

ADR Infrastrutture S.p.A.   (1)
Viale del Lago di, 00054, Fiumicino, RM,
Italy
Tel.: (39) 0344 349 3315
Web Site: https://www.adrinfrastrutture.it
Construction Services
N.A.I.C.S.: 236220
Fabio Capozio *(Chm)*

Aeroporto di Genova S.p.A.   (1)
Aeroporto C Colombo, Sestri, 16154,
Genoa, Italy
Tel.: (39) 0106 0151
Web Site: https://www.airport.genova.it
Airport Runway Maintenance Services
N.A.I.C.S.: 488119

Aerre S.r.l.   (1)
via della Meccanica n 9/4, 61122, Pesaro,
Italy
Tel.: (39) 072 148 1547
Web Site: https://www.aerresrl.it
Industrial Equipment Distr
N.A.I.C.S.: 423830

Autogrill Schweiz A.G.   (1)
Neuhardstrasse 31, 4601, Olten, Switzer-
land
Tel.: (41) 622868585
Web Site: https://www.autogrill.ch
Restaurant Operators
N.A.I.C.S.: 722511

Autogrill VFS F&B Co. Ltd.   (1)
Kiosk 1 1 16 1st Floor International Termi-
nal, Tan Son Nhat Airport, Ho Chi Minh
City, Vietnam
Tel.: (84) 2873067366
Web Site: https://www.autogrillvfs.com.vn
Restaurant Operators
N.A.I.C.S.: 722511
Simon Stansfield *(Mng Dir)*

Autostrada del Brennero S.p.A.   (1)
Via Berlino 10, 38121, Trento, Italy
Tel.: (39) 046 121 2611
Web Site: https://www.autobrennero.it
Road Construction Services
N.A.I.C.S.: 237310
Reichhalter Hartmann *(Pres)*

Autostrade Concessioni e Costruzioni
S.p.A.   (1)
via A Bergamini 50, 00159, Rome, Italy
Tel.: (39) 055 421 0452
Web Site: https://www.autostrade.it
Road Construction Services
N.A.I.C.S.: 237310
Giuliano Mari *(Chm)*

Benetton Asia Pacific Ltd.   (1)
Unit 401 Goldin Financial Global Centre 17
Kai Cheung Road, Kowloon Bay, Kowloon,
China (Hong Kong)
Tel.: (852) 2 175 2028
Cloth Distr
N.A.I.C.S.: 458110

Benetton Group S.p.A.   (1)
Villa Minelli, 31050, Ponzano Veneto, Tre-
viso, Italy   (100%)
Tel.: (39) 0422519111
Web Site: http://www.benetton.com
Emp.: 9,557
Casual Knitwear & Sportswear Mfr
N.A.I.C.S.: 315120
Carlo Benetton *(Deputy Chm)*

Subsidiary (US):

Benetton U.S.A. Corporation   (2)
601 Fifth Ave, New York, NY 10017-8260
Tel.: (212) 593-0290
Sales Range: $25-49.9 Million
Emp.: 60
Retail Sportswear Stores
N.A.I.C.S.: 315250
Diane Mrazcak *(VP)*

Edizione Property S.p.A.   (1)
20 Viale Felissent Gian Giacomo, 31020,
Villorba, Italy
Tel.: (39) 0422 3144
Property Management Services
N.A.I.C.S.: 531311
Valentina Zanatta *(Mgr-Asset)*

Edizione S.r.l.—(Continued)

Subsidiary (Non-US):

Cia De Tierras Sud Argentino S.A. (2)
Esmeralda 684, 1007, Buenos Aires, Argentina
Tel.: (54) 114 3932025
Emp.: 10
Sheep Farming Services
N.A.I.C.S.: 112410
Diego Perazzo (VP)

Maccarese S.p.A. (1)
Viale Maria 423 localita Maccarese Fiumicino, 00057, Rome, Italy
Tel.: (39) 06 66 72 336
Web Site: http://www.maccaresespa.com
Agricultural Equipment Mfr
N.A.I.C.S.: 333111

Mundys S.p.A. (1)
Piazza San Silvestro 8, 00187, Rome, Italy
Tel.: (39) 0644172652
Web Site: https://www.mundys.com
Rev.: $10,717,518,491
Assets: $72,772,933,005
Liabilities: $57,497,516,290
Net Worth: $15,275,416,715
Earnings: $683,298,377
Emp.: 4,979
Fiscal Year-end: 12/31/2023
Holding Company; Motorway Concession & Construction Services
N.A.I.C.S.: 488490
Tiziano Ceccarani (CFO)

Subsidiary (Domestic):

ADR Mobility Srl (2)
Via dell A Fiumicino Airport 320, 00054, Fiumicino, RM, Italy
Tel.: (39) 0665951
Passenger Parking Services
N.A.I.C.S.: 812930

Aeroporti di Roma S.p.A. (2)
Via Pier Paolo Racchetti 1, 00054, Fiumicino, Italy (95.9%)
Tel.: (39) 0665951
Web Site: http://www.adr.it
Rev.: $1,195,429,831
Assets: $3,668,863,124
Liabilities: $2,402,829,424
Net Worth: $1,266,033,700
Earnings: $281,646,850
Emp.: 3,453
Fiscal Year-end: 12/31/2018
Airport Management Services
N.A.I.C.S.: 488119
Guglielmo Bove (Gen Counsel & Sec)

Subsidiary (Domestic):

ADR Advertising S.p.A. (3)
Torre Uffici 1, Aeroporto Leonardo da Vinci, 00054, Fiumicino, Rome, Italy
Tel.: (39) 0665951
Web Site: http://www.adr.it
Sales Range: $25-49.9 Million
Emp.: 7
Airport Advertising Services
N.A.I.C.S.: 541810

ADR Tel S.p.A. (3)
Via Pier Paolo Racchetti 1, 00054, Fiumicino, Rome, Italy
Tel.: (39) 0665951
Web Site: http://www.adrtel.it
Sales Range: $25-49.9 Million
Emp.: 15
Telecommunication Servicesb
N.A.I.C.S.: 517810

Subsidiary (Domestic):

Autostrade Tec SpA (2)
Limite di Campi Bisenzio 39, 50123, Florence, Italy
Tel.: (39) 0554202111
Web Site: http://www.autostradetech.com
Hardware & Software System Services
N.A.I.C.S.: 541512

Autostrade per l'Italia S.p.A. (2)
Via Bergamini 50, 00159, Rome, Italy (100%)
Tel.: (39) 0643631
Web Site: http://www.autostrade.it
Toll Motorway Builder & Operator

N.A.I.C.S.: 237310
Paolo Berti (COO & Chief Maintenance Officer)

Essediesse Societa Di Servizi SpA (2)
Via Alberto Bergamini 50, 00159, Rome, Italy
Tel.: (39) 0643631
Web Site: http://www.essediessespa.it
Fiscal & Accounting Services
N.A.I.C.S.: 541219

Infoblu SpA (2)
via Bergamini 50, 00159, Rome, Italy
Tel.: (39) 0643631
Web Site: http://www.infoblu.it
Information Mobility Services
N.A.I.C.S.: 541511

K-Master Srl (2)
Via Alberto Bergamini n 50, 00159, Rome, Italy
Tel.: (39) 0110437951
Web Site: http://www.telepasskmaster.com
Fleet Management Services
N.A.I.C.S.: 561110

Subsidiary (Non-US):

Pavimental Polska SP Z.O.O. (2)
ul Dworcowa 2, 32-540, Trzebinia, Poland
Tel.: (48) 781999000
Web Site: http://www.pavimental.pl
Road Work & Environmental Construction Contractor Services
N.A.I.C.S.: 238910

Subsidiary (Domestic):

Pavimental SpA (2)
Via Giuseppe Donati 174, 00159, Rome, Italy
Tel.: (39) 0643631
Web Site: http://www.pavimental.it
Emp.: 700
Road Construction & Maintenance Services
N.A.I.C.S.: 237310
Gennarino Tozzi (Chm)

Subsidiary (Non-US):

Sociedad Concesionaria Autopista Nororiente SA (2)
Autopista Nororiente s/n Km 11 2, Chicureo Region Metropolitana, Colina, Chile
Tel.: (56) 224900900
Web Site: http://www.autopistanororiente.cl
Road Construction & Maintenance Services
N.A.I.C.S.: 237310

Sociedad Concesionaria Autopista Nueva Vespucio Sur SA (2)
Av Americo Vespucio 4665 frente al Metro Las Torres Linea 4, Macul, Chile
Tel.: (56) 223474900
Web Site: http://www.vespuciosur.cl
Road Construction & Maintenance Services
N.A.I.C.S.: 237310

Sociedad Concesionaria Constanera Norte SA (2)
General Prieto 1430 Independence Metropolitan Region, Santiago, Chile
Tel.: (56) 224900900
Web Site: http://web.costaneranorte.cl
Road Construction & Maintenance Services
N.A.I.C.S.: 237310

Sociedad Concesionaria de Los Lagos SA (2)
Ruta 5 Sur Km 993 Cruce Totoral, Llanquihue, Puerto Montt, Chile
Tel.: (56) 652423400
Web Site: http://www.scloslagos.cl
Road Construction & Maintenance Services
N.A.I.C.S.: 237310

Subsidiary (Domestic):

Societa Autostrada Tirrenica p.A. (2)
Via Alberto Bergamini 50, 00159, Rome, Italy
Tel.: (39) 0840042121
Web Site: http://www.tirrenica.it
Highway Construction & Maintenance Services
N.A.I.C.S.: 237310

Subsidiary (Non-US):

Spea do Brasil Projectos e Infraestrutura Limitada (2)

Leopoldo Couto de Magalhaes Junior Street 758-11th Floor-Suite 111/112, Itaim Bibi, Sao Paulo, 04542-000, Brazil
Tel.: (55) 1125059180
Highway Construction & Maintenance Services
N.A.I.C.S.: 237310

Subsidiary (Domestic):

Tangenziale di Napoli SpA (2)
Via Giovanni Porzio 4 Centro Direzionale di Napoli Isola A/7, 80143, Naples, Italy
Tel.: (39) 0817254111
Web Site: http://www.tangenzialedinapoli.it
Road Construction & Maintenance Services
N.A.I.C.S.: 237310

Telepass Pay SpA (2)
Branch 39, PO Box 2310, 50123, Florence, Italy
Tel.: (39) 0555104219
Web Site: http://www.telepasspay.com
Telepass Pay Services
N.A.I.C.S.: 541214

Olimpias Group S.r.l. (2)
Via Diritti dell'Infanzia 4, Ponzano Veneto, 31050, Treviso, Italy
Tel.: (39) 0422 6262
Web Site: https://www.olimpias.com
Cloth Distr
N.A.I.C.S.: 458110

Pallacanestro Treviso Societa Sportiva Dilettantistica a r.l. (1)
Strada del Nascimben 1/B, 31100, Treviso, Italy
Tel.: (39) 042 232 4235
Pub Operator
N.A.I.C.S.: 711310

Ponzano Children S.r.l. (1)
Via Diritti dell'Infanzia 4, Ponzano Veneto, 31050, Treviso, Italy
Tel.: (39) 042 296 3267
Web Site: https://www.ponzanochildren.com
Emp.: 21
Child Care Services
N.A.I.C.S.: 624410

Sintonia S.p.A (1)
Corso di Porta Vittoria 16, 20122, Milan, Italy
Tel.: (39) 0422599617
Web Site: http://www.sintoniaspa.it
Holding Company
N.A.I.C.S.: 551112
Gianni Mion (Chm)

Verde Sport S.p.A. (1)
La Ghirada Strada del Nascimben 1/B, 31100, Treviso, Italy
Tel.: (39) 0422 324111
Web Site: http://www.verdesport.it
Sports Club Operator
N.A.I.C.S.: 711310
Valerio Malavasi (Mgr-Sls)

Subsidiary (Domestic):

Asolo Golf Club S.r.l. (2)
Via Dei Borghi 1, Cavaso del Tomba, 31034, Treviso, Italy
Tel.: (39) 042 3942211
Web Site: http://www.asologolf.it
Golf Club Operator
N.A.I.C.S.: 713910
Gilberto Benetton (Chm-Mgmt Bd)

Benetton Rugby Treviso S.r.l. (2)
Strada Di Nascimben 1/B, 31100, Treviso, Italy
Tel.: (39) 0422 324238
Web Site: http://www.benettonrugby.it
Sports Club Operator
N.A.I.C.S.: 711211
Amino Zette (Gen Mgr)

EDMOND DE ROTHSCHILD HOLDING S.A.
8 rue de lArquebuse, 1211, Geneva, Switzerland
Tel.: (41) 582017500 CH
Web Site: http://www.edmond-de-rothschild.com
Year Founded: 1953
Holding Services
N.A.I.C.S.: 551111

Benjamin de Rothschild (Chm)

Subsidiaries:

Banque Privee Edmond de Rothschild S.A. (1)
18 rue de Hesse, 1204, Geneva, Switzerland
Tel.: (41) 588189111
Web Site: http://www.groupedr.eu
Sales Range: $25-49.9 Million
Emp.: 1,614
Asset & Wealth Management Services for Private Clients
N.A.I.C.S.: 523999

Subsidiary (Non-US):

Banque Privee Edmond de Rothschild Europe (2)
20 Boulevard Emmanuel Servais, 2535, Luxembourg, Luxembourg
Tel.: (352) 24881
Web Site: http://www.edmond-de-rothschild.eu
Sales Range: $25-49.9 Million
Emp.: 716
Investment Fund Administration, Wealth Management, Global Asset Management, Custody & Banking Services
N.A.I.C.S.: 523999
Elise Lethuillier (First VP-Family Office & Bus Dev)

Subsidiary (Domestic):

Adjutoris Conseil S.A. (3)
18 Blvd Emmanuel Servais, L-2535, Luxembourg, Luxembourg
Tel.: (352) 26262392
Web Site: http://www.adjutoris.lu
Brokerage Services
N.A.I.C.S.: 523150
Emeline Rodriguez (Mgr-Broker Svcs)

Subsidiary (Non-US):

BPER Europe Israel (3)
46 Rothschild Boulevard, 68883, Tel Aviv, Israel (100%)
Tel.: (972) 35669818
Web Site: http://www.edmond-de-rothschild.eu
Sales Range: $50-74.9 Million
Emp.: 3
Wealth Management, Family Advisory Services & Wealth Engineering
N.A.I.C.S.: 523999

Division (Domestic):

Edmond de Rothschild Investment Services Limited (4)
ALrov Tower 46 Rothschild Blvd, 66883, Tel Aviv, Israel
Tel.: (972) 37130300
Web Site: http://www.edris.co.il
Sales Range: $25-49.9 Million
Wealth Management, Corporate Advisory Services & Asset Management
N.A.I.C.S.: 523999

Edmond de Rothschild Private Equity Management Ltd. (4)
23 Menachem Begin Road Levenstein Tower 19th floor, Tel Aviv, 66183, Israel
Tel.: (972) 37979100
Web Site: http://www.edrpe.com
Sales Range: $50-74.9 Million
Emp.: 3
Private Equity Management Services
N.A.I.C.S.: 523999
Miki Kliger (Mng Dir)

Edmond de Rothschild (Bahamas) Ltd. (1)
Lyford Financial Centre Lyford Cay no 2 Western Road, PO Box SP-63948, Nassau, Bahamas
Tel.: (242) 702 80 00
Web Site: http://www.edmond-de-rothschild.bs
Commercial Banking Services
N.A.I.C.S.: 522110

Edmond de Rothschild (Europe) SA/NV (1)
Louizalaan 480 bus 16A, 1050, Brussels, Belgium
Tel.: (32) 2 645 57 57

Web Site: http://www.edmond-de-rothschild.be
Emp.: 40
Commercial Banking Services
N.A.I.C.S.: 522110
Moles Lebailly (Gen Mgr)

Edmond de Rothschild (Israel) Ltd. (1)
Alrov Tower 46 Rothschild Boulevard, 66883, Tel Aviv, Israel
Tel.: (972) 3 713 03 00
Web Site: http://www.edris.co.il
Commercial Banking Services
N.A.I.C.S.: 522110

Subsidiary (Domestic):

Edmond de Rothschild Private Equity Partners (Israel) Ltd. (2)
13 Rothschild Boulevard, 66881, Tel Aviv, Israel
Tel.: (972) 3 797 9100
Commercial Banking Services
N.A.I.C.S.: 522110

Edmond de Rothschild (Lugano) S.A. (1)
Via Ginevra 2 CP 5882, 6901, Lugano, Switzerland
Tel.: (41) 91 913 45 00
Web Site: http://privata.edmond-de-rothschild.ch
Commercial Banking Services
N.A.I.C.S.: 522110

Edmond de Rothschild (Monaco) Ltd. (1)
2 Avenue de Monte-Carlo Les Terrasses, BP 317, 98000, Monaco, Monaco
Tel.: (377) 93 10 47 47
Web Site: http://www.edmond-de-rothschild.mc
Commercial Banking Services
N.A.I.C.S.: 522110
Orgione Herve (CEO)

Edmond de Rothschild (UK) Limited (1)
4 Carlton Gardens, London, SW1Y 5AA, United Kingdom
Tel.: (44) 20 7845 5950
Web Site: http://www.edmond-de-rothschild.co.uk
Commercial Banking Services
N.A.I.C.S.: 522110

Edmond de Rothschild Advisory Management (Beijing) Co., Ltd. (1)
Unit 919 Winland International Finance Center 7 Financial Street, Beijing, China
Tel.: (86) 10 5796 5000
Asset Management Services
N.A.I.C.S.: 531390

Edmond de Rothschild Asset Management (C.I.) Limited (1)
Hirzel Court, Saint Peter Port, Channel Islands, Guernsey
Tel.: (44) 1481 716 336
Asset Management Services
N.A.I.C.S.: 531390

Edmond de Rothschild Asset Management (Luxembourg) SA (1)
20 Boulevard Emmanuel Servais, 2535, Luxembourg, Luxembourg
Tel.: (352) 24 88 1
Web Site: http://www.edram.lu
Asset Management Services
N.A.I.C.S.: 531390

Edmond de Rothschild Asset Management (Suisse) SA (1)
8 rue de l'Arquebuse, PO Box 5441, 1211, Geneva, Switzerland
Tel.: (41) 58 201 75 00
Web Site: http://www.edmond-de-rothschild.com
Financial Management Services
N.A.I.C.S.: 523999

Edmond de Rothschild Asset Management Chile S.A. (1)
Apoquindo 4001 oficina 305, Las Condes, Santiago, Chile
Tel.: (56) 2598 99 00
Web Site: http://www.groupedr.gg
Asset Management Services

N.A.I.C.S.: 531390

Edmond de Rothschild Investment Partners (Hong Kong) Ltd. (1)
Suite 5007 8 Connaught Place One Exchange Square, Central, Hong Kong, China (Hong Kong)
Tel.: (852) 3926 5288
Asset Management Services
N.A.I.C.S.: 531390

Edmond de Rothschild Investment Partners (Shanghai) Ltd. (1)
Room 02 28F China Insurance Building 166 East Lujiazui Road, Pudong New Area, Shanghai, 200120, China
Tel.: (86) 21 60 86 25 03
Asset Management Services
N.A.I.C.S.: 531390

La Compagnie Benjamin de Rothschild S.A. (1)
29 Route de Pre-Bois, Case Postale 490, 1215, Geneva, Switzerland
Tel.: (41) 227614640
Web Site: http://www.cbr.groupedr.ch
Sales Range: $50-74.9 Million
Emp.: 60
Financial Risk Management Services
N.A.I.C.S.: 523999
Benjamin de Rothschild (Chm)

La Compagnie Financiere Edmond de Rothschild (1)
47 rue du Faubourg Saint-Honore, 75401, Paris, Cedex, France
Tel.: (33) 140172525
Financial Holding Company
N.A.I.C.S.: 551111

Subsidiary (Domestic):

La Compagnie Financiere Edmond De Rothschild Banque (2)
47 rue du Faubourg, Saint Honore, Paris, 75401, France (91%)
Tel.: (33) 140172525
Web Site: http://www.groupedr.fr
Private Banking & Asset Management Services
N.A.I.C.S.: 523999

Subsidiary (Domestic):

Edmond de Rothschild Asset Management (3)
47 rue du Faubourg Saint-Honore, 75008, Paris, France
Tel.: (33) 140172525
Web Site: http://www.groupedr.fr
Asset Management Services
N.A.I.C.S.: 523999
Philippe Uzan (Chief Investment Officer)

Edmond de Rothschild Corporate Finance (3)
47 rue du Faubourg Saint-Honore, 75008, Paris, France (100%)
Tel.: (33) 140172111
Web Site: http://www.edrcf.com
Financial Services
N.A.I.C.S.: 523999

Edmond de Rothschild Enterprises Patrimoniales (3)
47 rue du Faubourg Saint-Honore, 75401, Paris, France
Tel.: (33) 140173163
Web Site: http://www.edrep.fr
Investment Management Service
N.A.I.C.S.: 523999
Francois Pailler (Mgr)

Edmond de Rothschild Enterprises Patrimoniales Croissance (3)
47 rue du Faubourg Saint-Honore, 75401, Paris, Cedex 08, France
Tel.: (33) 140172525
Web Site: http://www.edmond-de-rothschild.com
Investment
N.A.I.C.S.: 523999

Oncodesign SA (1)
20 rue Jean Mazen, BP 27627, 21076, Dijon, Cedex, France (61.58%)
Tel.: (33) 3 80 78 82 60
Web Site: http://www.oncodesign.com
Pharmaceuticals Mfr
N.A.I.C.S.: 325412

Philippe Genne (Founder, Chm & CEO)

EDMONDS CHEVROLET BUICK GMC
138 Hanes Rd, Huntsville, P1H 1M4, ON, Canada
Tel.: (705) 789-7500
Web Site: http://www.edmondsgm.ca
Rev.: $18,742,700
Emp.: 25
New & Used Vehicles
N.A.I.C.S.: 441227
Richard Janssen (Gen Mgr)

EDMONTON KENWORTH LTD.
17335 - 118 Avenue, Edmonton, T5S 2P5, AB, Canada
Tel.: (780) 453-3431
Web Site: https://www.edmkw.com
Year Founded: 1954
Rev.: $258,212,875
Emp.: 288
New & Used Truck Leasing, Sales & Service
N.A.I.C.S.: 532120
Jason MacLean (Mgr-Comml Fin)

Subsidiaries:

Edmonton Kenworth Ltd. - Kenworth Fort McMurray Division (1)
11-885 Memorial Drive, Fort McMurray, T9K 0K4, AB, Canada
Tel.: (780) 743-0819
Automobile Parts Distr
N.A.I.C.S.: 423120
Clay Willness (Mgr-Svc)

Edmonton Kenworth Ltd. - Kenworth Leduc Division (1)
8202-42 Street, Leduc, T9E 8M6, AB, Canada
Tel.: (780) 612-9855
Truck Leasing Services
N.A.I.C.S.: 532120
Gary King (Pres)

Edmonton Kenworth Ltd. - Kenworth Lloydminster Division (1)
6101-63 Avenue, Lloydminster, T9V 3T6, AB, Canada
Tel.: (780) 871-0950
Truck Leasing Services
N.A.I.C.S.: 532120
Brent Herman (Mgr-Parts)

EDMUND TIE & COMPANY (SEA) PTE. LTD.
5 Shenton Way 13-05 UIC Building, Singapore, 068808, Singapore
Tel.: (65) 6293 3228
Web Site: http://www.etcsea.com
Year Founded: 1995
Real Estate Manangement Services
N.A.I.C.S.: 531390
Choon Fah Ong (CEO)

Subsidiaries:

Edmund Tie & Company (Thailand) Co., Ltd. (1)
8th Floor Tonson Tower 900 Ploenchit Road Lumpini, Pathumwan, Bangkok, 10330, Thailand
Tel.: (66) 2 257 0499
Properties Management Services
N.A.I.C.S.: 531312
Hua Thong Heng (Mng Dir)

EDOARDOS MARTIN, S.A.B. DE C.V.
Tihuatlan 15 int 601 san jeronimo aculco, 10400, Mexico, DE, Mexico
Tel.: (52) 56584569   MX
Year Founded: 1948
EDOARDO---(MEX)
Sales Range: Less than $1 Million
Apparel Mfr & Whslr
N.A.I.C.S.: 315990

EDOKO FOOD IMPORTERS LTD.
1335 Kebet Way, Port Coquitlam, V3C 6G1, BC, Canada
Tel.: (604) 944-7332
Web Site: http://www.edokofood.ca
Year Founded: 1957
Rev.: $10,172,559
Emp.: 35
General Food Products Whslr
N.A.I.C.S.: 456191
Neal Letourneau (Pres)

EDOM TECHNOLOGY CO., LTD.
8F No 50 Ln 10 Jihu Rd, Neihu Dist, Taipei, 114, Taiwan
Tel.: (886) 226578811
Web Site: https://www.edomtech.com
3048—(TAI)
Rev.: $3,505,515,025
Assets: $974,056,505
Liabilities: $811,745,416
Net Worth: $162,311,090
Earnings: $200,334
Emp.: 800
Fiscal Year-end: 12/31/23
Electronic Components Mfr
N.A.I.C.S.: 334416
Lin Fei-Hung (Vice Chm)

Subsidiaries:

EDOM Electronic Technology (Shanghai) Co., Ltd. (1)
16F No 20 Building No 487 Tianlin Road Caohejing Hi-Tech Park, Xuhui District, Shanghai, 200233, China
Tel.: (86) 2133675222
Electronic Components Mfr & Distr
N.A.I.C.S.: 334419

EDOM TECHNOLOGY (SHANGHAI) LTD. (1)
16F No 20 Building No 487 Tianlin Road Caohejing Hi-Tech Park, Xuhui District, Shanghai, 200233, Guangdong, China
Tel.: (86) 21 3367 5222
Web Site: http://www.edom.com.tw
Integrated Circuit Distr
N.A.I.C.S.: 423690

EDOM TRADING (SHENZHEN) LTD. (1)
Room 2703 Hua Rong Building No 178 Mintian Road, Futian District, Shenzhen, 518048, Guangdong, China
Tel.: (86) 75583588188
Web Site: http://www.edomtechnology.com
Emp.: 100
Computer Peripheral Distr
N.A.I.C.S.: 423430

EDOM Technology Japan Co., Ltd. (1)
Nagai Building 3F 3-9-5 Kyobashi, Chuo-ku, Tokyo, 104-0031, Japan
Tel.: (81) 355799710
Electronic Components Mfr & Distr
N.A.I.C.S.: 334419

Goldenflash Electronics Co., Ltd. (1)
6F-2 No 103 RuiHu St, Neihu Dist, Taipei, Taiwan
Tel.: (886) 227988186
Web Site: https://www.goldenflash-elec.com
Electronic Equipment Mfr & Distr
N.A.I.C.S.: 335314

Sunjet Components Corp. (1)
1F No 50 Ln 10 Jihu Rd, Neihu Dist, Taipei, Taiwan (98.83%)
Tel.: (886) 226561399
Web Site: https://www.sunjettech.com
Electronic Components Distr
N.A.I.C.S.: 423690
Jodge Liu (VP-Sls)

iPro Technology Inc. (1)
No 69 Section 1 Jiafeng 6th Road, Zhubei, 30271, Hsinchu, Taiwan
Tel.: (886) 36585100
Web Site: https://www.iprotech.com.tw
Circuit Board Whslr
N.A.I.C.S.: 423690

EDOM Technology Co., Ltd—(Continued)

EDP - ENERGIAS DE PORTU-GAL, S.A.
Av 24 de Julho 12, 1249-300, Lisbon, Portugal
Tel.: (351) 210012834　　　　PT
Web Site: http://www.edp.pt
EDP—(EUR)
Sales Range: $15-24.9 Billion
Electric Power Generation, Supply & Distribution
N.A.I.C.S.: 221122
Miguel Stilwell d'Andrade *(Chm)*

Subsidiaries:

Agrupacion Eolica, S.L.U.　　　**(1)**
Plaza Antonio Beltran Martinez 1-Piso 4 F
Ct Emp, Zaragoza, 50002, Spain
Tel.: (34) 976210664
Eletric Power Generation Services
N.A.I.C.S.: 221118

Bon Vent de L Ebre, S.L.　　　**(1)**
Calle Navas De Tolosa 161, Terrassa, 08224, Barcelona, Spain
Tel.: (34) 937454400
Eletric Power Generation Services
N.A.I.C.S.: 221118

Desarrollos Eolicos Promocion, S.A.　　　**(1)**
Avenida Montes Sierra 36-2 Planta, Seville, 41007, Spain
Tel.: (34) 954269240
Web Site: http://www.edprenovaveis.com
Sales Range: $25-49.9 Million
Emp.: 55
Engineeering Services
N.A.I.C.S.: 541330

Desarrollos Eolicos, S.A.　　　**(1)**
Avenida Montes Sierra 36, Seville, 41007, Spain
Tel.: (34) 954269240
Sales Range: $25-49.9 Million
Emp.: 60
Wind Turbine Mfr
N.A.I.C.S.: 333611
Francisco Galvan *(Mng Dir)*

EDP - Energias do Brasil S.A.　**(1)**
Gomes de Carvalho Street No 1996 7th Floor, Olympia, 04532-001, Sao Paulo, SP, Brazil　　　　　　　　　**(100%)**
Tel.: (55) 1121855907
Web Site: http://www.edpbr.com.br
Rev.: $3,180,606,090
Assets: $6,690,166,784
Liabilities: $4,533,602,961
Net Worth: $2,156,563,822
Earnings: $247,601,395
Emp.: 3,254
Fiscal Year-end: 12/31/2023
Holding Company; Electric Power Generation, Supply & Distribution
N.A.I.C.S.: 551112
Antonio Luis Guerra Nunes Mexia *(Chm)*

Subsidiary (Domestic):

Bandeirante Energia SA　　　**(2)**
Rua Gomes de Carvalho Street No 1996 7th Floor Vila Olimpia, Sao Paulo, SP, Brazil　　　　　　　　　**(100%)**
Tel.: (55) 11 2185 5045
Web Site: http://www.bandeirante.com.br
Emp.: 1,080
Electricity Generation, Transmission, Distribution & Sale
N.A.I.C.S.: 221122
Miguel Nuno Simoes Nunes Ferreira Setas *(CEO)*

EDP Escelsa - Espirito Santo Centrais Eletricas S.A.　　　**(2)**
R Bandeira Paulista 530 3 andar, Chacara Itaim, Sao Paulo, CEP 04532-001, SP, Brazil　　　　　　　　　**(100%)**
Tel.: (55) 11 2185 5985
Web Site: http://www.edpescelsa.com.br
Electricity Distr
N.A.I.C.S.: 221122

EDP Espirito Santo Distribuicao De Energia S.A.　　　**(2)**
Rua Florentino Faller 80, Vitoria, 29050-310, ES, Brazil

Tel.: (55) 27 3325 4126
Natural Gas Distribution Services
N.A.I.C.S.: 221210
Michel Nunes Itkes *(Vice Chm & CEO)*

Empresa Energetica do Mato Grosso do Sul S.A.　　　**(2)**
Avenida Gury Marques no 8000, CEP 79072 900, Campo Grande, MS, Brazil
Tel.: (55) 6733984000
Web Site: http://www.enersul.com.br
Electricity Generation, Transmission & Distribution
N.A.I.C.S.: 221122

Enertrade　　　**(2)**
rua gomes de carvalho 1996 7F, Chacara Itaim, Sao Paulo, 04547006, Brazil
Tel.: (55) 1121855801
Web Site: http://www.edpcomercialieadao.com.br
Sales Range: $50-74.9 Million
Emp.: 25
Electricity Trading & Supply Services
N.A.I.C.S.: 221122
Esoani Portes *(Mgr-Comml)*

EDP - Gestao da Producao de Energia, S.A.　　　**(1)**
Avenida Jose Malhoa Lote A 13, Lisbon, 1070 157, Portugal
Tel.: (351) 21 001 2000
Eletric Power Generation Services
N.A.I.C.S.: 221118

EDP - Projectos S.G.P.S., S.A.　**(1)**
Praca Marques De Pombal 12, Lisbon, Portugal
Tel.: (351) 210015300
Eletric Power Generation Services
N.A.I.C.S.: 221118

Subsidiary (Domestic):

EDP GAS.Com - Comercio de Gas Natural, S.A.　　　**(2)**
Praca Marques De Pombal 12, 1250-162, Lisbon, Portugal
Tel.: (351) 225071400
Natural Gas Distr
N.A.I.C.S.: 221210

EDP Distribuicao　　　**(1)**
Rua Camilo Castelo Branco 43, 1050-044, Lisbon, Portugal　　　**(100%)**
Tel.: (351) 504394029
Web Site: http://www.edpdistribuicao.pt
Sales Range: $5-14.9 Billion
Emp.: 4,980
Distribution & Sale of Electric Power
N.A.I.C.S.: 221122

EDP Distribuicao de Energia, S.A.　　　**(1)**
R Camilo Castelo Branco 43, Lisbon, 1250-162, Portugal
Tel.: (351) 213172300
Web Site: http://www.edp.pt
Electric Power Distribution Services
N.A.I.C.S.: 221122
Antonio Mexia *(VP)*

EDP Gas Servico Universal, S.A.　**(1)**
Rua Linhas de Torres 41, Porto, Portugal
Tel.: (351) 225071400
Natural Gas Distribution Services
N.A.I.C.S.: 221210

EDP Inovacao, S.A.　　　**(1)**
Avenida Sidonio Pais 24 R/C Esq, 1050-215, Lisbon, Portugal
Tel.: (351) 210010260
Sales Range: $25-49.9 Million
Emp.: 21
Power Project Engineering Services
N.A.I.C.S.: 541330
Antonio Vidigal *(Gen Dir)*

EDP Renewables Canada, Ltd　**(1)**
449 Winchester Main, Winchester, K0C 2K0, ON, Canada
Tel.: (613) 774-4068
Eletric Power Generation Services
N.A.I.C.S.: 221118

EDP Renewables North America, L.L.C.　　　**(1)**
808 Travis St Ste 700, Houston, TX 77002
Tel.: (713) 265-0350

Wind Power Plant Construction Engineering Services
N.A.I.C.S.: 237130
Maria Beatriz Iglesias *(Engr-Energy Mgmt Sys)*

Subsidiary (Domestic):

Marble River, L.L.C.　　　**(2)**
5591 State Rte 11, Ellenburg Center, NY 12934
Tel.: (518) 497-0033
Wind Electric Power Generation Services
N.A.I.C.S.: 221118

Meadow Lake Wind Farm IV, L.L.C.　　　**(2)**
808 Travis St 700, Houston, TX 77002-5774
Tel.: (713) 265-0350
Sales Range: $200-249.9 Million
Emp.: 300
Wind Power Plant Operating Services
N.A.I.C.S.: 221118
Miguel Prado *(CEO)*

Meadow Lake Wind Farm, L.L.C.　**(2)**
808 Travis St Ste 700, Houston, TX 77002-5774
Tel.: (713) 265-0350
Web Site: http://www.edpr.com
Wind Power Plant Operating Services
N.A.I.C.S.: 221118

Paulding Wind Farm II, L.L.C.　　**(2)**
808 Travis St Ste 700, Houston, TX 77002-5774
Tel.: (713) 265-0350
Web Site: http://www.edpr.com
Emp.: 200
Eletric Power Generation Services
N.A.I.C.S.: 221118

EDP Renewables Polska, Sp. z o.o.　　　**(1)**
Al Jerozolimskie 98, 00 - 807, Warsaw, Poland
Tel.: (48) 222121950
Web Site: http://www.edpr.com
Sales Range: $50-74.9 Million
Emp.: 40
Eletric Power Generation Services
N.A.I.C.S.: 221118

EDP Renovaveis S.A.　　　**(1)**
Serrano Galvache 56 Parque Norte Business Center, Edificio Olmo 7th Floor, 28033, Madrid, Spain　　**(82.57%)**
Tel.: (34) 902830700
Web Site: https://www.edpr.com
Rev.: $2,125,784,978
Assets: $22,307,976,553
Liabilities: $11,715,842,366
Net Worth: $10,592,134,187
Earnings: $838,704,912
Emp.: 1,702
Fiscal Year-end: 12/31/2020
Power Distr
N.A.I.C.S.: 221118
Rui Antunes *(Dir-Investor Relations)*

EDP Servicos - Sistemas para a Qualidade e Eficiencia Energetica, S.A.　　　**(1)**
Praca Marques De Pombal 13, 1250-162, Lisbon, Portugal
Tel.: (351) 210012500
Business Management Consulting Services
N.A.I.C.S.: 541611
Juan Tosh *(Gen Mgr)*

EDP Serviner - Servicos de Energia, S.A.　　　**(1)**
Pc Marques Pombal Nr 13, Lisbon, 1250-162, Portugal
Tel.: (351) 210012500
Business Management & Consulting Services
N.A.I.C.S.: 541611

Electrica de la Ribera del Ebro, S.A.　　　**(1)**
Poligono Industrial Castejon Par M 04, Castejon, 31590, Spain
Tel.: (34) 948814400
Eletric Power Generation Services
N.A.I.C.S.: 221118

Energia e Industria de Toledo, S.A.　　　**(1)**

Plaza De La Gesta 2, Oviedo, 33007, Spain
Tel.: (34) 98 523 03 00
Eletric Power Generation Services
N.A.I.C.S.: 221118

Eolica Arlanzon, S.A.　　　**(1)**
Calle Serrano Galvache 56-Ed Encina, Madrid, 28033, Spain
Tel.: (34) 917819353
Wind Electric Power Generation Services
N.A.I.C.S.: 221118

Eolica Guadalteba, S.L.　　　**(1)**
Avenida Montes Sierra 36-Plt 2, Seville, 41007, Spain
Tel.: (34) 954269240
Web Site: http://www.edpr.com
Eletric Power Generation Services
N.A.I.C.S.: 221118

Greenwind, S.A.　　　**(1)**
Avenue Pasteur 6 Building H, Wavre, Louvain-la-Neuve, 1300, Belgium
Tel.: (32) 1 068 64 85
Web Site: http://www.edprenovapeis.com
Sales Range: $75-99.9 Million
Emp.: 1
Wind Electric Power Generation Services
N.A.I.C.S.: 221118
Frederic Lanoe *(Gen Mgr)*

HC Naturgas Comercializadora de Ultimo Recurso, S.A.　　　**(1)**
Plaza De La Gesta 2, Oviedo, 33007, Spain
Tel.: (34) 985230300
Natural Gas Distribution Services
N.A.I.C.S.: 221210

HidroElectrica del Cantabrico, S.A.　　　**(1)**
Plaza de la Gesta 2, 33007, Oviedo, Spain　　　　　　　　　**(100%)**
Tel.: (34) 985230300
Sales Range: $150-199.9 Million
Emp.: 200
Electricity Output, Transportation, Conversion & Distribution Services
N.A.I.C.S.: 221122
Manuel Menendez Menendez *(Chm)*

Subsidiary (Domestic):

HC Energia　　　**(2)**
Plaza de la Gesta 2, Oviedo, 33007, Spain　　　　　　　　　**(80%)**
Tel.: (34) 902830100
Engineering & Construction of Renewable Energy Plants
N.A.I.C.S.: 541330
Marcos Enrique Antuna Egocheaga *(CEO)*

HidroCantabrico Energia, S.A.U.　**(2)**
Plaza de la Gesta 2, Oviedo, 33007, Spain　　　　　　　　　**(100%)**
Tel.: (34) 902830100
Retail & Supply of Electricity
N.A.I.C.S.: 221121
João Manuel Manso Neto *(CEO)*

Naturgas Energia Grupo, S.A.　**(2)**
Plz de Pio Baroja 3, 48001, Bilbao, Spain　　　　　　　　　**(100%)**
Tel.: (34) 944035700
Web Site: http://www.naturgasenergia.com
Sales Range: $150-199.9 Million
Emp.: 200
Gas & Electricity Marketing & Supply
N.A.I.C.S.: 221210

Subsidiary (Domestic):

Naturgas Energia Comercializadoras Ultimo Recurso, S.A.　　　**(3)**
General Concha 20, Bilbao, 48010, Spain
Tel.: (34) 944035700
Natural Gas Distribution Services
N.A.I.C.S.: 221210

Hidrocantabrico Cogeneracion, S.L.　　　**(1)**
Plaza Gesta 2, Oviedo, 33007, Spain
Tel.: (34) 985230300
Eletric Power Generation Services
N.A.I.C.S.: 221118

O&M Servicos - Operacao e Manutencao Industrial, S.A.　　　**(1)**
Lugar Do Freixo Nr 45, Mortagua, 3450-116, Viseu, Portugal
Tel.: (351) 231927530

Web Site: http://www.edp.pt
Emp.: 30
Eletric Power Generation Services
N.A.I.C.S.: 221118

Parques Eolicos del Cantabrico S.A. (1)
Plaza De La Gesta 2-Planta 4, Oviedo, 33007, Spain
Tel.: (34) 917819353
Web Site: http://www.edpr.com
Eletric Power Generation Services
N.A.I.C.S.: 221118

Portgas-Sociedade de Producao e Distribuicao de Gas SA (1)
Rua Linhas de Torres 41, 4350 214, Porto, Portugal (72%)
Tel.: (351) 225071400
Web Site: http://www.portgas.pt
Sales Range: $125-149.9 Million
Emp.: 100
Natural Gas Distribution
N.A.I.C.S.: 221210

SARL LEMEE (1)
Bel-Air, 22100, Aucaleuc, France (58.91%)
Tel.: (33) 296394564
Web Site: http://www.lemee-sarl.fr
Grain & Animal Feed Whslr
N.A.I.C.S.: 424590

Santa Quiteria Energia, S.L.U. (1)
Pz Antonio Beltran Martinez 1, Zaragoza, 50002, Spain
Tel.: (34) 976216735
Web Site: http://www.edp.com
Wind Power Plant Construction Services
N.A.I.C.S.: 237130

EDPA KIMYA SAN. VE TIC. A.S.
Husrev Gerede Cad No 126, Tevikiye, 34365, Istanbul, Turkiye
Tel.: (90) 2122591791 TR
Real Estate Development Services
N.A.I.C.S.: 531390

EDPA TEKSTIL TICARET A.S.
Vali Konagi Cad Kocatas Ishani No 26, Nisantas, 34365, Istanbul, Turkiye
Tel.: (90) 2122196595 TR
Real Estate Development Services
N.A.I.C.S.: 531390

EDRAN BERHAD
No 2 Jalan 4/76C Desa Pandan, 55100, Kuala Lumpur, Malaysia
Tel.: (60) 392067200
Web Site: http://www.edaran.com
EDARAN—(KLS)
Rev.: $14,694,498
Assets: $13,921,743
Liabilities: $7,741,074
Net Worth: $6,180,668
Earnings: $428,004
Fiscal Year-end: 06/30/23
Information Technology Services
N.A.I.C.S.: 513210
Asbanizam Abu Bakar *(Head-Legal & Secretarial Grp)*

Subsidiaries:

Edaran IT Services Sdn. Bhd. (1)
No 2 Jalan 4/76C Desa Pandan, 55100, Kuala Lumpur, Malaysia
Tel.: (60) 392067200
Sales Range: $25-49.9 Million
Emp.: 100
Software Development Services
N.A.I.C.S.: 541511

Edaran Trade Network Sdn. Bhd. (1)
No 2 4 and 6 Jalan 4/76C, Desa Pandan, 55100, Kuala Lumpur, Malaysia
Tel.: (60) 392067200
Web Site: https://www.edarantrade.net
Electronic Data Exchange Services
N.A.I.C.S.: 522320

SIDIC Technology Sdn. Bhd. (1)
No 2 Jalan 4/76C, Desa Pandan, 55100, Kuala Lumpur, Malaysia
Tel.: (60) 392067200

Web Site: http://www.edaran.com
Emp.: 80
Surveillance System Installation Services
N.A.I.C.S.: 561990
Arif Hassan *(VP)*

Shinba-Edaran Sdn. Bhd. (1)
Unit 1 Level 3 Bangunan Dar Takaful IBB Utama Jalan Pemancha, Bandar Seri Begawan, Brunei Darussalam
Tel.: (673) 2236777
Sales Range: $25-49.9 Million
Emp.: 5
Software Development Services
N.A.I.C.S.: 541511

EDRASIS - C. PSALLIDAS S.A.
47th Km of Attiki Odos, 19400, Koropi, Greece
Tel.: (30) 2106680600
Web Site: http://www.edrasis.gr
Year Founded: 1974
Sales Range: $10-24.9 Million
Emp.: 504
Geo Technical Engineering Contract Services
N.A.I.C.S.: 541330
Constantinos Psallidas *(Chm & Mng Dir)*

Subsidiaries:

Enviprosystems S.A. (1)
47 Km Attiki Odos, Koropi, 19400, Greece
Tel.: (30) 2106680600
Web Site: http://www.edrasis.gr
Emp.: 150
Environmental Protection Systems Design & Construction Services
N.A.I.C.S.: 238210
Costas Psallidas *(Gen Mgr)*

Redra Construct Group S.A (1)
Bd Libertatii nr 8 bl 115 sc 1 ap 15, Sector 4, Bucharest, 062203, Romania
Tel.: (40) 213118365
Commercial Building Construction Services
N.A.I.C.S.: 236220

EDRI-EL ISRAEL ASSETS LTD.
37 Itzhak Sade Street, Tel Aviv, 37213, Israel
Tel.: (972) 36090772
Web Site: http://www.edrigroup.co.il
EDRL—(TAE)
Assets: $712,272
Liabilities: $557,182
Net Worth: $155,089
Earnings: ($9,994,577)
Fiscal Year-end: 12/31/22
Real Estate Investment Services
N.A.I.C.S.: 531390

EDS-R GMBH
Maybachstr 18, 90441, Nuremberg, Germany
Tel.: (49) 911424770
Web Site: http://www.eds-r.com
Environmental Support Services
N.A.I.C.S.: 541620
Johann Schmidt *(Mng Dir)*

EDSERV SOFTSYSTEMS LIMITED
New No 50 Old No 72 Arya Gowder Road West Mambalam, Chennai, 600 033, India
Tel.: (91) 44 3988 5533
Sales Range: $1-9.9 Million
Online Education Services
N.A.I.C.S.: 923110
S. Giridharan *(Chm, CEO & Mng Dir)*

EDTECHX HOLDINGS ACQUISITION CORP.
22 Soho Square, London, W1D 4NS, United Kingdom
Tel.: (44) 207 070 7080 DE
Web Site:
http://www.edtechxcorp.com
Year Founded: 2018

EDTXU—(NASDAQ)
Rev.: $1,509,120
Assets: $66,071,605
Liabilities: $61,071,595
Net Worth: $5,000,010
Earnings: $383,031
Emp.: 2
Fiscal Year-end: 12/31/19
Holding Company
N.A.I.C.S.: 551112
Charles McIntyre *(Chm & Chief Investment Officer)*

EDTRIN GROUP LIMITED
406 Queens Parade, Clifton Hill, Melbourne, 3068, VIC, Australia
Tel.: (61) 3 9481 2111
Web Site: http://www.edtrin.com
Education Services
N.A.I.C.S.: 611710
Koichiro Matsuura *(Chm)*

EDUARD KETTNER
Z I Metz Nord 57 B Avenue Des 2 Fontaines, 57050, Metz, Moselle, France
Tel.: (33) 387347373
Rev.: $36,700,000
Emp.: 80
N.A.I.C.S.: 459110
Francis Gerard *(Dir-Admin)*

EDUCATION CARTOGRAPHY & ILLUSTRATION JSC
45 Hang Chuoi Str Pham Dinh Ho Ward, Hai Ba Trung Dist, Hanoi, Vietnam
Tel.: (84) 439716096
Web Site:
http://www.bandotranhanh.vn
ECI—(HNX)
Rev.: $5,419,200
Assets: $5,819,200
Liabilities: $1,671,600
Net Worth: $4,147,600
Earnings: $265,900
Fiscal Year-end: 12/31/22
Office Equipments Mfr
N.A.I.C.S.: 333310
Vinh Trong Ngo *(Chm-Mgmt Bd)*

EDUCATION MEDIA & PUBLISHING GROUP (CHINA) LIMITED
75 Saint Stephens Green, Dublin, 2, Ireland
Tel.: (353) 1 511 0100 IE
Web Site: http://www.empgi.com
Media & Publishing Investment Holding Company
N.A.I.C.S.: 551112
Barry O'Callaghan *(Chm)*

EDUCATIONAL BOOK JSC
39 Trinh Dinh Thao Khue Trung Ward, Cam Le District, Da Nang, Vietnam
Tel.: (84) 2363797971
Web Site:
http://www.sachgiaoduc.com
DAE—(HNX)
Rev.: $2,335,628
Assets: $2,027,740
Liabilities: $310,936
Net Worth: $1,716,804
Earnings: $131,387
Emp.: 23
Fiscal Year-end: 12/31/23
Books Publishing Services
N.A.I.C.S.: 513130
Vinh Trong Ngo *(Chm)*

EDUCATIONAL BOOK JSC
Building D 2nd Floor Vinaconex1 289A Trung Hoa ward, Cau Giay District, Hanoi, Vietnam

Tel.: (84) 462534302
Web Site:
http://www.sachgiaoduchanoi.vn
EBS—(HNX)
Rev.: $4,568,670
Assets: $6,305,024
Liabilities: $771,995
Net Worth: $5,533,030
Earnings: $320,498
Fiscal Year-end: 12/31/20
Books Publishing Services
N.A.I.C.S.: 513130
Nguyen Thi Hoa *(Chief Acctg Officer)*

EDUCATIONAL BOOK JSC
No 363 Hung Phu Street Ward 9 District 8, Ho Chi Minh City, Vietnam
Tel.: (84) 839540600
Web Site:
http://www.sachgiaoduchcm.com.vn
SGD—(HNX)
Rev.: $20,396,100
Assets: $8,657,400
Liabilities: $2,694,300
Net Worth: $5,963,100
Earnings: $158,900
Emp.: 37
Fiscal Year-end: 12/31/23
Books Publishing Services
N.A.I.C.S.: 513130
Vinh Ngo *(Chm-Mgmt Bd)*

EDUCATIONPARTNER CO LTD
8th Floor 125 Yanghwa-ro Mapo-gu, Seoul, 121-838, Korea (South)
Tel.: (82) 263375433
Educational Service Provider
N.A.I.C.S.: 611710

EDUCOMP SOLUTIONS, LTD.
514 Udyog Vihar Phase III, Gurgaon, 122 001, India
Tel.: (91) 911244529000 In
Web Site: https://www.educomp.com
Year Founded: 1994
EDUCOMP—(NSE)
Sales Range: $50-74.9 Million
Educational Technology Products & Services
N.A.I.C.S.: 611710
Shantanu Prakash *(Chm & Mng Dir)*

Subsidiaries:

Edumatics Corporation Inc. (1)
1655 Mesa Verde Ave Ste 120, Ventura, CA 93003
Tel.: (805) 650-3000
Web Site: http://www.edusmart.com
Educational Support Services
N.A.I.C.S.: 611710

Learning Internet Inc. (1)
1618 SW 1st Ave 215, Portland, OR 97201
Web Site: http://www.learning.com
Educational Support Services
N.A.I.C.S.: 611710
Keith Oelrich *(CEO)*

Savvica Inc. (1)
116 Spadina Ave 701, Toronto, M5V 2K6, ON, Canada
Tel.: (416) 363-9510
Educational Support Services
N.A.I.C.S.: 611710

Wizlearn Technologies (1)
10 Science Park Road 03 13 The Alpha, Singapore Science Park II, Singapore, 117684, Singapore
Tel.: (65) 67762013
Web Site: http://www.wizlearn.com
Sales Range: $10-24.9 Million
Emp.: 100
Internet-Based E-Learning Solutions, Content & Services for Schools
N.A.I.C.S.: 611710

Wizlearn Technologies Pte Ltd. (1)
10 Science Park Road 03-13 Alpha Science Park II, Singapore, 117884, Singapore
Tel.: (65) 67762013
Educational Support Services

Educomp Solutions, Ltd.—(Continued)
N.A.I.C.S.: 611710

EDUEXEL INFOTAINMENT LIMITED

No 1 Wallers Lane 1st Floor Room No 3 Mataji Complex Near India, Silk House Mount Road, Chennai, 600 002, Tamil Nadu, India
Tel.: (91) 9003113372
Assets: $1,675,996
Liabilities: $202
Net Worth: $1,675,794
Earnings: ($6,141)
Fiscal Year-end: 03/31/18
Television Broadcasting Services
N.A.I.C.S.: 516120

EDULAB, INC.

13F W Building 1-8-15 Konan, Minato-ku, Tokyo, 108-0075, Japan
Tel.: (81) 366257700
Web Site: https://www.edulab-inc.com
Year Founded: 2015
4427—(TKS)
Rev.: $50,062,490
Assets: $42,688,890
Liabilities: $29,331,330
Net Worth: $13,357,560
Earnings: ($22,014,450)
Emp.: 153
Fiscal Year-end: 09/30/23
Educational Support Services
N.A.I.C.S.: 611710
Junichi Takamura (Pres & CEO)

Subsidiaries:

Edutech Lab AP Private Limited (1)
10 Collyer Quay 10-01 Ocean Financial Centre, Singapore, 049315, Singapore
Tel.: (65) 91078374
Software Development Services
N.A.I.C.S.: 541511

Edutech Lab, Inc. (1)
10900 NE 4th St Ste 2300, Bellevue, WA 98004
Tel.: (425) 440-2671
Web Site: https://www.edutech-lab.com
Software Development Services
N.A.I.C.S.: 541511

The Japan Institute for Educational Measurement, Inc. (1)
Shibuya Solasta Bldg 14F 1-21-1 Dōgen-zaka, Shibuya-ku, Tokyo, 150-0043, Japan
Tel.: (81) 366257720
Web Site: https://www.jiem.co.jp
Emp.: 170
Learning Services
N.A.I.C.S.: 611420
Hiroyuki Otake (Pres)

EDUN APPAREL LTD.

30 32 Sir John Rogersons Quay, Dublin, 2, Ireland
Tel.: (353) 12561289
Web Site: http://www.edun.com
Year Founded: 2005
Sales Range: $10-24.9 Million
Emp.: 20
Clothing Mfr & Retailer
N.A.I.C.S.: 315250
Ali Hewson (Founder)

EDUNIVERSAL SA

18-20 avenue Gabriel Peri, 93100, Montreuil, France
Tel.: (33) 148579744
Web Site: http://www.smbg.fr
Educational Support Services
N.A.I.C.S.: 611710
Martial Guiette (Chm & CEO)

EDUSPEC HOLDINGS BER-HAD

No 10 Jalan 15/ 22 Tiong Nam Indus-

trial Park Section 15, 40200, Shah Alam, Selangor Darul Ehsan, Malaysia
Tel.: (60) 355231781   **MY**
Web Site: https://www.eduspec.com.my
Year Founded: 1984
EDUSPEC—(KLS)
Rev.: $4,800,127
Assets: $24,737,436
Liabilities: $8,558,381
Net Worth: $16,179,055
Earnings: ($2,191,218)
Fiscal Year-end: 02/29/24
Information Technology & Educational Services
N.A.I.C.S.: 541512
Een Hong Lim (Chm & CEO)

EDVANCE INTERNATIONAL HOLDINGS LIMITED

39/F Montery Plaza 15 Chong Yip Street Kwun Tong, Kowloon, China (Hong Kong)
Tel.: (852) 3 184 9400   **Ky**
Web Site: http://www.edvancesecurity.com
Year Founded: 2002
1410—(HKG)
Rev.: $67,763,899
Assets: $69,693,440
Liabilities: $48,461,913
Net Worth: $21,231,527
Earnings: $2,716,577
Emp.: 112
Fiscal Year-end: 03/31/22
Software Development Services
N.A.I.C.S.: 541511
Raymond Yui Ting Liu (Co-Founder & Chm)

Subsidiaries:

Axion Global Digits Technology (Hong Kong) Limited (1)
20/F 8 Wyndham Street, Central, China (Hong Kong)
Tel.: (852) 3 184 9422
Web Site: https://www.agdigits.com
Asset Management Services
N.A.I.C.S.: 523940

ESH (Hong Kong) Limited (1)
18/F Prosperity Center 25 Chong Yip Street, Kwun Tong, Kowloon, China (Hong Kong)
Tel.: (852) 38998400
Information Technology Services
N.A.I.C.S.: 541511

Edvance Technology (Hong Kong) Limited (1)
25/F Tower 1 The Millennity 98 How Ming Street, Kwun Tong, Kowloon, China (Hong Kong)
Tel.: (852) 31849400
Web Site: https://www.edvance.hk
Software Development Services
N.A.I.C.S.: 513210

Edvance Technology (Singapore) Pte. Ltd. (1)
2 Sims Close 01-11/12 Gemini Sims, Singapore, 387298, Singapore
Tel.: (65) 62480600
Web Site: http://www.edvancesecurity.com
Emp.: 10
Software Development Services
N.A.I.C.S.: 513210
Andrew Lam (Mng Dir)

Green Radar (Hong Kong) Limited (1)
25/F Tower 1 The Millennity 98 How Ming Street, Kwun Tong, Kowloon, China (Hong Kong)
Tel.: (852) 31942200
Web Site: https://www.greenradar.com
Software Development Services
N.A.I.C.S.: 513210

Green Radar (SG) Pte Limited (1)
2 Sims Close 01-11/12, Singapore, 387298, Singapore

Tel.: (65) 62480600
Web Site: https://www.greenradar.com
Cyber Security Services
N.A.I.C.S.: 561621

EDVANTAGE GROUP HOLDINGS LIMITED

Room 1115 11/F Wing On Plaza 62 Mody Road, Tsim Sha Tsui, Kowloon, China (Hong Kong)
Tel.: (852) 3 168 6668   **Ky**
Web Site: http://www.edvantagegroup.com.hk
Year Founded: 2003
0382—(HKG)
Rev.: $191,764,377
Assets: $944,706,189
Liabilities: $478,035,424
Net Worth: $466,670,766
Earnings: $71,965,188
Emp.: 4,900
Fiscal Year-end: 08/31/21
Holding Company
N.A.I.C.S.: 551112
Yung Chau Liu (Chm)

Subsidiaries:

Edvantage Institute (Singapore) Pte. Ltd. (1)
91 Bencoolen Street 03-02/03 Sunshine Plaza, Singapore, 189652, Singapore
Tel.: (65) 63383533
Web Site: https://www.eis.edu.sg
Higher Education Support Services
N.A.I.C.S.: 611310

Edvantage Institute Australia Pty. Ltd. (1)
Queen St Campus 338 Queen St, Melbourne, 3000, VIC, Australia
Tel.: (61) 390413050
Web Site: https://www.eia.edu.au
Higher Education Support Services
N.A.I.C.S.: 611310
Celina Yu (Gen Mgr)

Global Business College of Australia Pty. Ltd. (1)
337-339 La Trobe Street 338 Queen Street, Melbourne, 3000, VIC, Australia
Tel.: (61) 390413050
Web Site: https://www.gbca.edu.au
Higher Education Support Services
N.A.I.C.S.: 611310
Celina Ping Yu (Mng Dir)

EDVENSWA ENTERPRISES LIMITED

H No 1-36/13 Manju Anurag Enclave, Malkajgiri, Hyderabad, 500047, India
Tel.: (91) 4042039977
Web Site: https://www.klk.co.in
Year Founded: 1980
517170—(BOM)
Rev.: $5,332,239
Assets: $3,372,377
Liabilities: $797,345
Net Worth: $2,575,031
Earnings: $512,649
Fiscal Year-end: 03/31/22
Electric Equipment Mfr
N.A.I.C.S.: 335999
R. Ravi Kumar Rao (Exec Dir)

EDWARD B. BEHARRY & CO. LTD.

191 Charlotte Street, Georgetown, Guyana
Tel.: (592) 2270632
Web Site: http://www.beharrygroup.com
Year Founded: 1935
Sales Range: $350-399.9 Million
Emp.: 1,500
Holding Company
N.A.I.C.S.: 551112
Suresh Beharry (Chm)

Subsidiaries:

Beharry Automotive Limited (1)

192 N1/2 Wellington Street, Lacytown, Georgetown, Guyana
Tel.: (592) 2272526
Automotive Spare Parts Distr
N.A.I.C.S.: 423120
Jan Verwey (Mgr)

Guyana Americas Merchant Bank Inc. (1)
GBTI Corporate Office High and Young Streets, Kingston, Georgetown, Guyana
Tel.: (592) 592 223 5193
Web Site: http://www.gasci.com
Emp.: 5
Financial Brokerage Services
N.A.I.C.S.: 523150
Richard Isava (Mng Dir)

North American Fire and General Insurance Company (1)
30/31 Regent & Hincks Streets, Robbstown, Georgetown, Guyana
Tel.: (592) 226 9241
Insurance Services
N.A.I.C.S.: 524113

Secure International Finance Co. Inc. (1)
191 Wellington & Charlotte Streets, Lacytown, Georgetown, Guyana
Tel.: (592) 2272526
Web Site: http://www.beharrygroup.com
Sales Range: $50-74.9 Million
Emp.: 9
Financial Management Services
N.A.I.C.S.: 523999

Subsidiary (Domestic):

Guyana Bank for Trade & Industry Ltd. (2)
47-48 Water St, PO Box 10280, Georgetown, Guyana (61%)
Tel.: (592) 2268430
Web Site: http://www.gbtibank.com
Sales Range: $1-9.9 Million
Emp.: 250
Banking Services
N.A.I.C.S.: 522110
Nolan Hendricks (Chief Security Officer)

Sterling Products Limited (1)
East Bank Public Road, Providence, Demerara, Guyana
Tel.: (592) 592 265 7403
Web Site: http://www.sterlingguyana.com
Saop & Detergent Mfr
N.A.I.C.S.: 325611

EDWARD BILLINGTON & SON LTD.

Cunard Building, Liverpool, L3 1EL, United Kingdom
Tel.: (44) 151 243 9000
Web Site: http://www.ebsgroup.co.uk
Year Founded: 1898
Sales Range: $350-399.9 Million
Emp.: 638
Investment Management Service
N.A.I.C.S.: 523940
Lloyd Whiteley (Chm)

EDWARD DILLON & CO. LTD.

Estuary House Block P7 East Point Business Park, Fairview, Dublin, 3, Ireland
Tel.: (353) 18193300
Web Site: http://www.edwarddillonco.ie
Wines & Spirit Distr
N.A.I.C.S.: 424820
Andy O'Hara (CEO)

EDWARDS DOORS SYSTEMS LIMITED

PO Box 607, Sarnia, N7T 7J4, ON, Canada
Tel.: (519) 336-4991
Web Site: http://www.edwardsdoors.com
Year Founded: 1972
Rev.: $10,617,200
Emp.: 30

Electronic High Security Locks Industrial Doors Mfr
N.A.I.C.S.: 423310
G. W. Cassidy *(CEO)*

EDWARDS GARAGE LTD.
4403 42nd Avenue, PO Box 880, Rocky Mountain House, T4T 1A6, AB, Canada
Tel.: (403) 845-3328
Web Site:
http://www.edwardsgarage.com
Rev.: $17,883,600
Emp.: 50
New & Used Car Dealers
N.A.I.C.S.: 441110
Ken Charlton *(Mgr-Fleet)*

EDYNAMICS SOLUTIONS LTD
103 Plot No 2 1st Floor Triveni Complex Veer Savarkar Block, Shakarpur, New Delhi, 110092, India
Tel.: (91) 1165670013
Web Site:
http://www.edynamicssolutions.com
Rev.: $164,578
Assets: $6,458,256
Liabilities: $925,369
Net Worth: $5,532,887
Earnings: $436
Fiscal Year-end: 03/31/18
Internet Retailer
N.A.I.C.S.: 541511

EE-HWA CONSTRUCTION CO., LTD.
371-14 Seokyo-Dong, Mapo-ku, Seoul, 121-838, Korea (South)
Tel.: (82) 23360041
Web Site: http://www.ee-hwa.co.kr
Year Founded: 1956
001840—(KRS)
Rev.: $149,226,180
Assets: $72,688,731
Liabilities: $36,672,487
Net Worth: $36,016,244
Earnings: $438,505
Emp.: 173
Fiscal Year-end: 12/31/22
Construction Engineering Services
N.A.I.C.S.: 541330
Jong Hoon Lee *(Deputy Head-Dept)*

EEI CORPORATION
12 Manggahan St Bagumbayan, Quezon City, 1110, Philippines
Tel.: (63) 3342677   PH
Web Site: http://www.eei.com.ph
Year Founded: 1931
EEI—(PHI)
Rev.: $333,637,725
Assets: $533,575,023
Liabilities: $303,754,890
Net Worth: $229,820,133
Earnings: $2,816,052
Emp.: 5,113
Fiscal Year-end: 12/31/23
Engineering & General Construction Services
N.A.I.C.S.: 333120
Oscar D. Mercado *(Sr VP-Engrg & Mktg)*

Subsidiaries:

EEI Construction & Marine Corp. **(1)**
12 Manggahan St, Bagumbayan, Quezon City, 1100, Manila, Philippines **(100%)**
Tel.: (63) 286360620
Web Site: https://www.eeicmi.com
Emp.: 150
Ship Repair; Ship Breaking; Ship Building
N.A.I.C.S.: 336611

EEI Power Corp. **(1)**
12 Mangahan St Brgy Bagumbayan Libis, Bagumbayan, Quezon City, 1100, Metro Manila, Philippines **(100%)**
Tel.: (63) 286350843

Emp.: 20
Power Generation
N.A.I.C.S.: 335312

EEI-Construction Division **(1)**
12 Mangahan St Brgy Bagumbayan Libis, Quezon City, 1110, Metro Manila, Philippines **(70%)**
Tel.: (63) 26350843
Web Site: http://www.eei.com
Sales Range: $25-49.9 Million
Emp.: 4,000
Large-Scale Industrial Construction
N.A.I.C.S.: 236220

Gulf Asia International Corporation **(1)**
Ground Fl Topy Bldg No 3 Economia St, Bagumbayan, Quezon City, 1110, Philippines **(100%)**
Tel.: (63) 286347551
Web Site: https://www.gaicgrp.com
Emp.: 37
Recruitment Agency
N.A.I.C.S.: 561311
Ricardo C. Reyes *(Pres)*

EEII AG
Alpenstrasse 15, PO Box 7863, 6302, Zug, Switzerland
Tel.: (41) 417294280
Web Site: https://www.eeii.ch
Year Founded: 1997
EEII—(SWX)
Rev.: $1,467
Assets: $586,204
Liabilities: $60,956
Net Worth: $525,248
Earnings: ($7,296,839)
Fiscal Year-end: 12/31/22
Energy & Commodity Service Sectors
N.A.I.C.S.: 541990
Victor Lorenz Gnehm *(Chm)*

EEKA FASHION HOLDINGS LIMITED
7/F B Block Hongsong Building Terra 9th Road Chegongmiao, Futian District, Shenzhen, Guangdong, China
Tel.: (86) 75583303808   Ky
Web Site:
http://wwww.eekagroup.com
Year Founded: 2012
3709—(HKG)
Rev.: $795,145,572
Assets: $878,578,693
Liabilities: $318,733,693
Net Worth: $559,845,000
Earnings: $52,709,670
Emp.: 10,327
Fiscal Year-end: 12/31/22
Holding Company
N.A.I.C.S.: 551112
Ming Jin *(Founder, Chm & CEO)*

Subsidiaries:

Shenzen Koradior Fashion Co., Ltd. **(1)**
Hong Song Building B Block 7th Floor Terra 9th Road Che Gong Miao, Futian District, Shenzhen, 518048, China
Tel.: (86) 75583303808
Web Site: http://www.en.koradior.com
Ladies Fashion Wear Mfr & Retailer
N.A.I.C.S.: 315250

EEMS ITALIA S.P.A
Viale delle Scienze 5, 02015, Cittaducale, Italy
Tel.: (39) 07466041
Web Site: https://www.eems.com
Year Founded: 1994
EEMS—(ITA)
Sales Range: $200-249.9 Million
Emp.: 1,431
Semiconductor Assembly & Test Solutions
N.A.I.C.S.: 333242
Pasquale Amido *(Dir-R&D)*

Subsidiaries:

Solsonica **(1)**
Viale delle Scienze 5, Cittaducale, 02015, Italy
Tel.: (39) 0746604500
Web Site: http://www.solsonica.com
Sales Range: $75-99.9 Million
Emp.: 236
Photovoltaic & Solar Energy Management
N.A.I.C.S.: 926130

EENERGY GROUP PLC
Salisbury House London Wall, London, EC2M 5PS, United Kingdom
Tel.: (44) 2070789564
Web Site: http://eenergyplc.com
EAAS—(AIM)
Rev.: $30,000,181
Assets: $67,469,180
Liabilities: $36,855,309
Net Worth: $30,613,871
Earnings: ($2,024,361)
Emp.: 128
Fiscal Year-end: 06/30/22
Metal Ore Mining
N.A.I.C.S.: 212290
Harvey Sinclair *(CEO)*

Subsidiaries:

Beond Group Limited **(1)**
Building 11 Chiswick Business Park 566 Chiswick High Road, London, W4 5YS, United Kingdom
Tel.: (44) 208 634 7533
Web Site: https://beondgroup.com
Environmental Consulting Services
N.A.I.C.S.: 541620
Alastair Huston *(Mng Dir)*

Compania Minera Molinetes SAC **(1)**
Av Paseo De La Republica No 3195 Dpto 906, San Isidro, Lima, Peru
Tel.: (51) 1 4422309
Mineral Mining Services
N.A.I.C.S.: 212390

MetaLeach Limited **(1)**
Martin Rosser and Matthew Sutcliffe 1st Fl 35 Piccadilly, London, W1J 0DW, United Kingdom
Tel.: (44) 2072921300
Web Site: http://www.metaleach.com
Sales Range: $25-49.9 Million
Hydrometallurgical Mineral Processing Services
N.A.I.C.S.: 541380

Renewable Solutions Lighting Limited **(1)**
Suite 2 St Frances House Olding Road, Bury Saint Edmunds, IP33 3TA, United Kingdom
Tel.: (44) 208 108 5975
Web Site: https://rslighting.co.uk
Turnkey Led Lighting Installation Services
N.A.I.C.S.: 238210
Karl Peachey *(Project Mgr)*

EESTECH, INC.
241 Adelaide Street Suite 471, Brisbane, 4000, QLD, Australia
Tel.: (61) 417079299   DE
Web Site:
https://www.eestechinc.com
Year Founded: 2000
EESH—(OTCIQ)
Sales Range: Less than $1 Million
Waste Management Services
N.A.I.C.S.: 562998
Murray Bailey *(Chm & CEO)*

EESTI ENERGIA AS
Lelle 22, 11318, Tallinn, Estonia
Tel.: (372) 46 52 222
Web Site: http://www.energia.ee
Year Founded: 1939
Rev.: $1,140,577,410
Assets: $3,883,786,466
Liabilities: $1,866,246,690
Net Worth: $2,017,539,776

Earnings: $25,868,766
Emp.: 5,020
Fiscal Year-end: 12/31/19
Electricity, Heat & Fuel Production & Sales
N.A.I.C.S.: 335311
Raine Pajo *(Member-Mgmt Bd)*

Subsidiaries:

Eesti Energia Tehnoloogiatoostus AS **(1)**
Malmi 8, 41537, Johvi, Estonia **(100%)**
Tel.: (372) 7166702
Web Site: http://www.enefit.com.ee
Sales Range: $25-49.9 Million
Emp.: 900
Plate Work Mfr
N.A.I.C.S.: 332313
Otto Richard Pukk *(Member-Mgmt Bd-Construction & Installation)*

Eesti Polevkivi AS **(1)**
Jaama tn 10, 41533, Johvi, Estonia **(100%)**
Tel.: (372) 3364801
Web Site: http://www.ep.ee
Sales Range: $1-4.9 Billion
Emp.: 3,000
Crude Petroleum & Natural Gas Extraction
N.A.I.C.S.: 211120
Andres Vainola *(Chm)*

Elektrilevi OU **(1)**
Veskiposti 2, 10138, Tallinn, Estonia **(100%)**
Tel.: (372) 7154230
Web Site: http://www.elektrilevi.ee
Sales Range: $200-249.9 Million
Emp.: 800
Electricity Supplier
N.A.I.C.S.: 221122
Jaanus Tiisvend *(Chm-Mgmt Bd)*

Elpec AS **(1)**
Kadaka 63, 12915, Tallinn, Estonia **(100%)**
Tel.: (372) 7154100
Web Site: http://www.elpec.ee
Sales Range: $25-49.9 Million
Emp.: 80
Architectural Services
N.A.I.C.S.: 541310
Mike Teske *(Mng Dir)*

Enefit Outotec Technology OU **(1)**
Ludwig-Erhard-Strasse 21, Oberursel, 61440, Germany
Tel.: (49) 617 12063521
Web Site: http://www.enefit.com
Emp.: 5
Eletric Power Generation Services
N.A.I.C.S.: 221118
Robert A. Mergler *(CTO)*

Enefit SIA **(1)**
Vesetas Street 7, Riga, LV-1013, Latvia
Tel.: (371) 677 80590
Web Site: http://www.enefit.lv
Eletric Power Generation Services
N.A.I.C.S.: 221118
Krists Mertens *(Head-Enefit)*

Iru Elektrijaam OU **(1)**
Peterburi tee 105, 74114, Maardu, Estonia **(100%)**
Tel.: (372) 7153222
Web Site: http://www.iruenergia.ee
Sales Range: $75-99.9 Million
Emp.: 51
Other Electric Power Generation
N.A.I.C.S.: 221118

Maetehnika AS **(1)**
8 Malmi, Johvi, 41537, Estonia **(100%)**
Tel.: (372) 3364301
Web Site: http://www.tehmoolgiatoost.ee
Sales Range: $100-124.9 Million
Emp.: 360
Mining Machinery & Equipment Mfr
N.A.I.C.S.: 333131

Narva Elektrijaamad As **(1)**
Elektrijaama Tee 59, Narva, Tallinn, 40101, Estonia **(100%)**
Tel.: (372) 7166100
Sales Range: $400-449.9 Million
Emp.: 1,300
Instrument Mfr for Measuring & Testing Electricity & Electrical Signals

Eesti Energia AS—(Continued)
N.A.I.C.S.: 334515

Narva Soojusvork AS (1)
Oru 2, Narva, 20203, Tallinn,
Estonia (34%)
Tel.: (372) 3591250
Produces, Sells & Transmits Electric &
Thermal Power
N.A.I.C.S.: 221122

Nordic Energy Link AS (1)
Laki 24, Tallinn, 12915, Estonia (100%)
Tel.: (372) 7152307
Electrical Apparatus & Equipment Wiring
Supplies & Construction Material Wholr
N.A.I.C.S.: 423610

Pohivork OU (1)
Kadaka tee 42, 12915, Tallinn,
Estonia (100%)
Tel.: (372) 7151209
Web Site: http://www.elering.ee
Emp.: 150
Instrument Mfr for Measuring & Testing
Electricity & Electrical Signals
N.A.I.C.S.: 334515

Solidus OY (1)
Toolonkatu 4, Helsinki, 00101, Finland
Tel.: (358) 969 306066
Electric Power Distr
N.A.I.C.S.: 221122

EF-ON INC.
17F Gran Tokyo South Tower 1-9-2
Marunouchi, Chiyoda-ku, Tokyo, 100-
6617, Japan
Tel.: (81) 345006450
Web Site: https://www.ef-on.co.jp
Year Founded: 1997
9514—(TKS)
Rev.: $108,682,060
Assets: $281,529,640
Liabilities: $168,114,160
Net Worth: $113,415,480
Earnings: $1,747,820
Emp.: 267
Fiscal Year-end: 06/30/24
Energy Conservation Support Services
N.A.I.C.S.: 541690
Tomotada Shimazaki (Pres)

EFACEC CAPITAL, SGPS, S.A.
Arroteia Leca do Balio Apartado 1018
4466-952, S Mamede de Infesta,
4466-952, Porto, Portugal
Tel.: (351) 229562300 PT
Web Site: http://www.efacec.pt
Year Founded: 1948
Sales Range: $1-4.9 Billion
Emp.: 150
Holding Company
N.A.I.C.S.: 551112
Angelo Manuel Da Cruz Ramalho
(Pres & CEO)

Subsidiaries:

Efacec ALGERIE EURL. (1)
Business Center Dar El Madina Tour A
etage 7, Micro zone d'activite Hydra Lote N
20, 16000, Algiers, Algeria
Tel.: (213) 23531481
Electrical Equipment Distr
N.A.I.C.S.: 423440

Efacec ASIA PACIFICO, Ltd., (1)
Av da Praia Grande 759 1 Andar, Beijing,
China
Tel.: (86) 283 0183
Electrical Equipment Distr
N.A.I.C.S.: 423440
Joao Sousa (Mng Dir)

Efacec Angola, Lda. (1)
Fidel Castro Avenue Viana Industrial Park,
Viana, 10409, Luanda, Angola
Tel.: (244) 226430210
Electrical Equipment Distr
N.A.I.C.S.: 423440

**Efacec C&S MV Components PvT.
Ltd.** (1)

H-155 Ambad, Nashik, 422010, Maharash-
tra, India
Tel.: (91) 120 435 8149 54
Electrical Equipment Distr
N.A.I.C.S.: 423440

Efacec Central Europe, Ltd, (1)
Dudesti-Pantelimon Street n 42 Rams Cen-
ter Building 3rd Floor, 3rd District, Bucha-
rest, Romania
Tel.: (40) 213233091
Electrical Equipment Distr
N.A.I.C.S.: 423440
Danut Adrian Adrian (Mgr-Ops)

Efacec Chile, SA (1)
Nuestra Senora de los Angeles 179 Las
Condes, 7550039, Santiago, Chile
Tel.: (56) 22484978
Electrical Equipment Distr
N.A.I.C.S.: 423440

**Efacec Contracting Central Europe
GmbH** (1)
Gablenzgasse 3/5 th floor, 1150, Vienna,
Austria
Tel.: (43) 133600040
Electrical Equipment Distr
N.A.I.C.S.: 423440

**Efacec Engenharia e Sistemas,
S.A.** (1)
Rua Eng Frederico Ulrich Guardeiras Apar-
tado 3078, 4471-907, Maia,
Portugal (100%)
Tel.: (351) 229402000
Power, Water Treatment & Waste Treatment
Plants, Renewable Energy Equipment &
Transport Systems Engineering & Construc-
tion Services
N.A.I.C.S.: 541330
Joao Afonso Ramalho Sopas Pereira Bento
(Chm)

Joint Venture (Non-US):

**Godrej Efacec Automation & Robotics
Ltd.** (2)
Plant 19-A Pirojshanagar, Vikhroli, Mumbai,
400 079, India (51%)
Tel.: (91) 2267965347
Web Site: http://www.godrejefacec.com
Automated Storage & Retrieval Systems
Developer & Mfr
N.A.I.C.S.: 333248

Efacec Equipos Electricos, S.L. (1)
Apartment 66 Poligono Industrial Barranc
del Lledo Parcel 09, Santa Barbara, 43570,
Tarragona, Spain
Tel.: (34) 977719811
Electrical Equipment Distr
N.A.I.C.S.: 423440

Efacec MAROC SARLAU (1)
28 Rue de Terves Mers Sultan 20 160, Rue
Moulay Youssef, Casablanca, Morocco
Tel.: (212) 522492494
Electrical Equipment Distr
N.A.I.C.S.: 423440

**Efacec Marketing Internacional,
SA** (1)
Rua Eng Frederico Ulrich Guardeiras Apar-
tado 3078, 4471-907, Moreira, Portugal
Tel.: (351) 229402000
Electric Equipment Mfr
N.A.I.C.S.: 423440

Efacec Mozambique, Lda. (1)
Av Fernao de Magalhaes 932, Maputo,
Mozambique
Tel.: (258) 21 322 035
Electrical Equipment Distr
N.A.I.C.S.: 423440
Victor Jose Muhale (Project Coord)

Efacec PRAHA s.r.o. (1)
U Spejcharu 503, Tuchomerice, 252 67,
Prague, Czech Republic
Tel.: (420) 242426999
Web Site: http://www.efacec.cz
Electrical Equipment Distr
N.A.I.C.S.: 423690

Efacec SINGAPORE Pte, Ltd (1)
1 Kaki Bukit View 02-11 Techview, Singapore, '415941, Singapore
Tel.: (65) 68417073
Web Site: http://www.efacec.com.sg

Emp.: 20
Conveying Equipment Distr
N.A.I.C.S.: 423830
Miguel Silva (Mgr-Engrg & Maintenance)

**Efacec Servicos Corporativos,
SA** (1)
Parque Empresarial Arroteia Poente - Ar-
roteia, Leca do Balio Apartado 1018, 4466-
952, Mamede de Infesta, Portugal
Tel.: (351) 229562300
Electric Equipment Mfr
N.A.I.C.S.: 423690
Luis Campilho (Mgr-Insurance)

Efacec Sistemas Espana, S.L. (1)
Avda de la Industria 4 Edificio 1 Escalera 2
-2 C, Natea Business Park, 28108, Al-
cobendas, Madrid, Spain
Tel.: (34) 916 626 826
Electrical Equipment Distr
N.A.I.C.S.: 423690
Blas Lopez (Bus Mgr)

Efacec TUNIS (1)
Rue du Lac Victoria Immeuble L'Arche du
Lac Bureau N A4 - 3eme etage, 1053, Tu-
nis, Tunisia
Tel.: (216) 71 963 387
Electrical Equipment Distr
N.A.I.C.S.: 423690

Efacec USA, inc. (1)
2755 Northwoods Pkwy Ste B, Norcross,
GA 30071
Tel.: (470) 395-3648
Web Site: http://www.efacecusa.com
Electrical Equipment Mfr & Distr
N.A.I.C.S.: 334416
Mike Anderson (Mgr-Sls-EV Chargers)

Efacec do Brasil, LTDA. (1)
Rua Sena Madureira n 930 - Vila Mariana,
Sao Paulo, 04021-001, Brazil
Tel.: (55) 11 5591 1999
Electrical Equipment Distr
N.A.I.C.S.: 423440

SESCO efacec SDN. BHD. (1)
Lot 755 Block 64-KTLD Jalan Sungai Priok
Off Jalan Pending, 93450, Kuching, Sara-
wak, Malaysia
Tel.: (60) 82 331868
Electrical Equipment Distr
N.A.I.C.S.: 423690

**EFAD REAL ESTATE COM-
PANY**
PO Box 21876, Kuwait, 13079, Ku-
wait
Tel.: (965) 22427060 KW
Web Site: http://www.efadre.com
Holding Company
N.A.I.C.S.: 551112
Rezam Mohamed Al Roumi (CEO)

Subsidiaries:

**Adeem Investment & Wealth Man-
agement Co., K.S.C.C.** (1)
PO Box 29092, 13151, Kuwait, Safat, Ku-
wait
Tel.: (965) 222 33 000
Web Site: http://www.adeeminv.com
Investment & Wealth Management Services
N.A.I.C.S.: 523999
Abdullah Zidan (Sr VP-Direct Investment)

Affiliate (Domestic):

**Investment Dar Company
K.S.C.C.** (2)
Sharq Al Shuhada Street Arraya Center
31st Floor, PO Box 5963, Safat, Kuwait,
13060, Kuwait
Tel.: (965) 22324000
Web Site: http://www.inv-dar.com
Sales Range: $650-699.9 Million
Emp.: 211
Financial, Real Estate & Investment Ser-
vices
N.A.I.C.S.: 523999

Holding (Non-US):

Aston Martin Lagonda Limited (3)
Banbury Road, Gaydon, CV35 0DB, Warks,
United Kingdom

Tel.: (44) 1926644644
Web Site: https://www.astonmartin.com
Sales Range: $350-399.9 Million
Emp.: 1,200
Luxury Sportscar Mfr
N.A.I.C.S.: 336110
Marek Reichman (Dir-Design)

Branch (Domestic):

Aston Martin Lagonda (4)
Tickford Street, Newport Pagnell, MK16
9AN, United Kingdom
Tel.: (44) 1908610620
Web Site: http://www.astonmartin.com
Sales Range: $25-49.9 Million
Emp.: 250
Automobiles Design Services
N.A.I.C.S.: 541330
Maximilian Szwaj (CTO)

Subsidiary (US):

**Aston Martin Lagonda of North
America, Inc.** (4)
9920 Ervine Center Dr, Irvine, CA 92618
Tel.: (949) 379-3100
Web Site: http://www.astonmartin.com
Automobiles & Parts Importer & Distr
N.A.I.C.S.: 423110

**EFANOR INVESTIMENTOS,
SGPS, SA**
Avenida da Boavista, 1277/81 4,
Porto, Portugal
Tel.: (351) 229487522 PT
Investment Holding Company
N.A.I.C.S.: 523999
Belmiro Mendes de Azevedo (Owner
& Chm)

Subsidiaries:

Sonae Capital, SGPS, SA (1)
Lugar do Espido Via Norte, 4471 907, Maia,
Portugal (92.3%)
Tel.: (351) 22 012 95 00
Web Site: http://www.sonaecapital.pt
Rev.: $161,030,396
Assets: $574,098,756
Liabilities: $267,531,322
Net Worth: $306,567,434
Earnings: ($3,729,715)
Emp.: 1,496
Fiscal Year-end: 12/31/2018
Investment Banking Services
N.A.I.C.S.: 523150
Pedro Manuel Bruno (Exec Dir)

Sonae SGPS, SA (1)
Lugar do Espido Via Norte, 4471-909, Maia,
Portugal (52.99%)
Tel.: (351) 220104000
Web Site: https://www.sonae.pt
Rev.: $8,901,141,408
Assets: $9,763,831,550
Liabilities: $5,942,461,641
Net Worth: $3,821,369,909
Earnings: $481,247,378
Emp.: 48,132
Fiscal Year-end: 12/31/2023
Shopping Center Retail Operations, Super-
market Chain Supplier, Real Estate Ser-
vices & Telecommunications
N.A.I.C.S.: 459999
Duarte Paulo Teixeira de Azevedo (Chm)

Subsidiary (Domestic):

Modelo Continente, SGPA, SA (2)
Rua Joao Mondoca 529-6, Serzedo, Portu-
gal
Tel.: (351) 229561958
Operates Supermarkets
N.A.I.C.S.: 445110

Holding (Domestic):

Sonae Industria, SGPS, S.A. (2)
Lugar do Espido - Via Norte Apartado 1096,
4470-177, Maia, Portugal
Tel.: (351) 220 106 300
Web Site: http://www.sonaeindustria.com
Rev.: $255,888,640
Assets: $471,174,280
Liabilities: $328,595,476
Net Worth: $142,578,804
Earnings: ($14,971,799)
Emp.: 3,316

Fiscal Year-end: 12/31/2019
Wood Panel Mfr
N.A.I.C.S.: 321212
Duarte Paulo Teixeira de Azevedo *(Chm)*

Sonae Sierra SGPS, SA **(2)**
Torre Ocidente R Galileu Galilei 2 3 Piso,
Lisbon, 1500-392, Portugal **(70%)**
Tel.: (351) 217515000
Web Site: http://www.sonaesierra.com
Sales Range: $300-349.9 Million
Emp.: 800
Shopping Center Owner, Manager & Developer
N.A.I.C.S.: 531312
Paulo Azevedo *(Chm)*

Subsidiary (Domestic):

Sonae.com **(2)**
Rua Henrique Pousao 432 - 7, Senhora da
Hora, 4460-841, Lisbon, Portugal
Tel.: (351) 229572000
Web Site: http://www.sonae.com
Wireless Communications Website
N.A.I.C.S.: 517810

EFC (I) LIMITED
32 Milan Park Society Nr Jawahar
Chowk, Maninagar, Ahmedabad, 380
008, India
Tel.: (91) 7925462907
Web Site: http://www.amanitrading.in
512008—(BOM)
Rev.: $21,632
Assets: $223,605
Liabilities: $422
Net Worth: $223,183
Earnings: $9,696
Emp.: 2
Fiscal Year-end: 03/31/21
Cotton Product Whslr
N.A.I.C.S.: 424990
Anish A. Shah *(Mng Dir)*

EFESAN GROUP
Visnezade Mahallesi Suleyman Seba
Caddesi Abac Latif Sokak No 26/8,
Besiktas, 34357, Istanbul, Turkiye
Tel.: (90) 2122887070
Web Site: http://www.efesan.com.tr
Year Founded: 1972
Sales Range: $125-149.9 Million
Emp.: 1,000
Steel Mfrs
N.A.I.C.S.: 331110
Kadir Efe *(Chm)*

Subsidiaries:

Efesan Demir Sanayi ve Ticaret
A.S. **(1)**
Guzeltepe Mahallesi Fatih Sultan Mehmet
Bulvari No 17 Alibeykoy, Eyup, 34060, Istanbul, Turkiye
Tel.: (90) 212 625 10 50
Web Site: http://www.efesandemircelik.com
Iron & Steel Product Mfr & Distr
N.A.I.C.S.: 331110
Ozgur Horasanli *(Mgr-Ops)*

EfesanPort **(1)**
Dilovasi Organize Sanayi Bolgesi 1 Kisim
D-1006 Sokak No 8 Dilovas, 41455, Gebze,
Kocaeli, Turkiye
Tel.: (90) 262 754 84 61
Web Site: http://www.efesanport.com
Freight Forwarding Services
N.A.I.C.S.: 488510

EFFICIENT E-SOLUTIONS
BERHAD
No 3 Jalan Astaka U8/82 Taman Perindustrian, Bukit Jelutong Seksyen
U8 Bukit Jelutong, 40150, Shah
Alam, Selangor Darul Ehsan, Malaysia
Tel.: (60) 378472777 MY
Web Site:
https://www.efficient.com.my
EFFICEN—(KLS)
Rev.: $3,998,343
Assets: $27,252,699

Liabilities: $1,711,750
Net Worth: $25,540,949
Earnings: ($263,858)
Emp.: 360
Fiscal Year-end: 12/31/22
Holding Company
N.A.I.C.S.: 551112
Vincent Chee Kong Cheah *(Mng Dir)*

Subsidiaries:

Vigilant Asia (M) Sdn Bhd **(1)**
No 3 Jalan Astaka U8/82, Bukit Jelutong,
40150, Shah Alam, Selangor, Malaysia
Tel.: (60) 358702252
Web Site: https://www.vigilantasia.com.my
Security Services
N.A.I.C.S.: 561612

EFFINGO TEXTILE & TRADING
LIMITED
502 Arcadia Building 195 Ncpa Marg
Nariman Point, Mumbai, 400021,
India
Tel.: (91) 2222836835
Web Site:
http://effingotextileandtradingltd.com
Year Founded: 1985
Rev.: $104,814
Assets: $2,200,380
Liabilities: $57,021
Net Worth: $2,143,359
Earnings: $32,285
Fiscal Year-end: 03/31/18
Textile Products Mfr
N.A.I.C.S.: 314999

EFG BANK EUROPEAN FI-
NANCIAL GROUP SA
24 quai du seujet1 1211 Geneva 2,
1211, Geneva, Switzerland
Tel.: (41) 29187272
Web Site: https://www.efggroup.com
Bank Holding Company : Deposit Accounts, Secured Lombard-type &
Mortgage Loans, Fiduciary Placements
N.A.I.C.S.: 551111

EFG HOLDING
Building No B129 Phase 3 Smart Village Km 28, Cairo Alexandria Desert
Road, 12577, Cairo, 12577, Egypt
Tel.: (20) 235356499 EG
Web Site: https://www.efghldg.com
Year Founded: 1984
BG79—(LSE)
Rev.: $383,334,202
Assets: $6,127,003,651
Liabilities: $5,029,265,677
Net Worth: $1,097,737,973
Earnings: $99,897,182
Emp.: 5,000
Fiscal Year-end: 12/31/21
Investment Banking & Financial Services
N.A.I.C.S.: 523150
Karim Awad *(CEO)*

Subsidiaries:

Beaufort Investments Company **(1)**
Tel.: (44) 3452415376
Web Site: https://you-asset.co.uk
Investment Management Service
N.A.I.C.S.: 523940
Shane Balkham *(Chief Investment Officer)*

EFG - Hermes Jordan Company **(1)**
Building No 85 Al Sharif Nasser Bin Jameel
St, Shmeisani, Amman, Jordan
Tel.: (962) 65543200
Investment Banking Services
N.A.I.C.S.: 523999
Tareq Adawi *(Fin Mgr)*

EFG - Hermes Kenya Ltd. **(1)**
8th Floor Orbit Place Westlands Road, PO
Box 349, 00623, Nairobi, Kenya
Tel.: (254) 203743040
Investment Banking Services

N.A.I.C.S.: 523999

EFG - Hermes UK Limited **(1)**
Tel.: (44) 2075182908
Investment Banking Services
N.A.I.C.S.: 523999

EFG Hermes Financial Management
(Egypt) Ltd **(1)**
C/o International Corporate Management Of
Bermuda 19 Par-La-Ville Road, Hamilton,
Bermuda
Tel.: (441) 292 3580
Investment Management Service
N.A.I.C.S.: 523999

EFG Hermes Pakistan Limited **(1)**
Office No 904 9th Floor Emerald Tower Plot
No G-19 Block-5, Clifton, Karachi, Pakistan
Tel.: (92) 213514110004
Web Site:
http://www.efghermespakistan.com
Rev.: $772,956
Assets: $4,275,757
Liabilities: $3,664,268
Net Worth: $611,489
Earnings: ($366,638)
Emp.: 45
Fiscal Year-end: 12/31/2022
Investment Management Service
N.A.I.C.S.: 523940
Kamal Shahid *(Sec)*

EFG Hermes UAE Ltd **(1)**
301 Gate Village 11 Exchange Building
DIFC, PO Box 30727, Dubai, United Arab
Emirates
Tel.: (971) 43634000
Emp.: 60
Investment Banking & Securities Brokerage
Services
N.A.I.C.S.: 523150
Moustafa Chiati *(CEO)*

EFG Hermes USA, Inc. **(1)**
3 Columbus Cir 15th Fl Ste 1604, New
York, NY 10019
Tel.: (212) 315-1372
Investment Banking Services
N.A.I.C.S.: 523999

EFG- Hermes Oman LLC **(1)**
Hormuz Building 3rd Floor, PO Box 1857,
Ruwi, 114, Oman
Tel.: (968) 24760076
Investment Banking Services
N.A.I.C.S.: 523999
Alaa Moustafa *(Gen Mgr)*

EFG- Hermes UAE LLC **(1)**
Office 106 The Offices 3 One Central
DWTC, PO Box 112736, Dubai, United Arab
Emirates
Tel.: (971) 43634000
Investment Banking Services
N.A.I.C.S.: 523999

EFG-Hermes Investment
Banking **(1)**
58 El Tahrir St, Gokki, Giza, Egypt **(100%)**
Web Site: http://www.efg-hermes.com
Sales Range: $50-74.9 Million
Emp.: 18
Provider of Investment Banking Services
N.A.I.C.S.: 523940

EFG-Hermes Leasing Company **(1)**
Building No B129 Phase 3 Smart Village,
Km 28 Cairo Alexandria Desert Road, 6th of
October City, 12577, Egypt
Tel.: (20) 235356743
Web Site: http://www.efghermesleasing.com
Financial Banking Services
N.A.I.C.S.: 522110
Ahmed El-Kholy *(CEO)*

Financial Brokerage Group **(1)**
58 El Tahrir St, Giza, Egypt **(100%)**
Tel.: (20) 23374713
Provider of Financial Services
N.A.I.C.S.: 523940

Hermes Financial Management
Egypt, Ltd. **(1)**
58 El Tahrir St, Giza, Egypt
Tel.: (20) 23365960
Web Site: http://www.efg-hermes.com
Sales Range: $50-74.9 Million
Emp.: 15
Provider of Financial Management Services
N.A.I.C.S.: 523940

Hermes Securities Brokerage **(1)**
Building No B129 Phase 3 Smart Village -
KM28 Cairo Alexandria road, Km 28 Cairo-
Alexandria Desert, Road 6 October, 12577,
6th of October City, Egypt **(100%)**
Tel.: (20) 23 535 6140
Web Site: http://www.efg-hermes.com
Online Securities Brokerage Services
N.A.I.C.S.: 523150

Paytabs **(1)**
Office L102 The Greek Campus 28 Falaki
St Downtown, Cairo Governorate, 11513,
Cairo, Egypt
Tel.: (20) 1007161169
Information Technology Services
N.A.I.C.S.: 541511

Vision Investment Services Co.
(S.A.O.C) **(1)**
PO Box 712, Sultanate of Oman, Muscat,
131, Oman
Tel.: (968) 2 472 6000
Web Site: https://www.investvis.co.om
Emp.: 40
Securities Brokerage Services
N.A.I.C.S.: 523150
Khalifa Saif Al Katbi *(Chm)*

EFG INTERNATIONAL AG
Bleicherweg 8, PO Box 6012, 8022,
Zurich, Switzerland
Tel.: (41) 442261850 CH
Web Site:
https://www.efginternational.com
Year Founded: 1997
EFGN—(SWX)
Rev.: $437,128,597
Assets: $2,416,092,238
Liabilities: $903,494,180
Net Worth: $1,512,598,057
Earnings: $236,629,428
Emp.: 3,025
Fiscal Year-end: 12/31/23
Asset Management & Private Banking Services
N.A.I.C.S.: 523150
Giorgio Pradelli *(CEO)*

Subsidiaries:

A&G Banca Privada S.A.U. **(1)**
Paseo de la Castellana 92, 28046, Madrid,
Spain
Tel.: (34) 915902121
Web Site: http://www.ayg.es
Asset Management & Private Banking Services
N.A.I.C.S.: 523150

Bank von Ernst (Liechtenstein)
AG **(1)**
Egertastrasse 10, 9490, Vaduz, Liechtenstein
Tel.: (423) 2655353
Web Site: http://www.efgbankvonernst.com
Sales Range: $50-74.9 Million
Emp.: 20
Banking Services
N.A.I.C.S.: 522110

Bull Wealth Management Group
Inc. **(1)**
410 - 4100 Yonge Street, Toronto, M2P
2B5, ON, Canada
Tel.: (416) 223-2053
Web Site: https://www.bullwealth.com
Sales Range: $50-74.9 Million
Emp.: 30
Investment Services
N.A.I.C.S.: 523999
James A. Bull *(Founder, Pres & CEO)*

EFG (Panama) S.A. **(1)**
Torre Generali Piso 14 Ave Samuel Lewis y
Calle 54 Obarrio Apartado, 832-1637,
Panama, Panama
Tel.: (507) 3669800
Asset Management & Private Banking Services
N.A.I.C.S.: 523150

EFG AG **(1)**
Bahrain Financial Harbour West Tower 14th
Floor, PO Box 11321, Manama, Bahrain
Tel.: (973) 17155155

EFG International AG—(Continued)

Asset Management & Private Banking Services
N.A.I.C.S.: 523150

EFG Asesorias Financieras SpA (1)
Av Isidora Goyenechea 2800 Piso 29 Edificio Titanium Las Condes, Santiago, Chile
Tel.: (56) 27975600
Asset Management & Private Banking Services
N.A.I.C.S.: 523150

EFG Asset Management (Americas) Corp. (1)
701 Brickell Ave Ste 900, Miami, FL 33131
Tel.: (305) 482-8000
Asset Management & Private Banking Services
N.A.I.C.S.: 523150

EFG Asset Management (Hong Kong) Ltd. (1)
18th Floor International Commerce Centre 1 Austin Road West, Kowloon, China (Hong Kong)
Tel.: (852) 22983000
Asset Management & Private Banking Services
N.A.I.C.S.: 523150
Amy Lai *(Sr Mgr-Ops)*

EFG Asset Management (Singapore) Pte. Ltd. (1)
25 North Bridge Road 07-00 EFG Bank Building, Singapore, 179107, Singapore
Tel.: (65) 65954888
Asset Management & Private Banking Services
N.A.I.C.S.: 523150

EFG Asset Management (Switzerland) S.A. (1)
24 Quai du Seujet, PO Box 2391, 1211, Geneva, Switzerland
Tel.: (41) 229187171
Asset Management Services
N.A.I.C.S.: 541611

EFG Asset Management Holding AG (1)
Bleicherweg 8, PO Box 6012, 8022, Zurich, Switzerland
Tel.: (41) 442261850
Web Site: http://www.efgbank.com
Investment Management Service
N.A.I.C.S.: 523999

EFG Asset Managers SAM (1)
Europa Residence Place des Moulins, 98000, Monaco, Monaco
Tel.: (377) 97973979
Asset Management & Private Banking Services
N.A.I.C.S.: 523150
Giorgio Ghersi *(Gen Mgr)*

EFG Bank (Gibraltar) Ltd (1)
Corral Road 1, PO Box 561, Gibraltar, Gibraltar
Tel.: (350) 200 40 117
Commercial Banking Services
N.A.I.C.S.: 522110

EFG Bank (Luxembourg) SA (1)
14 Allae Marconi, 2120, Luxembourg, Luxembourg
Tel.: (352) 26 454 1
Web Site: http://www.efgbank.lu
Commercial Banking Services
N.A.I.C.S.: 522110

EFG Bank (Monaco) (1)
Villa Les Aigles 15 Avenue d'Ostende, Boite postale 37, 98001, Monaco, Monaco
Tel.: (377) 93151111
Web Site: https://www.efginternational.com
Emp.: 80
Commercial Banking Services
N.A.I.C.S.: 522110

EFG Bank AB (1)
Jakobsbergsgatan 16, Box 55963, 102 16, Stockholm, Sweden
Tel.: (46) 855509400
Web Site: www.efgbank.se
Emp.: 5
Commercial Banking Services
N.A.I.C.S.: 522110

EFG Bank AG (1)
Via Magatti 2, 6900, Lugano, Switzerland
Tel.: (41) 588093111
Web Site: http://www.efgbank.com
Asset Management & Financial Planning Services
N.A.I.C.S.: 523940

Subsidiary (Non-US):

BSI (Panama) S.A. (2)
Torre Generali Piso 14 Ave Samuel Lewis y Calle 54 Obarrio, Apartado 832-1637 WTC, Panama, Panama
Tel.: (507) 366 9800
Web Site: http://www.efginternational.com
Investment Management Service
N.A.I.C.S.: 523999

BSI Trust Corporation (Malta) Limited (2)
35 St Zachary Street, VLT 1132, Valletta, Malta
Tel.: (356) 21225817
Web Site: http://www.efginternational.com
Asset Management & Trust Administration Services
N.A.I.C.S.: 523940

Affiliate (Domestic):

Dreieck Fiduciaria SA (2)
Viale Cantonale 19, PO Box 5518, 6900, Lugano, Switzerland
Tel.: (41) 912600303
Web Site: http://www.dreieckfid.ch
Asset Management & Investment Advisory Services
N.A.I.C.S.: 523940

Subsidiary (Non-US):

EFG Bank & Trust (Bahamas) Ltd. (2)
Goodmans Bay Corporate Center, PO Box CB 10956, West Bay Street and Sea View Drive, Nassau, Bahamas
Tel.: (242) 5025400
Web Site: https://www.efginternational.com
Banking, Investment & Trust Services
N.A.I.C.S.: 523150

EFG Bank (Luxembourg) S.A. (2)
56 Grand-Rue, PO Box 385, L-2013, Luxembourg, Luxembourg
Tel.: (352) 264541
Web Site: https://www.efginternational.com
Asset Management, Banking & Investment Advisory Services
N.A.I.C.S.: 523940
Lena Lascari *(CEO, Mng Dir & Sr VP)*

EOS Servizi Fiduciari SpA (2)
Via Paleocapa 5, 20121, Milan, Italy
Tel.: (39) 026369621
Web Site: http://www.eosfiduciaria.it
Financial Management Services
N.A.I.C.S.: 523999

Oudart SA (2)
10A rue de la Paix, 75002, Paris, France
Tel.: (33) 142862500
Web Site: http://www.oudart.fr
Asset Management, Financial Planning & Investment Advisory Services
N.A.I.C.S.: 523940
Alexis d'Arvieu *(Chm-Mgmt Bd)*

Subsidiary (Domestic):

Oudart Gestion SA (3)
10A rue de la Paix, Paris, 75002, France
Tel.: (33) 1 42 86 25 00
Web Site: http://www.oudart.fr
Financial Management Services
N.A.I.C.S.: 523999

Oudart Patrimoine (3)
10A rue de la Paix, 75002, Paris, France
Tel.: (33) 1 42 86 25 00
Web Site: http://www.oudart.fr
Financial Advisory Services
N.A.I.C.S.: 523940

Solidia Finance et Patrimoine S.A. (3)
10 A Rue de la Paix, 75002, Paris, France
Tel.: (33) 1 42 86 25 00
Web Site: http://www.oudart.fr
Financial Management Services
N.A.I.C.S.: 523999

Subsidiary (Domestic):

Thalia SA (2)
Via Cantonale 2, 6900, Lugano, Switzerland
Tel.: (41) 919129700
Web Site: http://www.thaliainvest.com
Emp.: 17
Asset Management Services
N.A.I.C.S.: 523940
Margrethe Rokkum-Testi *(Founder, CEO & CIO)*

EFG Bank AG (1)
Bleicherweg 8, PO Box 6012, 8022, Zurich, Switzerland (100%)
Tel.: (41) 442261717
Web Site: https://www.efginternational.com
Commericial Banking
N.A.I.C.S.: 522110

EFG Bank Ltd. (1)
Jl M H Thamrin Kav 28-30The Plaza Office Tower Level 20 Unit F2, 10350, Jakarta, Indonesia
Tel.: (62) 2129920304
Asset Management & Private Banking Services
N.A.I.C.S.: 523150

EFG Bank von Ernst AG (1)
Egertastrasse 10, 9490, Vaduz, Liechtenstein
Tel.: (423) 2655353
Web Site: https://www.efgbankvonernst.com
Sales Range: $50-74.9 Million
Emp.: 19
Investment Banking Services
N.A.I.C.S.: 523150
Daniel Taverna *(Chm-Exec Bd)*

EFG Banque Privee SA (1)
5 Boulevard de la Tour Maubourg, 75007, Paris, France
Tel.: (33) 1 44 11 13 00
Web Site: http://www.efgfrance.com
Investment Management Service
N.A.I.C.S.: 523999

EFG Capital Asesores Financieros S.A.C. (1)
Alberto del Campo 411 Oficina 604 Magdalena del Mar, Lima, Peru
Tel.: (51) 12125914
Asset Management & Private Banking Services
N.A.I.C.S.: 523150
Eliane Zilberman *(VP)*

EFG Capital International Corp. (1)
701 Brickell Ave 9th Fl Ste 1350, Miami, FL 33131
Tel.: (305) 482-8000
Web Site: https://www.efginternational.com
Sales Range: $100-124.9 Million
Emp.: 130
Investment Banking Services
N.A.I.C.S.: 523150

EFG Investment Bank (1)
Engelbrektsgatan 9-11, 114 32, Stockholm, Sweden
Tel.: (46) 84596400
Web Site: http://www.efgib.com
Investment Services
N.A.I.C.S.: 523150

EFG Oficina de Representacion Uruguay SA (1)
Av Dr Luis A de Herrera 1248 WTC Torre II Piso 20, 11300, Montevideo, Uruguay
Tel.: (598) 26286010
Asset Management & Private Banking Services
N.A.I.C.S.: 523150

EFG Platts Flello Ltd (1)
33 Great Charles Street, Birmingham, B3 3JN, West Midlands, United Kingdom
Tel.: (44) 121 200 2255
Sales Range: $50-74.9 Million
Emp.: 15
Financial Management Services
N.A.I.C.S.: 523940
John Male *(Mng Dir)*

EFG Private Bank Limited (1)
Park House 116 Park Street, Curzon Street, London, W1K 6AP, United Kingdom
Tel.: (44) 2074919111
Web Site: https://www.efginternational.com

Sales Range: $100-124.9 Million
Emp.: 250
Banking Services
N.A.I.C.S.: 522110

Subsidiary (Domestic):

EFG Asset Management (UK) Ltd. (2)
Park House 116 Park Street, London, W1K 6AP, United Kingdom
Tel.: (44) 2074919111
Asset Management Services
N.A.I.C.S.: 523150

EFG Harris Allday (2)
33 Great Charles Street, Birmingham, B3 3JN, United Kingdom
Tel.: (44) 121 233 1222
Web Site: http://www.efgwealthsolutions.com
Investment Banking Services
N.A.I.C.S.: 523150

EFG Independent Financial Advisers (2)
Waterloo Court 31 Waterloo Road, Wolverhampton, WV1 4DJ, United Kingdom
Tel.: (44) 1902710402
Web Site: http://www.efg-ifa.com
Sales Range: $50-74.9 Million
Emp.: 25
Investment Banking Services
N.A.I.C.S.: 523150
Phil Oaten *(Exec Dir)*

EFG Independent Financial Advisors Ltd (2)
33 Great Charles Street, Birmingham, B3 3JN, United Kingdom
Tel.: (44) 121 200 2255
Web Site: http://www.efg-ifa.com
Financial Advisory Services
N.A.I.C.S.: 523940
John Male *(Mng Dir)*

Subsidiary (Non-US):

EFG Offshore Limited (2)
Seaton Place, PO Box 641 1, Saint Helier, JE4 8YJ, Jersey
Tel.: (44) 1534605600
Web Site: http://www.efgoffshore.com
Sales Range: $50-74.9 Million
Emp.: 90
Investment Banking Services
N.A.I.C.S.: 523150
Gerard Gardner *(Mng Dir)*

Subsidiary (Domestic):

EFG Platts Fiello Limited (2)
33 Great Charls St, Birmingham, B3 3JN, United Kingdom
Tel.: (44) 1212002255
Web Site: http://www.efgl.com
Sales Range: $25-49.9 Million
Emp.: 15
Investment Banking Services
N.A.I.C.S.: 523150

Subsidiary (Non-US):

EFG Private Bank (Channel Islands) Limited (2)
EFG House St Julians Ave, PO Box 603, Saint Peter Port, GY1 4NN, Guernsey
Tel.: (44) 1481723432
Web Site: http://www.efgoffshore.com
Banking Services
N.A.I.C.S.: 522110

EFG SA (1)
Rue du Simplon 4, Martigny, Switzerland
Tel.: (41) 588087492
Asset Management & Private Banking Services
N.A.I.C.S.: 523150

EFG Wealth Management (Bermuda) Ltd. (1)
Windsor Place 22 Queen Street 1st Floor, Hamilton, Bermuda
Tel.: (441) 2963131
Asset Management & Private Banking Services
N.A.I.C.S.: 523150
Greg Soares *(Mng Dir & Chief Revenue Officer)*

EFG Wealth Management (Canada) Limited (1)
350 Sparks Street Suite 909, Ottawa, K1R 7S8, ON, Canada
Tel.: (613) 565-4334
Web Site: http://www.efgcanada.com
Investment Advisory Services
N.A.I.C.S.: 523940

EFG Wealth Management (Cayman) Ltd. (1)
Suite 3208 9 Forum Lane KY1 Grand Cayman, PO Box 10360, Camana Bay, 1003, Cayman Islands
Tel.: (345) 9433350
Asset Management & Private Banking Services
N.A.I.C.S.: 523150

EFG Wealth Management (India) Private Limited (1)
Strategy House 44 Mint Rd, Mumbai, 400001, Maharashtra, India
Tel.: (91) 22 6634 9946
Financial Management Services
N.A.I.C.S.: 523999
Pradeep Nair *(CEO)*

EFG Wealth Solutions (Singapore) Ltd. (1)
25 North Bridge Road 07-00 EFG Bank Building, Singapore, 179107, Singapore
Tel.: (65) 65954998
Asset Management & Private Banking Services
N.A.I.C.S.: 523150

On Finance SA (1)
Piazza Manzoni 3, 6900, Lugano, Switzerland
Tel.: (41) 91 910 20 60
Web Site: http://www.onfinance.ch
Emp.: 50
Financial Management Services
N.A.I.C.S.: 523999
Stefano Pezzoli *(Chm & Mng Partner)*

PRS International Consulting Inc (1)
801 Brickell Ave Ste 1600, Miami, FL 33131
Tel.: (305) 381-8340
Asset Management & Financial Consulting Services
N.A.I.C.S.: 541611
Gonzalo Rodriguez-Frail *(Co-Pres)*

Patrimony 1873 SA (1)
Via Canova 6, 6901, Lugano, Switzerland
Tel.: (41) 919127272
Web Site: http://www.patrimony1873.com
Asset Management Services
N.A.I.C.S.: 523940
Paolo Filippini *(CEO)*

Quesada Kapitalforvaltning AB (1)
Jakobsbergsgatan 16, 111 44, Stockholm, Sweden
Tel.: (46) 855509650
Web Site: http://www.quesada.com
Sales Range: $50-74.9 Million
Emp.: 30
Investment Management Service
N.A.I.C.S.: 523999
Per Molen *(Gen Mgr)*

SIF Swiss Investment Funds S.A. (1)
Quai du Seujet 26, CH 1211, Geneva, Switzerland
Tel.: (41) 229187388
Web Site: http://www.swiss-if.ch
Sales Range: $50-74.9 Million
Emp.: 6
Investment Services
N.A.I.C.S.: 523150

UBI Banca International S.A. (1)
37 A Av. John F. Kennedy, Kirchberg, Luxembourg, 1855, Luxembourg
Tel.: (352) 227851
Commericial Banking
N.A.I.C.S.: 522110

Subsidiary (Domestic):

UBI Management Company SA (2)
37 A Avenue J F Kennedy, 1855, Luxembourg, Luxembourg
Tel.: (352) 2686181
Sales Range: $50-74.9 Million
Emp.: 3
Financial Management Services

N.A.I.C.S.: 523940
Amato Massimo *(Chm)*

UBI Trustee SA (2)
Le President 37A Avenue J F Kennedy, Luxembourg, 1855, Luxembourg
Tel.: (352) 27 04 88 56
Web Site: http://www.ubibanca.lu
Sales Range: $50-74.9 Million
Emp.: 10
Financial Management Services
N.A.I.C.S.: 523999
Massimo Amato *(Mng Dir)*

EFORT INTELLIGENT EQUIPMENT CO., LTD.
No 96 East Wanchun Road, Jiujiang, Wuhu, 241000, Anhui, China
Tel.: (86) 4000528877
Web Site: https://efort.com.cn
Year Founded: 2007
688165—(SHG)
Rev.: $186,382,067
Assets: $466,938,529
Liabilities: $220,227,930
Net Worth: $246,710,599
Earnings: ($24,270,681)
Fiscal Year-end: 12/31/22
Robot Mfr
N.A.I.C.S.: 334512
Lijin Xu *(Chm & Dir)*

Subsidiaries:

Autorobot-Strefa Sp Z.O.O. (1)
ul L Wyczolkowskiego 29, 44-109, Gliwice, Poland
Tel.: (48) 327753390
Web Site: https://www.autorobotstrefa.pl
Automotive Body Welding Line Mfr
N.A.I.C.S.: 333992

CMA (Wuhu) Robotics Co., Ltd. (1)
No 96 East Wanchun Road, Jiujiang Economic Development District, Wuhu, Anhui, China
Tel.: (86) 5535670660
Web Site: http://www.cmarobot.com.cn
Spraying Robot Equipment & Machinery Mfr
N.A.I.C.S.: 333998

CMA Roboter GmbH (1)
Linprunstrasse 49, 80335, Munich, Germany
Tel.: (49) 8999216131
Web Site: http://www.cma-roboter.com
Painting Robotic Equipment Mfr & Distr
N.A.I.C.S.: 325510

CMA Robotics S.P.A. (1)
Viale del Lavoro 41 Z I U, 33050, Pavia di Udine, UD, Italy
Tel.: (39) 0432640172
Web Site: http://www.cmarobot.it
Painting Robotic Equipment Mfr
N.A.I.C.S.: 325510
Marco Zanor *(Supvr-Technical)*

Efort Europe S.R.L (1)
Borgaretto Plant-Via Gorizia 41, 10092, Beinasco, TO, Italy
Tel.: (39) 0110240413
Painting Robotic Equipment Mfr
N.A.I.C.S.: 325510

Efort France S.A.S (1)
6-8 Rue du 4 Septembre, 92130, Issy-les-Moulineaux, France
Tel.: (33) 626893475
Project Management Services
N.A.I.C.S.: 541611

Evolut (WUHU) Robotics Co., Ltd. (1)
No 96 Wanchun East Road, Jiujiang Economic Development District, Wuhu, Anhui, China
Tel.: (86) 18010735257
Machine Tools Mfr
N.A.I.C.S.: 333517

Evolut S.P.A. (1)
Via Padana Superiore 111/A, 25045, Castegnato, BS, Italy
Tel.: (39) 0302141193
Web Site: http://www.evolutspa.com
Machine Tools Mfr
N.A.I.C.S.: 333517

GME Aerospace Industria De Material Composto S.A. (1)
Alameda Bom Pastor 1683, Ouro Fino, Sao Jose dos Pinhais, 83015-140, Parana, Brazil
Tel.: (55) 4132992000
Web Site: https://www.gmebrasil.com.br
Automobile Parts Mfr
N.A.I.C.S.: 336390

O.L.C.I. Engineering India Private Limited (1)
Plot No E-14, Chakan Industrial Area PH-III Nighoje Khed, Pune, 410 501, MH, India
Tel.: (91) 3337378972
Automobile Parts Mfr
N.A.I.C.S.: 336390

OLCI Engineering S.r.l. (1)
Via I maggio 8, 10040, Rivalta di Torino, TO, Italy
Tel.: (39) 0115201320
Web Site: https://www.olcieng.eu
Automobile Body Parts Mfr
N.A.I.C.S.: 336211

Robox SpA (1)
Via Sempione 82, 28053, Castelletto Sopra Ticino, NO, Italy
Tel.: (39) 0331922086
Web Site: http://www.robox.it
Electronic Controller Mfr
N.A.I.C.S.: 335999

W.F.C. Holding S.P.A. (1)
Via I Maggio 8, 10040, Rivalta di Torino, TO, Italy
Tel.: (39) 03337378972
Automotive Equipment & Robotic System Distr
N.A.I.C.S.: 423830

Webb Robotica S.R.L. (1)
Via Triestina 44, 30024, Musile di Piave, VE, Italy
Tel.: (39) 0421332951
Web Site: http://www.webbrobotica.it
Industrial Robotic Machinery Mfr
N.A.I.C.S.: 333248

EFT CANADA INC.
801 Eglinton West Suite 400, Toronto, M5N 1E3, ON, Canada
Tel.: (416) 781-0666
Web Site: http://www.eftcanada.com
Year Founded: 2003
Electronic Payment Services
N.A.I.C.S.: 522320

EFT SOLUTIONS HOLDINGS LIMITED
Workshops B1 & B3 11/F Yip Fung Industrial Bldg 28-36 Kwai Fung Cres, Kwai Chung, New Territories, China (Hong Kong)
Tel.: (852) 37412116   Ky
Web Site: https://www.eftsolutions.com
Year Founded: 2004
8062—(HKG)
Rev.: $13,379,740
Assets: $19,585,226
Liabilities: $4,064,289
Net Worth: $15,520,937
Earnings: $1,379,312
Emp.: 73
Fiscal Year-end: 03/31/22
Electronic Fund Transfer Services
N.A.I.C.S.: 522320
Kelvin Ka Ming Lee *(COO)*

EFTEN CAPITAL AS
A Lauteri 5, 10114, Tallinn, Estonia
Tel.: (372) 655 9515   EE
Web Site: http://www.eften.ee
Emp.: 30
Commercial Real Estate Fund Management Services
N.A.I.C.S.: 531390
Viljar Arakas *(CEO & Member-Mgmt Bd)*

Subsidiaries:

Magistral Kaubanduskeskuse OU (1)
Sopruse pst 201/203, Tallinn, Estonia
Tel.: (372) 665 9100
Web Site: http://www.magistral.ee
Shopping Mall Operator
N.A.I.C.S.: 531120

EFTEN REAL ESTATE FUND III AS
A Lauteri 5, 10114, Tallinn, Estonia
Tel.: (372) 6559515
Web Site: http://www.eref.co
Year Founded: 2015
EFT1T—(TAL)
Rev.: $35,121,978
Assets: $420,514,406
Liabilities: $179,099,238
Net Worth: $241,415,167
Earnings: $1,103,875
Emp.: 12
Fiscal Year-end: 12/31/23
Real Estate Investment Trust Services
N.A.I.C.S.: 531190
Viljar Arakas *(Member-Mgmt Bd)*

EFU GENERAL INSURANCE LTD.
EFU House M A Jinnah Road, PO Box 5005, Karachi, 74000, Pakistan
Tel.: (92) 2132313471
Web Site: https://www.efuinsurance.com
Year Founded: 1932
EFUG—(LAH)
Rev.: $248,211,729
Assets: $1,121,989,410
Liabilities: $962,683,387
Net Worth: $159,306,022
Earnings: $21,698,923
Emp.: 1,207
Fiscal Year-end: 12/31/19
Insurance Services
N.A.I.C.S.: 525190
Saifuddin N. Zoomkawala *(Chm)*

Subsidiaries:

EFU General Insurance Ltd - Central Division (1)
1st Floor Kashif Centre Shahrah E F, Karachi, Pakistan
Tel.: (92) 21 35653907
Web Site: http://www.efuinsurance.com
General Insurance Services
N.A.I.C.S.: 524210

EFU LIFE ASSURANCE LIMITED
EFU Life House Plot No 112 8th East Street, Phase 1 DHA, Karachi, Pakistan
Tel.: (92) 21111338111   PK
Web Site: https://www.efulife.com
Year Founded: 1992
EFUL—(KAR)
Rev.: $200,552,123
Assets: $832,625,275
Liabilities: $794,578,142
Net Worth: $38,047,134
Earnings: $9,977,260
Emp.: 1,386
Fiscal Year-end: 12/31/19
General Insurance Services
N.A.I.C.S.: 524210
S. Shahid Abbas *(Exec Dir)*

Subsidiaries:

Jahangir Siddiqui Securities Services Limited (1)
20th Floor The Centre Plot No 28 SB-5 Abdullah Haroon Road, Saddar, Karachi, Pakistan
Tel.: (92) 21111574111
Web Site: https://www.jssslweb.com
Investment Management Service

EFU Life Assurance Limited—(Continued)

N.A.I.C.S.: 523999
Muhammad Uzair Marghoob (Sec)

EFUN TECHNOLOGY CO., LTD.
No 391 Section 2 Honda Road, Annan District, Tainan City, Taiwan
Tel.: (886) 63841313
Web Site: https://www.efun.com.tw
3523—(TPE)
Rev.: $4,732,452
Assets: $40,330,988
Liabilities: $30,979,020
Net Worth: $9,351,968
Earnings: ($3,926,461)
Fiscal Year-end: 12/31/22
Electronic Components Mfr
N.A.I.C.S.: 334419
I-Lin Tang (Chm)

EFUSION SOLUTIONS PTE. LTD.
1 Lorong 2 Toa Payoh 01 03, Singapore, 319637, Singapore
Tel.: (65) 65174920   SG
Web Site: http://www.efusion.com.sg
Year Founded: 2002
Ecommerce Services
N.A.I.C.S.: 541512

EG CORPORATION
118 Myeongdang 3-gil, Geumsangun, Gwangyang, 57815, Jeollanamdo, Korea (South)
Tel.: (82) 417507777
Web Site: https://www.egcorp.co.kr
Year Founded: 1987
037370—(KRS)
Rev.: $53,835,022
Assets: $118,228,810
Liabilities: $79,414,375
Net Worth: $38,814,435
Earnings: ($1,844,767)
Emp.: 81
Fiscal Year-end: 12/31/22
Chemicals Mfr
N.A.I.C.S.: 325180
Gyung-Hwan Moon (CEO)

Subsidiaries:

EG METAL Corporation   (1)
836 Hwangswong-dong, Nam-gu, Ulsan, 44495, Korea (South)
Tel.: (82) 522786800
Web Site: https://www.egmetal.co.kr
Chemical Products Mfr
N.A.I.C.S.: 325180

EG POTECH CO. LTD   (1)
6262 Dongchon-dong, Nam-Gu, Pohang, Gyeongbook, Korea (South)
Tel.: (82) 542209683
Web Site: http://www.egpotec.co.kr
Chemical Products Mfr
N.A.I.C.S.: 325180
Go Geuon-Su (CEO)

EG Tech Corp.   (1)
2nd floor 5-3 Majang 1-gil, Gwangyang, Jeollanam-do, Korea (South)
Tel.: (82) 617912051
Web Site: https://www.egtech.co.kr
Chemical Products Mfr
N.A.I.C.S.: 325180

EG INDUSTRIES BERHAD
Plot 102 Jalan 4 Bakar Arang Industrial Estate, 08000, Sungai Petani, Kedah, Malaysia
Tel.: (60) 44229881   MY
Web Site: https://www.eg.com.my
Year Founded: 1991
EG—(KLS)
Rev.: $285,766,610
Assets: $256,986,324
Liabilities: $163,978,588
Net Worth: $93,007,736
Earnings: $8,259,035

Emp.: 3,009
Fiscal Year-end: 06/30/23
Printed Circuit Board Mfr
N.A.I.C.S.: 334412
Churn Hwa Chai (Sec)

Subsidiaries:

Mastimber Industries Sdn. Bhd.   (1)
Lot 25 Kuala Ketil Industrial Estate, Kuala Ketil, Kedah, Malaysia
Tel.: (60) 44162828
Sales Range: $25-49.9 Million
Emp.: 45
Hardwood Parquetry Mfr
N.A.I.C.S.: 321999

SMT Industries Co. Ltd.   (1)
196 Moo 10 304 Industrial Park, Thatoom Sub district Srimahaphote District, Prachin Buri, 25140, Thailand
Tel.: (66) 37274423
Emp.: 300
Electronic Products Mfr
N.A.I.C.S.: 334511
Robert Teoh (Mgr-Production)

SMT Technologies Sdn. Bhd.   (1)
Plot 102 102A Bakar Arang Industrial Estate, 08000, Sungai Petani, Kedah, Malaysia
Tel.: (60) 44229881
Web Site: https://www.esmtt.com
Telecommunication Products Mfr
N.A.I.C.S.: 334210
Karupiah Mogan (Dir-Quality)

EG PENNER BUILDING CENTRES
200 Park Road West, Steinbach, R5G 1A1, MB, Canada
Tel.: (204) 326-1325
Web Site: https://www.egpenner.com
Year Founded: 1960
Rev.: $11,850,007
Emp.: 175
Building Construction Services
N.A.I.C.S.: 236220
Ernest Penner (Pres)

EGALAX-EMIPIA TECHNOLOGY, INC.
11F No 302 Rueiguang Rd, Neihu District, Taipei, Taiwan
Tel.: (886) 287515191
Web Site: https://www.eeti.com
3556—(TPE)
Rev.: $44,821,092
Assets: $54,957,665
Liabilities: $11,441,203
Net Worth: $43,516,462
Earnings: $10,210,112
Emp.: 200
Fiscal Year-end: 12/31/22
Semiconductor Devices Mfr
N.A.I.C.S.: 334413
Jing-Rong Tang (Chm & Gen Mgr)

EGAN VISUAL INC.
300 Hanlan Road, Woodbridge, L4L 3P6, ON, Canada
Tel.: (905) 851-2826
Web Site: http://www.egan.com
Year Founded: 1967
Visual Communication Systems & Furniture Mfr
N.A.I.C.S.: 334290
Sean Brown (Pres)

EGAT PUBLIC COMPANY LIMITED
EGCO Tower 222 Moo 5 Vibhavadi Rangsit Road, Tungsonghong Laksi, Bangkok, 10210, Thailand
Tel.: (66) 29985000
Web Site: http://www.egco.com
Year Founded: 1992
Sales Range: $350-399.9 Million
Emp.: 650
Electric Power Distr
N.A.I.C.S.: 335311

Jakgrich Pibulpairoj (Pres)

Subsidiaries:

Amata B. Grimm Power 1 Limited   (1)
Amata Nakorn Industrial Estate, 700-371 Moo 6 Nongmaidaeng, Ampur Muang, 20000, Chon Buri, Thailand
Tel.: (66) 3821 3317
Web Site: http://www.amatapower.com
Sales Range: $50-74.9 Million
Emp.: 35
Electric Power Generation
N.A.I.C.S.: 221118

EGCO Engineering and Service Co. Ltd   (1)
EGCO Tower 222 Moo 5 Vibhavadi Rangsit Road, Tungsonghong Laksi, 10210, Bangkok, Thailand   (99.99%)
Tel.: (66) 29985999
Web Site: http://www.egco.co.th
Electrical Contractor
N.A.I.C.S.: 238210

Gulf Electric Public Co. Ltd   (1)
11th Floor M Thai Tower All Seasons Place, 87 Wireless Road Phathumwan, 10330, Bangkok, Thailand   (50%)
Tel.: (66) 26540155
Sales Range: $75-99.9 Million
Emp.: 100
Electric Power Generation
N.A.I.C.S.: 221118
Sarath Ratanavadi (Pres)

Khanom Electricity Generating Co. Ltd.   (1)
EGCO Tower 222 Moo 5 Vibhavadi Rangsit Road, Tungsonghong Laksi, 10210, Bangkok, Thailand   (99.99%)
Tel.: (66) 29985997
Web Site: http://www.egco.co.th
Sales Range: $125-149.9 Million
Emp.: 150
Electric Power Generation
N.A.I.C.S.: 221118

Rayong Electricity Generating Co. Ltd.   (1)
EGCO Tower 222 Moo 5 Vibhavadi Rangsit Road, Tungsonghong Laksi, 10210, Bangkok, Thailand   (99.99%)
Tel.: (66) 29985999
Web Site: http://www.egco.com
Electrical Contractor
N.A.I.C.S.: 238210

Roi-Et Green Co. Ltd   (1)
13th Floor EGCO Tower, Tungsonghong Laksi, Bangkok, Thailand   (95%)
Tel.: (66) 29985000
Sales Range: $25-49.9 Million
Emp.: 5
Measuring & Testing Electricity & Electrical Signals Instrument Mfr
N.A.I.C.S.: 334515

EGE ENDUSTRI VE TICARET AS
Kemalpasa Caddesi No 280, Pinarbasi, 35060, Izmir, Turkiye
Tel.: (90) 2324911400
Web Site:
   https://www.egeendustri.com
Year Founded: 1974
EGEEN—(IST)
Rev.: $69,416,273
Assets: $96,207,236
Liabilities: $42,206,216
Net Worth: $54,001,020
Earnings: $27,759,843
Emp.: 500
Fiscal Year-end: 12/31/22
Motor Vehicle Part & Accessory Mfr
N.A.I.C.S.: 336390
Huseyin Bayraktar (Chm)

EGE GUBRE SANAYI A.S.
Nemrut Sanayi Bolgesi Cakmakli Mah 25 Cadde No 2, Aliaga, 35801, Izmir, Turkiye
Tel.: (90) 2326251250

Web Site:
   https://www.egegubre.com.tr
Year Founded: 1973
EGGUB—(IST)
Rev.: $76,756,610
Assets: $156,861,194
Liabilities: $15,645,764
Net Worth: $141,215,430
Earnings: $12,537,047
Fiscal Year-end: 12/31/23
Chemical Fertilizer Mfr & Distr
N.A.I.C.S.: 325314
Ahmet Gencer (Chm & Member-Exec Bd)

EGE SERAMIK SANAYI VE TICARET A.S.
Kemalpasa OSB Mahallesi Ansizca Sanayi Sitesi Sokak No 297/1, 35730, Izmir, Türkiye
Tel.: (90) 2328781700
Web Site:
   https://www.egeseramik.com
Year Founded: 1972
EGSER—(IST)
Rev.: $92,728,122
Assets: $102,376,648
Liabilities: $27,259,637
Net Worth: $75,117,012
Earnings: ($3,653,244)
Emp.: 919
Fiscal Year-end: 12/31/23
Ceramic Tile Mfr
N.A.I.C.S.: 327120
Murat Polat (Chm)

Subsidiaries:

Ege Seramik America Inc.   (1)
1721 Oakbrook Dr Ste C, Norcross, GA 30093
Tel.: (678) 291-0888
Web Site: https://www.egeseramik-usa.com
Ceramic Construction Material Distr
N.A.I.C.S.: 423320

Ege Seramik Ic ve Dis Ticaret A.S.   (1)
Buyukdere Cad Polat Han No 87/3, Mecidiyekoy, 34387, Istanbul, Turkiye
Tel.: (90) 2122166700
Building Materials Mfr
N.A.I.C.S.: 327120
Secil Mutlu (Sr Mgr-Area Export)

EGELI & CO ENERJI YATIRIMLARI A.S.
Merkez Mh Abide i Hurriyet Cd Sibel Apt No 161 K 2 D 3, Sisli, Istanbul, Turkiye
Tel.: (90) 2123430626
Investment Management Service
N.A.I.C.S.: 523940

EGELI & CO TARIM GIRISIM SERMAYESI YATIRIM ORTAKLIGI AS
Merkez Mh Abide i Hurriyet Cd Sibel Apt No 161 K 2 D 3, Sisli, Istanbul, Turkiye
Tel.: (90) 2123430626
Investment Management Service
N.A.I.C.S.: 523940

EGELI & CO. YATIRIM HOLDING A.S.
Abdi Ipekci Caddesi No 40, Nisantasi, 34367, Istanbul, Turkiye
Tel.: (90) 212 343 06 26
Web Site: http://www.egcyh.com
Year Founded: 1994
Sales Range: $1-9.9 Million
Holding Company
N.A.I.C.S.: 551112

EGEPLAST EGE PLASTIK SAN VE TIC. A.S.

10003 Sokak No 6 AOSB, Cigli,
Izmir, Turkiye
Tel.: (90) 2323768631
Web Site:
  https://www.egeplast.com.tr
Year Founded: 1959
EPLAS—(IST)
Rev.: $23,909,002
Assets: $44,833,414
Liabilities: $14,308,603
Net Worth: $30,524,810
Earnings: $1,179,977
Fiscal Year-end: 12/31/22
Plastic Pipe Fitting Mfr
N.A.I.C.S.: 326122
Kemal Zorlu *(Chm & Mng Dir)*

**EGERIA CAPITAL MANAGE-
MENT B.V.**
Sarphatikade 12, 1017 WV, Amster-
dam, Netherlands
Tel.: (31) 205306868   NI
Web Site: http://www.egeria.nl
Year Founded: 1997
Privater Equity Firm
N.A.I.C.S.: 523999
Peter Visser *(Partner)*

Subsidiaries:

Axent Nabestaandenzorg N.V.   **(1)**
Leonard Springerlaan 31, 9727 KB, Gronin-
gen, Netherlands
Tel.: (31) 58 2446416
Sales Range: $75-99.9 Million
General Insurance Services
N.A.I.C.S.: 524298

Boemer Rental Services Group   **(1)**
Oliemolen 2, 4671 HB, Dinteloord, Nether-
lands
Tel.: (31) 167 52 39 25
Web Site: http://www.boemer.eu
Commercial Property Rental Services
N.A.I.C.S.: 532490
Ardaan Spruijt *(Mgr-Bus Dev)*

Clondalkin Group Holdings BV   **(1)**
Beatrixgeboux - JIM 6th Floor Jaarbeur-
splein 6, 3521 AL, Utrecht, Netherlands
Tel.: (31) 204226911
Web Site: http://www.clondalkingroup.com
Sales Range: $900-999.9 Million
Holding Company
N.A.I.C.S.: 551112
Sebastiaan van den Steenhoven *(Mgr-Pur)*

Subsidiary (Non-US):

Clondalkin Group Holdings Ltd.   **(2)**
Siac Bldg Clondalkin, Dublin, 22, Ireland
Tel.: (353) 14591559
Web Site: http://www.clondalkin-group.com
Sales Range: $750-799.9 Million
Emp.: 3,000
Holding Company
N.A.I.C.S.: 551112

Subsidiary (Domestic):

Clondalkin Group plc   **(3)**
Siac Bldg Clondalkin, Monastery Rd, Dub-
lin, 22, Ireland
Tel.: (353) 4591559
Web Site: http://www.clondalkin-group.com
Sales Range: $550-599.9 Million
Emp.: 3,500
Mfr & Producer of Printing & Packaging
Products
N.A.I.C.S.: 333248
Colin J. Williams *(Chm)*

Subsidiary (US):

Clondalkin Pharma & Healthcare
Inc.   **(4)**
10500 Industrial Dr, Pineville, NC 28134
Tel.: (704) 889-7262
Web Site: http://www.clondalkingroup.com
Pharmaceutical & Healthcare Packaging
Products Mfr & Whslr
N.A.I.C.S.: 326112
David C. Lennon *(CEO)*

Subsidiary (Domestic):

Clondalkin Pharma & Healthcare
(Evv), Inc.   **(5)**

1100 E Louisiana St, Evansville, IN 47711
Tel.: (812) 464-2461
Web Site: http://www.clondalkingroup.com
Printed Packaging for Pharmaceutical &
Medical Device Industries
N.A.I.C.S.: 322220
Brian Emmons *(Dir-Ops)*

Clondalkin Pharma & Healthcare
(Port), Inc.   **(5)**
1072 Boulder Rd, Greensboro, NC 27409
Tel.: (336) 292-4555
Web Site: http://www.clondalkingroup.com
Mfr of Pressure-Sensitive Labels, Package
Outserts, Inserts & Folding Cartons
N.A.I.C.S.: 322212
Kevin Kenjarski *(VP-Sls & Mktg-North
America)*

Subsidiary (US):

Vaassen, Inc.   **(4)**
1200 Central Florida Pkwy, Orlando, FL
32837-9259
Tel.: (407) 859-7780
Web Site: http://www.spiralkote.com
Sales Range: $50-74.9 Million
Emp.: 90
Flex Graphic Tinting
N.A.I.C.S.: 323111
Bill Harris *(Mgr-Tech Sls)*

Dynniq Group B.V.   **(1)**
Basicweg 16, 3821 BR, Amersfoort, Nether-
lands
Tel.: (31) 33 454 1777
Web Site: http://www.dynniq.com
Holding Company; Traffic & Infrastructure
Engineering & Construction Services
N.A.I.C.S.: 551112
Cees de Wijs *(CEO)*

Branch (Domestic):

Dynniq Nederland BV   **(2)**
Hardwareweg 11, 3821 BL, Amersfoort,
Netherlands
Tel.: (31) 33 450 2211
Web Site: http://www.dynniq.nl
Traffic & Infrastructure Engineering & Con-
struction Services
N.A.I.C.S.: 541330
Ron van Laar *(CFO)*

Subsidiary (Domestic):

Dynniq Peek Traffic B.V.   **(2)**
Basicweg 16, 3821 BR, Amersfoort, Nether-
lands
Tel.: (31) 33 454 1777
Web Site: http://www.dynniq.com
Traffic System Software Development Ser-
vices
N.A.I.C.S.: 541511
Cees Zewis *(Gen Mgr)*

Subsidiary (Non-US):

Peek Promet d.o.o.   **(3)**
Sprecka ulica 8, 10000, Zagreb, Croatia
Tel.: (385) 7988 407
Web Site: http://www.peek.hr
Traffic Control System Distr
N.A.I.C.S.: 423610
Bojan Radosevic *(Mng Dir)*

Subsidiary (Non-US):

Dynniq UK Ltd   **(2)**
Hazelwood House Lime Tree Way Chine-
ham Business Park, Basingstoke, RG24
8WZ, Hampshire, United Kingdom
Tel.: (44) 1256 891800
Web Site: http://www.dynniq.co.uk
Transportation Systems Mfr & Services
N.A.I.C.S.: 334419
Tony O'Brien *(Mng Dir)*

IZICO Holding B.V.   **(1)**
Minervum 7035, 4817 ZL, Breda, Nether-
lands
Tel.: (31) 765784800
Web Site: http://www.izicosnacks.com
Sales Range: $125-149.9 Million
Emp.: 400
Holding Company; Snack Food Mfr
N.A.I.C.S.: 551112
Lydia Thomas *(Mgr-Mktg)*

Subsidiary (Domestic):

IZICO Nederland B.V.   **(2)**

Minervum 7035, 4817 ZL, Breda,
Netherlands   **(100%)**
Tel.: (31) 765784800
Web Site: http://www.izicosnacks.com
Sales Range: $25-49.9 Million
Baked Goods Mfr
N.A.I.C.S.: 311999
Hans Peter *(Gen Mgr)*

Subsidiary (Domestic):

IZICO Katwijk B.V.   **(3)**
Kalkbranderstraat 2, 2222 BH, Katwijk aan
Zee, Netherlands   **(100%)**
Tel.: (31) 714029214
Web Site: http://www.izicosnacks.com
Sales Range: $25-49.9 Million
Baked Goods Mfr
N.A.I.C.S.: 311999

Koninklijke Mosa bv.   **(1)**
Meerssenerweg 358, 6224AL, Maastricht,
Netherlands
Tel.: (31) 43 368 94 44
Web Site: http://www.mosa.nl
Flooring Installation Services
N.A.I.C.S.: 238330
Rene Vermeeren *(CFO)*

Muelink & Grol B.V.   **(1)**
Duinkerkenstraat 27, 9723 BP, Groningen,
Netherlands
Tel.: (31) 503139944
Web Site: http://www.muelink-grol.nl
Sales Range: $125-149.9 Million
Venting Product Mfr
N.A.I.C.S.: 333415

Subsidiary (US):

DuraVent, Inc.   **(2)**
877 Cotting Ct, Vacaville, CA 95688-9354
Tel.: (707) 446-1786
Web Site: http://www.duravent.com
Sales Range: $100-124.9 Million
Gas Vents, All-Fuel Chimneys, Stovepipes,
Chimney Liners & Pellet Vents Mfr
N.A.I.C.S.: 332322
Todd Lampey *(Mgr-Natl Sls)*

Subsidiary (Domestic):

Hart & Cooley, Inc.   **(3)**
5030 Corporate Exchange Blvd, Grand
Rapids, MI 49512
Web Site: http://www.hartandcooley.com
Air Distribution Products Mfr
N.A.I.C.S.: 334512
Curt Monhart *(Exec VP-Mktg & Sls)*

N.V. Nationale
Borg-Maatschappij   **(1)**
Keizersgracht 165, 1016 DP, Amsterdam,
Netherlands
Tel.: (31) 205533900
Web Site: http://www.nationaleborg.nl
Rev.: $579,698,529
Assets: $1,424,585,844
Liabilities: $1,367,820,626
Net Worth: $56,765,217
Earnings: $14,980,174
Emp.: 114
Fiscal Year-end: 12/31/2017
Non-Life Insurance & Reinsurance
N.A.I.C.S.: 524128
A. P. Jos C. Kroon *(CEO & Member-Mgmt
Bd)*

Sif Group bv.   **(1)**
Mijnheerkensweg 33, 6041 TA, Roermond,
Netherlands
Tel.: (31) 475 385 777
Web Site: http://www.sif-group.com
Oil & Gas Exploration Services
N.A.I.C.S.: 211120

EGERSUND GROUP AS
Svanavgveien 30, 4374, Egersund,
Norway
Tel.: (47) 51 46 29 00
Web Site:
  http://www.egersundgroup.no
Year Founded: 1952
Fishing, Aquaculture & Trade Ser-
vices
N.A.I.C.S.: 112511
Hans Kristian Mong *(Mng Dir)*

Subsidiaries:

AKVA Group ASA   **(1)**
Plogfabrikkvegen 11, 4353, Klepp, Stasjon,
Norway   **(51%)**
Tel.: (47) 51778500
Web Site: https://www.akvagroup.com
Rev.: $311,871,421
Assets: $330,726,584
Liabilities: $225,023,924
Net Worth: $105,702,660
Earnings: ($12,107,427)
Emp.: 1,466
Fiscal Year-end: 12/31/2022
Steel & Plastic Cages Mfr
N.A.I.C.S.: 331222
Andrew Campbell *(COO-Intl)*

Subsidiary (Non-US):

AKVA group Chile S.A.   **(2)**
Ruta 5 Sur Km 1030, Puerto Montt,
5480000, Llanquihue, Chile
Tel.: (56) 65250250
Sales Range: $125-149.9 Million
Emp.: 310
Fishing Equipment & Supplies Distr
N.A.I.C.S.: 423910
Christian Schafer *(Gen Mgr)*

AKVA group Denmark A/S   **(2)**
Navervej 10, Fredericia, 7000, Denmark
Tel.: (45) 75513211
Web Site: http://www.akvasmart.com
Sales Range: $25-49.9 Million
Emp.: 40
Fish Farming Products Distr
N.A.I.C.S.: 424460
Jacob Bregnballe *(Dir-Sls-Land Based Sys)*

AKVA group North America Inc.   **(2)**
1495 Baikie Rd, PO Box 397, Campbell
River, V9W0C2, BC, Canada
Tel.: (250) 286-8802
Sales Range: $25-49.9 Million
Emp.: 7
Fishing Equipment & Supplies Distr
N.A.I.C.S.: 423910
Wade Kaskiw *(Mng Dir)*

AKVA group Scotland Ltd.   **(2)**
36F Shore St, Inverness, IV1 1NF, Scot-
land, United Kingdom
Tel.: (44) 1463221444
Web Site: http://www.akvasmart.com
Sales Range: $25-49.9 Million
Emp.: 30
Commercial Fish Farming Products Distr
N.A.I.C.S.: 423910
Jason Cleaversmith *(Gen Mgr)*

Subsidiary (Domestic):

Helgeland Plast AS   **(2)**
Basmosjyen 4, Mo i Rana, 8616, Nordland,
Norway
Tel.: (47) 75143750
Web Site: http://www.akvagroup.com
Sales Range: $75-99.9 Million
Emp.: 200
Plastic Cages & Fishing Boats Distr
N.A.I.C.S.: 423830
Trond Severinsen *(Dir-Mktg)*

AS Fiskenett   **(1)**
Mangeroy, 5936, Manger, Norway
Tel.: (47) 56349860
Web Site: http://www.fiskenett.no
Emp.: 50
Fishing Net Mfr
N.A.I.C.S.: 314999
Hugo Ulvatn *(Gen Mgr)*

Egersund Heroy AS   **(1)**
Mjolstadneset, 6092, Fosnavag, Norway
Tel.: (47) 70080480
Ship Repair & Maintenance Services
N.A.I.C.S.: 336611

Egersund Iceland EHF   **(1)**
Hafnargata 5, 735, Eskifjorour, Iceland
Tel.: (354) 4706700
Web Site: http://www.egersund.is
Gear Mfr
N.A.I.C.S.: 336350
Stefan B. Ingvarsson *(Mng Dir)*

Egersund Trading AS   **(1)**
Hovedkontor -Rabben, 5397, Bekkjarvik,
Norway
Tel.: (47) 55088500

Web Site: http://www.egersundtrading.no
Farm Equipment Distr
N.A.I.C.S.: 423820
Monika Rabben *(Gen Mgr)*

OK Marine AS (1)
Mjavannsveien 73, 4628, Kristiansand, Norway
Tel.: (47) 92284091
Web Site: http://www.okmarine.no
Fishing Equipment Distr
N.A.I.C.S.: 423830

Plastsveis AS (1)
Mossaveien 6, 8920, Somna, Norway
Tel.: (47) 75027880
Web Site: http://www.plastsveis.no
Welding Services
N.A.I.C.S.: 811310
Sten Lorentzen *(Mgr)*

YesMaritime AS (1)
Stamsneset 100A, 5252, Hordaland, Norway
Tel.: (47) 55 91 04 67
Web Site: http://www.yesmaritime.no
Construction Engineering Services
N.A.I.C.S.: 541330

EGETAEPPER A/S

Industrivej Nord 25, Post Box 190, DK-7400, Herning, Denmark
Tel.: (45) 97118811
Web Site: http://www.egecarpets.com
Year Founded: 1938
Rev.: $186,162,965
Assets: $163,840,845
Liabilities: $81,598,722
Net Worth: $82,242,122
Earnings: $7,083,351
Emp.: 707
Fiscal Year-end: 04/30/18
Carpet Designing & Mfr
N.A.I.C.S.: 314110
Gitte Garner *(Sec & Head-IR)*

Subsidiaries:

Bentzon Carpets ApS (1)
Fabrikvej 15B Rojle, 5500, Middelfart, Denmark
Tel.: (45) 64402000
Web Site: http://www.bentzon.dk
Textile Products Mfr
N.A.I.C.S.: 314999
Tage Bajlum *(CEO & Mng Dir)*

Carpet Concept Objekt-Teppichboden GmbH (1)
Bunzlauer Strasse 7, 33719, Bielefeld, Germany
Tel.: (49) 521924590
Carpet Retailer
N.A.I.C.S.: 449121
Barbara Prussner *(Sec)*

Carpet Concept Teppichfabrik GmbH & Co. KG (1)
Jenaer Strasse 22, 07589, Munchenbernsdorf, Germany
Tel.: (49) 366049122
Carpet Retailer
N.A.I.C.S.: 449121
Axel Hucker *(CEO)*

Ege Carpets DACH GmbH (1)
Seiler Hofe Schanzenstrasse 39 D14, 51063, Cologne, Germany
Tel.: (49) 2219697270
Carpet Retailer
N.A.I.C.S.: 449121

Ege Carpets Norway AS (1)
Trondheimsveien 156, 0570, Oslo, Norway
Tel.: (47) 87876750
Carpet Retailer
N.A.I.C.S.: 449121

Ege Carpets Sweden AB (1)
Engelbrektsgatan 28, 411 37, Gothenburg, Sweden
Tel.: (46) 317780050
Carpet Retailer
N.A.I.C.S.: 449121

Ege Carpets UK Ltd. (1)
Matrix Business Park 12 Eaton Avenue,

Buckshaw Village, Chorley, PR7 7NA, Lancashire, United Kingdom
Tel.: (44) 1257239000
Carpet Retailer
N.A.I.C.S.: 449121

Ege Contract A/S (1)
PO Box 190, Industrivej Nord 25, 7400, Herning, Denmark
Tel.: (45) 97118811
Web Site: http://www.egecontract.dk
Carpet Title Distr
N.A.I.C.S.: 449121

Hammer Taepper A/S (1)
Industrivej Syd 17-19 Birk, 7400, Herning, Denmark
Tel.: (45) 96270000
Web Site: http://www.hammercarpets.com
Textile Products Mfr
N.A.I.C.S.: 314999
Tom Moller Jorgensen *(CEO)*

UAB Litspin (1)
Danu St 18 Andrusaiciai vil, LT-60162, Raseiniai, Lithuania
Tel.: (370) 42871393
Web Site: http://www.litspin.lt
Textile Products Mfr
N.A.I.C.S.: 314999

EGETIS THERAPEUTICS AB

Klara Norra Kyrkogata 26, SE111 22, Stockholm, Sweden
Tel.: (46) 86797210
Web Site: https://www.egetis.com
EGTX—(OMX)
Rev.: $5,718,030
Assets: $75,466,080
Liabilities: $21,303,632
Net Worth: $54,162,449
Earnings: ($32,451,804)
Emp.: 29
Fiscal Year-end: 12/31/23
Pharmaceuticals Product Mfr
N.A.I.C.S.: 325412

EGF THERAMED HEALTH CORP.

Suite 1600 609 Granville Street, PO Box 10068, Pacific Centre, Vancouver, V7Y 1C3, BC, Canada
Tel.: (778) 331-4303　　　BC
Web Site:
　　https://www.egftheramedhealth.com
Year Founded: 2011
AUH—(DEU)
Assets: $139,767
Liabilities: $1,966,628
Net Worth: ($1,826,862)
Earnings: ($1,066,963)
Fiscal Year-end: 06/30/22
Pharmaceuticals Mfr
N.A.I.C.S.: 325412
Usama Chaudhry *(CFO)*

EGGED ISRAEL TRANSPORT COOPERATIVE SOCIETY LTD.

Airport Complex Hayarden St, PO Box 43, Ben Gurion Intl Airport, Tel Aviv, 70150, Israel
Tel.: (972) 36948888　　　IL
Web Site: http://www.egged.co.il
Year Founded: 1933
Sales Range: $300-349.9 Million
Emp.: 6,200
Public Transportation Services
N.A.I.C.S.: 485999

Subsidiaries:

Egged Holding (1)
11 Hamelacha North Ind Z, Lod, Israel
Tel.: (972) 8 6220444
Transportation Route & Railway Line Operator
N.A.I.C.S.: 485111

Subsidiary (Non-US):

Egged Bulgaria (2)
74 Treti Mart Bul, Ruse, 7000, Bulgaria
Tel.: (359) 82 82 00 12

Transportation Route & Railway Line Operator
N.A.I.C.S.: 485111

PKS Ostroleka S.A. (1)
ul T Zawadzkiego Zoski 1, Ostroleka, 07-412, Poland
Tel.: (48) 2976026713
Public Transport Bus Services
N.A.I.C.S.: 485113

PKS Plock S.A. (1)
ul Bielska 53, 09-400, Plock, Poland
Tel.: (48) 24 267 65 00
Public Transport Bus Services
N.A.I.C.S.: 485113

EGGRICULTURE FOODS LTD.

1 Lim Chu Kang Lane 9, Singapore, 718845, Singapore
Tel.: (65) 67929745　　　Ky
Web Site:
　　https://www.eggstory.com.sg
Year Founded: 2002
8609—(HKG)
Rev.: $39,600,441
Assets: $44,325,799
Liabilities: $18,473,361
Net Worth: $25,852,438
Earnings: $5,633,586
Emp.: 255
Fiscal Year-end: 03/31/21
Egg Product Distr
N.A.I.C.S.: 424440
Chin Chew Ma *(Chm & CEO)*

EGHTESAD NOVIN BANK

No 24 Esfandiyar Blvd Valiasr Ave, PO Box 19395-3796, 1968655944, Tehran, Iran
Tel.: (98) 21 8233 0000
Web Site: http://www.enbank.ir
Year Founded: 2001
NOVN1—(THE)
Sales Range: Less than $1 Million
Banking Services
N.A.I.C.S.: 522110
Ali Reza Bolgouri *(CEO)*

EGIDE SA

Site Sactar - CS 20205, 84505, Bollene, Cedex, France
Tel.: (33) 490309711　　　FR
Web Site: https://www.egide-group.com
Year Founded: 1986
ALGID—(EUR)
Rev.: $39,921,485
Assets: $34,762,877
Liabilities: $20,547,227
Net Worth: $14,215,650
Earnings: $246,876
Emp.: 132
Fiscal Year-end: 12/31/21
Aluminum Hermetic Packages, Modulators, Multi-Chip Modules, Relay Headers & Infra-Red Detector Packages Designer Mfr & Distr
N.A.I.C.S.: 334419
Wladimir Muffato *(Dir-Ceramic Components)*

Subsidiaries:

Egide USA, LLC (1)
4 Washington St, Cambridge, MD 21613　　　(100%)
Tel.: (410) 901-6100
Web Site: http://www.egide.fr
Emp.: 72
Holding Company; Aluminum Hermetic Packages, Modulators, Multi-Chip Modules, Relay Headers & Infra-Red Detector Packages Mfr & Distr
N.A.I.C.S.: 551112
Philippe Bregi *(Chm)*

Subsidiary (Domestic):

Egide USA, Inc. (2)
4 Washington St, Cambridge, MD 21613　　　(100%)

Tel.: (410) 901-6100
Web Site: http://www.egide.fr
Aluminum Hermetic Packages, Modulators, Multi-Chip Modules, Relay Headers & Infra-Red Detector Packages Mfr & Distr
N.A.I.C.S.: 334419

Santier Inc. (1)
10103 Carroll Canyon Rd, San Diego, CA 92131
Tel.: (858) 271-1993
Web Site: https://www.santier.com
Electronic Component & Printer Mfr
N.A.I.C.S.: 334419

EGING PHOTOVOLTAIC TECHNOLOGY CO., LTD.

No 18 Jinwu Road, Jintan District, Changzhou, 213213, Jiangsu, China
Tel.: (86) 51982585558
Web Site: http://www.egingpv.com
Year Founded: 2003
600537—(SHG)
Rev.: $1,407,240,783
Assets: $1,656,550,846
Liabilities: $1,253,743,513
Net Worth: $402,807,333
Earnings: $17,843,619
Fiscal Year-end: 12/31/22
Solar Module Mfr
N.A.I.C.S.: 335999
Liu Qiang *(Chm & Gen Mgr)*

Subsidiaries:

Changzhou EGING PV Technology Co., Ltd. (1)
No 18 Jinwu Road, Yaotang Town Jintan District, Changzhou, 213213, Jiangsu, China
Tel.: (86) 51982585880
Web Site: https://www.egingpv.com
Emp.: 5,000
Crystalline Silicon Product Mfr & Distr
N.A.I.C.S.: 334413

EGing Photovoltaic Europe GmbH (1)
Lyoner Strasse 34, 60528, Frankfurt, Germany
Tel.: (49) 15154361810
Solar Module Distr
N.A.I.C.S.: 423720

EGing Photovoltaic Technology Co., Ltd. (1)
4199 Campus Dr Ste 550, Irvine, CA 92612-2224
Tel.: (949) 725-2948
Solar Panel Distr
N.A.I.C.S.: 423720

EGL HOLDINGS COMPANY LIMITED

15th Floor EGL Tower 83 Hung To Road, Kwun Tong, China (Hong Kong)
Tel.: (852) 23151955
Web Site: http://www.egltours.com
6882—(HKG)
Rev.: $25,051,073
Assets: $115,394,640
Liabilities: $112,784,843
Net Worth: $2,609,798
Earnings: ($9,626,123)
Emp.: 294
Fiscal Year-end: 12/31/22
Holding Company; Travel Services
N.A.I.C.S.: 551112
Man Ying Yuen *(Chm)*

EGLS CO., LTD.

Linjiang Industrial Park Yucheng New District, Hujia Bailongqiao Town, Jinhua, 321025, Zhejiang, China
Tel.: (86) 1082356080
Web Site: http://www.egls.cn
Year Founded: 2001
002619—(SSE)
Rev.: $27,868,899
Assets: $343,414,087
Liabilities: $11,453,980

Net Worth: $331,960,107
Earnings: ($191,103,429)
Fiscal Year-end: 12/31/20
Wireless Boutique Online Games Developer & Operator
N.A.I.C.S.: 513210

EGMONT FONDEN

Vognmagergade 11, 1148, Copenhagen, K, Denmark
Tel.: (45) 33 305550   DK
Web Site:
   http://www.egmontfonden.dk
Year Founded: 1878
Rev.: $1,883,234,966
Assets: $2,206,685,250
Liabilities: $1,214,579,999
Net Worth: $992,105,251
Earnings: $61,864,426
Emp.: 4,264
Fiscal Year-end: 12/31/19
Youth Education & Support Grant-making Foundation
N.A.I.C.S.: 813219

Subsidiaries:

Anglatroll AB   **(1)**
Cajsa Wargs Grand 4, 702 15, Orebro, Sweden
Tel.: (46) 19 321774
Child & Youth Services
N.A.I.C.S.: 624110

Bagaren och Kocken AB   **(1)**
Sorredsvagen 113, 418 78, Gothenburg, Sweden
Tel.: (46) 31 25 22 22
Web Site: http://www.bagarenochkocken.se
Household Appliance Distr
N.A.I.C.S.: 423620

Billetlugen A/S   **(1)**
Tel.: (45) 70263267
Web Site: http://www.billetlugen.dk
Event Management Services
N.A.I.C.S.: 711310

Egmont Creative Center A/S   **(1)**
Vognmagergade 11, 1148, Copenhagen, Denmark
Tel.: (45) 3330 5000
Web Site: http://www.egmontcreative.com
Magazine Publisher
N.A.I.C.S.: 513120
Lars Bastholm *(Chief Creative Officer)*

Egmont Ehapa Comic Collection GmbH   **(1)**
Gertrudenstr 30-36, 50667, Cologne, Germany
Tel.: (49) 221 20811 0
Web Site: http://www.egmont-comic-collection.de
Comic Book Publisher
N.A.I.C.S.: 513120

Egmont Ehapa Media GmbH   **(1)**
Jakobstrasse 83/84, 10179, Berlin, Germany
Tel.: (49) 30 24008 0
Web Site: http://www.ehapa.de
Magazine Publisher
N.A.I.C.S.: 513120
Dirk Eggert *(Head-Media Sls)*

Egmont Ehapa Verlag GmbH   **(1)**
Am Heumarkt 7 top 5, 1030, Vienna, Austria
Tel.: (43) 18 13 55 27 0
Magazine Publisher
N.A.I.C.S.: 513120

Egmont Holding Oy   **(1)**
Mechelininkatu 1, 00180, Helsinki, Finland
Tel.: (358) 9 4764460
Holding Company
N.A.I.C.S.: 551112

Egmont International Holding A/S **(1)**
Vognmagergade 11, 1148, Copenhagen, Denmark
Tel.: (45) 70240000
Web Site: http://www.egmont.com
Sales Range: $900-999.9 Million
Emp.: 3,533
Media Holding Company

N.A.I.C.S.: 551112

Affiliate (Non-US):

Bladcentralen ANS   **(2)**
Haraldrudveien 20, PO Box 53, 0581, Oslo, Norway   **(43%)**
Tel.: (47) 22726200
Web Site: http://www.bladcentralen.no
Sales Range: $25-49.9 Million
Emp.: 50
Freight Transportation Arrangement
N.A.I.C.S.: 488510
Paul Berddahl *(Mgr)*

Subsidiary (Domestic):

Bladcentralens Eiendomsselskap AS   **(3)**
Haraldrudveien 20, PO Box 53, 0581, Oslo, Norway
Tel.: (47) 22726200
Web Site: http://www.bladcentralens.no
Sales Range: $50-74.9 Million
Real Estate Agents & Brokers
N.A.I.C.S.: 531210

Subsidiary (Non-US):

Cappelen Damm AS   **(2)**
Akersgata 47/49, 0055, Oslo, Norway
Tel.: (47) 21616500
Web Site: http://www.cappelendamm.no
Sales Range: $100-124.9 Million
Emp.: 400
Book Publishers
N.A.I.C.S.: 513130
Tom Harald Jenssen *(Mng Dir)*

Drammen Kino AS   **(2)**
Bragernes torg 2A, 3017, Drammen, Norway
Tel.: (47) 32 21 78 60
Web Site: http://www.nfkino.no
Motion Picture & Video Producer & Distr
N.A.I.C.S.: 512110

Egmont AS   **(2)**
Nydalsveien 12 Nydalen, Oslo, 0055, Norway
Tel.: (47) 24051300
Web Site: http://www.egmont.no
Sales Range: $50-74.9 Million
Emp.: 150
Book Publishers
N.A.I.C.S.: 513130

Subsidiary (Domestic):

Egmont Administration A/S   **(2)**
Vognmagergade 11, 1148, Copenhagen, K, Denmark   **(100%)**
Tel.: (45) 33305550
Web Site: http://www.egmont.com
Sales Range: $200-249.9 Million
Emp.: 700
Office Administrative Services
N.A.I.C.S.: 561110

Subsidiary (Non-US):

Egmont Bulgaria EAD   **(2)**
21 Hristo Belchev street, 1000, Sofia, Bulgaria
Tel.: (359) 2988 01 37
Magazine Publisher
N.A.I.C.S.: 513120

Egmont CR s.r.o.   **(2)**
Zirovnicka 3124, 106 00, Prague, Czech Republic
Tel.: (420) 22 48 00 75 1
Web Site: http://www.egmont.cz
Newspaper & Magazine Publisher
N.A.I.C.S.: 513120

Subsidiary (Domestic):

Egmont Creative A/S   **(2)**
Vognmagergade 9 4th & 5th Fl, Copenhagen, 1148, Denmark   **(100%)**
Tel.: (45) 33305550
Web Site: http://www.egmont.com
Sales Range: $100-124.9 Million
Emp.: 400
Periodical Publishers
N.A.I.C.S.: 513130
Steffen Kragh *(Mng Dir)*

Subsidiary (Non-US):

Egmont Estonia AS   **(2)**

Laki 26, 12915, Tallinn, Estonia
Tel.: (372) 646 12 14
Web Site: http://www.egmont.ee
Magazine Publisher
N.A.I.C.S.: 513120
Svea Uusen *(Chm)*

Egmont Holding AB   **(2)**
Skeppsgatan 9, 20507, Malmo, Sweden   **(100%)**
Tel.: (46) 40385200
Web Site: http://www.egmont.se
Sales Range: $50-74.9 Million
Emp.: 100
Holding Company
N.A.I.C.S.: 551112

Egmont Hungary Kft.   **(2)**
Galagonya u 5, 1036, Budapest, Hungary
Tel.: (36) 6 1 464 3906
Web Site: http://www.egmont.hu
Magazine Publisher
N.A.I.C.S.: 513120

Subsidiary (Domestic):

Egmont Imagination A/S   **(2)**
Mosedalvej 14, 2500, Valby, Denmark
Tel.: (45) 36188200
Web Site: http://www.egmont.com
Sales Range: $25-49.9 Million
Emp.: 2
Motion Picture & Video Production
N.A.I.C.S.: 512110
Allan Hansen *(Mng Dir)*

Subsidiary (Non-US):

Egmont Karnan AB   **(2)**
Drottningtorget 14, 20508, Malmo, Sweden
Tel.: (46) 406939400
Web Site: http://www.egmontkarnan.se
Periodical Publishers
N.A.I.C.S.: 513120

Egmont Latvija SIA   **(2)**
Antonijas Street 24-11, Riga, 1010, Latvia
Tel.: (371) 67185785
Web Site: http://www.egmont.lv
Magazine Publisher
N.A.I.C.S.: 513120
Roman Filipov *(Chm)*

Egmont Polska sp. z o.o.   **(2)**
ul Dzielna 60, 01-029, Warsaw, Poland
Tel.: (48) 22 838 41 00
Web Site:
   http://www.wydawnictwoegmont.pl
Newspaper & Magazine Publisher
N.A.I.C.S.: 513120

Subsidiary (Domestic):

Egmont Publishing Magasiner A/S   **(2)**
Hellerupvej 51, 2900, Hellerup, Denmark
Tel.: (45) 39457500
Web Site: http://www.egmontmagasiner.dk
Sales Range: $50-74.9 Million
Emp.: 250
Periodical Publishers
N.A.I.C.S.: 513120
Torsten Bjerre Rasmussen *(CEO)*

Egmont Serieforlaget A/S   **(2)**
Vognmagergade 11, 1148, Copenhagen, Denmark   **(100%)**
Tel.: (45) 33305550
Web Site: http://www.egmont.com
Sales Range: $25-49.9 Million
Emp.: 50
Periodical Publishers
N.A.I.C.S.: 513120
Steffen Kragh *(Pres & CEO)*

Subsidiary (Non-US):

Egmont Serieforlaget AS   **(2)**
Fridtjof Nansens vei 14, 0055, Oslo, Norway
Tel.: (47) 24051300
Web Site: http://www.egmont.com
Sales Range: $50-74.9 Million
Emp.: 150
Book Publishers
N.A.I.C.S.: 513130

Egmont Sourcing (HK) Ltd.   **(2)**
Unit 1101 11/F Wing On Plaza 62 Mody Road, Tsim Sha Tsui, Kowloon, China (Hong Kong)

Tel.: (852) 2311 7268
Web Site: http://www.egmontsourcing.com
Magazine Publisher
N.A.I.C.S.: 513120
Winnie Ng *(Office Mgr)*

Egmont Tidskrifter AB   **(2)**
Skeppsgatan 9, 205 07, Malmo, Sweden   **(100%)**
Tel.: (46) 40385200
Web Site: http://www.egmont.se
Sales Range: $25-49.9 Million
Emp.: 100
Periodical Publishers
N.A.I.C.S.: 513120

Egmont Tidskrifter BM AB   **(2)**
Pyramidvagen 7, 169 56, Solna, Sweden
Tel.: (46) 8 692 01 00
Newspaper & Magazine Publisher
N.A.I.C.S.: 513120

Subsidiary (US):

Egmont US Inc.   **(2)**
443 Park Ave S Ste 806, New York, NY 10016
Tel.: (212) 685-0102
Web Site: http://www.egmontusa.com
Magazine Publisher
N.A.I.C.S.: 513120

Subsidiary (Non-US):

Egmont Ukraine LLC   **(2)**
67 Premogy avenue building K of 101, 03680, Kiev, Ukraine
Tel.: (380) 44 53 13 55 5
Magazine Publisher
N.A.I.C.S.: 513120

Egmont Verlagsgesellschaften mbH   **(2)**
Alte Jakobstrasse 83/84, 10179, Berlin, Germany
Tel.: (49) 30240080
Web Site: http://www.egmont.de
Newspaper & Magazine Publisher
N.A.I.C.S.: 513120

Egmont d.o.o.   **(2)**
Visnjevac 3, 10000, Zagreb, Croatia
Tel.: (385) 1 30 40 555
Web Site: http://www.egmont.hr
Magazine Publisher
N.A.I.C.S.: 513120

Subsidiary (Domestic):

Euro Broadcast Hire A/S   **(2)**
Titangade 1, 2200, Copenhagen, Denmark   **(100%)**
Tel.: (45) 35828220
Web Site: http://www.ebh.cc
Sales Range: $25-49.9 Million
Emp.: 10
Motion Picture & Video Production
N.A.I.C.S.: 512110
Thomas Niyi *(Gen Mgr)*

Subsidiary (Non-US):

Filmweb AS   **(2)**
Nedre gate 7, 551, Oslo, Norway
Tel.: (47) 21 50 48 00
Web Site: http://www.filmweb.no
Motion Picture & Video Producer & Distr
N.A.I.C.S.: 512110

Kanal 24 Norge AS   **(2)**
Pilestredet 8, Oslo, 0180, Norway
Tel.: (47) 69 70 76 00
Web Site: http://www.kanal24.no
Radio Broadcasting Services
N.A.I.C.S.: 516210

Subsidiary (Domestic):

Kino.dk A/S   **(2)**
Skt Peders Straede 30 C stuen, 1453, Copenhagen, Denmark
Tel.: (45) 71 99 32 48
Web Site: http://www.kino.dk
Theater Operator
N.A.I.C.S.: 512131

Lindhardt og Ringhof Forlag A/S **(2)**
Vognmagergade 11, 1148, Copenhagen, Denmark   **(100%)**
Tel.: (45) 33305550
Web Site: http://www.lindhardtogringhof.dk

Egmont Fonden—(Continued)

Sales Range: $200-249.9 Million
Emp.: 600
Periodical Publishers
N.A.I.C.S.: 513120
Steffen Kragh *(Mng Dir)*

Unit (Domestic):

Alinea   **(3)**
Vognmagergade 11 2 sal, 1148, Copenha-
gen, K, Denmark
Tel.: (45) 3369 4666
Web Site: http://www.alinea.dk
Sales Range: $25-49.9 Million
Emp.: 80
Textbook Publisher
N.A.I.C.S.: 513130

Subsidiary (Non-US):

Matila Rohr Productions (MRP)   **(2)**
Tallberginkatu 1A 141, Helsinki, 00180,
Finland   **(100%)**
Tel.: (358) 96689990
Web Site: http://www.nordiskfilmtv.fi
Sales Range: $25-49.9 Million
Emp.: 25
Motion Picture & Video Production
N.A.I.C.S.: 512110

Media Direct Norge AS   **(2)**
Graterudveien 1, 3036, Drammen, Norway
Tel.: (47) 32 20 56 00
Web Site: http://www.mdn.no
Motion Picture & Video Producer & Distr
N.A.I.C.S.: 512110

Neofilm AS   **(2)**
Wedel Jarlsbergsvei 36, PO Box 272, Jar,
1358, Baerum, Norway
Tel.: (47) 67 52 53 26
Motion Picture & Video Producer & Distr
N.A.I.C.S.: 512110

Subsidiary (Domestic):

Nordisk Film A/S   **(2)**
Mosedalvej 14, Valby, 2500, Denmark
Tel.: (45) 36188200
Web Site: http://www.nordiskfilm.com
Sales Range: $100-124.9 Million
Emp.: 550
Motion Picture & Video Production
N.A.I.C.S.: 512110
Allan Mathson Hansen *(CEO)*

Subsidiary (Non-US):

Nordisk Film AB   **(3)**
Karlsrovagen 2 D, Danderyd, Sweden
Tel.: (46) 86013200
Sales Range: $25-49.9 Million
Emp.: 50
Motion Picture & Video Production
N.A.I.C.S.: 512110

Nordisk Film AS   **(3)**
Nydalsveien 12A, 0484, Oslo, Norway
Tel.: (47) 21544700
Motion Picture & Video Producer & Distr
N.A.I.C.S.: 512110
Morten Christoffersen *(Dir-Theatrical Distr)*

Subsidiary (Domestic):

Nordisk Film Biografer A/S   **(3)**
Mosedalvej 14 2500, 1609, Valby, Denmark
Tel.: (45) 33147606
Web Site: http://www.nordiskfilm.com
Sales Range: $100-124.9 Million
Emp.: 300
Motion Picture Theater
N.A.I.C.S.: 512131
John Tonnes *(Mng Dir)*

Nordisk Film Post Production
A/S   **(3)**
Tagensvej 85 D, Copenhagen, 2200, Den-
mark
Tel.: (45) 35877777
Web Site: http://www.shorcut.com
Sales Range: $25-49.9 Million
Emp.: 50
Motion Picture & Video Production
N.A.I.C.S.: 512110

Subsidiary (Non-US):

Nordisk Film Post Production Stock-
holm AB   **(3)**

Tullvaktsvagen 2, Stockholm, Sweden
Tel.: (46) 84504500
Sales Range: $25-49.9 Million
Emp.: 60
Motion Picture & Video Production
N.A.I.C.S.: 512110

Nordisk Film Production Sverige
AB   **(3)**
Tegeluddsvagen 80, 10252, Stockholm,
Sweden
Tel.: (46) 86013200
Sales Range: $25-49.9 Million
Emp.: 100
Motion Picture & Video Production
N.A.I.C.S.: 512110

Oy Nordisk Film AB   **(3)**
Mechelininkatu 1a, Helsinki, 180, Finland
Tel.: (358) 94764460
Web Site: http://www.nordiskfilm.fi
Sales Range: $25-49.9 Million
Emp.: 30
Motion Picture & Video Production
N.A.I.C.S.: 512110
Allan Hansen *(Mng Dir)*

Subsidiary (Domestic):

Nordisk Film Shortcut A/S   **(2)**
Tagensvej 85D, 2200, Copenhagen, Den-
mark
Tel.: (45) 35 87 77 77
Web Site: http://www.shortcut.dk
Motion Picture & Video Producer
N.A.I.C.S.: 512110
Rikke Crosby *(CEO)*

Subsidiary (Non-US):

Nordisk Film ShortCut AB   **(3)**
Eriksbergsgatan 10, 114 30, Stockholm,
Sweden
Tel.: (46) 8 515 164 00
Web Site: http://se.nordiskfilm-shortcut.com
Motion Picture & Video Producer & Distr
N.A.I.C.S.: 512110
Mikael Frisell *(Mgr)*

Nordisk Film ShortCut AS   **(3)**
Nedre gate 7d, 551, Oslo, Norway
Tel.: (47) 21 421 030
Web Site: http://www.shortcutoslo.no
Motion Picture & Video Producer & Distr
N.A.I.C.S.: 512110
Kristin Hellebust *(Mng Dir)*

Subsidiary (Non-US):

Norsk Filmdistribusjon AS   **(2)**
Sagveien 23 C2, 459, Oslo, Norway
Tel.: (47) 23 35 82 00
Web Site:
    http://www.norskfilmdistribusjon.no
Motion Picture & Video Producer & Distr
N.A.I.C.S.: 512110
Jarle Namtvedt *(Officer-Press & Mktg Mgr)*

Oslo Kino AS   **(2)**
Essendrops gate 3 etasje, Oslo, 0368, Nor-
way
Tel.: (47) 99 43 20 00
Theater Operator
N.A.I.C.S.: 512131

Subsidiary (Domestic):

Scala Bio Nykobong F. ApS   **(2)**
Slotsbryggen 5, 4800, Copenhagen, Den-
mark
Tel.: (45) 70 13 12 11
Web Site: http://www.nfbio.dk
Theater Operator
N.A.I.C.S.: 512131

Subsidiary (Non-US):

TV 2 AS   **(2)**
Nostegaten 72, PO Box 7222, Bergen,
5020, Norway   **(100%)**
Tel.: (47) 55908070
Web Site: http://www.tv2.no
Sales Range: $200-249.9 Million
Emp.: 800
Television Broadcasting
N.A.I.C.S.: 516120
Olav Sandnes *(Mng Dir)*

UAB Egmont Lietuva   **(2)**
Algirdog 51 A, 03609, Vilnius, Lithuania
Tel.: (370) 52 13 12 65

Magazine Publisher
N.A.I.C.S.: 513120
Regina Komziene *(Mgr-Mktg)*

Subsidiary (Domestic):

Vaegtkonsulenterne A/S   **(2)**
Hellerupvej 51, 2900, Hellerup, Denmark
Tel.: (45) 39 45 75 90
Web Site: http://www.vaegtkonsulenterne.dk
Weight Reducing Center
N.A.I.C.S.: 812191

Subsidiary (Non-US):

Vagabond Media AB   **(2)**
Gotgatan 95, PO Box 20 123, 10460,
Stockholm, Sweden
Tel.: (46) 80 555 240 00
Web Site: http://www.vagabond.se
Periodical Publishers
N.A.I.C.S.: 513120

ZAO Egmont Russia Ltd.   **(2)**
8/6 Olsufievsky per, 119071, Moscow, Rus-
sia
Tel.: (7) 49 59 33 72 50
Magazine Publisher
N.A.I.C.S.: 513120
Lev Yelin *(Mng Dir & VP)*

Egmont Kids Media Nordic AS   **(1)**
Nydalsveien 12, 0484, Oslo, Norway
Tel.: (47) 22 77 20 00
Magazine Publisher
N.A.I.C.S.: 513120

Egmont Printing Service A/S   **(1)**
Hellerupvej 51, 2900, Hellerup, Denmark
Tel.: (45) 35 82 70 60
Book Printing Services
N.A.I.C.S.: 513120

Egmont Publishing Kids AB   **(1)**
Skeppsgatan 9, 205 07, Malmo, Sweden
Tel.: (46) 40385200
Web Site: http://www.egmont.com
Magazine Publisher
N.A.I.C.S.: 513120
Charlotta Borelius *(Mgr-Dev)*

Egmont Publishing Subsidiary
AB   **(1)**
Pyramidvagen 7, 169 56, Solna, Sweden
Tel.: (46) 8 58782200
Magazine Publisher
N.A.I.C.S.: 513120

Egmont Serbia   **(1)**
Zorza Klemansoa 24, 11000, Belgrade,
Serbia
Tel.: (381) 11 27 82 502
Web Site: http://www.egmont.rs
Magazine Publisher
N.A.I.C.S.: 513120

Gavekortet.dk A/S   **(1)**
Vesterbrogade 44 1, 1620, Copenhagen,
Denmark
Tel.: (45) 3823 7020
Web Site: http://www.gavekortet.dk
Gift Card Online Retailer
N.A.I.C.S.: 459420
Per Christoffersen *(Mgr-Bus Dev)*

MaxiKarty.pl. sp. z o.o   **(1)**
Emilii Plater 53, 00-113, Warsaw, Poland
Tel.: (48) 22 250 30 30
Web Site: http://www.maxikarty.pl
Gift Card Online Retailer
N.A.I.C.S.: 459420

Nordisk Film Kino AS   **(1)**
Fridtjof Nansens vei 6, 0369, Oslo, Norway
Tel.: (47) 994 32 000
Web Site: http://www.nfkino.no
Theater Operator
N.A.I.C.S.: 512131

Scala Bio Center Aalborg ApS   **(1)**
Vesterbro 49, 9000, Aalborg, Denmark
Tel.: (45) 96 30 36 90
Child & Youth Services
N.A.I.C.S.: 624110

TV 2 Torget AS   **(1)**
Nostegaten 78, 5020, Bergen, Norway
Tel.: (47) 815 22205
Web Site: http://www.tv2torget.no
Television Broadcasting Services
N.A.I.C.S.: 516120

Venuepoint AB   **(1)**
Avagen 25, 412 51, Gothenburg, Sweden
Tel.: (46) 771 130 150
Child & Youth Services
N.A.I.C.S.: 624110

Venuepoint AS   **(1)**
Mollergata 4, 0179, Oslo, Norway
Tel.: (47) 948 19 234
Child & Youth Services
N.A.I.C.S.: 624110

Vimond Media Solutions   **(1)**
Calle Trelawny 2 piso 10 puerta 2, 08003,
Barcelona, Spain
Tel.: (34) 647 465 714
Online Television Broadcasting Services
N.A.I.C.S.: 516120

Vimond Media Solutions Inc.   **(1)**
79 Madison Ave 2nd fl, New York, NY
10016
Tel.: (415) 366-1103
Online Television Broadcasting Services
N.A.I.C.S.: 516120
Andreas Helland *(Pres)*

EGR EXPLORATION LTD.
410 - 325 Howe Street, Vancouver,
V6C 1Z7, BC, Canada
Tel.: (604) 353-4080   **BC**
Web Site: https://www.egrexploration.com
Year Founded: 2006
Z0R—(DEU)
Assets: $614,329
Liabilities: $195,894
Net Worth: $418,435
Earnings: ($389,560)
Fiscal Year-end: 03/31/23
Gold, Silver & Copper Mining & Ex-
ploration Services
N.A.I.C.S.: 212220
Daniel Rodriguez *(CEO)*

EGREEN CO., LTD.
Icheon-si, Icheon, Gyeonggi, Korea
(South)
Tel.: (82) 31 7836733
Web Site: http://www.e-
    greenglobal.com
Animal Corn Feed Mfr
N.A.I.C.S.: 111150
Jong-Moon Park *(CEO)*

**EGUANA TECHNOLOGIES
INC.**
3636 7th Street SE, Calgary, T2G
2Y8, AB, Canada
Tel.: (403) 508-7177   **AB**
Web Site:
    https://www.eguanatech.com
Year Founded: 1999
EGT—(OTCIQ)
Rev.: $5,612,537
Assets: $11,667,073
Liabilities: $8,935,896
Net Worth: $2,731,177
Earnings: ($8,135,746)
Emp.: 43
Fiscal Year-end: 09/30/21
Power Electronics Products (Invert-
ers) for the Renewable Energy Indus-
try
N.A.I.C.S.: 335311
Brent Harris *(Founder & Exec VP)*

Subsidiaries:

Eguana GmbH   **(1)**
Marsdorfer Str 5, 01109, Dresden, Germany
Tel.: (49) 35188927033
Solar Photovoltaic Cell Distr
N.A.I.C.S.: 423690

Mainpower Hellas Ltd.   **(1)**
Argyrokastrou 21, 15234, Halandri, Greece
Tel.: (30) 2106007910
Web Site: http://www.mainpower.eu
Sales Range: $25-49.9 Million
Emp.: 4
Power Inverter Mfr & Distr
N.A.I.C.S.: 335999

Sustainable Energy Europa SL (1)
C Casanova 211 Entlo 2, 08021, Barcelona,
Spain
Tel.: (34) 93 200 2683
Sales Range: $25-49.9 Million
Emp.: 4
Power Inverter Mfr & Distr
N.A.I.C.S.: 335999

Sustainable Energy Systems Inc (1)
500-609 14th St NW, Calgary, T2N 2A1,
AB, Canada
Tel.: (403) 508-7177
Sales Range: $25-49.9 Million
Emp.: 18
Power Inverter Mfr & Distr
N.A.I.C.S.: 335999

EGUARANTEE, INC.
Akasaka Biz Tower 5-3-1 Akasaka,
Minato-ku, Tokyo, 107-6337, Japan
Tel.: (81) 363273577
Web Site:
https://www.eguarantee.co.jp
Year Founded: 2000
8771—(TKS)
Rev.: $60,580,650
Assets: $199,020,490
Liabilities: $39,547,630
Net Worth: $159,472,860
Earnings: $21,561,820
Emp.: 190
Fiscal Year-end: 03/31/24
Credit Intermediation
N.A.I.C.S.: 522390
Masanori Eto (Pres & CEO)

EGYM GMBH
Einsteinstrasse 172, 81677, Munich,
Germany
Tel.: (49) 89 9213105 99   De
Web Site: http://www.egym.com
Software Publisher
N.A.I.C.S.: 513210
Martin Fichter (Mng Dir)

EGYPT ALUMINIUM COMPANY
Naga Hammadi, Qena, Egypt
Tel.: (20) 962590009
Web Site:
https://www.egyptalum.com.eg
Year Founded: 1976
EGAL.CA—(EGX)
Sales Range: Less than $1 Million
Aluminum Mfr
N.A.I.C.S.: 331313
Mahmoud Aly Ahmed Salem (CEO &
Exec Mng Dir)

EGYPT FOR POULTRY
24 Misr-Helwan Road Al-Jazeerah
Tower 2, Maadi, Cairo, Egypt
Tel.: (20) 25244154
Web Site: https://www.epco-
chickina.com
Year Founded: 1977
EPCO.CA—(EGX)
Sales Range: Less than $1 Million
Poultry Processing Services
N.A.I.C.S.: 311615
Hisham Shawqi Ali Mohammed (Vice
Chm & Mng Dir)

EGYPT FREE SHOPS CO.
106 Gameat Al Dewal Al Arabia St
Mohandessin, Giza, Egypt
Tel.: (20) 1280818389
Web Site: https://efsco.com.eg
Year Founded: 1975
Speciality Store Operator
N.A.I.C.S.: 456120
Ashraf Ahmed Zain Ahmed (CEO)

EGYPT KUWAIT HOLDING CO. S.A.E
14 Hassan Mohamed El Razzaz
Street, Agouza, Giza, Egypt
Tel.: (20) 233363300

Web Site: https://www.ekholding.com
Year Founded: 1997
EKHOLDING—(KUW)
Rev.: $747,704,323
Assets: $1,745,727,760
Liabilities: $1,105,680,116
Net Worth: $640,047,644
Earnings: $217,811,907
Emp.: 6,700
Fiscal Year-end: 12/31/23
Private Equity Holdings
N.A.I.C.S.: 551112
Moataz Al-Alfi (Chm & Co-CEO)

Subsidiaries:

Delta Insurance (1)
14 Hassan Mohamed Al Razzaz Street,
Agouza, Giza, Egypt   (55.4%)
Tel.: (20) 2 3335 2045
Web Site: http://www.deltains.org
Sales Range: Less than $1 Million
Insurance Management Services
N.A.I.C.S.: 524298

EGYPTAIR HOLDING COMPANY
6 Adly Street, Cairo, Egypt
Tel.: (20) 23900999
Web Site: http://www.egyptair.com.eg
Year Founded: 1932
Holding Company; Air Transportation
Services
N.A.I.C.S.: 551112
Hossam Kamal (Chm & CEO)

Subsidiaries:

EGYPTAIR CARGO (1)
3rd Floor Middle Building Airport Road,
Cairo, Egypt
Tel.: (20) 222657304
Web Site: http://www.egyptair-cargo.com
Airport Cargo Handling Services
N.A.I.C.S.: 488119
Bassem Gohar (Chm & CEO)

EGYPTAIR MAINTENANCE &
ENGINEERING (1)
Cairo International Airport, Post Office 02,
Airport 1, 11776, Cairo, Egypt
Tel.: (20) 2 2267 4512
Web Site: http://www.egyptair-me.com
Aircraft Maintenance Services
N.A.I.C.S.: 488190
Abou Taleb Tawfik (Chm & CEO)

EGYPTIAN ARABIAN CMAR SECURITIES BROKERAGE
20 wezaret Alzeraa St, Dokki, Giza,
Egypt
Tel.: (20) 2 37626890
Web Site: http://www.eac-
finance.com
Year Founded: 1995
EASB.CA—(EGX)
Sales Range: Less than $1 Million
Securities Dealing Services
N.A.I.C.S.: 523150

EGYPTIAN FINANCIAL & INDUSTRIAL CO.
25 Sherif Street Abdeen Downtown,
PO BOX 11613, 11613, Cairo, Egypt
Tel.: (20) 23950678
Web Site: https://efic-eg.com
Year Founded: 1929
EFIC.CA—(EGX)
Rev.: $184,737,779
Assets: $178,747,145
Liabilities: $102,591,372
Net Worth: $76,155,772
Earnings: $22,659,454
Emp.: 1,524
Fiscal Year-end: 12/31/23
Chemical Products Mfr
N.A.I.C.S.: 325199
Abd Elaal Tolba AlBanna (CEO)

EGYPTIAN FOR DEVELOPING BUILDING MATERIALS

58 Thawra St, Heliopolis, Egypt
Tel.: (20) 2 24177553
Year Founded: 1978
Building Materials Mfr
N.A.I.C.S.: 327120

EGYPTIAN GULF BANK
El orman Plaza Building 8 10 Ahmed
Nessim St, PO Box 56, Giza, Egypt
Tel.: (20) 226733118
Web Site: https://www.eg-bank.com
Year Founded: 1981
EGBE.CA—(EGX)
Rev.: $250,293,766
Assets: $2,055,979,325
Liabilities: $1,899,117,314
Net Worth: $156,862,012
Earnings: $31,277,251
Emp.: 2,172
Fiscal Year-end: 12/31/23
Commercial Banking Services
N.A.I.C.S.: 522110
Mohamed Gamaleldin Mahmoud
(Chm)

EGYPTIAN INTERNATIONAL PHARMACEUTICAL INDUSTRIES COMPANY
Industrial Zone B 1, PO Box 149,
10th of Ramadan City, Egypt
Tel.: (20) 554499199
Web Site: https://www.eipico.com.eg
Year Founded: 1980
PHAR.CA—(EGX)
Sales Range: $150-199.9 Million
Emp.: 5,165
Pharmaceutical Product Mfr & Whslr
N.A.I.C.S.: 325412
Ahmed Borhan El Din Ismail (Chm &
Gen Mgr)

EGYPTIAN KUWAITI HOLDING
14 Hassan Mohamed El Razzaz
Street, Agouza, Giza, Egypt
Tel.: (20) 233363300
Web Site: http://www.ekholding.com
Year Founded: 1997
EKHO.CA—(EGX)
Rev.: $747,704,323
Assets: $1,745,727,760
Liabilities: $1,105,680,116
Net Worth: $640,047,644
Earnings: $217,811,907
Emp.: 5,000
Fiscal Year-end: 12/31/23
Investment Management Service
N.A.I.C.S.: 525990
Ahmed Farouk (Sr Mgr-HR)

Subsidiaries:

Alex Fert Co. - S.A.E. (1)
El Tabia Rashid Road, 21911, Alexandria,
Egypt
Tel.: (20) 35603238
Web Site: https://www.alexfert.com
Emp.: 488
Nitrogen Fertilizer Mfr
N.A.I.C.S.: 325311
Khaled Elsayed (Chm & Mng Dir)

Cooling Technology by Natural Gas
Co. (Gas Chill) S.A.E. (1)
97 omar ibn Al khattab st, Heliopolis, Cairo,
Egypt
Tel.: (20) 24159010
Web Site: https://www.gaschill.net
Cooling & Heating Equipment Mfr
N.A.I.C.S.: 333415
Eslam Ammar (Sr Engr-MEP Site)

EGYPTIAN MEDIA PRODUCTION CITY SAE
6th Of October City, PO Box 31,
12568, Cairo, 12568, Egypt
Tel.: (20) 238555064
Web Site: https://www.empc.com.eg
MPRC—(EGX)
Sales Range: $25-49.9 Million

Emp.: 650
Film & Television Producer & Distr
N.A.I.C.S.: 512110
Sayed Al Sayed (Chm)

EGYPTIAN RESORTS COMPANY
4A Aziz Abaza St, Zamalek, Cairo,
Egypt
Tel.: (20) 227358427
Web Site: https://www.erc-egypt.com
Year Founded: 1995
Sales Range: $1-9.9 Million
Hotel Operator
N.A.I.C.S.: 721110
Hazem Kassem (Chief Dev Officer)

EGYPTIAN TRANSPORT & COMMERCIAL SERVICES COMPANY S.A.E.
Down Town Katameya Mall Building
S3 3rd Floor Unit 4 El Teseen St, 5th
Settlement, Cairo, Egypt
Tel.: (20) 223146053   EG
Web Site: https://www.egytrans.com
Year Founded: 1973
ETRS.CA—(EGX)
Rev.: $13,705,009
Assets: $22,597,628
Liabilities: $6,514,602
Net Worth: $16,083,026
Earnings: $828,543
Emp.: 284
Fiscal Year-end: 12/31/20
Logistic Services
N.A.I.C.S.: 541614
Abir Wael Leheta (Chm & CEO)

Subsidiaries:

Egyptian Transportation & logistics
Company (1)
11 Dr Kamel Morsy St, Shatby, Alexandria,
21519, Egypt
Tel.: (20) 35908304
Web Site: http://www.etalegypt.com
Transport Equipment Whslr
N.A.I.C.S.: 423860

Egytrans Depot Solutions
Company (1)
Km 25 Alexandria-Cairo Desert Road, Alex-
andria, Egypt
Tel.: (20) 34702258
Web Site:
http://www.egytransdepotsolutions.com
Transport Equipment Whslr
N.A.I.C.S.: 423860

EGYPTIANS ABROAD INVESTMENT & DEVELOPMENT CO.
21 Al Giza St- Nile Business Tower -
Floor 24, Giza, Egypt
Tel.: (20) 2 35 35 624
Web Site:
http://www.egyptiansabroad.com
Year Founded: 1984
ABRD.CA—(EGX)
Sales Range: Less than $1 Million
Investment Management Service
N.A.I.C.S.: 523999
Ahmed Kamal Aboul Magd (Chm)

EGYPTIANS FOR HOUSING & DEVELOPMENT CO.
Smart Village Bld 1358, Financial
District, Giza, Egypt
Tel.: (20) 235372081
Web Site: https://www.egy-
housing.com
Year Founded: 1986
EHDR.CA—(EGX)
Sales Range: Less than $1 Million
Real Estate Development Services
N.A.I.C.S.: 531390
Ibrahim Fawzy (Chm)

EHANG HOLDINGS LIMITED

EHang Holdings Limited—(Continued)

Floor 11 Building One EHang Technology Park No 29 Bishan Blvd, Huangpu District, Guangzhou, 510700, China
Tel.: (86) 2029028899   **Ky**
Web Site: https://www.ehang.com
Year Founded: 2014
EH—(NASDAQ)
Rev.: $6,789,808
Assets: $81,334,133
Liabilities: $62,232,217
Net Worth: $19,101,916
Earnings: ($50,286,739)
Emp.: 341
Fiscal Year-end: 12/31/22
Holding Company
N.A.I.C.S.: 551112
Derrick Yifang Xiong (Co-Founder)

EHI CAR SERVICES LIMITED
Unit 12/F Building No 5 Guosheng Center 388 Daduhe Road, Shanghai, 200062, China
Tel.: (86) 21 6468 7000   **Ky**
Web Site: http://www.1hai.cn
Year Founded: 2006
Sales Range: $400-449.9 Million
Emp.: 7,195
Car Rental & Leasing Services
N.A.I.C.S.: 532111
Colin Chitnim Sung (CFO)

EHINGER-SCHWARZ GMBH & CO. KG
Am Hochstrass 8, Ulm, 89081, Germany
Tel.: (49) 731509750
Web Site: http://www.ehinger-schwarz.de
Year Founded: 1876
Sales Range: $10-24.9 Million
Emp.: 120
Jewelry Mfr
N.A.I.C.S.: 423940
Christoph Weiss (Owner & Manager)

EHL IMMOBILIEN GMBH
Prinz-Eugen-Strasse 8-10, 1040, Vienna, Austria
Tel.: (43) 1 512 7690   **AT**
Web Site: http://www.ehl.at
Real Estate Investment, Development, Brokerage & Property Management Services
N.A.I.C.S.: 531390
Michael Ehlmaier (Mng Partner)

Subsidiaries:

EHL Immobilien Management GmbH   **(1)**
Prinz-Eugen-Strasse 8-10, Vienna, 1040, Austria
Tel.: (43) 1 512 7690
Emp.: 52
Commercial Property Management Services
N.A.I.C.S.: 531312
Jorg F. Bitzer (Head-Retail)

EHOTEL AG
Greifswalder Strasse 208, 10405, Berlin, Germany
Tel.: (49) 30473730
Web Site: http://www.ehotel.com
Hotel Reservation Services
N.A.I.C.S.: 561599
Fritz Zerweck (CEO)

EHRMANN AG
Hauptstrasse 19, 87770, Augsburg, Germany
Tel.: (49) 83333010
Web Site: http://www.ehrmann.com
Dairy Products Mfr & Distr
N.A.I.C.S.: 424430

EHWA TECHNOLOGIES INFORMATION CO. LTD.
Seokho Bldg 7F Nonhyeonro 746, Gangnam-gu, Seoul, 06049, Korea (South)
Tel.: (82) 24148111
Web Site: https://www.eti21.com
Year Founded: 1956
024810—(KRS)
Rev.: $40,258,674
Assets: $275,120,035
Liabilities: $107,332,000
Net Worth: $167,788,035
Earnings: ($63,032,133)
Emp.: 166
Fiscal Year-end: 12/31/22
Electric Equipment Mfr & Whslr
N.A.I.C.S.: 335999
Ha Chun Lee (Mng Dir)

EI AUTOSERVIS A.D.
Bulevar Cara Konstantina 80-86, 18000, Nis, Serbia
Tel.: (381) 18 550 759
Year Founded: 1948
EIAS—(BEL)
Emp.: 2
Motor Vehicle Repair & Maintenance Services
N.A.I.C.S.: 811114

EI TOWERS S.P.A.
Via Zanella 21, 20851, Lissone, MB, Italy
Tel.: (39) 03924321   **IT**
Web Site: http://www.eitowers.it
Year Founded: 1999
Rev.: $315,861,308
Assets: $1,166,891,725
Liabilities: $574,874,575
Net Worth: $592,017,150
Earnings: $65,215,092
Emp.: 557
Fiscal Year-end: 12/31/17
Holding Company; Communication Tower & Transmission Equipment Mfr
N.A.I.C.S.: 551112
Guido Barbieri (CEO)

Subsidiaries:

Towertel S.p.A.   **(1)**
Via Zanella 21, Lissone, IT-20851, MB, Italy   **(100%)**
Tel.: (39) 03924321
Communication Tower Construction Services
N.A.I.C.S.: 334220
Guido Barbieri (CEO)

EICHER MOTORS LIMITED
3rd Floor-Select Citywalk A-3 District Centre Saket, New Delhi, 110 017, India
Tel.: (91) 1244445070
Web Site: https://www.eicher.in
505200—(BOM)
Rev.: $1,686,546,370
Assets: $1,371,326,659
Liabilities: $880,202,626
Net Worth: $491,124,033
Earnings: $314,440,381
Emp.: 4,995
Fiscal Year-end: 03/31/23
Automotive Components Mfr
N.A.I.C.S.: 336110
Lalit Malik (CFO)

Subsidiaries:

VE Commercial Vehicles Ltd   **(1)**
96 Sector 32, Gurgaon, 122 001, Haryana, India
Tel.: (91) 1244415600
Web Site: https://www.vecv.in
Automobile Parts Distr
N.A.I.C.S.: 423120
Siddhartha Lal (Chm)

VECV South Africa (Pty) Ltd.   **(1)**

Block C Lakefield Office Park 272A West Avenue, Die Hoewes, Centurion, 0157, South Africa
Tel.: (27) 761646340
Web Site: https://www.eichertrucksandbuses.co.za
Logistic Services
N.A.I.C.S.: 488510

EICKHOFF MASCHINENFABRIK GMBH
Am Eickhoffpark 1, PO Box 100629, 44789, Bochum, Germany
Tel.: (49) 2349750
Web Site: http://www.eickhoff-bochum.de
Year Founded: 1864
Sales Range: $125-149.9 Million
Emp.: 1,200
Drum Loaders for Stable & Rise Driving Machine Mfr
N.A.I.C.S.: 333922
Ulf Achenbach (Mng Dir)

Subsidiaries:

Eickhoff (G.B.) Ltd.   **(1)**
Darnall Works, Prince of Wales Road, Sheffield, S9 4EX, United Kingdom
Tel.: (44) 87 122 1164
Web Site: http://www.eickhoffcorp.com
Industrial Machinery Producer
N.A.I.C.S.: 333248

Eickhoff Australia Pty. Ltd   **(1)**
Prince William Dr 41, Seven Hills, 2147, NSW, Australia   **(100%)**
Tel.: (61) 296746733
Web Site: http://www.eickhoffcorp.com
Sales Range: $25-49.9 Million
Emp.: 30
Industrial Machinery Producer
N.A.I.C.S.: 333248

Eickhoff Bergbautechnik GmbH   **(1)**
Eickhoff Park 1, 44789, Bochum, Germany
Tel.: (49) 2349750
Web Site: http://www.eickhoff-bochum.de
Sales Range: $25-49.9 Million
Mining & Tunneling Shearer Loader Equipment Mfr
N.A.I.C.S.: 333248

Eickhoff Corporation   **(1)**
200 Parkwest Dr, Pittsburgh, PA 15275-1002   **(100%)**
Tel.: (412) 788-1400
Web Site: http://www.eickhoffcorp.com
Sales Range: $50-74.9 Million
Emp.: 12
Mfr & Wholesaler of Longwall Mining Machinery
N.A.I.C.S.: 423810
Richard Liconti (VP)

Eickhoff Giesserei GmbH   **(1)**
Hunscheidtstrasse 176, 44789, Bochum, Germany   **(100%)**
Tel.: (49) 2349752760
Web Site: http://www.eickhoff-bochum.de
Sales Range: $50-74.9 Million
Emp.: 200
Industrial Machinery Producer
N.A.I.C.S.: 333248
Ralf Funke (CEO)

Eickhoff Mining Technology GmbH   **(1)**
Magdeburger Strasse 37, 45881, Gelsenkirchen, Germany
Tel.: (49) 20998050
Web Site: http://www.eickhoff-bochum.de
Industrial Machinery Producer
N.A.I.C.S.: 333248

Eickhoff Polonia Ltd.   **(1)**
Ul Podleska 72, Mikolow, PL 43190, Mirkow, Poland   **(100%)**
Tel.: (48) 322066010
Web Site: http://www.eickhoffcorp.com
Industrial Machinery Producer
N.A.I.C.S.: 333248

Eickhoff Pty Ltd   **(1)**
12 Strauss Crescent Wadeville Ext 6, PO Box 74, Germiston, 4322, South Africa   **(100%)**
Tel.: (27) 1190256301

Web Site: http://www.eickhoffcorp.com
Sales Range: $25-49.9 Million
Emp.: 100
Industrial Machinery Producer
N.A.I.C.S.: 333248
Werner Mars (Mgr-Fin)

EICL LIMITED
TC 79/4 Veli, Thiruvananthapuram, 695021, Kerala, India
Tel.: (91) 4714095111
Web Site: http://www.eicl.in
Rev.: $18,089,491
Assets: $36,712,194
Liabilities: $15,673,449
Net Worth: $21,038,745
Earnings: ($2,950,789)
Fiscal Year-end: 03/31/22
Kaolin Clay Mining & Manufacturing
N.A.I.C.S.: 212323
Karan Thapar (Chm)

EIDAI CO., LTD.
2-10-60 Hirabayashi Minami, Suminoe-ku, Osaka, 559-8658, Japan
Tel.: (81) 666843000
Web Site: https://www.eidai.com
Year Founded: 1946
7822—(TKS)
Rev.: $473,705,650
Assets: $635,339,980
Liabilities: $352,359,270
Net Worth: $282,980,710
Earnings: $21,277,590
Emp.: 256
Fiscal Year-end: 03/31/24
Household & Interior Wooden Building Materials Mfr & Sales
N.A.I.C.S.: 321211
Nobuhiro Shien (Pres)

Subsidiaries:

Eidai Staff Service Co., Ltd.   **(1)**
4F Yongda Building No 10-60 Hirabayashi South 2-chome, Suminoe Ward, Osaka, 559-8658, Japan
Tel.: (81) 666843065
General Dispatch Services
N.A.I.C.S.: 488510

Eidai Vietnam Co., Ltd.   **(1)**
Dong Van II Industrial Park, Duy Minh Ward Duy Tien Town, Ha Nam, Vietnam
Tel.: (84) 2266266688
Web Site: http://www.eidaivietnam.com
Furniture Product Mfr
N.A.I.C.S.: 337121

PT. Eidai Industries Indonesia   **(1)**
Jl kenari Raya Blok G6-01 Kav 23D Delta Silicon 6 Cibatu, South Cikarang, Bekasi, 17530, West Java, Indonesia
Tel.: (62) 2189910073
Web Site: http://eidai-indonesia.business.site
Furniture Product Mfr
N.A.I.C.S.: 337121

EIDAI KAKO CO., LTD.
2-3-9 Hiranokita, Hirano-ku, Osaka, 547-0041, Japan
Tel.: (81) 667913355
Web Site: https://www.eidaikako.co.jp
Year Founded: 1956
7877—(TKS)
Rev.: $60,071,680
Assets: $63,317,190
Liabilities: $17,067,020
Net Worth: $46,250,170
Earnings: $1,183,190
Emp.: 140
Fiscal Year-end: 03/31/24
Mold Product Mfr
N.A.I.C.S.: 326291
Yoshinori Ura (Pres)

EIDESVIK HOLDING A/S
Vestvikvegen 1, 5443, Bomlo, Norway
Tel.: (47) 53448000

Web Site: http://www.eidesvik.no
Sales Range: $75-99.9 Million
Emp.: 400
Holding Company
N.A.I.C.S.: 551112
Erling Lodden *(VP-HR)*

Subsidiaries:

Eidesvik AS **(1)**
Vestvikvegen 1, NO-5443, Bomlo,
Norway **(100%)**
Tel.: (47) 53448000
Web Site: https://www.eidesvik.no
Sales Range: $125-149.9 Million
Vessels Fleet Operating Manager
N.A.I.C.S.: 488390
Helga Cotgrove *(CFO)*

NorSea Group AS **(1)**
Risavika Havnering 14, 4056, Tananger,
Norway
Tel.: (47) 40004321
Web Site: https://norseagroup.com
Holding Company; Support Activities for Oil
& Gas Operations
N.A.I.C.S.: 551112
May Britt Lilletvedt *(CEO-)*

Subsidiary (Domestic):

NorSea AS **(2)**
Risavika Havnering 14, 4056, Tananger,
Norway
Tel.: (47) 4 000 4321
Web Site: https://www.norseagroup.com
Sales Range: $75-99.9 Million
Emp.: 200
Supply Base Logistic & Onshore & Offshore
Industry Support Service
N.A.I.C.S.: 213112

Vestbase AS **(2)**
Omagaten 110 C, N 6500, Kristiansund,
Norway
Tel.: (47) 71572200
Web Site: http://www.vestbase.com
Sales Range: $50-74.9 Million
Emp.: 220
Logistics Supplier for Offshore Related Ac-
tivities
N.A.I.C.S.: 211120
Alf Dahl *(Mng Dir)*

EIDESVIK OFFSHORE ASA
Vestvikvegen 1, NO-5443, Bomlo,
Norway
Tel.: (47) 53448000
Web Site: https://www.eidesvik.no
EIOF—(OSL)
Rev.: $84,846,388
Assets: $216,057,085
Liabilities: $130,333,179
Net Worth: $85,723,905
Earnings: $37,570,294
Emp.: 405
Fiscal Year-end: 12/31/22
Shipping Vessel Parts Distr
N.A.I.C.S.: 488330
Helga Cotgrove *(CFO)*

EIENDOMSSPAR ASA
Olav Vs gate 6 inngang Radhuspas-
sasjen, Oslo, Norway
Tel.: (47) 22330550
Web Site:
http://www.eiendomsspar.no
Sales Range: $25-49.9 Million
Emp.: 35
Real Estate Services
N.A.I.C.S.: 531390
Christian Ringnes *(CEO)*

Subsidiaries:

Pandox AB **(1)**
Vasagatan 11 level 9, PO Box 15, 101 20,
Stockholm, Sweden
Tel.: (46) 850620550
Web Site: https://www.pandox.se
Rev.: $387,970,240
Assets: $7,912,615,200
Liabilities: $4,971,952,160
Net Worth: $2,940,663,040
Earnings: ($171,888,640)

Emp.: 982
Fiscal Year-end: 12/31/2020
Hotel Owner & Management Services
N.A.I.C.S.: 721110
Aldert Schaaphok *(Sr VP & Dir-Ops-Intl)*

Subsidiary (Non-US):

Norgani Finland Holding OY **(2)**
Etelaesplanadi 22B 3rd Floor, 00130, Hel-
sinki, Finland
Tel.: (358) 9 67 77 24
Hotel Management & Services
N.A.I.C.S.: 721110

Norgani Hotels ASA **(2)**
Stramdem 3 A 6th Fl, 0250, Oslo, Norway
Tel.: (47) 40004303
Web Site: http://www.norgani.no
Sales Range: $75-99.9 Million
Emp.: 19
Hotel Management & Services
N.A.I.C.S.: 721110

EIFFAGE S.A.
3-7 Place de l'Europe, 78140, Velizy-
Villacoublay, France
Tel.: (33) 134658989
Web Site: https://www.eiffage.com
Year Founded: 1844
FGR—(EUR)
Rev.: $20,935,782,700
Assets: $36,817,637,220
Liabilities: $29,839,789,560
Net Worth: $6,977,847,660
Earnings: $1,246,404,180
Emp.: 72,500
Fiscal Year-end: 12/31/19
Construction & Public Works Services
N.A.I.C.S.: 236220
Christian Cassayre *(CFO)*

Subsidiaries:

A lienor S.A., **(1)**
40 rue de Liege, 64000, Pau, France
Tel.: (33) 559814747
Web Site: http://www.a65-alienor.com
Road & Bridge Construction Services
N.A.I.C.S.: 237310

Alsatel **(1)**
Zone Aeroparc II 8 rue des Herons, 67960,
Entzheim, France
Tel.: (33) 3 88 76 22 22
Web Site: http://www.alsatel.fr
Telecommunication Engineering Services
N.A.I.C.S.: 517810

Armor Connectic SAS **(1)**
163 Quai du Docteur Dervaux, 92601,
Asnieres-sur-Seine, France
Tel.: (33) 141328264
Web Site: http://www.armorconnectic.com
Broadband Internet Service Provider
N.A.I.C.S.: 517810

COLLIGNON Luxembourg SARL **(1)**
Z I de Kehlen, 8287, Kehlen, Luxembourg
Tel.: (352) 26 10 30 20
Web Site: http://www.collignon.net
Sales Range: $25-49.9 Million
Emp.: 25
Electrical Equipment Distr
N.A.I.C.S.: 423610

Clemessy Emcs **(1)**
172 Av Aristide Briand, Mulhouse, 68200,
France
Tel.: (33) 389 323 720
Industrial Engineering Services
N.A.I.C.S.: 541330

Collignon Eng SA - Bruxelles
Division **(1)**
Parc Industriel 11, 1440, Wauthier Brain,
Belgium
Tel.: (32) 2 385 14 32
Electrical Equipment Distr
N.A.I.C.S.: 423610
Serge de Moffarts *(Mng Dir)*

Collignon Eng SA - Liege
Division **(1)**
Z I de Grace-Hollogne Rue de l'Expansion
45, 4460, Grace-Hollogne, Belgium
Tel.: (32) 4 388 15 15
Electrical Installation Services

N.A.I.C.S.: 238210
Mauh Phillip *(Gen Mgr)*

Compagnie Eiffage du Viaduc de
Millau **(1)**
Peage de Saint Germain, BP 60457, 12104,
Millau, France **(51%)**
Tel.: (33) 565616161
Web Site: http://www.leviaducdemillau.com
Bridge Construction Services
N.A.I.C.S.: 237310
Immanuel Cachot *(Mng Dir)*

ECV **(1)**
Rue du Travail 5, 4460, Grace-Hollogne,
Belgium
Tel.: (32) 4 247 22 05
Web Site: http://www.ecv-sa.be
Street & Highway Lightning Construction
Services
N.A.I.C.S.: 237130

EKB Groep B.V **(1)**
Wijkermeerweg 31, 1948 NT, Beverwijk,
Netherlands
Tel.: (31) 251 26 19 20
Web Site: http://www.ekb.nl
Emp.: 70
Industrial Automation Services
N.A.I.C.S.: 238210

Eiffage Construction **(1)**
3 Ave Morane Saulnier, 78141, Velizy-
Villacoublay, France **(100%)**
Tel.: (33) 134658989
Web Site:
http://www.eiffageconstruction.com
Sales Range: $1-4.9 Billion
Emp.: 100
Commercial & Institutional Construction
Services
N.A.I.C.S.: 236220
Philippe Content *(Deputy CEO)*

Subsidiary (Non-US):

Antwerpse Bouwwerken NV **(2)**
Bouwensstraat 35, 2140, Antwerp, Belgium
Tel.: (32) 3 205 28 00
Web Site:
http://www.antwerpsebouwwerken.be
Civil Engineering Construction Services
N.A.I.C.S.: 237990

Auto Park Poznan Sp. z o.o. **(2)**
ul Sw Michala 43, Poznan, 61-119, Poland
Tel.: (48) 618 50 18 40
Construction Engineering Services
N.A.I.C.S.: 237990

Collignon Eng SA **(2)**
Briscol 4, 6779, Erezee, Belgium
Tel.: (32) 86 47 77 00
Web Site: http://www.collignon.net
Electrical Lightning Installation Services
N.A.I.C.S.: 238210

De Graeve Entreprises Generales
SA **(2)**
Avenue Reine Elisabeth 16, Namur, 5000,
Belgium
Tel.: (32) 8 122 77 81
Construction Engineering Services
N.A.I.C.S.: 237990

Subsidiary (Domestic):

Eiffage Construction Alsace Franche
Comte S.N.C **(2)**
10 Rue Du Vallon, Ecole-Valentin, 25480,
Doubs, France
Tel.: (33) 381483434
Construction Engineering Services
N.A.I.C.S.: 541330

Eiffage Construction Artois Hainaut
S.N.C. **(2)**
Zone Industrielle Douai Dorignies 350 R F
Pilatre De Rozier, 59500, Douai, Nord,
France
Tel.: (33) 327991499
Construction Engineering Services
N.A.I.C.S.: 541330

Eiffage Construction Auvergne
SNC **(2)**
49 Rue Georges Besse, Clermont-Ferrand,
63100, Puy-de-Dome, France
Tel.: (33) 473980650
Construction Engineering Services

N.A.I.C.S.: 541330

Eiffage Construction Basse
Normandie **(2)**
Rue Roger Anne, Cherbourg-Octeville,
50100, Manche, France
Tel.: (33) 233876420
Construction Engineering Services
N.A.I.C.S.: 237990

Eiffage Construction Bourgogne **(2)**
4 Rue Lavoisier, 21600, Longvic, Cote-d Or,
France
Tel.: (33) 380692929
Construction Engineering Services
N.A.I.C.S.: 237990

Eiffage Construction Bretagne
S.N.C **(2)**
40 bd de La Tour d'Auvergne, Rennes,
35000, France
Tel.: (33) 299653131
Construction Engineering Services
N.A.I.C.S.: 237990

Eiffage Construction Centre **(2)**
5 Rue Claude Lewy, Orleans, 45077, Loiret,
France
Tel.: (33) 238226666
Construction Engineering Services
N.A.I.C.S.: 237990

Eiffage Construction Champagne **(2)**
19 rue Maurice Prevoteau, Reims, 51100,
France
Tel.: (33) 3 26 82 82 35
Construction Engineering Services
N.A.I.C.S.: 237990

Eiffage Construction Cote d Azur
S.N.C. **(2)**
Les Vaisseaux de Sophia Ba 300 Rue Du
Vallon, 6560, Valbonne, Alpes-Maritimes,
France
Tel.: (33) 492384600
Construction Engineering Services
N.A.I.C.S.: 237990

Eiffage Construction Limousin **(2)**
Les Hauts De Bel Air 50 Rue Pierre Et Ma-
rie Curie, Limoges, 87000, Haute-Vienne,
France
Tel.: (33) 555064949
Emp.: 300
Construction Engineering Services
N.A.I.C.S.: 541330
Michel Berthou *(Gen Mgr)*

Eiffage Construction Lorraine
S.N.C **(2)**
9 Rue Paul Langevin, Maxeville, 54320,
Meurthe-et-Moselle, France
Tel.: (33) 383574831
Construction Engineering Services
N.A.I.C.S.: 541330

Eiffage Construction Materiel **(2)**
11 Place de L Europe, Velizy-Villacoublay,
78140, Yvelines, France
Tel.: (33) 134658989
Construction Materials Distr
N.A.I.C.S.: 423320

Eiffage Construction Metallique
S.A. **(2)**
48/50 rue de Seine, 92707, Colombes,
France
Tel.: (33) 1 47 60 47 00
Web Site:
http://www.eiffageconstructionmetal.com
Sales Range: $800-899.9 Million
Civil Engineering Construction Services
N.A.I.C.S.: 237990

Eiffage Construction Midi Pyrenees
S.N.C **(2)**
Batiment C 109 Avenue De Lespinet, Tou-
louse, 31400, Haute-Garonne, France
Tel.: (33) 534312000
Construction Engineering Services
N.A.I.C.S.: 541330

Eiffage Construction Nord **(2)**
2 rue de l'hta, Lezennes, 59260, Nord,
France
Tel.: (33) 328389666
Construction Engineering Services
N.A.I.C.S.: 541330

Eiffage Construction Paris
Patrimoine **(2)**

Eiffage S.A.—(Continued)

423 Les Bureaux De La Colline, 92210,
Saint-Cloud, France
Tel.: (33) 147755873
Construction Engineering Services
N.A.I.C.S.: 541330

**Eiffage Construction Provence
S.N.C** 　　　　　　　　　　　　　**(2)**
Parc du Roy D Espagne 8 A 14 8 Allee Cer-
vantes, Marseille, 13009, Bouches-du-
Rhone, France
Tel.: (33) 491166900
Web Site: http://www.eiffage.com
Emp.: 100
Construction Engineering Services
N.A.I.C.S.: 541330
Luc Bouvet (Mgr)

**Eiffage Construction Rhone-Alpes
S.N.C** 　　　　　　　　　　　　　**(2)**
3 rue Hrant Dink, Lyon, 69002, Rhone,
France
Tel.: (33) 478601515
Sales Range: $75-99.9 Million
Construction Engineering Services
N.A.I.C.S.: 541330

Eiffage Construction Services 　**(2)**
361 Avenue du General de Gaulle, 92140,
Clamart, France
Tel.: (33) 1 40 83 17 50
Construction Engineering Services
N.A.I.C.S.: 237990

**Eiffage Construction Val de Seine
S.N.C** 　　　　　　　　　　　　　**(2)**
Zone Industrielle 3 Rue Ampere, 91430,
Igny, Essonne, France
Tel.: (33) 169337100
Construction Engineering Services
N.A.I.C.S.: 541330

Subsidiary (Non-US):

**Eiffage Immobilier Polska sp. z
oo** 　　　　　　　　　　　　　　**(2)**
ul Domaniewska 28, 02-672, Warsaw, Po-
land
Tel.: (48) 225664900
Web Site: https://eiffage-immobilier.pl
Real Estate Manangement Services
N.A.I.C.S.: 531390
Tymon Nowosielski (CEO)

Eiffage Polska Budownictwo SA **(2)**
ul Domaniewska 28, 02-672, Warsaw, Po-
land
Tel.: (48) 225664900
Rev.: $280,608,000
Emp.: 50
Construction Engineering Services
N.A.I.C.S.: 237990
Zbigniew Zajaczkowski (Chm-Mgmt Bd)

Eiffage Polska Koleje Sp. z o.o. **(2)**
ul Marynarska 19A, Warsaw, 02-674, Po-
land
Tel.: (48) 223 51 06 02
Web Site: http://www.tchaspolska.pl
Sales Range: $25-49.9 Million
Emp.: 15
Construction Engineering Services
N.A.I.C.S.: 237990

Subsidiary (Domestic):

Fougerolle S.A. 　　　　　　　　**(2)**
Rue de la longueraie Z A des Landelles,
35520, Melesse, France
Tel.: (33) 2 99 66 08 17
Web Site: http://www.fougerolle-fr.com
Audio & Video Equipment Mfr
N.A.I.C.S.: 334310

Genie Civil Industriel 　　　　　**(2)**
Zi Molina la Chazote Cplt Lieu Dit le Mont-
cel, 42650, Saint-Jean-Bonnefonds, Loire,
France
Tel.: (33) 477476080
Civil Engineering Services
N.A.I.C.S.: 237990

Subsidiary (Non-US):

Limpens SA 　　　　　　　　　　**(2)**
Rue Bara 71, Brussels, 1070, Belgium
Tel.: (32) 2 523 81 96
Web Site: http://www.limpens.be
Heating & Plumbing Services

N.A.I.C.S.: 238220

PIT Antwerpen NV 　　　　　　　**(2)**
Starrenhoflaan 27, Kapellen, 2950, Belgium
Tel.: (32) 3 605 14 33
Web Site: http://www.pitantwerpen.be
Sales Range: $25-49.9 Million
Emp.: 27
Apartment Building Construction Services
N.A.I.C.S.: 236117

Perrard S.A. 　　　　　　　　　　**(2)**
94 rue du Grunewald, 1912, Luxembourg,
Luxembourg
Tel.: (352) 4253531
Web Site: http://www.perrard.lu
Civil Engineering & Construction Services
N.A.I.C.S.: 237990

SA Eiffage Benelux 　　　　　　**(2)**
Avenue Brugmann 27A, 1060, Brussels,
Belgium
Tel.: (32) 2 543 45 00
Web Site: http://www.eiffagebenelux.be
Civil Engineering Construction Services
N.A.I.C.S.: 237990
Thierry Durbecq (Mgr-Fin)

Subsidiary (Domestic):

Socamip 　　　　　　　　　　　　**(2)**
Residence Le Bastion 49 rue du Rempart
Saint Claude, La Rochelle, 17000,
Charente-Maritime, France
Tel.: (33) 546341202
Web Site: http://www.socamip.fr
Construction Engineering Services
N.A.I.C.S.: 541330

Subsidiary (Non-US):

Yvan Paque S.A. 　　　　　　　　**(2)**
Rue de l'Arbre Courte Joie 48, Rocourt,
4000, Liege, Belgium
Tel.: (32) 42247724
Web Site: http://www.paque.be
Sales Range: $100-124.9 Million
Electronic Lightning Installation Services
N.A.I.C.S.: 238210

Plant (Domestic):

**Yvan Paque S.A. - Villeroux
Plant** 　　　　　　　　　　　　　　**(3)**
Parc Artisanal de Villeroux 3, B-6640, Vaux-
sur-Sure, Belgium
Tel.: (32) 61 28 85 07
Street & Traffic Light Construction Services
N.A.I.C.S.: 237310

Eiffage Energia S.L 　　　　　　**(1)**
Avda de la Mancha 280 Esquina C Trova-
dores, 02006, Albacete, Spain
Tel.: (34) 967 190 116
Web Site: http://www.energia.eiffage.es
Electrical System Installation Services
N.A.I.C.S.: 238210

Eiffage Energie S.A.S. 　　　　　**(1)**
117 rue du Landy, BP 80008, La Plaine
Saint-Denis, F-93213, France 　**(100%)**
Tel.: (33) 1 5587 5100
Web Site: http://www.eiffageenergie.com
Sales Range: $1-4.9 Billion
Power Plant Design, Construction & Opera-
tion Services
N.A.I.C.S.: 236210

Unit (Domestic):

Eiffage Energie Centre-est 　　**(2)**
3 rue Hrant Dink, F-69285, Lyon, Cedex 02,
France
Tel.: (33) 4 3724 2750
Web Site: http://www.eiffageenergie.com
Electrical Installation Services
N.A.I.C.S.: 238210

Subsidiary (Domestic):

**Eiffage Energie Electronique
S.A.S.** 　　　　　　　　　　　　　　**(2)**
Route Nationale 37, Verquin, 62131, France
Tel.: (33) 3 2164 6812
Web Site: http://www.eiffageenergie.com
Emp.: 100
Electrical System Installation Services
N.A.I.C.S.: 238210

Unit (Domestic):

Eiffage Energie Ile-de-France **(2)**

2 rue Flora Tristan, BP 30012, 93213, La
Plaine Saint-Denis, Cedex, France
Tel.: (33) 1 5869 2030
Web Site: http://www.eiffageenergie.com
Electrical System Installation Services
N.A.I.C.S.: 238210

Eiffage Energie Nord 　　　　　　**(2)**
36 Place Cormontaigne, F-59000, Lille,
Nord, France
Tel.: (33) 320223377
Web Site: http://www.eiffageenergie.com
Construction Engineering Services
N.A.I.C.S.: 541330

Subsidiary (Domestic):

**Eiffage Energie Poitou-Charentes
S.A.S.** 　　　　　　　　　　　　　　**(2)**
Zone Republique 1 3 Rue Des Entrepre-
neurs, F-86000, Poitiers, Vienne, France
Tel.: (33) 549384200
Web Site: http://www.eiffageenergie.com
Construction Engineering Services
N.A.I.C.S.: 541330

Eiffage Energie Thermie S.A.S. **(2)**
Rue Michel Manoll Zac Chantrerie, Ilot Per-
verie Erdrerie II, 44300, Nantes, France
Tel.: (33) 240254949
Web Site: http://www.eiffageenergie.com
Emp.: 230
Electrical System Installation Services
N.A.I.C.S.: 238210
Frederic Gantes (Mgr)

**Eiffage Energie Transport & Distribu-
tion S.A.S.** 　　　　　　　　　　　**(2)**
Route 937, F-62131, Verquin, France
Tel.: (33) 3 2164 6808
Web Site: http://www.eiffageenergie.com
Transportation Facilities Construction & In-
stallation Services
N.A.I.C.S.: 237310

**Eiffage Energie Val de Loire
S.A.S.** 　　　　　　　　　　　　　　**(2)**
6 8 rue Denis Papin, 37300, Joue-les-Tours,
France
Tel.: (33) 2 47 68 44 44
Electrical Engineering Services
N.A.I.C.S.: 541330

**Forclum Alsace Franche Comte
SAS** 　　　　　　　　　　　　　　　**(2)**
1 rue Pierre et Marie Curie, 67540, Ost-
wald, Bas-Rhin, France
Tel.: (33) 388555455
Institutional Building Construction Services
N.A.I.C.S.: 236220

Forclum Reseaux Nord S.A.S 　**(2)**
3 Route D'Estaires Zone Porte, BP 23, La
Bassee, 59480, France
Tel.: (33) 3 20 29 99 29
Electrical System Installation Services
N.A.I.C.S.: 238210

Forclum Rhone Alpes S.A.S 　　**(2)**
170 Allee Des Marais, 74130, Bonneville,
Haute-Savoie, France
Tel.: (33) 450257260
Construction Engineering Services
N.A.I.C.S.: 237990

Eiffage Immobilier 　　　　　　　**(1)**
11 place de l'Europe, BP 46, CS 50570,
78141, Velizy-Villacoublay, France
Tel.: (33) 134658989
Web Site: https://www.eiffage-immobilier.fr
Real Estate Manangement Services
N.A.I.C.S.: 531390

Eiffage Travaux Publics SAS 　**(1)**
2 rue Helene Boucher, BP 92, 92337,
Neuilly-sur-Marne, France
Tel.: (33) 149449000
Web Site:
　http://www.eiffagetravauxpublics.com
Highway Construction Services
N.A.I.C.S.: 237310

Subsidiary (Non-US):

Aglomerados Albacete SA 　　　**(2)**
Calle Madrid Km 594, Almansa, 2640, Al-
bacete, Spain
Tel.: (34) 967345727
Construction Engineering Services
N.A.I.C.S.: 237990

Aglomerados Los Serranos SA **(2)**
Calle Manuel Macia Juan 4, Elche, 03203,
Alicante, Spain
Tel.: (34) 966615242
Web Site:
　http://www.infraestructuras.eiffage.es
Emp.: 300
Construction Engineering Services
N.A.I.C.S.: 237990
Cesar Nohales (Gen Mgr)

Subsidiary (Domestic):

Antrope SNC 　　　　　　　　　　**(2)**
Hameau de Samson, 60150, Chevincourt,
France
Tel.: (33) 3 44 96 31 90
Civil Engineering Services
N.A.I.C.S.: 237990

Appia Grands Travaux SNC 　　**(2)**
3 Rue Hrant Dink, Lyon, 69002, Rhone,
France
Tel.: (33) 478036401
Civil Engineering Services
N.A.I.C.S.: 237990

**Appia Liants Emulsion Rhone
Alpes** 　　　　　　　　　　　　　　**(2)**
3 Rue Hrant Dink, Lyon, 69002, France
Tel.: (33) 4 78 03 64 01
Highway Construction Services
N.A.I.C.S.: 237310

Carriere de la Roche Blain 　　　**(2)**
La Roche Blain, BP 4, 14680, Fresney-le-
Puceux, Calvados, France
Tel.: (33) 2 31 15 36 00
Civil Engineering Services
N.A.I.C.S.: 237990
Philippe Boutteau (Gen Mgr)

Carriere des Chenes S.A. 　　　**(2)**
Route N 7 Rn 7, Andancette, France
Tel.: (33) 4 75 23 11 55
Construction Engineering Services
N.A.I.C.S.: 237990

Desquesnes SNC 　　　　　　　**(2)**
198 Au 212 198 Rue Casimir Beugnet,
Auchel, 62260, Pas-de-Calais, France
Tel.: (33) 321613600
Construction Engineering Services
N.A.I.C.S.: 237990

Dle Ouest 　　　　　　　　　　　　**(2)**
5 Rue de Catalogne, 44240, La
Chapelle-sur-Erdre, France
Tel.: (33) 240778989
Civil Engineering Services
N.A.I.C.S.: 237990

Subsidiary (Non-US):

Dle Outre-Mer 　　　　　　　　　**(2)**
Lieu Dit Sicama Chemin Gibelin, Matoury,
97351, Guyane, French Guiana
Tel.: (594) 594357090
Civil Engineering Construction Services
N.A.I.C.S.: 237990

Subsidiary (Domestic):

Dle Specialites 　　　　　　　　　**(2)**
78 A Rue de la Garde, Nantes, 44300,
France
Tel.: (33) 2 51 89 59 59
Civil Engineering Construction Services
N.A.I.C.S.: 237310

Subsidiary (Non-US):

**Eiffage Deutschland Bauholding
Gmbh** 　　　　　　　　　　　　　　**(2)**
Neumuhlenallee 32, Borken, 46325, Ger-
many
Tel.: (49) 2861800821
Civil Engineering Construction Services
N.A.I.C.S.: 237990

Subsidiary (Domestic):

Eiffage Genie Civil 　　　　　　　**(2)**
2 rue Helene-Boucher, 93330, Neuilly-sur-
Marne, France
Tel.: (33) 149449000
Civil Engineering Services
N.A.I.C.S.: 237990

Subsidiary (Non-US):

Eiffage Infra-Nordwest GmbH 　**(2)**

Hansastrasse 83, 49134, Wallenhorst, Germany
Tel.: (49) 54075010
Web Site: https://nordwest.eiffage-infra.de
Rev.: $169,896,000
Emp.: 500
Civil Engineering Construction Services
N.A.I.C.S.: 237990

Eiffage Infra-West GmbH **(2)**
Neumuhlenallee 32, 46325, Borken, Germany
Tel.: (49) 286180080
Web Site: https://west.eiffage-infra.de
Rev.: $89,336,980
Emp.: 236
Construction Engineering Services
N.A.I.C.S.: 237990

Eiffage Infraestructuras **(2)**
Pol Industrial Vicalvaro C/ Mir s/n, 28052, Madrid, Spain
Tel.: (34) 917 765 521
Web Site:
    http://www.infraestructuras.eiffage.es
Civil Engineering Construction Services
N.A.I.C.S.: 237990

Subsidiary (Domestic):

Eiffage International S.A. **(2)**
2 rue Helene Boucher, 93330, Neuilly-sur-Seine, France
Tel.: (33) 0134658989
Web Site: http://www.eiffage.com
Emp.: 1,600
Civil Construction & Engineering Services
N.A.I.C.S.: 237990

Eiffage Travaux Publics Est **(2)**
1 R W Et Catherine Booth, 10000, Troyes, France
Tel.: (33) 3 25 76 24 24
Road Construction Services
N.A.I.C.S.: 237310

Eiffage Travaux Publics Mediterranee **(2)**
Zone Industrielle Les Estroublans 4 rue de Copenhague, Vitrolles, 13127, Bouches-du-Rhone, France
Tel.: (33) 442023400
Construction Engineering Services
N.A.I.C.S.: 541330

Eiffage Travaux Publics Nord S.N.C **(2)**
53 Boulevard Faidherbe, 62033, Arras, France
Tel.: (33) 3 21 22 76 76
Road Construction Services
N.A.I.C.S.: 237310

Eiffage Travaux Publics Ouest S.N.C **(2)**
6 Place de Boston, 14200, Herouville-Saint-Clair, France
Tel.: (33) 2 35 66 43 43
Construction Engineering Services
N.A.I.C.S.: 237990

Eiffage Travaux Publics Reseaux **(2)**
Zi de la Petite Montagne Sud 1 3 rue du Bourbonnais, Lisses, 91090, Essonne, France
Tel.: (33) 169115020
Construction Engineering Services
N.A.I.C.S.: 237990

Eiffage Travaux Publics Sud Ouest S.N.C **(2)**
Parc de Canteranne 21 Avenue de Canteranne, Pessac, 33600, Gironde, France
Tel.: (33) 251273610
Construction Engineering Services
N.A.I.C.S.: 541330

Subsidiary (Non-US):

Hormigones Los Serranos S.L **(2)**
Calle Raco S/N-Part, Gandia, 46702, Spain
Tel.: (34) 966 61 54 44
Civil Engineering Construction Services
N.A.I.C.S.: 237990

Hormigones y Morteros Serrano SL **(2)**
Calle Clemente Gonzalvez Valls 38, Elche, 03202, Alicante, Spain
Tel.: (34) 966615444
Construction Engineering Services

N.A.I.C.S.: 237990

Lanwehr Asphalt Gmbh **(2)**
Sudstrasse 16, 48231, Warendorf, Germany
Tel.: (49) 2581937345
Construction Engineering Services
N.A.I.C.S.: 237990

Lanwehr Bau Gmbh **(2)**
Sudstrasse 16, 48231, Warendorf, Germany
Tel.: (49) 258193730
Web Site: http://www.lanwehr.de
Sales Range: $50-74.9 Million
Emp.: 250
Civil Engineering Construction Services
N.A.I.C.S.: 237310

Masfalt S.A **(2)**
Parque Comercial Malaga Nostrum C Jaen n 9 Edif Galia Ofic 105, 29004, Malaga, Spain
Tel.: (34) 952 122 633
Web Site: http://www.masfalt.com
Civil Engineering Construction Services
N.A.I.C.S.: 237990

Subsidiary (Domestic):

SNC Travaux Publics de Provence **(2)**
30 Quartier Prignan, Istres, 13800, Bouches-du-Rhone, France
Tel.: (33) 442569121
Marketing & Advertising Services
N.A.I.C.S.: 541890

Subsidiary (Non-US):

Serrano Aznar Obras Publicas S.L **(2)**
Lugar Paraje Tres Santos, Abanilla, 30640, Murcia, Spain
Tel.: (34) 965492799
Construction Engineering Services
N.A.I.C.S.: 541330

Subsidiary (Domestic):

Societe des Carrieres de la 113 **(2)**
Domaine De La Plaine, 11200, Raissac-d'Aude, Aude, France
Tel.: (33) 468901414
Construction Engineering Services
N.A.I.C.S.: 237990

Sopal **(2)**
15 rue Gen de Lattre de Tassigny, Eschau, 67114, France
Tel.: (33) 388640369
Painting Supplies Distr
N.A.I.C.S.: 424950

Stinkal **(2)**
Ham Beaulieu, 62250, Ferques, Pas-de-Calais, France
Tel.: (33) 321323945
Construction Engineering Services
N.A.I.C.S.: 541330

Tinel SA **(2)**
Zone Industrielle Chemin de Chomaget 10 Rue de Chomaget, 43100, Brioude, Haute-Loire, France
Tel.: (33) 471502705
Construction Engineering Services
N.A.I.C.S.: 237990

Transroute SA **(2)**
12 Rue De Molsheim, Wolxheim, 67120, France
Tel.: (33) 388479494
Highway Construction Services
N.A.I.C.S.: 237310

Travaux Publics et Assainissement **(2)**
Route de Chambry, 02840, Athies-sous-Laon, France
Tel.: (33) 3 23 24 66 00
Web Site: http://www.travauxpublics-picardie.fr
Highway & Bridge Construction Services
N.A.I.C.S.: 237310

Eiffel Industrie S.A.S **(1)**
48/50 rue de Seine, 92707, Colombes, France
Tel.: (33) 1 47 60 47 00
Web Site: http://www.eiffel-industrie.com
Industrial Maintenance & Engineering Services

N.A.I.C.S.: 541330

Elomech Elektroanlagen GmbH **(1)**
Mainstrasse 21, 45478, Mulheim an der Ruhr, Germany
Tel.: (49) 20858870
Web Site: http://www.elomech.de
Electrical Installation Services
N.A.I.C.S.: 238210
Andreas Bundschuh (Mng Dir)

Etcm SA **(1)**
Parc D Activites De La Brayell 481 R Du Faubourg D Esquerchin, 59553, Cuincy, Nord, France
Tel.: (33) 327957500
Construction Engineering Services
N.A.I.C.S.: 541330

Financiere Eiffarie **(1)**
163 quai du Docter Dervaux, Asnieres-sur-Seine, 92600, France
Tel.: (33) 141328000
Holding Company
N.A.I.C.S.: 551112

Subsidiary (Domestic):

Autoroutes Paris-Rhin-Rhone **(2)**
36 rue du Docteur-Schmitt, 21800, Saint Apollinaire, France
Tel.: (33) 380776700
Web Site: http://www.parisrhinrhone.com
Sales Range: $1-9.9 Million
Emp.: 3,800
Motorways, Telecoms, Secure Car Parks & Railroad Transportation Services
N.A.I.C.S.: 488999
Philippe Nourry (CEO)

Subsidiary (Domestic):

AREA Societe des Autoroutes Rhones-Alpes SA **(3)**
260 avenue Jean Monnet, BP 48, Bron, Cedex, Bron, France
Tel.: (33) 472353200
Web Site: http://www.appr.fr
Sales Range: $450-499.9 Million
Emp.: 150
Bus Terminal & Service Facilities
N.A.I.C.S.: 237310
Philippe Nourry (Pres)

Fontanie **(1)**
Zone Industrielle de Thibaud 4 rue Colomies, 31100, Toulouse, Haute-Garonne, France
Tel.: (33) 561190331
Industrial Engineering Services
N.A.I.C.S.: 541330

Forclumeca Antilles Guyane **(1)**
10 Zac La Marie 10 Rue Raymond Berger, Ducos, 97224, Martinique
Tel.: (596) 596561552
Construction Engineering Services
N.A.I.C.S.: 541330

Game Ingenierie S.A.S **(1)**
17 rue de la Belle Etoile, Ormoy, 91540, Essonne, France
Tel.: (33) 160905858
Construction Engineering Services
N.A.I.C.S.: 541330

Ger2i **(1)**
Zae Rue De Seine, 78260, Acheres, Yvelines, France
Tel.: (33) 139114530
Industrial Maintenance & Engineering Services
N.A.I.C.S.: 541330

JOAO JACINTO TOME, S.A. **(1)**
Rua Possidonio da Silva n 158 A, 1399-008, Lisbon, Portugal
Tel.: (351) 213 920 910
Web Site: http://www.jjtome-sa.com
Emp.: 6
Electrical Installation Services
N.A.I.C.S.: 238210
Patrick Steinfort (Gen Mgr)

Oostvlaams Milieubeheer **(1)**
Havennummer 4410B J Kennedylaan 50, 9042, Gent, Belgium
Tel.: (32) 93429567
Web Site: http://www.ovmb.be
Sales Range: $25-49.9 Million
Emp.: 14
Industrial Waste Management Services

N.A.I.C.S.: 562998
Nadia Casler (Gen Mgr)

Romarco NV **(1)**
Baaikensstraat 17 B, 9240, Zele, Belgium
Tel.: (32) 52 44 86 94
Web Site: http://www.romarco.be
Industrial Cleaning Services
N.A.I.C.S.: 561720
Peter Rooms (Gen Mgr)

SATRA SA **(1)**
Berismenil 93C, 6980, Berismenil, Belgium
Tel.: (32) 84 44 41 70
Web Site: http://www.collignon.net
Underground Cable Laying Construction Services
N.A.I.C.S.: 237130

Secauto S.A **(1)**
15 a 17 rue A Nobel chateau de l, 69552, Feyzin, France
Tel.: (33) 4 72 89 04 40
Web Site: http://www.secauto.fr
Sales Range: $75-99.9 Million
Emp.: 280
Engineering Project Consulting Services
N.A.I.C.S.: 541330
Jean-Marc Borrel (Mgr)

Soprano Oyj **(1)**
Mannerheimintie 15, 00260, Helsinki, Finland
Tel.: (358) 104321000
Web Site: https://www.soprano.fi
Rev.: $14,382,690
Assets: $16,298,745
Liabilities: $11,029,595
Net Worth: $5,269,150
Earnings: ($1,842,360)
Emp.: 83
Fiscal Year-end: 12/31/2020
Communications & Information Technology Marketing, Advertising & Consulting Services
N.A.I.C.S.: 541613
Pauliina Lautanen-Nissi (CEO-Acting)

Tpam SAS **(1)**
Impasse Edouard Branly ZI de la Peyenniere, Mayenne, 53100, France
Tel.: (33) 2 43 04 04 04
Road & Bridge Construction Services
N.A.I.C.S.: 237310

EIGHT CAPITAL PARTNERS PLC

Kemp House 160 City Road, London, EC1V 2NX, United Kingdom
Tel.: (44) 2076897888
Web Site: https://www.eight.capital
Asset Management Services
N.A.I.C.S.: 523940
Dominic White (Chm)

EIGHT PEAKS GROUP LTD.

37th Floor 1 Canada Square, London, E14 5AA, United Kingdom
Tel.: (44) 207 583 8304
Web Site: http://www.8pg.co
8PG—(LSE)
Assets: $7,299,054
Liabilities: $74,761
Net Worth: $7,224,293
Earnings: ($2,446,134)
Fiscal Year-end: 12/31/19
Investment Management Service
N.A.I.C.S.: 523999
Zafarullah Karim (Chm)

EIGHTY JEWELLERS LIMITED

A T Palace Near Kotawali Chowk, Raipur, 492001, Chhattisgarh, India
Tel.: (91) 7712234737
Web Site: https://www.eightyjewels.in
Year Founded: 2010
543518—(BOM)
Rev.: $10,741,032
Assets: $3,904,790
Liabilities: $2,636,970
Net Worth: $1,267,820
Earnings: $524,644
Fiscal Year-end: 03/31/21
Jewelry Product Distr

Eighty Jewellers Limited—(Continued)
N.A.I.C.S.: 423940
Tilok Chand Bardia *(COO)*

EIH ASSOCIATED HOTELS LIMITED
1/24 GST Road Meenambakkam,
Chennai, 600 027, India
Tel.: (91) 4422344747
Web Site:
　https://www.eihassociatedhotels.in
EIHAHOTELS—(NSE)
Rev.: $26,996,015
Assets: $56,243,597
Liabilities: $10,879,187
Net Worth: $45,364,410
Earnings: $1,758,393
Emp.: 451
Fiscal Year-end: 03/31/22
Home Management Services
N.A.I.C.S.: 721110
Vikramjit Singh Oberoi *(Mng Dir)*

EIH PLC
15-19 Athol Street, Douglas, IM1
1LB, Isle of Man
Tel.: (44) 2071078000　　IM
Web Site: http://www.eihplc.co.uk
Investment Management Service
N.A.I.C.S.: 523940
Rhys Davies *(Chm)*

EIK BANK P/F
Yvirivid Strond 2, PO Box 34, FO-
110, Torshavn, Faroe Islands
Tel.: (298) 348000
Web Site: http://www.eik.fo
Sales Range: $200-249.9 Million
Emp.: 330
Banking Services
N.A.I.C.S.: 522110
Ossur Nolsoe *(Head-Corp Banking)*

Subsidiaries:

P F Inni　　　　　　　　　　　　**(1)**
Niels Finsensgota 37, PO Box 364, FO 110,
Torshavn, Faroe Islands
Tel.: (298) 354200
Sales Range: $50-74.9 Million
Emp.: 6
Real Estate Services
N.A.I.C.S.: 531390

EIK FASTEIGNAFELAG HF
Soltun 26, 105, Reykjavik, Iceland
Tel.: (354) 590902200
Web Site: https://www.eik.is
EIK—(ICE)
Rev.: $128,672,986
Assets: $923,818,756
Liabilities: $609,701,278
Net Worth: $314,117,478
Earnings: $57,453,684
Emp.: 47
Fiscal Year-end: 12/31/22
Real Estate Services
N.A.I.C.S.: 531210

EIKEN CHEMICAL CO. LTD.
4-19-9 Taito, Taito-ku, Tokyo, 110-
8408, Japan
Tel.: (81) 358463305
Web Site: https://www.eiken.co.jp
Year Founded: 1939
4549—(TKS)
Rev.: $264,743,720
Assets: $407,513,110
Liabilities: $103,644,800
Net Worth: $303,868,310
Earnings: $17,410,740
Emp.: 1,432
Fiscal Year-end: 03/31/24
Clinical Diagnostics & Equipments
Mfr & Sales
N.A.I.C.S.: 334510
Morifumi Wada *(Pres & CEO)*

Subsidiaries:

Eiken China Co., Ltd.　　　　　**(1)**
Tel.: (86) 2151323333
Web Site: http://www.eiken.com.cn
Production Equipment Mfr
N.A.I.C.S.: 333248

EIKEN INDUSTRIES CO., LTD
1370 Kadoya, Omaezaki, 437-1698,
Shizuoka, Japan
Tel.: (81) 537854132
Web Site: https://www.eiken-kk.co.jp
Year Founded: 1967
7265—(TKS)
Emp.: 180
Oil Filter Mfr
N.A.I.C.S.: 213112
Y. Hayama *(Pres)*

EIKO LIFESCIENCES LIMITED
604 Centrum Opp TMC OfficeNear
Satkar Grande Hotel, Thane, 400
604, Maharashtra, India
Tel.: (91) 9082668855　　　In
Web Site:
　https://www.eikolifesciences.com
Year Founded: 1977
540204—(BOM)
Rev.: $3,560,630
Assets: $4,762,990
Liabilities: $855,063
Net Worth: $3,907,927
Earnings: $96,328
Emp.: 6
Fiscal Year-end: 03/31/22
Investment Management Service
N.A.I.C.S.: 523150

EIMCO ELECON INDIA LTD
Anand Sojitra Road Vallabh Vidyana-
gar, Anand, 388120, Gujarat, India
Tel.: (91) 2692230902
Web Site: https://eimcoelecon.in
523708—(NSE)
Rev.: $12,779,321
Assets: $49,885,304
Liabilities: $4,452,603
Net Worth: $45,432,701
Earnings: $1,184,533
Emp.: 121
Fiscal Year-end: 03/31/22
Underground & Opencast Mines
Equipment Marketing & Mfr
N.A.I.C.S.: 333131
Pradip M. Patel *(Chm)*

EIMSKIPAFELAG ISLANDS HF.
Sundabakki 2, 104, Reykjavik, Ice-
land
Tel.: (354) 5257000
Web Site: https://www.eimskip.com
EIM—(ICE)
Rev.: $893,083,315
Assets: $667,859,918
Liabilities: $331,067,343
Net Worth: $336,792,575
Earnings: $58,823,656
Emp.: 1,728
Fiscal Year-end: 12/31/23
Air, Land & Sea Transportation & Lo-
gistics Services
N.A.I.C.S.: 481112
David Ingi Jonsson *(Compliance Offi-
cer & Gen Counsel)*

Subsidiaries:

Air Atlanta Icelandic　　　　　　**(1)**
Hlidasmari 3, 201, Kopavogur, Iceland
Tel.: (354) 4584000
Web Site: http://www.atlanta.is
Sales Range: $550-599.9 Million
Airline Services
N.A.I.C.S.: 481111
Hannes Hilmarsson *(Chm)*

Eimskip　　　　　　　　　　　　**(1)**
Korngordum 2, 104, Reykjavik, Iceland
Tel.: (354) 5257000

Web Site: http://www.eimskip.is
Sales Range: $250-299.9 Million
Emp.: 1,000
Marine Shipping & Logistics Services
N.A.I.C.S.: 488320

Eimskip UK Ltd.　　　　　　　　**(1)**
Middleplatt Road, Immingham, DN40 1AH,
NE Lincolnshire, United Kingdom
Tel.: (44) 1469550200
Freight Forwarding Services
N.A.I.C.S.: 488510

Eimskip USA Inc.　　　　　　　**(1)**
1424 Baker Rd, Virginia Beach, VA 23455
Tel.: (207) 331-3300
Web Site: https://www.eimskip.com
Sales Range: $25-49.9 Million
Emp.: 15
Freight & Transportation Services
N.A.I.C.S.: 483111

Excel Airways Group plc　　　　**(1)**
Explorer House, Fleming Way, Crawley,
RH10 9EA, West Sussex, United Kingdom
Tel.: (44) 1293439100
Web Site:
　http://www.excelairwaysgroup.com
Sales Range: $450-499.9 Million
Airline Services
N.A.I.C.S.: 481111

Subsidiary (Non-US):

Star Airlines　　　　　　　　　**(2)**
10 allee Bienvenue, 93885, Noisy-le-Grand,
France
Tel.: (33) 148159000
Web Site: http://www.star-airlines.fr
Airline Services
N.A.I.C.S.: 481111

Saeferdir ehf.　　　　　　　　　**(1)**
Workshop path 3, 340, Stykkisholmur, Ice-
land
Tel.: (354) 4332254
Web Site: https://www.seatours.is
Tour Operator
N.A.I.C.S.: 561520

TVG-Zimsen ehf.　　　　　　　**(1)**
Sundabakka 2, 104, Reykjavik, Iceland
Tel.: (354) 5600700
Web Site: https://tvg.is
Transportation Services
N.A.I.C.S.: 485999

EINBECKER BRAUHAUS AG
Papenstrasse 4-7, 37574, Einbeck,
Germany
Tel.: (49) 5561 797 0
Web Site: http://www.einbecker.de
Sales Range: $50-74.9 Million
Emp.: 173
Beer Mfr
N.A.I.C.S.: 312120
Martin Deutsch *(Member-Mgmt Bd-
Sls & Mktg)*

EINDEC CORPORATION LIM-ITED
10 Bukit Batok Crescent 0605 The
Spire, Singapore, 118524, Singapore
Tel.: (65) 62651311
Web Site: https://www.eindec.com.sg
42Z—(CAT)
Rev.: $12,038,931
Assets: $12,747,103
Liabilities: $7,514,959
Net Worth: $5,232,144
Earnings: ($115,883)
Emp.: 165
Fiscal Year-end: 12/31/23
Air Conditioning & Clean Room
Equipment Design, Manufacture &
Distribution
N.A.I.C.S.: 334512
Shirley Tan Sey Liy *(Sec)*

EINFOCHIPS LIMITED
11 A-B Chandra Colony Off C G
Road, Ahmedabad, 380 006, India
Tel.: (91) 7926563705
Web Site: http://www.einfochips.com

Year Founded: 1994
Sales Range: $125-149.9 Million
Emp.: 1,500
Chip & Product Design Services
N.A.I.C.S.: 334413
Pratul Shroff *(Pres & CEO)*

Subsidiaries:

eInfochips, Inc.　　　　　　　　**(1)**
1230 Midas Way Ste 200, Sunnyvale, CA
94085
Tel.: (408) 496-1882
Web Site: http://www.einfochips.com
ASIC Design Embedded System Application
Software Services
N.A.I.C.S.: 334413
Parag Mehta *(Chief Bus Dev Officer)*

EINHELL GERMANY AG
Wiesenweg 22, 94405, Landau, Ger-
many
Tel.: (49) 99519420
Web Site: https://www.einhell.com
EIN3—(DEU)
Rev.: $1,114,304,986
Assets: $909,457,155
Liabilities: $513,562,487
Net Worth: $395,894,669
Earnings: $65,616,231
Emp.: 2,000
Fiscal Year-end: 12/31/22
Power Tool, Garden Equipment &
Heating & Air Conditioning Equipment
Mfr
N.A.I.C.S.: 333991
Markus Thannhuber *(CTO)*

Subsidiaries:

AS Espak　　　　　　　　　　　**(1)**
Viadukti tn 42, Tallinn, 11313, Estonia
Tel.: (372) 6512333
Web Site: http://www.espak.ee
Construction Materials Whslr
N.A.I.C.S.: 423390
Boris Poljak *(Mgr-Sls & Pur)*

Ardiles Import S.A.C.　　　　　**(1)**
Av Santa Maria 230 Urb La Aurora, Ate,
Lima, Peru
Tel.: (51) 3190660
Web Site: http://www.ardilesimport.com
Hardware Material Retailer
N.A.I.C.S.: 444140

Byko ehf　　　　　　　　　　　**(1)**
Skemmuvegur 2, 200, Kopavogur, Iceland
Tel.: (354) 5154094
Construction Product Retailer
N.A.I.C.S.: 444180
Hjalti Baldursson *(CEO)*

EINHELL d. o. o.　　　　　　　**(1)**
Vojvodjanska 386, 11 271, Belgrade,
Serbia　　　　　　　　　　　　**(100%)**
Tel.: (381) 112269171
Web Site: https://www.einhell.rs
Emp.: 17
Power Tool, Garden Equipment & Heating &
Air Conditioning Equipment Mfr
N.A.I.C.S.: 333991

Einhell Argentina S. A　　　　　**(1)**
Las Lilas 970 Manuel Alberti, Edificio BLUE
BUILDING - Piso 2 Ramal Pilar KM 42,
1629, Buenos Aires, Argentina
Tel.: (54) 2304440593
Web Site: https://www.einhell.com.ar
Sales Range: $25-49.9 Million
Emp.: 35
Business Services
N.A.I.C.S.: 561499

Einhell Australia Pty. Ltd.　　　**(1)**
1-23 Letcon Drive, Melbourne, 3175, VIC,
Australia　　　　　　　　　　　**(100%)**
Tel.: (61) 384134300
Web Site: http://www.einhell.com.au
Sales Range: $50-74.9 Million
Emp.: 10
Power Tool, Garden Equipment & Heating &
Air Conditioning Equipment Mfr
N.A.I.C.S.: 333991
Kai Schmid *(CEO)*

Einhell Benelux B.V.　　　　　　**(1)**

Mijkenbroek 16, 4824 AB, Breda, Netherlands **(100%)**
Tel.: (31) 765986470
Web Site: http://www.einhell.nl
Sales Range: $25-49.9 Million
Emp.: 12
Power Tool, Garden Equipment & Heating & Air Conditioning Equipment Mfr
N.A.I.C.S.: 333991

Einhell BiH d.o.o **(1)**
Poslovni centar 96, 72250, Vitez, Bosnia & Herzegovina **(66.7%)**
Tel.: (387) 30717251
Web Site: https://www.einhell.ba
Sales Range: $25-49.9 Million
Emp.: 15
Power Tool, Garden Equipment & Heating & Air Conditioning Equipment Mfr
N.A.I.C.S.: 333991

Einhell Bulgaria Ltd. **(1)**
Tsar Osvoboditel Blvd 331, 9023, Varna, Bulgaria **(67%)**
Tel.: (359) 52739038
Web Site: https://www.einhell.bg
Power Tool, Garden Equipment & Heating & Air Conditioning Equipment Mfr
N.A.I.C.S.: 333991

Einhell Chile S.A. **(1)**
Calle la Farfana N 400 Bodegas San Francisco Bodega G -10, Pudahuel, Santiago, Chile **(90%)**
Tel.: (56) 225448664
Power Tool, Garden Equipment & Heating & Air Conditioning Equipment Mfr
N.A.I.C.S.: 333991

Einhell Colombia S.A.S. **(1)**
Cra 106 No 15-25 Manzana 16 Warehouse 3-4 Lot 114 D-Free Zone, Bogota, Colombia
Tel.: (57) 14431620
Web Site: https://www.einhell.co
Emp.: 15
Power Tool & Electrical Garden Equipment Mfr & Retailer
N.A.I.C.S.: 335999
Paulo Restrepo *(Gen Dir)*

Einhell Croatia d.o.o **(1)**
Pustodol Zacretski 19/H, Sveti Kriz Zacretje, 49223, Lepajci, Croatia **(100%)**
Tel.: (385) 49342444
Web Site: https://www.einhell.hr
Sales Range: $25-49.9 Million
Emp.: 24
Power Tool, Garden Equipment & Heating & Air Conditioning Equipment Mfr
N.A.I.C.S.: 333991

Einhell Denmark ApS **(1)**
A C Illumsvej 21 A-B, 8600, Silkeborg, Denmark
Tel.: (45) 87 201200
Web Site: http://www.einhell.com
Automobile Parts Mfr
N.A.I.C.S.: 336390

Einhell Espana **(1)**
Pol Industrial El Nogal Travesia de Villa Esther 15, 28119, Algete, Madrid, Spain **(100%)**
Tel.: (34) 91 7294888
Web Site: http://www.einhell.es
Mfr, Sales & Training of Various Tools & Equipment for DIY Enthusiasts & Semi-Professionals
N.A.I.C.S.: 333991

Einhell Finland OY **(1)**
Haarlankatu 4 E 2 kerros, 33230, Tampere, Finland
Tel.: (358) 207698833
Web Site: https://www.einhell.fi
Garden Tool Mfr
N.A.I.C.S.: 333515

Einhell France S.A.S. **(1)**
Paris Nord 2 22 Rue Des Nations Batiment Rabelais, PO Box 59018, Villepinte CDG, 95945, Roissy-en-France, Cedex, France **(70%)**
Tel.: (33) 826101103
Web Site: http://www.einhell.fr
Sales Range: $25-49.9 Million
Emp.: 12
Power Tool, Garden Equipment & Heating & Air Conditioning Equipment Mfr
N.A.I.C.S.: 333991

Einhell Hellas S.A. **(1)**
Thessaloniki 77-79, Nea Filadelfia, 14342, Athens, Greece
Tel.: (30) 2102790930
Web Site: https://www.einhell.com.gr
Sales Range: $25-49.9 Million
Emp.: 20
Power Tool, Garden Equipment & Heating & Air Conditioning Equipment Mfr
N.A.I.C.S.: 333991

Einhell Holding Gesellschaft m.b.H. **(1)**
Brunnerstrasse 81a, Vienna, 1230, Austria
Tel.: (43) 18691480
Sales Range: $50-74.9 Million
Emp.: 30
Financial Investment Services
N.A.I.C.S.: 523999
Christoph Hinterecker *(Gen Mgr)*

Einhell Hungaria Ltd. **(1)**
Budaorsi utca 2749/2, 2092, Budakeszi, Hungary **(100%)**
Tel.: (36) 23920741
Web Site: https://www.einhell.hu
Sales Range: $25-49.9 Million
Emp.: 15
Power Tool, Garden Equipment & Heating & Air Conditioning Equipment Mfr
N.A.I.C.S.: 333991

Einhell Intratek Muhendislik ve Dis Ticaret A.S. **(1)**
Serifali Mah Bayraktar Bul Beyit Sok No 7, Umraniye, 34775, Istanbul, Türkiye
Tel.: (90) 216 456 60 60
Web Site: http://www.einhell.com.tr
Industrial Supplies Distr
N.A.I.C.S.: 423840

Einhell Italia s.r.l. **(1)**
Via delle Acacie sn, 22070, Beregazzo con Figliaro, Italy **(100%)**
Tel.: (39) 031992080
Web Site: https://www.einhell.it
Emp.: 25
Power Tool, Garden Equipment & Heating & Air Conditioning Equipment Mfr
N.A.I.C.S.: 333991

Einhell Middle East Trading FZC **(1)**
Rak Free Trade Zone Shed No 26 Technology Park, Ras al Khaimah, United Arab Emirates
Tel.: (971) 72447449
Web Site: http://www.einhell.com
Sales Range: $25-49.9 Million
Emp.: 12
Electronic Components Mfr
N.A.I.C.S.: 334419

Einhell Nordic ApS **(1)**
Rokhoj 26, 8520, Lystrup, Denmark
Tel.: (45) 32712425
Web Site: https://www.einhell.dk
Emp.: 30
Power Tool & Electrical Garden Equipment Mfr & Retailer
N.A.I.C.S.: 335999
Lars Baerentsen *(Gen Mgr)*

Einhell Norway AS **(1)**
Sondre Kullerod 6, 3241, Sandefjord, Norway
Tel.: (47) 33 11 35 40
Web Site: http://www.einhell.no
Emp.: 1
Automotive Components Mfr
N.A.I.C.S.: 336390

Einhell Osterreich Gesellschaft mbH **(1)**
Mellergasse 4, A-1230, Vienna, Austria
Tel.: (43) 18691480
Electrical Accessories Mfr & Distr
N.A.I.C.S.: 335999

Einhell Polska sp. Z.o.o. **(1)**
ul Wymyslowskiego 1, 55 080, Nowa Wies Wroclawska, Poland **(90%)**
Tel.: (48) 713603076
Web Site: https://www.einhell.pl
Sales Range: $25-49.9 Million
Emp.: 40
Power Tool, Garden Equipment & Heating & Air Conditioning Equipment Mfr
N.A.I.C.S.: 333991
Ryszard Turkiewicz *(Pres)*

Einhell Portugal - Comercio Int., Lda. **(1)**
Rua da Aldeia 225, Arcozelo, 4410-459, Vila Nova de Gaia, Portugal
Tel.: (351) 707917506
Web Site: https://www.einhell.pt
Power Tool & Electrical Garden Equipment Mfr
N.A.I.C.S.: 335999

Einhell Portugal Lda. **(1)**
Rua da Aldeia 225 Apartado 2100, P 4410 459, Arcozelo, Portugal **(100%)**
Tel.: (351) 220917500
Web Site: http://www.einhell.pt
Sales Range: $25-49.9 Million
Emp.: 13
Power Tool, Garden Equipment & Heating & Air Conditioning Equipment Mfr
N.A.I.C.S.: 333991

Einhell Romania S.R.L. **(1)**
A1 Business Park Dragomiresti-Deal, Hala B1 Judet Ilfov, 077096, Bucharest, Romania
Tel.: (40) 213185544
Web Site: https://www.einhell.ro
Sales Range: $25-49.9 Million
Emp.: 25
Power Tool, Garden Equipment & Heating & Air Conditioning Equipment Mfr
N.A.I.C.S.: 333991

Einhell SAS **(1)**
Schapenweide 1A3, 4824 AN, Breda, Netherlands
Tel.: (31) 885986470
Web Site: http://www.einhell.nl
Power Tool & Electrical Garden Equipment Mfr & Retailer
N.A.I.C.S.: 335999

Einhell SAS **(1)**
22 Avenue des Nations Immeuble Le Rabelais CDG, BP 59018, 95945, Roissy-en-France, Cedex, France
Tel.: (33) 148170053
Web Site: https://www.einhell.fr
Power Tool & Electrical Garden Equipment Mfr & Retailer
N.A.I.C.S.: 335999
Cynthia Lachens *(Gen Mgr)*

Einhell Schweiz AG **(1)**
St Gallerstrasse 182, 8404, Winterthur, Switzerland
Tel.: (41) 522358787
Web Site: https://www.einhell.ch
Emp.: 18
Power Tool, Garden Equipment & Heating & Air Conditioning Equipment Mfr
N.A.I.C.S.: 333991

Einhell Skandinavia Aps **(1)**
Bergsoesvej 36, 8600, Silkeborg, Denmark **(100%)**
Tel.: (45) 87201200
Power Tool, Garden Equipment & Heating & Air Conditioning Equipment Mfr
N.A.I.C.S.: 333991

Einhell Slovakia s.r.o. **(1)**
Dianicna Cesta 18, 903 01, Senec, Slovakia **(100%)**
Tel.: (421) 220903780
Web Site: http://www.einhell.sk
Sales Range: $50-74.9 Million
Emp.: 6
Power Tool, Garden Equipment & Heating & Air Conditioning Equipment Mfr
N.A.I.C.S.: 333991

Einhell Turkey Dis Ticaret A.S. **(1)**
Serifali Mah Find Bayraktar Beyit St No 7, 34775, Istanbul, Türkiye
Tel.: (90) 2164566060
Web Site: https://www.einhell.com.tr
Machine Tools Mfr
N.A.I.C.S.: 333517

Einhell UK Ltd. **(1)**
Morpeth Wharf Twelve Quays, Birkenhead, CH41 1LF, United Kingdom **(100%)**
Tel.: (44) 1516491500
Web Site: http://www.einhell-uk.co.uk
Power Tool, Garden Equipment & Heating & Air Conditioning Equipment Mfr
N.A.I.C.S.: 333991

Einhell Ukraine TOV **(1)**

16 Chaiki Street, 08130, Kiev, Ukraine **(100%)**
Tel.: (380) 503854820
Web Site: http://www.einhell.ua
Power Tool, Garden Equipment & Heating & Air Conditioning Equipment Mfr
N.A.I.C.S.: 333991

Einhell Unicore s.r.o. **(1)**
Zavodni 278, 360 18, Karlovy Vary, Czech Republic **(100%)**
Tel.: (420) 353440217
Web Site: https://www.einhell.cz
Sales Range: $25-49.9 Million
Emp.: 25
Power Tool, Garden Equipment & Heating & Air Conditioning Equipment Mfr
N.A.I.C.S.: 333991

Fakhroo International Trading Agencies Co. **(1)**
Bldg 7248 Prince Mansoor Street Cross 12 Northern, PO Box 79104, Al Khobar, 31952, Saudi Arabia
Tel.: (966) 17253529
Power Tool & Electrical Garden Equipment Mfr
N.A.I.C.S.: 335999

Fielex S.A. **(1)**
Cerro Largo 760, 11100, Montevideo, Uruguay
Tel.: (598) 29029929
Power Tool & Electrical Garden Equipment Mfr
N.A.I.C.S.: 335999

Hans Einhell (China) Chongqing Co., Ltd. **(1)**
Qinzhou North Rd No 1122, 92 Bld 1-3F, Shanghai, 200233, China **(100%)**
Tel.: (86) 2124122888
Sales Range: $50-74.9 Million
Emp.: 200
Power Tool, Garden Equipment & Heating & Air Conditioning Equipment Mfr
N.A.I.C.S.: 333991

Hans Einhell Osterreich GmbH **(1)**
Brunner Strasse 81 A, A 1230, Vienna, Austria **(100%)**
Tel.: (43) 18691480
Sales Range: $25-49.9 Million
Emp.: 25
Power Tool, Garden Equipment & Heating & Air Conditioning Equipment Mfr
N.A.I.C.S.: 333991

Hans Einhell Ukraine TOV **(1)**
StA V Chaika 16 p Chaika, Kyiv-Sviatoshynskyi District, 08135, Kiev, Ukraine
Web Site: http://www.einhell.ua
Power Tool & Electrical Garden Equipment Mfr & Retailer
N.A.I.C.S.: 335999

Hansi Anhai Far East Ltd. **(1)**
15 F OTB Building 160 Gloucester Rd, Wanchai, China (Hong Kong) **(100%)**
Tel.: (852) 25015556
Power Tool, Garden Equipment & Heating & Air Conditioning Equipment Mfr
N.A.I.C.S.: 333991

Ikhairi & Aljenabi Trading Co. **(1)**
Al Rasheed street al Shorja maket near of central bank Abbas shop, Baghdad, Iraq
Tel.: (964) 7907902383126
Power Tool & Electrical Garden Equipment Mfr
N.A.I.C.S.: 335999

Kauppahuone Harju Oy **(1)**
Myllypuronkatu 30, 33330, Tampere, Finland
Tel.: (358) 207431330
Web Site: http://www.harju.fi
Electronic Product Whslr
N.A.I.C.S.: 423690
Juha Pitkanen *(Sls Mgr)*

Lavabau LLC **(1)**
B-10 Hermes Center Peace Avenue, Bayangol District, Ulaanbaatar, Mongolia
Tel.: (976) 99004665
Power Tool & Electrical Garden Equipment Mfr
N.A.I.C.S.: 335999

Lawn Star Pty. Ltd. **(1)**

Einhell Germany AG—(Continued)

4 Bofors Two 98 Bofors Circle Eping 2
South, Cape Town, South Africa
Tel.: (27) 215355249
Web Site: https://lawnstar.co.za
Garden Tool Mfr
N.A.I.C.S.: 333515

Lee+Cho Trading Co. (1)
Buheung-roÅ 877 Gwangjeok-myeon
Gyeonggi-do, Yangju, Korea (South)
Tel.: (82) 318366303
Power Tool & Electrical Garden Equipment
Mfr
N.A.I.C.S.: 335999

Multicenter S.R.L. (1)
3rd Int Ring and Av Santos Doumont, Santa
Cruz, Bolivia
Tel.: (591) 33431700
Web Site: http://www.multicenter.com.bo
Household Furniture Mfr
N.A.I.C.S.: 337126

Ole Moe AS (1)
Hoie Naeringspark Setesdalsveien 620,
4619, Kristiansand, Norway
Tel.: (47) 38177080
Web Site: http://www.olemoe.no
Hardware & Paint Whslr
N.A.I.C.S.: 424950

Ozito Industries Pty. Ltd. (1)
1-23 Letcon Drive, Bangholme, Melbourne,
3175, VIC, Australia
Tel.: (61) 392385555
Power Tool & Electrical Garden Equipment
Mfr
N.A.I.C.S.: 335999
Lynton Aldrick (Head-Mktg)

Platinova Sarl (1)
Lot At-Tawfiq N 5 Rue Ibnou El Koutia Q I
Oukacha, Ain Sebaa, Casablanca, Morocco
Tel.: (212) 522674424
Web Site: http://www.platinova.ma
Plaster Product Distr
N.A.I.C.S.: 423320

**S&L Sealing Solutions Private
Limited** (1)
2 Bukit Batok Street 23 Bukit Batok Con-
nection 01-09, Singapore, 659554, Singa-
pore
Tel.: (65) 65155686
Power Tool & Electrical Garden Equipment
Mfr
N.A.I.C.S.: 335999

SPI Instrument Ltd. (1)
40 Let Pobedy 23A Office 44-12 V Boro-
vlyany, Minsk, Belarus
Tel.: (375) 175119818
Power Tool & Electrical Garden Equipment
Mfr
N.A.I.C.S.: 335999

Sarl Outilux (1)
RN n 5 Haouche EL Mekhfi W, Ouled Hed-
dadj, Boumerdes, Algeria
Tel.: (213) 21860357
Web Site: http://www.outilux.dz
Power Tool & Electrical Garden Equipment
Distr
N.A.I.C.S.: 423490

Shimal Service MMC (1)
White City Hayat Park 3, Baku, Azerbaijan
Tel.: (994) 502137770
Power Tool & Electrical Garden Equipment
Mfr
N.A.I.C.S.: 335999

**Societe Zeghondy pour le Commerce
S.A.R.L.** (1)
Sea Side, Byblos, Amchit, Lebanon
Tel.: (961) 9624040
Power Tool & Electrical Garden Equipment
Mfr
N.A.I.C.S.: 335999

Svenska Einhell AB (1)
Ostergarde Industriomrade 415, 41729,
Gothenburg, Sweden (100%)
Tel.: (46) 31550999
Web Site: http://www.einhell.se
Power Tool, Garden Equipment & Heating &
Air Conditioning Equipment Mfr
N.A.I.C.S.: 333991

**Swisstec Sourcing Vietnam Joint
Stock Company**
18L1-2 VSIP II Street 3, Singapore Indus-
trial park 2 Hoa Phu ward, Thu Dau Mot,
Vietnam
Tel.: (84) 2743865075
Web Site: https://swisstecsourcing.com
Emp.: 66
Machine Tools Mfr
N.A.I.C.S.: 333517

Tools Act Company Limited (1)
26/2 Leabklongsong Bangchan, Klong-
samwa, Bangkok, 10510, Thailand
Tel.: (66) 254859101
Power Tool & Electrical Garden Equipment
Mfr
N.A.I.C.S.: 335999

Vesna Trading Plc (1)
PO Box 62517, Addis Ababa, Ethiopia
Tel.: (251) 118282943
Power Tool & Electrical Garden Equipment
Mfr
N.A.I.C.S.: 335999
Lemma Berhane (Mng Dir)

Zana Tools SHPK (1)
Rruga Bekim Berisha, Dardani Peja, 30000,
Pristina, Kosovo
Tel.: (383) 44348303
Web Site: http://www.zanatools.com
Industrial Machinery Equipment Mfr
N.A.I.C.S.: 333248

iSC GmbH (1)
Eschenstrasse 6, 94405, Landau,
Germany (100%)
Tel.: (49) 99519593019
Web Site: https://www.isc-gmbh.info
Power Tool Distr
N.A.I.C.S.: 423710

Subsidiary (Non-US):

iSC Italia s.r.l. (2)
Corso Roma 7, Beregazzo con Figliaro,
22070, Italy
Tel.: (39) 031 800863
Industrial Machinery Distr
N.A.I.C.S.: 423830

kwb Germany GmbH (1)
Hauptstrasse 132, 28816, Stuhr, Germany
Tel.: (49) 42189940
Web Site: https://www.kwb.eu
Emp.: 200
Saw Blade & Hand Tool Mfr
N.A.I.C.S.: 332216
Matthias Kern (Mng Dir & Gen Mgr)

EION INC.
320 March Rd Ste 500, Ottawa, K2K
2E3, ON, Canada
Tel.: (613) 271-4400 Ca
Web Site:
http://www.eionwireless.com
Year Founded: 2001
Sales Range: $1-9.9 Million
IP Solutions for Data & Voice Over
Satellite, Wired & Wireless Networks
N.A.I.C.S.: 517410
Anastasia Pavlovic (CEO)

EIRCOM HOLDINGS (IRE-
LAND) LIMITED
1 Heuston South Quarter St John's
Road, Dublin, 8, Ireland
Tel.: (353) 16714444 IE
Web Site: http://www.eir.iewww.eir.ie
Year Founded: 2012
Rev.: $1,391,992,430
Assets: $2,944,115,460
Liabilities: $3,941,500,340
Net Worth: ($997,384,880)
Earnings: $34,313,700
Emp.: 1,678
Fiscal Year-end: 06/30/19
Holding Company; Fixed-Line & Mo-
bile Telecommunications Services
N.A.I.C.S.: 551112

Subsidiaries:

**Tetra Ireland Communications
Limited** (1)

Block 43a 2nd Floor Yeats Way, Parkwest
Business Park Nangor Road, Dublin, Ire-
land
Tel.: (353) 16400219
Web Site: https://www.tetraireland.ie
Radio Broadcasting Services
N.A.I.C.S.: 334220

eircom Limited (1)
1 Hueston South Quarter St John's Road,
Dublin, 8, Ireland
Tel.: (353) 16714444
Web Site: http://www.eir.ie
Fixed-Line & Mobile Telecommunications
Services
N.A.I.C.S.: 517111
Richard Moat (CEO)

EIRGENIX, INC.
No 101 Lane 169 Kangning St, Xizhi
Dist, New Taipei City, 22180, Taiwan
Tel.: (886) 277080123
Web Site: https://www.eirgenix.com
Year Founded: 2005
6589—(TPE)
Rev.: $46,306,382
Assets: $370,420,411
Liabilities: $36,403,027
Net Worth: $334,017,384
Earnings: ($3,612,544)
Emp.: 412
Fiscal Year-end: 12/31/22
Pharmaceuticals Product Mfr
N.A.I.C.S.: 325412
Lee-Cheng Liu (Pres & CEO)

Subsidiaries:

EirGenix Europe GmbH (1)
REGUS Business Center Theresienhohe
28, 80339, Munich, Germany
Tel.: (49) 89896798100
Biological Product Mfr
N.A.I.C.S.: 325414
Thomas Schulze (Mng Dir)

EISAI CO., LTD.
4-6-10 Koishikawa, Bunkyo-ku, To-
kyo, 112-8088, Japan
Tel.: (81) 338173700 JP
Web Site: https://www.eisai.com
Year Founded: 1941
4523—(TKS)
Rev.: $4,902,974,110
Assets: $9,213,011,390
Liabilities: $3,270,786,640
Net Worth: $5,942,224,750
Earnings: $280,303,660
Emp.: 10,000
Fiscal Year-end: 03/31/24
Pharmaceutical Products & Equip-
ment Mfr
N.A.I.C.S.: 325412
Yasushi Okada (COO)

Subsidiaries:

Arteryex Inc. (1)
4F VORT Asakusabashi Ekimae IV 1-10-6,
Asakusabashi Taito-ku, Tokyo, 111-0053,
Japan
Tel.: (81) 358294859
Web Site: https://arteryex.biz
Software Development Services
N.A.I.C.S.: 541511

Bracco-Eisai Co., Ltd. (1)
3-11-6 Ohtsuka, Bunkyo-ku, Tokyo, 112-
0012, Japan (49%)
Tel.: (81) 3 5319 3381
Sales Range: $1-9.9 Million
Emp.: 50
Medical Contrast Imaging Products Mfr &
Distr
N.A.I.C.S.: 325412
Neil Foust (Gen Mgr)

EA Pharma Co., Ltd. (1)
2-1-1 Irifune, Chuo-ku, Tokyo, 104-0042,
Japan
Tel.: (81) 362809500
Web Site: https://www.eapharma.co.jp
Emp.: 940
Pharmaceuticals Products Mfr & Distr
N.A.I.C.S.: 325412

Tetsuro Aramaki (Exec VP)

**Eisai (Liaoning) Pharmaceutical Co.,
Ltd.** (1)
39 Pingtai 2nd Street, Hi-Tech Industry De-
velopment Zone, Benxi, 117004, Liao Ning,
China
Tel.: (86) 2445598788
Web Site: http://www.eisai.com.cn
Emp.: 250
Pharmaceutical Product Mfr & Distr
N.A.I.C.S.: 325412

Eisai (Malaysia) Sdn. Bhd. (1)
Unit 701D Level 7 Tower Uptown 5 No 5
Jalan SS 21/30 Damanaora Uptown, 47400,
Petaling Jaya, Selangor,
Malaysia (98.09%)
Tel.: (60) 377320300
Web Site: https://eisaimal.com.my
Sales Range: $25-49.9 Million
Emp.: 36
Sales of Pharmaceuticals
N.A.I.C.S.: 424210

Eisai (Singapore) Pte. Ltd. (1)
152 Beach Road 15-07/08 Gateway East,
Singapore, 189721, Singapore
Tel.: (65) 62966977
Web Site: https://eisai.com.sg
Emp.: 10
Pharmaceutical Products Distr
N.A.I.C.S.: 424210

Eisai (Suzhou) Trading Co., Ltd. (1)
168 Xingpu Road, Industrial Park, Suzhou,
215126, Jiangsu, China
Tel.: (86) 51267903966
Pharmaceutical Product Mfr & Distr
N.A.I.C.S.: 325412

**Eisai (Thailand) Marketing Co.,
Ltd.** (1)
6th Floor GPF Witthaya Tower A 93/1 Wire-
less Road, Lumpini Patumwan, Bangkok,
10330, Thailand (50%)
Tel.: (66) 225662969
Web Site: https://www.eisai.co.th
Sales Range: $25-49.9 Million
Emp.: 20
Mfr & Sales of Pharmaceuticals
N.A.I.C.S.: 325412

Eisai Australia Pty. Ltd. (1)
Level 2 437 St Kilda Road, PO Box 33004,
Melbourne, 3004, VIC, Australia
Tel.: (61) 398329100
Web Site: https://www.eisai.com.au
Pharmaceutical Product Mfr & Distr
N.A.I.C.S.: 325412

Eisai China Holdings Ltd. (1)
No 168 Xingpu Road Suzhou Industrial
Park, Suzhou, 215021, China
Tel.: (86) 51269566776
N.A.I.C.S.: 325412
Yanhui Feng (Sr VP)

Eisai China Inc. (1)
39th-40th Floors Park Place 1601 Nanjing
West Road, Jing'an District, Shanghai,
200040, China (100%)
Tel.: (86) 2124192888
Web Site: https://www.eisai.com.cn
Sales Range: $50-74.9 Million
Emp.: 200
Pharmaceuticals Mfr & Sales
N.A.I.C.S.: 325412

Subsidiary (Domestic):

**Eisai China Inc. - Suzhou
Factory** (2)
168 Xingpu Road, Suzhou Industrial Park,
Suzhou, 215126, Jiangsu, China
Tel.: (86) 51269566776
Pharmaceuticals Product Mfr
N.A.I.C.S.: 325412

**Eisai Clinical Research Singapore
Pte Ltd.** (1)
152 Beach Road 15-05/08 Gateway East,
Singapore, 189721, Singapore
Tel.: (65) 62976624
Web Site: http://www.eisai.co.jp
Sales Range: $25-49.9 Million
Emp.: 8
Clinical Research
N.A.I.C.S.: 541715
Masashi Yoshikawa (Mng Dir)

Eisai Co., Ltd. - Kashima Plant (1)
Sunayama, Kamisu, 314-0255, Ibaraki, Japan
Tel.: (81) 479461155
Pharmaceuticals Product Mfr
N.A.I.C.S.: 325412

Eisai Corporation of North America (1)
100 Tice Blvd, Woodcliff Lake, NJ 07677
Tel.: (201) 692-1100
Web Site: http://us.eisai.com
Holding Company
N.A.I.C.S.: 551112

Subsidiary (Domestic):

Eisai Inc. (2)
100 Tice Blvd, Woodcliff Lake, NJ 07677
Tel.: (201) 692-1100
Web Site: http://www.eisai.com
Sales Range: $1-4.9 Billion
Emp.: 900
Pharmaceutical & Ethical Health Care Products Mfr
N.A.I.C.S.: 325412
Shaji Procida (Pres & COO)

Unit (Domestic):

Eisai Inc. - Andover Research Laboratory (3)
4 Corporate Dr, Andover, MA 01810-2447
Tel.: (978) 794-1117
Web Site: http://www.eisai.com
Mfr & Sale of Pharmaceuticals Prescriptions & Ethical Health Care Products
N.A.I.C.S.: 541720

Eisai Inc. - Research Triangle Park (3)
900 Davis Dr, Research Triangle Park, NC 27709
Tel.: (919) 941-6920
Web Site: http://www.eisai.com
Sales Range: $75-99.9 Million
Emp.: 300
Pharmaceuticals Prescriptions & Ethical Health Care Products
N.A.I.C.S.: 325412
Catherine Burke (Engr-Pkg)

Subsidiary (Domestic):

H3 Biomedicine Inc. (2)
300 Technology Sq FL 5, Cambridge, MA 02139
Tel.: (617) 252-5000
Web Site: http://www.h3biomedicine.com
Sales Range: $10-24.9 Million
Emp.: 40
Biotechnology Research & Development Services
N.A.I.C.S.: 541714
Yutaka Ishizaka (COO)

Morphotek, Inc. (2)
210 Welsh Pool Rd, Exton, PA 19341
Tel.: (610) 423-6100
Web Site: http://www.morphotek.com
Sales Range: $25-49.9 Million
Emp.: 100
Clinical Research
N.A.I.C.S.: 541715
Nicholas C. Nicolaides (Pres & CEO)

Eisai Distribution Co., Ltd. (1)
2-16-1 Iiyama Minami, Atsugi, 243-0218, Kanagawa, Japan (100%)
Tel.: (81) 462482655
Web Site: https://www.edc.eisai.co.jp
Sales Range: $50-74.9 Million
Emp.: 95
Pharmaceutical Drug Mfr
N.A.I.C.S.: 424210

Eisai Europe Ltd. (1)
EMEA Knowledge Centre Mosquito Way, Hatfield, AL10 9SN, Hertfordshire, United Kingdom
Tel.: (44) 2086001400
Web Site: https://www.eisai.eu
Emp.: 400
Holding Company
N.A.I.C.S.: 551112

Subsidiary (Non-US):

Eisai AB (2)
Svardvagen 3A, PO Box 23060, 104 35,
Danderyd, Stockholm, Sweden
Tel.: (46) 850101600
Web Site: http://www.eisai.se
Sales Range: $25-49.9 Million
Emp.: 25
Pharmaceutical Sales
N.A.I.C.S.: 424210
Erik Hagglund (Mng Dir)

Eisai B.V. (2)
Strawinskylaan 1141 Toren C 11e, 1077 XX, Amsterdam, Netherlands (100%)
Tel.: (31) 205753340
Web Site: http://www.eisai.com
Sales Range: $25-49.9 Million
Emp.: 3
Pharmaceutical Products Mfr & Distr
N.A.I.C.S.: 325412

Eisai Farmaceutica S.A. (2)
Cristalia Business Park Via de los Poblados Street 3 Building 7/8, 4th floor, 28033, Madrid, Spain
Tel.: (34) 914559455
Web Site: https://eisai.es
Sales Range: $10-24.9 Million
Emp.: 25
Pharmaceutical Sales Promotion
N.A.I.C.S.: 424210

Subsidiary (Non-US):

Eisai Farmaceutica, Unipessoal Lda. (3)
Lagoas Park Edificio 5A 6 Piso, 2740-245, Porto Salvo, Portugal
Tel.: (351) 214875540
Web Site: http://www.eisai.com
Pharmaceutical Products Distr
N.A.I.C.S.: 424210

Subsidiary (Non-US):

Eisai GesmbH (2)
Saturn Tower Leonard-Bernstein-Strasse 10, 1220, Vienna, Austria
Tel.: (43) 1535198011
Emp.: 1
Pharmaceutical Products Distr
N.A.I.C.S.: 424210

Eisai GmbH (2)
Edmund-Rumpler-Strasse 3, 60549, Frankfurt am Main, Germany (100%)
Tel.: (49) 69665850
Web Site: https://www.eisai.de
Sales Range: $25-49.9 Million
Emp.: 50
Pharmaceuticals Distr
N.A.I.C.S.: 424210

Subsidiary (Domestic):

Eisai Ltd. (2)
European Knowledge Centre Mosquito Way, Hatfield, AL10 9SN, Hertfordshire, United Kingdom (100%)
Tel.: (44) 2086001400
Web Site: http://www.eisai.co.uk
Sales Range: $25-49.9 Million
Emp.: 450
Pharmaceutical & Clinical Research
N.A.I.C.S.: 541715

Eisai Manufacturing Ltd. (2)
European Knowledge Centre Mosquito Way, Hatfield, AL10 9SN, Hertfordshire, United Kingdom
Tel.: (44) 2086001400
Pharmaceuticals
N.A.I.C.S.: 325412

Subsidiary (Non-US):

Eisai Pharma AG (2)
Leutschenbachstrasse 95, 8050, Zurich, Switzerland
Tel.: (41) 443061212
Web Site: https://www.eisai.ch
Pharmaceutical Sales
N.A.I.C.S.: 424210

Eisai S.A.S. (2)
1 terrasse Bellini, Courbevoie, 92800, Puteaux, Cedex, France (100%)
Tel.: (33) 147670005
Web Site: https://www.eisai.fr
Sales Range: $150-199.9 Million
Emp.: 70
Pharmaceuticals Mfr & Distr
N.A.I.C.S.: 424210

Eisai S.r.l. (2)
Centro Leoni - Palazzo A Via Giovanni Spadolini n 5, 20141, Milan, Italy
Tel.: (39) 025181401
Web Site: https://www.eisai.it
Sales Range: $25-49.9 Million
Emp.: 80
Pharmaceutical Sales
N.A.I.C.S.: 424210

Eisai Food & Chemicals Co., Ltd. (1)
2-13-10 Nihonbashi 2 chome, Chuo-ku, Tokyo, 103 0027, Japan
Tel.: (81) 335483560
Web Site: http://www.eisai-fc.co.jp
Sales Range: $25-49.9 Million
Emp.: 60
Development & Marketing of Pharmaceutical & Cosmetic Raw Materials, Food Ingredients & Food Additives, Supplements & Nutrition & Vitamins
N.A.I.C.S.: 325412
Hiroaki Ike (Pres)

Eisai Hong Kong Co., Ltd. (1)
Flat D 18/F Lee Man Commercial Center 169 Electric Road, North Point, China (Hong Kong) (100%)
Tel.: (852) 25166128
Web Site: http://www.eisai.com
Sales Range: $25-49.9 Million
Emp.: 13
Mfr & Sales of Pharmaceuticals
N.A.I.C.S.: 325412

Eisai Korea, Inc. (1)
10F Revessant 6 Bongeunsa-ro 86-gil, Gangnam-gu, Seoul, 135-878, Korea (South) (100%)
Tel.: (82) 234515500
Web Site: https://www.eisaikorea.com
Sales Range: $25-49.9 Million
Emp.: 80
Sales of Pharmaceuticals
N.A.I.C.S.: 424210

Eisai Laboratorios Ltda. (2)
Av Dr Cardoso de Melo 1628/1644, Vila Olimpia, Sao Paulo, 04548-005, Brazil
Tel.: (55) 1155553865
Pharmaceutical Product Mfr & Distr
N.A.I.C.S.: 325412

Eisai Laboratorios, S. de R.L. de C.V. (1)
Corporativo Punto Polanco Lago Alberto 319 5th Floor Int 501A, Col Granada Delegacion Miguel Hidalgo, 11520, Mexico, Mexico
Tel.: (52) 5541697580
Pharmaceutical Product Mfr & Distr
N.A.I.C.S.: 325412

Eisai Limited (1)
6925 Century Avenue Suite 701, Mississauga, L5N 7K2, ON, Canada
Tel.: (905) 361-7130
Web Site: http://ca.eisai.com
Pharmaceutical Product Mfr & Distr
N.A.I.C.S.: 325412

Eisai Pharmaceuticals India Private Ltd. (1)
Sales Range: $25-49.9 Million
Emp.: 60
Pharmaceutical Production & Sales
N.A.I.C.S.: 325412

Eisai Pharmatechnology & Manufacturing Pvt. Ltd. (1)
Ramky Pharma City SEZ Plot Nos 96 97 98 124 & 126 Parawada, 531 019, Visakhapatnam, Andhra Pradesh, India
Tel.: (91) 8924282500
Web Site: http://www.eisai.com
Sales Range: $125-149.9 Million
Emp.: 300
Pharmaceuticals Product Mfr
N.A.I.C.S.: 325412
Sanjit Singh Lamba (Mng Dir)

Eisai R&D Management Co., Ltd. (1)
4-6-10 Koishikawa, Tokyo, 112-8088, Japan
Tel.: (81) 338173658
Sales Range: $25-49.9 Million
Emp.: 2
Clinical Research

N.A.I.C.S.: 541715
Nobuo Deguchi (Sr VP-R&D)

Eisai SA/NV (1)
Brusselsestraat 190 bus 4, 3000, Leuven, Belgium
Tel.: (32) 16140490
Pharmaceutical Product Mfr & Distr
N.A.I.C.S.: 325412

Eisai Taiwan, Inc. (1)
Office 902 9F No 18 Sec 1 Chang'an East Rd, Taipei, 104, Taiwan (100%)
Tel.: (886) 225314175
Web Site: https://www.eisai.com.tw
Sales Range: $25-49.9 Million
Emp.: 96
Mfr & Sales of Pharmaceuticals
N.A.I.C.S.: 325412

Eisai Vietnam Co., Ltd. (1)
E Town 3 Building Unit 8 7 8th Floor 364 Cong Hoa Street, Ward 13 Tan Binh District, Ho Chi Minh City, Vietnam
Tel.: (84) 2838113797
Pharmaceutical Product Mfr & Distr
N.A.I.C.S.: 325412

Hi-Eisai Pharmaceuticals, Inc. (1)
Unit 2 22nd Floor Tower 6789 6789 Ayala Avenue, Makati, 1226, Metro Manila, Philippines (49.9%)
Tel.: (63) 288875160
Web Site: https://hieisai.com.ph
Sales Range: $50-74.9 Million
Emp.: 109
Marketer & Sales of Pharmaceuticals
N.A.I.C.S.: 325412

KAN Research Institute, Inc. (1)
6-8-2 Minatojima Minamimachi, Chuo-ku, Kobe, 650-0047, Hyogo, Japan (100%)
Tel.: (81) 783065910
Sales Range: $25-49.9 Million
Emp.: 61
Research of Pharmaceuticals & Research Related to Life Sciences
N.A.I.C.S.: 541715

Limited Liability Company Eisai (1)
Business Centre Lotte Profsouznaya str 65/1, 117342, Moscow, Russia
Tel.: (7) 4955807026
Web Site: http://eisai.ru
Pharmaceutical Product Mfr & Distr
N.A.I.C.S.: 325412

PT. Eisai Indonesia (1)
Eisai Indonesia Agro Plaza Lantai 14 Jl Rasuna Said Kav X-2 No 1, Jakarta, 12950, Indonesia (80%)
Tel.: (62) 215262520
Web Site: https://www.eisai.co.id
Sales Range: $50-74.9 Million
Emp.: 80
Pharmaceuticals & Cosmetics Mfr & Sales
N.A.I.C.S.: 325412

Subsidiary (Domestic):

PT. Eisai Indonesia - Bogor Factory (2)
Ji Lanbau Desa Karang Asem Barat Kecamatan Citeureup, Bogor, 16810, Jawa-Barat, Indonesia
Tel.: (62) 218753202
Pharmaceuticals Product Mfr
N.A.I.C.S.: 325412

Palma Bee'Z Research Institute Co., Ltd. (1)
3262-12 Yoshiwara Ami-machi, Inashiki-gun, Ibaraki, 300-1155, Japan
Tel.: (81) 29 833 6033
Web Site: http://www.eisai.com
Diagnostic Products Research & Development Services
N.A.I.C.S.: 541715

Sannova Co., Ltd. (1)
3038-2 Serada-cho, Ota, 370-0426, Gunma, Japan (80%)
Tel.: (81) 276523611
Web Site: http://www.sannova.co.jp
Emp.: 382
Pharmaceutical Products Mfr & Distr
N.A.I.C.S.: 424210
Toru Takekawa (Chm)

Sunplanet Co., Ltd. (1)
3-5-10 Otsuka, Bunkyo-ku, Tokyo, 112-

Eisai Co., Ltd.—(Continued)

0012, Japan   **(84.91%)**
Tel.: (81) 359781941
Web Site: https://www.sunplanet.co.jp
Emp.: 800
Real Estate Manangement Services
N.A.I.C.S.: 531210
Takatoshi Fukai (Mng Exec Officer)

Unlimit Health Limited   **(1)**
40th Floor Park Place No 1601 Nanjing Xi
Road, Shanghai, 200040, China
Tel.: (86) 2124192888
Pharmaceutical Product Mfr & Distr
N.A.I.C.S.: 325412

EISENBAU KRAMER GMBH

Karl-Kramer-Strasse 12, 57223,
Kreuztal, Germany
Tel.: (49) 27325880   De
Web Site: http://www.eisenbau-
    kraemer.de
Year Founded: 1921
Sales Range: $10-24.9 Million
Emp.: 400
Rolled & Welded Steel Pipe & Shell
Mfr
N.A.I.C.S.: 331221
Rainer Seelbach (Chm)

Subsidiaries:

Eisenbau Kramer GmbH - Littfeld
Plant   **(1)**
Karl-Kramer-Strasse 12, 57223, Kreuztal,
Germany
Tel.: (49) 27325880
Web Site: http://www.eisenbau-kraemer.de
Steel Pole Mfr
N.A.I.C.S.: 331210
Heinz-Walter Hesener (Plant Mgr)

Eisenbau Kramer GmbH - Reckling-
hausen Plant   **(1)**
Hellbachstrasse 84-86, 45661, Reckling-
hausen, Germany
Tel.: (49) 236 160850
Steel Pole Mfr
N.A.I.C.S.: 331210

EISENMANN AG

Tubinger Strasse 81, Boblingen,
71032, Germany
Tel.: (49) 7031780
Web Site: http://www.eisenmann.com
Year Founded: 1951
Rev.: $212,012,500
Emp.: 2,160
Industrial Equipment Distr
N.A.I.C.S.: 423840
Matthias von Krauland (Chm-Mgmt
Bd)

Subsidiaries:

EISENMANN Ingenieria S.A.   **(1)**
Parc de Negocis MAS BLAU / Edificio
Prima Muntadas B C/Solsones 2, El Prat de
Llobregat, 8820, Barcelona, Spain
Tel.: (34) 934796610
Industrial Machinery Equipment Distr
N.A.I.C.S.: 423830
Carlos Manzano Rey (Project Mgr)

Eisenmann Corporation   **(1)**
150 E Dartmoor Dr, Crystal Lake, IL 60014
Tel.: (815) 455-4100
Web Site: http://www.eisenmann.us.com
Emp.: 120
Industrial Machinery Equipment Distr
N.A.I.C.S.: 423830
Mark West (Gen Mgr)

Eisenmann DO Brasil Equipamentos
Industriais Ltda   **(1)**
Rodovia Dr Avelino Junior Km 26 Quadra C
Numero, 100 Distrito Industrial, Cruzeiro,
12720-730, Sao Paulo, Brazil
Tel.: (55) 1121611200
Industrial Machinery Equipment Distr
N.A.I.C.S.: 423830

Eisenmann France SARL   **(1)**
Espace Claude Monet 14 rue Ernest Gouin,
78290, Croissy-sur-Seine, France

Tel.: (33) 130159800
Industrial Machinery Equipment Distr
N.A.I.C.S.: 423830

Eisenmann India Pvt. Ltd.   **(1)**
Technosoft Knowledge Gateway 1st Floor
Plot No B-14, Road No 1 Wagle Industrial
Estate, Thane, 400604, Maharashtra, India
Tel.: (91) 2266148148
Commercial & Industrial Equipment Distr
N.A.I.C.S.: 423830
Somnath Bhattacharya (Assoc VP)

Eisenmann Italia S.r.l.   **(1)**
Via Ferrari 21, 21047, Saronno, Italy
Tel.: (39) 0296718626
Industrial Machinery Equipment Distr
N.A.I.C.S.: 423830
Giovanni Ferrari (Acct Mgr)

Eisenmann S.A. De C.V.   **(1)**
Blvd 15 de Mayo 2933 Fracc Las Hadas,
72070, Puebla, Mexico
Tel.: (52) 2222311712
Industrial Machinery Equipment Distr
N.A.I.C.S.: 423830
Jorge Tamborero (VP-Svcs)

Eisenmann Shanghai Co., Ltd.   **(1)**
Room 301 Gubei International Fortune Cen-
ter No 1452 Hong Qiao Rd, Changning,
Shanghai, China
Tel.: (86) 2131352188
Industrial Machinery Equipment Distr
N.A.I.C.S.: 423830
Yu Li (Project Mgr)

Eisenmann Surface Finishing Sys-
tems India Pvt. Ltd.   **(1)**
609 Mahatta Towers 6th Floor Plot No 54 B
Block Community Centre, Janakpuri, New
Delhi, 110 058, India
Tel.: (91) 1165636353
Industrial Machinery Equipment Distr
N.A.I.C.S.: 423830

Eisenmann Thermal Solutions GmbH
& Co. KG   **(1)**
Leinetal Auf der Mauer 1 Gewerbegebiet
AREA 3 Sud, 37120, Bovenden, Germany
Tel.: (49) 5518208300
Web Site: http://www.ruhstrat.com
Industrial Machinery Equipment Distr
N.A.I.C.S.: 423830
Balu Parcibale Shikida (Mgr-Sls)

Eisenmann U.K. Ltd.   **(1)**
Unit La Priestly Court Staffordshire Technol-
ogy Park, Beaconside, Stafford, ST18 0LQ,
Staffordshire, United Kingdom
Tel.: (44) 1785283790
Industrial Machinery Equipment Distr
N.A.I.C.S.: 423830

OOO Eisenmann   **(1)**
Ul Pyatnitskaya 47-1, 119017, Moscow,
Russia
Tel.: (7) 4959516824
Industrial Machinery Equipment Distr
N.A.I.C.S.: 423830

OOO Eisenmann Togliatti   **(1)**
Ul Frunze 8 Buro 902, 445051, Togliatti,
Russia
Tel.: (7) 8482557586
Commercial & Industrial Equipment Distr
N.A.I.C.S.: 423830

intec Bielenberg GmbH & Co.
KG   **(1)**
Otto-Hahn-Allee 9, Erftstadt, 50374, Co-
logne, Germany
Tel.: (49) 2235465580
Web Site: http://www.bielenberg.de
Automotive Spare Parts Distr
N.A.I.C.S.: 423120

EISO ENTERPRISE CO., LTD.

No 2 Zhonghua Ln Shanying Rd, Kui
Shan County, Taoyuan, Taiwan
Tel.: (886) 33596066
Web Site: https://eiso.com.tw
5291—(TPE)
Rev.: $42,620,223
Assets: $50,898,109
Liabilities: $22,146,736
Net Worth: $28,751,373
Earnings: $2,510,210

Fiscal Year-end: 12/31/20
Printed Circuit Board Mfr
N.A.I.C.S.: 334418
Jung-Kun Chien (Chm)

EISSMANN AUTOMOTIVE DEUTSCHLAND GMBH

Munsinger Strasse 150, 72574, Bad
Urach, Germany
Tel.: (49) 712593730
Web Site: http://www.eissmann.com
Year Founded: 1964
Sales Range: $350-399.9 Million
Emp.: 4,200
Automotive Interiors Mfr
N.A.I.C.S.: 336390
Klaus Elmer (CEO)

Subsidiaries:

Dagro Eissmann Automotive
GmbH   **(1)**
An der Silbergrube 2, 07551, Gera, Ger-
many
Tel.: (49) 365737740
Automobile Spare Parts Mfr
N.A.I.C.S.: 336360

Eissmann Automotive Ceska repub-
lika s.r.o.   **(1)**
Vysocany 56, 34802, Prague, Czech Re-
public
Tel.: (420) 374217311
Automotive Spare Parts Distr
N.A.I.C.S.: 423120

Eissmann Automotive Detroit Devel-
opment, LLC   **(1)**
5700 Crooks Rd Ste 300, Troy, MI 48098
Tel.: (810) 216-6253
Automobile Parts Mfr
N.A.I.C.S.: 336390
Bob Evard (Dir-Pur & Supplier Mgmt)

Eissmann Automotive Hungaria
Kft.   **(1)**
Bottyan J u 8/a, 4400, Nyiregyhaza, Hun-
gary
Tel.: (36) 42801100
Automotive Spare Parts Distr
N.A.I.C.S.: 423120

Eissmann Automotive North America,
Inc.   **(1)**
599 Ed Gardner Dr, Pell City, AL 35125
Tel.: (205) 338-4044
Automotive Spare Parts Distr
N.A.I.C.S.: 423120

Eissmann Automotive Slovensko
s.r.o   **(1)**
Lesna 880/1, 90851, Holic, Slovakia
Tel.: (421) 346900343
Automobile Parts Mfr
N.A.I.C.S.: 336390
Lukas Filin (Mgr-Pur)

Eissmann Automotive de Mexico S.A.
de C.V.   **(1)**
Reforma Sur 27 Nave 1, Papalotla de Xi-
cohtencatl, 90796, Panzacola, Tlaxcala,
Mexico
Tel.: (52) 2222633565
Automotive Spare Parts Distr
N.A.I.C.S.: 423120

Eissmann Cotesa GmbH   **(1)**
Bahnhofstrasse 70, 09648, Mittweida, Ger-
many
Tel.: (49) 712593730
Automobile Spare Parts Mfr
N.A.I.C.S.: 336360

Eissmann Individual GmbH   **(1)**
Munsinger Strasse 150, 72574, Bad
Urach, Germany
Tel.: (49) 712593730
Automobile Spare Parts Mfr
N.A.I.C.S.: 336360

Gearchief Eissmann Automotive Parts
Co., Ltd   **(1)**
No 5000 Guigu Street Hi-tech Development
Zone, Changchun, China
Tel.: (86) 43185886618
Automotive Spare Parts Distr
N.A.I.C.S.: 423120

EIT ENVIRONMENTAL DEVEL-OPMENT GROUP CO., LTD.

Building 5 E-commerce Industrial
Park, Zhumeng Town Tianxin Avenue
Yuexi County, Anqing, 518040, Anhui,
China
Tel.: (86) 75582734788
Web Site: https://www.eit-sz.com
Year Founded: 2010
300815—(SSE)
Rev.: $757,247,400
Assets: $859,065,480
Liabilities: $347,944,896
Net Worth: $511,120,584
Earnings: $69,402,528
Fiscal Year-end: 12/31/22
Property Management Services
N.A.I.C.S.: 531311
Ping Zhou (Chm)

EITA RESOURCES BERHAD

Lot 4 Block A Jalan SS13/7 Subang
Jaya Industrial Estate, 47500, Sub-
ang Jaya, Selangor, Malaysia
Tel.: (60) 356378099
Web Site: https://www.eita.com.my
EITA—(KLS)
Rev.: $67,062,434
Assets: $76,884,021
Liabilities: $31,508,571
Net Worth: $45,375,450
Earnings: $1,552,381
Emp.: 656
Fiscal Year-end: 09/30/23
Elevator Systems & Busduct Systems
N.A.I.C.S.: 333921
Wing Hoong Fu (Mng Dir-Grp)

Subsidiaries:

EITA Elevator (Malaysia) Sdn.
Bhd.   **(1)**
No 6 Jalan Astana 1/KU2 Bandar Bukit
Raja, Sunway Tunas, 41050, Klang, Selan-
gor Darul Ehsan, Malaysia
Tel.: (60) 333412112
Elevator Mfr
N.A.I.C.S.: 333921

EITA Power System Sdn. Bhd.   **(1)**
Lot 4 Block A Jalan SS 13/7, Subang Jaya
Industrial Estate, 47500, Subang Jaya, Se-
langor, Malaysia
Tel.: (60) 356357088
Electrical & Electronic Component Distr
N.A.I.C.S.: 423690

EITA Research & Development Sdn.
Bhd.   **(1)**
No 6 Jalan Astana 1/KU2, Bandar Bukit
Raja, 41050, Kelang, Selangor, Malaysia
Tel.: (60) 333411717
Elevator Mfr
N.A.I.C.S.: 333921

EITA Technologies (Malaysia) Sdn.
Bhd.   **(1)**
Lot 4 Block A Jalan SS 13/7, Subang Jaya
Industrial Estate, 47500, Subang Jaya, Se-
langor, Malaysia
Tel.: (60) 356378363
Fire Resistant Cable Mfr & Distr
N.A.I.C.S.: 335929

EITA Technologies Pte. Ltd.   **(1)**
49 Jalan Pemimpin 04-12 APS Industrial
Building, Singapore, 577203, Singapore
Tel.: (65) 62563080
Electrical Equipment Whslr
N.A.I.C.S.: 423610

EITA-Schneider (MFG) Sdn.
Bhd.   **(1)**
No 6 Jalan Astana 1/KU2, Bandar Bukit
Raja, 41050, Klang, Selangor, Malaysia
Tel.: (60) 333412112
Web Site: https://www.eitaelevator.com.my
Elevator Mfr & Distr
N.A.I.C.S.: 333921

Eita Electric Sdn. Bhd.   **(1)**
Lot 4 Block A Jalan SS 13/7 Subang Jaya
Industrial Estate, 47500, Subang Jaya, Se-
langor Darul Ehsan, Malaysia

Tel.: (60) 356378088
Emp.: 50
Electrical Equipment Distr
N.A.I.C.S.: 423610
See Wang *(Gen Mgr)*

Furutec Electrical Sdn. Bhd. (1)
Plot 89 Lorong Perindustrian Bukit Minyak
11, Kawasan Perindustrian Bukit Minyak
MK13, 14100, Penang, Selangor, Malaysia
Tel.: (60) 356357088
Web Site: https://furutec.com.my
Elevator Mfr & Distr
N.A.I.C.S.: 333921

EIWA CORPORATION
4-1-7 Kitahorie, Nishi-Ku, Osaka,
550-0014, Japan
Tel.: (81) 334934061
Web Site: https://www.eiwa-net.co.jp
Year Founded: 1947
9857—(TKS)
Rev.: $286,160,120
Assets: $211,116,790
Liabilities: $106,936,580
Net Worth: $104,180,210
Earnings: $11,018,870
Emp.: 757
Fiscal Year-end: 03/31/24
Industrial Measuring Instrument Mfr &
Distr
N.A.I.C.S.: 334513
Yoshinori Abe *(Pres & CEO)*

EIZO CORPORATION
153 Shimokashiwano, Hakusan, 924-
8566, Ishikawa, Japan
Tel.: (81) 762754121
Web Site: https://www.eizoglobal.com
Year Founded: 1968
6737—(TKS)
Rev.: $531,913,310
Assets: $1,089,453,590
Liabilities: $233,960,950
Net Worth: $855,492,640
Earnings: $36,050,940
Emp.: 2,495
Fiscal Year-end: 03/31/24
Computer Monitors & Peripherals Mfr
N.A.I.C.S.: 334118
Kazuhide Shimura *(Sr Exec Operating Officer)*

Subsidiaries:

Carina System Co., Ltd. (1)
7F Sannomiya Daiichi Seimei Bldg 69 Kyo-
machi, Chuo-ku, Kobe, 650-0034, Hyogo,
Japan
Tel.: (81) 783357601
Web Site: https://www.carinasystem.co.jp
Software Development Services
N.A.I.C.S.: 541511
Kotoh Mutsuo *(Pres & CEO)*

EIZO Austria GmbH (1)
Pfarrgasse 87, 1230, Vienna, Austria
Tel.: (43) 1615288610
Web Site: http://www.eizo.at
Visual Display Equipment Mfr & Whslr
N.A.I.C.S.: 334310

**EIZO Display Technologies (Suzhou)
Co., Ltd.** (1)
5B Zhongxin Science Technology Industrial
Zone 8 Zhanye Road, Suzhou Industrial
Park, Suzhou, 215121, China
Tel.: (86) 51262520100
Computer Monitors & Peripherals Mfr
N.A.I.C.S.: 334118

EIZO Europe GmbH (1)
Belgrader Strasse 2, 41069, Monchenglad-
bach, Germany
Tel.: (49) 216182100
Web Site: http://www.eizo.de
Visual Display Equipment Mfr & Whslr
N.A.I.C.S.: 334310

EIZO GmbH (1)
Siemensallee 84, 76187, Karlsruhe, Ger-
many
Tel.: (49) 721203210
Web Site: http://www.eizo.eu

Sales Range: $150-199.9 Million
Emp.: 300
Medical Monitors Distr
N.A.I.C.S.: 423430
Peter Ziegler *(CEO)*

EIZO Inc. (1)
5710 Warland Dr, Cypress, CA 90630
Tel.: (562) 431-5011
Web Site: https://www.eizo.com
Emp.: 20
Sales of Computer Monitors & Peripherals
N.A.I.C.S.: 423430
Toshimitsu Hamauchi *(Head-HR)*

EIZO Limited (1)
1 Queens Square Ascot Business Park
Lyndhurst Road, Ascot, SL5 9FE, Berkshire,
United Kingdom
Tel.: (44) 1344317480
Web Site: http://www.eizo.co.uk
Visual Display Equipment Mfr & Whslr
N.A.I.C.S.: 334310

EIZO Nordic AB (1)
Lovangsvagen 14, 194 45, Upplands Vasby,
Sweden
Tel.: (46) 859410500
Computer Monitors & Peripherals Mfr
N.A.I.C.S.: 334118

EIZO Technologies GmbH (1)
Benzweg 3, 82538, Geretsried, Germany
Tel.: (49) 817134920
Web Site: https://www.eizo-tech.com
Sales Range: $25-49.9 Million
Emp.: 100
Monitors & Converter Cards Mfr
N.A.I.C.S.: 334118
Andy Kuerz *(Pres)*

Eizo Engineering Corporation (1)
153 Shimokashiwanocho, Hakusan, 924-
8566, Ishikawa, Japan
Tel.: (81) 762742448
Web Site: http://www.eizoeg.com
Liquid Crystal Display Mfr
N.A.I.C.S.: 334419

Eizo Nanao AG (1)
Moosacherstrasse 6 Au, 8820, Wadenswil,
Zurich, Switzerland
Tel.: (41) 447822440
Web Site: https://www.eizo.ch
Sales Range: $25-49.9 Million
Emp.: 15
Monitors Distr
N.A.I.C.S.: 423430

Eizo Nanao MS Corporation (1)
Abu 8-2 Fujihashi, Nanao, 926-8566,
Ishikawa, Japan
Tel.: (81) 767522222
Sales Range: $50-74.9 Million
Emp.: 200
Liquid Crystal Display Mfr
N.A.I.C.S.: 334419

**Eizo Support Network
Corporation** (1)
153 Shimokashiwano, Hakusan, 924-8566,
Ishikawa, Japan
Tel.: (81) 762742424
Web Site: https://www.eizo-support.co.jp
Sales Range: $25-49.9 Million
Emp.: 86
Monitors Sales & Maintenance Services
N.A.I.C.S.: 811210
Yoshitaka Mimori *(Pres)*

Irem Software Engineering Inc. (1)
Tel.: (81) 352893055
Web Site: http://www.irem.co.jp
Sales Range: $50-74.9 Million
Emp.: 100
Video Game Software Development Ser-
vices
N.A.I.C.S.: 334610

Nanao Agency Corporation (1)
153 Shimokashiwano, Hakusan, 924-8566,
Ishikawa, Japan
Tel.: (81) 762740035
Web Site: http://www.eizo.com
Medical Imaging Monitors Distr
N.A.I.C.S.: 423450

Tech Source, Inc. (1)
442 Northlake Blvd, Altamonte Springs, FL
32701
Tel.: (407) 262-7100

Web Site: http://www.eico-ruggete.com
Sales Range: $25-49.9 Million
Emp.: 50
Air Traffic Control Components Mfr
N.A.I.C.S.: 334511
Selwyn L. Henriques *(Pres)*

EJ HOLDINGS INC.
Tsushima Kyomachi 3-chome 1-21,
Kita Ward, Okayama, 700-0087, Ja-
pan
Tel.: (81) 862527520
Web Site: https://www.ej-hds.co.jp
Year Founded: 2007
2153—(TKS)
Rev.: $245,938,270
Assets: $273,806,030
Liabilities: $58,372,910
Net Worth: $215,433,120
Earnings: $20,041,520
Emp.: 1,721
Fiscal Year-end: 05/31/24
Holding Company
N.A.I.C.S.: 551112
Yuji Kotani *(Pres & CEO)*

EJADA FOR FINANCIAL IN-
VESTMENTS PLC
AL Shemesani Alsalahat complex
building No 86, PO Box 962365, Am-
man, 11196, Jordan
Tel.: (962) 5623116
Year Founded: 1995
EJAD—(AMM)
Sales Range: Less than $1 Million
Emp.: 3
Investment Management Service
N.A.I.C.S.: 523999

EJE (HONG KONG) HOLDINGS
LIMITED
Eastern Section of Guangzhou Eco-
nomic and Technological Develop-
ment, Huangpu District, Guangzhou,
Guangdong, China
Tel.: (86) 2082998812
Web Site: http://www.jmbedding.com
8101—(HKG)
Rev.: $18,036,982
Assets: $117,522,887
Liabilities: $67,009,731
Net Worth: $50,513,155
Earnings: $10,707,339
Emp.: 231
Fiscal Year-end: 03/31/20
Mattresses & Soft Beds Mfr
N.A.I.C.S.: 337910
King Chung Wong *(Compliance Offi-
cer, Sec & Controller-Fin)*

EJECTA MARKETING LTD.
1 Old Court House Corner 1st Floor
Room No 15, Kolkata, 700001, India
Tel.: (91) 63723688
Web Site:
    http://www.ejectamarketing.com
Year Founded: 1983
Rev.: $155,664
Assets: $2,252,487
Liabilities: $83,399
Net Worth: $2,169,088
Earnings: $4,074
Emp.: 8
Fiscal Year-end: 03/31/19
General Marketing Services
N.A.I.C.S.: 541613
Jai Kumar Baid *(CFO)*

EJECTT INC
4F No 118 Sec 1 Neihu Rd, Neihu
Dist, Taipei, 11493, Taiwan
Tel.: (886) 287518337
Web Site: http://www.yuanjiu.com.tw
3089—(TPE)
Rev.: $4,130,788
Assets: $21,416,940
Liabilities: $5,737,298

Net Worth: $15,679,642
Earnings: ($7,586,655)
Fiscal Year-end: 12/31/22
Semiconductor Equipment Mfr
N.A.I.C.S.: 334413
Chun-Kuo Lin *(Chm)*

EJF INVESTMENTS LTD.
IFC1 The Esplanade, Saint Helier,
JE1 4BP, Jersey
Tel.: (44) 2037526774   JE
Web Site: https://www.ejfi.com
Year Founded: 2005
EJFI—(I SF)
Rev.: $10,184,596
Assets: $156,047,813
Liabilities: $31,304,593
Net Worth: $124,743,220
Earnings: ($10,163,641)
Fiscal Year-end: 12/31/23
Investment Management Service
N.A.I.C.S.: 523940
Joanna Dentskevich *(Chm)*

EKA NOODLES BERHAD
Lot 208 Phase II Kuala Ketil Industrial
Estate, Kuala Ketil, 09300, Kedah
Darul Aman, Malaysia
Tel.: (60) 44162222
Web Site:
    http://www.ekanoodles.com
EKA—(KLS)
Rev.: $10,202,556
Assets: $15,350,218
Liabilities: $23,934,123
Net Worth: ($8,583,905)
Earnings: ($301,937)
Emp.: 144
Fiscal Year-end: 12/31/20
Rice & Sago Sticks Mfr
N.A.I.C.S.: 311230
Tong Lang Tan *(Co-Sec)*

Subsidiaries:

**Bersatu Sago Industries (Mukah) Sdn
Bhd** (1)
Lot 122 Block 134 Mukah Land District
Sungai Metapus, Mukah, Sarawak, Malay-
sia
Tel.: (60) 84875030
Sales Range: $25-49.9 Million
Emp.: 40
Starch Mfr
N.A.I.C.S.: 339999

**Bersatu Sago Industries Sdn
Bhd** (1)
Lot 3161 3162 3164 3319 Retus Land Dis-
trict Ulu Sungai Danan, Batang Igan, Sibu,
Sarawak, Malaysia
Tel.: (60) 8 486 2464
Web Site: http://www.krb.com.my
Starch Mfr
N.A.I.C.S.: 339999

EKA Foodstuff Sdn. Bhd. (1)
Lot 208 Phase II, Kuala Ketil Industrial Es-
tate, 09300, Kuala Ketil, Kedah Darul
Aman, Malaysia
Tel.: (60) 192816893
Web Site: https://www.eka.com.my
Vermicelli Mfr
N.A.I.C.S.: 311991

**Kilang Bihun Bersatu (East Malaysia)
Sdn Bhd** (1)
Lot 1178 Block 19, Seduan Land District
Upper Lanang Industrial Estate, 96000,
Sibu, Sarawak, Malaysia
Tel.: (60) 8 421 4801
Web Site: http://www.krb.com.my
Emp.: 60
Plant Food Distr
N.A.I.C.S.: 424930
Frederick Law *(Gen Mgr)*

Kilang Bihun Bersatu Sdn Bhd (1)
Lot 208 Phase II, Kuala Ketil Industrial Es-
tate, 09300, Kuala Ketil, Kedah Darul
Aman, Malaysia
Tel.: (60) 44162222
Web Site: https://www.ekanoodles.com
Rice & Sago Sticks Mfr & Distr

EKA Noodles Berhad—(Continued)

N.A.I.C.S.: 311999
Cho Teing Ang *(Mng Dir)*

PT Bersatu International Food
Industries **(1)**
Jl Raya Cikande Rangkasbitung No 88 Km
45 Desa Kareo Kecamatan Jawilan, Se-
rang, Banten, Indonesia
Tel.: (62) 254401145
Rice Mfr
N.A.I.C.S.: 311212

**EKACHAI MEDICAL CARE
PCL**
99/9 Moo 4 Ekachai Rd Khok Kham,
Muang, Samut Sakhon, 74000, Thai-
land
Tel.: (66) 916626261
Web Site:
http://www.ekachaihospital.com
Year Founded: 2004
EKH—(THA)
Rev.: $36,729,390
Assets: $71,778,139
Liabilities: $9,656,155
Net Worth: $62,121,984
Earnings: $8,822,344
Emp.: 598
Fiscal Year-end: 12/31/23
Healtcare Services
N.A.I.C.S.: 622110
Amnuay Oerareemitr *(CEO)*

**EKAM LEASING & FINANCE
CO. LTD.**
No 11 Rani Jhansi Road Motia Khan,
M M Road, New Delhi, 110055, India
Tel.: (91) 1132033277
Web Site:
http://www.ekamleasing.com
Year Founded: 1993
530581—(BOM)
Rev.: $71,267
Assets: $1,300,149
Liabilities: $182,364
Net Worth: $1,117,785
Earnings: $42,219
Emp.: 2
Fiscal Year-end: 03/31/21
Financial Lending Services
N.A.I.C.S.: 522220
Rakesh Jain *(Chm & Mng Dir)*

EKANSH CONCEPTS LIMITED
A-403 Mittal Commercia A-Wing And-
heri Kurla Road, Marol Naka Andheri
East, Mumbai, 400059, India
Tel.: (91) 2240149792   In
Web Site:
https://ekanshconcepts.com
Year Founded: 1992
531364—(BOM)
Rev.: $8,816,603
Assets: $17,942,079
Liabilities: $14,493,092
Net Worth: $3,448,986
Earnings: $1,014,932
Fiscal Year-end: 03/31/21
Highway & Bridge Construction Ser-
vices
N.A.I.C.S.: 237310
Govind Ram Patodia *(Mng Dir)*

**EKARAT ENGINEERING PUB-
LIC COMPANY LIMITED**
9/291 UM Tower Ramkhamhaeng Rd,
Suanluang, Bangkok, 10250, Thai-
land
Tel.: (66) 27198777
Web Site: https://ekarat.co.th
Year Founded: 1981
AKR—(THA)
Rev.: $66,676,842
Assets: $65,598,055
Liabilities: $21,948,603
Net Worth: $43,649,452

Earnings: $6,442,008
Emp.: 698
Fiscal Year-end: 12/31/23
Transformer Mfr
N.A.I.C.S.: 334416
Danucha Noichaiboon *(Mng Dir)*

**EKATO RUHR- UND MIS-
CHTECHNIK GMBH**
Hohe-Flum-Strasse 37, 79650,
Schopfheim, Germany
Tel.: (49) 7622290   De
Web Site: http://www.ekato.com
Year Founded: 1933
Industrial Process Equipment Mfr
N.A.I.C.S.: 333248
Philip Mathon *(Mng Dir)*

**EKENNIS SOFTWARE SER-
VICE LTD.**
No 1&2 Second Floor Neeladri Circle
Doddathogur Vill, Electronic City
Phase-1, Bengaluru, 560100, Karna-
taka, India
Tel.: (91) 9986384219
Web Site: https://www.ekennis.com
Year Founded: 2019
543475—(BOM)
Rev.: $647,843
Assets: $758,831
Liabilities: $162,080
Net Worth: $596,751
Earnings: $148,430
Emp.: 56
Fiscal Year-end: 03/31/22
Software Development Services
N.A.I.C.S.: 541511
Manisha Sharma *(Mng Dir & Chm)*

**EKF DIAGNOSTICS HOLD-
INGS PLC**
Tel.: (44) 2920710570
Web Site:
https://www.ekfdiagnostics.com
EKF—(LSE)
Rev.: $82,747,343
Assets: $110,881,564
Liabilities: $18,338,902
Net Worth: $92,542,661
Earnings: ($11,891,477)
Emp.: 356
Fiscal Year-end: 12/31/22
Analytical Laboratory Instrument
Manufacturing
N.A.I.C.S.: 334516
Luke Daum *(Chief Scientific Officer)*

Subsidiaries:

EKF Diagnostics Inc. **(1)**
1261 N Main St, Boerne, TX 78006
Tel.: (830) 249-0772
Web Site: https://www.ekfusa.com
Clinical Diagnostic Product Mfr & Distr
N.A.I.C.S.: 334510

Senslab GmbH **(1)**
Bautzner Str 67, 04347, Leipzig, Germany
Tel.: (49) 3412341830
Web Site: https://senslab.de
Medical Device Mfr
N.A.I.C.S.: 334516
Olga Suckau *(Mng Dir)*

Separation Technology, Inc. **(1)**
570 Monroe Rd Ste 1008, Sanford, FL
32771
Tel.: (407) 788-8791
Web Site:
http://www.separationtechnology.com
Sales Range: $1-9.9 Million
Emp.: 15
Centrifugation Products Mfr
N.A.I.C.S.: 334516

Stanbio Laboratory LP **(1)**
1261 N Main St, Boerne, TX 78006
Tel.: (830) 249-0772
Web Site: https://www.stanbio.com

Sales Range: $25-49.9 Million
Emp.: 75
Pharmaceutical Preparations
N.A.I.C.S.: 325412

**EKI ENERGY SERVICES LIM-
ITED**
Plot 48 Scheme 78 Part-2 Behind
Vrindavan Hotel Vijay Nagar, Indore,
452010, Madhya Pradesh, India
Tel.: (91) 7314289086
Web Site: https://www.enkingint.org
Year Founded: 2008
543284—(BOM)
Rev.: $155,784,294
Assets: $106,508,279
Liabilities: $41,589,941
Net Worth: $64,918,338
Earnings: $14,345,219
Emp.: 232
Fiscal Year-end: 03/31/23
Management Consultancy Services
N.A.I.C.S.: 541618
Manish Dabkara *(CEO)*

Subsidiaries:

EKI Power Trading Private
Limited **(1)**
Plot- 48 Scheme No 78 Part-II Vijay Nagar,
Indore, 452010, Madhya Pradesh, India
Tel.: (91) 7314289086
Web Site: https://www.ekipowertrading.com
Electricity Generation Services
N.A.I.C.S.: 237130

GHG Reduction Technologies Private
Limited **(1)**
Flat 101 Plot 48 Scheme 78 Part 2 Vijay
Nagar, Indore, 452010, India
Tel.: (91) 11333015
Web Site: https://ghgreductiontech.com
Coal Stove Mfr
N.A.I.C.S.: 335220

Galaxy Certification Services Private
Limited **(1)**
Crescent 3 Prestige Shantiniketan Commer-
cial Complex 12th Floor Awfis, ITPL Road
Whitefield, Bengaluru, 560048, India
Tel.: (91) 9848335693
Web Site:
https://www.galaxycertification.com
Certification & Inspection Services
N.A.I.C.S.: 541380

EKINOPS S.A.
10 rue Edouard Branly, 22300, Lan-
nion, France
Tel.: (33) 296050030
Web Site: https://www.ekinops.com
Year Founded: 2003
EKI—(EUR)
Sales Range: $100-124.9 Million
Ethernet Services & Carrier Ethernet
Access Devices Mfr
N.A.I.C.S.: 334210
Didier Bredy *(Chm & CEO)*

Subsidiaries:

Ekinops Belgium NV **(1)**
Geldenaaksebaan 335, 3001, Leuven, Bel-
gium
Tel.: (32) 16799799
Telecommunication Servicesb
N.A.I.C.S.: 517810

Ekinops Corporation **(1)**
9200 Corporate Blvd Ste 360, Rockville,
MD 20850
Tel.: (571) 335-8700
Telecommunication Servicesb
N.A.I.C.S.: 517810

Ekinops Espana Srl. **(1)**
Paseo de la Castellana 143 Planta 10,
Modulo D, 28046, Madrid, Spain
Tel.: (34) 911935071
Telecommunication Servicesb
N.A.I.C.S.: 517810
Nacho Carcas *(Engr-Sls)*

Ekinops France SA **(1)**
Le Chavez 13 Avenue Morane Saulnier,

78140, Velizy-Villacoublay, France
Tel.: (33) 177711200
Telecommunication Servicesb
N.A.I.C.S.: 517810
Sebastien Bernard *(Acct Mgr)*

Ekinops India Pvt. Ltd. **(1)**
27 S V Towers Third Floor 80 Feet Road,
Koramangala 6th Block, Bengaluru,
560095, Karnataka, India
Tel.: (91) 8042590222
Telecommunication Servicesb
N.A.I.C.S.: 517810
Keerthi Raj R. *(Asst Mgr-HR & Admin)*

Ekinops Italia Srl. **(1)**
Via Savoia 78, 00198, Rome, Italy
Tel.: (39) 0685237241
Telecommunication Servicesb
N.A.I.C.S.: 517810
Fabrizio Nurra *(Mgr-Pre Sls)*

OneAccess SA **(1)**
13 Avenue Morane Saulnier, Velizy Villacou-
blay, Paris, 78140, France
Tel.: (33) 177711200
Web Site: https://www.oneaccess-net.com
Multi-Service Access Routers & Carrier Eth-
ernet Access Devices Mfr
N.A.I.C.S.: 334210
Denis Behaghel *(CTO)*

EKIP-98 HOLDING AD
Aleksandar Malinov 75, Sofia, 1712,
Bulgaria
Tel.: (359) 29434567
Web Site: http://www.ekip98.eu
5EKA—(BUL)
Sales Range: Less than $1 Million
Holding Company
N.A.I.C.S.: 551112

EKITAN & CO., LTD.
6-2-1 Ginza Chuo-ku, Tokyo, 104-
0061, Japan
Tel.: (81) 362523670
Web Site: http://www.ekitan.co.jp
Year Founded: 2003
3646—(TKS)
Rev.: $26,691,180
Assets: $18,078,350
Liabilities: $6,841,350
Net Worth: $11,237,000
Earnings: ($4,864,960)
Emp.: 252
Fiscal Year-end: 03/31/24
Network Communications
N.A.I.C.S.: 517810
Naoyuki Kaneda *(Pres & CEO)*

**EKIZ KIMYA SANAYI VE TI-
CARET A.S.**
Ismet Kaptan Neighborhood Martyr
Nevres Boulevard Deren Plaza No
10/11, Konak, Izmir, Turkiye
Tel.: (90) 2324645633
Web Site: https://www.ekizkimya.com
EKIZ—(IST)
Sales Range: Less than $1 Million
Food Products Distr
N.A.I.C.S.: 311999
Ibrahim Ekiz *(Chm)*

**EKIZ YAG VE SABUN SANAYI
A.S.**
Sehitler Caddesi 1508 Sokak 4 Al-
sancak, 35230, Izmir, Turkiye
Tel.: (90) 2324885700
Web Site: http://www.ekizyag.com
Year Founded: 1946
Sales Range: $10-24.9 Million
Emp.: 90
Olive & Vegetable Oil Refiner, Pro-
ducer & Marketer
N.A.I.C.S.: 311225
Husnu Ekiz *(Chm & Gen Mgr)*

EKO EXPORT S.A.
81 Strazacka street, 43-382, Bielsko-
Biala, Poland

Tel.: (48) 338196292
Web Site: https://ekoexport.com
EEX—(WAR)
Rev.: $7,833,866
Assets: $5,297,622
Liabilities: $8,468,897
Net Worth: ($3,171,274)
Earnings: ($10,012,906)
Fiscal Year-end: 12/31/22
Microspheres Distr & Exporter
N.A.I.C.S.: 424690
Jolanta Sidzina-Bokun (Deputy Chm-Supervisory Bd)

EKO FAKTORING A.S.
Maslak Mah Meydan Sok Veko Giz Plaza No 3 PK, 34398, Istanbul, Turkiye
Tel.: (90) 2123292100
Web Site:
    http://www.ekofaktoring.com
Year Founded: 1994
EKOFA—(IST)
Sales Range: Less than $1 Million
Financial Consulting Services
N.A.I.C.S.: 541611
Enver Gocay (Chm)

EKO-KOM, A.S.
Na Pankraci 1685/17, 140 21, Prague, Czech Republic
Tel.: (420) 729848111
Web Site: http://www.ekokom.cz
Year Founded: 1997
Recycling Services
N.A.I.C.S.: 423930
Zbynek Kozel (CEO)

EKOCORP PLC.
31 Mobolaji Bank Anthony Way, Ikeja, Lagos, Nigeria
Tel.: (234) 012716997
Web Site: http://www.ekocorp.net
Year Founded: 1991
EKOCORP—(NIGE)
Rev.: $2,560,460
Assets: $16,639,778
Liabilities: $10,132,894
Net Worth: $6,506,884
Earnings: ($907,842)
Emp.: 296
Fiscal Year-end: 12/31/20
Medical Insurance Services
N.A.I.C.S.: 524114
Ademolu Owoyele (CEO-Acting)

EKOPAK NV
Careelstraat 13, 8700, Tielt, Belgium
Tel.: (32) 51755105   BE
Web Site: https://ekopakwater.com
Year Founded: 1997
EKOP—(EUR)
Rev.: $40,538,528
Assets: $139,641,701
Liabilities: $81,885,387
Net Worth: $57,756,313
Earnings: ($3,319,663)
Emp.: 154
Fiscal Year-end: 12/31/23
Waste Treatment Services
N.A.I.C.S.: 221310
Els De Keukelaere (CFO)

EKOSEM-AGRAR GMBH
Johann-Jakob-Astor-Strasse 49, 69190, Walldorf, Germany
Tel.: (49) 6227 3585 919   De
Web Site: http://www.ekosem-agrar.de
Year Founded: 1993
Sales Range: $150-199.9 Million
Emp.: 5,326
Holding Company; Cattle, Dairy & Agricultural Farming
N.A.I.C.S.: 551112
Stefan Durr (Founder, Mng Partner & CEO)

Subsidiaries:

Ekosem Agrarprojekte GmbH   (1)
Alt-Moabit 41, 10555, Berlin, Germany
Tel.: (49) 3047473720
Web Site: http://www.ekosem-agrarprojekte.de
Agricultural Services
N.A.I.C.S.: 115116

Huck Finn GmbH   (1)
Kromsdorfer Str 17, 99427, Weimar, Germany
Tel.: (49) 3643515816
Web Site: http://www.huckfinn-weimar.de
Piano Moving Services
N.A.I.C.S.: 484210

MC EkoNiva-APK Holding   (1)
33A Engels st, 394036, Voronezh, Russia
Tel.: (7) 4732679777
Web Site: http://www.ekoniva-apk.ru
Emp.: 5,000
Holding Company; Cattle, Dairy & Agricultural Farming
N.A.I.C.S.: 551112
Stefan Durr (Pres & Dir Gen)

OOO Agrofirma Mezhdurechye   (1)
30 Tsentralnaya st, Gilyovo Yarkovo district, 626077, Tyumen, Russia
Tel.: (7) 3453137175
Emp.: 230
Dairy Farming Services
N.A.I.C.S.: 112120
Sergey Kamenev (Exec Dir)

OOO EkoNiva-Media   (1)
79-a Radishchev st, 305004, Kursk, Russia
Tel.: (7) 4712392660
Advertising & Marketing Services
N.A.I.C.S.: 541810
Svetlana Weber (Exec Dir)

OOO EkoNivaAgro   (1)
46 Tsentralnaya st, Zaluzhnoye Village Liskinsky district, 397920, Voronezh, Russia
Tel.: (7) 4739198138
Web Site: https://ekoniva-apk.ru
Emp.: 3,804
Dairy Farming Services
N.A.I.C.S.: 112120
Aleksander Rybenko (Reg Dir)

OOO Oka Moloko   (1)
44A Shchedrina st room N-1, 390000, Ryazan, Russia
Tel.: (7) 4912427123
Web Site: https://ekoniva-apk.ru
Emp.: 1,447
Dairy & Crop Farming Services
N.A.I.C.S.: 111998
Sergey Ivanov (Deputy Exec Dir)

OOO Peterburgskaya Niva   (1)
33 Chirkovitsi Village, Volosovskiy district, 188425, Saint Petersburg, Leningrad, Russia
Tel.: (7) 8137353717
Web Site: https://ekoniva-apk.ru
Emp.: 105
Milk Mfr
N.A.I.C.S.: 311511
Yuri Kinyakin (Exec Dir)

OOO Savinskaja Niva   (1)
2 Sadovaya st, Savino Mosalsky district, Kaluga, 249930, Russia
Tel.: (7) 4845226164
Emp.: 50
Organic Grain Product Distr
N.A.I.C.S.: 424510
Ivan Golikov (Deputy Dir-Production)

OOO Sibirskaya Niva   (1)
2 Tsentralnaya st Paivino, Maslyaninsky district, 633571, Novosibirsk, Russia
Tel.: (7) 3834751646
Web Site: https://ekoniva-apk.ru
Emp.: 1,361
Dairy Production Services
N.A.I.C.S.: 112120
Sergey Lyakhov (Reg Dir-Siberian Reg)

OOO Stupinskaya Niva   (1)
11 Novye doma St, Office 18 Stupino Dubnevo Village, 142825, Moscow, Russia
Tel.: (7) 4966458140
Web Site: https://ekoniva-apk.ru
Emp.: 245
Dairy Farming Services

N.A.I.C.S.: 112120
Yuri Kinyakin (Exec Dir)

OOO Zaschitnoe   (1)
Zashchitnoye, Shchigry district, 306513, Kursk, Russia
Tel.: (7) 4712748582
Web Site: https://ekoniva-apk.ru
Emp.: 541
Dairy Farming Services
N.A.I.C.S.: 112120
Yuriy Vasyukov (Reg Dir)

EKOSTAV A.S
Spitalska 10, 071 80, Michalovce, 071 80, Slovakia
Tel.: (421) 911248042
Web Site:
    https://www.eng.ekostav.eu
Year Founded: 1990
1ESM01AE—(BRA)
Sales Range: Less than $1 Million
Building Construction Services
N.A.I.C.S.: 236210
Jan Steso (Chm-Mgmt Bd)

EKOTAB AD KOCHERINOVO
Ul Jelyo Demirevski 1 obshtin, Kocherinovo Selo Barakovo, Kyustendil, 2634, Bulgaria
Tel.: (359) 70532207
Paper Products Mfr
N.A.I.C.S.: 322299
Kiril Hristov Baychev (Exec Dir)

EKOTECHNIKA AG
Johann-Jakob-Astor-Str 49, 69190, Walldorf, Germany
Tel.: (49) 62273585919
Web Site: http://www.ekotechnika.de
0EK2—(BER)
Rev.: $189,025,469
Assets: $172,435,787
Liabilities: $98,505,288
Net Worth: $73,930,499
Earnings: $9,948,198
Emp.: 844
Fiscal Year-end: 09/30/23
Agricultural Equipment Mfr
N.A.I.C.S.: 333111
Stefan Durr (Founder, Chm & Mng Dir)

EKOTON+ JSC
Nur-Sultan Korgalzhinskoe Highway 31A, Nur-Sultan, 010000, Kazakhstan
Tel.: (7) 7172695584
Web Site: http://www.ecoton.kz
EKTN—(KAZ)
Rev.: $20,501,635
Assets: $48,155,881
Liabilities: $24,179,531
Net Worth: $23,976,349
Earnings: $4,234,907
Fiscal Year-end: 12/31/21
Cellular Concrete Good Mfr
N.A.I.C.S.: 327390

EKOVEST BERHAD
Ground Floor Wisma EKOVEST Jalan Gombak, 53000, Kuala Lumpur, Malaysia
Tel.: (60) 340215948
Web Site:
    https://www.ekovest.com.my
EKOVEST—(KLS)
Rev.: $200,103,750
Assets: $2,778,749,078
Liabilities: $2,070,399,870
Net Worth: $708,349,208
Earnings: ($30,552,885)
Fiscal Year-end: 06/30/22
Civil Engineering Services
N.A.I.C.S.: 541330
Thiam Wah Lim (Sec)

Subsidiaries:

Binawani Sdn Bhd   (1)

No 33-35 2nd Floor Wisma Ekovest Jalan Desa Gombak 6 Taman Sri Setapak, Off Jalan Gombak, 53000, Kuala Lumpur, Wilayah Persekutuan, Malaysia
Tel.: (60) 340215948
Emp.: 290
Civil Engineering Services
N.A.I.C.S.: 541330
Lee Ban Hock (Gen Mgr)

Milan Resources Sdn. Bhd.   (1)
Ground Floor Wisma Ecovest No 33-35 Jalan 6/50A Taman Sri Setapak, 53000, Kuala Lumpur, Malaysia
Tel.: (60) 340246115
Sales Range: $25-49.9 Million
Emp.: 100
Civil Engineering Services
N.A.I.C.S.: 541330

EKS FRANCE
12 Rue De Baldenheim, Wittisheim, 67820, Strasbourg, France
Tel.: (33) 388858400
Web Site: http://www.eks-france.fr
Sales Range: $25-49.9 Million
Emp.: 193
Controlling Device Mfr
N.A.I.C.S.: 334519
Susan Lau (Gen Mgr)

Subsidiaries:

EKS Asia Ltd.   (1)
Room A 21/F Gaylord Commercial Building 114-118 Lockhart Road, Wan Chai, Kowloon, China (Hong Kong)
Tel.: (852) 2785 3930
Controlling Device Distr
N.A.I.C.S.: 423690

EKS International (UK) Ltd.   (1)
Unit 3 The Motte House Howton, Hereford, HR2 0BG, Herefordshire, United Kingdom
Tel.: (44) 1981 240033
Controlling Device Distr
N.A.I.C.S.: 423690
Cathy Morgan (Mgr-Export)

EKS International Sweden AB   (1)
Anderstorpsvagen 24, 332 36, Gislaved, Sweden
Tel.: (46) 371 336 00
Controlling Device Distr
N.A.I.C.S.: 423690

EKSONS CORPORATION BERHAD
TB 4327 Block 31 2nd Floor Fajar Complex Jalan Haji Karim, 91000, Tawau, Sabah, Malaysia
Tel.: (60) 89757911
Web Site:
    https://www.eksons.com.my
EKSONS—(KLS)
Rev.: $22,471,165
Assets: $108,747,624
Liabilities: $10,127,726
Net Worth: $98,619,898
Earnings: ($3,619,637)
Fiscal Year-end: 03/31/22
Plywood Mfr
N.A.I.C.S.: 321212
Philip Hon Keong Chan (Mng Dir-Grp)

Subsidiaries:

Rajang Plywood (Sabah) Sdn. Bhd.   (1)
TB4327 2nd Floor Fajar Complex Jalan Haji Karim, PO Box 62105, 91031, Tawau, Sabah, Malaysia
Tel.: (60) 89757913
Plywood & Veneer Mfr
N.A.I.C.S.: 321211

Rajang Plywood Sawmill Sdn. Bhd.   (1)
Engkilo Land Lot No 1632 Block 11, Engkilo Land District Sungai Dasan, 96000, Sibu, Sarawak, Malaysia
Tel.: (60) 84320909
Plywood Mfr
N.A.I.C.S.: 321211

Eksons Corporation Berhad—(Continued)

Viva Paradise Sdn. Bhd.   (1)
B-13A-3 Megan Avenue II No 12 Jalan Yap
Kwan Seng, 50450, Kuala Lumpur, Malaysia
Tel.: (60) 321611216
Property Development Services
N.A.I.C.S.: 531390

EKSPORTFINANS ASA
Dronning Mauds Gate 15, 0250,
Oslo, Norway
Tel.: (47) 22012201
Web Site:
   http://www.eksportfinans.no
Year Founded: 1962
Rev.: $47,691,000
Assets: $1,655,899,650
Liabilities: $921,571,800
Net Worth: $734,327,850
Earnings: $12,036,300
Emp.: 22
Fiscal Year-end: 12/31/19
Financial Services for Export Industries
N.A.I.C.S.: 522220
Jens Olav Feiring (Exec VP-Legal)

Subsidiaries:

Eiendomsselskapet Dronning Mauds
gate 15 AS   (1)
Dronning Mauds gate 15, PO Box 1601,
0250, Oslo, Norway
Tel.: (47) 22836486
Financial Services
N.A.I.C.S.: 523150

EKTER S.A.
15 Nikis Str, 105 57, Athens, Greece
Tel.: (30) 2103259700
Web Site: https://www.ekter.gr
Year Founded: 1959
EKTER—(ATH)
Rev.: $24,858,117
Assets: $38,862,125
Liabilities: $18,830,163
Net Worth: $20,031,962
Earnings: $610,532
Emp.: 63
Fiscal Year-end: 12/31/22
Civil Engineering Contract Services
N.A.I.C.S.: 237990
Konstantinos Stoumpos (VP)

EKTTITAB HOLDING COMPANY S.A.K.C.
East - Behbehani Tower - 16th floor,
PO Box 2799, Safat, Kuwait, 13028,
Kuwait
Tel.: (965) 22087928
Web Site: https://www.ektettab.com
Year Founded: 1999
EKTTITAB—(KUW)
Rev.: $677,320
Assets: $49,371,091
Liabilities: $5,942,005
Net Worth: $43,429,085
Earnings: ($1,492,658)
Emp.: 10
Fiscal Year-end: 12/31/19
Investment Services; Owned 26.8%
by Al-Madina For Finance & Investment Co. S.A.K.C.
N.A.I.C.S.: 523999
Saleh Nasser Al Saleh (Vice Chm)

EKUITI NASIONAL BERHAD
Level 16 Surian Tower No 1 Jalan
PJU 7/3, Mutiara Damansara, Petaling Jaya, 47810, Malaysia
Tel.: (60) 3 7710 7171   MY
Web Site:
   http://www.ekuinas.com.my
Year Founded: 2009
Private Equity Fund Management
Services
N.A.I.C.S.: 523940

Yasir Arafat Abdul Kadir (CEO)

Subsidiaries:

Davex (Malaysia) Sdn. Bhd.   (1)
No 65 Jalan PJS 11/7, Bandar Sunway,
46150, Petaling Jaya, Selangor Darul Ehsan, Malaysia
Tel.: (60) 356364348
Web Site: http://www.davislighting.com
Lighting Products & Accessories Mfr &
Whslr
N.A.I.C.S.: 335132

Subsidiary (Non-US):

Davex Australia Pty Ltd   (2)
123 Gardens Drive, Willawong, Brisbane,
4110, QLD, Australia
Tel.: (61) 737128988
Web Site: http://www.davislighting.com
Lighting Fixture Distr
N.A.I.C.S.: 335131

Subsidiary (Domestic):

Davex Engineering (M) Sdn Bhd   (2)
Plot 32 Lorong Perusahaan Maju 8 Bukit
Tengah Industrial Park, Prai, 13600, Penang, Malaysia
Tel.: (60) 4 5070 580
Web Site: http://www.davislighting.com
Lighting Accessories Mfr
N.A.I.C.S.: 335139

Subsidiary (Non-US):

Davex Singapore Pte Ltd   (2)
Blk 512 Chai Chee Lane #02-01, Singapore, 469028, Singapore
Tel.: (65) 67452511
Web Site: http://www.davislighting.com
Lighting Fixture Mfr
N.A.I.C.S.: 335132

Orkim Sdn. Bhd.   (1)
Suite 22 02 22nd Floor Plaza Permata,
Jalan Kampar, 50400, Kuala Lumpur,
Malaysia   (95.5%)
Tel.: (60) 4042929
Web Site: http://www.orkim.com.my
Investment Holding Company; Clean Petroleum Product & Liquefied Petroleum Gas
Shipping Services
N.A.I.C.S.: 551112
Sharifuddin Al-Manaf (CEO)

EKWB D.O.O.
Pod Iipami 18, SI-1218, Komenda,
Slovenia
Tel.: (386) 18284998
Year Founded: 1999
Computer Product Mfr
N.A.I.C.S.: 334118

EKWIENOX LIMITED
160 Brompton Road, Knightsbridge,
London, SW3 1HW, United Kingdom
Tel.: (44) 20 7594 0660
Web Site: http://www.ekwienox.com
Holding Company
N.A.I.C.S.: 551112
Geoffrey Ronald Mayhill (Gen Counsel)

Subsidiaries:

ASPone Ltd   (1)
Lloyds Chambers 5th Floor Office N 1 Portsoken Street, London, E1 8BT, United Kingdom
Tel.: (44) 2038180900
Web Site: http://www.aspone.co.uk
Information Technology Consulting Services
N.A.I.C.S.: 541512
Bill Pinfold (Mgr-Comml)

STX Services   (1)
Praha City Centre Klimentska 46, 100 02,
Prague, Czech Republic
Tel.: (420) 236073601
Commodity Brokerage Services
N.A.I.C.S.: 523160

STX Services B.V.   (1)
Vijzelstraat 79, 1017 HG, Amsterdam, Netherlands
Tel.: (31) 205357770

Web Site: http://www.services.stxgroup.com
Commodity Brokerage Services
N.A.I.C.S.: 523160
Tim van der Noordt (CEO)

EL AHRAM FOR PACKING S.A.E.
2nd Industrial zone land No 6 Block
No 11, Borg El Arab El-Gidida, Alexandria, Egypt
Tel.: (20) 34626441
Web Site: https://www.ahramco.com
Year Founded: 1993
EPPK.CA—(EGX)
Sales Range: Less than $1 Million
Paper Packaging Product Mfr
N.A.I.C.S.: 322220

EL AL AIRLINES LTD.
Ben Gurion Airport, PO Box 41, Tel
Aviv, 7015001, Israel
Tel.: (972) 39716202
Web Site: https://www.elal.com
Year Founded: 1948
ELAL—(TAE)
Rev.: $623,075,000
Assets: $3,006,761,000
Liabilities: $3,262,858,000
Net Worth: ($256,097,000)
Earnings: ($531,037,000)
Fiscal Year-end: 12/31/20
Oil Transportation Services
N.A.I.C.S.: 481111
Shlomi Karako (VP-Maintenance &
Engrg)

Subsidiaries:

Borenstein Caterers, Inc.   (1)
179-29 150th Rd, Jamaica, NY
11434   (100%)
Tel.: (718) 656-3600
Web Site: http://www.bcelal.com
Sales Range: $25-49.9 Million
Emp.: 110
Airline Food Services
N.A.I.C.S.: 722320
Issac Sabig (Pres)

El Al Israel Airlines, Ltd.   (1)
100 Wall St 4th Fl, New York, NY
10005   (100%)
Tel.: (212) 852-0708
Web Site: http://www.elal.com
Sales Range: $75-99.9 Million
Emp.: 160
International Airline Services
N.A.I.C.S.: 481111
Tamar Mozes Borovitz (Vice Chm-Mgmt Bd)

Superstar Holidays Ltd   (1)
UK House 180 Oxford Street, London, W1D
1EL, United Kingdom   (100%)
Tel.: (44) 20 7957 4300
Web Site: http://www.superstar.co.uk
Sales Range: $25-49.9 Million
Emp.: 10
Travel Agency
N.A.I.C.S.: 561510

EL CORTE INGLES, S.A.
Hermosilla 112, 28009, Madrid, Spain
Tel.: (34) 901122122   ES
Web Site:
   http://www.elcorteingles.com
Year Founded: 1940
Sales Range: $10-24.9 Million
Emp.: 72,000
Department Store Supermarket &
Travel Agency Operator
N.A.I.C.S.: 455110
Juan Hermoso (Mgr-Mktg & Promo)

Subsidiaries:

Convenience Shops, S.A.   (1)
Hermosilla 112, Madrid, Spain
Tel.: (34) 901122122
Web Site:
   http://www.elcorteinglescorporativo.es
Extended Hour Department Stores
N.A.I.C.S.: 455110

Correduria de Seguros, S.A.   (1)

c/o COnde de Penalver 45, Madrid, 28006,
Spain
Tel.: (34) 901 116 146
Web Site: http://www.elcorteingles.es
Insurance Brokers
N.A.I.C.S.: 524298

El Corte Ingles Life, Pensions and
Insurance, S.A.   (1)
Hermosilla 112, 28009, Madrid, Spain
Tel.: (34) 901 116 821
Life Insurance & Pension Plans
N.A.I.C.S.: 524113

El Corte Ingles, S.A. Computers   (1)
Hermosilla 112, 28009, Madrid, Spain
Tel.: (34) 901122122
Web Site: http://www.elcorteingles.es
Computer Solutions, Products & Services
N.A.I.C.S.: 541519

Gespevesa, S.A.   (1)
Paseo de la Castellana, 257, Madrid, Spain
Tel.: (34) 901122122
Gasoline Stations with Convenience Stores
N.A.I.C.S.: 457110

Hipercor, S.A.   (1)
Hermosilla 112, 28009, Madrid, Spain
Tel.: (34) 901122122
Web Site: http://www.hipercor.es
Supermarket
N.A.I.C.S.: 445110

Investronica, S.A.   (1)
Ronda de Valdecarrizo, 7, 28760, Madrid,
Spain
Tel.: (34) 902354435
Computer Products & Service Whslr
N.A.I.C.S.: 423430

Sfera Joven, S.A.   (1)
Hermosilla, 112, Madrid, Spain
Tel.: (34) 901 122 122
Web Site: http://www.elcorteingles.es
Women's, Men's & Childrens' Apparel
Stores
N.A.I.C.S.: 458110

Supercor, S.A.   (1)
Hermosilla 112, 28009, Madrid, Spain
Tel.: (34) 901122
Web Site:
   http://www.elcorteinglescorporativo.es
Supermarket Management
N.A.I.C.S.: 445110

Telecor, S.A.   (1)
Hermosilla, 112, 28009, Madrid, Spain
Tel.: (34) 902141500
Web Site: http://www.telecor.es
Telecommunications Services Marketing
N.A.I.C.S.: 517810

Viajes El Corte Ingles, S.A.   (1)
Calle Hermosilla 112, 28009, Madrid, Spain
Tel.: (34) 913298100
Web Site: http://www.viajeselcorteingles.es
Travel Agency
N.A.I.C.S.: 561510

EL FORGE LTD
Door No 21C A R K Colony Eldams
Road, Alwarpet, Chennai, 600018,
India
Tel.: (91) 4424334010
Web Site: https://www.elforge.com
Year Founded: 1934
Rev.: $6,718,792
Assets: $14,484,757
Liabilities: $26,328,422
Net Worth: ($11,843,665)
Earnings: ($1,809,939)
Emp.: 174
Fiscal Year-end: 03/31/18
Automobile Parts Mfr
N.A.I.C.S.: 441330
V. Srikanth (Chm)

Subsidiaries:

El Forge Ltd - Appur Division   (1)
1A Sriperumbudur High Rd Appur village
Singaperumal Kovil, Kancheepuram, Chennai, 603 204, Tamil Nadu, India
Tel.: (91) 4447112500
Web Site: http://www.elforge.com
Emp.: 280

Machine Part Mfr
N.A.I.C.S.: 336330
K. R. Srihari (VP-Mktg)

El Forge Ltd - Hosur Division　**(1)**
Denkanikottai Rd, PO Box 11, Hosur, 635
109, Tamil Nadu, India
Tel.: (91) 4344222486
Web Site: http://www.elforge.com
Machine Part Mfr
N.A.I.C.S.: 336330

EL NASR CLOTHING & TEX-TILES CO.

407 Canal El Mahmoudiah St El Ha-
dara, PO Box 829, Alexandria, Egypt
Tel.: (20) 3 4286585
Web Site: http://www.kabo.com.eg
Year Founded: 1940
KABO.CA—(EGX)
Sales Range: Less than $1 Million
Apparels Mfr
N.A.I.C.S.: 315120
Amro Mohammed Al Sharnoubi (Chm
& Mng Dir)

EL NASR FOR MANUFACTUR-ING AGRICULTURAL CROPS S.A.E.

4 Maarouf St, Cairo, Egypt
Tel.: (20) 2 25798081
Web Site: http://www.elnasr-
dehydration.com
Year Founded: 1997
ELNA.CA—(EGX)
Sales Range: Less than $1 Million
Crop Farming Services
N.A.I.C.S.: 111998
Safwat Salah Alddin Ali Al Nehas
(Chm)

EL OBOUR REAL ESTATE IN-VESTMENT

84 Merghani St, Heliopolis, Cairo,
Egypt
Tel.: (20) 22906031
Web Site: http://www.elobouregy.com
Year Founded: 1994
OBRI.CA—(EGX)
Sales Range: Less than $1 Million
Real Estate Manangement Services
N.A.I.C.S.: 531390

EL ORO LTD.

East Wing Trafalgar Court, Saint Pe-
ter Port, GY1 3PP, Guernsey
Tel.: (44) 20 7581 2782　　**GY**
Web Site: http://www.eloro.co.uk
Rev.: $1,829,864
Assets: $79,779,272
Liabilities: $7,373,439
Net Worth: $72,405,834
Earnings: ($2,158,056)
Emp.: 5
Fiscal Year-end: 06/30/18
Holding Company
N.A.I.C.S.: 551112
C. Robin Woodbine Parish (Chm &
Mng Dir)

EL PUERTO DE LIVERPOOL S.A.B. DE C.V.

Av Prolongacion Vasco de Quiroga
4800 Torre 2, Piso 3 Santa Fe Cuaji-
malpa de Morelos, Mexico, Mexico
Tel.: (52) 5552629999　　**MX**
Web Site:
　http://www.liverpool.com.mx
Year Founded: 1847
LIVEPOL—(MEX)
Sales Range: $1-4.9 Billion
Emp.: 25,887
Retail & Department Stores; Shop-
ping Outlets & Real Estate Seller &
Leaser
N.A.I.C.S.: 455110
Max David (Chm)

EL RAN FURNITURE

2751 Transcanada Highway, Pointe-
Claire, H9R 1B4, QC, Canada
Tel.: (514) 630-5656
Web Site: http://www.elran.com
Year Founded: 1967
Rev.: $65,905,893
Emp.: 625
Furniture Mfr & Distr
N.A.I.C.S.: 337126
Sheldon Lubin (Pres)

EL SEWEDY ELECTRIC COM-PANY

Plot no 27 1st District 5th Settlement
New Cairo, PO Box 311, Cairo,
11853, Egypt
Tel.: (20) 2 27599700　　**EG**
Web Site:
　http://www.elsewedyelectric.com
Year Founded: 1984
Rev.: $2,901,709,693
Assets: $3,322,938,425
Liabilities: $2,246,451,401
Net Worth: $1,076,487,024
Earnings: $259,070,209
Emp.: 10,000
Fiscal Year-end: 12/31/19
Integrated Cables & Electrical Prod-
ucts Mfr
N.A.I.C.S.: 335929
Ahmed Ahmed Sadek El Sewedy
(Mng Dir)

Subsidiaries:

Arab Cables Company　　**(1)**
14 Baghdad Street, El-Korba Heliopolis,
Cairo, Egypt　　**(99.99%)**
Tel.: (20) 2 22909430
Web Site: http://www.elsewedycables.com
Mfr of Power Cables, Control Cables &
Overhead Transmission Lines
N.A.I.C.S.: 335921

Egytec Cables Company　　**(1)**
Plot No 27 1st District 5th Settlement, New
Cairo, Cairo, Egypt　　**(99.98%)**
Tel.: (20) 2 27599700
Web Site: http://www.elsewedyelectric.com
Cable Networks
N.A.I.C.S.: 516210

Jeddah Cable Company　　**(1)**
Indus City Phase 3, PO Box 31248, Jed-
dah, 21497, Saudi Arabia　　**(100%)**
Tel.: (966) 26360770
Web Site: http://www.jeddah-cable.com
Sales Range: $200-249.9 Million
Emp.: 800
Mfr of Cables
N.A.I.C.S.: 331420

Sudanese Egyptian Electric Industries
Company Ltd　　**(1)**
El Kwaitia Buildings - 4th tower 7th stage,
Khartoum, Sudan　　**(69.97%)**
Tel.: (249) 183764118
Sales Range: $25-49.9 Million
Emp.: 10
Copper Foundries
N.A.I.C.S.: 331529

United Metals Company　　**(1)**
Plot no 27 1st District 5th Settlement New
Cairo, Cairo, Egypt　　**(99.8%)**
Tel.: (20) 27599700
Web Site: http://www.elsewedyelectric.com
Current-Carrying Wiring Device Mfr
N.A.I.C.S.: 335931

EL SHAMS PYRAMIDS CO. FOR HOTELS & TOURISTIC PROJECTS S.A.E.

Le meridian Pyramids El Remaya
Square Pyramids, POB 25, Giza,
Egypt
Tel.: (20) 233773388
Web Site:
　https://www.elshamspyramids.com
Year Founded: 1967
SPHT.CA—(EGX)
Sales Range: Less than $1 Million

Hotel Operator
N.A.I.C.S.: 721110

EL WADI FOR INTERNA-TIONAL AND INVESTMENT DEVELOPMENT SAE

140 26th of July St, Zamalek, Cairo,
Egypt
Tel.: (20) 2 27360147
Web Site: http://www.elwadi-inv.com
Year Founded: 1998
ELWA.CA—(EGX)
Sales Range: Less than $1 Million
Tourism Investment Services
N.A.I.C.S.: 523999
Tariq Ahmad Abbas Nadim (Chm &
Mng Dir)

EL-NILE CO. FOR PHARMA-CEUTICALS & CHEMICAL IN-DUSTRIES

Al-Sawah square ElAmeria, Cairo,
Egypt
Tel.: (20) 226023684
Web Site:
　http://www.nilepharma.com.eg
Year Founded: 1962
NIPH.CA—(EGX)
Sales Range: Less than $1 Million
Pharmaceuticals Product Mfr
N.A.I.C.S.: 325412
Hesham Abd Elaziz Elsayed (Chm &
Mng Dir)

EL. D. MOUZAKIS S.A.

Kifissou 41, 122 42, Aegaleo, Attiki,
Greece
Tel.: (30) 2103490500
Web Site: https://www.mouzakis.gr
Year Founded: 1968
MOYZK—(ATH)
Sales Range: Less than $1 Million
Cotton Yarn Mfr
N.A.I.C.S.: 313110
Eleftheria E. Mouzaki (Chm)

Subsidiaries:

ELVIP s.r.o.　　**(1)**
Tovarni 302, 26712, Lodenice u Berouna,
Czech Republic
Tel.: (420) 311 671799
Yarn & Thread Mfr
N.A.I.C.S.: 313110

HELIOS S.A.　　**(1)**
Plagiari, Thessaloniki, 54110, Greece
Tel.: (30) 3920 23161
Women Apparel Mfr
N.A.I.C.S.: 315250

MACOPLEX S.A.　　**(1)**
Pavlou Mela 19 & Manis, Vyronas, 16233,
Greece
Tel.: (30) 210 7648220
Women Apparel Mfr & Distr
N.A.I.C.S.: 315250

Serres Ginning S.A.　　**(1)**
Gazoros, 62050, Serres, Greece
Tel.: (30) 240 42430 3
Yarn & Thread Mfr
N.A.I.C.S.: 313110

EL.EN. S.P.A.

Via Baldanzese 17, 50041, Calen-
zano, Florence, Italy
Tel.: (39) 0558826807　　**IT**
Web Site: https://www.elengroup.com
Year Founded: 1981
ELN—(ITA)
Rev.: $508,267,361
Assets: $577,730,575
Liabilities: $282,136,809
Net Worth: $295,593,765
Earnings: $24,878,181
Emp.: 269
Fiscal Year-end: 12/31/20

Developer of Laser Systems for
Medical, Industrial & Scientific Appli-
cations
N.A.I.C.S.: 333517
Andrea Cangioli (Mng Dir)

Subsidiaries:

AQL Srl　　**(1)**
Via Iv Novembre 116, Solbiate Olona, Italy
Tel.: (39) 0331375385
Web Site: http://www.quantasystem.com
Sales Range: $25-49.9 Million
Emp.: 80
Measuring & Controlling Device Mfr
N.A.I.C.S.: 334519

ASA Srl　　**(1)**
Via Galileo Galilei 23, 36057, Arcugnano,
Vicenza, Italy
Tel.: (39) 0444289200
Web Site: https://www.asalaser.com
Emp.: 100
Laser Treatment Services
N.A.I.C.S.: 621999

Asclepion Laser Technologies
GmbH　　**(1)**
Brusseler Str 10, 07747, Jena, Germany
Tel.: (49) 36417700100
Web Site: https://asclepion.com
Electrical Equipment & Component Mfr
N.A.I.C.S.: 335999
Danilo Leggieri (Mng Dir)

Cutlite Penta Srl　　**(1)**
Via Guimaraes 7/9, 59100, Prato, Italy
Tel.: (39) 0574874302
Web Site: https://www.cutlitepenta.com
Emp.: 50
Laser Cutting Machinery Mfr
N.A.I.C.S.: 333515

Cutlite do Brasil Ltda　　**(1)**
General Osorio 4584Shed 16-Intercom
116Salto Weissbach, Blumenau, Brazil
Tel.: (55) 4732210800
Web Site: https://www.cutlite.com.br
Laser Cutting Machinery Mfr
N.A.I.C.S.: 333517

Cynosure GmbH　　**(1)**
Robert Bosch Str 11a, 63225, Langen, Ger-
many
Tel.: (49) 61032011100
Web Site: http://cynosure.de
Sales Range: $25-49.9 Million
Emp.: 3
Medical Equipment & Supplies Mfr
N.A.I.C.S.: 339112

Cynosure KK　　**(1)**
1-4-25 Koraku, Bunkyo-ku Nikkei Sales
Building, Tokyo, 112-0004, Japan
Tel.: (81) 358443651
Web Site: http://www.cynosure.co.jp
Medical Equipment & Supplies Mfr
N.A.I.C.S.: 339112

Cynosure Korea Limited　　**(1)**
Samwon Building 6F 651 Eonju-ro
Nonhyeon-dong, Gangnam-gu, Seoul, Ko-
rea (South)
Tel.: (82) 2 517 6267
Web Site: http://cynosure.co.kr
Laser Treatment & Health Care Services
N.A.I.C.S.: 621999

Cynosure Sarl　　**(1)**
Energy Park Batiment 6 132-134 Avenue de
Verdun, 92400, Courbevoie, France
Tel.: (33) 146672250
Laser Systems Equipment Mfr
N.A.I.C.S.: 334510

Cynosure Spain S.L.　　**(1)**
Avda de Quitapesares 17Edificio Ferbocar
1 derecha, Villaviciosa De Odon, 28670,
Madrid, Spain
Tel.: (34) 917888700
Web Site: http://cynosure.es
Laser Treatment Services
N.A.I.C.S.: 621999

Cynosure UK Ltd　　**(1)**
The Old Barn Offices Lower Mount Farm,
Cookham, SL6 9EE, Berkshire, United
Kingdom
Tel.: (44) 1628522252
Web Site: http://www.cynosureuk.com

El.En. S.pA.—(Continued)

Sales Range: $25-49.9 Million
Emp.: 10
Medical Equipment Mfr
N.A.I.C.S.: 334510

Deka Japan Co. Ltd   **(1)**
2-21-37 Minami-Aoyama, Minato-ku, Tokyo,
107-0062, Japan
Tel.: (81) 357852133
Web Site: https://www.dekajapan.jp
Sales Range: $50-74.9 Million
Emp.: 10
Medical Equipment Sales & Maintenance
Services
N.A.I.C.S.: 423450

Deka Laser Technologies LLC   **(1)**
2720 Loker Ave V Ste C, Carlsbad, CA
92010
Tel.: (760) 918-0297
Web Site: http://www.dekalaser.com
Medical Dental & Hospital Equipment &
Supplies Whslr
N.A.I.C.S.: 423450
Ted Hurley *(Mgr-Ops)*

Deka Lasertechnologie GmbH   **(1)**
Prielmayerstrasse 3, 84048, Mainburg, Ger-
many
Tel.: (49) 8751846156
Web Site: http://www.dekalaser.de
Medical Laser Equipment Mfr
N.A.I.C.S.: 339112

Deka M.E.L.A. Srl   **(1)**
Via Baldanzese 17, 50041, Calenzano, Fl,
Italy
Tel.: (39) 0558874942
Web Site: http://www.dekalaser.com
Surgical & Medical Instrument Mfr
N.A.I.C.S.: 339112

Deka Medical Inc   **(1)**
665 3rd St, San Francisco, CA 94107-1926
Tel.: (877) 844-5552
Web Site: http://www.dekamedinc.com
Medical Laser Equipment Mfr
N.A.I.C.S.: 339112

Deka Technologies Laser Sarl   **(1)**
99 cours Gambetta, 69003, Lyon, France
Tel.: (33) 478627148
Web Site: http://www.deka.fr
Sales Range: $25-49.9 Million
Emp.: 8
Medical Laser Equipment Mfr
N.A.I.C.S.: 339112
Igor Pellissier *(Dir-Comml & Mktg)*

Esthelogue Srl   **(1)**
Via Baldanzese 33, 50041, Calenzano, Fl,
Italy
Tel.: (39) 0557766691
Web Site: https://www.esthelogue.com
Emp.: 15
Health Care Srvices
N.A.I.C.S.: 621999

Galli Giovanni & C. S.r.l.   **(1)**
Tel.: (39) 0331887356
Web Site: https://www.galligiovannisrl.it
Mechanical Component Mfr
N.A.I.C.S.: 333613

HL S.r.l.   **(1)**
Via G Cimabue 9, I-20148, Milan, Italy
Tel.: (39) 03484206070
Plastics Product Mfr
N.A.I.C.S.: 326199

Lasercut Inc.   **(1)**
69 N Branford Rd, Branford, CT 06405-
2810
Tel.: (203) 488-0031
Web Site: http://www.lasercutinc.com
Electronic Components Mfr
N.A.I.C.S.: 334419

Lasit Laser Deutschland GmbH   **(1)**
Im Stockacker 7, 78194, Emmendingen,
Germany
Tel.: (49) 74622692041
Web Site: https://www.lasitlaser.de
Laser Cutting Machinery Mfr
N.A.I.C.S.: 334413

Lasit Laser Iberica, S.L.   **(1)**
Calle Bari 55, Plataforma Logistica, 50197,
Zaragoza, Spain

Tel.: (34) 876268713
Web Site: https://www.lasit.es
Laser Cutting Machinery Mfr
N.A.I.C.S.: 334413

Lasit Laser Polska Sp. z o.o.   **(1)**
Street Fabryczna 34, 43100, Tychy, Poland
Tel.: (48) 327070223
Web Site: https://www.lasitlaser.pl
Laser Cutting Machinery Mfr
N.A.I.C.S.: 334413

Lasit Laser Uk Ltd.   **(1)**
Im Stockacker 7, 78194, Emmendingen,
Germany
Tel.: (49) 74622692041
Automation Machinery Mfr
N.A.I.C.S.: 333248

Lasit SpA   **(1)**
Via Solferino 4, 80058, Torre Annunziata,
Italy
Tel.: (39) 0815368855
Web Site: http://www.lasit.it
Sales Range: $25-49.9 Million
Emp.: 84
Laser Marking Systems Mfr
N.A.I.C.S.: 333248

Lasit USA Inc.   **(1)**
69 N Branford Rd, Branford, CT 06405
Tel.: (508) 528-2542
Web Site: https://www.lasitusa.com
Sales Range: $25-49.9 Million
Emp.: 58
Laser Treatment Devices Mfr
N.A.I.C.S.: 339112
Robin Barbero *(Gen Mgr)*

Ot-las Srl   **(1)**
Via Guimaraes 7/9, 59100, Prato, PO, Italy
Tel.: (39) 0557760183
Web Site: https://www.otlas.com
Laser Marking Systems Mfr
N.A.I.C.S.: 333248

Penta Laser Zhejiang Co., Ltd.   **(1)**
No 398 Haitong Road Binhai Park, Eco-
nomic and Technological Development
Zone, Wenzhou, Zhejiang, China
Tel.: (86) 2781736331
Web Site: https://en.pentalaser.com
Laser Cutting Machinery Mfr
N.A.I.C.S.: 333517

Quanta System S.p.A.   **(1)**
Via Acquedotto 109, 21017, Samarate, VA,
Italy
Tel.: (39) 0331376797
Web Site: https://www.quantasystem.com
Sales Range: $25-49.9 Million
Emp.: 57
Measuring & Controlling Device Mfr
N.A.I.C.S.: 334519

Raylife Srl   **(1)**
Via Dante Alighieri 8, 50041, Calenzano, Fl,
Italy
Tel.: (39) 055 7766696
Web Site: http://www.raylife.it
Laser Treatment & Health Care Services
N.A.I.C.S.: 621999

**Shenzhen KBF Laser Tech Co.,
Ltd.**   **(1)**
2nd Floor Building C Comlong Science and
Technology Park No 5, Guansheng 5th
Road Longhua District, Shenzhen, Guang-
dong Province, China
Tel.: (86) 18819029912
Web Site: https://www.kbflaser.com
Laser Cutting Machinery Mfr
N.A.I.C.S.: 333517

Sotras Srl   **(1)**
Via Donatello 13, Borgaro Torinese, 10071,
Turin, To, Italy
Tel.: (39) 0112622222
Web Site: http://www.sotras.com
Sales Range: $50-74.9 Million
Emp.: 110
Machine Tool & Metal Cutting Types Mfr
N.A.I.C.S.: 333517

Valfivre Italia Srl   **(1)**
Via Baldanzese 17, 50041, Calenzano, Fl,
Italy
Tel.: (39) 0558874942
Emp.: 200
Machine Tools Mfr
N.A.I.C.S.: 333517

Andrea Cangioli *(Gen Mgr)*

With Us Co., Ltd.   **(1)**
Sumitomo Real Estate Shiba Building 2 5F
1-5-9 Shiba, Minato-ku, Tokyo, 105-0014,
Japan
Tel.: (81) 662644146
Web Site: https://www.with-us.co.jp
Emp.: 918
Educational Support Services
N.A.I.C.S.: 611710

ELAF ISLAMIC BANK
Al-Karada Kahramana Sq, Baghdad,
Iraq
Tel.: (964) 7500127848
Web Site: https://eib.iq
Year Founded: 2001
BELF—(IRAQ)
Sales Range: Less than $1 Million
Banking Services
N.A.I.C.S.: 522110

ELAGHMORE GP LLP
36 Hamilton Terrace, Leamington
Spa, London, CV32 4LY, Warks,
United Kingdom
Tel.: (44) 1926 430077
Web Site: http://elaghmore.com
Year Founded: 2016
Holding Company
N.A.I.C.S.: 551112
Michael Rice *(Dir-Investment)*

Subsidiaries:

Orchard House Foods Limited   **(1)**
79 Manton Road Earlstrees Industrial Es-
tate, Corby, NN17 4JL, United Kingdom
Tel.: (44)1536274000
Web Site: http://www.ohf.co.uk
Fruit Food Product Mfr & Distr
N.A.I.C.S.: 311991

**ELAHI COTTON MILLS LIM-
ITED**
270-Sector I-9 Industrial Area, Islam-
abad, Pakistan
Tel.: (92) 514433451
Web Site:
https://www.elahicotton.com
Year Founded: 1970
ELCM—(PSX)
Rev.: $3,611,762
Assets: $1,226,387
Liabilities: $831,228
Net Worth: $395,159
Earnings: $5,144
Emp.: 275
Fiscal Year-end: 06/30/19
Yarn Mfr & Whslr
N.A.I.C.S.: 313110
Mahboob Elahi *(Chm)*

ELAINE SECURITIES PLC
Finsgate 5-7 Cranwood Street, Lon-
don, EC1V 9EE, United Kingdom
Tel.: (44) 2036376616
Financial Lending Services
N.A.I.C.S.: 522390

ELAN A.D.
Ljubise Miodragovica 11, 31300,
Prijepolje, Serbia
Tel.: (381) 33781350
Web Site: https://www.elan.rs
Year Founded: 1997
ELAN—(BEL)
Sales Range: $1-9.9 Million
Emp.: 101
Chemical Products Mfr
N.A.I.C.S.: 325199
Goran Sekulic *(Exec Dir & Dir)*

**ELAN CONSTRUCTION LIM-
ITED**
100 3639 27 St NE, Calgary, T1Y
5E4, AB, Canada
Tel.: (403) 291-1165

Web Site:
http://www.elanconstruction.com
Year Founded: 1978
Rev.: $69,643,671
Emp.: 70
Building Construction Services
N.A.I.C.S.: 236220
Trevor R. Poulsen *(VP)*

**ELAN MICROELECTRONIC
CORP.**
No 12 Innovation 1st Rd Hsinchu Sci-
ence Park, Hsin-chu, 300092, Taiwan
Tel.: (886) 35639977
Web Site: https://www.emc.com.tw
Year Founded: 1994
2458—(TAI)
Rev.: $394,339,728
Assets: $458,466,087
Liabilities: $156,716,891
Net Worth: $301,749,196
Earnings: $64,914,808
Emp.: 1,301
Fiscal Year-end: 12/31/23
IC Chip Mfr
N.A.I.C.S.: 334419
I-Hau Yeh *(Chm & Pres)*

Subsidiaries:

Avisonic Technology Corp.   **(1)**
300 7th Floor No 12 Chuangxin 1st Road,
Science Industrial Park, Hsinchu, 308, Tai-
wan
Tel.: (886) 35778077
Web Site: https://www.avisonic.com
Electronic Product Mfr & Distr
N.A.I.C.S.: 334412

**ELAN (H.K.) Microelectronic
Corp.**   **(1)**
Flat A 19/F World Tech Centre 95 How
Ming Street, Kwun Tong, Kowloon,
(Hong Kong)
Tel.: (852) 27233376
Integrated Circuit Mfr & Distr
N.A.I.C.S.: 334413

**ELAN Microelectronic Corp Shanghai
Ltd.**   **(1)**
Room 703 No 3 Lane88 Shengrong Road,
Pudong New Area, Shanghai, 201203,
China
Tel.: (86) 2150803866
Integrated Circuit Mfr & Distr
N.A.I.C.S.: 334413

**Elan (H.K.) Microelectronics
Corp.**   **(1)**
Flat A 19/F World Tech Centre 95 How
Ming Street Kwun Tong Kowloon, Kowloon,
China (Hong Kong)
Tel.: (852) 85227233376
Semiconductor Product Mfr
N.A.I.C.S.: 334413

**Elan Information Technology
Group.**   **(1)**
Tel.: (408) 366-8225
Motor Vehicle Support Services
N.A.I.C.S.: 561990

**Elan Microelectronics (Shanghai) Co.,
Ltd.**   **(1)**
Room 703 No 3 Lane88 Shengrong Road,
Pudong New Area, Shanghai, 201203,
China
Tel.: (86) 2150803866
Information Technology Services
N.A.I.C.S.: 541519

**Elan Microelectronics (Shenzhen)
Co., Ltd.**   **(1)**
8A Floor Microprofit Building Gaoxin South
Road 6 Shenzhen, Hi-Tech Industrial Park
South Area, Shenzhen, 518057, China
Tel.: (86) 75526010565
Information Technology Services
N.A.I.C.S.: 541519

**Eminent Electronic Technology,Co.,
Ltd.**   **(1)**
5th Floor No 12 Chuangxin 1st Road Sci-
ence Park, Hsinchu, Taiwan
Tel.: (886) 35639986
Web Site: https://www.eminent-tek.com

Integrated Circuit Mfr & Distr
N.A.I.C.S.: 334413

Metanoia Communications Inc.   **(1)**
3F No 12 Innovations Rd 1, Hsinchu, 300,
Taiwan
Tel.: (886) 35776123
Web Site: http://www.metanoia-comm.com
Chip Mfr & Distr
N.A.I.C.S.: 334413

ELANA AGRICULTURAL LAND FUND REIT

Sopharma Business Towers 5 La-
chezar Stanchev St Tower B Floor
12, 1756, Sofia, Bulgaria
Tel.: (359) 28100092
Web Site: https://agrocredit.elana.net
EALF—(BUL)
Sales Range: Less than $1 Million
Real Estate Investment Services
N.A.I.C.S.: 531390

ELANA AGROCREDIT

Sopharma Business Towers tower B
floor 12 Lachezar Stanchev No 5,
1756, Sofia, Bulgaria
Tel.: (359) 28100092
Web Site:
  https://www.agrocredit.elana.net
EAC—(BUL)
Sales Range: Less than $1 Million
Agricultural Machinery Mfr
N.A.I.C.S.: 333111
Gergana Kostadinova *(Exec Dir)*

ELANGO INDUSTRIES LIMITED

5 Ranganathan Gardens Anna Nagar,
Chennai, 600 040, India
Tel.: (91) 4442172116   In
Web Site:
  https://www.elangoindustries.com
Year Founded: 1989
513452—(BOM)
Rev.: $49,475
Assets: $659,410
Liabilities: $13,293
Net Worth: $646,117
Earnings: $5,820
Emp.: 6
Fiscal Year-end: 03/31/21
Eletric Power Generation Services
N.A.I.C.S.: 221118
Elangovan S. *(Chm & Mng Dir)*

ELANIX BIOTECHNOLOGIES AG

Hanauer Landstrasse 291 B, 60314,
Frankfurt am Main, Germany
Tel.: (49) 61171627677
Web Site:
  http://www.elanixbiotechnologies.ch
ELNJ—(DEU)
Sales Range: Less than $1 Million
Pharmaceutical Preparation Mfr
N.A.I.C.S.: 325412
Geofrey De Visscher *(CTO & Member-Mgmt Bd)*

ELANOR INVESTORS GROUP

Level 38 259 George St, Sydney,
2000, NSW, Australia
Tel.: (61) 292398400
Web Site:
  https://www.elanorinvestors.com
ENN—(ASX)
Rev.: $101,082,651
Assets: $520,671,922
Liabilities: $285,468,430
Net Worth: $235,203,491
Earnings: ($20,477,962)
Fiscal Year-end: 06/30/23
Investment & Funds Management
N.A.I.C.S.: 525990
Paul Bedbrook *(Chm)*

ELANOR RETAIL PROPERTY FUND

Level 38, 259 George st, Sydney,
2000, NSW, Australia
Tel.: (61) 292398400
Web Site:
  http://www.elanorinvestors.com
Year Founded: 2009
ERF—(ASX)
Rev.: $19,949,289
Assets: $188,885,756
Liabilities: $69,093,482
Net Worth: $119,792,274
Earnings: $5,483,622
Fiscal Year-end: 06/30/21
Investment Management Service
N.A.I.C.S.: 525990
Glenn Norman Willis *(CEO & Mng Dir)*

ELARG AGRICULTURAL LAND OPPORTUNITY FUND REIT

16 Nikola Vaptsarov Blvd, 1164, So-
fia, Bulgaria
Tel.: (359) 28681868
Web Site: http://www.elarg.bg
Sales Range: $1-9.9 Million
Agricultural Investment Services
N.A.I.C.S.: 523999
Andrey Kruglyikhin *(Chm)*

ELASTRON S.A.

St Ag Ioannou St John, 193 00, As-
propyrgos, Greece
Tel.: (30) 2105515000
Web Site: https://www.elastron.gr
Year Founded: 1958
ELSTR—(ATH)
Rev.: $195,320,460
Assets: $203,613,984
Liabilities: $109,396,968
Net Worth: $94,217,016
Earnings: $12,544,063
Emp.: 90
Fiscal Year-end: 12/31/22
Steel & Steel Products Trading Ser-
vices
N.A.I.C.S.: 423510
Andreas Kalpinis *(Founder & CEO)*

ELATE HOLDINGS LIMITED

Unit 1002 10/F Euro Trade Centre
13-14 Connaught Road and 21-23,
Des Voeux Road, Central, China
(Hong Kong)
Tel.: (852) 28656863   HK
Web Site:
  http://www.southseapetro.com.hk
0076—(HKG)
Rev.: $100,189,000
Assets: $409,142,000
Liabilities: $23,970,000
Net Worth: $385,172,000
Earnings: $572,000
Emp.: 344
Fiscal Year-end: 12/31/22
Crude Oil Extraction Services
N.A.I.C.S.: 211120
Zhong Yun Feng *(Mng Dir)*

Subsidiaries:

Axiom Manufacturing Services
Limited   **(1)**
Technology Park Newbridge, Newport,
NP11 5AN, United Kingdom
Tel.: (44) 149 524 2130
Web Site: https://www.axiom-ms.com
Electronic Components Mfr
N.A.I.C.S.: 334419
David Davies *(Mng Dir)*

Greeve Limited   **(1)**
Unit 17-17a, Severn Farm Industrial Estate
Welshpool, Powys, SY21 7DF, United King-
dom
Tel.: (44) 1938559558
Web Site: https://www.greeve.co.uk
Electronic Components Mfr

N.A.I.C.S.: 334419

ELATERAL LTD.

Elateral House Crosby Way, Farn-
ham, GU9 7XX, Surrey, United King-
dom
Tel.: (44) 1252740740
Web Site: http://www.elateral.com
Sales Range: $10-24.9 Million
Emp.: 50
Marketing Software Development
Services
N.A.I.C.S.: 513210
Paul Goater *(CEO)*

Subsidiaries:

Elateral, Inc.   **(1)**
1 Westbrook Corporate Ctr Ste 352,
Westchester, IL 60154
Tel.: (877) 914-0789
Web Site: http://www.elateral.com
Cloud Marketing Services
N.A.I.C.S.: 518210

ELAUT INTERNATIONAL N.V.

Passtraat 223, 9100, Saint-Niklaas,
Belgium
Tel.: (32) 37809480   BE
Web Site: http://www.elaut-
amusement.com
Year Founded: 1959
Sales Range: $25-49.9 Million
Emp.: 40
Holding Company; Coin-Operated
Amusement & Gaming Equipment
Mfr & Concessionaire
N.A.I.C.S.: 551112
Eric Verstraeten *(CEO & Mgr-Intl Sls)*

Subsidiaries:

ELAUT GERMANY GmbH   **(1)**
In der Wolfshecke 9, 64653, Lorsch, Ger-
many
Tel.: (49) 6251 855 449
Web Site: http://www.elaut.de
Coin Operated Game Machine Distr
N.A.I.C.S.: 423990

ELAUT Spain SL   **(1)**
Resina 37, 28021, Madrid, Spain
Tel.: (34) 93 582 01 53
Web Site: http://www.elaut.be
Emp.: 2
Coin Operated Game Machine Distr
N.A.I.C.S.: 423990
Eric Verstraeten *(Mng Dir)*

Elaut N.V.   **(1)**
Passtraat 223, 9100, Saint-Niklaas,
Belgium   **(100%)**
Tel.: (32) 37809480
Web Site: http://www.elaut.com
Emp.: 60
Coin-Operated Amusement & Gaming
Equipment Mfr & Concessionaire
N.A.I.C.S.: 339999
Eric Verstraeten *(CEO & Mgr-Intl Sls)*

Elaut USA, Inc.   **(1)**
1000 Towbin Ave, Lakewood, NJ 08701
Tel.: (732) 364-9900
Web Site: http://www.elautusa.com
Amusement Park Coin-Operated Equipment
Concessionaire
N.A.I.C.S.: 423990

Subsidiary (Domestic):

Coast to Coast Entertainment
LLC   **(2)**
1000 Towbin Ave, Lakewood, NJ 08701
Tel.: (732) 238-0096
Web Site:
  http://www.coastentertainment.com
Crane Style Coin-Operated Machines Mfr
N.A.I.C.S.: 333310
John Maurer *(Owner)*

ELB GROUP LIMITED

14 Atlas Road, Anderbolt, Boksburg,
1459, South Africa
Tel.: (27) 11772 1400   ZA
Web Site: http://www.elb.co.za

ELR—(JSE)
Rev.: $156,921,942
Assets: $128,137,686
Liabilities: $92,636,005
Net Worth: $35,501,682
Earnings: ($2,211,548)
Emp.: 412
Fiscal Year-end: 06/30/19
Engineered Products Mfr & Related
Services In Mining & Process Indus-
tries
N.A.I.C.S.: 541330
Anthony Garth Fletcher *(Chm)*

Subsidiaries:

ELB Capital Investments (Pty)
Limited   **(1)**
55-6th Rd Hyde Park, Sandton, Johannes-
burg, 2196, Gauteng, South Africa
Tel.: (27) 117721400
Web Site: http://www.masterguardfpsa.co.za
Sales Range: $50-74.9 Million
Emp.: 100
Investment Management Service
N.A.I.C.S.: 523999

ELB Engineering Services (Pty)
Limited   **(1)**
345 Rivonia Road, Sandton, Johannesburg,
2191, Sandton, South Africa
Tel.: (27) 117721400
Sales Range: $25-49.9 Million
Emp.: 110
Engineeering Services
N.A.I.C.S.: 541330
Stephen John Meijers *(CEO)*

ELB Equipment Holdings Limited   **(1)**
4 Parin Rd, Ravensmead, Cape Town,
7493, South Africa
Tel.: (27) 113060700
Web Site: http://www.elbequipment.com
Investment Holding Services
N.A.I.C.S.: 551112
Graham Jones *(Sec)*

ELB Equipment Limited   **(1)**
14 Atlas Road, Anderbolt, Boksburg, 1459,
Gauteng, South Africa
Tel.: (27) 113060700
Web Site: http://www.elbequipment.co.za
Sales Range: $75-99.9 Million
Emp.: 120
Construction & Mining Equipments Distr
N.A.I.C.S.: 423810
Steven Crabbe *(Mgr-Brits)*

Division (Domestic):

ELB Equipment Limited - Construc-
tion Equipment Division   **(2)**
14 Atlas Rd, Boksburg, 1508, Gauteng,
South Africa
Tel.: (27) 113060700
Web Site: http://www.elbquip.co.za
Construction Equipment Distr
N.A.I.C.S.: 532412
Peter Blunden *(Gen Mgr)*

ELB Equipment Limited - Earthmov-
ing Equipment Division   **(2)**
14 Atlas Road, Boksburg, 1459, South Af-
rica
Tel.: (27) 113060704
Web Site: http://www.elbequipment.com
Earth Moving Equipments Distr
N.A.I.C.S.: 532412
Peter Blunden *(CEO)*

ELB Equipment Limited - Mining &
Quarrying Equipment Division   **(2)**
14 Atlas Rd, Boksburg, 1459, Gauteng,
South Africa
Tel.: (27) 113060705
Web Site: http://www.elbequipment.com
Emp.: 250
Mining Equipment Distr
N.A.I.C.S.: 423810
Peter Blunden *(CEO)*

ELB Power Systems Limited   **(1)**
PO Box 565, Boksburg, 1460, Gauteng,
South Africa
Tel.: (27) 132351200
Electrical Contracting Services
N.A.I.C.S.: 238210

ELB Group Limited—(Continued)

ELBAR INDUSTRIAL LIMITED
Syston Lane, Grantham, NG32 2LY, Lincs, United Kingdom
Tel.: (44) 01476581300   UK
Sales Range: $50-74.9 Million
Emp.: 150
Automobile Parts Mfr
N.A.I.C.S.: 336390
Steve Harris (Mng Dir)

ELBI S.P.A.
Via Buccia, 9, 35010, Limena, Italy
Tel.: (39) 0498840677
Web Site: https://www.elbi.it
Year Founded: 1965
Electronics Mfr
N.A.I.C.S.: 334419

Subsidiaries:

Elbi of America Inc   (1)
525 Mccarty St, Houston, TX 77029
Tel.: (713) 674-2900
Web Site: http://www.elbi.net
Rev.: $3,000,000
Emp.: 17
Business to Business Electronic Markets
N.A.I.C.S.: 425120
Paolo Brustio (Pres)

Subsidiary (Domestic):

Nda Distributors, LLC   (2)
1281 Puerta Del Sol, San Clemente, CA 92673-6310
Tel.: (949) 492-4399
Web Site: http://ndaonline.net
Sales Range: $1-9.9 Million
Emp.: 26
Electronic Appliance Whslr
N.A.I.C.S.: 423620

ELBISCO HOLDING S.A.
21st km Marathonas Avenue, 19009, Pikermi, Greece
Tel.: (30) 2106039703
Web Site: http://www.elbisco.gr
Year Founded: 1987
Sales Range: $150-199.9 Million
Emp.: 1,240
Cereal Products Mfr
N.A.I.C.S.: 311211
Dimosthenis Ramandanis (CEO)

Subsidiaries:

ELBISCO INDUSTRIAL & COMMERCIAL S.A.   (1)
21 Km Marathonos Pikermi Attikee, Athens, 19009, Greece
Tel.: (30) 2106039712
Web Site: http://www.elbisco.com.gr
Baked Goods Distr
N.A.I.C.S.: 445291
Dimosthenis Ramandanis (Gen Mgr)

Zito Luks A.D.   (1)
Makedonsko Kosovska Brigada no 44, 1000, Skopje, North Macedonia
Tel.: (389) 25270000
Web Site: http://www.zitoluks.com.mk
Rev.: $19,929,318
Assets: $17,959,911
Liabilities: $9,414,913
Net Worth: $8,544,999
Earnings: ($178,758)
Emp.: 367
Fiscal Year-end: 12/31/2019
Bakery Products Mfr
N.A.I.Q.S.: 311812
Kiro Risteski (Member-Mgmt Bd & Dir-Production-Bakery & Mill)

ELBIT IMAGING LTD.
3 Shimshon Street, Petah Tiqwa, 4900102, Israel
Tel.: (972) 36086000   II
Web Site:
http://www.elbitimaging.com
EMITF—(NASDAQ)
Rev.: $17,474,676
Assets: $43,345,274

Liabilities: $92,166,475
Net Worth: ($48,821,201)
Earnings: ($39,498,105)
Emp.: 16
Fiscal Year-end: 12/31/19
Shopping Mall Construction & Management Services; Hotel Management Services; Medical Imaging Product Mfr
N.A.I.C.S.: 721110
Ron Hadassi (CEO)

Subsidiaries:

Elscint Limited   (1)
Kinert 8 Bneibrak, Tel Aviv, 67442, Israel
Tel.: (972) 36086020
Web Site: http://www.elbitimaging.com
Hotel Owner & Operator
N.A.I.C.S.: 721110

InSightec Ltd.   (1)
5 Nachum Heth St, POB 2059, Tirat Karmel, 39120, Israel   (52%)
Tel.: (972) 48131313
Web Site: http://www.insightec.com
Magnetic Resonance Imaging Equipment Mfr
N.A.I.C.S.: 334510
Kobi Vortman (Founder & Vice Chm)

ELBIT MEDICAL TECHNOLOGIES LTD.
POB 539, Haifa, 3100401, Israel
Tel.: (972) 772940000
Web Site: https://elbitsystems.com
Year Founded: 1992
EMTC.M—(TAE)
Assets: $7,414,000
Liabilities: $197,000
Net Worth: $7,217,000
Earnings: ($17,794,000)
Fiscal Year-end: 12/31/23
Surgical & Medical Instrument Manufacturing
N.A.I.C.S.: 339112
Tzipi Sinai (CFO)

ELBIT SYSTEMS LIMITED
Advanced Technology Center, Haifa, 3100401, Israel
Tel.: (972) 772940000
Web Site:
https://www.elbitsystems.com
Year Founded: 1966
ESLT—(NASDAQ)
Rev.: $5,511,549,000
Assets: $9,215,651,000
Liabilities: $6,457,976,000
Net Worth: $2,757,675,000
Earnings: $275,448,000
Emp.: 18,407
Fiscal Year-end: 12/31/22
N.A.I.C.S.: 332912
Michael Federmann (Chm)

Subsidiaries:

AEL Sistemas S.A.   (1)
Tel.: (55) 5121011200
Sales Range: $125-149.9 Million
Emp.: 300
Aircraft Electronic Products Mfr & Distr
N.A.I.C.S.: 336320
Sergio Goncalves Horta (Pres)

Elbit Security Systems Ltd.   (1)
Industrial Park Sderot, Sderot, 80100, Israel
Tel.: (972) 8 689 1691
Security Device Mfr
N.A.I.C.S.: 334290

Elbit Systems Cyclone Ltd.   (1)
Bar Lev Industrial Park, PO B 114, Karmiel, 20100, Israel
Tel.: (972) 49960700
Web Site: http://www.elbitsystems.com
Emp.: 600
Aircraft Components Mfr
N.A.I.C.S.: 336413

Elbit Systems EW and SIGINT - Elisra Ltd   (1)

48 Mivtza Kadesh St, Bene Beraq, 51230, Israel
Tel.: (972) 3 6175 111
Defence Electronic System Mfr
N.A.I.C.S.: 334419

Elbit Systems Electro-Optics ELOP Ltd.   (1)
Advanced Technology Park, PO B 1165, Rehovot, 76111, Israel
Tel.: (972) 9 9386211
Web Site: http://www.elbitsystems.com
Electro Optics Systems Mfr & Distr
N.A.I.C.S.: 334419

Elbit Systems Land and C4I Ltd.   (1)
2 Ha'Machshev St, Netanya, 42507, Israel
Tel.: (972) 9 8898080
Web Site: http://www.elbitsystems.com
Electronic Products Mfr & Whslr
N.A.I.C.S.: 334419

Elbit Systems of America, LLC   (1)
4700 Marine Creek Pkwy, Fort Worth, TX 76179   (100%)
Tel.: (817) 234-6600
Web Site: https://www.elbitamerica.com
Sales Range: $125-149.9 Million
Emp.: 500
Advanced Avionics & Electro-optic Instruments & Systems Mfr
N.A.I.C.S.: 334511
Raanan Horowitz (Pres & CEO)

Subsidiary (Domestic):

EFW Inc.   (2)
4700 Marine Creek Pkwy, Fort Worth, TX 76179
Tel.: (817) 234-6600
Electronic Products Mfr & Distr
N.A.I.C.S.: 334419

Harris Corp. - Night Vision   (2)
7635 Plantation Rd, Roanoke, VA 24019
Tel.: (540) 563-0371
Military Night Vision Equipment Designer, Mfr & Whslr
N.A.I.C.S.: 334511
Jim Thurston (Sr Mgr-HR)

Innovative Concepts, Inc.   (2)
8200 Greensboro Dr Ste 700, McLean, VA 22102
Tel.: (703) 893-2007
Rev.: $7,500,000
Emp.: 74
Communication Equipment Mfr
N.A.I.C.S.: 334220

International Enterprises, Inc.   (2)
108 Allen St, Talladega, AL 35160
Tel.: (256) 362-8562
Web Site: http://www.ieionline.com
Sales Range: $25-49.9 Million
Emp.: 100
Electronic Components Mfr
N.A.I.C.S.: 334419

KMC Systems Inc.   (2)
220 Daniel Webster Hwy, Merrimack, NH 03054-4898
Tel.: (817) 234-6600
Web Site: https://www.kmcsystems.com
Sales Range: $50-74.9 Million
Emp.: 200
Provider of Contract Services for the Ddevelopment & Manufacture of Electromechanical Instruments for the Medical Industry
N.A.I.C.S.: 334511
Derek Kane (VP-Ops)

Kollsman, Inc.   (2)
220 Daniel Webster Hwy, Merrimack, NH 03054-4840
Tel.: (603) 889-2500
Navigation Equipment Mfr
N.A.I.C.S.: 334511

M7 Aerospace LP   (2)
10823 NE Entrance Rd, San Antonio, TX 78216-6001
Tel.: (210) 824-9421
Web Site: http://www.m7aerospace.com
Aircrafts Designer & Mfr
N.A.I.C.S.: 423860

Real-Time Laboratories, LLC   (2)
990 S Rogers Cir Ste 5, Boca Raton, FL 33487

Tel.: (561) 988-8826
Web Site: http://www.real-timelabs.com
Aerospace Hydraulic Assembly Mfr
N.A.I.C.S.: 334511

Sparton Corporation   (2)
5612 Johnson Lake Rd, De Leon Springs, FL 32130
Tel.: (386) 985-4631
Web Site: http://www.sparton.com
Technical Products Mfr for Worldwide Commercial Electronics, Telecommunications & Governmental Customers
N.A.I.C.S.: 334418
William J. Toti (Pres & CEO)

Subsidiary (Domestic):

Aubrey Group, Inc.   (3)
6 Cromwell Ste 100, Irvine, CA 92618
Tel.: (949) 581-0188
Web Site: http://www.aubreygroup.com
Sales Range: $1-9.9 Million
Emp.: 44
Medical Device Mfr
N.A.I.C.S.: 339112
David Mishelevich (Chief Medical Officer & VP-Engrg)

Aydin Displays, Inc.   (3)
1 Riga Ln, Birdsboro, PA 19508
Tel.: (610) 404-7400
Web Site: http://www.aydindisplays.com
Sales Range: $50-74.9 Million
Emp.: 72
Whslr of Display Terminals; Color, Digital & Graphic, CAD Systems, High Resolution Monitors
N.A.I.C.S.: 334118

Beckwood Services, Inc.   (3)
27 Hale Spring Road, Plaistow, NH 03865
Tel.: (603) 382-3840
Web Site: http://www.sparton.com
Rev.: $8,372,000
Emp.: 52
Machine Shops
N.A.I.C.S.: 332710

Creonix, LLC   (3)
2145 63rd Ave E, Bradenton, FL 34203
Tel.: (941) 758-3340
Web Site: http://www.creonixllc.com
Sales Range: $10-24.9 Million
Emp.: 50
Printed Circuit Boards
N.A.I.C.S.: 334412

Real Time Enterprises, Inc.   (3)
160 Office Pkwy, Pittsford, NY 14534
Tel.: (585) 383-1290
Web Site: http://www.rtemd.com
Sales Range: $1-9.9 Million
Emp.: 30
Medical Device Software Services
N.A.I.C.S.: 513210

Sparton Beckwood, LLC   (3)
27 Hale Spring Rd, Plaistow, NH 03865
Tel.: (603) 382-3840
Web Site: http://www.spartan.com
Emp.: 35
Semiconductor Equipment Mfr
N.A.I.C.S.: 334413
Joseph Aarptnet (CEO)

Sparton Brooksville, LLC   (3)
30167 Power Line Rd, Brooksville, FL 34602
Tel.: (352) 799-6520
Semiconductor Equipment Mfr
N.A.I.C.S.: 334413

Sparton Electronics Florida, Inc.   (3)
5612 Johnson Lake Rd, De Leon Springs, FL 32130   (100%)
Tel.: (386) 985-4631
Web Site: http://www.sparton.com
Sales Range: $150-199.9 Million
Emp.: 500
Electronics Contract Manufacturing & Design Services for Printed Circuit Boards, Sonobuoys, Transducers, Hydrophones, Full System Build & Test Capabilities
N.A.I.C.S.: 334419

Sparton Medical Systems, Inc.   (3)
22740 Lunn Rd, Strongsville, OH 44149
Tel.: (440) 878-4630
Web Site:
http://www.spartonmedicalsystems.com

Sales Range: $100-124.9 Million
Emp.: 800
Electronic Components Mfr
N.A.I.C.S.: 334419
Kevin Webb (Mgr-Mktg & Sls)

Subsidiary (Domestic):

Sparton Medical Systems Colorado,
LLC   (4)
4300 Godding Hollow Pkwy, Frederick, CO
80504
Tel.: (303) 678-8585
Web Site: http://www.sparton.com
Electronic Components Mfr
N.A.I.C.S.: 334419

Sparton Onyx, LLC   (4)
2920 Kelly Ave, Watertown, SD 57201
Tel.: (605) 886-2519
Web Site: http://www.sparton.com
Emp.: 210
Medical Device Mfr
N.A.I.C.S.: 334510

Subsidiary (Domestic):

electronic Manufacturing Technology,
LLC   (3)
2602 McGaw Ave, Irvine, CA 92614
Tel.: (949) 855-6625
Web Site: http://www.emtllc2.com
Sales Range: $10-24.9 Million
Emp.: 100
Electromechanical Controls & Electronic
Assemblies Mfr
N.A.I.C.S.: 334417

Elbit Systems of Australia Pty
Ltd.   (1)
Level 2 650 Lorimer Street, Port Melbourne,
Melbourne, 3207, VIC, Australia
Tel.: (61) 386441600
Sales Range: $25-49.9 Million
Emp.: 45
Aircraft Electronic Parts Mfr
N.A.I.C.S.: 336413

Ferranti Technologies Limited   (1)
Cairo House, Waterhead, Oldham, OL4
3JA, Lancashire, United Kingdom
Tel.: (44) 161 624 0281
Web Site: http://www.ferranti-
technologies.co.uk
Aerospace & Defense Electro-Mechanical
Equipment Mfr
N.A.I.C.S.: 334419

Kinetics Ltd.   (1)
Golan Street Airport City, Ben-Gurion Air-
port, 79100, Israel
Tel.: (972) 39720200
Web Site: http://www.kinetics.co.il
Emp.: 150
Automobile Parts Mfr
N.A.I.C.S.: 336390

OIP N.V.   (1)
Westerring 21, 9700, Oudenaarde,
Belgium   (100%)
Tel.: (32) 55333811
Sales Range: $10-24.9 Million
Emp.: 100
Mfr of Holographics & Night Vision Equip-
ment
N.A.I.C.S.: 333310

Opgal - Optronics Industries Ltd.   (1)
Industrial Zone 5, PO Box 462, 20101,
Karmiel, Israel   (50.1%)
Tel.: (972) 49953902
Web Site: http://www.opgal.com
Electro Optic Systems & Thermal Imaging
Mfr
N.A.I.C.S.: 333310
Sylvie Dasculi (VP-Defense Projects)

Telefunken Radio Communications
Systems GmbH   (1)
Eberhard-Finckh-Strsse 55, 89075, Ulm,
Germany
Tel.: (49) 73115530
Web Site: https://elbitsystems-de.com
Emp.: 100
Radio Communication Equipment Mfr
N.A.I.C.S.: 334220

UAV ENGINES LTD.   (1)
Lynn Lane, Shenstone, Lichfield, WS14
0DT, United Kingdom

Tel.: (44) 1543481819
Web Site: https://www.uavenginesltd.co.uk
Wankel Engine Mfr
N.A.I.C.S.: 336412

ELBRIDGE INVESTMENTS (CYPRUS) LTD.
Office no 303 Vesper Floor Akaman-
tis Building 10 Egypt Street, 1097,
Nicosia, Cyprus
Tel.: (357) 22662682
Web Site: http://www.elbridge.com.cy
Year Founded: 2001
Investment Services
N.A.I.C.S.: 523940
Nataliya Chistova (Exec Dir)

ELBROOK CASH & CARRY LTD.
105 Bond Rd, Mitcham, CR4 3HG,
Surrey, United Kingdom
Tel.: (44) 208 646 6502
Web Site:
http://www.elbrookcashandcarry.com
Year Founded: 1984
Sales Range: $200-249.9 Million
Emp.: 66
Cash & Carry Management Services
N.A.I.C.S.: 522299
Fukhera Khalid (Mng Dir)

ELCA HOLDING SA
Av de la Harpe 22 24, PO Box 519,
1001, Lausanne, Switzerland
Tel.: (41) 21 613 21 11   CH
Web Site: http://www.elca.ch
Year Founded: 1968
Sales Range: $100-124.9 Million
Emp.: 700
IT Services
N.A.I.C.S.: 541690
Cedric Moret (CEO)

Subsidiaries:

ELCA Information Technology
Ltd.   (1)
Jean-Paul Tschumi Melody-2 Tower N1
Dien Bien Phu, Binh Thanh District, Ho Chi
Minh City, Vietnam
Tel.: (84) 838994740
Information Technology Consulting Services
N.A.I.C.S.: 541512

ELCID INVESTMENTS LIMITED
414 Shah Nahar Worli Industrial Es-
tate B Wing Dr E Moses Road, Worli,
Mumbai, 400018, Maharashtra, India
Tel.: (91) 2266625602
Web Site:
https://www.elcidinvestments.com
Year Founded: 1981
503681—(BOM)
Rev.: $14,706,169
Assets: $1,481,978,234
Liabilities: $94,425,650
Net Worth: $1,387,552,585
Earnings: $11,063,229
Emp.: 2
Fiscal Year-end: 03/31/21
Investment Management Service
N.A.I.C.S.: 523999
Varun Amar Vakil (Chm)

ELCO LIMITED
Electra Tower 50th Floor 98 Yigal
Alon St, Tel Aviv, 978914, Israel
Tel.: (972) 36939670   Il
Web Site: https://www.elco.co.il
Year Founded: 1949
ELCO—(TAE)
Rev.: $5,156,507,000
Assets: $6,611,316,000
Liabilities: $5,236,728,000
Net Worth: $1,374,588,000
Earnings: ($140,893,000)
Emp.: 21,400
Fiscal Year-end: 12/31/23

Capacitor, Resistor, Coil, Transformer
& Other Inductor Manufacturing
N.A.I.C.S.: 334416
Daniel Salkind (Co-Mng Dir)

Subsidiaries:

Elco Contracting & Services (1973)
Ltd.   (1)
4 Haomanut Kiryat Nordau, Netanya,
42504, Israel
Tel.: (972) 98630888
Electric Equipment Mfr
N.A.I.C.S.: 335999

Elco Holland B.V.   (1)
Parktoren 6th floor Van Heuven Goedhart-
laan 11a, Amstelveen, 1181 LE, Nether-
lands
Tel.: (31) 207105000
Consumer Electronics Distr
N.A.I.C.S.: 423620

Elco Landmark Residential Holdings
LLC   (1)
3505 Frontage Rd Ste 150, Tampa, FL
33607
Tel.: (813) 281-2907
Web Site:
http://www.landmarkresidential.com
Apartment Leasing Services
N.A.I.C.S.: 531110
Joseph G. Lubeck (CEO & Mng Partner)

Electra Consumer Products (1970)
Ltd.   (1)
St losf Sfir 1, Rishon le Zion, 75 704,
Israel   (70%)
Tel.: (972) 36939696
Web Site: http://www.electra-consumer.co.il
Rev.: $1,797,201,519
Assets: $1,936,476,279
Liabilities: $1,659,510,404
Net Worth: $276,965,875
Earnings: ($65,003,729)
Emp.: 7,100
Fiscal Year-end: 12/31/2023
Air-Conditioning & Warm Air Heating Equip-
ment & Commercial & Industrial Refrigera-
tion Equipment Manufacturing
N.A.I.C.S.: 333415
Zvika Shwimmer (CEO)

Subsidiary (Domestic):

Electra Air Conditioning Industries
2006 Limited   (2)
1 Sapir Yosef New I Z, Rishon le Zion,
75704, Israel
Tel.: (972) 732220400
Consumer Electronics Distr
N.A.I.C.S.: 423620

Electra Ltd.   (1)
2 Jabotinsky Street Amot Atrium Building,
Ramat Gan, 5250501, Israel   (69%)
Tel.: (972) 37535666
Web Site: https://www.electra.co.il
Rev.: $3,209,017,217
Assets: $3,082,903,115
Liabilities: $2,554,621,593
Net Worth: $528,281,522
Earnings: $67,208,453
Emp.: 13,500
Fiscal Year-end: 12/31/2023
Plumbing, Heating & Air-Conditioning Con-
tractors
N.A.I.C.S.: 238220
Itamar Deutscher (Pres & CEO)

Subsidiary (US):

Electra America, Inc.   (2)
1331 S Killian Dr Unit A, Lake Park, FL
33403
Tel.: (561) 408-3442
Real Estate Services
N.A.I.C.S.: 531390
Joe Lubeck (CEO)

Subsidiary (Domestic):

Robbins Property Associates,
LLC   (3)
4890 W Kennedy Blvd Ste 270, Tampa, FL
33609
Tel.: (813) 443-4656
Web Site:
https://www.robbinspropertyllc.com

Sales Range: $25-49.9 Million
Apartment Management & Investment
N.A.I.C.S.: 531311
Steve Robbins (Pres)

Subsidiary (Domestic):

Electra Real Estate Ltd.   (2)
98 Yigal Alon St, Tel Aviv, 67891,
Israel   (80%)
Tel.: (972) 37101700
Web Site: https://electra-re.com
Rev.: $17,056,000
Assets: $786,395,000
Liabilities: $459,571,000
Net Worth: $326,824,000
Earnings: ($62,981,000)
Emp.: 1,120
Fiscal Year-end: 12/31/2023
Other Activities Related to Real Estate
N.A.I.C.S.: 531390
Amir Yaniv (CEO)

FagorBrandt SAS   (1)
89-91 Bd Franklin Roosevelt CS 30002,
92854, Rueil-Malmaison, Cedex, France
Tel.: (33) 1 47 16 65 65
Web Site: http://www.fagorbrandt.com
Sales Range: $100-124.9 Million
Emp.: 300
Mfr of Large Household Appliances; Joint
Venture of Elco-Holdings Ltd.(90%) & Fagor
Electrodomesticos(10%)
N.A.I.C.S.: 335220

Iliasi Ltd.   (1)
21 Hamel Shaul Blvd, Tel Aviv, 64367, Is-
rael
Tel.: (972) 36939671
Construction Engineering Services
N.A.I.C.S.: 541330

ELCOM TECHNOLOGY COM-MUNICATIONS CORPORATION
ELCOM Building Duy Tan Street, Cau
Giay District, Hanoi, Vietnam
Tel.: (84) 2438359359
Web Site: https://www.elcom.com.vn
Year Founded: 1995
ELC—(HOSE)
Rev.: $40,379,708
Assets: $75,029,897
Liabilities: $27,561,028
Net Worth: $47,468,868
Earnings: $3,474,025
Fiscal Year-end: 12/31/23
Software Development Services
N.A.I.C.S.: 541511

Subsidiaries:

Elcom Plus JSC   (1)
Elcom building Lane 15 Duy Tan Street,
Dich Vong Hau Ward Cau Giay District, Ha-
noi, Vietnam
Tel.: (84) 983266266
Software Development Services
N.A.I.C.S.: 541511

ELCOM TECHNOLOGY PTY LTD
SE 7101 2 Locomotive Street,
Eveleigh, Sydney, 2015, NSW, Aus-
tralia
Tel.: (61) 2 8064 0999
Web Site: http://www.elcomcms.com
Year Founded: 1996
Sales Range: $10-24.9 Million
Software Publisher
N.A.I.C.S.: 513210
John Anstey (CEO)

ELCOMTEC CO., LTD
231 Dongbu-daero Jinwi-myeon,
Pyeongtaek, 451-862, Gyeonggi-do,
Korea (South)
Tel.: (82) 313726740
Web Site: http://www.elcomtec.co.kr
Year Founded: 1983
037950—(KRS)
Rev.: $31,909,294
Assets: $57,689,428
Liabilities: $6,794,948

Elcomtec Co., Ltd—(Continued)

Net Worth: $50,894,480
Earnings: $6,015,782
Emp.: 60
Fiscal Year-end: 12/31/22
Electronic Components Mfr
N.A.I.C.S.: 334419
Choong-seop Kim (CEO)

ELCORA ADVANCED MATERI-ALS CORP.

Suite 10 275 Rocky Lake Drive, Bed-ford, B4A 2T3, NS, Canada
Tel.: (902) 802-8847 NS
Web Site:
https://www.elcoracorp.com
Year Founded: 2011
ECORF—(OTCIQ)
Assets: $1,302,068
Liabilities: $1,414,207
Net Worth: ($112,139)
Earnings: ($750,279)
Fiscal Year-end: 03/31/22
Mineral Exploration & Mining Development
N.A.I.C.S.: 213115
Troy Grant (CEO)

Subsidiaries:

Graphene Corporation (1)
118 Pall Mall, London, SW1Y 5ED, United Kingdom
Tel.: (44) 2071010733
Web Site:
http://www.thegraphenecorporation.com
Grapheme Composite Product Mfr
N.A.I.C.S.: 335991

ELCOT CAPITAL MANAGE-MENT LIMITED

6 Queripel House, 1 Duke of York Square, London, SW3 4LY, United Kingdom
Tel.: (44) 207 881 0684
Web Site: http://www.elcotcapital.com
Emp.: 6
Investment Services
N.A.I.C.S.: 523940
Mike Vogel (Chm & CEO)

ELDAN ELECTRONIC CO. LTD.

Neopharm Building 6 Hashiloach St, PO Box 7641, Petah Tiqwa, 4951439, Israel
Tel.: (972) 39371102
Web Site: http://www.eldan.biz
Year Founded: 1960
Sales Range: $10-24.9 Million
Emp.: 500
Equipment Instrumentation & Service for Scientific Research & Medical Field
N.A.I.C.S.: 334516
Moshe Ben Simon (Sr VP & Mgr-Life Science Div)

Subsidiaries:

Cure Medical & Technical Supply Ltd (1)
4 Baltimore Street Kiriat Arie, 49130, Petah Tiqwa, Israel
Tel.: (972) 39265960
Medical Equipment Distr
N.A.I.C.S.: 423450
Tal Rabinovich (Gen Mgr)

ELDAN TRANSPORTATION LTD.

6 Yehezkel Koipman St, Tel Aviv, Israel
Tel.: (972) 35654500
Web Site: https://www.eldan.co.il
ELDT—(TAE)
Rev.: $433,121,143
Assets: $908,136,745
Liabilities: $700,383,744
Net Worth: $207,753,001

Earnings: $35,424,229
Fiscal Year-end: 12/31/23
Investment Management Service
N.A.I.C.S.: 523999

ELDAV INVESTMENT LTD.

Ahad Ha'Am St 48, Tel Aviv, 65202, Israel
Tel.: (972) 35644717
Web Site: https://www.eldav.co.il
ELDAV.M—(TAE)
Rev.: $398,950
Assets: $32,632,960
Liabilities: $188,712
Net Worth: $32,144,218
Earnings: ($639,315)
Fiscal Year-end: 12/31/23
Miscellaneous Financial Investment Activities
N.A.I.C.S.: 523999
Rony Sternbach (Founder & Chm)

ELDECO HOUSING & INDUS-TRIES LTD

Corporate Chamber-I 2nd Floor Vibhuti Khand Opp Mandi Parishad, Gomti Nagar, Lucknow, 226010, Uttar Pradesh, India
Tel.: (91) 5224039999
Web Site:
https://www.eldecogroup.com
ELDEHSG—(NSE)
Rev.: $16,863,174
Assets: $66,817,913
Liabilities: $25,509,406
Net Worth: $41,308,507
Earnings: $5,319,369
Emp.: 50
Fiscal Year-end: 03/31/23
Real Estate Development Services
N.A.I.C.S.: 531210
Pankaj Bajaj (Chm & Mng Dir)

ELDER PHARMACEUTICALS LTD.

Elder House C-9 Dalia Industrial Estate, Off Veera Desai Road Andheri W, Mumbai, 400 053, India
Tel.: (91) 2226730058 In
Web Site: http://www.elderindia.com
Year Founded: 1989
Sales Range: $150-199.9 Million
Emp.: 3,215
Pharmaceutical & Medical Device Mfr
N.A.I.C.S.: 325412

Subsidiaries:

NeutraHealth plc (1)
180 Lifford Lane Kings Norton, Birmingham, B30 3NU, West Midlands, United Kingdom
Tel.: (44) 845 5219 190
Web Site: http://www.neutrahealthplc.co.uk
Sales Range: $50-74.9 Million
Emp.: 243
Holding Company: Pharmaceuticals
N.A.I.C.S.: 551112
James S. McEuen (CEO)

Subsidiary (Domestic):

BioCare Limited (2)
Lakeside 180 Lifford Lane, Kings Norton, B30 3NU, W Midlands, United Kingdom
Tel.: (44) 1214333727
Web Site: http://www.biocare.co.uk
Sales Range: $25-49.9 Million
Emp.: 50
Pharmaceutical Product Whslr
N.A.I.C.S.: 456110
Ema Ellis (Mng Dir)

Brunel Healthcare Manufacturing Limited (2)
William Nadin Way, Swadlincote, DE11 0BB, Derbys, United Kingdom
Tel.: (44) 1283228300
Web Site: http://www.brunelhealthcare.co.uk
Sales Range: $125-149.9 Million
Nutraceutical Products Mfr & Sales
N.A.I.C.S.: 325412

Matt Woodings (Dir-Ops)

ELDER PROJECTS LIMITED

Plot No A-38/1 Patalganga Industrial Area Village Khaire, Raigad, Khalapur, 410 220, Maharashtra, India
Tel.: (91) 2192 250020
Web Site:
http://www.elderprojectsindia.com
Year Founded: 1985
Sales Range: $1-9.9 Million
Pharmaceutical Preparation Mfr
N.A.I.C.S.: 325412
Anuj Saxena (Mng Dir)

ELDERS LIMITED

80 Grenfell Street, Adelaide, 5000, SA, Australia
Tel.: (61) 884254000
Web Site: https://elders.com.au
FTZ—(DEU)
Rev.: $2,639,719,162
Assets: $1,547,700,735
Liabilities: $888,227,977
Net Worth: $659,472,758
Earnings: $130,259,962
Emp.: 2,649
Fiscal Year-end: 09/30/22
Offices of Other Holding Companies
N.A.I.C.S.: 551112
Mark Charles Allison (CEO & Mng Dir)

Subsidiaries:

Ace Ohlsson Pty Limited (1)
Stores 7 and 8 Warehouse J, Bringelly, Sydney, 2556, NSW, Australia
Tel.: (61) 297466640
Web Site: https://www.aceohlsson.com.au
Emp.: 40
Seed Distr
N.A.I.C.S.: 424910
Charlie Horder (Gen Mgr)

Acehill Investments Pty. Ltd. (1)
27 Currie Street, Adelaide, 5000, SA, Australia
Tel.: (61) 884254999
Investment Management Service
N.A.I.C.S.: 523940

Agricultural Land Management Limited (1)
Level 3 27 Currie Street, Adelaide, 5000, SA, Australia
Tel.: (61) 884255100
Web Site:
http://www.agriculturallandtrust.com
Investment Management Service
N.A.I.C.S.: 523940

Ashwick (Vic) No 102 Pty. Ltd. (1)
880 Greenfield St, Adelaide, 5000, SA, Australia
Tel.: (61) 884254000
Emp.: 100
Real Estate Property Holding Services
N.A.I.C.S.: 531210

Eastern Rural Pty Ltd (1)
44 Drayton Street, Dalby, 4405, QLD, Australia
Tel.: (61) 745936050
Web Site: https://easternrural.com.au
Real Estate Services
N.A.I.C.S.: 531210
Jennifer Ziesemer (Ops Mgr)

Elders Fine Foods (Shanghai) Company (1)
No T52-4 Building 1201 Gui Qiao Road, Shanghai Pilot Free Trade Zone, Shanghai, 201206, China
Tel.: (86) 213 872 0368
Web Site: https://www.elders.com.cn
Sales Range: $25-49.9 Million
Emp.: 60
Convenience Food Distr
N.A.I.C.S.: 445131

Elders Real Estate (QLD) Pty. Ltd. (1)
SW1 Level 1 52 Merivale Street, Brisbane,

4101, QLD, Australia
Tel.: (61) 738405522
Web Site:
http://ruralqld.eldersrealestate.com.au
Real Estate Manangement Services
N.A.I.C.S.: 531311

Elders Real Estate (Tasmania) Pty. Ltd. (1)
74-76 Elizabeth Street, Launceston, 7250, TAS, Australia
Tel.: (61) 363312022
Web Site:
https://www.eldersrealestate.com.au
Real Estate Manangement Services
N.A.I.C.S.: 531312

Elders Real Estate (WA) Pty. Ltd. (1)
Level 2 195 Great Eastern Highway, Belmont, 6104, WA, Australia
Tel.: (61) 894222301
Web Site:
https://regionalwa.eldersrealestate.com.au
Real Estate Manangement Services
N.A.I.C.S.: 531312

Elders Rural Services Australia Limited (1)
80 Grenfell Street, Adelaide, 5000, SA, Australia (100%)
Tel.: (61) 884254000
Farming Industry Support Services
N.A.I.C.S.: 561499

Elders Rural Services Limited (1)
80 Grenfell Street, Adelaide, 5000, SA, Australia
Tel.: (61) 884254000
Farming Industry Support Services
N.A.I.C.S.: 561499

Killara Feedlot Pty. Ltd. (1)
Pine Ridge Road, PO Box 348, Quirindi, 2343, NSW, Australia
Tel.: (61) 262471700
Sales Range: $10-24.9 Million
Emp.: 30
Cattle Feedlot Services
N.A.I.C.S.: 112112
Tony Fitzgerald (Mgr)

Primac Pty. Ltd. (1)
109 Melbourne Street, Brisbane, 4350, QLD, Australia
Tel.: (61) 738405506
Real Estate Property Development Services
N.A.I.C.S.: 531210

The Hunter River Company Pty Ltd (1)
74-76 Drummond Road, Shepparton, 3630, VIC, Australia
Tel.: (61) 358208400
Web Site: https://www.hunterriverco.com.au
Pharmaceuticals Product Mfr
N.A.I.C.S.: 325412

Therm Air Australia Pty. Ltd. (1)
27 Currie St, Adelaide, 5000, SA, Australia
Tel.: (61) 884254999
Motor Vehicle Parts Mfr
N.A.I.C.S.: 336390

Titan Ag Pty Ltd (1)
Princes Street Marina Suite 15 / 16 Princes Street, Newport, 2106, NSW, Australia
Tel.: (61) 299996655
Web Site: https://www.titanag.com.au
Agricultural Chemical Mfr & Distr
N.A.I.C.S.: 325320

ELDERSTREET INVESTMENTS LTD.

20 Garrick Street, London, WC2E 9BT, United Kingdom
Tel.: (44) 2078315088
Web Site: http://www.elderstreet.com
Year Founded: 1990
Sales Range: $25-49.9 Million
Emp.: 10
Investment Services
N.A.I.C.S.: 523940
Michael Edward Wilson Jackson (Founder & Chm)

ELDORADO GOLD CORPORA-TION

1188 Bentall 5550 Burrard Street,
Vancouver, V6C 2B5, BC, Canada
Tel.: (604) 687-4018   Ca
Web Site:
   https://www.eldoradogold.com
EGO—(NYSE)
Rev.: $871,984,000
Assets: $4,457,916,000
Liabilities: $1,257,048,000
Net Worth: $3,200,868,000
Earnings: ($426,853,000)
Emp.: 2,937
Fiscal Year-end: 12/31/22
Gold Ore Exploration & Mining
N.A.I.C.S.: 212220
Nicolae Stanca *(VP & Gen Mgr-Romania)*

Subsidiaries:

Brazauro Recursos Minerais SA   (1)
Avenida Olegario Maciel 1846, Santo Agostinho, Belo Horizonte, 30180-112, MG,
Brazil
Tel.: (55) 3121013750
Gold Mining Services
N.A.I.C.S.: 212220

Deva Gold SA   (1)
89 Principala Str, Certeju de Sus, 337190,
Romania
Tel.: (40) 254233680
Web Site: http://www.eldoradogold.com
Gold Mining Services
N.A.I.C.S.: 212220

Hellas Gold SA   (1)
23A Vas Sofias Ave and N Vamva 2, 10674,
Athens, Greece
Tel.: (30) 2146870000
Web Site: https://www.hellas-gold.com
Gold Mining Services
N.A.I.C.S.: 212220

QMX Gold Corporation   (1)
1876 3e avenue, PO Box 370, Val d'Or,   (17.36%)
QC, Canada
Tel.: (819) 825-3412
Web Site: http://www.qmxgold.ca
Assets: $31,262,505
Liabilities: $7,196,391
Net Worth: $24,066,114
Earnings: ($1,124,306)
Emp.: 131
Fiscal Year-end: 12/31/2019
Gold Exploration & Mining Services
N.A.I.C.S.: 212220
David M. Rigg *(Sr VP)*

Thrace Minerals SA   (1)
Vasilissis Sofias 23a and N Vamva 2,
10674, Athens, Greece
Tel.: (30) 2146870012
Web Site: https://www.tmsa.gr
Gold Mining Services
N.A.I.C.S.: 212220

Thracean Gold Mining SA   (1)
23A Vassilissis Sofias Road, 10674, Athens,
Greece
Tel.: (30) 2146870012
Web Site: http://www.tgm.gr
Gold Mining Services
N.A.I.C.S.: 212220

Tuprag Metal Madencilik Sanayi ve
Ticaret Limited Sirketi   (1)
Iran Caddesi Turan Emeksiz Sok No 1, Ankara, Turkiye   (100%)
Tel.: (90) 3124684536
Web Site: http://www.tuprag.com.tr
Sales Range: $50-74.9 Million
Emp.: 50
Gold Exploration
N.A.I.C.S.: 212220

Unamgen Mineracao e Metalurgia
S/A   (1)
Avenida Olegario Maciel 1846, Santo Agostinho, Belo Horizonte, 30180-112, Minas
Gerais, Brazil
Tel.: (55) 31 2101 3750
Web Site: http://www.eldoradogold.com
Sales Range: $50-74.9 Million
Emp.: 25
Gold Mining Services
N.A.I.C.S.: 212220

Subsidiary (Domestic):

Sao Bento Mineracao SA   (2)
Rua Dr Geraldo De Campos Moreira, Barao
de Cocais, Brazil
Tel.: (55) 31 3837 7180
Gold Mining Services
N.A.I.C.S.: 212220

**ELEC-TECH INTERNATIONAL
CO., LTD.**
No 1 Jinfeng Road, Tangjiawan Town,
Zhuhai, 519000, Guangdong, China
Tel.: (86) 7563390000
Web Site:
   https://www_en.electech.com.cn
Year Founded: 1996
002005—(SSE)
Rev.: $166,437,180
Assets: $376,124,580
Liabilities: $198,501,732
Net Worth: $177,622,848
Earnings: ($51,757,056)
Emp.: 15,000
Fiscal Year-end: 12/31/22.
Household Cooking Product Mfr
N.A.I.C.S.: 335220
Xuebin Ji *(Chm & Gen Mgr)*

ELECNOR, S.A.
Maestro Alonso 21-23 planta 3,
28028, Madrid, Spain
Tel.: (34) 917260076   ES
Web Site: https://www.elecnor.com
Year Founded: 1958
ENO—(VAL)
Rev.: $3,835,082,369
Assets: $4,035,875,044
Liabilities: $3,257,582,345
Net Worth: $778,292,700
Earnings: $174,469,036
Emp.: 21,431
Fiscal Year-end: 12/31/21
Engineering Services & Construction
& Development of Infrastructure Projects
N.A.I.C.S.: 541330
Jaime Real de Asua Arteche *(Chm)*

Subsidiaries:

Adhorna Prefabricacion, SA   (1)
Avda Iparraguirre 102 A, 48940, Leioa,
Vizcaya, Spain
Tel.: (34) 94 480 64 84
Web Site: http://www.adhorna.es
Prefabricated Concrete & Fiberglass Reinforced Polyester Products Mfr & Sales for
Infrastructure Engineering Projects
N.A.I.C.S.: 327390

Aplicaciones Tecnicas de la Energia,
S.L.   (1)
P Ind Juan Carlos I Av de la Foia 14, Almussafes, 46440, Valencia, Spain
Tel.: (34) 961 038 430
Web Site: http://www.atersa.com
Emp.: 200
Engineering Services & Solutions for Solar
Systems
N.A.I.C.S.: 541330

Area 3 Equipamiento y Diseno Interiorismo, S.L.U.   (1)
Maestro Alonso 21-23, 28028, Madrid,
Spain
Tel.: (34) 917260076
Web Site: http://area3.elecnor.com
Interior Design Consulting Services
N.A.I.C.S.: 541410

Audeca, S.L.U.   (1)
Albasanz 65 4 Planta Edificio America III,
28037, Madrid, Spain
Tel.: (34) 913514587
Web Site: http://www.audeca.es
Road Restoration Services
N.A.I.C.S.: 488490

Celeo Concesiones E Inversiones,
S.L.U.   (1)
Av General Peron 38 Edificio Master's I
Planta 14, 28020, Madrid, Spain
Tel.: (34) 917703117

Financial Investment Services
N.A.I.C.S.: 523999

Celeo Redes Brasil, S.A.   (1)
Rua do Passeio 38 - Torre II Sala 1201,
Centro, Rio de Janeiro, 20021-290, RJ,
Brazil
Tel.: (55) 2139619400
Financial Investment Services
N.A.I.C.S.: 523999

Celeo Redes Chile Ltda.   (1)
Av Apoquindo 4501 of 1902, Las Condes,
Santiago, Chile
Tel.: (56) 232024300
Financial Investment Services
N.A.I.C.S.: 523999

Celeo Redes, S.L.U.   (1)
Av General Peron 38 planta 14 Edificio
Master's I, 28020, Madrid, Spain
Tel.: (34) 917703117
Construction & Engineering Services
N.A.I.C.S.: 541330

Deimos Space, S.L.U.   (1)
Ronda de Poniente 19 Edificio Fiteni VI
Portal 2 Planta 2, Tres Cantos, 28760, Madrid, Spain
Tel.: (34) 918063450
Web Site: http://www.elecnor-deimos.com
Construction & Engineering Services
N.A.I.C.S.: 541330

Ehisa Construcciones y Obras,
S.A.U.   (1)
Aznar de Molina 15, 57002, Zaragoza,
Spain
Tel.: (34) 976204530
Web Site: http://www.ehisa.com
Construction & Engineering Services
N.A.I.C.S.: 541330

Elecdor, S.A.   (1)
Av Republica de El Salvador N35-40 edf
Athos Piso 1, Aptdo 17-11-6357, Quito,
Ecuador
Tel.: (593) 22264113
Web Site: http://www.elecnor.ec
Construction & Engineering Services
N.A.I.C.S.: 541330

Elecnor Chile, S.A.   (1)
Avda Apoquindo 4501 Oficinas 1104 1601
1602, Las Condes, Santiago, Chile
Tel.: (56) 224304100
Web Site: http://www.elecnor.cl
Construction & Engineering Services
N.A.I.C.S.: 541330

Elecnor Hawkeye, LLC   (1)
100 Marcus Blvd Ste 1, Hauppauge, NY
11788
Tel.: (631) 447-3100
Construction Services to Utilities
N.A.I.C.S.: 237990
Dave Ranta *(VP)*

Elecven Construcciones, S.A.   (1)
Av Luis Roche with 3rd transversal Edif Seguros Nuevo Mundo 10th Floor, Urbanization Altamira Municipality Chacao Miranda
State, 1060, Caracas, Venezuela
Tel.: (58) 2122642262
Web Site: http://elecven.com
Construction & Engineering Services
N.A.I.C.S.: 541330

Enerfin Enervento, S.L.U.   (1)
Paseo de la Castellana 141, Edificio Cuzco
IV 16 Pl, 28046, Madrid, Spain
Tel.: (34) 914170980
Construction & Engineering Services
N.A.I.C.S.: 541330

Enerfin Renewables, LLC   (1)
117 4th St N E, Charlottesville, VA 22902
Tel.: (434) 394-0035
Web Site:
   https://www.enerfinrenewables.com
Emp.: 20,000
Solar Renewable Energy Services
N.A.I.C.S.: 541690

IQA Operatios Group, Ltd.   (1)
2 Centura Court Nasmyth Place, Hillington,
Glasgow, G52 4PR, United Kingdom
Tel.: (44) 8454335256
Web Site: http://www.iqagroup.co.uk
Emp.: 250
Electrical Installation Services

N.A.I.C.S.: 238210
Antonio Henarejos *(Mng Dir)*

Luzy Energia Renovable, S.L.U.   (1)
Calle Arturo Soria No 383 floor 4a, 28033,
Madrid, Spain
Tel.: (34) 900120020
Web Site:
   https://www.luzyenergiarenovable.com
Wind Farm Renewable Energy Services
N.A.I.C.S.: 221115

Montajes Electricos Arranz, S.L.   (1)
Pol Ind La Noria sector 1-8 warehouse 1,
50730, Zaragoza, Spain
Tel.: (34) 976105667
Electrical Equipment Installation Services
N.A.I.C.S.: 238210

Omninstal Electricidade, S.A.   (1)
Rua Consiglieri Pedroso 71, Edificio E R/C
Esq, 2730-555, Queluz De Baixo, Portugal
Tel.: (351) 214342130
Web Site: http://www.omninstal.com
Construction & Engineering Services
N.A.I.C.S.: 541330

ELECO PLC
Dawson House 5 Jewry street Pegasus Way, Haddenham, London,
EC3N 2EX, United Kingdom
Tel.: (44) 2074228000
Web Site: https://www.elecosoft.com
ELCO—(AIM)
Rev.: $37,125,496
Assets: $53,251,136
Liabilities: $20,874,945
Net Worth: $32,376,191
Earnings: $3,707,933
Emp.: 245
Fiscal Year-end: 12/31/21
Software Services
N.A.I.C.S.: 423430
John Ketteley *(Co-Chm)*

Subsidiaries:

Consultec Group AB   (1)
Storgatan 40, Box 709, 931 31, Skelleftea,
Sweden
Tel.: (46) 101308700
Web Site: http://www.consultec.se
Sales Range: $25-49.9 Million
Emp.: 4
Construction Software Development Services
N.A.I.C.S.: 541511

Subsidiary (Domestic):

Consultec Byggprogram AB   (2)
Lasarettsvagen 35, Box 709, Skelleftea,
931 27, Sweden
Tel.: (46) 910 87878
Web Site: http://www.consultec.se
Construction Software Development Services
N.A.I.C.S.: 541511

Consultec System AB   (2)
Lasarettsvagen 35, Box 709, Skelleftea,
931 27, Sweden
Tel.: (46) 910 878 00
Web Site: http://www.consultec.se
Construction Software Development Services
N.A.I.C.S.: 541511

Downer Cladding Systems Ltd.   (1)
Oaksmere Business Park, Yaxley, Eye,
IP23 8BW, Suffolk, United Kingdom
Tel.: (44) 01379787215
Sales Range: $50-74.9 Million
Emp.: 10
Rain Screen Systems Mfr
N.A.I.C.S.: 423810

Eleco Bauprodukte   (1)
Erdingerstrasse 82 A, 85359, Munich, Germany
Tel.: (49) 8161879620
Web Site: http://www.eleco.de
Sales Range: $25-49.9 Million
Emp.: 8
Timber Engineering Services
N.A.I.C.S.: 321999

Eleco Software Limited   (1)

Eleco Plc—(Continued)

Haslemere Business Centre 1A Causeway High Street, Haslemere, GU27 2JZ, Surrey, United Kingdom
Tel.: (44) 1252267788
Web Site: http://www.3dhomesoftware.co.uk
Construction Industry Software Developer
N.A.I.C.S.: 513210

Subsidiary (Domestic):

Asta Development plc   (2)
Parkway House Haddenham Business Park, Haddenham, HP17 8LJ, United Kingdom
Tel.: (44) 3456461735
Web Site: https://www.elecosoft.com
Sales Range: $25-49.9 Million
Emp.: 40
Project Management Software Development Services
N.A.I.C.S.: 541511
Peter Thompson (Dir-Fin)

Subsidiary (Non-US):

Asta Development GmbH   (3)
Egon-Eiermann-Allee 8, 76187, Karlsruhe, Germany
Tel.: (49) 72195250
Web Site: https://www.elecosoft.de
Emp.: 12
Business Management Software Publisher
N.A.I.C.S.: 513210

Subsidiary (Non-US):

ESIGN Software GmbH   (2)
Warmbuchenstrasse 17, Niedersachsen, 30159, Hannover, Germany
Tel.: (49) 51185614340
Web Site: http://www.e-sign.com
Emp.: 80
Flooring Industry Software Developer
N.A.I.C.S.: 513210

Eleco Software GmbH   (2)
Kastanienwall 56, 31785, Hameln, Germany
Tel.: (49) 5151822390
Web Site: http://www.arcon-eleco.ge
Sales Range: $25-49.9 Million
Construction Software Developer
N.A.I.C.S.: 513210
Jurgen Kruger (CEO-Germany)

Eleco Timber Frame Ltd.   (1)
Goodlass Road, Speke, Liverpool, L24 9HJ, United Kingdom
Tel.: (44) 01514480055
Sales Range: $25-49.9 Million
Emp.: 50
Engineered Timber Products
N.A.I.C.S.: 321215

Elecosoft BV   (1)
Bennekomseweg 41, 6717 LL, Ede, Netherlands
Tel.: (31) 31 821 0004
Web Site: https://www.elecosoft.nl
Software Development Services
N.A.I.C.S.: 541511

Lubekonsult AB   (1)
Instrumentvagen 29, Hagersten, 126 53, Stockholm, Sweden
Tel.: (46) 8 18 63 40
Web Site: http://www.lube.se
Building Design Software Development Services
N.A.I.C.S.: 541511

Milbury Systems Limited   (1)
Milbury Precast Lydney Industrial Estate Harbour Road, Lydney, GL15 4EJ, Glos, United Kingdom
Tel.: (44) 1594847500
Web Site: http://www.milbury.com
Concrete Products Mfr
N.A.I.C.S.: 327390

Stramit Industries Ltd.   (1)
Oaksmere Business Park, Eye, IP23 8BW, Suffolk, United Kingdom
Tel.: (44) 01379783465
Sales Range: $25-49.9 Million
Emp.: 40
Partitioning Products Mfr
N.A.I.C.S.: 236210

Veeuze GmbH   (1)

Warmbuchenstrasse 15-17, 30159, Hannover, Germany
Tel.: (49) 51185614340
Web Site: https://veeuze.com
Software Development Services
N.A.I.C.S.: 541511

ELECOM CO., LTD.
9F Meiji Yasuda Life Osaka Midosuji Building 4-1-1, Chuo-ku, Osaka, 541-8765, Japan
Tel.: (81) 662291418
Web Site: https://www.elecom.co.jp
Year Founded: 1986
6750—(TKS)
Rev.: $728,217,090
Assets: $775,802,480
Liabilities: $204,374,590
Net Worth: $571,427,890
Earnings: $66,000,850
Emp.: 765
Fiscal Year-end: 03/31/24
Computer Products Mfr & Distr
N.A.I.C.S.: 334118
Koichi Iwami (Pres, Co-CEO & COO)

Subsidiaries:

DX Antenna Co., Ltd.   (1)
1-2-2 Murotani, Nishi-ku, Kobe, 651-2241, Hyogo, Japan
Tel.: (81) 78 996 3302
Web Site: https://www.dxantenna.co.jp
Electronics & Electric Equipment Mfr & Whslr
N.A.I.C.S.: 335999
Teruhiko Nagashiro (Pres)

ELECON ENGINEERING COMPANY LTD.
Anand Sojitra Road, Vallabh Vidyanagar, 388120, Anand, Gujarat, India
Tel.: (91) 2692 236513
Web Site: http://www.elecon.com
Sales Range: $200-249.9 Million
Emp.: 200
Material Handling Equipment Mfr
N.A.I.C.S.: 423860
Parthiv Parikh (Sec)

Subsidiaries:

Benzler Antriebstechnik G.m.b.H   (1)
Schwannstrasse 6, 40476, Dusseldorf, Germany
Tel.: (49) 8003504000
Gear Box Whslr
N.A.I.C.S.: 423840
Lutz Engelbracht (Acct Mgr)

Benzler TBA B.V.   (1)
Jachthavenweg 2, 5928 NT, Venlo, Netherlands
Tel.: (31) 773245900
Gear Box Whslr
N.A.I.C.S.: 423840

Benzler Transmission A.S.   (1)
Dalager 1, 2605, Brondby, Denmark
Tel.: (45) 36340300
Gear Box Whslr
N.A.I.C.S.: 423840
Henrik Andersen (Acct Mgr)

Benzlers Italia s.r.l.   (1)
Viale Romagna 7, 20090, Rozzano, Milan, Italy
Tel.: (39) 028243511
Gear Box Whslr
N.A.I.C.S.: 423840
Omar Monti (Acct Mgr)

Benzlers Systems AB   (1)
Porfyrgatan 7, 254 68, Helsingborg, Sweden
Tel.: (46) 42186800
Web Site: http://www.benzlers.com
Gear Box Whslr
N.A.I.C.S.: 423840

Elecon Middle East FZCO   (1)
Office No 5EA420 Dubai Airport Free Zone, PO Box 54754, Dubai, United Arab Emirates
Tel.: (971) 46091424425
Gear Box Whslr

N.A.I.C.S.: 423840

Elecon Singapore Pte. Limited   (1)
10 Anson Road 24-03 International Plaza, Singapore, 079903, Singapore
Tel.: (65) 62278258
Gear Box Whslr
N.A.I.C.S.: 423840

Elecon US Transmission Limited   (1)
1599 Lunt Ave, Elk Grove Village, IL 60007
Tel.: (847) 593-9910
Gear Box Whslr
N.A.I.C.S.: 423840

Oy Benzler AB   (1)
Vanha Talvitie 3C, 00580, Helsingfors, Finland
Tel.: (358) 93401716
Gear Box Whslr
N.A.I.C.S.: 423840
Heikki Arffman (Acct Mgr)

Radicon Transmission UK Limited   (1)
Unit J3 Lowfields Business Park Lowfields Way, Elland, HX5 9DA, West Yorkshire, United Kingdom
Tel.: (44) 1484465800
Web Site: http://www.radicon.com
Gear Box Whslr
N.A.I.C.S.: 423840
Thilo Scheuermann (Gen Mgr)

ELECSTER OYJ
Sontulantie 382, 37801, Akaa, Finland
Tel.: (358) 201541211
Web Site: https://www.elecster.fi
ELEAV—(HEL)
Rev.: $46,060,868
Assets: $56,809,842
Liabilities: $27,126,052
Net Worth: $29,683,790
Earnings: $1,271,314
Emp.: 225
Fiscal Year-end: 12/31/22
Packaging Machinery Mfr
N.A.I.C.S.: 333993

Subsidiaries:

Elecster (Tianjin) Aseptic Packaging Co. Ltd.   (1)
No 7 Dongting Third Street TEDA, Tianjin, 300457, China
Tel.: (86) 2225320566
Packaging Material Mfr & Distr
N.A.I.C.S.: 326111

OOO Finnpack   (1)
st Zhdanovskaya 45 A room 23-N, Saint Petersburg, 197198, Russia
Tel.: (7) 8122400675
Web Site: https://finnpack.ru
Packaging Machinery Mfr & Distr
N.A.I.C.S.: 333993

ELECTRA BATTERY MATERIALS CORPORATION
Suite 602 133 Richmond Street West, Toronto, M5H 2L3, ON, Canada
Tel.: (416) 900-3891   BC
Web Site: https://electrabmc.com
Year Founded: 2011
ELBM—(NASDAQ)
Assets: $109,841,176
Liabilities: $48,307,601
Net Worth: $61,533,575
Earnings: ($47,769,816)
Emp.: 23
Fiscal Year-end: 12/31/23
Cobalt Ore Exploration
N.A.I.C.S.: 213114
Trent Charles Arthur Mell (Pres & CEO)

ELECTRA STONE LTD.
Suite 330 470 Granville Street, Vancouver, V6C 1V5, BC, Canada
Tel.: (604) 620-8589   BC
Web Site:
http://www.electrastone.com

N.A.I.C.S.: 423840

Year Founded: 1978
Rev.: $622,834
Assets: $466,430
Liabilities: $1,125,558
Net Worth: ($659,128)
Earnings: ($2,206,543)
Emp.: 5
Fiscal Year-end: 12/31/16
Gold Mining Services
N.A.I.C.S.: 212220
Tony Hu (Pres & CEO)

Subsidiaries:

Suquash Coal Ltd   (1)
1165 Burdett Ave, Victoria, V8V 3H3, BC, Canada
Tel.: (250) 381-6768
Web Site: http://www.suquash.com
Sales Range: $50-74.9 Million
Coal Mining Services
N.A.I.C.S.: 212115
Jo Shearer (Mgr)

ELECTRAWINDS SE
51 Boulevard Grande Duchesse Charlotte, 1331, Luxembourg, Luxembourg
Tel.: (352) 27177522   LU
Web Site:
http://www.ewi.electrawinds.be
Year Founded: 2010
EWI—(DEU)
Renewable Energy Development Services
N.A.I.C.S.: 541690
Paul Desender (Chm)

ELECTRECORD SA
11 Corneliu Coposu Boulevard, Bucharest, Romania
Tel.: (40) 213134185
Web Site: http://www.electrecord.ro
Recorded Media Reproduction
N.A.I.C.S.: 541840

ELECTREON WIRELESS LTD.
Hadassah Neurim Youth Village, Beit Yanai, Netanya, 4029800, Israel
Tel.: (972) 765409944
Web Site: https://www.electreon.com
Year Founded: 2013
ELWS—(TAE)
Rev.: $6,381,268
Assets: $35,685,039
Liabilities: $5,079,154
Net Worth: $30,605,884
Earnings: ($20,951,236)
Fiscal Year-end: 12/31/23
Wireless Charging Station Operator
N.A.I.C.S.: 516110
Hanan Rumbak (Co-Founder)

ELECTRIC CONNECTOR TECHNOLOGY CO., LTD.
1-3/F 8-A Block Jinxiu Industrial Park Gongming Street, Xitian Community Guangming District, Shenzhen, 518100, Guangdong, China
Tel.: (86) 75581735688
Web Site: https://www.ectsz.com
Year Founded: 2006
300679—(CHIN)
Rev.: $440,729,087
Assets: $886,565,902
Liabilities: $227,636,361
Net Worth: $658,929,541
Earnings: $50,164,319
Emp.: 8,000
Fiscal Year-end: 12/31/23
Electrical Component Mfr & Distr
N.A.I.C.S.: 335313
Chen Yuxuan (Chm)

Subsidiaries:

Electric Connector Technology Co., Ltd. - Carlsbad Branch   (1)

2205 Faraday Ave Ste B, Carlsbad, CA
92008
Tel.: (760) 585-2262
Electronic Parts & Equipment Whslr
N.A.I.C.S.: 423690

ELECTRIC GUITAR PLC
52 Lime Street, London, EC3M 7AF,
Berkshire, United Kingdom
Tel.: (44) 1189570444   UK
Web Site:
    https://www.electricguitarplc.com
Year Founded: 2021
FI FG—(I SE)
Digital Marketing Services
N.A.I.C.S.: 541810
Gregory Kuenzel *(Fin Dir)*

**ELECTRIC KHODRO SHARGH
COMPANY**
5 Kmof Asian Highway, Mashhad,
9187381723, Iran
Tel.: (98) 511 6514390
Web Site: http://www.eks.co.ir
Year Founded: 1997
KHSH—(THE)
Sales Range: Less than $1 Million
Wire Harnesses Mfr
N.A.I.C.S.: 339999
Saeed Hadizadeh Zargar *(Chm)*

**ELECTRIC POWER DEVELOP-
MENT CO., LTD.**
6-15-1 Ginza, Chuo-ku, Tokyo, 104-
8165, Japan
Tel.: (81) 335462211   JP
Web Site: https://www.jpower.co.jp
Year Founded: 1952
EPWDF—(OTCIQ)
Rev.: $8,315,366,780
Assets: $22,975,071,050
Liabilities: $14,163,048,700
Net Worth: $8,812,022,350
Earnings: $514,086,140
Emp.: 1,862
Fiscal Year-end: 03/31/24
Electric Power Whslr
N.A.I.C.S.: 221122
Hiromi Minaminosono *(Exec VP)*

Subsidiaries:

Dream-Up Tomamae Co., Ltd.   (1)
14 Uehira Tomamaecho, Tomamae-Gun,
Hokkaido, 078-3712, Japan
Tel.: (81) 335469615
Web Site: http://www.Epower.co.jp
Sales Range: $500-549.9 Million
Emp.: 1,000
Eletric Power Generation Services
N.A.I.C.S.: 221118
Akira Mihoya *(Pres)*

EPDC CoalTech and Marine Co.,
Ltd.   (1)
Building 4-1-6 Nihonbashi Muromachi,
Chuo-ku, Tokyo, 103-0022, Japan
Tel.: (81) 352032506
Sales Range: $25-49.9 Million
Emp.: 100
Marine Transportation Services
N.A.I.C.S.: 483111

Fresh Water Miike Co., Ltd.   (1)
74 Aobamachi, Omuta, 836-0897, Fukuoka,
Japan
Tel.: (81) 944572003
Water Supply Services
N.A.I.C.S.: 221310

Green Power Kuzumaki Co., Ltd. (1)
20-18-4 Kuzumaki, Kuzumaki-Machi, Iwate,
028-5402, Japan
Tel.: (81) 195663611
Sales Range: $75-99.9 Million
Emp.: 4
Eletric Power Generation Services
N.A.I.C.S.: 221118

J-POWER AUSTRALIA PTY.
LTD.   (1)
Riverside Centre 123 Eagle Street, Bris-
bane, 4000, QLD, Australia

Tel.: (61) 732117055
Coal Mining Services
N.A.I.C.S.: 213113

J-POWER Holdings (Thailand) Co.,
Ltd.   (1)
388 Sukhumvit Rd, Klong Toei, Bangkok,
10110, Thailand
Tel.: (66) 22598258
Sales Range: $50-74.9 Million
Emp.: 30
Investment Management Service
N.A.I.C.S.: 523940

J-POWER USA Development Co.,
Ltd.   (1)
1900 E Golf Rd Ste 1030, Schaumburg, IL
60173-5076
Tel.: (847) 908-2800
Web Site: https://www.jpowerusa.com
Eletric Power Generation Services
N.A.I.C.S.: 221112
Mark Condon *(Pres & CEO)*

J-Power EnTech, Inc.   (1)
No 4 Daiwa NishiShimbashi bldg 3-2-1,
Nishi-shinbashi Minato-ku, Tokyo, 105-0003,
Japan   (100%)
Tel.: (81) 334347081
Web Site: http://www.jpower.co.jp
Engineering Relating to Equipment for Re-
moval of Atmospheric & Water Pollutants
N.A.I.C.S.: 541330
Masao Sotooka *(Pres)*

J-Power Resources Co., Ltd.   (1)
Ginza 6, 4-chome, Chuo-ku, Tokyo, 104-
8165, Japan   (100%)
Tel.: (81) 351481315
Web Site: http://www.eoc.co.jp
Sales Range: $50-74.9 Million
Emp.: 20
Coal Surveying, Prospecting, Development
& Related Investments
N.A.I.C.S.: 212115
Takayukishi Yamamura *(Pres)*

JP Business Service Corporation (1)
4-6-4 Tsukiji, Chuo-ku, Tokyo, 104-0045,
Japan
Tel.: (81) 342132019
Web Site: https://www.jpbs.co.jp
Emp.: 770
General Administration, Industrial Relations,
Business Development & Accounting Ser-
vices
N.A.I.C.S.: 561499
Okazaki Masamichi *(Pres)*

JP Design Co., Ltd.   (1)
2-16-2 Sotokanda 2nd DIC Building 4th and
5th floor, Chiyoda-ku, Tokyo, 101-0021,
Japan   (100%)
Tel.: (81) 332556211
Web Site: https://www.jpde.co.jp
Emp.: 130
Power Generation Plant Construction Ser-
vices
N.A.I.C.S.: 237130
Koichiro Kikuchi *(Mng Dir)*

JPHYTEC Co., Ltd.   (1)
4-2-5 Kudankita, Chiyoda-ku, Tokyo, 102-
0073, Japan
Tel.: (81) 332372323
Web Site: https://www.jphytec.co.jp
Sales Range: $450-499.9 Million
Emp.: 1,200
Power Plant Construction Services
N.A.I.C.S.: 237990
Kanji Shimada *(Pres & CEO)*

JPec Co., Ltd.   (1)
Tsukiji 5-6-4 Hama Mitsui Building, Chuo-
ku, Tokyo, 104-0045, Japan   (100%)
Tel.: (81) 335455252
Web Site: http://www.jpec.co.jp
Thermal & Nuclear Power Plant Construc-
tion & Engineering Services
N.A.I.C.S.: 237130
Masaya Shigenori *(Pres & Dir)*

Japan Network Engineering Co.,
Ltd.   (1)
6F Ginza 7-15-5, Chuo-ku, Tokyo, 104-
0061, Japan
Tel.: (81) 335241721
Web Site: http://www.jne.co.jp
Telecommunication Engineering Services
N.A.I.C.S.: 517810

KEC Corporation   (1)
1-37-6 Hakusan, Bunkyo-ku, Tokyo, Japan
Tel.: (81) 338168211
Web Site: http://www.kec.co.jp
Rev.: $173,552,589
Assets: $282,581,202
Liabilities: $157,263,618
Net Worth: $125,317,584
Earnings: $434,487
Emp.: 650
Fiscal Year-end: 12/31/2015
Installation & Maintenance of Electronic &
Communications Equipment
N.A.I.C.S.: 811310
Kiyotaka Muramatsu *(Pres & CEO)*

Kaihatsuhiryou Co., Ltd.   (1)
2-1-1 Tadanouminagahama, Takehara, 729-
2315, Hiroshima, Japan
Tel.: (81) 84 624 1601
Web Site: http://www.jpower.co.jp
Production & Sales of Fertilizers Containing
Coal Ash
N.A.I.C.S.: 325311

**ELECTRIC POWER TECHNOL-
OGY LIMITED**
11F No 149 Sec 2 Keelung Road,
Xinyi District, Taipei, 11054, Taiwan
Tel.: (886) 223773200
Web Site: http://www.eptech.tw
Year Founded: 1987
4529—(TPE)
Rev.: $90,830
Assets: $17,399,712
Liabilities: $844,105
Net Worth: $16,555,608
Earnings: $765,469
Fiscal Year-end: 12/31/22
Electric Tool Mfr & Distr
N.A.I.C.S.: 336320
Shen Wei *(Chm)*

ELECTRIC ROYALTIES LTD.
1400-1040 West Georgia Street, Van-
couver, V6E 4H1, BC, Canada
Tel.: (604) 639-9200
Web Site:
    https://www.electricroyalties.com
ELEC—(TSXV)
Rev.: $125,207
Assets: $13,598,882
Liabilities: $3,389,805
Net Worth: $10,209,077
Earnings: ($4,530,150)
Fiscal Year-end: 12/31/23
Business Consulting Services
N.A.I.C.S.: 522299
Marchand Snyman *(Chm)*

ELECTRIC TRACTOR CORP.
59 Hunter Road, Niagara-on-the-
Lake, L0S 1J0, ON, Canada
Tel.: (905) 467-5531   WY
Web Site:
    http://www.electrictractor.com
Year Founded: 2006
Emp.: 1
Electric Tractor Mfr
N.A.I.C.S.: 333924
Richard A. Zirger *(CEO)*

ELECTRIC WORD PLC
7th Floor 133 Whitechapel High
Street, London, E1 7QA, United King-
dom
Tel.: (44) 845 450 6414
Web Site:
    http://www.electricwordplc.com
Sales Range: $1-9.9 Million
Emp.: 94
Magazine, Book & Website Publisher
N.A.I.C.S.: 513120
Julian J. C. Turner *(CEO)*

Subsidiaries:

Optimus Professional Publishing
Limited   (1)
2nd Floor 5 Thomas More Square, London,

E1W 1YW, United Kingdom
Tel.: (44) 2079543433
Web Site: http://www.optimus-
education.com
Sales Range: $25-49.9 Million
Emp.: 100
Professional Publishing Services
N.A.I.C.S.: 513130
Julian Turner *(Mng Dir)*

ELECTRICA PUNTILLA SA
Orinoco 90 of 1102, Las Condes,
Santiago, Chile
Tel.: (56) 225922300
Web Site:
    https://www.electricapuntilla.cl
PUNTILLA—(SGO)
Sales Range: Less than $1 Million
Electronic Services
N.A.I.C.S.: 221118
Alejandro Gomez Vidal *(CEO)*

**ELECTRICAL CONSTRUCTION
& MAINTENANCE AUSTRALIA
PTY LTD**
1 Channel Close, Henderson, 6166,
WA, Australia
Tel.: (61) 894552944
Web Site: http://www.ecm.com.au
Year Founded: 1986
Sales Range: $75-99.9 Million
Emp.: 500
Electrical Contractor
N.A.I.C.S.: 238210
Michael Hender *(Chm)*

Subsidiaries:

Electrical Construction & Mainte-
nance Australia Pty Ltd - Fabrication
Facility   (1)
31 Office Road, Kwinana, 6167, WA, Aus-
tralia
Tel.: (61) 894395600
Web Site: http://www.ecm.com.au
Electrical Contractor
N.A.I.C.S.: 238210

**ELECTRICAL EQUIPMENT
JOINT STOCK COMPANY**
Bien Hoa Industrial Zone No 1 Road
No 09, An Binh ward, Bien Hoa,
Dong Nai, Vietnam
Tel.: (84) 613836139
Web Site: http://www.thibidi.com.vn
Year Founded: 1980
THI—(HNX)
Rev.: $65,972,424
Assets: $95,948,076
Liabilities: $39,915,119
Net Worth: $56,032,957
Earnings: $1,869,751
Fiscal Year-end: 12/31/22
Specialty Transformer Mfr
N.A.I.C.S.: 335311

**ELECTRICAL INDUSTRIES
COMPANY**
First Industrial City of Dammam, PO
Box 6033, Dammam, 31442, Saudi
Arabia
Tel.: (966) 1381000280
Web Site: https://www.eic.com.sa
1303—(SAU)
Rev.: $415,815,839
Assets: $505,566,095
Liabilities: $306,958,482
Net Worth: $198,607,613
Earnings: $53,607,635
Emp.: 1,529
Fiscal Year-end: 12/31/23
Electric Equipment Mfr
N.A.I.C.S.: 335999
Yousuef Ali Al-Quraishi *(Chm)*

Subsidiaries:

Pauwels Transformers N.V.   (1)
Antwerpsesteenweg 167, 2800, Mechelen,
Belgium

Electrical Industries Company—(Continued)

Tel.: (32) 15283333
Web Site: https://pauwels.com
High Voltage Power Transformer Mfr & Distr
N.A.I.C.S.: 335311

Saudi Power Transformer Company Limited (1)
2nd Industrial City, PO Box 6140, Dammam, 32232, Saudi Arabia
Tel.: (966) 138144622
Web Site: http://www.sptc.com.sa
Transformer Mfr
N.A.I.C.S.: 335311

Saudi Transformer Company Limited (1)
1st Industrial City, PO Box 5785, Dammam, 31432, Saudi Arabia
Tel.: (966) 38473020
Web Site: http://www.sauditransformers.com
Transformer Mfr
N.A.I.C.S.: 335311
Medhat Adham (Exec VP-Fin & IT)

Wahah Electric Supply Company of Saudi Arabia Limited (1)
First Industrial City, PO Box 2389, Dammam, 31451, Saudi Arabia
Tel.: (966) 38474242
Web Site: https://www.wescosa.com
Electrical Cables Mfr
N.A.I.C.S.: 335929
Tariq M. Al-Tahini (Pres & CEO)

ELECTRICITE DE FRANCE S.A.
22-30 avenue de Wagram, 75008, Paris, France
Tel.: (33) 140422222   FR
Web Site: https://www.edf.fr
Year Founded: 1946
EDF—(EUR)
Rev.: $154,227,839,739
Assets: $402,706,700,575
Liabilities: $331,927,365,098
Net Worth: $70,779,335,477
Earnings: $8,402,693,455
Emp.: 171,862
Fiscal Year-end: 12/31/23
Electric Power Distr
N.A.I.C.S.: 221122
Simone Rossi (Sr Exec VP)

Subsidiaries:

Citelum SA (1)
Tour Pacific-11-13 Cours Valmy, La Defense, 92977, Paris, Cedex, France
Tel.: (33) 14 197 7200
Web Site: https://www.citelum.fr
Emp.: 2,500
Engineeering Services
N.A.I.C.S.: 541330
Carmen Munoz-Dormoy (CEO)

Dalkia France S.C.A. (1)
37 avenue du Marechal de Lattre de Tassigny, 59350, Saint-Andre-Lez-Lille, France
Tel.: (33) 1 71 00 71 00
Web Site: http://www.dalkia.fr
Power Plant Construction Engineering Services
N.A.I.C.S.: 237130

Subsidiary (US):

Aegis Energy Services, LLC (2)
59 Jackson St, Holyoke, MA 01040
Tel.: (413) 536-1156
Web Site: https://aegischp.com
Miscellaneous Electrical Equipment & Component Mfr
N.A.I.C.S.: 335999

Groom Energy Solutions, LLC (2)
200 Cummings Ctr Ste 177C, Salem, MA 01915   (100%)
Tel.: (978) 306-6052
Web Site: http://www.groomenergy.com
Engineering & Installation Services
N.A.I.C.S.: 541330
Jon Guerster (CEO)

Dalkia NV-SA (1)
Quai Fernand Demets 52, 1070, Brussels, Belgium

Tel.: (32) 25251002
Web Site: http://www.dalkia.com
Sales Range: $1-4.9 Billion
Emp.: 1,500
Provider of Energy Management Services
N.A.I.C.S.: 221122

Dunkerque LNG SAS (1)
30 Rue Lhemitte Centre Tertiaire Des Trois Ponts, 59140, Dunkerque, France
Tel.: (33) 328241663
Web Site: http://dunkerquelng.com
Liquefied Natural Gas Terminal Operator
N.A.I.C.S.: 424710

EDF DEMASZ Partner Kft (1)
Kossuth Lajos Sugarut 64-66, Szeged, 6724, Hungary
Tel.: (36) 62565565
Sales Range: $250-299.9 Million
Emp.: 500
Electric Power Distribution Services
N.A.I.C.S.: 221122

Subsidiary (Domestic):

DEMASZ Primavill Halozatszerelo Ipari Kft (2)
Pulcz Utca 42, Szeged, 6724, Hungary
Tel.: (36) 62565565
Electric Power Distribution Services
N.A.I.C.S.: 221122
Istvan Korponai (Mng Dir)

EDF Energies Nouvelles S.A. (1)
Coeur Defense Tour B 100 esplanade du General de Gaulle, La Defense, 92932, Paris, France
Tel.: (33) 140902300
Web Site: http://www.edf-renouvelables.com
Sales Range: $400-449.9 Million
Emp.: 2,839
Electronic Services
N.A.I.C.S.: 221118

Subsidiary (US):

EDF Renewables, Inc. (2)
15445 Innovation Dr, San Diego, CA 92128-3432
Tel.: (760) 740-7022
Web Site: https://www.edf-re.com
Wind Energy Developer, Mfr & Operator
N.A.I.C.S.: 221122
Tristan Grimbert (Pres & CEO)

Subsidiary (Domestic):

OwnEnergy, Inc. (3)
45 Main St Ste 536, Brooklyn, NY 11201
Tel.: (646) 898-3690
Web Site: http://www.ownenergy.net
Wind Electric Power Generation Services
N.A.I.C.S.: 221115
Jacob Susman (CEO & VP)

Subsidiary (Domestic):

Futuren SA (2)
Coeur Defense 100 esplanade du General de Gaulle, 92, Paris, France   (90.5%)
Tel.: (33) 442904904
Web Site: http://www.futuren-group.com
Rev.: $553,121,437,880
Assets: $580,579,982,660
Liabilities: $70,646,189,220
Net Worth: $509,933,793,440
Earnings: ($6,287,567,140)
Fiscal Year-end: 12/31/2017
Electric Power Distr
N.A.I.C.S.: 221122
Alexandre Morin (CEO)

Subsidiary (Non-US):

CWP GmbH (3)
Werderstrasse 32, D-78132, Hornberg, Baden-Wurttemberg, Germany
Tel.: (49) 78339609924
Web Site: http://www.cw-products.de
Eletric Power Generation Services
N.A.I.C.S.: 221118

Subsidiary (Domestic):

Centrale Eolienne de Fonds de Fresnes (3)
4 rue Jules Ferry Immeuble le Regent, 34000, Montpellier, Herault, France
Tel.: (33) 467582270
Eletric Power Generation Services

N.A.I.C.S.: 221118

Ecoval Technology SAS (3)
360 Rue Louis de Broglie, Les Milles, 13100, Aix-en-Provence, Bouches-du-Rhone, France
Tel.: (33) 4 42 90 49 04
Eletric Power Generation Services
N.A.I.C.S.: 221118

Subsidiary (Non-US):

Maestrale Green Energy Srl (3)
Corso Magenta 32, Milan, 20123, Italy
Tel.: (39) 0280500422
Web Site: http://www.futuren-group.com
Eletric Power Generation Services
N.A.I.C.S.: 221118

Natenco Windpark 1 Management GmbH (3)
Feldscheide 2, Sehestedt, 24814, Schleswig-Holstein, Germany   (100%)
Tel.: (49) 711238600
Electric Power Distribution Services
N.A.I.C.S.: 221122

RheinEnergie Windkraft GmbH (3)
Ulmer Strasse 4, Leinfelden-Echterdingen, 70771, Baden-Wurttemberg, Germany
Tel.: (49) 711 238600
Web Site: http://www.theolia.de
Emp.: 35
Investment Management Service
N.A.I.C.S.: 523999
Shaahriar Sateni (Gen Mgr)

Subsidiary (Domestic):

Seres Environnement S.A.S (3)
360 rue Louis de Broglie, BP 20087, La Duranne, 13793, Aix-en-Provence, Bouches-du-Rhone, France
Tel.: (33) 442973737
Web Site: http://www.seres-france.com
Environmental Control System Mfr
N.A.I.C.S.: 334512
Didier Suchet (Pres)

Subsidiary (Non-US):

Solarkraftwerk Merzig Gmbh & Co. Kg (3)
Ulmer Strasse 4, 70771, Leinfelden-Echterdingen, Baden-Wurttemberg, Germany
Tel.: (49) 68618390130
Eletric Power Generation Services
N.A.I.C.S.: 221118

Theolia Naturenergien GmbH (3)
Ulmer Strasse 4, 70771, Leinfelden-Echterdingen, Baden-Wurttemberg, Germany
Tel.: (49) 711 238600
Web Site: http://www.theolia.de
Electric Power Distribution Services
N.A.I.C.S.: 221122
Alexandre Morin (Mng Dir)

WP GROSS WARNOW GmbH & Co. KG (3)
Wimemuehlenbert, Sehestedt, 24814, Schleswig-Holstein, Germany   (100%)
Tel.: (49) 435799770
Eletric Power Generation Services
N.A.I.C.S.: 221118
Torften Lezfen (CEO)

WP HECKELBERG-BREYDIN GmbH & Co. KG (3)
Ulmer Strasse 4, Leinfelden-Echterdingen, 70771, Baden-Wurttemberg, Germany   (100%)
Tel.: (49) 7112 38600
Electric Power Distribution Services
N.A.I.C.S.: 221122

EDF Energy plc (1)
40 Grosvenor Place, London, SW1X 7EN, United Kingdom
Tel.: (44) 2072429050
Web Site: http://www.edfenergy.com
Sales Range: $5-14.9 Billion
Emp.: 20,000
Gas & Electricity Supplier
N.A.I.C.S.: 221118

Subsidiary (Domestic):

EDF Energy UK Ltd (2)

40 Grosvenor Place Victoria, London, SW1X 7EN, United Kingdom
Tel.: (44) 2072429050
Web Site: http://www.edfenergy.com
Emp.: 600
Electric Power Generation & Distribution Services
N.A.I.C.S.: 221118

EDF Production UK Ltd (2)
1B Blake Mews, Richmond, TW9 3GA, United Kingdom
Tel.: (44) 208 439 8810
Electric Power Generation & Distribution Services
N.A.I.C.S.: 221118

EDF Holding SAS (1)
22-30 Ave De Wagram, Paris, 75008, France
Tel.: (33) 143692200
Web Site: http://www.edf.com
Electric Power Distribution Services
N.A.I.C.S.: 221122

EDF International SA (1)
20 Place De La Defense Cedex Courbevoie, 92050, Paris, France
Tel.: (33) 156651111
Web Site: http://www.edf.com
Holding Company
N.A.I.C.S.: 551112

EDF Polska Sp. z o.o. (1)
UI Nowy Swiat 19, 00-029, Warsaw, Poland
Tel.: (48) 22 55 65 300
Web Site: http://www.polska.edf.com
Electric Power Generation & Distribution Services
N.A.I.C.S.: 221118
Philippe Castanet (Pres)

EDF Trading Limited (1)
3rd Floor Cardinal Place 80 Victoria Street, London, SW1E 5JL, United Kingdom
Tel.: (44) 207 061 4000
Web Site: https://www.edftrading.com
Emp.: 800
Commodities Wholesale Trade Broker
N.A.I.C.S.: 425120
Philipp Bussenschutt (Chief Comml Officer-Origination & Bus Dev)

Subsidiary (US):

EDF Trading North America, LLC (2)
601 Travis St Ste 1700, Houston, TX 77002
Tel.: (281) 781-0333
Web Site: http://www.edftrading.com
Commodities Wholesale Trade Broker
N.A.I.C.S.: 425120
Mary Anne Brelinsky (Pres)

Edf Belgium SA (1)
Bd Bischoffsheim 11 (Boite 5), B-1000, Bruxelles, Belgium
Web Site: http://be.edf.com
Electricity And Other Forms of Energy
N.A.I.C.S.: 221118

Subsidiary (Domestic):

EDF Luminus nv (2)
Markiesstraat 1, 1000, Brussels, Belgium   (68.63%)
Tel.: (32) 22291950
Web Site: http://www.luminus.be
Emp.: 1,583
Hydroelectric Power Generation Services
N.A.I.C.S.: 221111
Gregoire Dallemagne (CEO)

Edison S.p.A. (1)
Foro Buonaparte 31, 20121, Milan, Italy
Tel.: (39) 0262221
Web Site: http://www.edison.it
Rev.: $12,078,022,380
Assets: $12,361,915,200
Liabilities: $4,931,589,620
Net Worth: $7,430,325,580
Earnings: ($195,251,180)
Emp.: 5,144
Fiscal Year-end: 12/31/2017
Electric Power Generation & Distr
N.A.I.C.S.: 221122
Lucrezia Geraci (Dir-Corp Affairs & Governance)

Joint Venture (Non-US):

ED INA d.o.o. (2)

Subiceva 29, 10000, Zagreb,
Croatia **(50%)**
Tel.: (385) 14552474
Sales Range: $50-74.9 Million
Emp.: 20
Research, Development & Hydrocarbon
Production
N.A.I.C.S.: 213112

Fahrenheit **(1)**
1 Rue Du Commerce, Cosne-Cours-sur-
Loire, 58200, France
Tel.: (33) 386266014
Electric Power Generation & Distribution
Services
N.A.I.C.S.: 221122

Fenice S.p.A. **(1)**
Via del Lavoro 1, 36078, Valdagno, VI, Italy
Tel.: (39) 044 542 4888
Web Site: https://www.fenice.it
Sales Range: $25-49.9 Million
Emp.: 100
Specialty Chemicals Mfr
N.A.I.C.S.: 325180
Giuseppe Pisi *(Founder & Pres)*

Framatome SAS **(1)**
1 Place Jean Millier, 92400, Courbevoie,
France **(75.5%)**
Tel.: (33) 13 496 1000
Web Site: https://www.framatome.com
Nuclear Power Plant Components Designer,
Mfr & Installer
N.A.I.C.S.: 332410
Bernard Fontana *(CEO)*

Subsidiary (US):

**BWXT Nuclear Operations Group,
Inc.** **(2)**
2016 Mount Athos Rd, Lynchburg, VA
24504
Tel.: (434) 522-6000
Web Site: https://www.bwxt.com
Nuclear Power Component Mfr & Nuclear
Power Support Services
N.A.I.C.S.: 332410

Subsidiary (Domestic):

BWXT Nuclear Energy, Inc. **(3)**
800 Main St, Lynchburg, VA 24504
Tel.: (434) 522-6800
Web Site: http://www.bwxt.com
Nuclear Power Generation Component Mfr
N.A.I.C.S.: 332410

Subsidiary (Domestic):

Intech, Inc. **(4)**
2802 Belle Arbor Ave, Chattanooga, TN
37406
Tel.: (423) 622-3700
Nuclear Facility Inspection & Maintenance
Services
N.A.I.C.S.: 541330

Subsidiary (Domestic):

Ivey-Cooper Services LLC **(5)**
11135 Dayton Pike, Soddy Daisy, TN 37379
Tel.: (423) 493-0097
Web Site: http://iveycooper.com
Sales Range: $25-49.9 Million
Emp.: 29
Testing Laboratories
N.A.I.C.S.: 541380
David Ivey *(CFO)*

Subsidiary (Domestic):

Nuclear Fuel Services, Inc. **(3)**
1205 Banner Hill Rd, Erwin, TN 37650
Tel.: (423) 743-9141
Web Site:
   http://www.nuclearfuelservices.com
Emp.: 1,200
Nuclear Reactor Fuel & Cores Production
N.A.I.C.S.: 325180
John A. Stewart *(Pres)*

Subsidiary (Non-US):

Framatome GmbH **(2)**
Paul-Gossen-Strasse 100, 91052, Erlangen,
Germany
Tel.: (49) 91319000
Web Site: http://www.framatome.com
Nuclear Power Plant Components Designer,
Mfr & Installer

N.A.I.C.S.: 237130
Carsten Haferkamp *(Mng Dir)*

Subsidiary (Domestic):

Advanced Nuclear Fuels GmbH **(3)**
Am Seitenkanal 1, 49811, Lingen, Germany
Tel.: (49) 5 919 1450
Web Site: https://www.framatome.com
Fuel Assemblies Mfr
N.A.I.C.S.: 237130

Subsidiary (US):

Framatome Inc. **(3)**
3315 Old Forest Rd, Lynchburg, VA 24501
Tel.: (434) 832-3000
Web Site: http://www.framatome.com
Nuclear Power Plant Equipment Mfr
N.A.I.C.S.: 334513
Robert Ryan *(Supervisor-Quality Ops)*

Subsidiary (Non-US):

Framatome Canada Ltd. **(3)**
925 Brock Road, Pickering, L1W 2X9, ON,
Canada
Tel.: (905) 421-2600
Web Site: http://www.framatome.co
Nuclear Power Services & Engineering Ser-
vices Provider
N.A.I.C.S.: 237130
Joel Drennan *(Sls Dir)*

Subsidiary (Non-US):

Framatome Spain SLU **(2)**
Iberia Mart I Pedro Teixeira 8, 28020, Ma-
drid, Spain
Tel.: (34) 917 02 71 63
Web Site: http://www.framatome.com
Nuclear Systems & Equipment
N.A.I.C.S.: 221113

Subsidiary (Domestic):

Intercontrole SA **(2)**
76 rue des Gemeaux, 94583, Rungis, Ce-
dex, France
Tel.: (33) 149 78 40 40
Web Site: http://www.intercontrole.com
Nuclear Power Plant Testing Services
N.A.I.C.S.: 541380

Valinox Nucleaire S.A.S. **(2)**
5 Avenue Du General Leclerc, BP 50, Mont-
bard, 21500, France
Tel.: (33) 3 80 89 82 82
Web Site: http://www.valinoxnucleaire.com
Stainless Steel Tube Mfr
N.A.I.C.S.: 331210
Carole le Couedic *(Pres)*

Imtech Engineering Services Ltd. **(1)**
Hooton Street Carlton Road, Nottingham,
NG3 5GL, United Kingdom
Tel.: (44) 1159505100
Web Site: http://www.imtech.co.uk
Electrical & Mechanical Engineering Ser-
vices
N.A.I.C.S.: 541330
Jacqui Cook *(Mgr-HR)*

Subsidiary (Non-US):

Axians Informa GmbH **(2)**
Horvelsinger Weg 17, 89081, Ulm, Ger-
many
Tel.: (49) 73115510
Web Site: http://www.axians-infoma.com
Software & System Solutions Developer &
Marketer
N.A.I.C.S.: 513210
Daniel Riss *(Mng Dir)*

Subsidiary (Non-US):

Axians AB **(3)**
Rsundavagen 4, 169 67, Stockholm, Swe-
den
Tel.: (46) 86725000
Web Site: http://www.axians.se
IT Outsourcing & Consulting Services
N.A.I.C.S.: 541519

Axians Infoma (Schweiz) A.G. **(3)**
Riedstrasse 1, 6343, Rotkreuz, Switzerland
Tel.: (41) 41 725 09 00
Web Site: http://www.axians-infoma.com
Information Technology Consulting Services
N.A.I.C.S.: 541512

Subsidiary (Non-US):

**Deutsche van Rietschoten & Houw-
ens GmbH** **(2)**
12 Junkerstrasse, Hannover, 30179,
Germany **(100%)**
Tel.: (49) 511372070
Web Site: http://www.rietschoten.de
Engineers of Power Transmission Equip-
ment; Importers & Distributors of Industrial
Disc Brakes & Clutches
N.A.I.C.S.: 541330
H. P. Ravens *(Mng Dir)*

**Elkon Elektrik Sanayi Ve Ticaret
AS** **(2)**
Rauf Orbay Cad No 39, Tuzla, 39944, Is-
tanbul, Turkiye
Tel.: (90) 216 3956695
Web Site: http://www.elkon-tr.com
Electronic Components Mfr
N.A.I.C.S.: 334419
Ertug Yasar *(Mng Dir)*

Groupe Techsol Marine Inc. **(2)**
4800 Rue Rideau, Quebec, G1P 4P4, QC,
Canada
Tel.: (418) 688-2230
Web Site: http://www.techsolmarine.com
Maritime Engineering Services
N.A.I.C.S.: 541330

Subsidiary (Domestic):

Imtech Aqua Ltd. **(2)**
G&H House Hooton Street Carlton Road,
Nottingham, NG3 5GL, England, United
Kingdom
Tel.: (44) 1159505100
Web Site: http://www.imtech.co.uk
Mechanical & Electrical Engineering Ser-
vices
N.A.I.C.S.: 541330

Subsidiary (Non-US):

Imtech Belgium N.V. **(2)**
Industrielaan 28, B-1070, Brussels,
Belgium **(100%)**
Tel.: (32) 25585911
Web Site: http://www.imtech.be
Emp.: 800
Building & Engineering Services
N.A.I.C.S.: 541330

Subsidiary (Domestic):

Imtech Maintenance N.V. **(3)**
Industrie Blvd 26, 1070, Anderlecht, Bel-
gium
Tel.: (32) 25585900
Web Site: http://www.imtech.be
Technical Maintenance & Management Mar-
ket
N.A.I.C.S.: 541330

Imtech Projects N.V. **(3)**
Frank Van Dyckelaan, 17 9140, Temse,
Belgium
Tel.: (32) 3 771 36 92
Web Site: http://www.imtech.be
Engineers/Contractors of Installations for
Airconditioning, Heating, Ventilation, Cool-
ing, Energy-Saving & Heat Pump Installa-
tions, Building-Automation & Installation
Control Systems
N.A.I.C.S.: 238210

Imtech Projects N.V. **(3)**
Hendrikstraat 120, Alken, 3570, East Flan-
ders, Belgium **(100%)**
Tel.: (32) 3 771 36 92
Web Site: http://www.imtech.be
Provider of Climatization Services
N.A.I.C.S.: 541330

Imtech Projects N.V. **(3)**
Koralenhoeve 9, 2160, Wommelgem,
Belgium **(100%)**
Tel.: (32) 33506161
Web Site: http://www.imtech.be
Provider or Engineering Services Including
Automation, Electrical & Data Networks
N.A.I.C.S.: 541330

Van Looy Group N.V. **(3)**
Noordersingel 19, 2140, Antwerp, Borger-
hout, Belgium **(100%)**
Tel.: (32) 32353508
Web Site: http://www.vanlooygroup.com

Design, Engineering, Project Management
& Turn-Key Construction of Automated Stor-
age, Distribution & Sorting Centres
N.A.I.C.S.: 541330
Paul Vanlooy *(Mng Dir)*

Subsidiary (Non-US):

Van Looy Group B.V. **(4)**
Lemelerberg 29, Alphen, 2402 ZN, Rijn,
Netherlands
Tel.: (31) 172 418 866
Design, Engineering, Project Management
& Turn-Key Construction of Automated Stor-
age, Distribution & Sorting Centres
N.A.I.C.S.: 541330

Subsidiary (Domestic):

**Imtech Engineering Services London
and South Ltd.** **(2)**
20 Kingston Road, Staines-Upon-Thames,
TW18 4LG, Middlesex, United Kingdom
Tel.: (44) 1784411600
Web Site: http://www.imtech.co.uk
Electrical Engineering Services
N.A.I.C.S.: 541330
Martin McEvoy *(Dir-Bus Improvement)*

Subsidiary (Non-US):

Imtech Hungary Kft **(2)**
Buda West Irodahaz Retkoz u 5, Budapest,
1118, Hungary
Tel.: (36) 1 248 21 35
Engineeering Services
N.A.I.C.S.: 541330

Subsidiary (Domestic):

Imtech Inviron Ltd. **(2)**
3100 Park Square Solihull Parkway Bir-
mingham Business Park, Birmingham, B37
7YN, United Kingdom
Tel.: (44) 121 779 7005
Web Site: http://www.imtech.co.uk
Electrical System Installation Services
N.A.I.C.S.: 238210

Subsidiary (Non-US):

Imtech Spain S.L. **(2)**
Avda. De Manoteras 44 Delta Norte Busi-
ness Park Building I 15, Rivas Vaciamadrid,
Madrid, 28050, Spain
Tel.: (34) 91 102 27 26
Web Site: http://www.imtech.es
Air Conditioning Installation & Construction
Services
N.A.I.C.S.: 238220

Imtech Technology Srl **(2)**
Bulevardul Marasti, Bucharest, Romania
Tel.: (40) 374 833 391
Electrical Automation System Installation
Services
N.A.I.C.S.: 238210

Subsidiary (Domestic):

Knowsley SK Ltd. **(2)**
Unit C Centrepoint Westinghouse Rd, Traf-
ford Park, Manchester, M17 1AE, United
Kingdom **(100%)**
Tel.: (44) 618727511
Web Site: http://www.knowsleysk.co.uk
Mfr & Distributor of Manual & Remote Con-
trolled Monitors, Pillar Hydrants, Fire Valves
& Nozzles; Designer & Manufacturer of Fire
Protection Systems
N.A.I.C.S.: 922160
Stephen Wood *(Mng Dir)*

Subsidiary (Non-US):

Koninklijke Dirkzwager B.V. **(2)**
Govert van Wijnkade 50, Maassluis, 3144
EG, Netherlands
Tel.: (31) 10 59 31 600
Web Site: http://www.dirkzwager.com
Maritime Shipping Information Services
N.A.I.C.S.: 519290

LVI Helin Oy **(2)**
Kinkomaantie 140, Saynatsalo, 40900, Jy-
vaskyla, Finland
Tel.: (358) 14 374 1300
Web Site: http://www.lvihelin.fi
Plumbing & Heating Equipment Installation
Services
N.A.I.C.S.: 238220

Electricite de France S.A.—(Continued)

Paul Wagner et Fils   **(2)**
9 Rue Robert Stumper, 2557, Luxembourg,
Luxembourg   **(60%)**
Tel.: (352) 4819911
Web Site: http://www.pwagner.lu
Electrical Installation Services
N.A.I.C.S.: 238210
Hegerl Guido (CEO)

Saval B.V.   **(2)**
Huifakkerstraat 22, 4815 PN, Breda, Noord
Braband, Netherlands   **(100%)**
Tel.: (31) 765487000
Web Site: http://www.saval.nl
Mfr & Distributor of Portable & Wheeled Ex-
tinguishers, Hose Reels, Fire Hoses &
Foam Making Equipment; Designer &
Manufacturer of Fire Protection & Detection
Systems
N.A.I.C.S.: 922160
Fulco De Vries (Dir-BU High Value Asset
Protection)

Subsidiary (Non-US):

Saval N.V.   **(3)**
Oostkaai 25-6, Merksem, 2170,
Belgium   **(100%)**
Tel.: (32) 36452510
Web Site: http://www.saval.be
Distr of Portable & Wheeled Fire Fighting
Equipment, Fire Detection Systems & Extin-
guishing Systems; Sales Office for Fire
Fighting Trucks
N.A.I.C.S.: 922160

Subsidiary (Non-US):

Ventilex B.V.   **(2)**
Europaweg 8, 8181 BH, Heerde,
Netherlands   **(100%)**
Tel.: (31) 578698200
Web Site: http://www.ventilex.com
Food Product Machinery Mfr
N.A.I.C.S.: 333241
Herman Vis (Mng Dir)

WPS Parking Systems BV   **(2)**
Hoevenweg 11, 5052 AW, Eindhoven,
Netherlands   **(100%)**
Tel.: (31) 402509111
Web Site:
  http://www.wpsparkingsolutions.com
Mfr & Supplier of Automated Parking Sys-
tems
N.A.I.C.S.: 238290

Mekong Energy Company Ltd.   **(1)**
Unit 01 Floor 20 Bitexco Financial Tower,
District 1, Ho Chi Minh City, Vietnam
Tel.: (84) 83 821 9390
Web Site: https://www.mekong-energy.com
Electricity Power Distribution Services
N.A.I.C.S.: 221122

Oceane Re SA   **(1)**
534 Rue de Neudorf, 2220, Luxembourg,
Luxembourg
Tel.: (352) 26684575
Electric Power Distribution Services
N.A.I.C.S.: 221122

PEI Group, LLC   **(1)**
1916 Hwy 22 W, Madisonville, LA 70447
Tel.: (985) 898-6343
Web Site: http://peigroup.com
Mfr & Technical Products Distr
N.A.I.C.S.: 811310

**Porterbrook Leasing Company
Limited**   **(1)**
Ivatt House 7 The Point Pinnacle Way,
Pride Park, Derby, DE24 8ZS, United King-
dom
Tel.: (44) 1332285050
Web Site: https://www.porterbrook.co.uk
Rolling Stock Leasing Services
N.A.I.C.S.: 532411

Protertia FM   **(1)**
Tour Edf 20 Pl De la Defense, Puteaux,
92800, France
Tel.: (33) 141454201
Web Site: http://www.protertia.com
Sales Range: $10-24.9 Million
Emp.: 50
Facilities Management Services
N.A.I.C.S.: 561210

**Societe pour le Conditionnement des
Dechets et Effluents Industriels**   **(1)**
Site de CENTRACO Codolet-Marcoule,
30204, Bagnols-sur-Ceze, Cedex,
France   **(100%)**
Tel.: (33) 4 66 50 58 00
Web Site: http://www.socodei.fr
Rev.: $53,357,080
Emp.: 200
Industrial Waste Management Services
N.A.I.C.S.: 562998

Sofinel   **(1)**
Blvd Du Docteur Postel, 27400, Louviers,
France
Tel.: (33) 232251085
Engineeering Services
N.A.I.C.S.: 541330

Thyssengas GmbH   **(1)**
Emil-Moog-Platz 13, 44137, Dortmund,
Germany   **(50%)**
Tel.: (49) 231912910
Web Site: http://www.thyssengas.com
Natural Gas Logistics & Transmission
N.A.I.C.S.: 486210
Thomas Gossmann (Chm-Exec Bd)

**Total Infrastructures Gaz France
SA**   **(1)**
40 avenue de l'Europe, CS 20522, 64010,
Pau, Cedex, France   **(18%)**
Tel.: (33) 559133400
Web Site: https://www.terega.fr
Sales Range: $400-449.9 Million
Emp.: 500
Natural Gas Transportation & Storage Ser-
vices
N.A.I.C.S.: 486210
Bernard Clement (Chm)

UTE Norte Fluminense S.A.   **(1)**
Av Almirante Barroso 52/17 Andar Centro,
20031-000, Rio de Janeiro, Brazil
Tel.: (55) 21 3974 6100
Web Site:
  http://www.edfnortefluminense.com.br
Sales Range: $75-99.9 Million
Emp.: 30
Electric Power Generation & Distribution
Services
N.A.I.C.S.: 221122
Yann des Longchamps (CEO & Country
Dir)

ELECTRICITE DE STRAS-
BOURG
26 boulevard du President Wilson,
67932, Strasbourg, cedex 9, France
Tel.: (33) 388206020
ELEC—(EUR)
Web Site: https://www.es.fr
Sales Range: $1-4.9 Billion
Electric Power Distribution Services
N.A.I.C.S.: 221122
Marc Kugler (CEO)

ELECTRICITE ET EAUX DE
MADAGASCAR SA
40 Rue du Louvre, 75001, Paris,
France
Tel.: (33) 153839560
Web Site: http://www.eem-group.com
EEM—(EUR)
Sales Range: Less than $1 Million
Real Estate Manangement Services
N.A.I.C.S.: 531210
Helene Tronconi (Chm & CEO)

ELECTRICITY GENERATING
PUBLIC CO., LTD.
222 Vibhavadi Rangsit Road Thung
Song Hong, Laksi, Bangkok, 10210,
Thailand
Tel.: (66) 29985000
Web Site: https://investor-
th.egco.com
EYGPF—(OTCIQ)
Rev.: $1,372,021,306
Assets: $7,100,440,806
Liabilities: $4,028,694,919
Net Worth: $3,071,745,886
Earnings: ($244,813,465)

Emp.: 1,267
Fiscal Year-end: 12/31/23
Electric Power Generation
N.A.I.C.S.: 221118
Somsiri Yoosook (Exec VP-Fin)

Subsidiaries:

B. Grimm & Co., R.O.P.   **(1)**
Dr Gerhard Link Building 5 Krungthep-
kreetha Road, Huamark Bangkapi, Bang-
kok, 10240, Bangkapi, Thailand   **(50%)**
Tel.: (66) 2 710 3000
Web Site: https://bgrimmgroup.com
Electric Bulk Power Transmission
N.A.I.C.S.: 221121

BLCP Power Ltd.   **(1)**
No 9 I-8 Road, Map Ta Phut Industrial Es-
tate Tumbol Map Ta Phut Amphur Muang,
Rayong, 21150, Thailand   **(50%)**
Tel.: (66) 3 892 5100
Web Site: https://www.blcp.co.th
Other Electric Power Generation
N.A.I.C.S.: 221118
Yuthana Charoenwong (Mng Dir)

Banpong Utilities Co., Ltd.   **(1)**
19/300 Moo19 Tha Pha, Banpong, Ratch-
aburi, 70110, Thailand
Tel.: (66) 29985000
Electricity Generating & Supply Services
N.A.I.C.S.: 221118

Boco Rock Wind Farm Pty. Ltd.   **(1)**
Block E 34 Thynne St, PO Box 731, Jami-
son Centre, Jamison, 2614, ACT, Australia
Tel.: (61) 1300855985
Web Site:
  https://www.bocorockwindfarm.com.au
Renewable Energy Services
N.A.I.C.S.: 221118

EGCO Cogeneration Co., Ltd.   **(1)**
222 Moo 8, Mabkha Sub-district Nikhom
Pattana District, Rayong, 21180, Thailand
Tel.: (66) 29985000
Natural Gas Distribution Services
N.A.I.C.S.: 221210

EGCO Green Energy Co., Ltd   **(1)**
EGCO Tower, Bangkok, Thailand
Tel.: (66) 29985000
Eletric Power Generation Services
N.A.I.C.S.: 221118

EGCO Pearl Co., Ltd.   **(1)**
4F No 200 Sec 1 Keelung Rd, Xinyi Dist,
Taipei, 110, Taiwan
Tel.: (886) 29985000
Holding Company
N.A.I.C.S.: 551111

**Egco Engineering & Service Co.,
Ltd**   **(99.99%)**
Tel.: (66) 386826114
Web Site: https://www.egco-
engineering.com
Sales Range: $250-299.9 Million
Emp.: 300
Electric Bulk Power Transmission & Control
N.A.I.C.S.: 221121

Subsidiary (Domestic):

Agro Energy Co., Ltd   **(2)**
EGCO Tower, Bangkok, Thailand
Tel.: (66) 2998 5000
Eletric Power Generation Services
N.A.I.C.S.: 221118

**Khanom Electricity Generating Co.,
Ltd.**   **(1)**
112 Moo 8 Tongnean, Khanom Nakhon Sri
Thammarat, 80210, Bangkok,
Thailand   **(99.99%)**
Tel.: (66) 75529173
Sales Range: $125-149.9 Million
Emp.: 105
Electric Power Generation
N.A.I.C.S.: 221118

Klongluang Utilities Co., Ltd.   **(1)**
1/9 Moo 3, Klongnueng Klongluang, Pa-
thumthani, 12120, Thailand
Tel.: (66) 29985000
Electricity Generating & Supply Services
N.A.I.C.S.: 221118

**Natural Energy Development Co.,
Ltd.**   **(1)**
188 Moo 3, Wang Ploeng Sub-District Khok
Samrong District, Lopburi, 15120, Thailand
Tel.: (66) 36418400
Web Site: https://www.ned.co.th
Renewable Energy Services
N.A.I.C.S.: 221118

New Growth Plus B.V.   **(1)**
Buitenveldertselaan 106, 1081 AB, Amster-
dam, Netherlands
Tel.: (31) 29985000
Holding Company
N.A.I.C.S.: 551112

**North Pole Investment Company
Limited**   **(1)**
6th Floor Tower A 1 CyberCity, Ebene,
Mauritius
Tel.: (230) 29985000
Holding Company
N.A.I.C.S.: 551112

**Pearl Energy Philippines Operating,
Inc.**   **(1)**
Buitenveldertselaan 106, 1081 AB, Amster-
dam, Netherlands
Tel.: (31) 29985000
QPL Maintenance & Operation Services
N.A.I.C.S.: 561210

**Quezon Management Service
Inc.**   **(1)**
14/F Zuellig Building Makati Avenue corner
Paseo de Roxas, Makati, 1225, Philippines
Tel.: (63) 286872180
Web Site: https://www.qmsi.com.ph
Management Services
N.A.I.C.S.: 541611

**Quezon Power (Philippines) Limited
Co.**   **(1)**
62 H Dela Costa Street, Barangay Daungan
Mauban, Quezon City, 4330, Philippines
Tel.: (63) 427840295
Web Site: https://www.qpl.com.ph
Electricity Power Supply Services
N.A.I.C.S.: 221122
Frank Thiel (Mng Dir)

**Rayong Electricity Generating Co.,
Ltd.**   **(1)**
222 Mu 5 vibhavadi Rangsit Rd, Kwaeng
Tungsonghong Khet Laksi, 10210, Bang-
kok, Thailand   **(99.99%)**
Tel.: (66) 38681012
Web Site: http://www.egco.co.th
Sales Range: $125-149.9 Million
Emp.: 102
Electric Power Generation
N.A.I.C.S.: 221118
Chumsak Desudjit (Dir-Rayong Power
Plant)

South Pacific Power Pty. Limited   **(1)**
One International Towers Watermans Quay,
Barangaroo, 2000, NSW, Australia
Tel.: (61) 282660000
Holding Company
N.A.I.C.S.: 551112

ELECTRO ACO ALTONA S.A.
Rua Eng Paul Werner 925, Blu-
menau, 89030-900, SC, Brazil
Tel.: (55) 4733217766
Web Site: https://www.altona.com.br
Year Founded: 1924
EALT4—(BRAZ)
Rev.: $102,107,985
Assets: $115,553,632
Liabilities: $65,357,651
Net Worth: $50,195,981
Earnings: $10,162,390
Emp.: 638
Fiscal Year-end: 12/31/23
Steel Casting Mfr
N.A.I.C.S.: 331511

ELECTRO MECHANICAL SYS-
TEMS LTD.
Eros House Calleva Park, Aldermas-
ton, RG7 8LN, Berkshire, United
Kingdom
Tel.: (44) 118 9817391

Web Site: http://www.ems-limited.co.uk
Year Founded: 1985
Electromechanical Equipment Distr
N.A.I.C.S.: 423690
Stewart Goulding *(Dir-Sls & Mktg)*

ELECTRO OPTIC SYSTEMS HOLDINGS LIMITED

18 Wormald Street, Symonston, 2609, ACT, Australia
Tel.: (61) 62227900   AU
Web Site: https://www.eos-aus.com
Year Founded: 1983
EOPSF—(OTCIQ)
Rev.: $93,311,787
Assets: $278,654,905
Liabilities: $123,042,686
Net Worth: $155,612,219
Earnings: ($77,148,524)
Emp.: 404
Fiscal Year-end: 12/31/22
Electro Optic Products Mfr
N.A.I.C.S.: 334419
Frederick Bart *(Chm)*

Subsidiaries:

EOS Defense Systems Pte Limited   **(1)**
456 Alexandra Road Fragrance Empire Building 21-02, Singapore, 119962, Singapore
Tel.: (65) 63043130
Space & Defence Equipment Distr
N.A.I.C.S.: 423690
Henry Heng *(Gen Mgr)*

EOS Optronics GmbH   **(1)**
Ulrichsberger Str 17, 94469, Deggendorf, Germany
Tel.: (49) 99128921964
Space & Defence Equipment Distr
N.A.I.C.S.: 423690

EOS Space Systems Pty Limited   **(1)**
18 Wormald Street, Symonston, 2609, ACT, Australia
Tel.: (61) 262227900
Space & Defence Equipment Mfr
N.A.I.C.S.: 334511
Craig Smith *(CEO)*

EOS Technologies, Inc.   **(1)**
2500 N Tucson Blvd Ste 114, Tucson, AZ 85716
Tel.: (520) 624-6399
Space & Defence Equipment Distr
N.A.I.C.S.: 423690
Marcia Strait *(Gen Mgr)*

Electro Optic Systems Pty Limited   **(1)**
18 Wormald Street, Symonston, 2609, ACT, Australia
Tel.: (61) 262227900
Web Site: https://www.eos-aus.com
Space & Defence Equipment Mfr
N.A.I.C.S.: 334511
Neil Carter *(Chief Strategy Officer)*

ELECTRO PUNO SAA

Jr Mariano H Cornejo N 160, Puno, Peru
Tel.: (51) 352552
Web Site: https://www.gob.pe
Year Founded: 1999
EPUNOBC1—(LIM)
Sales Range: Less than $1 Million
Electric Power Distribution Services
N.A.I.C.S.: 221122

ELECTRO SONIC INC.

60 Renfrew Drive Suite 110, Markham, L3R 0E1, ON, Canada
Tel.: (905) 946-0100
Web Site: https://www.e-sonic.com
Year Founded: 1952
Rev.: $38,935,881
Emp.: 210
Electronic Components & Equipment Distr
N.A.I.C.S.: 423690

ELECTRO SUR ESTE SAA

Av Mariscal Sucre N 400 Bancopat, Santiago, Lima, Cusco, Peru
Tel.: (51) 84223070
Web Site: https://www.gob.pe
Year Founded: 1984
ESUREBC1—(LIM)
Sales Range: Less than $1 Million
Electricity Power Distribution Services
N.A.I.C.S.: 221122
Frantz Luis Olazabal Ibanez *(Chm)*

ELECTROAPARATAJ S.A.

Calea Campulung nr 121 C7, Targoviste, Bucharest, Romania
Tel.: (40) 245217981
Web Site: https://www.electroaparataj.ro
Year Founded: 1948
ELJ—(BUC)
Rev.: $2,624,922
Assets: $3,024,341
Liabilities: $786,148
Net Worth: $2,238,193
Earnings: ($29,351)
Emp.: 45
Fiscal Year-end: 12/31/22
Low Voltage Switching Equipment Mfr
N.A.I.C.S.: 335999

ELECTROARGES SA

12 Albesti St, 115300, Arges, Romania
Tel.: (40) 248724000
Web Site: https://www.electroarges.ro
Sales Range: $25-49.9 Million
Emp.: 479
Household Appliances & Electrical Portable Tools Mfr
N.A.I.C.S.: 335210

Subsidiaries:

Renewable Holding Management S.A.   **(1)**
          (67.02%)
Tel.: (40) 758839312
Web Site: https://esgholdings.ro
Rev.: $660
Assets: $44,070
Liabilities: $13,069
Net Worth: $31,001
Earnings: ($16,339)
Emp.: 1
Fiscal Year-end: 12/31/2022
Building Construction Services
N.A.I.C.S.: 236116

ELECTROCONSTRUCTIA ELCO ALBA IULIA SA

Ion Arion St No 62, Alba Iulia, Alba, Romania
Tel.: (40) 258811607
EEAI—(BUC)
Rev.: $2,279,849
Assets: $469,008
Liabilities: $197,069
Net Worth: $271,939
Earnings: $82,566
Emp.: 13
Fiscal Year-end: 12/31/23
Construction Engineering Services
N.A.I.C.S.: 541330
Alin Sandor *(Dir Gen)*

ELECTROCONSTRUCTIA ELCO SA

Str 22 Decembrie Nr 1, Suceava, Romania
Tel.: (40) 230516416
ELEL—(BUC)
Rev.: $882,322
Assets: $1,104,658
Liabilities: $102,357
Net Worth: $1,002,301
Earnings: ($75,670)
Emp.: 22
Fiscal Year-end: 12/31/23
Construction Engineering Services

N.A.I.C.S.: 541330

ELECTROCONSTRUCTIA ELCO TIMISOARA S.A.

Str Cerna Nr 5, Timis, Timisoara, Romania
Tel.: (40) 256223367
Web Site: http://www.elco.ro
Rev.: $63,085
Assets: $477,426
Liabilities: $121,694
Net Worth: $355,732
Earnings: ($3,979)
Emp.: 8
Fiscal Year-end: 12/31/18
Electrical Installation Services
N.A.I.C.S.: 238210
Maria Ghinda *(Pres)*

ELECTROLUX PROFES-SIONAL AB

Metallgatan 2-4, Alingsas, 44182, Sweden
Tel.: (46) 32274000
Web Site: http://www.electrolux.se
EPRO.B—(OMX)
Rev.: $1,176,166,955
Assets: $1,126,432,008
Liabilities: $659,360,307
Net Worth: $467,071,702
Earnings: $76,935,296
Emp.: 3,930
Fiscal Year-end: 12/31/23
Laundry & Foodservice Equipment & Supplies Mfr
N.A.I.C.S.: 423850

Subsidiaries:

Electrolux Professional AG   **(1)**
Bleichematt Strasse 31, CH 5001, Aarau, Switzerland   **(100%)**
Tel.: (41) 628376161
Web Site: http://www.electrolux-professional.com
Sales Range: $75-99.9 Million
Laundry & Foodservice Equipment & Supplies Mfr
N.A.I.C.S.: 423850

Tosei Corporation   **(1)**
Toranomon Tosei Bldg 4-2-3 Toranomon, Minato-ku, Tokyo, 105-0001, Japan
Tel.: (81) 354398801
Web Site: https://www.toseicorp.co.jp
Rev.: $686,825,040
Assets: $2,042,044,400
Liabilities: $1,342,277,200
Net Worth: $699,767,200
Earnings: $83,315,760
Emp.: 663
Fiscal Year-end: 11/30/2022
Real Estate Management Services
N.A.I.C.S.: 523999
Seiichiro Yamaguchi *(Pres & CEO)*

Unified Brands Inc.   **(1)**
88 Armory Rd, Vicksburg, MS 39183
Tel.: (601) 372-3903
Web Site: http://www.unifiedbrands.net
Steam Jacketed Kettles, Braising Pans, Steamers, Cooker Mixers, Continuous Process Equipment, Combination Steamer-Ovens & Cook-Chill Systems Mfr
N.A.I.C.S.: 333241
Dave Herring *(Pres)*

ELECTROMAGNETIC GEO-SERVICES ASA

Karenslyst Alle 4 4th Floor, N-0278, Oslo, Norway
Tel.: (47) 91141149
Web Site: https://www.emgs.com
E2M—(DEU)
Rev.: $34,979,000
Assets: $42,681,000
Liabilities: $34,000,000
Net Worth: $8,681,000
Earnings: $11,192,000
Emp.: 20
Fiscal Year-end: 12/31/22
Oil & Gas Exploration Services

N.A.I.C.S.: 211120
Bjorn Petter Lindhom *(CEO)*

Subsidiaries:

EMGS AS   **(1)**
Stiklestadveien 1, 7041, Trondheim, Norway
Tel.: (47) 73568810
Sales Range: $25-49.9 Million
Emp.: 120
Electromagnetic Geophysical Surveying Services
N.A.I.C.S.: 541360

EMGS Americas Inc.   **(1)**
15021 Katy Freeway Ste 500, Houston, TX 77094
Tel.: (281) 920-5601
Web Site: http://www.emgs.com
Sales Range: $25-49.9 Million
Emp.: 30
Geophysical Surveying Services
N.A.I.C.S.: 541360

EMGS Asia Pacific Sdn Bhd   **(1)**
Unit E-15 2-4 15th Floor East Wing Wisma Rohas Perkasa, No 8 Jalan Perak, 50450, Kuala Lumpur, Malaysia
Tel.: (60) 321660613
Sales Range: $25-49.9 Million
Emp.: 26
Electromagnetic Geophysical Surveying Services
N.A.I.C.S.: 541360

EMGS International BV   **(1)**
Rokin 55, 1012 KK, Amsterdam, North Holland, Netherlands
Tel.: (31) 206278983
Business Consulting Services
N.A.I.C.S.: 541611

EMGS do Brasil Ltda.   **(1)**
Praia de Botafogo 501 2 andar, Rio de Janeiro, 22250-040, Brazil
Tel.: (55) 21 2546 9936
Electromagnetic Geophysical Surveying Services
N.A.I.C.S.: 541360

ELECTROMAGNETICA S.A.

Calea Rahovei 266-268 Sector 5, 50912, Bucharest, Romania
Tel.: (40) 214042102
Web Site: https://www.electromagnetica.ro
ELMA—(BUC)
Rev.: $41,984,393
Assets: $84,886,675
Liabilities: $10,450,678
Net Worth: $74,435,997
Earnings: ($6,681,110)
Emp.: 350
Fiscal Year-end: 12/31/23
Electric & Electronic Devices Mfr
N.A.I.C.S.: 334515
Octavian Macovei *(Mgr-Technical)*

Subsidiaries:

Procetel SA   **(1)**
Calea Rahovei 266-268 Sector 5, 050912, Bucharest, Romania
Tel.: (40) 733381884
Web Site: https://www.procetel.ro
Office Space Rental Services
N.A.I.C.S.: 531120

ELECTROMINING SA

Calea Nationala Nr 6 Bis, Botosani, Romania
Tel.: (40) 231515444
Sales Range: Less than $1 Million
Emp.: 4
Real Estate Management Services
N.A.I.C.S.: 531390
Viorica Munteanu *(Pres)*

ELECTRON MEC S.A.R.L

2 rue Alphonse Bouffard Roupe Zac de Champfeuillet, 38500, Voiron, France
Tel.: (33) 476670280   FR
Electronic Product Distr
N.A.I.C.S.: 449210

Electron Mec S.a.r.l—(Continued)

ELECTRON MEC S.A.R.L
Via negroli 51A, 20133, Milan, MI,
Italy
Tel.: (39) 0276110156   IT
Web Site: http://www.electron-
mec.com
Year Founded: 2005
Electronic Product Distr
N.A.I.C.S.: 449210
Giampaolo Calligarich *(Pres)*

ELECTRONIC BUSINESS SYS-TEM
100 rue de Paris, 91300, Massy,
France
Tel.: (33) 164472150
Sales Range: $10-24.9 Million
Emp.: 25
Postal Printing Engineering
N.A.I.C.S.: 491110

Subsidiaries:

Societe de Services de Maintenance
Industriels   (1)
ZI Du Sous Biscain, Villers Sous St Leu,
60340, Saint Leu d'Esserent,
France   (100%)
Tel.: (33) 344568570
Provider of Maintenance Services
N.A.I.C.S.: 811412

ELECTRONIC INDUSTRIES CO.
Hai Babil Sec 931 St 30, Baghdad,
Iraq
Tel.: (964) 1 7197023
Year Founded: 1973
Electric Equipment Mfr
N.A.I.C.S.: 334419

ELECTRONICPARTNER HAN-DEL SE
Mundelheimer Weg 40, 40472, Dus-
seldorf, Germany
Tel.: (49) 21141560   De
Web Site:
http://www.electronicpartner.com
Year Founded: 1937
Home Electronic Retailer
N.A.I.C.S.: 449210
Karl Trautmann *(Member-Exec Bd)*

Subsidiaries:

ElectronicPartner Austria GmbH   (1)
IZ NO Sud Strasse 2 Objekt M 21/1, 2355,
Wiener Neudorf, Austria
Tel.: (43) 2236 90 55 0
Web Site: http://www.electronicpartner.at
Electronic Product Retailer
N.A.I.C.S.: 449210

ElectronicPartner Belgie N.V.   (1)
Leuvensesteenweg 542 Planet 2 A5, 1930,
Zaventem, Belgium
Tel.: (32) 800 16955
Web Site: http://www.ep-shop.be
Electronic Product Retailer
N.A.I.C.S.: 449210

ElectronicPartner GmbH   (1)
Mundelheimer Weg 40, 40472, Dusseldorf,
Germany
Tel.: (49) 211 4156 0
Web Site: http://www.electronicpartner.com
Emp.: 200
Electronics, Information Technology & Tele-
communications Products Wholesale Trade
Distr & Retailer
N.A.I.C.S.: 423620
Jorg Ehmer *(CEO & Chm-Mgmt Bd)*

ElectronicPartner Nederland B.V. (1)
Marconiweg 2c, 4131 PD, Vianen, Nether-
lands
Tel.: (31) 347 364433
Web Site: http://www.electronicpartner.nl
Electronic Product Retailer
N.A.I.C.S.: 449210

ElectronicPartner Schweiz AG   (1)

Industriestrasse 6, 8305, Dietlikon, Switzer-
land
Tel.: (41) 44 805 96 66
Web Site: http://www.ep-online.ch
Electronic Product Retailer
N.A.I.C.S.: 449210

MEDIMAX Online GmbH   (1)
Mundelheimer Weg 40, 40472, Dusseldorf,
Germany
Tel.: (49) 21141568080
Electric Device Mfr
N.A.I.C.S.: 811310
Jurgen Welke *(Head-Cust Svc & Logistics)*

Subsidiary (Domestic):

notebooksbilliger.de AG   (2)
Wiedemannstrasse 3, D-31157, Sarstedt,
Germany
Tel.: (49) 1805 99971 31
Web Site: http://www.notebooksbilliger.de
Online Consumer Electronics
N.A.I.C.S.: 449210
Gerardus Marinus van Os *(Chm-
Supervisory Bd)*

ELECTRONICS INDUSTRY PUBLIC COMPANY LIMITED
349 SJ Infinite I Business Complex
Unit 1507 15th Floor Vibhavadi-Rang,
Chompol, Bangkok, 10900, Thailand
Tel.: (66) 2 075 5667
Web Site: http://www.eicasia.net
Year Founded: 1984
Rev.: $5,826,225
Assets: $23,737,714
Liabilities: $6,690,144
Net Worth: $17,047,570
Earnings: $160,050
Emp.: 221
Fiscal Year-end: 12/31/18
Semiconductor Devices Mfr
N.A.I.C.S.: 334413
Nakorn Aranyanark *(Chm)*

Subsidiaries:

EIC International Co., Ltd   (1)
Room 702 Block B Hoi Luen Industrial Cen-
tre 55 Hoi Yuen Road, Kowloon, Hong
Kong, China (Hong Kong)
Tel.: (852) 2341 6681
Semiconductor Distr
N.A.I.C.S.: 423690

EIC Semiconductor, Inc.   (1)
15705 Arrow Hwy Ste 4 5, Irwindale, CA
91706
Tel.: (626) 960-0877
Emp.: 6
Semiconductor Distr
N.A.I.C.S.: 423690
Olumide Adefope *(Gen Mgr)*

ELECTRONICS MART INDIA LIMITED
M No 6-3-666/A1 To 7-3rd & 4th floor
Opp NIMS Hospital, Panjagutta Main
Road, Hyderabad, 500082, Telan-
gana, India
Tel.: (91) 4023242512
Web Site:
https://www.electronicsindia.com
Year Founded: 1980
EMIL—(NSE)
Rev.: $594,194,192
Assets: $249,077,283
Liabilities: $167,653,532
Net Worth: $81,423,752
Earnings: $14,181,122
Emp.: 2,200
Fiscal Year-end: 03/31/22
Consumer Electronic Products Distr
N.A.I.C.S.: 423620

ELECTROPRECIZIA S.A.
Electroprecizia No 3 Street, 505600,
Sacele, 505600, Brasov, Romania
Tel.: (40) 268273775
Web Site:
https://www.electroprecizia.ro
Year Founded: 1936

ELZY—(BUC)
Rev.: $6,580,036
Assets: $43,908,258
Liabilities: $9,688,484
Net Worth: $34,219,774
Earnings: $116,045
Emp.: 16
Fiscal Year-end: 12/31/23
Electric Motor Mfr
N.A.I.C.S.: 336390
Karoly Katona *(Deputy Dir)*

ELECTROPRIVOD LTD.
Sverdlovckaya nab 14/2 Litor A room
17N, 195009, Saint Petersburg, Rus-
sia
Tel.: (7) 9516583396   RU
Motion Controller Mfr
N.A.I.C.S.: 335314

ELECTROPUTERE S.A.
80 Calea Bucuresti Street, Dolj
County, 200440, Craiova, Romania
Tel.: (40) 372703450
Web Site:
https://www.electroputere.ro
Year Founded: 1949
EPT—(BUC)
Rev.: $2,956,700
Assets: $59,393,463
Liabilities: $128,486,336
Net Worth: ($69,092,873)
Earnings: $8,677
Emp.: 18
Fiscal Year-end: 12/31/20
Railway Transport Electrotechnical
Equipments Mfr
N.A.I.C.S.: 335312
Liliana Hallabrin *(Dir-HR & Admin)*

ELECTROPUTERE VFU PAS-CANI S.A.
Str Garii nr 18, 705200, Iasi, Roma-
nia
Tel.: (40) 232718300
Web Site:
http://www.electroputerevfu.ro
Sales Range: $10-24.9 Million
Emp.: 750
Railroad Car Mfr
N.A.I.C.S.: 336510

ELECTROSTEEL CASTINGS LTD
GK Tower 19 Camac Street, Kolkata,
700 017, India
Tel.: (91) 3322839990
Web Site:
https://www.electrosteel.com
ELECTCAST—(NSE)
Rev.: $481,678,265
Assets: $980,267,488
Liabilities: $466,112,447
Net Worth: $514,155,041
Earnings: ($12,539,777)
Emp.: 1,520
Fiscal Year-end: 03/31/21
Ductile Iron Spun Pipes Mfr
N.A.I.C.S.: 339992
Pradip Kumar Khaitan *(Chm)*

Subsidiaries:

Electrosteel Algerie SPA   (1)
Hai Alioua Fodil Villa No-130, Cheraga, Al-
giers, 16002, Algeria
Tel.: (213) 770964858
Web Site: http://www.electrosteel.fr
Sales Range: $25-49.9 Million
Emp.: 14
Ductile Iron Pipes Mfr
N.A.I.C.S.: 331511

Electrosteel Castings (UK)
Limited   (1)
Ambrose House Broombank Road Trading
Estate Broombank Road, Off Carrwood
Road, Chesterfield, S41 9QJ, Derbyshire,
United Kingdom

Tel.: (44) 1246264222
Web Site: http://www.electrosteel.co.uk
Sales Range: $25-49.9 Million
Emp.: 50
Ductile Iron Pipes Mfr
N.A.I.C.S.: 331511
Glenn Wheeler *(Mgr-Sls)*

Electrosteel Castings Gulf FZE.   (1)
No LB09021 Lob 9, PO Box 261462, Jebel
Ali Free Zone, Dubai, United Arab Emirates
Tel.: (971) 505928405
Cast Iron Mfr & Distr
N.A.I.C.S.: 331511

Electrosteel Europe S.A.   (1)
Velazquez 19 3 Fl, Madrid, 28001, Spain
Tel.: (34) 935830522
Sales Range: $25-49.9 Million
Emp.: 20
Ductile Iron Pipes Mfr
N.A.I.C.S.: 331511

Electrosteel USA, LLC   (1)
1101 Louisville Road, Savannah, GA 31415
Tel.: (912) 387-0613
Web Site: https://electrosteelusa.com
Sales Range: $25-49.9 Million
Emp.: 25
Ductile Iron Pipes Mfr
N.A.I.C.S.: 331511
Danny Swalley *(Mng Dir)*

Singardo International Pte Ltd   (1)
2 Kallang Ave 09-23 CT Hub, Singapore,
339407, Singapore
Tel.: (65) 62945875
Web Site: http://www.singardo.com.sg
Sales Range: $25-49.9 Million
Emp.: 15
Ductile Iron Pipes Mfr
N.A.I.C.S.: 331511
Alan Chua *(Pres)*

ELECTROTEL S.A.
279 Dunarii Street, Teleorman,
140103, Alexandria, Romania
Tel.: (40) 247 306 200
Web Site: http://www.electrotel.ro
Year Founded: 1970
Sales Range: $10-24.9 Million
Emp.: 450
Electricity Distribution & Control Ap-
paratus Mfr
N.A.I.C.S.: 335313

ELECTROTHERM INDIA LTD
A-1 Skylark Apartment Satellite Road,
Satellite, Ahmedabad, 380015, India
Tel.: (91) 2717660550
Web Site:
https://www.electrotherm.com
Year Founded: 1983
ELECTHERM—(NSE)
Rev.: $344,291,220
Assets: $258,902,280
Liabilities: $401,187,150
Net Worth: ($142,284,870)
Earnings: $6,755,385
Emp.: 2,841
Fiscal Year-end: 03/31/21
Electrical & Steel Equipment Mfr
N.A.I.C.S.: 334416
Shailesh Bhandari *(Mng Dir)*

Subsidiaries:

Electrotherm India Ltd - Electric Ve-
hicle Division   (1)
No 72 Palodia, Ahmedabad, 382115, Guja-
rat, India
Tel.: (91) 2717660550
Web Site: http://www.electrotherment.com
Electric Vehicle Component Mfr
N.A.I.C.S.: 336390

Electrotherm India Ltd - Electrotherm
Renewables   (1)
Surv No 72 Palodia Via Thaltej, Ahmeda-
bad, 382 115, Gujarat, India
Tel.: (91) 2717660550
Web Site: http://www.etrenewables.com
Electricity Generation Services

N.A.I.C.S.: 221118
Sanjai Joshi *(Head-HR)*

Electrotherm India Ltd - Engineering & Project Division (1)
Surv No 72 Vlg Palodia Taluka Kalol Dist, Gandhinagar, 382 115, Gujarat, India
Tel.: (91) 2717234553
Web Site: http://www.electrotherm.com
Sales Range: $400-449.9 Million
Emp.: 2,500
Induction Furnace Mfr
N.A.I.C.S.: 333994

ELECTROVAYA INC.
6688 Kitimat Road, Mississauga, L5N 1P8, ON, Canada
Tel.: (905) 855-4627   ON
Web Site:
    https://www.electrovaya.com
ELVA—(NASDAQ)
Rev.: $44,615,000
Assets: $39,482,000
Liabilities: $30,897,000
Net Worth: $8,585,000
Earnings: ($1,485,000)
Emp.: 97
Fiscal Year-end: 09/30/24
Rechargeable Battery Mfr
N.A.I.C.S.: 335910
Alexander McLean *(Chm)*

Subsidiaries:

Electrovaya Company (1)
107 Hermes Rd Ste 100 Malta, New York, NY 12020
Tel.: (518) 899-7300
Sales Range: $25-49.9 Million
Emp.: 3
BatteryDesign & Mfr
N.A.I.C.S.: 335910

Electrovaya Corp., (1)
6688 Kitimat Road, Mississauga, L5N 1P8, ON, Canada
Tel.: (905) 855-4610
Web Site: https://www.electrovaya.com
Emp.: 40
Battery Design & Mfr
N.A.I.C.S.: 335910
Amit Majumdar *(Mgr-Bus Dev)*

Electrovaya USA Inc. (1)
107 Hermes Rd Ste 100, Malta, NY 12020
Tel.: (518) 899-7300
Web Site: http://www.electrovaya.com
Sales Range: $25-49.9 Million
Emp.: 2
Battery Design & Mfr
N.A.I.C.S.: 335910

ELEFIRST SCIENCE AND TECHNOLOGY CO., LTD.
86 Runqi Road Dongshan Street, Ji-angning District, Nanjing, China
Tel.: (86) 2568531928
Web Site: http://www.elefirst.com
300356—(CHIN)
Rev.: $60,214,594
Assets: $286,502,700
Liabilities: $136,340,047
Net Worth: $150,162,653
Earnings: ($15,013,048)
Fiscal Year-end: 12/31/20
Electricity Signals Testing Instruments & Meter Reading Systems Software & Hardware
N.A.I.C.S.: 334515

ELEGANCE OPTICAL INTERNATIONAL HOLDINGS LTD.
Unit 2405 24/F World Wide House 19 Des Voeux Road Central, Central, China (Hong Kong)
Tel.: (852) 2 342 0826
0907—(HKG)
Rev.: $6,955,891
Assets: $51,657,780
Liabilities: $16,511,762
Net Worth: $35,146,018
Earnings: ($2,343,051)

Emp.: 235
Fiscal Year-end: 03/31/21
Optical Frames & Sunglasses Mfr
N.A.I.C.S.: 333310

Subsidiaries:

Elegance Optical Investments Limited (1)
Rm 2 8 F Mai Hing Indus Bldg Block B 16-18 Hing Yip St, Kwun Tong, Kowloon, China (Hong Kong)
Tel.: (852) 23420826
Web Site: http://www.elegance-group.com
Investment Holding Services
N.A.I.C.S.: 551112

Elegance Optical Manufactory Limited (1)
Rm B2 & B4 8 Fl Mai Hing Indus Bldg 16-18 Hing Yip St, Kwun Tong, Kowloon, China (Hong Kong)
Tel.: (852) 23420826
Optical Frames Mfr & Sales
N.A.I.C.S.: 339115

Sandwalk Far East Limited (1)
B1 B2 6 F Block B Mai Hing Indus Bldg 16-18 Hing Yip St, Kwun Tong, Kowloon, China (Hong Kong)
Tel.: (852) 2951 6074
Web Site: http://www.sandwalkstudio.com
Leather Accessories Sales
N.A.I.C.S.: 458320

ELEGANT MARBLES & GRANI INDUSTRIES LTD.
Elegant House Raghuvanshi Mills Compound Senapati Bapat Marg, Lower Parel West, Mumbai, 400013, Maharastra, India
Tel.: (91) 2224960771
Web Site:
    https://www.elegantmarbles.com
Year Founded: 1984
526705—(BOM)
Rev.: $4,070,075
Assets: $14,833,578
Liabilities: $433,155
Net Worth: $14,400,422
Earnings: $366,994
Emp.: 59
Fiscal Year-end: 03/31/22
Marbles & Granites Mfr
N.A.I.C.S.: 327991
Rajesh Agrawal *(Chm & Mng Dir)*

ELEKTA AB
Kungstensgatan 18, PO Box 7593, 103 93, Stockholm, Sweden
Tel.: (46) 858725400   SE
Web Site: https://www.elekta.com
EKTAF—(OTCIQ)
Rev.: $1,697,059,966
Assets: $2,942,201,265
Liabilities: $1,932,619,645
Net Worth: $1,009,581,620
Earnings: $121,947,794
Emp.: 4,584
Fiscal Year-end: 04/30/24
Medical Radiation Treatment Equipment Mfr
N.A.I.C.S.: 339112
Laurent Leksell *(Founder & Chm)*

Subsidiaries:

3D Line Research and Development S.r.l. (1)
Via Bernardo Rucellai 23, Milan, 20126, Italy
Tel.: (39) 022550161
Web Site: http://www.3dline.com
Medical Equipment Research & Development Services
N.A.I.C.S.: 541715

Elekta (Pty) Ltd (Southern Africa) (1)
Maxwell Office Park First Floor Building 3 Magwa Crescent, Private Bag X81, Waterfall City Midrand, Johannesburg, 2090, South Africa
Tel.: (27) 110751900

Sales Range: $25-49.9 Million
Emp.: 10
Medical Radiation Therapy Equipment Mfr & Sales
N.A.I.C.S.: 339112
Erik Leksell *(Mng Dir)*

Elekta / IMPAC Medical Systems, Inc. (1)
13723 Riverport Dr Ste 100, Maryland Heights, MO 63043
Tel.: (314) 993-0003
Web Site: http://www.elekta.com
Sales Range: $25-49.9 Million
Emp.: 155
Radiation Treatment Planning Systems Mfr
N.A.I.C.S.: 339112
Tomas Puusepp *(Dir-Board)*

Subsidiary (Non-US):

CMS GmbH (2)
Heinrich von Stephan Str 5 B, Freiburg, 79100, Germany
Tel.: (49) 761881880
Sales Range: $25-49.9 Million
Emp.: 30
Radiation Treatment Planning Software Mfr
N.A.I.C.S.: 339112
David Paton *(Mng Dir)*

CMS Japan K.K. (2)
Nagatacho Bldg 2 4 3 Nagata cho, Chiyoda Ku, Tokyo, 100-0014, Japan
Tel.: (81) 3 3580 7100
Sales Range: $25-49.9 Million
Emp.: 30
Radiation Treatment Planning Software Mfr
N.A.I.C.S.: 339112

Elekta Asia Ltd (1)
Unit 1201-1203 12/F Railway Plaza 39 Chatham Road South, TsimShaTsui, Kowloon, China (Hong Kong)
Tel.: (852) 58140159
Surgical Equipment Distr
N.A.I.C.S.: 423450

Elekta B.V. (1)
De Maas 26, 5684, Best, Netherlands
Tel.: (31) 499336161
Sales Range: $25-49.9 Million
Emp.: 23
Medical Radiation Therapy Equipment Mfr & Sales
N.A.I.C.S.: 339112

Elekta BMEI (Beijing) Medical Equipment Co., Ltd (1)
No 21 Chuang Xin Road Science Park, Chang Ping, Beijing, 102200, China
Tel.: (86) 1080125012
Web Site: http://www.elekta.com
Sales Range: $50-74.9 Million
Emp.: 115
Medical Radiation Therapy Equipment Mfr & Sales
N.A.I.C.S.: 339112

Elekta GmbH (1)
Klostergasse 4, 6020, Innsbruck, Austria
Tel.: (43) 512560220
Sales Range: $25-49.9 Million
Emp.: 15
Medical Radiation Therapy Equipment Mfr & Sales
N.A.I.C.S.: 339112

Elekta GmbH (1)
Borsteler Chaussee 49, 22453, Hamburg, Germany
Tel.: (49) 40 59 38 30
Web Site: http://www.elekta.de
Emp.: 100
Pharmaceuticals Product Mfr
N.A.I.C.S.: 325412
Rolf Kuster *(Mng Dir)*

Elekta Hellas EPE (1)
17-19 AG Konstantinou and AG Anargyron 42, Marousi, 151 24, Athens, Greece
Tel.: (30) 2108067901
Medical Scanning Equipment Mfr
N.A.I.C.S.: 334510

Elekta Inc. (1)
400 Perimeter Center Ter NE Ste 50, Atlanta, GA 30346
Tel.: (770) 300-9725
Sales Range: $50-74.9 Million
Emp.: 200
Medical Technology Systems & Solutions

N.A.I.C.S.: 339112

Elekta Instrument (Shanghai) Ltd (1)
B2 No 1000 Jihai Road, Pudong, Shanghai, 201206, China
Tel.: (86) 2158997200
Sales Range: $25-49.9 Million
Emp.: 100
Medical Radiation Therapy Equipment Mfr & Sales
N.A.I.C.S.: 339112

Elekta Instrument AB (1)
Kungstensgatan 18, PO Box 7593, 103 93, Stockholm, Sweden
Tel.: (46) 858725400
Web Site: http://www.elekta.com
Emp.: 150
Medical & Surgical Instrument Mfr
N.A.I.C.S.: 339112

Elekta KK (1)
3-9-1 Shibaura Shibaura Rene Site Tower 7F, Minato-Ku, Tokyo, 108-0023, Japan
Tel.: (81) 367486180
Web Site: https://www.elekta.co.jp
Medical Equipment Sales & Maintenance
N.A.I.C.S.: 423450

Elekta LLC (1)
premises I 11 Floor bld 4 Kosmodamianskaya nab 52, 115035, Moscow, Russia
Tel.: (7) 4957888045
Medical Scanning Equipment Mfr
N.A.I.C.S.: 334510

Elekta Limited (1)
Cornerstone London Road, Crawley, RH10 9BL, W Sussex, United Kingdom
Tel.: (44) 1293544422
Sales Range: $200-249.9 Million
Emp.: 900
Medical Radiation Treatment Equipment Mfr & Sales
N.A.I.C.S.: 339112

Elekta Limited (1)
No 824 Mikeum Park Building 150 Geumgok-Dong, 463-805, Seongnam, Gyeonggi-Do, Korea (South)
Tel.: (82) 31 716 0080
Surgical & Medical Equipment Mfr
N.A.I.C.S.: 339113

Elekta Ltd. (1)
2050 Bleury Suite 200, Montreal, H3A 2J5, QC, Canada
Tel.: (514) 840-9600
Medical Scanning Equipment Mfr
N.A.I.C.S.: 334510

Elekta Medical S.A. (1)
Calle Manuel Tovar 43, 28034, Madrid, Spain
Tel.: (34) 915562025
Web Site: https://www.elekta.com
Sales Range: $25-49.9 Million
Emp.: 47
Medical Radiation Therapy Equipment Mfr & Sales
N.A.I.C.S.: 339112

Elekta Medical SA de CV (1)
Av Mariano Escobedo 476 piso 10 oficina 1001, Colonia Nueva Anzures Delegacion Miguel Hidalgo, 11590, Mexico, Mexico
Tel.: (52) 5555648184
Medical Scanning Equipment Mfr
N.A.I.C.S.: 334510

Elekta Medical Systems Comercio e Prestacao de Servicos para Radiologia, Radiocirurgia e Radioterapia Ltda. (1)
Avenida Brigadeiro Faria Lima 1355 - 20 andar, Sao Paulo, 01452 919, Brazil
Tel.: (55) 1150544550
Sales Range: $25-49.9 Million
Emp.: 5
Medical & Surgical Equipment Distr
N.A.I.C.S.: 423450
Antonio Ponce *(Gen Mgr)*

Elekta Medical Systems India PVT. Ltd. (1)
12TH Floor Vatika Professional Point Sector 66, Golf Course Extension Road, Gurgaon, 122001, Haryana, India
Tel.: (91) 1244933222
Web Site: http://www.elekta.com

Elekta AB—(Continued)

Sales Range: $25-49.9 Million
Emp.: 100
Medical Radiation Therapy Equipment Mfr & Sales
N.A.I.C.S.: 339112

Elekta Medical Systems SRL (1)
12th Menuetului street Building D 4th floor, Bucharest Business Park, 01185, Bucharest, Romania
Tel.: (40) 318284830
Medical Care Services
N.A.I.C.S.: 621610

Elekta Medikal Sistemler Ticaret A.S. (1)
Barbaros Mah Begonya Sokak Nidakule Atasehir Kuzey Kat 18, Atasehir, 34746, Istanbul, Turkiye
Tel.: (90) 2164743500
Medical Scanning Equipment Mfr
N.A.I.C.S.: 334510

Elekta Neuromag Oy (1)
Siltasaarenkatu 18 20 A, PO Box 34, 00531, Helsinki, Finland
Tel.: (358) 97562400
Web Site: http://www.elekta.com
Emp.: 20
Medical Imaging Equipment Mfr & Sales
N.A.I.C.S.: 339112

Elekta Pte Ltd. (1)
238A Thomson Road 12-06/07 Novena Square Tower A, Singapore, 307684, Singapore
Tel.: (65) 62212322
Medical Scanning Equipment Mfr
N.A.I.C.S.: 334510

Elekta Pty. Ltd. (1)
Suite 10 02 Level 10 146 Arthur Street, North Sydney, 2060, NSW, Australia
Tel.: (61) 289071800
Web Site: http://www.elekta.com.au
Sales Range: $25-49.9 Million
Emp.: 13
Medical Radiation Therapy Equipment Mfr & Sales
N.A.I.C.S.: 339112

Elekta S.A./N.V. (1)
Belgicastraat 11, 1930, Zaventem, Belgium
Tel.: (32) 27212010
Emp.: 9
Medical & Surgical Equipment Distr
N.A.I.C.S.: 423450

Elekta S.p.A. (1)
Centro Direzionale Colleonib Palazzo Andromeda ingr 3, 20864, Agrate Brianza, MB, Italy
Tel.: (39) 0398889130
Web Site: https://www.elekta.com
Surgical & Medical Equipment Distr
N.A.I.C.S.: 423450

Elekta SA (1)
19-21 rue du Dome, 92100, Boulogne-Billancourt, France
Tel.: (33) 155958340
Sales Range: $25-49.9 Million
Emp.: 5
Medical Device Mfr & Distr
N.A.I.C.S.: 339112

Elekta Services S.R.O. (1)
Prazakova 1000/60, 619 00, Brno, Czech Republic
Tel.: (420) 547213603
Medical Scanning Equipment Mfr
N.A.I.C.S.: 334510

Elekta Solutions AB (1)
Hagaplan 4, Box 7593, 113 68, Stockholm, Sweden
Tel.: (46) 858725400
Medical Scanning Equipment Mfr
N.A.I.C.S.: 334510

Elekta sp.Z.O.O (1)
Inflancka 4C building D Gdanski Business Center, 00-189, Warsaw, Poland
Tel.: (48) 225591360
Medical Scanning Equipment Mfr
N.A.I.C.S.: 334510

IMPAC Medical Systems, Inc. (1)
100 Methilda Pl, Sunnyvale, CA 94086

Tel.: (650) 623-8800
Web Site: http://www.elekta.com
Sales Range: $50-74.9 Million
Emp.: 200
Computer Software Development
N.A.I.C.S.: 513210
Rob MacMillan (VP-Product Mktg)

Subsidiary (Non-US):

Elekta IMPAC Software (2)
Linac House Fleming Way, Crawley, RH10 9RR, W Sussex, United Kingdom (100%)
Tel.: (44) 1293544422
Web Site: http://www.elekta.co.uk
Sales Range: $25-49.9 Million
Emp.: 150
Computer Software Developer
N.A.I.C.S.: 334610

Subsidiary (Domestic):

IMPAC Global Systems (2)
100 Mathilda Pl FI 5, Sunnyvale, CA 94086
Tel.: (650) 623-8800
Sales Range: $50-74.9 Million
Emp.: 200
Computer Software Development
N.A.I.C.S.: 513210
David A. Auerbach (Pres)

Nucletron B.V. (1)
Waardgelder 1, 3905 TH, Veenendaal, Netherlands
Tel.: (31) 31 855 7133
Web Site: http://www.nucletron.com
Sales Range: $150-199.9 Million
Emp.: 250
Cancer Treatment Device Mfr, Sales & Service
N.A.I.C.S.: 339112
Jos Lamers (CEO)

Subsidiary (Non-US):

Nucletron A/S (2)
Fyrstikkalleen 3A, PO Box 6651, 0609, Oslo, Norway
Tel.: (47) 2270 7970
Web Site: http://www.nucletron.com
Sales Range: $25-49.9 Million
Emp.: 20
Cancer Treatment Device Mfr & Sales
N.A.I.C.S.: 339112

Nucletron Asia Pacific Ltd. (2)
Room 1005 Tower II Silvercord, 30 Canton Rd Tsim Sha Tsui, Kowloon, China (Hong Kong)
Tel.: (852) 23112683
Web Site: http://www.nucletron.com.hk
Sales Range: $25-49.9 Million
Emp.: 25
Cancer Treatment Device Mfr & Sales
N.A.I.C.S.: 339112

Nucletron Canada Inc. (2)
411 Legget Drive Suite 502, Kanata, K2K 3C9, ON, Canada
Tel.: (613) 886-1100
Sales Range: $25-49.9 Million
Emp.: 7
Cancer Treatment Device Mfr & Sales
N.A.I.C.S.: 339112

Nucletron Poland SP z.o.o. (2)
Oddzial w Warszawie, Al Krakowska 285, 02 133, Warsaw, Poland
Tel.: (48) 228681782
Cancer Treatment Device Mfr & Sales
N.A.I.C.S.: 339112

Nucletron Pty. Ltd. (2)
1b Little Commodore Street, Newtown, 2042, NSW, Australia
Tel.: (61) 295171300
Web Site: http://www.nucletron.com
Sales Range: $25-49.9 Million
Emp.: 9
Cancer Treatment Device Mfr & Sales
N.A.I.C.S.: 339112
Peter Douglas (Mng Dir)

Nucletron SAS (2)
Parc d'Activites Bernard Vergnaud, 15 Rue Paul Langevin, 93274, Sevran, Cedex, France
Tel.: (33) 149362060
Web Site: http://www.nucletron.com

Sales Range: $25-49.9 Million
Emp.: 18
Cancer Treatment Device Mfr & Sales
N.A.I.C.S.: 339112

Nucletron UK Ltd. (2)
Nucletron House Chowley Oak, Tattenhall, Chester, CH3 9EX, United Kingdom
Tel.: (44) 1829771111
Web Site: http://www.nucletron.com
Sales Range: $25-49.9 Million
Emp.: 26
Cancer Treatment Device Mfr & Sales
N.A.I.C.S.: 339112
Mark Hitchman (Mng Dir)

Theranostic Medizintechnik GmbH (2)
Obere Dammstrasse 8 10, 42653, Solingen, Germany
Tel.: (49) 2125875153
Web Site: http://www.theranostic.de
Sales Range: $25-49.9 Million
Emp.: 50
Cancer Treatment Device Mfr & Sales
N.A.I.C.S.: 339112

RRTS Unipessoal Lda (1)
Alameda dos Oceanos 27 Escritorio 8, Parque das Nacoes, 1990-197, Lisbon, Portugal
Tel.: (351) 211910797
Medical Scanning Equipment Mfr
N.A.I.C.S.: 334510

ELEKTRIM S.A.
ul Panska 77/79, 00-834, Warsaw, Poland
Tel.: (48) 224328801
Web Site: http://www.elektrim.pl
Year Founded: 1945
Sales Range: $200-249.9 Million
Emp.: 15
Holding Company Telecommunications Energy & Cable Mfr
N.A.I.C.S.: 551112
Wojciech Piskorz (Chm)

Subsidiaries:

Elektrim-Megadex S.A. (1)
Mickiewicza 63, Warsaw, 010625, Poland (99%)
Tel.: (48) 225605700
Web Site: http://www.emsa.com.pl
Sales Range: $25-49.9 Million
N.A.I.C.S.: 238210

Elektrim-Volt S.A. (1)
ul Panska 85, 00-834, Warsaw, Poland (100%)
Tel.: (48) 224378655
Web Site: http://www.elektrim-volt.eu
N.A.I.C.S.: 238210

ELEKTRISOLA DR. GERD SCHILDBACH GMBH & CO. KG
Zur Steinagger 3, 51580, Reichshof, Germany
Tel.: (49) 2265120
Web Site: http://www.elektrisola.com
Year Founded: 1948
Sales Range: $75-99.9 Million
Emp.: 300
Silo Mfr
N.A.I.C.S.: 331318

Subsidiaries:

Elektrisola (Hangzhou) Co., Ltd. (1)
Xiao Ling Tou, Yuhang, 311115, Hangzhou, Pingyao, China
Tel.: (86) 571 8852 0788
Copper Wire Mfr & Distr
N.A.I.C.S.: 331318
Bernt Gramann (Gen Mgr)

Elektrisola (M) Sdn. Bhd. (1)
Jalan Damai 1 Janda Baik, 28750, Bentung, Pahang, Malaysia
Tel.: (60) 9 221 0888
Wire Mfr & Distr
N.A.I.C.S.: 331318
I-Kwang Chang (Mgr-R&D)

Elektrisola Atesina S.r.l. (1)
Molini di Tures - Zona Industriale 13, Others, Campo Tures, Bolzano, Italy
Tel.: (39) 0474 689111
Web Site: http://www.elektrisola.it
Wire Mfr & Distr
N.A.I.C.S.: 331318

Elektrisola Company Limited (1)
Flat M 8/F Yue Cheung Centre 1 - 3 Wong Chuk Yeung Street, Fotan, New Territories, China (Hong Kong)
Tel.: (852) 29593270
Pipe Distr
N.A.I.C.S.: 423610

Elektrisola Feindraht AG (1)
Hauptstrasse 35, 6182, Escholzmatt-Marbach, Switzerland
Tel.: (41) 41 487 77 00
Web Site: http://www.textile-wire.ch
Emp.: 200
Wire Mfr & Distr
N.A.I.C.S.: 331318
Benno Zemp (Mng Dir)

Elektrisola France Sa (1)
107-111 Rue du Moulin Sarrazin, BP 83, 95101, Argenteuil, France
Tel.: (33) 1 34110506
Web Site: http://www.elektrisola.fr
Pipe Distr
N.A.I.C.S.: 423610

Elektrisola Inc. (1)
126 High St, Boscawen, NH 03303-2808
Tel.: (603) 796-2114
Web Site: http://www.elektrisola.com
Sales Range: $50-74.9 Million
Emp.: 170
Provider of Nonferrous Wiredrawing & Insulating Services
N.A.I.C.S.: 335929
Pete Grondin (Controller)

Elektrisola India Pvt. Ltd (1)
41 Sheetal Adiabad Estate Off A B Nair Road, Juhu, 400 049, Mumbai, India
Tel.: (91) 22 26210400
Pipe Distr
N.A.I.C.S.: 423610

Elektrisola Korea Co. Ltd. (1)
314 Bangsan-dong, Siheung, Kyunggi-do, Korea (South)
Tel.: (82) 31 316 0611
Pipe Distr
N.A.I.C.S.: 423610

Elektrisola S.A. de C.V. (1)
Periferico Manuel Gomez Morin 1800, Cuauhtemoc, 31500, Chihuahua, Mexico
Tel.: (52) 625 581 9000
Wire Mfr & Distr
N.A.I.C.S.: 331318

Nippon Elektrisola Ltd. (1)
4F MY Atsugi Bldg 3-11-18 Naka-cho, Atsugi, 243-0018, Kanagawa-Ken, Japan
Tel.: (81) 46 296 2130
Web Site: http://www.elektrisola.com.jp
Emp.: 10
Pipe Distr
N.A.I.C.S.: 423610

ELEKTRIZITATSWERK DER STADT ZURICH
Tramstrasse 35, 8050, Zurich, Switzerland
Tel.: (41) 58 319 41 11
Web Site: http://www.ewz.ch
Energy Service Company
N.A.I.C.S.: 221122
Harry Graf (Head-Media & Public Affairs)

Subsidiaries:

SunTechnics Fabrisolar AG (1)
Untere Heslibachstrasse 39, Kusnacht, 8700, Zurich, Switzerland
Tel.: (41) 44 9142 88 0
Web Site: http://www.suntechnics.ch
Power Plant Management Services
N.A.I.C.S.: 221118

ELEKTRO GRUPA D.D.

Kneza Branimira 2, 88000, Mostar,
Bosnia & Herzegovina
Tel.: (387) 36313824
ELGJR—(SARE)
Rev.: $170,461
Assets: $4,201,870
Liabilities: $3,390,039
Net Worth: $811,831
Earnings: ($78,778)
Emp.: 1
Fiscal Year-end: 12/31/20
Electrical Installation Services
N.A.I.C.S.: 238210

ELEKTRO INDUSTRIJSKA SERVISNA MREZA A.D.
NH Milorada Bondzulica 1, Belgrade,
Serbia
Tel.: (381) 112452252
Year Founded: 1975
EISV—(BEL)
Rev.: $434,965
Assets: $826,977
Liabilities: $325,297
Net Worth: $501,679
Earnings: $13,381
Emp.: 42
Fiscal Year-end: 12/31/22
Household Goods Repair & Mainte-
nance Services
N.A.I.C.S.: 811490
Mirjana Milic (Dir)

ELEKTRO MACK GMBH
Kiesgrubenstr 18, 88255, Baindt,
Germany
Tel.: (49) 750294010
Web Site: http://www.elektro-
mack.com
Year Founded: 1973
Rev.: $10,000,000
Emp.: 75
Industrial Electric Installation Services
N.A.I.C.S.: 221122
Karl Mack (Co-Mng Dir)

ELEKTRO SLOVENIA D.O.O.
Hajdrihova Ulica 2, 1000, Ljubljana,
Slovenia
Tel.: (386) 14743000
Web Site: http://www.eles.si
Sales Range: $200-249.9 Million
Emp.: 500
Electric Power Transmission Services
N.A.I.C.S.: 221122

Subsidiaries:

Borzen, d.o.o. (1)
Dunajska 156, Ljubljana, 1000, Slovenia
Tel.: (386) 16207600
Web Site: http://www.borzen.si
Sales Range: $50-74.9 Million
Emp.: 30
Electricity Trading
N.A.I.C.S.: 523210

Education Centre of the Slovenian (1)
Electric Power Authority
Hajdrihova Ulica 2, 1000, Ljubljana, Slove-
nia
Tel.: (386) 014742631
Web Site: http://www.ices.se
Sales Range: $25-49.9 Million
Emp.: 3
Personnel Training
N.A.I.C.S.: 541612

Eles-Gen, d.o.o. (1)
Hajdrihova Ulica 2, 1000, Ljubljana, Slove-
nia
Tel.: (386) 014743000
Web Site: http://www.eles.si
Sales Range: $500-549.9 Million
Electric Power Generation
N.A.I.C.S.: 221121
Vitoslav Turk (CEO & Mng Dir)

STELKOM d.o.o. (1)
Spruha 19, 1236, Trzin, Slovenia
Tel.: (386) 1 620 22 00
Telecommunication Servicesb

N.A.I.C.S.: 517810
Janko Janezic (Gen Mgr)

TALUM d.d. (1)
Tovarniska cesta 10, Kidricevo, 2325, Ptuj,
Slovenia
Tel.: (386) 2 7995 100
Web Site: http://www.talum.si
Emp.: 1,200
Primary Aluminium Production Services
N.A.I.C.S.: 331313
Marko Drobnic (Chm-Mgmt Bd)

ELEKTRODIZALICA A.D.
Kralja Petra 77, Belgrade, Serbia
Tel.: (381) 112623179
Year Founded: 1979
ELDZ—(BEL)
Rev.: $142,838
Assets: $63,374
Liabilities: $63,328
Net Worth: $46
Earnings: ($3,432)
Fiscal Year-end: 12/31/22
Metal Structure Mfr
N.A.I.C.S.: 331221
Branko Stankovic (Exec Dir)

ELEKTROIMPORTOREN AS
Nedre Kalbakkvei 88B, 1081, Oslo,
Norway
Tel.: (47) 22812770
Web Site:
https://www.elektroimportoren.no
Year Founded: 1994
ELIMP—(OSL)
Rev.: $148,186,403
Assets: $134,093,017
Liabilities: $92,619,804
Net Worth: $41,473,213
Earnings: ($1,096,804)
Emp.: 412
Fiscal Year-end: 12/31/23
Electrical Products Distr
N.A.I.C.S.: 423610
Amund Skarholt (Chm)

ELEKTROKRAJINA A.D. BANJA LUKA
Kralja Petra I Karadordevica 95,
78000, Banja Luka, Republika
Srpska, Bosnia & Herzegovina
Tel.: (387) 51246300
Web Site:
https://www.elektrokrajina.com
Year Founded: 1947
EKBL—(BANJ)
Sales Range: $1-4.9 Billion
Emp.: 1,684
Electrical Energy Distr
N.A.I.C.S.: 221122
Rajko Srdic (Pres & Exec Dir-Legal
Issues)

ELEKTROMETAL A.D.
Vlajkoviceva 12, Belgrade, Serbia
Tel.: (381) 113347000
Year Founded: 1952
ELKR—(BEL)
Sales Range: $1-9.9 Million
Emp.: 28
Hardware Product Whslr
N.A.I.C.S.: 423710

ELEKTROMETAL AD
ul Milyo voyvoda 1, 4400, Pazard-
zhik, Bulgaria
Tel.: (359) 443430
ELMT—(BUL)
Sales Range: Less than $1 Million
Rubber Products Mfr
N.A.I.C.S.: 326291

ELEKTROMONT A.D.
F Visnjica 4a, Novi Sad, Serbia
Tel.: (381) 21 6612 911
Web Site:
http://www.elektromont.co.rs

Year Founded: 1987
Sales Range: Less than $1 Million
Emp.: 2
Electrical Contracting Services
N.A.I.C.S.: 238210

ELEKTROPORCELAN A.D.
Marka Miljanova 15, 21000, Novi
Sad, Serbia
Tel.: (381) 21 661 5556
Web Site:
http://www.elektroporcelan.com
Year Founded: 1922
ELPO—(BEL)
Sales Range: Less than $1 Million
Emp.: 180
Insulator Mfr
N.A.I.C.S.: 423330
Marko Pejcic (Chm)

ELEKTROPORCELAN ARAN-DELOVAC A.D.
Put 1300 Kaplara bb, 34300, Arande-
lovac, Serbia
Tel.: (381) 34 542 003
Web Site: http://www.epa.rs
Year Founded: 1952
Sales Range: Less than $1 Million
Insulator Product Mfr
N.A.I.C.S.: 327110

ELEKTROREMONT D.D.
Omazici bb, 75290, Banovici, Bosnia
& Herzegovina
Tel.: (387) 35875495
Web Site:
http://www.elektroremont.ba
Year Founded: 1962
ELRMRK3—(SARE)
Rev.: $2,933,182
Assets: $2,301,759
Liabilities: $884,668
Net Worth: $1,417,091
Earnings: $3,719
Emp.: 111
Fiscal Year-end: 12/31/20
Industrial Machinery Repair Services
N.A.I.C.S.: 811310

ELEKTROS, INC.
229 Tongda Avenue, Economic &
Technological Development Zone,
Suqian, 223800, Jiangsu, China
Tel.: (86) 527 8437 0508 NV
Web Site: http://www.cxfee.com
Year Founded: 2011
ELEK—(OTCIQ)
Sales Range: Less than $1 Million
Emp.: 1
Environmental Engineering Services
N.A.I.C.S.: 541330
Li Yuan (Chm, CEO & CFO)

ELEKTROSERVIS A.D.
Bulevar Srpske Vojske 13, 78000,
Banja Luka, Bosnia & Herzegovina
Tel.: (387) 51300881
Year Founded: 2001
ELSR-R-A—(BANJ)
Sales Range: Less than $1 Million
Electrical Product Repair Services
N.A.I.C.S.: 811210
Miroslav Jaslar (Chm-Mgmt Bd)

ELEKTROTIM S.A.
ul Stargardzka 8, 54-156, Wroclaw,
Poland
Tel.: (48) 713521341
Web Site: https://www.elektrotim.pl
Year Founded: 1998
ELT—(WAR)
Rev.: $138,960,111
Assets: $68,242,632
Liabilities: $42,030,742
Net Worth: $26,211,890
Earnings: $4,988,567

Emp.: 334
Fiscal Year-end: 12/31/23
Electric Installations & Automatic Sys-
tems
N.A.I.C.S.: 238210
Andrzej Diakun (Chm-Mgmt Bd)

ELEKTROVEZE PROIZ-VODNJA A.D.
Svetog Nikole 27, Belgrade, Serbia
Tel.: (381) 11 2416 543
Year Founded: 1993
ELVPR—(BEL)
Sales Range: Less than $1 Million
Emp.: 2
Communication Equipment Mfr
N.A.I.C.S.: 334220
Snezana Vrzic-Orlovic (Gen Mgr)

ELEKTROWNIA BELCHATOW S.A.
Rogowiec 5, 97-406, Belchatow, Po-
land
Tel.: (48) 446325132
Year Founded: 1960
Sales Range: $900-999.9 Million
Emp.: 5,000
Electronic Services
N.A.I.C.S.: 221122

Subsidiaries:

Bot Elektrownia Turow SA (1)
ul Mlodych Energetykow 12, Bogatynia, 59-
916, Warsaw, Poland
Tel.: (48) 757734900
Web Site: http://www.elturow.bot.pl
Other Electric Power Generation
N.A.I.C.S.: 221118

Bot Gornictwo I Energetyka SA (1)
Al J Pilsudskiego 12, 90-051, Lodz, Poland
Tel.: (48) 422828000
Web Site: http://www.bot.pl
Sales Range: $75-99.9 Million
Emp.: 150
Other Holding Companies Offices
N.A.I.C.S.: 551112

ELBIS Sp. z o.o. (1)
ul Instalacyina 2, 97-427, Rogowiec, Poland
Tel.: (48) 447353320
Web Site: https://www.elb2.pl
Electric Power Distribution
N.A.I.C.S.: 221122

ELEMENT 25 LIMITED
Park 355 Scarborough Beach Road,
Osborne Park, 6017, WA, Australia
Tel.: (61) 863752525 AU
Web Site:
https://www.element25.com.au
Year Founded: 2006
E25—(ASX)
Rev.: $8,878,807
Assets: $43,528,988
Liabilities: $5,380,309
Net Worth: $38,148,679
Earnings: ($14,366,287)
Fiscal Year-end: 06/30/24
Gold & Copper Exploration
N.A.I.C.S.: 213114
Justin Brown (Mng Dir)

ELEMENT 29 RESOURCES INC.
1005-409 Granville Street, Vancou-
ver, V6C 1T2, BC, Canada BC
Web Site:
https://www.e29copper.com
Year Founded: 2017
EMTRF—(OTCQB)
Assets: $10,849,068
Liabilities: $343,708
Net Worth: $10,505,360
Earnings: $3,910,485
Fiscal Year-end: 12/31/22
Mineral Mining Services
N.A.I.C.S.: 213115
Duane Lo (CFO)

Element Alpha SA—(Continued)

ELEMENT ALPHA SA
6 Rue du Rhône, 1207, Geneva,
Switzerland
Tel.: (41) 225522460   CH
Web Site: http://www.element-
alpha.com
Year Founded: 2015
Investment Services
N.A.I.C.S.: 523999
Ninu Mendiburu *(Founder & CEO)*

Subsidiaries:

Origin International Inc.   **(1)**
5501 Pennington Ave, Baltimore, MD 21226
Tel.: (410) 354-9500
Web Site: http://www.origin-international.us
Oil Storage Terminals & Processing Facilities Mfr
N.A.I.C.S.: 333132

ELEMENT FLEET MANAGEMENT CORPORATION
161 Bay Street Suite 3600, Toronto,
M5J 2S1, ON, Canada
Tel.: (416) 386-1067   ON
Web Site:
https://www.elementfleet.com
Year Founded: 2011
EFN—(TSX)
Rev.: $760,726,614
Assets: $13,337,829,400
Liabilities: $10,420,240,940
Net Worth: $2,917,588,460
Earnings: $74,764,713
Emp.: 2,500
Fiscal Year-end: 12/31/19
Equipment Finance Services
N.A.I.C.S.: 532412
Jim Halliday *(COO & Exec VP)*

Subsidiaries:

Element Fleet Management Corporation Mexico S.A. de C.V   **(1)**
Avenida Vasco De Quiroga 3000 Planta
Baja, Centro De Santa Fe, 1530, Mexico,
Mexico
Tel.: (52) 5550187100
Web Site: http://www.elementfleet.com.mx
Equipment Finance Services
N.A.I.C.S.: 532412

Element Vehicle Management Services, LLC   **(1)**
940 Ridgebrook Rd, Sparks, MD
21152-9390   **(100%)**
Tel.: (410) 771-1900
Web Site: http://www.elementfleet.com
Sales Range: $200-249.9 Million
Fleet Management Services
N.A.I.C.S.: 561110

Gelco Corporation   **(1)**
3 Capital Dr, Eden Prairie, MN 55344
Tel.: (952) 828-1000
Financial Consulting Services
N.A.I.C.S.: 523940

ELEMENT LIFESTYLE RETIREMENT INC.
438 West King Edward Avenue, Vancouver, V5Y 2J4, BC, Canada
Tel.: (604) 676-1418   BC
Web Site:
https://www.elementlifestyle.com
Year Founded: 2007
ELM—(TSXV)
Rev.: $252,668
Assets: $1,552,220
Liabilities: $1,903,005
Net Worth: ($350,785)
Earnings: ($1,195,533)
Fiscal Year-end: 05/31/21
Metal Mining
N.A.I.C.S.: 212290
Michael Diao *(CEO)*

ELEMENT NUTRITIONAL SCIENCES INC.

1100 Walkers Line Suite 401, Burlington, L7N 2G3, ON, Canada
Tel.: (416) 467-5229   BC
Web Site: https://www.elmtinc.com
Year Founded: 2018
MUSL—(CNSX)
Rev.: $361,062
Assets: $120,608
Liabilities: $6,515,442
Net Worth: ($6,394,834)
Earnings: ($4,385,231)
Fiscal Year-end: 12/31/23
Pharmaceutical Product Mfr & Distr
N.A.I.C.S.: 325412
Dean Pipher *(Chief Sls Officer)*

ELEMENT TECHNICAL SERVICES INC.
810 530-8th Ave SW, Calgary, T2P
3S8, AB, Canada
Tel.: (403) 930-0246
Web Site: https://www.element-
technical.com
Emp.: 100
Fracturing & Coiled Tubing Services
N.A.I.C.S.: 213112
Jason Nikish *(Pres)*

Subsidiaries:

Essential Energy Services Ltd.   **(1)**
Livingston Place West 1100 250 2nd St
SW, Calgary, T2P 0C1, AB, Canada
Tel.: (403) 263-6778
Web Site: https://www.essentialenergy.ca
Rev.: $121,208,000
Assets: $159,086,000
Liabilities: $36,260,000
Net Worth: $122,826,000
Earnings: $11,397,000
Emp.: 382
Fiscal Year-end: 12/31/2021
Oil Field Services
N.A.I.C.S.: 213112
Garnet K. Amundson *(Pres & CEO)*

Division (Domestic):

Essential Energy Services Ltd. - Tryton Rentals Division   **(2)**
1203-4th Street, Nisku, T9E 7L3, AB,
Canada
Tel.: (780) 955-9420
Web Site: http://www.trytonrentals.com
Oilfield Rental Equipment Distr
N.A.I.C.S.: 423830

Subsidiary (Domestic):

Tryton Tool Services Ltd.   **(2)**
1100 250-2nd St SW, Calgary, T2P 0C1,
AB, Canada
Tel.: (403) 263-6778
Web Site: http://www.trytontoolservices.com
Oilfield Rental Equipment Distr
N.A.I.C.S.: 423830
Wes Lyster *(Mgr-Sls & Mktg)*

ELEMENT79 GOLD CORP.
Suite 1100-1111 Melville Street, Vancouver, V6E 3V6, BC, Canada
Tel.: (403) 850-8050   BC
Web Site:
https://www.element79.gold
Year Founded: 2020
ELEM—(CNSX)
Assets: $20,106,920
Liabilities: $7,407,861
Net Worth: $12,699,060
Earnings: ($3,697,967)
Fiscal Year-end: 08/31/22
Gold Exploration Services
N.A.I.C.S.: 212220
James C. Tworek *(CEO)*

ELEMENTAL ALTUS ROYALTIES CORP.
1020 - 800 West Pender, Vancouver,
V6C 2V6, BC, Canada
Tel.: (604) 243-6511   BC
Web Site:
https://www.elementalaltus.com

Year Founded: 2004
ELEM—(OTCBB)
Rev.: $1,614,321
Assets: $1,790,278
Liabilities: $2,986,746
Net Worth: ($1,196,468)
Earnings: ($2,330,535)
Fiscal Year-end: 09/30/19
Fertilizer Producer
N.A.I.C.S.: 325312
Steven Poulton *(Chm)*

Subsidiaries:

Altus Strategies Plc   **(1)**
14 Station Road The Orchard Centre, Didcot, OX11 7LL, Oxfordshire, United Kingdom
Tel.: (44) 1235511767
Web Site: http://www.altus-strategies.com
Rev.: $2,632,096
Assets: $15,669,068
Liabilities: $1,683,060
Net Worth: $13,986,008
Earnings: ($2,823,228)
Emp.: 30
Fiscal Year-end: 12/31/2020
Mining Exploration Services
N.A.I.C.S.: 213114
Will Slater *(VP-Exploration)*

ELEMENTAL ENERGIES HOLDINGS LIMITED
12-16 Albyn Place Aberdeen, Aberdeenshire, AB10 1PS, United Kingdom
Tel.: (44) 1224025448
Web Site:
https://www.elementalenergies.com
Year Founded: 2022
Technical & Environmental Consulting
Services
N.A.I.C.S.: 541690
Martyn Fear *(Chm)*

Subsidiaries:

Norwell Engineering Limited   **(1)**
78 Queens Road, Aberdeen, AB15 4YE,
United Kingdom
Tel.: (44) 1224498400
Web Site:
https://www.norwellengineering.com
Engineering Project Management Services
N.A.I.C.S.: 541330
Ken Fraser *(Founder & Chm)*

ELEMENTAL HOLDING S.A.
ul Traugutta 42, 05-825, Grodzisk
Mazowiecki, Poland
Tel.: (48) 22 390 91 35
Web Site: http://www.elemental-
holding.pl
Recycling Services & Recyclable Materials Distr
N.A.I.C.S.: 562998
Pawel Jarski *(Chm-Mgmt Bd)*

Subsidiaries:

Elemental Resource Management
Ltd.   **(1)**
Unit 5 Gelderd Trading Estate, Leeds, LS12
6BD, United Kingdom
Tel.: (44) 1132450511
Web Site: http://www.elementalrm.com
Metal Product Distr
N.A.I.C.S.: 423510
Marcin Szczypka *(Mng Dir)*

Elemental USA Inc.   **(1)**
2371 Church St, Philadelphia, PA 19124
Tel.: (215) 289-1475
Web Site: http://www.eleminc.com
Sales Range: $1-9.9 Million
Emp.: 12
Computer Peripheral Recycling Services
N.A.I.C.S.: 811210
Karen Petherbridge *(Pres)*

Evciler Kimya Madencilik ve Degerli
Metaller San.Tic A.S.   **(1)**
KaracaOren Mah 1645 Cad No 9, Altindag,
Ankara, Turkiye
Tel.: (90) 3125282015

FINEX SICAV SIF S.A. - Private Equity VII   **(1)**
25A Boulevard Royal, 2449, Luxembourg,
Luxembourg
Tel.: (352) 202129
Web Site: http://www.finexis.lu
Fund Management Services
N.A.I.C.S.: 523940
Christian Denizon *(Chm & Mng Dir)*

PGM Group Sp. z o.o.   **(1)**
ul Słowackiego 22A, 05-825, Grodzisk Mazowiecki, Poland
Tel.: (48) 511353535
Web Site: http://www.pgmg.eu
Recycling Metal Services
N.A.I.C.S.: 423510

PGM of Texas LLC   **(1)**
2809 S I-35, San Marcos, TX 78666
Tel.: (512) 829-4194
Web Site: http://www.pgmoftexas.com
Recycling Metal Services
N.A.I.C.S.: 423510
Allen Hickman *(Gen Mgr-Sls & Pur)*

Platinium M.M. spolka z ograniczona
odpowiedzialnoscia sp.k.   **(1)**
ul Szparagowa nr 3, 62-081, Wysogotowo,
Poland
Tel.: (48) 533650650
Web Site: http://www.platiniummm.pl
Recycling Metal Services
N.A.I.C.S.: 423510

RECAT GmbH   **(1)**
Ochsenburger Strasse 19 EGO Business
Park Under the Ravensburg, 75056,
Sulzfeld, Germany
Tel.: (49) 7269960930
Web Site: http://www.recat.de
Recycling Metal Services
N.A.I.C.S.: 423510
Marta Rutkowska *(Mng Dir)*

Syntom Metal Recycling Sp. z
o.o.   **(1)**
ul Wysoka 61/65, 97-200, Tomaszow Mazowiecki, Poland
Tel.: (48) 447244648
Web Site: http://www.syntom.pl
Recycling Metal Services
N.A.I.C.S.: 423510
Grzegorz Bartus *(Pres)*

Terra Recycling Sp. z o.o.Sp.k.   **(1)**
ul Traugutta 42, 05-825, Grodzisk Mazowiecki, Poland
Tel.: (48) 223797431
Web Site: http://www.terrarecycling.pl
Electronic Device Recycling Services
N.A.I.C.S.: 562920

ELEMENTIS PLC
Aspect House Spencer Road, Lancing, BN99 6DA, West Sussex, United
Kingdom
Tel.: (44) 2070672999   UK
Web Site:
https://www.elementisplc.com
Year Founded: 1908
ELM—(LSE)
Rev.: $736,400,000
Assets: $1,627,000,000
Liabilities: $843,100,000
Net Worth: $783,900,000
Earnings: ($62,600,000)
Fiscal Year-end: 12/31/22
Specialty Chemicals, Pigments &
Chromium Mfr
N.A.I.C.S.: 325998
Paul Waterman *(CEO)*

Subsidiaries:

Adentatec GmbH   **(1)**
Konrad-Adenauer-Str 13, 50996, Cologne,
Germany
Tel.: (49) 221 359 6100
Web Site: https://adentatec.com
Dental Material Mfr & Distr
N.A.I.C.S.: 339114

Elementis Chromium (1)
Eaglescliffe, Stockton-on-Tees, TS16 0QG,
United Kingdom (100%)
Tel.: (44) 1642780682
Web Site:
http://www.elementischromium.com
Sales Range: $650-699.9 Million
Emp.: 180
Chromium Chemicals Sales; Financial & IT
Services
N.A.I.C.S.: 325998

Elementis Chromium, LP (1)
3800 Buddy Lawrence Dr, Corpus Christi,
TX 78407 (100%)
Tel.: (361) 880-7706
Web Site:
http://www.elementischromium.com
Rev.: $30,000,000
Emp.: 50
Chromium Chemicals Mfr
N.A.I.C.S.: 325180

Elementis LTP, LT (1)
546 S Water St, Milwaukee, WI
53204-1646 (100%)
Tel.: (414) 278-8844
Web Site:
http://www.elementischromium.com
Sales Range: $50-74.9 Million
Emp.: 10
Leather Tanning Product Mfr
N.A.I.C.S.: 325180

Elementis Pharma GmbH (1)
Giulinistrasse 2, 67065, Ludwigshafen, Ger-
many
Tel.: (49) 6215 709 6990
Web Site:
https://www.elementispharma.com
Aluminum Hydroxide Powder Mfr
N.A.I.C.S.: 325180

**Elementis S.E.A. (Malaysia) Sdn
Bhd** (1)
62-1 JalanTasik Utama 5 Medan Niaga Ta-
sik Damai The Trillium, Lakefields Sungei
Besi, 57000, Kuala Lumpur, Selangor, Ma-
laysia
Tel.: (60) 39 054 6690
Chemical Products Mfr
N.A.I.C.S.: 325180

Elementis Specialties, Inc. (1)
329 Wyckoffs Mills Rd, Hightstown, NJ
08520-1007
Tel.: (609) 443-2500
Web Site: http://www.elementis-
specialties.com
Sales Range: $75-99.9 Million
Emp.: 250
Specialty Chemicals Mfr
N.A.I.C.S.: 325510

Subsidiary (Domestic):

Hi-Mar Specialty Chemicals, LLC (2)
3939 W McKinley Ave, Milwaukee, WI
53208
Tel.: (414) 342-5443
Web Site: http://www.hi-mar.net
Sales Range: $10-24.9 Million
Emp.: 28
Surface Active Agent Mfr
N.A.I.C.S.: 325613
Debarah Jones *(Acct Mgr)*

Mondo Minerals B.V. (1)
Kajuitweg 8, 1041 AR, Amsterdam, Nether-
lands
Tel.: (31) 20 448 7 448
Web Site: http://www.mondominerals.com
Sales Range: $25-49.9 Million
Emp.: 80
Talc Product Mfr
N.A.I.C.S.: 327992

ELEMENTOS LIMITED
Level 7 167 Eagle St, PO Box 10555,
Adelaide Street, Brisbane, 4000,
QLD, Australia
Tel.: (61) 732126299
Web Site:
https://www.elementos.com.au
ELT—(ASX)
Rev.: $11,257
Assets: $14,651,693
Liabilities: $1,320,620

Net Worth: $13,331,074
Earnings: ($852,392)
Emp.: 6
Fiscal Year-end: 06/30/24
Metal Mining Services
N.A.I.C.S.: 212290
Christopher James Dunks *(Exec Dir)*

ELENICA AD
str Marshal Tito no 222, 2400, Stru-
mica, North Macedonia
Tel.: (389) 34345046
Web Site:
https://www.elenica.com.mk
Year Founded: 1954
Building Materials Mfr
N.A.I.C.S.: 327120

ELENSYS CO., LTD.
30 Parang-ro 466beon-gil, Seo-gu,
Incheon, 22111, Korea (South)
Tel.: (82) 325737542
Web Site: http://www.elensys.co.kr
Year Founded: 2002
264850—(KRS)
Rev.: $63,350,366
Assets: $47,061,536
Liabilities: $14,310,388
Net Worth: $32,751,149
Earnings: $3,967,487
Emp.: 132
Fiscal Year-end: 12/31/22
Motor Mfr
N.A.I.C.S.: 335312
Jae-Gue Sim *(Pres)*

ELENTEC CO,. LTD.
37 Samsung-ro 268beon-gil,
Yeongtong-gu, Suwon, Gyeonggi,
Korea (South)
Tel.: (82) 7070988071
Web Site: http://www.elentec.co.kr
Year Founded: 1982
054210—(KRS)
Rev.: $765,417,641
Assets: $465,606,213
Liabilities: $266,146,024
Net Worth: $199,460,189
Earnings: $41,965,361
Emp.: 324
Fiscal Year-end: 12/31/22
Battery Pack Mfr
N.A.I.C.S.: 335910
Se Yong Lee *(Board of Directors &
CEO)*

Subsidiaries:

Elentec India Technologies Pvt.
Ltd. (1)
Eou Unit-57/1 2 Ecotech-1 Extension-1
Greater Noida G B Nagar, Noida, 201308,
Uttar Pradesh, India
Tel.: (91) 1202447098
Battery & Wire Mfr
N.A.I.C.S.: 335999

Plant (Domestic):

Elentec India Technologies Pvt. Ltd. -
Charger Factory (2)
Plot No B-37 Sector-80 Phase-II, Noida,
201305, Uttar Pradesh, India
Tel.: (91) 1204057800
Battery & Wire Mfr
N.A.I.C.S.: 335999

ELEPHANT CAPITAL PLC
Norfolk House 31 St James's Square,
London, SW1Y 4JJ, United Kingdom
Tel.: (44) 207 629 9524 IM
Web Site:
http://www.elephantcapital.com
Sales Range: Less than $1 Million
Investment Management Service
N.A.I.C.S.: 523940
Vincent Campbell *(Sec)*

**ELEPHANT HILL CAPITAL,
INC.**
639-5th Avenue Southwest Suite
1250, Calgary, T2P 0M9, AB, Canada
Tel.: (403) 613-7310
EH.P—(TSXV)
Rev.: $2,328
Assets: $291,796
Liabilities: $12,115
Net Worth: $279,681
Earnings: ($39,109)
Fiscal Year-end: 12/31/19
Asset Management Services
N.A.I.C.S.: 523040
Eamon Hurley *(CFO & Sec)*

ELEROM S.A. ROMAN
Strada Uzina de Tevi nr 13 Comuna
Cordun, 617135, Roman, 617135,
Neamt, Romania
Tel.: (40) 233748169
Web Site: http://www.elerom.ro
Year Founded: 1960
ELER—(BUC)
Rev.: $4,311,395
Assets: $3,509,032
Liabilities: $574,615
Net Worth: $2,934,417
Earnings: ($40,098)
Emp.: 63
Fiscal Year-end: 12/31/23
Transformer Mfr
N.A.I.C.S.: 334416
Iosif Mihoc *(Pres)*

ELES S.P.A.
Zona Bodoglie 148/1/Z, Todi, 06059,
Perugia, Italy
Tel.: (39) 075898000
Web Site: https://www.eles.com
Year Founded: 1988
ELES—(ITA)
Sales Range: Less than $1 Million
Semiconductor Equipment Distr
N.A.I.C.S.: 423690
Antonio Zaffarami *(Pres)*

ELEVATE URANIUM LTD.
Suite 2 5 Ord Street, West Perth,
6005, WA, Australia
Tel.: (61) 865551816 AU
Web Site:
https://www.elevateuranium.com.au
Year Founded: 1978
EL8—(ASX)
Rev.: $318,128
Assets: $8,854,029
Liabilities: $988,966
Net Worth: $7,865,063
Earnings: ($7,179,537)
Emp.: 11
Fiscal Year-end: 06/30/24
Gold Ore & Silver Ore Mining
N.A.I.C.S.: 212220
Murray Hill *(CEO & Mng Dir)*

ELEXXION AG
Otto-Hahn-StraSSe 7, 78224, Singen,
Germany
Tel.: (49) 773190733
Web Site: https://www.elexxion.com
E8X—(MUN)
Rev.: $469,128
Assets: $4,872,534
Liabilities: $9,052,038
Net Worth: ($4,179,504)
Earnings: ($1,044,876)
Emp.: 9
Fiscal Year-end: 12/31/22
Dental Laser System Mfr & Distr
N.A.I.C.S.: 334510
Xianlin Song *(Chm-Mgmt Bd)*

ELGAR ELECTRIC LTD.
7728 134 Street, Surrey, V3W 6Y5,
BC, Canada

Tel.: (604) 590-2771
Web Site:
http://www.elgarelectric.com
Year Founded: 1955
Rev.: $13,924,559
Emp.: 80
Electrical Contractor
N.A.I.C.S.: 238210
Robert Klein *(Pres & Gen Mgr)*

ELGEKA S.A.
Industrial Area of Sindos DA 13 OT
31 B FASI, Delta Municipality, 570
22, Thessaloniki, Greece
Tel.: (30) 2310779700
Web Site: http://www.elgeka.gr
ELGEK—(ATH)
Rev.: $200,704,669
Assets: $176,300,680
Liabilities: $171,083,252
Net Worth: $5,217,428
Earnings: $2,072,861
Emp.: 866
Fiscal Year-end: 12/31/19
Food Products Distr
N.A.I.C.S.: 424420
Alexander G. Katsiotis *(Chm & CEO)*

Subsidiaries:

Diakinisis S.A. (1)
Xenodochoipalilon Str 81, 136 77, Acha-
rnes, Greece
Tel.: (30) 2105538300
Web Site: http://www.diakinisis.gr
Logistics & Supply Chain Services
N.A.I.C.S.: 541614

Elgeka Ferfelis Romania S.A. (1)
150-158 Drum Intre Tarlale Street, 3rd Dis-
trict, Bucharest, Romania
Tel.: (40) 212046600
Web Site: http://www.elgeka-ferfelis.ro
Emp.: 480
Logistics & Supply Chain Services
N.A.I.C.S.: 541614
Adriana Mihailescu *(Mgr-HR)*

Global Synergy Buying Group
S.A. (1)
A 13-OT 31 - Boaon TK, Sindos, 570 22,
Thessaloniki, Greece
Tel.: (30) 2310752392
Web Site: http://www.gsbuyinggroup.gr
Logistics & Supply Chain Services
N.A.I.C.S.: 541614

ELGI EQUIPMENTS LIMITED
ELGI Industrial Complex Trichy Road,
Singanallur, Coimbatore, 641 005,
India
Tel.: (91) 4222589555 In
Web Site: https://www.elgi.com
Year Founded: 1960
522074—(BOM)
Rev.: $265,840,302
Assets: $241,155,915
Liabilities: $122,416,476
Net Worth: $118,739,439
Earnings: $13,989,203
Emp.: 1,285
Fiscal Year-end: 03/31/21
Air Compressors & Automotive Ser-
vice Station Equipment Mfr
N.A.I.C.S.: 333912
Jairam Vardaraj *(Mng Dir)*

Subsidiaries:

ATS Elgi Limited (1)
Private Industrial Estate, Kurichy, Coim-
batore, 641021, India
Tel.: (91) 422 258 9999
Web Site: https://www.ats-elgi.com
Automotive Equipment Mfr & Distr
N.A.I.C.S.: 333912

ELGI Compressors (M) Sdn.
Bhd. (1)
No 2A-1 Jalan Eco Santuari 8/2B Eco San-
tuari, 42500, Teluk Panglima Garang, Se-
langar, Malaysia
Tel.: (60) 386821258

ELGI Equipments Limited—(Continued)

Air Compressor Mfr & Distr
N.A.I.C.S.: 333912

**ELGI Equipments Limited - Pressure
Vessel Division** (1)
1473-TrichyRoad, Coimbatore, 641018,
India
Tel.: (91) 422 2589777
Air Compressor Mfr
N.A.I.C.S.: 333912

ELGI Equipments Ltd. (1)
223/66 14th Floor Country Complex Bldg A
Sanphawut Rd, Bangna Tai 5 Bangna,
Bangkok, 10260, Thailand
Tel.: (66) 27455160
Web Site: https://www.elgi.com
Air Compressor Mfr & Distr
N.A.I.C.S.: 333912
Bheemsingh Melchisedec *(Dir-Operations)*

ELGI Equipments Pty Ltd. (1)
Unit 1 33 Kingsbury Street, Brendale, 4500,
QLD, Australia
Tel.: (61) 731060589
Web Site: https://www.elgi.com
Air Compressor Mfr & Distr
N.A.I.C.S.: 333912

**Elgi Compressores do Brazil
Ltda** (1)
Rua Quinze de Novembro 200 Galpao II,
Bairro Paineiras, Itupeva, 13295 000, Sao
Paulo, Brazil
Tel.: (55) 114 496 5519
Web Site: https://www.elgi.com.br
Compressors Sales, Distr & Repair
N.A.I.C.S.: 423830

**Elgi Compressors Trading (Shanghai)
Co., Ltd** (1)
Room 402 No 19 Lane 1500 South Lianhua
Road, Min Hang District, Shanghai, 201108,
China
Tel.: (86) 21 33581191
Air Compressors & Automotive Service Sta-
tion Equipment Distr
N.A.I.C.S.: 423830

Elgi Compressors USA Inc. (1)
4610 Entrance Dr Ste A, Charlotte, NC
28273
Tel.: (704) 943-7966
Web Site: http://www.elgi.us
Air Compressor Mfr
N.A.I.C.S.: 333912

**Elgi Equipments (Zhejiang)
Limited** (1)
West of 1st Floor Building 2 No 232 Yunhai
Road, Jiaxing, 314033, Zhejiang, China
Tel.: (86) 5738 255 1120
Web Site: https://www.elgi.com.cn
Air Compressor Mfr
N.A.I.C.S.: 333912
Mandinder Singh Anand *(Gen Mgr)*

**Elgi Equipments Australia Pty
Ltd.** (1)
Unit 1 33 Kingsbury Street, Brendale, 4500,
QLD, Australia
Tel.: (61) 73 106 0589
Web Site: https://www.elgi.com.au
Air Compressor Mfr & Distr
N.A.I.C.S.: 333912

Elgi Gulf FZE (1)
PO Box 120695, Q4-081 Saif Zone,
Sharjah, United Arab Emirates
Tel.: (971) 6 557 9970
Compressors Sales, Distr & Repair
N.A.I.C.S.: 423440

Elgitread (USA) LLC (1)
600 N Magnolia, Luling, TX 78648
Tel.: (704) 332-4634
Sales Range: $25-49.9 Million
Emp.: 40
Tires Recapping & Retreading & Repairing
Services
N.A.I.C.S.: 326212

PT ELGI Equipments Indonesia (1)
Kawasan Pergudangan BIZPARK Commercial Estate Pulogadung Jl, Raya Bekai KM
21 5 Blok A3 No 12 Kel Rawa Terate Kec
Cakung Pulogadung, Jakarta, 13920, Indonesia

Tel.: (62) 4 682 2216
Web Site: https://www.elgi.com
Air Compressor Mfr
N.A.I.C.S.: 333912
Nitin Sharma *(Country Mgr)*

Patton's, Inc. (1)
4610 Entrance Dr Ste H, Charlotte, NC
28273
Tel.: (704) 523-4122
Web Site: https://www.pattonsinc.com
Sales Range: $25-49.9 Million
Emp.: 130
Compressed Air, Gas & Vacuum Systems
Mfr & Distr
N.A.I.C.S.: 423830
Scott Sutton *(VP & Gen Mgr)*

Rotair S.p.A. (1)
Via Bernezzo 67, 12023, Caraglio, CN, Italy
Tel.: (39) 017 161 9676
Web Site: https://www.rotairspa.com
Air Compressor Mfr & Distr
N.A.I.C.S.: 333912

SAS Belair, (1)
ZI de Moutti sud, 74540, Alby-sur-Cheran,
France
Tel.: (33) 4 50 68 20 57
Air Compressor Mfr
N.A.I.C.S.: 333912

ELGI RUBBER COMPANY LIM-
ITED

Super A Unit Coimbatore Private In-
dustrial Estate, Coimbatore, 641 021,
India
Tel.: (91) 4224321000   In
Web Site: https://www.elgirubber.com
Year Founded: 2006
ELGIRUBCO—(NSE)
Rev.: $50,315,449
Assets: $63,898,687
Liabilities: $41,832,144
Net Worth: $22,066,543
Earnings: $809,304
Emp.: 436
Fiscal Year-end: 03/31/23
Rubber Mfr
N.A.I.C.S.: 326291
Sudarsan Varadaraj *(Chm & Mng Dir)*

Subsidiaries:

**Borrachas e Equipamentos Elgi
Ltda** (1)
Estrada Chiquito De Aquino 150 Bairro
Mondesir Lorena, Sao Paulo, CEP 12 612
550, Brazil
Tel.: (55) 1231522414
Rubber Distr
N.A.I.C.S.: 424990

Elgi Rubber Company BV (1)
Schoenerweg 36, 6222 NX, Maastricht,
Netherlands
Tel.: (31) 433290444
Rubber Distr
N.A.I.C.S.: 424990

Elgi Rubber Company LLC (1)
600 N Magnolia Ave, Luling, TX 78648
Tel.: (830) 875-5539
Rubber Distr
N.A.I.C.S.: 424990

**Elgi Rubber Company Limited - Cin-
cinnati Retread Systems Division** (1)
4990 Factory Dr, Fairfield, OH 45014
Tel.: (513) 829-2248
Retreading Equipment Mfr
N.A.I.C.S.: 333248

Pincott International Pty Limited (1)
20 Churchill Street, Silverwater, 2128,
NSW, Australia
Tel.: (61) 296484009
Rubber Distr
N.A.I.C.S.: 424990

Subsidiary (US):

Pincott Sales Company Inc (2)
1140 S Jason St, Denver, CO 80223
Tel.: (303) 722-2623
Retread Tire Distr
N.A.I.C.S.: 423130

**Rubber Compounding Holland
B.V.** (1)
Koolhaaspark 15, 3864 PW, Nijkerkerveen,
Netherlands
Tel.: (31) 332580674
Web Site:
http://www.rubbercompoundholland.com
Rubber Mfr
N.A.I.C.S.: 325212

ELHIM ISKRA JSC

9 Iskra St, 4400, Pazardzhik, Bulgaria
Tel.: (359) 34441751
Web Site: https://www.elhim-
iskra.com
Year Founded: 1960
ELHM—(BUL)
Sales Range: Less than $1 Million
Motor Vehicle Equipment Mfr
N.A.I.C.S.: 336320

ELHO BV

Atlasstraat 11, 5047 RG, Tilburg,
Netherlands
Tel.: (31) 135157800
Web Site: http://www.elho.nl
Year Founded: 1964
Synthetic Pottery Mfr
N.A.I.C.S.: 327110

Subsidiaries:

Fiskars Germany GmbH (1)
Oststrasse 23, 32051, Herford, Germany
Tel.: (49) 5221 935 0
Web Site: http://www.fiskars.com
Sales Range: $50-74.9 Million
Emp.: 15
Gardening Tool Mfr & Distr
N.A.I.C.S.: 333112

ELIA GROUP SA

Boulevard de l Empereur 20, 1000,
Brussels, Belgium
Tel.: (32) 478901316   BE
Web Site: https://www.elia.be
ELI—(EUR)
Rev.: $3,902,439,024
Assets: $22,225,663,717
Liabilities: $16,013,274,336
Net Worth: $6,212,389,381
Earnings: $440,535,290
Emp.: 3,127
Fiscal Year-end: 12/31/22
Electric Power Distr
N.A.I.C.S.: 221122
Claude Gregoire *(Vice Chm)*

Subsidiaries:

50Hertz Transmission GmbH (1)
Heidestrasse 2, 10557, Berlin, Germany
Tel.: (49) 3051500
Web Site: https://www.50hertz.com
Sales Range: $500-549.9 Million
Emp.: 615
Power Transmission Grid Operation & Main-
tenance Services
N.A.I.C.S.: 221121
Boris Schucht *(CEO)*

Subsidiary (Domestic):

50Hertz Offshore GmbH (2)
Heidestrasse 2, 10557, Berlin, Germany
Tel.: (49) 3051502401
Sales Range: $150-199.9 Million
Offshore Power Structure Installation Ser-
vices
N.A.I.C.S.: 237130

Elia Asset SA (1)
Boulevard de l'Empereur 20, Brussels,
1000, Belgium
Tel.: (32) 2 546 70 11
Asset Management Services
N.A.I.C.S.: 523940

Elia Engineering SA (1)
boulevard de l'Empereur 20, 1000, Brus-
sels, Belgium
Tel.: (32) 2 5467711
Electrical Engineering Services
N.A.I.C.S.: 541330

Elia Grid International NV/SA (1)
Rue Joseph Stevens 7 Joseph Ste-
vensstraat, 1000, Brussels, Belgium
Tel.: (32) 22043811
Investment Holding Services
N.A.I.C.S.: 551112

Subsidiary (Non-US):

Elia Grid International GmbH (2)
Heidestrasse 41, 10557, Berlin, Germany
Tel.: (49) 30166379911
Investment Holding Services
N.A.I.C.S.: 551112

Elia Grid International LLC (2)
Office 905 9th Floor Al Fardan Office Tower
Al Funduq St West Bay, PO Box 31316,
Doha, Qatar
Tel.: (974) 800100739
Investment Holding Services
N.A.I.C.S.: 551112

Elia Grid International Pte. Ltd. (1)
20 Collyer Quay 09-01, Singapore, 049319,
Singapore
Tel.: (65) 31570670
Engineering Consultancy Services
N.A.I.C.S.: 813920

Eurogrid GmbH (1)
Heidestrasse 2, 10557, Berlin, Germany
Tel.: (49) 3051503201
Web Site: https://www.eurogrid.com
Rev.: $1,051,826,440
Electric Utility Asset Investment Services
N.A.I.C.S.: 523940

**Eurogrid International
CVBA/SCRL** (1)
Sablon Tower Joseph Stevensstraat 7,
1000, Brussels, Belgium
Tel.: (32) 25467570
Web Site: https://www.eurogrid-int.net
Investment Holding Services
N.A.I.C.S.: 551112

Re.Alto-Energy B.V./S.R.L. (1)
Boulevard de l Empereur 20, 1000, Brus-
sels, Belgium
Tel.: (32) 28918072
Web Site: https://www.realto.io
Digital Energy Services
N.A.I.C.S.: 541990

ELIANCE (PTY) LIMITED

Eliance House Glen Gables Building,
c/o Lynnwood Road & January
Masilela Dr, Pretoria, 40, South Africa
Tel.: (27) 124712500
Web Site: http://www.eliance.co.za
Sales Range: $25-49.9 Million
Emp.: 84
Software Consulting & Web Hosting
Services
N.A.I.C.S.: 518210
Claudio Camera *(CEO)*

ELICA S.P.A.

Via Ermanno Casoli 2, 60044, Fab-
riano, Italy
Tel.: (39) 07326101
Web Site:
https://www.elicagroup.com
Year Founded: 1970
ELC—(ITA)
Rev.: $594,595,708
Assets: $510,576,631
Liabilities: $361,041,622
Net Worth: $149,535,010
Earnings: $18,001,301
Emp.: 2,685
Fiscal Year-end: 12/31/22
Kitchen Cooker Hoods, Boiler Motors
& Home Heating Systems Mfr
N.A.I.C.S.: 335220
Francesco Casoli *(Chm)*

Subsidiaries:

Airforce S.p.A. (1)
Via Ca' Maiano 140/E, 60044, Fabriano,
AN, Italy
Tel.: (39) 0732250468
Web Site: http://www.airforcespa.it
Household Appliance Mfr & Whslr

Ariafina Co. Ltd. (1)
2-1-9 Fuchinobe, Chuo-ku, Sagamihara, 252-0206, Kanagawa, Japan
Tel.: (81) 427535340
Web Site: https://www.ariafina.jp
Household Appliance Mfr & Whslr
N.A.I.C.S.: 335220
Kosuke Kashimura *(Pres)*

Elica France S.A.S. (1)
11 Rue Louis Philippe, 92200, Neuilly-sur-Seine, France
Tel.: (33) 185533060
Household Appliance Mfr & Whslr
N.A.I.C.S.: 335220

Elica Group Polska (1)
ul Inzynierska 3, Jelcz Laskowice, 55-221, Wroclaw, Poland
Tel.: (48) 713386530
Cooker Hoods & Motor Assembly Sets Mfr
N.A.I.C.S.: 336390

Elica Trading LLC (1)
Tel.: (7) 4956403560
Household Appliance Mfr & Whslr
N.A.I.C.S.: 335220

Elicamex (1)
Jose Maria Arteaga No 57, 76220, Queretaro, Mexico
Tel.: (52) 4421531300
Furniture Mfr
N.A.I.C.S.: 337126

Fime (1)
Via Jesina 56, 60022, Castelfidardo, AN, Italy
Tel.: (39) 0717204301
Web Site: http://www.fimemotors.com
Sales Range: $100-124.9 Million
Emp.: 300
Cooker Hood Motors Mfr
N.A.I.C.S.: 335220

The Gutmann Company (1)
Muhlacker Strasse 77, Muhlacker, 75417, Germany
Tel.: (49) 704188241
Exhaust Hoods Mfr
N.A.I.C.S.: 337126

ELICERA THERAPEUTICS AB
Massans gata 10 Floor 7, World Trade Center, 412 51, Gothenburg, Sweden
Tel.: (46) 703319051
Web Site: https://www.elicera.com
Year Founded: 2014
ELIC—(OMX)
Rev.: $1,051,829
Assets: $2,826,718
Liabilities: $1,290,526
Net Worth: $1,536,192
Earnings: ($1,535,866)
Emp.: 2
Fiscal Year-end: 12/31/23
Biotechnology Research & Development Services
N.A.I.C.S.: 541714
Agneta Edberg *(Chm)*

ELIFE HOLDINGS LIMITED
Unit 806 Level 8 Core D Cyberport 3 100 Cyberport Road, Hong Kong, China (Hong Kong)
Tel.: (852) 25196668   Ky
Web Site: https://elife.com.hk
Year Founded: 2001
0223—(HKG)
Rev.: $19,682,348
Assets: $13,071,349
Liabilities: $7,475,552
Net Worth: $5,595,797
Earnings: ($6,368,388)
Emp.: 45
Fiscal Year-end: 03/31/22
Exhibition & Trade Fair Organizer
N.A.I.C.S.: 561920
Feng Gao *(Vice Chm)*

ELIGO S.P.A.

Via Pietro Mascagni 15, 20121, Milan, Italy
Tel.: (39) 0283488708
Web Site: https://www.eligo.style
ELG—(EUR)
Employee Recruitment Services
N.A.I.C.S.: 561311
Alessandra Rubino *(COO)*

ELIN VERD S.A.
24 Adrianou Str, 14561, Kifissia, Greece
Tel.: (30) 2144440144
Web Site: http://www.elinverd.gr
Year Founded: 2005
Biodiesel Mfr & Distr
N.A.I.C.S.: 325199
Yannis Courouclis *(Chm, CEO & Mng Dir)*

ELINI BVBA
Vestingstraat 49, 2018, Antwerp, Belgium
Tel.: (32) 032318640
Web Site: http://www.elini.com
Year Founded: 1989
Sales Range: $150-199.9 Million
Emp.: 700
Jewelry Mfr, Designer, Marketer & Sales
N.A.I.C.S.: 458310
Nisso Barokas *(Owner)*

Subsidiaries:

Elini Designs Corp. (1)
7950 Nw 53rd St Ste 215, Miami, FL 33166-4638
Tel.: (305) 466-7855
Web Site: http://www.elini.com
Jewelry Retailer
N.A.I.C.S.: 458310

ELINOIL S.A.
Pigon 33, Kifisia, 14564, Kifissia, Greece
Tel.: (30) 2106241500
Web Site: https://www.elin.gr
Year Founded: 1989
ELIN—(ATH)
Rev.: $2,741,671,526
Assets: $262,299,942
Liabilities: $177,675,748
Net Worth: $84,624,194
Earnings: $7,169,355
Emp.: 226
Fiscal Year-end: 12/31/23
Fuel, Lubricant & Gas Distr
N.A.I.C.S.: 424720
Georgios Tsounias *(Vice Chm)*

Subsidiaries:

Elin Technical SA (1)
Pigon St, Kifissia, 14564, Athens, Greece
Tel.: (30) 2106241570
Web Site: http://www.elintech.gr
Construction Services
N.A.I.C.S.: 236220

ELION CLEAN ENERGY CO., LTD.
30 E'erduosi St West Dongsheng, Ordos, 017000, China
Tel.: (86) 10 56632432
Web Site: http://english.elion.com.cn
Sales Range: $1-4.9 Billion
Emp.: 3,071
Holding Company
N.A.I.C.S.: 551112
Chengguo Yin *(Chm)*

ELISA CORPORATION
Ratavartijankatu 5, PO Box 1, FIN-00061, Helsinki, FIN-00061, Finland
Tel.: (358) 1026000
Web Site: https://www.elisa.com
Year Founded: 1882

ELISA—(HEL)
Rev.: $2,298,186,920
Assets: $3,346,427,801
Liabilities: $1,995,359,378
Net Worth: $1,351,068,422
Earnings: $402,331,103
Emp.: 5,523
Fiscal Year-end: 12/31/22
Telecommunication, Mobile & Voice Services
N.A.I.C.S.: 517112
Veli-Matti Mattila *(CEO)*

Subsidiaries:

Ecosite Oy (1)
Kutomotie 18, 00380, Helsinki, Finland
Tel.: (358) 1026056
Web Site: http://www.ecosite.fi
Radio Transmitting Tower Construction Services
N.A.I.C.S.: 237130

Elisa Eesti As (1)
Friendship pst 145, 13425, Tallinn, Estonia
Tel.: (372) 6811963
Web Site: https://www.elisa.ee
Sales Range: $100-124.9 Million
Emp.: 300
Mobile Phone Network Operation Services
N.A.I.C.S.: 517112
Marika Raiski *(Head-PR)*

Elisa Santa Monica Oy (1)
Derby Business Park training and negotiation rooms 4th Floor, Tarvonsalmenkatu 15-17, 02600, Espoo, Finland
Tel.: (358) 102665400
Web Site: http://www.elisasantamonica.fi
Software Development Services
N.A.I.C.S.: 541511

Elisa Videra Norge As (1)
Parkveien 2B, Langhus, 1405, Oslo, Norway
Tel.: (47) 21403766
Information Technology Services
N.A.I.C.S.: 541519

Elisa Videra Oy (1)
Kaarlenkatu 9-11, 00530, Helsinki, Finland
Tel.: (358) 103226200
Information Technology Services
N.A.I.C.S.: 541519

Elisa Videra Spain S.L (1)
Gran Via 39 3, 28013, Madrid, Spain
Tel.: (34) 627715498
Information Technology Services
N.A.I.C.S.: 541519

Elisa Videra UK Ltd. (1)
The Triangle 5-17 Hammersmith Grove, Hammersmith, London, W6 0LG, United Kingdom
Tel.: (44) 2084356524
Information Technology Services
N.A.I.C.S.: 541519

Elisa camLine Holding GmbH (1)
Fraunhoferring 9, 85238, Petershagen, Germany
Tel.: (49) 81379350
Web Site: https://www.camline.com
Software Development Services
N.A.I.C.S.: 541519

Fenix Solutions Oy (1)
Brahenkatu 20, 20100, Turku, Finland
Tel.: (358) 28800180
Web Site: https://www.fenixsolutions.fi
Information Technology Services
N.A.I.C.S.: 541511

Fonum Oy (1)
Kaarlenkatu 9-11, 00530, Helsinki, Finland
Tel.: (358) 201321400
Web Site: https://www.fonum.fi
Mobile Phone Retailer
N.A.I.C.S.: 449210

Frinx s.r.o. (1)
Mlynske nivy 4959/48, 821 09, Bratislava, Slovakia
Tel.: (421) 220910141
Web Site: https://frinx.io
Software Development Services
N.A.I.C.S.: 541511

Kepit Systems Oy (1)

Beach House promenade, 65100, Vaasa, Finland
Tel.: (358) 443321322
Web Site: http://www.kepit.fi
Software Development Services
N.A.I.C.S.: 541511

Kiinteisto Oy Raision Luolasto (1)
Kuninkaanvayla 3, 21200, Raisio, Finland
Tel.: (358) 1026000
Real Estate Management Services
N.A.I.C.S.: 531390

LNS Kommunikation AB (1)
Lindetorpsvagen 19, 12163, Johanneshov, Sweden   **(100%)**
Tel.: (46) 854490650
Web Site: http://www.lnscom.net
Telecommunications
N.A.I.C.S.: 517810

OOO LNR (1)
15 Liter A Ul Chapaeva, Saint Petersburg, 197101, Russia
Tel.: (7) 8123323108
Web Site: http://www.elisa.ru
Sales Range: $25-49.9 Million
Emp.: 15
Telecommunication Software Development Services
N.A.I.C.S.: 541511
Olga Valentinovna Kaledina *(Dir Gen)*

P-OSS Solutions S.L.U. (1)
4 Rodriguez Arias Street, 48008, Bilbao, Spain
Tel.: (34) 689014259
Web Site: http://www.p-oss.com
Telecommunication Servicesb
N.A.I.C.S.: 517810

Polystar Asia Private Ltd. (1)
101 Thomson Road 08-05A United Square, Singapore, 307591, Singapore
Tel.: (65) 67379667
Polystyrene Product Mfr
N.A.I.C.S.: 326140

Polystar Instruments Inc. (1)
2591 Dallas Pkwy Ste 300, Frisco, TX 75034
Tel.: (972) 731-4398
Polystyrene Product Mfr
N.A.I.C.S.: 326140

Polystar Osix AB (1)
Hammarby alle 29, 120 32, Stockholm, Sweden
Tel.: (46) 850600600
Web Site: https://elisapolystar.com
Polystyrene Product Mfr
N.A.I.C.S.: 326140

Polystar Ryssland LLC (1)
Prechistenka Str bld 40/2 block 1, 119034, Moscow, Russia
Tel.: (7) 4957881130
Polystyrene Product Mfr
N.A.I.C.S.: 326140

Preminet Oy (1)
Atomitie 2C, 00370, Helsinki, Finland
Tel.: (358) 405757772
Web Site: https://www.primanet.fi
Information Technology Services
N.A.I.C.S.: 541511

Saunalahti Group Oyj (1)
Ratabartikankatu 3, 00520, Helsinki, Finland
Tel.: (358) 942430001
Web Site: http://www.saunalahti.fi
Cellular & Wireless Telecommunications
N.A.I.C.S.: 517112

Sutaria Services Inc. (1)
13140 Coit Rd Ste 335, Dallas, TX 75240
Tel.: (909) 278-8233
Web Site: https://www.calcuquote.com
Software Development Services
N.A.I.C.S.: 541511
Chintan Sutaria *(Founder)*

Tampereen Tietoverkko Oy (1)
Nasinlinnankatu 41, Tampere, 33200, Finland
Tel.: (358) 103095300
Web Site: http://www.ttv.fi
Cable Television Distribution Services
N.A.I.C.S.: 517111
Matias Castren *(Pres)*

Elisa Corporation—(Continued)

Videra Oy (1)
Elektroniikkatie 2 B, 90590, Oulu, Finland
Tel.: (358) 424 6761
Web Site: http://www.videra.com
Video Conferencing Services
N.A.I.C.S.: 561499

Xenetic Oy (1)
Mannerheiminaukio 1B, 00100, Helsinki, Finland
Tel.: (358) 106178500
Web Site: http://www.xenetic.fi
Sales Range: $25-49.9 Million
Emp.: 30
Data Storage Services
N.A.I.C.S.: 518210

camLine Dresden GmbH (1)
An den Ellerwiesen 11, 01109, Dresden, Germany
Tel.: (49) 3514188510
Software Development Services
N.A.I.C.S.: 541511

camLine GmbH (1)
Fraunhoferring 9, Petershausen, 85238, Dachau, Germany
Tel.: (49) 81379350
Software Development Services
N.A.I.C.S.: 541511
Heinz Linsmaier (CEO)

camLine Pte. Ltd. (1)
18 Kaki Bukit Road 3 04-20 Entrepreneur Business Center, Singapore, 415978, Singapore
Tel.: (65) 67476038
Software Development Services
N.A.I.C.S.: 541511

camLine USA Inc. (1)
519 Johnson Ferry Rd Ste 100, Marietta, GA 30068-4659
Tel.: (404) 566-2927
Software Development Services
N.A.I.C.S.: 541511

ELITE ADVANCED LASER CORPORATION
10F No 35 Qiao an St, Zhonghe Dist, New Taipei City, 235026, Taiwan
Tel.: (886) 282456186
Web Site: https://www.elaser.com.tw
Year Founded: 2000
3450—(TAI)
Rev.: $176,565,512
Assets: $292,448,238
Liabilities: $97,680,332
Net Worth: $194,767,905
Earnings: $4,310,180
Emp.: 2,572
Fiscal Year-end: 12/31/23
Electronic Manufacturing Service Provider
N.A.I.C.S.: 334419
Chu-Liang Cheng (Chm & CEO)

Subsidiaries:

Centera Photonics Inc. (1)
3F No 6-3 Dusing Rd Hsinchu Science Park, Hsinchu, 30078, Taiwan
Tel.: (886) 36213966
Web Site: https://www.centera-photonics.com
Electronic Parts Mfr & Distr
N.A.I.C.S.: 334419

ELITE BMW
1040 Ogilvie Road, Ottawa, K1J 8G9, ON, Canada
Tel.: (613) 749-7700
Web Site: http://www.elite.bmw.ca
Rev.: $18,519,274
Emp.: 40
New & Used Car Dealers
N.A.I.C.S.: 441110
Julie Wright (Gen Mgr-Sls)

ELITE COLOR ENVIRONMENTAL RESOURCES SCIENCE & TECHNOLOGY CO., LTD.
29 Huanxi Road, Zhutang Town, Wuxi, 214415, Jiangsu, China
Tel.: (86) 51068836881
Web Site: https://www.elitecolor.cn
Year Founded: 2003
002998—(SSE)
Rev.: $316,481,256
Assets: $363,144,600
Liabilities: $133,742,232
Net Worth: $229,402,368
Earnings: $10,896,444
Fiscal Year-end: 12/31/22
Polyester Fiber Product Mfr & Distr
N.A.I.C.S.: 325211
Zexin Dai (Founder & Chm)

ELITE COMMERCIAL REIT
8 Temasek Boulevard 37-02 Suntec Tower Three, Singapore, 038988, Singapore
Tel.: (65) 69559999
Web Site: https://www.elitecreit.com
Year Founded: 2018
MXNU—(SES)
Rev.: $47,914,704
Assets: $565,299,811
Liabilities: $301,465,310
Net Worth: $263,834,501
Earnings: ($28,224,061)
Emp.: 6
Fiscal Year-end: 12/31/23
Real Estate Investment Services
N.A.I.C.S.: 531190
Shaldine Wang (CEO)

ELITE EMAIL INC.
5511 Steeles Ave W Suite 200, Toronto, M9L 1S7, ON, Canada
Tel.: (416) 747-6111
Web Site: http://www.eliteemail.com
Sales Range: $10-24.9 Million
Email Marketing Software, Website Hosting, Website Design & Search Engine Optimization
N.A.I.C.S.: 513210
Robert Burko (Founder & CEO)

ELITE KSB HOLDINGS LIMITED
6 Senoko Way, Singapore, 758029, Singapore
Tel.: (65) 6757 2121
Sales Range: $50-74.9 Million
Chicken Processing Services & Meat Products Distr
N.A.I.C.S.: 311615

ELITE MATERIAL CO., LTD.
No 18 Datong 1st Rd, Guanyin Dist, Taoyuan, 328417, Taiwan
Tel.: (886) 34837937
Web Site: https://www.emctw.com
Year Founded: 1992
2383—(TAI)
Rev.: $1,350,476,322
Assets: $1,747,167,173
Liabilities: $870,438,373
Net Worth: $876,728,800
Earnings: $179,479,669
Emp.: 3,020
Fiscal Year-end: 12/31/23
Copper Clad Laminates Mfr
N.A.I.C.S.: 334419
Ding Yu Dong (Chm, Pres & CEO)

Subsidiaries:

Elite Electronic Material (Kunshan) Co., Ltd. (1)
No 368 Yubi Road, Zhoushi Town, Kunshan, Jiangsu, China
Tel.: (86) 51257663671
Copper Clad Laminate Mfr & Distr
N.A.I.C.S.: 334412

Elite Electronic Material (Zhongshan) Co., Ltd. (1)
No 7 Technology Avenue, Huo-Ju Development Zone, Zhongshan, Guangdong, China
Tel.: (86) 76088297988
Copper Clad Laminate Mfr & Distr
N.A.I.C.S.: 334412

Elite Electronic Material Co., Ltd.-Kunshan Plant (1)
368 You Bi Road, Zhou Shi Town, Kunshan, 215300, Jiangsu, China
Tel.: (86) 51257663671
Printed Circuit Board Mfr
N.A.I.C.S.: 334412

Elite Material Co., Ltd. - Hsinchu Plant (1)
No 14 Wenhua Rd, Hukou Township, Hsinchu, 30352, Taiwan
Tel.: (886) 3 5981688
Web Site: http://www.emctw.com
Printed Circuit Board Mfr
N.A.I.C.S.: 334412

Elite Material Co., Ltd. - Taoyuan Plant (1)
No 18 Datong 1st Rd, Guanyin Dist, Taoyuan, 32849, Taiwan
Tel.: (886) 34837937
Web Site: http://www.emctw.com
Printed Circuit Board Mfr
N.A.I.C.S.: 334418

ELITE SEMICONDUCTOR MICROELECTRONICS TECHNOLOGY INC.
No 23 Industry E Rd IV Science Park, Hsinchu, 30077, Taiwan
Tel.: (886) 35781970
Web Site: https://www.esmt.com.tw
Year Founded: 1998
3006—(TAI)
Rev.: $388,636,664
Assets: $591,818,219
Liabilities: $267,409,585
Net Worth: $324,408,634
Earnings: ($39,535,660)
Emp.: 603
Fiscal Year-end: 12/31/23
Integrated Circuits Mfr
N.A.I.C.S.: 334412

ELITE SPORTSWEAR & AWARDS LTD.
14703 118th Avenue, Edmonton, T5L 2M7, AB, Canada
Tel.: (780) 454-9775
Web Site: http://www.elitesportswear.com
Year Founded: 1952
Rev.: $13,407,400
Emp.: 110
Sportswear Supplier
N.A.I.C.S.: 459999
Drew Schamehorn (Pres)

ELITE SURFACE TECHNOLOGIES PTY. LTD.
305 Frankston-Dandenong Rd, Dandenong, 3175, VIC, Australia
Tel.: (61) 3 9548 3661
Web Site: http://www.elitesurfacetech.com.au
Metal Finishing Services
N.A.I.C.S.: 423510
Anne Yozin (Mng Dir)

ELITE WORKWEAR UK LIMITED
38 Corringham Road Industrial Estate Longwood Road, Gainsborough, DN21 1QB, Lincolnshire, United Kingdom
Tel.: (44) 1427810555
Web Site: http://www.eliteworkwearuk.co.uk
Year Founded: 2006
Sales Range: $10-24.9 Million
Emp.: 7
Health & Safety Consulting Services
N.A.I.C.S.: 541618
Colin Emerson (Co-Owner & Gen Mgr)

ELITE WORLD S.A.
28 Boulevard d'Avranches, L-1160, Luxembourg, Luxembourg
Tel.: (352) 140443222
Web Site: http://www.elitemodelworld.com
Sales Range: $75-99.9 Million
Human Resource Consulting Services
N.A.I.C.S.: 541612
Christophe Chenut (Co-CEO)

Subsidiaries:

Angels Model Management SARL (1)
34 rue du Faugbourg Saint Honore, 75008, Paris, France
Tel.: (33) 42 68 24 44
Web Site: http://www.angels-models.com
Model Management Services
N.A.I.C.S.: 711410

Elite Licensing Company S.A. (1)
Route Des Arsenaux 15, 1700, Fribourg, Switzerland
Tel.: (41) 263224815
Model Management Services
N.A.I.C.S.: 711410

Elite Management S.A. (1)
Paseo de Gracia 81 4-2, Barcelona, 8008, Spain
Tel.: (34) 932720909
Web Site: http://www.elitemodel.es
Emp.: 12
Model Management Services
N.A.I.C.S.: 711410
Anna Vicent (Mgr-Acctg)

Elite Model Management Amsterdam B.V. (1)
Keizersgracht 448, Amsterdam, 1016 GD, Netherlands
Tel.: (31) 20 627 9929
Web Site: http://www.elitemodel.nl
Sales Range: $50-74.9 Million
Emp.: 4
Model Management Services
N.A.I.C.S.: 711410
Manon Kosterman (Head-Acctg)

Elite Model Management Bratislava Sro. (1)
Klemensova 4, Bratislava, 81102, Slovakia
Tel.: (421) 252 968 300
Web Site: http://www.elitemodels.cz
Model Management Services
N.A.I.C.S.: 711410

Elite Model Management Copenhagen (1)
Bredgade 23B 4th Floor, Copenhagen, 1260, Denmark
Tel.: (45) 33151414
Web Site: http://www.elitemodel.dk
Sales Range: $50-74.9 Million
Emp.: 6
Model Management Services
N.A.I.C.S.: 711410
Munir Bouylud (Mng Dir)

Elite Model Management London Ltd. (1)
3-5 Islington High Street, London, N1 9LQ, United Kingdom
Tel.: (44) 207 841 3288
Web Site: http://www.elitemodellondon.co.uk
Sales Range: $50-74.9 Million
Emp.: 22
Model Management Services
N.A.I.C.S.: 711410
Michelangelo Chiacchio (Mng Dir)

Elite Model Management Prague Sro (1)
Na Perstyne 2, 110 00, Prague, Czech Republic
Tel.: (420) 222 212 394
Web Site: http://www.elitemodel.cz
Sales Range: $50-74.9 Million
Emp.: 6
Model Management Services
N.A.I.C.S.: 711410

Sasa Jany *(Gen Mgr)*

Elite Model Management SARL (1)
19 Avenue George V, 75008, Paris, France
Tel.: (33) 1 4044 3222
Web Site: http://www.elitemodel.fr
Model Management Services
N.A.I.C.S.: 711410

Elite Model Management SARL (1)
via Tortona 35, 20144, Milan, Italy
Tel.: (39) 02 467 521
Web Site: http://www.elitemodel.it
Model Management Services
N.A.I.C.S.: 711410
Roberto Valensin *(Mng Dir)*

ELITECON INTERNATIONAL LIMITED
152 Shivani Apartments Plot No 63 I
P Extension, Patparganj East Delhi,
Delhi, 110092, Assam, India
Tel.: (91) 919871761020
Web Site:
https://www.eliteconinternation.com
539533—(BOM)
Rev.: $13,106
Assets: $492,043
Liabilities: $69,615
Net Worth: $422,428
Earnings: ($5,473)
Fiscal Year-end: 03/31/21
Financial Investment Services
N.A.I.C.S.: 523999
Bishnu Agarwal *(Chm, Mng Dir & CFO)*

ELITEGROUP COMPUTER SYSTEMS CO., LTD.
9F No 22-1 Sec 3 Zhongshan N Rd,
Zhongshan Dist, Taipei, 104427, Taiwan
Tel.: (886) 221621177
Web Site: https://www.ecs.com.tw
Year Founded: 1987
2331—(TAI)
Rev.: $645,598,099
Assets: $752,559,931
Liabilities: $358,394,375
Net Worth: $394,165,556
Earnings: $33,158,441
Emp.: 7,000
Fiscal Year-end: 12/31/23
Computer Motherboard Mfr
N.A.I.C.S.: 541512
Wkang-Hsiang Wang *(Chm)*

Subsidiaries:

Advazone International Ltd. (1)
House 285 Road 04 5th Floor Baridhara
DOHS, Dhaka, Bangladesh
Tel.: (880) 1911009132
Web Site: http://www.advazone.com
Holding Company
N.A.I.C.S.: 551112

ECS Industrial Computer Co., Ltd. (1)
9F No 22 Sec 3 Zhongshan N Rd, Zhongshan Dist, Taipei, 104427, Taiwan
Tel.: (886) 227972829
Web Site: https://www.ecsipc.com
Automotive Parts Mfr & Distr
N.A.I.C.S.: 336390

Elitegroup Computer Systems (HK) Co., Ltd. (1)
Rm A&d 12/f Roxy Indl Ctr 58 - 66 Tai Lin Pai Rd, Kwai Chung, China (Hong Kong)
Tel.: (852) 29538838
Computer Peripheral Equipment Distr
N.A.I.C.S.: 423430

Elitegroup Computer Systems (Japan) Co., Ltd. (1)
2F Sakura Bldg 4-6-1, Oi Shinagawa-Ku,
Tokyo, 140-0014, Japan
Tel.: (81) 357430421
Web Site: https://www.ecsjpn.co.jp
Computer Product Mfr & Distr
N.A.I.C.S.: 334111

ELITETELE.COM HOLDINGS PLC
Dawson House Matrix Business Park,
Chorley, PR7 7NA, Lancashire,
United Kingdom
Tel.: (44) 844 875 8880
Web Site: http://www.elitetele.com
Year Founded: 2000
Sales Range: $10-24.9 Million
Emp.: 170
Telecommunication Servicesb
N.A.I.C.S.: 517810
Matt Newing *(Founder & CEO)*

ELIVISION CO., LTD.
230 Harmony-Ro, Yeonsu-Gu, Incheon, Korea (South)
Tel.: (82) 322353050
Web Site: https://www.elivision.com
Year Founded: 1995
276240—(KRS)
Construction Equipment Mfr
N.A.I.C.S.: 333120
Dukgeun Ahn *(Board of Directors & CEO)*

ELIXENS S.A.
28 Boulevard Kellermann, 75013,
Paris, France
Tel.: (33) 134485757
Web Site: http://www.elixens.com
Year Founded: 1987
Sales Range: $25-49.9 Million
Emp.: 200
Organic Molecular Chemicals Mfr & Sales
N.A.I.C.S.: 325199
Emmanuel Alves *(Chm & CEO)*

Subsidiaries:

ELIXENS America Inc. (1)
1443 Pinewood St, Rahway, NJ 07065
Tel.: (732) 388-3555
Web Site: http://www.elixensamerica.com
Emp.: 10
Oil Mfr
N.A.I.C.S.: 325199

ELIXENS UK Ltd (1)
No 1 Essence House Crabtree Road
Thorpe Industrial Estate, Egham, TW20 8RN, United Kingdom
Tel.: (44) 1784485600
Oil Mfr
N.A.I.C.S.: 325199

ELIXINOL WELLNESS LIMITED
Level 12 680 George Street, Sydney,
2000, NSW, Australia
Year Founded: 2017
E8M—(DEU)
Rev.: $4,709,918
Assets: $9,002,586
Liabilities: $2,888,705
Net Worth: $6,113,881
Earnings: ($7,057,200)
Fiscal Year-end: 12/31/22
Medicinal Product Mfr & Distr
N.A.I.C.S.: 325411
Ron Dufficy *(Grp CEO & Mng Dir)*

Subsidiaries:

Ananda Food Pty. Ltd. (1)
PO Box 3276, Thornton, 2322, NSW, Australia
Tel.: (61) 249663736
Web Site: https://www.anandafood.com
Hemp Seed Product Mfr & Distr
N.A.I.C.S.: 311119

Elixinol BV (1)
Techniekweg 34, 3542 DT, Utrecht, Netherlands
Tel.: (31) 202993179
Web Site: http://www.elixinol.eu
CBD Oil & Capsule Product Mfr
N.A.I.C.S.: 325411

ELIXIR CAPITAL LTD.
58 Mittal Chambers 5th Floor 228
Nariman Point, Mumbai, 400 021,
India
Tel.: (91) 2261151919
Web Site: https://www.elixircapital.in
531278—(BOM)
Rev.: $2,670,186
Assets: $9,941,365
Liabilities: $4,390,814
Net Worth: $5,550,551
Earnings: $1,669,215
Fiscal Year-end: 03/31/21
Security Brokerage Services
N.A.I.C.S.: 523150
Dipan Mehta *(Chm)*

Subsidiaries:

Elixir Equities Private Limited (1)
58 Mittal Chambers 5th Floor 228, Nariman Point, Mumbai, 400021, India
Tel.: (91) 2261151919
Web Site: www.elixirequities.com
Stock Broking Services
N.A.I.C.S.: 523150

ELIXIR ENERGY LIMITED
Unit 3B Level 3 60 Hindmarsh
Square, Adelaide, 5000, SA, Australia
Tel.: (61) 870795610　　AU
Web Site: https://elixirenergy.com.au
EXR—(ASX)
Rev.: $1,116,107
Assets: $41,617,461
Liabilities: $5,875,967
Net Worth: $35,741,494
Earnings: ($1,064,699)
Emp.: 1
Fiscal Year-end: 06/30/23
Oil & Gas Exploration Services
N.A.I.C.S.: 211120
Achitsan Buyannemekh *(Mgr)*

Subsidiaries:

GOH Clean Energy LLC (1)
801 8th Floor Naiman Zovkhis Building
Seoul Street 21, Ulaanbaatar, Mongolia
Tel.: (976) 75951331
Web Site: https://www.cleanenergy.mn
Renewable Energy Services
N.A.I.C.S.: 221114

ELIXIRR INTERNATIONAL PLC
12 Helmet Row, London, EC1V 3QJ,
United Kingdom
Tel.: (44) 2072205410
Web Site: https://www.elixirr.com
Year Founded: 2009
ELIX—(AIM)
Marketing Consulting Services
N.A.I.C.S.: 541613

Subsidiaries:

Elixirr, Inc. (1)
2600 Network Blvd Ste 570, Frisco, TX 75034
Tel.: (214) 618-5000
Web Site: https://www.elixirr.com
General Management Consulting Services
N.A.I.C.S.: 541611

Subsidiary (Domestic):

Insigniam Performance, L.P. (2)
301 Woodbine Ave, Narberth, PA 19072
Tel.: (610) 667-7822
Web Site: http://www.insigniam.com
Rev.: $9,700,000
Emp.: 60
Lessors of Nonfinancial Intangible Assets, except Copyrighted Works
N.A.I.C.S.: 533110
Bonnie Wingate *(Partner-US)*

iOLAP, Inc. (1)
2591 Dallas Pkwy Ste 107, Frisco, TX 75034
Tel.: (214) 618-8082
Web Site: http://www.iolap.com
Custom Computer Programing
N.A.I.C.S.: 541511
Douglas C. Slemmer *(Co-Founder & CTO)*

ELIZA TINSLEY LTD.
Potters Lane, Wednesbury, WS10 0AS, West Midlands, United Kingdom
Tel.: (44) 1215020055
Web Site:
http://www.elizatinsley.co.uk
Sales Range: $125-149.9 Million
Emp.: 100
Assemblies Designer & Mfr; Chains, Ropes & Related Flexible Connectors Distr
N.A.I.C.S.: 332999
Rythm Jain *(CEO)*

ELIZADE NIGERIA LIMITED
Elizade Toyota Plaza 322A Ikorodu
Road AnthonyVillage, Maryland, Lagos, Nigeria
Tel.: (234) 17603012
Web Site: http://www.elizade.net
Sales Range: $75-99.9 Million
Emp.: 300
Automobile Dealership Operator
N.A.I.C.S.: 441110
Michael Ade-Ojo *(Founder)*

Subsidiaries:

Toyota Nigeria Limited (1)
Plot 2 Block G Oshodi Isolo Expressway
Oshodi, Lagos, Nigeria (75%)
Tel.: (234) 1 4528320
Web Site: http://www.toyotanigeria.com
Automotive Distr
N.A.I.C.S.: 423110
Michael Ade-Ojo *(Chm)*

ELK CORPORATION
687 Gwanpyeong-dong, Yuseong-gu,
Daejeon, 305-509, Korea (South)
Tel.: (82) 42 939 9300
Web Site: http://www.elk.co.kr
Year Founded: 1999
Rev.: $176,430,112
Assets: $114,085,757
Liabilities: $97,103,624
Net Worth: $16,982,133
Earnings: ($27,417,697)
Emp.: 200
Fiscal Year-end: 12/31/18
Sensor Mfr
N.A.I.C.S.: 334413
Dong-Hyuk Shin *(CEO)*

ELK ORTHOBIOLOGICS LIMITED
123 Camberwell Road Level 1, Hawthorn, 3123, VIC, Australia
Tel.: (61) 3 9811 9966
Web Site: http://www.elkortho.com
Biotechnology Product Developer & Researcher
N.A.I.C.S.: 541714
Andrew M. Bray *(CEO & Mng Dir)*

ELK PETROLEUM LIMITED
Suite 4 Level 9 341 George Street,
Sydney, 2000, NSW, Australia
Tel.: (61) 2 9299 9690
Web Site: http://www.elkpet.com
EKPTF—(OTCIQ)
Sales Range: $75-99.9 Million
Oil Exploration
N.A.I.C.S.: 211120
Andrew William Bursill *(Co-Sec)*

Subsidiaries:

Elk Petroleum Inc (1)
123 W 1st St, Casper, WY 82601
Tel.: (307) 265-3328
Sales Range: $50-74.9 Million
Oil & Gas Production Services
N.A.I.C.S.: 211120
Chris Mullen *(Pres)*

ELK-DESA RESOURCES BHD
No 15 17 Jalan Brunei UtaraOff Jalan

ELK-Desa Resources Bhd—(Continued)

Pudu, 55100, Kuala Lumpur, Malaysia
Tel.: (60) 321457000
Web Site: https://www.elk-desa.com.my
Year Founded: 2012
ELKDESA—(KLS)
Rev.: $32,855,461
Assets: $146,677,091
Liabilities: $46,830,988
Net Worth: $99,846,102
Earnings: $10,102,747
Emp.: 194
Fiscal Year-end: 03/31/23
Financial Investment Services
N.A.I.C.S.: 522299
Tew Hock Chai Teoh (CEO)

Subsidiaries:

ELK-Desa Furniture Sdn. Bhd. **(1)**
Lot 755 Jalan Haji Sirat, 42100, Klang, Selangor Darul Ehsan, Malaysia
Tel.: (60) 332901288
Web Site: https://www.elk-desafurniture.com.my
Furniture Product Whslr
N.A.I.C.S.: 423210

ELKA BETEILIGUNGS GMBH
Hasenkampstrasse 11b, 44795, Bochum, Germany
Tel.: (49) 171 553 0565   De
Web Site: http://www.elka-beteiligungs.de
Year Founded: 2010
Investment Holding Company
N.A.I.C.S.: 551112
Ludger Kramer (Founder, Owner & Mng Dir)

Subsidiaries:

Plant Systems & Services PSS
GmbH **(1)**
c/o ELKA Beteiligungs - Hasenkampstrasse 11b, 44795, Bochum, Germany
Tel.: (49) 171 553 0565
Holding Company; Energy & Process Industry Support Services
N.A.I.C.S.: 551112
Ludger Kramer (Mng Dir)

Subsidiary (Domestic):

ETABO Energietechnik und Anlagenservice GmbH **(2)**
Harpener Feld 16, 44805, Bochum,
Germany **(75%)**
Tel.: (49) 234 5067 0
Web Site: http://www.eta-bochum.de
Engineering Services
N.A.I.C.S.: 541330
Nicolas Korte (Chm-Mgmt Bd)

Veltec GmbH **(2)**
Ruttelweg 7, Niedernberg, 63843, Aschaffenburg, Germany
Tel.: (49) 6028 9797 0
Web Site: https://www.veltec-services.com
Process & Power Plant Technical Maintenance Services
N.A.I.C.S.: 541990
Martin Kaus (Member-Mgmt Bd)

Subsidiary (Non-US):

Veltec AS **(3)**
Litlaas 2, 5954, Mongstad, Norway
Tel.: (47) 56167450
Process & Power Plant Technical Maintenance Services
N.A.I.C.S.: 541990

Veltec Industrial Services A/S **(3)**
Odinsvej 35, 4100, Ringsted, Denmark
Tel.: (45) 57666000
Process & Power Plant Technical Maintenance Services
N.A.I.C.S.: 541990
Gert Nielsen (Mng Dir)

Veltec N.V. **(3)**
Starrenhoflaan 13, 2950, Kapellen, Belgium
Tel.: (32) 3660 1250

Process & Power Plant Technical Maintenance Services
N.A.I.C.S.: 541990

ELKOK A.D.
3 Olge Grbic Street, 31260, Kosjeric, Serbia
Tel.: (381) 38131781121
Web Site: https://www.elkok.co.rs
Year Founded: 2003
ELKK—(BEL)
Rev.: $19,442,147
Assets: $5,343,648
Liabilities: $4,552,037
Net Worth: $791,610
Earnings: $181,096
Fiscal Year-end: 12/31/22
Electronic Connector Mfr
N.A.I.C.S.: 335931
Vladimir Lojanica (Dir)

ELKOP S.A.
ul Zygmunta Padlewskiego 18C, 09-402, Plock, Poland
Tel.: (48) 243660626
Web Site: https://www.elkop.pl
Year Founded: 1950
EKP—(WAR)
Rev.: $4,817,581
Assets: $35,831,555
Liabilities: $11,633,892
Net Worth: $24,197,663
Earnings: $1,623,222
Fiscal Year-end: 12/31/21
Electrical Installation Services
N.A.I.C.S.: 238210
Jacek Koralewski (Chm & Chm-Mgmt Bd)

ELL ENVIRONMENTAL HOLDINGS LIMITED
Unit 5 7th Floor Westlands Centre 20 Westlands Road, Hong Kong, China (Hong Kong)
Tel.: (852) 37582210   Ky
Web Site: http://www.ellhk.com
1395—(HKG)
Rev.: $25,966,523
Assets: $67,709,640
Liabilities: $29,090,910
Net Worth: $38,618,730
Earnings: ($280,755)
Emp.: 185
Fiscal Year-end: 12/31/22
Holding Company
N.A.I.C.S.: 551112
On Ta Yuen Chau (Chm)

Subsidiaries:

PT. Rimba Plama Sejahtera **(1)**
Jalan Jenderal Sudirman 52 Tanah Abang - Karet Tengsin, 10220, Jakarta, Indonesia
Tel.: (62) 2129035373
Emp.: 100
Palm Kernel Oil Mfr & Distr
N.A.I.C.S.: 311225
Alice Ma (Gen Mgr)

ELLAH LAKES PLC.
No 12 Ihama Road GRA, Edo State, Benin City, Nigeria
Tel.: (234) 84233938
Web Site: https://www.ellahlakes.com
Year Founded: 1980
ELLAHLAKES—(NIGE)
Assets: $50,175,789
Liabilities: $7,535,459
Net Worth: $42,640,329
Earnings: ($1,818,919)
Fiscal Year-end: 07/31/23
Fish Farming Services
N.A.I.C.S.: 112511

ELLAKTOR S.A.
Ermou St 25 Nea Kifissia Amia National Road, Olympic Village Interchange, 14564, Athens, Greece

Tel.: (30) 2108185000
Web Site: https://www.ellaktor.com
Year Founded: 1997
ELLKF—(OTCIQ)
Rev.: $1,126,207,641
Assets: $2,646,673,861
Liabilities: $1,660,785,668
Net Worth: $985,888,193
Earnings: $559,667,602
Emp.: 7,329
Fiscal Year-end: 12/31/22
Holding Company
N.A.I.C.S.: 551112
Anastassios Kallitsantsis (Mng Dir)

Subsidiaries:

AEOLIKI KANDILIOU SA **(1)**
25 Ermou St Athens - Lamia National Road, Olympic Village Interchange, 145 64, Nea Kifissia, Greece
Tel.: (30) 2108184600
Eletric Power Generation Services
N.A.I.C.S.: 221118
Theodoros Sietis (Mng Dir)

AEOLIKI OLYMPUS EVIA S.A. **(1)**
25 Ermou St Athens Lamia National Road Olympic Village Interchange, 14564, Nea Kifissia, Greece
Tel.: (30) 2108184600
Web Site: http://www.en.ellaktor.gr
Real Estate & Construction Management Services
N.A.I.C.S.: 531390
Theodore Sietis (Mng Dir)

AEOLIKI PARNONOS SA **(1)**
25 Ermou St Athens - Lamia National Road, Olympic Village Interchange, 145 64, Nea Kifissia, Greece
Tel.: (30) 2108184600
Construction Engineering Services
N.A.I.C.S.: 541330

AKTOR BULGARIA SA **(1)**
Residential Complex Maritza Gardens Block 10 Office 1, 4003, Plovdiv, Bulgaria
Tel.: (359) 32396760
Web Site: https://www.aktor.bg
Sales Range: $25-49.9 Million
Emp.: 5
Building Construction & Mining Services
N.A.I.C.S.: 236220
Simos Banagiogis (Gen Mgr)

AKTOR FACILITY MANAGEMENT
S.A. **(1)**
25 Ermou Str Athens - Lamia National Road, Olympic Village Interchange, 145 64, Nea Kifissia, Greece
Tel.: (30) 2108185261
Sales Range: $25-49.9 Million
Emp.: 60
Construction Engineering Services
N.A.I.C.S.: 541330
Kelpies Mitosis (Pres)

AKTOR KUWAIT WLL **(1)**
Fahed Al Salem Street Sheraton Round About Kuwait Flag Plaza, AKTOR Site Office, Kuwait, Kuwait
Tel.: (965) 24921068
Web Site: https://en.aktor.gr
Road Construction Services
N.A.I.C.S.: 237310

ALPHA AEOLIKI MOLAON LAKONIA
S.A **(1)**
25 Ermou St Athens - Lamia National Road, Olympic Village Interchange, Nea Kifissia, DR14564, Greece
Tel.: (30) 210 8184600
Web Site: http://www.eltechanemos.com
Construction Engineering Services
N.A.I.C.S.: 541330

ANEMOS ATALANTIS SA **(1)**
25 Ermou St Athens Lamia National Rd, Olympic Village Interchange, 145 64, Nea Kifissia, Greece
Tel.: (30) 210 8184600
Web Site: http://www.en.ellaktor.gr
Construction Engineering Services
N.A.I.C.S.: 541330

ANEMOS THRAKIS SA **(1)**
25 Ermou St, GR 145 64, Nea Kifissia, Greece

Tel.: (30) 210 8184600
Web Site: http://www.eltechanemos.com
Real Estate & Construction Management Services
N.A.I.C.S.: 531390
Akliicsantsin Nanstanios (CEO)

APOTEFROTIRAS SA **(1)**
25 Ermou Street Nea Kifissia Lamia National Road, Olympic Village Node, 14564, Athens, Greece
Tel.: (30) 21055776645
Web Site: https://www.apotefrotiras.gr
Medical Waste Transportation & Disposal Services
N.A.I.C.S.: 562000

ATTIKI ODOS S.A **(1)**
41 9 km Attiki Odos Motorway, Attica, 19002, Peania, Greece
Tel.: (30) 2106682200
Web Site: https://www.aodos.gr
Sales Range: $150-199.9 Million
Emp.: 1,000
Construction Engineering Services
N.A.I.C.S.: 541330

Aktor S.A. **(1)**
25 Ermou Lamia National Road, Nea Kifissia Olympic Village Interchange, GR 145 64, Athens, Greece
Tel.: (30) 2108184000
Web Site: http://www.ellaktor.com
Rev.: $1,009,750,885
Assets: $904,364,220
Liabilities: $786,645,657
Net Worth: $117,718,563
Earnings: ($134,525,422)
Emp.: 3,664
Fiscal Year-end: 12/31/2019
Construction Services
N.A.I.C.S.: 237310

Subsidiary (Domestic):

AKTOR CONCESSIONS S.A. **(2)**
25 Ermou Street, Kifissia, 14564, Greece
Tel.: (30) 2108184000
Web Site: http://www.aktor.com
Construction Engineering Services
N.A.I.C.S.: 541330
Dimitris Koutras (Gen Mgr)

Subsidiary (Non-US):

AKTOROM SRL **(2)**
11 Preciziei Blvd the 6th district, Bucharest, 062202, Romania
Tel.: (40) 213141943
Real Estate & Construction Management Services
N.A.I.C.S.: 531390
Patros Katias (Gen Mgr)

Subsidiary (Domestic):

HELLENIC QUARRIES SA **(2)**
25 Ermou Str Lamia National Road Olympic Village Interchange, 145 64, Nea Kifissia, Greece
Tel.: (30) 2108184350
Web Site: https://en.ellaktor.gr
Sales Range: $150-199.9 Million
Emp.: 500
Real Estate & Construction Management Services
N.A.I.C.S.: 531390
Vassilis Lambos (Gen Mgr)

Kastor S.A. **(2)**
25 Ermou Str, 14564, Kifissia, Greece
Tel.: (30) 2108184300
Web Site: http://www.kastor.gr
Sales Range: $1-9.9 Million
Emp.: 50
Construction Services
N.A.I.C.S.: 237110
Kare Fylakif Molen (Pres)

Biosar America LLC **(1)**
5962 LaPlace Ct Ste 220, Carlsbad, CA 92008
Tel.: (760) 517-6151
Construction & Electrical Equipment Services
N.A.I.C.S.: 811310
George Kanetakis (Mng Dir)

Biosar Australia Pty Ltd **(1)**
Level 1 Suite 1202 1 Queens Road, Melbourne, 3004, VIC, Australia

Tel.: (61) 398636212
Construction & Electrical Equipment Services
N.A.I.C.S.: 811310
Manos Chaviaras *(Country Mgr)*

Biosar Brasil - Energia Renovavel Ltda **(1)**
R Bela Cintra 756 Conj 101 Consolacao, 01415-002, Sao Paulo, Brazil
Tel.: (55) 1125320418
Construction & Electrical Equipment Services
N.A.I.C.S.: 811310

Biosar Chile SpA **(1)**
Avenue Alonso de Cordoba 5870 Office 921, Las Condes, Santiago, Chile
Tel.: (56) 227552724
Construction & Electrical Equipment Services
N.A.I.C.S.: 811310

Biosar Energy (UK) Ltd. **(1)**
Level 30 40 Bank Street, Canary Wharf, London, E14 5NR, United Kingdom
Tel.: (44) 2031029626
Construction & Electrical Equipment Services
N.A.I.C.S.: 811310
Anastasios Gkinis *(Country Mgr)*

Biosar Holdings Ltd. **(1)**
Photiades Business Centre 8 Stassinos Avenue, Nicosia, Cyprus
Tel.: (357) 22751555
Construction & Electrical Equipment Services
N.A.I.C.S.: 811310

Biosar Panama Inc. **(1)**
PH Omega Building 6th Floor Office 6D Samuel Lewis Navarro Ave, Obarrio, Panama, Panama
Tel.: (507) 2644188
Construction & Electrical Equipment Services
N.A.I.C.S.: 811310

CORREA HOLDING LTD **(1)**
9A Falirou Str Pallouriotissa, 1046, Nicosia, Cyprus
Tel.: (357) 22751555
Financial Management Consulting Services
N.A.I.C.S.: 541611

DIMITRA SA **(1)**
Antheia of Alexandroupolis, Alexandroupoli, Evros, Greece
Tel.: (30) 25510 51388
Web Site: http://www.dimitra-sa.gr
Sales Range: $25-49.9 Million
Emp.: 25
Pet Food Mfr
N.A.I.C.S.: 311111

Development Of New Alimos Marina S.A. **(1)**
25 Ermou Street, Attica, Kifissia, Greece
Tel.: (30) 2109880000
Web Site: https://www.alimos-marina.gr
Marina Development Services
N.A.I.C.S.: 237990

ELLINIKI TECHNODOMIKI ANEMOS S.A **(1)**
25 Ermou St Athens - Lamia National Road, Olympic Village Interchange, 145 64, Nea Kifissia, Greece
Tel.: (30) 2108184600
Construction Engineering Services
N.A.I.C.S.: 541330
Theodore Siepis *(Gen Mgr)*

ELLINIKI TECHNODOMIKI ENERGIAKI S.A **(1)**
25 Ermou Str Athens - Lamia National Road, Olympic Village Interchange, 145 64, Nea Kifissia, Greece
Tel.: (30) 2108184600
Construction Engineering Services
N.A.I.C.S.: 541330

EOLIKI ZARAKA METAMORFOSSIS SA **(1)**
25 Ermou St Athens - Lamia National Road, Olympic Village Interchange, 145 64, Nea Kifissia, Greece
Tel.: (30) 2108184600
Web Site: http://www.en.ellaktor.gr

Eletric Power Generation Services
N.A.I.C.S.: 221118
Theodore Sietis *(Mng Dir)*

Epadym S.A. **(1)**
Lignite Center of Western Macedonia, 501 00, Kozani, Greece
Tel.: (30) 2461440960
Web Site: https://en.epadym.gr
Construction Services
N.A.I.C.S.: 541330

European Finance Associates S.A. **(1)**
7 Stratigi Street, 154 51, Psychiko, Greece
Tel.. (30) 2100772281
Investment Banking Services
N.A.I.C.S.: 523150
Evangelos Boutlas *(Owner)*

HELECTOR SA **(1)**
25 Ermou str N, 145 64, Kifissia, Greece
Tel.: (30) 2108184700
Web Site: https://www.helector.gr
Sales Range: $50-74.9 Million
Emp.: 40
Eletric Power Generation Services
N.A.I.C.S.: 221118
Leonidas Mpompolas *(Chm & CEO)*

Subsidiary (Non-US):

HELECTOR CYPRUS **(2)**
PO Box 42096, 6530, Larnaca, Cyprus
Tel.: (357) 22818494
Sales Range: $25-49.9 Million
Emp.: 115
Waste Treatment Services
N.A.I.C.S.: 562998
Harris Eleftheriadis *(Mgr)*

HELECTOR GMBH **(2)**
Kalkgraben 2, 35606, Solms, Germany
Tel.: (49) 64 42 207 0
Web Site: http://www.herhof.de
Sales Range: $25-49.9 Million
Emp.: 25
Waste Management Services
N.A.I.C.S.: 562998

HERHOF RECYCLING CENTER OSNABRUCK GMBH **(2)**
Furstenauer Weg 73, Osnabruck, 49090, Germany
Tel.: (49) 541349790
Waste Management Services
N.A.I.C.S.: 562998

Herhof GmbH **(1)**
Kalkgraben 2, 35606, Solms, Germany
Tel.: (49) 64422070
Web Site: https://herhof.com
Plant Engineering & Construction Services
N.A.I.C.S.: 237130

KARTEREDA HOLDING LTD **(1)**
9A Falirou Str Pallouriotissa, 1046, Nicosia, Cyprus
Tel.: (357) 22751555
Web Site: http://en.ellaktor.gr
Financial Management Consulting Services
N.A.I.C.S.: 541611

Moreas S.A. **(1)**
149 4 km Athens-Kalamata Motorway, Nestani, 22100, Athens, Greece
Tel.: (30) 2710562000
Web Site: https://www.moreas.com.gr
Emp.: 280
Construction Services
N.A.I.C.S.: 541330
Giorgos Bobolas *(Mgr-Procurement)*

PANTECNIKI SA **(1)**
25 Ermou St, 145 64, Athens, Greece
Tel.: (30) 2108184450
Web Site: http://www.pantechniki.gr
Construction Engineering Services
N.A.I.C.S.: 541330

PROFIT CONSTRUCT SRL **(1)**
Splaiul Unirii nr 96 Etaj 2 ap 10 Sector 4, Bucharest, Romania
Tel.: (40) 213137742
Emp.: 6
Real Estate & Construction Management Services
N.A.I.C.S.: 531390

Promas S.A **(1)**

64 Kifisias Ave, Marousi, 151 25, Athens, Greece
Tel.: (30) 2110125031
Web Site: http://www.promas.gr
Specialty Trade Contractors
N.A.I.C.S.: 238990

S.C. INSCUT BUCURESTI S.A. **(1)**
B-dul Preciziei Nr 11 Sector 6, Bucharest, 62202, Romania   **(96.63%)**
Tel.: (40) 21 318 20 80
Web Site: http://www.inscut.ro
Sales Range: $1-9.9 Million
Emp.: 100
Construction Services
N.A.I.C.S.: 237310
Dimitrios Kourtas *(Mgr)*

SC CLH ESTATE SRL **(1)**
11 Preciziei Bld Sector 6 3rd Floor, Bucharest, 62203, Romania
Tel.: (40) 213137742
Web Site: https://www.ellaktor.gr
Sales Range: $50-74.9 Million
Emp.: 3
Real Estate & Construction Management Services
N.A.I.C.S.: 531390

STATHMOI PANTECHNIKI SA **(1)**
25 Ermou Str Athens-Lamia National Road, Olympic Village Interchange, 145 64, Nea Kifissia, Greece
Tel.: (30) 2108184455
Construction Engineering Services
N.A.I.C.S.: 541330

TOMI SA **(1)**
25 Ermou Str Athens - Lamia National Road, Olympic Village Interchange, 145 64, Nea Kifissia, Greece
Tel.: (30) 2108184500
Construction Engineering Services
N.A.I.C.S.: 541330
Karefylakis Timoleom *(Mng Dir)*

VIOTIKOS ANEMOS SA **(1)**
25 Ermou St Athens - Lamia National Road, Olympic Village Interchange, 145 64, Nea Kifissia, Greece
Tel.: (30) 210 8184600
Web Site: http://www.en.ellaktor.gr
Sales Range: $50-74.9 Million
Emp.: 35
Eletric Power Generation Services
N.A.I.C.S.: 221118

ELLERINE HOLDINGS LTD.
14 Charles Cresent Eastgate Ext. 14, PO Box 122, 2148, Sandton, South Africa
Tel.: (27) 102012000
Web Site: http://www.ellerines.co.za
Sales Range: $300-349.9 Million
Emp.: 200
Holding Company
N.A.I.C.S.: 551112
Bruce Sinclair *(Dir-Support Svcs)*

ELLERMAN INVESTMENTS LTD.
20 Saint James Street 3rd Floor, London, SW1A 1ES, United Kingdom
Tel.: (44) 12 2435 0733
Holding Company
N.A.I.C.S.: 551112
Frederick Barclay *(Co-Owner)*

Subsidiaries:

The Ritz Hotel (London) Limited **(1)**
150 Piccadilly, London, W1J 9BR, United Kingdom   **(100%)**
Tel.: (44) 2074938181
Web Site: http://www.theritzlondon.com
Sales Range: $25-49.9 Million
Emp.: 300
Hotel Operator
N.A.I.C.S.: 721199

ELLERSTON ASIAN INVESTMENTS LIMITED
Level 11 179 Elizabeth Street, Sydney, 2000, NSW, Australia
Tel.: (61) 290217701   AU

Web Site:
http://www.ellerstoncapital.com
Year Founded: 2015
EAI—(ASX)
Rev.: $1,797,211
Assets: $97,309,791
Liabilities: $767,345
Net Worth: $96,542,446
Earnings: ($22,519,774)
Fiscal Year-end: 06/30/22
Investment Management Service
N.A.I.C.S.: 523940
Ian Kelly *(Sec)*

ELLERSTON GLOBAL INVESTMENTS LIMITED
Level 11 179 Elizabeth Street, Sydney, 2000, NSW, Australia
Tel.: (61) 2 9021 7797
Web Site:
http://ellerstonegi.arkade.com.au
Investment Services
N.A.I.C.S.: 523999

ELLEX MEDICAL LASERS LIMITED
3-4 Second Avenue Mawson Lakes, Salisbury, 5095, SA, Australia
Tel.: (61) 870748200
Web Site: http://www.ellex.com
EYE—(ASX)
Rev.: $15,998,932
Assets: $19,953,258
Liabilities: $5,710,470
Net Worth: $14,242,788
Earnings: ($5,869,391)
Fiscal Year-end: 06/30/24
Lasers & Diagnostic Ultrasound Systems Mfr
N.A.I.C.S.: 334510
Victor Previn *(Chm)*

Subsidiaries:

Ellex (Japan) Corporation **(1)**
Harumi Center Bldg 5F 2-5-24 Harumi, Chuo-ku, Tokyo, 104-0053, Japan
Tel.: (81) 663962250
Web Site: http://www.ellex.jp
Sales Range: $25-49.9 Million
Emp.: 25
Diagnostic Ultrasound System Sales & Services
N.A.I.C.S.: 423450

Ellex (USA) Inc. **(1)**
7138 Shady Oak Rd, Minneapolis, MN 55344-3517
Tel.: (952) 881-9100
Sales Range: $50-74.9 Million
Emp.: 8
Diagnostic Ultrasound System Sales
N.A.I.C.S.: 423450
Bill Swaim *(Pres)*

Ellex Deutschland Gmbh **(1)**
Ostring 45, 63533, Mainhausen, Hesse, Germany
Tel.: (49) 61828296
Sales Range: $50-74.9 Million
Emp.: 7
Diagnostic Ultrasound Systems Sales & Services
N.A.I.C.S.: 423450

Ellex Medical Pty Ltd. **(1)**
82 Gilbert St, Adelaide, 5000, SA, Australia
Tel.: (61) 881045200
Web Site: http://www.ellex.com
Sales Range: $50-74.9 Million
Emp.: 120
Diagnostic System Mfr
N.A.I.C.S.: 334510

Ellex Services Europe S.A.R.L **(1)**
555 Chemin Du Bois, 69140, Rillieux-la-Pape, France
Tel.: (33) 473341855
Sales Range: $25-49.9 Million
Emp.: 7
Diagnostic Ultrasound Systems Mfr
N.A.I.C.S.: 334510

ELLIES HOLDINGS LIMITED

Ellies Holdings Limited—(Continued)

94 Eloff Street Ext, Village Deep, Johannesburg, 2001, South Africa
Tel.: (27) 114903800   ZA
Web Site:
http://www.elliesholdings.com
Year Founded: 1979
ELI—(JSE)
Rev.: $51,824,670
Assets: $21,896,889
Liabilities: $19,395,370
Net Worth: $2,501,519
Earnings: ($4,436,881)
Emp.: 010
Fiscal Year-end: 04/30/23
Electronic Component Mfr & Whslr
N.A.I.C.S.: 334419
Christiaan Booyens (CFO)

Subsidiaries:

Archsat Investments (Gauteng)(Pty)
Ltd   (1)
94 Eloff St Ext, Johannesburg, 2190, Gauteng, South Africa
Tel.: (27) 114903800
Electronic Products Mfr
N.A.I.C.S.: 334419

Archsat Investments (Natal) (Pty)
Ltd   (1)
94 Ellof Street, Johannesburg, 2137, Gauteng, South Africa
Tel.: (27) 114903959
Web Site: http://www.ellies.co.za
Sales Range: $25-49.9 Million
Emp.: 600
Electronic Products Mfr
N.A.I.C.S.: 334419
Wayne Samson (CEO)

Ellies (Pty) Ltd   (1)
94 Eloff Street Ext, Village Deep, 2001, Johannesburg, South Africa
Tel.: (27) 11 490 3800
Web Site: http://www.ellies.co.za
Sales Range: $200-249.9 Million
Emp.: 600
Electronic Products Mfr
N.A.I.C.S.: 334419

Subsidiary (Domestic):

Megatron Holdings (Pty) Ltd.   (2)
198 Element Road, Kempton Park, 1624, South Africa
Tel.: (27) 11 976 3003
Web Site: http://www.megatronfederal.com
Sales Range: $125-149.9 Million
Emp.: 200
Power Generation & Distribution Services
N.A.I.C.S.: 221118
Carlos Fidalgo (Gen Mgr)

Ellies Electronics (Bloemfontein)(Pty)
Ltd   (1)
27-29 Grey Street, Hilton, Bloemfontein, 9300, Free State, South Africa
Tel.: (27) 51 403 5200
Web Site: https://www.ellies.co.za
Emp.: 80
Electronic Products Mfr
N.A.I.C.S.: 334419

Ellies Electronics (Cape)(Pty) Ltd (1)
47 Morningside Road, Ndabeni, Cape Town, 7405, Western Cape, South Africa
Tel.: (27) 21 100 3329
Web Site: https://www.ellies.co.za
Emp.: 80
Electronic Products Mfr
N.A.I.C.S.: 334419

Ellies Electronics (Natal)(Pty) Ltd (1)
911 Umngeni Road, Durban, 4001, Kwazulu-Natal, South Africa
Tel.: (27) 313033298
Electronic Products Mfr
N.A.I.C.S.: 334419

Ellies Electronics (Nelspruit)(Pty)
Ltd   (1)
8 Christie Crescent, Nelspruit, 1201, Mpumalanga, South Africa
Tel.: (27) 137553000
Electronic Products Mfr
N.A.I.C.S.: 334419

Ellies Electronics (Pietersburg)(Pty)
Ltd   (1)
Gypsum Tagore Street Nirvana, Polokwane, 0700, South Africa
Tel.: (27) 152921096
Electronic Products Mfr
N.A.I.C.S.: 334419
Peter van Vuuren (Exec Dir)

**ELLINAS FINANCE PUBLIC
COMPANY LTD**
Theotoki 6, PO Box 21357-1507, 1055, Nicosia, Cyprus
Tel.: (357) 22349801
Web Site:
https://www.ellinasfinance.com
Year Founded: 1992
ELF—(CYP)
Rev.: $1,908,584
Assets: $15,361,474
Liabilities: $5,420,458
Net Worth: $9,941,016
Earnings: $626,234
Fiscal Year-end: 12/31/20
Financial Services
N.A.I.C.S.: 523999

**ELLIOTT MATSUURA
CANADA, INC.**
2120 Buckingham Road, Oakville, L6H 5X2, ON, Canada
Tel.: (905) 829-2211
Web Site:
http://www.elliottmachinery.com
Year Founded: 1950
Rev.: $16,019,231
Emp.: 60
Industrial Equipment Whsr
N.A.I.C.S.: 423830
Frank Bolieiro (VP-Sls & Mktg)

**ELLIPSIZ COMMUNICATIONS
LTD.**
Suite 208 340 Ferrier Street, Markham, L3R 2Z5, ON, Canada
Tel.: (905) 470-8800
Web Site: http://www.ellipsiz-comms.com
ECT—(TSXV)
Sales Range: Less than $1 Million
Telecommunication Servicesb
N.A.I.C.S.: 517810
Tan Chong Gin (Pres & CEO)

ELLIPSIZ LTD.
54 Serangoon North Avenue 4 05 02, Singapore, 555854, Singapore
Tel.: (65) 65182200   SG
Web Site: https://www.ellipsiz.com
Year Founded: 1992
BIX—(SES)
Rev.: $43,825,861
Assets: $104,125,232
Liabilities: $15,408,670
Net Worth: $88,716,562
Earnings: $517,229
Emp.: 106
Fiscal Year-end: 06/30/23
Probe Card Designer & Mfr, Silicon Wafer Reclaim Services, Semiconductor Manufacturing Equipment Distr & Test Systems Integration
N.A.I.C.S.: 334419
Kelvin Wen-Sum Lum (CEO)

Subsidiaries:

Axis-Tec Pte. Ltd.   (1)
Blk 5008 07-19 Ang Mo Kio Ave 5, Singapore, 569874, Singapore
Tel.: (65) 69140500
Web Site: https://www.axis-tec.com.sg
Automobile Parts Mfr
N.A.I.C.S.: 336390

Ellipsiz (Shanghai) International
Ltd   (1)
Room 1406 Building 2 Lane 289 Zheqiao Road, Pudong, Shanghai, 201206, China

Tel.: (86) 2150270969
Web Site: http://www.ellipsizdss.com
Sales Range: $50-74.9 Million
Emp.: 25
Semiconductor Devices Mfr & Distr
N.A.I.C.S.: 423690

Ellipsiz Communications (NZ)
Limited   (1)
Marion Square, PO Box 9348, Wellington, 6141, New Zealand
Tel.: (64) 2 168 6377
Web Site: https://www.ellipsiz.co.nz
Sales Range: $25-49.9 Million
Emp.: 4
Electronic Components Distr
N.A.I.C.S.: 334419

Ellipsiz Communications Taiwan
Ltd   (1)
8F No 96 Section 1 Jianguo North Road, Jhongshan District, Taipei, 10489, Taiwan
Tel.: (886) 225159596
Emp.: 25
Electronic Components Distr
N.A.I.C.S.: 423690

Ellipsiz DSS Pte. Ltd.   (1)
54 Serangoon North Avenue 4 05-02, Singapore, 555854, Singapore
Tel.: (65) 65182200
Web Site: https://www.ellipsizdss.com
Semiconductor & Electronics Industry Products Distr & Services
N.A.I.C.S.: 423690
Ray Ling Hwee Goh (Gen Mgr-Singapore)

Subsidiary (Non-US):

Ellipsiz iNETest (Shanghai) Co.,
Ltd   (2)
Building 2 Room 2402 1406 No 289 ZheQiao Road, Pudong New District, Shanghai, 201206, China
Tel.: (86) 2152383300
Web Site: http://www.ellipsizdss.com
Sales Range: $25-49.9 Million
Emp.: 32
Semiconductor & Electronics Industry Products Distr & Services
N.A.I.C.S.: 423690
Jeff Chu Mou Chuang (Gen Mgr)

Ellipsiz iNETest (Suzhou) Co.,
Ltd   (2)
No 501 5F Building 2 OET Park No 69 Weixin Road, Suzhou Industrial Park, Suzhou, 215021, Jiangsu, China
Tel.: (86) 51267623789
Web Site: http://www.ellipsizdss.com
Semiconductor & Electronics Industry Products Distr & Services
N.A.I.C.S.: 423690
Jeff Chu Mou Chuang (Gen Mgr)

iNETest Malaysia Sdn. Bhd.   (2)
50 Persiaran Bayan Indah Bayan Bay, 11900, Bayan Lepas, Penanag, Malaysia
Tel.: (60) 46425035
Web Site: http://www.ellipsizdss.com
Sales Range: $25-49.9 Million
Emp.: 40
Semiconductor & Electronics Industry Products Distr & Services
N.A.I.C.S.: 423690
Gim Poay Boey (Gen Mgr)

Ellipsiz Second Source Inc   (1)
251 Chen Ju Road Lin 9 Ta Tso Li Chunan Chen Miaoli, 35057, Miao-li, Taiwan
Tel.: (886) 37460087
Pump Sales & Refurbishment Services
N.A.I.C.S.: 423830

Ellipsiz Semilab (Shanghai) Co.,
Ltd   (1)
4F No 2 Jia Li Building 201 Keyuan Road Zhang Jiang Hi-Tech Park,, Pudong, Shanghai, 201203, China
Tel.: (86) 21 5027 0969
Web Site: http://www.ellipsiz.com
Semiconductor Devices Mfr
N.A.I.C.S.: 334413

Ellipsiz Singapore Pte Ltd   (1)
54 Serangoon North Avenue 4, Singapore, 555854, Singapore
Tel.: (65) 63118500
Semiconductor Devices Mfr
N.A.I.C.S.: 334413

Chan Melvin (Gen Mgr)

Subsidiary (Domestic):

E+HPS Pte. Ltd   (2)
152 Paya Lebar Road 06-03 Citipoint Paya Lebar, Singapore, 409020, Singapore
Tel.: (65) 6 841 4833
Web Site: https://www.ehps.com.sg
Sales Range: $25-49.9 Million
Emp.: 20
Electronic Components Distr
N.A.I.C.S.: 423690

Subsidiary (Non-US):

E+HPS Engineering (Suzhou) Co.,
Ltd   (3)
Unit 14 3F No 5 XingHan Street Block A, Suzhou, 215021, Jiangsu, China
Tel.: (86) 512 6767 2671
Web Site: https://www.ehps.com.sg
Electronic Components Mfr
N.A.I.C.S.: 334413

**ELLIPTIC LABORATORIES
ASA**
Hausmannsgate 21, 182, Oslo, Norway
Tel.: (47) 92410137
Web Site:
https://www.ellipticlabs.com
Year Founded: 2006
EIP—(DEU)
Rev.: $4,808,978
Assets: $32,267,135
Liabilities: $2,189,359
Net Worth: $30,077,776
Earnings: ($3,048,125)
Emp.: 72
Fiscal Year-end: 12/31/22
Software Development Services
N.A.I.C.S.: 541511
Laila B. Danielsen (Pres, CEO & Co-Founder)

ELLISDON CORPORATION
1004 Middlegate Rd Suite 1000, Mississauga, L4Y 1M4, ON, Canada
Tel.: (905) 896-8900
Web Site: https://www.ellisdon.com
Year Founded: 1951
Sales Range: $1-4.9 Billion
Emp.: 1,500
General Contractor & Construction Services
N.A.I.C.S.: 236220
Geoffrey Smith (Pres & CEO)

Subsidiaries:

EllisDon Corporation   (1)
2045 Oxford Street East, London, N5V 2Z7, ON, Canada
Tel.: (519) 455-6770
Web Site: http://www.ellisdon.com
Sales Range: $25-49.9 Million
Emp.: 100
General Contractors
N.A.I.C.S.: 236220

Branch (Non-US):

EllisDon Construction Inc.   (1)
Pergamou 3, Nea Smyrni, GR-171 21, Athens, Greece
Tel.: (30) 2109313372
General Contractors
N.A.I.C.S.: 236220

EllisDon Construction Inc.   (2)
Office No 501 Al Barsha Business Centre, PO Box 112208, Dubai, 112208, United Arab Emirates
Tel.: (971) 45153400
Web Site: http://www.ellisdon.com
Sales Range: $50-74.9 Million
General Contractors
N.A.I.C.S.: 236220
Paul Kirby (VP-Intl)

Branch (Domestic):

EllisDon Construction Services
Inc.   (2)

300 7330 Fisher St SE, Calgary, T2H 2H8,
AB, Canada
Tel.: (403) 259-6627
Sales Range: $25-49.9 Million
Emp.: 50
General Contractors
N.A.I.C.S.: 236220
Vince Davoli *(VP)*

EllisDon Corporation   **(2)**
7071 Bayers Road Suite 5007, Halifax, B3L
2C2, NS, Canada
Tel.: (902) 422-4587
Web Site: http://www.ellisdon.com
Sales Range: $25-49.9 Million
Emp.: 28
General Contractors
N.A.I.C.S.: 236220
Shaun Stiles *(VP)*

EllisDon Corporation   **(2)**
2680 Queensview Drive, Ottawa, K2B 8J9,
ON, Canada
Tel.: (613) 565-2680
Sales Range: $25-49.9 Million
Emp.: 50
General Contractor Services
N.A.I.C.S.: 236220

EllisDon Corporation   **(2)**
13775 Commerce Parkway Suite 350, Rich-
mond, V6V 2V4, BC, Canada
Tel.: (604) 247-1072
Web Site: https://www.ellisdon.com
General Contractors
N.A.I.C.S.: 236220

Oxford Builders Supplies   **(2)**
2045 Oxford St E, London, N5V 2Z7, ON,
Canada
Tel.: (519) 455-6109
Web Site: http://www.oxfordbuilders.ca
Sales Range: $25-49.9 Million
Emp.: 20
Building Supplies
N.A.I.C.S.: 423840
Mike Demelo *(VP-Svc)*

Branch (Non-US):

Windjammer Landing Villa Beach Re-
sort & Spa   **(2)**
Labrelotte Bay, PO Box 1504, Castries,
Saint Lucia
Tel.: (758) 4569000
Web Site: http://www.windjammer-
landing.com
Resort & Spa Hotel
N.A.I.C.S.: 721110

EllisDon Services Inc.   **(1)**
Office No 12 Manal Centre 2 Al Basatin Ma-
dina Road, Jeddah, Saudi Arabia
Tel.: (966) 11 486 8321
Construction Engineering Services
N.A.I.C.S.: 541330

ELLISON TRAVEL & TOURS
LTD.
311 Main Street, Exeter, N0M 1S7,
ON, Canada
Tel.: (519) 235-2000
Web Site: http://www.ettravel.com
Year Founded: 1980
Sales Range: $10-24.9 Million
Emp.: 60
Tour & Travel Services
N.A.I.C.S.: 561510
Doug Ellison *(Pres)*

ELLOMAY CAPITAL LTD.
18 Rothschild Boulevard 1st Floor,
Tel Aviv, 6688121, Israel
Tel.: (972) 37971111   II
Web Site: https://www.ellomay.com
ELLO—(NYSEAMEX)
Rev.: $65,538,886
Assets: $707,659,074
Liabilities: $605,620,579
Net Worth: $102,038,494
Earnings: $171,954
Emp.: 25
Fiscal Year-end: 12/31/22
Holding Company
N.A.I.C.S.: 551112

Shlomo Nechama *(Chm)*

ELLWEE AB
Kardanvagen 38, 461 38, Trollhattan,
Sweden
Tel.: (46) 709909966
Web Site: https://www.ellwee.com
Year Founded: 2015
9U2—(DEU)
Electric Vehicle Mfr
N.A.I.C.S.: 336320

ELMA ELECTRONIC AG
Hofstrasse 93, CH-8620, Wetzikon,
Switzerland
Tel.: (41) 449334111
Web Site: https://www.elma.com
Year Founded: 1960
ELMN—(SWX)
Rev.: $198,645,116
Assets: $131,773,236
Liabilities: $67,696,696
Net Worth: $64,076,539
Earnings: $5,959,116
Emp.: 770
Fiscal Year-end: 12/31/23
Electronic Computer Manufacturing
N.A.I.C.S.: 334111
Edwin Wild *(CFO)*

Subsidiaries:

ELMA Electronic GmbH   **(1)**
Stuttgarter Str 11, 75179, Pforzheim,
Germany   **(100%)**
Tel.: (49) 723197340
Web Site: https://www.elma.com
Sales Range: $25-49.9 Million
Emp.: 18
Electronic Components Mfr
N.A.I.C.S.: 334419
Paolo Putzolu *(Mng Dir)*

Elma Asia Pacific Pte. Ltd.   **(1)**
8 Ubi Road 2 07-14 Zervex Building, Singa-
pore, 408538, Singapore
Tel.: (65) 64798552
Sales Range: $25-49.9 Million
Emp.: 4
Back Planes & Rotary Component Mfr
N.A.I.C.S.: 332999
Jason Chua *(Sls Dir)*

Elma Bustronic Corp.   **(1)**
44350 Grimmer Blvd, Fremont, CA
94538   **(100%)**
Tel.: (510) 490-7388
Web Site: http://www.bustronic.com
Sales Range: $25-49.9 Million
Emp.: 50
Bare Printed Circuit Board Mfr
N.A.I.C.S.: 334412
Boris Micha *(Gen Mgr)*

Elma Electronic France SASU   **(1)**
16 rue Hannah Arendt, Parc des Forges,
67200, Strasbourg, France   **(100%)**
Tel.: (33) 388567250
Sales Range: $25-49.9 Million
Emp.: 6
Electronic Parts & Equipment Whslr
N.A.I.C.S.: 423690

Elma Electronic GmbH   **(1)**
Stuttgarter Str 11, 75179, Pforzheim, Ger-
many
Tel.: (49) 72 319 7340
Hardware Mfr
N.A.I.C.S.: 332510
Paolo Putzolu *(Mng Dir)*

Elma Electronic Inc.   **(1)**
44350 S Grimmer Blvd, Fremont, CA 94538
Tel.: (510) 656-3400
Sales Range: $50-74.9 Million
Emp.: 155
Electronic Enclosure & Passive Electronic
Component Designer & Mfr
N.A.I.C.S.: 334111

Elma Electronic Israel Ltd   **(1)**
34 Modiin St, Sgula, Petach Tikva, 49271,
Israel   **(100%)**
Tel.: (972) 39305025
Web Site: http://www.elma.co.il

Sales Range: $50-74.9 Million
Emp.: 80
Electronic Parts & Equipment Whslr
N.A.I.C.S.: 423690

Elma Electronic Romania SRL   **(1)**
Chisoda DN 59 Km 8 550 m, 307221, Ti-
mis, Romania
Tel.: (40) 256306046
Hardware Mfr
N.A.I.C.S.: 332510
Gerhard Kerner *(Mng Dir)*

Elma Electronic Technology (Shang-
hai) Co., Ltd.   **(1)**
Building 11 No 198 Chang Jian Road, Bao
Shan District, Shanghai, 200949, China
Tel.: (86) 2158665908
Hardware Mfr
N.A.I.C.S.: 332510

Elma Electronic UK Ltd.   **(1)**
Solutions House Fraser Road, Priory Busi-
ness Park, Bedford, MK44 3BF, United
Kingdom
Tel.: (44) 1234838822
Web Site: https://www.elma.com
Hardware Mfr
N.A.I.C.S.: 332510
Stuart Young *(Mng Dir)*

Optima Eps Corp   **(1)**
2305 Newpoint Pkwy, Lawrenceville, GA
30043   **(100%)**
Tel.: (770) 496-4000
Web Site: http://www.elma.com
Sales Range: $25-49.9 Million
Emp.: 50
Electronic Parts & Equipment Whslr
N.A.I.C.S.: 423690

Optima Stantron Corp.   **(1)**
2305 Newpoint Pkwy, Lawrenceville, GA
30043
Tel.: (770) 496-4000
Hardware Mfr
N.A.I.C.S.: 332510

ELMA HANS SCHMIDBAUER
GMBH & CO. KG
Kolpingstr 1 7, D-78224, Singen, Ger-
many
Tel.: (49) 77318820
Web Site: http://www.elma-
ultrasonic.com
Year Founded: 1948
Rev.: $24,584,970
Emp.: 15
Cleaning Equipment Mfr
N.A.I.C.S.: 335999
Manfred H. Schmidbauer *(Mng Dir)*

Subsidiaries:

Elma Schmidbauer Suisse AG   **(1)**
Feldstrasse 4, 5506, Magenwil, Switzerland
Tel.: (41) 628872500
Web Site: http://www.elma-suisse.ch
Cleaning Equipment Mfr
N.A.I.C.S.: 335999

ELMA HOLDINGS PUBLIC
COMPANY LTD
54 Grivas Digenis Avenue, PO Box
22333, 1096, Nicosia, Cyprus
Tel.: (357) 2 202 0200
Web Site: http://www.elma.com.cy
Investment Management Service
N.A.I.C.S.: 523999

Subsidiaries:

Dodoni Portfolio Investments Public
Company Ltd.   **(1)**
                                         (65%)
Tel.: (357) 22020200
Sales Range: Less than $1 Million
Financial Services
N.A.I.C.S.: 523999
Michalakis Ioannidis *(Pres)*

Jupiter Portfolio Investments Public
Company Ltd.   **(1)**
54 Griva Dhigenis Avenue Silvex House 6th
floor, 1096, Nicosia, Cyprus
Tel.: (357) 22020200

Sales Range: Less than $1 Million
Financial Services
N.A.I.C.S.: 523999
Antonis Kallis *(CFO & Sec)*

ELMAT - SCHLAGHECK GMBH
& CO. KG
Alte Ziegelei 27, 51491, Overath,
Germany
Tel.: (49) 220494810
Web Site: http://www.elmat.de
Emp.: 50
Cable Mfr
N.A.I.C.S.: 332618
Bodo Schlagheck *(Mng Partner)*

ELMERA GROUP ASA
Folke Bernadottesvei 38, Fyllings-
dalen, 5147, Bergen, Norway
Tel.: (47) 920153577   NO
Web Site:
    https://investor.elmeragroup.no
Year Founded: 2001
1ZK—(DEU)
Rev.: $2,357,427,859
Assets: $1,327,550,157
Liabilities: $1,212,999,446
Net Worth: $114,550,711
Earnings: $6,821,264
Emp.: 412
Fiscal Year-end: 12/31/22
Electricity Power Generation Services
N.A.I.C.S.: 237130
Rolf Barmen *(Pres & CEO)*

Subsidiaries:

Energismart Norge AS   **(1)**
Mariboes gate 8, 183, Oslo, Norway
Tel.: (47) 23109610
Web Site: https://www.energismart.no
Electricity Distribution Services
N.A.I.C.S.: 221122

Steddi Payments AS   **(1)**
PO Box 3507, Fyllingsdalen, 5845, Bergen,
Norway
Tel.: (47) 55907350
Web Site: https://www.steddi.no
Payment Processing Services
N.A.I.C.S.: 522320

Switch Nordic Green AB   **(1)**
Katarinavagen 20, 116 45, Stockholm, Swe-
den
Tel.: (46) 8205100
Web Site: https://www.nordicgreen.se
Electricity Distribution Services
N.A.I.C.S.: 221122

ELMONT A.D.
Karadordeva 2, 78000, Banja Luka,
Bosnia & Herzegovina
Tel.: (387) 51316297
Year Founded: 2001
ELMT-R-A—(BANJ)
Rev.: $50,633
Assets: $1,684,425
Liabilities: $471,705
Net Worth: $1,212,720
Earnings: $4
Emp.: 2
Fiscal Year-end: 12/31/13
Electrical Wiring Installation Services
N.A.I.C.S.: 238210
Tomislav Bojaniae *(Chm-Mgmt Bd)*

ELMORE LTD.
Tel.: (61) 863232310   AU
Web Site:
    https://www.elmoreltd.com.au
ELE—(ASX)
Rev.: $654,907
Assets: $6,800,459
Liabilities: $5,261,883
Net Worth: $1,538,576
Earnings: $(9,094,790)
Fiscal Year-end: 06/30/22
Thermal Coal Mining Services
N.A.I.C.S.: 213113
Sean P. Henbury *(Sec)*

Elmore Ltd.—(Continued)

Subsidiaries:

NSL Mining Resources India (Pvt) Ltd **(1)**
Shahahi Residency 3rd Floor Flat No 3 6-3-680/8/3 Plot No 1, Thakur Mansion Lane Somajiguda, Hyderabad, 500 082, India
Tel.: (91) 40 23418396
Coal Mining Services
N.A.I.C.S.: 212114

ELMOS SEMICONDUCTOR AG
Heinrich Hertz Strasse 1, 44227, Dortmund, Germany
Tel.: (49) 23175490
Web Site: https://www.elmos.com
Year Founded: 1984
ELG—(MUN)
Rev.: $634,736,289
Assets: $896,783,988
Liabilities: $402,868,395
Net Worth: $493,915,593
Earnings: $109,448,710
Emp.: 1,282
Fiscal Year-end: 12/31/23
Integrated Circuits Mfr
N.A.I.C.S.: 334413
Klaus G. Weyer (Chm-Supervisory Bd)

Subsidiaries:

Area 21 Software GmbH **(1)**
Hauert 12a, 44227, Dortmund, Germany
Tel.: (49) 75490
Web Site: https://www.area21-software.com
Software Designing & Testing Services
N.A.I.C.S.: 541511

DMOS Dresden MOS Design GmbH **(1)**
Bergstrasse 4, 01069, Dresden, Germany
Tel.: (49) 351479420
Web Site: https://www.dmos2002.de
Emp.: 14
Management Consulting Services
N.A.I.C.S.: 541618

ELMOS Korea Ltd **(1)**
C-301 Innovalley 253 Pangyo-ro, Bundang-Gu, Seongnam, 13486, Gyeonggi-do, Korea (South)
Tel.: (82) 317141131
Web Site: http://www.elmos.com
Sales Range: $50-74.9 Million
Emp.: 7
Semiconductor Equipment Distr
N.A.I.C.S.: 423690

ELMOS N.A. Inc **(1)**
32255 Northwestern Hwy Ste 45, Farmington Hills, MI 48334
Tel.: (248) 865-3200
Web Site: http://www.elmosna.com
Emp.: 6
Semiconductor Devices Mfr
N.A.I.C.S.: 334413

ELMOS Semiconductor Sud GmbH **(1)**
Heinrich-Hertz-Str 1, Dortmund, 44227, Germany **(100%)**
Tel.: (49) 23175490
Sales Range: $200-249.9 Million
Emp.: 800
Electronic Components Mfr
N.A.I.C.S.: 334419
Anton Mindl (Mgr)

Elmos Central IT Services GmbH & Co. KG **(1)**
Heinrich-Hertz-Str 1, 44227, Dortmund, Germany **(100%)**
Tel.: (49) 23175490
Web Site: http://www.elmos.com
Emp.: 800
Computer Programming Services
N.A.I.C.S.: 541511
Anton Mindl (Mng Dir)

Elmos Japan K.K. **(1)**
Tamachi 16th Fujishima Bldg 6F 4-13-4 Shiba, Minato-ku, Tokyo, 108-0014, Japan
Tel.: (81) 334517101
Semiconductor Product Mfr

N.A.I.C.S.: 334413

Elmos Semiconductor Singapore Pte. Ltd. **(1)**
29 International Business Park 05-03 Acer, Singapore, 609923, Singapore
Tel.: (65) 69081261
Semiconductor Product Mfr
N.A.I.C.S.: 334413

Elmos Semiconductor Technology (Shanghai) Co., Ltd. **(1)**
Unit 1601 16F Zhao Feng World Trade Building No 369 Jiang Su Road, Chang Ning District, Shanghai, 200050, China
Tel.: (86) 2162100908
Semiconductor Product Mfr
N.A.I.C.S.: 334413
Ling Jun Wang (Engr-Sls)

GED Gartner Electronic Design GmbH **(1)**
Im Technologiepark 27, 15236, Frankfurt, Germany **(100%)**
Tel.: (49) 3355572050
Web Site: http://www.ged.de
Sales Range: $25-49.9 Million
Emp.: 35
Computer System Design Services
N.A.I.C.S.: 541512

IndustrieAlpine Bautrager GmbH **(1)**
Am Geflugelhof 12, 85716, Unterschleissheim, Germany
Tel.: (49) 893183700
Semiconductor Mfr
N.A.I.C.S.: 334413

MAZ Mikroelektronik-Anwendungszentrum GmbH im Land Brandenburg **(1)**
Pascalstrasse 10 A, 10587, Berlin, Germany
Tel.: (49) 303151886
Web Site: http://www.mazbr.de
Electronics Retailer
N.A.I.C.S.: 449210

Mechaless GmbH **(1)**
TRIWO Technopark Bruchsal Building 5108 Werner-von-Siemens-Str 2-6, 76646, Bruchsal, Germany **(51%)**
Tel.: (49) 725 150 5130
Web Site: https://www.mechaless.com
Sales Range: $25-49.9 Million
Emp.: 20
Research & Development in the Physical Engineering & Life Sciences
N.A.I.C.S.: 541715

Mechaless Systems GmbH **(1)**
Building 5108 Werner-von-Siemens-Str 2-6, TRIWO Technopark Bruchsal, 76646, Bruchsal, Germany
Tel.: (49) 725150513
Web Site: https://www.mechaless.com
Automobile Parts Distr
N.A.I.C.S.: 423120

Online Engineering GmbH **(1)**
Alter Hellweg 48, 44379, Dortmund, Germany
Tel.: (49) 23128667690
Web Site: https://www.online-engineering.de
Emp.: 20
Electric Equipment Mfr
N.A.I.C.S.: 335999

ELNET TECHNOLOGIES LIMITED
Elnet Software City TS 140 Block No 2 and 9, Rajiv Gandhi Salai Taramani, Chennai, 600 113, Tamil Nadu, India
Tel.: (91) 4422541098
Web Site:
https://www.elnettechnologies.com
Year Founded: 1990
517477—(BOM)
Rev.: $3,603,068
Assets: $15,835,188
Liabilities: $2,615,040
Net Worth: $13,220,148
Earnings: $1,636,212
Emp.: 12
Fiscal Year-end: 03/31/21

Business Process Outsourcing Services
N.A.I.C.S.: 561990
Unnamalai Thiagarajan (Mng Dir)

ELODRIVE GMBH
Potsdamer Str 12, 32423, Minden, Germany
Tel.: (49) 571934300
Web Site: http://www.elodrive.de
Actuator Mfr
N.A.I.C.S.: 334512
Stefan Sohn (Mng Dir)

ELOF HANSSON AB
Forsta Langgatan 17, 413 80, Gothenburg, Sweden
Tel.: (46) 31856000
Web Site:
http://www.elofhansson.com
Year Founded: 1897
Sales Range: $700-749.9 Million
Emp.: 120
Electronics Appliances Electric Product Mfr
N.A.I.C.S.: 335999

Subsidiaries:

Adexi A/S **(1)**
Grenavej 635A, 8541, Skodstrup, Denmark
Tel.: (45) 87 41 71 00
Web Site: http://www.adexi.dk
Emp.: 15
Home Appliance Product Whlsr
N.A.I.C.S.: 423620
Erik Peschardt (Mng Dir)

Elof Hansson (Australia) Pty Ltd **(1)**
Suite 3 265-271 Pennant Hills Road, PO Box 130, Thornleigh, 2120, NSW, Australia
Tel.: (61) 2 9980 2800
Paper Product Distr
N.A.I.C.S.: 424120
Stephen Hiwkey (Mng Dir)

Elof Hansson (India) Pvt Ltd **(1)**
New no 149 Chamiers Road, R A Puram, 600 028, Chennai, Tamil Nadu, India
Tel.: (91) 44 2431 5110
Paper Product Distr
N.A.I.C.S.: 424120
Ramanathan Thanthoni (Mgr-Bus Dev)

Elof Hansson AB-Suc. **(1)**
Libertad 567 7 piso, C1012AAK, Buenos Aires, Argentina
Tel.: (54) 11 4382 2771
Paper Product Distr
N.A.I.C.S.: 424120

Elof Hansson Fiber LLC **(1)**
145 W Wisconsin Ave, Neenah, WI 54956
Tel.: (920) 727-1177
Paper Product Distr
N.A.I.C.S.: 424120

Elof Hansson Inc. **(1)**
127 W Main St, Tarrytown, NY, 10591 **(100%)**
Tel.: (914) 345-8380
Web Site: http://www.elofhansson.com
Sales Range: $25-49.9 Million
Emp.: 15
Paper & Wood Pulp
N.A.I.C.S.: 424130
Thomas Driscoll (CFO)

Division (Domestic):

Elof Hansson Inc. - Fiber Division **(2)**
3070 Bristol Pike Ste 222, Bensalem, PA 19020
Tel.: (215) 639-6622
Paper Products Mfr
N.A.I.C.S.: 322299

Subsidiary (Domestic):

Elof Hansson Paper & Board, Inc. **(2)**
400 Tech Centre Dr Ste 220, Milford, OH 45150 **(100%)**
Tel.: (513) 965-5090

Sales Range: $25-49.9 Million
Paper & Board
N.A.I.C.S.: 424130

Elof Hansson International AB **(1)**
Forsta Langgatan 17, 413 80, Gothenburg, Sweden
Tel.: (46) 31 85 60 00
Web Site: http://www.elofhansson.com
Paper Product Distr
N.A.I.C.S.: 424120
Jonas Heiman (Mgr-Sls-ECA Projects)

Elof Hansson K.K. **(1)**
3F Sawa Building 2-2 Nishi-Shinbashi 2-chome, Minato-Ku, Tokyo, 105-0003, Japan
Tel.: (81) 3 3503 6161
Paper Product Distr
N.A.I.C.S.: 424120

Elof Hansson Ltda **(1)**
Rua Libero Badaro 293 10 andar CJ 10-B, 01009-000, Sao Paulo, Brazil
Tel.: (55) 11 3101 5257
Paper Product Distr
N.A.I.C.S.: 424120

Elof Hansson Pulp & Paper Singapore Pte Ltd **(1)**
298 Tiong Bahru Road 08-04 Central Plaza, 168730, Singapore, Singapore
Tel.: (65) 6223 4393
Web Site: http://www.elofhansson.com
Paper Product Distr
N.A.I.C.S.: 424120
Shyam Sunder (Mng Dir)

Elof Hansson Pulp and Paper Ltd **(1)**
Unit 22 Carlson Court 116 Putney Bridge Road, London, SW15 2NQ, United Kingdom
Tel.: (44) 20 8877 8840
Paper Product Distr
N.A.I.C.S.: 424120
Roth-Kielund Anne (Mgr-Sls)

ELOMATIC OY
Itainen Rantakatu 72, 20810, Turku, Finland
Tel.: (358) 103957000
Web Site: https://www.elomatic.com
Emp.: 100
Engineeering Services
N.A.I.C.S.: 541330
Markku S. Lehtinen (Sr VP-Process & Energy)

Subsidiaries:

Elron Oy **(1)**
Yliopistonkatu 5, Helsinki, 00100, Finland
Tel.: (358) 503719052
Web Site: http://www.elron.fi
Sales Range: $50-74.9 Million
Emp.: 20
Financial & Project Development Advisory Services
N.A.I.C.S.: 523940
Martti Lehtinen (Mng Partner)

ELON AB
Trangsundsvagen 20, 392 39, Kalmar, 392 39, Sweden
Tel.: (46) 102204000
Web Site: https://www.elongroup.se
ELEC—(OMX)
Rev.: $195,225,159
Assets: $68,151,546
Liabilities: $46,498,920
Net Worth: $21,652,627
Earnings: $1,884,049
Emp.: 135
Fiscal Year-end: 12/31/19
Electronic Product Whlsr
N.A.I.C.S.: 423690

ELONEX
Z I Rousset 85 Avenue De La Plaine, 13790, Rousset, Bouches-du-Rhone, France
Tel.: (33) 442535400
Web Site: http://www.elonex.com
Rev.: $39,600,000
Emp.: 55

Computer Equipment
N.A.I.C.S.: 423430
Veronique Gardy *(Dir-Mktg)*

ELONG POWER HOLDING LIMITED
Gushan Standard Factory Buldg Project W Gushan Road & N Xingguang Road, Ganzhou New Energy Vehicle Technology City, Ganzhou, 341000, Jiangxi, China
Tel.: (86) 13011896849　　　Ky
Web Site:
　https://www.elongpower.com
Year Founded: 2014
ELPW—(NASDAQ)
Rev.: $3,162,739
Assets: $37,503,085
Liabilities: $36,524,749
Net Worth: $978,336
Earnings: ($7,446,001)
Emp.: 93
Fiscal Year-end: 12/31/23
Holding Company
N.A.I.C.S.: 551112

ELORO RESOURCES LTD.
20 Adelaide Street East Suite 200, Toronto, M5C 2T6, ON, Canada
Tel.: (416) 868-9168　　　ON
Web Site:
　https://www.elororesources.com
Year Founded: 1975
ELO—(TSX)
Rev.: $170,300
Assets: $43,635,709
Liabilities: $1,398,743
Net Worth: $42,236,967
Earnings: ($5,958,676)
Emp.: 126
Fiscal Year-end: 03/31/23
Gold Exploration Services
N.A.I.C.S.: 213114
Alexander S. Horvath *(CTO)*

ELP CORPORATION
29 Samsung 1-ro 2-gil, Hwaseong, 445-170, Gyeonggi-do, Korea (South)
Tel.: (82) 3180365800
Web Site: https://www.elp.co.kr
Year Founded: 1999
063760—(KRS)
Rev.: $18,110,121
Assets: $64,983,450
Liabilities: $15,677,760
Net Worth: $49,305,690
Earnings: ($1,232,070)
Emp.: 132
Fiscal Year-end: 12/31/22
LCD & AMOLED Product Mfr
N.A.I.C.S.: 334419
Jaehyuk Lee *(CEO)*

ELPHINSTONE PTY LTD
91 Terra Nova Drive, PO Box 717, Wynyard, Hobart, 7325, TAS, Australia
Tel.: (61) 3 6442 7777
Web Site: http://elphinstone.com
Industrial Machinery & Equipment Design & Mfr
N.A.I.C.S.: 333131
Dale Elphinstone *(Founder & Exec Chm)*

Subsidiaries:

United Equipment Pty Ltd　　　**(1)**
49 Pilbara Street, Welshpool, Perth, 6106, WA, Australia　　　**(100%)**
Tel.: (61) 8 6166 9800
Web Site:
　http://www.unitedequipment.com.au
Access Equipment, Industrial & Mining Machinery Distr
N.A.I.C.S.: 423830
Peter Court *(Mng Dir)*

ELPITIYA PLANTATIONS PLC
Level 09 Aitken Spence Tower I No 305 Vauxhall Street, Colombo, Sri Lanka
Tel.: (94) 114693000
Web Site: https://www.elpitiya.com
ELPL.N0000—(COL)
Rev.: $27,789,927
Assets: $40,003,466
Liabilities: $11,668,760
Net Worth: $28,334,706
Earnings: $6,094,092
Emp.: 4,597
Fiscal Year-end: 03/31/23
Tea Mfr
N.A.I.C.S.: 311920
Parakrama Dissanayake *(Chm)*

ELPO AD
Osvobozhdenie 2, Nikolaevo, 6190, Bulgaria
Tel.: (359) 4330 687 70
ELPO—(BUL)
Sales Range: Less than $1 Million
Electrical Component Mfr
N.A.I.C.S.: 335999

ELPRO INTERNATIONAL LTD.
17th Floor Nirmal Nariman Point, Mumbai, 400 021, India
Tel.: (91) 2222023075
Web Site: https://www.elpro.co.in
Year Founded: 1962
504000—(BOM)
Rev.: $9,071,312
Assets: $62,704,251
Liabilities: $39,347,040
Net Worth: $23,357,211
Earnings: $2,694,660
Emp.: 42
Fiscal Year-end: 03/31/21
Electric Equipment Mfr
N.A.I.C.S.: 335999
Sambhaw Kumar Jain *(CFO)*

Subsidiaries:

Elpro Estates Limited　　　**(1)**
The Metro Pliitan Chapekar Chowk, Chinchwad, Pune, 411 019, India
Tel.: (91) 20 32319113
Apartment Construction Services
N.A.I.C.S.: 236116

ELQ S.A.
ul Jagiellonska 81/83, 42-200, Czestochowa, Poland
Tel.: (48) 513291160
Web Site: https://elq.pl
Year Founded: 1976
Eletric Power Generation Services
N.A.I.C.S.: 221112
Ryszard Bobrowski *(CEO)*

ELRINGKLINGER AG
Max-Eyth-Strasse 2, 72581, Dettingen an der Erms, Germany
Tel.: (49) 71237240
Web Site:
　https://www.elringklinger.de
Year Founded: 1879
ZIL2—(DEU)
Rev.: $2,038,980,354
Assets: $2,216,769,657
Liabilities: $1,286,063,744
Net Worth: $930,705,913
Earnings: $43,393,130
Emp.: 9,600
Fiscal Year-end: 12/31/23
Exhaust Equipment Mfr
N.A.I.C.S.: 336310
Stefan Wolf *(Chm-Mgmt Bd & CEO)*

Subsidiaries:

Changchun ElringKlinger Ltd.　　**(1)**
118 Jinzhou Street, Economic and Technic Development Zone, Changchun, 130033, China

Tel.: (86) 43185878500
Exhaust Equipment Mfr
N.A.I.C.S.: 336310

EKASER, S.A. de C.V.　　　**(1)**
Mz 9 L-13 Y 14, 50200, Toluca, Mexico
Tel.: (52) 17222731912
Automobile Parts Mfr & Distr
N.A.I.C.S.: 336390

EKPO Fuel Cell Technologies
GmbH　　　**(1)**
Max-Eyth-Strasse 2, 72581, Dettingen an der Erms, Germany
Tel.: (49) 7123724200
Web Site: https://www.ekpo-fuelcell.com
Fuel Cell Mfr
N.A.I.C.S.: 334413

Elring Italia S.r.l.　　　**(1)**
Via De Nicola 7/ter, 10036, Settimo Torinese, TO, Italy
Tel.: (39) 0118022111
Electric Equipment Mfr
N.A.I.C.S.: 335999

Elring Klinger (Great Britain) Ltd.　**(1)**
Kirkleatham Business Park, Redcar, TS10 5RX, N Yorkshire, United Kingdom
Tel.: (44) 1642492492
Cylinder Head Gaskets Mfr
N.A.I.C.S.: 339991

Elring Klinger Mexico, S.A. de
C.V.　　　**(1)**
Alfonso Gomez de Orozco No 122 Col Exportec II, 50223, Toluca, Estado de Mexico, Mexico
Tel.: (52) 7222622800
Web Site: https://www.elringklinger.com.mx
Gaskets & Shielding Parts Mfr
N.A.I.C.S.: 335991

Elring Klinger Motortechnik
GmbH　　　**(1)**
Richard-Klinger-Strasse 8, 65510, Idstein, Germany
Tel.: (49) 612622305
Web Site: http://www.elringklinger.de
Automotive Engineering Services
N.A.I.C.S.: 811192

Elring Klinger, S.A.U.　　　**(1)**
Carrer de Tarrega num 19, 43204, Reus, Spain
Tel.: (34) 977770096
Web Site: http://www.elringklinger.es
Plastic Cup Mfr
N.A.I.C.S.: 326199

Elring Parts Ltd.　　　**(1)**
Unit 2 Derwent Ct Earlsway Team Vly Trading Estate, Gateshead, NE11 0TF, Tyne and Wear, United Kingdom
Tel.: (44) 1914915678
Web Site: http://www.elringparts.co.uk
Sales Range: $25-49.9 Million
Emp.: 29
Gaskets Distr
N.A.I.C.S.: 423840
Garry Waite *(Mng Dir)*

ElringKlinger Abschirmtechnik
(Schweiz) AG　　　**(1)**
Schildstrasse 20, 9475, Sevelen, Switzerland
Tel.: (41) 817501210
Web Site: http://www.elringklinger.com
Sales Range: $75-99.9 Million
Emp.: 400
Industrial Engineering Services
N.A.I.C.S.: 541330

ElringKlinger Automotive Components (India) Pvt. Ltd.　　　**(1)**
Plot No G2 Ranjangaon Ind Area, Tal Shirur Dist, Pune, 412220, Maharashtra, India
Web Site: http://www.elringklinger.in
Sales Range: $75-99.9 Million
Emp.: 120
Automobile Component Distr
N.A.I.C.S.: 423840

ElringKlinger Automotive Manufacturing, Inc.　　　**(1)**
47912 Halyard Dr Ste 111, Plymouth, MI 48170
Tel.: (734) 738-1800
Automotive Stamping Products Mfr & Distr
N.A.I.C.S.: 336370

ElringKlinger Canada, Inc.　　　**(1)**
1 Seneca Rd RR 4, Leamington, N8H 5P2, ON, Canada
Tel.: (519) 326-6113
Web Site: http://www.elringklinger.ca
Sales Range: $50-74.9 Million
Emp.: 130
Injection Molding Automotive Parts Mfr
N.A.I.C.S.: 336390

ElringKlinger China, Ltd.　　　**(1)**
660 Lu Shan Rd Snd, Suzhou, 215129, Jiangsu, China
Tel.: (86) 51285667745
Exhaust Equipment Mfr
N.A.I.C.S.: 336310
Humphrey Chen *(Gen Mgr)*

ElringKlinger Chongqing Ltd.　　**(1)**
Tel.: (86) 51285566299
Exhaust Equipment Mfr
N.A.I.C.S.: 336310

ElringKlinger Engineered Plastics (Qingdao) Co., Ltd.　　　**(1)**
101/201 Building A2 National Quality Inspection Park No 1000, Yuntaishan Road Zhongde Ecological Park Huangdao District, Qingdao, 266500, Shandong, China
Tel.: (86) 53255582832
Web Site: https://www.elringklinger-ep.cn
Plastics Product Mfr & Distr
N.A.I.C.S.: 326199

ElringKlinger Engineered Plastics North America, Inc.　　　**(1)**
4971 Golden Pkwy, Buford, GA 30518
Tel.: (678) 730-8190
Plastics Product Mfr
N.A.I.C.S.: 326199

ElringKlinger Holding USA, Inc.　**(1)**
4961 Golden Pkwy, Buford, GA 30518
Tel.: (678) 730-8169
Automotive Parts Mfr & Distr
N.A.I.C.S.: 336390

ElringKlinger Italia Srl　　　**(1)**
Via Verga 49, 10036, Settimo Torinese, Italy
Tel.: (39) 0118022111
Exhaust Equipment Mfr
N.A.I.C.S.: 336310
Fabrizio Goria *(Mgr-Pur)*

ElringKlinger Korea Co., Ltd.　　**(1)**
23-7 4 Gongdan-ro 10-gil, Gumi, 39424, Gyeongsanbuk-do, Korea (South)
Tel.: (82) 547161080
Web Site: http://www.elringklinger.kr
Electric Motor Engine Mfr
N.A.I.C.S.: 336320
Stefan Spreu *(Gen Mgr)*

ElringKlinger Kunststofftechnik
GmbH　　　**(1)**
Etzelstrasse 10, 74321, Bietigheim-Bissingen, Germany
Tel.: (49) 71425830
Web Site: http://www.elringklinger.com
Sales Range: $125-149.9 Million
Emp.: 570
Polytetrafluoroethylene Products Mfr
N.A.I.C.S.: 336310

Subsidiary (Non-US):

Elring Gaskets (Pty) Ltd.　　　**(2)**
81 Mimetes Rd, Denver, Johannesburg, 2094, Gauteng, South Africa
Tel.: (27) 116225660
Sales Range: $25-49.9 Million
Emp.: 12
Gaskets Retailer
N.A.I.C.S.: 423840
Hennie Lotter *(Gen Mgr)*

Elring Klinger do Brasil Ltda.　　**(2)**
Rua Francisco Carlos de Castro Neves 945, Piracicaba, 13522170, Sao Paulo, Brazil
Tel.: (55) 1931249000
Web Site: http://www.elringklinger.com.br
Sales Range: $75-99.9 Million
Emp.: 350
Gaskets Mfr
N.A.I.C.S.: 339991

ElringKlinger Engineered Plastics (Qingdao) Commercial Co., Ltd.　　**(2)**

ElringKlinger AG—(Continued)

No 101 & 201 Room A2 Building 1000 Yuntai Shan Road, International Innovation Park Sino German Ecopark Huangdao District, Qingdao, 266500, Shandong, China
Tel.: (86) 53255582832
Web Site: http://www.elringklinger-engineered-plastics.com
Plastics Product Mfr
N.A.I.C.S.: 326199

ElringKlinger Logistic Service GmbH **(1)**
Mercedesstrasse 40, 72108, Rottenburg am Neckar, Baden-Wurttemberg, Germany
Tel.: (49) 7457956010
Web Site: http://www.ek-ls.de
Sales Range: $550-599.9 Million
Emp.: 1,500
Cylinder Head Gaskets Supplier
N.A.I.C.S.: 423840

ElringKlinger South Africa (Pty) Ltd. **(1)**
13 Bentonite Street, Alrode, 1450, South Africa
Tel.: (27) 116227823
Exhaust Equipment Mfr
N.A.I.C.S.: 336310
Hennie Lotter (Gen Mgr)

ElringKlinger Switzerland AG **(1)**
Schildstrasse 20, 9475, Sevelen, Switzerland
Tel.: (41) 817501210
Electric Equipment Mfr
N.A.I.C.S.: 335999

ElringKlinger TR Otomotiv Sanayi ve Ticaret A.S. **(1)**
Tel.: (90) 2242753900
Web Site: http://www.elringklinger.com.tr
Emp.: 181
Electric Motor Engine Mfr
N.A.I.C.S.: 336310
Yavuz Gunaydin (Gen Mgr)

ElringKlinger Texas, LLC **(1)**
Ridgeview 35 4210 IH-35, San Antonio, TX 78218
Tel.: (210) 253-8182
Automotive Parts Mfr & Distr
N.A.I.C.S.: 336390

ElringKlinger USA, Inc. **(1)**
4961 Golden Pkwy, Buford, GA 30518
Tel.: (678) 730-8000
Automobile Parts Mfr
N.A.I.C.S.: 336310

Hofer Powertain Products UK Ltd. **(1)**
2 Titan Business Centre Spartan Close, Warwick, CV34 6RR, United Kingdom
Tel.: (44) 1926674500
Web Site: http://www.hofer-powertrain.co.uk
Train Product Distr
N.A.I.C.S.: 423840
William Hartley (Mng Dir)

Hofer Powertrain Products GmbH **(1)**
Ohmstr 15, 72622, Nurtingen, Germany
Tel.: (49) 70222178840
Web Site: http://hofer-powertrain.eu
Train Product Distr
N.A.I.C.S.: 423840
Johann Hofer (CEO & Mng Dir)

PT Natarang Mining **(1)**
Jalan Ciputat Raya No 16 Pondok Pinang Kebayoran Lama, Jakarta Selatan, Jakarta, 12310, Indonesia
Tel.: (62) 21 751 0125
Gold Mining Services
N.A.I.C.S.: 212220

ELRON VENTURES LTD
ToHa Tower 114 Yigal Alon St 27th Floor, Tel Aviv, 6744320, Israel
Tel.: (972) 36075555
Web Site: https://elronventures.com
Year Founded: 1962
ELRNF—(OTCEM)
Rev.: $16,085,000
Assets: $159,821,000
Liabilities: $18,256,000

Net Worth: $141,565,000
Earnings: ($10,991,000)
Emp.: 8
Fiscal Year-end: 12/31/23
Technology Investment Services
N.A.I.C.S.: 523999
Saul Zang (Vice Chm)

Subsidiaries:

RDC Rafael Development Corporation Ltd. **(1)**
3 Azrieli Center The Triangle Tower 42nd Floor, Tel Aviv, 6702301, Israel
Tel.: (972) 36075500
Web Site: http://www.rdc.co.il
Defense & Security System Services
N.A.I.C.S.: 561621
Arie Mientkavich (Chm)

ELSA SOLUTIONS SPA
Via P Patarini 15, 40026, Imola, BO, Italy
Tel.: (39) 0542362470
Web Site: https://www.elsaweb.it
Year Founded: 1982
ELSA—(EUR)
Electric Equipment Mfr
N.A.I.C.S.: 335312

ELSAN LTD.
Bellbrook Park, Uckfield, TN22 1QF, Sussex, United Kingdom
Tel.: (44) 825748200   UK
Web Site: http://www.elsan.co.uk
Year Founded: 1924
Sales Range: $1-9.9 Million
Emp.: 20
Chemical Sanitation Products Mfr & Supplier
N.A.I.C.S.: 325612
Peter Warwick-Smith (Mng Dir)

Subsidiaries:

Horton Hygiene Co. **(1)**
Bellbrook Pk, Uckfield, TN22 4LW, Sussex, United Kingdom
Tel.: (44) 825748200
Sanitation Products Mfr
N.A.I.C.S.: 325612

Lautus Trading bvba **(1)**
Guido Gezellelaan 109, 8800, Roeselare, Belgium
Tel.: (32) 51 22 41 27
Web Site: http://www.lautustrading.com
Toilet Fluid Cleaner Mfr
N.A.I.C.S.: 325612

The Trailerbarrow Co. **(1)**
Buxted, Uckfield, TN22 4LW, Sussex, United Kingdom
Tel.: (44) 825733291
Wheelbarrow Mfr
N.A.I.C.S.: 333112

ELSECO LIMITED
Level 7 Gate Village Bldg 8 Dubai International Financial Centre, PO Box 506639, Dubai, United Arab Emirates
Tel.: (971) 4 384 2800
Web Site: http://www.else.co
Year Founded: 2006
Commercial Space, Aviation & Energy Insurance Underwriting Services
N.A.I.C.S.: 524298
Laurent Lemaire (Founder & CEO)

ELSMORE RESOURCES LIMITED
Suite 1306 Level 13 370 Pitt Street, Sydney, 2000, NSW, Australia
Tel.: (61) 2 92670004
Web Site: http://www.elsmore.com.au
Tin & Gems Mining & Exploration
N.A.I.C.S.: 212290
John Patrick Gaffney (Chm)

ELSO HAZAI ENERGIA-

PORTFOLIO PLC
Cziraki u 26-32 II 144, Budapest, 1163, Hungary
Tel.: (36) 20 219 3364
EHEP—(BUD)
Sales Range: Less than $1 Million
Investment Management Service
N.A.I.C.S.: 525990
Kis Andor (Chm-Mgmt Bd)

ELSOFT RESEARCH BERHAD
Plot 85B Lintang Bayan Lepas 9 Bayan Lepas Industrial Park Phase 4, Bayan Lepas, 11900, Penang, Malaysia
Tel.: (60) 46468122   MY
Web Site: https://www.elsoftresearch.com
Year Founded: 1996
ELSOFT—(KLS)
Rev.: $5,945,955
Assets: $32,039,222
Liabilities: $2,637,017
Net Worth: $29,402,206
Earnings: $9,093,990
Emp.: 68
Fiscal Year-end: 12/31/22
Embedded System Development Services
N.A.I.C.S.: 334118
Eng Keat Chong (Chm)

Subsidiaries:

Elsoft Systems Sdn. Bhd. **(1)**
Plot 85B Lintang Bayan Lepas 9 Phase 4, Bayan Lepas Industrial Park, 11900, Bayan Lepas, Penang, Malaysia
Tel.: (60) 46468122
Semiconductor Product Mfr
N.A.I.C.S.: 334413

ELSPEC ENGINEERING LTD.
4 Hashoham St Zone 23 Caesarea Industrial Park, PO Box 3019, Caesarea, Israel
Tel.: (972) 46272470
Web Site: https://www.elspec-ltd.com
Year Founded: 1988
ELSPC—(TAE)
Rev.: $24,697,057
Assets: $27,821,522
Liabilities: $6,737,671
Net Worth: $21,083,851
Earnings: $3,013,676
Emp.: 116
Fiscal Year-end: 12/31/23
Instrument Manufacturing for Measuring & Testing Electricity & Electrical Signals
N.A.I.C.S.: 334515

Subsidiaries:

ELSPEC Engineering India Pvt. Ltd. **(1)**
Tulsi Chambers 4-5/2 Old Palasia Greater Kailash Road, Indore, 452018, Madhya Pradesh, India
Tel.: (91) 7314020081
Electrical Power Quality Machine Mfr
N.A.I.C.S.: 334515

ELSPEC Portugal Lda. **(1)**
Zona Industrial-Fase 1 Avenida de S Romao do Neiva, 197 C/D I Estrada Nacional 13 Neiva, 4935-546, Viana do Castelo, Portugal
Tel.: (351) 258351920
Electrical Power Quality Machine Mfr
N.A.I.C.S.: 334515

Elspec Andina S.A.S **(1)**
Avenida 6 BIS 35-100 Oficina 412 Centro empresarial, Chipichape, Cali, Colombia
Tel.: (57) 4868672
Electrical Engineering Services
N.A.I.C.S.: 541330

Elspec Ltd. **(1)**
4 Hashoham St, PO Box 3019, Zone 23 Caesarea Industrial Park, Caesarea, Israel
Tel.: (972) 46272470

Web Site: https://www.elspec-ltd.com
Software Development Services
N.A.I.C.S.: 541511

Elspec North America, Inc. **(1)**
2900 W Pearl City Rd Ste 104, Freeport, IL 61032
Tel.: (815) 266-4210
Testing Electricity Instrument Mfr
N.A.I.C.S.: 334515

ELTA TECHNOLOGY CO., LTD
4F No 41 Sec 1 Jhonghua Road, Taipei, 100, ROC, Taiwan
Tel.: (000) 223411100
Web Site: http://www.elta.com.tw
Year Founded: 2000
Sales Range: $25-49.9 Million
Emp.: 120
Computer Related Services
N.A.I.C.S.: 541519
Sally Chen (Pres & CEO)

ELTE
80 Ronald Ave, Toronto, M6E 5A2, ON, Canada
Tel.: (416) 785-7885
Web Site: http://www.elte.com
Year Founded: 1919
Rev.: $50,051,310
Emp.: 150
Home Furnishings Retailer
N.A.I.C.S.: 423220
Alan Goldberg (Pres)

ELTEL AB
Adolfsbergsvagen 13 Bromma, PO Box 126 23, 112 92, Stockholm, Sweden
Tel.: (46) 858537600   SE
Web Site: https://www.eltelgroup.com
ELTEL—(OMX)
Rev.: $77,139,940
Assets: $58,229,603
Liabilities: $38,438,843
Net Worth: $19,790,759
Earnings: ($1,395,562)
Emp.: 5,063
Fiscal Year-end: 12/31/22
Holding Company
N.A.I.C.S.: 551112
Juha Luusua (Mng Dir-Finland)

Subsidiaries:

Eltel Group Corporation **(1)**
Laturinkuja 8, Box 50, 02650, Espoo, Finland   **(100%)**
Tel.: (358) 20411211
Holding Company
N.A.I.C.S.: 551112
Axel Hjarne (Pres & CEO)

Division (Non-US):

Eltel Infranet GmbH **(2)**
Rendsburger Strasse 16, 30659, Hannover, Germany   **(100%)**
Tel.: (49) 511 655 125 50
Web Site: http://www.eltelnetworks.com
Emp.: 170
Electrical & Telecommunications Network Maintenance & Transmission Services
N.A.I.C.S.: 237130

Eltel Networks A/S **(2)**
Horkaer 3, 2730, Herlev, Denmark **(100%)**
Tel.: (45) 8 813 5000
Web Site: https://www.eltelnetworks.dk
Electrical & Telecommunications Network Maintenance & Transmission Services
N.A.I.C.S.: 237130

Eltel Networks AS **(2)**
Haavard Martinsens vei 30, PO Box 343, Alnabru, 0978, Oslo, Norway **(100%)**
Tel.: (47) 9 870 2530
Web Site: http://www.eltelnetworks.no
Electrical & Telecommunications Network Maintenance & Transmission Services
N.A.I.C.S.: 237130

Eltel Networks Infranet AB **(2)**
Adolfsbergsvagen 13, PO Box 126 23, Bro-

mma, 168 67, Bromma, Sweden   **(100%)**
Tel.: (46) 858537600
Web Site: https://www.eltelnetworks.se
Emp.: 5,400
Electrical & Telecommunications Network
Maintenance & Transmission Services
N.A.I.C.S.: 237130

Subsidiary (Domestic):

Eltel Networks Oy   **(2)**
Laturinkuja 8, 02650, Espoo,
Finland   **(100%)**
Tel.: (358) 20411211
Web Site: https://www.eltelnetworks.fi
Emp.: 200
Electrical & Telecommunications Network
Maintenance & Transmission Services
N.A.I.C.S.: 237130
Juha Luusua (Mng Dir)

Division (Non-US):

Eltel Networks SIA   **(2)**
Lubanas Road 9km Stopinu parish, LV-
1012, Riga, Latvia   **(100%)**
Tel.: (371) 7317 500
Web Site: http://www.eltelnetworks.com
Electrical & Telecommunications Network
Maintenance & Transmission Services
N.A.I.C.S.: 237130

Eltel Networks Telecom Sp. z
o.o.   **(2)**
Ul Zupnicza 17, 03-821, Warsaw,
Poland   **(100%)**
Tel.: (48) 225189500
Web Site: http://www.eltelnetworks.com
Electrical & Telecommunications Network
Maintenance & Transmission Services
N.A.I.C.S.: 237130

UAB Eltel Networks   **(2)**
Vilkpedes St 4, 03151, Vilnius,
Lithuania   **(100%)**
Tel.: (370) 5 213 1221
Web Site: https://www.eltelnetworks.lt
Telecommunication Network Operator
N.A.I.C.S.: 517111
Ramunas Bendikas (Pres)

Eltel Networks GmbH   **(1)**
Wanner Strasse 30, 45661, Reckling-
hausen, Germany
Tel.: (49) 2361497920
Web Site: https://www.eltelnetworks.de
Wireless Telecommunication Services
N.A.I.C.S.: 517112

Eltel Networks TE AB   **(1)**
Adolfsbergsvagen 13 Bromma, POB 126
23, 112 92, Stockholm, Sweden
Tel.: (46) 858537600
Emp.: 150
Fiscal Year-end: 12/31/2003
Power & Communication Network Services
N.A.I.C.S.: 237130

Energoprojekt-Krakow S.A.   **(1)**
Ul Mazowlecka 21, 30-019, Krakow, Poland
Tel.: (48) 122997222
Web Site:
   http://www.energoprojekt.krakow.pl
Construction Services
N.A.I.C.S.: 236220
Slawomir Samek (Pres & CEO)

ELTES CO., LTD.
3-2-5 Kasumigaseki Chiyoda-ku, To-
kyo, Japan
Tel.: (81) 365509280
Web Site: http://www.eltes.co.jp
Year Founded: 2004
3967—(TKS)
Rev.: $46,333,150
Assets: $48,906,820
Liabilities: $30,409,010
Net Worth: $18,497,810
Earnings: $1,822,130
Emp.: 788
Fiscal Year-end: 02/29/24
Digital Technology Consulting Ser-
vices
N.A.I.C.S.: 541512
Takahiro Sugawara (Pres)

**ELTEX ENTERPRISES 2002
LTD.**

211- 14770 64th Avenue, Surrey,
V3S 1X7, BC, Canada
Tel.: (604) 599-5088
Web Site: http://www.eltex.ca
Year Founded: 1988
Rev.: $16,385,920
Emp.: 80
Drywall & Insulation Contracting Ser-
vices
N.A.I.C.S.: 238310
James Hatch (Founder)

**ELTON INTERNATIONAL
TRADING COMPANY S.A.**
Draseza Place Industrial Park, Avlo-
nas Attica, 19011, Athens, Greece
Tel.: (30) 2295029350
Web Site: https://www.elton-
group.com
Year Founded: 1981
ELTON—(ATH)
Rev.: $209,982,842
Assets: $129,141,705
Liabilities: $55,926,594
Net Worth: $73,215,111
Earnings: $11,805,400
Emp.: 253
Fiscal Year-end: 12/31/22
Chemical Products Distr
N.A.I.C.S.: 424690
Nestor Dimitris Papathanasiou (Chm
& CEO)

Subsidiaries:

ELTON CORPORATION LTD   **(1)**
Eurogate Logistics Park 12 Prodan
Tarakchiev Str. Sofia Airport, 1540, Sofia,
Bulgaria
Tel.: (359) 2 9488 602
Chemical Products Distr
N.A.I.C.S.: 424690
Vencislav Karakostov (Mgr-Sls)

ELTON CORPORATION S.A.   **(1)**
5 Campului street, Ilfov, 077145, Panteli-
mon, Bucharest, Romania
Tel.: (40) 2135072578
Web Site: http://www.elton.ro
Chemical Products Distr
N.A.I.C.S.: 424690

ELTON Corporation D.O.O.   **(1)**
Sanje Zivanovica 28 D, 11000, Belgrade,
Serbia
Tel.: (381) 116555113
Chemical Products Distr
N.A.I.C.S.: 424690

ELTRAK S.A.
15 Thivaidos St, 14564 N, Nea Kifis-
sia, Athens, Greece
Tel.: (30) 2108196800
Web Site: http://www.eltrak.gr
Rev.: $125,820,331
Assets: $129,806,440
Liabilities: $67,143,904
Net Worth: $62,662,535
Earnings: $2,050,815
Emp.: 369
Fiscal Year-end: 12/31/18
Machinery & Motor Vehicle Spare
Parts Distr
N.A.I.C.S.: 423120
Fragkiskos Doukeris (CFO)

Subsidiaries:

Elastrak S.A.   **(1)**
15 Thivaidos St, Nea Kifissia, 14564, Ath-
ens, Greece
Tel.: (30) 2108196800
Sales Range: $50-74.9 Million
Emp.: 80
Tire Distr
N.A.I.C.S.: 423130
Takis Diamantopoulos (Mng Dir)

Eltrak Bulgaria Ltd.   **(1)**
43000 Europa Blvd, 1331, Sofia, Bulgaria
Tel.: (359) 28183000
Web Site: http://www.eltrakbulgaria.com

Sales Range: $25-49.9 Million
Emp.: 53
Construction & Mining Equipment Mfr
N.A.I.C.S.: 333120
Plamen Stoychev (Mng Dir)

ELTROTREC S.A.C.
Av Aviacion 3040 Int 2, San Borja,
Peru
Tel.: (51) 14124738   Pe
Web Site: http://www.eltrotec.com.pe
Electrical Equipment Distr
N.A.I.C.S.: 423610

ELUMEO SE
Erkelenzdamm 59/61, 10999, Berlin,
Germany
Tel.: (49) 30695979   De
Web Site: https://www.elumeo.com
Year Founded: 2008
ELB—(MUN)
Rev.: $50,104,659
Assets: $24,461,759
Liabilities: $15,553,528
Net Worth: $8,908,231
Earnings: ($3,620,694)
Emp.: 285
Fiscal Year-end: 12/31/23
Online Jewelry Distr
N.A.I.C.S.: 449210
Wolfgang Boye (Chm-Exec Bd)

Subsidiaries:

Jooli.com GmbH   **(1)**
Erkelenzdamm 59/61, 10999, Berlin, Ger-
many
Tel.: (49) 306959790
Web Site: https://www.jooli.com
Personal Care Services
N.A.I.C.S.: 812990

Juwelo Italia S.R.L.   **(1)**
Via Albalonga 27, 00183, Rome, Italy
Tel.: (39) 06899700613
Web Site: http://www.juwelo.it
Costume Jewellery Services
N.A.I.C.S.: 458310
Annette Freising (Program Mgr)

ELUON CORPORATION
A-905 U Space1 660
Daewangpangyo-ro, Bundang-gu,
Seongnam, Gyeonggi, Korea (South)
Tel.: (82) 7044891000
Web Site: https://www.eluon.com
Year Founded: 1998
065440—(KRS)
Rev.: $43,382,879
Assets: $49,517,916
Liabilities: $17,432,841
Net Worth: $32,085,075
Earnings: $1,324,328
Emp.: 134
Fiscal Year-end: 12/31/22
Wireless Communication Solution
Services
N.A.I.C.S.: 541511
SeungKu Yi (Pres & CEO)

Subsidiaries:

Eluon INS Co., Ltd.   **(1)**
660 Daewangpangyo-ro Room 905 Building
A U-Space 1, Bundang-gu, Seongnam,
Gyeonggi-do, Korea (South)
Tel.: (82) 7044891078
Web Site: https://www.eluonins.com
Electronic Machine Mfr
N.A.I.C.S.: 336320

Eluon LBS Corp.   **(1)**
Room 905 Building A U-Space 1 660
Daewangpangyo-ro, Room 905 Building A
U-Space 1 670 Sampyeong-dong Bundang-
gu, Seongnam, 463-400, Gyeonggi-do, Ko-
rea (South)
Tel.: (82) 7044891065
Web Site: https://www.eluonlbs.com
Call Mart Services
N.A.I.C.S.: 561421

ELVE S.A.

Agios Andreas, Peramos, 64007,
Thessaloniki, Greece
Tel.: (30) 2594023600
Web Site: https://www.elvesa.gr
Year Founded: 1987
ELBE—(ATH)
Sales Range: Less than $1 Million
Apparel Mfr & Distr
N.A.I.C.S.: 315250
Telemachos Kitsikopoulos (Chm &
Co-CEO)

ELVICTOR GROUP, INC.
Vasileos Konstantinou, Voulao Vario
Vouliagmenis, 7916672, Athens,
Greece
Tel.: (30) 6464916601   NV
Web Site:
   https://www.elvictorgroup.com
Year Founded: 2017
ELVG—(OTCIQ)
Rev.: $2,475,660
Assets: $1,479,331
Liabilities: $1,026,740
Net Worth: $452,591
Earnings: ($238,858)
Emp.: 23
Fiscal Year-end: 12/31/22
Business Development Consulting
Services
N.A.I.C.S.: 541611
Konstantinos S. Galanakis (CEO &
CFO)

**ELVIEMEK LAND DEVELOP-
MENT - LOGISTICS PARKS -
ENERGY - RECYCLING SA**
40 Agiou Konstantinou Street, Ma-
roussi, 151 24, Greece
Tel.: (30) 2106108491
Real Estate Manangement Services
N.A.I.C.S.: 531210
Nikolaos D. Remantas (Chm)

ELVILA S.A.
Str Siriului Nr 74-76 Sector 1, Bucha-
rest, Romania
Tel.: (40) 372131810
Web Site: https://www.elvila.ro
ELV—(BUC)
Rev.: $5,886,546
Assets: $14,109,296
Liabilities: $790,761
Net Worth: $13,318,534
Earnings: ($1,468,429)
Emp.: 142
Fiscal Year-end: 12/31/22
Furniture Product Mfr
N.A.I.C.S.: 321999
Viorel Catarama (Pres)

**ELYS GAME TECHNOLOGY,
CORP.**
130 Adelaide Street West Suite 701,
Toronto, M5H 2K4, ON, Canada
Tel.: (628) 258-5148   DE
Web Site: http://www.elysgame.com
Year Founded: 1998
ELYS—(NASDAQ)
Rev.: $42,678,659
Assets: $21,357,269
Liabilities: $14,206,854
Net Worth: $7,150,415
Earnings: ($18,258,218)
Emp.: 87
Fiscal Year-end: 12/31/22
Casino, Gaming & Wagering Opera-
tions
N.A.I.C.S.: 713210
Carlo Reali (Interim CFO & Principal
Acctg Officer)

Subsidiaries:

Multigioco Srl   **(1)**
Tel.: (39) 0690201126
Web Site: http://www.newgioco.it

Elys Game Technology, Corp.—(Continued)

Gambling Services
N.A.I.C.S.: 713290

ELYSEE DEVELOPMENT CORP.
9th Floor -1021 West Hastings Street, Vancouver, V6E 0C3, BC, Canada
Tel.: (778) 373-1562   **AB**
Web Site:
https://www.elyseedevelopment.com
Year Founded: 1996
ASXSF—(OTCIQ)
Rev.: $3,752,639
Assets: $14,680,953
Liabilities: $252,158
Net Worth: $14,428,795
Earnings: $3,143,704
Fiscal Year-end: 12/31/20
Investment Services
N.A.I.C.S.: 523999
Gordon Steblin (CFO)

ELYSIAN CAPITAL LLP
Manfield House 1 Southampton Street, London, WC2R 0LR, United Kingdom
Tel.: (44) 207 925 8050   **UK**
Web Site:
http://www.elysiancapital.com
Privater Equity Firm
N.A.I.C.S.: 523999
Chai Patel (Chm)

Subsidiaries:

Aspirations Care Ltd.   **(1)**
Unit B2 Elmbridge Court Cheltenham Road, Gloucester, GL3 1JZ, United Kingdom
Tel.: (44) 1452 399190
Web Site: http://www.aspirationscare.com
Health Care Srvices
N.A.I.C.S.: 622210
Christine Cameron (CEO)

Brand Addition Limited   **(1)**
Trafford Wharf Road, Manchester, M17 1DD, United Kingdom   **(100%)**
Tel.: (44) 845 266 6616
Web Site: http://www.brandaddition.com
Branded Merchandise Design & Distribution Services
N.A.I.C.S.: 423990
Chris Lee (CEO)

United Living Group   **(1)**
Media House Azalea Drive, Swanley, WS9 8TU, Kent, United Kingdom
Tel.: (44) 1322665522
Web Site: http://www.unitedliving.co.uk
Construction & Engineering Services
N.A.I.C.S.: 541330
Neil Armstrong (CEO)

ELYSIUM FUND MANAGEMENT LIMITED
1st Floor Royal Chambers Saint Julian's Avenue, PO Box 650, Saint Peter Port, GY1 3JX, Guernsey
Tel.: (44) 1481 810 100   **GY**
Web Site:
http://www.elysiumfundman.com
Year Founded: 2006
Investment Management Service
N.A.I.C.S.: 523940
Steve Mann (Mgr-Acctg)

ELZAY READY WEAR MANUFACTURING COMPANY
Rusaifeh-Awajan Main Street, PO Box 3151, Amman, 11181, Jordan
Tel.: (962) 53740200
Web Site: http://www.elzay.com
Year Founded: 1992
ELZA—(AMM)
Sales Range: $10-24.9 Million
Emp.: 1,087
Mens Apparel Mfr & Distr
N.A.I.C.S.: 315250
Qustandi Yagnem (Gen Mgr)

EM KOREA CO., LTD.
767 Ungnam-ro, Seongsan-gu, Changwon, Gyeongnam, Korea (South)
Tel.: (82) 552119600
Web Site: https://www.yesemk.com
Year Founded: 1987
095190—(KRS)
Rev.: $73,270,447
Assets: $132,913,860
Liabilities: $71,215,560
Net Worth: $61,698,300
Earnings: ($7,252,832)
Emp.: 277
Fiscal Year-end: 12/31/22
Machine Tools Mfr
N.A.I.C.S.: 333517
Sam Su Kang (CEO)

EM SHIPPING SDN. BHD.
Lease 3815 Lot 10914 Section 64 KTLD Jalan Datuk, Abang Abdul Rahim, 93450, Kuching, Sarawak, Malaysia
Tel.: (60) 82335393
Marine Shipping Services
N.A.I.C.S.: 488320
Dennis Ling (Mng Dir)

EM SYSTEMS CO., LTD.
6-1 Miyahara 1-chome, Yodogawa-ku, Osaka, 532-0003, Japan
Tel.: (81) 663971888
Web Site:
https://www.emsystems.co.jp
Year Founded: 1980
4820—(TKS)
Rev.: $144,316,950
Assets: $208,353,830
Liabilities: $62,540,890
Net Worth: $145,812,940
Earnings: $13,910,580
Emp.: 765
Fiscal Year-end: 12/31/23
Pharmacy System Devalopment Services
N.A.I.C.S.: 541512
Kenji Oishi (Chm)

Subsidiaries:

ChoQi Co., Ltd.   **(1)**
Shin- Osaka Brick Building 1-6-1 Miyahara, Yodogawa-ku, Osaka, 532-0003, Japan
Tel.: (81) 66 397 5210
Web Site: https://choqi.co.jp
Medical Insurance Services
N.A.I.C.S.: 524114

LASANTE Co., Ltd.   **(1)**
5F Suzuki Building 1-8-14 Nishikicho, Tachikawa, 190-0022, Tokyo, Japan
Tel.: (81) 425401616
Web Site: https://www.lasante.co.jp
Footwear Distr
N.A.I.C.S.: 424340

EMA INDIA LTD.
C-37 Panki Industrial Area PO Udyog Nagar, Kanpur, 208 022, Uttar Pradesh, India
Tel.: (91) 5122691210
Web Site: https://www.eiltd.info
522027—(BOM)
Rev.: $18,682
Assets: $117,976
Liabilities: $69,831
Net Worth: $48,145
Earnings: ($50,427)
Emp.: 4
Fiscal Year-end: 03/31/21
Induction Heating Equipment Mfr
N.A.I.C.S.: 333414
Ranjana Bhargava (CFO)

EMA S.A.R.
Baltagului Street No 1, Piatra Neamt, Neamt, Romania
Tel.: (40) 233214020

Web Site: http://www.ema.ro
Year Founded: 1907
EPN—(BUC)
Rev.: $802,257
Assets: $1,659,520
Liabilities: $323,124
Net Worth: $1,336,396
Earnings: ($360,111)
Emp.: 87
Fiscal Year-end: 12/31/22
Knitwear Mfr
N.A.I.C.S.: 313240

EMAAR MISR FOR DEVELOPMENT S.A.E.
Mivida Business Park Building 1 end of road 90 next to AUC campus, PO Box 229, 11571, Cairo, Egypt
Tel.: (20) 225032000
Web Site:
https://www.emaarmisr.com
EMFD.CA—(EGX)
Sales Range: Less than $1 Million
Real Estate Services
N.A.I.C.S.: 531390
Mohamed Ali Rashed Alabbar (Founder)

EMAAR PROPERTIES PJSC
Level 7 Emaar Business Park 1 Dubai Hills Estate, PO Box 9440, Dubai, United Arab Emirates
Tel.: (971) 43661688   **AE**
Web Site: https://www.emaar.com
EMAAR—(DFM)
Rev.: $6,692,536,278
Assets: $31,813,292,673
Liabilities: $14,541,725,238
Net Worth: $17,271,567,435
Earnings: $2,234,665,802
Emp.: 240
Fiscal Year-end: 12/31/19
Real Estate Services
N.A.I.C.S.: 531210
Mohamed Rashid Alabbar (Founder & Chm)

Subsidiaries:

Amelkis Resorts S.A.   **(1)**
Hattan Villa, Marrakech, Morocco
Tel.: (212) 524403601
Real Estate Agent & Broker Services
N.A.I.C.S.: 531210

Amlak Finance PJSC   **(1)**
Office No 1803 Grosvenor Business Tower Barsha Heights, Dubai, United Arab Emirates
Tel.: (971) 80026525
Web Site: https://www.amlakfinance.com
Rev.: $48,216,013
Assets: $1,444,697,955
Liabilities: $1,224,557,101
Net Worth: $220,140,855
Earnings: ($87,047,858)
Fiscal Year-end: 12/31/2019
Financial Management Services
N.A.I.C.S.: 523999
Arif Abdulla Alharmi Albastaki (CEO)

Emaar Development PJSC   **(1)**
Emaar Square Building 3 Level 1, PO Box 9440, Dubai, United Arab Emirates
Tel.: (971) 43673333
Rev.: $2,656,399,798
Assets: $9,176,247,102
Liabilities: $5,501,340,802
Net Worth: $3,674,906,301
Earnings: $559,556,377
Fiscal Year-end: 12/31/2020
Property Development Services
N.A.I.C.S.: 531312
Adnan Abdulfattah Kazim (Chm)

Emaar Dha Islamabad Limited   **(1)**
Emaar Sales Centre DHA Phase 2-Extension Islamabad Highway, Islamabad, Pakistan
Tel.: (92) 512096036
Real Estate Agent & Broker Services
N.A.I.C.S.: 531210

Emaar Giga Karachi Limited   **(1)**

Emaar Sales Centre Abdul Sattar Edhi Avenue DHA Phase-8 EXT, Karachi, Pakistan
Tel.: (92) 512096036
Real Estate Agent & Broker Services
N.A.I.C.S.: 531210

Emaar Hospitality Group LLC   **(1)**
Down Town Burj Khalifa Emaar Square Building 3 Level 2, PO Box 9440, Dubai, United Arab Emirates
Tel.: (971) 80036227
Hospital & Leisure Facility Development & Management Services
N.A.I.C.S.: 236220
Olivier Harnisch (CEO)

Emaar Hotels & Resorts LLC   **(1)**
Building 3 Emaar Business Park Sheikh Zayed Road, PO Box 9440, Dubai, United Arab Emirates
Tel.: (971) 43673392
Hotel & Resort Management Services
N.A.I.C.S.: 721110

Emaar India Limited   **(1)**
Mehrauli Gurgaon Road Sikandarpur Chowk Sector-28, Emaar Business Park, Gurgaon, 122002, Haryana, India
Tel.: (91) 1244041155
Web Site: https://in.emaar.com
Real Estate Services
N.A.I.C.S.: 531210

Emaar International Jordan   **(1)**
Al Rabia Towers Fifth Floor, PO Box 4434, Amman, 11953, Jordan
Tel.: (962) 65501800
Web Site: http://www.emaar.jo
Sales Range: $50-74.9 Million.
Emp.: 22
Real Estate Manangement Services
N.A.I.C.S.: 531390

Emaar Lebanon S.A.   **(1)**
PO Box 16-6622, Beirut, Lebanon
Tel.: (961) 1212121
Residential Property Development Services
N.A.I.C.S.: 236116

Emaar MGF Land Limited   **(1)**
306-308 3rd Floor Square One C-2 District Centre, Saket, New Delhi, 110017, India
Tel.: (91) 1141521155
Web Site: http://www.emaarmgf.com
Sales Range: $50-74.9 Million.
Emp.: 80
Real Estate Services
N.A.I.C.S.: 531390

Emaar Malls Group LLC   **(1)**
Burj Khalifa Square Building 3 Floor 2, PO Box 9440, Dubai, United Arab Emirates
Tel.: (971) 43675588
Mall Property Development Services
N.A.I.C.S.: 236220
Patrick Bousquet-Chavanne (CEO)

Subsidiary (Domestic):

Emaar International Malls LLC   **(2)**
Downtown Burj Dubai Emaar Square, PO Box 9007, Dubai, United Arab Emirates
Tel.: (971) 43673333
Web Site: http://www.emaar.com
Commercial Property Management Services
N.A.I.C.S.: 531312

Emaar Retail LLC   **(2)**
Emaar Square Building 3 Near Bur Dubai, Dubai, United Arab Emirates
Tel.: (971) 43673333
Mall Property Development Services
N.A.I.C.S.: 236220

Emaar Pakistan Group   **(1)**
Canyon Views Emaar Sales Centre Islamabad Highway DHA Phase II, Islamabad, 44000, Pakistan
Tel.: (92) 512803188
Web Site: http://www.emaar.ae
Emp.: 80
Property Development Services
N.A.I.C.S.: 531390
Wazirzada M. Owais (Sec & Sr Dir-Legal)

Emaar Properties Canada LTD   **(1)**
Suite 1420 Guiness Twr 1055 West Hasting Street, Vancouver, V6E 2E9, BC, Canada
Tel.: (604) 630-2008
Web Site: http://www.emaarcanada.com
Property Development Services

N.A.I.C.S.: 531190
Robert D. Booth *(Mng Dir)*

Emaar Technologies LLC (1)
Emaar Business Park Building 3 4th Floor,
PO Box 9440, Dubai, United Arab Emirates
Tel.: (971) 44384888
Web Site:
http://www.emaartechnologies.com
Real Estate Agent & Broker Services
N.A.I.C.S.: 531210

Emaar Turkey (1)
Unalan Mahallesi Libadiye Caddesi No 82F
Kat 1 Uskudar, Sisli, 34700, Istanbul, Tur-
kiye
Tel.: (90) 2165471730
Web Site: http://careers.emaar.com.tr
Real Estate Property Development Services
N.A.I.C.S.: 531390

Emaar USA (1)
5505 Cancha de Golf, Rancho Santa Fe,
CA 92091
Tel.: (858) 755-0216
Web Site: http://properties.emaar.com
Property Development Services
N.A.I.C.S.: 531390

**Mirage Leisure & Development
Inc.** (1)
Emaar Business Park, Dubai, United Arab
Emirates
Tel.: (971) 44538835
Web Site: http://mirageglobal.com
Real Estate Agent & Broker Services
N.A.I.C.S.: 531210

**EMAAR THE ECONOMIC CITY
JSC**
2211-Hejaz Boulevard-Bay La Sun
Unit No 1, King Abdullah Economic
City, 23965-7373, Saudi Arabia
Tel.: (966) 125106600   SA
Web Site: https://www.kaec.net
Year Founded: 2006
4220—(SAU)
Rev.: $96,858,286
Assets: $4,054,383,416
Liabilities: $2,280,012,798
Net Worth: $1,774,370,617
Earnings: ($308,569,524)
Fiscal Year-end: 12/31/22
Real Estate Manangement Services
N.A.I.C.S.: 531390
Abdulaziz Alnowaiser *(CEO)*

**EMAE - EMPRESA METRO-
POLITANA DE AGUAS E EN-
ERGIA S.A.**
Av Jornalista Roberto Marinho 85
16th floor, Cidade Moncoes, 04576-
010, Sao Paulo, 04576-010, Brazil
Tel.: (55) 1127636750
Web Site: https://www.emae.com.br
Year Founded: 1899
EMAE4—(BRAZ)
Rev.: $107,850,411
Assets: $373,123,459
Liabilities: $178,545,427
Net Worth: $194,578,032
Earnings: $26,899,769
Fiscal Year-end: 12/31/23
Eletric Power Generation Services
N.A.I.C.S.: 221111
Marcio Rea *(CEO)*

EMAGINE GMBH
Spittelmarkt 10, 10117, Berlin, Ger-
many
Tel.: (49) 30 2091 651   De
Web Site: http://www.emagine.de
Year Founded: 1988
Third Party Business Management
Services
N.A.I.C.S.: 561110
Jean-Francois Bodin *(Mng Dir)*

Subsidiaries:

emagine GmbH (1)

Neumannstrasse 4, 40235, Dusseldorf,
Germany
Tel.: (49) 2118632660
Web Site: http://www.emagine.org
Information Technology Freelancers Place-
ment Services
N.A.I.C.S.: 561311

EMAK S.P.A.
Via Fermi 4 Bagnolo in Piano, 42011,
Reggio Emilia, Italy
Tel.: (39) 0522956611   IT
Web Site:
https://www.emakgroup.com
Year Founded: 1992
EM—(ITA)
Rev.: $653,704,943
Assets: $732,912,799
Liabilities: $433,984,459
Net Worth: $298,928,340
Earnings: $32,665,659
Emp.: 2,284
Fiscal Year-end: 12/31/22
Garden Machinery & Equipment Mfr
N.A.I.C.S.: 333112
Fausto Bellamico *(Chm & CEO)*

Subsidiaries:

Agres Sistemas Eletronicos S.A. (1)
Av Com Franco 6720, Uberaba, Curitiba,
81560-000, Parana, Brazil
Tel.: (55) 4131323300
Web Site: https://en.agres.com.br
Agricultural Machinery Mfr
N.A.I.C.S.: 333111

Comet S.p.A. (1)
Via G Dorso 4, IT-42124, Reggio
nell'Emilia, Italy
Tel.: (39) 0522386111
Web Site: https://www.comet-spa.com
Pumps & Pumping Equipment Mfr & Distr
N.A.I.C.S.: 333914

Subsidiary (US):

Comet USA, Inc. (2)
1601 Hwy 13 E Ste 100, Burnsville, MN
55337
Tel.: (952) 707-1894
Web Site: https://www.cometpump.com
Pump & Pumping Equipment Mfr & Distr
N.A.I.C.S.: 333914

Subsidiary (Domestic):

Valley Industries, LLP (3)
180 N Lake Ave, Paynesville, MN
56362   **(90%)**
Tel.: (320) 243-8500
Web Site: https://www.valleyind.com
Sales Range: $10-24.9 Million
Industrial Fluid Components, Agricultural
Parts & Pressure Washer Accessories Mfr
& Distr
N.A.I.C.S.: 332912

Emak Deutschland GmbH (1)
Max-Eyth-Str 5, Oeffingen, 70736, Fellbach,
Germany
Tel.: (49) 711 510 9830
Web Site: https://www.efco-motorgeraete.de
Gardening Equipment Distr
N.A.I.C.S.: 423820

Emak France SAS (1)
1 rue de l'industrie, BP 9, Region Alsace,
68170, Rixheim, France
Tel.: (33) 389645151
Web Site: https://www.emak.fr
Agricultural Management Services
N.A.I.C.S.: 115116

Emak U.K. Ltd. (1)
Unit 8 Zone 4, Burntwood Business Park,
Burntwood, WS7 3XD, Staffordshire, United
Kingdom
Tel.: (44) 154 368 7660
Web Site: https://www.oleo-mac.co.uk
Gardening Equipment Distr
N.A.I.C.S.: 423820

**Lavorwash Brasil Ind. E Com.
Ltda** (1)
Estrada General Motors 852 Galpao 13
Cond Business Caldeira, Neighborhood
Caldeira, Indaiatuba, 13347-500, Sao

Paulo, Brazil
Tel.: (55) 193 115 0200
Web Site: https://lavorwash.com.br
Cleaning Equipment Mfr
N.A.I.C.S.: 333310

Lavorwash Brasil Ind. Ltda. (1)
Rodovia Eng Ermenio de Oliveira Penteado
SP-075 56 Km 56 Galpao 02, Helvetia, In-
daiatuba, SP, Brazil
Tel.: (55) 8007702715
Web Site: https://www.lavorwash.com.br
Industry Machinery Mfr
N.A.I.C.S.: 333248

Lavorwash France S.A.S. (1)
Immeuble Renoir Hall B 22 avenue des Na-
tions, CS 49041, 93120, Villepinte, France
Tel.: (33) 148910729
Web Site: https://www.lavorwash-
france.com
High Pressure Cleaner Mfr
N.A.I.C.S.: 333310

Lavorwash Iberica S.L. (1)
C / President Companys 2 Local 2, La
Selva del Camp, 3470, Tarragona, Spain
Tel.: (34) 977845321
Vacuum Cleaner Mfr
N.A.I.C.S.: 333310

Lavorwash Polska S.P. z o.o. (1)
ul Jana Pawla II 146, 85-151, Bydgoszcz,
Poland
Tel.: (48) 523210123
Web Site: https://www.lavorwash.pl
High Pressure Cleaner Mfr & Distr
N.A.I.C.S.: 333310

**Markusson Professional Grinders
AB** (1)
Tegelbruksvagen 6, Rimbo, 762 31, Stock-
holm, Sweden
Tel.: (46) 17571326
Web Site: https://home.markusson.se
Automatic Chain Slip Machine Mfr
N.A.I.C.S.: 333517
Oscar Lowenhielm *(CEO)*

PTC Srl (1)
Via Mantegna 4, 42048, Rubiera, Reggio
Emilia, Italy
Tel.: (39) 0522626477
Web Site: https://www.ptcitaliana.com
Water Blasting Equipment Distr
N.A.I.C.S.: 423720

Sabart Srl (1)
Via F Zoboli 18, 42124, Reggio Emilia, RE,
Italy
Tel.: (39) 0522508511
Web Site: https://www.sabart.it
Chain Saw Mfr & Distr
N.A.I.C.S.: 332216

**Speed Line South Africa (Pty)
Ltd.** (1)
15 Wiganthorpe Road, Pietermaritzburg,
3201, South Africa
Tel.: (27) 333421246
Monofilament Mfr
N.A.I.C.S.: 325220

Speed North America Inc. (1)
1700A Old Mansfield Rd, Wooster, OH
44691
Tel.: (330) 202-7775
Web Site: https://www.speedgroupe.com
Gardening Equipment Mfr & Distr
N.A.I.C.S.: 332216

Speed South America S.p.A. (1)
Camino lo Echevers No 891 - Bodega 13
and 14, Quilicura, Santiago, Chile
Tel.: (56) 227390050
Monofilament Mfr
N.A.I.C.S.: 325220

**Spraycom comercio de pecas para
agricoltura S.A.** (1)
Av Said Tuma 600, Distrito Industrial Jose
Antonio Boso, Catanduva, 15803-150, Sao
Paulo, Brazil
Tel.: (55) 1735312340
Web Site: https://spraycom.com.br
Polypropylene Material Distr
N.A.I.C.S.: 424610

Tecomec S.r.l. (1)
Strada della Mirandola 11, 42124, Reggio
Emilia, RE, Italy

Tel.: (39) 0522959001
Web Site: https://www.tecomec.com
Farming Component Mfr
N.A.I.C.S.: 335999

**Trebol Maquinaria y Suministros
S.A.** (1)
Eduardo Pondal Parc 46 - Pol Ind, Sigueiro
Oroso, 15688, A Coruna, Spain
Tel.: (34) 981696453
Web Site: https://trebolmaquinaria.com
Farming Component Mfr
N.A.I.C.S.: 335999

Victus Emak Sp. z o.o. (1)
ul Karpia 37, 61-619, Poznan, Poland
Tel.: (48) 618238369
Web Site: https://www.victus.pl
Gardening Equipment Distr
N.A.I.C.S.: 423820

**Yong Kang Lavorwash Equipment
Co., Ltd.** (1)
Tel.: (86) 57987205326
Web Site: https://en.lavorchina.cn
Emp.: 150
Cleaning Equipment Mfr
N.A.I.C.S.: 333310

EMAKINA GROUP S.A.
64A Rue Middelbourg, 1170, Brus-
sels, Belgium
Tel.: (32) 2 400 40 00
Web Site: http://www.emakina.com
Year Founded: 2001
ALEMK—(EUR)
Rev.: $121,703,725
Assets: $69,396,033
Liabilities: $56,837,575
Net Worth: $12,558,458
Earnings: $813,386
Emp.: 1,046
Fiscal Year-end: 12/31/20
Website Development Services
N.A.I.C.S.: 518210
Brice Le Blevennec *(CEO & Exec
Mng Dir)*

Subsidiaries:

Design Is Dead BVBA (1)
Duboisstraat 50, 2060, Antwerp, Belgium
Tel.: (32) 3 260 66 55
Web Site: http://www.designisdead.com
Website Development Services
N.A.I.C.S.: 518210
Annouck Hendrickx *(Mgr-Client Svc)*

Emakina BV (1)
Danzigerkade 4, 1013 AP, Amsterdam,
Netherlands
Tel.: (31) 204637766
Web Site: http://www.emakina.nl
Website Development Services
N.A.I.C.S.: 518210

Subsidiary (Domestic):

Emakina.NL BV (2)
Las Palmas - Wilhelminakade 314, 3072
AR, Rotterdam, Netherlands
Tel.: (31) 10 217 15 00
Web Site: http://www.emakina.nl
Website Development Services
N.A.I.C.S.: 518210

Emakina.CH SA. (1)
13 Rue le Royer, 1227, Geneva, Switzer-
land
Tel.: (41) 223426030
Web Site: http://www.emakina.ch
Website Development Services
N.A.I.C.S.: 518210
Arnaud Grobet *(Partner)*

Emakina.FR SA. (1)
84 Boulevard de Sebastopol, 75003, Paris,
France
Tel.: (33) 1 44 54 52 80
Web Site: http://www.emakina.fr
Website Development Services
N.A.I.C.S.: 518210
Jerome Piot *(Chief Strategy Officer)*

EMAMI GROUP
Emami Tower 687 Anandapur, EM

Emami Group—(Continued)

Bypass, 700107, Kolkata, West Bengal, India
Tel.: (91) 33 6613 6264
Web Site:
http://www.emamigroup.com
Holding Company
N.A.I.C.S.: 551112

Subsidiaries:

Emami Realty Limited (1)
Acropolis 13th Floor 1858/1 Rajdanga Main Road, Kasba, Kolkata, 700 107, West Bengal, India
Tel.: (91) 3366251200
Web Site: https://www.emamirealty.com
Rev.: $45,210,302
Assets: $268,625,093
Liabilities: $253,264,707
Net Worth: $15,360,386
Earnings: $83,647
Emp.: 100
Fiscal Year-end: 03/31/2021
Real Estate Development Services
N.A.I.C.S.: 531390
Abhijit Datta (Chm)

Subsidiary (Domestic):

Zandu Realty Limited (2)
Akash Tower 3rd Floor 781 Anandapur E M Bypass, Kolkata, 700 107, West Bengal, India (35.51%)
Tel.: (91) 33 66251200
Web Site: http://www.emamirealty.com
Sales Range: $1-9.9 Million
Real Estate Manangement Services
N.A.I.C.S.: 531390
Abhijit Datta (Chm)

EMAMI LTD

Emami Tower 687 Anandapur EM Bypass, Kolkata, 700107, West Bengal, India
Tel.: (91) 3366136264
Web Site: https://www.emamiltd.in
531162—(NSE)
Rev.: $402,783,941
Assets: $343,937,535
Liabilities: $103,456,899
Net Worth: $240,480,636
Earnings: $62,067,751
Emp.: 3,133
Fiscal Year-end: 03/31/21
Health Care Consumer Products
N.A.I.C.S.: 424210
R. S. Goenka (Co-Founder)

Subsidiaries:

Emami Bangladesh Limited (1)
Aqua Tower Level 6 43 Mohakhali C/A, Dhaka, 1212, Bangladesh
Tel.: (880) 29899056
Personal Care & Healthcare Product Distr
N.A.I.C.S.: 456199

Emami Indo Lanka Pvt Ltd (1)
No 200 Lukmanjee Square Grandpass Road, Colombo, Sri Lanka
Tel.: (94) 112432675
Personal Care & Healthcare Product Distr
N.A.I.C.S.: 456199

Emami International FZE (1)
904 and 905 Bel Rasheed Tower, PO Box 77884, Buhaira Corniche RoadNmc Hospital Building, Sharjah, United Arab Emirates
Tel.: (971) 65756731
Web Site: http://www.emamigroup.com
Sales Range: $25-49.9 Million
Emp.: 30
Health Care Products Mfr
N.A.I.C.S.: 325411

Subsidiary (Non-US):

Creme 21 GmbH (2)
Kaiser-Friedrich-Promenade 28, 61348, Bad Homburg, Germany
Tel.: (49) 6172764210
Web Site: http://www.creme21.com
Skin Care Product Retailer
N.A.I.C.S.: 456120
Amitabh Goenka (Co-CEO)

Subsidiary (Domestic):

Emami Overseas FZE (2)
Elob Office No E-85G-06 Hamriyah Free Zone NMC Hospital Building, PO Box 52338, Sharjah, United Arab Emirates
Tel.: (971) 65756731
Personal Care & Healthcare Product Distr
N.A.I.C.S.: 456199

Subsidiary (Non-US):

Emami Rus (LLC) (2)
Leninskiy prospect st house 113/1 office 703A, 117198, Moscow, Russia
Tel.: (7) 4954343181
Personal Care & Healthcare Product Distr
N.A.I.C.S.: 456199

Emami Paper Mills Ltd. (1)
Emami Tower 687 Anandapur E M Bypass, Kolkata, 700 107, India
Tel.: (91) 3366136264
Web Site: https://www.emamipaper.com
Rev.: $277,030,154
Assets: $236,930,640
Liabilities: $153,156,286
Net Worth: $83,774,354
Earnings: $8,293,268
Emp.: 690
Fiscal Year-end: 03/31/2023
Newsprint Mfr
N.A.I.C.S.: 322120
R. S. Goenka (Co-Founder)

Emami Realty Limited (1)
8-2-598 Ground Fl Uma Dev Raj Villa Rd No 10, Banjara Hills, Hyderabad, 500034, India
Tel.: (91) 4040262889
Health Care Products Mfr
N.A.I.C.S.: 325411
Nitesh Kumar Gupta (CEO)

Subsidiary (Domestic):

Orbit Projects Private Limited (2)
1 Garstin Pl, Kolkata, 700001, West Bengal, India
Tel.: (91) 3340119050
Web Site: http://www.orbitgroup.net
Sales Range: $25-49.9 Million
Emp.: 50
Real Estate Consultant
N.A.I.C.S.: 531390
Basant Kumar Parakh (Mng Dir)

Pharma Derm SAE Co. (1)
3rd Zone Part no 5 Block-11, New Borg El Arab Industria City, Alexandria, Egypt
Tel.: (20) 1001183882
Personal Care & Healthcare Product Distr
N.A.I.C.S.: 456199

EMAN A.S.

U Pergamenky 1145/12, 170 00, Prague, Czech Republic
Tel.: (420) 222202222
Web Site:
https://www.emanprague.com
EMAN—(PRA)
Sales Range: Less than $1 Million
Emp.: 120
Software Development Services
N.A.I.C.S.: 541511
Jiri Horyna (Founder & CEO)

Subsidiaries:

eMan Solutions LLC (1)
1334 Brittmoore Rd, Houston, TX 77043
Tel.: (346) 232-2867
Web Site: http://www.emanglobal.com
Emp.: 100
Software Development Services
N.A.I.C.S.: 541511

EMANUEL UNGARO

2 Avenue Montaigne, 75008, Paris, France
Tel.: (33) 153570000
Web Site:
http://www.emanuelungaro.com
Sales Range: $25-49.9 Million
Emp.: 10

Perfume, Clothing & Accessories Designer & Retailer
N.A.I.C.S.: 315990
Mary Fornier (Mng Dir)

EMAS KIARA SDN. BHD.

Lot 13A Rawang Industrial Estate, 48000, Rawang, Selangor, Malaysia
Tel.: (60) 360926881
Sales Range: $25-49.9 Million
Emp.: 40
Textile Products Mfr
N.A.I.C.S.: 314999
Roger Kong Foo Wong (Mng Dir)

EMASZ

Dozsa Gyorgy ut 13, 3525, Miskolc, Hungary
Tel.: (36) 46535000
Electric Power Distribution Services
N.A.I.C.S.: 221122
Marie Theres Thiell (Chm-Mgmt Bd)

EMATEC II S. DE R. L. DE C.V.

Avenida Isidoro Sepulveda 540, Apodaca, 66603, NL, Mexico
Tel.: (52) 81 81312500
Web Site: http://www.ematec.com.mx
Sales Range: $75-99.9 Million
Emp.: 480
Molded Fiber Packaging Mfr
N.A.I.C.S.: 325211
Alejandro Paez Jimenez (CEO)

Subsidiaries:

Ematec - Cuernavaca Plant (1)
Paseo de los clavelaes #74, Col Bugambilias, Jiutepec, Morelos, Mexico
Tel.: (52) 777 3295900
Web Site: http://www.ematec.com.mx
Sales Range: $25-49.9 Million
Emp.: 100
Molded Fiber Packaging Mfr
N.A.I.C.S.: 325211

Ematec II S. de R. L. de C.V. - Guadalajara Plant (1)
Carretera a San Martin De las Flores Km 1 5, El Salto, Jalisco, Mexico
Tel.: (52) 3336970103
Plastic Material & Resin Mfr
N.A.I.C.S.: 325211

Ematec II S. de R. L. de C.V. - Guadalupe Plant (1)
San Antonio 140 between Antiguo Camino, Cadereyta Jimenez, Mexico
Tel.: (52) 8182824173
Plastic Material & Resin Mfr
N.A.I.C.S.: 325211

Ematec II S. de R. L. de C.V. - Hermosillo Plant (1)
Calle Nogales between Plomo St and Plata St Parque Industrial de, Hermosillo, Sonora, Mexico
Tel.: (52) 8008365500
Plastic Material & Resin Mfr
N.A.I.C.S.: 325211

EMB CO., LTD.

4F 93 Jeonpa-ro 24beon-gil, Manan-gu Gyeonggi-do, Anyang, 14087, Korea (South)
Tel.: (82) 314638983
Web Site:
https://www.fineemtech.co.kr
Year Founded: 2013
Electronic Component Mfr & Distr
N.A.I.C.S.: 334419
Nam Yoon Myung (Dir)

EMBARK GROUP LIMITED

7th Floor 100 Cannon Street, London, EC4N 6EU, United Kingdom
Tel.: (44) 20 7382 4741
Web Site:
http://www.embarkgroup.co.uk
Year Founded: 2013
Rev.: $20,236,800,000
Emp.: 500

Retirement Solutions Provider
N.A.I.C.S.: 523999
Richard Wohanka (Chm)

Subsidiaries:

EBS Pension Limited (1)
100 Cannon Street, London, EC4N 6EU, United Kingdom
Tel.: (44) 2039531060
Web Site: http://www.ebspensions.co.uk
Pension Fund Management
N.A.I.C.S.: 524292
David Etherington (Chm)

Subsidiary (Domestic):

EBS Pensioneer Trustees Limited (2)
100 Cannon Street, London, EC4N 6EU, United Kingdom
Tel.: (44) 2039531060
Pension Funds
N.A.I.C.S.: 525110

EBS Self-Administered Personal Pension Plan Trustees Limited (2)
100 Cannon Street, London, EC4N 6EU, United Kingdom
Tel.: (44) 2039531060
Pension Funds
N.A.I.C.S.: 525110

EMBASSY OFFICE PARKS REIT

Royal Oak Embassy Golflinks Business Park Off Intermediate Ring Road, Bengaluru, 560 071, Karnataka, India
Tel.: (91) 8047222222
Web Site:
https://www.embassyofficeparks.com
Year Founded: 2017
EMBASSY—(NSE)
Rev.: $338,362,479
Assets: $6,154,014,594
Liabilities: $2,455,810,949
Net Worth: $3,698,203,646
Earnings: $95,325,185
Fiscal Year-end: 03/31/21
Real Estate Manangement Services
N.A.I.C.S.: 531210
Michael Holland (CEO)

EMBEDWAY TECHNOLOGIES (SHANGHAI) CORPORATION

6F Building 8 No 2388 Chenhang Rd, Shanghai, 201114, China
Tel.: (86) 2161002300
Web Site:
https://www.embedway.com
Year Founded: 2003
603496—(SHG)
Rev.: $108,182,173
Assets: $239,767,595
Liabilities: $62,140,886
Net Worth: $177,626,709
Earnings: $10,701,569
Fiscal Year-end: 12/31/22
Networking Component Mfr & Distr
N.A.I.C.S.: 334413

EMBELLENCE GROUP AB

Ryssnasgatan 8, 504 94, Boras, Sweden
Tel.: (46) 33 23 64 00
Web Site:
https://www.embellencegroup.com
Emp.: 100
Interior Design Services
N.A.I.C.S.: 541410
Olle Svensk (CEO)

EMBELTON LIMITED

147 Bakers Road, Coburg, 3058, VIC, Australia
Tel.: (61) 393534811
Web Site: https://www.embelton.com
Year Founded: 1925

EMB—(ASX)
Rev.: $46,623,670
Assets: $19,568,011
Liabilities: $6,103,032
Net Worth: $13,464,979
Earnings: $841,687
Emp.: 100
Fiscal Year-end: 06/30/24
Flooring Product Mfr
N.A.I.C.S.: 321918
George R. Embelton *(Chm)*

Subsidiaries:

G.P. Embelton & Company Pty
Ltd. **(1)**
3/100-108 Asquith Street, Silverwater, 2140,
NSW, Australia
Tel.: (61) 2 9748 3188
Web Site: http://www.embelton.com
Emp.: 50
Flooring Product Mfr
N.A.I.C.S.: 321918

Genmech Engineering (S) Pte.
Ltd. **(1)**
21 Toh Guan Road East 07-14/15/16 Toh
Guan Centre, Singapore, 608609, Singapore
Tel.: (65) 67630200
Web Site: https://www.genmech-singapore.com
Engineering Consulting Services
N.A.I.C.S.: 541330

NAP Acoustics Far East Limited **(1)**
Units 1301-1305 13/F Peninsula Tower 538
Castle Peak Road, Kowloon, China (Hong
Kong)
Tel.: (852) 28662886
Web Site: https://www.napacoustics.com.hk
Environmental Services
N.A.I.C.S.: 541620

Vibration Control Ltd. **(1)**
Unit 8B/16 Saturn Place, PO Box 302 592,
Rosedale, Auckland, 0632, New Zealand
Tel.: (64) 94146508
Web Site: https://www.vibrationcontrol.co.nz
Isolator Product Distr
N.A.I.C.S.: 423610

EMBENTION SISTEMAS IN-TELIGENTES, S.A.
Poligono Industrial Las Atalayas calle
Chelin 16, 03114, Alicante, Spain
Tel.: (34) 965115421   ES
Web Site:
  https://www.embention.com
Year Founded: 2007
MLUAV—(EUR)
Rev.: $3,692,748
Assets: $6,896,112
Liabilities: $4,075,419
Net Worth: $2,820,692
Earnings: $430,625
Emp.: 60
Fiscal Year-end: 12/31/21
Drone Mfr
N.A.I.C.S.: 336411
David Julian Benavente Sanchez
(CEO)

EMBOTELLADORA ANDINA S.A.
Miraflores 9153 7th Floor, Renca,
Santiago, Chile
Tel.: (56) 23380520   CL
Web Site: https://www.koandina.com
Year Founded: 1946
AKO.A—(NYSE)
Rev.: $3,719,629,753
Assets: $4,214,980,850
Liabilities: $2,978,217,137
Net Worth: $1,236,763,713
Earnings: $179,842,582
Emp.: 17,315
Fiscal Year-end: 12/31/22
Soft-Drink Bottler
N.A.I.C.S.: 312111
Juan Claro Gonzalez *(Chm)*

Subsidiaries:

Andina Bottling Investments SA **(1)**
Av Miraflores 9153 piso 7, Renca, Santiago,
Chile **(99.9%)**
Tel.: (56) 223380520
Holding Company; Food & Beverage Mfr &
Bottler
N.A.I.C.S.: 551112

Comercializadora Novaverde
S.A. **(1)**
Carretera General San Martin Km 16 5
Calle Simon Bolivar Sitio 19, Colina, Santiago, Chile
Tel.: (56) 224110150
Juices & Sports Drink Distr
N.A.I.C.S.: 424420

Envases CMF S.A. **(1)**
(50%)
Tel.: (56) 25448222
Sales Range: $50-74.9 Million
Emp.: 200
All Other Plastics Product Mfr
N.A.I.C.S.: 326199

Envases Central S.A. **(1)**
Av Miraflores 8755, Renca, Santiago,
Chile **(49.91%)**
Tel.: (56) 225999300
Sales Range: $25-49.9 Million
Emp.: 60
Metal Tank Mfr
N.A.I.C.S.: 332431

Re-Ciclar S.A. **(1)**
La Martina 390, Pudahue, Santiago, Chile
Tel.: (56) 225448222
Juices & Sports Drink Distr
N.A.I.C.S.: 424420

Rio de Janeiro Refrescos Ltda. **(1)**
(99.99%)
Sales Range: $100-124.9 Million
Emp.: 300
Production & Sale of Alcoholic & Non-
Alcoholic Beverages
N.A.I.C.S.: 312112

Servicios Multivending Ltda. **(1)**
Av Miraflores 9153 piso 4, Renca, Santiago,
Chile **(99.9%)**
Tel.: (56) 226115838
Service Establishment Equipment & Supplies Merchant Whslr
N.A.I.C.S.: 423850

Vital Aguas S.A. **(1)**
Av Americo Vespucio 1651, Rengo, Chile
Tel.: (56) 6003603600
Web Site: http://www.vital-sa.cl
Vitamin Water Mfr
N.A.I.C.S.: 312112

EMBRACE CHANGE ACQUISI-TION CORP.
74 Block D Beijing Fund Town Build-
ing, Fangshan District, Beijing, China
Tel.: (86) 1089353650   Ky
Year Founded: 2021
EMCG—(NASDAQ)
Rev.: $764,689
Assets: $76,944,986
Liabilities: $79,286,003
Net Worth: ($2,341,017)
Earnings: $410,646
Emp.: 2
Fiscal Year-end: 12/31/22
Investment Services
N.A.I.C.S.: 523999
Yoann Delwarde *(CEO)*

EMBRACER GROUP AB
Alvgatan 1, Karlstad, SE-652 25,
Sweden
Tel.: (46) 554 854 763
Web Site: http://www.embracer.com
Online Game Developer & Publisher
N.A.I.C.S.: 541511
Lars Wingefors *(Founder & CEO)*

Subsidiaries:

S3D Interactive, Inc. **(1)**
4 Winthrop Pl, Maplewood, NJ 07040

Tel.: (877) 681-3973
Web Site: http://saber3d.com
Video Game Developer
N.A.I.C.S.: 513210
Matthew Karch *(Co-Founder & CEO)*

Subsidiary (Non-US):

3D Realms Entertainment ApS **(2)**
, Aalborg, 9000, Denmark
Web Site: http://www.3drealms.com
Software Publisher
N.A.I.C.S.: 513210
George Broussard *(Pres)*

Subsidiary (Domestic):

Aspyr Media, Inc. **(2)**
1250 S Capital of Texas Hwy Bldg 1 Ste
650, Austin, TX 78746
Tel.: (512) 708-8100
Web Site: http://www.aspyr.com
Sales Range: $1-9.9 Million
Emp.: 130
Ret Computers/Software
N.A.I.C.S.: 513210
Michael Rogers *(Co-Founder & CEO)*

Demiurge Studios, LLC **(2)**
226 Causeway St,, Boston, MA 02114
Tel.: (617) 354-7772
Web Site: https://demiurgestudios.com
Video Game Developer
N.A.I.C.S.: 513210
Tom Lin *(Creative Dir)*

EMBRAER S.A.
Av Nacoes Unidas 8501 Eldorado
Business Towers 30 andar, Pinheiros,
Sao Paulo, 05425-070, Brazil
Tel.: (55) 1130406874   BR
Web Site: https://embraer.com
Year Founded: 1969
ERJ—(NYSE)
Rev.: $4,540,400,000
Assets: $10,142,100,000
Liabilities: $7,317,800,000
Net Worth: $2,824,300,000
Earnings: ($203,500,000)
Emp.: 19,475
Fiscal Year-end: 12/31/22
Commercial Aircraft Mfr
N.A.I.C.S.: 336411
Alexandre Goncalves Silva *(Chm)*

Subsidiaries:

EAI-Embraer Aviation
International **(1)**
33 Rue Des Vanesses, Paris Nord 2 - Bat
Eddington, 93420, Villepinte,
France **(100%)**
Tel.: (33) 149384400
Web Site: http://www.embraer.com
Rev.: $17,237,000
Emp.: 2,050
Sales, Support, Assistance
N.A.I.C.S.: 425120

ECC do Brasil Cia de Seguros **(1)**
av Faria Lima Brig 2170 Prd F 56 SI Eixo C
15, Jd da Granja, Sao Jose dos Campos,
12227-901, Sao Paulo, Brazil
Tel.: (55) 12 3927 1040
General Insurance Services
N.A.I.C.S.: 524298

Eleb-Embraer **(1)**
Rua Itabaiana 40 Parque Industrial, Sao
Jose dos Campos, 12237-540, SP,
Brazil **(51%)**
Tel.: (55) 1239355494
Web Site: http://www.eleb.net
Sales Range: $100-124.9 Million
Emp.: 500
Production of Landing Gears & Pylons,
Wheels, Brakes & Hydraulic System Components
N.A.I.C.S.: 333995

Embraer Aircraft Holding Inc. **(1)**
276 SW 34th St, Fort Lauderdale, FL
33315-3603
Tel.: (954) 359-3700
Sales Range: $150-199.9 Million
Emp.: 300
Aircraft Mfr
N.A.I.C.S.: 423860

Frederico C. Pinheiro Fleury Curado *(Pres
& CEO)*

Subsidiary (Domestic):

Embraer Aircraft Maintenance Ser-
vices, **(2)**
10 Airways Blvd, Nashville, TN 37217
Tel.: (615) 367-2100
Aircraft Maintenance Services
N.A.I.C.S.: 488190

Embraer Executive Aircraft, Inc. **(2)**
1205 General Aviation Dr, Melbourne, FL
32935
Tel.: (321) 426-2623
Emp.: 100
Aircraft Mfr
N.A.I.C.S.: 336411

Embraer Executive Jet Services,
LLC **(2)**
276 SW 34th St, Fort Lauderdale, FL
33315-3603
Tel.: (954) 359-3700
Web Site:
  http://www1.embraerexecutivejets.com
Sales Range: $25-49.9 Million
Emp.: 200
Aircraft Mfr
N.A.I.C.S.: 336411

Embraer Services, Inc. **(2)**
276 SW 34th St, Fort Lauderdale, FL
33315-3603
Tel.: (954) 359-3700
Aircraft Mfr
N.A.I.C.S.: 336411

Embraer Aviation Europe SAS **(1)**
33 rue des Vanesses Paris Nord 2 Bat Ed-
dington Roissy CDG, Villepinte, 95943,
France
Tel.: (33) 1 49 38 44 00
Aircraft Repair & Maintenance Services
N.A.I.C.S.: 488190

Subsidiary (Domestic):

Embraer Aviation International
SAS **(2)**
33 Rue Des Vanesses, Villepinte, 93420,
France
Tel.: (33) 1 49 38 44 00
Aircraft Repair & Maintenance Services
N.A.I.C.S.: 488190

Embraer China **(1)**
Suite 1806 Tower 2 China Central Place
Office Building, No 79 Jianguo Road Cha-
oyang District, Beijing, 100025,
China **(100%)**
Tel.: (86) 1065989988
Web Site: http://www.embraer.com
Sales Range: $50-74.9 Million
Emp.: 120
Aircraft & Flight Operations
N.A.I.C.S.: 336411

Embraer Spain Holding Co., SL **(1)**
Pafeodeloa 3 Tilos, Barcelona, Spain
Tel.: (34) 934150522
Financial Management Services
N.A.I.C.S.: 523999

Subsidiary (Non-US):

ECC Leasing Company Ltd. **(2)**
202 Q House 76 Furze Road, Sandyford,
Dublin, Ireland
Tel.: (353) 1 245 3980
Web Site: http://www.eccleasing.com
Emp.: 3
Aircraft Leasing Services
N.A.I.C.S.: 532411

Liebherr-Aerospace Brasil Ltda. **(1)**
Rua Dr Hans Liebherr 1 Vila Bela, Guarat-
ingueta, 12522-635, SP, Brazil
Tel.: (55) 1221314774
Sales Range: $25-49.9 Million
Emp.: 24
Joint Venture of Embraer-Empresa Brasile-
ira de Aeronautica S/A (60%) & Liebherr-
International AG (40%)
N.A.I.C.S.: 332911

OGMA - Industria Aeronautica De
Portugal S.A. **(1)**
Parque Aeronautico de Alverca, Lisbon,
2615173, Portugal

Embraer S.A.—(Continued)

Tel.: (351) 219579000
Web Site: http://www.ogma.pt
Sales Range: $450-499.9 Million
Emp.: 1,600
Aircraft Mfr
N.A.I.C.S.: 336411

Orbisat Industria e Aerolevantamento
S.A.   (1)
Avenida Jose de Souza Campos 1815 / An
6, Cambui, 12244-000, Campinas, Sao
Paulo, Brazil
Tel.: (55) 19 3295 8844
Electric Equipment Mfr
N.A.I.C.S.: 334419

EMBRUDIS
La Clapiere, Embrun, 0700, Hautes
Alpes, France
Tel.: (33) 492432850
Rev.: $22,600,000
Emp.: 49
Grocery Stores
N.A.I.C.S.: 445110
Alain Vappereau (Pres)

EMBRY HOLDINGS LIMITED
7th Floor Wyler Centre II 200 Tai Lin
Pai Road, Kwai Chung, NT, China
(Hong Kong)
Tel.: (852) 24188288
Web Site:
  https://www.embryform.com
Year Founded: 1975
1388—(HKG)
Rev.: $170,119,298
Assets: $379,542,638
Liabilities: $89,820,308
Net Worth: $289,722,330
Earnings: ($6,532,973)
Emp.: 4,568
Fiscal Year-end: 12/31/22
Women's Clothing Retailer
N.A.I.C.S.: 458110
Ming Chu Ngok (Exec Dir)

EMC LIMITED
Constantia Office Complex 11 Dr U N
Brahmachari Street 8th Floor, South
Block, Kolkata, 700017, India
Tel.: (91) 33 22893122
Web Site: http://www.emcpower.com
Year Founded: 1953
Sales Range: $800-899.9 Million
Emp.: 1,500
Power Transmission & Distribution
Services
N.A.I.C.S.: 221121
Manoj Toshniwal (Chm & Mng Dir)

Subsidiaries:

Advanced Steel & Crane Inc.   (1)
6420 S 39th W Ave, Tulsa, OK 74132
Tel.: (918) 445-0260
Web Site: http://www.advancedsteelinc.com
Steel Product Mfr & Distr
N.A.I.C.S.: 332999
Ron Ledford (Head-Sls & Mfg)

Quatro Rail Tech Solutions Pvt.
Ltd.   (1)
756 4th Block 80 Feet Road, Koramangala,
Bengaluru, 560034, India
Tel.: (91) 8041657588
Web Site: http://www.quatrorail.com
Telecommunication Servicesb
N.A.I.C.S.: 517112
Subroto Chaudhury (Chm)

Technolines S.R.L.   (1)
Via Palazzolo/ 109, Brescia, 25031, Italy
Tel.: (39) 0302054536
Web Site: http://www.tecnoline-srl.it
Industrial Equipment Distr
N.A.I.C.S.: 423830

**EMC PUBLIC COMPANY LIM-
ITED**

140/66 ITF Tower Building 28th Floor-
Silom Road Suriyawong Subdistrict,
Suriyawong Subdistrict, Bangkok,
10500, Thailand
Tel.: (66) 26156100
Web Site: https://www.emc.co.th
Year Founded: 1979
EMC—(THA)
Rev.: $13,327,886
Assets: $69,163,951
Liabilities: $41,296,712
Net Worth: $27,867,238
Earnings: ($16,330,572)
Emp.: 217
Fiscal Year-end: 12/31/23
Engineering Services Contractor
N.A.I.C.S.: 238210
Chanachai Leenabanchong (Chm)

EMCO INDUSTRIES LIMITED
4th-Floor National Tower 28-Edgerton
Road, Lahore, 54000, Pakistan
Tel.: (92) 4236306545
Web Site: https://www.emco.com.pk
Year Founded: 1954
EMCO—(PSX)
Rev.: $9,950,710
Assets: $17,644,591
Liabilities: $9,273,994
Net Worth: $8,370,597
Earnings: $1,037,793
Emp.: 471
Fiscal Year-end: 06/30/19
Insulators Mfr
N.A.I.C.S.: 335999
Tariq Rehman (CEO)

EMCO LTD.
N-104 MIDC Area, Mehrun, Jalgaon,
425003, Maharashtra, India
Tel.: (91) 2572272462
Web Site: http://www.emco.co.in
EMCO—(NSE)
Rev.: $3,983,056
Assets: $20,945,529
Liabilities: $43,501,089
Net Worth: ($22,555,560)
Earnings: ($217,431,696)
Fiscal Year-end: 03/31/20
Power Transmission Equipment Mfr &
Distr
N.A.I.C.S.: 333613
Rajesh S. Jain (Chm)

EMCOM HOLDINGS CO., LTD.
KSS Gotanda Building 5F 1-21-8
Nishigotanda, Shinagawa-ku, Tokyo,
141-0031, Japan
Tel.: (81) 50 3155 4370
Web Site: http://www.hd.emcom.jp
Year Founded: 1974
Sales Range: $25-49.9 Million
Emp.: 10
Business Strategy Support Services
N.A.I.C.S.: 561499
Yanji Yan (Pres)

Subsidiaries:

EMCOM ENTERTAINMENT Co.,
Ltd.   (1)
Kojimachi Center Building 3F 3-5-8 Koji-
machi, Chiyoda-ku, Tokyo, 102-0083, Japan
Tel.: (81) 50 3155 4368
Business Management Services
N.A.I.C.S.: 541611
Yanji Yang (Pres)

EMD MUSIC S.A.
boulevard General Wahis 16a, 1030,
Brussels, Belgium
Tel.: (32) 2 745 0970
Web Site: http://www.emdmusic.com
EMD—(EUR)
Sales Range: $50-74.9 Million
Emp.: 120
Musical Instrument Distr
N.A.I.C.S.: 423990

**EMDOOR INFORMATION CO.,
LTD.**
16/17F Emdoor Building No 8
Guangke 1st road, Pingshan District,
Shenzhen, 518101, Guangdong,
China
Tel.: (86) 75523722880
Web Site:
  https://www.emdoorrugged.com
Year Founded: 2002
001314—(SSE)
Rev.: $386,653,176
Assets: $246,182,976
Liabilities: $110,034,200
Net Worth: $128,148,696
Earnings: $27,684,072
Emp.: 800
Fiscal Year-end: 12/31/22
Electronic Product Mfr & Distr
N.A.I.C.S.: 334111
Zhiyu Zhang (Chm)

EME CAPITAL LLP
Berkeley Street, London, W1J ADJ,
United Kingdom
Tel.: (44) 20 3468 1900
Web Site: http://www.eme-
  capital.com
Privater Equity Firm
N.A.I.C.S.: 523999

EMECO HOLDINGS LIMITED
Level 3 133 Hasler Road, Osborne
Park, 6017, WA, Australia
Tel.: (61) 894200222
Web Site:
  https://www.emecogroup.com
Year Founded: 1972
EHL—(ASX)
Rev.: $551,827,589
Assets: $784,427,080
Liabilities: $358,918,935
Net Worth: $425,508,145
Earnings: $35,162,927
Emp.: 832
Fiscal Year-end: 06/30/24
Mining Equipment Rental & Mainte-
nance Services
N.A.I.C.S.: 532412
Peter Richards (Chm)

Subsidiaries:

Force Equipment Pty Ltd   (1)
897 Abernethy Road, Forrestfield, 6058,
WA, Australia
Tel.: (61) 436034740
Web Site:
  http://www.forceequipment.com.au
Earthmoving Equipment & Component Re-
pair Services
N.A.I.C.S.: 811310

Pit N Portal Mining Services Pty
Ltd   (1)
Level 3 133 Hasler Road, Osborne Park,
Perth, 6017, WA, Australia
Tel.: (61) 894938100
Web Site: https://www.pitnportal.com.au
Mining Services
N.A.I.C.S.: 213114
Steve Versteegen (CEO)

**EMEI SHAN TOURISM COM-
PANY LIMITED**
No 639 Mingshan South Road,
Emeishan City, Leshan, 614200, Si-
chuan, China
Tel.: (86) 8335528888
Web Site: https://www.emslg.com
Year Founded: 1997
000888—(SSE)
Rev.: $60,525,036
Assets: $432,573,804
Liabilities: $111,782,268
Net Worth: $320,791,536
Earnings: ($20,474,532)
Fiscal Year-end: 12/31/22
Tourism Operator

N.A.I.C.S.: 561520
Xu Ladi (Chm & Sec-Party Committee)

EMEIS SA
12 Rue Jean Jarues, FR-92813, Pu-
teaux, Cedex, France
Tel.: (33) 147757807
Web Site: https://www.emeis-
  group.com
Year Founded: 1989
EMEIS—(EUR)
Rev.: $5,555,364,819
Assets: $14,864,870,400
Liabilities: $12,846,518,554
Net Worth: $2,018,351,846
Earnings: $1,454,280,890
Emp.: 47,658
Fiscal Year-end: 12/31/23
Retirement Homes, Outpatient, Reha-
bilitation Clinics & Psychiatric Care
Facilities Operator
N.A.I.C.S.: 623110
Guillaume Pepy (Chm)

Subsidiaries:

Casamia Immobiliare SAS   (1)
Piazza Carlo Zinelli 1 Torre Galileo - piano
1, 37057, San Giovanni Lupatoto, VR, Italy
Tel.: (39) 0458205070
Web Site:
  http://www.casamiaimmobiliare.net
Real Estate Agency Services
N.A.I.C.S.: 531210

Grupo Care SA   (1)
Paseo de la Reforma 2355-A, 11930, Lo-
mas de Chapultepec, Mexico
Tel.: (52) 5510841989
Web Site: http://www.grupo-care.com
Construction Piling Services
N.A.I.C.S.: 238910

ORPEA POLSKA Sp. z o. o   (1)
ul Prosta 69, 00-838, Warsaw, Poland
Tel.: (48) 228885942
Web Site: https://www.orpea.pl
Health Care Srvices
N.A.I.C.S.: 621999

Orpea Deutschland GmbH   (1)
De-Saint-Exupery-Strasse 8, 60549, Frank-
furt am Main, Germany
Tel.: (49) 6964357000
Web Site: https://orpea-deutschland.de
Health Care Srvices
N.A.I.C.S.: 621999

Orpea Iberica S.A.U   (1)
Paseo del General Martinez Campos 46 7
Planta, 28010, Madrid, Spain
Tel.: (34) 914260952
Web Site: https://www.boucomayores.es
Health Care Srvices
N.A.I.C.S.: 621999

SARL Residence de Balbigny   (1)
33 Bis Rue du 8 Mai 1945, Balbigny,
42510, Roanne, France
Tel.: (33) 477272854
Web Site: http://www.orpea.com
Health Care Srvices
N.A.I.C.S.: 621999

Senevita AG   (1)
Worbstrasse 46, Postfach 345, Muri b Bern,
CH-3074, Bern, Switzerland
Tel.: (41) 319609999
Web Site: https://www.senevita.ch
Health Care Srvices
N.A.I.C.S.: 621999

emeis Belgium   (1)
Alsembergsesteenweg 1037, 1180, Ukkel,
Belgium
Tel.: (32) 23334550
Web Site: https://emeis.be
Emp.: 4,200
Health Care Srvices
N.A.I.C.S.: 621999
Katleen Bogaerts (Chief HR Officer)

**EMEK ELEKTRIK ENDUSTRISI
A.S.**
Balikhisar Mahallesi Koyici

Kumeevleri No 574, Akyurt, 06750, Ankara, Turkiye
Tel.: (90) 3123980181
Web Site: https://emek.com
EMKEL—(IST)
Rev.: $14,324,249
Assets: $38,803,137
Liabilities: $18,567,012
Net Worth: $20,236,125
Earnings: ($703,983)
Emp.: 250
Fiscal Year-end: 12/31/23
Electro Mechanical Product Mfr
N.A.I.C.S.: 334416
Huseyin Arabul *(Chm)*

Subsidiaries:

APS Power Solutions LLC   (1)
319 Vann Dr St E196, Jackson, TN 38305
Tel.: (731) 891-1139
Web Site: https://www.apsps.net
Electric Power Transmission Distr
N.A.I.C.S.: 423610

Emek USA Inc.   (1)
1200 Woodruff Rd A-3, Greenville, SC 29607
Tel.: (404) 993-1208
Electromechanical Product Mfr & Distr
N.A.I.C.S.: 335999

Performance Electrical Products,Inc.   (1)
1121 Boyce Rd Ste 1800A, Pittsburgh, PA 15241
Tel.: (412) 835-1508
Web Site: https://www.pepincpower.com
Electric Power Distr
N.A.I.C.S.: 423610

Power-Equip Sales Reps, Ltd.   (1)
209 Camille Ct, Pflugerville, TX 78660
Tel.: (281) 393-0300
Web Site: https://www.power-equipsalesreps.com
Electric Power Distribution Services
N.A.I.C.S.: 221122

Velpa Soluciones Integrales S.A.   (1)
Cra 48A No 25AA Sur - 70 Of 517 Edificio Complex Las Vegas, Envigado, Colombia
Tel.: (57) 6043329234
Web Site: https://velpa-si.com
Electric Equipment Assembly Services
N.A.I.C.S.: 238210

EMEMORY TECHNOLOGY, INC.
8F No 5 Tai-Yuan 1st St, Hsinchu County, Zhubei, 302082, Taiwan
Tel.: (886) 35601168
Web Site:
   https://www.ememory.com.tw
3529—(TPE)
Rev.: $100,575,650
Assets: $121,880,718
Liabilities: $25,162,962
Net Worth: $96,717,756
Earnings: $50,156,052
Emp.: 333
Fiscal Year-end: 12/31/22
Semiconductor Mfr
N.A.I.C.S.: 334413
Charles Hsu *(Chm)*

Subsidiaries:

PUF Security Corporation   (1)
8F 1 No 5 Taiyuan 1st St, Hsinchu County, Zhubei, 30288, Taiwan
Tel.: (886) 35601010
Web Site: http://www.pufsecurity.com
Security Services
N.A.I.C.S.: 561612
Charles Hsu *(Chm)*

EMERA, INC.
5151 Terminal Road, Halifax, B3J 1A1, NS, Canada
Tel.: (902) 428-6096   NS
Web Site: https://www.emera.com
Year Founded: 1998

EMAB—(BISX)
Rev.: $7,563,000,000
Assets: $39,480,000,000
Liabilities: $27,392,000,000
Net Worth: $12,088,000,000
Earnings: $978,000,000
Emp.: 7,366
Fiscal Year-end: 12/31/23
Electricity Distribution Services
N.A.I.C.S.: 551112
Jacqueline Sheppard *(Chm)*

Subsidiaries:

Bangor Hydro-Electric Company   (1)
PO Box 932, Bangor, ME 04402-0932
Tel.: (207) 973-2000
Web Site: https://www.versantpower.com
Sales Range: $500-549.9 Million
Emp.: 600
Operator of Electricity Transmission & Distribution System
N.A.I.C.S.: 221121

Division (Domestic):

Bangor Hydro-Electric Company-Hancock County Division   (2)
PO Box 932, Bangor, ME 04402
Tel.: (207) 947-2414
Web Site: http://www.bhe.com
Sales Range: $75-99.9 Million
Emp.: 100
Electronic Services
N.A.I.C.S.: 221121

Bangor Hydro-Electric Company-Northern Division   (2)
PO Box 932, Bangor, ME 04402
Tel.: (207) 945-5621
Web Site: http://www.bhe.com
Sales Range: $200-249.9 Million
Emp.: 272
Electronic Services
N.A.I.C.S.: 221121

Dominica Electricity Services Ltd.   (1)
18 Castle Street, Roseau, Dominica
Tel.: (767) 2556000
Web Site: https://www.domlec.dm
Emp.: 208
Electric Power Distribution Services
N.A.I.C.S.: 221122
David McGregor *(Chm)*

Emera (Caribbean) Incorporated   (1)
PO Box 142, Garrison Hil, Saint Michael, BB11000, Barbados
Tel.: (246) 6265013
Web Site: http://www.emeracaribbean.com
Electric Utility Services
N.A.I.C.S.: 221122
Rick Janega *(Pres)*

Emera Brunswick Pipeline Co Ltd   (1)
1 Germain St Ste 1204, Saint John, E2L 4V1, NB, Canada
Tel.: (506) 693-4214
Web Site: http://www.brunswickpipeline.com
Natural Gas Distribution Services
N.A.I.C.S.: 486210

Emera Energy   (1)
1223 Lower Water Street, Halifax, B3J 2A8, NS, Canada   **(100%)**
Tel.: (866) 474-7800
Web Site: http://www.emeraenergy.com
Energy Marketing & Trading Services
N.A.I.C.S.: 561499
Judy Steele *(Pres & COO)*

Emera Utility Services Inc.   (1)
31 Dominion Crescent, PO Box 40, Lakeside, B3T 1M0, NS, Canada
Tel.: (902) 832-7999
Electrical Engineering Services
N.A.I.C.S.: 238210

Grand Bahama Power Company Limited   (1)
Pioneers Way East Mall Drive, PO Box F-40888, Freeport, Grand Bahama, Bahamas   **(80.4%)**
Tel.: (242) 3508900
Web Site: https://www.gb-power.com
Sales Range: $125-149.9 Million
Emp.: 200
Electricity Supplier

N.A.I.C.S.: 221122
Franklyn Woodworth *(VP)*

NSP Maritime Link Inc.   (1)
1223 Lower Water Street, Halifax, B3J 3S8, NS, Canada
Maritime Construction Services
N.A.I.C.S.: 336611
Rick Janega *(Pres & CEO)*

Nova Scotia Power Inc.   (1)
1223 Lower Water St, Halifax, B3J 3S8, NS, Canada   **(100%)**
Tel.: (902) 428-6230
Web Site: http://www.nspower.ca
Rev.: $1,094,293,200
Assets: $4,216,472,400
Liabilities: $3,112,231,080
Net Worth: $1,104,241,320
Earnings: $105,603,120
Emp.: 2,000
Fiscal Year-end: 12/31/2019
Electricity Production, Transmission & Distribution Services
N.A.I.C.S.: 221122
Scott C. Balfour *(Chm)*

TECO Energy, Inc.   (1)
702 N Franklin St, Tampa, FL 33602
Tel.: (813) 228-1111
Web Site: http://www.tecoenergy.com
Emp.: 3,713
Holding Company; Independent Power Generation, River & Ocean Transportation, Energy Services, Coal Mining & Alternative Fuels
N.A.I.C.S.: 221122
Gregory W. Blunden *(CFO & Sr VP-Fin & Acctg)*

Subsidiary (Domestic):

New Mexico Gas Company, Inc.   (2)
PO Box 97500, Albuquerque, NM 87199-7500
Tel.: (506) 697-3335
Web Site: http://www.nmgco.com
Natural Gas Distr
N.A.I.C.S.: 221210
Ryan Shell *(Pres)*

Peoples Gas System (Florida), Inc.   (2)
PO Box 2562, Tampa, FL 33601-2562
Tel.: (813) 275-3700
Web Site: https://www.peoplesgas.com
N.A.I.C.S.: 486210
Helen Wesley *(Pres)*

TECO Diversified, Inc.   (2)
702 N Franklin St, Tampa, FL 33602
Tel.: (813) 228-1111
Fuel Production & Coal Mining Services
N.A.I.C.S.: 212114

TECO Guatemala, Inc.   (2)
702 N Franklin St, Tampa, FL 33602
Tel.: (813) 228-1111
Power Plant Operator
N.A.I.C.S.: 221122

TECO Partners, Inc.   (2)
702 N Franklin St, Tampa, FL 33602
Web Site: https://www.tecopartners.com
N.A.I.C.S.: 221114
Kevin Nordlund *(Mgr-Energy)*

TECO Peoples Gas   (2)
702 N Franklin St Plz 4, Tampa, FL 33602
Tel.: (813) 275-3700
Web Site: http://www.tecoenergy.com
Emp.: 548
Natural Gas Distr
N.A.I.C.S.: 221210
Luke Buzard *(VP-Regulatory Affairs)*

TECO Solutions, Inc.   (2)
3801 SW 47th Ave Ste 503, Davie, FL 33314
Tel.: (954) 651-6208
Web Site: https://www.tecosolutions.no
N.A.I.C.S.: 213112
Michael Rasmussen *(CTO)*

Tampa Electric Company   (2)
TECO Plz 702 N Franklin St, Tampa, FL 33602   **(100%)**
Tel.: (813) 228-1111
Web Site: https://www.tampaelectric.com
Rev.: $3,169,000,000
Assets: $13,803,000,000

Liabilities: $4,649,000,000
Net Worth: $9,154,000,000
Earnings: $540,000,000
Emp.: 2,469
Fiscal Year-end: 12/31/2022
Electric Power Distribution & Generation Services
N.A.I.C.S.: 221122
Karen M. Mincey *(CIO & VP-IT & Telecom)*

Subsidiary (Non-US):

Tecnologia Maritima, S.A.   (2)
3rd Avenue 12-38 Zone 10 Paseo Plaza Building Level 11, 01010, Guatemala, Guatemala
Tel.: (502) 24286000
Web Site: https://tecnologiamaritima.com
N.A.I.C.S.: 541519

The Barbados Light & Power Company Limited   (1)
Garrison Hill, PO Box 142, Saint Michael, BB11000, Barbados   **(79.7%)**
Tel.: (246) 6261800
Web Site: https://www.blpc.com.bb
Emp.: 500
Electric Power Generation & Distr
N.A.I.C.S.: 221122
Roger Blackman *(Mng Dir)*

EMERALD AIRWAYS LTD.
Speke Hall Avenue, Liverpool John Lennon Airport, Liverpool, L24 1YW, Merseyside, United Kingdom
Tel.: (44) 151 448 0844
Web Site: http://www.emerald-airways.co.uk
Year Founded: 1987
Sales Range: $25-49.9 Million
Emp.: 250
Oil Transportation Services
N.A.I.C.S.: 488510

EMERALD LEISURES LIMITED
Club Emerald Sports Complex Plot No 366/15 Swastik Park, Near Mangal Anand Sushrut Hospital Chembur, Mumbai, 400071, India
Tel.: (91) 2225265800
Web Site:
   https://corporate.clubemerald.in
Year Founded: 1933
507265—(BOM)
Rev.: $676,710
Assets: $10,605,232
Liabilities: $19,973,094
Net Worth: ($9,367,862)
Earnings: ($1,475,998)
Emp.: 63
Fiscal Year-end: 03/31/21
Property Development & Securities Trading Services
N.A.I.C.S.: 531390
Rajesh Motilal Loya *(Exec Dir)*

EMERALD PLANTATION HOLDINGS LIMITED
18/F Cigna Tower, 482 Jaffe Road, Causeway Bay, China (Hong Kong)
Tel.: (852) 28770078   Ky
Web Site:
   https://www.emeraldplantation.com
EMEXF—(OTCIQ)
Sales Range: Less than $1 Million
Holding Company; Wood & Wood-Based Products Distr; Plantations & Downstream Manufacturing Operator
N.A.I.C.S.: 551112
James Michael Dubow *(CEO)*

Subsidiaries:

Guangzhou Panyu Dacheng Wood Co., Ltd.   (1)
No 23 Liye Road DongChong, Nansha District, Guangzhou, 511453, Guangdong, China
Tel.: (86) 2084780089
Engineered Wood Veneer Mfr
N.A.I.C.S.: 321211

Emerald Plantation Holdings Limited—(Continued)

Jiafeng Wood (Suzhou) Co., Ltd. (1)
No 28 East Shihu Road Wuzhong Economic Development Zone, Suzhou, 215128, Jiangsu, China
Tel.: (86) 51265655365
Wood Flooring Mfr
N.A.I.C.S.: 321918

Jiangxi Jiachang Forestry Development Co., Ltd. (1)
2-A Jingwei Mansion No 37 Erjing Road, Nanchang, China
Tel.: (86) 7916827143
Wood Products Mfr
N.A.I.C.S.: 321999

Sino-Forest (Suzhou) Trading Co., Ltd. (1)
Room 6018 Business Building No 3, Zhangjiagang Port, Suzhou, 215633, Jiangsu, China
Tel.: (86) 512 58700861
Lumber Product Whslr
N.A.I.C.S.: 423990

Sino-Maple (Shanghai) Co., Ltd. (1)
Room 302 Fenghuang Mansion Building 19 No 1515 Gumei Road Xuhui, Shanghai, 200233, China
Tel.: (86) 2161281800
Wood Flooring Mfr
N.A.I.C.S.: 321918
Ella Chen *(Mgr)*

Sino-Maple (Shanghai) Trading Co., Ltd. (1)
No 28 East Shihu Road Wuzhong Economic Development Zone, Suzhou, 215128, Jiangsu, China
Tel.: (86) 51265655365
Wood Flooring Sales
N.A.I.C.S.: 423310

Sino-Panel (Asia) Inc. (1)
Unit 5 17th Fl Tai Yau Bldg 181 Johnston Rd, Wanchai, China (Hong Kong)
Tel.: (852) 2877 0078
Web Site: http://www.sinopanel.com
Sales Range: $25-49.9 Million
Emp.: 30
Wood Products Mfr
N.A.I.C.S.: 321918

Sino-Panel (China) Investments Limited (1)
767 Dongfeng, 510600, Guangzhou, China
Tel.: (86) 20 3836 1982
Wood Products Mfr
N.A.I.C.S.: 321999

Sino-Panel (Guangxi) Limited (1)
Beihai Road West, Beihai, 536000, Guangxi, China
Tel.: (86) 779 3928068
Forestry Services
N.A.I.C.S.: 115310

Sino-Panel (Guangzhou) Limited (1)
767 Dongfeng, 510600, Guangzhou, Guangdong, China
Tel.: (86) 2038361982
Forestry Services
N.A.I.C.S.: 115310

Sino-Wood Partners Limited (1)
Room 3815-29 38th Floor Sun Hung Kai Center, 30 Harbour Road, Wanchai, China (Hong Kong)
Tel.: (852) 28770078
Web Site: http://www.sinoforest.com
Durable Goods Whslr
N.A.I.C.S.: 423990

Sino-Wood Trading Limited (1)
2nd Floor R G Hodge Plaza, Road Town, Tortola, Virgin Islands (British)
Tel.: (284) 284 494 4693
Wood Fiber Products Mfr
N.A.I.C.S.: 321999

Sinowood Limited (1)
1526 17th Fl Taya Bldg 181 Johnston Rd, Wanchai, China (Hong Kong)
Tel.: (852) 28770078
Sales Range: $25-49.9 Million
Emp.: 100
Forestry Services
N.A.I.C.S.: 115310

James Lau *(VP)*

EMERALD RESOURCES NL
1110 Hay Street, West Perth, 6005, WA, Australia
Tel.: (61) 892866300
Web Site:
https://www.emeraldresources.com
EMR—(ASX)
Rev.: $247,778,444
Assets: $475,709,133
Liabilities: $103,134,348
Net Worth: $372,574,785
Earnings: $53,881,216
Emp.: 310
Fiscal Year-end: 06/30/24
Crude Petroleum Extraction Services
N.A.I.C.S.: 211120
Morgan Hart *(Mng Dir)*

Subsidiaries:

Bullseye Mining Limited (1)
Ground Floor 1110 Hay Street, West Perth, 6005, WA, Australia **(100%)**
Tel.: (61) 892866300
Web Site:
https://www.bullseyemining.com.au
Gold Mining Services
N.A.I.C.S.: 212321

Dingo Range Pty. Ltd. (1)
9 Owen St East, Dalby, 4405, QLD, Australia
Tel.: (61) 746725400
Web Site: https://www.dingo.com.au
Construction & Light Equipment Mfr
N.A.I.C.S.: 333120

EMERAM CAPITAL PARTNERS GMBH
Muhlbaurstrasse 1, 81677, Munich, Germany
Tel.: (49) 89 41999 67 0
Web Site: http://www.emeram.com
Year Founded: 2012
Private Investment Firm
N.A.I.C.S.: 523999
Korbinian Knoblach *(Partner)*

Subsidiaries:

Hussel Susswarenfachgeschafte GmbH (1)
Kabeler Strasse 4, 58099, Hagen, Germany **(100%)**
Tel.: (49) 2331 690 8181
Web Site: http://www.hussel.de
Chocolate & Confectionery Stores
N.A.I.C.S.: 445292
Sven Ekloeh *(CEO)*

Subsidiary (Domestic):

Cerrini Confiserie GmbH (2)
Kabeler Str 4, 58099, Hagen, Germany
Tel.: (49) 23316900
Cosmetics & Perfume Distr
N.A.I.C.S.: 424210

Hussel Geschenkstudio GmbH (2)
Kabeler Strasse 4, 58099, Hagen, Germany
Tel.: (49) 23316908008
Web Site: http://www.hussel.de
Confectionery Gifts Distr
N.A.I.C.S.: 424450

frostkrone Tiefkuhlkost GmbH (1)
Konrad-Adenauer-Strasse 28, D-33397, Rietberg, Germany
Tel.: (49) 5244 90 36 0
Web Site: http://www.frostkrone.de
Frozen Finger Food & Snack Products Mfr & Distr
N.A.I.C.S.: 311412
Frederic Dervieux *(CEO & Mng Partner)*

Subsidiary (US):

Rite Stuff Foods, Inc. (2)
2155 S Lincoln, Jerome, ID 83338
Tel.: (208) 324-8410
Web Site: http://www.ritestuff.com
Emp.: 230
Dried Or Canned Foods Frozen Potatoes
N.A.I.C.S.: 445110

Thomas J. Madden *(Founder & Pres)*

EMERGE COMMERCE LTD.
77 King Street West Suite 700 TD North Tower, Toronto, M5K 1G8, ON, Canada
Tel.: (416) 644-9964
ECOM—(TSXV)
Rev.: $17,993,798
Assets: $17,359,787
Liabilities: $24,809,822
Net Worth: ($7,450,035)
Earnings: ($16,384,156)
Fiscal Year-end: 12/01/20
Financial Services
N.A.I.C.S.: 523999
Ghassan Halazon *(Pres & CEO)*

EMERGENCY ASSISTANCE JAPAN CO., LTD.
NRK Koishikawa Building 1-21-14 Koishikawa, Bunkyo-ku, Tokyo, 112-0002, Japan
Tel.: (81) 338118121
Web Site:
https://www.emergency.co.jp
6063—(TKS)
Rev.: $25,509,820
Assets: $26,126,650
Liabilities: $13,981,480
Net Worth: $12,145,170
Earnings: $843,710
Emp.: 116
Fiscal Year-end: 12/31/23
Emergency Medical Services
N.A.I.C.S.: 624230
Kiyoshi Kurata *(CEO)*

Subsidiaries:

Emergency Assistance Beijing Co., Ltd. (1)
Room 2303-2305 23F Tower A Ocean International Center 56, Dongsihuanzhonglu Chaoyang District, Beijing, 100025, China
Tel.: (86) 215 213 2303
Medical Assistance Services
N.A.I.C.S.: 621112

Emergency Assistance Japan (Singapore), Pte. Ltd (1)
101 Cecil Street 16-04 Tong Eng Building, Singapore, 069533, Singapore
Tel.: (65) 67325810
Emp.: 10
Medical Assistance Services
N.A.I.C.S.: 624229

Emergency Assistance Japan (U.S.A.), Inc. (1)
7130 Glen Forest Dr Ste 201, Richmond, VA 23226
Tel.: (804) 249-9907
Medical Assistance Services
N.A.I.C.S.: 624229

Emergency Assistance Thailand Co., Ltd (1)
9th Floor Prime Building 24 Sukhumvit Soi 21 Asoke Klongtoey-Nua, Wattana, Bangkok, 10110, Thailand
Tel.: (66) 26657280
Medical Assistance Services
N.A.I.C.S.: 624229

EMERGENT INDUSTRIAL SOLUTIONS LIMITED
8B Sagar Apartments 6 Tilak Marg, New Delhi, 110001, India
Tel.: (91) 1123782022
Web Site: https://www.eesl.in
506180—(BOM)
Rev.: $18,515,425
Assets: $3,447,995
Liabilities: $777,915
Net Worth: $2,670,080
Earnings: $167,220
Emp.: 13
Fiscal Year-end: 03/31/23
Educational Support Services
N.A.I.C.S.: 611710

Sabina Nagpal *(Officer-Compliance & Sec)*

EMERGENT METALS CORP.
789 West Pender Street Suite 1010, Vancouver, V6C 1H2, BC, Canada
Web Site:
https://emergentmetals.com
EML—(BER)
Rev.: $54,900
Assets: $5,359,775
Liabilities: $2,756,382
Net Worth: $2,603,393
Earnings: ($057,007)
Emp.: 1
Fiscal Year-end: 12/31/20
Gold Exploration Services
N.A.I.C.S.: 212220
David G. Watkinson *(Pres, CEO & Dir-Emgold Mining Corp & Subsidiaries)*

Subsidiaries:

Idaho-Maryland Mining Corporation (1)
431 Crown Point Cir Ste 150, Grass Valley, CA 95945
Tel.: (530) 271-0679
Gold Exploration Services
N.A.I.C.S.: 212220
David Watkinson *(Pres & CEO)*

EMERGEO SOLUTIONS WORLDWIDE INC.
1001 1166 Alberni Street, Vancouver, V6E 3Z3, BC, Canada
Tel.: (604) 336-8120
Web Site: http://www.emergeo.com
Year Founded: 1997
Sales Range: $1-9.9 Million
Security Software Solution Services
N.A.I.C.S.: 541511
Timothy Webb *(CTO & VP)*

EMERGEVEST LIMITED
190 Elgin Avenue, Georgetown, KY1-9005, Cayman Islands
Tel.: (345) 852 9186 6152
Web Site:
http://www.emergevest.com
Year Founded: 2013
Privater Equity Firm
N.A.I.C.S.: 523999
Craig Sears-Black *(Operating Partner)*

Subsidiaries:

NFT Distribution Operations Limited (1)
Azalea Close Clover Nook Industrial Estate, Somercotes, Alfreton, DE55 4QX, Derbyshire, United Kingdom
Tel.: (44) 1773523623
Web Site: http://www.nft.co.uk
Sales Range: $250-299.9 Million
Emp.: 2,000
Refrigerated Transportation Services
N.A.I.C.S.: 484121
David Frankish *(CEO)*

EMERGIA INC.
402 - 185 Avenue Dorval, Dorval, H9S 5J9, QC, Canada
Tel.: (514) 420-1414
Web Site: https://emergia.com
Year Founded: 2015
EMER—(CNSX)
Rev.: $434,429
Assets: $102,713,445
Liabilities: $48,521,648
Net Worth: $54,191,798
Earnings: $25,539,213
Fiscal Year-end: 12/31/21
Real Estate Services
N.A.I.C.S.: 531390
Henri Petit *(Chm, Pres & CEO)*

EMERGING DISPLAY TECH-

NOLOGIES CORP.
No 5 Central 1st Rd, Cianjhen Dist,
Kaohsiung, Taiwan
Tel.: (886) 78124832
Web Site: https://www.edtc.com
Year Founded: 1994
3038—(TAI)
Rev.: $143,455,438
Assets: $135,833,181
Liabilities: $49,890,675
Net Worth: $85,942,506
Earnings: $13,688,969
Emp.: 750
Fiscal Year-end: 12/31/23
Touch Panel Mfr
N.A.I.C.S.: 334419
Tseng Ray *(Founder & Chm)*

Subsidiaries:

EDT-Europe ApS   **(1)**
Raadhustorvet 3 3520, 3520, Farum, Denmark
Tel.: (45) 44346300
Web Site: http://www.edtc.com
Emp.: 10
Electronic Parts Mfr & Distr
N.A.I.C.S.: 334419
Micheal Melvang *(Mng Dir)*

EDT-Japan Corp.   **(1)**
2-21-41 Takanawa Takanawa No1 Building,
Minatoku, Tokyo, 108-0074, Japan
Tel.: (81) 364085780
Electronic Parts Mfr & Distr
N.A.I.C.S.: 334419

Emerging Display Technologies
Co.,   **(1)**
No 5 Central 1st Rd K E P Z, Kaohsiung,
Taiwan
Tel.: (886) 78124832
Electronic Parts Mfr & Distr
N.A.I.C.S.: 334419

Emerging Display Technologies
Corp.   **(1)**
A-1111 Pyunchon Acro Tower 1591
Gwanyang-Dong, Dongan-Ku, Anyang,
Kyunggi Do, Korea (South)
Tel.: (82) 314789923
Electronic Parts Mfr & Distr
N.A.I.C.S.: 334419

EMERGING GLORY SDN BHD
Lot 2.08 2nd Floor Wisma Westcourt,
126 Jalan Kelang Lama, Kuala Lumpur, 58000, Malaysia
Tel.: (60) 3 7980 1304
Investment Holding Company
N.A.I.C.S.: 551112
Bong Wong Lau *(Co-Owner)*

Subsidiaries:

Leong Hup Holdings Berhad   **(1)**
2nd Fl Wisma Westcourt No 126 Jalan Kelang Lama, 58000, Kuala Lumpur, Malaysia
Tel.: (60) 379801304
Web Site: http://www.lhhb.com
Sales Range: $300-349.9 Million
Emp.: 1,000
Holding Company; Poultry Farming Services
N.A.I.C.S.: 551112
Fei San Seow *(Co-Sec)*

Holding (Non-US):

Kendo Trading Pte. Ltd.   **(2)**
233 Pandan Loop, Singapore, 128421, Singapore
Tel.: (65) 67787477
Web Site: https://www.kendo.com.sg
Poultry Distr
N.A.I.C.S.: 424440
Lee Thaison *(Dir)*

Subsidiary (Domestic):

Safa Gourmet Food Pte Ltd   **(3)**
6 Senoko Way, Singapore, Singapore
Tel.: (65) 65553838
Marinated Chicken Distr
N.A.I.C.S.: 424440
Steven Tan *(Mgr-Bus Dev)*

Soonly Food Processing Industries
Pte Ltd   **(3)**
Senoko Industrial Estate 4 Senoko Way,
Singapore, 758028, Singapore
Tel.: (65) 67572121
Web Site: http://www.ksbdist.com
Chicken Processing Services
N.A.I.C.S.: 311615
Steven Tan *(Gen Mgr)*

Subsidiary (Non-US):

PT Malindo Feedmill Tbk   **(2)**
Jl RS Fatmawati No 15 Komplek Golden
Plaza Blok G No 17-22, Jakarta, 12420,
Selatan, Indonesia
Tel.: (62) 217661727
Web Site: https://www.malindofeedmill.com
Rev.: $783,048,019
Assets: $358,293,259
Liabilities: $219,303,356
Net Worth: $138,989,903
Earnings: $4,101,789
Emp.: 3,616
Fiscal Year-end: 12/31/2023
Animal Feed Mfr
N.A.I.C.S.: 311119
Lau Tuang Nguang *(Chm)*

Holding (Domestic):

Teo Seng Capital Berhad   **(2)**
Lot PTD 25740 Batu 4 Jalan Air Hitam,
Yong Peng, 83700, Johor,
Malaysia   **(51%)**
Tel.: (60) 74672289
Web Site: https://www.teoseng.com.my
Rev.: $118,374,403
Assets: $146,262,365
Liabilities: $70,023,906
Net Worth: $76,238,460
Earnings: $1,036,632
Fiscal Year-end: 12/31/2020
Holding Company; Poultry Farming Services; Egg Tray & Animal Feeds Mfr & Distr;
Pet Food, Medicine & Other Related Products Distr
N.A.I.C.S.: 551112
Wee Ching Loh *(Exec Dir)*

Subsidiary (Non-US):

Ritma Prestasi Sdn Bhd   **(3)**
   (100%)
Sales Range: $25-49.9 Million
Emp.: 40
Veterinary Products Whslr
N.A.I.C.S.: 541940
Tim Nam Ya Jun *(Gen Mgr)*

Subsidiary (Domestic):

Success Century Sdn Bhd   **(3)**
No 8 Jln Sutera 1, Johor Bahru,
Malaysia   **(100%)**
Tel.: (60) 74681982
Poultry Farming Services
N.A.I.C.S.: 112340

Teo Seng Farming Sdn Bhd   **(3)**
Lot 7850 Mukim Tanjung Sembrong Batu 1
Jalan Muar, Yong Peng, 83700, Johor,
Malaysia   **(100%)**
Tel.: (60) 74672289
Web Site: http://www.lhhb.com
Sales Range: $75-99.9 Million
Emp.: 450
Egg Production & Marketing
N.A.I.C.S.: 112310
Wee Ching Loh *(Dir-Mktg)*

Teo Seng Feedmill Sdn Bhd   **(3)**
Lot 7850 Mukim Tanjung Sembrong Batu 1,
Jalan Muar Yong Peng, 83700, Johor,
Malaysia   **(100%)**
Tel.: (60) 74681690
Web Site: http://www.lhhb.com
Emp.: 700
Poultry Feedmill
N.A.I.C.S.: 311119
Hiok Joo Nam *(Gen Mgr)*

Teo Seng Paper Products Sdn
Bhd   **(3)**
Lot 7850 Mukim Tanjung Sembrong Batu
1 Jalan Muar, Yong Peng, Johor, 83700,
Malaysia
Tel.: (60) 74672289
Web Site: http://www.teoseng.com.my

Sales Range: $25-49.9 Million
Emp.: 100
Paper Products Mfr
N.A.I.C.S.: 322299
Laujui Peng *(CEO)*

EMERGING INVESTMENT PARTNERS
Abdul Razzak Building 2nd Floor
Abdul Hamid Karami St, Bab Idriss,
Beirut, Lebanon
Tel.: (961) 1 998598
Web Site: http://www.eip-capital.com
Investment Advice
N.A.I.C.S.: 523940
Wassim Heneine *(Mng Dir)*

Subsidiaries:

General Cable Egypt S.A.E.   **(1)**
Industrial Zone Abdelmoumen Center Abu
Rawash Km 28 Misr, Alexandria Desert
Road, Cairo, Egypt
Tel.: (20) 222580202
Cable & Wire Mfr & Distr
N.A.I.C.S.: 332618
Ahmed Soliman Mohamed Rabie *(Mgr-Plng)*

EMERGING MARKETS HORIZON CORP.
30 Ekaterinis Kornarou street 3rd
floor, Stovolos, 2024, Nicosia, Cyprus
Tel.: (357) 22150494   Ky
Year Founded: 2021
Investment Services
N.A.I.C.S.: 523999
Jonathan Neill *(Interim CEO)*

EMERGING TOWNS & CITIES SINGAPORE LTD.
80 Robinson Road 17-02, Singapore,
68898, Singapore
Tel.: (65) 65849411   SG
Web Site:
   https://www.etcsingapore.com
Year Founded: 1980
1C0—(CAT)
Rev.: $13,522,045
Assets: $157,984,439
Liabilities: $115,092,256
Net Worth: $42,892,182
Earnings: ($31,471,656)
Emp.: 42
Fiscal Year-end: 12/31/22
Holding Company
N.A.I.C.S.: 551112
Thiam Hee Tan *(CEO)*

EMERGN LIMITED
40 Bank Street Level 18 Canary
Wharf, London, E14 5NR, United
Kingdom
Tel.: (44) 20 8444 4503
Web Site: http://www.emergn.com
Year Founded: 2009
Sales Range: $1-9.9 Million
Emp.: 50
IT-Development Related Advisory,
Consulting, Delivery & Education
Services
N.A.I.C.S.: 519290
Alex Adamopoulos *(Co-Founder & CEO)*

Subsidiaries:

Emergn Limited   **(1)**
1 International Pl Ste 1400, Boston, MA
02110
Web Site: http://www.emergn.com
IT-Development Related Advisory Consulting Delivery & Education Services
N.A.I.C.S.: 519290
Amy Welsh *(Sr VP-Sls Enablement & Inside Sls)*

Emergn Limited   **(1)**
Kapelsestraat 192, Kapellen, 2950, Belgium
Tel.: (32) 249 958 2561
Web Site: http://www.emergn.com

IT Development Related Advisory, Consulting, Delivery & Education Services
N.A.I.C.S.: 519290
Philip Black *(COO)*

EMERISQUE BRANDS UK LIMITED
53 Davies Street, London, W1K 5JH,
United Kingdom
Tel.: (44) 2071526347   UK
Web Site: http://www.emerisque.com
Year Founded: 2009
Private Equity Firm & Investment
Services
N.A.I.C.S.: 523999
Ajay Khaitan *(Founder)*

EMERITA RESOURCES CORP.
36 Lombard Street Floor 4, Toronto,
M5C 2X3, ON, Canada
Tel.: (647) 910-2500   BC
Web Site:
   https://www.emeritaresources.com
Year Founded: 2009
EMO—(TSXV)
Rev.: $280,913
Assets: $9,895,708
Liabilities: $1,176,278
Net Worth: $8,719,430
Earnings: ($16,034,387)
Fiscal Year-end: 06/30/23
Mineral Exploration & Development
Services
N.A.I.C.S.: 212220
Joaquin Merino-Marquez *(Pres)*

EMERSON DEVELOPMENTS (HOLDINGS) LIMITED
Emerson House Hayes Lane, Alderley Edge, SK9 7LF, Cheshire, United
Kingdom
Tel.: (44) 1625 588400
Web Site: http://www.emerson.co.uk
Year Founded: 1959
Sales Range: $250-299.9 Million
Emp.: 600
Residential & Commercial Property
Developer
N.A.I.C.S.: 237210
Anne Weatherby *(Sec)*

Subsidiaries:

Boavista Golf & Spa Resort Empreendimentos Tur isticos, SA   **(1)**
Quinta da Boavista, 8601-901, Lagos, Portugal
Tel.: (351) 282000111
Web Site: http://www.boavistaresort.pt
Resort Management Services
N.A.I.C.S.: 721110
Filipe Goncalves *(Mgr-Estate)*

Emerson International, Inc.   **(1)**
370 CenterPointe Cir Ste 1136, Altamonte
Springs, FL 32701
Tel.: (407) 834-9560
Web Site: http://www.emerson-us.com
Residential & Commercial Property Developer
N.A.I.C.S.: 237210
Marla Lamb *(Controller)*

FE Jones (Builders) Limited   **(1)**
303 Mount Road, Levenshulme, Manchester, M19 3ET, United Kingdom
Tel.: (44) 1612248001
Web Site: http://www.fejones.co.uk
Industrial Machinery Distr
N.A.I.C.S.: 423830

Holidays Select Limited   **(1)**
3 Grove Street, Wilmslow, SK9 1DU,
Cheshire, United Kingdom
Tel.: (44) 1625539505
Property Development Services
N.A.I.C.S.: 237210

Jones Homes (Northern) Limited   **(1)**
Green Bank House Green Bank, Cleckheaton, BD19 5LQ, West Yorkshire, United
Kingdom
Tel.: (44) 1274852700

Emerson Developments (Holdings)
Limited—(Continued)

Residential Building Development Services
N.A.I.C.S.: 236116

Jones Homes (Southern) Limited (1)
3 White Oak Square, Swanley, BR8 7AG,
Kent, United Kingdom
Tel.: (44) 1322665000
Residential Building Development Services
N.A.I.C.S.: 236116
Sara Stanhope (Dir-Sls & Mktg)

Newfield Construction Limited (1)
5 Fleet Street, Lytham Saint Anne's, FY8
2DQ, Lancashire, United Kingdom
Tel.: (44) 1253728760
Property Development Services
N.A.I.C.S.: 237210
Alex Kharia

**Orbit Developments (Southern)
Limited** (1)
Building 3 Heathrow Boulevard 282 Bath
Road, Sipson, West Drayton, UB7 0DQ,
United Kingdom
Tel.: (44) 2087501410
Web Site: http://www.orbit-
developments.co.uk
Property Development Services
N.A.I.C.S.: 237210
Tony Jones (Mng Dir)

**Rosewood Development
Corporation** (1)
3740 Via Cara Loma, Encinitas, CA 92024
Tel.: (760) 519-2138
Web Site:
http://www.therosewooddevelopment.com
Property Development Services
N.A.I.C.S.: 237210

Stargaze Windows Limited (1)
Stockport Rd Cheadle Heath, Stockport,
SK3 0PL, Cheshire, United Kingdom
Tel.: (44) 1614911648
Web Site:
http://www.stargazewindows.co.uk
Window & Door Mfr
N.A.I.C.S.: 321911

EMETALS LIMITED
Level 3 88 William Street, Perth,
6000, WA, Australia
Tel.: (61) 894632463
Web Site:
https://www.emetalslimited.com.au
Year Founded: 2010
EMT—(ASX)
Rev.: $61,363
Assets: $3,521,892
Liabilities: $28,940
Net Worth: $3,492,953
Earnings: ($3,813,327)
Fiscal Year-end: 06/30/24
Investment Services
N.A.I.C.S.: 523999
Sonu Cheema (Sec)

**EMF CAPITAL PARTNERS LIM-
ITED**
Capital Tower 91 Waterloo Road,
London, SE1 8RT, United Kingdom
Tel.: (44) 20 7448 3540   UK
Web Site: http://www.emfcp.com
Investment Management Service
N.A.I.C.S.: 523940
Peter Lovas (Founder)

Subsidiaries:

EMF Capital (UK) Limited (1)
43 London Wall, London, EC2M 5TF,
United Kingdom
Tel.: (44) 20 7448 3540
Web Site: http://www.emfcp.com
Privater Equity Firm
N.A.I.C.S.: 523999
Peter Lovas (CEO)

Unico Sigorta A.S. (1)
Nida Kule Goztepe Is Merkezi Merdivenkoy
Mah Bora Sokak, No 1 Kat: 22 & 24, Istan-
bul, Turkiye
Tel.: (90) 216 547 75 75
Web Site: http://www.unicosigorta.com.tr

Long-Term Savings, Fund Management &
General Insurance Services
N.A.I.C.S.: 524298
Rabia Kocaaku (Head-HR & Trng)

EMFRONTIER INC.
14 F Poonglim Bldg 823 Yeoksam 1
Dong, Gangnam-Gu, Seoul, 135784,
Korea (South)
Tel.: (82) 2 3016 7300
Web Site: http://www.emfrontier.com
Year Founded: 2000
Sales Range: $25-49.9 Million
Emp.: 150
Information Technology Consulting
Services
N.A.I.C.S.: 541512
Jae Hwan Ahn (CEO)

EMG HOLDINGS LTD
5 Fornham Road, Bury St. Edmunds,,
Suffolk, IP32 6AL, United Kingdom
Tel.: (44) 01284330544
Web Site:
https://www.emgmotorgroup.com
Year Founded: 1999
Automobile Mfr
N.A.I.C.S.: 336110

Subsidiaries:

EMG Motor Group Ltd (1)
3-5 Fornham Road Bury St Edmunds, Suf-
folk, IP32 6AL, United Kingdom
Tel.: (44) 01284330544
Web Site: https://www.emgmotorgroup.com
Car Dealer
N.A.I.C.S.: 441110

Subsidiary (Domestic):

Murketts of Cambridge Limited (2)
5 Fornham Road St. Edmunds, Suf-
folk, England, IP32 6AL, United Kingdom
Tel.: (44) 01284775905
Web Site: https://www.emgmotorgroup.com
Automobile Mfr
N.A.I.C.S.: 336110

**EMGEE CABLES & COMMUNI-
CATIONS LTD.**
T-16 3rd Floor, Alankar Plaza Central
Spine Vidhyadhar Nagar, Jaipur, 302
023, India
Tel.: (91) 1413240104
Web Site:
http://www.emgeecables.com
Year Founded: 1965
Rev.: $25,747,208
Assets: $19,200,110
Liabilities: $16,496,988
Net Worth: $2,703,122
Earnings: $109,823
Emp.: 39
Fiscal Year-end: 03/31/17
Wire & cable Product Mfr
N.A.I.C.S.: 332618

EMH PARTNERS GMBH
Alter Hof Dienerstr 12, 80331, Mu-
nich, Germany
Tel.: (49) 89 2388 68 0
Web Site: http://emh.com
Investment Services
N.A.I.C.S.: 523999
Maximilian Kuss (Co-Founder & Mng
Partner)

Subsidiaries:

Cleverbridge AG (1)
Brabanter Str 2-4, Cologne, 50674, Ger-
many
Tel.: (49) 221 222 45 0
Web Site: http://www.cleverbridge.com
Sales Range: $125-149.9 Million
Emp.: 100
E-Commerce Software & Services
N.A.I.C.S.: 513210
Martin Trzaskalik (Co-Founder & CTO)

Subsidiary (US):

Cleverbridge, Inc. (2)
360 N Michigan Ave Ste 1900, Chicago, IL
60601-3805
Tel.: (312) 922-8693
Web Site: http://www.cleverbridge.com
Sales Range: $25-49.9 Million
E-Commerce Software & Services
N.A.I.C.S.: 513210
Christian Blume (Pres)

EMICO HOLDINGS BERHAD
18 Lebuhraya Kampung Jawa Bayan
Lepas, 11900, Penang, Malaysia
Tel.: (60) 46438501
Web Site: https://www.emico.com.my
EMICO—(KLS)
Rev.: $12,952,777
Assets: $18,328,507
Liabilities: $6,037,341
Net Worth: $12,291,166
Earnings: $124,159
Emp.: 221
Fiscal Year-end: 03/31/23
Property Development & Manage-
ment Services
N.A.I.C.S.: 531312
Chiew Keem P'ng (Co-Sec)

Subsidiaries:

Emico Asia Sdn. Bhd. (1)
18 Lebuhraya Kampong Jawa, Bayan
Lepas, 11900, Penang, Malaysia
Tel.: (60) 46443888
Web Site: http://www.emicoasia.com
Sales Range: $25-49.9 Million
Emp.: 8
Household Product Distr
N.A.I.C.S.: 449210
Lucinda Lim (Dir-Bus Dev)

Emico Development Sdn. Bhd. (1)
741 Jalan 1/1 Bandar Mutiara Jalan Len-
cong Timur, 8000, Sungai Petani, Kedah
Darul Aman, Malaysia
Tel.: (60) 44480888
Web Site: http://www.emicoproperty.com
Sales Range: $25-49.9 Million
Emp.: 11
Residential Building Construction Services
N.A.I.C.S.: 236116
Jimmy Ong (Mng Dir)

Emico Marketing Sdn. Bhd. (1)
Plot 18 Lebuhraya Kampung Jawa, 11900,
Bayan Lepas, Penang, Malaysia
Tel.: (60) 46448202
Sales Range: $75-99.9 Million
Emp.: 200
Trophies Distr
N.A.I.C.S.: 424990
Seifoon Kow (Mgr-HR)

Emico Melaka Sdn. Bhd. (1)
41-D Jalan Ong Kim Wee, 75300, Melaka,
Malaysia
Tel.: (60) 62847880
Sales Range: $25-49.9 Million
Emp.: 4
Clothing Apparel Retailer
N.A.I.C.S.: 458110

Emico Penang Sdn. Bhd. (1)
18 Lebuhraya Kampung Jawa, 11900,
Bayan Lepas, Penang, Malaysia
Tel.: (60) 46448202
Web Site: http://emicotrophy.com
Emp.: 200
Plastics Product Mfr
N.A.I.C.S.: 326199
Tracey Lim (Dir-Bus Dev)

**EMIDS TECHNOLOGIES PVT.
LTD. CORP.**
Survey No 3/2 Hosur Main Road,
Bommanahalli, Pune, 560068, India
Tel.: (91) 80 4098 0000   In
Web Site: http://www.emids.com
Year Founded: 1999
Healthcare Industry-Focused Informa-
tion Technology Services
N.A.I.C.S.: 541519
Saurabh Sinha (Chm)

Subsidiaries:

emids Technologies Pvt. Ltd. Corp. -
Headquarters (1)
318 Seaboard Ln Ste 110, Franklin, TN
37037
Tel.: (615) 332-7701
Web Site: http://www.emids.com
Healthcare Industry-Focused Information
Technology Services
N.A.I.C.S.: 541519
Saurabh Sinha (Founder & CEO)

Subsidiary (Domestic):

Flextech, Inc. (2)
930 Tahoe Blvd Ste 802-213, Incline Vil-
lage, NV 89451
Tel.: (616) 392-9726
Web Site: http://www.flextech.com
Sales Range: $1-9.9 Million
Emp.: 55
Custom Computer Programming Services
N.A.I.C.S.: 541511
Craig Pfent (Pres & CEO)

EMIL FREY HOLDING AG
Badenerstrasse 600, 8048, Zurich,
Switzerland
Tel.: (41) 444952111   CH
Web Site: https://www.emilfrey.ch
Year Founded: 1924
Motor Vehicles Mfr
N.A.I.C.S.: 423110
Emil Frey (Chm)

Subsidiaries:

Emil Frey Nederland NV (1)
Plesmanstraat 36, 3905KZ, Veenendaal,
Netherlands
Tel.: (31) 318581310
Web Site: https://www.emilfrey.nl
Automotive Retail Services
N.A.I.C.S.: 423110

EMILIA DEVELOPMENT LTD.
11 Menahem Begin St, Ramat Gan,
526814, Israel
Tel.: (972) 37533777
Web Site: https://www.emilia.co.il
Year Founded: 1952
EMDV—(TAE)
Rev.: $565,445,771
Assets: $718,025,959
Liabilities: $432,803,143
Net Worth: $285,222,816
Earnings: $17,032,739
Emp.: 1,800
Fiscal Year-end: 12/31/23
Freight Transportation Arrangement
N.A.I.C.S.: 488510
Oded Feller (CEO)

**EMINENCE ORGANIC SKIN
CARE INC.**
300-530 West Broadway, Vancouver,
V5Z 1E9, BC, Canada
Tel.: (604) 602-4787
Web Site:
https://www.eminenceorganics.com
Year Founded: 1958
Sales Range: $25-49.9 Million
Emp.: 200
Beauty Product Mfr
N.A.I.C.S.: 325620

EMINENT GOLD CORP.
3849 Thurston Street, Burnaby, V5H
1H9, BC, Canada
Tel.: (312) 539-0843   Ca
Web Site:
https://eminentgoldcorp.com
Year Founded: 2011
EMNT—(OTCIQ)
Assets: $1,888,492
Liabilities: $104,531
Net Worth: $1,783,961
Earnings: ($995,520)
Fiscal Year-end: 12/31/20
Metal Ore Mining Services

N.A.I.C.S.: 212290

EMINENT LUGGAGE CORP.
No 1 Sec 2 Zhongzheng S Rd, Guiren Dist, Tainan City, 711, Taiwan
Tel.: (886) 62303952
Year Founded: 1979
9950—(TPE)
Rev.: $71,679,924
Assets: $136,024,857
Liabilities: $125,905,075
Net Worth: $10,119,782
Earnings: ($7,019,823)
Fiscal Year-end: 12/31/22
Luggage Bag Product Mfr
N.A.I.C.S.: 314910
Hsieh Ming Chen (Chm & CEO)

EMINIS AMBALAJ SANAYI VE TICARET A.S.
Dilovasi Organize Sanayi Bolgesi 1 Kisim D-1003 Sokak No 4 PK, Kocaeli, 41455, Dilovasi, Turkiye
Tel.: (90) 2627545238
Web Site: https://eminis.com.tr
Year Founded: 1970
EMNIS—(IST)
Packaging Machinery Mfr
N.A.I.C.S.: 333993
Mustafa Feridun Uzunyol (Chm & Gen Mgr)

EMIRA PROPERTY FUND
1st Floor Building A Knightsbridge 33 Sloane Street, Bryanston, 2191, South Africa
Tel.: (27) 110283100
Web Site: https://www.emira.co.za
EMI—(JSE)
Rev.: $99,407,699
Assets: $960,102,812
Liabilities: $423,382,979
Net Worth: $536,719,832
Earnings: $66,181,940
Emp.: 24
Fiscal Year-end: 06/30/22
Property Trust Fund Services
N.A.I.C.S.: 525990
Ulana van Biljon (COO)

EMIRATE INTEGRATED TELE-COMMUNICATIONS COMPANY PJSC
Al Salam Tower Dubai Media City, PO Box 502666, Dubai, United Arab Emirates
Tel.: (971) 555678155
Web Site: https://www.du.ae
Year Founded: 2006
Rev.: $3,539,790,058
Assets: $4,853,716,879
Liabilities: $2,665,790,156
Net Worth: $2,187,926,724
Earnings: $465,948,149
Emp.: 1,614
Fiscal Year-end: 12/31/17
Telecommunication Services Provider
N.A.I.C.S.: 517410
Farid Faraidooni (Deputy CEO-Enterprise Solutions)

EMIRATES ADVANCED IN-VESTMENTS GROUP LLC
Emirates Post Building Khalifa Commercial Center, 29th & 54th Street, Abu Dhabi, United Arab Emirates
Tel.: (971) 2 5565027
Web Site: http://www.eaig.ae
Private Investment Firm
N.A.I.C.S.: 523999
Hussain Ibrahim Al Hammadi (Chm & CEO)

Subsidiaries:

Marmum Dairy Farm LLC **(1)**

PO Box 31671, Dubai, United Arab Emirates **(100%)**
Tel.: (971) 48326440
Web Site: http://www.marmum.ae
Dairy Products, except Dried or Canned Whslr
N.A.I.C.S.: 424430

EMIRATES CEMENT LLC
PO Box 1333, Al Ain, United Arab Emirates
Tel.: (971) 37012644   AE
Cement Mfr
N.A.I.C.S.: 327310

EMIRATES DRIVING COM-PANY PJSC
PO Box 2943, Abu Dhabi, United Arab Emirates
Tel.: (971) 25027207
Web Site: http://www.edcad.ae
Year Founded: 2000
DRIVE—(EMI)
Rev.: $56,984,003
Assets: $216,813,273
Liabilities: $25,509,027
Net Worth: $191,304,246
Earnings: $30,891,095
Fiscal Year-end: 12/31/19
Driving School Operator
N.A.I.C.S.: 611692

EMIRATES ENVIRONMENTAL GROUP
Villa No JMR 68-117A Jumeirah 1, PO Box 7013, Dubai, United Arab Emirates
Tel.: (971) 43448622
Web Site: http://www.eeg-uae.org
Year Founded: 1991
Emp.: 1,000
Environmental Protection Organization
N.A.I.C.S.: 813312
Habiba Al Marashi (Chm)

EMIRATES GLOBAL ALU-MINIUM PJSC
PO Box 3627, Dubai, United Arab Emirates
Tel.: (971) 4 884 6666
Web Site: http://www.ega.ae
Year Founded: 2014
Aluminium Smelter Operations
N.A.I.C.S.: 331410
Saeed Mohammed Al Tayer (Vice Chm)

EMIRATES INSURANCE COM-PANY
EIC Bldg Al Zahiya Tourist CLub, PO Box 3856, Abu Dhabi, United Arab Emirates
Tel.: (971) 26440400
Web Site: https://www.eminsco.com
Year Founded: 1982
EIC—(ABU)
Rev.: $308,724,203
Assets: $653,388,782
Liabilities: $305,166,893
Net Worth: $348,221,889
Earnings: $34,384,155
Emp.: 312
Fiscal Year-end: 12/31/23
Insurance Services
N.A.I.C.S.: 524128
Abdullah Mohamed Al Mazrouei (Chm)

EMIRATES INVESTMENT & DEVELOPMENT COMPANY PSC
PO Box 62220, Dubai, United Arab Emirates
Tel.: (971) 43257705
Web Site: http://www.emivest.ae

Year Founded: 1997
Private Equity Investment Services
N.A.I.C.S.: 523999
Buti Saeed Al Ghandi (Chm)

Subsidiaries:

Emivest Aerospace Corporation **(1)**
1770 Skyplace Blvd, San Antonio, TX 78216
Tel.: (210) 258-3900
Web Site:
    http://www.emivestaerospace.com
Sales Range: $100-124.9 Million
Emp.: 300
Aircraft Designer & Mfr
N.A.I.C.S.: 336411

EMIRATES ISLAMIC BANK PJSC
3rd Floor Building 16 Dubai Health-care City, PO Box 6564, Dubai, United Arab Emirates
Tel.: (971) 43834726
Web Site:
    https://www.emiratesislamic.ae
EIB—(DFM)
Rev.: $1,270,119,001
Assets: $23,908,661,573
Liabilities: $20,792,862,139
Net Worth: $3,115,799,434
Earnings: $577,547,111
Emp.: 1,720
Fiscal Year-end: 12/31/23
Banking Services
N.A.I.C.S.: 522110
Buti Obaid Buti Al Mulla (Vice Chm)

EMIRATES NATIONAL OIL COMPANY LIMITED
ENOC Complex, PO Box 6442, Dubai, United Arab Emirates
Tel.: (971) 43374400
Web Site: http://www.enoc.com
Sales Range: $500-549.9 Million
Emp.: 9,000
Producer of Oil & Related Products
N.A.I.C.S.: 213112
Sheikh Hamdan Bin Rashid Al Maktoum (Chm)

Subsidiaries:

Cylingas Company LLC **(1)**
Al Quoz Industrial Area 3 Sheikh Zayed Road, PO Box 5698, Dubai, United Arab Emirates
Tel.: (971) 4 3472648
Web Site: http://www.cylingas.ae
Gas Cylinder Mfr
N.A.I.C.S.: 332420

Dragon Oil Plc **(1)**
ENOC House II 3rd Floor Right Wing, PO Box 34666, Sheikh Rashid Road, Dubai, United Arab Emirates **(66.7%)**
Tel.: (971) 43053600
Web Site: http://www.dragonoil.com
Rev.: $1,093,057,000
Assets: $4,960,056,000
Liabilities: $1,251,852,000
Net Worth: $3,708,204,000
Earnings: $650,528,000
Emp.: 1,504
Fiscal Year-end: 12/31/2014
Oil & Gas Production & Exploration
N.A.I.C.S.: 213112
Eldar Kazimov (Deputy Gen Mgr-Turkmenistan)

ENOC Processing Company LLC **(1)**
3rd Roundabout Near Gate 2, PO Box 31288, Jebel Ali, United Arab Emirates
Tel.: (971) 4 8814400
Petroleum Product Mfr
N.A.I.C.S.: 324199
Aju Thomas (Mgr-Tech Procurement)

Emirates Gas LLC **(1)**
PO Box 7736, Dubai, United Arab Emirates
Tel.: (971) 4 267 3299
Web Site: http://www.emiratesgas.com
Gas Distr

N.A.I.C.S.: 221210
Zahed Hussain (Mgr-IT Sys)

Emirates National Oil Company Singapore Pte Ltd **(1)**
3 Temasek Avenue 24-02 Centennial Tower, Singapore, 039190, Singapore
Tel.: (65) 6235 1551
Oil Whslr
N.A.I.C.S.: 424720

Emirates Petroleum Products Company LLC **(1)**
ENOC Complex Sheikh Rashed Road, Zaabeel Area, Dubai, United Arab Emirates
Tel.: (971) 4 3372131
Gasoline Services
N.A.I.C.S.: 457120

Horizon Terminals Limited **(1)**
ENOC House, PO Box 6442, Jebel Ali, Dubai, United Arab Emirates
Tel.: (971) 43134840
Web Site: http://www.horizon-terminals.com
Logistics Consulting Servies
N.A.I.C.S.: 541614
Mounir Chouaieb (Mgr-Comml)

Subsidiary (Non-US):

Horizon Singapore Terminals Private Limited **(2)**
11 Meranti Crescent, Singapore, 627806, Singapore
Tel.: (65) 6303 8200
Petrochemical Products Mfr
N.A.I.C.S.: 325110
Cuthbert Choo (Mgr-Comml)

EMIRATES NBD PJSC
11th Floor Beniyas Road, PO Box 777, Deira, United Arab Emirates
Tel.: (971) 800456
Web Site:
    http://www.emiratesnbd.com
Year Founded: 2007
EMIRATESNBD—(DFM)
Rev.: $6,102,543,968
Assets: $186,006,690,726
Liabilities: $163,792,487,094
Net Worth: $22,214,203,633
Earnings: $3,948,047,549
Emp.: 14,000
Fiscal Year-end: 12/31/19
Commercial Banking Services
N.A.I.C.S.: 522110
Abdulla Qassem (COO)

Subsidiaries:

DenizBank A.S. **(1)**
Buyukdere Cad No 141, Esentepe, 34394, Istanbul, Turkiye **(99.85%)**
Tel.: (90) 2123482000
Web Site: http://www.denizbank.com
Rev.: $1,705,822,242
Assets: $19,304,755,571
Liabilities: $17,610,172,445
Net Worth: $1,694,583,126
Earnings: $535,163,040
Emp.: 15,609
Fiscal Year-end: 12/31/2022
Commercial & Corporate Banking Services
N.A.I.C.S.: 522110
Hakan Ates (Pres & CEO)

Subsidiary (Non-US):

DenizBank AG **(2)**
Thomas-Klestil-Platz 1, 1030, Vienna, Austria
Tel.: (43) 5051052000
Web Site: https://www.denizbank.at
Emp.: 485
Commercial Banking Services
N.A.I.C.S.: 522110
Hakan Ates (Chm-Supervisory Bd)

Diners Club UAE LLC **(1)**
Network International Building, PO Box 4487, Al Barsha 2, Dubai, United Arab Emirates
Tel.: (971) 43032431
Web Site: http://dinersclub.ae
Credit Card Issuing Services
N.A.I.C.S.: 522210

E.T.F.S. LLC **(1)**

Emirates NBD PJSC—(Continued)

PO Box 46046, Bur Dubai, Dubai, United
Arab Emirates
Tel.: (971) 4 237 3344
Web Site: http://etfs.ae
Investment Banking Services
N.A.I.C.S.: 523150

**Emirates NBD Asset Management
Ltd** (1)
8th floor East Wing The Gate Building, PO
Box 506578, Dubai International Financial
Centre, Dubai, United Arab Emirates
Web Site: https://www.emiratesnbd.com
Sales Range: $25-49.9 Million
Emp.: 50
Asset Management Services
N.A.I.C.S.: 541618

Emirates NBD Bank PJSC (1)
Baniyas Road, Deira, United Arab Emirates
Tel.: (971) 43160333
Web Site: http://www.emiratesnbd.com
Sales Range: $400-449.9 Million
Emp.: 1,700
Banking Services
N.A.I.C.S.: 522110
Ahmed Saeed Al Maktoum *(Chm)*

Subsidiary (Non-US):

**Emirates Investment Services
Ltd** (2)
Prince Mohamed bin Abdul Aziz St, PO Box
341777, Mansouriah Commercial Center,
Riyadh, 11333, Saudi Arabia
Tel.: (966) 12993600
Web Site: http://www.eisksa.com
Securities Brokerage
N.A.I.C.S.: 523150

Subsidiary (Domestic):

Network International LLC (2)
Level 1 Network Building, PO Box 4487, Al
Barsha 2, Dubai, United Arab
Emirates (51%)
Tel.: (971) 43032431
Web Site: https://www.network.ae
Commercial Banking
N.A.I.C.S.: 522110

Subsidiary (Non-US):

Emerging Markets Payments (3)
92 Tahrir Street Saridar Business Tower 3rd
Floor, Dokki, Cairo, Egypt (100%)
Tel.: (20) 2 3333 1400
Web Site: http://www.emp-group.com
Electronic Payment Software & Systems
Soutions
N.A.I.C.S.: 518210
Paul Edwards *(Exec Chm)*

Subsidiary (Domestic):

Union Properties PJSC (2)
Union Business Park 1 Green Community
East Dubai Investment Park 1, Dubai,
24649, United Arab Emirates
Tel.: (971) 800886466
Web Site: http://up.ae
Sales Range: $100-124.9 Million
Emp.: 9,110
Property Investment & Development Ser-
vices
N.A.I.C.S.: 531110
Khalifa Hasan Ali Saleh Al Hammadi *(Chm)*

Subsidiary (Domestic):

Edara L.L.C. (3)
P O Box 27642, Dubai, United Arab Emir-
ates
Tel.: (971) 44028106
Web Site: http://www.edara.ae
Sales Range: $25-49.9 Million
Emp.: 100
Project Management Services
N.A.I.C.S.: 541618

Emirates NBD Capital KSA LLC (1)
Signature Center 2nd Floor Prince Turki Al
Awwal Road, Hittin, Riyadh, 11333, Saudi
Arabia
Tel.: (966) 1 299 3900
Web Site:
http://www.emiratesnbdcapital.com.sa
Securities Brokerage Services

N.A.I.C.S.: 523150
Tariq Linjawi *(Chm)*

Emirates NBD Capital Ltd. (1)
DIFC The Gate West Wing Level 12, Dubai,
United Arab Emirates
Tel.: (971) 43032800
Investment Banking Services
N.A.I.C.S.: 523150

Emirates NBD Securities LLC (1)
2nd Fl Emirates NBD Bldg Dubai Police
Training Academy Al Wasl Road, PO Box
9409, Dubai, United Arab Emirates
Tel.: (971) 4 303 2233
Web Site: http://www.eisecurities.ae
Emp.: 37
Securities Brokerage Services
N.A.I.C.S.: 523150
Hamad Ali Almajidi *(VP)*

**Emirates NBD Trust Company (Jer-
sey) Limited** (1)
RBC Trust Company International Limited
La Motte Chambers, JE1 1PB, Saint Helier,
Jersey
Tel.: (44) 1534501000
Investment Banking Services
N.A.I.C.S.: 523150

National Bank of Dubai PJSC (1)
Floor 11 Headquarters Baniyas Road Deira,
PO Box 777, Dubai, United Arab Emirates
Tel.: (971) 43160018
Web Site: https://www.emiratesnbd.com
Sales Range: $700-749.9 Million
Emp.: 1,540
Banking Services
N.A.I.C.S.: 522110

Tanfeeth LLC (1)
Building Q Meydan Nad Al Sheba 1, PO
Box 777, Dubai, United Arab Emirates
Tel.: (971) 43843515
Banking Services
N.A.I.C.S.: 522110

EMIRATES POST
Deira Main Post Office, PO Box
99999, Dubai, United Arab Emirates
Tel.: (971) 42622222
Web Site:
http://www.emiratespost.gov.ae
Sales Range: $200-249.9 Million
Emp.: 1,500
Postal Service
N.A.I.C.S.: 491110
Yousuf Alkhaja *(Chief Happiness &
Positivity Officer & Acting Exec Dir-
Network)*

Subsidiaries:

**Wall Street Exchange Centre
L.L.C** (1)
Naif Road Deira central bldg, Dubai, United
Arab Emirates
Tel.: (971) 42284889
Web Site: http://www.wallstreet.ae
Currency Exchange Services
N.A.I.C.S.: 523160
Rajendra Srivastava *(CIO)*

Wall Street Forex London Ltd (1)
39A South Road, Southall, UB1 1SW,
Middlesex, United Kingdom
Tel.: (44) 2088679444
Web Site: http://www.wallstreetforexuk.com
Currency Exchange Services
N.A.I.C.S.: 523160

EMIRATES PROPERTIES REIT
Balgariya 132 Vh A, 1618, Sofia,
1618, Bulgaria
Tel.: (359) 878110862
Web Site: https://www.adsic-
emirates-properties.bg
EMPR—(BUL)
Sales Range: Less than $1 Million
Real Estate Investment Services
N.A.I.C.S.: 531210

EMIRATES REEM INVEST-
MENTS COMPANY P.J.S.C
Al Asayel Street Al Quoz Industrial

Area, PO Box 5567, Al Quoz, Dubai,
United Arab Emirates
Tel.: (971) 43335566 AE
Web Site: https://erc.ae
Year Founded: 1980
ERC—(DFM)
Rev.: $10,919,574
Assets: $14,366,894
Liabilities: $7,259,446
Net Worth: $7,107,448
Earnings: ($2,752,051)
Fiscal Year-end: 12/31/19
Mineral Water Mfr & Whslr
N.A.I.C.S.: 312112

EMIRATES REIT (CEIC) PLC
Level 23 - East Entrance Index Tower
DIFC, PO Box 482015, Dubai Inter-
national Financial Centre, Dubai,
United Arab Emirates
Tel.: (971) 44057348
Web Site: https://www.reit.ae
Year Founded: 2010
REIT—(NASDAQDBAI)
Rev.: $67,330,000
Assets: $929,582,000
Liabilities: $556,992,000
Net Worth: $372,590,000
Earnings: $81,990,000
Fiscal Year-end: 12/31/22
Real Estate Investment Services
N.A.I.C.S.: 525990
Abdulla Al Hamli *(Chm & Chm-Mgmt
Bd)*

EMIRATES TECHNOLOGY
COMPANY (EMITAC)
Emitac Bldg Al Ghroud, PO Box
8391, Dubai, United Arab Emirates
Tel.: (971) 42827577
Web Site: http://www.emitac.ae
Sales Range: $250-299.9 Million
Emp.: 400
Computer Technology Services
N.A.I.C.S.: 334118
Abdulrahman Bukhatir *(Chm)*

Subsidiaries:

Qatar Datamation Systems (1)
PO Box 13856, Doha, Qatar
Tel.: (974) 4439900
Sales Range: $25-49.9 Million
Emp.: 50
Computer Technology Services
N.A.I.C.S.: 334118

EMIRATES TELECOMMUNICA-
TIONS GROUP COMPAPNY
PJSC
Intersection of Zayed The 1st Street
and Sheikh Rashid Bin, PO Box
3838, Saeed Al Marktoum Street, Abu
Dhabi, United Arab Emirates
Tel.: (971) 26283333
Web Site: http://www.etisalat.com
Year Founded: 1976
EAND—(ABU)
Rev.: $14,637,180,514
Assets: $40,003,337,146
Liabilities: $26,095,512,894
Net Worth: $13,907,824,252
Earnings: $3,034,667,647
Emp.: 682
Fiscal Year-end: 12/31/23
Telecommunication Servicesb
N.A.I.C.S.: 517112
Khalifa Hassan Al Forah Al Shamsi
*(Chief Corp Strategy & Governance
Officer)*

Subsidiaries:

**Emirates Telecommunications & Ma-
rine Services FZE** (1)
Etisalat Business Center Bank Street, PO
Box 282727, Dubai, United Arab Emirates
Tel.: (971) 4 881 4433
Web Site: https://www.emarine.ae

Telecommunication Servicesb.

Maroc Telecom S.A. (1)
Avenue Annakhil Hay Riad, Rabat,
Morocco (53%)
Tel.: (212) 537719000
Web Site: https://www.iam.ma
Rev.: $1,742,148,531
Assets: $6,273,638,699
Liabilities: $4,808,163,346
Net Worth: $1,465,475,352
Earnings: $88,654,416
Fiscal Year-end: 12/31/2022
Telecommunication Servicesb
N.A.I.C.S.: 517810
Abdeslam Ahizoune *(Chm-Mgmt Bd)*

Subsidiary (Non-US):

Gabon Telecom SA (2)
Quartier Agondje Immeuble Delta Postal,
Libreville, Gabon
Tel.: (241) 78 70 00
Telecommunication Servicesb
N.A.I.C.S.: 517810

Mauritel SA (2)
Avenue Roi Faycal, BP 7000, Nouakchott,
Mauritania
Tel.: (222) 5257600
Web Site: http://www.mauritel.mr
Telecommunication Servicesb
N.A.I.C.S.: 517810

Onatel SA (2)
705 Avenue of the Nation 01, PO Box
10000, Ouagadougou, Burkina Faso
Tel.: (226) 25334001
Web Site: http://www.onatel.bf
Telecommunication Servicesb
N.A.I.C.S.: 517810

Sotelma SA (2)
Hamdallaye ACI 2000 pres du Palais des
Sports, PO Box 740, Bamako, Mali
Tel.: (223) 20215280
Web Site: https://www.moov-africa.ml
Telecommunication Servicesb
N.A.I.C.S.: 517810

EMIS GROUP PLC
Fulford Grange Micklefield Lane,
Rawdon, Leeds, LS19 6BA, United
Kingdom
Tel.: (44) 3300241269 UK
Web Site:
http://www.emisgroupplc.com
Year Founded: 2008
EMIS—(AIM)
Rev.: $228,403,805
Assets: $267,393,450
Liabilities: $92,957,658
Net Worth: $174,435,792
Earnings: $39,477,067
Emp.: 1,429
Fiscal Year-end: 12/31/21
Holding Company; Medical Software
& Record Management Services
N.A.I.C.S.: 551112
Peter Southby *(CFO)*

Subsidiaries:

EMIS Health (1)
Fulford Grange Micklefield Lane, Rawdon,
Leeds, LS19 6BA, W Yorkshire, United
Kingdom
Tel.: (44) 3300241269
Web Site: https://www.emishealth.com
Sales Range: $150-199.9 Million
Emp.: 500
Healthcare Software Development Services
N.A.I.C.S.: 541511

Division (Domestic):

**Egton Medical Information Systems
Ltd. - Egton Division** (2)
Stafford House Unit 2 Leathley Road,
Leeds, LS10 1BG, W Yorkshire, United
Kingdom
Tel.: (44) 8451245245
Web Site: http://www.egton.net
Sales Range: $150-199.9 Million
Emp.: 500
Healthcare Software Development Services

N.A.I.C.S.: 541511

Edenbridge Healthcare Limited (1)
1 Mariner Court Calder Business Park,
Wakefield, WF4 3FL, United Kingdom
Tel.: (44) 3003731246
Web Site:
https://www.edenbridgehealthcare.com
Healthcare Software Development Services
N.A.I.C.S.: 541511

Healthcare Gateway Limited (1)
Unit 3 Rawdon Park Green Lane, Rawdon,
Leeds, LS19 7BA, United Kingdom
Tel.: (44) 845 601 2642
Web Site: https://healthcaregateway.co.uk
Healtcare Services
N.A.I.C.S.: 621999
Melissa George *(Dir-Ops)*

Patient Platform Limited (1)
Fulford Grange Micklefield Lane, Rawdon,
Leeds, LS19 6BA, United Kingdom
Tel.: (44) 2037510486
Web Site: http://patient.info
Healtcare Services
N.A.I.C.S.: 621999

Pinnacle Health Partnership LLP (1)
Upper Floors 86-88 High Street, Isle of
Wight, Newport, PO30 1BH, United King-
dom
Tel.: (44) 3454506279
Web Site: https://www.phpartnership.com
Software Development Services
N.A.I.C.S.: 541511

EMIVEST BERHAD
Lot 13A Jalan PBR 1 Fasa 1, Ka-
wasan Perindustrian Bukit Rambai,
75250, Melaka, Malaysia
Tel.: (60) 63512992
Sales Range: $150-199.9 Million
Livestock Feed Mfr
N.A.I.C.S.: 311119
Shew Meng Kang *(Co-Sec)*

Subsidiaries:

Beaming Agrotrade Sdn. Bhd. (1)
No 9569 Jln Pbr 6 Fasa 1 Kaw Perindus-
trian Bkt Ramba, 75260, Melaka, Malaysia
Tel.: (60) 63512616
Animal Feed Mfr
N.A.I.C.S.: 311119

Gymtech Feedmill (M) Sdn. Bhd. (1)
Lot 13a Jalan Pbr 1 Phase 1 Kawasan Per-
industrian Bukit Rambai, 75250, Melaka,
Malaysia
Tel.: (60) 63512992
Web Site: http://www.gym-tech.com
Sales Range: $25-49.9 Million
Emp.: 150
Livestock Feed Mfr
N.A.I.C.S.: 311119

Ideal Multifeed (Malaysia) Sdn
Berhad (1)
9578 9578 Kaw Perindustrian Tangga Bt
Tanjong Kling, 76400, Melaka, Malaysia
Tel.: (60) 63518303
Sales Range: $25-49.9 Million
Emp.: 100
Livestock Feed Mfr
N.A.I.C.S.: 311119

Prima Anjung Sdn. Bhd. (1)
29 Jln Gopeng Gopeng Industrial Park,
Gopeng, 31600, Perak, Malaysia
Tel.: (60) 53576088
Sales Range: $25-49.9 Million
Emp.: 70
Animal Farming Services
N.A.I.C.S.: 115210
Law Jui Peng *(Mng Dir)*

United Global Resources Limited (1)
1st 2nd and Pent Floor 86 A Allen Avenue,
Ikeja, Lagos, Nigeria
Tel.: (234) 17900854
Web Site: http://www.ugrl.net
Computer Education & Training Services
N.A.I.C.S.: 611420

EMKA JSC
30 Nikola Petkov Str, 5400, Sevlievo,
Bulgaria

Tel.: (359) 67532868
Web Site: https://www.emka-bg.com
Year Founded: 1936
EMKA—(BUL)
Sales Range: Less than $1 Million
Cable & Wires Mfr
N.A.I.C.S.: 332618

EMKA-BESCHLAGTEILE GMBH & CO. KG
Langenberger Str 32, Velbert, 42551,
Germany
Tel.: (49) 20512730
Web Site: http://www.emka.com
Year Founded: 1932
Sales Range: $200-249.9 Million
Emp.: 1,050
Lock & Security Systems Mfr
N.A.I.C.S.: 561621
Friedhelm Runge *(Owner & Mng Dir)*

Subsidiaries:

EMKA (UK) Ltd. (1)
Patricia House Bodmin Road, Coventry,
CV2 5DG, United Kingdom
Tel.: (44) 24 766 16505
Web Site: http://www.emka.co.uk
Emp.: 20
Hardware Mfr
N.A.I.C.S.: 332510
Andy Billingham *(Mng Dir)*

EMKA Benelux B.V. (1)
Marconiweg 2, 5466 AS, Veghel, Nether-
lands
Tel.: (31) 413 323510
Web Site: http://www.emka.com
Emp.: 16
Hardware Whslr
N.A.I.C.S.: 423710
Rob Van Leeuwarden *(Pres)*

EMKA Beschlagteile AG (1)
Kammistr 5, 3800, Interlaken, Switzerland
Tel.: (41) 33 826 02 20
Web Site: http://www.emka.ch
Hardware Whslr
N.A.I.C.S.: 423710

EMKA Beschlagteile Ges.m.b.H. (1)
Intercity Park 4, 2421, Kittsee, Austria
Tel.: (43) 2143 4 30 63
Web Site: http://www.emka-beschlagteile.at
Hardware Whslr
N.A.I.C.S.: 423710

EMKA Beschlagteile Iberica S.L. (1)
Pol Ind Planarresano Carretera de Prejano
n 78, Arnedo, 26580, La Rioja, Spain
Tel.: (34) 672 262672
Web Site: http://www.emka-iberica.es
Hardware Mfr
N.A.I.C.S.: 332510

EMKA Beschlagteile SRL (1)
Soseaua Alba Iulia 110, 550052, Sibiu, Ro-
mania
Tel.: (40) 269 222700
Web Site: http://www.emka.ro
Hardware Whslr
N.A.I.C.S.: 423710

EMKA Bosnia d.o.o. (1)
Ibrahima Popovica br 32, 73000, Gorazde,
Bosnia & Herzegovina
Tel.: (387) 38 241 310
Web Site: http://www.emka.ba
Hardware Mfr
N.A.I.C.S.: 332510

EMKA France SA (1)
Parc d activite Megazone Moselle Est,
57450, Henriville, France
Tel.: (33) 3 87 29 66 66
Web Site: http://www.emka-france.com
Hardware Mfr
N.A.I.C.S.: 332510
Kuklinski Ullerich *(Gen Mgr)*

EMKA Inc. (1)
1961 Fulling Mill Rd, Middletown, PA 17057
Tel.: (717) 986-1111
Web Site: http://www.emkausa.com
Hardware Mfr
N.A.I.C.S.: 332510
Scott Ulp *(Territory Mgr)*

EMKA India Panel Accessories Pvt
Ltd (1)
No 32/33/5 3rd Floor Annapoorna Industrial
Compound Kanakapura Road, Jaragana-
halli, Bengaluru, 560 078, Karnataka, India
Tel.: (91) 80 26660212
Web Site: http://www.emka.in
Hardware Whslr
N.A.I.C.S.: 423710
S. M. Venkatraman *(Exec Mgr)*

EMKA Industrial Hardware Co.
Ltd. (1)
No 15 Fuyuan Road Wuqing Development
Area, Tianjin, 301700, China
Tel.: (86) 22 82 12 37 59
Web Site: http://www.emka.cn
Hardware Mfr
N.A.I.C.S.: 332510

EMKA Italia S.r.l. (1)
Via Isidora 10, Lazise, 37017, Verona, Italy
Tel.: (39) 045 6471070
Web Site: http://www.emka.it
Hardware Whslr
N.A.I.C.S.: 423710

EMKA Kilit Sistemleri Metal San. ve
Tic. Ltd. Sti. (1)
IMES Organize Sanayi Bolgesi 10 Cadde
No 41, Cerkesli-Dilovasi, 41455, Kocaeli,
Turkiye
Tel.: (90) 262 290 90 97
Web Site: http://www.emkakilit.com.tr
Hardware Whslr
N.A.I.C.S.: 423710

EMKA Mexico Beschlagteile S. de
R.L. de C.V. (1)
Ano de Juarez No 340 Of 10 Col Granjas
San Antonio, Iztapalapa, 09070, Mexico,
Mexico
Tel.: (52) 55 54469664
Web Site: http://www.emka.mx
Hardware Whslr
N.A.I.C.S.: 423710

EMKA Middle East LLC (1)
PO Box 36293, Dubai, United Arab Emir-
ates
Tel.: (971) 4 2844 528
Web Site: http://www.emka.ae
Hardware Whslr
N.A.I.C.S.: 423710
V. A. Shaffi *(Reg Mgr)*

EMKA Okovi d.o.o. (1)
Branimirova 64, 35000, Slavonski Brod,
Croatia
Tel.: (385) 35 27 00 73
Web Site: http://www.emka-okovi.hr
Hardware Whslr
N.A.I.C.S.: 423710

EMKA Polska Sp. z. o. o. (1)
ul Katowicka 72, 41-406, Myslowice, Poland
Tel.: (48) 326663300
Web Site: http://www.emka.com
Hardware Whslr
N.A.I.C.S.: 423710

EMKA Scandinavia AB (1)
Industrigatan 10 B, 55302, Jonkoping, Swe-
den
Tel.: (46) 36 31 41 30
Web Site: http://www.emka.com
Hardware Whslr
N.A.I.C.S.: 423710

Emka Hellas S.A. (1)
47-49 Hatzikiriakou Ave, 185-38, Piraeus,
Greece
Tel.: (30) 21041 83183
Web Site: http://www.emka-hellas.com
Hardware Whslr
N.A.I.C.S.: 423710

Fort Securite s.a. (1)
Megazone de Freyming Merlebach Zone
Industrielle, BP 12, 57450, Henriville,
France
Tel.: (33) 387 29 6666
Web Site: http://www.emka.com
Sales Range: $25-49.9 Million
Emp.: 50
Security System Mfr
N.A.I.C.S.: 332510
Kudulenske Ulreca *(Gen Mgr)*

ILS Speth GmbH (1)

Industriestr 21 - 23, 42327, Wuppertal, Ger-
many
Tel.: (49) 202 74 96 0
Web Site: http://www.ils-fertigungstechnik.de
Hardware Mfr
N.A.I.C.S.: 332510

EMKAY GLOBAL FINANCIAL SERVICES LIMITED
7th Floor The Ruby Senapati Bapat
Marg, Dadar - West, Mumbai,
400028, India
Tel.: (91) 2266121212
Web Site:
https://www.emkayglobal.com
Year Founded: 1995
EMKAY—(NSE)
Rev.: $22,520,412
Assets: $77,101,097
Liabilities: $54,387,633
Net Worth: $22,713,464
Earnings: $1,519,641
Emp.: 424
Fiscal Year-end: 03/31/21
Securities Brokerage & Investment
Banking Services
N.A.I.C.S.: 523150
Sushil Kumar Saboo Madan Lal
(Chm)

EMKAY TAPS & CUTTING TOOLS LTD.
Plot No B-27 and B-27/1 MIDC
Hingna, Industrial Estate, Nagpur,
440016, Maharashtra, India
Tel.: (91) 7104237584
Web Site: https://www.etctl.com
Year Founded: 1995
EMKAYTOOLS—(NSE)
Rev.: $8,959,399
Assets: $21,677,232
Liabilities: $1,782,388
Net Worth: $19,894,844
Earnings: $3,252,530
Emp.: 71
Fiscal Year-end: 03/31/21
Cutting Tool Mfr
N.A.I.C.S.: 333515
Ajayprakash Kanoria *(Chm & Mng
Dir)*

EML PAYMENTS LIMITED
Level 12 333 Ann Street, Brisbane,
4000, QLD, Australia
Tel.: (61) 735571100   AU
Web Site:
https://www.emlpayments.com
EML—(ASX)
Rev.: $145,126,869
Assets: $1,658,579,721
Liabilities: $1,552,395,159
Net Worth: $106,184,562
Earnings: ($6,417,601)
Emp.: 458
Fiscal Year-end: 06/30/24
Financial Services
N.A.I.C.S.: 522210
Paul Wenk *(Gen Counsel-)*

Subsidiaries:

EML Payment Solutions Limited (1)
Level 12 333 Ann Street, Brisbane, 4000,
QLD, Australia
Tel.: (61) 73 557 1100
Payment Solutions Services
N.A.I.C.S.: 541511

Flex-e-Card Limited (1)
2 St James Gate, Newcastle upon Tyne,
NE1 4BE, United Kingdom
Tel.: (44) 844 774 4277
Web Site: https://www.flex-e-card.com
Card Transaction Processing Services
N.A.I.C.S.: 522320

Sentenial B.V.B.A. (1)
Lenniksebaan 451, B-1070, Brussels, Bel-
gium
Tel.: (32) 28948286

EML Payments Limited—(Continued)

Payment Financial Services
N.A.I.C.S.: 522320

Sentenial Limited (1)
4th Floor 35 Great, St Helens, London,
EC3A 6AP, United Kingdom
Tel.: (44) 2034811260
Payment Financial Services
N.A.I.C.S.: 522320

Sentenial S.A.R.L. (1)
4 Place Louis Armand, 75012, Paris,
France
Tel.: (33) 567806081
Payment & Banking Services
N.A.I.C.S.: 522110

Store Financial Services, LLC (1)
7171 W 95th St, Overland Park, KS 66212
Tel.: (913) 648-2214
Web Site: http://www.storefinancial.com
Rev.: $5,100,000
Emp.: 65
Data Processing, Hosting & Related Services
N.A.I.C.S.: 518210
Michelle Young (VP-Mktg & Sls Support)

EMLAK KATILIM VARLIK KIRALAMA A.S.
Barbaros Mah Begonya Sok No 9/A,
Atasehir, Istanbul, Turkiye
Tel.: (90) 2162662626
Web Site:
http://www.emlakkatilimvks.com.tr
EKTVK—(IST)
Real Estate Investment Services
N.A.I.C.S.: 531190
Abdullah Erdem Cantimur (Chm)

EMLAK KONUT GAYRIMENKUL YATIRIM ORTAKLIGI AS
Barbaros Mah Mor Sumbul Sok No
7/2 B, Atasehir, Istanbul, Turkiye
Tel.: (90) 2165791515
Web Site:
https://www.emlakkonut.com
Year Founded: 1953
EKGYO—(IST)
Rev.: $250,894,998
Assets: $1,450,454,171
Liabilities: $883,110,871
Net Worth: $567,343,300
Earnings: $92,574,107
Emp.: 563
Fiscal Year-end: 12/31/22
Residential Property Developer & Investment Services
N.A.I.C.S.: 237210
Ertan Keles (Chm)

Subsidiaries:

**Emlak Konut Asansor Sistemleri
Sanayi ve Ticaret A.S.** (1)
Finanskent Mahallesi Finans Caddesi Sarphan, Finanspark Plaza No 5/A Kat 7 Umraniye, Istanbul, Turkiye
Tel.: (90) 8505024747
Web Site: https://www.ekaelevator.com
Elevator Mfr & Distr
N.A.I.C.S.: 333921

EMMA VILLAS S.P.A.
Via Antonio Bertoloni 8, 00142,
Rome, Italy
Tel.: (39) 05781901639
Web Site:
https://www.emmavillas.com
Year Founded: 2006
EAV—(EUR)
Real Estate Development Services
N.A.I.C.S.: 531190

EMMAR INVESTMENTS & REAL ESTATE DEVELOPMENT COMPANY
Zahran Street-6th Circle-Emmar Towers Building A 2nd Floor, Amman,
11195, Jordan

Tel.: (962) 65777251
Web Site: http://www.emmar.jo
Year Founded: 2005
EMAR—(AMM)
Rev.: $539,907
Assets: $16,409,416
Liabilities: $5,711,644
Net Worth: $10,697,772
Earnings: ($586,595)
Emp.: 8
Fiscal Year-end: 12/31/21
Real Estate Development Services
N.A.I.C.S.: 531390
Munjed Sukhtian (Chm)

EMMBI INDUSTRIES LIMITED
99/2/1 and 9 Madhuban Industrial
Estate Madhuban Dam Road, Rakholi
Union Territory of Dadra and Nagar
Haveli, Silvassa, 396230, India
Tel.: (91) 2246725555
Web Site: https://emmbi.com
Year Founded: 1994
533161—(BOM)
Rev.: $43,658,024
Assets: $44,838,203
Liabilities: $26,388,726
Net Worth: $18,449,477
Earnings: $1,047,501
Emp.: 250
Fiscal Year-end: 03/31/21
Jumbo Bags & Woven Sacks Mfr &
Sales
N.A.I.C.S.: 314910
Makrand M. Appalwar (Chm & Mng Dir)

EMMENDINGER MASCHINENBAU GMBH
Am Elzdamm 32, Emmendingen,
79312, Germany
Tel.: (49) 764192420
Web Site:
http://www.emmendinger.de
Year Founded: 1957
Rev.: $12,414,600
Emp.: 75
Engineering Parts Mfr
N.A.I.C.S.: 423690
Jurgen Stadler (Mng Dir)

EMMERSON PLC
55 Athol Street, Douglas, Isle of Man,
IM1 1LA, United Kingdom
Tel.: (44) 71383204 IM
Web Site:
https://www.emmersonplc.com
Year Founded: 2016
EML—(AIM)
Assets: $23,510,000
Liabilities: $350,000
Net Worth: $23,160,000
Earnings: ($2,990,000)
Fiscal Year-end: 12/31/23
Investment Brokerage Services
N.A.I.C.S.: 523150
Robert Wrixon (Exec Dir)

EMMERSON RESOURCES LIMITED
Level 2 43 Ventnor Avenue, West
Perth, 6005, WA, Australia
Tel.: (61) 893817838
Web Site:
https://www.emmerson.com.au
ERM—(ASX)
Rev.: $289,123
Assets: $3,808,787
Liabilities: $627,787
Net Worth: $3,181,000
Earnings: ($1,961,941)
Emp.: 20
Fiscal Year-end: 06/30/24
Minerals Exploration
N.A.I.C.S.: 213115
Robert Bills (CEO & Mng Dir)

EMMESSAR BIOTECH & NUTRITION LTD.
29 Kamer Building 4th Floor 38 Oawasji Patel Street Fort, Mumbai, 400
001, Maharashtra, India
Tel.: (91) 9004870100
Web Site: https://www.ebnl.org
524768—(BOM)
Rev.: $1,154,300
Assets: $1,065,591
Liabilities: $287,436
Net Worth: $778,155
Earnings: $197,890
Fiscal Year-end: 00/31/21
Chemical Products Mfr
N.A.I.C.S.: 325180
Mathurakavi Srinivasa Raghavan
Ayyangar (Founder, CEO & Mng Dir)

EMMI AG
Landenbergrstrasse 1, CH-6005, Lucerne, Switzerland
Tel.: (41) 582272727 CH
Web Site: http://group.emmi.com
EMMN—(SWX)
Rev.: $4,689,588,692
Assets: $2,921,772,727
Liabilities: $1,498,373,614
Net Worth: $1,423,399,113
Earnings: $202,379,157
Emp.: 9,368
Fiscal Year-end: 12/31/22
Dairy & Creamery Products Producer
N.A.I.C.S.: 112120
Urs Riedener (Chm)

Subsidiaries:

A-27 S.p.A. (1)
Via Vittor Pisani 20,124, Milan, Italy
Tel.: (39) 0332999811
Web Site: http://www.a27.it
Pastry Dessert Mfr
N.A.I.C.S.: 311813

AVH Dairy Trade B.V. (1)
Stationsplein 63, 1703 WE, Heerhugowaard, Netherlands
Tel.: (31) 725020946
Web Site: https://www.avhdairy.com
Milk Product Distr
N.A.I.C.S.: 424430
Franck Van Dalen (Mng Dir)

Baumann Kase AG (1)
Zurichstrasse 9, CH-3052, Zollikofen, Switzerland
Tel.: (41) 582272828
Web Site: https://www.baumann-kaese.ch
Cheese Distr
N.A.I.C.S.: 424430

Bettinehoeve B.V. (1)
Nieuwe Donk 6, 4879 AC, Etten-Leur, Netherlands
Tel.: (31) 765022247
Web Site: https://www.bettine.nl
Milk Product Distr
N.A.I.C.S.: 424430
Rico Ter Voert (Mgr-Sls & Export)

Cowgirl Creamery (1)
2080 Lakeville Hwy, Petaluma, CA 94954
Tel.: (707) 789-9433
Web Site: http://www.cowgirlcreamery.com
Sales Range: $1-9.9 Million
Emp.: 30
Specialty Food Stores
N.A.I.C.S.: 445298
Sue Connley (Co-Founder)

Cypress Grove Chevre, Inc. (1)
1330 Q St, Arcata, CA 95521
Tel.: (707) 825-1100
Web Site:
https://www.cypressgrovecheese.com
Restaurant Operators
N.A.I.C.S.: 722511
Mary Keehn (Founder)

Emmi Benelux B.V. (1)
Zuiderhavenweg 4, 4004 JJ, Tiel, Netherlands
Tel.: (31) 344744400
Web Site: https://benelux.emmi.com

Emp.: 5,500
Dairy Products Mfr
N.A.I.C.S.: 311514
Barend Van Kesteren (Gen Mgr)

Emmi Canada Inc. (1)
1250 Nobel Street Suite 200, Boucherville,
J4B 5H1, QC, Canada
Web Site: http://www.ca.emmi.com
Emp.: 20
Dairy Products Mfr
N.A.I.C.S.: 311514
Patrick Méunier (VP-Sls & Mktg-Natl)

Emmi Dessert Italia S.p.A (1)
Via Gascinetta 44, Gattico, 28013, Gattico-Veruno, NO, Italy
Tel.: (39) 03221918111
Web Site: https://www.emmidessert.it
Emp.: 450
Pastry Dessert Mfr
N.A.I.C.S.: 311813

Emmi Deutschland GmbH (1)
Im Teelbruch 130, 45219, Essen, Germany
Tel.: (49) 20189045800
Web Site: https://group.emmi.com
Dairy Products Mfr
N.A.I.C.S.: 311514
Elisabeth Wagner-Wehrborn (Mng Dir)

Emmi Osterreich GmbH (1)
Illweg 8, Nuziders, A-6714, Bludenz, Austria
Tel.: (43) 555262232
Web Site: https://group.emmi.com
Emp.: 53
Dairy Products Mfr
N.A.I.C.S.: 311514
Bernd Kammerlander (Head-Fin, Acct & HR)

Emmi Roth USA Inc. (1)
5525 Nobel Dr Ste 100, Fitchburg, WI
53711
Tel.: (608) 285-9800
Web Site: http://www.emmiroth.com
Cheese Mfr
N.A.I.C.S.: 311513
Kerry Olson (VP-FoodSvcs Sls)

Emmi Roth USA Inc. (1)
1325 6th Ave, Monroe, WI 53566
Tel.: (608) 328-2122
Web Site: http://www.emmiroth.com
Cheese Mfr
N.A.I.C.S.: 311513
Kerry Olson (VP-FoodSvcs Sls)

Emmi UK Limited (1)
111 Upper Richmond Road, Putney, London, SW15 2TJ, United Kingdom
Tel.: (44) 2084325480
Web Site: https://group.emmi.com
Emp.: 25
Dairy Products Mfr
N.A.I.C.S.: 311514
Julie Plant (Mng Dir)

Goat Milk Powder B.V. (1)
Stationsplein 63, 1703 WE, Heerhugowaard, Netherlands
Tel.: (31) 725020946
Web Site: http://www.goatmilkpowder.com
Milk Product Distr
N.A.I.C.S.: 424430

Italian Fresh Foods S.p.A. (1)
Via Cassina 5, Lasnigo, 22030, Como, Italy
Tel.: (39) 0321031131
Web Site: http://www.italianfreshfoods.it
Frozen Dessert Mfr
N.A.I.C.S.: 311520

Jackson-Mitchell, Inc. (1)
PO Box 934, Turlock, CA 95381
Tel.: (209) 667-2019
Web Site: https://www.meyenberg.com
Sales Range: $25-49.9 Million
Emp.: 30
Dairy Products Distr
N.A.I.C.S.: 311511
Carol Jackson (CMO & VP)

Kaiku Km0 S.L. (1)
Pole Ind Aparcabisa, 48510, Valle de Trapaga, Spain
Tel.: (34) 944180956
Web Site: http://www.kaikukm0.rest
Food Products Distr
N.A.I.C.S.: 424490

Kaserei Studer AG (1)
Romanshornerstrasse 253, Hefenhofen TG,
8580, Amriswil, Switzerland
Tel.: (41) 582273060
Web Site: https://www.kaeserei-studer.ch
Cheese Distr
N.A.I.C.S.: 424430
Mathias Lustenberger (Gen Sls Mgr)

Lesa Lataria Engiadinaisa SA (1)
Via Charels Suot 18, CH-7502, Bever, Swit-
zerland
Tel.: (41) 818524545
Web Site: https://www.lesa.ch
Dairy Products Mfr
N.A.I.C.S.: 311514

Llet Nostra Alimentaria S.L. (1)
C/Valencia Num 3B Central Pavilion, 08015,
Barcelona, Spain
Tel.: (34) 932265794
Web Site: https://www.lletnostra.cat
Milk Product Distr
N.A.I.C.S.: 424430
Marta Domingo Enrich (Product Mgr)

Molkerei Biedermann AG (1)
Steigstrasse 2, 9220, Bischofszell, Switzer-
land
Tel.: (41) 582275656
Web Site: http://biomolkerei.ch
Dairy Products Mfr
N.A.I.C.S.: 311514

Rachelli Italia S.r.l. (1)
Via Leonardo Da Vinci 10, 20016, Pero,
Milan, Italy
Tel.: (39) 0238100444
Web Site: http://www.rachelli.com
Ice Cream Parlor Services
N.A.I.C.S.: 722515

**Redwood Hill Farm & Creamery,
Inc.** (1)
2064 Gravenstein Hwy N Bldg 1 Ste 130,
Sebastopol, CA 95472
Tel.: (707) 823-8250
Web Site: https://redwoodhill.com
Sales Range: $1-9.9 Million
Emp.: 32
Dairy Products Mfr
N.A.I.C.S.: 311514
Rich Martin (Mng Dir)

Regio Molkerei Beider Basel AG (1)
Flachsackerstrasse 100, 4402, Frenkendorf,
Switzerland
Tel.: (41) 582273030
Web Site: https://www.regiomolkerei.ch
Emp.: 13
Milk Product Distr
N.A.I.C.S.: 445298

Tomales Bay Foods Inc. (1)
2080 Lakeville Hwy, Petaluma, CA 94954
Tel.: (707) 789-9433
Web Site: https://www.tomalesbayfoods.com
Cheese Product Whslr
N.A.I.C.S.: 424430
Debra Dickerson (Mgr-Sls)

EMMSONS INTERNATIONAL LIMITED
10112 Community Centre
Zamarudpur, New Delhi, 110048,
India
Tel.: (91) 1129247721
Web Site: https://www.emmsons.com
532038—(BOM)
Sales Range: Less than $1 Million
Emp.: 72
Food Products Distr
N.A.I.C.S.: 311999
Anil Monga (Co-Founder & Mng Dir)

Subsidiaries:

Emmsons Asia Pte. Ltd. (1)
150 Cecil St 07-01 AXA Life Bldg, Singa-
pore, 069543, Singapore
Tel.: (65) 62212090
Grain Farming Services
N.A.I.C.S.: 111199

EMNET INC.
14F Daeryung PostTower III Digital-ro

34-gil 27, Guro-gu, Seoul, Korea
(South)
Tel.: (82) 222778877
Web Site: https://www.emnet.co.kr
Year Founded: 2000
123570—(KRS)
Rev.: $33,910,073
Assets: $98,346,508
Liabilities: $26,376,578
Net Worth: $71,969,929
Earnings: $5,154,422
Emp.: 354
Fiscal Year-end: 12/31/22
Advetising Agency
N.A.I.C.S.: 541810
Young-Won Kim (CEO)

Subsidiaries:

eMnet Japan Co., Ltd. (1)
10F Nitto Nishi-Shinjuku Building 6-10-1
Nishi-Shinjuku, Shinjuku-Ku, Tokyo, 160-
0023, Japan
Tel.: (81) 362794111
Web Site: https://www.emnet.co.jp
Advertising Agency Services
N.A.I.C.S.: 541810
Shinichiro Yamamoto (Chm, Pres & CEO)

EMNI CO., LTD
Rm 306 308 705 Haean-ro, Sangnok-
gu, Ansan, Gyeonggi-do, Korea
(South)
Tel.: (82) 313269941
Web Site: https://www.emni.co.kr
Year Founded: 1999
083470—(KRS)
Rev.: $26,440,775
Assets: $15,031,753
Liabilities: $5,456,045
Net Worth: $9,575,708
Earnings: ($93,909)
Emp.: 28
Fiscal Year-end: 12/31/22
Backlight Unit Mfr
N.A.I.C.S.: 334419

Subsidiaries:

Juken Kogyo Co. Ltd. (1)
140-1 Komukai cho aza Kitakomukai, Toyo-
hashi, 441-8003, Aichi, Japan
Tel.: (81) 532312061
Web Site: https://en.juken.com
Electronic Components Mfr
N.A.I.C.S.: 334419

Juken Optics (Yantai) Co. Ltd. (1)
No 19 Sanghai Road Development Zone,
Yantai, 264006, Shandong, China
Tel.: (86) 5352163366
Electronic Components Mfr
N.A.I.C.S.: 334419

**Juken Technology (Dong-Guan) Co.
Ltd.** (1)
The Zhengchong Industrial Development
Zone, Shatou Chang-an Town, Dongguan,
Shandong, China
Tel.: (86) 76985093538
Electronic Components Mfr
N.A.I.C.S.: 334419

**Juken Technology (Huizhou) Co.
Ltd.** (1)
Block A Wu Yi Industrial Zone, ChenJing
Town, Huizhou, 516229, Guangdong, China
Tel.: (86) 7523896360
Electronic Components Mfr
N.A.I.C.S.: 334419

**Juken Technology Engineering Sdn.
Bhd.** (1)
Lot 12 Jalan BRP 9/1C Bukit Rahman Putra
Industrial Park, 47000, Sungai Buloh, Se-
langor, Malaysia
Tel.: (60) 361562386
Electronic Components Mfr
N.A.I.C.S.: 334419

KJ Pretech Asia Holding Co. Ltd. (1)
R1103 11/F CFC Tower 22-28 Mody Road,
Tsim Sha Tsui, Kowloon, China (Hong
Kong)
Tel.: (852) 27210777

Electronic Components Mfr
N.A.I.C.S.: 334419

Taiwan Juken Co. Ltd. (1)
No 14 Ching Ho Street Tuu Cherng City,
Taipei, Taiwan
Tel.: (886) 222605966
Electronic Components Mfr
N.A.I.C.S.: 334419

EMO
12 Whiteladies Rd, Clifton, BS8 1PD,
Bristol, United Kingdom
Tel.: (44) 117 311 9009   UK
Web Site: http://www.emo.uk.com
Year Founded: 1977
Rev.: $15,000,000
Emp.: 20
N.A.I.C.S.: 541810
Glenn Orr (Chm)

EMOVA GROUP
145 Rue Jean Jacques Rousseau,
92130, Paris, France
Tel.: (33) 180002034   FR
Web Site: https://www.emova-
group.com
Year Founded: 1965
ALEMV—(EUR)
Sales Range: $25-49.9 Billion
Florist Shop Owner & Operator
N.A.I.C.S.: 459310
Laurent Pfeiffer (CEO)

EMP METALS CORP.
208A - 980 West 1st Street, North
Vancouver, V7P 3N4, BC, Canada
Tel.: (604) 689-7422   Ca
Web Site: https://empmetals.com
Year Founded: 2018
EMPPF—(CNSX)
Rev.: $279
Assets: $461,501
Liabilities: $35,314
Net Worth: $426,187
Earnings: ($2,873,391)
Fiscal Year-end: 04/30/21
Metal Mining & Exploration Services
N.A.I.C.S.: 213114
Robin Gamley (Pres & CEO)

EMP. CONST. MOLLER Y PEREZ-COTAPOS S.A.
Av Los Leones 957, Providencia,
Santiago, Chile
Web Site: http://www.mpc.cl
MOLLER—(SGO)
Sales Range: Less than $1 Million
Engineering & Construction Services
N.A.I.C.S.: 541330
Marcos Retamal Munoz (CEO)

EMPEE DISTILLERIES LIMITED
Empee Tower No 59 Harris Road
Pudupet, Chennai, 600 002, India
Tel.: (91) 44 2853 1111
Web Site:
    http://www.empeegroup.co.in
Rev.: $97,023,291
Assets: $126,627,233
Liabilities: $89,709,593
Net Worth: $36,917,640
Earnings: ($13,150,627)
Emp.: 536
Fiscal Year-end: 03/31/18
Alcoholic Beverages Mfr
N.A.I.C.S.: 312140
M. P. Purushothaman (Founder)

Subsidiaries:

EDL Properties Limited (1)
59 Harris Road, Pudupet, Chennai, 600
002, India
Tel.: (91) 44 28522510
Web Site: http://www.edlproperties.in
Sales Range: $25-49.9 Million
Emp.: 4

Residential & Commercial Property Devel-
opment Services
N.A.I.C.S.: 236117
M. P. Purushothaman (Chm & Mng Dir)

EMPEE SUGARS & CHEMICALS LTD.
Empee Tower No 59 Harris Road
Pudupet, Chennai, 600 002, India
Tel.: (91) 4428531111
Sugar Mfr
N.A.I.C.S.: 311314
M. P. Purushothaman (Chm & Mng
Dir)

EMPERIA HOLDING S.A
ul Projektowa 2 Building B, 02-566,
Warsaw, Poland
Tel.: (48) 817451778
Web Site: http://www.emperia.pl
Year Founded: 2002
Rev.: $738,463,245
Assets: $327,794,396
Liabilities: $141,082,963
Net Worth: $186,711,434
Earnings: $9,992,433
Emp.: 8,610
Fiscal Year-end: 12/31/17
Food Products Whslr & Retailer
N.A.I.C.S.: 445298

Subsidiaries:

Ambra Sp. z o.o. (1)
Ul Hutnicza 7, 43-502, Czechowice-
Dziedzice, Silesian, Poland
Tel.: (48) 322144340
Web Site: http://www.ambra-czechowice.pl
Cosmetics Distr
N.A.I.C.S.: 424990

Detal Koncept Sp. z o.o. (1)
ul Melgiewska 7-9, 20-952, Lublin, Poland
Tel.: (48) 817465757
Web Site: http://www.detalkoncept.pl
Fast Moving Consumer Goods Distr
N.A.I.C.S.: 425120

Emperia Info Sp. z o.o. (1)
Ul Melgiewska 7-9, 20-952, Lublin, Poland
Tel.: (48) 817450024
Web Site: http://www.dls.pl
Sales Range: $25-49.9 Million
Emp.: 108
Enterprise Management Software Develop-
ment Services
N.A.I.C.S.: 541511

Euro Sklep S.A. (1)
Ul Bystrzanska 94/A, 43-309, Bielsko-Biala,
Silesian, Poland
Tel.: (48) 338150204
Web Site: http://www.eurosklep.eu
Delicatessens Retailer
N.A.I.C.S.: 445110

Groszek Sp.z.o.o (1)
Melgiewska 7-9, 20-952, Lublin,
Poland   (100%)
Tel.: (48) 817465757
Web Site: http://www.groszek.com.pl
Supermarkets & Grocery Stores
N.A.I.C.S.: 445110

**Lewiatan Czestochowa Sp. z
o.o.** (1)
Ul Wreczycka 22 /26, 42-200, Czesto-
chowa, Silesian, Poland
Tel.: (48) 343694013
Supermarkets Operation Services
N.A.I.C.S.: 445110

Lewiatan Holding S.A. (1)
ul Kilinskiego 10, 87-800, Wloclawek, Wlo-
clawek, Poland
Tel.: (48) 544127821
Web Site: http://www.lewiatan.pl
Sales Range: $25-49.9 Million
Emp.: 40
Grocery Stores Operation Services
N.A.I.C.S.: 445110

Lewiatan Kujawy Sp. z o.o. (1)
Komunalna 6, 87-800, Wloclawek,
Kuyavian-Pomeranian, Poland
Tel.: (48) 54 411 30 45
Web Site: http://www.kujawy.lewiatan.pl

EMPERIA HOLDING S.A

Emperia Holding S.A—(Continued)

Grocery Stores Operation Services
N.A.I.C.S.: 445110

Lewiatan Slask Sp. z o.o. **(1)**
Ul Lenartowicza 39, Sosnowiec, 41219,
Silesian, Poland
Tel.: (48) 322947025
Web Site: http://www.slask.lewiatan.pl
Sales Range: $25-49.9 Million
Emp.: 30
Grocery Stores Operation Services
N.A.I.C.S.: 445110

Lewiatan-Orbita Sp.z o.o. **(1)**
Ul Lubelska 33, 10-080, Olsztyn, Warmian-
Masurian, Poland
Tel.: (48) 895328242
Web Site: http://www.orbita.lewiatan.pl
Grocery Stores Operation Services
N.A.I.C.S.: 445110

Maro Markety Sp. z o.o. **(1)**
Ul Skwierzynska 20, 61-615, Poznan, Po-
land
Tel.: (48) 618204204
Web Site: http://www.maromarkety.pl
Sales Range: $100-124.9 Million
Emp.: 400
Delicatessens Retailer
N.A.I.C.S.: 445110

Subsidiary (Domestic):

Lewiatan Opole Sp. z o.o. **(2)**
ul Swiatowida 2, 45-325, Opole, Poland
Tel.: (48) 774416505
Web Site: http://www.opole.lewiatan.pl
Sales Range: $25-49.9 Million
Emp.: 15
Grocery Stores Operation Services
N.A.I.C.S.: 445110

Lewiatan Wielkopolska Sp. z o.o. **(2)**
Winiary 54, 60-479, Poznan, Poland
Tel.: (48) 618460890
Web Site:
http://www.wielkopolska.lewiatan.pl
Sales Range: $25-49.9 Million
Emp.: 15
Grocery Stores Operation Services
N.A.I.C.S.: 445110
Jolanta Rewers *(Mgr)*

Spolem Tychy Sp. z o.o. **(1)**
Ul Ks Damrota 72, 43-100, Tychy, Silesian,
Poland
Tel.: (48) 322272210
Web Site: http://www.spolem.tychy.pl
Sales Range: $150-199.9 Million
Emp.: 411
Vegetables & Fruits Retailer
N.A.I.C.S.: 424480

Subsidiary (Domestic):

Piccolo Sp. z o.o. **(2)**
Grota Roweckiego 60 A, 43-100, Tychy,
Silesian, Poland
Tel.: (48) 323283639
Bakery Goods Retailer
N.A.I.C.S.: 445291

Stokrotka Sp.z o.o **(1)**
Melgiewska 7-7, Lublin, Poland **(100%)**
Tel.: (48) 817460725
Web Site: http://www.stokrotka.pl
Sales Range: $200-249.9 Million
Emp.: 700
Supermarkets & Grocery Stores
N.A.I.C.S.: 445110

EMPEROR CAPITAL GROUP LIMITED

23-24/F Emperor Group Centre 288
Hennessy Road, Wanchai, China
(Hong Kong)
Tel.: (852) 29192919
Web Site:
http://www.emperorcapital.com
Financial Services
N.A.I.C.S.: 523999
Daisy Yeung *(CEO & Mng Dir)*

EMPEROR CULTURE GROUP LIMITED

28/F Emperor Group Centre 288

Hennessy Road, Wanchai, China
(Hong Kong)
Tel.: (852) 28356688 **BM**
Web Site:
https://www.empculture.com
Year Founded: 1992
0491—(HKG)
Rev.: $39,559,843
Assets: $233,351,003
Liabilities: $276,133,411
Net Worth: ($42,782,408)
Earnings: ($28,169,490)
Emp.: 745
Fiscal Year-end: 06/30/22
Multimedia Electronic Products Mfr
N.A.I.C.S.: 334419
Vanessa Man seung Fan *(Chm & Exec Dir)*

Subsidiaries:

Icon International Model Management
Limited **(1)**
15/F Parkview Commercial Bldg, 9 Shelter
St, Causeway Bay, Sheung Wan, China
(Hong Kong)
Tel.: (852) 35270369
Web Site: http://www.iconmodel.com.hk
Sales Range: $50-74.9 Million
Emp.: 8
Modeling Agencies
N.A.I.C.S.: 711410

Media Platform Limited **(1)**
128a Uxbridge Road, London, W13 8QS,
United Kingdom
Tel.: (44) 208 840 8844
Web Site:
https://www.mediaplatformltd.co.uk
Sales Range: $25-49.9 Million
Emp.: 3
Accounting Services
N.A.I.C.S.: 541219

Mega-Vision Pictures Limited **(1)**
Unit 606 6/F Tower B Manulife Financial
Centre, Kwun Tong, Kowloon, China (Hong
Kong)
Tel.: (852) 27900381
Web Site: http://www.mvphk.biz
Sales Range: $25-49.9 Million
Emp.: 25
Motion Picture Production
N.A.I.C.S.: 512110
Angela Wong *(Gen Mgr)*

Talent Bang Limited **(1)**
15 F Parkview Commericial Bldg 9-11 Shel-
ter St, Hong Kong, China (Hong Kong)
Tel.: (852) 35270369
Web Site: http://www.talentbang.com.hk
Modeling Agencies
N.A.I.C.S.: 711410

EMPEROR ENERGY LIMITED

Level 4 55 York Street, Sydney,
2000, NSW, Australia
Tel.: (61) 402277282 **AU**
Web Site:
https://www.emperorenergy.com.au
EMP—(ASX)
Rev.: $2,831
Assets: $3,935,234
Liabilities: $167,223
Net Worth: $3,768,011
Earnings: ($537,073)
Fiscal Year-end: 06/30/24
Oil & Gas Producer & Development
N.A.I.C.S.: 213112
Carl Dumbrell *(Sec & Sec)*

Subsidiaries:

Canning Basin Oil Limited **(1)**
Level 4 100 Albert Road, South Melbourne,
3205, VIC, Australia
Tel.: (61) 396927222
Web Site:
http://www.canningbasinoil.com.au
Sales Range: $50-74.9 Million
Emp.: 15
Oil & Gas Exploration Services
N.A.I.C.S.: 213110
Neil Doyle *(Mgr)*

EMPEROR ENTERTAINMENT HOTEL LIMITED

28/F Emperor Group Centre 288
Hennessy Road, Wanchai, China
(Hong Kong)
Tel.: (852) 28356699 **BM**
Web Site: https://www.emp296.com
0296—(HKG)
Rev.: $53,642,008
Assets: $648,823,959
Liabilities: $50,133,494
Net Worth: $598,690,464
Earnings: ($83,094,720)
Emp.: 876
Fiscal Year-end: 03/31/22
Holding Company
N.A.I.C.S.: 551112
Liu Chui Ying *(Sec)*

Subsidiaries:

Grand Emperor Entertainment & Ho-
tel (Macau) Limited **(1)**
No 288 Avenida Comercial De, Macau,
China (Macau)
Tel.: (853) 28889988
Web Site: http://www.grandemperor.com
Hotel Operator
N.A.I.C.S.: 721110

Inn Hotel Macau Limited **(1)**
822 Estrada Governador Nobre Carvalho,
Taipa, China (Macau)
Tel.: (853) 28821666
Web Site: http://www.innhotel.com
Hotel Operator
N.A.I.C.S.: 721110

EMPEROR INTERNATIONAL HOLDINGS LIMITED

28th Floor Emperor Group Centre
288 Hennessy Road, Wanchai, China
(Hong Kong)
Tel.: (852) 28356688
Web Site:
https://www.emperorint.com
0163—(HKG)
Rev.: $300,436,210
Assets: $7,055,916,035
Liabilities: $3,345,483,498
Net Worth: $3,710,432,537
Earnings: ($95,399,025)
Emp.: 1,208
Fiscal Year-end: 03/31/22
Real Estate Industry
N.A.I.C.S.: 237210
Ping Keung Cheung *(Exec Dir)*

Subsidiaries:

The Emperor Hotel Limited **(1)**
373 Queen's Road East, Wanchai, China
(Hong Kong)
Tel.: (852) 28933693
Web Site: https://www.emperorhotel.com.hk
Hotel Operator
N.A.I.C.S.: 721110

The Unit Serviced Apartments
Limited **(1)**
17 Yik Yam Street Happy Valley, Hong
Kong, China (Hong Kong)
Tel.: (852) 22678901
Apartment Building Rental & Leasing Ser-
vices
N.A.I.C.S.: 531110

EMPEROR METALS INC.

10545-45 Avenue Northwest 250
South Ridge Suite 300, Edmonton,
T6H 4M9, AB, Canada
Tel.: (780) 966-7015 **BC**
Web Site:
https://www.emperormetals.com
Year Founded: 2020
EMAUF—(OTCQB)
Rev.: $87,267
Assets: $5,383,106
Liabilities: $662,863
Net Worth: $4,720,243
Earnings: ($802,921)
Emp.: 2

Fiscal Year-end: 01/31/24
Mineral Exploration Services
N.A.I.C.S.: 213115

EMPEROR OIL LTD.

Suite 1100 743 7th Avenue SW, Cal-
gary, T2P 3P8, AB, Canada
Tel.: (403) 850-3450
Web Site: http://www.emperoroil.com
Sales Range: Less than $1 Million
Oil & Gas Exploration Services
N.A.I.C.S.: 211120
Gregory Fedun *(Pres & CEO)*

EMPEROR WATCH & JEWELLERY LIMITED

25th Floor Emperor Group Centre
288 Hennessy Road, Wanchai, China
(Hong Kong)
Tel.: (852) 25222918
Web Site:
https://www.emperorwatchjewels.com
0887—(HKG)
Rev.: $469,743,278
Assets: $686,183,198
Liabilities: $68,438,175
Net Worth: $617,745,023
Earnings: $28,320,938
Emp.: 839
Fiscal Year-end: 12/31/22
Watches & Jewelry Retailer
N.A.I.C.S.: 458310
Cindy Yeung *(Chm, CEO, Exec Dir & Dir)*

Subsidiaries:

EWJ Macau Company Limited **(1)**
Shop 1 G/F Grand Emperor Hotel, 288
Avenida Comercial De Macau, Macau,
China (Macau)
Tel.: (853) 28755238
Jewelry & Watch Whslr
N.A.I.C.S.: 423940

Emperor Watch & Jewellery (HK)
Company Limited **(1)**
G F & Bsmt Comm House, 35 Queen,
Hong Kong, China (Hong Kong)
Tel.: (852) 28100988
Web Site: http://www.emperor.com.hk
Emp.: 200
Jewelry & Watch Mfr & Retailer
N.A.I.C.S.: 334519
Cindy Yeung *(CEO)*

EMPHOR FZCO

Jebel Ali free Zone, PO Box 61232,
Dubai, United Arab Emirates
Tel.: (971) 43392603 **AE**
Web Site: http://www.emphor.biz
Year Founded: 1980
Marine Equipment Distr
N.A.I.C.S.: 423860

EMPICA LTD.

The Courtyard Wraxall Hill, Wraxall,
Bristol, BS48 1NA, United Kingdom
Tel.: (44) 1275 394400
Web Site: http://www.empica.com
Year Founded: 1989
Sales Range: $10-24.9 Million
Emp.: 8
Advertising Services
N.A.I.C.S.: 541810
Martin Powell *(Mng Dir)*

EMPIRE COMPANY LIMITED

115 King Street, Stellarton, B0K 1S0,
NS, Canada
Tel.: (902) 752-8371 **NS**
Web Site: https://www.empireco.ca
Year Founded: 1963
EMP.A—(TSX)
Rev.: $22,113,725,724
Assets: $11,870,238,492
Liabilities: $8,351,543,052
Net Worth: $3,518,695,440
Earnings: $597,818,376

Emp.: 62,000
Fiscal Year-end: 05/01/21
Real Estate Manangement Services
N.A.I.C.S.: 551112
L. Jane McDow *(Asst Sec)*

Subsidiaries:

Crombie REIT **(1)**
610 East River Rd Suite 200, New Glasgow, B2H 3S2, NS, Canada **(41.6%)**
Tel.: (902) 755-8100
Web Site: https://www.crombie.ca
Rev.: $332,961,858
Assets: $3,132,666,668
Liabilities: $1,754,789,388
Net Worth: $1,377,877,281
Earnings: ($44,762,003)
Emp.: 286
Fiscal Year-end: 12/31/2023
Commercial Real Estate Investment Trust
N.A.I.C.S.: 525990
Donald E. Clow *(Pres & CEO)*

ECL Developments Limited **(1)**
115 King St, Stellarton, B0K 1S0, NS, Canada
Tel.: (902) 755-4440
Web Site: http://www.empirecompany.com
Emp.: 99
Shopping Center & Other Commercial Real Estate Development Services
N.A.I.C.S.: 237210

ECL Western Holdings limited **(1)**
115 King Street, Stellarton, B0K 1S0, NS, Canada
Tel.: (902) 755-4440
Holding Company
N.A.I.C.S.: 551112
Donald Clow *(Gen Mgr)*

Empire Theaters Limited **(1)**
610 E River Rd., New Glasgow, B2H 3S2, NS, Canada **(100%)**
Tel.: (902) 755-7620
Web Site: http://www.empiretheaters.com
Sales Range: $25-49.9 Million
Emp.: 40
Movie Theaters
N.A.I.C.S.: 512132

Sobeys Group Inc. **(1)**
115 King Street, Stellarton, B0K 1S0, NS, Canada
Tel.: (902) 752-8371
Web Site: https://corporate.sobeys.com
Sales Range: $125-149.9 Million
Emp.: 800
Holding Company; Food Distribution & Grocery Store Operator
N.A.I.C.S.: 551112

Subsidiary (Domestic):

Sobeys Inc. **(2)**
293 Foord Street, Box 1140, Stellarton, B0K 1S0, NS, Canada
Tel.: (902) 755-1830
Web Site: http://www.sobeys.com
Sales Range: $15-24.9 Billion
Food Distribution & Grocery Store Operator
N.A.I.C.S.: 424490
L. Jane McDow *(Asst Sec)*

Subsidiary (Domestic):

Canada Safeway Limited **(3)**
1020 64th Ave NE, Calgary, T2E 7V8, AB, Canada
Tel.: (403) 730-3500
Web Site: http://www.safeway.ca
Sales Range: $5-14.9 Billion
Emp.: 30,000
Supermarkets Owner & Operator
N.A.I.C.S.: 445110
Patrick Lauzon *(Dir-Loyalty & Mktg Strategy)*

Lawtons Drug Stores Limited **(3)**
535 Portland Street Unit 1, Dartmouth, B2Y 4B1, NS, Canada **(100%)**
Tel.: (902) 468-1000
Web Site: http://www.lawtons.ca
Sales Range: $25-49.9 Million
Emp.: 150
Operator of Drug Stores
N.A.I.C.S.: 456110

Sobeys Capital Incorporated. **(3)**

115 King Street Shelburne Mall, Shelburne, B0T 1W0, NS, Canada
Tel.: (902) 875-2458
Web Site: https://www.sobeys.com
Packaging Services
N.A.I.C.S.: 561910
Clinton Keay *(Exec VP-Fin)*

Division (Domestic):

Sobeys Ontario Division **(3)**
4980 Tahoe Blvd, Mississauga, L4W 0C7, ON, Canada **(100%)**
Tel.: (905) 238-7124
Web Site: http://www.sobeysweb.com
Sales Range: $125-149.9 Million
Emp.: 500
N.A.I.C.S.: 457110

Sobeys Quebec Division **(3)**
11281 Albert-Hudon Boulevard, Montreal, H1G 3J5, QC, Canada **(100%)**
Tel.: (514) 324-1010
Web Site: http://www.sobeys.com
Sales Range: $200-249.9 Million
Emp.: 1,000
Distr of Groceries
N.A.I.C.S.: 424490

Subsidiary (Domestic):

Sobeys West, Inc. **(3)**
1020-64 Avenue NE, Calgary, T2E 7V8, AB, Canada
Tel.: (780) 486-4800
Web Site: http://www.sobeys.com
Sales Range: $50-74.9 Million
Emp.: 200
N.A.I.C.S.: 457110
Barbara Dewes *(Mgr)*

Thrifty Foods Inc. **(3)**
7860 Wallace Drive, Saanichton, V8M 2B3, BC, Canada
Tel.: (250) 544-0980
Web Site: http://www.thriftyfoods.com
Sales Range: $10-24.9 Million
Emp.: 300
Grocery Store Owner & Operator
N.A.I.C.S.: 445110
Jim Jimtores *(Pres)*

EMPIRE ENERGY GROUP LIMITED
Level 5 6 10 OConnell Street, Sydney, 2000, NSW, Australia
Tel.: (61) 292511846
Web Site:
https://www.empireenergygroup.net
Year Founded: 1984
EEG—(OTCIQ)
Rev.: $8,947,208
Assets: $128,871,677
Liabilities: $41,756,994
Net Worth: $87,114,683
Earnings: ($3,914,198)
Emp.: 40
Fiscal Year-end: 12/31/22
Oil & Gas Exploration
N.A.I.C.S.: 211120
Alex Underwood *(Mng Dir)*

Subsidiaries:

Imperial Resources, LLC **(1)**
380 Southpointe Blvd Ste 130, Canonsburg, PA 15317
Tel.: (724) 483-2070
Rev.: $25,886,371
Assets: $113,606,342
Liabilities: $71,333,761
Net Worth: $42,272,581
Earnings: $91,031
Emp.: 48
Fiscal Year-end: 12/31/2013
Oil & Gas Exploration
N.A.I.C.S.: 211120
Bruce W. McLeod *(CEO)*

EMPIRE MAINTENANCE INDUSTRIES INC.
695 90e Avenue, LaSalle, Montreal, H8R 3A4, QC, Canada
Tel.: (514) 341-6161
Web Site:
http://www.empiremaintenance.ca

Year Founded: 1938
Rev.: $72,826,310
Emp.: 4,000
Janitorial Services
N.A.I.C.S.: 561720
Mario W. Levasseur *(Pres & CEO)*

EMPIRE METALS CORP.
702-889 West Pender Street, Vancouver, V6C 3B2, BC, Canada
Tel.: (604) 683-3288
Web Site:
http://www.empiremetalscorp.com
EP—(TSXV)
Assets: $2,190,461
Liabilities: $1,302,112
Net Worth: $888,349
Earnings: ($883,292)
Fiscal Year-end: 12/31/23
Mineral Exploration Services
N.A.I.C.S.: 213115
Mark Patchett *(Pres & CEO)*

EMPIRE METALS LIMITED
6 Heddon Street, London, W1B 4BT, United Kingdom
Tel.: (44) 2079079327 **VG**
Web Site:
https://www.empiremetals.co.uk
Year Founded: 2010
EEE—(LSE)
Assets: $6,055,501
Liabilities: $136,976
Net Worth: $5,918,526
Earnings: ($1,443,866)
Emp.: 1
Fiscal Year-end: 12/31/22
Support Activities for Nonmetallic Minerals (except Fuels) Mining
N.A.I.C.S.: 213115
Gregory Kuenzel *(Fin Dir)*

EMPIRE RESOURCES LIMITED
159 Stirling Highway, PO Box 1104, Nedlands, 6009, WA, Australia
Tel.: (61) 63891032
Web Site:
https://www.resourcesempire.com
ERL—(ASX)
Rev.: $4,767
Assets: $536,826
Liabilities: $126,848
Net Worth: $409,977
Earnings: ($657,991)
Emp.: 2
Fiscal Year-end: 06/30/24
Minerals Exploration
N.A.I.C.S.: 213115
Simon Jonathan Storm *(Sec)*

EMPIRED LTD
Level 7 The Quadrant 1 William Street, Perth, 6000, WA, Australia
Tel.: (61) 863332200
Web Site: http://www.empired.com
EPD—(ASX)
Rev.: $123,776,822
Assets: $76,569,674
Liabilities: $33,025,244
Net Worth: $43,544,431
Earnings: ($10,767,597)
Emp.: 53
Fiscal Year-end: 06/30/19
Software Services
N.A.I.C.S.: 513210
Russell Baskerville *(CEO & Mng Dir)*

Subsidiaries:

eSavvy Pty Ltd **(1)**
15 Young St, Sydney, 2000, NSW, Australia
Tel.: (61) 292512880
Web Site: http://www.esavvy.com.au
Consulting Services
N.A.I.C.S.: 541612

EMPIRIC STUDENT PROPERTY PLC

72 Borough High Street 1st Floor, London, SE1 1XF, United Kingdom
Tel.: (44) 2080788791 **UK**
Web Site: https://www.empiric.co.uk
Year Founded: 2014
ESP—(LSE)
Rev.: $80,708,308
Assets: $1,432,049,739
Liabilities: $572,236,891
Net Worth: $859,812,848
Earnings: ($32,544,548)
Emp.: 324
Fiscal Year-end: 12/31/20
Investment Management Service
N.A.I.C.S.: 523940
Lynne Fennah *(CFO & COO)*

EMPLOCITY S.A.
ul Nowogrodzka 51 3rd floor, 00-695, Warsaw, Poland
Tel.: (48) 222139511
Web Site: https://www.emplocity.com
Year Founded: 2013
V6A—(DEU)
Software Development Services
N.A.I.C.S.: 541511
Krzysztof Sobczak *(CEO)*

EMPORIO HOTELS & RESORTS S.A. DE C.V.
Paseo de la Reforma No 124, Mexico, Mexico
Tel.: (52) 5062 6161
Web Site:
http://www.emporiohotels.com
Hotel Operator
N.A.I.C.S.: 721110
Liliana Mendez *(Mgr-E-Commerce)*

Subsidiaries:

Emporio Acapulco, S.A. de C.V. **(1)**
Costera Miguel Aleman Ave No 121 Fracc Magallanes, 39670, Acapulco, Guerrero, Mexico
Tel.: (52) 7444690505
Hotel & Resort Operator
N.A.I.C.S.: 721110

Emporio Ixtapa S.A. de C.V., Lic. **(1)**
Ixtapa Blvd s/n Mpio Tnte Jose Azueta, 40880, Ixtapaluca, Ixhuatanejo, Mexico
Tel.: (52) 7555531066
Hotel & Resort Operator
N.A.I.C.S.: 721110

Emporio Mazatlan, S.A. de C.V. **(1)**
Camaron Sabalo Ave 51 Golden Zone, 82110, Mazatlan, Sinaloa, Mexico
Tel.: (52) 6699834611
Hotel & Resort Operator
N.A.I.C.S.: 721110

Emporio Veracruz S.A. De C.V. **(1)**
Paseo del Malecon 244, 91709, Veracruz, Veracruz, Mexico
Tel.: (52) 2299893300
Hotel & Resort Operator
N.A.I.C.S.: 721110

Emporio Zacatecas, S.A. de C.V. **(1)**
Hidalgo Ave No 703 Historical Center, 98000, Zacatecas, Zacatecas, Mexico
Tel.: (52) 4929256500
Hotel & Resort Operator
N.A.I.C.S.: 721110

Samba Vallarta **(1)**
Av Costera y La Playa y Nuevo Vallarta s/n, Residencial Flamingos Nayarta cp 63732 Bahia de Banderas, Nayarit, Mexico
Tel.: (52) 3222268250
Web Site: http://www.sambavallarta.com
Sales Range: $10-24.9 Million
Emp.: 300
Hotel Operations
N.A.I.C.S.: 721110

EMPOWER CLINICS INC.
505-1771 Robson Street, Vancouver, V6G 1C9, BC, Canada
Tel.: (604) 359-9058 **Ca**
Web Site:
https://www.empowerclinics.com

Empower Clinics Inc.—(Continued)

Year Founded: 1997
EPW—(CNSX)
Rev.: $4,368,916
Assets: $5,037,376
Liabilities: $11,430,317
Net Worth: ($6,392,941)
Earnings: ($32,256,315)
Emp.: 58
Fiscal Year-end: 12/31/21
Oil & Gas Exploration Services
N.A.I.C.S.: 211120
Steven McAuley *(Chm & CEO)*

Subsidiaries:

Adira Energy Corp **(1)**
Unit 1204 120 Adelaide St W, Toronto, M4V
3A1, ON, Canada
Tel.: (416) 250-1955
Web Site: http://www.adiraenergy.com
Oil & Gas Exploration Services
N.A.I.C.S.: 211120

Adira Energy Israel Ltd. **(1)**
12 Abba Hillel Silver 12th Floor, Ramat
Gan, 52506, Israel
Tel.: (972) 3 373 0166
Oil & Gas Exploration Services
N.A.I.C.S.: 213112

Kai Medical Laboratory, LLC **(1)**
8230 Elmbrook Dr Ste 200, Dallas, TX
75247
Tel.: (469) 447-8956
Web Site:
https://www.kaimedicallaboratory.com
Medical Testing Services
N.A.I.C.S.: 621511
Yoshi Tyler *(Pres & Founder)*

Lawrence Park Health & Wellness
Clinic Inc. **(1)**
88 Eglinton Ave W 101, Toronto, M4R 1A2,
ON, Canada
Tel.: (416) 486-6662
Web Site: https://lawrenceparkhealth.com
Physiotherapy Services
N.A.I.C.S.: 621340

Sun Valley Health, LLC **(1)**
12801 W Bell Rd 145, Surprise, AZ 85378
Tel.: (623) 847-6652
Web Site: http://www.sunvalleyhealth.com
Primary Care Services
N.A.I.C.S.: 621111

EMPOWER INDIA LIMITED
25/25A 2nd Floor Nawab Building
327 D N Road, Fort, Mumbai,
400001, India
Tel.: (91) 2222045055
Web Site:
https://www.empowerindia.in
Year Founded: 1981
Rev.: $164,638
Assets: $77,252,778
Liabilities: $28,724,870
Net Worth: $48,527,908
Earnings: $3,872
Emp.: 7
Fiscal Year-end: 03/31/19
Information Technology Support Services
N.A.I.C.S.: 541512
Rajgopalan Iyengar *(CFO)*

**EMPRESA AGRARIA AZU-
CARERA ANDAHUASI S.A.A.**
Carretera Huaura Sayan Km 40 5,
Sayan, Lima, Huaura, Peru
Tel.: (51) 2371159
Web Site: http://www.andahuasi.com
Year Founded: 1996
ANDAHUC1—(LIM)
Sales Range: Less than $1 Million
Sugar Mfr
N.A.I.C.S.: 311313
Greco Vladimir Augusto Quiroz Diaz
(Vice Chm)

**EMPRESA AGRICOLA SAN
JUAN SA**

Kilometro 56 Carretera a Chongoy-
ape, Chiclayo, Peru
Tel.: (51) 74433149
Web Site:
https://www.agricolasanjuan.com.pe
Year Founded: 1998
ASJUANC1—(LIM)
Sales Range: Less than $1 Million
Food Products Distr
N.A.I.C.S.: 424420
Jorge Luis Grandez Fernandez
(Chm)

**EMPRESA CONSTRUCTORA
BELFI SA**
Puerta del Sol 55 floor 3, Las Con-
des, Santiago, Chile
Tel.: (56) 25604800
Web Site: http://www.belfi.cl
Year Founded: 1950
General Construction Services
N.A.I.C.S.: 237990

Subsidiaries:

Terminal Puerto Arica S.A. **(1)**
Av Maximo Lira 389, Arica, Chile **(50%)**
Tel.: (56) 58 2 202000
Web Site: http://www.tpa.cl
Cost Management Services
N.A.I.C.S.: 488320
Diego Bulnes *(Gen Mgr)*

**EMPRESA DE GENERACION
ELECTRICA DEL SUR SA**
Av Ejercito s/n Para Sub Station,
Tacna, Peru
Tel.: (51) 52315300
Web Site: http://www.egesur.com.pe
Year Founded: 1994
EGESUBC1—(LIM)
Rev.: $18,655,709
Assets: $56,777,859
Liabilities: $13,976,466
Net Worth: $42,801,393
Earnings: $6,427,010
Fiscal Year-end: 12/31/23
Eletric Power Generation Services
N.A.I.C.S.: 221118
Victor Murillo Huaman *(Chm)*

**EMPRESA DE GENERACION
ELECTRICA SAN GABAN S.A.**
Av Floral 245 Bellavista, Puno, Peru
Tel.: (51) 51364401
Web Site: http://www.sangaban.com
Year Founded: 1994
SANGABC1—(LIM)
Sales Range: Less than $1 Million
Hydroelectric Power Generation Ser-
vices
N.A.I.C.S.: 221111
Jose Mercedes Mosquera Castillo
(Chm)

**EMPRESA DE SERVICIOS
SANITARIOS DE LOS LAGOS
SA**
Covadonga No 52, De Los Lagos,
Puerto Montt, Chile
Tel.: (56) 65281200
ESSAL-A—(SGO)
Sales Range: Less than $1 Million
Water Supply Services
N.A.I.C.S.: 221310
Gustavo Mayor Lemarie *(Chm)*

**EMPRESA DE TELECOMUNI-
CACIONES DE BOGOTA SA**
Cra 8 20-56 First Floor, Bogota, Co-
lombia
Tel.: (57) 13777777
Web Site: https://www.etb.com
Year Founded: 1884
ETB—(COLO)
Sales Range: Less than $1 Million
Telecommunication Servicesb

N.A.I.C.S.: 517112
Jorge Castellanos Rueda *(Pres)*

**EMPRESA ELECTRICA PIL-
MAIQUEN S.A.**
Malaga 50 Piso 2 Oficina 21, Las
Condes, Santiago, Chile
Tel.: (56) 2063133
Web Site: http://www.epilmaiquen.cl
Hydroelectric Power Transmission
Services
N.A.I.C.S.: 221111
Luis Arqueros Wood *(CEO)*

**EMPRESA ELECTRICIDAD
DEL PERU-ELECTROPERU SA**
Prol Pedro Miota 421, San Juan de
Miraflores, Lima, Peru
Tel.: (51) 17083400
Web Site:
http://www.electroperu.com.pe
Year Founded: 1972
ELECPBC1—(LIM)
Sales Range: Less than $1 Million
Hydroelectric Power Generation Ser-
vices
N.A.I.C.S.: 221111
Luis Alberto Haro Zavaleta *(Chm &
Pres)*

**EMPRESA GENERAL DE IN-
VERSIONES, S.A.**
Edificio Torre Banco General Aquilino
de la Guardia Street E2 floor, PO Box
0816-00843, 5th Avenue South B
Marbella Apartado 4592, Panama,
Panama
Tel.: (507) 3035322
Web Site: https://www.egi.com.pa
Year Founded: 1973
EGIN—(PAN)
Sales Range: Less than $1 Million
Holding Company
N.A.I.C.S.: 551112
Leopoldo Arosemena *(Treas)*

**EMPRESA NACIONAL DE CO-
MERCIO REDITO E PARTICI-
PACOES, S.A.-ENCORPAR**
R Aimores 981, 30140071, Belo Hori-
zonte, MG, Brazil
Tel.: (55) 31 2129 9877
ECPR3—(BRAZ)
Sales Range: Less than $1 Million
Emp.: 1,614
Investment Management Service
N.A.I.C.S.: 523940
Joao Batista Da Cunha Bomfim
(Dir-IR)

**EMPRESA NACIONAL DEL PE-
TROLEO**
Av Apoquindo 2929 5th floor Las
Condes, Santiago, Chile
Tel.: (56) 222803000
Web Site: http://www.enap.cl
Year Founded: 1950
Exploration & Production of Energy
N.A.I.C.S.: 221118
Loreto Silva *(Chm)*

Subsidiaries:

ENAP Refinerias SA **(1)**
Av Borgono 25 777, Concon, Chile
Tel.: (56) 322650200
Refining & Selling Crude Oil
N.A.I.C.S.: 211120
Maria Loreta Silva Rojas *(Chm)*

**EMPRESA REGIONAL DE
SERVICIO PU DE EL SA**
Agustinas 1343 Casilla 297, San-
tiago, Chile
Tel.: (56) 24412000
ELESUDC1—(LIM)
Rev.: $74,821,202

Assets: $97,919,467
Liabilities: $46,040,806
Net Worth: $51,878,660
Earnings: $6,848,298
Fiscal Year-end: 12/31/23
Wood Products Mfr
N.A.I.C.S.: 322220
Francisco Ruiz-Tagle Edwards *(CEO)*

EMPRESARIA GROUP PLC
Old Church House Sandy Lane,
Crawley Down, Crawley, RH10 4HS,
West Sussex, United Kingdom
Tel.: (44) 1342711430
Web Site:
https://www.empresaria.com
EMR—(LSE)
Rev.: $348,255,180
Assets: $165,777,612
Liabilities: $108,210,284
Net Worth: $57,567,328
Earnings: ($4,344,704)
Emp.: 1,764
Fiscal Year-end: 12/31/20
Recruitment Services
N.A.I.C.S.: 541612
Anthony Martin *(Chm)*

Subsidiaries:

2nd City Resourcing Limited **(1)**
37 - 39 Ludgate Hill St Pauls Square, Bir-
mingham, B3 1EH, United Kingdom
Tel.: (44) 1216656768
Web Site: http://www.2ndcityresourcing.com
Sales Range: $25-49.9 Million
Emp.: 5
Employment Placement Agencies
N.A.I.C.S.: 561311

Alternativa Empresa De Servicios
Transitorios Limitada **(1)**
Alcalde Jorge Monckeberg 77, Nunoa, Chile
Tel.: (56) 93 911 6365
Web Site: https://www.alternattiva.cl
Human Resouce Services
N.A.I.C.S.: 541612

Become Recruitment Limited **(1)**
Rhodesia House 52 Princess St, Man-
chester, M1 6JX, United Kingdom
Tel.: (44) 161 974 7460
Web Site:
https://www.becomerecruitment.com
Employment Placement Agency Services
N.A.I.C.S.: 561311
Justin Moore *(Assoc Dir)*

Beresford Wilson & Partners
FZ-LLC **(1)**
1004-217 Swiss Tower Jumeirah Lakes
Towers, PO Box 643718, Dubai, United
Arab Emirates
Tel.: (971) 4 279 8352
Web Site: https://www.bwpltd.com
Recruitment Services
N.A.I.C.S.: 561311
Nick Kingston *(Mng Dir)*

ConSol Partners LLC **(1)**
4th Floor 35 New Broad Street, London,
EC2M 1NH, United Kingdom **(82.5%)**
Tel.: (44) 203 207 7999
Web Site: http://www.consolpartners.com
Employee Recruitment Services
N.A.I.C.S.: 561311
Ben Wallin *(Dir-Permanent Recruitment &
Cloud)*

Empresaria Limited **(1)**
Old Church House Sandy Lane, Crawley
Down, Crawley, RH10 4HS, West Sussex,
United Kingdom
Tel.: (44) 134 271 1430
Staffing & Recruiting Services
N.A.I.C.S.: 561311

Fast Track Management Services
(London) Limited **(1)**
Unit 4 Century Court Tolpits Lane, Watford,
WD18 9RS, United Kingdom
Tel.: (44) 1923813101
Web Site: http://www.ftrack.co.uk
Sales Range: $25-49.9 Million
Emp.: 100
Industrial Building Construction

N.A.I.C.S.: 236210

Fast Track Management Services (Midlands) Limited (1)
The Saturn Centre, 101 Lockhurst Lane, Coventry, CV65SF, United Kingdom
Tel.: (44) 2476708110
Web Site: http://www.ftrack.co.uk
Industrial Building Construction
N.A.I.C.S.: 236210

Greycoat Lumleys Ltd. (1)
Uncommon Offices N101 126/128 New Kings Road, London, SW6 4LZ, United Kingdom
Tel.: (44) 207 233 9950
Web Site:
https://www.greycoatlumleys.co.uk
Sales Range: $25-49.9 Million
Emp.: 25
International Recruitment Agencies
N.A.I.C.S.: 561311
Debbie Salter (Mng Dir)

HEC Resources Limited (1)
Suite 2 James Yard 480 Larkshall Road, Highams Park, London, E4 9UA, United Kingdom (100%)
Tel.: (44) 2085233561
Web Site: http://www.hecresources.com
Human Resources & Executive Search Consulting Services
N.A.I.C.S.: 541612

Headway Holding GmbH (1)
landshuter strasse 73, 84030, Ergolding, Germany
Tel.: (49) 871 9 75 28 0
Web Site: http://www.headway-group.com
Sales Range: $25-49.9 Million
Emp.: 18
Employment Agency Services
N.A.I.C.S.: 561311
Spencer Wreford (Mng Dir)

ITC Apt Sp. Z.o.o. (1)
ul Kurniki 4, 31-156, Krakow, Poland
Tel.: (48) 126192822
Human Resources & Executive Search Consulting Services
N.A.I.C.S.: 541612

ITC Cs Sp. Z.o.o. (1)
ul Kurniki 4, 31-156, Krakow, Poland
Tel.: (48) 12 357 22 88
Web Site: http://www.itcpraca.pl
Human Resources & Executive Search Consulting Services
N.A.I.C.S.: 541612

Interactive Manpower Solutions Private Limited (1)
1/2 Indraprasth Business Park Near DAV School, Prahladnagar Extension Makarba, Ahmedabad, 380051, Gujarat, India
Tel.: (91) 796 827 4444
Web Site: https://www.imspeople.com
Sales Range: $25-49.9 Million
Emp.: 14
Human Resource Consulting Services
N.A.I.C.S.: 541612

LMA Recruitment Limited (1)
9 Cloak Lane, London, EC4R 2RU, United Kingdom (80%)
Tel.: (44) 207 236 4999
Web Site: https://www.lmarecruitment.com
Sales Range: $25-49.9 Million
Emp.: 20
Human Resources & Executive Search Consulting Services
N.A.I.C.S.: 541612
Nefino Joannides (Mng Dir)

LMA Recruitment Singapore Pte. Limited (1)
Level 28 Clifford Centre 24 Raffles Place, Singapore, 048621, Singapore
Tel.: (65) 6 632 4699
Web Site: https://www.lmarecruitment.asia
Recruitment Services
N.A.I.C.S.: 561311
Tanu Booluck (Office Mgr)

Lindsay Morgan Associates Ltd. (1)
Ground Floor Prince Rupert House, 64 Queen Street, London, EC4R 2RU, United Kingdom
Tel.: (44) 2072364999
Web Site: http://www.lmassoc.com

Sales Range: $25-49.9 Million
Emp.: 18
Recruitment Services
N.A.I.C.S.: 541612
Russell Thompson (Mng Dir)

Mansion House Recruitment Ltd. (1)
Ground Floor Pellipar House, 9 Cloak Lane, London, EC4R 2RU, United Kingdom
Tel.: (44) 207 332 5870
Web Site: http://www.mansionhouse.co.uk
Sales Range: $25-49.9 Million
Emp.: 15
Recruitment Services
N.A.I.C.S.: 541612
Jayne Coles (Mng Dir)

Marketing y Promociones S.A. (1)
Alcalde Jorge Monckeberg 77, Nunoa, Santiago, Chile
Tel.: (56) 2 482 3800
Temporary Staffing Services
N.A.I.C.S.: 561320

McCall Limited (1)
9 Cloak Lane, London, EC4R 2RU, United Kingdom
Tel.: (44) 207 029 3800
Web Site: https://www.mccall.co.uk
Sales Range: $10-24.9 Million
Emp.: 10
Vocational Rehabilitation Services
N.A.I.C.S.: 624310
Julie O'Neill (Co-Mng Dir)

Medical Recruitment Strategies, LLC (1)
477 Main St, Stoneham, MA 02180
Web Site:
https://www.medicalrecruitment.com
Recruitment Services
N.A.I.C.S.: 561311
Elisa Ciardiello (CEO)

Medikumppani Oy (1)
Hameenkatu 30 C 32, 20700, Turku, Finland
Tel.: (358) 29 170 1370
Web Site: https://medikumppani.fi
Healtcare Services
N.A.I.C.S.: 621111

Mediradix Oy (1)
PL 299, 20101, Turku, Finland
Tel.: (358) 22813150
Web Site: http://www.mediradix.fi
Sales Range: $25-49.9 Million
Emp.: 20
Healthcare Staffing Services
N.A.I.C.S.: 561320
Jaana Kiviniemi (Bus Dir)

Monroe Consulting Group (1)
South Quarter Building Tower C Level 10 Jl RA Kartini Kav 8, RT 010 RW 004 Cilandak, 12430, Jakarta Selatan, DKI Jakarta, Indonesia
Tel.: (62) 215 098 2629
Web Site:
https://www.monroeconsulting.com
Sales Range: $25-49.9 Million
Emp.: 30
Human Resource Consulting Services
N.A.I.C.S.: 541612
James Palin (Mng Dir)

Monroe Consulting Group Vietnam Limited Liability Company (1)
HD Tower 6th floor 25bis Nguyen Thi Minh Khai Street, Ben Nghe Ward District 1, Ho Chi Minh City, 700000, Vietnam
Tel.: (84) 283 911 6268
Recruitment Services
N.A.I.C.S.: 561311
Lhorlan El Laurel (Mng Dir)

Monroe Recruitment Consulting Group Co Limited (1)
Lake Rajada Office Complex Building 28th Floor 193/119, Ratchadapisek Road Klongtoey, 10110, Bangkok, Thailand
Tel.: (66) 2 055 4759
Web Site:
https://www.monroeconsulting.com
Sales Range: $50-74.9 Million
Emp.: 13
Commericial Banking
N.A.I.C.S.: 522110

Monroe Recruitment Consulting Group Company Limited (1)

Lake Rajada Office Complex Building 28th Floor, 193/119 Ratchadapisek Road Klongtoey, Bangkok, 10110, Thailand
Tel.: (66) 2 055 4759
Web Site:
https://www.monroeconsulting.com
Recruitment Services
N.A.I.C.S.: 561311
John Stuart Tolmie (Mng Dir)

PT. Learning Resources (1)
Jl Wijaya I No 71 Kebayoran Baru, Jakarta Selatan, 12170, Indonesia
Tel.: (62) 21 723 2388
Web Site: https://www.lresources.co.id
Professional Training Services
N.A.I.C.S.: 611430

Reflex HR Limited (1)
Delta House Bridge Road, Haywards Heath, RH16 1UA, West Sussex, United Kingdom
Tel.: (44) 1444414164
Web Site: http://www.reflexhr.co.uk
Sales Range: $25-49.9 Million
Emp.: 12
Industrial Building Construction
N.A.I.C.S.: 236210
Simon Lanaway (Mng Dir)

Resolve Interim Solutions Limited (1)
Oakhurst 23 Harrogate Road, Chapel Allerton, Leeds, LS73PD, United Kingdom
Tel.: (44) 1133836207
Web Site: http://www.resolveltd.co.uk
Sales Range: $25-49.9 Million
Emp.: 5
Employment Placement Agencies
N.A.I.C.S.: 561311

Skillhouse Staffing Solutions K.K. (1)
Tomoecho Annex No 2 Building 3-8-27 Toranomon, Minato-ku, Tokyo, 105-0001, Japan
Tel.: (81) 35 408 5070
Web Site: https://www.skillhouse.co.jp
Sales Range: $10-24.9 Million
Emp.: 180
Employment Placement Agencies
N.A.I.C.S.: 561311
Mark Smith (Pres)

Social Work Associates Limited (1)
16 Brune Street, 004 Coppergate House, London, E17NJ, United Kingdom (100%)
Tel.: (44) 2079537878
Web Site:
http://www.socialworkassociates.co.uk
Sales Range: $25-49.9 Million
Emp.: 4
Employment Placement Agencies
N.A.I.C.S.: 561311

Teamsales Limited (1)
25 Princess Road, Primrose Hill, London, NW1 8JR, United Kingdom (100%)
Tel.: (44) 2072092499
Web Site: http://www.team-sales.co.uk
Sales Range: $25-49.9 Million
Emp.: 12
Employment Placement Agencies
N.A.I.C.S.: 561311

The Recruitment Business Limited (1)
17-18 Henrietta Street, London, WC2E 8QH, United Kingdom
Tel.: (44) 20 7240 0088
Web Site: http://www.becomeuk.com
Emp.: 14
Human Resource Consulting Services
N.A.I.C.S.: 541612
Dianne Lang (Mgr-HR & Fin)

EMPRESAS CABO DE HORNOS S.A.
Agustinas 814 Of 706, PO Box 1388, Santiago, Chile
Tel.: (56) 6338481
Web Site:
http://www.cabodehornos.cl
HORNOS—(SGO)
Sales Range: Less than $1 Million
Grape Plantation Services
N.A.I.C.S.: 115112

EMPRESAS CMPC S.A.

Agustinas 1343, Santiago, Chile
Tel.: (56) 224412000 **CL**
Web Site: http://www.cmpc.cl
Year Founded: 1920
CMPC—(SGO)
Rev.: $5,670,277,000
Assets: $14,955,796,000
Liabilities: $6,820,221,000
Net Worth: $8,135,575,000
Earnings: $84,391,000
Emp.: 18,921
Fiscal Year-end: 12/31/19
Paper & Paper Product Mfr
N.A.I.C.S.: 322120
Luis Felipe Gazitua (Pres)

Subsidiaries:

CMPC Celulosa S.A. (1)
Tel.: (56) 224412030
Web Site: https://www.cmpccelulosa.cl
Sales Range: $200-249.9 Million
Emp.: 1,000
Pulp Milling Services
N.A.I.C.S.: 322110

Subsidiary (Domestic):

CMPC Maderas SpA (2)
Agustinas 1343 P 4, Santiago, Chile
Tel.: (56) 224412832
Web Site: https://www.cmpcmaderas.com
Wood Product Mfr & Distr
N.A.I.C.S.: 321999
Victor Argomedo Georgi (Dir-Sls Domestic Market)

CMPC Europe Limited (1)
5 Dukes Gate Acton Lane Chiswick, London, W4 5DX, United Kingdom
Tel.: (44) 2089969960
Web Site: http://www.cmpc.co.uk
Sales Range: $50-74.9 Million
Emp.: 3
Paper Products Sales
N.A.I.C.S.: 424130

CMPC Papeles S.A. (1)
Agustinas 1343 Piso 5 Correo Central, PO Box 297, 6500587, Santiago, Chile
Tel.: (56) 24412000
Web Site: http://www.cmpc.cl
Sales Range: $125-149.9 Million
Emp.: 500
Folding Boxboard, Corrugating Materials & Newsprint Mfr & Marketer
N.A.I.C.S.: 322120
Hernan Rodriguez (Mng Dir)

Subsidiary (Domestic):

Empresa Distribuidora de Papeles y Cartones SpA (2)
Las Esteras Sur 2501, Quilicura, Santiago, Chile
Tel.: (56) 223752400
Web Site:
http://edipac.cmpcbiopackaging.com
Tape Distr
N.A.I.C.S.: 424130

Papeles Cordillera SpA (2)
Avda Eyzaguirre 01098, Casilla 23, Puente Alto, Chile
Tel.: (56) 223675700
Web Site:
https://corrugados.cmpcbiopackaging.com
Paper Mfr
N.A.I.C.S.: 322120

CMPC Productos de Papel S.A. (1)
Agustinas 1343 Piso 6, PO Box 297, Santiago, 8340412, Chile
Tel.: (56) 24412000
Web Site: http://www.cmpc.cl
Sales Range: $25-49.9 Million
Emp.: 6
Corrugated Box Mfr
N.A.I.C.S.: 322211

CMPC Tissue S.A. (1)
Agustinia 1343 Piso 6, Santiago, Chile
Tel.: (56) 24412000
Web Site: http://www.cmpctissue.cl
Toilet Paper, Paper Towels, Napkins, Disposable Handkerchiefs & Disposable Diaper Mfr
N.A.I.C.S.: 322291

Empresas CMPC S.A.—(Continued)

Subsidiary (Non-US):

Protisa Colombia S.A.　(2)
Calle 134 7 - 83 Oficina 151 Edificio Altos
del Bosque, Bogota, Colombia
Tel.: (57) 15893333
Web Site: http://www.ompc.co
Baby Diaper Mfr & Distr
N.A.I.C.S.: 322291

CMPC USA, Inc.　(1)
1050 Crown Point Pkwy Ste 1590, Atlanta,
GA 30338
Tel.: (770) 551-2640
Web Cite: http://www.cmpcmaderas.com
Sales Range: $50-74.9 Million
Emp.: 13
Paper Products Sales
N.A.I.C.S.: 424130
Nadia Lakhani (Coord-Logistics)

Chilena de Moldeados S.A.　(1)
Jose Luis Coo 01162 Puente Alto Apartado
208, Santiago, Chile
Tel.: (56) 224331900
Web Site: http://www.chimolsa.cl
Sales Range: $50-74.9 Million
Emp.: 150
Molded Pulp Packaging Production Ser-
vices
N.A.I.C.S.: 322110

Envases Impresos S.A.　(1)
Lo Echevers 221 Clasificador No 3 Quili-
cura, Santiago, Chile
Tel.: (56) 24442309
Web Site: http://www.envases.cl
Sales Range: $125-149.9 Million
Emp.: 360
Mfr & Distr of Corrugated Cardboard Boxes
N.A.I.C.S.: 322130
Pablo Sufan (Mng Dir)

FABI Bolsas Industriales S.A.　(1)
Virasoro 2656 Edificio Uruguay III,
B1643HDB, Buenos Aires,
Argentina　(100%)
Tel.: (54) 1147371001
Corrugated & Solid Fiber Box Mfr
N.A.I.C.S.: 322211
Adrian Saj (Mgr)

Forestal Bosques del Plata S.A.　(1)
Av Juan Manuel Fangio 3873, Barrio San
Isidro, Posadas, Misiones, Argentina
Tel.: (54) 3764451911
Web Site: https://bosquesdelplata.com.ar
Seed Mfr
N.A.I.C.S.: 333112

Forestal Mininco S.A.　(1)
Agustinas 1343 Piso 4, PO Box 297,
Correo Central, Santiago, 8340432, Chile
Tel.: (56) 24412000
Sales Range: $25-49.9 Million
Emp.: 7
Forest Management Services
N.A.I.C.S.: 115310
Francisco Ruiz-Tagle (Mng Dir)

**Forestal y Agricola Monteaguila
S.A.**　(1)
Avenida Francisco Encina s/n, PO Box
32-D, Pallihue, Los Angeles, Chile
Tel.: (56) 43 631 000
Flour Milling Services
N.A.I.C.S.: 311211

Forsac MExico S.A. de C.V.　(1)
Calle Benjamin Franklin block 3 lot 5 and 6
Carretera a Chapala, Km 16 5 Parque In-
dustrial Aeropuerto Tlajomulco de Zuniga,
45645, Jalisco, Mexico
Tel.: (52) 3332841100
Pulp & Paper Distr
N.A.I.C.S.: 424130

Industrias Forestales S.A.　(1)
Agustinas 1357 Piso 9, PO Box 9201, San-
tiago, 341, Chile
Tel.: (56) 24412050
Web Site: http://www.inforsa.cl
Sales Range: $200-249.9 Million
Emp.: 1,000
Newsprint & Wood-Containing Paper Mfr
N.A.I.C.S.: 322120
Andres Larain Marchant (CEO)

**Productos Tissue del Ecuador
S.A.**　(1)

Km 24 5 Via Daule Solar 1-1 Mz 13,
Guayaquil, 090708, Ecuador
Tel.: (593) 45000160
Web Site: http://protisaecuador.negocio.site
Personal Hygiene Paper Mfr
N.A.I.C.S.: 322291

EMPRESAS HITES S.A.
Moneda 970 Piso 4, Santiago, Chile
Tel.: (56) 7265000
Web Site: http://www.hites.cl
HITES—(SGO)
Sales Range: Less than $1 Million
Retail Store Operator
N.A.I.C.O.O.: 459999
Enrique Bone Soto (Chm & Pres)

EMPRESAS ICA S.A.B. DE C.V.
Av Patriotismo 201 Torre Metropoli
6th Floor Col, San Pedro de los Pi-
nos A. Benito Juarez, 03800, Mexico,
Mexico
Tel.: (52) 5552729991　MX
Web Site: https://www.ica.com.mx
Year Founded: 1947
ICA—(MEX)
Sales Range: Less than $1 Million
Engineering & Construction for Public
& Private Sectors
N.A.I.C.S.: 237990
Guadalupe Phillips Margain (CEO)

Subsidiaries:

**AEROPUERTO CULIACAN, S.A. DE
C.V.**　(1)
Carret A Navolato Km 4 5 Col Bachilaguato,
Culiacan, 80130, Sinaloa, Mexico
Tel.: (52) 667 480 7000
Airport Management Services
N.A.I.C.S.: 488119
Hector Cortes (Mng Dir)

**AEROPUERTO MAZATLAN, S.A. DE
C.V.**　(1)
Carretera Internacional al Sur S/N, Mazat-
lan, 82000, Sinaloa, Mexico
Tel.: (52) 669 982 23 99
Airport Management Services
N.A.I.C.S.: 488119

**AEROPUERTO REYNOSA SA DE
CV**　(1)
Carretera a Matamoros-Mazatlan, Reynosa,
88780, Tamaulipas, Mexico
Tel.: (52) 899 478 7000
Airport Management Services
N.A.I.C.S.: 488119

**AEROPUERTO TORREON S.A. DE
C.V.**　(1)
Carretera Torreon San Pedro km 9 S/N,
27016, Torreon, Coahuila, Mexico
Tel.: (52) 871 4787000
Web Site: http://www.oma.aero
Airport Operation Services
N.A.I.C.S.: 488119

**Aeropuerto Acapulco S.A. de
C.V.**　(1)
Blvd De las Naciones s/n Poblado de Los
Amates, Acapulco, 39931, Guerrero,
Mexico
Tel.: (52) 744 435 2060
Airport Management Services
N.A.I.C.S.: 488119

**Aeropuerto Chihuahua, S.A. de
C.V.**　(1)
Blvd Juan Pablo II Km 14, 31390, Chihua-
hua, Mexico
Tel.: (52) 6144787000
Web Site: http://www.oma.aero
Sales Range: $25-49.9 Million
Emp.: 90
Airport Management Services
N.A.I.C.S.: 488119

**Aeropuerto Ciudad Juarez, S.A. de
C.V.**　(1)
Carretera Panamericana Km 18 5, 32690,
Ciudad Juarez, Chihuahua, Mexico
Tel.: (52) 6564787000
Web Site: http://www.oma.aero
Airport Operation Services
N.A.I.C.S.: 488119

Aeropuerto Durango　(1)
Autopista Gomez Palacios Dgo km 15 5,
Durango, 34304, Mexico
Tel.: (52) 618 118 7012
Airport Management Services
N.A.I.C.S.: 488119

Aeropuerto Monterrey　(1)
Carretera Miguel Aleman km 24, Apodaca,
66600, Nuevo Leon, Mexico
Tel.: (52) 81 82 88 7700
Airport Management Services
N.A.I.C.S.: 488119

**Aeropuerto Tampico, S. A. de C.
V.**　(1)
Blvd Adolfo Lopez Mateos No 1001, Tam-
pico, 89339, Mexico
Tel.: (52) 833 478 7000
Airport Management Services
N.A.I.C.S.: 488119

**Aeropuerto Zacatecas, S.A. de
C.V.**　(1)
Carretera Panamericana Zacatecas-
Fresnillo Km 23, 98000, Zacatecas, Mexico
Tel.: (52) 478 985 0338
Web Site: http://www.oma.aero
Emp.: 40
Airport Management Services
N.A.I.C.S.: 488119
Gerardo Vernalmarcint (Gen Mgr)

**Asesoria Tecnica y Gestion Adminis-
trativa, S.A. de C.V.**　(1)
Mineria No 145 Edificio F P B, Mexico,
11800, Mexico
Tel.: (52) 5552729991
Business Management Consulting Services
N.A.I.C.S.: 541611

**Autovia Mitla- Tehuantepec, S.A. de
C.V.**　(1)
Blvd Manuel Avila Camacho No 36 Lomas
de Chapultepec, Delegacion Miguel Hi-
dalgo, Mexico, 11000, DF, Mexico
Tel.: (52) 55 5272 9991
Construction Materials Whslr
N.A.I.C.S.: 423390

**Autovia Paradores y Servicios, S.A.
de C.V.**　(1)
Blvd Manuel Avila Camacho No 36, Col Lo-
mas de Chapultepec, Mexico, 11000,
Mexico
Tel.: (52) 55 52729991
Construction Materials Whslr
N.A.I.C.S.: 423390

**Caminos y Carreteras del Mayab,
S.A.P.I. de C.V.**　(1)
Blvd Manuel Avila Camacho No 36 Lomas
de Chapultepec, Seccion Miguel Hidalgo,
Mexico, 11000, Mexico
Tel.: (52) 55 5272 9991
Construction Materials Whslr
N.A.I.C.S.: 423390

**Carceri e Infraestructura, S.A.P.I. de
C.V.**　(1)
Blvd Manuel Avila Camacho No 36 Lomas
de Chapultepec, Seccion Miguel Hidalgo,
Mexico, 11000, Mexico
Tel.: (52) 55 5272 9991
Construction Materials Whslr
N.A.I.C.S.: 423390

Centro Sur, S.A. de C.V.　(1)
Mineria No 145 Escandon, Seccion Miguel
Hidalgo, Mexico, 11800, Mexico
Tel.: (52) 55 52729991
Investment Management Service
N.A.I.C.S.: 523940

**Compania Hidroelectrica La Yesca,
S.A. de C.V.**　(1)
Manuel Avila Camacho No 36 Piso 2,
Mexico, 11000, Mexico
Tel.: (52) 5552729991
Industrial Construction Services
N.A.I.C.S.: 236220

**Compania Integradora Mercantil Agri-
cola, S.A. de C.V.**　(1)
Mineria 145 Edif G 3o Piso Escandon, Sec-
cion Miguel Hidalgo, Mexico, 11800, Mexico
Tel.: (52) 5552729991
Agricultural Product Whslr
N.A.I.C.S.: 926140

**Concesionaria de Ejes Terrestres de
Coahuila, S.A. de C.V.**　(1)
Mineria 145 Edif F Planta Baja Escandon,
Seccion Miguel Hidalgo, Mexico, 11800,
Mexico
Tel.: (52) 5552275000
Road Construction Services
N.A.I.C.S.: 237990

**Constructora El Cajon, S.A. de
C.V.**　(1)
Mineria No 145 Edif G 3o piso Escandon,
Seccion Miguel Hidalgo, Mexico, 11800,
Mexico
Tel.: (52) 5552729991
Industrial Construction Services
N.A.I.C.S.: 236220

**Constructora Hidroelectrica La Yesca,
S.A. de C.V.**　(1)
Manuel Avila Camacho No 36 Piso 2,
Mexico, 11000, Mexico
Tel.: (52) 5552729991
Industrial Plant Construction Services
N.A.I.C.S.: 237990

**Constructora de Proyectos Hidroelec-
tricos, S.A. de C.V.**　(1)
Manuel Avila Camacho No 36 Piso 2,
Mexico, 11000, Mexico
Tel.: (52) 5552729991
Industrial Construction Services
N.A.I.C.S.: 236220

**Constructora ICA, S. A. de C.
V.**　(1)
Blvd Manuel Avila Camacha No 36 Tower 2
Fl 9, Miguel Hidalgo, Mexico, 11870,
Mexico
Tel.: (52) 555 272 9991
Sales Range: $25-49.9 Million
Emp.: 70
Construction Engineering Services
N.A.I.C.S.: 541330

Construexport, S.A. de C.V.　(1)
Mineria No 145 Escandon, 11800, Mexico,
Mexico
Tel.: (52) 55 52729991
Industrial Building Construction Services
N.A.I.C.S.: 236210

**Controladora de Empresas de Vivi-
enda, S. A. de C.V.**　(1)
Mineria No 145 Edif G 3o piso Escandon,
Mexico, 11800, Miguel Hidalgo, Mexico
Tel.: (52) 5552729991
Industrial Construction Services
N.A.I.C.S.: 236220

**Controladora de Operaciones de In-
fraestructura, S. A. de C. V.**　(1)
Blvd Manuel Avila Camacha No 36 Tower 2
Fl 9, Mexico, 11800, Mexico
Tel.: (52) 5552729991
Sales Range: $50-74.9 Million
Emp.: 70
Investment Management Service
N.A.I.C.S.: 523940

Facchina Construction Co., Inc.　(1)
102 Centennial St Ste 201, La Plata, MD
20646
Tel.: (240) 776-7000
Web Site: http://www.facchina.com
Sales Range: $300-349.9 Million
Emp.: 300
Highway Construction, Concrete Frames,
Site Development & Commercial Building
Construction
N.A.I.C.S.: 237990
George Nash (Dir-Bus Dev)

**Grupo Aeroportuario Centro Norte,
S.A. de C.V.**　(1)
Carretera Miguel Aleman S/N Km 24, Apo-
daca, 66600, Mexico
Tel.: (52) 8186254300
Airport Management Services
N.A.I.C.S.: 488119

**Ica Construccion Civil, S.A. de
C.V.**　(1)
Mineria 145 Colonia Escandon Edificio B
Piso 2, Delegacion Miguel Hidalgo,
11800, DF, Mexico
Tel.: (52) 5552729991
Industrial Construction Services
N.A.I.C.S.: 236220

Ica Infraestructura, S.A. de C.V. **(1)**
Mineria No 145, Mexico, 11800, Mexico
Tel.: (52) 5552729991
Industrial Construction Services
N.A.I.C.S.: 236220

Ica Ingenieria, S.A. de C.V. **(1)**
Mineria No 145 Edif A Piso 3, Mexico,
11800, Mexico
Tel.: (52) 5552729991
Industrial Construction Services
N.A.I.C.S.: 236220

Ica Propiedades Inmuebles, S.A. de
C.V. **(1)**
Manuel Avila Camacho 36, Mexico, 11800,
Mexico
Tel.: (52) 5552729991
Real Estate Development Services
N.A.I.C.S.: 531390

Ica Servicios de Direccion Corpora-
tiva, S.A. de C.V. **(1)**
Minera No 145, Mexico, 11800, Mexico
Tel.: (52) 5552729991
Construction Engineering Services
N.A.I.C.S.: 541330

Ica- Miramar Corporation **(1)**
444 Calle De Diego Ste 105, San Juan, PR
00923
Tel.: (787) 622-3040
Highway & Street Construction Services
N.A.I.C.S.: 237310

Ica- Miramar Metro San Juan
Corp. **(1)**
Carr 2 Km 6 4, Guaynabo, PR 00966
Tel.: (787) 782-9711
Highway Construction Services
N.A.I.C.S.: 237310

Icapital, S.A. de C.V. **(1)**
Mineria No 145 Escandon, Seccion Miguel
Hidalgo, Mexico, 11800, Mexico
Tel.: (52) 55 52729991
Industrial Construction Services
N.A.I.C.S.: 236220

Ingenieros Civiles Asociados Mexico,
S.A. **(1)**
Cl 102 A 50 49, Bogota, Colombia
Tel.: (57) 12574079
Residential Building Construction Services
N.A.I.C.S.: 236116

Ingenieros Civiles Asociados, S. A.
de C. V. **(1)**
Mineria 145 Edificio Central, Mexico, 11800,
Mexico
Tel.: (52) 5 272 9991
Civil Engineering Construction Services
N.A.I.C.S.: 237990

Inmobiliaria Baja, S.A. de C.V. **(1)**
Blvd Manuel Avila Camacho No 36, Mexico,
11000, Mexico
Tel.: (52) 5552729991
Real Estate Manangement Services
N.A.I.C.S.: 531390

Libramiento ICA La Piedad, S.A. de
C.V. **(1)**
Manuel Avila Camacho No 36, Mexico,
11000, Mexico
Tel.: (52) 5552729991
Industrial Construction Services
N.A.I.C.S.: 236220

Operadora de la Autopista del Occi-
dente, S.A. de C.V. **(1)**
Blvd Manuel Avila Camacho No 36, Mexico,
11000, Mexico
Tel.: (52) 5552729991
Commercial Building Construction Services
N.A.I.C.S.: 236220

Prefabricados y Transportes, S.A. de
C.V. **(1)**
Blvd Manuel Avila Camacho No 36 5o Piso
Lomas de Chapultepec, Mexico, 11000,
Mexico
Tel.: (52) 5552729991
Industrial Construction Services
N.A.I.C.S.: 236220

Promotora e Inversora Adisa, S.A. de
C.V. **(1)**
Mineria No 145 Edif G 3er Piso, Mexico,
11800, Mexico

Tel.: (52) 5552729991
Investment Management Service
N.A.I.C.S.: 523940

Rodio Cimentaciones Especiales,
S.A. **(1)**
Velazquez 50 6th Fl, 28001, Madrid,
Spain **(100%)**
Tel.: (34) 915624610
Web Site: http://www.rodio.com
Sales Range: $25-49.9 Million
Emp.: 80
N.A.I.C.S.: 237310
Jose Luex Rogo (Gen Mgr)

San Martin Contratistas Generales
S.A. **(1)**
Jr Morro Solar 1010, Santiago de Surco,
Lima, Peru
Tel.: (51) 511 450 1999
Web Site: http://www.sanmartinperu.pe
Mining Engineering Services
N.A.I.C.S.: 541330

Sondagens Rodio Ltda. **(1)**
Av dos Combatentes 52 Abrunheira, 2710,
Sintra, Portugal
Tel.: (351) 219158210
Web Site: http://www.rodio.pt
Sales Range: $25-49.9 Million
Emp.: 70
Civil Engineering & Construction
N.A.I.C.S.: 237310

Tuneles Concesionados de Acapulco,
S.A. de C.V. **(1)**
Domicilio Conocido Caseta de Cobro, Las
Cruces, Coyuca de Catalan, 39760, Guer-
rero, Mexico
Tel.: (52) 7444411766
Industrial Construction Services
N.A.I.C.S.: 236220

Viveica, S.A. de C.V. **(1)**
Mineria 145 Edif D 4to Piso Col Escandon,
Miguel Hidalgo, Mexico, 11800, Mexico
Tel.: (52) 656 681 7295
Web Site: http://www.viveica.com.mx
Real Estate Manangement Services
N.A.I.C.S.: 531390

EMPRESAS JUAN YARUR
S.A.C.
Avenida Apoquindo 3721, Las Con-
des, Santiago, Chile
Tel.: (56) 2 206 9999 CL
Bank Holding Company
N.A.I.C.S.: 551111
Luis Enrique Yarur Rey (Chm)

Subsidiaries:

Banco de Credito e Inversiones
S.A. **(1)**
The Golf 125, Las Condes, Chile **(55.13%)**
Tel.: (56) 223835471
Web Site: https://www.bci.cl
Rev.: $2,962,497,577
Assets: $79,629,769,933
Liabilities: $74,756,229,149
Net Worth: $4,873,540,785
Earnings: $837,651,380
Emp.: 11,514
Fiscal Year-end: 12/31/2022
Commercial Banking Services
N.A.I.C.S.: 522110
Luis Enrique Yarur Rey (Chm)

Subsidiary (Domestic):

BCI Seguros Generales S.A. **(2)**
Huerfanos 1189 Piso 2-8, Santiago,
Chile **(60%)**
Tel.: (56) 2 2679 9200
Web Site: http://www.bciseguros.cl
Sales Range: $75-99.9 Million
Property & Casualty Insurance Products &
Services
N.A.I.C.S.: 524126
Mario Gazitua Swett (Gen Mgr)

BCI Seguros Vida S.A. **(2)**
Huerfanos 1189 Pisos 2-8, Santiago,
Chile **(60%)**
Tel.: (56) 2 2679 9200
Web Site: http://www.bciseguros.cl
Rev.: $1,781,242,020
Assets: $37,950,905,460
Liabilities: $25,079,909,520

Net Worth: $12,870,995,940
Earnings: $545,325,480
Fiscal Year-end: 12/31/2014
Life Insurance Products & Services
N.A.I.C.S.: 524113
Mario Gazitua Swett (CEO)

Subsidiary (US):

City National Bank of Florida **(2)**
25 W Flagler St, Miami, FL 33130-1712
Tel.: (305) 577-7333
Web Site: http://www.citynationalcm.com
Sales Range: $125-149.9 Million
Emp.: 434
Commercial Banking
N.A.I.C.S.: 522110
Daniel Kushner (CFO)

EMPRESAS LA POLAR S.A.
Nueva de Lyon 72 piso 6, Providen-
cia, Santiago, Chile
Tel.: (56) 6003913000 CL
Web Site: https://www.lapolar.cl
NUEVAPOLAR—(SGO)
Sales Range: Less than $1 Million
Departmental Store Operator
N.A.I.C.S.: 455110
Gonzalo Ceballos Guzman (Gen Mgr)

EMPRESAS LIPIGAS SA
Apoquindo 5400 Piso 15, Los Con-
des, Santiago, Chile
Tel.: (56) 226503620
Web Site: https://www.lipigas.cl
Year Founded: 1950
LIPIGAS—(SGO)
Rev.: $839,369,508
Assets: $834,684,561
Liabilities: $610,413,559
Net Worth: $224,271,002
Earnings: $43,217,600
Emp.: 2,475
Fiscal Year-end: 12/31/23
Liquefied Petroleum Distr
N.A.I.C.S.: 457210
Osvaldo Rosa Ageitos (CFO)

Subsidiaries:

Limagas Natural Peru S.A. **(1)**
Calle Bernini N 149 Torre Trazo Piso 4, San
Borja, Lima, Peru
Tel.: (51) 16408888
Natural Gas Distribution Services
N.A.I.C.S.: 221210

EMPRESAS PENTA S.A.
Avda El Bosque Norte 0440 Piso
9-15, Las Condes, Santiago,
7550000, Chile
Tel.: (56) 2 2203 5606 CL
Web Site:
http://www.empresaspenta.cl
Holding Company
N.A.I.C.S.: 551112

Subsidiaries:

Penta Las Americas Administradora
de Fondos de Inversion SA **(1)**
Av El Bosque Norte 0440 Piso 6 Of 602,
Las Condes, Santiago, Chile
Tel.: (56) 2 2496 7200
Web Site: http://www.lasamericas.cl
Financial & Fund Investments
N.A.I.C.S.: 523999
Horacio Pena Novoa (CEO)

Subsidiary (Domestic):

Sociedad Concesionaria Ruta del Ca-
nal, S.A. **(2)**
Ruta 5 Sur Km 1053 4, Puerto Montt, Chile
Tel.: (56) 65 2438888
Web Site: http://www.rutadelcanal.cl
Road Construction Services
N.A.I.C.S.: 237310

EMPRESAS PETROLEO IPI-
RANGA
Av Dolores Alcaraz Caldas 90, CEP
901-180, Porto Alegre, RS, Brazil

Tel.: (55) 5132164411
Web Site: http://www.ipiranga.com.br
Sales Range: $150-199.9 Million
Emp.: 384
Oil & Gas Exploration & Development
Services
N.A.I.C.S.: 211120

EMPRESAS POLAR
2 Da Avenida De Los Cortijos, Ed
Centro Empresarial Polar, Caracas,
1071, Venezuela
Tel.: (58) 212202311
Web Site: http://www.empresas-
polar.com
Sales Range: $1-4.9 Billion
Emp.: 10,001
Holding Company
N.A.I.C.S.: 551112

Subsidiaries:

Mavesa, S.A. **(1)**
Avenida Principal De Los Ruces Centro, Ed
Centro Empresarial Polar, Caracas, 1071,
Venezuela
Tel.: (58) 2122023111
Web Site: http://www.empresas-polar.com
Sales Range: $350-399.9 Million
Emp.: 1,800
Mfr & Distributor of Consumer Products
such as Food, Soaps & Cleaning Products
N.A.I.C.S.: 311423

EMPRESAS PUBLICAS DE
MEDELLIN ESP
Carrera 58 42-125, Antioquia, Medel-
lin, Colombia
Tel.: (57) 4 34444 115 Co
Web Site: http://www.epm.com.co
Gas & Energy Distribution & Tele-
communications Services
N.A.I.C.S.: 221210
Juan Esteban Calle Restrepo (CEO &
Gen Mgr)

Subsidiaries:

Aguas de Antofagasta S.A. **(1)**
Avda Pedro Aguirre Cerda 6496, Antofa-
gasta, Chile
Tel.: (56) 6007000101
Web Site: http://www3.aguasantofagasta.cl
Waste Water Treatment Services
N.A.I.C.S.: 221320

COMEGSA **(1)**
6a Avenida 8-14 zona 1, Guatemala, Gua-
temala
Tel.: (502) 24204200
Web Site: http://www.comegsa.com.gt
Electric Power Distribution Services
N.A.I.C.S.: 221122

EPM Capital Mexico S.A. de C.V **(1)**
WTC Montecito 38 Piso 37 Oficina 26 Na-
poles, Benito Juarez, 03810, Mexico,
Mexico
Tel.: (52) 55 9000 4084
Telecommunication Servicesb
N.A.I.C.S.: 517810

Subsidiary (Domestic):

Technologia Intercontinenetal S.A. De
C.V. **(2)**
Rio Lerma 171 piso 4 Col, Cuauhtemoc,
06500, Mexico, Mexico
Tel.: (52) 55 3098 5600
Web Site: http://www.ticsa.com.mx
Plant Construction Service
N.A.I.C.S.: 236210

Subsidiary (Domestic):

Aquasol Morelia S.A. de C.V. **(3)**
Aristeo Mercado No 754, Morelia, 58280,
Mexico
Tel.: (52) 4513590211
Telecommunication Servicesb
N.A.I.C.S.: 517810

Corporacion de Personal Administra-
tivo S. A. de C. V. **(3)**
Spencer No 425, Mexico, 11580, Mexico
Tel.: (52) 30985209

Empresas Publicas de Medellin ESP—(Continued)

Telecommunication Servicesb
N.A.I.C.S.: 517810

Proyectos de Ingenieria Corporativa, S.A. de C.V. (3)
Rio Marne No 17, Mexico, 06500, Mexico
Tel.: (52) 30985609
Telecommunication Servicesb
N.A.I.C.S.: 517810

EPM Chile S.A. (1)
Edificio New Century Avda Pdte Kennedy No 4700 oficina 902, Vitacura, Santiago, Chile
Tel.: (56) 229536631
Plant Construction Service
N.A.I.C.S.: 236210

Elektra Noreste S.A. (1)
Sede Corporativa Costa del Este Business Park, Torre Oeste Piso 3, Panama, Panama
Tel.: (507) 3404600
Web Site: http://www.ensa.com.pa
Electrical Component Distr
N.A.I.C.S.: 423610

Empresas Publicas de Oriente Antio-queno S.A. (1)
Carrera 47 Cl 74 18, Rionegro, Colombia
Tel.: (57) 45611313
Telecommunication Servicesb
N.A.I.C.S.: 517810

Hidroecologica del Teribe S.A. (1)
Ave Balboa con Aquilino de la Guardia Torre BICSA Financial Center, piso 35 oficina 10 Panama, Changuinola, Bocas del Toro, Panama
Tel.: (507) 7588034
Web Site: http://www.hidroecologicadelteribe.com
Hydroelectric Power Generation Services
N.A.I.C.S.: 221111

Trelec, S. A. (1)
2a Avenida 9-27 Zona 1, Guatemala, Guatemala
Tel.: (502) 22231800
Electric Power Transmission Services
N.A.I.C.S.: 221121

UNE EPM Telecomunicaciones SA (1)
Carrera 16 # 11a Sur 100, Medellin, Colombia
Tel.: (57) 4 382 2020
Web Site: http://www.une.com.co
Telecommunication Servicesb
N.A.I.C.S.: 517810

Subsidiary (Domestic):

Colombia Movil S.A.E.S.P. (2)
Carrera 13 2700, Piso 3, 810, Bogota, Colombia
Tel.: (57) 1 587 0000
Web Site: http://www.tigo.com.co
Telecommunication Servicesb
N.A.I.C.S.: 517810

Subsidiary (Non-US):

Multivision S.A. (3)
Calle 22 de Calacoto 7810, La Paz, Bolivia (100%)
Tel.: (591) 2 2157777
Cable Television Broadcasting Services
N.A.I.C.S.: 516210

Tigo Pvt Ltd. (3)
109 Galle Rd 3, Grandpass Rd, Colombo, Sri Lanka
Tel.: (94) 112541541
Web Site: http://www.etisalat.lk
Cellular & Wireless Telecommunications
N.A.I.C.S.: 517112
Beryl Hammond Appiah (Dir-HR)

EMPRESAS TAGAROPULOS, S.A.
Via Ricardo J Alfaro La Loceria, PO Box 6-4000, Panama, Panama
Tel.: (507) 360 0316
Holding Company
N.A.I.C.S.: 551112

EMPRESAS TRICOT SA
Vicuna Mackenna 3600, Macul, 7810967, Santiago, Chile
Tel.: (56) 2223503600
Web Site: https://www.tricot.cl
Year Founded: 1952
TRICOT—(SGO)
Sales Range: Less than $1 Million
Apparels Mfr
N.A.I.C.S.: 315990

EMPRESS MINING INC.
492 Gilbert Road, Preston, 3072, VIC, Australia
Tel.: (61) 3 9605 3907   NV
Year Founded: 2010
Mineral Exploration Services
N.A.I.C.S.: 212290

EMPRESS ROYALTY CORP.
Suite 3123 595 Burrad Street, Vancouver, V7X 1J1, BC, Canada
Tel.: (604) 331-2080   BC
Web Site: https://www.empressroyalty.com
Year Founded: 2020
EMPYF—(OTCQB)
Rev.: $1,825,049
Assets: $19,934,102
Liabilities: $3,294,649
Net Worth: $16,639,453
Earnings: ($3,379,960)
Fiscal Year-end: 12/31/22
Mineral Mining Services
N.A.I.C.S.: 213115
Alexandra Woodyer Sherron (Pres)

EMPTEEZY LTD
Empteezy Houstoun Industrial Estate 4 Muir Road, Houstoun Industrial Estate, Livingston, EH54 5DR, W Lothian, United Kingdom
Tel.: (44) 1506430309
Web Site: http://www.empteezy.co.uk
Year Founded: 1986
Sales Range: $10-24.9 Million
Emp.: 60
Material Handling & Storage Container Mfr
N.A.I.C.S.: 332439
Bruce Wishart (Founder & Mng Dir)

Subsidiaries:

Delahaye Industries S.A.S. (1)
Zone DIA Nantes Atlantique Avenue Antoine de Saint Exupery, Saint Aignan de Grand Lieu, 44860, Nantes, France
Tel.: (33) 2 40 32 34 00
Web Site: http://www.delahaye-industries.fr
Storage Container Mfr
N.A.I.C.S.: 332420

Empteezy Benelux BVBA (1)
Zwaaikomstraat 5, 8800, Roeselare, Belgium
Tel.: (32) 51 63 68 54
Web Site: http://www.empteezy.be
Storage Container Mfr
N.A.I.C.S.: 332420

Empteezy Holland BV (1)
Waalhaven N-Z 83 Havennr 2078, 3087 BJ, Rotterdam, Netherlands
Tel.: (31) 10 303 00 40
Web Site: http://www.empteezy.nl
Storage Container Mfr
N.A.I.C.S.: 332420

Empteezy Iberica S.L. (1)
Pol Ind Can Prunera Calle Solsones s/n nave 18, Villirana, 08759, Barcelona, Spain
Tel.: (34) 93 683 51 75
Web Site: http://www.empteezy-iberica.com
Storage Container Mfr
N.A.I.C.S.: 332420

Empteezy Italia S.r.l (1)
Via Enrico Fermi 8/10, Settimo Milanese, 20019, Milan, Italy
Tel.: (39) 02 32 88 131
Web Site: http://www.empteezy.it
Storage Container Mfr

N.A.I.C.S.: 332420

Empteezy UAE Fze (1)
Warehouse No WN-05, PO Box 42429, Hamriyah Free Zone, Sharjah, United Arab Emirates
Tel.: (971) 6 526 1997
Web Site: http://www.empteezyme.com
Storage Container Mfr
N.A.I.C.S.: 332420

Romold Ltd (1)
4 Maxwell Square Brucefield Industrial Park, Livingston, EH54 9BL, Scotland, United Kingdom
Tel.: (44) 1506 409973
Web Site: http://www.romold.co.uk
Storage Container Mfr
N.A.I.C.S.: 332420

Schoeller Industries (1)
Z I Rue De La Maziere, 67130, Wisches, France
Tel.: (33) 388473500
Web Site: http://www.schoellerindustries.fr
Engineered Papers & Specialized Printing Papers Mfr
N.A.I.C.S.: 322120

EMPYREAN CASHEWS LIMITED
Opposite MTNL Office 1309 Lodha Supremus Saki Vihar Rd, Powai, Mumbai, 400072, Maharashtra, India
Tel.: (91) 7625098406
Web Site: https://www.krishival.com
Year Founded: 2014
KRISHIVAL—(NSE)
Rev.: $7,126,419
Assets: $7,527,170
Liabilities: $1,774,500
Net Worth: $5,752,670
Earnings: $453,016
Emp.: 32
Fiscal Year-end: 03/31/22
Cashew Product Mfr
N.A.I.C.S.: 333111

EMPYREAN ENERGY PLC
2nd Floor 38-43 Lincoln's Inn Fields, London, WC2A 3PE, United Kingdom
Tel.: (44) 2071821746
Web Site: https://www.empyreanenergy.com
EME—(AIM)
Assets: $6,353,000
Liabilities: $10,712,000
Net Worth: ($4,359,000)
Earnings: ($9,586,000)
Fiscal Year-end: 03/31/24
Energy Resource Exploration & Development In Geopolitically Stable Environments
N.A.I.C.S.: 926110
John Laycock (Dir-Fin)

EMPYREAN TECHNOLOGY CO., LTD.
2nd Floor Building A Wangjing Science Park No 2 Lizehong 2nd Road, Chaoyang District, Beijing, 100102, China
Tel.: (86) 1084776888
Web Site: https://www.empyrean.com.cn
Year Founded: 2009
301269—(CHIN)
Rev.: $139,898,386
Assets: $766,440,172
Liabilities: $104,147,195
Net Worth: $662,292,977
Earnings: $27,791,704
Fiscal Year-end: 12/31/23
Software Development Services
N.A.I.C.S.: 541511
Weiping Liu (Chm)

EMQTEC AG
Innere Industriestr 22, Friedberg, 86316, Germany

Tel.: (49) 821808510
Plastics Product Mfr
N.A.I.C.S.: 326111
Erwin Franz Mueller (Chm-Mgmt Bd)

EMR CAPITAL PTY LTD
Level 2 150 Collins Street, Melbourne, 3000, VIC, Australia
Tel.: (61) 396699999
Web Site: http://www.emrcapital.com
Private Equity Firm Services
N.A.I.C.S.: 523999
Owen Hegarty (Chm)

EMRO CO. LTD.
5th Fl Dangsan SK V1 Center E Unit 11 41-gil Dangsan-ro, Yongdeungpo-gu, Seoul, 07217, Korea (South)
Tel.: (82) 27859848
Web Site: https://www.emro.co.kr
Year Founded: 2000
Software Development Services
N.A.I.C.S.: 541511
Jay Song (CEO)

EMS ENERGY LIMITED
25 International Business Park, German Centre No 02-57, Singapore, 639916, Singapore
Tel.: (65) 6861 2722
Web Site: http://www.emsenergy.com.sg
Sales Range: $25-49.9 Million
Emp.: 100
Marine, Oil & Gas Engineering Services
N.A.I.C.S.: 237990
Teck Jin Ting (Chm & CEO)

Subsidiaries:

EMS Offshore Pte. Ltd. (1)
10 Tuas Ave 11, Singapore, 639076, Singapore
Tel.: (65) 68621062
Web Site: http://www.emsenergy.com.sg
Vessel Products Mfr
N.A.I.C.S.: 322219
Ting Teck Jin (CEO)

Subsidiary (Domestic):

Engineering & Marine Services (Pte) Ltd (2)
10 Tuas Ave 11, Singapore, 639076, Singapore
Tel.: (65) 68621062
Web Site: http://www.emsenergy.com.sg
Offshore Natural Gas Production Services
N.A.I.C.S.: 211120
Teckjin Ting (Mng Dir)

EMS Water Pte Ltd (1)
10 Tuas Ave 11, Singapore, Singapore
Tel.: (65) 68621062
Web Site: http://www.emsenergy.com.sg
Sales Range: $25-49.9 Million
Emp.: 30
General Trading Company
N.A.I.C.S.: 238990

EMS LIMITED
C-88 Raj Nagar Distt Centre Raj Nagar, Ghaziabad, 201 002, Uttar Pradesh, India
Tel.: (91) 1204235555
Web Site: https://www.ems.co.in
Year Founded: 1998
EMSLIMITED—(NSE)
Rev.: $65,440,463
Assets: $77,996,003
Liabilities: $77,739,841
Net Worth: $256,163
Earnings: $13,236,318
Emp.: 316
Fiscal Year-end: 03/31/23
Construction Engineering Services
N.A.I.C.S.: 541330
Ashish Tomar (Mng Dir)

EMS WIRING SYSTEMS PTE LTD
240 MacPherson Road 02-04, Singapore, 348574, Singapore
Tel.: (65) 64442988   SG
Web Site: http://www.emsgroup.biz
Year Founded: 1990
Telecommunication Servicesb
N.A.I.C.S.: 517810
Raphael Teo *(Chm)*

EMS-CHEMIE HOLDING AG
Fuederholzstrasse 34, 8704, Herrliberg, Switzerland
Tel.: (41) 449157000   CH
Web Site: https://www.ems-group.com
Year Founded: 1936
EMSN—(SWX)
Rev.: $2,041,105,040
Assets: $2,352,746,061
Liabilities: $513,331,664
Net Worth: $1,839,414,398
Earnings: $497,902,893
Emp.: 2,521
Fiscal Year-end: 12/31/20
Polymer Plastics & Fiber Mfr
N.A.I.C.S.: 326199
Bernhard Merki *(Chm)*

Subsidiaries:

EFTEC (Changshu) Engineering Co., Ltd.   **(1)**
Building 7 No 20 Wanhe Road, Wanhe Indual Park, Changshu, 215513, China
Tel.: (86) 51252978590
Automotive Equipment Distr
N.A.I.C.S.: 423120

EFTEC (Czech Republic) A.S.   **(1)**
U Tescomy 206, 760 01, Zlin, Czech Republic
Tel.: (420) 577004411
Automotive Equipment Distr
N.A.I.C.S.: 423120

EFTEC North America, L.L.C.   **(1)**
20219 Northline Rd, Taylor, MI 48180
Tel.: (248) 585-2200
Automotive Equipment Distr
N.A.I.C.S.: 423120

EMS-CHEMIE (China) Ltd.   **(1)**
227 Songbei Road, Suzhou Industrial Park, Suzhou, 215126, Jiangsu, China
Tel.: (86) 51286668180
Polymer Plastics & Fiber Mfr
N.A.I.C.S.: 326199

EMS-CHEMIE (Japan) Ltd.   **(1)**
M Building 2-11-20 Higashikojiya, Ota-ku, Tokyo, 144-0033, Japan   **(70%)**
Tel.: (81) 357350611
Web Site: https://www.emsgrivory.co.jp
Sales Range: $50-74.9 Million
Emp.: 15
Performance Polymers & Fine Chemicals/Engineering
N.A.I.C.S.: 325199

EMS-CHEMIE (Korea) Ltd.   **(1)**
817 Doosan Venturedigm 415 Heungan Daero, Dongan-gu, Anyang, 14059, Gyeonggi-do, Korea (South)
Tel.: (82) 314783159
Polymer Plastics & Fiber Mfr
N.A.I.C.S.: 326199

EMS-CHEMIE (Neumunster) GmbH Co. KG   **(1)**
Tungendorfer Str 10, 24536, Neumunster, Germany
Tel.: (49) 4321302500
Web Site: http://www.emsgriltech.com
Polymer Plastics & Fiber Mfr
N.A.I.C.S.: 326199
Carsten Scheffler *(Mng Dir)*

EMS-CHEMIE (Suzhou) Ltd.   **(1)**
227 Songbei Road, Suzhou Industrial Park, Suzhou, 215126, Jiangsu, China
Tel.: (86) 51286668181
Polymer Plastics & Fiber Mfr
N.A.I.C.S.: 326199

EMS-CHEMIE (Taiwan) Ltd.   **(1)**
36 Kwang Fu South Road, Hsin Chu Industrial Park Fu Kou Hsiang, Hsin-chu, 30351, Hsien, Taiwan   **(100%)**
Tel.: (886) 35985335
Web Site: http://www.emsgrivory.com
Sales Range: $50-74.9 Million
Emp.: 65
Polymer Plastics & Fiber Mfr
N.A.I.C.S.: 326199

EMS-Chemie (Deutschland) GmbH   **(1)**
Warthweg 14, 64823, Gross-Umstadt, Germany   **(100%)**
Tel.: (49) 60787830
Sales Range: $75-99.9 Million
Emp.: 150
N.A.I.C.S.: 326199

EMS-Chemie (France) S.A.   **(1)**
855 Avenue Roger Salengro, 92370, Chaville, France   **(100%)**
Tel.: (33) 141100610
Web Site: http://www.ems-group.com
Sales Range: $25-49.9 Million
Emp.: 25
Chemical Polymers Mfr
N.A.I.C.S.: 325180

EMS-Chemie (North America) Inc.   **(1)**
2060 Corporate Way, Sumter, SC 29151   **(100%)**
Tel.: (803) 481-9173
Sales Range: $50-74.9 Million
Emp.: 100
Mfr of Polyhydrocarbonic Chemicals
N.A.I.C.S.: 325211

EMS-Chemie (Produktion) AG   **(1)**
Via Innovativa 1, 7013, Domat/Ems, Switzerland
Tel.: (41) 816326111
Chemical Product Mfr & Distr
N.A.I.C.S.: 325998

EMS-Chemie (Switzerland) AG   **(1)**
Hofstrasse 31, 8590, Romanshorn, Switzerland
Tel.: (41) 714664277
Chemical Product Mfr & Distr
N.A.I.C.S.: 325998

EMS-Chemie (UK) Ltd.   **(1)**
Forest Lodge, Dunston Business Village Dunston, Stafford, ST18 9AB, United Kingdom   **(100%)**
Tel.: (44) 1785283739
Sales Range: $50-74.9 Million
Emp.: 10
N.A.I.C.S.: 326199

EMS-Chemie AG   **(1)**
Via Innovativa 1, 7013, Domat/Ems, Switzerland   **(100%)**
Tel.: (41) 816326111
Sales Range: $600-649.9 Million
Emp.: 1,600
N.A.I.C.S.: 326199
Morf Christian *(VP-Sales-Marketing)*

Subsidiary (Domestic):

EMS-Griltech AG   **(2)**
Via Innovativa 1, 7013, Domat/Ems, Switzerland
Tel.: (41) 816327202
Web Site: http://www.emsgriltech.com
Chemical Product Mfr & Distr
N.A.I.C.S.: 325998

EMS-INTERNATIONAL FINANCE (Guernsey) Ltd.   **(1)**
Trafalger Court 3rd Floor West Wing, Saint Peter Port, GY1 2JA, Guernsey
Tel.: (44) 1481712704
Financial Services
N.A.I.C.S.: 561499

EMS-PATENT AG   **(1)**
Via Innovativa 1, 7013, Domat/Ems, Switzerland
Tel.: (41) 816326826
Web Site: http://www.emspatent.com
Plastics Product Mfr
N.A.I.C.S.: 326199
Magdalena Martullo *(Gen Mgr)*

EMS-UBE Ltd.   **(1)**

1978-10 Kogushi, Ube, 755-8633, Yamaguchi, Japan
Tel.: (81) 836310213
Polymer Plastics & Fiber Mfr
N.A.I.C.S.: 326199

Eftec AG   **(1)**
Hofstrasse 31, PO Box 46, 8590, Romanshorn, Switzerland   **(100%)**
Tel.: (41) 714664000
Sales Range: $25-49.9 Million
Emp.: 100
Adhesives, Sealants & Coatings Mfr for the Automotive Industry
N.A.I.C.S.: 325520

Subsidiary (Non-US):

Changchun EFTEC Chemical Products Ltd.   **(2)**
No 808 Chuangxin Road, New High Tech Ind Development Zone, Changchun, 130012, China
Tel.: (86) 43185080800
Sales Range: $25-49.9 Million
Emp.: 16
N.A.I.C.S.: 326199

D PLAST-EFTEC UA   **(2)**
St Gorkeho 27/29, 69063, Zaporizhzhya, Ukraine
Tel.: (380) 612138568
Web Site: http://www.eftec.ch
Adhesives, Sealants & Coatings Mfr
N.A.I.C.S.: 325520

D Plast-Eftec NN   **(2)**
ul Kovpaka 1, 603 053, Nizhniy Novgorod, Russia
Tel.: (7) 8312530515
Web Site: http://www.ems-group.com
N.A.I.C.S.: 326199

D Plast-Eftec a.s.   **(2)**
Utescomy 206, 76001, Zlin, Czech Republic   **(52%)**
Tel.: (420) 577004411
Web Site: http://www.dplast-eftec.cz
Sales Range: $500-549.9 Million
Emp.: 85
Mfr of Automotive Products & Parts
N.A.I.C.S.: 336340
Richard Valko *(Gen Mgr)*

EFTEC (Elabuga) OOO   **(2)**
Industrial Zone Alabuga Street 20 1 case 1/1, Yelabuga, 423 603, Russia
Tel.: (7) 8555751940
Automotive Equipment Distr
N.A.I.C.S.: 423120

EFTEC (India) Pvt. Ltd.   **(2)**
G-9 MIDC Area Ranjangaon Pune-Ahmednagar Highway, Ranjangaon Tal-Shirur Dist, Pune, 412220, Maharashtra, India
Tel.: (91) 2138663400
Emp.: 5
Adhesives, Sealants & Coatings Mfr
N.A.I.C.S.: 325520

EFTEC (Nizhniy Novgorod) OOO **(2)**
Ul Shuvalovsky kanal 6, Nizhniy Novgorod, 603 053, Russia
Tel.: (7) 8312996892
Automotive Equipment Distr
N.A.I.C.S.: 423120

EFTEC (Romania) S.R.L.   **(2)**
Budeasa Mare, Arges County, RO-117151, Budeasa, Romania
Tel.: (40) 248236377
Adhesives, Sealants & Coatings Mfr
N.A.I.C.S.: 325520

EFTEC Brasil Ltda.   **(2)**
Av Charles Goodyear 521 Cururuquara, Santana de Parnaiba, 06524-115, SP, Brazil
Tel.: (55) 1141559191
Adhesives, Sealants & Coatings Mfr
N.A.I.C.S.: 325520

EFTEC China Ltd.   **(2)**
3313-3317 Jardine House, 1 Connaught Place, Central, China (Hong Kong)
Tel.: (852) 2526 4868
Adhesives, Sealants & Coatings Mfr
N.A.I.C.S.: 325520

Subsidiary (Non-US):

EFTEC (Changshu) Automotive Materials Limited   **(3)**

No 88 Wanfu Road, Changshu Economic and Technological Development Zone, Changshu, 215513, Jiangsu, China
Tel.: (86) 51252978550
Automotive Equipment Distr
N.A.I.C.S.: 423120

EFTEC (Shanghai) Services Co., Ltd.   **(3)**
Floor 16 V-Capital Mansion 333 Xian Xia Road, Shanghai, CN-200336, China
Chemical Product Mfr & Distr
N.A.I.C.S.: 325998

Foshan EFTEC Automotive Materials Co., Ltd.   **(3)**
Plant 2 No 4 in Area A Lubao Park, Sanshui Central Science and Industry Park, Foshan, 528139, Guangdong, China
Tel.: (86) 75787266735
Chemical Product Mfr & Distr
N.A.I.C.S.: 325998

Subsidiary (Non-US):

EFTEC Engineering GmbH   **(2)**
Dornierstrasse 7, 88677, Markdorf, Germany
Tel.: (49) 75449200
Adhesives, Sealants & Coatings Mfr
N.A.I.C.S.: 325520

EFTEC Mexico S.A. de C.V.   **(2)**
Calle 56 Sur 11 CIVAC, 62578, Jiutepec, Morelos, Mexico
Tel.: (52) 7773193477
Automotive Equipment Distr
N.A.I.C.S.: 423120

EFTEC-PLACOSA   **(2)**
Calle 56 sur #11 CIVAC, 62578, Jiutepec, Morelos, Mexico
Tel.: (52) 777 319 3477
Adhesives, Sealants & Coatings Mfr
N.A.I.C.S.: 325520

Eftec (Thailand) Co. Ltd.   **(2)**
109/10 Moo 4 Pluakdaeng, Eastern Seaboard Industrial Estate, Rayong, 21140, Thailand   **(100%)**
Tel.: (66) 33211301
Sales Range: $25-49.9 Million
Emp.: 20
Mfr of Adhesives, Sealants & Coatings for the Automotive Industry
N.A.I.C.S.: 326199

Eftec Asia Pte. Ltd.   **(2)**
15 Beach Road, #03-07 Beach Centre, Singapore, 189677, Singapore   **(100%)**
Tel.: (65) 65458201
Web Site: http://www.ems-group.com
Plastics Product Mfr
N.A.I.C.S.: 326199

Eftec Engineering AB   **(2)**
Spangatan 3, 28121, Hassleholm, Sweden   **(100%)**
Tel.: (46) 45188000
Web Site: http://www.eftec.se
Sales Range: $10-24.9 Million
Emp.: 40
Mfr of Adhesives, Sealants & Coatings for the Automotive Industry
N.A.I.C.S.: 326199

Eftec Ltd.   **(2)**
Mid Glamorgan, Rhigos, Aberdare, CF44 9UE, Great Britain, United Kingdom   **(100%)**
Tel.: (44) 1685815400
Sales Range: $25-49.9 Million
Emp.: 30
Mfr of Adhesives, Sealants & Coatings for the Automotive Industry
N.A.I.C.S.: 326199

Eftec Market GmbH   **(2)**
Pyrmonter Strasse 76, Lugde, 32676, Germany   **(100%)**
Tel.: (49) 5281982980
Web Site: http://www.eftec.de
Rev.: $10,396,854
Emp.: 65
Mfr of Polymer Plastics & Fiber
N.A.I.C.S.: 326199
Edmond Robeyn *(Mng Dir)*

Eftec N.V.   **(2)**
Henry Fordlaan 1, 3600, Genk, Limburg, Belgium   **(99%)**

EMS-CHEMIE HOLDING AG

EMS-Chemie Holding AG—(Continued)
Tel.: (32) 89651400
Sales Range: $25-49.9 Million
Emp.: 100
Mfr of Polymer Plastics & Fiber
N.A.I.C.S.: 326199

Eftec S.A. (2)
Carretera Logrono Km 29 2, Figueruelas,
50639, Zaragoza, Spain (100%)
Tel.: (34) 976656269
Web Site: http://www.ems-group.com
Sales Range: $25-49.9 Million
Emp.: 35
Mfr of Adhesives, Sealants & Coatings for
the Automotive Industy
N.A.I.C.S.: 326199

Eftec S.a.r.l. (2)
Velizy Espace Immeuble Le Blériot 13 av-
enue Morane Saulnier, Boite postale 16,
Velizy-Villacoublay, 78140, Chaville, France
Tel.: (33) 141100610
Sales Range: $125-149.9 Million
Emp.: 8
Mfr of Polymer Plastics & Fiber
N.A.I.C.S.: 326199

Eftec Shroff India Limited (2)
Plot No 645-646 4th FL Oberoi Chambers
II, New Link Road, Mumbai, 400053,
India (49%)
Tel.: (91) 2138663400
Web Site: http://www.eftec.com
Emp.: 120
Bonding, Coating, Sealing & Damping Sys-
tems
N.A.I.C.S.: 339991
Sagar Kulkarni (Pres)

**Shanghai Eftec Chemical Products
Ltd.** (2)
Humin Road 521 Guang Hua Road, Shang-
hai, 201108, China (60%)
Tel.: (86) 2164891122
Sales Range: $10-24.9 Million
Emp.: 70
Sealant, Adhesive & Coating Mfr
N.A.I.C.S.: 325510

**Wuhu EFTEC Chemical Products
Ltd.** (2)
Yinhu North Road East, Wuhu, 241009, An-
hui, China
Tel.: (86) 5535965152
Adhesives, Sealants & Coatings Mfr
N.A.I.C.S.: 325520

EMSLAND-STARKE GMBH

Emslandstrasse 58, D-49824, Emlich-
heim, Germany
Tel.: (49) 5943 81 0 De
Web Site: http://www.emsland-
group.de
Year Founded: 1928
Emp.: 976
Mfr of Products from Renewable Raw
Materials Like Potato Starches,
Flakes & Granules
N.A.I.C.S.: 111211
Gerrit-Jan Wesselink (COO)

Subsidiaries:

**Emsland-Starke Asia Pacific Pte
Ltd.** (1)
25 International Business Park 02-58 Ger-
man Center, Singapore, 609916, Singapore
Tel.: (65) 65628066
Starch Mfr
N.A.I.C.S.: 311221

**Emsland-Starke GmbH Golssen
Factory** (1)
Am Bahnhof 34, 15938, Berlin, Germany
Tel.: (49) 354523830
Starch Mfr
N.A.I.C.S.: 311221

**Emsland-Starke GmbH Kyritz
Factory** (1)
Pritzwalker Strasse 10, 16866, Berlin, Ger-
many
Tel.: (49) 33971680
Starch Mfr
N.A.I.C.S.: 311221

**Emsland-Starke GmbH Wietzendorf
Factory** (1)
Klein Amerika, 29649, Berlin, Germany
Tel.: (49) 519698800
Starch Mfr
N.A.I.C.S.: 311221

**Emsland-Starke Logistics GmbH &
Co. KG** (1)
Rudolf-Diesel-Strasse 8, 49824, Emlich-
heim, Germany
Tel.: (49) 5943810
Starch Mfr
N.A.I.C.S.: 311221

EMSTEEL BUILDING MATERI-ALS PJSC

PO Box 9022, Musaffah, Abu Dhabi,
United Arab Emirates
Tel.: (971) 25511187
Web Site: https://www.emsteel.com
Year Founded: 2005
Rev.: $263,457,709
Assets: $907,565,215
Liabilities: $419,255,776
Net Worth: $488,309,438
Earnings: $14,555,554
Fiscal Year-end: 12/31/18
Construction Product Mfr
N.A.I.C.S.: 339999
Jamal Obaid Salem Al Dhaheri (Chm)

EMTEK (SHENZHEN) CO., LTD.

Unit 01 6/F Buiding 11A Shenzhen
bay Eco-Technology Park, Keji South
Road Nanshan District, Shenzhen,
518057, Guangdong, China
Tel.: (86) 4008838258
Web Site: https://www.emtek.com.cn
Year Founded: 2000
300938—(SSE)
Rev.: $76,533,444
Assets: $206,654,760
Liabilities: $39,104,208
Net Worth: $167,550,552
Earnings: $16,574,220
Fiscal Year-end: 12/31/22
Testing Services
N.A.I.C.S.: 541380
Jiezhong Lv (Chm)

Subsidiaries:

EMTEK (Dongguan) Co., Ltd. (1)
1 2/F Building 2 Zone A No 9 XinCheng Av-
enue, ZhongDa Marine Biotechnology Re-
search and Development Base, Dongguan,
Guangdong, China
Tel.: (86) 76922807078
Laboratory Testing Services
N.A.I.C.S.: 541380

EMTEK (Guangzhou) Co., Ltd. (1)
4/F Building A Hongtao Science and Tech-
nology Park No 38, Nanxiang 3rd Road
Huangpu District, Guangzhou, China
Tel.: (86) 2082553111
Laboratory Testing Services
N.A.I.C.S.: 541380

EMTEK (Ningbo) Co., Ltd. (1)
No 8 Building 8 Lane 216 QingYi Road
High-Tech Zone, Ningbo, Zhejiang, China
Tel.: (86) 57427907998
Laboratory Testing Services
N.A.I.C.S.: 541380

EMTEK (Suzhou) Co., Ltd. (1)
No 1388 Songjia Road, Wuzhong Economic
and Technological Development Zone, Su-
zhou, China
Tel.: (86) 51280996798
Laboratory Testing Services
N.A.I.C.S.: 541380

EMTEK (Wuhan) Co., Ltd. (1)
Incubation Park No 17 Gutian 5th Road,
Qiaokou District, Wuhan, Hubei, China
Tel.: (86) 2784733628
Laboratory Testing Services
N.A.I.C.S.: 541380

EMU NL

10 Walker Avenue, West Perth, 6005,
WA, Australia
Tel.: (61) 419833604
Web Site: https://www.emunl.com.au
EMU—(ASX)
Rev.: $12,496
Assets: $134,858
Liabilities: $157,356
Net Worth: ($22,498)
Earnings: ($1,358,409)
Emp.: 10
Fiscal Year-end: 06/30/24
Diamond Mining Services
N.A.I.C.S.: 212311
Damien Kelly (Sec)

EMUDHRA LIMITED

eMudhra Digital Campus No 12-P1-A
& 12-P1-B, Hi-Tech Defence and
Aerospace Park IT sector Jala Hobli
B K Palya, Bengaluru, 562149, India
Tel.: (91) 8046156902
Web Site: https://www.emudhra.com
Year Founded: 2008
543533—(BOM)
Rev.: $25,079,828
Assets: $35,509,110
Liabilities: $14,545,713
Net Worth: $20,963,397
Earnings: $5,615,201
Fiscal Year-end: 03/31/22
Information Technology Services
N.A.I.C.S.: 541512

Subsidiaries:

eMudhra, Inc. (1)
97 Cedar Grove Ln Ste 202, Somerset, NJ
08873
Tel.: (559) 546-4889
Information Technology Services
N.A.I.C.S.: 541512

EMUGE-WERK RICHARD GLIMPEL GMBH & CO. KG

Nurnberger Strasse 96 100, 91207,
Lauf an der Pegnitz, Germany
Tel.: (49) 91231860
Web Site: http://www.emuge.de
Rev.: $100,696,200
Emp.: 761
Threading Equipment Mfr
N.A.I.C.S.: 333517
Helmut Glimpel (Co-Mng Dir)

Subsidiaries:

**EMUGE Prazisionswerkzeuge
GmbH** (1)
Im Astenfeld 10, 4490, Sankt Florian, Aus-
tria
Tel.: (43) 722480001
Web Site: http://www.emuge-franken.at
Machine Tool Distr
N.A.I.C.S.: 423830
Josef Kroll (Mgr-Sls)

**EMUGE-FRANKEN (Bulgaria)
e.o.o.d.** (1)
Neofil Rilski Str No 1 Ap 25, 5500, Lovech,
Bulgaria
Tel.: (359) 68624546
Web Site: http://www.emuge-franken-
bg.com
Machine Tool Distr
N.A.I.C.S.: 423830

EMUGE-FRANKEN AB (1)
Hagalundsvägen 43, 70230, Orebro, Swe-
den
Tel.: (46) 19245000
Web Site: http://www.emuge-franken.se
Machine Tool Distr
N.A.I.C.S.: 423830
Magnus Andersson (Mng Dir)

EMUGE-FRANKEN AB (1)
Toldbodgade 18 5 sal, 1253, Copenhagen,
Denmark
Tel.: (45) 70257220
Web Site: http://www.emuge-franken.dk
Machine Tool Distr
N.A.I.C.S.: 423830
Magnus Andersson (Mng Dir)

EMUGE-FRANKEN B.V. (1)
Handelsstraat 28, 6851 EH, Huissen, Neth-
erlands
Tel.: (31) 263259020
Web Site: http://www.emuge-franken.nl
Machine Tools Mfr
N.A.I.C.S.: 333517
Johan Vlietstra (Mng Dir)

**EMUGE-FRANKEN Hassas Kesici
Takim Sanayi Ltd. Sti.** (1)
Ataturk Mah 3 Cad No 1/1 D 7, Atasehir,
34758, Istanbul, Turkiye
Tel.: (90) 2164551272
Web Site: http://www.emuge-franken.com
Machine Tools Mfr
N.A.I.C.S.: 333517
Atilla Sinan Sayginer (Country Mgr)

EMUGE-FRANKEN S.r.l. (1)
Via Cantinotti 25, Cormano, 20032, Milan,
Italy
Tel.: (39) 0239324402
Machine Tool Distr
N.A.I.C.S.: 423830

EMUGE-FRANKEN SARL (1)
2 Bd de la Libération, 93284, Paris, Cedex,
France
Tel.: (33) 155872222
Web Site: http://www.emuge-franken.fr
Machine Tool Distr
N.A.I.C.S.: 423830

EMUGE-FRANKEN Technik (1)
ul Marysinska 29, 04-606, Warsaw, Poland
Tel.: (48) 228796731
Web Site: http://www.emuge-franken.com.pl
Machine Tool Distr
N.A.I.C.S.: 423830

**EMUGE-FRANKEN Tooling Service
d.o.o.** (1)
Adi Endre ul 77, 24400, Senta, Serbia
Tel.: (381) 24817000
Machine Tool Distr
N.A.I.C.S.: 423830

**EMUGE-FRANKEN Tools Romania
SRL** (1)
Str Tabacarilor nr 15B/104 Ansamblu River
Tower, 400139, Cluj-Napoca, Romania
Tel.: (40) 264597600
Web Site: http://www.emuge.ro
Machine Tool Distr
N.A.I.C.S.: 423830

EMUGE-FRANKEN UK LIMITED (1)
Unit G The Point Bradmarsh Way, Rother-
ham, S60 1BP, United Kingdom
Tel.: (44) 1709364494
Web Site: http://www.emuge-franken.co.uk
Machine Tool Distr
N.A.I.C.S.: 423830
Paula Ellis (Mgr-Technical)

**EMUGE-FRANKEN nastroje spol. s
r.o** (1)
Lubovnikova 19, 841 07, Bratislava, Slova-
kia
Tel.: (421) 264536635
Web Site: http://www.emuge.sk
Machine Tool Distr
N.A.I.C.S.: 423830

**EMUGE-FRANKEN servisni centrum,
s.r.o.** (1)
Molakova 8, 628 00, Brno, Czech Republic
Tel.: (420) 544423261
Web Site: http://www.emugefranken.cz
Machine Tool Distr
N.A.I.C.S.: 423830

**EMUGE-FRANKEN tehnika
d.o.o.** (1)
Streliska ul 25, 1000, Ljubljana, Slovenia
Tel.: (386) 14301040
Web Site: http://www.emuge-franken.si
Machine Tool Distr
N.A.I.C.S.: 423830

EMUGE-FRANKEN, S.L. (1)
Calle Fructuos Gelabert 1, Sant Joan De-
spi, 8970, Barcelona, Spain
Tel.: (34) 934774690
Machine Tool Distr
N.A.I.C.S.: 423830
Eduard Farran (Gen Mgr)

OOO EMUGE-FRANKEN (1)

Office 711 713 715 Business Center
Obukhov-Center, Pr Obukhovskoy oborony
271 A, 192012, Saint Petersburg, Russia
Tel.: (7) 8123193019
Web Site: http://www.emuge-franken.ru
Machine Tool Distr
N.A.I.C.S.: 423830

EMVISION MEDICAL DEVICES LTD.

Suite 4 65 Epping Rd Macquarie
Park, Sydney, 2113, NSW, Australia
Tel.: (61) 286675337   AU
Web Site: https://emvision.com.au
Year Founded: 2017
EMV—(ASX)
Rev.: $7,719,292
Assets: $16,006,549
Liabilities: $3,642,935
Net Worth: $12,363,614
Earnings: ($1,822,656)
Fiscal Year-end: 06/30/24
Medical Instrument Mfr
N.A.I.C.S.: 339112
Robert Tiller *(Head-Design)*

EMW

155 Namdongseo-ro Namdong-gu,
Incheon, Korea (South)
Tel.: (82) 221075500
Web Site: http://www.emw.co.kr
Year Founded: 1988
079190—(KRS)
Rev.: $42,625,209
Assets: $39,620,469
Liabilities: $27,792,731
Net Worth: $11,827,739
Earnings: ($8,327,593)
Emp.: 94
Fiscal Year-end: 12/31/22
Electric Device Mfr
N.A.I.C.S.: 334419

EMX ENTERPRISES LIMITED

250 Granton Drive, Richmond Hill,
L4B 1H7, ON, Canada
Tel.: (905) 764-0040
Web Site: http://www.emx.ca
Year Founded: 1970
Sales Range: $25-49.9 Million
Emp.: 36
Printed Circuit Supplies & Electronic
Components Whslr
N.A.I.C.S.: 423690
Arthur Legiehn *(Founder)*

EMX ROYALTY CORPORATION

Suite 501 - 543 Granville Street, Van-
couver, V6C 1X8, BC, Canada
Tel.: (604) 688-6390   BC
Web Site:
   https://www.emxroyalty.com
Year Founded: 2001
EMX—(NYSEAMEX)
Rev.: $18,277,000
Assets: $168,830,000
Liabilities: $45,629,000
Net Worth: $123,201,000
Earnings: $3,349,000
Emp.: 40
Fiscal Year-end: 12/31/22
Mineral Exploration Services
N.A.I.C.S.: 213114
Michael D. Winn *(Chm)*

Subsidiaries:

Bronco Creek Exploration, Inc.   **(1)**
1815 E Winsett St, Tucson, AZ
85719-6547   **(100%)**
Tel.: (520) 624-4153
Web Site: http://www.broncocreek.com
Mineral Exploration Services
N.A.I.C.S.: 213114
David A. Johnson *(Co-Founder & Pres-Bus Unit)*

EMX (USA) Services Corp.   **(1)**
6624 Willow Broom Trl, Littleton, CO 80125
Tel.: (303) 948-5100

Mineral Exploration & Mining Services
N.A.I.C.S.: 212312

Norra Metals Corp.   **(1)**
510 – 580 Hornby St., Vancouver, V6C
3B6, BC, Canada   **(52.37%)**
Tel.: (604) 684-4691
Mineral Exploration Services
N.A.I.C.S.: 212290
Cyrus H. Driver *(CFO)*

EMYRIA LIMITED

D2 661 Newcastle Street, Leederville,
6007, WA, Australia
Tel.: (61) 865592800   AU
Web Site: https://www.emyria.com
Year Founded: 2018
EMD—(ASX)
Rev.: $1,461,565
Assets: $6,627,084
Liabilities: $2,197,524
Net Worth: $4,429,559
Earnings: ($3,345,581)
Fiscal Year-end: 06/30/23
Biotechnology Research & Develop-
ment Services
N.A.I.C.S.: 541714
Joseph Ohayon *(CFO)*

EN+ GROUP INTERNATIONAL PJSC

1 Vasilisy Kozhinoy St, 121096, Mos-
cow, 121096, Russia
Tel.: (7) 4956427937   RU
Web Site: https://enplusgroup.com
Year Founded: 2002
ENPL—(LSE)
Rev.: $16,549,000,000
Assets: $30,678,000,000
Liabilities: $17,946,000,000
Net Worth: $12,732,000,000
Earnings: $1,846,000,000
Emp.: 96,617
Fiscal Year-end: 12/31/22
Natural Gas Distribution Services
N.A.I.C.S.: 221210
Vladimir Kiriukhin *(CEO)*

EN+ GROUP LTD.

1 Vasilisy Kozhinoy St, 121096, Mos-
cow, Russia
Tel.: (7) 4956427937
Web Site:
   http://www.enplusgroup.com
Year Founded: 2002
Sales Range: $15-24.9 Billion
Emp.: 100,000
Holding Company; Electricity, Coal,
Uranium, Aluminum & Silicon
N.A.I.C.S.: 551112
Jivko Savov *(Deputy CEO)*

Subsidiaries:

EuroSibEnergo PLC   **(1)**
3 Schepkina Street, Moscow, 129090, Rus-
sia
Tel.: (7) 495 720 50 85
Web Site: http://www.eurosib.ru
Hydroelectric Power Generation Services
N.A.I.C.S.: 221111
Alexander Kolokoltsev *(CEO)*

Subsidiary (Domestic):

ZAO MAREM   **(2)**
3 Ul shchepkina, Moscow, 129090, Russia
Tel.: (7) 4957204915
Hydroelectric Power Generation Services
N.A.I.C.S.: 221111

KraMZ   **(1)**
42 Pogranichnikov Street, 660111, Krasno-
yarsk, Russia
Tel.: (7) 3912564071
Web Site: http://www.kramz-trade.ru
Iron & Steel Mfr
N.A.I.C.S.: 331110
Kleymenova Elena *(Deputy Head-Sls)*

Strikeforce Mining & Resources
Ltd   **(1)**
1 Vasilisa Kozhina St Floor 3, Moscow,

121096, Russia
Tel.: (7) 495 720 50 30
Web Site: http://www.smr-company.ru
Metal Ore Mining Services
N.A.I.C.S.: 212290

EN-JAPAN INC.

Shinjuku I-land Tower 6-5-1 Nishi-
Shinjuku, Shinjuku-ku, Tokyo, 163-
1335, Japan
Tel.: (81) 333424506
Web Site: https://corp.en-japan.com
Year Founded: 2000
4849—(TKS)
Rev.: $447,049,759
Assets: $323,581,013
Liabilities: $111,086,854
Net Worth: $212,494,159
Earnings: $28,073,993
Emp.: 3,317
Fiscal Year-end: 03/31/24
Recruitment Consultation Services
N.A.I.C.S.: 541618
Michikatsu Ochi *(Chm)*

Subsidiaries:

Cbase corporation   **(1)**
7F Hulic Shinjuku Gyoen Building 2-8-8
Shinjuku, Shinjuku-ku, Tokyo, 160-0022,
Japan
Tel.: (81) 352823554
Web Site: https://www.cbase.co.jp
Recruitment Services
N.A.I.C.S.: 561311

Future Focus Infotech Pvt. Ltd.   **(1)**
Old No 62/1 New No 169 Habibullah Road
T Nagar, Chennai, 600034, Tamil Nadu,
India
Tel.: (91) 4443931900
Web Site: https://www.focusinfotech.com
Staffing Services
N.A.I.C.S.: 561320
Kensuke Ogata *(Chm)*

Insight Tech Inc.   **(1)**
6-5-1 Nishi-Shinjuku Shinjuku Island Tower,
Shinjuku-ku, Tokyo, 163-1335, Japan
Tel.: (81) 333426710
Web Site: https://www.insight-tech.co.jp
Marketing Research Service
N.A.I.C.S.: 541910

Navigos Group Joint Stock
Company   **(1)**
Floor 20 E Town Central 11 Doan Van Bo,
Ward 13 District 4, Ho Chi Minh City, Viet-
nam
Tel.: (84) 2839255000
Web Site: http://www.navigosgroup.com
Emp.: 602
Recruitment Services
N.A.I.C.S.: 561311
Jonah Levey *(Founder)*

Subsidiary (Domestic):

Navigos Search   **(2)**
7th Floor V-Building 125 -127 Ba Trieu
Street, Hai Ba Trung District, Hanoi, Viet-
nam
Tel.: (84) 1800585826
Web Site: http://www.navigossearch.com
Employment Placement Agency
N.A.I.C.S.: 561311
Nguyen Thi Van Anh *(Mng Dir)*

New Era India Consultancy Pvt.
Ltd.   **(1)**
Plot No 246 2nd Floor Okhla Industrial Es-
tate Phase 3, New Delhi, 110020, India
Tel.: (91) 1133265000
Web Site: http://www.enworld.co.in
Recruitment Services
N.A.I.C.S.: 561311

Owls, Inc.   **(1)**
33rd Floor Shinjuku Island Tower 6-5-1
Nishi-Shinjuku, Shinjuku-ku, Tokyo, 163-
1333, Japan
Tel.: (81) 367098355
Web Site: http://owls-inc.com
Website & Application Design Services
N.A.I.C.S.: 541511

The Capstone Group Recruitment
and Consulting (Thailand) Ltd.   **(1)**

Trendy Building 7th Floor Sukhumvit Soi 13,
Bangkok, Thailand
Tel.: (66) 2 168 7070
Web Site: http://www.thecapstonegroup.com
Employment Placement Agency
N.A.I.C.S.: 561311

ZEKU Corporation   **(1)**
3-19-26 SOC Takanawa Building 7f, Taka-
nawa Minato-ku, Tokyo, 108-0074, Japan
Tel.: (81) 366811650
Web Site: https://www.zeku.co.jp
Recruitment Services
N.A.I.C.S.: 561311

en Konkatsu Agent Co., Ltd.   **(1)**
3-23-4 Yoyogi VORT Nishi-Shinjuku 2 Build-
ing 10F, Shibuya-ku, Tokyo, Japan **(100%)**
Tel.: (81) 120974835
Web Site: http://en-konkatsu.com
Online Dating Services
N.A.I.C.S.: 812090

en world Hong-Kong Limited.   **(1)**
Level 27 World Wide House 19 Des Voeux
Road, Central, China (Hong Kong)
Tel.: (852) 3972 6580
Web Site: http://www.enworld.com
Recruitment Services
N.A.I.C.S.: 561311
Robert England *(Pres)*

en world Japan K.K.   **(1)**
12F Tokyo Square Garden 3-1-1, Kyobashi
Chuo-ku, Tokyo, 104-0061, Japan
Tel.: (81) 345783500
Web Site: http://www.enworld.com
Employment Placement Agency
N.A.I.C.S.: 561311
Craig Saphin *(Pres)*

en world Korea Co., Ltd   **(1)**
10F Seoul Finance Center 136 Sejong-
Daero, Jung-gu, Seoul, 100-768, Korea
(South)
Tel.: (82) 2 3782 4680
Web Site: http://www.enworld.com
Recruitment Services
N.A.I.C.S.: 561311
Simon Kim *(Pres)*

ENABLENCE TECHNOLOGIES INC.

390 March Road Suite 119, Ottawa,
K2K 0G7, ON, Canada
Tel.: (613) 656-2850
Web Site:
   https://www.enablence.com
ENA—(TSXV)
Rev.: $1,424,000
Assets: $2,174,000
Liabilities: $25,574,000
Net Worth: ($23,400,000)
Earnings: ($9,780,000)
Fiscal Year-end: 06/30/19
Optical Component Mfr
N.A.I.C.S.: 333310
Derek H. Burney *(Chm)*

Subsidiaries:

Enablence USA Components,
Inc.   **(1)**
2933 Bayview Dr, Fremont, CA 94538
Tel.: (510) 226-8900
Optical Chip Design & Mfr
N.A.I.C.S.: 334413

Suzhou Enablence Photonic Tech-
nologies Co., Ltd.   **(1)**
99 Jinji Lake Avenue NW-13 Suite 301B,
Suzhou Industrial Park, Suzhou, 215123,
Jiangsu, China
Tel.: (86) 51269995886
Optical Chip Design & Mfr
N.A.I.C.S.: 334413

ENABLES IT GROUP LIMITED

Unit 5 Mole Business Park Randalls
Road, Leatherhead, KT22 7BA, Sur-
rey, United Kingdom
Tel.: (44) 1372453232
Web Site: http://www.enablesit.com
Year Founded: 1991
Information Technology Services
N.A.I.C.S.: 541512

Enables IT Group Limited—(Continued)

Michael Walliss *(Mng Dir)*

ENAGAS, S.A.
Paseo de los Olmos 19, 28005, Madrid, Spain
Tel.: (34) 902443700   ES
Web Site: https://www.enagas.es
Year Founded: 1972
ENG—(BIL)
Rev.: $974,205,668
Assets: $9,131,891,373
Liabilities: $5,911,881,711
Not Worth: $3,220,009,002
Earnings: $368,192,357
Emp.: 1,316
Fiscal Year-end: 12/31/23
Pipeline Infrastructure Construction & Operation & Natural Gas Transportation & Storage
N.A.I.C.S.: 486210
Antonio Llarden Carratala *(Chm)*

Subsidiaries:

Bahia de Bizkaia Gas, S.L.   **(1)**
Punta Ceballos 2, 48508, Zierbena, Spain   **(50%)**
Tel.: (34) 946366020
Web Site: http://www.bbg.es
Sales Range: $75-99.9 Million
Emp.: 71
Natural Gas Distr
N.A.I.C.S.: 221210

Compania Operadora de Gas del Amazonas, S.A.C.   **(1)**
Av Republica de Panama 3461 Piso 4 Interior 401, San Isidro, Lima, Peru
Tel.: (51) 1 617 7888
Web Site: https://www.coga.pe
Oil & Gas Distr
N.A.I.C.S.: 424720

Efficiency for LNG Applications, S.L.   **(1)**
Paseo de los Olmos 19, 28005, Madrid, Spain
Tel.: (34) 619383451
Web Site: https://e4efficiency.es
Natural Gas Liquefaction & Regasification Services
N.A.I.C.S.: 221210

Naturgas Energia Servicios Comunes, S.A.   **(1)**
General Concha 20, Bilbao, 48010, Spain
Tel.: (34) 944035700
Web Site: http://www.edpenergia.es
Eletric Power Generation Services
N.A.I.C.S.: 221118

Naturgas Energia Transporte, S.A.U.   **(1)**
General Concha 20, Bilbao, 48010, Spain
Tel.: (34) 944 03 57 00
Web Site: http://www.edpenergia.es
Natural Gas Transportation Services
N.A.I.C.S.: 486210

Scale Gas Solutions, S.L.   **(1)**
Paseo de los Olmos 19, 28005, Madrid, Spain
Tel.: (34) 917099230
Web Site: https://www.scalegas.com
Natural Gas Distribution Services
N.A.I.C.S.: 221210

Sercomgas Gas Solutions, S.L.   **(1)**
Calle Titan 8, Arganzuela, 28045, Madrid, Spain
Tel.: (34) 679357793
Web Site: https://www.sercomgas.com
Oil & Gas Distr
N.A.I.C.S.: 424720

ENAIRE
Avenida de Aragon 402, 28022, Madrid, Spain
Tel.: (34) 912 967 551   ES
Web Site: http://www.enaire.es
Year Founded: 1990
Air Transit Services
N.A.I.C.S.: 926120
Julio Gomez-Pomar Rodriguez *(Chm)*

Subsidiaries:

Aena SME, S.A.   **(1)**
Calle Peonias 12, 28042, Madrid, Spain   **(51%)**
Tel.: (34) 913211000
Web Site: https://www.aena.es
Rev.: $5,497,937,621
Assets: $18,946,930,714
Liabilities: $10,790,106,842
Net Worth: $8,156,823,872
Earnings: $1,759,997,842
Emp.: 8,654
Fiscal Year-end: 12/31/2023
Airline Services
N.A.I.C.S.: 561599
Juan Carlos Alfonso Rubio *(Sec)*

Joint Venture (Non-US):

London Luton Airport Group Limited   **(2)**
Airport Way, Luton, LU2 9LY, Beds, United Kingdom   **(51%)**
Tel.: (44) 1582405100
Web Site: http://www.london-luton.co.uk
Sales Range: $200-249.9 Million
Emp.: 600
Air Transportation Management Services
N.A.I.C.S.: 488190
Elliot Renton *(CFO)*

Subsidiary (Domestic):

London Luton Airport Operations Limited   **(3)**
Airport Way, Luton, LU2 9LY, Bedfordshire, United Kingdom
Tel.: (44) 1582405100
Web Site: http://www.london-luton.co.uk
Airport Operation Services
N.A.I.C.S.: 488119
Glyn Jones *(Mng Dir)*

ENALYZER A/S
Refshalevej 147, 1432, Copenhagen, Denmark
Tel.: (45) 70107006
Web Site: http://www.enalyzer.com
Year Founded: 2000
ENALYZ—(OMX)
Rev.: $3,943,077
Assets: $3,862,337
Liabilities: $3,032,079
Net Worth: $830,259
Earnings: $77,556
Emp.: 33
Fiscal Year-end: 12/31/22
Software Development Services
N.A.I.C.S.: 541511
Frederik Borg *(Head-Dev)*

ENAPTER AG
Reinhardtstrasse 35, 10117, Berlin, Germany
Tel.: (49) 30921008130
Web Site: https://www.enapterag.de
Year Founded: 2004
H2O—(DEU)
Rev.: $34,109,118
Assets: $152,610,021
Liabilities: $65,986,132
Net Worth: $86,623,888
Earnings: $(7,731,682)
Emp.: 203
Fiscal Year-end: 12/31/23
Hydrogen Generator Mfr
N.A.I.C.S.: 325120

ENAUTA PARTICIPACOES S.A.
Av Almirante Barroso No 52 Sala 1301, Centro, Rio de Janeiro, 20031-918, RJ, Brazil
Tel.: (55) 2135095800
Web Site: https://www.enauta.com
ENAT3—(BRAZ)
Rev.: $276,909,363
Assets: $1,622,711,138
Liabilities: $849,463,157
Net Worth: $773,247,981
Earnings: $(9,052,348)
Emp.: 163

Fiscal Year-end: 12/31/23
Oil & Gas Exploration Services
N.A.I.C.S.: 213112
Antonio Augusto de Queiroz Galvao *(Chm)*

ENAV S.P.A.
Via Salaria 716, 00138, Rome, Italy
Tel.: (39) 0681661
Web Site: https://www.enav.it
Year Founded: 2001
ENAV—(ITA)
Rev.: $1,028,254,099
Assets: $2,610,605,897
Liabilities: $1,308,108,394
Net Worth: $1,302,497,503
Earnings: $112,774,579
Emp.: 250
Fiscal Year-end: 12/31/22
Air Traffic Management Services
N.A.I.C.S.: 488111
Nicola Maione *(Chm)*

Subsidiaries:

D-Flight S.p.A.   **(1)**
Funzione Comunicazione Via Salaria 716, 00138, Rome, Italy
Tel.: (39) 0644596200
Web Site: https://www.d-flight.it
Traffic Management Services
N.A.I.C.S.: 561990

IDS AirNav S.r.l.   **(1)**
Via del Casale Cavallari 200, 00156, Rome, RM, Italy
Tel.: (39) 0681661
Web Site: https://www.idsairnav.com
Traffic Management Services
N.A.I.C.S.: 561990

ENBD REIT CEIC PLC
8th floor East Wing The Gate Building, Dubai International Financial Centre, 506578, Dubai, United Arab Emirates
Tel.: (971) 45093010
Web Site: https://www.enbdreit.com
Year Founded: 2016
Rev.: $38,040,334
Assets: $467,115,474
Liabilities: $197,048,598
Net Worth: $270,066,876
Earnings: $(9,349,130)
Fiscal Year-end: 03/31/19
Asset Management Services
N.A.I.C.S.: 523940
Asif Siddique *(CFO)*

ENBEE TRADE & FINANCE LIMITED
B4 /C5 Gods Gift Chs Ltd N M Joshi Marg Lower Parel Mumbai, Mumbai, 400013, Maharashtra, India
Tel.: (91) 2224965566
Web Site:
   https://www.enbeetrade.com
512441—(BOM)
Rev.: $267,021
Assets: $1,380,452
Liabilities: $85,899
Net Worth: $1,294,552
Earnings: $9,323
Fiscal Year-end: 03/31/21
Investment Management Service
N.A.I.C.S.: 523940
Amar Narendra Gala *(Chm & Mng Dir)*

ENBIO CO., LTD.
37-20 Beonyeong-Ro 28 Beon-Gil, Gunpo, Gyeonggi-do, Korea (South)
Tel.: (82) 314776011
Web Site: https://www.enbio.co.kr
Year Founded: 1997
352940—(KRS)
Rev.: $26,261,935
Assets: $67,004,821
Liabilities: $31,348,156

Net Worth: $35,656,664
Earnings: ($2,642,071)
Emp.: 167
Fiscal Year-end: 12/31/22
Agricultural Chemical Mfr
N.A.I.C.S.: 325320
Inseon Jo *(CFO)*

ENBIO HOLDINGS INC.
Kanda Park Plaza 8th floor 2-2-2 Kajicho, Chiyoda-ku, Tokyo, 1010044, Japan
Tel.: (81) 352977155
Web Site: https://www.enbio-holdings.com
Year Founded: 1999
6092—(TKS)
Rev.: $63,290,750
Assets: $127,639,100
Liabilities: $70,852,590
Net Worth: $56,786,510
Earnings: $4,679,880
Fiscal Year-end: 03/31/24
Environmental Services
N.A.I.C.S.: 541620
Minoru Nishimura *(Chm, Pres & CEO)*

Subsidiaries:

Altair Solar, LLC   **(1)**
2372 Morse Ave Ste 176, Irvine, CA 92614
Tel.: (877) 886-0601
Web Site: http://www.altairsolar.com
Real Estate Manangement Services
N.A.I.C.S.: 531210

EnBio Engineering, Inc.   **(1)**
Kanda Park Plaza 8th Floor 2-2-2 Kajicho, Chiyoda-ku, Tokyo, 101-0044, Japan
Tel.: (81) 35 297 7288
Web Site: https://enbio-eng.com
Environmental Consulting Services
N.A.I.C.S.: 541620
Wang Ning *(Gen Mgr)*

Enbio Real Estate, Inc.   **(1)**
8F Kanda Park Plaza 2-2-2 Kajicho, Chiyoda-ku, Tokyo, 101-0044, Japan
Tel.: (81) 335265170
Web Site: https://www.enbio-realestate.com
Real Estate Manangement Services
N.A.I.C.S.: 531210

In Situ Solutions Co., Ltd.   **(1)**
2-5-2 Kandasudacho Sudamachisashita Bldg 9F Chiyoda-ku, Tokyo, 101-0041, Japan
Tel.: (81) 352977288
Web Site: http://www.is-solution.com
Emp.: 30
Soil Remediation Services
N.A.I.C.S.: 562910
Shusaku Kusaba *(Gen Mgr)*

Land Concierge, Inc.   **(1)**
2-11 Kandatacho Chiyoda-Ku, Tokyo, 101-0044, Japan
Tel.: (81) 355775528
Web Site: http://www.land-concierge.com
Soil Remediation Services
N.A.I.C.S.: 562910

ENBRIDGE INC.
200 Fifth Avenue Place 425 - 1st Street S W, Calgary, T2P 3L8, AB, Canada
Tel.: (403) 231-3900   Ca
Web Site: https://www.enbridge.com
Year Founded: 1949
ENB—(NYSE)
Rev.: $36,822,701,880
Assets: $132,098,929,920
Liabilities: $82,527,410,880
Net Worth: $49,571,519,040
Earnings: $4,939,315,920
Emp.: 10,900
Fiscal Year-end: 12/31/21
Holding Company; Energy Resource Transportation, Distribution & Services
N.A.I.C.S.: 551112

Laura J. Buss-Sayavedra (Chief Admin Officer & Sr VP-Projects)

Subsidiaries:

Algonquin Gas Transmission, LLC (1)
54 Algonquin Ln, Pascoag, RI 02859
Tel.: (401) 568-1698
Crude Oil & Natural Gas Distr
N.A.I.C.S.: 486210

Alliance Pipeline L.P. (1)
6385 Old Shady Oak Rd Ste 150, Eden Prairie, MN 55344
Tel.: (952) 944-3183
Web Site: http://www.alliancepipeline.com
Pipeline Transportation Services
N.A.I.C.S.: 486990
Brian Trojcuk (Mgr-Regulatory Affairs)

Alliance Pipeline Limited Partnership (1)
200 Fifth Avenue Place 425-1st Street SW, Calgary, T2P 3L8, AB, Canada
Tel.: (403) 231-3900
Web Site: http://www.alliancepipeline.com
Natural Gas Pipeline Transportation Services
N.A.I.C.S.: 486210

Aux Sable Canada L.P (1)
8th Ave Place, Calgary, T2P 3H5, AB, Canada
Tel.: (403) 231-7500
Web Site: http://www.auxsable.com
Pipeline Transportation Services
N.A.I.C.S.: 486990

Aux Sable Canada Ltd. (1)
8th Ave Place, Calgary, T2P 3H5, AB, Canada
Tel.: (403) 231-7500
Web Site: http://www.auxsable.com
Natural Gas Pipeline Transportation Services
N.A.I.C.S.: 486210
Scott Seibert (Mgr-Environmental, Regulatory & Govt Affairs)

East Tennessee Natural Gas, LLC (1)
5400 Westheimer Ct, Houston, TX 77056
Tel.: (713) 627-5400
Natural Gas Pipeline Operator
N.A.I.C.S.: 221210

Enbridge Energy Company, Inc. (1)
1100 Louisiana St Ste 3300, Houston, TX 77002-5217
Tel.: (713) 650-8900
Sales Range: $250-299.9 Million
Emp.: 500
Natural Gas Pipeline Company Services
N.A.I.C.S.: 221210
Mark Andrew Maki (Pres)

Affiliate (Domestic):

Enbridge Energy Management, LLC (2)
5400 Westheimer Ct, Houston, TX 77056 (11.1%)
Tel.: (713) 627-5400
Web Site: http://www.enbridgemanagement.com
Assets: $1,000,000
Net Worth: $1,000,000
Earnings: ($29,000,000)
Fiscal Year-end: 12/31/2017
Energy Management & Operation Services
N.A.I.C.S.: 213112
Mark Andrew Maki (Pres & CEO)

Affiliate (Domestic):

Enbridge Energy Partners, L.P. (3)
5400 Westheimer Court, Houston, TX 77056 (15.2%)
Tel.: (713) 627-5400
Web Site: http://www.enbridgepartners.com
Rev.: $2,428,000,000
Assets: $14,828,000,000
Liabilities: $8,089,000,000
Net Worth: $6,739,000,000
Earnings: $651,000,000
Fiscal Year-end: 12/31/2017
Oil Transportation
N.A.I.C.S.: 423860
Wanda Marie Opheim (Treas)

Subsidiary (Domestic):

ELTM, L.P. (4)
1374 Hwy 11 N, Petal, MS 39465-1184 (100%)
Tel.: (601) 583-9991
Sales Range: $25-49.9 Million
Emp.: 95
Natural Gas, Petroleum Products & Chemicals Marketer & Transporter
N.A.I.C.S.: 424720
Gary Worone (Pres)

Enbridge G & P (North Texas) L P (4)
1100 Louisiana St Ste 3300, Houston, TX 77002
Tel.: (713) 821-2000
Business Support Services
N.A.I.C.S.: 561499

Enbridge Pipeline Corporation (4)
13688 Hwy 82 E, Duncanville, AL 35456 (100%)
Tel.: (205) 758-5926
Natural Gas Pipelines
N.A.I.C.S.: 221210

Enbridge Gas Inc. (1)
500 Consumers Road, North York, M2J 1P8, ON, Canada (100%)
Tel.: (877) 362-7434
Web Site: http://www.uniongas.com
Sales Range: $75-99.9 Million
Emp.: 100
Natural Gas Distribution
N.A.I.C.S.: 221210

Enbridge Income Fund Holdings Inc. (1)
3000 Fifth Avenue Place 425 - 1st Street SW, Calgary, T2P 3L8, AB, Canada (100%)
Tel.: (403) 231-3900
Web Site: http://www.enbridgeincomefund.com
Sales Range: $75-99.9 Million
Financial Investment Services
N.A.I.C.S.: 523999
Wanda Marie Opheim (CFO)

Subsidiary (Domestic):

Enbridge Pipelines, Inc. (2)
10201 Jasper Ave, Edmonton, T5J 2J9, AB, Canada (100%)
Tel.: (780) 420-8554
Web Site: http://www.enbridge.com
Sales Range: $125-149.9 Million
Emp.: 425
Liquid Hydrocarbon & Crude Oil Distr
N.A.I.C.S.: 486110
Melissa M. LaForge (VP-Fin)

Enbridge Pipelines (Athabasca) Inc. (1)
Franklin Ave, Fort McMurray, T9H 0A5, AB, Canada
Tel.: (780) 788-2051
Natural Gas Pipeline Transportation Services
N.A.I.C.S.: 486210
Daniel Huntley (Mgr-Ops)

Express Pipeline Ltd. (1)
300 5th Avenue Southwest, Calgary, T2P 5J2, AB, Canada
Tel.: (403) 691-6000
Crude Oil Pipelines
N.A.I.C.S.: 486110

Gazifere Inc. (1)
706 Boulevard Greber, Gatineau, J8V 3P8, QC, Canada
Tel.: (819) 771-8321
Web Site: http://www.gazifere.com
Emp.: 110
Natural Gas Distribution Services
N.A.I.C.S.: 221210

Genalta Power Inc. (1)
Suite 1470 400-3 Avenue SW, Calgary, T2P 4H2, AB, Canada
Tel.: (403) 237-9740
Web Site: http://www.genaltapower.com
Eletric Power Generation Services
N.A.I.C.S.: 221118
Paul Miller (Pres & CEO)

Hi-Fi Engineering Inc. (1)

2 816 - 46th Avenue SE, Calgary, T2G 2A6, AB, Canada
Tel.: (403) 264-8930
Web Site: http://hifieng.com
Electrical Engineering Services
N.A.I.C.S.: 541330
Steven Koles (Pres & CEO)

IntelliView Technologies Inc. (1)
205 327 - 41st Ave NE, Calgary, T2E 2N4, AB, Canada
Tel.: (403) 338-0001
Web Site: http://intelliviewtech.com
Oil & Gas Leak Detector Mfr & Distr
N.A.I.C.S.: 334519
Tariq Ahmed (CMO)

Islander East Pipeline Company, L.L.C. (1)
5400 Westheimer Court, Houston, TX 77056
Tel.: (713) 627-5400
Oil & Gas Pipeline Developer
N.A.I.C.S.: 237120

Maritimes & Northeast Pipeline Limited Partnership (1)
1801 Hollis Street Suite 1600, Halifax, B3J 3N4, NS, Canada
Tel.: (902) 425-4474
Web Site: http://www.mnpp.com
Natural Gas Distr
N.A.I.C.S.: 221210
Steve Rankin (Dir-External Rels)

Morgan Solar Inc. (1)
100 Symes Road Unit 100 A, Toronto, M6N 0A8, ON, Canada
Tel.: (416) 203-1655
Web Site: http://morgansolar.com
Solar Cell Mfr
N.A.I.C.S.: 334413
Mike Andrade (CEO)

Moss Bluff Hub, LLC (1)
5400 Westheimer Ct, Houston, TX 77056
Tel.: (713) 627-5400
Gas Storage Services
N.A.I.C.S.: 493190

NextBridge Infrastructure LP (1)
1 Pinewood Drive, Wawa, P0S 1K0, ON, Canada
Web Site: http://www.nextbridge.ca
Natural Gas Transmission Services
N.A.I.C.S.: 486210

Questar Gas Company (1)
333 S State St, Salt Lake City, UT 84145-0433
Tel.: (801) 324-5000
Web Site: https://www.questargas.com
Rev.: $921,300,000
Assets: $2,506,500,000
Liabilities: $1,848,900,000
Net Worth: $657,600,000
Earnings: $57,200,000
Emp.: 900
Fiscal Year-end: 12/31/2016
Natural Gas Distr
N.A.I.C.S.: 221210

Rabaska Inc. (1)
2388 Einstein Street, Quebec, G1P 4T1, QC, Canada
Tel.: (418) 659-6000
Web Site: http://www.rabaska.net
Natural Gas Distribution Services
N.A.I.C.S.: 221210

Saltville Gas Storage Company L.L.C. (1)
889 Ader Ln, Saltville, VA 24370
Tel.: (276) 496-7004
Natural Gas Transportation Services
N.A.I.C.S.: 486990

Spectra Energy Canada Exchangeco Inc. (1)
1055 West Georgia Street Suite 1100, PO Box 11162, Vancouver, V6E 3R5, BC, Canada
Tel.: (604) 488-8016
Web Site: http://www.spectraenergy.com
Natural Gas Transportation, Processing & Distr
N.A.I.C.S.: 486210

Spectra Energy Partners, L.P. (1)
5400 Westheimer Ct, Houston, TX 77056 (100%)

Tel.: (713) 627-5400
Natural Gas Transportation & Storage Services
N.A.I.C.S.: 486210

Syscor Controls & Automation Inc. (1)
Suite 201 60 Bastion Square, Victoria, V8W 1J2, BC, Canada
Tel.: (250) 361-1681
Web Site: http://syscor.com
Wireless Sensor System Mfr
N.A.I.C.S.: 334511

Temporal Power Ltd. (1)
2-3750A Laird Rd, Mississauga, L5L 0A6, ON, Canada
Tel.: (905) 581-4474
Web Site: http://temporalpower.com
Electricity Storage System Mfr
N.A.I.C.S.: 335910
Pierre Rivard (Chm)

The East Ohio Gas Company (1)
Tel.: (800) 362-7557
Natural Gas Distr
N.A.I.C.S.: 221210

Tidal Energy Marketing Inc. (1)
2000 237 - 4th Ave SW, Calgary, T2P 4K3, AB, Canada
Tel.: (403) 205-7770
Web Site: http://www.tidal-energy.com
Natural Gas Distribution Services
N.A.I.C.S.: 221210
Judd Florence (Pres)

Tri Global Energy LLC (1)
17300 Dallas Pkwy Ste 2060, Dallas, TX 75248-7703
Tel.: (972) 290-0825
Web Site: http://www.triglobalenergy.com
Electrical Contractor
N.A.I.C.S.: 238210
John Billingsley (Chm & CEO)

Vector Pipeline, L.P. (1)
38705 7th Mile Rd Ste 490, Livonia, MI 48152
Tel.: (734) 462-0230
Web Site: https://www.vector-pipeline.com
Sales Range: $25-49.9 Million
Emp.: 10
Gas Pipeline; Owned 50% by DTE Energy Company & 50% by Enbridge, Inc.
N.A.I.C.S.: 486210
Peter Cianci (Pres)

Westcoast Energy, Inc. (1)
425-1st Street Southwest 200 5th Avenue Place, Calgary, T2P 3L8, AB, Canada
Tel.: (403) 231-3900
Web Site: https://noms.wei-pipeline.com
Natural Gas Extraction Services
N.A.I.C.S.: 211130

Wexpro Company (1)
180 E 100 S, Salt Lake City, UT 84111
Tel.: (801) 324-5000
Web Site: http://www.questar.com
Emp.: 100
Oil Production & Distr
N.A.I.C.S.: 211120

ENBW ENERGIE BADEN-WURTTEMBERG AG
Durlacher Allee 93, 76131, Karlsruhe, Germany
Tel.: (49) 7216300   De
Web Site: https://www.enbw.com
Year Founded: 1997
EBK—(DEU)
Rev.: $47,950,248,219
Assets: $69,845,564,429
Liabilities: $59,799,481,977
Net Worth: $10,046,082,452
Earnings: $1,977,768,185
Emp.: 28,630
Fiscal Year-end: 12/31/23
Natural Gas Extraction Services
N.A.I.C.S.: 551112
Thomas Kusterer (CFO & Member-Mgmt Bd)

Subsidiaries:

AWISTA Gesellschaft fur Abfallwirtschaft und Stadtreinigung

EnBW Energie Baden-Wurttemberg
AG—(Continued)

mbH (1)
Hoherweg 100, 40233, Dusseldorf, Germany
Tel.: (49) 2118 309 9099
Web Site: https://www.awista.de
Waste Management Services
N.A.I.C.S.: 562998

AWISTA Logistik GmbH (1)
Hoherweg 222, 40233, Dusseldorf, Germany
Tel.: (49) 21183099150
Web Site: https://www.awistalogistik.de
Waste Collection & Transportation Services
N.A.I.C.S.: 562998

AutenSys GmbH (1)
Karlstrasse 52-54, 76133, Karlsruhe, Germany
Tel.: (49) 7212 766 9000
Web Site: https://www.autensys.de
Renewable & Environment Services
N.A.I.C.S.: 221118

BEN Fleet Services GmbH (1)
Gartenstr 7, 10115, Berlin, Germany
Tel.: (49) 302 000 3585
Web Site: https://www.benfleetservices.com
Logistic & Supply Chain Services
N.A.I.C.S.: 484121
Florian Schon (Head-Ops)

CarbonBW (Thailand) Ltd. (1)
29/7 Ekkamai Soi 10 Soi Charoen Mit
Sukhumvit 63 Road, North Klongton Wattana, Bangkok, 10110, Thailand
Tel.: (66) 2 711 7527
Web Site: https://www.carbonbw.co.th
Green Energy Supply Services
N.A.I.C.S.: 221118

Connected Wind Services A/S (1)
Langs Skoven 37, 8541, Skodstrup, Denmark
Tel.: (45) 86230155
Web Site: https://www.connectedwind.com
N.A.I.C.S.: 811310
Oliver Auras (CEO)

Connected Wind Services Danmark A/S (1)
Nyballevej 8, 8444, Ballerup, Denmark
Tel.: (45) 86230155
Renewable & Environment Services
N.A.I.C.S.: 221115
Kent Hougaard (Mng Dir)

Connected Wind Services Deutschland GmbH (1)
Muhlenberg 19, Rantrum, 25873, Schleswig, Germany
Tel.: (49) 4848901280
Renewable & Environment Services
N.A.I.C.S.: 221115
Bernd Paulsen (Mng Dir)

ED Netze GmbH (1)
Schildgasse 20, 79618, Rheinfelden, Germany
Tel.: (49) 762 392 1800
Web Site: https://www.ednetze.de
Power Supply Services
N.A.I.C.S.: 221122

ESD Energie Service Deutschland GmbH (1)
Zeller Strasse 38, 77654, Offenburg, Germany
Tel.: (49) 78193 689 8100
Web Site: https://www.energie-service-deutschland.de
Call Center Services
N.A.I.C.S.: 561422

Elektrizitatswerk Aach eG, (1)
Eltastr 1-5, 78532, Tuttlingen, Germany
Tel.: (49) 7 461 7090
Web Site: https://www.ew-aach.de
Eletric Power Generation Services
N.A.I.C.S.: 221111

Elektrizitatswerk Weissenhorn AG (1)
Illerberger Strasse 6 a, Weissenhorn, 89264, Neu-Ulm, Germany
Tel.: (49) 73 099 6100
Web Site: https://www.ewag-weissenhorn.de
Electricity Power Supply Services

N.A.I.C.S.: 221122

EnAlpin AG (1)
Bahnhofplatz 1b, 3930, Visp, Switzerland
Tel.: (41) 27 945 7500
Web Site: https://www.enalpin.com
Electric Power Generator & Distr
N.A.I.C.S.: 221122
Michel Schwery (Mng Dir)

Subsidiary (Domestic):

Aletsch AG (2)
Furkastrasse 8, 3983, Morel, Switzerland
Power Station
N.A.I.C.S.: 221118

ERAG Elektrizitatswerk Rheinau AG (2)
Parkstrasse 23, 8462, Rheinau, Switzerland
Tel.: (41) 523191454
Power Station
N.A.I.C.S.: 221122

Energie De Sion Region SA (2)
Rue De La Industrie 43, 1950, Sion, Switzerland
Tel.: (41) 273240111
Web Site: http://www.esr.ch
Sales Range: $100-124.9 Million
Services & Natural Gas Distribution
N.A.I.C.S.: 221210

Gaznat SA (2)
Av General-Guisan 28, 1800, Vevey, Switzerland
Tel.: (41) 58 274 0484
Web Site: https://www.gaznat.ch
Sales Range: $75-99.9 Million
Emp.: 10
Services & Natural Gas Distribution
N.A.I.C.S.: 221210
Rene Bautz (CEO)

RKN Rheinkraftwerk Neuhausen AG (2)
c/o EnAlpine AG, Bahnhofplatz 1b, Visp, CH-3930, Switzerland
Tel.: (41) 27 945 7500
Web Site: http://www.enalpin.com
Power Station
N.A.I.C.S.: 221122

EnBW Asia Pacific Ltd. (1)
11F No 168 Sec 3 Nanjing East Rd, Zhongshan District, Taipei, 10488, Taiwan
Tel.: (886) 227785500
Web Site: http://www.enbw.com.tw
Renewable & Environment Services
N.A.I.C.S.: 221115
Markus Wild (Mng Dir)

EnBW Baltic 1 GmbH & Co. KG (1)
Kronenstr. 26, Stuttgart, 70173, Baden-Wurttemberg, Germany
Tel.: (49) 71112800
Eletric Power Generation Services
N.A.I.C.S.: 221118

EnBW Baltic 1 Verwaltungs gesellschaft mbH (1)
Durlacher Allee 93, Karlsruhe, Germany
Tel.: (49) 7216307
Eletric Power Generation Services
N.A.I.C.S.: 221111

EnBW Benelux B.V. (1)
West Black 89, Rotterdam, 3012KG, Netherlands
Tel.: (31) 102245333
Energy Consulting Services
N.A.I.C.S.: 541690

EnBW Biomasse GmbH (1)
Am Erlengraben 5, 76275, Ettlingen, Germany
Tel.: (49) 7243 505 7890
Web Site: https://www.enbw-biomasse.com
Biomass Power Supply Services
N.A.I.C.S.: 221117

EnBW Energy Factory GmbH (1)
Schelmenwasenstrasse 15, 70567, Stuttgart, Germany
Tel.: (49) 7112 898 7225
Web Site: https://www.energyfactory.de
Electric Power Supply Services
N.A.I.C.S.: 221122
Mark Baldinus (Mng Dir)

EnBW EnergyWatchers GmbH (1)

Friedrichstr 13, 70174, Stuttgart, Germany
Tel.: (49) 7111283683
Sales Range: $75-99.9 Million
Emp.: 20
Electric Power Distribution Services
N.A.I.C.S.: 221122

EnBW Gasnetz GmbH (1)
Talstrasse 117, 70188, Stuttgart, Germany
Tel.: (49) 711 289 46883
Web Site: http://www.enbw.com
Gas Distribution Services
N.A.I.C.S.: 221210

EnBW Holding A.S. (1)
Gumussuyu No 43/9 Inonu Cad, Istanbul, 34437, Turkiye
Tel.: (90) 2122455015
Eletric Power Generation Services
N.A.I.C.S.: 221111

EnBW Kernkraft GmbH (1)
Kraftwerkstrasse 1, Obrigheim, 74847, Germany
Tel.: (49) 6261650
Electrcity & Natural Gas
N.A.I.C.S.: 221122

EnBW Kommunale Beteiligungen GmbH (1)
Schelmenwasenstrasse 15, 70567, Stuttgart, Germany
Tel.: (49) 71128944710
Electric Power Distr
N.A.I.C.S.: 221122

EnBW Kraftwerke AG (1)
Schelmenwasenstrasse 15, 70567, Stuttgart, Germany
Tel.: (49) 7112181500
Sales Range: $75-99.9 Million
Emp.: 72
Power Stations Operator
N.A.I.C.S.: 221122

EnBW Mainfrankenpark GmbH (1)
Mainfrankenpark 2, 97337, Dettelbach, Germany
Tel.: (49) 930 293 1003
Web Site: https://www.mainfrankenpark.de
Leisure Services
N.A.I.C.S.: 713990

EnBW North America Inc. (1)
311 Summer St Ste 200, Boston, MA 02110
Tel.: (617) 415-4111
Web Site: http://www.enbw.us
Offshore Wind Development Services
N.A.I.C.S.: 221115
Bill White (Pres & CEO)

EnBW Omega Dreiundzwanzigste Verwaltungsgesellschaft mbH (1)
Durlacher Allee 93, Karlsruhe, 76131, Baden-Wurttemberg, Germany
Tel.: (49) 7216300
Eletric Power Generation Services
N.A.I.C.S.: 221118

EnBW Omega Elfte Verwaltungsgesellschaft mbH (1)
Durlacher Allee 93, Karlsruhe, 76131, Baden-Wurttemberg, Germany
Tel.: (49) 7216300
Eletric Power Generation Services
N.A.I.C.S.: 221118
Kusterer Thomas (CFO)

EnBW Omega Siebzehnte Verwaltungsgesellschaft mbH (1)
Durlacher Allee 93, Karlsruhe, 76131, Baden-Wurttemberg, Germany
Tel.: (49) 7216307
Energy Consulting Services
N.A.I.C.S.: 541690

EnBW Ostwurttemberg DonauRies AG (1)
Unterer Bruhl 2, 73479, Ellwangen, Germany
Tel.: (49) 796 1820
Web Site: https://www.odr.de
Emp.: 300
Electric Power & Natural Gas Distr
N.A.I.C.S.: 221122

EnBW Perspektiven GmbH (1)
Durlacher Allee 93, 76131, Karlsruhe, Germany
Tel.: (49) 71128948607

N.A.I.C.S.: 517810

EnBW Sverige AB (1)
Akarevagen 17, 311 32, Falkenberg, Sweden
Tel.: (46) 104540890
Web Site: https://www.enbw.se
N.A.I.C.S.: 221114

EnBW Systeme Infrastruktur Support GmbH (1)
Durlacher Allee 93, 76131, Karlsruhe, Germany
Tel.: (49) 721 63 00
Web Site: http://www.enbw.com
Energy Consulting Services
N.A.I.C.S.: 541690

EnBW Trading GmbH (1)
Durlacher Allee 93, D-76131, Karlsruhe, Germany (100%)
Tel.: (49) 7216307
Risk Management Services; Trades in Electricity, Gas, Coal & Oil
N.A.I.C.S.: 561499

EnBW Vertrieb GmbH (1)
Schelmenwasenstrasse 15, 70567, Stuttgart, Germany
Tel.: (49) 800 3629 000
Web Site: http://www.enbw.com
Electric Power Distribution Services
N.A.I.C.S.: 221122

EnergieDienst Holding AG (1)
Baslerstrasse 44, CH-5080, Laufenburg, Switzerland
Tel.: (41) 628692510
Web Site: https://www.naturenergie-holding.ch
Sales Range: $1-4.9 Billion
Emp.: 770
Holding Company; Hydroelectric Power Generation Services
N.A.I.C.S.: 551112
Martin Steiger (CEO)

Subsidiary (Non-US):

Energiedienst AG (2)
Schonenbergerstrasse 10, 79618, Rheinfelden, Germany
Tel.: (49) 7623 92 0
Web Site: http://www.energiedienst.de
Hydroelectric Power Generation Services
N.A.I.C.S.: 221111

Subsidiary (Domestic):

ED Immobilien GmbH & Co. KG (3)
Rheinbruckstr 5/7, Rheinfelden, 79618, Germany
Tel.: (49) 776381 2640
Natural Gas Distr
N.A.I.C.S.: 221210

Energiedienst Netze GmbH (3)
Schildgasse 20, 79618, Rheinfelden, Germany
Tel.: (49) 7623921800
Web Site: https://www.ednetze.de
Sales Range: $150-199.9 Million
Emp.: 750
Energy Consulting Services
N.A.I.C.S.: 541690

EnergieFinanz GmbH (1)
Werderstrasse 74b, 19055, Schwerin, Germany
Tel.: (49) 385 592 9201
Web Site: https://www.energiefinanz.eu
Trading Platform Services
N.A.I.C.S.: 523160

Energieversorgung Gaildorf OHG der EnBW Kommunale Beteiligungen GmbH (1)
Burg 2, 74405, Gaildorf, Germany
Tel.: (49) 7971260920
Web Site: https://www.ev-gaildorf.de
Electric Power Distr
N.A.I.C.S.: 221122

Energieversum GmbH & Co. KG (1)
Friedrichsdorfer Str 111, 33335, Gutersloh, Germany
Tel.: (49) 5241 224 9960
Web Site: https://www.energieversum.de
Photovoltaic Solar System Services
N.A.I.C.S.: 221114

Erdgas Sudwest GmbH (1)
Siemensstrasse 9, 76275, Ettlingen, Germany
Tel.: (49) 724 321 6100
Web Site: https://www.erdgas-suedwest.de
Emp.: 261
Natural Gas Distr
N.A.I.C.S.: 221210

Erdgas-Beteiligungsgesellschaft Sud mbH (1)
Schulze-Delitzsch-Strasse 7, 70565, Stuttgart, Germany
Tel.: (49) 71178125
Web Site: https://www.gvs-erdgas.de
Electric Power Distribution Services
N.A.I.C.S.: 221122

FoxInsights GmbH (1)
Ridlerstrsse 57, 80339, Munich, Germany
Tel.: (49) 8921540220
Web Site: https://foxinsights.ai
Emp.: 50
Software Development Services
N.A.I.C.S.: 513210
Sylvia Kerscher (Head-Bus Dev)

Frontier Technologies S.r.o. (1)
Na Hroude 2149/19, 100 00, Prague, Czech Republic
Tel.: (420) 27 700 2333
Web Site: https://www.frontier-technologies.eu
Lighting System Services
N.A.I.C.S.: 238210
Stanislav Smejdir (Exec Dir)

GVS Netz GmbH (1)
Schulze Delitzsch Strasse 7, Stuttgart, 705659, Germany
Tel.: (49) 71178120
Web Site: http://www.gvs-netz.de
Emp.: 75
Oil & Gas Field Engineering Services
N.A.I.C.S.: 213112
Helmut Oehoer (Mgr)

GasVersorgung Suddeutschland GmbH (1)
Schulze-Delitzsch-Strasse 7, 70565, Stuttgart, Germany
Tel.: (49) 7 117 8125
Web Site: https://www.gvs-erdgas.de
Emp.: 75
Natural Gas Distr
N.A.I.C.S.: 221210

Gasversorgung Unterland GmbH (1)
Weipertstrasse 41, 74076, Heilbronn, Germany
Tel.: (49) 7131 610 1515
Web Site: https://www.gasversorgung-unterland.de
Natural Gas Distr
N.A.I.C.S.: 221210

Grunwerke GmbH (1)
Hoherweg 200, 40233, Dusseldorf, Germany
Tel.: (49) 211 821 8088
Web Site: https://www.gruenwerke.de
Sales Range: $25-49.9 Million
Emp.: 10
Solar Power Plant Construction Services
N.A.I.C.S.: 237130
Ralf Zischke (CEO)

HEV Hohenloher Energie Versorgung GmbH (1)
Orlacher Strasse 1, Ishofen Obersteinach, 74532, Schwabisch Hall, Germany
Tel.: (49) 790 694 0613
Web Site: https://www.hev-energie.de
Energy Supply Services
N.A.I.C.S.: 221118

Hidiv Elektrik Enerjisi Toptan Satis A.S (1)
Purtelas Hasan Mah Meclisi Mebusan Cd N 35 K 7, Istanbul, Turkiye
Tel.: (90) 2123935297
Eletric Power Generation Services
N.A.I.C.S.: 221111

Intepe Elektrik Uretim Ve Tic. A.S (1)
Purtelas Hasan Mah Meclisi Mebusan Cad No 35 K 7, Istanbul, Turkiye
Tel.: (90) 2123935200
Eletric Power Generation Services

N.A.I.C.S.: 221111

Interconnector GmbH (1)
Durlacher Allee 93, 76131, Karlsruhe, Germany
Tel.: (49) 71196883918
Web Site: http://www.interconnector.de
Solar Power Equipment Retailer
N.A.I.C.S.: 423690

JatroSolutions GmbH (1)
Echterdinger Str 30, 70599, Stuttgart, Germany
Tel.: (49) 7114 599 9760
Web Site: https://www.jatrosolutions.com
Agricultural Services
N.A.I.C.S.: 115116
Sebastian Held (Mng Dir)

KIC InnoEnergy S.E. (1)
Kennispoort 6th Floor John F Kennedylaan 2, 5612 AB, Eindhoven, Netherlands
Tel.: (31) 402406031
Web Site: https://www.innoenergy.com
Education Services
N.A.I.C.S.: 611710
Diego Pavia (CEO)

KNG Kraftwerks- und Netzgesellschaft mbH (1)
Am Kuhlturm 1, 18147, Rostock, Germany
Tel.: (49) 3 816 7020
Web Site: https://www.kraftwerk-rostock.de
Sales Range: $125-149.9 Million
Emp.: 121
Eletric Power Generation Services
N.A.I.C.S.: 221111
Lars Eigenmann (Mgr-Tech)

Kernkraftwerk Obrigheim GmbH (1)
Kraftwerkstrasse 1, Obrigheim, 74847, Germany
Tel.: (49) 6261650
Web Site: http://www.enbw.com
Eletric Power Generation Services
N.A.I.C.S.: 221111
Joseph Zimmer (Gen Mgr)

Kormak Praha a.s. (1)
namesti Bratri Jandusu 34/34, Uhrineves, 104 00, Prague, Czech Republic
Tel.: (420) 26 705 1399
Web Site: https://www.kormak.cz
Electrical Engineering Services
N.A.I.C.S.: 541330

Le Val Energie SARL (1)
609 Route De La Roquette, CS 50105, 06254, Mougins, France
Tel.: (33) 492283220
Web Site: https://www.valenergies.com
N.A.I.C.S.: 221114

Leoni Cable Inc (1)
2800 Livernois Rd Ste D600-B, Troy, MI 48083
Tel.: (248) 650-3328
Fiber Optic Cable Mfr
N.A.I.C.S.: 335921
Mary DeCook (Acct Mgr)

MSE Mobile Schlammentwasserungs GmbH (1)
Auf der Hub 35-39, Karlsbad, 76307, Ittersbach, Germany
Tel.: (49) 724892700
Web Site: https://www.mse-mobile.de
Sales Range: $25-49.9 Million
Emp.: 60
Sewage Disposal Services
N.A.I.C.S.: 562219
Michael Part (Mng Dir)

Maya Enerji Yatirimlari A.S. (1)
Buyukdere Caddesi No 112, Esentepe, 34394, Istanbul, Turkiye
Tel.: (90) 2123402760
Eletric Power Generation Services
N.A.I.C.S.: 221111

Messerschmid Energiesysteme GmbH (1)
Im Breitenfeld 20, 79848, Bonndorf, Germany
Tel.: (49) 7703 931 7790
Web Site: https://www.messerschmid-energiesysteme.de
Natural Gas Boiler Mfr & Distr
N.A.I.C.S.: 333414

NHF Netzgesellschaft Heilbronn-Franken mbH (1)

Weipertstrasse 39, 74076, Heilbronn, Germany
Tel.: (49) 7131 649 9188
Web Site: https://www.n-hf.de
Electric Power Distribution Services
N.A.I.C.S.: 221122

NHL Netzgesellschaft Heilbronner Land GmbH & Co. KG (1)
Weipertstrasse 39, 74076, Heilbronn, Germany
Tel.: (49) 7131 898 1188
Web Site: https://www.n-hl.de
Energy Power Supply Services
N.A.I.C.S.: 221122

Nahwarme Dusseldorf GmbH (1)
Hoherweg 100, 40233, Dusseldorf, Germany
Tel.: (49) 211 821 2553
Web Site: https://www.nwd-gmbh.de
Heating Supply Services
N.A.I.C.S.: 238220

NaturlichEnergie EMH GmbH (1)
Im Haag 2a, Wengerohr, 54516, Wittlich, Germany
Tel.: (49) 6571 958 9077
Web Site: https://www.natuerlich-energie-emh.de
Hydroelectric Power Generation Services
N.A.I.C.S.: 221111

NaturlichEnergie Swiss NES GmbH (1)
Baslerstrasse 44, 5080, Laufenburg, Switzerland
Tel.: (41) 62 869 2680
Web Site: https://www.natuerlichenergie-swiss.ch
Gas Distr
N.A.I.C.S.: 424720
Marco Ruegg (Acct Mgr)

NeckarCom Telekommunikation GmbH (1)
Stockachstr 48, 70190, Stuttgart, Germany
Tel.: (49) 711 22 55 78 0
Web Site: http://www.neckarcom.de
Telecommunication Servicesb
N.A.I.C.S.: 517810

NetCom BW GmbH (1)
Unterer Bruhl 2, 73479, Ellwangen, Germany
Tel.: (49) 71134034034
Web Site: https://www.netcom-bw.de
Telecommunication Servicesb
N.A.I.C.S.: 517810

NetCom BW GmbH (1)
Unterer Bruhl 2, 73479, Ellwangen, Germany
Tel.: (49) 800 362 9266
Web Site: https://www.netcom-bw.de
Emp.: 380
Telecommunication Servicesb
N.A.I.C.S.: 517810

Netze BW GmbH (1)
Schelmenwasenstrasse 15, 70567, Stuttgart, Germany
Tel.: (49) 800 362 9900
Web Site: https://www.netze-bw.de
Electricity Power Supply Services
N.A.I.C.S.: 221122

Netze BW Wasser GmbH (1)
Poststrasse 43, 70190, Stuttgart, Germany
Tel.: (49) 7112890
Electricity Power Supply Services
N.A.I.C.S.: 221122

Netze-Gesellschaft Sudwest mbH (1)
Siemensstr 9, 76275, Ettlingen, Germany
Tel.: (49) 7243 342 7100
Web Site: https://www.netze-suedwest.de
Natural Gas Supply Services
N.A.I.C.S.: 221210

Netzgesellschaft Dusseldorf mbH (1)
Hoherweg 100, 40233, Dusseldorf, Germany
Tel.: (49) 211 821 6389
Web Site: https://www.netz-duesseldorf.de
Electricity Power Supply Services
N.A.I.C.S.: 221122

Netzgesellschaft Elz-Neckar GmbH & Co. KG (1)

Hauptstrasse 7, 74847, Obrigheim, Germany
Tel.: (49) 62 616 4672
Web Site: https://www.netz-elz-neckar.de
Electricity Power Grid Services
N.A.I.C.S.: 221122

Netzgesellschaft Ostwurttemberg DonauRies GmbH (1)
Unterer Bruhl 2, 73479, Ellwangen, Germany
Tel.: (49) 796193361401
Web Site: https://www.netze-odr.de
Electric Power Distribution Services
N.A.I.C.S.: 221122

Netzgesellschaft Steinheim GmbH & Co. KG (1)
Hauptstr 24, Steinheim, 89555, Baden-Wurttemberg, Germany
Tel.: (49) 796193360
Electric Power Distribution Services
N.A.I.C.S.: 221122

Netzgesellschaft Steinheim Verwaltungsgesellschaft mbH. (1)
Unterer Bruhl 2, Ellwangen, 73479, Baden-Wurttemberg, Germany
Tel.: (49) 796193360
Electric Power Distribution Services
N.A.I.C.S.: 221122

P2 Plant & Pipeline Engineering GmbH (1)
Paul-Klinger-Strasse 1, 45127, Essen, Germany
Tel.: (49) 201 240 9710
Web Site: https://www.p2-engineering.de
Engineeering Services
N.A.I.C.S.: 541330

PREdistribuce a.s. (1)
Svornosti 3199/19a, 150 00, Prague, Czech Republic
Tel.: (420) 22 491 9473
Web Site: https://www.predistribuce.cz
Electricity Power Supply Services
N.A.I.C.S.: 221122
Karel Jiranek (CIO)

PREmereni a.s. (1)
Na Hroude 2149/19, 100 05, Prague, Czech Republic
Tel.: (420) 73 314 3143
Web Site: https://www.premereni.cz
Electricity Power Supply Services
N.A.I.C.S.: 221122

PREnetcom a.s. (1)
Na Hroude 1492/4, 100 00, Prague, 10, Czech Republic
Tel.: (420) 800550055
Web Site: https://www.prenetcom.cz
N.A.I.C.S.: 517810
Petr Dvorak (Chm)

PREservisnf s.r.o. (1)
Na Hroude 1492/4, 100 00, Prague, 10, Czech Republic
Tel.: (420) 800550055
Web Site: https://www.preservisni.cz
N.A.I.C.S.: 517810
Pavel Elis (Chm-Supervisory Bd)

PREzakaznicka a.s. (1)
Na Hroude 1492/4, Vrsovice, 100 05, Prague, Czech Republic
Tel.: (420) 26 705 1111
Web Site: https://www.prezakaznicka.cz
Call Center Services
N.A.I.C.S.: 561422

Plusnet Infrastruktur GmbH & Co. KG (1)
Mathias-Bruggen-Str 55, 50829, Cologne, Germany
Tel.: (49) 221 669 8050
Web Site: https://www.plusnet.de
Broadband Communication Services
N.A.I.C.S.: 517810

Q-DSL home GmbH (1)
Mathias-Bruggen-Str 55, 50829, Cologne, Germany
Tel.: (49) 221 669 8000
Web Site: https://www.q-dsl-home.de
Telecommunication Servicesb
N.A.I.C.S.: 517810

RBS wave GmbH (1)

EnBW Energie Baden-Wurttemberg
AG—(Continued)

Tel.: (49) 7111 857 1500
Web Site: https://www.rbs-wave.de
Sales Range: $25-49.9 Million
Emp.: 150
Engineering Services
N.A.I.C.S.: 541330

Rheinkraftwerk Iffezheim GmbH (1)
Lautenschlagerstr 20, Stuttgart, 70173,
Baden-Wurttemberg, Germany
Tel.: (49) 7229188300
Web Site: http://www.enbw.com
Electric Power Generation Services
N.A.I.C.S.: 221111

Rieger Beteiligungs-GmbH (1)
Friedrichstr 16, 72805, Lichtenstein, Ger-
many
Tel.: (49) 712992510
Web Site: http://www.ewr-rieger.de
Electric Power Distr
N.A.I.C.S.: 221122

Rieger GmbH & Co. KG (1)
Kochertalstr 32, 73431, Aalen, Germany
Tel.: (49) 73 615 7020
Web Site: https://www.rr-rieger.com
Aluminum Foundry Product Mfr
N.A.I.C.S.: 331524
Regina Ritter (Sls Dir-Operational)

SENEC GmbH (1)
Wittenberger Strasse 15, 04129, Leipzig,
Germany
Tel.: (49) 341870570
Power Storage Equipment Mfr
N.A.I.C.S.: 335999
Nils Buntrock (Dir-Mktg & Comm)

Senec Australia Pty. Ltd. (1)
Level 1 5 Collingwood Street, Osborne
Park, 6017, WA, Australia
Tel.: (61) 862801206
Storage Battery Mfr
N.A.I.C.S.: 335910
Patricia Cavalcanti (COO)

Solarinvest - Green Energy S.r.o. (1)
Na Hroude 2419/19, Strasnice, 100 00,
Prague, Czech Republic
Tel.: (420) 72 498 1004
Web Site: https://www.solarinvest.cz
Household Photovoltaic Installation Services
N.A.I.C.S.: 238210
Ales Hradecky (CEO)

Stadtwerke Dusseldorf AG (1)
Hoherweg 100, 40233, Dusseldorf,
Germany **(54.95%)**
Tel.: (49) 21 182 1821
Web Site: https://www.swd-ag.de
Emp.: 1,548
Electricity, Water, Heat & Gas Utility Admin-
istration Services
N.A.I.C.S.: 926130
Udo Brockmeier (CEO & Member-Mgmt Bd)

Subsidiary (Domestic):

**Stadtwerke Dusseldorf Netz
GmbH** (2)
Hoherweg 200, 40233, Dusseldorf, Ger-
many
Tel.: (49) 211 821 6389
Web Site: http://www.swd-netz.de
Electric Power Distribution Services
N.A.I.C.S.: 221122

**Stadtwerke Sinsheim Versorgungs
GmbH & Co. KG** (1)
Duhrener Str 23, 74889, Sinsheim,
Germany **(60%)**
Tel.: (49) 7 261 4040
Web Site: https://www.sw-sinsheim.de
Electricity, Gas & Other Utility Administra-
tion Services
N.A.I.C.S.: 926130
Andreas Uhler (Mng Dir)

Subsidiary (Domestic):

**Stadtwerke Sinsheim Verwaltungs
GmbH** (2)
Duhrener Strasse 23, 74889, Sinsheim,
Germany
Tel.: (49) 7261404301
Electric Power & Gas Distribution Services
N.A.I.C.S.: 221122

**Stromnetzgesellschaft Herrenberg
mbH & Co. KG** (1)
Stuttgarter Str 80, 71083, Herrenberg, Ger-
many
Tel.: (49) 8003629396
Web Site: https://stromnetz-herrenberg.de
N.A.I.C.S.: 221114

T-plus GmbH (1)
Am Erlengraben 5, 76275, Ettlingen, Ger-
many
Tel.: (49) 7243 505 7890
Web Site: https://www.tplusgmbh.de
Sales Range: $25-49.9 Million
Emp.: 11
Waste Materials Disposal Services
N.A.I.C.S.: 562998

TRITEC AG (1)
Heckenweg 29, 3270, Aarberg, Switzerland
Tel.: (41) 32 665 3535
Web Site: https://www.tritec.ch
Emp.: 50
Solar Power Generation Services
N.A.I.C.S.: 221114
Roland Hofmann (CEO)

**Thermogas Gas- und
Geratevertriebs-GmbH** (1)
Talstr 117, 70188, Stuttgart, Germany
Tel.: (49) 71128941700
Web Site: http://www.thermogas.de
Emp.: 18
Liquefied Petroleum Gas Distr
N.A.I.C.S.: 424720
Bernd Mazzoli (Chm)

TransnetBW GmbH (1)
Pariser Platz Osloer Strasse 15-17, 70173,
Stuttgart, Germany
Tel.: (49) 71 121 8580
Web Site: https://www.transnetbw.de
Emp.: 1,205
Electricity Transmission Services
N.A.I.C.S.: 221121
Werner Gotz (Chm)

TransnetBW GmbH (1)
Pariser Platz Osloer Strasse 15-17, 70173,
Stuttgart, Germany
Tel.: (49) 711218580
Web Site: https://www.transnetbw.de
Energy Consulting Services
N.A.I.C.S.: 541690

VNG AG (1)
Braunstrasse 7, 04347, Leipzig, Germany
Tel.: (49) 3414430
Web Site: http://www.vng.de
Rev.: $11,814,299,028
Assets: $7,486,936,016
Liabilities: $6,025,294,744
Net Worth: $1,461,641,272
Earnings: $131,135,606
Emp.: 1,155
Fiscal Year-end: 12/31/2019
Natural Gas Distr
N.A.I.C.S.: 221210
Ulf Heitmuller (Chm-Exec Bd)

Subsidiary (Domestic):

**Balance Erneuerbare Energien
GmbH** (2)
Braunstrasse 7, 04347, Leipzig, Germany
Tel.: (49) 341 443 2968
Web Site: https://www.balance-vng.de
Natural Gas Storage Distr
N.A.I.C.S.: 221112
Sebastian Schuritz (Head-Fin & Controlling)

Energieunion GmbH (2)
Werderstrasse 74b, 19055, Schwerin, Ger-
many
Tel.: (49) 38 559 2920
Web Site: https://www.energieunion.de
Electricity & Gas Distr
N.A.I.C.S.: 221112
Steffen Rothe (Mng Dir)

Subsidiary (Non-US):

G.EN. Gaz Energia Sp. z o.o. (2)
Ul Dorczyka 1, 62-080, Tarnowo Podgorne,
Poland
Tel.: (48) 61 829 9820
Web Site: https://www.gen.com.pl
Natural Gas Storage Distr
N.A.I.C.S.: 221210
Falko Thormeier (Chm)

Handen Sp. z o.o. (2)
Ul Domaniewska 37, 02-672, Warsaw, Po-
land
Tel.: (48) 22 305 8800
Web Site: https://www.handen.pl
Electricity & Gas Distr
N.A.I.C.S.: 221112
Emilia Smieciuch (Mktg Mgr)

Subsidiary (Domestic):

**Infracon Infrastruktur Service GmbH
& Co. KG** (2)
Maximilianallee 4, 04129, Leipzig, Germany
Tel.: (49) 34127 111 7994
Web Site: https://www.infracon-service.de
Natural Gas Storage Distr
N.A.I.C.S.: 221210
Philipp Pillmaier (Mgr-Contract)

MGMTree GmbH (2)
Braunstrasse 7, 04347, Leipzig, Germany
Tel.: (49) 3412 410 8931
Web Site: https://www.mgmtree.de
Management Consulting Services
N.A.I.C.S.: 541618

Moviatec GmbH (2)
Maximilianallee 4, 04129, Leipzig, Germany
Tel.: (49) 34127 111 1234
Web Site: https://www.moviatec.de
Natural Gas Storage Distr
N.A.I.C.S.: 221210

ONTRAS Gastransport GmbH (2)
Maximilianallee 4, 04129, Leipzig, Germany
Tel.: (49) 34 127 1110
Web Site: https://www.ontras.com
Emp.: 379
Oil & Energy Services
N.A.I.C.S.: 213112
Ralph Bahke (Mng Dir-Controlling & Dev)

Subsidiary (Domestic):

GDMcom GmbH (3)
Maximilianallee 4, 04129, Leipzig, Germany
Tel.: (49) 3 413 5040
Web Site: https://www.gdmcom.de
Telecommunication Contractor Services
N.A.I.C.S.: 238210

Subsidiary (Non-US):

Spigas S.r.l. (2)
Via Nazario Sauro 8, 40121, Bologna, BO,
Italy
Tel.: (39) 018 725 7105
Web Site: https://www.spigas.com
Natural Gas Storage Distr
N.A.I.C.S.: 221210
Francesco Rezzaghi (Acct Mgr-Sls)

VNG Austria GmbH (2)
Pirching 95/1, 8200, Gleisdorf, Austria
Tel.: (43) 31 122 1075
Web Site: https://www.vng-austria.at
Emp.: 15
Natural Gas Storage Distr
N.A.I.C.S.: 221210

VNG Energie Czech s.r.o. (2)
Opletalova 1284/37, 110 00, Prague, Czech
Republic
Tel.: (420) 22 281 4630
Web Site: https://www.vng.cz
Emp.: 205
Natural Gas Storage Distr
N.A.I.C.S.: 221210
Lubos Capousek (Portfolio Mgr)

Subsidiary (Domestic):

VNG Gasspeicher GmbH (2)
Maximilianallee 2, 04129, Leipzig, Germany
Tel.: (49) 341 443 5353
Web Site: https://www.vng-gasspeicher.de
Natural Gas Storage Distr
N.A.I.C.S.: 221210
Bernd Protze (Mng Dir)

VNG Handel & Vertrieb GmbH (2)
Braunstrasse 7, 04347, Leipzig, Germany
Tel.: (49) 341 443 1910
Web Site: https://www.vng-handel.de
Emp.: 205
Natural Gas Storage Distr
N.A.I.C.S.: 221210
Kerstin Schultheiss (Mng Dir)

Subsidiary (Non-US):

goldgas GmbH (2)
Mariahilfer Strasse 62/26, 1070, Vienna,
Austria
Tel.: (43) 1 522 0909
Web Site: https://www.goldgas.at
Electricity & Gas Distr
N.A.I.C.S.: 221112
P. Martin (Sls Mgr)

Subsidiary (Domestic):

goldgas GmbH (2)
Ginnheimer Strasse 4, 65760, Eschborn,
Germany
Tel.: (49) 61 967 7400
Web Site: https://www.goldgas.de
Electricity & Gas Distr
N.A.I.C.S.: 221112
Grazia Friedrich (Sls Mgr-Support)

VNG Innovation GmbH (1)
Braunstr 7, 04347, Leipzig, Germany
Tel.: (49) 341 443 2304
Web Site: https://www.vng-innovation.de
Emp.: 1,200
Natural Gas Distr
N.A.I.C.S.: 424720
Bernhard Kaltefleiter (Dir-Comm)

VNG ViertelEnergie GmbH (1)
Braunstrasse 7, 04347, Leipzig, Germany
Tel.: (49) 3414434444
Web Site: http://www.vng-viertelenergie.de
Engineering Services
N.A.I.C.S.: 541330
Andreas Franke (Mng Dir)

VOLTCOM spol. s r.o. (1)
Otevrena 1092/2, 169 00, Prague, Czech
Republic
Tel.: (420) 26 705 1635
Web Site: https://www.voltcom.cz
Electric Power Distribution Services
N.A.I.C.S.: 221122

WTT CampusONE GmbH (1)
Konigsallee 37, 71638, Ludwigsburg, Ger-
many
Tel.: (49) 7141 505 3020
Web Site: https://www.wtt-campusone.com
Computer Training Services
N.A.I.C.S.: 611420
Rana Abdallah (Mgr-HR)

Watt Deutschland GmbH (1)
Lyoner Strasse 44-48, 60528, Frankfurt am
Main, Germany
Tel.: (49) 8009288787
Web Site: http://www.watt.de
Energy Consulting Services
N.A.I.C.S.: 541690

Watt Synergia GmbH (1)
Lyoner Strasse 44-48, 60528, Frankfurt am
Main, Germany
Tel.: (49) 6924437188112
Web Site: http://www.wattsynergia.de
Sales Range: $25-49.9 Million
Emp.: 10
Energy Consulting Services
N.A.I.C.S.: 541690
Michael Georgi (CEO & CFO)

Winsun AG (1)
Beeschi Mattenstrasse 2, Hohtenn, 3940,
Steg, Switzerland
Tel.: (41) 27 934 3254
Web Site: https://www.winsun.ch
Emp.: 50
Photovoltaic Solar System Services
N.A.I.C.S.: 221114

Yello Strom GmbH (1)
Siegburger Strasse 229, 50679, Cologne,
Germany
Tel.: (49) 2212 711 7777
Web Site: https://www.yello.de
Electric Power Distribution Services
N.A.I.C.S.: 221122

**Yello Strom Verwaltungsgesellschaft
mbH** (1)
Durlacher Allee 93, Karlsruhe, 76131,
Baden-Wurttemberg, Germany
Tel.: (49) 8001900019
Electric Power Distr
N.A.I.C.S.: 221122

ZEAG Energie AG (1)

Weipertstrasse 41, 74076, Heilbronn, Germany
Tel.: (49) 7 131 6100
Web Site: https://www.zeag-energie.de
Electric Power Distribution Services
N.A.I.C.S.: 221122

ZEAG Energie AG **(1)**
Weipertstrasse 41, 74076, Heilbronn, Germany
Tel.: (49) 71316100
Web Site: https://www.zeag-energie.de
Sales Range: $75-99.9 Million
Emp.: 235
Provider of Cement & Electricity Services
N.A.I.C.S.: 221122

ZEAG Engineering GmbH **(1)**
Theresienstrasse 2, 74072, Heilbronn, Germany
Tel.: (49) 713 1670
Web Site: https://www.zeag-engineering.de
Engineeering Services
N.A.I.C.S.: 541330

Zentraldeponie Hubbelrath GmbH **(1)**
Erkrather Landstr 81, 40629, Dusseldorf, Germany
Tel.: (49) 211 302 6930
Web Site: https://www.zentraldeponie-hubbelrath.de
Waste Management Services
N.A.I.C.S.: 562998

backnangstrom GmbH & Co. KG **(1)**
Schlachthofstrasse 6 - 10, 71522, Backnang, Germany
Tel.: (49) 71 911 7620
Web Site: https://www.backnangstrom.de
Eletric Power Generation Services
N.A.I.C.S.: 221122

bmp greengas GmbH **(1)**
Ganghoferstrasse 68a, 80339, Munich, Germany
Tel.: (49) 893 090 5870
Web Site: https://www.bmp-greengas.de
Natural Gas Distribution Services
N.A.I.C.S.: 221210
Thomas Hardtl *(Head-Portfolio Mgmt)*

eYello CZ k.s. **(1)**
Kubanske Namesti 1391/11, 100 00, Prague, Czech Republic
Tel.: (420) 26 705 6704
Web Site: https://www.yello.cz
Gas Distr
N.A.I.C.S.: 424720
Zdenek Vachel *(Mgr)*

effizienzcloud GmbH **(1)**
Lohrstrasse 15, 04105, Leipzig, Germany
Tel.: (49) 3414432211
Web Site: http://www.effizienz.cloud
Software Development Services
N.A.I.C.S.: 513210

fonial GmbH **(1)**
Kaiser-Wilhelm-Ring 7-9, 50672, Cologne, Germany
Tel.: (49) 2216 695 1100
Web Site: https://www.fonial.de
Telecommunication Servicesb
N.A.I.C.S.: 517810
Jennifer Schmitz *(Mktg Mgr)*

grunES GmbH **(1)**
Fleischmannstr 50, 73728, Esslingen am Neckar, Germany
Tel.: (49) 7 113 9070
Web Site: https://www.gruen-es.de
Natural Gas Distr
N.A.I.C.S.: 424720

terranets bw GmbH **(1)**
Am Wallgraben 135, 70565, Stuttgart, Germany
Tel.: (49) 71178120
Web Site: http://www.terranets-bw.de
Emp.: 235
Natural Gas Supply Services
N.A.I.C.S.: 221210
Katrin Flinspach *(Mng Dir)*

ENC DIGITAL TECHNOLOGY CO., LTD.
Xinao Building Sichuan Nanlu Railway Bridge South, Guangxi Zhuang

Autonomous Region, Beihai, 200120, China
Tel.: (86) 2150688096
Web Site: https://www.encdata.cn
Year Founded: 1986
603869—(SHG)
Rev.: $135,195,358
Assets: $684,330,000
Liabilities: $122,541,780
Net Worth: $561,788,220
Earnings: $2,509,102
Fiscal Year-end: 12/31/22
Tour Operator
N.A.I.C.S.: 561520
Xilin Ju *(Vice Chm)*

ENCANTO POTASH CORP.
595 Burrard Street Suite 3123, Vancouver, V7X 1J1, BC, Canada
Tel.: (514) 826-6662
Web Site: https://epotash.com
ENCTF—(OTCEM)
Assets: $71,847
Liabilities: $21,649,906
Net Worth: ($21,578,059)
Earnings: ($1,312,756)
Fiscal Year-end: 12/31/23
Potash Exploration Services
N.A.I.C.S.: 212390
Aref Kanafani *(CFO)*

Subsidiaries:

Encanto Resources Ltd **(1)**
Ste 380 580 Hornby St, Vancouver, V6C 3B6, BC, Canada
Tel.: (604) 683-2402
Sales Range: $50-74.9 Million
Potash Mining Services
N.A.I.C.S.: 212390

ENCASH ENTERTAINMENT LIMITED
12 Free School Street, Mercantile Building, Kolkata, 700016, West Bengal, India
Tel.: (91) 3322303313
Web Site:
http://www.encashentertain.com
Rev.: $766,463
Assets: $4,573,654
Liabilities: $3,239,981
Net Worth: $1,333,673
Earnings: ($25,085)
Fiscal Year-end: 03/31/19
Film Production & Distribution
N.A.I.C.S.: 512110
Swati Ganguly *(Gen Mgr)*

ENCAVIS AG
Grosse Elbstrasse 59, 22767, Hamburg, 22767, Germany
Tel.: (49) 403785620
Web Site: https://www.encavis.com
Year Founded: 1998
ECV—(DEU)
Rev.: $518,421,507
Assets: $3,944,745,677
Liabilities: $2,914,040,181
Net Worth: $1,030,705,496
Earnings: $58,869,387
Emp.: 368
Fiscal Year-end: 12/31/23
Private Investment Firm
N.A.I.C.S.: 523999
Manfred Kruper *(Chm-Supervisory Bd)*

Subsidiaries:

Casette S.r.l. **(1)**
Via Archimede 10, 37036, San Martino Buon Albergo, VR, Italy
Tel.: (39) 0457085030
Web Site: http://www.casettesrl.it
Real Estate Services
N.A.I.C.S.: 531390

Encavis Asset Management AG **(1)**
Prof-Messerschmitt-Str 3, 85579, Neubib-

erg, Germany
Tel.: (49) 8944230600
Web Site: http://www.encavis.com
Wind Electric Power Generation Services
N.A.I.C.S.: 221115
Karsten Mieth *(Member-Mgmt Bd)*

Encavis Portfolio Management GmbH **(1)**
Prof-Messerschmitt-Str 3, 85579, Neubiberg, Germany
Tel.: (49) 1715540097
Investment Banking Services
N.A.I.C.S.: 523150

Encavis Technical Services GmbH **(1)**
Delitzscher Strasse 72, 06112, Halle, Germany
Tel.: (49) 34568579061
Technical Services
N.A.I.C.S.: 541990
Holger Baumgartel *(Mng Dir)*

Stern Energy Ltd. **(1)**
Unit 6 Union Way Aston, Birmingham, B6 7FH, West Midlands, United Kingdom
Tel.: (44) 1323819944
Web Site: https://www.stern-energy.com
Photovoltaic System Construction Services
N.A.I.C.S.: 237130

Stern Energy S.p.A. **(1)**
Largo Novaro 1/A, 43121, Parma, Italy
Tel.: (39) 0521229761
Photovoltaic System Construction Services
N.A.I.C.S.: 237130

Vallone S.r.l. **(1)**
Via Francesco Denza 20, 00197, Rome, Italy
Tel.: (39) 0766879624
Web Site: http://www.vallone.it
Industrial & Commercial Waste Management Services
N.A.I.C.S.: 562998

ENCE ENERGIA Y CELULOSA, S.A.
Beatriz de Bobadilla 14, 28040, Madrid, Spain
Tel.: (34) 913378500 ES
Web Site: https://www.ence.es
Year Founded: 1957
ENC—(MAD)
Rev.: $915,777,680
Assets: $1,877,110,057
Liabilities: $1,160,045,259
Net Worth: $717,064,798
Earnings: ($23,258,638)
Emp.: 1,148
Fiscal Year-end: 12/31/23
Cellulose & Wood Products Producer
N.A.I.C.S.: 113210
Ignacio de Colmenares y Brunet *(Chm & Mng Dir)*

Subsidiaries:

Celulosa Energia, S.L. **(1)**
Carretera A-5000 Km 7.5, Apartado 223, 21007, Huelva, Spain
Tel.: (34) 959367700
Web Site: http://www.ence.es
Electric Power Generation
N.A.I.C.S.: 221118

Celulosas de Asturias, S.A. **(1)**
Calle Armental, Navia, 33710, Asturias, Spain
Tel.: (34) 985630200
Sales Range: $125-149.9 Million
Emp.: 300
Pulp Mill
N.A.I.C.S.: 322110
Diec Arto *(Mng Dir)*

Ence, Energia y Celulosa, S.A. - Pontevedra Mill **(1)**
Marisma de Lourizan s/n Apartado 157, 36153, Pontevedra, Spain
Tel.: (34) 986856000
Wood Products Mfr
N.A.I.C.S.: 321211

Iberflorestal - Comercio E ServiCos Florestais, S A **(1)**

Avenida Antonio Augusto De Aguiar130 2, 2nd Fl, Lisbon, Portugal
Tel.: (351) 217800269
Sales Range: $25-49.9 Million
Emp.: 20
Forest Nurseries & Gathering
N.A.I.C.S.: 113210

Ibersilva, S.A.U. **(1)**
Avenida Antonio Augusto De Aguiar 130 St 2, 1050 020, Lisbon, Portugal
Tel.: (351) 217800269
Web Site: http://www.ibersilva.es
Sales Range: $25-49.9 Million
Emp.: 17
Forestry
N.A.I.C.S.: 115310

SEGEPER, S.A. **(1)**
Avda del Partenon 12, 28042, Madrid, Spain
Tel.: (34) 91 337 60 00
Oil & Gas Exploration Services
N.A.I.C.S.: 213112

ENCHEM CO., LTD.
107 Bio-valley-ro, Jecheon, 27159, Chungbuk, Korea (South)
Tel.: (82) 436530910
Web Site: https://www.enchem.net
Year Founded: 2012
348370—(KRS)
Chemicals Mfr
N.A.I.C.S.: 325998
Eun-Gi Shim *(Dir-Tech Res Center)*

ENCHO CO., LTD.
12-12 2-chome Chuo-cho, Fuji, 417-0052, Shizuoka, Japan
Tel.: (81) 545570808
Web Site: http://www.encho.co.jp
Year Founded: 1939
8208—(TKS)
Rev.: $226,798,747
Assets: $241,473,338
Liabilities: $179,986,735
Net Worth: $61,486,603
Earnings: ($2,728,774)
Emp.: 1,354
Fiscal Year-end: 03/31/24
Construction Materials Distr
N.A.I.C.S.: 423320
Takeo Endo *(Chm)*

Subsidiaries:

Jumbo Co., Ltd. **(1)**
Jumbo Bldg 1474-4 Eda-Cho, Aoba-Ku, Yokohama, 225-8501, Kanagawa, Japan
Tel.: (81) 459122112
Web Site: https://www.jmb.co.jp
Market Research Services
N.A.I.C.S.: 541613
Tadashi Omura *(Pres)*

ENCO SPOL. S R.O.
Michalska 7, Bratislava, 811 01, Slovakia
Tel.: (421) 254435144
Web Site: http://www.enco.sk
Year Founded: 1993
Sales Range: $150-199.9 Million
Emp.: 600
Large Pressing Tool, Moulded Rubber Product & Automotive Industry Mfr
N.A.I.C.S.: 332322
Jozef Medved *(Mng Dir)*

Subsidiaries:

METALLFORM, s.r.o. **(1)**
Tovarenska 422, 018 61, Belusa, Slovakia
Tel.: (421) 424459201
Web Site: http://www.enco.sk
Sales Range: $75-99.9 Million
Emp.: 130
Automotive Rubber & Plastic Composite Mfr
N.A.I.C.S.: 326299
Monica Budjacova *(Gen Mgr)*

ZVS ENCO a.s. **(1)**
Sturova 1, 018 41, Dubnica nad Vahom, Slovakia
Tel.: (421) 42 442 66 39

Enco spol, s r.o.—(Continued)

Metal Products Mfr
N.A.I.C.S.: 332312

ENCODE PACKAGING INDIA LIMITED
D-82 Focal Point Extension, Jalandhar, 144 004, Punjab, India
Tel.: (91) 1815007630
Web Site:
https://encodepackaging.com
Year Founded: 1994
530733—(BOM)
Rev.: $144,648
Assets: $471,767
Liabilities: $24,512
Net Worth: $447,254
Earnings: $6,367
Fiscal Year-end: 03/31/22
Books Publishing Services
N.A.I.C.S.: 513130
Sunil Kumar Chopra (Mng Dir)

ENCORE ART GROUP
Unit 110 6311 Westminster Hwy,
Richmond, V7C 4V4, BC, Canada
Tel.: (604) 276-4551
Web Site:
http://www.capandwinnbevon.com
Sales Range: $10-24.9 Million
Emp.: 40
Fine Art Reproductions, Limited Edition Prints, Imprints, Monoprints & Upscale Posters Publisher
N.A.I.C.S.: 513199
Hall Krieger (Pres)

Subsidiaries:

Canadian Art Prints, Inc. **(1)**
6311 Westminster Hwy Ste 110, Richmond,
V7C 4V4, BC, Canada
Tel.: (604) 276-4551
Web Site: http://www.canadianartprints.com
Art Publisher
N.A.I.C.S.: 513140
Joseph Halby Krieger (CEO)

Winn Devon Art Group **(1)**
Unit 110 6311 Westminster Hwy, Richmond,
V7C 4V4, BC, Canada
Tel.: (604) 276-4551
Web Site: http://www.winndevon.com
Fine Art Reproductions, Limited Edition Prints, Imprints, Monoprints & Upscale Posters Publisher
N.A.I.C.S.: 513199

ENCORE ENERGY CORP.
250-200 Burrard Street, Vancouver,
V6C 3L6, BC, Canada
Tel.: (604) 802-4759
Web Site: https://encoreuranium.com
Year Founded: 2009
EU—(NYSEAMEX)
Rev.: $406,132
Assets: $223,529,458
Liabilities: $8,479,219
Net Worth: $215,050,239
Earnings: ($16,515,389)
Fiscal Year-end: 12/31/22
Uranium Ore Exploration Services
N.A.I.C.S.: 213114
William Morris Sheriff (Chm)

ENCOUNTER RESOURCES LIMITED
Suite 2 1 Alvan Street, Subiaco,
6008, WA, Australia
Tel.: (61) 894869455
Web Site:
https://www.encounter.com.au
Year Founded: 2004
ENR—(ASX)
Rev.: $412,711
Assets: $25,330,115
Liabilities: $1,124,794
Net Worth: $24,205,322
Earnings: ($2,892,447)

Emp.: 11
Fiscal Year-end: 06/30/24
Mineral Exploration Services
N.A.I.C.S.: 212290
William Robinson (Mng Dir)

ENCOURAGE TECHNOLOGIES CO., LTD.
7F Tornare Nihonbashi Hamacho
3-3-2 Nihonbashi Hamacho, Chuo-ku,
Tokyo, 103-0007, Japan
Tel.: (81) 356232622
Web Site: https://www.et-x.jp
Year Founded: 2002
3682—(TKS)
Rev.: $17,679,760
Assets: $35,552,090
Liabilities: $5,722,080
Net Worth: $29,830,010
Earnings: $761,110
Fiscal Year-end: 03/31/20
Software Developer
N.A.I.C.S.: 513210
Shinya Ishii (Pres)

Subsidiaries:

Acrotech Co., Ltd **(1)**
3-42-3 Nihonbashi-Hamacho, Sumitomo Realty & Development Hamacho Building
6F Chuo-ku, Tokyo, 103-0007, Japan
Tel.: (81) 368108377
Web Site: http://www.acrotech.co.jp
Emp.: 37
Software Development Services
N.A.I.C.S.: 541511

ENCRES DUBUIT SA
1 rue Isaac Newton, 77290, Mitry-Mory, France
Tel.: (33) 164674160 **FR**
Web Site:
https://www.encresdubuit.com
Year Founded: 1970
ALDUB—(EUR)
Sales Range: $10-24.9 Million
Emp.: 77
Screen Printing Services
N.A.I.C.S.: 323113
Chrystelle Ferrari (Chm-Mgmt Bd, CFO & Chief Admin Officer)

Subsidiaries:

Publivenor BVBA **(1)**
Suikerkaai 40, 1500, Halle, Belgium
Tel.: (32) 23630920
Web Site: http://www.publivenor.be
Textile Printer Product Mfr
N.A.I.C.S.: 314999
Olivier De Brauwer (Mng Dir)

ENDAVA PLC
125 Old Broad Street, London, EC2N 1AR, United Kingdom
Tel.: (44) 2073671000 **UK**
Web Site: https://www.endava.com
Year Founded: 2000
DAVA—(NYSE)
Rev.: $936,243,679
Assets: $1,281,459,806
Liabilities: $473,250,757
Net Worth: $808,209,048
Earnings: $21,640,546
Emp.: 12,085
Fiscal Year-end: 06/30/24
Information Technology Services
N.A.I.C.S.: 541512
John Cotterell (Founder & CEO)

Subsidiaries:

Endava (US) LLC **(1)**
441 Lexington Ave Ste 702, New York, NY, 10017
Tel.: (212) 920-7240
Information Technology Consulting Services
N.A.I.C.S.: 541511
Simon Whittington (Mng Dir)

Endava DOOEL Skopje **(1)**
Kale Building Ul 11 Mart Br 2, 1000, Sko-

pje, North Macedonia
Tel.: (389) 2 510 2300
Information Technology Consulting Services
N.A.I.C.S.: 541511
Magdalena Milosevic (Project Mgr)

Endava GmbH **(1)**
Eschersheimer Landstrasse 10, 60322, Frankfurt, Germany
Tel.: (49) 69 999 911 5 0
Information Technology Consulting Services
N.A.I.C.S.: 541511
Thorsten Junike (Mng Dir)

Endava Limited **(1)**
The Stables 112 Preston, Crowmarsh, Wallingford, OX10 6SL, Oxon, United Kingdom
Tel.: (44) 1491 820900
IT Services
N.A.I.C.S.: 541512

Endava Limited **(1)**
3rd Floor 151 West George Street, Glasgow, G2 2JJ, United Kingdom
Tel.: (44) 20 7367 1000
IT Services
N.A.I.C.S.: 541512
Lori Coretchi (Office Mgr)

Endava Romania SRL **(1)**
75B Nicolae Caramfil St Floor 2-3 Sector 1, 14142, Bucharest, Romania
Tel.: (40) 372 363 291
Web Site: http://www.endava.com
IT Services
N.A.I.C.S.: 541512

Endava Romania SRL **(1)**
AFI Business Park 1 4E Vasile Milea BLV floor 6, 6th district, 061344, Bucharest, Romania
Tel.: (40) 372 363 291
Web Site: http://www.endava.com
Emp.: 400
Information Technology Consulting Services
N.A.I.C.S.: 541511

Endava, LLC **(1)**
11714 Northcreek Pkwy N 175, Bothell, WA 98011
Tel.: (425) 454-2686
Web Site: http://www.endava.com
Software Developer
N.A.I.C.S.: 513210

ICS Endava SRL **(1)**
15 Sfatul Tarii St, 2012, Chisinau, Moldova
Tel.: (373) 22 806 700
Information Technology Consulting Services
N.A.I.C.S.: 541511
Valentina Vremes (Dir-HR)

Levvel, LLC **(1)**
101 N Tryon St Ste 1500, Charlotte, NC 28202
Tel.: (980) 278-3065
Web Site: http://www.levvel.io
Sales Range: $25-49.9 Million
Emp.: 172
Application Software Development Services
N.A.I.C.S.: 541511
Chris Hart (Co-Founder & CEO)

ENDEAVOUR FINANCIAL LTD.
Plough Court 37 Lombard Street,
London, EC3V 9BQ, United Kingdom
Tel.: (44) 2075902720
Web Site:
http://www.endeavourfinancial.com
Year Founded: 1988
Emp.: 10
Debt Finance & Merger Advisory Services
N.A.I.C.S.: 522299
David Rhodes (Mng Partner)

ENDEAVOUR GROUP LIMITED
26 Waterloo Street, Surry Hills, 2010,
NSW, Australia
Tel.: (61) 293338008 **AU**
Web Site:
https://www.endeavourgroup.com
Year Founded: 2019
EDV—(ASX)
Rev.: $7,748,581,861
Assets: $7,609,702,028
Liabilities: $5,191,367,282

Net Worth: $2,418,334,746
Earnings: $344,917,520
Emp.: 30,000
Fiscal Year-end: 06/25/23
Alcoholic Drink Distr
N.A.I.C.S.: 424820
Kate Beattie (Deputy CFO)

Subsidiaries:

Chapel Hill Winery Pty. Ltd. **(1)**
Chaffey Rd & Chapel Hill Road, McLaren Vale, 5171, SA, Australia
Tel.: (61) 883244404
Web Site:
https://www.chapelhillwine.com.au
Wine Mfr & Distr
N.A.I.C.S.: 312130

ENDEAVOUR MINING PLC.
94 Solaris Avenue Camana Bay, PO
Box 1348, Georgetown, KY1-1108,
Grand Cayman, Cayman Islands
Tel.: (345) 9433100 **Ky**
Web Site:
https://www.endeavourmining.com
Year Founded: 2002
EDVMF—(OTCIQ)
Rev.: $2,114,600,000
Assets: $5,858,500,000
Liabilities: $2,310,200,000
Net Worth: $3,548,300,000
Earnings: $42,700,000
Emp.: 4,820
Fiscal Year-end: 12/31/23
Gold & Other Mineral Exploration & Mining
N.A.I.C.S.: 212220
Morgan Carroll (Gen Counsel & Exec VP-Corp Fin)

Subsidiaries:

SEMAFO Inc. **(1)**
100 Boulevard Alexis-Nihon 7th floor, Saint Laurent, H4M 2P3, QC, Canada
Tel.: (514) 744-4408
Web Site: http://www.semafo.co
Gold & Iron Ore Mining & Exploration Services
N.A.I.C.S.: 212220
Patrick Moryoussef (VP-Mining Ops)

Subsidiary (Non-US):

Mana Mineral S.A. **(2)**
Sector 13 Babanguida Avenue Benda Street Door 21101 Ouagadougou 01, PO Box 390, Ouagadougou, Burkina Faso
Tel.: (226) 50 36 95 92
Mineral Exploration Services
N.A.I.C.S.: 212390

SEMAFO Guinee S.A. **(2)**
Boulevard du Commerce Immeuble ETI face Ambassade de France, PO BOX 2073, Conakry, Papua New Guinea
Tel.: (675) 30435241
Web Site: http://www.semafo.com
Explorer & Developer of Mining
N.A.I.C.S.: 213113

SEMAFO Mineral S.A. **(2)**
Avenue Wemtenga Rue 2906 Porte N 619, Ouagadougou, Burkina Faso
Tel.: (226) 36 95 92
Explorer & Developer of Mining
N.A.I.C.S.: 213113

Teranga Gold Corporation **(1)**
77 King Street West Suite 2110, Toronto, M5K 2A1, ON, Canada
Tel.: (416) 594-0000
Web Site: http://www.terangagold.com
Rev.: $353,490,000
Assets: $1,175,810,000
Liabilities: $596,907,000
Net Worth: $578,903,000
Earnings: ($29,952,000)
Emp.: 2,600
Fiscal Year-end: 12/31/2019
Gold Exploration & Mining Services
N.A.I.C.S.: 212220
Richard S. Young (Pres & CEO)

ENDEAVOUR SILVER CORP.

1130-609 Granville Street, Vancouver, V7Y 1G5, BC, Canada
Tel.: (604) 685-9775   BC
Web Site: https://www.edrsilver.com
EXK—(NYSE)
Rev.: $210,160,000
Assets: $399,437,000
Liabilities: $83,543,000
Net Worth: $315,894,000
Earnings: $6,201,000
Emp.: 1,298
Fiscal Year-end: 12/31/22
Silver Mining & Production Services
N.A.I.C.S.: 212220
Rex John McLennan *(Chm)*

Subsidiaries:

Metales Interamericanos S.A. de
C.V.   **(1)**
Heraclito No 307 Chapultepec Morales, 11570, Mexico, Mexico
Tel.: (52) 5552035238
Web Site:
    https://www.interamericanademetales.com
Aluminium Products Mfr
N.A.I.C.S.: 331315

Minera Santa Cruz y Garibaldi SA de
CV   **(1)**
Miguel De Cervantes Saavedra No 106 Sur Centro, Durango, Mexico
Tel.: (52) 6188114668
Silver Mining Services
N.A.I.C.S.: 212220
David Howe *(VP)*

ENDEAVOUR VENTURES LIMITED
41 Devonshire Street, London, W1G 7AJ, United Kingdom
Tel.: (44) 207 637 4102   UK
Web Site: http://www.endven.com
Venture Capital Investment Firm
N.A.I.C.S.: 523999
Richard Hargreaves *(Co-Founder)*

ENDLESS LLP
3 Whitehall Quay, Leeds, LS1 4BF, United Kingdom
Tel.: (44) 1132104000   UK
Web Site: http://www.endlessllp.com
Year Founded: 2005
Rev.: $789,645,000
Emp.: 120
Privater Equity Firm
N.A.I.C.S.: 523999
Garry Wilson *(Mng Partner)*

Subsidiaries:

ASCO Group Limited   **(1)**
11 Harvest Avenue, Dyce, Aberdeen, AB21 0BQ, Scotland, United Kingdom
Tel.: (44) 1224580396
Web Site: http://www.ascoworld.com
Logistic & Supply Chain Management Services
N.A.I.C.S.: 213112
Mike Pettigrew *(CEO)*

Subsidiary (US):

ASCO Freight Management   **(2)**
1755 Federal Rd, Houston, TX 77015
Tel.: (713) 451-0008
Web Site: http://www.ascoworld.com
Sales Range: $25-49.9 Million
Emp.: 40
Freight Management & Logistics Services
N.A.I.C.S.: 488510
Gary L. Morris *(Gen Mgr-Packing Div)*

Subsidiary (Domestic):

ASCO Freight Management Ltd.   **(2)**
Unit B1/B2 Lombard Centre Kirkhill Industrial Estate, Dyce, Aberdeen, AB21 0GU, United Kingdom
Tel.: (44) 1224280022
Web Site: http://www.ascoworld.com
Emp.: 20
Freight Transportation & Logistics Management
N.A.I.C.S.: 488510

Accrofab Holdings Limited   **(1)**
Stoney Cross Industrial Park Stoney Gate Road Spondon, Derby, DE21 7RX, United Kingdom
Tel.: (44) 1332666878
Web Site: https://www.accrofab.co.uk
Aerospace Component Mfr
N.A.I.C.S.: 332999
Simon Ward *(Chm)*

Subsidiary (Domestic):

RTI Advanced Forming, Ltd.   **(2)**
Watchmead Welwyn, Garden City, AL7 1LT, United Kingdom
Tel.: (44) 1707351500
Titanium Sheets Mfr
N.A.I.C.S.: 332322

Adare Group Limited   **(1)**
1 Meridian South Meridian Business Park, Leicester, LE19 1WY, United Kingdom
Tel.: (44) 1484863411
Web Site: http://www.adare.com
Sales Range: $300-349.9 Million
Emp.: 1,100
Global Marketing Services & Secure & Essential Communications Solutions
N.A.I.C.S.: 541890

Subsidiary (Domestic):

Adare SEC Limited   **(2)**
Park Mill Clayton West, Huddersfield, HD8 9QQ, United Kingdom
Tel.: (44) 1484863411
Web Site: http://www.adaresec.com
Business Critical Communications Solutions
N.A.I.C.S.: 561499
Barry Crich *(Mng Dir)*

Subsidiary (Domestic):

Adare SEC Limited - Redditch   **(3)**
Unit 1 Arrow Valley Claybrook Drive, Redditch, B98 0FY, Worcs, United Kingdom
Tel.: (44) 1527838890
Web Site: http://shop.kalamazoodirect.co.uk
Security Products & Solutions
N.A.I.C.S.: 561621
Tim Dyer *(Site Dir)*

BSW Timber Ltd.   **(1)**
East End, Berwick-upon-Tweed, TD4 6JA, Berwickshire, United Kingdom
Tel.: (44) 8005878887
Web Site: http://www.bsw.co.uk
Sawmill Operator; Timber Decking, Fencing, Landscaping & Construction Products Mfr
N.A.I.C.S.: 321113
Tony Hackney *(CEO)*

Brabant Alucast International
B.V.   **(1)**
De Grens 45, Heijen, 6598 DK, Gennep, Netherlands   **(100%)**
Tel.: (31) 485 550 234
Web Site: http://www.brabantalucast.com
Aluminum Casting Mfr
N.A.I.C.S.: 331523
H. Schuitema *(Dir-Sls)*

Cinesite (Europe) Limited   **(1)**
Medius House 2 Sheraton Street, London, W1F 8BH, United Kingdom
Tel.: (44) 2079734000
Web Site: http://www.cinesite.co.uk
Sales Range: $50-74.9 Million
Emp.: 100
Digital Imaging Services
N.A.I.C.S.: 512120
Antony Hunt *(Grp CEO)*

EVO Business Supplies Limited   **(1)**
K House Sheffield Business Park, Europa Link, Sheffield, S9 1XU, United Kingdom
Tel.: (44) 114 256 6000
Web Site: http://www.evo-group.co.uk
Business Supplies Distr
N.A.I.C.S.: 424120
Steve Haworth *(CEO)*

Subsidiary (Domestic):

Banner Business Services
Limited   **(2)**
K House Sheffield Business Park Europa Link, Sheffield, S9 1XU, United Kingdom
Tel.: (44) 1603691000
Web Site: http://www.bbanner.co.uk

Stationery & Office Supplies Distr
N.A.I.C.S.: 424120
Richard Costin *(Mng Dir)*

Findel Education Limited   **(1)**
2 Gregory Street, Hyde, SK14 4TH, Cheshire, United Kingdom   **(100%)**
Tel.: (44) 3451203603
Web Site: http://www.findel-education.co.uk
Sales Range: $150-199.9 Million
Emp.: 500
Stationery & Office Supplies Merchant Whslr
N.A.I.C.S.: 424120
Chris Mahady *(Mng Dir)*

Interserve Learning Employment Services Ltd.   **(1)**
12 Europa View Sheffield Business Park, Sheffield, S9 1XH, United Kingdom
Tel.: (44) 3334445055
Web Site: http://www.learning-employment.com
Emp.: 300
Education & Employment Services
N.A.I.C.S.: 611710

KTC (Edibles) Limited   **(1)**
Moorcroft Drive, Wednesbury, WS10 7DE, West Midlands, United Kingdom
Tel.: (44) 121 505 9200
Web Site: http://www.ktc-edibles.com
Sales Range: $350-399.9 Million
Emp.: 223
Edible Oil Mfr
N.A.I.C.S.: 311225
Mike Baldrey *(Dir-Sls)*

Subsidiary (Non-US):

Trilby Trading Limited   **(2)**
No 2 Northwood Avenue Northwood Business Park, Santry, D09 X5N9, Dublin, 9, Ireland
Tel.: (353) 419832137
Sales Range: $25-49.9 Million
Emp.: 9
Specialty Trade Contractors
N.A.I.C.S.: 238990
Seamus Goomley *(Mng Dir)*

Kesslers International Ltd.   **(1)**
11 Rick Roberts Way, London, E15 2NF, United Kingdom
Tel.: (44) 2085223000
Web Site: http://www.kesslers.com
Miscellaneous General Merchandise Stores,
N.A.I.C.S.: 455219
John Wood *(Chm)*

Menzies Distribution Limited   **(1)**
Unit E Twelvetrees Business Park Twelvetrees Crescent, London, E3 3JG, United Kingdom   **(52%)**
Tel.: (44) 1314678070
Web Site:
    http://www.menziesdistribution.com
Magazines, Books, Home Entertainment Products; Computer & Multimedia Software & Games, Toys; Air Transport & Air Cargo Handling Services
N.A.I.C.S.: 481212
Martyn R. Smith *(Fin Dir)*

Subsidiary (Domestic):

Bibby Distribution Limited   **(2)**
105 Duke Street, Liverpool, L1 5JQ, United Kingdom
Tel.: (44) 151 794 1074
Web Site: http://www.bibbydist.co.uk
Sales Range: $350-399.9 Million
Emp.: 200
Logistics & Distr
N.A.I.C.S.: 541614
Paul Kavanagh *(COO)*

Division (Domestic):

John Menzies Distribution   **(2)**
2 Lochside Ave, Edinburgh, EH12 9DJ, United Kingdom   **(100%)**
Tel.: (44) 1314678070
Web Site:
    http://www.menziesdistribution.com
Sales Range: $75-99.9 Million
Emp.: 250
Newspapers, Magazines & Periodicals Distribution & Marketing Services
N.A.I.C.S.: 541870

The Works Stores Ltd.   **(1)**
5 Midpoint Park Kingsbury Road Minworth, Sutton Coldfield, B76 1RN, W Midlands, United Kingdom
Tel.: (44) 12 1313 6000
Web Site: http://www.theworks.co.uk
Sales Range: $200-249.9 Million
Emp.: 2,100
Discount Book, Toy, Art & Craft, Gift & Stationery Stores Operator
N.A.I.C.S.: 455110
Victoria Reid Norrish *(Dir-Supply Chain)*

ENDLESS SOLAR CORPORATION PTY LIMITED
Level 9 406 Collins Street, Melbourne, 3000, VIC, Australia
Tel.: (61) 3 9600 3242   AU
Web Site: http://www.endless-solar.com
Rev.: $157,230
Assets: $3,361,876
Liabilities: $1,247,076
Net Worth: $2,114,800
Earnings: ($118,063)
Fiscal Year-end: 06/30/17
Evacuated Tube Solar Hot Water Mfr
N.A.I.C.S.: 333414
David Harold Allen Craig *(Exec Dir)*

ENDO FINANCE PLC
10 Timber Wharf, Marsa, MRS 1443, Malta
Tel.: (356) 22068000
Web Site:
    http://www.endofinance.com
Year Founded: 2018
EN29A—(MAL)
Rev.: $143,410
Assets: $11,735,176
Liabilities: $2,175,763
Net Worth: $9,559,413
Earnings: $47,082
Fiscal Year-end: 12/31/23
Financial Investment Services
N.A.I.C.S.: 523940
Christopher Frendo *(Exec Dir)*

ENDO INTERNATIONAL PLC
First Floor Minerva House Simmonscourt Road Ballsbridge, Dublin, 4, Ireland
Tel.: (353) 12682000   IE
Web Site: https://www.endo.com
Year Founded: 2013
ENDP—(NASDAQ)
Rev.: $2,993,206,000
Assets: $8,767,415,000
Liabilities: $10,011,401,000
Net Worth: ($1,243,986,000)
Earnings: ($613,245,000)
Emp.: 3,103
Fiscal Year-end: 12/31/21
Holding Company; Pharmaceutical Mfr & Distr
N.A.I.C.S.: 551112
Blaise Coleman *(Pres & CEO)*

Subsidiaries:

BIOSPECIFICS TECHNOLOGIES CORP.   **(1)**
35 Wilbur St, Lynbrook, NY 11563
Tel.: (516) 593-7000
Web Site: http://www.biospecifics.com
Rev.: $38,187,755
Assets: $126,653,268
Liabilities: $2,162,166
Net Worth: $124,491,102
Earnings: $24,469,808
Emp.: 7
Fiscal Year-end: 12/31/2019
Dermatological Pharmaceuticals Mfr
N.A.I.C.S.: 325412
Patrick Hutchison *(CFO)*

Subsidiary (Domestic):

Advance Biofactures Corp.   **(2)**
35 Wilbur St, Lynbrook, NY
11563-2358   **(100%)**

Endo International plc—(Continued)

Tel.: (516) 593-7000
Sales Range: $75-99.9 Million
Collagen Therapeutic Enzymes Mfr
N.A.I.C.S.: 541715
Thomas L. Wegman (Pres)

Endo Health Solutions Inc.   **(1)**
1400 Atwater Dr, Malvern, PA 19355
Tel.: (484) 216-0000
Web Site: http://www.endo.com
Rev.: $2,616,907,000
Assets: $6,571,856,000
Liabilities: $5,986,640,000
Net Worth: $585,216,000
Earnings: ($632,414,000)
Emp.: 3,371
Fiscal Year-end: 12/31/2013
Holding Company for Pharmaceutical Mfr
N.A.I.C.S.: 325412
Suketu P. Upadhyay (CFO & Exec VP)

Subsidiary (Domestic):

American Medical Systems Holdings, Inc.   **(2)**
10700 Bren Rd W, Minnetonka, MN 55343
Tel.: (952) 930-6000
Web Site:
  http://www.americanmedicalsystems.com
Sales Range: $250-299.9 Million
Emp.: 1,255
Medical Device Mfr
N.A.I.C.S.: 339112
Joe W. Martin (Sr VP & Gen Mgr-BPH Therapy)

Subsidiary (Non-US):

AMS - American Medical Systems do Brasil Produtos Urologicos e Ginecologicos Ltda.   **(3)**
Av Ibirapuera 2907 Conj 1212, Sao Paulo, 04029-200, Brazil
Tel.: (55) 1150919753
Web Site:
  http://www.americanmedicalsystems.com
Sales Range: $25-49.9 Million
Emp.: 6
Medical Therapy Apparatus & Medical Devices Mfr
N.A.I.C.S.: 423450

AMS Medical Systems Ireland Limited   **(3)**
Unit A Athlone Business & Technology Park Garrycastle Dublin Road, Athlone, Westmeath, Ireland
Tel.: (353) 906465300
Web Site: http://www.bzams.com
Emp.: 50
Medical Therapy Apparatus & Medical Devices Mfr
N.A.I.C.S.: 423450

American Medical Systems Canada Inc.   **(3)**
381 Elmira Rd N, PO Box 461, Guelph, N1K 1H3, ON, Canada
Tel.: (519) 826-5333
Medical Device Distr
N.A.I.C.S.: 423450

American Medical Systems Deutschland GmbH   **(3)**
Voss Strasse 20, 10117, Berlin, Germany
Tel.: (49) 302064390
Web Site:
  http://www.americanmedicalsystems.de
Medical Therapy Apparatus & Medical Devices Mfr
N.A.I.C.S.: 423450

American Medical Systems Europe B.V.   **(3)**
Haarlerbergweg 23/G Riverbuilding 6th Floor, 1101 CH, Amsterdam, Netherlands
Tel.: (31) 346258100
Emp.: 50
Medical Therapy Apparatus & Medical Devices Mfr
N.A.I.C.S.: 423450

American Medical Systems France S.A.S   **(3)**
19 Avenue de Norvege, Courtaboeuf, 91953, France
Tel.: (33) 169599700

Sales Range: $25-49.9 Million
Emp.: 30
Medical Device Mfr
N.A.I.C.S.: 339112
Gerome Augustin (Mng Dir)

American Medical Systems Iberica S.L.   **(3)**
C/Joaquin Turina 21 Planta Oficina 6, Pozuelo de Alarcon, 28224, Spain
Tel.: (34) 917994970
Medical Therapy Apparatus & Devices Mfr
N.A.I.C.S.: 339112

American Medical Systems UK Limited   **(3)**
13th Floor GW1 Great West House Great West Road, Brentford, TW8 9DF, United Kingdom
Tel.: (44) 2089963100
Web Site:
  http://www.americanmedicalsystems.co.uk
Sales Range: $25-49.9 Million
Emp.: 40
Medical Therapy Apparatus & Medical Devices Mfr
N.A.I.C.S.: 423450

Subsidiary (Domestic):

American Medical Systems, Inc.   **(3)**
10700 Bren Rd W, Minnetonka, MN 55343-9679
Tel.: (952) 930-6000
Web Site:
  http://www.americanmedicalsystems.com
Sales Range: $75-99.9 Million
Emp.: 500
Urological Devices Mfr
N.A.I.C.S.: 339113

Branch (Domestic):

American Medical Systems, Inc.-San Jose   **(4)**
3052 Orchard Dr, San Jose, CA 95134-2011
Tel.: (408) 943-0636
Web Site:
  http://www.americanmedicalsystems.com
Sales Range: $75-99.9 Million
Emp.: 296
Medical Laser Equipment & Systems Designer, Mfr, Sales & Servicer
N.A.I.C.S.: 334510

Subsidiary (Domestic):

CPEC LLC   **(2)**
3326 Hwy 51 N, Fort Mill, SC 29715-8348
Tel.: (803) 548-4348
Pharmaceuticals Product Mfr
N.A.I.C.S.: 325412

Endo Pharmaceuticals Solutions Inc.   **(2)**
100 Endo Blvd, Chadds Ford, PA 19317
Tel.: (610) 558-9800
Web Site: http://www.endo.com
Sales Range: $75-99.9 Million
Emp.: 246
Pharmaceuticals Mfr
N.A.I.C.S.: 325412

Unit (Domestic):

Endo Pharmaceuticals Solutions Inc. - New Jersey   **(3)**
7 Clarke Dr, Cranbury, NJ 08512
Tel.: (609) 409-9010
Web Site: http://www.endo.com
Sales Range: $25-49.9 Million
Emp.: 101
Pharmaceuticals Mfr
N.A.I.C.S.: 325412

Subsidiary (Non-US):

Paladin Labs Inc.   **(2)**
100 Alexis-Nihon Blvd 600, Saint Laurent, H4M 2P2, QC, Canada
Tel.: (514) 340-1112
Web Site: http://www.paladin-labs.com
Sales Range: $200-249.9 Million
Emp.: 88
Biotechnological & Pharmaceutical Products Mfr
N.A.I.C.S.: 325412
Isabelle Trempe (VP-Bus Dev)

Subsidiary (Non-US):

Labopharm Europe Limited   **(3)**
5 The Seapoint Building 44 Clomtars Road, Dublin, Ireland   **(100%)**
Tel.: (353) 018540140
Sales Range: $25-49.9 Million
Emp.: 12
Pharmaceutical Research & Development
N.A.I.C.S.: 541715

Subsidiary (Domestic):

Par Pharmaceutical Companies, Inc.   **(2)**
1 Ram Ridgo Rd, Chootnut Ridge, NY 10977
Tel.: (845) 573-5500
Web Site: http://www.parpharm.com
Holding Company; Pharmaceutical Mfr
N.A.I.C.S.: 551112
Keri Mattox (Sr VP-Investor Rels & Corp Affairs)

Subsidiary (Domestic):

Par Pharmaceutical Holdings, Inc.   **(3)**
One Ram Rdg Rd, Chestnut Ridge, NY 07677
Tel.: (845) 573-5500
Web Site: http://www.parpharm.com
Emp.: 1,600
Pharmaceutical Preparation Mfr
N.A.I.C.S.: 325412

Par Pharmaceutical, Inc.   **(3)**
1 Ram Rdg Rd, Chestnut Ridge, NY 10977
Tel.: (845) 573-5500
Web Site: http://www.parpharm.com
Pharmaceuticals Research & Development & Mfr
N.A.I.C.S.: 325412
Keri Mattox (Sr VP-IR & Corp Affairs)

Par Sterile Products, LLC   **(3)**
6 Ram Ridge Rd, Chestnut Ridge, NY 10977
Tel.: (845) 573-5500
Web Site: http://www.parsterileproducts.com
Sterile Injectable Pharmaceuticals Developer, Mfr & Distr
N.A.I.C.S.: 325412

Endo Management Limited   **(1)**
301-400 St Mary Ave, Winnipeg, R3C 4K5, MB, Canada
Tel.: (204) 943-8863
Health Care Srvices
N.A.I.C.S.: 621610

Endo U.S. Inc.   **(1)**
1400 Atwater Dr, Malvern, PA 19355
Tel.: (484) 216-0000
Health Care Srvices
N.A.I.C.S.: 621610

Innoteq, Inc.   **(1)**
312 New Jersey 38 Ste 120, Moorestown, NJ 08057
Tel.: (856) 440-1031
Web Site: http://www.innoteq.us
Marketing Agent Services
N.A.I.C.S.: 541613

Litha Healthcare Group Limited   **(1)**
No 106 16th Road, PO Box 8356, Midrand, 1686, Gauteng, South Africa
Tel.: (27) 115161700
Emp.: 279
Health Care Srvices
N.A.I.C.S.: 621610

Par Active Technologies Private Limited   **(1)**
Plot No 16 17 31 and 32 Sidco Phamaceutical Complex, Kanchipuram District, Alathur, 603110, Tamilnadu, India
Tel.: (91) 4467300300
Pharmaceuticals Mfr
N.A.I.C.S.: 325412

Par Biosciences Private Limited   **(1)**
RVI Tower-5th Floor No 149 Velachery Tambaram Main Road, Pallikaranai, Chennai, 600100, Tamilnadu, India
Tel.: (91) 4449273300
Pharmaceuticals Mfr
N.A.I.C.S.: 325412

Par Formulations Private Limited   **(1)**

9/215 Pudupakkam-Vandalur Main Road, Pudupakkam Kelambakkam, Chennai, 603103, Tamilnadu, India
Tel.: (91) 4467480100
Pharmaceuticals Mfr
N.A.I.C.S.: 325412

ENDO LIGHTING CORPORATION
1-7-3 Bingomachi, Chuo-ku, Osaka, 541-0051, Japan
Tel.: (81) 662677055
Web Site: https://www.endo-lighting.com
Year Founded: 1967
6932—(TKS)
Rev.: $341,776,660
Assets: $414,797,330
Liabilities: $159,869,460
Net Worth: $254,927,870
Earnings: $30,729,890
Emp.: 1,389
Fiscal Year-end: 03/31/24
Lighting Equipment Mfr & Distr
N.A.I.C.S.: 335132
Kunihiko Endo (Pres)

Subsidiaries:

Ansell (Sales & Distribution) Limited   **(1)**
Unit 2 M2 Business Park Duncrue Street, Belfast, BT3 9AR, United Kingdom
Tel.: (44) 289 077 3750
Light Fixture Mfr & Distr
N.A.I.C.S.: 335131

Ansell Electrical Products Limited   **(1)**
Unit 6B Stonecross Ind Park Yew Tree Way, Warrington, WA3 3JD, Cheshire, United Kingdom
Tel.: (44) 194 243 3333
Light Fixture Mfr & Distr
N.A.I.C.S.: 335131

ENDO Lighting (Thailand) Public Company Ltd.   **(1)**
Floor 27 Unit 2711 Sathorn Square 98 North Sathorn Rd Silom, Bangrak, Bangkok, 10500, Thailand
Tel.: (66) 2 108 1565
Light Fixture Mfr & Distr
N.A.I.C.S.: 335131

ENDO Lighting SE Asia Pte. Ltd   **(1)**
8 Eu Tong Sen Street 11-86 The Central, Singapore, 059818, Singapore
Tel.: (65) 63339051
Light Fixture Distr
N.A.I.C.S.: 423610

ENDO TRADE (BEIJING) CO., LTD.   **(1)**
Room 905 -906 Floor 9 Tower F Shi Ji Hua Teng Headquarters Park, No 9 yard Chen Jia Lin Gao Bei Dian Chaoyang District, Beijing, 100125, China
Tel.: (86) 1087732770
Light Fixture Distr
N.A.I.C.S.: 423610

ENDO TRADE (BEIJING) SHANGHAI CO., LTD   **(1)**
Room 302 No 679 Ningxia road, Putuo District, Shanghai, 200070, China
Tel.: (86) 2152049106
Light Fixture Distr
N.A.I.C.S.: 423610

Endo Lighting Accessories India Private Limited   **(1)**
Survey No 131/1B/3/2 1st Floor Akshay Electronics Building, Ram Indu Park Lane Building Opp Sapling School Off Baner Mhalunge Road, Pune, 411045, India
Tel.: (91) 2048583400
Light Fixture Distr
N.A.I.C.S.: 423610
Abhinav Kanthale (Head-Product)

Endo Lighting Vietnam Co. Ltd.   **(1)**
5th floor Somerset Chancellor Court 21-23 Nguyen Thi Minh Khai Street, District 1, Ho Chi Minh City, Vietnam
Tel.: (84) 2838221183
Light Fixture Distr

N.A.I.C.S.: 423610
Yoshio Takamori *(Gen Mgr)*

Kunshan Endo Lighting Co., Ltd. **(1)**
No 333 Yunque Road Economic Development Zone, Kunshan, China
Tel.: (86) 51257721080
Web Site: http://www.chinaendolighting.com
Emp.: 700
Light Fixture Mfr
N.A.I.C.S.: 335139

ENDO MANUFACTURING CO., LTD.
987 Higashiota, Tsubame, 959-1289, Niigata, Japan
Tel.: (81) 256636111
Web Site: https://www.endo-mfg.co.jp
Year Founded: 1950
7841—(TKS)
Rev.: $111,376,810
Assets: $170,287,620
Liabilities: $28,700,320
Net Worth: $141,587,300
Earnings: $5,402,580
Emp.: 1,251
Fiscal Year-end: 12/31/23
Golf Club Heads, Stainless Products & Forged Products Mfr & Sales
N.A.I.C.S.: 332999

Subsidiaries:

ENDO STAINLESS STEEL (VIETNAM) CO., LTD. **(1)**
Plot 74 - Noi Bai Industrial Zone Quang Tien, Soc Son District, Hanoi, Vietnam
Tel.: (84) 435824784
Stainless Steel Products Mfr
N.A.I.C.S.: 331110

EPON GOLF CORPORATION **(1)**
1137 Higashiota, Tsubame, 959-1289, Niigata, Japan
Tel.: (81) 25 664 5551
Web Site: https://www.epongolf.co.jp
Sales Range: $25-49.9 Million
Emp.: 13
Golf Clubs Mfr & Distr
N.A.I.C.S.: 339920

Endo Forging (Thailand) Co. Ltd. **(1)**
179/2 Moo 7 Gateway Industrial Estate General Zone Highway Rd, No 331 Huasamrong Plangyao District, Chachoengsao, 24190, Thailand **(100%)**
Tel.: (66) 38575223
Sales Range: $50-74.9 Million
Emp.: 460
All Other Motor Vehicle Parts Mfr
N.A.I.C.S.: 336390

Endo Metal Sleeve (Thailand) Co., Ltd. **(1)**
179 Moo 7 Gateway Industrial Estate, Xport Zone Plangyao District, Chachoengsao, 24190, Thailand
Tel.: (66) 38575016
Metal Sleeve Product Mfr
N.A.I.C.S.: 332999

Endo Stainless Steel (Thailand) Co. Ltd. **(1)**
179 Moo 7 Gateway Industrial Estate, Export Zone , Plangyao District, 24190, Chachoengsao, Thailand **(100%)**
Tel.: (66) 8575016
Web Site: http://www.endo-mfg.co.jp
Sales Range: $25-49.9 Million
Emp.: 90
Structural Steel Erection Contractors
N.A.I.C.S.: 238120

Endo Thai Co.Ltd. **(1)**
179-1 Moo 9 Gate Way City Industrial Estat, Plangyao, 24190, Chachoengsao, Thailand **(100%)**
Tel.: (66) 23260342
Web Site: http://www.endothai.com
Sales Range: $25-49.9 Million
Emp.: 80
Sporting & Athletic Goods Mfr
N.A.I.C.S.: 339920

ENDOCEUTICS INC.

2989 de la Promenade, Quebec, G1W 2J5, QC, Canada
Tel.: (418) 652-0197 **Ca**
Web Site:
http://www.endoceutics.com
Sales Range: $1-9.9 Million
Emp.: 1
Hormone Therapy Biopharmaceutical Product Developer
N.A.I.C.S.: 325412
Fernand Labrie *(Pres, CEO & Chief Scientific Officer)*

ENDOGENE LTD.
Suite 10 2 St Andrews Street, Brighton, 3186, VIC, Australia
Tel.: (61) 395932022
Web Site:
https://www.endogene.com.au
Medical Device Mfr
N.A.I.C.S.: 339112

ENDOMINES AB
PO BOX 5822, 10248, Stockholm, Sweden
Tel.: (46) 86116645
Web Site: http://www.endomines.com
ENDO—(HEL)
Rev.: $1,320,906
Assets: $71,409,475
Liabilities: $31,037,619
Net Worth: $40,371,856
Earnings: ($24,032,669)
Emp.: 43
Fiscal Year-end: 12/31/20
Gold Mining
N.A.I.C.S.: 212220
Ingmar Haga *(Chm)*

Subsidiaries:

Endomines Oy **(1)**
Pampalontie 11, 82967, Hattu, Finland
Tel.: (358) 13 83 01 72
Gold Mining Services
N.A.I.C.S.: 212220
Janne Muttonen *(Mgr-Resident)*

ENDRESS+HAUSER (INTERNATIONAL) HOLDING AG
Kagenstrasse 2, CH 4153, Reinach, Switzerland
Tel.: (41) 61 7 15 75 75 **CH**
Web Site: http://www.endress.com
Year Founded: 1953
Sales Range: $1-4.9 Billion
Emp.: 10,000
Industrial Process Control Devices & Systems Mfr
N.A.I.C.S.: 334513
Klaus Endress *(Pres)*

Subsidiaries:

ARIS Mauritius Limited **(1)**
The Cubicle 35-37 Royal Road 105 E, Phoenix, Mauritius
Tel.: (230) 698 7247
Measurement Instrumentation Mfr & Distr
N.A.I.C.S.: 334513

ARIS Trading Ltd. **(1)**
Lot VB 72 Z HB Ambatoroka 101, Antananarivo, Madagascar
Tel.: (261) 20 222 9024
Measurement Instrumentation Mfr & Distr
N.A.I.C.S.: 334513

Analytik Jena AG **(1)**
Konrad-Zuse-Strasse 1, 07745, Jena, Germany
Tel.: (49) 36 41 77 70
Web Site: http://www.analytik-jena.de
Instruments & Products for Analytical Measuring Technology, Life Science & Optoelectronics
N.A.I.C.S.: 334516
Andreas Krey *(Chm-Supervisory Bd)*

Subsidiary (Domestic):

AJ Innuscreen GmbH **(2)**

Robert-Rossle-Strasse 10, 13125, Berlin, Germany
Tel.: (49) 3094893380
Web Site: http://www.aj-innuscreen.com
Sales Range: $25-49.9 Million
Emp.: 20
Diagnostic Products Mfr
N.A.I.C.S.: 325413

AJ Roboscreen GmbH **(2)**
Hohmannstr 7, 04129, Leipzig, Germany
Tel.: (49) 30 94 89 33 80
Web Site: http://www.aj-roboscreen.com
Diagnostic Test Kits Mfr & Distr
N.A.I.C.S.: 423450

Subsidiary (Non-US):

Analytik Jena Japan Co., Ltd. **(2)**
YBP East Tower 11F 134 Goudo-cho, Hodogaya-ku, Yokohama, 240-0005, Kanagawa, Japan
Tel.: (81) 453405740
Web Site: http://www.analytik-jena.co.jp
Emp.: 40
Analytical Laboratory Equipment & Software Distr
N.A.I.C.S.: 423450
Marco Tilgner *(Mng Dir)*

Analytik Jena Shanghai Instruments Co. Ltd. **(2)**
Rm B 10th Fl No 91 Bldg No 1122 N Quinzhou Rd, Shanghai, 200233, China
Tel.: (86) 2154261977
Web Site: http://www.analytikjena.com.cn
Sales Range: $25-49.9 Million
Emp.: 30
Analytical Instrument Mfr
N.A.I.C.S.: 334516
Zhao Tai *(Gen Mgr)*

Subsidiary (US):

Analytik Jena US, Inc. **(2)**
500 W Cummings Park Ste 1800, Woburn, MA 01801
Tel.: (781) 376-9899
Web Site: http://www.analytik-jena.de
Diagnostic Equipment Distr
N.A.I.C.S.: 423450

Subsidiary (Domestic):

Biometra GmbH **(2)**
Rudolf-Wissell-Str 30, 37079, Gottingen, Lower Saxony, Germany
Tel.: (49) 551506860
Web Site: http://www.biometra.com
Sales Range: $25-49.9 Million
Emp.: 45
Laboratory Products Mfr & Distr
N.A.I.C.S.: 334516
Jurgen Otte *(Mgr-Quality)*

Subsidiary (Non-US):

CyBio Northern Europe Ltd. **(2)**
8 James Whatman Ct Turkey Mill Ashford Rd, Maidstone, ME 14 5SS, Kent, United Kingdom
Tel.: (44) 1622662118
Web Site: http://www.cybio-ag.com
Sales Range: $50-74.9 Million
Emp.: 5
Diagnostic Equipment Distr
N.A.I.C.S.: 423450

Subsidiary (Domestic):

ETG Entwicklungs- und Technologie Gesellschaft mbH **(2)**
Am Eichicht 1A, D 98693, Ilmenau, Germany **(80%)**
Tel.: (49) 36 77 46 12 0
Analytical Laboratory Instrument Mfr
N.A.I.C.S.: 334516
Ulrich Riegel *(Mng Dir)*

Subsidiary (US):

UVP, LLC **(2)**
2066 W 11th St, Upland, CA 91786-3509
Tel.: (909) 946-3197
Web Site: http://www.uvp.com
Sales Range: $10-24.9 Million
Emp.: 110
Ultraviolet Products Mfr
N.A.I.C.S.: 334516

Subsidiary (Non-US):

Ultra-Violet Products Ltd. **(3)**
Unit 1 Trinity Hall Farm Estate, Nuffield Road, Cambridge, CB4 1TG, United Kingdom
Tel.: (44) 1223 420022
Web Site: http://www.uvp.com
Emp.: 10
Ultraviolet Products Distr
N.A.I.C.S.: 423450
Bjorn Sundberg *(Gen Mgr)*

Anasia - Egypt (S.A.E.) **(1)**
9 Mostafa Refaat St, PO Box 2443, Sheraton Heliopolis, 11361, Cairo, Egypt
Tel.: (20) 22 268 4159
Emp.: 15
Measurement Instrumentation Mfr & Distr
N.A.I.C.S.: 334513
Magdy M. Habib *(Mng Dir)*

Arabian Darb General Trading & Contracting Company **(1)**
Sultan Sons Commercial Complex 6th Ring Road, Dajeej, Al Farwaniyah, Kuwait
Tel.: (965) 2 433 8094
Web Site: https://www.adcokuwait.com
Emp.: 50
Oil & Gas Services
N.A.I.C.S.: 213112
Lawrence Saldanha *(Mng Dir)*

Arya Instrument Co. **(1)**
Unit 63 and 64 6 Floor of Oaj Tower No 485 Above 63 St, Tehran, 1434964655, Iran
Tel.: (98) 219 107 0076
Web Site: https://www.aryainstrument.com
Measurement Instrumentation Mfr & Distr
N.A.I.C.S.: 334513

Automation Solutions Ltd. **(1)**
3 Becca Villa Behind Cal Bank Spintex Road, Accra, Ghana
Tel.: (233) 30 281 2680
Emp.: 6
Measurement Instrumentation Mfr & Distr
N.A.I.C.S.: 334513
Kweku Asmah *(Mng Dir)*

Avanceon LP **(1)**
19KM Main Multan Road, Lahore, 54660, Punjab, Pakistan
Tel.: (92) 4211 194 0940
Emp.: 215
Industrial Automation Services
N.A.I.C.S.: 541330
Bakhtiar H. Wain *(Mng Dir)*

Avas Engineering LLC **(1)**
St Rahmona Nabieva 119A, Dushanbe, Tajikistan
Tel.: (992) 44 610 7727
Web Site: https://www.avas.tj
Industrial Automation Services
N.A.I.C.S.: 541330

C.I.M.C.I Sarl **(1)**
Cite des Arts Rue C46 Villa 19 28, BP 1271, 28 Abidjan Codody, Abidjan, Cote d'Ivoire
Tel.: (225) 2 248 5554
Measurement Instrumentation Mfr & Distr
N.A.I.C.S.: 334513

CENTRIX Control Solutions Limited Partnership **(1)**
Unit 115 1551 Broadway Street, Port Coquitlam, V3C 6N9, BC, Canada
Tel.: (604) 942-0288
Web Site: https://www.centrixcs.com
Measurement & Control Equipment Mfr
N.A.I.C.S.: 334519
Dom Sacco *(Gen Mgr)*

Changsha High-tech Development Zone Kaiquan Mechanical & Electrical Technology Co., Ltd. **(1)**
Unit 202 2F Block 5 Oak Park 8 Lutian Road, Changsha High-tech Development Zone, Changsha, 410205, Hunan, China
Tel.: (86) 7318 876 2128
Measurement Instrumentation Mfr & Distr
N.A.I.C.S.: 334513

Chengdu Huamaokexin Automation Control Engineering Co., Ltd. **(1)**
No 16 4F Kehuanan Consulate 222 Tianren Road, High-tech Zone, Chengdu, 610000, Sichuan, China

Endress+Hauser (International) Holding
AG—(Continued)

Tel.: (86) 286 780 3384
Measurement Instrumentation Mfr & Distr
N.A.I.C.S.: 334513

Comin Khmere Co., Ltd. (1)
No 8b Down Town Road No 7, Phnom
Penh, Cambodia
Tel.: (855) 23 982 5401
Emp.: 1,400
Measurement Instrumentation Mfr & Distr
N.A.I.C.S.: 334513
Ngorn Saing (Mng Dir)

**Dalian New Oriental International In-
strument Industry & Trade Co.,
Ltd.** (1)
The International Financial Building 10C 15
Renmin Road, Zhongshan District, She-
nyang, 116001, Dalian, China
Tel.: (86) 4118 210 8168
Measurement Instrumentation Mfr & Distr
N.A.I.C.S.: 334513

Diffusion Sarl (1)
Rue de la Martinique 21, Sainte Clotilde,
97490, Reunion
Tel.: (262) 216870
Measurement Instrumentation Mfr & Distr
N.A.I.C.S.: 334513

**ECN Automation El Salvador S.A. de
C.V.** (1)
Av Albert Einstein 17 local 1-4, Lomas de
San Francisco Antiguo Cuscatlan La Liber-
tad, San Salvador, El Salvador
Tel.: (503) 7 803 0111
Measurement Instrumentation Mfr & Distr
N.A.I.C.S.: 334513

EMC Industrial Group Limited (1)
56 Tarndale Grove, PO Box 101-444, 0632,
Auckland, New Zealand
Tel.: (64) 94155110
Web Site: http://www.emc.co.nz
Sales Range: $25-49.9 Million
Emp.: 25
Inorganic Chemical Mfr
N.A.I.C.S.: 325180
Chris Gailer (Mng Dir)

**Endress & Hauser Process Automa-
tion (UAE) Trading LLC** (1)
Control Tower Dubai Motor City 17th Floor,
PO Box 473547, Dubai, United Arab Emir-
ates
Tel.: (971) 4 402 0600
Emp.: 43
Measurement Instrumentation Mfr & Distr
N.A.I.C.S.: 334513
Tariq Bakeer (Mng Dir)

**Endress + Hauser Mexico, S.A. De
C.V.** (1)
Fernando Montes de Oca 21 Edificio A Piso
3, San Nicolas, Tlalnepantla, 54030, Estado
de Mexico, Mexico
Tel.: (52) 5553212080
Web Site: http://www.mx.endress.com
Measuring Instrument Distr
N.A.I.C.S.: 423830
Jaime Lezama (Mng Dir)

Endress Hauser A.S. (1)
Buyukdere Cad No 103 Sarli Is Center 8th
Floor, Mecidiyekoy, 34394, Istanbul, Türkiye
Tel.: (90) 212 403 6300
Web Site: https://www.tr.endress.com
Electronics Instrument Mfr
N.A.I.C.S.: 336320

Endress and Hauser Arabia LLC (1)
King Faysal Road Titanium Tower within
Down Town Complex, Ground Floor Office
SH05, Al Khobar, Saudi Arabia
Tel.: (966) 1 384 944 71
Emp.: 39
Measuring Instrument Distr
N.A.I.C.S.: 423830
Craig Horan (Mng Dir)

Endress y Hauser, S.A. (1)
Constitucio 3 A, Barcelona, 8960, Spain
Tel.: (34) 934803366
Web Site: http://www.es.endress.com
Sales Range: $50-74.9 Million
Emp.: 64
Electrical Appliance Television & Radio Set
Whslr

N.A.I.C.S.: 423620
Antonio Carrillo (Gen Mgr)

**Endress+Hauser (BRASIL) Instru-
mentacao e Automacao Ltda** (1)
Estrada Municipal Antonio Sesti 600 Rec-
reio Costa Verde, 13254-085, Itatiba, Brazil
Tel.: (55) 11 3183 5340
Emp.: 12
Measuring Instrument Distr
N.A.I.C.S.: 423830
Rogerio Jeronymo (Mng Dir)

Endress+Hauser (Baltic) UAB (1)
Europos av 50, 46366, Kaunas, Lithuania
Tel.: (370) 37 26 94 44
Emp.: 8
Measuring Instrument Distr
N.A.I.C.S.: 423830
Romualdas Razbadauskas (Mng Dir)

**Endress+Hauser (China) Automation
Instrumentation Co. Ltd.** (1)
Suzhou Industrial Park No 491 Su Hong
Zhong Road No, Suzhou, 215021, Jiangsu,
China
Tel.: (86) 512 625 896 38
Emp.: 88
Measuring Instrument Distr
N.A.I.C.S.: 423830
Jian Gong (Mng Dir)

**Endress+Hauser (Deutschland)
GmbH+Co. KG.** (1)
Colmarer Strasse 6, 79576, Weil am Rhein,
Germany
Tel.: (49) 76 219 7501
Web Site: https://www.de.endress.com
Emp.: 668
Measurement Instrumentation Mfr & Distr
N.A.I.C.S.: 334513
Oliver K. Stockl (Mng Dir)

Endress+Hauser (H.K.) Ltd. (1)
Unit 1211 12th-Floor Tower I Silvercord, 30
Canton Road Tsimshatsui, Kowloon, China
(Hong Kong)
Tel.: (852) 25283120
Web Site: http://www.hk.endress.com
Sales Range: $25-49.9 Million
Emp.: 13
Inorganic Chemical Mfr
N.A.I.C.S.: 325180
Ken Wong (Dir-Mktg)

Endress+Hauser (Hellas) S.A. (1)
4 Leoforoskimis Ilektras 4B, Marousi,
15122, Athens, Greece
Tel.: (30) 2108002320
Web Site: http://www.endress.com
Sales Range: $50-74.9 Million
Emp.: 11
Electrical Apparatus & Equipment Wiring
Supplies & Construction Material Whslr
N.A.I.C.S.: 423610
George Karageorges (Gen Mgr)

**Endress+Hauser (India) Automation
Instrumentation Pvt. Ltd.** (1)
Plot No M-192 MIDC Waluj, Aurangabad,
431 136, Maharashtra, India
Tel.: (91) 240 256 3800
Web Site: http://www.in.endress.com
Emp.: 51
Measuring Instrument Distr
N.A.I.C.S.: 423830
Sriram Narayanan (Mng Dir)

Endress+Hauser (India) Pvt. Ltd. (1)
5th Floor Wing A and B Raj Plaza, LBS
Marg Vikhroli - West, Mumbai, 400083,
India
Tel.: (91) 2266481111
Web Site: http://www.in.endress.com
Sales Range: $50-74.9 Million
Emp.: 80
Industrial Machinery & Equipment Whslr
N.A.I.C.S.: 423830
Sajiv Nath (Mng Dir)

Endress+Hauser (Ireland) Ltd. (1)
Kilcock Road Clane, Kilcock Rd Clane Busi-
ness Pk, Kildare, Ireland
Tel.: (353) 45868615
Web Site: http://www.ie.endress.com
Sales Range: $25-49.9 Million
Emp.: 24
Engineering Services
N.A.I.C.S.: 541330
Christophe Roche (Gen Mgr)

Endress+Hauser (M) Sdn. Bhd. (1)
Lot 10 4th Floor, Jalan Astaka U8-84
Seksyen U8, Shah Alam, 40150, Selangor,
Malaysia
Tel.: (60) 378433888
Web Site: http://www.my.endress.com
Sales Range: $50-74.9 Million
Emp.: 55
Industrial Machinery & Equipment Whslr
N.A.I.C.S.: 423830

**Endress+Hauser (Magyarorszag)
Kft.** (1)
Forgach u 9 / b, 1139, Budapest, Hungary
Tel.: (36) 1 412 0421
Web Site: https://www.hu.endress.com
Measurement Instrumentation Mfr & Distr
N.A.I.C.S.: 334513

Endress+Hauser (Pty.) Ltd. (1)
5 Commerce Crescent West Eastgate Ext
13, PO Box 783996, 2146, Sandton, South
Africa
Tel.: (27) 112628000
Web Site: http://www.za.endress.com
Sales Range: $50-74.9 Million
Emp.: 80
Electrical Appliance Television & Radio Set
Whslr
N.A.I.C.S.: 423620
Rob MacKenzie (Mng Dir)

Endress+Hauser (Qatar) L.L.C. (1)
Al Wafid Street C-Ring Road Financial
Square Building No 2, PO Box 31539, Al
Wafid Street C-Ring Road Financial Square
Building No 2, Doha, Qatar
Tel.: (974) 4 421 09 44
Web Site: http://www.endress.com
Emp.: 15
Measuring Instrument Distr
N.A.I.C.S.: 423830
Bahman Dastvareh (Mng Dir)

Endress+Hauser (SEA) Pte Ltd. (1)
1 International Business Park, #01-11-12
The Synergy, 609917, Singapore, Singa-
pore
Tel.: (65) 65668222
Web Site: http://www.sg.endress.com
Sales Range: $25-49.9 Million
Emp.: 38
Industrial Machinery & Equipment Whslr
N.A.I.C.S.: 423830
Neal Watmough (Mng Dir)

Endress+Hauser (Schweiz) AG (1)
Kaegenstrasse 2, Reinach, 4153, Switzer-
land
Tel.: (41) 617157575
Web Site: http://www.ch.endress.com
Sales Range: $75-99.9 Million
Emp.: 800
Industrial Machinery & Equipment Whslr
N.A.I.C.S.: 423830
Klaus Endress (CEO)

**Endress+Hauser (Slovenija)
D.o.o.** (1)
Pot k sejmiscu 26A, 1000, Ljubljana,
Slovenia
Tel.: (386) 15140250
Web Site: http://www.si.endress.com
Sales Range: $25-49.9 Million
Emp.: 9
Instrument Mfr for Measuring & Testing
Electricity & Electrical Signals
N.A.I.C.S.: 334515
Bozo Vihar (Gen Mgr)

**Endress+Hauser (Suzhou) Automa-
tion Instrumentation Co., Ltd.** (1)
Suzhou Industrial Park 491 Su Hong Zhong
Road, Suzhou, 215021, Jiangsu, China
Tel.: (86) 5126 258 9638
Emp.: 106
Measurement Instrumentation Mfr & Distr
N.A.I.C.S.: 334513
Tao Shen (Mng Dir)

Endress+Hauser (Thailand) Ltd. (1)
111 Moo 4 Bangkruai - Jongthanom Road,
Mahasawat Bangkruai, 11130, Nonthaburi,
Thailand
Tel.: (66) 244769009
Web Site: http://www.th.endress.com
Sales Range: $25-49.9 Million
Emp.: 44
Instrument Mfr for Measuring & Testing
Electricity & Electrical Signals

N.A.I.C.S.: 334515

Endress+Hauser (UAE) LLC (1)
Dubai Investment Park European Business
Center Office 344 3rd Floor, PO Box
473547, Dubai, United Arab Emirates
Tel.: (971) 4 808 76 00
Web Site: http://www.endress.com
Emp.: 50
Measuring Instrument Distr
N.A.I.C.S.: 423830
Jens Winkelmann (Mng Dir)

**Endress+Hauser (Vietnam) Co.
Ltd.** (1)
106 Nguyen Van Troi Street Unit 3 1st Floor
CentrePoint Building, Phu Nhuan District,
Ho Chi Minh City, Vietnam
Tel.: (84) 283 842 0026
Emp.: 32
Measurement Instrumentation Mfr & Distr
N.A.I.C.S.: 334513
Rolf Leber (Mng Dir)

Endress+Hauser A/S (1)
Poppelgardvej 10-12, Soborg, 2860, Den-
mark
Tel.: (45) 70131132
Web Site: http://www.dk.endress.com
Sales Range: $25-49.9 Million
Emp.: 30
Electrical Appliance Television & Radio Set
Whslr
N.A.I.C.S.: 423620
Felix Langkjaer (Mng Dir)

Endress+Hauser AB (1)
Sundbybergsvagen 1, 171 73, Solna, Swe-
den
Tel.: (46) 855511600
Web Site: http://www.se.endress.com
Sales Range: $25-49.9 Million
Emp.: 25
Industrial Machinery & Equipment Distr
N.A.I.C.S.: 423830
Stefan Bgorkegrem (CEO)

Endress+Hauser AG (1)
Kagenstrasse 2, 4153, Reinach, BL, Swit-
zerland
Tel.: (41) 617157700
Web Site: https://www.endress.com
Rev.: $3,993,093,671
Assets: $4,897,019,275
Liabilities: $970,476,591
Net Worth: $3,926,542,684
Earnings: $361,720,943
Emp.: 15,817
Fiscal Year-end: 12/31/2023
Industrial Engineering Services
N.A.I.C.S.: 541330

Endress+Hauser AS (1)
PO Box 62, 3421, Oslo, Norway
Tel.: (47) 32 85 98 50
Emp.: 20
Measuring Instrument Distr
N.A.I.C.S.: 423830
Tore Sandvoll (Mng Dir)

Endress+Hauser Algerie SARL (1)
24 rue du Stade - Hydra, 16035, Algiers,
Algeria
Tel.: (213) 21 48 3299
Measuring Instrument Distr
N.A.I.C.S.: 423830

**Endress+Hauser Analytical Instru-
ments (Suzhou) Co., Ltd.** (1)
Suzhou Industrial Park 491 Su-Hong Zhong
Lu, Suzhou, 215021, Jiangsu, China
Tel.: (86) 5126 258 9010
Emp.: 40
Measurement Instrumentation Mfr & Distr
N.A.I.C.S.: 334513
Baoyong Luan (Mng Dir)

Endress+Hauser Argentina S.A. (1)
Av Ruiz Huidobro 4771, 1430, Buenos Ai-
res, Argentina
Tel.: (54) 1145434500
Web Site: http://www.ar.endress.com
Industrial Machinery & Equipment Whslr
N.A.I.C.S.: 423830

**Endress+Hauser Australia Pty
Ltd.** (1)
Level 1 16 Giffnock Avenue, North Ryde-
Link Business Park, Macquarie Park, 2113,
NSW, Australia

Tel.: (61) 288777000
Web Site: http://www.endress.com.au
Sales Range: $25-49.9 Million
Emp.: 40
Engineeering Services
N.A.I.C.S.: 541330
Chris Gailer *(Mng Dir)*

Endress+Hauser B.V. (1)
Nikkelstraat 6-12, PO Box 5102, 1410AC,
Naarden, Netherlands
Tel.: (31) 356958611
Web Site: http://www.nl.endress.com
Sales Range: $75-99.9 Million
Emp.: 125
Warm Air Heating & Air-Conditioning Equip-
ment & Supplies Whslr
N.A.I.C.S.: 423730
R. Homnersen *(Gen Mgr)*

Endress+Hauser Canada Ltd. (1)
1075 Sutton Drive, Burlington, L7L 5Z8,
ON, Canada
Tel.: (905) 681-9292
Web Site: http://www.ca.endress.com
Sales Range: $75-99.9 Million
Emp.: 125
Industrial Machinery & Equipment Whslr
N.A.I.C.S.: 423830

Endress+Hauser Chile Ltd. (1)
Maria Luisa Santander 0447, Providencia,
7500859, Santiago, Chile
Tel.: (56) 27849800
Web Site: http://www.cl.endress.com
Sales Range: $25-49.9 Million
Emp.: 43
Electrical Apparatus & Equipment Wiring
Supplies & Construction Material Whslr
N.A.I.C.S.: 423610

**Endress+Hauser Colombia
S.A.S.** (1)
Edificio Ecotower Carrera 17 93-9 Oficina
201, Bogota, Colombia
Tel.: (57) 1 390 4425
Web Site: https://www.co.endress.com
Measurement Instrumentation Mfr & Distr
N.A.I.C.S.: 334513

**Endress+Hauser Conducta
GmbH+Co. KG** (1)
Dieselstrasse 24, 70839, Gerlingen, Ger-
many
Tel.: (49) 71562090
Web Site: http://www.conducta.endress.com
Sales Range: $25-49.9 Million
Industrial Liquid Analysis
N.A.I.C.S.: 541990
Manfred Jagiella *(CEO)*

Subsidiary (US):

Endress+Hauser Conducta, Inc. (2)
4123 East La Palma Ave Ste 200, Anaheim,
CA 92807
Tel.: (800) 835-5474
Emp.: 100
Measuring Instrument Distr
N.A.I.C.S.: 423830
Brian Costelloe *(Mng Dir)*

Endress+Hauser Consult AG (1)
Kaegenstrasse 2, 4153, Reinach, Switzer-
land
Tel.: (41) 617157575
Web Site: http://www.ch.endress.com
Sales Range: $75-99.9 Million
Emp.: 425
Management Consulting Services
N.A.I.C.S.: 541618
Klaus Endress *(CEO)*

**Endress+Hauser Controle e Automa-
cao Ltda.** (1)
Av Ibirapuera 2033 3rd Walk, Moema, Sao
Paulo, 04029-901, Brazil
Tel.: (55) 1150334333
Web Site: http://www.br.endress.com
Sales Range: $50-74.9 Million
Emp.: 60
Industrial Machinery & Equipment Whslr
N.A.I.C.S.: 423830
Carlos Behrends *(Gen Mgr)*

Endress+Hauser Czech S.r.o. (1)
Olbrachtova 2006-9, 14000, Prague, Czech
Republic
Tel.: (420) 241080450
Web Site: http://www.cz.endress.com

Sales Range: $25-49.9 Million
Emp.: 24
Industrial Machinery & Equipment Whslr
N.A.I.C.S.: 423830

Endress+Hauser D.o.o. (1)
Froudeova 94, 10020, Zagreb, Croatia
Tel.: (385) 16591780
Web Site: http://www.endress.com
Sales Range: $25-49.9 Million
Emp.: 9
Management Consulting Services
N.A.I.C.S.: 541618
Drazen Kolenc *(Mng Dir)*

**Endress+Hauser Elektronik San.ve
Tic. A.S.** (1)
Buyukdere Cad No 103 Sarli is Merk 8 Kat,
Mecidiyekoy, 34394, Istanbul, Turkiye
Tel.: (90) 2124036300
Web Site: http://www.tr.endress.com
Industrial Process Control Device & System
Distr
N.A.I.C.S.: 423830

**Endress+Hauser Flowtec (Brasil)
Fluxometros Ltda.** (1)
Estrada Municipal Antonio Sesti 600 Bairro
Recreio Costa Verde, Itatiba, 13254-085,
Sao Paulo, Brazil
Tel.: (55) 113 183 5360
Emp.: 19
Measurement Instrumentation Mfr & Distr
N.A.I.C.S.: 334513
Andre Nucci Riesemberg *(Mng Dir)*

**Endress+Hauser Flowtec (China)
Co., Ltd.** (1)
China-Singapore-Suzhou Industrial Park
SIP Su-Hong-Zhong-Lu No 465, 215021,
Suzhou, China
Tel.: (86) 512 625 80208
Emp.: 119
Measuring Instrument Distr
N.A.I.C.S.: 423830
Qinxue Wei *(Mng Dir)*

**Endress+Hauser Flowtec (India) Pvt.
Ltd.** (1)
M-171/176 Waluj Industrial Area MIDC, 431
136, Aurangabad, India
Tel.: (91) 240 2563 603
Emp.: 122
Measuring Instrument Distr
N.A.I.C.S.: 423830
Kulathu Mng Dir *(Mng Dir)*

Endress+Hauser Flowtec AG (1)
Christoph Merian-Ring 4, Basel-Landschaft,
4153, Reinach, Switzerland
Tel.: (41) 61 715 6111
Measurement Instrumentation Mfr & Distr
N.A.I.C.S.: 334513

Endress+Hauser Ges.m.b.H. (1)
Lehnergasse 4, PO Box 173, Vienna, 1230,
Austria
Tel.: (43) 1880560
Web Site: http://www.at.endress.com
Sales Range: $25-49.9 Million
Emp.: 68
Instrument Mfr for Measuring & Testing
Electricity & Electrical Signals
N.A.I.C.S.: 334515
Wolfgang Maurer *(Mng Dir)*

**Endress+Hauser Group Services
AG** (1)
Kagenstrasse 2, 4153, Reinach, Switzer-
land
Tel.: (41) 61 715 7700
Measurement Instrumentation Mfr & Distr
N.A.I.C.S.: 334513

Endress+Hauser Inc. (1)
2350 Endress Pl, Greenwood, IN 46143
Tel.: (317) 535-7138
Web Site: http://www.us.endress.com
Sales Range: $50-74.9 Million
Emp.: 250
Instruments & Related Products Mfr for
Measuring Displaying & Controlling Indus-
trial Process Variables
N.A.I.C.S.: 334513
Codd Lucey *(Gen Mgr)*

Subsidiary (Domestic):

**Endress+Hauser (USA) Automation
Instrumentation Inc.** (2)

2340 Endress Pl, Greenwood, IN 46143
Tel.: (317) 535-7138
Emp.: 103
Measuring Instrument Distr
N.A.I.C.S.: 423830
John Schnake *(Mng Dir)*

Unit (Domestic):

**Endress+Hauser Inc. - Northeast Re-
gional Center** (2)
500 Horizon Dr Ste 502, Chalfont, PA
18914
Tel.: (215) 712-9050
Web Site: http://www.endress.com
Emp.: 0
Industrial Supplies Merchant Whslr
N.A.I.C.S.: 423840
Stephen McGee *(Reg Mgr)*

Subsidiary (Domestic):

Kaiser Optical Systems, Inc. (2)
371 Parkland Plz, Ann Arbor, MI
48103   (100%)
Tel.: (734) 665-8083
Web Site: http://www.kosi.com
Sales Range: $10-24.9 Million
Emp.: 75
Spectrographic Instrumentation & Applied
Holographic Technology
N.A.I.C.S.: 333310
Harry Owen *(Dir-Bus Dev)*

SpectraSensors, Inc. (2)
4333 W Sam Houston Pkwy Ste 100, Hous-
ton, TX 77043
Tel.: (713) 300-2700
Web Site: http://www.spectrasensors.com
Sales Range: $10-24.9 Million
Emp.: 80
Laser-Based Test Instruments for Natural
Gas & Petrochemical Companies
N.A.I.C.S.: 334516
Jorge Jones *(VP-Sls & Mktg)*

**Endress+Hauser InfoServe
GmbH+Co. KG** (1)
Colmarer Strasse 6, 79576, Weil am Rhein,
Germany
Tel.: (49) 76 219 7503
Emp.: 360
Measurement Instrumentation Mfr & Distr
N.A.I.C.S.: 334513
Pieter F. de Koning *(Mng Dir)*

**Endress+Hauser International
AG** (1)
Kaegenstrasse 2, 4153, Reinach, Switzer-
land
Tel.: (41) 61 715 8100
Emp.: 10
Measurement Instrumentation Mfr & Distr
N.A.I.C.S.: 334513
Dirk Bogner *(Mng Dir)*

Endress+Hauser Italia S.p.A. (1)
Via Donat Cattin 2-a, Cernusco, Milan,
20063, Italy
Tel.: (39) 02921921
Web Site: http://www.it.endress.com
Sales Range: $25-49.9 Million
Emp.: 144
Environmental Consulting Services
N.A.I.C.S.: 541620
Ivano Mazzoletti *(Mng Dir)*

Endress+Hauser Japan Co.,Ltd. (1)
5-70-3 Nisshincho Fuchu-shi, Tokyo, 183-
0036, Japan
Tel.: (81) 423141911
Web Site: http://www.jp.endress.com
Sales Range: $75-99.9 Million
Emp.: 154
Industrial Machinery & Equipment Whslr
N.A.I.C.S.: 423830
Sito Yujiro *(Pres)*

Endress+Hauser Korea Co., Ltd. (1)
5th Floor Kocom Building, 260-7
Yeomchang-dong Kangseo-g, 157-040,
Seoul, Korea (South)
Tel.: (82) 226587200
Web Site: http://www.endress.co.kr
Sales Range: $25-49.9 Million
Emp.: 40
Industrial Machinery & Equipment Whslr
N.A.I.C.S.: 423830

Endress+Hauser Ltd. (1)

Floats Rd, Manchester, M239NF, United
Kingdom
Tel.: (44) 1612865000
Web Site: http://www.uk.endress.com
Sales Range: $50-74.9 Million
Emp.: 190
Instruments & Related Products Mfr for
Measuring Displaying & Controlling Indus-
trial Process Variables
N.A.I.C.S.: 334513
David Newell *(Mng Dir)*

**Endress+Hauser Magyarorszag
Folyamatmuszerezesi Kft.** (1)
Forgach u 9/b, 1139, Budapest, Hungary
Tel.: (30) 412 0421
Measuring Instrument Distr
N.A.I.C.S.: 423830

**Endress+Hauser Messtechnik
GmbH+Co. KG** (1)
Colmarer Strasse 6, 79576, Weil am Rhein,
Germany
Tel.: (49) 7621 9 75 01
Web Site: http://www.de.endress.com
Emp.: 668
Measuring Instrument Distr
N.A.I.C.S.: 423830
Kurt Johannsen *(Mng Dir)*

Endress+Hauser Oy (1)
Robert Huberin tie 3 B, 01510, Vantaa, Fin-
land
Tel.: (358) 20 110 3600
Web Site: https://www.fi.endress.com
Emp.: 49
Measurement Instrumentation Mfr & Distr
N.A.I.C.S.: 334513
Tuomo Saukkonen *(Mng Dir)*

Endress+Hauser Panama Inc. (1)
Avenida Marina Norte Plaza Real 3er piso
Oficina 314, Panama, Panama
Tel.: (507) 275 5800
Emp.: 4
Measurement Instrumentation Mfr & Distr
N.A.I.C.S.: 334513
Gustavo Jordan *(Mng Dir)*

Endress+Hauser Philippines Inc. (1)
32nd St Bonifacio Global City Unit 803 One
World Place Bld, Taguig, Metro Manila, Phil-
ippines
Tel.: (63) 28 809 3299
Emp.: 14
Measurement Instrumentation Mfr & Distr
N.A.I.C.S.: 334513
Miles Umlas *(Mng Dir)*

**Endress+Hauser Polska Sp. Z
o.o.** (1)
ul J Pilsudskiego 49-57, Wroclaw, 54116,
Poland
Tel.: (48) 717803700
Web Site: http://www.pl.endress.com
Sales Range: $25-49.9 Million
Emp.: 69
Totalizing Fluid Meter & Counting Device
Mfr
N.A.I.C.S.: 334514
Andrzej Frosztega *(Gen Mgr)*

Endress+Hauser Portugal, Lda (1)
Condominio Empresarial da Moita, Fraccao
K, 2860-579, Moita, Portugal
Tel.: (351) 214253070
Web Site: http://www.endress.com
Sales Range: $25-49.9 Million
Emp.: 15
Warm Air Heating & Air-Conditioning Equip-
ment & Supplies Whslr
N.A.I.C.S.: 423730
Fandro Silva *(Mng Dir)*

**Endress+Hauser Process Solutions
AG** (1)
Christoph Merian-Ring 12, 4153, Reinach,
Switzerland
Tel.: (41) 61 715 7378
Emp.: 180
Measurement Instrumentation Mfr & Distr
N.A.I.C.S.: 334513
Rolf Birkhofer *(Mng Dir)*

Endress+Hauser Romania SRL (1)
319C Splaiul Independentei, 060044, Bucharest, Romania
Tel.: (40) 213159067
Web Site: http://www.endress.com

Endress+Hauser (International) Holding AG—(Continued)

Sales Range: $25-49.9 Million
Emp.: 17
Industrial Machinery & Equipment Whslr
N.A.I.C.S.: 423830
Rudolf Moos (Mng Dir)

Endress+Hauser SAS (1)
3 rue du Rhin, BP 150, 68330, Huningue, France
Tel.: (33) 825 888 001
Web Site: http://www.endress.com
Emp.: 256
Measuring Instrument Distr
N.A.I.C.S.: 423830
Urs Endress (Mng Dir)

Plant (Domestic):

Endress+Hauser SAS - Cernay (2)
35 rue de l'Europe, 68700, Cernay, France
Tel.: (33) 389 75 35 00
Measuring Instrument Distr
N.A.I.C.S.: 423830
Matthias Aschberger (Mng Dir)

Endress+Hauser SE+Co. KG. (1)
Hauptstrasse 1, 79689, Maulburg, Germany
Tel.: (49) 762 2280
Measurement Instrumentation Mfr & Distr
N.A.I.C.S.: 334513

Endress+Hauser Shanghai Automation Equipment Co. Ltd. (1)
No 458 East Jiang Chuan Road, 200241, Shanghai, China
Tel.: (86) 2124039600
Web Site: http://www.cn.endress.com
Sales Range: $75-99.9 Million
Emp.: 170
Industrial Machinery & Equipment Whslr
N.A.I.C.S.: 423830

Endress+Hauser Sicestherm S.r.L. (1)
Via Martin Luther King 7, Pessano con Bornago, 20060, Milan, Italy
Tel.: (39) 0295 9641
Emp.: 190
Measurement Instrumentation Mfr & Distr
N.A.I.C.S.: 334513
Martin Benoliel (Mng Dir)

Endress+Hauser Systemplan GmbH (1)
Wagnerstrasse 14, 76448, Durmersheim, Germany
Tel.: (49) 724 591 5720
Measurement Instrumentation Mfr & Distr
N.A.I.C.S.: 334513

Endress+Hauser Venezuela S.A. (1)
Av Francisco de Miranda c/c San Juan Bosco Edificio Seguros Adriatica, Caracas, Venezuela
Tel.: (58) 212 266 26 85
Emp.: 11
Measuring Instrument Distr
N.A.I.C.S.: 423830
Gustavo Padron (Mng Dir)

Endress+Hauser Wetzer (Suzhou) Co. Ltd. (1)
China Singapore-Suzhou Industry Park 31 Jiang-Tian-Li-lu, Suzhou, 215126, Jiangsu, China
Tel.: (86) 5126 258 9791
Emp.: 29
Measurement Instrumentation Mfr & Distr
N.A.I.C.S.: 334513
Liu Peng (Mng Dir)

Endress+Hauser Wetzer GmbH + Co. KG (1)
Obere Wank 1, 87484, Nesselwang, Germany
Tel.: (49) 8361 308 0
Emp.: 350
Measuring Instrument Distr
N.A.I.C.S.: 423830
Harald Hertweck (Mng Dir)

Endress+Hauser Wetzer India Pvt. Ltd. (1)
M 171-173 Waluj MIDC Industrial Area, Aurangabad, 431 136, Maharashtra, India
Tel.: (91) 240 255 1600
Emp.: 15

Measuring Instrument Distr
N.A.I.C.S.: 423830
Narendra Kulkarni (Mng Dir)

Endress+Hauser Wetzer USA Inc. (1)
2375 Endress Pl, Greenwood, IN 46143
Tel.: (317) 535-2772
Emp.: 28
Measurement Instrumentation Mfr & Distr
N.A.I.C.S.: 334513
Patrick McGlothlen (Mng Dir)

Endress+Hauser Yamanashi Co. Ltd. (1)
862-1 Mitsukunugi Sakaigawa-cho, Fuefuki-shi, Yamanashi, 406-0846, Japan
Tel.: (81) 552 66 49 11
Emp.: 80
Measuring Instrument Distr
N.A.I.C.S.: 423830
Yasuyuki Inoue (Mng Dir)

Endress+Hauser sa/nv (1)
Rue Carli Straat 13, Brussels, 1140, Belgium
Tel.: (32) 22480600
Web Site: http://www.be.endress.com
Sales Range: $50-74.9 Million
Emp.: 55
Electrical Apparatus & Equipment Wiring Supplies & Construction Material Whslr
N.A.I.C.S.: 423610
Johan Puimege (Gen Mgr)

Euroinstruments Cia. Ltda. (1)
Av Eugenio Espejo 24-10 y Av Interoceanica, Centro Comercial Plaza del Rancho of B1-105 Via a Tanda, Quito, Ecuador
Tel.: (593) 99 866 2710
Web Site:
https://www.euroinstruments.com.ec
Emp.: 18
Industrial Automation Services
N.A.I.C.S.: 541330
A. Luis Anibal Ortiz (Mng Dir)

Everest Ingenieria SRL (1)
Colonia Elisa N 202, Villa Elisa, Asuncion, 2610, Paraguay
Tel.: (595) 2 194 0080
Measurement Instrumentation Mfr & Distr
N.A.I.C.S.: 334513

Fagkaup ehf. (1)
Klettagardar 12, 104, Reykjavik, Iceland
Tel.: (354) 520 0800
Measurement Instrumentation Mfr & Distr
N.A.I.C.S.: 334513

Fast Equipamentos e Servicos Lda. (1)
Centralidade do Kilamba Edificio U22, Luanda, Angola
Tel.: (244) 94 134 3184
Web Site: https://fast.co.ao
Measurement Instrumentation Mfr & Distr
N.A.I.C.S.: 334513

Gia Caucasia Logistics Ltd. (1)
40 Skhvitaridze Str, Tbilisi, Georgia
Tel.: (995) 32 237 5863
Web Site: https://giacaucasia.ge
Automobile Parts Distr
N.A.I.C.S.: 441330

Golden Palm Petroleum Services Company W.L.L. (1)
24 3rd Floor Block B Al-Hashan Commercial Complex, PO Box 251, Abu Halifa, Fahaheel, 54753, Kuwait
Tel.: (965) 2 392 6283
Web Site: https://www.goldenpalm.com.kw
Electrical & Instrumentation Mfr & Distr
N.A.I.C.S.: 334515

Hefei Hengchang Automation Control Co., Ltd. (1)
71 Building B3 Phase II West Section of Fanhua Avenue Gongtou Liheng, Industrial Plaza Hefei Economic and Technological Development Zone, Hefei, 230092, Anhui, China
Tel.: (86) 5516 523 0340
Measurement Instrumentation Mfr & Distr
N.A.I.C.S.: 334513

Hefei Qunying Science & Technology Co., Ltd. (1)
A907 Jiahua Center 1 East Suixi Road, Hefei, 230011, Anhui, China
Tel.: (86) 5516 421 8819
Measurement Instrumentation Mfr & Distr
N.A.I.C.S.: 334513

I B E Junuzovic d.o.o. (1)
Zelimira Vidovica Kelija 4F, 71000, Sarajevo, Bosnia & Herzegovina
Tel.: (387) 3 376 4975
Web Site: https://www.ibej.ba
Emp.: 9
Measurement Instrumentation Mfr & Distr
N.A.I.C.S.: 334513
Hasan Junuzovic (Mng Dir)

I+G Electrical Services Co. Ltd. (1)
Laxia Industrial Estate, PO Box 12666, Nicosia, Cyprus
Tel.: (357) 2 248 4787
Measurement Instrumentation Mfr & Distr
N.A.I.C.S.: 334513

INTEK Honduras, S.A. de C.V. (1)
100 mts antes del Peaje a La Lima Edificio PWC-14B, Ofi-Bodegas Premier Warehouse Complex, San Pedro Sula, Honduras
Tel.: (504) 2 559 4748
Web Site: https://intek-ca.com.hn
Industrial Electronic Product Mfr & Distr
N.A.I.C.S.: 334419

INTEK Nicaragua, S.A. (1)
Reparto El Carmen De Iglesia El Carmen 1/2 Cuadra al, Managua, Nicaragua
Tel.: (505) 202 222 2451
Web Site: https://intek-ca.com.ni
Industrial Electronic Product Mfr & Distr
N.A.I.C.S.: 334419

Industrial Sales & Service-GC S.R.L. (1)
Ave Nunez de Caceres Esq Pablito Mirabal Plaza Castellana, Suite 305 Sector La Castellana, Santo Domingo, Dominican Republic
Tel.: (809) 227 7184
Emp.: 7
Measurement Instrumentation Mfr & Distr
N.A.I.C.S.: 334515
Gensley Capella (Mng Dir)

Innovative Sensor Technology IST AG (1)
Stegrutistrasse 14, Ebnat-Kappel, 9642, Saint Gallen, Switzerland
Tel.: (41) 71 992 0100
Web Site: https://www.ist-ag.com
Measurement Instrumentation Mfr & Distr
N.A.I.C.S.: 334513
Jorn Luten (CEO)

Instrumetrics Industrial Control Ltd. (1)
PO Box 8696, Netanya, 4250543, Israel
Tel.: (972) 9 835 7090
Web Site: https://www.inst-ic.com
Measurement Instrumentation Mfr & Distr
N.A.I.C.S.: 334513

Isotek S.R.L. (1)
Barrio 23 de Junio Avenida San Juan Entre Calle 4 y 5, A2 cuadras de la Av Banzer entrando por Valtra frente a laboratios IFA, Santa Cruz, Bolivia
Tel.: (591) 3 311 2470
Web Site: https://www.isotek.bo
Lighting Equipment Distr
N.A.I.C.S.: 423610

Jiangsu Wanlong Automation Equipment Co., Ltd. (1)
Room 2019 Central International Plaza 105-6 North Zhongshan Road, Nanjing, 210009, Jiangsu, China
Tel.: (86) 258 320 6616
Measuring Equipment Mfr & Distr
N.A.I.C.S.: 334515

Jinan Zhengte Automation Technology Co., Ltd. (1)
Room 1201 Building 2 Ginza Center No 22799 Jingshi Road, Jinan, 250022, China
Tel.: (86) 5318 715 6600
Web Site: https://www.jnzhengte.com
Measuring Equipment Distr
N.A.I.C.S.: 423830

Kingjarl Corporation (1)
9F-2 No 307 Dunhua N Rd, Taipei, 10583, Taiwan

Tel.: (886) 22 718 3938
Web Site: https://www.kingjarl.com.tw
Measuring Equipment Distr
N.A.I.C.S.: 423830

Kunming Condell Electronics Co., Ltd. (1)
Century Square F8 C1 88 Nanping Street, Kunming, 650011, Yunnan, China
Tel.: (86) 8716 363 4650
Measurement Instrumentation Mfr & Distr
N.A.I.C.S.: 334513

MH Instrument OU (1)
RK 11410563 Oru, Enno Village Noo District, 01005, Tartu, Estonia
Tel.: (372) 506 2876
Web Site: https://mhinstruments.ee
Measurement Instrumentation Mfr
N.A.I.C.S.: 334519

MMI Business Services FZE (1)
S Turkmenbashi Avenue 81 Floor 13 Business Center, 744017, Ashgabat, Turkmenistan
Tel.: (993) 1 222 7434
Emp.: 150
Measurement Instrumentation Mfr & Distr
N.A.I.C.S.: 334513
Gaurav Brahmwar (Mng Dir)

MT Industrial Supplies & Services Co. Ltd. (1)
Building 16/13 Block 43 The Heart Hospital St Erkowit, PO Box 8418, Khartoum, Sudan
Tel.: (249) 15 518 3770
Emp.: 47
Measurement Instrumentation Mfr & Distr
N.A.I.C.S.: 334513
Mohamed Taha Hassan (Mng Dir)

Meris d.o.o. (1)
Dunavska 78a, 11070, Belgrade, Serbia
Tel.: (381) 11 314 8800
Web Site: https://www.meris.rs
Measuring Equipment Distr
N.A.I.C.S.: 423830

Metso Endress+Hauser Oy (1)
Laippatie 4C, Helsinki, Finland
Tel.: (358) 20483160
Web Site: http://www.metsoendress.com
Sales Range: $50-74.9 Million
Emp.: 100
Electronic Parts & Equipment Whslr
N.A.I.C.S.: 423690
Tuomo Saukkonen (Gen Mgr)

Mexatronika-TES Ltd. (1)
1 Tallimarjon Street, Tashkent, 100105, Uzbekistan
Tel.: (998) 71 291 3760
Web Site: https://mtes.uz
Industrial Equipment Mfr & Distr
N.A.I.C.S.: 333248

NK Engineering Co., Ltd. (1)
466/4 Le Quang Dinh Street, Ward 2 Tan Binh District, Ho Chi Minh City, Vietnam
Tel.: (84) 286 294 0280
Web Site: https://nkengineering.com.vn
Measurement Instrumentation Mfr & Distr
N.A.I.C.S.: 334513
Do Trong Nguyen (CEO)

Nogoon Tolgoi Uul LLC (1)
Galaxy Tower 5005 Mahatma Gandhi Str, 15th Khoroo Khan-Uul District, Ulaanbaatar, 17010, Mongolia
Tel.: (976) 7 711 8485
Web Site: https://www.ntu.mn
Industrial Equipment Mfr & Distr
N.A.I.C.S.: 333248

Onyx For Engineering & Integrated Solutions PLC (1)
Afework Building 2nd Floor, Addis Ababa, Ethiopia
Tel.: (251) 11 522 6060
Web Site: https://www.onyxethiopia.com
Measurement Instrumentation Distr
N.A.I.C.S.: 423830

PE Energy Limited (1)
54 Emekuku Street D Line, Port Harcourt, Rivers, Nigeria
Tel.: (234) 702 600 0116
Web Site: https://www.pe-ng.com
Electrical & Instrumentation Mfr & Distr
N.A.I.C.S.: 334515

C. Igilar *(Chief Comml Officer)*

PH Trading W.L.L. (1)
Block 428 Building No 198 Road 2803, PO
Box 815, Seef, Manama, Bahrain
Tel.: (973) 1 758 7654
Emp.: 6
Measurement Instrumentation Mfr & Distr
N.A.I.C.S.: 334513
Abbas Shirazi *(Mng Dir)*

PT. Endress+Hauser Indonesia (1)
Tempo Scan Tower 29th and B2 Floor Jl
HR Rasuna Said Kav 3-4, Jakarta, 12950,
Indonesia
Tel.: (62) 215 084 3929
Web Site: https://www.id.endress.com
Measurement Instrumentation Mfr & Distr
N.A.I.C.S.: 334513
Henry Chia *(Mng Dir)*

Photonika LLC (1)
Vyshgorodskaya str 45-B/1, Kiev, Ukraine
Tel.: (380) 44 485 1102
Web Site: https://fotonika.kiev.ua
Measurement Instrumentation Mfr & Distr
N.A.I.C.S.: 334513

**Prime Atlantic Global Instruments
Limited** (1)
9 Younis Bashorun Street Off Ajose Adeo-
gun Street, Victoria Island, Lagos, Nigeria
Tel.: (234) 1 460 6130
Web Site: https://pagi-ng.com
Measurement Instrumentation Mfr & Distr
N.A.I.C.S.: 334513

**Process & Energy Solutions,
S.A.** (1)
22 Av 3-95 Z13 Canadas del Rio, San
Miguel Petapa, Guatemala, Guatemala
Tel.: (502) 6 675 7279
Web Site: https://proceso.com.gt
Measurement Instrumentation Mfr & Distr
N.A.I.C.S.: 334513

Process Automation Ltd. (1)
Islam House 1st Floor House-197 Road-1
Block-K Bashundhara R/A, 1212, Dhaka,
Bangladesh
Tel.: (880) 171 306 6374
Emp.: 15
Measurement Instrumentation Mfr & Distr
N.A.I.C.S.: 334513
Mazidul Islam *(Mng Dir)*

Pumps & Motors of Belize Ltd. (1)
3 1/2 mls Philip Goodson Hwy, Belize, Be-
lize
Tel.: (501) 223 6687
Web Site: https://www.pumpsandmotors.bz
Pumping Equipment Mfr
N.A.I.C.S.: 333914

**Qingdao Aikete Automation Instru-
ment Co., Ltd.** (1)
Room 606 Block B Ruban Plaza 177 Shan-
dong Road, Qingdao, 266033, Shandong,
China
Tel.: (86) 5328 565 2336
Measurement Instrumentation Mfr & Distr
N.A.I.C.S.: 334513

**Quanzhou Fengze Nice Mechanical &
Electrical Equipment Co., Ltd.** (1)
Waidai Building F4 Tianan Road, Quan-
zhou, 362000, Fujian, China
Tel.: (86) 5952 255 9386
Measurement Instrumentation Mfr & Distr
N.A.I.C.S.: 334513

Rangooners Company Limited (1)
No 959 Yathawaddy Street, Ward South
Okkalapa Township, Yangon, 11091, Myan-
mar
Tel.: (95) 944 881 1216
Web Site: https://www.rangooners.com
Building Construction Services
N.A.I.C.S.: 236220

S-IU - COR - Cominvestment AG (1)
Miramar Playa Calle 14 113 1ra y 3ra, Ha-
vana, Cuba
Tel.: (53) 7 204 5775
Measurement Instrumentation Mfr & Distr
N.A.I.C.S.: 334513

SATA Sarl (1)
Avenue Birago Diop x - Rue G - Point E
Dakar Fann, BP 5344, Dakar, Senegal
Tel.: (221) 33 864 2626

Measurement Instrumentation Mfr & Distr
N.A.I.C.S.: 334513

**Shaanxi Haifeng Energy Automation
Co., Ltd.** (1)
Road 10701 Block D Urban Gate 1 Jinye
Road, High-tech Zone, Xi'an, 710075,
Shaanxi, China
Tel.: (86) 298 889 3366
Measurement Instrumentation Mfr & Distr
N.A.I.C.S.: 334513

Standard for Trading Co. (1)
PO Box 4297, Aden, Yemen
Tel.: (967) 77 737 2900
Web Site: https://www.standardyemen.com
Measurement Instrumentation Mfr & Distr
N.A.I.C.S.: 334513

Summit Valve & Controls Inc. (1)
107 343 - 70th Street E, Saskatoon, S7P
0E1, SK, Canada
Tel.: (306) 373-4134
Web Site: https://www.summitvalve.com
Industrial Equipment Mfr & Distr
N.A.I.C.S.: 333248

**Technical Associates Services P.
Ltd.** (1)
Aspen Marg Maitighar St Xavier College
Rd, 44600, Kathmandu, Nepal
Tel.: (977) 1 423 9555
Web Site: https://tas.com.np
Waste Treatment Services
N.A.I.C.S.: 221310

Technical Services Bureau Co. (1)
Al Azraq Highway 200m Before Grain Silos,
PO Box 113, Amman, 11636, Jordan
Tel.: (962) 6 412 7967
Web Site: https://tsb.com.jo
Waste Treatment Services
N.A.I.C.S.: 221310

Techno Solutions Private Limited (1)
No 09 D W Rupasinghe Mawatha, Nuge-
goda, Colombo, Sri Lanka
Tel.: (94) 11 282 4604
Web Site: https://www.technospl.com
Construction Engineering Services
N.A.I.C.S.: 541330

Techno Test S.R.L. (1)
66 M Eminescu Str, MD2012, Chisinau,
Moldova
Tel.: (373) 2 222 8313
Web Site: https://technotest.md
Measuring Equipment Mfr & Distr
N.A.I.C.S.: 334515
Sergiu Gurievschi *(Sys Engr-Sales)*

TecnoSagot S.A. (1)
La Uruca diagonal a la rotonda Juan Pablo
II, San Jose, Costa Rica
Tel.: (506) 4 001 6540
Web Site: https://tecnosagot.com
Construction Engineering Services
N.A.I.C.S.: 541330

Transcom Technik, spol. s r.o. (1)
Bojnicka 18, PO Box 25, Bratislava, 830 00,
Slovakia
Tel.: (421) 23 544 8810
Web Site: https://transcom.sk
Measurement Equipment Distr
N.A.I.C.S.: 423830

Trigla Ltd. (1)
Prospect Pobedy 56, Kiev, Ukraine
Tel.: (380) 44 366 2423
Web Site: https://trigla.net.ua
Measuring Equipment Mfr & Distr
N.A.I.C.S.: 334515

TrueDyne Sensors AG (1)
Christoph-Merian-Ring 20, 4153, Reinach,
Switzerland
Tel.: (41) 44 366 2423
Web Site: https://www.truedyne.com
Micro Sensor System Distr
N.A.I.C.S.: 423690
Josua Ritter *(Mng Dir)*

**Valuetec Engineering Solutions
Limited** (1)
B-08 A MIC Building - KN 2 Avenue, Kigali,
Rwanda
Tel.: (250) 78 145 7957
Web Site: https://valuetec.rw
Engineeering Services
N.A.I.C.S.: 541330

Mohamed Salah *(Head-PMO)*

Varma & Velaverk ehf. (1)
Knarrarvogi 4, 104, Reykjavik, Iceland
Tel.: (354) 585 1070
Web Site: https://vov.is
Pump Equipment Mfr & Distr
N.A.I.C.S.: 333914
Arni Dan Einarsson *(Mng Dir)*

**Viet An Environment Technology Joint
Stock Company** (1)
No 4E Street 6, An Phu Ward Thu Duc City,
Ho Chi Minh City, Vietnam
Tel.: (84) 287 777 1616
Web Site: https://www.vietan-enviro.com
Automatic Environmental Monitoring System
Mfr
N.A.I.C.S.: 334512

**Wuxi Kedi Automation Equipment
Co., Ltd.** (1)
Building 67 489 Xinjie Street Greengarden
lv2yuan2 Road, Yixing, Wuxi, 214205, Ji-
angsu, China
Tel.: (86) 5108 706 1554
Measurement Instrumentation Mfr & Distr
N.A.I.C.S.: 334513

Yashyl Dunya LLC (1)
54 Gulyyev Avenue Hilli Hyzmat BC,
Ashgabat, 744015, Turkmenistan
Tel.: (993) 1 275 4568
Web Site: https://yashyl-dunya.tm
Industrial Equipment Distr
N.A.I.C.S.: 423830

**Zhejiang Helihua Technology Co.,
Ltd.** (1)
Room 203 West Lake Radio and Television
Center 7 Gudun Road, Hangzhou, 310023,
Zhejiang, China
Tel.: (86) 5718 777 0812
Measurement Instrumentation Mfr & Distr
N.A.I.C.S.: 334513

**Zhuzhou Huasheng Technology Co.,
Ltd.** (1)
Room 1805 Lushanlian Complex Building
69 Lushan Road, Tianyuan District, Zhu-
zhou, 412007, Hunan, China
Measurement Instrumentation Mfr & Distr
N.A.I.C.S.: 334513

ENDRICH BAUELEMENTE
VERTRIEBS GMBH
Hauptstrasse 56, 72202, Nagold,
Germany
Tel.: (49) 745260070
Web Site: http://www.endrich.com
Year Founded: 1976
Rev.: $88,675,606
Emp.: 106
Electrochemical Components Whlsr
N.A.I.C.S.: 334419
Wolfgang Endrich *(Founder)*

Subsidiaries:

ENDRICH BAUELEMENTE S.L. (1)
C/ Balmes 243, 8006, Barcelona, Spain
Tel.: (34) 932173144
Electronic Parts Distr
N.A.I.C.S.: 423690
Oriol Veas *(Engr-Sls)*

Endrich Ges.m.b.H (1)
Liebermannstrasse A01 / 303-4, 2345,
Brunn am Gebirge, Austria
Tel.: (43) 16652525
Electronic Parts Distr
N.A.I.C.S.: 423690

ENDUR ASA
Damsgardsveien 119, 5160, Lak-
sevag, Norway
Tel.: (47) 55542400   NO
Web Site: https://www.endur.no
ENDUR—(OSL)
Rev.: $194,457,556
Assets: $288,928,872
Liabilities: $171,778,541
Net Worth: $117,150,331
Earnings: ($2,654,241)
Emp.: 730
Fiscal Year-end: 12/31/23

Holding Company; Ship Building, Offshore Engineering & Maritime Services
N.A.I.C.S.: 551112
Morten Riiser *(Co-CFO)*

Subsidiaries:

Artec Aqua AS (1)
Postvegen 13 No-6018, Alesund, Norway
Tel.: (47) 70135400
Web Site: https://www.artec-aqua.com
Onshore Aquaculture Services
N.A.I.C.S.: 518210

BG Amia Sp. z o.o. (1)
Batorego 23, 81-365, Gdynia, Pomeranian,
Poland
Tel.: (48) 583500200
Web Site: http://www.amia.com
Sales Range: $25-49.9 Million
Emp.: 6
Shipbuilding Industry Staff Hiring Services
N.A.I.C.S.: 561311

BMO Entreprenor AS (1)
Skrubbmoen 6, Skollenborg, 3619, Kongs-
berg, Norway
Tel.: (47) 32770930
Web Site: https://bmoe.no
Bridge Construction Services
N.A.I.C.S.: 237310

Bergen Group Hanoytangen AS (1)
Hanoytangen 128, 5310, Hauglandshella,
Hordaland, Norway
Tel.: (47) 56150000
Sales Range: $25-49.9 Million
Emp.: 40
Drydocks Operation Services
N.A.I.C.S.: 488390

Bergen Group Kimek AS (1)
Storgata 4, 9900, Kirkenes, Norway
Tel.: (47) 78977100
Sales Range: $25-49.9 Million
Emp.: 75
Ship Repair & Maintenance Services
N.A.I.C.S.: 336611

**Bergen Group Kimek Offshore
AS** (1)
Storgata 4, 9900, Kirkenes, Norway
Tel.: (47) 78977260
Sales Range: $25-49.9 Million
Emp.: 90
Ship Building & Repair Services
N.A.I.C.S.: 336611

Bergen Group Services AS (1)
Damsgardsv 119, 5162, Laksevag, Norway
Tel.: (47) 55948200
Sales Range: $25-49.9 Million
Emp.: 35
Maritime & Industrial Services
N.A.I.C.S.: 541330
Jonny Arefjord *(Mgr-Svc)*

Division (Domestic):

**Bergen Group Services AS - Indus-
trial Service** (2)
PO Box 14 Laksevag, Nesttun, 5224, Ber-
gen, Norway
Tel.: (47) 55925140
Industrial Engineering Services
N.A.I.C.S.: 541330
Frode Johansson *(Gen Mgr)*

**Bergen Group Services AS - Maritime
Service** (2)
Damsgardsv 119, Laksevag, 5163, Norway
Tel.: (47) 5594 8200
Marine Engineering Services
N.A.I.C.S.: 541330
Rhode Johansson *(Dir Gen)*

Bergen Group Skarveland AS (1)
Sunde industriomrade 3, Sunde, Hordaland,
Norway
Tel.: (47) 53477070
Sales Range: $75-99.9 Million
Emp.: 110
Ship & Industrial Pipes Distr
N.A.I.C.S.: 423510

DYKAB Varv & Mek AB (1)
Stationsgatan 2-4, 972 38, Lulea, Sweden
Tel.: (46) 92089025
Steel Construction Services

ENDUR ASA

Endur ASA—(Continued)
N.A.I.C.S.: 541310

DYKAB i Lulea AB   **(1)**
Stationsgatan 2-4, 97238, Lulea, Sweden
Tel.: (46) 92089025
Construction Services
N.A.I.C.S.: 237110

Endur Maritime AS   **(1)**
Damsgardsveien 119, 5160, Laksevag, Norway
Tel.: (47) 55542400
Maritime Transportation Services
N.A.I.C.S.: 488390
Jonny Arefjord *(Mng Dir)*

Installit AS   **(1)**
Harbitzalleen 2A, 0275, Oslo, Norway
Tel.: (47) 2 308 4340
Web Site: https://www.installit.no
Emp.: 15
Engineeering Services
N.A.I.C.S.: 541330
Christine S. Amland *(CEO & Gen Mgr)*

Marcon Gruppen i Sverige AB   **(1)**
Ekhogsvagen 5, 262 74, Angelholm, Sweden
Tel.: (46) 43125620
Web Site: https://www.marcon.se
Emp.: 240
Water Construction & Maintenance Services
N.A.I.C.S.: 532411

ENDURANCE GOLD CORPORATION

Suite 520 - 800 West Pender Street, Vancouver, V6C 2V6, BC, Canada
Tel.: (604) 682-2707
Web Site:
http://www.endurancegold.com
Year Founded: 2003
Sales Range: Less than $1 Million
Mineral Exploration Services
N.A.I.C.S.: 213114
Robert T. Boyd *(Pres & CEO)*

ENDURANCE MOTIVE SA

Calle la Bernia 1, Canet De Berenguer, 46529, Valencia, Spain
Tel.: (34) 961343044
Web Site:
https://www.endurancemotive.com
Year Founded: 2018
END—(BYMA)
Battery Mfr
N.A.I.C.S.: 335910
Jorge Novella Vera *(Sec)*

ENDYMED LTD.

Bareket Street 7, Caesarea, 30889, Israel
Tel.: (972) 46309100
Medical Equipment Mfr
N.A.I.C.S.: 339112
Yossi Bar-On *(CEO)*

ENE TECHNOLOGY INC.

4th Floor No 21 Lixing Road Hsinchu City Hsinchu Industrial Park, Hsinchu, 300, Taiwan
Tel.: (886) 36662888
Web Site: https://www.ene.com.tw
Year Founded: 1998
6243—(TAI)
Rev.: $28,625,592
Assets: $37,523,364
Liabilities: $10,707,969
Net Worth: $26,815,395
Earnings: $2,180,451
Emp.: 130
Fiscal Year-end: 12/31/23
Integrated Circuits Mfr & Distr
N.A.I.C.S.: 334412
Jason Weng *(Founder & Chm)*

ENEA AB

Jan Stenbecks Torg 17, PO Box 1033, SE-164 21, Kista, Sweden
Tel.: (46) 850714000
Web Site: http://www.enea.se
Year Founded: 1968
ENEA—(OMX)
Rev.: $90,360,036
Assets: $310,767,278
Liabilities: $96,169,041
Net Worth: $214,598,237
Earnings: $21,056,132
Emp.: 619
Fiscal Year-end: 12/31/22
Software Developer
N.A.I.C.S.: 513210
Anders Lidbeck *(Chm)*

Subsidiaries:

AdaptiveMobile Security Ltd.   **(1)**
Ferry House 48-52 Lower Mount Street, Dublin, 2, Ireland
Tel.: (353) 15249000
Software Development Services
N.A.I.C.S.: 541511

Enea GmbH   **(1)**
Konrad-Zuse-Platz 8, 81829, Munich, Germany
Tel.: (49) 895446760
Software Development Services
N.A.I.C.S.: 541511

Enea KK   **(1)**
The Gate Ichigaya 3F 3-6 Ichigaya Tamachi, Shinjuku-ku, Tokyo, 162-0843, Japan
Tel.: (81) 352072610
Software Development Services
N.A.I.C.S.: 541511

Enea Netbricks SAS   **(1)**
15 avenue du Hoggar, 91969, Les Ulis, France
Tel.: (33) 1 76 91 58 20
Web Site: http://www.netbricks.com
Software Development Services
N.A.I.C.S.: 541511

Enea Polyhedra Ltd   **(1)**
The Malt Ho Malt Ho Sq, Princes Risborough, HP27 9AB, Buckinghamshire, United Kingdom
Tel.: (44) 1749346784
Software Development Services
N.A.I.C.S.: 541511

Enea Software & Services, Inc   **(1)**
402 Amherst St Ste 300, Nashua, NH 03063
Tel.: (480) 753-9200
Software Development Services
N.A.I.C.S.: 541511

Enea Software (Beijing) Co., Ltd.   **(1)**
Room 1203 Silver Tower No 218 South Xi-Zang Road, Shanghai, 200021, China
Tel.: (86) 21 6334 3406
Software Development Services
N.A.I.C.S.: 541511

Enea Software SRL   **(1)**
319 Splaiul Independentei, OB403A District 6, 060044, Bucharest, Romania
Tel.: (40) 213114300
Communication Software Development Services
N.A.I.C.S.: 541511

Enea TekSci Inc.   **(1)**
1711 W Greentree Dr Ste 108, Tempe, AZ 85284
Tel.: (480) 753-9200
Web Site: http://www.enea.com
Sales Range: $10-24.9 Million
Emp.: 65
Software Design Services
N.A.I.C.S.: 541511

Openwave Mobility, Inc.   **(1)**
303 Twin Dolphin Dr 6th Fl, Redwood City, CA 94065
Tel.: (650) 480-7200
Web Site: http://www.owmobility.com
Wireless Telecommunications Carriers
N.A.I.C.S.: 517112
Indranil Chatterjee *(Sr VP-Products, Sls & Mktg)*

Qosmos SA   **(1)**

6 rue Casteres, Clichy, 92110, Paris, France
Tel.: (33) 17 081 1900
Web Site: https://www.qosmos.com
Computer Networking Product Mfr
N.A.I.C.S.: 334118

ENEA S.A.

ul Gorecka 1, 60-201, Poznan, Poland
Tel.: (48) 618845544
Web Site: https://www.enea.pl
Year Founded: 2001
ENA—(WAR)
Rev.: $11,205,059,931
Assets: $9,936,672,993
Liabilities: $6,014,010,655
Net Worth: $3,922,662,338
Earnings: ($112,455,030)
Emp.: 10,000
Fiscal Year-end: 12/31/23
Electric Power Generator Distr
N.A.I.C.S.: 221122

Subsidiaries:

ENEA Bioenergia Sp. z o.o.   **(1)**
Zawada 26, 28-230, Polaniec, Poland
Tel.: (48) 158657022
Electricity & Heat Generation Services
N.A.I.C.S.: 221118

ENEA Cieplo Serwis Sp. z o.o.   **(1)**
Ul Starosielce 2/1, 15-670, Bialystok, Poland
Tel.: (48) 856549800
Electricity & Heat Generation Services
N.A.I.C.S.: 221118

ENEA Cieplo Sp. z o.o.   **(1)**
Ul WarsZawska 27, 15-062, Bialystok, Poland
Tel.: (48) 856549868
Electricity & Heat Generation Services
N.A.I.C.S.: 221118

ENEA Elektrownia Polaniec S.A.   **(1)**
Zawada 26, 28-230, Polaniec, Poland
Tel.: (48) 158656701
Electricity & Heat Generation Services
N.A.I.C.S.: 221118

ENEA Innowacje Sp. z o.o.   **(1)**
Ul Wisniowa 40, 02-520, Warsaw, Poland
Tel.: (48) 228712970
Electricity Distribution Services
N.A.I.C.S.: 221122

ENEA Logistyka Sp. z o.o.   **(1)**
Ul StrZesZynska 58, 60-479, Poznan, Poland
Tel.: (48) 618845660
Web Site: https://sklep-elog.enea.pl
Electricity Distribution Services
N.A.I.C.S.: 221122

ENEA Operator Sp. z o.o.   **(1)**
ul Strzeszynska 58, 60 479, Poznan, Poland
Tel.: (48) 618504000
Web Site: https://www.operator.enea.pl
Electricity Distribution Services
N.A.I.C.S.: 221122

ENEA Oswietlenie Sp. z o.o.   **(1)**
Ul Ku Sloncu 34, 71-080, Szczecin, Poland
Tel.: (48) 913321720
Electricity & Heat Generation Services
N.A.I.C.S.: 221118

ENEA Polaniec Serwis Sp. z o.o.   **(1)**
Zawada 26, 28-230, Polaniec, Poland
Tel.: (48) 158656110
Electricity & Heat Generation Services
N.A.I.C.S.: 221118

ENEA Serwis Sp. z o.o.   **(1)**
Gronowko 30, Lipno, 64-111, Leszno, Poland
Tel.: (48) 618843400
Electricity Distribution Services
N.A.I.C.S.: 221122

ENEA Trading Sp. z o.o.   **(1)**
Kozienice 1, Swierze Gorne, 26-900, Kozienice, Poland
Tel.: (48) 486115600
Electricity Trading Services
N.A.I.C.S.: 221122

Elektrownia Kozienice S.A.   **(1)**
Swierze Upper Vlg Kozienice, 26 900, Kozienice, Masovian, Poland
Tel.: (48) 486141627
Web Site: http://www.elko.com.pl
Electric Power Distribution Services
N.A.I.C.S.: 221122

Elektrownie Wodne Sp. z o.o.   **(1)**
Samociazek 92, 86 010, Koronowo, Kuyavian-Pomeranian, Poland
Tel.: (48) 523825800
Web Site: http://www.koronowo.pl
Sales Range: $125-149.9 Million
Emp.: 176
Eletric Power Generation Services
N.A.I.C.S.: 221118

Energetyka Poznanska Przedsiebiorstwo Uslug Energetycznych Energobud Leszno Sp. z o.o.   **(1)**
Gronowko 30, 64-111, Lipno, Poland
Tel.: (48) 655256900
Web Site: http://www.energobud.pl
Sales Range: $25-49.9 Million
Emp.: 100
Energy Consulting Services
N.A.I.C.S.: 541690
Paul Mularczyk *(Branch Mgr & Sec)*

Energetyka Poznanska Zaklad Obslugi Socjalnej ENERGO-TOUR Sp. z o.o.   **(1)**
Glogowska 55 57, 60 738, Poznan, Poland
Tel.: (48) 618561630
Airline Ticket Services
N.A.I.C.S.: 561599

EnergoPartner Sp. z o.o.   **(1)**
ul Krzysztofa Gotowskiego 6, 85-030, Bydgoszcz, Poland
Tel.: (48) 606 959 222
Web Site: http://www.energopartner.com.pl
Sales Range: $75-99.9 Million
Emp.: 12
Electricity Supplier
N.A.I.C.S.: 221118

Energomiar Sp. z o.o.   **(1)**
Ul Strzeszynska 58, 60479, Poznan, Poland
Tel.: (48) 618561730
Web Site: http://www.energomiar.pl
Sales Range: $125-149.9 Million
Emp.: 200
Power Supplier Services
N.A.I.C.S.: 221122
Alexander Wilski *(Mgr)*

Kozienice II Sp. z o.o.   **(1)**
Swierze Gorne, 26 900, Kozienice, Masovian, Poland
Tel.: (48) 486141097
Sales Range: $75-99.9 Million
Emp.: 10
Electricity Distribution Services
N.A.I.C.S.: 221122

Miejska Energetyka Cieplna Sp. z o.o.   **(1)**
ul Armii Krajowej 81, 78 400, Szczecinek, Poland
Tel.: (48) 943726650
Web Site: http://www.mec-szczecinek.com.pl
Heating System Distr
N.A.I.C.S.: 221330

Przedsiebiorstwo Energetyki Cieplnej - Gozdnica Sp. z o.o.   **(1)**
Wybudowanie 56, 64 600, Oborniki, Poland
Tel.: (48) 612961519
Heating System Distr
N.A.I.C.S.: 221330

Zaklad Uslug Teleinformatycznych ZZE S.A. ITSERWIS sp. z o.o.   **(1)**
Zacisze 28, 65 792, Zielona Gora, Lubusz, Poland
Tel.: (48) 683281898
Web Site: http://www.itserwis.com.pl
Sales Range: $25-49.9 Million
Emp.: 100
Telecommunication Servicesb
N.A.I.C.S.: 517810

ENEABBA GAS LIMITED

Ground Floor 50 Ord St, West Perth, 6005, WA, Australia

Tel.: (61) 8 9467 4220   AU
Web Site:
http://www.eneabbagas.com.au
Sales Range: Less than $1 Million
Emp.: 5
Mineral Exploration & Electricity Generation
N.A.I.C.S.: 237990
Gabriel Chiappini *(Sec)*

ENECO ENERGY LIMITED
300 Tampines Ave 5, 45414, Singaporo, 520653, Singapore
Tel.: (65) 62238022
Web Site: https://enecoenergy.com
Year Founded: 1992
R14—(SES)
Rev.: $23,148,527
Assets: $23,846,096
Liabilities: $8,611,679
Net Worth: $15,234,416
Earnings: $62,865
Emp.: 276
Fiscal Year-end: 12/31/23
Oil & Gas Exploration & Production;
Logistics Services
N.A.I.C.S.: 211120
Colin Moran *(CEO-Logistics)*

Subsidiaries:

RichLand Logistics Services Pte.
Ltd.   **(1)**
300 Tampines Ave 5 Unit 05-02, Singapore,
529653, Singapore
Tel.: (65) 64197500
Web Site: http://www.richlandlogistics.com
Logistics Transportation Services
N.A.I.C.S.: 541614

ENECO HOLDING N.V.
Antwoordnummer 5166, 3000 VB,
Rotterdam, Netherlands
Tel.: (31) 888951111   NI
Web Site:
http://www.enecogroup.com
Year Founded: 1995
Emp.: 100
Holding Company; Wind & Solar
Power Production & Distribution
N.A.I.C.S.: 551112
Hiroshi Sakuma *(Chief Collaboration
& Intl Officer & Member-Mgmt Bd)*

Subsidiaries:

Eneco Belgium N.V.   **(1)**
Battelsesteenweg 455i, 2800, Mechelen,
Belgium
Tel.: (32) 80015534
Web Site: http://eneco.be
Electricity Generation & Distribution
N.A.I.C.S.: 221122

Eneco Zuid Nederland B.V.   **(1)**
Dr Holtroplaan 2-28, Eindhoven, 5652 XR,
Netherlands
Tel.: (31) 9000601
Electric Power & Natural Gas Distribution
Services
N.A.I.C.S.: 221122

ENECO REFRESH LIMITED
17 Denninup Way, Malaga, 6090,
WA, Australia
Tel.: (61) 892487222   AU
Web Site: https://www.eneco-
refresh.com.au
ERG—(ASX)
Rev.: $10,318,078
Assets: $9,336,795
Liabilities: $3,722,576
Net Worth: $5,614,219
Earnings: ($1,058,922)
Fiscal Year-end: 06/30/24
Distilled Drinking Water Distr
N.A.I.C.S.: 325998
Henry Eng Chye Heng *(Founder,
Chm & Mng Dir)*

Subsidiaries:

AridTec Pte Ltd.   **(1)**
Block 514 Chai Chee Ln No 05-01, Singapore, Singapore
Tel.: (65) 64428022
Web Site: http://www.aridtec.com
Sales Range: $75-99.9 Million
Emp.: 12
Clean & Potable Water Distr
N.A.I.C.S.: 221310

Hydr8 Water   **(1)**
3 Salisbury Street, Silverwater, 2128, NSW,
Australia
Tel.: (01) 1000707900
Web Site: https://www.hydr8water.com.au
Sales Range: $50-74.9 Million
Emp.: 1
Distilled Waters Distr
N.A.I.C.S.: 424490

Refresh Plastics Pty Ltd   **(1)**
9-11 Olive Grove, Keysborough, 3173, VIC,
Australia
Tel.: (61) 39 701 5600
Web Site: https://refreshplastics.com.au
Plastics Product Mfr
N.A.I.C.S.: 326199

Refresh Waters Pty Ltd.   **(1)**
17 Denninup Way, Malaga, 6090, WA, Australia
Tel.: (61) 892487222
Web Site: https://refreshwaters.com.au
Distilled Waters Distr
N.A.I.C.S.: 424490

Division (Domestic):

Refresh Waters Pty Ltd. - Oz Water
Filters   **(2)**
17 Denninup Way, Malaga, 6090, WA, Australia
Tel.: (61) 892487222
Web Site: http://www.ozwaterfilters.com.au
Water Filters Mfr
N.A.I.C.S.: 333310

Refresh Waters Queensland Pty
Ltd.   **(1)**
600 Boundary St, Toowoomba, 4350, QLD,
Australia   **(100%)**
Tel.: (61) 746590400
Web Site:
http://www.refreshtoowoomba.com.au
Distilled Waters Distr
N.A.I.C.S.: 424490

ENECSYS PLC
5 New Street Square, London, EC4A
3TW, United Kingdom
Tel.: (44) 1223 792 101
Web Site: http://www.enecsys.com
Micro Inverters & Monitoring Systems
Mfr
N.A.I.C.S.: 334413

Subsidiaries:

Enecsys LLC   **(1)**
39684 Eureka Dr, Newark, CA 94560
Tel.: (510) 933-9700
Web Site: http://www.enecsys.com
Micro Inverter & Monitoring System Distr
N.A.I.C.S.: 423690

Enecsys Taiwan Limited   **(1)**
9F No 8 Ln 321 Yangguang St, Neihu District, Taipei, 114, Taiwan
Tel.: (886) 226276118
Micro Inverter & Monitoring System Distr
N.A.I.C.S.: 423690

ENEFI VAGYONKEZELO NYRT
Web Site: http://www.e-star.hu
EST—(WAR)
Rev.: $1,140,525
Assets: $9,914,728
Liabilities: $1,829,173
Net Worth: $8,085,555
Earnings: ($633,334)
Emp.: 26
Fiscal Year-end: 12/31/23
Eletric Power Generation Services
N.A.I.C.S.: 221111

ENEFIT GREEN AS
Lelle 22, 11318, Tallinn, Estonia
Tel.: (372) 58654999
Web Site: https://www.enefitgreen.ee
Year Founded: 2016
EGR1T—(TAL)
Rev.: $222,055,903
Assets: $1,405,053,961
Liabilities: $631,052,234
Net Worth: $774,001,727
Earnings: $60,212,605
Emp.: 194
Fiscal Year-end: 12/31/23
Natural Gas Distribution Services
N.A.I.C.S.: 221210
Aavo Karmas *(CEO)*

ENEGEX LIMITED
Unit 24 589 Stirling Highway, PO Box
556, Cottesloe, 6911, WA, Australia
Tel.: (61) 861531861   AU
Web Site: https://www.enegex.com
Year Founded: 2012
ENX—(ASX)
Rev.: $30,258
Assets: $1,963,580
Liabilities: $164,744
Net Worth: $1,798,836
Earnings: ($597,336)
Fiscal Year-end: 06/30/24
Oil & Natural Gas Exploration
N.A.I.C.S.: 213112
Raewyn L. Clark *(Exec Dir)*

ENEL S.P.A.
Viale Regina Margherita 137, 00198,
Rome, Italy
Tel.: (39) 0683054000   IT
Web Site: https://www.enel.com
Year Founded: 1962
ENEL—(ITA)
Rev.: $103,135,117,634
Assets: $210,688,538,744
Liabilities: $162,006,259,443
Net Worth: $48,682,279,301
Earnings: $4,605,007,555
Emp.: 61,055
Fiscal Year-end: 12/31/23
Natural Gas Distribution Services
N.A.I.C.S.: 551112
Claudio Machetti *(Head-Trading-
Global)*

Subsidiaries:

Albany Solar LLC   **(1)**
15 Farrell Rd, Troy, NY 12180
Tel.: (518) 720-7779
Web Site:
https://www.albanysolarsolutions.com
Solar Installation Services
N.A.I.C.S.: 238210

Beijing Tecnatom Nuclear Power
Safety Technology Services Company
Limited   **(1)**
E-806 Sanlitun SOHO No 8 Gongti Beilu,
Chaoyang District, Beijing, 100027, China
Tel.: (86) 1056301310
Nuclear Power Plants Services
N.A.I.C.S.: 541690

Bolonia Real Estate SL   **(1)**
Calle Ribera Del Loira 60, Madrid, 28042,
Spain
Tel.: (34) 912131000
Real Estate Manangement Services
N.A.I.C.S.: 531390

Boott Hydropower Inc.   **(1)**
1 Tech Dr Ste 220, Andover, MA 01810
Tel.: (978) 454-8074
Hydroelectric Power Generation Services
N.A.I.C.S.: 221111
Wayne Pincence *(Mgr)*

Bypass Power Company   **(1)**
1 Tech Dr, Andover, MA 01810-2453
Tel.: (828) 452-5346
Management Consulting Services
N.A.I.C.S.: 541611

Subsidiary (Domestic):

CHI Operations Inc.   **(2)**
97 Industrial Ave, Sanford, ME 04073-5820
Tel.: (207) 490-1980
Sales Range: $10-24.9 Million
Emp.: 10
Hydro Electric Services
N.A.I.C.S.: 221122

Consolidated Hydro New York
Inc   **(2)**
Pine St, Schuylerville, NY 12871
Tel.: (518) 695-3035
Hydroelectric Power Generation Services
N.A.I.C.S.: 221111

Hydro Development Group Inc.   **(2)**
16472 NYS Route 12F, Dexter, NY 13634
Tel.: (315) 639-6700
Web Site: http://www.enel.com
Rev.: $8,600,000
Emp.: 40
Hydro Electric Power Generation
N.A.I.C.S.: 221118

TKO Power Inc.   **(2)**
9485 Deschutes Rd, Palo Cedro, CA
96073-9758
Tel.: (203) 425-8850
Rev.: $2,500,000
Emp.: 11
Electronic Services
N.A.I.C.S.: 221122

Carvemagere Manutencao e Energias Renovaveis Lda   **(1)**
Lugar Pedreira, 4750-625, Braga, Portugal
Tel.: (351) 253860030
Natural Gas Mfr
N.A.I.C.S.: 325120

Central Dock Sud SA   **(1)**
Av Agustin Debenedetti 1636, Dock Sud,
Avellaneda, B1871AAL, Argentina
Tel.: (54) 1142291000
Web Site: http://www.cdssa.com.ar
Thermal Electric Power Generation Services
N.A.I.C.S.: 221118

Centrum Pre Vedu A Vyskum
s.r.o.   **(1)**
Mochovce 6, Kalna nad Hronom, 935 32,
Levice, Slovakia
Tel.: (421) 258663635
Web Site: https://cvv.sk
Nuclear Power Plants Services
N.A.I.C.S.: 541690

Chi West Inc.   **(1)**
20020 Tamarack Rd, Burney, CA 96013
Tel.: (530) 335-4305
Sales Range: $75-99.9 Million
Emp.: 5
Eletric Power Generation Services
N.A.I.C.S.: 221118

Consolidated Hydro Southeast
Inc.   **(1)**
11 Anderson St, Piedmont, SC 29673
Tel.: (978) 681-1900
Hydroelectric Power Generation Services
N.A.I.C.S.: 221111

Deval SpA   **(1)**
Via Clavalite 8, 11100, Aosta, Italy
Tel.: (39) 0165647211
Electric Power Distribution Services
N.A.I.C.S.: 221122

E.S.CO. Comuni Srl   **(1)**
Piazza Salvo D Acquisto 80, Trescore Balneario, 24069, Bergamo, Italy
Tel.: (39) 0354274281
Web Site: https://www.escocomuni.it
Solar Energy Services
N.A.I.C.S.: 221114

Edistribucion Redes Digitales SL   **(1)**
C/ Ribera del Loira 60, 28042, Madrid,
Spain
Tel.: (34) 900878119
Web Site: https://www.edistribucion.com
Electric Power Distribution Services
N.A.I.C.S.: 221122

Empresa de Alumbrado Electrico de
Ceuta Energia S.L.U.   **(1)**
Calle Gral Serrano Orive 19, 51001, Ceuta,
Spain

Enel S.p.A.—(Continued)

Tel.: (34) 900103306
Web Site: https://www.electricadeceuta.es
N.A.I.C.S.: 238210

Empresa de Alumbrado Electrico de Ceuta SA **(1)**
Calle Gral Serrano Orive 19, 51001, Ceuta, Spain
Tel.: (34) 900103306
Web Site: http://www.electricadeceuta.com
Electric Power Distribution Services
N.A.I.C.S.: 221122

Endesa Energia SA **(1)**
Calle Ribera Del Loira No 60, 28042, Madrid, Spain
Tel.: (34) 912131503
Web Site: https://www.endesa.com
Natural Gas Distribution Services
N.A.I.C.S.: 221210

Endesa X Servicios SLU **(1)**
Ribera del Loire 60, 28042, Madrid, Spain
Tel.: (34) 912131102
Web Site: https://www.endesax.com
Natural Gas Distribution Services
N.A.I.C.S.: 221210

Endesa X Way S.L. **(1)**
C/Ribera Del Loire 60, 28042, Madrid, Spain
Tel.: (34) 912131102
Web Site: https://www.endesaxway.com
N.A.I.C.S.: 423620

Endesa, S.A. **(1)**
Ribera del Loira 60, 28042, Madrid, Spain **(70.1%)**
Tel.: (34) 912131503
Web Site: https://www.endesa.com
Rev.: $1,069,501,403
Assets: $26,255,126,268
Liabilities: $18,220,375,567
Net Worth: $8,034,750,701
Earnings: $752,212,389
Emp.: 1,241
Fiscal Year-end: 12/31/2022
Electric Utility Services
N.A.I.C.S.: 221122
Jose Damian Bogas Galvez *(CEO)*

Subsidiary (Domestic):

Carboex, S.A. **(2)**
Manuel Cortina 2 2, Madrid, Spain **(100%)**
Tel.: (34) 915668800
Sales Range: $25-49.9 Million
Emp.: 23
Coal Supply Services
N.A.I.C.S.: 423520

Endesa Desarrollo SL **(2)**
Calle Ribera Del Loira 60, Madrid, 28042, Spain
Tel.: (34) 912131000
Eletric Power Generation Services
N.A.I.C.S.: 221118

Endesa Financiacion Filiales SAU **(2)**
Calle Ribera Del Loira 60, Madrid, 28042, Spain **(100%)**
Tel.: (34) 912131000
Financial Management Services
N.A.I.C.S.: 525990

Subsidiary (Non-US):

Sociedad Inversora Dock Sud SA **(3)**
Debenedetti 1636, Dock Sud, Buenos Aires, 1871, Argentina
Tel.: (54) 1142018011
Eletric Power Generation Services
N.A.I.C.S.: 221118

Subsidiary (Domestic):

Endesa Generacion, S.A. **(2)**
Ribera del Loira 60, 28042, Madrid, Spain **(100%)**
Tel.: (34) 91 213 1503
Web Site: http://www.endesaclientes.com
Electric Power Generation & Distribution
N.A.I.C.S.: 221118

Subsidiary (Non-US):

Endesa Generacion Portugal, S.A. **(3)**

Quinta Da Fonte Edificio Dom Manuel I Piso Ala B, Paco d'Arcos, 2770-192, Portugal **(100%)**
Tel.: (351) 211102700
Sales Range: $75-99.9 Million
Emp.: 12
Geothermal Electric Power Generation Services
N.A.I.C.S.: 221116

Subsidiary (Domestic):

Endesa Ingenieria SLU **(2)**
C/Inca Garcilaso s/n Edif EXPO Isla de la Cartuja, 41092, Sevilla, Spain
Tel.: (34) 954217991
Web Site: http://www.endesaingenieria.es
Sales Range: $150-199.9 Million
Emp.: 70
Electric Power Generation & Distribution Services
N.A.I.C.S.: 221118

Endesa Red SA **(2)**
Av Del Paralelo 51, Barcelona, 08004, Spain
Tel.: (34) 91 566 88 00
Electric Power Distribution Services
N.A.I.C.S.: 221122

Subsidiary (Domestic):

Distribuidora de Energia Electrica del Bages SA **(3)**
Bda Riera 1, Rajadell, 8289, Barcelona, Spain
Tel.: (34) 938368000
Electric Power Distribution Services
N.A.I.C.S.: 221122

Subsidiary (Domestic):

Endesa Servicios SL **(2)**
Calle Ribera del Loira 60, Madrid, 28042, Spain
Tel.: (34) 91 213 10 00
Consulting Management Services
N.A.I.C.S.: 541611

Subsidiary (Domestic):

Endesa Network Factory SL **(3)**
Avenida Paral Lel 51, Barcelona, Spain
Tel.: (34) 912131000
Electric Power Transmission Services
N.A.I.C.S.: 221122

Subsidiary (Non-US):

International Endesa BV **(2)**
Herengracht 471, Amsterdam, 1017BS, Netherlands
Tel.: (31) 20 521 8771
Web Site: http://www.endesa.com
Sales Range: $50-74.9 Million
Emp.: 2
Financial Management Services
N.A.I.C.S.: 523999
Ernesto Di Giacomo *(Mng Dir)*

Subsidiary (Non-US):

Enel Americas S.A. **(1)**
Avenida Santa Rosa 76, PO Box 1557, 833-009, Santiago, Chile **(82.3%)**
Tel.: (56) 223534000
Web Site: https://www.enelamericas.com
Rev.: $16,192,336,000
Assets: $34,958,938,000
Liabilities: $19,928,845,000
Net Worth: $15,030,093,000
Earnings: $740,859,000
Emp.: 16,461
Fiscal Year-end: 12/31/2021
Electricity Generation & Distr
N.A.I.C.S.: 221122
Jose Antonio Vargas Lleras *(Bd of Dirs & Vice Chm)*

Subsidiary (Non-US):

Central Geradora Termeletrica Fortaleza SA **(2)**
Rodovia Ce 422 s/n Km 1 Complexo Industrial Do Pecem, Caucaia, 61600-000, Ceara, Brazil
Tel.: (55) 85 3464 4100
Web Site: http://www.enelbrasil.com
Eletric Power Generation Services
N.A.I.C.S.: 221118
Martelo Falcucci *(Office Mgr)*

Empresa Distribuidora Sur S.A. **(2)**

San Jose 140, 1076, Buenos Aires, Argentina **(72.12%)**
Web Site: http://www.edesur.com.ar
Sales Range: $1-4.9 Billion
Emp.: 2,400
Electric Power Distr
N.A.I.C.S.: 221122
Hector Ruiz Moreno *(Dir-HR)*

Empresa de Distribucion Electrica de Lima Norte S.A.A. **(2)**
(75.68%)
Tel.: (51) 15612001
Sales Range: $450-499.9 Million
Emp.: 625
Electricity Generation & Distribution
N.A.I.C.S.: 221122

Enel Brasil S.A. **(2)**
Praca Leoni Ramos 1 Sao Domingos, 24210-200, Rio de Janeiro, Niteroi, Brazil **(53.9%)**
Tel.: (55) 2136079500
Web Site: http://www.enel.com.br
Holding Company
N.A.I.C.S.: 551112
Mario Fernando de Melo Santos *(Chm)*

Subsidiary (Domestic):

Ampla Energia e Servicos, S.A. **(3)**
Avenida Oscar Niemeyer 2000 bl 01 sl 701, Santo Cristo, Rio de Janeiro, 20220-297, RJ, Brazil **(99.64%)**
Tel.: (55) 2126137031
Web Site: http://www.enel.com.br
Sales Range: Less than $1 Million
Emp.: 1,500
Electricity Distribution
N.A.I.C.S.: 221122
Francesco Tutoli *(Dir-Investor Relations)*

Eletropaulo Metropolitana Eletricidade de Sao Paulo S.A. **(3)**
Av Dr Marcos Penteado de Ulhoa Rodrigues 939, 06460 040, Barueri, SP, Brazil **(100%)**
Tel.: (55) 11 2195 7048
Sales Range: $1-4.9 Billion
Emp.: 7,355
Electric Power Distr
N.A.I.C.S.: 221122
Britaldo Pedrosa Soares *(Chm)*

Enel Distribucion Cear S.A. **(3)**
Rua Padre Valdevino 150, Bairro Dionisio Torres, Fortaleza, Ceara, Brazil **(74.5%)**
Tel.: (55) 8532161350
Web Site: http://www.coelce.com.br
Sales Range: $1-4.9 Billion
Emp.: 1,297
Electric Power Distribution
N.A.I.C.S.: 221122

Subsidiary (Non-US):

Synapsis Argentina Ltda **(2)**
Olga Cossettini 1551, Buenos Aires, 1425, Argentina
Tel.: (54) 11 4021 8300
Web Site: http://www.synapsis.com.ar
Emp.: 50
Information Technology Services
N.A.I.C.S.: 541512
Claudio Stasi *(Dir)*

Enel Chile S.A. **(1)**
Santa Rosa 76, Santiago, Chile **(60.6%)**
Tel.: (56) 223534400
Web Site: https://www.enel.cl
Rev.: $6,939,004,608
Assets: $16,611,811,625
Liabilities: $10,467,296,601
Net Worth: $6,144,515,024
Earnings: $1,752,915,161
Emp.: 498
Fiscal Year-end: 12/31/2022
Electric Power Generation & Distr
N.A.I.C.S.: 221122
Giulio Fazio *(Vice Chm)*

Subsidiary (Domestic):

Enel Distribucion Chile SA **(3)**
Roger de Flor 2725 Torre 2 piso 17, Las Condes, Chile **(99%)**
Tel.: (56) 223534680
Web Site: http://www.chilectra.cl
Sales Range: $1-4.9 Billion
Emp.: 720
Electric Power Distr

N.A.I.C.S.: 221122

Subsidiary (Domestic):

Compania Electrica Tarapaca SA **(3)**
Santa Rosa 76 Piso 13, Santiago, 8330099, Chile
Tel.: (56) 2 630 9448
Electric Power Generation & Distribution Services
N.A.I.C.S.: 221118

Enel Colina SA **(1)**
Chacabuco 31, Lampa, Chile
Tel.: (56) 223534500
Web Site: https://www.enelcolina.cl
Electricity Bill Services
N.A.I.C.S.: 926130

Enel Cove Fort LLC **(1)**
1 Main St, Beaver, UT 84713
Tel.: (978) 681-1900
Hydroelectric Power Generation Services
N.A.I.C.S.: 221111

Enel Distribucion Chile SA **(1)**
Avenida Santa Rosa 76, 8330099, Santiago, Chile
Tel.: (56) 223534500
N.A.I.C.S.: 221114

Enel Distribucion Peru SAA **(1)**
Paseo Del Bosque N 500 Urb Chacarilla Del Estanque, San Borja, 15037, Lima, Peru
Tel.: (51) 5612001
Web Site: https://www.enel.pe
N.A.I.C.S.: 221114

Enel Energia S.p.A. **(1)**
Tel.: (39) 0683051
Electric Power Generator & Distr; Natural Gas Distr
N.A.I.C.S.: 221122

Subsidiary (Domestic):

Enel Distribuzione S.p.A. **(2)**
Via Ombrone 2, Rome, Italy
Tel.: (39) 0685091
Web Site: http://www.enel.it
Electric Power Distr
N.A.I.C.S.: 221122

Enel Produzione S.p.A. **(2)**
Viale Regina Margherita 125, 00198, Rome, Italy
Tel.: (39) 0683051
Thermal Electric Power Generation Services
N.A.I.C.S.: 221116

Subsidiary (Non-US):

Slovenske elektrarne AS **(3)**
Mlynske nivy 47, 821 09, Bratislava, Slovakia
Tel.: (421) 258661111
Nuclear Electric Power Generation Services
N.A.I.C.S.: 221113
Branislav Strycek *(Chm)*

Subsidiary (Domestic):

Ochrana A Bezpecnost Se AS **(4)**
Seas 83538, 935 39, Mochovce, Slovakia
Tel.: (421) 366355811
Web Site: http://www.oabse.sk
Emp.: 46
Nuclear Electric Power Generation Services
N.A.I.C.S.: 221113

Subsidiary (Non-US):

Slovenske elektrarne Finance BV **(4)**
Herengracht 471, Amsterdam, 1017 BS, Netherlands
Tel.: (31) 205218777
Web Site: http://www.seas.sk
Emp.: 3
Financial Investment Services
N.A.I.C.S.: 523999

Subsidiary (Domestic):

Enel Servizio Elettrico SpA **(2)**
Viale Regina Margherita 125, Rome, 198, Italy
Tel.: (39) 0683051
Web Site: http://www.enel.it
Electric Power Distribution Services

N.A.I.C.S.: 221122

Enel Finance International NV   **(1)**
Tel.: (31) 205218777
Web Site: http://www.enel.com
Sales Range: $50-74.9 Million
Emp.: 1
Financial Management Services
N.A.I.C.S.: 523999

Enel Generacion Chile S.A.   **(1)**
Santa Rosa 76, Santiago, Chile   **(95.55%)**
Tel.: (56) 223534682
Web Site: http://www.enelgeneracion.cl
Rev.: $2,195,421,742
Assets: $4,806,846,361
Liabilities: $2,161,881,473
Net Worth: $2,644,964,888
Earnings: $269,776,924
Emp.: 710
Fiscal Year-end: 12/31/2019
Electricity Generation & Distribution
N.A.I.C.S.: 221122
Luis Ignacio Quinones Sotomayor *(Gen Counsel)*

Subsidiary (Domestic):

Empresa Electrica Pehuenche, S.A.   **(2)**
Santa Rosa No 76 piso 17, 833-0099, Santiago, Chile   **(92.65%)**
Tel.: (56) 226309606
Rev.: $4,971,885,819
Assets: $13,432,101,736
Liabilities: $8,028,162,556
Net Worth: $5,403,939,181
Earnings: $771,862,800
Fiscal Year-end: 12/31/2023
Electricity Generation & Distribution
N.A.I.C.S.: 221122

Subsidiary (Non-US):

Endesa Argentina SA   **(2)**
Avenida Espana 3301, Buenos Aires, C1107ANA, Argentina
Tel.: (54) 1143073040
Eletric Power Generation Services
N.A.I.C.S.: 221118

Subsidiary (Domestic):

Endesa Cemsa SA   **(3)**
Ing Enrique Butty 220 Piso 16, C1001AFB, Buenos Aires, Argentina
Tel.: (54) 11 4875 0600
Web Site: http://www.endesacemsa.com
Electric Power Distribution Services
N.A.I.C.S.: 221122

Subsidiary (Domestic):

Endesa Eco SA   **(2)**
Avda Santa Rosa 76 Piso 12, Santiago, Chile
Tel.: (56) 26309000
Eletric Power Generation Services
N.A.I.C.S.: 221118

Gasoducto Atacama Argentina SA   **(2)**
Av Isidora Goyenechea 3365 Piso 8, Las Condes, 7550120, Santiago, Chile
Tel.: (56) 23663800
Web Site: http://www.gasatacama.cl
Emp.: 5
Natural Gas Distribution & Transmission Services
N.A.I.C.S.: 221210
Dawn Hancock *(Office Mgr)*

Subsidiary (Non-US):

Southern Cone Power Argentina SA   **(2)**
Avenida Costanera Espana 3301 Ciudad de 1107, Buenos Aires, Argentina
Tel.: (54) 1143073040
Eletric Power Generation Services
N.A.I.C.S.: 221118

Enel Green Power Chile Ltda.   **(1)**
Santa Rosa 76, Santiago, Chile
Tel.: (56) 228479000
Eletric Power Generation Services
N.A.I.C.S.: 221118

Enel Green Power Costa Rica SA   **(1)**

200 Mts Sur del parqueo de Cine Mark Multiplaza Escazu, Edificio Terraforte 2 do Piso Escazu, San Jose, Costa Rica
Tel.: (506) 22014500
Eletric Power Generation Services
N.A.I.C.S.: 221118

Enel Green Power Espana SL   **(1)**
Ribera del Loira 60 3D, 28042, Madrid, Spain
Eletric Power Generation Services
N.A.I.C.S.: 221118

Subsidiary (Domestic):

Compania Eolica Tierras Altas SA   **(2)**
C/ Diputacion 1, 42002, Soria, Spain
Tel.: (34) 975213704
Web Site: https://www.cetasaeolica.com
Renewable Energy Services
N.A.I.C.S.: 221118

Enel Green Power Guatemala SA   **(1)**
Diagonal 6 10-65 Zona 10 Centro Gerencial Las Margaritas Torre I, Nivel 8 Oficina 801, 01010, Guatemala, Guatemala
Tel.: (502) 23277000
Eletric Power Generation Services
N.A.I.C.S.: 221118

Enel Green Power Hellas SA   **(1)**
4 Gravias Str Maroussi, 15125, Athens, Greece   **(50%)**
Tel.: (30) 2111808500
Eletric Power Generation Services
N.A.I.C.S.: 221118

Enel Green Power Mexico S de RL de Cv   **(1)**
Av National Army No 769 Tower B Floor 17 Col, Granada, 11520, Mexico, Mexico
Tel.: (52) 5511014900
Eletric Power Generation Services
N.A.I.C.S.: 221118

Enel Green Power Panama SA   **(1)**
Costa del Este Avenida Felipe Motta PH GMT piso 3, Panama, Panama
Tel.: (507) 8316000
Eletric Power Generation Services
N.A.I.C.S.: 221118

Enel Green Power Peru SA   **(1)**
Forest Walk No 500 Borja's dream, San Miguel, Lima, Peru
Tel.: (51) 12156374
Eletric Power Generation Services
N.A.I.C.S.: 221118

Enel Green Power Rome Villoresi Srl   **(1)**
Viale Regina Margherita 125, Rome, Italy
Tel.: (39) 0683051
Eletric Power Generation Services
N.A.I.C.S.: 221118

Enel Green Power S.p.A.   **(1)**
Viale Regina Margherita 125, 00198, Rome, Italy   **(68.29%)**
Tel.: (39) 0683051
Web Site: http://www.enelgreenpower.com
Rev.: $3,278,738,120
Assets: $22,294,548,080
Liabilities: $11,808,248,480
Net Worth: $10,486,299,600
Earnings: $287,474,880
Emp.: 3,599
Fiscal Year-end: 12/31/2015
Renewable Energy Generation Services
N.A.I.C.S.: 221111
Antonio Cammisecra *(CEO)*

Subsidiary (Non-US):

Enel Brasil Participacoes Ltda   **(2)**
Praca Leoni Ramos andar bloco 2, 20090 010, Niteroi, Brazil
Tel.: (55) 21 2206 5600
Sales Range: $150-199.9 Million
Emp.: 20
Electric Power Generation & Distribution Services
N.A.I.C.S.: 221118
Nicola Cotugno *(Country Mgr)*

Enel Green Power France SAS   **(2)**
Le Bonnel - 20 rue de la Villette, 39003, Lyon, France
Tel.: (33) 4 78 92 68 70

Web Site: http://www.enelgreenpower.com
Sales Range: $50-74.9 Million
Emp.: 5
Wind Farm Electric Power Generation Services
N.A.I.C.S.: 221118

Subsidiary (US):

Enel Green Power North America, Inc.   **(2)**
100 Brickstone Sq Ste 300, Andover, MA 01810
Tel.: (978) 681-1900
Sales Range: $75-99.9 Million
Emp.: 260
Renewable Energy Plants Owner & Operator
N.A.I.C.S.: 221118
Lisa Zarek *(Treas, VP & Controller)*

Subsidiary (Domestic):

Demand Energy Networks, Inc.   **(3)**
23403 E Mission Ave Ste 111, Liberty Lake, WA 99019-7553
Tel.: (509) 255-7150
Web Site:
  http://www.demandenergynetworks.com
Software Developer for Energy Market
N.A.I.C.S.: 513210
Doug Staker *(VP- Sls-Global)*

Subsidiary (Non-US):

Enel Green Power Canada, Inc.   **(3)**
1110-1255 Robert-Bourassa Blvd, Montreal, H3B 3W7, QC, Canada
Tel.: (514) 397-0463
Web Site: http://www.enelgreenpower.com
Eletric Power Generation Services
N.A.I.C.S.: 221118

Subsidiary (Domestic):

Newind Group Inc.   **(4)**
1255 Rue University Bureau 1204, Montreal, H3B 3W9, QC, Canada
Tel.: (514) 397-0463
Web Site: http://www.enel.com
Eletric Power Generation Services
N.A.I.C.S.: 221118

Subsidiary (Non-US):

Enel X North America, Inc.   **(3)**
Tel.: (617) 224-9900
Web Site: http://www.enelx.com
Cloud-based Energy Intelligence Software Services
N.A.I.C.S.: 513210
Michael I. Storch *(Pres & CEO)*

Subsidiary (Non-US):

EnerNOC GmbH   **(4)**
Berliner Allee 65, 64295, Darmstadt, Germany
Tel.: (49) 61513975475
Web Site: http://www.enernoc.com
Energy Management Services
N.A.I.C.S.: 238210

EnerNOC Korea Limited   **(4)**
7F AIA Tower Tongil-ro 2-gil, Jung-gu, Seoul, Korea (South)
Tel.: (82) 2 6190 5801
Web Site: http://www.enernoc.com
Energy Management Services
N.A.I.C.S.: 238210

EnerNOC New Zealand Limited   **(4)**
15-17 Murphy Street Level 8, Thorndon, Wellington, NZ 6011, New Zealand
Tel.: (64) 49097546
Web Site: http://www.enernoc.com
Energy Consulting Services
N.A.I.C.S.: 541690

EnerNOC Pty Ltd   **(4)**
535 Bourke Street Level 18, Melbourne, 3000, VIC, Australia
Tel.: (61) 386435900
Web Site: http://www.enernoc.com
Energy Management & Consulting Services
N.A.I.C.S.: 541690

EnerNOC UK Limited   **(4)**
360-364 City Road, London, EC1V 2PY, United Kingdom
Tel.: (44) 2078333353

Web Site: http://www.enernoc.com
Energy Management Services
N.A.I.C.S.: 238210

Entelios AG   **(4)**
Claudius-Keller Str 3c, 81669, Munich, Germany
Tel.: (49) 895529968
Energy Management Services
N.A.I.C.S.: 238210

Subsidiary (Non-US):

Enel Green Power Romania SRL   **(2)**
62-64 Strada Buzesti Et 6 Sector 1, Bucharest, 427206, Romania
Tel.: (40) 263350298
Sales Range: $50-74.9 Million
Emp.: 50
Hydroelectric Power Generation Services
N.A.I.C.S.: 221111
Francesco Lazzeri *(Gen Mgr)*

Energias de Graus SL   **(2)**
Argualas street 1 Edificio Torreon 1 Planta, Barcelona, 50012, Spain
Tel.: (34) 976760011
Web Site: http://www.enelgreenpower.com
Emp.: 20
Hydroelectric Plants
N.A.I.C.S.: 221111

Generadora de Occidente Ltda   **(2)**
A Diagonal 6 10-65 Zona 10, Centro Gerencial Las Margaritas Torre 1 Nivel 8, Guatemala, 1010, Guatemala
Tel.: (502) 23277000
Web Site: http://www.enelgreenpower.com
Sales Range: $75-99.9 Million
Emp.: 12
Eletric Power Generation Services
N.A.I.C.S.: 221118

Enel Guatemala SA   **(1)**
Diagonal 6 10-65 Zona 10 Centro Gerencial Las Margaritas, Torre I Nivel 8 Oficina 801, 1010, Guatemala, Guatemala
Tel.: (502) 23277000
Sales Range: $50-74.9 Million
Emp.: 4
Hydroelectric Power Generation Services
N.A.I.C.S.: 221111

Enel Iberoamerica SL   **(1)**
Ribera del Loira 60, 28042, Madrid, Spain   **(100%)**
Tel.: (34) 912131000
Holding Company
N.A.I.C.S.: 551112

Subsidiary (Domestic):

Enel Latinoamerica SA   **(2)**
Ribera del Loira 60, 28042, Madrid, Spain   **(100%)**
Tel.: (34) 912 13 10 00
Holding Company
N.A.I.C.S.: 551112

Enel M@P Srl   **(1)**
Via Ombrone 2, 198, Rome, Italy
Tel.: (39) 0683051
Eletric Power Generation Services
N.A.I.C.S.: 221118

Enel Panama SA   **(1)**
Calle 50 Edificio Dresdner Tower Floor 7 & 9, Panama, 507, Panama
Tel.: (507) 2693555
Web Site: http://www.mauad.com.pa
Emp.: 10
Eletric Power Generation Services
N.A.I.C.S.: 221118
Jose Alberto *(Gen Mgr)*

Enel Stillwater LLC   **(1)**
4785 Lawrence Ln, Fallon, NV 89406
Tel.: (775) 423-0322
Hydroelectric Power Generation Services
N.A.I.C.S.: 221111

Enel Washington DC Ltd.   **(1)**
816 Connecticut Ave NW Ste 600, Washington, DC 20006
Tel.: (202) 609-7798
Fuel Electric Power Generation Services
N.A.I.C.S.: 221112

Enel X Argentina SAU   **(1)**
190 oficina 303-Ciudad Autonoma de, Buenos Aires, C1076AAD, Argentina

Enel S.p.A.—(Continued)
Tel.: (54) 1140000000
Web Site: http://www.enelx.com
Electric Power Generation Services
N.A.I.C.S.: 221118

Enel X Australia (Pty) Ltd. (1)
Level 34 140 William Street, Melbourne,
3000, VIC, Australia
Tel.: (61) 386435900
Power Generation Services
N.A.I.C.S.: 221118

Enel X Brasil SA (1)
United Nations Avenue 23rd Floor - Suite
234 Tower B1, Aroeira - Vila Gertrudes, São
Paulo, 14401, SP, Brazil
Tel.: (55) 982226125
N.A.I.C.S.: 221114

Enel X Japan KK (1)
4-3 Nihonbashi - Muromachi 4 Chome,
Chuo-ku, Tokyo, 103-0022, Japan
Tel.: (81) 362627272
Power Generation Services
N.A.I.C.S.: 221118

Enel X Korea Limited (1)
Junggu Tongilro 2-Gil AIA Tower 7, Seoul,
Korea (South)
Tel.: (82) 261905801
N.A.I.C.S.: 221114

Enel X Way Romania S.r.l. (1)
30 Mircea Voda Bd Room 411 4th floor, Bu-
charest, Romania
Tel.: (40) 372115694
Software Development Services
N.A.I.C.S.: 541519

Enel de Costa Rica SA (1)
200 Mts Sur del Parqueo de CineMark Mul-
tiplaza Escazu, Edificio Terraforte 2do Piso,
San Jose, 1631255, San Jose, Costa Rica
Tel.: (506) 2201 4500
Sales Range: $50-74.9 Million
Emp.: 6
Electric Power Generation Services
N.A.I.C.S.: 221118
Joseph Benavidez *(Gen Mgr)*

**Energia Ceuta XXI Comercializadora
de Referencia SA** (1)
Calle Gral Serrano Orive 19, 51001, Ceuta,
Spain
Tel.: (34) 900106004
Web Site: https://www.energiaceutaxxi.com
Electric Power Distribution Services
N.A.I.C.S.: 221122

**Energia Nueva Energia Limpia
Mexico Srl de Cv** (1)
Miguel De Cervantes Saavedra No 193 4th
Fl Office 901, Mexico, 11520, Mexico
Tel.: (52) 5552809361
Web Site: http://www.enelgreenpower.com
Sales Range: $50-74.9 Million
Emp.: 10
Electric Power Generation Services
N.A.I.C.S.: 221118

**Energie Electrique de Tahaddart
SA** (1)
25 Centre Ibn Batouta Avenue Youssef Ben
Tachine Stage 3 Bureau B3 10, 90013,
Tangiers, Morocco
Tel.: (212) 539343400
Web Site: https://eet.ma
Electric Power Distribution Services
N.A.I.C.S.: 221122

**Eolflor - Producao de Energia Eo lica
Lda** (1)
Avenida Sidonio Pais 379 - 2 Andar, Porto,
4100-468, Portugal
Tel.: (351) 226080180
Web Site: http://www.enel.com
Sales Range: $50-74.9 Million
Emp.: 3
Wind Farm Electric Power Generation Ser-
vices
N.A.I.C.S.: 221118

Fermicaise SA de Cv (1)
Reforma No 873 San Nicolas Tolentino
Iztapalapa, Mexico, 9850, Mexico
Tel.: (52) 5556322235
Electric Power Generation Services
N.A.I.C.S.: 221118

GNL Chile S.A. (1)
Cerro Colorado 5240 Torre I Oficina 1003,
Las Condes, Chile
Tel.: (56) 228928000
Web Site: https://www.gnlchile.com
Natural Gas Distr
N.A.I.C.S.: 486210

Gas Atacama Chile SA (1)
Santa Rosa 76, Santiago, Chile
Tel.: (56) 228565300
Gas Pipeline Services
N.A.I.C.S.: 541990

**Gas y Electricidad Generacion
SAU** (1)
Calle Sant Joan De Deu 1, Palma de Mal-
lorca, 7007, Spain
Tel.: (34) 971467711
Electric Power Generation Services
N.A.I.C.S.: 221118

Genability, Inc. (1)
455 Market St Ste 650, San Francisco, CA
94105
Tel.: (415) 371-0136
Web Site: http://www.genability.com
Software Program Services
N.A.I.C.S.: 541511
Jason Riley *(Founder & CEO)*

Gesa Gas SAU (1)
Calle Juan Maragall 16, 07006, Palma de
Mallorca, Spain
Tel.: (34) 971 467 711
Natural Gas Distr
N.A.I.C.S.: 221210

**Hidroelectricidad del Pacifico Srl de
Cv** (1)
Boulevard Miguel De Cervantes Saavedra
No 193 901 Granada, Miguel Hidalgo,
Mexico, 11520, Mexico
Tel.: (52) 5552809361
Sales Range: $75-99.9 Million
Emp.: 6
Electric Power Generation Services
N.A.I.C.S.: 221118

High Noon Solar Project LLC (1)
415 N M St, Poynette, WI 53955
Tel.: (608) 444-7815
Web Site:
https://highnoonsolarenergycenter.com
Solar Power Generation Services
N.A.I.C.S.: 221114

Hydro Energies Corporation (1)
Deweys Mills Rd, Quechee, VT 05059
Tel.: (802) 295-1490
Electric Power Distribution Services
N.A.I.C.S.: 221122

**Hydrogen Park Marghera Per
L'idrogeno Scrl** (1)
Via Delle Industrie 19, Marghera, 30175,
Venice, Italy
Tel.: (39) 041 5499152
Web Site: http://www.hydrogenpark.com
Hydroelectric Power Generation & Distribu-
tion Services
N.A.I.C.S.: 221111
Silvia Michela Castronovo *(Pres)*

Hydromac Energy BV (1)
Herengracht 471, Amsterdam, 1017 BS,
Netherlands
Tel.: (31) 205218777
Web Site: http://www.enel.it
Emp.: 2
Investment Management Service
N.A.I.C.S.: 523999
Ernesto Dingiaco *(CEO)*

Subsidiary (Non-US):

Enel Latin America (Chile) Ltda. (2)
Rosario Norte 530, Las Condes, Santiago,
Chile
Tel.: (56) 2 8999200
Electric Power Generation Services
N.A.I.C.S.: 221118

Ifx Networks Argentina Srl (1)
498 Del Libertador Avenue floor 26 Torre
Prourban Ciudad de, Buenos Aires, Argen-
tina
Tel.: (54) 1150312400
Telecommunication Servicesb
N.A.I.C.S.: 517810

Ifx Networks Chile SA (1)
92 El Bosque Central Avenue Floor 10,
Santiago, Chile
Tel.: (56) 225894500
Telecommunication Servicesb
N.A.I.C.S.: 517810

**Inmobiliaria Manso de Velasco
Ltda** (1)
Calle Miraflores 383 Fl 29, Piso, Santiago,
8320149, Chile
Tel.: (56) 2 378 4700
Sales Range: $25-49.9 Million
Emp.: 34
Real Estate Development Services
N.A.I.C.S.: 531390
Andres Salas *(Gen Mgr)*

**Inspectores y Consultores Ibercal
S.L.U.** (1)
Ctra Ugarte Galindo s/n, Trapagaran, Bi-
zkaia, Spain
Tel.: (34) 944418954
Web Site: https://ibercalconsultores.es
Electronic Equipment Mfr & Distr
N.A.I.C.S.: 334419

Minas Gargallo SL (1)
Calle Ribera Del Loira 60, Madrid, 28042,
Spain
Tel.: (34) 912131165
Electric Power Generation Services
N.A.I.C.S.: 221118

Mooney S.p.A. (1)
Via Privata Nino Bonnet 6/A, 20154, Milan,
Italy
Tel.: (39) 0291673001
Web Site: https://mooneygroup.it
Investment Finance Services
N.A.I.C.S.: 523999

Mooney Servizi S.p.A. (1)
Via Privata Nino Bonnet 6/A, 20154, Milan,
Italy
Tel.: (39) 0291673001
Investment Finance Services
N.A.I.C.S.: 523999

Negocios y Telefonia Nedetel SA (1)
Av Perimetral Km 4 and Av Francisco de
Orellana, Guayaquil, Ecuador
Tel.: (593) 46008192
Web Site: https://www.nedetel.net
Telecommunication Servicesb
N.A.I.C.S.: 517810

Northwest Hydro Inc. (1)
31 Cougar Creek Rd, Stevenson, WA
98648
Tel.: (509) 427-5081
Electric Power Generation Services
N.A.I.C.S.: 221118

Nuove Energie Srl (1)
Via della Meccanica 23/25, 36100, Vicenza,
Italy
Tel.: (39) 0444963453
Web Site: https://www.nuoveenergie.com
Emp.: 2
Micro Filter Mfr
N.A.I.C.S.: 333413

**Ottauquechee Hydro Company
Inc.** (1)
One Tech Dr Ste 220, Andover, MA 01810
Tel.: (978) 681-1900
Hydroelectric Power Generation Services
N.A.I.C.S.: 221118

**Oyster Bay Wind Farm (RF) (Pty.)
Ltd.** (1)
102 Rivonia Road Tower 2 EY Building, Jo-
hannesburg, South Africa
Tel.: (27) 103440200
Solar Energy Services
N.A.I.C.S.: 562213

Parque Eolico Pampa SA (1)
Pampa Energia Building Maipu 1,
C1084ABA, Buenos Aires, Argentina
Tel.: (54) 1143446000
Web Site: https://ri.pampaenergia.com
Electric Power Generation Services
N.A.I.C.S.: 221116

Planta Eolica Europea SA (1)
Calle Balbino Marron 1, Seville, 41018,
Spain
Tel.: (34) 954171101

Electric Power Generation Services
N.A.I.C.S.: 221118

**Proyectos Eolicos Valencianos
SA** (1)
Plaza America 2, 46004, Valencia, Spain
Tel.: (34) 963 16 21 42
Electric Power Generation Services
N.A.I.C.S.: 221118

Reaktortest Sro (1)
Frantiskanska 22, 917 01, Trnava, Slovakia
Tel.: (421) 335521030
Web Site: https://www.reaktortest.sk
Technical Control & Consultancy Services
N.A.I.C.S.: 541690
Vladimir Chmelik *(Mgr)*

Roadrunner Storage LLC (1)
170 S Roadrunner Pkwy, Las Cruces, NM
88011
Tel.: (575) 936-2949
Web Site:
https://www.roadrunnerselfstoragelc.com
Self Storage Services
N.A.I.C.S.: 493110

**Sealve - Sociedade Electrica de Al-
vaiazere SA** (1)
Avenida Sidonio Pais 379 2, 4100-468,
Porto, Portugal
Tel.: (351) 226080180
Emp.: 25
Electric Power Generation Services
N.A.I.C.S.: 221118
Rue Neves *(Gen Mgr)*

Servizio Elettrico Nazionale SpA (1)
Piazza Venezia 11, 00187, Rome, Italy
Tel.: (39) 0230172011
Web Site:
https://www.servizioelettriconazionale.it
Electricity Bill Services
N.A.I.C.S.: 926130

Smoky Hills Wind Farm LLC (1)
223 N Hwy 14, Lincoln, KS 67455
Tel.: (978) 681-1900
Electric Power Generation Services
N.A.I.C.S.: 221118

Smoky Hills Wind Project II LLC (1)
16105 W 113th St Ste 105, Shawnee Mission, KS 66219-2307
Tel.: (978) 681-1900
Wind Farm Electric Power Generation Services
N.A.I.C.S.: 221118

Snyder Wind Farm LLC (1)
1 Tech Dr Ste 220, Andover, MA 01810-
2452
Tel.: (978) 296-6827
Wind Farm Electric Power Generation Services
N.A.I.C.S.: 221118

Suministro de Luz y Fuerza SL (1)
Rambla D Anselm Viola 7, 17257, Torroella
de Montgri, Spain
Tel.: (34) 972 75 92 56
Electric Power Distribution Services
N.A.I.C.S.: 221122

Tecnatom France S.A.S. (1)
Pavb Rue des Artisans, 71240, Saint Loup
de Varennes, France
Tel.: (33) 385900750
Petrochemical Inspection Engineering Ser-
vices
N.A.I.C.S.: 926150

Tecnatom S.A. (1)
Avda Montes de Oca 1, San Sebastian de
los Reyes, 28703, Madrid, Spain
Tel.: (34) 916598600
Web Site: https://www.tecnatom.es
Inspection Equipment Mfr & Distr
N.A.I.C.S.: 334519

Teploprogress OJSC (1)
ul Fryazevskaya 10, 111 396, Moscow,
Russia
Tel.: (7) 4953032981
Heat Exchange Block Mfr
N.A.I.C.S.: 332410

Termica Colleferro SpA (1)
Via Ariana Km 5 2, Colleferro, 00034,
Rome, Italy
Tel.: (39) 0697710901

Web Site: https://www.termicacolleferro.it
Thermal Power Services
N.A.I.C.S.: 541380

**Termoelectrica Jose de San Martin
S.A.** (1)
Av Cacique Mangore 12580, Timbues Pcia,
Santa Fe, Argentina
Tel.: (54) 3476495700
Web Site: https://www.tsm.com.ar
Electricity Power Plants Services
N.A.I.C.S.: 562213

Ufinet Brasil SA (1)
Alameda Araguaia 3972 Alphaville Indus-
trial, Baruori, 06455-000, Sao Paulo, Brazil
Tel.: (55) 1130808900
Telecommunication Servicesb
N.A.I.C.S.: 517810

Ufinet Colombia SA (1)
Bogota Calle 72 No 5 - 83 Of 1202, Bogota,
Colombia
Tel.: (57) 6017434200
Telecommunication Servicesb
N.A.I.C.S.: 517810

Ufinet FTTH Guatemala Ltda. (1)
Avenida Reforma 6-39 Zona 10 C Corpora-
tivo Guayacan Oficina 701, Guatemala,
Guatemala
Tel.: (502) 23173300
Telecommunication Servicesb
N.A.I.C.S.: 517810

Ufinet Latam SLU (1)
Conde de Aranda 5 4D, 28001, Madrid,
Spain
Tel.: (34) 910888570
Telecommunication Servicesb
N.A.I.C.S.: 517810

Subsidiary (US):

Ifx Networks LLC (2)
520 S Dixie Hwy, Hallandale, FL 33009
Telecommunication Servicesb
N.A.I.C.S.: 517810

Subsidiary (Non-US):

Rsl Telecom Panama SA (2)
Ultima Park Guachipelin, San Jose, Costa
Rica
Tel.: (506) 40710388
Web Site: http://www.rsltelecom.com
Submarine Cable Telecommunication Ser-
vices
N.A.I.C.S.: 517111
Mario A. Montero (Gen Mgr)

Ufinet Argentina SA (1)
Av Del Libertador No 498 Piso 26 Torre
Prourban Ciudad de, Buenos Aires, Argen-
tina
Tel.: (54) 1139867400
Telecommunication Servicesb
N.A.I.C.S.: 517810

Ufinet Chile SA (2)
Tel.: (56) 232510160
Telecommunication Servicesb
N.A.I.C.S.: 517810

Ufinet Costa Rica SA (2)
Tel.: (506) 41070300
Telecommunication Servicesb
N.A.I.C.S.: 517810
Laura Perez Lopera (Acct Mgr-Global)

Ufinet Ecuador Ufiec SA (2)
Tel.: (593) 324016300
Telecommunication Servicesb
N.A.I.C.S.: 517810

Ufinet El Salvador SA de Cv (2)
Edificio Redes 251 Colonia San Benito
Calle Loma Linda, San Salvador, El Salva-
dor
Tel.: (503) 22739552
Telecommunication Servicesb
N.A.I.C.S.: 517810

Ufinet Guatemala SA (2)
Avenida Reforma 6-39 Zona 10 C Corpora-
tivo Guayacan Oficina 701, Guatemala,
Guatemala
Tel.: (502) 23173300
Telecommunication Servicesb
N.A.I.C.S.: 517810

Ufinet Honduras SA (2)

Edificio Torre Morazan 1 Nivel 15 Local
11504-6 Boulevard Morazan, Tegucigalpa,
Honduras
Tel.: (504) 22710313
Telecommunication Servicesb
N.A.I.C.S.: 517810

Ufinet Mexico S de RL de Cv (2)
Av Insurgentes Sur 730 Piso 2 Oficina 206,
Colonia Del Valle Alcaldia Benito Juarez,
03104, Mexico, Mexico
Tel.: (52) 5576986888
Telecommunication Servicesb
N.A.I.C.S.: 517810

Ufinet Nicaragua SA (2)
Colonial Los Robles 39 Semaforos Monte
de los Olivos 1/2 c al sur, 1/2 c este 1c al
sur, Managua, Nicaragua
Tel.: (505) 22744706
Telecommunication Servicesb
N.A.I.C.S.: 517810

Ufinet Panama SA (2)
Urb Obarrio Ave Ricardo Arango Edif Victo-
ria Plaza 1er Piso, Panama, Panama
Tel.: (507) 3760100
Telecommunication Servicesb
N.A.I.C.S.: 517810
Jose Quintas Garcia (Country Mgr)

Ufinet Paraguay SA (2)
Av Aviadores del Chaco 2581 c/ Tte Vicente
Oddone Edif Skypark, Torre 1 Piso 18,
Asuncion, Paraguay
Tel.: (595) 216587000
Telecommunication Servicesb
N.A.I.C.S.: 517810

Ufinet Peru SAC (2)
Telecommunication Servicesb
N.A.I.C.S.: 517810
Camargo Edwin (Acct Mgr)

**Union Electrica de Canarias Genera-
cion SAU** (1)
Calle Albareda Plaza Woermann 38, Las
Palmas, 35008, Spain
Tel.: (34) 928309900
Eletric Power Generation Services
N.A.I.C.S.: 221118

WP Bulgaria 12 EOOD (1)
R-N Triaditsa Distr Floor 5 2 Pl Pozitano,
Sofia, 1000, Bulgaria
Tel.: (359) 29032300
Electric Power Plant Construction & Mainte-
nance Services
N.A.I.C.S.: 237130

**Water & INDUSTRIAL Services Com-
pany SpA** (1)
Jiulane 5, Monza, 20052, Italy
Tel.: (39) 0392096411
Sales Range: $75-99.9 Million
Emp.: 23
Sewage Treatment Services
N.A.I.C.S.: 221320

ENENSYS TECHNOLOGIES SA
4A Rue des Buttes CS37734, 35577,
Cesson Sevigne, 35577, France
Tel.: (33) 170725170
Web Site: https://www.enensys.com
Year Founded: 2004
ALNN6—(EUR)
Sales Range: Less than $1 Million
Broadcasting Equipment Mfr
N.A.I.C.S.: 334220
Regis Le Roux (Founder, Pres &
CEO)

ENENTO GROUP PLC
Hermannin Rantatie 6, PO Box 16,
FI-00580, Helsinki, Finland
Tel.: (358) 102707100
Web Site: https://enento.com
Year Founded: 1905
ENENTO—(OMX)
Rev.: $15,691,084
Assets: $46,743,938
Liabilities: $19,126,790
Net Worth: $27,617,148
Earnings: $1,625,502
Emp.: 428
Fiscal Year-end: 12/31/22

Business & Consumer Information
Services
N.A.I.C.S.: 541611
Heikki Koivula (Dir-Risk Decisions)

Subsidiaries:

Emaileri Oy (1)
Yliopistonkatu 11 a A 8, 20100, Turku, Fin-
land
Tel.: (358) 207809220
Web Site: https://www.emaileri.com
Advertising Services
N.A.I.C.S.: 541890

Proff AB (1)
Stromgatan 2, Kalmar, 392 32, Sweden
Tel.: (46) 770111335
Web Site: https://insikt.proff.se
Advertising Services
N.A.I.C.S.: 541890

Proff AS (1)
Olaf Helsets Vei 5, Oslo, Norway
Tel.: (47) 81544428
Web Site: http://www.proff.no
Book Publishers
N.A.I.C.S.: 513130

Proff ApS (1)
Sct Mathias Gade 38, 8800, Viborg, Den-
mark
Tel.: (45) 89875112
Web Site: https://indsigt.proff.dk
Advertising Services
N.A.I.C.S.: 541890

Suomen Asiakastieto Oy (1)
Hermanni rantatie 6, PO Box 16, 00580,
Helsinki, Finland
Tel.: (358) 102707200
Web Site: https://www.asiakastieto.fi
Financial Services
N.A.I.C.S.: 523999

ENEOS HOLDINGS, INC.
1-1-2 Otemachi, Chiyoda-ku, Tokyo,
100-8162, Japan
Tel.: (81) 120568704   JP
Web Site: https://www.hd.eneos.co.jp
Year Founded: 2010
JXHGF—(OTCIQ)
Rev.: $98,246,366,346
Assets: $71,870,029,994
Liabilities: $45,609,256,648
Net Worth: $26,260,773,345
Earnings: $2,449,533,022
Emp.: 44,617
Fiscal Year-end: 03/31/24
Holding Company; Oil & Gas Explo-
ration, Extraction & Refining; Metal
Mining & Manufacturing
N.A.I.C.S.: 551112
Someya Yoshiyuki (Exec Officer, Sr
VP & Gen Mgr-Procurement Dept)

Subsidiaries:

Abu Dhabi Oil Co., Ltd. (1)
9th Floor Hamamatsucho Building 1-1
1-Chome, Shibaura Minato-ku, Tokyo, 105-
0023, Japan
Tel.: (81) 97126661100
Web Site: http://adocauh.cts-co.net
Emp.: 194
Oil Exploration Services
N.A.I.C.S.: 213111
Hiroshi Hosoi (Chm)

Dai Nippon Construction (1)
6-16-6 Nishi-Shinjuku, Shinjuku-ku, Tokyo,
160-0023, Japan   **(79.5%)**
Tel.: (81) 35 326 3932
Web Site: https://www.dnc.co.jp
Sales Range: $300-349.9 Million
Emp.: 944
Civil Engineering & Building Construction
Subcontractor
N.A.I.C.S.: 238990
Baba Yoshio (Pres & CEO)

**ENEOS Career Support
Corporation** (1)
3-4-2 Marunouchi Shin-Nisseki Building 6th
Floor, Chiyoda-ku, Tokyo, 100-0005, Japan
Tel.: (81) 368035500
Web Site: http://www.cs.eneos.co.jp

Staffing Services
N.A.I.C.S.: 561320

ENEOS Celltech Co., Ltd. (1)
1-1-1 Sakada Oizumimachi Sanyodenkito-
kyoseisakusho, Oura, 370-0596, Gunma,
Japan
Tel.: (81) 276 61 9459
Web Site: http://www.eneoscelltech.co.jp
Fuel Cell System Mfr
N.A.I.C.S.: 335999

ENEOS Corporation (1)
1-1-2 Otemachi, Chiyoda-ku, Tokyo, 100-
8162, Japan
Tel.: (81) 362577174
Web Site: https://www.eneos.co.jp
N.A.I.C.S.: 325110

ENEOS Globe Corporation (1)
15F Sanno Park Tower 11-1 2-chome Na-
gatacho, Chiyoda-ku, Tokyo, 100-6115, Ja-
pan
Tel.: (81) 352539330
Web Site: http://www.eneos-globe.co.jp
Emp.: 300
Petroleum Product Distr
N.A.I.C.S.: 424720
Seisuke Iwai (Pres)

**ENEOS Insurance Service
Corporation** (1)
6th Floor of Shin-Nisseki Building 3-4-2,
Marunouchi Chiyoda-ku, Tokyo, 100-8340,
Japan
Tel.: (81) 368038120
Web Site: http://www.is.eneos.co.jp
Insurance Services
N.A.I.C.S.: 524210

ENEOS Real Estate Corporation (1)
1-1-8 Sakuragicho, Naka-ku, Yokohama,
231-0062, Kanagawa, Japan
Tel.: (81) 456832800
Web Site: https://www.re.eneos.co.jp
N.A.I.C.S.: 531311
Itsuo Niwa (Chm)

**ENEOS Trading Company
Limited** (1)
1-3-13 12th Floor of Tokyo Building Nihon-
bashi Building, Nihonbashi Chuo- ku, Tokyo,
103-0027, Japan
Tel.: (81) 362622500
Web Site: http://www.etr.eneos.co.jp
Natural Gas Producer
N.A.I.C.S.: 221210

ENEOS Wing Corporation (1)
3-6-1 Sakae, Naka-ku, Nagoya, 460-0008,
Japan
Tel.: (81) 522693210
Web Site: http://www.eneos-wing.co.jp
Petroleum Product Distr
N.A.I.C.S.: 424720

JX Advanced Metals Corporation (1)
The Okura Prestige Tower 10-4 Toranomon
2-chome, Minato-ku, Tokyo, 105-8417,
Japan   **(100%)**
Tel.: (81) 364336000
Web Site: https://www.jx-nmm.com
Sales Range: $700-749.9 Million
Emp.: 1,500
Non-Ferrous Metal Mining, Smelting, Refin-
ing, Product Fabrication & Recycling Ser-
vices
N.A.I.C.S.: 331410
Shigeru Oi (Pres & CEO)

Joint Venture (Non-US):

BioSigma S.A. (2)
Carretera General San Martin 16 500 Lote
#106 Colina Parque, Industrial Los Liberta-
dores, Santiago, Chile
Tel.: (56) 24379030
Web Site: http://www.biosigma.cl
Sales Range: $25-49.9 Million
Emp.: 70
Mining Proteomics & Bioinformatics Re-
search & Development; Owned by Corpora-
cion Nacional del Cobre de Chile & by JX
Holdings, Inc.
N.A.I.C.S.: 541715

Subsidiary (Non-US):

Compania Minera Quechua S.A. (2)
Avenida Amador Merino Reyna 267 Edificio
Parque Plaza, Piso 12 Oficina 1201, San

ENEOS Holdings, Inc.—(Continued)

Isidro, 27, Lima, Peru **(100%)**
Tel.: (51) 12028484
Emp.: 20
Copper Mining
N.A.I.C.S.: 212230

Gould Electronics GmbH **(2)**
Hauptstrasse 3, D-79356, Eichstetten, Germany
Tel.: (49) 7663620
Web Site: http://www.gould.com
Sales Range: $25-49.9 Million
Emp.: 180
Copper Foil Mfr & Marketer
N.A.I.C.S.: 331420

Subsidiary (US):

**High Performance Copper Foil,
Inc.** **(3)**
2555 W Fairview St Ste 103, Chandler, AZ 85214
Tel.: (480) 223-0870
Web Site: http://www.gould.com
Sales Range: $50-74.9 Million
Emp.: 2
Copper Foil Mfr
N.A.I.C.S.: 331420
Rolland D. Savage *(Dir-Sls)*

Subsidiary (Non-US):

**Nippon Mining & Metals (Suzhou)
Co., Ltd.** **(3)**
536 Fengting Road Weiting Town, Suzhou Industrial Park, Suzhou, Jiangsu, China **(100%)**
Tel.: (86) 51262750188
Rolled & Fabricated Metal Products Mfr
N.A.I.C.S.: 332999

Subsidiary (Non-US):

JX Metals Philippines, Inc. **(2)**
117 E Science Ave, Laguna Technopark Phase III, Binan, 4024, Laguna, Philippines **(100%)**
Tel.: (63) 495411606
Sales Range: $100-124.9 Million
Emp.: 500
Electro-Deposited & Treated Copper Foils Mfr & Distr
N.A.I.C.S.: 331420
Masafumi Ishii *(Pres)*

Subsidiary (Domestic):

JX Metals Trading Co., Ltd. **(2)**
Sumitomo Fudosan Yotsuya Building 6F 13-4 Araki-cho, Shinjuku-ku, Tokyo, 160-0007, Japan **(100%)**
Tel.: (81) 35 368 3150
Web Site: https://www.jx-kinzokushoji.com
Emp.: 291
Non-Ferrous Metals, Fabricated Metal Products & Chemical Products Wholesale Trade Distr
N.A.I.C.S.: 425120
Takashi Ando *(Mng Dir)*

JX Nippon Coil Center Co., Ltd. **(2)**
3 Kurami Samukawa-machi, Kouza-gun, Koza, 253-0101, Kawagawa, Japan **(100%)**
Tel.: (81) 46 775 7005
Web Site: http://www.nikko-coil.co.jp
Emp.: 200
Copper, Copper Alloy & Steel Products Mfr & Distr
N.A.I.C.S.: 334416
Ryochi Nobuyoshi *(Gen Mgr)*

**JX Nippon Environmental Services
Co., Ltd.** **(2)**
3453 Miyata-cho, Hitachi, 317-0055, Ibaraki, Japan **(100%)**
Tel.: (81) 29 421 1711
Web Site: https://jx-kinzokukankyo.co.jp
Emp.: 71
Recycling & Environmental Services
N.A.I.C.S.: 562920

JX Nippon Exploration & Development Co., Ltd. **(2)**
1-9 Kanda nishikicho, Chiyoda-ku, Tokyo, 101-0054, Japan **(100%)**
Tel.: (81) 35 577 4916
Web Site: https://www.tankai.co.jp

Emp.: 90
Specialty Geologic & Environmental Engineering Services
N.A.I.C.S.: 541360

Subsidiary (Domestic):

JX Nippon Drilling Co., Ltd. **(3)**
7-10 Toranomon 2-chome, Minato-ku, Tokyo, 105-0001, Japan
Tel.: (81) 335037788
Oil Well Drilling Services
N.A.I.C.S.: 213111

Subsidiary (Domestic):

JX Nippon Foundry Co., Ltd. **(2)**
187-4 Usuba Hanakawa-cho, Kitaibaraki, 319-1535Kitaiba, Ibaraki, Japan **(100%)**
Tel.: (81) 293427775
Copper & Other Non-Ferrous Metal Foundry Operator
N.A.I.C.S.: 331529

Subsidiary (Non-US):

JX Nippon Mining & Metals Singapore Pte. Ltd. **(2)**
16 Raffles Quay 33-04 Hong Leong Bldg, Singapore, 048581, Singapore **(100%)**
Tel.: (65) 62255413
Electronic Material Distr
N.A.I.C.S.: 423690
Toshihiko Yoneda *(Gen Mgr)*

Subsidiary (US):

**JX Nippon Mining & Metals USA,
Inc.** **(2)**
125 N Price Rd, Chandler, AZ 85224-4912
Tel.: (480) 732-9857
Web Site: http://www.nikkometals.com
Sales Range: $25-49.9 Million
Emp.: 100
Compound Semiconductor Materials Distr
N.A.I.C.S.: 423690

Subsidiary (Domestic):

**JX Nippon Mining Ecomanagement,
Inc.** **(2)**
6-3 Otemachi 2-chome, Chiyoda-ku, Tokyo, 100-0004, Japan **(100%)**
Tel.: (81) 352997326
Emp.: 20
Closed Mine Administrative & Environmental Management Services
N.A.I.C.S.: 561110

Subsidiary (Non-US):

**Nikko Fuji Electronics Dongguan Co.,
Ltd.** **(2)**
Section B 1st Yinghua Industrial Zone Hongjin Road, Hongmei Town, Dongguan, Guangdong, China **(100%)**
Tel.: (86) 769 8843 1720
Electrode Components Mfr & Whslr
N.A.I.C.S.: 334419

**Nikko Fuji Precision (Wuxi) Co.,
Ltd.** **(2)**
Wuxi Metal Surface Processing Sci & Tech Indus Park, Luoshezhen Huishan, Wuxi, 10154, Jiangsu, China **(100%)**
Tel.: (86) 51083569918
Surface-Treated Materials Mfr & Whslr
N.A.I.C.S.: 332811

Nikko Metals Hong Kong Ltd. **(2)**
36-38 Wang Lok Street, Yuen Long Industrial Estate, Yuen Long, NT, China (Hong Kong) **(100%)**
Tel.: (852) 2443 0038
Web Site: http://www.nmm.jx-group.co.jp
Sales Range: $25-49.9 Million
Electro-Deposited Copper Foil Warehousing, Processing & Distr
N.A.I.C.S.: 423510

Nikko Metals Shanghai Co., Ltd. **(2)**
Section C Building 37 No 378 Meigui North Road, Waigaoqiao Free Trade Zone, Shanghai, China **(100%)**
Tel.: (86) 21 5046 3646
Rolled Copper, Copper Alloy & Specialty Steel Products Distr
N.A.I.C.S.: 423510

Nikko Metals Taiwan Co., Ltd. **(2)**

62 You-Lian St, Bade, Tao-Yuan, Taiwan **(83.7%)**
Tel.: (886) 33682303
Electronics Materials Mfr & Marketer; Recycled Materials Collector & Distr
N.A.I.C.S.: 332999

Plant (Domestic):

**Nikko Metals Taiwan Co., Ltd. -
Kuanyin Works** **(3)**
No 45 Ching Chien 4th Rd Kuan Yin Industrial Park, Taoyuan, Taiwan
Tel.: (886) 3 483 8570
Precision Rolled Products Mfr
N.A.I.C.S.: 332721

Subsidiary (Non-US):

**Nikko Metals Trading & Services
(Shanghai) Co., Ltd.** **(2)**
2304 Ruijing Bldg 205 Maoming Road, Shanghai, 200020, China **(100%)**
Tel.: (86) 2154659258
Sales Range: $25-49.9 Million
Emp.: 4
Business Support, Information Collection & Market Research Services
N.A.I.C.S.: 561499
Seiichi Murayama *(Gen Mgr)*

Subsidiary (Domestic):

Nippon Marine Co., Ltd. **(2)**
Matsuoka Tamuracho Bldg 4F 22-10 Shimbashi 5-chome, Minato-ku, Tokyo, 105-0004, Japan **(100%)**
Tel.: (81) 35 402 7270
Web Site: https://www.nipponmarine.co.jp
Emp.: 60
Non-Ferrous Metal Product Sea Transportation Services
N.A.I.C.S.: 483111
Shinichi Igata *(Pres)*

Pan Pacific Copper Co., Ltd. **(2)**
10-4 Toranomon 2-chome The Okura Prestige Tower, Minato-ku, Tokyo, 105-8418, Japan **(66%)**
Tel.: (81) 36 433 6600
Web Site: https://www.ppcu.co.jp
Emp.: 764
Copper Mining & Refining Services
N.A.I.C.S.: 212230
Akira Miura *(Pres & CEO)*

Subsidiary (Domestic):

Keihin Kasehin Center Co., Ltd. **(3)**
7-1 Ebisu-cho, Kanagawa-ku, Yokohama, 221-0024, Kanagawa, Japan **(60%)**
Tel.: (81) 454415431
Web Site: http://www.ppcu.co.jp
Transportation Control of Sulphuric Acid & Sales of Diluted Sulphuric Acid
N.A.I.C.S.: 424690

Subsidiary (Non-US):

**Pan Pacific Copper Shanghai Co.,
Ltd.** **(2)**
1907A Ruijing Bldg 205 Maoming Road S, Shanghai, 200020, China **(100%)**
Tel.: (86) 2154659208
Refined Copper Wholesale Trading Distr
N.A.I.C.S.: 425120

Subsidiary (Domestic):

**Tatsuta Electric Wire & Cable Co.,
Ltd.** **(2)**
2-3-1 Iwata-cho, Higashiosaka, 578-8585, Osaka, Japan **(87.64%)**
Tel.: (81) 667213331
Web Site: https://www.tatsuta.co.jp
Rev.: $423,826,590
Assets: $403,996,540
Liabilities: $65,657,130
Net Worth: $338,339,460
Earnings: $11,666,650
Emp.: 1,050
Fiscal Year-end: 03/31/2024
Electric Wire & Cable Mfr
N.A.I.C.S.: 332618
Tetsuya Shibata *(Sr Exec Officer)*

Subsidiary (Non-US):

**Changzhou Tatsuta China Electric
Wire & Cable Co., Ltd.** **(3)**

Unit B & Unit C Factory Building 13 Yuehai Industrial Park, 388 Huang He Xi Lu Xin Bei Qu, Changzhou, Jiangsu, China
Tel.: (86) 509 6888 1308
Wire & Cable Mfr
N.A.I.C.S.: 332618

Subsidiary (Domestic):

**Chugoku Electric Wire & Cable Co.,
Ltd.** **(3)**
2-4-56 Ko, Fujiidera, Osaka, 583-0006, Japan
Tel.: (81) 729540901
Web Site: https://www.chugokudensen.co.jp
Emp.: 124
Wire & Cable Mfr
N.A.I.C.S.: 332618

Plant (Domestic):

**Tatsuta Electric Wire & Cable Co.,
Ltd. - Kyoto Works** **(3)**
3-17 Osadano-cho Fukuchiyama, Kyoto, 620-0853, Japan
Tel.: (81) 773273331
Electrical Wire & Cable Mfr
N.A.I.C.S.: 332618

Subsidiary (Non-US):

**Tatsuta Electronic Materials Malaysia
Sdn. Bhd.** **(3)**
No 8 Jalan Pendaftar U1/54, Temasya Industrial Park, 40150, Shah Alam, Selangor, Malaysia
Tel.: (60) 355670715
Web Site: https://tatsuta.com.my
Emp.: 18
Electronic Materials Mfr
N.A.I.C.S.: 334419

Subsidiary (Domestic):

Tatsuta Environmental Analysis Center Co., Ltd. **(3)**
2-3-1 Iwat-cho, Higashiosaka, 578-8585, Osaka, Japan
Tel.: (81) 667256688
Research Services
N.A.I.C.S.: 541715

**JX Metals Precision Technology Co.,
Ltd.** **(1)**
1-10-12 Commercial and Industrial Chukin, Daiichi Seimei Ueno Building 4th Floor Ueno Taito-ku, Tokyo, 110-0005, Japan
Tel.: (81) 358122715
Web Site: http://www.jxpt.co.jp
Electronic Component Mfr & Distr
N.A.I.C.S.: 334419

**JX Nippon Business Services
Corporation** **(1)**
2-6-3 Otemachi, Chiyoda-Ku, Tokyo, 100-0004, Japan
Tel.: (81) 368038144
Payroll Management Services
N.A.I.C.S.: 541214

**JX Nippon Information Technology
Co., Ltd.** **(1)**
1-1-8 Sakuragicho Nisseki Yokohama Building, Naka-ku, Yokohama, 231-0062, Kanagawa, Japan
Tel.: (81) 456832411
Web Site: http://www.it.eneos.co.jp
Software Services
N.A.I.C.S.: 541511

**JX Nippon Oil & Gas Exploration
Corporation** **(1)**
ENEOS Building 1-2 Otemachi 1-chome, Chiyoda-ku, Tokyo, 100-8163, Japan **(100%)**
Tel.: (81) 36 257 6000
Web Site: https://www.nex.jx-group.co.jp
Holding Company; Oil & Natural Gas Exploration, Development & Extraction
N.A.I.C.S.: 551112
Hidetoshi Ohashi *(Exec Officer & Exec VP)*

Subsidiary (Non-US):

**JX Nippon Oil & Gas Exploration
(Malaysia), Ltd.** **(2)**
Level 15 17 Menara Prestige No 1, Jalan Pinang, 50450, Kuala Lumpur, Malaysia **(78.7%)**
Tel.: (60) 32 168 9596

Web Site: https://www.nex.jx-group.co.jp
Oil & Natural Gas Exploration, Development
& Extraction
N.A.I.C.S.: 211120

Subsidiary (US):

JX Nippon Oil Exploration (U.S.A.)
Limited **(2)**
3040 Post Oak Blvd Ste 1600, Houston, TX
77056
Tel.: (713) 260-7400
Web Site: https://www.nex.jx-group.co.jp
Sales Range: $75-99.9 Million
Emp.: 60
Oil & Natural Gas Exploration, Development
& Extraction
N.A.I.C.S.: 211120

Subsidiary (Non-US):

Japan Energy E&P Australia Pty.
Ltd. **(2)**
Level 2 33 Colin St, West Perth, 6005, WA,
Australia
Tel.: (61) 894838200
Web Site: http://www.nex.jx-group.co.jp
Sales Range: $75-99.9 Million
Emp.: 8
Oil & Natural Gas Exploration, Development
& Extraction
N.A.I.C.S.: 211120
Yoshinori Iino *(Gen Mgr)*

Japan Vietnam Petroleum Co.,
Ltd. **(2)**
PetroVietnam Towers 7th Floor No 8 Hoang
Dieu St, Vung Tau, Vietnam **(97.1%)**
Tel.: (84) 254 385 6937
Web Site: http://www.nex.jx-group.co.jp
Sales Range: $100-124.9 Million
Emp.: 150
Oil & Natural Gas Exploration, Development
& Extraction
N.A.I.C.S.: 211120

Subsidiary (US):

Petra Nova Parish Holdings LLC **(2)**
1000 Main St Ste 2300, Houston, TX 77002
Tel.: (832) 357-5890
Emp.: 7
Holding Company
N.A.I.C.S.: 551112

JX Nippon Procurement
Corporation **(1)**
2-6-3 Otemachi Jieiekkusu Bldg 15kai,
Chiyoda-Ku, Tokyo, 100-0004, Japan
Tel.: (81) 3 6275 5063
Web Site: http://www.pr.jx-group.co.jp
Construction Engineering Services
N.A.I.C.S.: 541330

JX Nippon Research Institute,
Ltd. **(1)**
9F Kyobashi Trust Tower 1-3-3 Kyobashi,
Chuo-ku, Tokyo, 104-0031, Japan
Tel.: (81) 362626200
Web Site: http://www.rs.jx-group.co.jp
Sales Range: $25-49.9 Million
Emp.: 85
Energy Consulting Services
N.A.I.C.S.: 541690
Hatsunori Sakurai *(Pres)*

JXTG Nippon Oil & Energy
Corporation **(1)**
6-3 Otemachi 2-chome, Chiyoda-ku, Tokyo,
100-8162, Japan **(100%)**
Tel.: (81) 362755046
Web Site: http://www.noe.jx-group.co.jp
Holding Company; Oil & Gas Refining &
Marketing
N.A.I.C.S.: 551112
Takashi Noro *(Exec VP)*

Subsidiary (Domestic):

ENEOS Frontier Company,
Limited **(2)**
1-7-2 Kyobashi, Chuo-ku, Tokyo, 104-8218,
Japan
Tel.: (81) 335639211
Web Site: http://www.eneos-frontier.co.jp
Emp.: 2,500
Petroleum Product Distr
N.A.I.C.S.: 424720

J-Quest Co., Ltd. **(2)**

2-31-27 Yushima Yushimadai Bldg 7f,
Bunkyo-Ku, Tokyo, 113-0034, Japan
Tel.: (81) 358422530
Petroleum Product Distr
N.A.I.C.S.: 424720

JOMO Retail Service Co., Ltd. **(2)**
12-7 Nihombashikoamicho Nihomba-
shikoami Bldg, Chuo-Ku, Tokyo, 103-0016,
Japan
Tel.: (81) 356236831
Petroleum Product Distr
N.A.I.C.S.: 424720

JOMO-NET Co., Ltd. **(2)**
1-1-12 Nihombashihamacho Plaza Mamu
Bldg 8f, Chuo-Ku, Tokyo, 103-0007, Japan
Tel.: (81) 358212600
Web Site: http://www.jomo-net.co.jp
Business Support Services
N.A.I.C.S.: 561499

JX Nippon ANCI Corporation **(2)**
Arca Central 7F 2-1 Kinshi 1-chome,
Sumida-ku, Tokyo, 130-0013,
Japan **(100%)**
Tel.: (81) 356194920
Web Site: http://www.an.jx-group.co.jp
Sales Range: $50-74.9 Million
Emp.: 16
Synthetic Resin Products Mfr & Distr
N.A.I.C.S.: 325991
Alvin Everson *(Pres & CEO)*

Plant (Domestic):

JX Nippon ANCI Corp. - Narita
Plant **(3)**
2700-72 Koike, Shibayama-cho, Narita,
289-1624, Chiba, Japan
Tel.: (81) 47 977 1521
Web Site: https://www.tmc.eneos.co.jp
Synthetic Resin Products Mfr
N.A.I.C.S.: 325991

Subsidiary (US):

JX Nippon ANCI, Inc. **(3)**
600 Town Park Ln Ste 075, Kennesaw, GA
30144 **(100%)**
Tel.: (404) 891-1300
Web Site: http://www.clafusa.com
Sales Range: $25-49.9 Million
Emp.: 10
Nonwoven Synthetic Resin Materials Mfr
N.A.I.C.S.: 325991
Alvin Everson *(Pres & CEO)*

Subsidiary (Non-US):

JX Nippon Oil & Energy (Australia)
Pty. Ltd. **(2)**
L 19 Chifley Tower 2 Chifley sq, Sydney,
2000, NSW, Australia
Tel.: (61) 292213366
Coal Mining Services
N.A.I.C.S.: 213113

JX Nippon Oil & Energy Asia Pte.
Ltd. **(2)**
9 Temasek Blvd 2301 Suntec Tower Two,
Singapore, 038989, Singapore **(100%)**
Tel.: (65) 63367330
Petroleum Products Wholesale Trade Distr
N.A.I.C.S.: 425120

Subsidiary (Domestic):

JX Nippon Oil & Energy Trading
Corporation **(2)**
2-6-3 Ootemachi Tiyoda-Ku, Chiyoda-ku,
Tokyo, 100-8168, Japan **(100%)**
Tel.: (81) 368038128
Motor Vehicle-Related Parts Sales & Leas-
ing Services
N.A.I.C.S.: 423120

Subsidiary (US):

JX Nippon Oil & Energy USA
Inc. **(2)**
300 Park Blvd Ste 105, Itasca, IL 60143-
2604
Tel.: (630) 875-9701
Web Site: http://www.eneos.us
Petroleum Product Distr
N.A.I.C.S.: 424720

Subsidiary (Domestic):

Nippon Oil Lubricants (America)
LLC **(3)**

100 Nippon Dr, Childersburg, AL 35044-
9004
Tel.: (256) 378-0131
Sales Range: $25-49.9 Million
Emp.: 50
Lubricant Oil Mfr & Distr
N.A.I.C.S.: 324199
Takahiro Yoshida *(Pres)*

Subsidiary (Domestic):

Japan Gas Energy Corporation **(2)**
17th floor of Hibiya Kokusai Building 2-2-3
Uchisaiwaicho, Chiyoda-ku, Tokyo, 100-
0011, Japan **(51%)**
Tel.: (81) 36 206 6222
Web Site: https://www.j-gasenergy.co.jp
Sales Range: $25-49.9 Million
Emp.: 115
Liquefied Petroleum Gas Distr
N.A.I.C.S.: 424720

Kashima Aromatics Co., Ltd. **(2)**
6-3 Otemachi 2-chome Chiyoda-ku,
Chiyoda-ku, Tokyo, 100-8162,
Japan **(80%)**
Tel.: (81) 3 6275 5201
Holding Company; Petrochemical Mfr
N.A.I.C.S.: 551112
Masumi Takashi *(Gen Mgr)*

Kashima Oil Co., Ltd. **(2)**
6-3 Otemachi 2-chome, Chiyoda-ku, Tokyo,
100-0004, Japan **(70.7%)**
Tel.: (81) 362755078
Web Site: http://www.kashima-oil.co.jp
Sales Range: $150-199.9 Million
Emp.: 400
Holding Company; Petroleum Refinery &
Products Mfr
N.A.I.C.S.: 551112
Keizou Takeuchi *(Pres & CEO)*

NUC Corporation **(2)**
12-1 Ekimae Honcho Kawasaki Ekimae
Tower Riverk 10th floor, Kawasaki-ku, Ka-
wasaki, 210-0007, Kanagawa,
Japan **(100%)**
Tel.: (81) 44 221 1610
Web Site: https://www.eneos-nuc.co.jp
Emp.: 305
Low-Density Polyethylene Mfr & Distr
N.A.I.C.S.: 325211
Keiki Satoh *(Pres)*

Nippon Global Tanker Co., Ltd. **(2)**
6-3 Otemachi 2-chome, Chiyoda-Ku, Tokyo,
100-0004, Japan **(65%)**
Tel.: (81) 362755093
Web Site: http://www.noe.jx-group.co.jp
Crude Oil Transportation Services
N.A.I.C.S.: 213112
Hiroshi Okuda *(Gen Mgr)*

Subsidiary (Non-US):

Nippon Oil (U.K.) plc **(2)**
2nd Fl New Livapool House 15 Eadon St,
London, EC2N 7LB, United Kingdom
Tel.: (44) 2073096960
Web Site: http://www.eneos.co.jp
Sales Range: $25-49.9 Million
Emp.: 7
Providers of Petroleum Refining Services
N.A.I.C.S.: 324110

Nippon Oil Finance (Netherlands)
B.V. **(2)**
World Trade Ctr, Amsterdam Tower A,
Strawinskylaan 1205, 1077XX, Amsterdam,
Netherlands
Tel.: (31) 3052626
Providers of Petroleum Refining Services
N.A.I.C.S.: 324110

Nippon Oil-Dhabi **(2)**
Al Masaood Tower Suite 503 5th Floor,
Sheikh Hamdan Street, Abu Dhabi, United
Arab Emirates
Tel.: (971) 2314991
Web Site: http://www.eneos.co.jp
Providers of Petroleum Refining Services
N.A.I.C.S.: 324110

Subsidiary (Domestic):

Nippon Petroleum Refining Co.,
Ltd. **(2)**
3 12 Nishin Shinbashi 1 Chome, Minato-ku,
Tokyo, 105 8412, Japan

Tel.: (81) 335021111
Web Site: http://www.eneos.co.jp
Sales Range: $800-899.9 Million
Emp.: 2,621
Refinery
N.A.I.C.S.: 324110

Nissho Shipping Co., Ltd. **(2)**
No 33 Mori Bldg 3-8-21 Toranomon, Minato-
Ku, Tokyo, 105-0001, Japan
Tel.: (81) 334383515
Web Site: http://www.nissho-shipping.co.jp
Sales Range: $25-49.9 Million
Emp.: 88
Marine Shipping Agencies
N.A.I.C.S.: 488510

Subsidiary (Non-US):

Shanxi Japan Energy Lubricants Co.,
Ltd. **(2)**
East District of Economic Development
Area, Yangquan, 045000, Shanxi, China
Tel.: (86) 3532160144
Petroleum Lubricating Oil Mfr
N.A.I.C.S.: 324191

Subsidiary (Domestic):

Space Energy Corporation **(2)**
Suzunoya Murotate Bldg 8F 1-20-11 Ueno,
Taito-ku, Tokyo, 110-0005, Japan
Tel.: (81) 3 3839 7676
Web Site: http://www.space-energy.co.jp
Rev.: $91,677,600
Emp.: 250
Solar Wafer Mfr
N.A.I.C.S.: 332999

Subsidiary (Non-US):

Taiwan Nisseki Co., Ltd. **(2)**
Room A1 24F No 6 Su Wei 3rd Road, Ka-
ohsiung, 802, Taiwan
Tel.: (886) 75357458
Web Site: http://www.eneos.co.jp
Sales Range: $25-49.9 Million
Emp.: 4
Sale, Import & Export of Lubricants & Other
Products
N.A.I.C.S.: 424720

Subsidiary (Domestic):

Tonen Chemical Corporation **(2)**
7-1 Ukishima cho, Kawasaki, 210-8523,
Japan
Tel.: (81) 4 4288 8301
Sales Range: $125-149.9 Million
Emp.: 385
Petrochemical Mfr
N.A.I.C.S.: 325110
Yasushi Onoda *(Pres)*

Joint Venture (Domestic):

Tozai Oil Terminal Co., Ltd. **(2)**
1-10-2 Nishi-Shimbashi Sumitomo Life
Nishi-Shimbashi Building 8F, Minato-ku, To-
kyo, 105-0003, Japan
Tel.: (81) 33 539 1451
Web Site: https://www.tozai-ot.jp
Emp.: 278
Petroleum Terminal Operator
N.A.I.C.S.: 424710

Subsidiary (Domestic):

Wakayama Petroleum Refining Co.,
Ltd. **(2)**
758 Fujishiro, Kainan, 642 0034, Wa-
kayama, Japan **(99.8%)**
Tel.: (81) 734825211
Sales Range: $50-74.9 Million
Emp.: 140
Lubricants & Other Petroleum Products Mfr
& Whslr
N.A.I.C.S.: 324191
Junya Hadayama *(Mgr)*

Kawasaki Natural Gas Power Gen-
eration Co., Ltd. **(1)**
12-1 Ogimachi, Kawasaki-ku, Kawasaki,
210-0867, Kanagawa, Japan
Tel.: (81) 443668671
Web Site: http://www.kngg.co.jp
Natural Gas Producer
N.A.I.C.S.: 221210

Nichiyo Engineering Corporation **(1)**
3-17-35 Niizominami, Toda, 335-8502, Sai-

ENEOS Holdings, Inc.—(Continued)
tama, Japan
Tel.: (81) 484201000
Web Site: http://www.ny-eng.co.jp
Civil Engineering Construction Services
N.A.I.C.S.: 237990

Nippo Corporation　　　　　　　　　**(1)**
1-19-11 Kyobashi, Chuo-ku, Tokyo, 104-
8380, Japan　　　　　　　　　　　　　**(50.1%)**
Tel.: (81) 33 563 6743
Web Site: https://www.nippo-c.co.jp
Sales Range: Less than $1 Million
Emp.: 2,105
Road, Civil Engineering Works & Petroleum
Facilities Design & Construction Services
N.A.I.C.S.: 237990
Hiromi Iwata *(Chm)*

**Osaka International Refining Com-
pany, Limited**　　　　　　　　　　　　**(1)**
1 Chigusakaigan, Ichihara, Chiba, Japan
Tel.: (81) 436239580
Web Site: http://www.oirec.co.jp
Petroleum Refining Distr
N.A.I.C.S.: 424720

Showa Nittan Corp.　　　　　　　　**(1)**
Shin-Nisseki Building 3F 3-4-2, Marunouchi
Chiyoda-ku, Tokyo, 100-0005, Japan
Tel.: (81) 362680391
Web Site: http://www.showa-nittan.co.jp
Oil Transportation Services
N.A.I.C.S.: 488510
Kenji Tsutsui *(Pres & CEO)*

**United Petroleum Development Co.,
Ltd.**
ENEOS Building 1-2 1-chome, Otemachi
Chiyoda-ku, Tokyo, Japan
Tel.: (81) 362577010
Oil Exploration Services
N.A.I.C.S.: 213111

ENERAQUA TECHNOLOGIES
PLC
2 Windmill Street, Fitzrovia, London,
W1T 2HX, United Kingdom　　　　**UK**
Web Site:
　　https://www.eneraquatech.com
Year Founded: 2012
ETP—(AIM)
Rev.: $74,775,071
Assets: $65,664,770
Liabilities: $31,701,404
Net Worth: $33,963,366
Earnings: $11,560,986
Emp.: 168
Fiscal Year-end: 01/31/23
Software Development Services
N.A.I.C.S.: 541511

Subsidiaries:

Cenergist BV　　　　　　　　　　　**(1)**
Constructieweg 21 a, 8305 AA, Emmeloord,
Netherlands
Tel.: (31) 527618345
Web Site: https://www.cenergist.com
Environmental Management Services
N.A.I.C.S.: 541620

Cenergist Limited　　　　　　　　**(1)**
8 Bede House Tower Road, Washington,
NE37 2SH, Tyne and Wear, United King-
dom
Tel.: (44) 1912610406
Web Site: https://www.cenergist.com
Municipalities & Housing Associations Con-
sultancy Services
N.A.I.C.S.: 541820

Cenergist Spain SL　　　　　　　**(1)**
Avenida de la Constitucion 218, Casarru-
bios del Monte, Toledo, Spain
Tel.: (34) 915621159
Hot Water Heating System Whslr
N.A.I.C.S.: 238220

HGP International BV　　　　　　**(1)**
Huizermaatweg 27-2, 1273, Huizen, Nether-
lands
Tel.: (31) 355235070
Hot Water Heating System Whslr
N.A.I.C.S.: 238220

Luxe Lights Limited　　　　　　　**(1)**

25 Wildmoor Mill Mill Lanelux New Office 3
Wildmoor, Bromsgrove, B61 0BX, Worces-
tershire, United Kingdom
Tel.: (44) 1527878327
Web Site: https://www.luxlighting.co.uk
Lighting Design Services
N.A.I.C.S.: 541490

Welltherm Drilling Ltd.　　　　　　**(1)**
8 Bede House Tower Road, Washington,
NE37 2SH, Tyne and Wear, United King-
dom
Tel.: (44) 1919062930
Web Site: https://www.wellthermdrilling.com
Site Investigation Services
N.A.I.C.S.: 561611

ENERCHEM INTERNATIONAL,
INC.
Bow Valley Square 2 Ste 3900 205
5th Avenue SW, Calgary, T2P 2V7,
AB, Canada
Tel.: (403) 266-1985　　　　　　　**Ca**
Web Site: http://www.enerchem.com
Year Founded: 1988
Sales Range: $100-124.9 Million
Emp.: 55
Hydrocarbon Fluid Mfr
N.A.I.C.S.: 325110
Nigel Richardson *(CFO & VP-Fin)*

Subsidiaries:

Millard Trucking Ltd.　　　　　　　**(1)**
TWP Road 32/5 B, PO Box 960, Sundre,
T0M 1X0, AB, Canada
Tel.: (403) 638-4500
Sales Range: $25-49.9 Million
Emp.: 125
Trucking Service
N.A.I.C.S.: 484110
Jody Millard *(Mgr-Transportation)*

ENEREV5 METALS INC.
141 Adelaide W Suite 340, Toronto,
M5H 3L5, ON, Canada
Tel.: (416) 500-3670　　　　　　　**ON**
Web Site: https://www.enerev5.com
Year Founded: 1980
ENEV—(TSXV)
Assets: $541,917
Liabilities: $662,185
Net Worth: ($120,269)
Earnings: ($308,073)
Fiscal Year-end: 05/31/21
Peat Fuel Exploration Services
N.A.I.C.S.: 213112
Peter Hooper *(CEO)*

ENERFLEX LTD.
904 1331 Macleod Trail SE, Calgary,
T2G 0K3, AB, Canada
Tel.: (403) 387-6377　　　　　　　**Ca**
Web Site: https://www.enerflex.com
Year Founded: 2010
EFXT—(NYSE)
Rev.: $1,390,735,819
Assets: $3,340,014,083
Liabilities: $2,133,028,013
Net Worth: $1,206,986,070
Earnings: ($78,965,690)
Emp.: 4,900
Fiscal Year-end: 12/31/22
Natural Gas, Oil & CO2 Compres-
sion, Production & Processing
N.A.I.C.S.: 211120
Greg Stewart *(Pres-USA)*

Subsidiaries:

EFX Global KL Sdn Bhd　　　　　**(1)**
Level 28 The Gardens South Tower Mid
Valley City Lingkaran Syed Putra, 59200,
Kuala Lumpur, Malaysia
Tel.: (60) 3 2298 7236
Oil & Gas Field Equipment Mfr & Distr
N.A.I.C.S.: 333132
Sock Cheng Goh *(Mgr-Ops)*

**Enerflex Australasia Holdings Pty.
Ltd.**　　　　　　　　　　　　　　　　**(1)**

64 Irvine Drive, Malaga, Perth, 6090, WA,
Australia
Tel.: (61) 86 465 5700
Web Site: http://www.enerflex.com
Oil & Gas Field Equipment Mfr & Distr
N.A.I.C.S.: 333132

Enerflex Energy Systems Inc.　**(1)**
10815 Telge Rd, Houston, TX
77095　　　　　　　　　　　　　　　　**(100%)**
Tel.: (281) 345-9300
Sales Range: $125-149.9 Million
Emp.: 300
Gas Compression Units & Commercial Re-
frigeration Systems Mfr
N.A.I.C.S.: 333912

Subsidiary (Domestic):

**Enerflex Energy Systems (Wyoming)
Inc.**　　　　　　　　　　　　　　　　**(2)**
885 S Burma Ave, Gillette, WY
82718　　　　　　　　　　　　　　　　**(100%)**
Tel.: (307) 682-2405
Gas Compression Units & Commercial Re-
frigeration Systems Mfr
N.A.I.C.S.: 333912

Enerflex MENA Ltd　　　　　　　**(1)**
Barclays Tower A Muroor Road, PO Box
48294, Abu Dhabi, United Arab Emirates
Tel.: (971) 2 443 0015
Oil & Gas Field Equipment Mfr & Distr
N.A.I.C.S.: 333132
Toufic Khalik *(Mng Dir)*

Enerflex Process Pty. Ltd.　　　**(1)**
115 Schneider Road, Eagle Farm, 4009,
QLD, Australia
Tel.: (61) 733189000
Emp.: 60
Oil & Gas Field Equipment Mfr & Distr
N.A.I.C.S.: 333132

Enerflex Pte. Ltd.　　　　　　　**(1)**
3 Anson Road 27-01 Springleaf Tower, Sin-
gapore, 079909, Singapore
Tel.: (65) 9093 9954
Oil & Gas Field Equipment Mfr & Distr
N.A.I.C.S.: 333132
Jonathan Jonis *(Mng Dir)*

Enerflex Service Pty. Ltd.　　　**(1)**
25 Prime Drive, Seven Hills, 2147, NSW,
Australia
Tel.: (61) 2 8887 8500
Oil & Gas Field Equipment Mfr & Distr
N.A.I.C.S.: 333132
Shaun McCullough *(Gen Mgr)*

Exterran Corporation　　　　　　**(1)**
11000 Equity Dr, Houston, TX 77041
Tel.: (281) 836-7000
Web Site: http://www.exterran.com
Rev.: $630,245,000
Assets: $1,179,197,000
Liabilities: $995,605,000
Net Worth: $183,592,000
Earnings: ($112,708,000)
Emp.: 2,800
Fiscal Year-end: 12/31/2021
Compression, Production & Processing
Products & Services for Production &
Transportation of Oil & Natural Gas
N.A.I.C.S.: 213112
Roger George *(Sr VP-Global Engrg & Prod-
uct Lines)*

Subsidiary (Non-US):

Belleli Energy F.Z.E.　　　　　　**(2)**
2nd Roundabout Hamriya Free Zone
Sharjah, Near Unique Maritime Co, Sharjah,
41697, United Arab Emirates
Tel.: (971) 65263734
Web Site: http://www.exterran.com
Sales Range: $1-4.9 Billion
Emp.: 1,000
Crude Petroleum & Gas Extraction Services
N.A.I.C.S.: 211120
Sergio Jerome *(CEO)*

Exterran (Singapore) Pte. Ltd.　**(2)**
49 Gul Road, Singapore, 629360, Singa-
pore
Tel.: (65) 68610344
Web Site: http://www.exterran.com
Emp.: 50
Oil & Gas Processing Equipment Mainte-
nance Services
N.A.I.C.S.: 213112

Exterran Argentina S.r.l.　　　　**(2)**
Ruta Nacional 22 km 1234, Santa Fe Sur
esquina Avenida de los Constituyentes Plot-
tier, 8316, Neuquen, Argentina
Tel.: (54) 92994937900
Web Site: http://www.exterran.com
Natural Gas Compression; Contract Natural
Gas Handling Service, Fabrication & Equip-
ment
N.A.I.C.S.: 423830

Exterran Bahrain S.P.C.　　　　　**(2)**
Flat No 141 Building No 95 Road No 1702
Block No 317, The Diplomatic Area, Ma-
nama, Bahrain
Tel.: (973) 17570400
Industrial Machinery & Equipment Distr
N.A.I.C.S.: 423830

Exterran Bolivia Ltda.　　　　　　**(2)**
Carretera al Norte Km 9 1/2, Santa Cruz,
Bolivia
Tel.: (591) 363 0200
Web Site: http://www.exterran.com
Sales Range: $50-74.9 Million
Emp.: 70
Natural Gas Compression; Contract Natural
Gas Handling Service, Fabrication & Equip-
ment
N.A.I.C.S.: 423830

**Exterran Eastern Hemisphere
FZE**　　　　　　　　　　　　　　　　**(2)**
East Wing 5B 4th Floor Dubai Airport Free
Zone, PO Box 293509, Dubai, 293509,
United Arab Emirates
Tel.: (971) 4 602 7100
Web Site: http://www.exterran.com
Sales Range: $150-199.9 Million
Emp.: 200
Natural Gas Compression; Contract Natural
Gas Handling Service, Fabrication & Equip-
ment
N.A.I.C.S.: 423830

Subsidiary (Domestic):

Exterran Energy Solutions, L.P.　**(2)**
16666 Northchase Dr, Houston, TX
77060　　　　　　　　　　　　　　　　**(100%)**
Tel.: (281) 836-7671
Web Site: http://www.exterran.com
Oil & Gas Field Machinery & Equipment Mfr
N.A.I.C.S.: 333132
D. Bradley Childers *(Pres & CEO)*

Subsidiary (Non-US):

**Compression Services de Mexico,
S.A. de C.V.**　　　　　　　　　　　　**(3)**
Boulevard Prolongacion Loma Real 1160,
88715, Reynosa, Mexico　　　　**(100%)**
Tel.: (52) 8999093306
Sales Range: $150-199.9 Million
Natural Gas Compression; Contract Natural
Gas Handling Service, Fabrication & Equip-
ment
N.A.I.C.S.: 423830

Unit (Domestic):

Exterran　　　　　　　　　　　　　**(3)**
3333 Gibson St, Bakersfield, CA 93308
Tel.: (661) 321-0271
Web Site: http://www.exterran.com
Sales Range: $150-199.9 Million
Emp.: 40
Natural Gas Compression; Contract Natural
Gas Handling Service, Fabrication & Equip-
ment
N.A.I.C.S.: 423830

Exterran　　　　　　　　　　　　　**(3)**
1114 Hughes Rd, Broussard, LA 70518
Tel.: (337) 359-3400
Web Site: http://www.exterran.com
Sales Range: $150-199.9 Million
Emp.: 350
Natural Gas Compression; Contract Natural
Gas Handling Service, Fabrication & Equip-
ment
N.A.I.C.S.: 423830

Exterran　　　　　　　　　　　　　**(3)**
20602 E 81st St S, Broken Arrow, OK
74014
Tel.: (918) 251-8571
Web Site: http://www.exterran.com
Sales Range: $150-199.9 Million
Emp.: 300

Natural Gas Compression; Contract Natural Gas Handling Service, Fabrication & Equipment
N.A.I.C.S.: 423830

Exterran (3)
8304 Mckee Industrial Rd, Davis, OK 73030
Tel.: (580) 369-2646
Web Site: http://www.exterran.com
Sales Range: $150-199.9 Million
Emp.: 40
Natural Gas Compression; Contract Natural Gas Handling Service, Fabrication & Equipment
N.A.I.C.S.: 423830

Exterran (3)
11000 NW 10th St, Yukon, OK 73099
Tel.: (405) 324-8787
Web Site: http://www.exterran.com
Sales Range: $150-199.9 Million
Emp.: 200
Natural Gas Compression; Contract Natural Gas Handling Service, Fabrication & Equipment
N.A.I.C.S.: 423830

Exterran (3)
2207 FM 949, Alleyton, TX 78935
Tel.: (979) 732-2327
Web Site: http://www.exterran.com
Sales Range: $75-99.9 Million
Emp.: 30
Natural Gas Compression; Contract Natural Gas Handling Service, Fabrication & Equipment
N.A.I.C.S.: 423830

Exterran (3)
9704 W Interstate 20, Midland, TX 79706-2620
Tel.: (432) 567-1050
Web Site: http://www.exterran.com
Sales Range: $50-74.9 Million
Emp.: 100
Natural Gas Compression; Contract Natural Gas Handling Service, Fabrication & Equipment
N.A.I.C.S.: 423830

Exterran (3)
11000 Equity Dr, Houston, TX 77041
Tel.: (281) 836-7000
Web Site: http://www.exterran.com
Sales Range: $800-899.9 Million
Emp.: 2,000
Natural Gas Compression; Contract Natural Gas Handling Service, Fabrication & Equipment
N.A.I.C.S.: 423830

Subsidiary (Non-US):

Exterran Brasil Ltda (3)
Rua Mexico n 3 12 Andar Centro, Rio de Janeiro, 20031-144, Brazil
Tel.: (55) 2121267800
Web Site: http://www.exterran.com
Sales Range: $50-74.9 Million
Emp.: 150
Natural Gas Compression; Contract Natural Gas Handling Service, Fabrication & Equipment
N.A.I.C.S.: 423830

Exterran Energy Malaysia SDN. BHD. (3)
1 Sentral Level 16 Jalan Stesen Sentral 5 KL Sentral, KL Sentral, 50470, Kuala Lumpur, Malaysia
Tel.: (60) 12 303 1357
Web Site: http://www.exterran.com
Natural Gas Compression; Contract Natural Gas Handling Service, Fabrication & Equipment
N.A.I.C.S.: 423830

Plant (Domestic):

Exterran Energy Solutions, L.P. - Houston (Brittmoore) Plant (3)
4444 Brittmoore Rd, Houston, TX 77041
Tel.: (713) 335-7000
Web Site: http://www.exterran.com
Sales Range: $150-199.9 Million
Emp.: 6,250
Natural Gas Compression; Contract Natural Gas Handling Service, Fabrication & Equipment
N.A.I.C.S.: 423830

Exterran Energy Solutions, L.P. - Houston (Rosslyn) Plant (3)
12001 N Houston Rosslyn Rd, Houston, TX 77086
Tel.: (281) 447-8787
Web Site: http://www.exterran.com
Natural Gas Compression; Contract Natural Gas Handling Service, Fabrication & Equipment
N.A.I.C.S.: 423830

Subsidiary (Non-US):

Exterran Holding Company NL B.V. (3)
Dokter Kuyperstraat 1, 2514 BA, Hague, Netherlands
Tel.: (31) 70 311 1900
Industrial Machinery & Equipment Distr
N.A.I.C.S.: 423830

Exterran Peru Selva S.r.l. (3)
Calle Coronel Andres Reyes 360 - Piso 7, San Isidro, Lima, 27, Peru (100%)
Tel.: (51) 1 712 9100
Web Site: http://www.exterran.com
Sales Range: $10-24.9 Million
Emp.: 29
Natural Gas Compression Equipment Mfr
N.A.I.C.S.: 333912

PT. Exterran Indonesia (3)
Jl Gandaria Tengah III No 25, Kebayoran Baru, Jakarta Selatan, 12160, Indonesia (100%)
Tel.: (62) 217 280 0604
Web Site: http://www.exterran.com
Natural Gas Compression; Contract Natural Gas Handling Services, Fabrication & Equipment
N.A.I.C.S.: 423830

Servi-Compresores, C.A. (3)
Carrera 3 entre calles 2 y 4 Galpones MP-17 y 20 Zona Industrial 2, Estado Lara, Barquisimeto, Venezuela (100%)
Tel.: (58) 2512692706
Web Site: https://servicompresores.com
Natural Gas Compression Equipment Mfr
N.A.I.C.S.: 333912

Subsidiary (Non-US):

Exterran Energy de Mexico, S.A. de C.V. (2)
Blvd Loma Real No 1160 Fracc Loma Real, Reynosa, 88715, Mexico
Tel.: (52) 8999093358
Oil & Gas Processing Equipment Maintenance Services
N.A.I.C.S.: 213112

Subsidiary (Domestic):

Exterran General Holdings LLC (2)
12001 N Houston Rosslyn Rd, Houston, TX 77086
Tel.: (281) 921-9337
Web Site: http://www.exterran.com
Oil & Gas Field Machinery & Equipment Mfr
N.A.I.C.S.: 333132

Subsidiary (Non-US):

Exterran International SA (2)
Chemin des Primeveres 45, PO Box 592, Fribourg, 1700, Switzerland (100%)
Tel.: (41) 264755005
Web Site: http://exterran.com
Industrial Machinery & Equipment Distr
N.A.I.C.S.: 423830

Exterran Offshore Pte. Ltd. (2)
49 Gul Road, Singapore, 629360, Singapore
Tel.: (65) 6 861 0344
Web Site: http://www.exterran.com
Emp.: 131
Oil & Gas Production Equipment Distr
N.A.I.C.S.: 423830

Exterran Servicos de Oleo e Gas Ltda. (2)
Rua Mexico n 3 12 andar Centro, Rio de Janeiro, 20031-144, Brazil
Tel.: (55) 212 126 7800
Web Site: http://www.exterran.com.br
Oil & Gas Processing Equipment Maintenance Services
N.A.I.C.S.: 213112

Exterran Water Solutions ULC (2)
1721 27th Avenue NE, Calgary, T2E 7E1, AB, Canada
Tel.: (403) 219-2210
Web Site:
http://www.exterranwatersolutions.com
Waste Management Services
N.A.I.C.S.: 213112

ExterranEnergy Solutions Ecuador Cia. Ltda. (2)
Edif Renazzo Plaza Ofc 708 Av de los Shyris and Sweden, Quito, Pichincha, Ecuador
Tel.: (593) 26044165
Sales Range: $50-74.9 Million
Emp.: 7
Oil & Natural Gas Processing Equipment Maintenance Services
N.A.I.C.S.: 213112

Gas Conditioning of Mexico, S. de R.L. de C.V. (2)
Blvd Prolongacion Loma Real 1160 Tamaulipas, 88715, Reynosa, Tamaulipas, Mexico
Tel.: (52) 8999093327
Industrial Machinery & Equipment Distr
N.A.I.C.S.: 423830

LLC Exterran Vostok (2)
23 Novoslobodskaya Str Business Center named by Vs Meyerhold Floor 7, Office 723, 127055, Moscow, Russia
Tel.: (7) 495 287 0410
Web Site: http://www.exterran.com
Emp.: 30
Industrial Machinery & Equipment Distr
N.A.I.C.S.: 423830

Gas Drive Global LP (1)
10121 Barlow Trail NE, Calgary, T3J 3C6, AB, Canada
Tel.: (403) 387-6300
Web Site: http://www.gasdriveglobal.com
Emp.: 150
Gas Engine Distr
N.A.I.C.S.: 423860
Trevor Kramer (Gen Mgr)

ENERGEAN PLC
3rd Floor Accurist House 44 Baker Street, London, W1U 7AL, United Kingdom
Tel.: (44) 2036557200   UK
Web Site: https://www.energean.com
Year Founded: 2007
ENOG—(LSE)
Rev.: $737,081,000
Assets: $5,731,427,000
Liabilities: $5,081,229,000
Net Worth: $650,198,000
Earnings: $17,271,000
Emp.: 536
Fiscal Year-end: 12/31/22
Oil & Gas Exploration Services
N.A.I.C.S.: 213112
Karen Simon (Chm)

Subsidiaries:

Energean Israel Finance Ltd. (1)
Matam Park Building 23 First Floor Andre Sacharov 9, Haifa, 3508409, Israel
Tel.: (972) 768835700
Oil & Gas Exploration Services
N.A.I.C.S.: 213112

Energean Israel Transmission Ltd. (1)
Tel.: (972) 36715000
Oil & Gas Exploration Services
N.A.I.C.S.: 213112

Energean Oil & Gas S.A. (1)
32 Kifissias Avenue Atrina Center, 151 25, Maroussi, Athens, Greece
Tel.: (30) 2108174200
Oil & Gas Exploration Services
N.A.I.C.S.: 213112

ENERGEIA A.S.
Cort Adelers gate 33, 0254, Oslo, Norway
Tel.: (47) 48023214
Web Site: https://www.energeia.no
Year Founded: 2010

ENERG—(OSL)
Rev.: $6,991,074
Assets: $22,969,310
Liabilities: $11,381,287
Net Worth: $11,588,023
Earnings: ($1,616,236)
Emp.: 55
Fiscal Year-end: 12/31/23
Solar Electric Power Generation Services
N.A.I.C.S.: 221114
Earl Egil Markussen (Deputy CEO)

ENERGETIC SERVICES INC.
13366 Thompkins Frontage Road, Charlie Lake, V0C 1H0, BC, Canada
Tel.: (250) 785-4761
Web Site:
http://www.energeticservices.com
Year Founded: 1996
Rev.: $12,259,238
Emp.: 68
Transportation Services
N.A.I.C.S.: 488999
Brennan Ross (Pres & CEO)

Subsidiaries:

Energetic Services Inc. - Edson Facility (1)
3-5039 5th Ave, PO Box 30188, Edson, T7E 1Y2, AB, Canada
Tel.: (780) 723-4937
Basic Chemicals Mfr
N.A.I.C.S.: 325180

Energetic Services Inc. - Fort Nelson Facility (1)
Mile 293 Alaska Hwy BCR Industrial Park Lot 1629, Fort Nelson, V0C 1R0, BC, Canada
Tel.: (250) 774-4761
Basic Chemicals Mfr
N.A.I.C.S.: 325180
Colin Harbin (Area Mgr)

Energetic Services Inc. - Grande Prairie Facility (1)
13701 99th Street, Grande Prairie, T8V 7N9, AB, Canada
Tel.: (780) 532-9195
Basic Chemicals Mfr
N.A.I.C.S.: 325180
Don Hamaluk (Area Mgr)

ENERGETICKY A PRUMYS-LOVY HOLDING, A.S.
Parizska 26, 110 00, Prague, Czech Republic
Tel.: (420) 232005200   CZ
Web Site: http://www.epholding.cz
Year Founded: 2009
Emp.: 25,000
Energy & Industrial Investment Holding Company
N.A.I.C.S.: 551112
Daniel Kretinsky (Chm)

Subsidiaries:

Budapesti Eromu Zrt (1)
Budafoki ut 52, 1117, Budapest, Hungary (95.6%)
Tel.: (36) 6 1 577 84 39
Web Site: http://www.budapestieromu.hu
Sales Range: $150-199.9 Million
Power & Heating Plants Operator
N.A.I.C.S.: 221118
Vinkovits Andras (Chm & CEO)

ENERGZET, a.s. (1)
Jedovnicka 4303/2a, 628 00, Brno, Czech Republic
Tel.: (420) 606 718 488
Web Site: http://www.energzet.cz
Electric Power Distribution Services
N.A.I.C.S.: 221122

EP Commodities, a.s. (1)
Klimentska 1216/46, 11000, Prague, Czech Republic
Tel.: (420) 232 005 100
Commodity Trading Services
N.A.I.C.S.: 523160

Energeticky a Prumyslovy Holding, a.s.—(Continued)

Daniel Pexidr *(Mng Dir)*

EP ENERGY TRADING, a.s. (1)
Klimentska 46, 110 02, Prague, Czech Republic
Tel.: (420) 255 707 099
Web Site: http://www.epet.cz
Electric Power Distribution Services
N.A.I.C.S.: 221122
Zanet Mullerova *(Head-Sls)*

EP Power Europe, a.s. (1)
Parizska 26, 110 00, Prague, 1, Czech Republic
Tel.: (420) 232 005 200
Web Site: http://www.eppowereurope.cz
Electric Power Distr
N.A.I.C.S.: 221122
Daniel Kretinsky *(Chm)*

Subsidiary (Non-US):

STEAG Power Minerals GmbH (2)
Duisburger Strasse 170, 46535, Dinslaken, Germany
Tel.: (49) 2064608330
Web Site: http://www.steag-powerminerals.com
Sales Range: $75-99.9 Million
Emp.: 150
Waste Management
N.A.I.C.S.: 924110

Eggborough Power Ltd (1)
Eggborough Power Station, Eggborough, Goole, DN14 0BS, E Yorkshire, United Kingdom
Tel.: (44) 1977 782 500
Web Site:
    http://www.eggboroughpower.co.uk
Coal-Fired Electricity Generation
N.A.I.C.S.: 221112
Alan Beeston *(Dir-Ops)*

GALA-MIBRAG-Service GmbH (1)
Platz der Freiheit 4, 06729, Elsteraue, Germany
Tel.: (49) 34424 81416
Web Site: http://www.gamise.de
Coal Mining Services
N.A.I.C.S.: 212114

Helmstedter Revier GmbH (1)
Schoninger Strasse 2 -3, 38350, Helmstedt, Germany
Tel.: (49) 5352 9439 4500
Web Site: http://www.helmstedterrevier.de
Coal Mining Services
N.A.I.C.S.: 212114

Kraftwerk Mehrum GmbH (1)
Triftstrasse 25, 31249, Hohenhameln, Germany
Tel.: (49) 5128740
Web Site: http://www.kraftwerk-mehrum.de
Electric Power Production
N.A.I.C.S.: 221122

Mitteldeutsche Braunkohlengesellschaft mbH (1)
Gluck-Auf-Strasse 1, 06711, Zeitz, Germany   (50%)
Tel.: (49) 34416840
Web Site: https://www.mibrag.de
Coal Mining
N.A.I.C.S.: 212114
Armin Eichholz *(Chm-Mgmt Bd)*

PRVNI MOSTECKA a.s. (1)
Stavbaru 32, 434 01, Most, Czech Republic
Tel.: (420) 476 447 83
Web Site: http://www.prvnimostecka.cz
Electricity Generation & Distribution Services
N.A.I.C.S.: 221116

PT Holding Investment B.V. (1)
Weteringschans 26, 1017 SG, Amsterdam, Netherlands
Tel.: (31) 205301260
Emp.: 3
Holding Company
N.A.I.C.S.: 551112
Nicolaas Scholtens *(Mng Dir)*

Plzenska energetika a.s. (1)
Tylova 1/57, 316 00, Plzen, Czech Republic
Tel.: (420) 378 133 790
Web Site: http://www.pe.cz

Electricity Generation & Distribution Services
N.A.I.C.S.: 221116
Jiri Beran *(Head-Purchase Dept)*

Przedsiebiorstwo Gornicze SILESIA Sp. z o.o. (1)
ul Gornicza 60, PL-43 502, Czechowice-Dziedzice, Poland
Tel.: (48) 32 737 3311
Web Site: http://www.pgsilesia.pl
Coal Mining Services
N.A.I.C.S.: 212114
Jan Marinov *(Chm)*

Tynagh Energy Ltd. (1)
Northwood Park, Santry, Dublin, 9, Ireland   (80%)
Tel.: (353) 1 857 8700
Web Site: http://www.tynaghenergy.ie
Eletric Power Generation Services
N.A.I.C.S.: 221118
John O'Connor *(CEO)*

United Energy a.s. (1)
Teplarenska 2, PO Box 22, 434 03, Most, Czech Republic
Tel.: (420) 476 447 111
Web Site: http://www.ue.cz
Electricity Generation & Distribution Services
N.A.I.C.S.: 221116

ENERGETICS & ENERGY SAVINGS FUND - FEEI SPV
gk Geo Milev 20 Kosta Lulchev St, Slatina district Stolichna municipality, 1113, Sofia, Bulgaria
Tel.: (359) 885920426
Year Founded: 2006
FEEI—(BUL)
Sales Range: Less than $1 Million
Real Estate Investment Services
N.A.I.C.S.: 531190
Krasimir Dimitrov Todorov *(Chm)*

ENERGIA DE CASABLANCA SA
Avenida Portales N 187, Box 41, Casablanca, Valparaiso, Chile
Tel.: (56) 322742652
Web Site: https://www.casablanca.cl
Year Founded: 1995
CASABLANCA—(SGO)
Sales Range: Less than $1 Million
Construction Equipment Distr
N.A.I.C.S.: 423830

ENERGIA INNOVACION Y DESARROLLO FOTOVOLTAICO S.A.
Orense Street 11 1 A, Mud, 36692, Pontevedra, Spain
Tel.: (34) 900535037
Web Site: https://www.eidfsolar.es
Year Founded: 2008
F63—(DEU)
Solar Component Mfr & Distr
N.A.I.C.S.: 334413
Fernando Romero *(Pres)*

ENERGIA LATINA SA
Francisco de Aguirre 3720 Office 63, Vitacura, 7630446, Santiago, Chile
Tel.: (56) 229632900
Web Site: https://www.enlasa.com
Year Founded: 2007
ENLASA—(SGO)
Sales Range: Less than $1 Million
Eletric Power Generation Services
N.A.I.C.S.: 221118
Rodrigo Saez *(CEO)*

ENERGIE AG
Bohmerwaldstrasse 3, PO Box 298, A-4021, Linz, Austria
Tel.: (43) 0590000   AT
Web Site: http://www.energieag.at
Year Founded: 1892
Rev.: $2,074,204,031

Assets: $3,403,253,926
Liabilities: $1,904,501,739
Net Worth: $1,498,752,187
Earnings: $64,564,429
Emp.: 4,506
Fiscal Year-end: 09/30/19
Electric Power & Water Distr; Waste Disposal Services
N.A.I.C.S.: 221122

ENERGIE STEIERMARK AG
Leonhardgurtel 10, 8010, Graz, Austria
Tel.: (43) 316 9000   AT
Web Site: http://www.e-steiermark.com
Holding Company Services
N.A.I.C.S.: 551112
Christian Purrer *(CEO)*

Subsidiaries:

Energie Steiermark Kunden GmbH (1)
Leonhardgurtel 10, 8010, Graz, Austria
Tel.: (43) 316 9000 0
Web Site: http://www.e-steiermark.com
Electricity Gas & Heat Sale & Customer Support Services
N.A.I.C.S.: 561422
Hannes Zeichen *(Mng Dir)*

Energie Steiermark Service GmbH (1)
Leonhardgurtel 10, 8010, Graz, Austria
Tel.: (43) 316 9000 0
Web Site: http://www.e-steiermark.com
Energy Industry Technical Support Services
N.A.I.C.S.: 561422
Dietmar Mauschitz *(Mng Dir)*

ENERGIEKONTOR AG
Mary-Somerville-Strasse 5, 28359, Bremen, Germany
Tel.: (49) 42133040   De
Web Site:
    https://www.energiekontor.de
Year Founded: 1990
EKT—(DEU)
Rev.: $266,915,766
Assets: $796,596,747
Liabilities: $592,104,829
Net Worth: $204,491,917
Earnings: $91,974,448
Emp.: 173
Fiscal Year-end: 12/31/23
Wind Farm Operator
N.A.I.C.S.: 238220
Guenter Eschen *(Member-Mgmt Bd)*

Subsidiaries:

Energiekontor UK Ltd. (1)
4330 Park Approach Thorpe Park, Leeds, LS15 8GB, United Kingdom
Tel.: (44) 1132044850
Web Site: https://energiekontor.co.uk
Solar Power Generation Services
N.A.I.C.S.: 221114
Michael Briggs *(Mgr-Project)*

Energiekontor US Inc. (1)
201 Main St Ste 103, Rapid City, SD 57701
Solar Power Generation Services
N.A.I.C.S.: 221114
Brenda G. Moore *(Gen Mgr-US Wind Markets)*

ENERGISME S.A.
88 Avenue du General Leclerc, 92100, Boulogne-Billancourt, France
Tel.: (33) 181893390
Web Site:
    https://www.energisme.com
Year Founded: 2004
ALNRG—(EUR)
Software Development Services
N.A.I.C.S.: 541511

ENERGIX RENEWABLE ENERGIES LTD.

Atrium Building 2 Jabotinsky St, Ramat Gan, 5250501, Israel
Tel.: (972) 35668855
Web Site: https://www.energix-group.com
Year Founded: 2009
ENRG—(TAE)
Rev.: $188,397,842
Assets: $2,710,561,637
Liabilities: $2,055,456,246
Net Worth: $655,105,391
Earnings: $71,299,350
Emp.: 230
Fiscal Year-end: 12/31/23
Other Electric Power Generation
N.A.I.C.S.: 221118
Nathan Hetz *(Chm)*

Subsidiaries:

Energix US LLC (1)
1201 Wilson Blvd Ste 2200, Arlington, VA 22209
Tel.: (703) 373-7345
Web Site:
    https://www.energixrenewables.com
Wind Energy Generation Services
N.A.I.C.S.: 541350

ENERGO-PRO A.S.
Na Porici 3a, 110 00, Prague, Czech Republic
Tel.: (420) 222310245   CZ
Web Site: http://www.energo-pro.com
Year Founded: 1994
Sales Range: $1-4.9 Billion
Emp.: 9,000
Electricity & Hydropower Plant Distr Operator
N.A.I.C.S.: 221122
Jiri Krushina *(Chm)*

Subsidiaries:

ENERGO-PRO Bulgaria EAD (1)
2 Pozitano Sq 5th Floor, 1000, Sofia, Bulgaria
Tel.: (359) 29817050
Web Site: http://www.energo-pro.com
Hydroelectric Power Plant Operator, Construction & Maintenance Services
N.A.I.C.S.: 221111

ENERGO-PRO Caucasus LLC (1)
AUA Center office 404 9 Alek Manukyan Str, 0070, Yerevan, Armenia
Tel.: (374) 10 512262
Hydroelectric Power Generation Services
N.A.I.C.S.: 221111

ENERGO-PRO Czech s.r.o. (1)
Edisonova 5, CZ-612 00, Brno, Czech Republic
Tel.: (420) 510 000 050
Web Site: http://www.energo-pro.com
Hydroelectric Power Plant Operator, Construction & Maintenance Services
N.A.I.C.S.: 221111

ENERGO-PRO EAD (1)
Varna Towers Tower G 258 Vladislav Varnenchik Blvd, 9009, Varna, Bulgaria   (100%)
Tel.: (359) 700 161 61
Web Site: http://www.energo-pro.bg
Electric Power Distr
N.A.I.C.S.: 221122

ENERGO-PRO Georgia JSC (1)
1 Sandro Euli Str, 0186, Tbilisi, Georgia
Tel.: (995) 32319800
Web Site: http://www.energo-pro.ge
Hydroelectric Power Plant Operator, Construction & Maintenance Services
N.A.I.C.S.: 221111

ENERGO-PRO Guney Elektrik Uretim San. ve Tic. A.S.
Iran Caddesi No 21 Karum Is Merkezi D Blok 6 Kat No 448 Kavaklidere, 06700, Ankara, Turkiye
Tel.: (90) 312 468 00 57
Hydroelectric Power Generation Services
N.A.I.C.S.: 221111

ENERGOAPARATURA S.A.

ul gen K Pulaskiego 7, 40-273, Katowice, Poland
Tel.: (48) 327285492
Web Site: https://www.enap.com.pl
Year Founded: 1955
ENP—(WAR)
Rev.: $11,795,732
Assets: $9,606,199
Liabilities: $4,256,606
Net Worth: $5,349,593
Earnings: $829,268
Fiscal Year-end: 12/31/23
Electrical Installation Services
N.A.I.C.S.: 238210
Malgorzata Gegotek-Rapak (Vice Chm-Supervisory Bd & Sec)

ENERGOAQUA A.S.
1 maje 823, 75661, Roznov pod Radhostem, 75661, Czech Republic
Tel.: (420) 571844389
Web Site: https://www.energoaqua.cz
Year Founded: 1992
Electric Power Generation & Distribution Services
N.A.I.C.S.: 221111

ENERGOINSTAL S.A.
Al Rozdzienskiego 188d, 40-203, Katowice, Poland
Tel.: (48) 327357200
Web Site:
  https://www7.energoinstal.pl
Year Founded: 1949
ENI—(WAR)
Rev.: $27,938,770
Assets: $36,237,805
Liabilities: $24,270,579
Net Worth: $11,967,226
Earnings: ($595,783)
Fiscal Year-end: 12/31/23
Power Boiler Mfr
N.A.I.C.S.: 332410
Tomasz Lampert (Dir-Mktg Dept)

Subsidiaries:

Enizo Sp. z o.o.   (1)
Al Rozdzienskiego 188D, 40-203, Katowice, Poland
Tel.: (48) 327298353
Web Site: https://www.enizo.pl
Advertising Services
N.A.I.C.S.: 541810
Pawel Szajner (Pres)

ENERGOINVEST AUTOMATIKA A.D.
Vuka Karadzica br 28, 71123, Istocno Sarajevo, Bosnia & Herzegovina
Tel.: (387) 57340203
Web Site: https://eautomatica.com
ATMK—(BANJ)
Sales Range: Less than $1 Million
Emp.: 10
Industrial Machinery & Equipment Rental Services
N.A.I.C.S.: 532490
Miro Grgic (Chm)

ENERGOINVEST TVORNICA DALEKOVODNIH STUBOVA D.D.
Dzemala Bijedica 164, Sarajevo, 71000, Bosnia & Herzegovina
Tel.: (387) 33 460 354
Web Site: http://www.energoinvest-tds.com
Year Founded: 1953
ETDSRK1—(SARE)
Sales Range: Less than $1 Million
Emp.: 143
Metal Structure Mfr
N.A.I.C.S.: 332312

ENERGOINVEST, D.D.
Hamdije Cemerlica 2, 71000, Sarajevo, Bosnia & Herzegovina

Tel.: (387) 33703301
Web Site: http://www.energoinvest.ba
Year Founded: 1951
ENISR—(SARE)
Rev.: $113,147,554
Assets: $80,263,973
Liabilities: $69,754,316
Net Worth: $10,509,657
Earnings: ($3,507,312)
Emp.: 211
Fiscal Year-end: 12/31/22
Engineeering Services
N.A.I.C.S.: 541330
Bisera Hadzialjevic (Dir)

ENERGOINVEST-DALEKOVODIZGRADNJA, D.D.
Zujevinska 6 Sarajevo, 71 215, Blazuj, Bosnia & Herzegovina
Tel.: (387) 33 761 395
Web Site:
  http://www.dalekovodizgradnja.com
EDVIRK1—(SARE)
Sales Range: Less than $1 Million
Emp.: 2
Construction Engineering Services
N.A.I.C.S.: 237990

ENERGOLD DRILLING CORP.
1602-700 W Pender St, Vancouver, V6C 1G8, BC, Canada
Tel.: (604) 681-9501   BC
Web Site: https://www.energold.com
Year Founded: 1973
Sales Range: $50-74.9 Million
Drilling Services
N.A.I.C.S.: 212311
Richard Thomas (Pres-EMEA)

Subsidiaries:

E Global Drilling Corp   (1)
PO Box 11004, Alcester, B49 6WE, Warwickshire, United Kingdom
Tel.: (44) 1926650376
Web Site: http://www.eglobaldrilling.com
Oil & Gas Wells Drilling Services
N.A.I.C.S.: 213111

Energold de Mexico S.A. de C.V.   (1)
Neiva 949 Lindavista Gustavo A Madero, Mexico, 7300, Mexico
Tel.: (52) 15555862523
Diamond Mining Services
N.A.I.C.S.: 212390

ENERGOMASHBANK, PLC
Ul Karavannaya 1, Saint Petersburg, 191011, Russia
Tel.: (7) 8126357487
Web Site:
  http://www.energomashbank.ru
Sales Range: Less than $1 Million
Commercial Banking Services
N.A.I.C.S.: 522110

ENERGOMONTAJ S.A.
Calea Dorobantilor 103-105 sector 1, 010561, Bucharest, Romania
Tel.: (40) 213189303
Web Site: http://www.saem.ro
Year Founded: 1949
Sales Range: $1-4.9 Billion
Emp.: 5,897
Power Station Installation & Construction Services
N.A.I.C.S.: 237990
Iosif Falup (Dir-Tech)

Subsidiaries:

Energomontaj S.A. - Electrical, Automation & Telecommunication Installations Division   (1)
103-105 Calea Dorobantilor, District 1, 010561, Bucharest, Romania
Tel.: (40) 213460238
Web Site: http://www.saem.ro
Sales Range: $400-449.9 Million
Emp.: 1,300

Telecommunication Installation, Repair & Technical Assistance Services
N.A.I.C.S.: 237130
Florin Kessler (Pres)

Energomontaj S.A. - FEE   (1)
103-105 Calea Dorobantilor, District 1, 10561, Bucharest, Romania
Tel.: (40) 21 3469449
Web Site: http://www.saem.ro
Sales Range: $150-199.9 Million
Emp.: 350
Metallic Structures, Protective Coatings, Machine Tools & Equipment Mfr
N.A.I.C.S.: 332312

Energomontaj S.A. - Hidro
Division   (1)
103-105 Calea Dorbantilor, District 1, Bucharest, 10561, Romania
Tel.: (40) 213189310
Sales Range: $400-449.9 Million
Emp.: 1,100
Hydro Mechanical & Power Equipment Installer & Mfr
N.A.I.C.S.: 333613
Viorel Popoescu (Mgr-Div)

Energomontaj S.A. - Thermo
Division   (1)
103-105 Calea Dorbbantilor Dt 1, Bucharest, 010561, Romania
Tel.: (40) 213189300
Sales Range: $50-74.9 Million
Emp.: 200
Water & Gas Power Plant Engineering Services
N.A.I.C.S.: 237990

ENERGONOVA D.D.
Semizovac bb, 71 321, Vogosca, Bosnia & Herzegovina
Tel.: (387) 33475180
EGNSR—(SARE)
Rev.: $472,540
Assets: $9,361,076
Liabilities: $3,353,462
Net Worth: $6,007,614
Earnings: $26,991
Emp.: 7
Fiscal Year-end: 12/31/21
Electric Power Generation & Distribution Services
N.A.I.C.S.: 221111

ENERGOPROJEKT HOLDING A.D.
Bulevar Mihaila Pupina 12, 11070, Belgrade, Serbia
Tel.: (381) 113101010
Web Site:
  http://www.energoprojekt.rs
ENHL—(BEL)
Rev.: $182,533,971
Assets: $320,021,967
Liabilities: $142,138,469
Net Worth: $177,883,498
Earnings: $7,972,462
Emp.: 1,274
Fiscal Year-end: 12/31/21
Civil Engineering Services
N.A.I.C.S.: 541330

Subsidiaries:

302 Enlisa S.A.   (1)
Amador Merino Reyna 460 piso 17, San Isidro, Lima, Peru
Tel.: (51) 14429033
Web Site: http://eng.energoprojekt.rs
Sales Range: $25-49.9 Million
Emp.: 32
Construction Engineering Services
N.A.I.C.S.: 541330

EP Industrija a.d.   (1)
Bulevar Mihaila Pupina 12, Belgrade, 11070, Serbia
Tel.: (381) 11 310 14 01
Web Site: http://www.ep-industry.com
Sales Range: $50-74.9 Million
Emp.: 130
Industrial Plants & Facilities Engineering Services
N.A.I.C.S.: 236210

Vitomir Peric (Pres)

EP Urbanizam i arh. a.d.   (1)
Bulevar Mihaila Pupina 12, 11070, Belgrade, Serbia
Tel.: (381) 11 311 33 45
Web Site: http://www.eparhitektura.rs
Sales Range: $25-49.9 Million
Emp.: 170
Architectural Design Services
N.A.I.C.S.: 541310

EP-Holding Guinee S.A.   (1)
Rue MA-019 Coleah, BP 251, Matam, Conakry, Guinea
Tel.: (224) 63 403 525
Construction Engineering Services
N.A.I.C.S.: 541330

Encom GmbH   (1)
Zeppelinallee 71, 60487, Frankfurt am Main, Hesse, Germany
Tel.: (49) 699706050
Web Site: http://www.encom.info
Engineering Consulting Services
N.A.I.C.S.: 541330

Energo Consult L.L.C.   (1)
Al Qubaissi Building Office No 202, PO Box 52473, Abu Dhabi, United Arab Emirates
Tel.: (971) 26763554
Sales Range: $25-49.9 Million
Emp.: 40
Energy Consulting Services
N.A.I.C.S.: 541690

Energo Nigerija Ltd.   (1)
138 Aminu Kano Crescent, Abuja, Nigeria
Tel.: (234) 94611362
Web Site: http://www.energonigeria.com
Sales Range: $25-49.9 Million
Emp.: 200
Construction Engineering Services
N.A.I.C.S.: 541330
Dejan Jerotic (Vice Chm)

Energoprojekt - Entel a.d.   (1)
Bulevar Mihajla Pupina 12, PO Box 20, 11070, Belgrade, Serbia   (86.26%)
Tel.: (381) 113101200
Web Site: https://www.ep-entel.com
Sales Range: $25-49.9 Million
Emp.: 192
Consulting, Engineering, Design & Project Management Services
N.A.I.C.S.: 541330
Mladen Simovic (Mng Dir)

Energoprojekt Energodata a.d.   (1)
Bulevar Mihaila Pupina 12, Belgrade, 11070, Serbia
Tel.: (381) 113113351
Web Site: http://www.energodata.rs
Sales Range: $25-49.9 Million
Emp.: 70
Financial Software Development Services
N.A.I.C.S.: 541511

Energoprojekt Entel Company   (1)
Area 315 Avenue 336 Building 27 Flat No 62, PO Box 21153, Manama, Bahrain
Tel.: (973) 1 729 6449
Construction Services
N.A.I.C.S.: 236220

Energoprojekt Entel L.L.C.   (1)
Al Khuwair South Block 42 Complex No 225 357 Al Maha Street, Bld No 3886, Muscat, Oman
Tel.: (968) 24488011
Construction Services
N.A.I.C.S.: 236220

Energoprojekt Entel Ltd.   (1)
Palm Tower B 21st Floor Al Dafna Area, PO Box 4769, Doha, Qatar
Tel.: (974) 44477321
Web Site: https://www.ep-entel.com
Construction Services
N.A.I.C.S.: 236220

Energoprojekt Garant a.d.o.   (1)
Bulevar Mihaila Pupina 12, Belgrade, 11000, Serbia
Tel.: (381) 113101066
Web Site: http://www.garant.rs
Sales Range: $50-74.9 Million
Emp.: 10
General Insurance Services
N.A.I.C.S.: 524126
Mirjana Bogicevic (CEO & Gen Mgr)

Energoprojekt Holding a.d.—(Continued)

Energoprojekt Hidroinzenjering a.d. (1)
Bulevar Mihajla Pupina 12, 11000, Belgrade, Serbia
Tel.: (381) 113101150
Web Site: https://www.ephydro.com
Sales Range: $25-49.9 Million
Emp.: 211
Engineering Consulting Services
N.A.I.C.S.: 541330
Bratislav Stisovic (Mng Dir)

Energoprojekt Holding Guinee S.A. (1)
Rue Ma-019 Coleah, Conakry, Matam, Guinea
Tel.: (224) 622407301
Construction Services
N.A.I.C.S.: 236220

Energoprojekt Niskogradnja Joint Stock Co. (1)
12 Boulevard of Mihajlo Pupin, PO Box 20, 11070, Belgrade, Serbia
Tel.: (381) 112146424
Web Site: https://www.energoprojekt-ng.rs
Public Utility Construction & Engineering Services
N.A.I.C.S.: 237110
Milan Ristic (Exec Dir-Construction Mgmt)

Energoprojekt Oprema a.d. (1)
Bulevar Mihajla Pupina 12, 11070, Belgrade, Serbia
Tel.: (381) 113101600
Web Site: http://www.energoprojekt-oprema.com
Sales Range: $75-99.9 Million
Emp.: 300
Electrical & Mechanical Engineering Services
N.A.I.C.S.: 541330

INEC ENGINEERING CO. Ltd. (1)
73 Mornington Street, London, NW1 7QE, United Kingdom
Tel.: (44) 2073832385
Construction Engineering Services
N.A.I.C.S.: 541330

ENERGOPROJEKT INDUSTRIJA A.D.
Bulevar Mihajla Pupina 12, 11070, Belgrade, Serbia
Tel.: (381) 11 310 14 01
Web Site: http://www.ep-industry.com
Engineeering Services
N.A.I.C.S.: 541330
Dejan Pantovic (Dir-Mktg & Construction Mgmt)

ENERGOPROJEKT URBANIZAM I ARHITEKTURA A.D.
Bulevar Mihaila Pupina 12, Belgrade, Serbia
Tel.: (381) 11 311 33 45
Web Site: http://www.eparhitektura.rs
Year Founded: 1989
Sales Range: $1-9.9 Million
Emp.: 106
Engineering Consultancy Services
N.A.I.C.S.: 541330
Zoran Radojicic (Mng Dir)

ENERGOPROJEKT VISOKOGRADNJA A.D.
Bulevar Mihaila Pupina 12, 11070, Belgrade, Serbia
Tel.: (381) 11 310 15 02
Web Site: http://www.energovg.rs
Year Founded: 1951
Sales Range: $25-49.9 Million
Construction Consulting Services
N.A.I.C.S.: 541330
Ljiljana Gnjatovic (Sec)

ENERGOSBYT PLUS JSC
Building 52a Ul Ordzhonikidze, Izhevsk, 426063, Russia
Tel.: (7) 3412681864

Web Site: http://www.udm.esplus.ru
Sales Range: Less than $1 Million
Electric Power Distribution Services
N.A.I.C.S.: 237130

ENERGROUP HOLDINGS CORPORATION
No 9 Xin Yi Street, Ganjinzgi District, Dalian, 116039, Liaoning, China
Tel.: (86) 41186716696
Meat Product Distr
N.A.I.C.S.: 424470
Huashan Shi (Pres & CEO)

ENERGULF RESOURCES INC.
15444 Royal Avenue, White Rock, V4B 1N1, BC, Canada
Tel.: (604) 408-1990   BC
Web Site:
     https://www.keyfactsenergy.com
Year Founded: 1981
ENG—(TSXV)
Oil & Gas Exploration Services
N.A.I.C.S.: 213112
Clive Brookes (CFO)

ENERGY ABSOLUTE PUBLIC COMPANY LIMITED
16th Floor AIA Capital Center Building 89 Ratchadaphisek Road, Dindaeng, Bangkok, 10400, Thailand
Tel.: (66) 22482488
Web Site:
     https://www.energyabsolute.co.th
Year Founded: 2006
EA—(THA)
Rev.: $922,400,735
Assets: $3,334,579,334
Liabilities: $2,049,851,980
Net Worth: $1,284,727,354
Earnings: $218,943,844
Emp.: 257
Fiscal Year-end: 12/31/23
Biodiesel Production
N.A.I.C.S.: 324199
Amorn Sapthaweekul (Deputy CEO)

Subsidiaries:

Absolute Assembly Co., Ltd. (1)
8/8 Moo 1, Tumbol Klong Prawet Amphur Ban Pho, Chachoengsao, 24140, Thailand
Tel.: (66) 33050733
Electric Vehicle Component Mfr & Distr
N.A.I.C.S.: 336320

Amita Technologies Inc. (1)
No 6 Chazhuan Rd, Gueishan, Taoyuan, 333-49, Taiwan
Tel.: (886) 32631212
Web Site: https://www.amitatech.com
Lithium Polymer Battery Mfr
N.A.I.C.S.: 335910

Amita Technology (Thailand) Co., Ltd. (1)
No 89 AIA Capital Center Building 16th Floor Ratchadapisek Road, Din Daeng Sub-district, Bangkok, 10400, Thailand
Tel.: (66) 2248248892
Web Site: https://www.amitathailand.co.th
Lithium Battery Mfr
N.A.I.C.S.: 335910

Battery Electric Vehicle & Electronic Products Testing Center Co., Ltd. (1)
No 89 AIA Capital Center Building 16th Floor, Daeng Sub-District Din Daeng District, Bangkok, 10400, Thailand
Tel.: (66) 2248248892
Wind Power Energy Mfr & Distr
N.A.I.C.S.: 333611

EA Palm Network Co., Ltd. (1)
No 89 AIA Capital Center Building 16th Floor, Din Dang Sub-District Din Dang District, Bangkok, 10400, Thailand
Tel.: (66) 2248248892
Crude Palm Oil Mfr & Distr
N.A.I.C.S.: 311225

Energy Mahanakhon Co., Ltd. (1)

16th Floor AIA Capital Center Building 89 Ratchadaphisek Road, Dindaeng, Bangkok, 10400, Thailand
Tel.: (66) 20266133
Web Site: https://www.eaanywhere.com
Electric Charging Stations For Electric Vehicle Services
N.A.I.C.S.: 532120

Energy Solution Management Co., Ltd. (1)
No 89 AIA Capital Center Building 16th Floor, Din Daeng Sub-District Din Daeng District, Bangkok, 10400, Thailand
Tel.: (66) 2248248892
Power Plant Electricity Services
N.A.I.C.S.: 221118

Kanjanadit Palm Oil Co., Ltd. (1)
No 179/1 Tha U Thae Sub-distrot, Kanchanadit District, Surat Thani, 84160, Thailand
Tel.: (66) 77953012
Electric Battery Mfr & Distr
N.A.I.C.S.: 335311

Mine Mobility Corporation Co., Ltd. (1)
No 89 AIA Capital Center Building 16th Floor, Din Dang Sub-District Din Dang District, Bangkok, 10400, Thailand
Tel.: (66) 2248248892
Web Site: https://www.minemobility.com
Electric Vehicle Mfr
N.A.I.C.S.: 336320
Kant Suadtummakit (Mgr-Ops)

Paypop Co., Ltd. (1)
No 89 AIA Capital Center Building 16th Floor, Din Dang Sub-District Din Dang District, Bangkok, 10400, Thailand
Tel.: (66) 2248248892
Electronic Financial Transaction Services
N.A.I.C.S.: 522320

Surachai (1997) Co., Ltd. (1)
No 89 AIA Capital Center Building 16th Floor Ratchadapisek Road, Din Dang Sub-District Din Dang District, Bangkok, 10400, Thailand
Tel.: (66) 2248248892
Solar Power Electricity Distribution Services
N.A.I.C.S.: 221114

ENERGY ACTION LIMITED
Level 5 56 Station Street, Parramatta, 2150, NSW, Australia
Tel.: (61) 296336451
Web Site:
     https://www.energyaction.com.au
Year Founded: 2000
EAX—(ASX)
Rev.: $7,629,943
Assets: $6,976,863
Liabilities: $5,418,457
Net Worth: $1,558,406
Earnings: $390,229
Emp.: 150
Fiscal Year-end: 06/30/24
Energy Procurement & Management Services
N.A.I.C.S.: 213112
John Huggart (CEO)

Subsidiaries:

Energy Action (Australia) Pty Limited (1)
Level 5 56 Station Street, Dharug Country, Parramatta, 2150, NSW, Australia
Tel.: (61) 298916911
Sales Range: $50-74.9 Million
Eltric Power Generation Services
N.A.I.C.S.: 221118

ENERGY DEVELOPMENT COMPANY LIMITED
EDCL House 1A Elgin Road, Kolkata, 700 020, West Bengal, India
Tel.: (91) 3340411983
Web Site: https://www.edclgroup.com
Year Founded: 1995
ENERGYDEV—(NSE)
Rev.: $4,575,152
Assets: $47,163,071
Liabilities: $35,858,141

Net Worth: $11,304,930
Earnings: ($862,707)
Emp.: 37
Fiscal Year-end: 03/31/21
Eletric Power Generation Services
N.A.I.C.S.: 221111
Vijayshree Binnani (Officer-Compliance & Sec)

ENERGY DEVELOPMENT CORPORATION
38/F One Corporate Centre Julia Vargas corner Meralco Ave Ortigas Ctr, Pasig, 1605, Philippines
Tel.: (63) 26677332
Web Site: http://www.energy.com.ph
Rev.: $665,103,814
Assets: $2,751,742,436
Liabilities: $1,579,827,238
Net Worth: $1,171,915,199
Earnings: $158,829,941
Emp.: 1,866
Fiscal Year-end: 12/31/17
Power Generation Services
N.A.I.C.S.: 221111
Richard B. Tantoco (Pres & COO)

ENERGY EARTH PUBLIC COMPANY LIMITED
889 Thai CC Tower 125-128 F12, South Sathorn Road, Bangkok, 10120, Thailand
Tel.: (66) 2 673 9631
Web Site:
     http://www.energyearth.co.th
Sales Range: $500-549.9 Million
Bituminous Coal Whslr
N.A.I.C.S.: 423520
Phisudhi Phihakendr (Chm)

ENERGY INTERNATIONAL INVESTMENTS HOLDINGS LIMITED
Units 4307-08 Office Tower Convention Plaza 1 Harbour Road, Wanchai, China (Hong Kong)
Tel.: (852) 2 169 3104   Ky
Web Site:
     http://website.energyintinv.com
0353—(HKG)
Rev.: $67,144,279
Assets: $303,008,845
Liabilities: $143,090,670
Net Worth: $159,918,175
Earnings: $5,408,905
Emp.: 71
Fiscal Year-end: 03/31/22
Investment Management Service
N.A.I.C.S.: 523940
Wai Cheung Chan (Sec)

ENERGY LAB S.P.A.
Via Cividal 12, 33040, Moimacco, Italy
Tel.: (39) 0432 734175
Web Site: http://www.e-labgroup.it
Power Plant Construction
N.A.I.C.S.: 237130

ENERGY METALS LIMITED
Level 2 5 Ord Street, West Perth, 6005, WA, Australia
Tel.: (61) 893226904
Web Site:
     https://www.energymetals.net
EME—(ASX)
Rev.: $411,264
Assets: $33,925,466
Liabilities: $128,727
Net Worth: $33,796,739
Earnings: ($262,590)
Fiscal Year-end: 12/31/23
Uranium Exploration
N.A.I.C.S.: 212290
Shuqing Xiao (Mng Dir)

ENERGY ONE LIMITED

Level 13 77 Pacific Highway, Sydney, 2060, NSW, Australia
Tel.: (61) 289162200　　　　　AU
Web Site:
　https://www.energyone.com
EOL—(ASX)
Rev.: $35,028,045
Assets: $61,736,111
Liabilities: $26,268,696
Net Worth: $35,467,414
Earnings: $962,206
Emp.: 100
Fiscal Year-end: 06/30/24
Software Development Services
N.A.I.C.S.: 541511
Andrew Bonwick (Chm)

Subsidiaries:

CQ Energy Pty. Ltd.　　　　　(1)
143/220 Greenhill Road, Eastwood, 5063, SA, Australia
Tel.: (61) 884640300
Web Site: https://www.cqenergy.com.au
Eletric Power Generation Services
N.A.I.C.S.: 221118

Contigo Software Limited　　　(1)
4th Floor Radcliffe House Blenheim Court, Solihull, B91 2AA, United Kingdom
Tel.: (44) 8458386848
Web Site: http://www.contigosoftware.com
Software Services
N.A.I.C.S.: 541511
Simon Wheeler (CEO)

eZ-nergy SAS　　　　　　　(1)
24 rue de l'Est, 75020, Paris, France
Tel.: (33) 184177565
Web Site: http://www.ez-nergy.com
Emp.: 20
Oil Trading Services
N.A.I.C.S.: 523160
Johann Zamboni (Co-Founder & CEO)

ENERGY POWER SYSTEMS AUSTRALIA PTY. LTD.

227 Wellington Road, Mulgrave, 3170, VIC, Australia
Tel.: (61) 385624100
Web Site:
　http://www.energypower.com.au
Year Founded: 1992
Sales Range: $500-549.9 Million
Emp.: 220
Medium-Speed Engine & High-Speed Diesel Engine Supplier
N.A.I.C.S.: 423120
Rob Siegrist (Bus Mgr-Oil & Gas)

Subsidiaries:

Energy Power Systems PNG Limited　　　　　　　(1)
Spring Garden Road, Port Moresby, Hohola, Papua New Guinea
Tel.: (675) 3008358
Web Site:
　http://www.energysystems.com.au
Sales Range: $25-49.9 Million
Emp.: 50
Electric Power Distribution
N.A.I.C.S.: 221122

ENERGY SOURCE NATURAL GAS SERVICES INC.

102 75 Farquhar St, Guelph, N1H 3N4, ON, Canada
Tel.: (519) 826-0777
Web Site:
　http://www.energysource.ca
Rev.: $80,032,798
Emp.: 11
Natural Gas Distr
N.A.I.C.S.: 221210
Dave Cornies (Pres)

ENERGY TECHNOLOGIES LIMITED

J/134-140 Old Pittwater Road, Brookvale, 2100, NSW, Australia
Tel.: (61) 289782610　　　　　AU
Web Site:
　https://www.energytechnologies.com
EGY—(ASX)
Rev.: $8,612,905
Assets: $13,440,485
Liabilities: $15,984,911
Net Worth: ($2,544,426)
Earnings: ($7,037,079)
Emp.: 73
Fiscal Year-end: 06/30/24
Energy Infrastructure Products Mfr
N.A.I.C.S.: 541330
Alfred J. Chown (Mng Dir & Chm)

Subsidiaries:

Bambach Wires & Cables Pty Ltd　　　　　　　　(1)
J/134-140 Old Pittwater Road, Brookvale, 2100, NSW, Australia
Tel.: (61) 29 938 5622
Web Site: https://bambachcables.com.au
Carrying Wiring Device Mfr
N.A.I.C.S.: 335931

Dulhunty Poles Pty Ltd　　　　(1)
35 Buckley Grove, Moolap, Geelong, 3224, VIC, Australia
Tel.: (61) 35 248 1661
Web Site: https://dulhuntypoles.com
Cement Mfr & Distr
N.A.I.C.S.: 327390
Phil Scott (Gen Mgr)

Dulhunty Power (Aust) Pty Limited　　　　　　　(1)
Tel.: (61) 298707277
Web Site: http://www.dulhuntypower.com
Electricity Transmission & Distribution Products Mfr
N.A.I.C.S.: 335139

Subsidiary (Non-US):

Dulhunty Power (NZ) Limited　(2)
Tel.: (64) 94247295
Web Site: http://www.dulhuntypower.com
Transmission & Disribution Equipment Mfr
N.A.I.C.S.: 335311

Dulhunty Power (Thailand) Limited　　　　　　　(1)
105/1-2 Moo 1 Bang Sao Thong District, Srisa Chorakhe Yai, Samut Prakan, 10570, Thailand
Tel.: (66) 639874564
Web Site: http://www.dulhuntypower.com
Emp.: 30
Electricity Transmission & Distribution Products Mfr
N.A.I.C.S.: 335139
Pana Pong Pairoj (Gen Mgr)

ENERGY TRANSITION MINERALS LTD

Tel.: (61) 893822322
Web Site: https://www.ggg.gl
ETM—(ASX)
Rev.: $230,229
Assets: $15,197,138
Liabilities: $1,015,595
Net Worth: $14,181,543
Earnings: ($4,159,783)
Emp.: 28
Fiscal Year-end: 12/31/23
Specialty Metals & Uranium Exploration Services
N.A.I.C.S.: 212290
John Lefroy Mair (Mng Dir)

ENERGY TRANSITION PARTNERS B.V.

Luna Arena Herikerbergweg 238, 1101, Amsterdam, Netherlands
Tel.: (31) 205755600　　　　　Nl
Web Site: https://www.entpa.nl
Year Founded: 2021
ENTPA—(EUR)
Assets: $219,374,132
Liabilities: $237,289,090
Net Worth: ($17,914,958)
Earnings: ($11,658,546)

Fiscal Year-end: 12/31/22
Asset Management Services
N.A.I.C.S.: 523999
Anthony Bryan Hayward (Chm)

ENERGY WORLD CORPORATION LTD

9A Seaforth Crescent, Seaforth, Sydney, 2092, NSW, Australia
Tel.: (61) 292476888　　　　　AU
Web Site:
　https://www.energyworldcorp.com
Year Founded: 1985
EWCLF—(OTCIQ)
Rev.: $149,365,000
Assets: $1,705,679,000
Liabilities: $913,416,000
Net Worth: $792,263,000
Earnings: $1,842,000
Fiscal Year-end: 06/30/21
Oil & Gas Exploration Services
N.A.I.C.S.: 211120
Stewart William George Elliott (Chm, CEO & Mng Dir)

Subsidiaries:

Central Energy Australia Pty Ltd　(1)
PO Box 3482, Alice Springs, 0871, NT, Australia
Tel.: (61) 889522511
Oil & Gas Exploration Services
N.A.I.C.S.: 213112

PT South Sulawesi LNG　　　　(1)
Fajar Graha Pena 18th Floor, Makassar, South Sulawesi, Indonesia
Tel.: (62) 411422131
Oil & Gas Exploration Services
N.A.I.C.S.: 213112

ENERGYO SOLUTIONS INVEST AB

Styckjunkargatan 1, 114 35, Stockholm, Sweden
Tel.: (46) 84073150
Web Site: https://www.eosinv.com
V38—(BER)
Rev.: $629,408
Assets: $23,387,564
Liabilities: $11,114,764
Net Worth: $12,272,800
Earnings: ($42,568,116)
Emp.: 1
Fiscal Year-end: 12/31/22
Asset Management Services
N.A.I.C.S.: 523940
Ulf-Henrik Svensson (CEO)

ENERGYPATHWAYS PLC

Highdown House Yeoman Way, Worthing, BN99 3HH, West Sussex, United Kingdom
Tel.: (44) 1615299910　　　　　UK
Web Site: https://energypathways.uk
Year Founded: 2021
EPP—(LSE)
Investment Management Service
N.A.I.C.S.: 523999

ENERKEM INC.

1130 Sherbrooke Street West Suite 1500, Montreal, H3A 2M8, QC, Canada
Tel.: (514) 875-0284　　　　　Ca
Web Site: http://www.enerkem.com
Sales Range: $1-9.9 Million
Emp.: 136
Chemicals Mfr
N.A.I.C.S.: 325998
Joshua Ruch (Chm)

ENERO GROUP LIMITED

Level 2 100 Harris Street, Pyrmont, 2009, NSW, Australia
Tel.: (61) 282133031　　　　　AU
Web Site: https://www.enero.com
Year Founded: 2000

EGG—(ASX)
Rev.: $537,175,479
Assets: $200,912,793
Liabilities: $92,018,563
Net Worth: $108,894,230
Earnings: ($24,798,344)
Emp.: 650
Fiscal Year-end: 06/30/24
Advertising Services
N.A.I.C.S.: 551112
Brendan York (Acting Co-CFO, Co-CEO & Co-Sec)

Subsidiaries:

BMF　　　　　　　　　　(1)
Level 2 100 Harris Street, Pyrmont, 2009, NSW, Australia
Tel.: (61) 295527000
Web Site: https://www.bmf.com.au
Sales Range: $75-99.9 Million
Emp.: 230
N.A.I.C.S.: 541810
Matthew Melhuish (Chm)

BMF Advertising Pty Limited　(1)
Level 2 63 Miller Street, Pyrmont, 2009, NSW, Australia
Tel.: (61) 295527000
Web Site: http://www.bmf.com.au
Sales Range: $25-49.9 Million
Emp.: 200
Advertising Agency Services
N.A.I.C.S.: 541810
Matthew Melhuish (Chm)

City Public Relations Pty Limited　(1)
Level 6 155 George Street, Sydney, 2000, NSW, Australia
Tel.: (61) 2 8916 4848
Web Site:
　http://www.citypublicrelations.com.au
Public Relations Services
N.A.I.C.S.: 541820
Tim Allerton (Mng Dir)

DVL Smith Limited　　　　　(1)
106 Charter Avenue, Ilford, IG2 7AD, United Kingdom
Tel.: (44) 2033972552
Web Site: https://www.dvlsmith.com
Emp.: 5
Marketing Consulting Services
N.A.I.C.S.: 541613

Dark Blue Sea Limited　　　　(1)
Level 1 91 Bridge Street, Fortitude Valley, 4006, QLD, Australia
Tel.: (61) 730070000
Web Site: http://www.darkbluesea.com
Sales Range: $10-24.9 Million
Online Direct Navigation Supplier
N.A.I.C.S.: 541890

Subsidiary (Domestic):

DBS Administration Pty Limited　(2)
Level 1 91 Birch Street, PO Box 278, Brisbane, 4006, QLD, Australia
Tel.: (61) 730070000
Web Site: http://www.darkbluesea.com
Emp.: 4
Online Marketing Services
N.A.I.C.S.: 541613
Peter Stevenson (Mgr-Ops)

Darkblue.com Pty Limited　　(2)
Level 1 91 Bridge St, Fortitude Valley, 4006, QLD, Australia
Tel.: (61) 7 3007 0070
Web Site: http://www.darkbluesea.com
Online Marketing Services
N.A.I.C.S.: 541613

Domain Active Pty Limited　　(2)
Level 10 243 Edward St, PO Box 262, Clayfield, Brisbane, 4000, QLD, Australia
Tel.: (61) 730185100
Emp.: 5
Online Marketing Services
N.A.I.C.S.: 541613

Fabulous.com Pty Limited　　(2)
Level 1 91 Bridge Street Fortitude Valley, Brisbane, 4006, QLD, Australia
Tel.: (61) 7 3007 0070
Web Site: http://www.fabulous.com
Emp.: 10
Online Marketing Services

Enero Group Limited—(Continued)

N.A.I.C.S.: 541613

Roar.com Pty Limited (2)
Level 10, 243 Edward St, Brisbane, 4000,
Queensland, Australia
Tel.: (61) 7 3007 0070
Web Site: http://www.roar.com
Contextual Advertising Network & Online
Marketing Services
N.A.I.C.S.: 541613

**Whois Privacy Services Pty
Limited** (2)
PO Box 1717, Brisbane, Queensland, Aus-
tralia
Tel.: (61) 730070090
Domain Privacy Services
N.A.I.C.S.: 518210

Energo Group Limited (1)
Level 2 100 Harris Street, Pyrmont, 2009,
NSW, Australia
Tel.: (61) 282133031
Web Site: https://enero.com
Sales Range: $25-49.9 Million
Emp.: 20
Marketing Consulting Services
N.A.I.C.S.: 541613

Findology Interactive Media (1)
1158 26th St Ste 464, Santa Monica, CA
90403
Tel.: (310) 556-4440
Web Site: http://www.findology.com
Sales Range: $25-49.9 Million
Emp.: 20
N.A.I.C.S.: 541890
George Coo (Acct Mgr)

Frank PR Australia Pty Limited (1)
Level 2 1 Miller Lane, Surry Hills, Pyrmont,
2009, NSW, Australia
Tel.: (61) 2 8202 0555
Web Site: http://www.frankpr.com.au
Sales Range: $25-49.9 Million
Emp.: 20
Public Relations Consulting Services
N.A.I.C.S.: 541820
Graham Goodkind (Co-Founder & Chm)

Frank PR Limited (1)
Centro 4 20-23 Mandela St, London, NW1
0DU, United Kingdom
Tel.: (44) 2076936999
Web Site: http://www.frankpr.it
Sales Range: $25-49.9 Million
Emp.: 65
Public Relation Agency Services
N.A.I.C.S.: 541820
Graham Goodkind (Co-Founder & Chm)

Hotwire Public Relations Limited (1)
69 Wilson Street, London, EC2A 2BB,
United Kingdom
Tel.: (44) 2076082500
Web Site: https://www.hotwireglobal.co.uk
Public Relations Consulting Services
N.A.I.C.S.: 541820
John Brown (Grp Sr VP-Strategy &
Innovation-New York)

Subsidiary (Non-US):

**Hotwire Public Relation Italy
S.R.L.** (2)
Via Nino Bixio 7, 20122, Milan, Italy
Tel.: (39) 027729968
Web Site: http://www.hotwirepr.it
Sales Range: $25-49.9 Million
Emp.: 4
Public Relations Consulting Services
N.A.I.C.S.: 541820

Hotwire Public Relations GmbH (2)
Stephanstrasse 1, 60313, Frankfurt am
Main, Germany
Tel.: (49) 6925669370
Web Site: http://www.hotwirepr.de
Public Relations Consulting Services
N.A.I.C.S.: 541820

Hotwire Public Relations SARL (2)
105 rue du Faubourg Saint-Honore, 75008,
Paris, France
Tel.: (33) 143125555
Web Site: http://www.hotwirepr.fr
Emp.: 25
Public Relation Agency Services
N.A.I.C.S.: 541820

Hotwire Public Relations SL (2)
C de la Libertad 15 bajo b, 28004, Madrid,
Spain
Tel.: (34) 917441265
Web Site: https://www.hotwireglobal.es
Sales Range: $25-49.9 Million
Emp.: 15
Public Relations Consulting Services
N.A.I.C.S.: 541820
Yashim Zavaleta (Country Mgr)

ISS Marketing Pty Limited (1)
Suite 102 490 Crown Street, Surry Hills,
2010, NSW, Australia
Tel.: (61) 2 9018 8730
Web Site: http://www.issmarketing.com.au
Sales Range: $25-49.9 Million
Emp.: 5
Marketing Consulting Services
N.A.I.C.S.: 541613
Michael Blumberg (Mng Dir)

ImageBox Group Pty Limited (1)
112 Buckhurst Street, South Melbourne,
3205, VIC, Australia
Tel.: (61) 396969022
Web Site: https://www.imagebox.com.au
Sales Range: $25-49.9 Million
Emp.: 22
Graphic Design Services
N.A.I.C.S.: 541430
David Asker (Co-Mng Dir)

**Naked Communications Australia Pty
Limited** (1)
Level 1 63 Miller St Tyrmond, Pyrmont,
2009, NSW, Australia
Tel.: (61) 292133400
Web Site:
    http://www.nakedcommunications.com.au
Emp.: 25
Marketing Consulting Services
N.A.I.C.S.: 541613
Paul Ward (Grp Chief Production Officer-
Sydney)

Subsidiary (Non-US):

Naked NZ Limited (2)
150 Karangahape Rd Suite 602, Auckland,
1010, New Zealand
Tel.: (64) 9 307 3860
Sales Range: $25-49.9 Million
Emp.: 10
Business Consulting Services
N.A.I.C.S.: 541618

Naked Communications Ltd. (1)
Tel.: (44) 207 336 8084
Web Site: http://www.nakedcomms.com
Sales Range: $25-49.9 Million
Emp.: 60
Advetising Agency
N.A.I.C.S.: 541810

Subsidiary (Non-US):

Lunch Communications Limited (2)
Tel.: (44) 20 7663 1650
Web Site: http://www.lunchcomms.com
Marketing Consulting Services
N.A.I.C.S.: 541613

Branch (Non-US):

Naked Communications Nordic (2)
Tel.: (47) 2299 2150
Sales Range: $25-49.9 Million
Emp.: 10
N.A.I.C.S.: 541810

Ne Kid Paris (2)
Tel.: (33) 143381548
Sales Range: $25-49.9 Million
Emp.: 10
N.A.I.C.S.: 541810

OB Media LLC (1)
3740 Greenbriar Dr No 540901, Houston,
TX 77098
Tel.: (713) 850-0607
Web Site: https://www.obmedia.com
Online Advertising Services
N.A.I.C.S.: 541613

**Photon Group Singapore Pte
Limited** (1)
28 Maxwell Road 04-08 Reddot Traffic, Sin-
gapore, 069120, Singapore
Tel.: (65) 64356116
Marketing Research Service

N.A.I.C.S.: 541910

**Powerforce Field Marketing & Retail
Services Ltd** (1)
650 Wharfedale Road Winnersh Triangle,
Winnersh, RG41 5TP, Berkshire, United
Kingdom
Tel.: (44) 1189271090
Web Site: https://www.powerforcegb.com
Emp.: 15
Marketing Agency & Research Services
N.A.I.C.S.: 541910
Jane Wood (Dir-Acct)

Precinct (1)
6 Bond St, Yarra, VIC 3141, Australia
Tel.: (61) 3 9856 2977
Web Site: http://www.precinct.com.au
N.A.I.C.S.: 541810
Jaime Nelson (Mng Dir)

Sledge (1)
7 Glenthorne Mews, London, W6 0LJ,
United Kingdom
Tel.: (44) 2087404550
Web Site: https://www.sledge.co.uk
Rev.: $22,000,000
Emp.: 30
Advetising Agency
N.A.I.C.S.: 541810
Robin Fawcett (Co-Founder & CEO)

**The Leading Edge Market Research
Consultants Pty Limited** (1)
Level 6 76 Commonwealth Street, Millers
Point, Sydney, 2010, NSW, Australia
Tel.: (61) 292584444
Web Site:
    http://www.theleadingedge.com.au
Sales Range: $25-49.9 Million
Emp.: 30
Marketing Research Service
N.A.I.C.S.: 541910
Lee Naylor (Mng Partner-Asia Pacific)

ENERPLUS CORPORATION
The Dome Tower 3000 333 7th Av-
enue SW, Calgary, T2P 2Z1, AB,
Canada
Tel.: (403) 298-2200
Web Site: http://www.enerplus.com
Year Founded: 1986
ERF—(NYSE)
Rev.: $1,694,333,000
Assets: $2,068,476,000
Liabilities: $841,127,000
Net Worth: $1,227,349,000
Earnings: $456,076,000
Emp.: 404
Fiscal Year-end: 12/31/23
Oil & Gas Refining
N.A.I.C.S.: 211120
Ian C. Dundas (Pres & CEO)

Subsidiaries:

Enerplus Resources (USA)
Corporation (1)
950 17th St Ste 2200, Denver, CO
80202-2805 (100%)
Tel.: (720) 279-5500
Web Site: http://www.enerplus.com
Sales Range: $1-9.9 Million
Emp.: 150
Oil & Gas Refining
N.A.I.C.S.: 211120
Edward L. McLaughlin (Pres)

ENERSENSE INTERNATIONAL
OYJ
Konepajanranta 2, 28100, Pori, Fin-
land
Tel.: (358) 26337722 FI
Web Site:
    https://www.enersense.com
Year Founded: 2005
ESENSE—(HEL)
Rev.: $401,057,512
Assets: $235,942,157
Liabilities: $178,421,459
Net Worth: $57,520,698
Earnings: ($10,099,349)
Emp.: 1,982
Fiscal Year-end: 12/31/23

Reduced Emissions Consulting, Engi-
neering & Support Services
N.A.I.C.S.: 541330
Jyri Laakso (Acct Mgr)

ENERSIZE OYJ
Friitalantie 13, Ulvila, FI-28400, Fin-
land
Tel.: (358) 207980310
ENERS—(OMX)
Rev.: $194,259
Assets: $2,169,221
Liabilities: $1,046,838
Not Worth: $1,122,383
Earnings: ($2,611,699)
Emp.: 3
Fiscal Year-end: 12/31/22
Software Development Services
N.A.I.C.S.: 541511
Daniel Winkler (Head-Sls & Mktg)

ENERSPAR CORP.
22 Coulson Avenue, Toronto, M4V
1Y5, ON, Canada
Tel.: (416) 410-5297 AB
Web Site: http://enerspar.com
Year Founded: 2011
ENER—(TSXV)
Assets: $13,897
Liabilities: $79,107
Net Worth: ($65,210)
Earnings: ($21,725)
Fiscal Year-end: 12/31/20
Investment Services
N.A.I.C.S.: 523999
James A. Richardson (CEO)

ENERTIME SAS
1 Rue du Moulin des Bruyeres,
92400, Courbevoie, France
Tel.: (33) 175431540
Web Site: https://www.enertime.com
Year Founded: 2008
ALENE—(EUR)
Sales Range: $1-9.9 Million
Emp.: 42
Industrial Machinery Mfr & Distr
N.A.I.C.S.: 334513
Gilles David (Co-Founder & CEO)

ENERTOPIA CORPORATION
7 1873 Spall Rd, Kelowna, V1Y 4R2,
BC, Canada
Tel.: (250) 870-2219 NV
Web Site: https://www.enertopia.com
Year Founded: 2004
ENRT—(CSE)
Assets: $342,630
Liabilities: $316,032
Net Worth: $26,598
Earnings: ($999,010)
Fiscal Year-end: 08/31/24
Oil & Gas Exploration & Other Re-
lated Services
N.A.I.C.S.: 211120
Robert G. McAllister (Chm, Pres &
CEO)

ENERTORK LTD.
344 Neungyouro, Sejeongdaewang-
myeon, Yeoju, Gyeonggi, Korea
(South)
Tel.: (82) 25550883
Web Site: https://www.enertork.com
Year Founded: 1987
019990—(KRS)
Rev.: $20,162,188
Assets: $39,684,582
Liabilities: $5,629,967
Net Worth: $34,054,615
Earnings: $582,992
Emp.: 96
Fiscal Year-end: 12/31/22
Actuator & Decelerator Mfr
N.A.I.C.S.: 333995
Minchan Kim (CTO)

ENERTRONICA SANTERNO S.P.A.
Via della Concia, 7, 40023, Castel Guelfo, Italy
Tel.: (39) 0542489711
Web Site:
https://enertronicasanterno.it
ENT—(ITA)
Solar Power Plant Construction
N.A.I.C.S.: 237130
Vito Nardi (CEO)

Subsidiaries:

Elettronica Santerno S.p.A. (1)
Strada Statale Selice 47, Imola, 40026, Bologna, Italy
Tel.: (39) 0542668611
Web Site: http://www.elettronicasanterno.it
Sales Range: $75-99.9 Million
Emp.: 66
Other Electric Power Generation
N.A.I.C.S.: 221118

ENERVIT S.P.A.
Viale Achille Papa 30, 20149, Milan, Italy
Tel.: (39) 02485631 IT
Web Site: https://www.enervit.com
Year Founded: 1954
ENV—(ITA)
Sales Range: $50-74.9 Million
Emp.: 140
Sports Nutrition Products Researcher, Developer, Mfr & Marketer
N.A.I.C.S.: 311999

ENERZENT CO., LTD.
30 Techno 1-ro, Yuseong-gu, Daejeon, Korea (South)
Tel.: (82) 426208000
Web Site:
http://www.gemvaxtech.com
Year Founded: 1998
041590—(KRS)
Rev.: $29,519,877
Assets: $96,551,170
Liabilities: $39,988,068
Net Worth: $56,563,101
Earnings: ($19,174,810)
Emp.: 126
Fiscal Year-end: 12/31/22
LCD Module Mfr
N.A.I.C.S.: 334419
Sang Jae Kim (CEO)

ENEVA S.A.
Empresarial Mourisco-Praia de Botafogo 501 Torre Corcovado sala 404, Rio de Janeiro, 22250-040, Brazil
Tel.: (55) 2137213000 BR
Web Site: https://www.eneva.com.br
ENEV3—(BRAZ)
Rev.: $2,012,343,205
Assets: $8,687,980,656
Liabilities: $5,709,092,233
Net Worth: $2,978,888,424
Earnings: $60,510,918
Emp.: 1,551
Fiscal Year-end: 12/31/23
Power Generation Services
N.A.I.C.S.: 221112
Marcelo Habibe (Fin Dir)

ENEX CO., LTD.
40 Seocho-daero 73-gil, Seocho-gu, Seoul, Korea (South)
Tel.: (82) 221852000
Web Site: https://www.enex.co.kr
Year Founded: 1976
011090—(KRS)
Rev.: $157,968,510
Assets: $98,237,480
Liabilities: $64,227,858
Net Worth: $34,009,622
Earnings: ($18,002,558)
Emp.: 241

Fiscal Year-end: 12/31/22
Home Furniture Mfr & Whlsr
N.A.I.C.S.: 337122
Sung-Soo Song (CEO & VP)

ENEX ENERGY CORP
4F 6750 Office Tower Ayala Avenue, Makati, 1226, Philippines
Tel.: (63) 277306300
Web Site: http://enexor.com.ph
Year Founded: 1994
ENEX—(PHI)
Assets: $2,579,780
Liabilities: $4,612,587
Net Worth: ($2,032,807)
Earnings: $932,024
Emp.: 1
Fiscal Year-end: 12/31/23
Renewable Power Generation Services
N.A.I.C.S.: 221118
John Eric T. Francia (Chm & CEO)

ENEX INFRASTRUCTURE INVESTMENT CORP.
29th floor Kasumigaseki Building 325 Kasumigaseki, Chiyoda-ku, Tokyo, 100-6008, Japan
Tel.: (81) 342338330
Web Site: https://www.enexinfra.com
Year Founded: 2018
9286—(TKS)
Rev.: $11,529,111
Assets: $184,281,246
Liabilities: $107,068,746
Net Worth: $77,212,500
Earnings: $2,833,337
Fiscal Year-end: 11/30/19
Asset Management Services
N.A.I.C.S.: 523940
Keiichi Matsuzuka (Exec Officer)

ENEXOMA AG
Dalbker Strasse 138, D-33813, Oerlinghausen, Germany
Tel.: (49) 5205 879 2630
Web Site: http://www.enexoma.de
Emp.: 15
Software Publisher
N.A.I.C.S.: 513210
Nikolaus Brakowski (Mng Dir)

ENF TECHNOLOGY CO., LTD.
14 Tapsil-ro 35beon-gil, Giheung-gu, Yongin, 17084, Gyeonggi-do, Korea (South)
Tel.: (82) 318818200
Web Site: https://www.enftech.com
Year Founded: 2000
102710—(KRS)
Rev.: $521,718,754
Assets: $507,968,087
Liabilities: $207,552,456
Net Worth: $300,415,631
Earnings: $35,899,779
Emp.: 568
Fiscal Year-end: 12/31/22
Chemical Products Mfr
N.A.I.C.S.: 325998
Yong-Seok Chi (CEO)

Subsidiaries:

ENF Technology Co., Ltd. - Asan Plant (1)
123-38 Injusandan-ro, Inju-myeon, Asan, Chungcheongnam-do, Korea (South)
Tel.: (82) 415383700
Chemical Products Mfr
N.A.I.C.S.: 325998

ENF Technology Co., Ltd. - Ulsan Plant (1)
66 Sanggae-ro, Nam-gu, Ulsan, Korea (South)
Tel.: (82) 522594800
Chemical Products Mfr
N.A.I.C.S.: 325998
Yong-Seok Chi (CEO)

ENFIELD EXPLORATION CORP.
2408 Pine Street, Vancouver, V6J 0A9, BC, Canada
Tel.: (604) 721-3000 BC
Web Site:
http://enfieldexploration.com
Year Founded: 2013
Metal Mining
N.A.I.C.S.: 212290
John Bevilacqua (Pres & CEO)

ENFINITY N.V.
Henri Lebbestraat 188, Waregem, 8790, Belgium
Tel.: (32) 56288888 BE
Web Site: http://www.enfinity.be
Year Founded: 2005
Sales Range: $100-124.9 Million
Emp.: 100
Renewable Energy Project Development, Management & Financing Services
N.A.I.C.S.: 237130
Patrick Decuyper (Founder)

Subsidiaries:

Enfinity Corporation (1)
1414 S St, Sacramento, CA 95814 (100%)
Tel.: (916) 339-7003
Web Site: http://www.enfinitycorp.com
Renewable Energy Project Development, Management & Financing Services
N.A.I.C.S.: 237130

Enfinity France SARL (1)
Les Lofts du Vieux Port 7 Cours Jean Ballard, 13001, Marseille, France
Tel.: (33) 4 86 95 97 25
Web Site: http://www.enfinity.fr
Solar Product Mfr & Distr
N.A.I.C.S.: 333414

Enfinity Italia srl (1)
Via Colico 36, 20158, Milan, Italy
Tel.: (39) 02 36 590 400
Web Site: http://www.enfinity.it
Solar Product Mfr & Distr
N.A.I.C.S.: 333414

Enfinity Philippines Renewable Resources Inc. (1)
9th Floor Unit 9D Ayala-Life FGU Center Ayala Avenue, 6811, Makati, Philippines
Tel.: (63) 2 576 9007
Solar Product Mfr & Distr
N.A.I.C.S.: 333414
Dennis Ibarra (Pres)

Enfinity Thailand Limited (1)
Jasmine International Tower 5th floor room no 507, No 200 Moo 4 Chaengwatthana Rd, 11100, Nonthaburi, Thailand
Tel.: (66) 2 964 9996
Solar Product Mfr & Distr
N.A.I.C.S.: 333414

ENFO OYJ
Viestikatu 7, 70600, Kuopio, Finland
Tel.: (358) 2054321
Web Site: http://www.enfo.fi
Year Founded: 1964
Rev.: $136,013,716
Assets: $133,897,181
Liabilities: $85,325,493
Net Worth: $48,571,688
Earnings: ($1,518,530)
Emp.: 884
Fiscal Year-end: 12/31/19
Information Technology & Information Logistics Services
N.A.I.C.S.: 541512
Nina Annila (Member-Mgmt Bd & Exec VP-Care & Data Platforms)

Subsidiaries:

Enfo AB (1)
Anders Carlssons Gata 9, nind hollnstiren 3B, 417 55, Gothenburg, Sweden
Tel.: (46) 774404400
Web Site: http://www.enfo.se

Sales Range: $200-249.9 Million
IT Infrstructure & Integration Services
N.A.I.C.S.: 513210

Subsidiary (Domestic):

Enfo Zystems (2)
Lindholmspiren 3B, Box 9792, 41755, Gothenburg, Sweden
Tel.: (46) 77 440 44 00
Web Site: http://www.enfo.se
Sales Range: $75-99.9 Million
Emp.: 300
Computer Systems Integration
N.A.I.C.S.: 541519
Fredrik Bergman (Mng Dir)

Zingle by Enfo AB (2)
Anders Carlssons Gata 9, PO Box 8792, 402 76, Gothenburg, Sweden
Tel.: (46) 774404400
Web Site: http://www.zingle.se
Sales Range: $75-99.9 Million
Emp.: 350
IT User Integration
N.A.I.C.S.: 541519

Zipper by Enfo AB (2)
Lindholmspiren 4B, 417 55, Gothenburg, Sweden
Tel.: (46) 774404400
Web Site: http://www.enfo.se
Sales Range: $50-74.9 Million
Emp.: 120
IT Infrastructure
N.A.I.C.S.: 513210
Lauris Aboliver (CEO)

Enfo EnjoyIT Intergration AB (1)
Farogatan 33 A, 164 51, Kista, Sweden
Tel.: (46) 8 410 337 70
Information Technology Consulting Services
N.A.I.C.S.: 541512

ENG KAH CORPORATION BERHAD
Plot 95 and 97 Hala Kampung Jawa 2 Kawasan Perindustrian Bayan Lepas, 11900, Bayan Lepas, Penang, Malaysia
Tel.: (60) 46435180
Web Site: https://www.engkah.com
ENGKAH—(KLS)
Rev.: $10,609,267
Assets: $15,208,794
Liabilities: $2,356,033
Net Worth: $12,852,761
Earnings: ($805,506)
Emp.: 96
Fiscal Year-end: 12/31/23
Personal Care Product Mfr
N.A.I.C.S.: 325620
Lay Hoon Ch'ng (Sec)

Subsidiaries:

Eng Kah Enterprise (KL) Sdn. Bhd. (1)
Lot 152 Jalan Permata 1 Arab Malaysia Industrial Park, 71800, Nilai, Negeri Sembilan, Malaysia
Tel.: (60) 67999121
Web Site: http://engkah.com
Emp.: 60
Household Cosmetic Products Mfr
N.A.I.C.S.: 325620

Eng Kah Enterprise Sdn. Bhd. (1)
Plot 95 & 97 Hala Kampung Jawa 2 Kawasan Perindustrian Bayan Lepas, 11900, Bayan Lepas, Penang, Malaysia
Tel.: (60) 46435180
Sales Range: $125-149.9 Million
Emp.: 400
Household Cosmectics Mfr
N.A.I.C.S.: 325620
Lim Mei Ning (Gen Mgr)

ENG KONG HOLDINGS PTE LTD.
13 Tuas Avenue 11, Jurong, 639079, Singapore
Tel.: (65) 68616355
Web Site: http://www.engkong.com
Year Founded: 1978

Eng Kong Holdings Pte Ltd.—(Continued)

Sales Range: $25-49.9 Million
Emp.: 600
Warehouse & Container Services
N.A.I.C.S.: 541614
Eddie Hung Li (Co-Founder & Co-Chm)

Subsidiaries:

Eng Kong Container Agencies (Pte) Ltd   (1)
8A Tuas Ave 13, Singapore, Singapore
Tel.: (65) 68610843
General Warehousing Services
N.A.I.C.S.: 493110
Danny Gan (Mgr)

Eng Kong Container Services (Johor) Sdn Bhd   (1)
PLO 704 Jalan Keluli Pasir Gudang Indust Area, 81700, Pasir Gudang, Johor Bahru, Malaysia
Tel.: (60) 72551870
Container Sales & Services
N.A.I.C.S.: 423840

Eng Kong Container Services (Penang) Sdn Bhd.   (1)
Lot 1332 Mukim 14 Jalan Bagan Lallang, Mak Mandin Indus Estate, 13400, Butterworth, Penang, Malaysia
Tel.: (60) 43249268
Web Site: http://www.engkong.com
Emp.: 200
Container Sales & Services
N.A.I.C.S.: 423840
Ronny Tan (Mng Dir)

Eng Kong Container Services (Shenzhen) Company Limited   (1)
1st Gang Cheng Rd Mawan Gang Ave, Shekou, Shenzhen, 518067, Guangdong, China
Tel.: (86) 75526451148
Container Services
N.A.I.C.S.: 484110

Grand Pacific Warehouse Limited   (1)
Unit 508-509 Hutchison Logistics Ctr 18 Container Port Rd, Kwai Chung, China (Hong Kong)
Tel.: (852) 26152228
Web Site: http://www.ekh-gpw.com.hk
Emp.: 25
Warehousing & Container Freight Services
N.A.I.C.S.: 484110

Ming Fung Container Limited   (1)
16-26 Kwai Tak St Golden Indus Bldg 5th Fl Rm 12, Kwai Chung, New Territories, China (Hong Kong)
Tel.: (852) 24182882
Sales Range: $25-49.9 Million
Emp.: 14
Refrigeration Equipment Maintenance Services
N.A.I.C.S.: 811310
Danny Hung (Gen Mgr & Mng Dir)

New Eng Kong Container Logistic Services (M) Sdn Bhd   (1)
Lot 4 Lingkaran Sultan Muhamed 1 Kawasan Perusahaan, Bandar Sultan Suleiman, 42000, Port Klang, Selangor Darul Ehsan, Malaysia
Tel.: (60) 331764142
Web Site: http://www.engkong.com
Emp.: 30
Container & Logistics Consulting Services
N.A.I.C.S.: 541614
Ronny Tan (Gen Mgr)

PCL (Pte) Ltd   (1)
13 Tuas Ave 11, Singapore, 639079, Singapore
Tel.: (65) 65587106
Web Site: http://www.engkong.com
Sales Range: $50-74.9 Million
Emp.: 2
Container Sales
N.A.I.C.S.: 423840

PCL Container Services Limited   (1)
Unit 310-311A Hutchison Logistics Ctr 18 Container Port Rd, Kwai Chung, New Territories, China (Hong Kong)

Tel.: (852) 24022180
Container Depot Services
N.A.I.C.S.: 493110

Reefertec Pte Ltd   (1)
13 Tuas Ave 11, Singapore, 639079, Singapore
Tel.: (65) 68620400
Web Site: http://www.engkong.com
Emp.: 15
Refrigeration Equipment Repair & Maintenance Services
N.A.I.C.S.: 423840
Michael Ho (Gen Mgr)

Shanghai Eng Kong Container Services Ltd   (1)
1800-1 Yun Chuan Rd, Bao Shan, Shanghai, China
Tel.: (86) 2156497060
Container Trucking Services
N.A.I.C.S.: 484110

Smartz Pte Ltd   (1)
13 Tuas Ave 11, Singapore, 639079, Singapore
Tel.: (65) 68978577
Web Site: http://www.engkong.com.sg
Sales Range: $75-99.9 Million
Emp.: 200
Container Parts Whslr
N.A.I.C.S.: 423840
Terry Chan (Mgr)

Techni-con Container Survey Limited   (1)
1800-1 Yun Chuan Rd, Bao Shan, Shanghai, 201901, China
Tel.: (86) 2166760090
Web Site: http://www.engkong.com.sg
Sales Range: $25-49.9 Million
Emp.: 17
Container Surveying Services
N.A.I.C.S.: 484110
Molin Ohou (Mgr)

Tricool Reefer Sdn Bhd   (1)
Lot 51 & 52 Jalan Perigi Nanas 8/7 Taman Perindustrian, 42920, Pulau Indah, Selangor, Malaysia
Tel.: (60) 331012678
Sales Range: $25-49.9 Million
Emp.: 8
Reefer Repair Services
N.A.I.C.S.: 811310

ENG. SHABAH AL-SHAMMERY & PARTNERS CO.
Al-Mansoor Al-Ameerat St, District No 609 St No 1 House No 21, Baghdad, Iraq
Tel.: (964) 15412787
Web Site: http://www.shammery.com
Sales Range: $100-124.9 Million
Emp.: 260
General Trading Services
N.A.I.C.S.: 425120

Subsidiaries:

Al-Sawam General Contracting Company Ltd.   (1)
Dawoodi Hay Al Andalus District 611 St 79 House no 49, PO Box 50300, Al Maamoon, Baghdad, Iraq
Tel.: (964) 1 5426133
Building Construction Services
N.A.I.C.S.: 236220

Al-Ta'aluf General Transportation Co. Ltd.   (1)
2nd Floor Office No 2 Al-Noor Building, Al-Tahsinniyah, Basrah, Iraq
Tel.: (964) 40 621245
Freight Transportation Services
N.A.I.C.S.: 484110

Al-Usool General Trading Company Ltd.   (1)
Al-Wahda District no 904 Steet 99 Building 88, Baghdad, Iraq
Tel.: (964) 7400242468
Web Site: http://www.usoolgroup.com
Industrial Equipment Distr
N.A.I.C.S.: 423830

URUK for computer services & office equipment Co. Ltd.   (1)

Al-Mansour District 609 Street 1 Building 25, PO Box 50300, Baghdad, Iraq
Tel.: (964) 1 5432384
Web Site: http://www.urukco.com
Information Technology Consulting Services
N.A.I.C.S.: 541512
Nameer Al Ani (Mgr-Logistics)

ENGAGE MOBILITY, INC.
15C China Merchants Tower No 1166 Wanghai Road, Nansha, Guangdong, 518067, China
Tel.: (86) 75586575200
Year Founded: 2011
Software Development Services
N.A.I.C.S.: 541511
Hua Zhang (Pres, CEO & Treas)

ENGAGE XR HOLDINGS PLC
Unit 9 Cleaboy Business Park Old Kilmeaden Road, Waterford, X91 Ax83, Ireland
Tel.: (353) 51585837
Web Site: https://engagevr.io
Year Founded: 2017
EXR—(AIM)
Rev.: $1,739,884
Assets: $4,223,861
Liabilities: $511,636
Net Worth: $3,712,225
Earnings: ($3,351,182)
Emp.: 39
Fiscal Year-end: 12/31/20
Software Development Services
N.A.I.C.S.: 541511
Sandra Whelan (COO)

ENGAGE:BDR LIMITED
Level 4 90 William Street, Melbourne, 3000, VIC, Australia
Tel.: (61) 396927222
EN1—(ASX)
Rev.: $7,615,065
Assets: $6,931,054
Liabilities: $3,466,596
Net Worth: $3,464,458
Earnings: ($4,125,124)
Fiscal Year-end: 12/31/21
Advertising Agency Services
N.A.I.C.S.: 541810
Ted Dhanik (Chm & CEO)

ENGCON AB
Godsgatan 6, 833 36, Stromsund, Sweden
Tel.: (46) 67017800
Web Site: https://www.engcon.com
Year Founded: 1990
ENGCON.B—(OMX)
Rev.: $177,770,285
Assets: $94,785,842
Liabilities: $37,464,760
Net Worth: $57,321,082
Earnings: $25,757,022
Emp.: 406
Fiscal Year-end: 12/31/23
Construction Machinery Mfr
N.A.I.C.S.: 333120
Jens Blom (CFO)

Subsidiaries:

Engcon Austria GmbH   (1)
Geidorfgurtel 20, 8010, Graz, Austria
Tel.: (43) 6763786239
Excavator Attachment Equipment Distr
N.A.I.C.S.: 423810

Engcon France S.A.S   (1)
Parc des Erables - Batiment C 12 Avenue de Norvege, 91140, Villebon-sur-Yvette, France
Tel.: (33) 7861901
Excavator Attachment Equipment Distr
N.A.I.C.S.: 423810

Engcon Germany GmbH   (1)
Obere Gruben 7, DE-97877, Wertheim, Germany
Tel.: (49) 9342934850
Excavator Attachment Equipment Distr

N.A.I.C.S.: 423810

Engcon Ireland Ltd.   (1)
Bellview 1 Station Road, Leixlip, Kildare, W23 N6C6, Ireland
Tel.: (353) 15686742
Tilt Rotator System Mfr & Distr
N.A.I.C.S.: 333120

Engcon North America Inc.   (1)
2666 State St, Hamden, CT 06517, China
Tel.: (203) 691-5920
Excavator Attachment Equipment Distr
N.A.I.C.S.: 423810

Engcon Poland Sp. z o.o.   (1)
Cisowa 15, PL-64-320, Niepruszewo, Poland
Tel.: (48) 618940047
Excavator Attachment Equipment Mfr
N.A.I.C.S.: 333120

Engcon United Kingdom Ltd.   (1)
Unit 5 Ashchurch Business Centre Alexandra Way, Tewkesbury, GL20 8NB, United Kingdom
Tel.: (44) 1684297168
Excavator Attachment Equipment Distr
N.A.I.C.S.: 423810

ENGEL CONSTRUCTION & DEVELOPMENT GROUP
85 Medinat Hayehudim Street, Herzliyya, 46140, Israel
Tel.: (972) 99707000
Sales Range: $25-49.9 Million
Emp.: 70
Building & Housing Construction Services
N.A.I.C.S.: 236220
Yael Miller (CEO)

Subsidiaries:

Engel General Developers Ltd.   (1)
66 Hahistadrut Avenue, Haifa, 32960, Israel
Tel.: (972) 48422777
Sales Range: $25-49.9 Million
Emp.: 52
Residential Construction Services
N.A.I.C.S.: 236115

ENGENCO LIMITED
L14 140 William Street, Melbourne, 3000, VIC, Australia
Tel.: (61) 386208900
Web Site: https://www.engenco.com.au
EGN—(ASX)
Rev.: $143,460,870
Assets: $127,200,854
Liabilities: $62,475,961
Net Worth: $64,724,893
Earnings: $2,624,199
Emp.: 500
Fiscal Year-end: 06/30/24
Engineeering Services
N.A.I.C.S.: 541330
Vincent De Santis (Chm)

Subsidiaries:

Asset Kinetics Pty. Ltd.   (1)
6 Sandhill St, Wedgefield, Port Hedland, 6721, WA, Australia
Tel.: (61) 891722255
Sales Range: $25-49.9 Million
Emp.: 5
Transport & Logistics Services
N.A.I.C.S.: 541614
Jeff Coote (Mng Dir)

Centre for Excellence in Rail Training Pty. Ltd.   (1)
1359 Albany Highway, PO Box 270, Maddington, Cannington, 6107, WA, Australia
Tel.: (61) 892518080
Web Site: http://www.certrail.com.au
Sales Range: $10-24.9 Million
Emp.: 7
Training & Assessment Services
N.A.I.C.S.: 611430
Mark Haigh (Mgr-Natl)

Convair Engineering Pty. Ltd.   (1)

91-93 Miller Street, Epping, 3076, VIC, Australia
Tel.: (61) 394087255
Web Site: http://www.convair.com.au
Sales Range: $25-49.9 Million
Emp.: 35
Pneumatic Bulk Tanker Mfr
N.A.I.C.S.: 332420
Peter Swann *(Gen Mgr)*

Drivetrain Australia Pty. Ltd. (1)
13 Firebrick Drive, Thornton, 2322, NSW, Australia
Tel.: (61) 240882310
Web Site: https://www.drivetrainpower.com
Sales Range: $25-40.9 Million
Emp.: 30
Industrial Equipment Repair & Maintenance Services
N.A.I.C.S.: 811310

Subsidiary (Non-US):

Drivetrain Philippines Inc. (2)
325 Gregorio Araneta Ave, Quezon City, Manila, Philippines
Tel.: (63) 27145820
Web Site: http://www.drivetrainpower.com
Sales Range: $25-49.9 Million
Emp.: 4
Engine Repair & Maintenance Services
N.A.I.C.S.: 811198

Drivetrain Singapore Pte. Ltd. (2)
69N Tuas South Avenue 1, No 02-07 Eunos Technolink, Singapore, 637504, Singapore
Tel.: (65) 386126722
Web Site: http://www.drivetrainpower.com
Sales Range: $25-49.9 Million
Emp.: 4
Industrial Equipment Repair & Maintenance Services
N.A.I.C.S.: 811310

Drivetrain Power and Propulsion Pty. Ltd. (1)
Level 8 15 Talavera Rd, North Ryde, 2113, NSW, Australia
Tel.: (61) 298054000
Web Site: http://www.drivetrainpower.com.au
Sales Range: $25-49.9 Million
Emp.: 15
Engine Maintenance & Repair Services
N.A.I.C.S.: 811198
Ross Dunning *(Mng Dir)*

Eureka 4WD Training Pty. Ltd. (1)
77A Great Eastern Hwy, Bellevue, 6056, WA, Australia
Tel.: (61) 894612300
Web Site: https://www.eureka4wd.com.au
Four Wheel Drive Training Services
N.A.I.C.S.: 611519

Gemco Rail Pty. Ltd. (1)
860-870 Abernethy Road, Forrestfield, 6058, WA, Australia (100%)
Tel.: (61) 893656901
Web Site: https://www.gemcorail.com.au
Sales Range: $25-49.9 Million
Emp.: 250
Products & Services to Rail Industry
N.A.I.C.S.: 488210

Hedemora Diesel AB (1)
Sturegatan 2, 776 35, Hedemora, Dalarna, Sweden
Tel.: (46) 225595800
Web Site: http://www.hedemoratd.com
Sales Range: $25-49.9 Million
Emp.: 28
Diesel Engine Mfr
N.A.I.C.S.: 333618

Hedemora Turbo & Diesel AB (1)
Sturegatan 2, 776 35, Hedemora, Sweden
Tel.: (46) 22 559 5800
Web Site: https://www.hedemoratd.com
Turbocharger Whslr
N.A.I.C.S.: 423610
Johan Kallstrom *(Gen Dir)*

PC Diesel Pty. Ltd. (1)
Tel.: (61) 893583003
Sales Range: $25-49.9 Million
Emp.: 13
Diesel Engine Equipment Mfr
N.A.I.C.S.: 333618

Subsidiary (Non-US):

Industrial Powertrain Pty. Ltd. (2)

Tel.: (61) 893771880
Sales Range: $25-49.9 Million
Industrial Equipment Repair & Maintenance Services
N.A.I.C.S.: 811310

Total Momentum Pty. Ltd. (1)
77A Great Eastern Highway, Bellevue, 6056, WA, Australia
Tel.: (61) 1300117778
Web Site: https://www.momentumrail.com
Railroad Construction Services
N.A.I.C.S.: 482111

ENGENE HOLDINGS INC.
4868 Rue Levy Suite 220 Saint-Laurent, Montreal, H4R 2P1, QC, Canada
Tel.: (514) 332-4888   BC
Web Site: https://www.engene.com
Year Founded: 2021
ENGN—(NASDAQ)
Rev.: $10,413,000
Assets: $311,173,000
Liabilities: $38,561,000
Net Worth: $272,612,000
Earnings: ($55,142,000)
Emp.: 56
Fiscal Year-end: 10/31/24
Holding Company
N.A.I.C.S.: 551112
Ronald H. W. Cooper *(CEO)*

ENGHOUSE SYSTEMS LIMITED
80 Tiverton Court Suite 800, Markham, L3R 0G4, ON, Canada
Tel.: (905) 946-3200   ON
Web Site: https://www.enghouse.com
Year Founded: 1984
EGHSF—(OTCIQ)
Rev.: $334,491,194
Assets: $551,505,835
Liabilities: $153,978,519
Net Worth: $397,527,316
Earnings: $73,923,895
Emp.: 1,729
Fiscal Year-end: 10/31/22
Automated Mapping & Facilities Management Through Geographic Information Systems Engineering Software Products
N.A.I.C.S.: 541512
Stephen J. Sadler *(Chm & CEO)*

Subsidiaries:

CTI Group (Holdings) Inc. (1)
333 N Alabama St Ste 240, Indianapolis, IN 46204
Tel.: (317) 262-4666
Sales Range: $10-24.9 Million
Holding Company; Telephone Management & Billing Software Publisher & Whslr
N.A.I.C.S.: 551112

CustomCall Data Systems, Inc. (1)
1009 S Whitney Way, Madison, WI 53711
Tel.: (608) 274-3009
Web Site: http://www.customcall.com
Sales Range: $25-49.9 Million
Emp.: 40
Billing, OSS & Business Process Management Solutions
N.A.I.C.S.: 541519
Robert M. Whritenour *(VP & Gen Mgr)*

Enghouse (U.K.) Limited (1)
Enterprise House Ocean Village, Southampton, SO14 3XB, Hampshire, United Kingdom
Tel.: (44) 2380488752
Emp.: 1
Computer Software Development Services
N.A.I.C.S.: 541511

Enghouse Interactive (1)
216 Route 17 N Ste 301, Rochelle Park, NJ 07662
Tel.: (602) 789-2800
Sales Range: $10-24.9 Million
Emp.: 78
Communications Software
N.A.I.C.S.: 513210

Enghouse Interactive (1)
Imperium Imperial Way, Reading, RG2 0TD, Berks, United Kingdom
Tel.: (44) 2033573040
Sales Range: $25-49.9 Million
Emp.: 150
Communications Software
N.A.I.C.S.: 513210

Subsidiary (Domestic):

Arc Solutions (International) Limited (2)
Innovation House Pincents Lane, Reading, RG31 4UH, Berkshire, United Kingdom
Tel.: (44) 1189439200
Web Site: http://www.enghouse.com
Emp.: 80
Software Development Services
N.A.I.C.S.: 541511

Datapulse Limited (2)
Progression House Pincents Lane, Reading, RG31 4UH, Berkshire, United Kingdom
Tel.: (44) 1189728400
Web Site: http://www.datapulse.co.uk
Sales Range: $25-49.9 Million
Emp.: 10
Information Technology Consulting Services
N.A.I.C.S.: 541512
Iain McKenzie *(Grp Mng Dir-EMEA)*

Exxcom Limited (2)
Kingsmede House 1 Southbridge Street, Shefford, SG17 5DB, Bedfordshire, United Kingdom
Tel.: (44) 1462850912
Web Site: https://www.exxcom.co.uk
Web Hosting Services
N.A.I.C.S.: 518210

Enghouse Networks (Germany) GmbH (1)
Willi-Bleicher-Str 9, Duren, 52353, Cologne, Germany
Tel.: (49) 242198570
Telecommunication Servicesb
N.A.I.C.S.: 517810

Enghouse Transportation LLC (1)
800-80 Tiverton Court, Markham, L3R 0G4, ON, Canada
Tel.: (905) 946-3200
Web Site: http://www.enghousetransportation.com
Transportation Software Development Services
N.A.I.C.S.: 541511

Espial Group Inc. (1)
200 Elgin Street Suite 1000, Ottawa, K2P 1L5, ON, Canada
Tel.: (613) 230-4770
Web Site: http://www.espial.com
Rev.: $26,632,444
Assets: $43,010,502
Liabilities: $6,471,449
Net Worth: $36,539,054
Earnings: ($6,789,304)
Emp.: 174
Fiscal Year-end: 12/31/2017
On-Demand Television Software & Services
N.A.I.C.S.: 513210
Kirk Edwardson *(Dir-Mktg)*

Subsidiary (Non-US):

Espial (UK) Limited (2)
First Floor 335 Cambridge Science Park, Milton Road, Cambridge, CB4 0WN, United Kingdom (100%)
Tel.: (44) 1223716400
Web Site: http://www.espial.com
On-Demand Television Software Whslr
N.A.I.C.S.: 423430

Gamma Projects Ltd. (1)
The Brewery, Magor, NP26 3DJ, Monmouthshire, United Kingdom
Tel.: (44) 1633883000
Web Site: http://www.gammaprojects.com
Telecommunication Software Consulting Services
N.A.I.C.S.: 541512

Information Access Technology, Inc. (1)
6671 South Redwood Rd, West Jordan, UT 84084
Web Site: http://www.iatsmartdial.com

Sales Range: $1-9.9 Million
Emp.: 30
Software Publisher
N.A.I.C.S.: 513210

Jinny Software Ltd. (1)
29 North Anne Street, Dublin, Ireland
Tel.: (353) 18872626
Web Site: http://www.jinnysoftware.com
Sales Range: $25-49.9 Million
Emp.: 250
Telecommunication Software Development Services
N.A.I.C.S.: 541511
Antoine Ghaoui *(Chief Software Officer)*

Mediasite KK (1)
Tel.: (81) 364529043
Web Site: http://www.mediasite.co.jp
Emp.: 50
Video Creation Services
N.A.I.C.S.: 518210
Nakagawa Hisashi *(Chm)*

Moore Resource Systems (Ontario) Limited (1)
80 Tiverton Crt Ste 800, Markham, L3R 0G4, ON, Canada
Tel.: (905) 854-1607
Software Development Services
N.A.I.C.S.: 541511

Pulse Teleservice Inc. (1)
90 Nolan Crt, Markham, L3R 4L9, ON, Canada
Tel.: (905) 695-3500
Telecommunication Servicesb
N.A.I.C.S.: 517810

Pulse Voice Inc (1)
90 Nolan Ct Ste 1A, Markham, L3R 4L9, ON, Canada
Tel.: (905) 754-4100
Web Site: http://www.pulsenetworks.com
Enterprise Software Development Services
N.A.I.C.S.: 541511

Qumu Corporation (1)
400 S 4th St Ste 401-412, Minneapolis, MN 55415
Tel.: (612) 638-9100
Web Site: http://www.qumu.com
Rev.: $24,022,000
Assets: $37,096,000
Liabilities: $24,500,000
Net Worth: $12,596,000
Earnings: ($16,365,000)
Emp.: 108
Fiscal Year-end: 12/31/2021
Computer Hardware & Related Devices
N.A.I.C.S.: 334118

Subsidiary (Non-US):

Qumu (Singapore) Pte. Ltd (2)
9 Temasek Boulevard 31st Floor Suntec City Tower 2, Singapore, 038989, Singapore
Tel.: (65) 65595377
Software Development Services
N.A.I.C.S.: 541511

Qumu Japan Co., Ltd. (2)
20F Nakameguro GT Tower 2-1-1 Kamimeguro, Meguro-Ku, Tokyo, 153-0051, Japan
Tel.: (81) 367734267
Software Development Services
N.A.I.C.S.: 541511
Yoshi Oyamada *(Mng Dir)*

Qumu Ltd. (2)
Third Floor 1 West Smithfield, London, EC1A 9JU, United Kingdom
Tel.: (44) 2072538080
Telecommunication Servicesb
N.A.I.C.S.: 517810

Subsidiary (Domestic):

Qumu, Inc. (2)
1100 Grundy Ln Ste 110, San Bruno, CA 94066
Tel.: (650) 396-8530
Web Site: http://www.qumu.com
Software Development Services
N.A.I.C.S.: 513210

Sonic Foundry International B.V. (1)
Merelstraat 2bis, 3514 CN, Utrecht, Netherlands
Tel.: (31) 302753000

Enghouse Systems Limited—(Continued)

Web Site: http://www.sonicfoundry.com
Data Processing & Hosting Services
N.A.I.C.S.: 518210

Syntellect, Inc.   (1)
2095 W Pinnacle Peak Rd Ste 110, Phoenix, AZ 85027
Tel.: (602) 789-2800
Sales Range: $25-49.9 Million
Emp.: 50
Speech-Enabled Customer, Employee &
Supply-Chain Self-Service Software Solutions & Hosted Services
N.A.I.C.S.: 334111
Keith Gussler (VP)

Subsidiary (Non-US):

Syntellect Ltd   (1)
Technology House Fleetwood Pk, Barley
Way Fleet, Hampshire, GU51 2QJ, United
Kingdom   (100%)
Tel.: (44) 256685100
Sales Range: $25-49.9 Million
Emp.: 45
N.A.I.C.S.: 334418

Subsidiary (Domestic):

Syntellect Technology Corp.   (2)
Ste 110 30 Mansell Ct, Roswell, GA 30076-
1580
Mfr of Telephone Systems
N.A.I.C.S.: 541219

Tollgrade Communications, Inc.   (1)
260 Executive Dr Ste 150, Cranberry Township, PA 16066
Tel.: (724) 720-1400
Testing Equipment for the Telecommunications Industry
N.A.I.C.S.: 334210
Thomas Kolb (COO & Gen Mgr-Broadband
Solutions)

Subsidiary (Non-US):

Tollgrade Germany GmbH   (2)
Ludwig-Richter-Strasse 20, 42329, Wuppertal, Germany
Tel.: (49) 202273340
Web Site: http://www.tollgrade.com
Testing Equipment Mfr for the Telecommunications Industry
N.A.I.C.S.: 334210

Tollgrade UK Limited   (2)
Richmond House, Oldbury, Bracknell,
RG128TQ, Berkshire, United Kingdom
Tel.: (44) 1344469800
Testing Equipment Mfr for the Telecommunications Industry
N.A.I.C.S.: 334210

Trio Danmark A/S   (1)
Rodkaervej 18, Sabro, 8471, Arhus, Denmark
Tel.: (45) 4488 0050
Web Site: http://www.trio.com
Communication Software Development Services
N.A.I.C.S.: 541511

Trio Enterprise AB   (1)
St Eriksgatan 117, Box 6795, 113 85,
Stockholm, Sweden
Tel.: (46) 8 457 30 00
Web Site: http://www.trio.com
Sales Range: $25-49.9 Million
Emp.: 45
Telephony System Software Development
Services
N.A.I.C.S.: 541511
Michael Stubbing (CEO)

Trio Norge AS   (1)
Fornebuvn 46, PB 493, 1327, Lysaker, Norway
Tel.: (47) 67 83 00 80
Communication Software Development Services
N.A.I.C.S.: 541511

Vidyo, Inc.   (1)
433 Hackensack Ave, Hackensack, NJ
07601
Tel.: (201) 289-8597
Web Site: https://de.vidyo.com

Sales Range: $25-49.9 Million
Emp.: 200
Video Conferencing Software
N.A.I.C.S.: 513210
Roi Sasson (Sr VP-Engrg)

Subsidiary (Non-US):

Vidyo Asia Pacific   (2)
Unit 06A 22nd Floor West Tower Shun Tak
Center 200 Connaught Road, Central,
China (Hong Kong)
Tel.: (852) 22765863
Video Conferencing Software
N.A.I.C.S.: 513210

Vidyo EMEA   (2)
Europarc Pichaury Batiment B5, 13856, Aix-en-Provence, France
Tel.: (33) 488 718 823
Video Conferencing Software
N.A.I.C.S.: 513210

Vidyo India   (2)
306 Suncity Business Tower Golf Course
Road Sector 54, Gurgaon, 122011, Haryana, India
Tel.: (91) 124 4111671
Video Conferencing Software
N.A.I.C.S.: 513210
Ruchir Godura (Mng Dir)

Vidyo Italy   (2)
Via Leopardi 1, 20123, Milan, Italy
Tel.: (39) 0334 6113620
Video Conferencing Software
N.A.I.C.S.: 513210

Vidyo Japan   (2)
Global Business Hub Tokyo 3F Otemachi
Financial City Grand Cube, 1-9-2 otemachi
Chiyoda-ku, Tokyo, 100-0013, Japan
Tel.: (81) 342436088
Video Conferencing Software
N.A.I.C.S.: 513210

Vidyo Netherlands   (2)
Crystalic Building Francois Haverschmidtwei
2, 8914 BC, Leeuwarden, Netherlands
Tel.: (31) 58 291 1351
Video Conferencing Software
N.A.I.C.S.: 513210

Vidyo Nordics & Baltics   (2)
Jarnbrottsgatan 11, 42668, Vastra Frolunda,
Sweden
Tel.: (46) 76 148 4242
Video Conferencing Software
N.A.I.C.S.: 513210

Vidyo United Kingdom   (2)
20 Eastbourne Terrace, Apsley, London, W2
6LG, Hertfordshire, United Kingdom
Tel.: (44) 2038712873
Video Conferencing Software
N.A.I.C.S.: 513210

Voiceport, LLC   (1)
500 Lee Rd, Ste 200, Rochester, NY 14606
Tel.: (585) 218-0550
Web Site: http://www.voiceport.net
Sales Range: $1-9.9 Million
Emp.: 25
Prepackaged Software
N.A.I.C.S.: 513210
Chris Mann (Pres & CEO)

ENGIE SA
1 place Samuel de Champlain, Faubourg de l'Arche La Defense, 92930,
Paris, Cedex, France
Tel.: (33) 144220000   FR
Web Site: https://www.engie.com
Year Founded: 1946
ENGI—(ITA)
Rev.: $91,141,406,349
Assets: $214,858,152,144
Liabilities: $175,423,335,934
Net Worth: $39,434,816,210
Earnings: $3,204,547,964
Emp.: 89,240
Fiscal Year-end: 12/31/23
Holding Company; Natural Gas Extractor, Refiner & Wholesale Distr &
Other Low-carbon Energy & Services
N.A.I.C.S.: 551112

Sebastien Arbola (CEO-ENGIE-
Middle East, South, Central Asia &
Turkey Bus)

Subsidiaries:

ABM Energie Conseil SAS.   (1)
ZAD du Taure Avenue L de Vinci, 31880, La
Salvetat-Saint-Gilles, France
Tel.: (33) 562130050
Web Site: http://www.abmec.fr
Thermal Electric Power Generation Services
N.A.I.C.S.: 221118

Banque Solfea SA   (1)
49 Avenue de l'Opera Cedex 02, Paris,
75083, France
Tel.: (33) 1 40 17 55 00
Web Site: http://www.banquesolfea.fr
Sales Range: $25-49.9 Million
Emp.: 85
Gas Equipment Installation Services
N.A.I.C.S.: 238290

CIE Dupaquier SARL.   (1)
1 Avenue de Verdun Centre d'affaires Pont
Jean Richard, 71100, Chalon-sur-Saone,
France
Tel.: (33) 38 594 7736
Web Site: https://www.ciedupaquier.fr
Sales Range: $75-99.9 Million
Emp.: 16
Eletric Power Generation Services
N.A.I.C.S.: 221118
Denis Dupaquier (Gen Mgr)

CLIPSOL S.A.   (1)
Parc d'Activite des Combaruches, 73100,
Aix-les-Bains, France
Tel.: (33) 4 79 34 35 36
Web Site: http://www.clipsol.com
Sales Range: $25-49.9 Million
Emp.: 10
Photovoltaic Device Mfr
N.A.I.C.S.: 334413
Jean-Claude Toucas (Mng Dir)

Calliance Gestion   (1)
22 Rue Marius Aufan, 92300, Levallois-
Perret, France
Tel.: (33) 810638856
Eletric Power Generation Services
N.A.I.C.S.: 221118

Compagnie Nationale du Rhone   (1)
2 rue Andre Bonin, 69004, Lyon, France
Tel.: (33) 472006969
Web Site: https://www.cnr.tm.fr
Sales Range: $1-4.9 Billion
Emp.: 600
Energy, Navigation & Engineering Services
N.A.I.C.S.: 488330
Pierre-Jean Grangette (Dir-Energy Dev)

ELENGY S.A.   (1)
11 Avenue Michel Ricard TSA 90100,
92276, Bois-Colombes, Cedex, France
Tel.: (33) 1 46 52 36 25
Web Site: http://www.elengy.com
Rev.: $299,955,530
Emp.: 20
Liquefied Natural Gas Terminal Operator
N.A.I.C.S.: 424710
Marc Haestier (Chm)

ENERGIA, SAS   (1)
39 Route De Chaluzy Zone Industrielle De
St Eloi, 58000, Nevers, France
Tel.: (33) 3 86 59 25 13
Web Site: http://www.energia.fr
Eletric Power Generation Services
N.A.I.C.S.: 221118

ENGIE Axima Germany GmbH   (1)
Ruwoldtweg 12, 22309, Hamburg, Germany
Tel.: (49) 408 5440
Web Site: https://marine.engie-axima.com
Vessel Heating, Ventilation, Air Conditioning
& Refrigeration Systems Installation Services
N.A.I.C.S.: 238220
Harald Knoth (Head-Pur)

ENGIE Energia Peru S.A.   (1)
Av Republica de Panama 3490, 15047, San
Isidro, Peru
Tel.: (51) 16167979
Web Site: https://www.engie-energia.pe
Power Generation Services

N.A.I.C.S.: 221118

ENGIE Energie Nederland N.V.   (1)
Grote Voort 291, 8041 BL, Zwolle, Netherlands
Tel.: (31) 884446622
Web Site: https://www.engie.nl
N.A.I.C.S.: 221111

ENGIE North America Inc.   (1)
1990 Post Oak Blvd Ste 1900, Houston, TX
77056-3831
Tel.: (713) 636-0000
Web Site: http://www.engie-na.com
Holding Company; Regional Managing Office
N.A.I.C.S.: 551112
David Carroll (Chief Renewables Officer)

Subsidiary (Domestic):

ENGIE Energy Marketing NA,
Inc.   (2)
1990 Post Oak Blvd Ste 1900, Houston, TX
77056-3831   (100%)
Tel.: (713) 636-1700
Web Site: http://www.suezenergyna.com
Energy Marketing Services
N.A.I.C.S.: 541613

ENGIE Gas & LNG LLC   (2)
1990 Post Oak Blvd Ste 1900, Houston, TX
77056-3831   (100%)
Tel.: (713) 636-0000
Web Site: http://www.engie-na.com
Liquefied Natural Gas Distr
N.A.I.C.S.: 221210

Subsidiary (Domestic):

ENGIE Gas & LNG Holdings
LLC   (3)
20 City Sq Ste 3, Charlestown, MA 02129
Tel.: (617) 886-8700
Web Site: http://www.engie-na.com
Liquefied Natural Gas Terminal Operator
N.A.I.C.S.: 424710
Edward Cahill (VP-Mktg, Sls & Transportation)

Subsidiary (Domestic):

Distrigas of Massachusetts LLC   (4)
18 rover st, Everett, MA 02109
Tel.: (617) 526-8300
Web Site: http://www.suezenergy.com
Sales Range: $50-74.9 Million
Emp.: 100
Importer of Liquefied Natural Gas from Algeria
N.A.I.C.S.: 221210

Neptune LNG LLC   (4)
20 City Sq Ste 3, Charlestown, MA 02129
Tel.: (617) 886-8700
Natural Gas Distribution Services
N.A.I.C.S.: 221210

Subsidiary (Domestic):

ENGIE Resources LLC   (2)
1360 Post Oak Blvd Ste 400, Houston, TX
77056-3030   (100%)
Tel.: (713) 636-0000
Web Site: https://www.engieresources.com
Sales Range: $450-499.9 Million
Emp.: 550
Retail Electric Power Distribution Services
N.A.I.C.S.: 221122
J.D. Burrows (VP-Mktg)

ENGIE Services U.S. Inc   (2)
500 12th St Ste 300, Oakland, CA 94607
Web Site: https://engieservices.us
National Sustainable Energy Investment
Services
N.A.I.C.S.: 523999
John Mahoney (CEO)

Subsidiary (Domestic):

Energy Control, Inc.   (3)
2600 American Rd SE Ste 360, Rio Rancho, NM 87124
Tel.: (505) 890-2888
Web Site: http://www.energyctrl.com
Building Systems Contractor & Services
N.A.I.C.S.: 238220
Jose Martinez II (Mgr-Construction)

Subsidiary (Domestic):

Fred Williams, Inc. (2)
80 Research Rd, Hingham, MA 02043
Tel.: (781) 961-1500
Web Site: https://ww.engiemep.com
Heating, Ventilation & Air-Conditioning Contractor
N.A.I.C.S.: 238220
James Williams (Pres)

H.T. Lyons, Inc. (2)
7165 Ambassador Dr, Allentown, PA 18106
Tel.: (610) 530-2600
Web Site: http://www.htlyons.com
Engineering Services
N.A.I.C.S.: 541330
Rick Perosa (Pres)

Nassau Energy Corp. (2)
185 Charles Lindbergh Blvd, Garden City,
NY 11530-4819
Tel.: (516) 222-2884
Web Site: http://www.suezenergyna.com
Sales Range: $25-49.9 Million
Emp.: 28
Electric Power Supply Services
N.A.I.C.S.: 221118
David Petty (Gen Mgr)

Systecon LLC (2)
6121 Schumacher Park Dr, West Chester,
OH 45069
Tel.: (513) 777-7722
Web Site: https://www.systecon.com
Sales Range: $25-49.9 Million
Emp.: 83
Water Management System Mfr
N.A.I.C.S.: 333914
Terry Moses (CEO)

ENGIE Romania SA (1)
Bd Marasesti nr 4-6 Sector 4, Bucharest,
Romania
Tel.: (40) 212640100
Web Site: http://www.engie.ro
Electric power distribution services
N.A.I.C.S.: 221122

Eco-Metering (1)
Le Jean Monnet 11 Place Des Vosges, La
Defense, Paris, 92061, France
Tel.: (33) 1 46 67 82 00
Web Site: http://www.ecometering-gdfsuez.com
Measuring Instruments Mfr
N.A.I.C.S.: 334515
Bernard Cheze (Gen Mgr)

Engie Eps S.A. (1)
28 rue de Londres, 75009, Paris, France
Tel.: (33) 970467135
Web Site: http://www.engie-eps.com
Rev.: $22,626,559
Assets: $49,077,203
Liabilities: $46,460,309
Net Worth: $2,616,893
Earnings: ($16,399,549)
Emp.: 110
Fiscal Year-end: 12/31/2019
Hydrogen-Based Energy Storage Systems
N.A.I.C.S.: 335311
Carlalberto Guglielminotti (CEO & Gen Mgr)

Eole Generation SAS (1)
Immeuble Le Nautilus 14 Rue du Sous-marin Venus, 56100, Lorient, France
Tel.: (33) 2 97 88 35 20
Web Site: http://www.eole-generation.com
Wind Electric Power Generation Services
N.A.I.C.S.: 221115

First Hydro Holdings Company (1)
Llanberis, Caernarfon, Gwynedd, LL55 4TY,
United Kingdom
Tel.: (44) 1286870166
Web Site: http://www.fhc.co.uk
Generate Electricity & Pumped Storage
Services
N.A.I.C.S.: 221118

Fosmax LNG SAS (1)
Batiment EOLE 11 Avenue Michel Ricard
TSA 10200, 92276, Bois-Colombes, Cedex,
France
Tel.: (33) 146523574
Web Site: http://www.fosmax-lng.com
Liquefied Natural Gas Distribution Services
N.A.I.C.S.: 221210
Sabah Hamdani (Compliance Officer)

GASAG AG (1)
Henriette-Herz-Platz 4, 10178, Berlin,
Germany (31.57%)
Tel.: (49) 3078723050
Web Site: http://www.gasag.de
Rev.: $1,401,660,451
Assets: $2,365,415,326
Liabilities: $1,610,674,481
Net Worth: $754,740,846
Earnings: $36,177,077
Emp.: 1,708
Fiscal Year-end: 12/31/2019
Liquid Natural Gas Distr
N.A.I.C.S.: 211120

Subsidiary (Domestic):

**BAS Kundenservice GmbH & Co.
KG** (2)
Euref-Campus 23-24, 10829, Berlin, Germany
Tel.: (49) 3078724444
Web Site: https://www.bas-kundenservice.de
Telephone Meter Reading, Billing & Collection Services
N.A.I.C.S.: 561990

**DSE Direkt-Service-Energie
GmbH** (2)
Henriette-Herz-Platz 4, 10178, Berlin, Germany
Tel.: (49) 3078721540
Web Site: http://www.dse-vertrieb.de
Energy Consulting Services
N.A.I.C.S.: 541690

GASAG Contracting GmbH (2)
Im Teelbruch 55, 45219, Essen, Germany
Tel.: (49) 20 54 96 954 0
Web Site: http://www.gasag-contracting.de
Sales Range: $25-49.9 Million
Emp.: 20
Energy Solutions & Contracting Projects
N.A.I.C.S.: 221118
Frank Mattat (Mgr)

GASAG Solution Plus GmbH (2)
Euref-Campus 23-24, 10829, Berlin, Germany
Tel.: (49) 3078724444
Web Site: https://www.gasag-solution.de
Sales Range: $25-49.9 Million
Emp.: 20
Electricity Meter Reading Services
N.A.I.C.S.: 561990

**NBB Netz gesellschaft Berlin-
Brandenburg mbH** (2)
An der Spandauer Brucke 10, 10178, Berlin, Germany
Tel.: (49) 30 81876 0
Web Site: http://www.nbb-netzgesellschaft.de
Gas Supply & Meter Reading Services
N.A.I.C.S.: 221210

**SpreeGas Gesellschaft fur Gasver-
sorgung und Energiedienstleistung
mbH** (2)
Nordparkstrasse 30, 03044, Cottbus, Germany
Tel.: (49) 35578220
Web Site: http://www.spreegas.de
Natural Gas Services
N.A.I.C.S.: 221210

Stadtwerke Forst GmbH (2)
Euloer Strasse 90, 03149, Forst, Germany
Tel.: (49) 35629500
Web Site: http://www.stadtwerke-forst.de
Electricity, Gas, Water & Heat Administration Services
N.A.I.C.S.: 926130

GDF SUEZ Trading SAS (1)
1 place Samuel de Champlain, 92400,
Courbevoie, France (100%)
Tel.: (33) 156656565
Web Site: https://www.engie-globalmarkets.com
Petroleum Products & Coal Wholesale
Trade Distr
N.A.I.C.S.: 425120
Edouard Neviaski (CEO)

GDF Suez Energie Services SA (1)
Le Voltaire 1 Pl des degres, 92059, Paris,
Cedex, France
Tel.: (33) 141201000

Web Site: http://www.gdfsuez.com
Rev.: $18,471,550,000
Emp.: 77,900
Energy Services
N.A.I.C.S.: 221122

Subsidiary (Non-US):

COFELY Fabricom S.A. (2)
World Trade Center Tower 1 30 Boulevard
du Roi Albert II, B 1000, Brussels, Belgium
Tel.: (32) 23703111
Web Site: http://www.cofelyfabricom-gdfsuez.com
Sales Range: $900-999.9 Million
Emp.: 5,000
Energy Efficiency & Technical Installations
& Services
N.A.I.C.S.: 541330
Louis Martens (CFO)

Subsidiary (Non-US):

**Fabricom Oil, Gas & Power
Limited** (3)
Origin 3 Origin Way, Europac, Grimsby,
DN37 9TZ, South Humberside, United Kingdom
Tel.: (44) 1469576411
Web Site: http://www.fabricom-gdfsuez.co.uk
Sales Range: $150-199.9 Million
Emp.: 775
Technical Installations & Services
N.A.I.C.S.: 541330
Michel Hanson (Pres)

Subsidiary (Domestic):

Fabricom Offshore Services Ltd. (4)
Q16 Quorum Business Park, Benton Lane,
Newcastle upon Tyne, NE12 8BX, Tyne &
Wear, United Kingdom
Tel.: (44) 1912381460
Web Site: http://www.fabricom-gdfsuez.co.uk
Sales Range: $25-49.9 Million
Emp.: 100
Offshore Oil & Gas Facilities Engineering
N.A.I.C.S.: 541330
Allan Cairns (Dir-Engrg)

Subsidiary (Non-US):

COFELY Services SA/NV (2)
World Trade Ctr Twr 1, 30 Blvd du Roi Albert II, 1000, Brussels, 1000, Belgium
Tel.: (32) 22060211
Web Site: http://www.cofelyservices-gdfsuez.be
Sales Range: $350-399.9 Million
Emp.: 1,900
Energy Management, Long-Term Technical
Management & Facilities Management Services
N.A.I.C.S.: 561990
Xavier Sinechal (Mng Dir)

Subsidiary (Non-US):

COFELY AG (3)
Thurgauerstrasse 56, CH-5080, Zurich,
Switzerland
Tel.: (41) 443878500
Web Site: http://www.cofely.ch
Emp.: 200
Energy Management, Long-Term Technical
Management & Facilities Management Services
N.A.I.C.S.: 561990
Patrick Meili (Head-Fin & Controller)

Branch (Domestic):

COFELY AG - Winterthur (4)
Zeughausstrasse 70, CH 8411, Winterthur,
Switzerland
Tel.: (41) 522695012
Web Site: http://www.cofely.ch
Sales Range: $150-199.9 Million
Emp.: 1,000
Energy Management, Long-Term Technical
Management & Facilities Management Services
N.A.I.C.S.: 561990

Subsidiary (Domestic):

Caliqua AG (4)
Bruderholzstrasse 31, PO Box 31, 4053,
Basel, Switzerland

Tel.: (41) 613663500
Web Site: https://www.caliqua.ch
Sales Range: $25-49.9 Million
Emp.: 95
Heating & Air Conditioning Systems Installation & Maintenance
N.A.I.C.S.: 333415
Klaus Zietler (Mng Dir)

Subsidiary (Non-US):

Caliqua Powertec GmbH (5)
Dammstrasse 1, 79576, Weil am Rhein,
Germany
Tel.: (49) 7621974270
Web Site: http://www.caliqua.ch
Sales Range: $75-99.9 Million
Emp.: 70
Heating & Air Conditioning Systems Installation & Maintenance
N.A.I.C.S.: 333415
Klaus Zietler (Mng Dir)

Subsidiary (Non-US):

**COFELY Airport & Logistics Services
SA** (3)
69 Rue de la Belle Etoile, PO Box 59320,
95 700, Roissy-en-France, France
Tel.: (33) 148170570
Web Site: http://www.cofely-gdfsuez.com
Sales Range: $25-49.9 Million
Emp.: 150
Logistics Consulting Servies
N.A.I.C.S.: 541614

COFELY Axima (3)
46 Boulevard Prairie Au Duc, BP 40119,
44201, Nantes, Cedex 2, France
Tel.: (33) 240410000
Web Site: http://www.cofelyaxima-gdfsuez.com
Refrigeration Products Mfr
N.A.I.C.S.: 333415

COFELY Deutschland GmbH (3)
Durener Strasse 403-405, 50858, Cologne,
Germany
Tel.: (49) 221469050
Web Site: http://www.cofely.de
Sales Range: $50-74.9 Million
Emp.: 170
Energy Management, Long-Term Technical
Management & Facilities Management Services
N.A.I.C.S.: 561990
Manfred Schmitz (CEO)

Subsidiary (Domestic):

H.G.S. GmbH & Co. KG (4)
Hessenstrasse 55, 47809, Krefeld, Germany
Tel.: (49) 21515255600
Web Site: http://www.hgspartner.de
Sales Range: $25-49.9 Million
Emp.: 80
Industrial Engine & Generator Installation &
Maintenance Services
N.A.I.C.S.: 811310
Jan Voelkel (Mgr-Svc)

Subsidiary (Non-US):

COFELY District Energy Ltd (3)
Garrett House Manor Royal, Crawley, RH10
9UT, West Sussex, United Kingdom
Tel.: (44) 1293549944
Web Site: http://www.cofely-gdfsuez.co.uk
Sales Range: $125-149.9 Million
Emp.: 16
Eletric Power Generation Services
N.A.I.C.S.: 221118
Paul Laidlaw (Mng Dir)

COFELY Endel (3)
1 Place Des Degres, 92059, Paris, France
Tel.: (33) 157609000
Web Site: http://www.engie.com
Emp.: 30
Eletric Power Generation Services
N.A.I.C.S.: 221118
Pascal Weil (Mgr-Publ)

COFELY Epuletgepeszeti Kft. (3)
Ulloi Ut 206, 1191, Budapest, 1191, Hungary
Tel.: (36) 14601030
Web Site: http://www.cofely.hu
Construction Design Services

ENGIE SA—(Continued)

N.A.I.C.S.: 541490
Csanady Zsolt (Mng Dir)

COFELY Espana, S.A.U. (3)
Torrelaguna 79, 28043, Madrid, Spain
Tel.: (34) 917498200
Web Site: http://www.cofely.es
Sales Range: $50-74.9 Million
Emp.: 150
Energy Management, Long-Term Technical
Management & Facilities Management Services
N.A.I.C.S.: 561990
Loretto Orgonez (Dir Gen)

Branch (Domestic):

**COFELY Espana, S.A.U. -
Barcelona** (4)
Torre Realia BCN Plaza Europa 41-43,
L'Hospitalet de Llobregat, Barcelona, 8908,
Spain
Tel.: (34) 933638686
Web Site: http://www.cofely-gdfsuez.es
Energy Management, Long-Term Technical
Management & Facilities Management Services
N.A.I.C.S.: 561990
Didier Maurice (Dir Gen)

Subsidiary (Non-US):

COFELY FM s.r.o. (3)
Lhotecka c 3, 143 00, Prague, Czech Republic
Tel.: (420) 257941652
Web Site: http://www.cofelyfm.cz
Construction Facility Management Services
N.A.I.C.S.: 237990

COFELY Hellas A.E. (3)
Thermopylae 2, 152 35 Vrilissia, Athens,
152 35, Greece
Tel.: (30) 2106084176
Web Site: http://www.cofely-gdfsuez.gr
Sales Range: $25-49.9 Million
Emp.: 100
Energy Management, Long-Term Technical
Management & Facilities Management Services
N.A.I.C.S.: 561990
George Daniolos (Mng Dir)

COFELY Ineo (3)
1 Place Des Degres, 92059, Paris, France
Tel.: (33) 157604200
Web Site: http://www.injeie.com
Electrical Engineering & Telecommunication
Services
N.A.I.C.S.: 541330
Guy Lacroix (Chm & CEO)

Division (Domestic):

**COFELY Ineo - Ineo Engineering &
Systems Division** (4)
Z I Sud Est 16 Rue de la Tremblaie, 35000,
Rennes, France
Tel.: (33) 299532155
Web Site: http://www.cofelyineo-
gdfsuez.com
Sales Range: $50-74.9 Million
Emp.: 280
Information Technology Consulting Services
N.A.I.C.S.: 541512

Subsidiary (Domestic):

Ineo Defense (4)
23 Rue General Valerie Andre', 78140,
Velizy-Villacoublay, France
Tel.: (33) 139269200
Emp.: 700
Defense Security System Services
N.A.I.C.S.: 561621
Jean-Louis Marucci (CEO)

Subsidiary (Non-US):

COFELY Italia S.p.A. (3)
Via Miramare 15, 20126, Milan, Italy
Tel.: (39) 02380821
Web Site: http://www.cofely-gdfsuez.it
Energy Services
N.A.I.C.S.: 221122

COFELY Kaltetechnik GmbH (3)
Langegasse 19, Lauterach, 6923, Austria
Tel.: (43) 557467050

Web Site: http://www.cofely.info
Industrial Refrigeration Mfr
N.A.I.C.S.: 333415
Karl Guldenschuh (Office Mgr)

COFELY Limited (3)
Stuart House Coronation Road, High Wycombe, HP12 3TA, Bucks, United Kingdom
Tel.: (44) 1494472902
Web Site: http://www.cofely-gdfsuez.co.uk
Energy Management Services
N.A.I.C.S.: 221122
Simon Woodward (Mng Dir)

Subsidiary (Domestic):

Cofely WorkPlace Limited (4)
Fourth Floor West Block 1 Angel Square 1
Torrens Street, London, EC1V 1NY, United
Kingdom
Tel.: (44) 2078223720
Web Site: http://www.cofely-gdfsuez.co.uk
Sales Range: $700-749.9 Million
Facilities Management & Maintenance Services
N.A.I.C.S.: 561210

Subsidiary (Non-US):

COFELY Morocco (3)
20 Boulevard Rachidi, 20000, Casablanca,
Morocco
Tel.: (212) 522224423
Web Site: http://www.cofely-gdfsuez.com
Eletric Power Generation Services
N.A.I.C.S.: 221118

COFELY Nederland N.V. (3)
Kosterijland 20, 3981 AJ, Bunnik, 3981 AJ,
Netherlands
Tel.: (31) 306569459
Web Site: http://www.cofely-gdfsuez.nl
Emp.: 200
Energy Management, Long-Term Technical
Management & Facilities Management Services
N.A.I.C.S.: 561990
J. Han Blokland (Mng Dir)

Subsidiary (Domestic):

COFELY Delta Controls BV (4)
Pieter de Keyserstraat 6, 7825 VE, Emmen,
Netherlands
Tel.: (31) 591678800
Web Site: http://www.deltacontrols.nl
Emp.: 5
Valve & Actuator Mfr
N.A.I.C.S.: 332911
Gerald Gommers (Gen Mgr)

COFELY Energy Solutions BV (4)
Kosterijland 20, 3981 AJ, Bunnik, Netherlands
Tel.: (31) 884840484
Sales Range: $200-249.9 Million
Emp.: 50
Eletric Power Generation Services
N.A.I.C.S.: 221113

COFELY Noord BV (4)
Exportweg 1, 9301 ZV, Roden, Netherlands
Tel.: (31) 505023456
Web Site: http://www.cofely-gdfsuez.nl
Sales Range: $350-399.9 Million
Emp.: 1,000
Eletric Power Generation Services
N.A.I.C.S.: 221118
F. Deboer (Mng Dir)

COFELY Refrigeration BV (4)
Industrieweg 1, 2712 LA, Zoetermeer, 2712
LA, Netherlands
Tel.: (31) 793462727
Web Site: http://www.cofely-gdfsuez.nl
Refrigeration Product Distr
N.A.I.C.S.: 423740
J. Nieuwenhuis (Gen Mgr)

COFELY West Industrie BV (4)
Willingestraat 4, 3087 AD, Rotterdam, Netherlands
Emp.: 20
Eletric Power Generation Services
N.A.I.C.S.: 221118

COFELY West Nederland BV (4)
Albert Heijnweg 1, 1507 EH, Zaandam,
Netherlands
Tel.: (31) 756537000
Eletric Power Generation Services

N.A.I.C.S.: 221118

COFELY Zuid Nederland BV (4)
Vlamoven 40, 6826 TN, Arnhem, Netherlands
Tel.: (31) 263763800
Web Site: http://www.cofely-gdfsuez.nl
Sales Range: $350-399.9 Million
Emp.: 300
Eletric Power Generation Services
N.A.I.C.S.: 221118
Hans Boot (Gen Mgr)

Subsidiary (Non-US):

COFELY Pacific (3)
Cofely Pacific 19 Rue Auer - Ducos, BP
1085, 98845, Noumea, New Caledonia
Tel.: (687) 272227
Web Site: http://www.cofely-gdfsuez.com
Eletric Power Generation Services
N.A.I.C.S.: 221118

COFELY Portugal (3)
Rua do Arco a Alcantara 44, 1350-021, Lisbon, Portugal
Tel.: (351) 213928030
Web Site: http://www.cofely-gdfsuez.pt
Sales Range: $125-149.9 Million
Emp.: 25
Eletric Power Generation Services
N.A.I.C.S.: 221118
Pedro Alves (Dir-Sls & Mktg)

COFELY Refrigeration GmbH (3)
Kemptener Str 11-15, 88131, Lindau, Germany
Tel.: (49) 83827060
Web Site: http://www.cofely-refrigeration.de
Sales Range: $125-149.9 Million
Emp.: 34
Refrigeration Product Distr
N.A.I.C.S.: 423740
Manfred Schmitz (Head-Germany)

COFELY Services (3)
Le Voltaire 1 Place Des Degres, 92059,
Paris, France
Tel.: (33) 141201000
Web Site: http://www.cofelyservices-
gdfsuez.fr
Eletric Power Generation Services
N.A.I.C.S.: 221118
Marie-Laurence Berlioz (Mgr-Publ)

COFELY Services Inc. (3)
550 Sherbrooke Street West Suite 400,
Montreal, H3A 1B9, QC, Canada
Tel.: (514) 876-8780
Web Site: http://www.cofelyservices-
gdfsuez.net
Emp.: 70
Energy Management, Long-Term Technical
Management & Facilities Management Services
N.A.I.C.S.: 561990
Francois Depelteau (Pres)

Subsidiary (Domestic):

Adelt Mechanical Works Ltd. (4)
2640 Argentia Rd, Mississauga, L5N 6C5,
ON, Canada
Tel.: (905) 812-7900
Web Site: http://www.adeltmechanical.com
Sales Range: $10-24.9 Million
Emp.: 135
Mechanical Contractor
N.A.I.C.S.: 333415
Scott Munro (VP)

Subsidiary (Non-US):

COFELY Services S.A. (3)
Zare Ilot Ouest, 4384, Ehlerange, Luxembourg
Tel.: (352) 2655331
Web Site: http://www.cofelyservices-
gdfsuez.lu
Sales Range: $25-49.9 Million
Emp.: 87
Energy Management, Long-Term Technical
Management & Facilities Management Services
N.A.I.C.S.: 561990
Gilbert Lentz (Dir-Indus Engrg)

Branch (Domestic):

COFELY Services SA/NV - Liege (3)

Bld du Roi Albert II 30, 4100, Brussels, Belgium
Tel.: (32) 43859450
Web Site: http://www.cofelyservices-
gdfsuez.be
Sales Range: $25-49.9 Million
Emp.: 100
Energy Management, Long-Term Technical
Management & Facilities Management Services
N.A.I.C.S.: 561990

**COFELY Services SA/NV -
Mechelen** (3)
Egide Walschaertsstraat 15 1, Mechelen,
1000, Belgium
Tel.: (32) 15450400
Web Site: http://www.cofelyservices-
gdfsuez.be
Sales Range: $400-449.9 Million
Emp.: 1,800
Energy Management, Long-Term Technical
Management & Facilities Management Services
N.A.I.C.S.: 561990
Stanislas de Pierpont (Mng Dir)

Subsidiary (Non-US):

COFELY Services Sp. z o.o. (3)
Centrum Milenium ul Kijowska 1, 03 738,
Warsaw, Poland
Tel.: (48) 225180186
Web Site: http://www.cofely.pl
Sales Range: $25-49.9 Million
Emp.: 25
Energy Management, Long-Term Technical
Management & Facilities Management Services
N.A.I.C.S.: 561990
Jan Wrzniak (Mng Dir)

**COFELY South East Asia Pte.
Ltd.** (3)
146B Paya Lebar Road 03-01 ACE Bldg,
Singapore, 409017, Singapore
Tel.: (65) 64401818
Web Site: http://www.cofely.com.sg
Emp.: 160
Energy Management, Long-Term Technical
Management & Facilities Management Services
N.A.I.C.S.: 561990

Affiliate (Non-US):

COFELY (Thailand) Pte. Ltd. (4)
Eastern Seaboard Industrial Estates 107/1
Moo 4 T Pluakdaeng, A Pluakdaeng, Rayong, 21140, Thailand (40%)
Tel.: (66) 38955353
Web Site: http://www.cofely.co.th
Energy Management, Long-Term Technical
Management & Facilities Management Services
N.A.I.C.S.: 561990
Sawat Macmyraxa (Gen Mgr)

Subsidiary (Domestic):

Cofely FMO (4)
108 Pasir Panjang Road 05-04 Golden Agri
Plaza, Singapore, 118535, Singapore
Tel.: (65) 65138288
Web Site: http://www.cofely.com.sg
Facility Management Services
N.A.I.C.S.: 561210

Subsidiary (Non-US):

COFELY Termika (3)
Avenida Blanco 15 i 2 - Parque Industrial
Los Libertadores, Colina, Santiago, Chile
Tel.: (56) 24804400
Web Site: http://www.cofely-termika.ch
Electrical Engineering Services
N.A.I.C.S.: 541330

COFELY Vanuatu (3)
BP 6, Port-Vila, Vanuatu
Tel.: (678) 26000
Eletric Power Generation Services
N.A.I.C.S.: 221118
David Lefebvre (Gen Mgr)

COFELY a.s. (3)
Mlynske Nivy 61, Bratislava, 82711, Slovakia
Tel.: (421) 258316223
Web Site: http://www.cofely.sk

Sales Range: $50-74.9 Million
Emp.: 180
Energy Management, Long-Term Technical Management & Facilities Management Services
N.A.I.C.S.: 561990
Peter Strycek (Reg Mgr)

COFELY a.s. (3)
Lhotecka 793/3, 143 00, Prague, Czech Republic
Tel.: (420) 267054909
Web Site: http://www.cofely.cz
Sales Range: $75-99.9 Million
Emp.: 365
Energy Infrastructure Services, Electricity Production & Distribution & Facility Management Services
N.A.I.C.S.: 221122
Ales Damm (CEO)

Cofely Gebaudetechnik GmbH (3)
Leberstrasse 120, A-1110, Vienna, Austria
Tel.: (43) 1740360
Web Site: http://www.axima.at
Sales Range: $150-199.9 Million
Emp.: 900
Construction Technology & Facilities Management Services
N.A.I.C.S.: 561210
Adolf Lauber (Mng Dir)

ENGIE Services Australia & New Zealand Holdings Pty. Ltd. (3)
Suite B 225 Rawson Street, Auburn, 2144, NSW, Australia
Tel.: (61) 297144700
Web Site: http://www.engie-anz.com
Holding Company
N.A.I.C.S.: 551112

Subsidiary (Domestic):

ENGIE Fire Services Australia Pty Limited (4)
Suite B 255 Rawson Street, Auburn, 2144, NSW, Australia
Tel.: (61) 297144700
Web Site: http://www.engie-anz.com
Fire Protection Facilities Support Services
N.A.I.C.S.: 922160

ENGIE Mechanical Services Australia Pty Limited (4)
Unit E 225 Rawson Street, Auburn, 2144, NSW, Australia
Tel.: (61) 297144700
Web Site: http://www.engie-anz.com
Heating, Ventilation, Air-Conditioning & Refrigeration Services Contractor
N.A.I.C.S.: 238220
Mark Williamson (Mng Dir-Svcs)

Subsidiary (Non-US):

ENGIE Services New Zealand Limited (4)
1 Gabador Place, Mt Wellington, Auckland, 1060, New Zealand
Tel.: (64) 5082321338
Web Site: http://www.engie-anz.com
Commercial & Industrial Refrigeration Systems Designer, Whslr & Installation Services
N.A.I.C.S.: 423740

Subsidiary (US):

ENGIE Services Inc. (3)
Louisville International Airport 600 Terminal Dr Upper Level Door L225, Louisville, KY 40209-1595
Tel.: (877) 455-8780
Web Site: http://www.cofelyservices-gdfsuez.net
Emp.: 80
Engineeering Services
N.A.I.C.S.: 541330
Pierre Loyer (Grp Dir-Airport)

Subsidiary (Domestic):

Ecova, Inc. (4)
1313 N Atlantic St Ste 5000, Spokane, WA 99201
Tel.: (509) 329-7600
Web Site: http://www.ecova.com
Sales Range: $150-199.9 Million
Energy Consulting Services
N.A.I.C.S.: 541690

Hossein Nikdel (CTO & VP)

Subsidiary (Domestic):

Retroficiency, Inc. (5)
Summer Exchange Bldg 101 Arch St Ste 30, Boston, MA 02110
Tel.: (857) 753-4840
Web Site: http://www.retroficiency.com
Energy Conservation Software Services
N.A.I.C.S.: 541511

Subsidiary (Domestic):

Climespace (2)
185 rue de Bercy, 75579, Paris, France
Tel.: (33) 144748940
Web Site: http://www.climespace.fr
Rev.: $76,434,000
Emp.: 85
Cooling Energy Services
N.A.I.C.S.: 333415
Carole Le Gall (Chm)

Subsidiary (Non-US):

Climaespaco (3)
Rua do Mar Vermelho n 2, 1990-152, Lisbon, Portugal
Tel.: (351) 213171170
Web Site: https://www.climaespaco.pt
Sales Range: $10-24.9 Million
Emp.: 30
Heating & Air Conditioning Services
N.A.I.C.S.: 333415
Joao Castanheira (Gen Dir)

Subsidiary (Domestic):

Compagnie Parisienne de Chauffage Urbain (2)
185 avenue de Bercy, 75012, Paris, 75012, France
Tel.: (33) 144686820
Web Site: https://www.cpcu.fr
Sales Range: $200-249.9 Million
Emp.: 590
Energy Services
N.A.I.C.S.: 221122
Marc Ballier (Gen Mgr)

Subsidiary (Non-US):

Electricite De Tahiti (2)
Route de Puurai, BP 8021, 98702, Faaa, French Polynesia
Tel.: (689) 40867786
Web Site: https://www.edt.pf
Sales Range: $200-249.9 Million
Emp.: 450
Electric Power Distr
N.A.I.C.S.: 221122

Subsidiary (Domestic):

Endel SAS (2)
165 Blvd de Valmy, 1Places degree, 92059, Paris, France
Tel.: (33) 157609000
Web Site: http://www.endel.fr
Sales Range: $700-749.9 Million
Emp.: 5,000
Industrial Equipment Installation & Maintenance
N.A.I.C.S.: 811310

GEPSA (2)
23 avenue Jules Rimet OLYMPE Building, 93210, La Plaine Saint-Denis, France
Tel.: (33) 155994325
Web Site: https://www.gepsa.fr
Sales Range: $75-99.9 Million
Emp.: 370
Facility Management Services
N.A.I.C.S.: 561210

Subsidiary (Non-US):

Togo Electricite (2)
Ave Leopold Sedar Senghor, PO Box 42, Lome, Togo
Tel.: (228) 2212744
Web Site: http://www.togoelectricite.com
Electricity Producer & Distr
N.A.I.C.S.: 221122

GDF Suez Energy International (1)
Place du Trone 1, 1000, Brussels, Belgium
Tel.: (32) 25107111
Web Site: http://www.suezenergy.com

Sales Range: $1-4.9 Billion
Emp.: 5,450
Holding Company; Electricity & Gas Energy Services
N.A.I.C.S.: 551112

Subsidiary (Non-US):

Carbopego - Abastecimento de combustiveis, S.A. (2)
Quinta Da Fonte Edificio D Maria Piso 0 Ala B, 2780-730, Paco d'Arcos, Portugal
Tel.: (351) 214403200
Web Site: http://www.tejoenergia.com
Sales Range: $75-99.9 Million
Emp.: 3
Electric Power Distribution Services
N.A.I.C.S.: 221118
Fernando Pinto Teixeira (Gen Mgr)

Castelnou Energia S.L (2)
Carretera CV - 407 Al Apeadero De Escatron s/n, 44592, Castelnou, Teruel, Spain
Tel.: (34) 978 82 80 15
Sales Range: $50-74.9 Million
Emp.: 3
Eletric Power Generation Services
N.A.I.C.S.: 221118

Distrigaz Confort SRL (2)
Str Arhitect Harjeu Nr 57 Sect 2, Bucharest, Romania
Tel.: (40) 374222270
Web Site: http://www.distrigazconfort-gdfsuez.ro
Gas Installation Services
N.A.I.C.S.: 238220
Frederic Gerard Bellon (Gen Mgr)

EGAZ-DEGAZ FOLDGAZELOSZTO ZRT. (2)
Puskas Tivadar u 37, 9027, Gyor, Hungary
Tel.: (36) 6 96 503 100
Web Site: http://www.egaz-degaz-foldgazeloszto.hu
Natural Gas Distribution Services
N.A.I.C.S.: 221210

ENGIE Deutschland AG (2)
Friedrichstrasse 200, 10117, Berlin, Germany
Tel.: (49) 30726153500
Web Site: http://www.engie-deutschland.de
Sales Range: $1-4.9 Billion
Emp.: 600
Gas Distribution
N.A.I.C.S.: 221210
Manfred Schmitz (Chm-Exec Bd & Mng Dir)

Subsidiary (Domestic):

Energieversorgung Gera GmbH (3)
De-Smit-Strasse 18, 07545, Gera, Germany
Tel.: (49) 365 8560
Web Site: https://www.energieversorgung-gera.de
Sales Range: $150-199.9 Million
Emp.: 200
Eletric Power Generation Services
N.A.I.C.S.: 221118
Andre Grieser (Mng Dir)

Subsidiary (Non-US):

GDF Suez E&P Deutschland GmbH (3)
(100%)
Sales Range: $75-99.9 Million
Emp.: 101
Natural Gas & Oil Distr
N.A.I.C.S.: 211120
Heinz Wendel (Head-Tech)

Subsidiary (Domestic):

GDF Suez Gas Energy Sales GmbH (3)
Friedrichstrasse 200, D 10117, Berlin, Germany
(100%)
Tel.: (49) 3059006100
Web Site: http://www.gdfsuez-energysales.de
Sales Range: $50-74.9 Million
Emp.: 70
Gas Supplier
N.A.I.C.S.: 221210
Olga Ivanova (Mng Dir)

Joint Venture (Domestic):

MEGAL Mittel-Europaische-Gasleitungsgesellschaft mbH & Co.

KG (3)
Kallenbergstrasse 5, D-45141, Essen, Germany
Tel.: (49) 20136420
Web Site: http://www.open-grid-europe.com
Natural Gas Pipeline Transportation Services
N.A.I.C.S.: 486210
Hans Jurgen Plattner (Mng Dir)

Subsidiary (Domestic):

Electrabel S.A. (2)
Boulevard Simon 34, Brussels, 1000, Belgium
Tel.: (32) 25186111
Web Site: http://www.electrabel.be
Sales Range: $15-24.9 Billion
Power Generation & Distribution
N.A.I.C.S.: 221122

Subsidiary (Domestic):

Electrabel Blue Sky Investments SCRL (3)
Simon Bolivarlaan 34, 1000, Brussels, Belgium
Tel.: (32) 2 509 64 63
Financial Investment Services
N.A.I.C.S.: 523999

Electrabel Customer Solutions N.V./S.A (3)
Ave Simon Boulevar 34, 1000, Brussels, Belgium
Tel.: (32) 25186111
Web Site: http://www.electrabel.be
Emp.: 3,000
Electric Power & Natural Gas Distribution Services
N.A.I.C.S.: 221122
Philippe Van Troeye (CEO)

Subsidiary (Non-US):

Electrabel France S.A. (3)
20 Pl Louis Pradel, 69001, Lyon, France
Tel.: (33) 472982100
Sales Range: $75-99.9 Million
Emp.: 100
Electronic Services
N.A.I.C.S.: 221122

Electrabel Nederland Retail N.V. (3)
Grote Voort 291, 8041 BL, Zwolle, Netherlands
Tel.: (31) 887692900
Web Site: http://www.electrabel.nl
Emp.: 400
Electric Power Distr
N.A.I.C.S.: 221122
Erik Bockweg (Head-Mktg & Sls)

Subsidiary (Domestic):

Cogas Energie B.V. (4)
Rohofstraat 83, 7605 AT, Almelo, Netherlands
Tel.: (31) 546836666
Web Site: http://www.cogas.nl
Sales Range: $100-124.9 Million
Emp.: 230
Gas & Power Distr
N.A.I.C.S.: 221122
Michiel Kirch (CEO)

Subsidiary (Domestic):

Laborelec C.V. (3)
Rodestraat 125, Linkebeek, 1630, Belgium
Tel.: (32) 23820211
Web Site: http://www.laborelec.com
Sales Range: $25-49.9 Million
Emp.: 250
Scientific & Technical Research & Assessment Services to Electricity Industry
N.A.I.C.S.: 541715
B. Boesmans (Gen Mgr)

SUEZ-Tractebel SA (3)
Avenue Ariane 7, 1200, Brussels, Belgium
Tel.: (32) 2 773 99 11
Web Site: http://www.tractebel-engineering-gdfsuez.com
Sales Range: $600-649.9 Million
Emp.: 1,500
Holding Company; Engineering Services
N.A.I.C.S.: 551112
Daniel Develay (CEO)

ENGIE SA—(Continued)

Subsidiary (Domestic):

Electrabel Green Projects Flanders
SCRL **(4)**
Rodenhuizekaai 3, 9042, Gent, Belgium
Tel.: (32) 53760711
Wind Electric Power Generation Services
N.A.I.C.S.: 221118

Tractebel Engineering **(4)**
Boulevard Simon Bolivar 34, gdfsuez, Brussels, 1200, Belgium
Tel.: (32) 2 773 9911
Sales Range: $500-549.9 Million
Engineering Consulting Services
N.A.I.C.S.: 541330
Georges Cornet *(CEO)*

Subsidiary (Non-US):

Engie Brasil Energia SA **(5)**
Rua Paschoal Apostolo Pisca no 5064 Agronomica, Florianopolis, 88025 255, SC, Brazil
Tel.: (55) 4832217000
Web Site:
https://www.tractebelenergia.com.br
Rev.: $58,940,076,071
Assets: $189,032,059,750
Liabilities: $147,251,520,316
Net Worth: $41,780,539,434
Earnings: $13,190,144,514
Emp.: 1,215
Fiscal Year-end: 12/31/2022
Electric Power Generation & Distribution
N.A.I.C.S.: 221122
Paulo Jorge Tavares Almirante *(VP)*

Plant (Domestic):

Tractebel Energia S.A. - HPP CANA
BRAVA - UHCB Plant **(6)**
Caixa Postal 52, 76450-000, Minacu, Brazil
Tel.: (55) 6233798600
Hydroelectric Power Generation Services
N.A.I.C.S.: 221111

Tractebel Energia S.A. - HPP
MACHADINHO - UHMA Plant **(6)**
Linha Sao Paulo s/n Caixa Postal 3, Piratuba, 89667 000, Santa Catarina, Brazil
Tel.: (55) 4935536000
Web Site:
http://www.tractebelenergia.com.br
Hydroelectric Power Generation Services
N.A.I.C.S.: 221111
Roberto Deboni *(Office Mgr)*

Tractebel Energia S.A. - HPP PONTE
DE PEDRA - UHPP Plant **(6)**
Est da Usina Hidreletrica Ponte de Pedra s/n Antiga BR 163, 78790-000, Itiquira, Brazil
Tel.: (55) 5435441166
Hydroelectric Power Generation Services
N.A.I.C.S.: 221111

Tractebel Energia S.A. - HPP SALTO
OSORIO - UHSO Plant **(6)**
Rodovia PR 475 Km 3, 85460-000, Quedas do Iguacu, Parana, Brazil
Tel.: (55) 4635598100
Sales Range: $10-24.9 Million
Emp.: 38
Hydroelectric Power Generation Services
N.A.I.C.S.: 221111
Antonio Carlos Martins *(Gen Mgr)*

Tractebel Energia S.A. - HPP SALTO
SANTIAGO - UHSS Plant **(6)**
Rodovia BR 158 Km 41, 85568-000, Saudade do Iguacu, Brazil
Tel.: (55) 4632468300
Hydroelectric Power Generation Services
N.A.I.C.S.: 221111

Tractebel Energia S.A. - HPP SAO
SALVADOR - UHSA Plant **(6)**
Rod TO 387 PRN/Sao Salvador Km 40 to left 20Km Zona Rural S/N, 77360-000, Parana, Brazil
Tel.: (55) 4632468300
Hydroelectric Power Generation Services
N.A.I.C.S.: 221111

Tractebel Energia S.A. - JORGE
LACERDA THERMOELECTRIC
COMPLEX - CJL Plant **(6)**

Av Paulo Santos Mello s/n, Caixa Postal n
38, 88745 000, Capivari de Baixo, Santa
Catarina, Brazil
Tel.: (55) 4836214000
Thermal Electric Power Generation Services
N.A.I.C.S.: 221118

Tractebel Energia S.A. - Lages Cogeneration Unit - UCLA Plant **(6)**
Rua Vivanderio Santos do Vale s/n, 85516-600, Lages, Santa Catarina, Brazil
Tel.: (55) 4932214500
Eletric Power Generation Services
N.A.I.C.S.: 221118

Tractebel Energia S.A. - TPP ALEGRETE - UTAL Plant **(6)**
Rua Joao Galant s/n Bairro Ibirapuita, 97546-330, Alegrete, Rio Grande do Sul, Brazil
Tel.: (55) 5534224600
Thermal Electric Power Generation Services
N.A.I.C.S.: 221118

Tractebel Energia S.A. - TPP CHARQUEADAS - UTCH Plant **(6)**
Geologo White s/n, Bairro Centro, 96745-000, Charqueadas, Rio Grande do Sul, Brazil
Tel.: (55) 5136581899
Thermal Electric Power Generation Services
N.A.I.C.S.: 221116

Tractebel Energia S.A. - TPP WILLIAM ARJONA - UTWA Plant **(6)**
Rodovia BR 060 s/n Estrada Vicinal, Imbirussu, 79008-970, Campo Grande, Mato Grosso do Sul, Brazil
Tel.: (55) 6733249091
Web Site:
http://www.tractebelenergia.com.br
Thermal Electric Power Generation Services
N.A.I.C.S.: 221118

Subsidiary (Domestic):

Techum-Tractabel Engineering
N.V. **(5)**
Coveliersstraat 15, B 2600, Antwerp, Belgium
Tel.: (32) 32709292
Web Site: http://www.technum.be
Sales Range: $200-249.9 Million
Emp.: 400
Engineering & Consulting Services
N.A.I.C.S.: 541330

Subsidiary (Domestic):

Technum-Tractebel Engineering
N.V. **(6)**
Ilgatlaan 23, 3500, Hasselt, Limburg, Belgium
Tel.: (32) 1 128 8600
Web Site: https://www.tractebel-engie.be
Sales Range: $10-24.9 Million
Emp.: 140
Urban Building & Infrastructure Engineering Services
N.A.I.C.S.: 541330

Subsidiary (Domestic):

Tractebel Development Engineering
S.A. **(5)**
Ave Ariane 7, B-1200, Brussels, Belgium
Tel.: (32) 27737589
Web Site: http://www.tde.tractebel.com
Sales Range: $700-749.9 Million
Emp.: 1,500
Engineering Services; Building & Infrastructure
N.A.I.C.S.: 541330

Subsidiary (Non-US):

Tractebel S.A. **(5)**
API World Tower Fl 31, Sheikh Zayed Rd, Dubai, 66235, United Arab Emirates
Tel.: (971) 43314486
Sales Range: $150-199.9 Million
Emp.: 50
Electric Power Generation
N.A.I.C.S.: 221122
G. Cornet *(CEO)*

Subsidiary (Non-US):

Baymina Enerji AS **(6)**
Malikoy Mahallesi Malikoy Kume Evleri No 506, PO Box 40 K, Sincan, 06900, Ankara, Turkiye
Tel.: (90) 3126309100
Web Site: https://www.bayenerji.com
Emp.: 47
Electricity Generation Services
N.A.I.C.S.: 221122
Kemal Taragay *(CEO & CFO)*

Subsidiary (Non-US):

Energie Saarlorlux AG **(2)**
Richard-Wagner-Strasse 14-16, Saarbrucken, 66111, Germany
Tel.: (49) 6815874777
Web Site: http://www.energie-saarlorlux.com
Electric Power Generation & Distribution Services
N.A.I.C.S.: 221118
Jochen Starke *(CEO)*

Energy Consulting Services S.A. **(2)**
Olga Cossettini 340-1st floor, C1106ABL, Buenos Aires, Argentina
Tel.: (54) 115 071 8800
Web Site: https://en.ecs.com.ar
Energy Consulting Services
N.A.I.C.S.: 541690

GDF Britain Ltd. **(2)**
40 Holborn Viaduct, London, EC1 2PB, United Kingdom **(100%)**
Tel.: (44) 2070674400
Web Site: http://www.gazdefrance.co.uk
Sales Range: $75-99.9 Million
Emp.: 120
Natural Gas Distribution
N.A.I.C.S.: 211130

Subsidiary (Domestic):

International Power plc **(3)**
Level 20 25 Canada Square, London, E145LQ, United Kingdom **(70%)**
Tel.: (44) 2073208600
Web Site: http://www.iprplc-gdfsuez.com
Emp.: 400
Holding Company; Power Generation & Distribution Services
N.A.I.C.S.: 551112
Gerard Mestrallet *(Chm)*

Joint Venture (Domestic):

Deeside Power (UK) Limited **(4)**
Weighbridge Road Zone 4, Deeside Industrial Park, Deeside, CH5 2UL, Flintshire, United Kingdom **(75%)**
Tel.: (44) 1244286000
Web Site: http://www.deesidepower.com
Sales Range: $50-74.9 Million
Emp.: 60
Electric Power Generator & Distr
N.A.I.C.S.: 221112

Subsidiary (Domestic):

First Hydro Finance plc **(4)**
Senator House 85 Queen Victoria Street, London, EC4V 4DP, United Kingdom
Tel.: (44) 8702385500
Financial Investment Services
N.A.I.C.S.: 523999

GDF SUEZ Energy UK Limited **(4)**
1 City Walk, Leeds, LS12 1BE, United Kingdom
Tel.: (44) 8001303600
Web Site: https://www.engie.co.uk
Emp.: 22
Eletric Power Generation Services
N.A.I.C.S.: 221118
Luciana Andriani *(Mng Dir)*

Subsidiary (Domestic):

GDF SUEZ Sales Ltd **(5)**
26 Whitehall Road, Leeds, LS12 1BE, West Yorkshire, United Kingdom
Tel.: (44) 1133062000
Sales Range: $250-299.9 Million
Natural Gas Distribution Services
N.A.I.C.S.: 221210

GDF SUEZ Services Limited **(5)**
26 Whitehall Road, Leeds, LS12 1BE, United Kingdom

Tel.: (44) 11 33 06 20 00
Web Site: http://www.gdfsuez-energy.co.uk
Natural Gas Distribution Services
N.A.I.C.S.: 221210

GDF SUEZ Shotton Limited **(5)**
1 City Walk, Leeds, LS11 9DX, United Kingdom
Tel.: (44) 113306 2000
Web Site: http://www.gdfsuezuk.com
Electric Power Distribution Services
N.A.I.C.S.: 221122

GDF SUEZ Solutions Limited **(5)**
1 City Walk, Leeds, LS11 9DX, United Kingdom
Tel.: (44) 1133062000
Sales Range: $300-349.9 Million
Electric Power & Natural Gas Distribution Services
N.A.I.C.S.: 221122

Gdf Suez Teesside Ltd **(5)**
Teesside Power Station Greystone Road, Eston, Middlesbrough, TS6 9JF, Cleveland, United Kingdom
Tel.: (44) 1642440440
Sales Range: $150-199.9 Million
Emp.: 4
Eletric Power Generation Services
N.A.I.C.S.: 221118

Joint Venture (Non-US):

Hidd Power Company BSC **(4)**
Hidd Power Station, Hidd Industrial Area, Hidd, Bahrain **(30%)**
Tel.: (973) 1 767 9479
Web Site: https://www.hpc.com.bh
Water & Electric Utility Services
N.A.I.C.S.: 221112
Radhakrishnan Kaiparambath *(Mgr-Engrg, Plng & Performance)*

Subsidiary (Domestic):

IPM Energy Trading Limited **(4)**
Senator House 85 Queen Victoria Street, London, EC4V 4D, United Kingdom
Tel.: (44) 113 306 2000
Eletric Power Generation Services
N.A.I.C.S.: 221118

Subsidiary (Non-US):

IPR - GDF SUEZ Australia Pty
Ltd **(4)**
Level 3 Rialto South Tower 525 Collins Street, Melbourne, 3000, VIC, Australia
Tel.: (61) 3 9617 8400
Web Site: http://www.gdfsuez.com.au
Sales Range: $350-399.9 Million
Emp.: 750
Eletric Power Generation Services
N.A.I.C.S.: 221118
Tony Concannon *(CEO)*

Subsidiary (Domestic):

HAZELWOOD POWER
PARTNERSHIP **(5)**
PO Box 195, Morwell, 3840, VIC, Australia
Tel.: (61) 39617 8400
Web Site: http://www.gdfsuezau.com
Emp.: 80
Eletric Power Generation Services
N.A.I.C.S.: 221118

Plant (Domestic):

IPR - GDF SUEZ Australia Pty Ltd -
Kwinana Cogeneration Plant **(5)**
Locked Bag 66, Rockingham, 6967, WA, Australia
Tel.: (61) 8 9439 8111
Emp.: 19
Eletric Power Generation Services
N.A.I.C.S.: 221118

Subsidiary (Domestic):

Latrobe Power Partnership **(5)**
Bartons Lane, Traralgon, 3844, VIC, Australia
Tel.: (61) 351732917
Electric Power Distribution Services
N.A.I.C.S.: 221122

Subsidiary (Non-US):

IPR - GDF SUEZ Latin America **(4)**

Av Apoquindo 3721 - Piso 8, Las Condes,
755 0177, Santiago, Chile
Tel.: (56) 2 290 0400
Web Site: http://www.iprplc-gdfsuez.com
Eletric Power Generation Services
N.A.I.C.S.: 221118
Pierre Devillers (Sr VP-HR & Comm)

Subsidiary (Non-US):

**Comphania Energetica Sao Salvador
S.A.** (5)
Rua Paschoal Apostolo Pitsica 5064, Flori-
anopolis, 88025-255, Brazil
Tel.: (55) 4832217000
Web Site:
http://www.tractebelenergia.com.br
Emp.: 300
Eletric Power Generation Services
N.A.I.C.S.: 221118
Manoel Varoni (Pres)

**Tractebel Energia Comercializadora
Limitada** (5)
Al Santos 905 4 And, Sao Paulo, 01419-
001, Brazil
Tel.: (55) 1132624141
Eletric Power Generation Services
N.A.I.C.S.: 221118

Subsidiary (Non-US):

**IPR - GDF SUEZ Middle East, Turkey
& Africa** (4)
Business Central Towers - B 50th Floor Me-
dia City Sheikh Zayed Road, PO Box
66235, Dubai, United Arab Emirates
Tel.: (971) 4 4570 777
Web Site: http://www.iprplc-gdfsuez-
meta.com
Eletric Power Generation Services
N.A.I.C.S.: 221118

Subsidiary (Non-US):

IPR - GDF SUEZ North Africa (5)
Rue Kadi Iass N6 - 3d Floor Maarif, 20100,
Casablanca, Morocco
Tel.: (212) 659817557
Web Site: http://www.iprplc-gdfsuez-
meta.com
Sales Range: $200-249.9 Million
Emp.: 5
Eletric Power Generation Services
N.A.I.C.S.: 221118
Jeremy Hughes (Gen Mgr)

Subsidiary (US):

IPR - GDF SUEZ North America (4)
1990 Post Oak Ste 1900, Houston, TX
77056
Tel.: (713) 636-1962
Eletric Power Generation Services
N.A.I.C.S.: 221118
Bill Beck (Supvr-Coal Handling)

Subsidiary (Domestic):

**ANP Blackstone Energy Company,
LLC** (5)
204 Elm St, Blackstone, MA 01504-1399
Tel.: (508) 876-8100
Eletric Power Generation Services
N.A.I.C.S.: 221118

Choctaw Gas Generation LLC (5)
2510 Pensacola Rd, Ackerman, MS 39735-
8902
Tel.: (662) 387-5691
Natural Gas Generation Services
N.A.I.C.S.: 211130

**Chowtaw Generation Limited
Partnership** (5)
1990 Post Oak Blvd Ste 1900, Houston, TX
77056
Tel.: (713) 636-1276
Power Plant Operator
N.A.I.C.S.: 221118

Coleto Creek Power, LP (5)
45 FM 2987, Houston, TX 77960
Tel.: (361) 788-5100
Thermal Electric Power Generation Ser-
vices
N.A.I.C.S.: 221118

**Colorado Energy Nations Company,
LLLP** (5)

1003 Vasquez St, Golden, CO 80401
Tel.: (303) 277-5455
Eletric Power Generation Services
N.A.I.C.S.: 221118
Michael Gwyther (Plant Mgr)

Ennis Power Company LLC (5)
4001 W Ennis Ave, Ennis, TX 75119
Tel.: (972) 875-2993
Eletric Power Generation Services
N.A.I.C.S.: 221118

**GDF SUEZ Gas NA Holdings
LLC** (5)
1990 Post Oak Blvd Ste 1900, Houston, TX
77056-3831
Tel.: (713) 636-0000
Investment Management Service
N.A.I.C.S.: 523999
Robert Wilson (Pres & CEO)

Hays Energy Limited Partnership (5)
1601 Frances Harris Ln, San Marcos, TX
78666-8967
Tel.: (512) 805-7200
Eletric Power Generation Services
N.A.I.C.S.: 221118

Hopewell Cogeneration LP (5)
1114 Hercules Rd, Hopewell, VA 23860-
5244
Tel.: (804) 458-0700
Web Site: http://www.gdfsuez.com
Eletric Power Generation Services
N.A.I.C.S.: 221118
Charles Davis (VP)

**Hot Spring Power Company,
LLC** (5)
410 Henderson Rd, Malvern, AR 72104
Tel.: (501) 467-3232
Eletric Power Generation Services
N.A.I.C.S.: 221118

International Power America, Inc. (5)
62 Forest St Ste 102, Marlborough, MA
01752 (100%)
Tel.: (508) 382-9300
Production & Distribution of Power
N.A.I.C.S.: 221122
Robert M. Chiste (Founder)

**Midlothian Energy Limited
Partnership** (5)
4601 Brookhollow Dr, Midlothian, TX
76065-5359
Tel.: (972) 923-7404
Emp.: 47
Eletric Power Generation Services
N.A.I.C.S.: 221118
Mike Stanley (Plant Mgr)

**Mt. Tom Generating Company
LLC** (5)
20 Church St Fl 16, Hartford, CT 06103-
1221
Tel.: (860) 895-6900
Eletric Power Generation Services
N.A.I.C.S.: 221118

Syracuse Energy Corporation (5)
56 Industrial Dr, Syracuse, NY 13204-1091
Tel.: (315) 487-4473
Electric Power Distribution Services
N.A.I.C.S.: 221122

Subsidiary (Domestic):

Indian Queens Power Ltd. (4)
Gaverigan, Saint Dennis, Saint Austell,
PL26 8BY, Cornwall, United
Kingdom (75%)
Tel.: (44) 1726860202
Sales Range: $10-24.9 Million
Emp.: 8
Power Generation & Distribution Services
N.A.I.C.S.: 221112
Vic Tanks (Mgr)

Subsidiary (Non-US):

**International Power Australia Pty
Ltd.** (4)
Level 33 Rialto North Tower, 525 Collins St,
Melbourne, 3000, VIC, Australia (100%)
Tel.: (61) 396178400
Web Site: http://www.gdfsuez.com
Sales Range: $50-74.9 Million
Emp.: 50
Generates & Sells Electricity

N.A.I.C.S.: 221122
Tony Concannon (Pres & CEO)

Levanto GSEF (Lux) S.a.r.l. (4)
Rue Guillaume Kroll 5, Luxembourg, 1882,
Luxembourg
Tel.: (352) 48 18 28 1
Eletric Power Generation Services
N.A.I.C.S.: 221118

Subsidiary (Domestic):

Rugeley Power Ltd (4)
Rugeley Power Station, Rugeley, WS15
1PR, Staffordshire, United
Kingdom (75%)
Tel.: (44) 1889572100
Web Site: http://www.rugeleypower.com
Sales Range: $100-124.9 Million
Emp.: 200
Generates & Sells Electricity
N.A.I.C.S.: 221122

**Saltend Cogeneration Company
Limited** (4)
Saltend Energy Centre Hedon Road, Hull,
HU12 8GA, United Kingdom
Tel.: (44) 1482 895 500
Sales Range: $50-74.9 Million
Emp.: 50
Thermal Electric Power Generation Ser-
vices
N.A.I.C.S.: 221118
Mick Farr (Gen Mgr)

Subsidiary (Non-US):

Sociedad GNL Mejillones S.A. (4)
Av Rosario Norte No 532 Of 1601 Piso 16,
Las Condes, Santiago, Chile
Tel.: (56) 23538800
Web Site: http://www.gnlm.cl
Natural Gas Transmission Services
N.A.I.C.S.: 486210

Thai National Power Co., Ltd. (4)
Siam Eastern Industrial Park 60 19 Moo 3
Mabyangporn, Rayong, 21140,
Thailand (100%)
Tel.: (66) 38891324
Sales Range: $50-74.9 Million
Emp.: 30
Power Generation
N.A.I.C.S.: 221118

**Turbogas - Produtora Energia
S.A.** (4)
Central de Ciclo Combinado da Tapada do
Outeiro Broalhos, 4515-430, Medas, Portu-
gal
Tel.: (351) 22 476 71 00
Web Site: http://www.turbogas.pt
Sales Range: $25-49.9 Million
Emp.: 48
Natural Gas Mfr.
N.A.I.C.S.: 325120

Subsidiary (Domestic):

GDF SUEZ CC SCRL (2)
Place Du Trone 1, Brussels, 1000, Belgium
Tel.: (32) 23703111
Sales Range: $1-4.9 Billion
Emp.: 1,500
Natural Gas Distribution Services
N.A.I.C.S.: 221210

Subsidiary (Non-US):

GDF SUEZ E&P NORGE AS (2)
Vestre Svanholmen 6, Sandnes, 4300, Nor-
way
Tel.: (47) 52 03 10 00
Web Site: http://www.gdfsuezep.no
Oil & Natural Gas Exploration & Distribution
Services
N.A.I.C.S.: 213112
Ulf Rosenberg (Head-Comm)

GDF SUEZ E&P Nederland B.V. (2)
Einsteinlaan 10, 2719 EP, Zoetermeer,
Netherlands
Tel.: (31) 79368 68 68
Web Site: http://www.gdfsuezep.nl
Sales Range: $200-249.9 Million
Emp.: 150
Oil & Gas Exploration Services
N.A.I.C.S.: 213112

GDF SUEZ E&P UK LTD (2)

40 Holborn Viaduct, London, EC1N2PB,
United Kingdom
Tel.: (44) 20 3122 1400
Gas Exploration & Electric Power Genera-
tion Services
N.A.I.C.S.: 213112
Ruud Zoon (Mng Dir)

**GDF SUEZ ENERGIA POLSKA
SA** (2)
Ul Domaniewska 42, 02-672, Warsaw, Po-
land
Tel.: (48) 22 43 42 800
Web Site: http://www.gdfsuez-energia.pl
Wind Electric Power Generation Services
N.A.I.C.S.: 221118
Mateusz Madejski (Acct Mgr)

Subsidiary (Domestic):

GDF SUEZ Bioenergia Sp. z o.o. (3)
Zawada 26, 28-230, Polaniec, Poland
Tel.: (48) 15 865 70 22
Eletric Power Generation Services
N.A.I.C.S.: 221118

Subsidiary (Non-US):

**GDF SUEZ ENERGY UK
RETAIL** (2)
26 Whitehall Road, Leeds, LS12 1BE,
United Kingdom
Tel.: (44) 113 306 2000
Web Site: http://www.gdfsuez-energy.co.uk
Emp.: 22
Electric Power Distribution Services
N.A.I.C.S.: 221122
Alexandre Caron (Mng Dir)

GDF SUEZ Energia Espana SLU (2)
General Castanos N4-3 Planta, 28004, Ma-
drid, Spain
Tel.: (34) 91 310 62 70
Web Site: http://www.gdfsuez-energia.es
Sales Range: $100-124.9 Million
Emp.: 10
Electric Power Generation & Distribution
Services
N.A.I.C.S.: 221118
Miguel Bascones Perez-Fragero (CFO)

GDF SUEZ Energy Asia (2)
26 Fl M Thai Tower All Seasons Place 87,
Wireless Road, Limpini Prathumwan, Bang-
kok, 10330, Thailand
Tel.: (66) 2 253 6466
Electricity Generator & Distributor; Natural
Gas Supplier
N.A.I.C.S.: 221122

Joint Venture (Domestic):

**PTT Natural Gas Distribution Co.,
Ltd.** (3)
3rd Floor Building A Energy Complex 555/1
Vibhavadi - Rangsit Road, Chatuchak,
Bangkok, 10900, Thailand (42%)
Tel.: (66) 2 140 1500
Web Site: https://www.pttngd.co.th
Sales Range: $75-99.9 Million
Emp.: 80
Natural Gas Distr
N.A.I.C.S.: 221210
Somnuek Phangwapee (Co-Chm)

Affiliate (Non-US):

Sohar Power Company (3)
Jawharat A'Shatti, PO Box 147, 134, Mus-
cat, Oman (45%)
Tel.: (968) 2 407 3800
Web Site: https://www.soharpower.com
Sales Range: $75-99.9 Million
Emp.: 15
Electric Power Distr
N.A.I.C.S.: 221122
Guillaume Baudet (CEO)

Subsidiary (Non-US):

**GDF SUEZ Energy Latin
America** (2)
Paschoal Pitch 5064, 88025 255, Florian-
opolis, Santa Catarina, Brazil
Tel.: (55) 4832122200
Sales Range: $900-999.9 Million
Emp.: 1,200
Electric Power Distr
N.A.I.C.S.: 221122
Jan Franciscus Maria Flachet (Pres & CEO)

ENGIE SA—(Continued)

Subsidiary (Non-US):

GDF SUEZ Energy Andino S.A.　**(3)**
Ave Apoquindo Oficina 3721 18th Fl Offc
81, Santiago, 7550177, Chile
Tel.: (56) 22900400
Web Site: http://www.gdfsuiz.com
Sales Range: $50-74.9 Million
Emp.: 60
Electric Power Distr
N.A.I.C.S.: 221122
Juan Clavia (CEO)

Affiliate (Domestic):

E.CL S.A.　**(4)**
Avenida Apoquindo 3721 Piso 6, Las Con-
des, Santiago, Chile　**(52.77%)**
Tel.: (56) 2 353 32 01
Web Site: http://www.e-cl.cl
Rev.: $967,444,000
Assets: $3,313,078,000
Liabilities: $1,306,912,000
Net Worth: $2,006,166,000
Earnings: $254,830,000
Emp.: 886
Fiscal Year-end: 12/31/2016
Electric Power Generation & Distribution
N.A.I.C.S.: 221122
Axel Leveque (CEO)

Subsidiary (Domestic):

**Gasoducto Nor Andino Chile
S.A.**　**(4)**
Ave Apoquindo 3721 Oficina 81, Santiago,
Chile　**(85%)**
Tel.: (56) 22900400
Sales Range: $25-49.9 Million
Emp.: 4
Gas Transportation Services
N.A.I.C.S.: 486210

Subsidiary (Non-US):

GDF SUEZ Energy Argentina　**(3)**
Bouchard 710 9th floor, 1013, Buenos Ai-
res, Argentina
Tel.: (54) 1157899500
Web Site: http://www.engie.com
Sales Range: $75-99.9 Million
Emp.: 3
Electric Power Distr
N.A.I.C.S.: 221122
Dante Del Elce (CEO)

Subsidiary (Domestic):

**ECS - Energy Consulting
Services**　**(4)**
Olga Cossettini 340 - 1st Floor, C1106ABL,
Buenos Aires, Argentina
Tel.: (54) 1150718800
Web Site: https://www.ecs.com.ar
Sales Range: $75-99.9 Million
Emp.: 30
Gas & Electricity Management & Consulting
N.A.I.C.S.: 221122
Gustavo Schettini (CEO)

Gasoducto Nor Andino Argentina　**(4)**
Talcahuano 833 Piso 5 Oficina D, Buenos
Aires, C1013AAQ, Argentina
Tel.: (54) 1157899789
Sales Range: $25-49.9 Million
Gas Pipeline Transportation
N.A.I.C.S.: 486210

Litoral Gas SA　**(4)**
Mitre 635, 2000, Rosario, Santa Fe,
Argentina　**(65%)**
Tel.: (54) 341 420 0100
Web Site: https://www.litoral-gas.com.ar
Natural Gas Distr
N.A.I.C.S.: 221210
Ricardo Fraga (CEO)

Subsidiary (Domestic):

GDF SUEZ Energy Brasil　**(3)**
Av Almirante Barroso 52 Sala 1401, 20031-
000, Rio de Janeiro, Brazil
Tel.: (55) 2139745400
Sales Range: $50-74.9 Million
Emp.: 33
Electric Power Distr
N.A.I.C.S.: 221122
Mauricio Bahr (CEO)

Subsidiary (Non-US):

GDF SUEZ Energy Peru　**(3)**
Av Republica De Panama 3490, San Isidro,
Lima, Peru
Tel.: (51) 16167979
Web Site: http://www.suezenergy.com.pe
Sales Range: $50-74.9 Million
Emp.: 30
Electricity Distribution
N.A.I.C.S.: 221122
Willem van Twembeke (CEO)

Subsidiary (Non-US):

Energia del Sur S.A.　**(4)**
Central Termica Patagonia Ruta 39 Km 12,
Comodoro Rivadavia, Ciudadela, Chubut,
Argentina
Tel.: (54) 297 454 9046
Web Site: https://web.edssa.com.ar
Electricity Generator & Distr
N.A.I.C.S.: 221122

Subsidiary (Non-US):

Tamauligas S.A. de C.V.　**(3)**
Calle 14 y Rayon Ste 1401 Zona Centro,
Matamoros, 87300, Tamaulipas, Mexico
Tel.: (52) 868 8113100
Web Site:
　　http://www.maxigasnatural.com.mx
Natural Gas Supplier
N.A.I.C.S.: 211130

Subsidiary (Non-US):

**GDF SUEZ GAS SUPPLY & SALES
NEDERLAND BV**　**(2)**
Einsteinlaan 10, 2719 EP, Zoetermeer,
Netherlands
Tel.: (31) 79 3686868
Web Site:
Natural Gas Distribution Services
N.A.I.C.S.: 221210
Ruud Zoon (Gen Mgr)

**INTERNATIONAL POWER AUSTRA-
LIA FINANCE**　**(2)**
Level 33 Rialto South Tower 525 Collins
Street, Melbourne, 3000, VIC, Australia
Tel.: (61) 3 9617 8400
Web Site: http://www.gdfsuezau.com
Emp.: 200
Financial Investment Services
N.A.I.C.S.: 523999

**INTERNATIONAL POWER CON-
SOLIDATED HOLDINGS
LIMITED**　**(2)**
25 Canada Square, London, E145 ALQ,
United Kingdom
Tel.: (44) 2073208600
Investment Management Service
N.A.I.C.S.: 523940

NOORDGASTRANSPORT B.V.　**(2)**
Einsteinlaan 10, 2719 EP, Zoetermeer,
Netherlands
Tel.: (31) 793686868
Sales Range: $25-49.9 Million
Emp.: 150
Natural Gas Pipeline Transportation Ser-
vices
N.A.I.C.S.: 486210
Roods Bos (Mng Dir)

PEGOP - Energia Electrica, S.A.　**(2)**
Estrada Nacional 118 Km 142 1, Pego,
Portugal
Tel.: (351) 241830500
Electric Power Generation Services
N.A.I.C.S.: 221118

PT Paiton Energy　**(2)**
Sentral Senayan II 5th Floor Jl Asia Afrika
No 8, Jakarta, 10270, Indonesia
Tel.: (62) 2157974524
Emp.: 20
Electric Power Generation Services
N.A.I.C.S.: 221118

Portgas　**(2)**
Rua Linhas De Torres 41, 4350 214, Porto,
Portugal　**(100%)**
Tel.: (351) 225071400
Web Site: http://www.portgas.pt
Sales Range: $75-99.9 Million
Emp.: 100
Natural Gas Supplier
N.A.I.C.S.: 221210

ROSIGNANO ENERGIA SPA　**(2)**
via Piave 6, Rosignano Solvay, 57016,
Livorno, Italy
Tel.: (39) 0586 7251
Web Site: http://www.rosenspa.com
Eletric Power Generation Services
N.A.I.C.S.: 221118

Roumanie SRL　**(2)**
Str CoriolanBrediceanu 10 City Business
Centre Block A Etaj 3, 300011, Timisoara,
Romania
Tel.: (40) 256 204422
Sales Range: $75-99.9 Million
Emp.: 3
Eletric Power Generation Services
N.A.I.C.S.: 221118

SALTEND　**(2)**
Senator House 85 Queen Victoria Street,
London, EC4V 4DP, United Kingdom
Tel.: (44) 113 306 2000
Eletric Power Generation Services
N.A.I.C.S.: 221118

SC AMGAZ S.A.　**(2)**
1 Tamas Erno Street, 540307, Targu Mures,
Mures, Romania
Tel.: (40) 265 762 146
Web Site: http://www.amgaz.ro
Emp.: 3
Natural Gas Terminal Operator
N.A.I.C.S.: 424710
Dorini Dorini-Giovanni (Gen Dir)

**SC GDF SUEZ ENERGY ROMANIA
SA**　**(2)**
Bd Marasesti nr 4-6 sector 4 Corp A,
040254, Bucharest, Romania
Tel.: (40) 213012000
Web Site: http://www.gdfsuez.ro
Natural Gas Distribution Services
N.A.I.C.S.: 221210

Subsidiary (Domestic):

Depomures SA　**(3)**
Str Tamas Erno nr 1, Mures, 540307, Targu
Mures, Romania
Tel.: (40) 26 521 7055
Web Site: https://www.depomures.ro
Sales Range: $25-49.9 Million
Emp.: 21
Natural Gas Storage Services
N.A.I.C.S.: 486210
Razvan Georgescu (Gen Mgr)

Subsidiary (Non-US):

SOLGAS S.A.　**(2)**
Apoquindo 3721 Piso 8, Las Condes,
7550000, Santiago, Chile
Tel.: (56) 22900400
Web Site: http://www.solgas.cl
Natural Gas Distribution Services
N.A.I.C.S.: 221210
Juan Claveria (Gen Mgr)

Senoko Energy Pte Ltd.　**(2)**
31 Senoko Rd, Singapore, 758103, Singa-
pore
Tel.: (65) 6 750 0000
Web Site: https://www.senokoenergy.com
Electric Power Generation & Distribution
Services
N.A.I.C.S.: 221118
Koji Kuroda (Chm)

TIRRENO POWER SPA　**(2)**
Via Barberini 47, 187, Rome, Italy
Tel.: (39) 06 83022800
Web Site: http://www.tirrenopower.com
Sales Range: $550-599.9 Million
Emp.: 60
Electric Power Generation & Distribution
Services
N.A.I.C.S.: 221118
Giovanni Gosio (CEO)

Subsidiary (Domestic):

Tirreno Solar S.r.l.　**(3)**
Stradone Vigliena 9, 80146, Naples, Italy
Tel.: (39) 081 3455 899
Solar Electric Power Generation Services
N.A.I.C.S.: 221114

Subsidiary (Non-US):

Telca 2000　**(2)**
Rua Paula e Silva 11 - Sao Cristovao, Rio

de Janeiro, 20910-120, Brazil
Tel.: (55) 2125051105
Web Site: http://www.telca2000.com.br
Emp.: 9
Electric Equipment Mfr
N.A.I.C.S.: 334419
Jeroen Visser (Office Mgr)

GDF Suez Global Gas & LNG　**(1)**
1 place samuel de champplain, 75392,
Paris, France
Tel.: (33) 144220000
Rev.: $13,758,120,000
Emp.: 2,200
Natural Gas Exploration, Production & Pro-
curement Contract Services
N.A.I.C.S.: 221210
Jean-Marie Dauger (Exec VP)

GDF Suez Infrastructures　**(1)**
22 rue du docteur Lancereaux, 75392,
Paris, Cedex 08, France
Tel.: (33) 157040000
Natural Gas Terminals, Storage Site &
Transmission Management
N.A.I.C.S.: 221210

GRTGAZ SA　**(1)**
Building Bora 6 Rue Raoul Nordling, 92270,
Bois-Colombes, France
Tel.: (33) 15 566 4000
Web Site: https://www.grtgaz.com
Natural Gas Distribution Services
N.A.I.C.S.: 221210

Subsidiary (Non-US):

GRTgaz Deutschland GmbH　**(2)**
Rosenthaler Strasse 40/41, 10178, Berlin,
Germany
Tel.: (49) 308 009 3300
Web Site: https://www.grtgaz-
　　deutschland.de
Emp.: 30
Natural Gas Transmission Services
N.A.I.C.S.: 486210
Nicolas Delaporte (Gen Mgr)

Gaz Electricite de Grenoble SE　**(1)**
8 Place Robert Schuman, 38042, Grenoble,
France
Tel.: (33) 4 76 84 38 38
Web Site: http://www.geg.fr
Electric Power Generation & Distribution
Services
N.A.I.C.S.: 221118

GrDF　**(1)**
6 Rue Condorcet, 75009, Paris, France
Tel.: (33) 9 69 36 35 34
Web Site: http://www.grdf.fr
Natural Gas Distribution Services
N.A.I.C.S.: 221210

La Compagnie du Vent SAS　**(1)**
The Triad II - Millennium Bus Pk II, 215 rue
Samuel Morse, 34967, Montpellier, Cedex
2, France
Tel.: (33) 499526470
Web Site: http://www.compagnieduvent.com
Sales Range: $10-24.9 Million
Emp.: 150
Renewable Energy Services
N.A.I.C.S.: 221115

SAVELYS GDF Suez　**(1)**
23 rue Philibert Delorme, 75816, Paris, Ce-
dex 17, France
Tel.: (33) 153387964
Web Site: http://www.savelys.fr
Rev.: $452,665,704
Emp.: 1,700
Heating & Air Conditioning Services
N.A.I.C.S.: 333415

SAVELYS Group　**(1)**
23 Rue Philibert Delorme, 75816, Paris,
France
Tel.: (33) 1 58 57 31 00
Web Site: http://www.savelys.fr
Boiler Repair & Maintenance Services
N.A.I.C.S.: 811198

Societe Hydro-Electrique du Midi　**(1)**
1 rue Louis Renault, BP 13383, BP 13383,
31133, Balma, Cedex, France
Tel.: (33) 561171500
Web Site: https://www.shem.fr
Emp.: 320
Electricity Production
N.A.I.C.S.: 221122

Societe Hydroelectrique du Midi (1)
1 rue Louis Renault, BP 13383, 31133,
Balma, Cedex, France
Tel.: (33) 56 117 1500
Web Site: https://www.shem.fr
Hydroelectric Power Generation Services
N.A.I.C.S.: 221111
Pierre Boulestreau (Mng Dir)

Storengy Deutschland GmbH (1)
Zimmerstrasse 56, 10117, Berlin, Germany
Tel.: (49) 302888340
Web Site: http://www.storengy.de
Natural Gas Storage Services
N.A.I.C.S.: 486210
Catherine Gras (Chm & Mng Dh)

Storengy SA (1)
Immeuble Djinn 12 rue Raoul Nordling, CS
70001, 92274, Bois-Colombes, Cedex,
France
Tel.: (33) 14 652 3390
Web Site: http://www.storengy.fr
Natural Gas Storage Services
N.A.I.C.S.: 486210
Jean-Marc Leroy (CEO)

Subsidiary (Non-US):

Storengy UK Ltd (2)
King Street, Northwich, CW9 7SE, Chesh-
ire, United Kingdom
Tel.: (44) 1606 814680
Web Site: http://www.storengy.co.uk
Sales Range: $25-49.9 Million
Emp.: 3
Natural Gas Storage Services
N.A.I.C.S.: 486210
Charlotte Roule (Mng Dir)

Synatom SA (1)
Boulevard Simon Bolivar 34, 1000, Brus-
sels, Belgium
Tel.: (32) 25050711
Web Site: http://www.synatom.be
Fuel Power Generation Services
N.A.I.C.S.: 221112

UCH Power Limited (1)
2-B I and T Center Sector G-6/1-1, Islam-
abad, 44000, Pakistan
Tel.: (92) 51262484045
Web Site: http://www.uchpower.com
Electric power distribution services
N.A.I.C.S.: 221122

ENGINEER GOLD MINES LTD.
Suite 1100 - 1111 Melville Street,
Vancouver, V6E 3V6, BC, Canada
Tel.: (604) 669-6463
Web Site:
  https://www.engineergoldmines.com
Year Founded: 2018
9EG0—(DEU)
Assets: $3,604,597
Liabilities: $254,537
Net Worth: $3,350,059
Earnings: ($266,973)
Emp.: 2
Fiscal Year-end: 11/30/22
Gold Exploration & Mining Services
N.A.I.C.S.: 212220

ENGINEERING AIDS SDN BHD
No 16 Jalan Hujan Rahmat 3 Taman
Overseas Union Garden, Jalan Klang
Lama, 58200, Kuala Lumpur, Malay-
sia
Tel.: (60) 377822355   MY
Web Site: http://www.engrgaids.com
Year Founded: 1978
Welding Machine & Equipment Mfr
N.A.I.C.S.: 333992

ENGINEERING.COM INCOR-
PORATED
5285 Solar Drive Suite 101, Missis-
sauga, L4W 5B8, ON, Canada
Tel.: (905) 273-9991   ON
Web Site:
  https://www.engineering.com
Year Founded: 2000
Sales Range: $1-9.9 Million
Emp.: 7

Online Engineering Information & Re-
source Services
N.A.I.C.S.: 513140
John Hayes (CEO)

ENGINEERS INDIA LTD.
EI Bhavan 1 Bhikaiji Cama Place,
New Delhi, 110 066, India
Tel.: (91) 1126762121
Web Site:
  https://www.engineersindia.com
Year Founded: 1965
ENGINERSIN—(NSE)
Rev.: $454,947,170
Assets: $606,259,549
Liabilities: $367,287,962
Net Worth: $238,971,587
Earnings: $33,976,160
Emp.: 2,814
Fiscal Year-end: 03/31/21
Heavy Engineering Services
N.A.I.C.S.: 237990
Rakesh Kumar Sabharwal (Dir-
Comml)

Subsidiaries:

Certification Engineers International
Limited   (1)
Engineers India Bhavan 1st Floor Plot No
85 Sector 11, Kharghar Dist, Raigad, 410
210, Maharashtra, India
Tel.: (91) 2227528700
Web Site: https://ceil.co.in
Certification & Third Party Inspection Ser-
vices
N.A.I.C.S.: 541380

ENGINES ENGINEERING
S.R.L.
Via Pasquali 6, Castenaso, 40055,
Bologna, Italy
Tel.: (39) 0516050312
Web Site:
  http://www.enginesengineering.com
Year Founded: 1979
Sales Range: $10-24.9 Million
Emp.: 50
Motorcycle Mfr
N.A.I.C.S.: 336991
Alberto Strazzari (Founder)

ENGIS TECHNOLOGIES, INC
501 505 Forhu 58 Wangsimni-ro,
Seongdong-gu, Seoul, 04778, Korea
(South)
Tel.: (82) 215229060   KR
Web Site: https://www.engistech.com
Year Founded: 1998
208860—(KRS)
Rev.: $2,679,860
Assets: $25,966,894
Liabilities: $20,839,894
Net Worth: $5,127,000
Earnings: ($725,943)
Emp.: 34
Fiscal Year-end: 12/31/22
Navigation Software Development
Services
N.A.I.C.S.: 541511
Minsu Lee (CTO)

ENGLEWOOD LAB
Gangnam Building 5th Floor 217
bankruptcies in Gangnam-gu, Seoul,
Korea (South)
Tel.: (82) 234452900
Web Site:
  http://www.englewoodlab.kr
950140—(KRS)
Rev.: $114,371,312
Assets: $99,622,872
Liabilities: $46,828,724
Net Worth: $52,794,148
Earnings: $1,946,160
Emp.: 269
Fiscal Year-end: 12/31/19
Skin Care Product Mfr

N.A.I.C.S.: 325620

ENGLISH LEASING LIMITED
Office 203 Park Avenue 24-A Block-6
PECHS Sharea Faisal, Karachi, Paki-
stan
Tel.: (92) 21 34326515
Emp.: 13
Consumer Financial Services
N.A.I.C.S.: 522291

ENGLISH NATIONAL OPERA
The London Coliseum, London,
WC2N 4ES, United Kingdom
Tel.: (44) 2078360111
Web Site: http://www.eno.org
Year Founded: 1931
Sales Range: $25-49.9 Million
Emp.: 1,000
Music Producer
N.A.I.C.S.: 711130
John Cooke (Sec)

ENGOLD MINES LTD.
Suite 1507 - 1030 West Georgia St,
Vancouver, V6E 2Y3, BC, Canada
Tel.: (604) 682-2421   Ca
Web Site: https://www.engold.ca
Year Founded: 1987
EGM—(TSXV)
Rev.: $460,263
Assets: $2,144,266
Liabilities: $1,337,239
Net Worth: $807,027
Earnings: ($648,287)
Fiscal Year-end: 09/30/23
Gold Exploration Services
N.A.I.C.S.: 213114
Rob Shives (VP-Exploration)

ENGRO CORPORATION LIM-
ITED
8th Floor The Harbour Front Building
HC 3, Marine Drive Block 4 Clifton,
Karachi, Pakistan
Tel.: (92) 111211211   PK
Web Site: http://www.engro.com
ENGRO—(PSX)
Rev.: $1,282,249,469
Assets: $2,696,025,844
Liabilities: $1,830,524,084
Net Worth: $865,501,760
Earnings: $165,885,506
Emp.: 2,342
Fiscal Year-end: 12/31/22
Fertilizer Mfr
N.A.I.C.S.: 325314
Abdul Samad Dawood (Vice Chm)

Subsidiaries:

Engro Energy Limited   (1)
16th Floor Harbor Front Building Marine
Drive Block 4, Clifton, Karachi, Pakistan
Tel.: (92) 215297501
Web Site: http://www.engroenergy.com
Eletric Power Generation Services
N.A.I.C.S.: 221118
Ghias Khan (Chm)

Engro Enfrashare (Private)
Limited   (1)
Office 1 top Floor-Beverly Centre Jinnah
Avenue, Blue area, Islamabad, Pakistan
Tel.: (92) 51831380080
Web Site: http://www.engroenfrashare.com
Telecom Infrastructure Services
N.A.I.C.S.: 517810
Ghias Khan (Chm)

Engro Fertilizers Limited   (1)
6th Floor Harbor Front Building Marine
Drive Block 4, Clifton, Karachi, Pakistan
Tel.: (92) 21111211211
Web Site: https://www.engrofertilizers.com
Rev.: $781,524,642
Assets: $818,181,463
Liabilities: $539,461,740
Net Worth: $278,719,722
Earnings: $108,650,676
Emp.: 1,260

Fiscal Year-end: 12/31/2019
Fertilizers Mfr & Distr
N.A.I.C.S.: 325314
Ghias Khan (Chm)

Engro Polymer & Chemicals
Limited   (1)
12th Floor Ocean Tower G-3 Scheme No 5
Main Clifton Road Block 9, Clifton, Karachi,
Pakistan   (56.2%)
Tel.: (92) 2135166863
Web Site: https://www.engropolymer.com
Rev.: $243,670,280
Assets: $370,422,360
Liabilities: $255,944,920
Net Worth: $114,477,440
Earnings: $23,802,240
Emp.: 455
Fiscal Year-end: 12/31/2019
Plastics Material & Resin Mfr
N.A.I.C.S.: 325211
Ghias Khan (Chm)

Engro Powergen Qadirpur
Limited   (1)
16th Floor Harbor Front Building Marine
Drive Block 4 Clifton, Karachi, Pakistan
Tel.: (92) 2135297501
Web Site: https://www.engroenergy.com
Rev.: $47,689,870
Assets: $83,021,321
Liabilities: $30,920,083
Net Worth: $52,101,237
Earnings: $9,033,761
Emp.: 107
Fiscal Year-end: 12/31/2023
Eletric Power Generation Services
N.A.I.C.S.: 221111
Shahab Qader (CEO & VP-Comml)

Engro Vopak Terminal Ltd   (1)
Corporate Office Block 4th Floor Office
Number 5 Dolmen City, HC 3 Block 4
Scheme 5 Clifton, 74000, Karachi, Pakistan
Tel.: (92) 213 529 3901
Web Site: http://www.vopak.com
Sales Range: $50-74.9 Million
Emp.: 80
Other Chemical & Allied Products Merchant
Whslr
N.A.I.C.S.: 424690

ENGRO CORPORATION LIM-
ITED
29 International Business Park 08 05
06 Acer Building Tower B, Singapore,
609923, Singapore
Tel.: (65) 65617978
Web Site: https://www.engro-
  global.com
Year Founded: 1973
S44—(SES)
Rev.: $121,454,215
Assets: $240,028,781
Liabilities: $37,752,026
Net Worth: $202,276,755
Earnings: ($4,262,668)
Emp.: 247
Fiscal Year-end: 12/31/23
Cement Mfr
N.A.I.C.S.: 327310
Cheng Gay Tan (Chm & CEO)

Subsidiaries:

Resin & Pigment Technologies Pte
Ltd   (1)
1 Banyan Place, Jurong Island, Singapore,
627841, Singapore
Tel.: (65) 68624588
Web Site: http://www.resinpts.com
Sales Range: $25-49.9 Million
Emp.: 60
Polymer Processing & Compounding Ser-
vices
N.A.I.C.S.: 325991
Tai Bonchen (Mgr-Ops)

Sancem Investment Pte Ltd   (1)
29 International Business Park 08-05/06
Acer Building, Singapore, 609923, Singa-
pore
Tel.: (65) 65617978
Investment Management Service
N.A.I.C.S.: 523999

EnGro Corporation Limited—(Continued)

Shanghai S3 Building Materials Co Ltd (1)
18 Nan Wen Zao Bang Road Ye Qiao, Baoshan District, Shanghai, 200435, China
Tel.: (86) 21 5641 3366
Web Site: http://www.s3asia.com
Building Materials Mfr & Distr
N.A.I.C.S.: 325520

SsangYong Cement (S) Pte Ltd (1)
Acer Building, Singapore, 609923, Singapore
Tel.: (65) 65617978
Web Site: http://www.engro-global.com
Sales Range: $75-99.9 Million
Emp.: 200
Construction Materials Sales
N.A.I.C.S.: 423320

SsangYong Cement Singapore (China) Pte Ltd (1)
Acer Building 29 08-05/06 International Business Park, Singapore, 609923, Singapore
Tel.: (65) 65617978
Cement Mfr
N.A.I.C.S.: 327310

Top Mix Concrete Pte Ltd (1)
29 International Business Park 08-05/06 Acer Building Tower B, Acer Bldg Tower B # 08-05/06, Singapore, 609923, Singapore (100%)
Tel.: (65) 65617978
Sales Range: $25-49.9 Million
Emp.: 53
Concrete Mfr
N.A.I.C.S.: 327320
Tan Cheng Gay (CEO)

ENGTEX GROUP BERHAD
Lot 36 Jalan BRP 9/2B Putra Industrial Park Bukit Rahman Putra, 47000, Sungai Buloh, Selangor Darul Ehsan, Malaysia
Tel.: (60) 361401111
Web Site: https://www.engtex.com.my 5056—(KLS)
Rev.: $305,591,746
Assets: $324,294,392
Liabilities: $151,527,196
Net Worth: $172,767,196
Earnings: $7,264,339
Emp.: 1,507
Fiscal Year-end: 12/31/22
Hardware Distr & Precision Components Mfr
N.A.I.C.S.: 444140
Kevin Chi Hoe Tang (Co-Sec)

Subsidiaries:

Alimach Holdings Sdn. Bhd. (1)
No 2 Level 10 Wisma Menjalara Jalan 7A/62A, Bandar Menjalara, 52200, Kuala Lumpur, Malaysia
Tel.: (60) 362772288
Pipe & Valve Fitting Mfr & Distr
N.A.I.C.S.: 331511

Allpipes Technology Sdn. Bhd. (1)
Lot 36 Jalan Brp 9/2B PUTRA Industrial park Bkt rahman Putra, Sungai Buloh, 47000, Selangor, Malaysia
Tel.: (60) 361401111
Sales Range: $25-49.9 Million
Emp.: 100
Iron Pipe Fittings & Mfr
N.A.I.C.S.: 331511
Cheah Hock Kee (Mgr-Sls)

Subsidiary (Domestic):

Canova Manufacturing Sdn. Bhd. (2)
Lot 3757 Batu 29 Jalan Ipoh-Kuala Lumpur, 48200, Serendah, Selangor Darul Ehsan, Malaysia
Tel.: (60) 360813836
Sales Range: $25-49.9 Million
Steel Water Tank & Pipe Fittings Mfr
N.A.I.C.S.: 331511
Cheah Hock Kee (Gen Mgr)

Nagasari Bitumen Products Sdn. Bhd. (2)
Lot 3757 Batu 29 Jalan Ipoh-Kuala Lumpur, 48200, Serendah, Selangor Darul Ehsan, Malaysia
Tel.: (60) 360813836
Iron Pipe & Fittings Mfr
N.A.I.C.S.: 331511
Cheah Hock Kee (Gen Mgr)

Benton Corporation Sdn. Bhd. (1)
Tel.: (60) 361575757
Sales Range: $25-49.9 Million
Emp.: 8
Iron Pipe Fittings Mfr
N.A.I.C.S.: 331511
Chong Keong Khoo (Acct Mgr-Fin)

East Coast Manufacturing Sdn. Bhd. (1)
Lot 10769 Jalan Gebeng 1/2, Kawasan Perindustrian Gebeng, 26080, Kuantan, Pahang, Malaysia
Tel.: (60) 95839898
Web Site: https://www.eastcoastmalaysia.com
Sales Range: $25-49.9 Million
Emp.: 50
Steel Products Mfr
N.A.I.C.S.: 331221

East Coast Metals Sdn. Bhd. (1)
Lot 10769 Jalan Gebeng 1/2 Kawasan Perindustrian Gebeng, 26080, Kuantan, Pahang, Malaysia
Tel.: (60) 95839898
Iron Pipe Fittings Mfr
N.A.I.C.S.: 332996

Eng Lian Hup Manufacturing Sdn. Bhd. (1)
No 910 Jalan Perindustrian Bukit Minyak Mukim 13 Kawasan Perindustrian, Bukit Minyak Tengah Seberang Perai, 14100, Bukit Minyak, Penang, Malaysia
Tel.: (60) 45071222
Pipe & Valve Fitting Mfr & Distr
N.A.I.C.S.: 331511

Eng Lian Hup Trading Sdn. Bhd. (1)
No 910 Jalan Perindustrian Bukit Minyak Mukim 13, Kawasan Perindustrian Bukit Minyak Bukit Minyak Seberang Prai Tengah, 14100, Bukit Mertajam, Penang, Malaysia
Tel.: (60) 45071222
Iron Pipe Fittings Mfr
N.A.I.C.S.: 331210

Subsidiary (Domestic):

Apsonic Sdn. Bhd. (2)
910 Jalan Perindustrian Bukit Minyak Mukim 13 Kawasan Perindustrian, Bukit Minyak, 14100, Bukit Mertajam, Penang, Malaysia
Tel.: (60) 45071222
Emp.: 50
Financial & Real Estate Planning Services
N.A.I.C.S.: 523999
Boon Yew Yong (Mgr)

EngLen Manufacturing Sdn. Bhd. (1)
Lot 5 Industrial Zone 7 Ph-1 Jalan Norowot Kota Kinabalu Ind Park Kkip, 88460, Kota Kinabalu, Sabah, Malaysia
Tel.: (60) 88497550
Pipe & Valve Fitting Mfr & Distr
N.A.I.C.S.: 331511

Engtex Ductile Iron Marketing Sdn. Bhd. (1)
Lot 68 Jalan Gebeng 1/6 Gebeng Industrial Estate, 26080, Kuantan, Pahang, Malaysia
Tel.: (60) 95837822
Pipe & Valve Fitting Mfr & Distr
N.A.I.C.S.: 331511

Engtex Ductile Iron Pipes Industry Sdn. Bhd. (1)
Lot 68 Kawasan Perindustrian Gebeng, 26080, Kuantan, Pahang, Malaysia (100%)
Tel.: (60) 95837822
Sales Range: $25-49.9 Million
Emp.: 100
Iron Pipe Fittings Mfr
N.A.I.C.S.: 332919
Tnay Sam (Mgr-Bus Dev)

Engtex Metals (Utara) Sdn. Bhd. (1)
Pmt 1171 Lorong Perindustrian Bukit Minyak 11, Taman Perindustrian Bukit Minyak Simpang Ampat, 14100, Penang, Malaysia
Tel.: (60) 45057802
Web Site: https://engtexutara.com.my
Wire Mesh Mfr
N.A.I.C.S.: 331222

Engtex Metals Sdn. Bhd. (1)
Lot 36 Jalan BRP9/2B Putra Industrial Park, Bukit Rahman Putra, 47000, Sungai Buloh, Selangor, Malaysia
Tel.: (60) 361401554
Web Site: https://engtexmetals.com.my
Sales Range: $25-49.9 Million
Emp.: 70
Iron Pipe Fittings Mfr
N.A.I.C.S.: 331210

Engtex Pipe Industry Sdn. Bhd. (1)
Lot 3757 Batu 29 Jalan Ipoh- Kuala Lumpur, 48200, Serendah, Selangor Darul Ehsan, Malaysia
Tel.: (60) 360813836
Pipe & Valve Fitting Mfr & Distr
N.A.I.C.S.: 331511

Engtex Properties Sdn. Bhd. (1)
No 2 Level 10 Wisma Menjalara Jalan 7A/62A, Bandar Manjalara, 52200, Kuala Lumpur, Federal Territory, Malaysia
Tel.: (60) 362801594
Web Site: http://www.engtexproperties.com.my
Sales Range: $50-74.9 Million
Emp.: 15
Property Development Services
N.A.I.C.S.: 531390

Engtex Sdn Berhad (1)
Lot 36 Jalan BRP 9/2B Putra Industrial Park, Bukit Rahman Putra, 47000, Sungai Buloh, Selangor, Malaysia
Tel.: (60) 361401111
Pipe & Valve Fitting Mfr & Distr
N.A.I.C.S.: 331511

Subsidiary (Domestic):

Engtex Industries Sdn. Bhd. (2)
Lot 36 Jalan BRP 9/2B Putra Industrial Park, Bukit Rahman Putra, 47000, Sungai Buloh, Selangor, Malaysia
Web Site: http://www.engtexwire.com.my
Stainless Steel Bolt & Nut Mfr
N.A.I.C.S.: 332722

Engtex Marketing Sdn. Bhd. (2)
Lot 36 Jalan BRP 9/2B Putra Industrial Park, Bukit Rahman Putra, 47000, Sungai Buloh, Selangor, Malaysia
Tel.: (60) 361576938
Pipe & Valve Fitting Mfr & Distr
N.A.I.C.S.: 331511

Hachita Enterprise Sdn. Bhd. (2)
Lot 36 Jalan BRP 9/2B Putra Industrial Park, Bukit Rahman Putra, 47000, Sungai Buloh, Selangor, Malaysia
Tel.: (60) 361405540
Pipe & Valve Fitting Mfr & Distr
N.A.I.C.S.: 331511

LYE Manufacturing Sdn. Bhd. (2)
Lot 1844 Jalan Kpb 8 Kawasan Perindustrian Kg Baru Balakong, Seri Kembangan, 43300, Kajang, Selangor, Malaysia
Tel.: (60) 389611623
Web Site: https://www.lye.com.my
Pipe & Valve Fitting Mfr & Distr
N.A.I.C.S.: 331511

Wiki Pratama Sdn. Bhd. (2)
Lot 36 Jalan BRP 9/2B Putra Industrial Park, Bukit Rahman Putra, 47000, Sungai Buloh, Malaysia
Tel.: (60) 361572388
Web Site: http://www.imbaco.work
Food Processing Machinery Equipment Mfr
N.A.I.C.S.: 333241

Engtex Steel Industries Sdn. Bhd. (1)
Lot 1A Kawasan Perindustrian Merlimau, Merlimau, 77300, Melaka, Malaysia
Tel.: (60) 62633069
Pipe & Valve Fitting Mfr & Distr
N.A.I.C.S.: 331511

LYE Marketing Sdn. Bhd. (1)

Lot 36 Jalan Brp 9/2b Putra Industrial Park, Bukit Rahman Putra, 47000, Sungai Buloh, Selangor, Malaysia
Tel.: (60) 361403030
Web Site: http://www.lye.com.my
Sales Range: $200-249.9 Million
Emp.: 200
Valves Mfr & Distr
N.A.I.C.S.: 332911

Mega Alliance Builder Supplies Sdn. Bhd. (1)
Lot 36 Jalan BRP 9/2B Putra Industrial Park, Bukit Rahman Putra, 47000, Sungai Buloh, Selangor Darul Ehsan, Malaysia (100%)
Tel.: (60) 361403722
Sales Range: $25-49.9 Million
Emp.: 12
Iron Pipe Fittings Mfr
N.A.I.C.S.: 331511

ENGYCO PLC
22 Grenville Street, Saint Helier, JE4 8PX, Jersey
Tel.: (44) 1534609556
Web Site: http://www.engyco.com
Solar Power
N.A.I.C.S.: 221118
John Roberts (Chm)

ENI S.P.A.
Piazzale Mattei 1, 00144, Rome, Italy
Tel.: (39) 0659821 IT
Web Site: https://www.eni.com
Year Founded: 1953
E—(NYSE)
Rev.: $55,205,703,280
Assets: $134,674,059,520
Liabilities: $88,623,657,200
Net Worth: $46,050,402,320
Earnings: ($10,605,852,400)
Emp.: 31,495
Fiscal Year-end: 12/31/20
Petroleum & Natural Gas Products & Services
N.A.I.C.S.: 211120
Claudio Descalzi (CEO & Gen Mgr)

Subsidiaries:

Adriaplin Podjetje Za Distribucijo Zemeljskega Plina d.o.o. (1)
Dunajska cesta 7, 1000, Ljubljana, Slovenia
Tel.: (386) 13300100
Web Site: http://www.adriaplin.si
Natural Gas Producer
N.A.I.C.S.: 221210

Agenzia Giornalistica Italia SpA (1)
Via Ostiense 72, 00154, Rome, Italy
Tel.: (39) 06519961
Web Site: https://www.agi.it
Sales Range: $25-49.9 Million
Emp.: 82
News Agency Management Services
N.A.I.C.S.: 516210

Agip Caspian Sea BV (1)
Tel.: (31) 205707100
Oil & Gas Production Services
N.A.I.C.S.: 211120

Agip S.p.A. (1)
Via Emilia 1, 20097, San Donato Milanese, Italy (100%)
Tel.: (39) 025201
Web Site: http://www.agip.it
Rev.: $5,986,000,000
Hydrocarbon Exploration & Production
N.A.I.C.S.: 324110

Joint Venture (Domestic):

Cam Petroli S.r.l. (2)
Via Sempione 230, 20016, Pero, Italy (50%)
Tel.: (39) 02353741
Web Site: http://www.gruppocamfin.it
Petroleum Bulk Stations & Terminals
N.A.I.C.S.: 424710

Banque Eni SA (1)
Emp.: 40
Oil & Gas Exploration Services
N.A.I.C.S.: 237120

Carboil Srl (1)
Via Lucania 13, 00187, Rome, Italy
Tel.: (39) 0652205553
Web Site: https://www.carboil.it
Fueling Services in Airports
N.A.I.C.S.: 457210

Subsidiary (Domestic):

Skytanking S. R. L. (2)
Via Francesco De Pinedo 48/50 Aeroporto
Fiumicino, 00054, Rome, Italy
Tel.: (39) 06 6595 4226
Petroleum Product Distr
N.A.I.C.S.: 424720
Rolٮand Casall (Mng Dir)

**Compagnia Napoletana di illuminazi-
one e Scaldamento col Gas SpA** (1)
Via Galileo Ferraris 66/F, 80142, Naples,
Italy
Tel.: (39) 0815831909
Natural Gas Distribution Services
N.A.I.C.S.: 221210

Eni Algeria Production BV (1)
Strawinskylaan 1725, Amsterdam, 1077 XX,
Netherlands
Tel.: (31) 20719600
Web Site: http://www.eni.com
Emp.: 2
Liquid & Gas Whslr
N.A.I.C.S.: 457210

Eni Angola Exploration (1)
Strawinskylaan 1725, 1077 XX, Amsterdam,
Netherlands
Tel.: (31) 20719600
Emp.: 3
Oil & Gas Exploration Services
N.A.I.C.S.: 213112
Davide Maria Colombo (Mgr-Fin)

**Eni Argentina Exploracion y Explota-
cion SA** (1)
Calle Bartolome Mitre 699 - Piso 4, Buenos
Aires, Argentina
Tel.: (54) 13341136
Natural Gas Producer
N.A.I.C.S.: 221210

Eni Australia Limited (1)
226 Adelaide Terrace, Perth, 6000, WA,
Australia
Tel.: (61) 9 320 1111
Web Site: http://www.eni.com
Oil & Gas Exploration Services
N.A.I.C.S.: 213112

Subsidiary (Domestic):

Eni JPDA 06-105 Pty Ltd (2)
226 Adelaide Terrace, Perth, 6000, WA,
Australia
Tel.: (61) 893201111
Oil & Gas Exploration Services
N.A.I.C.S.: 213112
Ernie Delfos (Mng Dir)

Eni Austria GmbH (1)
Millennium Tower Handelskai 94-96, 1200,
Vienna, Osterreich, Austria
Tel.: (43) 1240700
Oil Refining & Distr
N.A.I.C.S.: 213112
Ricardo Piunti (Gen Mgr)

Subsidiary (Domestic):

Eni Austria Marketing GmbH (2)
Millennium Tower Handelskai 94-96, 1200,
Vienna, Austria
Tel.: (43) 1240700
Oil Refining Services & Distr
N.A.I.C.S.: 324110

**Eni Austria Tankstellenbetrieb
GmbH** (2)
Millennium Tower Handelskai 94-96, 1200,
Vienna, Austria
Tel.: (43) 1240700
Sales Range: $125-149.9 Million
Emp.: 180
Natural Gas Product Mfr & Distr
N.A.I.C.S.: 324110
Ricardo Piunti (Gen Mgr)

Eni Ceska Republika, s.r.o. (1)
Sokolovska 394/17, CZ 186 00, Prague, 8,
Czech Republic (100%)
Tel.: (420) 224495111

Web Site: http://www.eniceska.cz
Sales Range: $50-74.9 Million
Emp.: 80
Crude Oil Processor & Petroleum Products
Mfr
N.A.I.C.S.: 211120

Eni Corporate University SpA (1)
Via S Salvo 1, 20097, San Donato Mila-
nese, Milan, Italy
Tel.: (39) 025201
Human Resource Consulting Services
N.A.I.C.S.: 541612

Eni Deutschland GmbH (1)
Theresienhohe 30, 80339, Munich,
Germany (100%)
Tel.: (49) 8959070
Web Site: https://www.eni.com
Sales Range: $1-4.9 Billion
Emp.: 300
Petroleum Refining & Wholesaling
N.A.I.C.S.: 324110

Subsidiary (Domestic):

**Bronberger & Kessler Handelsgesell-
schaft GmbH** (2)
Dreimuhlen Strasse, 82065, Munich,
Germany (100%)
Tel.: (49) 8972901
Web Site: http://www.bronberger-kessler.de
Sales Range: $25-49.9 Million
Emp.: 20
Fuel Distribution
N.A.I.C.S.: 457210

Eni Schmiertechnik GmbH (2)
Paradiesstrasse 14, 97080, Wurzburg, Ger-
many
Tel.: (49) 931900980
Oil & Gas Exploration Services
N.A.I.C.S.: 213112

Eni Finance International SA (1)
Rue Guimard 1/A, 1040, Brussels, Belgium
Tel.: (32) 25510380
Sales Range: $50-74.9 Million
Emp.: 40
Financial Services
N.A.I.C.S.: 523999

Eni France Sarl (1)
12 Avenue Tony Garnier, CS 40720, 69367,
Lyon, Cedex, France
Tel.: (33) 472407878
Natural Gas Producer
N.A.I.C.S.: 221210

Eni Fuel Nord SpA (1)
26 V Maritano, San Donato Milanese,
20097, Milan, Italy
Tel.: (39) 02 5201
Heating Fuel Whslr
N.A.I.C.S.: 457210

Eni Gas & Power Belgium SA (1)
Guimardstraat 1A Rue Guimard, BE-1040,
Brussels, Belgium
Tel.: (32) 25112344
Web Site: http://www.eni.it
Gas & Power Services
N.A.I.C.S.: 213112

Eni Indonesia Ltd. (1)
Atrium Mulia Building 3 and 3A Floors, Jl
HR Rasuna Said Kav B10-11, Jakarta,
12910, Indonesia (100%)
Tel.: (62) 2130003200
Web Site: http://www.eni.com
Oil & Gas Exploration & Production
N.A.I.C.S.: 211120

Eni International B.V. (1)
Strawinskylaan 1725, 1077 XX, Amsterdam,
Netherlands (54%)
Tel.: (31) 207196000
Sales Range: $25-49.9 Million
Emp.: 40
Holding Company
N.A.I.C.S.: 551112

Eni International Resources Ltd (1)
Eni House 10 Ebury Bridge Road, London,
SW1W 8PZ, United Kingdom
Tel.: (44) 2073444100
Emp.: 70
Employee Assessment Consulting Services
N.A.I.C.S.: 541612
Claudio Descalzi (Pres)

Eni Magyarorszagon (1)
Agip Komplexum, 1 PF 164 H 2041 Deli
Oldal Pos, 2040, Budapest,
Hungary (65%)
Tel.: (36) 23415550
Web Site: http://www.eni.com
Sales Range: $50-74.9 Million
Emp.: 50
Petroleum & Natural Gas
N.A.I.C.S.: 211120

**Eni S.p.A. - Gas & Power
Division** (1)
Villa De Gasperi 16 San Donato Milanese,
20097, Milan, San Donato Milanese,
Italy (100%)
Tel.: (39) 025201
Rev.: $9,500,000,000
Emp.: 100
Purchaser, Transporter, Distributor & Seller
of Imported & Domestic Natural Gas; Oil
Transportation by Sea & Land; Gasoline &
Oil Pipeline
N.A.I.C.S.: 221210

Affiliate (Domestic):

**Acquedotto di Domodossola
S.p.A.** (2)
Via San Quintono 14, Turin, Italy (25.84%)
Tel.: (39) 01155941
Water Transport & Distribution
N.A.I.C.S.: 221310

Acquedotto di Savona S.p.A. (2)
Via Schiantapetto 21, Savona, 17100,
Italy (26.29%)
Tel.: (39) 019 840171
Sales Range: $50-74.9 Million
Emp.: 62
Water Transport & Distribution
N.A.I.C.S.: 221310
Gianluigi Devoto (Gen Mgr)

Subsidiary (Domestic):

Immobiliare Metanopoli S.p.A. (2)
Via Martiri di Cefalonia N 67, 20097, San
Donato Milanese, Italy (90.39%)
Tel.: (39) 0252054014
Sales Range: $50-74.9 Million
Emp.: 6
Provider of Real Estate Services
N.A.I.C.S.: 531210

Subsidiary (Non-US):

**Scogat SA Societe Pour la Construc-
tion du Gazoduc Transt** (2)
Centre Urbain Du Nord Boulevard 7 No-
vembre 1082, Tunis, Tunisia (100%)
Tel.: (216) 71 238522
Web Site: http://www.ttpc.it
Rev.: $8,867,000
Emp.: 48
Pipeline Construction
N.A.I.C.S.: 237120

Affiliate (Non-US):

Societa Italiana Per Il Gas (2)
(100%)
Tel.: (39) 01123941
Web Site: http://www.italgas.it
Sales Range: $700-749.9 Million
Hydrocarbon Transport & Gas Distribution
N.A.I.C.S.: 221210

Affiliate (Domestic):

Veneziana Gas S.p.A. (2)
Forte Marghera 140 Mestre, 30173, Venice,
Italy (64%)
Tel.: (39) 0412389111
Hydrocarbons Transport & Gas Distribution
N.A.I.C.S.: 221210

**Eni S.p.A. - Refining & Marketing
Division** (1)
Via Laurentina 449, I 00142, Rome,
Italy (100%)
Tel.: (39) 0659881
Web Site: http://www.agippetroli.it
Petroleum Refining; Operator of Service
Stations
N.A.I.C.S.: 211120

Subsidiary (US):

Eni Petroleum (2)

1201 Louisiana St Ste 3500, Houston, TX
77002-5617
Tel.: (504) 593-7000
Sales Range: $200-249.9 Million
Emp.: 407
Energy Exploration & Production
N.A.I.C.S.: 213112

Eni Slovensko Spol Sro (1)
Prievozska 2/A, 811 09, Bratislava, Slovakia
Tel.: (421) 250700411
Sales Range: $50-74.9 Million
Emp.: 5
Oil & Gas Exploration Services
N.A.I.C.S.: 213112
Massimo Bechi (Gen Mgr)

Eni Suisse S.A. (1)
Av de Gratta-Paille 1, 1018, Lausanne,
Switzerland (100%)
Tel.: (41) 216443111
Web Site: https://www.eni.com
Rev.: $245,000,000
Emp.: 80
Petroleum Wholesaling
N.A.I.C.S.: 424720

Subsidiary (Domestic):

Snam International Holding A.G. (2)
Banhofstrasse 18, Zurich, Switzerland
Owned by Eni International Holding B.V.
(51%) & Snam S.p.A. (49%); Joint Venture
N.A.I.C.S.: 551112

Eni Tunisia BV (1)
Immeuble Iris Rue du Lac de Come, Berges
Du Lac, 1053, Tunis, Tunisia
Tel.: (216) 205753399
Oil & Gas Exploration Services
N.A.I.C.S.: 213112

Eni UK Ltd (1)
Eni House 10 Ebury Bridge Road, 10 Ebury
Bridge Rd, London, SW1W 8PZ, United
Kingdom (100%)
Tel.: (44) 2073446000
Sales Range: $75-99.9 Million
Emp.: 200
Holding Company for Exploration & Produc-
tion of Oil & Gas
N.A.I.C.S.: 551112

Subsidiary (Domestic):

Burren Energy (2)
Kierran Cross 2nd Fl, London, WC2N 5HR,
United Kingdom
Tel.: (44) 2074841900
Exploration & Production Services
N.A.I.C.S.: 541360

Subsidiary (Non-US):

Eni Turkmenistan Ltd (3)
Business Centre Archabil Shayoly 41,
Ashgabat, 744036, Turkmenistan (100%)
Tel.: (993) 12488522
Sales Range: $150-199.9 Million
Emp.: 1,000
Oil & Gas Field Machinery & Equipment Mfr
N.A.I.C.S.: 333132
Enrico Trovato (Mng Dir)

Ieoc Production BV (3)
Building No 200 and 201 Second Sector of
City Centre, PO Box 2, Fifth Settlement,
11835, Cairo, Egypt
Tel.: (20) 27057171
Oil & Gas Field Machinery & Equipment
Mfg
N.A.I.C.S.: 333132

Subsidiary (Domestic):

Eni BTC Ltd (2)
10 Ebury Bridge Road, London, SW1W
8PZ, United Kingdom
Tel.: (44) 2073446000
Oil & Gas Exploration Services
N.A.I.C.S.: 213112

Eni ULT Ltd (2)
ENI House 10 Ebury Bridge Road, West-
minster, London, SW1W 8PZ, United King-
dom
Tel.: (44) 20 7344 6000
Web Site: http://www.eni.com
Emp.: 200
Investment Management Service
N.A.I.C.S.: 523999

Eni S.p.A.—(Continued)

Eni ULX Ltd (2)
Eni House 10 Ebury Bridge Road, London,
SW1W 8PZ, United Kingdom
Tel.: (44) 2073446372
Oil & Gas Exploration Services
N.A.I.C.S.: 213112

Subsidiary (Non-US):

Eni Venezuela (2)
(100%)
Tel.: (58) 2123182000
Sales Range: $50-74.9 Million
Emp.: 70
Oil & Gas Exploration
N.A.I.C.S.: 211120
Biagio Pietraroia (Gen Mgr)

Eni USA Inc (1)
Tel.: (713) 393-6100
Oil & Gas Exploration Services
N.A.I.C.S.: 213112

Subsidiary (Non-US):

Eni Oil & Gas Inc (2)
Tel.: (713) 393-6100
Management Consulting Services
N.A.I.C.S.: 541611

Eni Trading & Shipping Inc (2)
Tel.: (713) 393-6100
Web Site: http://www.eni.com
Petroleum Product Whslr
N.A.I.C.S.: 424720

Eni US Operating Co Inc (2)
Tel.: (713) 393-6100
Crude Petroleum & Natural Gas Extraction
Services
N.A.I.C.S.: 211120

Eni USA R&M Co Inc (2)
Tel.: (724) 352-4451
Oil Refinery Services
N.A.I.C.S.: 324110

EniPower Mantova SpA (1)
Via Taliercio 14, 46100, Mantua, Italy
Tel.: (39) 025201
Eletric Power Generation Services
N.A.I.C.S.: 221118

EniPower SpA (1)
Piazza Vanoni 1, San Donato Milanese,
20097, Milan, Italy
Tel.: (39) 025201
Electric Power Generation & Distribution
Services
N.A.I.C.S.: 221118

EniProgetti SpA (1)
Via dell'Industria 39, Marghera, 30175, Ven-
ice, Italy
Tel.: (39) 041796711
Natural Gas Producer
N.A.I.C.S.: 221210
Zarri Francesca (Chm)

**Gas Supply Company Thessaloniki -
Thessalia SA** (1)
256 Monastiriou St and 7 D Glinou St, Men-
emeni, 54628, Thessaloniki, Greece
Tel.: (30) 2310520309
Web Site: http://www.edathess.gr
Natural Gas Producer
N.A.I.C.S.: 221210
Leonidas Bakouras (Gen Mgr)

LNG Shipping SpA (1)
Piazza Vanoni 1, 20097, San Donato Mila-
nese, Milan, Italy
Web Site: http://www.eni.com
Natural Gas Transportation Services
N.A.I.C.S.: 486210

Neptune Energy Group Limited (1)
Nova North 11 Bressenden Place, London,
SW1E 5BY, United Kingdom
Tel.: (44) 2078323900
Web Site: https://www.neptuneenergy.com
Emp.: 100
Holding Company
N.A.I.C.S.: 551112

OOO Eni Energhia (1)
Bolshoy Levshinskiy pereulok 10/1, 119034,
Moscow, Russia
Tel.: (7) 4959165314
Web Site: http://www.eni.com

Natural Gas Producer
N.A.I.C.S.: 221210

Petrolig Srl (1)
Calata Canzio, 16126, Genoa, Italy
Tel.: (39) 010265178
Oil & Gas Exploration Services
N.A.I.C.S.: 213112

Polimeri Europa SpA (1)
Piazza Boldrini 1, 20097, San Donato Mila-
nese, Milano, Italy
Tel.: (39) 025201
Web Site: https://www.versalis.eni.com
Petrochemical Product Mfr & Distr
N.A.I.C.S.: 325110

Subsidiary (Non-US):

Polimeri Europa GmbH (2)
Dusseldorferstrasse 13, 65760, Eschborn,
Germany
Tel.: (49) 61964920
Web Site: http://www.eni.com
Petrochemical Product Distr
N.A.I.C.S.: 424720

Polimeri Europa UK Ltd (2)
Cadland Road Hardley - Hythe, Inghilterra,
Southampton, SO45 3YY, United Kingdom
Tel.: (44) 23 80387000
Web Site: http://www.eni.com
Natural Gas Distribution Services
N.A.I.C.S.: 221210

Saipem S.p.A. (1)
Via Luigi Russolo 5, 20097, San Donato
Milanese, Milan, Italy
Tel.: (39) 0244231 (43%)
Web Site: https://www.saipem.com
Rev.: $9,098,801,920
Assets: $13,832,438,880
Liabilities: $10,211,587,360
Net Worth: $3,620,851,520
Earnings: ($1,371,944,080)
Emp.: 29,522
Fiscal Year-end: 12/31/2020
Offshore Construction, Pipe Laying & Drill-
ing
N.A.I.C.S.: 541330
Alessandro Puliti (CEO, COO & Gen Mgr)

Subsidiary (Non-US):

Moss Maritime A/S (2)
Vollsveien 17 A, PO Box 120, 1366, Ly-
saker, Norway (100%)
Tel.: (47) 67526250
Web Site: https://www.mossww.com
Sales Range: $75-99.9 Million
Emp.: 70
Gas Technology, Gas Carriers & Rigs Mfr
N.A.I.C.S.: 221210
Ida Husem (CEO)

Petrex S.A. (2)
Avenida Republica de Panama 3050 San
Isidro, 27, Lima, Peru
Tel.: (51) 12215050
Sales Range: $650-699.9 Million
Emp.: 1,200
Oil Field Services
N.A.I.C.S.: 213112

Saipem (Malaysia) Sdn. Bhd. (2)
Level 16 Menara Shell No 211 Jalan Tun
Sambathan, No 19 Jalan Pinang, 50470,
Kuala Lumpur, Malaysia
Tel.: (60) 327206000
Oil Field Services
N.A.I.C.S.: 213112
Massimiliano Bellotti (Mng Dir)

Subsidiary (US):

Saipem America, Inc. (2)
1311 Broadfield Blvd, Houston, TX 77084
Tel.: (281) 552-5600
Engineeering Services
N.A.I.C.S.: 541330

Subsidiary (Non-US):

Saipem UK Ltd (2)
Saipem House - 12-42 Wood Street, Mot-
spur Park, Kingston upon Thames, KT1
1TG, Surrey, United Kingdom
Tel.: (44) 2082965000
Sales Range: $25-49.9 Million
Emp.: 100

Oilfield Services, Construction & Engineering
N.A.I.C.S.: 541330

Sonsub Ltd. (2)
Tern Place Denmore Rd, Bridge of Don,
Aberdeen, AB23 8JX, United Kingdom
Tel.: (44) 1224843434
Web Site: http://www.sonsub.com
Sales Range: $100-124.9 Million
Emp.: 500
Subsea Construction & Engineering Ser-
vices
N.A.I.C.S.: 237120

Servizi Aerei SpA (1)
Via Carlo Simeoni Snc, Ciampino, 40,
Rome, Italy
Tel.: (39) 0679348601
Web Site: http://www.eni.com
Sales Range: $75-99.9 Million
Emp.: 58
Electric Power Distribution Services
N.A.I.C.S.: 221122

Snam S.p.A. (1)
Piazza Santa Barbara 7, 20097, San Do-
nato Milanese, MI, Italy (51.07%)
Tel.: (39) 0237031
Web Site: https://www.snam.it
Rev.: $4,580,185,625
Assets: $36,180,660,479
Liabilities: $27,892,294,410
Net Worth: $8,288,366,070
Earnings: $1,235,700,410
Emp.: 3,798
Fiscal Year-end: 12/31/2023
Oil & Gas Distribution Services
N.A.I.C.S.: 551112
Patrizia Rutigliano (Exec VP-Institutional
Affairs, Comm & Mktg)

Subsidiary (Domestic):

GNL Italia S.p.A. (2)
Piazza S Barbara 7, 20097, San Donato
Milanese, Italy (100%)
Tel.: (39) 025201
Web Site: http://www.gnlitalia.it
Natural Gas Pipeline Transportation
N.A.I.C.S.: 486210

Joint Venture (Non-US):

Gas Connect Austria GmbH (2)
Floridsdorfer Hauptstrasse 1, Floridsdorfer
Hauptstrasse 1, 1210, Vienna,
Austria (19.6%)
Tel.: (43) 1275000
Web Site: https://www.gasconnect.at
Sales Range: $75-99.9 Million
Emp.: 240
Petroleum Services
N.A.I.C.S.: 213112
Harald Stindl (Mng Dir)

Subsidiary (Domestic):

Serfactoring S.p.A. (2)
Via Maastricht 1, San Donato Milanese,
Italy
Tel.: (39) 0252045690
Credit Intermediation
N.A.I.C.S.: 522390

Snam Rete Gas S.p.A. (2)
Piazza Santa Barbara 7, 20097, San Do-
nato Milanese, MI, Italy
Tel.: (39) 0237038300
Natural Gas Pipeline Transportation Ser-
vices
N.A.I.C.S.: 486210

Stoccaggi Gas Italia S.p.A. (2)
Via Dell Unione Europea 4, 20097, San Do-
nato Milanese, Italy
Tel.: (39) 025201
Natural Gas Distribution
N.A.I.C.S.: 221210

Joint Venture (Non-US):

**Total Infrastructures Gaz France
SA** (2)
40 avenue de l'Europe, CS 20522, 64010,
Pau, Cedex, France (40.5%)
Tel.: (33) 559133400
Web Site: https://www.terega.fr
Sales Range: $400-449.9 Million
Emp.: 500

Natural Gas Transportation & Storage Ser-
vices
N.A.I.C.S.: 486210
Bernard Clement (Chm)

Subsidiary (Non-US):

Trans Austria Gasleitung GmbH (2)
Wiedner Hauptstrasse 120, 1050, Vienna,
Austria (89%)
Tel.: (43) 15975116
Web Site: https://www.taggmbh.at
Sales Range: $50-74.9 Million
Emp.: 10
Gas Pipeline Services
N.A.I.C.S.: 486210

**Societe de Service du Gazoduc Tran-
stunisien SA - Sergaz SA** (1)
Boulevard 7 Novembre, 1082, Tunis, Tuni-
sia
Tel.: (216) 31205707100
Natural Gas Producer
N.A.I.C.S.: 221210

Sofidsim S.p.A. (1)
Via M Ghetaldi 64, 143, Rome,
Italy (100%)
Tel.: (39) 0645474547
Sales Range: $50-74.9 Million
Emp.: 50
Fuel Distr
N.A.I.C.S.: 211120

Syndial servizi ambientali S.p.A. (1)
(100%)
Tel.: (39) 025201
Web Site: http://www.syndial.it
Natural Gas Extraction Services
N.A.I.C.S.: 211120

Trans Tunisian Pipeline Co Ltd (1)
Piazza Ezio Vanoni 1, 20097, San Donato
Milanese, MI, Italy
Tel.: (39) 0252059089
Oil & Gas Pipeline Transportation Services
N.A.I.C.S.: 486990

Var Energi AS (1)
Vestre Svanholmen 1, 4313, Sandnes,
Norway (69.6%)
Tel.: (47) 51606060
Web Site: https://varenergi.no
Rev.: $6,849,716,000
Assets: $19,289,199,000
Liabilities: $17,521,173,000
Net Worth: $1,768,026,000
Earnings: $610,229,000
Emp.: 1,055
Fiscal Year-end: 12/31/2023
Exploration & Production Company
N.A.I.C.S.: 213110
Philip D. Hemmens (Chm)

Subsidiary (Domestic):

Neptune Energy Norge AS (2)
Botnaneset Bygg 59, Floro, Norway
Tel.: (47) 52031000
Web Site: http://www.neptuneenergy.com
Emp.: 100
Oil & Gas Exploration Services
N.A.I.C.S.: 211130
Sam Laidlaw (Chm)

Subsidiary (Domestic):

Neptune E&P Norge (3)
Laberget 22, 4020, Stavanger, Norway
Tel.: (47) 51538900
Web Site: http://www.neptuneenergy.com
Oil & Gas Support Services
N.A.I.C.S.: 213112
Ulf Rosenberg (Mgr-Public Affairs & Comm)

**Versalis Pacific Trading (Shanghai)
Co. Ltd.** (1)
Unit 1502 and 1504 Hongyi Plaza 288 Jiuji-
ang Road, Huang Pu District, Shanghai,
200001, China
Tel.: (86) 2123137555
Natural Gas Producer
N.A.I.C.S.: 221210

Versalis S.p.A. (1)
Piazza Boldrini 1, 20097, San Donato Mila-
nese, MI, Italy
Tel.: (39) 025201
Web Site: https://www.versalis.eni.com
Chemical Products Mfr & Distr
N.A.I.C.S.: 325998

ENIBLOCK S.A.
Tour W-102 Terrasse Boieldieu, la-
Defense, 92800, Puteaux, France
Tel.: (33) 187666269
Web Site: https://www.eniblock.com
ALENI—(EUR)
Software Development Services
N.A.I.C.S.: 541511

ENIKON A.D.
Gradiliste bb, 15300, Loznica, Serbia
Tel.: (381) 64 8559514
Web Site: http://www.enikon.rs
Year Founded: 1992
Sales Range: $1-9.9 Million
Emp.: 91
Power Plant Parts Mfr
N.A.I.C.S.: 333611
Budimir Gacic *(Exec Dir)*

ENIRO GROUP AB
Kistagangen 12, SE-164 40, Kista,
Sweden
Tel.: (46) 855331000
Web Site: https://www.eniro.com
ENRO—(OMX)
Rev.: $107,674,560
Assets: $145,397,280
Liabilities: $124,643,680
Net Worth: $20,753,600
Earnings: ($8,301,440)
Emp.: 614
Fiscal Year-end: 12/31/20
Directories, Directory Assistance, In-
ternet & Mobile Information Services
N.A.I.C.S.: 513140
Magdalena Bonde *(Pres & CEO)*

Subsidiaries:

Din Del AB   **(1)**
Gustav III Boulevard 40, Stockholm, 16987,
Sweden
Tel.: (46) 8 58 50 23 00
Web Site: http://www.dindel.se
Directory & Periodical Publishing Services
N.A.I.C.S.: 513140
Tobias Johannson *(Mgr-Customer Service)*

Subsidiary (Domestic):

Din Del Forsaljning AB   **(2)**
Gustav III S Boulevard 40, 169 87, Solna,
Sweden
Tel.: (46) 858502300
Web Site: http://www.eniro.com.sd
Advertising Agency Services
N.A.I.C.S.: 541810
Sedsan Kercza *(Gen Mgr)*

Eniro 118 118 AB   **(1)**
Kistagangen 12, 164 40, Kista,
Sweden   **(100%)**
Tel.: (46) 770779797
Web Site: http://www.eniro.se
Sales Range: $200-249.9 Million
Emp.: 1,000
Wired Telecommunications Carriers
N.A.I.C.S.: 517111
Stefan Kercza *(Gen Mgr)*

Eniro Emfas AB   **(1)**
Gustav IIIs Boulevard 40, 16987, Solna,
Stockholm, Sweden   **(100%)**
Tel.: (46) 855331000
Web Site: http://www.eniro.com
Sales Range: $400-449.9 Million
Emp.: 1,500
Book Publishers
N.A.I.C.S.: 513130
Johan Lindgren *(Pres & CEO)*

Eniro International AB   **(1)**
Kistagangen 12, 164 40, Kista,
Sweden   **(100%)**
Tel.: (46) 855331000
Web Site: http://www.eniro.com
Emp.: 1,500
Holding Company
N.A.I.C.S.: 551112

Subsidiary (Non-US):

1880 Nummeropplysning AS   **(2)**

Ringvegen 3, 2815, Gjovik,
Norway   **(100%)**
Tel.: (47) 93435829
Sales Range: $50-74.9 Million
Emp.: 150
Information Services
N.A.I.C.S.: 519290

Bedriftskatalogen AS   **(2)**
Olaf Helsets Vei 5, Oslo, Norway
Tel.: (47) 81544418
Book Publishers
N.A.I.C.S.: 513130

Ditt Distrikt AS   **(2)**
Langkaia 1, Oslo, 0150, Norway
Tel.: (47) 81544418
Web Site: http://www.dittdistrikt.no
Emp.: 200
Book Publishers
N.A.I.C.S.: 513130
Donald Stefan *(Mng Dir)*

Editorium AS   **(2)**
Gjerdrums Vei 19, Oslo, Norway   **(100%)**
Tel.: (47) 21508000
Book Publishers
N.A.I.C.S.: 513130

Eniro Danmark A/S   **(2)**
Sydmarken 44a, 2860, Soborg, Denmark
Tel.: (45) 88383800
Web Site: http://www.eniro.dk
Sales Range: $75-99.9 Million
Emp.: 510
Directories, Directory Assistance, Internet &
Mobile Information Services
N.A.I.C.S.: 513140
Mathias Wedar *(Pres)*

Eniro Norge AS   **(2)**
Olaf Helsets Vei 5, Oslo, 0694, Norway
Tel.: (47) 81544418
Web Site: http://www.eniro.no
Sales Range: $200-249.9 Million
Emp.: 800
N.A.I.C.S.: 513110

Eniro Norway   **(2)**
Olaf Helsets Vai 5, N 0694, Oslo,
Norway   **(100%)**
Tel.: (47) 22583800
Web Site: http://www.eniro.no
Sales Range: $50-74.9 Million
Emp.: 210
N.A.I.C.S.: 513110

Eniro Sentraali Oy   **(2)**
Valimotie 9-11, 00380, Helsinki, Finland
Tel.: (358) 29 0100 100
Web Site: http://www.sentraali.fi
Sales Range: $100-124.9 Million
Emp.: 50
Directory Assistance & Mobile Search Ser-
vices
N.A.I.C.S.: 513140
Kaj Lindholm *(Mng Dir)*

Findexa Forlag AS   **(2)**
Sandakerveien 116 D, Oslo, 0484, Nydalen,
Norway   **(100%)**
Tel.: (47) 21508000
Book Publishers
N.A.I.C.S.: 513130

Grenseguiden AS   **(2)**
Olaf Helsets Vei 5, Oslo, Norway
Tel.: (47) 81544418
Book Publishers
N.A.I.C.S.: 513130

Gule Sider AS   **(2)**
Langkaia 1, 0150, Oslo, Norway
Tel.: (47) 22749280
Web Site: http://www.gulesider.no
Book Publishers
N.A.I.C.S.: 513130

Subsidiary (Domestic):

Gule Sider Internett AS   **(3)**
Olaf Helsets Vei 5, Oslo, Norway
Tel.: (47) 81544418
Web Site: http://www.gulesider.no
Book Publishers
N.A.I.C.S.: 513130

Subsidiary (Non-US):

Index Publishing AS   **(2)**
Gjerdrums Vei 19, Oslo, Norway   **(100%)**

Tel.: (47) 21508000
Book Publishers
N.A.I.C.S.: 513130

Telefonkatalogens Gule Sider AS   **(2)**
Iankala 1, Oslo, 0150, Norway
Tel.: (47) 81544448
Web Site: http://www.eniro.no
Book Publishers
N.A.I.C.S.: 513130
Wenche Holen *(Mng Dir)*

Eniro Sverige AB   **(1)**
Guftav 3 Boulevard 40, 16973, Solna,
Sweden   **(100%)**
Tel.: (46) 855331000
Web Site: http://www.enrio.com
Sales Range: $350-399.9 Million
Emp.: 1,550
Advertising Agencies
N.A.I.C.S.: 541810
Matthias Wedrar *(Mng Dir)*

Subsidiary (Domestic):

Eniro Gula Sidorna AB   **(2)**
Gustav III S Boulevard 40, Stockholm, 169
87, Sweden
Tel.: (46) 85533 1000
Web Site: http://www.eniro.com
Directory Publishing Services
N.A.I.C.S.: 513140

Subsidiary (Domestic):

Eniro Gula Sidorna Forsaljning
AB   **(3)**
Gustav III S Boulevard 40, Solna, SE-169
87, Stockholm, Sweden
Tel.: (46) 855331000
Web Site: http://www.eniro.se
Directory Sales
N.A.I.C.S.: 424920
Stefan Kerza *(CEO)*

Subsidiary (Domestic):

Eniro Passagen AB   **(2)**
Gustav Iii S Boulevard 40, Solna, 169 87,
Sweden
Tel.: (46) 8 55331000
Web Site: http://www.eniro.se
Advertising Agency Services
N.A.I.C.S.: 541810

Eniro Sverige Forsaljning AB   **(2)**
Justav 3rd Blvd 40, 16973, Solna, Sweden
Tel.: (46) 855331000
Web Site: http://www.eniro.se
Sales Range: $300-349.9 Million
Emp.: 1,000
Advertising Agencies
N.A.I.C.S.: 541810
Nils Carlsson *(Mng Dir)*

Kataloger i Norr AB   **(1)**
Hornellgatan 17, 93130, Skelleftea,
Sweden   **(100%)**
Tel.: (46) 910714350
Web Site: http://www.katalogerinorr.se
Plate Work Mfr
N.A.I.C.S.: 332813

Leta Information Eniro AB   **(1)**
Gustav Iii S Boulevard 40, Solna, 16987,
Sweden
Tel.: (46) 855331000
Directory Publishing Services
N.A.I.C.S.: 513140

ENISH INC.
6F/8F Fujikikai Hiroo Building 1-13-1
Hiroo, Shibuya-ku, Tokyo, 150-0012,
Japan
Tel.: (81) 357912131
Web Site: http://www.enish.jp
Year Founded: 2009
3667—(TKS)
Sales Range: $25-49.9 Million
Emp.: 71
Social Gaming Software
N.A.I.C.S.: 513210
Kan Sato *(Auditor)*

ENJAZ FOR DEVELOPMENT &
MULTI PROJECTS COMPANY
P.L.C.

Yathreb Commercial Complex - Build-
ing No 41 - 1st Floor - Office No 5,
PO Box 910776, Al Shahid Wasfi Al
Tal Street, Amman, 11191, Jordan
Tel.: (962) 5537503
Year Founded: 1976
ATCO—(AMM)
Rev.: $60,769,393
Assets: $223,608,576
Liabilities: $155,173,015
Net Worth: $68,435,561
Earnings: $473,177
Emp.: 3
Fiscal Year-end: 12/31/21
Real Estate Development Services
N.A.I.C.S.: 531390
Hazem Mohammad Al-Qadi *(Gen*
Mgr)

Subsidiaries:

Arab Tower Contracting Company
Ltd.   **(1)**
Wasfi Al Tal St 41, PO Box 06 593, Yathreb
Commercial Complex, Amman, 11953, Jor-
dan
Tel.: (962) 65530381
Web Site: https://www.atcco.com.jo
Construction Services
N.A.I.C.S.: 236220

ENJET CO., LTD.
No 45 Saneop-ro 92beon-gil,
Gwonseon-gu, Suwon, Gyeonggi-do,
Korea (South)
Tel.: (82) 7048928111
Web Site: https://enjet.co.kr
Year Founded: 2009
419080—(KRS)
Printing Ink Mfr
N.A.I.C.S.: 325910
Doyoung Byun *(CEO & Mng Dir)*

ENJOYOR TECHNOLOGY CO.,
LTD.
Building A1 Fuchun Park China Zhigu
Jiulong Avenue Yinhu Street, Fuyang
District, Hangzhou, 311400, Zhejiang,
China
Tel.: (86) 57189716117
Web Site: https://www.enjoyor.net
Year Founded: 1992
300020—(CHIN)
Rev.: $164,664,622
Assets: $981,186,509
Liabilities: $384,591,686
Net Worth: $596,594,824
Earnings: ($32,951,998)
Fiscal Year-end: 12/31/23
Information Technology Services
N.A.I.C.S.: 541512
Caijun Chen *(Chm)*

ENK DRUCK & MEDIA GMBH
Brinkstegge 33, 46395, Bocholt, Ger-
many
Tel.: (49) 287124800
Web Site: http://www.enk-media.de
Sales Range: $25-49.9 Million
Emp.: 80
Printing Services
N.A.I.C.S.: 323111
Franz-Hermann Enk *(Mng Dir)*

ENKA INSAAT VE SANAYI A.S.
Balmumcu Mahallesi Zincirlikuyu Yolu
No 10 Besiktas, 34349, Istanbul, Tur-
kiye
Tel.: (90) 2123761000   **TR**
Web Site: https://www.enka.com
Year Founded: 1957
ENKAI—(IST)
Rev.: $3,769,514,000
Assets: $9,023,621,000
Liabilities: $2,119,725,000
Net Worth: $6,903,896,000
Earnings: $16,140,000
Emp.: 19,582

Enka Insaat ve Sanayi A.S.—(Continued)

Fiscal Year-end: 12/31/22
Industrial Building Construction
N.A.I.C.S.: 236220
M. Sinan Tara *(Chm)*

Subsidiaries:

**Adapazari Elektrik Uretim Limited
Sirketi**   **(1)**
Enka Caddesi TN1 No13 Adres No
2169458698, Adapazari, 54000, Sakarya,
Turkiye   **(100%)**
Tel.: (90) 2642890100
Sales Range: $25-49.9 Million
Emp.: 100
Heavy & Civil Engineering Construction
N.A.I.C.S.: 237990

Airenka Hava Tasimaciligi A.S.   **(1)**
Bestekar Sevki Bey Sokak Enka 1 Bina
Zemin Kat, Balmumcu, Besiktas, Istanbul,
Turkiye
Tel.: (90) 212 274 25 40
Air Taxi Operator
N.A.I.C.S.: 481211

**Cimtas (Ningbo) Steel Processing
Company Ltd.**   **(1)**
No 16 Yangzijiang South Road, Export Pro-
cessing Zone, Ningbo, 315806, Zhejiang,
China
Tel.: (86) 57456215599
Web Site: https://www.cimtasnbo.com
Fabricated Steel Pipe Mfr
N.A.I.C.S.: 331210

**Cimtas Borulama Sanayi ve Ticaret
Ltd. Sti.**   **(1)**
Bursa Serbest Bolgesi Liman Yolu Hisar
Mevkii, Bursa, 16600, Turkiye
Tel.: (90) 2245248731
Industrial Pipe Distr
N.A.I.C.S.: 423830

**Cimtas Celik Imalat Montaj Ve Tesisat
A.S.**   **(1)**
Enka 2 Binasi Kat 3, Bestekar Sevkibey,
Sokak, Istanbul, 34349, Turkiye
Tel.: (90) 2123403535
Web Site: http://www.cimtas.com.tr
Sales Range: $200-249.9 Million
Emp.: 1,000
Fabricated Structural Metal Mfr
N.A.I.C.S.: 332312

Subsidiary (Non-US):

IBH Engineering GmbH   **(2)**
Donnersbergweg 2, Ludwigshafen, 67059,
Germany
Tel.: (49) 621659010
Web Site: http://www.ibh-engineers.de
Sales Range: $25-49.9 Million
Emp.: 10
Business Support Services
N.A.I.C.S.: 561990

**Cimtas Gemi Insa Sanayi ve Ticaret
A.S.**   **(1)**
2 Ada Kocaeli Serbest Bolgesi, 41275,
Izmit, Kocaeli, Turkiye
Tel.: (90) 2623414282
Web Site: http://www.cimtasshipyard.com
Emp.: 50
Civil Engineering Construction Services
N.A.I.C.S.: 237990

**Cimtas Steel Metal Konstruksiya
MMC**   **(1)**
Ata Mah Sanayi Cad No 52, Gemlik, 16600,
Bursa, Turkiye
Tel.: (90) 2245190250
Web Site: https://www.cimtas.com
Construction Engineering Services
N.A.I.C.S.: 541330

Enka Finansal Kiralama A.S.   **(1)**
Ata 4 Carsi Plaza K 3 No 39 Atasehir,
Kadikoy, 34749, Istanbul, Turkiye
Tel.: (90) 216 455 10 00
Sales Range: $50-74.9 Million
Emp.: 16
Automotive Financial Leasing Services
N.A.I.C.S.: 522220
Fikri Aca *(Gen Mgr)*

Enka Holding B.V.   **(1)**
Evert van de Beekstraat 310, 1118 CX,

Schiphol, Netherlands   **(100%)**
Tel.: (31) 206541938
Holding Company; Real Estate Investment
Trusts
N.A.I.C.S.: 551112
Nanne Refos *(Gen Mgr)*

Subsidiary (Domestic):

Capital City Investment B.V.   **(2)**
Evert van de Beekstraat 310, Schiphol,
1118CX, Netherlands   **(100%)**
Tel.: (31) 206541938
Real Estate Investment Trust
N.A.I.C.S.: 525990
N. Resos *(Office Mgr)*

Edco Investment B.V.   **(2)**
Evert van de Beekstraat 310, 1118 CX,
Schiphol, Netherlands   **(100%)**
Tel.: (31) 206541938
Real Estate Investment Trust
N.A.I.C.S.: 525990

**Enka Adapazari Power Investment
B.V.**   **(2)**
Evert van de Beekstraat 310, Schiphol,
1118 CX, Netherlands   **(100%)**
Tel.: (31) 206541938
Real Estate Investment Trust
N.A.I.C.S.: 525990
Anne Refos *(CEO)*

**Enka Construction & Development
B.V.**   **(2)**
Evert van de Beekstraat 310, 1118 CX,
Schiphol, Netherlands   **(100%)**
Tel.: (31) 206541938
Real Estate Investment Trust
N.A.I.C.S.: 525990

**Enka Gebze Power Investment
B.V.**   **(2)**
Evert van de Beekstraat 310, 1118 CX,
Schiphol, Netherlands   **(100%)**
Tel.: (31) 206541938
Real Estate Investment Trust
N.A.I.C.S.: 525990

**Enka Izmir Power Investment
B.V.**   **(2)**
Evert van de Beekstraat 310, 1118 CX,
Schiphol, Netherlands   **(100%)**
Tel.: (31) 206541938
Real Estate Investment Trust
N.A.I.C.S.: 525990

Enka Power Investment B.V.   **(2)**
Evert van de Beekstraat 310, 1118 CX,
Schiphol, Netherlands   **(100%)**
Tel.: (31) 206541938
Real Estate Investment Trust
N.A.I.C.S.: 525990

Enru Development B.V.   **(2)**
Evert van de Beekstraat 310, 1118 CX,
Schiphol, Netherlands   **(100%)**
Tel.: (31) 206541938
Real Estate Investment Trust
N.A.I.C.S.: 525990

Far East Development B.V.   **(2)**
Evert van de Beekstraat 310, 1118 CX,
Schiphol, Netherlands
Tel.: (31) 206541938
Real Estate Investment Trust
N.A.I.C.S.: 525990

**Enka Pazarlama Ihracat Ithalat
AS**   **(1)**
Istasyon Mah Araplar Cad No 6, 34940,
Istanbul, Turkiye
Tel.: (90) 2164466464
Web Site: https://www.enka.com
Construction Engineering Services
N.A.I.C.S.: 541330

Enka TC LLC   **(1)**
Presnenskaya naberezhnaya 10 Naber-
ezhnaya Tower Block C floor 58, Moscow,
123112, Russia
Tel.: (7) 4959370440
Web Site: https://enkatc.com
Shopping Mall Operation Services
N.A.I.C.S.: 531210

Enka Teknik A.S.   **(1)**
Enka 2 Balmumcu Besiktas, Bolg Plaza
Ofis N 710, Istanbul, 3449, Turkiye
Tel.: (90) 2122741800
Web Site: http://www.enkateknik.com

Sales Range: $25-49.9 Million
Emp.: 85
New Single-Family Housing Construction
N.A.I.C.S.: 236115

**Enka Teknik Genel Muteahhitlik Ba-
kim Isletme Sevk ve Idare Anonim
Sirketi**   **(1)**
Balmumcu Mahallesi Zincirlikuyu Yolu Enka
2 Binasi, Besiktas, 34349, Istanbul, Turkiye
Tel.: (90) 2122741800
Web Site: http://www.enkateknik.com
Emp.: 30
Civil Engineering Construction Services
N.A.I.C.S.: 237990

Enmar Trading Ltd   **(1)**
10 Coldbath Square, London, EC1R 5HL,
United Kingdom
Tel.: (44) 2081331920
Sales Range: $50-74.9 Million
Emp.: 1
Nondurable Goods Merchant Whslr
N.A.I.C.S.: 424990

**Entas Nakliyat ve Turizm Anonim
Sirketi**   **(1)**
Buyukdere Caddesi No 108/A Enka Binasi
Gayrettepe, 34394, Istanbul,
Turkiye   **(99.93%)**
Tel.: (90) 2123542424
Web Site: http://www.entas.com.tr
Sales Range: $10-24.9 Million
Emp.: 50
Travel Agencies
N.A.I.C.S.: 561510

**Gebze Elektrik Uretim Limited
Sirketi**   **(1)**
Balmumcu Mah Zincirlikuyu Yolu Sok Enka
A S No 10, Besiktas, Istanbul,
Turkiye   **(100%)**
Tel.: (90) 2122889998
Web Site: http://www.enkapower.com
Sales Range: $25-49.9 Million
Emp.: 33
Heavy & Civil Engineering Construction
N.A.I.C.S.: 237990

**Izmir Elektrik Uretim Limited
Sirketi**   **(1)**
9 Cadde No 11, Bozkoy / Aliaga, 35800,
Izmir, Turkiye   **(100%)**
Tel.: (90) 2326252150
Web Site: http://www.izmir-elektrik.com
Sales Range: $75-99.9 Million
Emp.: 22
Electric Power Generation
N.A.I.C.S.: 221118

**Kasktas Kayar Kalip Altyapi Sondaj
Kazik ve Tecrit Anonim Sirketi**   **(1)**
Balmumcu Mah Zincirlikuyu Yolu Sk Enka A
S No 10, Besiktas, 34349, Istanbul, Turkiye
Tel.: (90) 2122745842
Web Site: https://www.kasktas.com.tr
Sales Range: $75-99.9 Million
Emp.: 50
Geotechnical Engineering Services
N.A.I.C.S.: 541330

MCC Investment SA.   **(1)**
C/o Fidinam Geneve Sa Avenue Blanc 53,
Geneva, 1202, Switzerland
Tel.: (41) 227051130
Investment Management Service
N.A.I.C.S.: 523999

Metra Akdeniz Dis Ticaret A.S.   **(1)**
Istasyon Mah Araplar Cad No 6, Tuzla, Is-
tanbul, 34940, Turkiye
Tel.: (90) 2164466464
Web Site: http://www.metra-akdeniz.com
Civil Engineering Construction Services
N.A.I.C.S.: 237990

Mosenka LLC   **(1)**
Kosmodamianskaya Nab 52 Bldg 11, Mos-
cow, 115035, Russia
Tel.: (7) 4957872288
Web Site: https://www.mosenka.ru
Emp.: 75
Real Estate Investment Services
N.A.I.C.S.: 531120

Mosenka OAO   **(1)**
Str 3 25 Bul Tsvetnoi Blvd, Moscow,
127051, Russia
Tel.: (7) 4957872288
Web Site: http://www.mosenka.ru

Sales Range: $25-49.9 Million
Emp.: 50
Heavy & Civil Engineering Construction
N.A.I.C.S.: 237990

Moskva Krasnye Holmy LLC   **(1)**
Kosmodamianskay Nab 52 Bldg 11, Mos-
cow, 115035, Russia
Tel.: (7) 4952586840
Web Site: https://www.mkh.ru
Emp.: 98
Real Estate Manangement Services
N.A.I.C.S.: 531210

Rumos S.A.   **(1)**
Mirage Building - EntrecamposRua Dr Edu-
ardo Neves 3, 1050-077, Lisbon, Portugal
Tel.: (351) 217824100
Web Site: https://www.rumos.pt
Information Technology Consulting Services
N.A.I.C.S.: 541512
Andy Thomson *(Mng Dir)*

**Titas Toprak Insaat ve Taahhut
Anonim Sirketi**   **(1)**
Balmumcu Besiktas Apartment 525, Besik-
tas, 80700, Istanbul, Turkiye
Tel.: (90) 2122742342
Civil Engineering Construction Services
N.A.I.C.S.: 237990

ENKEI WHEELS (INDIA) LTD.

Gat No 1425 Shikrapur, Tal-Shirur
Dist, Pune, 412208, Maharashtra,
India
Tel.: (91) 2137618700
Web Site: https://www.enkei.in
Year Founded: 2009
533477—(BOM)
Rev.: $61,821,260
Assets: $66,650,493
Liabilities: $38,309,544
Net Worth: $28,340,949
Earnings: $2,221,811
Emp.: 418
Fiscal Year-end: 12/31/21
Auto Parts & Equipment Mfr
N.A.I.C.S.: 423110
Jitendra Parmar *(CFO)*

ENKER D.D.

Bukva bb, Tesanj, 74260, Bosnia &
Herzegovina
Tel.: (387) 32650189
Web Site: http://www.enker.ba
Year Founded: 1974
ENKTRK2—(SARE)
Rev.: $3,705,855
Assets: $11,690,451
Liabilities: $999,339
Net Worth: $10,691,112
Earnings: ($330,547)
Emp.: 203
Fiscal Year-end: 12/31/21
Electronic Equipment Distr
N.A.I.C.S.: 423690

ENKSZ ELSO NEMZETI KOZ-MUSZOLGALTATO ZRT.

Nador u 31, 1051, Budapest, Hun-
gary
Tel.: (36) 6 40 474 474
Web Site: http://www.enksz.hu
Natural Gas & Electricity Distr
N.A.I.C.S.: 221210
Peter Horvath *(Pres & CEO)*

Subsidiaries:

FOGAZ Zrt.   **(1)**
Janos Pal papa ter 20, 1081, Budapest,
Hungary
Tel.: (36) 40 454 454
Web Site: http://www.fogaz.hu
Natural Gas Transmission & Distribution
Services
N.A.I.C.S.: 221210
Kobor Gyorgy *(Chm-Mgmt Bd)*

ENL LIMITED

ENL House Vivea Business Park,
Moka, Mauritius

Tel.: (230) 4049500
Web Site: http://www.enl.mu
Year Founded: 1944
ENLG—(MAU)
Rev.: $449,429,177
Assets: $1,967,507,210
Liabilities: $899,136,373
Net Worth: $1,068,370,836
Earnings: $64,476,961
Emp.: 54,427
Fiscal Year-end: 06/30/23
Holding Company; Agricultural Services; Manufacturing Services; General Business Services
N.A.I.C.S.: 551112
Eric Espitalier-Noel *(CEO-ENL Commercial Limited)*

Subsidiaries:

Bagatelle Hotel Operations Company Limited   **(1)**
Bagatelle Mall, PO Box 30, Reduit, Mauritius
Tel.: (230) 4068000
Web Site: https://www.voilahotel.mu
Hotel & Resort Services
N.A.I.C.S.: 721110

Blue Sky Reunion SAS   **(1)**
7 Rue Francois de Mahy, 97410, Saint-Pierre, Reunion
Tel.: (262) 808810
Web Site: https://www.bluesky.re
Travel Agency Services
N.A.I.C.S.: 561510

Box Manufacturing Co   **(1)**
201 Spring St, Peoria, IL 61603
Tel.: (309) 637-6228
Rev.: $1,335,000
Emp.: 5
Corrugated & Solid Fiber Box Mfr
N.A.I.C.S.: 322211
Jay Streid *(Mgr)*

Box Manufacturing Company Limited   **(1)**
Royal Road, Morcellement Saint Andre, Mauritius
Tel.: (230) 2611742
Carton Box Mfr
N.A.I.C.S.: 322212

Croisieres Australes Ltee   **(1)**
Rue Breard Bagatelle, 80832, Moka, Mauritius
Tel.: (230) 2026660
Web Site: https://www.croisieres-australes.com
Catamaran Cruise Services
N.A.I.C.S.: 487210

ENL Commercial Limited   **(1)**
7th Floor Swan Group Centre, Intendance Street, Port Louis, Mauritius
Tel.: (230) 2133800
Holding Company
N.A.I.C.S.: 551112

Subsidiary (Domestic):

Axess Limited   **(2)**
Grewals Lane, Les Pailles, Mauritius
Tel.: (230) 2064300
Web Site: https://www.axess.mu
Emp.: 400
Automobile Sales
N.A.I.C.S.: 441227
Antoine M. d'Unienville *(Office Mgr)*

Charabia Ltd.   **(2)**
Virgile Naz Street, Curepipe, Mauritius
Tel.: (230) 696 2772
Web Site: http://www.charabia.mu
Emp.: 9
Decorator Fabric Sales
N.A.I.C.S.: 449129
Nathalie Hardy *(Gen Mgr)*

Cogir Limitee   **(2)**
Grewals Lane, Les Pailles, Mauritius   **(56%)**
Tel.: (230) 286 5633
Building & Civil Engineering Construction Services
N.A.I.C.S.: 236220

Grewals (Mauritius) Limited   **(2)**

Grewals Lane, Les Pailles, Mauritius
Tel.: (230) 2866619
Web Site: https://www.grewals.mu
Emp.: 91
Lumbering & Saw Mill Operations
N.A.I.C.S.: 321912

Subsidiary (Domestic):

Grewals Rodrigues Ltd.   **(3)**
Camp de Roi, Rodrigues, Mauritius
Tel.: (230) 831 0178
Lumbering & Milling Services
N.A.I.C.S.: 321912

Subsidiary (Domestic):

Pack Plastics Limited   **(2)**
Anse Courtois, Les Pailles, Mauritius
Tel.: (230) 286 2826
Web Site: http://www.elit_spationery.com
Emp.: 10
Plastics Product Mfr
N.A.I.C.S.: 326199
Arnaud Boulle *(Mgr)*

Packestate Limited   **(2)**
Anse Courtois, Les Pailles, Mauritius
Tel.: (230) 286 2826
Plastics Product Mfr
N.A.I.C.S.: 326199
Arnaud Boulle *(Mgr)*

Plastinax Austral Limitee   **(2)**
Industrial Zone, Saint Pierre, Mauritius
Tel.: (230) 4334638
Emp.: 350
Sunglasses & Reading Glasses Mfr
N.A.I.C.S.: 339115
Nicolas Park *(Mgr)*

Plastinax Madagascar Ltd.   **(2)**
Industrial Zone, Saint Pierre, Mauritius
Tel.: (230) 433 4638
Sunglasses & Reading Glasses Mfr
N.A.I.C.S.: 339115

Plastintco International Ltd,   **(2)**
Industrial Zone, Saint Pierre, Mauritius
Tel.: (230) 433 4638
Web Site: http://www.plastinax.com
Sunglasses & Reading Glasses Mfr
N.A.I.C.S.: 339115
Nicolas Park *(Mgr)*

Rennel Limited   **(2)**
Anse Courtois, Les Pailles, Mauritius
Tel.: (230) 2965914
Web Site: https://rennel.mu
Emp.: 60
Air Courier Services
N.A.I.C.S.: 492110
Ludovic Desvaux de Marigny *(Gen Mgr)*

Savi Shop Ltd.   **(2)**
7th Floor Swan Group Centre, Intendance Street, Port Louis, Mauritius
Tel.: (230) 213 3800
Business Support Services
N.A.I.C.S.: 561499

Versatech Limited   **(2)**
Anse Courtois, Les Pailles, Mauritius
Tel.: (230) 2333479
Emp.: 4
Water Purifier Rental Services
N.A.I.C.S.: 221310
Cedric Deweer *(Gen Mgr)*

ENL Finance Limited   **(1)**
7th Floor Swan Group Centre, Intendance Street, Port Louis, Mauritius
Tel.: (230) 213 3800
Financial Services
N.A.I.C.S.: 561499

ENL Foundation   **(1)**
Bldg 1827, Moka, 0230, Mauritius
Tel.: (230) 433 4231
Community Support Services
N.A.I.C.S.: 561499
Mario Radegonde *(Mgr)*

ENL House Limited   **(1)**
Vivea Business Park, Moka, Mauritius
Tel.: (230) 4049500
Web Site: http://www.enl.mu
Emp.: 4
Business Support Services
N.A.I.C.S.: 561499

Pascal Grosse *(Gen Mgr)*

ENL Land Ltd   **(1)**
Vivea Business Park, Moka, Mauritius
Tel.: (230) 4049500
Web Site: http://www.enl.mu
Sales Range: $200-249.9 Million
Emp.: 5,940
Crop Farming Services
N.A.I.C.S.: 111998
Hector Espitalier-Noel *(CEO)*

Subsidiary (Domestic):

ENL Agri Limited   **(2)**
Royal Road, Saint Pierre, Mauritius
Tel.: (230) 4334304
Agricultural Services
N.A.I.C.S.: 424930
Jean-Raymond Hardy *(CEO)*

Subsidiary (Domestic):

Agrex Limited   **(3)**
Nehru road, Belle Terre, Phoenix, Mauritius
Tel.: (230) 54523515
Web Site: https://www.agrex.mu
Emp.: 10
Flower Grower & Exporter
N.A.I.C.S.: 424930

Anthurium and Orchids Limited   **(3)**
Royal Road, Henrietta, Vacoas, 252, Mauritius
Tel.: (230) 684 7147
Web Site: http://www.agri.com.mu
Flower Grower & Exporter
N.A.I.C.S.: 424930

ESP Landscapers Ltd.   **(3)**
Vivea Business Park, Moka, Mauritius
Tel.: (230) 4049780
Web Site: https://www.esplandscapers.com
Emp.: 20
Landscaping Services
N.A.I.C.S.: 561730
Benoit Mariette *(Mgr)*

Enquickfix Limited   **(3)**
Royal Road, Saint Pierre, Mauritius
Tel.: (230) 4334304
Agricultural Services
N.A.I.C.S.: 926140

Exotiflors Limited   **(3)**
Henrietta, Vacoas, 230, Mauritius
Tel.: (230) 684 7147
Emp.: 13
Flower Growing Services
N.A.I.C.S.: 424930
Bernard Audibert *(Gen Mgr)*

Mon Desert-Alma Sugar Milling Company Limited   **(3)**
Vivea Business Park, Intendance Street, Moka, Mauritius
Tel.: (230) 4049500
Sugar Refining Services
N.A.I.C.S.: 311314

The Savannah Sugar Milling Company Ltd.   **(3)**
Royal Road, Saint Pierre, Mauritius
Tel.: (230) 433 4304
Sugar Milling Services
N.A.I.C.S.: 311314

ENL Property Limited   **(1)**
ENL House Vivea Business Park, Moka, Mauritius
Tel.: (230) 4049500
Property Management Services
N.A.I.C.S.: 531390

Subsidiary (Domestic):

Bagaprop Limited   **(2)**
Stone House Mon Desert Alma, Saint Pierre, Mauritius
Tel.: (230) 4332929
Real Estate Services
N.A.I.C.S.: 531390

Bagatelle Hotel Operation Limited   **(2)**
Stone House Mon Desert Alma, Saint Pierre, Mauritius
Tel.: (230) 433 2939
Hotel Owner & Operator
N.A.I.C.S.: 721110

Ensejour Ltd.   **(2)**
Stone House Mon Desert Alma, Saint Pierre, Mauritius
Tel.: (230) 433 2929
Real Estate Services
N.A.I.C.S.: 531390

Enstyle Management Limited   **(2)**
7th Floor Swan Group Centre, Intendance Street, Port Louis, Mauritius
Tel.: (230) 213 3800
Property Management Services
N.A.I.C.S.: 531390

Espral Ltd.   **(2)**
6th Floor Anglo-Mauritius House, Intendance Street, Port Louis, Mauritius
Tel.: (230) 210 8669
Land Management Services
N.A.I.C.S.: 237210

Subsidiary (Domestic):

Espral International Ltd.   **(3)**
Old Factory, Saint Pierre, Mauritius
Tel.: (230) 433 4030
Web Site: http://www.espral.com
Emp.: 25
Land Management Services
N.A.I.C.S.: 237210
Samuel Dejersigny *(Office Mgr)*

International Valuers Ltd.   **(3)**
6th Floor Anglo-Mauritius House, Intendance Street, Port Louis, Mauritius
Tel.: (230) 210 8669
Real Estate Services
N.A.I.C.S.: 531390

Subsidiary (Domestic):

Helvetia Sport Ltd.   **(2)**
Stone House Mon Desert Alma, Saint Pierre, Mauritius
Tel.: (230) 433 2929
Real Estate Management Services
N.A.I.C.S.: 531390

Kendra Saint Pierre Limited   **(2)**
Stone House Mon Desert Alma, Saint Pierre, Mauritius
Tel.: (230) 433 2929
Real Estate Management Services
N.A.I.C.S.: 531390

Les Allees D'Helvetia Commercial Centre Limited   **(2)**
Stone House Mon Desert Alma, Saint Pierre, Mauritius
Tel.: (230) 433 2929
Real Estate Management Services
N.A.I.C.S.: 531390

MDA Properties Ltd.   **(2)**
Stone House Mon Desert Alma, Saint Pierre, Mauritius
Tel.: (230) 433 2929
Real Estate Management Services
N.A.I.C.S.: 531390

Mall of (Mauritius) at Bagatelle Ltd.   **(2)**
Stone House Mon Desert Alma, Saint Pierre, Mauritius
Tel.: (230) 433 2929
Real Estate Management Services
N.A.I.C.S.: 531390

Robin's Nest Interiors (Mauritius) Ltd.   **(2)**
Place Dumoulin Coastal Road, Bel Ombre, Mauritius
Tel.: (230) 623 5620
Web Site: http://robinsnestmauritius.com
Emp.: 11
Interior Design Services
N.A.I.C.S.: 541410
Subi Ramburrun *(Mgr)*

SB Cattle Ltd.   **(2)**
Stone House Mon Desert Alma, Saint Pierre, Mauritius
Tel.: (230) 4332929
Real Estate Development Services
N.A.I.C.S.: 531390

Savannah Properties Limited   **(2)**
Stone House Mon Desert Alma, Saint Pierre, Mauritius
Tel.: (230) 4332929
Real Estate Services

ENL Limited—(Continued)
N.A.I.C.S.: 531390

The Gardens of Bagatelle Ltd. **(2)**
Stone House Mon Desert Alma, Saint
Pierre, Mauritius
Tel.: (230) 433 2929
Real Estate Manangement Services
N.A.I.C.S.: 531390

The Old Factory Limited **(2)**
Stone House Mon Desert Alma, Saint
Pierre, Mauritius
Tel.: (230) 433 2929
Real Estate Manangement Services
N.A.I.C.S.: 531300

Valetta Locoshed Offices Ltd. **(2)**
Stone House Mon Desert Alma, Saint
Pierre, Mauritius
Tel.: (230) 433 2929
Real Estate Manangement Services
N.A.I.C.S.: 531390

Enex (Mauritius) Limited **(1)**
7th Floor Swan Group Centre, Intendance
Street, Port Louis, Mauritius
Tel.: (230) 213 3800
Business Support Services
N.A.I.C.S.: 561499

Enfyn Management Limited **(1)**
Stone House Mon Desert Alma, Saint
Pierre, Mauritius
Tel.: (230) 433 2929
Real Estate Services
N.A.I.C.S.: 531390

Island Living Ltd. **(1)**
Rue Breard Bagatelle, Moka, Mauritius
Tel.: (230) 4608950
Hotel & Resort Services
N.A.I.C.S.: 721110
Reshmee Boodhooa (CFO)

Islandian SARL **(1)**
7 Rue Francois de Mahy, 97410, Saint-
Pierre, France
Tel.: (33) 184781009
Travel Reservation Services
N.A.I.C.S.: 561599

Les Villas de Bel Ombre Ltee **(1)**
Chateau Gardens Coastal Road, Bel Om-
bre, Mauritius
Tel.: (230) 6235620
Web Site: http://www.illasvalriche.com
Hotel & Resort Services
N.A.I.C.S.: 721110
Seepursaund Kunal (Sec)

Oficea Company Limited **(1)**
ENL House Vivea Business Park, Moka,
Mauritius
Tel.: (230) 4049660
Web Site: https://www.oficea.com
Emp.: 2,000
Real Estate Development Services
N.A.I.C.S.: 531390
Johan Pilot (CEO)

Rogers Capital Ltd. **(1)**
Rogers House 5 President John Kennedy
Street, Port Louis, Mauritius
Tel.: (230) 2031100
Web Site: https://www.rogerscapital.mu
Financial Advisory Services
N.A.I.C.S.: 523940
Kabir Ruhee (CEO)

Rogers Shipping Ltd. **(1)**
3F La Capitainerie Building Quay D, 11615,
Port Louis, Mauritius
Tel.: (230) 2176229
Web Site: https://www.rogersshipping.com
Freight Forwarding Services
N.A.I.C.S.: 488510

Societe Reunion **(1)**
7th Floor Swan Group Centre, Intendance
Street, Port Louis, Mauritius
Tel.: (230) 2133800
Business Services
N.A.I.C.S.: 561499

Sygeco Limited **(1)**
Vivea Business Park, Moka, Mauritius
Tel.: (230) 4049770
Web Site: https://www.sygeco.com
Property Management Services
N.A.I.C.S.: 531390

Turbine Incubator Limited **(1)**
La Turbine Vivea Business Park, Moka,
Mauritius
Tel.: (230) 4815365
Web Site: https://www.turbine.mu
Business Coaching & Professional Services
N.A.I.C.S.: 611430
Sohashnee Kowal (Coord-Comm)

Villas Valriche Resorts Ltd. **(1)**
Administration Block Coastal Road, Bel
Ombre, Mauritius
Tel.: (230) 6055000
Web Site: http://www.myvillasvalriche.com
Real Estate Rental Services
N.A.I.C.S.: 531110

ENLIGHT CORPORATION
Room E 9th Floor No 111 Section 2
Qingpu Road, Guishan Dist, Taoyuan,
333, Taiwan
Tel.: (886) 33508001
Web Site:
　https://www.enlightcorp.com.tw
Year Founded: 1973
2438—(TAI)
Rev.: $3,854,508
Assets: $44,702,245
Liabilities: $21,851,041
Net Worth: $22,851,204
Earnings: ($2,311,913)
Fiscal Year-end: 12/31/23
Hardware Product Mfr
N.A.I.C.S.: 332510
Chih-Yung Wang (Chm)

ENLIGHT RENEWABLE EN-ERGY LTD.
13 Haamal St Afek Industrial Park,
PO Box 11659, Rosh Ha'Ayin,
4809249, Israel
Tel.: (972) 39008700
Web Site:
　https://www.enlightenergy.co.il
Year Founded: 1981
ENLT—(TAE)
Rev.: $192,172,000
Assets: $3,533,367,000
Liabilities: $2,483,333,000
Net Worth: $1,050,034,000
Earnings: $38,113,000
Emp.: 217
Fiscal Year-end: 12/31/22
Solar Electric Power Generation Ser-
vices
N.A.I.C.S.: 221114
Gilad Yavetz (Co-Founder & CEO)

ENLIGHTA INC.
2270 - 8788 McKim Way, Vancouver,
V6X 4E2, BC, Canada
Tel.: (604) 377-7575　　　　BC
Web Site:
　http://www.libertybiopharma.com
Year Founded: 2010
NLTA—(TSXV)
Assets: $35,602
Liabilities: $1,987,655
Net Worth: ($1,952,054)
Earnings: ($2,837,105)
Fiscal Year-end: 06/30/22
Biotechnology Research & Develop-
ment Services
N.A.I.C.S.: 541714

ENLIVEX THERAPEUTICS LTD.
14 Einstein St, Ness Ziona, 7403618,
Israel
Tel.: (972) 26708072　　　　Il
Web Site: https://www.enlivex.com
Year Founded: 2012
ENLV—(NASDAQ)
Assets: $67,642,000
Liabilities: $10,801,000
Net Worth: $56,841,000
Earnings: ($31,060,000)
Emp.: 77
Fiscal Year-end: 12/31/22

Pharmaceuticals Mfr
N.A.I.C.S.: 325412
Oren Elmaliah (Executives)

ENM HOLDINGS LIMITED
Suites 3301-3302 33/F Tower 2 Nina
Tower 8 Yeung Uk Road, Tsuen Wan,
New Territories, China (Hong Kong)
Tel.: (852) 25940600
Web Site:
　https://www.enmholdings.com
0128—(OTCIQ)
Rev.: $12,062,699
Assets: $151,550,932
Liabilities: $5,609,928
Net Worth: $145,950,004
Earnings: ($19,317,290)
Emp.: 115
Fiscal Year-end: 12/31/22
Resort & Recreation Club Holding
Company
N.A.I.C.S.: 551112
Pui Man Cheng (Sec)

Subsidiaries:

Hill Top Country Club Limited **(1)**
10 Hilltop Road, Lo Wai, Tsuen Wan, New
Territories, China (Hong Kong)
Tel.: (852) 2 412 0201
Web Site:
　https://www.hilltopcountryclub.com
Country Club Services
N.A.I.C.S.: 713910

The Swank Shop Limited **(1)**
Shops 102-106 110 1/F Central Building 1-3
Pedder Street, Central, China (Hong Kong)
Tel.: (852) 2 868 6990
Web Site: https://www.swank.hk
Sales Range: $50-74.9 Million
Emp.: 150
Fashion Apparels Retailer
N.A.I.C.S.: 458110

Subsidiary (Non-US):

The Swank Shop (Beijing)
Limited **(2)**
Shop 210-211 Jinbao Pi Shopping Ctr 88
Jinbao St, Dong Cheng Dist, Beijing,
100005, China
Tel.: (86) 1085221398
Fashion Wears Retailer
N.A.I.C.S.: 458110

ENMAX CORPORATION
141 50 Avenue SE, Calgary, T2G
4S7, AB, Canada
Tel.: (403) 514-3000　　　　Ca
Web Site: https://www.enmax.com
Year Founded: 1905
Rev.: $1,932,154,476
Assets: $5,184,730,572
Liabilities: $3,394,298,544
Net Worth: $1,790,432,028
Earnings: $119,530,488
Emp.: 1,800
Fiscal Year-end: 12/31/19
Holding Company; Energy Distribu-
tion, Transmission & Support Ser-
vices
N.A.I.C.S.: 551112
Gregory Melchin (Chm)

Subsidiaries:

ENMAX Commercial Services
Inc. **(1)**
311-6th Avenue SW Suite 1650, Calgary,
T2P 3H2, AB, Canada
Tel.: (403) 770-1170
Electric Power Distribution Services
N.A.I.C.S.: 221122

ENMAX Encompass Inc. **(1)**
141 50th Ave SE, Calgary, T2G 4S7, AB,
Canada　　　　　　　　　**(100%)**
Tel.: (403) 514-3000
Sales Range: $350-399.9 Million
Emp.: 1,200
Energy Billing & Customer Care Services
N.A.I.C.S.: 561499
Gianna Manes (CEO)

ENMAX Energy Corporation **(1)**
141 50th Ave SE, Calgary, T2G 4S7, AB,
Canada　　　　　　　　　**(100%)**
Tel.: (403) 514-3000
Web Site: https://www.enmax.com
Sales Range: $1-4.9 Billion
Emp.: 1,500
Electric Power Generation, Retail & Whole-
sale Energy Distribution & Transmission
Services
N.A.I.C.S.: 221122

Subsidiary (Domestic):

ENMAX Commercial Energy Market-
ing Inc. **(2)**
141 50th Ave SE, Calgary, T2G 4S7, AB,
Canada　　　　　　　　　**(100%)**
Tel.: (403) 514-3000
Sales Range: $500-549.9 Million
Emp.: 800
Commercial Electric Power & Natural Gas
Wholesale Transmission
N.A.I.C.S.: 221121

ENMAX Energy Marketing Inc. **(2)**
141 50th Avenue SE, Calgary, T2G 4S7,
AB, Canada　　　　　　　**(100%)**
Tel.: (403) 514-3000
Sales Range: $1-4.9 Billion
Electric Power & Natural Gas Wholesale
Transmission
N.A.I.C.S.: 221121

ENMAX Green Power Inc. **(2)**
141 50 Avenue Southeast, ENMAX Place,
Calgary, T2G 4S7, AB, Canada **(100%)**
Tel.: (403) 689-6150
Sales Range: $75-99.9 Million
Emp.: 100
Electric Power Generation
N.A.I.C.S.: 221118

ENMAX Power Corporation **(1)**
141 50 Avenue Southeast, Calgary, T2G
4S7, AB, Canada　　　　　　**(100%)**
Tel.: (403) 514-3000
Web Site: http://www.enmax.com
Sales Range: $350-399.9 Million
Emp.: 800
Holding Company; Electricity Distribution &
Transmission Network Owner & Operator
N.A.I.C.S.: 551112

Emera Maine **(1)**
PO Box 932, Bangor, ME 04401-0932
Tel.: (207) 973-2000
Web Site: http://www.emeramaine.com
Electronic Services
N.A.I.C.S.: 221121
Mike Herrin (Pres & COO)

ENN ENERGY HOLDINGS LIM-ITED
Rooms 3101-04 31st Floor Tower I
Lippo Centre 89 Queensway, Eco-
nomic and Technological Develop-
ment Zone, Hong Kong, Hebei, China
Tel.: (86) 225285666
Web Site: https://ir.ennenergy.com
2688—(HKG)
Rev.: $15,451,160,400
Assets: $14,370,080,400
Liabilities: $7,974,158,400
Net Worth: $6,395,922,000
Earnings: $935,625,600
Emp.: 34,812
Fiscal Year-end: 12/31/22
Gas Distr
N.A.I.C.S.: 221210
Yusuo Wang (Founder & Chm)

Subsidiaries:

Changzhou Xinao Gas Engineering
Company Limited **(1)**
Gaoxin Tech Industry Dvpt Zone, Wujing
District, Changshu, 213101, China
Tel.: (86) 51986322733
Natural Gas Distribution Services
N.A.I.C.S.: 221210

ENN NATURAL GAS CO., LTD.
No 118 Huaxiang Road Tower B,
ENN Science Park Economic and

Technical Development Zone, Langfang, Hebei, China
Tel.: (86) 3162597115
Web Site: https://www.enn-ng.com
600803—(SHG)
Rev.: $19,916,077,758
Assets: $18,632,795,193
Net Worth: $8,104,875,111
Earnings: $981,821,832
Emp.: 38,321
Fiscal Year-end: 12/31/23
Natural Gas Distribution Services
N.A.I.C.S.: 551112
Han Jishen *(Co-CEO)*

Subsidiaries:

Shanghai International Engineering Construction Consulting Co., Ltd. **(1)**
7/F Zhong Yi Building No2 Lane 1040 Cao Yang Road, Shanghai, 200063, China
Tel.: (86) 2162857069
Web Site: https://www.siecc.com
Engineering Equipment Mfr & Distr
N.A.I.C.S.: 333248

Xindi Energy Engineering Technology Co., Ltd. **(1)**
Block B No 118 Huaxiang Road, South District Technology Park Langfang Development Zone, Langfang, Hebei, China
Tel.: (86) 3162591132
Web Site: https://en.xindny.com
Technical Research & Development Services
N.A.I.C.S.: 541990

ENNO ROGGEMANN GMBH & CO. KG

Ahrensstrasse 4, 28197, Bremen, Germany
Tel.: (49) 42151850   De
Web Site: http://www.roggemann.de
Year Founded: 1948
Sales Range: $150-199.9 Million
Emp.: 220
Plywood & Timber Product Whslr
N.A.I.C.S.: 423310
Jurgen Roggemann *(Mng Dir)*

Subsidiaries:

Sperrholz Koch GmbH **(1)**
Otterkamp 11, Coesfeld, 48653, Germany **(100%)**
Tel.: (49) 25418090
Web Site: http://www.sperrholzkoch.de
Sales Range: $10-24.9 Million
Emp.: 75
Based Panel Products & Flush Doors Whslr
N.A.I.C.S.: 423310
Juergen Roggemann *(CEO)*

ENNOCONN CORPORATION

6F No10 Jiankang Rd, Zhonghe Dist, New Taipei City, 23586, Taiwan
Tel.: (886) 255908050
Web Site: https://www.ennoconn.com
Year Founded: 1999
6414—(TAI)
Rev.: $3,383,939,374
Assets: $3,725,879,780
Liabilities: $2,390,439,390
Net Worth: $1,335,440,390
Earnings: $319,157,521
Emp.: 9,455
Fiscal Year-end: 12/31/22
Computer Parts & Equipment Mfr
N.A.I.C.S.: 334118
Fu-Chuan Chu *(Chm)*

Subsidiaries:

Dexatek Technology Ltd. **(1)**
16F-1 No 81 Sec 1 Xintai 5th Rd, Xizhi Dist, New Taipei City, 22101, Taiwan
Tel.: (886) 286984245
Web Site: https://www.dexatek.com
Electronic Products Mfr
N.A.I.C.S.: 334419
Kate Chen *(Sls Mgr)*

Ennoconn (Suzhou) Technology Co., Ltd. **(1)**
Room 1 No 299 Nansong Road, Yushan Town, Kunshan, Jiangsu, China
Tel.: (86) 51286183888
Hardware System Services
N.A.I.C.S.: 541512

Subsidiary (Domestic):

Ennoconn (Kunshan) Technology Co., Ltd. **(2)**
Room 3 No 299 Nansong Road, Yushan Town, Kunshan, 215300, Jiangsu, China
Tel.: (86) 4008680008
Hardware Electronic Product Mtr
N.A.I.C.S.: 334419

Ennowyse Corporation **(1)**
3F No 10 Jiankang Rd, Zhonghe, New Taipei City, 23586, Taiwan
Tel.: (886) 255908050
Web Site: http://www.ennowyse.com
Bank Services
N.A.I.C.S.: 522110

Goldtek Technology (Shenzheng) Co., Ltd. **(1)**
16F No166 Jian 1st Rd, Zhonghe, New Taipei City, 23511, Taiwan
Web Site: http://www.goldtek.com
Engineeering Services
N.A.I.C.S.: 541330
Francesca Tang *(Mgr-Bus Dev)*

HighAim (Kunshan) Technology Inc. **(1)**
278 Chensong Rd, Kunshan, Jiangsu, China
Tel.: (86) 51257562971
Automotive Product Mfr & Distr
N.A.I.C.S.: 332119

HighAim Technology Inc. **(1)**
278 Jinsong Rd, Kunshan, Jiangsu, China
Tel.: (86) 51257562971
Electronic Products Mfr
N.A.I.C.S.: 334111

Nera Telecommunications Ltd. **(1)**
19 Tai Seng Ave 06-01, Singapore, 534054, Singapore **(63.77%)**
Tel.: (65) 62332433
Web Site: https://www1.nera.net
Rev.: $98,206,002
Assets: $112,938,125
Liabilities: $82,508,336
Net Worth: $30,429,789
Earnings: ($5,402,742)
Emp.: 292
Fiscal Year-end: 12/31/2022
Telecommunication, Internet & Information Technology Services
N.A.I.C.S.: 517111
Su-yen Wong *(Chm)*

Subsidiary (Non-US):

Nera (Malaysia) Sdn. Bhd. **(2)**
No 11 Jalan Jurukur U1/19 Hicom Glenmarie Industrial Park, Shah Alam, 40150, Selangor Darul Ehsan, Malaysia
Tel.: (60) 3 5569 0233
Web Site: http://www.neratel.com.sg
Sales Range: $25-49.9 Million
Emp.: 55
Telecommunications & Mobile Services
N.A.I.C.S.: 517111

Nera (Thailand) Ltd **(2)**
253 Asoke 26th Floor Sukhumvit 21 Road, Klongtoeynua Wattana, Bangkok, 10110, Thailand
Tel.: (66) 26641464
Web Site: http://www.neratel.com
Sales Range: $25-49.9 Million
Emp.: 60
Telecommunication, Internet & Information Technology Services
N.A.I.C.S.: 517810

Nera Infocom (M) Sdn Bhd **(2)**
Hicom Glenmarie Industrial Park No 11 Jalan juru Ukur U1/19, 40150, Shah Alam, Selangor, Malaysia
Tel.: (60) 355690233
Web Site: http://www.neratel.com
Sales Range: $25-49.9 Million
Telecommunication Power Transmission Equipment Mfr

N.A.I.C.S.: 333613
Ahmad Fauzan *(Mng Dir)*

Nera Philippines, Inc. **(2)**
8 Fl Multinational Bank Corporation Ctr, 6805 Ayala Ave, Makati, 9417, Philippines
Tel.: (63) 28496372
Web Site: http://www.neraphil.com.ph
Sales Range: $1-9.9 Million
Emp.: 94
Telecommunication, Internet & Information Technology Services
N.A.I.C.S.: 517111
Nimfa Tancioco-Mariano *(Mgr)*

Nera Telecommunications (India) Pvt Ltd **(2)**
2nd Fl 256 Okhla Industrial Estate Phase III, New Delhi, 110 020, India
Tel.: (91) 1126310705
Emp.: 7
Telecommunication Network Services
N.A.I.C.S.: 517111

Nera Telecommunications (Taiwan) Co. Ltd **(2)**
Suite 1006 No 333 Sec 1 Jilung Road, Taipei, Taiwan
Tel.: (886) 2 8789 8338
Web Site: http://www.neratel.com.sg
Telecommunication Power Transmission Equipment Mfr
N.A.I.C.S.: 333613

Nera Telecommunications Ltd. **(2)**
Intl Ctr Unit 03B 4 17 Ngo Quyen St, Hanoi, Vietnam
Tel.: (84) 49341926
Web Site: http://www.neratel.com.sg
Sales Range: $25-49.9 Million
Emp.: 2
Telecommunication, Internet & Information Technology Services
N.A.I.C.S.: 517111

Nera Telecommunications Ltd. (Indonesia) **(2)**
Level 12 Ste 1201 Plz Lippo, JL Jend Sudirman Kav 25, Jakarta, 12920, Indonesia
Tel.: (62) 215201355
Web Site: http://www.neraindo.co.id
Sales Range: $25-49.9 Million
Emp.: 30
N.A.I.C.S.: 334220

Pt. Nera Indonesia **(2)**
Plaza Lippo 12th Floor Suite 1201 Jl Jend Sudirman Kav 25, Jakarta, 12920, Indonesia
Tel.: (62) 215201355
Web Site: http://www.neratel.com.sg
Sales Range: $25-49.9 Million
Emp.: 80
Telecommunication Power Transmission Equipment Mfr
N.A.I.C.S.: 333613

Poslab Technology Corporation **(1)**
11F-1 No 258 Liancheng Rd, Zhonghe Dist, New Taipei City, 23553, Taiwan
Tel.: (886) 277337789
Web Site: https://www.poslab.com.tw
Hardware Mfr
N.A.I.C.S.: 332510

Thecus Technology Corp. **(1)**
16F 6 No 81 Sec 1 Xintai 5th Rd, Xizhi Dist, New Taipei City, 23845, Taiwan
Tel.: (886) 277058888
Web Site: https://www.thecus.com
Electronic Products Mfr
N.A.I.C.S.: 334111

Subsidiary (US):

Thecus U.S.A., Inc. **(2)**
4011 Clipper Ct, Fremont, CA 94538
Tel.: (510) 246-8987
Electronic Products Mfr
N.A.I.C.S.: 334111

Vecow Co., Ltd. **(1)**
3F No 10 Jiankang Rd, Zhonghe Dist, New Taipei City, 23586, Taiwan
Tel.: (886) 222685658
Web Site: https://www.vecow.com
Computer Product Mfr
N.A.I.C.S.: 334111

ENNOGIE SOLAR GROUP A/S

Orebygardvej 16, 7400, Herning, Denmark
Tel.: (45) 69153990
Web Site: https://ennogie.com
ESG—(CSE)
Rev.: $8,843,744
Assets: $8,285,222
Liabilities: $6,559,014
Net Worth: $1,726,209
Earnings: ($1,694,376)
Emp.: 46
Fiscal Year-end: 12/31/22
Financial Investment Services
N.A.I.C.S.: 523999

ENNOSTAR INC.

7F 5 No 1 Sec 3 Gongdao 5th Rd, East Dist, Hsinchu, 300042, Taiwan
Tel.: (886) 35679000
Web Site: https://www.ennostar.com
Year Founded: 2021
3714—(TAI)
Rev.: $729,444,362
Assets: $2,096,290,251
Liabilities: $489,150,248
Net Worth: $1,607,140,003
Earnings: ($239,469,300)
Emp.: 8,545
Fiscal Year-end: 12/31/23
Compound Semiconductors Developer & Mfr
N.A.I.C.S.: 334413
Biing-Jye Lee *(Chm)*

Subsidiaries:

Epistar Corporation **(1)**
21 Li-hsin Rd, Hsinchu Science Park, Hsinchu, 300, Taiwan
Tel.: (886) 35678000
Web Site: http://www.epistar.com.tw
Rev.: $530,664,381
Assets: $1,952,792,783
Liabilities: $383,547,129
Net Worth: $1,569,245,654
Earnings: ($130,922,540)
Emp.: 3,319
Fiscal Year-end: 12/31/2019
Optoelectronic Light Emitting Diode Products Developer, Mfr & Marketer
N.A.I.C.S.: 335139
Biing-Jye Lee *(Chm & Officer-Strategy)*

Subsidiary (Non-US):

Epicrystal Corporation (Changzhou) Ltd. **(2)**
No 518 Yancheng South Road, Wujin National Hi-tech Industrial Zone, Changzhou, 213166, Jiangsu, China
Tel.: (86) 51981182968
Electronic Components Mfr
N.A.I.C.S.: 334419

Episky Corporation (Xiamen) Ltd. **(2)**
No 99 Xiang Xing Road, Industrial Zone Xiamen Torch High-tech Zone, Xiamen, 361101, China
Tel.: (86) 5927615988
Web Site: http://www.epi-sky.com
Electronic Components Mfr
N.A.I.C.S.: 334419

Subsidiary (Domestic):

Formosa Epitaxy Incorporation **(2)**
No 99 Lun Yuan 1st Road, Longtan, Taoyuan, Taiwan
Tel.: (886) 34994555
Web Site: http://www.forepi.com.tw
Sales Range: $125-149.9 Million
Light Emitting Diode Mfr
N.A.I.C.S.: 334413
C. Lo *(Sr Dir-Mktg & Plng Div)*

Huga Optotech Inc. **(2)**
22 Keya Rd Daya Dist Central Taiwan Science Park, Taichung, Taiwan
Tel.: (886) 4 25598999
Web Site: http://www.hugaopto.com.tw
Sales Range: $150-199.9 Million
Emp.: 1,200
Light Emitting Diode (LED) Semiconductor Device Mfr

Ennostar Inc.—(Continued)

N.A.I.C.S.: 334413
T. P. Chen *(Chm)*

Subsidiary (Non-US):

Jiangsu Canyang Optoelectronics
Ltd.   **(2)**
No 9 Branch Zhouzhuanghe Road,
Yangzhou Economic and Technological De-
velopment Zone, Jiangsu, China
Tel.: (86) 51487976999
Web Site: http://www.canyangopto.com
Electronic Components Mfr
N.A.I.C.S.: 334419

Luxlite (Shenzhen) Corporation
Limited   **(2)**
Room 1501 Jin Qi Zhi Gu Building 1 Tang
Ling St Liu Xian Rd, Nanshan District,
Shenzhen, 518055, China
Tel.: (86) 75533355666
Electronic Components Mfr
N.A.I.C.S.: 334419

Subsidiary (Domestic):

Unikorn Semiconductor
Corporation   **(2)**
1st Floor No 5 Lixing 5th Road, Hsinchu
Science Park, Hsinchu, 30078, Taiwan
Tel.: (886) 35635666
Web Site: http://www.unikornsemi.com
Semiconductor Components Mfr
N.A.I.C.S.: 334413

Subsidiary (Non-US):

United LED Corporation (Shandong)
Limited   **(2)**
No 6688 Chong Wen Road, Jining High and
New Technology Industry Development
Zone, Jining, 272000, Shandong, China
Tel.: (86) 5373286000
Electronic Components Mfr
N.A.I.C.S.: 334419

Lextar Electronics Corp.   **(2)**
No 3 Gongye E 3rd Road Hsinchu Science
Park, Hsin-chu, 30075, Taiwan
Tel.: (886) 35658800
Web Site: http://www.lextar.com
Light Emitting Diode (LED) Products Mfr
N.A.I.C.S.: 334419
David Su *(Chm & CEO)*

Subsidiary (Non-US):

Lextar Electronics (Suzhou) Co.,
Ltd.   **(2)**
No 259 Changyang St, Suzhou Industrial
Park, Suzhou, 215024, Jiangsu, China
Tel.: (86) 51285558800
Electronic Components Distr
N.A.I.C.S.: 423690

Subsidiary (Domestic):

Lextar Electronics (Chuzhou)
Corp.   **(3)**
No 2168 Qingliu East Road, Suzhou-
Chuzhou Modern Industrial Park, Chuzhou,
239001, Anhui, China
Tel.: (86) 5502598800
Electronic Components Mfr
N.A.I.C.S.: 334419

Subsidiary (Non-US):

Lextar Electronics (Xiamen)
Corp.   **(2)**
No 3089 XiangAn North Road XiangAn
Branch, Torch Hi-tech Industrial Develop-
ment Zone, Xiamen, 361101, Fujian, China
Tel.: (86) 5923758800
Electronic Components Mfr
N.A.I.C.S.: 334419

Subsidiary (Domestic):

Trendylite Corporation   **(2)**
No 20-1 Guangfu N Rd, Hukou Township,
Hsinchu, 303, Taiwan
Tel.: (886) 36669565
Web Site: http://www.trendylite.com
Electronic Components Mfr
N.A.I.C.S.: 334419

ENNOX GROUP LTD.

Level 13 200 Queen Street, Mel-
bourne, 300, VIC, Australia
Tel.: (61) 38 600 6946
Web Site: http://ennoxgroup.com.au
Year Founded: 1987
EXO—(ASX)
Sales Range: Less than $1 Million
Investment Management Service
N.A.I.C.S.: 523999
David Low *(Chm)*

ENO S.A.S.

95 rue de la Terraudiere, PO Box
8632, 70026, Niort, France
Tel.: (33) 549286001   **FR**
Web Site: http://www.eno.fr
Year Founded: 1909
Sales Range: $10-24.9 Million
Emp.: 80
Home & Marine Heating & Cooking
Equipment Designer, Mfr & Distr
N.A.I.C.S.: 333415
Antoine Thomas *(Mng Dir)*

Subsidiaries:

Force 10 Manufacturing
Corporation   **(1)**
Unit A 19169 21st Ave, Surrey, V3S 3M3,
BC, Canada
Tel.: (604) 536-0379
Web Site: http://www.force10.com
Sales Range: $1-9.9 Million
Emp.: 20
Gas & Electric Cooking Appliances Mfr
N.A.I.C.S.: 335220

ENOGIA SA

19 Avenue Paul Heroult, 13015, Mar-
seille, France
Tel.: (33) 484256017
Web Site: https://www.enogia.com
Year Founded: 2009
ALENO—(EUR)
Emp.: 60
Electric Equipment Mfr
N.A.I.C.S.: 333414
Alaaeddine Ghazzali *(CFO)*

ENOMOTO CO., LTD.

8154-19 Uenohara, Uenohara City,
Yamanashi, 409-0198, Japan
Tel.: (81) 554625111
Web Site: https://www.enomoto.co.jp
Year Founded: 1967
6928—(TKS)
Rev.: $166,862,840
Assets: $213,972,310
Liabilities: $75,314,340
Net Worth: $138,657,970
Earnings: $799,810
Emp.: 1,264
Fiscal Year-end: 03/31/24
Electronic Parts Mfr & Sales
N.A.I.C.S.: 334419
Nobuyuki Takeuchi *(Chm & Pres)*

Subsidiaries:

Enomoto Hong Kong Co.Ltd.   **(1)**
Room 1805 Starlight Line No 3 Starlight
Road, Tsim Sha Tsui, Kowloon, China
(Hong Kong)
Tel.: (852) 21997848
Emp.: 4
Other Electronic Component Mfr
N.A.I.C.S.: 334419

Enomoto Philippine Manufacturing
Inc.   **(1)**
PEZA-Gateway Business Park Javalera
Gen, 4107, Cavite, Philippines
Tel.: (63) 464330263
Web Site: http://www.enomoto.co.gp
Sales Range: $100-124.9 Million
Emp.: 500
Semiconductor & Related Device Mfr
N.A.I.C.S.: 334413
Hitoshi Sakamoco *(Sr VP)*

Enomoto Precision Engineering (S)
Pte.Ltd   **(1)**

30 Loyang Drive, 508945, Singapore, Sin-
gapore
Tel.: (65) 65424542
Web Site: http://www.enomoto.com.cn
Sales Range: $25-49.9 Million
Emp.: 70
Mfg & Indus Building Construction
N.A.I.C.S.: 236210

Zhong Shan Enomoto Co. Ltd.   **(1)**
No 36 Yixian Road Torch Development
Zone, Zhongshan, Guangdong, China
Tel.: (86) 76085335111
Web Site: http://www.enomoto.com.cn
Sales Range: $50-74.9 Million
Emp.: 200
Semiconductor & Related Device Mfr
N.A.I.C.S.: 334413

**ENOVOS INTERNATIONAL
S.A.**

2 Rue Thomas Edison, 1445, Stras-
sen, Luxembourg
Tel.: (352) 27371   **LU**
Web Site: http://www.enovos.eu
Sales Range: $450-499.9 Million
Emp.: 745
Holding Company; Electricity Genera-
tion & Distribution Services; Natural
Gas Distribution
N.A.I.C.S.: 551112
Claude Seywert *(Co-Vice Chm)*

Subsidiaries:

CASC EU S.A.   **(1)**
2 Rue de Bitbourg, Hamm, 1273, Luxem-
bourg, Luxembourg
Tel.: (352) 27 62 38 01
Web Site: http://www.casc.eu
Power Generation Services
N.A.I.C.S.: 221118
Frank Vandenberghe *(Chm)*

City Mov S.a r.l.   **(1)**
9 Avenue des Hauts-Fourneaux, 4362,
Esch-sur-Alzette, Luxembourg
Tel.: (352) 27 62 06 20
Natural Gas Distr
N.A.I.C.S.: 221210

Creos Deutschland GmbH   **(1)**
Am Halberg 4, 66121, Saarbrucken, Ger-
many
Tel.: (49) 681 2106 0
Web Site: http://www.creos-net.de
Natural Gas Distr
N.A.I.C.S.: 221210

EnergieSudwest Netz GmbH   **(1)**
Industriestr 18, 76829, Landau, Germany
Tel.: (49) 6341289109
Web Site: http://esw-netz.de
Natural Gas Distr
N.A.I.C.S.: 221210

Energiepark Trelder Berg GmbH   **(1)**
Ritscherstrasse 22, 21244, Berlin, Germany
Tel.: (49) 4186 8958930
Emp.: 12
Power Generation Services
N.A.I.C.S.: 221118
Aamir Reiner Wuerth *(Gen Mgr)*

Enovos Balance Deutschland
GmbH   **(1)**
Konrad-adenauer-ring 33, Wiesbaden,
65187, Germany
Tel.: (49) 611267850
Natural Gas Distr
N.A.I.C.S.: 221210

Enovos Deutschland SE   **(1)**
Am Halberg 3, 66121, Saarbrucken,
Germany   **(88.98%)**
Tel.: (49) 681810500
Web Site: http://www.enovos.de
Gas & Electricity Distr
N.A.I.C.S.: 221122
Hans-Martin Huber-Ditzel *(Mng Dir & CEO-
Germany)*

Enovos Luxembourg S.A.   **(1)**
2 rue Thomas Edison, Strassen, L-2089,
Luxembourg
Tel.: (352) 27371
Web Site: http://www.enovas.eu

Sales Range: $150-199.9 Million
Emp.: 111
Gas & Electricity Distr
N.A.I.C.S.: 221122
Lucius Jean *(Mng Dir)*

Subsidiary (Domestic):

Cegedel Participations S.A.   **(2)**
Rue Thomas Edison 2, Strassen,
Luxembourg   **(100%)**
Tel.: (352) 27371
Web Site: http://www.enovo.eu
Sales Range: $25-49.9 Million
Emp.: 100
Holding Company
N.A.I.C.S.: 551112

Subsidiary (Domestic):

LuxEnergie S.A.   **(3)**
23 avenue John F Kennedy, Luxembourg,
1855, Luxembourg   **(60.35%)**
Tel.: (352) 2254741
Web Site: http://www.luxenergie.lu
Sales Range: $25-49.9 Million
Emp.: 60
Power Plant Design Services
N.A.I.C.S.: 541330

Subsidiary (Domestic):

Leo S.A.   **(2)**
9 Boulevard Roosevelt, 2450, Luxembourg,
Luxembourg
Tel.: (352) 2639 4848
Web Site: http://www.leoenergy.lu
Natural Gas Distr
N.A.I.C.S.: 221210
Eric von Scholz *(Chm)*

NPG energy nv   **(1)**
Tongersesteenweg 99, 3770, Amsterdam,
Netherlands
Tel.: (31) 12 441 999
Web Site: http://www.npgenergy.be
Power Generation Services
N.A.I.C.S.: 221118
Jacques Adam *(Co-Founder)*

PNE Biogas Ohretal GmbH   **(1)**
Oberwiesachstrasse 3, 72290, Berlin, Ger-
many
Tel.: (49) 745594680
Power Generation Services
N.A.I.C.S.: 221118

ENOX BIOPHARMA, INC.

1687 West Broadway Suite 303, Van-
couver, V6J 1X2, BC, Canada
Tel.: (604) 637-9744   **NV**
Web Site:
http://www.enoxbiopharma.com
Year Founded: 2007
Biopharmaceutical Developer & Mfr
N.A.I.C.S.: 325412
Yossef Av-Gay *(Founder & Pres)*

ENPLAS CORPORATION

2-30-1 Namiki, Kawaguchi, 332-0034,
Saitama, Japan
Tel.: (81) 482533131
Web Site: https://www.enplas.co.jp
Year Founded: 1962
6961—(TKS)
Rev.: $249,891,050
Assets: $396,785,080
Liabilities: $48,656,210
Net Worth: $348,128,870
Earnings: $22,758,230
Fiscal Year-end: 03/31/24
Plastic Mfr
N.A.I.C.S.: 326199
Daisuke Yokota *(Pres)*

Subsidiaries:

Enplas (Hong Kong) Limited   **(1)**
Ste 515 5 F World Com Ctr Harbour City 11
Canton Rd, Tsim Sha Tsui, Kowloon, China
(Hong Kong)
Tel.: (852) 23698661
Web Site: http://www.enplas.com
Sales Range: $25-49.9 Million
Emp.: 4
Optical Devices Mfr & Whslr

N.A.I.C.S.: 334112
Yoshihiko Sato *(Mgr)*

Enplas (U.S.A.), Inc. **(1)**
1901 W Oak Cir, Marietta, GA 30062
Tel.: (770) 795-1100
Web Site: http://www.enplasusa.com
Sales Range: $25-49.9 Million
Emp.: 50
Injection Molding Solutions
N.A.I.C.S.: 333511

Enplas (Vietnam) Co., Ltd. **(1)**
K-3 Plot Thang Long Industrial Park, Dong
Anh District, Hanoi, Vietnam
Tel.: (84) 2439516485
Sales Range: $125-149.9 Million
Optical & Semiconductor Peripherals Mfr
N.A.I.C.S.: 333310

**Enplas Corporation - Engineering
Plastics Products Division** **(1)**
2-30-1 Namiki, Kawaguchi, 332-0034, Sai-
tama, Japan
Tel.: (81) 48 497 2986
Web Site: http://www.enplas.com
Engineering Plastic Product Mfr
N.A.I.C.S.: 326199

**Enplas Corporation - Kanuma
Plant** **(1)**
7-2 Satsuki-Cho, Kanuma, 322-0014,
Tochigi, Japan
Tel.: (81) 289720600
Web Site: http://www.enplas.co.jp
Sales Range: $50-74.9 Million
Emp.: 157
Engineering Plastic Product Mfr
N.A.I.C.S.: 326199
Daifuki Yokota *(Pres)*

**Enplas Corporation - LED Business
Division** **(1)**
2-30-1 Namiki, Kawaguchi, 332-0034, Sai-
tama, Japan
Tel.: (81) 482568619
Web Site: http://www.enplas.co.jp
Sales Range: $50-74.9 Million
Emp.: 250
Light Enhancer Cap Module Mfr
N.A.I.C.S.: 335139
Daisuae Yokoca *(Pres)*

**Enplas Corporation - Plastic Optics
Division** **(1)**
2-30-1 Namiki, Kawaguchi, 332-0034, Sai-
tama, Japan
Tel.: (81) 482501311
Web Site: http://www.enplas.com
Sales Range: $50-74.9 Million
Emp.: 200
Optical Fiber Components Whslr
N.A.I.C.S.: 335921
Masanori Watanabe *(Gen Mgr)*

**Enplas Hi-Tech (Singapore) Pte.
Ltd.** **(1)**
28 Genting Lane 07-06 Platinum 28, Singa-
pore, 349585, Singapore
Tel.: (65) 6 213 0588
Optical Product Mfr
N.A.I.C.S.: 333310

**Enplas Hy-cad Electronic (Shanghai)
Co., Ltd.** **(1)**
Part B Standard Building 70 No 36 Yi Wei
Road Waigaoqiao, Free Trade Zone,
Shanghai, 200131, China
Tel.: (86) 2150461686
Web Site: http://www.enplasusa.com
Sales Range: $25-49.9 Million
Emp.: 100
Engineering Plastic Product Mfr
N.A.I.C.S.: 326220

Enplas Laboratories, Inc. **(1)**
2-38-5 Namiki, Kawaguchi, 332-0034, Sai-
tama, Japan
Tel.: (81) 48 256 8515
Optical Product Mfr
N.A.I.C.S.: 333310

Enplas Life Tech, Inc. **(1)**
230 Sardis Rd, Asheville, NC 28806
Tel.: (828) 633-2250
Web Site: https://www.enplaslifetech.com
Plastics Product Mfr
N.A.I.C.S.: 326199

Enplas Microtech, Inc. **(1)**

3211 Scott Blvd Ste 103, Santa Clara, CA
95054
Tel.: (669) 243-3610
Electronic Components Mfr
N.A.I.C.S.: 334419

**Enplas Niching Technology
Corporation** **(1)**
Tel.: (886) 35505858
Web Site: http://www.enplas.com
Sales Range: $25-49.9 Million
Emp.: 7
Testing Equipment Mfr
N.A.I.C.S.: 334515

**Enplas Precision (Malaysia) Sdn.
Bhd.** **(1)**
No 9 9A Jalan Hasil 2 Kawasan Perindus-
trian, Jalan Hasil, 81200, Johor Bahru, Jo-
hor, Malaysia
Tel.: (60) 72365253
Plastic Engineering Products Mfr
N.A.I.C.S.: 326199

**Enplas Precision (Thailand) Co.,
Ltd.** **(1)**
Web Site: http://www.enplas.co.jp
Sales Range: $50-74.9 Million
Emp.: 150
Plastic Injection Molding Machine Mfr
N.A.I.C.S.: 326199

Enplas Seiki Corporation **(1)**
827-3 Moro, Kanuma, 322-0026, Tochigi,
Japan
Tel.: (81) 289765315
Semiconductor Peripherals Mfr
N.A.I.C.S.: 334413

**Enplas Semiconductor Peripheral
Corporation** **(1)**
1-19-57 Kamiaoki, Kawaguchi, 333-0844,
Saitama, Japan
Tel.: (81) 482506680
Web Site: http://www.enplas.com
Sales Range: $25-49.9 Million
Emp.: 85
Semiconductor Peripherals Mfr
N.A.I.C.S.: 334413
Ryoji Maruyama *(Pres)*

**Enplas Semiconductor Peripherals
Pte. Ltd.** **(1)**
No 28 Genting Lane 07-03/04/05, Singa-
pore, 349585, Singapore
Tel.: (65) 6 213 0588
Electronic Components Mfr
N.A.I.C.S.: 334419

Enplas Tesco, Inc. **(1)**
765 N Mary Ave, Sunnyvale, CA 94085-
2909
Tel.: (408) 749-8124
Web Site: http://www.enplas-ets.com
Sales Range: $25-49.9 Million
Emp.: 11
Sockets Mfr
N.A.I.C.S.: 335999

**Guangzhou Enplas Mechatronics Co.,
Ltd.** **(1)**
10 Yongsheng Road Yong He Economic
Zone, Guangzhou Economic Technological
Development District, Guangzhou, 511356,
China
Tel.: (86) 2032225678
Web Site: http://www.enplas.com
Sales Range: $25-49.9 Million
Emp.: 70
Engineering Plastic Product Mfr
N.A.I.C.S.: 326199

PT. Enplas Indonesia **(1)**
Kawasan Industri Jababeka 3Jl Tekno Bou-
levard BlokB 6F, Desa Pasirgombong Kec
Cikarang Utara, Bekasi, 17530, Indonesia
Tel.: (62) 218 984 2416
Electronic Components Mfr
N.A.I.C.S.: 334419

QMS Co., Ltd. **(1)**
1-3-12 Kamiaoki, Kawaguchi, 333-0844,
Saitama, Japan
Tel.: (81) 482550051
Web Site: https://qms-co.com
Sales Range: $25-49.9 Million
Emp.: 50
Sockets Mfr
N.A.I.C.S.: 335999

ENPLUS CO., LTD.
818-11 Hyundaikia-ro, Bibong-myeon,
Hwaseong, 18284, Gyeonggi-do, Ko-
rea (South)
Tel.: (82) 313669600
Web Site: https://www.en3.co.kr
Year Founded: 2003
074610—(KRS)
Rev.: $20,628,679
Assets: $92,291,302
Liabilities: $42,599,850
Net Worth: $49,691,453
Earnings: ($27,809,181)
Emp.: 61
Fiscal Year-end: 12/31/22
Fire Truck & Fire Fighting Product Mfr
N.A.I.C.S.: 336120
Ahn Young Yong *(Pres)*

ENQUEST PLC
2nd Floor Charles House 5-11 Re-
gent Street, London, SW1Y 4LR,
United Kingdom
Tel.: (44) 2079254900
Web Site: https://www.enquest.com
ENQ—(LSE)
Rev.: $1,853,622,000
Assets: $4,024,275,000
Liabilities: $3,540,034,000
Net Worth: $484,241,000
Earnings: ($41,234,000)
Emp.: 715
Fiscal Year-end: 12/31/22
Crude Petroleum Extraction Services
N.A.I.C.S.: 211120
Amjad Bseisu *(CEO)*

**ENR ASSET MANAGEMENT
INC.**
1 Westmount Square Suite 1400,
Westmount, H3Z 2P9, QC, Canada
Tel.: (514) 989-8027   QC
Web Site:
   http://www.enrassetmanage.com
Year Founded: 1991
Rev.: $303,176,100
Emp.: 10
Investment Advisory & Management
Services
N.A.I.C.S.: 523940

ENR RUSSIA INVEST SA
rue du Rhone 118, 1204, Geneva,
Switzerland
Tel.: (41) 225102626
Web Site: https://www.enr.ch
Year Founded: 1995
RUS—(SWX)
Rev.: $4,351,580
Assets: $51,915,396
Liabilities: $17,515,373
Net Worth: $34,400,023
Earnings: ($9,446,053)
Emp.: 10
Fiscal Year-end: 12/31/23
Portfolio Management & Investment
Advice
N.A.I.C.S.: 523940
Gustav Stenbolt *(Chm)*

Subsidiaries:

Petrovsky Fort LLC **(1)**
4a Finlyandsky Avenue, Saint Petersburg,
194044, Russia
Tel.: (7) 88123321535
Web Site: https://www.petrofort.ru
Property Rental Services
N.A.I.C.S.: 531311
Nikolay Lobas *(Gen Dir)*

ENRA GROUP BERHAD
D3-U6-15 Block D3 Solaris Dutamas
No 1, Jalan Dutamas 1, 50480, Kuala
Lumpur, Malaysia
Tel.: (60) 323003555   MY
Web Site: https://www.enra.my
Year Founded: 1992

ENRA—(KLS)
Rev.: $6,450,582
Assets: $32,406,561
Liabilities: $14,157,672
Net Worth: $18,248,889
Earnings: ($8,367,619)
Emp.: 31
Fiscal Year-end: 03/31/23
Investment Services
N.A.I.C.S.: 523999
Kamaluddin Abdullah *(Pres & CEO-
Grp)*

Subsidiaries:

Enra IOL Sdn. Bhd. **(1)**
34-G Jalan Tasik Selatan 3, 57000, Kuala
Lumpur, Malaysia
Tel.: (60) 390583388
Web Site: http://www.enra-iol.com
Power & Communication Network Services
N.A.I.C.S.: 237130

Enra Kimia Sdn. Bhd. **(1)**
D3-U6-11 Block D3 Solaris Dutamas No 1
Jalan Dutamas 1, 50480, Kuala Lumpur,
Malaysia **(100%)**
Tel.: (60) 323003500
Web Site: http://www.enrakimia.enra.my
Chemical Distr
N.A.I.C.S.: 424690
Rayburn Azhar Ali *(CEO)*

International Chemicals Engineering
Pty. Ltd. **(1)**
18-20 Kilkenny Court, Dandenong, Victoria,
3175, VIC, Australia
Tel.: (61) 397924844
Web Site: https://www.iceng.net.au
Chemical Metering Pump & Gas Odorant
Distr
N.A.I.C.S.: 424690
Chris Ulrik *(Mng Dir)*

ENRAD AB
Verkstadsgatan 10, 504 62, Boras,
Sweden
Tel.: (46) 33297550
Web Site: https://www.enrad.se
Year Founded: 2008
Commercial Refrigeration Mfr
N.A.I.C.S.: 333415
Andreas Backang *(CEO)*

ENRG ELEMENTS LIMITED
Suite 10 44 Kings Park Road, West
Perth, 6005, WA, Australia
Tel.: (61) 862634451
Web Site: https://enrg-elements.com
EEL—(ASX)
Rev.: $18,256
Assets: $1,790,240
Liabilities: $108,614
Net Worth: $1,681,626
Earnings: ($1,273,766)
Fiscal Year-end: 06/30/24
Gold Ore & Silver Ore Mining
N.A.I.C.S.: 212220
Shannon Coates *(Co-Sec)*

ENRO ENERGIE SE
Huyssenallee 86-88, 45128, Essen,
Germany
Tel.: (49) 2012453615
Power Distr
N.A.I.C.S.: 221122
Thomas Neu *(Mng Dir)*

ENS TOYOTA
285 Venture Crescent, Saskatoon,
S7K 6N8, SK, Canada
Tel.: (306) 653-5611
Web Site: http://enstoyota.ca
Rev.: $35,299,650
Emp.: 72
New & Used Car Dealers
N.A.I.C.S.: 441110

**ENSA STEEL INDUSTRIES
LIMITED**

Ensa Steel Industries Limited—(Continued)

43 Atlanta Nariman Point, Mumbai,
400 021, Maharashtra, India
Tel.: (91) 22 66306732
Web Site: http://www.ensasteel.com
Sales Range: Less than $1 Million
Iron & Steel Product Whslr
N.A.I.C.S.: 423510

ENSEMBLE SYSTEMS INC.
2268 - 13353 Commerce Parkway,
Richmond, V6V 3A1, BC, Canada
Tel.: (604) 231-9510
Web Site: http://www.ensemble.com
Year Founded: 1995
Rev.: $10,172,559
Emp.: 86
Software Development & Services
N.A.I.C.S.: 449210
Mike Bacinschi (Pres)

ENSHU LIMITED
4888 Takatsuka-cho, Chuo-ku, Ha-
mamatsu, 432-8522, Shizuoka, Japan
Tel.: (81) 534472111
Web Site: https://www.enshu.co.jp
Year Founded: 1920
6218—(TKS)
Rev.: $159,241,510
Assets: $219,465,220
Liabilities: $141,414,340
Net Worth: $78,050,880
Earnings: $1,460,810
Fiscal Year-end: 03/31/24
Machine Tool Mfr & Whslr
N.A.I.C.S.: 333517
Atsushi Suzuki (Pres)

Subsidiaries:

BANGKOK ENSHU MACHINERY **(1)**
CO., Ltd.
19/22 25 Unit A3 A4 Moo 10 Tambol Klong-
neung, Amphur Klongluang, Pathumthani,
12120, Thailand
Tel.: (66) 25204052
Machine Tool Distr
N.A.I.C.S.: 423830

ENSHU (Qingdao) Limited **(1)**
West side of Shuangyuan Road Liuting
Street, Chengyang, Qingdao, 266109,
Shangdong, China
Tel.: (86) 53266962386
Web Site: https://www.enshu-ql.com
Emp.: 21
Industrial Machinery Distr
N.A.I.C.S.: 423830
Hiroya Ono (Accountant)

ENSHU (Thailand) LIMITED **(1)**
19/25 Unit A4 Moo 10 Phahonyothin Road
Tambol Klongneung, Amphur Klongluang,
Pathumthani, 12120, Thailand
Tel.: (66) 25205229
Industrial Machinery Distr
N.A.I.C.S.: 423830

ENSHU GmbH **(1)**
Raiffeisenstrase 7b, 63225, Langen, Ger-
many
Tel.: (49) 6103 20 690
Web Site: http://www.enshugmbh.de
Industrial Machinery Distr
N.A.I.C.S.: 423830

ENSHU VIETNAM Co., Ltd. **(1)**
No 19 Street 3 VSIP Bac Ninh, Tu Son, Bac
Ninh, Vietnam
Tel.: (84) 2223906116
Industrial Machinery Distr
N.A.I.C.S.: 423830

Enshu (Qingdao) Machine Co.,
Ltd. **(1)**
West side of Shuangyuan Road Liuting
Street, Chengyang District Qingdao, Shang-
dong, China
Tel.: (86) 5326 696 2386
Web Site: https://www.enshu-ql.com
Emp.: 17
Business Consulting Services
N.A.I.C.S.: 541611
Yoshinori Tada (CEO)

Enshu (USA) Corporation Mexico
R.O.W.I. **(1)**
Hercules 301A-3 Poligono Industrial Santa
Rosa Jauregui Interseccion, Carretera Fed-
eral No 57 Qro-Slp Con Libramiento sur
Poniente, 76220, Queretaro, Mexico
Tel.: (52) 442 256 2502
Metal Sleeve Product Mfr
N.A.I.C.S.: 332999

Enshu India Private Limited **(1)**
Unit No 229-230 2nd Floor DLF Star Tower
Sector 30, Gurgaon, 122001, India
Tel.: (91) 124 479 8235
Metal Sleeve Product Mfr
N.A.I.C.S.: 332999

Enshu Limited - Hamakita
Factory **(1)**
788 Negata, Hamakita-ku, Hamamatsu,
434-0016, Shizuoka, Japan
Tel.: (81) 535882670
Machine Tools Mfr
N.A.I.C.S.: 333517
Kato Takeshi (Gen Mgr)

Enshu USA Corporation **(1)**
404 E State Pkwy, Schaumburg, IL 60173
Tel.: (847) 839-8105
Industrial Machinery Distr
N.A.I.C.S.: 423830

PT. ENSHU INDONESIA **(1)**
Ruko Festive Garden Grand Wisata Blok
AA16 No 1 Lambangsari, Tambun Selatan,
Bekasi, 17510, Jawa Barat, Indonesia
Tel.: (62) 2185504104
Industrial Machinery Distr
N.A.I.C.S.: 423830

ENSIGN CHRYSLER DODGE JEEP
1061 Yates Street, Victoria, V8V3M5,
BC, Canada
Tel.: (250) 386-2411
Web Site:
　　http://www.ensignchrysler.com
Year Founded: 1957
Rev.: $28,700,000
Emp.: 52
New & Used Car Dealers
N.A.I.C.S.: 441110
Brett Gallagher (Coord-Five Star)

ENSIGN ENERGY SERVICES INC.
400 - 5th Avenue SW Suite 1000,
Calgary, T2P 0L6, AB, Canada
Tel.: (403) 262-1361
Web Site:
　　https://www.ensignenergy.com
Year Founded: 1987
ENB—(DEU)
Rev.: $1,352,999,097
Assets: $2,226,083,188
Liabilities: $1,237,810,827
Net Worth: $988,272,361
Earnings: $31,488,504
Emp.: 3,862
Fiscal Year-end: 12/31/23
Drilling, Well Servicing, Manufacturing
& Production Service
N.A.I.C.S.: 213111
N. Murray Edwards (Chm)

Subsidiaries:

Champion Drilling, Inc. **(1)**
1 Tree Rd, Brooks, T1R1B9, AB,
Canada **(100%)**
Tel.: (403) 362-4400
Web Site: http://www.ensignenergy.com
Sales Range: $350-399.9 Million
Emp.: 525
Provider of Drilling, Well Servicing, Manu-
facturing & Production Services to Crude
Oil & Natural Gas Industry
N.A.I.C.S.: 213111

Continuous Tubing **(1)**
Ste 1000 400 5th Ave SW, Calgary, T2P
0L6, AB, Canada **(100%)**
Tel.: (403) 265-6361

Sales Range: $50-74.9 Million
Emp.: 30
N.A.I.C.S.: 211120

Enhanced Petroleum Services
Partnership **(1)**
1000 400-5th Avenue SW, Calgary, T2P
0L6, AB, Canada
Tel.: (403) 262-1361
Web Site: http://www.ensignenergy.com
Oil & Gas Well Drilling Services
N.A.I.C.S.: 213111

Enhanced Petroleum Services Part-
nership - Chandel Equipment Rentals
Division **(1)**
400 - 5th Avenue SW Ste 1000, Calgary,
T2P 0L6, AB, Canada
Tel.: (403) 262-1361
Web Site: http://www.chandelrentals.com
Emp.: 130
Drilling Equipment Rental Services
N.A.I.C.S.: 532412

Ensign Argentina S.A. **(1)**
Cerrito 836 Piso 9 Office 22, C1010AAR,
Buenos Aires, Argentina
Tel.: (54) 11 4816 0067
Sales Range: $50-74.9 Million
Emp.: 5
Oil & Gas Well Drilling Services
N.A.I.C.S.: 213111
Ricardo Lopez Olaciregu (Gen Mgr)

Ensign Australia Pty Limited **(1)**
461 Greenwattle Street, Toowoomba, 4350,
QLD, Australia
Tel.: (61) 746991888
Web Site: http://www.ensignenergy.com
Sales Range: $50-74.9 Million
Emp.: 15
Oil, Gas & Geothermal Drillings
N.A.I.C.S.: 213111

Subsidiary (Domestic):

Ensign International Energy
Services **(2)**
Level 1 5 Elizabeth Street, 15 17 West
Court Rd Elizabeth, Sydney, 2000, NSW,
Australia **(100%)**
Tel.: (61) 292233755
Sales Range: $50-74.9 Million
Emp.: 4
Oil & Gas Drilling Services
N.A.I.C.S.: 213111

Ensign Drilling, Inc. **(1)**
400 - 5th Avenue SW Suite 1000, Calgary,
T2P 0L6, AB, Canada **(100%)**
Tel.: (403) 262-1361
Web Site: http://www.ensignenergy.com
Sales Range: $1-4.9 Billion
Emp.: 150
Provider of Drilling, Well Servicing, Manu-
facturing & Production Services to Crude
Oil & Natural Gas Industry
N.A.I.C.S.: 213111

Division (Domestic):

Ensign Drilling Partnership - Encore
Coring & Drilling Division **(2)**
400 5 Ave SW Ste 1000, Calgary, T2P 0L6,
AB, Canada
Tel.: (403) 262-1361
Web Site: http://www.ensignenergy.com
Sales Range: $50-74.9 Million
Emp.: 130
Oil & Gas Well Drilling Services
N.A.I.C.S.: 213111
Tom Connors (VP)

Ensign Drilling Partnership - Engi-
neering, Procurement & Construction
Division **(2)**
2000-5th Street, Nisku, T9E 7X3, AB,
Canada
Tel.: (780) 955-8808
Web Site: http://www.ensignenergy.com
Emp.: 40
Engineeering Services
N.A.I.C.S.: 541330

Ensign Drilling Partnership - Ensign
Atlantic Directional Services
Division **(2)**
14 10672-46th St SW, Calgary, T2C 1G1,
AB, Canada

Tel.: (403) 290-1570
Web Site: http://www.ensignenergy.com
Oil & Gas Well Drilling Services
N.A.I.C.S.: 213111

Ensign Drilling Partnership - Ensign
Canadian Drilling Division **(2)**
2000-5th Street, Nisku, T9E 7X3, AB,
Canada
Tel.: (780) 955-8808
Web Site: http://www.ensignenergy.com
Emp.: 70
Oil & Gas Well Drilling Services
N.A.I.C.S.: 213111

Ensign Drilling Partnership - Ensign
Directional Services Division **(2)**
14 10672-46th Street SE, Calgary, T2C
1G1, AB, Canada
Tel.: (403) 290-1570
Web Site: http://www.ensignenergy.com
Oil & Gas Well Drilling Services
N.A.I.C.S.: 213111

Subsidiary (Domestic):

Ensign Drilling, Inc.-Nisku Operations
Centre **(2)**
3059 - 4th Street, Nisku, T9E 8L1, AB,
Canada **(100%)**
Tel.: (780) 955-8808
Web Site: http://www.ensignenergy.com
Sales Range: $50-74.9 Million
Emp.: 100
Provider of Drilling, Well Servicing, Manu-
facturing & Production Services to Crude
Oil & Natural Gas Industry
N.A.I.C.S.: 213111

Ensign Energy Services International
Limited **(1)**
15-17 Westport Rd Edinburgh North, Eliza-
beth West, Adelaide, 5113, SA, Australia
Tel.: (61) 8 8255 3011
Web Site: http://www.ensignenergy.com
Sales Range: $50-74.9 Million
Emp.: 50
Oil & Gas Exploration Services
N.A.I.C.S.: 213112

Ensign Energy Services International
Limited - Eastern Hemisphere
Division **(1)**
15-17 Westport Road, Edinburgh North, Ad-
elaide, 5113, SA, Australia
Tel.: (61) 8 8255 3011
Web Site: http://www.ensignenergy.com
Sales Range: $50-74.9 Million
Emp.: 40
Oil & Gas Exploration Services
N.A.I.C.S.: 213112
Peter Koutsoukos (VP-Australian Ops)

Ensign Europa Sp. Z.O.O. **(1)**
Horizon Business Centre Entrance A Floor
5 Domaniewska Street, 39A Room 501,
Warsaw, 02-672, Poland
Tel.: (48) 22 208 2756
Sales Range: $50-74.9 Million
Emp.: 3
Oil & Gas Exploration Services
N.A.I.C.S.: 213112

Ensign International Energy Services
Inc. **(1)**
450 Gears Rd Ste 777, Houston, TX 77065
Tel.: (281) 872-7770
Web Site: http://www.ensignenergy.com
Oil & Gas Drilling Services
N.A.I.C.S.: 213111

Division (Domestic):

Ensign International Energy Services
Inc. - Latin America Division **(2)**
450 Gears Rd Ste 777, Houston, TX 77067
Tel.: (281) 872-7770
Web Site: http://www.ensignenergy.com
Sales Range: $50-74.9 Million
Emp.: 25
Oil & Gas Well Drilling Services
N.A.I.C.S.: 213111

Ensign Operating Company Inc. **(1)**
1225 17th St Ste 1900, Denver, CO 80202
Tel.: (303) 293-9999
Sales Range: $50-74.9 Million
Emp.: 40
Crude Petroleum Production

N.A.I.C.S.: 213112

Ensign Rockwell Services (1)
6302 - 53 Avenue, Lloydminster, T9V 2E2, AB, Canada
Tel.: (780) 875-5278
Web Site: http://www.ensignenergy.com
Sales Range: $50-74.9 Million
Emp.: 100
Provider of Oil Well Services
N.A.I.C.S.: 213111

Ensign US Southern Drilling LLC (1)
450 Gears Rd Ste 777, Houston, TX 77065
Tel.: (281) 872-7770
Web Site: http://www.ensignenergy.com
Emp.: 150
Oil & Gas Wells Drilling Services
N.A.I.C.S.: 213111

Ensign United States Drilling, Inc. (1)
1700 Broadway Ste 777, Denver, CO 80290
Tel.: (303) 292-1206
Web Site: http://www.ensignusd.com
Sales Range: $50-74.9 Million
Emp.: 95
Drilling, Well Servicing, Manufacturing & Production Services
N.A.I.C.S.: 213111
Michael Nuss *(Gen Mgr-Ops)*

Division (Domestic):

Ensign United States Drilling Inc. - Ensign Directional Drilling Services Division (2)
200 S 2nd St, La Salle, CO 80645
Tel.: (303) 292-1206
Web Site: http://www.ensignenergy.com
Emp.: 75
Oil & Gas Well Drilling Services
N.A.I.C.S.: 213111

Ensign United States Drilling Inc. - Ensign Well Services Division (2)
1700 Broadway Ste 777, Denver, CO 80290
Tel.: (303) 292-1206
Web Site: http://www.ensignenergy.com
Oil & Gas Well Drilling Services
N.A.I.C.S.: 213111

Ensign United States Drilling Inc. - Rocky Mountain Oilfield Rentals Division (2)
1700 Broadway Ste 777, Denver, CO 80290
Tel.: (303) 292-1206
Web Site: http://www.ensignenergy.com
Sales Range: $50-74.9 Million
Emp.: 95
Oil & Gas Well Drilling Services
N.A.I.C.S.: 213111

Ensign United States Drilling-California (1)
7001 Charity Ave, Bakersfield, CA 93308-5824
Tel.: (661) 589-0111
Web Site: http://www.ensignusd.com
Sales Range: $200-249.9 Million
Emp.: 500
Drilling, Well Servicing, Manufacturing & Production Services to Crude Oil & Natural Gas Industry
N.A.I.C.S.: 213111

Division (Domestic):

Ensign United States Drilling (California) Inc. - Ensign California Well Services Division (2)
3701 Fruitvale Ave, Bakersfield, CA 93308
Tel.: (661) 387-8400
Web Site: https://www.ensignenergy.com
Sales Range: $150-199.9 Million
Emp.: 350
Oil & Gas Well Drilling Services
N.A.I.C.S.: 213111
Graham Klaiber *(Mng Dir)*

Ensign United States Drilling (California) Inc. - West Coast Oilfield Rentals Divison (2)
7001 Charity Ave, Bakersfield, CA 93308
Tel.: (661) 589-0111

Sales Range: $300-349.9 Million
Oil & Gas Well Drilling Services
N.A.I.C.S.: 213111

Ensign de Venezuela C.A. (1)
Av Espana Ensign Nro S/N Sector Pueblo Nuevo, El Tigre, 6050, Estado Anzoategui, Venezuela
Tel.: (58) 283 500 5000
Web Site: http://www.ensignenergy.com
Oil & Gas Drilling Services
N.A.I.C.S.: 213111

Rockwell Service (1)
52 Hwy 39 E, Estevan, S4A 2A5, SK, Canada **(100%)**
Tel.: (403) 267-1463
Web Site: http://www.ensignenergy.com
Sales Range: $50-74.9 Million
Emp.: 60
Provider of Drilling, Well Servicing, Manufacturing & Production Services to Crude Oil & Natural Gas Industry
N.A.I.C.S.: 213111

Rockwell Servicing, Inc. (1)
400 - 5th Avenue SW Suite 1000, Calgary, T2P 0L6, AB, Canada **(100%)**
Tel.: (403) 262-1361
Web Site: http://www.ensignenergy.com
Sales Range: $50-74.9 Million
Emp.: 25
Provider of Drilling, Well Servicing, Manufacturing & Production Services to Crude Oil & Natural Gas Industry
N.A.I.C.S.: 213111

Trinidad Drilling Ltd. (1)
400 250 2 Street SW, Calgary, T2P 0C1, AB, Canada
Tel.: (403) 265-6525
Web Site: http://www.trinidaddrilling.com
Oil & Gas Drilling Equipment Services
N.A.I.C.S.: 213111
Ken Stickland *(Chm)*

Holding (Non-US):

Trinidad Colombia SAS (2)
Carrera 7 71 52 Piso 9, Bogota, Colombia
Tel.: (57) 13137800
Emp.: 70
Oil & Gas Drilling Services
N.A.I.C.S.: 213111
Francisco Lopez *(Gen Mgr)*

Subsidiary (US):

Trinidad Drilling Limited Partnership (2)
15015 Vickery Dr, Houston, TX 77032
Tel.: (281) 872-7770
Web Site: http://www.trinidaddrilling.com
Petroleum & Natural Gas Extraction
N.A.I.C.S.: 211120
Thomas Horton *(VP-Bus Dev & Contracts-US & Intl)*

Subsidiary (Domestic):

Axxis Drilling Inc. (3)
229 Development St, Houma, LA 70363
Tel.: (985) 868-6969
Web Site: http://www.axxisdrilling.com
Petroleum & Natural Gas Drilling & Extraction Services
N.A.I.C.S.: 213111

CanElson Drilling (US), Inc. (3)
137 Industrial Ave, Mohall, ND 58761-4101
Tel.: (701) 756-7260
Web Site: http://www.canelsondrilling.com
Emp.: 75
Petroleum & Natural Gas Drilling & Extraction Services
N.A.I.C.S.: 213111

ENSILICA PLC

100 Park Drive Milton Park, Abingdon, OX14 4RY, Oxfordshire, United Kingdom
Tel.: (44) 1183217310   **UK**
Web Site: https://www.ensilica.com
Year Founded: 2001
ENSI—(AIM)
Rev.: $25,847,008
Assets: $34,697,046
Liabilities: $14,546,832
Net Worth: $20,150,215

Earnings: $2,262,055
Emp.: 168
Fiscal Year-end: 05/31/23
Electronic Components Mfr
N.A.I.C.S.: 334419

Subsidiaries:

Ensilica India Private Limited (1)
2064 Siri Iris 2nd Floor 24th Main HSR Layout 1st sector, Bengaluru, 560102, India
Tel.: (91) 8022584450
Electronic Printed Circuit Board Mfr
N.A.I.C.S.: 334412

ENSINGER GMBH

Rudolf-Diesel-Str 8, 71154, Nufringen, Germany
Tel.: (49) 70328190
Web Site: http://www.ensinger-online.com
Year Founded: 1966
Sales Range: $150-199.9 Million
Emp.: 2,500
Laminated Plastics Mfr
N.A.I.C.S.: 326130

Subsidiaries:

Elekem Ltd. (1)
Wellbank Works 68 Blackburn Road, Haslingden, Rossendale, BB4 5QF, Lancashire, United Kingdom
Tel.: (44) 1706831535
Web Site: http://www.elekem.com
Plastic Tube Product Mfr
N.A.I.C.S.: 326199
Joanna Hawarden *(Office Mgr)*

Ensinger (China) Co., Ltd. (1)
1F Building A3 No 1528 Gumei Road, Shanghai, 200233, China
Tel.: (86) 21 52285111
Web Site: http://www.ensinger-china.com
Plastic Product Distr
N.A.I.C.S.: 424610
Carl Chen *(Mgr-Sls)*

Ensinger (Shanghai) Engineering Plastics Co., Ltd. (1)
NoC3 Jinxi Park Lane 180 Jinxi Road, Songjiang Industrial Zone, Shanghai, 201613, China
Tel.: (86) 2133528111
Engineering Plastic Product Mfr
N.A.I.C.S.: 326199

Ensinger Asia Holding Pte Ltd (1)
63 Hillview Avenue 02-03, Singapore, 669569, Singapore
Tel.: (65) 6552 4177
Web Site: http://www.ensinger.com.sg
Emp.: 20
Plastic Product Distr
N.A.I.C.S.: 424610
Jan van Schaik *(Mng Dir)*

Subsidiary (Non-US):

Ensinger Malaysia (2)
Setia Business Park I & II No 1&3 Jalan Pesisirian Laman Setia, 7/1 Laman Setia, 81550, Johor Bahru, Johor, Malaysia
Tel.: (60) 7 509 0186
Web Site: http://www.ensinger.my
Plastic Product Distr
N.A.I.C.S.: 424610

Ensinger Building Products Ltd. (1)
Wilfried Way, Mid Glamorgan, Tonyrefail, CF39 8JQ, United Kingdom
Tel.: (44) 1443678400
Insulation Profile for Window & Door Mfr
N.A.I.C.S.: 332321

Ensinger Composites Schweiz GmbH (1)
Libernstrasse 24, 8112, Otelfingen, Switzerland
Tel.: (41) 435382378
Thermoplastic Composite Material Mfr
N.A.I.C.S.: 325211
Niccolo Pini *(Mng Dir)*

Ensinger Danmark A/S (1)
Rugvaenget 6B, 4100, Ringsted, Denmark
Tel.: (45) 7810 4410
Web Site: http://www.ensinger.dk

Plastic Product Distr
N.A.I.C.S.: 424610

Ensinger France S.A.R.L. (1)
ZAC les Batterses ZI Nord, 01700, Beynost, France
Tel.: (33) 4 78554574
Web Site: http://www.ensinger.fr
Plastic Product Distr
N.A.I.C.S.: 424610
Gauby Olivier *(Gen Mgr)*

Ensinger Group Limited (1)
Wilfried Way, Mid Glamorgan, Tonyrefail, CF39 8JQ, United Kingdom
Tel.: (44) 1443678400
Emp.: 290
Engineering Plastic Product Mfr
N.A.I.C.S.: 326210
Paul David *(Mng Dir)*

Ensinger India Engineering Plastics Private Ltd. (1)
RK Plaza Survey No 206/3 Plot No 17 Near Rosary School, Viman Nagar, Pune, 411 014, India
Tel.: (91) 2049131000
Web Site: http://www.ensingerplastics.com
Plastic Product Distr
N.A.I.C.S.: 424610

Ensinger Industria de Plasticos Tecnicos Ltda. (1)
Av Sao Borja 3185, 032-000, Sao Leopoldo, Brazil
Tel.: (55) 51 35798800
Web Site: http://www.ensinger.com.br
Plastic Product Distr
N.A.I.C.S.: 424610

Ensinger Italia S.r.l. (1)
Via Franco Tosi 1/3 Olcella di Busto, 20020, Busto Garolfo, Italy
Tel.: (39) 0331 568348
Web Site: http://www.ensinger.it
Plastic Product Distr
N.A.I.C.S.: 424610
Flavio M. Granato *(Mgr-Engrg-Shapes Div)*

Ensinger Japan Co., Ltd. (1)
3-5-1 Rinkaicho, Edogawa-ku, Tokyo, 134-0086, Japan
Tel.: (81) 3 5878 1903
Web Site: http://www.ensinger.jp
Plastic Product Distr
N.A.I.C.S.: 424610

Ensinger Korea Ltd. (1)
3dong 4 Songsan-ro 515beon-gil, Ilsanseo-gu, Goyang, 10212, Gyeonggi-do, Korea (South)
Tel.: (82) 319263512
Engineering Plastic Product Mfr
N.A.I.C.S.: 326199

Ensinger Limited (1)
Wilfried Way, Tonyrefail, CF39 8JQ, Mid Glamorgan, United Kingdom
Tel.: (44) 1443 678400
Web Site: http://www.ensinger.co.uk
Plastic Product Distr
N.A.I.C.S.: 424610
Tracy Bennett *(Head-Personnel)*

Ensinger Machining SA (1)
ZAC le Batterses ZI Nord rue des Petites Combes, 01700, Beynost, France
Tel.: (33) 478554574
Thermoplastic Composite Material Mfr
N.A.I.C.S.: 325211

Ensinger Penn Fibre Inc. (1)
2434 Bristol Rd, Bensalem, PA 19020
Web Site: http://www.pennfibre.com
Engineering Thermoplastic Mfr
N.A.I.C.S.: 325211
Mike Cherubini *(Gen Mgr)*

Ensinger Polska Sp. z o.o. (1)
ul Geodetow 2, 64-100, Leszno, Poland
Tel.: (48) 65 5295810
Web Site: http://www.ensinger.pl
Emp.: 45
Plastic Mfr
N.A.I.C.S.: 325211
Cézary Michalczyk *(Gen Mgr)*

Ensinger Precision Components Inc. (1)
11 Danco Rd, Putnam, CT 06260
Tel.: (860) 928-7911

Ensinger GmbH—(Continued)

Web Site: http://www.ensinger-pc.com
Thermoplastic Product Mfr & Distr
N.A.I.C.S.: 325211
Christine Campbell *(Sls Mgr-Plastock)*

Ensinger Precision Engineering Ltd. (1)
Wilfried Way, Mid Glamorgan, Tonyrefail, CF39 8JQ, United Kingdom
Tel.: (44) 1443678500
Engineering Plastic Product Mfr
N.A.I.C.S.: 326199
Graeme Timms *(Mgr-Quality)*

Encingor S.A. (1)
Girona 21-27, La Llagosta, 08120, Barcelona, Spain
Tel.: (34) 93 5745726
Web Site: http://www.ensinger.es
Plastic Product Distr
N.A.I.C.S.: 424610
Klaus Ensinger *(Mng Dir)*

Ensinger Sintimid GmbH (1)
Werkstrasse 3, 4860, Lenzing, Austria
Tel.: (43) 7672 7012800
Web Site: http://www.ensinger-sintimid.at
Plastic Product Distr
N.A.I.C.S.: 424610

Ensinger Special Polymers, Inc. (1)
12331 Cutten Road, Houston, TX 77066
Tel.: (281) 580-3600
Web Site: http://www.ensingerspi.com
Electric Equipment Mfr
N.A.I.C.S.: 334515

Ensinger Sweden AB (1)
Stenvretsgatan 5, 749 40, Enkoping, Sweden
Tel.: (46) 171 477 050
Web Site: http://www.ensinger.se
Plastic Product Distr
N.A.I.C.S.: 424610
Per Jelensek *(Mgr-Sls)*

Ensinger Tecarim GmbH (1)
Flotzerweg 184, 4030, Linz, Austria
Tel.: (43) 73238638411
Engineering Plastic Product Mfr
N.A.I.C.S.: 326199

Ensinger Turkey Teknik Danismanlik Ltd. Sti. (1)
Cerkesli OSB Mh imes-17 Cd Kucuk Sanayi Sitesi D8 Blok No 6/2, Dilovasi, Kocaeli, Turkiye
Tel.: (90) 2629996967
Engineering Plastic Product Mfr
N.A.I.C.S.: 326199

Ensinger s.r.o. (1)
Prumyslova 991, PO Box 15, 33441, Dobrany, Czech Republic
Tel.: (420) 37 7972056
Web Site: http://www.ensinger.cz
Plastic Product Distr
N.A.I.C.S.: 424610

Ensinger, Inc. (1)
365 Meadowlands Blvd, Washington, PA 15301
Tel.: (724) 746-6050
Web Site: http://www.shopforplastics.com
Sales Range: $50-74.9 Million
Emp.: 100
Laminated Plastics Mfr
N.A.I.C.S.: 326130
Peter Fowler *(Controller)*

Subsidiary (Domestic):

Ensinger-Hyde (2)
1 Main St, Grenloch, NJ 08032
Tel.: (856) 227-0500
Sales Range: $25-49.9 Million
Emp.: 60
Custom OEM Plastic Injection Molding, Extruded Mill Shapes
N.A.I.C.S.: 326130
Bruce Dickinson *(Dir-Mktg & Sls)*

Moll Engineering GmbH (1)
Seelandstr 14-16, 23569, Lubeck, Germany
Tel.: (49) 45139689280
Web Site: http://www.moll-engineering.de
Carbon Fiber & Stainless Steel Product Mfr
N.A.I.C.S.: 335991
Stefan Moll *(CEO)*

Trig Engineering Limited (1)
Huntworth Business Park, Bridgwater, TA6 6TS, United Kingdom
Tel.: (44) 1278440000
Emp.: 90
Precision Plastic Component Mfr
N.A.I.C.S.: 326199
Terry Maggs *(Mng Dir)*

Wenglon Sp. z o.o. (1)
Ul Sportowa 12, Dobra, 72-003, Szczecin, Poland
Tel.: (48) 914324520
Web Site: http://www.wenglon.eu
Carbon Fiber & Stainless Steel Product Mfr
N.A.I.C.S.: 335991

ENSO GROUP
19th Floor Nirmal Building, Mumbai, 400021, Maharashtra, India
Tel.: (91) 2222823142
Web Site: http://www.ensogroup.com
Year Founded: 2005
Holding Company
N.A.I.C.S.: 551112
Vinay Maloo *(Founder & Chm)*

Subsidiaries:

Enso Oil & Gas Ltd. (1)
74 Jolly Maker Chambers II 220 Nariman Point, Mumbai, 400005, Maharashtra, India
Tel.: (91) 22 2281 5665
Web Site: http://www.ensogroup.com
Petroleum & Natural Gas Exploration, Development & Extraction
N.A.I.C.S.: 211120
Vaibhav Maloo *(Mng Dir)*

Enso WZHI Pte Limited (1)
26-04 Marina Bay Financial Centre Tower 3 12 Marina Boulevard, Singapore, 018982, Singapore
Tel.: (65) 65715686
Investment Management Service
N.A.I.C.S.: 523940

Globerer Inc (1)
23 Buckingham Court, Buckingham Gate, London, SW1E 6PE, United Kingdom
Tel.: (44) 2072229077
Investment Management Service
N.A.I.C.S.: 523940

ENSOL BIOSCIENCES, INC.
51 Techno 10-ro, Yuseong-gu, Daejeon, 34036, Korea (South)
Tel.: (82) 429394500
Web Site: https://www.ensolbio.co.kr
Year Founded: 2001
Pharmaceuticals Product Mfr
N.A.I.C.S.: 325412
Hae-Jin Kim *(CEO)*

ENSPERT INC.
2F 7F Daewha Bldg 169 Samsung-Dong, Gangnam-Gu, Seoul, Korea (South)
Tel.: (82) 260039300
Web Site: http://www.enspert.com
Software Development Services
N.A.I.C.S.: 541511
Chang-Seok Lee *(CEO)*

ENSSOLUTIONS GROUP INC.
4306 Bartlett Rd, Beamsville, L0R 1B1, ON, Canada
Tel.: (905) 312-8422   Ca
Web Site:
    http://www.enssolutions.com
Year Founded: 2007
ENV—(OTCIQ)
Sales Range: $1-9.9 Million
Organic Pine Rosin Emulsion Product Mfr & Distr
N.A.I.C.S.: 115112
James D. Staudohar *(Pres & CEO)*

Subsidiaries:

EnsSolutions Ltd. (1)
450 Sherman Avenue North, Hamilton, L8L 8J6, ON, Canada
Tel.: (905) 312-8422

Construction Equipment & Supplies Distr
N.A.I.C.S.: 423810

ENSTAR GROUP LIMITED
Windsor Place 3rd Floor 22 Queen Street, Hamilton, HM JX, Bermuda
Tel.: (441) 2923645   BM
Web Site:
    http://www.enstargroup.com
ESGR—(NASDAQ)
Rev.: $1,429,000,000
Assets: $20,913,000,000
Liabilities: $15,265,000,000
Net Worth: $5,648,000,000
Earnings: $1,218,000,000
Emp.: 805
Fiscal Year-end: 12/31/23
Insurance Acquisitions & Management
N.A.I.C.S.: 524298
Nazar Alobaidat *(Chief Investment Officer)*

Subsidiaries:

American Concept Insurance Company (1)
475 Kilvert St 330, Warwick, RI 02886
Tel.: (401) 453-7000
Reinsurance Services
N.A.I.C.S.: 524130

Arena SA (1)
Brand Whitlocklaan 165, 1200, Brussels, Belgium
Tel.: (32) 25120304
Web Site: https://arena-nv.be
N.A.I.C.S.: 524113

Atrium Risk Management Services (Washington) Ltd. (1)
Ste 740 1st Sansome St, San Francisco, CA 94104
Tel.: (415) 376-4700
Insurance Related Services
N.A.I.C.S.: 524298

Atrium Underwriters Ltd. (1)
Lloyd's Building 1 Lime Street, London, EC3M 7DQ, United Kingdom
Tel.: (44) 2073274877
Insurance Related Services
N.A.I.C.S.: 524298

Atrium Underwriting Group Ltd. (1)
Level 20 8 Bishopsgate, London, EC2N 4BQ, United Kingdom
Tel.: (44) 2070503000
Web Site: https://www.atrium-uw.com
N.A.I.C.S.: 524210
John Fowle *(CEO)*

Brake Systems, Inc. (1)
2221 NE Hoyt, Portland, OR 97232
Tel.: (503) 236-2116
Web Site: https://www.brakesystemsinc.com
Other Management Consulting Services
N.A.I.C.S.: 541618

Companion Property & Casualty Insurance Group (1)
51 Clemson Rd, Columbia, SC 29229
Tel.: (800) 845-2724
Web Site: http://www.companiongroup.com
Fire, Marine & Casualty Insurance Services
N.A.I.C.S.: 524126

Cranmore (UK) Limited (1)
8th Floor One Creechurch Place, London, EC3A 5AY, United Kingdom
Tel.: (44) 2076804100
Insurance Related Services
N.A.I.C.S.: 524298
Steven Norrington *(Pres & CEO-Cranmore Grp)*

Cranmore (US) Inc. (1)
150 2nd Ave N 3rd Fl, Saint Petersburg, FL 33701
Tel.: (727) 217-2970
Web Site: http://cranmore.co
Reinsurance Services
N.A.I.C.S.: 524130
Steven Norrington *(Pres & CEO)*

Cranmore Europe BVBA (1)
Sint Michielswarande 30B, 1040, Etterbeek, Belgium

Tel.: (32) 22203211
N.A.I.C.S.: 524210

Dunmore LLLP (1)
145 Wharton Rd, Bristol, PA 19007
Tel.: (215) 781-8895
Web Site: https://www.dunmore.com
N.A.I.C.S.: 326112

EPE, Inc (1)
8461 Lk St, Omaha, NE 68134
Tel.: (402) 399-8282
Web Site: https://epe-inc.com
Fiscal Year-end: 12/31/2013
Other Management Consulting Services
N.A.I.C.S.: 541618

Enstar (EU) Limited (1)
Tel.: (44) 1483452622
Web Site: http://www.enstargroup.com
Emp.: 10
Reinsurance Services
N.A.I.C.S.: 524130

Enstar (US) Inc. (1)
150 2nd Ave N 3rd Fl, Saint Petersburg, FL 33701
Tel.: (727) 217-2900
Investment Management Service
N.A.I.C.S.: 523940
Linda Reinking *(VP-Claims)*

Enstar Australia Limited (1)
6th Floor Suite 6 06 3 Spring Street, Sydney, 2000, NSW, Australia
Tel.: (61) 280624200
N.A.I.C.S.: 524210

Enstar Holdings (US) LLC (1)
150 2nd Ave N 3rd Fl, Saint Petersburg, FL 33701
Tel.: (727) 217-2900
Marketing Solutions
N.A.I.C.S.: 541613

Subsidiary (Domestic):

BorgWarner Morse TEC, LLC (2)
800 Warren Rd, Ithaca, NY 14850
Tel.: (607) 257-6700
Automotive Chains & Pump Systems Mfr
N.A.I.C.S.: 336350

Subsidiary (Non-US):

Borg-Warner Automotive Taiwan Co., Ltd. (3)
No 8 Lane 316 Chung Shan S Road, Yung Kan, Tainan Hsien, Taiwan
Tel.: (886) 6 201 6149
Web Site: http://www.morsetec.com
Powertrain Components & Systems Mfr
N.A.I.C.S.: 336350

BorgWarner Morse TEC Japan K.K. (3)
1300-50 Yabata, Nabari, 518-0495, Japan
Tel.: (81) 595641300
Automotive Chains & Pump Systems Mfr
N.A.I.C.S.: 336390

BorgWarner Morse TEC Korea Ltd. (3)
47-18 Cheongbuksandanro, Cheongbuk-Eup, Pyeongtaek, 017-792, Gyonggi-do, Korea (South)
Tel.: (82) 31 680 0000
Web Site: http://www.morsetec.com
Automotive Chains & Pump Systems Mfr
N.A.I.C.S.: 336390

BorgWarner Morse TEC Mexico, S.A. de C.V. (3)
Calle 2 No 10543 Parque Industrial El Salto, El Salto, 45680, Jalisco, Mexico
Tel.: (52) 3336880750
Sales Range: $100-124.9 Million
Emp.: 240
Automotive Chains & Pump Systems Mfr
N.A.I.C.S.: 336350

Morse TEC Europe S.r.l. (3)
Via Cesare Battisti 122, 20862, Arcore, Italy
Tel.: (39) 0396271
Web Site: http://www.morsetec.it
Drive Train Components & Engine Timing Systems & Components Mfr & Distr
N.A.I.C.S.: 336390

Enstar New York, Inc (1)

55 W 46th St Ste 2805, New York, NY 10036
Tel.: (212) 790-9700
N.A.I.C.S.: 524210

Forsakringsaktiebolaget Assuransinvest MF (1)
Wallingatan 33, 10397, Stockholm, Sweden
Tel.: (46) 856219930
Reinsurance Services
N.A.I.C.S.: 524130

Harper Holding Sarl (1)
B/d de la Foire 11-13, 1528, Luxembourg, Luxembourg
Tel.: (352) 35226262154
Web Site: https://harperholdingsarl.com
Holding Company
N.A.I.C.S.: 551112

Subsidiary (Non-US):

Alpha Insurance SA (2)
Sint-Michielswarande 30B, 1040, Brussels, Belgium
Tel.: (32) 22203211
Web Site: https://www.alpha-insurance.be
Insurance Support Services
N.A.I.C.S.: 524298

Kinsale Brokers Limited (1)
2nd Floor 3 Guildford Business Park, London, GU2 8XG, United Kingdom
Tel.: (44) 1483452622
Direct Insurance Services
N.A.I.C.S.: 524128

Maiden Reinsurance North America, Inc. (1)
6000 Midlantic Dr, Mount Laurel, NJ 08054
Holding Company; Reinsurance Products & Services
N.A.I.C.S.: 551112
Patricia McInerney (Sr VP-HR)

Monument Re Limited (1)
Crown House 4 Par-La-Ville Road, Hamilton, HM08, Bermuda
Tel.: (441) 4009300
Web Site:
https://www.monumentregroup.com
Insurance Support Services
N.A.I.C.S.: 524298

Subsidiary (Non-US):

Laguna Life d.a.c. (2)
Europa House Block 9 Harcourt Centre Harcourt Street, Dublin, 2, Ireland
Tel.: (353) 00 0969 127
Fire Insurance Services
N.A.I.C.S.: 524113

Subsidiary (Domestic):

Inora Life DAC (3)
IFSC House International Financial Services Centre, Dublin, Ireland
Tel.: (353) 1 675 0300
Web Site: http://www.inoralife.com
Insurance Management Services
N.A.I.C.S.: 524298

Subsidiary (Non-US):

Monument Assurance Luxembourg S.A. (2)
Atrium Business Park 29 rue du Puits Romain, Bertrange, L-8070, Luxembourg, Luxembourg
Tel.: (352) 264981
Web Site:
https://www.monumentassurance.lu
Insurance Support Services
N.A.I.C.S.: 524298
Oliver Schmidt-Berteau (CEO)

Subsidiary (Domestic):

AME Life Lux SA (3)
Atrium Business Park 41 Rue du Puits Romain, 8070, Bertrange, Luxembourg
Tel.: (352) 47 46 93
Web Site: http://www.amelife.lu
Emp.: 24
Fire Insurance Services
N.A.I.C.S.: 524113

Rombalds Run-Off Limited (1)
2nd Floor 3 Guildford Business Park, Guildford, GU2 8XG, United Kingdom

Tel.: (44) 1483452622
Other Management Consulting Services
N.A.I.C.S.: 541618

SeaBright Holdings, Inc. (1)
1501 4th Ave Ste 2600, Seattle, WA 98101
Tel.: (206) 269-8500
Web Site: http://www.sbic.com
Sales Range: $250-299.9 Million
Emp.: 325
Insurance Services; Holding Company
N.A.I.C.S.: 551112
Jeffrey C. Wanamaker (Sr VP-Underwriting & VP)

Subsidiary (Domestic):

SeaBright Insurance Company (2)
1501 4th Ave Ste 2600, Seattle, WA 98101
Tel.: (206) 269-8500
Web Site: http://www.sbic.com
Sales Range: $75-99.9 Million
Emp.: 115
Workers' Compensation Insurance Services
N.A.I.C.S.: 524126

Shelbourne Group Limited (1)
America House, London, EC3N 2LU, United Kingdom
Tel.: (44) 2076804123
Emp.: 10
Direct Insurance Services
N.A.I.C.S.: 524128

StarStone Insurance SE (1)
88 Leadenhall Street, London, EC3A 3BP, United Kingdom
Tel.: (44) 2032068000
Insurance Support Services
N.A.I.C.S.: 524298

StarStone Insurance Services Limited (1)
Beursplein 37-Office 658, Rotterdam, 3011 AA, Netherlands
Tel.: (31) 102244700
Other Management Consulting Services
N.A.I.C.S.: 541618

Subsidiary (Non-US):

Vander Haeghen & Co SA (2)
Avenue des Nerviens 85 Bte 2, 1040, Brussels, Belgium
Tel.: (32) 25260010
Web Site: https://www.vdh.be
Insurance Support Services
N.A.I.C.S.: 524298

StarStone Specialty Insurance Company (1)
88 Pine St 16th Fl Wall St Plz, New York, NY 10005
Tel.: (212) 790-9706
Insurance Support Services
N.A.I.C.S.: 524298

Subsidiary (Domestic):

StarStone National Insurance Company (2)
Harborside Plz 5 185 Hudson St Ste 2600, Jersey City, NJ 07311
Tel.: (201) 743-7700
Insurance Support Services
N.A.I.C.S.: 524298
Mike Gunter (Mgr-Loss Control)

Sussex Insurance Company (1)
221 Dawson Rd, Columbia, SC 29223
Tel.: (803) 735-0672
Web Site: http://www.sussexgroup.com
Insurance Related Services
N.A.I.C.S.: 524298

Torus Corporate Capital Ltd. (1)
Plantation Place - 4th Floor 30 Fenchurch Street, London, EC3M 3AD, United Kingdom
Tel.: (44) 2071058033
Insurance Related Services
N.A.I.C.S.: 524298

Torus National Insurance Company (1)
250 Commercial St Ste 5000, Manchester, NH 03101
Tel.: (603) 656-2200
Insurance Related Services
N.A.I.C.S.: 524298

Torus US Intermediaries Inc (1)
Harborside Financial Ctr Plz 5 Ste 2900, Jersey City, NJ 07311
Tel.: (201) 743-7729
Insurance Related Services
N.A.I.C.S.: 524298

Torus Underwriting Management Ltd. (1)
Langham Street 88, W1B3, London, United Kingdom
Tel.: (44) 2032068000
Insurance Related Services
N.A.I.C.S.: 524298

ENSUIKO SUGAR REFINING CO., LTD.

New ESR Bldg 2-9-6 Nihombashi Horidome, Chuo-ku, Tokyo, 103-0012, Japan
Tel.: (81) 332492381
Web Site: https://www.ensuiko.co.jp
Year Founded: 1950
2112—(TKS)
Rev.: $208,545,500
Assets: $181,821,270
Liabilities: $91,191,560
Net Worth: $90,629,710
Earnings: $9,749,750
Emp.: 74
Fiscal Year-end: 03/31/24
Sugar Mfr & Distr
N.A.I.C.S.: 311314
Shuji Hisano (Pres & Chm)

ENSURANCE LTD.

Level 21 Westfield Tower 2 101 Grafton Street, Bondi Junction, 2022, NSW, Australia
Tel.: (61) 291678050
Web Site:
http://www.ensurance.com.au
ENA—(ASX)
Rev.: $5,589,387
Assets: $23,238,234
Liabilities: $19,489,750
Net Worth: $3,748,483
Earnings: $209,741
Emp.: 27
Fiscal Year-end: 06/30/22
Insurance Services
N.A.I.C.S.: 524298
Sam Hallab (Sec)

Subsidiaries:

Ensurance Underwriting Pty. Limited (1)
Suite 4/400 Canterbury Rd, Surry Hills, 3127, VIC, Australia
Tel.: (61) 1300794079
Web Site:
http://www.ensuranceunderwriting.com.au
Construction Insurance Services
N.A.I.C.S.: 524298
Michael Huntly (Head-Insurance Underwriting)

TK Specialty Risks Pty. (1)
Suite 1920 Level 19 1 O'Connell Street, Sydney, 2000, NSW, Australia
Tel.: (61) 881203289
Web Site: https://au.ensurance.ltd
Insurance Agencies Services
N.A.I.C.S.: 524210

ENSURE GLOBAL CORP. LTD.

2nd Floor No 2 Section 4 Huanzhong Road, Beidou, Taichung, 114, Taiwan
Tel.: (886) 437076327
Web Site:
https://www.ensureglobal.com.tw
Year Founded: 1991
4419—(TPE)
Rev.: $222,399
Assets: $13,216,678
Liabilities: $10,332,458
Net Worth: $2,884,220
Earnings: ($780,196)
Fiscal Year-end: 12/31/22
Fiber Product Mfr & Distr

N.A.I.C.S.: 313310
Ruei-Min Sie (CEO)

ENSURE RECRUITMENT PTY LIMITED

Level 3 28 O'Connell Street, Sydney, 2000, NSW, Australia
Tel.: (61) 29346 5280
Web Site:
http://www.ensurerecruitment.com.au
Year Founded: 2009
Recruitment Services
N.A.I.C.S.: 561311
Paul Murphy (Mng Dir-Life Insurance)

ENSURGE MICROPOWER ASA

Fridtjof Nansen Plass 4, 0160, Oslo, Norway
Tel.: (47) 22424500
Web Site: https://www.ensurge.com
ENSU—(OTCIQ)
Rev.: $513,000
Assets: $7,729,000
Liabilities: $54,594,000
Net Worth: ($46,865,000)
Earnings: ($38,794,000)
Emp.: 22
Fiscal Year-end: 12/31/20
Thim Film Electronic Mfr
N.A.I.C.S.: 334419
Morten Opstad (Chm)

ENTAIN PLC

2a Lord Street, Douglas, IM1 2BD, Isle of Man
Tel.: (44) 35020078700   IM
Web Site:
https://www.entaingroup.com
Year Founded: 2004
ENT—(LSE)
Rev.: $6,108,569,251
Assets: $13,714,105,132
Liabilities: $10,184,403,420
Net Worth: $3,529,701,713
Earnings: ($1,110,591,505)
Emp.: 23,650
Fiscal Year-end: 12/31/23
Holding Company; Online Gaming
N.A.I.C.S.: 551112
Rob Wood (CFO)

Subsidiaries:

49's Limited (1)
Suite Z 82 Portland Place, PO Box 7835, London, WIB 1NS, United Kingdom
Tel.: (44) 1924792388
Web Site: https://www.49s.co.uk
Gaming & Restaurant Operator
N.A.I.C.S.: 721120
Miles Phillips (COO)

Bwin Latam S.A.S. (1)
Carrera 15 106-32 Of P H 3, Bogota, Colombia
Tel.: (57) 3584216
Web Site: https://help.bwin.co
Gaming Entertainment Services
N.A.I.C.S.: 721120

GVC Corporation B.V. (1)
New Haven E-Zone Emancipatie Boulevard 29 Suite 07, Willemstad, Curacao
Tel.: (599) 97341105
Online Sports Betting & Gaming Services
N.A.I.C.S.: 713290

Gaming VC Corporation Limited (1)
Palazzo Ca Brungnera 2nd Floor Valley Road, Birkirkara, BKR 9024, Malta
Tel.: (356) 27799221
Online Sports Betting & Gaming Services
N.A.I.C.S.: 713290

IVY Comptech Private Limited (1)
5th 6th Floor B Block Divyasree Omega Plot No 13/E Survey No 13 part, Kondapur, Hyderabad, 500084, Telangana, India
Tel.: (91) 4044721000
Web Site: http://www.ivy.global
Application Software Services
N.A.I.C.S.: 541511
Ananth Krishnan C. Subramanian (CFO)

Entain PLC—(Continued)

IVY Global Shared Services Private Limited (1)
5th & 6th Floor B Block Plot No 13/E Survey No 13 Part, Divyasree Omega Kondapur, Hyderabad, 500084, Telangana, India
Tel.: (91) 4044721000
Software Development Services
N.A.I.C.S.: 541511

IVY Software Development Services Private Limited (1)
5th Floor B Block Divyasree Omega Plot No 13/E Survey No 13 Part, Kondapur, Hyderabad, 500084, Telangana, India
Tel.: (91) 4044721000
Application Software Development Services
N.A.I.C.S.: 541511

Impala Digital Limited (1)
3rd Floor One New Change, London, EC4M 9AF, United Kingdom
Tel.: (44) 8448706477
Web Site: https://www.impaladigital.co.uk
Digital Marketing Services
N.A.I.C.S.: 541613

Interactive Sports (CI) Limited (1)
Tudor House Le Bordage, Saint Peter Port, GY1 1DB, Guernsey
Tel.: (44) 1481 735900
Web Site: http://www.sportingbet.com
Online Gambling Services
N.A.I.C.S.: 713290

Intertronic Limited (1)
Suite 313 14/19 Vincenti Buildings Strait Street, Valletta, VLT 1432, Malta
Tel.: (356) 25572557
Online Sports Betting & Gaming Services
N.A.I.C.S.: 713290

Kahnawake Management Services Inc. (1)
2006 Old Malone Road, PO Box 1539, Mohawk Territory, Kahnawake, J0L 1B0, QC, Canada
Web Site: https://www.kmservices.org
Business Management Consulting Services
N.A.I.C.S.: 541611

Ladbrokes Coral Group Limited (1)
7th Floor, One Stratford Place, Westfield Stratford City, Montfichet Road, London, E20 1EJ, United Kingdom
Tel.: (44) 442032887000
Holding Company; Gambling & Betting Services
N.A.I.C.S.: 551112

Subsidiary (Domestic):

Coral Stadia Limited (2)
3rd Floor One New Change, PO Box EC4M 9AF, London, EC4M 9AF, United Kingdom (100%)
Tel.: (44) 1708762345
Recreational Services
N.A.I.C.S.: 713990

Subsidiary (Non-US):

Eurobet Italia SRL (2)
Viale Alessandro Marchetti 105, Rome, 00148, Italy (100%)
Tel.: (39) 0664893050
Web Site: http://www.eurobet.it
Gambling Outlet Operator
N.A.I.C.S.: 713290
Paolo Bazzocchi (CIO)

Gala Interactive (Gibraltar) Limited (2)
2nd Floor Regal House, Gibraltar, Gibraltar (100%)
Tel.: (350) 20010400
Recreational Services
N.A.I.C.S.: 713990

Subsidiary (Domestic):

Ladbrokes Betting & Gaming Limited (2)
Imperial House Imperial Drive, Rayners Lane, Harrow, HA2 7JW, Mddx, United Kingdom (100%)
Tel.: (44) 2088688899
Web Site: http://www.ladbrokes.co.uk

Gambling & Betting Activities Management Services
N.A.I.C.S.: 713290

Ladbrokes Group Finance plc (2)
3rd Floor One New Change, London, EC4M 9AF, United Kingdom
Tel.: (44) 2088688899
Gambling & Betting Transaction Processing & Bookkeeping Services
N.A.I.C.S.: 522320

Romford Stadium Limited (2)
London Rd, Romford, RM7 9DU, United Kingdom (100%)
Tel.: (44) 1708 773444
Web Site: http://www.romfordgreyhoundstadium.com
Recreational Services
N.A.I.C.S.: 713990

Martingale Malta 2 Limited (1)
Penthouse Palazzo Spinola Business Centre 46 St Christopher Street, Valletta, VLT 1464, Malta
Tel.: (356) 27780102
Web Site: http://www.login.casinoclub.com
Casino Hotel Operator
N.A.I.C.S.: 721120

Minus5 d.o.o. (1)
Ulica Josipa Marohnica 1 HoB 8th floor, 10000, Zagreb, Croatia
Tel.: (385) 16445925
Web Site: https://minus5.hr
Software Development Services
N.A.I.C.S.: 541511

Sportingbet Australia Pty Limited (1)
PO Box 700, Parap, Darwin, 804, NT, Australia
Tel.: (61) 8 8923 8068
Web Site: http://www.sportingbet.com.au
Sales Range: $25-49.9 Million
Emp.: 50
Holding Company
Michael Sullivan (CEO)

Sports Interactive Ltd. (1)
Here East International Broadcast Centre, 313-314 Upper St, London, E20 3BS, United Kingdom
Tel.: (44) 2077040091
Web Site: http://www.sigames.com
Spectator Sports
N.A.I.C.S.: 711219

Stadium Technology Group, LLC (1)
7251 Amigo St Ste 100, Las Vegas, NV 89119
Tel.: (702) 302-4071
Web Site: https://www.stadiumtechnologygroup.net
Application Software Development Services
N.A.I.C.S.: 541511
Glenn Clark (Gen Mgr)

ENTATECH UK LTD.
Stafford Park 6, Telford, TF3 3AT, Shropshire, United Kingdom
Tel.: (44) 3301003551 UK
Web Site: http://www.enta.net
Sales Range: $150-199.9 Million
Emp.: 160
Information Technology Components, Systems & Software Distr
N.A.I.C.S.: 423430
Dave Stevinson (Mng Dir)

Subsidiaries:

EntaMedia Ltd. (1)
Stafford Park 6, Telford, TF3 3AT, Shropshire, United Kingdom
Tel.: (44) 333 101 5000
Web Site: http://www.entamedia.com
Emp.: 20
Digital Media Design & Marketing Services
N.A.I.C.S.: 541430
Ryan Lee (Mng Dir)

ENTE VASCO DE LA ENERGIA
Alameda de Urquijo 36 1 Edificio Plaza Bizkaia, 48011, Bilbao, Spain
Tel.: (34) 944035600
Web Site: http://www.eve.es

Year Founded: 1982
Rev.: $36,041,253
Assets: $214,809,335
Liabilities: $9,375,173
Net Worth: $205,434,161
Earnings: $25,533,632
Emp.: 72
Fiscal Year-end: 12/31/18
Energy Services
N.A.I.C.S.: 221121

Subsidiaries:

Bahia de Bizkaia Electricidad S.L. (1)
Punta Ceballos n 8, 48508, Zierbena, Spain (25%)
Tel.: (34) 946366000
Web Site: https://www.bbe.es
Emp.: 49
Electricity Generation Services
N.A.I.C.S.: 221112

Bahia de Bizkaia Gas, S.L. (1)
Punta Ceballos 2, 48508, Zierbena, Spain (50%)
Tel.: (34) 946366020
Web Site: http://www.bbg.es
Sales Range: $75-99.9 Million
Emp.: 71
Natural Gas Distr
N.A.I.C.S.: 221210

BioArtigas (1)
Plaza Ernesto Erkoreka 7, 48007, Bilbao, Spain
Tel.: (34) 946338132
Project Management Services
N.A.I.C.S.: 561110

Gecasa (1)
Zona Industriale Via Colle San Giovanni 5/7, Oricola, L'Aquila, 67063, Italy
Tel.: (39) 0863996134
Project Management Services
N.A.I.C.S.: 561110

IBIL (1)
Torre BEC Ronda de Azkue 1 planta 14, 48902, Barakaldo, Biscay, Spain
Tel.: (34) 902540810
Web Site: http://www.ibil.es
Project Management Services
N.A.I.C.S.: 561110

Zabalgarbi, S.A. (1)
Artigabidea 10, 48002, Bilbao, Spain
Tel.: (34) 944155288
Web Site: http://www.zabalgarbi.com
Emp.: 68
Project Management Services
N.A.I.C.S.: 561110

ENTECH SA
11 allee Jean-Francois de la Perouse ZA de Menez Prat, 29000, Quimper, France
Tel.: (33) 298944448
Web Site: https://www.entech-se.com
Year Founded: 2016
ALESE—(EUR)
Emp.: 135
Electrical Equipment Mfr & Distr
N.A.I.C.S.: 333414
Jean Blavot (COO)

ENTEGRA LIMITED
606 6th Floor Raheja Chambers Free Press Journal Marg Nariman Point, Mumbai, 400021, India
Tel.: (91) 02266044242 In
Web Site: http://www.entegra.co.in
Year Founded: 1995
Eletric Power Generation Services
N.A.I.C.S.: 221118

ENTEQ TECHNOLOGIES PLC
7 Albert Buildings 49 Queen Victoria Street, London, EC4N 4SA, Bucks, United Kingdom
Tel.: (44) 2080872202
Web Site: https://www.enteq.com
NTQ—(AIM)
Rev.: $7,306,000

Assets: $17,392,000
Liabilities: $1,863,000
Net Worth: $15,529,000
Earnings: ($787,000)
Emp.: 16
Fiscal Year-end: 03/31/22
Oil & Gas Exploration Services
N.A.I.C.S.: 211120
Martin Gordon Perry (Founder)

Subsidiaries:

Enteq Upstream USA Inc. (1)
9302-A Lambright Rd, Houston, TX 77075
Tel.: (713) 044 6100
Oil & Gas Drilling Equipment Mfr & Distr
N.A.I.C.S.: 333132

ENTER AIR SP ZOO
ul 17 Stycznia 74, 02-146, Warsaw, Poland
Tel.: (48) 223551570
Web Site: http://www.enterair.pl
Year Founded: 2009
ENT—(WAR)
Rev.: $667,160,313
Assets: $502,875,761
Liabilities: $411,982,977
Net Worth: $90,892,784
Earnings: $49,907,266
Fiscal Year-end: 12/31/23
Aircraft Charter Services
N.A.I.C.S.: 481219
Grzegorz Wojciech Polaniecki (CEO & Member-Mgmt Bd)

ENTERA BIO LTD
Hadassah Bio Park 5th Floor, Jerusalem, 9112002, Israel
Tel.: (972) 25327151 II
Web Site: https://www.enterabio.com
Year Founded: 2010
ENTX—(NASDAQ)
Rev.: $134,000
Assets: $13,127,000
Liabilities: $1,373,000
Net Worth: $11,754,000
Earnings: ($13,071,000)
Emp.: 15
Fiscal Year-end: 12/31/22
Biotechnology Research & Development Services
N.A.I.C.S.: 541714
Gerald M. Lieberman (Chm)

ENTEREX INTERNATIONAL LIMITED
10F No 573 Qingping Road, Anping District, T'ainan, 70842, Taiwan
Tel.: (886) 62931556
1592—(TAI)
Rev.: $152,112,333
Assets: $154,498,845
Liabilities: $124,929,970
Net Worth: $29,568,875
Earnings: ($50,408,211)
Emp.: 2,000
Fiscal Year-end: 12/31/20
Radiators, Condensers & Evaporators Mfr
N.A.I.C.S.: 333415
Wen-Chung Wong (Chm & Gen Mgr)

Subsidiaries:

AVA Benelux B.V. (1)
Smaragdweg 40, 5527 LB, Hapert, Netherlands
Tel.: (31) 13 505 81 00
Web Site: http://www.ava.eu
Radiator Distr
N.A.I.C.S.: 423120

Subsidiary (Non-US):

AVA Danmark A/S (2)
Finlandsvej 4, 8700, Horsens, Denmark
Tel.: (45) 75621077
Web Site: http://www.ava.eu
Emp.: 3
Radiator Distr

N.A.I.C.S.: 423120
Inger Nielsen *(Gen Mgr)*

AVA Kuhlercenter Austria GmbH (2)
Karntnerstr 100, 8053, Graz, Austria
Tel.: (43) 316273993
Radiator Distr
N.A.I.C.S.: 423120

Enterex America LLC (1)
2046 Boston Post Rd, Westbrook, CT 06498
Tel.: (860) 661-4635
Web Site:
   http://www.enterexinternational.com
Radiator Dictr
N.A.I.C.S.: 423120

Subsidiary (Domestic):

Automotive Parts Distribution International, LLC. (2)
3000 East Pioneer Pkwy Ste 160, Arlington, TX 76010
Tel.: (817) 394-6424
Radiator Distr
N.A.I.C.S.: 423120

Enterex Europe Holding B.V. (1)
Slibbroek 15, 5081 NR, Hilvarenbeek, Netherlands
Tel.: (31) 13 5058100
Web Site: http://www.ava.eu
Emp.: 50
Radiator Distr
N.A.I.C.S.: 423120
Ronald Van Herpen *(Pres)*

Subsidiary (Non-US):

AVA Cooling UK Limited (2)
Unit 2 Eastwood Trading Estate Chesterton Road, Rotherham, S65 1SU, United Kingdom
Tel.: (44) 1909550944
Radiator Distr
N.A.I.C.S.: 423120

AVA Italia S.R.L. (2)
46 Via Dorsale, 54100, Massa, Italy
Tel.: (39) 0 585 79 34 58
Radiator Distr
N.A.I.C.S.: 423120

AVA Moradia SAS (2)
7 Route du Mole 03 02 - BAT B29 F, 92230, Gennevilliers, France
Tel.: (33) 147941414
Radiator Distr
N.A.I.C.S.: 423120

Enterex Polska Sp. z o.o. (1)
Skosna 20 Street, 30-383, Krakow, Poland
Tel.: (48) 122524949
Motor Vehicle Parts Distr
N.A.I.C.S.: 441330

Subsidiary (Domestic):

AVA CEE Sp. z o.o. (2)
Ul Grabska 10A, 32-005, Niepolomice, Poland
Tel.: (48) 123858888
Motor Vehicle Parts Mfr & Distr
N.A.I.C.S.: 336390

Fruitage International Co., Ltd (1)
60 Market Square, PO Box 364, Belize, Belize
Tel.: (501) 6 293 1556
Radiator Distr
N.A.I.C.S.: 423120

Fruitage International Co., Ltd. (1)
60 Market Square, PO Box 364, Belize, Belize
Tel.: (501) 62931556
Radiator Distr
N.A.I.C.S.: 423120

Merit Wise International Limited (1)
12th Floor Ruttonjee House 11 Duddell Street, Central, China (Hong Kong)
Tel.: (852) 6 293 1556
Radiator Distr
N.A.I.C.S.: 423120

Subsidiary (Non-US):

Yangzhou Chung-Mei Auto Parts Co., Ltd. (2)
No 5 Jinyuan Rd Guangling Economic Development Zone, Yangzhou, Jiangsu, China
Tel.: (86) 51487812768
Radiator Distr
N.A.I.C.S.: 423120

Yangzhou Enterex Industrial Co., Ltd. (2)
5 Jinyuan Rd Guangling Economic Development Zone, Yangzhou, Jiangsu, China
Tel.: (86) 51487812768
Radiator Distr
N.A.I.C.S.: 423120

ENTERPARTNERS CO., LTD
13 Floor 702 Eonju-ro, Gangnam-gu, Seoul, Korea (South)
Tel.: (82) 7052203960
Web Site: http://www.ilya.co.kr
Year Founded: 1978
058450—(KRS)
Rev.: $8,538,901
Assets: $18,775,555
Liabilities: $11,567,874
Net Worth: $7,207,681
Earnings: ($6,138,291)
Emp.: 23
Fiscal Year-end: 12/31/22
Mobile Phone Parts Mfr
N.A.I.C.S.: 517112
Yangmyung Kang *(Mng Dir)*

Subsidiaries:

ILYA Co., Ltd. - Pyeongtaek Factory (1)
979-8 Suworam-ri, Seotan-Myeon, Pyeongtaek, Gyeonggi-do, Korea (South)
Tel.: (82) 316104300
Telecommunication Equipment & Accessory Mfr
N.A.I.C.S.: 334210

ILYA Co., Ltd. - Weihai Factory (1)
Jangchonjin Changwha-Road, Weihai, China
Tel.: (86) 2423711912
Telecommunication Equipment & Accessory Mfr
N.A.I.C.S.: 334210

ENTERPRISE DEVELOPMENT HOLDINGS LIMITED
Flat B 11/F Hing Lung Commercial Building 68-74 Bonham Strand, Sheung Wan, China (Hong Kong)
Tel.: (852) 36116042
Web Site: http://www.1808.com.hk
1808—(HKG)
Rev.: $6,726,424
Assets: $28,498,111
Liabilities: $5,035,306
Net Worth: $23,462,806
Earnings: ($3,511,966)
Emp.: 89
Fiscal Year-end: 12/31/22
Investment Holding Company
N.A.I.C.S.: 551112
Kai Tai Lam *(Chm)*

ENTERPRISE GROUP PLC
Advantage Place Mayor Road Ridge West, PMB 150 GPO, Accra, Ghana
Tel.: (233) 302634777
Web Site:
   https://myenterprisegroup.io
EGL—(GHA)
Rev.: $42,361,732
Assets: $367,785,523
Liabilities: $225,930,029
Net Worth: $141,855,494
Earnings: $20,886,069
Emp.: 431
Fiscal Year-end: 12/31/21
Insurance Services
N.A.I.C.S.: 524298
Trevor Trefgarne *(Chm)*

ENTERPRISE GROUP, INC.
64 Riel Drive Suite 2, Saint Albert, T8N 4A4, AB, Canada

Tel.: (780) 418-4400   AB
Web Site:
   https://www.enterprisegrp.ca
Year Founded: 2004
E—(TSX)
Rev.: $12,141,068
Assets: $40,875,039
Liabilities: $13,489,976
Net Worth: $27,385,063
Earnings: ($3,937,770)
Emp.: 80
Fiscal Year-end: 12/31/20
Pipeline Construction & Maintenance Services
N.A.I.C.S.: 237120
Leonard D. Jaroszuk *(Chm, Pres & CEO)*

Subsidiaries:

Enterprise Energy Services Inc. (1)
900 8th St NW, PO Box 652, Slave Lake, T0G 2A0, AB, Canada
Tel.: (780) 849-3865
Sales Range: $25-49.9 Million
Emp.: 15
Energy Supply Services
N.A.I.C.S.: 541690
Leonard Jaroszuk *(Pres)*

Enterprise Pipeline Company Inc. (1)
64 Riel Dr Unit 2, Saint Albert, T8N 5B3, AB, Canada
Tel.: (780) 418-4400
Web Site: http://www.enterpriseoil.ca
Sales Range: $25-49.9 Million
Emp.: 13
Pipeline Transportation Services
N.A.I.C.S.: 486990
Leonard Jaroszuk *(Pres)*

Pro Tech Construction, Inc. (1)
7429 ACC Blvd Ste 109, Raleigh, NC 27617
Tel.: (919) 848-9035
Web Site:
   https://www.protechconstruction.net
Sales Range: $10-24.9 Million
Emp.: 16
Commercial & Institutional Building Construction Services
N.A.I.C.S.: 236220
Linda Wilkerson *(Pres)*

Westar Oilfield Rentals, Inc. (1)
11650 MacLean Rd, Fort Saint John, V1J 4M7, BC, Canada
Tel.: (250) 263-9444
Web Site:
   https://www.westaroilfieldrentals.com
Construction Services
N.A.I.C.S.: 236220

ENTERPRISE INTERNATIONAL LIMITED
Malayalay Unit No 2A S 2nd Floor 3 Woodburn Park, Kolkata, 700 020, India
Tel.: (91) 3340447872
Web Site: https://www.eilgroup.co.in
Year Founded: 1989
526574—(BOM)
Rev.: $1,090,335
Assets: $1,459,231
Liabilities: $64,234
Net Worth: $1,394,997
Earnings: $94,350
Emp.: 6
Fiscal Year-end: 03/31/21
Textile Product Whslr
N.A.I.C.S.: 424990
Gopal Das Sarda *(Chm)*

ENTERPRISE INVESTMENT FUND SLHF.
Lagmuli 9, 108, Reykjavik, Iceland
Tel.: (354) 571 7080   IS
Web Site:
   http://www.framtakssjodur.is
Year Founded: 2009
Emp.: 5
Investment Management Service

N.A.I.C.S.: 523999
Herdis Fjeldsted *(CEO)*

Subsidiaries:

Advania Holding hf (1)
Gudrunartun 10, 105, Reykjavik, Iceland   (73.95%)
Tel.: (354) 440 9000
Web Site: http://www.advania.com
Emp.: 1,100
Information Technology Services
N.A.I.C.S.: 541519
Gestur G. Gestsson *(CEO)*

Icelandic Group HF (1)
Borgartun 27, 105, Reykjavik, Iceland
Tel.: (354) 5607800
Web Site: http://www.icelandic.com
Holding Company
N.A.I.C.S.: 551112
Orkell Sigurlaugsson *(Chm)*

Subsidiary (Non-US):

Icelandic Germany GmbH (2)
Osterbekstrasse 90 B, D 22083, Hamburg, Germany   (100%)
Tel.: (49) 402783940
Web Site: http://www.icelandic.de
Sales Range: $1-9.9 Million
Importer, Wholesaler & Supplier of Frozen Seafood Products to Industry & Retail
N.A.I.C.S.: 445250

Icelandic Iberica SA (2)
Edificio Muntadas, Parque Empresarial Mas Blau, Llobregat, 08820, Spain   (100%)
Tel.: (34) 934788000
Web Site: http://www.icelandic.com
Sales Range: $25-49.9 Million
Distr of Frozen Seafood Products
N.A.I.C.S.: 445250
Hjorleifur Asgeirsson *(Mng Dir)*

Icelandic Japan KK (2)
Landic Toranomon Bldg 6F 3 7 10 Toranomon, Minato Ku, Tokyo, 105 0001, Japan   (100%)
Tel.: (81) 354720450
Web Site: http://www.icelandic.is
Sales Range: $25-49.9 Million
Emp.: 10
Trader of Frozen Fish
N.A.I.C.S.: 445250
Eythor Eyjolfsson *(Mng Dir)*

Icelandic UK Limited (2)
Estate Rd No 2 S Humberside, Industrial Estate, Grimsby, DN31 2TG, United Kingdom   (100%)
Tel.: (44) 1472582900
Web Site: http://www.icelandic.co.uk
Sales Range: $450-499.9 Million
Frozen Seafood Products Distr
N.A.I.C.S.: 445250
Magni Thor Geirsson *(Mng Dir-Procurement & Deputy CEO)*

Subsidiary (Domestic):

Coldwater Seafood (UK) Limited (3)
Est Rd No 2 S Humberside Industrial Est, N E Limcs, DN312TG, Grimsby, United Kingdom   (100%)
Tel.: (44) 472321100
Sales Range: $150-199.9 Million
Producer of Frozen Seafood
N.A.I.C.S.: 311710

IFP Trading Ltd. (3)
Estate Road No 2, South Humberside Ind Est, Grimsby, DN31 2TG, NE Lincolnshire, United Kingdom   (100%)
Tel.: (44) 224878099
Sales Range: $25-49.9 Million
Fish Processing
N.A.I.C.S.: 311710

ENTERPRISE INVESTORS SP. Z O.O.
Warsaw Financial Center 53 Emilii Plater St, 00-113, Warsaw, Poland
Tel.: (48) 224588500   PL
Web Site: http://www.ei.com.pl
Year Founded: 1990
Sales Range: $1-9.9 Million
Emp.: 60
Privater Equity Firm

ENTERPRISE INVESTORS SP. Z O.O.

Enterprise Investors Sp. z o.o.—(Continued)
N.A.I.C.S.: 523999
Jacek Siwicki (Pres)

Subsidiaries:

Danwood S.A.   (1)
Biuro i dom pokazowy ul Rysia 5, 80-175,
Gdansk, Poland
Tel.: (48) 536 560 000
Web Site: http://www.danwood.pl
Emp.: 2,000
Interior Decoration Services
N.A.I.C.S.: 541410
Jaroslaw Jurak (Pres & CEO)

INTERSPORT ISI, d.o.o.   (1)
Cesta na Okroglo 3, 4202, Ljubljana,
Slovenia   (100%)
Tel.: (386) 4 256 84 29
Web Site: http://www.intersport.si
Sporting Goods Distr
N.A.I.C.S.: 423910
Mateja Jesenek (CEO & Dir)

Polish Stem Cell Bank S.A.   (1)
ul Grzybowska 2/41, 00-131, Warsaw, Po-
land
Tel.: (48) 22 436 40 50
Web Site: http://www.pbkm.pl
Biotechnology Research & Development
Services
N.A.I.C.S.: 541714

it WORKS S.A.   (1)
ul Prof Michala Zyczkowskiego 19, 31-864,
Krakow, Poland
Tel.: (48) 12 39 51 300
Web Site: http://www.itworks.pl
Information Technology Consulting Services
N.A.I.C.S.: 541511

ENTERPRISE METALS LIMITED

Suite 4 Level 1 7 Ventnor Avenue,
West Perth, 6005, WA, Australia
Tel.: (61) 863810392
Web Site:
  https://www.enterprisemetals.com
ENT—(ASX)
Rev.: $47,544
Assets: $3,977,656
Liabilities: $457,612
Net Worth: $3,520,045
Earnings: ($781,480)
Emp.: 2
Fiscal Year-end: 06/30/24
Uranium Producer
N.A.I.C.S.: 325180
Allan Trench (Chm)

ENTERSOFT S.A.

362 Sygrou St, Kallithea, Greece
Tel.: (30) 11015000
Web Site: https://www.entersoft.gr
Software Development Services
N.A.I.C.S.: 541511
Pandelis Nikolopoulos (Chm)

Subsidiaries:

Entersoft Bulgaria EOOD   (1)
Evrotur Business Center 12 Mihail Tenev
Str 6th Floor Office 21, 1784, Sofia, Bul-
garia
Tel.: (359) 879920002
Software Development Services
N.A.I.C.S.: 541511

Entersoft Middle East FZ LLC   (1)
IMPZ Publishing Pavilion Office 220, PO
Box 500424, Dubai, United Arab Emirates
Tel.: (971) 45519388
Software Development Services
N.A.I.C.S.: 541511

Entersoft Romania Software Srl   (1)
Polona Street No 43 Floor 6 Intercom 2,
Bucharest, 010493, Romania
Tel.: (40) 212301201
Web Site: http://www.entersoft.ro
Software Development Services
N.A.I.C.S.: 541511

ENTERTAINMENT MAGPIE LIMITED

Black & White House Hulley Rd Hur-
dsfield Industrial Estate, Macclesfield,
SK10 2AF, United Kingdom
Tel.: (44) 870 495 1283
Web Site:
  http://www.musicmagpie.co.uk
Year Founded: 2007
Sales Range: $100-124.9 Million
Emp.: 750
Online CD, DVD & Video Game Trad-
ing Services
N.A.I.C.S.: 713000
Steve Oliver (Co-Founder & CEO)

ENTEST GROUP, INC.

No 911 Baoan Book City Xinqiao
Street Central Road, Baoan District,
Shenzhen, China
Tel.: (86) 13709631109   NV
Year Founded: 2008
ETNI—(OTCIQ)
Rev.: $231,736
Liabilities: $32,671
Net Worth: ($32,671)
Earnings: $191,618
Emp.: 1
Fiscal Year-end: 08/31/19
Veterinary Medicinal Products Mfr
N.A.I.C.S.: 325412
Peiwen Yu (Pres & CEO)

ENTHEON BIOMEDICAL CORP.

Suite 720 999 W Broadway Street,
Vancouver, V5Z 1K5, BC, Canada
Tel.: (604) 562-3932   BC
Web Site:
  https://www.entheonbiomedical.com
Year Founded: 2010
ENTBF—(OTCQB)
Rev.: $141,499
Assets: $573,840
Liabilities: $115,369
Net Worth: $458,471
Earnings: $6,356,467
Emp.: 2
Fiscal Year-end: 11/30/22
Biotechnology Research & Develop-
ment Services
N.A.I.C.S.: 541714

ENTHEOS CAPITAL CORP.

Suite 1500 409 Granville Street, Van-
couver, V6C 1T2, BC, Canada
Tel.: (778) 656-0377
Web Site:
  http://waterfrontcapitalcorp.com
Year Founded: 2000
ENTH.H—(TSXV)
Rev.: $4,284
Assets: $60,359
Liabilities: $100,033
Net Worth: ($39,674)
Earnings: ($223,830)
Fiscal Year-end: 12/31/19
Financial Services
N.A.I.C.S.: 523910
Brayden Sutton (CEO)

ENTHUSIAST GAMING HOLD-INGS, INC.

90 Eglinton Ave E Unit 805, Toronto,
M4P2Y3, ON, Canada
Tel.: (416) 623-9360   ON
Web Site:
  https://www.enthusiastgaming.com
Year Founded: 2014
EGLX—(NASDAQ)
Rev.: $158,674,484
Assets: $267,099,763
Liabilities: $67,891,373
Net Worth: $199,208,390
Earnings: ($60,103,202)
Emp.: 210

Fiscal Year-end: 12/31/22
Video Game Development Services
N.A.I.C.S.: 551112
Adrian Montgomery (Chm & Interim
CEO)

Subsidiaries:

Enthusiast Gaming (TSR) Inc.   (1)
90 Eglinton Ave E Unit 805, Toronto, M4P
2Y3, ON, Canada
Tel.: (416) 623-9360
Web Site:
  https://www.enthusiastgaming.com
Gaming Technology Services
N.A.I.C.S.: 541511

ENTIE COMMERCIAL BANK, LTD.

40F Tower No 7 Sec 5 Hsinyi Rd,
Taipei, 11049, Taiwan
Tel.: (886) 281012277
Web Site:
  https://www.entiebank.com.tw
Year Founded: 1992
2849—(TAI)
Rev.: $285,467,761
Assets: $11,048,524,322
Liabilities: $9,951,888,371
Net Worth: $1,096,635,951
Earnings: $36,005,983
Emp.: 1,514
Fiscal Year-end: 12/31/23
Commercial Bank Services
N.A.I.C.S.: 522110
Jeff Chang (Pres & Co-Chief Credit
Officer)

ENTIRE TECHNOLOGY CO., LTD.

No 12 Kung-Yeh 5th Road Ping-Zhen
Industrial Park, Taoyuan, 32459, Tai-
wan
Tel.: (886) 32623311
Web Site: http://www.entire.com.tw
Sales Range: $100-124.9 Million
Liquid Crystal Display Mfr
N.A.I.C.S.: 334419
Jack Huang (Chm)

ENTOURAGE HEALTH CORP.

250 Elm Street, Aylmer, N5H 2M8,
ON, Canada   ON
Web Site: https://www.weedmd.com
Year Founded: 2014
ETRGF—(OTCIQ)
Rev.: $40,863,267
Assets: $23,705,153
Liabilities: $134,929,688
Net Worth: ($111,224,535)
Earnings: ($34,862,199)
Emp.: 211
Fiscal Year-end: 12/31/23
Medical Marijuana Producer
N.A.I.C.S.: 325411
George Scorsis (Chm & CEO)

Subsidiaries:

Starseed Medicinal Inc.   (1)
250 Elm St, Aylmer, N5H 2M8, ON, Canada
Web Site: https://www.starseed.com
Insurance Consulting Services
N.A.I.C.S.: 524298

ENTOURAGE MINING LTD.

1390A William Road, Montreal, H3C
1R4, QC, Canada
Tel.: (514) 419-5221
Web Site:
  http://www.entouragemining.com
Year Founded: 1995
Mineral Exploration Services
N.A.I.C.S.: 213115

ENTR RATIONNELLE INSTAL-LATION ELECTRIQUE

102 B Rue Danielle Casanova,
93300, Aubervilliers, France

Tel.: (33) 148113750
Web Site: http://www.entra.fr
Rev.: $23,000,000
Emp.: 178
Specialty Trade Contractors
N.A.I.C.S.: 238990
Christine Desbrueres (Dir-Pur)

ENTRA ASA

Biskop Gunnerus gate 14 A, 0185,
Oslo, Norway
Tel.: (47) 21605100
Web Site: https://www.entra.no
Year Founded: 2000
ENTRA—(OSL)
Rev.: $336,007,242
Assets: $7,209,311,614
Liabilities: $4,697,121,717
Net Worth: $2,512,189,897
Earnings: ($548,739,738)
Emp.: 198
Fiscal Year-end: 12/31/23
Office Property Management & De-
velopment
N.A.I.C.S.: 531312
Anders Olstad (CFO)

Subsidiaries:

Papirbredden Eiendom AS   (1)
Gronland 58, 3045, Drammen, Norway
Tel.: (47) 91660518
Web Site: https://www.papirbredden.no
Property Management Services
N.A.I.C.S.: 531311

Ribekk AS   (1)
Akersgata 32, 0180, Oslo, Norway
Tel.: (47) 21 60 51 00
Property Management Services
N.A.I.C.S.: 531311

ENTRECAMPOS CUATRO SO-CIMI SA

C/ Rosario Pino 18-3, 28020, Madrid,
28020, Spain
Tel.: (34) 917709650
Web Site:
  https://entrecamposcuatro.com
YENT—(MAD)
Sales Range: Less than $1 Million
Real Estate Manangement Services
N.A.I.C.S.: 531390

ENTREE RESOURCES LTD.

1650-1066 West Hastings Street,
Vancouver, V6E 3X1, BC, Canada
Tel.: (604) 687-4777   BC
Web Site:
  https://www.entreeresourcesltd.com
ERLFF—(OTCQB)
Rev.: $147,000
Assets: $7,493,000
Liabilities: $65,027,000
Net Worth: ($57,534,000)
Earnings: ($9,061,000)
Emp.: 2
Fiscal Year-end: 12/31/22
Gold & Copper Mining Services
N.A.I.C.S.: 212220
Stephen Victor Scott (Pres & CEO)

Subsidiaries:

Entree Gold (US) Inc.   (1)
5B Hwy 95A E, Yerington, NV
89447   (100%)
Tel.: (775) 463-4467
Web Site: http://www.entreegold.com
Mineral Resource Exploration Services
N.A.I.C.S.: 213114

Entree LLC   (1)
Suite 409 Gurvan Gal Office Center 8/1 Ch-
inggis Avenue, Sukhbaatar District 1st
county, Ulaanbaatar, Mongolia
Tel.: (976) 11318562
Emp.: 16
Mineral Resource Exploration Services
N.A.I.C.S.: 212390
Munkhtulga Buyannemekh (Mng Dir)

ENTREPARTICULIERS.COM SA
20 Rue Cambon, 75001, Paris, France
Tel.: (33) 147155050   FR
Web Site: https://www.enteparticuliers.com
ALENT—(EUR)
Sales Range: Less than $1 Million
Emp.: 13
Online Advertising Service Provider
N.A.I.C.S.: 513140
Stephane Romanyszyn *(Chm & CEO)*

ENTREPRENDRE SA
53 rue du Chemin Vert, 92100, Boulogne-Billancourt, France
Tel.: (33) 146102121   FR
Web Site: https://www.entreprendre.fr
Year Founded: 1984
ALENR—(EUR)
Sales Range: Less than $1 Million
Magazine Publisher
N.A.I.C.S.: 513120

ENTREPRISE GUIBAN SA
Rue de Kerlo -ZI de Kerpont-Bras, 56850, Caudan, France
Tel.: (33) 297760588
Web Site: http://www.guiban.com
Year Founded: 1970
Sales Range: $10-24.9 Million
Emp.: 171
Plumbing, Heating, Air-Conditioning & Water Treatments
N.A.I.C.S.: 238220
Lionel Guiban *(CEO)*

Subsidiaries:

ENTREPRISE GUIBAN
ANTILLES   (1)
ZI de Jarry - Rue Ferdinand Forest Prolongee, 97122, La Baie Mahault, Guadeloupe
Tel.: (590) 41 35 81
Heating & Ventilation System Installation Services
N.A.I.C.S.: 238220

ENTREPRISE GUILLERM
Le Gueven 5, 29420, Plouvorn, France
Tel.: (33) 298613022
Web Site: http://www.guillerm.fr
Rev.: $20,300,000
Emp.: 108
Nonresidential Construction
N.A.I.C.S.: 236220
Alain Guillerm *(Pres)*

ENTREPRISE MINIERE ET CHIMIQUE SA
62 Rue Jeanne d'Arc, F 75641, Paris, Cedex 13, France
Tel.: (33) 144065200   FR
Year Founded: 1967
Sales Range: $1-4.9 Billion
Emp.: 2,270
Holding Company; Producer of Potash, Derivatives & Chemicals; Environment & Waste Management
N.A.I.C.S.: 212390

Subsidiaries:

Societe Commerciale des Potasses et de L'azote   (1)
2 Pl Du General De Gaulle, BP 1170, F 68053, Mulhouse, Cedex, France   **(100%)**
Tel.: (33) 389363600
Web Site: http://www.scpa.com
Fertilizer Production & Distribution
N.A.I.C.S.: 325314

ENTREPRISE PAUL CALIN
25 Rue Voltaire, Harchechamp, 88300, Nancy, France
Tel.: (33) 329069009
Web Site: http://www.paul-calin.fr

Sales Range: $10-24.9 Million
Emp.: 113
Mixed Concrete
N.A.I.C.S.: 327320
Guy Calin *(Mng Dir)*

ENTREPRISE ROBERT THIBERT INC.
200 Saint Jean Baptiste Boulevard, Mercier, J6R 2L2, QC, Canada
Tel.: (800) 361-9805
Web Site: http://www.rthibert.com
Year Founded: 1976
Automotive Parts & Components Distr
N.A.I.C.S.: 441330
Robert Thibert *(Founder)*

ENTREPRISES ET CHEMINS DE FER EN CHINE SA
Rue du Bois Sauvage 17, 1000, Brussels, Belgium
Tel.: (32) 22275450
Real Estate Manangement Services
N.A.I.C.S.: 531210

ENTRETENIMIENTO GM DE MEXICO SA DE CV
Campos Eliseos No 400 Oficina 1102 Chapultepec Polanco, Miguel Hidalgo, Mexico, 11560, DF, Mexico
Tel.: (52) 55 1103 5000
Holding Company
N.A.I.C.S.: 551112
German Larrea Mota Velasco *(CEO)*

Subsidiaries:

Grupo Cinemex SA de CV   (1)
Av Santa Fe No 481 piso 12 Cruz Manoa, Cuajimalpa de Morelos, Mexico, 05349, DF, Mexico
Tel.: (52) 55 5201 5800
Web Site: http://www.cinemex.com
Sales Range: $150-199.9 Million
Emp.: 9,000
Owns & Operates Motion Picture Theaters
N.A.I.C.S.: 512131
Miguel Angel Davila Guzman *(CEO)*

Affiliate (Domestic):

Cinemark de Mexico, S.A. de C.V.   (2)
Calderon de la Barca 89 Piso 3 Colonia Polanco, Delegacion Miguel Hidalgo, Mexico, 11560, DF, Mexico
Tel.: (52) 5552801882
Sales Range: $50-74.9 Million
Owns, Operates & Leases Motion Picture Theaters
N.A.I.C.S.: 512131
Roberto Jenkins *(Gen Mgr)*

Subsidiary (US):

Cinemex Holdings USA, Inc.   (2)
400 62nd St, New York, NY 10065
Tel.: (646) 964-0572
Web Site: http://www.cmxcinemas.com
Entertainment Services
N.A.I.C.S.: 512131
Rogelio Velez *(CEO)*

ENTRUST SECURITIES PLC
National Savings Bank No 255 Galle Road, Colombo, 03, Sri Lanka
Tel.: (94) 114444999
Year Founded: 2000
Banking Services
N.A.I.C.S.: 522110

ENVASES DEL PACIFICO S.A.
Camino A Melipilla 13320, PO Box 45, Maipu, Santiago, Chile
Tel.: (56) 23854500   CL
Web Site: https://www.edelpa.cl
EDELPA—(SGO)
Sales Range: Less than $1 Million
Packaged Product Mfr
N.A.I.C.S.: 424420

Renato Ramirez Fernandez *(Chm & Pres)*

ENVI-PAK A.S.
Galvaniho 7/B, 821 04, Bratislava, Slovakia
Tel.: (421) 233322710
Web Site: http://www.envipak.sk
Recycling Services
N.A.I.C.S.: 423930
Hana Novakova *(Chm)*

ENVICONTROL-ENVITEC N.V.
Kromstraat 64C 5A 12A, Ranst, Antwerp, 2520, Belgium
Tel.: (32) 34301698
Web Site: http://www.envicontrol.com
Year Founded: 1992
Sales Range: $10-24.9 Million
Emp.: 10
Measuring Instruments Mfr
N.A.I.C.S.: 334519
Eric Callaert *(Founder & Mgr-Bus Dev)*

ENVICTUS INTERNATIONAL HOLDINGS LIMITED
4 Shenton Way 17-01 SGX Centre II, Singapore, 068807, Singapore
Tel.: (65) 65350550
Web Site: https://www.envictus-intl.com
BQD—(CAT)
Rev.: $119,804,021
Assets: $120,311,323
Liabilities: $87,638,307
Net Worth: $32,673,016
Earnings: ($6,953,228)
Emp.: 2,300
Fiscal Year-end: 09/30/23
Condensed Milk & Other Food Products
N.A.I.C.S.: 311514
Alan York Keng Pok *(COO-Frozen Food Trading)*

Subsidiaries:

Etika Beverages Sdn. Bhd.   (1)
Lot 17225 Jalan Haruan 6 Kawasan Perindustrian Oakland, Seremban, 70300, Negeri Sembilan, Malaysia
Tel.: (60) 67677830
Web Site: http://www.etika-intl.com
Sales Range: $25-49.9 Million
Emp.: 54
Canned Beverages Mfr
N.A.I.C.S.: 312111
Wong Swee Peng *(Gen Mgr)*

Etika Dairies NZ Limited   (1)
Whakatu Industrial Park 37-44 Johnston Way Whakatu, Hastings, 4180, Hawke's Bay, New Zealand   **(63.4%)**
Tel.: (64) 66503000
Sales Range: $25-49.9 Million
Emp.: 8
Fluid Milk & Fruit Beverage Mfr
N.A.I.C.S.: 311511

Pok Brothers Sdn. Bhd.   (1)
2 Jalan U1/24, Hicom-Glenmarie Industrial Park, 40150, Shah Alam, Selangor, Malaysia
Tel.: (60) 378051001
Sales Range: $50-74.9 Million
Emp.: 220
Frozen Food Whslr
N.A.I.C.S.: 424420

Subsidiary (Domestic):

De-Luxe Food Services Sdn. Bhd.   (2)
No 9 Jalan Korporat KU9, Taman Perindustrian Meru, 42200, Kelang, Selangor, Malaysia
Tel.: (60) 3 3393 1001
Web Site: http://www.de-luxefood.com
Sales Range: $25-49.9 Million
Emp.: 50
Frozen Baked Goods Mfr
N.A.I.C.S.: 311813

ENVIONEER CO., LTD.
604 158 Jeongjail-ro, Bundang-Gu, Seongnam, 13558, Gyeonggi-do, Korea (South)
Tel.: (82) 317163670
Web Site: https://www.envioneer.com
Year Founded: 2001
317870—(KRS)
Rev.: $8,455,266
Assets: $30,669,110
Liabilities: $14,578,506
Net Worth: $16,090,604
Earnings: ($125,030)
Emp.: 84
Fiscal Year-end: 12/31/22
Pollution Control Equipment Mfr & Distr
N.A.I.C.S.: 335314
Jeong-Cheol Han *(Pres & CEO)*

ENVIPCO HOLDING N.V.
Van Asch van Wijckstraat 4, 3811 LP, Amersfoort, Netherlands
Tel.: (31) 332851773
Web Site: https://www.envipco.com
ENVI—(EUR)
Rev.: $96,710,454
Assets: $108,620,157
Liabilities: $62,286,124
Net Worth: $46,334,032
Earnings: $663,429
Emp.: 411
Fiscal Year-end: 12/31/23
Reverse Vending Machines Mfr
N.A.I.C.S.: 333248
Dilraj S. Chawla *(CFO)*

Subsidiaries:

Envipco Automaten GmbH   (1)
Anton-Storch-Strasse 15, 49080, Osnabruck, Germany
Tel.: (49) 5416688760
Material Recycling Services
N.A.I.C.S.: 562920

Envipco Pickup & Processing Services Inc.   (1)
99 Great Hill Rd, Naugatuck, CT 06770
Tel.: (203) 720-4059
Emp.: 90
Logistics Consulting Servies
N.A.I.C.S.: 541614

Envipco Portugal Unipessoal Lda.   (1)
Passeio do Adamastor 13 Loja 1 - Parque das Nacoes, 1990-007, Lisbon, Portugal
Tel.: (351) 911881884
Reverse Vending Machine Mfr & Distr
N.A.I.C.S.: 334111

Envipco Slovakia s.r.o.   (1)
Panonska cesta 17, 851 04, Bratislava, Slovakia
Tel.: (421) 902987698
Reverse Vending Machine Mfr & Distr
N.A.I.C.S.: 335311

Posada Holding B.V.   (1)
Herengracht 458, 1017 CA, Amsterdam, Netherlands
Tel.: (31) 20 521 6342
Investment Management Service
N.A.I.C.S.: 523940

Sorepla Industrie S.A.   (1)
100 Chemin de Grety, BP 89, Rebeuville, 88300, Neufchateau, Cedex, France
Tel.: (33) 3 29 06 11 80
Web Site: http://www.sorepla.com
Plastic Recycling Services
N.A.I.C.S.: 562920

ENVIPRO HOLDINGS INC.
3507-19 Yamamiya, Fujinomiya-shi, Shizuoka, 418-0111, Japan
Tel.: (81) 544585800
Web Site: https://www.envipro.jp
5698—(TKS)
Rev.: $324,771,080
Assets: $210,148,920
Liabilities: $104,172,560

Envipro Holdings Inc.—(Continued)

Net Worth: $105,976,360
Earnings: $3,340,140
Emp.: 20
Fiscal Year-end: 06/30/24
Holding Company; Solid Waste Services
N.A.I.C.S.: 551112
Tomikazu Sano (Pres & CEO)

Subsidiaries:

3WM UGANDA LIMITED (1)
Jinja Road Katwe Makindye Division, Kampala, Uganda
Tel.: (256) 703784451
Automobile Parts Distr
N.A.I.C.S.: 423110
Shigeru Kawachi (Gen Mgr)

ASTOCO Inc. (1)
MT3 Bldg 2F 1-12-24 Mita Meguro-ku, Tokyo, 153-0062, Japan
Tel.: (81) 364522670
Web Site: http://www.ecommit.jp
Disabled Welfare Services
N.A.I.C.S.: 624120

Cyterrace Co., Ltd. (1)
Yokohama Aioi-cho Building 10F 6-104 Aioi-cho, Naka-ku, Yokohama, 231-0012, Kanagawa, Japan
Tel.: (81) 453196125
Web Site: https://www.cyterrace.co.jp
Logistics Customs Clearance Services
N.A.I.C.S.: 541614

E3 Co., Ltd. (1)
2 Chome-8-11 Nishishinbashi Minato-ku, Tokyo, 105-0003, Japan
Tel.: (81) 362057501
Web Site: https://www.envipro-e3.jp
Solar Power Generation Services
N.A.I.C.S.: 221114

Econecol Inc. (1)
3507-19 Yamamiya, Fujinomiya, 418-0111, Shizuoka, Japan
Tel.: (81) 54 458 5801
Web Site: https://www.econecol.com
Recycling Center Services
N.A.I.C.S.: 562920
Fumikatsu Sano (Pres & CEO)

Kuroda Recycle Co., Ltd. (1)
274-246 Nishikikyo-cho, Hakodate, 041-0824, Hokkaido, Japan
Tel.: (81) 138498880
Web Site: http://www.kurodarecycle.co.jp
Emp.: 76
Waste Recycling Services
N.A.I.C.S.: 562920

NEWSCON Inc. (1)
Kyobashi RK Building 8F 2-5-15, Kyobashi Chuo-ku, Tokyo, 104-0031, Japan
Tel.: (81) 335286223
Web Site: https://www.newscon.co.jp
Recyclable Material Trading Services
N.A.I.C.S.: 541870

SYNECO Inc. (1)
2346 Shimadzu, Matsumoto, 390-0852, Nagano, Japan
Tel.: (81) 263473211
Web Site: http://www.syneco.co.jp
Emp.: 60
Waste Recycling Services
N.A.I.C.S.: 562920

Toyo Rubber Chip Co., Ltd. (1)
1573 Fukatsu, Kasukawa-cho, Maebashi, 371-0215, Japan
Tel.: (81) 272853131
Web Site: https://www.envipro-toyo.co.jp
Rubber Mfr
N.A.I.C.S.: 326220

ENVIRO ENERGY INTERNATIONAL HOLDINGS LIMITED

Room 1603-5 16th Floor Harcourt House, 39 Gloucester Road, Wanchai, China (Hong Kong)
Tel.: (852) 39166700   Ky
Web Site: http://www.enviro-energy.com.hk
Rev.: $7,304,346

Assets: $104,161,954
Liabilities: $35,042,319
Net Worth: $69,119,636
Earnings: ($3,221,293)
Emp.: 18
Fiscal Year-end: 12/31/19
Up-Stream Petroleum & Natural Gas Developer
N.A.I.C.S.: 324199
Sen Li (Chm)

ENVIRO TECH JAPAN CO., LTD.

Ozu Main Building 3-6-2 Nihonbashi-honcho, Chuo-ku, Tokyo, 103-8435, Japan
Tel.: (81) 336618925   JP
Web Site:
http://www.envirotechjp.com
Year Founded: 2017
Peracetic Acid Mfr
N.A.I.C.S.: 325180

ENVIRO-HUB HOLDINGS LTD.

3 Gul Crescent, Singapore, 629519, Singapore
Tel.: (65) 68632100
Web Site: https://www.enviro-hub.com
L23—(SES)
Rev.: $30,516,549
Assets: $108,745,740
Liabilities: $43,463,607
Net Worth: $65,282,133
Earnings: $2,955,389
Emp.: 125
Fiscal Year-end: 12/31/23
Environmental Services
N.A.I.C.S.: 541330
Raymond Ah Hua Ng (Chm)

Subsidiaries:

Cimelia Resource Recovery Pte. Ltd. (1)
99 Tuas Bay Drive, Singapore, 637426, Singapore
Tel.: (65) 68980808
Web Site: https://www.cimeliaglobal.com
Sales Range: $10-24.9 Million
Emp.: 50
Electronic Waste Management & Recycling Services
N.A.I.C.S.: 562998

EH Property Management Pte Ltd (1)
1 Selegie Road B1-15 PoMo, Singapore, 188306, Singapore
Tel.: (65) 63394253
Web Site: http://www.ehpm.com.sg
Real Estate Services
N.A.I.C.S.: 531390

Enviro-Metals Pte Ltd (1)
No 3 Tuas Avenue 2, Singapore, 639443, Singapore
Tel.: (65) 68632100
Web Site: http://www.enviro-hub.com
Sales Range: $25-49.9 Million
Emp.: 100
Metal Waste Recycling Services
N.A.I.C.S.: 562920

HLS Electronics Pte Ltd (1)
99 Tuas Bay Drive, Singapore, 637426, Singapore
Tel.: (65) 6 792 5333
Web Site: https://hls.com.sg
Emp.: 22
Electronic Waste Recycling Services
N.A.I.C.S.: 562920
Jess Tai (Mgr-Mktg)

Leong Hin Piling (Pte) Ltd (1)
200 Pandan Loop 05-01 Pantec 21, Singapore, 128388, Singapore
Tel.: (65) 68632100
Web Site: https://www.leonghin.com
Sales Range: $50-74.9 Million
Emp.: 130
Piling Contractors
N.A.I.C.S.: 238190

Pastel Glove Sdn. Bhd. (1)
PT 285724 Jalan Pusing Taman Perindustrian Perabot Negeri Perak, Pusing, 31550, Perak, Malaysia
Tel.: (60) 53227000
Web Site: https://www.pastel.my
Rubber Glove Mfr & Distr
N.A.I.C.S.: 339113

ENVIROGOLD GLOBAL LIMITED

1890 1075 West Georgia Street, Vancouver, V6E 3C9, BC, Canada
Tel.: (281) 851-7743   BC
Web Site:
https://envirogoldglobal.com
Year Founded: 2005
ESGLF—(OTCQB)
Assets: $2,387,287
Liabilities: $498,700
Net Worth: $1,888,587
Earnings: $6,856,758
Emp.: 6
Fiscal Year-end: 12/31/22
Oil & Gas Exploration Services
N.A.I.C.S.: 211120
Allan J. Bezanson (CEO)

ENVIROLOGIC AB

Rapsgatan 33, 754 54, Uppsala, Sweden
Tel.: (46) 18398230
Web Site: https://www.envirologic.se
Year Founded: 1999
Automatic Washing Equipment Distr
N.A.I.C.S.: 423690
Jan Sandberg (CEO)

ENVIROMETAL TECHNOLOGIES INC.

Unit 114 8331 Eastlake Drive, Burnaby, V5A 4W2, BC, Canada
Tel.: (604) 428-2400
Web Site:
http://www.enviroleach.com
EVLLF—(OTCQB)
Rev.: $638,955
Assets: $12,959,976
Liabilities: $1,668,310
Net Worth: $11,291,667
Earnings: ($5,343,935)
Fiscal Year-end: 12/31/20
Mining & Electronic Waste Sector Services
N.A.I.C.S.: 562998
Nathalie Pilon (CFO & Corp Sec)

ENVIROMISSION LIMITED

238 Albert Road, South Melbourne, 3205, VIC, Australia
Tel.: (61) 396935666
Web Site:
http://www.enviromission.com.au
Year Founded: 2000
Rev.: $479,401
Assets: $974,947
Liabilities: $3,173,173
Net Worth: ($2,198,226)
Earnings: ($916,133)
Fiscal Year-end: 06/30/18
Solar Tower Technology
N.A.I.C.S.: 926130
Roger Chalmers Davey (Chm, CEO & Exec Dir)

Subsidiaries:

Pure Solar Power (IP) Pty. Ltd. (1)
3 Raglan Street, Melbourne, 3205, VIC, Australia
Tel.: (61) 396935666
Sales Range: $25-49.9 Million
Emp.: 1
Solar Tower Development Services
N.A.I.C.S.: 237130

ENVIRON GROUP (INVESTMENTS) PLC

5 Furlong Parade Burslem, Stoke-on-Trent, Staffs, United Kingdom
Tel.: (44) 1782 826939   UK
Web Site:
http://www.environgroup.co.uk
Sales Range: $25-49.9 Million
Emp.: 288
Holding Company; Investment Services
N.A.I.C.S.: 551112
Mark Sims (CEO)

Subsidiaries:

Fenhams Ltd. (1)
James Richardson House Gosforth Pkwy, Gosforth Bus Park, Newcastle upon Tyne, NE12 8DG, Tyne and Wear, United Kingdom
Tel.: (44) 1912561066
Sales Range: $50-74.9 Million
Emp.: 175
Heating System Installation & Plumbing Services
N.A.I.C.S.: 238220

Ronald Thompson Limited (1)
Albany Rd E Gateshead Indus Estate, Gateshead, NE8 3EH, Tyne & Wear, United Kingdom
Tel.: (44) 191 477 8000
Sales Range: $25-49.9 Million
Emp.: 20
Electrical & Mechanical Contractors
N.A.I.C.S.: 238210

ENVIRONMENT ECOLOGY HOLDING COMPANY OF CHINA

391 Hua Yu Lane Dong Xin Street, Xi'an, Shaanxi, China
Tel.: (86) 29 88265109   FL
Year Founded: 1989
Sales Range: $25-49.9 Million
Emp.: 68
Landscape Architectural Services
N.A.I.C.S.: 541320
Sheng Li Liu (Chm & Pres)

ENVIRONMENT FRIENDLY HOLDINGS CORP.

Nishi Shinbashi Tokyoiida Building 9th Floor, Minato-ku, Tokyo, 105-0003, Japan
Tel.: (81) 362610190
Web Site: https://www.ef-hd.com
Year Founded: 1995
3777—(TKS)
Rev.: $120,522,910
Assets: $23,928,750
Liabilities: $1,779,590
Net Worth: $22,149,160
Earnings: $1,084,770
Fiscal Year-end: 12/31/23
Internet Technology Services
N.A.I.C.S.: 541519

ENVIRONMENTAL CLEAN TECHNOLOGIES LIMITED

Suite 37 209 Toorak Rd, PO Box 482, South Yarra, 3141, VIC, Australia
Tel.: (61) 398496203
Web Site: https://www.ectltd.com.au
ECT—(ASX)
Rev.: $974,025
Assets: $3,975,057
Liabilities: $1,688,357
Net Worth: $2,286,700
Earnings: ($2,479,997)
Emp.: 48
Fiscal Year-end: 06/30/24
Waste Management Services
N.A.I.C.S.: 924110
Ashley Moore (Head-Engrg)

Subsidiaries:

ECT Finance Ltd. (1)

388 Punt Road, South Yarra, 3141, VIC, Australia
Tel.: (61) 398496203
Web Site: http://www.ectfinance.com.au
Financial Services
N.A.I.C.S.: 523999

ENVIRONMENTAL CONTROL CENTER CO., LTD.
3-7-23 Sanda-machi, Hachioji, 193-0832, Tokyo, Japan
Tel.: (81) 426730500
Web Site: https://www.kankyo-kanri.co.jp
Year Founded: 1971
4657—(TKS)
Rev.: $34,794,680
Assets: $34,844,440
Liabilities: $19,717,400
Net Worth: $15,127,040
Earnings: $1,355,960
Emp.: 260
Fiscal Year-end: 06/30/24
Environmental Measurement Services
N.A.I.C.S.: 541620
Kengo Mizuochi *(Pres)*

ENVIRONMENTAL WASTE INTERNATIONAL INC.
1751 Wentworth Street Unit 1, Whitby, L1N 8R6, ON, Canada
Tel.: (905) 686-8689
Web Site: https://www.ewi.ca
Year Founded: 1992
EWS—(TSXV)
Rev.: $62,297
Assets: $2,307,794
Liabilities: $4,350,209
Net Worth: ($2,042,415)
Earnings: ($1,405,065)
Fiscal Year-end: 12/31/23
Waste Treatment Services
N.A.I.C.S.: 562998
Emanuel Gerard *(Chm)*

Subsidiaries:

Ellsin Environmental Ltd.   **(1)**
360 Frankcom Street, Ajax, L1S 1R5, ON, Canada
Tel.: (905) 686-8689
Web Site: http://www.ewi.ca
Sales Range: $25-49.9 Million
Emp.: 8
Tire Recycling Services
N.A.I.C.S.: 562920

Plant (Domestic):

Ellsin Environmental Ltd. - Ellsin Plant 1   **(2)**
Sault Ste Marie Facility 155 Yates Avenue, Sault Sainte Marie, P6C 1G1, ON, Canada
Tel.: (705) 575-4662
Web Site: http://www.ellsin.com
Sales Range: $25-49.9 Million
Emp.: 1
Tire Recycling Services
N.A.I.C.S.: 562920

ENVIROSUITE LIMITED
Tel.: (61) 1300987009
Web Site:
    https://www.envirosuite.com
EVS—(ASX)
Rev.: $39,649,066
Assets: $79,633,337
Liabilities: $22,850,731
Net Worth: $56,782,606
Earnings: ($21,533,280)
Emp.: 250
Fiscal Year-end: 06/30/24
Environmental Consulting Services
N.A.I.C.S.: 541620

Subsidiaries:

Commercial Energy Services Pty Ltd   **(1)**
Ste 8 76 Reserve Road, Artarmon, 2064, NSW, Australia
Tel.: (61) 2 9425 1800

Web Site:
    http://www.energyservices.com.au
Facilities Management Consulting Services
N.A.I.C.S.: 541618
Lincoln James Young *(Co-Founder & CEO)*

EMS Bruel & Kjaer Iberica S.A.   **(1)**
Teide 5 28703 San Sebastian de los, Reyes, Madrid, Spain
Tel.: (34) 91 163 4003
Software Services
N.A.I.C.S.: 541511

EMS Bruel & Kjaer Taiwan Ltd.   **(1)**
13F-1 No 128 Sec 3 Min Sheng East Road, Taipei, Taiwan
Tel.: (886) 7 742 6488
Software Services
N.A.I.C.S.: 541511

Envirosuite Denmark ApS   **(1)**
Generatorvej 6A 2nd Floor, Soborg, 2860, Denmark
Tel.: (45) 8 082 6875
Software Services
N.A.I.C.S.: 541511

Envirosuite Taiwan Ltd.   **(1)**
17 F-1A No 77 Sec 2 Dunhua S Rd, Daan Dist, Taipei, Taiwan
Tel.: (886) 932148020
Web Site: https://envirosuite.com
Wastewater Treatment Software Services
N.A.I.C.S.: 221320

Pacific Air & Environment Pty Ltd   **(1)**
Level 1 La Melba 59 Melbourne Street, South Brisbane, Brisbane, 4101, QLD, Australia
Tel.: (61) 730046400
Web Site: http://www.paeholmes.com
Sales Range: $25-49.9 Million
Emp.: 18
Environmental Consulting Services
N.A.I.C.S.: 541620
Chaim Kolominskas *(Mgr-Bus Dev-Tech)*

Queensland Environment Pty Ltd   **(1)**
Level 1 La Melba 59 Melbourne St, South Brisbane, Brisbane, 4101, QLD, Australia
Tel.: (61) 730046400
Web Site: http://www.pelgrout.com
Sales Range: $25-49.9 Million
Emp.: 20
Environmental Consulting Services
N.A.I.C.S.: 541620

Toxikos Pty Ltd   **(1)**
Ste G62 63 Turner St, Port Melbourne, 3207, VIC, Australia
Tel.: (61) 395693088
Web Site: http://www.toxikos.com
Sales Range: $25-49.9 Million
Emp.: 6
Environmental Consulting Services
N.A.I.C.S.: 541620

ENVISION GROUP
Building B One East Plaza 736 South Zhongshan 1st Road, Shanghai, 200023, China
Tel.: (86) 2160318000   CN
Web Site: http://www.envision-group.com
Year Founded: 2007
Emp.: 100
Wind Turbines, Energy Management Software & Technology Services
N.A.I.C.S.: 221115
Lei Zhang *(CEO & Founder)*

Subsidiaries:

Envision Energy USA Limited   **(1)**
1201 Louisiana St Ste 500, Houston, TX 77002
Tel.: (832) 879-2349
Web Site: http://www.envision-group.com
Wind Power, Energy Management & Technology Services
N.A.I.C.S.: 221115

ENVITEC BIOGAS AG
Industriering 10a, 49393, Lohne, Germany
Tel.: (49) 444280168100

Web Site: https://www.envitec-biogas.com
ETG—(MUN)
Rev.: $460,115,093
Assets: $460,667,028
Liabilities: $248,701,911
Net Worth: $211,965,117
Earnings: $64,532,240
Emp.: 660
Fiscal Year-end: 12/31/23
Tank Construction
N.A.I.C.S.: 238990
Jorg Fischer *(CFO & Member-Mgmt Bd-Controlling, Fin, IR, Mktg, PR & SIs)*

Subsidiaries:

A3 Water Solutions GmbH   **(1)**
Boschstrasse 2, 48369, Saerbeck, Germany
Tel.: (49) 257488758200
Web Site: https://www.a3-gmbh.com
Sales Range: $25-49.9 Million
Emp.: 15
Water Treatment Equipment Mfr & Wastewater Treatment Services
N.A.I.C.S.: 237110
Ulrich Bruess *(Mng Dir)*

Subsidiary (Domestic):

MaxFlow Membran Filtration GmbH   **(2)**
Boschstrasse 2, 48369, Saerbeck, Germany
Tel.: (49) 257488758260
Web Site: http://www.maxflow-gmbh.com
Sales Range: $25-49.9 Million
Emp.: 10
Filtration Membrane Modules Distr
N.A.I.C.S.: 424130

Biogas Friedland GmbH & Co. KG   **(1)**
Industriering 10a, 49393, Lohne, Germany
Tel.: (49) 444280650
Biogas Mfr & Distr
N.A.I.C.S.: 221210

Biogas Herzberg GmbH & Co. KG   **(1)**
Industriering 10a, 49393, Lohne, Germany
Tel.: (49) 444280650
Web Site: http://www.envited-biogas.com
Sales Range: $25-49.9 Million
Emp.: 100
Biogas Mfr
N.A.I.C.S.: 324110

Biogas Nieheim GmbH & Co. KG   **(1)**
Steinheimer Strasse 99, 33039, Nieheim, Germany
Tel.: (49) 527495840
Biogas Mfr
N.A.I.C.S.: 324110

ETFT EnviTec Filtration Technik GmbH   **(1)**
Industriering 10a, 49393, Lohne, Nordrhein-Westfalen, Germany
Tel.: (49) 444280650
Sales Range: $25-49.9 Million
Emp.: 2
Biogas Mfr
N.A.I.C.S.: 324110

EnviTec Biogas Baltic SIA   **(1)**
Atmodas iela 19, Jelgava, 3001, Latvia
Tel.: (371) 27507497
Biogas Mfr
N.A.I.C.S.: 325120

EnviTec Biogas Baltics SIA   **(1)**
Mokslininku Str 9A-16, Vilnius, Lithuania
Tel.: (370) 64055888
Sales Range: $25-49.9 Million
Emp.: 10
Biogas Mfr
N.A.I.C.S.: 324110

EnviTec Biogas Central Europe s.r.o.   **(1)**
Prumyslova 2051, Velke Mezirici, 594 01, Czech Republic
Tel.: (420) 566520800
Web Site: http://www.envitec-biogas.cz

Sales Range: $25-49.9 Million
Emp.: 15
Biogas Mfr
N.A.I.C.S.: 324110

EnviTec Biogas China Ltd.   **(1)**
Office C617 Bejing Lufthansa Center No 50 Liangmaqiao Road, Chaoyang District, Beijing, 100125, China
Tel.: (86) 1064607150
Biogas Mfr
N.A.I.C.S.: 325120

EnviTec Biogas France S.A.R.L.   **(1)**
Parc d Activites Les Chatelets 7 rue des Compagnons, 22960, Saint-Brieuc, France
Tel.: (33) 296766170
Web Site: http://www.envitec-biogas.fr
Sales Range: $25-49.9 Million
Emp.: 3
Biogas Mfr
N.A.I.C.S.: 324110

EnviTec Biogas Nederland B.V.   **(1)**
Bornerbroekseweg 1d, 7468 RM, Enter, Overijssel, Netherlands
Tel.: (31) 547380523
Sales Range: $125-149.9 Million
Emp.: 300
Biogas Mfr
N.A.I.C.S.: 324110

EnviTec Biogas Romania S.R.L   **(1)**
Str Corneliu Coposu 9, 310003, Arad, Romania
Tel.: (40) 357445946
Web Site: http://www.envitec-biogas.ro
Sales Range: $25-49.9 Million
Emp.: 5
Biogas Mfr
N.A.I.C.S.: 324110

EnviTec Biogas Service Baltic SIA   **(1)**
Kalnciema iela 175, Riga, 1046, Latvia
Tel.: (371) 27722967
Web Site: http://www.envitec-biogas.lv
Biogas Mfr
N.A.I.C.S.: 325120

EnviTec Biogas South East Europe Ltd.   **(1)**
62 Cegledi Str, 6000, Kecskemet, Bacs-Kiskun, Hungary
Tel.: (36) 76505590
Web Site: http://www.envitec-biogas.hu
Sales Range: $25-49.9 Million
Emp.: 10
Biogas Mfr
N.A.I.C.S.: 324110

EnviTec Biogas UK Ltd.   **(1)**
Colton Road, Rugeley, WS15 3HF, Staffordshire, United Kingdom
Tel.: (44) 1889584459
Web Site: http://www.envitec-biogas.de
Sales Range: $25-49.9 Million
Emp.: 4
Biogas Plant Construction Management Services
N.A.I.C.S.: 237120
John Day *(Mgr-SIs)*

EnviTec Biogas s.r.l.   **(1)**
Via J Monnet 17, 37136, Verona, Italy
Tel.: (39) 0458969899
Web Site: https://www.envitec-biogas.it
Biogas Mfr
N.A.I.C.S.: 325120

EnviTec Green Power GmbH & Co. KG   **(1)**
Industriering 10a, 49393, Lohne, Nordrhein-Westfalen, Germany
Tel.: (49) 44428065100
Web Site: http://www.envitech-biogas.de
Sales Range: $125-149.9 Million
Biogas Mfr
N.A.I.C.S.: 324110

EnviTec Green Power Verwaltungs GmbH   **(1)**
Industriering 10a, 49393, Lohne, Nordrhein-Westfalen, Germany
Tel.: (49) 44428065100
Web Site: http://www.envitec-biogas.de
Sales Range: $25-49.9 Million
Emp.: 100
Biogas Mfr
N.A.I.C.S.: 324110

EnviTec Biogas AG—(Continued)

EnviTec Service ApS (1)
Port 14 / Kloftehoj 3, 8680, Ry, Denmark
Tel.: (45) 51703099
Biogas Mfr
N.A.I.C.S.: 325120

EnviTec Service GmbH (1)
Tel.: (49) 444280650
Web Site: http://www.envitec-biogas.de
Emp.: 150
Industrial Equipments & Machinery Mainte-
nance Services
N.A.I.C.S.: 811310

EnviTec Service SARL (1)
760 Chemin, Coudon, Pont-Saint-Maxence,
60150, France
Tel.: (33) 611563495
Biogas Mfr
N.A.I.C.S.: 325120

Kiinteisto Oy Piispanpiha 5 (1)
Korkeavuorenkatu 45, Helsinki, 00130, Fin-
land
Tel.: (358) 400 472272
Biogas Plant Construction Services
N.A.I.C.S.: 237120

RePro Beber GmbH & Co. KG (1)
Industriering 10 a, 49393, Lohne, Germany
Tel.: (49) 444280650
Biogas Mfr
N.A.I.C.S.: 324110

Renagen Inc. (1)
8F 3-2-3 Kanda Jinbo, Chiyoda, Tokyo,
101-0051, Japan
Tel.: (81) 335560173
Biogas Mfr
N.A.I.C.S.: 325120

**Zweite EnviTec Beteiligungs GmbH &
Co. KG** (1)
Industriering 10a, 49393, Lohne, Germany
Tel.: (49) 44428065100
Web Site: http://www.envitec-biogas.de
Sales Range: $200-249.9 Million
Biogas Mfr
N.A.I.C.S.: 211120

ENVIZION MEDICAL LTD.
7 Haarad St, 6971060, Tel Aviv, Is-
rael
Tel.: (972) 722288240
Web Site:
   http://www.envizionmed.com
Year Founded: 2017
ENVM.L—(TAE)
Rev.: $1,152,000
Assets: $375,000
Liabilities: $4,509,000
Net Worth: ($4,134,000)
Earnings: ($4,875,000)
Fiscal Year-end: 06/30/23
Surgical & Medical Instrument Manu-
facturing
N.A.I.C.S.: 339112
Doron Besser (Founder, Pres & CEO)

ENVOY TEXTILES LTD.
Envoy Tower 18/E Lake Circus Kala-
bagan West Panthapath, Dhaka,
1205, Bangladesh
Tel.: (880) 241021684
Web Site:
   https://www.envoytextiles.com
Year Founded: 1995
ENVOYTEX—(CHT)
Rev.: $101,203,967
Assets: $188,838,160
Liabilities: $129,824,682
Net Worth: $59,013,478
Earnings: $2,985,336
Emp.: 3,376
Fiscal Year-end: 06/30/23
Fashion Designing Services
N.A.I.C.S.: 541490
Kutubuddin Ahmed (Chm)

ENWAVE CORPORATION
Unit 1-1668 Derwent Way, Delta,
V3M 6R9, BC, Canada

Tel.: (604) 806-6110
Web Site: https://www.enwave.net
Year Founded: 1996
NWVCF—(OTCIQ)
Rev.: $32,784,412
Assets: $33,096,630
Liabilities: $9,417,043
Net Worth: $23,679,587
Earnings: ($1,519,767)
Emp.: 45
Fiscal Year-end: 09/30/19
Dehydrated Food Mfr
N.A.I.C.S.: 311423
John P. A. Budreski (Chm)

Subsidiaries:

**Hans Binder Maschinenbau
GmbH** (1)
Isarstrasse 8, Freising, Marzling, 85417,
Germany
Tel.: (49) 816196810
Web Site: http://www.binder-trockner.de
Sales Range: $25-49.9 Million
Emp.: 3
Belt Dryer Mfr
N.A.I.C.S.: 333922
Fred Hoen (Mng Dir)

**ENWEI PHARMACEUTICAL
CO., LTD.**
Enwei Building Chuangye Avenue,
Dam Area A Changdu Economic De-
velopment Zone, Chengdu, 854000,
China
Tel.: (86) 2885887067
Web Site: https://www.enwei.com.cn
Year Founded: 2005
301331—(CHIN)
Rev.: $110,590,324
Assets: $188,303,957
Liabilities: $33,001,662
Net Worth: $155,378,295
Earnings: $12,156,662
Emp.: 1,000
Fiscal Year-end: 12/31/23
Pharmaceutical Product Mfr & Distr
N.A.I.C.S.: 325412
Yongjiang Xue (Chm & CEO)

ENWELL ENERGY PLC
16 Old Queen Street, London, SW1H
9HP, United Kingdom
Tel.: (44) 2034273550   UK
Web Site: https://www.enwell-
   energy.com
RGPMF—(OTCIQ)
Rev.: $121,353,000
Assets: $208,590,000
Liabilities: $30,073,000
Net Worth: $178,517,000
Earnings: $51,119,000
Emp.: 300
Fiscal Year-end: 12/31/21
Crude Petroleum Extraction Services
N.A.I.C.S.: 211120
Sergii Glazunov (CEO)

Subsidiaries:

Regal Group Services Limited (1)
Lansdowne House 57, Berkeley Sq, Lon-
don, W1J 6ER, United Kingdom
Tel.: (44) 2074089500
Sales Range: $50-74.9 Million
Emp.: 15
Oil & Gas Services
N.A.I.C.S.: 211120

ENX GROUP LIMITED
9th Floor Kathryn Towers 1 Park
Lane Sandton, Elandsfontein, South
Africa
Tel.: (27) 119662000
Web Site:
   https://www.enxgroup.co.za
ENX—(JSE)
Rev.: $221,526,579
Assets: $294,256,276
Liabilities: $157,852,428

Net Worth: $136,403,849
Earnings: $10,078,529
Emp.: 386
Fiscal Year-end: 08/31/23
Industrial & Construction Products
Sales
N.A.I.C.S.: 423830
Paul Mansour (Chief Investment Offi-
cer)

Subsidiaries:

**AUSTRO WOOD (PTY)
LIMITED** (1)
1125 Leader Avenue Stormill ext 4, Roode-
poort, 2148, Gauteng, South Africa
Tel.: (27) 11 222 8300
Web Site: http://www.austro.co.za
Sales Range: $75-99.9 Million
Emp.: 140
Woodworking Machinery Distr
N.A.I.C.S.: 423830

Division (Domestic):

**Austro Woodworking Machines &
Tools** (2)
1125 Leader Avenue Stormill Ext 4, Roode-
poort, 1724, Gauteng, South Africa
Tel.: (27) 112228300
Web Site: http://www.austro.co.za
Sales Range: $25-49.9 Million
Emp.: 100
Woodworking Machinery & Tools Distr
N.A.I.C.S.: 423830
Peter Ivanoff (Mgr-Mktg)

Gearing Moss Supplies (Pty) Ltd (2)
1127 Leader Ave Stormill Ext 8, Roode-
poort, Johannesburg, 1710, Gauteng, South
Africa
Tel.: (27) 11 222 8350
Portable Sawmills Distr
N.A.I.C.S.: 321113

Austro (Pty) Limited (1)
1125 Leader Avenue, Stormill, Roodepoort,
South Africa
Tel.: (27) 11 222 8300
Web Site: https://www.austro.co.za
Sales Range: $50-74.9 Million
Emp.: 10
Woodworking Machinery & Tools Distr
N.A.I.C.S.: 423830

**Austro Engineering Cape (Pty)
Limited** (1)
28 Cabernet Rd Saxenburg Park 1,
Rustdal, Cape Town, 7580, Western Cape,
South Africa
Tel.: (27) 21 905 0430
Web Site: https://www.austro.co.za
Sales Range: $25-49.9 Million
Emp.: 15
Woodworking Machinery & Tools Distr
N.A.I.C.S.: 423830

Division (Domestic):

Neptune Plant Hire (Pty) Limited (2)
23 Neptune Street, Paarden Eiland, Cape
Town, 7405, Western Cape, South Africa
Tel.: (27) 215112733
Web Site: http://www.neptuneplanthire.co.za
Sales Range: $50-74.9 Million
Emp.: 7
Generator Leasing Services
N.A.I.C.S.: 532490

**New Way Motor & Diesel Engineering
(Pty) Ltd** (2)
30 Jacoba Street Alberton North, Johannes-
burg, 2023, Excom, South Africa
Tel.: (27) 116805632
Web Site: http://www.newway.co.za
Generators Mfr & Distr
N.A.I.C.S.: 332994

**Quad Technical Services (Pty)
Limited** (2)
1626 Harriet Ave, Driehoek, Germiston,
1401, Gauteng, South Africa
Tel.: (27) 117768320
Web Site: http://www.qts.co.za
Electrical Control Panels & Generators Mfr
& Distr
N.A.I.C.S.: 335312

**NEW WAY POWER (PTY)
LIMITED** (1)
30-38 Jacoba Str Alberton North, Johannes-
burg, 1449, South Africa
Tel.: (27) 102162600
Sales Range: $25-49.9 Million
Emp.: 100
Power Turbines Mfr
N.A.I.C.S.: 333611

**enX Leasing Investments Proprietary
Limited** (1)
61 Maple Street, Kempton Park, 1619, Jo-
hannesburg, South Africa
Tel.: (27) 11 966 2000
Web Site: http://www.enxgroup.co.za
Emp.: 61
Holding Company; Industrial Equipment,
Fleet Management & Logistics Products &
Services
N.A.I.C.S.: 551112

Subsidiary (Domestic):

600SA Holdings (Pty) Ltd. (2)
62 Maple Street, Pomona, Kempton Park,
1619, South Africa
Tel.: (27) 11 966 2400
Web Site: https://www.600sa.co.za
Holding Company; Industrial Equipment Mfr
& Distr
N.A.I.C.S.: 551112
Clive Forrester (Reg Sls Mgr-Equipment
Sls)

**ENZAL CHEMICALS (INDIA)
LTD.**
159 1st Fl Bldg 6 Mittal Industrial Es-
tate Sir MV Rd, Kalina Santa Cruz E,
Mumbai, 400 098, India
Tel.: (91) 2256926478   In
Web Site: http://www.enzal.com
Year Founded: 1992
Sales Range: $10-24.9 Million
Emp.: 200
Specialty Drug Intermediates Mfr
N.A.I.C.S.: 325412
Arun Gupta (Chm & Mng Dir)

**ENZYCHEM LIFESCIENCES
CORPORATION**
10F aT Center 27 Gangnamdae-ro,
Seocho-gu, Seoul, Korea (South)
Tel.: (82) 25011084
Web Site:
   https://www.enzychem.com
Year Founded: 1999
183490—(KRS)
Rev.: $20,431,063
Assets: $189,874,675
Liabilities: $35,136,965
Net Worth: $154,737,710
Earnings: ($19,246,415)
Emp.: 85
Fiscal Year-end: 12/31/22
Pharmaceuticals Product Mfr
N.A.I.C.S.: 325412
Insu Kang (VP)

Subsidiaries:

**Enzychem Lifesciences Corporation -
Jecheon Factory** (1)
59 Bio Valley-ro, Jecheon,
Chungcheongbuk-do, Korea (South)
Tel.: (82) 436522845
Web Site: https://www.enzychem.com
Pharmaceuticals Product Mfr
N.A.I.C.S.: 325412

Enzychem Lifesciences Inc. (1)
440 Sylvan Ave Ste 290B, Englewood
Cliffs, NJ 07632
Tel.: (201) 591-1008
Pharmaceuticals Product Mfr
N.A.I.C.S.: 325412

ENZYMATICA AB
Ideon Science Park Scheelevaagen
19 Delta 5, SE-223 70, Lund, Swe-
den
Tel.: (46) 462863100
Web Site: https://www.enzymatica.se

ENZY—(OMX)
Rev.: $4,584,750
Assets: $16,335,572
Liabilities: $4,507,011
Net Worth: $11,828,561
Earnings: ($6,430,826)
Emp.: 21
Fiscal Year-end: 12/31/22
Pharmaceuticals Mfr
N.A.I.C.S.: 325412
Ulf Blom (Exec VP-Mktg & Ops)

Subsidiaries:

Zymetech ehf   (1)
Fiskisloo 39, 101, Reykjavik, Iceland
Tel.: (354) 551 5400
Web Site: https://www.enzymatica.se
Pharmaceuticals Product Mfr
N.A.I.C.S.: 325412
Agusta Gudmundsdottir (Mgr-R&D)

EO TECHNICS CO., LTD.
91 Dongpyeonro, Anyang, 13930,
Gyeonggi-do, Korea (South)
Tel.: (82) 314222501
Web Site:
   https://www.eotechnics.com
Year Founded: 1989
039030—(KRS)
Rev.: $342,969,871
Assets: $472,370,290
Liabilities: $58,869,449
Net Worth: $413,500,841
Earnings: $58,693,409
Emp.: 653
Fiscal Year-end: 12/31/22
Water Equipment Mfr
N.A.I.C.S.: 333517
Kyu-Dong Sung (CEO)

Subsidiaries:

EM TECH Co., Ltd.   (1)
864-2 Gwanyang 2-dong, Dongan-gu, Any-
ang, 431-804, Gyeonggi-do, Korea (South)
Tel.: (82) 31 423 9501
Web Site: http://www.em21.com
Electronic Components Mfr
N.A.I.C.S.: 334419
YoungHwan Choi (Dir-Global Mfg)

EO Technics Co., Ltd.   (1)
Eguchi Bld 3F Kanata 2-7-6, Kokurakita-ku
Kitakyushu-Si, Fukuoka, Japan
Tel.: (81) 934822992
Electronic Components Mfr
N.A.I.C.S.: 334419

EO Technics India Pvt. Ltd   (1)
1014 10th Floor Tower-A1 Plot No 7A Ansal
Corporate Park Sector-142, Noida, 201301,
Uttar Pradesh, India
Tel.: (91) 1206650415
Electronic Components Mfr
N.A.I.C.S.: 334419
Rajesh Tuli (Gen Mgr)

EO Technics International, Inc.   (1)
219 S William Dillards Dr Ste 121, Gilbert,
AZ 85233
Tel.: (480) 598-8660
Electronic Components Distr
N.A.I.C.S.: 423690

EO Technics Singapore Pte.,
Ltd.   (1)
07-27 CT-HUB 2 Kallang Avenue, Singa-
pore, 339407, Singapore
Tel.: (65) 62983844
Electronic Components Mfr
N.A.I.C.S.: 334419

EO Technics Taiwan Co., Ltd.   (1)
10F No 5 Lane91 Dongmei Rd, Taipei, Tai-
wan
Tel.: (886) 3 573 6612
Electronic Components Mfr
N.A.I.C.S.: 334419

TIANJIN EO TECHNICS CO.,
LTD   (1)
Rm 305 fl 3 Bldg E2 XEDA Sci-tech Park,
Xiqing Development Area, Tianjin, 300385,
China
Tel.: (86) 2223889020

Electronic Components Mfr
N.A.I.C.S.: 334419

WINTECH Co., Ltd.   (1)
SK Ventium Building 104 Room 1001 SK
Ventium 166, Gosan-ro, Gunpo, 15850,
Gyeonggi-do, Korea (South)
Tel.: (82) 314292401
Web Site: https://www.wintec.co.kr
Electronic Components Mfr
N.A.I.C.S.: 334419

EO2 S.A.
36 Avenue Pierre Brossolette, 92240,
Malakoff, France
Tel.: (33) 17700500
Web Site: https://www.eo2.fr
ALEO2—(EUR)
Rev.: $29,133,475
Earnings: $704,575
Fiscal Year-end: 02/28/19
Wood Pellet Mfr
N.A.I.C.S.: 321999

EOFLOW CO., LTD.
216 Hwangsaeul-ro, Bundang-Gu,
Seongnam, 13595, Gyeonggi-do, Ko-
rea (South)
Tel.: (82) 317380200
Web Site: https://www.eoflow.com
Year Founded: 2011
294090—(KRS)
Rev.: $5,144,941
Assets: $116,776,082
Liabilities: $41,051,739
Net Worth: $75,724,343
Earnings: ($23,555,499)
Emp.: 113
Fiscal Year-end: 12/31/22
Medical Device Mfr & Distr
N.A.I.C.S.: 339112
Jesse J. Kim (Founder & CEO)

EOH HOLDINGS LIMITED
Tel.: (27) 116078100
Web Site: http://www.eoh.co.za
EOH—(JSE)
Rev.: $469,027,485
Assets: $369,833,483
Liabilities: $357,702,598
Net Worth: $12,130,885
Earnings: ($19,090,890)
Emp.: 10,578
Fiscal Year-end: 07/31/21
Business & Technology Solutions
Provider
N.A.I.C.S.: 518210
Stephen van Coller (CEO)

Subsidiaries:

CA Southern Africa (Pty) Limited   (1)
Block F Gilloolys View Ofc Park 1 Osborne
Ln, Bedfordview, 2007, Gauteng, South
Africa
Tel.: (27) 114178699
Web Site: http://www.caafrica.co.za
Sales Range: $25-49.9 Million
Emp.: 120
Business Management Software Solutions
N.A.I.C.S.: 541511
Gary Lawrence (Mng Dir)

E-Secure (Pty) Limited   (1)
Block C Cent Park 400 16th Rd,
Randjespark, Midrand, 1685, Gauteng,
South Africa
Tel.: (27) 115456200
Web Site: http://www.esecuredist.co.za
Sales Range: $25-49.9 Million
Emp.: 9
Secured Software Application Development
Services
N.A.I.C.S.: 541511
John Hindley (Mgr)

EOH Consulting (Pty) Limited   (1)
Plot 67977 KPMG Building off Tlokweng
Road, PO Box AD6, Gaborone, Botswana
Tel.: (267) 3191039
Sales Range: $25-49.9 Million
Emp.: 18
Business Management Consulting Services

N.A.I.C.S.: 541611
Kenneth Molosi (CEO)

EOH Consulting Services (Eastern
Cape) (Pty) Limited   (1)
36 Pickerling St, Port Elizabeth, 6045, East-
ern Cape, South Africa
Tel.: (27) 413930700
Web Site: http://www.eoh.co.za
Sales Range: $25-49.9 Million
Emp.: 51
Business Software Consulting Services
N.A.I.C.S.: 541512

EOH Consulting Services (Western
Cape) (Pty) Limited   (1)
Block C The Estuaries Oxbow Ln Century
Ave, Century City, Cape Town, 7441, West-
ern Cape, South Africa
Tel.: (27) 215056800
Business Software Consulting Services
N.A.I.C.S.: 541512

EOH Mthombo (Pty) Limited   (1)
1 Osborne Rd Block F Gilloolys View, Bed-
fordview, 2007, Gauteng, South Africa
Tel.: (27) 116078100
Sales Range: $700-749.9 Million
Emp.: 3,000
Information Technology Solutions
N.A.I.C.S.: 541512

Subsidiary (Domestic):

Bromide Technologies (Pty) Ltd   (2)
Block C Cent Park 400 16th Rd,
Randjespark, Midrand, 1685, Gauteng,
South Africa
Tel.: (27) 115456000
Web Site: http://www.bromide.co.za
Sales Range: $25-49.9 Million
Emp.: 100
Business Management Software Solutions
N.A.I.C.S.: 541511
Delfim Alves (Mng Dir)

Enterprise Softworks (Pty)
Limited   (1)
Block F Gilloolly, Johannesburg, 2007, Gau-
teng, South Africa
Tel.: (27) 116078299
Web Site: http://www.esoftworx.co.za
Sales Range: $25-49.9 Million
Emp.: 81
Business & Information Technology Solu-
tions
N.A.I.C.S.: 541512
Jane Thomson (Mng Dir)

Enterweb (Pty) Limited   (1)
Gilloolys View Office Park 1 Osborne Lane,
Bedfordview, 2007, South Africa
Tel.: (27) 116078400
Business & Information Technology Solu-
tions
N.A.I.C.S.: 541512
Asher Bobhot (CEO)

Intellient (Pty) Limited   (1)
Block D Gilloolly's View Office Park 1 Os-
borne Lane, Bedfordview, 2007, South Af-
rica
Tel.: (27) 116078200
Business Management Software Solution-
sde Villiers
N.A.I.C.S.: 541511
Carl Janse Van Rensburg (Dir-Ops)

Mthombo IT Services (Pty)
Limited   (1)
Block E Gilloolys View Ofc Park 1 Osborne
Ln, Bedfordview, 2007, Gauteng, South
Africa
Tel.: (27) 114796300
Web Site: http://www.mit.co.za
Sales Range: $75-99.9 Million
Emp.: 500
Business Management Services
N.A.I.C.S.: 561110

EOLE, INC.
RONDO Nihonbashi Building 4F 6-16
Yokoyamacho Nihonbashi, Chuo-ku,
Tokyo, 103-0003, Japan
Tel.: (81) 5018027135
Web Site: https://www.eole.co.jp
Year Founded: 2001
2334—(TKS)

Sales Range: Less than $1 Million
Emp.: 76
Software Development Services
N.A.I.C.S.: 541511
Toru Ohyama (Auditor)

EOLUS VIND AB
Tredje Avenyn 3, 281 48, Hassle-
holm, Sweden
Tel.: (46) 101998800
Web Site: https://www.eolusvind.com
Year Founded: 1990
EOLU.B—(OMX)
Rev.: $316,272,656
Assets: $220,747,742
Liabilities: $94,277,257
Net Worth: $126,470,485
Earnings: $24,208,708
Emp.: 45
Fiscal Year-end: 12/31/20
Wind Power
N.A.I.C.S.: 221115
Per Witalisson (CEO)

Subsidiaries:

Eolus North America Inc.   (1)
5538A La Jolla Blvd, La Jolla, CA 92037
Tel.: (858) 842-5800
Web Site:
   https://www.eolusnorthamerica.com
Wind Power Project Development Services
N.A.I.C.S.: 237130

OU Baltic Wind Energy   (1)
Lossi 3, Kuressaare, 93819, Estonia
Tel.: (372) 5077788
Wind Power Project Development Services
N.A.I.C.S.: 237130
Peeter Kukk (Mgr)

SIA Eolus   (1)
Kalku iela 7, Riga, 1050, Latvia
Tel.: (371) 29 22 68 03
Wind Power Project Development Services
N.A.I.C.S.: 237130

EOMJIHOUSE CO., LTD.
25 Teheranro 28-Gil, Gangnam-Gu,
Seoul, Korea (South)
Tel.: (82) 25507800
Web Site:
   https://www.eomjihouse.co.kr
Year Founded: 1985
224810—(KRS)
Construction Services
N.A.I.C.S.: 236220
Jae-Ho Jeong (CEO)

EON ELECTRIC LTD.
6th Floor VB Capitol Building Range
Hill Rd, opp Hotel Symphony Bhos-
lenagar Shivajinagar, Pune, 411007,
Maharashtra, India
Tel.: (91) 7709003344
Web Site: https://www.efclimited.in
Year Founded: 1984
Rev.: $12,043,929
Assets: $28,416,645
Liabilities: $14,077,212
Net Worth: $14,339,432
Earnings: ($3,440,558)
Emp.: 215
Fiscal Year-end: 03/31/19
Lighting Equipment Mfr
N.A.I.C.S.: 335132
Ved Prakash Mahendru (Chm & Co-
Mng Dir)

Subsidiaries:

Indo Asian Fusegear Ltd - Haridwar
Lighting Plant   (1)
Plot No 2 Sector-2 IIE SIDCUL, Haridwar,
249403, India
Tel.: (91) 1334308369
Web Site: http://www.indoasian.com
Sales Range: $125-149.9 Million
Emp.: 173
Eletric Power Generation Services
N.A.I.C.S.: 221118

EON Electric Ltd.—(Continued)

Indo Asian Fusegear Ltd - Indo Simon Plant Haridwar (1)
Plot No 26 Sector 4, Sidcul, Haridwar, 249 403, Uttarakhand, India
Tel.: (91) 1334329801
Eletric Power Generation Services
N.A.I.C.S.: 221118

Indo Asian Fusegear Ltd - Jalandhar Switchgear Plant (1)
By Ln Nakodar Rd, Jalandhar, 144 003, Punjab, India
Tel.: (91) 1814639900
Eletric Power Generation Services
N.A.I.C.S.: 221118

Indo Asian Fusegear Ltd - Noida Lighting Plant (1)
V J Business Towers A-6 Ground Floor Sector 125, Noida, 201 301, Uttar Pradesh, India
Tel.: (91) 1203365300
Web Site: http://www.indoasian.com
Sales Range: $125-149.9 Million
Emp.: 210
Eletric Power Generation Services
N.A.I.C.S.: 221118

EON HADAPSAR INFRA-STRUCTURE PVT. LTD.
Tech Park One Tower E 191 Yerwada Off Airport Road, Pune, 411 006, India
Tel.: (91) 2066473200
Real Estate Support Services
N.A.I.C.S.: 531390
Sagar Ishwardas Chordia (Mng Dir)

EON MOTORS GROUP SA
Batiment 1 - Ecoparc - Parcs dActivites du Prieure, 04350, Malijai, France
Tel.: (33) 492318368
Web Site: http://www.eon-motors.com
Motor Vehicle Body Mfr
N.A.I.C.S.: 336211
Denis Mergin (Chm & CEO)

EON NRG LIMITED
Suite 2 20 Howard St, Perth, 6000, WA, Australia
Tel.: (61) 8 6144 0590   AU
Web Site:
   http://www.incrementaloil.com
Year Founded: 2009
Rev.: $4,981,781
Assets: $15,945,274
Liabilities: $11,983,628
Net Worth: $3,961,646
Earnings: ($1,426,435)
Fiscal Year-end: 12/31/18
Oil & Gas Exploration & Production Services
N.A.I.C.S.: 211120
Gerard McGann (Dir-Technical)

EONE DIAGNOMICS GENOME CENTER CO., LTD.
291 Harmony-Ro, Yeonsu-Gu, Incheon, 22014, Korea (South)
Tel.: (82) 327132100
Web Site: https://www.edgc.com
Year Founded: 2013
245620—(KRS)
Rev.: $72,284,912
Assets: $147,272,120
Liabilities: $122,087,356
Net Worth: $25,184,764
Earnings: ($22,906,267)
Emp.: 119
Fiscal Year-end: 12/31/22
Medical Device Mfr & Distr
N.A.I.C.S.: 339112
Min-Seob Lee (Co-CEO)

EONMETALL GROUP BERHAD
Lot 1258 Mk 12 Jalan Seruling Ka-

wasan Perusahaan Valdor, 14200, Sungai Bakap, Penang, Malaysia
Tel.: (60) 45828323
Web Site: https://www.eonmetall.com
EMETALL—(KLS)
Rev.: $54,375,564
Assets: $128,733,096
Liabilities: $59,771,746
Net Worth: $68,961,351
Earnings: $3,164,475
Emp.: 250
Fiscal Year-end: 12/31/22
Cold Rolled Steel Mfr
N.A.I.C.S.: 331110
Cheng Chye Yeoh (CEO & Mng Dir)

Subsidiaries:

Eonmetall Industries Sdn. Bhd. (1)
Lot 1258 Mk12 Jalan Seruling, 14200, Sungai Bakap, Pulau Pinang, Malaysia
Tel.: (60) 45828323
Web Site: https://www.eonmetall.com
Sales Range: $50-74.9 Million
Emp.: 200
Steel Products Mfr & Distr
N.A.I.C.S.: 331110

Eonmetall Systems Sdn. Bhd. (1)
Lot 1258 Mk12 Jalan Seruling Kawasan Perusahaan Valdor, Sungai Bakap, 14200, Pulau Pinang, Malaysia
Tel.: (60) 45828323
Web Site: http://www.eonmetall.com
Sales Range: $50-74.9 Million
Emp.: 200
Steel Products Mfr & Distr
N.A.I.C.S.: 331210

Eonmetall Technology Sdn. Bhd. (1)
Lot 1258 Mk12 Jalan Seruling Kawasan Perusahaan Valdor, Sungai Jawi, 14200, Pulau Pinang, Malaysia
Tel.: (60) 45828322
Sales Range: $50-74.9 Million
Emp.: 200
Metalworks Machinery Mfr
N.A.I.C.S.: 333517
Cheng Huat Goh (Pres)

Eontarr IT Solutions Sdn. Bhd. (1)
Lot 1258 MK 12 Jalan Seruling Kawasan Perusahaan Valdor, Sungai Bakap, 14200, Penang, Malaysia
Tel.: (60) 45828323
Web Site: http://www.eonmetall.com
Sales Range: $25-49.9 Million
Software Development Services
N.A.I.C.S.: 541511

Lienteh Technology Sdn. Bhd. (1)
Lot 6483 Jalan Sungai Puloh KU 5 Kawasan Perindustrian Sungai Puloh, 42100, Klang, Selangor, Malaysia
Tel.: (60) 332901235
Web Site: https://lienteh.com
Latex Gloves Mfr & Distr
N.A.I.C.S.: 339113

Norimax Sdn. Bhd. (1)
No 2 Jalan TPP 5/17 Taman Perindustrian Seksyen 5, 47160, Puchong, Selangor Darul Ehsan, Malaysia
Tel.: (60) 380602334
Web Site: http://www.norimax.com.my
Sales Range: $25-49.9 Million
Emp.: 40
Corrosion Control Products Mfr
N.A.I.C.S.: 339999

EOS GMBH ELECTRO OPTICAL SYSTEMS
Robert Stirling Ring 1, Krailling, 82152, Germany
Tel.: (49) 89893360
Web Site: http://www.eos.info
Year Founded: 1989
Rev.: $89,173,000
Emp.: 280
Optical Instruments & Lenses Mfr
N.A.I.C.S.: 333310
Glynn Fletcher (Member-Exec Bd)

Subsidiaries:

EOS Electro Optical Systems
Ltd. (1)

The Innovation Centre Warwick Technology Park, Warwick, CV34 6UW, United Kingdom
Tel.: (44) 19 26 62 31 07
Sales Range: $25-49.9 Million
Emp.: 12
Laser Sintering System & Equipment Mfr
N.A.I.C.S.: 332312
Adrian Keppler (Mng Dir)

EOS Singapore Pte Ltd (1)
8 Admiralty Street 06-12/13 Admirax, Singapore, 757438, Singapore
Tel.: (65) 6430 0552
Web Site: http://www.eos.info
Emp.: 16
Laser Sintering System & Equipment Mfr
N.A.I.C.S.: 332312

EOS of North America, Inc. (1)
28970 Cabot Dr Ste 700, Novi, MI 48377-2978
Tel.: (248) 306-0143
Web Site: http://www.eos.info
Sales Range: $25-49.9 Million
Emp.: 25
Laser Sintering System & Equipment Mfr
N.A.I.C.S.: 332312
Donnie Vanelli (Pres)

EOS s.r.l. Electro Optical Systems (1)
Via Gallarate 94, 20151, Milan, Italy
Tel.: (39) 02 33 40 16 59
Emp.: 7
Laser Sintering System & Equipment Mfr
N.A.I.C.S.: 332312

Electro Optical Systems Nordic AB (1)
Stena Center 1 C, Gothenburg, 41292, Sweden
Tel.: (46) 31 760 46 40
Sales Range: $25-49.9 Million
Emp.: 7
Laser Sintering System & Equipment Mfr
N.A.I.C.S.: 332312
Micael Amandusson (Reg Mgr-Sls)

EOS INC.
2F No 157 Sec 2 Nanjing E Rd, Zhongshan District, Taipei, 104075, Taiwan
Tel.: (886) 225868300   NV
Web Site: https://eosinc999.us
Year Founded: 2015
EOSS—(OTCIQ)
Rev.: $652,547
Assets: $546,492
Liabilities: $1,462,784
Net Worth: ($916,292)
Earnings: ($1,870,865)
Emp.: 9
Fiscal Year-end: 12/31/22
Skin Care Products Distr
N.A.I.C.S.: 456120
Yu Cheng Yang (Gen Mgr)

EP BIOCOMPOSITES LIMITED
First Floor BR Commercial Centre Opp Campal Parade Grounds, Campal Panaji, Goa, 403001, India
Tel.: (91) 9158005202
Web Site:
   https://www.epbiocomposites.com
Year Founded: 1991
543595—(BOM)
Rev.: $1,102,306
Assets: $1,266,297
Liabilities: $993,515
Net Worth: $272,782
Earnings: $110,483
Fiscal Year-end: 03/31/22
Polymer Product Mfr
N.A.I.C.S.: 325211

EP MANUFACTURING BHD.
No 8 10 Jalan Jurutera U123 Seksyen U1, Kawasan Perindustrian HICOM Glenmarie, 40150, Shah Alam, Selangor Darul Ehsan, Malaysia
Tel.: (60) 378036663

Web Site: https://www.epmb.com.my
EPMB—(KLS)
Rev.: $141,513,497
Assets: $134,437,310
Liabilities: $68,302,787
Net Worth: $66,134,524
Earnings: $4,401,611
Emp.: 842
Fiscal Year-end: 12/31/23
Automobile Parts Mfr
N.A.I.C.S.: 441330
Saiful Azhar Sabilan (Asst Mgr-Maintenance)

Subsidiaries:

EP Polymers (M) Sdn Bhd (1)
No 8 & 10 Jalan Jurutera U1/23 Seksyen U1, Shah Alam, 40150, Selangor, Malaysia
Tel.: (60) 378036663
Web Site: http://www.epmb.com.my
Sales Range: $50-74.9 Million
Emp.: 100
Automotive Part Whslr
N.A.I.C.S.: 423120

PEPS - JV (M) Sdn Bhd (1)
Lot 1403 1406 & 1409 Batu 29 Jalan Ipoh, Batang Kali, 44300, Selangor, Malaysia
Tel.: (60) 360753190
Sales Range: $250-299.9 Million
Emp.: 900
Automobile Parts Distr
N.A.I.C.S.: 423120

Peps-JV (Kedah) Sdn. Bhd. (1)
Plant No 2 Lot 333 Jalan PKNK 3/5 Kawasan Perindustrian Sungai Petani, 08000, Sungai Petani, Malaysia
Tel.: (60) 44400414
Automotive Part & Accessory Mfr
N.A.I.C.S.: 336390
Vincent Paul Lai Vin Pau (Deputy Gen Mgr-Bus & Dev)

EP&T GLOBAL LIMITED
Level 11 213 Miller Street, North Sydney, 2060, NSW, Australia
Tel.: (61) 284226000
Web Site: https://www.eptglobal.com
Year Founded: 1993
EPX—(ASX)
Rev.: $8,701,903
Assets: $9,960,384
Liabilities: $6,667,281
Net Worth: $3,293,103
Earnings: ($3,234,066)
Fiscal Year-end: 06/30/24
Custom Computer Programming Services
N.A.I.C.S.: 541511
Keith Gunaratne (Founder)

EPAPYRUS, INC.
Room 408 4th Floor 230, Pangyoyeok-ro, Bundang-gu, Seongnam-si, 13493, Gyeonggi-do, Korea (South)
Tel.: (82) 02 2051 5207   KR
Year Founded: 2003
Emp.: 100
Software Publisher
N.A.I.C.S.: 513210
Jeong Hee Kim (Founder & CEO)

Subsidiaries:

Artifex Software Inc. (1)
7 Mount Lassen Dr Ste A134, San Rafael, CA 94903-1149
Tel.: (415) 492-9861
Web Site: http://www.artifex.com
Electronics Stores
N.A.I.C.S.: 449210
Scott Sackett (VP)

EPCO CO., LTD.
Olinas Tower 12th Floor 4-1-3 Taihei, Sumida-ku, Tokyo, 130-0012, Japan
Tel.: (81) 368539165
Web Site: https://www.epco.co.jp
Year Founded: 1990

2311—(TKS)
Rev.: $35,868,310
Assets: $39,718,180
Liabilities: $6,558,250
Net Worth: $33,159,930
Earnings: $4,438,340
Emp.: 260
Fiscal Year-end: 12/31/23
Construction Services
N.A.I.C.S.: 541330
Yoshiyuki Iwasaki *(CEO-Grp)*

Subsidiaries:

EPCO (HK) LIMITED   (1)
Rm 3914 39/F Cosco Tower 183 Queen's
Road C, Sheung Wan, China (Hong Kong)
Tel.: (852) 2907 6920
Architectural Design Services
N.A.I.C.S.: 541310

Subsidiary (Non-US):

EPCO (Shenzhen) Ltd.   (2)
14F Baoyunda Logistics Information Build-
ing Bao'an District, Shenzhen, 518102,
China
Tel.: (86) 75527960696
Architectural Design Services
N.A.I.C.S.: 541310

EPCO (Jilin) Ltd.   (1)
Pioneer Park A8F No 86 Shenzhen Street,
Jilin, China
Tel.: (86) 43262260029
Architectural Design Services
N.A.I.C.S.: 541310

Enechange Co., Ltd.   (1)
3F Nihon Building 2-6-2 Otemachi,
Chiyoda-ku, Tokyo, 100-0004, Japan
Tel.: (81) 367746601
Web Site: http://www.enechange.co.jp
Data Processing Services
N.A.I.C.S.: 518210
Yohei Shiroguchi *(CEO)*

EPCOR UTILITIES, INC.
2000-10423 101 Street NW, Edmon-
ton, T5H 0E8, AB, Canada
Tel.: (780) 412-3414   AB
Web Site: http://www.epcor.com
Year Founded: 1996
Rev.: $1,426,407,360
Assets: $8,739,806,040
Liabilities: $5,905,357,080
Net Worth: $2,834,448,960
Earnings: $176,770,440
Fiscal Year-end: 12/31/19
Electric Power & Water Solutions
N.A.I.C.S.: 221122
Stephen John Stanley *(Sr VP-
Drainage Svcs)*

Subsidiaries:

Arizona-American Water
Company   (1)
19820 N 7th St Ste 201, Phoenix, AZ
85024
Tel.: (623) 445-2400
Sales Range: $50-74.9 Million
Emp.: 50
Water Utility
N.A.I.C.S.: 221310

EPCOR Energy   (1)
2000-10423 101 Street NW, Edmonton,
T5H 0E8, AB, Canada
Tel.: (780) 412-3414
Web Site: http://www.epcor.com
Sales Range: $1-9.9 Million
Emp.: 20
Regulated Electricity Services
N.A.I.C.S.: 221122

EPCOR Merchant & Capital, L.P.   (1)
EPCOR Place 505 2nd Street Southwest
8th Floor, Calgary, T2P 1N8, AB, Canada
Tel.: (403) 717-4600
Web Site: http://www.epcor.com
Sales Range: $125-149.9 Million
Emp.: 200
Non-regulated Electricity Services
N.A.I.C.S.: 221122

EPCOR USA Inc.   (1)

Tel.: (623) 445-2400
Web Site: http://www.epcor.com
Water & Wastewater Services
N.A.I.C.S.: 221310
Rebecca Stenholm *(Dir-Pub & Govt Affairs)*

Subsidiary (Domestic):

EPCOR Water Arizona Inc.   (2)
2355 W Pinnacle Peak Rd Ste 300, Phoe-
nix, AZ 85027
Tel.: (623) 445-2400
Electrical Transmission & Water Distr
N.A.I.C.S.: 221121
Troy Day *(VP-Ops)*

Subsidiary (Domestic):

Johnson Utilities, LLC   (3)
968 E Hunt Hwy, San Tan Valley, AZ 85143
Tel.: (480) 987-9870
Web Site: http://www.johnsonutilities.com
Sewage Treatment Facilities
N.A.I.C.S.: 221320
Chad Small *(Project Mgr)*

EPCOR Water Services, Inc.   (1)
215 10451 Shellbridge Way, Richmond,
V6X 2W8, BC, Canada
Tel.: (604) 270-9236
Sales Range: $1-9.9 Million
Emp.: 20
Water & Wastewater Services
N.A.I.C.S.: 924110

New Mexico American Water   (1)
1005 N Norris St, Clovis, NM 88101-6372
Tel.: (575) 763-5538
Sales Range: $75-99.9 Million
Emp.: 17
Water Supply
N.A.I.C.S.: 221310

Primary Energy Ventures LLC   (1)
2000 York Rd Ste 129, Oak Brook, IL
60523
Tel.: (630) 371-0505
Web Site: http://www.epcorusa.com
Sales Range: $100-124.9 Million
Emp.: 200
Investment Services
N.A.I.C.S.: 523999

Subsidiary (Domestic):

Portside Energy Corp.   (2)
6290 US Hwy 12, Portage, IN 46368
Tel.: (219) 763-7426
Sales Range: $50-74.9 Million
Emp.: 15
Provider of Electric Services
N.A.I.C.S.: 221118

Thunder Mountain Water
Company   (1)
51 Dinkle Ct, Edgewood, NM 87015
Tel.: (505) 281-7978
Electrical Transmission & Water Distr
N.A.I.C.S.: 221121

EPE SPECIAL OPPORTUNI-
TIES LIMITED
Clarendon House 2 Church Street,
Hamilton, HM 11, Bermuda   IM
Web Site:
    https://www.epeopportunities.com
Year Founded: 2003
EO.P—(AQSE)
Rev.: $4,775,638
Assets: $146,732,248
Liabilities: $23,396,823
Net Worth: $123,335,425
Earnings: ($504,726)
Fiscal Year-end: 01/31/24
Investment Management Service
N.A.I.C.S.: 523999

EPENDION AB
Stora Varvsgatan 13a, 201 24,
Malmo, Sweden
Tel.: (46) 40358600
Web Site: https://www.ependion.com
Year Founded: 1981
EPEN—(OMX)
Rev.: $199,348,675
Assets: $227,860,013

Liabilities: $134,749,501
Net Worth: $93,110,512
Earnings: $13,682,130
Emp.: 827
Fiscal Year-end: 12/31/22
Industrial Automation & Data Commu-
nication Services
N.A.I.C.S.: 334118
Bo Elisson *(Chm)*

Subsidiaries:

Beijer Electronics A/S   (1)
Betonvej 10, 4000, Roskilde, Denmark
Tel.: (45) 46757666
Web Site: http://www.beijerelectronics.dk
Electronic Products Mfr
N.A.I.C.S.: 334111

Beijer Electronics AS   (1)
Tegelverksveien 1, 3413, Lier, Norway
Tel.: (47) 32243000
Web Site: http://www.beijerelectronics.no
Electronic Products Mfr
N.A.I.C.S.: 334111

Beijer Electronics Corp.   (1)
14F No 215 Sec 3 Beixin Rd, Xindian Dist,
New Taipei City, 21341, Taiwan
Tel.: (886) 222183600
Web Site: http://www.beijerelectronics.tw
Electronic Products Mfr
N.A.I.C.S.: 334111

Beijer Electronics GmbH & Co.
KG   (1)
Max-Eyth-Strasse 21, 72622, Nurtingen,
Germany
Tel.: (49) 70 229 6600
Web Site: https://www.beijerelectronics.de
Electronic Products Mfr
N.A.I.C.S.: 334111

Beijer Electronics Inc.   (1)
1865 W 2100 S Ste200, Salt Lake City, UT
84119
Tel.: (801) 466-8770
Rev.: $7,500,000
Emp.: 50
Industrial Control Systems Distr
N.A.I.C.S.: 423610

Beijer Electronics Korea Co.,
Ltd.   (1)
1712 SK V1 Center 171, Geumcheon-gu,
Seoul, Korea (South)
Tel.: (82) 28530602
Electronic Products Mfr
N.A.I.C.S.: 334111

Beijer Electronics Trading (Shanghai)
Co., Ltd.   (1)
3rd Floor Building 11 No 99 Tianzhou Road,
Xuhui District, Shanghai, China
Tel.: (86) 216 145 0400
Web Site: https://www.beijerelectronics.cn
Electronic Products Mfr
N.A.I.C.S.: 334111

Beijer Electronics UK Ltd.   (1)
15 Oak Street, Carrington, Nottingham,
NG5 2AT, United Kingdom
Tel.: (44) 1158224863
Electronic Products Mfr
N.A.I.C.S.: 334111

Beijer Elektronik ve Tic. A.S.   (1)
Aydinevler Mah Aslanbey Cad No 5-7 Mert
Plaza B Blok Kat 2, Ofis 5-6-7-8 Maltepe,
34854, Istanbul, Turkiye
Tel.: (90) 216 366 3202
Web Site:
    https://www.beijerelektronik.com.tr
Electronic Products Mfr
N.A.I.C.S.: 334111

Virtual Access (Ireland) Ltd.   (1)
9B Beckett Way Park West Business Park,
Dublin, D12 PK44, Ireland
Tel.: (353) 16041800
Telecommunication Equipment Services
N.A.I.C.S.: 811210

Westermo Neratec AG   (1)
Rosswiesstrasse 29, 8608, Bubikon, Swit-
zerland
Tel.: (41) 552532000
Web Site: https://www.neratec.com
Fiscal Year-end: 12/31/2015
Wireless Product Mfr

N.A.I.C.S.: 334220

Westermo Network Technologies
AB   (1)
Metallverksgatan 6, SE-721 30, Vasteras,
Sweden
Tel.: (46) 16428000
Web Site: http://www.westermo.com
Industrial Automation Services
N.A.I.C.S.: 333998
Jenny Sjodahl *(CEO)*

EPH EUROPEAN PROPERTY
HOLDINGS PLC
RG Hodge Plaza 3rd Floor, PO Box
3483, Road Town, Tortola, Virgin Is-
lands (British)
Tel.: (284) 4944692   CY
Web Site:
    http://www.easternholdings.com
EPH—(SWX)
Rev.: $27,047,616
Assets: $1,676,278,672
Liabilities: $1,158,981,691
Net Worth: $517,296,981
Earnings: $6,995,180
Fiscal Year-end: 12/31/22
Real Estate Services & Developer
N.A.I.C.S.: 531210
Olga Melnikova *(Chm)*

Subsidiaries:

City Gate Stuttgart GmbH   (1)
Westendstrasse 28, 60325, Frankfurt, Ger-
many
Tel.: (49) 71121954549
Web Site: http://www.citygate-stuttgart.de
Property Development Services
N.A.I.C.S.: 531390

EPHRAIM RESOURCES LIM-
ITED
C- Nexia Perth Level 3 88 William
Street, Perth, 6000, WA, Australia
Tel.: (61) 894632463   AU
Web Site:
    http://www.ephraimresources.com.au
Agricultural Biogenetics Research
Services
N.A.I.C.S.: 541715
Steven Pynt *(Chm)*

EPI (HOLDINGS) LIMITED
Room 2107 21st Floor Great Eagle
Centre, 23 Harbour Road, Wanchai,
China (Hong Kong)
Tel.: (852) 26967799
Web Site:
    http://www.epiholdings.com
0689—(HKG)
Rev.: $5,750,505
Assets: $55,295,348
Liabilities: $7,315,440
Net Worth: $47,979,908
Earnings: ($5,960,115)
Emp.: 23
Fiscal Year-end: 12/31/22
Telecommunications Equipment
N.A.I.C.S.: 334290
Chun Kong Yiu *(Exec Dir)*

EPI BIOTECH CO., LTD.
M-1903 32 Songdogwahak-ro,
Yeonsu-gu, Incheon, 21984, Korea
(South)
Tel.: (82) 7042090556
Web Site:
    https://www.epibiotech.com
Year Founded: 2015
446440—(KRS)
Biotechnology Research & Develop-
ment Services
N.A.I.C.S.: 541714
Jonghyuk Seong *(CEO)*

EPI ENVIRONMENTAL TECH-
NOLOGIES INC.

EPI Environmental Technologies Inc.—(Continued)

Suite 801-1788 West Broadway, Vancouver, V6J 1Y1, BC, Canada
Tel.: (604) 738-6281　　　　BC
Web Site: https://www.epi-global.com
Year Founded: 1991
Oxo-biodegradable Plastic Technology; Chemical Additives Mfr & Distr
N.A.I.C.S.: 325998
Joseph G. Gho *(Chm & CEO)*

Subsidiaries:

EPI (Europe) Limited　　　　(1)
McLintocks Summer Lane, Barnsley, S70 2NZ, South Yorkshire, United Kingdom
Tel.: (44) 1629760168
Web Site: http://www.epi-global.com
Emp.: 1
Degradable & Biodegradable Chemical Additives Distr
N.A.I.C.S.: 424690
Joseph Gho *(CEO)*

EPI Environmental Products Inc.　(1)
Unit 207 102 Grover St, Lynden, WA 98264
Tel.: (604) 738-6281
Web Site: http://www.epi-global.com
Degradable & Biodegradable Chemical Additives Mfr
N.A.I.C.S.: 325998

EPI Environmental Products Inc.　(1)
Unit 210 - 27090 Gloucester Way, Langley, V4W 3Y5, BC, Canada
Tel.: (604) 856-8812
Degradable & Biodegradable Chemical Additives Mfr
N.A.I.C.S.: 325998

EPI S.A.
1 rue de l'Europe, 67520, Marlenheim, France
Tel.: (33) 388592989
Web Site: http://www.epi.fr
Sales Range: $250-299.9 Million
Emp.: 770
Household Furniture & Flooring Mfr & Distr
N.A.I.C.S.: 337122
Gerard Voirin *(Chm-Exec Bd)*

EPIC BPIFRANCE
27-31 avenue du General Leclerc, 94710, Maisons-Alfort, Cedex, France
Tel.: (33) 1 4179 8000　　　FR
Web Site: http://www.bpifrance.fr
Year Founded: 2005
Sales Range: Less than $1 Million
Public Finance Activities Organization
N.A.I.C.S.: 921130
Pierre Lepetit *(Chm, CEO & Gen Mgr)*

Subsidiaries:

SA BPI-Groupe　　　　　　(1)
27-31 Avenue du General Leclerc, 94710, Maisons-Alfort, Cedex, France　(50%)
Tel.: (33) 1 4179 8000
Web Site: http://www.bpifrance.fr
Holding Company; Private Equity & Equity Investment Services
N.A.I.C.S.: 551112
Arnaud Caudoux *(Dir-Fin & Warranty Mgmt)*

Subsidiary (Domestic):

Bpifrance Financement　　　(2)
27-31 avenue du General Leclerc, 94710, Maisons-Alfort, Cedex, France　(89.7%)
Tel.: (33) 1 4179 8000
Web Site: http://www.bpifrance.fr
Investment Financing Services
N.A.I.C.S.: 522299
Nicolas Dufourcq *(Chm & Dir Gen)*

Bpifrance Participations　　(2)
27-31 avenue du General Leclerc, 94710, Maisons-Alfort, Cedex, France
Tel.: (33) 1 4179 8000
Web Site: http://www.bpifrance.fr
Emp.: 2,000
Equity Investment Firm
N.A.I.C.S.: 523999

Nicolas Dufourcq *(Chm & Dir Gen)*

Subsidiary (Domestic):

Bpifrance Investissement SAS　(3)
27-31 avenue du General Leclerc, 94710, Maisons-Alfort, Cedex, France
Tel.: (33) 1 4179 8000
Web Site: http://www.bpifrance.fr
Emp.: 1,300
Investment Management Service
N.A.I.C.S.: 523940
Nicolas Dufourcq *(Chm)*

Subsidiary (Domestic):

BAOBAG SAS　　　　　　(4)
2-16 Boulevard de Vintimille, 13015, Marseilles, France
Tel.: (33) 491627719
Web Site: http://www.baobag.eu
Plastics Bag Mfr
N.A.I.C.S.: 326111
Alain Cavalier *(Pres)*

EPIC ENERGY LTD.
Sai Pooja Apt Office No 2 Plot No 374 Sector 19 C, Kopar Khairane, Navi Mumbai, 400709, India
Tel.: (91) 9833832664
Web Site: https://epicenergy.in
530407—(BOM)
Rev.: $196,901
Assets: $1,235,857
Liabilities: $245,454
Net Worth: $990,403
Earnings: ($87,155)
Emp.: 5
Fiscal Year-end: 03/31/21
Renewable Energy Devices Mfr
N.A.I.C.S.: 333613
Nikhil Morsawala *(Chm & CFO)*

Subsidiaries:

Epic Energy Ltd. - Navi Mumbai Works　　　　　　　　(1)
119 Patil Wadi Station Road Rabale West, Navi Mumbai, 400 701, India
Tel.: (91) 22 27692611
Solar Product Mfr
N.A.I.C.S.: 333414

EPICENTRE HOLDINGS LIMITED
48 Toh Guan Road East No 01-100 Enterprise Hub, Singapore, 608586, Singapore
Tel.: (65) 6259 5647　　　SG
Web Site:
　　http://www.epicentreasia.com
Year Founded: 2002
5MQ—(CAT)
Sales Range: $10-24.9 Million
Emp.: 50
Computer & Computer Products Retailer & Distr
N.A.I.C.S.: 449210
Tiong Hian Lim *(Chm & CEO-Acting)*

Subsidiaries:

Afor Sdn. Bhd.　　　　　(1)
No 34 17th Fl Cent Plz, Jln Sultan Ismail, Kuala Lumpur, 50250, Malaysia
Tel.: (60) 321411781
Web Site: http://www.epicentreasia.com
Sales Range: $25-49.9 Million
Emp.: 9
Computer Peripherals Mfr
N.A.I.C.S.: 334118
Ling Chuan Goh *(Exec Dir)*

EpiCentre Pte. Ltd.　　　　(1)
545 Orchard Rd Far E Shopping Ctr No 12-11, Singapore, 238882, Singapore
Tel.: (65) 62389376
Computer Peripherals Mfr
N.A.I.C.S.: 334118

EpiCentre Solutions Pte. Ltd.　(1)
Far E Shopping Ctr, 545 Orchard Rd No 12-11, Singapore, 238882, Singapore
Tel.: (65) 62389376
Computer Peripherals Mfr

N.A.I.C.S.: 334118

EPIGENOMICS AG
Ziegelhauser Landstrasse 3, 69120, Heidelberg, Germany
Tel.: (49) 62216492487　　De
Web Site:
　　https://www.epigenomics.com
Year Founded: 1998
EPGNY—(OTCIQ)
Rev.: $1,034,178
Assets: $8,348,347
Liabilities: $3,602,428
Net Worth: $4,745,919
Earnings: ($14,353,213)
Emp.: 37
Fiscal Year-end: 12/31/20
Cancer Blood Diagnostics & Specialty Applications
N.A.I.C.S.: 541380
Heino von Prondzynski *(Chm-Supervisory Bd)*

Subsidiaries:

Epigenomics Inc.　　　　(1)
11055 Flintkote Ave Ste A, San Diego, CA 92121
Tel.: (858) 429-6199
Molecular Diagnostic Product Mfr
N.A.I.C.S.: 325413

EPILEDS TECHNOLOGIES, INC.
No 7 Kanxi Rd, Xinshi Dist, T'ainan, Taiwan
Tel.: (886) 65050101
Web Site: https://www.epileds.com.tw
Year Founded: 2006
4956—(TAI)
Rev.: $37,033,878
Assets: $90,733,278
Liabilities: $34,423,982
Net Worth: $56,309,295
Earnings: ($4,537,493)
Emp.: 351
Fiscal Year-end: 12/31/23
LED Wafer & Chip Mfr
N.A.I.C.S.: 334413

Subsidiaries:

Suzhou Epileds Co., Ltd.　　(1)
Room 1812 Building 1 Lejia Building No 8 Jiarui Lane, Suzhou Industrial Park, Suzhou, Jiangsu, China
Tel.: (86) 51265755803
Light Emitting Diode Wafer & Chip Mfr
N.A.I.C.S.: 334413

EPINAL AUTO
91 Rue D Alsace, 88000, Epinal, Vosges, France
Tel.: (33) 329291515
Web Site:
　　http://www.epinalauto.peugeot.fr
Rev.: $31,000,000
Emp.: 78
N.A.I.C.S.: 441110
Johann Choux *(Dir-Pur)*

EPIPROCARE GMBH
Krausenstrasse 37, 10117, Berlin, Germany
Tel.: (49) 1729748880
Medical Product Mfr & Distr
N.A.I.C.S.: 339112

EPIRIS MANAGERS LLP
Forum St Pauls 33 Gutter Lane, London, EC2V 8AS, United Kingdom
Tel.: (44) 20 7214 4200　　UK
Web Site: http://www.epiris.co.uk
Private Equity Fund Management Services
N.A.I.C.S.: 523940
Alex Cooper-Evans *(Partner)*

Subsidiaries:

Bonhams 1793 Ltd.　　　　(1)
101 New Bond St, London, W1S 1SR, United Kingdom
Tel.: (44) 2074477447
Web Site: http://www.bonhams.com
Sales Range: $50-74.9 Million
Emp.: 481
Fine Art, Antiques & Collectibles Auction Services
N.A.I.C.S.: 459920
Caroline Oliphant *(Dir-Pictures)*

Subsidiary (US):

Bonhams & Butterfields　　(2)
220 San Bruno Ave, San Francisco, CA 94103
Tel.: (415) 861-7500
Web Site: http://www.bonhams.com
Sales Range: $50-74.9 Million
Emp.: 250
Fine Art, Antiques & Collectibles Auction Services
N.A.I.C.S.: 459920
Patrick Meade *(Sr VP-Bus Dev)*

Casual Dining Group Ltd　　(1)
163 Eversholt Street, London, NW1 1BU, United Kingdom
Tel.: (44) 20 7121 3200
Web Site:
　　http://www.casualdininggroup.com
Restaurant Operators
N.A.I.C.S.: 722511
Nick White *(Mng Dir-Bella Italia)*

Delinian Limited　　　　　(1)
8 Bouverie Street, London, EC4Y 8AX, United Kingdom
Tel.: (44) 2077798888
Web Site: https://www.delinian.com
Rev.: $432,841,136
Assets: $1,325,542,036
Liabilities: $527,609,992
Net Worth: $797,932,044
Earnings: $48,063,288
Emp.: 2,748
Fiscal Year-end: 09/30/2022
Holding Company; Trade Magazine, Newsletter, Journal & Book Publisher; Conference, Seminar & Training Course Organizer
N.A.I.C.S.: 551112
Tim Bratton *(Sec)*

Subsidiary (US):

Euromoney Training, Inc.　　(2)
225 Park Ave S 8th Fl, New York, NY 10003　　　　　　　　　(100%)
Tel.: (212) 361-3299
Web Site:
　　http://www.euromoneytraining.com
Legal, Information Technology Audit, Information Security, Banking & Financial Training Services
N.A.I.C.S.: 611430

MIS Training Institute, LLC　(2)
153 Cordaville Rd, Southborough, MA 01772-1834
Tel.: (508) 879-7999
Web Site: http://www.misti.com
Audit & Information Security Training Courses & Services; Conference & Trade Show Organizer
N.A.I.C.S.: 611430
Fred Roth *(VP-IT Audit Div)*

Subsidiary (Domestic):

Metal Bulletin Limited　　　(2)
Nestor House PlayHouse Yard, London, EC4V 5EX, United Kingdom
Tel.: (44) 2078279977
Web Site: http://www.metalbulletin.com
Sales Range: $100-124.9 Million
Emp.: 460
Data Management & Publishing Services
N.A.I.C.S.: 513140

Subsidiary (US):

American Metal Market　　(3)
707 Grant St Ste 1340, Pittsburgh, PA 15219
Tel.: (412) 765-2580
Web Site: http://www.amm.com

Sales Range: $25-49.9 Million
Emp.: 15
Journal Publisher
N.A.I.C.S.: 513120
Raju Daswani *(Mng Dir)*

Subsidiary (Non-US):

Metal Bulletin Japan **(3)**
Rm 701 Oak Mansions, Negishi 5 16 5,
Taito Ku, Tokyo, 1100003, Japan
Tel.: (81) 338765760
Web Site: http://www.metalbulletin.com
Data Management & Publishing
N.A.I.C.S.: 513140

Metal Bulletin Singapore **(3)**
3 Raffles Pl 08-01, Singapore, 048617, Singapore
Tel.: (65) 63335523
Web Site: http://www.metalbulletin.com
Sales Range: $25-49.9 Million
Emp.: 10
Data Management & Publishing
N.A.I.C.S.: 513140

Subsidiary (US):

Ned Davis Research Inc. **(2)**
600 Bird Bay Dr W, Venice, FL 34285
Tel.: (941) 412-2300
Web Site: http://www.ndr.com
Sales Range: $10-24.9 Million
Emp.: 90
Investment Research & Advisory Services
N.A.I.C.S.: 541910
Brian Frohn *(Mng Dir)*

RISI, Inc **(2)**
4 Alfred Cir, Bedford, MA 01730
Tel.: (322) 536-0748
Web Site: http://www.risiinfo.com
Price Reporting, Analytics & Events Organization & Services
N.A.I.C.S.: 519290
Matt Graves *(Sr VP-Fastmarkets Indices)*

Random Lengths Publications,
Inc. **(2)**
450 Country Club Road Ste 315, Eugene,
OR 97401
Tel.: (541) 686-9925
Web Site: https://www.rlmyprint.com
Periodical Publishers
N.A.I.C.S.: 513120

The Deal, LLC **(2)**
Hippodrome Bldg 1120 Ave of the Americas, New York, NY 10036
Tel.: (212) 224-3069
Web Site: http://www.thedeal.com
Internet Advertising Services
N.A.I.C.S.: 541810
Robert Kondracki *(Chief Acctg Officer)*

IFG Group plc **(1)**
70 Sir John Rogerson's Quay Grand Canal
Dock, Dublin, 2, Ireland
Tel.: (353) 1 632 4800
Web Site: http://www.ifggroup.com
Rev.: $111,208,030
Assets: $136,191,226
Liabilities: $42,252,021
Net Worth: $93,939,206
Earnings: ($1,210,645)
Emp.: 834
Fiscal Year-end: 12/31/2018
Financial Services
N.A.I.C.S.: 523940
Kathryn Purves *(CEO)*

Subsidiary (Non-US):

Associated Risk Consultants
Limited **(2)**
Unit 322 Vale Enterprise Centre Hayes
Road Sully, Penarth, CF64 5SY, United
Kingdom
Tel.: (44) 1446745245
Web Site: http://www.tcbrokers.com
Sales Range: $25-49.9 Million
Emp.: 2
Administrative Management Consulting Services
N.A.I.C.S.: 541611

DK Wild & Company Limited **(2)**
7 Woolgate Court 55-57 Saint Benedicts
Street, Norwich, NR2 4AP, United Kingdom
Tel.: (44) 1603760033
Web Site: http://www.wildandco.net

Sales Range: $50-74.9 Million
Emp.: 11
Financial Advisory Services
N.A.I.C.S.: 523940

Subsidiary (US):

FNTC America Limited **(2)**
Birch Pond Park Ste 349 410 Amherst St,
Nashua, NH 03063-1237
Tel.: (866) 978-2571
Web Site: http://www.fntcamerica.com
Trust Services
N.A.I.C.S.: 541199

Subsidiary (Non-US):

First National Trustee Company
Limited **(2)**
International House Castle Hill Victoria
Road, Douglas, Isle of Man
Tel.: (44) 1624630630
Web Site: http://www.fntc.com
Legal Support Services
N.A.I.C.S.: 541199
Declan Kenny *(CEO)*

Foster & Cranfield Ltd. **(2)**
25 Britton Street, London, EC1M 5NY,
United Kingdom **(100%)**
Tel.: (44) 2076081941
Web Site: http://www.foster-and-cranfield.co.uk
Emp.: 3
Second-hand Endowment Policies Auctioneer
N.A.I.C.S.: 524298

IFG Asia Limited **(2)**
8 F Shimbashi Kato Building 5-26-8 Shimbashi, Minato-ku, Tokyo, 105-0004, Japan
Tel.: (81) 334362001
Web Site: http://www.ifg-asia.com
Investment Advisory Services
N.A.I.C.S.: 523999

Subsidiary (Domestic):

IFG Quigley Limited **(2)**
Ifg House Booterstown Hall, Blackrock, Ireland
Tel.: (353) 12752915
Web Site: http://www.ifg.ie
Investment Advisory Services
N.A.I.C.S.: 523940

Subsidiary (Non-US):

IPS Pensions Limited **(2)**
1 Castlepark Tower Hill, Bristol, BS2 0JA,
United Kingdom
Tel.: (44) 1179290941
Sales Range: $50-74.9 Million
Emp.: 50
Pension Fund Management Services
N.A.I.C.S.: 524292
Richard Valentine *(Gen Mgr)*

The IPS Partnership plc **(2)**
4th Fl Boundary House 91-93 Charterhouse
Street, London, EC1M 6HR, United Kingdom
Tel.: (44) 2073156600
Financial Investment Management Services
N.A.I.C.S.: 523999

TI Media Limited **(1)**
3rd Floor 161 Marsh Wall, London, E14
9AP, United Kingdom
Tel.: (44) 2031485000
Web Site: http://www.ti-media.com
Digital Magazine Publishing Services
N.A.I.C.S.: 513120
Sam Finlay *(Chief Revenue Officer)*

Subsidiary (Domestic):

Time Inc. (UK) Property Investments
Ltd **(2)**
3rd Floor 161 Marsh Wall, London, E14
9AP, United Kingdom
Tel.: (44) 2031485000
Periodical Publishing Services
N.A.I.C.S.: 513120

Unbound Group plc **(1)**
17 Old Park Lane, London, W1K 1QT,
United Kingdom
Tel.: (44) 2038748300
Web Site: http://www.electraequity.com

Sales Range: $1-9.9 Million
Private Equity Investment Trust
N.A.I.C.S.: 525990
Neil Anthony Johnson *(Chm)*

Holding (Domestic):

AXIO Group Management Ltd. **(2)**
Tallis House 2 Tallis Street, London, EC4Y
0AB, United Kingdom **(69%)**
Tel.: (44) 20 7975 1600
Web Site: http://www.axiogroup.net
Investment Management Service
N.A.I.C.S.: 523940
Hans Gieskes *(Chm)*

Beaconsfield Footwear Limited **(2)**
2 Peel Road, West Pimbo, Skelmersdale,
WN8 9PT, Lancs, United Kingdom **(61%)**
Tel.: (44) 1695 712 720
Web Site: http://www.hottershoes.com
Sales Range: $100-124.9 Million
Emp.: 1,000
Footwear Mfr
N.A.I.C.S.: 316210
Stewart Houlgrave *(Founder)*

EPIROC AB
Sickla Industrivag 19, SE-131 54,
Nacka, Sweden
Tel.: (46) 107550000 SE
Web Site:
  https://www.epirocgroup.com
Year Founded: 1873
EPI.A—(OMX)
Rev.: $5,651,839,988
Assets: $6,348,778,181
Liabilities: $2,863,618,908
Net Worth: $3,485,159,272
Earnings: $885,854,243
Emp.: 18,211
Fiscal Year-end: 12/31/23
Industrial Machinery Mfr
N.A.I.C.S.: 333120
Anders Linden *(CFO & Sr VP-Controlling & Fin)*

Subsidiaries:

CQMS Razer Pty. Ltd. **(1)**
Level 5 828 Pacific Highway, Gordon, 2072,
NSW, Australia
Tel.: (61) 294185600
Web Site: https://crmining.com
Mining Equipment Mfr
N.A.I.C.S.: 333131
John Barbagallo *(CEO)*

Construction Tools GmbH **(1)**
Hambacher Str 5 OT Stadtlengsfeld, Dermbach, 36466, Stadtlengsfeld, Germany
Tel.: (49) 3695851090
Web Site: https://www.erkat.com
Construction Equipment Mfr
N.A.I.C.S.: 333120
Martina Schierholz *(Gen Mgr)*

Construction Tools GmbH **(1)**
Helenenstrasse 149, 45143, Essen, Germany
Tel.: (49) 2016330
Construction Equipment Mfr
N.A.I.C.S.: 333120

Corescan Pty. Ltd. **(1)**
1/127 Grandstand Road, Ascot Vale, 6104,
WA, Australia
Tel.: (61) 892772355
Web Site: https://corescan.com.au
Geological Logging Services
N.A.I.C.S.: 213114

Corescan S.A. de C.V. **(1)**
Rosa de Castilla Poniente 5 Col Quinta
Emilia, 83214, Hermosillo, Sonora, Mexico
Tel.: (52) 5553505577
Geological Logging Services
N.A.I.C.S.: 213114

Corescan S.A.C. **(1)**
Jr Sta Catalina Zona E Mz 29 - Lote 3A
-Grupo Zonal 14 y 15, Semi Rural
Pachacutec-Arequipa, Arequipa, Peru
Tel.: (51) 17003328
Mining Services
N.A.I.C.S.: 213114

Corescan SpA **(1)**

San Pablo 9900 Oficina 5 Edificio 1, Pudahuel, Chile
Tel.: (56) 227125057
Mining Services
N.A.I.C.S.: 213114

Coreshed Pty. Ltd. **(1)**
1/127 Grandstand Road, Ascot Vale, 6105,
WA, Australia
Tel.: (61) 892772355
Web Site: https://coreshed.com
Data Management & Storage Services
N.A.I.C.S.: 541513

Epiroc (Thailand) Ltd. **(1)**
405 Soi Bangna-Trad 12, Bangna, Bangkok, 10260, Thailand
Tel.: (66) 20266770
Web Site: https://www.epiroc.com
Construction Equipment Mfr
N.A.I.C.S.: 333120

Epiroc Argentina S.A.C.I. **(1)**
Estados Unidos 5335, Buenos Aires,
B1667JHQ, Argentina
Tel.: (54) 3327525300
Web Site: https://www.epiroc.com
Engineering Services
N.A.I.C.S.: 541330
Ricardo Ornelas *(Gen Mgr)*

Epiroc Armenia LLC **(1)**
St Ghazar Parpetsi 11-2, Yerevan, 0002,
Armenia
Tel.: (374) 10530669
Web Site: https://www.epiroc.com
Engineering Services
N.A.I.C.S.: 541330
Arsen Vardanyan *(Country Mgr)*

Epiroc Australia Pty Ltd. **(1)**
19 Reid Road International Airport, Perth,
6105, WA, Australia
Tel.: (61) 300366880
Web Site: https://www.epiroc.com
Engineering Services
N.A.I.C.S.: 541330

Epiroc B-H d.o.o. **(1)**
Doglodi 1, 71000, Sarajevo, Bosnia & Herzegovina
Tel.: (387) 33674391
Web Site: https://www.epiroc.com
Engineering Services
N.A.I.C.S.: 541330

Epiroc Bolivia Equipos y Servicios
S.A. **(1)**
Av 20 de Octubre Esquina Calle Campos
No 2665 Edificio Torre Azul, Mezannine
Norte, La Paz, Bolivia
Tel.: (591) 2112000
Engineering Services
N.A.I.C.S.: 541330

Epiroc Botswana (Pty) Ltd. **(1)**
Plot 175 Unit 1 Gaborone International
Commerce Park, PO Box 41565, Gaborone, Botswana
Tel.: (267) 3959155
Web Site: https://www.epiroc.com
Engineering Services
N.A.I.C.S.: 541330

Epiroc Brasil Comercializacao De
Produtos E Servicos Para Mineracao
E Construcao Ltda. **(1)**
Alameda Tocantins 125 Andar 8 Sala
801/802 Alphaville, Barueri, 06455-931, SP,
Brazil
Tel.: (55) 1134788200
Web Site: https://www.epiroc.com
Engineering Services
N.A.I.C.S.: 541330

Epiroc Bulgaria EOOD **(1)**
Bul Iskarsko Shose 7 Sgrada No 3 Ofis 4,
1528, Sofia, Bulgaria
Tel.: (359) 24896050
Web Site: https://www.epiroc.com
N.A.I.C.S.: 333517

Epiroc Burkina Faso SARL **(1)**
Quartier Dassasgho Rue 27-67 Porte 150,
Ouagadougou, Burkina Faso
Tel.: (226) 25429900
Web Site: https://www.epiroc.com
Engineering Services
N.A.I.C.S.: 541330

Epiroc Canada Inc. **(1)**

Epiroc AB—(Continued)

1025 Tristar Drive, Mississauga, L5T 1W5, ON, Canada
Tel.: (289) 562-0100
Web Site: https://www.epiroc.com
Engineeering Services
N.A.I.C.S.: 541330
Nathalie Gaudet (Mgr-HR)

Epiroc Central America S.A. (1)
Carrera 85 K 46-66 San Cayetano Business Complex-Building B, Office 201, Bogota, Colombia
Tel.: (57) 17433728
Mining Equipment Mfr
N.A.I.C.S.: 333131
Juan Carlos Valencia (Project Mgr)

Epiroc Central Asia LLP (1)
St Iliyas Zhansugiruly 14, Nur-Sultan, 010000, Kazakhstan
Tel.: (7) 7172738260
Mining Equipment Mfr
N.A.I.C.S.: 333131

Epiroc Chile S.A.C. (1)
Panamericana Norte N 5001, Conchali, Santiago, Chile
Tel.: (56) 224423600
Web Site: https://www.epiroc.com
Engineeering Services
N.A.I.C.S.: 541330
Charlie Ekberg (Gen Mgr)

Epiroc Colombia S.A.S. (1)
Oficina Principal Colombia Carrera 85 K 46-66, Complejo Empresarial San Cayetano-Edificio B-Oficina 201, Bogota, Colombia
Tel.: (57) 17433728
Web Site: https://www.epiroc.com
Engineeering Services
N.A.I.C.S.: 541330

Epiroc Croatia d.o.o. (1)
Zagrebacka cesta 143/A, 10000, Zagreb, Croatia
Tel.: (385) 16111288
Web Site: https://www.epiroc.com
Engineeering Services
N.A.I.C.S.: 541330
Nikolina Vrabec (Country Mgr)

Epiroc Czech Republic s.r.o. (1)
Antala Staska 510/38, Krc, 140 00, Prague, 4, Czech Republic
Tel.: (420) 234713900
Web Site: https://www.epiroc.com
Engineeering Services
N.A.I.C.S.: 541330

Epiroc DRC SARL (1)
23 Avenue Lac Kipopo, Lubumbashi, Congo, Democratic Republic of
Tel.: (243) 991004430
Web Site: https://www.epiroc.com
Engineeering Services
N.A.I.C.S.: 541330
Kennedy Ngandu (Mgr-Bus Line)

Epiroc Deutschland GmbH (1)
Helenenstrasse 149, 45143, Essen, Germany
Tel.: (49) 20124678268
Web Site: https://www.epiroc.com
Construction Equipment Mfr
N.A.I.C.S.: 333120
Baki Attila (Mgr-Bus Line Capital Equipment)

Epiroc Drilling Solutions LLC (1)
2100 N 1st St, Garland, TX 75040
Tel.: (972) 496-7400
N.A.I.C.S.: 333517

Epiroc Drilling Tools AB (1)
Bjornbacksvagen 2, 737 30, Fagersta, Sweden
Tel.: (46) 22346100
N.A.I.C.S.: 333517

Epiroc Drilling Tools LLC (1)
13278 Lincoln Way W, Fort Loudon, PA 17224
Tel.: (717) 369-3177
N.A.I.C.S.: 333517

Epiroc Eastern Africa Ltd. (1)
Sameer Business Park Block C1 2nd Floor, PO Box 38884, 00100, Nairobi, Kenya

Tel.: (254) 709556000
Web Site: https://www.epiroc.com
Engineeering Services
N.A.I.C.S.: 541330
Saidi Gloria (Engr-Sls)

Epiroc FVT Inc. (1)
103 - 19055 Airport Way, Pitt Meadows, V3Y 0G4, BC, Canada
Tel.: (604) 465-0529
Web Site: https://www.fvtresearch.com
Electric Mining Vehicle Mfr
N.A.I.C.S.: 336320

Epiroc Finland Oy Ab (1)
Itainen Valkoisenlahteentie 14 A, 01380, Vantaa, Finland
Tel.: (358) 207189380
Web Site: https://www.epiroc.com
Mining Equipment Mfr
N.A.I.C.S.: 333131

Epiroc France S.A.S. (1)
Campus Saint-Christophe Batiment Galilee 3-10 Avenue de l Entreprise, Pontoise, 95863, Cergy, Cedex, France
Tel.: (33) 134333050
Web Site: https://www.epiroc.com
Mining Equipment Mfr
N.A.I.C.S.: 333131

Epiroc Hellas S.A. (1)
95 Koropiou Varis Avenue, 19400, Koropi, Greece
Tel.: (30) 2146878560
Web Site: https://www.epiroc.com
Engineeering Services
N.A.I.C.S.: 541330

Epiroc Hong Kong Ltd. (1)
36A Ko Po Tsuen Kam Tin Road, Yuen Long, Hong Kong, China (Hong Kong)
Tel.: (852) 24880103
Web Site: https://www.epiroc.com
Engineeering Services
N.A.I.C.S.: 541330

Epiroc Italia S.r.l. (1)
Via Galileo Galilei 40, 20092, Cinisello Balsamo, MI, Italy
Tel.: (39) 026606731
Web Site: https://www.epiroc.com
Engineeering Services
N.A.I.C.S.: 541330

Epiroc Japan KK (1)
Kawawa-cho 50-1, Tsuzuki-ku, Yokohama, 224-0057, Kanagawa, Japan
Tel.: (81) 459336541
Mining Equipment Mfr
N.A.I.C.S.: 333131
Tom Ross (Mktg Mgr)

Epiroc Korea Co., Ltd. (1)
6F Yemiji Building 14-1 Pangyoyeok-ro 192beon-gil, Bundang-gu, Seongnam, Gyeonggi-do, Korea (South)
Tel.: (82) 316258970
Web Site: https://www.epiroc.com
Construction Equipment Mfr
N.A.I.C.S.: 333120

Epiroc Makina S.A. (1)
Icerenkoy Quarter Karaman Farm Road Street Snow Plaza No 47/11, Atasehir, Istanbul, 34572, Turkiye
Tel.: (90) 2165241000
Web Site: https://www.epiroc.com
Construction Equipment Mfr
N.A.I.C.S.: 333120

Epiroc Mali SARL (1)
Route de Sotuba Rue 78 Porte 239, Bamako, Mali
Tel.: (223) 44980600
Web Site: https://www.epiroc.com
Construction Equipment Mfr
N.A.I.C.S.: 333120
Moussa Diakite (Product Mgr-Parts)

Epiroc Maroc SARL (1)
N 21 Lotissement Attawfiq Rue Ibnou El Koutia, Quartier Industriel Oukacha, 20580, Casablanca, Morocco
Tel.: (212) 520439900
Web Site: https://www.epiroc.com
Mining Equipment Mfr
N.A.I.C.S.: 333131

Epiroc Mexico, S.A. de C.V. (1)

Oficina Central -Jose Luis Lagrange 103 Piso 2 Col Polanco, Alcaldia Miguel Hidalgo Ciudad de, 11560, Mexico, Mexico
Tel.: (52) 4789852322
Web Site: https://www.epiroc.com
Engineeering Services
N.A.I.C.S.: 541330

Epiroc Meyco AG (1)
Buetigenstrasse 80, 2557, Studen, Switzerland
Tel.: (41) 325550010
Web Site: https://www.epiroc.com
Engineeering Services
N.A.I.C.S.: 541330

Epiroc Middle East FZE (1)
Flr 17 Jafza View 18 Building, PO Box 263681, Dubai, United Arab Emirates
Tel.: (971) 48213700
Web Site: https://www.epiroc.com
Construction Equipment Mfr
N.A.I.C.S.: 333120

Epiroc Mineria e Ingenieria Civil Espana, S.L.U (1)
Avda Jose Garate n 3-P I de Coslada, 28823, Coslada, Madrid, Spain
Tel.: (34) 919908538
Web Site: https://www.epiroc.com
Construction Equipment Mfr
N.A.I.C.S.: 333120

Epiroc Mining (Namibia) (Pty) Ltd. (1)
6 Jan Marais Street, Northern Industrial Area, Windhoek, Namibia
Tel.: (264) 840009400
Web Site: https://www.epiroc.com
Mining Equipment Mfr
N.A.I.C.S.: 333131

Epiroc Mining India Ltd. (1)
14th Floor Tower 1 Fountainhead Phoenix Market City Nagar Road, Viman Nagar, Pune, 411 014, Maharashtra, India
Tel.: (91) 7219722200
Mining Equipment Mfr
N.A.I.C.S.: 333131

Epiroc Mocambique Limitada (1)
Rua Beijo da Mulata n 111 Sommerschield 2, 1102, Maputo, Mozambique
Tel.: (258) 21494383
Web Site: https://www.epiroc.com
Engineeering Services
N.A.I.C.S.: 541330

Epiroc Mongolia LLC (1)
G Center building 8th floor 1, Sukhbaatar District, Ulaanbaatar, Mongolia
Tel.: (976) 70129294
Web Site: https://www.epiroc.com
Engineeering Services
N.A.I.C.S.: 541330
Batzorig Jamsranjav (Mgr-Bus Line)

Epiroc Norge AS (1)
Svarthagsveien 7, Vestby, 1543, Langhus, Norway
Tel.: (47) 64860300
Web Site: https://www.epiroc.com
Mining Equipment Mfr
N.A.I.C.S.: 333131

Epiroc Peru S.A. (1)
Francisco Grana 150-152 Urb Santa Catalina La Victoria, Lima, Peru
Tel.: (51) 14116100
Web Site: https://www.epiroc.com
Mining Equipment Mfr
N.A.I.C.S.: 333131

Epiroc Philippines Inc. (1)
2nd and 4th Floor LIIP Business Center Building B10 L4 LIIP Avenue, LIIP Maplasan, Binan, Philippines
Tel.: (63) 282499480
Web Site: https://www.epiroc.com
Construction Equipment Mfr
N.A.I.C.S.: 333120

Epiroc Portugal Unipessoal Lda (1)
Lake Towers-Building D Rua Daciano Baptista Marques 245, 4400-617, Vila Nova de Gaia, Portugal
Tel.: (351) 221202374
Construction Equipment Mfr
N.A.I.C.S.: 333120

Epiroc RUS LLC (1)

Sergeya Makeeva St Hom 13, Moscow, 123022, Russia
Tel.: (7) 84959335552
N.A.I.C.S.: 333517

Epiroc Srbija a.d. (1)
Milutina Milankovica 23, 11070, Novi Beograd, Serbia
Tel.: (381) 112201640
Construction Equipment Mfr
N.A.I.C.S.: 333120

Epiroc Sweden AB (1)
Sjobodavagen 9, 145 53, Norsborg, Sweden
Tel.: (46) 20784455
Web Site: https://www.epiroc.com
Mining Equipment Distr
N.A.I.C.S.: 423810

Epiroc Tajikistan LLC (1)
Avenue Koshkarbaeva 1/5, 010000, Nur-Sultan, Kazakhstan
Tel.: (7) 7172649815
N.A.I.C.S.: 333517

Epiroc Tanzania Ltd. (1)
Plot 35 Nyakato Industrial Area, Mwanza, Tanzania
Tel.: (255) 746983401
Web Site: https://www.epiroc.com
Construction Equipment Mfr
N.A.I.C.S.: 333120
Joseph Wainaina (Mgr-Bus Line)

Epiroc Tashkent LLC (1)
St Shota Rustaveli 53B, Tashkent, 100100, Uzbekistan
Tel.: (998) 711204764
Construction Equipment Mfr
N.A.I.C.S.: 333120

Epiroc Trading Co., Ltd. (1)
No 2 Hengtai Road Economic and Technological Development Zone, Nanjing, Jiangsu, China
Tel.: (86) 4008287608
Web Site: https://www.epiroc.cn
Construction Equipment Services
N.A.I.C.S.: 811310

Epiroc USA LLC (1)
8001 Arista Pl Ste 400, Broomfield, CO 80021
Web Site: https://www.epiroc.com
Industrial Equipment Distr
N.A.I.C.S.: 423830

Epiroc Ukraine LLC (1)
9 Stepana Bandery Building 3, 04073, Kiev, Ukraine
Tel.: (380) 444991870
Web Site: https://www.epiroc.com
Mining Equipment Mfr
N.A.I.C.S.: 333131

Epiroc Zambia Ltd. (1)
Plot 210 Kabundi Road, PO Box 11291, Chingola, Zambia
Tel.: (260) 760474100
Web Site: https://www.epiroc.com
Construction Equipment Mfr
N.A.I.C.S.: 333120
Tusho Aponde (Mgr-Safety Health Environmental & Quality)

Epiroc Zimbabwe (Private) Ltd. (1)
122 Lytton Road, Workington, Harare, Zimbabwe
Tel.: (263) 772140566
Web Site: https://www.epiroc.com
Construction Equipment Mfr
N.A.I.C.S.: 333120
Davis Nongera (Country Mgr)

Fordia Group Inc. (1)
3 Hotel-de-Ville, Dollard des Ormeaux, H9B 3G4, QC, Canada
Tel.: (514) 336-9211
Web Site: http://www.fordia.com
Industrial Equipment Distr
N.A.I.C.S.: 423830

GIA (Shanghai) Mining Equipment Co., Ltd. (1)
Room 401 Building 6 No 138 Xinjun Ring Road, Minhang District, Shanghai, 201114, China
Tel.: (86) 2134786216
Web Site: http://www.giaproduct.com
Construction Equipment Services

N.A.I.C.S.: 811310
Jackey Lee *(Natl Dir-Sls & Svcs)*

Italparts Italia S.r.l. (1)
Via Grandi 4/16, 20068, Peschiera Borromeo, MI, Italy
Tel.: (39) 0299291476
Web Site: https://www.ital-parts.it
Industrial Machinery Distr
N.A.I.C.S.: 423830

JCAC Technologies Inc (1)
8 Manning Close NE Suite 200, Calgary, T2E 7N5, AB, Canada
Tel.: (403) 203-2018
Web Site: https://3d-p.com
Open-Sourced Computing Platforms & Multiple Application Wireless Networks to Various Industries
N.A.I.C.S.: 513210
Evan Hansen *(CTO)*

Subsidiary (US):

3D-P (2)
4500 E Aviation Way, Safford, AZ 85546 (100%)
Web Site: http://www.3d-p.com
Open-Sourced Computing Platforms
N.A.I.C.S.: 513210
Evan Hansen *(COO)*

Subsidiary (Non-US):

3D-P (2)
207 Bank St Unit 1 East Victoria Park, Perth, 6101, WA, Australia (100%)
Tel.: (61) 18009559337
Web Site: http://www.3d-p.com
Open-Sourced Computing Platforms & Wireless Networks
N.A.I.C.S.: 513210
Mal Jones *(Gen Mgr & VP)*

JTMEC Pty Ltd. (1)
50 Boulder Rd, Malaga, 6090, WA, Australia
Tel.: (61) 892056400
Web Site: https://jtmec.com.au
Electrical Contracting Services
N.A.I.C.S.: 238210

Meglab Electronique Inc. (1)
281 19th Street, Val-d'Or, J9P 0L7, QC, Canada
Tel.: (819) 824-7710
Web Site: https://meglab.ca
N.A.I.C.S.: 334419
Eric Dessureault *(VP-Operations)*

MineRP Canada Limited (1)
432 Westmount Ave Unit AB, Sudbury, P3A 5Z8, ON, Canada
Tel.: (705) 525-4774
Software Development Services
N.A.I.C.S.: 541511

Mining Tag S.A. (1)
Suecia 172 Floor 2, Providencia, Chile
Tel.: (56) 942913983
Web Site: https://miningtag.com
Polymetallic Mining Services
N.A.I.C.S.: 213114

New Concept Mining (Pty) Ltd. (1)
109 Adcock Ingram Avenue, Aeroton, Johannesburg, South Africa
Tel.: (27) 114946000
Web Site:
https://www.newconceptmining.com
Mining Equipment Mfr
N.A.I.C.S.: 333131

New Concept Mining Chile SpA (1)
Don Carlos 2939 Oficina 208, Las Condes, Santiago, Chile
Tel.: (56) 25966406
Metal Mining Services
N.A.I.C.S.: 213114

New Concept Mining Peru S.A.C. (1)
Av Venezuela 2415-2419, El Cercado, Lima, Peru
Tel.: (51) 13397517
Mining Equipment Mfr
N.A.I.C.S.: 333131

PT Epiroc Southern Asia (1)
South Quarter Building Tower C11th Floor Unit H Jl RA Kartini Kav 8, Jakarta Selatan,

12560, Indonesia
Tel.: (62) 2122722212
Web Site: https://www.epiroc.com
Engineeering Services
N.A.I.C.S.: 541330

ProReman Pty Ltd. (1)
9 Formation Street, Wacol, 4076, QLD, Australia
Tel.: (61) 733546700
Web Site: https://www.hyperfluid.com.au
Hay-Performance Fluid Power Product Mfr & Distr
N.A.I.C.S.: 333996

RCT Global SpA (1)
Reyes Lavalle 3170 Office 28, Las Condes, Chile
Tel.: (56) 352299409
Mining Services
N.A.I.C.S.: 213114

Radlink Pty. Ltd. (1)
22 Oxleigh Drive, Malaga, 6090, WA, Australia
Tel.: (61) 1300735583
Web Site: https://radlink.com.au
Emp.: 423
Satellite Telecommunication Services
N.A.I.C.S.: 517410

Remote Control Technologies Pty Ltd. (1)
Unit 1-6/511 Abernethy Rd, Kewdale, 6105, WA, Australia
Tel.: (61) 893536577
Web Site: https://rct-global.com
Mining Services
N.A.I.C.S.: 213114

Sautec AS (1)
Tule 10, 76505, Saue, Estonia
Tel.: (372) 6709670
Web Site: https://www.sautec.ee
N.A.I.C.S.: 333517

Secoroc Ghana Ltd. (1)
Block B Plot Nos 10A/11A/12A/13A Gausu, Obuasi, Ghana
Tel.: (233) 308251085
Web Site: https://www.epiroc.com
Construction Equipment Mfr
N.A.I.C.S.: 333120
Eric Nyarko Mensah *(Mgr-Supply & Logistics)*

SensIR Inc. (1)
104 S Estes Dr Ste 301K, Chapel Hill, NC 27514
Tel.: (919) 308-7731
Web Site: https://www.sensir.com
N.A.I.C.S.: 334510
Mike Sullivan *(Pres)*

Shandong Rock Drilling Tools Co., Ltd. (1)
No 3 Sanshan Road, Xihu Yanggu, Liaocheng, Shandong, China
Tel.: (86) 6356511658
Web Site: https://www.cnrocktool.cn
Emp.: 262
Construction Equipment Mfr
N.A.I.C.S.: 333120

Stanley Infrastructure, LLC (1)
3810 SE Naef Rd, Milwaukie, OR 97267
Tel.: (503) 659-5660
Web Site:
https://www.stanleyinfrastructure.com
Cutlery & Hand Tool Mfr
N.A.I.C.S.: 332216

EPISIL HOLDINGS, INC.
No 18 Innovation Road I, Science Based Industrial Park, Hsin-chu, 30076, Taiwan
Tel.: (886) 35779245
Web Site: https://www.episil.com
Year Founded: 2014
3707—(TPE)
Rev.: $277,643,780
Assets: $401,729,231
Liabilities: $151,951,068
Net Worth: $249,778,163
Earnings: $34,583,591
Emp.: 600
Fiscal Year-end: 12/31/22
Financial Investment Services

N.A.I.C.S.: 523999
J. H. Shyu *(CEO)*

EPISIL PRECISION INC.
No 10 Dusing Road I Hsinchu Science Park, Hsinchu, 30078, Taiwan
Tel.: (886) 35632255
Web Site: https://www.epi.episil.com
Year Founded: 1998
3016—(TAI)
Rev.: $138,542,851
Assets: $222,766,792
Liabilities: $62,616,205
Net Worth: $160,150,587
Earnings: $5,364,433
Emp.: 271
Fiscal Year-end: 12/31/23
Silicon Wafers Mfr
N.A.I.C.S.: 333242
Jian-Hua Syu *(Chm)*

Subsidiaries:

PRECISION SILICON JAPAN CO., LTD. (1)
2F Kawai Building 1-32-6 Higashiikebukuro, Toshima-ku, Tokyo, 170-0013, Japan
Tel.: (81) 359798731
Sales Range: $25-49.9 Million
Emp.: 4
Silicon Wafers Mfr
N.A.I.C.S.: 334413
Joseph Lee *(Pres)*

EPISIL TECHNOLOGIES, INC.
No. 3 Innovation Road I Science Based Industrial Park, Hsin-chu, 300, Taiwan
Tel.: (886) 35779245
Web Site: http://www.tech.episil.com
Year Founded: 1985
Semiconductor Components Mfr
N.A.I.C.S.: 334419
Daniel Wang *(Mgr-Sls)*

EPISURF MEDICAL AB
Karlavagen 60, 114 49, Stockholm, Sweden
Tel.: (46) 86120020
Web Site: https://episurf.com
Year Founded: 2008
EPIS.B—(OMX)
Rev.: $842,352
Assets: $33,034,848
Liabilities: $2,173,024
Net Worth: $30,861,824
Earnings: ($8,460,144)
Emp.: 29
Fiscal Year-end: 12/31/21
Implants & Surgical Instruments Mfr
N.A.I.C.S.: 339112
Pall Ryfors *(CEO)*

EPLAY DIGITAL INC.
Suite 970 - 777 Hornby Street, Vancouver, V6Z 1S4, BC, Canada
Tel.: (403) 775-9475 BC
Web Site:
https://www.eplaydigital.com
Year Founded: 2013
EPY—(CNSX)
Rev.: $39,992
Assets: $40,595
Liabilities: $1,207,395
Net Worth: ($1,166,799)
Earnings: ($529,047)
Fiscal Year-end: 12/31/22
E-Sports, Gaming & Digital Media Services
N.A.I.C.S.: 541715

Subsidiaries:

PokerVision Media Inc. (1)
1025 10th Street, Calgary, T2G 3E1, AB, Canada
Tel.: (403) 723-2800
Web Site: http://www.pokervisionmedia.com
Social Media Services
N.A.I.C.S.: 541840

EPOCH CHEMTRONICS CORP.
5F-1 No 35 Xintai Rd, Hsinchu County, Zhubei, 302, Taiwan
Tel.: (886) 35545488
Web Site: https://www.epoch-optic.com
Year Founded: 1997
3633—(TAI)
Emp.: 900
Led Lighting Product Mfr
N.A.I.C.S.: 335132
J. P. Hsu *(Chm)*

EPOCH CO. LTD.
2-2 Komagata 2 chome, Taitoku, Tokyo, 111 8618, Japan
Tel.: (81) 338438812
Web Site: http://www.epoch.jp
Year Founded: 1958
Sales Range: $10-24.9 Million
Emp.: 200
Toy & Game Mfr
N.A.I.C.S.: 339930
Michihiro Maeda *(Pres & CEO)*

Subsidiaries:

International Playthings, LLC (1)
75D Lackawanna Ave, Parsippany, NJ 07054
Tel.: (973) 316-5883
Web Site: http://www.intplay.com
Toy Developer & Supplier
N.A.I.C.S.: 423920
Michael Varda *(CEO)*

EPOCH ENERGY TECHNOLOGY SDN BHD
9 Jalan Shamelin Niaga 1 Shamelin Heights Business Park, Taman Shamelin Perkasa Cheras, 56100, Kuala Lumpur, Malaysia
Tel.: (60) 3 9200 3368
Year Founded: 2001
Cleaning Equipment Mfr & Distr
N.A.I.C.S.: 333131

EPOWER METALS INC.
Suite 440 580 Hormby St, Vancouver, V6C 3B6, BC, Canada
Tel.: (604) 764-7094 Ca
Web Site:
http://www.argusmetalscorp.com
Year Founded: 2009
Sales Range: Less than $1 Million
Mineral Exploration Services
N.A.I.C.S.: 213114
Murray John *(Chm)*

EPOXY BASE ELECTRONIC MATERIAL CORPORATION LIMITED
2 Of No 1 Yunpu 1st Rd, Luogang District, Guangzhou, 510530, China
Tel.: (86) 2082266156
Web Site:
https://www.graceepoxy.com
Year Founded: 1994
603002—(SHG)
Rev.: $424,350,225
Assets: $505,190,593
Liabilities: $160,440,387
Net Worth: $344,750,206
Earnings: $78,172,431
Emp.: 220
Fiscal Year-end: 12/31/22
Epoxy Resin Mfr & Distr
N.A.I.C.S.: 325211
Lin Ruirong *(Chm)*

EPPENDORF AG
Barkhausenweg 1, 22339, Hamburg, Germany
Tel.: (49) 40538010 De
Web Site: http://www.eppendorf.com
Year Founded: 1945
Rev.: $900,245,375
Assets: $1,237,584,163

Eppendorf AG—(Continued)

Liabilities: $414,277,649
Net Worth: $823,306,514
Earnings: $109,073,244
Emp.: 3,567
Fiscal Year-end: 12/31/19
Medical Equipment & Supplies Whslr
N.A.I.C.S.: 339112

Subsidiaries:

Bio-ITech B.V. (1)
Kieler Bocht 9e, 9723 JA, Groningen, Netherlands
Tel.: (31) 507200055
Web Site: http://www.bio-itech.nl
Software Services
N.A.I.C.S.: 541511
Erwin Seinen (Mng Dir)

Brinkmann Instruments, Inc. (1)
1 Cantiague Rock Rd, Westbury, NY 11590-2826
Tel.: (516) 334-7500
Web Site: http://www.brinkmann.com
Sales Range: $75-99.9 Million
Emp.: 260
Importer & Distributor of Scientific Instruments Used in Laboratories, for Quality Control of Manufacturing Processes & for Environmental Monitoring
N.A.I.C.S.: 423490

Subsidiary (Non-US):

Brinkmann Instruments (Canada), Ltd. (2)
6670 Campobello Rd, Mississauga, L5N 2L8, ON, Canada (100%)
Tel.: (905) 826-5525
Web Site: http://www.brinkmann.com
Sales Range: $25-49.9 Million
Emp.: 30
U.S. & Canadian Distribution & Marketing of Scientific Instruments Such as Laboratory Analysis Equipment; Distribution & Marketing of Process & Quality Control Equipment
N.A.I.C.S.: 423490

Calibration Technology Ltd. (1)
InnovationWorks National Technology Park, Castletroy, Limerick, Ireland
Tel.: (353) 61503132
Web Site: http://www.calibrationtech.ie
Laboratory Instrument Services
N.A.I.C.S.: 334516

Eppendorf (Thailand) Co. Ltd. (1)
5 Soi Krungthepkreetha 4, Huamark Bankapi, Bangkok, 10240, Thailand
Tel.: (66) 237942125
Web Site: http://www.eppendorf.com
Medical Equipment Distr
N.A.I.C.S.: 423450
Pitikarn Wongphanit (Mng Dir)

Eppendorf Asia Pacific Sdn. Bhd. (1)
10th Floor Menara Symphony No 5 Jalan Prof Khoo Kay Kim Seksyen 13, 46200, Petaling Jaya, Selangor, Malaysia
Tel.: (60) 376105200
Web Site: http://www.eppendorf.com
Medical Equipment Distr
N.A.I.C.S.: 423450
Shim Yok Lam (Mng Dir)

Eppendorf Austria GmbH (1)
Ignaz Kock Strasse 10, 1210, Vienna, Austria
Tel.: (43) 1 890 13 64 0
Web Site: http://www.eppendorf.com
Medical Equipment Distr
N.A.I.C.S.: 423450
Hamid Heidari (Mgr-Operational Mktg-Central & Eastern Europe)

Eppendorf Belgium NV/SA (1)
Nijverheidslaan 22, 3200, Aarschot, Belgium
Tel.: (32) 16525810
Web Site: http://www.eppendorf.be
Emp.: 12
Medical Equipment Distr
N.A.I.C.S.: 423450

Eppendorf Biotechnology International Trade (Shanghai) Company Ltd. (1)
Shanghai Pudong Century Boulevard, 1600 Pohang Business Plaza 151, 200122,

Shanghai, China
Tel.: (86) 2168760880
Professional Equipment & Supplies Whslr
N.A.I.C.S.: 423490

Eppendorf Canada Ltd. (1)
2810 Argentia Road 2, Mississauga, L5N 8L2, ON, Canada
Web Site: http://www.eppendorf.com
Medical Equipment Distr
N.A.I.C.S.: 423450

Eppendorf China Ltd. (1)
10th Floor Century Commercial Plaza No 989 Changle Road, Xuhui District, Shanghai, 200031, China
Tel.: (86) 4008856070
Web Site: http://www.eppendorf.com
Sales Range: $25-49.9 Million
Professional Equipment & Supplies Whslr
N.A.I.C.S.: 423450

Eppendorf China Ltd. (1)
Unit 1801-05 Westin Centre 26 Hung To Road, Kwun Tong, Kowloon, China (Hong Kong)
Tel.: (852) 35288900
Web Site: http://www.eppendorf.hk
Laboratory Instrument Services
N.A.I.C.S.: 334516

Eppendorf Co., Ltd. (1)
2-4-5 Higashikanda Horisho Building, Higashikanda Chiyoda-ku, Tokyo, 101-0031, Japan (100%)
Tel.: (81) 358252361
Web Site: http://www.eppendorf.com
Professional Equipment & Supplies Whslr
N.A.I.C.S.: 423490

Eppendorf Czech & Slovakia s.r.o. (1)
Voderadska 2552/16, 251 01, Ricany, Czech Republic
Tel.: (420) 323 605 454
Web Site: http://www.eppendorf.com
Medical Equipment Distr
N.A.I.C.S.: 423450

Eppendorf France S.A.R.L. (1)
2/6 Rue du Chateau d'Eau, 78360, Montesson, France (100%)
Tel.: (33) 130156740
Web Site: http://www.eppendorf.com
Sales Range: $25-49.9 Million
Medical Dental & Hospital Equipment & Supply Services
N.A.I.C.S.: 423450

Eppendorf Iberica S.L. (1)
Avenida Tenerife 2 Edificio 1, San Sebastian de los Reyes, 28703, Madrid, Spain (100%)
Tel.: (34) 916517694
Web Site: http://www.eppendorf.com
Sales Range: $25-49.9 Million
Laboratory Apparatus & Furniture Mfr
N.A.I.C.S.: 334516

Eppendorf India Ltd. (1)
Plot No 18 19 20 Part Ambit Park Road, Sidco Industrial Estate South Ambattur, Chennai, 600 058, India (100%)
Tel.: (91) 4466312222
Web Site: http://www.eppendorf.com
Sales Range: $25-49.9 Million
Emp.: 158
Surgical & Medical Instrument Mfr
N.A.I.C.S.: 339112

Eppendorf Korea Ltd. (1)
10F Megazone Building 46 85-gil, Gangnam-gu Nonhyeon, Seoul, 06235, Korea (South)
Tel.: (82) 1577 4395
Web Site: http://www.eppendorf.com
Medical Equipment Distr
N.A.I.C.S.: 423450

Eppendorf Middle East FZ-LLC (1)
Dubai Science Park - Nucleotide Complex Office G08A Ground Floor, PO Box 502019, Al Barsha South 2 Um Suqeim Road, Dubai, United Arab Emirates
Tel.: (971) 43692954
Web Site: http://www.eppendorf.com
Sales Range: $50-74.9 Million
Emp.: 7
Medical Dental & Hospital Equipment & Supplies Whslr

N.A.I.C.S.: 423450
Erich Mueller (Mng Dir)

Eppendorf Nordic ApS (1)
Slotsmarken 12, 2970, Horsholm, Denmark (100%)
Tel.: (45) 43240000
Web Site: http://www.eppendorf.com
Sales Range: $50-74.9 Million
Emp.: 20
Industrial Supplies Whslr
N.A.I.C.S.: 423840
Mathias Brodersen (Mgr-Acct)

Eppendorf Norge AS (1)
Forskningsparken Gaustadalleen 21, 0349, Oslo, Norway
Tel.: (47) 22566632
Laboratory Instrument Services
N.A.I.C.S.: 334516

Eppendorf North America, Inc. (1)
175 Freshwater Blvd, Enfield, CT 06082
Tel.: (516) 334-7500
Web Site: http://www.eppendorf.com
Sales Range: $50-74.9 Million
Laboratory Apparatus & Furniture Mfr
N.A.I.C.S.: 334516

Eppendorf Poland Sp. zo.o. (1)
Al Jerozolimskie 212, 02-486, Warsaw, Poland
Tel.: (48) 22 571 40 20
Web Site: http://www.eppendorf.com
Medical Equipment Distr
N.A.I.C.S.: 423450

Eppendorf Russia OOO (1)
Derbenevskaya Nab 11 Office B301, 115114, Moscow, Russia
Tel.: (7) 4957435123
Web Site: http://www.eppendorf.com
Laboratory Instrument Services
N.A.I.C.S.: 334516

Eppendorf S.r.l. (1)
Via Zante 14, 20138, Milan, Italy
Tel.: (39) 02554041
Web Site: http://www.eppendorf.com
Sales Range: $50-74.9 Million
Electrical Apparatus & Equipment Wiring Supplies & Construction Material Whslr
N.A.I.C.S.: 423610

Eppendorf Scientific, Inc. (1)
102 Motor Pkwy, Hauppauge, NY, 11788
Tel.: (516) 334-7500
Web Site: http://www.eppendorf.com
Sales Range: $25-49.9 Million
Emp.: 70
Analytical Laboratory Instrument Mfr
N.A.I.C.S.: 334516
Martin Farb (Pres)

Eppendorf South Pacific Pty. Ltd. (1)
Level 1 97 Waterloo Road, Macquarie Park, 2113, NSW, Australia
Tel.: (61) 298895000
Web Site: http://www.eppendorf.com
Sales Range: $25-49.9 Million
Professional Equipment & Supplies Whslr
N.A.I.C.S.: 423490
Matthew Banfield (Mng Dir & Head-Sls-East Asia & Pacific)

Eppendorf UK Ltd. (1)
Eppendorf House Gateway 1000 Arlington Business Park Whittle Way, Vision Park Histon, Stevenage, SG1 2FP, United Kingdom (100%)
Tel.: (44) 1438735888
Web Site: http://www.eppendorf.com
Sales Range: $25-49.9 Million
Emp.: 40
Measuring & Controlling Device Mfr
N.A.I.C.S.: 334519

Eppendorf Vertrieb Deutschland GmbH (1)
Peter-Henlein-Str 2, Berzdorf, 50389, Wesseling, Germany (100%)
Tel.: (49) 22324180
Web Site: http://www.eppendorf.com
Sales Range: $25-49.9 Million
Emp.: 60
Laboratory Apparatus & Furniture Mfr
N.A.I.C.S.: 333248

Eppendorf Zentrifugen GmbH (1)
Portitzer Allee 15, 04319, Leipzig, Germany

Tel.: (49) 3412574500
Medical Equipment Mfr & Distr
N.A.I.C.S.: 339112

Eppendorf do Brasil Ltda. (1)
Rua Presidente Antonio Candido n 80, Alto Da Lapa, Sao Paulo, 05083-060, SP, Brazil (100%)
Tel.: (55) 1136485400
Web Site: http://www.eppendorf.com
Sales Range: $50-74.9 Million
Medical Dental & Hospital Equipment & Supplies Whslr
N.A.I.C.S.: 423450

New Brunswick Scientific Co., Inc. (1)
44 Talmadge Rd, Edison, NJ 08817-3319
Tel.: (732) 287-1200
Web Site: http://www.nbsc.com
Sales Range: $75-99.9 Million
Emp.: 437
Designer, Mfr & Marketer of High-Technology Equipment & Instruments for Research & Development to Produce Therapeutic Drugs, Enzymes, Biochemicals, Antibiotics, Vaccines & Other Biological Products
N.A.I.C.S.: 334516

Subsidiary (Non-US):

New Brunswick Scientific (UK) Ltd. (2)
17 Alban Pk Hatfield Road, Saint Albans, AL4 0JJ, United Kingdom
Tel.: (44) 1727833855
Web Site: http://www.nbsuk.co.uk
Rev.: $1,632,685
Emp.: 20
Laboratory Equipment Sales & Services
N.A.I.C.S.: 423490

New Brunswick Scientific B.V. (2)
Kerkenbos 1101, 6546 BC, Nijmegen, Netherlands
Tel.: (31) 243717600
Web Site: http://www.nbsc.com
Sales Range: $25-49.9 Million
Emp.: 25
Laboratory Equipment Sales & Service
N.A.I.C.S.: 423490

New Brunswick Scientific Co., Inc. (2)
9 Building Qijiayuan No 9-42 Diplomatic Compound, 9 Jianguomenwai Dajie, Beijing, 100600, China
Tel.: (86) 1085325665
Web Site: http://www.nbsc.com
Sales Range: $25-49.9 Million
Emp.: 4
Pharmaceuticals Mfr
N.A.I.C.S.: 325412

New Brunswick Scientific GmbH (2)
In der Au 14, D 72622, Nurtingen, Germany
Tel.: (49) 7022932490
Web Site: http://www.nbsgmbh.de
Sales Range: $25-49.9 Million
Emp.: 15
Laboratory Equipment Sales & Services
N.A.I.C.S.: 423490

Starlab (UK) Limited (1)
5 Tanners Drive, Blakelands, Milton Keynes, MK14 5BU, United Kingdom
Tel.: (44) 1908283800
Laboratory Instrument Services
N.A.I.C.S.: 334516

Starlab France S.a.r.l. (1)
30 Rue Jean Rostand, 91400, Orsay, France
Tel.: (33) 160137170
Laboratory Instrument Services
N.A.I.C.S.: 334516

Starlab International GmbH (1)
Neuer Holtigbaum 38, 22143, Hamburg, Germany
Tel.: (49) 4067599390
Web Site: http://www.starlabgroup.com
Laboratory Instrument Services
N.A.I.C.S.: 334516
Klaus Ambos (Mng Dir)

Starlab s.r.l. (1)
Via Pinturicchio 1, 20133, Milan, Italy
Tel.: (39) 0270201040

Laboratory Instrument Services
N.A.I.C.S.: 334516

USA Scientific, Inc.   (1)
PO Box 3565, Ocala, FL 34478-3565
Tel.: (352) 237-6288
Web Site: http://www.usascientific.com
Sales Range: $25-49.9 Million
Surgical & Medical Instrument Mfr
N.A.I.C.S.: 339112

Vaudaux-Eppendorf AG   (1)
Im Kirschgarten 30, Schonenbuch, 4124,
Basel, Switzerland
Tel.: (41) 61 482 14 14
Web Site: http://www.eppendorf.com
Medical Equipment Distr
N.A.I.C.S.: 423450

EPRCOMUNICAZIONE S.P.A.
Via Arenula 29, 00186, Rome, Italy
Tel.: (39) 06681621
Web Site:
https://www.eprcomunicazione.it
Year Founded: 2011
EPRB—(ITA)
Communication Service
N.A.I.C.S.: 517410

EPRICE S.P.A.
Via San Marco 29, 20121, Milan, Italy
Tel.: (39) 0230315400   IT
Web Site: http://corporate.eprice.it
Year Founded: 2007
EPR—(ITA)
Sales Range: $200-249.9 Million
Emp.: 170
E-Commerce & Digital Publishing
Services
N.A.I.C.S.: 513199
Pietro Scott Jovane *(CEO & Gen Mgr)*

EPRINT GROUP LIMITED
Flat A and B 4/F Phase 3 Kwun Tong
Industrial Centre Kwun Tong Road,
Kowloon, China (Hong Kong)
Tel.: (852) 2319 7107   Ky
Web Site:
http://www.eprintgroup.com.hk
Year Founded: 2001
1884—(HKG)
Rev.: $34,425,020
Assets: $42,711,985
Liabilities: $10,382,503
Net Worth: $32,329,482
Earnings: $2,494,344
Emp.: 302
Fiscal Year-end: 03/31/21
Printing Services
N.A.I.C.S.: 323120
Cheuk Ki Chong *(Exec Dir)*

Subsidiaries:

Ebanner Solution Sdn. Bhd.   (1)
No 51-53 Jalan PBS 14/9, Taman Perindus-
trian Bukit Serdang, 43300, Seri Kemban-
gan, Selangor, Malaysia
Tel.: (60) 389583776
Web Site: https://my.e-banner.com
Digital Printing Services
N.A.I.C.S.: 561439

**Promise Network Printing
Limited**   (1)
Shop B G/F Phase 4 KwunTong Ind Ctr
436-446 KwunTong Rd, Kwun Tong MTR
Exit D4, Kwun Tong, China (Hong Kong)
Tel.: (852) 23446668
Printing Services
N.A.I.C.S.: 323120

EPS BIO TECHNOLOGY CORP.
No 8 R&D RD III Hsinchu Science
Park, Hsin-Chu, Hsinchu, 30076,
Taiwan
Tel.: (886) 36686868
Web Site: https://www.epsbio.com
4183—(TPE)
Rev.: $14,490,573
Assets: $16,501,329

Liabilities: $6,860,113
Net Worth: $9,641,216
Earnings: $792,921
Fiscal Year-end: 12/31/22
Healtcare Services
N.A.I.C.S.: 423450
Feng-Lin Kuo *(Chm)*

EPS HOLDINGS, INC.
6F Kagurazaka AK Building 1-8
Tsukudo-cho, Shinjuku-ku, Tokyo,
162-0822, Tokyo, Japan
Tel.: (81) 356847873   JP
Web Site: http://www.eps-
holdings.co.jp
Year Founded: 1991
Rev.: $47,432,000
Assets: $49,009,840
Liabilities: $24,887,280
Net Worth: $24,122,560
Earnings: $1,694,000
Emp.: 6,220
Fiscal Year-end: 09/30/21
Medical & Pharmaceutical Industry
Outsourcing Services
N.A.I.C.S.: 561499
Yan Hao *(Chm)*

Subsidiaries:

All Right Software Inc.   (1)
3rd Fl Takara Bldg, 4 18 13 Iidabashi
Chiyoda ku, Tokyo, 102 0072, Japan
Tel.: (81) 352262581
Web Site: http://www.allrightsoft.co.jp
Sales Range: $50-74.9 Million
Emp.: 120
Software Reproducing
N.A.I.C.S.: 334610

**Beijing Global Pharmaceutical Re-
search Co., Ltd.**   (1)
No 4 Building 903-904 Guancheng Midtown
Plaza, Dong Cheng District, Beijing,
100022, China
Tel.: (86) 1067044158
Clinical Development Services
N.A.I.C.S.: 541714

E -Trial Co., Ltd.   (1)
9th Fl Tsuruya Bldg 2-23 Shimomiyabi-cho,
Shinjuku, Tokyo, 162-0822, Japan
Tel.: (81) 352259771
Web Site: http://www.e-trial.co.jp
Sales Range: $25-49.9 Million
Emp.: 20
Software Reproducing
N.A.I.C.S.: 334610

EMS Co., Ltd   (1)
Okudo 3-19-14, Katushika Ward, Tokyo,
124-0022, Japan
Tel.: (81) 356706925
Web Site: http://www.ems-esd.co.jp
Business Process Outsourcing Services
N.A.I.C.S.: 561499

EP Mediate Co., Ltd.   (1)
1-8 Tsukudocho, Shinjuku-ku, Tokyo, 162-
0821, Japan
Tel.: (81) 356579130
Web Site: http://www.ep-mediate.co.jp
Medical Research & Development Services
N.A.I.C.S.: 541714

EP Trading Co., Ltd.   (1)
1-8 Kagurazaka AK Building Eighth Floor
Tsukudo-cho, Shinjuku-ku, Tokyo, 162-0821,
Japan
Tel.: (81) 335136530
Web Site: http://www.eptrading.co.jp
Non-Clinical Research Product Distr
N.A.I.C.S.: 423450

EP Yamanashi Co., Ltd.   (1)
Aria 101 Kawadamachi, Kofu, 400-0811,
Yamanashi, Japan
Tel.: (81) 552255110
Web Site: http://www.epsym.co.jp
Clinical Research Services
N.A.I.C.S.: 541715

EP-CRSU Co., Ltd.   (1)
6-29 Shinogawamachi Acropolis Tokyo 3rd
Floor, Shinjuku, Tokyo, 162-0814, Japan
Tel.: (81) 356847809
Web Site: http://www.ep-crsu.co.jp

Clinical Research Services
N.A.I.C.S.: 541715

EP-Force Co., Ltd.   (1)
KDX Ikebukuro 9F 2-6-1, Ikebukuro
Toshima-Ku, Tokyo, 171-0014, Japan
Tel.: (81) 359561971
Web Site: http://www.epforce.co.jp
Recruitment Services
N.A.I.C.S.: 561311
Akiyoshi Ogasawara *(Chm)*

EP-Mint Co., Ltd.   (1)
Sumitomo Fudousan Otowa Bldg, 2-9-3 Ot-
suka Bunkyo-ku, Tokyo, 112-0012,
Japan   (100%)
Tel.: (81) 353193530
Web Site: http://www.epmint.co.jp
Sales Range: $25-49.9 Million
Emp.: 535
Medical Development Support & Associated
Services
N.A.I.C.S.: 325412
Hidetaka Ando *(Pres)*

EP-PharmaLine Co., Ltd   (1)
Ikebukuro Westpark Bldg 3-27-12 Nishiike-
bukuro, Toshima-ku, Tokyo, 171-0021, Ja-
pan
Tel.: (81) 120 861 664
Web Site: http://www.eppharmaline.co.jp
General Medical Services
N.A.I.C.S.: 621491
Junichi Nishizuka *(Chm)*

EP-SOGO Co., Ltd.   (1)
Kagurazaka AK Bldg 1-8 Tsukudocho,
Shinjuku-ku, Tokyo, 162-0821, Japan
Tel.: (81) 342183500
Web Site: http://www.epsogo.co.jp
Emp.: 1,640
Management Consulting Services
N.A.I.C.S.: 541611
Tatsuma Nagaoka *(Chm)*

EPBiz Co., Ltd.   (1)
Kagurazaka AK Building 3rd Floor 1-8 Tsu-
kudocho, Shinjuku-ku, Tokyo, 162-0821,
Japan
Tel.: (81) 356847879
Web Site: http://www.epbiz.co.jp
Medical Equipment Rental Services
N.A.I.C.S.: 532490

EPMate Co., Ltd.   (1)
S&S Building 4th Floor 6-36 Shin Ogawa-
cho, Shinjuku-ku, 162-0814, Tokyo, Japan
Tel.: (81) 3 5229 8992
Web Site: http://www.epmate.co.jp
Medical Staffing Services
N.A.I.C.S.: 561320

EPMedical Co., Ltd.   (1)
5th Floor Ishikinnihonbashi Building, 4-14-7
Nihonbashi-honcho, Chuo-ku, 103-0023,
Tokyo, Japan
Tel.: (81) 358477725
Sales Range: $25-49.9 Million
Emp.: 92
Testing Laboratories
N.A.I.C.S.: 541380

EPS Americas Corp.   (1)
103 Carnegie Ctr Ste 300, Princeton, NJ
08540
Tel.: (708) 657-4321
Clinical Development Services
N.A.I.C.S.: 541714

EPS China Co., Ltd.   (1)
Floor 5 Building 5 B No 329 Tianyaoqiao
Road, Xuhui District, Shanghai, 200030,
China
Tel.: (86) 2133632793
Web Site: http://www.epscn.com
Contract Research Services
N.A.I.C.S.: 541715

**EPS Creative Health Technology
Group Ltd.**   (1)
Flat A 17/F Gemstar Tower 23 Man Lok
Street Hung Hom, Kowloon, China (Hong
Kong)   (75%)
Tel.: (852) 23342088
Web Site: http://www.speedapparel.com.hk
Rev.: $54,772,131
Assets: $32,105,702
Liabilities: $15,763,420
Net Worth: $16,342,282
Earnings: ($2,375,167)
Emp.: 70

Fiscal Year-end: 03/31/2022
Clothing Product Mfr & Distr
N.A.I.C.S.: 315250
Wing Kai Chan *(Chm, CEO & Compliance
Officer)*

EPS Digital-Share Co., Ltd.   (1)
1-8 Kagurazaka AK building 3F / 4F
Tsukudo-cho, Shinjuku-ku, Tokyo, 162-0821,
Japan
Tel.: (81) 345865350
Web Site: http://www.eps-digitalshare.co.jp
Information Technology Services
N.A.I.C.S.: 541511

EPS EKISHIN Co., Ltd.   (1)
Kagurazaka Plaza Building 4-8, Kagurazaka
Shinjuku-ku, Tokyo, 162-0825, Japan
Tel.: (81) 356847869
Web Site: http://www.epsekishin.co.jp
Medical Device Mfr & Distr
N.A.I.C.S.: 339112

EPS Global Research Pte. Ltd.   (1)
150 Beach Rd 06-02/04, Singapore,
189720, Singapore   (51%)
Tel.: (65) 6737 3642
Web Site: http://www.epsgr.com
Emp.: 50
Clinical Research Services
N.A.I.C.S.: 621511

**EPS International (China) Co.,
Ltd.**   (1)
Floor 3 Bio-tech Science Park No 1326 Yan
An Xi Road, Shanghai, 200052, China
Tel.: (86) 2152668666
Clinical Development Services
N.A.I.C.S.: 541714

EPS International Co., Ltd.   (1)
128 Tsukudo Cho Shinjuku AK Building 8th
Fl, 2-23 Shimomiyabi-cho Shinjuku, Tokyo,
1620821, Japan
Tel.: (81) 356847882
Web Site: http://www.eps.co.jp
Emp.: 1,000
Chemical & Allied Products Merchant Whslr
N.A.I.C.S.: 424690

Subsidiary (Non-US):

**Taiwan Total Management Consulting
Ltd.**   (2)
4F-2 No 26 Sec 3 Zhung-Shan N Road,
Taipei, Taiwan
Tel.: (886) 2 25866090
Web Site: http://www.ttmc.com.tw
Site Management Organization Services
N.A.I.C.S.: 541618

EPS International Korea Limited   (1)
5F Justco Tower 431 Teheran-ro,
Gangnam-gu, Seoul, Korea (South)
Tel.: (82) 263030068
Clinical Development Services
N.A.I.C.S.: 541714

**EPS Tigermed (Suzhou) Co.,
Ltd.**   (1)
88 Suzhou Industrial Park, Suzhou,
215213, China
Tel.: (86) 51262621231
Web Site: http://www.epi-china.com
Clinical Research Services
N.A.I.C.S.: 541715

**EPSI Global Research (Taiwan) Co.,
Ltd.**   (1)
9F No 156 Sec 3 Mingsheng East Road,
Songshan District, Taipei, 105, Taiwan
Tel.: (886) 266011330
Clinical Development Services
N.A.I.C.S.: 541714

ES-Link Co., Ltd.   (1)
Kagurazaka AK Building 1-8 Tsukudocho,
Shinjuku-ku, Tokyo, 162-0821, Japan
Tel.: (81) 359798143
Web Site: http://www.eslink.co.jp
BPO Services
N.A.I.C.S.: 561990

**Ever Progressing System Pte.
Ltd.**   (1)
6 Raffles Boulevard 03-308 Marina Square,
Singapore, 039594, Singapore
Tel.: (65) 69322738
Clinical Development Services
N.A.I.C.S.: 541714

EPS Holdings, Inc.—(Continued)

LSG Co., Ltd. (1)
Kagurazaka AK Building 1-8 Tsukudo-cho,
Shinjuku-ku, Shinjuku-ku, Tokyo, 162-0821,
Japan
Tel.: (81) 335136533
Web Site: http://www.lsg.co.jp
Emp.: 1
Surface Active Agent Mfr
N.A.I.C.S.: 325613
Takeshi Tadano (Pres)

**Shanghai Huaxin Biotechnology Co.,
Ltd.** (1)
No 1150 Guiqiao Road, Pudong New Area,
Shanghai, China
Tel.: (86) 2160571066
Web Site: http://www.huaxin-bio.com
Pharmaceutical Product Mfr & Distr
N.A.I.C.S.: 325414

**Total Trial Management Consulting
Co., Ltd.** (1)
10F No 156 Sec 3 Ming Sheng E Road,
Taipei, 105, Taiwan
Tel.: (886) 266011322
Web Site: http://www.ttmcsmo.com
Management Consulting Services
N.A.I.C.S.: 541611
Sammy Yu (Sr Dir-Clinical Operation)

EPSILON HEALTHCARE LTD.
Level 1 1 Jamison Street, Sydney,
2000, NSW, Australia
Tel.: (61) 288393000
Web Site:
　https://epsilonhealthcare.com.au
Year Founded: 2016
EPN—(ASX)
Rev.: $4,637,278
Assets: $13,366,342
Liabilities: $7,322,203
Net Worth: $6,044,139
Earnings: ($8,664,381)
Fiscal Year-end: 12/31/22
Medicinal Cannabis Mfr & Distr
N.A.I.C.S.: 325412
Peter Giannopoulos (CEO & Exec
Dir)

Subsidiaries:

Canna Clinics Pty. Ltd. (1)
903 50 Clarence Street, Sydney, 2000,
NSW, Australia
Tel.: (61) 283241382
Web Site: http://cannabis-
　clinics.business.site
Medical Practice Services
N.A.I.C.S.: 621111

Crystal Mountain Products Ltd. (1)
200 Carnegie Drive Suite 234, Saint Albert,
T8N 5A7, AB, Canada
Tel.: (780) 454-4545
Web Site: https://www.crystalcoolers.com
Water Dispenser Mfr
N.A.I.C.S.: 333914

EPSILON NET S.A.
Parodos 17th November 87 EMO
Zone, 55534, Thessaloniki, Greece
Tel.: (30) 2310981700
Web Site: https://www.epsilonnet.gr
EPSIL—(ATH)
Rev.: $100,076,949
Assets: $134,183,787
Liabilities: $68,951,614
Net Worth: $65,232,173
Earnings: $21,490,338
Emp.: 1,231
Fiscal Year-end: 12/31/23
Software Development Services
N.A.I.C.S.: 541511
Ioannis Michos (Chm & CEO)

Subsidiaries:

Epsilon Europe PLC (1)
2 Agias Fylaxeos and Zenonos Rossidi, Li-
massol, 3082, Cyprus
Tel.: (357) 2 582 3330
Web Site: https://www.epsilonplc.eu
Computer Programming Services

N.A.I.C.S.: 541511

Hoteliga Int. Sp. z o.o. (1)
Aleja Jana Pawla II 43b, 31-864, Krakow,
Poland
Tel.: (48) 12 350 6544
Web Site: https://www.hoteliga.com
Management Consulting Services
N.A.I.C.S.: 541611
Dimitris Van Leusden (CEO)

EPSOM PROPERTIES LIMITED
Old No 249 New No 339 Safi House
2nd Floor Anna Salai Teynampet,
Teynampet West, Chennai, 600 006,
Tamil Nadu, India
Tel.: (91) 4443021233
Web Site: https://www.epsom.in
Year Founded: 1987
531155—(BOM)
Assets: $8,048
Liabilities: $86,557
Net Worth: ($78,509)
Earnings: ($44,517)
Emp.: 3
Fiscal Year-end: 03/31/22
Construction Services
N.A.I.C.S.: 236220
C. Sivakumar Reddy (Mng Dir)

EPTA S.P.A.
Via Mecenate 86, 20138, Milan, Italy
Tel.: (39) 02 55 403 211
Web Site:
　http://www.eptarefrigeration.com
Commercial & Industrial Refrigeration
Equipment Mfr
N.A.I.C.S.: 333415

Subsidiaries:

Kysor Warren Epta US Corp. (1)
5201 Transport Blvd, Columbus, GA 31907
Tel.: (706) 568-1514
Web Site: http://www.kysorwarren.com
Commercial Refrigeration Equipment Mfr
N.A.I.C.S.: 333415
Park Adamson (VP & Gen Mgr)

Subsidiary (Domestic):

Kysor Warren Corp. (2)
5201 Transport Blvd, Columbus, GA 31907
Tel.: (706) 568-1514
Web Site: http://www.kysorwarren.com
Sales Range: $150-199.9 Million
Emp.: 600
Commercial Refrigeration Equipment Mfr
N.A.I.C.S.: 333415
Parke Adamson (VP & Gen Mgr)

EPUJA SPIRITECH LTD.
Unit No 402 Plot B/65 Stanford Plaza
New Link Road, Opp City Mall And-
heri W, Mumbai, 400053, India
Tel.: (91) 67199122
Web Site: https://epuja.co.in
Year Founded: 1980
532092—(BOM)
Rev.: $169,318
Assets: $878,041
Liabilities: $150,890
Net Worth: $727,151
Earnings: ($26,677)
Fiscal Year-end: 03/31/23
Financial Investment Services
N.A.I.C.S.: 523999
Kalakad Sundaram Sathi (Exec Dir)

EPWIN GROUP PLC
Friars Gate 1011 Stratford Road,
Cranmore Boulevard, Solihull, B90
4BN, United Kingdom
Tel.: (44) 1217463700
Web Site: https://www.epwin.co.uk
EPWN—(AIM)
Rev.: $439,718,378
Assets: $370,845,291
Liabilities: $240,864,844
Net Worth: $129,980,447
Earnings: $11,839,551

Fiscal Year-end: 12/31/23
Extrusions, Mouldings & Fabricated
Building Products
N.A.I.C.S.: 326199
Jonathan Albert Bednall (CEO)

Subsidiaries:

Kestrel-BCE Limited (1)
Billet Lane Normanby Enterprise Park, Nor-
manby Road, Scunthorpe, DN15 9YH, N
Lincolnshire, United Kingdom
Tel.: (44) 1724400440
Web Site: http://www.kestrelbce.com
Emp.: 220
Building Product Mfr
N.A.I.C.S.: 326199
David Johnstone (Mgr-Export)

Saltire Trade Plastics Limited (1)
Block 8 Unit 1 Roseberry Road Chapelhall
Industrial Estate, Airdrie, ML6 8QH, United
Kingdom
Tel.: (44) 1236606600
Web Site: https://www.saltiretrade.co.uk
All Window & Door Distr
N.A.I.C.S.: 423310

Swish Building Products Limited (1)
Pioneer House, Lichfield Road Indl Estate,
Tamworth, B79 7TF, Staffordshire, United
Kingdom
Tel.: (44) 1827 31700
PVC Windows, Doors & Conservatory Sys-
tems Mfr
N.A.I.C.S.: 326199

Ultraframe (UK) Ltd. (1)
Enterprise Works Salthill Rd, Clitheroe, BB7
1PE, Lancs, United Kingdom
Tel.: (44) 1200443311
Web Site: http://www.ultraframe.co.uk
Sales Range: $150-199.9 Million
Emp.: 250
Conservatory Roofing Systems Mfr
N.A.I.C.S.: 337212

Subsidiary (US):

Four Seasons Sunroom (2)
5005 Veterans Memorial Hwy, Holbrook, NY
11741-4506
Tel.: (631) 563-4000
Web Site:
　https://www.fourseasonssunrooms.com
Sales Range: $50-74.9 Million
Emp.: 200
Mfr & Distr of Sunrooms, Enclosures &
Large-Scale Skylights
N.A.I.C.S.: 332311

Subsidiary (Domestic):

Fisher Skylights, Inc. (3)
5005 Veterans Memorial Hwy, Holbrook, NY
11741-4506
Tel.: (631) 563-4001
Sales Range: $50-74.9 Million
Emp.: 150
Mfr of Custom Metal Framed Skylights
N.A.I.C.S.: 332311

EQ INC.
1255 Bay Street Suite 401, Toronto,
M5R 3K4, ON, Canada
Tel.: (416) 260-4326　　　　ON
Web Site: https://www.eqworks.com
EQ—(TSXV)
Rev.: $9,454,636
Assets: $14,903,999
Liabilities: $5,951,586
Net Worth: $8,952,412
Earnings: ($4,658,477)
Emp.: 58
Fiscal Year-end: 12/31/21
Internet Software Development Ser-
vices
N.A.I.C.S.: 513210
Geoffrey Rotstein (Pres & CEO)

Subsidiaries:

Cyberplex Inc.-Boston (1)
15 Dartmouth Pl, Boston, MA 02116-6106
Tel.: (617) 859-9361
Provider of Internet Advertising Services
N.A.I.C.S.: 517810

WebAffairs Inc (1)
1255 Bay St Ste 400, Toronto, M5R 2A9,
ON, Canada　　　　　　　　　　　(100%)
Tel.: (416) 597-8889
Web Site: http://www.webaffairs.ca
Sales Range: $25-49.9 Million
Emp.: 20
Data Processing & Hosting Services
N.A.I.C.S.: 518210

EQ OYJ
Aleksanterinkatu 19 A 5th fl, 00100,
Helsinki, Finland
Tel.: (358) 968178777
Web Site: https://www.eq.fi
EQV1V—(HEL)
Rev.: $84,592,057
Assets: $119,639,542
Liabilities: $31,382,474
Net Worth: $88,257,069
Earnings: $39,199,223
Emp.: 94
Fiscal Year-end: 12/31/22
Investment Services
N.A.I.C.S.: 523999
Georg Ehrnrooth (Chm)

Subsidiaries:

Advium Corporate Finance Oy (1)
Aleksanterinkatu 19 A 5th floor, 00100, Hel-
sinki, Finland
Tel.: (358) 968178900
Web Site: https://www.advium.fi
Investment Services
N.A.I.C.S.: 523940

eQ Life Oy (1)
Aleksanterinkatu 19 A 5th floor, 00100, Hel-
sinki, Finland
Tel.: (358) 968178777
Asset Management Services
N.A.I.C.S.: 531390

EQ RESOURCES LIMITED
Tel.: (61) 740943072
Web Site:
　https://www.eqresources.com.au
Year Founded: 2006
EQR—(ASX)
Rev.: $20,250,611
Assets: $111,036,087
Liabilities: $73,224,870
Net Worth: $37,811,217
Earnings: ($18,869,586)
Emp.: 231
Fiscal Year-end: 06/30/24
Mineral Exploration Services
N.A.I.C.S.: 213115
Russell Krause (Chm)

Subsidiaries:

Saloro S.L.U. (1)
Carretera DSA-573 Km 13 66, Barruecop-
ardo, 37255, Salamanca, Spain
Tel.: (34) 923520367
Web Site: https://www.saloro.com
Mineral Exploration Services
N.A.I.C.S.: 213115

EQB INC.
30 St Clair Avenue West Suite 700,
Toronto, M4V 3A1, ON, Canada
Tel.: (416) 515-7000
Web Site:
　https://www.equitablebank.ca
EQB—(TSX)
Rev.: $913,404,209
Assets: $28,286,517,280
Liabilities: $26,759,010,754
Net Worth: $1,527,506,526
Earnings: $228,840,368
Emp.: 1,161
Fiscal Year-end: 12/31/21
Mortgage Financing
N.A.I.C.S.: 522310
Kimberley Kukulowicz (Sr VP)

EQOLOGY ASA
Kirkeveien 59b, 1363, Hovik, Norway

Tel.: (47) 67102190
Web Site: http://www.eqology.com
Year Founded: 2010
Health & Skincare Products
N.A.I.C.S.: 325620
Borre Gjersvik *(Pres-Res, Dev & Comm-Health Concepts)*

EQT AB

Regeringsgatan 25, SE-111 53,
Stockholm, Sweden
Tel.: (46) 850655300   SE
Web Site: https://www.eqtgroup.com
Year Founded: 2011
EQT—(OMX)
Rev.: $195,228,863
Assets: $862,466,867
Liabilities: $300,158,289
Net Worth: $562,308,578
Earnings: $12,166,681
Emp.: 1,777
Fiscal Year-end: 12/31/23
Real Estate Manangement Services
N.A.I.C.S.: 551112
Christian Sinding *(CEO)*

Subsidiaries:

Benesse Holdings, Inc.   **(1)**
3-7-17 Minamigata, Kita-ku, Okayama, 700-0807, Japan
Web Site: http://www.benesse-hd.co.jp
Rev.: $2,953,158,090
Assets: $3,882,985,200
Liabilities: $2,726,794,020
Net Worth: $1,156,191,180
Earnings: $81,401,010
Emp.: 16,637
Fiscal Year-end: 03/31/2023
Holding Company
N.A.I.C.S.: 551112
Hitoshi Kobayashi *(Exec VP)*

Subsidiary (Domestic):

Benesse BE studio Inc.   **(2)**
1-53-6 Hatsudai Mitsuyama Building 4F,
Hatsudai Shibuya-ku, Tokyo, 151-0061,
Japan
Tel.: (81) 368333843
Web Site: http://benesse-bestudio.co.jp
Kindergarten & Nursery School Services
N.A.I.C.S.: 611110

Benesse Business-mate, Inc.   **(2)**
Benesse Corporation Tokyo Building 1-34,
Ochiai, Tama, 206-0033, Tokyo, Japan
Tel.: (81) 423553536
Web Site: http://www.benesse-bizmate.jp
Outsourcing & Support Services
N.A.I.C.S.: 561499

Benesse Corporation   **(2)**
3-7-17 Minamigata, Kita-ku, Okayama, 700-8686, Japan   **(100%)**
Tel.: (81) 86 225 1100
Web Site: https://www.benesse.co.jp
Emp.: 1,000
Educational Materials Publisher & Support Services
N.A.I.C.S.: 513199

Co-Headquarters (Domestic):

Benesse Corporation - Tokyo Head Office   **(3)**
1-34 Ochiai, Tama, 206-8686, Tokyo, Japan
Tel.: (81) 42 356 1100
Web Site: http://www.benesse.co.jp
Administrative & Executive Office
N.A.I.C.S.: 561110

Subsidiary (Domestic):

Benesse Music Publishing Co.   **(3)**
1-34 Ochiai, Tama, 206 8686, Tokyo,
Japan   **(100%)**
Tel.: (81) 42 356 7134
Sales Range: Less than $1 Million
Emp.: 25
Music Publication Rights Management Services
N.A.I.C.S.: 533110

Benesse Style Care Co., Ltd.   **(3)**
2-3-1 Nishi-Shinjuku Shinjuku Monolith

Building 5F, Shinjuku-ku, Tokyo, 160-0023,
Japan
Tel.: (81) 36 836 1111
Web Site: https://www.benesse-style-care.co.jp
Emp.: 18,053
Senior Citizen Welfare Services
N.A.I.C.S.: 624120
Shinya Takiyama *(Pres)*

Tokyo Individualized Educational Institute, Inc.   **(3)**
25F Shinjuku Nomura Building, 2-26-2
Nishi-Shinjuku Shinjuku-ku, Tokyo, 163-0525, Japan   **(61.91%)**
Tel.: (81) 369113248
Web Site: https://www.tkg-jp.com
Rev.: $153,576,490
Assets: $82,867,920
Liabilities: $23,028,320
Net Worth: $59,839,600
Earnings: $6,799,310
Emp.: 582
Fiscal Year-end: 02/29/2024
Preparatory School Operator
N.A.I.C.S.: 611699
Katsuki Saito *(Chm & Pres)*

Subsidiary (Non-US):

Benesse Corporation China   **(2)**
5F Block B Honghui International Plaza
1602 Zhongshan West Road, Xuhui District,
Shanghai, China
Tel.: (86) 4008205099
Web Site: http://www.benesse.com.cn
Study Material Mfr & Whslr
N.A.I.C.S.: 322230

Benesse Hong Kong Co., Ltd.   **(2)**
Unit 808 Tower 1 Grand Central Plaza 138
Shatin Rural Committee Rd, Sha Tin, China
(Hong Kong)
Tel.: (852) 25988800
Web Site: http://www.benesse-hk.com
Educational Toy Mfr & Distr
N.A.I.C.S.: 339930
Hiroyuki Hayashi *(Mng Dir)*

Subsidiary (Domestic):

Benesse InfoShell Co., Ltd.   **(2)**
10-1 Takayanagi Higashimachi, Kita-ku,
Okayama, 700-0034, Japan
Tel.: (81) 862143131
Web Site: http://www.benesse-infoshell.co.jp
Information System Development Services
N.A.I.C.S.: 541511

Benesse MCM Corp.   **(2)**
26th Floor Shinjuku Monolith Building 2-3-1,
Nishi-Shinjuku Shinjuku-ku, Tokyo, 163-0926, Japan
Tel.: (81) 368361155
Web Site: http://corporate.benesse-mcm.co.jp
Health Care & Nursing Services
N.A.I.C.S.: 621610

Benesse Palette Co., Ltd.   **(2)**
Shinjuku Monolith Building 2-3-1, Nishi-Shinjuku Shinjuku-ku, Tokyo, 163-0905,
Japan
Tel.: (81) 368361080
Web Site: http://www.benesse-palette.co.jp
Food Distribution For Elderly Services
N.A.I.C.S.: 624120

Benesse Senior Support Co.,
Ltd.   **(2)**
Shinjuku Monolith Building 5F 2-3-1, Nishi-Shinjuku Shinjuku-ku, Tokyo, 163-0905,
Japan
Tel.: (81) 368361165
Web Site: http://www.benesse-senior-support.co.jp
Home Care Nursing Services
N.A.I.C.S.: 621610

Benesse i-Career, Co., Ltd.   **(2)**
32nd Floor Shinjuku Mitsui Building 2-1-1,
Nishi-Shinjuku Shinjuku-ku, Tokyo, 163-0432, Japan
Tel.: (81) 353201299
Web Site: http://www.benesse-i-career.co.jp
Career Educational Support Services
N.A.I.C.S.: 611710

EDUCOM Corporation   **(2)**
7-7-5 Nyoisaru-cho, Kasugai, 486-0918,
Aichi, Japan

Tel.: (81) 568357601
Web Site: http://www.educom.co.jp
Computer Education Support Services
N.A.I.C.S.: 611420

Heart Medical Care Co., Ltd.   **(2)**
Taihei Dengyo 2nd Building 5F 2-4 Kanda
Jimbocho, Chiyoda-ku, Tokyo, 101-0051,
Japan
Tel.: (81) 332221800
Web Site: http://www.heart-mc.co.jp
Health Care Srvices
N.A.I.C.S.: 621999

Learn-S Co., Ltd.   **(2)**
3-7-17 Minamigata, Kita-ku, Okayama, 700-0807, Japan
Tel.: (81) 862215410
Web Site: http://www.learn-s.co.jp
Study Material Mfr & Whslr
N.A.I.C.S.: 322230

Naoshima Benesse   **(2)**
Gotanji Naoshima-cho, Kagawa-gun,
Kagawa, 761 3110, Japan   **(100%)**
Tel.: (81) 878922030
Sales Range: $1-9.9 Million
Emp.: 50
Hotel & Campsite Operation & Management
N.A.I.C.S.: 721110
Soichiro Fukutake *(Pres)*

Naoshima Cultural Village Co.,
Ltd.   **(2)**
Gotanji Naoshima-cho, Kagawa-gun,
Kagawa, 761-3110, Japan
Tel.: (81) 878922887
Web Site: https://www.benesse-artsite.jp
Home Management Services
N.A.I.C.S.: 721110

Ochanomizu Seminar Co., Ltd.   **(2)**
2-21-11 Misakicho, Kanda Chiyoda-ku, Tokyo, 101-0061, Japan
Tel.: (81) 120404424
Web Site: http://www.ochazemi.co.jp
Education Services
N.A.I.C.S.: 611110

Plandit Co., Ltd.   **(2)**
1-34 Ochiai 10F, Tama, 206-0033, Tokyo,
Japan   **(100%)**
Tel.: (81) 42 357 3211
Web Site: https://www.plandit.co.jp
Sales Range: $1-9.9 Million
Emp.: 109
Developer of Published Study Materials
N.A.I.C.S.: 513130
Tamotsu Fukushima *(Pres)*

Shinken-AD Co., Ltd.   **(2)**
2-4-27 Dojima JRE Dojima Tower, Kita-ku,
Osaka, 530-0003, Japan   **(76.35%)**
Tel.: (81) 66 345 7170
Web Site: https://www.shinken-ad.co.jp
Sales Range: $75-99.9 Million
Emp.: 200
Advertising Services
N.A.I.C.S.: 541810

Sympres Co., Ltd.   **(2)**
10 1 Takayanagi Higashi Cho, Okayana
Shi, Okayama, 700 0034, Japan   **(11.8%)**
Tel.: (81) 862556660
Sales Range: $25-49.9 Million
Emp.: 50
Provider of Prepress Operations
N.A.I.C.S.: 323120

Synform Co., Ltd.   **(2)**
10 1 Takayanagi Higashi Cho, Okayama,
700 0034, Japan   **(100%)**
Tel.: (81) 862560202
Web Site: http://www.synform.co.jp
Sales Range: $150-199.9 Million
Emp.: 400
Machine Tooling Equipment Mfr
N.A.I.C.S.: 333248

Tokyo Educational Institute Co.,
Ltd.   **(2)**
1-55-8 Yoyogi, Shibuya-ku, Tokyo, 151-0053, Japan
Tel.: (81) 333756893
Web Site: http://www.tetsuryokukai.co.jp
Entrance Examination Training Services
N.A.I.C.S.: 611691

Affiliate (Domestic):

Zip Inc.   **(2)**

301-11 Osafune, Osafune-cho, Setouchi,
701-4271, Okayama, Japan   **(67%)**
Tel.: (81) 86 926 8217
Web Site: https://www.zip-inc.co.jp
Emp.: 3,290
Distribution Services
N.A.I.C.S.: 541870
Seijiro Iwatsubo *(Chm)*

EBV Explosives Environmental
Company   **(1)**
4174 Country Rd 180, Carthage, MO 64801
Tel.: (417) 624-0212
Web Site: http://dnr.mo.gov
Aircraft Mfr
N.A.I.C.S.: 336411

EQT Partners AB   **(1)**
Regeringsgatan 25, SE-111 53, Stockholm,
Sweden   **(100%)**
Tel.: (46) 850655300
Web Site: https://www.eqtgroup.com
Privater Equity Firm
N.A.I.C.S.: 523999
Marcus Wallenberg *(Deputy Chm)*

Holding (US):

Acumatica, Inc.   **(2)**
3933 Lake Washington Blvd NE #350, Kirkland, WA 98033
Tel.: (888) 228-8300
Web Site: http://www.acumatica.com
Computer System Design Services
N.A.I.C.S.: 541512
Sanket Akerkar *(Chief Revenue Officer)*

Holding (Domestic):

Anticimex International AB   **(2)**
Arstaangsvagen 21B, Stockholm, 11743,
Sweden   **(92%)**
Tel.: (46) 851763300
Web Site: http://www.anticimex.com
Holding Company; Hygiene, Pest Control,
Safety & Fire Protection Services
N.A.I.C.S.: 551112
Thomas Hilde *(Pres-Reg Continental Europe)*

Subsidiary (US):

American Pest Management,
Inc.   **(3)**
11820 West Market Pl, Fulton, MD 20759
Tel.: (240) 377-0253
Web Site: http://www.americanpest.net
General Pest Control
N.A.I.C.S.: 561710
Ravi Sachdeva *(CEO)*

Subsidiary (Domestic):

American Pest Control-Mntgmry   **(4)**
401 N Stonestreet Ave, Rockville, MD
20850
Tel.: (800) 585-7378
Web Site: http://www.pestcentral.com
Rev.: $1,248,000
Emp.: 16
Exterminating & Pest Control Services
N.A.I.C.S.: 561710
Doug Wade *(Owner)*

Innovative Pest Management,
LLC   **(4)**
500 Greenbridge Rd, Brookeville, MD
20833-1912
Tel.: (301) 570-3900
Web Site: http://www.ipm4u.com
Exterminating & Pest Control Services
N.A.I.C.S.: 561710
Richard D. Kramer *(Pres)*

Subsidiary (Non-US):

Anticimex A/S   **(3)**
Pilestredet 28, 0166, Oslo, Norway
Tel.: (47) 81548250
Hygiene, Pest Control, Safety & Fire Protection Services
N.A.I.C.S.: 561710

Subsidiary (Domestic):

Anticimex AB   **(3)**
Halsingegatan 40, 113 43, Stockholm, Sweden
Tel.: (46) 851763300
Web Site: http://www.anticimex.com

EQT AB—(Continued)

Sales Range: $250-299.9 Million
Emp.: 70
Hygiene, Pest Control, Safety & Fire Protection Services
N.A.I.C.S.: 561710
Mikael Roos (Pres)

Subsidiary (Domestic):

Anticimex Forsakringar AB (4)
Lovholmsvagen 61, 117 65, Stockholm, Sweden
Tel.: (46) 851763300
Web Site: http://www.anticimex.com
Insurance Services
N.A.I.C.S.: 524298
Mats Samuelsson (Pres)

Subsidiary (Non-US):

Anticimex AS (3)
Kvaglundvej 82, 6705, Esbjerg, Denmark
Tel.: (45) 75145822
Web Site: http://www.anticimex.com
Emp.: 100
Hygiene, Pest Control, Safety & Fire Protection Services
N.A.I.C.S.: 561710
Rune Sejersen (Mgr-Fin)

Anticimex Benelux B.V. (3)
Schapenweide 6, 4824 AN, Breda, Netherlands
Tel.: (31) 765486660
Web Site: http://www.anticimex.com
Sales Range: $25-49.9 Million
Emp.: 56
Hygiene, Pest Control, Safety & Fire Protection Services
N.A.I.C.S.: 561710
Sascha Suijkerbuijk (Mng Dir)

Anticimex GmbH & Co. KG (3)
Havighorster Weg 8d, Hamburg, 21031, Germany
Tel.: (49) 407392450
Web Site: http://www.anticimex.com
Hygiene, Pest Control, Safety & Fire Protection Services
N.A.I.C.S.: 561710

Subsidiary (US):

JP McHale Pest Management, LLC (3)
241 Bleakley Ave, Buchanan, NY 10511
Tel.: (914) 734-7413
Web Site: http://nopests.com
Exterminating & Pest Control Services
N.A.I.C.S.: 561710
James P. McHale Sr. (Founder)

Northwest Exterminating Co., Inc. (3)
4954 N Shamrock Pl, Tucson, AZ 85705-1498
Tel.: (520) 888-5779
Web Site: http://www.nwexterminating.com
Rev.: $4,000,000
Emp.: 95
Exterminating & Pest Control Services
N.A.I.C.S.: 561710
Dena Berg (Dir-Ops)

Viking Termite & Pest Control, LLC (3)
97 Mount Bethel Rd, Warren, NJ 07059
Tel.: (732) 479-7289
Web Site: http://www.vikingpest.com
Exterminating & Pest Control Services
N.A.I.C.S.: 561710
Frank Modrick (Mgr)

Subsidiary (Domestic):

ChemTec Pest Control Corp. (4)
250 Market St, Saddle Brook, NJ 07663
Tel.: (201) 843-0780
Web Site: http://chemtecpest.com
Exterminating & Pest Control Services
N.A.I.C.S.: 561710
Stanley Saltzman (Chm)

Holding (Non-US):

Apleona GmbH (2)
An der Gehespitz 50, 63263, Neu-Isenburg, Germany
Tel.: (49) 6102453400

Web Site: http://www.apleona.com
Holding Company; Facilities Management & Support Services
N.A.I.C.S.: 551112
Jochen Keysberg (Chm-Mgmt Bd & CEO)

Subsidiary (Domestic):

Apleona Ahr Healthcare & Services GmbH (3)
Lindnerstrasse 96, 46149, Oberhausen, Germany
Tel.: (49) 20865900
Web Site: http://www.ahr.apleona.com
Emp.: 8,000
Healthcare Industry Facility Management & Operational Support Services
N.A.I.C.S.: 561210
Martin Buerger (Chm-Mgmt Bd & CEO)

Subsidiary (Domestic):

Apleona Ahr Carecatering GmbH (4)
Lindnerstrasse 96, 46149, Oberhausen, Germany
Tel.: (49) 20865900
Healthcare Industry Catering Services
N.A.I.C.S.: 722320
Martin Buerger (Mng Dir)

Apleona Ahr Careclean GmbH (4)
Lindnerstrasse 96, 46149, Oberhausen, Germany
Tel.: (49) 20865900
Healthcare Industry Janitorial & Specialist Cleaning Services
N.A.I.C.S.: 561720

Subsidiary (Domestic):

Apleona HSG GmbH (3)
An der Gehespitz 50, 63263, Neu-Isenburg, Germany (100%)
Tel.: (49) 6102 45 3400
Web Site: http://www.hsg.apleona.com
Sales Range: $1-4.9 Billion
Emp.: 17,000
Facility Support & Property Management Services
N.A.I.C.S.: 561210
Otto Kajetan Weixler (Mng Dir)

Subsidiary (Non-US):

Apleona HSG A/S (4)
Strandvejen 100 4 sal, 2900, Hellerup, Denmark
Tel.: (45) 70200577
Web Site: http://www.hsg.apleona.com
Emp.: 22
Facility Management Services
N.A.I.C.S.: 561210

Apleona HSG AG (4)
Alte Winterthurerstrasse 14b, 8304, Wallisellen, Switzerland
Tel.: (41) 445674000
Web Site: http://www.ch-hsg.apleona.com
Facility Management Services
N.A.I.C.S.: 561210
Markus Faber (Co-COO)

Subsidiary (Domestic):

Apleona HSG Culinaress GmbH (4)
Maria-Merian-Strasse 10, 85521, Ottobrunn, Germany
Tel.: (49) 89444927968
Web Site: http://www.hsg.apleona.com
Catering Services
N.A.I.C.S.: 722320

Subsidiary (Non-US):

Apleona HSG EOOD (4)
Petra Street 6-8, 1504, Sofia, Bulgaria
Tel.: (359) 887950504
Web Site: http://www.hsg.apleona.com
Sales Range: $10-24.9 Million
Emp.: 38
Facility Management Services
N.A.I.C.S.: 561210
Georgi Hristov (Country Mgr)

Subsidiary (Domestic):

Apleona HSG Event Services GmbH (4)
Isarstrasse 1, 65451, Kelsterbach, Germany
Tel.: (49) 6142835550

Web Site: http://www.eventservices.apleona.com
Sales Range: $50-74.9 Million
Emp.: 40
Event Management Services
N.A.I.C.S.: 561920
Tom Frerik Bauerfeind (Mng Dir)

Subsidiary (Non-US):

Apleona HSG GmbH (4)
Leonard-Bernstein-Strasse 10, 1220, Vienna, Austria
Tel.: (43) 1211470
Web Site: http://www.hsg.apleona.com
Emp.: 60
Facility Management Services
N.A.I.C.S.: 561210
Gerhard Schenk (Mng Dir)

Apleona HSG Kft. (4)
Akna u 2-4, 1106, Budapest, Hungary
Tel.: (36) 14333624
Web Site: http://www.hsg.apleona.com
Facility Management Services
N.A.I.C.S.: 561210
Eniko Vano-Huszar (Mng Dir)

Apleona HSG Limited (4)
Landscape House Landscape Road, Churchtown, Dublin, Ireland (100%)
Tel.: (353) 12157000
Web Site: http://www.hsg.apleona.com
Sales Range: $25-49.9 Million
Emp.: 200
Facility Management Services
N.A.I.C.S.: 561210
Dirk Van Breda (CFO & Dir-Comml)

Apleona HSG Limited (4)
Fifth Floor City Reach 5 Greenwich View Place, London, E14 9NN, United Kingdom
Tel.: (44) 2087901000
Web Site: http://www.uk-hsg.apleona.com
Sales Range: $150-199.9 Million
Emp.: 1,900
Building & Facilities Management Services
N.A.I.C.S.: 561210
Jacqui Paice (Mng Dir-FM)

Subsidiary (Domestic):

Apleona PPP Limited (5)
Gloucestershire Royal Hospital, Great Western Road, Gloucester, GL1 3NN, Gloucestershire, United Kingdom
Tel.: (44) 8454228391
Facility Management Services
N.A.I.C.S.: 561210
Brian Jenkinson (Dir-Ops)

Europa Workspace Solutions Limited (5)
Unit A 1 Watt Place Hamilton International Technology Park, Blantyre, G72 0AH, United Kingdom
Tel.: (44) 1698720520
Sales Range: $25-49.9 Million
Emp.: 35
Facilities Support Services
N.A.I.C.S.: 541410
David Eastlake (Mng Dir)

Subsidiary (Domestic):

Apleona HSG Nord GmbH (4)
An der Gehespitz 50, 63263, Neu-Isenburg, Germany
Tel.: (49) 6102453400
Web Site: http://www.hsg.apleona.com
Facility Management Services
N.A.I.C.S.: 561210
Jorn Ettenhofer (Mng Dir)

Apleona HSG Nordost GmbH (4)
Oberlandstrasse 88, 12099, Berlin, Germany
Tel.: (49) 303009180
Web Site: http://www.hsg.apleona.com
Facility Management Services
N.A.I.C.S.: 561210
Erich Zanoni (Mng Dir)

Subsidiary (Non-US):

Apleona HSG O.O.O. (4)
Zemlyanoy Val str 9, 105064, Moscow, Russia
Tel.: (7) 4952299550
Web Site: http://www.ru-hsg.apleona.com

Sales Range: $150-199.9 Million
Emp.: 800
Facility Management Services
N.A.I.C.S.: 561210
Victor Efremov (CEO)

Subsidiary (Domestic):

Apleona HSG Ost GmbH (4)
Zum Frischemarkt 2a, 04158, Leipzig, Germany
Tel.: (49) 341521130
Web Site: http://www.hsg.apleona.com
Facility Management Services
N.A.I.C.S.: 561210
Hauke Disselbeck (Mng Dir)

Apleona HSG Rhein-Main GmbH (4)
Admiral-Rosendahl-Strasse 1, 63263, Neu-Isenburg, Germany
Tel.: (49) 69697647100
Web Site: http://www.hsg.apleona.com
Facility Management Services
N.A.I.C.S.: 561210
Peter Panzof (Mng Dir)

Subsidiary (Non-US):

Apleona HSG S.A. (4)
C/ Monasterio de Suso y Yuso 34 3rd Fl, 28049, Madrid, Spain
Tel.: (34) 917911000
Web Site: http://www.es-hsg.apleona.com
Facilities Support Services
N.A.I.C.S.: 561210
Jaime Pire (Mng Dir)

Apleona HSG S.p.A. (4)
via VIII Strada 9 ZI, Fosso, 30030, Venice, Italy
Tel.: (39) 0415170039
Web Site: http://www.hsg.apleona.com
Facilities Support Services
N.A.I.C.S.: 561210
Alessandro Lunardi (Mng Dir)

Apleona HSG SRL (4)
17 Thomas Masaryk Str 3rd Floor Sector 2, 020983, Bucharest, Romania
Tel.: (40) 212692164
Web Site: http://www.hsg.apleona.com
Facilities Support Services
N.A.I.C.S.: 561210
Bianca Radulescu (Country Mgr)

Subsidiary (Domestic):

Apleona HSG Security & Services GmbH (4)
An der Gehespitz 50, 63263, Neu-Isenburg, Germany
Tel.: (49) 6102453900
Web Site: http://www.hsg.apleona.com
Security System Services
N.A.I.C.S.: 561621
Klaus-Rolf Vogt (Gen Mgr)

Subsidiary (Non-US):

Apleona HSG Sp. z o.o. (4)
Al Armii Ludowej 26, 00-609, Warsaw, Poland
Tel.: (48) 225793232
Web Site: http://www.hsg.apleona.com
Sales Range: $25-49.9 Million
Emp.: 20
Facility Management Services
N.A.I.C.S.: 561210
Thorsten Bruedigam (Mng Dir)

Subsidiary (Domestic):

Apleona HSG Sudost GmbH (4)
Nordring 69, 90409, Nuremberg, Germany
Tel.: (49) 91136080
Web Site: http://www.hsg.apleona.com
Facility Management Services
N.A.I.C.S.: 561210
Juergen Wohlrab (Mng Dir)

Subsidiary (Non-US):

Apleona HSG TOV (4)
24-V Moskovsky Avenue, 04073, Kiev, Ukraine
Tel.: (380) 445036329
Web Site: http://www.hsg.apleona.com
Facility Management Services
N.A.I.C.S.: 561210

Subsidiary (Domestic):

Apleona HSG Wurttemberg GmbH (4)
Industriestrasse 74, 70565, Stuttgart, Germany
Tel.: (49) 711722440
Web Site: http://www.hsg.apleona.com
Facility Management Services
N.A.I.C.S.: 561210
Dirk Christophel (Mng Dir)

Subsidiary (Non-US):

Apleona HSG s.a.r.l. (4)
7 rue de Luxembourg, 0130, Luxembourg, Luxembourg
Tel.: (352) 28550520
Web Site: http://www.hsg.apleona.com
Facility Management Services
N.A.I.C.S.: 561210
Johannes Schwarz (Mng Dir)

Apleona HSG s.r.o. (4)
Za Strahovem 19, 169 00, Prague, Czech Republic
Tel.: (420) 233090520
Web Site: http://www.cz-hsg.apleona.com
Sales Range: $25-49.9 Million
Emp.: 170
Facility Management Services
N.A.I.C.S.: 561210
Jiri Folta (Mng Dir)

Apleona HSG s.r.o. (4)
Rontgenova 26, 851 01, Bratislava, Slovakia
Tel.: (421) 244640014
Web Site: http://www.hsg.apleona.com
Sales Range: $25-49.9 Million
Emp.: 55
Facility Management Services
N.A.I.C.S.: 561210
Stefan Melikant (Country Mgr)

Joint Venture (Domestic):

CSG GmbH (4)
Godesberger Allee 157, 53175, Bonn, Germany
Tel.: (49) 228 5289 0
Web Site: http://www.csg-gmbh.com
Property & Facility Management Services
N.A.I.C.S.: 561210
Georg Behrens (Mng Dir)

Subsidiary (Domestic):

HSG Zander FS GmbH (4)
An Der Gehespitz 50, 63263, Neu-Isenburg, Hessen, Germany
Tel.: (49) 6102453400
Facility Management Services
N.A.I.C.S.: 561210

Subsidiary (Non-US):

Siemens Gebaudemanagement & -Services G.m.b.H. (3)
Europastrasse 4, 9524, Villach, Austria
Tel.: (43) 424290032000
Web Site: http://www.sgs.at
Facility Management Services
N.A.I.C.S.: 561210

Holding (Non-US):

Azelis Group NV (2)
Posthofbrug 12, 2600, Berchem, 2600, Belgium
Tel.: (32) 36130120
Web Site: https://www.azelis.com
Rev.: $4,583,535,711
Assets: $6,151,040,955
Liabilities: $3,196,434,485
Net Worth: $2,954,606,469
Earnings: $208,976,708
Fiscal Year-end: 12/31/2023
Chemicals Mfr
N.A.I.C.S.: 325199
Hans-Joachim Muller (CEO-Grp)

Subsidiary (Domestic):

Azelis S.A. (3)
Posthofbrug 12, PO Box 6, 2600, Antwerp, Belgium
Tel.: (32) 36130120
Web Site: http://www.azelis.com
Emp.: 1,100
Specialty Chemicals Distr

N.A.I.C.S.: 424690
Hans-Joachim Muller (CEO)

Subsidiary (Non-US):

Azelis A/S (4)
Lundtoftegaardsvej 95, 2800, Kongens Lyngby, Denmark
Tel.: (45) 45263333
Web Site: http://www.azelis.com
Chemicals Mfr & Distr
N.A.I.C.S.: 325998
Gert Schnoor (Mng Dir)

Subsidiary (US):

Azelis Americas (4)
262 Harbor Dr 3rd Fl, Stamford, CT 06902
Tel.: (203) 274-8691
Web Site: http://www.azelisamericas.com
Specialty Chemicals Distr
N.A.I.C.S.: 424690
Frank Bergonzi (Pres & CEO)

Subsidiary (Domestic):

ADAPCO, LLC (5)
550 Aero Ln, Sanford, FL 32771-6342
Web Site: http://www.myadapco.com
Emp.: 10
Chemical Products Distr
N.A.I.C.S.: 424690
Jason Trumbetta (Gen Mgr)

Subsidiary (Non-US):

Azelis Canada, Inc. (5)
1570 rue Ampere Suite 106, Boucherville, J4B 7L4, QC, Canada
Tel.: (450) 449-6363
Web Site: http://www.azelis.com
Specialty Chemicals Distr
N.A.I.C.S.: 424690
Jean-Pierre Pelchat (Mng Dir)

Subsidiary (Domestic):

GMZ, Inc. (5)
225 Pictoria Dr, Springdale, OH 45246
Tel.: (513) 860-9300
Web Site: http://www.gmzinc.com
Emp.: 41
Specialty Chemical Distribution
N.A.I.C.S.: 424690
William Robinson (Mgr-Bus Dev-Southwest)

Gillco Products, Inc. (5)
1701 La Costa Meadows Dr, San Marcos, CA 92078-5105
Tel.: (760) 759-7900
Web Site: https://www.gillco.com
Sales Range: $10-24.9 Million
Emp.: 13
Chemical & Allied Product Whslr
N.A.I.C.S.: 424690
Matthew Berry (Acct Mgr)

Monson Companies Inc. (5)
154 Pioneer Dr, Leominster, MA 01453
Tel.: (978) 534-1425
Web Site: http://www.monsonco.com
Industrial Chemical Distr
N.A.I.C.S.: 424690
Holly Daley (Pres)

P.T. Hutchins Co., Ltd. (5)
901 S Stimson Ave, City of Industry, CA 91745
Tel.: (626) 333-3329
Web Site: http://www.pthutchins.com
Chemical Products Distr
N.A.I.C.S.: 424690
Doug Kercher (Pres)

Ribelin Sales Inc. (5)
3857 Miller Park Dr, Garland, TX 75042
Tel.: (972) 272-1594
Web Site: http://www.ribelin.com
Chemicals & Allied Products Distr
N.A.I.C.S.: 424690
Jordan Muller (Gen Mgr)

Ross Organic Specialty Sales, Inc. (5)
9770 Bell Ranch Dr, Santa Fe Springs, CA 90670
Tel.: (562) 236-5700
Web Site: http://www.rossorg.com
Sales Range: $1-9.9 Million
Emp.: 38

Drugs & Druggists' Sundries Merchant Whslr
N.A.I.C.S.: 424210
William C. Ross (Founder)

Vigon International, Inc. (5)
127 Airport Rd, East Stroudsburg, PA 18301-9629
Tel.: (570) 476-6300
Web Site: http://www.vigon.com
Sales Range: $25-49.9 Million
Emp.: 55
Basic Organic & Chemical Mfr
N.A.I.C.S.: 325199
Danna Ward (Mgr-Quality Sys)

Subsidiary (Non-US):

Azelis Australia Pty. Limited (4)
Suite 217 117 Old Pittwater Road, Sydney, 2100, NSW, Australia
Tel.: (61) 299392188
Web Site: http://www.azelis.com
Sales Range: $25-49.9 Million
Emp.: 3
Chemical Distr
N.A.I.C.S.: 424690

Azelis Bulgaria EAD (4)
World Trade Centre Interprd Office 410B 36 Dragan Tzankov Blvd, 1040, Sofia, Bulgaria
Tel.: (359) 29712130
Web Site: http://www.azelis.com
Sales Range: $25-49.9 Million
Emp.: 4
Chemical Distr
N.A.I.C.S.: 424690

Azelis Czech Republic, s.r.o. (4)
Evropska 2590/33 C, 160 00, Prague, Czech Republic
Tel.: (420) 224313303
Web Site: http://www.azelis.com
Sales Range: $25-49.9 Million
Emp.: 12
Chemical Distr
N.A.I.C.S.: 424690
Jakub Matys (Reg Mng Dir)

Azelis Deutschland GmbH (4)
Zum Siegblick 37-45, 53757, Saint Augustin, Germany
Tel.: (49) 224154970
Web Site: http://www.azelis.com
Emp.: 120
Chemical Distr
N.A.I.C.S.: 424690
Michael van Dermairen (Mng Dir)

Azelis Deutschland Kosmetik GmbH (4)
Galmesweg 65, 47445, Moers, Germany
Tel.: (49) 2841880360
Web Site: http://www.azelis-kosmetik.de
Sales Range: $25-49.9 Million
Emp.: 30
Personal Care Applications Specialty Chemicals Distr
N.A.I.C.S.: 424690

Azelis Espana, S.A. (4)
World Trade Center Almeda Park Placa de la Pau s/n Edificio 8 1 planta, Cornella de Llobregat, 08940, Barcelona, Spain
Tel.: (34) 934099070
Web Site: http://www.impexquimica.com
Chemical Products Distr
N.A.I.C.S.: 424690

Azelis Food & Health (4)
Foxholes Business Park John John Tate Road, Hertford, SG13 7YH, Beds, United Kingdom
Tel.: (44) 1767677666
Web Site: http://www.azelis.co.uk
Sales Range: $25-49.9 Million
Emp.: 30
Food Processing Services
N.A.I.C.S.: 325998
David Gray (Mng Dir)

Azelis France SAS (4)
8-14 avenue de l Arche, 92400, Courbevoie, Cedex 19, France
Tel.: (33) 144731000
Web Site: http://www.azelis.com
Sales Range: $25-49.9 Million
Emp.: 100
Compound Semiconductor Substrates Mfr

N.A.I.C.S.: 334413
Laurent Nataf (Pres & CEO-Asia Pacific)

Azelis India Private Limited (4)
Liberty Tower Unit No 801 B 8th Floor Plot No K 10, Kalwa Industrial Area Airoli Navi, Mumbai, 400 708, India
Tel.: (91) 2261294700
Web Site: http://www.azelis.com
Emp.: 19
Chemicals & Polymers Marketing
N.A.I.C.S.: 424690

Subsidiary (Domestic):

Chemo India (5)
707 8th Floor Ecstasy Business Park City Of Joy J S D Road, Opp Lok Everest Mulund W, 400080, Mumbai, Maharashtra, India
Tel.: (91) 2264556100
Web Site: http://www.chemoindia.com
Chemical Products Distr
N.A.I.C.S.: 424690
Dhirubhai Shah (Founder)

Subsidiary (Non-US):

Azelis Russia (4)
Butirsky val 68/70 bld 1 Office 64 Business Center Baker Plaza, 127055, Moscow, Russia
Tel.: (7) 495 228 1779
Web Site: http://www.azelis.com.ru
Chemical Distr
N.A.I.C.S.: 424690
Andrey Zhukov (Mng Dir)

Azelis Serbia (4)
Toplicin venac 3/2, 11000, Belgrade, Serbia
Tel.: (381) 113283390
Web Site: http://www.azelis.com
Chemical Distr
N.A.I.C.S.: 424690
Dubravka Mirkovic (Mng Dir)

Azelis UK Life Sciences Ltd (4)
Foxholes Business Park, John Tate Road, Hertford, SG13 7YH, Herts, United Kingdom
Tel.: (44) 1992825555
Web Site: http://www.azelis.com
Chemical Distr
N.A.I.C.S.: 424690
Trevor Bridger (Reg Mgr-Pharma Bus Unit-UK & Ireland)

Chesham Specialty Ingredients Ltd (4)
Cunningham House, Westfield Lane, Harrow, HA3 9ED, Middlesex, United Kingdom
Tel.: (44) 2089078822
Web Site: http://www.chesham-ingredients.com
Cosmetic & Toiletry Markets Raw Materials Distr
N.A.I.C.S.: 424690

Subsidiary (Non-US):

BPEA EQT Limited (2)
Suite 3801 Two International Finance Centre, 8 Finance Street, Central, China (Hong Kong)
Tel.: (852) 28439300
Web Site: http://www.bpeasia.com
Emp.: 190
Privater Equity Firm
N.A.I.C.S.: 523999
Jean Eric Salata (CEO)

Holding (Non-US):

Bushu Pharmaceuticals Ltd. (3)
1 Oaza Takeno, Kawagoe, Saitama, Japan
Tel.: (81) 492334651
Web Site: http://www.bushu-seiyaku.co.jp
Sales Range: $200-249.9 Million
Contract Pharmaceutical Mfr
N.A.I.C.S.: 325412
Jun Yokohama (Pres & CEO)

Plant (Domestic):

Bushu Pharmaceuticals Ltd. - Misato Plant (4)
950 Oaza-Hiroki Misato-machi, Kodamagun, Misato, 367-0198, Saitama, Japan
Tel.: (81) 495763111
Emp.: 210
Pharmaceuticals Product Mfr
N.A.I.C.S.: 325412

EQT AB—(Continued)

Joint Venture (Non-US):

Courts Singapore Limited (3)
50 Tampines North Drive 2, Singapore, Singapore
Tel.: (65) 63097888
Web Site: http://www.courts.com.sg
Household Products Retailer; Owned by
Baring Private Equity Asia & The International Investor Company K.S.C.
N.A.I.C.S.: 459999
Jasmine Seow (Dir-Mdse)

Holding (Non-US):

Hexaware Technologies Ltd (3)
Bldg No 152 Millennium Business Park A
Block TTC Industrial Area, Sector-3 Mahape, Navi Mumbai, 400 710,
India (71%)
Tel.: (91) 2241599595
Web Site: http://www.hexaware.com
Rev.: $785,501,780
Assets: $583,623,600
Liabilities: $196,458,780
Net Worth: $387,164,820
Earnings: $89,788,020
Emp.: 15,879
Fiscal Year-end: 12/31/2019
Information Technology & Business Process
Outsourcing Services
N.A.I.C.S.: 541690
Atul K. Nishar (Founder & Chm)

Subsidiary (Domestic):

Caliber Point Business Solutions (4)
Bldg No 3 Sector II Millennium Bus Park A
Block, TTC Industrial Area Mahape, Navi
Mumbai, 400710, Maharashtra, India
Tel.: (91) 2227783300
Web Site: http://www.caliberpoint.com
Sales Range: $50-74.9 Million
Business Management Services
N.A.I.C.S.: 541611
Shyam Mansukhani (Assoc VP)

Subsidiary (US):

Hexaware Technologies Inc. (4)
101 Wood Ave S Ste 600, Iselin, NJ 08830
Tel.: (609) 409-6950
Web Site: http://www.hexaware.com
Sales Range: $25-49.9 Million
Emp.: 215
Information Technology & Business Process
Outsourcing Services
N.A.I.C.S.: 541690
Vijay Iyer (Chief Sls Officer-Americas)

Mobiquity, Inc. (4)
51 Sawyer Rd 410, Waltham, MA 02453
Tel.: (781) 591-4800
Web Site: http://www.mobiquityinc.com
Enterprise Mobile Application Solutions
N.A.I.C.S.: 513210
Andrew Norman (COO)

Joint Venture (Domestic):

Nord Anglia Education, Inc. (3)
Level 12 St George's Building 2 Ice House
Street, Central, China (Hong Kong)
Tel.: (852) 39511100
Web Site:
    http://www.nordangliaeducation.com
Holding Company; Private Elementary &
Secondary Schools Operator
N.A.I.C.S.: 551112
Andrew Fitzmaurice (CEO)

Subsidiary (Non-US):

Nord Anglia Education Limited (4)
St Clements House 27-28 Lane, London,
EC4N 7AE, United Kingdom
Tel.: (44) 2075319696
Web Site: http://www.nordanglia.com
Holding Company; Education Services
N.A.I.C.S.: 551112
Andrew Fitzmaurice (CEO)

Subsidiary (Non-US):

**English International School
Prague** (5)
Brunelova 960/12, 14200, Prague, Czech
Republic
Tel.: (420) 272181911

Web Site:
    http://www.nordangliaeducation.com
Colleges Universities & Professional
Schools
N.A.I.C.S.: 611310
Mel Curtis (Principal)

Subsidiary (US):

IMG Academy, LLC
5650 Bollettieri Blvd, Bradenton, FL 34210
Tel.: (941) 749-8660
Web Site: https://www.imgacademy.com
Boarding School Services
N.A.I.C.S.: 611110

Subsidiary (Non-US):

**The British International School
Bratislava** (5)
J Valastana Dolinskeho 1, 84102, Bratislava, Slovakia
Tel.: (421) 269307081
Web Site:
    http://www.nordangliaeducation.com
Colleges Universities & Professional
Schools
N.A.I.C.S.: 611310
Bárbara Kanclerova (Bus Mgr)

**The British International School
Budapest** (5)
Kiscelli Koz 17, Budapest, 1037, Hungary
Tel.: (36) 12009971
Web Site:
    http://www.nordangliaeducation.com
Colleges Universities & Professional
Schools
N.A.I.C.S.: 611310
Eszter Valko (Bus Mgr)

**The British International School
Shanghai** (5)
Puxi Campus No 111 Jinguang Road, Huacao Town Minhang, 201107, Shanghai,
China
Tel.: (86) 2152263211
Web Site:
    http://www.nordangliaeducation.com
Colleges Universities & Professional
Schools
N.A.I.C.S.: 611310
Neil Hopkin (Principal)

The British School Sp. z o.o. (5)
ul Limanowskiego 15, 02943, Warsaw, Poland
Tel.: (48) 228423281
Web Site:
    http://www.nordangliaeducation.com
Colleges Universities & Professional
Schools
N.A.I.C.S.: 561499
Alun Yorath (Principal)

Holding (Non-US):

Pioneer Corporation (3)
28-8 Honkomagome 2-chome, Bunkyo-ku,
Tokyo, 113-0021, Japan
Tel.: (81) 366348777
Web Site: http://www.pioneer.jp
Rev.: $3,244,902,960
Assets: $2,553,088,800
Liabilities: $1,798,874,880
Net Worth: $754,213,920
Earnings: ($63,252,240)
Emp.: 16,798
Fiscal Year-end: 03/31/2018
Consumer & Commercial Electronics Mfr
N.A.I.C.S.: 334310
Kyotaro Sato (Sr Exec Officer)

Subsidiary (Non-US):

**INCREMENT P Shanghai
Co.,Ltd** (4)
4F 40 333 Qinjiang Lu Caohejing Hi Tech
Park Development Zone, Shanghai,
200233, China
Tel.: (86) 2164851828
Web Site: http://www.incrementp.com.cn
Emp.: 130
Geophysical Mapping Services
N.A.I.C.S.: 541360
Cxi Qiao (Gen Mgr)

Subsidiary (Domestic):

Increment P Corp (4)

Bunkyo Green Court Center Office 2-28-8
Honkomagome, Bunkyo-ku, Tokyo, 113-
0021, Japan
Tel.: (81) 366294850
Web Site: http://www.incrementp.co.jp
Sales Range: $150-199.9 Million
Emp.: 550
Geophysical Mapping Services
N.A.I.C.S.: 541360
Takumi Jinguji (Pres & CEO)

Mogami Denki Corporation (4)
954-1 Aramachi, Mamurogawa Mogami,
Yamagata, 999-5312, Japan
Tel.: (81) 233622261
Speaker Diaphragm Mfr & Retailer
N.A.I.C.S.: 334310

Subsidiary (Non-US):

**Mogami Dongguan Electronics Co.,
Ltd.** (4)
Tangxiazhen Tangxiazhen Industrial Zone,
Dongguan, Guangdong, China
Tel.: (86) 76987883718
Speaker Diaphragm Mfr & Retailer
N.A.I.C.S.: 334310

Mogami HongKong Co., Ltd. (4)
5/F 909 Cheung Sha Wan Road, Cheung
Sha Wan, Kowloon, China (Hong Kong)
Tel.: (852) 23753712
Speaker Diaphragm Retailer
N.A.I.C.S.: 449210

Pioneer (HK) Ltd. (4)
5/F 909 Cheung Sha Wan Road, Kowloon,
China (Hong Kong)
Tel.: (852) 28486488
Web Site:
    http://www.pioneerhongkong.com.hk
Audio & Video Equipment Mfr
N.A.I.C.S.: 334310

Division (US):

Pioneer Automotive Technology (4)
100 S Pioneer Blvd, Springboro, OH 45066-
1177
Tel.: (937) 746-6600
Web Site:
    http://www.pioneerelectronicsi.com
Sales Range: $125-149.9 Million
Emp.: 300
Mfr of Automotive Radios
N.A.I.C.S.: 334310
Tina McFarland Groves (Supvr-Production)

Subsidiary (Non-US):

Pioneer China Holding Co Ltd (4)
Room 808 Yian Plaza No 33 Jianshe No 6
Road, Dongshan, Guangzhou, 510061,
Guangdong, China
Tel.: (86) 2083633158
Web Site: http://www.pioneerchina.com
Sales Range: $25-49.9 Million
Emp.: 100
Consumer Electronics Product Mfr
N.A.I.C.S.: 334419

Subsidiary (Domestic):

Pioneer Communications Corp (4)
2-70-1 Hayashi Tokorozawa, Kawagoe,
359-1167, Japan
Tel.: (81) 429495111
Web Site: http://www.pioncomm.net
Telephone Apparatus Mfr
N.A.I.C.S.: 334210

Plant (Domestic):

**Pioneer Corporation - Kawagoe
Plant** (4)
25-1 Aza Nishimachi Yamada, Kawagoe,
350 8555, Saitama, Japan
Tel.: (81) 492231111
Emp.: 2,000
Electronic Products Mfr & Sales
N.A.I.C.S.: 335999
Susumu Kotani (Pres)

Subsidiary (US):

Pioneer Electronics (USA) Inc. (4)
1925 E Dominguez, Long Beach, CA
90810 (100%)
Tel.: (310) 952-2000
Web Site:
    http://www.pioneerelectronics.com

Sales Range: $150-199.9 Million
Emp.: 300
Consumer Electronics Sales
N.A.I.C.S.: 423620
Roberta Tapp (Dir-Mktg Comm)

Subsidiary (Domestic):

Pioneer North America Inc. (5)
1925 E Dominguez St, Long Beach, CA
90810-1639
Tel.: (310) 952-2000
Web Site:
    http://www.pioneerelectronics.com
Sales Range: $75-99.9 Million
Emp.: 200
Mfr of High Fidelity Equipment
N.A.I.C.S.: 423620
Gregory Pierson (Sec)

**Pioneer Research Center USA
Inc.** (5)
6170 Cornerstone Ct E Ste 330, San Diego,
CA 92121
Tel.: (858) 824-0790
Rev.: $3,000,000
Emp.: 10
Electronic Research
N.A.I.C.S.: 541715

Subsidiary (Non-US):

**Pioneer Electronics Asiacentre Pte.
Ltd.** (4)
258 Alexandra Rd 04 01, Singapore,
159936, Singapore (100%)
Tel.: (65) 64721111
Web Site: http://www.pioneer.com.sg
Sales Range: $100-124.9 Million
Emp.: 160
Coordination of Asian Subsidiaries' Operations & Financial Activities
N.A.I.C.S.: 523999
Tanaka Seiya (Mng Dir)

**Pioneer Electronics Australia Pty
Ltd** (4)
5 Arco Lane, Heatherton, 3202, VIC, Australia
Tel.: (61) 395866380
Web Site: http://www.pioneer.com.au
Emp.: 50
Consumer Electronics Product Mfr
N.A.I.C.S.: 334310
Bruce Blythe (CFO)

Division (US):

Pioneer Electronics Service (4)
1925 E Dominguez St, Long Beach, CA
90810
Tel.: (213) 746-6337
Web Site:
    http://www.pioneerelectronics.com
Sales Range: $75-99.9 Million
Emp.: 151
Electronic Equipment Repair
N.A.I.C.S.: 423620
Ken S Okano (Treas)

Pioneer Electronics Technology (4)
1800 West Holt Ave, Pomona, CA 91768-
3303
Tel.: (909) 623-3271
Web Site:
    http://www.pioneerelectronics.com
Sales Range: $75-99.9 Million
Emp.: 130
Mfr Big Screen Television
N.A.I.C.S.: 423620

Subsidiary (Non-US):

**Pioneer Electronics of Canada
Inc.** (4)
300 Allstate Pkwy, Markham, L3R 0P2, ON,
Canada (100%)
Tel.: (905) 479-4411
Web Site:
    http://www.pioneerelectronics.com
Sales Range: $50-74.9 Million
Emp.: 80
Distr For Consumer Products
N.A.I.C.S.: 922190

**Pioneer Electronics(Thailand) Co
Ltd** (4)
1 50 Moo 5 Soi Rojana Industrial Estate
Rojana Road, Uthai, Phra Nakhon Si Ayutthaya, 13210, Thailand

Tel.: (66) 35330990
Consumer Electronics Product Mfr
N.A.I.C.S.: 334419

Pioneer Europe N.V **(4)**
Haven 1087 Keetberglaan 1, Melsele, 9120,
Belgium
Tel.: (32) 35700511
Web Site: http://www.pioneer.eu
Sales Range: $50-74.9 Million
Emp.: 120
Electronic Products Mfr
N.A.I.C.S.: 334310
Masahiro Kawamura *(Gen Mgr)*

Pioneer Gulf, FZE **(4)**
Pioneer Gulf Free Zone, PO Box 61226,
Jebel Ali, Dubai, United Arab Emirates
Tel.: (971) 48815756
Web Site: http://www.pioneer-mea.com
Audio & Video Equipment Mfr
N.A.I.C.S.: 334310

**Pioneer High Fidelity Taiwan
Co.,Ltd** **(4)**
Taipei City Neihu District Ruig Uang Rd No
407 8th Fl, Taipei, 11492, Taiwan
Tel.: (886) 225213588
Web Site: http://www.pioneer-twn.com.tw
Emp.: 40
Consumer Electronics Product Mfr
N.A.I.C.S.: 334419
Shannon Yu *(Gen Mgr)*

**Pioneer India Electronics Private
Ltd** **(4)**
1-10-197 G Ashoka Nagar X Cross Roads,
Hyderabad, Andhra Pradesh, India
Tel.: (91) 4027678736
Electronic Products Mfr
N.A.I.C.S.: 334310

**Pioneer Industrial Components (Hong
Kong) Co., Ltd.** **(4)**
5/F 909 Cheung Sha Wan Road, Cheung
Sha Wan, Kowloon, China (Hong Kong)
Tel.: (852) 27988512
Electronic Parts & Component Distr
N.A.I.C.S.: 423690

**Pioneer Manufacturing (Thailand)
Co., Ltd.** **(4)**
1/31 Moo 5 Tambol Kanham Ambphur, Ro-
jana Industrial Park U-Thai, Phra Nakhon Si
Ayutthaya, 13210, Thailand
Tel.: (66) 35226160
Car Electronic Product Mfr
N.A.I.C.S.: 336320

Subsidiary (Domestic):

Pioneer Marketing Corp **(4)**
1-1 Shin Ogura Saiwai Ku, Kawasaki, 212-
0031, Kanagawa, Japan
Tel.: (81) 445806045
Electronic Equipments Mfr & Sales
N.A.I.C.S.: 423440

Subsidiary (Non-US):

**Pioneer RUS Limited Liability
Company** **(4)**
Nizhniy Susalny pereulok 5 building 19
Business Center ARMA, 105064, Moscow,
Russia
Tel.: (7) 4959568901
Web Site: http://www.pioneer-rus.ru
Automotive Electronic Product Mfr
N.A.I.C.S.: 336320

Subsidiary (Domestic):

Pioneer Service Network Corp **(4)**
1-1 Shin Ogura, Saiwai-Ku, Kawasaki, 212-
0031, Japan
Tel.: (81) 445803151
Web Site: http://www.pioneer.jp
Sales Range: $25-49.9 Million
Emp.: 220
Electronic Equipment Repair & Maintenance
Mfr
N.A.I.C.S.: 811210

Subsidiary (Non-US):

**Pioneer Technology (Dongguan) Co.,
Ltd.** **(4)**
GNo57-101 Liaobu Baiye Street, Liaobu-
Town, Dongguan, 523411, Guangdong,
China

Tel.: (86) 7693287700
Home Electronic Product Mfr
N.A.I.C.S.: 335220

**Pioneer Technology (Malaysia) Sdn.
Bhd.** **(4)**
16th Floor Menara Uni Asia 1008, Jalan
Sultan Ismail, 50250, Kuala Lumpur, Malay-
sia
Tel.: (60) 326972920
Web Site:
http://my.pioneercarentertainment.com
Car Audio Visual Equipment Mfr & Retailer
N.A.I.C.S.: 334310

**Pioneer Technology (Shanghai) Co.,
Ltd.** **(4)**
1-Huancheng Road North, Shanghai Com-
prehensive Industrial Development Zone,
Shanghai, 201401, China
Tel.: (86) 2167104188
Car Electronic Product Mfr
N.A.I.C.S.: 336320

Pioneer do Brasil Ltda **(4)**
Torquato Tapajos 4 920, Manaus, 69093-
018, Brazil
Tel.: (55) 9221217400
Audio & Video Equipment Mfr
N.A.I.C.S.: 334310

Subsidiary (Domestic):

PioneerFa Corp **(4)**
5-7-1 Chiyoda, Sakado, 350-0286, Saitama,
Japan
Tel.: (81) 492805000
Web Site: http://www.pioneerfa.co.jp
Sales Range: $50-74.9 Million
Emp.: 120
Electronic Equipment Mfr & Distr
N.A.I.C.S.: 334419
Hideaki Nishiyama *(Pres)*

Subsidiary (Non-US):

**Shanghai Pioneer Speakers Co.,
Ltd.** **(4)**
642 Xinghua Road, Jiangqiao Jiading Ward,
Shanghai, 201812, China
Tel.: (86) 2169133300
Speaker Mfr
N.A.I.C.S.: 334310

**Tohoku Pioneer (Thailand) Co.,
Ltd.** **(4)**
1/50 Moo 5 Tambol Khanham Amphur, Ro-
jana Industrial Park Uthai, Ayutthaya,
13210, Thailand
Tel.: (66) 35330990
Car Audio Visual Equipment Mfr & Retailer
N.A.I.C.S.: 334310

**Tohoku Pioneer (Vietnam) Co.,
Ltd.** **(4)**
Land Plot G Nomura-Haiphong Industrial
Zone, An Hung Ward An Duong District,
Haiphong, Vietnam
Tel.: (84) 313743245
Car Audio Visual Equipment Mfr & Retailer
N.A.I.C.S.: 334310

Subsidiary (Domestic):

Tohoku Pioneer Corporation **(4)**
1105 Kunomoto, Tendo, 994-8585, Yama-
gata, Japan
Tel.: (81) 236541211
Rev.: $511,416,960
Emp.: 6,591
Fiscal Year-end: 03/31/2017
Electronic Products Mfr
N.A.I.C.S.: 334419
Hiroyuki Mineta *(Pres & CEO)*

Plant (Domestic):

**Tohoku Pioneer Corporation -
Yonezawa Plant** **(5)**
4-3146-7 Hachimanpara, Yonezawa, 992-
1128, Yamagata, Japan
Tel.: (81) 238281211
Sales Range: $150-199.9 Million
Emp.: 1,000
Audio Devices Mfr
N.A.I.C.S.: 334310

Holding (Non-US):

SAI Global Pty. Limited **(3)**
Suite 7 01 Level 7 45 Clarence Street, Syd-

ney, 2000, NSW, Australia
Web Site: https://saiassurance.com.au
Risk Management, Compliance & Business
Development Information Services
N.A.I.C.S.: 519290
Kim Jenkins *(COO)*

Subsidiary (Non-US):

BWise B.V. **(4)**
Magistratenlaan 2, 5223 MD, 's-
Hertogenbosch, Netherlands
Tel.: (31) 737042000
Web Site: http://www.bwise.com
Risk Management, Internal Audit & Regula-
tory Compliance Management Software &
Services
N.A.I.C.S.: 541511
Jonathan Deeks *(CEO)*

Subsidiary (Domestic):

Bwise Beheer B.V. **(5)**
Magistratenlaan 2, 5223 MD, 's-
Hertogenbosch, Netherlands
Tel.: (31) 737042000
Web Site: http://www.bwise.com
Regulatory Compliance & Enterprise Risk
Management Software Solutions
N.A.I.C.S.: 541519

Bwise Development B.V. **(5)**
Rietbeemdenborcha14, 5241 LG, Ros-
malen, Netherlands
Tel.: (31) 736464922
Software Publishing Services
N.A.I.C.S.: 541519
Peter de Verdier *(CEO)*

Subsidiary (Non-US):

Bwise Germany GmbH **(5)**
Kaiserswerther Str 115, 40880, Ratingen,
Germany
Tel.: (49) 2102420663
Stock Management Services
N.A.I.C.S.: 523210

Subsidiary (US):

Bwise Internal Control Inc. **(5)**
195 Broadway 9th Fl, New York, NY 10007
Tel.: (212) 584-2260
Compliance Software Services
N.A.I.C.S.: 541519

Subsidiary (Domestic):

Espreon Limited **(4)**
680 George St Level 37, Sydney, 2000,
NSW, Australia
Tel.: (61) 282066060
Property, Legal & Accounting Business Sup-
port Services
N.A.I.C.S.: 561499

Subsidiary (Non-US):

PT Sai Global Indonesia **(4)**
Graha Iskandarsyah 4th Floor Jl Iskan-
darsyah Raya No 66 C, Kebayoran Baru,
Jakarta, 12160, Indonesia
Tel.: (62) 217206186
Web Site: https://saiassurance.id
Business Management Consulting Services
N.A.I.C.S.: 541611

QMI - SAI Canada Limited **(4)**
20 Carlson Court Suite 100, Toronto, M9W
7K6, ON, Canada
Tel.: (416) 401-8700
Business Support Services
N.A.I.C.S.: 561499

SAI Global Czech s.r.o **(4)**
Na Pankraci 1062/58, 140 00, Prague, 4,
Czech Republic
Tel.: (420) 267317053
Web Site: http://www.saiglobal.com
Information & Advisory Services
N.A.I.C.S.: 519290

SAI Global GmbH **(4)**
Friedrich-Ebert-Anlage 36, Frankfurt am
Main, 60325, Germany
Tel.: (49) 69244333222
Web Site: http://www.saiglobal.com
Information Services
N.A.I.C.S.: 519290

Subsidiary (US):

SAI Global Inc. **(4)**
2 Summit Park Dr Ste 425, Independence,
OH 44131-6919
Tel.: (216) 654-0900
Web Site: http://www.saiglobal.com
Information Services
N.A.I.C.S.: 519290

Subsidiary (Non-US):

SAI Global India **(4)**
11/12 Swastik Disa Business Park LBS
Marg Near Vadhani Estate, Ghatkopar,
Mumbai, 400086, India
Tel.: (91) 2240911563
Web Site: http://www.saiglobal.com
Information Services
N.A.I.C.S.: 519290

SAI Global Italia Srl **(4)**
C so Tazzoli 235/3 Torre A, 10137, Turin,
Italy
Tel.: (39) 0115165700
Web Site: http://www.saiglobal.it
Quality Management & Certification Ser-
vices
N.A.I.C.S.: 561990
Marta Escudero *(Mng Dir)*

SAI Global Japan Co Ltd **(4)**
5-3-2 Ise Shiba Building 3F, Minato-Ku, To-
kyo, 108-0014, Japan
Tel.: (81) 364360897
Web Site: http://www.saiglobal.com
Business Management Consulting Services
N.A.I.C.S.: 541611

SAI Global Limited **(4)**
Partis House Ground Floor 16 Davy Av-
enue, Knowlhill, Milton Keynes, MK5 8HJ,
United Kingdom
Tel.: (44) 1908249973
Web Site: http://www.saiglobal.com
Business Compliance Solutions
N.A.I.C.S.: 561499

Subsidiary (US):

Strategic BCP, Inc. **(4)**
960 Harvest Dr Bldg B Ste 250, Blue Bell,
PA 19422
Tel.: (610) 275-4227
Web Site: http://www.strategicbcp.com
Business Continuity Management Solutions
N.A.I.C.S.: 541512
Frank Perlmutter *(Founder & Pres)*

Holding (US):

Virtusa Corporation **(3)**
132 Turnpike Rd, Southborough, MA 01772
Tel.: (508) 389-7300
Web Site: http://www.virtusa.com
Rev.: $1,312,283,000
Assets: $1,337,067,000
Liabilities: $939,626,000
Net Worth: $397,441,000
Earnings: $48,352,000
Emp.: 22,830
Fiscal Year-end: 03/31/2020
IT Consulting Services
N.A.I.C.S.: 541690
Rajeev Mehta *(Chm)*

Subsidiary (Domestic):

Apparatus, Inc. **(4)**
1401 N Meridian St, Indianapolis, IN 46202
Tel.: (317) 254-8488
Web Site: http://www.apparatus.net
Information Technology Services
N.A.I.C.S.: 541511
Ben Frame *(CTO)*

Subsidiary (Non-US):

**Polaris Consulting & Services
Limited** **(4)**
No 34 IT Highway, Navallur, Chennai, 600
130, India **(77.7%)**
Tel.: (91) 4439874000
Web Site: http://www.polarisft.com
Sales Range: $250-299.9 Million
Banking & Insurance Software Developer &
Distr
N.A.I.C.S.: 513210
Rama Sivaraman *(COO)*

EQT AB—(Continued)

Subsidiary (Non-US):

Polaris Consulting & Services B.V. (5)
Newtonlaan 115, 3584 BH, Utrecht, Netherlands
Tel.: (31) 302106099
Web Site: http://www.polarisft.com
Banking & Insurance Software Developer & Distr
N.A.I.C.S.: 513210

Polaris Consulting & Services FZ LLC (5)
Room 113 Level 1 Building 12 Dubai Internet City, PO Box 501801, Dubai, United Arab Emirates
Tel.: (971) 43753637
Web Site: http://www.polarisft.com
Banking & Insurance Software Developer & Distr
N.A.I.C.S.: 513210

Polaris Consulting & Services GmbH (5)
2 Etage Herriotstrasse 1, 60528, Frankfurt am Main, Germany
Tel.: (49) 6967733410
Web Site: http://www.polaris-europe.com
Management Consulting Services
N.A.I.C.S.: 541618

Polaris Consulting & Services Inc. (5)
Suite 1800 The Exchange Tower, 130 King Street, Toronto, M5X 1E3, ON, Canada
Tel.: (416) 865-3365
Web Site: http://www.virtusapolaris.com
Banking & Insurance Software Developer & Distr
N.A.I.C.S.: 513210

Polaris Consulting & Services Ireland Ltd. (5)
Atlas Court Bray Business Park, Southern Cross, Bray, Co Wicklow, Ireland
Tel.: (353) 12041024
Web Site: http://www.polarisft.com
Custom Computer Programming Services
N.A.I.C.S.: 541511

Polaris Consulting & Services Limited (5)
6th Floor 1 Harbour Exchange Square, London, E14 9GE, United Kingdom
Tel.: (44) 2075315500
Web Site: http://www.polarisft.com
Software Development Services
N.A.I.C.S.: 541511
Vikrant Patankar *(Project Mgr)*

Representative Office (US):

Polaris Consulting & Services Ltd (5)
20 Corporate Pl S, Piscataway, NJ 08854
Tel.: (732) 590-8100
Web Site: http://www.virtusapolaris.com
Banking & Insurance Software Developer & Distr
N.A.I.C.S.: 541511

Subsidiary (Non-US):

Polaris Consulting & Services Pte. Ltd. (5)
3 Changi Business Park Vista #04-02 Akzonobel House, Singapore, 486051, Singapore
Tel.: (65) 64966565
Web Site: http://www.virtusapolaris.com
Banking & Insurance Software Developer & Distr
N.A.I.C.S.: 513210

Polaris Consulting & Services Pty Ltd (5)
Level 12 31 Market Street, Sydney, 2000, NSW, Australia
Tel.: (61) 292671955
Web Site: http://www.virtusapolaris.com
Emp.: 100
Banking & Insurance Software Developer & Distr
N.A.I.C.S.: 513210

Polaris Consulting & Services SA (5)

Avenue de la Gare 49, Case Postale 2607, 2001, Neuchatel, Switzerland
Tel.: (41) 327221990
Web Site: http://www.polarisft.com
Management Consulting Services
N.A.I.C.S.: 541618

Polaris Consulting and Services Japan K.K. (5)
32 Shiba Koen building 8th Floor Shiba Koen, Minato-ku, Tokyo, 105-0011, Japan
Tel.: (81) 354059410
Web Site: http://www.polarisft.com
Banking & Insurance Software Developer & Distr
N.A.I.C.S.: 513210

Polaris Software (Shanghai) Company Limited (5)
Level 26 Shanghai City Time Square Office TowerSuite 26-03A Level 26, No 93 Huaihai Zhong Road Luwan District, Shanghai, 200021, China
Tel.: (86) 2151176391
Web Site: http://www.polarisft.com
Banking & Insurance Software Developer & Distr
N.A.I.C.S.: 513210

Polaris Software Consulting & Services Sdn Bhd (5)
Suite 6 Level 21 Block 3B Plaza Sentral, Jalan Stesen Sentral 5, 50470, Kuala Lumpur, Malaysia
Tel.: (60) 327735628
Web Site: http://www.virtusapolaris.com
Banking & Insurance Software Developer & Distr
N.A.I.C.S.: 513210

Subsidiary (Non-US):

TechChefs Software Private Limited (4)
62 4th Floor The High Street 11th Main Road Jayanagar 4th Block, Bengaluru, 560011, India
Tel.: (91) 9008255228
Web Site: http://www.techchefs.in
Software Services
N.A.I.C.S.: 541511
Vikram Pawar *(Co-CEO)*

TradeTech Consulting Scandinavia AB (4)
Strandvagen 5B, 114 51, Stockholm, Sweden
Tel.: (46) 854582070
Business Management Consulting Services
N.A.I.C.S.: 541611

Virtusa (Private) Limited (4)
752 Dr Danister De Silva Mawatha, Colombo, 00900, Sri Lanka
Tel.: (94) 114605500
Information Technology Services
N.A.I.C.S.: 541519

Virtusa Austria GmbH (4)
Tuchlauben 7a, 1010, Vienna, Austria
Tel.: (43) 12051073103
Business Management Consulting Services
N.A.I.C.S.: 541611
Norbert Mayerhofer *(Head-Virtusa Academy & Project Mgr)*

Virtusa Consulting & Services Limited (4)
Level 8 26 Finsbury Square, London, EC2A 1DS, United Kingdom
Tel.: (44) 2036517800
Information Technology Consulting Services
N.A.I.C.S.: 541512

Virtusa Consulting Services Private Limited (4)
The Campus Sy No 115 / Part Plot No 10 TSIIC Limited SEZ, Nanakramguda Village Serilingampalli Mandal Ranga Reddy District, Hyderabad, 500 008, India
Tel.: (91) 4044528000
Information Technology Services
N.A.I.C.S.: 541519
Vasu Pendyala *(Dir-Fin & Controller)*

Branch (Domestic):

Virtusa Corporation - Connecticut (4)

100 Northfield Dr Ste 305, Windsor, CT 06095
Tel.: (860) 688-9900
Business Management Consulting Services
N.A.I.C.S.: 541611

Subsidiary (Non-US):

Virtusa Hungary KFT. (4)
Regus House Kalman Imre utca 1, Budapest, 1054, Hungary
Tel.: (36) 14751203
Web Site: http://www.virtusa.com
Software Development Services
N.A.I.C.S.: 541715

Virtusa International, B.V. (4)
Schiphol Boulevard 231, 1118 BH, Amsterdam, Netherlands
Tel.: (31) 885609950
Software Development Services
N.A.I.C.S.: 513210

Virtusa Malaysia Private Limited (4)
Unit 5-1 Level-5 Tower 6 Avenue 5 Bangsar South No 8 Jalan Kerinchi, 59200, Kuala Lumpur, Malaysia
Tel.: (60) 323860906
Business Management Consulting Services
N.A.I.C.S.: 541611

Virtusa Mexico S DE RL DE CV (4)
Av Prolongacion Americas 1600 Piso 4 Col Country Club, 44610, Guadalajara, Jalisco, Mexico
Tel.: (52) 3336789125
Information Technology Consulting Services
N.A.I.C.S.: 541512

Virtusa Middle East FZ LLC (4)
Room 306 Building 3 Dubai Internet City, PO Box 501801, Dubai, United Arab Emirates
Tel.: (971) 44518399
IT Services
N.A.I.C.S.: 541519
Laksh Narayanan *(Assoc Dir-HR)*

Virtusa Philippines, Inc (4)
6th Floor Science Hub Tower 2, Mckinley Hill Fort Bonifacio, Taguig, Philippines
Tel.: (63) 26431000
Business Management Consulting Services
N.A.I.C.S.: 541611

Virtusa QFC IT Consulting LLC (4)
Office 137 1st Floor Al-Jaidah Square Building Airport Road, PO Box 55743, Doha, Qatar
Tel.: (974) 44267369
Information Technology Consulting Services
N.A.I.C.S.: 541512

Virtusa Singapore Private Limited (4)
3 Changi Business Park Vista Akzonobel House 02-03/04/05, Singapore, 486051, Singapore
Tel.: (65) 64966565
Web Site: http://www.virtusa.com
Software Development Services
N.A.I.C.S.: 513210

Virtusa Switzerland GmbH (4)
Stadelhoferstrasse 22, Oberengstringen, 8001, Zurich, Switzerland
Tel.: (41) 435080069
Business Management Consulting Services
N.A.I.C.S.: 541611

Virtusa UK Limited (4)
Orchard Lea, Drift Road, Winkfield, Berkshire, SL4 4RU, United Kingdom
Tel.: (44) 1344887417
Web Site: http://virtusa.com
Sales Range: $10-24.9 Million
Emp.: 55
Information Technology Services
N.A.I.C.S.: 541519

Holding (Non-US):

Vistra Group Holdings S.A. (3)
15 Rue Edward Steichen 4th Floor, 2540, Luxembourg, Luxembourg
Tel.: (352) 422229
Web Site: http://www.vistra.com
Emp.: 4,600
Holding Company; Trust, Fiduciary, Fund Administration & Corporate Services
N.A.I.C.S.: 551112

Vincent Bremmer *(Mng Dir-Europe)*

Subsidiary (US):

Vistra Holdings (USA) LLC (4)
31 St James Ave, Boston, MA 02116
Tel.: (617) 474-1600
Web Site: http://www.vistra.com
International Business Management Advisory Services
N.A.I.C.S.: 561499

Subsidiary (Domestic):

Montage Services, Inc. (5)
281 Ellis St, San Francisco, CA 94102
Tel.: (415) 659-9236
Web Site: http://www.montage-services.com
Business Financial Services
N.A.I.C.S.: 561499
Scott Wentz *(Mng Dir)*

Subsidiary (Non-US):

Vistra IE UK Ltd. (5)
11th Floor Whitefriars, Lewins Mead, Bristol, BS1 2NT, United Kingdom
Tel.: (44) 1179299661
Web Site: http://www.vistra.com
Accounting, Tax, Finance, Human Resource, Legal & Compliance Consulting, Software & Support Services
N.A.I.C.S.: 561499

Subsidiary (Non-US):

Vistra Management Services (Netherlands) B.V. (4)
Atrium Building 8th Floor Strawinskylaan 3127, 1077 ZX, Amsterdam, Netherlands
Tel.: (31) 885609950
Web Site: http://www.vistra.com
Trust, Fiduciary, Fund Administration & Corporate Services
N.A.I.C.S.: 523991
Ron Arendsen *(Mng Dir & Country Head-Netherlands)*

Holding (US):

BTRS Holdings Inc. (2)
1009 Lenox Dr Ste 101, Lawrenceville, NJ 08648
Tel.: (609) 235-1010
Web Site: http://www.billtrust.com
Rev.: $166,405,000
Assets: $470,649,000
Liabilities: $161,015,000
Net Worth: $309,634,000
Earnings: ($61,200,000)
Emp.: 687
Fiscal Year-end: 12/31/2021
Investment Services
N.A.I.C.S.: 523999
Grant Johnson *(CMO)*

Subsidiary (Domestic):

Factor Systems, Inc. (3)
1009 Lenox Dr Ste 101, Lawrenceville, NJ 08648
Tel.: (609) 235-1010
Web Site: http://www.billtrust.com
Outsource Billing Services
N.A.I.C.S.: 541219
Flint A. Lane *(Founder & CEO)*

Joint Venture (Non-US):

Carl Zeiss Vision International GmbH (2)
Gartenstrasse 97, 73430, Aalen, Germany
Web Site: http://www.vision.zeiss.com
Sales Range: $1-4.9 Billion
Emp.: 10,000
Mfr of Eyeglasses & Lenses
N.A.I.C.S.: 333310
Michael Hoffmann *(CEO)*

Subsidiary (Non-US):

Alpha Lens Company Ltd. (3)
76-77 Capitol Industrial Park Capitol Way, London, NX9 0EW, United Kingdom
Tel.: (44) 2089491901
Sales Range: $25-49.9 Million
Emp.: 50
Ophthalmic Products Mfr & Supply
N.A.I.C.S.: 333310

Carl Zeiss Vision (3)

5th Fl Nissei Fushimi Machi Building, 4 4 1 Fushimi Machi Chuo Ku, Osaka, 541 0044, Japan
Tel.: (81) 662022672
Sales Range: $25-49.9 Million
Emp.: 100
Eyeglass Lenses Mfr
N.A.I.C.S.: 333310

Carl Zeiss Vision (3)
Calle 7 Sur No 1111, Tijuana, 22500, Mexico
Tel.: (52) 6646233734
Optical Lense Services
N.A.I.C.S.: 456130

Carl Zeiss Vision (3)
Avenida San Andres Atoto 165-B, Naucalpan de Juarez, Mexico, 53550, Mexico
Tel.: (52) 5555767033
Web Site: http://www.aolens.com
Sales Range: $25-49.9 Million
Emp.: 100
Optical Lense Services
N.A.I.C.S.: 333310

Carl Zeiss Vision (Guangzhou) Ltd. (3)
No 1389 Jui Fo West Road, Baiyun District, Guangzhou, 510555, China
Tel.: (86) 2087490088
Web Site: http://www.joffray.com
Eyeglass Lenses Mfr
N.A.I.C.S.: 333310

Carl Zeiss Vision Australia Ltd. (3)
24 Heath St, Lonsdale, 5160, SA, Australia
Tel.: (61) 883928899
Sales Range: $150-199.9 Million
Eyeglass Lenses Mfr
N.A.I.C.S.: 333310

Carl Zeiss Vision Brasil Industria Optica Ltda. (3)
Rua Luiz Winter 222 Duarte da Silveira, 25665-431, Petropolis, RJ, Brazil
Tel.: (55) 24 2233 7012
Eyeglass Lenses Mfr
N.A.I.C.S.: 333310

Subsidiary (Domestic):

Carl Zeiss Vision GmbH (3)
Turnstrasse 27, 73430, Aalen, Germany
Tel.: (49) 7361 598 5000
Web Site: http://www.vision.zeiss.com
Sales Range: $25-49.9 Million
Emp.: 8
Eyeglass Lenses Mfr
N.A.I.C.S.: 333310
Spiller Rudols (Gen Mgr)

Subsidiary (US):

Carl Zeiss Vision Inc. (3)
12121 Scripps Summit Dr, San Diego, CA 92130-4682
Tel.: (858) 790-7700
Web Site: http://www.vision.zeiss.com
Sales Range: $650-699.9 Million
Plastic & Glass Eyeglass Lenses Mfr & Sales
N.A.I.C.S.: 339115
Cindy Brown (Mgr-Trade Show & Events)

Subsidiary (Domestic):

Great Lakes Coating Laboratory (4)
1784 Larchwood Dr, Troy, MI 48083-2223
Tel.: (248) 524-0550
Web Site: http://www.carl-zeiss.com
Sales Range: $50-74.9 Million
Emp.: 120
Optical Goods Mfr & Sales
N.A.I.C.S.: 333310

Kansas City Opthalmics LLC (4)
13731 E 42nd Ter, Independence, MO 64055
Tel.: (816) 478-4901
Sales Range: $25-49.9 Million
Emp.: 6
Optical Services
N.A.I.C.S.: 456130

Subsidiary (Non-US):

Carl Zeiss Vision Ireland Ltd. (3)
Whitemill Industrial Estate, Wexford, Ireland
Tel.: (353) 5363700

Sales Range: $75-99.9 Million
Optical Lense Services
N.A.I.C.S.: 456130

Carl Zeiss Vision Italia SPA (3)
Via SEP Mazzucchelli No 17, Castiglione Olona, 21043, Varese, Lombardia, Italy
Tel.: (39) 0331851111
Web Site: http://www.zeiss.it
Sales Range: $75-99.9 Million
Emp.: 400
Eyeglass Lenses & Magnifying Vision Mfr
N.A.I.C.S.: 333310
Michele D'adamo (Gen Mgr)

Carl Zeiss Vision Swiss AG (3)
Helsinkistrasse 9, Basel, 4142, Switzerland
Tel.: (41) 613388100
Sales Range: $25-49.9 Million
Emp.: 15
Optical Products Mfr & Sales
N.A.I.C.S.: 333310

Carl Zeiss Vision UK Ltd. (3)
Unit 9 Holford Way, Holford, Birmingham, B6 7AX, United Kingdom
Tel.: (44) 1213324404
Web Site: http://www.vision.zeiss.co.uk
Sales Range: $75-99.9 Million
Eyeglass Lenses Mfr
N.A.I.C.S.: 333310

Carl Zeiss Vision Venezuela Industria Optica C.A. (3)
Av Francisco de Miranda, Centro Profesional Miranda, piso 2 ofc 2C, Caracas, 1060, Venezuela
Tel.: (58) 212 264 6231
Web Site: http://www.solaven.com
Sales Range: $25-49.9 Million
Emp.: 5
Eyeglass Lenses Mfr
N.A.I.C.S.: 333310

Holding (US):

Cast & Crew Entertainment Services LLC (2)
2300 Empire Ave 5 Fl, Burbank, CA 91504
Tel.: (818) 848-6022
Web Site: http://www.castandcrew.com
Payroll Services & Accounting Solutions to the Entertainment Industry
N.A.I.C.S.: 541214
Eric Belcher (Vice Chm)

Subsidiary (Domestic):

Final Draft, Inc. (3)
26707 W Agoura Rd Ste 205, Calabasas, CA 91302
Tel.: (818) 995-8995
Web Site: http://www.finaldraft.com
Prepackaged Screenwriting Software Services
N.A.I.C.S.: 513210
Marc Madnick (Founder)

Holding (US):

Contanda, LLC (2)
365 Canal St Ste 2900, New Orleans, LA 70130
Tel.: (504) 525-9741
Web Site: http://www.westway.com
Emp.: 50
Holding Company; Liquid Animal Feed Products Mfr & Bulk Liquid Storage Services
N.A.I.C.S.: 551112
Gene McClain (CEO)

Subsidiary (Domestic):

Contanda Steel, LLC (3)
16335 Peninsula Blvd, Houston, TX 77015
Tel.: (281) 452-0063
Web Site: http://www.contandasteel.com
Marine Terminals
N.A.I.C.S.: 488320
Carmen Geiger (Pres)

Westway Terminal Company LLC (3)
365 Canal St Ste 2900, New Orleans, LA 70130
Tel.: (504) 525-9741
Web Site: http://www.westway.com
Emp.: 35

Bulk Liquid Storage & Other Related Services
N.A.I.C.S.: 493190
Gene McClain (CEO)

Holding (US):

Covanta Holding Corporation (2)
445 S St, Morristown, NJ 07960
Tel.: (862) 345-5000
Web Site: http://www.covanta.com
Rev.: $1,904,000,000
Assets: $3,706,000,000
Liabilities: $3,396,000,000
Net Worth: $310,000,000
Earnings: ($28,000,000)
Emp.: 4,000
Fiscal Year-end: 12/31/2020
Holding Company; Waste Disposal & Energy Services; Specialty Insurance
N.A.I.C.S.: 524126
Timothy J. Simpson (Chief Admin Officer & Exec VP)

Subsidiary (Domestic):

Advanced Waste Services of Indiana, Inc. (3)
5625 Old Porter Rd, Portage, IN 46368
Tel.: (219) 763-7600
Waste Collection Services
N.A.I.C.S.: 562111

CIRCON Holdings, Inc. (3)
428 Hwy 146 S, La Porte, TX 77571
Tel.: (281) 474-4210
Web Site: https://circonenviro.com
Environmental Services; Waste Management & Recycling
N.A.I.C.S.: 562998
Marc Sansom (COO)

Subsidiary (Domestic):

Intergulf Corporation (4)
428 Hwy 146 S, La Porte, TX 77571
Tel.: (281) 474-4210
Petroleum Refinery Services
N.A.I.C.S.: 324110
Marc Sansom (COO)

Subsidiary (Domestic):

Lonestar Ecology, LLC (5)
12901 Baypark Rd Ste A, Pasadena, TX 77507-1100
Tel.: (281) 204-1268
Waste Water Treatment Services
N.A.I.C.S.: 221310
Walt Stringer (Mgr)

Subsidiary (Domestic):

Camden County Energy Recovery Associates, L.P. (3)
600 Morgan St, Camden, NJ 08104-2510
Tel.: (856) 966-7174
Power, Communication Line & Related Structures Construction Services
N.A.I.C.S.: 237130

Plant (Domestic):

Camden Resource Recovery Facility (3)
600 Morgan Blvd, Camden, NJ 08104
Tel.: (856) 966-7174
Solid Waste Incineration Electric Power Plant
N.A.I.C.S.: 221118

Subsidiary (Domestic):

Covanta Abington Transfer Solutions LLC (3)
995 Fitzwatertown Rd, Dublin, PA 19038
Tel.: (215) 517-4112
Waste Material Recycling Services
N.A.I.C.S.: 562920

Covanta Alexandria/Arlington, Inc. (3)
5301 Eisenhower Ave, Alexandria, VA 22304
Tel.: (703) 370-7722
Web Site: http://www.covanta.com
Waste Material Recycling Services
N.A.I.C.S.: 562920

Covanta Babylon, Inc. (3)

125 Gleam St, West Babylon, NY 11704-1204
Tel.: (631) 491-1976
Web Site: http://www.covanta.com
Recyclable Material Whslr
N.A.I.C.S.: 423930

Covanta Bristol, Inc. (3)
170 Enterprise Dr, Bristol, CT 06010-7493
Tel.: (860) 589-6470
Emp.: 35
Recyclable Material Whslr
N.A.I.C.S.: 423930
Joe Vitale (Bus Mgr)

Subsidiary (Non-US):

Covanta Burnaby Renewable Energy, Inc. (3)
5150 Riverbend Dr, Burnaby, V3N 4V3, BC, Canada
Tel.: (604) 521-1025
Web Site: https://www.covanta.com
Sales Range: $25-49.9 Million
Waste-to-Energy Facility Operator
N.A.I.C.S.: 221118
Stephen McKinney (Gen Mgr)

Subsidiary (Domestic):

Covanta Company of SEMASS, LLC (3)
247 A Commercial St, Lynn, MA 01905-3018
Tel.: (781) 593-8107
Web Site: http://www.covanta.com
Waste Material Recycling Services
N.A.I.C.S.: 562920

Covanta Dade Renewable Energy, LLC (3)
6990 NW 97th Ave, Doral, FL 33178
Tel.: (305) 593-7000
Biomass Fuel & Renewable Electricity Providing Services
N.A.I.C.S.: 221118

Covanta Delaware Valley LLC (3)
10 Highland Ave, Chester, PA 19013-2231
Tel.: (610) 497-8100
Recyclable Material Whslr
N.A.I.C.S.: 423930

Subsidiary (Non-US):

Covanta Durhan York Renewable Energy Limited Partnership (3)
1835 Energy Drive, Courtice, L1E 2R2, ON, Canada
Tel.: (905) 404-4030
Renewable Energy Generation Services
N.A.I.C.S.: 221114

Subsidiary (Domestic):

Covanta Energy Corporation (3)
40 Ln Rd, Fairfield, NJ 07004
Tel.: (973) 882-9000
Sales Range: $1-4.9 Billion
Emp.: 1,500
Energy Services; Electric Steam Generation & Water Treatment Facilities
N.A.I.C.S.: 562920

Covanta Environmental Solutions (3)
210 Tower Rd, Winneconne, WI 54986
Tel.: (920) 582-7596
Web Site: http://www.covanta.com
Refuse Collection & Disposal Services
N.A.I.C.S.: 562211

Covanta Haverhill, Inc. (3)
100 Recovery Way, Haverhill, MA 01835-3516
Tel.: (978) 372-6288
Web Site: http://www.covanta.com
Waste Material Recycling Services
N.A.I.C.S.: 562920

Covanta Hudson Valley Renewable Energy LLC (3)
98 Sand Dock Rd, Poughkeepsie, NY 12601-5443
Tel.: (845) 462-4650
Recyclable Material Whslr
N.A.I.C.S.: 423930

Covanta Huntsville, Inc. (3)
5251 Triana Blvd SW, Huntsville, AL 35805
Tel.: (256) 882-1019
Waste Material Recycling Services

EQT AB—(Continued)

N.A.I.C.S.: 562920

Covanta Indianapolis, Inc. (3)
2320 Harding St, Indianapolis, IN 46221-2028
Tel.: (317) 378-8700
Web Site: http://www.covanta.com
Emp.: 80
Freight & Transportation Services
N.A.I.C.S.: 484110

Covanta Kent, Inc. (3)
950 Market Ave SW, Grand Rapids, MI 49503
Tel.: (616) 235-3210
Web Site: http://www.covanta.com
Waste Material Recycling Services
N.A.I.C.S.: 562920

Covanta Lancaster, Inc. (3)
1911 River Rd, Bainbridge, PA 17502-9360
Tel.: (717) 397-9968
Emp.: 50
Waste Material Recycling Services
N.A.I.C.S.: 562920

Covanta Long Beach Renewable Energy Corp. (3)
118 Pier S Ave, Long Beach, CA 90802
Tel.: (562) 436-0636
Web Site: http://www.covanta.com
Waste Material Recycling Services
N.A.I.C.S.: 562920

Covanta Marion, Inc. (3)
4850 Brooklake Rd NE, Brooks, OR 97305
Tel.: (503) 393-0890
Waste Material Recycling Services
N.A.I.C.S.: 562920

Covanta Mendota, L.P. (3)
400 Guillen Pkwy, Mendota, CA 93640
Tel.: (559) 655-4921
Electric Power Distribution Services
N.A.I.C.S.: 221122

Covanta Montgomery, Inc. (3)
21204 Martinsburg Rd, Dickerson, MD 20842
Tel.: (301) 691-9001
Waste Material Recycling Services
N.A.I.C.S.: 562920

Covanta Niagara I, LLC (3)
100 Energy Blvd, Niagara Falls, NY 14304
Tel.: (716) 278-8500
Waste Collection Services
N.A.I.C.S.: 562111

Covanta Niagara, L.P. (3)
100 Energy Blvd, Niagara Falls, NY 14304-3100
Tel.: (716) 278-8500
Waste Material Recycling Services
N.A.I.C.S.: 562920

Covanta Onondaga Limited Partnership (3)
5801 Rock Cut Rd, Jamesville, NY 13078
Tel.: (315) 498-4111
Recyclable Material Whslr
N.A.I.C.S.: 423930

Covanta Pittsfield, LLC (3)
500 Hubbard Ave, Pittsfield, MA 01201
Tel.: (413) 464-9270
Recyclable Material Whslr
N.A.I.C.S.: 423930
Kevin Rousseau *(Mgr-Facility)*

Covanta Plymouth Renewable Energy LP (3)
1155 Conshohocken Rd, Conshohocken, PA 19428-1028
Tel.: (610) 569-9372
Web Site: http://www.convanta.com
Sales Range: $1-9.9 Million
Emp.: 46
Waste-to-Energy Facility Operator
N.A.I.C.S.: 221118

Covanta Projects of Wallingford, L.P. (3)
530 S Cherry St, Wallingford, CT 06492
Tel.: (203) 294-1649
Waste Material Recycling Services
N.A.I.C.S.: 562920

Covanta Renewable Fuels LLC (3)

445 S St, Morristown, NJ 07960-6454
Tel.: (973) 882-9000
Waste Material Recycling Services
N.A.I.C.S.: 562920

Covanta Southeastern Florida Renewable Energy LLC (3)
6990 Nw 97th Ave, Doral, FL 33178-2500
Tel.: (305) 593-7000
Waste Material Recycling Services
N.A.I.C.S.: 562920

Covanta Stanislaus, Inc. (3)
4040 Fink Rd, Crows Landing, CA 95313
Tel.: (209) 837-4423
Web Site: http://www.covanta.com
Waste Material Recycling Services
N.A.I.C.S.: 562920

Covanta Tulsa Renewable Energy LLC (3)
2122 S Yukon Ave, Tulsa, OK 74107
Tel.: (918) 699-0011
Power, Communication Line & Related Structures Construction Services
N.A.I.C.S.: 237130

Covanta Union, LLC (3)
1499 US Hwy 1, Rahway, NJ 07065-5619
Tel.: (732) 499-0101
Web Site: http://www.covanta.com
Recyclable Material Whslr
N.A.I.C.S.: 423930

Covanta Warren Energy Resource Co., LLC (3)
218 Mt Pisgah Ave, Oxford, NJ 07863
Tel.: (908) 453-2195
Web Site: http://www.covanta.com
Recyclable Material Whslr
N.A.I.C.S.: 423930

Covanta York Renewable Energy Limited Partnership (3)
2651 Black Bridge Rd, York, PA 17406-9702
Tel.: (717) 843-2902
Web Site: http://www.covanta.com
Waste Material Recycling Services
N.A.I.C.S.: 562920

GARCO, Inc. (3)
17724 Industriplex Blvd Ste D, Baton Rouge, LA 70809
Tel.: (225) 372-2502
Web Site: http://www.garco-inc.com
General Contractor Services
N.A.I.C.S.: 238990

Mount Kisco Transfer Station, Inc. (3)
10 Lincoln Pl, Mount Kisco, NY 10549
Tel.: (914) 666-6350
Waste Material Recycling Services
N.A.I.C.S.: 562920

National American Insurance Company of California (100%)
444 W Ocean Blvd 18th Fl, Long Beach, CA 90802
Tel.: (562) 279-1300
Web Site: http://www.naicc.com
Sales Range: $25-49.9 Million
Emp.: 50
Commercial Auto Insurance
N.A.I.C.S.: 524126

Pacific Oroville Power, Inc. (3)
Francisco Barriga 3050 S 5th Ave, Oroville, CA 95965
Tel.: (530) 532-0597
Recyclable Material Whslr
N.A.I.C.S.: 423930

Palm Beach Resource Recovery Corporation (3)
6501 N Jog Rd, West Palm Beach, FL 33412
Tel.: (561) 478-3800
Industrial Equipment & Machinery Repair Services
N.A.I.C.S.: 811310
Clyde Herrell *(Engr-Project)*

Holding (US):

Data Intensity, LLC (2)
22 Crosby Dr Ste 100, Bedford, MA 01730
Tel.: (859) 283-2520
Web Site: http://www.dataintensity.com

Emp.: 800
Software Development Services
N.A.I.C.S.: 513210
Marc Caruso *(CTO)*

Subsidiary (Non-US):

Dechra Pharmaceuticals PLC (2)
24 Cheshire Avenue Cheshire Business Park, Lostock Gralam, Northwich, CW9 7UA, United Kingdom
Tel.: (44) 1606814730
Web Site: http://www.dechra.com
Rev.: $925,693,496
Assets: $1,755,939,276
Liabilities: $850,611,580
Net Worth: $905,327,696
Earnings: $178,811,724
Emp.: 2,036
Fiscal Year-end: 06/30/2022
Holding Company; Veterinary Pharmaceutical & Supplement Mfr & Distr
N.A.I.C.S.: 551112
Ian Page *(CEO)*

Subsidiary (Non-US):

AST Farma B.V. (3)
Wilgenweg 7, 3421 TV, Oudewater, Netherlands
Tel.: (31) 348563434
Web Site: https://www.astfarma.nl
Veterinary Pharmaceutical Equipment Distr
N.A.I.C.S.: 423490

Subsidiary (Domestic):

Dechra Limited (3)
Keighley Road, Snaygill Industrial Estate, Skipton, BD23 2RW, United Kingdom
Tel.: (44) 1756791311
Web Site: http://www.dechra.com
Veterinary Pharmaceutical & Supplement Mfr & Distr; Veterinary Services
N.A.I.C.S.: 325412

Plant (Domestic):

Dechra Pharmaceuticals Manufacturing - UK (4)
Keighley Road, Snaygill Industrial Estate, Skipton, BD23 2RW, North Yorkshire, United Kingdom
Tel.: (44) 1756791311
Web Site: http://www.dechrapharmaceuticals.com
Emp.: 200
Pharmaceuticals Mfr
N.A.I.C.S.: 325412

Subsidiary (Domestic):

Dechra Veterinary Products Limited (4)
Sansaw Business Park, Hadnall, Shrewsbury, SY4 4AS, Shropshire, United Kingdom
Tel.: (44) 1939211200
Web Site: https://www.dechra.co.uk
Veterinary Products Marketer, Distr & Technical Support Services
N.A.I.C.S.: 424990

Subsidiary (Non-US):

Dechra Veterinary Products AB (5)
Stora Wasby Orangeriet 3, 194 37, Upplands Vasby, Sweden
Tel.: (46) 8325355
Web Site: https://www.dechra.se
Sales Range: $75-99.9 Million
Veterinary Products Marketer, Distr & Technical Support Services
N.A.I.C.S.: 424990

Dechra Veterinary Products AS (5)
Henrik Ibsensgate 90, 0255, Oslo, Norway
Tel.: (47) 48020798
Web Site: https://www.dechra.no
Veterinary Products Marketer, Distr & Technical Support Services
N.A.I.C.S.: 424990

Dechra Veterinary Products BV (5)
Minervum 7071, 4817 ZK, Breda, Netherlands
Tel.: (31) 765798100
Web Site: http://www.dechra.nl
Sales Range: $50-74.9 Million
Emp.: 7

Veterinary Products Marketer, Distr & Technical Support Services
N.A.I.C.S.: 424990

Dechra Veterinary Products OY (5)
Linnoitustie 4, 02600, Espoo, Finland
Tel.: (358) 22510500
Web Site: https://www.dechra.fi
Sales Range: $75-99.9 Million
Veterinary Products Marketer, Distr & Technical Support Services
N.A.I.C.S.: 424990

Dechra Veterinary Products SAS (5)
60 avenue du Centre, 78940, Montigny-le-Bretonneux, France
Tel.: (33) 130487140
Veterinary Products Marketer, Distr & Technical Support Services
N.A.I.C.S.: 424990

Dechra Veterinary Products SLU (5)
C/Tuset 20 6 planta, 08006, Barcelona, Spain
Tel.: (34) 935448507
Web Site: https://www.dechra.es
Veterinary Products Marketer, Distr & Technical Support Services
N.A.I.C.S.: 424990

Subsidiary (US):

Dechra Veterinary Products, LLC (5)
7015 College Blvd Ste 525, Overland Park, KS 66211
Tel.: (913) 327-0015
Web Site: https://www.dechra-us.com
Sales Range: $25-49.9 Million
Emp.: 35
Veterinary Products Marketer, Distr & Technical Support Services
N.A.I.C.S.: 424990
Chris Huettner *(Mgr-HR)*

Subsidiary (Non-US):

Dechra Productos Veterinarios, S.A. de C.V. (3)
Av Coyoacan 1622 Interior 401 B Del Valle Benito Juarez, 03100, Mexico, Mexico
Tel.: (52) 15555635022
Web Site: https://www.dechra.mx
Veterinary Pharmaceutical Product Mfr & Distr
N.A.I.C.S.: 325412

Dechra Veterinary Products (Australia) Pty Limited (3)
2 Cal Close, Somersby, 2250, NSW, Australia
Tel.: (61) 243721661
Web Site: https://www.dechra.com.au
Veterinary Pharmaceutical Product Mfr & Distr
N.A.I.C.S.: 325412

Dechra Veterinary Products Sp. z o.o. (3)
ul Modlinska 61 lok 3, 03-199, Warsaw, Poland
Tel.: (48) 224312890
Web Site: https://www.dechra.pl
Veterinary Pharmaceutical Product Mfr & Distr
N.A.I.C.S.: 325412

Dechra Veterinary Products, Inc. (3)
1 Holiday Avenue East Tower Suite 345, Pointe-Claire, H9R 5N3, QC, Canada
Tel.: (44)
Web Site: https://www.dechra.ca
Veterinary Pharmaceutical Product Mfr & Distr
N.A.I.C.S.: 325412
Vincent Martel *(Mgr)*

Genera Pharma d.o.o. (3)
Gostivarska 70, 11 000, Novi Beograd, Serbia
Tel.: (381) 653587998
Veterinary Pharmaceutical Product Mfr & Distr
N.A.I.C.S.: 325412

Genera d.d. (3)
Svetonedeljska cesta 2, 10436, Rakov Potok, Croatia
Tel.: (385) 13388888
Web Site: https://www.genera.hr
Holding Company; Pharmaceutical Mfr & Whslr

N.A.I.C.S.: 551112

Subsidiary (Non-US):

Genera d.o.o. Sarajevo (4)
Hamdije Cemerlica 2, 71000, Sarajevo, Bosnia & Herzegovina
Tel.: (387) 33652434
Web Site: https://genera.hr
Pharmaceuticals Product Mfr
N.A.I.C.S.: 325412

Subsidiary (US):

Med-Pharmex, Inc. (3)
2727 Thompson Creek Rd, Pomona, CA 91767
Tel.: (909) 593-7875
Sales Range: $1-9.9 Million
Emp.: 130
Pharmaceuticals Product Mfr
N.A.I.C.S.: 325412
Vince Palasota (CEO)

Subsidiary (Non-US):

EQT Funds Management Ltd (2)
Level 4 North St Julian's Court St Julian's Avenue, PO Box 269, Saint Peter Port, GY1 1WA, Guernsey
Tel.: (44) 1481722278
Financial Management Services
N.A.I.C.S.: 523999
Deon Van der Ploeg (Mng Dir)

EQT Management S.a r.l. (2)
23 Rue Aldringen, 1118, Luxembourg, Luxembourg
Tel.: (352) 267326
Financial Management Services
N.A.I.C.S.: 523999
Stefan Holmer (Mng Dir)

Subsidiary (Domestic):

EQT Fund Management S.a.r.l. (3)
51A Boulevard Royal, L-2449, Luxembourg, Luxembourg
Tel.: (352) 267326
Investment Fund Management Services
N.A.I.C.S.: 541690

Subsidiary (Domestic):

EQT Northern Europe Private Equity Funds (2)
Hovflagar Jagas 3, Stockholm, 10327, Sweden (100%)
Tel.: (46) 84405300
Web Site: http://www.eqt.fi
Sales Range: $50-74.9 Million
Emp.: 80
Provider of Equity Management & Funding
N.A.I.C.S.: 525910

Subsidiary (Non-US):

EQT Partners A/S (2)
Strandvejen 58 5th Floor, 2900, Hellerup, Denmark
Tel.: (45) 33121236
Financial Management Services
N.A.I.C.S.: 523999
Jannik Kruse Petersen (Co-Partner)

EQT Partners AG (2)
Bahnhofstrasse 20, 8001, Zurich, Switzerland
Tel.: (41) 442666800
Web Site: http://www.eqtgroup.com
Financial Management Services
N.A.I.C.S.: 523999
Lennart Blecher (Co-Partner)

EQT Partners Asia Ltd (2)
1708 Hutchison House 10 Harcourt Road, Central, China (Hong Kong)
Tel.: (852) 28016823
Web Site: http://www.eqt.hk
Financial Management Services
N.A.I.C.S.: 523999
Sylvia Chong (Dir-HR)

EQT Partners Australia Pty. Ltd. (2)
Level 42 Quay Quarter Tower 50 Bridge St, Sydney, 2000, NSW, Australia
Tel.: (61) 290524851
Investment Fund Management Services
N.A.I.C.S.: 525910

EQT Partners GmbH (2)
Leopoldpalais Leopoldstrasse 8, 80802,

Munich, Germany
Tel.: (49) 8925549900
Web Site: http://www.eqtgroup.com
Emp.: 55
Financial Management Services
N.A.I.C.S.: 523999
Andreas Huber (Partner-Infrastructure)

Subsidiary (US):

EQT Partners Inc. (2)
1114 Avenue of the Americas 38th Fl, New York, NY 10036
Tel.: (917) 281-0850
Web Site: http://www.eqt.se
Emp.: 30
Financial Management Services
N.A.I.C.S.: 523999
Alex Darden (Co-Partner)

Subsidiary (Non-US):

EQT Partners Japan KK (2)
37F Roppongi Hills Mori Tower 10-1 Roppongi 6-chome, Minato-ku, Tokyo, Japan
Tel.: (81) 8075582324
Investment Fund Management Services
N.A.I.C.S.: 525910

EQT Partners Korea Co., Ltd. (2)
27th Floor West Tower Center 1 26 Euljiro 5-gil, Jung-gu, Seoul, 04539, Korea (South)
Tel.: (82) 260300330
Investment Fund Management Services
N.A.I.C.S.: 525910

EQT Partners Netherlands B.V. (2)
Johannes Vermeerplein 9, 1071 DV, Amsterdam, Netherlands
Tel.: (31) 205776647
Investment Fund Management Services
N.A.I.C.S.: 525910

EQT Partners Oy (2)
Etelaesplanadi 20 3rd Floor, 00130, Helsinki, Finland
Tel.: (358) 96962470
Web Site: http://www.eqt.fi
Emp.: 11
Financial Management Services
N.A.I.C.S.: 523999
Eeva-Riitta Leino (Office Mgr)

EQT Partners Shanghai Ltd (2)
Unit 907 CITIC Square 1168 Nanjing Road West, Shanghai, 200041, China
Tel.: (86) 2161135868
Web Site: http://www.eqt.se
Financial Management Services
N.A.I.C.S.: 523999

EQT Partners Singapore Pte Ltd (2)
80 Raffles Place 44-02 UOB Plaza 1, Singapore, 048624, Singapore
Tel.: (65) 65951830
Financial Management Services
N.A.I.C.S.: 523999
Simon Griffiths (Partner)

EQT Partners Sp. z o.o. (2)
Grzybowska Park 7th floor Grzybowska 5A, 00-132, Warsaw, Poland
Tel.: (48) 223245828
Financial Management Services
N.A.I.C.S.: 523999

EQT Partners Spain S.L.U. (2)
Torre Serrano Calle Marques de Villamagna 3 - Planta 5, 28001, Madrid, Spain
Tel.: (34) 910830551
Investment Fund Management Services
N.A.I.C.S.: 541690

EQT Partners UK Advisors LLP (2)
15 Golden Square, London, W1F 9JG, United Kingdom
Tel.: (44) 2074305510
Financial Management Services
N.A.I.C.S.: 523999
Caroline Conder (Head-Tax)

Subsidiary (Domestic):

EQT Services (UK) Limited (3)
30 Broadwick Street 3rd Floor, London, W1F 8JB, United Kingdom
Tel.: (44) 2074305510
Investment Fund Management Services
N.A.I.C.S.: 541690

Subsidiary (Domestic):

EQT Scandinavian Partners Ltd. (2)

Hovslagargatan 3, PO Box 16409, Stockholm, 11148, Sweden (100%)
Tel.: (46) 850655300
Sales Range: $50-74.9 Million
Portfolio Management
N.A.I.C.S.: 523940
Conni Jonsson (Chm)

Holding (Domestic):

Eton AB (2)
Stora Vagen 8, Ganghester, 507 71, Boras, Sweden (90%)
Tel.: (46) 105006010
Web Site: http://www.etonshirts.com
Sales Range: $75-99.9 Million
Men's Shirts Mfr & Retailer
N.A.I.C.S.: 315250
Hans Davidson (CEO)

Holding (US):

First Transit, Inc. (2)
600 Vine St Ste 1400, Cincinnati, OH 45202
Tel.: (513) 241-2200
Web Site: https://www.firsttransit.com
Sales Range: $700-749.9 Million
Emp.: 7,300
Transit Management & Contracting; Airport Shuttle Bus Services, Paratransit Operations & Light Transit Activities
N.A.I.C.S.: 485991
Robert James (VP-Tech & Innovation)

FocusVision Worldwide, Inc. (2)
1266 E Main St, Stamford, CT 06902
Tel.: (203) 961-1715
Web Site: http://www.focusvision.com
Sales Range: $10-24.9 Million
Emp.: 300
Market Research Technology Software Developer, Publisher & Whslr
N.A.I.C.S.: 513210
Duke Perrucci (Chief Customer Officer)

Subsidiary (Non-US):

Confirmit ASA (3)
Karenslyst Alle 56, Oslo, 277, Norway
Tel.: (47) 21502500
Web Site: http://www.confirmit.com
Market Research Services
N.A.I.C.S.: 541910
Arnt Feruglio (COO)

Subsidiary (US):

CustomerSat, Inc. (4)
150 Spear St, San Francisco, CA 94105
Tel.: (415) 536-3300
Web Site: http://www.customersat.com
Sales Range: $10-24.9 Million
Emp.: 20
Data Processing, Hosting & Related Services
N.A.I.C.S.: 518210

Subsidiary (Domestic):

Decipher Inc. (3)
259 Granby St Ste 250, Norfolk, VA 23510-1810
Tel.: (757) 615-1111
Web Site: http://www.decipher.com
Games & Hobby Products Developer & Marketer
N.A.I.C.S.: 339930
Warren Holland (Chm & CEO)

Holding (Non-US):

Health Management International Ltd. (2)
7 Temasek Boulevard 12-10 Suntec Tower One, Singapore, 038987, Singapore
Tel.: (65) 68049888
Web Site: http://www.hmi.com.sg
Rev.: $115,127,057
Assets: $145,075,796
Liabilities: $84,501,734
Net Worth: $60,574,061
Earnings: $14,782,941
Emp.: 1,220
Fiscal Year-end: 06/30/2018
Hospital Owner & Operator; Medical Training & Education Services
N.A.I.C.S.: 622110
Wei Jia Chin (Grp CEO)

Subsidiary (Domestic):

HMI Institute of Health Sciences Pte. Ltd. (3)
167 Jalan Bukit Merah Connection 1 Tower 5 05-10, Singapore, 150167, Singapore
Tel.: (65) 62533818
Web Site: http://www.hmi-ihs.com
Sales Range: $10-24.9 Million
Emp.: 35
Healthcare Education & Training Services
N.A.I.C.S.: 611310
See Khem Gan (Chm)

Subsidiary (Non-US):

Mahkota Medical Centre Sdn. Bhd. (3)
3 Mahkota Melaka Jalan Merdeka, Melaka, 75000, Malaysia
Tel.: (60) 62852880
Web Site: http://www.mahkotamedical.com
Sales Range: $350-399.9 Million
Emp.: 900
Healthcare Education & Training Services
N.A.I.C.S.: 524114
See Khem Gan (Chm)

Regency Specialist Hospital Sdn.Bhd. (3)
No 1 Jalan Suria Bandar Seri Alam, Masai, 81750, Johor, Malaysia
Tel.: (60) 73817700
Web Site: http://www.regencyspecialist.com
Sales Range: $50-74.9 Million
Emp.: 500
Healtcare Services
N.A.I.C.S.: 622110
Serena Yong (CEO)

Holding (Domestic):

Hector Rail AB (2)
Svardvagen 27, 182 33, Danderyd, Sweden
Tel.: (46) 854496720
Web Site: http://www.hectorrail.com
Sales Range: $75-99.9 Million
Emp.: 190
Line Haul Railroad Operator
N.A.I.C.S.: 482111
Jonas Swartling (Mgr-Comml)

Subsidiary (Non-US):

GB Railfreight Limited (3)
3rd Floor 55 Old Broad Street, London, EC2M 1RX, United Kingdom
Tel.: (44) 2079043393
Web Site: http://www.gbrailfreight.com
Emp.: 750
Rail Freight Transportation Services
N.A.I.C.S.: 482111
John Smith (Mng Dir)

Holding (Domestic):

IP-Only Telecommunication AB (2)
Baverns Grand 17 753 19, 753 20, Uppsala, Sweden
Tel.: (46) 188431000
Web Site: http://www.ip-only.com
Sales Range: $50-74.9 Million
Emp.: 350
Data Center Services
N.A.I.C.S.: 518210
Mikael Philipsson (CEO)

Subsidiary (Domestic):

Availo AB (3)
St Persgatan 6, 753 20, Uppsala, Sweden
Tel.: (46) 18 8431000
Web Site: http://www.availo.com
Sales Range: $10-24.9 Million
Virtual Telecommunications Services
N.A.I.C.S.: 517810
Mikael Philipsson (CEO)

Subsidiary (Domestic):

Availo Networks AB (4)
Hammarby Fabriksvag 25, 120 30, Stockholm, Sweden
Tel.: (46) 850003000
Web Site: http://www.availo.com
Sales Range: $10-24.9 Million
Emp.: 20
Virtual Telecommunications Services
N.A.I.C.S.: 517810
Mikael Philipsson (Mng Dir)

EQT AB—(Continued)

Joint Venture (Non-US):

ISS Holding A/S (2)
Bredgade 30, DK-1260, Copenhagen,
Denmark (54%)
Tel.: (45) 38170000
Web Site: http://www.issworld.com
Sales Range: $5-14.9 Billion
Emp.: 520,000
Holding Company
N.A.I.C.S.: 551112
Charles L. Allen (Chm-ISS World Services
A/S)

Subsidiary (Domestic):

ISS A/S (3)
Buddingevej 197, 2860, Soborg, Denmark
Tel.: (45) 38170000
Web Site: https://www.issworld.com
Rev.: $11,650,403,463
Assets: $7,061,967,849
Liabilities: $5,503,960,894
Net Worth: $1,558,006,955
Earnings: $48,123,195
Emp.: 352,749
Fiscal Year-end: 12/31/2023
Holding Company; Commercial Facility
Maintenance & Business Support Services
N.A.I.C.S.: 551112
Bjorn Raasteen (Gen Counsel-Grp)

Subsidiary (Domestic):

ISS Global A/S (4)
Buddingevej 197, Soborg, 2860, Denmark
Tel.: (45) 38170000
Web Site: http://www.issworld.com
Sales Range: $50-74.9 Million
Emp.: 160
Holding Company
N.A.I.C.S.: 551112
Bjorn Raasteen (Grp Gen Counsel & Sr VP)

Subsidiary (Non-US):

ISS Facility Services A.E. (5)
14 Thrasimachou Str, GR-104 42, Athens,
Greece
Tel.: (30) 2102705600
Web Site: http://www.gr.issworld.com
Sales Range: $75-99.9 Million
Emp.: 100
Commercial Facility Maintenance & Business Support Services
N.A.I.C.S.: 561210

ISS Facility Services A/S (5)
PO Box 132 OKern, 0509, Oslo, Norway
Tel.: (47) 22885000
Web Site: http://www.no.issworld.com
Commercial Facility Maintenance & Business Support Services
N.A.I.C.S.: 561210
Bjorn Nilsen (Mng Dir)

Subsidiary (Domestic):

ISS Facility Services A/S (5)
Gyngemose Parkvej 50, 2860, Soborg,
Denmark
Tel.: (45) 38171717
Web Site: http://www.dk.issworld.com
Emp.: 11,000
Commercial Facility Maintenance & Business Support Services
N.A.I.C.S.: 561210
Maarten van Engeland (Mng Dir)

Subsidiary (Non-US):

ISS Facility Services AB (5)
Arstaangsvagen 11, Stockholm, 11743,
Sweden
Tel.: (46) 86816000
Web Site: http://www.se.issworld.com
Emp.: 300
Commercial Facility Maintenance & Business Support Services
N.A.I.C.S.: 561210
Majken Daugaard Larsen (CFO)

**ISS Facility Services Australia
Limited** (5)
Units 1 & 2 12 Mars Road, Lane Cove,
2066, NSW, Australia
Tel.: (61) 286449700
Web Site: http://www.au.issworld.com
Emp.: 21,000

Commercial Facility Maintenance & Business Support Services
N.A.I.C.S.: 561210
Ian Scanlon (CFO)

ISS Facility Services GmbH (5)
Brunner Strasse 85, 1210, Vienna, Austria
Tel.: (43) 57400
Web Site: http://www.at.issworld.com
Sales Range: $75-99.9 Million
Emp.: 300
Commercial Facility Maintenance & Business Support Services
N.A.I.C.S.: 561210

ISS Facility Services GmbH (5)
Wanheimer Strasse 92, Dusseldorf, 40468,
Germany
Tel.: (49) 211302780
Web Site: http://www.de.issworld.com
Commercial Facility Maintenance & Business Support Services
N.A.I.C.S.: 561210
Frank Merry (Gen Mgr-HR)

ISS Facility Services Lda. (5)
Rua Moinho da Barrunchada 4 1st Dt, Carnaxide, 2790-109, Portugal
Tel.: (351) 214246760
Web Site: http://www.pt.issworld.com
Commercial Facility Maintenance & Business Support Services
N.A.I.C.S.: 561210

ISS Facility Services Limited (5)
6F Dorset House Taikoo Place 979 Kings
Road, Quarry Bay, China (Hong Kong)
Tel.: (852) 2826 9166
Web Site: http://www.hk.issworld.com
Commercial Facility Maintenance & Business Support Services
N.A.I.C.S.: 561210
William Fung (CFO & Exec Dir)

Subsidiary (Domestic):

**ISS EastPoint Facility Services
Limited** (6)
18/F Warwick House West Taikoo Place
979 King's Road, Quarry Bay, China (Hong
Kong)
Tel.: (852) 28269166
Web Site: http://www.hk.issworld.com
Sales Range: $50-74.9 Million
Commercial Facility Maintenance & Support
Services
N.A.I.C.S.: 561210
Keith Futcher (CEO)

Subsidiary (Non-US):

ISS Facility Services S.A. (5)
Rue Christophe Plantin 5, 2339, Gasperich,
Luxembourg
Tel.: (352) 4246201
Web Site: http://www.lu.issworld.com
Sales Range: $75-99.9 Million
Commercial Facility Maintenance & Business Support Services
N.A.I.C.S.: 561210
Kris Cloots (Country Mgr)

ISS Facility Services s.r.o. (5)
Antala Staska 38/510, Prague, 14000,
Czech Republic
Tel.: (420) 261392311
Web Site: http://www.cz.issworld.com
Sales Range: $50-74.9 Million
Commercial Facility Maintenance & Business Support Services
N.A.I.C.S.: 561210

ISS Facility Services spol. s r.o. (5)
Dubraska Cesta 14, 841 04, Bratislava,
Slovakia
Tel.: (421) 232630111
Web Site: http://www.sk.issworld.com
Sales Range: $75-99.9 Million
Emp.: 60
Commercial Facility Maintenance & Business Support Services
N.A.I.C.S.: 561210
Peter Szavo (Mng Dir)

Subsidiary (US):

ISS Facility Services, Inc. (5)
1017 Central Pkwy N Ste 100, San Antonio,
TX 78232-5027
Tel.: (210) 495-6021
Web Site: http://www.us.issworld.com

Sales Range: $300-349.9 Million
Emp.: 10,000
Commercial Facility Maintenance & Support
Services
N.A.I.C.S.: 561210

Subsidiary (Domestic):

Guckenheimer Enterprise, Inc. (6)
1850 Gateway Dr Ste 500, San Mateo, CA
94404
Tel.: (650) 592-3800
Web Site: http://www.guckenheimer.com
Emp.: 3,200
Holding Company; Corporate Food Service
Contracting Services
N.A.I.C.S.: 551112
Randall Boyd (CEO & COO)

Branch (Domestic):

**ISS Facility Services, Inc. - Austin
Regional Office** (6)
10435 Burnet Rd Ste 102, Austin, TX
78758-3818
Tel.: (512) 836-9516
Web Site: http://www.us.issworld.com
Sales Range: $50-74.9 Million
Emp.: 170
Commercial Facility Maintenance & Support
Services
N.A.I.C.S.: 561210
Trent Harr (Gen Mgr)

**ISS Facility Services, Inc. - Dallas
Regional Office** (6)
1620 N I 35 E Ste 311, Carrollton, TX
75006
Tel.: (972) 446-1223
Web Site: http://www.us.issworld.com
Sales Range: $125-149.9 Million
Emp.: 500
Commercial Facility Maintenance & Support
Services
N.A.I.C.S.: 561210
Amy Vaughan (Gen Mgr)

ISS Facility Services, Inc. - Greensboro Regional Office (6)
18-A Oak Branch Dr, Greensboro, NC
27407
Tel.: (336) 855-8480
Web Site: http://www.us.issworld.com
Sales Range: $75-99.9 Million
Emp.: 218
Commercial Facility Maintenance & Support
Services
N.A.I.C.S.: 561210
Randy Jordan (Gen Mgr)

**ISS Facility Services, Inc. - Houston
Regional Office** (6)
320 Garden Oaks Blvd, Houston, TX 77018
Tel.: (713) 956-2277
Web Site: http://www.us.issworld.com
Sales Range: $25-49.9 Million
Emp.: 14
Commercial Facility Maintenance & Support
Services
N.A.I.C.S.: 561210
Jim Roll (Gen Mgr)

**ISS Facility Services, Inc. - Kansas
City Regional Office** (6)
1225 E 18th St, Kansas City, MO 64108
Tel.: (816) 421-8088
Web Site: http://www.us.issworld.com
Emp.: 600
Commercial Facility Maintenance & Support
Services
N.A.I.C.S.: 561210
John Combs (Mgr-Bus Dev)

ISS Facility Services, Inc. - Las Vegas Regional Office (6)
2700 E Patrick Ln Ste 3, Las Vegas, NV
89120
Tel.: (702) 822-2133
Web Site: http://www.us.issworld.com
Sales Range: $75-99.9 Million
Commercial Facility Maintenance & Support
Services
N.A.I.C.S.: 561210

**ISS Facility Services, Inc. - Memphis
Regional Office** (6)
3043 Broad Ave, Memphis, TN 38112-3003
Tel.: (901) 452-3770

Sales Range: $25-49.9 Million
Emp.: 10
Commercial Facility Maintenance & Support
Services
N.A.I.C.S.: 561210
Remiro Alvarev (Gen Mgr)

**ISS Facility Services, Inc. - Phoenix
Regional Office** (6)
3800 N Central Ave Ste 460, Phoenix, AZ
85012
Tel.: (602) 222-2555
Web Site: http://www.us.issworld.com
Commercial Facility Maintenance & Support
Services
N.A.I.C.S.: 561210

ISS Facility Services, Inc. - San Antonio Regional Office (6)
8506 Speedway Dr, San Antonio, TX
78230-5331
Tel.: (210) 349-4647
Web Site: http://www.us.issworld.com
Sales Range: $250-299.9 Million
Emp.: 800
Commercial Facility Maintenance & Support
Services
N.A.I.C.S.: 561210

Subsidiary (Domestic):

ISS TMC Services, Inc. (6)
81 Dorsa Ave, Livingston, NJ 07039
Tel.: (973) 740-0032
Web Site: http://www.us.issworld.com
Emp.: 1,500
Commercial Facility Maintenance & Support
Services
N.A.I.C.S.: 561210
Lisa Ostermann (Gen Mgr)

Subsidiary (Non-US):

ISS Ireland Ltd. (5)
4-6 Riverwalk Citywest Business Campus,
Dublin, Ireland
Tel.: (353) 1 468 2900
Web Site: http://www.ie.issworld.com
Emp.: 3,700
Commercial Facility Maintenance & Business Support Services
N.A.I.C.S.: 561210
Eric Doyle (Mng Dir)

ISS Island ehf. (5)
Austurhrauni 7, 210, Gardabaer, Iceland
Tel.: (354) 5800600
Web Site: http://www.is.issworld.com
Emp.: 50
Commercial Facility Maintenance & Business Support Services
N.A.I.C.S.: 561210
Gudmundur Gudmundsson (Country Mgr)

ISS N.V. (5)
Leuvensesteenweg 248C, 1800, Vilvoorde,
Belgium
Tel.: (32) 22636611
Web Site: https://www.be.issworld.com
Sales Range: $75-99.9 Million
Emp.: 500
Commercial Facility Maintenance & Business Support Services
N.A.I.C.S.: 561210

ISS Nederland B.V. (5)
Rijnzathe 8, 3454 PV, De Meern, Netherlands
Tel.: (31) 302424344
Web Site: http://www.nl.issworld.com
Emp.: 110
Commercial Facility Maintenance & Business Support Services
N.A.I.C.S.: 561210

Subsidiary (Domestic):

**De Loge Schoonmaakdiensten
B.V.** (6)
Van Deventerlaan 30-40, NL-3528 AE,
Utrecht, Netherlands
Tel.: (31) 30 242 4344
Web Site: http://www.nl.issworld.com
Sales Range: $75-99.9 Million
Facility Janitorial & Specialty Cleaning Services
N.A.I.C.S.: 561720

Subsidiary (Domestic):

ISS Facility Services (7)

Rijnzathe 8, 3454 PV, De Meern, Netherlands
Tel.: (31) 302424344
Web Site: https://www.nl.issworld.com
Sales Range: $50-74.9 Million
Emp.: 200
Food Industry Facility Sanitizing & Maintenance Services
N.A.I.C.S.: 561210
Peter Vorm *(Gen Mgr)*

Subsidiary (Domestic):

ISS Integrated Facility Services B.V. **(6)**
Rijnzathe 8, NL-3528, De Meern, Netherlands
Tel.: (31) 302424344
Web Site: http://www.nl.issworld.com
Sales Range: $50-74.9 Million
Integrated Facility Support Management Services
N.A.I.C.S.: 541611

Subsidiary (Domestic):

ISS Hospital Services B.V. **(7)**
Rijnzathe 8, 3454 PV, De Meern, Netherlands
Tel.: (31) 302424800
Web Site: http://www.nl.issworld.com
Sales Range: $50-74.9 Million
Emp.: 200
Management of Integrated Hospital Support Services
N.A.I.C.S.: 541611

Subsidiary (Non-US):

ISS Palvelut Oy **(5)**
Karvaamokuja 2 A, PO Box 100, 01055, Helsinki, Finland
Tel.: (358) 205155
Web Site: https://www.fi.issworld.com
Emp.: 12,000
Commercial Facility Maintenance & Business Support Services
N.A.I.C.S.: 561210

ISS Schweiz AG **(5)**
Vulkanplatz 3, PO Box 8010, 8010, Zurich, Switzerland
Tel.: (41) 587878000
Web Site: https://www.ch.issworld.com
Holding Company; Facility Support Services
N.A.I.C.S.: 551112
David Macherel *(Mng Dir)*

Subsidiary (Domestic):

ISS Facility Services AG **(6)**
Buckhauserstrasse 22, CH-8010, Zurich, Switzerland
Tel.: (41) 587878000
Web Site: http://www.iss.ch
Sales Range: $75-99.9 Million
Emp.: 500
Commercial Facility Support Services
N.A.I.C.S.: 561210
Andre Nauer *(CEO)*

Subsidiary (Non-US):

ISS Servisystem Kft. **(5)**
Peterdy utca 15, Budapest, 1071, Hungary
Tel.: (36) 1 413 3140
Web Site: http://www.hu.issworld.com
Sales Range: $75-99.9 Million
Commercial Facility Maintenance & Business Support Services
N.A.I.C.S.: 561210
Peter Szabo *(Country Mgr)*

ISS Servisystem d.o.o. **(5)**
Ptujska Cesta 95, SI-2000, Maribor, Slovenia
Tel.: (386) 24503300
Web Site: http://www.si.issworld.com
Sales Range: $10-24.9 Million
Commercial Facility Maintenance & Business Support Services
N.A.I.C.S.: 561210
Rudi Zupan *(Mng Dir)*

ISS Servisystem do Brasil Ltda. **(5)**
Estrada Kaiko 8 Embu, 06843-195, Sao Paulo, Brazil
Tel.: (55) 1121353700
Web Site: http://www.br.issworld.com

Sales Range: $25-49.9 Million
Commercial Facility Maintenance & Business Support Services
N.A.I.C.S.: 561210

ISS UK Limited **(5)**
Velocity 1 Brooklands Drive Brooklands, Weybridge, KT13 0SL, Surrey, United Kingdom
Tel.: (44) 8450576500
Web Site: https://www.uk.issworld.com
Emp.: 200
Holding Company; Commercial Facility Maintenance & Business Support Services
N.A.I.C.S.: 551112
David Openshaw *(Middle East & South Africa)*

Subsidiary (Domestic):

ISS Facility Services Limited **(6)**
Velocity 1 Brooklands Brooklands Drive, Weybridge, KT13 0SL, Surrey, United Kingdom
Tel.: (44) 8450576400
Web Site: http://www.uk.issworld.com
Sales Range: $750-799.9 Million
Commercial Facility Maintenance & Business Support Services
N.A.I.C.S.: 561210
Phil Jones *(Mng Dir)*

Branch (Domestic):

ISS Facility Services Ltd. - London **(7)**
9- 10- 11th Fl South Keuy Plz, London, E14 9FH, United Kingdom
Tel.: (44) 8449361030
Web Site: http://www.uk.issworld.com
Sales Range: $50-74.9 Million
Commercial Facility Maintenance & Support Services
N.A.I.C.S.: 561210

Holding (Domestic):

Industrial and Financial Systems, IFS AB **(2)**
Teknikringen 5, Box 1545, SE-581 15, Linkoping, Sweden **(96%)**
Tel.: (46) 013 460 3600
Web Site: http://www.ifsworld.com
Software Products & Services
N.A.I.C.S.: 334610
Darren Roos *(CEO)*

Subsidiary (Non-US):

Axios Systems plc. **(3)**
60 Melville Street, Edinburgh, EH3 7HF, United Kingdom
Tel.: (44) 1312204748
Web Site: http://www.axiossystems.com
Emp.: 250
Information Technology Consultancy Services
N.A.I.C.S.: 541512
Tasos Symeonides *(Founder & CEO)*

Subsidiary (US):

Customerville, Inc. **(3)**
800 5th Ave Ste 4100, Seattle, WA 98104-3100
Tel.: (206) 224-6200
Web Site: http://www.elliottslistens.com
Public Relations Agencies
N.A.I.C.S.: 541820
Max Israel *(Founder & CEO)*

IFS Americas, Inc. **(3)**
300 Park Blvd Ste 555, Chicago, IL 60143
Tel.: (847) 592-0200
Software Mfr
N.A.I.C.S.: 513210
Darren Roos *(CEO)*

Subsidiary (Domestic):

Astea International Inc. **(4)**
240 Gibraltar Rd, Horsham, PA 19044
Tel.: (215) 682-2500
Web Site: http://www.astea.com
Sales Range: Less than $1 Million
Customer Relations Management Software & Services Developer, Marketer & Supporter
N.A.I.C.S.: 513210
John Hunt *(Mng Dir-EMEA)*

Subsidiary (Non-US):

Astea (UK) Ltd. **(5)**
Ground Floor North Suite The Place Bridge Avenue, Maidenhead, SL6 1AF, United Kingdom
Tel.: (44) 1628915100
Web Site: http://www.astea.com
Service Management Software Provider
N.A.I.C.S.: 513210

Astea France **(5)**
109 Chemin De Ronde, BP 48, 78290, Croissy-sur-Seine, France **(100%)**
Tel.: (33) 130154444
Web Site: http://www.dix.axo.fr
Sales Range: $10-24.9 Million
Emp.: 16
Prepackaged Software
N.A.I.C.S.: 334610

Astea International Australian Pty Ltd. **(5)**
Level 3 Suite 7 100 Walker Street, North Sydney, 2060, NSW, Australia
Tel.: (61) 294360855
Emp.: 9
Management Software Development Services
N.A.I.C.S.: 513210
Ben Hartman *(Gen Mgr)*

Astea International Japan, Inc. **(5)**
1-15 Minami Aoyama Minato-ku, Tokyo Shin Aoyama Building East Building 15F, Tokyo, 107-0062, Japan
Tel.: (81) 357750130
Web Site: http://www.astea.com
Emp.: 14
Service Management Software Publisher
N.A.I.C.S.: 513210

Astea International, Inc. **(5)**
Level 3 Ste 7 100 Walker St, North Sydney, 2060, Australia **(100%)**
Tel.: (61) 294360855
Web Site: http://www.astea.com
Sales Range: $10-24.9 Million
Emp.: 30
Prepackaged Software
N.A.I.C.S.: 334610

Astea Israel Ltd. **(5)**
Hanapach St 12, PO Box 1146, Karmiel, 21653, Israel **(100%)**
Tel.: (972) 49088500
Web Site: http://www.astea.co.il
Sales Range: $10-24.9 Million
Emp.: 40
Prepackaged Software
N.A.I.C.S.: 334610

Astea Service & Distribution Systems, BV **(5)**
Lange Dreef 11, 4131, Vianen, Netherlands
Tel.: (31) 347715070
Web Site: http://www.astea.nl
Sales Range: $100-124.9 Million
Prepackaged Software
N.A.I.C.S.: 334610

Subsidiary (Domestic):

Network Data, Inc. **(5)**
103 Foulk Rd, Wilmington, DE 19803
Tel.: (302) 778-2895
Computer & Computer Peripheral Equipment Whslr
N.A.I.C.S.: 423430

Subsidiary (Non-US):

IFS Applications Iberica, S.A. **(3)**
Parque Euronova Ronda de Poniente 16 Planta 2a Modulo B, 28760, Tres Cantos, Spain
Tel.: (34) 918062345
Web Site: http://www.ifsworld.com
Application Software Development Services
N.A.I.C.S.: 541511

IFS Benelux B.V. **(3)**
Flight Forum 3450, Eindhoven, 5657 EW, Netherlands **(100%)**
Tel.: (31) 402923292
Web Site: http://www.ifsworld.com
Software Publisher
N.A.I.C.S.: 513210

IFS Beteiligungsges Mbh **(3)**

Weichselgarten 16, 91058, Erlangen, Germany **(100%)**
Tel.: (49) 913177340
Web Site: http://www.ifsworld.com
Management Services
N.A.I.C.S.: 562998

IFS Central & Eastern Europe Sp. Z.o.o. **(3)**
Marcina Flisa 4, Warsaw, 2247, Poland **(100%)**
Tel.: (48) 225774500
Computer & Software Stores
N.A.I.C.S.: 449210
Marcin Taranek *(Pres)*

Subsidiary (Non-US):

IFS Czech s.r.o. **(4)**
Budejovicka 778/3a, 140 00, Prague, Czech Republic **(100%)**
Tel.: (420) 227031280
Web Site: http://www.ifsworld.com
Information Technology Consulting Services
N.A.I.C.S.: 541512
Nicola Spicak *(Mgr-Dev)*

IFS Hungary kft. **(4)**
Vaci ut 22-24, 1132, Budapest, Hungary **(100%)**
Tel.: (36) 12363700
Web Site: http://www.ifsworld.com
Application Software Development Services
N.A.I.C.S.: 541511
Balint Vrabel *(Sls Mgr)*

IFS Slovakia, SPOL. s.r.o. **(4)**
Legionarska, 010 01, Zilina, Slovakia
Tel.: (421) 417233559
Web Site: http://www.ifsworld.com
Information Technology Consulting Services
N.A.I.C.S.: 541512

Subsidiary (Non-US):

IFS Danmark A/S **(3)**
Arne Jacobsens Alle 15-17, 2300, Copenhagen, Denmark **(100%)**
Tel.: (45) 43288950
Web Site: http://www.ifsworld.com
Information Technology Consulting Services
N.A.I.C.S.: 541512

IFS Deutschland GmbH & Co KG **(3)**
Weichselgarten 16, 91058, Erlangen, Germany **(100%)**
Tel.: (49) 913177340
Web Site: http://www.ifsworld.com
Computer Programming Services
N.A.I.C.S.: 541511

IFS Finland OY AB **(3)**
Keilaranta 13 A, 02150, Espoo, Finland **(100%)**
Tel.: (358) 102179300
Web Site: http://www.ifsworld.com
Computer Programming Services
N.A.I.C.S.: 541511

IFS France SA **(3)**
52 Rue De Dornach, 40077, Mulhouse, France **(100%)**
Tel.: (33) 389507272
Web Site: https://www.ifs.com
Software Publisher
N.A.I.C.S.: 513210

IFS Industrial Financial Systems Canada, Inc **(3)**
420 Weber St N Unit A, Waterloo, ON, Canada **(100%)**
Tel.: (888) 437-4968
Web Site: http://www.ifsworld.com
Software Publisher
N.A.I.C.S.: 513210

IFS Italia S.r.l. **(3)**
Via G B Pergolesi 4, Milan, 20124, Italy **(100%)**
Tel.: (39) 0229062264
Web Site: http://www.ifsworld.com
Management Consulting Services
N.A.I.C.S.: 541618
Mansrento Locatelli *(Country Mgr)*

IFS Japan K.K. **(3)**
PMO Tamachi Shiba 5-31-17, Minato-Ku, 108-0014, Tokyo, Japan **(100%)**
Tel.: (81) 354197900
Web Site: http://www.ifsworld.com

EQT AB—(Continued)

Software Publisher
N.A.I.C.S.: 513210
Stefan Gustafsson (Pres)

IFS Middle East FZ-LLC (3)
Office 109 First Floor DIB Building, Dubai
Internet City, Dubai, United Arab
Emirates (100%)
Tel.: (971) 43900888
Web Site: http://www.ifsworld.com
Software Publisher
N.A.I.C.S.: 513210
Ian F. Fleming (Mng Dir)

IFS New Zealand Pty Ltd (3)
Level 5 369 Queen Street, 1141, Auckland,
New Zealand (100%)
Tel.: (64) 93035577
Web Site: http://www.ifsworld.com
Information Technology Consulting Services
N.A.I.C.S.: 541512

IFS Norge AS (3)
Skysstasjonen 11, 1371, Asker,
Norway (100%)
Tel.: (47) 40485956
Web Site: http://www.ifsworld.com
Software Publisher
N.A.I.C.S.: 513210

Subsidiary (US):

IFS North America Inc. (3)
300 Park Blvd Ste 555, Itasca, IL
60143 (100%)
Tel.: (847) 592-0200
Web Site: http://www.ifsworld.com
Software Publisher
N.A.I.C.S.: 513210

Subsidiary (Domestic):

WorkWave LLC (4)
101 Crawfords Corner Rd Ste 2511-W,
Holmdel, NJ 07733
Tel.: (866) 794-1658
Web Site: http://www.workwave.com
Software Solutions
N.A.I.C.S.: 513210
Kelly Gliatta (VP-Talent Mgmt)

Subsidiary (Non-US):

IFS Philippines Inc. (3)
Regus Global City, 14th Floor, Net Cube
Center, 3rd Ave cor 30th Street, E Square
Zone Bonifacito, 1634, Makati, Taguig,
Philippines (100%)
Tel.: (63) 24795555
Web Site: http://www.ifsworld.com
Sales Range: $50-74.9 Million
Emp.: 3
Computer Equipment & Software Whslr
N.A.I.C.S.: 423430
Jan Brunaes (VP)

IFS Schweiz AG (3)
Althardstrasse 10, 8105, Zurich, Switzerland
Tel.: (41) 448716000
Web Site: http://www.ifsworld.com
Financial Management Services
N.A.I.C.S.: 523999

IFS Solutions (Shanghai) Co Ltd (3)
Room 2706 Suite 2 Of Ganghui Plaza,
Shanghai, China (100%)
Tel.: (86) 2164483398
Computer Programming Services
N.A.I.C.S.: 541511
Raymond Lan (Mng Dir)

IFS Solutions (Thai) Ltd. (3)
98 Sathorn Square Office Tower 30th Fl
Unit 3007 North Sathorn Rd, Silom, Bang-
kok, 10500, Thailand
Tel.: (66) 22332112
Web Site: http://www.ifsworld.com
Computer Equipment & Software Whslr
N.A.I.C.S.: 423430

**IFS Solutions Asia Pacific Pte
Ltd** (3)
80 Anson Road 34-07-08 Suji Zerox Tow-
ers, 79907, Singapore, Singapore (100%)
Tel.: (65) 63333000
Web Site: http://www.ifs.com
Computer Equipment & Software Whslr
N.A.I.C.S.: 423430

Subsidiary (Non-US):

IFS Solution India Pvt Ltd (4)
Office No 14 Ground Floor Tower 1 Stellar
IT Park C 25 Sector 62, Noida, 201301,
India
Tel.: (91) 1204146444
Web Site: http://www.ifsworld.com
Information Technology Consulting Services
N.A.I.C.S.: 541512
Nilesh Kumar (Dir)

Subsidiary (Non-US):

IFS Solutions Malaysia Sdn Bhd (3)
Level 4 Wisma MyKasih No 15 Jalan P,II
7/5 Mutiara Damansara, 46200, Petaling
Jaya, Selangor Darul Ehsan, Malaysia
Tel.: (60) 379571901
Web Site: http://www.ifsworld.com
Computer Equipment & Software Whslr
N.A.I.C.S.: 423430
Jan Brunaes (Pres-Asia Pacific)

IFS Sri Lanka Ltd (3)
18th Floor Orion Towers 1 736 Dr Danister
De Silva Mawatha, 600, Colombo, Sri.
Lanka
Tel.: (94) 112364400
Web Site: http://www.ifs.com
Application Software Development Services
N.A.I.C.S.: 541511

Subsidiary (Domestic):

IFS Sverige AB (3)
Teknikringen 5, Box 1545, Linkoping, 581
15, Sweden (100%)
Tel.: (46) 134603600
Web Site: http://www.ifsworld.com
Application Software Development Services
N.A.I.C.S.: 541511
Roger Arnroth (Dir-HR)

Subsidiary (Non-US):

IFSAR S.A. (3)
Av Sargento Mayor Cayetano Beliera 3025
RN8 Parque Austral Edificio, B1629WWA,
Buenos Aires, Argentina
Tel.: (54) 1152786343
Web Site: http://www.ifsworld.com
Software Development Services
N.A.I.C.S.: 541511
Juan Carlos Vottero (Dir-Comml)

**Industrial and Financial Systems, IFS
UK Ltd** (3)
Artisan Hillbottom Road High Wycombe,
Buckingham, HP12 4HJ, United Kingdom
Tel.: (44) 1159000444
Web Site: http://www.ifsworld.com
Financial Advisory Services
N.A.I.C.S.: 523940

Subsidiary (Domestic):

IFS UK Ltd. (4)
Artisan Hillbottom Road Sands Industrial
Estate High Wycombe, Buckingham, HP12
4HJ, United Kingdom
Tel.: (44) 1494 428 900
Web Site: http://www.ifsworld.com
Mobile Scheduling Software Development
Services
N.A.I.C.S.: 541511

Holding (Domestic):

Iver AB (2)
Sveavagen 145, 113 46, Stockholm, Swe-
den
Tel.: (46) 850610600
Web Site: http://www.iver.com
Telecommunication Servicesb
N.A.I.C.S.: 517810
Magdalena Persson (Chm)

Karo Pharma AB (2)
Klara Norra Kyrkogata 33, 111 22, Stock-
holm, Sweden
Tel.: (46) 103302310
Web Site: http://www.karopharma.se
Rev.: $351,940,403
Assets: $1,528,136,278
Liabilities: $839,789,419
Net Worth: $688,346,859
Earnings: $10,121,042
Emp.: 243
Fiscal Year-end: 12/31/2020

Pharmaceutical Research & Development
Services
N.A.I.C.S.: 325412
Carl Lindgren (VP-Bus Dev)

Subsidiary (Domestic):

MedCore AB (3)
Nybrokajen 7, 111 48, Stockholm,
Sweden (99%)
Tel.: (46) 86310830
Web Site: http://www.medcore.se
Diabetes Medical Products Mfr
N.A.I.C.S.: 339112

Holding (US):

Kodiak Gas Services, Inc. (2)
9950 Woodloch Forest Dr 19th Fl, The
Woodlands, TX 77380
Tel.: (936) 539-3300
Web Site: https://kodiakgas.com
Holding Company; Contract Oil & Gas
Compression Infrastructure Support Ser-
vices
N.A.I.C.S.: 551112
Ewan Hamilton (Chief Acctg Officer)

Subsidiary (Domestic):

CSI Compressco LP (3)
1735 Hughes Landing Blvd Ste 200, The
Woodlands, TX 77380
Tel.: (832) 365-2257
Rev.: $353,398,000
Assets: $722,403,000
Liabilities: $747,677,000
Net Worth: ($25,274,000)
Earnings: ($22,095,000)
Emp.: 792
Fiscal Year-end: 12/31/2021
Wellhead Compression-Based Production
Enhancement Services & Equipment &
Parts Distr
N.A.I.C.S.: 213112

Subsidiary (Non-US):

Compressco Canada, Inc. (4)
605 McCool Street, Crossfield, T0M 0S0,
AB, Canada
Tel.: (403) 279-5866
Web Site: https://www.csicompressco.com
Sales Range: $50-74.9 Million
Emp.: 5
Petroleum & Natural Gas Production En-
hancement Equipment Mfr
N.A.I.C.S.: 213112

Subsidiary (Domestic):

Compressor Systems Inc. (4)
24955 Interstate 45 N, The Woodlands, TX
77380
Tel.: (281) 364-2244
Web Site: http://www.csicompressco.com
Sales Range: $300-349.9 Million
Air & Gas Compressor Mfr
N.A.I.C.S.: 333912

Subsidiary (Domestic):

**Rotary Compressor Systems,
Inc.** (5)
5909 NW Expy Ste 570, Oklahoma City,
OK 73132
Tel.: (405) 621-1509
Rotary Screw Gas Compressor Packages
Design, Fabrication & Marketing
N.A.I.C.S.: 423830

Subsidiary (Domestic):

Kodiak Gas Services, LLC (3)
303 Longmire Rd Ste 1001, Conroe, TX
77304
Tel.: (936) 539-3300
Web Site: http://www.kodiakgas.com
Scientific & Technical Consulting Services
N.A.I.C.S.: 541690
Mickey McKee (Co-Founder & Pres)

Holding (Non-US):

Kuoni Reisen Holding AG (2)
c/o BLR & Partners AG Stockerstrasse 23,
8002, Zurich, Switzerland
Tel.: (41) 44 722 6020
Web Site: http://www.kuoni.ch
Holding Company; Travel Booking & Vacation Planning Services

N.A.I.C.S.: 551112

Subsidiary (Non-US):

Hellenic Tours S.A. (3)
4 Priinis St, N Smyrni, 17122, Athens,
Greece
Tel.: (30) 2109477000
Travel Services
N.A.I.C.S.: 561510

**Regale International Travel Company
Ltd.** (3)
191/1-2 Soi Suksaviddhaya Sathorn Nua
Rd, Kwaeng Silom, Khet Bangrak, Bangkok,
10500, Thailand (100%)
Tel.: (66) 2635245069
Web Site: http://www.regale-travel.com
Travel Agency
N.A.I.C.S.: 561510
Chumphon Chadawat (Mng Dir)

Reiseburo Kuoni Ges.m.b.H. (3)
Kamtner Ring 15, 1010, Vienna, Austria
Tel.: (43) 1515330
Web Site: http://www.kuoni.at
Travel Agency
N.A.I.C.S.: 561510
Franz Pech (Mgr)

Restplatzborse Ges.m.b.H. (3)
Kamtner Ring 15, 1010, Vienna,
Austria (100%)
Tel.: (43) 158085555
Web Site: http://www.restplatzboerse.at
Travel Agency
N.A.I.C.S.: 561510
Helmut Schoenbacher (Mng Dir)

VF Worldwide Holdings Ltd. (3)
Unit 3205 32nd Floor Jumeirah Business
Centre 1 Tower Cluster G, PO Box 114100,
Jumeirah Lakes Towers, Dubai, United Arab
Emirates
Tel.: (971) 4 396 1066
Web Site: http://www.vfsglobal.com
Holding Company; Governmental Outsourc-
ing & Technology Services
N.A.I.C.S.: 551112
Chris Dix (Head-Bus Dev)

Subsidiary (Non-US):

VFS Global Services Pvt. Ltd. (4)
20th Floor Urmi Estate, Mumbai, 400 013,
India
Tel.: (91) 2267289000
Web Site: http://www.vfsglobal.com
Business Outsourcing & Information Tech-
nology Services
N.A.I.C.S.: 561499
Jose Manuel Aisa Mancho (CFO)

Subsidiary (Non-US):

Viajes Kuoni, S.A. (3)
Paseo Infanta Isabel 17, 28014, Madrid,
Spain (100%)
Tel.: (34) 912092045
Web Site: http://www.kuoni.es
Travel Services
N.A.I.C.S.: 561510

Holding (Non-US):

Melita Capital PLC (2)
Gasan Centre Mriehel By-Pass, Mriehel By-
Pass, Mriehel, BKR 3000, Malta
Tel.: (356) 27270000
Web Site: http://www.melita.com
Holding Company; Cable Television Ser-
vices
N.A.I.C.S.: 551112
Harald Rosch (CEO)

Subsidiary (Domestic):

Melita Ltd. (3)
Gasan Centre, Mriehel By-Pass, Mriehel,
BKR 3000, Malta
Tel.: (356) 27270000
Web Site: http://www.melitacable.com
Cable Programming Services
N.A.I.C.S.: 516210
Harald Rosch (CEO)

Holding (Non-US):

Nautisk Forlag AS (2)
Universitetsgata 8, Oslo, 0164, Norway
Tel.: (47) 55706170

Web Site: http://www.stormgeo.com
Publisher of Nautical Charts, Logbooks &
Literature for the International Merchant
Navy & Leisure Craft
N.A.I.C.S.: 513110

Holding (US):

Osmose Utilities Services, Inc. (2)
2475 Gerorge Urban Blvd Ste 160, Depew,
NY 14043
Tel.: (716) 882-5905
Web Site: http://www.osmose.com
Holding Company; Railroad & Utilities Infra-
structure Services; Wood Preservation
N.A.I.C.S.: 551112
Ron Childress *(Pres & CEO)*

Subsidiary (US):

Osmose Utilities Services, Inc. (2)
635 Hwy 74 S, Peachtree City, GA 30269
Tel.: (770) 632-6700
Web Site: http://www.osmoseutilities.com
Utility Infrastructure Inspection, Mainte-
nance & Rehabilitation Services
N.A.I.C.S.: 237130
Chuck Musciano *(CIO)*

Subsidiary (Domestic):

**Mclean Engineering Company,
Inc.** (3)
2929 S Main St, Moultrie, GA 31768
Tel.: (229) 985-1148
Web Site:
 https://www.mcleanengineering.com
Emp.: 100
Engineeering Services
N.A.I.C.S.: 541330

Branch (Domestic):

**Osmose Utilities Services, Inc. -
Syracuse** (3)
5703B Enterprise Pkwy, East Syracuse, NY
13057
Tel.: (315) 433-1010
Web Site: http://www.osmose.com
Utility Infrastructure Inspection, Mainte-
nance & Rehabilitation Services
N.A.I.C.S.: 237130
David Mohammed *(Dir-Sls & Bus Dev)*

Holding (Non-US):

Qinterra AS (2)
Lagerveien 30, NO-4066, Stavanger, Nor-
way
Tel.: (47) 51951600
Web Site: http://www.qinterra.com
Sales Range: $50-74.9 Million
Wireline, Tractor & Cased Hole Logging
Services Supplier
N.A.I.C.S.: 213112
Jorgen Peter Rasmussen *(CEO)*

Holding (US):

RIMES Technologies Corporation (2)
84 Wooster St, New York, NY 10012
Tel.: (212) 334-6866
Web Site: http://www.rimes.com
Software Publisher
N.A.I.C.S.: 513210
Steve Davey *(Head-IT Infrastructure & Info
Security)*

Joint Venture (US):

Radius Global Infrastructure, Inc. (2)
3 Bala Plz E Ste 502, Bala Cynwyd, PA
19004
Tel.: (610) 660-4910
Web Site: https://www.radiusglobal.com
Rev.: $135,456,000
Assets: $2,453,490,000
Liabilities: $1,770,696,000
Net Worth: $682,794,000
Earnings: ($60,687,000)
Emp.: 399
Fiscal Year-end: 12/31/2022
Holding Company
N.A.I.C.S.: 551112
Richard I. Goldstein *(COO)*

Subsidiary (Domestic):

**AP WIP Investments Holdings,
LP** (3)

9373 Towne Ctr Dr Ste 200, San Diego, CA
92121
Web Site: http://www.apwip.com
Holding Company
N.A.I.C.S.: 551112
Dan Hasselman *(Co-Founder & Pres)*

Subsidiary (Domestic):

**APWireless Infrastructure Partners,
LLC** (4)
4250 Executive Sq Ste 900, La Jolla, CA
92037
Web Site: https://www.apwip.com
Real Estate Credit
N.A.I.C.S.: 522292
Scott E. Langeland *(CEO)*

Subsidiary (Non-US):

AP Wireless (UK) Limited (3)
2nd Floor 16-18 Conduit Street, Lichfield,
WS13 6JR, Staffordshire, United Kingdom
Tel.: (44) 1543547901
Web Site: https://www.apwireless.co.uk
Tower Infrastructure Services
N.A.I.C.S.: 517810
Thomas Evans *(Exec VP-Global Asset
Mgmt)*

AP Wireless Australia Pty Ltd (3)
64 York Street, Sydney, 2000, NSW, Aus-
tralia
Tel.: (61) 1800983402
Web Site: http://www.apwireless.com.au
Wireless Telecommunication Services
N.A.I.C.S.: 517112

AP Wireless Belgium, BVBA (3)
Suikerui 16, 2000, Antwerp, Belgium
Tel.: (32) 35470115
Web Site: https://www.apwbelgium.be
Wireless Telecommunication Services
N.A.I.C.S.: 517112
Thomas Evans *(Exec VP-Global Asset
Mgmt)*

AP Wireless Canada, ULC (3)
3080 Yonge Street Suite 6060, Toronto,
M4N 3N1, ON, Canada
Web Site: https://www.apwip.ca
Wireless Telecommunication Services
N.A.I.C.S.: 517112
Jeanne Lagueux *(Dir-Acquisitions & Site
Dev)*

**AP Wireless Ireland Investments
Ltd.** (3)
Gray Office Park Galway Retail Park Head-
ford Road, Galway, Ireland
Tel.: (353) 91457880
Web Site: https://www.apwireless.ie
Tower Infrastructure Services
N.A.I.C.S.: 517810
Linda Evans *(Mgr-Site Acquisition & Dev)*

APWPT II Investimentos, S.A. (3)
Rua Luciano Cordeiro 123 - 5E, 1050 139,
Lisbon, Portugal
Tel.: (351) 210200105
Web Site: http://www.apwportugal.pt
Tower Infrastructure Services
N.A.I.C.S.: 517810
Fernando Alves *(Country Mgr)*

Cell: CM Ltd. (3)
16-18 Conduit Street, Lichfield, WS13 6JR,
Staffordshire, United Kingdom
Tel.: (44) 1926298187
Web Site: https://www.cellcm.com
Wireless Telecommunication Services
N.A.I.C.S.: 517112
Marc Blake *(Mgr-Accounts)*

Dacia Antena, S.R.L. (3)
General David Praporgescu Street no 1-5
Sector 2, Bucharest, Romania
Tel.: (40) 312294646
Web Site: https://www.daciaantena.ro
Tower Infrastructure Services
N.A.I.C.S.: 517810

Pannon Antenna, Kft (3)
Benczur utca 47 1 em 313, 1068, Buda-
pest, Hungary
Tel.: (36) 15507374
Web Site: https://www.pannonantenna.hu
Tower Infrastructure Services
N.A.I.C.S.: 517810

**Telecom Iberica De Inversiones,
S.L.** (3)
Parque Empresarial Via Norte Calle Quinta-
navides No 15, Building 2 PB Module D
Door A, 28050, Madrid, Spain
Tel.: (34) 900838542
Web Site: http://www.telecomiberica.es
Tower Infrastructure Services
N.A.I.C.S.: 517810

Telecom Vastgoed, B.V. (3)
Bisonspoor 3002-C801, 3605 LT, Maarssen,
Netherlands
Tel.: (31) 733690553
Web Site: https://www.apwnetherlands.nl
Tower Infrastructure Services
N.A.I.C.S.: 517810
Thomas Evans *(Exec VP-Global Asset
Mgmt)*

Holding (Non-US):

SUSE S.A. (2)
11-13 Boulevard de la Foire, 1528, Luxem-
bourg, Luxembourg **(79.1%)**
Web Site: https://www.suse.com
Rev.: $653,023,000
Assets: $3,771,102,000
Liabilities: $1,521,390,000
Net Worth: $2,249,712,000
Earnings: ($39,490,000)
Emp.: 2,319
Fiscal Year-end: 10/31/2022
Software Development Services
N.A.I.C.S.: 541511
Andy Myers *(CFO)*

Holding (Domestic):

Scandic Hotels AB (2)
Halsingegatan 40, PO Box 3, SE 102 33,
Stockholm, Sweden
Tel.: (46) 851735000
Web Site: http://www.scandic-hotels.com
Sales Range: $800-899.9 Million
Hotel Operator
N.A.I.C.S.: 721110
Thomas Engelhart *(Chief Comml Officer)*

Subsidiary (Non-US):

**Scandic Hotel Deutschland
GmbH** (3)
Ferdinand-Sauerbruch-Strasse 14, 56073,
Koblenz, Germany
Tel.: (49) 261947310
Hotel Operator
N.A.I.C.S.: 721110

Scandic Hotels A/S (3)
Nansensgade 19 7th Fl, DK 1366, Copen-
hagen, Denmark
Tel.: (45) 23680461
Web Site: http://www.scandichotels.dk
Sales Range: $10-24.9 Million
Emp.: 20
Hotel Operator
N.A.I.C.S.: 721110
Soren Faerber *(Mng Dir)*

Scandic Hotels AS (3)
173 Skoyen, 0212, Oslo, Norway
Tel.: (47) 23155050
Web Site: http://www.scandichotels.no
Sales Range: $10-24.9 Million
Emp.: 30
Hotel Operator
N.A.I.C.S.: 721110

Scandic Hotels Oy (3)
Lars Sonckin Kaari 10, 02600, Espoo, Fin-
land
Tel.: (358) 207664107
Web Site: http://www.scandic-hotels.fi
Sales Range: $10-24.9 Million
Emp.: 30
Hotel Operator
N.A.I.C.S.: 721110

Holding (Non-US):

Schulke & Mayr GmbH (2)
Robert-Koch-Str 2, 22851, Norderstedt,
Germany
Tel.: (49) 40521000
Web Site: http://www.schuelke.com
Sales Range: $75-99.9 Million
Emp.: 300
Infection Control Products Mfr
N.A.I.C.S.: 339112

Christian Last *(CEO)*

Subsidiary (Non-US):

Schulke & Mayr (Asia) Pte. Ltd. (3)
10 Jalan Kilang 04-01/02/03 Sime Darby
Enterprise Centre, Singapore, 159410, Sin-
gapore
Tel.: (65) 62572388
Web Site: http://www.schuelke.com
Sales Range: $50-74.9 Million
Emp.: 10
Pharmaceutical Products Mfr & Distr
N.A.I.C.S.: 325412
Alexander Muller *(Dir)*

Schulke & Mayr (Asia) Sdn.Bhd. (3)
Block A Plaza Glomac Lot A-06-01 &
A-06-02 No 6 Jalan SS7/19, Kelana Jaya,
47301, Petaling Jaya, Selangor, Malaysia
Tel.: (60) 378858020
Web Site: http://www.schuelke.com
Hygiene & Infection Control Products Mfr
N.A.I.C.S.: 325613

Schulke & Mayr AG (3)
Sihlfeldstr 58, 8003, Zurich, Switzerland
Tel.: (41) 444665544
Hygiene & Preservation Products Mfr
N.A.I.C.S.: 325412

Schulke & Mayr Belgium NV (3)
Bourgetlaan 44, 1130, Brussels,
Belgium **(100%)**
Tel.: (32) 24797335
Web Site: http://www.schuelke.com.au
Sales Range: $25-49.9 Million
Emp.: 11
Mfr of Infection Control Products
N.A.I.C.S.: 339113
Gerard Vanmaurs *(Gen Mgr)*

Schulke & Mayr Benelux BV (3)
Oudeweg 8d, PO Box 9546, 2031 CC,
Haarlem, Netherlands **(100%)**
Tel.: (31) 235352634
Web Site: http://www.schuelke.com.au
Sales Range: $25-49.9 Million
Emp.: 10
Mfr of Infection Control Products
N.A.I.C.S.: 339113

Schulke & Mayr Ges.m.b.H (3)
Seidengasse 9, 1070, Vienna,
Austria **(100%)**
Tel.: (43) 152325010
Web Site: http://www.schuelke.com
Sales Range: $25-49.9 Million
Emp.: 27
Mfr of Infection Control Products
N.A.I.C.S.: 339113

Schulke & Mayr Italia S.r.l. (3)
Via Calabria 31, 20158, Milan, Italy
Tel.: (39) 024026590
Web Site: http://www.schuelke.com
Sales Range: $25-49.9 Million
Emp.: 7
Mfr of Infection Control Products
N.A.I.C.S.: 339113

Schulke & Mayr UK Ltd (3)
Cygnet House 1 Jenkin Rd, Sheffield, S9
1AT, S Yorkshire, United Kingdom **(100%)**
Tel.: (44) 01142543500
Web Site: http://www.uk.schulke-mayr.com
Sales Range: $25-49.9 Million
Emp.: 30
Mfr of Infection Control Products
N.A.I.C.S.: 339112

Schulke France SARL (3)
22 Terrasse Bellini, Paris La Defense,
92800, Puteaux, France
Tel.: (33) 142914242
Web Site: http://www.schuelke.com
Pharmaceutical Products Distr
N.A.I.C.S.: 424210

Schulke Polska Sp.z o.o. (3)
ul Rydygiera 8, 01-793, Warsaw, Poland
Tel.: (48) 225682202
Web Site: http://www.schuelke.com.au
Sales Range: $25-49.9 Million
Emp.: 11
Pharmaceutical Products Distr
N.A.I.C.S.: 424210

Subsidiary (US):

schulke inc. (3)

EQT AB—(Continued)

30 Two Bridges Rd Ste 225, Fairfield, NJ 07004
Tel.: (973) 770-7300
Web Site: http://www.schulke-us.com
Pension Fund Management Services
N.A.I.C.S.: 524292

Holding (US):

Segra **(2)**
1500 Hampton St, Columbia, SC 29201
Tel.: (833) 467-3472
Web Site: http://www.segra.com
Telecommunication Servicesb
N.A.I.C.S.: 517810
Timothy Biltz (CEO)

Subsidiary (Domestic):

Lumos Networks Corp. **(3)**
1 Lumos Plz, Waynesboro, VA 22980
Tel.: (800) 320-6144
Web Site: http://www.lumosnetworks.com
Fiber Optic Network Services
N.A.I.C.S.: 517111
Diego B. Anderson (Sr VP & Gen Mgr-RSMB)

Subsidiary (Domestic):

Lumos Networks Inc. **(4)**
1 Lumos Plz, Waynesboro, VA 22980
Web Site: http://www.lumosnetworks.com
Fiber Optic Network Services
N.A.I.C.S.: 517111

Lumos Networks Operating
Company **(4)**
1 Lumos Pl, Waynesboro, VA 22980
Web Site: http://www.lumosnetworks.com
Fiber Optic Network Services
N.A.I.C.S.: 517111

R & B Telephone LLC **(4)**
401 Spring Ln Ste, Waynesboro, VA 22980
Tel.: (540) 699-0167
Telecommunication Servicesb
N.A.I.C.S.: 517810

Subsidiary (Domestic):

North State Telecommunications
Corporation **(3)**
111 N Main St, High Point, NC 27260-5007
Tel.: (336) 886-3600
Web Site: http://www.northstate.net
Telecommunication Servicesb
N.A.I.C.S.: 517810
J. Patrick Harman (Chm)

Subsidiary (Domestic):

North State Communications,
LLC **(4)**
111 N Main St, High Point, NC 27260-5007
Tel.: (336) 886-3600
Web Site: http://www.northstate.net
Sales Range: $75-99.9 Million
Emp.: 400
Telephone Communications, Products &
Services
N.A.I.C.S.: 517121
Jonathan M. Cage (CFO, Treas, Sec & VP)

Subsidiary (Domestic):

DataChambers LLC **(5)**
3310 Old Lexington Rd, Winston Salem, NC 27107
Tel.: (336) 499-6000
Web Site: http://www.datachambers.com
Sales Range: $1-9.9 Million
Emp.: 26
IT Services
N.A.I.C.S.: 541430

Stalwart Systems, LLC **(5)**
6000 Fairview Rd Ste 1200, Charlotte, NC 28210
Tel.: (704) 358-2004
Web Site: http://www.stalwartsystems.com
Information Retrieval Services
N.A.I.C.S.: 517810
Jim S. Guido (CTO)

Holding (Non-US):

Sitecore Corporation A/S **(2)**
Vester Farimagsgade 3, 1606, Copenha-

gen, V, Denmark
Tel.: (45) 7023 6660
Web Site: http://www.sitecore.net
Emp.: 1,000
Holding Company; Web Content Manage-
ment & Portal Software Development Ser-
vices
N.A.I.C.S.: 551112
Jonas Persson (Chm)

Subsidiary (Non-US):

Sitecore Australia Pty Ltd **(3)**
Level 1 27-31 King St, Melbourne, 3000, VIC, Australia
Tel.: (61) 280148857
Web Site: http://www.sitecore.net
Software Development Services
N.A.I.C.S.: 541511
Louise Frederiksen (Bus Mgr-Greater Asia Sls Ops)

Sitecore Canada Ltd **(3)**
65 Queen Street W Suite 615, Toronto, M5H 2M5, ON, Canada
Tel.: (855) 748-3267
Web Site: http://www.sitecore.net
Software Development Services
N.A.I.C.S.: 541511

Sitecore Deutschland GmbH **(3)**
Otto-Lilienthal-Strasse 25, DE-28199, Bremen, Germany
Tel.: (49) 42183944400
Web Site: http://www.sitecore.net
Software Development Services
N.A.I.C.S.: 541511
Timo Wolters (Sls Dir)

Sitecore Japan **(3)**
2-11-16 Minamiaoyama, Minato-ku, Tokyo, 107-0062, Japan
Tel.: (81) 354136900
Web Site: http://www.sitecore.net
Software Development Services
N.A.I.C.S.: 541511

Sitecore Nederland BV **(3)**
Barbara Strozzilaan 101, 1083 HN, Amster-
dam, Netherlands
Tel.: (31) 202292363
Web Site: http://www.sitecore.net
Software Development Services
N.A.I.C.S.: 541511

Sitecore New Zealand **(3)**
Level 27 PWC Tower 188 Quay Street, Auckland, 1010, New Zealand
Tel.: (64) 2041613698
Web Site: http://www.sitecore.net
Software Development Services
N.A.I.C.S.: 541511

Sitecore Sverige AB **(3)**
Barnhusgatan 3, 111 23, Stockholm, Swe-
den
Tel.: (46) 852031400
Web Site: http://www.sitecore.net
Software Development Services
N.A.I.C.S.: 541511

Sitecore UK Ltd. **(3)**
4th Floor International House 1 St Katha-
rine's Way, London, E1W 1UN, United Kingdom
Tel.: (44) 2033270630
Web Site: http://www.sitecore.net
Software Development Services
N.A.I.C.S.: 541511

Subsidiary (US):

Sitecore USA, Inc. **(3)**
101 California Street Suite 1600, San Fran-
cisco, CA 94111
Tel.: (415) 380-0600
Web Site: http://www.sitecore.net
Web Content Management & Portal Soft-
ware Development Services
N.A.I.C.S.: 513210
Scott Anderson (CMO)

Holding (Non-US):

Sivantos GmbH **(2)**
Henri-Dunant-Str 100, 91058, Erlangen, Germany
Tel.: (49) 91313080
Web Site: http://www.sivantos.de
Hearing Aid Mfr & Distr
N.A.I.C.S.: 334510

Roger Radke (CEO)

Subsidiary (Non-US):

Sivantos India Pvt. Ltd. **(3)**
Unit 14 7th Floor Innovator International Tech Park Whitefield Road, Bengaluru, 560066, Karnataka, India
Tel.: (91) 8028015700
Web Site: http://www.sivantos.in
Hearing Equipment Mfr
N.A.I.C.S.: 334510
Avinash Pawar (CEO & Mng Dir)

Subsidiary (US):

Truhearing, Inc. **(3)**
12936 S Frontrunner Blvd Ste 100, Draper, UT 84020
Tel.: (877) 372-4960
Other Health & Personal Care Stores
N.A.I.C.S.: 456199

Subsidiary (Non-US):

Widex A/S **(3)**
Nymoellevej 6, 3540, Lynge, Denmark
Tel.: (45) 44355600
Web Site: http://global.widex.com
Hearing Aid Mfr
N.A.I.C.S.: 339112
Jan Topholm (Co-Owner & Chm)

Subsidiary (Non-US):

000 Widex **(4)**
Argunovskaya str 3 bld 1, 129075, Moscow, Russia
Tel.: (7) 4959566416
Web Site: http://www.widex.ru
Hearing Aid Distr
N.A.I.C.S.: 423450

AB Widex **(4)**
PO Box 16015, 200 25, Malmo, Sweden
Tel.: (46) 406801400
Web Site: http://www.widex.se
Hearing Aid Distr
N.A.I.C.S.: 423450

Centro Auditivo Widex Brasitom
Ltda. **(4)**
Rua Alameda Santos 745 1Andar, Sao Paulo, CEP01419 - 001, Brazil
Tel.: (55) 1133660033
Web Site: http://www.widex.com.br
Hearing Aid Distr
N.A.I.C.S.: 423450
Marcos Pohlmann (CEO)

Instituto Auditivo Widex S.A. **(4)**
Edf Centro Seguros La Paz Piso 5 Oficina Norte 51-E Av Fco De Miranda, Urb Boleita Sur, Caracas, Venezuela
Tel.: (58) 2122386362
Web Site: http://www.widexvenezuela.com
Hearing Aid Distr
N.A.I.C.S.: 423450

WIDEX A.S. **(4)**
Omer Avni Mah Inonu Cad No 12 Ucler Apt Kat 1 Daire 3, Gumussuyu Taksim, Istanbul, Turkiye
Tel.: (90) 2122445872
Hearing Aid Distr
N.A.I.C.S.: 423450

Widex - Reabilitacao Auditiva,
Lda. **(4)**
Edificio Omni Avenida Duque d'Avila 141 - 6, 1050-081, Lisbon, Portugal
Tel.: (351) 213538215
Web Site: http://www.widex.pt
Hearing Aid Distr
N.A.I.C.S.: 423450

Widex Akustik OY **(4)**
Uusiporvoontie 623, 01120, Vasterskog, Finland
Tel.: (358) 95915200
Web Site: http://www.widex.fi
Hearing Aid Distr
N.A.I.C.S.: 423450

Widex Algerie eurl **(4)**
18 rue Didouche Mourad, Algiers, 16009, Algeria
Tel.: (213) 21634951
Hearing Aid Distr
N.A.I.C.S.: 423450

Widex Argentina SA **(4)**
Tucuman 1321 4 piso A 1050, CP 1050, Buenos Aires, Argentina
Tel.: (54) 1143754522
Web Site: http://www.widex.com.ar
Hearing Aid Distr
N.A.I.C.S.: 423450

Widex Audifonos S.A. **(4)**
Edificio Widex C/ Escoles Pies 103, 08017, Barcelona, Spain
Tel.: (34) 932547930
Web Site: http://www.widex.es
Hearing Aid Distr
N.A.I.C.S.: 423450

Widex Australia Pty Ltd **(4)**
Unit 4/660 Lorimer st, Port Melbourne, 3207, VIC, Australia
Tel.: (61) 394112900
Web Site: http://www.widex.com.au
Hearing Aid Distr
N.A.I.C.S.: 423450
Justin Gow (CFO)

Widex Canada Ltd. **(4)**
5041 Mainway, Burlington, L7L 5H9, ON, Canada
Tel.: (905) 315-8303
Web Site: http://www.widex.ca
Hearing Aid Distr
N.A.I.C.S.: 423450

Widex Chile SpA. **(4)**
Hernando de Aguirre 201 oficina 301 - 603, Providencia, Santiago, Chile
Tel.: (56) 6008929000
Web Site: http://www.widex.cl
Hearing Aid Distr
N.A.I.C.S.: 423450

Widex Co., Ltd. **(4)**
Riverside Sumida Central Tower 1-19-9, Tsutsumi-dori Sumida-ku, Tokyo, Japan
Tel.: (81) 356312851
Web Site: http://japan.widex.com
Hearing Aid Distr
N.A.I.C.S.: 423450

Widex Colombia Ltda. **(4)**
Carrera 42 Numero 5C-95, Barrio Tequen-
dama, Cali, Colombia
Tel.: (57) 25518108
Web Site: http://www.widexcolombia.com
Hearing Aid Distr
N.A.I.C.S.: 423450

Widex Dominicana, SRL **(4)**
Abraham Lincoln No 1003 Edificio Profe-
sional Biltmore Suite 406, Ensanche Pian-
tini, Santo Domingo, 10150, Dominican Republic
Tel.: (809) 5407454
Web Site: http://www.widex.com.do
Emp.: 8
Hearing Aid Distr
N.A.I.C.S.: 423450
Victoria Acosta (Mgr)

Widex Emirates Hearing Care **(4)**
Buhaira corniche junior tower building 307 Apartment 203, PO Box 26402, Sharjah, United Arab Emirates
Tel.: (971) 65447332
Web Site:
　http://www.emirateshearingcare.ae
Emp.: 13
Hearing Aid Distr
N.A.I.C.S.: 423450
Julie Padros (Gen Mgr)

Widex France SAS **(4)**
14-16 rue du Taille Fer Z A Les Pouards, 91160, Champlan, France
Tel.: (33) 169741740
Web Site: http://www.widex.fr
Hearing Aid Distr
N.A.I.C.S.: 423450

Widex Hearing Aid (Shanghai) Co.
Ltd. **(4)**
Huaihai China Tower Room 1908 885 Ren-
min Road, Shanghai, 200010, China
Tel.: (86) 2163265101
Web Site: http://www.widex.com.cn
Hearing Aid Distr
N.A.I.C.S.: 423450

Subsidiary (US):

Widex Hearing Aid Co., Inc. **(4)**

3553 24th St, Long Island City, NY 11106
Tel.: (718) 392-6020
Web Site: http://www.widexmail.com
Rev.: $100,000,000
Emp.: 5
Hearing Aids
N.A.I.C.S.: 334510

Subsidiary (Non-US):

Widex Hong Kong Hearing & Speech Centre Ltd. (4)
Room 1101 Hang Shing Bldg 363 Nathan Road, Yaumatei, Kowloon, China (Hong Kong)
Tel.: (852) 27710501
Web Site: http://www.widex.pro
Healtcare Services
N.A.I.C.S.: 621340

Widex Horgerate AG (4)
Hertistrasse 21, 8304, Wallisellen, Switzerland
Tel.: (41) 432334242
Web Site: http://www.widex.ch
Hearing Aid Mfr
N.A.I.C.S.: 334510

Widex Horgerate GmbH (4)
Albstadtweg 6, 70567, Stuttgart, Germany
Tel.: (49) 71178950
Web Site: http://www.widex-hoergeraete.de
Hearing Aid Distr
N.A.I.C.S.: 423450

Widex India Private Limited (4)
54 Delta Tower 4th Floor Sector 44, Gurgaon, 122003, Haryana, India
Tel.: (91) 1244038544
Web Site: http://www.widexindia.com
Hearing Aid Distr
N.A.I.C.S.: 423450
Surajit Mukherjee (CEO-Retail)

Widex Ireland Ltd. (4)
9 North Earl Street, Dublin, Ireland
Tel.: (353) 16857000
Web Site: http://www.widex.ie
Hearing Aid Distr
N.A.I.C.S.: 423450

Widex Italia S.P.A (4)
Via Pontina km 29, Pomezia, 00040, Rome, Italy
Tel.: (39) 069125291
Web Site: http://www.widex.it
Hearing Aid Distr
N.A.I.C.S.: 423450

Widex Korea ltd. (4)
B-2303 Woolim Blue9, 240-21 YeomChang dong Gangsuh-Gu, Seoul, Korea (South)
Tel.: (82) 220931388
Web Site: http://www.widexkorea.com
Hearing Aid Distr
N.A.I.C.S.: 423450

Widex Libya (4)
Jaafer Ben Abitaleb St Menshia 7, PO Box 10, Tripoli, Libya
Tel.: (218) 927310296
Hearing Aid Distr
N.A.I.C.S.: 423450

Widex Line S.R.O. (4)
Bohusovicka 230/12, Strizkov, 190 00, Prague, Czech Republic
Tel.: (420) 283882217
Web Site: http://www.widex.pro
Hearing Aid Distr
N.A.I.C.S.: 423450

Widex Macau Hearing & Speech Centre Limited (4)
Avenida de Coronel Mesquita no 5C, R/C Jade Garden, Macau, China (Macau)
Tel.: (853) 28533530
Healtcare Services
N.A.I.C.S.: 621340

Widex Maroc (4)
18 Avenue Moulay Youssef, 10000, Rabat, Morocco
Tel.: (212) 537705951
Hearing Aid Distr
N.A.I.C.S.: 423450

Widex Medical Equipment (4)
Saeed Tower II Flat 702 Sheikh Zayed Road, Dubai, United Arab Emirates
Tel.: (971) 43433950

Emp.: 3
Hearing Aid Distr
N.A.I.C.S.: 423450
Julie Padrose (Gen Mgr)

Widex New Zealand Ltd. (4)
22 Williamson Avenue, Ponsonby, New Zealand
Tel.: (64) 93603412
Web Site: http://www.widex.co.nz
Hearing Aid Distr
N.A.I.C.S.: 423450

Widex Panama (4)
Calle Manuel Maria Icaza Edificio 7 Planta Baja, Area Bancaria, Panama, Panama
Tel.: (507) 2092969
Web Site: http://www.widexpanama.com
Hearing Aid Distr
N.A.I.C.S.: 423450

Widex Polska Sp. z.o.o. (4)
Sleza ul Szyszkowa 4, 55-040, Kobierzyce, Poland
Tel.: (48) 713882200
Web Site: http://www.widex.pl
Hearing Aid Distr
N.A.I.C.S.: 423450

Widex Singapore Pte Ltd (4)
14 Eng Hoon Street, Singapore, 169764, Singapore
Tel.: (65) 62228577
Web Site: http://sg.widex.com
Hearing Aid Distr
N.A.I.C.S.: 423450

Widex Slusni Aparati d.o.o (4)
ul Mustafe Kamerica br 10, 71000, Sarajevo, Bosnia & Herzegovina
Tel.: (387) 33450102
Web Site: http://www.widex.com.ba
Hearing Aid Distr
N.A.I.C.S.: 423450

Widex South Africa (Pty) Ltd. (4)
1st Floor Island Office Block 22 Island Circle, Riverhorse Valley, 4107, Durban, Kwa-Zulu Natal, South Africa
Tel.: (27) 873515105
Web Site: http://www.widex.co.za
Emp.: 25
Hearing Aid Distr
N.A.I.C.S.: 423450
David Charmer (Mng Dir)

Widex d.o.o. (4)
Resljeva 32, 1000, Ljubljana, Slovenia
Tel.: (386) 12345702
Web Site: http://www.widex.si
Emp.: 10
Hearing Aid Distr
N.A.I.C.S.: 423450
Katja Tapuer (Dir)

Widex-Egypt (4)
2A El- Noor Building- El Nasr St 3rd floor, Nasr, Cairo, Egypt
Tel.: (20) 22903406
Web Site: http://ab.widex.com
Hearing Aid Distr
N.A.I.C.S.: 423450

Widex-H Kft. (4)
Petofi utca 75, 1196, Budapest, Hungary
Tel.: (36) 13480551
Web Site: http://www.widex.hu
Hearing Aid Distr
N.A.I.C.S.: 423450

Holding (Domestic):

Stendorren Fastigheter AB (2)
Strandvagen 5a, 114 51, Stockholm, Sweden
Tel.: (46) 851833100
Web Site: http://www.stendorren.se
Property Development & Mgmt Svcs
N.A.I.C.S.: 531390
Fredrik Brodin (CEO)

Holding (Non-US):

StormGeo AS (2)
Norde Nostekaien 1, 5011, Bergen, Norway
Tel.: (47) 55706170
Web Site: http://www.stormgeo.com
Weather & Meteorology Forcasting Services
N.A.I.C.S.: 541620
Soren Andersen (CEO)

SuSE Linux GmbH (2)
Maxfeldstrasse 5, 90409, Nuremberg, Germany
Tel.: (49) 911740530
Web Site: https://www.suse.com
Technology Solutions & Software Design Services
N.A.I.C.S.: 541512
Ralf Flaxa (Pres-Engrg)

Holding (US):

Synagro Technologies, Inc. (2)
435 Williams Ct Ste 100, Baltimore, MD 21220
Tel.: (443) 489-9000
Web Site: http://www.synagro.com
Sales Range: $300-349.9 Million
Waste Water Treatment & Residual Management Services
N.A.I.C.S.: 562219
Pamela K. Racey (Chief Comml Officer)

Subsidiary (Non-US):

Tion Renewables AG (2)
Bavariafilmplatz 7 Building 49, Gruenwald, 82031, Munich, Germany (82.1%)
Tel.: (49) 89693191190
Web Site: https://www.tion-renewables.com
Rev.: $36,394,278
Assets: $336,080,603
Liabilities: $220,206,055
Net Worth: $115,874,548
Earnings: ($10,732,361)
Fiscal Year-end: 12/31/2022
Renewable Energy Services
N.A.I.C.S.: 221210
Christoph Strasser (CIO)

Holding (Non-US):

Utimaco GmbH (2)
Germanusstrasse 4, 52080, Aachen, Germany
Tel.: (49) 24116960
Web Site: http://www.utimaco.com
Emp.: 170
Information Security & Management Software
N.A.I.C.S.: 513210
Cynthia Curtis (Exec VP-Mktg)

Subsidiary (Domestic):

exceet Secure Solutions GmbH (3)
Rethelstrasse 47, 40237, Dusseldorf, Germany (100%)
Tel.: (49) 2114369890
Web Site: http://www.exceet-secure-solutions.de
Business Communication Software Services
N.A.I.C.S.: 561499
Christian Schmitz (Mng Dir)

Holding (US):

WASH Multifamily Laundry Systems, LLC (2)
Pacific Corp Towers 100 N Sepulveda Blvd 12th Fl, El Segundo, CA 90245
Tel.: (310) 643-8491
Web Site: http://www.washlaundry.com
Sales Range: $100-124.9 Million
Emp.: 900
Coin-Operated Laundries Operator; Laundry Equipment Maintenance & Repair Services
N.A.I.C.S.: 812310
Cathy Jackson (VP-Mktg)

Waystar, Inc. (2)
888 W Market St Louisville, Louisville, KY 40202
Tel.: (844) 492-9782
Web Site: http://www.waystar.com
Computer Software (for Healthcare Services); Claims & Revenue Cycle Management & Healthcare Information
N.A.I.C.S.: 541511
Matthew Hawkins (CEO)

Subsidiary (Domestic):

Navicure, Inc. (3)
2055 Sugarloaf Cir Ste 600, Duluth, GA 30097
Tel.: (770) 342-0200
Web Site: http://www.navicure.com
Automated Web-Based Claims Management Solutions

N.A.I.C.S.: 513210

Recondo Technology, Inc. (3)
7900 E Union Ave 4th Fl, Denver, CO 80237
Tel.: (303) 974-2800
Web Site: http://www.recondotech.com
Software Solutions Provider
N.A.I.C.S.: 541511
Mike Mulcahy (VP-Payer Rels)

ZirMed, Inc. (3)
888 W Main St Ste 400, Louisville, KY 40202
Tel.: (844) 492-9782
Rev.: $2,665,973,183
Assets: $4,072,036,518
Liabilities: $2,724,669,054
Net Worth: $1,347,367,463
Earnings: $355,183,396
Emp.: 10,416
Fiscal Year-end: 12/31/2018
Healthcare Patient Billing Services
N.A.I.C.S.: 561499

eSolutions, Inc. (3)
8215 W 108th Ter, Olathe, KS 66210
Tel.: (866) 633-4726
Web Site: http://www.esolutionsinc.com
Healthcare Software Services
N.A.I.C.S.: 541511
Gerry McCarthy (CEO)

Subsidiary (Domestic):

Practice Insight, LLC (4)
1 Greenway Plz Ste 350, Houston, TX 77046
Tel.: (713) 333-6000
Web Site: http://www.practiceinsight.net
Health Care Software Systems
N.A.I.C.S.: 541511
J. Michael Reeves (Co-Founder & Chm)

Holding (US):

XP Solutions Inc. (2)
5415 SW Westgate Dr Ste 150, Portland, OR 97221-2429
Tel.: (503) 234-9203
Web Site: http://www.xpsolutions.com
Electronics Stores
N.A.I.C.S.: 449210
Colby T. Manwaring (Pres)

Joint Venture (US):

Zayo Group Holdings, Inc. (2)
1821 30th Unit A, Boulder, CO 80301
Tel.: (303) 381-4683
Web Site: http://www.zayo.com
Rev.: $2,578,000,000
Assets: $9,334,600,000
Liabilities: $7,993,100,000
Net Worth: $1,341,500,000
Earnings: $150,000,000
Emp.: 3,781
Fiscal Year-end: 06/30/2019
Holding Company; Bandwidth Infrastructure
N.A.I.C.S.: 551112
Michael Strople (Pres-Allstream-Zayo Group LLC)

Subsidiary (Domestic):

Indiana Fiber Network, LLC (3)
722 North High School Rd, Indianapolis, IN 46214-2076
Tel.: (317) 280-4636
Web Site: http://www.indianafiber.net
Rev.: $7,700,000
Emp.: 8
Electrical Contractor
N.A.I.C.S.: 238210
Kelly Dyer (Pres & CEO)

Latisys-Ashburn, LLC (3)
21635 Red Rum Dr Ste 100, Ashburn, VA 20147-7504
Tel.: (703) 574-7223
Emp.: 20
Data Management Services
N.A.I.C.S.: 518210

Latisys-Chicago, LLC (3)
1808 Swift Dr Unit C, Oak Brook, IL 60523
Tel.: (630) 242-3500
Data Management Services
N.A.I.C.S.: 518210

QOS Networks LLC (3)
5 Park Plz Ste 350, Irvine, CA 92614

EQT AB—(Continued)

Tel.: (310) 436-6970
Web Site: http://www.qosnet.com
Information Technology Consulting Services
N.A.I.C.S.: 541512
Frank Cittadino *(CEO)*

Subsidiary (Non-US):

Serenisys SARL   **(3)**
19 - 21 Rue Poissonniere, 75002, Paris, France
Tel.: (33) 176772740
Web Site: https://www.serenisys.com
Management Consulting Services
N.A.I.C.S.: 541611
Jean-Claude Janvier *(CEO)*

Zayo France SAS   **(3)**
19/21 Rue Poissonniere, 75002, Paris, France
Tel.: (33) 179979646
Web Site: http://www.zayo.com
Software Development Services
N.A.I.C.S.: 541511

Subsidiary (Domestic):

Zayo Group, LLC   **(3)**
1821 30th St Ste A, Boulder, CO 80301
Tel.: (303) 381-4683
Web Site: https://www.zayo.com
Emp.: 3,000
Wired & Wireless Telecommunications Infrastructure Developer & Operator
N.A.I.C.S.: 517121
Daniel P. Caruso *(Co-Founder, Chm & CEO)*

Subsidiary (Non-US):

Allstream Inc.   **(4)**
5160 Orbitor Drive, Mississauga, L4W 5H2, ON, Canada
Web Site: http://www.allstream.com
Telecommunication Servicesb
N.A.I.C.S.: 517111

Subsidiary (Domestic):

IdeaTek Systems, Inc.   **(4)**
111 Old Mill St, Buhler, KS 67522-0258
Web Site: https://www.ideatek.com
Holding Company; Fiber-Based Telecommunications Services
N.A.I.C.S.: 551112
Jerrod Reimer *(Pres & CEO)*

Subsidiary (Domestic):

IdeaTek Telecom, LLC   **(5)**
111 Old Mill Ln, Buhler, KS 67522
Web Site: https://www.ideatek.com
Fiber-Based Telecommunications Services
N.A.I.C.S.: 517121

Subsidiary (Non-US):

Zayo Group UK Limited   **(4)**
100 New Bridge Street, London, EC4V 6JA, United Kingdom
Tel.: (44) 2072203822
Web Site: http://www.zayo.com
High Bandwidth Connectivity Solutions
N.A.I.C.S.: 517810

Subsidiary (Domestic):

Zayo Group, LLC-Louiseville   **(4)**
400 Centennial Pkwy Ste 200, Louisville, CO 80027
Tel.: (303) 381-4683
Web Site: http://www.zayo.com
Bandwidth & Telecom Services
N.A.I.C.S.: 517112

Subsidiary (Non-US):

upstreamNet Communications GmbH   **(3)**
Ruckergasse 30 - 32, 1120, Vienna, Austria
Tel.: (43) 50182180
Web Site: https://www.upstreamnet.at
Electronic Components Mfr
N.A.I.C.S.: 334419

Holding (Non-US):

ZeelandNet B.V.   **(2)**
Het Rip 9, 4493 RL, Kamperland, Netherlands

Tel.: (31) 113377778
Web Site: http://www.zeelandnet.nl
Internet Portal Operator
N.A.I.C.S.: 519290

Holding (US):

Zemax, LLC   **(2)**
10230 NE Points Dr Ste 500, Kirkland, WA 98033
Tel.: (425) 305-2800
Web Site: http://www.zemax.com
Software Publisher
N.A.I.C.S.: 513210
S. Subbiah *(CEO)*

Heritage Environmental Services, LLC   **(1)**
7901 W Morris St, Indianapolis, IN 46231
Tel.: (317) 486-2948
Web Site: https://www.heritage-enviro.com
Sales Range: $100-124.9 Million
Emp.: 1,000
Provider of Scrap & Waste Material Whslr
N.A.I.C.S.: 423930
Craig Hogarth *(Dir-Environmental Compliance)*

Subsidiary (Domestic):

Heritage Interactive Services, LLC   **(2)**
3719 W 96th St, Indianapolis, IN 46268
Tel.: (317) 334-2300
Web Site: https://www.heritage-interactive.com
Waste Material Disposal Services
N.A.I.C.S.: 562219
Wes Rodman *(Dir-Ops)*

Heritage Transport LLC   **(2)**
1626 Research Way, Indianapolis, IN 46231
Tel.: (317) 243-0811
Web Site: https://www.heritage-enviro.com
Rev.: $11,200,000
Emp.: 400
Liquid Petroleum Transport, Non-Local
N.A.I.C.S.: 484230
David Manley *(Gen Mgr)*

Subsidiary (Domestic):

Frank's Vacuum Truck Service, Inc.   **(3)**
1717 New Rd, Niagara Falls, NY 14304
Tel.: (716) 284-2132
Web Site: https://www.franksvac.com
Sales Range: $1-9.9 Million
Emp.: 50
General Freight Trucking, Long-Distance, Truckload
N.A.I.C.S.: 484121
Frank Jurek *(Pres)*

Subsidiary (Domestic):

Heritage-WTI, Inc.   **(2)**
1250 Saint George St, East Liverpool, OH 43920-3400
Tel.: (330) 385-7337
Web Site: https://www.heritage-wti.com
Emp.: 169
Waste Material Disposal Services
N.A.I.C.S.: 562219
Keith Moyer *(Mgr-Field Svcs)*

Joint Venture (Domestic):

Reclamation Technologies, Inc.   **(2)**
10005 Flanders Ct NE, Blaine, MN 55449
Tel.: (877) 407-2910
Web Site: https://www.reclamationtech.com
Emp.: 100
Refrigerants Merchant Whslr
N.A.I.C.S.: 424690

Subsidiary (Domestic):

Reclamation Technologies USA, LLC   **(3)**
10005 Flanders Ct NE, Blaine, MN 55449
Tel.: (877) 407-2910
Web Site: https://www.reclamationtech.com
Refrigerants Merchant Whslr
N.A.I.C.S.: 424690
Rodney Pierce *(Pres)*

Subsidiary (Domestic):

AllCool Refrigerant Reclaim, LLC   **(4)**

8606 Hunters Dr, Frederick, MD 21701-2614
Tel.: (301) 898-0808
Web Site: http://www.allcool.us
Plumbing, Heating & Air-Conditioning Contractors
N.A.I.C.S.: 238220
Jimmy Trout *(Pres)*

Novent Refrigerant Services, Inc.   **(4)**
10311 Woodberry Rd Ste 101, Tampa, FL 33619-8019
Tel.: (813) 679-9470
Web Site: http://www.noventing.com
Hazardous Waste Collection
N.A.I.C.S.: 562112
Robert P. Sheehan Sr. *(Pres)*

Subsidiary (Domestic):

Rineco Chemical Industries   **(2)**
607 N Market St, Benton, AR 72015
Tel.: (501) 778-9089
Web Site: https://www.rineco.com
Sales Range: $50-74.9 Million
Hazardous Waste Collection & Disposal
N.A.I.C.S.: 562211

Keywords Studios Plc   **(1)**
Whelan House South County Business Park, Dublin, 18, Ireland
Tel.: (353) 19022730
Web Site: https://www.keywordsstudios.com
Rev.: $745,432,765
Assets: $870,610,835
Liabilities: $269,390,244
Net Worth: $601,220,591
Earnings: $51,122,383
Emp.: 12,000
Fiscal Year-end: 12/31/2022
Video Game Technical Services
N.A.I.C.S.: 541990
Ross Graham *(Chm)*

Subsidiary (Non-US):

AMC RO Studios S.R.L.   **(2)**
36 Stirbei Voda St 1st Floor DOMUS I Building, 1st District, 010113, Bucharest, Romania
Tel.: (40) 752219585
Web Site: https://amcstudio.ro
Digital Art Design Services
N.A.I.C.S.: 541430

Babel Media India Private Limited   **(2)**
D-32 Infocity 2 Sector-33, Gurgaon, 122001, Haryana, India
Tel.: (91) 1244410482
Web Site: https://www.babelmedia.com
Outsourced Services
N.A.I.C.S.: 541214

Babel Media Limited   **(2)**
4th Floor 110 High Holborn, London, WC1V 6JS, United Kingdom
Tel.: (44) 1273764100
Web Site: https://www.babelmedia.com
Video Game Technical Services
N.A.I.C.S.: 541990

Binari Sonori S.r.l.   **(2)**
Viale Fulvio Testi 11, Cinisello Balsamo, 20092, Milan, Italy
Tel.: (39) 0261866310
Web Site: https://binarisonori.info
Audio Production Services
N.A.I.C.S.: 512240

Subsidiary (US):

Binari Sonori America Inc.   **(2)**
350 N Glenoaks Blvd, Burbank, CA 91502
Tel.: (818) 729-8508
Video Game Technical Services
N.A.I.C.S.: 541990
Kirk Lambert *(Pres & Mgr-Ops)*

Subsidiary (US):

Blindlight LLC   **(2)**
8335 Sunset Blvd, West Hollywood, CA 90069
Tel.: (323) 337-9090
Web Site: http://www.blindlight.com
Motion Picture Services
N.A.I.C.S.: 512110

Subsidiary (Non-US):

Cord Worldwide Ltd.   **(2)**

4th Floor 110 High Holborn, London, WC1V 6JS, United Kingdom
Tel.: (44) 2035975350
Web Site: https://www.cordww.com
Musical Troop Services
N.A.I.C.S.: 711130

Descriptive Video Works Inc.   **(2)**
147 W 3rd Avenue, Vancouver, V5Y 1E6, BC, Canada
Web Site: https://descriptivevideoworks.com
Entertainment & Studio Services
N.A.I.C.S.: 512110

Subsidiary (US):

GameSim, Inc.   **(2)**
13501 Ingenuity Dr, Orlando, FL 32826
Tel.: (407) 688-0587
Web Site: http://www.gamesim.com
Game Development & Terrain Databases
N.A.I.C.S.: 513210
Derek Minton *(CTO)*

Heavy Iron Studios, Inc.   **(2)**
1600 Rosecrans Ave Bldg 7 Ste 300, Manhattan Beach, CA 90266
Tel.: (310) 216-7703
Web Site: http://www.heavyiron.games
Motion Picture & Video Production
N.A.I.C.S.: 512110
Lyle Hall *(VP)*

High Voltage Software, Inc.   **(2)**
2345 Pembroke Ave, Hoffman Estates, IL 60169
Tel.: (847) 490-9567
Web Site: https://www.high-voltage.com
Entertainment & Studio Services
N.A.I.C.S.: 512110

Subsidiary (Non-US):

Indigo Pearl Limited   **(2)**
Indigo Pearl Keywords Studios 4th Floor, 110 High Holborn, London, WC1V 6JS, United Kingdom
Tel.: (44) 2089644545
Web Site: https://www.indigopearl.com
Entertainment & Studio Services
N.A.I.C.S.: 512110

Jinglebell S.r.l.   **(2)**
Via Marco d Oggiono 12, 20123, Milan, Italy
Tel.: (39) 028331141
Web Site: https://jinglebell.com
Entertainment & Studio Services
N.A.I.C.S.: 512110

Keywords International Co. Limited   **(2)**
2F Toshin Building 4-33-10 Yoyogi, Shibuya-ku, Tokyo, 151-0053, Japan
Tel.: (81) 3 4588 6760
Video Game Technical Services
N.A.I.C.S.: 541990

Keywords International Corporation Inc.   **(2)**
410 St-Nicolas Suite 600, Montreal, H2Y 2P5, QC, Canada
Tel.: (514) 789-0404
Video Game Technical Services
N.A.I.C.S.: 541990

Subsidiary (US):

Keywords International Inc.   **(2)**
Plz Ctr 10900 NE 8th St Ste 1000 Bellevue, Seattle, WA 98004
Tel.: (425) 633-3226
Video Game Technical Services
N.A.I.C.S.: 541990

Subsidiary (Non-US):

Keywords International Pte. Limited   **(2)**
20 Kallang Avenue 06-6A Lobby B Pico Creative Centre, Singapore, 339411, Singapore
Tel.: (65) 67098680
Emp.: 50
Video Game Technical Services
N.A.I.C.S.: 541990

Keywords Italia Srl   **(2)**
Viale delle Province 2, 00162, Rome, Italy
Tel.: (39) 06 44 20 25 21
Web Site: http://www.keywordsintl.it
Video Game Technical Services

N.A.I.C.S.: 541990

Subsidiary (US):

Liquid Development LLC **(2)**
4200 Montrose Blvd 300, Houston, TX
77006
Tel.: (713) 521-9574
Web Site: http://www.liquiddev.com
Computer System Design Services
N.A.I.C.S.: 541512

Subsidiary (Non-US):

Liquid Violet Limited **(2)**
1st Floor 39 Earlham Street, London,
WC2H 9LT, United Kingdom
Tel.: (44) 2039590770
Web Site: https://www.liquidviolet.co.uk
Audio Production Services
N.A.I.C.S.: 512240

Maverick Media Limited **(2)**
110 High Holborn, London, WC1V 6JS,
United Kingdom
Tel.: (44) 2072913450
Web Site: https://maverickmedia.co.uk
Emp.: 12,000
Video Games Design & Development Ser-
vices
N.A.I.C.S.: 512110

SPOV Ltd. **(2)**
4th Floor 110 High Holborn, London, WC1V
6JS, United Kingdom
Tel.: (44) 2077395862
Motion Picture Services
N.A.I.C.S.: 512110

Snowed In Studios, Inc. **(2)**
250 City Centre Ave, Ottawa, K1R 6K7,
ON, Canada
Tel.: (613) 656-3372
Web Site: https://www.snowedin.ca
Video Game Design Services
N.A.I.C.S.: 532282

TV+SYNCHRON Berlin GmbH **(2)**
Moriz Seeler Str 5-7 Franz Ehrlich Haus,
12489, Berlin, Germany
Tel.: (49) 30677749415
Web Site: https://tv-synchron.de
Recording Studio Services
N.A.I.C.S.: 512240

Tantalus Media Pty. Limited **(2)**
12 Spring Street, Fitzroy, 3065, VIC, Austra-
lia
Tel.: (61) 396940900
Web Site: https://www.tantalus.com.au
Video Games Design & Development Ser-
vices
N.A.I.C.S.: 512110

The TrailerFarm Limited **(2)**
Lees Housethird Floor West 22 - 33 Dyke
Road, Brighton, BN1 3FE, United Kingdom
Tel.: (44) 1273329727
Web Site: https://thetrailerfarm.com
Video Game Design Services
N.A.I.C.S.: 532282

Subsidiary (US):

VMC Consulting Corporation **(2)**
11601 Willows Rd NE, Redmond, WA
98052 **(100%)**
Tel.: (425) 558-7700
Web Site: http://www.vmc.com
Quality Assurance, Localization & Support
Services
N.A.I.C.S.: 541614

Subsidiary (Non-US):

Wizcorp Inc. **(2)**
Higashi-Nihonbashi 3-10-14 Sunrise
Tachibana 6F, Chuo-ku, Tokyo, 103-0004,
Japan
Tel.: (81) 34 550 1448
Web Site: https://www.wizcorp.jp
Sales Range: $1-9.9 Million
Emp.: 35
Mobile Application Development Services
N.A.I.C.S.: 541511
Guillaume Hansali *(Founder & CEO)*

d3t Ltd. **(2)**
Daresbury Point Greenwood Drive, Manor
Park, Runcorn, WA7 1UG, Cheshire, United
Kingdom

Tel.: (44) 1928575742
Web Site: https://www.d3tltd.com
Scientific & Technical Services
N.A.I.C.S.: 541990

Perficient, Inc. **(1)**
555 Maryville University Dr Ste 500, Saint
Louis, MO 63141
Tel.: (314) 529-3600
Web Site: https://www.perficient.com
Rev.: $905,062,000
Assets: $995,888,000
Liabilities: $585,761,000
Net Worth: $410,127,000
Earnings: $104,392,000
Emp.: 6,893
Fiscal Year-end: 12/31/2022
Information Technology & Services
N.A.I.C.S.: 541511
John Jenkins *(VP)*

Subsidiary (Domestic):

Ameex Technologies Corporation **(2)**
1701 E Woodfield Rd Ste 710, Schaum-
burg, IL 60173
Tel.: (804) 920-1956
Web Site: http://www.ameexusa.com
Application Software Development Services
N.A.I.C.S.: 541511
Dan Venkatesan *(Co-Founder, CEO & Mng
Dir)*

Inflection Point Systems Inc. **(2)**
CIRQL2 - 7142 Columbia Gateway Dr Ste
120, 21046, Columbia, MD
Tel.: (443) 283-8715
Web Site: http://www.ipointsystems.com
Software Development Services
N.A.I.C.S.: 541511

MedTouch LLC **(2)**
450 Artisan Way Ste 310, Somerville, MA
02145
Tel.: (617) 621-8670
Web Site: http://www.medtouch.com
Health Industry Internet Marketing, Advertis-
ing & Related Services
N.A.I.C.S.: 541613
Paul Griffiths *(CEO & Partner)*

Subsidiary (Non-US):

Perficient Canada Corp. **(2)**
90 Sheppard Avenue East Suite 501, To-
ronto, M2N 3A1, ON, Canada
Tel.: (734) 274-8233
Sales Range: $1-9.9 Million
Emp.: 12
Information Technology Consulting Services
N.A.I.C.S.: 541618

Perficient UK Ltd. **(2)**
Sandford Gate East Point Business Park,
Oxford, OX4 6LB, United Kingdom
Tel.: (44) 1865910200
Management Consulting Services
N.A.I.C.S.: 541618

Perficient d.o.o. **(2)**
Futoska 1A, 21000, Novi Sad, Serbia
Tel.: (381) 213017750
Digital Consulting Services
N.A.I.C.S.: 541611

Branch (Domestic):

Perficient, Inc. - Atlanta **(2)**
1200 Ashwood Pkwy 4th Fl, Atlanta, GA
30338
Tel.: (678) 587-9900
Web Site: http://www.perficient.com
Sales Range: $25-49.9 Million
Emp.: 95
Business Consulting & Technology Services
N.A.I.C.S.: 541690

Perficient, Inc. - Chicago **(2)**
20 N Wacker Dr Ste 1450 & 1560, Chicago,
IL 60606
Tel.: (312) 863-3100
Web Site: http://www.pointbridge.com
Sales Range: $10-24.9 Million
Emp.: 55
Information Technology Consulting Services
N.A.I.C.S.: 541690

Perficient, Inc. - Denver **(2)**
1422 Delgany St Ste 300, Denver, CO
80202
Tel.: (720) 946-2204

Web Site: http://www.perficient.com
Sales Range: $50-74.9 Million
Emp.: 200
Technology Consulting Services
N.A.I.C.S.: 541511

Perficient, Inc. - New Orleans **(2)**
1615 Poydras St, New Orleans, LA 70112
Tel.: (504) 523-5157
Web Site: http://www.perficient.com
Sales Range: $25-49.9 Million
Emp.: 35
Information Technology Consulting Services
N.A.I.C.S.: 541512

Perficient, Inc. - New York **(2)**
111 Broadway Ste 1802, New York, NY
10006
Tel.: (646) 760-2201
Sales Range: $10-24.9 Million
Emp.: 75
Financial Services
N.A.I.C.S.: 523999
Andrew Tsai *(Mgr-Tech)*

Perficient, Inc. - Plano **(2)**
5340 Legacy Dr Ste 125, Plano, TX 75024
Tel.: (469) 277-3650
Web Site: http://www.nascentsystems.com
Sales Range: $25-49.9 Million
Emp.: 70
Software Integration Services & Consulting
N.A.I.C.S.: 541512

Perficient, Inc. - San Francisco **(2)**
345 California St Ste 480, San Francisco,
CA 94104
Tel.: (415) 590-8550
Web Site: http://www.cleartask.com
Sales Range: $1-9.9 Million
Emp.: 25
Customizable Software Programs
N.A.I.C.S.: 513210

Subsidiary (Domestic):

RAS Associates LLC **(2)**
1706 Cottage St, Hainesport, NJ 08036
Tel.: (609) 267-4861
Web Site: https://www.raspr.com
Public Relations Services
N.A.I.C.S.: 541820

Sundog Interactive, Inc. **(2)**
2000 44th St S Ste 6, Fargo, ND 58103
Tel.: (701) 235-5525
Web Site: http://www.sundoginteractive.com
Specialized Design Services
N.A.I.C.S.: 541490
Brent Teiken *(CEO)*

Solarpack Corp Tecnologica SA **(1)**
Avenida de Algorta 16 3, 48992, Getxo,
Vizcaya, Spain
Tel.: (34) 944309204
Web Site: http://www.solarpack.es
Rev.: $100,706,256
Assets: $790,149,458
Liabilities: $604,038,289
Net Worth: $186,111,170
Earnings: $13,335,497
Emp.: 244
Fiscal Year-end: 12/31/2019
Eletric Power Generation Services
N.A.I.C.S.: 221118
Leonardo Moreno *(CEO)*

EQTEC PLC
Building 1000 City Gate Mahon,
Cork, Ireland
Tel.: (353) 212409056
Web Site: https://www.eqtecplc.com
Year Founded: 2008
EQT—(AIM)
Rev.: $8,555,251
Assets: $53,267,722
Liabilities: $13,408,728
Net Worth: $39,858,994
Earnings: ($11,297,891)
Emp.: 27
Fiscal Year-end: 12/31/22
Renewable Energy Services
N.A.I.C.S.: 221118

Subsidiaries:

Haverton WTV Limited **(1)**
LABS Triangle Stables Market Chalk Farm

Road, London, NW1 8AH, United Kingdom
Tel.: (44) 2038837009
Renewable Energy Semiconductor Mfr
N.A.I.C.S.: 334413

Kedco Power Limited **(1)**
Portgate Business Park, Monkstown, Cork,
Ireland
Tel.: (353) 214670427
Sales Range: $75-99.9 Million
Power Generation Services
N.A.I.C.S.: 221112

EQUAL EXPERTS UK LTD.
30 Brock Street, London, NW1 3FG,
United Kingdom
Tel.: (44) 203 603 7830
Web Site:
http://www.equalexperts.com
Year Founded: 2007
Sales Range: $10-24.9 Million
Emp.: 140
Software Development Services
N.A.I.C.S.: 541511
Thomas Granier *(Co-Founder &
CEO)*

Subsidiaries:

Equal Experts Devices Inc **(1)**
205 - 279 Midpark way S E, Calgary, T2X
1M2, AB, Canada
Tel.: (403) 775-4861
Software Development Services
N.A.I.C.S.: 541511

Equal Experts India Private Ltd **(1)**
Office No 4-C Cerebrum IT Park No B3,
Kumar City Kalyani Nagar, Pune, 411006,
India
Tel.: (91) 2066077763
Software Development Services
N.A.I.C.S.: 541511

EQUALS GROUP PLC
Vintners Place 68 Upper Thames
Street, London, EC4V 3BJ, United
Kingdom
Tel.: (44) 2077789300
Web Site: https://www.equalsplc.com
Year Founded: 2007
EQLS—(AIM)
Rev.: $87,960,111
Assets: $85,295,380
Liabilities: $31,141,126
Net Worth: $54,154,254
Earnings: $4,482,454
Emp.: 255
Fiscal Year-end: 12/31/22
Payment Services
N.A.I.C.S.: 522390
Ian Alexander Irving Strafford-Taylor
(Founder & CEO)

Subsidiaries:

Equals Money PLC **(1)**
3rd Floor Vintners Place 68 Upper Thames
Street, London, EC4V 3BJ, United Kingdom
Tel.: (44) 2077789302
Web Site: https://equalsmoney.com
Payment Transaction Services
N.A.I.C.S.: 522320

EQUATERRA BV
Rijnzathe 14, 3454 PV, De Meern,
Netherlands
Tel.: (31) 30 658 3090
Investment Advisory Services
N.A.I.C.S.: 523940

EQUATORIAL ENERGIA SA
SCS Block09 Lot C Tower A Rooms 1
201 1 202 1 204 and 1 205, Asa Sul
DF, Brasilia, 70308-200, Brazil
Tel.: (55) 6134261000
Web Site:
https://www.equatorialenergia.com
Year Founded: 1999
EQTL3—(BRAZ)
Rev.: $8,340,463,169
Assets: $21,091,442,482

Equatorial Energia SA—(Continued)

Liabilities: $15,946,217,875
Net Worth: $5,145,224,607
Earnings: $585,323,794
Emp.: 10
Fiscal Year-end: 12/31/23
Electrical Energy Distr.
N.A.I.C.S.: 221122
Carlos Augusto Leone Piani (Chm)

Subsidiaries:

CEMAR - Companhia Energetica do
Maranhao   (1)
Al A Qda Sqs Loteamento Quitandinha,
65071680, Sao Luis, MA, Brazil
Tel.: (55) 98 3217 8000
Web Site: http://www.cemar-ma.com.br
Rev.: $267,426,079,280
Liabilities: $782,111,471,600
Net Worth: $480,522,052,720
Earnings: $30,444,994,960
Emp.: 1,250
Fiscal Year-end: 12/31/2015
Electric Power Distribution Services
N.A.I.C.S.: 221122

Companhia Energetica do Piaui
SA   (1)
Ave Maranhao 759 Sul, Sao Miguel, Brazil
Tel.: (55) 8602212769
Web Site: http://www.cepisa.com.br
Electric Company
N.A.I.C.S.: 926130

Companhia Estadual de Distribuicao
de Energia Eletrica   (1)
Av Clovis Paim Grivot 11 - Humaita, Porto
Alegre, 90250-020, Rio Grande do Sul,
Brazil   (65.9%)
Tel.: (55) 5133824580
Web Site:
  https://www.equatorialenergia.com.br
Rev.: $856,766,034,320
Assets: $1,367,843,942,115
Liabilities: $1,967,517,868,362
Net Worth: ($599,673,926,247)
Earnings: ($80,720,578,466)
Fiscal Year-end: 12/31/2023
Electric Power Distribution Services
N.A.I.C.S.: 221122
Marco da Camino Ancona Lopez Soligo
(CEO)

Equatorial Energia Alagoas   (1)
Av Fernandes Lima 3349 Gruta de Lourdes,
57057-900, Maceio, Alagoas,
Brazil   (89.9%)
Tel.: (55) 82 2126 9300
Web Site: http://www.ceal.com.br
Electric Power Generation & Distribution
Services
N.A.I.C.S.: 221118

Equatorial Para   (1)
Rod Augusto Montenegro - Km 8 5,
66823010, Belem, PA, Brazil
Tel.: (55) 11 3216 1201
Web Site: http://ri.equatorialenergia.com.br
Electric Power Generation & Distribution
Services
N.A.I.C.S.: 221118

EQUATORIAL RESOURCES LIMITED

Level 9 BGC Centre 28 The Espla-
nade, Perth, 6000, WA, Australia
Tel.: (61) 893226322   **AU**
Web Site:
  https://www.equatorialresource.com
EQX—(ASX)
Rev.: $529,038
Assets: $10,613,663
Liabilities: $1,232,280
Net Worth: $9,381,383
Earnings: ($1,178,323)
Fiscal Year-end: 06/30/24
Iron Ore Exploration & Development
Services
N.A.I.C.S.: 212210
Ian Middlemas (Chm)

EQUBE GAMING LIMITED

10493 - 184 Street NW Suite 100,
Edmonton, T5S 2L1, AB, Canada
Tel.: (780) 414-8890   **HK**
Web Site: http://www.eqube.ca
Year Founded: 2011
Rev.: $9,207,398
Assets: $1,655,922
Liabilities: $3,796,564
Net Worth: ($2,140,642)
Earnings: $525,330
Fiscal Year-end: 02/28/19
Software for Electronic & Social
Gaming
N.A.I.C.S.: 513210
Andrew Janko (CEO-Interim)

EQUI=MEDIA LIMITED

60-61 Cherry Orchard E, Kembrey
Park, Swindon, SN2 8UQ, Wiltshire,
United Kingdom
Tel.: (44) 1793 715440   **UK**
Web Site:
  http://www.equimedia.co.uk
Advetising Agency
N.A.I.C.S.: 541810
Andrew Burgess (Mng Dir)

EQUICARE HEALTH INC.

201-2020 Yukon Street, Vancouver,
V5Y 3N8, BC, Canada
Tel.: (604) 708-9075   **BC**
Web Site:
  http://www.equicarehealth.com
Healthcare Web-Based Solutions
N.A.I.C.S.: 513210
Len Grenier (Pres & CEO)

EQUINOR ASA

Forusbeen 50, N-4035, Stavanger,
Norway
Tel.: (47) 114751990000   **NO**
Web Site: https://www.equinor.com
Year Founded: 1972
EQNR—(NYSE)
Rev.: $107,174,000,000
Assets: $143,580,000,000
Liabilities: $95,080,000,000
Net Worth: $48,500,000,000
Earnings: $11,885,000,000
Emp.: 23,449
Fiscal Year-end: 12/31/23
Natural Gas Distribution Services
N.A.I.C.S.: 551112
Lars Valdresbraten (Officer-IR)

Subsidiaries:

Danske Commodities Deutschland
GmbH   (1)
Grosse Elbstrasse 42, 22767, Hamburg,
Germany
Tel.: (49) 40299993400
Web Site: http://danskecommodities.de
Energy Trading Services
N.A.I.C.S.: 523160

Danske Commodities Turkey Enerji
Ticaret A.S.   (1)
Ali Kaya Sk Polat Plaza B Blok No1 B75,
Sisli, 34394, Istanbul, Turkiye
Tel.: (90) 2122707115
Web Site: http://danskecommodities.com.tr
Energy Trading Services
N.A.I.C.S.: 523160

Danske Commodities UK Limited   (1)
Waverley House One Kingdom Street, Lon-
don, W2 6BD, United Kingdom
Tel.: (44) 2122707115
Web Site: https://danskecommodities.com
N.A.I.C.S.: 221117
Jens Tang (Head-European Origination)

Danske Commodities US LLC   (1)
600 Washington Blvd, Stamford, CT 06901
Tel.: (203) 978-6900
N.A.I.C.S.: 541611
Thor Kalstrup (Head-Power Trading)

Earth Science Analytics AS   (1)
Professor Olav Hanssens vei 7a, 4021, Stavanger, Norway

Tel.: (47) 51731511
Web Site: https://www.earthanalytics.ai
Analytical Services
N.A.I.C.S.: 541380
Eirik Larsen (CEO)

Equinor Algeria AS   (1)
1 chemin Doudou Mokhtar, 16035, Ben Ak-
noun, Algeria
Tel.: (213) 770240645
Emp.: 25
Oil & Gas Exploration Services
N.A.I.C.S.: 213112

Equinor Angola AS   (1)
Belas Business Park Edificio Luanda 3 An-
dar - Talatona, Luanda, Angola
Tel.: (244) 222640939
N.A.I.C.S.: 213112

Equinor Apsheron AS   (1)
Tel.: (47) 51990000
Web Site: http://www.statoil.com
Oil & Gas Exploration Services
N.A.I.C.S.: 213112

Equinor Argentina AS   (1)
255 Cecilia Grierson Boulevard 4 Floor,
C1107CPE, Buenos Aires, Argentina
Tel.: (54) 1145902200
N.A.I.C.S.: 213112

Equinor Asia Pacific Pte. Ltd.   (1)
8 Marina View 41-05 Asia Square Tower 1,
Singapore, 018960, Singapore   (100%)
Tel.: (65) 62336533
Sales Range: $50-74.9 Million
Emp.: 30
Petroleum & Natural Gas Products Market-
ing & Trading Services
N.A.I.C.S.: 425120

Equinor Asset Management ASA   (1)
Forusbeen 50, 4035, Stavanger, Norway
Tel.: (47) 981363876
Web Site: https://www.equinorfondene.no
N.A.I.C.S.: 213112
Morten Faerevag (Mng Dir)

Equinor Azerbaijan AS   (1)
Marine Plaza Business Center 62 Uzeyir
Hajibeyli Street 16th Floor, 1095, Baku,
Azerbaijan   (100%)
Tel.: (994) 12 4977 340
Web Site: http://www.equinor.com
Petroleum & Natural Gas Exploration, Drill-
ing, Extraction & Pipeline Transportation
N.A.I.C.S.: 211120

Equinor Canada Ltd.   (1)
Steers Cove, Saint John's, A1C 6J5, NL,
Canada
Tel.: (709) 726-9091
N.A.I.C.S.: 213112

Equinor China AS   (1)
28th Floor West Tower Twin Towers B-12
Jianwai Ave, Chaoyang District, Beijing,
China
Tel.: (86) 1059632588
N.A.I.C.S.: 213112

Equinor Danmark A/S   (1)
Melbyvej 10, DK-4400, Kalundborg,
Denmark   (100%)
Tel.: (45) 59574500
Petroleum Refinery, Gas Service Station
Operator & Natural Gas Distr
N.A.I.C.S.: 457120

Subsidiary (Domestic):

Equinor Refining Denmark A/S   (2)
Melbyvej 10, Kalundborg, 4400, Denmark
Tel.: (45) 59574500
Petroleum Refiner
N.A.I.C.S.: 324110

Equinor Deutschland GmbH   (1)
Conradsweg 5, Friedeburg- Etzel, 26446,
Wittmund, Germany   (100%)
Tel.: (49) 446594420
Web Site: https://www.equinor.de
Sales Range: $50-74.9 Million
Emp.: 100
Natural Gas Pipeline Distr
N.A.I.C.S.: 486210

Equinor Energy AS   (1)
Forusbeen 50, 4035, Stavanger, Norway
Tel.: (47) 51990000
Emp.: 6,000

Oil & Gas Exploration Services
N.A.I.C.S.: 213112

Equinor Energy Belgium NV   (1)
Kortenberghlaan 120, 1000, Brussels, Bel-
gium
Tel.: (32) 27748254
Emp.: 25
Natural Gas Distribution Services
N.A.I.C.S.: 221210
Eldar Sartre (CEO)

Branch (Domestic):

Equinor Energy Belgium NV -
Mechelen Office   (2)
Bedrijvenlaan 5, 2800, Mechelen, Belgium
Tel.: (32) 15741010
Eletric Power Generation Services
N.A.I.C.S.: 221118

Equinor Energy do Brasil Ltda   (1)
Rua do Russel 804, Gloria, 22210-010, Rio
de Janeiro, Brazil   (100%)
Web Site: http://www.equinor.com.br
Sales Range: $100-124.9 Million
Emp.: 176
Petroleum & Natural Gas Exploration, Drill-
ing & Extraction
N.A.I.C.S.: 211120

Equinor Holding Netherlands
B.V.   (1)
Weena 760 8th Floor, 3014 DA, Rotterdam,
Netherlands
Tel.: (31) 102229770
N.A.I.C.S.: 213112

Equinor Insurance AS   (1)
Tel.: (47) 51990000
Web Site: http://www.statoil.com
Emp.: 25
Reinsurance Services
N.A.I.C.S.: 524130

Equinor Norsk LNG AS   (1)
Forusbeen 50, 4033, Stavanger, Norway
Tel.: (47) 51990000
Emp.: 6,000
Liquefied Natural Gas Distribution Services
N.A.I.C.S.: 221210

Equinor Polska Sp.zo.o.   (1)
Marszalkowska 107, Central Point, 00-110,
Warsaw, Poland   (100%)
Tel.: (48) 225640000
Web Site: https://www.equinor.pl
Gas Service Stations Operator
N.A.I.C.S.: 457120

Equinor Service Center Belgium
NV   (1)
Bedrijvenlaan 5, 2800, Mechelen,
Belgium   (100%)
Tel.: (32) 15741010
Sales Range: $75-99.9 Million
Emp.: 100
Corporate Cash Management & Accounting
Services
N.A.I.C.S.: 525990

Equinor South Korea Co., Ltd.   (1)
22F 79 Centum Jungang-Ro, Haeundae-gu,
Busan, 48058, Korea (South)
Tel.: (82) 1083235480
Web Site: https://www.equinor.co.kr
N.A.I.C.S.: 221111

Equinor Storage Deutschland
GmbH   (1)
Conradsweg 5, Friedeburg-Etzel, 26446,
Wittmund, Germany
Tel.: (49) 446594420
Web Site: https://www.equinorstorage.de
Storage Facility Services
N.A.I.C.S.: 531130

Equinor Tanzania AS   (1)
429 Mahando street Block A, Msasani Pen-
insula, Dar es Salaam, Tanzania
Tel.: (255) 684226203
Web Site: https://www.equinor.com
Petroleum Refining Mfr
N.A.I.C.S.: 324110

Equinor Technology Ventures AS (1)
Forusbeen 50, Stavanger, 4035, Norway
Tel.: (47) 51990000
Web Site: http://www.statoil.com
Investment Management Service
N.A.I.C.S.: 523999

Equinor UK Limited (1)
1Kingdom Street, London, W26 6BD,
United Kingdom (100%)
Tel.: (44) 2032043200
Web Site: http://www.equinor.com
Sales Range: $125-149.9 Million
Emp.: 200
Petroleum & Natural Gas Exploration, Drilling, Extraction & Marketing
N.A.I.C.S.: 211120

Equinor US Holdings Inc. (1)
120 Long Ridge Rd, Stamford, CT
06905 (100%)
Tel.: (203) 978-6900
Sales Range: $75-99.9 Million
Emp.: 80
Holding Company: Marketing & Trading In
Oil & Natural Gas
N.A.I.C.S.: 551112
Ole Johan Gillebo (Analyst)

Subsidiary (Domestic):

Equinor E&P Americas LP (2)
2107 City West Blvd Ste 100, Houston, TX
77042 (100%)
Tel.: (713) 918-8200
Web Site: http://www.statoil.com
Petroleum & Natural Gas Exploration, Development & Production
N.A.I.C.S.: 211120

Equinor Marketing & Trading (US)
Inc. (2)
1055 Washington Blvd 7th Fl, Stamford, CT
06901 (100%)
Tel.: (203) 978-6900
Sales Range: $50-74.9 Million
Emp.: 80
Petroleum & Natural Gas Products Marketing & Trading Services
N.A.I.C.S.: 425120

Equinor USA Onshore Properties
Inc. (1)
2107 City W Blvd Ste 100, Houston, TX
77042
Petroleum Refining Mfr
N.A.I.C.S.: 324110

Octio AS (1)
Kanalveien 119, 5068, Bergen, Norway
Tel.: (47) 55383000
Web Site: https://www.octio.com
Monitoring Services
N.A.I.C.S.: 561621

Statholding AS (1)
Forusbeen 50, PO Box 8500, 4035, Stavanger, Norway
Tel.: (47) 51990000
Web Site: http://www.statoil.com
Investment Management Service
N.A.I.C.S.: 523999

Wento Sp. z o.o. (1)
Miodowa 10, 00-252, Warsaw, Poland
Tel.: (48) 22 395 65 80
Web Site: http://www.wento.eu
Investment Management Service
N.A.I.C.S.: 523940
Marcin Guzik (Dir-Dev)

EQUINOX GOLD CORP.
Suite 1501 700 West Pender St, Vancouver, V6C 1G8, BC, Canada
Tel.: (604) 558-0560 BC
Web Site:
https://www.equinoxgold.com
Year Founded: 2007
EQX—(NYSEAMEX)
Rev.: $952,196,000
Assets: $3,856,397,000
Liabilities: $1,503,313,000
Net Worth: $2,353,084,000
Earnings: ($106,027,000)
Emp.: 3,317
Fiscal Year-end: 12/31/22
Gold Ore Exploration & Mining
N.A.I.C.S.: 213114
Gregory D. Smith (Co-Founder &
CEO)

Subsidiaries:

Premier Gold Mines Limited (1)

Suite 200 1100 Russell Street, Thunder
Bay, P7B 5N2, ON, Canada
Tel.: (807) 346-1390
Web Site: http://www.premiergoldmines.com
Rev.: $93,750,000
Assets: $408,641,000
Liabilities: $130,340,000
Net Worth: $278,301,000
Earnings: ($19,952,000)
Emp.: 520
Fiscal Year-end: 12/31/2019
Gold Mining & Exploration Services
N.A.I.C.S.: 212220
Stephen McGibbon (Exec VP-Corp & Project Dev)

Subsidiary (US):

Au-reka Gold Corporation (2)
2080 E Frontage Rd, Battle Mountain, NV
89820
Tel.: (775) 635-8641
Gold Ore Mining Services
N.A.I.C.S.: 212220

Subsidiary (Non-US):

Meridian Gold Holdings Mexico S.A.
de C.V. (2)
Reyes 126, 83190, Hermosillo, Senora,
Mexico
Tel.: (52) 6622158100
Gold Ore Mining Services
N.A.I.C.S.: 212220

Western Mesquite Mines, Inc. (1)
6502 E US Highway 78, Brawley, CA 92227
Tel.: (928) 341-4653
Web Site: http://newgold.com
Sales Range: $10-24.9 Million
Emp.: 20
Primary Smelting & Refining of Nonferrous
Metal (except Copper & Aluminum)
N.A.I.C.S.: 331410

EQUINOX RESOURCES LIMITED
Level 50 108 St Georges Terrace,
Perth, 6000, WA, Australia
Tel.: (61) 861096689 AU
Web Site: https://www.eqnx.com.au
Year Founded: 2021
EQN—(ASX)
Rev.: $1,342
Assets: $10,369,482
Liabilities: $312,653
Net Worth: $10,056,829
Earnings: ($798,135)
Fiscal Year-end: 06/30/23
Exploration & Mining Services
N.A.I.C.S.: 213115
Harry Spindler (Sec)

EQUIOM (ISLE OF MAN) LIMITED
Jubilee Buildings Victoria Street,
Douglas, IM1 2SH, Isle of Man
Tel.: (44) 1624 699000
Web Site:
http://www.equiomgroup.com
Year Founded: 1978
Sales Range: $10-24.9 Million
Emp.: 350
Business Management Services
N.A.I.C.S.: 561499
Larry Kearns (Chm)

Subsidiaries:

Equiom (Guernsey) Limited (1)
Frances House Sir William Place, Saint Peter Port, GY1 4HQ, Guernsey
Tel.: (44) 1481723573
Business Management Services
N.A.I.C.S.: 561110
Karen Gillen (Mgr-HR)

Equiom (Jersey) Limited (1)
One The Esplanade, Saint Helier, JE2 3QA,
Jersey
Tel.: (44) 1534760100
Business Management Services
N.A.I.C.S.: 561110
Paul Embery (Dir-Client Svcs)

Equiom (Malta) Limited (1)
2nd Floor Tower Business Centre Tower
Street, Swatar, Birkirkara, BKR 4013, Malta
Tel.: (356) 25466614
Business Management Services
N.A.I.C.S.: 561110

Equiom Marine & Aviation Services
(Jersey) Limited (1)
1st Floor Channel House Green Street,
Saint Helier, JE2 4UH, Jersey
Tel.: (44) 1534 720555
Business Management Services
N.A.I.C.S.: 561499

Equiom Trust Company (Cyprus)
Limited (1)
18 Spyrou Kyprianou Avenue 2nd & 3rd
Floors, 1075, Nicosia, Cyprus
Tel.: (357) 22 451317
Business Management Services
N.A.I.C.S.: 561499

EQUIPCERAMIC, S.A.
Ctra de la Pobla 64, Vilanova del
Cami, 08788, Spain
Tel.: (34) 938070717
Web Site:
http://www.equipceramic.com
Year Founded: 1998
Sales Range: $25-49.9 Million
Emp.: 85
Industrial Machinery Mfr
N.A.I.C.S.: 333248
Francisco Pain (Mng Dir)

EQUIPEMENTS FDS INC.
3050 rue Anderson, Terrebonne, J6Y
1W1, QC, Canada
Tel.: (450) 621-2649
Web Site:
http://www.drapeaucorporation.com
Year Founded: 2005
Sales Range: $1-9.9 Million
Crane Distr
N.A.I.C.S.: 423810

EQUIPEMENTS PIERRE
CHAMPIGNY LTEE
280 Bonin Street, Acton Vale, J0H
1A0, QC, Canada
Tel.: (450) 546-0999
Web Site: http://mobilicab.com
Year Founded: 1989
Rev.: $16,495,116
Emp.: 18
Automobile Dealers
N.A.I.C.S.: 811121

EQUIPMAKE HOLDINGS PLC
Unit 7 Snetterton Business Park,
Snetterton, Norfolk, NR16 2JU,
United Kingdom
Tel.: (44) 1953661200 UK
Web Site:
https://www.equipmake.co.uk
Year Founded: 1997
U8O—(DEU)
Rev.: $4,603,086
Assets: $5,718,221
Liabilities: $6,977,341
Net Worth: ($1,259,121)
Earnings: ($6,594,245)
Emp.: 69
Fiscal Year-end: 05/31/22
Holding Company
N.A.I.C.S.: 551112
Ian David Foley (Founder)

Subsidiaries:

Equipmake Limited (1)
Unit 7 Snetterton Business Park, Norfolk,
NR16 2JU, United Kingdom
Tel.: (44) 1953661200
Web Site: https://equipmake.co.uk
Motor Vehicles Mfr
N.A.I.C.S.: 336320

EQUIPMENT HOLDING COMPANY K.S.C.C.
Sector 8 Plot No 43 Street No 341
East Ahmadi, PO Box 192, Safat, Kuwait, 64002, Kuwait
Tel.: (965) 23987837
Web Site: https://equipment-holding.com
EQUIPMENT—(KUW)
Rev.: $229,513
Assets: $53,304,466
Liabilities: $38,449,969
Net Worth: $14,854,496
Earnings: ($1,530,752)
Emp.: 3
Fiscal Year-end: 12/31/22
Investment Services
N.A.I.C.S.: 523999

Subsidiaries:

Equipment Co. W.L.L. (1)
Sector 8 Plot No 43 Street No 341 East Ahmadi, PO Box 192, Safat, 13002, Kuwait,
Kuwait
Tel.: (965) 23987837
Web Site: http://www.equipcokuwait.com
Construction & Industrial Machines & Spare
Parts Distr
N.A.I.C.S.: 423830

EQUIPMENT WORLD INC.
988 Alloy Drive, Thunder Bay, P7B
6A5, ON, Canada
Tel.: (807) 623-9561
Web Site: http://www.equipworld.com
Year Founded: 1973
Rev.: $12,495,232
Emp.: 63
Industrial Machinery Whslr
N.A.I.C.S.: 423830
Ernie Ukrainec (Mgr-Construction &
Technical Sls)

EQUIPMENTS CELL CO., LTD.
181 Sanup-ro 155beon-gil,
Gwonseon-gu, Suwon, Gyeonggi-Do,
Korea (South)
Tel.: (82) 312993888
Web Site: https://eqcell.co.kr
160600—(KRS)
Rev.: $45,580,366
Assets: $96,166,353
Liabilities: $61,546,374
Net Worth: $34,619,979
Earnings: $4,405,006
Emp.: 92
Fiscal Year-end: 12/31/22
Semiconductor Devices Mfr
N.A.I.C.S.: 334413

EQUIPPP SOCIAL IMPACT
TECHNOLOGIES LTD
8th Floor Western Pearl Building
Near Google Building Hitech City
Road, Manikonda Ranga Reddy Dist
Telangana, Hyderabad, 500081, Telangana, India
Tel.: (91) 4029882855
Web Site: https://equippp.in
590057—(BOM)
Assets: $445,913
Liabilities: $3,771,137
Net Worth: ($3,325,224)
Earnings: ($43,077)
Emp.: 160
Fiscal Year-end: 03/31/20
Agricultural Biotechnology Services
N.A.I.C.S.: 541714
Dasigi Venkata Surya Prakash Rao
(CEO)

Subsidiaries:

Social Media India Limited (1)
8-2-334 1st Floor SDE Serene Chambers
Road No 5 Banjara Hills, Hyderabad,
500034, India
Tel.: (91) 4023548353

Equippp Social Impact Technologies Ltd—(Continued)

Web Site: http://www.socialmediaindia.com
Sales Range: $25-49.9 Million
Internet Technology Services
N.A.I.C.S.: 517810

EQUISTONE PARTNERS EUROPE LIMITED

One New Ludgate 60 Ludgate Hill,
London, EC4M 7AW, United Kingdom
Tel.: (44) 2076535300   **UK**
Web Site:
  https://www.equistonepe.com
Year Founded: 1979
Privater Equity Firm
N.A.I.C.S.: 523999
Owen Clarke (Chm-Supervisory Bd &
Sr Partner)

Subsidiaries:

Acuity Knowledge Partners (UK)
Limited   **(1)**
12th Floor One Canada Square Canary
Wharf, London, E14 5FA, United Kingdom
Tel.: (44) 2077721000
Web Site: http://www.acuitykp.com
Credit Rating Agency Services
N.A.I.C.S.: 561450
Ian Mullen (CFO)

Subsidiary (Non-US):

Acuity Knowledge Partners Costa
Rica Sociedad Anonima   **(2)**
3rd Floor West Tower in front of Cenade
Barreal de Heredia, Business Executive
Center Eurocenter Diursa, San Jose, 935-
1007, Costa Rica
Tel.: (506) 25092700
Credit Rating Agency Services
N.A.I.C.S.: 561450

Moodys Analytics Knowledge Services (India) Pvt. Ltd.   **(2)**
Elixir Chancery 135/1-2/21 Residency
Road, Bengaluru, 560 025, India
Tel.: (91) 8061133000
Credit Rating Agency Services
N.A.I.C.S.: 561450

Moodys Analytics Knowledge Services Lanka (Private) Limited   **(2)**
Level 32 West Tower World Trade Centre
Echelon Square, Colombo, Sri Lanka
Tel.: (94) 112356000
Credit Rating Agency Services
N.A.I.C.S.: 561450

Bien-Zenker GmbH   **(1)**
Am Distelrasen 2, 36381, Schluchtern, Germany
Tel.: (49) 6661 980
Web Site: http://www.bien-zenker.de
Building Construction Services
N.A.I.C.S.: 236116

Breteche Industrie SAS   **(1)**
1 rue Eugene Varlin, 44100, Nantes, France
Tel.: (33) 2 40 73 26 04
Web Site: http://www.breteche.com
Sales Range: $200-249.9 Million
Industrial Equipment Mfr
N.A.I.C.S.: 333248
Didier Soumet (Chm & CEO)

Subsidiary (US):

Shick Tube-Veyor Corporation   **(2)**
4346 Clary Blvd, Kansas City, KS 64130
Tel.: (816) 861-7224
Web Site: http://www.shicksolutions.com
Sales Range: $50-74.9 Million
Industrial Machinery Mfr
N.A.I.C.S.: 333248
Tim Cook (CEO)

ChartCo Ltd.   **(1)**
Unit 4 Voltage Mollison Avenue, Enfield,
EN3 7XQ, United Kingdom
Tel.: (44) 1992805400
Web Site: http://www.chartco.com
Maritime Charts
N.A.I.C.S.: 334511
Martin Taylor (CEO)

Equistone Partners Europe (Schweiz)
AG   **(1)**
General-Guisan-Quai 34, 8002, Zurich,
Switzerland
Tel.: (41) 44 289 8090
Investment Management Service
N.A.I.C.S.: 523940

Equistone Partners GmbH   **(1)**
Prannerstrasse 4, 80333, Munich, Germany
Tel.: (49) 892420640
Web Site: https://www.equistonepe.com
Investment Management Service
N.A.I.C.S.: 523940
Marc Arens (Sr Partner)

Eschenbach Holding GmbH   **(1)**
Schopenhauerstrasse 10, 90409, Nuremberg, Germany   **(70%)**
Tel.: (49) 911 3600 0
Web Site: http://www.eschenbach-optik.com
Sales Range: $150-199.9 Million
Emp.: 650
Holding Company
N.A.I.C.S.: 551112
Peter Schwind (Mng Dir)

Subsidiary (Domestic):

Eschenbach Optik GmbH   **(2)**
Schopenhauerstrasse 10, 90409, Nuremberg, Germany
Tel.: (49) 911 3600 0
Web Site: http://www.eschenbach-optik.com
Optical Lens & Electronic Magnification Device Mfr
N.A.I.C.S.: 333310
Wolfgang Rebstock (Chm & Mng Dir)

Subsidiary (Non-US):

Eschenbach Optik A/S   **(3)**
Boeskaervej 18, 7100, Vejle, Denmark
Tel.: (45) 70203888
Web Site: http://www.eschenbach.dk
Optical Lens Distr
N.A.I.C.S.: 423460

Eschenbach Optik BV   **(3)**
Osloweg 134, 9723 BX, Groningen, Netherlands
Tel.: (31) 50 541 2500
Web Site: http://www.eschenbach-optik.nl
Optical Lens Distr
N.A.I.C.S.: 423460

Eschenbach Optik GmbH   **(3)**
Brunnenfeldstrasse 15, 4030, Linz, Austria
Tel.: (43) 732 314930 0
Web Site: http://www.eschenbach-optik.at
Optical Lens Distr
N.A.I.C.S.: 423460

Eschenbach Optik Polen
sp.z.o.o.   **(3)**
ul Biedronki 60, 02-959, Warsaw, Poland
Tel.: (48) 22 885 4221
Web Site: http://www.eschenbach-optik.pl
Optical Lens Distr
N.A.I.C.S.: 423460

Eschenbach Optik S.L.   **(3)**
Consell de Cent 106-108 4 3a, 8015, Barcelona, Spain
Tel.: (34) 93 423 3112
Web Site: http://www.eschenbach-optik.com
Emp.: 7
Optical Lens Distr
N.A.I.C.S.: 423460
Sergi Noguera (Gen Mgr)

Subsidiary (US):

Eschenbach Optik of America,
Inc.   **(3)**
22 Shelter Rock Ln, Danbury, CT 06810
Tel.: (203) 702-1600
Web Site: http://www.eschenbach.com
Sales Range: $1-9.9 Million
Emp.: 12
Optical Instrument Mfr
N.A.I.C.S.: 333310
Ken Bradley (Pres)

Subsidiary (Non-US):

Eschenbach Optik of Japan Co.
Ltd.   **(3)**
2-15-4 Kanda-Tsukasamachi, Chiyoda-ku,
Tokyo, 101-0048, Japan

Tel.: (81) 3 3293 8570
Web Site: http://www.eschenbach-optik.co.jp
Optical Lens Distr
N.A.I.C.S.: 423460

Eschenbach Optik s.a.r.l.   **(3)**
64 rue Claude CHAPPE, 78340, Plaisir,
France
Tel.: (33) 1 3007 7900
Web Site: http://www.eschenbach-optik.fr
Optical Lens Distr
N.A.I.C.S.: 423460

Eschenbach Optik s.r.l.   **(3)**
Via C Colombo 10, 20066, Melzo, Milan,
Italy
Tel.: (39) 02 9573 7689
Web Site: http://www.eschenbach-optik.it
Optical Lens Distr
N.A.I.C.S.: 423460

Eschenbach Optik spol s.r.o.   **(3)**
K Fialce 276/35, 155 00, Prague, Czech
Republic
Tel.: (420) 251 614 213
Web Site: http://www.eschenbach.cz
Optical Lens Distr
N.A.I.C.S.: 423460

International Eyewear Ltd.   **(3)**
Atelier House 27 Blackberry Lane, Halesowen, B63 4NX, West Midlands, United
Kingdom
Tel.: (44) 121 585 6565
Web Site:
  http://www.internationaleyewear.co.uk
Optical Frame Distr
N.A.I.C.S.: 423460

Subsidiary (US):

Tura Inc.   **(3)**
123 Girton Dr, Muncy, PA 17756-6375
Tel.: (570) 546-9583
Web Site: http://www.tura.com
Sales Range: $10-24.9 Million
Eyeglass Frames
N.A.I.C.S.: 423460
Mike Pasnello (VP-Fin)

FirstPort Limited   **(1)**
Queensway House 11 Queensway, New
Milton, BH25 5NR, Hamps, United Kingdom
Tel.: (44) 1582 393751
Facilities Services
N.A.I.C.S.: 561210
Nigel Howell (CEO)

Subsidiary (Domestic):

Mainstay Group Limited   **(2)**
Whittington Hall Whittington Road, Worcester, WR5 2ZX, United Kingdom
Tel.: (44) 1905 357777
Web Site: http://www.mainstaygroup.co.uk
Facilities Management
N.A.I.C.S.: 531312
Paul Stevenson (Dir-Fin)

Hanse Haus GmbH & Co. KG   **(1)**
Ludwig-Weber-Strasse 18, D-97789, Oberleichtersbach, Bavaria, Germany   **(100%)**
Tel.: (49) 97418080
Web Site: http://www.hanse-haus.de
Prefabricated Home Mfr
N.A.I.C.S.: 321991
Marco Hammer (Mng Dir)

Heras B.V.   **(1)**
Hekdam 1, 5688 JE, Oirschot, Netherlands
Tel.: (31) 882740274
Web Site: https://www.heras.com
Sales Range: $200-249.9 Million
Emp.: 1,100
Security Fencing Services
N.A.I.C.S.: 331222

MPS Meat Processing Systems
B.V.   **(1)**
Albert Schweitzerstraat 33, 7131 PG, Lichtenvoorde, Netherlands
Tel.: (31) 544 390500
Web Site: http://www.mps-group.nl
Emp.: 420
Slaughter Plant Construction Services
N.A.I.C.S.: 311611
Remko Rosman (Mng Dir)

Subsidiary (Non-US):

MPS France, S.A.R.L.   **(2)**

ZI Calouet, CS 70621, 22606, Loudeac,
Cedex, France
Tel.: (33) 2 96 28 07 69
Web Site: http://www.mps-abattoir-france.fr
Animal Slaughtering Services
N.A.I.C.S.: 311611

MPS Germany GmbH   **(2)**
Kreuzackerstrasse 6, 35232, Dautphetal,
Germany
Tel.: (49) 6468 911937
Animal Slaughtering Services
N.A.I.C.S.: 311611

Subsidiary (US):

MPS North America, Inc.   **(2)**
8226 Nieman Rd, Lenexa, KS 66214
Tel.: (913) 310-0055
Animal Slaughtering Services
N.A.I.C.S.: 311611
Rick Dickerson (Engr-Field Svc)

Subsidiary (Non-US):

MPS Red Meat Slaughtering Co.,
Ltd.   **(2)**
SOHO New Town No 0508 Building B No
88 Jianguolu, Chaoyang District, Beijing,
100022, China
Tel.: (86) 10 8580 6058
Animal Slaughtering Services
N.A.I.C.S.: 311611
Jiang Hu (Project Mgr)

MPS Spain, S.A.U.   **(2)**
Rafael de Campalans 170 ent 1a, L Hospitalet del Llobregat, 8903, Barcelona, Spain
Tel.: (34) 93 2981550
Emp.: 110
Animal Slaughtering Services
N.A.I.C.S.: 311611
Jordi Elvira (Mgr)

OOO MPS Rus   **(2)**
Electrolitniy proezd 3 building 42, 115230,
Moscow, Russia
Tel.: (7) 495 245 56 00
Animal Slaughtering Services
N.A.I.C.S.: 311611

Meilleurtaux SA   **(1)**
19/29 rue du Capitaine Guynemer, 92903,
Paris, la Defense Cedex, France
Tel.: (33) 1 41 97 98 99
Web Site: http://www.meilleurtaux.com
Sales Range: $50-74.9 Million
Emp.: 400
Investment Related Services Through On-line
N.A.I.C.S.: 522310

Nexus Vehicle Management
Limited   **(1)**
Nexus House Owlcotes Court 141 Richardshaw Lane, Leeds, LS28 6AA, United Kingdom
Tel.: (44) 8719841940
Web Site: http://www.nexusrental.co.uk
Vehicle Rental Services
N.A.I.C.S.: 532111
John Ellis (Mng Dir)

Novares Group SA   **(1)**
361 avenue de Generak De Gaulle, 92140,
Clamart, France
Web Site: http://www.novaresteam.com
Automobile Equipment Mfr
N.A.I.C.S.: 336211
Emmanuel Vouturet (Dir-Bus Unit)

Subsidiary (Non-US):

Mecaplast India Pvt Ltd.   **(2)**
P43 8th Avenue Mahindra World City,
Chengalpet, Kanchipuram, 603 002, Tamil
Nadu, India
Tel.: (91) 4437475000
Web Site: http://www.mecaplastgroup.com
Automobile Parts Distr
N.A.I.C.S.: 423120
Ragu Raman (Engr-Validation)

Mecaplast Serbia d.o.o.   **(2)**
Lazarevicki drum bb, 23000, Zrenjanin, Serbia
Tel.: (381) 233150270
Automobile Parts Distr
N.A.I.C.S.: 423120
Mirjana Mikavica (Mgr-Logistics)

Mecaplast Shanghai (2)
No 6819 Chuansha Road, Pudong District, 201202, Shanghai, China
Tel.: (86) 2160203900
Web Site: http://www.mecaplastgroup.com
Automobile Parts Distr
N.A.I.C.S.: 423120
Debbie Yang *(Engr-Validation)*

Mecaplast Shenyang Car Components Co., Ltd. (2)
No 60 Yuelianghu Jie, Dadong District, Shenyang, 110122, Liaoning, China
Tel.: (86) 2431910780
Web Site: http://www.mecaplastgroup.com
Automobile Parts Distr
N.A.I.C.S.: 423120
Sebastian le Goueff *(Dir-Plant)*

Subsidiary (US):

Miniature Precision Components, Inc. (2)
820 Wisconsin St, Walworth, WI 53184
Tel.: (262) 275-5791
Web Site: http://www.mpc-inc.com
Sales Range: $250-299.9 Million
Emp.: 1,600
Plastics Product Mfr
N.A.I.C.S.: 326199
Jay Brost *(Founder)*

Subsidiary (Non-US):

Autopartes de Precision de Santana, S.A. de C.V. (3)
Ave Serna Y Calle 13 Santa Ana, Santa Ana, Sonora, 84600, Mexico (100%)
Tel.: (52) 5553237407
Web Site: http://www.mpc-inc.com
Sales Range: $25-49.9 Million
Emp.: 800
Mfr of Plastic Parts for Automobiles
N.A.I.C.S.: 326199
Jofe Maleonado *(Gen Mgr)*

Subsidiary (US):

Novares US LLC (2)
19575 Victor Pkwy Ste 400, Livonia, MI 48152
Tel.: (248) 449-6100
Web Site: http://www.novaresteam.com
Plastic Component Mfr
N.A.I.C.S.: 326199
Kevin Koshowsky *(Sr Mgr-HR)*

Plant (Domestic):

Novares US LLC - Felton (3)
12367 Mt Olivet Rd, Felton, PA 17322-8449
Tel.: (717) 244-4581
Web Site: http://www.novaresteam.com
Plastic Component Mfr
N.A.I.C.S.: 326199
Teresa Lewis *(Mgr-HR)*

Joint Venture (Non-US):

TBMECA Poland Sp. z o.o. (2)
ul Jaworzynska 291 a, 59-220, Legnica, Poland (25.1%)
Tel.: (48) 768508120
Web Site: http://www.tbmeca.pl
Emp.: 115
Automotive Components Mfr
N.A.I.C.S.: 336390

Subsidiary (Non-US):

Wuhan Mecaplast Co Ltd (2)
Zhang Jia Wang Road, Hong Shan District, Wuhan, 430065, China
Tel.: (86) 2788139007
Web Site: http://www.mecaplastgroup.com
Automobile Parts Distr
N.A.I.C.S.: 423120
Huang Xiwei *(Engr-Project & Pur)*

YanTai Mecaplast Car Components Co., Ltd. (2)
No 192 G-2 Block Qinhuaihe Road, Yantai, 264006, Shandong, China
Tel.: (86) 5353410777
Web Site: http://www.mecaplastgroup.com
Automobile Parts Distr
N.A.I.C.S.: 423120
Grace Lin *(Mgr-HR)*

Performance Interactive Alliance GmbH (1)
ABC Strasse 21, 20354, Hamburg, Germany
Tel.: (49) 40 524 70 59 0
Marketing Services
N.A.I.C.S.: 541613

Subsidiary (Domestic):

Feed Dynamix GmbH (2)
Ludwigstrasse 31, D-60327, Frankfurt am Main, Germany
Tel.: (49) 69 25 49 49 10
Web Site: http://www.feed-dynamix.de
Software Consulting Management Services
N.A.I.C.S.: 541512
Tobias Jungcurt *(Mng Dir)*

Rhodius GmbH (1)
Treuchtlinger Strasse 23, 91781, Weissenburg, Germany
Tel.: (49) 9141 919 0
Web Site: http://www.rhodius.com
Emp.: 400
Holding Company; Automotive, Environmental & Industrial Products Mfr
N.A.I.C.S.: 551112
Robert Kopetzky *(Mng Dir)*

Subsidiary (Non-US):

Rhodius Magyarorszag Kft. (2)
Halasto u 5, 8300, Tapolca, Hungary
Tel.: (36) 87 510 976
Network Cable Installation Services
N.A.I.C.S.: 238210

Rhodius Safety and Environmental Solutions (Kunshan) Co., Ltd (2)
Bldg 1A 99 Mingtong Street Zhouzhuang Town, Kunshan, 215325, Jiangsu, China
Tel.: (86) 512 572 00 281
Web Site: http://www.rhodius.com
Network Cable Installation Services
N.A.I.C.S.: 238210

Sicame SA (1)
1 Avenue Basile Lachaud, 19230, Arnac-Pompadour, France (60%)
Tel.: (33) 555738956
Web Site: http://www.sicame.com
Electrical Equipment Manufacturing & Distribution
N.A.I.C.S.: 335999
Nadine Valet *(Dir-HR)*

Subsidiary (US):

ASK Products, Inc. (2)
544 N Highland Ave, Aurora, IL 60506
Tel.: (630) 896-4056
Web Site: http://www.asklug.com
Rev.: $2,000,000
Emp.: 30
Metal Stamping
N.A.I.C.S.: 332119
Steve Kase *(Pres & CEO)*

Subsidiary (Non-US):

Hydel Inc. (2)
206 Great Gulf Drive, Vaughan, L4K 5W1, ON, Canada
Tel.: (403) 258-2011
Web Site: https://www.hydelinc.com
Rev.: $23,777,401
Assets: $17,591,913
Liabilities: $7,195,411
Net Worth: $10,396,501
Earnings: $1,308,754
Emp.: 151
Fiscal Year-end: 12/31/2020
Voice & Data Telecommunications Services
N.A.I.C.S.: 517112

Subsidiary (Domestic):

Circa Metals Inc. (3)
206 Great Gulf Drive, Vaughan, L4K 5W1, ON, Canada
Tel.: (905) 669-7553
Web Site: https://www.circametals.com
Fabricated Metal Products Mfr
N.A.I.C.S.: 332312

Subsidiary (US):

Circa Telecom USA Inc (3)
6293 W Linebaugh Ave, Tampa, FL 33625
Tel.: (813) 676-2050

Sales Range: $10-24.9 Million
Emp.: 16
Provider of Voice & Data Telecommunications Services
N.A.I.C.S.: 423690
Ivan Smith *(Pres & CEO)*

TriStyle Mode GmbH (1)
Erika-Mann-Strasse 11, 80636, Munich, Germany
Tel.: (49) 89 599 7890 0
Web Site: http://www.tristylegroup.com
Emp.: 1,742
Holding Company; Women's Fashion Online & Mail-Order Retailer
N.A.I.C.S.: 551112
Daniel Gutting *(Mng Dir)*

Subsidiary (Domestic):

Madeleine Mode GmbH (2)
Im Pinderpark 7, 90513, Zirndorf, Germany
Tel.: (49) 911 2550 998 0
Web Site: http://www.madeleine.de
Sales Range: $150-199.9 Million
Emp.: 272
Women's Fashion Online & Mail-Order Retailer
N.A.I.C.S.: 458110
Alexander Weih *(CEO & Mng Dir)*

Peter Hahn GmbH (2)
Peter-Hahn-Platz 1, 73649, Winterbach, Germany
Tel.: (49) 800 7 444 555
Web Site: http://www.peterhahn.de
Sales Range: $350-399.9 Million
Emp.: 1,004
Women's Fashion Online & Mail-Order Retailer
N.A.I.C.S.: 458110
Stefan Kober *(Mng Dir)*

UNITHER Pharmaceuticals SAS (1)
41 Rue de la Chaussee d'Antin, Paris, 75009, France
Tel.: (33) 1 4463 5170
Web Site: http://www.unither-pharma.com
Sales Range: $200-249.9 Million
Pharmaceuticals Mfr
N.A.I.C.S.: 325412
Eric Goupil *(CEO)*

United Initiators GmbH & Co. KG (1)
Dr-Gustav-Adolph-Strasse 3, Pullach, DE-82049, Munich, Germany
Tel.: (49) 89 744 220
Web Site: http://www.united-initiators.com
Organic Peroxide & Persulfates Mfr & Distr
N.A.I.C.S.: 325199
Ed Hoozemans *(Mng Dir)*

Subsidiary (Non-US):

United Initiators Pty. Ltd. (2)
20-22 McPherson Street, Banksmeadow, Sydney, 2019, NSW, Australia
Tel.: (61) 293160046
Web Site: http://www.united-initiators.com
Organic Peroxide & Persulfates Mfr & Distr
N.A.I.C.S.: 325199

Subsidiary (US):

United Initiators, Inc. (2)
555 Garden St, Elyria, OH 44035
Tel.: (440) 323-3112
Web Site: http://www.united-initiators.com
Organic Peroxide & Persulfates Mfr & Distr
N.A.I.C.S.: 325199
Diana Navarro *(Mgr-Customer Svc)*

EQUITA GROUP S.P.A.
Via Filippo Turati 9, 20121, Milan, Italy
Tel.: (39) 0262041
Web Site: https://www.equita.eu
Year Founded: 2015
EQUI—(ITA)
Rev.: $1,168,022
Assets: $387,661,401
Liabilities: $265,686,069
Net Worth: $121,975,333
Earnings: $27,108,597
Emp.: 173
Fiscal Year-end: 12/31/21
Investment Banking Services
N.A.I.C.S.: 523150

Francesco Perilli *(Exec Dir)*

EQUITAL LTD.
Granite 8, PO Box 7313, Petah Tikva, 4951407, Israel
Tel.: (972) 39229225
Year Founded: 1977
EQTL—(TAE)
Rev.: $854,093,646
Assets: $6,789,280,734
Liabilities: $3,310,661,642
Net Worth: $3,478,619,092
Earnings: $227,623,701
Emp.: 409
Fiscal Year-end: 12/31/23
Offices of Other Holding Companies
N.A.I.C.S.: 551112
Eran Lendner *(CEO)*

Subsidiaries:

J.O.E.L. Jerusalem Oil Exploration Ltd. (1)
Hagranit 8 Kiriyat Ariye Ta Do'ar 10188, Petah Tiqwa, 49222, Israel
Tel.: (972) 39229225
Oil & Gas Exploration Services
N.A.I.C.S.: 213112
Eran Saar *(CEO)*

Subsidiary (Domestic):

Airport City Ltd. (2)
8 Granit St Kiryat Arie, Petach Tikva, Israel
Tel.: (972) 732333900
Web Site: http://www.nitsba.com
Rev.: $282,061,606
Assets: $5,130,731,236
Liabilities: $2,403,925,643
Net Worth: $2,726,805,594
Earnings: $70,702,306
Emp.: 122
Fiscal Year-end: 12/31/2023
Other Activities Related to Real Estate
N.A.I.C.S.: 531390
Haim Tsuff *(Chm)*

Naphtha Israel Petroleum Corporation Ltd. (2)
Granite 8, PO Box 7313, Petah Tikva, 4951407, Israel (65.08%)
Tel.: (972) 39229225
Rev.: $564,866,962
Assets: $1,581,900,514
Liabilities: $804,098,344
Net Worth: $777,802,170
Earnings: $153,780,354
Emp.: 287
Fiscal Year-end: 12/31/2023
Support Activities for Oil & Gas Operations
N.A.I.C.S.: 213112
Eran Lendner *(CEO)*

Subsidiary (US):

ISRAMCO, INC. (3)
1001 W Loop S Ste 750, Houston, TX 77027
Tel.: (713) 621-6785
Web Site: http://www.isramcousa.com
Rev.: $81,339,000
Assets: $111,614,000
Liabilities: $118,973,000
Net Worth: ($7,359,000)
Earnings: $17,934,000
Emp.: 297
Fiscal Year-end: 12/31/2018
Oil & Gas Exploration & Production Services
N.A.I.C.S.: 211120
Haim Tsuff *(Chm, Pres & Co-CEO)*

Subsidiary (Domestic):

Jay Petroleum LLC (4)
2425 W Loop S Ste 810, Houston, TX 77027
Tel.: (713) 621-5946
Sales Range: $250-299.9 Million
Oil & Gas Exploration & Production
N.A.I.C.S.: 211120

EQUITAS HOLDINGS LIMITED
410A 4th Floor Spencer Plaza Phase II No 769 Mount Road Anna Salai, Chennai, 600002, India

Equitas Holdings Limited—(Continued)

Tel.: (91) 4442995000   In
Web Site: http://www.equitas.in
Year Founded: 2007
EQUITAS—(NSE)
Rev.: $521,524,185
Assets: $3,492,105,435
Liabilities: $2,990,892,450
Net Worth: $501,212,985
Earnings: $70,132,335
Emp.: 16,629
Fiscal Year-end: 03/31/21
Financial Holding Company
N.A.I.C.S.: 551112
N. Rangachary *(Chm)*

Subsidiaries:

Equitas Small Finance Bank
Limited   (1)
4th Floor Spencer Plaza No 769 Phase II
Anna Salai, Chennai, 600 002,
India   (100%)
Tel.: (91) 444 299 5000
Web Site: https://www.equitasbank.com
Commericial Banking
N.A.I.C.S.: 522110
Vasudevan P. N. *(Founder, CEO & Mng Dir)*

**EQUITES PROPERTY FUND
LIMITED**
14th Fl Portside Tower 4 Bree St,
Cape Town, 8001, South Africa
Tel.: (27) 214600404
Web Site: https://www.equites.co.za
Year Founded: 2014
EQU—(JSE)
Rev.: $135,288,770
Assets: $1,645,953,294
Liabilities: $723,101,473
Net Worth: $922,851,821
Earnings: $82,922,702
Emp.: 40
Fiscal Year-end: 02/29/24
Investment Management Service
N.A.I.C.S.: 525990
Andrea Taverna-Turisan *(CEO)*

**EQUITIX INVESTMENT MAN-
AGEMENT LIMITED**
Welken House 10-11 Charterhouse
Square, London, EC1M 6EH, United
Kingdom
Tel.: (44) 2072507333
Web Site: http://www.equitix.co.uk
Building Infrastructure Bidding & Proj-
ect Development Services
N.A.I.C.S.: 238390
Geoff Jackson *(CEO)*

EQUITY BANK LIMITED
Equity Centre Hospital Road Upper
Hill, PO Box 75104-00200, Nairobi,
Kenya
Tel.: (254) 763063000
Web Site:
   http://www.equitybank.co.ke
Rev.: $627,123,905
Assets: $4,105,119,509
Liabilities: $3,413,331,289
Net Worth: $691,788,220
Earnings: $165,939,970
Fiscal Year-end: 12/31/15
Personal Banking Services
N.A.I.C.S.: 522291
Gerald Warui *(Mng Dir)*

Subsidiaries:

Equity Investment services Ltd   (1)
7575 Doctor Philips Blvd Ste 390, Orlando,
FL 32819
Tel.: (407) 573-0711
Web Site:
   http://www.equityinvestmentservices.com
Emp.: 8
Investment Banking Services
N.A.I.C.S.: 523999
Christopher M. Savino *(Mng Dir)*

**EQUITY GROUP HOLDINGS
PLC**
Upper Hill Hospital Road, PO Box
75104, Equity Centre 9th floor, Nai-
robi, 00200, Kenya
Tel.: (254) 763026000
Web Site:
   http://www.equitybankgroup.com
Year Founded: 1984
Commercial Banking Services
N.A.I.C.S.: 522110
James Mwangi *(Grp Mng Dir & CEO)*

**EQUITY METALS CORPORA-
TION**
1100-1199 West Hastings Street,
Vancouver, V6E 3T5, BC, Canada
Tel.: (604) 806-0626   BC
Web Site:
   https://www.equitymetalscorp.com
Year Founded: 1964
EQTY—(OTCQB)
Rev.: $223
Assets: $1,698,929
Liabilities: $76,717
Net Worth: $1,622,212
Earnings: ($3,291,462)
Fiscal Year-end: 08/31/21
Mineral Exploration Services
N.A.I.C.S.: 213114
Robert W. J. MacDonald *(VP-
Exploration)*

EQUITY STORY GROUP LTD.
44 North Fort Road The Barracks
Precinct, Manly, 2095, NSW, Austra-
lia
Tel.: (61) 299079652   AU
Web Site:
   https://www.equitystory.com.au
Year Founded: 2007
EQS—(ASX)
Rev.: $736,529
Assets: $1,663,179
Liabilities: $1,032,706
Net Worth: $630,473
Earnings: ($1,673,035)
Fiscal Year-end: 06/30/23
Investment Management Service
N.A.I.C.S.: 523999
David Tildesley *(Founder, Chm, CEO
& Exec Dir)*

Subsidiaries:

Equity Story Pty Ltd.   (1)
501/70 Castlereagh Street, Sydney, 2000,
NSW, Australia
Tel.: (61) 299079652
Web Site: https://equitystory.com.au
Education & Fund Management Services
N.A.I.C.S.: 525110

EQUITY TRUSTEES LIMITED
Level 1 575 Bourke St, Melbourne,
3000, VIC, Australia
Tel.: (61) 1300133472   AU
Web Site: https://www.eqt.com.au
Year Founded: 1888
Rev.: $69,039,023
Assets: $243,512,100
Liabilities: $45,381,591
Net Worth: $198,130,508
Earnings: $15,167,262
Emp.: 241
Fiscal Year-end: 06/30/18
Trustee & Executor Services
N.A.I.C.S.: 523991
Ian Westley *(Exec Gen Mgr-Trustee
& Wealth Svcs Private Clients Bus)*

EQUUS MINING LIMITED
Level 2 66 Hunter Street, Sydney,
2000, NSW, Australia
Tel.: (61) 293003366
Web Site:
   https://www.equusmining.com

EQE—(ASX)
Rev.: $11,969,956
Assets: $29,018,281
Liabilities: $13,355,967
Net Worth: $15,662,314
Earnings: ($3,052,689)
Emp.: 10
Fiscal Year-end: 06/30/22
Copper, Nickel, Lead & Zinc Mining
N.A.I.C.S.: 212230
Marcelo Mora *(Sec)*

EQVA ASA
Ilandelandsvegen 75, 5451, Fus-
navag, Norway
Tel.: (47) 70084550   NO
Web Site: https://www.eqva.no
EQVA—(OSL)
Rev.: $42,397,377
Assets: $65,801,404
Liabilities: $36,969,333
Net Worth: $28,832,071
Earnings: ($1,814,798)
Emp.: 410
Fiscal Year-end: 12/31/22
Holding Company; Ship Design, Engi-
neering & Building Services
N.A.I.C.S.: 551112
Gisle Vinjevoll Thrane *(VP-Sls)*

EQVITEC PARTNERS OY
PO Box 65, 00131, Helsinki, Finland
Tel.: (358) 50 66563
Web Site: http://www.eqvitec.com
Privater Equity Firm
N.A.I.C.S.: 523999
Jukka Makinen *(Mng Dir)*

ER&GE GMBH
Halberstadter Strasse 75, 33106,
Paderborn, Germany
Tel.: (49) 525117560
Web Site: http://www.ergeplas.de
Year Founded: 1982
Rev.: $14,843,516
Emp.: 29
Electrical Equipment Manufacturing
N.A.I.C.S.: 326199
Christian Raatz *(CEO)*

Subsidiaries:

ER&GE (UK) Limited   (1)
Unit 8 Gelderd Trading Estate West Vale,
Leeds, LS12 6BD, United Kingdom
Tel.: (44) 1132427341
Web Site: http://www.erge.co.uk
Polyethylene Sheet Distr
N.A.I.C.S.: 424610

ERA CO., LTD.
No 1118 Huangjiao Road, Huangyan,
Taizhou, 318020, Zhejiang, China
Tel.: (86) 57684279933
Web Site: https://www.yonggao.com
Year Founded: 1993
002641—(SSE)
Rev.: $1,120,184,208
Assets: $1,182,051,468
Liabilities: $467,588,160
Net Worth: $714,463,308
Earnings: $11,424,348
Emp.: 7,000
Fiscal Year-end: 12/31/22
Plastic Piping Mfr
N.A.I.C.S.: 326122
Zhou Xianpeng *(Chm)*

ERA D.O.O.
Presernova 10, 3320, Velenje, Slove-
nia
Tel.: (386) 3 62 03100
Web Site: http://www.era.si
Year Founded: 1951
Sales Range: $350-399.9 Million
Emp.: 100
Food Procurement Agency Whslr
N.A.I.C.S.: 455211

Gvido Omladic *(CEO)*

Subsidiaries:

Eko Energetika DOO   (1)
Belasica 2, PO Box 356, 1000, Skopje,
North Macedonia
Tel.: (389) 2 3218 388
Electric Power Generation & Distribution
Services
N.A.I.C.S.: 221114

ERA RESOURCES INC.
1st Floor Landmark Square 64 Earth
Close Grand Cayman, PO Box 715,
Georgetown, KY1-1107, Cayman
Islands
Tel.: (345) 7694423   AU
Web Site:
   http://www.eraresources.com
Year Founded: 2012
Sales Range: Less than $1 Million
Copper Mining Services
N.A.I.C.S.: 212230
Irena Al-Shameri *(Controller-Fin)*

ERAAYA LIFESPACES LIMITED
B-1 34/1 Vikas House Vikas Path
Marg East Punjabi Bagh, Janakpuri,
New Delhi, 110026, India
Tel.: (91) 7065084854   In
Web Site: https://www.eraayalife.com
Year Founded: 1967
531035—(BOM)
Rev.: $29,195
Assets: $25,970
Liabilities: $103,423
Net Worth: ($77,453)
Earnings: $9,196
Fiscal Year-end: 03/31/23
Bicycle Mfr
N.A.I.C.S.: 336991
Harish Agarwal *(CFO)*

ERAMET SA
10 Boulevard de Grenelle CS 63205,
FR-75015, Paris, France
Tel.: (33) 145384242
Web Site: https://www.eramet.com
ER7—(DEU)
Rev.: $3,588,696,325
Assets: $6,927,916,990
Liabilities: $4,726,791,037
Net Worth: $2,201,125,952
Earnings: $13,246,495
Emp.: 10,700
Fiscal Year-end: 12/31/23
Nonferrous Metals & Chemical De-
rivatives Producer
N.A.I.C.S.: 331491
Christel Bories *(Chm & CEO)*

Subsidiaries:

Brown Europe SAS   (1)
Zone artisanale, Laval-de-Cere, 46130,
Figeac, France
Tel.: (33) 56 533 8484
Web Site: https://www.brown-europe.com
Alloy Steel Mfr
N.A.I.C.S.: 331110

Comilog SA   (1)
Zone Industrielle de Moanda, BP 27/28,
Moanda, Port-Gentil, Gabon
Tel.: (241) 11664015
Web Site: https://comilog.eramet.com
Metallurgical Product Mfr
N.A.I.C.S.: 332117

Eramet Alloys   (1)
Tour Maine Montparnesse, 33 Avenue du
Maine, Paris, Cedex 15, France
Tel.: (33) 145386300
Web Site: http://www.eramet.fr
Sales Range: $50-74.9 Million
Emp.: 100
Steel Products Mfr
N.A.I.C.S.: 332111
Georges Duval *(CEO)*

Subsidiary (Domestic):

Aubert & Duval **(2)**
Tour Maine Montparnasse, 33 avenue du
Maine, Paris, Cedex 15, France
Tel.: (33) 145383888
Web Site: http://www.aubertduval.fr
Sales Range: $25-49.9 Million
Emp.: 30
Steel Alloy Products Mfr
N.A.I.C.S.: 332111

Plant (Domestic):

**Aubert & Duval SAS - Firminy
Plant** **(3)**
Rue du Colonel Riez, BP 141, 42704,
Firminy, Cedex, France
Tel.: (33) 47 740 3606
Web Site: https://www.aubertduval.com
Fabricated Steel Product Mfr
N.A.I.C.S.: 331110

**Aubert & Duval SAS - Gennevilliers
Plant** **(3)**
22 rue Henri Vuillemin, BP 63, 92233,
Gennevilliers, Hauts-de-Seine, France
Tel.: (33) 1 55 02 58 00
Fabricated Steel Product Mfr
N.A.I.C.S.: 331110

**Aubert & Duval SAS - Imphy
Plant** **(3)**
Avenue Jean Jaures, BP 02, 58160, Imphy,
Nievre, France
Tel.: (33) 3 86 90 74 00
Fabricated Steel Product Mfr
N.A.I.C.S.: 331110

**Aubert & Duval SAS - Issoire Inter-
forge Plant** **(3)**
ZA de la Maze, BP 75, 63501, Issoire, Ce-
dex, France
Tel.: (33) 47 389 0783
Web Site: http://www.aubertduval.fr
Fabricated Steel Product Mfr
N.A.I.C.S.: 331110

**Aubert & Duval SAS - Les Ancizes
Plant** **(3)**
BP 1, 63770, Les Ancizes-Comps, Puy-de-
Dome, France
Tel.: (33) 4 73 67 30 00
Fabricated Steel Product Mfr
N.A.I.C.S.: 331110

**Aubert & Duval SAS - Pamiers
Plant** **(3)**
75 boulevard de la Liberation, BP 173,
09102, Pamiers, Ariege, France
Tel.: (33) 5 61 68 44 00
Metal Stamping Mfr
N.A.I.C.S.: 332119

Eramet Manganese **(1)**
Tour Maine-Montparnasse, 33 Avenue du
Maine, 75755, Paris, Cedex,
France **(100%)**
Tel.: (33) 153912400
Web Site: http://www.erachem-comilog.com
Sales Range: $1-4.9 Billion
Emp.: 6,800
Manganese Chemicals Production & Sup-
plier; Copper Recycling
N.A.I.C.S.: 325998

Eramet Marietta Inc. **(1)**
16705 OH-7, Marietta, OH 45750
Tel.: (740) 374-1000
Web Site: https://marietta.eramet.com
Mineral Mining Services
N.A.I.C.S.: 213114

Eramet Nickel **(1)**
Tour Maine Montparnasse, 33 Avenue du
Maine, 75755, Paris, Cedex 15, France
Tel.: (33) 145384200
Web Site: http://www.eramet.com
Sales Range: $100-124.9 Million
Emp.: 200
Nickel Production
N.A.I.C.S.: 212230

Eramet Norway A/S **(1)**
Rolighetsv 11, 3933, Porsgrunn, Norway
Tel.: (47) 35561800
Web Site: https://www.eramet.no
Emp.: 530
Metal Alloy Mfr
N.A.I.C.S.: 331110

Erasteel Inc. **(1)**
95 Fulton St, Boonton, NJ 07005-1909
Tel.: (973) 335-8400
Steel Product Distr
N.A.I.C.S.: 423510

**Gulf Chemical & Metallurgical
Corporation**
302 Midway Road, Freeport, TX 77542-
2290
Tel.: (979) 415-1500
Spent Ptroleum Catalysts Recycling & Fer-
roalloys Mfr
N.A.I.C.S.: 331110

Minoral Doposite Limited **(1)**
Level 17 530 Collins Street, Melbourne,
3000, VIC, Australia
Tel.: (61) 396182500
Web Site:
    http://www.mineraldeposits.com.au
Rev.: $6,584,000
Assets: $261,447,000
Liabilities: $1,719,000
Net Worth: $259,728,000
Earnings: ($20,612,000)
Emp.: 715
Fiscal Year-end: 12/31/2017
Mineral Sand Exploration Services
N.A.I.C.S.: 212319

PT Weda Bay Nickel **(1)**
Wisma Pondok Indah 2 11th Floor Suites
1101 JI Sultan Iskandar Muda, Kav V-TA
Pondok Indah, Jakarta, 12310, Indonesia
Tel.: (62) 2175922802
Web Site: http://www.wedabay.co.id
Emp.: 50
Nickel Ore Mine Site Development Services
N.A.I.C.S.: 212230

Societe Le Nickel **(1)**
2 rue Desjardins-Doniambo, BP E5- 9 48,
Noumea, New Caledonia
Tel.: (687) 245555
Web Site: http://www.sln.nc
Mineral Mining Services
N.A.I.C.S.: 213114

TiZir Ltd. **(1)**
Nova South 9th Floor 160 Victoria Street,
London, SW1E 5LB, United Kingdom
Tel.: (44) 2039071155
Web Site: https://www.tizir.co.uk
Mineral Mining Services
N.A.I.C.S.: 213114
Kleber Silva *(Chm)*

TiZir Titanium & Iron A/S **(1)**
Naustbakken 1, Tyssedal, 5770, Vestby,
Norway
Tel.: (47) 53652500
Mineral Mining Services
N.A.I.C.S.: 213114

ERATAT LIFESTYLE LIMITED
Liupu Industrial Park Yangdai Chen-
dai Town, Jingjiang, 362218, Fujian,
China
Tel.: (86) 595 85086888
Web Site:
    http://www.eratatgroup.com
FO8—(SES)
Sales Range: $150-199.9 Million
Sports Footwear & Apparel Designer,
Mfr & Distr
N.A.I.C.S.: 316210
Jiancheng Lin *(Chm & CEO)*

ERAYAK POWER SOLUTION
GROUP INC.
No 528 4th Avenue Binhai Industrial
Park, Wenzhou, 325025, Zhejiang,
China
Tel.: (86) 57786829999   Ky
Web Site: https://erayakpower.com
Year Founded: 2019
RAYA—(NASDAQ)
Rev.: $20,322,498
Assets: $35,285,266
Liabilities: $15,083,179
Net Worth: $20,202,087
Earnings: $1,218,714
Emp.: 290
Fiscal Year-end: 12/31/23

Holding Company
N.A.I.C.S.: 551112
Lingyi Kong *(CEO & Chm)*

ERBACON INVESTMENT
HOLDINGS LIMITED
Block 3 Unit 6 The Willows Office
Park 276, George Road Erand Gar-
dens Midrand, Durban, KwaZulu-
Natal, South Africa
Tel.: (27) 11 206 9660
Commercial & Industrial Building
Construction Services
N.A.I.C.S.: 236220
Andrew N. Langham *(Interim CEO)*

ERBOSAN ERCIYAS BORU
SANAYII VE TICARET A.S.
895 Sokak No 9, Anbar Mahallesi,
Kayseri, Turkiye
Tel.: (90) 3523113511   TR
Web Site: https://www.erbosan.com.tr
Year Founded: 1974
ERBOS—(IST)
Rev.: $131,067,872,329
Assets: $85,582,447,811
Liabilities: $32,669,963,218
Net Worth: $52,912,484,593
Earnings: $23,533,515,636
Emp.: 303
Fiscal Year-end: 12/31/22
Steel Pole Mfr
N.A.I.C.S.: 331210
Mahmut Ozbiyik *(Chm)*

ERBUD S.A.
ul Franciszka Klimczaka 1, 02-797,
Warsaw, Poland
Tel.: (48) 225487000   PL
Web Site: https://www.erbud.pl
Year Founded: 1990
ERB—(WAR)
Rev.: $821,738,565
Assets: $501,481,960
Liabilities: $330,001,778
Net Worth: $171,480,182
Earnings: $5,918,445
Emp.: 1,600
Fiscal Year-end: 12/31/23
Commercial & Institutional Building
Construction
N.A.I.C.S.: 236220
Jozef Adam Zubelewicz *(Member-
Mgmt Bd)*

Subsidiaries:

GWI Bauunternehmung GmbH **(1)**
Schiessstrasse 55, 40549, Dusseldorf,
Germany **(85%)**
Tel.: (49) 21195599850
Web Site: http://www.gwi-bau.de
Residential, Office & Industrial Building
Construction Services
N.A.I.C.S.: 236220
Axel A. Wahl *(Mng Dir)*

MOD21 GmbH **(1)**
Hansaallee 247b, 40549, Dusseldorf, Ger-
many
Tel.: (49) 2119559980
Web Site: https://www.mod21.com
Emp.: 3,000
Real Estate Building Construction Services
N.A.I.C.S.: 541330

Onde S.A. **(1)**
ul Wapienna 40, 87-100, Torun,
Poland **(94.27%)**
Tel.: (48) 566122510
Web Site: https://onde.pl
Road Construction, Energy & Engineering
Services
N.A.I.C.S.: 237310

ERCO INTERIEURBOUW B.V.
JF Kennedylaan 51, PO Box 175,
5550 AD, Valkenswaard, Netherlands
Tel.: (31) 402084222
Web Site: http://www.erco-ib.nl
Sales Range: $10-24.9 Million

Office Furnishings Designer & Mfr
N.A.I.C.S.: 337214

ERCROS SA
Avda Diagonal, 08014, Barcelona,
Spain
Tel.: (34) 934393009
Web Site: https://www.ercros.es
Year Founded: 1989
ECR—(MAD)
Rev.: $836,324,098
Assets: $754,294,072
Liabilities: $353,460,647
Net Worth: $400,833,425
Earnings: $31,789,381
Emp.: 1,313
Fiscal Year-end: 12/31/23
Chemicals, Plastics & Pharmaceuti-
cals Mfr
N.A.I.C.S.: 325998
Eduardo Gual de Diego *(Dir-Sys)*

Subsidiaries:

**Ercros SA - Animal Feed
Division** **(1)**
Avda Diagonal 595, 08014, Barcelona,
Spain
Tel.: (34) 934393009
Animal Feed Mfr
N.A.I.C.S.: 311119

Plant (Domestic):

**Ercros SA - Animal Feed Division -
Cartagena Factory** **(2)**
C Los Parales S N Valle de Escombreras,
30350, Cartagena, Murcia, Spain
Tel.: (34) 968 333 400
Web Site: http://www.ercros.es
Animal Feed Mfr
N.A.I.C.S.: 311119

**Ercros SA - Animal Feed Division -
Flix Factory** **(2)**
Calle Afores S N, 43750, Flix, Tarragona,
Spain
Tel.: (34) 93 439 3009
Web Site: http://www.ercros.es
Sales Range: $50-74.9 Million
Emp.: 245
Phosphates Mfr
N.A.I.C.S.: 325180

**Ercros SA - Basic Chemicals
Division** **(1)**
Avda Diagonal 595, 08014, Barcelona,
Spain
Tel.: (34) 934393009
Sales Range: $25-49.9 Million
Emp.: 100
Basic Chemicals Mfr
N.A.I.C.S.: 325411
Jose Luismuniz *(Gen Mgr)*

Plant (Domestic):

**Ercros SA - Basic Chemicals Division
- Flix Factory** **(2)**
C Afores S N, 43750, Flix, Tarragona, Spain
Tel.: (34) 977 410 125
Web Site: http://www.ercros.es
Chlorine Compounds Mfr
N.A.I.C.S.: 325180
Francisco Garcia Bru *(Reg Dir)*

**Ercros SA - Basic Chemicals Division
- Sabinanigo Factory** **(2)**
C/ Serrablo 102, 22600, Sabinanigo, Hu-
esca, Spain
Tel.: (34) 974498000
Web Site: http://www.ercros.es
Chlorine Derivatives Mfr
N.A.I.C.S.: 325180
Luis Gallego *(Dir)*

**Ercros SA - Basic Chemicals Division
- Tarragona Factory** **(2)**
Apartado de Correos 450, 43080, Tarra-
gona, Spain
Tel.: (34) 977548011
Web Site: http://www.ercros.es
Chemicals Mfr
N.A.I.C.S.: 325199
Agustin Franco Blasco *(Dir & Gen Mgr)*

Ercros SA—(Continued)

Ercros SA - Basic Chemicals Division - Vila-seca I Factory (2)
Tarragona-Salou C-31 B Km 6, 43480, Vila-seca, Tarragona, Spain
Tel.: (34) 977370354
Web Site: http://www.ercros.es
Chemicals Mfr
N.A.I.C.S.: 325199

Ercros SA - Intermediate Chemicals Division (1)
Avda Diagonal 595, 8014, Barcelona, Spain
Tel.: (34) 934 393 009
Web Site: http://www.ercros.es
Formaldehyde & Derivatives Mfr
N.A.I.C.S.: 325199
Cerda Ignacio (Product Mgr)

Plant (Domestic):

Ercros SA - Intermediate Chemicals Division - Cerdanyola Factory (2)
C Santa Anna 105, 08290, Cerdanyola del Valles, Barcelona, Spain
Tel.: (34) 935803353
Web Site: http://www.ercros.com
Sales Range: $25-49.9 Million
Emp.: 90
Chemicals & Resins Mfr
N.A.I.C.S.: 325211
Angel Punzano (Mng Dir)

Ercros SA - Intermediate Chemicals Division - Tortosa Factory (2)
Poligon Industrial Baix Ebre carrer A, 43897, Tortosa, Tarragona, Spain
Tel.: (34) 977454022
Web Site: http://www.ercros.es
Sales Range: $50-74.9 Million
Emp.: 110
Organic Compounds Mfr
N.A.I.C.S.: 325199
Santiago Rodriguez (Gen Mgr)

Ercros SA - Pharmaceutical Division-Fyse (1)
Paseo del Deleite S N, 28300, Aranjuez, Madrid, Spain
Tel.: (34) 918 090 344
Web Site: http://www.ercros.es
Sales Range: $75-99.9 Million
Emp.: 200
Generic Pharmaceutical Products Mfr & Distr
N.A.I.C.S.: 325412
Antonio Zabalza (Mgr)

Ercros SA - Plastics Division (1)
Avda Diagonal 595, 8014, Barcelona, Spain
Tel.: (34) 933230554
Web Site: http://www.ercros.es
Plastic Mfr
N.A.I.C.S.: 326199
Jose Miguel Falcon (Gen Mgr)

Ercros SA - Water Treatment Division (1)
Avda Diagonal 595, 08014, Barcelona, Spain
Tel.: (34) 934532179
Web Site: http://www.ercros.es
Sales Range: $25-49.9 Million
Emp.: 30
Swimming Pool Chemicals Mfr
N.A.I.C.S.: 325998
Natalia Torrents (Mgr-Sls)

Plant (Domestic):

Ercros SA - Water Treatment Division - Sabinanigo Factory (2)
C Serrablo 102, Sabinanigo, 22600, Huesca, Spain
Tel.: (34) 974498000
Web Site: http://www.ercros.es
Emp.: 200
Swimming Pool Chemicals Mfr
N.A.I.C.S.: 325998
Luis Galleo (Mgr)

ERDENE RESOURCE DEVELOPMENT CORP.
Metropolitan Place 99 Wyse Road Suite 1480, Dartmouth, B3A 4S5, NS, Canada
Tel.: (902) 423-6419   Ca

Web Site: https://www.erdene.com
Year Founded: 2002
ERD—(TSX)
Rev.: $49,173
Assets: $33,492,403
Liabilities: $544,395
Net Worth: $32,948,008
Earnings: ($10,260,665)
Emp.: 23
Fiscal Year-end: 12/31/20
Metal Mining & Exploration Services
N.A.I.C.S.: 212290
D. Suzan Frazer (Sec)

Subsidiaries:

Erdene Mongol LLC (1)
Monrud LLC Building 2nd Floor United Nations Street 6/6, Chingeltei District, Ulaanbaatar, Mongolia
Tel.: (976) 11318532
Web Site: http://www.erdene.com
Metal Exploration Services
N.A.I.C.S.: 213114
Michael Gillis (VP-Ops)

ERDENET MINING CORPORATION
Amarlin Square 1, Erdenet, 213900, Mongolia
Tel.: (976) 135273501   Mn
Web Site: http://www.erdenetmc.mn
Year Founded: 1978
Sales Range: $1-4.9 Billion
Emp.: 5,900
Copper & Molybdenum Ore Mining & Processing
N.A.I.C.S.: 212290
Tserevsamba Davaatseren (Dir Gen)

ERECTION ELECTROMECHANICS TESTING JSC
434-436 Nguyen Trai Trung Van Tu Liem, Tu Lien District, Hanoi, Vietnam
Tel.: (84) 435543839
Web Site: https://www.emetc.com.vn
LCD—(HNX)
Rev.: $3,811,800
Assets: $13,161,500
Liabilities: $10,062,000
Net Worth: $3,099,500
Earnings: $12,700
Fiscal Year-end: 12/31/22
Electrical Testing Services
N.A.I.C.S.: 334515
Le Van Dinh (Gen Mgr)

EREGLI DEMIR VE CELIK FABRIKALARI T.A.S.
Uzunkum Caddesi No 7 Karadeniz, 67330, Eregli, 67330, Zonguldak, Turkiye
Tel.: (90) 3723232500
Web Site: https://www.erdemir.com.tr
Year Founded: 1960
EREGL—(IST)
Rev.: $9,249,589,160
Assets: $17,141,782,204
Liabilities: $5,679,663,530
Net Worth: $11,462,118,674
Earnings: $2,105,006,507
Emp.: 11,428
Fiscal Year-end: 12/31/21
Steel Producer
N.A.I.C.S.: 332111
Suleyman Savas Erdem (Chm)

Subsidiaries:

Celbor Celik Cekme Boru Sanayi Ve Ticaret A.S. (1)
Kayseri yolu 7 km PK 21, 71300, Kirikkale, Turkiye
Tel.: (90) 3182254696
Web Site: http://www.celbor.com.tr
Sales Range: $25-49.9 Million
Emp.: 100
Iron & Steel Pipe & Tube Mfr from Purchased Steel
N.A.I.C.S.: 331210

Erdemir Lojistik A.S. (1)
19 Mayis Mah Ataturk Cad Sitki Bey Plaza No 82 K 8, Kozyatagi-Kadikoy, Istanbul, Turkiye
Tel.: (90) 2164688090
Web Site: http://www.erdemirlojistik.com.tr
Sales Range: $25-49.9 Million
Emp.: 20
Activities for Transportation
N.A.I.C.S.: 488999

Erdemir Madencilik Sanayi Ve Ticaret A.S. (1)
Curek Yolu 5 Km, 58330, Divrigi, Sivas, Turkiye
Web Site: http://www.erdemirmaden.com.tr
Sales Range: $100-124.9 Million
Emp.: 300
Iron & Steel Mills
N.A.I.C.S.: 331110

Erdemir Muhendislik Yonetim Ve Danismanlik Hizmetleri A.S. (1)
Barboros Mah Ardig Sok No 6 Bati, Kucukbakkalkoy, 34750, Istanbul, Atasehir, Turkiye
Tel.: (90) 2165788000
Web Site: http://www.erenco.com
Sales Range: $25-49.9 Million
Emp.: 200
Engineering Services
N.A.I.C.S.: 541330

Erdemir Romania S.R.L. (1)
18 Soseaua Gaesti, Dimbovita, Targoviste, 130087, Romania
Tel.: (40) 245607100
Web Site: http://www.erdemir.ro
Sales Range: $100-124.9 Million
Emp.: 300
Iron & Steel Mills
N.A.I.C.S.: 331110
Ion Georgescu (Dir-Ops)

Iskenderun Demir Ve Celik A.S. (1)
Karsi Mahalle sehit Yuzbasi Ali Oguz Bulvari No 1, Payas, 31900, Iskenderun, Hatay, Turkiye
Tel.: (90) 3267584040
Web Site: https://www.isdemir.com.tr
Sales Range: $1-4.9 Billion
Emp.: 6,037
Steel Foundries
N.A.I.C.S.: 331513
Suleyman Savas Erdem (Chm)

Kumas Manyezit Sanayi A.S. (1)
Eskisehir Karayolu 9 Km Merkez, 43001, Kutahya, Turkiye
Tel.: (90) 2742250050
Web Site: https://www.kumasref.com
Building Material Mfr & Distr
N.A.I.C.S.: 327120

EREGLI TEKSTIL TURIZM SANAYI VE TICARET A.S.
Yenidogan Mahallesi Kizilay Sokak No 39 Zemin Kat-A, Bayrampasa, 34149, Istanbul, Turkiye
Tel.: (90) 2124681975
ERGLI—(IST)
Rev.: $115,325,059
Assets: $118,905,500
Liabilities: $66,727,372
Net Worth: $52,178,128
Earnings: $5,233,618
Fiscal Year-end: 12/31/22
Textile Products Mfr
N.A.I.C.S.: 314999
Fahri Aydin (Mgr-Factory)

EREN GROUPE SA
4 rue Willy Goergen, 1636, Luxembourg, Luxembourg
Tel.: (352) 285624200
Web Site: http://www.eren-groupe.lu
Holding Company
N.A.I.C.S.: 551112
Paris Mouratoglou (Founder & Chm-Supervisory Bd)

Subsidiaries:

Orege SA (1)
Parc Val Saint Quentin 2 Rue Rene

Caudron, 78960, Voisins-le-Bretonneux, France   (55.46%)
Tel.: (33) 139466432
Web Site: https://www.orege.com
Sales Range: $1-9.9 Million
Emp.: 30
Waste Treatment Services
N.A.I.C.S.: 221310
George Gonsalves (CFO)

Division (Domestic):

Orege SA - Scientific Division (2)
645 Rue Mayor de Montricher TechIndus Batiment C, Zone d Activite Aix les Milles, 13854, Aix-en-Provence, France
Tel.: (33) 442262816
Sales Range: $75-99.9 Million
Emp.: 18
Water Treatment Solutions
N.A.I.C.S.: 221310

EREX CO., LTD.
Kyobashi Edogrand 14th Floor 2-2-1 Kyobashi, Chuo-ku, Tokyo, 104-0031, Japan
Tel.: (81) 332431118
Web Site: https://www.erex.co.jp
9517—(TKS)
Rev.: $1,619,297,970
Assets: $959,639,800
Liabilities: $594,549,670
Net Worth: $365,090,130
Earnings: ($147,118,770)
Emp.: 269
Fiscal Year-end: 03/31/24
Electric Power Distr & Retailer
N.A.I.C.S.: 221122
Hitoshi Honna (Pres)

Subsidiaries:

T'dash G.K. (1)
14F Kyobashi Edogrand 2-2-1 Kyobashi, Chuo-ku, Tokyo, 104-0031, Japan
Tel.: (81) 120227297
Web Site: https://t-dash-erex.co.jp
Energy Retail Services
N.A.I.C.S.: 221118

ERG CAP 3 REIT
bul Brussels No 1, 1592, Sofia, Bulgaria
Tel.: (359) 882548324
Web Site: https://www.ergcapital-3.bg
5ER—(BUL)
Assets: $10,644,262
Liabilities: $2,285,167
Net Worth: $8,359,095
Earnings: ($1,403,966)
Fiscal Year-end: 12/31/19
Real Estate Investment Services
N.A.I.C.S.: 531190
Anna Tsankova-Boneva (Exec Dir)

ERG EXPLORATION JSC
47 Gornyakov St, Rudny, 111500, Kostanai region, Kazakhstan
Tel.: (7) 7143175578
SKLK—(KAZ)
Assets: $7,092,085,140
Liabilities: $4,129,526,340
Net Worth: $2,962,558,800
Earnings: ($313,252,200)
Fiscal Year-end: 12/31/19
Mineral Exploration Services
N.A.I.C.S.: 213115

ERG S.A.
Chemiczna 6, 42-520, Dabrowa Gornicza, Poland
Tel.: (48) 322640281
Web Site: https://www.erg.com.pl
Year Founded: 1896
ERG—(WAR)
Rev.: $23,951,219
Assets: $18,891,260
Liabilities: $8,369,919
Net Worth: $10,521,341
Earnings: $812,754
Emp.: 170

Fiscal Year-end: 12/31/23
Plastic Product Mfr & Distr
N.A.I.C.S.: 326199
Anna Koczur-Purgal *(Chm-Supervisory Bd)*

ERG S.P.A.

WTC Tower - Via De Marini, 16149, Genoa, Italy
Tel.: (39) 01024011   IT
Web Site: https://www.erg.eu
Year Founded: 1938
ERG—(ITA)
Rev.: $770,386,359
Assets: $5,640,389,596
Liabilities: $3,422,947,334
Net Worth: $2,217,442,262
Earnings: $413,444,852
Emp.: 573
Fiscal Year-end: 12/31/22
Renewable Sources of Energy Production, Management & Services
N.A.I.C.S.: 551112
Alessandro Garrone *(Deputy Chm)*

Subsidiaries:

ERG Developpement France S.a.s.   **(1)**
16 Boulevard Montmartre, 75009, Paris, France
Tel.: (33) 80877432
Web Site: https://www.ergfrance.fr
Eletric Power Generation Services
N.A.I.C.S.: 221118

ERG Renew S.p.A.   **(1)**
Torre WTC Via de Marini 1, 16149, Genoa, Italy   **(93%)**
Tel.: (39) 01024011
Web Site: http://www.ergrenew.it
Sales Range: $450-499.9 Million
Emp.: 203
Waste Disposal & Renewable Energy Services
N.A.I.C.S.: 562998

Subsidiary (Domestic):

ERG Eolica Italia Srl   **(2)**
Torre WTC via De Marini, 16149, Genoa, Italy
Tel.: (39) 01024011
Emp.: 100
Electric Power Generating Wind Turbines Operator
N.A.I.C.S.: 221115
Alessandro Garrone *(Gen Mgr)*

Eolo Srl   **(2)**
Via Broile 545, Atina, 03042, Frosinone, Frosinone, Italy   **(51%)**
Tel.: (39) 0776610413
Land Subdivision
N.A.I.C.S.: 237210

Subsidiary (Non-US):

Fim Inox Sas   **(2)**
3 Rue des Freres Montgolfier, 95500, Gonesse, France
Tel.: (33) 134452323
Web Site: http://www.fim-inox.com
Sales Range: $25-49.9 Million
Emp.: 12
Seal Products Distr
N.A.I.C.S.: 423510

Subsidiary (Domestic):

Sodai Italia SpA   **(2)**
Via Raimondo Montecuccoli 32, 20147, Milan, Italy   **(51%)**
Tel.: (39) 02475464
Web Site: http://www.sodai.com
Sales Range: $25-49.9 Million
Emp.: 10
Other Heavy & Civil Engineering Construction
N.A.I.C.S.: 237990

Subsidiary (Non-US):

Sorepla Srl   **(2)**
BP 89 - Chemin de Grety - Rebeuville, Neufchateau, 88300, Nancy, France
Tel.: (33) 329061180

Web Site: http://www.sorepla.com
Sales Range: $25-49.9 Million
Emp.: 70
All Other Plastics Product Mfr
N.A.I.C.S.: 326199

TAD Inox Service BV   **(2)**
Sourethweg 5, 6422 PC, Heerlen, Netherlands
Tel.: (31) 455436161
Web Site: http://www.tadinox.nl
Sales Range: $25-49.9 Million
Emp.: 100
Metal Service Centers & Offices
N.A.I.C.S.: 423510

Subsidiary (Non-US):

TAD Inox Service GmbH   **(3)**
Ewald-Renz-Str 1, 76669, Bad Schonborn, Germany
Tel.: (49) 725380200
Web Site: http://www.tadinox.de
Sales Range: $25-49.9 Million
Emp.: 30
Metal Service Centers & Offices
N.A.I.C.S.: 423510

Subsidiary (US):

TCT Stainless Steel Inc   **(2)**
6300 19 Mile Rd, Sterling Heights, MI 48314
Tel.: (586) 254-5333
Web Site: http://www.tctstainless.com
Metal Service Centers & Offices
N.A.I.C.S.: 423510
Andrea Mazzarini *(Gen Mgr)*

Subsidiary (Domestic):

TCT Stainless Steel of Nashville Inc   **(3)**
711 Maddox Simpson Pkwy, Lebanon, TN 37090
Tel.: (615) 443-4657
Web Site: http://www.tctstainless.com
Sales Range: $25-49.9 Million
Emp.: 20
Metal Service Centers & Offices
N.A.I.C.S.: 423510

ERG Wind 6 S.r.l.   **(1)**
via Leonida Bissolati 76, 00187, Rome, Italy
Tel.: (39) 06845571
Wind Energy Services
N.A.I.C.S.: 221115

ERG Wind Sicilia 3 S.r.l.   **(1)**
Torre WTC via De Marini 1, 16149, Genoa, Italy
Tel.: (39) 01024011
Wind Energy Services
N.A.I.C.S.: 221115

Epuron S.a.s.   **(1)**
16 Boulevard Montmartre, 75009, Paris, France
Tel.: (33) 180877432
Web Site: http://www.epuron.fr
Emp.: 52
Wind Energy Services
N.A.I.C.S.: 221115

Longburn Wind Farm Ltd.   **(1)**
1 Saint Colme Street St Colme St, Edinburgh, EH3 6AA, United Kingdom
Tel.: (44) 1315163501
Web Site: http://www.longburnwindfarm.com
Wind Energy Services
N.A.I.C.S.: 221115

ERGIS S.A.

ul Tamka 16, 00-349, Warsaw, Poland
Tel.: (48) 228280410
Web Site: http://www.ergis.eu
Sales Range: $150-199.9 Million
Emp.: 798
Polyethylene Stretch Films & Laminated Fabrics Mfr
N.A.I.C.S.: 326113
Marek Kaplucha *(Vice Chm-Mgmt Bd)*

Subsidiaries:

Ergis-Recycling Sp. z o.o.   **(1)**
Ul Tamka 16, 00-349, Warsaw, Poland

Tel.: (48) 243675000
Web Site: http://www.ergis-recycling.eu
Plastics Product Mfr
N.A.I.C.S.: 326199

Flexergis Sp. z o.o.   **(1)**
Ul Elektrodowa 45C, 33-300, Nowy Sacz, Poland
Tel.: (48) 184492950
Web Site: http://www.flexergis.eu
Plastics Product Mfr
N.A.I.C.S.: 326199

MKF-Ergis Sp. z o.o.   **(1)**
Ul Tamka 16, 00-349, Warsaw, Poland
Tel.: (48) 566884145
Web Site: http://www.mkf-ergis.eu
Plastics Product Mfr
N.A.I.C.S.: 326199
Malgorzata Pozniak *(Mgr-Bus Dev-Central & Eastern Europe)*

MKF-Schimanski-Ergis GmbH   **(1)**
Miraustrasse 42, 13509, Berlin, Germany
Tel.: (49) 304140720
Packaging Services
N.A.I.C.S.: 561910

Numeratis Sp. z o.o.   **(1)**
Ul Grudziadzka 110-114, 87-100, Torun, Poland
Tel.: (48) 566210789
Web Site: http://www.numeratis.eu
Bookkeeping Services
N.A.I.C.S.: 541219

ERGO-FIT GMBH & CO. KG

Blocksbergstrasse 165, 66955, Pirmasens, Germany
Tel.: (49) 633124610
Web Site: http://www.ergo-fit.de
Year Founded: 1947
Sales Range: $10-24.9 Million
Emp.: 100
Fitness Products Supplier
N.A.I.C.S.: 713940
Michael Resch *(Mng Dir)*

ERGON ENERGY CORPORATION LIMITED

PO Box 1090, Townsville, 4810, QLD, Australia
Tel.: (61) 30694100
Web Site: http://www.ergon.com.au
Sales Range: $1-4.9 Billion
Electric Power Distr
N.A.I.C.S.: 221122

Subsidiaries:

Ergon Energy Telecommunications Pty Ltd   **(1)**
22 Walker Street, Townsville, 4810, QLD, Australia
Tel.: (61) 1300 798 976
Web Site: http://www.nexium.net.au
Telecommunication Servicesb
N.A.I.C.S.: 517810
Kevin Boylan *(Mgr)*

ERI HOLDINGS CO., LTD.

5F 8-10-24 Akasaka, Minato-ku, Tokyo, 107-0052, Japan
Tel.: (81) 357701520   JP
Web Site: https://www.h-eri.co.jp
Year Founded: 2013
6083—(TKS)
Rev.: $119,125,420
Assets: $75,810,090
Liabilities: $37,630,730
Net Worth: $38,179,360
Earnings: $8,150,130
Emp.: 1,512
Fiscal Year-end: 05/31/24
Holding Company; Building Inspection Services
N.A.I.C.S.: 551112
Akiyo Masuda *(Pres & COO)*

Subsidiaries:

Japan ERI Co., Ltd.   **(1)**
Sumitomo Fudosan Aoyama Building South Building 8-10-24, Akasaka Minato-ku, To-

kyo, 107-0052, Japan
Tel.: (81) 337960223
Web Site: https://www.j-eri.co.jp
Sales Range: $100-124.9 Million
Emp.: 792
Building Inspection Services
N.A.I.C.S.: 541350
Yoshiki Nakazawa *(Chm & CEO)*

ERICH NETZSCH GMBH & CO. HOLDING KG

Gebruder-Netzsch-Strasse 19, 95100, Selb, Germany
Tel.: (49) 9287750   De
Web Site: http://www.netzsch.com
Year Founded: 1873
Sales Range: $200-249.9 Million
Emp.: 2,000
Industrial Machinery & Product Mfr & Distr
N.A.I.C.S.: 334513
Felix Kleinert *(Mng Dir-Bus Unit Pumps & Sys)*

Subsidiaries:

Ecutec Barcelona S.L.   **(1)**
Gran Via Corts Catalanes 641 6e 4, 08010, Barcelona, Spain
Tel.: (34) 932477700
Web Site: http://www.ecutec.eu
Grinding Product Mfr
N.A.I.C.S.: 327910
Sergio Alegre *(Mng Dir)*

NETZSCH (Shanghai) Machinery and Instruments Co. Ltd.   **(1)**
8 Yuan Da Rd An Ting, 201805, Shanghai, China   **(100%)**
Tel.: (86) 2169576008
Web Site: http://www.netzschgrinding.com.cn
Sales Range: $1-9.9 Million
Emp.: 80
Mfr of Industrial Machinery, Pumps, Filtration System Equipment, Grinding & Dispersing Equipment & Thermal Analysis Equipment
N.A.I.C.S.: 333914

NETZSCH Argentina S. A.   **(1)**
Ruta Panamericana Km 33 5 Ramal Escobar, Grand Bourg Partido De Islas, 1615, Buenos Aires, Argentina
Tel.: (54) 3327444935
Web Site: http://www.netzsch.com
Industrial Machinery, Pumps, Filtration System Equipment, Grinding & Dispersing Equipment & Thermal Analysis Equipment Mfr
N.A.I.C.S.: 333914
Fernando Fernandez *(Mng Dir)*

NETZSCH Asia Pacific PTE Ltd.   **(1)**
7 Toh Guan Road East unit 07-01/02, Alpha Industrial Building, 608599, Singapore, Singapore
Tel.: (65) 68634453
Web Site: http://www.netzsch.com.sg
Sales Range: $25-49.9 Million
Emp.: 19
Industrial Machinery, Pumps, Filtration System Equipment, Grinding & Dispersing Equipment & Thermal Analysis Equipment Mfr
N.A.I.C.S.: 333914
Edwin Chng *(Gen Mgr)*

NETZSCH Australia Pty Ltd   **(1)**
Unit 3 21 Binney Road, Kings Park, 2148, NSW, Australia
Tel.: (61) 296412840
Web Site: http://www.netzsch.com.au
Industrial Machinery & Equipment Distr
N.A.I.C.S.: 423830
Rafael Navarrete *(Dir-Sls)*

NETZSCH Canada, Inc.   **(1)**
740 Huronia Rd Unit 10, Barrie, L4N 6C6, ON, Canada
Tel.: (705) 797-8426
Web Site: http://www.netzsch.ca
Emp.: 1,000
Industrial Machinery Mfr & Distr
N.A.I.C.S.: 333998
Jason Balcerczyk *(Mng Dir)*

NETZSCH Espana S.A.   **(1)**

Erich Netzsch GmbH & Co, Holding
KG—(Continued)

Poligono Industrial Norte, C Provenza 194,
Terrassa, 8226, Spain **(99%)**
Tel.: (34) 937355065
Web Site: http://www.netzsch.com
Sales Range: $25-49.9 Million
Emp.: 10
Mfr of Industrial Machinery, Pumps, Filtration System Equipment, Grinding & Dispersing Equipment & Thermal Analysis Equipment
N.A.I.C.S.: 333914
Santiago Requena (Mng Dir)

NETZSCH Froroo S.a.r.l. **(1)**
32 34 Av Des Chardons, 77348, Paris,
France **(100%)**
Tel.: (33) 164435400
Web Site: http://www.netzsch.com
Sales Range: $25-49.9 Million
Emp.: 15
Mfr of Industrial Machinery, Pumps, Filtration System Equipment, Grinding & Dispersing Equipment & Thermal Analysis Equipment
N.A.I.C.S.: 333914
Catherine Stoganoysk (Mng Dir)

NETZSCH Geratebau GmbH **(1)**
Wittelsbacherstrasse 42, 95100, Selb,
Germany **(100%)**
Tel.: (49) 92878810
Web Site: http://www.netzsch-thermal-analysis.com
Sales Range: $50-74.9 Million
Emp.: 200
Industrial Machinery, Pumps, Filtration System Equipment, Grinding & Dispersing Equipment & Thermal Analysis Equipment Mfr
N.A.I.C.S.: 333914
Thomas Denner (Mng Dir)

NETZSCH Industria e Comercio de Equipamentos de Moagem Ltda. **(1)**
Rua Luiz Abry 2511-Centro, 89107-000,
Pomerode, Brazil
Tel.: (55) 47 3387 7000
Emp.: 100
Industrial Machinery Distr
N.A.I.C.S.: 423830
Rafael Ferriera (Mgr-Sls)

NETZSCH Instruments Sp.zo.o. **(1)**
Halicka 9, 31065, Krakow, Poland
Tel.: (48) 124240920
Web Site: http://www.netzsch.com.pl
Sales Range: $25-49.9 Million
Emp.: 10
Mfr of Industrial Machinery, Pumps, Filtration System Equipment, Grinding & Dispersing Equipment & Thermal Analysis Equipment
N.A.I.C.S.: 333914

NETZSCH Japan K.K. **(1)**
3-9-13 Moriya-cho, Yokohama, 221-0022,
Kanagawa, Japan
Tel.: (81) 45 453 1962
Web Site: http://www.netzsch.co.jp
Industrial Machinery Distr
N.A.I.C.S.: 423830
Yoshio Shinoda (Mng Dir)

NETZSCH Korea Co. Ltd **(1)**
5 F Jaeneung Bldg No 1294 3 Beaksuk
Dong, ROK Ilsan Gu Koyang, Seoul,
410816, Korea (South) **(100%)**
Tel.: (82) 319073193
Web Site: http://www.netzsch.com
Sales Range: $25-49.9 Million
Emp.: 25
Mfr of Industrial Machinery, Pumps, Filtration System Equipment, Grinding & Dispersing Equipment & Thermal Analysis Equipment
N.A.I.C.S.: 333914

NETZSCH Lanzhou Pumps Co. Ltd. **(1)**
506 Liu Jia Tan Lanzhou High Development
Zone, Lanzhou, 730000, Gansu, China
Tel.: (86) 9318555000
Web Site: http://www.netzsch.com.cn
Emp.: 208
Mfr of Industrial Machinery, Pumps, Filtration System Equipment, Grinding & Dispersing Equipment & Thermal Analysis Equipment

N.A.I.C.S.: 333914
Chris Gwalchmai (Mgr-Export Sls-Intl)

NETZSCH Lohnmahltechnik GmbH **(1)**
Max-Fischer-Str 20b, 86399, Bobingen,
Germany
Tel.: (49) 8234966150
Industrial Machinery & Equipment Distr
N.A.I.C.S.: 423830

NETZSCH Makine Sanayi ve Ticaret Ltd. Sti. **(1)**
A O S B 10016 Sokak No 72, Cigli, 35620,
Izmir, Turkiye
Tel · (90) 232 325 46 46
Industrial Machinery Distr
N.A.I.C.S.: 423830

NETZSCH Malaysia Sdn.Bhd **(1)**
No 49 2 Jalan PJU 1 37, Dataran Prima,
Petaling Jaya, 47301, Kuala Lumpur,
Malaysia **(100%)**
Tel.: (60) 378800882
Web Site: http://www.netzsch-pumps.com
Sales Range: $25-49.9 Million
Emp.: 4
Mfr of Industrial Machinery, Pumps, Filtration System Equipment, Grinding & Dispersing Equipment & Thermal Analysis Equipment
N.A.I.C.S.: 333914

NETZSCH Mastermix Ltd. **(1)**
23 Lombard Street, Lichfield, WS13 6DP,
Staffordshire, United Kingdom
Tel.: (44) 1543418938
Web Site: http://www.netzsch-grinding.com
Sales Range: $25-49.9 Million
Emp.: 15
Mfr of Industrial Machinery, Pumps, Filtration System Equipment, Grinding & Dispersing Equipment & Thermal Analysis Equipment
N.A.I.C.S.: 333914
David Tomlinson (Mng Dir)

NETZSCH Mexico S.A. DE C.V. **(1)**
Via Gustavo Baz 47 Col Parque Ind Naucalpan, Naucalpan, 53489, Mexico
Tel.: (52) 5551191046
Web Site: http://www.netzsch.com
Industrial Machinery Distr
N.A.I.C.S.: 423830
Paulo Roque (Gen Mgr)

NETZSCH Milantecnica S.R.L. **(1)**
Via Fleming 17, Verona, 37135,
Italy **(100%)**
Tel.: (39) 0458200755
Web Site: http://www.milantecnica.it
Sales Range: $25-49.9 Million
Emp.: 12
Industrial Machinery, Pumps, Filtration System Equipment, Grinding & Dispersing Equipment & Thermal Analysis Equipment Mfr
N.A.I.C.S.: 333914

NETZSCH Peru Sociedad Anonima Cerrado **(1)**
Calle Bolivar Nr 472 Edificio Business Club
oficina nr 503, Miraflores, Lima, 18, Peru
Tel.: (51) 1 446 5487
Industrial Machinery Distr
N.A.I.C.S.: 423830
Welington Serra Ferreira (Gen Mgr)

NETZSCH Pompe & Sistemi Italia Srl **(1)**
Via Fleming 17, 37135, Verona, Italy
Tel.: (39) 0458200755
Industrial Machinery & Equipment Distr
N.A.I.C.S.: 423830

NETZSCH Pompen Nederland B.V. **(1)**
Albert Schweitzerlaan 10 a, 3451 EC, Vleuten, Netherlands
Tel.: (31) 30 230 7160
Industrial Machinery Distr
N.A.I.C.S.: 423830

NETZSCH Premier Technologies, LLC. **(1)**
125 Pickering Way, Exton, PA 19341
Tel.: (610) 280-1229
Industrial Machinery Mfr & Distr
N.A.I.C.S.: 333998

Stephen Miranda (Dir-Sls-Grinding & Dispersing)

NETZSCH Pumpen & Systeme GmbH **(1)**
Geretsrieder Strasse 1, 84478,
Waldkraiburg, Germany
Tel.: (49) 8638 63 1010
Emp.: 600
Industrial Machinery Distr
N.A.I.C.S.: 423830
Bernhard Murrenhoff (Dir-Sls & Mktg)

NETZSCH Pumps & Systems Ltd. **(1)**
Horchester, Holywell, Dorchester, DT2 0LL,
Dorset, United Kingdom
Tel.: (44) 1935 483900
Emp.: 20
Industrial Machinery Distr
N.A.I.C.S.: 423830
Jerry Bradshaw (Mgr-Sls)

NETZSCH Pumps Bellux BVBA **(1)**
Brusselbaan 209, 1790, Affligem, Belgium
Tel.: (32) 53 66 33 01
Industrial Machinery Distr
N.A.I.C.S.: 423830
Hans Van der Gracht (Acct Mgr)

NETZSCH Pumps North America, LLC **(1)**
119 Pickering Way, Exton, PA 19431-1393
Tel.: (610) 363-8010
Web Site: http://www.netzschusa.com
Sales Range: $25-49.9 Million
Emp.: 60
Mfr of Special Industrial Machinery, Pumps, Grinding & Filtration System Equipments
N.A.I.C.S.: 333914
John Maguire (VP-Ops)

NETZSCH Pumps RUS OOO **(1)**
Leninski Prospekt 113/1 Office 505e - Tower
E, 117198, Moscow, Russia
Tel.: (7) 4959569086
Web Site: http://www.netzsch.ru
Industrial Machinery Distr
N.A.I.C.S.: 423830
Karl-Heinz Mommert (Mng Dir)

NETZSCH Scientific Instruments Trading (Shanghai) Ltd. **(1)**
Section A 4th Floor Building 1 No 456 Fute
Road N, Waigaoqiao Free Trade Zone,
Shanghai, 200131, China
Tel.: (86) 21 51089255
Industrial Machinery Distr
N.A.I.C.S.: 423830

NETZSCH Service Nordeste Ltda. **(1)**
Rua Martins Correia 155, 59054-204, Natal,
Brazil
Tel.: (55) 843 213 3229
Industrial Machinery Distr
N.A.I.C.S.: 423830
Sidney Guedes (Pres & CEO)

NETZSCH Southern Africa (PTY) Ltd. **(1)**
No 3 Eagle Mini Units Erf 167 Voorraadskip
Avenue, Honeydew, 2040, Johannesburg,
South Africa
Tel.: (27) 11 794 8975
Industrial Machinery Distr
N.A.I.C.S.: 423830
Tyron Adam (Mgr-Intl Sls)

NETZSCH Technologies, India Pvt. Ltd. **(1)**
No 39 2nd Street Spartan Nagar, Mogappair, Chennai, 600 037, India
Tel.: (91) 44 4296 5100
Web Site: http://www.netzschindia.com
Emp.: 100
Industrial Machinery Mfr & Distr
N.A.I.C.S.: 333998
Vivek Norman (Mng Dir)

Plant (Domestic):

NETZSCH Technologies India Pvt. Ltd. - Salcette Factory **(2)**
L -10 Verna Industrial Estate, Verna Salcette, Goa, 403 722, India
Tel.: (91) 8326627800
Industrial Machinery & Equipment Distr
N.A.I.C.S.: 423830

NETZSCH Thailand Ltd. **(1)**
1559 Town in Town Soi Srivara (Ladprow
94), Ladprow Road Wangthonglang, 10310,
Bangkok, Thailand
Tel.: (66) 23073858
Web Site: http://www.netzsch.com
Mfr of Industrial Machinery, Pumps, Filtration System Equipment, Grinding & Dispersing Equipment & Thermal Analysis Equipment
N.A.I.C.S.: 333914

NETZSCH Tula ZAO **(1)**
Settlement Shatsk 1B, 301107, Tula, Russia
Tel.: (7) 4872252820
Industrial Machinery Distr
N.A.I.C.S.: 423830

NETZSCH USA Holdings, Inc. **(1)**
129 Middlesex Tpke, Burlington, MA 01803
Tel.: (781) 272-5353
Sales Range: $25-49.9 Million
Emp.: 30
Holding Company; Monitoring Instrumentation Mfr
N.A.I.C.S.: 551112
Dave Shepard (Reg Mgr-Sls)

NETZSCH Vakumix GmbH **(1)**
Zeppelinstrasse 1, 28844, Weyhe, Germany
Tel.: (49) 421849560
Industrial Machinery & Equipment Distr
N.A.I.C.S.: 423830
Fabian Stapper (Mgr-Intl Sls)

NETZSCH Werbe- und Service-GmbH **(1)**
Gebruder-Netzsch-Strasse 19, PO Box
1460, 95100, Selb, Germany **(100%)**
Tel.: (49) 928775163
Web Site: http://www.netzsch.com
Sales Range: $200-249.9 Million
Emp.: 700
Industrial Machinery Pump Filtration System Equipment Grinding & Dispersing Equipment & Thermal Analysis Equipment Mfr
N.A.I.C.S.: 333914

NETZSCH do Brasil Ltda. **(1)**
Rua Hermann Weege 2383, PO Box 51,
BR 89107-000, Pomerode, SC,
Brazil **(100%)**
Tel.: (55) 47 3387 8222
Web Site: http://www.netzsch.com.br
Sales Range: $1-9.9 Million
Emp.: 100
Mfr of Industrial Machinery, Pumps, Filtration System Equipment, Grinding & Dispersing Equipment & Thermal Analysis Equipment
N.A.I.C.S.: 333914

NETZSCH-CONDUX Mahltechnik GmbH **(1)**
Rodenbacher Chaussee 1, 63457, Hanau,
Germany
Tel.: (49) 6181 506 01
Industrial Machinery Mfr & Distr
N.A.I.C.S.: 333998

NETZSCH-Feinmahltechnik GmbH **(1)**
Sedanstrasse 70, PO Box 1460, 95100,
Selb, Germany **(100%)**
Tel.: (49) 92877970
Web Site: http://www.netzschgrinding.com
Sales Range: $25-49.9 Million
Emp.: 100
Mfr of Industrial Machinery, Pumps, Filtration System Equipment, Grinding & Dispersing Equipment & Thermal Analysis Equipment
N.A.I.C.S.: 333914
Dimitrios Makrakis (Mng Dir)

NETZSCH-Oilfield Products GmbH **(1)**
Gebrueder Netzsch Str 19, 95100, Selb,
Germany **(100%)**
Tel.: (49) 928775424
Web Site: http://www.oil.netzsch.com
Sales Range: $25-49.9 Million
Emp.: 20
Mfr of Industrial Machinery, Pumps, Filtration System Equipment, Grinding & Dispersing Equipment & Thermal Analysis Equipment
N.A.I.C.S.: 333914

Nedgex GmbH **(1)**

Gebruder-Netzsch-Strasse 19, 95100, Selb,
Germany
Tel.: (49) 9287750
Web Site: http://www.nedgex.com
Information Technology Services
N.A.I.C.S.: 541511
Moritz Netzsch (Mng Dir)

Netzsch Ceska Republika S.R.O.   (1)
Ringhofferova 115/1, 155 21, Prague,
Czech Republic
Tel.: (420) 608701537
Pumping Equipment Mfr
N.A.I.C.S.: 333914
Jurgen Blumm (Mng Dir)

Netzsch Instruments North America,
LLC   (1)
129 Middlesex Tpke, Burlington, MA 01803
Tel.: (781) 272-5353
Polymer Product Mfr
N.A.I.C.S.: 325211
Michael Ward (Engr-Svc)

Netzsch Taurus Instruments
GmbH   (1)
Doebereinerstrasse 21, Industrial Area Wei-
mar Nord, 99427, Weimar, Germany
Tel.: (49) 364341740
Web Site: http://www.taurus-instruments.de
Emp.: 25
Optical Measuring Device Mfr
N.A.I.C.S.: 334513
Andre Lindemann (Mng Dir)

Netzsch Trockenmahltechnik
GmbH   (1)
Rodenbacher Chaussee 1, 63457, Hanau,
Germany
Tel.: (49) 618150601
Pumping Equipment Mfr
N.A.I.C.S.: 333914
Gerhard Kolb (Mng Dir)

Netzsch Vietnam Limited   (1)
3-5 Vu Tong Phan Street, An Phu Ward-
District 2, Ho Chi Minh City, Vietnam
Tel.: (84) 2862811042
Cavity Pump Product Mfr
N.A.I.C.S.: 333996

OOO Netzsch Pumps Rus   (1)
188 Dostyk Avenue Kulan Business Center
Office 605, Almaty, 117198, Kazakhstan
Tel.: (7) 7788040596
Pumping Equipment Mfr
N.A.I.C.S.: 333914
Karl-Heinz Mommert (Mgr)

PT NETZSCH Indonesia   (1)
Ruko Permata Kota Blok D No 6 Jl
Pangeran Tubagus Angke No 170, Jakarta,
14450, Indonesia
Tel.: (62) 21 6667 1513
Industrial Machinery Distr
N.A.I.C.S.: 423830
Lois Monnica Maleachi (Mgr-Fin & Admin)

ERICH UTSCH AG
Marienhutte 49, 57080, Siegen, Ger-
many
Tel.: (49) 27131910
Web Site: http://www.utsch.com
Year Founded: 1961
Rev.: $62,769,671
Emp.: 196
License Plate Mfr
N.A.I.C.S.: 332313
Dominic Hoffgen (CFO)

Subsidiaries:

Shimnit Utsch India Pvt. Ltd.   (1)
8th Floor Regent Chambers Nariman Point,
Mumbai, 400021, India
Tel.: (91) 2222795400
Web Site: http://www.shimnitutsch.co.in
Automobile Spare Parts Mfr
N.A.I.C.S.: 336330
Hemant Thaker (VP-Fin & Acct)

UTSCH Tonnjes International AG   (1)
Neuer Zollhof 3, 40221, Dusseldorf, Ger-
many
Tel.: (49) 21122059551
Web Site: http://www.uti-ag.com
Automotive Spare Parts Distr
N.A.I.C.S.: 423120

Utsch International Ltd.   (1)
Unit 2 Monavalley Industrial Estate, Tralee,
County Kerry, Ireland
Tel.: (353) 667126560
Automotive Spare Parts Distr
N.A.I.C.S.: 423120

Utsch do Brasil   (1)
Av das Americas 3434 Bloco 4 - Sala 307,
Rio de Janeiro, 22640-101, Brazil
Tel.: (55) 2134313469
Web Site: http://www.utschbrasil.com
Automotive Spare Parts Distr
N.A.I.C.S.: 423120

ERICKSEN NISSAN
10982 101 Street, Edmonton, T5H
2S8, AB, Canada
Tel.: (780) 429-4611
Web Site: http://gonissan.ca
Rev.: $25,747,905
Emp.: 35
New & Used Car Dealers
N.A.I.C.S.: 441110
Dwayne Bateman (VP)

**ERICOM TELEKOMU-
NIKASYON VE ENERJI
TEKNOLOJILERI A.S.**
Buyukdere Cd No 15/A Hur Han B
Blok Kat 3, Maslak, Istanbul, 34381,
Turkiye
Tel.: (90) 344 2213300
Sales Range: $1-9.9 Million
Emp.: 70
Energy & Communications Products
Mfr
N.A.I.C.S.: 335910
Ilker Aydin (Chm & Gen Mgr)

ERICPOL SP. Z O.O.
Targowa 9A, 90-042, Lodz, Poland
Tel.: (48) 42 6642500
Web Site: http://www.ericpol.com
Year Founded: 1991
Sales Range: $50-74.9 Million
Emp.: 1,001
Telecommunication Consultancy Ser-
vices
N.A.I.C.S.: 541618
Jan Smela (Founder, Owner & Pres)

Subsidiaries:

Ericpol AB   (1)
Teknikringen 10, 583 30, Linkoping, Swe-
den
Tel.: (46) 135602502
Emp.: 1,800
Engineering Consulting Services
N.A.I.C.S.: 541330
Patrik Jigblad (Mng Dir)

Ericpol TZOV   (1)
Sholom Aleykhem 11, 79007, Lviv, Ukraine
Tel.: (380) 322424420
Engineering Consulting Services
N.A.I.C.S.: 541330
Orest Kossak (Mng Dir)

IOOO ERICPOL BREST   (1)
Dzerzhynskogo 52, 224030, Minsk, Belarus
Tel.: (375) 162220019
Engineering Consulting Services
N.A.I.C.S.: 541330
Valery Tsilind (Mng Dir)

ERIDGE CAPITAL LIMITED
Ogier House The Esplanade, Saint
Helier, JE4 9WG, Jersey
Tel.: (44) 5149 612247   JE
Web Site: http://www.nwoilgas.com
Oil & Gas Exploration Services
N.A.I.C.S.: 213112

ERIK THUN AB
Ostra Hamnen 7, 531 32, Lidkoping,
Sweden
Tel.: (46) 51084800   SE
Web Site: http://www.thun.se
Year Founded: 1938
Sales Range: $1-4.9 Billion

Emp.: 600
Marine Cargo Handling, Aircraft Leas-
ing, Real Estate Management Ser-
vices; Processed Meat Mfr
N.A.I.C.S.: 488320
Anders Kallsson (Mng Dir)

Subsidiaries:

Thun Tankers B.V   (1)
Hogelandsterweg 14, 9936 BH, Farmsum,
Netherlands
Tel.: (31) 596633911
Web Site: http://www.thuntankers.com
Marine Shipping Services
N.A.I.C.S.: 488510
Karin Orsel (Mng Dir)

Thun Tankers B.V.   (1)
Hogelandsterweg 14, 9936 BH, Farmsum,
Netherlands
Tel.: (31) 596 633 911
Web Site: http://www.thuntankers.com
Shipping Vessel Operator
N.A.I.C.S.: 483111
Karin Orsel (Mng Dir)

ERIKA B-CURE LASER LTD.
5 Nahum Heth St, PO Box 15141,
Haifa, 3508504, Israel
Tel.: (972) 2070483765   II
Web Site:
   https://www.bcurelaser.com
BCUR—(TAE)
Rev.: $8,256,113
Assets: $12,959,525
Liabilities: $6,404,199
Net Worth: $6,555,325
Earnings: ($5,310,402)
Fiscal Year-end: 12/31/23
Electromedical & Electrotherapeutic
Apparatus Manufacturing
N.A.I.C.S.: 334510

ERIMA GMBH
Carl Zeiss Strasse 10, 72793, Pfullin-
gen, Germany
Tel.: (49) 71213420
Web Site: http://www.erima.de
Sales Range: $25-49.9 Million
Emp.: 200
Sports Apparel Mfr
N.A.I.C.S.: 339920
Wolfram Mannherz (Mng Dir)

ERIN DODGE CHRYSLER LTD.
2365 Motorway Boulevard, Missis-
sauga, L5L 2M4, ON, Canada
Tel.: (905) 828-2004
Web Site: http://www.erindodge.com
Year Founded: 1983
Sales Range: $25-49.9 Million
New & Used Car Dealer
N.A.I.C.S.: 441110
Mark Keenan (Principal-Dealer)

**ERIN PARK AUTOMOTIVE
PARTNERSHIP**
2360 Motorway Blvd, Mississauga,
L5L 1X3, ON, Canada
Tel.: (905) 828-7727
Web Site:
   https://www.erinparklexus.com
Rev.: $70,084,137
Emp.: 138
New & Used Car Dealers
N.A.I.C.S.: 441110
Stacey Cohen (Gen Mgr)

ERIN VENTURES INC.
645 Fort Street Suite 203, Victoria,
V8W 1G2, BC, Canada
Tel.: (250) 384-1999
Web Site:
   https://www.erinventures.com
Year Founded: 1993
EKV—(DEU)
Assets: $8,093,860
Liabilities: $510,335

Net Worth: $7,583,525
Earnings: ($709,575)
Fiscal Year-end: 06/30/24
Mineral Exploration Services
N.A.I.C.S.: 213114
Tim Daniels (Pres)

**ERINMOTORWAY INVEST-
MENTS LIMITED**
2380 Motorway Blvd, Mississauga,
L5L 1X3, ON, Canada
Tel.: (905) 828-2336
Web Site:
   http://www.mississaugahonda.com
Rev.: $54,340,594
Emp.: 105
New & Used Car Dealers
N.A.I.C.S.: 441110
Matt Rende (Mgr-Sls)

ERIS LIFESCIENCES LIMITED
Shivarth Ambit Plot No 142/2 Ram-
das Road Off SBR Near Swati Bun-
galows, Bodakdev, Ahmedabad, 380
054, Gujarat, India
Tel.: (91) 7971841000   In
Web Site: https://www.eris.co.in
Year Founded: 2007
ERIS—(NSE)
Rev.: $166,607,942
Assets: $250,447,470
Liabilities: $35,265,731
Net Worth: $215,181,740
Earnings: $48,475,928
Emp.: 3,246
Fiscal Year-end: 03/31/21
Pharmaceutical Product Mfr & Distr
N.A.I.C.S.: 325412
Amit Bakshi (Founder, Chm & Mng
Dir)

Subsidiaries:

Aprica Healthcare Private
Limited   (1)
A/4 4th Floor Safal Profitaire Corporate
Road Nr Prahladnagar Garden, Ahmeda-
bad, 380015, Gujarat, India
Tel.: (91) 794 008 4035
Web Site: https://www.aprica.in
Healtcare Services
N.A.I.C.S.: 621999
Maharshi Vyas (CEO)

Biocon Biologics Limited   (1)
Biocon House Semicon Park Electronics
City Phase - II Hosur Road, Bengaluru, 560
100, Karnataka, India
Tel.: (91) 8067756775
Web Site: https://www.bioconbiologics.com
Biopharmaceutical Mfr
N.A.I.C.S.: 325412

**ERIS PHARMACEUTICALS
AUSTRALIA PTY LTD.**
6 Eastern Road, Melbourne, 3205,
VIC, Australia
Tel.: (61) 396908473
Web Site: http://www.eris-
   pharma.com
Year Founded: 2009
Emp.: 50
Pharmaceuticals Product Mfr
N.A.I.C.S.: 325412
Panos Athanasiou (CEO)

ERISBEG HOLDINGS LIMITED
38-39 Fitzwilliam Square, 2, Dublin,
Ireland
Tel.: (353) 15079625
Web Site: https://erisbeg.com
Privater Equity Firm
N.A.I.C.S.: 523999
Andrew Murphy (Partner)

Subsidiaries:

PageOne Communications
Limited   (1)
12th Floor GW1 Great West House Great

Erisbeg Holdings Limited—(Continued)

West Road, Brentford, TW8 9DF, Middlesex, United Kingdom
Tel.: (44) 3332005033
Web Site: https://www.pageone.co.uk
Integrated Messaging Services
N.A.I.C.S.: 561421
Chris Jones *(CEO)*

ERITH GROUP

Erith House Queen St, Erith, DA8
1RP, Kent, United Kingdom
Tel.: (44) 8709508800
Web Site: http://www.erith.net
Sales Range: $75-99.9 Million
Emp.: 200
Demolition & Civil Engineering Services
N.A.I.C.S.: 237990
Steve Darsey *(Chm)*

ERLEBNIS AKADEMIE AG

Hafenberg 4, Bad Koetzting, 93444, Cham, Germany
Tel.: (49) 99419084840
Web Site: https://www.eak-ag.de
Year Founded: 2001
EAD—(MUN)
Rev.: $26,272,106
Assets: $65,382,220
Liabilities: $41,284,738
Net Worth: $24,097,482
Earnings: ($2,031,121)
Emp.: 245
Fiscal Year-end: 12/31/23
Educational Support Services
N.A.I.C.S.: 611710
Bernd Bayerkohler *(CEO)*

Subsidiaries:

Zazitkova Akademie s.r.o.　　　　**(1)**
Csl Armady 200, 253 01, Hostivice, Czech Republic
Tel.: (420) 233342309
Web Site: https://www.z-ak.cz
Emp.: 100
Travel Tour Operator
N.A.I.C.S.: 561520

ERMENEGILDO ZEGNA HOLD- ITALIA S.P.A.

Via Savona 56/A, 20144, Milan, Italy
Tel.: (39) 02422091　　　　　　**IT**
Web Site: http://www.zegna.com
Sales Range: $500-549.9 Million
Emp.: 5,000
High-End Menswear & Sportswear Mfr
N.A.I.C.S.: 315250
Ermenegildo Zegna *(Dir-Admin)*

ERMEWA INTERSERVICES SARL

Espace Seine 26 Guai Charles Pasqua, 92300, Levallois-Perret, France
Tel.: (33) 1 49 07 26 00　　　　**FR**
Web Site: http://www.ermewa-group.com
Year Founded: 1956
Sales Range: $500-549.9 Million
Emp.: 650
Tank Container & Locomotives Leasing Services
N.A.I.C.S.: 488510
Josef Kuttel *(Vice Chm-Supervisory Bd)*

Subsidiaries:

ATELIERS D ORVAL SA　　　　　**(1)**
Route de l Ombree, BP 64, 18202, Saint-Amand-Montrond, France
Tel.: (33) 2 48 96 07 39
Web Site: http://www.ermewa-workshops.com
Railway Construction Services
N.A.I.C.S.: 332312

ERMEWA Berlin　　　　　　　　**(1)**
Markgrafenstr 62, 10969, Berlin, Germany
Tel.: (49) 30 319 853 0
Container Leasing Services
N.A.I.C.S.: 532411

ERMEWA Geneve　　　　　　　　**(1)**
Rue du Mont Blanc, PO Box 1464, 1211, Geneva, Switzerland
Tel.: (41) 22 906 04 28
Oil & Gas Transportation Services
N.A.I.C.S.: 486210

ERMEWA LIMITED　　　　　　　**(1)**
The Sanderum Centre 30A Upper High Street, Thame, OX9 3EX, Oxfordshire, United Kingdom
Tel.: (44) 1844 211044
Container Leasing Services
N.A.I.C.S.: 532411

ERMEWA S.R.L.　　　　　　　　**(1)**
Via della Moscova 40, 20121, Milan, Italy
Tel.: (39) 02 29000721
Container Leasing Services
N.A.I.C.S.: 532411

ERMEWA srl　　　　　　　　　　**(1)**
Avenida Alberto Alcocer 46 6B, 28016, Madrid, Spain
Tel.: (34) 91 457 70 67
Container Leasing Services
N.A.I.C.S.: 532411

Ermewa France　　　　　　　　**(1)**
Le Stratege 172 rue de la Republique, 92817, Puteaux, Cedex, France
Tel.: (33) 1 4907 2531
Web Site: http://www.ermewa.com
Sales Range: $25-49.9 Million
Emp.: 16
Tank Container Services
N.A.I.C.S.: 488510
Etienne Fallou *(Mgr-Admin & Legal)*

Eurotainer SA　　　　　　　　　**(1)**
Le Stratege 172 Rue De La Republique, 92817, Puteaux, France
Tel.: (33) 0149072410
Web Site: http://www.eurotainer.com
Sales Range: $25-49.9 Million
Emp.: 25
Tank Container Services
N.A.I.C.S.: 488510
Vincent Martin *(Mng Dir)*

FERIFOS SA　　　　　　　　　　**(1)**
Zi Ventillon, 13270, Fos-sur-Mer, France
Tel.: (33) 442 11 30 00
Railway Equipment Mfr
N.A.I.C.S.: 336510

SARI SA　　　　　　　　　　　　**(1)**
Rue de Paris, 62121, Paris, France
Tel.: (33) 3 21 24 08 60
Container Leasing Services
N.A.I.C.S.: 532411

SEGI SA　　　　　　　　　　　　**(1)**
Rue des Marais, 94034, Creteil, France
Tel.: (33) 1 49 80 09 21
Container Leasing Services
N.A.I.C.S.: 532411

ERNEST DOE & SONS LIM- ITED

Ulting, Maldon, CM9 6QH, Essex, United Kingdom
Tel.: (44) 1245380311
Web Site: http://www.ernestdoe.com
Sales Range: $125-149.9 Million
Emp.: 526
Agricultural Machinery Distr
N.A.I.C.S.: 423820
Graham Parker *(Dir-Sls)*

ERNI ELECTRONICS GMBH

Seestrasse 9, Adelberg, 73099, Germany
Tel.: (49) 7166500　　　　　　　**De**
Web Site: http://www.erni.com
Year Founded: 1956
Sales Range: $200-249.9 Million
Emp.: 650
Telecommunications & Information Technology Interconnect Products Designer, Mfr & Distr

N.A.I.C.S.: 334417
Martin Seidenfuss *(CEO)*

Subsidiaries:

ELSA ERNI System　　　　　　　**(1)**
No 14th Jiuxianqiao Road A2-3-A2316 Zhaoweihuadeng Building, Chaoyang District, 100016, Beijing, China
Tel.: (86) 10 84799656
Electronic Products Mfr
N.A.I.C.S.: 334417

ERNI Asia Holding Pte Ltd　　　**(1)**
Blk 4008 Ang Mo Kio Avenue 10, 04-01/02 Techplace I, Singapore, 569625, Singapore
Tel.: (65) 6 555 5885
Electronic Product Distr
N.A.I.C.S.: 423690
Yong Hong Koh *(Dir-Engrg)*

ERNI Electronics (Thailand) Co. Ltd.　　　　　　　　　　　　　　**(1)**
179 M 4 T Ban Klang A Muang, 51000, Lamphun, Thailand
Tel.: (66) 53581750
Web Site: http://www.erni.co.th
Electronic Product Mfr & Distr
N.A.I.C.S.: 334417
B. Ukkit *(Exec Mgr-Technical)*

ERNI Electronics AG　　　　　　**(1)**
Zurichstrasse 72, Bruttisellen, 8306, Zurich, Switzerland
Tel.: (41) 448353391
Web Site: http://www.erni.com
Emp.: 15
Electronic Product Distr
N.A.I.C.S.: 423690
Gian Tomaso *(CEO)*

ERNI Electronics China　　　　　**(1)**
Room 319 Building 2 NanGuang City Garden ChuangYe Road, NanShan District, 518054, Shenzhen, China
Tel.: (86) 755 86171751
Electronic Product Distr
N.A.I.C.S.: 423690

ERNI Electronics Ltd.　　　　　　**(1)**
Room 1306 World-Wide Industrial Centre 43-47 Shan Mei Street, Fotan, Sha Tin, New Territories, China (Hong Kong)
Tel.: (852) 2690 4646
Electronic Product Distr
N.A.I.C.S.: 423690

ERNI Electronics, Inc.　　　　　　**(1)**
2201 Westwood Ave, Richmond, VA 23230
Tel.: (804) 228-4100
Web Site: http://www.erni.com
Sales Range: $10-24.9 Million
Emp.: 30
Telecommunications & Information Technology Interconnect Products Designer, Mfr & Distr
N.A.I.C.S.: 334417
Michael Singer *(Dir-Mktg)*

ERNI cable systems AG　　　　　**(1)**
Zeughausstrasse 10, 8887, Mels, Switzerland
Tel.: (41) 81 725 80 80
Web Site: http://www.erni-cs.ch
Electronic Product Distr
N.A.I.C.S.: 423690

ERNST & YOUNG GLOBAL LIMITED

1 More London Place, London, SE1 2AF, United Kingdom
Tel.: (44) 2079512000　　　　　**UK**
Year Founded: 1989
Sales Range: $25-49.9 Billion
Emp.: 300,000
Accounting, Audit, Tax & Financial Advisory Services Organization
N.A.I.C.S.: 813920
Mark Otty *(Deputy Chm-Emerging Markets-Global)*

ERNST & YOUNG GMBH WIRTSCHAFTSPRUFUNGSGE- SELLSCHAFT

Flughafenstrabe 61, Stuttgart, 70499, Germany

Tel.: (49) 71198810　　　　　　**De**
Accounting, Tax Preparation & Consulting Services
N.A.I.C.S.: 541211
Alexander Kron *(Mng Partner-Transaction Advisory Svc)*

Subsidiaries:

Ernst & Young J&M Management Consulting GmbH　　　　　　　**(1)**
Willy-Brandt-Platz 5, 68161, Mannheim, Germany
Tel.: (49) 621420845400
Sales Range: $50-74.9 Million
Emp.: 320
Supply Chain Management Consulting Services
N.A.I.C.S.: 541614
Frank Jenner *(Co-Founder & Mng Partner)*

ERNST & YOUNG INC.

Ernst and Young Twr 222 Bay St, Toronto, M5K 1J7, ON, Canada
Tel.: (416) 864-1234　　　　　　**ON**
Year Founded: 1989
Sales Range: $200-249.9 Million
Emp.: 2,000
Auditing & Accounting Services
N.A.I.C.S.: 541211
Jay Hutchison *(Chief Dev Officer & Mng Partner-Acct & Markets)*

ERNST & YOUNG LLP

1 More London Place, London, SE1 2AF, United Kingdom
Tel.: (44) 20 7951 2000
Web Site: https://www.ey.com
Year Founded: 1989
Emp.: 100
Accounting Services
N.A.I.C.S.: 541211
Hywel Ball *(Chm)*

ERNST & YOUNG PVT LTD.

3rd & 6th Floor Worldmark-1, IGI Airport Hospitality District, Aerocity, New Delhi, 110037, India
Tel.: (91) 11 4731 8000　　　　　**In**
Web Site: https://www.ey.com
Emp.: 100
Accounting, Audit, Tax & Financial Advisory Services
N.A.I.C.S.: 541211
Rajiv Memani *(Reg Mng Partner)*

Subsidiaries:

Pangea3 Legal Database Systems Pvt. Ltd.　　　　　　　　　　**(1)**
102B Ground Floor Leela Business Park Andheri-Kurla Road, Andheri East, Mumbai, 400059, India
Tel.: (91) 2230922206
Web Site: http://www.pangea3.com
Legal Process Outsourcing Solutions
N.A.I.C.S.: 541199
Jaideep Kewalramani *(VP-Ops)*

ERNST DELLO GMBH & CO. KG

Nedderfeld 75-93, 22529, Hamburg, Germany
Tel.: (49) 40 4712 0　　　　　　**De**
Web Site: http://www.dello.de
Year Founded: 1898
Sales Range: $250-299.9 Million
Emp.: 900
New & Used Car Dealerships Owner & Operator
N.A.I.C.S.: 441110
Kurt Kroger *(Mng Partner)*

Subsidiaries:

Autohaus Hansa Nord GmbH　　**(1)**
Berliner Str 8-10, 23560, Lubeck, Germany
Tel.: (49) 451 58375 0
Web Site: http://www.bmw-hansa-nord.de
New & Used Car Dealer
N.A.I.C.S.: 441110

Bjorn Heilmann *(Mng Dir)*

ERNST GOHNER STIFTUNG
Artherstrasse 19, 6300, Zug, Switzerland
Tel.: (41) 7296633   CH
Web Site: https://www.ernst-goehner-stiftung.ch
Holding Company; Real Estate Services
N.A.I.C.S.: 551112

Subsidiaries:

Bauwerk Group AG   **(1)**
Neudorfstrasse 49, 9430, St. Margrethen, Switzerland
Tel.: (41) 717477474
Web Site: https://www.bauwerk-group.com
Parquet Mfr & Supplier
N.A.I.C.S.: 238330

Subsidiary (US):

Somerset Hardwood Flooring, Inc.   **(2)**
70 W Racetrack Rd, Somerset, KY 42502
Tel.: (606) 561-4146
Web Site: http://www.somersetfloors.com
Sales Range: $25-49.9 Million
Emp.: 101
Hardwood Flooring & Other Unfinished Wood Products Mfr
N.A.I.C.S.: 321211
Timothy V. Bullock *(Controller)*

Subsidiary (Domestic):

Somerset Hardwood Lumber, Inc.   **(3)**
138 E Antioch Dr, Burnside, KY 42519
Tel.: (606) 561-4146
Web Site: http://www.somersetwood.com
Sales Range: $1-9.9 Million
Sawmills
N.A.I.C.S.: 321113
Michael Wang *(Dir-Sls Asia & Pacific)*

ERNST KLETT AG
Rotebuhlstrasse 77, Stuttgart, 70178, Germany
Tel.: (49) 7 11 66 72 18 97
Web Site: http://www.klett-gruppe.de
Year Founded: 1897
Sales Range: $600-649.9 Million
Emp.: 2,763
Educational Materials Publisher
N.A.I.C.S.: 513130
Philipp Haussmann *(Member-Mgmt Bd)*

Subsidiaries:

AAP Lehrerfachverlage GmbH   **(1)**
Veritaskai 3, Hamburg, 21079, Germany
Tel.: (49) 40325083040
Web Site: http://www.aap-lehrerfachverlage.de
Book Publishers
N.A.I.C.S.: 513130
Christian Glaser *(Mng Dir)*

APOLLON Hochschule der Gesundheitswirtschaft GmbH   **(1)**
Universitatsallee 18, 28359, Bremen, Germany
Tel.: (49) 4213782660
Web Site: http://www.apollon-hochschule.de
Educational Support Services
N.A.I.C.S.: 611710

Auer Verlag GmbH   **(1)**
Memminger Str 6, 86159, Augsburg, Germany
Tel.: (49) 82159977990
Web Site: http://www.auer-verlag.de
Educational Support Services
N.A.I.C.S.: 611710

Balmer Bucherdienst AG   **(1)**
Kobiboden, 8840, Einsiedeln, Germany
Tel.: (49) 554188989
Web Site: http://www.balmer-bd.ch
Book Publishers
N.A.I.C.S.: 513130

C. Bange Verlag GmbH   **(1)**

Marienplatz 12, 96142, Hollfeld, Germany
Tel.: (49) 9274808990
Web Site: http://www.bange-verlag.de
N.A.I.C.S.: 513130

Campe Bildungszentrum Hannover gGmbH   **(1)**
Expo Plaza 9 B, 30539, Hannover, Germany
Tel.: (49) 51127949290
Web Site: http://www.campe-bildungszentrum.de
Book Publishers
N.A.I.C.S.: 513130

Difusion Centro de Investigacion y Publicaciones de Idiomas, S.L.   **(1)**
C/ Trafalgar 10 Entlo 1A, 8010, Barcelona, Spain
Tel.: (34) 932680300
Web Site: http://www.difusion.com
Book Publishers
N.A.I.C.S.: 513130

Dr Josef RAABE Spolka Wydawnicza Sp. z o.o.   **(1)**
Mynarska 8/12, Warsaw, Poland
Tel.: (48) 222448400
Web Site: http://www.raabe.com.pl
Book Publishers
N.A.I.C.S.: 513130

Dr. Josef Raabe Slovensko, s. r. o.   **(1)**
Heydukova 12-14, 811 08, Bratislava, Slovakia
Tel.: (421) 232661840
Web Site: http://www.raabe.sk
Book Publishers
N.A.I.C.S.: 513130

Editions Maison des Langues S.A.R.L.   **(1)**
78 Rue de Turbigo, 75003, Paris, France
Tel.: (33) 146338559
Web Site: http://www.emdl.fr
Book Publishers
N.A.I.C.S.: 513130

Editions RAABE S.a.r.l.   **(1)**
34 rue Sommeiller, 74000, Annecy, France
Tel.: (33) 450882400
Web Site: http://www.editions-raabe.fr
Book Publishers
N.A.I.C.S.: 513130

Ernst Klett Vertriebsgesellschaft   **(1)**
Stockachstrasse 11, 70190, Stuttgart, Germany
Tel.: (49) 71189462141
Web Site: http://www.klett-vertrieb.de
Book Publishers
N.A.I.C.S.: 513130

Europaische Fernhochschule Hamburg GmbH   **(1)**
Doberaner Weg 20, 22143, Hamburg, Germany
Tel.: (49) 40675700
Web Site: http://www.euro-fh.de
Educational Support Services
N.A.I.C.S.: 611710

Ferdinand Porsche FernFH   **(1)**
Lothringerstrasse 4-8, 1040, Vienna, Austria
Tel.: (43) 15057778
Web Site: http://www.fernfh.at
Educational Support Services
N.A.I.C.S.: 611710

Fernakademie fur Erwachsenenbildung GmbH   **(1)**
Doberaner Weg 22, 22143, Hamburg, Germany
Tel.: (49) 406778078
Web Site: http://www.fernakademie-klett.de
Educational Support Services
N.A.I.C.S.: 611710

HAF Hamburger Akademie fur Fernstudien GmbH   **(1)**
Doberaner Weg 18, 22143, Hamburg, Germany
Tel.: (49) 40675709000
Web Site: http://www.akademie-fuer-fernstudien.de
Educational Support Services
N.A.I.C.S.: 611710

K.lab educmedia GmbH   **(1)**
Karl-Marx-Strasse 100, 12043, Berlin, Germany
Tel.: (49) 3094054635
Web Site: http://www.meinunterricht.de
Book Publishers
N.A.I.C.S.: 513130

Klett Bulgaria EOOD   **(1)**
Ul Petar Delayn no 22, 1124, Sofia, Bulgaria
Tel.: (359) 28432070
Web Site: http://www.pons.bg
Book Publishers
N.A.I.C.S.: 513130

Klett Hellas E.M.E.   **(1)**
Pindarou & Leof Ionias 110, 174 56, Alimos, Greece
Tel.: (30) 2109902700
Web Site: http://www.klett.gr
Book Publishers
N.A.I.C.S.: 513130

Klett nakladatelstvi s.r.o.   **(1)**
Prumyslova 1472/11 CTY Logistic Park, 102 00, Prague, Czech Republic
Tel.: (420) 233084110
Web Site: http://www.klett.cz
Book Publishers
N.A.I.C.S.: 513130

Klett und Balmer AG   **(1)**
Grabenstrasse 17, Postfach 1464, 6341, Baar, Switzerland
Tel.: (41) 417262800
Web Site: http://www.klett.ch
Book Publishers
N.A.I.C.S.: 513130

Nakladatelstvi Dr. Josef Raabe, s.r.o.   **(1)**
Radlicka 2487/99, 150 00, Prague, Czech Republic
Tel.: (420) 28940941
Web Site: http://www.raabe.cz
Book Publishers
N.A.I.C.S.: 513130

RAABE Bulgarien EOOD   **(1)**
Tzarigradsko-Chausee-Blcd Nr 133 A, 1040, Sofia, Bulgaria
Tel.: (359) 29741793
Web Site: http://www.raabebg.com
Book Publishers
N.A.I.C.S.: 513130

RAABE Tanacsado es Kiado Kft.   **(1)**
Klapka utca 11, 1134, Budapest, Hungary
Tel.: (36) 13200750
Web Site: http://www.raabe.hu
Book Publishers
N.A.I.C.S.: 513130

Wydawnictwo LektorKlett sp. z o.o.   **(1)**
Ul Polska 114, 60-401, Poznan, Poland
Tel.: (48) 618496201
Web Site: http://www.lektorklett.com.pl
Book Publishers
N.A.I.C.S.: 513130

Zalozba Rokus Klett, d.o.o.   **(1)**
Stegne 9b, 1000, Ljubljana, Slovenia
Tel.: (386) 1 513 46 00
Book Publishers
N.A.I.C.S.: 513130
Wojtek Grudzinski *(Dir-Mktg)*

Subsidiary (Non-US):

KLETT IZDAVACKA KUCA d.o.o.   **(2)**
Marsala Birjuzova 3-5 IV sprat, 11000, Belgrade, Serbia
Tel.: (381) 113348384
Web Site: http://www.klett.rs
Book Publishers
N.A.I.C.S.: 513130

obv Osterreichischer Bundesverlag Schulbuch GmbH & Co. KG   **(1)**
Lassallestrasse 9b, 1020, Vienna, Austria
Tel.: (43) 1401360
Web Site: http://www.oebv.at
Book Publishers
N.A.I.C.S.: 513130

ERNST RUSS AG
Elbchaussee 370, D-22609, Hamburg, Germany

Tel.: (49) 40888810
Web Site: https://www.ernst-russ.de
HXCK—(MUN)
Rev.: $223,721,333
Assets: $375,613,845
Liabilities: $187,205,313
Net Worth: $188,408,532
Earnings: $60,801,160
Emp.: 80
Fiscal Year-end: 12/31/23
Financial Services
N.A.I.C.S.: 522291
Alexander Stuhlmann *(Chm-Supervisory Bd)*

Subsidiaries:

Assetando Real Estate GmbH   **(1)**
Elbchaussee 370, 22609, Hamburg, Germany
Tel.: (49) 40888810
Web Site: http://www.assetando.de
Asset Management Services
N.A.I.C.S.: 523940
Thomas Deutsch *(Mng Dir)*

HCI Asset GmbH   **(1)**
Burchardstrasse 8, Hamburg, 20095, Germany
Tel.: (49) 40888810
Web Site: http://www.hci.de
Sales Range: $50-74.9 Million
Emp.: 100
Investment Management Service
N.A.I.C.S.: 523940
Ralf Friedrichs *(CEO)*

HCI Hanseatische Capitalberatungsgesellschaft fur Beteiligungskapital mbH   **(1)**
Burchardstrabe 8, D-20095, Hamburg, many
Tel.: (49) 40888810
Web Site: http://www.hci.de
Equity Investment Management Services
N.A.I.C.S.: 523940

HCI Hanseatische Capitalberatungsgesellschaft mbH   **(1)**
Burchardstrasse 8, 20095, Hamburg, many
Tel.: (49) 40888810
Investment Management Service
N.A.I.C.S.: 523999

HCI Hanseatische Capitalberatungsgesellschaft mbH   **(1)**
Annagasse 5 Stiege 2 Top 16, 1010, Vienna, Austria
Tel.: (43) 15120348
Sales Range: $50-74.9 Million
Emp.: 2
Property Management Services
N.A.I.C.S.: 531312

HCI Hanseatische Immobilienbeteiligungsgesellschaft mbH   **(1)**
Burchardstrasse 8, 20095, Hamburg, many
Tel.: (49) 40888810
Sales Range: $50-74.9 Million
Emp.: 60
Real Estate Investment Services
N.A.I.C.S.: 531190

HCI Hanseatische Schiffsconsult GmbH   **(1)**
Burchard strasse 8, Hamburg, 20095, Germany
Tel.: (49) 40888810
Web Site: http://www.hci.de
Emp.: 68
Financial Consulting Services
N.A.I.C.S.: 541611
David Landgrebe *(Mng Dir)*

HCI Immobilien Geschaftsfuhrungsgesellschaft mbH   **(1)**
Haupstrasse 47, 65719, Hofheim, Germany
Tel.: (49) 61927093
Web Site: http://www.hci-immobilien.de
Real Estate Services
N.A.I.C.S.: 531390

HCI Institutional Funds GmbH   **(1)**
Burchardstraase 8, 20095, Hamburg, Germany
Tel.: (49) 40888810

Ernst Russ AG—(Continued)

Web Site: http://www.hci-capital.com
Sales Range: $100-124.9 Million
Emp.: 130
Financial Investment Advisory Services
N.A.I.C.S.: 523940

HCI Real Estate Finance I GmbH & Co. KG (1)
Burchardstrasse 8, 20095, Hamburg, Germany
Tel.: (49) 40888810
Sales Range: $50-74.9 Million
Emp.: 60
Real Estate Investment Management Services
N.A.I.C.S.: 531390

HCI Treuhand GmbH (1)
Herdentorsteinweg 7, Bremen, 28195, Germany
Tel.: (49) 421369100
Web Site: http://www.hci-capital.de
Sales Range: $50-74.9 Million
Emp.: 100
Financial Investment Services
N.A.I.C.S.: 523940
Ingo Kuhlmann (Mng Dir)

HSC Hanseatische Management GmbH (1)
Burchardstrasse 8, Hamburg, 20095, Germany
Tel.: (49) 40888810
Web Site: http://www.hci-capital.de
Sales Range: $50-74.9 Million
Emp.: 60
Asset Management Services
N.A.I.C.S.: 531390
Andreas Arndt (Gen Mgr)

HSC Hanseatische Sachwert Concept GmbH (1)
Burchardstrasse 8, 20095, Hamburg, Germany
Tel.: (49) 4088881480
Web Site: http://www.hci-capital.de
Sales Range: $50-74.9 Million
Emp.: 60
Financial Investment Services
N.A.I.C.S.: 525990
Ralf Friedrichs (Chm)

Hanseatische Immobilien Management GmbH (1)
Rosa-Luxemburg-Strasse 14, 18055, Rostock, Germany
Tel.: (49) 3813644554
Web Site: http://www.him-rostock.de
Real Estate Manangement Services
N.A.I.C.S.: 531390

Hanseatische Immobilien Management Niederlande GmbH (1)
Herdentorsteinweg 7, 28195, Bremen, Germany
Tel.: (49) 4213691070
Web Site: http://www.hci-capital.de
Sales Range: $50-74.9 Million
Emp.: 100
Investment Management Service
N.A.I.C.S.: 523940
Ingo Kuhlmann (Mng Dir)

ERNSTING'S FAMILY GMBH & CO. KG
Industriestrasse 1, 48653, Coesfeld, Lette, Germany
Tel.: (49) 25 4677 0
Web Site: http://www.ernstings-family.de
Sales Range: $1-4.9 Billion
Emp.: 11,000
Clothing Retailer
N.A.I.C.S.: 458110

ERO COPPER CORP.
1050 - 625 Howe Street, Vancouver, V6C 2T6, BC, Canada
Tel.: (604) 449-9244 — Ca
Web Site: https://www.erocopper.com
Year Founded: 2016
ERO—(NYSE)
Rev.: $426,392,000
Assets: $1,188,076,000

Liabilities: $645,911,000
Net Worth: $542,165,000
Earnings: $103,067,000
Emp.: 3,253
Fiscal Year-end: 12/31/22
Metal Mining Services
N.A.I.C.S.: 213114
Christopher Noel Dunn (Chm)

Subsidiaries:

NX Gold S.A. (1)
Estrada Garimpo do Araes KM18, Nova Xavantina, Mato Grosso, 78690-000, MT, Brazil
Tel.: (55) 6634387500
Web Site: https://www.nxgold.com.br
Gold Mining Services
N.A.I.C.S.: 212321

EROAD LIMITED
260 Oteha Valley Road, Albany, Auckland, New Zealand
Tel.: (64) 99274700 — NZ
Web Site: https://www.eroad.co.nz
Year Founded: 2000
ERD—(ASX)
Rev.: $104,605,263
Assets: $240,909,091
Liabilities: $92,105,263
Net Worth: $148,803,828
Earnings: ($1,794,258)
Emp.: 493
Fiscal Year-end: 03/31/23
Transport Services
N.A.I.C.S.: 488490
Tony Warwood (Gen Mgr-Australia & New Zealand)

Subsidiaries:

Coretex Limited (1)
73 Remuera Rd, Remuera, Auckland, 1050, New Zealand
Tel.: (64) 9 373 7250
Web Site: http://www.coretex.com
Fleet Management Technology
N.A.I.C.S.: 334220
Tracey Herman (CFO)

Subsidiary (US):

Air-Trak (2)
11353 Sorrento Valley Rd, San Diego, CA 92121-1303
Tel.: (858) 677-9950
Web Site: http://www.air-trak.com
Sales Range: $1-9.9 Million
Emp.: 17
GPS Tracker Device Solutions & Fleet Management Services
N.A.I.C.S.: 334220
Dave Gelvin (Pres & CEO)

Coretex USA Inc. (1)
15110 Ave of Science Ste 100, San Diego, CA 92128
Web Site: https://www.coretex.com
Software Development Services
N.A.I.C.S.: 541511

EROGLU HOLDING AS
Zafer Mahallesi Cinar Sokak No 2 Kat 1, Istanbul, Turkiye
Tel.: (90) 212 653 27 00
Web Site: http://www.erogluholding.com
Year Founded: 1983
Holding Company
N.A.I.C.S.: 551112
Nurettin Eroglu (Chm)

Subsidiaries:

Colin's Belarus (1)
Veri Kharujey 25-3 Floor 9 Office No 901, Minsk, Belarus
Tel.: (375) 172377597
Emp.: 165
Clothing Accessory Distr
N.A.I.C.S.: 458110

Colin's Russia (1)
Vil Rumyantsevo Business Centre Building 1 Enterance 1-2 Floor 5, Leninsky, 142784,

Moscow, Russia
Tel.: (7) 4959338469
Clothing Accessory Distr
N.A.I.C.S.: 458110
Umit Degirmenci (Dir-Fin)

Colin's Ukraine (1)
Lukyanivskaya Street No 23, 04071, Kiev, Ukraine
Tel.: (380) 444999407
Clothing Accessory Distr
N.A.I.C.S.: 458110

Collins GmbH & Co. KG. (1)
Domstrasse 10, 20095, Hamburg, Germany
Tel.: (49) 406385690
Web Site: http://www.project-collins.com
Online Shopping Services
N.A.I.C.S.: 424130
Linda Dettmann (Head-Product Mgmt)

ERKA-AS (1)
Mutlukent Mahallesi Hekimkoy Sitesi 1934 Sok No 6 Umitkoy, Cankaya, 06810, Ankara, Turkiye
Tel.: (90) 3124728958
Web Site: http://www.erkaas.com.tr
Construction Management Services
N.A.I.C.S.: 236220

EROGLU GIYIM SAN. TIC. INC. - AKSARAY FACTORY (1)
Organize Sanayi Bolgesi Mehmet Altinsoy Bulvari No 19, Aksaray, Turkiye
Tel.: (90) 3822662113
Apparel Distr
N.A.I.C.S.: 458110

EROGLU GIYIM SAN. TIC. INC. - CORLU FACTORY (1)
Yulafli Koyu Tavsantepe Mevki Corlu-Tekirdag, Corlu, Turkiye
Tel.: (90) 2826764285
Apparel Distr
N.A.I.C.S.: 458110

EROGLU GIYIM SAN. TIC. INC. - EGYPT FACTORY (1)
Public Free Zone Ismailia, Ismailia, Egypt
Tel.: (20) 1724277
Apparel Distr
N.A.I.C.S.: 458110

ERPA Dis Ticaret Paz, VE San LTD STI (1)
Arikoy Toplu Yapi Alisveris Merkezy Macka SK 628/6, Uskumrukoy-Syriyter, Istanbul, Turkiye
Tel.: (90) 2122030065
Consumer Products Distr
N.A.I.C.S.: 423620
Aykut Dolgun (Gen Mgr)

Eryap Construction and Trade Inc. (1)
Mutlukent Quarter 1943 Street No 14 Umitkoy Cankaya, Ankara, Turkiye
Tel.: (90) 312 440 79 63
Web Site: http://www.eryap.com.tr
Construction Management Services
N.A.I.C.S.: 236220

Loft Magazacilik INC. (1)
Zafer Mahallesi Bahargulu Sokak No 2 Kat 2, Istanbul, Turkiye
Tel.: (90) 4445969
Web Site: http://www.loft.com.tr
Apparel Distr
N.A.I.C.S.: 458110
Aydin Suha (Head-Sls & Mktg)

Mexx Pazarlama INC. (1)
Zafer Mh Cinar Sk 2/5, Yenibosna Bahcelievler, Istanbul, Turkiye
Tel.: (90) 2126532700
Apparel Distr
N.A.I.C.S.: 458110

EROS INTERNATIONAL PLC
IQ EQ First Names House Victoria Road, Douglas, IM2 4DF, Isle of Man
Tel.: (44) 1624630630 — IM
Web Site: http://www.erosplc.com
EROS—(NYSE)
Rev.: $155,452,000
Assets: $607,656,000
Liabilities: $299,170,000
Net Worth: $308,486,000

Earnings: ($491,704,000)
Emp.: 340
Fiscal Year-end: 03/31/20
Holding Company; Film Production & Distribution Services
N.A.I.C.S.: 551112
Kishore Arjan Lulla (Chm, CEO & Mng Dir)

Subsidiaries:

Big Screen Entertainment Pvt. Limited (1)
201 Kailash Plz Plot No A-12 Opp Laxmi Indus Estate Link Rd, Andheri W, Mumbai, 400 058, Maharashtra, India (64%)
Tel.: (91) 2266918500
Web Site: http://www.bigscreen.co.in
Sales Range: $25-49.9 Million
Emp.: 50
Movies Production & Distribution Services
N.A.I.C.S.: 512110
Kumar Mangat (Mng Dir)

Eros (Pacific) Pvt. Ltd. (1)
92 Kennedy Avenue, PO Box 1802, Nadi, Fiji
Tel.: (679) 6707722
Web Site: http://www.erosentertainment.com
Sales Range: $25-49.9 Million
Emp.: 3
Film Production & Distribution Services
N.A.I.C.S.: 512110
Jack Raniga (Mng Dir)

Eros Australia Pvt. Ltd. (1)
U6/16 Mercer St, Castle Hill, 2154, NSW, Australia
Tel.: (61) 286266863
Motion Picture Distr
N.A.I.C.S.: 512120

Eros International (1)
Unit 23 Sovereign Park Coronation Road Park Royal, London, NW10 7QP, United Kingdom
Tel.: (44) 2079352727
Web Site: http://www.erosentertainment.com
Sales Range: $25-49.9 Million
Emp.: 20
Film Production & Distribution Services
N.A.I.C.S.: 512110

Subsidiary (Domestic):

Eros Network Limited (2)
Unit 23 Sovereign Park Coronation Rd Park Royal, London, NW10 7QP, United Kingdom
Tel.: (44) 2079352727
Film Production & Distribution Services
N.A.I.C.S.: 512110

Eros International Media Ltd. (1)
901902 Supreme Chambers, Off Veera Desai Road, Mumbai, 400053, Maharashtra, India (62.39%)
Tel.: (91) 2266021500
Web Site: https://erosmediaworld.com
Rev.: $53,061,645
Assets: $329,497,350
Liabilities: $185,676,855
Net Worth: $143,820,495
Earnings: ($24,687,390)
Emp.: 191
Fiscal Year-end: 03/31/2021
Movie Production & Distribution Services
N.A.I.C.S.: 512110
Sunil Lulla (Vice Chm & Mng Dir)

Eros International Pte Ltd. (1)
3 Phillip Street 18-00 Commerce Point, Singapore, 048693, Singapore
Tel.: (65) 6734 4993
Oil Distr
N.A.I.C.S.: 512120

Eros International USA Inc. (1)
550 County Ave, Secaucus, NJ 07094
Tel.: (201) 558-9001
Holding Company; Entertainment Media Production & Distribution
N.A.I.C.S.: 551112
Prem Parameswaran (Grp Pres-North America)

Subsidiary (Domestic):

Eros Entertainment, Inc. (2)
550 County Ave, Secaucus, NJ 07094

Tel.: (201) 558-9001
Film Production & Distribution Services
N.A.I.C.S.: 512110
Kishore Arjan Lulla *(Chm)*

Eros Worldwide FZ LLC **(1)**
529 Bldg No 8 Dubai Media City, PO Box
502121, Dubai, United Arab Emirates
Tel.: (971) 43902825
Web Site: http://www.erosentertainment.com
Sales Range: $25-49.9 Million
Emp.: 7
Film Production & Distribution Services
N.A.I.C.S.: 512110
Surender Sadhwani *(Head-Middle East Ops & Syndication)*

Subsidiary (Domestic):

Eros Digital FZ LLC **(2)**
3902 Tower A Business Central Tower,
Dubai Internet City Sheikh Zayed Road,
Dubai, United Arab Emirates
Tel.: (971) 43902825
Motion Picture Production & Distribution
Services
N.A.I.C.S.: 512120
Bishwarup Chakrabarti *(Head-Legal)*

EyeQube Studios Pvt. Ltd. **(1)**
Ground Fl Satyadev Bldg Off New Link Rd,
Andheri W, Mumbai, 400053, Maharashtra,
India
Tel.: (91) 2240538600
Sales Range: $50-74.9 Million
Emp.: 150
Movie Visual Effects Creation Services
N.A.I.C.S.: 512110

Universal Power Systems Private
Limited **(1)**
Gee Gee Plaza Flat No 20 3rd Floor No1
Wheatcrofts Road, Nungambakkam, Chen-
nai, 600 034, India
Tel.: (91) 4442806060
Web Site: http://www.56060.in
Mobile Operator Services
N.A.I.C.S.: 517112

EROS RESOURCES CORP.
Suite 420 - 789 West Pender Street,
Vancouver, V6C 1H2, BC, Canada
Tel.: (604) 688-8115 BC
Web Site:
https://www.erosresourcescorp.com
Year Founded: 1981
EROSF—(OTCQB)
Rev.: $4,662
Assets: $18,554,208
Liabilities: $2,980,683
Net Worth: $15,573,525
Earnings: $848,525
Fiscal Year-end: 12/31/21
Mineral Exploration Services
N.A.I.C.S.: 213114
Ronald Kort Netolitzky *(Pres & CEO)*

EROTIK ABWICKLUNGSGES
AG
Suhrenkamp 59, 22335, Hamburg,
Germany
Tel.: (49) 40 5555080 De
Web Site: http://www.beate-uhse.ag
Year Founded: 1946
Sales Range: $150-199.9 Million
Emp.: 470
Adult Products Retailer
N.A.I.C.S.: 459999

ERPSOFT SYSTEMS LTD.
10A Tranquill Nest Kamakoti Nagar,
Pallikaranai, Chennai, 500100, India
Tel.: (91) 7338855022 In
Web Site: http://www.erpsoft.com
Year Founded: 1994
Sales Range: $1-9.9 Million
Information Technology Consulting
Services
N.A.I.C.S.: 541512
Kallurupalli Parvathi *(Mng Dir)*

Subsidiaries:

Libertycom LLC **(1)**

303 West Capitol Ste 325, Little Rock, AR
72201
Tel.: (501) 960-3302
Web Site: http://www.libertycom.com
Information Technology Consulting Services
N.A.I.C.S.: 541512

ERPSOFT SYSTEMS LTD.
10A Tranquill Nest Kamakoti Nagar,
3rd Main Road, Chennai, 600100,
India
Tel.: (91) 7338855022
Web Site: https://www.erpsoft.com
530909—(BOM)
Rev.: $1,742,054
Assets: $2,773,380
Liabilities: $579,920
Net Worth: $2,193,459
Earnings: $49,290
Emp.: 13
Fiscal Year-end: 03/31/21
Information Technology Services
N.A.I.C.S.: 541512
Radha Krishna Reddy Kakuturu
(CFO)

ERRAWARRA RESOURCES
LTD.
Level 2 10 Ord Street, West Perth,
6005, WA, Australia
Tel.: (61) 893223383 AU
Web Site: https://www.errawarra.com
Year Founded: 2012
ERW—(ASX)
Rev.: $11,195
Assets: $948,198
Liabilities: $470,826
Net Worth: $477,372
Earnings: ($1,804,131)
Fiscal Year-end: 06/30/23
Exploration & Mining Services
N.A.I.C.S.: 213115
Mindy Ku *(Sec)*

ERRE DUE S.P.A.
Via G Gozzano 3, 57121, Livorno,
Italy
Tel.: (39) 0586444066
Web Site: https://www.erreduegas.it
Year Founded: 2000
RDUE—(ITA)
Hydrogen Mfr
N.A.I.C.S.: 325120

ERRECINQUE S.R.L.
Via Meucci 31/A, 10040, Turin, TO,
Italy
Tel.: (39) 011 99 69 260
Web Site: http://www.errecinque.it
Year Founded: 1981
Sales Range: $25-49.9 Million
Emp.: 160
Rubber & Plastic Hose Mfr
N.A.I.C.S.: 326220
Piero Lovera *(CEO)*

Subsidiaries:

Errecinque S.r.l. - Bologna Plant **(1)**
Via Cimarosa 55, 40033, Casalecchio di
Reno, Bolgona, Italy
Tel.: (39) 0516133358
Plastics Product Mfr
N.A.I.C.S.: 326220

Errecinque S.r.l. - Cosenza Plant **(1)**
Loc Piano Lago, Mangone, 87050,
Cosenza, Italy
Tel.: (39) 0984969708
Plastics Product Mfr
N.A.I.C.S.: 326220

Errecinque S.r.l. - Volpiano Plant **(1)**
Via Brandizzo 176, 10088, Volpiano, Turin,
Italy
Tel.: (39) 0119881833
Plastics Product Mfr
N.A.I.C.S.: 326220

ERRIA A/S

Torvet 21 A 1st, 4600, Koge, Den-
mark
Tel.: (45) 33364400
Web Site: https://www.erria.dk
Year Founded: 1992
ERRIA—(CSE)
Rev.: $22,852
Assets: $10,004
Liabilities: $9,446
Net Worth: $558
Earnings: $1,352
Emp.: 244
Fiscal Year-end: 12/31/22
Cargo Handling Services
N.A.I.C.S.: 488320
Henrik N. Andersen *(CEO)*

Subsidiaries:

Cathy Seal Pte. Ltd. **(1)**
167 Jalan Bukit Merah 05-12 SR11 Tower
4, Singapore, 150167, Singapore
Tel.: (65) 62744041
Web Site: https://cathyseal.com
Seal Product Mfr & Distr
N.A.I.C.S.: 339991

Ibex Maritime Ltd **(1)**
Bagdat Caddesi Gokce Sok Toksoy Apt No
10/17-18, Caddebostan, 34728, Kadikoy,
Istanbul, Turkiye
Tel.: (90) 216 302 5900
Web Site: http://www.ibexmaritime.com
Ship Chartering Services
N.A.I.C.S.: 483111
Evren Ugursoy *(Mgr-Chartering)*

Mermaid Maritime Vietnam Company
Ltd. **(1)**
Road 12 Dong Xuyen Industrial Park, Rach
Dua Ward, Vung Tau, Vietnam
Tel.: (84) 2543613305
Web Site: https://www.mermaid-safety.vn
Fire Fighting Equipment Distr
N.A.I.C.S.: 423850

ERSTE ABWICKLUNGSAN-
STALT AOR
Elisabethstrasse 65, Dusseldorf,
40217, Germany
Tel.: (49) 211 826 7800 De
Web Site: http://www.aa1.de
Emp.: 130
Corporate Restructuring &
Winding-up Services
N.A.I.C.S.: 525990
Matthias Wargers *(Member-Mgmt Bd)*

Subsidiaries:

Basinghall Finance Plc. **(1)**
Gateway House Gargrave Road, Skipton,
BD23 1UD, United Kingdom
Tel.: (44) 345 130 4386
Web Site: http://www.basinghall.com
Financial Investment Services
N.A.I.C.S.: 523999

CBAL S.A. **(1)**
Boulevard De France 9, Braine-l'Alleud,
1420, Brabant Wallon, Belgium
Tel.: (32) 23528742
Financial Investment Services
N.A.I.C.S.: 523999

Dussinvest2 Beteiligungsgesellschaft
mbH **(1)**
Herzogstrasse 15, 40217, Dusseldorf, Ger-
many
Tel.: (49) 21182601
Emp.: 3
Financial Investment Services
N.A.I.C.S.: 523999

EAA Covered Bond Bank Plc **(1)**
IFSC House, Dublin, Ireland
Tel.: (353) 1 612 7133
Financial Investment Services
N.A.I.C.S.: 523999

EAA Japan K.K. **(1)**
Ark Hills Mori Tower 3f 4-5 Roppongi 1cho-
Me, Minato-Ku, Tokyo, 106-0032, Japan
Tel.: (81) 351148488
Financial Investment Services
N.A.I.C.S.: 523999

MFC Real Estate LLC **(1)**
7 World Trade Ctr 250 Greenwich St, New
York, NY 10007
Tel.: (212) 852-6000
Real Estate Development Services
N.A.I.C.S.: 531390

PE Projekt-Entwicklungsgesellschaft
mbH **(1)**
Moskauer Str 27, 40227, Dusseldorf,
Nordrhein-Westfalen, Germany
Tel.: (49) 211 9010107
Financial Investment Services
N.A.I.C.S.: 523999

Portigon Financial Services
GmbH **(1)**
Schiessstrasse 43, 40549, Dusseldorf, Ger-
many
Tel.: (49) 211 826 02
Financial Investment Services
N.A.I.C.S.: 523999
Kerstin Heidler *(Mng Dir)*

Projektentwicklungsgesellschaft Gar-
tenstadt Wildau Rothegrund II
mbH **(1)**
Wildbahn 140, 15745, Wildau, Branden-
burg, Germany
Tel.: (49) 33762 56400
Financial Investment Services
N.A.I.C.S.: 523999

WestGKA Management Gesellschaft
fur kommunale Anlagen mbH **(1)**
Martin-Luther-Platz 28, 40212, Dusseldorf,
Germany
Tel.: (49) 211 130659 0
Web Site: http://www.westgka.de
Financial Investment Services
N.A.I.C.S.: 523999

ERSTE GROUP BANK AG
Am Belvedere 1, A-1100, Vienna,
Austria
Tel.: (43) 5010010100 AT
Web Site:
https://www.erstegroup.com
Year Founded: 2007
EBS—(DUS)
Rev.: $9,305,741,420
Assets: $349,519,749,622
Liabilities: $322,210,554,716
Net Worth: $27,309,194,906
Earnings: $2,336,175,264
Emp.: 41,045
Fiscal Year-end: 12/31/22
Bank Holding Company
N.A.I.C.S.: 551111
Friedrich Rodler *(Chm-Supervisory Bd)*

Subsidiaries:

BCR Procesare SRL **(1)**
18-20 Str Lipscani, Bucharest, 030153,
Romania
Tel.: (40) 213112761
Financial Management Services
N.A.I.C.S.: 523999

BCR Social Finance IFN S.A. **(1)**
D Cantemir Street no 2/c, Oradea, Romania
Tel.: (40) 752152746
Web Site: https://www.bcr-socialfinance.ro
Financial Services
N.A.I.C.S.: 522320

Bad Leonfelden Hotelbetriebs Gesell-
schaft mbH **(1)**
Wallseerstr 10, Leonfelden, 4190, Austria
Tel.: (43) 7213 20687
Web Site:
http://www.badleonfelden.falkensteiner.com
Emp.: 50
Financial Management Services
N.A.I.C.S.: 523999

Balance Resort AG **(1)**
Panoramaweg 1, 7551, Stegersbach, Bur-
genland, Austria
Tel.: (43) 332655155
Web Site: http://www.falkensteiner.com
Financial Investment Management Services
N.A.I.C.S.: 523999

Banca Comerciala Romana S.A. **(1)**

Erste Group Bank AG—(Continued)

159 Calea Plevnei Business Garden Building A 6th floor 6th District, RO-030016, Bucharest, Romania　**(69%)**
Tel.: (40) 214074200
Web Site: https://www.bcr.ro
Sales Range: $900-999.9 Million
Emp.: 9,012
Retail & Commercial Banking Services
N.A.I.C.S.: 522110
Andreas Treichl *(Deputy Chm-Supervisory Bd)*

CSSC Customer Sales Service Center GmbH　**(1)**
Ernst-Melchior-Gasse 24, 1020, Vienna, Austria
Tel.: (43) 5010055000
Customer Care Services
N.A.I.C.S.: 561422
Andreas Konrad *(Gen Mgr)*

Ceska Sporitelna a.s.　**(1)**
Olbrachtova 1929/62, Praha 4, 140 00, Prague, Czech Republic　**(97.99%)**
Tel.: (420) 956777666
Web Site: https://www.csas.cz
Rev.: $1,009,509,840
Assets: $42,202,433,820
Liabilities: $37,385,577,720
Net Worth: $4,816,856,100
Earnings: $611,633,490
Emp.: 10,299
Fiscal Year-end: 12/31/2016
Retail, Commercial & Investment Banking Services
N.A.I.C.S.: 522110
John James Stack *(Chm-Supervisory Bd)*

Subsidiary (Domestic):

Penzijni fond Ceske sporitelny, a.s　**(2)**
Polackova 1976/2, 140 21, Prague, Czech Republic
Tel.: (420) 956777444
Web Site: http://www.csps.cz
Pension Fund Management Services
N.A.I.C.S.: 525110

Czech TOP Venture Fund B.V.　**(1)**
Postweg 11, Groesbeek, 6561 KJ, Gelderland, Netherlands
Tel.: (31) 243977577
Investment Management Service
N.A.I.C.S.: 523999

DIE ERSTE Immobilienvermietungsgesellschaft m.b.H.　**(1)**
Graben 21, Vienna, 1010, Austria
Tel.: (43) 5010020111
Investment Management Service
N.A.I.C.S.: 523999

EB-Restaurantsbetriebe Ges.m.b.H.　**(1)**
Petersplatz 4, 1010, Vienna, Austria
Tel.: (43) 5 0100 18129
Web Site: http://www.ebr.at
Sales Range: $10-24.9 Million
Emp.: 85
Restaurant Operating Services
N.A.I.C.S.: 722511

EBB Hotelbetriebs GmbH　**(1)**
Teilwiesen 1, 6460, Imst, Tyrol, Austria
Tel.: (43) 5412 66415
Financial Management Services
N.A.I.C.S.: 523999

EBV - Leasing Gesellschaft m.b.H. & Co. KG.　**(1)**
Am Belvedere 1, 1100, Vienna, Austria
Tel.: (43) 5 0100 76700
Web Site: http://www.ebv-leasing.at
Sales Range: $100-124.9 Million
Emp.: 130
Automobile Finance Leasing Services
N.A.I.C.S.: 522220

EBV-Beteiligungen GmbH　**(1)**
Linke Wienzeile 120, Vienna, 1061, Austria
Tel.: (43) 5010076700
Web Site: http://www.ebv-leasing.at
Emp.: 120
Investment Management Service
N.A.I.C.S.: 523999

ERSTE BANK AD NOVI SAD　**(1)**

Bulevar Oslobodenja No 5, 21101, Novi Sad, Serbia
Tel.: (381) 800201201
Web Site: https://www.erstebank.rs
Rev.: $214,841,161
Assets: $3,760,376,284
Liabilities: $3,299,276,448
Net Worth: $461,099,836
Earnings: $52,422,231
Fiscal Year-end: 12/31/2023
Commercial Banking Services
N.A.I.C.S.: 522110
Jasna Terzic *(Chm)*

ERSTE BANK AD PODGORICA　**(1)**
Novaka Miloseva 40, Podgorica, 81000, Montenegro
Tel.: (382) 20440440
Web Site: http://www.erstebank.me
Commercial Banking Services
N.A.I.C.S.: 522110
Lalovic Predrag *(Exec Dir)*

ERSTE CARD CLUB d.d.　**(1)**
Ulica Frana Folnegovica 6, 10000, Zagreb, Croatia
Tel.: (385) 1 4929 000
Web Site: http://www.erstecardclub.hr
Sales Range: $100-124.9 Million
Emp.: 250
Credit Card Issuing Services
N.A.I.C.S.: 522210

ERSTE DMD d.o.o.　**(1)**
Ulica Ivana Lucica 2/a, Zagreb, 10000, Croatia
Tel.: (385) 14877381
Web Site: http://www.ersteplavi.hr
Sales Range: $50-74.9 Million
Emp.: 19
Commercial Banking Services
N.A.I.C.S.: 522110
Senka Fekeza Klemen *(Member-Mgmt Bd)*

ERSTE NEKRETNINE d.o.o.　**(1)**
Ivana Lucica 2, 10000, Zagreb, Croatia
Tel.: (385) 800345346
Web Site: http://www.erstenekretnine.hr
Real Estate Development Services
N.A.I.C.S.: 531390

ESPA-Financial Advisors GmbH　**(1)**
Habsburgergasse 1a, 1010, Vienna, Austria
Tel.: (43) 5010011490
Financial Management Services
N.A.I.C.S.: 523999

Erste & Steiermarkische Bank d.d.　**(1)**
Jadranski trg 3a, 51000, Rijeka, Croatia　**(51.4%)**
Tel.: (385) 62375000
Web Site: https://www.erstebank.hr
Sales Range: $200-249.9 Million
Emp.: 2,265
Retail, Commercial & Investment Banking Services
N.A.I.C.S.: 522110
Borislav Centner *(Member-Mgmt Bd)*

Erste Alapkezelo Zrt.　**(1)**
Nepfurdo U 24-26 9 Emelet, 1138, Budapest, Hungary
Tel.: (36) 19202193
Web Site: http://www.erstebroker.hu
Securities Brokerage Services
N.A.I.C.S.: 523150
Gyorgy Tibor Mesterhazy *(CEO)*

Erste Asset Management GmbH　**(1)**
Am Belvedere 1, 1100, Vienna, Austria
Tel.: (43) 5010019054
Web Site: http://www.erste-am.com
Emp.: 150
Asset Management Services
N.A.I.C.S.: 523940
Heinz Bednar *(CEO & Member-Mgmt Bd)*

Subsidiary (Non-US):

Asset Management Slovenskej sporitelne sprav spol a s.　**(2)**
Tomasikova 48, 832 65, Bratislava, Slovakia
Tel.: (421) 850 111 888
Web Site: http://www.amslsp.sk
Asset Management Services
N.A.I.C.S.: 523940

Erste Asset Management GmbH　**(2)**
Zugspitzstrasse 2a, 85591, Vaterstetten, Germany

Tel.: (49) 8106210160
Web Site: http://www.erste-am.com
Emp.: 5
Mutual Fund Management Services
N.A.I.C.S.: 524292

Erste Bank (Malta) Limited　**(1)**
72 Regent House Bisazza Street, Sliema, SLM 1641, Malta
Tel.: (356) 21347161
Sales Range: $50-74.9 Million
Emp.: 5
Commercial Banking Services
N.A.I.C.S.: 522110

Erste Bank Hungary Nyrt.　**(1)**
Nepfurdo U 24-26, 1138, Budapest, Hungary　**(99.95%)**
Tel.: (36) 12980222
Web Site: http://www.erstebank.hu
Sales Range: $300-349.9 Million
Emp.: 3,181
Retail, Commercial & Investment Banking Services
N.A.I.C.S.: 522110

Subsidiary (Domestic):

Commerzbank Zrt.　**(2)**
Szechenyi Rakpart 8, 1054, Budapest, Hungary
Tel.: (36) 13748100
Web Site: http://www.commerzbank.hu
Commercial Banking Services
N.A.I.C.S.: 522110
Krisztina Fulopne Bogdan *(Member-Mgmt Bd)*

Erste Bank d.d.　**(1)**
Bulevar oslobodenja 5, 21000, Novi Sad, Serbia
Tel.: (381) 214873510
Web Site: http://www.erstebank.rs
Sales Range: $400-449.9 Million
Emp.: 909
Retail & Commercial Banking Services
N.A.I.C.S.: 522110

Erste Bank der oesterreichischen Sparkassen AG　**(1)**
Am Belvedere 1, 1100, Vienna, Austria
Tel.: (43) 5010020111
Web Site: https://www.sparkasse.at
Emp.: 14,900
Retail, Commercial & Investment Banking Services
N.A.I.C.S.: 522110
Friedrich Rodler *(Chm-Supervisory Bd)*

Subsidiary (Domestic):

Erste Bank AG　**(2)**
Graben 21, 2020, Vienna, Austria
Tel.: (43) 5 0100 25800
Retail & Commercial Banking Services
N.A.I.C.S.: 522180
Volker Dahlhausen *(Second Vice Chm-Supervisory Bd)*

Salzburger Sparkasse Bank AG　**(2)**
Alter Markt 3, PO Box 180, 5021, Salzburg, Austria
Tel.: (43) 5010041000
Web Site: http://www.sparkasse.at
Retail & Commercial Banking Services
N.A.I.C.S.: 522180

Sparkasse Hainburg-Bruck-Neusiedl AG　**(2)**
Hauptplatz 1, A D Donau, 2410, Hainburg, Austria
Tel.: (43) 5010020216
Web Site: http://www.sparkasse.at
Retail & Commercial Banking Services
N.A.I.C.S.: 522180

Tiroler Sparkasse Bank AG　**(2)**
Sparkassenplatz 1, PO Box 245, 6010, Innsbruck, Austria
Tel.: (43) 5010070000
Web Site: http://www.sparkasse.at
Retail & Commercial Banking Services
N.A.I.C.S.: 522180

Erste Corporate Finance, a.s.　**(1)**
Na Perstyne 1/342, 11000, Prague, Czech Republic
Tel.: (420) 224 995 166
Commercial Banking Services
N.A.I.C.S.: 522110

Erste Digital GmbH　**(1)**
Am Belvedere 1, 1100, Vienna, Austria
Tel.: (43) 5010010400
Web Site: https://www.erstedigital.com
Information Technology Services
N.A.I.C.S.: 541511

Erste Faktor Penzugyi Szolgaltato Zrt.　**(1)**
Vaci ut 48, 1132, Budapest, Hungary
Tel.: (36) 40 222 228
Financial Management Services
N.A.I.C.S.: 523999

Erste Group Procurement　**(1)**
Am Heumarkt 4, 1030, Vienna, Austria
Tel.: (43) 5 0100 28000
Web Site: http://www.s-proserv.at
Sales Range: $25-49.9 Million
Emp.: 60
Procurement Services
N.A.I.C.S.: 561990

Erste Kereskedohaz Kft.　**(1)**
Nepfurdo Utca 24-26, Budapest, 1138, Hungary
Tel.: (36) 12684139
Investment Management Service
N.A.I.C.S.: 523999

Erste Private Equity Limited　**(1)**
68 Cornhill, London, EC3V 3QE, United Kingdom
Tel.: (44) 2076215000
Sales Range: $50-74.9 Million
Emp.: 50
Security Brokerage Services
N.A.I.C.S.: 523150
Aduard Oxwald *(Gen Mgr)*

Erste Securities Istanbul Menkul Degerler AS　**(1)**
Buyukdere Cad No 14 Kanyon Ofis Blogu, 34394, Istanbul, Levent, Turkiye
Tel.: (90) 2123712500
Web Site: http://www.erstesecuritiesistanbul.com.tr
Sales Range: $50-74.9 Million
Emp.: 20
Mutual Fund Management Services
N.A.I.C.S.: 524292

Erste Securities Polska S.A.　**(1)**
ul Krolewska 16, 00-103, Warsaw, Poland
Tel.: (48) 225386200
Web Site: http://www.esp.pl
Securities Brokerage Services
N.A.I.C.S.: 523150
Piotr Prazmo *(CFO & Member-Mgmt Bd)*

Erste-Sparinvest Kapitalanlagegesellschaft m.b.H.　**(1)**
Habsburgergasse 1a, 1010, Vienna, 1010, Austria
Tel.: (43) 5010019881
Web Site: http://www.erste-am.com
Emp.: 300
Financial Management Services
N.A.I.C.S.: 523999

F&S Finance and Service Leasing GmbH　**(1)**
Blumenstrasse 22, 70736, Fellbach, Germany
Tel.: (49) 711 933 83 0
Web Site: http://www.finance-and-service.com
Financial Lending Services
N.A.I.C.S.: 522220

Factoring Ceske sporitelny a.s.　**(1)**
Budejovicka 1912/64b, Praha 4, 140 00, Prague, Czech Republic
Tel.: (420) 956770711
Web Site: https://www.factoringcs.cz
Factoring Services
N.A.I.C.S.: 522299
Martin Stepka *(Dir-Sls)*

Financiara SA　**(1)**
15 Calea Victoriei, Bucharest, 030023, Romania
Tel.: (40) 213130154
Financial Management Services
N.A.I.C.S.: 523999

Flottenmanagement GmbH　**(1)**
Am Belvedere 1, 1100, Vienna, Austria
Tel.: (43) 5010027652

Web Site:
   http://www.flottenmanagement.co.at
Fleet Leasing Services
N.A.I.C.S.: 532112

GRANTIKA Ceske sporitelny,
a.s.   (1)
Jakubske nam 127/5, 602 00, Brno, Czech
Republic
Tel.: (420) 542210148
Web Site: http://www.grantikacs.cz
Sales Range: $50-74.9 Million
Emp.: 40
Commercial Banking Services
N.A.I.C.S.: 522110
Lukas Nemec *(Gen Mgr)*

Hochkonig Bergbahnen
Ges.m.b.H   (1)
Schloglberg 63, Muhlbach am Hochkonig,
5505, Austria
Tel.: (43) 64677214
Web Site: http://www.hochkonig.at
Sales Range: $50-74.9 Million
Emp.: 100
Financial Investment Management Services
N.A.I.C.S.: 523999
Michael Emberger *(Gen Mgr)*

IMMORENT Aktiengesellschaft   (1)
Windmuhlgasse 22-24, Vienna, 1060, Aus-
tria
Tel.: (43) 5010027000
Web Site: http://www.immorent.at
Real Estate Management Services
N.A.I.C.S.: 531390

IMMORENT BETA, leasing druzba,
d.o.o.   (1)
Cesta v Klece 15, Ljubljana, 1000, Slovenia
Tel.: (386) 1 513 88 00
Commercial Banking Services
N.A.I.C.S.: 522110
Mateja Sitar *(Head-Fin & Ops)*

IMMORENT
S-Immobilienmanagement
GesmbH   (1)
Windmuhlgasse 22-24, 1060, Vienna, Aus-
tria
Tel.: (43) 5 0100 27000
Financial Management Services
N.A.I.C.S.: 523999

IMMORENT-RAMON Grundverw-
ertungsgesellschaft m.b.H.   (1)
Windmuhlgasse 22-24, Vienna, 1060, Aus-
tria
Tel.: (43) 1588940
Investment Management Service
N.A.I.C.S.: 523999

Immorent-
Mobilienvermietungsgesellschaft
m.b.H. & Co Leasing 89 KG   (1)
Windmuhlgasse 22-24, Vienna, 1060, Aus-
tria
Tel.: (43) 1588940
Web Site: http://www.erstegroup.com
Sales Range: $100-124.9 Million
Emp.: 200
Financial Management Services
N.A.I.C.S.: 523999

Informations Technologie Austria SK
spol. s r.o.   (1)
Lassallestrabe 5, Vienna, 1020, Austria
Tel.: (43) 12171730
Commercial Banking Services
N.A.I.C.S.: 522110

Luitpoldpark-Hotel Betriebs- und
Vermietungsgesellschaft mbH   (1)
Bahnhofstr 1-3, Fussen, 87629, Germany
Tel.: (49) 83629040
Web Site: http://www.luitpoldpark-hotel.de
Sales Range: $10-24.9 Million
Emp.: 50
Home Management Services
N.A.I.C.S.: 721110

OM Objektmanagement GmbH   (1)
Traungasse 12, 1030, Vienna, Austria
Tel.: (43) 5 0100 13025
Web Site: http://www.objektmanagement.at
Sales Range: $25-49.9 Million
Emp.: 220
Facilities Management Services
N.A.I.C.S.: 561210

PARAGON Hotelbetriebs GmbH   (1)
Paragonstrabe 1, 1110, Vienna, Austria
Tel.: (43) 17431777
Web Site: http://www.roomshotels.com
General Insurance Services
N.A.I.C.S.: 524210
Stefanie Karbe *(Gen Mgr)*

Public Company Erste Bank   (1)
Polova 24 D, Kiev, Ukraine
Tel.: (380) 44 593 00 00
Web Site: http://www.erstebank.ua
Commercial Banking Services
N.A.I.C.S.: 522110

REICO investicni spolecnost Ceske
sporitelny, a.s.   (1)
Budejovicka alej Antala Staska 79, 140 00,
Prague, Czech Republic
Tel.: (420) 956786511
Web Site: http://www.reico.cz
Sales Range: $50-74.9 Million
Emp.: 9
Real Estate Fund Management Services
N.A.I.C.S.: 522292

RINGTURM Kapitalanlagegesell-
schaft m.b.H.   (1)
Habsburgergasse 2, Vienna, 1010, Austria
Tel.: (43) 5010019709
Web Site: http://www.ringturm.at
Sales Range: $50-74.9 Million
Emp.: 17
Mutual Fund Management Services
N.A.I.C.S.: 523940

RUTAR INTERNATIONAL trgovinska
d.o.o.   (1)
15 Cesta V Klece, Ljubljana, 1000, Slovenia
Tel.: (386) 15138800
Web Site:
   http://www.earthgroupimmorant.com
Sales Range: $50-74.9 Million
Emp.: 8
Real Estate Lending Services
N.A.I.C.S.: 531190
Andreja Tonin *(Gen Mgr)*

S MORAVA Leasing, a.s.   (1)
Horni namesti 264/18, 669 02, Znojmo,
Czech Republic
Tel.: (420) 515200511
Web Site: http://www.smorava.cz
Sales Range: $50-74.9 Million
Emp.: 60
Financial Lending Services
N.A.I.C.S.: 522220

S Servis, s.r.o.   (1)
Horni Namesti 264/18, 669 02, Znojmo,
Czech Republic
Tel.: (420) 737270438
Web Site: http://www.s-servis.cz
Insurance Brokerage Services
N.A.I.C.S.: 524210

S-Immobilien Weinviertler Sparkasse
GmbH   (1)
Hauptplatz 10, Hollabrunn, 2020, Austria
Tel.: (43) 5010025800
Financial Management Services
N.A.I.C.S.: 523999

S-Real Morava spol. s.r.o.   (1)
Horni Namesti 264/18, Znojmo, 66902,
Czech Republic
Tel.: (420) 515261950
Financial Management Services
N.A.I.C.S.: 523999

S-Tourismusfonds Management
Aktiengesellschaft   (1)
Fleischmarkt 18/14, 1010, Vienna, Austria
Tel.: (43) 5010025251
Web Site: http://www.s-tourismusfonds.at
Sales Range: $50-74.9 Million
Emp.: 12
Tourism Funding Services
N.A.I.C.S.: 525990
Johann Lassachaer *(Mng Dir)*

SAI Erste Asset Management
S.A.   (1)
92 Aviatorilor Bvd, Bucharest, Romania
Tel.: (40) 372269999
Web Site: https://www.erste-am.ro
Asset Management Services
N.A.I.C.S.: 523940
Heinz Bednar *(Chm-Supervisory Bd)*

SC Bucharest Financial Plazza
SRL   (1)
Calea Victoriei 15, Bucharest, Romania
Tel.: (40) 213104020
Financial Management Services
N.A.I.C.S.: 523999

SPV-Druck Gesellschaft m.b.H   (1)
Grimmelshausengasse 1, 1030, Vienna,
Austria
Tel.: (43) 5010028203
Book Printing Services
N.A.I.C.S.: 323117

Slovenska Sporitelna, a.s.   (1)
Tomasikova 48, 832 37, Bratislava,
Slovakia   (100%)
Tel.: (421) 850111888
Web Site: https://www.slsp.sk
Sales Range: $350-399.9 Million
Emp.: 4,238
Retail, Commercial & Investment Banking
Services
N.A.I.C.S.: 522110
Peter Krutil *(Chm & CEO)*

Sparkasse Kremstal Pyhrn
Aktiengesellschaft   (1)
Hauptplatz 18, 4560, Kirchdorf am Inn, Aus-
tria
Tel.: (43) 5010049126
Web Site: http://www.sparkasse.at
Asset Management Services
N.A.I.C.S.: 523940

Sparkasse Muhlviertel West Bank
Aktiengesellschaft   (1)
Markt 17, Ulrichsberg, 416, Austria
Tel.: (43) 72882226
Commercial Banking Services
N.A.I.C.S.: 522110

Sparkassenbeteiligungs und Service
AG fur Oberosterreich und
Salzburg   (1)
Promenade 11-13, 4020, Linz, Austria
Tel.: (43) 73273912725
Web Site: http://www.sparkasse-ooe.at
Financial Management Services
N.A.I.C.S.: 523999

Steiermarkische Bank und Sparkas-
sen AG   (1)
Sparkassenplatz 4, A-8010, Graz, Austria
Tel.: (43) 5 0100 36000
Web Site: http://www.steiermaerkische.at
Rev.: $318,712,156
Assets: $19,258,456,392
Liabilities: $17,201,497,544
Net Worth: $2,056,958,848
Earnings: $221,284,336
Emp.: 2,719
Fiscal Year-end: 12/31/2019
Banking Services
N.A.I.C.S.: 522110
Gerhard Fabisch *(CEO & Member-Mgmt
Bd)*

Subsidiary (Non-US):

Ohridska Banka A.D.   (2)
Orce Nikolov 54, 1000, Skopje, North
Macedonia
Tel.: (389) 23167600
Web Site: http://www.ohridskabanka.mk
Sales Range: Less than $1 Million
Banking Services
N.A.I.C.S.: 522110

Sparkasse Bank d.d.   (2)
Zmaja od Bosne 7, Sarajevo, Bosnia &
Herzegovina   (97.02%)
Tel.: (387) 33280300
Web Site: http://www.sparkasse.ba
Rev.: $32,893,047
Assets: $1,146,751,692
Liabilities: $1,003,865,295
Net Worth: $142,886,398
Earnings: $13,932,737
Emp.: 504
Fiscal Year-end: 12/31/2022
Banking Services
N.A.I.C.S.: 523150
Nedim Alihodzic *(Exec Dir-Corp, IT & Org,
Property & Security Mgmt & Assests)*

Tirolinvest Kapitalanlagegesellschaft
mbH   (1)
Sparkassenplatz 1, Innsbruck, 6010, Tyrol,
Austria

Tel.: (43) 5010070094
Web Site: http://www.tirolinvest.at
Asset Management Services
N.A.I.C.S.: 523940

good.bee Holding GmbH   (1)
Friedrichstrasse 10 4th Level, 1010, Vienna,
Austria
Tel.: (43) 5010016364
Web Site: http://www.goodbee.com
Financial Support Services
N.A.I.C.S.: 525990

good.bee Service RO SRL   (1)
6C Timisoara Blv 3rd Floor Sector 6, Bu-
charest, 061328, Romania
Tel.: (40) 21 266 77 01
Web Site: http://www.goodbee.ro
Financial Transaction Services
N.A.I.C.S.: 522320
Catalan Moisie *(Gen Mgr)*

s Autoleasing GmbH   (1)
Linke Wienzeile 120, 1061, Vienna, Austria
Tel.: (43) 5010027700
Web Site: http://www.sautoleasing.at
Emp.: 120
Automobile Finance Leasing Services
N.A.I.C.S.: 522220
Michael Steiner *(Mgr-Site)*

s Autoleasing a.s.   (1)
Budejovicka 1912/64B, 140 00, Prague,
Czech Republic
Tel.: (420) 956785111
Web Site: http://www.sautoleasing.cz
Finance Leasing Services
N.A.I.C.S.: 522220

s IT Solutions CZ, s.r.o.   (1)
Antala Staska 32/1292, Prague, 14000,
Czech Republic
Tel.: (420) 956 783 102
Web Site: http://www.s-itsolutions.cz
Sales Range: $150-199.9 Million
Emp.: 600
Information Technology Consulting Services
N.A.I.C.S.: 541512

s IT Solutions HR drustvo s ograni-
cenom odgovornoscu za usluge infor-
macijskih tehnologija   (1)
Jurja Haulika 19A, 43000, Bjelovar, Croatia
Tel.: (385) 62 37 3388
Web Site: http://www.s-itsolutions.hr
Emp.: 90
Information Technology Consulting Services
N.A.I.C.S.: 541512

s Proserv Hungary - Procurement
Services HU Kft.   (1)
Nepfurdo str 24-26, 1138, Budapest, Hun-
gary
Tel.: (36) 13732780
Emp.: 11
Real Estate Development Services
N.A.I.C.S.: 531390
Calin Valcea *(Mng Dir)*

s Proserv Slovakia - Procurement
Services SK, s.r.o.   (1)
Mileticova 60, 816 10, Bratislava, Slovakia
Tel.: (421) 2 5850 6610
Real Estate Development Services
N.A.I.C.S.: 531390

s Real Sparkasse d.o.o.   (1)
Cesta v Klece 1515, 1000, Ljubljana, Slove-
nia
Tel.: (386) 15832330
Web Site: http://www.sreal.si
Real Estate Management Services
N.A.I.C.S.: 531390

s Wohnbaubank AG   (1)
Am Belvedere 1, 1100, Vienna, Austria
Tel.: (43) 5010029157
Web Site: http://www.swohnbaubank.at
Commercial Banking Services
N.A.I.C.S.: 522110

s Wohnfinanzierung Beratungs
GmbH   (1)
Am Belvedere 1, 1100, Vienna, Austria
Tel.: (43) 5010029097
Web Site: http://www.swohnfinanz.at
Financial Investment Management Services
N.A.I.C.S.: 523999

**ERSU MEYVE VE GIDA
SANAYI A.S.**

Ersu Meyve ve Gida Sanayi A.S.—(Continued)
Ziya Gokalp Mah Irmak Sokak No 3,
Eregli, 42310, Konya, Turkiye
Tel.: (90) 3327345656
Web Site: https://www.ersu.com.tr
Year Founded: 1969
ERSU—(IST)
Juice Concentrate Mfr & Whslr
N.A.I.C.S.: 311411
Kamile Tunc (Vice Chm)

ERWE IMMOBILIEN AG
Herriotstrasse 1, 60528, Frankfurt am
Main, Germany
Tel.: (49) 69963768690
Web Site: https://www.erwe-ag.com
Year Founded: 2000
ERWE—(STU)
Rev.: $8,515,903
Assets: $237,536,679
Liabilities: $179,745,090
Net Worth: $57,791,590
Earnings: ($10,965,689)
Emp.: 47
Fiscal Year-end: 12/31/21
Real Estate Investment Services
N.A.I.C.S.: 531210

ERWEKA GMBH
Otto Strasse 20-22, Heusenstamm,
63150, Germany
Tel.: (49) 610469030
Web Site: http://www.erweka.com
Year Founded: 1951
Rev.: $17,448,261
Emp.: 75
Pharmaceutical Testing Equipment
Mfr
N.A.I.C.S.: 339112
Werner G. Muller (Co-Owner & Mng
Dir)

ERWIN HALDER KG
Erwin Halder Strasse 5-9, Bronnen,
88480, Achstetten, Germany
Tel.: (49) 739270090
Web Site: http://www.halder.com
Year Founded: 1938
Rev.: $40,107,434
Emp.: 200
Industrial Product Distr
N.A.I.C.S.: 339999
Subsidiaries:

Halder Schneidtechnik GmbH **(1)**
Gleiwitzer Strasse 2a, Eching, 85386, Ger-
many
Tel.: (49) 8937499480
Web Site:
http://www.halderschneidtechnik.de
Machine Tool Distr
N.A.I.C.S.: 423830

ERWIN MULLER GRUPPE GMBH
Breslauer Strasse 34-38, 49808, Lin-
gen, Germany
Tel.: (49) 59191400
Web Site: http://www.emco-group.de
Year Founded: 1949
Sales Range: $150-199.9 Million
Emp.: 1,200
Art Photo Presentation & Office Prod-
uct Distr
N.A.I.C.S.: 459410
Subsidiaries:

Dahle Burotechnik GmbH **(1)**
Karchestrasse 3 7, Coburg, 96450, Ger-
many
Tel.: (49) 95612780
Web Site: http://www.dahle.de
Sales Range: $50-74.9 Million
Emp.: 190
Mfr of Art, Photo, Presentation & Office
Products
N.A.I.C.S.: 459410

Novus Dahle GmbH & Co. KG **(1)**
Breslauer Strasse 34-38, D-49803, Lingen,
Germany
Tel.: (49) 591 9140 0
Web Site: http://www.novus-dahle.com
Mfr of Art, Photo, Presentation & Office
Products
N.A.I.C.S.: 459410

Subsidiary (US):

Dahle North America, Inc. **(2)**
49 Vose Farm Rd, Peterborough, NH
03458-1792
Tel.: (603) 924-0003
Web Site: http://www.dahle.com
Sales Range: $25-49.9 Million
Emp.: 13
Mfr of Art & Photo Tools & Other Office Re-
lated Products
N.A.I.C.S.: 333310
Scott Prokop (VP & Gen Mgr)

ERYMA SOGETREL GROUP
143 Avenue de Verdun, 92130, Issy-
les-Moulineaux, France
Tel.: (33) 1 69 10 78 40
Web Site: http://ww.eryma.com
Year Founded: 2007
Electronic Equipment Distr
N.A.I.C.S.: 423690
Xavier Hebert (Sls Dir)

ES CERAMICS TECHNOLOGY BHD
Lot 37 39 & 41 Lengkok Rishah 2
Kawasan Perindustrian Silibin, 30100,
Ipoh, Perak Darul Ridzua, Malaysia
Tel.: (60) 55283041
Web Site:
https://www.esceramics.com.my
ESCERAM—(KLS)
Rev.: $57,410,186
Assets: $63,298,258
Liabilities: $29,212,243
Net Worth: $34,086,015
Earnings: $4,828,399
Emp.: 415
Fiscal Year-end: 05/31/23
Ceramic Materials Mfr
N.A.I.C.S.: 327110
Fook Lin Wong (CEO)
Subsidiaries:

Easy Sun Sdn. Bhd. **(1)**
37 39 41 Lengkok Rishah 2, Kawasan Perindustrian Silibin, 30100, Ipoh, Perak, Malaysia
Tel.: (60) 55283041
Latex Gloves Mfr
N.A.I.C.S.: 326299

Euroceramic Technologies Co.,
Ltd. **(1)**
138 Moo 5 Kanchanawanich Road, Samna-
kkham, Sadao, 90320, Songkhla, Thailand
Tel.: (66) 74301536
Latex Gloves Mfr
N.A.I.C.S.: 326299

Evermix Concrete Sdn. Bhd. **(1)**
C-3-G One Kesas Jalan Bayu Laut
15d/Ks09 Kota Bayu Emas Pendamar,
41200, Klang, Selangor Darul Ehsan, Ma-
laysia
Tel.: (60) 331656748
Web Site: https://www.evermixconcrete.com
Ready Mix Mfr
N.A.I.C.S.: 327320

ES CUBE CO., LTD.
12th Fl Nonhyeon Building 556
Gangnam-daero, Gangnam-gu,
Seoul, Korea (South)
Tel.: (82) 234464875
Web Site: http://www.liveplex.co.kr
Year Founded: 1977
050120—(KRS)
Rev.: $57,688,871
Assets: $93,348,052
Liabilities: $8,671,825
Net Worth: $84,676,227

Earnings: $19,703,495
Emp.: 25
Fiscal Year-end: 12/31/22
Camping Tent Mfr & Whslr
N.A.I.C.S.: 336214
Ahn Kyung Hwan (CEO)
Subsidiaries:

Seouleaguer Co. Ltd. **(1)**
4F Bedro Bldg 10 Nonhyeon-ro 163-gil,
Gangnam-gu, Seoul, Korea (South)
Tel.: (82) 221385281
Web Site: http://www.playtech.co.kr
Rev.: $7,752,020
Assets: $29,272,072
Liabilities: $6,182,928
Net Worth: $23,089,143
Earnings: ($4,897,550)
Emp.: 21
Fiscal Year-end: 12/31/2022
Mobile Phone Accessories Mfr
N.A.I.C.S.: 335999
Jaekyu Lee (Gen Dir)

ES GLOBAL LTD
3 Vyner Street, London, E2 9DG,
United Kingdom
Tel.: (44) 20 7055 7200
Web Site:
http://www.esglobalsolutions.com
Sales Range: $50-74.9 Million
Outdoor Staging
N.A.I.C.S.: 711310
Jeff Burke (Co-CEO)

ES GROUP (HOLDINGS) LIMITED
8 Ubi Road 2 06-26 Zervex, Singa-
pore, 408538, Singapore
Tel.: (65) 67489111
Web Site:
https://www.esgroup.com.sg
Year Founded: 1975
5RC—(SES)
Rev.: $24,053,609
Assets: $25,749,574
Liabilities: $8,391,695
Net Worth: $17,357,879
Earnings: ($1,568,955)
Fiscal Year-end: 12/31/22
Cargo Handling Services
N.A.I.C.S.: 488320
Ken Chee Wee Low (CEO & COO)
Subsidiaries:

Dalian ES Marine & Offshore Engi-
neering Co., Ltd. **(1)**
Tel.: (86) 41182529272
Web Site: http://www.esgroup.com
Emp.: 20
Marine & Offshore Engineering Services
N.A.I.C.S.: 541330
Marco Chanz (Gen Mgr)

Eng Soon Engineering (1999) Pte
Ltd **(1)**
8 Ubi Road 2 No 06-26 Zervex, Singapore,
408538, Singapore
Tel.: (65) 67528017
Mechanical Engineering Services
N.A.I.C.S.: 541330

Eng Soon Investment Pte Ltd **(1)**
8 Ubi Rd 2, Singapore, 408538, Singapore
Tel.: (65) 67489111
Marine Supply Whslr
N.A.I.C.S.: 441222

ES INDUSTRY CO LTD
104-10 Bongsin-ro, Asan, Dunpo-
myeon, Korea (South)
Tel.: (82) 7086674522
Year Founded: 2007
Electric Drill Mfr
N.A.I.C.S.: 333515

ES NETWORKS CO., LTD.
JP Tower 23rd floor 2-7-2
Marunouchi, Chiyoda-ku, Tokyo, 100-
7023, Japan

Tel.: (81) 368266000
Web Site: https://www.esnet.co.jp
Year Founded: 1999
5867—(TKS)
Rev.: $19,220,990
Assets: $15,725,620
Liabilities: $5,835,070
Net Worth: $9,890,550
Earnings: $964,240
Emp.: 1,512
Fiscal Year-end: 12/31/23
Management Consulting Services
N.A.I.C.S.: 541613
Yoshinori Takabatake (Pres & CEO)

ES-CON JAPAN LTD.
20F Okura Prestige Tower 2-10-4
Toranomon, Minato-ku, Tokyo, 105-
0001, Japan
Tel.: (81) 362309303
Web Site: https://www.es-
conjapan.co.jp
Year Founded: 1995
8892—(TKS)
Rev.: $785,671,210
Assets: $2,641,990,560
Liabilities: $2,174,650,340
Net Worth: $467,340,220
Earnings: $66,430,500
Emp.: 398
Fiscal Year-end: 03/31/24
Real Estate Services
N.A.I.C.S.: 531390
Takatoshi Ito (Pres)
Subsidiaries:

ES-CON Asset Management Co.,
Ltd. **(1)**
The Okura Prestige Tower 20F 2-10-4 Tora-
nomon, Minato-ku, Tokyo, 105-0001, Japan
Tel.: (81) 362309338
Web Site: https://www.esconam.jp
Real Estate Investment Services
N.A.I.C.S.: 531210
Sumihiko Makino (Dir-Investment)

ES-CON Living Service Ltd. **(1)**
5-1-4 Toranomon, Minato-ku, Tokyo, 105-
0001, Japan,
Tel.: (81) 343357331
Web Site: https://www.esconls.co.jp
Real Estate Services
N.A.I.C.S.: 531210
Masaru Tanaka (CEO)

ESCON Japan REIT Investment
Corp. **(1)**
The Okura Prestige Tower 20F 2 10 4,
Toranomon Minato-ku, Tokyo, 1050001,
Japan
Tel.: (81) 362309338
Web Site: https://www.escon-reit.jp
Sales Range: $10-24.9 Million
Real Estate Management Services
N.A.I.C.S.: 531390
Satoshi Omori (Exec Dir)

Yuki Sangyo Co., Ltd. **(1)**
Picasso Kitahama Building 4F 1-5-7 Do-
shomachi, Chuo-ku, Osaka, Osaka, Japan
Tel.: (81) 662053500
Web Site: https://yuki-sangyo.co.jp
Emp.: 4
Building Property Management Services
N.A.I.C.S.: 561110

ESA CO., LTD.
Taeyang Bulding 8floor 413 Taehe-
rangro, Gangnamgu, Seoul, Korea
(South)
Tel.: (82) 25982554
Web Site: http://www.softmax.co.kr
Year Founded: 1994
052190—(KRS)
Rev.: $88,040
Assets: $2,836,442
Liabilities: $1,340,693
Net Worth: $1,495,748
Earnings: ($415,629)
Emp.: 6
Fiscal Year-end: 12/31/22

Game Development Services
N.A.I.C.S.: 513210
Jongpil Jin *(CEO)*

ESAAR (INDIA) LIMITED
204 B-Wing New Prabhat SRA CHS
LTD Chikuwadi Plot-115, Next to
Bisleri Factory W E Highway Andheri
East, Mumbai, 400066, Maharashtra,
India
Tel.: (91) 2240676000
Web Site: https://www.esaar.in
Year Founded: 1951
531502—(BOM)
Rev.: $5,161,904
Assets: $8,122,987
Liabilities: $5,479,316
Net Worth: $2,643,671
Earnings: $211,059
Emp.: 3
Fiscal Year-end: 03/31/21
Financial Services
N.A.I.C.S.: 523999
Raghvendra Kumar *(Exec Dir)*

ESANG NETWORKS CO., LTD.
ES Tower 9 World Cup Buk-ro 58-gil,
Mapo-gu, Seoul, Korea (South)
Tel.: (82) 261216200
Web Site: https://www.e-sang.net
Year Founded: 2002
080010—(KRS)
Rev.: $53,661,012
Assets: $125,894,853
Liabilities: $29,411,290
Net Worth: $96,483,564
Earnings: $9,141,833
Emp.: 50
Fiscal Year-end: 12/31/22
Electronic Shopping Services
N.A.I.C.S.: 425120
Wonpyo Cho *(Co-CEO)*

ESAOTE S.P.A.
Via E Melen 77, 16152, Genoa, Italy
Tel.: (39) 01065471   IT
Web Site: http://www.esaote.com
Year Founded: 1982
Sales Range: $350-399.9 Million
Emp.: 1,360
Biomedical Equipment Mfr
N.A.I.C.S.: 334510
Mariangela Dellepiane *(Head-Comm)*

Subsidiaries:

ESAOTE BENELUX N.V.   (1)
Diegemstraat 46, 1930, Zaventem, Belgium
Tel.: (32) 27 214476
Web Site: http://www.esaote.be
Medical Diagnostic Device Mfr
N.A.I.C.S.: 334510
Stijn Dhondt *(Mgr-Sls)*

ESAOTE HEALTHCARE DO
BRASIL   (1)
Rua Dr Tomas Carvalhal 711, 04006-001,
Sao Paulo, Brazil
Tel.: (55) 11 27890400
Web Site: http://www.esaotedobrasil.com.br
Medical Diagnostic Device Mfr
N.A.I.C.S.: 334510

ESAOTE MEDICAL SAS   (1)
10 rue de Temara CS 40343, 78105, Saint
Germain-en-Laye, Cedex, France
Tel.: (33) 1 82048950
Web Site: http://www.esaote.fr
Medical Diagnostic Device Mfr
N.A.I.C.S.: 334510

ESAOTE UK   (1)
14 Cambridge Science Park Milton Road,
Cambridge, CB4 0FQ, United Kingdom
Tel.: (44) 1223 424499
Web Site: http://www.esaote.co.uk
Medical Diagnostic Device Mfr
N.A.I.C.S.: 334510

Esaote Asia Pacific Diagnostic Private Limited   (1)
F1 Level 1 Global Arcade Near Global Business Park, MG Road, Gurgaon, 122002,
India
Tel.: (91) 1244775600
Web Site: http://www.esaote.com
Sales Range: $25-49.9 Million
Emp.: 3
Biomedical Equipment Mfr
N.A.I.C.S.: 334510

Esaote Biomedica Deutschland
GmbH   (1)
Max Planck Str 27 a, Cologne, Germany
Tel.: (49) 22192680000
Web Site: http://www.esaote.de
Sales Range: $25-49.9 Million
Emp.: 15
Biomedical Equipment Mfr
N.A.I.C.S.: 334510
Wim van Kemenade *(Mng Dir-Italy)*

Esaote China Ltd.   (1)
18F 135 Bonham Strand Trade Centre, 135
Bonham Strand, Sheung Wan, China (Hong
Kong)
Tel.: (852) 25458386
Web Site: http://www.esaote.com
Biomedical Equipment Mfr
N.A.I.C.S.: 334510
Alberto Boni *(Gen Mgr)*

Esaote Espana S.A.   (1)
Avda San Sebastian sn 08960 Sant Just
Desvern, Barcelona, 09860, Spain
Tel.: (34) 934732090
Web Site: http://www.esaote.es
Biomedical Equipment Mfr
N.A.I.C.S.: 334510

Esaote Europe B.V   (1)
Philipsweg 1, 6227 AJ, Maastricht, Netherlands
Tel.: (31) 433824600
Web Site: http://www.esaote.com
Sales Range: $50-74.9 Million
Emp.: 120
Biomedical Equipment Mfr
N.A.I.C.S.: 334510
Anton Esseling *(Gen Mgr)*

Esaote France S.A.R.L.   (1)
Za Du Bel Air 10 Ruegetemara, 78105,
Saint Germain-en-Laye, France
Tel.: (33) 148712525
Web Site: http://www.esaote.fr
Biomedical Equipment Mfr
N.A.I.C.S.: 334510

Esaote Latinoamerica S.A.   (1)
San Martin 551 Cuerpo C Piso 8, 1004,
Buenos Aires, Argentina
Tel.: (54) 1143261832,
Biomedical Equipment Mfr
N.A.I.C.S.: 334510

Esaote North America Inc.   (1)
8000 Castleway Dr, Indianapolis, IN 46250
Tel.: (317) 813-6000
Web Site: http://www.esaoteusa.com
Biomedical Equipment Mfr
N.A.I.C.S.: 334510
Kim Akers *(Controller)*

ESAS HOLDING A.S.
Esas Plaza Ruzgarlibahce Mh Kavak
Sk No 29, Beykoz, 34805, Istanbul,
Turkiye
Tel.: (90) 2166818500
Web Site: http://www.esas.com.tr
Year Founded: 2000
Emp.: 100
Investment Holding Services
N.A.I.C.S.: 551112
Inan Tanriover *(CFO)*

Subsidiaries:

Esas Gayrimenkul   (1)
Esas Plaza Ruzgarlibahce Mah Kavak Sok
No 29, Kavacik, 34805, Istanbul, Turkiye
Tel.: (90) 16 681 85 11
Web Site:
   http://www.esasgayrimenkul.com.tr
Real Estate Consulting Service
N.A.I.C.S.: 531210
Erhan Kamisli *(Chm)*

Esasligrup   (1)
Antalya Organize Sanayi Bolgesi Akdeniz
Bulvari NO2, Antalya, Turkiye
Tel.: (90) 242 258 18 80
Web Site: http://www.esasligrup.com.tr
Food Catering Services
N.A.I.C.S.: 722310

Gidaser Gida Dagitim Sanayi ve Ticaret A.S.   (1)
Ayazaga Kemerburgaz Caddesi No 45, Sariyer, 34398, Istanbul, Turkiye
Tel.: (90) 4440961
Web Site: http://www.bonservis.com.tr
Food Catering Services
N.A.I.C.S.: 722310

Kiraz 1 Gayrimenkul Yatirzm Danzsmanligi A.S.   (1)
Ruzgarlibahce Mah Poplar Sok No 29,
Beykoz, Istanbul, Turkiye
Tel.: (90) 216 681 8500
Real Estate Investment Services
N.A.I.C.S.: 531210

Subsidiary (Non-US):

ESSA Limited   (2)
61 London Road, Maidstone, ME16 8TX,
Kent, United Kingdom
Tel.: (44) 7847 387048
Oil Transportation Services
N.A.I.C.S.: 485999

Medline Healthcare Group   (1)
Kemerburgaz Caddesi No 45, Ayazaga Sariyer, 34396, Istanbul, Turkiye
Tel.: (90) 212 331 80 80
Web Site: http://www.medline.com.tr
Healtcare Services
N.A.I.C.S.: 622110
A. Gurkan Ergenekon *(Gen Mgr)*

Pegasus Hava Tasimaciligi A.S.   (1)
Aeropark Yenisehir Mahallesi Osmanli Bulvari No 11/A, Kurtkoy Pendik, 34912, Istanbul, Turkiye
Tel.: (90) 8882281212
Web Site: https://www.flypgs.com
Rev.: $1,319,893,552
Assets: $2,959,121,757
Liabilities: $2,401,763,776
Net Worth: $557,357,981
Earnings: $219,306,116
Emp.: 6,765
Fiscal Year-end: 12/31/2022
Airline
N.A.I.C.S.: 481111
Ali Ismail Sabanci *(Chm)*

Subsidiary (Non-US):

Air Manas Air Company LLC   (2)
75 Maldybaeva street, Bishkek, 720020,
Kyrgyzstan
Tel.: (996) 312 56 40 40
Web Site: http://airmanas.com
Aircraft Charter Services
N.A.I.C.S.: 481211

Subsidiary (Domestic):

IHY Izmir Havayollari A.S.   (2)
9 Eylul Mah Akcay Cad No 289 / 1 Adnan
Menderes, Havalimani Girisi Gaziemir,
35410, Izmir, Turkiye
Tel.: (90) 232 298 35 00
Web Site: http://www.izair.com.tr
Oil Transportation Services
N.A.I.C.S.: 485999

ESAUTOMOTION S.P.A.
Via Della Meccanica 23/1, 41012,
Carpi, MO, Italy
Tel.: (39) 059851414
Web Site:
   https://www.esautomotion.com
Year Founded: 1962
ESAU—(ITA)
Sales Range: Less than $1 Million
Industrial Machinery Mfr & Distr
N.A.I.C.S.: 334513
Franco Fontana *(Chm)*

**ESCALA COMUNICACAO &
MARKETING LTDA.**
Carlos Gomes 300 2 andar, 90480
000, Porto Alegre, Brazil
Tel.: (55) 5132014044

Web Site:
   http://www.agenciaescala.com.br
Emp.: 500
Advetising Agency
N.A.I.C.S.: 541810

ESCHA BAUELEMENTE GMBH
Elberfelder Str 32, Halver, 58553,
Germany
Tel.: (49) 2353708800
Web Site: https://www.escha.net
Rev.: $31,726,200
Emp.: 296
Electronic Connector Mfr
N.A.I.C.S.: 334417
Dietrich Turck *(Mng Dir)*

ESCO FINANCIAL & ENGINEERING COMPANY S.A/N.V.
Square de Meeus 38/40, 1000, Brussels, Belgium
Tel.: (32) 2 717 64 05
Web Site: http://www.efeco.com
Sales Range: $50-74.9 Million
Emp.: 200
Electric Drive, Inverter, Switch & Control Mfr
N.A.I.C.S.: 335314
Thierry Schmidt *(CEO)*

Subsidiaries:

Esco Aandrijvingen B.V.   (1)
Ondernemingsweg 19, 2404 HM, Alphen
aan den Rijn, Netherlands
Tel.: (31) 172 42 33 33
Web Site: http://www.esco-aandrijvingen.nl
Machinery Sales, Distribution Services
N.A.I.C.S.: 423830

Esco Couplings (Jinan) Ltd   (1)
Airport road No 2168, licheng district, Jinan,
250107, Shandong, China
Tel.: (86) 53155711596
Web Site: http://www.esco-couplings.cn
Seal Distr
N.A.I.C.S.: 423120

Esco Couplings N.V.   (1)
Kouterveld Culliganlaan 3, B 1831, Diegem,
Belgium
Tel.: (32) 2 715 65 60
Web Site: http://www.escocoupling.com
Couplings Mfr
N.A.I.C.S.: 333613

Subsidiary (Non-US):

Esco Couplings & Transmissions Private Limited   (2)
Plot 22/A 1st Stage Peenya Industrial Estate, Bengaluru, 560058, India
Tel.: (91) 80 49256000
Web Site: http://www.esco-couplings.co.in
Couplings Mfr
N.A.I.C.S.: 333613

Esco Drives & Automation N.V.   (1)
Kouterveld Culliganlaan 3, 1831, Diegem,
Flemish Brabant, Belgium
Tel.: (32) 27176460
Web Site: http://www.esco.be
Sales Range: $25-49.9 Million
Emp.: 9
Automation Electric Controls Mfr
N.A.I.C.S.: 335313

Esco Financial and Transmissions
Ltd.   (1)
38th Floor Central Plaza 18 Harbour Road,
Wanchai, China (Hong Kong)
Tel.: (852) 53155711597
Electrical Component Distr
N.A.I.C.S.: 423610

Esco Power N.V.   (1)
3 Rue des Gaulois, 7822, Ghislenghien,
Belgium
Tel.: (32) 2 717 64 90
Web Site: http://www.escopower.be
Gearbox & Transmission Equipment Mfr
N.A.I.C.S.: 333613

Esco Transmisja Mocy Sp. z o.o.   (1)
ul M Sklodowskiej-Curie 4A lok 1, 90-505,
Lodz, Poland

Esco Financial & Engineering Company
S.A/N.V.—(Continued)

Tel.: (48) 426375080
Web Site: http://www.escotransmisja.pl
Electrical Component Distr
N.A.I.C.S.: 423610

Esco Transmissions N.V.   **(1)**
Kouterveld Culliganlaan 3, Diegem, 1831,
Belgium
Tel.: (32) 2 717 64 60
Web Site: http://www.esco.be
Emp.: 20
Transmission Equipment Mfr
N.A.I.C.S.: 333613
Polspoel Patrick *(Mng Dir)*

Esco Transmissions S.A.   **(1)**
ZII 34 rue Ferme Saint-Ladre Saint Witz,
95471, Fosses, France
Tel.: (33) 1 34 31 95 95
Web Site: http://www.esco-transmissions.fr
Emp.: 19
Transmission Equipment Mfr
N.A.I.C.S.: 333613
Terry Smith *(Gen Mgr)*

esco antriebstechnik gmbh   **(1)**
Biberweg 10, D 53842, Troisdorf, Germany
Tel.: (49) 2241 48070
Web Site: http://www.esco-
antriebstechnik.de
Electrical Drive System Mfr
N.A.I.C.S.: 335999
Michael Reuter *(Mng Dir)*

ESCO GLOBAL REALTY CORP.
1081 Cole Harbour Road Suite 6,
Dartmouth, B2V 1E8, NS, Canada
Tel.: (902) 434-9381   CO
Web Site:
http://www.escorealtyspecialists.com
Year Founded: 2003
Sales Range: Less than $1 Million
Emp.: 1
Real Estate Brokerage Services
N.A.I.C.S.: 531210
Edward Gaius Carmichael *(CEO & Co-Owner)*

ESCO MARGINALEN AB
Trappstigen 3, Lidingo, Stockholm,
181 31, Sweden
Tel.: (46) 8 765 70 15
Consulting Services
N.A.I.C.S.: 541618

ESCORP ASSET MANAGEMENT LIMITED
60 Khatau Building Alkesh Dinesh
Marg Fort, Mumbai, 400 001, India
Tel.: (91) 2262166999
Web Site:
https://www.escorpamc.co.in
540455—(BOM)
Rev.: $23,792
Assets: $3,549,819
Liabilities: $183,906
Net Worth: $3,365,913
Earnings: $369
Emp.: 4
Fiscal Year-end: 03/31/21
Asset Management Services
N.A.I.C.S.: 523940
Shripal Shah *(Exec Dir)*

ESCORT TEKNOLOJI YATIRIM A.S.
Atakan Street No 14, Mecidiyekoy
Sisli, Istanbul, Turkiye
Tel.: (90) 2123406000
Web Site: https://www.escort.com.tr
Year Founded: 1991
ESCOM—(IST)
Electronic Device Mfr & Whslr
N.A.I.C.S.: 334419
H. Ibrahim Ozer *(Chm)*

ESCORTS INVESTMENT BANK LIMITED
Ground Floor 26 Davis Road LHR,
Lahore, Pakistan
Tel.: (92) 111003425
Web Site:
https://www.escortsbank.net
ESBL—(LAH)
Rev.: $809,873
Assets: $10,303,475
Liabilities: $9,946,609
Net Worth: $356,866
Earnings: ($361,129)
Emp.: 59
Fiscal Year-end: 06/30/19
Banking Services
N.A.I.C.S.: 522110
Kamran Chughtai *(Head-IT)*

Subsidiaries:

Escorts Capital Limited   **(1)**
26 Davis Rd, Lahore, Pakistan
Tel.: (92) 426371931
Banking Services
N.A.I.C.S.: 522110

ESCORTS KUBOTA LIMITED
15/5 Mathura Road, Faridabad, 121
003, India
Tel.: (91) 1292250222
Web Site:
https://www.escortskubota.com
Year Founded: 1994
ESCORTS—(NSE)
Rev.: $979,360,200
Assets: $938,870,205
Liabilities: $252,927,675
Net Worth: $685,942,530
Earnings: $118,977,495
Emp.: 3,764
Fiscal Year-end: 03/31/21
Agricultural & Industrial Machinery
Mfr & Distr
N.A.I.C.S.: 333111
Dipankar Ghosh *(CEO-Railway Equipment Div)*

Subsidiaries:

Escorts Crop Solution Limited   **(1)**
2nd Floor Plot No 4 Near Metro Pillar 599
15/1 Mathura Road NH-2, Faridabad,
121003, Haryana, India
Tel.: (91) 7240288888
Web Site:
https://www.escortscropsolutions.com
Mechanized Farming Services
N.A.I.C.S.: 115113
Rajan Chugh *(CEO)*

Escorts Finance Limited   **(1)**
SCO - 198-200 2nd Floor Sector - 34A,
Chandigarh, 160022, India
Tel.: (91) 1141895500
Web Site: https://ibcl.ltd
Rev.: $37,292
Assets: $662,557
Liabilities: $25,023,917
Net Worth: ($24,361,360)
Earnings: ($1,433)
Emp.: 3
Fiscal Year-end: 03/31/2021
Financial Services
N.A.I.C.S.: 523999
Donald Fernandez *(CFO)*

Escorts Securities Limited   **(1)**
202 Okhla Industrial Estate Phase III, New
Delhi, 110 020, India
Tel.: (91) 114 358 7400
Web Site: https://www.escortssecurities.com
Security Brokerage Services
N.A.I.C.S.: 541611
Vinod Dixit *(CEO, Mng Dir & Principal Officer)*

Farmtrac Tractors Europe Spolka z
o.o.   **(1)**
Przemyslowa 11 Str, 11-700, Mragowo,
Poland
Tel.: (48) 531249466
Web Site: https://farmtrac.pl
Tractor Mfr

N.A.I.C.S.: 333111

ESCRIT INC.
Yamamambiru 6-1 Nihombashikoam-
icho, Chuo-ku, Tokyo, 103-0016, Ja-
pan
Tel.: (81) 5017433418
Web Site: https://www.escrit.jp
Year Founded: 2003
2196—(TKS)
Rev.: $176,083,790
Assets: $153,345,390
Liabilities: $112,092,380
Net Worth: $41,253,010
Earnings: $4,091,590
Emp.: 398
Fiscal Year-end: 03/31/24
Wedding Ceremonies & Wedding Re-
ceptions Planner & Operator
N.A.I.C.S.: 812990
Hiroshi Iwamoto *(Chm)*

ESCROW AGENT JAPAN, INC.
4F Shin-Otemachi Building 2-2-1
Otemachi, Chiyoda-ku, Tokyo, 100-
0004, Japan
Tel.: (81) 367030500
Web Site: https://www.ea-j.jp
Year Founded: 2007
6093—(TKS)
Rev.: $29,339,206
Assets: $31,530,075
Liabilities: $6,962,567
Net Worth: $24,567,508
Earnings: $2,119,967
Fiscal Year-end: 02/29/24
Real Estate Financial Services
N.A.I.C.S.: 531390
Hideaki Honma *(Chm, Pres & CEO)*

ESCUDO CAPITAL CORPORA-
TION
#3507 1033 Marinaside Crescent,
Vancouver, V6Z 3A3, BC, Canada
Tel.: (604) 893-8784   BC
Web Site:
http://www.escudocapital.ca
Year Founded: 2011
Investment Services
N.A.I.C.S.: 523999
John Boddie *(CEO & Sec)*

ESDEC BV
Londenstraat 16, 7418EE, Deventer,
Netherlands
Tel.: (31) 850702000
Web Site:
https://esdecsolargroup.com
Year Founded: 2004
Solar Mounting Systems Installation
Services
N.A.I.C.S.: 238160

Subsidiaries:

Esdec USA   **(1)**
2700 Mitchell Dr, Walnut Creek, CA 94598
Tel.: (855) 373-3228
Web Site: http://usa.esdec.com
Rooftop Solar Mounting Solutions
N.A.I.C.S.: 221114

Subsidiary (Domestic):

PanelClaw, Inc.   **(2)**
1570 Osgood St Ste 2100, North Andover,
MA 01845
Tel.: (978) 688-4900
Web Site: http://www.panelclaw.com
Sales Range: $25-49.9 Million
Emp.: 26
Energy Consulting Services
N.A.I.C.S.: 541690
Thomas Ringler *(CEO)*

Ironridge Inc.   **(1)**
28357 Industrial Blvd, Hayward, CA 94545
Tel.: (855) 367-6233
Web Site: http://www.ironridge.com
Fabricated Structural Metal Mfr
N.A.I.C.S.: 332312
Craig Carni *(Founder)*

ESE ENTERTAINMENT, INC.
409 Granville Street Suite 1000, Van-
couver, V6C 1T2, BC, Canada
Tel.: (778) 238-4988
Web Site:
https://www.esegaming.com
ENTEF—(OTCQX)
Rev.: $46,012,603
Assets: $16,780,307
Liabilities: $15,032,776
Net Worth: $1,747,531
Earnings: ($23,341,538)
Emp.: 101
Fiscal Year-end: 10/31/22
Online Gambling Services
N.A.I.C.S.: 541511
Konrad Wasiela *(Founder & CEO)*

Subsidiaries:

ESE Europe SP. Z O.O.   **(1)**
ul Postepu 21, 02-676, Warsaw, Poland
Tel.: (48) 224300471
Waste Management Services
N.A.I.C.S.: 562111

ESENBOGA ELEKTRIK URE-
TIM A.S.
Kizilirmak Mahallesi 1450 Sokak ATM
Plaza B Blok No 1/68-69, Cukuram-
bar, Ankara, Turkiye
Tel.: (90) 3124671833
Web Site:
https://www.esenbogaelektrik.com.tr
Year Founded: 2015
ESEN—(IST)
Rev.: $31,366,604
Assets: $455,618,051
Liabilities: $156,947,466
Net Worth: $298,670,585
Earnings: $10,405,705
Fiscal Year-end: 12/31/23
Energy Distribution Services
N.A.I.C.S.: 221122
Yusuf Senel *(Chm)*

ESENCIA GROUP
1st Floor St Peter House Le Bourd-
age, Saint Peter Port, Guernsey
Tel.: (44) 1481 714 898
Web Site:
http://www.esenciagroup.com
Investment Holding Company
N.A.I.C.S.: 551112
Andrew MacDonald *(CEO)*

Subsidiaries:

Esencia Group   **(1)**
Edificio Melior Diego de Leon 47, 28006,
Madrid, Spain
Tel.: (34) 91 838 8558
Investment Holding Company
N.A.I.C.S.: 551112

Esencia Group   **(1)**
Miramar Trade Center Edificio Barcelona
Piso 2 Oficina 204, Havana, Cuba
Tel.: (53) 2047710
Investment Holding Company
N.A.I.C.S.: 551112

ESENSE-LAB LTD
8 Sapir Street, Ness Ziona, Israel
Tel.: (972) 506610402
Web Site: http://www.esense-lab.com
Year Founded: 2016
ESE—(ASX)
Rev.: $262,000
Assets: $636,000
Liabilities: $255,000
Net Worth: $381,000
Earnings: ($1,471,000)
Fiscal Year-end: 12/31/19
Pharmaceuticals Product Mfr
N.A.I.C.S.: 325411
Yoav Elishoov *(CEO)*

ESENTIRE, INC.

451 Phillip St Ste 135, Waterloo, N2L 3X2, ON, Canada
Tel.: (196) 12200
Web Site: http://www.esentire.com
Year Founded: 2001
Computer & Network Security Services
N.A.I.C.S.: 561621
J. Paul Haynes (*Pres*)

Subsidiaries:

CyFIR, LLC (1)
20130 Lakeview Ctr Plz Ste 120, Ashburn, VA 20147
Tel.: (703) 936-4170
Web Site: http://www.cyfir.com
Software Development Services
N.A.I.C.S.: 541511
Ben Cotton (*Founder*)

ESFAHAN'S MOBARAKEH STEEL COMPANY

Saadat Abad St Azadi SQ, Isfahan, Iran
Tel.: (98) 3152732200
Web Site: http://www.en.msc.ir
Year Founded: 1981
FOLD1—(THE)
Sales Range: Less than $1 Million
Steel Products Mfr
N.A.I.C.S.: 331110

ESG GLOBAL IMPACT CAPITAL INC.

Suite 1000 409 Granville Street, Vancouver, V6C 1T2, BC, Canada
Tel.: (604) 398-4485 BC
Web Site: https://esgcapitalinc.com
Year Founded: 2010
ESGW—(OTCIQ)
Rev.: $4,691,583
Assets: $8,254,651
Liabilities: $752,897
Net Worth: $7,501,754
Earnings: ($1,016,093)
Fiscal Year-end: 08/31/21
Investment Services
N.A.I.C.S.: 523999
David Andrew Berg (*CEO*)

ESGL HOLDINGS LIMITED

101 Tuas South Avenue 2, Singapore, 637226, Singapore
Tel.: (65) 66532299 Ky
Web Site: https://www.esgl.asia
Year Founded: 1999
ESGL—(NASDAQ)
Rev.: $6,164,173
Assets: $25,632,266
Liabilities: $17,611,509
Net Worth: $8,020,757
Earnings: ($94,979,338)
Emp.: 72
Fiscal Year-end: 12/31/23
Holding Company
N.A.I.C.S.: 551112

ESGOLD CORP.

1500-1505 West Georgia Street, Vancouver, V6E 4N7, BC, Canada
Tel.: (604) 506-7555
Web Site: https://esgold.com
ESAU—(CNSX)
Assets: $5,201,062
Liabilities: $2,695,270
Net Worth: $2,505,792
Earnings: ($2,695,740)
Fiscal Year-end: 06/30/24
Mineral Exploration Services
N.A.I.C.S.: 213114
P. Bradley Kitchen (*Chm & CEO*)

ESGTI AG

Bosch 37, 6331, Hunenberg, Switzerland
Tel.: (41) 415009983
Web Site: http://www.esgti.com

ESGTI—(SWX)
Rev.: $253,003
Assets: $265,547,754
Liabilities: $81,197,070
Net Worth: $184,350,684
Earnings: $28,771,158
Fiscal Year-end: 04/30/23
Investment Management Service
N.A.I.C.S.: 523940
Andreas R. Bihrer (*Chm*)

ESHA MEDIA RESEARCH LIMITED

T 1416 A Wing 2nd Floor Satyam Shopping Centre, Chembur West, Mumbai, 400 089, India
Tel.: (91) 2240966666
Web Site:
   https://www.eshamedia.com
531259—(BOM)
Rev.: $23,315
Assets: $238,090
Liabilities: $1,173,336
Net Worth: ($935,246)
Earnings: $7,172
Emp.: 110
Fiscal Year-end: 03/31/21
Media Monitoring Services
N.A.I.C.S.: 541910

ESHIPPERS MANAGEMENT LTD.

1620 W 8th Ave Ste 302, Vancouver, V6J 1V4, BC, Canada
Tel.: (604) 639-4457
Year Founded: 1992
Software Development Services
N.A.I.C.S.: 541511
Edward Leung (*CFO*)

ESHRAQ INVESTMENTS PJSC

Units 3 and 4 Ground Floor Marina Rise Tower, PO Box 108737, Sector RT2 Ras Mughayrej Street Reem Island, Abu Dhabi, United Arab Emirates
Tel.: (971) 26354854
Web Site: https://eshraquae.com
ESHRAQ—(EMI)
Rev.: $8,607,057
Assets: $619,874,219
Liabilities: $44,623,449
Net Worth: $575,250,770
Earnings: ($148,415,652)
Fiscal Year-end: 12/31/23
Real Estate Manangement Services
N.A.I.C.S.: 531390
Jassim Alseddiqi (*Chm*)

ESJOT GOLDENBERG

Rue Du Zornhoff, Monswiller, 67700, Saverne, France
Tel.: (33) 388715502
Web Site: http://www.esjot-group.com
Rev.: $20,900,000
Emp.: 68
Sheet Metalwork
N.A.I.C.S.: 332322
Jean Bonnelye (*Pres*)

ESKANDAR LTD.

134 Lots Rd, London, SW10 0RJ, United Kingdom
Tel.: (44) 2073517333
Web Site: http://www.eskandar.com
Sales Range: $10-24.9 Million
Emp.: 50
Clothing & Accessories Retailer
N.A.I.C.S.: 458110
Eskandar Nabavi (*Mng Dir*)

ESKAY MINING CORPORATION

82 Richmond Street East, Toronto, M5C 1P1, ON, Canada
Tel.: (416) 907-4605 Ca

Web Site:
   https://www.eskaymining.com
ESKYF—(OTCIQ)
Rev.: $3,020,464
Assets: $4,570,230
Liabilities: $286,252
Net Worth: $4,283,978
Earnings: ($2,112,643)
Fiscal Year-end: 02/29/24
Metal Mining Services
N.A.I.C.S.: 213114
Hugh M. Balkam (*Pres & CEO*)

ESKEN LIMITED

Third Floor 15 Stratford Place, Carlisle Lake District Airport, London, CA6 4NZ, United Kingdom
Tel.: (44) 2037939632 GY
Web Site: https://www.esken.com
Year Founded: 2002
ESKN—(LSE)
Rev.: $162,931,831
Assets: $595,859,861
Liabilities: $541,665,109
Net Worth: $54,194,752
Earnings: ($34,264,780)
Emp.: 778
Fiscal Year-end: 02/28/23
Holding Company; Transportation & Logistics Services
N.A.I.C.S.: 551112
Warwick Brady (*CEO*)

Subsidiaries:

Stobart Air (UK) Limited (1)
Third Floor 15 Stratford Place, London, W1C 1BE, United Kingdom (85%)
Tel.: (44) 1228 573641
Web Site: http://www.carlisleairport.co.uk
Emp.: 20
Airport Operator
N.A.I.C.S.: 488119
Martin Saxton (*Chief Comml Officer*)

Subsidiary (Domestic):

London Southend Airport Company Limited (2)
Third Floor 15 Stratford Place, London, W1C 1BE, Essex, United Kingdom
Tel.: (44) 3332205436
Web Site: https://londonsouthendairport.com
Sales Range: $25-49.9 Million
Commercial Airport Operator
N.A.I.C.S.: 488119

ESKER S.A.

113 Boulevard de la Bataille de Stalingrad, Villeurbanne, 69100, Lyon, France
Tel.: (33) 472834646 FR
Web Site: https://content.esker.fr
Year Founded: 1985
ALESK—(EUR)
Rev.: $197,101,225
Assets: $190,207,528
Liabilities: $70,574,015
Net Worth: $119,633,514
Earnings: $16,400,265
Emp.: 1,021
Fiscal Year-end: 12/31/23
Computer Software Publisher
N.A.I.C.S.: 513210
Jean-Michel Berard (*Founder & CEO-Exec Bd*)

Subsidiaries:

Esker Australia Pty. Ltd. (1)
Suite 1502 Level 15 227 Elizabeth Street, Sydney, 2000, NSW, Australia (100%)
Tel.: (61) 285965100
Web Site: http://www.esker.com.au
Sales Range: $1-9.9 Million
Emp.: 10
Provider of Computer Software
N.A.I.C.S.: 541511
Christophe Dumonet (*Mng Dir*)

Esker Documents Automation Asia Pte Ltd (1)
101 Thomson Road 11-01 United Square,

Singapore, 307591, Singapore
Tel.: (65) 67356882
Web Site: https://www.esker.com.sg
Emp.: 5
Document Process Automation Software Development Services
N.A.I.C.S.: 561410
Albert Leong (*Mng Dir*)

Esker GmbH (1)
Dornacher Str 3A, 80686, Feldkirchen, Germany (100%)
Tel.: (49) 897008870
Web Site: http://www.esker.de
Sales Range: $25-49.9 Million
Emp.: 8
Provider of Computer Software
N.A.I.C.S.: 541511
Jeanmichel Berard (*Gen Mgr*)

Esker Iberica (1)
Calle Chile 8 oficina 206, Las Rozas, 28290, Madrid, Spain (100%)
Tel.: (34) 915529265
Web Site: https://www.esker.es
Sales Range: $25-49.9 Million
Emp.: 55
Provider of Computer Software
N.A.I.C.S.: 541511
Jesus Midon (*Mng Dir*)

Esker Italia S.r.l. (1)
Via Guido Gozzano, 21052, Busto Arsizio, VA, Italy (100%)
Tel.: (39) 033165141
Web Site: https://www.esker.it
Sales Range: $25-49.9 Million
Emp.: 7
Provider of Computer Software
N.A.I.C.S.: 541511
Giovanni Gavioli (*Mng Dir*)

Esker Ltd. (1)
Durham Wyvern Business Park Spaniel Way, Shardlow, Derby, DE72 2GH, Derbyshire, United Kingdom (100%)
Tel.: (44) 332548181
Web Site: http://www.esker.co.uk
Sales Range: $25-49.9 Million
Emp.: 22
Provider of Computer Software
N.A.I.C.S.: 541511

Esker, Inc. (1)
1850 Deming Way Ste 150, Middleton, WI 53562 (100%)
Tel.: (608) 828-6000
Web Site: http://www.esker.com
Sales Range: $25-49.9 Million
Emp.: 120
Developer of Computer Network Connectivity Software
N.A.I.C.S.: 541511
Kevin Kniess (*Chief Compliance Officer & Gen Counsel*)

ESKMUIR PROPERTIES LTD

8 Queen Anne Street, London, W1G 9LD, United Kingdom
Tel.: (44) 2074362339
Web Site: http://www.eskmuir.com
Year Founded: 1990
Commercial Property Investment Services
N.A.I.C.S.: 531390
Paul Hodgson (*Mng Dir*)

Subsidiaries:

Eskmuir Securities Ltd (1)
8 Queen Anne Street, London, W1G 9LD, United Kingdom
Tel.: (44) 207 436 2339
Web Site: http://www.eskmuir.com
Sales Range: $50-74.9 Million
Emp.: 5
Securities Brokerage Services
N.A.I.C.S.: 523150
Paul Hodgson (*Mng Dir*)

ESKOM HOLDINGS SOC LIMITED

Megawatt Park Maxwell Drive Sunninghill, Sandton, 2157, South Africa
Tel.: (27) 118008111
Web Site: http://www.eskom.co.za

Eskom Holdings SOC Limited—(Continued)

Year Founded: 1923
Rev.: $14,122,791,240
Assets: $53,331,843,040
Liabilities: $38,605,352,760
Net Worth: $14,726,490,280
Earnings: ($1,291,866,820)
Emp.: 42,749
Fiscal Year-end: 03/31/21
Electricity Generation Services
N.A.I.C.S.: 221122
Calib Cassim *(CFO)*

Subsidiaries:

Rotek Engineering (Pty) Ltd.　　**(1)**
3 Lower Germiston Road Roshewill,
Rosherville, 40099, Johannesburg, South
Africa　　　　　　　　　　**(100%)**
Tel.: (27) 00116294000
Web Site: http://www.rotekengineering.com
Sales Range: $1-4.9 Billion
Emp.: 1,500
Maintenance & Service
N.A.I.C.S.: 221122

ESLEAD CORP.

6-25-19 Fukushima, Fukushima-ku,
Osaka, 553-0003, Japan
Tel.: (81) 663451880
Web Site: https://www.eslead.co.jp
Year Founded: 1968
8877—(TKS)
Rev.: $530,690,460
Assets: $1,116,785,940
Liabilities: $674,755,410
Net Worth: $442,030,530
Earnings: $49,693,980
Emp.: 10,866
Fiscal Year-end: 03/31/24
Real Estate Manangement Services
N.A.I.C.S.: 531390
Yuzo Inoue *(Sr Mng Dir)*

ESLITE SPECTRUM CORP.

B1 No 204 Songde Rd, Hsin-i, Taipei,
110027, Taiwan
Tel.: (886) 266385168
2926—(TPE)
Rev.: $174,616,546
Assets: $417,773,880
Net Worth: $21,339,680
Earnings: ($6,005,722)
Fiscal Year-end: 12/31/22
Department Store Retailer
N.A.I.C.S.: 455110
Min-Chieh Wu *(Chm)*

ESMO CORPORATION

91-1 Ungbigongdan-gil, Ulju-gun, Ul-
san, Korea (South)
Tel.: (82) 522598300
Web Site: http://www.esmo.co.kr
Year Founded: 1994
Rev.: $43,505,315
Assets: $102,891,584
Liabilities: $64,128,914
Net Worth: $38,762,670
Earnings: ($49,188,175)
Emp.: 146
Fiscal Year-end: 12/31/19
Motor Vehicle Parts Mfr
N.A.I.C.S.: 336390
In-Seok Kim *(CEO)*

ESO PARTNERS L.P.

Palladium House 2nd Floor 1-4 Argyll
Street, London, W1F 7TA, United
Kingdom
Tel.: (44) 2036422600
Web Site: http://www.esocapital.com
Sales Range: $25-49.9 Million
Emp.: 20
Miscellaneous Investment Manage-
ment Services
N.A.I.C.S.: 523999
Alex Schmid *(CEO)*

Subsidiaries:

Gardien Pacific Ltd.　　　　**(1)**
Ste 1022-23 Level 10 Landmark N 39, Lung
Sum Ave, Sheung Shui, China (Hong Kong)
Tel.: (852) 29675980
Web Site: http://www.gardien.com
Sales Range: $75-99.9 Million
Printed Circuit Board Testing Services
N.A.I.C.S.: 541380
Jan Lipton *(Pres)*

Subsidiary (Non-US):

Gardien　　　　　　　　**(2)**
79 Milliken Blvd, Toronto, M1V1V3, ON,
Canada
Tel.: (416) 292-0726
Printed Circuit Board Testing Services
N.A.I.C.S.: 541380

Gardien Japan Co., Ltd.　　**(2)**
2-4-3 Takanodai, 177-0033, Tokyo, Nerima
Ku, Japan
Tel.: (81) 339046282
Printed Circuit Board Testing Services
N.A.I.C.S.: 541380

Ucamco N.V.　　　　　　**(1)**
Bijenstraat 19, Gent, 9051, Belgium
Tel.: (32) 92169900
Web Site: http://www.ucamco.com
Sales Range: $25-49.9 Million
Designer & Mfr of PCB CAM & Laser Pho-
toplotting Systems
N.A.I.C.S.: 334118
Karel Tavernier *(Mng Dir)*

ESOL CO., LTD.

Harmony Tower 24F 1-32-2 Honcho,
Nakano-ku, Tokyo, 164-8721, Japan
Tel.: (81) 353651560
Web Site: https://www.esol.com
Year Founded: 1975
4420—(TKS)
Rev.: $68,262,520
Assets: $54,132,150
Liabilities: $13,995,660
Net Worth: $40,136,490
Earnings: $964,240
Emp.: 500
Fiscal Year-end: 12/31/23
Software Development Services
N.A.I.C.S.: 541511
Masaki Gondo *(CTO & VP)*

Subsidiaries:

eSOL Europe S.A.S.　　　**(1)**
2 Rue Racine, 02200, Soissons, France
Tel.: (33) 188320526
Software Development Services
N.A.I.C.S.: 541511

ESON PRECISION IND. CO., LTD.

12F 3 No 2 Sec 4 Zhongyang Rd,
Tucheng Dist, Taipei, Taiwan
Tel.: (886) 222673272
Web Site: http://www.eson.com.cn
5243—(TAI)
Rev.: $438,718,569
Assets: $374,798,330
Liabilities: $159,714,098
Net Worth: $215,084,232
Earnings: $25,041,897
Emp.: 2,857
Fiscal Year-end: 12/31/22
Consumer Electronics Parts Mfr
N.A.I.C.S.: 334419

Subsidiaries:

Ample Wealth Enterprise Ltd.　**(1)**
Suite 802 St James Court St Denis Street,
Port Louis, Mauritius
Tel.: (230) 222673272
Molded Plastic Product Distr
N.A.I.C.S.: 423840

ESON Precision Engineering S.A. de
C.V.　　　　　　　　　　**(1)**
Cinco Norte 115 Ciudad Industrial, Tijuana,
CP22444, Baja California, Mexico
Tel.: (52) 526642506721

Industrial Mold Mfr
N.A.I.C.S.: 333511

Eson Europe S.R.O.　　　**(1)**
Rontgenova 26, 851 02, Bratislava, Slova-
kia
Tel.: (421) 222673272
Investment Management Service
N.A.I.C.S.: 523940

Eson Precision Engineering (Malay-
sia) Sdn. Bhd.　　　　　**(1)**
Lot 3 Jalan P/10 Kawasan Perusahaan
Seksyen 10, 43650, Bandar Baru Bangi,
Selangor, Malaysia
Tel.: (60) 389200270
Hardware Product Mfr & Distr
N.A.I.C.S.: 332510

Eson Slovakia A.S.　　　**(1)**
Nitrianska 1881/17, 958 01, Partizanske,
Slovakia
Tel.: (421) 385000500
Industrial Mold Mfr
N.A.I.C.S.: 333511

Grand Liberty Co., Ltd.　　**(1)**
Suite 802 St James Court St Denis Street,
Port Louis, Mauritius
Tel.: (230) 222673272
Investment Management Service
N.A.I.C.S.: 523940

Kunshan Eson Precision Engineering
Co., Ltd.　　　　　　　**(1)**
No 88 Yuanfeng Road, High-tech Zone,
Kunshan, Jiangsu, China
Tel.: (86) 51257572938
Industrial Mold Mfr
N.A.I.C.S.: 333511

Kunshan Kuangrui Package Material
Co., Ltd.　　　　　　　**(1)**
No 88 Yuanfeng Road, Yushan Town, Kun-
shan, Jiangsu, China
Tel.: (86) 51257572938
Packaging Material Distr
N.A.I.C.S.: 423840

Multiwin De Mexico S.A. de C.V.　**(1)**
Blvd La Jolla 4432 Parque Industrial La
Jolla, 22525, Tijuana, Baja California,
Mexico
Tel.: (52) 6646876088
Industrial Mold Mfr
N.A.I.C.S.: 333511

Suntool Co., Ltd.　　　　**(1)**
No 6 Xin Yuan South Rd Ke Yuancheng
Tangxia Town, Dongguan, Guang Dong,
China
Tel.: (86) 76987919391
Industrial Mold Mfr
N.A.I.C.S.: 333511

Wuxi Singuan Metal Science & Tech-
nology Co., Ltd.　　　　**(1)**
No 218 Furong 4th Road, Xishan Economic
Development Zone, Wuxi, Jiangsu, China
Tel.: (86) 51083809000
Industrial Mold Mfr
N.A.I.C.S.: 333511

Yantai JIRAY Electronic Technology
Co., Ltd.　　　　　　　**(1)**
No 50 Beijing Central Rd Yantai Economic
Technological Development Zone, Yantai,
Shandong, China
Tel.: (86) 5356115378
Industrial Mold Mfr
N.A.I.C.S.: 333511

Yantai Zhengyi Precision Electronic
Co., Ltd.　　　　　　　**(1)**
No 88 Tianjin South Road, Economic and
Technological Development Zone, Yantai,
Shandong, China
Tel.: (86) 5352168888
Industrial Mold Mfr
N.A.I.C.S.: 333511

Zeal International Co., Ltd.　**(1)**
Suite 802 St James Court St Denis Street,
Port Louis, Mauritius
Tel.: (230) 222673272
Molded Plastic Product Distr
N.A.I.C.S.: 423840

ESOR LIMITED

16 Industry Road Clayville Industrial,
Olifantsfontein, South Africa
Tel.: (27) 10 880 5283　　ZA
Web Site: http://www.esor.co.za
Year Founded: 1994
ESR—(JSE)
Sales Range: $100-124.9 Million
Road & Earthwork Construction Ser-
vices
N.A.I.C.S.: 541330
Wessel C. van Zyl *(CEO)*

Subsidiaries:

Brookmay Properties (Pty)
Limited　　　　　　　　**(1)**
33 Setter Rd, Midrand, 1685, Gauteng,
South Africa
Tel.: (27) 113101900
Real Estate Property Investment Services
N.A.I.C.S.: 531210

Esor Africa (Pty) Limited　　**(1)**
30 Activia Rd, Activia Park, Germiston,
1401, Gauteng, South Africa
Tel.: (27) 118223906
Sales Range: $25-49.9 Million
Emp.: 28
Civil & Geotechnical Engineering Services
N.A.I.C.S.: 541330

Esorfranki Civils (Pty) Limited　**(1)**
33 Setter Rd Midrand Indus Park, Commer-
cia, Midrand, 1685, Gauteng, South Africa
Tel.: (27) 11 310 1901
Sales Range: $350-399.9 Million
Emp.: 1,100
Civil Engineering Services
N.A.I.C.S.: 541330
Richard Maynard *(Mng Dir)*

Esorfranki Pipelines (Pty) Limited　**(1)**
30 Activia Road Activia Park, Germiston,
1401, South Africa
Tel.: (27) 11 776 8700
Web Site: http://www.esorfranki.co.za
Sales Range: $25-49.9 Million
Emp.: 30
Construction & Rehabilitation Services of
Onshore Pipelines Including Operations in
Water, Sewerage & Stormwater Sectors &
Gas & Petrochemicals
N.A.I.C.S.: 237120
David Gibbons *(Mng Dir)*

Franki Africa (Pty) Limited　**(1)**
674 Main Pretoria Rd Wynberg, Wynberg,
Sandton, 2019, Gauteng, South Africa
Tel.: (27) 115312700
Web Site: http://www.franki.co.za
Geo Technical Engineering Contract Ser-
vices
N.A.I.C.S.: 541330
Roy McLintock *(Mng Dir)*

Frankipile International Projects
Limited　　　　　　　　**(1)**
4th Fl Barkly Whart Ste 410 Le Caudan,
Port Louis, Mauritius
Tel.: (230) 2100983
Sales Range: $25-49.9 Million
Emp.: 40
Geo Technical Engineering Contract Ser-
vices
N.A.I.C.S.: 238140

Subsidiary (Domestic):

Frankipile Mauritius International
Limited　　　　　　　　**(2)**
4th Fl Barkly Whart Ste 410 Le Caudan,
Port Louis, Mauritius
Tel.: (230) 2100983
Geo Technical Engineering Contract Ser-
vices
N.A.I.C.S.: 238140

Geo Compaction Dynamics (Pty)
Limited　　　　　　　　**(1)**
Unit 9 Hentha Indus Park Wolverhampton
St, Benoni, 1504, Gauteng, South Africa
Tel.: (27) 11 422 1219
Sales Range: $25-49.9 Million
Emp.: 30
Civil & Geotechnical Engineering Services
N.A.I.C.S.: 238140

ESOTIQ & HENDERSON SA

Ul Budowlanych 31C, 80-298,
Gdansk, Poland
Tel.: (48) 587284800
Web Site:
https://www.esotiqhenderson.com
Year Founded: 1998
EAH—(WAR)
Rev.: $69,993,648
Assets: $36,591,971
Liabilities: $20,975,610
Net Worth: $15,616,362
Earnings: $1,876,524
Fiscal Year-end: 12/31/23
Fashion Apparel Mfr & Distr
N.A.I.C.S.: 315990
Adam Skrzypek *(Chm)*

ESP SYSTEX LTD.
68 74 Holderness Road, Hull, HU9
1ED, United Kingdom
Tel.: (44) 1482384500
Web Site: http://www.espsystex.co.uk
Year Founded: 1994
Sales Range: $10-24.9 Million
Emp.: 60
Smart Card Solutions
N.A.I.C.S.: 541512
Michael Longman *(Mng Dir)*

ESPEC CORP.
3-5-6 Tenjinbashi, Kita-Ku, Osaka,
530 8550, Japan
Tel.: (81) 663584741
Web Site: https://www.espec.co.jp
Year Founded: 1947
6859—(TKS)
Rev.: $410,652,860
Assets: $517,133,350
Liabilities: $168,687,200
Net Worth: $348,446,150
Earnings: $32,845,090
Emp.: 1,775
Fiscal Year-end: 03/31/24
Industrial, Electronic & Semiconductor Machinery, Equipment & Accessories Mfr
N.A.I.C.S.: 333248
Masaaki Ishida *(Pres)*

Subsidiaries:

DAINAN TECH (S) PTE LTD (1)
66 Tannery Lane 01-01B Sindo Building,
Singapore, 347805, Singapore
Tel.: (65) 68978977
Web Site: https://www.dainan.com.sg
Sales Range: $25-49.9 Million
Emp.: 27
Environmental Testing Services
N.A.I.C.S.: 541380

DEVICE ENG CO., LTD. (1)
169 Eumbong-ro Eumbong-myeon, Asan,
31415, Chungcheongnam-do, Korea
(South)
Tel.: (82) 416295200
Web Site: https://www.deviceeng.co.kr
Rev.: $55,791,388
Assets: $129,121,770
Liabilities: $26,016,997
Net Worth: $103,104,773
Earnings: $8,283,456
Emp.: 158
Fiscal Year-end: 12/31/2022
Industrial Supplies Distr
N.A.I.C.S.: 423840
Sung-jin Lee *(CFO)*

ENVIRONMATE TECH CORP. (1)
Unit 3 Sycamore Arcs 2 Buencamino Street
Corner Alabang-Zapote Road, Muntinlupa,
1770, Philippines
Tel.: (63) 28426195
Web Site: https://www.environmate.com
Sales Range: $25-49.9 Million
Emp.: 12
Environmental Test Chambers Distr
N.A.I.C.S.: 423830
Lilia Duma-o *(Mgr-HR)*

ESPEC (CHINA) LIMITED (1)
Suite 618 6th F Ocean Centre, Harbour
City, Kowloon, China (Hong Kong)

Tel.: (852) 2620 0830
Web Site: http://www.espec-global.com
Environmental Test Chambers Distr
N.A.I.C.S.: 423830

ESPEC Corp. - FUKUCHIYAMA
PLANT (1)
1-7 Osadano-cho, Fukuchiyama, 620-0853,
Kyoto, Japan
Tel.: (81) 773273131
Environmental Testing Equipment Mfr
N.A.I.C.S.: 334513

ESPEC Environmental Equipment
(Shanghai) Co , Ltd. (1)
Unit A 5F Building B No 207 Songhong
Road, Changning District, Shanghai,
200335, China
Tel.: (86) 2151036677
Web Site: https://www.espec.cn
Sales Range: $25-49.9 Million
Emp.: 40
Residential Commercial & Appliance Use
Automatic Environmental Control Mfr
N.A.I.C.S.: 334512

ESPEC Europe GmbH (1)
Wahlerstr 32, 40472, Dusseldorf, Germany
Tel.: (49) 2113618500
Web Site: http://www.espec.de
Sales Range: $25-49.9 Million
Emp.: 5
Analytical Laboratory Instrument Mfr
N.A.I.C.S.: 334516
Koichi Higuchi *(Mng Dir)*

ESPEC Korea Corp. (1)
67 Hyeongoksandan-ro 93beon-gil
Cheongbuk-eup, Pyeongtaek, 17812,
Gyeonggi-do, Korea (South)
Tel.: (82) 3168685235
Web Site: https://www.espec-korea.com
Environmental Test Chambers Mfr
N.A.I.C.S.: 334512

ESPEC Kyushu Corp. (1)
2-6-15 Katano Shinmachi, Kokura Kita-ku,
Kitakyushu, 802-0062, Japan
Tel.: (81) 939411731
Web Site: https://www.espec-q.co.jp
Sales Range: $25-49.9 Million
Emp.: 23
Professional Equipment & Supplies Merchant Whslr
N.A.I.C.S.: 423490

ESPEC Mic Corp. (1)
1-233-1 Omido, Oguchi-cho, Niwa, 480-
0138, Aichi, Japan
Tel.: (81) 587956369
Web Site: https://www.especmic.co.jp
Sales Range: $25-49.9 Million
Emp.: 40
Florists
N.A.I.C.S.: 459310

ESPEC North America Inc. (1)
4141 Central Pkwy, Hudsonville, MI 49426
Tel.: (616) 896-6100
Web Site: http://www.espec.com
Sales Range: $50-74.9 Million
Emp.: 200
Environmental Chambers Mfr, Servicer &
Sales
N.A.I.C.S.: 334512
Ken Walter *(Pres)*

Subsidiary (Domestic):

Qualmark Corporation (2)
10390 E 48th Ave, Denver, CO 80238-2620
Tel.: (303) 254-8800
Web Site: http://www.qualmark.com
Sales Range: $10-24.9 Million
Emp.: 45
Testing Equipment Mfr & Marketer
N.A.I.C.S.: 334516

ESPEC SOUTH EAST ASIA SDN.
BHD.
No 10-1 Jalan Dagang SB 4/2 Taman Sungai Besi Indah, Off Jalan Sungai Besi,
43300, Seri Kembangan, Selangor, Malaysia
Tel.: (60) 3 8945 1377
Web Site: http://www.espec.dm1beta.com
Electronic Chambers Distr
N.A.I.C.S.: 423830
Shimata Taneo *(Gen Mgr)*

ESPEC Techno Corp. (1)
5-2-5 Kanokodaiminamimachi, Kita-ku,
Kobe, 651-1514, Hyogo, Japan
Tel.: (81) 789510960
Web Site: http://www.espec-global.com
Emp.: 30
Electrical Apparatus & Equipment Wiring
Supplies & Construction Materials Whslr
N.A.I.C.S.: 423610

ESPEC Test Technology (Shanghai)
Co., Ltd. (1)
Room 101 Building 2 No 1295 ChuanQiao
Road, PuDong New Area, Shanghai,
201206, China
Tel.: (86) 2168798008
Web Site: http://www.espec.com
Sales Range: $25-49.9 Million
Emp.: 8
Analytical Laboratory Instrument Mfr
N.A.I.C.S.: 334516

EST-SMT LLC (1)
St Novgorodskaya 1 bldg G sub 2, Moscow,
Russia
Tel.: (7) 4959884648
Web Site: http://www.est-smt.ru
Electronic Components Distr
N.A.I.C.S.: 423690

Espec Environmental Chambers
Sales & Engineering Ltd. Sti. (1)
Orucreis Mah Tekstilkent Ticaret Merkezi A
11 Blok no 31 Esenler, 34235, Istanbul,
Turkiye
Tel.: (90) 212 438 1841
Engineeering Services
N.A.I.C.S.: 541330

FURNACE ENGINEERING PTY
LTD (1)
50 Howleys Road, Notting Hill, 3168, VIC,
Australia
Tel.: (61) 395442922
Web Site: http://www.furnace.com.au
Sales Range: $25-49.9 Million
Emp.: 90
Furnaces & Industrial Oven Mfr
N.A.I.C.S.: 333994

H. BENTZ ELECTRONICS LTD. (1)
2 Faran St, Yavne, Israel
Tel.: (972) 8 9422923
Web Site: http://www.hbentz.com
Sales Range: $25-49.9 Million
Emp.: 15
Electric Equipment Mfr
N.A.I.C.S.: 335999

HIELKEMA TESTEQUIPMENT
B.V. (1)
Vluchtoord 23, 5406 XP, Uden, Netherlands
Tel.: (31) 413255243
Web Site: http://www.hielkematest.nl
Sales Range: $50-74.9 Million
Emp.: 10
Environmental Test Chambers Distr
N.A.I.C.S.: 423830

J&S ENGINEERING CORP. (1)
3F JS B/D 26 Samseong-ro 82-gil,
Gangnam-gu, Seoul, 135-881, Korea
(South)
Tel.: (82) 25570505
Environmental Test Chambers Distr
N.A.I.C.S.: 423830

JSC VO MASHPRIBORINTORG (1)
19 Tkatskaya st, Moscow, 105318, Russia
Tel.: (7) 495 363 2327
Web Site: http://www.espec-global.com
Electronic Equipment Distr
N.A.I.C.S.: 423690

OSTEC ENTERPRISE Ltd. (1)
Moldavskaya str 5/2, 121467, Moscow,
Russia
Tel.: (7) 4957884444
Web Site: http://www.ostec-group.ru
Sales Range: $25-49.9 Million
Emp.: 520
Engineering Consulting Services
N.A.I.C.S.: 541330

PRECISE TECH ELECTRONICS
LTD. (1)
Unit 1305 13/F Workingfield Commercial
Bldg 408-412 Jaffe Road, Causeway Bay,
China (Hong Kong)
Tel.: (852) 21239023

Environmental Test Chambers Distr
N.A.I.C.S.: 423830

PSP BRASIL (1)
R Coronel Arbues 98, Santana, Sao Paulo,
02403-040, SP, Brazil
Tel.: (55) 1137295023
Web Site: https://www.pspbrasil.com.br
Sales Range: $50-74.9 Million
Emp.: 10
Printed Circuit Board Distr
N.A.I.C.S.: 423690

SAMS ADVANCE CLIMATIC
TECHNOLOGIES (1)
Plot No 8 9/29 Mirra Industrial Estate, IDA
Patancheru, Hyderabad, 502319, India
Tel.: (91) 8688901255
Web Site: https://www.samsact.com
Sales Range: $25-49.9 Million
Emp.: 35
Environmental Test Chambers Distr
N.A.I.C.S.: 423830
Pilli Rajavardhana Rao *(Founder)*

SCHOELLER INSTRUMENTS,
S.R.O. (1)
Videnska 1398/124, 148 00, Prague, 4,
Czech Republic
Tel.: (420) 261009111
Web Site: http://www.schoeller.cz
Emp.: 30
Industrial Equipment Distr
N.A.I.C.S.: 423830

SENECO SRL (1)
Via Marcello Prestinari 2/4, 20158, Milan,
Italy
Tel.: (39) 0239313031
Web Site: http://www.seneco.it
Laboratory & Scientific Instruments Mfr
N.A.I.C.S.: 334516

Shanghai ESPEC Environmental
Equipment Co., Ltd. (1)
1518 Hao Hua xin Zhen Hua zhi Road,
Qing pu Qu, Shanghai, 201708, China
Tel.: (86) 21 69791178
Web Site: http://www.sh-espec.com
Environmental Test Chambers Mfr
N.A.I.C.S.: 333248

THERMOTEC Weilburg GmbH & Co.
KG (1)
Friedenbachstrasse 18, 35781, Weilburg,
Germany
Tel.: (49) 647162930
Web Site: https://www.ttwe.de
Sales Range: $25-49.9 Million
Emp.: 70
Environmental Test Chambers Mfr
N.A.I.C.S.: 333248
Karl-Heinz Habich *(Founder)*

UNITEMP LIMITED (1)
Unit 14 Treadaway Technical Centre Treadaway Hill, Loudwater, High Wycombe,
HP10 9RS, Bucks, United Kingdom
Tel.: (44) 1628850611
Web Site: https://www.unitemp.co.uk
Sales Range: $25-49.9 Million
Emp.: 7
Environmental Test Chambers Mfr
N.A.I.C.S.: 333248
Ron Brown *(Mng Dir)*

ESPERA-WERKE GMBH
Moltkestrasse 17-33, 47058, Duisburg, Germany
Tel.: (49) 20330540
Web Site: http://www.espera.com
Year Founded: 1924
Rev.: $23,449,800
Emp.: 125
Labelling Machinery Mfr
N.A.I.C.S.: 333993
Marcus Korthauer *(Mng Dir)*

Subsidiaries:

ESPERA IBERICA S.A. (1)
C/Fresadora 2 Pol Ind Santa Ana, 28522,
Rivas-Vaciamadrid, Spain
Tel.: (34) 916666778
Web Site: http://www.espera.de
Industrial Machinery & Equipment Distr
N.A.I.C.S.: 423830

ESPERA-WERKE GMBH—(Continued)

ESPERA Schweiz GmbH (1)
Zurcherstrasse 322, 8406, Winterthur, Switzerland
Tel.: (41) 522133838
Web Site: http://www.espera.de
Industrial Machinery & Equipment Distr
N.A.I.C.S.: 423830

ESPERA-BELGIUM B.V.B.A. (1)
Pleinstraat 33, 3220, Holsbeek, Belgium
Tel.: (32) 16449201
Web Site: http://www.espera.com
Industrial Machinery & Equipment Distr
N.A.I.C.S.: 423830

Espera S.a.r.l. (1)
12 rue des Gardes ZAC des Petits Ruisseaux, 91370, Verrieres-le-Buisson, France
Tel.: (33) 164532720
Industrial Machinery & Equipment Distr
N.A.I.C.S.: 423830

Espera-Nederland B.V. (1)
Industriegebied De Poortmannen De Boelakkers 6, 5591 RA, Heeze, Netherlands
Tel.: (31) 402530665
Web Site: http://www.espera.de
Industrial Machinery & Equipment Distr
N.A.I.C.S.: 423830

ESPERITE N.V.
Herengracht 282, 1016 BX, Amsterdam, Netherlands
Tel.: (31) 575 548 998
Web Site: http://www.esperite.com
Year Founded: 2000
ESP—(AIM)
Adult Stem Cell Collection & Storage Services
N.A.I.C.S.: 541715

Subsidiaries:

Archiv Bunek s.r.o. (1)
Podolske embankment 157/36, Praha 4 Podoli, 147 00, Prague, Czech Republic
Tel.: (420) 241 430 241
Sales Range: $10-24.9 Million
Emp.: 20
Stem Cell Storage Services
N.A.I.C.S.: 621491
Zoltan Merhala (CEO)

Cryo-Save (Pty) Ltd. (1)
Ground Floor Acacia House, Green Hill Village Office Park, Pretoria, 0001, South Africa
Tel.: (27) 878080170
Web Site: http://www.cryo-save.co.za
Stem Cell Storage Services
N.A.I.C.S.: 621491

Cryo-Save AG (1)
Churerstrasse 65B, 8808, Pfaffikon, Schwyz, Switzerland
Tel.: (41) 552220255
Sales Range: $10-24.9 Million
Emp.: 5
Stem Cell Storage Services
N.A.I.C.S.: 621491
Amar Fedrick (Mgr-HR)

Cryo-Save Espana S.A. (1)
Josep Argemi 13-15, 08950, Esplugues de Llobregat, Barcelona, Spain
Tel.: (34) 934705656
Web Site: http://www.2.cryo-save.com
Stem Cell Storage Services
N.A.I.C.S.: 621491

Cryo-Save GmbH (1)
Pauwelsstrasse 19, 52074, Aachen, Germany
Tel.: (49) 24198092750
Stem Cell Storage Services
N.A.I.C.S.: 621491

Output Pharma Services GmbH (1)
Pauwelsstrasse 19, 52074, Aachen, Germany
Tel.: (49) 2419632680
Web Site: http://www.output.eu
Sales Range: $50-74.9 Million
Emp.: 9
Medicinal Products Trading Services
N.A.I.C.S.: 424210

Stichting Cryo-Save (1)
Pyet Hein Straat 11, 7204, Zutphen, Gelderland, Netherlands
Tel.: (31) 575509100
Web Site: http://www.cryo-save.com
Sales Range: $10-24.9 Million
Emp.: 20
Stem Cell Storage Services
N.A.I.C.S.: 621491
Arnoud Van Tulder (CEO)

The Cell-Factory NV (1)
Molenberglei 20, 2627, Schelle, Antwerpen, Belgium
Tel.: (32) 38801540
Web Site: http://www.cell-factory.com
Sales Range: $10-24.9 Million
Emp.: 4
Stem Cell Storage Services
N.A.I.C.S.: 621491

ESPIGA CAPITAL GESTION S.G.E.C.R, S.A.
Montalban 5 Bajo Izdaq, 28014, Madrid, Spain
Tel.: (34) 91 531 7277
Web Site: http://www.espiga.com
Year Founded: 1998
Sales Range: $25-49.9 Million
Emp.: 7
Privater Equity Firm
N.A.I.C.S.: 523999
Carlos Prado (Mng Partner)

Subsidiaries:

Enjoy Wellness, S.L. (1)
Avenida Septima 68, 28022, Madrid, Spain
Tel.: (34) 917462995
Web Site: http://www.enjoywellness.es
Sport Center Operator
N.A.I.C.S.: 713940
Ana Jara Martin (Mgr-Mktg)

Industrial Veterinaria, S.A. (1)
Carrer de l'Esmaragda 19, 8950, Esplugues de Llobregat, Spain (91%)
Tel.: (34) 93 470 62 71
Web Site: http://www.invesagroup.eu
Sales Range: $50-74.9 Million
Emp.: 13
Veterinary Pharmaceutical Product Mfr
N.A.I.C.S.: 325412
Patrick Mochel (Gen Mgr)

Lekue, S.L. (1)
C/ Barcelona 16, La Llagosta, 08120, Barcelona, Spain
Tel.: (34) 93 574 26 40
Web Site: http://www.lekue.com
Kitchen Utensil Mfr
N.A.I.C.S.: 332215
Blanca Soler Marcos (Dir-Sls)

Subsidiary (US):

Lekue USA, Inc. (2)
802 Centerpoint Blvd, New Castle, DE 19720
Tel.: (302) 326-4805
Web Site: http://www.lekueusa.com
Kitchen Utensil Mfr
N.A.I.C.S.: 332215

M30 STANDS 2003 S.A. (1)
Ctra Santa Creu de Calafell 86, Sant Boi de Llobregat, 08830, Barcelona, Spain
Tel.: (34) 936305511
Web Site: http://www.m30stands.com
Construction Engineering Services
N.A.I.C.S.: 236220

Ydilo Advanced Voice Solutions S.A. (1)
Calle Jose Echegaray 8 Block 3 Floor 2 Office 2, Las Rozas, 28232, Madrid, Spain
Tel.: (34) 912528400
Web Site: http://www.ydilo.com
Application Software Development Services
N.A.I.C.S.: 541511
Jorge Porras (Mgr-Acctg & Reporting)

ESPIJNEIRA, PACHECO Y ASOCIADOS
Urb El Parque Calle Los Comuneros Centro Ejecutivo Los Leones Piso 5,

3001, Barquisimeto, Estado Lara, Venezuela
Tel.: (58) 251 255 49 83　　　VE
Web Site: http://www.pwc.com
Accounting, Tax & Business Consulting Services
N.A.I.C.S.: 541211

ESPIRE HOSPITALITY LIMITED
A-41 Mohan Co-Operative Industrial Area, Bhikaji Cama Place, New Delhi, 110 044, India
Tel.: (91) 8860707273
Web Site:
　　https://www.espirehospitality.com
532016—(BOM)
Rev.: $12,415
Assets: $180,099
Liabilities: $6,718
Net Worth: $173,381
Earnings: ($13,173)
Emp.: 2
Fiscal Year-end: 03/31/20
Real Estate Related Services
N.A.I.C.S.: 531390
Gyanendra Prakash (Mng Dir)

ESPLANADE LIMITED
Medina Avenue, Newport, PO30 1HG, Isle of Wight, United Kingdom
Tel.: (44) 1983523232
Web Site:
　　http://www.esplanade.co.uk
Year Founded: 1946
Rev.: $10,701,972
Emp.: 39
New & Used Car Dealer
N.A.I.C.S.: 441110
Neil Doble (Mgr-Sls)

ESPORTS ENTERTAINMENT GROUP, INC.
Block 6 Triq Paceville, Saint Julian's, STJ 3109, Malta
Tel.: (356) 2685629111　　NV
Web Site:
　　http://www.esportentertainment.com
Year Founded: 2008
GMBL—(NASDAQ)
Rev.: $22,965,804
Assets: $22,101,291
Liabilities: $17,305,032
Net Worth: $4,796,259
Earnings: ($33,632,161)
Emp.: 100
Fiscal Year-end: 06/30/23
Multi-Player Video Game Gambling
N.A.I.C.S.: 713290
Janis L. Jones Blackhurst (Chm)

ESPRESSIF SYSTEMS SHANGHAI CO., LTD.
Room 204 Building No 2 No 690 Bibo Road, Filot Free Trade Zone, Shanghai, 201203, China
Tel.: (86) 2161065218
Web Site: http://www.espressif.com
Year Founded: 2008
688018—(SHG)
Rev.: $178,466,259
Assets: $292,424,671
Liabilities: $35,959,150
Net Worth: $256,465,521
Earnings: $13,664,163
Fiscal Year-end: 12/31/22
Semiconductor Product Mfr
N.A.I.C.S.: 334413
Teo Swee Ann (Founder, Chm, CEO & Gen Mgr)

ESPRINET S.P.A.
Via Energy Park, 20-20871, Vimercate, MB, Italy
Tel.: (39) 0240498800
Web Site: https://www.esprinet.com
Year Founded: 1999

PRT—(ITA)
Rev.: $4,399,119,109
Assets: $2,026,106,635
Liabilities: $1,620,532,068
Net Worth: $405,574,567
Earnings: ($13,108,511)
Emp.: 1,776
Fiscal Year-end: 12/31/23
IT Hardware & Software
N.A.I.C.S.: 423430
Maurizio Rota (Chm)

Subsidiaries:

Celly S.p.A. (1)
Via Energy Park 20, 20871, Vimercate, MB, Italy
Tel.: (39) 0240498100
Web Site: http://www.celly.com
Smartphone Accessory Mfr & Distr
N.A.I.C.S.: 334210

Itway VAD (1)
Via L Braille 15, 48100, Ravenna, Italy
Tel.: (39) 0544288711
Web Site: http://www.itwayvad.com.tr
Internet Solutions Services
N.A.I.C.S.: 541512
Cesare Valenti (Exec VP)

Nilox (1)
Via Energy Park 20, 20871, Vimercate, MB, Italy (100%)
Tel.: (39) 03624961
Web Site: https://www.nilox.com
Sales Range: $250-299.9 Million
Emp.: 800
IT Hardware & Software
N.A.I.C.S.: 423430

V-Valley Advanced Solutions Espana, S.A. (1)
PE San Fernando-Ed Europe Floor 2 Staircase A, C/Sierra de Guadarrama 3 A2-Exit 17A, 28830, San Fernando de Henares, Madrid, Spain
Tel.: (34) 902444777
Web Site: http://www.gti.es
Software Development Services
N.A.I.C.S.: 541511

Subsidiary (Non-US):

GTI Software & Networking SARLAU (2)
Zenith Millenium Imm 1 Lot Attaoufik, Sidi Maarouf, 20270, Casablanca, Morocco
Tel.: (212) 522879490
Logistics Software & Networking Services
N.A.I.C.S.: 541519

Vinzeo Technologies S.A.U. (1)
Plaza Euskadi n 5 9th Floor, 48009, Bilbao, Vizcaya, Spain
Tel.: (34) 902380480
Web Site: http://www.vinzeo.com
Computer Products Whslr
N.A.I.C.S.: 423430

ESPRIT HOLDINGS LIMITED
Unit 1101 11/F Goldin Financial Global Centre, 17 Kai Cheung Road Kowloon Bay, Kowloon, China (Hong Kong)
Tel.: (852) 27654321
Web Site: http://www.esprit.com
0330—(HKG)
Rev.: $1,072,597,680
Assets: $1,295,862,060
Liabilities: $635,871,400
Net Worth: $659,990,660
Earnings: $491,413,800
Emp.: 2,260
Fiscal Year-end: 12/31/21
Holding Company; Clothing, Accessories, Footwear & Housewares
N.A.I.C.S.: 424350
Thomas Wing yung Tang (CFO)

Subsidiaries:

ESP Clothing Finland OY (1)
Kornetintie 6, 00380, Helsinki, Finland
Tel.: (358) 941700700

Sales Range: $25-49.9 Million
Emp.: 24
Apparel Retailer
N.A.I.C.S.: 458110
Piia Rossi (Mng Dir)

Esprit (Hong Kong) Limited (1)
Ground floor 142 Keking Rd 7 Ashley Rd,
Kowloon Bay, Kowloon, China (Hong Kong)
Tel.: (852) 23779114
Clothing Apparel Retailer
N.A.I.C.S.: 458110

Esprit Asia (Distribution) Limited (1)
43/F Enterprise Square Three 39 Wang
Chiu Road, Kowloon Bay, Kowloon, 052,
China (Hong Kong) (100%)
Tel.: (852) 27654232
Web Site: http://www.esprit.com
Quality & Lifestyle Products Sourcing, Retail
& Wholesale
N.A.I.C.S.: 458110

Esprit Belgie Retail N.V. (1)
Hessenstraatje 19, 2000, Antwerp, Belgium
Tel.: (32) 32336020
Web Site: http://www.espirit.be
Emp.: 35
Apparel Retailer
N.A.I.C.S.: 458110

**Esprit Canada Distribution
Limited** (1)
135 Liberty St Ste 300, Toronto, M6K 1A7,
ON, Canada
Tel.: (416) 913-0505
Casual Apparels Distr
N.A.I.C.S.: 315990

Esprit Canada Retail Limited (1)
1 Bass Pro Mills Dr, Vaughan, L4K 5W4,
ON, Canada
Tel.: (905) 738-2218
Casual Apparels Retailer
N.A.I.C.S.: 315210

Esprit Canada Wholesale Inc. (1)
2452 Chomedey A-13 O, Laval, H7X 4G8,
QC, Canada
Tel.: (450) 689-3613
Clothing Apparel Retailer
N.A.I.C.S.: 458110

Esprit Card Services GmbH (1)
Esprit-Allee, Ratingen, 40882, Nordrhein-
Westfalen, Germany
Tel.: (49) 21021230
Web Site: http://www.espirit.com
Sales Range: $400-449.9 Million
Emp.: 1,200
Apparel Retailer
N.A.I.C.S.: 458110

**Esprit Design & Product Development
GmbH** (1)
Esprit Allee 1, Ratingen, 40882, Nordrhein-
Westfalen, Germany
Tel.: (49) 210212345780
Web Site: http://www.esprit.com
Sales Range: $400-449.9 Million
Emp.: 1,300
Apparel Retailer
N.A.I.C.S.: 458110

Esprit Europe B.V. (1)
Marktstraat 6, 5211 SL, 's-Hertogenbosch,
Noord-Brabant, Netherlands
Tel.: (31) 736241244
Apparel Retailer
N.A.I.C.S.: 458110
Elf Wingerden (Mng Dir)

Esprit GB Limited (1)
178-182 Regent Street, London, W1B 5TH,
United Kingdom
Tel.: (44) 2070257700
Clothing Apparel Retailer
N.A.I.C.S.: 458110

Esprit Global Image GmbH (1)
Esprit-Allee, 40882, Ratingen, Germany.
Tel.: (49) 3022380663
Image Direction & Design Services
N.A.I.C.S.: 541490
Mark Daley (Mng Dir)

Esprit Handelsgesellschaft mbH. (1)
Soellheimer St-16, 5020, Salzburg, Austria
Tel.: (43) 662454700
Web Site: http://www.esprit.at

Sales Range: $25-49.9 Million
Emp.: 60
Clothing Apparel Retailer
N.A.I.C.S.: 458110
Karen Seldpauschsturm (Mng Dir)

Esprit International GP, Inc. (1)
1370 Broadway Fl 14, New York, NY 10018
Tel.: (212) 401-1122
Sales Range: $1-9.9 Million
Emp.: 15
Holding Company
N.A.I.C.S.: 551112

Esprit Italy Distribution S.R.L. (1)
Via Tortona 27, Milan, 20140, Italy
Tel.: (39) 0281881701
Web Site: http://www.espirit.com
Sales Range: $25-49.9 Million
Emp.: 34
Apparels & Accessories Distr
N.A.I.C.S.: 424310
Marco Bonanni (Gen Mgr)

Esprit Luxembourg S.a.r.L. (1)
Grand-Rue 23-25, 1661, Luxembourg, Lux-
embourg
Tel.: (352) 26262176
Web Site: http://www.espirit.com
Sales Range: $25-49.9 Million
Emp.: 15
Apparel Retailer
N.A.I.C.S.: 458110

**Esprit Macao Commercial Offshore
Limited** (1)
Room A-C L-N 15F Edi Zhu Kuan Avenida
Xian Xing Hai, Macau, China (Macau)
Tel.: (853) 87913600
Sales Range: $25-49.9 Million
Emp.: 70
Casual Apparels Retailer
N.A.I.C.S.: 458110

Esprit Regional Services Limited (1)
40F Enterprise Square Three 39 Wang Chiu
Road, Kowloon Bay, Kowloon, China (Hong
Kong)
Tel.: (852) 35113511
Clothing Apparel Retailer
N.A.I.C.S.: 458110
Fook Aun Chew (Exec Dir & Grp CFO)

Esprit Retail B.V. & Co. KG. (1)
Esprit-Allee 1, 40882, Ratingen,
Germany (100%)
Tel.: (49) 302 238 0663
Web Site: https://www.esprit.de
Online Apparel Retailer
N.A.I.C.S.: 458110

Esprit Retail Pte. Ltd. (1)
70 Bendemeer Road 05-01 Luzerne, Singa-
pore, 339940, Singapore (100%)
Tel.: (65) 62971211
Web Site: http://www.esprit.com
Sales Range: $50-74.9 Million
Emp.: 200
Casual Apparels Retailer
N.A.I.C.S.: 458110
Connie Chow (Mgr-Admin & Fin)

**Esprit Switzerland Distribution
AG** (1)
Thurgauerstrasse 113, 8152, Glattbrugg,
Zurich, Switzerland
Tel.: (41) 448281616
Web Site: http://www.espirit.com
Sales Range: $25-49.9 Million
Emp.: 50
Apparel & Accessories Wholesale Distribu-
tion Services
N.A.I.C.S.: 424350
Andrea Koller (Mgr-Sls)

Esprit Switzerland Retail AG (1)
Thurgauerstrasse 113, 8152, Zurich, Swit-
zerland
Tel.: (41) 448281616
Sales Range: $25-49.9 Million
Emp.: 30
Apparel & Accessories Retailer
N.A.I.C.S.: 458110
Stefan Kohlbauer (Head-Retail)

Esprit US Online Shop Limited (1)
1370 Broadway 16th Fl, New York, NY
10018
Tel.: (212) 401-1125
Online Apparel Retailer

N.A.I.C.S.: 458110

Esprit de Corp (Far East) Limited (1)
43F Enterprise Sq Three 39 Wang Chiu Rd,
Kowloon Bay, Kowloon, 852, China (Hong
Kong)
Tel.: (852) 27654321
Casual Apparels Retailer
N.A.I.C.S.: 458110

Esprit de Corp Danmark A/S (1)
Pohjoisesplanadi 33a, 00100, Helsinki, Fin-
land
Tel.: (358) 9780781
Apparel Retailer
N.A.I.C.S.: 458110

Esprit de Corp France S.A.S. (1)
N 29 Au 33 29 Rue du Louvre, Paris,
75002, France
Tel.: (33) 140285500
Apparel Retailer
N.A.I.C.S.: 458110

Esprit de Corp. (Spain) S.L. (1)
Calle Jose Abascal 45 5th Floor, Madrid,
28003, Spain
Tel.: (34) 914292213
Web Site: http://www.esprit.com
Sales Range: $25-49.9 Million
Emp.: 30
Apparel Retailer
N.A.I.C.S.: 458110
Tamara Reach (Asst Mgr)

ESPRO INFORMATION TECH-
NOLOGIES LTD.
17 Atir Yeda Street, Kfar Saba,
4464313, Israel
Tel.: (972) 9 763 4400
Web Site:
http://www.acoustiguide.com
Multimedia Guide Production Ser-
vices
N.A.I.C.S.: 512110
Shmuel Shalem (CTO)

Subsidiaries:

Acoustiguide Asia Ltd. (1)
10/F 143 Nanking East Road Section 4,
Taipei, 00105, Taiwan
Tel.: (886) 227135355
Software Development Services
N.A.I.C.S.: 541511
Jasper Lin (Gen Mgr)

Acoustiguide GmbH (1)
Martin-Luther-Strasse 111, 10825, Berlin,
Germany
Tel.: (49) 30 78 77 36 0
Web Site: http://www.acoustiguide.de
Emp.: 7
Multimedia Guide Production Services
N.A.I.C.S.: 512110
Jorg Bruckner (Mng Dir)

Acoustiguide Inc. (1)
102 W 38th St, New York, NY 10018
Tel.: (212) 279-1300
Web Site: http://www.acoustiguide.com
Sales Range: $25-49.9 Million
Emp.: 12
Multimedia Guide Production Services
N.A.I.C.S.: 512110
Julie Twitmyer (Mng Dir-Americas)

Acoustiguide Japan Ltd. (1)
Jingu Gaien Building 7F 2-7-25, Minato
Kita-aoyama, Tokyo, 107-0061, Japan
Tel.: (81) 357714081
Software Development Services
N.A.I.C.S.: 541511
Kaori Kurata (Mng Dir)

Acoustiguide Ltd. (1)
2 3 North Mews, London, WC1N 2JP,
United Kingdom
Tel.: (44) 20 7269 5150
Web Site: http://www.acoustiguide.co.uk
Multimedia Guide Production Services
N.A.I.C.S.: 512110
Louisa Matthews (Mng Dir)

Acoustiguide SAS (1)
15 bis Rue Sainte-Anne, 75002, Paris,
France
Tel.: (33) 142606968
Software Development Services

N.A.I.C.S.: 541511
Agnes Alfandari (VP-Digital Strategy Acoustiguide Grp)

**Acoustiguide of Australia Pty.,
Ltd.** (1)
Suite 1 768 Old Princes Highway, Suther-
land, 2232, NSW, Australia
Tel.: (61) 6295893240
Software Development Services
N.A.I.C.S.: 541511
Maryanne Leigh (Gen Mgr)

Espro Acoustiguide SAS (1)
171 quai de Valmy, 75010, Paris, France
Tel.: (33) 1 4260 6968
Web Site: http://www.acoustiguide.com
Multimedia Guide Production Services
N.A.I.C.S.: 512110

ESQUIRE KNIT COMPOSITE
LTD.
Ideal Trade Centre 9th Floor 102
Shaheed Tajuddin Ahmed Sharani,
Tejgaon I/A, Dhaka, 1208, Bangla-
desh
Tel.: (880) 9602333888
Web Site:
https://www.esquireknit.com
Year Founded: 2001
ESQUIRENIT—(DHA)
Rev.: $117,747,208
Assets: $181,982,296
Liabilities: $79,939,912
Net Worth: $102,042,384
Earnings: $3,696,543
Emp.: 8,428
Fiscal Year-end: 06/30/22
Garments Mfr
N.A.I.C.S.: 315990
Mofazzal Hossain (Chm)

ESR GROUP LIMITED
2406-07 Man Yee Building 68 Des
Voeux Road, Central, China (Hong
Kong)
Tel.: (852) 23769600   Ky
Web Site: http://www.esr.com
Year Founded: 2011
1821—(HKG)
Rev.: $821,154,000
Assets: $16,199,374,000
Liabilities: $7,059,060,000
Net Worth: $9,140,314,000
Earnings: $631,109,000
Emp.: 2,237
Fiscal Year-end: 12/31/22
Real Estate Development Services
N.A.I.C.S.: 541614
Jeffrey Jinchu Shen (Co-Founder &
Co-CEO)

Subsidiaries:

**APM Property Management Pte.
Ltd.** (1)
1 Raffles Boulevard Level 2 Crescent 1
Suntec City, Singapore, 039593, Singapore
Tel.: (65) 62952888
Web Site: https://www.apm-asia.com
Commercial Real Estate Services
N.A.I.C.S.: 531210

ARA Asset Management Limited (1)
5 Temasek Boulevard 12-01 Suntec Tower
Four, Singapore, 038986, Singapore
Tel.: (65) 68359232
Web Site: http://www.ara-group.com
Rev.: $263,751,034
Assets: $2,646,676,435
Liabilities: $812,593,840
Net Worth: $1,834,082,595
Earnings: $139,528,271
Fiscal Year-end: 12/31/2020
Real Estate Investment Fund Management
Services
N.A.I.C.S.: 523940
Pauline Lim (Sr Dir-HR & Admin)

Subsidiary (Non-US):

**ARA Asset Management (Prosperity)
Limited** (2)
Rm 5508-9 55/F The Ctr 99 Queens Rd,

ESR Group Limited—(Continued)

Central, China (Hong Kong)
Tel.: (852) 21690928
Sales Range: $25-49.9 Million
Emp.: 35
Real Estate Investment Trust Management Services
N.A.I.C.S.: 523940
Mavis Wong *(CEO)*

ARA Korea Limited **(2)**
20F Two IFC 10 Gukjegeumyung-ro, Yeongdeungpo-gu, Seoul, 150-010, Korea (South)
Tel.: (82) 2 6137 3700
Real Estate Investment Fund Management Services
N.A.I.C.S.: 523940
Anthony D. Kang *(CEO)*

Subsidiary (Domestic):

ARA Real Estate Investors XVIII Pte. Ltd **(2)**
5 Temasek Boulevard 12-01 Suntec Tower 5, Singapore, 038985, Singapore
Tel.: (65) 68359232
Holding Company
N.A.I.C.S.: 551112

ARA Trust Management (Suntec) Limited **(2)**
6 Temasek Boulevard 16-02 Suntec Tower Four, Singapore, 038986, Singapore
Tel.: (65) 6835 9232
Web Site: http://www.ara-asia.com
Sales Range: $25-49.9 Million
Emp.: 80
Real Estate Investment Trust Management Services
N.A.I.C.S.: 523940
Poh Choo Low *(Sr Dir-Fin)*

Suntec International Convention & Exhibition Services Pte. Ltd. **(2)**
1 Raffles Boulevard Suntec City, Singapore, 039593, Singapore
Tel.: (65) 63372888
Web Site: http://www.suntecsingapore.com
Sales Range: $150-199.9 Million
Emp.: 300
Convention & Exhibition Center Management Services
N.A.I.C.S.: 531312
Arun Madhok *(CEO)*

Suntec Singapore International Convention & Exhibition Services Pte. Ltd. **(2)**
1 Raffles Boulevard, Suntec City, Singapore, 039593, Singapore
Tel.: (65) 6337 2888
Web Site: http://www.suntecsingapore.com
Sales Range: $75-99.9 Million
Emp.: 300
Exhibition Venue Rental & Operation Services
N.A.I.C.S.: 711310
Arun Madhok *(CEO)*

Venn Partners LLP **(1)**
13 George Street, London, W1U 3QJ, United Kingdom
Tel.: (44) 2070739350
Web Site: https://www.ara-venn.com
Investment Management Service
N.A.I.C.S.: 541690

ESR INVESTMENT MANAGEMENT (S) PTE. LTD.
138 Market Street 26-03/04 CapitaGreen, Singapore, 048946, Singapore
Tel.: (65) 6222 3339　　　　SG
Real Estate Investment Trust Management Services
N.A.I.C.S.: 523940
Adrian Wai Yin Chui *(CEO)*

Subsidiaries:

ESR-LOGOS REIT **(1)**
138 Market Street 26-03/04 CapitaGreen, Singapore, 048946, Singapore
Tel.: (65) 62223339
Web Site: https://www.esr-logosreit.com.sg
Rev.: $254,506,528

Assets: $4,192,558,157
Liabilities: $2,079,960,147
Net Worth: $2,112,598,011
Earnings: ($201,272,019)
Emp.: 79
Fiscal Year-end: 12/31/2022
Real Estate Investment Trust
N.A.I.C.S.: 525990
Adrian Wai Yin Chui *(CEO)*

ESR KENDALL SQUARE REIT CO., LTD.
35F Three Ifc 10 Gukjegeumyung-Ro, Yeongdeungpo-Gu, Seoul, Korea (South)
Tel.: (82) 262050467
Web Site: https://www.esrks-reit.com
Year Founded: 2020
365550—(KRS)
Real Estate Investment Trust Services
N.A.I.C.S.: 531390
Dongjin Lee *(Head-IR)*

ESREY RESOURCES LTD
Suite 1000 - 355 Burrard Street, Vancouver, V6C 2G8, BC, Canada
Tel.: (604) 925-5136　　　　BC
Web Site: https://www.esreyresources.com
Year Founded: 2000
ESR—(TSXV)
Sales Range: Less than $1 Million
Oil & Gas Exploration & Development Services
N.A.I.C.S.: 213112
Allen Leschert *(CEO)*

ESS ASIA LTD
Lot 2-1 Incubator 3 Technology Park Malaysia, Bukit Jalil, 57000, Kuala Lumpur, Malaysia
Tel.: (60) 389941919　　　　MY
Web Site: http://www.essasia.net
Year Founded: 2002
Information Technology Consulting Services
N.A.I.C.S.: 541511
Mansor Mohammed *(Mng Dir)*

ESS ENN TIMBER AB
Skruvbyvagen 2A, 360 53, Lessebo, Sweden
Tel.: (46) 478 208 00
Web Site: http://www.ess-enn.se
Building Construction Materials Mfr
N.A.I.C.S.: 113110

ESSA PHARMA INC.
Suite 720 999 West Broadway, Vancouver, V5Z 1K5, BC, Canada
Tel.: (778) 331-0962　　　　BC
Web Site: https://www.essapharma.com
Year Founded: 2009
EPIX—(NASDAQ)
Assets: $128,112,003
Liabilities: $3,506,233
Net Worth: $124,605,770
Earnings: ($28,542,821)
Emp.: 35
Fiscal Year-end: 09/30/24
Pharmaceuticals Mfr
N.A.I.C.S.: 325412
Richard M. Glickman *(Founder & Chm)*

ESSAR GLOBAL LIMITED
Essar House 11 Keshavrao Khadya Marg, Mahalaxmi, Mumbai, 400 034, India
Tel.: (91) 2266601100　　　　In
Web Site: http://www.essar.com
Sales Range: $5-14.9 Billion
Emp.: 20,000
Holding Company
N.A.I.C.S.: 551112

Rajiv Sawhney *(CEO-Telecom Bus Grp)*

Subsidiaries:

Essar Energy plc **(1)**
Essar House 10 Frere Felix de Valois Street, Port Louis, Mauritius **(78.02%)**
Tel.: (230) 4051400
Web Site: https://www.essar.com
Sales Range: $25-49.9 Billion
Emp.: 3,951
Holding Company; Petroleum Exploration, Production, Refining & Marketing Services; Power Generation & Transmission Services
N.A.I.C.S.: 551112
Sushil K. Maroo *(CEO)*

Subsidiary (Non-US):

Essar Exploration & Production Ltd. **(2)**
Equinox Business Park off Bandra Kurla Complex LBS Marg Kurla West, Mumbai, 400 070, India
Tel.: (91) 22 6733 5000
Web Site: http://www.essarenergy.com
Gas Exploration
N.A.I.C.S.: 213112

Essar Investments Ltd. **(1)**
Essar House 11 KK Marg Mahalaxmi, Mumbai, 400034, India
Tel.: (91) 2 2425 0606
Investment Services
N.A.I.C.S.: 523999

Essar Ports Limited **(1)**
Salaya Administrative Building ER 2 Building Salaya, Taluka Khambhalia District Devbhumi Dwarka, Jamnagar, 361305, Gujarat, India
Tel.: (91) 2833664440
Web Site: http://www.essarports.com
Rev.: $23,444,820
Assets: $149,626,764
Liabilities: $120,768,480
Net Worth: $28,858,284
Earnings: ($4,392,290)
Emp.: 8,000
Fiscal Year-end: 03/31/2020
Ports & Terminals, Logistics Services, Sea Transportation & Oilfield Drilling Services
N.A.I.C.S.: 488310
K. K. Sinha *(Exec Dir)*

Subsidiary (Domestic):

Essar International Ltd. **(2)**
Equinox Business Park Peninsula Techno Park Off Bandra Kurla Complex, LBS Marg Kurla West, Mumbai, 400 070, Maharashtra, India
Tel.: (91) 22 6733 5000
Web Site: http://www.essar.com
Ports & Harbor Operation
N.A.I.C.S.: 488310
Rakesh Kankanala *(Mgr-Fin)*

Essar Oilfields Services Limited **(2)**
Essar House 11 Keshavrao Khadye Marg, Mahalaxmi, Mumbai, 400 034, India **(100%)**
Tel.: (91) 22 2495 0606
Emp.: 800
Oil Rig Operator
N.A.I.C.S.: 213112
Rajeev Nayyer *(CEO)*

Essar Port & Terminals Ltd. **(2)**
11 Keshavrao Khadye Marg Mahalaxmi, Mumbai, 400 034, India
Tel.: (91) 22 2495 0606
Port & Terminal Operations
N.A.I.C.S.: 488310

Essar Power Ltd. **(1)**
Essar House 11 Keshavrao Khadye Marg, Opp Race Course Mahalakshmi, Mumbai, 400 034, India
Tel.: (91) 22673350
Power Generation
N.A.I.C.S.: 211120

Essar Steel Ltd. **(1)**
Essar House 11 Keshavrao Khadye Marg, Opposite Mahalakshmi, Mumbai, 400 034, India
Tel.: (91) 2266601100
Web Site: http://www.essarsteel.com

Sales Range: $300-349.9 Million
Steel Production & Export
N.A.I.C.S.: 332111
Shashi Ruia *(Chm)*

Subsidiary (US):

Essar Steel Minnesota LLC **(2)**
555 W 27th St, Hibbing, MN 55746
Tel.: (218) 263-3331
Web Site: http://www.essarsteelmn.com
Sales Range: $25-49.9 Million
Emp.: 20
Steel Mining
N.A.I.C.S.: 332111
Matthew Stook *(CEO)*

Subsidiary (Non-US):

PT Essar Indonesia **(2)**
Bekasi Fajar Industrial Estate Industri 3 Area Kav B1, Bekasi, 17520, Indonesia
Tel.: (62) 218980152
Web Site: http://www.essar.co.id
Sales Range: $75-99.9 Million
Emp.: 400
Cold Rolled Steel
N.A.I.C.S.: 331221
Shireesh Sharma *(Gen Mgr-Mktg)*

Essar Teleholding Ltd. **(1)**
Equinox Business Park off Bandra Kurla Complex LBS Marg Kurla West, Mumbai, 400 070, Maharashtra, India
Tel.: (91) 22 6733 5000
Web Site: http://www.essar.com
Telecommunications
N.A.I.C.S.: 517810
Rajiv Sawhney *(CEO)*

Subsidiary (Domestic):

The MobileStore Ltd. **(2)**
Essar Techno Park Building 'B' 1st Floor Pyramid Infotech Park, Swan Mill Compound LBS Marg, Mumbai, 400 070, Kurla (W), India
Tel.: (91) 2260006363
Web Site: http://www.themobilestore.in
Mobile Phones & Equipment Stores
N.A.I.C.S.: 517810

Hutchison Essar Limited **(1)**
Hutch House Peninsula Corporate Park, Ganpatrao Kdam Marg, Lower Parel, Mumbai, 400 013, India
Tel.: (91) 2256661200
Wireless Telecommunication Services
N.A.I.C.S.: 517112

ESSAR SECURITIES LIMITED
Essar House 11 K K Marg, Mahalaxmi, Mumbai, 400034, India
Tel.: (91) 2266601100　　　　UK
Web Site: https://www.essar.com
Rev.: $144,174
Assets: $143,099
Liabilities: $3,657
Net Worth: $139,442
Earnings: $102,617
Emp.: 50,000
Fiscal Year-end: 03/31/19
Financial Services
N.A.I.C.S.: 921130
Shashi Ruia *(Co-Founder)*

ESSAR SHIPPING LIMITED
Essar House 11 kk Marg Mahalaxmi, PO Box No 7, Taluka Khambalia Devbhumi Dwarka, Mumbai, 400 034, Maharashtra, India
Tel.: (91) 2266601100
Web Site: https://www.essar.com
Year Founded: 2010
ESSARSHPNG—(NSE)
Rev.: $69,363,840
Assets: $284,471,460
Liabilities: $905,434,530
Net Worth: ($620,963,070)
Earnings: ($84,706,440)
Emp.: 35
Fiscal Year-end: 03/31/21
Chartering & Shipping Services
N.A.I.C.S.: 483111
Ranjit Singh *(Pres & CEO)*

Subsidiaries:

Essar Oilfields Services Limited (1)
Essar House 10 Frere Felix de Valois
Street, Port Louis, Mauritius
Tel.: (230) 4051400
Maritime Services
N.A.I.C.S.: 488390

ESSBIO SA
Avenida Prat 199 Torre B Piso 15,
Concepcion, Chile
Tel.: (56) 412263700
Web Site: http://www.essbio.cl
Water Utility Services
N.A.I.C.S.: 221310
Cristian Vergara Castillo *(CEO)*

ESSECO GROUP SRL
Via S Cassiano 99, San Martino,
28069, Trecate, Novara, Italy
Tel.: (39) 03217901   IT
Web Site:
   http://www.essecogroup.com
Year Founded: 1982
Sales Range: $1-4.9 Billion
Holding Company; Chemicals Re-
search & Development & Mfr
N.A.I.C.S.: 325180
Piero Nulli *(Chm & CEO)*

Subsidiaries:

Altair Chimica SpA (1)
Via Moie Vecchie 13, 56048, Pisa, Italy
Tel.: (39) 0588 9811
Web Site: http://www.altairchimica.com
Chemical Products Mfr
N.A.I.C.S.: 325199
Roberto Vagheggi *(Mng Dir)*

ENARTIS ARGENTINA S.A. (1)
Rodriguez Pena 1437, Luzuriaga Maipu,
Mendoza, Argentina
Tel.: (54) 261 493 0301
Chemical Products Distr
N.A.I.C.S.: 424690

ENARTIS CENTRAL EUROPE
s.r.o. (1)
Nam A Hlinku 1, 831 06, Bratislava, Slova-
kia
Tel.: (421) 33 6422606
Chemical Products Distr
N.A.I.C.S.: 424690

ENARTIS CHILE LTDA (1)
440 Antillaca Ave, 13200, Santiago, Quili-
cura, Chile
Tel.: (56) 9 77061643
Chemical Products Distr
N.A.I.C.S.: 424690

ENARTIS PACIFIC PTY LTD (1)
30-38 Tanunda rd, PO Box 886, Sydney,
5355, SA, Australia
Tel.: (61) 8 85657244
Chemical Products Distr
N.A.I.C.S.: 424690

ENARTIS PORTUGAL UNIPES-
SOAL, LDA (1)
Rua de Sao Joao de Brito no 605 E 4 - 4 1,
4100 - 455, Porto, Portugal
Tel.: (351) 220 992 192
Web Site: http://www.enartis.com.pt
Wine Mfr
N.A.I.C.S.: 312130

ENARTIS SEPSA S.A.U. (1)
Pol Ind Clot de Moja c/Garnatxa 13-15,
08734, Olerdola, Spain
Tel.: (34) 938 199100
Web Site: http://www.enartis.es
Chemical Products Distr
N.A.I.C.S.: 424690

ENARTIS SOUTH AFRICA LTD (1)
10 Distillery Street, Dal Josaphat, 7646,
Paarl, South Africa
Tel.: (27) 21 8701181
Web Site: http://www.enartis.co.za
Wine Mfr
N.A.I.C.S.: 312130
Jaco Cockrell *(Key Acct Mgr)*

ENARTIS VINQUIRY INC. (1)

7795 Bell Rd, Windsor, CA 95492
Tel.: (707) 838-6312
Web Site: http://www.enartisvinquiry.com
Wine Mfr
N.A.I.C.S.: 312130
Amy Kolberg *(Bus Mgr-Central Coast)*

ESSECO DO BRASIL INDUSTRIA E
COMERCIO DE PRODUTOS QUIMI-
COS LTDA (1)
Estrada do Zilo 1509 Bairro da Ronda, Ara-
cariguama, Sao Paulo, Brazil
Tel.: (55) 11 41363200
Chemical Products Distr
N.A.I.C.S.: 327910

ESSECO USA LLC (1)
Gatehall IV 4 Gatehall Dr, Parsippany, NJ
07054
Tel.: (973) 267-3330
Web Site: http://www.essecousa.com
Chemical Products Mfr
N.A.I.C.S.: 325199
Mark Dulik *(Sr Engr)*

EVER BRASIL INDUSTRIA E COM-
ERCIO LTDA (1)
Rua Eca de Queiroz 150, Bairro Garibal-
dina, Rio Grande, Brazil
Tel.: (55) 5434649300
Web Site: http://www.everbrasil.com.br
Wine Mfr
N.A.I.C.S.: 312130

EVER S.r.l. (1)
via Pacinotti 37, Pramaggiore, 30020, Ven-
ice, Italy
Tel.: (39) 0421 200455
Web Site: http://www.ever.it
Chemical Products Mfr
N.A.I.C.S.: 325199

EVER TRADE S.r.o. (1)
Jesenskeho 16, 902 01, Pezinok, Slovakia
Tel.: (421) 33 64 22 606
Web Site: http://www.evertrade.sk
Wine Mfr
N.A.I.C.S.: 312130

EVERINTEC GMBH (1)
Gustav Freytag Strasse 13, 65189, Wies-
baden, Germany
Tel.: (49) 611 36024823
Chemical Products Distr
N.A.I.C.S.: 424690

Esseco UK Limited (1)
Calder Vale Road, Wakefield, WF1 5PH,
West Yorkshire, United Kingdom   **(100%)**
Tel.: (44) 1924371919
Web Site: http://www.essecouk.com
Sales Range: $10-24.9 Million
Emp.: 55
Ammonium Compound Mfr
N.A.I.C.S.: 325180
Chris Mckenfia *(Mng Dir)*

RUBBER NANO PRODUCTS EU-
ROPE SRL (1)
Via San Cassiano 99, 28069, Novara, Italy
Tel.: (39) 0321 790201
Emp.: 3
Chemical Products Distr
N.A.I.C.S.: 424690
Alessandro Lanfranchi *(Mng Dir)*

ESSEL CORPORATE RE-
SOURCES PVT. LTD.
18th Floor A-Wing Marathon Futurex
N M Joshi Marg, Lower Parel, Mum-
bai, 400 013, India
Tel.: (91) 2271061234   In
Web Site: http://www.esselgroup.com
Sales Range: $50-74.9 Million
Emp.: 8,000
Holding Company
N.A.I.C.S.: 551112
Subhash Chandra *(Chm)*

Subsidiaries:

Asia TV Limited (1)
Hygeia Building 3rd Floor 66/68 College
Road, Harrow, HA1 1BE, United Kingdom
Tel.: (44) 20 8839 4000
Web Site: http://www.zeetv.co.uk
Television Broadcasting Services
N.A.I.C.S.: 516120

Taha Coburn Kutay *(CEO-India)*

Subsidiary (Non-US):

Taj TV Limited (2)
Dubai Media City Tensports Bldg, PO Box
502018, Dubai, United Arab Emirates
Tel.: (971) 4 3919500
Web Site: http://www.tensports.com
Television Broadcasting Services
N.A.I.C.S.: 516120
Ali Obbajja *(Mgr-Studio ops)*

Cyquator Technologies Limited (1)
Tower No 2 4th Floor International Infotech
Park, Above Vashi Rly stn, Navi Mumbai,
400703, India
Tel.: (91) 49186500
Web Site: http://www.cyquator.com
Software Development Services
N.A.I.C.S.: 541511

E-City Bioscope Entertainment Pvt
Ltd (1)
Rani Sati Road, 332001, Sikar, Rajasthan,
India
Tel.: (91) 1572 271444
Building Construction Services
N.A.I.C.S.: 236116

E-City Property Management & Ser-
vices Pvt. Ltd. (1)
Fun Republic Level 5 Plot No 844/4 Shah
Indl Estate Veera Desai Road, Andheri
West, Mumbai, 400053, Maharashtra, India
Tel.: (91) 22 66755705
Web Site: http://www.epms.in
Emp.: 40
Real Estate Development Services
N.A.I.C.S.: 531390
Girish Pande *(COO)*

Essel Infraprojects Limited (1)
513/A 5th floor Kohinoor City Kirol Road L
B S Marg, Kurla W, Mumbai, 400 070, India
Tel.: (91) 22 66012323
Web Site: http://www.esselinfraprojects.com
Solar Electric Power Generation Services
N.A.I.C.S.: 221114
Ashok Agarwal *(CEO)*

Essel Utilities Distribution Company
Ltd (1)
Kohinoor City 513 A-Wing Off LBS Road,
Kurla, Mumbai, 400 070, India
Tel.: (91) 226 601 2323
Web Site: http://www.esselutilities.com
Water & Power Distribution Services
N.A.I.C.S.: 221310

Subsidiary (Domestic):

Essel Vidyut Vitaran (Gwalior) Pvt.
Ltd. (2)
2nd Floor Bahadura Residency Kailash Vi-
har City Center, Gwalior, 474 011, Madhya
Pradesh, India
Tel.: (91) 751 66 11 000
Power Distribution Services
N.A.I.C.S.: 221122

Essel Vidyut Vitaran (Muzaffarpur)
Limited (2)
Pandey Motors Plot No 28 Near Gobarsahi
Chowk, New Delhi, 842 003, Bihar, India
Tel.: (91) 621 3031444
Electric Power Distribution Services
N.A.I.C.S.: 221122
Sujit Sinha *(Head-Matls & Contract)*

Essel Vidyut Vitaran (Sagar) Private
Limited (2)
Power House Near Main Bus Stand
Krishnaganj Ward, Sagar, 470 001, Madhya
Pradesh, India
Tel.: (91) 1860 233 0000
Web Site:
   http://www.cppsagar.esselutilities.com
Power Distribution Services
N.A.I.C.S.: 221122

Essel Vidyut Vitaran (Ujjain) Pvt.
Ltd. (2)
B-116 Divine Valley Dewas Road Near
Lotus Showroom, Ujjain, 456 010, Madhya
Pradesh, India
Tel.: (91) 734 66 11 000
Web Site:
   http://www.cpujjain.esselutilities.com
Power Distribution Services

N.A.I.C.S.: 221122

SND Limited (2)
5th floor Narang Tower Palm Road Civil
lines, Nagpur, Maharashtra, India
Tel.: (91) 712 6662700
Power Distribution Services
N.A.I.C.S.: 221122
Neelesh Upadhyay *(Asst Mgr-HR)*

Natural Wellness USA, Inc. (1)
701 Highlander Blvd Ste 200, Arlington, TX
76015
Tel.: (817) 804-4650
Web Site: http://www.veria.com
Sales Range: $50-74.9 Million
Emp.: 40
Holding Company; Natural Health Center
Operator & Health Food & Herbal Supple-
ment Whslr
N.A.I.C.S.: 551112
Subhash Chandra *(Chm)*

Subsidiary (Domestic):

Natural Wellness Corporation
Ltd. (2)
701 Highlander Blvd Ste 200, Arlington, TX
76015
Tel.: (817) 804-4650
Web Site: http://www.veria.com
Sales Range: $50-74.9 Million
Natural Health Center Operator & Health
Food & Supplement Whslr
N.A.I.C.S.: 713940

Pan India Paryatan Limited (1)
14th Floor Times Tower Kamala Mills Com-
pound Lower Parel, Mumbai, 400 013, Ma-
harashtra, India
Tel.: (91) 22 6112 5900
Web Site: http://www.esselworld.com
Amusement Park Operator
N.A.I.C.S.: 713110
R. P. Tyagi *(VP-Projects)*

SITI Networks Limited (1)
FC - 19 & 20 Upper Ground Floor Sector -
16A, Film City, Noida, 201301, India
Tel.: (91) 1204526707
Web Site: https://sitinetworks.com
Rev.: $165,461,663
Assets: $169,134,944
Liabilities: $256,495,774
Net Worth: ($87,360,830)
Earnings: $37,820,275
Emp.: 205
Fiscal Year-end: 03/31/2023
Cable Television Services
N.A.I.C.S.: 517111
Suresh Kumar *(Officer-Compliance & Sec)*

Subsidiary (Domestic):

Central Bombay Cable Network
Limited (2)
Essel House B-10 Lawrence Road Indus-
trial Area, New Delhi, 110 035, India
Tel.: (91) 1127101145
Web Site: http://www.wwil.net
Cable Television Services
N.A.I.C.S.: 517111

Indian Cable Net Company
Limited (2)
J 1/15 Block EP 4th Floor Sector V, Saltlake
Electronics Complex, Kolkata, 700 091,
India
Tel.: (91) 33 22828169
Web Site: http://www.wwil.net
Cable Television Services
N.A.I.C.S.: 517111

Subsidiary (Domestic):

Siti Maurya Cable Net Private
Limited (3)
J-1/15 Block EP 4th Floor Sector-V, Salt
Lake, Kolkata, 700091, West Bengal, India
Tel.: (91) 33 40025020
Television Broadcasting Services
N.A.I.C.S.: 516120

Subsidiary (Domestic):

Master Channel Community Network
Private Limited (2)
T-4 Vijaya Apartments Jammichettu Centre,
Mogalrajpuram, Vijayawada, 520 010, India
Tel.: (91) 866 2491955

Essel Corporate Resources Pvt.
Ltd.—(Continued)

Web Site: http://www.wwil.net
Sales Range: $25-49.9 Million
Emp.: 10
Cable Television Services
N.A.I.C.S.: 517111
B. Nagamani *(Mgr-Sls)*

SITI Cable Tisai Satellite Limited　　(2)
3rd Floor TISAI House Poona Link Road,
Opp Ashirwad Hospital, Kalyan, 421 306,
India
Tel.: (91) 251 2356225
Television Broadcasting Services
N.A.I.C.S.: 516120

**Siti Bhatia Network Entertainment
Private Limited**　　(2)
Near Bank of India Dayalband, Bilaspur,
495001, Chhattisgarh, India
Tel.: (91) 775 2417770
Television Broadcasting Services
N.A.I.C.S.: 516120

Siti Energy Limited　　(2)
Suncity Business Tower Second floor Sec-
tor - 54 Golf Course Road, Gurgaon,
122002, Haryana, India
Tel.: (91) 124 4691000
Web Site: http://www.sitienergy.com
Natural Gas Distribution Services
N.A.I.C.S.: 486210
A. K. Gupta *(CEO)*

**Siti Guntur Digital Network Private
Limited**　　(2)
B-10 Lawrence Road Industrial Area, New
Delhi, 110035, India
Tel.: (91) 11 47502600
Television Broadcasting Services
N.A.I.C.S.: 516120

**Siti Krishna Digital Media Private
Limited**　　(2)
G-366 Preet Vihar, Delhi, 110092, India
Tel.: (91) 9911104212
Television Broadcasting Services
N.A.I.C.S.: 516120

**Siti Vision Digital Media Private
Limited**　　(2)
6-2-935/2 1st Floor Zee News Building
Rajbhavan Road, Behind BPCL Petrol
pump Khairatabad, Hyderabad, 500004,
India
Tel.: (91) 40 23376967
Television Broadcasting Services
N.A.I.C.S.: 516120

**Siticable Broadband South
Limited**　　(2)
United Mansions 3rd Floor, 39 Mahatma
Gandhi Road, Bengaluru, 560 001, India
Tel.: (91) 8025581234
Web Site: http://www.wwil.net
Cable Television Services
N.A.I.C.S.: 517111

**Wire and Wireless Tisai Satellite
Limited**　　(2)
3rd Floor TISAI House opp Ashirwad Hospi-
tal, Poona Link Road, Kalyan, 421 306,
East, India
Tel.: (91) 2512356255
Web Site: http://www.wwil.net
Cable Television Services
N.A.I.C.S.: 517111

**Zee Entertainment Enterprises
Ltd.**　　(1)
18th Floor A Wing Marathon Futurex Lower
Parel, Worli, Mumbai, 400 013, India
Tel.: (91) 2271061234
Web Site: https://www.zee.com
Rev.: $1,177,890,000
Assets: $1,732,318,000
Liabilities: $422,632,000
Net Worth: $1,309,686,000
Earnings: $73,444,000
Emp.: 3,429
Fiscal Year-end: 03/31/2020
Television Broadcasting
N.A.I.C.S.: 516120
Subhash Chandra *(Founder)*

Subsidiary (Non-US):

Asia Today Limited　　(2)

2nd Fl Ebene House 33 Cybercity, Ebene
City, Ebene, 72201, Mauritius
Tel.: (230) 4642222
Web Site: http://www.zeetelevision.com
Emp.: 10
Television Broadcasting Services
N.A.I.C.S.: 516120
Rajesh Hotwani *(Gen Mgr)*

Subsidiary (Non-US):

**Expand Fast Holdings (Singapore)
Pte. Limited**　　(3)
500 Rifle Range Road # 01-09, Singapore,
588397, Singapore
Tel.: (65) 6465 2406
Holding Company
N.A.I.C.S.: 551112

Taj TV Limited　　(3)
Dubai Media City Tensports Bldg, PO Box
502018, Dubai, United Arab Emirates
Tel.: (971) 4 3919500
Television Broadcasting Services
N.A.I.C.S.: 516120
Ali Obbajja *(Mgr-Studio Ops)*

Subsidiary (Domestic):

**Zee Multimedia (Maurice)
Limited**　　(3)
2nd Floor Ebene House 33 Cybercity,
Ebene, 5572, Mauritius
Tel.: (230) 2304642222
Television Broadcasting Services
N.A.I.C.S.: 516120

Subsidiary (Non-US):

Zee TV South Africa Pty. Ltd.　　(3)
110 Atrium Terraces, 272 Oak Avenue,
Randburg, RSA 2194, South Africa
Tel.: (27) 117813352
Web Site: http://www.zeetv.co.za
Sales Range: $25-49.9 Million
Emp.: 8
Television Broadcasting Services
N.A.I.C.S.: 516120
Vishwa Mohan *(Head-Territory)*

**Zee Telefilms Middle East
FZ-LLC**　　(3)
Dubai Media City Zee Tower Building 2nd
Floor, Dubai, 202-204, United Arab Emir-
ates
Tel.: (971) 4 4264100
Television Broadcasting Services
N.A.I.C.S.: 516120

Subsidiary (Domestic):

ETC Networks Ltd.　　(2)
Continental Building 135, Dr Annie Besant
Road Worli, Mumbai, 400 018, India
Tel.: (91) 2266971234
Web Site: http://www.etc.in
Sales Range: $100-124.9 Million
Emp.: 400
Television Broadcasting Services
N.A.I.C.S.: 516120

Division (Domestic):

**ETC Networks Ltd.-Broadcasting
Division**　　(3)
7B Shah Industrial Estate, Off Veera Desai
Road Andheri, Mumbai, 400053, India
Tel.: (91) 2267813737
Web Site: http://www.etc.in
Sales Range: $50-74.9 Million
Emp.: 200
Television Broadcasting Services
N.A.I.C.S.: 516120
Anurag Bedi *(Head-Bus)*

**ETC Networks Ltd.-Education
Division**　　(3)
3rd Floor Valecha Chambers Plot B6, And-
heri Link Road Andheri, Mumbai, 400 053,
India
Tel.: (91) 2226743900
Web Site: http://www.zeelearn.com
Educational Television Programming &
Broadcasting Services
N.A.I.C.S.: 516120

Subsidiary (Non-US):

Taj Television Ltd.　　(2)
Dubai Media City ten sports Bld, PO Box

502018, Dubai Media City, Dubai, United
Arab Emirates
Tel.: (971) 4 426 4100
Web Site: http://www.tensports.com
Sales Range: $50-74.9 Million
Emp.: 150
Sports Television Broadcasting
N.A.I.C.S.: 516120
Rajesh Sethi *(CEO)*

**Zee Multimedia Worldwide (Mauritius)
Limited**　　(2)
2nd Fl Ebene House 33 Cybercity Ebene
City, Port Louis, Mauritius
Tel.: (230) 4642222
Web Site: http://www.zeetelevision.com
Sales Range: $25-49.9 Million
Emp.: 10
Holding Company; Television Broadcasting
Services
N.A.I.C.S.: 551112
Deepak Jain *(Gen Mgr)*

Joint Venture (Domestic):

Zee Turner Limited　　(2)
2nd Floor Plot 9, Film City Sector 16 A,
Noida, 201301, India
Tel.: (91) 1206766466
Web Site: http://www.zeeturner.com
Emp.: 500
Television Broadcasting Services
N.A.I.C.S.: 516120
Akash Deep Ahluwalia *(VP-Ops)*

Zee Media Corporation Ltd.　　(1)
14th Floor A Wing Marathon Futurex, NM
Joshi Marg Lower Parel, Mumbai, 400013,
Maharashtra, India　　　　**(69.11%)**
Tel.: (91) 2271061234
Web Site: https://www.zeemedia.in
Rev.: $89,308,947
Assets: $150,829,634
Liabilities: $78,218,186
Net Worth: $72,611,448
Earnings: $10,338,647
Emp.: 1,893
Fiscal Year-end: 03/31/2021
Television Broadcasting Services
N.A.I.C.S.: 516120
Pushpal Sanghavi *(Officer-Compliance &
Sec)*

ESSEN TECH CO., LTD.
15 Jayumuyeok 2-gil, Gunsan,
Jeollabuk-do, Korea (South)
Tel.: (82) 634406500
Web Site:
　　https://www.essentech.co.kr
Year Founded: 1985
043340—(KRS)
Rev.: $47,992,555
Assets: $63,897,409
Liabilities: $45,515,885
Net Worth: $18,381,523
Earnings: $283,424
Emp.: 212
Fiscal Year-end: 12/31/22
Container Valve Mfr
N.A.I.C.S.: 332911
Si-young Cho *(CEO)*

**ESSENCE INFORMATION
TECHNOLOGY CO., LTD.**
4F Building No 12 Shuyuan Software
Park No 1 Jiaogong Road, Xihu,
Hangzhou, 310007, Zhejiang, China
Tel.: (86) 5718 731 8958
Web Site: http://www.sino-
essence.com
Year Founded: 2013
688555—(SHG)
Rev.: $50,409,154
Assets: $180,104,483
Liabilities: $49,424,014
Net Worth: $130,680,470
Earnings: $7,058,385
Fiscal Year-end: 12/31/21
Information Technology Services
N.A.I.C.S.: 541512
Ying Lin *(Chm & Gen Mgr)*

ESSENSYS PLC

1 Finsbury Avenue, London, EC2M
2PF, United Kingdom
Tel.: (44) 2031025252　　UK
Web Site: https://www.essensys.tech
Year Founded: 2006
ESYS—(AIM)
Rev.: $29,083,060
Assets: $59,077,306
Liabilities: $14,192,034
Net Worth: $44,885,272
Earnings: ($13,480,560)
Fiscal Year-end: 07/31/22
Software Development Services
N.A.I.C.S.: 541611
Mark Furness *(Founder & CEO)*

ESSENT GROUP LTD.
Clarendon House 2 Church Street,
Hamilton, HM 11, Bermuda
Tel.: (441) 2979901　　BM
Web Site: https://ir.essentgroup.com
Year Founded: 2008
ESNT—(NYSE)
Rev.: $1,109,759,000
Assets: $6,426,673,000
Liabilities: $1,324,123,000
Net Worth: $5,102,550,000
Earnings: $696,386,000
Emp.: 536
Fiscal Year-end: 12/31/23
Holding Company; Mortgage Insur-
ance Services
N.A.I.C.S.: 551112
Mark A. Casale *(Founder, Chm, Pres
& CEO)*

Subsidiaries:

Essent Guaranty, Inc.　　(1)
2 Radnor Corporate Ctr 100 Matsonford Rd,
Radnor, PA 19087
Tel.: (336) 776-3906
Web Site: https://www.essent.us
Mortgage Insurance Services
N.A.I.C.S.: 524298
Mark A. Casale *(Chm & CEO)*

ESSENTIAL METALS LIMITED
Ground Floor 72 Kings Park Road,
West Perth, 6005, WA, Australia
Tel.: (61) 893226974
Web Site:
　　http://www.pioneerresources.com.au
ESS—(ASX)
Rev.: $403,016
Assets: $21,622,648
Liabilities: $1,484,876
Net Worth: $20,137,772
Earnings: ($1,078,029)
Emp.: 5
Fiscal Year-end: 06/30/22
Nickel Exploration & Mining Services
N.A.I.C.S.: 212230
Timothy Gerard Spencer *(Mng Dir)*

ESSENTRA PLC
Langford Locks, Kidlington, OX5
1HX, United Kingdom
Tel.: (44) 1908359100　　UK
Web Site:
　　https://www.essentraplc.com
ESNT—(LSE)
Rev.: $266,400,360
Assets: $704,356,560
Liabilities: $385,764,120
Net Worth: $318,592,440
Earnings: ($144,907,920)
Emp.: 2,559
Fiscal Year-end: 12/31/22
Specialty Plastic & Fiber Products Mfr
N.A.I.C.S.: 326199
Scott Fawcet *(Mng Dir-Components)*

Subsidiaries:

3C! Packaging Company　　(1)
1000 CCC Dr, Clayton, NC 27520
Tel.: (919) 553-4113
Web Site: https://www.3cpackaging.com
Setup Paperboard Box Mfr

N.A.I.C.S.: 322219
Joseph Elphick *(Founder)*

Essentra (Bangor) Ltd. **(1)**
15 Balloo Drive, Bangor, BT19 7QY, Co
Down, United Kingdom
Tel.: (44) 2891463015
Specialty Plastic & Fiber Product Mfr
N.A.I.C.S.: 326199

Essentra Component Solutions **(1)**
3123 Station Rd, Erie, PA 16510
Tel.: (814) 899-9263
Web Site: http://www.essentra.com
Emp.: 20
Custom Moulded Plastic Product Mfr
N.A.I.C.S.: 326199

Essentra Components (Pty) Ltd. **(1)**
PO Box 50181, Randjiesfontein, Midrand,
1683, Gauteng, South Africa
Tel.: (27) 113148750
Specialty Plastic & Fiber Product Distr
N.A.I.C.S.: 424690

**Essentra Components Japan
Inc.** **(1)**
8F Tobu Tateno Building 2-10-27 Kitasaiwai,
Nishi-ku, Yokohama, 220-0004, Kanagawa,
Japan
Tel.: (81) 453212752
Web Site:
    https://www.essentracomponents.jp
Specialty Plastic & Fiber Product Distr
N.A.I.C.S.: 424690

Essentra Components Kft **(1)**
Gyar U 2, 2040, Budaors, Hungary
Tel.: (36) 23886990
Specialty Plastic & Fiber Product Mfr
N.A.I.C.S.: 326199

Essentra Components Ltd. **(1)**
Langford Locks, Kidlington, OX5 1HX,
Oxon, United Kingdom
Tel.: (44) 3455280474
Web Site:
    https://www.essentracomponents.com
Sales Range: $125-149.9 Million
Emp.: 350
Industrial Plastic Products Mfr & Distr
N.A.I.C.S.: 326199
Scot Fawcett *(Mng Dir)*

Subsidiary (Non-US):

Essentra Components B.V. **(2)**
Dragonder 3, 5554 GM, Valkenswaard,
Netherlands
Tel.: (31) 497572002
Web Site:
    https://www.essentracomponents.com
Sales Range: $25-49.9 Million
Emp.: 20
Industrial Plastic Products Distr
N.A.I.C.S.: 424610

Essentra Components GmbH **(2)**
Montel-Allee 3, D-41334, Nettetal, Germany
Tel.: (49) 215789690
Web Site:
    https://www.essentracomponents.com
Sales Range: $25-49.9 Million
Emp.: 30
Industrial Plastic Products Distr
N.A.I.C.S.: 424610

Essentra Components s.r.o. **(2)**
Videnska 101/119, 619 00, Brno, Czech
Republic
Tel.: (420) 545221660
Web Site:
    https://www.essentracomponents.com
Industrial Plastic Products Mfr & Distr
N.A.I.C.S.: 326199

Essentra Malaysia Sdn. Bhd. **(2)**
D5-5-6 Solaris Dutamas 1 Jalan Dutamas
1, 50480, Kuala Lumpur, Malaysia
Tel.: (60) 36 207 3333
Web Site:
    http://www.essentracomponents.com.my
Bearing Product Distr
N.A.I.C.S.: 423840

Essentra Sp. z o.o. **(2)**
ul Slaska 126D, 93 237, Lodz, Poland
Tel.: (48) 42 639 52 64
Web Site:
    http://www.essentracomponents.pl

Sales Range: $25-49.9 Million
Emp.: 20
Industrial Plastic Products Distr
N.A.I.C.S.: 326199

Moss Pieces Plastiques S.A.R.L. **(2)**
Strategic Parc 1 Rue du Gue, 77990, Le
Mesnil-Amelot, Seine-et-Marne, France
Tel.: (33) 160038484
Web Site: http://www.essentracomponents.fr
Sales Range: $25-49.9 Million
Emp.: 14
Industrial Plastic Products Distr
N.A.I.C.S.: 424610

Essentra Components SAS **(1)**
280 Rue De La Belle Etolle, Roissy En
France, 95700, Paris, France
Tel.: (33) 800302092
Specialty Plastic & Fiber Product Distr
N.A.I.C.S.: 424690

Essentra Corporation **(1)**
2 Westbrook Corporate Ctr, Westchester, IL
60154
Tel.: (773) 527-0943
Web Site:
    https://www.essentracomponents.com
Specialty Plastic & Fiber Product Mfr
N.A.I.C.S.: 326199

Essentra Extrusion B.V. **(1)**
Beatrixstraat 7/9, Postbus 1, 9285 TV,
Buitenpost, Friesland, Netherlands
Tel.: (31) 511541700
Web Site: http://www.essentraextrusion.com
Sales Range: $150-199.9 Million
Emp.: 200
Plastic Extrusions Mfr & Distr
N.A.I.C.S.: 326199
Nico Loonstra *(Mgr-Sls)*

Essentra Filter Products Limited **(1)**
Avebury House 201-249 Avebury Boule-
vard, Milton Keynes, MK9 1AU, Bucks,
United Kingdom
Tel.: (44) 1908359100
Web Site: http://www.filtronafilters.com
Cigarette Filters Mfr
N.A.I.C.S.: 322299

Essentra Filter Products S.A. **(1)**
Calle 12-Acaray KM12-Ruta 7, Ciudad del
Este, Paraguay
Tel.: (595) 61580077
Specialty Plastic & Fiber Product Distr
N.A.I.C.S.: 424690

Essentra Limited **(1)**
116/3 Soi Thiantalay 24 Bangkhunthian-
Chaitalay Road, Thakam Bangkhunthian,
Bangkok, Thailand
Tel.: (66) 20072192
Web Site:
    https://www.essentracomponents.com
Specialty Plastic & Fiber Product Mfr
N.A.I.C.S.: 326199

**Essentra Packaging & Security
Limited** **(1)**
Wildmere Road, Banbury, OX16 3JU, Oxon,
United Kingdom
Tel.: (44) 1295265601
Web Site:
    http://www.essentrapackaging.com
Sales Range: $10-24.9 Million
Emp.: 50
Brand Protection & Document Security Ser-
vices
N.A.I.C.S.: 561621

Subsidiary (Non-US):

Essentra (India) Private Limited **(2)**
Brigade Rubix No 20 Unit 302 HMT Main
Rd, Jalahalli, Bengaluru, 560 058, Karna-
taka, India
Tel.: (91) 7899739157
Web Site:
    https://www.essentracomponents.co.in
Tear Tapes & Coated Films Distr
N.A.I.C.S.: 424120
N. K. Ramprasad *(Mgr-Fin)*

Branch (Domestic):

Essentra Packaging - Cardiff **(2)**
Imperial Park Celtic Way, Newport, NP10
8BE, United Kingdom
Tel.: (44) 292 010 0600

Web Site:
    http://www.essentrapackaging.com
Sales Range: $10-24.9 Million
Emp.: 35
Self Adhesive Label Printing Services
N.A.I.C.S.: 561910

**Essentra Packaging -
Nottingham** **(2)**
Giltway, Giltbrook, Nottingham, NG16 2GT,
Nottinghamshire, United Kingdom
Tel.: (44) 1159759000
Emp.: 200
Document Protection Services
N.A.I.C.S.: 561612
Sue Jones *(Mgr-I IR)*

Subsidiary (US):

Essentra Packaging Inc. **(2)**
1625 Ashton Park Dr, Colonial Heights, VA
23834
Tel.: (804) 518-1803
Web Site:
    http://www.essentrapackaging.com
Tear Tapes & Coated Films Distr
N.A.I.C.S.: 424120

Subsidiary (Non-US):

Essentra Packaging Pte. Limited **(2)**
238A Thomson Road #25-04/05, Singapore,
307684, Singapore
Tel.: (65) 65429993
Web Site:
    http://www.essentrapackaging.com
Tear Tapes & Coated Films Distr
N.A.I.C.S.: 424120

Essentra Packaging B.V. **(1)**
Celsiusweg 37, 8912 AM, Leeuwarden,
Netherlands
Tel.: (31) 582332121
Specialty Plastic & Fiber Product Mfr
N.A.I.C.S.: 326199

Essentra Packaging GmbH **(1)**
Filmstrasse 5, 06766, Bitterfeld-Wolfen,
Germany
Tel.: (49) 3494634020
Specialty Plastic & Fiber Product Mfr
N.A.I.C.S.: 326199

Essentra Packaging Srl **(1)**
Via N Copernico 54 Placenda, Podenzano,
29027, Piacenza, Italy
Tel.: (39) 0523523901
Specialty Plastic & Fiber Product Distr
N.A.I.C.S.: 424690

**Essentra Pipe Protection
Technologies** **(1)**
Lote 1 MZNA 4 AV Framboyanes Esq Al-
mendros CD Industrial, Bruno Pagliai, Vera-
cruz, CP 91697, VER, Mexico
Tel.: (52) 229 989 6731
Web Site: http://www.essentra.com
Sales Range: $25-49.9 Million
Emp.: 87
Component & Protection Solutions & Pipe
Mfr
N.A.I.C.S.: 332996

**Essentra Pipe Protection
Technologies** **(1)**
9035 Solon Rd, Houston, TX 77064
Tel.: (281) 890-4595
Web Site:
    http://www.essentrapipeprotection.com
Emp.: 150
Drilling Thread & Pipe Protection Products
Mfr
N.A.I.C.S.: 333132
Mauro Hernandez *(VP-Global Bus Dev)*

Essentra Pte. Ltd. **(1)**
36 Robinson Road 17-01 City House, Sin-
gapore, 068877, Singapore
Tel.: (65) 62580918
Specialty Plastic & Fiber Product Distr
N.A.I.C.S.: 424690

Essentra Pty. Ltd. **(1)**
503 Victoria St, Wetherill Park, 2164, NSW,
Australia
Tel.: (61) 296380100
Web Site:
    https://www.essentracomponents.com
Specialty Plastic & Fiber Product Mfr &
Distr

N.A.I.C.S.: 326199

**Filtrona Special Fiber Products
Ningbo Co., Ltd.** **(1)**
99 Huanghai Road, Beilun District, Ningbo,
315800, Zhejiang, China
Tel.: (86) 574 2688 3377
Web Site:
    http://www.filtronaporoustechnologies.com
Sales Range: $25-49.9 Million
Emp.: 80
Fluid & Vapor Handling Components Mfr
N.A.I.C.S.: 332912

Innovative Components, Inc. **(1)**
1050 National Pkwy, Schaumburg, IL 60173
Tel.: (847) 885-9050
Web Site: https://www.innovative-
    components.com
Plastic Pipe & Pipe Fitting Mfr
N.A.I.C.S.: 326122

Mesan Kilit A.S. **(1)**
Mimar Sinan Mahallesi Ulubey Caddesi
Fabrikalar Sitesi No 7, Silivri, 34570, Istan-
bul, Turkiye
Tel.: (90) 2127214444
Web Site: https://www.mesanlocks.com
Specialty Plastic & Fiber Product Mfr
N.A.I.C.S.: 326199
Mustafa Mertoz *(Gen Mgr)*

**Micro Plastics International
Limited** **(1)**
Henley Road, Unit 2 Henley Industrial Park,
Coventry, CV2 1SR, United Kingdom
Tel.: (44) 2476614320
Plastics Product Mfr
N.A.I.C.S.: 326199
Cheryl Lully *(Mgr-Ops)*

**Micro Plastics International S.A. de
C.V. de R.L.** **(1)**
Carretera a Huinala 510 Fracc Ind, 66640,
Apodaca, Nuevo Leon, Mexico
Tel.: (52) 8180003760
Screw & Nut Distr
N.A.I.C.S.: 423710

Micro Plastics, Inc. **(1)**
111 Industry Ln, Flippin, AR 72634
Tel.: (870) 453-2261
Web Site: http://secure.microplastics.com
Emp.: 400
Threaded Nylon Fasteners Mfr
N.A.I.C.S.: 326199
Tom Hill *(Pres & CEO)*

PT Essentra **(1)**
Jalan Berbek Industri I No 18-20, Industrial
Estate, Surabaya, Indonesia
Tel.: (62) 318432018
Specialty Plastic & Fiber Product Mfr
N.A.I.C.S.: 326199

Richco, Inc. **(1)**
8145 River Dr, Morton Grove, IL 60053
Tel.: (773) 539-4060
Web Site: http://www.richco-inc.com
Sales Range: $125-149.9 Million
Emp.: 300
Plastic Installation Hardware Mfr
N.A.I.C.S.: 326199

Skiffy B.V. **(1)**
Transformatorweg 37, 1014 AJ, Amsterdam,
North Holland, Netherlands
Tel.: (31) 206868711
Web Site: http://www.skiffy.com
Sales Range: $50-74.9 Million
Emp.: 235
Industrial Plastic & Metal Products Mfr &
Distr
N.A.I.C.S.: 326121

Subsidiary (Non-US):

**Essentra Sp. z o.o. Oddzial
Skiffy** **(2)**
Ul Slaska 126D, 93-237, Lodz, Poland
Tel.: (48) 426395264
Web Site: http://www.skiffy.com
Industrial Plastic & Metal Products Distr
N.A.I.C.S.: 423510

Skiffy GmbH **(2)**
Memelerstrasse 26, 42781, Haan,
Nordrhein-Westfalen, Germany
Tel.: (49) 212994313
Web Site: http://www.skiffy.com

Essentra plc—(Continued)

Metal Screws Mfr
N.A.I.C.S.: 332722

Skiffy Ltd. (2)
Unit 12 Old Forge Trading Estate Dudley
Road, Stourbridge, DY9 8EL, United Kingdom
Tel.: (44) 1902894658
Web Site: http://www.skiffy.com
Sales Range: $25-49.9 Million
Emp.: 3
Transmission Equipment Mfr
N.A.I.C.S.: 333613

Skiffy S.A. (Pty) Ltd. (2)
Unit 2 Corner Suni & Tsessebe Streets
Sage Corporate Park South, Randjiesfontein, Midrand, 1685, Gauteng, South Africa
Tel.: (27) 113148750
Web Site: http://www.skiffy.com
Sales Range: $25-49.9 Million
Emp.: 5
Industrial Plastic & Metal Products Distr
N.A.I.C.S.: 423510

Skiffy S.A.S. (2)
7 allee des Foulons, BP 305, 67832, Lingolsheim, Bas-Rhin, France
Tel.: (33) 388789130
Web Site: http://www.skiffy.com
Industrial Plastic & Metal Products Mfr
N.A.I.C.S.: 326121

ESSERE BENESSERE SPA
Via Calabria 22/24, 20090, Segrate,
MI, Italy
Tel.: (39) 02 26 92 30 10
Web Site:
  http://www.esserebenessere.it
Sales Range: $125-149.9 Million
Emp.: 500
Pharmaceutical & Personal Care
Products Distr
N.A.I.C.S.: 424210
Danilo Giuseppe Salsi (Chm & CEO)

ESSEX BIO-TECHNOLOGY LIMITED
Room 2818 China Merchants Tower
Shun Tak Centre 168-200 Connaught
Road, Central, China (Hong Kong)
Tel.: (852) 25877838   Ky
Web Site: http://www.essexbio.com
1061—(HKG)
Rev.: $168,008,104
Assets: $345,830,634
Liabilities: $125,081,367
Net Worth: $220,749,268
Earnings: $28,739,942
Emp.: 1,471
Fiscal Year-end: 12/31/22
Biopharmaceutical Mfr
N.A.I.C.S.: 325412
Patrick Mia Je Ngiam (Founder &
Chm)

Subsidiaries:

Essex Medipharma (Zhuhai) Company Limited (1)
No 88 Keji 6th Road Hi-Tech Zone, Zhuhai,
519085, Guangdong, China
Tel.: (86) 7563911112
Biopharmaceutical Product Distr
N.A.I.C.S.: 424210
Haizhou Fang (Gen Mgr)

ESSEX MINERALS, INC.
3002-1211 Melville Street, Vancouver,
V6E 0A7, BC, Canada
Tel.: (416) 842-9003
Web Site:
  https://www.essexminerals.com
OPTG—(TSXV)
Rev.: $1,044
Assets: $1,015,467
Liabilities: $291,935
Net Worth: $723,532
Earnings: ($1,953,862)
Fiscal Year-end: 09/30/23
Mineral Exploration Services

N.A.I.C.S.: 213115
Paul Loudon (CEO)

ESSEX SERVICES GROUP PLC
Viking Business Centre Danes Road,
Romford, RM7 0HL, Essex, United
Kingdom
Tel.: (44) 1708708888   UK
Web Site: http://www.esgplc.com
Year Founded: 1975
Mechanical, Electrical & Maintenance
Services Contractor
N.A.I.C.S.: 238990
John Sampson (CEO)

ESSILORLUXOTTICA SA
147 Rue de Paris, 75008, Paris,
France
Tel.: (33) 149774224   FR
Web Site:
  https://www.essilorluxottica.com
Year Founded: 1971
EL—(EUR)
Rev.: $28,032,895,467
Assets: $66,809,802,416
Liabilities: $23,879,015,347
Net Worth: $42,930,787,069
Earnings: $2,677,999,780
Emp.: 77,500
Fiscal Year-end: 12/31/23
Eyeglass Lenses & Other Ophthalmic
Products Mfr & Whslr
N.A.I.C.S.: 333310
Paul du Saillant (Deputy CEO)

Subsidiaries:

20 20 Optics Pvt Ltd (1)
Plot No A 30 2nd Floor Shankar Towers
Near Allahabad Bank, Apiie Main Road Bala
Nagar, Hyderabad, 500037, Andhra
Pradesh, India
Tel.: (91) 40 64633922
Web Site: http://www.essilor2020.com
Sales Range: $25-49.9 Million
Emp.: 70
Optical Lens Mfr
N.A.I.C.S.: 333310
Ratan Kumar (Gen Mgr)

Amico (1)
Building 27 - Block A 5th Floor Room 501,
PO Box 505014, Dubai Healthcare City,
Dubai, 55320, United Arab Emirates
Tel.: (971) 43624727
Web Site: http://www.amicogroup.com
Sales Range: $50-74.9 Million
Emp.: 80
Medical Equipment Whslr
N.A.I.C.S.: 423450
Mihran Hazarian (Pres & CEO)

Aries Optical Ltd. (1)
77 Stonebridge Ct, Fredericton, E3A 1J4,
NB, Canada
Tel.: (506) 458-1902
Web Site: http://www.ariesoptical.ca
Ophthalmic Laboratory Services
N.A.I.C.S.: 541380

BBGR GmbH (1)
Von-Ketteler-Str 1, 96050, Bamberg, Germany
Tel.: (49) 951 1860
Sales Range: $50-74.9 Million
Emp.: 35
Investment Management Service
N.A.I.C.S.: 523999
Steven Landry (Gen Mgr)

BBGR S.A. (1)
22 rue de Montmorency, 75003, Paris,
France   (99.99%)
Tel.: (33) 144783100
Web Site: https://www.bbgr.com
Sales Range: $25-49.9 Million
Emp.: 750
Glass & Plastic Lenses Mfr & Marketer
N.A.I.C.S.: 333310

BBGR Skandinaviska AB (1)
Hedegaardsvej 88, Limhamn, Copenhagen,
2300, Sweden
Tel.: (46) 40 36 38 60

Web Site: http://www.bbgr.se
Emp.: 15
Optical Product Mfr
N.A.I.C.S.: 339115
Olivier Rabeyrin (Gen Mgr)

BNL Eurolens SA (1)
ZI Avenue Paul Langevin, 1200, Bellegarde-sur-Valserine, France
Tel.: (33) 4 50 48 02 80
Web Site: http://www.bnl-eurolens.com
Sales Range: $25-49.9 Million
Emp.: 6
Polarized Lenses Mfr
N.A.I.C.S.: 339115
Frank Ledion (Gen Mgr)

Canoptec Inc. (1)
371 Deslauriers, Saint Laurent, H4N 1W2,
QC, Canada
Tel.: (514) 337-0673
Web Site: http://www.canoptecservices.ca
Ophthalmic Lens Whslr
N.A.I.C.S.: 423460
Ronald Pepin (Mgr)

Cascade Optical Ltd (1)
7475 Hedley Ave Ste 206, Burnaby, V5E
2R1, BC, Canada
Tel.: (604) 437-3937
Optical Lens Distr
N.A.I.C.S.: 423460

Chapter 4 Corp. (1)
190 Bowery, New York, NY 10012
Tel.: (212) 966-7799
Web Site: https://jp.supreme.com
Sales Range: $10-24.9 Million
Emp.: 50
Sporting Goods Retailer
N.A.I.C.S.: 459110

City Optical Pty Ltd. (1)
10 Marlow Rd, Keswick, Adelaide, 5035,
SA, Australia
Tel.: (61) 1800882176
Ophthalmic Photographic Equipment Mfr
N.A.I.C.S.: 333310

De Ceunynck & Co nv (1)
Brandekensweg 2b, 2627, Schelle, Belgium
Tel.: (32) 38703711
Web Site: https://www.deceunynck.be
Sales Range: $25-49.9 Million
Emp.: 80
Glass Mfr
N.A.I.C.S.: 327211
Stefan Laridon (Mng Dir)

Eastern Optical Laboratories Ltd. (1)
101 Ilsley Avenue, PO Box 115, Dartmouth,
B3B 1S8, NS, Canada
Tel.: (902) 468-4567
Web Site: http://www.easternoptical.ca
Sales Range: $25-49.9 Million
Emp.: 3
Optical Lens Mfr
N.A.I.C.S.: 333310
Tom Allen (Gen Mgr)

Easy Vision (1)
Hope Street 78, George, 6530, Western
Cape, South Africa
Tel.: (27) 448744210
Web Site: http://www.easy.co.za
Sales Range: $50-74.9 Million
Emp.: 2
Contact Lens Whslr
N.A.I.C.S.: 423460
Brian Randall (Gen Mgr)

Joint Venture (Non-US):

Nikon-Essilor Co., Ltd. (2)
10-8 Ryogoku 2-chome, Sumida-ku, Tokyo,
130-0026, Japan
Tel.: (81) 570025230
Web Site: https://www.nikon-essilor.co.jp
Sales Range: $25-49.9 Million
Developer, Manufacturer & Sales of Ophthalmic Lenses & Related Products; Joint
Venture of Essilor International S.A. (50%)
& Nikon Corporation (50%)
N.A.I.C.S.: 333310

Subsidiary (Domestic):

Nasu Nikon Co., Ltd. (3)
1956 3 Oaza Kyono Karasuyama Machi,
Nasu Gun, Tochigi, 321 0611,
Japan   (100%)

Tel.: (81) 287801122
Sales Range: $75-99.9 Million
Mfr of Ophthalmic Lenses
N.A.I.C.S.: 333310

Subsidiary (Non-US):

Optodev, Inc. (2)
Block 2 Lot 2 Star Avenue corner Interstar
Street, LIIP Mamplasan, Laguna,
Philippines   (99.99%)
Mfr & Sales of Ophthalmic Goods
N.A.I.C.S.: 339113

Essilor AB (1)
Fagerstagatan 18A, Box 8169, 163 08,
Spanga, Sweden
Tel.: (46) 86212600
Web Site: https://www.essilor.se
Optical Goods Distr
N.A.I.C.S.: 423460

Essilor Asia Pacific Pte Ltd. (1)
215 Kallang Bahru 06-00 Essilor Building,
Singapore, 339346, Singapore   (100%)
Tel.: (65) 62936801
Web Site: http://www.essilor.com.sg
Sales Range: $300-349.9 Million
Emp.: 8,752
Eyeglass Lenses & Other Ophthalmic Products Mfr & Whslr
N.A.I.C.S.: 333310
Patrick Cherrier (Reg Pres)

Essilor Austria Gmbh (1)
Liebermann Street 1 A01/401, 2355, Brunn,
Austria
Tel.: (43) 22366800
Web Site: http://www.essilor.at
Emp.: 3
Optical Instruments Whslr
N.A.I.C.S.: 423460
Wolfgang Smith (Gen Mgr)

Essilor Canada Ltd. (1)
371 Rue Deslauriers, Saint Laurent, H4N
1W2, QC, Canada   (100%)
Tel.: (514) 337-2943
Web Site: http://www.essilor.ca
Sales Range: $50-74.9 Million
Emp.: 200
Mfr of Optical Lens
N.A.I.C.S.: 339113
Marie-France Desnoyers (VP-HR)

Essilor D.O.O (1)
Zagrebska Cesta 022, Maribor, 2000, Slovenia
Tel.: (386) 22283620
Web Site: https://www.essilor.si
Optical Lens Mfr
N.A.I.C.S.: 333310

Essilor Danmark A.S. (1)
Hassellunden 13, Smorum, 2765, Denmark
Tel.: (45) 70 20 84 44
Emp.: 20
Optical Instruments Mfr & Whslr
N.A.I.C.S.: 339115
Henrik Bense Petersens (Mgr)

**Essilor European Shared Service
Center Ltd.** (1)
St Lukes House Emerson Way Emersons
Green, Bristol, BS16 7AR, Avon, United
Kingdom
Tel.: (44) 1179709618
Accounting Services
N.A.I.C.S.: 541219
Isabell Serval (Gen Mgr)

**Essilor Group The Netherlands
B.V** (1)
Marconistraat 9, 6902 PC, Zevenaar, Netherlands
Tel.: (31) 402065858
Web Site: http://www.essilor.nl
Sales Range: $25-49.9 Million
Emp.: 3
Optical Goods Distr
N.A.I.C.S.: 423460
R. Cersteeg (VP)

Essilor India Pvt Ltd (1)
No 71/1 S C Road Brigade Plaza 6th Floor
Anand Rao Circle Gandhinagar, Bengaluru,
560009, Karnataka, India
Tel.: (91) 80 40921800
Web Site: http://www.essilorindia.com
Emp.: 300

Optical Lens Mfr
N.A.I.C.S.: 333310
Shiv Kumar Janardhanan (CEO)

Essilor Ireland Ltd. (1)
Bay 1 Raheen Industrial Park, Raheen,
Limerick, Ireland (100%)
Tel.: (353) 61227533
Sales Range: $25-49.9 Million
Emp.: 70
Eyeglass Lenses Mfr
N.A.I.C.S.: 333310

Essilor Lens & Spects P Ltd (1)
Shed No 2 Chashmawala Compound Behind Vihar Cinema, Pratap Nagar, Vadodara, 390004, Gujarat, India
Tel.: (91) 265 2439006
Optical Goods Distr
N.A.I.C.S.: 423460

Essilor Logistik GmbH (1)
Voltastrasse 12, 63457, Hanau, Germany
Tel.: (49) 618150010
Web Site: http://www.essilor.de
Logistics Consulting Servies
N.A.I.C.S.: 541614
Stefan Rudiger (Gen Mgr)

Essilor Ltd. (1)
Cooper Road, Thornbury, Bristol, BS35
3UW, United Kingdom (100%)
Tel.: (44) 1454417100
Web Site: https://global.essilor.com
Sales Range: $100-124.9 Million
Emp.: 500
Ophthalmic Lenses
N.A.I.C.S.: 333310
Tim Precious (Mng Dir)

Essilor Mexico S.A DE CV (1)
sevilla 40 floor 5 colonial juarez, Mexico,
6000, Mexico
Tel.: (52) 55 5130 7310
Web Site: http://www.essilor.com.mx
Sales Range: $50-74.9 Million
Emp.: 200
Ophthalmic Lens Whslr
N.A.I.C.S.: 423460
Ingrid Arias (Dir-Logistics)

Essilor Norge A.S. (1)
Hermann Foss Gate 4, Kongsberg, 3611,
Norway
Tel.: (47) 32726000
Web Site: https://www.essilor.no
Emp.: 31
Eyeglass & Frame Whslr
N.A.I.C.S.: 423460
John Hanssen (Gen Mgr)

**Essilor Optical laboratory Polska Sp.
Z.o.o.** (1)
Annopol 3, 03-236, Warsaw, 03-236, Poland
Tel.: (48) 225105900
Corrective Lens Mfr
N.A.I.C.S.: 333310

Essilor Polonia Sp. z o.o (1)
Biuro Centralne Ul Annopol 3, 03-236, Warsaw, Poland
Tel.: (48) 225 10 59 00
Eyeglass & Contact Lenses Mfr
N.A.I.C.S.: 339115

Essilor Romania SRL (1)
266-268 Calea Rahovei, Bucharest, 10011,
Romania
Tel.: (40) 214048244
Web Site: http://www.Essilor.ro
Sales Range: $25-49.9 Million
Emp.: 3
Optical Glasses Mfr & Whslr
N.A.I.C.S.: 333310
Tudor Baciu (Gen Mgr)

Essilor S.A. (1)
Rue des Avouil 30, Les Acacias, 1196,
Gland, Switzerland
Tel.: (41) 848847748
Web Site: https://www.essilor.ch
Ophthalmic Lens Mfr
N.A.I.C.S.: 339115

Essilor South Africa (Pty) Ltd. (1)
137 Kuschke St, Meadowdale, Johannesburg, 1614, South Africa
Tel.: (27) 873652077
Web Site: https://www.essilor.co.za
Emp.: 25

Optical Lens Mfr
N.A.I.C.S.: 333310
Darren Duggan (Gen Mgr)

Essilor of America, Inc. (1)
13555 N Stemmons Fwy, Dallas, TX
75234 (100%)
Tel.: (214) 496-4000
Web Site: https://www.essilorusa.com
Eyeglass Lenses & Other Ophthalmic Products Mfr & Whslr
N.A.I.C.S.: 333310
Kevin A. Rupp (Sr VP-Fin & Admin)

Subsidiary (Domestic):

Cherry Optical, Inc. (2)
2429 Oakwood, Melvindale, MI 48122
Tel.: (313) 388-7622
Web Site: https://cherryoptical.com
Sales Range: $1-9.9 Million
Emp.: 28
Mfr of Prescription Eyeglass Lenses
N.A.I.C.S.: 423490
Adam Cherry (Pres)

Costa Inc. (2)
2361 Mason Ave Ste 100, Daytona Beach,
FL 32117
Tel.: (386) 274-4000
Web Site: http://www.costadelmar.com
Holding Company; Polarized Sunglasses
Mfr & Distr
N.A.I.C.S.: 551112

Subsidiary (Domestic):

Costa Del Mar, Inc. (3)
2361 Mason Ave Ste 100, Daytona Beach,
FL 32117 (100%)
Tel.: (386) 274-4000
Web Site: https://www.costadelmar.com
Sales Range: $10-24.9 Million
Emp.: 100
Polarized Sunglasses Mfr & Distr
N.A.I.C.S.: 339115
Terri Ossi (VP-Mktg)

Subsidiary (Domestic):

Dioptics Medical Products Inc. (2)
500 George Washington Hwy, Smithfield, RI
02917
Tel.: (800) 959-9038
Web Site: http://www.diopticssunwear.com
Sunwear Optical Mfr
N.A.I.C.S.: 333310
Henry Lane (CEO & Pres)

**ELOA California Acquisition
Corp.** (2)
2101 S Atlantic Blvd, Commerce, CA
90040-1319
Tel.: (323) 266-3030
Eyewear Products Distr
N.A.I.C.S.: 423460

**Essilor Laboratories of America,
Inc.** (2)
13555 N Stemmons Fwy, Dallas, TX 75234
Tel.: (214) 496-4000
Web Site: http://www.eloa.com
Optical Laboratory Services
N.A.I.C.S.: 621511
Rick Long (Sr VP-Partner Lab Div)

Subsidiary (Domestic):

Advance Optical (3)
37 Goodway Dr, Rochester, NY 14623
Tel.: (585) 427-0800
Web Site: https://www.advanceoptical.com
Sales Range: $25-49.9 Million
Emp.: 30
Optical Goods Mfr & Distr
N.A.I.C.S.: 333310
Brian Bartlett (Mgr-Ops)

Apex Optical Company Inc. (3)
306 Goodland St, Orlando, FL 32811
Tel.: (407) 298-1200
Sales Range: $25-49.9 Million
Emp.: 9
Ophthalmic Lenses Mfr & Whslr
N.A.I.C.S.: 339115
Michele Freeman (Gen Mgr)

BSA Industries, Inc. (3)
6510 Huntley Rd, Columbus, OH 43229-
1012
Tel.: (614) 846-5750

Holding Company; Ophthalmic Goods Mfr &
Whslr
N.A.I.C.S.: 551112

Subsidiary (Domestic):

Select Optical, Inc. (4)
6510 Huntley Rd, Columbus, OH 43229-
1012
Tel.: (614) 846-5515
Web Site: http://www.selectoptical.com
Emp.: 115
Ophthalmic Goods Mfr & Whslr
N.A.I.C.S.: 339115
Chip Lothes (Pres)

Subsidiary (Domestic):

Beitler McKee Company (3)
160 S 22nd St, Pittsburgh, PA 15203
Tel.: (800) 989-4700
Web Site: http://www.beitlermckee.com
Optical Products Mfr & Whslr
N.A.I.C.S.: 333310
Michael Klaphake (Mgr-Gas Permeable
Lab)

CSC Laboratories, Inc. (3)
180 Westgate Dr, Watsonville, CA 95076
Tel.: (831) 763-6931
Web Site: http://www.csclabs.com
Sales Range: $25-49.9 Million
Emp.: 200
Eyeglass Lens & Frame Mfr & Distr
N.A.I.C.S.: 339115
Francious Gloin (Pres & CEO)

Classic Optical Laboratories, Inc. (3)
3710 Belmont Ave, Youngstown, OH 44505
Tel.: (330) 759-8245
Web Site: https://www.classicoptical.com
Sales Range: $10-24.9 Million
Emp.: 170
Ophthalmic Goods Mfr
N.A.I.C.S.: 339115
Dawn Friedkin (Pres)

Collard Rose (3)
12402 Philadelphia, Whittier, CA 90601
Tel.: (562) 698-2286
Web Site: https://www.collardrose.com
Optical Laboratory Services
N.A.I.C.S.: 541380
Jennifer Hernandez (Dir-Sls & Mktg)

Custom Optical (3)
661 Duling Ave, Jackson, MS 39216
Tel.: (601) 362-6675
Web Site: https://www.customoptical.net
Optical Goods Distr
N.A.I.C.S.: 456130

Dunlaw Optical Laboratories Inc. (3)
1313 Sw A Ave, Lawton, OK 73501
Tel.: (580) 355-8410
Sales Range: $25-49.9 Million
Emp.: 14
Optical Goods Mfr & Whslr
N.A.I.C.S.: 339115
Jeffrey Foster (Gen Mgr)

Empire Optical of California Inc (3)
7633 Varna Ave, North Hollywood, CA
91605
Tel.: (818) 997-6474
Web Site: https://www.empireoptical.org
Sales Range: $25-49.9 Million
Emp.: 50
Optical Laboratory Equipment Whslr
N.A.I.C.S.: 423440
Maria J. Galvan (Dir-Sls)

Eye Care Express Lab Inc. (3)
6119 Clarewood Dr, Houston, TX 77081
Tel.: (713) 774-2314
Web Site: http://www.eye-care-express-
lab.com
Sales Range: $25-49.9 Million
Emp.: 30
Optical Glasses Mfr
N.A.I.C.S.: 327215
Ty Dinh (Founder & Pres)

Homer Optical Company, Inc. (3)
2401 Linden Ln, Silver Spring, MD 20910
Tel.: (301) 585-9060
Web Site: http://www.homeroptical.com
Optical Laboratory Lens Whslr
N.A.I.C.S.: 423460
Bill White (VP-Ops)

Interstate Optical Co Inc (3)
680 Lindaire Ln, Ontario, OH 44906
Tel.: (419) 529-6800
Web Site: http://www.interstateoptical.com
Sales Range: $75-99.9 Million
Emp.: 150
Optical Laboratory Equipment Whslr
N.A.I.C.S.: 423440
John Art (Pres)

Jorgenson Optical Supply Cy. (3)
1901 S Union Ave B1001, Tacoma, WA
98405-1879
Tel.: (253) 572-4522
Optical Goods Retailer
N.A.I.C.S.: 466130

**KBco, The Polarized Lens
Company** (3)
7328 S Revere Pkwy Unit 208, Centennial,
CO 80112
Tel.: (303) 253-6600
Web Site: https://www.kbco.net
Sales Range: $25-49.9 Million
Emp.: 50
Polarized Optical Lens Mfr & Whslr
N.A.I.C.S.: 333310
Chris Bailey (Mgr-Mktg)

Katz & Klein (3)
9901 Horn Rd, Sacramento, CA 95827
Tel.: (916) 444-2024
Web Site: http://www.katzandklein.com
Sales Range: $1-9.9 Million
Emp.: 45
Ophthalmic Goods Mfr
N.A.I.C.S.: 339115
Candy Corcoran (Controller)

McLeodd Optical Company Inc. (3)
50 Jefferson Park Rd, Warwick, RI 02888
Tel.: (401) 467-3000
Web Site: https://www.mcleodoptical.com
Emp.: 50
Laboratory Equipment Whslr
N.A.I.C.S.: 423450

**Midland Optical Chicago Labs,
Inc.** (3)
2600 Beverly Dr Ste 101, Aurora, IL 60502
Tel.: (630) 820-6800
Web Site: http://www.focusoptical.com
Emp.: 50
Testing Laboratory Operating Services
N.A.I.C.S.: 541380

NEA Optical LLC (3)
1426 E Washington, Jonesboro, AR 72401
Tel.: (800) 535-7774
Web Site: http://www.neaoptical.com
Sales Range: $25-49.9 Million
Emp.: 20
Ophthalmic Goods Mfr
N.A.I.C.S.: 339115
Jim Evans (Mng Dir)

OMNI Optical Lab (3)
3255 Executive Blvd Ste 100, Beaumont,
TX 77705
Tel.: (409) 842-4113
Web Site: http://www.omnioptical.com
Rev.: $1,500,000
Emp.: 40
Optical Goods Stores
N.A.I.C.S.: 456130
Welton McGallion (Supvr-Maintenance)

Omega Optical Holdings Inc. (3)
13515 N Stemmons Fwy, Dallas, TX 75234-
5765
Tel.: (972) 241-4141
Investment Management Service
N.A.I.C.S.: 523999

Optical One Inc (3)
1751 Houret Ct, Milpitas, CA 95035
Tel.: (408) 263-0933
Web Site: http://www.opticalone.com
Eyewear Lens & Frames Mfr
N.A.I.C.S.: 339115

Ozarks Optical Laboratories Inc (3)
1845 W Arbor Ct, Springfield, MO 65807
Tel.: (417) 890-5367
Optical Lens Whslr
N.A.I.C.S.: 456130
John Vannoy (Pres & Gen Mgr)

Perferx Optical Co. Inc. (3)
25 Downing 3, Pittsfield, MA 01201
Tel.: (800) 649-2550

EssilorLuxottica SA—(Continued)

Web Site: http://www.perferxoptical.com
Eyewear Products Mfr
N.A.I.C.S.: 333310
Joe Yannone (Mgr-General Lab)

Plunkett Optical, Inc. (3)
1705 N A St, Fort Smith, AR 72901
Tel.: (479) 783-2001
Sales Range: $1-9.9 Million
Emp.: 26
Ophthalmic Goods Merchant Whslr
N.A.I.C.S.: 423460

Professional Ophthalmic Laboratories, Inc. (3)
2126 Winston Ave SW, Roanoke, VA 24014
Tel.: (540) 345-7303
Sales Range: $1-9.9 Million
Emp.: 25
Ophthalmic Goods Developer & Distr
N.A.I.C.S.: 339115
Diane Strickler (Treas & Sec)

RD Cherry, Inc. (3)
2429 Oakwood, Melvindale, MI 48122
Tel.: (313) 388-7622
Web Site: https://www.cherryoptical.com
Sales Range: $1-9.9 Million
Emp.: 23
Ophthalmic Goods Mfr
N.A.I.C.S.: 339115
Richard Cherry (Pres)

Southwest Lens Corp. (3)
4735 Memphis St, Dallas, TX 75207
Tel.: (214) 634-8109
Web Site: http://www.southwestlens.com
Optical Lens Mfr
N.A.I.C.S.: 333310
Matthew Herod (Gen Mgr)

Stereo Optical Co. Inc. (3)
8623 W Bryn Mawr Ave Ste 703, Chicago, IL 60656
Tel.: (773) 867-0380
Web Site: https://www.stereooptical.com
Vision Testing Equipment Whslr
N.A.I.C.S.: 423490
Mackenzie Rakers (Mgr-Sls-Natl Mktg)

Sutherlin Optical Company (3)
1941 Central, Kansas City, MO 64108
Tel.: (816) 421-0369
Web Site: https://www.sutherlinoptical.com
Sales Range: $10-24.9 Million
Emp.: 150
Eyeglass Lenses Mfr
N.A.I.C.S.: 333310
John Sutherlin (VP)

Tri Supreme Optical LLC (3)
91 Carolyn Blvd, Farmingdale, NY 11735
Tel.: (631) 249-2020
Web Site: https://www.trisupreme.com
Sales Range: $25-49.9 Million
Emp.: 10
Ophthalmic Product Whslr
N.A.I.C.S.: 456130
Larry Yellin (Acct Mgr)

VIP Optical Laboratories, Inc. (3)
4700 33rd St, Long Island City, NY 11101
Tel.: (908) 523-1422
Web Site: http://www.vipopticallabs.com
Sales Range: $1-9.9 Million
Ophthalmic Goods Mfr
N.A.I.C.S.: 339115
Morris Cohen (Mgr-Lab)

Subsidiary (Domestic):

FGX Direct LLC (2)
500 Washington Hwy, Smithfield, RI 02917
Tel.: (401) 231-3800
Optical Goods Mfr & Whslr
N.A.I.C.S.: 423460

FGX International, Inc. (2)
500 George Washington Hwy, Smithfield, RI 02917
Tel.: (401) 231-3800
Web Site: https://www.fgxi.com
Sales Range: $250-299.9 Million
Emp.: 500
Non-Prescription Reading Glasses, Sunglasses & Costume Jewelry Designer & Marketer
N.A.I.C.S.: 551112
Mark A. Williams (VP & Controller)

Subsidiary (Domestic):

Corinne McCormark, Inc (3)
7 W 36th St, New York, NY 10018
Tel.: (212) 868-7919
Web Site:
http://www.corinnemccormack.com
Sales Range: $25-49.9 Million
Emp.: 9
Optical Accessories Mfr & Whslr
N.A.I.C.S.: 333310
Corinne McCormark (Pres)

Subsidiary (Non-US):

FGX Canada-FosterGrant (3)
555 Richmond St W Ste 1005, PO Box 201, Toronto, M5V 3B1, ON, Canada
Tel.: (416) 504-5533
Web Site: http://www.fgxi.com
Sales Range: $100-124.9 Million
Non-Prescription Eyewear Mfr
N.A.I.C.S.: 333310

FGX Europe, Ltd. (3)
Longbridge Hayes Road Longport, Stoke-on-Trent, ST6 4DS, United Kingdom
Tel.: (44) 1782577055
Web Site: https://www.fostergrant.co.uk
Sales Range: $10-24.9 Million
Emp.: 40
Non-Prescription Eyewear Mfr
N.A.I.C.S.: 333310
Chris Jones (Mng Dir)

FGX International Limited China (3)
Rm 1004 Block A Carrianna Friendship Sq Chun Feng Rd, Shenzhen, 518001, Luo Hu District, China
Tel.: (86) 75582219328
Web Site: http://www.fgxi.com
Sales Range: $100-124.9 Million
Emp.: 50
Non-Prescription Eyewear Mfr
N.A.I.C.S.: 333310
James Mg (Gen Mgr)

Suntech Optics Inc. (3)
758 Harbourside Drive, North Vancouver, V7P 3R7, BC, Canada
Tel.: (604) 929-8141
Sales Range: $10-24.9 Million
Emp.: 75
Eye Wears & Lenses
N.A.I.C.S.: 333310

Subsidiary (Domestic):

Frames For America Inc (2)
501 E Corporate Dr, Lewisville, TX 75057
Tel.: (512) 402-8557
Web Site: https://www.framesdirect.com
Emp.: 70
Eyewear Product Whslr
N.A.I.C.S.: 423490

Future Optics FL Inc (2)
11333 47th St, Clearwater, FL 33762
Tel.: (727) 571-1941
Web Site: https://futureopticsinc.com
Emp.: 40
Lab Optical Instruments Mfr
N.A.I.C.S.: 333310

Gentex Optics, Inc. (2)
183 W Main St, Dudley, MA 01571 (100%)
Tel.: (570) 282-3550
Web Site:
https://www.gentexopticscareers.com
Rev.: $20,000,000
Emp.: 450
Mfr Optical Products, Safety Lenses, Welding Filter Plates, Polycarbonate RX Lenses
N.A.I.C.S.: 339115
L. Peter Frieder Jr. (Chm)

MOC Acquisition Corporation (2)
1833 Knox Ave St, Saint Louis, MO 63139
Tel.: (314) 533-2020
Web Site: http://www.midlandoptical.com
Sales Range: $50-74.9 Million
Emp.: 200
Ophthalmic Goods Equipment Mfr & Whslr
N.A.I.C.S.: 339115

OOGP, Inc. (2)
557 Westbrook Way, PO Box 724, Grants Pass, OR 97528 (80%)
Tel.: (541) 479-4743
Web Site: http://www.oogp.com

Sales Range: $25-49.9 Million
Emp.: 125
Contact Lenses & Other Ophthalmic Products Distr
N.A.I.C.S.: 423460

Optical Dimension Inc (2)
6750 Airport Blvd Ste A, Mobile, AL 36608-3792
Tel.: (251) 342-1905
Ophthalmic Goods Mfr
N.A.I.C.S.: 339115
Paul Milewski (Gen Mgr)

Optifacts Inc. (2)
18 Riverside Ave S Ste 100, Sartell, MN 56377
Tel.: (320) 258-3559
Web Site: http://www.optifacts.com
Sales Range: $25-49.9 Million
Emp.: 14
Optical Laboratory Software Management Services
N.A.I.C.S.: 541511
Steve Morris (Pres)

Satisloh North America Inc (2)
Ste 200 N106 W13131 Bradley Way, Germantown, WI 53022
Tel.: (262) 255-6001
Web Site: http://www.satisloh.com
Emp.: 60
Ophthalmic Lens Mfr & Distr
N.A.I.C.S.: 423460
Pete Lothes (CEO)

Signet Armorlite, Inc. (2)
1001 Armorlite Dr, San Marcos, CA 92069-1431 (100%)
Tel.: (760) 744-4000
Web Site: http://www.signetarmorlite.com
Sales Range: $125-149.9 Million
Emp.: 200
Ophthalmic Lens Mfr
N.A.I.C.S.: 339115
M. Kathryn Bernard (VP-Fin)

Subsidiary (Non-US):

Crossbows Optical Ltd (3)
Unit 1 Halfpenny Valley Industrial Estate, Craigavon, Lurgan, BT66 8TP, Co Armagh, United Kingdom
Tel.: (44) 2838322301
Web Site:
https://www.crossbowsoptical.com
Emp.: 30
Optical Lens Mfr
N.A.I.C.S.: 333310
Mervyn McCrea (Mng Dir)

Subsidiary (Domestic):

Skaggs and Gruber, Ltd (2)
2970 Sutro St, Reno, NV 89512-1616
Tel.: (775) 359-6667
Optical Goods Distr
N.A.I.C.S.: 423460
Jeffrey Skaggs (Pres)

Transitions Optical, Inc. (2)
9251 Belcher Rd Ste B, Pinellas Park, FL 33782-4200
Tel.: (727) 545-0400
Web Site: https://www.transitions.com
Rev.: $250,000,000
Emp.: 200
Photochromic Ophthalmic Products Mfr & Distr
N.A.I.C.S.: 339115
Patience Cook (Assoc Dir-Mktg-North America)

Subsidiary (Non-US):

Transitions Optical (S) Pte. Ltd (3)
201 Kallenge Bahru X 02-02, Singapore, 339338, Singapore
Tel.: (65) 65366878
Web Site: http://www.transitions.com
Sales Range: $10-24.9 Million
Emp.: 12
Optical Lens Mfr
N.A.I.C.S.: 333310

Transitions Optical (Thailand) Ltd. (3)
700/15 Moo 1 Amata Nakorn Industrial Estate, Bankao Panthong, Chon Buri, 20160, Thailand
Tel.: (66) 38468999

Web Site: http://www.transitions.com
Optical Lens Mfr
N.A.I.C.S.: 333310

Transitions Optical Limited (3)
IDA Industrial Estate Dunmore Road, Tuam, H54 RD25, Co Galway, Ireland
Tel.: (353) 9370600
Web Site: http://www.transitions.com
Emp.: 105
Photochromic Coated Lenses Mfr
N.A.I.C.S.: 333310
Kevin Menton (Gen Mgr)

Transitions Optical Philippines, Inc. (3)
Block 4 Lot 1 Star Avenue Laguna International Industrial Park, Mamplasan, Binan, 4024, Laguna, Philippines
Tel.: (63) 495390999
Lens Mfr
N.A.I.C.S.: 333310

Subsidiary (Domestic):

e.magine Optical, Inc. (2)
4139 S 88th E Ave, Tulsa, OK 74147
Tel.: (918) 627-0593
Web Site: http://www.emagineoptical.com
Optical Instrument & Lens Mfr
N.A.I.C.S.: 333310
Tom Yancy (Pres)

FGX Canada Corp (1)
555 Richmond St W Suite 1005, Toronto, M5V 3B1, ON, Canada
Tel.: (416) 504-5533
Sales Range: $25-49.9 Million
Emp.: 3
Sunglasses Whslr
N.A.I.C.S.: 339115

Groupe Vision Optique (1)
535 Boulevard Laurier Suite 314, Beloeil, G3G 5E9, QC, Canada
Tel.: (450) 446-9898
Web Site: http://www.essilor.com
Emp.: 5
Ophthalmic Lens Mfr
N.A.I.C.S.: 339115
Michelle Morin (Gen Mgr)

Heidelberg Engineering GmbH (1)
Max-Jarecki-Strasse 8, 69115, Heidelberg, Germany (80%)
Tel.: (49) 622164630
Web Site:
http://www.heidelbergengineering.com
Sales Range: $25-49.9 Million
Emp.: 150
Diagnostic Instrument Mfr & Distr
N.A.I.C.S.: 339112
Gerhard Zinser (Founder & Mng Dir)

Subsidiary (US):

Heidelberg Engineering Inc. (2)
1808 Aston Ave Ste 130, Carlsbad, CA 92008
Tel.: (800) 931-2230
Web Site:
http://www.heidelbergengineering.com
Sales Range: $25-49.9 Million
Emp.: 20
Medical Diagnostic Equipment Distr
N.A.I.C.S.: 423450
Gerhard Zinser (Mng Dir)

Subsidiary (Non-US):

Heidelberg Engineering Ltd. (2)
55 Marlowes, Hemel Hempstead, HP1 1LE, Hertfordshire, United Kingdom
Tel.: (44) 1442 502 330
Web Site:
http://www.heidelbergengineering.co.uk
Medical Equipment Distr
N.A.I.C.S.: 423450
Christopher Mody (Dir-Clinical Affairs)

Heidelberg Engineering Pty. Ltd. (2)
404 Albert St, Melbourne, 3002, VIC, Australia
Tel.: (61) 396 392 125
Medical Equipment Distr
N.A.I.C.S.: 423450

Holland Optical Instruments BV (1)
Verrijn Stuartweg 42, 1112 AX, Diemen, Netherlands
Tel.: (31) 205696555

Quality Lenses Distr
N.A.I.C.S.: 423460

Horizon Optical Company Ltd (1)
9-11 Apex Business Centre Boscombe
Road, Dunstable, LU5 4SA, United King-
dom
Tel.: (44) 1582472733
Web Site: http://www.horizonoptical.co.uk
Sales Range: $25-49.9 Million
Emp.: 6
Eyeglass Mfr & Whslr
N.A.I.C.S.: 339115
Ian Wooster (Mng Dir)

Infiold Safoty GmbH (1)
Nordstrasse 10 a, 42719, Solingen, Ger-
many
Tel.: (49) 212232340
Web Site: https://www.infield-safety.com
Sales Range: $25-49.9 Million
Emp.: 3
Optical Product Distr
N.A.I.C.S.: 423460
Stefan Find (Mng Dir)

Infield safety UK, Ltd. (1)
Unit 1-7 Apollo Olympus Park, Quedgeley,
Gloucester, GL2 4NF, United Kingdom
Tel.: (44) 1223 836222
Web Site: http://www.infield-safety.co.uk
Protective Eyewear Mfr & Whslr
N.A.I.C.S.: 339115
Chris Stewart (Gen Mgr)

**Integrated Lens Technology Pte
Ltd** (1)
201 Kallang Bahru 02-01 Essilor Building I,
Singapore, 339338, Singapore
Tel.: (65) 65542242
Web Site: https://www.iltoptics.com
Sales Range: $25-49.9 Million
Emp.: 3
Optical Lens Mfr & Distr
N.A.I.C.S.: 339115

Intercast Europe S.r.l. (1)
Via Giulio Natta 10/A, Parma, 43100, Italy
Tel.: (39) 0521 60 75 55
Web Site: http://www.intercast.it
Optical Lens Mfr
N.A.I.C.S.: 333310

K & W Optical Ltd. (1)
1770 Courtwood Crescent, Ottawa, K2C
2B5, ON, Canada
Tel.: (800) 361-1106
Web Site: http://www.kwoptical.ca
Ophthalmic Product Mfr
N.A.I.C.S.: 339115

Luxottica Group S.p.A. (1)
Piazzale L Cadorna 3, 20123, Milan,
Italy (100%)
Tel.: (39) 02863341
Web Site: http://www.luxottica.com
Rev.: $10,212,773,949
Assets: $11,968,889,638
Liabilities: $4,755,568,853
Net Worth: $7,213,320,785
Earnings: $1,029,828,483
Emp.: 55,035
Fiscal Year-end: 12/31/2018
Eyeglass Frames & Sunglasses Mfr
N.A.I.C.S.: 333310
Stefano Grassi (Exec Dir)

Subsidiary (Domestic):

Giorgio Fedon & Figli SpA (2)
Via Dell Industria 5/9, 32016, Pieve
d'Alpago, Belluno, Italy (90.9%)
Tel.: (39) 0437 9823
Web Site: http://www.fedongroup.com
Sales Range: Less than $1 Million
Plastics Product Mfr
N.A.I.C.S.: 326199
Callisto Fedon (Chm & CEO)

Subsidiary (Non-US):

Edgar Kleine Kapunkt GmbH (3)
Liebigstr 5, 85551, Kirchheim, Germany
Tel.: (49) 89 9446890
Web Site: http://www.fe19.de
Eyeglass Case Whslr
N.A.I.C.S.: 424990

Subsidiary (US):

FEDON AMERICA, INC (3)

389 5th Ave, New York, NY 10016
Tel.: (212) 683-6220
Packaging Case & Accessories Distr
N.A.I.C.S.: 424130

Subsidiary (Non-US):

Fedon Far East Limited (3)
Room 15 12/F China Minmetals Tower 79
Chatham Road South, Tsim Sha Tsui, Kow-
loon, China (Hong Kong)
Tel.: (852) 25444700
Web Site: http://www.fedongroup.com
Sales Range: $50-74.9 Million
Emp.: 10
Investment Management Service
N.A.I.C.S.: 523940

genetier SAS (3)
Carre Haussmann II 10/12 Allee de la Con-
naissance, 77127, Lieusaint, France
Tel.: (33) 178482140
Web Site: http://www.genetier.com
Sales Range: $25-49.9 Million
Emp.: 15
Optical Goods Distr
N.A.I.C.S.: 423460
Fianck Champion (Gen Mgr)

Branch (Domestic):

Luxottica (2)
Corso Torino 7, 10020, Lauriano,
Italy (100%)
Tel.: (39) 0119198900
Web Site: http://www.luxottica.com
Sales Range: $100-124.9 Million
Emp.: 500
N.A.I.C.S.: 339113

Subsidiary (Non-US):

Luxottica (Switzerland) A.G. (2)
Hohlstrasse 560, Postfach 3322, 8048, Zu-
rich, Schonbuhl, Switzerland (100%)
Tel.: (41) 800552848
Web Site: http://www.luxottica.com
Sales Range: $25-49.9 Million
Emp.: 15
N.A.I.C.S.: 339113

Luxottica Australia Pty. Ltd. (2)
75 Talavera Road, Macquarie Park, 2113,
NSW, Australia (100%)
Tel.: (61) 2 9815 2333
Web Site: http://www.luxottica.com.au
Emp.: 100
N.A.I.C.S.: 339113

Subsidiary (Domestic):

**Luxottica Retail Australia Pty.
Limited** (3)
Level 6 75 Talavera Road, North Ryde,
2113, NSW, Australia
Tel.: (61) 298152333
Web Site: http://www.opsm.com.au
Emp.: 2,500
Eye Care Service
N.A.I.C.S.: 456130
Suzanne McCracken (Mgr-Store)

Subsidiary (Non-US):

Luxottica Belgium N.V. (2)
Luchthavenlei 78, 2600, Berchem, Antwer-
pen, Belgium (100%)
Tel.: (32) 32868000
Sales Range: $25-49.9 Million
Emp.: 35
Distr of Frames
N.A.I.C.S.: 423460

Luxottica Canada, Inc. (2)
947 Verbena Rd, Mississauga, L5T 1T5,
ON, Canada (100%)
Tel.: (905) 564-2400
Web Site: http://www.luxotticagroup.com
Sales Range: $25-49.9 Million
Emp.: 41
Distr of Frames
N.A.I.C.S.: 423460

**Luxottica Fashion Brillen Virties
GmbH** (2)
Hans Pinsel Strasse 9 A 85540 Haar Beix,
85530, Munich, Germany (100%)
Tel.: (49) 894569150
Sales Range: $25-49.9 Million
Emp.: 20
Distr of Frames

N.A.I.C.S.: 423460

Luxottica France S.a.r.l. (2)
80 Rte Des Lucioles Les Espaces De So-
phia, Sophia Antipolis, 06560, Valbonne,
France (100%)
Tel.: (33) 492966600
Sales Range: $50-74.9 Million
Emp.: 63
Distr of Eyeglass Frames
N.A.I.C.S.: 423460

Luxottica Hellas AE (2)
Anthousas Ave 3, 153 51, Athens,
Greece (70%)
Tel.: (30) 2106669300
Web Site: http://www.luxottica.gr
Sales Range: $25-49.9 Million
Emp.: 50
Distr of Eyeglass Frames
N.A.I.C.S.: 423460
Stefano Mattiello (Country Mgr)

Luxottica Iberica S.A. (2)
Plaza de la pau, Barcelona, 08940,
Spain (100%)
Tel.: (34) 934741989
Web Site: http://www.luxotticaiberica.com
Sales Range: $50-74.9 Million
Emp.: 64
Distr of Eyeglass Frames
N.A.I.C.S.: 423460

Luxottica Mexico SA de C.V. (2)
Monte Elbruz 132 9 Piso, Col Lomas De
Chapultepec, 11000, Mexico, DF,
Mexico (100%)
Tel.: (52) 5552807244
Web Site: http://www.luxottica.com
Sales Range: $25-49.9 Million
Emp.: 43
N.A.I.C.S.: 339113

Luxottica Nederland B.V. (2)
Van De Eijndekade 2, PO Box 506, 2100
AM, Heemstede, Netherlands (51%)
Tel.: (31) 235232800
Sales Range: $25-49.9 Million
Emp.: 50
Eyeglass Frames & Sunglasses Mfr
N.A.I.C.S.: 423460

Luxottica Portugal S.A. (2)
Rua Joao De Freitas Branco 32 C, 1500
359, Lisbon, Portugal (100%)
Tel.: (351) 217221300
Sales Range: $25-49.9 Million
Emp.: 25
Distr of Eyeglass Frames
N.A.I.C.S.: 423460

Subsidiary (US):

**Luxottica Retail North America
Inc.** (2)
4000 Luxottica Pl, Mason, OH 45040
Tel.: (513) 765-6000
Web Site: http://www.luxottica.com
Eyewear Retailer
N.A.I.C.S.: 446130

Subsidiary (Domestic):

Oakley, Inc. (3)
1 Icon, Foothill Ranch, CA 92610-3000
Tel.: (949) 951-0991
Web Site: http://www.oakley.com
Sales Range: $750-799.9 Million
Emp.: 3,400
Eyewear & Athletic Equipment Mfr; De-
signer & Distr
N.A.I.C.S.: 339115
Colin Baden (CEO)

Subsidiary (Non-US):

Luxottica Sweden A.B. (2)
Hangovagen 19, Hus 1 Plan 6, 115 41,
Stockholm, Vastra Frolunda,
Sweden (100%)
Tel.: (46) 852297150
Web Site: http://www.luxottica.com
Sales Range: $25-49.9 Million
Emp.: 20
Distr of Eyeglass Frames
N.A.I.C.S.: 423460

Luxottica U.K. Ltd. (2)
Iron Bridge Close, Great Central Way, Ne-
asden, NW10 0NW, United
Kingdom (100%)

Tel.: (44) 2088300066
Sales Range: $25-49.9 Million
Emp.: 40
Distr of Eyeglass Frames
N.A.I.C.S.: 423460

Subsidiary (US):

Luxottica USA LLC (2)
44 Harbor Park Dr, Port Washington, NY
11050-4625
Tel.: (516) 484-3800
Web Site: http://www.luxottica.com
Prescription Frames & Sunglasses Distr
Jane Lehman (VP-Corp Comm)

Subsidiary (Non-US):

Luxottica Vertriebs GmbH (2)
Inkustrasse 1 7 Stg 3, A 3400, Klosterneu-
burg, Austria (75%)
Tel.: (43) 2243308880
Sales Range: $25-49.9 Million
Emp.: 25
Distr of Eyeglass Frames
N.A.I.C.S.: 423460

Luxottica do Brasil Ltda. (2)
Ave Tambore 1180, PO Box 3, Barueri, Sao
Paulo, 06460-000, Brazil (100%)
Tel.: (55) 141918240
Sales Range: $25-49.9 Million
Emp.: 15
Distr of Frames
N.A.I.C.S.: 423460

Mirari Japan Ltd (2)
Aobadai Bldg 8F 10 9 Aobadai 3 Chome
Meguro Ku, Tokyo, 153 0042,
Japan (50%)
Tel.: (81) 337806833
Web Site: http://www.mirari-japan.co.jp
Sales Range: $25-49.9 Million
Emp.: 37
Distr of Eyeglass Frames
N.A.I.C.S.: 423460
Giorgio Armani (Dir-Sls)

Oy Luxottica Finland AB (2)
Sinikalliontie 12, 02630, Espoo,
Finland (100%)
Tel.: (358) 94391050
Web Site: http://www.luxottica.com.fi
Sales Range: $1-9.9 Million
Emp.: 10
Distr of Eyeglass Frames
N.A.I.C.S.: 423460
Kim Morelaos (Mng Dir)

RayBan Sun Optics India Limited (2)
DLF Building No 9 Tower B 7th Floor,
Phase III DLF Cyber City, Gurgaon,
122002, India
Tel.: (91) 12 4454 5600
Web Site: http://www.luxottica.com
Emp.: 70
Optical Frames & Sunglasses Mfr & Sales
N.A.I.C.S.: 339115

MyOptique Group Ltd. (1)
40 Clifton St, London, EC2A 4DX, United
Kingdom
Tel.: (44) 7930393363
Web Site: https://myoptique.co.uk
Optical Goods Stores
N.A.I.C.S.: 456130
Barney Streeting (CEO)

Subsidiary (Non-US):

4CARE GmbH (2)
Wissenschaftspark, 24118, Kiel, Germany
Tel.: (49) 4318811801
Web Site: https://www.4care.de
Ophthalmic Products Mfr & Distr
N.A.I.C.S.: 339115
Ling Fan-Montzka (Exec Dir)

OMI (1)
101 Boulevard Des Liberateurs, 13011,
Marseille, Bouches-du-Rhone, France
Tel.: (33) 491892601
Emp.: 4
Optical Lens Mfr
N.A.I.C.S.: 333310

OPSG Ltd. (1)
2100 Oxford Street East Unit 27 & 29, London, N5V 4A4, ON, Canada
Tel.: (519) 451-9943
Web Site: http://www.opsg.ca

EssilorLuxottica SA—(Continued)

Sales Range: $50-74.9 Million
Emp.: 6
Optical Laboratory Equipment Whslr
N.A.I.C.S.: 423440

Omega Optix S.R.O. **(1)**
Komenskeho 12B, 974 01, Banska Bystrica,
Slovakia
Tel.: (421) 48 411 30 74
Web Site: http://www.omega-optix.sk
Sales Range: $25-49.9 Million
Emp.: 11
Spectacle Lenses Mfr & Distr
N.A.I.C.S.: 333310
Jiri Peterka *(Mgr-Sls)*

Optical Laboratories Ltd. **(1)**
Unit 1 76 Porana Road, Glenfield, Auckland, 627, New Zealand
Tel.: (64) 33666420
Emp.: 12
Optical Laboratory Services
N.A.I.C.S.: 541380

Optikos SP Zoo **(1)**
Traugutta 24-3, Krakow, 30-549, Poland
Tel.: (48) 126562769
Optical Goods Whslr
N.A.I.C.S.: 423460

Optique Cristal Inc **(1)**
197 Avenue Riverin, Chicoutimi, Saguenay,
G7H 4R2, QC, Canada
Tel.: (418) 545-8556
Optical Lens Mfr
N.A.I.C.S.: 333310

Optique Lison Inc. **(1)**
6980 rue Dalpe, Trois Rivieres, G9A 5C9,
QC, Canada
Tel.: (819) 691-4110
Emp.: 5
Optical Products Whslr
N.A.I.C.S.: 423460
Claude Perreault *(Gen Mgr)*

Optique de l'Estrie Inc **(1)**
417-T Rue Bel Vedere S, Sherbrooke, J1H-4B7, QC, Canada
Tel.: (819) 569-5533
Web Site: http://www.essilor.ca
Emp.: 2
Ophthalmic Lens Mfr & Whslr
N.A.I.C.S.: 339115
Tom Enge Winger *(Office Mgr)*

Perspectics **(1)**
1393 Border St Unit 1, Winnipeg, R3H 0N1,
MB, Canada
Tel.: (204) 474-2684
Web Site: http://www.perspectics.ca
Sales Range: $25-49.9 Million
Emp.: 15
Lens & Frames Mfr
N.A.I.C.S.: 333310
Volker Hues *(Gen Mgr)*

Pioneer Optical Inc. **(1)**
100-2825 Saskatchewan Dr, Regina, S4T
1H3, SK, Canada
Tel.: (306) 525-5201
Sales Range: $50-74.9 Million
Emp.: 6
Ophthalmic Lens Whslr
N.A.I.C.S.: 423460

Pro Optic Canada Inc. **(1)**
551 Boulevard Laurier Suite 100, Laval,
H7L 5C7, QC, Canada
Tel.: (800) 361-4010
Sales Range: $25-49.9 Million
Emp.: 40
Optical Lens Mfr
N.A.I.C.S.: 333310

Subsidiary (Non-US):

Satisloh do Brasil Ltda **(2)**
Rua Caramuru 525 - Cj Saude, Sao Paulo,
04138-001, Brazil
Tel.: (55) 1129308600
Web Site: https://satisloh.com.br
Emp.: 1
Optical Lenses Whslr
N.A.I.C.S.: 423460
Christian Vogil *(Gen Mgr)*

R & R Optical Laboratory Ltd. **(1)**
4500 Sheppard Avenue East Unit 43, Scar-

borough, M1S 3R6, ON, Canada
Tel.: (416) 291-8811
Web Site: http://www.rroptical.ca
Sales Range: $25-49.9 Million
Emp.: 2
Lens Whslr
N.A.I.C.S.: 423460
Ed McGrath *(Gen Mgr)*

Rupp & Hubrach Optik Gmbh **(1)**
Von-Ketteler-Strasse 1, 96050, Bamberg,
Germany
Tel.: (49) 9511860
Web Site: https://www.rh-brillenglas.de
Sales Range: $100-124.9 Million
Emp.: 50
Spectacle Lenses Mfr
N.A.I.C.S.: 339115
Ralf Thiehofe *(Mng Dir)*

Satisloh AG **(1)**
Neuhofstrasse 12, 6340, Baar, Switzerland
Tel.: (41) 7661616
Web Site: http://www.satisloh.com
Emp.: 505
Optical Goods Mfr
N.A.I.C.S.: 333310
Peter Lothes *(Pres & CEO)*

Satisloh Asia Ltd. **(1)**
Suite 3802 38/F Skyline Tower 39 Wang
Kwong Road, Kowloon Bay, Kowloon,
China (Hong Kong)
Tel.: (852) 27567711
Web Site: http://www.satisloh.com
Emp.: 100
Optical Goods Mfr
N.A.I.C.S.: 333310

Satisloh Gmbh **(1)**
Wilhelm-Loh-Str 2-4, 35578, Wetzlar, Germany
Tel.: (49) 64419120
Web Site: http://www.satisloh.com
Emp.: 150
Optical Lens Mfr
N.A.I.C.S.: 339115
Rene Leroux *(Member-Mgmt Bd)*

Satisloh Iberica SL **(1)**
Les Sagraments 22 Pol Ind Sant Ermengol,
08630, Abrera, Barcelona, Spain
Tel.: (34) 93 773 80 28
Optical Lens Mfr
N.A.I.C.S.: 333310
Jan Pohl *(Gen Mgr)*

Satisloh Italy Spa **(1)**
Via Campaccio 0013, 20019, Settimo Milanese, 20019, Milan, Italy
Tel.: (39) 02335561
Web Site: http://www.satisloh.com
Emp.: 7
Optical Lens Mfr
N.A.I.C.S.: 333310

Satisloh Photonics AG **(1)**
Neugasse 10, 8810, Horgen, Switzerland
Tel.: (41) 432441544
Emp.: 8
Optical Instrument & Machine Tool Mfr
N.A.I.C.S.: 333517
Marc Peter *(Head-R&D & Photonics)*

Satisloh Zhongshan Ltd **(1)**
Ground Floor 4th Building Sinda-Jiahu Industrial Park, Jiang Wei Tou Village Hi-Tech
Development Zone, Zhongshan, 528437,
Guangdong, China
Tel.: (86) 76088580781
Web Site: http://www.satisloh.com
Emp.: 40
Optical Lens Mfr
N.A.I.C.S.: 333310
Zhou Zhang *(Gen Mgr)*

Sentralslip AS **(1)**
Gladengveien 3B, Oslo, 601, Norway
Tel.: (47) 23 12 24 00
Web Site: http://www.sentralslip.no
Emp.: 9
Optical Lens Distr
N.A.I.C.S.: 423460

Shamir Optical Industry Ltd. **(1)**
Kibbutz Shamir, Shamir, 1213500, Upper
Galilee, Israel **(50%)**
Tel.: (972) 46947777
Web Site: https://www.shamir.com
Sales Range: $150-199.9 Million
Emp.: 1,764
Progressive Eyeglass Lenses Mfr

N.A.I.C.S.: 333310
Lior Regev *(CFO)*

Subsidiary (Domestic):

Eyal Optical Ind. Ltd. **(2)**
Kibbutz Eyal, Hasharon Hatihon, 45840,
Israel
Tel.: (972) 97639000
Web Site: http://www.shamir.co.il
Sales Range: $25-49.9 Million
Emp.: 200
Optical Lens Mfr
N.A.I.C.S.: 333310
Amos Nezer *(Mng Dir)*

Subsidiary (US):

Shamir Insight, Inc. **(2)**
9938 Via Pasar, San Diego, CA
92126 **(100%)**
Tel.: (858) 514-8330
Web Site: http://www.shamirlens.com
Sales Range: $25-49.9 Million
Emp.: 40
Optical Lens Marketing & Distribution Services
N.A.I.C.S.: 333310

Shamir USA, Inc. **(2)**
9938 Via Pasar, San Diego, CA 92126
Tel.: (818) 889-6292
Web Site: http://www.shamir.co.il
Sales Range: $25-49.9 Million
Emp.: 3
Optical Lens Research, Development, Mfr &
Marketing
N.A.I.C.S.: 333310
Michael Latzer *(Pres)*

Signet Armorlite (Asia) Pte Ltd **(1)**
215 Kallang Bahru 06-00, Singapore,
349281, Singapore
Tel.: (65) 62936801
Sales Range: $25-49.9 Million
Emp.: 100
Optical Goods Mfr & Whslr
N.A.I.C.S.: 333310

Signet Armorlite (Holland) BV **(1)**
Parellaan 56, 2132 WS, Hoofddorp, 2132
WS, Netherlands
Tel.: (31) 235650304
Web Site: https://www.signetarmorlite.com
Ophthalmic Lens Mfr
N.A.I.C.S.: 339115

Signet Armorlite Canada, Inc **(1)**
349 Evans Avenue, Etobicoke, M8Z 1K2,
ON, Canada
Tel.: (905) 828-8798
Optical Goods Mfr & Whslr
N.A.I.C.S.: 339115

**Signet Armorlite Germany Holding
GmbH** **(1)**
Bevenroder Str 150, Braunschweig, 38108,
Germany
Tel.: (49) 531370020
Web Site: http://www.signet-armorlite.de
Sales Range: $50-74.9 Million
Emp.: 25
Financial Investment Services
N.A.I.C.S.: 523999
Stephan Find *(Mng Dir)*

Signet Armorlite Iberica SA **(1)**
Manuel Tovar 7, 28034, Madrid, Spain
Tel.: (34) 913581513
Optical Lens Mfr
N.A.I.C.S.: 333310

Signet Armorlite Optic Gmbh **(1)**
Bevenroder Strasse 150, 38108, Braunschweig, Germany
Tel.: (49) 5313700259
Web Site: http://www.signet-armorlite.de
Emp.: 10
Optical Instrument Mfr
N.A.I.C.S.: 333310
Marcus Manegold *(Mng Dir)*

Spherical Optics (Pty) Ltd. **(1)**
10 The Avenue Orchards, 2196, Johannesburg, South Africa
Tel.: (27) 114833584
Web Site: http://www.shamir.co.il
Sales Range: $25-49.9 Million
Emp.: 20
Optical Lens Distr
N.A.I.C.S.: 333310

Philip Rabinowitz *(Mng Dir)*

Tasmanian Optical Cy Pty LTD **(1)**
71 Murray St, Hobart, 7000, TAS, Australia
Tel.: (61) 3 6234 5044
Optical Goods Whslr
N.A.I.C.S.: 456130

UAB JZP Optika Lituania **(1)**
Savanoriu Pr 187, Vilnius, 2300, Lithuania
Tel.: (370) 52653704
Sales Range: $50-74.9 Million
Emp.: 6
Optical Goods Distr
N.A.I.C.S.: 423460
Donatas Guzys *(Gen Mgr)*

**Wholesale Lens Corporation
Limited** **(1)**
73-77 Gloucester Road, Croydon, CR0
2DL, Surrey, United Kingdom
Tel.: (44) 2086832902
Web Site: https://www.wlclens.co.uk
Emp.: 4
Optical Goods Distr
N.A.I.C.S.: 423460

ESSITY AKTIEBOLAG
Klarabergsviadukten 63, PO Box 200,
111 64, Stockholm, Sweden
Tel.: (46) 87885100 **SE**
Web Site: https://www.essity.com
Year Founded: 1929
ESSITY—(OMX)
Rev.: $14,877,523,360
Assets: $21,370,104,000
Liabilities: $13,006,769,440
Net Worth: $8,363,334,560
Earnings: $1,197,604,800
Emp.: 46,000
Fiscal Year-end: 12/31/21
Personal Care Product Services
N.A.I.C.S.: 424130
Magnus Groth *(Pres & CEO)*

Subsidiaries:

Asaleo Care Limited **(1)**
30-32 Westall Road, Springvale, 3171, VIC,
Australia
Tel.: (61) 95502999
Web Site: http://www.asaleocare.com
Rev.: $294,325,692
Assets: $336,387,706
Liabilities: $209,011,303
Net Worth: $127,376,404
Earnings: $15,448,126
Emp.: 688
Fiscal Year-end: 12/31/2019
Personal Care & Hygiene Products Mfr &
Distr
N.A.I.C.S.: 322291
David Griss *(Exec Gen Mgr-People & Corp
Svcs)*

Branch (Non-US):

Asaleo Care Limited **(2)**
2nd Floor 103 Carlton Gore Road, Newmarket, 1023, Auckland, New Zealand
Tel.: (64) 9 302 5200
Web Site: http://www.asaleocare.com
Sales Range: $150-199.9 Million
Emp.: 600
Personal Care & Hygiene Products Mfr &
Distr
N.A.I.C.S.: 812199

BSN Radiante SAS **(1)**
57 Boulevard Demorieux, 72100, Le Mans,
France
Tel.: (33) 549214091
Web Site: https://medical.essity.fr
N.A.I.C.S.: 621111
Valere Weiss *(Dir-Publication)*

Essity Canada Inc. **(1)**
1275 North Service Road West Suite 800,
Oakville, L6M 3G4, ON, Canada
Web Site: https://medical.essity.ca
N.A.I.C.S.: 621111

Essity Chile SA **(1)**
Panamericana Norte 22 550, Metropolitan
Region, 9391279, Lampa, Chile
Tel.: (56) 80020097
N.A.I.C.S.: 621111

Essity Czech Republic s.r.o. (1)
BU Professional Hygiene Sokolovska 94,
186 00, Prague, Czech Republic
Tel.: (420) 221706111
Hygiene & Sanitary Paper Mfr
N.A.I.C.S.: 322291
Vit Ulrich *(Mgr-Sls)*

Essity Denmark A/S (1)
Gydevang 33, 3450, Allerod, Denmark
Tel.: (45) 48168220
Sanitary Paper Product Mfr
N.A.I.C.S.: 322291
Nielsen Susanne *(Mgr-Fin)*

Essity Franco SAS (1)
151 Boulevard Victor Hugo, 93588, Saint-
Ouen, Cedex, France
Tel.: (33) 185079000
Web Site: https://www.essity.fr
N.A.I.C.S.: 621111

Essity Germany GmbH (1)
Adalperostrasse 31, Ismaning, 85737, Mu-
nich, Germany
Tel.: (49) 89970060
Sanitary Paper Product Mfr
N.A.I.C.S.: 322291

Essity Hijyen Urunleri Sanayi ve Ti-
caret A.S. (1)
Kuris Kule Business Center Cevizli Mah,
D-100 Guney Yan Yol Cad No 2 K 9 Kartal,
34953, Istanbul, Turkiye
Tel.: (90) 2165601300
Sanitary Paper Product Mfr
N.A.I.C.S.: 322291

Essity Hungary Kft (1)
Professional Hygiene Budakeszi ut 51,
1021, Budapest, Hungary
Tel.: (36) 13922115
Sanitary Paper Product Mfr
N.A.I.C.S.: 322291

Essity Italy S.p.A. (1)
Via XXV Aprile 2, Badia Pozzeveri Altopas-
cio, 55011, Lucca, Italy
Tel.: (39) 0583938611
Web Site: https://www.essity.it
N.A.I.C.S.: 621111

Essity Norway AS (1)
Fredrik Selmers vei 6, 0603, Oslo, Norway
Tel.: (47) 22706200
Sanitary Paper Product Mfr
N.A.I.C.S.: 322291

Essity Operations Poland Sp. z
o.o. (1)
Ul 3 Maja 30A, 55-200, Olawa, Poland
Tel.: (48) 713013000
N.A.I.C.S.: 621111

Essity Operations Witzenhausen
GmbH (1)
Sandhofer Strasse 176, 68305, Mannheim,
Germany
Tel.: (49) 6217780
Web Site: https://www.essity.de
Healthcare Product Distr
N.A.I.C.S.: 423450

Essity Poland Sp. z o.o. (1)
Ul Pulawska Nr 435 A, 02-801, Warsaw,
Poland
Tel.: (48) 225437500
N.A.I.C.S.: 621111

Essity Professional Hygiene North
America LLC (1)
Cira Ctr Ste 2600 2929 Arch St, Philadel-
phia, PA 19104
N.A.I.C.S.: 621111

Essity Switzerland AG (1)
Parkstrasse 1b, Schenkon, 6214, Sursee,
Switzerland
Tel.: (41) 84 022 0222
Web Site: https://www.tena.ch
Incontinence Care & Healthcare Services
N.A.I.C.S.: 621610

Legacy Converting, Inc. (1)
1 Advantage Ct, Bordentown, NJ 08512
Web Site: http://www.everwipe.com
Non-Woven & Paper Goods Mfr
N.A.I.C.S.: 322299
Jason Slosberg *(Pres)*

OY Essity Finland AB (1)

Itsehallintokuja 6, 02600, Espoo, Finland
Tel.: (358) 9506881
Sanitary Paper Product Mfr
N.A.I.C.S.: 322291
Olli Oksa *(Acct Mgr)*

Productos Familia S.A. (1)
Carrero 50 No 8 Sur 117, Medellin,
Colombia (95.8%)
Tel.: (57) 4 360 9500
Web Site:
   http://www.familiainstitucional.com
Designer, Mfr & Distr of Personal Hygiene &
Paper Products
N.A.I.C.S.: 322291
Dario Rey Mora *(CEO)*

Subsidiary (Non-US):

Sancela Chile S.A. (2)
Avenida Gladys Marin 6366 Estacion Cen-
tral, Santiago, Chile
Tel.: (56) 2 2389 2131
Sanitary Paper Product Mfr
N.A.I.C.S.: 322291

Vinda International Holdings
Limited (1)
Penthouse East Ocean Centre 98 Granville
Road Tsim Sha Tsui East, Kowloon, China
(Hong Kong) (51.59%)
Tel.: (852) 23669853
Web Site: https://www.vindapaper.com
Holding Company; Paper Products Mfr
N.A.I.C.S.: 551112
Yi Ping Dong *(CTO)*

Subsidiary (Domestic):

Forton Enterprises Limited (2)
Room 605 Phase 1 Hong Leong Plaza No
33 Lok Yip Road, Fanling, New Territories,
China (Hong Kong) (100%)
Tel.: (852) 2782 5512
Holding Company; Household Consumable
Paper Sales
N.A.I.C.S.: 424130

Vinda Household Paper (Hong Kong)
Limited (2)
Room 506 Tower 1 South Seas Centre 75
Mody Road, Tsimshatsui East, Kowloon,
China (Hong Kong) (100%)
Tel.: (852) 2366 9853
Sales Range: $25-49.9 Million
Emp.: 1
Holding Company
N.A.I.C.S.: 551112
Paul Psang *(CFO)*

Subsidiary (Non-US):

Vinda North Paper (Beijing) Company
Limited (2)
No 16 Hangyu Street, Pinggu District, Bei-
jing, 101200, China (100%)
Tel.: (86) 1069934888
Household Consumable Paper Products Mfr
& Sales
N.A.I.C.S.: 322299

Vinda Paper (Beijing) Limited (2)
No 16 Hangyu Street, Pinggu District, Bei-
jing, China
Tel.: (86) 10 69934888
Web Site: http://www.vindapaper.com
Household Consumable Paper Sales
N.A.I.C.S.: 424990

Vinda Paper (China) Company
Limited (2)
Donghou Industrial Development Zone, Xin-
hui District, Jiangmen, 529100,
China (100%)
Tel.: (86) 7506168333
Sales Range: $450-499.9 Million
Emp.: 130
Paper Products Mfr
N.A.I.C.S.: 322299

Vinda Paper (Sichuan) Limited (2)
No 19 Section 3 Longquanshan Road, Dey-
ang, 618000, Sichuan, China
Tel.: (86) 838 2906199
Web Site: http://www.vindapaper.com
Sanitary Paper Product Mfr
N.A.I.C.S.: 322291

Vinda Paper (Zhejiang) Company
Limited (2)

No 9 Fengkun Rd Longyou Industrial Park,
Longyou, Quzhou, 324404, China (100%)
Tel.: (86) 5707788805
Household Consumable Paper Products Mfr
& Sales
N.A.I.C.S.: 322291

ESSIX BIOSCIENCES LIMITED
B-4 & 5 Industrial Focal Point, Mo-
hali, Derabassi, India
Tel.: (91) 1762281278   In
Web Site:
   https://essixbiosciences.com
Emp.: 100
Pharmaceutical Preparation Mfr
N.A.I.C.S.: 325412

ESSTRA INDUSTRIES INC.
2110 650 West Georgia St, PO Box
1831, Garibaldi Highlands, Vancou-
ver, V6B 4N8, BC, Canada
Tel.: (604) 689-1280   BC
Year Founded: 1996
MIVO—(TSXV)
Assets: $32,916
Liabilities: $119,436
Net Worth: ($86,521)
Earnings: ($30,089)
Fiscal Year-end: 05/31/24
Financial Investment Services
N.A.I.C.S.: 523999
Virginia Olnick *(CEO & Sec)*

Subsidiaries:

412688 B.C. Ltd. (1)
510 Burrard St Ste 575, Vancouver, V6C
3A8, BC, Canada
Tel.: (604) 662-3230
Financial Investment Services
N.A.I.C.S.: 523999
Teter Dickson *(Pres)*

EST GLOBAL APPAREL CO.,
LTD.
8F No 252 Sec 2 New Taipei Blvd,
Sanchong Dist, New Taipei City,
241553, Taiwan
Tel.: (886) 225637238
Web Site: https://www.estga.com
Year Founded: 1987
4413—(TPE)
Rev.: $14,650,152
Assets: $15,972,857
Liabilities: $4,534,223
Net Worth: $11,438,634
Earnings: $593,381
Fiscal Year-end: 12/31/23
Apparel Product Mfr
N.A.I.C.S.: 315990
Dennis Huang *(Mng Dir)*

EST IMPRIMERIE
Z D''activite Tournebride Zone De
Tournebride, 57160, Metz, France
Tel.: (33) 387383400
Web Site: http://www.est-
   imprimerie.fr
Rev.: $21,300,000
Emp.: 64
Commercial Printing
N.A.I.C.S.: 323111

EST TOOLS CO., LTD.
No 68 Haixing East Road, Haiyan
County, Jiaxing, 314300, Zhejiang,
China
Tel.: (86) 57386169512
Web Site: https://www.esttools.com
Year Founded: 1990
300488—(CHIN)
Rev.: $79,045,936
Assets: $223,948,613
Liabilities: $28,858,080
Net Worth: $195,090,532
Earnings: $19,042,328
Fiscal Year-end: 12/31/23
Industrial Machinery Mfr
N.A.I.C.S.: 333248

Chen Errong *(Chm)*

ESTABLISHMENT LABS
HOLDINGS, INC.
Coyol Free Zone B15, Coyol Free
Zone, Alajuela, Costa Rica
Tel.: (506) 24342400   VG
Web Site:
   https://www.establishmentlabs.com
Year Founded: 2013
ESTA—(NASDAQ)
Rev.: $161,700,000
Assets: $211,061,000
Liabilities: $219,246,000
Net Worth: ($8,185,000)
Earnings: ($75,209,000)
Emp.: 958
Fiscal Year-end: 12/31/22
Holding Company
N.A.I.C.S.: 551112
Juan Jose Chacon Quiros *(CEO)*

ESTATE MANAGEMENT COM-
PANY JSC
240g Nursultan Nazarbaev ave, Al-
maty, 050000, Kazakhstan
Tel.: (7) 273551111
Web Site: http://www.emc-
   company.kz
ESMC—(KAZ)
Rev.: $54,285
Assets: $203,486,040
Liabilities: $1,783,374
Net Worth: $201,702,666
Earnings: ($26,929,604)
Fiscal Year-end: 12/31/19
Real Estate Manangement Services
N.A.I.C.S.: 531210
Erbol Zhamanbayev *(Chm-Mgmt Bd)*

ESTATIA AG
Gubelstrasse 17, 6304, Zug, Switzer-
land
Tel.: (41) 223628852   CH
Holding Company
N.A.I.C.S.: 551112
Jostein Eikeland *(Founder & Chm)*

ESTEEM BIO ORGANIC FOOD
PROCESSING LTD
49 Gujrawala Town Part II, New
Delhi, 110009, India
Tel.: (91) 11 32961926
Web Site:
   http://www.esteembioorganic.com
Rev.: $538,609
Assets: $7,068,021
Liabilities: $475,327
Net Worth: $6,592,694
Earnings: $222,835
Emp.: 13
Fiscal Year-end: 03/31/18
Farm Management & Food Process-
ing
N.A.I.C.S.: 115116
Sanjay Lohra *(CFO)*

ESTELLE HOLDINGS CO.,
LTD.
6F JRE Ginza 1 chome East Bldg
1-19-7 Ginza, Chuo-ku, Tokyo, 104-
0061, Japan
Tel.: (81) 366288480
Web Site: https://www.estelle.co.jp
Year Founded: 1946
7872—(TKS)
Rev.: $209,530,390
Assets: $211,731,520
Liabilities: $128,253,830
Net Worth: $83,477,690
Earnings: ($6,471,190)
Emp.: 2,759
Fiscal Year-end: 03/31/24
Jewelry Product Mfr & Distr
N.A.I.C.S.: 339910
Katsuyoshi Hirano *(Exec Mng Dir)*

Estelle Holdings Co., Ltd.—(Continued)

ESTER INDUSTRIES LTD

Plot No-11-A Infocity -1 Sector - 33-34, Gurgaon, 122001, Haryana, India
Tel.: (91) 1244572100
Web Site:
  https://www.esterindustries.com
500136—(BOM)
Rev.: $136,464,114
Assets: $117,621,914
Liabilities: $47,731,306
Net Worth: $69,890,607
Earnings: $18,767,876
Emp.: 520
Fiscal Year-end: 03/31/21
Polyester Films & Plastics Production
& Marketing
N.A.I.C.S.: 326113
Arvind Kumar Singhania (Founder,
Chm & CEO)

ESTERAD INVESTMENT COMPANY BSC

GFH Tower 3rd floor, PO Box 1080,
Manama, Bahrain
Tel.: (973) 17585400
Web Site: https://www.esterad.net
Year Founded: 1973
ESTERAD—(BAH)
Rev.: $11,666,200
Assets: $142,174,706
Liabilities: $48,007,939
Net Worth: $94,166,767
Earnings: $5,732,554
Emp.: 12
Fiscal Year-end: 12/31/22
Equity Investment Services
N.A.I.C.S.: 523999
Abdulrahman M. S. Jamsheer
(Deputy Chm)

Subsidiaries:

Venture Capital Bank BSC   **(1)**
GFH Tower 3rd Floor Road 4626 Block 346
Building 1411, PO Box 11755, Sea Front,
Manama, Bahrain
Tel.: (973) 17518888
Web Site: https://www.vc-bank.com
Investment Services
N.A.I.C.S.: 523940

ESTERCHEM LTD.

Brooklands Way Basford Lane Industrial Estate, Leek, ST13 7QF,
Staffordshire, United Kingdom
Tel.: (44) 1538383997
Web Site:
  http://www.esterchem.co.uk
Year Founded: 1998
Emp.: 100
Chemical Products Mfr
N.A.I.C.S.: 325199
Adam Bray (Mng Dir)

ESTERFORM PACKAGING LTD.

Boraston Lane Burford, Tenbury
Wells, WR15 8LE, Worcestershire,
United Kingdom
Tel.: (44) 1584812000   UK
Web Site: http://www.esterform.com
Year Founded: 1999
Sales Range: $75-99.9 Million
Plastics Bottle Mfr
N.A.I.C.S.: 326160
Simon Hartley (Dir-Fin)

ESTEVE PHARMACEUTICALS S.A.

Passeig de la Zona Franca 109 4
Planta, 08038, Barcelona, Spain
Tel.: (34) 93 446 60 00
Web Site: http://www.esteve.com
Year Founded: 1787
Pharmaceuticals Mfr
N.A.I.C.S.: 325412

Staffan Schuberg (CEO)

ESTHETICS INTERNATIONAL GROUP BERHAD

Lot 11 Jalan Astaka U8/88 Bukit Jelutong, Seksyen U8, 40150, Shah
Alam, Selangor Darul Ehsan, Malaysia
Tel.: (60) 378096688
Web Site:
  https://www.estheticsgroup.com
EIG—(KLS)
Rev.: $34,942,646
Assets: $56,387,090
Liabilities: $22,167,196
Net Worth: $34,219,894
Earnings: ($1,201,270)
Emp.: 700
Fiscal Year-end: 03/31/23
Skin Care Product Mfr
N.A.I.C.S.: 812112
Wai Ngan Lee (Sec)

Subsidiaries:

AsterSpring International Sdn.
Bhd.   **(1)**
Lot 11 Jalan Astaka U8/88 Bukit Jelutong
Seksyen U8, 40150, Shah Alam, Selangor,
Malaysia
Tel.: (60) 378096777
Web Site: https://asterspring.com
Skin Care Services
N.A.I.C.S.: 812112

EIG GLOBAL PTE LTD   **(1)**
60 Paya Lebar Road 09-28, Paya Lebar
Square, Singapore, 409051, Singapore
Tel.: (65) 62714733
Health Care & Cosmetic Products Distr
N.A.I.C.S.: 424210

EIG Global (China) Co. Ltd.   **(1)**
Room Unit 04 15th Floor Teem Tower No
208 Tianhe Road, Tianhe District,
Guangzhou, China
Tel.: (86) 2038103628
Web Site: http://www.estheticsgroup.com
Skin & Hair Care Products Distr
N.A.I.C.S.: 424210

EIG Global (HK) Ltd.   **(1)**
Suite 1808 22 Hung To Road Elite Centre,
Kwung Tong, Kowloon, China (Hong Kong)
Tel.: (852) 6 022 0255
Web Site: http://www.estheticsgroup.com
Cosmetics Distr
N.A.I.C.S.: 424210

EIG Pharma Asia Sdn. Bhd.   **(1)**
Lot 11 Jalan Astaka U8/88 Bukit Jelutong,
40150, Shah Alam, Selangor, Malaysia
Tel.: (60) 378096688
Web Site: http://www.estheticsgroup.com
Pharmaceutical Products Distr
N.A.I.C.S.: 424210
Susan Siok Wee Lim (Sr Gen Mgr)

Esthetics Concept Sdn.Bhd.   **(1)**
Lot 11 Jalan Astaka U8/88 Seksyen U8
Bukit Jelutong, 40150, Shah Alam, Selangor, Malaysia
Tel.: (60) 378096688
Web Site: http://www.estheticsgroup.com
Emp.: 200
Cosmetic Product Distr
N.A.I.C.S.: 424210
Mitchell Lam (Gen Mgr)

Esthetics and Wellness International
Sdn. Bhd.   **(1)**
Lot 11 Jalan Astaka U8/88 Bukit Jelutong
Seksyen U8, Shah Alam, 40150, Selangor,
Malaysia
Tel.: (60) 3 78096688
Web Site: http://www.estheticsgroup.com
Sales Range: $10-24.9 Million
Emp.: 100
Educational Support Services
N.A.I.C.S.: 611710
Eddy Chieng (Mng Dir)

Klientec International Sdn. Bhd.   **(1)**
Lot 11 Jalan Astaka U8/88 Bukit Jelutong
Seksyen U8, 40150, Shah Alam, Selangor,
Malaysia
Tel.: (60) 378096689

Web Site: http://www.klientec.com
Marketing Automation Solutions
N.A.I.C.S.: 518210

Leonard Drake (HK) Ltd.   **(1)**
HK Pacific Centre Fl 9, Tsim Tsa Tsui, Kowloon, China (Hong Kong)
Tel.: (852) 31151132
Hair & Skin Care Services
N.A.I.C.S.: 812112

Leonard Drake (M) Sdn. Bhd.   **(1)**
Lot 11 Jalan Astaka U8/88 Bukit Jelutong
Seksyen U8, 40150, Shah Alam, Malaysia
Tel.: (60) 378006666
Web Site: http://www.leonarddrake.com.my
Sales Range: $125-149.9 Million
Emp.: 400
Cosmetics Products Mfr
N.A.I.C.S.: 325620

Medklinn International Sdn. Bhd.   **(1)**
22 Jalan Pengacara U1/48, Kawasan Perindustrian Temasya, 40150, Shah Alam, Selangor, Malaysia
Tel.: (60) 355670788
Web Site: https://www.medklinn.com
Healthcare Product Distr
N.A.I.C.S.: 424210

ESTI CHEM A/S

Sondre Molevej 14-16, Koge, 4600,
Denmark
Tel.: (45) 56653372
Web Site: http://www.dow.com
Sales Range: $150-199.9 Million
Emp.: 15
Chemicals Mfr
N.A.I.C.S.: 325998

ESTIC CORPORATION

1-2-16 Togodori, Moriguchi, 570-0041, Osaka, Japan
Tel.: (81) 669938855
Web Site: https://www.estic-global.com
Year Founded: 1993
6161—(TKS)
Rev.: $47,109,470
Assets: $70,925,300
Liabilities: $8,903,670
Net Worth: $62,021,630
Earnings: $7,489,130
Emp.: 213
Fiscal Year-end: 03/31/24
Electric Power Tool Mfr & Whslr
N.A.I.C.S.: 333991
Hiroshi Suzuki (Founder & Chm)

Subsidiaries:

ESTIC (Thailand) Co., Ltd.   **(1)**
19 Naradhiwas Rajanakarin Road Chong
Nonsi, Yannawa, Bangkok, 10120, Thailand
Tel.: (66) 26780171
Electric Power Tool Whslr
N.A.I.C.S.: 423710
Nawin Boonsaenunt (Engr-Sls)

ESTIC America, Inc.   **(1)**
Ste 120 1895 Airport Exchange Blvd, Erlanger, KY 41018
Tel.: (859) 746-8800
Industrial Machinery Mfr
N.A.I.C.S.: 333248

Shanghai ESTIC Co., Ltd.   **(1)**
No 6 51Gate 1159Lane Kanqiao East Road,
Pudong, Shanghai, 201315, China
Tel.: (86) 2168130333
Electric Power Tool Whslr
N.A.I.C.S.: 423710

ESTNATION INC.

6-10-2 Roppongi Minato-ku 1F-2F
Keyakizaka Complex Roppongi Hills,
Tokyo, 106-0032, Japan
Tel.: (81) 3 5159 7800
Web Site: http://www.estnation.co.jp
Year Founded: 2000
Sales Range: $25-49.9 Million
Emp.: 200
Clothing, Accessories, Sundries &
Gift Items Retailer

N.A.I.C.S.: 458110
Shunsuki Nagaoka (CEO)

ESTORE CORPORATION

Midtown Tower 9-7-1 Akasaka,
Minato-ku, Tokyo, 107-6205, Japan
Tel.: (81) 364345196
Web Site: https://estore.jp
Year Founded: 1999
4304—(TKS)
Rev.: $83,061,260
Assets: $84,879,010
Liabilities: $60,653,360
Net Worth: $24,225,650
Earnings: $3,053,820
Emp.: 284
Fiscal Year-end: 03/31/24
Internet-Related Services
N.A.I.C.S.: 517810
Mikio Ohki (Exec Officer & Sls Mgr)

ESTORIL SOL, SGPS, S.A.

Dr Stanley Ho Avenue Estoril Casino
Building, Estoril, 2765-190, Cascais,
Portugal
Tel.: (351) 214667700   PT
Web Site: https://www.estoril-solsgps.com
Year Founded: 1958
ESON—(EUR)
Rev.: $150,999,558
Assets: $188,377,768
Liabilities: $43,181,361
Net Worth: $145,196,407
Earnings: $46,264,334
Emp.: 900
Fiscal Year-end: 12/31/22
Holding Company
N.A.I.C.S.: 551112
Carlos Alberto Francisco Farinha
(Sec)

Subsidiaries:

Desenvolvimento Turistico e Hoteleiro, SA   **(1)**
Rua Melo e Sousa 535, Estoril, Lisbon,
2765-253, Portugal
Tel.: (351) 214 670 770
Investment Management Service
N.A.I.C.S.: 523940

ESTRE AMBIENTAL S.A.

4509 Brigadeiro Faria Lima Avenue 8
Floor, 04538-132, Sao Paulo, SP,
Brazil
Tel.: (55) 1121243100
Web Site: http://www.estre.com.br
Year Founded: 1999
Waste Management Services
N.A.I.C.S.: 562119
Sergio Messias Pedreiro (CEO)

ESTRELLA GROUP LTD

Number 7 Mill Pool Nash Lane, Belbroughton, Stourbridge, DY9 9AF, W
Midlands, United Kingdom
Tel.: (44) 1562 730871
Web Site:
  http://www.estrellagroup.co.uk
Sales Range: $50-74.9 Million
Emp.: 270
Engineeering Services
N.A.I.C.S.: 541330
Steve Hayes (Chm)

ESTRELLA INTERNATIONAL ENERGY SERVICES LTD.

1136 Cerrito Street 9th Floor, Buenos
Aires, C1010AAX, Argentina
Tel.: (54) 11 5217 5250   AB
Web Site: http://www.estrellasp.com
Year Founded: 2007
Sales Range: $125-149.9 Million
Investment Services
N.A.I.C.S.: 523999
Javier Vedoya (CEO)

ESTRELLA RESOURCES LIMITED

Level 11 216 St Georges Terrace, Perth, 6000, WA, Australia
Tel.: (61) 894810389
Web Site:
https://www.estrellaresources.com
ESR—(ASX)
Rev.: $5,471
Assets: $14,095,107
Liabilities: $260,576
Net Worth: $13,834,531
Earnings: ($1,997,289)
Emp.: 2
Fiscal Year-end: 06/30/24
Gold & Copper Mining
N.A.I.C.S.: 212220
Christopher Daws (Mng Dir)

Subsidiaries:

Estrella Resources (Chile) SpA (1)
Av Vitacura 5250 Oficina 802, Vitacura, Santiago, Chile
Tel.: (56) 2 242 1157
Gold & Copper Mining
N.A.I.C.S.: 212220

ESTRIMA S.P.A.

Via Roveredo 20/b, 33170, Pordenone, Italy
Web Site: https://www.estrima.com
Year Founded: 2008
BIRO—(EUR)
Automobile Parts Mfr
N.A.I.C.S.: 336110
Ludovico Maggiore (CEO)

ESTSOFT CORP

6 78 F 3 Banpo-daero, Seocho-gu, Seoul, 6711, Korea (South)
Tel.: (82) 25834620
Web Site: https://estsoft.ai
Year Founded: 1993
047560—(KRS)
Rev.: $4,148,302
Assets: $141,915,243
Liabilities: $77,856,179
Net Worth: $64,059,064
Earnings: ($4,680,132)
Emp.: 188
Fiscal Year-end: 12/31/22
Software Producer
N.A.I.C.S.: 334610
Sangwon Chung (CEO)

Subsidiaries:

DeepEye Co., Ltd. (1)
4F 34 Gangnam-daero 94-gil, Gangnam-gu, Seoul, Korea (South)
Tel.: (82) 1 522 0416
Web Site: https://www.deep-eye.co.kr
Eyewear Distr
N.A.I.C.S.: 423460

ESTsecurity Corp. (1)
Tel.: (82) 25834616
Information Technology Security Software Services
N.A.I.C.S.: 541519
Sangwon Chung (CEO)

Exponential Investments Co., Ltd. (1)
Room 710A 7th Floor CCMM Building 101 Yeouigongwon-ro, Yeongdeungpo-gu, Seoul, Korea (South)
Tel.: (82) 269541505
Investment Management Service
N.A.I.C.S.: 523940

ESVAL SA

Cochrane No 751, Valparaiso, Chile
Tel.: (56) 322209000
Web Site: http://www.esval.cl
Year Founded: 2014
Drinking Water Purification Mfr
N.A.I.C.S.: 312112
Jose Luis Murillo Collado (CEO)

ETA ELECTRIC INDUSTRY CO., LTD.

2-16-10 Hon-Haneda, Ohta-Ku, Tokyo, 144-8611, Japan
Tel.: (81) 3 3745 7771
Web Site: http://www.eta.co.jp
Year Founded: 1979
Sales Range: $25-49.9 Million
Emp.: 87
Customized Power Production & Sales
N.A.I.C.S.: 221122
Hiroshi Takahashi (Pres & CEO)

Subsidiaries:

ETA-POWER EUROPE LTD. (1)
Sennweidstrasse 45, 6312, Steinhausen, Switzerland
Tel.: (41) 41 747 0111
Web Site: http://www.etapower.com
Power Conversion Device Mfr
N.A.I.C.S.: 335999

ETA-USA Inc. (1)
16170 Vineyard Blvd Ste 180, Morgan Hill, CA 95037
Tel.: (408) 778-2793
Web Site: http://www.eta-usa.com
Electric Equipment Mfr
N.A.I.C.S.: 335999

ETABLISSEMENTS ALLIN

28 Rue De Cardurand, 44600, Saint Nazaire, Loire Atlantique, France
Tel.: (33) 549350003
Web Site: http://www.allin.fr
Rev.: $22,200,000
Emp.: 100
Wood Products
N.A.I.C.S.: 321999

ETABLISSEMENTS CHAZAUD

ZI N 2 Les Grands Danjons, 2 Allee Evariste Galois, 18000, Bourges, France
Tel.: (33) 248505050
Sales Range: $10-24.9 Million
Emp.: 23
Meat Packing Plants
N.A.I.C.S.: 311611
Carlo Rui (Dir-Pur)

ETABLISSEMENTS EMILE GEORGET

Z D''activite Tournebride Zone De Tournebride, 57160, Metz, France
Tel.: (33) 549200088
Sales Range: $10-24.9 Million
Emp.: 64
New & Used Car Dealers
N.A.I.C.S.: 441110
Focazanf Denes (Pres)

ETABLISSEMENTS EMILE LLAU

ZI du Couserans Voie Haussmann, 09160, Caumont, France
Tel.: (33) 561044444
Rev.: $24,100,000
Emp.: 35
Scrap & Waste Materials
N.A.I.C.S.: 423930
Valerie Llau (Dir-Personnel & HR)

ETABLISSEMENTS GAS-CHEAU

895 Rue Louis Saillant, 26800, Portes-les-Valence, France
Tel.: (33) 475577074
Sales Range: $10-24.9 Million
Emp.: 168
Nonresidential Construction
N.A.I.C.S.: 236220
Jean-Louis Morel (Dir)

ETABLISSEMENTS GOUT-OULY ET FILS

Le Bearnais, 47330, Saint-Quentin, France
Tel.: (33) 553368283
Rev.: $23,900,000
Emp.: 46
Canned Fruits & Specialties
N.A.I.C.S.: 311421
Marilyne Lesca (Personnel Mgr)

ETABLISSEMENTS J. SOUFFLET

Quai Du General Sarrail, 10400, Nogent-sur-Seine, France
Tel.: (33) 325394111   FR
Web Site: http://www.soufflet-group.com
Year Founded: 1900
Sales Range: $650-699.9 Million
Emp.: 3,300
Malting, Milling & Maize Processing
N.A.I.C.S.: 311213
Jean-Michel Soufflet (Chm-Mgmt Bd)

Subsidiaries:

Ceres S.A. (1)
Avenue de Vilvorde 300, 1130, Brussels, Belgium
Tel.: (32) 22400600
Web Site: http://www.ceres.be
Sales Range: $150-199.9 Million
Emp.: 130
Flour Milling
N.A.I.C.S.: 311211

Heinrich Durst Malzfabriken GmbH & Co. KG (1)
Markgrafenstrasse 41-43, 76646, Bruchsal, Germany
Tel.: (49) 72515060
Web Site: http://www.durst-malz.de
Malt Mfr
N.A.I.C.S.: 311213
Christophe Passelande (Mng Dir)

Lyven S.A. (1)
ZAC Normandial - 11 avenue du Pays de Caen, 14460, Colombelles, France
Tel.: (33) 231 350 530
Web Site: http://www.lyven.com
Enzyme Mfr
N.A.I.C.S.: 325199
Ivan Pestretzoff (Gen Mgr)

Malteries Franc-Belges S.A. (1)
Quai Sarrail BP 12, 10400, Nogent-sur-Seine, France
Tel.: (33) 325394111
Web Site:
http://www.malteriesfrancobelges.fr
Sales Range: $100-124.9 Million
Emp.: 141
Malt Beverage Mfr
N.A.I.C.S.: 311213

Moulins Soufflet Pantin S.A. (1)
Quai du General Sarrail, Nogent-sur-Seine, F-10402, France
Tel.: (33) 325394111
Web Site: http://www.soufflet.com
Sales Range: $75-99.9 Million
Emp.: 360
Flour Milling
N.A.I.C.S.: 311211
Jean-Michel Soufflet (Pres)

Soufflet Agriculte Limited (1)
Quai Sarrail, Nogent-sur-Seine, 10402, France
Tel.: (33) 325394111
Web Site: http://www.soufflet-group.com
Sales Range: $700-749.9 Million
Emp.: 738
Grain & Field Beans Whslr
N.A.I.C.S.: 424510
Jean Soufflet (Gen Mgr)

Soufflet Agro Polska Sp. z o.o. (1)
ul Szwajcarska 13, 61-285, Poznan, Poland
Tel.: (48) 61 650 10 96
Web Site: http://www.soufflet.pl
Agricultural Consulting Services
N.A.I.C.S.: 541690

Soufflet Agro s.r.o. (1)
3145/56 Vrahovicka, 796 01, Prostejov, Czech Republic

Tel.: (420) 582 328 320
Web Site: http://www.soufflet-agro.cz
Agricultural Consulting Services
N.A.I.C.S.: 541690
Adina Slechtova (Vice Chm)

Soufflet Alimentaire S.A. (1)
41 Rue de Petit Bruxelles, Valenciennes, F-49300, France
Tel.: (33) 327200909
Web Site: http://www.soufflet.com
Sales Range: $100-124.9 Million
Emp.: 200
Raw Materials Importer
N.A.I.C.S.: 424590
Theirry Lievin (Pres)

Soufflet Biotechnologies SAS (1)
Zac Normandial 11 avenue du Pays de Caen, 14460, Colombelles, France
Tel.: (33) 231350530
Web Site:
http://www.souffletbiotechnologies.com
Food Product Whslr
N.A.I.C.S.: 424490

Soufflet Negoce S.A. (1)
BP 12, Quai Sarrail, 10402, Nogent-sur-Seine, France
Tel.: (33) 325394111
Web Site: http://www.soufflet.com
Cereals, Oil-Seeds & Dairy Products Transporter & Exporter
N.A.I.C.S.: 424510

Soufflet Vigne S.A. (1)
Le Pont Rouge CS 20125, Villefranche Sue Saone, Limas, 69654, Cedex, France
Tel.: (33) 4 74 65 31 04
Web Site: http://www.lesouffletvert.fr
Sales Range: $50-74.9 Million
Emp.: 176
Wine Making Products; Wine Mfr & Distr
N.A.I.C.S.: 312130

ETABLISSEMENTS MARTI-NENQ

2 rue Georges Charpak, ZAC Universite Gare, Lieusaint, 77127, France
Tel.: (33) 1 60 188900
Web Site: http://www.martinenq.com
Year Founded: 1921
Rev.: $20,800,000
Emp.: 80
Commercial Printing
N.A.I.C.S.: 323111
Jean-Christophe Martinenq (Dir Gen)

ETABLISSEMENTS R. BLANCHET

17 rue de l'Esperance, Les Hautes Rivieres, 08800, Charleville-Mezieres, France
Tel.: (33) 254310182
Sales Range: $10-24.9 Million
Emp.: 141
Trucking Except Local
N.A.I.C.S.: 484121
Emmanuelle Pilon (Mng Partner)

ETABLISSEMENTS R. LEGRAND

91 Rue Jean Chossegros, 69270, Lyon, France
Tel.: (33) 478222696
Web Site: http://www.btp-legrand.com
Sales Range: $10-24.9 Million
Emp.: 188
Water, Sewer & Utility Lines
N.A.I.C.S.: 237110

ETABLISSEMENTS ROCHE ET COMPAGNIE

105 Rue Basse Saint Martin, 16100, Cognac, Charente, France
Tel.: (33) 478788210
Sales Range: $10-24.9 Million
Emp.: 216
Painting & Paper Hanging
N.A.I.C.S.: 238320
Michele Garin (Gen Mgr)

Etablissements Roche et Compagnie—(Continued)

ETALON GROUP PLC
2-4 Arch Makariou III Avenue Capital
Center 9th floor, 1065, Nicosia, Cyprus
Tel.: (357) 2081231328 **GY**
Web Site:
http://www.etalongroup.com
Year Founded: 1987
ETLN—(LSE)
Rev.: $1,173,748,860
Assets: $2,991,660,060
Liabilities: $2,165,140,860
Net Worth: $826,519,200
Earnings: $40,504,290
Emp.: 4,765
Fiscal Year-end: 12/31/21
Real Estate Development Services
N.A.I.C.S.: 531390
Gennadiy Shcherbina *(CEO)*

Subsidiaries:

CJSC "SSMO LenSpetsSMU" (1)
2 lit a Bogatyrskiy prospect, Saint Petersburg, 197348, Russia
Tel.: (7) 812 348 11 85
Real Estate Development Services
N.A.I.C.S.: 531390

LLC "Etalon-Invest" (1)
Uzbekistan Avenue 16 A Shaykhantakhur
Area, 100027, Tashkent, Uzbekistan
Tel.: (998) 2391346
Real Estate Development Services
N.A.I.C.S.: 531390

ETALON-LENSPETSSMU CONSTRUCTION HOLDING COMPANY
2 lit a Bogatyrskiy Prospect, 197348,
Saint Petersburg, Russia
Tel.: (7) 8123493840
Web Site:
http://www.finance.lenspecsmu.ru
Year Founded: 1987
Sales Range: $550-599.9 Million
Holding Company; Real Estate Services
N.A.I.C.S.: 551112
Dmitry V. Zarenkov *(Pres & CEO)*

ETAM DEVELOPPEMENT SCA
78 rue de Rivoli, 75004, Paris,
France
Tel.: (33) 15 590 7070
Web Site:
http://www.etamdeveloppement.com
Women's Clothing Mfr & Retailer
N.A.I.C.S.: 315250

Subsidiaries:

ETAM POLAND SP (1)
Ul Nowogrodzka 50, 00-695, Warsaw, Poland
Tel.: (48) 226290116
Women Apparel Mfr
N.A.I.C.S.: 315250

Elan Industries (1)
57 Rue Henri Barbusse 59, Clichy, 92110,
France
Tel.: (33) 1 55 90 70 70
Women Apparel Mfr
N.A.I.C.S.: 315250

Etam Italia Srl (1)
Centro Direzionale Colleoni Palazzo Andromeda 2, 20041, Agrate Brianza, Italy
Tel.: (39) 039 68 92 236
Web Site: http://www.etam.it
Women's Clothing Retailer
N.A.I.C.S.: 458110

GROUPE ETAM SUISSE (1)
Neue Jonastrasse 20, Rapperswil, 8640,
Switzerland
Tel.: (41) 552106726
Web Site: http://www.1-2-3.com
Apparels Mfr
N.A.I.C.S.: 315990
Kakec Alken *(Mgr-Store)*

Shanghai Intermoda Clothing Co.,
Ltd. (1)
Room 304-305 Golden Gate Square No
389 Jinwan Road Pudong New A, Shanghai, 201206, China
Tel.: (86) 2158999333
Women Apparel Mfr
N.A.I.C.S.: 315250

ETASK TECHNOLOGIES LIMITED
IIQ Farnborough Business Park The
Hub Regus Floor 1, Fowler Avenue,
Farnborough, GU14 7JF, United Kingdom
Tel.: (44) 12 5230 2354
Web Site: http://www.etask.it
Project Management Services
N.A.I.C.S.: 541611
Juan Manrique *(CEO)*

Subsidiaries:

Hydra Management Limited (1)
Riverview Ct Castlegate, Wetherby, Leeds,
LS22 6LE, West Yorkshire, United Kingdom
Tel.: (44) 1937589560
Web Site: http://www.hydra-management.com
Sales Range: $25-49.9 Million
Emp.: 10
Software Sales & Support Services
N.A.I.C.S.: 541511
Juan Manrique *(CEO)*

ETERNA PLC.
5a Oba Adeyinka Oyekan Avenue,
Ikoyi, Lagos, Nigeria
Tel.: (234) 9085511111 **NG**
Web Site: http://www.eternaplc.com
Year Founded: 1989
ETERNA—(NIGE)
Rev.: $86,212,660
Assets: $39,964,043
Liabilities: $30,244,812
Net Worth: $9,719,231
Earnings: $749,267
Emp.: 92
Fiscal Year-end: 12/31/22
Petroleum Product Mfr
N.A.I.C.S.: 324199
Kudi Badmus *(CFO & Exec Dir-Fin)*

Subsidiaries:

Eterna Industries Limited (1)
25/103 F Gandhi Nagar, Agra, 282004,
India
Tel.: (91) 9897256005
Web Site: https://www.eternaindustries.com
Construction Machinery Mfr
N.A.I.C.S.: 333120

ETERNAL ASIA SUPPLY CHAIN MANAGEMENT LTD.
Building 1 Eternal Asia Integrated
Supply Chain Base, No 3 Lilang
Road Nanwan Street Longgang District, Shenzhen, 518114, Guangdong,
China
Tel.: (86) 4008309031
Web Site: https://www.eascs.com
Year Founded: 1997
002183—(SSE)
Rev.: $11,989,844,100
Assets: $7,294,006,044
Liabilities: $5,807,073,168
Net Worth: $1,486,932,876
Earnings: $35,955,036
Fiscal Year-end: 12/31/22
Supply Chain Management Services
N.A.I.C.S.: 541618
Guohui Zhou *(Chm, Pres & Gen Mgr)*

ETERNAL BEST INDUSTRIAL LIMITED
Room F 16th Floor Block 2 Sheung
Shui Centre, Sheung Shui New Territories, Kowloon, China (Hong Kong)
Tel.: (852) 26722348 **HK**

Year Founded: 2000
Holding Company
N.A.I.C.S.: 551112

ETERNAL ENERGY PUBLIC COMPANY LIMITED
No 888 iTower Building 8th Floor Vibhavadi Rangsit Road, Chatuchak
Subdistrict, Bangkok, 10900, Thailand
Tel.: (66) 25548000
Web Site:
https://www.eternalenergy.co.th
Year Founded: 1987
EE—(THA)
Rev.: $199,965
Assets: $29,373,836
Liabilities: $636,093
Net Worth: $28,737,743
Earnings: ($19,066,151)
Emp.: 10
Fiscal Year-end: 12/31/23
Methanol Mfr
N.A.I.C.S.: 325193
Borwornsak Uwanno *(Co-Chm)*

ETERNAL MATERIALS CO., LTD.
No 578 Jiangong Rd, Sanmin Dist,
Kaohsiung, 807, Taiwan
Tel.: (886) 73838181
Web Site: https://www.eternal-group.com
Year Founded: 1964
1717—(TAI)
Rev.: $1,388,259,080
Assets: $1,914,328,519
Liabilities: $1,089,711,362
Net Worth: $824,617,157
Earnings: $48,794,792
Emp.: 1,158
Fiscal Year-end: 12/31/23
Electronic Chemical Materials & Special Chemicals Mfr
N.A.I.C.S.: 333517
Kuo-Lun Kao *(Chm)*

Subsidiaries:

Changhe International Trading
(GZFTZ) Co,. Ltd. (1)
No 8 Ruihe Road Science City, New and
High Technology Industrial Development
Zone, Guangzhou, 510535, Guangdong,
China
Tel.: (86) 2032206688
Web Site: http://www.eternal-group.com
Copper Clad Laminates & Speciality Chemicals Mfr
N.A.I.C.S.: 325992

Chou-Kou Materials Co., Ltd. (1)
507 Concurred Yokohama 3-1 Kinkocho,
Kanagawa-Ku, Yokohama, 221-0056, Kanagawa, Japan
Tel.: (81) 456248864
Resin Material Distr
N.A.I.C.S.: 424610

ESCO Specialty Coatings
(Guangzhou) Co., Ltd. (1)
182 Junda Road Eastern Zone GETDD,
Guangzhou, 510530, Guangdong, China
Tel.: (86) 20 2820 7118
Web Site: http://www.eternal.com.tw
Specialty Chemical Coating Services
N.A.I.C.S.: 332812

Eternal (China) Investment Co.,
Ltd. (1)
Room 1401 Floor 14 Building A No 1397
Yishan Rd, Xuhui Dist, Shanghai, 200233,
China
Tel.: (86) 2133671177
Copper Clad Laminate Mfr & Distr
N.A.I.C.S.: 331420

Eternal Chemical (Chengdu) Co.,
Ltd. (1)
15 Yangheng Si Road, Yang'an Industrial
Park Qionglai City, Chengdu, 611535,
China
Tel.: (86) 2888776333
Synthetic Resin Mfr

N.A.I.C.S.: 325211
Eternal Chemical (Guangdong) Co.,
Ltd. (1)
Dalang Bay Industrial Zone, Nanshui Town,
Zhuhai, 519050, Guangdong, China
Tel.: (86) 756 726 5566
Web Site: http://www.eternal.com.tw
Sales Range: $50-74.9 Million
Emp.: 200
Resin Mfr
N.A.I.C.S.: 325211

Eternal Chemical (Guangzhou) Co.,
Ltd. (1)
Γl £ 1st Bldg Scientech Pk Chuangyie Rd
GETDD, Guangzhou, 510720, Guangdong,
China
Tel.: (86) 2082221885
Web Site: http://www.eternal.com.tw
Sales Range: $125-149.9 Million
Emp.: 400
Dry Film Photoresist Mfr
N.A.I.C.S.: 325992

Eternal Chemical (Japan) Co.,
Ltd. (1)
Kijmon Building 5F 6-26-9 Haramachida,
Machida, 194-0013, Tokyo, Japan
Tel.: (81) 427241745
Sales Range: $25-49.9 Million
Emp.: 6
Resin Mfr
N.A.I.C.S.: 325211

Eternal Chemical (Tianjin) Co.,
Ltd. (1)
Room 1711 Smart Valley Building No 220
Hongqi Road, Nankai District, Tianjin,
300190, China
Tel.: (86) 2287630036
Resin Material Mfr & Distr
N.A.I.C.S.: 325211

Eternal Chemical Co., Ltd. -TPING-
NAN Plant (1)
No 23 Pingnan Rd, Pingtung County, Fangliao, 940, Taiwan
Tel.: (86) 88669009
Web Site: http://www.eternal.com.tw
Emp.: 350
Synthetic Resin Mfr
N.A.I.C.S.: 325211

Eternal Chemical Co., Ltd. - TA-FA
Plant (1)
30 Yumin St, Daliao Dist, Kaohsiung, 831,
Taiwan
Tel.: (886) 77873645
Web Site: http://www.eternal.com.tw
Sales Range: $125-149.9 Million
Emp.: 400
Dry Film Photoresist Mfr
N.A.I.C.S.: 325992

Eternal Electronic (Suzhou) Co.,
Ltd. (1)
No 2 Huaqiao Road SND, Xushuguan
Town, Suzhou, 215151, Jiangsu, China
Tel.: (86) 51267373188
Dry Film Photoresist Mfr & Distr
N.A.I.C.S.: 325992

Eternal Electronic Material
(Guangzhou) Co., Ltd. (1)
69 Dongpeng Road, Eastern Zone GETDD,
Guangzhou, 510765, Guangdong, China
Tel.: (86) 208 226 4378
Dry Film Photoresist Mfr & Distr
N.A.I.C.S.: 325992

Eternal Electronic Material (Thailand)
Co., Ltd. (1)
335/8 Moo 9 Bangna-Trad Rd KM19, Tambol Bangchalong Amphur Bangplee, Bang
Phli, 10540, Samut Prakan, Thailand
Tel.: (66) 27509086
Emp.: 50
Industrial Chemicals Mfr
N.A.I.C.S.: 324110
Dean Shu *(Gen Mgr)*

Eternal Materials (Guangdong) Co.,
Ltd. (1)
No 9523 Zhuhai Road, Nanshui Town, Zhuhai, 519050, Guangdong, China
Tel.: (86) 7567265566
Resin Material Mfr & Distr
N.A.I.C.S.: 325211

Eternal Materials (Malaysia) Sdn. Bhd. (1)
PTD 5044 Jalan Rumbia 2, Tanjung Langsat Industrial Estate Mukim Sungai Tiram, 81700, Pasir Gudang, Johor, Malaysia
Tel.: (60) 72778600
Resin Material Mfr & Distr
N.A.I.C.S.: 325211

Eternal Optical Material (Suzhou) Co., Ltd. (1)
No 111 Songshan Road SND, Suzhou, 215129, Jiangsu, China
Tel.: (86) 51268050026
Web Site: http://www.eternal.com.tw
Optical Materials Mfr
N.A.I.C.S.: 333310

Eternal Photo Electronic Materials (Guangzhou) Co., Ltd. (1)
No 8 Ruihe Road Science City, New and High Technology Industrial Development Zone, Guangzhou, 510535, Guangdong, China
Tel.: (86) 2032206688
Electronic High Tech Chemical Product Mfr & Distr
N.A.I.C.S.: 325998

Eternal Photoelectric Material Industry (Yingkou) Co., Ltd. (1)
No 102 Xinhai Street Coastal Industrial Base, Yingkou, 115002, Liaoning, China
Tel.: (86) 4172935000
Web Site: http://www.eternal-up.com
Dry Film Photoresist Mfr
N.A.I.C.S.: 325992

Eternal Specialty Chemical (Zhuhai) Co., Ltd. (1)
Biyang Road Gaolan Petrochemical Sector of Harbor Industrial Zone, Zhuhai, 519060, Guangdong, China
Tel.: (86) 7563985888
Web Site: http://www.eternal.com.tw
Monomer Specialty & OPV Mfr
N.A.I.C.S.: 325211

Eternal Specialty Materials (Suzhou) Co., Ltd. (1)
Building No 2 15 Xinggang Road, Economic Development Zone Riverside Industrial Park, Changshu, 215536, Jiangsu, China
Tel.: (86) 5125 201 6201
Chemical Product Mfr & Distr
N.A.I.C.S.: 325998

Eternal Specialty Materials (Zhuhai) Co., Ltd. (1)
307 petrochemical 9th Road, Gaolan Port Economic Zone, Zhuhai, 519050, Guangdong, China
Tel.: (86) 7563985888
Acrylic Resin Mfr & Distr
N.A.I.C.S.: 325211

Eternal Synthetic Resins (Changshu) Co., Ltd. (1)
15 Xinggang Road, Riverside Industrial Park, Changshu, 215536, Jiangsu, China
Tel.: (86) 51252860006
Unsaturated Polyester Resin Mfr & Distr
N.A.I.C.S.: 325211

Eternal Technology Corporation (1)
1800 Touchstone Rd, Colonial Heights, VA 23834
Tel.: (804) 524-8555
Web Site: https://eternaltechcorp.com
Sales Range: $25-49.9 Million
Emp.: 40
Dry Film Photoresist Distr
N.A.I.C.S.: 423420

Nikko Materials Co., Ltd. (1)
Concurred Yokohama 5F 3-1, Kinko-cho, Yokohama, 221-0056, Kanagawa, Japan
Tel.: (81) 456209480
Web Site: http://www.nikko-materials.com
Emp.: 61
Dry Film Photoresist, Products & Equipment Mfr & Sales
N.A.I.C.S.: 326112

Nikko Mechanics Co., Ltd. (1)
3-1 Kofukada Shinbayashi-cho, Chiryu, 472-0017, Aichi, Japan
Tel.: (81) 566826011
Precision Machinery Mfr & Distr

N.A.I.C.S.: 333248

P.T. Eternal Materials Indonesia (1)
The St Moritz Office Tower Unit 1101 Jl Puri Indah Boulevard Blok U1, Jakarta Barat, 11610, Indonesia
Tel.: (62) 2129185108
Coating Synthetic Resin Mfr & Distr
N.A.I.C.S.: 325998

ETERNAL SPEECH, INC.
156/13 Moo 10 Nongprue, Bang Lamung, 20150, Chonburi, Thailand
Tel.: (66) 775 562 0589   NV
Year Founded: 2015
Assets: $18
Liabilities: $39,771
Net Worth: ($39,753)
Earnings: ($26,952)
Fiscal Year-end: 02/28/18
Internet Communication Services
N.A.I.C.S.: 517121
Suthep Thepchit (Chm, Pres, CEO, CFO, Treas & Sec)

ETERNIT S.A.
R Dr Fernandes Coelho 85 8 Andar, 05423 040, Sao Paulo, 05423 040, Brazil
Tel.: (55) 8000211709
Web Site: https://www.eternit.com.br
ETER3—(BRAZ)
Rev.: $201,857,845
Assets: $232,453,114
Liabilities: $94,842,778
Net Worth: $137,610,336
Earnings: $22,741,995
Emp.: 2,000
Fiscal Year-end: 12/31/23
Construction Materials Mfr
N.A.I.C.S.: 327331
Luis Augusto Barcelos Barbosa (CEO & Member-Exec Bd)

Subsidiaries:

Precon Goias Industrial Ltda. (1)
Distrito Indus de Anapolis, Quadra, Anapolis, Goias, Brazil
Tel.: (55) 62 3328 4444
Asbestos Cement Sheets Mfr
N.A.I.C.S.: 327999

Sama S.A. (1)
Cana Brava Mine, PO Box 01, Minacu, 76450000, Goias, Brazil
Tel.: (55) 62 3379 8100
Web Site: http://www.sama.com.br
Sales Range: $350-399.9 Million
Emp.: 530
Asbestos Mining Services
N.A.I.C.S.: 212390

ETERNITY INVESTMENT LIMITED
Unit 1211 Shun Tak Centre West Tower 168-200 Connaught Road, Central, China (Hong Kong)
Tel.: (852) 22688236   BM
0764—(HKG)
Rev.: $19,903,133
Assets: $440,827,425
Liabilities: $212,166,885
Net Worth: $228,660,540
Earnings: ($34,778,940)
Emp.: 102
Fiscal Year-end: 12/31/22
Holding Company
N.A.I.C.S.: 551112
Hong Wai Lei (Chm & CEO)

ETEX SA/NV
Luchthaven Brussel Nationaal Gebouw 1K, 1930, Zaventem, Belgium
Tel.: (32) 2 778 12 11   BE
Web Site: http://www.etexgroup.com
Year Founded: 1905
Rev.: $3,292,481,348
Assets: $3,368,081,977
Liabilities: $2,069,712,934

Net Worth: $1,298,369,044
Earnings: $202,397,897
Emp.: 13,260
Fiscal Year-end: 12/31/19
Building Materials & Systems Mfr & Marketer
N.A.I.C.S.: 326199
Jean-Louis de Cartier de Marchienne (Chm)

Subsidiaries:

Batiroc S.A.S. (1)
Avenue Jean Monnet, 54920, Villers la Montagne, France   (100%)
Tel.: (33) 382440408
Web Site: http://www.batiroc.fr
Sales Range: $25-49.9 Million
Mfr of Metal Profiled Sheets
N.A.I.C.S.: 332322

Baupro GmbH (1)
Industriehalle 4 Schwesterstrasse 58c, 42285, Wuppertal, Germany
Tel.: (49) 202 2480450
Fire Protection System Distr
N.A.I.C.S.: 423990

CERAMICAS CORDILLERA S.A. (1)
Av Las Condes 9765 local 206, Santiago, Chile
Tel.: (56) 223874200
Web Site: https://www.cordillera.cl
Building Materials Distr
N.A.I.C.S.: 423390

Ceramica San Lorenzo Colombia S.A. (1)
Kilometro 1 Via Sopo Canavita Vereda a Carolina, Sopo, Cundinamarca, Colombia
Tel.: (57) 6684490
Web Site: http://www.sanlorenzo.com.co
Building Materials Mfr
N.A.I.C.S.: 339999

Ceramica San Lorenzo I.C.S.A (1)
Avda del Libertador 6550 - Piso 6, C1428ARV, Buenos Aires, Argentina
Tel.: (54) 91157772230
Web Site: http://www.ceramicasanlorenzo.com.ar
Building Materials Mfr
N.A.I.C.S.: 339999

Ceramica San Lorenzo U.S.A. Inc. (1)
1150 Red Gum St Unit C, Anaheim, CA 92806
Tel.: (562) 222-2345
Web Site: http://www.csanlorenzo.com
Fiscal Year-end: 12/31/2011
Building Materials Mfr
N.A.I.C.S.: 339999
Josue Maya (Office Mgr)

Ceramica San Lorenzo de Mexico S.A. de C.V. (1)
Carretera Ejido Michoacan KM 2750 Ejido Puebla, Baja California, Mexicali, 21260, Mexico
Tel.: (52) 686 8433300
Building Materials Mfr
N.A.I.C.S.: 339999

Ciments Renforces Industries S.A.S.U. (1)
rue Bahon Rault, 35768, Saint-Gregoire, France
Tel.: (33) 2 99 84 81 70
Web Site: http://www.ciments-renforces.fr
Building Material Mfr & Distr
N.A.I.C.S.: 339999

Comais S.r.l. (1)
Via Provinciale 10, 24040, Filago, Bergamo, Italy
Tel.: (39) 035 99 37 37
Web Site: http://www.comais.it
Chemical Products Mfr
N.A.I.C.S.: 325998
Mirrefori Frenchesco (Mgr)

Comptoir du Batiment NV (1)
Heiveldekens 6 b Industrieterrein Blauwsteen, 2550, Kontich, Belgium
Tel.: (32) 3 451 07 91
Web Site: http://www.comptoirdubatiment.com
Cement Product Mfr

N.A.I.C.S.: 327390

Creaton & Eternit S.R.L. (1)
B-dul Ion Ionescu de la Brad nr 2B, 013813, Bucharest, Romania
Tel.: (40) 21 26 92 174
Web Site: http://www.creaton.com.ro
Roofing & Tile Mfr
N.A.I.C.S.: 327120
Dreier Engelbert Robert (Area Mgr-Sls)

Creaton AG (1)
Dillinger Strasse 60, 86637, Wertingen, Germany
Tel.: (49) 827286461
Web Site: http://www.creaton.de
Sales Range: $150-199.9 Million
Emp.: 1,000
Roofing Tile Mfr
N.A.I.C.S.: 327120

Creaton Hungary Kft. (1)
Cserepgyar Utca 1, 8960, Lenti, Hungary
Tel.: (36) 9255 155 0
Web Site: http://www.creaton.hu
Building Materials Mfr
N.A.I.C.S.: 339999

Creaton Kera-Dach GmbH & Co. KG (1)
Dillinger Str 60, 86637, Wertingen, Germany
Tel.: (49) 8272 860
Building Materials Whslr
N.A.I.C.S.: 423390

Durlock S.A. (1)
Av Gral J Manuel de Rosas, San Justo, 2720, Buenos Aires, Argentina
Tel.: (54) 11 4480 6090
Web Site: http://www.durlock.com
Gypsum Product Mfr
N.A.I.C.S.: 327420

EASA S.A. (1)
42 rue de l Avenir, 1147, Luxembourg, Luxembourg
Tel.: (352) 47 4402 1
Building Materials Distr
N.A.I.C.S.: 423390

Edilit S.r.l. (1)
Via Lungargine Muson 5, Vigodarzere, 35010, Padua, Italy
Tel.: (39) 049 8881311
Web Site: http://www.edilit.com
Cement Product Distr
N.A.I.C.S.: 423320

Emenite Ltd. (1)
7 Old Abakaliki Road, PMB 01646, Emene, Enugu, Nigeria
Tel.: (234) 8035506214
Web Site: http://www.emenite.com
Cement Roofing Mfr & Distr
N.A.I.C.S.: 324122

Eternit B.V. (1)
Haven 12, 7471 LV, Goor, Netherlands
Tel.: (31) 547 288 888
Web Site: http://www.eternit.nl
Emp.: 150
Cement Product Mfr & Distr.
N.A.I.C.S.: 325998

Eternit Guangzhou Building Systems Co. Ltd. (1)
No 2 Taihua Street, Yonghe Economic District, Guangzhou, 511356, China
Tel.: (86) 20 32225600
Web Site: http://www.eternit.com.cn
Fiber Cement Board Mfr
N.A.I.C.S.: 327310

Eternit Kaluga OOO (1)
Ul Stroitel naya 2, Detchino Kaluga, Maloyaroslavets, 249080, Russia
Tel.: (7) 4843 156 200
Web Site: http://www.eternit.ru
Emp.: 20
Building Materials Distr
N.A.I.C.S.: 423990
Dmitry Svidlov (Mgr-Logistics)

Eternit Ltd. (1)
102 Sapele Warri Road, PO Box 483, Sapele, Delta State, Nigeria
Tel.: (234) 8067640464
Web Site: http://www.eternitsap.com
Concrete Products Mfr
N.A.I.C.S.: 327390

Etex SA/NV—(Continued)

Bemigho Malvis (Gen Mgr)

Eternit NV (1)
Kuiermansstraat 1, 1880, Kapelle-op-den-Bos, Belgium
Tel.: (32) 15 71 71 71
Web Site: http://www.eternit.be
Roofing Tile Mfr
N.A.I.C.S.: 327390

Eternit S.A.S. (1)
Amange, PO Box 33, Vernouillet, 78540, France (100%)
Tel.: (33) 139796085
Web Site: http://www.eternit.fr
Sales Range: $25-49.9 Million
Emp.: 50
Mfr of Fibre Cement Products
N.A.I.C.S.: 327310

Etex Building Materials Polska Sp. z o.o. (1)
ul Wspolna 6, 32-300, Olkusz, Poland
Tel.: (48) 326249500
Web Site: http://www.ebmpolska.pl
Roofing Tile Mfr
N.A.I.C.S.: 327390
Maciej Dyja (Gen Mgr)

Euro Panels Overseas NV (1)
Kuiermansstraat 1, 1880, Kapelle-op-den-Bos, Belgium
Tel.: (32) 15 71 73 80
Web Site: http://www.europanels.net
Concrete Products Mfr
N.A.I.C.S.: 327390
Patricia Kringhs (Officer-Comml & Logistical Svc)

Euronit Fachadas y Cubiertas S.L. (1)
Apartado de Correos 3 019 Autovia Segovia-Valladolid A-60, 1 km 21 Parque Empresarial, 47160, Valladolid, Spain
Tel.: (34) 91 272 49 02
Web Site: http://www.euronit.es
Roof & Ventilated Wall Mfr
N.A.I.C.S.: 327390

FIBROCEMENTOS PUDAHUEL S.A. (1)
Camino a Melipilla 10803, Maipu, Chile
Tel.: (56) 2 23912316
Web Site:
http://www.fibrocementospudahuel.cl
Roofing Product Whslr
N.A.I.C.S.: 423330

Fabrica Peruana Eternit S.A. (1)
Jr Republica del Ecuador 448, Lima, Peru
Tel.: (51) 6196400
Web Site: http://www.eternit.com.pe
Cement Product Mfr
N.A.I.C.S.: 327390

Fibrolith Dammstoffe GmbH (1)
An der L83, 56746, Kempenich, Germany
Tel.: (49) 265595920
Web Site: http://www.fibrolith.de
Building Material Mfr & Distr
N.A.I.C.S.: 339999

Giwarite Ltd. (1)
Plot H4 Kakuri Industrial Area, Kaduna, Nigeria
Tel.: (234) 62 23 25 52
Concrete Pile Mfr
N.A.I.C.S.: 327390

IVARSSON SVERIGE AB (1)
Hastvagen 2, 212 35, Malmo, Sweden
Tel.: (46) 40 49 02 50
Web Site: http://www.ivarssonsverige.se
Roofing Product Whslr
N.A.I.C.S.: 423330

Intumex s.r.o. (1)
VP Ckalova 22/784, 160 00, Prague, 6, Czech Republic
Tel.: (420) 224 390 811
Web Site: http://www.intumex.cz
Fire Protection System Distr
N.A.I.C.S.: 423990

Ivarsson A/S (1)
Kometvej 36, 6230, Rodekro, Denmark
Tel.: (45) 73 66 19 99
Web Site: http://www.ivarsson.dk
Emp.: 60

Roofing Tile Whslr
N.A.I.C.S.: 423330
Thomas Bendgsen (Gen Mgr)

MARLEY ROOFING (PTY) LTD (1)
44 - 50 Industry Road Clayville Ext 4, Olifantsfontein, 1665, Gauteng, South Africa
Tel.: (27) 11 316 2121
Web Site: http://www.marleyroofing.co.za
Emp.: 500
Concrete Product Mfr & Distr
N.A.I.C.S.: 327390

Marley Contract Services (1)
Cadder Bishopbriggs, Glasgow, G64 2PY, United Kingdom
Tel.: (44) 141 761 4321
Web Site:
http://www.marleycontractservices.co.uk
Roofing & Cladding Contracting Services
N.A.I.C.S.: 238160

Marley Ltd. (1)
Nepicar Works London Road, Wrotham Heath, Sevenoaks, TN15 7RW, Kent, United Kingdom
Tel.: (44) 01732455255
Web Site: http://www.marley.com
Sales Range: $25-49.9 Million
Emp.: 15
Mfr of Roof Tiles, Blocks, Floor Coverings, Plastic Rainwater Guttering, Pipes Underground Drainage Products, Plastic Moldings & Ventilation Equipment
N.A.I.C.S.: 327120
Terry Helmore (Mgr-Pension)

Subsidiary (Non-US):

Marley Polska Ltd. (2)
Ul Gdanska 40, 70660, Szczecin, Poland (100%)
Tel.: (48) 914624987
Web Site: http://www.marley.com.pl
Sales Range: $25-49.9 Million
Emp.: 4
Mfr & Distr of Thermoplastic Pipes, Valves, Fittings, Metal Couplings & Rubber Components for Pipe Lines & Systems
N.A.I.C.S.: 332919

Microtherm Engineered Solutions N.V. (1)
Industriepark-Noord 1, 9100, Saint-Niklaas, Belgium
Tel.: (32) 3 7601980
Web Site: http://www.microthermgroup.com
Thermal Insulation Mfr & Distr
N.A.I.C.S.: 326140

Nidaplast-Honeycombs S.A.S. (1)
rue Paul Vaillant Couturier, BP 3, 59224, Thiant, France
Tel.: (33) 327447200
Web Site: http://www.nidaplast.com
Sales Range: $25-49.9 Million
Mfr of Plastic Products
N.A.I.C.S.: 326199

Nippon Microtherm Co. Ltd. (1)
Korakuen Shinjuku Bldg 4-15-7 Nishi, Shinjuku, Tokyo, 160-0023, Japan
Tel.: (81) 333 772 821
Web Site: http://www.microtherm.co.jp
Emp.: 10
Thermal Insulation Mfr & Distr
N.A.I.C.S.: 326140

PROMAT S.P.A. (1)
Viale Milanofiori Strada 2 Palazzo C4, 20057, Assago, Italy
Tel.: (39) 02 99 77 86 11
Web Site: http://www.promat.it
Building Material Mfr & Distr
N.A.I.C.S.: 339999

Promat (Malaysia) Sdn. Bhd. (1)
Unit 19-02-01 2 PNB Damansara No Lorong Dungun Damansara Heights, 50490, Kuala Lumpur, Malaysia
Tel.: (60) 3 2095 8555
Web Site: http://www.promat-ap.com
Emp.: 50
Building Materials Mfr
N.A.I.C.S.: 339999

Promat AG (1)
Industriestrasse 3, 9542, Munchwilen, Switzerland
Tel.: (41) 52 320 94 00
Web Site: http://www.promat.ch

Building Materials Mfr
N.A.I.C.S.: 339999

Promat Australia Pty Ltd. (1)
Unit 1 175 Briens Road, Northmead, 2152, NSW, Australia
Tel.: (61) 2 9630 4922
Web Site: http://www.promat.com.au
Building Materials Mfr
N.A.I.C.S.: 339999

Promat B.V. (1)
Vleugrlboot 22, 3991 CL, Houten, Netherlands
Tel.: (31) 302410770
Web Site: http://www.promat.nl
Building Materials Mfr
N.A.I.C.S.: 339999

Promat Building System Pte Ltd. (1)
10 Science Park Road 03-14 The Alpha Singapore Science Park II, Singapore, 117684, Singapore
Tel.: (65) 6776 7635
Web Site: http://www.promat.com
Emp.: 8
Building Materials Mfr
N.A.I.C.S.: 339999

Promat China Ltd. (1)
Room 506 Block A Qi Lin Plaza 13-35 Pan Fu Road, Guangzhou, 510180, China
Tel.: (86) 20 8136 1167
Web Site: http://www.promat.com.cn
Building Materials Mfr
N.A.I.C.S.: 339999

Promat Glasgow Ltd. (1)
348 Petershill Road Springburn, Glasgow, G21 4AU, United Kingdom
Tel.: (44) 141 558 6144
Building Materials Mfr
N.A.I.C.S.: 339999
Stephen Fulton (Mgr-Pur)

Promat GmbH (1)
St Peter-Strasse 25, 4021, Linz, Austria
Tel.: (43) 732 6912 0
Web Site: http://www.promat.at
Building Materials Mfr
N.A.I.C.S.: 339999

Promat GmbH (1)
Scheifenkamp 16, 40878, Ratingen, Germany
Tel.: (49) 2102 4 93 0
Web Site: http://www.promat.de
Emp.: 80
Building Materials Mfr
N.A.I.C.S.: 339999
Bernhard Ludecke (Mng Dir)

Promat Iberica S.A. (1)
C/ Velazquez 47-6 izq, 28001, Madrid, Spain
Tel.: (34) 917811550
Web Site: http://www.promat.es
Emp.: 25
Building Materials Distr
N.A.I.C.S.: 423390
Carlos Fernandez (Dir Gen)

Promat S.A.S. (1)
Rue de l Amandier 3, 78540, Vernouillet, France
Tel.: (33) 1 39796160
Web Site: http://www.promat.fr
Building Materials Mfr
N.A.I.C.S.: 339999

Promat Shangai Ltd. (1)
5528 Songjin Road, Tinglin Jinshan, Shanghai, 201505, China
Tel.: (86) 21 5723 8899
Building Materials Mfr
N.A.I.C.S.: 339999
Peter Pi (Mgr-Acctg)

Promat TOP Sp. z o.o. (1)
ul Przeclawska 8, 03 879, Warsaw, Poland
Tel.: (48) 222 122280
Building Materials Mfr
N.A.I.C.S.: 339999
Piotr Michalak (Product Mgr)

Promat UK Ltd. (1)
The Sterling Centre Eastern Road, Bracknell, Berkshire, United Kingdom
Tel.: (44) 134 4381300
Building Materials Mfr
N.A.I.C.S.: 339999

Promat s.r.o. (1)
VPCkalova 22/784, Bubenec, 160 00, Prague, Czech Republic
Tel.: (420) 224390811
Web Site: http://www.promatpraha.cz
Building Materials Mfr
N.A.I.C.S.: 339999

SEA S.A. (1)
14 Ave De Ille De France, BP N 204, 27202, Vernon, France
Tel.: (33) 232643130
Web Site: http://www.seavernon.com
Sales Range: $25-49.9 Million
Emp.: 43
Mfr of Paints & Adhesives
N.A.I.C.S.: 325520
Bruno Oget (Gen Mgr)

SOCIEDAD INDUSTRIAL PIZARRENO S.A (1)
Road to Melipilla 10 803, Maipu, Santiago, Chile
Tel.: (56) 223812071
Web Site: http://www.pizarreno-romeral.cl
Emp.: 500
Building Materials Mfr
N.A.I.C.S.: 339999

Siniat SA (1)
500 rue Marcel Demonque, 84915, Avignon, Cedex, France (80%)
Tel.: (33) 432 444 444
Web Site: http://www.siniat.fr
Sales Range: $1-4.9 Billion
Emp.: 4,200
Plasterboard & Accessories Mfr
N.A.I.C.S.: 327420

Subsidiary (Domestic):

Siniat International SA (2)
500 rue Marcel Demonque, 84000, Avignon, France (100%)
Tel.: (33) 432 444 444
Web Site: http://www.siniat.fr
Sales Range: $500-549.9 Million
Emp.: 1,370
Holding Company
N.A.I.C.S.: 551112

Subsidiary (Non-US):

Siniat B.V. (3)
Oosterhorn 32-34, 9936 HD, Farmsum, Netherlands
Tel.: (31) 596 649300
Building Materials Mfr
N.A.I.C.S.: 339999
Jeroen Holman (Mgr-Nordics Countries)

Siniat GmbH (3)
Frankfurter Landstrasse 2-4, 61440, Oberursel, Germany (100%)
Tel.: (49) 6171613000
Web Site: http://www.siniat.de
Drywall Mfr
N.A.I.C.S.: 327420
Bernhard Ludecke (Mng Dir)

Siniat Limited (3)
Marsh Lane, Easton-in-Gordano, Bristol, BS20 0FB, United Kingdom (100%)
Tel.: (44) 1275 377 773
Web Site: http://www.siniat.co.uk
Sales Range: $150-199.9 Million
Mfr of Gypsum Products
N.A.I.C.S.: 327420

Siniat NV (3)
Bormstraat 24, Tisselt, 2830, Willebroek, Belgium
Tel.: (32) 15718050
Web Site: http://www.siniat.be
Building Materials Mfr
N.A.I.C.S.: 339999

Siniat S.pA (3)
Via G G Winckelmann 2, 20146, Milan, Italy
Tel.: (39) 02 42 41 51
Web Site: http://www.siniat.it
Gypsum Product Mfr
N.A.I.C.S.: 327420

Skinco Colombit S.A. (1)
Parque Industrial Juanchito, Manizales, Colombia
Tel.: (57) 687 47747
Web Site: http://www.skinco.co
Building Material & Equipment Mfr
N.A.I.C.S.: 333120

Nicolas Jaramillo *(Mgr-Foreign Trade)*

Sociedad Industrial Romeral S.A. **(1)**
Avda Santa Rosa N, 01998, Puente Alto,
Chile
Tel.: (56) 251 061 00
Building Materials Mfr
N.A.I.C.S.: 339999

Sociedad Industrial Tejas de Chena
S.A. **(1)**
Nueva Costanera 4269, 7630122, Santiago,
Chile
Tel.: (56) 2 381 20 70
Building Materials Mfr
N.A.I.C.S.: 000000

Tegral Holdings Ltd. **(1)**
Tegral Building Products Ltd, Athy,
014VN84, Ireland
Tel.: (353) 598 631316
Building Materials Mfr
N.A.I.C.S.: 339999

UAB Eternit Baltic **(1)**
J Dalinkeviciaus g 2, 85118, Naujoji Ak-
mene, Lithuania
Tel.: (370) 842 55684
Building Materials Mfr
N.A.I.C.S.: 339999
Dainius Krivickas *(Mgr-Logistics)*

Vinilit S.A. **(1)**
Av Pdte Jorge Alessandri Rodrrguez,
Casilla 251, 10900, San Bernardo, Chile
Tel.: (56) 25924000
Web Site: http://www.vinilit.cl
Sales Range: Less than $1 Million
Plastic Pipe & Fitting Mfr; Joint Venture of
S.A. Etex Group N.V. (60%) & Aliaxis
S.A./N.V. (40%)
N.A.I.C.S.: 425120

Wanit Fulgurit GmbH **(1)**
Im Breitspiel 20, 69126, Heidelberg, Ger-
many
Tel.: (49) 303 485370
Building Materials Mfr
N.A.I.C.S.: 339999

ETGA GROUP LTD.
Harokim St Azrieli Business Park
Building D 5th Floor, Holon, 5885849,
Israel
Tel.: (972) 35594050   II
Web Site: https://www.etga.co.il
ETGA—(TAE)
Rev.: $98,022,101
Assets: $134,228,759
Liabilities: $65,981,764
Net Worth: $68,246,994
Earnings: $7,343,832
Emp.: 170
Fiscal Year-end: 12/31/23
Process, Physical Distribution & Lo-
gistics Consulting Services
N.A.I.C.S.: 541614

ETHANOL TECHNOLOGIES LIMITED
249 Park Street, Victoria, 3205,
South Melbourne, Australia
Tel.: (61) 747765300
Web Site: http://www.ethtec.com.au
Year Founded: 2004
Ethanol Fuel Mfr
N.A.I.C.S.: 325193
Robert Michael Carey *(Chm)*

ETHERNITY NETWORKS LTD.
Beit Golan 3rd Floor 1 Golan Street,
Airport City, 7019900, Israel
Tel.: (972) 37489846   II
Web Site:
   https://www.ethernitynet.com
Year Founded: 2003
ENET—(AIM)
Rev.: $3,777,919
Assets: $9,676,341
Liabilities: $3,759,168
Net Worth: $5,917,173
Earnings: ($6,364,747)
Fiscal Year-end: 12/31/23

Network Processing Technology Ser-
vices
N.A.I.C.S.: 513199
Mark Reichenberg *(CFO)*

ETHERSTACK PLC
93A Shepherd Street, Chippendale,
2008, NSW, Australia
Tel.: (61) 283997500
Web Site:
   https://www.etherstack.com
ESK—(ASX)
Rev.: $9,419,000
Assets: $16,223,000
Liabilities: $6,396,000
Net Worth: $9,827,000
Earnings: $522,000
Emp.: 40
Fiscal Year-end: 12/31/23
Radio & Wireless Communications
Software
N.A.I.C.S.: 513210
David Deacon *(CEO & Exec Dir)*

Subsidiaries:

Auria Wireless Pty Limited **(1)**
64 Rose Street, Chippendale, 2008, NSW,
Australia
Tel.: (61) 283997555
Web Site: https://www.auriawireless.com.au
Communication Software Development Ser-
vices
N.A.I.C.S.: 541511

Etherstack Inc. **(1)**
16 Madison Sq W FL12 Ste 1200, New
York, NY 10010
Tel.: (917) 661-4110
Communication Software Development Ser-
vices
N.A.I.C.S.: 541511

Etherstack Japan Limited **(1)**
12F Daiwa Jisho Building 74-1 Yamashita-
cho, Naka-ku, Yokohama, 231-0023, Kanagawa, Japan
Tel.: (81) 453429050
Communication Software Development Services
N.A.I.C.S.: 541511

Etherstack Limited **(1)**
1st Floor 28 Poland Street, London, W1F
8QN, United Kingdom
Tel.: (44) 2077340200
Communication Software Development Services
N.A.I.C.S.: 541511

ETHIAS FINANCE SA/NV
Rue des Croisiers 24, 4000, Liege,
Belgium
Tel.: (32) 42203111
Sales Range: $1-4.9 Billion
Emp.: 1,800
Holding Company; Insurance
N.A.I.C.S.: 551112
Bernard Thiry *(Gen Dir)*

Subsidiaries:

Ethias SA **(1)**
Rue des Croisiers 24, 4000, Liege, Belgium
Tel.: (32) 42203111
Web Site: http://www.ethias.be
Insurance Services
N.A.I.C.S.: 524210
Dries Olemans *(Head-Claims Dept)*

ETHIOPIAN AIRLINES ENTER-PRISE
Bole International Airport, PO Box
1755, Addis Ababa, 1755, Ethiopia
Tel.: (251) 116652222
Web Site:
   http://www.ethiopianairlines.com
Year Founded: 1945
Sales Range: $350-399.9 Million
Emp.: 4,587
Airline Services
N.A.I.C.S.: 481111
Mesfin Tassew *(COO)*

ETHOS CAPITAL PARTNERS LIMITED
6th Floor Tower A 1 Cybercity,
Ebene, Mauritius
Tel.: (230) 4648866
Web Site:
   https://www.ethoscapital.mu
Year Founded: 2016
Asset Management Services
N.A.I.C.S.: 523940
Peter Hayward-Butt *(CEO)*

ETHOS LIMITED
SCO 88-89 Sector 8-C, Chandigarh,
160009, India
Tel.: (91) 1722548223
Web Site:
   https://www.ethoswatches.com
Year Founded: 2003
543532—(BOM)
Rev.: $80,543,463
Assets: $68,844,717
Liabilities: $37,219,728
Net Worth: $31,624,989
Earnings: $3,192,462
Emp.: 424
Fiscal Year-end: 03/31/22
Watch Product Distr
N.A.I.C.S.: 423940

ETIHAD AIRWAYS P.J.S.C.
Khailfa City A, PO Box 35566, Abu
Dhabi, United Arab Emirates
Tel.: (971) 25110000
Web Site:
   http://www.etihadairways.com
Year Founded: 2003
Sales Range: $1-4.9 Billion
Emp.: 9,000
Oil Transportation Services
N.A.I.C.S.: 481111
Geert W. Boven *(Sr VP-Global Airport Svcs)*

ETIHAD ATHEEB TELECOM-MUNICATION CO
3704 King Abdul Aziz Street, PO Box
12482, 6488, Riyadh, 6488, Saudi
Arabia
Tel.: (966) 115111100
Web Site: https://www.go.com.sa
7040—(SAU)
Rev.: $75,123,230
Assets: $275,659,114
Liabilities: $245,903,018
Net Worth: $29,756,096
Earnings: ($10,386,499)
Fiscal Year-end: 03/31/21
Telecommunication Servicesb
N.A.I.C.S.: 517112
Fahad Abdul Rahman Al Bawardi
(CTO)

ETIHAD ETISALAT COMPANY
26th Floor The Kingdom Tower, PO
Box 9979, Riyadh, 12214, Saudi Ara-
bia
Tel.: (966) 560314099
Web Site: https://www.mobily.com.sa
Year Founded: 2004
7020—(SAU)
Rev.: $4,177,820,291
Assets: $10,603,694,174
Liabilities: $6,241,999,733
Net Worth: $4,361,694,441
Earnings: $441,791,761
Emp.: 2,430
Fiscal Year-end: 12/31/22
Mobile Network Service Providers
N.A.I.C.S.: 334220
Abdullah Mohammed Al-Issa *(Vice Chm)*

ETILER GIDA VE TICARI YATIRIMLAR SAN VE TIC A.S.
Cevizli Mh Yesil Sk No 4 Kat 17 D 88

Adakule Residence, Maltepe, 34846,
Istanbul, Turkiye
Tel.: (90) 4449384
Web Site:
   http://www.etilermarmaris.com.tr
ETILR—(IST)
Rev.: $11,197,956
Assets: $15,002,472
Liabilities: $9,030,126
Net Worth: $5,972,346
Earnings: ($451,362)
Emp.: 1,000
Fiscal Year-end: 12/31/23
Frozen Food Distr
N.A.I.C.S.: 424490
Izzettin Kaplan *(Chm)*

ETIMEX GMBH
Martin Adolff Strasse 44, D 89165,
Dietenheim, Germany
Tel.: (49) 7347670
Web Site: http://www.etimex.de
Sales Range: $200-249.9 Million
Emp.: 900
Plastic Mfr
N.A.I.C.S.: 326199
Michael Joy *(Mng Dir)*

Subsidiaries:

ETIMEX Primary Packaging
GmbH **(1)**
Martin-Adolff-Strasse 44, 89165, Dieten-
heim, Germany
Tel.: (49) 7347 67 437
Web Site: http://www.etimex-pp.com
Food Packaging Services
N.A.I.C.S.: 561910

ETIMEX Technical Components
GmbH **(1)**
Ehinger Strasse 30, 89616, Rottenacker,
Germany
Tel.: (49) 7393 52 0
Web Site: http://www.etimex-tc.com
Molded Plastic Components & Assemblies
Mfr
N.A.I.C.S.: 326199

Etimex USA, Inc. **(1)**
10925 Westlake Dr, Charlotte, NC 28273
Tel.: (704) 583-0002
Web Site: http://www.etimex-tc.com
Sales Range: $10-24.9 Million
Emp.: 37
Plastics Product Mfr
N.A.I.C.S.: 326199
Nick Pignatiello *(Mgr-Sls)*

ETION LIMITED
85 Regency Drive Route 21, Corpo-
rate Park Irene, Centurion, 0157,
South Africa
Tel.: (27) 12 749 1800   ZA
Web Site: http://www.etion.co.za
Year Founded: 1987
ETO—(JSE)
Rev.: $28,606,724
Assets: $42,240,647
Liabilities: $17,592,560
Net Worth: $24,648,088
Earnings: $3,590,467
Emp.: 281
Fiscal Year-end: 03/31/21
Engineeering Services
N.A.I.C.S.: 541330
Teddy Daka *(CEO-Grp)*

Subsidiaries:

Etion Connect (Pty) Ltd. **(1)**
21 Warehouse 4 Unit C16 Purlin St N
Sterkfontein Ext 6, Industrial Estate, Kemp-
ton Park, South Africa
Tel.: (27) 127491800
Electronic Sensor Product Mfr
N.A.I.C.S.: 334513

Law Trusted Third Party Services
(Pty) Ltd **(1)**
85 Regency Drive Route 21 Corporate
Park, Irene, Centurion, 0157, South Africa
Tel.: (27) 126769240

Etion Limited—(Continued)

Web Site: http://www.lawtrust.co.za
Network Security Services
N.A.I.C.S.: 541519

ETO GRUPPE BETEILIGUN-GEN GMBH

Hardtring 8, 78333, Stockach, Germany
Tel.: (49) 7771 809 0
Web Site: http://www.etogroup.com
Year Founded: 1948
Emp.: 1,800
Vehicle Technology & Components
Mfr
N.A.I.C.S.: 336390
Michael Schwabe *(Mng Dir)*

Subsidiaries:

ETO Magnetic Corp.　　　　　　　**(1)**
4311 Patterson Ave SE, Grand Rapids, MI
49512
Tel.: (616) 957-2570
Web Site: http://www.etomagnetic.com
Sales Range: $25-49.9 Million
Emp.: 150
Solenoid Switches Mfr
N.A.I.C.S.: 335314
Michael Ignaczak *(Pres)*

ETOBICOKE IRONWORKS LIMITED

141 Rivalda Road, Weston, M9M
2M6, ON, Canada
Tel.: (416) 742-7111
Web Site: http://www.eiw.ca
Year Founded: 1955
Rev.: $26,651,142
Emp.: 100
Structural Steel Fabricator & Scaffolds Mfr
N.A.I.C.S.: 332323
Luc Leveille *(Mgr-Sls)*

ETREND HIGHTECH CORP.

4F-1 No 35 Hsin-Tai Road, Chu-pei
City, Hsinchu, 302, Taiwan
Tel.: (886) 35544308
Web Site: https://www.etrendtech.tw
3567—(TPE)
Rev.: $11,517,775
Assets: $21,811,337
Liabilities: $3,148,141
Net Worth: $18,663,196
Earnings: $2,505,581
Emp.: 861
Fiscal Year-end: 12/31/22
Electronic Component Mfr & Distr
N.A.I.C.S.: 334419
Hsiao-Hua Kuo *(Chm & VP-Bus)*

ETRION CORPORATION

Rue du Commerce 4, 1204, Geneva,
Switzerland
Tel.: (41) 227152090　　　　　　　　AB
Web Site: http://www.etrion.com
Year Founded: 1996
ETRXF—(OTCEM)
Rev.: $74,000
Assets: $10,217,000
Liabilities: $2,860,000
Net Worth: $7,357,000
Earnings: ($5,267,000)
Fiscal Year-end: 12/31/23
Power Plant Operator
N.A.I.C.S.: 221118
Marco Antonio Northland *(CEO)*

Subsidiaries:

Etrion Services Japan KK　　　　　**(1)**
Embassy of Sweden Compound 1-10-3-204
Roppongi, Minato-ku, Tokyo, 106-0032,
Japan
Tel.: (81) 335603090
Eletric Power Generation Services
N.A.I.C.S.: 221118

ETRO S.P.A.

Via Spartaco 3, 20135, Milan, Italy
Tel.: (39) 02550201
Web Site: http://www.etro.com
Year Founded: 1968
Sales Range: $150-199.9 Million
Emp.: 250
Textile Goods Mfr
N.A.I.C.S.: 313210

Subsidiaries:

ETRO USA Inc.　　　　　　　　　**(1)**
41 W 56th St, New York, NY 10019
Tel · (212) 247-1200
Leather Goods Mfr & Distr
N.A.I.C.S.: 316990
Marco Pievani *(Gen Mgr)*

ETROPAL JSC

Bul Ruski 191, 2180, Etropole, Bulgaria
Tel.: (359) 72063422
Web Site: https://www.etropal.eu
Year Founded: 1976
ETR—(BUL)
Sales Range: Less than $1 Million
Medicinal Product Mfr
N.A.I.C.S.: 423450
Milena Stoyanova *(Dir-IR)*

ETRUSCUS RESOURCES CORP.

Suite 604-850 West Hastings Street,
Vancouver, V6C 3J1, BC, Canada
Tel.: (604) 336-9088
Web Site:
　　https://www.etruscusresources.com
ETRUF—(OTCIQ)
Rev.: $2,780
Assets: $3,706,675
Liabilities: $176,994
Net Worth: $3,529,680
Earnings: ($339,905)
Fiscal Year-end: 03/31/23
Mining Services
N.A.I.C.S.: 212290
Fiore Aliperti *(Chm, Interim Pres & Interim CEO)*

ETS GROUP LIMITED

4/F China Paint Building 1163 Canton
Road, Mongkok, Kowloon, China
(Hong Kong)　　　　　　　　　　Ky
Web Site:
　　https://www.etsgroup.com.hk
Year Founded: 2011
8031—(HKG)
Rev.: $11,109,047
Assets: $15,374,674
Liabilities: $3,785,692
Net Worth: $11,588,982
Earnings: ($1,198,998)
Emp.: 237
Fiscal Year-end: 12/31/22
Multimedia Contact Services
N.A.I.C.S.: 541840
Carol Men Yee Chang *(COO)*

Subsidiaries:

Epro Telecom Holdings Limited　　**(1)**
4/F China Paint Building 1163 Canton
Road, Mongkok, Kowloon, China (Hong
Kong)
Tel.: (852) 27990202
Web Site: https://www.eprotel.com.hk
Multi Media Contact Centre Services
N.A.I.C.S.: 561422

Gear Asset Management Limited　**(1)**
7/F China Paint Building 1163 Canton
Road, Mongkok, Kowloon, China (Hong
Kong)
Tel.: (852) 35763228
Securities Investment & Asset Management
Services
N.A.I.C.S.: 525910

Gear Securities Investment
Limited　　　　　　　　　　　　**(1)**

7/F China Paint Building 1163 Canton
Road, Mongkok, Kowloon, China (Hong
Kong)
Tel.: (852) 37000088
Securities Investment & Asset Management
Services
N.A.I.C.S.: 525910

ETS HOLDINGS CO., LTD.

1-10-13 Minamilkebukuro, Toshima-
Ku, Tokyo, 171-0022, Japan
Tel.: (81) 359577661
Web Site: https://www.ets-
holdings.co.jp
Year Founded: 1935
1789—(TKS)
Rev.: $50,600,060
Assets: $36,900,080
Liabilities: $16,496,830
Net Worth: $20,403,250
Earnings: $990,360
Fiscal Year-end: 09/30/19
Power Line Work Services
N.A.I.C.S.: 237130
Noriaki Kato *(Pres)*

ETS MOUSSIER

21 Avenue Fontcouverte, BP 20773,
84036, Avignon, Cedex, France
Tel.: (33) 490132120　　　　　　JP
Web Site: http://www.moussier.com
Year Founded: 1952
Rev.: $28,100,000
Emp.: 74
Electrical Appliances Mfr & Distr
N.A.I.C.S.: 423620
Patricia Giraud *(Pres)*

ETS RAYMOND BARRE

17 rue de l'Esperance, Les Hautes
Rivieres, 08800, Charleville-Mezieres,
France
Tel.: (33) 324534218
Rev.: $22,900,000
Emp.: 141
Metal Stamping
N.A.I.C.S.: 332119
Gerard Barre *(Mng Dir)*

ETT LIMITED

17 Hemkunt Colony, New Delhi,
110048, India
Tel.: (91) 9911089289
Web Site: https://www.ettgroup.in
537707—(BOM)
Rev.: $480,494
Assets: $4,322,000
Liabilities: $767,458
Net Worth: $3,554,542
Earnings: $5,870
Emp.: 8
Fiscal Year-end: 03/31/21
Infrastructure Development Services
N.A.I.C.S.: 237310
Puniti Sharma *(Compliance Officer & Sec)*

ETTEPLAN OYJ

Tekniikantie 4 D, 2150, Espoo, Finland
Tel.: (358) 103070
Web Site: https://www.etteplan.com
Year Founded: 1983
ETTE—(HEL)
Rev.: $368,607,106
Assets: $311,911,548
Liabilities: $190,426,330
Net Worth: $121,485,218
Earnings: $24,613,930
Emp.: 3,993
Fiscal Year-end: 12/31/21
Software Design & Development Services
N.A.I.C.S.: 541512
Juha Nakki *(Pres & CEO)*

Subsidiaries:

Cognitas GmbH　　　　　　　　　**(1)**
Chausseestrasse 86, 10115, Berlin, Germany
Tel.: (49) 30340600200
Media Insight Services
N.A.I.C.S.: 518210

Cool Engineering AB　　　　　　　**(1)**
Arods Industrivag 60, 422 43, Hisings
Backa, Sweden
Tel.: (46) 31 744 90 80
Web Site: http://www.cool-engineering.se
Sales Range: $25-49.9 Million
Emp.: 50
Product Testing & Consulting Services
N.A.I.C.S.: 541380
Morgan Henriksson *(Mgr-Test Lab Svcs)*

Ette-Consulting Oy　　　　　　　**(1)**
Terveystie 18, Hollola, 15860,
Finland　　　　　　　　　　　**(100%)**
Tel.: (358) 103070
Web Site: http://www.ette.com
Sales Range: $25-49.9 Million
Emp.: 100
Engineeering Services
N.A.I.C.S.: 541330

Ette-Engineering Oy　　　　　　　**(1)**
Terveystie 18, 15860, Hollola,
Finland　　　　　　　　　　　**(100%)**
Tel.: (358) 103070
Web Site: http://www.etteplan.com
Sales Range: $25-49.9 Million
Emp.: 100
Engineeering Services
N.A.I.C.S.: 541330

Etteplan　　　　　　　　　　　　**(1)**
Vretenvagen 10, 171-54, Solna,
Sweden　　　　　　　　　　　**(80%)**
Tel.: (46) 10 722 4000
Web Site: https://www.etteplan.com
Sales Range: $25-49.9 Million
Emp.: 20
Engineeering Services
N.A.I.C.S.: 541330

Etteplan B.V.　　　　　　　　　　**(1)**
Dillenburgstraat 25-09, 5652 AM, Eindhoven, Netherlands
Tel.: (31) 402677677
Information Management & Digital Engineering Services
N.A.I.C.S.: 541810

Etteplan Consulting (Shanghai) Co.,
Ltd　　　　　　　　　　　　　**(1)**
Tel.: (86) 2164804828
Industrial Engineering Services
N.A.I.C.S.: 541330

Etteplan Denmark A/S　　　　　　**(1)**
Horkaer 28 1, 2730, Herlev, Denmark
Tel.: (45) 103072876
Software Development Services
N.A.I.C.S.: 541511

Etteplan Design Center Oy　　　　**(1)**
Muovitie 1, 15860, Hollola, Finland
Tel.: (358) 103071010
Web Site: http://www.etteplan.com
Sales Range: $25-49.9 Million
Emp.: 75
Engineering Design Services
N.A.I.C.S.: 541330

Etteplan Deutschland GmbH　　　**(1)**
Weserstrasse 4, 47506, Neukirchen-Vluyn,
Germany
Tel.: (49) 2845949800
Software Development & Design Services
N.A.I.C.S.: 541512
Frank Wischnewski *(Mgr-Area)*

Etteplan Engineering Solutions Netherlands B.V.　　　　　　　　　　**(1)**
High Tech Campus 85, 5656 AG, Eindhoven, Netherlands
Tel.: (31) 402677677
Information Management & Digital Engineering Services
N.A.I.C.S.: 541810

Etteplan Germany GmbH　　　　　**(1)**
Werkstattenstrasse 37, 51379, Leverkusen,
Germany
Tel.: (49) 2143230
Software Development Services

N.A.I.C.S.: 541511

Etteplan Industriteknik AB (1)
Gjuterigatan 28, 65221, Karlstad,
Sweden (100%)
Tel.: (46) 54852600
Web Site: http://www.etteplan.se
Sales Range: $25-49.9 Million
Emp.: 27
Engineeering Services
N.A.I.C.S.: 541330

Etteplan Industry AB (1)
Iggebygatan 12, PO Box 1089, 721 27,
Vasteras, Sweden
Tel.: (46) 21 171 000
Web Site: http://www.etteplan.com
Sales Range: $25-49.9 Million
Emp.: 100
Mechanical Engineering Services
N.A.I.C.S.: 541330

Etteplan Sweden AB (1)
Ostra Ringvagen 2 Plan A, 722 14, Vast-
eras, Sweden
Tel.: (46) 107224000
Information Management & Digital Engi-
neering Services
N.A.I.C.S.: 541810

Etteplan Tech Poland S.A. (1)
Sobieskiego 2, 40-082, Katowice, Poland
Tel.: (48) 575500498
Information Management & Digital Engi-
neering Services
N.A.I.C.S.: 541810

Etteplan Technical Systems AB (1)
Stora Torget 3, 44130, Alingsas,
Sweden (100%)
Tel.: (46) 322669900
Web Site: http://www.etteplan.com
Sales Range: $25-49.9 Million
Emp.: 20
Engineeering Services
N.A.I.C.S.: 541330

Etteplan Technology Center Ltd. (1)
No 88 Zhonghua Road, Shipai Town, Kun-
shan, 215312, China
Tel.: (86) 51236633508
Software Development & Design Services
N.A.I.C.S.: 541512
Martin Zachrisson (Reg Dir)

Etteplan USA Inc. (1)
16238 Ranch Rd 620 Ste 380, Austin, TX
78717
Tel.: (512) 762-0475
Software Development & Design Services
N.A.I.C.S.: 541512
Berry Braster (Dir-Tech)

F.I.T. Fahrzeug Ingenieurtechnik
GmbH (1)
Rudolf-Virchow-Str 11, 56073, Koblenz,
Germany
Tel.: (49) 2612918580
Information Management & Digital Engi-
neering Services
N.A.I.C.S.: 541810

Innovation Team Sweden AB (1)
Sperlingsgatan 5, 302 48, Halmstad, Swe-
den
Tel.: (46) 35 17 47 00
Web Site: http://www.innovationteam.se
Sales Range: $25-49.9 Million
Emp.: 50
Medical Equipment Mfr
N.A.I.C.S.: 339112

LCA Consulting Oy (1)
Lauritsalantie 1, 53100, Lappeenranta, Fin-
land
Tel.: (358) 103070
Software Development Services
N.A.I.C.S.: 541511

Lutab AB (1)
Gavlegatan 22, 113 30, Stockholm, Sweden
Tel.: (46) 86741200
Web Site: http://www.lutab.se
Sales Range: $25-49.9 Million
Emp.: 45
Technical Consulting Services
N.A.I.C.S.: 541690

ProTang AB (1)
Iggebygatan 12, 1089, 72127, Vasteras,
Sweden (73.16%)

Tel.: (46) 21171000
Web Site: http://www.protang.se
Sales Range: $25-49.9 Million
Emp.: 200
Other Scientific & Technical Consulting Ser-
vices
N.A.I.C.S.: 541690
Tom Anderson (Mng Dir)

ProTang Teknikinformation Ab (1)
Iggebygatan 12 1089, 72127, Vasteras,
Sweden (100%)
Tel.: (46) 21171000
Web Site: http://www.protang.se
Sales Range: $25-49.9 Million
Emp.: 250
Other Management Consulting Services
N.A.I.C.S.: 541618

Syncore technologies AB (1)
Teknikringen 2 Mjardevi Science Park, 583
30, Linkoping, Sweden
Tel.: (46) 107224000
Software Development Services
N.A.I.C.S.: 541511

ETTYL LIMITED
1st Floor Queen Victoria House Vic-
toria Street, Douglas, IM1 2LF, Isle of
Man
Tel.: (44) 1624 820615
Web Site: http://www.ettyl.im
Year Founded: 2020
Airlines/Aviation Services
N.A.I.C.S.: 488119
Jason Scales (CEO)

ETUDES INSTALLATIONS ET MAINTENANCE INDUSTRI-ELLES SAS
ZI Technoland 169 Rue du Breuil, BP
51004, 25461, Etupes, Cedex,
France
Tel.: (33) 381942323   FR
Web Site: http://www.eimi.fr
Year Founded: 1979
Sales Range: $150-199.9 Million
Emp.: 800
Industrial Heating, Ventilation, Air
Conditioning & Electrical Engineering
Contractor
N.A.I.C.S.: 238220
Bartolino Nardis (Founder)

EU YAN SANG INTERNA-TIONAL LTD.
Eu Yan Sang Centre 21 Tai Seng
Drive, Singapore, 535223, Singapore
Tel.: (65) 62253211   SG
Web Site: http://www.euyansang.com
Year Founded: 1879
Holding Company; Traditional Chi-
nese Medicinal Products Mfr & Distr
N.A.I.C.S.: 551112
Caryn Peh (Mng Dir-Clinic Svcs-
Singapore)

Subsidiaries:

Bod International Pty. Limited (1)
316 Horsley Rd, PO Box 4034, Milperra,
2214, NSW, Australia
Tel.: (61) 297727155
Web Site: http://www.bod.com.au
Sales Range: $25-49.9 Million
Emp.: 50
Healthcare Products Mfr & Sales
N.A.I.C.S.: 456199
Amy Thompson (Brand Mgr)

EYS KangHong Herbal Pte Ltd (1)
269a South Bridge Road, Singapore,
58818, Singapore
Tel.: (65) 62253211
Sales Range: $25-49.9 Million
Emp.: 45
Herbal Products Whslr
N.A.I.C.S.: 424210

Eu Yan Sang (Hong Kong)
Limited (1)
Eu Yan Sang Centre 10 Wang Lee Street
Yuen Long Industrial Park, Yuen Long, New

Territories, China (Hong Kong)
Tel.: (852) 2544 3268
Healthcare Product Distr
N.A.I.C.S.: 424210

Eu Yan Sang (Singapore) Pte
Ltd (1)
21 Tai Seng Drive, Singapore, 535223, Sin-
gapore
Tel.: (65) 6749 8830
Traditional Chinese Medicinal Products Mfr
& Distr
N.A.I.C.S.: 325411
Serene Scow (Mng Dir)

Eu Yan Sang Integrative Health Pte.
Ltd. (1)
221 Taiseng Drive, Singapore, 535223, Sin-
gapore
Tel.: (65) 6225 1887
Web Site: http://www.euyansangclinic.com
General Medical Services
N.A.I.C.S.: 621111
Caryn Peh (Mng Dir)

Eu Yan Sang Marketing Pte Ltd (1)
Eu Yan Sang Ctr 21 Tai Seng, Singa-
pore, 535223, Singapore
Tel.: (65) 6225 3211
Medicinal Products Marketer
N.A.I.C.S.: 541910
Richard Eu (CEO)

Healthy Life Group Pty. Ltd. (1)
Locked Bag 1123, Milperra, 2214, NSW,
Australia
Tel.: (61) 1300 135 900
Web Site: http://www.healthylifegroup.net.au
Health Food Stores
N.A.I.C.S.: 456191
Chad Braithwaite (Gen Mgr)

Synco (H.K.) Limited (1)
3 On Yip Street 3/F Block D Sunview Indus-
trial Building, Chai Wan, China (Hong Kong)
Tel.: (852) 2556 0157
Web Site: http://www.synco-pharma.com
Pharmaceutical Products Mfr & Distr
N.A.I.C.S.: 325412

Weng Li Sdn. Bhd. (1)
No 2 And 4 Persiaran 1/118C Fasa 2 Desa
Tun Razak Industrial Park, Cheras, 56000,
Kuala Lumpur, Malaysia (100%)
Tel.: (60) 3 9173 1984
Web Site: http://www.wengli.com.my
Medicinal Herbal Soup & Tea Mfr
N.A.I.C.S.: 325411

Yin Yang Spa Products Pte Ltd (1)
21 Taiseng Drive, Singapore, 535223, Sin-
gapore
Tel.: (65) 6749 8830
Web Site: http://www.yinyangspa.com.sg
Traditional Chinese Medicinal Products Mfr
N.A.I.C.S.: 325411
Eugena Ng (Mgr-Sls & Mktg)

EUBIOLOGICS CO., LTD.
8F Seongdo B/D 207 Dosan-daero
Sinsa-dong, Gangnam-gu, Seoul, Ko-
rea (South)
Tel.: (82) 25726675
Web Site: http://www.eubiologics.com
Year Founded: 2010
206650—(KRS)
Rev.: $42,542,954
Assets: $124,304,557
Liabilities: $32,697,845
Net Worth: $91,606,712
Earnings: ($2,636,471)
Emp.: 314
Fiscal Year-end: 12/31/22
Vaccine Mfr & Distr
N.A.I.C.S.: 325414
Ik-Pyo Hong (Co-COO)

EUCATEX S.A. INDUSTRIA E COMERCIO
Av Pres Juscelino Kubitschek 1830 -
Torre I - 11 Andar, Vila Nova Concei-
cao, Sao Paulo, 04543-900, SP, Bra-
zil
Tel.: (55) 1130492331

Web Site:
https://www.eucatex.com.br
Year Founded: 1951
EUCA3—(BRAZ)
Rev.: $533,968,691
Assets: $819,307,010
Liabilities: $339,250,573
Net Worth: $480,056,436
Earnings: $84,199,422
Emp.: 3,000
Fiscal Year-end: 12/31/23
Insulating Material Mfr & Whslr
N.A.I.C.S.: 321999
Jose Antonio Goulart de Carvalho
(Officer-IR & Exec VP)

Subsidiaries:

Eucatex S.A. Industria e Comercio -
Eucatex Paints and Varnishes
Plant (1)
Estrada do Guaruja 3150, Bairro Jardim
Marilia, Sao Paulo, 13323-902, Brazil
Tel.: (55) 11 4602 7000
Insulation Material Mfr
N.A.I.C.S.: 321999

Eucatex S.A. Industria e Comercio -
Fiberboard Facilty (1)
Rua Ribeirao Preto 811/909, Bairro Jardim
Marilia, Sao Paulo, 13323-010, Brazil
Tel.: (55) 11 4028 9000
Insulation Material Mfr
N.A.I.C.S.: 321999

Eucatex S.A. Industria e Comercio -
MDP and Laminate Flooring
Facilty (1)
Estrada Municipal Botucatu/Itatinga s/n,
Sao Paulo, 18603-970, Brazil
Tel.: (55) 14 3811 5000
Insulation Material Mfr.
N.A.I.C.S.: 321999

Eucatex S.A. Industria e Comercio -
Seedlings Nursery Unit (1)
Fazenda Santa Terezinha Bairro Sao
Roque Novo, Sao Paulo, 18590-000, Brazil
Tel.: (55) 14 6852 1196
Insulation Material Mfr
N.A.I.C.S.: 321999

Eucatex Tintas e Vernizes Ltda. (1)
Rua Guaruja 3150 Jardim Marilia, Salto,
Sao Paulo, 13323-005, Brazil
Tel.: (55) 11 4602 7000
Insulation Material Distr
N.A.I.C.S.: 424990

Eucatex of North America, Inc (1)
2500 Northwinds Pkwy Ste 685, Alpharetta,
GA 30009
Tel.: (678) 624-0160
Web Site: http://www.eucatex.com.br
Emp.: 5
Insulation Material Distr
N.A.I.C.S.: 423990
Tetro Furlanetto (Mng Dir)

EUCLID LABS S.R.L.
Via Newton 5G, 31040, Nervesa della
Battaglia, TV, Italy
Tel.: (39) 0422887075   IT
Web Site: http://www.euclidlabs.it
Year Founded: 2005
Automation Product Mfr
N.A.I.C.S.: 334512
Roberto Polesel (CEO)

EUCODIS BIOSCIENCE GMBH
Campus Vienna Biocenter II, Vieh-
marktgasse 2 a/ 2 OG, Vienna, 1030,
Austria
Tel.: (43) 18900804
Web Site: http://www.eucodis.com
Biotechnology Researcher & Devel-
oper
N.A.I.C.S.: 541714

EUDA HEALTH HOLDINGS LIMITED
1 Pemimpin Drive 1207 One Pemimpin, Singapore, 576151, Singapore

EUDA Health Holdings Limited—(Continued)

Tel.: (65) 82618261 VG
Web Site: https://euda.com
Year Founded: 2021
EUDA—(NASDAQ)
Rev.: $222,912
Assets: $86,775,601
Liabilities: $90,499,151
Net Worth: ($3,723,550)
Earnings: ($1,762,838)
Emp.: 2
Fiscal Year-end: 07/31/22
Digital Healthcare Ecosystem
N.A.I.C.S.: 513210

Subsidiaries:

EUDA Health Ltd. (1)
Tel.: (65) 82618261
Health Technology Company
N.A.I.C.S.: 621610

EUGEN LAGLER GMBH

Kappelrain 2 Frauenzimmern, 74363,
Guglingen, Germany
Tel.: (49) 713598900
Web Site: http://www.laegler.com
Year Founded: 1956
Sales Range: $10-24.9 Million
Emp.: 60
Floor Sanding Machine Mfr
N.A.I.C.S.: 333310
Karleugen Lagler (Mng Dir)

Subsidiaries:

Lagler Australia (1)
28 Parkhurst Drive, Knoxfield, 3180, VIC,
Australia
Tel.: (61) 398872344
Web Site: http://www.lagler.com.au
Industrial Machinery Distr
N.A.I.C.S.: 423830
Yirun Lu (Project Mgr)

EUGENE ALLARD CUISINE ET TENDANCES

2448 Rue des roitelets, Chicoutimi,
G7H 7X3, QC, Canada
Tel.: (418) 549-4747
Web Site: https://eugeneallard.com
Emp.: 100
Cooking Utensils & Appliances Whslr
N.A.I.C.S.: 423220

EUGENE CORPORATION

23rd Fl Park-One Tower 1 108
Yeoeui-daero, Yeongdeungpo-gu,
Seoul, Korea (South)
Tel.: (82) 237043300
Web Site:
https://www.eugenecorp.co.kr
Year Founded: 1984
023410—(KRS)
Rev.: $1,079,719,291
Assets: $1,557,333,566
Liabilities: $838,197,244
Net Worth: $719,136,322
Earnings: $23,877,927
Emp.: 703
Fiscal Year-end: 12/31/22
Construction Materials Mfr
N.A.I.C.S.: 423320
Kom Jin Gu (VP)

EUGENE INVESTMENT & SE-CURITIES CO., LTD.

24 Gukjegeumyung-ro,
Yeongdeungpo-gu, Seoul, 150 710,
Korea (South)
Tel.: (82) 23686114
Web Site: https://www.eugenefn.com
Year Founded: 1954
001200—(KRS)
Rev.: $1,439,045,466
Assets: $6,380,362,556
Liabilities: $5,609,603,781
Net Worth: $770,758,775
Earnings: $12,381,149

Emp.: 832
Fiscal Year-end: 12/31/22
Investment Banking & Brokerage
N.A.I.C.S.: 523150
Sangsik Lee (Mng Dir)

Subsidiaries:

Eugene Investment & Futures Co.,
Ltd. (1)
A23-9 Yeouido-Dong Yeongdeungpo-Gu,
Seoul, 150 710, Korea (South)
Tel.: (82) 237718721
Web Site:
http://www.eng.eugenefutures.com
Sales Range: $50-74.9 Million
Emp.: 80
Brokerage & Investment Services
N.A.I.C.S.: 523150

EUGENE SPECIAL PURPOSE ACQUISITION 3 CO., LTD

28 Gukjegeumyung-ro 2-gil,
Yeongdeungpo-gu, Seoul, Korea
(South)
Tel.: (82) 23686296
Year Founded: 2015
Assets: $11,497,510
Liabilities: $1,111,034
Net Worth: $10,386,476
Earnings: $22,219
Emp.: 4
Financial Investment Management
Services
N.A.I.C.S.: 523940
Eul Jin Nam (CEO)

EUGENE TECHNOLOGY CO., LTD.

42 Chugye-Ro Yangji-myeon, Cheoin-gu, Yongin, Gyeonggi-do, Korea
(South)
Tel.: (82) 313235700
Web Site:
https://www.eugenetech.co.kr
Year Founded: 2000
084370—(KRS)
Rev.: $238,255,448
Assets: $332,888,591
Liabilities: $66,968,128
Net Worth: $265,920,463
Earnings: $29,095,247
Emp.: 305
Fiscal Year-end: 12/31/22
Semiconductor Machinery Mfr
N.A.I.C.S.: 333242
Pyung Yong Um (CEO)

EUGLENA CO., LTD.

G-BASE Tamachi 2nd and 3rd floor
5-29-11 Shiba, Minato-ku, Tokyo,
108-0014, Japan
Tel.: (81) 334534907
Web Site: https://www.euglena.jp
Year Founded: 2005
2931—(TKS)
Rev.: $329,557,380
Assets: $422,698,710
Liabilities: $279,381,450
Net Worth: $143,317,260
Earnings: ($18,802,680)
Emp.: 1,070
Fiscal Year-end: 12/31/23
Bio-Fuel Production & Research
N.A.I.C.S.: 324199
Mitsuru Izumo (Founder, Pres &
CEO)

Subsidiaries:

Daikyo Fertilizer Co., Ltd. (1)
2-1-29 Kawakita, Osaka, 583-0001, Japan
Tel.: (81) 729723951
Web Site: https://www.daikyo-hiryo.co.jp
Organic Fertilizer Mfr & Distr
N.A.I.C.S.: 325311

Epauler Co., Ltd. (1)
1383-1 Kisumicho, Matsuyama, 791-1102,
Ehime, Japan

Tel.: (81) 899557511
Web Site: https://www.epauler.jp
Cosmetic Product Mfr & Distr
N.A.I.C.S.: 325620

Flemish Co., Ltd. (1)
Garlic Building Sangubashi 102 3-43-1,
Yoyogi Shibuya-ku, Tokyo, Japan
Tel.: (81) 344054551
Web Site: https://frembassy.jp
Food Products Distr
N.A.I.C.S.: 424420

LIGUNA Inc. (1)
5-8-26 Kajinocho, Koganei, 184-0002, To-kyo, Japan
Tel.: (81) 423828527
Web Site: https://liguna.jp
Cosmetic Product Mfr & Distr
N.A.I.C.S.: 325620

Q'sai Co., Ltd. (1)
1-7-16 Kusagae, Chuo-ku, Fukuoka, 810-8606, Japan
Tel.: (81) 927240831
Web Site: http://corporate.kyusai.co.jp
Sales Range: $50-74.9 Million
Emp.: 498
Health Food Products Mfr & Distr
N.A.I.C.S.: 311999
Satoshi Kambe (Pres)

Shanghai Euglena Biotechnology Co.,
Ltd. (1)
Far East International Plaza Room 1512
1513 No 317 Xianxia Road, Building B
Changning District, Shanghai, China
Tel.: (86) 2162345117
Web Site: https://www.euglena.cn
Food Products Mfr
N.A.I.C.S.: 311412

Yaeyama Shokusan Co., Ltd. (1)
287-14 Shiraho, Ishigaki, Okinawa, 907-0242, Japan
Tel.: (81) 980867154
Web Site:
https://www.yaeyamachlorella.com
Pharmaceuticals Product Mfr
N.A.I.C.S.: 325412
Ryohei Nakano (CEO)

EUKALIN SPEZIAL-KLEBSTOFF FABRIK GMBH

Ernst-Abbe-Str 10, D – 52249,
Eschweiler, Germany
Tel.: (49) 2403 6450 51 De
Web Site: https://www.eukalin.de
Emp.: 100
Adhesive Mfr
N.A.I.C.S.: 325520
Jan Schulz-Wachler (Pres)

Subsidiaries:

Adhesives Specialists, Inc. (1)
739 Roble Rd, Allentown, PA 18109
Tel.: (610) 266-8910
Web Site:
http://www.adhesivesspecialists.com
Rev.: $5,300,000
Emp.: 34
Adhesive Mfr
N.A.I.C.S.: 325520
Laurett Elfand (Mgr-Inside Sls)

EUKEDOS S.P.A.

via Benedetto da Foiano 14, 50125,
Florence, Italy
Tel.: (39) 0550682844
Web Site: https://www.eukedos.it
EUK—(ITA)
Sales Range: Less than $1 Million
Healtcare Services
N.A.I.C.S.: 621610
Carlo Iuculano (Chm & CEO)

EUMUNDI GROUP LIMITED

Ashmore Tavern 161 Cotlew Street,
Ashmore, 4214, QLD, Australia
Tel.: (61) 732297222 AU
Web Site:
https://eumundigroup.com.au
Year Founded: 2000

EBG—(ASX)
Rev.: $20,320,513
Assets: $71,257,345
Liabilities: $26,649,973
Net Worth: $44,607,372
Earnings: $2,417,869
Emp.: 24
Fiscal Year-end: 06/30/24
Holding Company; Tavern Operator &
Property Investment
N.A.I.C.S.: 551112
Joseph Michael Ganim (Bd of Dirs &
Chm)

EUNISELL INTERLINKED PLC

50 B Oladipo Bateye Street, Ikeja
GRA, Lagos, Nigeria
Tel.: (234) 9086641616
Web Site: https://interlinkedplc.com
Year Founded: 1981
EUNISELL—(NIGE)
Rev.: $205,119
Assets: $470,657
Liabilities: $325,726
Net Worth: $144,931
Earnings: $6,546
Emp.: 15
Fiscal Year-end: 06/30/23
Porcelain & Jointing Material Mfr
N.A.I.C.S.: 327110
Fabian C. Nnadozie (Chm)

EUPE CORPORATION BER-HAD

5th Floor Wisma Ria Taman Ria,
08000, Sungai Petani, Kedah Darul
Aman, Malaysia
Tel.: (60) 44414888
Web Site: https://www.eupe.com.my
Year Founded: 1986
EUPE—(KLS)
Rev.: $74,047,671
Assets: $175,898,129
Liabilities: $66,959,513
Net Worth: $108,938,616
Earnings: $8,997,170
Emp.: 386
Fiscal Year-end: 02/29/24
Property Development Services
N.A.I.C.S.: 531312
Hiang Joo Tan (Chm)

Subsidiaries:

Esteem Glory Sdn. Bhd. (1)
94 Lorong Ria 5/2 Taman Ria Padang Se-rai, 09400, Kulim, Kedah, Malaysia
Tel.: (60) 44855884
Residential Building Construction Services
N.A.I.C.S.: 236117

Eupe Golf Management Bhd. (1)
No 552 Taman Ria, 08000, Sungai Petani,
Kedah, Malaysia
Tel.: (60) 44414666
Web Site: http://www.cintasayangresort.com
Sales Range: $75-99.9 Million
Emp.: 200
Golf Club Management Services
N.A.I.C.S.: 713910

Ria Food Centre Sdn. Bhd. (1)
57-61 Lrg 2 Taman Ria, 08000, Sungai
Petani, Kedah, Malaysia
Tel.: (60) 44412705
Sales Range: $50-74.9 Million
Emp.: 15
Operator of Complex for Rental of Stalls
N.A.I.C.S.: 531312
Beh Huck Boon (Mng Dir)

Riacon Sdn. Bhd. (1)
5th Floor Wisma Ria Taman Ria, 08000,
Sungai Petani, Kedah, Malaysia
Tel.: (60) 44414888
Web Site: http://www.eupe.com.my
Sales Range: $50-74.9 Million
Emp.: 150
Residential Construction Services
N.A.I.C.S.: 236116

EUPHON COMMUNICATIONS S.P.A.

Via Nizza 280, 10126, Turin, Italy
Tel.: (39) 011 6311790   IT
Web Site: http://www.euphon.it
Audio Video Communications Systems Design Services
N.A.I.C.S.: 334310

EURALIS COOP
Avenue Gaston Phoebus, 64231, Lescar, Cedex, France
Tel.: (33) 5 5992 3838   FR
Web Site: http://www.euralis.fr
Emp.: 4,835
Agricultural Cooperative
N.A.I.C.S.: 493130
Christian Pees *(Pres & Mng Dir-Acting)*

Subsidiaries:

Biogemma S.A.S.   (1)
5 rue Saint-Germain l'Auxerrois, 75001, Paris, France
Tel.: (33) 155349400
Web Site: http://www.biogemma.com
Emp.: 80
Agricultural Seed Genetic Research & Development
N.A.I.C.S.: 541715

EURALIS ESPACES VERTS   (1)
163 rue de la vallee d'Ossau, 64 121, Serres-Castet, France
Tel.: (33) 5 59 33 58 99
Web Site: http://www.euralis-espacesverts.fr
Environmental Consulting Services
N.A.I.C.S.: 541620

EURALIS SEMILLAS, S.A.   (1)
Ctra del Copero, 41012, Seville, Spain
Tel.: (34) 954 295 000
Web Site: http://www.euralis-semillas.com
Agricultural Product Mfr
N.A.I.C.S.: 111199

EURALIS Saaten GmbH   (1)
Oststrasse 122, 22844, Norderstedt, Germany
Tel.: (49) 40 60 88 77 0
Web Site: http://www.euralis.de
Agricultural Product Mfr
N.A.I.C.S.: 111998

Euralis Semences SAS   (1)
Avenue Gaston Phoebus, 64231, Lescar, France
Tel.: (33) 5 59 92 38 38
Web Site: http://www.euralis-semences.fr
Agricultural Product Mfr
N.A.I.C.S.: 111199

EURASIA DRILLING COMPANY LIMITED
Boundary Hall Cricket Square, PO Box 1111, Georgetown, Ky1-1102, Grand Cayman, Cayman Islands
Tel.: (345) 19495122
Web Site:
http://www.eurasiadrilling.com
Sales Range: $1-4.9 Billion
Emp.: 21,850
Oil & Gas Exploration
N.A.I.C.S.: 213112
Alexander Shokhin *(Chm)*

Subsidiaries:

BKE Shelf Ltd.   (1)
ul N Kachuevskoy 9, Astrakhan, 414000, Russia
Tel.: (7) 8512 391008
Web Site: http://www.bkeshelf.ru
Sales Range: $100-124.9 Million
Emp.: 200
Offshore Drilling Contract Services
N.A.I.C.S.: 213111
Sergey Polousov *(Deputy Dir Gen)*

EURASIA ENERGY LIMITED
294 Heywood House, South Hill, Anguilla
Tel.: (264) 476 5202   NV
Web Site:
http://www.eurasiaenergy.com
Year Founded: 2003

EUENF—(OTCIQ)
Assets: $1,393
Liabilities: $61,704
Net Worth: ($60,311)
Earnings: ($21,233)
Fiscal Year-end: 12/31/20
Oil & Gas Exploration Services
N.A.I.C.S.: 213112
Nicholas Baxter *(Pres & CEO)*

EURASIA FONCIERE INVESTISSEMENTS SA
164 boulevard Haussmann, 75008, Paris, France
Tel.: (33) 148392161   FR
Web Site:
https://www.eurasiafonciereinvest.fr
Year Founded: 1984
EFI—(EUR)
Sales Range: $10-24.9 Million
Financial Investment Services
N.A.I.C.S.: 523940

EURASIA GROUPE SA
72 Rue de la Haie Coq, 93300, Aubervilliers, France
Tel.: (33) 48392161   FR
Web Site:
https://cn.eurasiagroupe.com
Year Founded: 1993
ALEUA—(EUR)
Sales Range: Less than $1 Million
Commercial Real Estate Owner & Manager
N.A.I.C.S.: 531312
Hsueh Sheng Wang *(Chm & CEO)*

EURASIA MINING PLC
International House 142 Cromwell Road, London, SW7 4EF, United Kingdom
Tel.: (44) 2079320418
Web Site:
https://www.eurasiamining.co.uk
EUA—(AIM)
Rev.: $150,877
Assets: $31,978,741
Liabilities: $3,688,266
Net Worth: $28,290,476
Earnings: ($9,126,594)
Emp.: 116
Fiscal Year-end: 12/31/22
Gold & Metals Exploration
N.A.I.C.S.: 212220
Christian Schaffalitzky *(Chm)*

EURASIA TRAVEL CO., LTD.
4F Sabo Kaikan Bekkan 2-7-4 Hirakawa-cho, Chiyoda-Ku, Tokyo, 102-8642, Japan
Tel.: (81) 332651691
Web Site: https://www.eurasia.co.jp
Year Founded: 1986
9376—(TKS)
Rev.: $20,880,050
Assets: $18,611,250
Liabilities: $6,756,770
Net Worth: $11,854,480
Earnings: ($389,950)
Fiscal Year-end: 09/30/23
Travel Arrangement Services
N.A.I.C.S.: 561510
Toshio Inoue *(Pres)*

EURASIAN BANK JSC
56 Kunaev Str, Medeu district, Almaty, 050002, Kazakhstan
Tel.: (7) 7272508684
Web Site: http://www.eurasian-bank.kz
Year Founded: 1994
EUBN—(KAZ)
Rev.: $425,523,798
Assets: $5,268,504,651
Liabilities: $4,827,266,164
Net Worth: $441,238,487

Earnings: $186,306,900
Emp.: 5,000
Fiscal Year-end: 12/31/22
Banking Services
N.A.I.C.S.: 522110
Ivan Belokhvostikov *(Deputy CEO & Member-Mgmt Bd)*

Subsidiaries:

Eurasian Bank PJSC   (1)
Multifunctional complex Capital City South block 6-th floor, Moskow International business center, Moscow, Russia
Tel.: (7) 4952879966
Commercial Banking Services
N.A.I.C.S.: 522110

Insurance Company Eurasia JSC   (1)
Zheltoksan 59, Almaty, 050004, Kazakhstan
Tel.: (7) 7272584336
Web Site: http://www.theeurasia.kz
Emp.: 221
Insurance Services
N.A.I.C.S.: 524210
Samat Kabdolov *(Exec Dir)*

EURASIAN DEVELOPMENT BANK
220 Dostyk Ave, Almaty, 050051, Kazakhstan
Tel.: (7) 7272444044
Web Site: http://www.eabr.org
EABR—(KAZ)
Rev.: $206,208,000
Assets: $8,167,342,000
Liabilities: $6,179,336,000
Net Worth: $1,988,006,000
Earnings: $125,192,000
Fiscal Year-end: 12/31/23
Commercial Banking Services
N.A.I.C.S.: 522110
Berik Mukhambetzhanov *(Member-Mgmt Bd & Dir-Fin)*

EURASIAN NATURAL RESOURCES CORPORATION LIMITED
16 Saint James's Street, London, SW1A 1ER, United Kingdom
Tel.: (44) 2073891440   UK
Web Site: http://www.enrc.com
Sales Range: $5-14.9 Billion
Emp.: 78,484
Diversified Natural Resource Holding Company
N.A.I.C.S.: 551112

Subsidiaries:

Africo Resources Ltd.   (1)
520 - 800 West Pender St, Vancouver, V6C 2V6, BC, Canada   (100%)
Tel.: (604) 646-3225
Web Site: http://www.africoresources.com
Sales Range: Less than $1 Million
Emp.: 9
Mineral Exploration & Development Services
N.A.I.C.S.: 327999
Chris Theodoropoulos *(Chm, Pres & CEO)*

Subsidiary (Domestic):

Africo Resources (B.C.) Ltd.   (2)
Suite 1108 1030 Georgia St W, Vancouver, V6E 3B9, BC, Canada
Tel.: (604) 646-3225
Mineral Exploration Services
N.A.I.C.S.: 213115

ENRC Leasing BV   (1)
Jan Luijkenstraat 8, 1071 CM, Amsterdam, Netherlands
Tel.: (31) 205707590
Financial Management Services
N.A.I.C.S.: 523940

ENRC Logistics LLP   (1)
76 Abai Ave, Almaty, 050057, Kazakhstan
Tel.: (7) 7272582858
Freight Transportation Services
N.A.I.C.S.: 481212

ENRC Management (UK) Limited   (1)
2nd Fl 16 St James, London, SW1A 1ER, United Kingdom
Tel.: (44) 2073891440
Web Site: http://www.enrc.com
Sales Range: $25-49.9 Million
Emp.: 70
Business Management Services
N.A.I.C.S.: 561499

ENRC Marketing AG   (1)
Balz Zimmermann Strasse 7, Zurich, 8058, Switzerland
Tel.: (41) 434994100
Sales Range: $25-49.9 Million
Emp.: 80
Transportation Services
N.A.I.C.S.: 481112

TransCom LLP   (1)
76 Abai Ave, 050057, Almaty, Kazakhstan
Tel.: (7) 7272509952
Freight Transportation Services
N.A.I.C.S.: 481212

Universal Service LLP   (1)
76 Abai Ave, 050057, Almaty, Kazakhstan
Tel.: (7) 7272582188
Freight Transportation Services
N.A.I.C.S.: 481212

EURAZEO SE
66 rue Pierre Charron, 75008, Paris, France
Tel.: (33) 144150111   FR
Web Site: https://www.eurazeo.com
Year Founded: 2001
EUQ—(DEU)
Rev.: $367,346,560
Assets: $10,438,256,710
Liabilities: $1,508,978,867
Net Worth: $8,929,277,843
Earnings: $1,980,685,197
Emp.: 445
Fiscal Year-end: 12/31/23
Investment Services
N.A.I.C.S.: 523999
Olivier Merveilleux du Vignaux *(Vice Chm-Supervisory Bd)*

Subsidiaries:

3S Photonics S.A.S.   (1)
Route de Villejust, F 91625, Nozay, Cedex, France   (86%)
Tel.: (33) 169805750
Web Site: http://www.3spgroup.com
Sales Range: $50-74.9 Million
Emp.: 100
Optical & Optoelectronic Components Mfr
N.A.I.C.S.: 333310
Yannick Bailly *(Deputy Gen Mgr-France)*

Branch (Domestic):

3S Photonics S.A.S - Marcoussis   (2)
Batiment A1, Route de Nozay, F-91460, Marcoussis, France
Tel.: (33) 169805830
Electronic Components Mfr
N.A.I.C.S.: 334418

Albingia SA   (1)
109/111 rue Victor Hugo, 92532, Levallois-Perret, Cedex, France
Tel.: (33) 141067000
Web Site: http://www.albingia.fr
Insurance Services
N.A.I.C.S.: 524210

Clinique Bon Secours SAS   (1)
67 Bis Avenue Du Marechal Foch, 43009, Le Puy, Cedex, France
Tel.: (33) 471098800
Web Site: http://www.clinique-bon-secours.fr
Gastroenterology Clinic Services
N.A.I.C.S.: 621111

Clinique Nouvelle du Forez SA   (1)
28 Route Nouvelle, 42600, Montbrison, France
Tel.: (33) 477968600
Web Site: http://www.clinique-du-forez.fr
Gastroenterology Clinic Services
N.A.I.C.S.: 621111

Clinique Saint Martin SA   (1)

Eurazeo SE—(Continued)

183 route des Camoins, 13396, Marseilles, Cedex, France
Tel.: (33) 491273000
Web Site: http://www.cliniques-saint-martin.fr
Gastroenterology Clinic Services
N.A.I.C.S.: 621111

Clinique du Jura SAS (1)
9 Rue Louis Rousseau, Lons le Saunier, 39000, Lons, France
Tel.: (33) 384351600
Web Site: http://www.cliniquedujura.fr
Gastroenterology Clinic Services
N.A.I.C.S.: 621111

Clinique du Parc Lyon SA (1)
155 Boulevard Stalingrad, 69006, Lyon, France
Tel.: (33) 472448800
Web Site:
   http://www.cliniqueduparclyon.com
Emp.: 220
Gastroenterology Clinic Services
N.A.I.C.S.: 621111

Clinique du Renaison SAS (1)
75 Rue General Giraud, 42300, Roanne, France
Tel.: (33) 477444500
Web Site: http://www.clinique-renaison.fr
Gastroenterology Clinic Services
N.A.I.C.S.: 621111

Cranial Technologies, Inc. (1)
1395 W Auto Dr, Tempe, AZ 85284
Tel.: (480) 505-1840
Web Site: http://www.cranialtech.com
Custom Cranial Orthotic Remodeling Bands Mfr
N.A.I.C.S.: 339112
Carol Erickson (Pres)

DBA SAS (1)
Via Provinciale Est 34, Salgareda, 31040, Treviso, Italy
Tel.: (39) 04221830469
Computer Repair Services
N.A.I.C.S.: 811210

EFESO Consulting S.A. (1)
117 avenue des Champs-Elysees, 75008, Paris, France
Tel.: (33) 1 53535700
Web Site: http://www.efeso.com
Business Consulting Services
N.A.I.C.S.: 541618
Filippo Mantegazza (Chm-Mgmt Bd & CEO)

EU Taxfree Deutschland GmbH (1)
Paul-Ehrlich-Str 38, 63322, Rodermark, Germany
Tel.: (49) 60744852865
Web Site: http://www.taxfreegermany.de
Payment Services
N.A.I.C.S.: 522320
Iveta Muller (Mng Dir)

Elemica, Inc. (1)
550 E Swedesford Rd Ste 310, Wayne, PA 19087
Tel.: (484) 253-4674
Web Site: http://www.elemica.com
Supply Chain Operating Network
N.A.I.C.S.: 541519
Mark Kerschner (CFO)

Subsidiary (Non-US):

Elemica International B.V. (2)
Building Officia I De Boelelaan 7 7th Floor, 1083 HJ, Amsterdam, Netherlands
Tel.: (31) 20 504 1500
Web Site: http://www.elemica.com
Supply Chain Operating Network
N.A.I.C.S.: 541519
Sergio Juarez (Chief Comml Officer)

Elemica International Inc. (2)
Herriotstrasse 1 5th Floor, 60528, Frankfurt am Main, Germany **(100%)**
Tel.: (49) 69 66123 0
Web Site: http://www.elemica.com
Sales Range: $10-24.9 Million
Emp.: 30
Provider of E-Commerce for Chemical Industry
N.A.I.C.S.: 541511

Elis S.A. (1)
5 Boulevard Louis Loucheu, 92210, Saint-Cloud, France
Tel.: (33) 175499400
Web Site: https://www.fr.elis.com
Rev.: $4,123,570,041
Assets: $9,300,669,113
Liabilities: $5,831,858,407
Net Worth: $3,468,810,706
Earnings: $220,807,252
Emp.: 45,126
Fiscal Year-end: 12/31/2022
Linens, Professional Garments, Hygiene & Wellness Equipment Rental & Maintenance
N.A.I.C.S.: 812332
Xavier Martire (Chm-Mgmt BU & CEO)

Subsidiary (Non-US):

Berendsen Limited (2)
Intec 3 Intec Business Park Wade Road, Basingstoke, RG24 8NE, United Kingdom
Tel.: (44) 1256 339200
Web Site: http://uk.elis.com
Textile Maintenance Services
N.A.I.C.S.: 812320

Subsidiary (Domestic):

Berendsen UK Limited (3)
Intec 3 Wade Road, Intec Business Park, Basingstoke, RG24 8NE, Hants, United Kingdom
Tel.: (44) 1256 339 200
Web Site: http://www.berendsen.co.uk
Linen Hire & Laundry Services
N.A.I.C.S.: 812331

Subsidiary (Non-US):

Elis Danmark A/S (3)
Tobaksvejen 22, 2860, Soborg, Denmark
Tel.: (45) 70133331
Web Site: https://dk.elis.com
Textile Services & Solutions & Protective Gear
N.A.I.C.S.: 333996

Subsidiary (Non-US):

Berendsen GmbH (4)
Holsteiner Chaussee 303a, 22457, Hamburg, Germany
Tel.: (49) 403562520
Web Site: http://www.berendsen.de
Laundry & Textile Service
N.A.I.C.S.: 812332

Elis Nederland B.V. (4)
Pieter Calandweg 2, 6827 BK, Arnhem, Netherlands
Tel.: (31) 263848140
Web Site: http://www.nl.elis.com
Garments, Industrial Wipers, Roller Towel Cabinets, Mats & Personal Safety Equipment Mfr
N.A.I.C.S.: 423620
Eric Verstappan (COO & Country Mgr-Workwear)

Elis Norge AS (4)
Smeltedigelen 1 Kvaernerbyen, 0195, Etterstad, Norway
Tel.: (47) 22384000
Web Site: http://www.berendsen.no
Laundry & Textile Service
N.A.I.C.S.: 812320

Elis Textil Service AB (4)
St Johannesgatan 2, 211 46, Malmo, Sweden
Tel.: (46) 20740101
Web Site: http://www.berendsen.se
Textile Handling Equipment for Hotels, Hospitals & Industry
N.A.I.C.S.: 532490

Eurazeo North America Inc. (1)
745 5th Ave Fl 32, New York, NY 10151
Tel.: (212) 653-9743
Financial Investment Services
N.A.I.C.S.: 523999
Jill Granoff (CEO)

Eurazeo PME SAS (1)
1 Rue Georges Berger, 75017, Paris, France
Tel.: (33) 144150111
Web Site: http://www.eurazeo-pme.com
Small Market Enterprise Investment Firm
N.A.I.C.S.: 523999

Olivier Millet (Chm-Exec Bd)

Holding (Domestic):

EasyVista Holding SAS (2)
Immeuble Horizon 10 Allee Bienvenue, 93885, Noisy-le-Grand, Cedex, France
Tel.: (33) 1 55 85 9100
Holding Company
N.A.I.C.S.: 551112

Subsidiary (Domestic):

EasyVista S.A. (3)
Immeuble Horizon 10 Allee Bienvenue, 93885, Noisy-le-Grand, Cedex, France **(100%)**
Tel.: (33) 155859100
Web Site: http://www.easyvista.com
Sales Range: $10-24.9 Million
Information Technology Services
N.A.I.C.S.: 541512
Sylvain Gauthier (CEO)

Subsidiary (US):

EasyVista Inc. (4)
3 Columbus Cir 15th Flr Ste 1532, New York, NY 10019
Tel.: (888) 398-4876
Information Technology Services
N.A.I.C.S.: 541512
Evan Carlson (Chief Revenue Officer)

Subsidiary (Non-US):

EasyVista Italy (4)
Via Conservatorio 22, Milan, 20122, Italy
Tel.: (39) 02 77297552
Information Technology Services
N.A.I.C.S.: 541512

EasyVista Portugal S.A. (4)
Av Eng Duarte Pachero Torre 2 6 Andar Escritorio 7, 1070-102, Lisbon, Portugal
Tel.: (351) 21 805 13 20
Information Technology Services
N.A.I.C.S.: 541512

EasyVista Spain (4)
Avenida de la Industria N 4 Edif 3 - 2 B, 28108, Alcobendas, Spain
Tel.: (34) 902 430 412
Information Technology Consulting Services
N.A.I.C.S.: 541512
Luis Camiro Perales (Mgr-Presales)

EasyVista United Kingdom (4)
Berkhamsted House 121 High Street, Berkhamsted, HP4 2DJ, United Kingdom
Tel.: (44) 1442 200 120
Information Technology Services
N.A.I.C.S.: 541512

Easyvista Gmbh (4)
Maximilianstrasse 13, 80539, Munich, Germany
Tel.: (49) 89203006277
Computer Software Development Services
N.A.I.C.S.: 513210

Easyvista SL (4)
Avenida de la Industria N 4 Edif 3-2 B, 28108, Alcobendas, Spain
Tel.: (34) 902430412
Computer Software Development Services
N.A.I.C.S.: 513210

Easyvista Srl (4)
Via Cechov 48 CC Bonola Uffici 2 Piano, 20151, Milan, Italy
Tel.: (39) 0245390680
Computer Software Development Services
N.A.I.C.S.: 513210

Easyvista, S.A. (4)
Rua Tierno Galvan Amoreiras Torre 3 10 Andar Fracao A, 1070-274, Lisbon, Portugal
Tel.: (351) 218051320
Computer Software Development Services
N.A.I.C.S.: 513210
Joana Gaspar (Mgr-Inside Sls)

Logiciels EasyVista Inc (4)
2001 McGill College Avenue, Montreal, H3A 3P9, QC, Canada
Tel.: (888) 398-4876
Information Technology Services
N.A.I.C.S.: 541512

Holding (Domestic):

Financiere Dessange SASU (2)

39 avenue Franklin Roosevelt, 75008, Paris, France
Tel.: (33) 1 53 83 99 10
Holding Company
N.A.I.C.S.: 551112

Holding (Domestic):

DESSANGE International SA (3)
39 avenue Franklin Roosevelt, 75008, Paris, France
Tel.: (33) 1 53 83 99 10
Sales Range: $1-4.9 Billion
Hair Salon
N.A.I.C.S.: 812112

Subsidiary (US):

Fantastic Sams International Corporation (4)
50 Dunham Rd 3rd Fl, Beverly, MA 01915
Tel.: (978) 232-5600
Web Site: http://www.fantasticsams.com
Sales Range: $10-24.9 Million
Emp.: 48
Hair Salon Operator
N.A.I.C.S.: 812112

Holding (Domestic):

Orolia SA (2)
Parc Technopolis Bat Sigma 3 Avenue du Canada, 2405 route des Dolines, 91974, Les Ulis, Cedex, France **(51.9%)**
Tel.: (33) 164533980
Web Site: http://www.orolia.com
Sales Range: $75-99.9 Million
Emp.: 425
High-Precision Time & Frequency Systems Designer, Mfr & Marketer
N.A.I.C.S.: 334519
Jean-Yves Courtois (CEO)

Subsidiary (US):

McMurdo, Inc. (3)
4296 Forbes Blvd, Lanham, MD 20706
Tel.: (240) 790-0600
Web Site: http://www.mcmurdogroup.com
Emp.: 500
Search & Rescue, Defense & Systems Engineering Technology Development Services
N.A.I.C.S.: 334290
Jean-Yves Courtois (CEO)

Subsidiary (Non-US):

Orolia Switzerland SA (3)
Vauseyon 29, 2000, Neuchatel, Switzerland
Tel.: (41) 327321666
Web Site: http://www.spectratime.com
GPS Design & Mfr
N.A.I.C.S.: 334220
Jean-Luc Schwizgebel (Ops Mgr)

T4 Science SA (3)
Vauseyon 29, 2000, Neuchatel, Switzerland **(85%)**
Tel.: (41) 327318008
Web Site: http://www.t4science.com
Maser Design & Mfr
N.A.I.C.S.: 335999
P. Rochat (Pres & CEO)

Holding (Domestic):

Smile SAS (2)
20 rue des Jardins, 92600, Asnieres-sur-Seine, France
Tel.: (33) 1 41 40 11 00
Web Site: http://www.smile.eu
Information Technology Consultancy Services
N.A.I.C.S.: 541512
Gregory Becue (Gen Dir- Strategy & Dev)

Fonroche Energie SAS (1)
ZAC des champs de Lescaze, PO Box 90021, 47310, Roquefort, France
Tel.: (33) 559716552
Web Site: http://www.fonrochegroup.com
Sales Range: $100-124.9 Million
Emp.: 28
Semiconductor Devices Mfr
N.A.I.C.S.: 334413

GHO Creteil Le Lac SAS (1)
Rue Jean Gabin RN 186, 94000, Creteil, France
Tel.: (33) 156725672

Web Site: http://www.all.accor.com
Room & Restaurant Operator
N.A.I.C.S.: 721110

GHO Grenoble Nord Voreppe SAS (1)
1625 Route de Veurey, 38340, Voreppe,
France
Tel.: (33) 476505555
Room & Restaurant Operator
N.A.I.C.S.: 721110

GHO Reims Parc des Expositions SAS (1)
2 rue Gabriel Voisin, BP 308, 51688, Reims, France
Tel.: (33) 326050008
Room & Restaurant Operator
N.A.I.C.S.: 721110

GHO Vitry sur Seine A86 Bords de Seine SAS (1)
19 Rue Leon Geoffroy Z I les Ardoines,
94400, Vitry-sur-Seine, France
Tel.: (33) 892683027
Room & Restaurant Operator
N.A.I.C.S.: 721110

Idinvest Partners SA (1)
117 Avenue des Champs Elysees, PO Box
293, 75008, Paris, France (80%)
Tel.: (33) 158185656
Web Site: http://www.idinvest.com
Emp.: 270
Privater Equity Firm
N.A.I.C.S.: 523999
Christophe Baviere (Founding Partner &
CEO)

Lakeland Tours, LLC (1)
218 W Water St Ste 400, Charlottesville, VA
22902
Tel.: (434) 982-8600
Web Site: http://www.worldstrides.org
Educational Travel Programs
N.A.I.C.S.: 561510
Bob Gogel (Pres & CEO)

Subsidiary (Domestic):

Explorica, Inc. (2)
101 Federal St Ste 900, Boston, MA 02110
Tel.: (888) 310-7121
Web Site: http://www.explorica.com
Educational Travel Products & Services
N.A.I.C.S.: 561520

Leon de Bruxelles SA (1)
5 rue de Chartres, 92200, Neuilly-sur-Seine,
France
Tel.: (33) 155612400
Web Site: http://www.leon-de-bruxelles.fr
Restaurant Services
N.A.I.C.S.: 722511

Subsidiary (Domestic):

Resto Belle Epine SNC (2)
Avenue du Luxembourg Centre Commercial
Belle Epine, 94320, Thiais, France
Tel.: (33) 146872020
Restaurant Operators
N.A.I.C.S.: 722511

Resto Clermont-Ferrand SNC (2)
93 Boulevard Gustave Flaubert, 63000,
Clermont-Ferrand, France
Tel.: (33) 473140594
Restaurant Operators
N.A.I.C.S.: 722511

Resto L'Isle Adam SNC (2)
Zac du Pont ofs Rayons Zone Du Grand
Val, 95290, L'Isle-Adam, France
Tel.: (33) 134080607
Restaurant Operators
N.A.I.C.S.: 722511

Resto Les Halles SNC (2)
120 Rue Rambuteau, 75001, Paris, France
Tel.: (33) 142361850
Restaurant Operators
N.A.I.C.S.: 722511

Resto Mareuil SNC (2)
400 Route Cote of La Justice Zone of La
Haute Borne, Mareuil-les-Meaux, 77100,
Meaux, France
Tel.: (33) 160232400
Restaurant Operators
N.A.I.C.S.: 722511

Resto Montlhery SNC (2)
113 Route D Orleans, 91310, Montlhery,
France
Tel.: (33) 169016312
Restaurant Operators
N.A.I.C.S.: 722511

Resto Pessac SNC (2)
4 Bis Avenue Antoine Becquerel, 33600,
Pessac, France
Tel.: (33) 556076478
Restaurant Operators
N.A.I.C.S.: 722511

Resto Rosny SNC (2)
02 Rue Jules Ferry, 03110, Rosny sous
Bois, France
Tel.: (33) 148541289
Restaurant Operators
N.A.I.C.S.: 722511

Resto Saint-Germain SNC (2)
131 Boulevard Saint Germain, 75006, Paris,
France
Tel.: (33) 143264595
Restaurant Operators
N.A.I.C.S.: 722511

Resto Tours SNC (2)
7 Rue Thomas Edison Lieu Dit Marsin,
37170, Chambray les Tours, France
Tel.: (33) 247746638
Restaurant Operators
N.A.I.C.S.: 722511

Resto Trappes SNC (2)
Route Nationale 10 Zone Immobiliere Parc,
78190, Trappes, France
Tel.: (33) 130503100
Restaurant Operators
N.A.I.C.S.: 722511

Resto Velizy SNC (2)
31 Avenue of L Europe, 78140, Velizy-
Villacoublay, France
Tel.: (33) 130708550
Restaurant Operators
N.A.I.C.S.: 722511

Resto Villiers SNC (2)
Boulevard of Friedberg ZAC Ofs Portes of
Villiers, 94350, Villiers-sur-Marne, France
Tel.: (33) 149306036
Restaurant Operators
N.A.I.C.S.: 722511

Resto Wasquehal SNC (2)
Avenue du Grand Cottignies Lotissement of
l Ecluse, 59290, Wasquehal, France
Tel.: (33) 320726634
Restaurant Operators
N.A.I.C.S.: 722511

SAS Amiens Glisy (2)
34 Avenue of La Ville Ideale ZAC of La
Croix of Fer-Route Nationale 29, Glisy,
80440, Amiens, France
Tel.: (33) 322463503
Restaurant Operators
N.A.I.C.S.: 722511

SAS Lyon Mezieu (2)
2 Rue du 24 Avril 1915, 69330, Meyzieu,
France
Tel.: (33) 472057506
Restaurant Operators
N.A.I.C.S.: 722511

SAS Resto Besancon (2)
Rue Rene Char Lieu-dit A Prabey, 25000,
Besancon, France
Tel.: (33) 381870807
Restaurant Operators
N.A.I.C.S.: 722511

SAS Resto DEV Leon 6 - Arras (2)
4 Rue of La Symphorine ZAC ofs Bon-
nettes, 62000, Arras, France
Tel.: (33) 321504652
Restaurant Operators
N.A.I.C.S.: 722511

SAS Resto Metz (2)
Rue du Patural ZAC Euromoselle, Seme-
court, 57280, Metz, France
Tel.: (33) 387515913
Restaurant Operators
N.A.I.C.S.: 722511

SAS Resto Nantes (2)
13-17 Route of Paris Secteur Paridis-La
Beaujoire, 44300, Nantes, France

Tel.: (33) 251890506
Restaurant Operators
N.A.I.C.S.: 722511

SNC Resto Chartres (2)
43 Rue ofs Pierres Missigault Lieu-dit La
Torche, Barjouville, 28630, Chartres, France
Tel.: (33) 237286940
Restaurant Operators
N.A.I.C.S.: 722511

**Societe de restauration Montpar-
nasse SAS** (2)
82 Bis Boulevard Du Montparnasse, 75014,
Paris, France
Tel.: (33) 143216662
Restaurant Operators
N.A.I.C.S.: 722511

NEST Fragrances, LLC (1)
3 E 54th St 5th Fl, New York, NY 10022-
0022
Tel.: (212) 759-0047
Web Site: http://www.nestfragrances.com
Candles & Other Scented Home Products
Designer, Mfr, Whslr & Online Retailer
N.A.I.C.S.: 339999

Peters Surgical SASU (1)
42 rue Benoit Frachon, 93013, Bobigny,
Cedex, France
Tel.: (33) 148106262
Web Site: http://www.peters-surgical.com
Medical Device Mfr & Whslr
N.A.I.C.S.: 339112
Thierry Herbreteau (CEO)

**Planet Payment (Greece) Tax Ser-
vices Single Partner Limited** (1)
246 Mesogeion, Holargos, 155 61, Athens,
Greece
Tel.: (30) 2106749481
Payment Services
N.A.I.C.S.: 522320

Planet Payment Austria GmbH (1)
Wollzeile 1-3 Stiege 2 Top 4 3, 1010, Vi-
enna, Austria
Tel.: (43) 59904444
Payment Services
N.A.I.C.S.: 522320

Planet Payment Belgium SA (1)
Avenue Louise 523, 1050, Brussels, Bel-
gium
Tel.: (32) 25368805
Payment Services
N.A.I.C.S.: 522320

Planet Payment Denmark APS (1)
Ostergade 24A 2 Sal Kobenhavn K, 1100,
Copenhagen, Denmark
Tel.: (45) 70277844
Payment Services
N.A.I.C.S.: 522320

Planet Payment Finland OY (1)
Itamerenkatu 1, 00180, Helsinki, Finland
Tel.: (358) 105044050
Payment Services
N.A.I.C.S.: 522320

Planet Payment France SAS (1)
140 Boulevard Malesherbes, 75017, Paris,
France
Tel.: (33) 183799010
Payment Services
N.A.I.C.S.: 522320

Planet Payment Germany GmbH (1)
Sapporobogen 6-8, 80637, Munich, Ger-
many
Tel.: (49) 89244109810
Payment Services
N.A.I.C.S.: 522320

Planet Payment Iceland ehf. (1)
Aoalstraeti 2, 101, Reykjavik, Iceland
Tel.: (354) 5646400
Payment Services
N.A.I.C.S.: 522320

Planet Payment Ireland Limited (1)
8 Claremont Road, Sandymount, Dublin,
Ireland
Tel.: (353) 15133800
Payment Services
N.A.I.C.S.: 522320
Peter Daly (Sec)

Planet Payment Italy S.R.L. (1)

Via Gregoriana 54, 00187, Rome, Italy
Tel.: (39) 0669923383
Payment Services
N.A.I.C.S.: 522320

**Planet Payment Luxembourg
Sarl** (1)
21 rue Glesener, 1631, Luxembourg, Lux-
embourg
Tel.: (352) 25368805
Payment Services
N.A.I.C.S.: 522320

Planet Payment Malta Limited (1)
3rd Floor 293 Republic Street, Valletta, VLT
1110, Malta
Tel.: (356) 22035500
Payment Services
N.A.I.C.S.: 522320

**Planet Payment Netherlands
B.V.** (1)
Luna Arena Herikerbergweg 238, 1101 CM,
Amsterdam, Netherlands
Tel.: (31) 205207909
Payment Services
N.A.I.C.S.: 522320

Planet Payment Norway A/S (1)
Tollbugata 8b, 0152, Oslo, Norway
Tel.: (47) 21995460
Payment Services
N.A.I.C.S.: 522320

**Planet Payment Poland Sp. z
o.o.** (1)
Domaniewska 39, 02-672, Warsaw, Poland
Tel.: (48) 223075222
Payment Services
N.A.I.C.S.: 522320

**Planet Payment Portugal Unipessoal
Lda.** (1)
Rua Duque de Palmela N 2-4 esq, 1250-
098, Lisbon, Portugal
Tel.: (351) 213827140
Payment Services
N.A.I.C.S.: 522320

Planet Payment Sweden AB (1)
Kungsgatan 37 4tr, 111 56, Stockholm,
Sweden
Tel.: (46) 855803017
Payment Services
N.A.I.C.S.: 522320

**Planet Payment Switzerland
GmbH** (1)
Buchholzstrasse 2, 9435, Heerbrugg, Swit-
zerland
Tel.: (41) 717409390
Payment Services
N.A.I.C.S.: 522320

Planet Payment UK Limited (1)
Somerset House 47-49 London Road, Re-
dhill, RH1 1LU, United Kingdom
Tel.: (44) 2035304100
Payment Services
N.A.I.C.S.: 522320

Polyclinique Saint-Odilon, SA (1)
32 Avenue Etienne Sorrel, 03000, Moulins,
France
Tel.: (33) 470443242
Web Site: http://www.polyclinique-st-odilon.fr
Gastroenterology Clinic Services
N.A.I.C.S.: 621111

Polyclinique du Parc Drevon, SA (1)
18 Cours General De Gaulle, 21000, Dijon,
France
Tel.: (33) 380294500
Web Site: http://www.cliniquedrevon.fr
Gastroenterology Clinic Services
N.A.I.C.S.: 621111

**Polyclinique du Val de Saone
SAS** (1)
44 rue Ambroise Pare, 71031, Macon, Ce-
dex, France
Tel.: (33) 385232323
Web Site: http://www.cliniquevaldesaone.fr
Gastroenterology Clinic Services
N.A.I.C.S.: 621111

Seqens SAS (1)
21 chemin de la Sauvegarde 21 Ecully
Parc, CS 33167, 69134, Ecully, Cedex,
France (67%)
Tel.: (33) 426991800

Eurazeo SE—(Continued)

Web Site: http://www.sequens.eu
Emp.: 2,750
Holding Company; Chemicals Mfr & Distr
N.A.I.C.S.: 551112
Pierre Luzeau (CEO)

Subsidiary (Non-US):

CU Chemie Uetikon GmbH   (2)
Raiffeisenstrasse 4, D 77933, Lahr, Germany
Tel.: (49) 7821 585 0
Web Site: http://www.uetikon.com
Emp.: 144
Active Pharmaceutical Ingredients & Fine Chemicals Mfr
N.A.I.C.S.: 325998
Heinz Sieger (Chm-Supervisory Bd)

Subsidiary (Domestic):

PCAS SA   (2)
BP 181-23 Rue Bossuet ZI La Vigne aux Loups, 91160, Longjumeau, France
Tel.: (33) 169097785
Web Site: http://www.pcas.com
Sales Range: $1-9.9 Million
Complex Molecules Mfr
N.A.I.C.S.: 325998

Subsidiary (Domestic):

Expansia S.A.S.   (3)
23 rue Bossuet, BP 181, ZI de la Vigne-aux-Loups, 91160, Longjumeau, Essonne, France
Tel.: (33) 466570101
Web Site: http://www.pcas.com
Pharmaceutical Chemicals Mfr
N.A.I.C.S.: 325998

Subsidiary (US):

PCAS America Inc.   (3)
208 3rd St, Hoboken, NJ 07030-3838
Tel.: (201) 633-0290
Web Site: http://www.pcas.com
Sales Range: $25-49.9 Million
Emp.: 1
Pharmaceutical Preparation Mfr
N.A.I.C.S.: 325412

Subsidiary (Non-US):

PCAS China   (3)
Qi Hua Building 6F 1375 Huai Hai Zhong Lu, Shanghai, China
Tel.: (86) 2164331616
Web Site: http://www.pcaschina.com
Fine Chemicals Mfr
N.A.I.C.S.: 325199

PCAS Finland Oy   (3)
Messukentankatu 8, PO Box 979, 20101, Turku, Finland
Tel.: (358) 23305542
Web Site: https://www.pcasfinland.com
Sales Range: $50-74.9 Million
Emp.: 120
Pharmaceutical Chemicals Mfr
N.A.I.C.S.: 325998

PCAS GmbH   (3)
De-Saint-Exupery-Strasse 8, 60549, Frankfurt am Main, Germany
Tel.: (49) 21028924307
Web Site: http://www.pcas.com
Pharmaceutical Chemicals Mfr
N.A.I.C.S.: 325998

Plant (Domestic):

Produits Chimiques Auxiliaires et de Synthese SA - Usine de Bourgoin Plant   (3)
15 Avenue Des Freres-Lumiere, Bourgoin-Jallieu, 38300, Isere, France
Tel.: (33) 4 74 93 63 33
Web Site: http://www.pcas.com
Sales Range: $25-49.9 Million
Emp.: 70
Pharmaceutical Chemicals Mfr
N.A.I.C.S.: 325998

Produits Chimiques Auxiliaires et de Synthese SA - Usine de Couterne Plant   (3)
Route de Lassay, 61410, Couterne, Orne, France

Tel.: (33) 2 33 37 50 20
Web Site: http://www.pcas.com
Sales Range: $50-74.9 Million
Emp.: 245
Pharmaceutical Chemicals Mfr
N.A.I.C.S.: 325412

Produits Chimiques Auxiliaires et de Synthese SA - Usine de Limay Plant   (3)
19 route de Meulan, 78520, Limay, Yvelines, France
Tel.: (33) 1 34 78 87 87
Web Site: http://www.pcas.com
Pharmaceutical Chemicals Mfr
N.A.I.C.S.: 325199

Subsidiary (Domestic):

VLG Chem S.A.S.   (3)
35 Avenue Jean-Jaures, 92390, Villeneuve-la-Garenne, France
Tel.: (33) 146859191
Pharmaceutical Chemicals Mfr
N.A.I.C.S.: 325998

Vignal Systems SA   (1)
19 Avenue du 24 Aout 1944, BP 594, 69960, Corbas, France   (71%)
Tel.: (33) 4 72 90 29 29
Web Site: http://www.vignal-systems.com
Sales Range: $50-74.9 Million
Emp.: 230
Vehicular Signaling Products & Systems Designer, Mfr & Distr
N.A.I.C.S.: 336320
Fabrice Jahan (Dir-Sls)

WorldStrides Pty. Ltd.   (1)
264 Keilor Road, Essendon North, Melbourne, 3041, VIC, Australia
Tel.: (61) 383250000
Web Site: http://www.worldstrides.com.au
Travel Agency Services
N.A.I.C.S.: 561510
Bob Gogel (Pres & CEO)

Subsidiary (Non-US):

Explorica Canada Inc.   (2)
3080 Yonge Street Suite 5052, Toronto, M4N 3N1, ON, Canada
Web Site: http://www.explorica.ca
Travel Agency Services
N.A.I.C.S.: 561510

iM Global Partner SAS   (1)
20 Rue Treilhard, 75008, Paris, France
Tel.: (33) 188407500
Investment Services
N.A.I.C.S.: 523999
Philippe Couvrecelle (Founder & CEO)

EUREKA 93 INC.

1400-340 Albert Street, Ottawa, K1R 0A5, ON, Canada
Tel.: (613) 566-2831   Ca
Year Founded: 2014
Financial Investment Services
N.A.I.C.S.: 523999

EUREKA DESIGN PUBLIC COMPANY LIMITED

19 MOO 11 Tambon Ladsawai, Amphoe Lamlukka, Pathumthani, 12150, Thailand
Tel.: (66) 21923737
Web Site:
  https://www.eurekadesign.co.th
Year Founded: 2002
UREKA—(THA)
Rev.: $9,285,279
Assets: $51,861,453
Liabilities: $9,853,563
Net Worth: $42,007,890
Earnings: $1,655,577
Fiscal Year-end: 12/31/23
Automotive Machinery Mfr
N.A.I.C.S.: 336390
Awoot Aemwong (Chm)

EUREKA GROUP HOLDINGS LIMITED

Level 5 120 Edward Street, Brisbane, 4000, QLD, Australia

Tel.: (61) 721456322
Web Site:
  https://www.eurekaholdings.com.au
EGH—(ASX)
Rev.: $27,613,515
Assets: $183,780,715
Liabilities: $80,788,595
Net Worth: $102,992,120
Earnings: $8,818,777
Emp.: 12
Fiscal Year-end: 06/30/24
Retirement Facilities Property Asset Management & Catering Services
N.A.I.C.S.: 531390
Tracey Campion (Gen Mgr-Operations)

EUREKA INDUSTRIES LIMITED

1001 Shitiratna Opp Panchwati Apartment, Ellisbridge, Ahmedabad, 380009, Gujarat, India
Tel.: (91) 8052653720   In
Web Site:
  https://www.eurekaindltd.com
Year Founded: 1992
521137—(BOM)
Rev.: $8,504
Assets: $198,347
Liabilities: $15,209
Net Worth: $183,138
Earnings: ($228)
Fiscal Year-end: 03/31/21
Textile Products Mfr
N.A.I.C.S.: 314999
Vinay Nishad (Chm)

EUREKA LITHIUM CORP.

Suite 2300 550 Burrard Street, Vancouver, V6C 2B5, BC, Canada
Tel.: (604) 837-5440   BC
Web Site:
  https://www.eurekalithiumcorp.com
Year Founded: 2021
ERKA—(CNSX)
Rev.: $174,108
Assets: $7,610,761
Liabilities: $715,981
Net Worth: $6,894,780
Earnings: ($4,576,377)
Fiscal Year-end: 12/31/23
Mineral Mining Services
N.A.I.C.S.: 213115
Jeff Wilson (CEO)

EUREKING SA

128 Rue de la Boetie, 75008, Paris, France
Tel.: (33) 153707470   FR
Web Site: https://www.eureking.com
Year Founded: 2022
KINGS—(EUR)
Investment Management Service
N.A.I.C.S.: 523999
Gerard Le Fur (Chm)

EUREMIS HOLDING SA

Avenue Greiner 1, Seraing, 4100, Belgium
Tel.: (32) 498442411   BE
Sales Range: $800-899.9 Million
Emp.: 3,500
Holding Company
N.A.I.C.S.: 551112
Pierre Meyers (CEO & Mng Dir)

Subsidiaries:

Cockerill Maintenance & Ingenierie SA   (1)
Ave Greiner 1, 4100, Seraing, Belgium   (80.65%)
Tel.: (32) 43302243
Web Site: http://www.cmigroupe.com
Sales Range: $750-799.9 Million
Emp.: 2,700
Designs, Maintains, Engineers & Supplies Technical Equipment, Including Boilers,

Weapon Systems, Processing Lines, Chemical & Thermal Process Systems for Energy, Defence & Industry Sectors
N.A.I.C.S.: 333613
Bernard Serin (Chm & Mng Dir)

Holding (US):

CMI Industry Americas Inc.   (2)
435 W Wilson St, Salem, OH 44460
Tel.: (330) 332-4661
Web Site: http://www.cmigroupe.com
Sales Range: $300-349.9 Million
Emp.: 66
Residential Construction Services
N.A.I.C.S.: 236115
Pat Simonsic (Controller)

Subsidiary (Domestic):

CMI Nesa   (2)
Rue Edouard Belin 1, Box 4, 1435, Mont-Saint-Guibert, Belgium
Tel.: (32) 10 47 5611
Web Site: http://www.cmigroupe.com
Sales Range: $25-49.9 Million
Emp.: 75
Engineeering Services
N.A.I.C.S.: 541330

Subsidiary (Non-US):

John Cockerill India Limited   (2)
Mehta House 64 Road No 13 MIDC, Andheri E, Mumbai, 400 093, India
Tel.: (91) 2266762727
Web Site:
  https://www.johncockerillindia.com
Rev.: $59,985,984
Assets: $102,000,719
Liabilities: $78,938,541
Net Worth: $23,062,179
Earnings: $1,544,919
Emp.: 413
Fiscal Year-end: 03/31/2023
Metal Processing Equipment Mfr
N.A.I.C.S.: 333248
Haresh Vala (Compliance Officer & Sec)

EURO ARAB INSURANCE

Wadi Saqra Sharif Nasser Bin Jameel Street Building No 41, PO Box 1435, Amman, 11953, Jordan
Tel.: (962) 65518935
Web Site:
  https://www.euroarabins.com
Year Founded: 1996
AMMI—(AMM)
Rev.: $38,705,654
Assets: $52,462,135
Liabilities: $35,691,380
Net Worth: $16,770,755
Earnings: $1,717,996
Emp.: 90
Fiscal Year-end: 12/31/20
Insurance Services
N.A.I.C.S.: 524298
Fouad Bajjali (Chm)

EURO ASIA EXPORTS LIMITED

PLOT NO 3-A 1st Floor BLK-X Loha Mandi, Naraina Industrial Area, New Delhi, 110028, India
Tel.: (91) 1125894805
Web Site:
  https://www.euroasiaexportsltd.com
530929—(BOM)
Rev.: $261,363
Assets: $107,520
Liabilities: $49,510
Net Worth: $58,011
Earnings: $570
Emp.: 2
Fiscal Year-end: 03/31/21
Textile Product Mfr & Distr
N.A.I.C.S.: 315250
Rakesh Kumar Singhal (Mng Dir)

EURO CERAMICS LTD

208 Sangam Arcade 2nd Floor Vallabhbhai Road, Vile Parle West, Mumbai, 400056, India

Tel.: (91) 2240194019
Web Site:
   https://www.eurovitrified.com
Sales Range: $1-9.9 Million
Emp.: 261
Ceramic Tile Mfr
N.A.I.C.S.: 327120
Nenshi Ladhabhai Shah *(CEO)*

Subsidiaries:

Euro Merchandise (India) Limited **(1)**
208 Sangam Arcade 2nd Floor Vallabhbhai
Road Vile Parle West, Mumbai, 400056,
Maharashtra, India
Tel.: (91) 2240194019
Web Site: http://www.eurotilesindia.com
Sales Range: $25-49.9 Million
Emp.: 50
Wall & Floor Tiles Mfr
N.A.I.C.S.: 327120
Nitesh P. Shah *(Mng Dir)*

EURO CHEMO-PHARMA SDN BHD

2408 and 2809 Lorong Perusahaan
Satu, Prai Industrial Estate, 13600,
Prai, Penang, Malaysia
Tel.: (60) 43901941   MY
Web Site: http://www.eurochemo.com
Year Founded: 1975
Chemical Products Distr
N.A.I.C.S.: 424690

EURO EKSPERTS AD

bul Kocho Racin 38-3/13, Skopje,
North Macedonia
Tel.: (389) 2 3 217 217
Web Site:
   http://www.euroexperts.com.mk
General Insurance Services
N.A.I.C.S.: 524210
Goce Atanasov *(Gen Mgr)*

EURO FRIGO A.D.

Barijeciflicki Put Bb, Pirot, Serbia
Tel.: (381) 10 320 816
Year Founded: 2003
EFRG—(BEL)
Sales Range: Less than $1 Million
Emp.: 31
Fruit & Vegetable Processing Services
N.A.I.C.S.: 311411
Slavisa Nikolic *(Exec Dir)*

EURO HOLDINGS BERHAD

Lot 21 Jalan RP3 Rawang Industrial
Estate, 48000, Rawang, Selangor
Darul Ehsan, Malaysia
Tel.: (60) 360926666
Web Site:
   https://www.euroholdings.com.my
EURO—(KLS)
Rev.: $15,915,983
Assets: $31,381,515
Liabilities: $14,544,090
Net Worth: $16,837,425
Earnings: $366,300
Emp.: 413
Fiscal Year-end: 12/31/20
Office Furniture Mfr
N.A.I.C.S.: 337211
Yuen Keong Choong *(Exec Dir)*

Subsidiaries:

Euro Chairs Manufacturer (M) Sdn
Bhd.   **(1)**
Wisma Euro Lot 21 Rawang Industrial Estate, 48000, Rawang, Selangor Darul Ehsan, Malaysia
Tel.: (60) 360926666
Web Site: https://www.eurochairs.com
Sales Range: $100-124.9 Million
Emp.: 200
Office Furniture Mfr & Distr
N.A.I.C.S.: 337214

Euro Space Industries (M) Sdn
Bhd   **(1)**

Wisma Euro Lot 21 Rawang Industrial Estate, Rawang, 48000, Selangor, Malaysia
Tel.: (60) 360927777
Office Furniture Mfr & Distr
N.A.I.C.S.: 337214

EURO INDIA FRESH FOODS LTD.

4408 Central Tower Kohinoor Square
N C Kelkar Marg R G Gadkari
Chowk, Chhatrapati Shivaji Maharaj
Park, Mumbai, 400059, India
Tel.: (91) 2612913021
Wob Site:
   https://www.euroindiafoods.com
EIFFL—(NSE)
Rev.: $13,448,814
Assets: $15,366,340
Liabilities: $6,939,906
Net Worth: $8,426,435
Earnings: $180,461
Emp.: 434
Fiscal Year-end: 03/31/21
Prepared Food Mfr
N.A.I.C.S.: 311991
Manharbhai Jivanbhai Sanspara
(Chm)

EURO KAPITAL YATIRIM OR-TAKLIGI A.S.

Oguzlar Mah Ceyhun Atif Kansu St
No 66 Floor 2, Balgat, Ankara, Türkiye
Tel.: (90) 3122018800
Web Site:
   https://www.eurokapitalyo.com
EUKYO—(IST)
Financial Investment Services
N.A.I.C.S.: 523999
Ismail Guner *(Gen Mgr)*

EURO MANGANESE, INC.

709 - 700 West Pender Street, Vancouver, V6C 1G8, BC, Canada
Tel.: (604) 681-1010   Ca
Web Site: https://www.mn25.ca
Year Founded: 2014
EMN—(OTCIQ)
Assets: $33,900,644
Liabilities: $4,640,887
Net Worth: $29,259,757
Earnings: ($7,463,281)
Emp.: 17
Fiscal Year-end: 09/30/21
Mining & Mineral Exploration Services
N.A.I.C.S.: 213114
Fausto Taddei *(Sec & VP-Corp Dev)*

EURO MECHANICAL & ELECTRICAL CONTRACTORS LTD.

1st Floor Moh'd Al Hurr Al Suweidi
Bldg, PO Box 46153, Abu Dhabi,
46153, United Arab Emirates
Tel.: (971) 26781133
Web Site:
   http://www.euromechanical.com
Year Founded: 1976
Sales Range: $75-99.9 Million
Emp.: 500
Mechanical & Electrical Contractor
N.A.I.C.S.: 238210
Matt Greenslade *(Gen Mgr-Plant Hire)*

EURO MENKUL KIYMET YATIRIM ORTAKLIGI AS

Oguzlar Mah Ceyhun Atif Kansu St
No 66 Floor 2 Balgat, Ankara, Türkiye
Tel.: (90) 03122018800
Web Site:
   https://www.euroyatirimortakligi.com
EUYO—(IST)
Sales Range: Less than $1 Million
Commercial Banking Services
N.A.I.C.S.: 522110

Coskun Arik *(Chm)*

EURO MULTIVISION LTD.

F12 Ground Floor Sangam Arcade
Vallabhbhai Road, Vile Parle West,
Mumbai, 400056, India
Tel.: (91) 2240364036
Web Site:
   https://www.euromultivision.com
Rev.: $1,247,252
Assets: $14,167,969
Liabilities: $59,334,579
Net Worth: ($45,166,610)
Earnings: ($2,441,346)
Emp.: 4
Fiscal Year-end: 03/31/19
Interior & Exterior Building Materials
Mfr & Distr
N.A.I.C.S.: 321999
Uday Thoria *(CFO)*

EURO STEEL DANMARK A/S

Lundagervej 31, 8722, Hedensted,
Denmark
Tel.: (45) 75890166   DK
Web Site: https://euro-steel.eu
Year Founded: 1988
Steel Products Whslr
N.A.I.C.S.: 331221

Subsidiaries:

Valmont SM A/S   **(1)**
Vaerksvej 5, 6230, Rodekro, Denmark
Tel.: (45) 74393333
Industrial Machinery Mfr
N.A.I.C.S.: 333248

EURO SUN MINING INC.

198 Davenport Road, Box 48, Toronto, M5R 1J2, ON, Canada
Tel.: (416) 843-2099
Web Site:
   https://www.eurosunmining.com
Year Founded: 2003
ESM—(OTCIQ)
Assets: $2,913,193
Liabilities: $4,278,834
Net Worth: ($1,365,641)
Earnings: ($11,213,682)
Emp.: 422
Fiscal Year-end: 12/31/19
Mineral Exploration & Development
Services
N.A.I.C.S.: 327999
Grant Sboros *(CEO)*

EURO TECH HOLDINGS COMPANY LIMITED

Unit D 18/F Gee Chang Hong Centre
65 Wong Chuk Hong Road, Hong
Kong, China (Hong Kong)   VG
Tel.: (852) 28140311
Web Site: https://www.euro-tech.com
Year Founded: 1971
CLWT—(NASDAQ)
Rev.: $21,388,000
Assets: $21,250,000
Liabilities: $6,449,000
Net Worth: $14,801,000
Earnings: $989,000
Emp.: 67
Fiscal Year-end: 12/31/21
Analytical Instrument Distr
N.A.I.C.S.: 333310
T. C. Leung *(Chm & CEO)*

Subsidiaries:

Euro Tech (Far East) Ltd.   **(1)**
Room C D 18/F Gee Chang Hong Centre
65 Wong Chuk Hang Road, 65 Wong Chuk
Hong Road, Hong Kong, China (Hong
Kong)
Tel.: (852) 28140311
Web Site: https://www.euro-tech.com
Sales Range: $25-49.9 Million
Analytical Instrument Distr
N.A.I.C.S.: 551112

Shanghai Euro Tech Ltd.   **(1)**
Unit 305 building 2 Xinguang kech-
uangyuan 177 JiangKai Road, Minhang District, Shanghai, 201206, PR, China **(100%)**
Tel.: (86) 2158347460
Emp.: 20
Business Support Services
N.A.I.C.S.: 561499

EURO TREND YATIRIM OR-TAKLIGI AS

Oguzlar Mah Ceyhun Atif Kansu St
No 66 Floor 2, Balgat, 6520, Ankara,
Turkiye
Tel.: (90) 3122018800
Web Site:
   https://www.eurotrendyo.com
ETYAT—(IST)
Sales Range: Less than $1 Million
Investment Management Service
N.A.I.C.S.: 523940
Orkun Sahin *(Chm)*

EURO YATIRIM HOLDING AS

Yildiz Posta Caddesi Cerrahogullari Is
Merkezi No 17 Kat 4, Sisli, Istanbul,
Turkiye
Tel.: (90) 2123540700
Web Site: https://euroyatirim.com.tr
Year Founded: 1996
EUHOL—(IST)
Sales Range: Less than $1 Million
Holding Company
N.A.I.C.S.: 551112
Ali Arslan *(Vice Chm)*

EURO-CYCLES SA

Zone Industrielle, Kalaa Kebira, 4060,
Sousse, Tunisia
Tel.: (216) 36408806
Web Site: https://www.euro-
   cycles.com
Year Founded: 1993
ECYCL—(BVT)
Assemble Kid Bike Product Mfr
N.A.I.C.S.: 336991
Mourad Ghazi *(Gen Mgr)*

EURO-FINANCE LTD.

43 Christopher Columbus Blvd floor
5, Sofia, 1592, Bulgaria
Tel.: (359) 70015656   BG
Web Site: http://www.eurofinance.bg
Year Founded: 1993
Sales Range: Less than $1 Million
Emp.: 30
Financial Services
N.A.I.C.S.: 525990
Toma Kavroshilov *(Dir-Securities)*

EURO-M FLEXIBLE PACKAGING SA

140 Route De Wallonie, 7011, Ghlin,
Belgium
Tel.: (32) 6576 0000   BE
Web Site: http://www.eurom.be
Sales Range: $10-24.9 Million
Emp.: 60
Flexible Packaging Products Mfr
N.A.I.C.S.: 326112
Silvio Pignone *(Mng Dir)*

EURO-MED LABORATORIES PHIL., INC.

2nd Floor PPL Bldg UN Avenue corner San Marcelino, Manila, Philippines
Tel.: (63) 285240091
Web Site:
   https://www.euromedlab.net
EURO—(PHI)
Rev.: $79,645,726
Assets: $209,490,033
Liabilities: $96,175,280
Net Worth: $113,314,753
Earnings: $4,369,044
Emp.: 1,118

Euro-Med Laboratories Phil., Inc.—(Continued)

Fiscal Year-end: 12/31/20
Intravenous Fluids Mfr
N.A.I.C.S.: 325412
Janice R. Ong (Sec)

Subsidiaries:

Hemotek Renal Center, Inc. (1)
3rd Flr PPL Bldg 1000 United Nations Ave,
Paco, Manila, 1007, Philippines
Tel.: (63) 5361091.
Web Site: http://www.hemotek.net
Kidney Dialysis Services
N.A.I.C.S.: 621492

EURO-PRO CORPORATION
4400 Bois Franc, Saint Laurent, H4S
IA7, QC, Canada
Tel.: (514) 842-8691
Web Site: http://www.euro-pro.com
Year Founded: 1950
Sales Range: $25-49.9 Million
Emp.: 100
Vacuum Cleaner & Household Appliance Designer, Mfr & Distr
N.A.I.C.S.: 335210

EUROAMERICA SEGUROS DE VIDA, S.A.
Agustinas 1127 3rd Floor, Santiago,
8340418, Chile
Tel.: (56) 27827000
Web Site: http://www.euroamerica.cl
Year Founded: 1900
Sales Range: $50-74.9 Million
Emp.: 400
Insurance & Financial Products
N.A.I.C.S.: 524128
Jaime Artigas Celis (Dir-Admin & Fin)

EUROAPI SAS
15 Rue Traversiere, 75012, Paris,
France
Tel.: (33) 189206200
Web Site: https://www.euroapi.com
Year Founded: 2020
EAPI—(EUR)
Rev.: $1,093,459,961
Assets: $1,740,125,189
Liabilities: $738,938,053
Net Worth: $1,001,187,136
Earnings: ($204,726,959)
Emp.: 3,650
Fiscal Year-end: 12/31/23
Pharmaceutical Product Mfr & Distr
N.A.I.C.S.: 325412
Antoine Delcour (CFO)

EUROBANK ERGASIAS SERVICES AND HOLDINGS S.A.
8 Othonos Street, 10557, Athens,
Greece
Tel.: (30) 2144061000   **GR**
Web Site:
https://www.eurobankholdings.gr
Year Founded: 1990
EUROB—(ATH)
Rev.: $2,498,381,179
Assets: $87,912,799,482
Liabilities: $80,662,637,600
Net Worth: $7,250,161,882
Earnings: $1,435,355,062
Emp.: 11,328
Fiscal Year-end: 12/31/22
Holding Company
N.A.I.C.S.: 551112
Stavros E. Ioannou (Deputy CEO & COO-Intl Activities)

Subsidiaries:

Bancpost S.A. (1)
6A Dimitrie Pompeiu Boulevard Sector 2,
020337, Bucharest, Romania
Tel.: (40) 213020789
Web Site: http://www.bancpost.ro

Sales Range: $1-4.9 Billion
Emp.: 3,500
Commercial Banking Services
N.A.I.C.S.: 522110
Andreea Argentina Anghel (Mgr)

Be-Business Exchanges S.A. (1)
be24 Panagouli and Siniosoglou, Nea Ionia,
142 34, Athens, Greece
Tel.: (30) 214 404 5981
Web Site: https://www.be24.gr
Sales Range: $50-74.9 Million
Emp.: 10
Ecommerce Services
N.A.I.C.S.: 425120
Alkiviadis Trigas (CFO)

EFG Business Services d.o.o.
Beograd (1)
Eurobank EFG Centar 10 Vuka Karadzica
Str, 11000, Belgrade, Serbia
Tel.: (381) 11 320 7572
Payroll Processing Services
N.A.I.C.S.: 541214

EFG Eurobank Finance S.A. (1)
America House 4-8 Nicolae Titulescu Blvd,
West Wing 4th Floor, 011141, Bucharest,
Romania
Tel.: (40) 212062300
Web Site: http://www.efgfinance.ro
Sales Range: $50-74.9 Million
Emp.: 2
Financial Advisory Services
N.A.I.C.S.: 523940

EFG Eurobank Property Services
S.A. (1)
6A Dimitrie Pompeiu Blvd Olympus House
Fifth Fl, District 2, 020337, Bucharest, Romania
Tel.: (40) 213086100
Web Site:
http://www.eurobankpropertyservices.ro
Sales Range: $50-74.9 Million
Emp.: 25
Real Estate Mariangement Services
N.A.I.C.S.: 531210
Stefanos Doulas (Gen Mgr)

EFG Leasing IFN S.A. (1)
6A Dimitrie Pompeiu Boulevard Sector 2 5
th Floor, 020337, Bucharest, 020337, Romania
Tel.: (40) 213086121
Web Site: http://www.efgleasing.ro
Emp.: 20
Financial Lending Services
N.A.I.C.S.: 522220
Constantin Gina (Principal)

EFG Leasing Poland Sp. z o o
19 Mokotowska Street, 00-560, Warsaw,
Poland
Tel.: (48) 22 347 75 30
Web Site: http://www.efgleasing.com.pl
Financial Lending Services
N.A.I.C.S.: 522220

EFG Property Services Polska
Sp.z o.o. (1)
Mokotowska 19, 00 560, Warsaw, Poland
Tel.: (48) 223438084
Web Site: http://www.efgpropertyservices.pl
Real Estate Mariangement Services
N.A.I.C.S.: 531210

EFG Property Services Ukraine
LLC (1)
54/19 Avtozavodska Street, 4114, Kiev,
Ukraine
Tel.: (380) 443915604
Web Site:
http://www.efgpropertyservices.net.ua
Sales Range: $50-74.9 Million
Emp.: 3
Real Estate Mariangement Services
N.A.I.C.S.: 531210
George Vasilantonakis (Gen Mgr)

EFG Property Services d.o.o.
Belgrade (1)
10 Vuka Karadzica Str, 11000, Belgrade,
Serbia
Tel.: (381) 11 3207 580
Web Site: http://www.efgpropertyservices.rs
Real Estate Mariangement Services
N.A.I.C.S.: 531210

EFG Retail Services IFN S.A. (1)

6A Dimitrie Pompeiu Boulevard Sector 2
3rd & 4th Floor, 020337, Bucharest, Romania
Tel.: (40) 21 308 4000
Web Site: http://www.euroline-cards.ro
Credit Card Issuing Services
N.A.I.C.S.: 522210

Eurobank Bulgaria AD (1)
260 Okolovrasten Pat Str, 1766, Sofia, Bulgaria
Tel.: (359) 2 816 6000
Web Site: https://www.postbank.bg
Sales Range: $350-399.9 Million
Emp.: 2,998
Banking Services
N.A.I.C.S.: 522110
Anthony C. Hassiotis (Chm-Mgmt Bd & CEO)

Subsidiary (Domestic):

BNP Paribas Personal Finance
EAD (2)
Residential Complex Mladost 4 Business
Park Sofia Building 14, 1766, Sofia, Bulgaria
Tel.: (359) 70011811
Web Site: http://www.bnpparibas-pf.bg
Financial Management Services
N.A.I.C.S.: 523999

EFG Auto Leasing E.O.Q.D. (2)
14 Tzar Osvoboditel Blvd, 1000, Sofia, Bulgaria
Tel.: (359) 2 937 5858
Web Site: http://www.postbank.bg
Sales Range: $25-49.9 Million
Emp.: 30
Automobile Leasing Services
N.A.I.C.S.: 532112
Gergana Gerdzhikova (Gen Mgr)

EFG Securities Bulgaria E.A.D. (2)
14 Tzar Osvoboditel Boulevard, 1048, Sofia, Bulgaria
Tel.: (359) 2 811 6601
Securities Brokerage Services
N.A.I.C.S.: 523150

Piraeus Bank Bulgaria AD (2)
115 E Tsarigradsko Shosse Blvd, 1784, Sofia, Bulgaria
Tel.: (359) 70012002
Web Site: http://www.piraeusbank.bg
Sales Range: $125-149.9 Million
Banking Services
N.A.I.C.S.: 522110

Eurobank Cyprus Ltd. (1)
28 Spyrou Kyprianou Avenue, 1075, Nicosia, Cyprus
Tel.: (357) 22208000
Web Site: https://www.eurobank.com.cy
Banking Services
N.A.I.C.S.: 522110

Eurobank Direktna A.D (1)
10 Vuka Karadzica Street, 11000, Belgrade,
Serbia
Tel.: (381) 112023353
Web Site: https://www.eurobank-direktna.rs
Emp.: 11,762
Retail & Corporate Banking Services
N.A.I.C.S.: 541430

Eurobank EFG A.D. Belgrade (1)
10 Vuka Karadzica Street, 11000, Belgrade,
Serbia
Tel.: (381) 112023353
Web Site: http://www.eurobankefg.rs
Commercial Banking Services
N.A.I.C.S.: 522110
Slavica Pavlovic (Member-Exec Bd & CFO)

Subsidiary (Domestic):

EFG Leasing A.D. Belgrade (2)
Vuka Karadzica 10, Belgrade, 11000, Serbia
Tel.: (381) 113027555
Web Site: http://www.eurobank.rs
Sales Range: $25-49.9 Million
Emp.: 13
Financial Lending Services
N.A.I.C.S.: 522220
Baldan Milanovic (Mng Dir)

Eurobank EFG Business Services
S.A. (1)
21 Kallirois Street, Athens, 11743, Greece

Tel.: (30) 2109008500
Web Site: http://www.eurobank-bs.gr
Sales Range: $25-49.9 Million
Emp.: 60
Payroll Processing Services
N.A.I.C.S.: 541214
George Katiniotis (CEO)

Eurobank EFG Cyprus Ltd. (1)
41 Arch Makarios Avenue, Nicosia, 1065,
Cyprus
Tel.: (357) 22 20 8000
Web Site: http://www.eurobank.com.cy
Sales Range: $50-74.9 Million
Emp.: 70
Commercial Banking Services
N.A.I.C.S.: 522110

Eurobank EFG Equities Investment
Firm S.A. (1)
Filellinon 10, 105 57, Athens, Greece
Tel.: (30) 2103720000
Web Site: https://www.eurobankequities.gr
Equities Investment Services
N.A.I.C.S.: 531110
Nikolaos Andrianopoulos (CEO & Pres)

Eurobank EFG Factors S.A. (1)
16 Laodikias and 1-3 Nymfeou Str, 115 28,
Athens, Greece
Tel.: (30) 2144060700
Web Site: https://www.eurobankfactors.gr
Sales Range: $50-74.9 Million
Emp.: 50
Factoring & Forfaiting Services
N.A.I.C.S.: 522299
George Karagiannopoulos (CEO)

Eurobank EFG Fund Management
Company (Luxembourg) S.A. (1)
5 rue Jean Monnet Str, PO Box 438, 2180,
Luxembourg, Luxembourg
Tel.: (352) 2609151
Web Site: http://www.eurobankefg-fmc.lu
Sales Range: $50-74.9 Million
Emp.: 10
Mutual Fund Management Services
N.A.I.C.S.: 525910
Georgios Vlachakis (Mng Dir)

Eurobank EFG Mutual Funds Management Company S.A. (1)
10 Stadiou St, 105 64, Athens, Greece
Tel.: (30) 2103352800
Web Site: http://www.eurobank.gr
Emp.: 62
Mutual Fund Management Services
N.A.I.C.S.: 525910
Elena Griga (Head-IT Ops & Sys Admin)

Eurobank Fin and Rent S.A. (1)
34 El Venizelou, 106 79, Athens, Greece
Tel.: (30) 210 366 0800
Web Site: http://www.eurobank.gr
Automobile Leasing Services
N.A.I.C.S.: 532112
Konstantinos Kanakis (CEO)

Eurobank Leasing Single-Member
SA (1)
7-13 Eslin 20 Amaliados Streets, 11523,
Athens, Greece
Tel.: (30) 2144057200
Web Site: https://www.eurobank-leasing.gr
Sales Range: $50-74.9 Million
Emp.: 57
Financial Lending Services
N.A.I.C.S.: 523999
Zacharias Vlachos (CEO)

Eurobank Private Bank Luxembourg
SA (1)
534 rue de Neudorf, 2220, Luxembourg,
Luxembourg
Tel.: (352) 4207241
Web Site: https://www.eurobankpb.lu
Emp.: 80
Private Banking & Investment Advisory Services
N.A.I.C.S.: 522110
Haris Hambakis (CEO)

Grivalia Properties Real Estate Investments Company S.A. (1)
117 Kifissias Avenue Agiou Konstantinou,
Maroussi, 151 24, Athens,
Greece   (51.43%)
Tel.: (30) 2108129600
Web Site: https://www.grivalia.com
Rev.: $77,842,932
Assets: $1,281,528,125

Liabilities: $193,626,882
Net Worth: $1,087,901,243
Earnings: $75,641,265
Emp.: 31
Fiscal Year-end: 12/31/2017
Real Estate Property Services
N.A.I.C.S.: 531210
Natalia Strafti *(Mng Partner-Ops)*

IMO Property Investments A.D. **(1)**
Vuka Karadzica 10 260 Okolovrasten Pat
Building C Floor 3 Office 7, 11000, Beo-
grad, Serbia
Tel.: (381) 3027521
Real Estate Fund Services
N.A.I.C.S.: 522292

Open 24 S.A. **(1)**
188 Syngrou Avenue, 176 71, Kallithea,
Athens, Greece
Tel.: (30) 210 955 8100
Web Site: http://www.open24.gr
Financial & Insurance Services
N.A.I.C.S.: 522291

SC EFG Eurolife Asigurari Generale
S.A. **(1)**
6A Dimitrie Pompeiu Boulevard Sector 2,
020337, Bucharest, Romania
Tel.: (40) 21 320 0640
Web Site: http://www.efgeurolife.ro
Sales Range: $50-74.9 Million
Emp.: 17
General Insurance Services
N.A.I.C.S.: 524210

SC EFG Eurolife Asigurari de Viata
S.A. **(1)**
6A Dimitrie Pompeiu Boulevard Sector 2
Olympus House 5 Floor, 020337, Bucha-
rest, 020337, Romania
Tel.: (40) 314184083
Web Site: http://www.eurolife-asigurari.ro
Sales Range: $50-74.9 Million
Emp.: 12
Fire Insurance Services
N.A.I.C.S.: 524113
Anita Laura Nitulescu *(Gen Dir)*

Seferco Development S.A. **(1)**
1 No 17 Fagaras Street Attic Room 3, Bu-
charest, Romania
Tel.: (40) 213002831
Own & Leased Real Estate Operator
N.A.I.C.S.: 531190

T Bank S.A. **(1)**
Omirou 22, 106 72, Athens, Greece
Tel.: (30) 21 0336 4000
Sales Range: $100-124.9 Million
International Banking Services
N.A.I.C.S.: 522299
George Dayantis *(Gen Mgr-Ops & IT)*

Subsidiary (Domestic):

Aspis Insurance Brokerage SA **(2)**
330 Venizelou Avenue, 176 75, Athens,
Greece
Tel.: (30) 2109402265
Insurance Services
N.A.I.C.S.: 524298

Aspis International AEDAK **(2)**
23-25 Lekka Str, 105 62, Athens, Greece
Tel.: (30) 2103727800
Web Site: http://www.aspisfunds.gr
Sales Range: $50-74.9 Million
Emp.: 20
Financial Services
N.A.I.C.S.: 523999

Aspis Leasing S.A. **(2)**
23-25 Lekka St, 105 62, Athens, Greece
Tel.: (30) 2103364451
Web Site: http://www.tbank.gr
Sales Range: $50-74.9 Million
Emp.: 17
Leasing Services
N.A.I.C.S.: 532490

EUROBATTERY MINERALS AB
Strandvagen 7A, 114 56, Stockholm,
Sweden
Tel.: (46) 31131190
Web Site:
    https://www.eurobatterymineral.com
Year Founded: 2009
EBM—(STU)

Mineral Exploration Services
N.A.I.C.S.: 213115
Roberto Garcia Martinez *(CEO)*

EUROBIO SCIENTIFIC SA
7 avenue de Scandinavie ZA de
Courtaboeuf, Les Ulis, 91953, Paris,
France
Tel.: (33) 1 69 79 64 80
Web Site: http://www.diaxonhit.com
Year Founded: 1997
ALEHT.PA—(EUR)
Sales Range: $10-24.9 Million
Biomedical Diagnostic Equipment
Distr
N.A.I.C.S.: 423450
Herve Duchesne de Lamotte *(CFO &
Gen Mgr)*

Subsidiaries:

Innominata **(1)**
15222 Avenue of Science, San Diego, CA
92128
Tel.: (858) 592-9300
Web Site: http://www.genbio.com
Sales Range: $1-9.9 Million
Emp.: 18
Biomedical Diagnostic Product Mfr
N.A.I.C.S.: 325413
Fred Adler *(Principal)*

EUROBROKERS S.A.
100 Kifissias Av Marathonodromou
83 St, Marousi, 15125, Athens,
Greece
Tel.: (30) 210 8123800
Web Site: http://www.eurobrokers.gr
Year Founded: 1992
EUBRK—(ATH)
Sales Range: $1-9.9 Million
Emp.: 50
Insurance Brokerage & Advisory Ser-
vices
N.A.I.C.S.: 524210
George Koumbas *(Chm)*

EUROCASH S.A.
ul Wisniowa 11, 62-052, Komorniki,
Poland
Tel.: (48) 616513313
Web Site: http://www.eurocash.pl
Year Founded: 1995
EUSHF—(OTCIQ)
Rev.: $6,851,070,953
Assets: $2,174,617,308
Liabilities: $1,904,241,308
Net Worth: $270,376,000
Earnings: $18,353,326
Emp.: 21,067
Fiscal Year-end: 12/31/20
Grocery Store Owner & Operator
N.A.I.C.S.: 457110
Rui Amaral *(Member-Mgmt Bd)*

Subsidiaries:

ABC Na Kolach Sp. z o.o. **(1)**
ul Wisniowa 11, 62-052, Komorniki, Poland
Tel.: (48) 500063241
Web Site: http://www.abcnakolach.pl
Food Distr
N.A.I.C.S.: 424490
Marta Krolikowska *(Mng Dir)*

ABC Sp. z o.o. **(1)**
ul Powstancow Warszawskich 45, 80-165,
Gdansk, Poland
Tel.: (48) 587187187
Web Site: http://www.amber-hotel.pl
Hotel Operator
N.A.I.C.S.: 721110

Akademia Umiejetnosci Eurocash Sp.
z o.o. **(1)**
Marynarska Business Park ul Tasmowa 7a,
02-677, Warsaw, Poland
Tel.: (48) 502004024
Web Site:
    http://www.akademiaeurocash.com.pl
Professional Training Services
N.A.I.C.S.: 611430

Cerville Investments Sp. z o.o. **(1)**
Ul Czerniowiecka 2B, 02-705, Warsaw,
Poland
Tel.: (48) 224282011
Web Site: http://www.cerville.com.pl
Alcohol Mfr
N.A.I.C.S.: 312140

EKO Holding SA **(1)**
Ul Ryszarda Chomicza 13C Nowa Wies
Wroclawska, 55-080, Katy Wroclawskie,
Poland **(100%)**
Tel.: (48) 717491101
Web Site: http://www.eko.pl
Holding Company; Food, Pharmaceuticals
& Household Chemicals, Cosmetics & Per-
sonal Care Products Retailer & Distr
N.A.I.C.S.: 551112

Inmedio Sp. z o.o. **(1)**
Aleje Jerozolimskie 174, 02-486, Warsaw,
Poland
Tel.: (48) 506015353
Web Site: http://www.inmediotrendy.pl
Professional Training Services
N.A.I.C.S.: 611430

Innowacyjna Platforma Handlu Sp. z
o.o. **(1)**
Ul Wisniowa 11, 62-052, Komorniki, Poland
Tel.: (48) 795183602
Web Site: https://www.iph.com.pl
Publishing Services
N.A.I.C.S.: 541511

Lewiatan Podkarpacie Sp. z o.o. **(1)**
ul Krakowska 47, 39-200, Debica, Poland
Tel.: (48) 146815199
Grocery Product Distr
N.A.I.C.S.: 445110

Lewiatan Podlasie Sp. z o.o. **(1)**
ul Porosly 70 A, Choroszcz, 16-070, Bialys-
tok, Poland
Tel.: (48) 857465712
Grocery Product Distr
N.A.I.C.S.: 445110

Lewiatan Polnoc Sp. z o.o. **(1)**
ul of The 1st Division of The Polish Army
98, 84-230, Rumia, Poland
Tel.: (48) 585728576
Grocery Product Distr
N.A.I.C.S.: 445110

Lewiatan Zachod Sp. z o.o. **(1)**
ul Przemyslowa 5, 73-110, Stargard Szc-
zecinski, Poland
Tel.: (48) 915778558
Grocery Product Distr
N.A.I.C.S.: 445110

Mila S.A. **(1)**
Ul Swietokrzyska 22, 88-100, Inowroclaw,
Poland
Tel.: (48) 523042422
Web Site: http://www.mila.pl
Fresh Food & Vegetable Distr
N.A.I.C.S.: 445230

EUROCASTLE INVESTMENT LIMITED
Oak House Hirzel Street, Saint Peter
Port, GY1 2NP, Guernsey
Tel.: (44) 2072905600
Web Site:
    https://www.eurocastleinv.com
ECT—(EUR)
Rev.: $3,602,428
Assets: $41,186,572
Liabilities: $738,172
Net Worth: $40,448,400
Earnings: $1,306,841
Fiscal Year-end: 12/31/21
Investment Services
N.A.I.C.S.: 523999

EUROCHARM HOLDINGS CO., LTD.
No 15 Lane 315 XinShu Road, Xin-
Zhuang District, New Taipei City, 242,
Taiwan
Tel.: (886) 222080151
Web Site:
    https://www.eurocharm.com.tw
Year Founded: 1974

5288—(TAI)
Rev.: $165,717,322
Assets: $187,801,810
Liabilities: $78,570,217
Net Worth: $109,231,593
Earnings: $19,677,395
Emp.: 3,400
Fiscal Year-end: 12/31/20
Medical Equipment & Motorcycle
Parts Mfr
N.A.I.C.S.: 339112
Steven Yu *(Chm & Gen Mgr)*

Subsidiaries:

Eurocharm Innovation Co., Ltd. **(1)**
No 15 Lane 315 XinShu Road, XinZhuang
District, New Taipei City, 242, Taiwan
Tel.: (886) 222028393
Motorcycle Parts Distr
N.A.I.C.S.: 423110

Subsidiary (Non-US):

Vietnam Precision Industrial No.1
Co., Ltd. **(2)**
Khai Quang Industrial Zone, Khai Quang,
Vinh Yen, Vinh Phuc, Vietnam
Tel.: (84) 2113842897
Motorcycle Parts Distr
N.A.I.C.S.: 423110

EUROCHEM MINERAL CHEMI-CAL COMPANY, OJSC
53 p 6 Dubininskaya Street, 115054,
Moscow, Russia
Tel.: (7) 4957952527 RU
Web Site: http://www.eurochem.ru
Year Founded: 2001
Sales Range: $200-249.9 Million
Emp.: 25,700
Holding Company; Fertilizer Mfr
N.A.I.C.S.: 551112
Dmitry Strezhnev *(CEO)*

Subsidiaries:

EuroChem - Belorechenskie Minudo-
brenia, LLC **(1)**
Chemical Site, 352636, Belorechensk, Kras-
nodar, Russia **(100%)**
Tel.: (7) 86155 2 31 31
Web Site: http://www.eurochem.ru
Phosphate & Compound Fertilizers Mfr
N.A.I.C.S.: 325312

EuroChem Antwerpen NV **(1)**
Scheldelaan 600, Zandvliet, 2040, Antwerp,
Belgium **(100%)**
Tel.: (32) 32105500
Web Site: http://www.werkenbijeurochem.be
Fertilizer Mfr
N.A.I.C.S.: 325314

EuroChem Trading GmbH **(1)**
Bundesstrasse 5, 6301, Zug,
Switzerland **(100%)**
Tel.: (41) 41 727 7608
Web Site: http://www.eurochem.ru
Sales of Fertilizers
N.A.I.C.S.: 424690

Subsidiary (Non-US):

EuroChem Agro GmbH **(2)**
Reichskanzler-Mueller-Strasse 23, 68165,
Mannheim, Germany **(100%)**
Tel.: (49) 621 87209 0
Web Site: http://www.eurochemagro.com
Emp.: 100
Nitrogenous Fertilizer Mfr
N.A.I.C.S.: 325311
Andriy Savchuk *(Gen Mgr)*

Subsidiary (Non-US):

EuroChem Agro Hellas SA **(3)**
Mesogeion 249, Neo Psichiko, 154 51, Ath-
ens, Greece
Tel.: (30) 211 1769 142
Web Site: http://eurochemagro.com
Nitrogen Fertilizer Mfr
N.A.I.C.S.: 325311

Subsidiary (Non-US):

EuroChem Agro Iberia, S.L. **(2)**

EuroChem Mineral Chemical Company,
OJSC—(Continued)

Joan dAustria 39-47 6 planta, 08005, Bar-
celona, Spain　　　　　　　　　**(100%)**
Tel.: (34) 932247222
Web Site: http://www.es.eurochemagro.com
Nitrogenous Fertilizer Mfr
N.A.I.C.S.: 325311

EuroChem Comercio de Produtos
Quimicos Ltda　　　　　　　　　**(2)**
888 Rua Tabapua 2nd Floor, Sao Paulo,
04533 003, Brazil　　　　　　　**(50%)**
Tel.: (55) 11 3562 1486
Sales of Fertilizers
N.A.I.C.S.: 424690

EuroChem Trading USA Corp.　　**(1)**
2701 N Rocky Point Dr Ste 600, Tampa, FL
33607　　　　　　　　　　　　　**(100%)**
Tel.: (813) 549-3400
Web Site: http://www.eurochem.ru
Fertilizer Mfr & Distr
N.A.I.C.S.: 424690
Kathie Ditri (Mgr)

Lifosa AB　　　　　　　　　　　**(1)**
Juodkiskio str 50, 57502, Kedainiai,
Lithuania　　　　　　　　　　　**(96.35%)**
Tel.: (370) 347 66483
Web Site: http://www.lifosa.com
Fertilizer Mfr
N.A.I.C.S.: 325311
Juozas Baniota (Dir-Admin)

Novomoskovskiy Azot, OJSC　　**(1)**
10 Svyasi St, Novomoskovsk, Moscow,
31660, Tula Region, Russia
Tel.: (7) 48762 2 22 22
Web Site: http://www.eurochem.ru
Ammonia & Nitrogen Fertilizer Mfr
N.A.I.C.S.: 325311

Phosphorit Industrial Group, LLC　**(1)**
Phosphorit Industrial Site, Kingisepp,
188452, Leningrad Region, Russia **(100%)**
Tel.: (7) 81375 9 53 12
Web Site: http://www.eurochem.ru
Phosphate Fertilizers & Feed Phosphates
Mfr
N.A.I.C.S.: 325312

EUROCLEAR S.A./N.V.

1 Boulevard du Roi Albert II, 1210,
Brussels, Belgium
Tel.: (32) 23261211　　　　　　BE
Web Site: http://www.euroclear.com
Year Founded: 1968
Rev.: $1,607,510,876
Assets: $30,872,958,958
Liabilities: $26,136,386,783
Net Worth: $4,736,572,174
Earnings: $482,399,852
Emp.: 3,989
Fiscal Year-end: 12/31/19
Securities Settlement Services
N.A.I.C.S.: 523210
Lieve Mostrey (CEO)

Subsidiaries:

Calar Belgium S.A./N.V.　　　　**(1)**
1 Blvd Du Roi Albert II, B 1210, Brussels,
Belgium　　　　　　　　　　　**(100%)**
Tel.: (32) 22241211
Sales Range: $1-4.9 Billion
Emp.: 3,000
Financial Services
N.A.I.C.S.: 523940

Euroclear Finland Oy　　　　　**(1)**
Urho Kekkosen katu 5C, 101, Helsinki, Fin-
land
Tel.: (358) 20 770 6000
Securities & Commodity Exchange Services
N.A.I.C.S.: 523210
Jani Viskari (Mgr-Settlement & Debt Ops)

Euroclear Sweden AB　　　　　**(1)**
Klarabergsviadukten 63, Box 191, Stock-
holm, 101 23, Sweden
Tel.: (46) 84 02 90 00
Securities & Commodity Exchange Services
N.A.I.C.S.: 523210

Euroclear UK & Ireland　　　　**(1)**
33 Cannon St, London, EC4M 5SB, United
Kingdom

Tel.: (44) 2078490000
Web Site: http://www.euroclear.com
Sales Range: $200-249.9 Million
Emp.: 500
Provider of Securities Settlement Services
N.A.I.C.S.: 523210

TradeGO S.A./N.V.　　　　　　**(1)**
1 Boulevard du Roi Albert II, B-1210, Brussels, Belgium
Investment Banking Services
N.A.I.C.S.: 523150

EUROCOM CORPORATION

148 Colonnado Road, Nopoan, K2E
7R4, ON, Canada
Tel.: (613) 224-6122
Web Site: https://www.eurocom.com
Year Founded: 1989
Sales Range: $100-124.9 Million
Portable Computer & Mobile Servers
Mfr
N.A.I.C.S.: 334111
Mark Bialic (Pres)

EUROCOMMERCIAL PROPER-
TIES N.V.

Herengracht 469, 1017 BS, Amster-
dam, Netherlands
Tel.: (31) 205306030
Web Site:
　　https://www.europroperties.com
ECMPM—(ITA)
Rev.: $283,537,918
Assets: $4,223,624,021
Liabilities: $2,007,949,001
Net Worth: $2,215,675,020
Earnings: ($28,806,712)
Emp.: 97
Fiscal Year-end: 12/31/23
Real Estate Investment Services
N.A.I.C.S.: 531210
Jeremy P. Lewis (CEO & Founder)

Subsidiaries:

Aktiebolaget Norrkoping Silvret 1　**(1)**
PO Box 1147, 11181, Stockholm, Sweden
Tel.: (46) 84535046
Miscellaneous Financial Investment Activi-
ties
N.A.I.C.S.: 523999

Bergvik Kopet 3 K.B.　　　　　**(1)**
Timmergatan 1, 65115, Karlstad, Sweden
Tel.: (46) 54220000
Other Real Estate Property Lessors
N.A.I.C.S.: 531190

Burlov Centre Fastighets A.B.　**(1)**
PO Box 1147, 11181, Stockholm, Sweden
Tel.: (46) 84535046
Other Real Estate Property Lessors
N.A.I.C.S.: 531190

ECP Karlskrona AB　　　　　　**(1)**
Norrlandsgatan 22, Stockholm, 111 43,
Sweden
Tel.: (46) 86785360
Web Site: http://www.ecpnb.com
Sales Range: $50-74.9 Million
Emp.: 8
Investment Management Service
N.A.I.C.S.: 523999

ECP Moraberg K.B.　　　　　　**(1)**
PO Box 1147, 11181, Stockholm, Sweden
Tel.: (46) 84535046
Other Real Estate Property Lessors
N.A.I.C.S.: 531190
Martin Bjoorn (Mng Dir)

Ecp Collestrada S.R.L.　　　　**(1)**
Via Valtiera 181, Collestrada, 06135, Peru-
gia, Italy
Tel.: (39) 0758420434
Web Site: https://www.collestrada.it
Shopping Centre Services
N.A.I.C.S.: 531120

Eurocommercial Properties Azur
S.a.r.l　　　　　　　　　　　　　**(1)**
66 Avenue des Champs Elysees (Chez Abc
Liv), 75008, Paris, France
Tel.: (33) 140687002

Miscellaneous Financial Investment Activities
N.A.I.C.S.: 523999

Eurocommercial Properties Caumar-
tin S.N.C.　　　　　　　　　　**(1)**
107 Rue Saint Lazare, 75009, Paris, 75009,
France
Tel.: (33) 153219672
Properties Leasing Services
N.A.I.C.S.: 531190

Eurocommercial Properties Italia
S.r.l.　　　　　　　　　　　　　**(1)**
A Via della Moscova 3, 20121, Milan,
Italy　　　　　　　　　　　　　**(100%)**
Tel.: (39) 027607591
Sales Range: $50-74.9 Million
Emp.: 15
Real Estate Investment Trust
N.A.I.C.S.: 525990
Tim Samtini (Mng Dir)

Eurocommercial Properties Ltd　**(1)**
4 Carlton Gardens, London, SW1Y 5AB,
United Kingdom
Tel.: (44) 2079257860
Web Site:
　　http://www.eurocommercialproperties.com
Sales Range: $50-74.9 Million
Miscellaneous Financial Investment Activi-
ties
N.A.I.C.S.: 523999
Kate Spiro (Mgr-IR)

Eurocommercial Properties Sweden
AB　　　　　　　　　　　　　　**(1)**
A Kungsgatan 48, 111 35, Stockholm, Swe-
den
Tel.: (46) 86785360
Sales Range: $50-74.9 Million
Emp.: 8
Other Real Estate Property Lessors
N.A.I.C.S.: 531190
Jeremi Lewis (CEO)

Kronan Fastigheter i Karlskrona
AB　　　　　　　　　　　　　　**(1)**
Box 1147, 111 81, Stockholm, Sweden
Tel.: (46) 45510755
Property Leasing Services
N.A.I.C.S.: 531190

Samarkandfastigheter AB　　　**(1)**
PO Box 1147, 11181, Stockholm, Sweden
Tel.: (46) 84535046
Other Real Estate Property Lessors
N.A.I.C.S.: 531190

Sentinel Holdings B.V.　　　　**(1)**
Herengracht 469, Amsterdam, 1017 BS,
Netherlands
Tel.: (31) 205306030
Web Site: http://www.ecpnv.com
Emp.: 12
Investment Management Service
N.A.I.C.S.: 523999

Sentinel Holdings II B.V.　　　**(1)**
Herengracht 469, 1017 BS, Amsterdam,
Netherlands　　　　　　　　　**(100%)**
Tel.: (31) 205306030
Web Site: http://www.ecpnv.com
Sales Range: $50-74.9 Million
Emp.: 12
Real Estate Investment Trust
N.A.I.C.S.: 525990
J. Louis (Mng Dir)

EUROCONSULTANTS S.A.

Antoni Tritsi Str 21, 570 01, Thessa-
loniki, Greece
Tel.: (30) 2310804000
Web Site:
　　https://www.euroconsultants.gr
Year Founded: 1993
EUROC—(ATH)
Sales Range: Less than $1 Million
Emp.: 36
Business Management Consulting
Services
N.A.I.C.S.: 541618
Efstathios Tavridis (Co-Mng Dir & VP)

EUROCRANE (CHINA) CO.,
LTD.

No 288-388 Fenyue Road Fenhu
High-tech Industrial Development
Zone, Suzhou, 215211, Jiangsu,
China
Tel.: (86) 51282072666
Web Site:
　　https://www.eurocrane.com.cn
Year Founded: 2002
603966—(SHG)
Rev.: $262,603,809
Assets: $458,517,815
Liabilities: $255,359,309
Net Worth: $203,158,505
Earnings: $28,638,011
Emp.: 1,000
Fiscal Year-end: 12/31/22
Crane Equipment Mfr & Distr
N.A.I.C.S.: 333924

EURODEV BV

Windmolen 22, 7609 NN, Almelo,
Netherlands
Tel.: (31) 546 660 000
Web Site: http://www.eurodev.com
Year Founded: 1996
Sales Range: $10-24.9 Million
Emp.: 80
Business Services
N.A.I.C.S.: 561499
Mark de Vries (CEO)

Subsidiaries:

EuroDev SARL　　　　　　　　**(1)**
Villantipolis Bat 5 Rez de chaussee, 473
route des Dolines, 6560, Sophia-Antipolis,
France
Tel.: (33) 4 92 91 07 91
Emp.: 8
Business Services
N.A.I.C.S.: 561499
Mark de Vries (CEO)

EURODRY LTD.

Messogiou Thallasis 4 & Evropis, 151
24, Maroussi, Greece
Tel.: (30) 2111804004　　　　　　MH
Web Site: https://www.eurodry.gr
Year Founded: 2018
EDRY—(NASDAQ)
Rev.: $70,183,369
Assets: $199,505,159
Liabilities: $85,564,042
Net Worth: $113,941,117
Earnings: $33,542,671
Emp.: 226
Fiscal Year-end: 12/31/22
Holding Company
N.A.I.C.S.: 551112
Anastasios Aslidis (CFO & Treas)

EUROESPES S.A.

Santa Marta de Babio s/n, Bergondo,
15165, La Coruna, Spain
Tel.: (34) 981780505
Web Site:
　　https://www.euroespes.com
Year Founded: 1991
EEP—(MAD)
Sales Range: Less than $1 Million
Pharmaceutical Researcher, Devel-
oper & Mfr
N.A.I.C.S.: 325412
Ramon Cacabelos Garcia (Chm)

EUROEYES INTERNATIONAL
EYE CLINIC LIMITED

Suite A155 16/F Tower 5 The Gate-
way Harbour City 15 Canton Road,
Tsim Sha Tsui, Kowloon, China (Hong
Kong)
Tel.: (852) 21113956　　　　　　Ky
Web Site: http://www.euroeyes.hk
Year Founded: 2018
1846—(HKG)
Rev.: $81,635,440
Assets: $176,576,458
Liabilities: $42,375,734

Net Worth: $134,200,723
Earnings: $17,074,888
Emp.: 225
Fiscal Year-end: 12/31/21
Health Care Srvices
N.A.I.C.S.: 621610
Jorn Slot Jorgensen *(Chm & CEO)*

Subsidiaries:

EuroEyes AugenLaserZentrum Berlin
GmbH   **(1)**
Berlin Sonycenter Bellevuestr 5, 10785,
Berlin, Germany
Tel.: (49) 302009050
Eye Treatment Services
N.A.I.C.S.: 621320

EuroEyes AugenLaserZentrum
Bremen GmbH   **(1)**
Parkallee 301 Universitatsallee, 28213,
Bremen, Germany
Tel.: (49) 4216391977
Eye Treatment Services
N.A.I.C.S.: 621320

EuroEyes AugenLaserZentrum City
Hamburg GmbH   **(1)**
Valentinskamp 90, 20355, Hamburg, Ger-
many
Tel.: (49) 4034809290
Eye Treatment Services
N.A.I.C.S.: 621320

EuroEyes AugenLaserZentrum Han-
nover GmbH   **(1)**
Georgstrasse 34, 30159, Hannover, Ger-
many
Tel.: (49) 5115194990
Eye Treatment Services
N.A.I.C.S.: 621320

EuroEyes AugenLaserZentrum Stutt-
gart GmbH   **(1)**
Koenigstrasse 70, 70173, Stuttgart, Ger-
many
Tel.: (49) 7113277940
Eye Treatment Services
N.A.I.C.S.: 621320

EuroEyes Deutschland Holding
GmbH & Co. KG   **(1)**
Valentinskamp 90, 20355, Hamburg, Ger-
many
Tel.: (49) 4086648870
Web Site: http://www.euroeyes.com
Eye Treatment Services
N.A.I.C.S.: 621320
Jorn Slot Jorgensen *(Founder, Chm &
CEO)*

EuroEyes Hong Kong Co.
Limited   **(1)**
Suite A155 16/F Tower 5 The Gateway Har-
bour City 15 Canton Road, Tsim Sha Tsui,
Kowloon, China (Hong Kong)
Tel.: (852) 21113956
Eye Treatment Services
N.A.I.C.S.: 621320

Euroeyes Aps   **(1)**
Gyngemose Parkvej 66, 2860, Soborg,
Denmark
Tel.: (45) 70274553
Web Site: http://www.euroeyes.dk
Eye Treatment Services
N.A.I.C.S.: 621320

LASIK Germany GmbH   **(1)**
Hohe Bleichen 10, 20354, Hamburg, Ger-
many
Tel.: (49) 4035017519
Web Site: http://www.lasik-germany.de
Lasik Surgery Services
N.A.I.C.S.: 621493

EUROFIMA

Rittergasse 20, 4001, Basel, Switzer-
land
Tel.: (41) 612873340
Web Site: http://www.eurofima.org
Year Founded: 1956
Rev.: $493,709,319
Assets: $18,044,974,976
Liabilities: $16,333,266,726
Net Worth: $1,711,708,250
Earnings: $25,462,257

Fiscal Year-end: 12/31/19
Railway Development Lending & Fi-
nancial Services
N.A.I.C.S.: 525990
Harry Muller *(CEO)*

EUROFINANCE INVESTMENT
COMPANY JSC

52/4 Kosmodamianskaya Nab, Mos-
cow, 115035, Russia
Tel.: (7) 495 545 35 35
Web Site: http://www.eufn.ru
Investment Brokerage Services
N.A.I.C.S.: 523150

EUROFINS SCIENTIFIC S.E.

Val Fleuri 23, 1526, Luxembourg,
Luxembourg
Tel.: (352) 26185320   LU
Web Site: https://www.eurofins.com
Year Founded: 1987
ERF—(EUR)
Rev.: $6,010,369,960
Assets: $10,045,822,360
Liabilities: $5,306,057,120
Net Worth: $4,739,765,240
Earnings: $283,976,280
Emp.: 61,379
Fiscal Year-end: 12/31/23
Holding Company; Bio-Analytical
Testing Services
N.A.I.C.S.: 551112
Laurent Lebras *(Grp Dir-Fin & Admin)*

Subsidiaries:

AQL EMC limited   **(1)**
16 Cobham Road Ferndown Industrial Es-
tate, Wimborne, BH21 7PG, Dorset, United
Kingdom
Tel.: (44) 1202861175
Web Site: https://www.aql-emc.co.uk
Electromagnetic Compatibility Testing &
Certification Services
N.A.I.C.S.: 541380

AQM Vietnam Limited   **(1)**
14th Floor Hapro Building No 11B Cat Linh
Street, Quoc Tu Giam Ward Dong Da Dis-
trict, 10000, Hanoi, Vietnam
Tel.: (84) 1656252120
Laboratory Testing Services
N.A.I.C.S.: 541380

AgeaCare Switzerland S.A.   **(1)**
Chemin Sous le Bois 12a, 1197, Prangins,
Switzerland
Tel.: (41) 225189736
Web Site: https://www.vaterschaftstest24.de
Deoxyribonucleic Acid Testing Services
N.A.I.C.S.: 621511

Agrartest GmbH   **(1)**
Carl-Goerdeler-Weg 5, 21684, Stade, Ger-
many
Tel.: (49) 1622727681
Laboratory Testing Services
N.A.I.C.S.: 541380

Agrohuarpes - Eurofins Agrosciences
Services S.A.   **(1)**
Los Aromos 2060, Las Higueras, X5805,
Cordoba, Argentina
Tel.: (54) 93584371732
Laboratory Testing Services
N.A.I.C.S.: 541380

Ajal Medical Specialty Company
Ltd.   **(1)**
King Abdullah Dr King Abdullah Dt, Riyadh,
12411, Saudi Arabia
Tel.: (966) 920033304
Medical Specialty Services
N.A.I.C.S.: 621999

Alpa Chimie Alimentaire SAS   **(1)**
49 rue Mustel, 76000, Rouen, France
Tel.: (33) 278775021
Laboratory Testing Services
N.A.I.C.S.: 541380

Alpa Hygiene Alimentaire SAS   **(1)**
230 rue des Eglantiers ZAC des Barillettes,
73230, Saint-Alban-Leysse, France
Tel.: (33) 969370102
Laboratory Testing Services

N.A.I.C.S.: 541380

Alpa Microbiologie Alimentaire
SAS   **(1)**
6 Rue des Aeronefs, 37210, Parcay-
Meslay, France
Tel.: (33) 609315182
Laboratory Testing Services
N.A.I.C.S.: 541380

Alpabio SAS   **(1)**
4 rue des A Aircraft, 37210, Parcay-Meslay,
France
Tel.: (33) 6713701
Laboratory Testing Services
N.A.I.C.S.: 541380

Amar Immunodiagnostics Pvt Ltd   **(1)**
Plot No 242/1 Road No 18 Jubilee Hills,
Hyderabad, 500 033, Telangana, India
Tel.: (91) 4023552954
Laboratory Testing Services
N.A.I.C.S.: 541380

Amatsiaquitaine SAS   **(1)**
Avenue Gay Lussac, ZI Artigues Artigues-
pres-Bordeaux, 33370, Bordeaux, France
Tel.: (33) 557021920
Laboratory Testing Services
N.A.I.C.S.: 541380

Analclinic SA   **(1)**
Calle Emparrado N 3, Mislata, 46920, Va-
lencia, Spain
Tel.: (34) 963134110
Web Site: http://www.analclinic.es
Healtcare Services
N.A.I.C.S.: 621999

Analytico BV   **(1)**
Bergschot 71, PO Box 5510, 4817 PA,
Breda, Netherlands   **(100%)**
Tel.: (31) 765737373
Web Site: http://www.eurofins.com
Sales Range: $25-49.9 Million
Emp.: 200
Testing Laboratories
N.A.I.C.S.: 541380

Analytico Milieu NV   **(1)**
Fotografielaan 43, 2610, Antwerp,
Belgium   **(100%)**
Tel.: (32) 38275111
Web Site: http://www.eurofins.be
Sales Range: $25-49.9 Million
Emp.: 50
Testing Laboratories
N.A.I.C.S.: 541380
Bart van Boven *(Mng Dir)*

Ars Probata GmbH   **(1)**
Mollendorffstrasse 47, 10367, Berlin, Ger-
many
Tel.: (49) 3047004632
Web Site: https://www.ars-probata.com
Food Testing & Certification Services
N.A.I.C.S.: 541380

Ascend Clinical LLC   **(1)**
1400 Industrial Way, San Francisco, CA
94145-0001
Web Site: http://www.ascendclinical.com
Research & Development in Biotechnology
N.A.I.C.S.: 541714
Paul F. Beyer *(CEO)*

Ashwood UK Limited   **(1)**
Tweedside Park Tweedbank, Galashiels,
TD1 3TE, United Kingdom
Tel.: (44) 1721724833
Laboratory Testing Services
N.A.I.C.S.: 541380

Bacteriologisch Controle Station
BV   **(1)**
Heerenveg 7, Katwijk, 2222AM, Hague,
Netherlands   **(100%)**
Tel.: (31) 714024234
Research & Development in the Physical
Engineering & Life Sciences
N.A.I.C.S.: 541715

Bio Search (N.I.) Limited   **(1)**
31 Dufferin Rd, Belfast, BT3 9AA, United
Kingdom
Tel.: (44) 2890352066
Web Site: https://www.biosearch.co.uk
Environmental & Food Analytical Services
N.A.I.C.S.: 541380

Biomnis Empreintes Genetiques
SAS   **(1)**

N.A.I.C.S.: 541380

17/19 avenue Tony Garnier, 69007, Lyon,
France
Tel.: (33) 472801010
Laboratory Testing Services
N.A.I.C.S.: 541380

Blue Heron Biotech, LLC   **(1)**
22310 20th Ave SE 100, Bothell, WA 98021
Tel.: (425) 368-5000
Web Site: http://www.blueheronbio.com
Bio Technology Services
N.A.I.C.S.: 541714

Boston Heart Diagnostics
Corporation   **(1)**
200 Crossing Blvd, Framingham, MA 01702
Web Site:
    https://www.bostonheartdiagnostics.com
Advanced Diagnostic Testing Services
N.A.I.C.S.: 621511
Pat Noland *(Pres)*

Bureau de Wit BV   **(1)**
Televisieweg 32, 1322 AL, Almere, Nether-
lands
Tel.: (31) 365367420
Web Site: http://www.bureaudewit.nl
Food Testing Laboratory Services
N.A.I.C.S.: 541380

CLL Chemnitzer Laborleistungs
GmbH   **(1)**
Dammweg 10, 09114, Chemnitz, Germany
Tel.: (49) 3714893232
Web Site: https://www.c-labor.de
Laboratory Analytical Services
N.A.I.C.S.: 621511

CPA Laboratories Ltd.   **(1)**
318 Worple Road, Raynes Park, London,
SW20 8QU, United Kingdom   **(100%)**
Tel.: (44) 2089468621
Web Site: http://www.cpalaboratories.com
Sales Range: $25-49.9 Million
Emp.: 10
Biological Product Mfr
N.A.I.C.S.: 325414

Centro de Analise e Tipagem de Ge-
nomas Ltda.   **(1)**
R Leandro Dupre 967 VI Clementino, Sao
Paulo, 04025-014, SP, Brazil
Tel.: (55) 8007711137
Laboratory Testing Services
N.A.I.C.S.: 541380

Chemical Control Srl   **(1)**
Via L da Vinci 5, 57123, Livorno,
Italy   **(100%)**
Tel.: (39) 0586401204
Web Site: http://www.chemicalcontrols.net
Sales Range: $25-49.9 Million
Emp.: 50
Research & Development in the Physical
Engineering & Life Sciences
N.A.I.C.S.: 541715

Chemtest Limited   **(1)**
Depot Road, Newmarket, Cambridge, CB8
0AL, United Kingdom
Tel.: (44) 1638606070
Web Site: http://www.chemtest.com
Environmental Testing Laboratory Services
N.A.I.C.S.: 541380

City Analysts Limited   **(1)**
Pigeon House Road, Ringsend, Dublin,
Ireland
Tel.: (353) 16136003
Web Site: http://www.cityanalysts.ie
Environmental Analysis Laboratory Services
N.A.I.C.S.: 541380

Clinical Enterprise, Inc.   **(1)**
175 Crossing Blvd Ste 400, Framingham,
MA 01702
Web Site: https://www.clinicalenterprise.com
Genetic Research Services
N.A.I.C.S.: 541714

Clinilab Laboratorio Clinico Huelva,
S.L.U.   **(1)**
Calle Sor Paula Alzola 20, 21002, Huelva,
Spain
Tel.: (34) 959244709
Web Site: https://www.clinilabhuelva.es
Clinical Laboratory Analysis Services
N.A.I.C.S.: 621511

Confidentia - Tecnologias Informaticas Aplicadas, Ltda.   **(1)**

Eurofins Scientific S.E.—(Continued)

R do Ateneu Comercial de Santarem Lote
12 Loja, 2000-215, Santarem, Portugal
Tel.: (351) 243356550
Web Site: https://www.confidentia.pt
Information Technology Support Services
N.A.I.C.S.: 541512

**DERMA Tronnier Institut fur experi-
mentelle Dermatologie GmbH & Co.
KG**   **(1)**
Alfred-Herrhausen-Str 44, 58455, Witten,
Germany
Tel.: (49) 23022826300
Web Site: http://www.derma-tronnier.de
Dermatology Research Services
N.A.I.C.S.: 541714
Nicole Braun *(Mgr-Scientific)*

Dermscan Poland Sp. z.o.o.   **(1)**
Piecewska 34B, 80-288, Gdansk, Poland
Tel.: (48) 587320290
Web Site: http://www.dermscan.pl
Laboratory Testing Services
N.A.I.C.S.: 541380

Dia-Go B.V.   **(1)**
HJE Wenckebachweg 120, 1114 AD, Am-
sterdam, Netherlands
Tel.: (31) 205976680
Web Site: https://dia-go.nl
Software Development Services
N.A.I.C.S.: 541511

Diatherix Laboratories, LLC   **(1)**
601 Genome Way Ste 2100, Huntsville, AL
35806
Web Site: http://www.eurofins-diatherix.com
Diagnostic Testing Services
N.A.I.C.S.: 621511
Pete Carothers *(Pres)*

Discoverybiomed Inc.   **(1)**
1500 1st Ave N Ste 29, Birmingham, AL
35203-1876
Tel.: (205) 918-8138
Web Site: http://www.discoverybiomed.com
Medical Laboratories
N.A.I.C.S.: 621511
Erik Schwiedert *(Owner)*

Disposable Lab SAS   **(1)**
Technopole Montesquieu 7 Allee Isaac
Newton, 33650, Martillac, France
Tel.: (33) 557120732
Laboratory Testing Services
N.A.I.C.S.: 541380

Dr. Lauk & Dr. Breitling GmbH   **(1)**
Gewerbepark 13, 72218, Wildberg, Ger-
many
Tel.: (49) 7054932250
Web Site: https://www.lauk-breitling.de
Veterinary Diagnostic & Food Analysis Ser-
vices
N.A.I.C.S.: 541380

EGL Genetic Diagnostics LLC   **(1)**
2460 Mountain Industrial Blvd, Tucker, GA
30084
Tel.: (470) 378-2200
Diagnostic Testing Services
N.A.I.C.S.: 621511

EMLab P&K LLC   **(1)**
6000 Shoreline Ct Ste 205, San Francisco,
CA 94080-7606
Environmental Testing Services
N.A.I.C.S.: 541380

ESL prelevement SAS   **(1)**
122 rue Marcel Hartmann Z I Lea Park-
Batiment A, 94853, Ivry-sur-Seine, France
Tel.: (33) 143901885
Laboratory Testing Services
N.A.I.C.S.: 541380

**EmpowerDX Umweltanalytik
Deutschland GmbH**   **(1)**
Vorgebirgsstrasse 20, 50389, Wesseling,
Germany
Tel.: (49) 2236897187
Web Site:
  https://www.umwelt.empowerdx.de
Environmental Analysis Services
N.A.I.C.S.: 541380

EmpowerDX, Inc.   **(1)**
175 Crossing Blvd, Framingham, MA 01702
Web Site: http://www.empowerdxlab.com

Medical Laboratory Testing Services
N.A.I.C.S.: 621511
Delia Vallejo *(VP & Gen Mgr)*

Envira Ingenieros Asesores SL   **(1)**
Parque Tecnologico de Asturias 39 Calle
Faya 4, 33428, Llanera, Spain
Tel.: (34) 985980050
Web Site: http://www.envira.es
Laboratory Testing Services
N.A.I.C.S.: 541380

Environmental Laboratories BV   **(1)**
Koopvaardijweg 34, 4906CV, Oosterhout,
Netherlands   **(100%)**
Tel.: (31) 235677950
Testing Laboratories
N.A.I.C.S.: 541380

**Environmental Laboratory Services
Limited**   **(1)**
Acorn Business Campus, Mahon Industrial
Park Co Cork, Blackrock, Ireland
Tel.: (353) 214536141
Laboratory Testing Services
N.A.I.C.S.: 541380

**Environmental Sampling Supply,
Inc.**   **(1)**
640-143rd Ave, San Leandro, CA 94578
Tel.: (510) 614-8312
Web Site: https://www.essvial.com
Environmental Testing Services
N.A.I.C.S.: 541380
Matt Macy *(VP)*

**Eurofins - Ofi Lebensmittelanalytik
GmbH**   **(1)**
Palmersstrasse 2, 2351, Wiener Neudorf,
Austria
Tel.: (43) 19043344100
Web Site: http://www.eurofins.at
Emp.: 50
Food Testing Services
N.A.I.C.S.: 541380
Barbara Csandl *(Head-Customer Svc)*

**Eurofins 1. Verwaltungsgesellschaft
mbH**   **(1)**
Grossmoorbogen 25, Hamburg, 21079,
Germany
Tel.: (49) 40 30086201
Web Site: http://www.eurofins.de
Emp.: 200
Bio Analytical Testing Services
N.A.I.C.S.: 541380

**Eurofins 2. Verwaltungsgesellschaft
mbH**   **(1)**
Stenzelring 14b, Hamburg, 21107, Germany
Tel.: (49) 40 49294 0
Management Consulting Services
N.A.I.C.S.: 541618

Eurofins 3 Ohms SAS   **(1)**
5 Parc du Grand Pont 1900 Avenue Jean
Pallet, 13880, Velaux, France
Tel.: (33) 669581669
Laboratory Testing Services
N.A.I.C.S.: 541380

Eurofins A/S   **(1)**
Smedeskovvej 38, Galten, 8464, Arhus,
Denmark   **(100%)**
Tel.: (45) 70224266
Web Site: http://www.eurofins.dk
Sales Range: $200-249.9 Million
Emp.: 750
Analytical Laboratory Instrument Mfr
N.A.I.C.S.: 334516

Eurofins Abraxis, Inc.   **(1)**
124 Railroad Dr, Warminster, PA 18974
Tel.: (215) 357-3911
Web Site: http://abraxis.eurofins-
  technologies.com
Rapid Testing Kit Mfr
N.A.I.C.S.: 325413

Eurofins Acmaa Inspectie B.V.   **(1)**
T Haarboer 6, 7561 BL, Deurningen, Neth-
erlands
Tel.: (31) 742455040
Web Site: https://www.acmaa.nl
Pharmaceutical Research & Testing Ser-
vices
N.A.I.C.S.: 541380

Eurofins Acmaa Laboratoria B.V.   **(1)**
T Haarboer 6, 7561 BL, Deurningen, Netherlands

Tel.: (31) 742455040
Pharmaceutical Research & Testing Ser-
vices
N.A.I.C.S.: 541380

**Eurofins Advantar Laboratories,
Inc.**   **(1)**
5451 Oberlin Dr 100, San Diego, CA 92121
Tel.: (858) 228-7788
Clinical Diagnostic Testing Services
N.A.I.C.S.: 621512

**Eurofins Advinus AgroSciences Ser-
vices India Private Limited**   **(1)**
21 & 22 Phase II Peenya Industrial Area,
Bengaluru, 560058, India
Tel.: (91) 866552700
Environmental & Food Analytical Testing
Services
N.A.I.C.S.: 541380

**Eurofins Advinus BioPharma Services
India Pvt Ltd**   **(1)**
Plot 17-F, Bidadi, Bengaluru, 562109, India
Tel.: (91) 8066552700
Laboratory Testing Services
N.A.I.C.S.: 541380

**Eurofins Advinus Discovery Services
Private Limited**   **(1)**
203 12th Main Rd Phase III Peenya, Ben-
galuru, 560058, India
Tel.: (91) 8044172085
Environmental & Food Analytical Testing
Services
N.A.I.C.S.: 541380

**Eurofins Agraranalytik Deutschland
GmbH**   **(1)**
Lobstedter Strasse 78, D-07749, Jena, Ger-
many
Tel.: (49) 3641464985
Laboratory Testing Services
N.A.I.C.S.: 541380

**Eurofins Agro Testing Belgium
NV**   **(1)**
Venecoweg 5, B-9810, Nazareth, Belgium
Tel.: (32) 50833731
Laboratory Testing Services
N.A.I.C.S.: 541380

**Eurofins Agro Testing Denmark
A/S**   **(1)**
Ladelundvej 85, DK-6600, Vejen, Denmark
Tel.: (45) 76604242
Web Site: https://www.eurofins.dk
Laboratory Testing Services
N.A.I.C.S.: 541380
Steen Jensen *(Mng Dir)*

Eurofins Agro Testing Norway AS   **(1)**
Mollebakken 50, PO Box 303, Kambo, NO-
1538, Moss, Norway
Tel.: (47) 92239999
Laboratory Testing Services
N.A.I.C.S.: 541380

**Eurofins Agro Testing Sweden
AB**   **(1)**
Estrids Vag 1, 291 65, Kristianstad, Sweden
Tel.: (46) 104908410
Environmental & Food Analytical Services
N.A.I.C.S.: 541380

Eurofins Agro Testing UK Limited   **(1)**
154 Business Park Valiant Way, Wolver-
hampton, WV9 5GB, United Kingdom
Tel.: (44) 8456046740
Food & Consumer Product Testing Services
N.A.I.C.S.: 541611

**Eurofins Agro Testing Wageningen
BV**   **(1)**
Binnenhaven 5, 6709 PD, Wageningen,
Netherlands
Tel.: (31) 888761010
Laboratory Testing Services
N.A.I.C.S.: 541380

Eurofins Agro-Analyses S.A.S.   **(1)**
40 Route de Rombas, 57140, Woippy,
France
Tel.: (33) 387759150
French Food Testing & Support Services
N.A.I.C.S.: 541380

**Eurofins AgroScience Services
Ltd.**   **(1)**
Door no 58 Idigarai-mol Road Vadakku

Thottam area, Idikarai, Coimbatore,
641031, Tamil Nadu, India
Tel.: (91) 8067223200
Crop Efficacy Testing Services
N.A.I.C.S.: 541380

Eurofins Agroambiental SA   **(1)**
Partida Setsambs s/n, Sidamon, 25222,
Lleida, Spain
Tel.: (34) 973717000
Laboratory Testing Services
N.A.I.C.S.: 541380

**Eurofins Agroscience Services Austria
GmbH**   **(1)**
Am Tieberhof 21, A 8200, Gloiedorf, Austria
Tel.: (43) 311220383
Laboratory Testing Services
N.A.I.C.S.: 541380

**Eurofins Agroscience Services Chem
GmbH**   **(1)**
Am Neulander Gewerbepark 2, 21079,
Hamburg, Germany
Tel.: (49) 40881448666
Laboratory Testing Services
N.A.I.C.S.: 541380

**Eurofins Agroscience Services Chem
SAS**   **(1)**
75 B Avenue du Pascalet, 30310, Vergeze,
France
Tel.: (33) 466730097
Analytical Testing Services
N.A.I.C.S.: 541380

**Eurofins Agroscience Services Chile
S.A**   **(1)**
Salvador Allende 0109 6 region, Rancagua,
Chile
Tel.: (56) 994392608
Laboratory Testing Services
N.A.I.C.S.: 541380

**Eurofins Agroscience Services EAG
Laboratories GmbH**   **(1)**
Eiselauer Weg 4 Building 5, 89081, Ulm,
Germany
Tel.: (49) 73140069348
Pharmaceutical & Cosmetic Product Testing
Services
N.A.I.C.S.: 541611

**Eurofins Agroscience Services Eco-
Chem GmbH**   **(1)**
Eutinger Strasse 24, D-75223, Niefern-
Oschelbronn, Germany
Tel.: (49) 72339627710
Sales Range: $25-49.9 Million
Emp.: 115
Agricultural Chemical Testing Services
N.A.I.C.S.: 541380

**Eurofins Agroscience Services Ecotox
GmbH**   **(1)**
Eutinger Strasse 24, D-75223, Niefern-
Oschelbronn, Germany
Tel.: (49) 72339627710
Laboratory Testing Services
N.A.I.C.S.: 541380

**Eurofins Agroscience Services
GmbH**   **(1)**
Am Neulander Gewerbepark 2, 21079,
Hamburg, Germany
Tel.: (49) 40881448666
Web Site: http://www.eurofins.com
Sales Range: $25-49.9 Million
Emp.: 40
Laboratory Testing Services
N.A.I.C.S.: 541380

Subsidiary (Non-US):

**Eurofins Agroscience Services Sp.
z.o.o.**   **(2)**
ul Parkowa 6, Kazmierz, 64-530, Sza-
motuly, Poland
Tel.: (48) 612927081
Web Site: https://www.eurofins.pl
Chemical Testing Services
N.A.I.C.S.: 541380

**Eurofins Agroscience Services Italy
S.R.L.**   **(1)**
Via XXV Aprile 8/2-8/3 San Giorgio di Piano
Localita Stiatico, 40016, Bologna, Italy
Tel.: (39) 0516650637
Pharmaceutical & Consumer Product Ana-
lytical Services

N.A.I.C.S.: 541611

Eurofins Agroscience Services Kft (1)
Uj Varalja sor 16, H-8000, Szekesfehervar, Hungary
Tel.: (36) 22501684
Web Site: https://www.eurofins.hu
Sales Range: $25-49.9 Million
Emp.: 20
Agricultural Chemical Testing Services
N.A.I.C.S.: 541380

Eurofins Agroscience Services Ltd (1)
Slade Lane Wilson, Melbourne, DE73 8AG, Derby, United Kingdom
Tel.: (44) 7584529033
Sales Range: $25-49.9 Million
Emp.: 100
Agricultural Chemical Mfr
N.A.I.C.S.: 325320

Eurofins Agroscience Services Maroc SARL (1)
N 182 Tranche K Riad Ismailia N2 AITOUL-LAL, 5000, Meknes, Morocco
Tel.: (212) 535512347
Laboratory Testing Services
N.A.I.C.S.: 541380

Eurofins Agroscience Services NZ Limited (1)
1139 Maraekakaho Road Longlands, 4175, Hastings, New Zealand
Tel.: (64) 78495109
Laboratory Testing Services
N.A.I.C.S.: 541380

Eurofins Agroscience Services Regulatory France SAS (1)
Site de la Geraudiere Rue Pierre-Adolphe Bobierre, 44300, Nantes, France
Tel.: (33) 476492274
Laboratory Testing Services
N.A.I.C.S.: 541380

Eurofins Agroscience Services Regulatory Germany GmbH (1)
Eutinger Strasse 24, 75223, Niefern-Oschelbronn, Germany
Tel.: (49) 72339627626
Laboratory Testing Services
N.A.I.C.S.: 541380

Eurofins Agroscience Services Regulatory Spain SL (1)
Sorolla Center 4th floor - Office Av Cortes Valencianas 58, E-46015, Valencia, Spain
Tel.: (34) 961002084
Chemical Testing Services
N.A.I.C.S.: 541380

Eurofins Agroscience Services S.A.S. (1)
Z I des Sabotiers, 49350, Migennes, France
Tel.: (33) 241385353
Pharmaceutical & Cosmetic Product Testing Services
N.A.I.C.S.: 541611

Eurofins Agroscience Services SL (1)
Parque Industrial Parque Plata Camino Empedrado 37-39, Camas, ES-41900, Seville, Spain
Tel.: (34) 954187014
Web Site: https://www.eurofins.com
Agricultural Chemical Testing Services
N.A.I.C.S.: 541380

Eurofins Agroscience Services Seeds France SAS (1)
3 rue de la Porte du Bearn, 64330, Garlin, France
Tel.: (33) 785624854
Laboratory Testing Services
N.A.I.C.S.: 541380

Eurofins Agroscience Services Srl (1)
Via XXV Aprile 8/3 Localito Stiatico, San Giorgio di Piano, 40016, Bologna, Italy
Tel.: (39) 0516650637
Analytical Laboratory Testing Services
N.A.I.C.S.: 541380

Eurofins Agroscience Services Thailand Co. Ltd. (1)

98/2 Moo 19 Tumbol Takhli, Takhli District, Nakhon Sawan, 60140, Thailand
Tel.: (66) 56374563
Laboratory Testing Services
N.A.I.C.S.: 541380

Eurofins Agroscience Testing NZ Limited (1)
12-14 Pukete Road, Te Rapa, Hamilton, 3240, New Zealand
Tel.: (64) 61299008449
Laboratory Testing Services
N.A.I.C.S.: 541380

Eurofins Agroscience Testing Pty Ltd (1)
Unit F6 Building F 16 Mars Road, Lane Cove West, Sydney, 2066, NSW, Australia
Tel.: (61) 299008442
Laboratory Testing Services
N.A.I.C.S.: 541380

Eurofins Agrosciences Services Srl (1)
Via XXV Aprile 8/2- 8/3, 40016, San Giorgio di Piano, Bologna, Italy
Tel.: (39) 051 66 50 637
Web Site: http://www.eurofins.com
Sales Range: $25-49.9 Million
Emp.: 20
Pesticide & Agricultural Chemical Mfr
N.A.I.C.S.: 325320

Eurofins Ahma Oy (1)
PL 96 Teollisuustie 6, 96320, Rovaniemi, Finland
Tel.: (358) 401333800
Laboratory Testing Services
N.A.I.C.S.: 541380

Eurofins Air Monitoring Belgium N.V. (1)
Venecoweg 5, 9810, Nazareth, Belgium
Tel.: (32) 92227759
Food Testing Services
N.A.I.C.S.: 541380

Eurofins Alba Science Limited (1)
24 Broughton Street, Edinburgh, EH1 3RH, United Kingdom
Tel.: (44) 1312970000
Web Site: https://www.albascience.com
Pharmaceutical & Cosmetic Product Testing Services
N.A.I.C.S.: 541611

Eurofins Amatsi Analytics SAS (1)
14 route des Champs Jarennes, Le Bourg, 19390, Saint-Augustin, France
Tel.: (33) 555273770
Laboratory Testing Services
N.A.I.C.S.: 541380

Eurofins Amatsiaquitaine S.A.S. (1)
Avenue Gay Lussac ZI Artigues, Artigues Pres, 33370, Bordeaux, France
Tel.: (33) 557021920
Pharmaceutical & Cosmetic Product Testing Services
N.A.I.C.S.: 541611

Eurofins Amatsigroup NV (1)
Industriepark Zwijnaarde 7B, 9052, Gent, Belgium
Tel.: (32) 92776200
Laboratory Testing Services
N.A.I.C.S.: 541380

Eurofins Amatsigroup S.A.S. (1)
17 Parc des Vautes, 34980, Saint Gely-du-Fesc, France
Tel.: (33) 499583860
Pharmaceutical & Cosmetic Product Testing Services
N.A.I.C.S.: 541611

Eurofins Analisis Agro, S.A. (1)
Partida Setsambs S/N, Sidamon, 25222, Lleida, Spain
Tel.: (34) 973717000
Agriculture & Environment Analysis Services
N.A.I.C.S.: 541620

Eurofins Analisis Alimentario Nordeste SL (1)
Avd de Marcelo Celayeta 75 Entrada 6 nave AA3 oficina 37 bis, 31007, Pamplona, Spain
Tel.: (34) 948175271

Laboratory Testing Services
N.A.I.C.S.: 541380

Eurofins Analisis Alimentario SL (1)
C/Josep Rodoreda 39, 08950, Esplugues de Llobregat, Barcelona, Spain
Tel.: (34) 935527777
Laboratory Testing Services
N.A.I.C.S.: 541380

Eurofins Analisis Clinicos Canarias, SL (1)
Avda Primero De Mayo 17 Bajo Canaria, 35002, Las Palmas, Spain
Tel.: (34) 928364699
Laboratory Testing Services
N.A.I.C.S.: 541380

Eurofins Analyses Nutritionnelles France S.A.S. (1)
Rue Pierre Adolphe Bobierre, BP 42301, 44323, Nantes, France
Tel.: (33) 251832100
Environmental & Food Analysis Services
N.A.I.C.S.: 541380

Eurofins Analyses Pour Le Batiment Nord-Ouest CEBAT S.A.S. (1)
B1 1294 Rue Achille Peres ZI de Petite Synthe, 59640, Dunkerque, France
Tel.: (33) 643623608
Environmental & Laboratory Testing Services
N.A.I.C.S.: 621511

Eurofins Analyses Pour Le Batiment Sud SAS (1)
75C avenue de Pascalet, 30310, Vergeze, France
Tel.: (33) 466731684
Asbestos Testing Services
N.A.I.C.S.: 541380

Eurofins Analyses Pour le batiment Sud-Ouest SAS (1)
4 Chemin des Maures, CS 60134, 33172, Gradignan, Cedex, France
Tel.: (33) 688052916
Asbestos Testing Services
N.A.I.C.S.: 541380

Eurofins Analyses des Materiaux et Combustibles France SAS (1)
3 Rue d'Ottersviller, 67700, Saverne, France
Tel.: (33) 388021562
Laboratory Testing Services
N.A.I.C.S.: 541380

Eurofins Analyses pour le Batiment Nord SAS (1)
557 chemin de Noyelles-PA du Pommier, CS 20013, 62110, Henin-Beaumont, France
Tel.: (33) 321088020
Asbestos Testing Services
N.A.I.C.S.: 541380

Eurofins Analyses pour le Batiment Ouest SAS (1)
7 rue Pierre Adolphe Bobierre, CS 90827, 44308, Nantes, Cedex 3, France
Tel.: (33) 251834948
Asbestos Testing Services
N.A.I.C.S.: 541380

Eurofins Analyses pour le Batiment Sud Est SAS (1)
2 rue Chanoine Ploton, CS 40265, 42016, Saint-Etienne, Cedex, France
Tel.: (33) 672979492
Asbestos Testing Services
N.A.I.C.S.: 541380

Eurofins Analytical Laboratories, Inc. (1)
2219 Lakeshore Dr Ste 500, New Orleans, LA 70122
Tel.: (504) 297-3400
Food Safety & Environmental Testing Services
N.A.I.C.S.: 541380

Eurofins Analytical Services Hungary Kft. (1)
Anonymus utca 6, 1045, Budapest, Hungary
Tel.: (36) 18723600
Food Safety & Environmental Health Analysis Services
N.A.I.C.S.: 541380

Eurofins Analytical Services India Pvt Ltd (1)
540/1 Doddanakundi Industrial Area 2 Graphite India Road Hoodi, Whitefield, Bengaluru, 560048, India
Tel.: (91) 9886690048
Sales Range: $25-49.9 Million
Emp.: 35
Analytical Laboratory Testing Services
N.A.I.C.S.: 541380

Eurofins Analytico (1)
Gildeweg 32-46, 3771 NB, Barneveld, Netherlands (100%)
Tel.: (31) 342426300
Web Site: https://www.analytico.com
Sales Range: $75-99.9 Million
Emp.: 270
Research & Development in the Physical Engineering & Life Sciences
N.A.I.C.S.: 541715

Eurofins Analytico Food BV (1)
Leeuwarderstraatweg 129, PO Box 766, 8441 PK, Heerenveen, Netherlands (100%)
Tel.: (31) 888310000
Web Site: http://www.eurofins.nl
Sales Range: $25-49.9 Million
Emp.: 250
Research & Development in the Physical Engineering & Life Sciences
N.A.I.C.S.: 541715

Eurofins Analytics & Services Austria GmbH (1)
Sankt-Peter-Strasse 25, 4020, Linz, Austria
Tel.: (43) 73269112974
Laboratory Testing Services
N.A.I.C.S.: 541380

Eurofins Analytics LLC (1)
10329 Stony Run Ln, Ashland, VA 23005
Tel.: (804) 365-3000
Pharmaceutical & Cosmetic Product Testing Services
N.A.I.C.S.: 541611

Eurofins Analytik GmbH (1)
Neulander Kamp 1, 21079, Hamburg, Germany (100%)
Tel.: (49) 40492941770
Sales Range: $25-49.9 Million
Emp.: 130
Testing Laboratories
N.A.I.C.S.: 541380

Subsidiary (Domestic):

Eurofins Umwelt West GmbH (2)
Hasenpfuhlerweide 16, 67346, Speyer, Germany (100%)
Tel.: (49) 6232876770
Testing Laboratories
N.A.I.C.S.: 541380

Eurofins Animal Health Australia Pty Ltd (1)
Unit F10 Building F 16 Mars Rd, Lane Cove, 2066, NSW, Australia
Tel.: (61) 299008400
Laboratory Testing Services
N.A.I.C.S.: 541380

Eurofins Apal Pty. Ltd. (1)
Unit 3 11 Ridley St, Hindmarsh, 5007, SA, Australia
Tel.: (61) 883320199
Web Site: https://www.apal.com.au
Water Analytical Services
N.A.I.C.S.: 541380

Eurofins Aquatic Ecotoxicology GmbH (1)
Eutinger Strasse 24, D-75223, Niefern-Oschelbronn, Germany
Tel.: (49) 72339627615
Food Testing Services
N.A.I.C.S.: 541380

Eurofins Asbestos Testing Belgium NV (1)
Venecoweg 5, B-9810, Nazareth, Belgium
Tel.: (32) 498171673
Laboratory Testing Services
N.A.I.C.S.: 541380

Eurofins Asbestos Testing Europe SAS (1)
Parc Heliopolis - Batiment B3 1103 Avenue

Eurofins Scientific S.E.—(Continued)

Jacques Cartier, CS 40392, 44819, Saint-Herblain, France
Tel.: (33) 228067779
Web Site: https://www.myeasylab.fr
Asbestos Testing Services
N.A.I.C.S.: 541380

Eurofins Assurance China Co., Ltd. (1)
Shanghai Technology Building No 705 Yishan Road, Shanghai, 200233, China
Tel.: (86) 2160901227
Food Testing Services
N.A.I.C.S.: 541380

Eurofins Assurance India Pvt Ltd. (1)
Tower A 12th floor Vatika Mindscapes Sarai Sector 27 D, Faridabad, Delhi, 121003, India
Tel.: (91) 8861973031
Web Site: https://www.eurofins.in
Laboratory Testing Services
N.A.I.C.S.: 541380

Eurofins Assurance Myanmar Ltd. (1)
6th Floor No 91 Marlarmyaing 4th Street, Hlaing Township Ward 16, Yangon, Myanmar
Tel.: (95) 9952842970
Pharmaceutical & Cosmetic Product Testing Services
N.A.I.C.S.: 541611

Eurofins Assurance Turkey Kalite ve Denetim Hizmetleri Limited Sirketi
Ali Riza Gurcan Cad Cirpici Yolu Merter, Meridyen Is Merkezi No 403-406-419-420, 34010, Istanbul, Turkiye
Tel.: (90) 2125039355
Environmental & Consumer Product Testing Services
N.A.I.C.S.: 541611

Eurofins BIOMI Kft. (1)
Szent-Gyorgyi Albert u 4, 2100, Godollo, Hungary
Tel.: (36) 204010165
Web Site: https://www.biomi.hu
Molecular Biology Services
N.A.I.C.S.: 541714

Eurofins BLC Leather Technology Centre Limited
Kings Park Road Moulton Park, Northampton, NN3 6JD, United Kingdom
Tel.: (44) 1604679999
Web Site: https://www.blcleathertech.com
Laboratory Testing Services
N.A.I.C.S.: 541380

Eurofins Bacteriologisch Adviesburo BV (1)
Meeboerserf 1, 3851 SR, Ermelo, Netherlands
Tel.: (31) 341562176
Web Site: https://www.bacburo.nl
Laboratory Testing Services
N.A.I.C.S.: 541380

Eurofins Bactimcm BV (1)
Middenkampweg 19, 6545 CH, Nijmegen, Netherlands
Tel.: (31) 243715280
Medical Device Mfr
N.A.I.C.S.: 339112

Eurofins Bactup SAS (1)
97 allee Alexandre Borodine, 69800, Saint Priest, France
Tel.: (33) 426784888
Web Site: https://www.bactup.com
Bio Technology Services
N.A.I.C.S.: 541714
Arnaud Carlotti (Pres)

Eurofins Bay Of Plenty Limited (1)
Tel.: (64) 75491044
Laboratory Testing Services
N.A.I.C.S.: 541380

Eurofins Beacon Discovery, Inc. (1)
6118 Nancy Ridge Dr, San Diego, CA 92121
Tel.: (858) 247-0001

Pharmaceutical & Cosmetic Product Testing Services
N.A.I.C.S.: 541611

Eurofins Becewa NV (1)
Venecoweg 5, 9810, Nazareth, Belgium
Tel.: (32) 9 222 77 59
Biotechnology Research & Development Services
N.A.I.C.S.: 541714

Eurofins Bel/Novamann s.r.o. (1)
Kollarovo nam 9, SK-811 07, Bratislava, Slovakia
Tel.: (421) 911810533
Laboratory Testing Services
N.A.I.C.S.: 541380

Eurofins Belgium NV (1)
Parc Crealys CRI Cassiopee Rue Jean Jonet 21 bte 1, Isnes, 5032, Gembloux, Belgium
Tel.: (32) 81728850
Web Site: https://www.eurofins.be
Laboratory Testing Services
N.A.I.C.S.: 541380

Eurofins BioPharma Product Testing Columbia, Inc. (1)
4780 Discovery Dr, Columbia, MO 65201
Tel.: (573) 777-6100
Medical Testing Laboratory Services
N.A.I.C.S.: 621511

Eurofins BioPharma Product Testing Czech Republic s.r.o. (1)
Videnska 204/125, 619 00, Brno, Czech Republic
Tel.: (420) 515800011
Pharmaceutical Research & Development Services
N.A.I.C.S.: 541714

Eurofins BioPharma Product Testing Enco, Inc. (1)
102-A Woodwinds Industrial Ct, Cary, NC 27511
Tel.: (919) 467-3090
Pharmaceutical & Cosmetic Product Testing Services
N.A.I.C.S.: 541611

Eurofins BioPharma Product Testing Hamburg GmbH (1)
Am Neulander Gewerbepark 2, 21079, Hamburg, Germany
Tel.: (49) 40492945900
Laboratory Testing Services
N.A.I.C.S.: 541380

Eurofins BioPharma Product Testing Hungary Kft. (1)
Anonymus u 6, 1045, Budapest, Hungary
Tel.: (36) 18723600
Pharmaceutical & Cosmetic Product Testing Services
N.A.I.C.S.: 541611

Eurofins BioPharma Product Testing India Private Limited (1)
7 Pugalendi Street Muthulakshmi Nagar Chitlapakkam, Chennai, 600 064, India
Tel.: (91) 4448649124
Environmental & Food Analytical Testing Services
N.A.I.C.S.: 541380

Eurofins BioPharma Product Testing Munich GmbH (1)
Behringstrasse 6/8, D-82152, Planegg, Germany
Tel.: (49) 898996500
Laboratory Testing Services
N.A.I.C.S.: 541380

Eurofins BioPharma Product Testing NZ Limited (1)
Tel.: (64) 95792669
Laboratory Testing Services
N.A.I.C.S.: 541380

Eurofins BioPharma Product Testing Spain SLU (1)
C/Josep Argemi 13-15, ES-08028, Esplugues de Llobregat, Barcelona, Spain
Tel.: (34) 934707272
Laboratory Testing Services
N.A.I.C.S.: 541380

Eurofins BioPharma Product Testing Switzerland AG (1)

Parkstrasse 10, CH-5012, Schonenwerd, Switzerland
Tel.: (41) 628587150
Laboratory Testing Services
N.A.I.C.S.: 541380

Eurofins BioTesting Services Nord GmbH (1)
Neulander Kamp 1a, D-21079, Hamburg, Germany
Tel.: (49) 40492941805
Laboratory Testing Services
N.A.I.C.S.: 541380

Eurofins BioTesting Services Ost GmbH (1)
Edisonstrasse 63, 12459, Berlin, Germany
Tel.: (49) 30241899260
Laboratory Testing Services
N.A.I.C.S.: 541380

Eurofins Biooffice SELAS (1)
24 Rue des Cavailles, Lormont, 33310, Bordeaux, France
Tel.: (33) 556338700
Laboratory Testing Services
N.A.I.C.S.: 541380

Eurofins Biofuel & Energy Testing Sweden AB (1)
Sjohagsgatan 3, 531 40, Linkoping, Sweden
Tel.: (46) 104908110
Laboratory Testing Services
N.A.I.C.S.: 541380

Eurofins Biologie Medicale Ile de France SAS (1)
58 avenue Debourg, 69007, Lyon, France
Tel.: (33) 472801010
Web Site: https://www.eurofins-biologie-medicale.com
Laboratory Testing Services
N.A.I.C.S.: 541380

Eurofins Biologie moleculaire France SAS (1)
Rue Pierre-Adolphe Bobierre, BP 42301, F-44323, Nantes, France
Tel.: (33) 251832100
Laboratory Testing Services
N.A.I.C.S.: 541380

Eurofins Biomnis Ireland Limited (1)
Three Rock Road, Sandyford Industrial Estate, Dublin, D18 A4C0, Ireland
Tel.: (353) 800252966
Laboratory Testing Services
N.A.I.C.S.: 541380

Eurofins Biomnis SELAS (1)
17/19 Avenue Tony Garnier, 69007, Lyon, France
Tel.: (33) 472801010
Web Site: https://www.eurofins-biomnis.com
Clinical Testing Services
N.A.I.C.S.: 541380
Francois Cornu (Dir-Publication)

Eurofins Biomnis UK Limited (1)
90 Priestly Road The Surrey Research Park, Guildford, GU2 7AU, Surrey, United Kingdom
Tel.: (44) 1276414522
Medical Laboratory Services
N.A.I.C.S.: 621511

Eurofins Biopharma Product Testing Denmark A/S (1)
Ornebjergvej 1, DK-2600, Glostrup, Denmark
Tel.: (45) 70224296
Laboratory Testing Services
N.A.I.C.S.: 541380

Eurofins Biopharma Product Testing Sweden AB (1)
Rapsgatan 21, 754 50, Uppsala, Sweden
Tel.: (46) 18572200
Laboratory Testing Services
N.A.I.C.S.: 541380

Eurofins Biopharma Product Testing UK Limited (1)
6-8 Cochrane Square, Brucefield Industry Park, Livingston, EH54 9DR, United Kingdom
Tel.: (44) 1506534240
Laboratory Testing Services
N.A.I.C.S.: 541380

Eurofins Bioskin GmbH (1)
Messberg 4, 20095, Hamburg, Germany
Tel.: (49) 406068970
Pharmaceutical & Cosmetic Product Testing Services
N.A.I.C.S.: 541611

Eurofins Biotalde, S.L.U. (1)
Poligono Industrial San Isidro II Idorsolo 15 - Dpto 3 2, 48160, Derio, Spain
Tel.: (34) 944566589
Web Site: https://www.biotalde.com
Food Safety & Environmental Health Analysis Services
N.A.I.C.S.: 541380

Eurofins Bureau de Wit B.V. (1)
Transistorstraat 20, 1322 CE, Almere, Netherlands
Tel.: (31) 365367420
Web Site: https://www.bureaudewit.nl
Food Safety & Testing Services
N.A.I.C.S.: 541380

Eurofins C Mark BV (1)
Munsterstraat 2 L, PO Box 766, 7418 EV, Deventer, Netherlands (100%)
Tel.: (31) 888310500
Web Site: https://www.c-mark.nl
Sales Range: $25-49.9 Million
Emp.: 120
Research & Development in the Physical Engineering & Life Sciences
N.A.I.C.S.: 541715

Eurofins CBM69 SELAS (1)
158 Rue Leon Blum Medipole Lyon, 69100, Villeurbanne, France
Tel.: (33) 487650100
Microbiological Testing Services
N.A.I.C.S.: 541380

Eurofins CDMO Alphora, Inc. (1)
2240 Speakman Drive, Mississauga, L5K 1A9, ON, Canada
Tel.: (905) 403-0477
Pharmaceutical & Cosmetic Product Testing Services
N.A.I.C.S.: 541611

Eurofins CEBAT SAS (1)
B1 1294 Rue Achille Peres, ZI de Petite Synthe, 59640, Dunkerque, France
Tel.: (33) 643623608
Asbestos Testing Services
N.A.I.C.S.: 541380

Eurofins CEF SELAS (1)
37 Rue Boulard, 75014, Paris, France
Tel.: (33) 144125930
Microbiological Testing Services
N.A.I.C.S.: 541380

Eurofins CLF Specialised Nutrition Testing Services GmbH (1)
Professor-Wagner-Str 11, 61381, Friedrichsdorf, Germany
Tel.: (49) 617217970
Web Site: https://www.eurofins.de
Laboratory Testing Services
N.A.I.C.S.: 541380

Eurofins CRA Co., Ltd. (1)
303 2018 Cheongnam-Ro, Seowon-gu Bunpyeong-Dong Mujin Building, Cheongju, Chungcheongbuk-do, Korea (South)
Tel.: (82) 432988460
Web Site: https://www.crakorea.co.kr
Pharmaceutical & Cosmetic Product Testing Services
N.A.I.C.S.: 541611

Eurofins CRL Cosmetics, Inc. (1)
371 Hoes Ln Ste 100, Piscataway, NJ 08854
Tel.: (732) 981-1616
Web Site: https://crlresearchlabs.com
Emp.: 75
Clinical Research & Testing Services
N.A.I.C.S.: 621511

Eurofins CRL Inc. (1)
371 Hoes Ln Ste #100, Piscataway, NJ 08854
Tel.: (732) 981-1616
Web Site: https://crlresearchlabs.com
Sales Range: $1-9.9 Million
Medical Laboratories
N.A.I.C.S.: 621511
Lenore Coyle (Pres)

Eurofins Calixar S.A.S. (1)
Batiment Laennec 60A Avenue Rockefeller, 69008, Lyon, France
Tel.: (33) 481076460
Web Site: https://www.calixar.com
Biotechnology Research & Development Services
N.A.I.C.S.: 541714

Eurofins Cavendish, S.L.U. (1)
Ctra Bailen-Motril Parcela 102-B Pol Juncaril, Peligros, 18210, Granada, Spain
Tel.: (34) 958490045
Food Testing Services
N.A.I.C.S.: 541380

Eurofins CellTx, Inc. (1)
9052 S Rita Rd Ste 1400, Tucson, AZ 85747
Tel.: (520) 633-4125
Pharmaceutical & Cosmetic Product Testing Services
N.A.I.C.S.: 541611

Eurofins Central Laboratory (1)
Bergschot 71, 4817 PA, Breda, Netherlands
Tel.: (31) 765727272
Emp.: 200
Laboratory Testing Services Supporting Clinical Trials
N.A.I.C.S.: 541380
Elena Logan (Sr VP-Bio Pharma Svcs)

Subsidiary (US):

Eurofins Genomics Inc. (2)
2211 Seminole Dr, Huntsville, AL 35805
Tel.: (800) 688-2248
Laboratory Testing Services
N.A.I.C.S.: 541380
Martin Kunz (Gen Mgr)

Eurofins Central Laboratory China Co., Ltd. (1)
6/F Building 18 No 2168 ChenHang Road, MinHang District, Shanghai, 201100, China
Tel.: (86) 2136202828
Laboratory Testing Services
N.A.I.C.S.: 541380

Eurofins Central Laboratory LLC (1)
2430 New Holland Pike Bldg D Ste 100, Lancaster, PA 17601
Tel.: (717) 556-7350
Web Site: https://www.eurofinscentrallaboratory.com
Laboratory Testing Services
N.A.I.C.S.: 541380
Tracy Hendershott (VP-Comml Ops)

Eurofins Central Laboratory Pte. Ltd. (1)
01-16 The Synergy 1 International Business Park, Singapore, 609917, Singapore
Tel.: (65) 65623858
Laboratory Testing Services
N.A.I.C.S.: 541380

Eurofins Centro Analitico Miguez Muinos, S.L.U. (1)
Calle Zaragoza No 6 Bajo, Pontevedra, 36203, Vigo, Spain
Tel.: (34) 986402729
Pharmaceutical & Cosmetic Product Testing Services
N.A.I.C.S.: 541611

Eurofins Chemtest Limited (1)
Depot Road, Newmarket, Cambridge, CB8 0AL, United Kingdom
Tel.: (44) 1638606070
Web Site: https://www.chemtest.com
Environmental & Laboratory Testing Services
N.A.I.C.S.: 621511

Eurofins Chimie Alimentaire Rouen S.A.S. (1)
72 Rue Aristide Briand, 76650, Petit-Couronne, France
Tel.: (33) 232102246
Environmental & Food Analysis Services
N.A.I.C.S.: 541380

Eurofins Cidesal, S.L.U. (1)
Gremi Teixidors No 17 Local No 1 Son Castello Industrial Estate, Illes Balears, 07009, Palma de Mallorca, Spain
Tel.: (34) 971718776
Web Site: https://www.cidesal.com

Agri Food & Environmental Analysis Services
N.A.I.C.S.: 541380

Eurofins Cimera Estudios Aplicados, S.L.U. (1)
C/ Santiago Grisolia 2, Tres Cantos, 28760, Madrid, Spain
Tel.: (34) 911280968
Pharmaceutical & Cosmetic Product Testing Services
N.A.I.C.S.: 541611

Eurofins Clinical Diagnostics Bangalore Private Limited (1)
No - S-1 First Floor GNEPIP Surajpur Industrial Area Site-V Kasna Road, Noida, 201310, Uttar Pradesh, India
Tel.: (91) 1206925600
Pharmaceutical Research & Testing Services
N.A.I.C.S.: 541380

Eurofins Clinical Diagnostics Kortrijk N.V. (1)
Engelse Wandeling 7, 8500, Kortrijk, Belgium
Tel.: (32) 56258401
Web Site: https://eurofins-clinicaldiagnostics.be
Clinical Diagnostic Centre Operator
N.A.I.C.S.: 621512

Eurofins Clinical Diagnostics Pte. Ltd. (1)
1 International Business Park 03-17 The Synergy, Singapore, 609917, Singapore
Tel.: (65) 67978898
Web Site: https://www.eurofins.sg
Laboratory Testing Services
N.A.I.C.S.: 541380

Eurofins Clinical Diagnostics UK Limited (1)
90 Priestley Road The Surrey Research Park, Guildford, GU2 7AU, Surrey, United Kingdom
Tel.: (44) 1483450388
Food & Consumer Product Testing Services
N.A.I.C.S.: 541611

Eurofins Clinical Genetics India Pvt Ltd (1)
540/1 Graphite India Road, Doddanakundi Industrial Area 2 Hoodi Whitefield, Bengaluru, 560048, India
Tel.: (91) 8067223200
Medical Laboratory Services
N.A.I.C.S.: 621511

Eurofins Clinical Genetics KK (1)
Chiyoda First Building East Building 12F 3-8-1 Nishi-Kanda, Chiyoda-ku, Tokyo, 101-0065, Japan
Tel.: (81) 366310111
Web Site: https://www.eurofinsclinicalgenetics.co.jp
Laboratory Testing Services
N.A.I.C.S.: 541380

Eurofins Clinical Genetics UK Limited (1)
90 Priestley Road Surrey Research Park, Guildford, GU2 7AU, United Kingdom
Tel.: (44) 7501805142
Genetic Research & Testing Services
N.A.I.C.S.: 541715

Eurofins Clinical Testing Sweden AB (1)
Rapsgatan 23, 754 50, Uppsala, Sweden
Tel.: (46) 730718831
Pharmaceutical Research & Testing Services
N.A.I.C.S.: 541380

Eurofins Consult GmbH (1)
Grossmoorbogen 25, Hamburg, 21079, Germany (100%)
Tel.: (49) 4030086200
Web Site: http://www.eurofins.de
Sales Range: $25-49.9 Million
Emp.: 30
Management Consulting Services
N.A.I.C.S.: 541618

Eurofins Consulting Agroalimentaire SAS (1)
1 bis Avenue Guy de Maupassant, 13170, Les Pennes-Mirabeau, France

Tel.: (33) 442246190
Food Safety Consulting Services
N.A.I.C.S.: 541690

Eurofins Consumer Product Testing (Guangzhou) Co., Ltd. (1)
Room 408 4/F Nanzhou Venture Investment Centre No 339 Nanzhou Road, Haizhu District, Guangzhou, 510000, Guangdong, China
Tel.: (86) 2031955765
Laboratory Testing Services
N.A.I.C.S.: 541380

Eurofins Consumer Product Testing IBLSC US, Inc. (1)
11822 N Creek Pkwy N Ste 110, Bothell, WA 98011
Pharmaceutical & Cosmetic Product Testing Services
N.A.I.C.S.: 541611

Eurofins Consumer Product Testing Vietnam Co. Ltd. (1)
1/4 Tan Thoi Nhat 18 Street, Tan Thoi Nhat Ward District 12, Ho Chi Minh City, Vietnam
Tel.: (84) 2871098828
Web Site: https://www.eurofins.vn
Laboratory Testing Services
N.A.I.C.S.: 541380

Eurofins Control Ambiental y Ecogestor, S.L.U. (1)
39 Calle Faya 4, Parque Tecnologico de Asturias, 33428, Llanera, Spain
Tel.: (34) 985980050
Web Site: https://www.ecogestor.com
Food Testing Services
N.A.I.C.S.: 541380

Eurofins Convet, S.L.U. (1)
Corregidor Escofet 83-85, 25005, Lleida, Spain
Tel.: (34) 973234461
Web Site: https://www.convet.net
Food Testing Services
N.A.I.C.S.: 541380

Eurofins Cosmetic & Personal Care Italy Srl (1)
Lungotevere Arnaldo da Brescia 11, 00196, Rome, Italy
Tel.: (39) 0636006629
Laboratory Testing Services
N.A.I.C.S.: 541380

Eurofins Cosmetics & Personal Care Italy S.R.L. (1)
Lungotevere Arnaldo da Brescia 11, 00196, Rome, Italy
Tel.: (39) 0636006629
Cosmetic Product Testing Services
N.A.I.C.S.: 541611

Eurofins Cosmetics & Personal Care Testing Canada, Inc. (1)
1111 Flint Rd Unit 36, Toronto, M3J 3C7, ON, Canada
Tel.: (416) 665-2134
Laboratory Testing Services
N.A.I.C.S.: 541380

Eurofins County Pathology Limited (1)
90 Priestley Road The Surrey Research Park, Guildford, GU2 7AU, United Kingdom
Tel.: (44) 1483450388
Pathology Testing Laboratory Services
N.A.I.C.S.: 621511

Eurofins Croatiakontrola d.o.o. (1)
Karlovacka cesta 4 L, 10000, Zagreb, Croatia
Tel.: (385) 14817215
Web Site: https://www.eurofins.hr
Laboratory Testing Services
N.A.I.C.S.: 541380

Eurofins Cyber Security Netherlands Holding BV (1)
Diakenhuisweg 37, 2033 AP, Haarlem, Netherlands
Tel.: (31) 858222800
Cyber Security Services
N.A.I.C.S.: 541519

Eurofins DSC Forensics SAS (1)
Rue Pierre Adolphe Bobierre, BP 42301, 44323, Nantes, France
Tel.: (33) 272642195

Pesticide Testing Services
N.A.I.C.S.: 541380

Eurofins Danmark A/S (1)
Smedeskovvej 38, Galten, 8464, Arhus, Denmark (100%)
Tel.: (45) 70224266
Web Site: http://www.eurofins.dk
Sales Range: $25-49.9 Million
Emp.: 100
Analytical Laboratory Instrument Mfr
N.A.I.C.S.: 334516
Coston Yanson (Mng Dir)

Eurofins De Bredelaar B.V. (1)
Reethsestraat 17, 6662 PK, Elst, Netherlands
Tel.: (31) 481462379
Agriculture & Horticulture Research Services
N.A.I.C.S.: 541720

Eurofins Derma Tronnier GmbH (1)
Alfred-Herrhausen-Strasse 44, 58455, Witten, Germany
Tel.: (49) 23022826300
Pharmaceutical & Cosmetic Product Testing Services
N.A.I.C.S.: 541611

Eurofins Dermatest Pty Ltd (1)
20-22 King St, Rockdale, Sydney, 2216, NSW, Australia
Tel.: (61) 295562601
Web Site: https://www.eurofins.com.au
Laboratory Testing Services
N.A.I.C.S.: 541380
John Staton (CEO)

Eurofins Dermscan Poland Sp. z o.o. (1)
Ul Matuszewskiego 12, 80-288, Gdansk, Poland
Tel.: (48) 587320290
Web Site: https://www.dermscan.pl
Medical Device & Cosmetic Product Testing Services
N.A.I.C.S.: 541611

Eurofins Dermscan Tunisie S.A.R.L. (1)
Avenue Tahar Ben Ammar E2 Centre Esthetical, El Menzah 9, 1013, Tunis, Tunisia
Tel.: (216) 70814503
Pharmaceutical Research & Testing Services
N.A.I.C.S.: 541380

Eurofins Diatherix Laboratories, LLC (1)
601 Genome Way Ste 2100, Huntsville, AL 35806
Web Site: https://eurofins-diatherix.com
Molecular Biological Diagnostic Services
N.A.I.C.S.: 621512

Eurofins Digital Media Services, LLC (1)
3515 W Pacific Ave, Burbank, CA 91505
Tel.: (818) 559-7200
Web Site: http://www.eurofins-dms.com
Motion Picture & Post Production Services
N.A.I.C.S.: 512110

Eurofins Digital Testing UK Holding Limited (1)
Castlemead Lower Castle Street, Bristol, BS1 3AG, United Kingdom
Tel.: (44) 1179 896100
Web Site: http://www.eurofins-digitaltesting.com
Quality Assurance & Testing Services
N.A.I.C.S.: 513210

Subsidiary (Domestic):

Edge Testing Solutions Limited (2)
Willow House Kestrel View Strathclyde Business Park, Bellshill, ML4 3PB, United Kingdom
Tel.: (44) 1698 464280
Web Site: http://www.edgetesting.co.uk
Emp.: 250
Software Testing Services
N.A.I.C.S.: 541511
Sharon Hamilton (Mng Dir)

Eurofins Digital Product Testing UK Limited (2)
Castlemead Lower Castle Street, Bristol,

Eurofins Scientific S.E.—(Continued)

BS1 3AG, United Kingdom
Tel.: (44) 179896100
Digital TV Testing Services
N.A.I.C.S.: 541380

Subsidiary (Non-US):

Eurofins Digital Testing Belgium NV (2)
Kempische Steenweg 303, PO Box 100, 3500, Hasselt, Belgium
Tel.: (32) 11303600
Laboratory Testing Services
N.A.I.C.S.: 541380

Eurofins Digital Testing Sweden AB (2)
Diskettgatan 11b, 583 35, Linkoping, Sweden
Tel.: (46) 134602727
Laboratory Testing Services
N.A.I.C.S.: 541380

Eurofins DiscoverX Corporation, Inc. (1)
42501 Albrae St, Fremont, CA 94538
Tel.: (510) 979-1415
Drug Discovery & Development Services
N.A.I.C.S.: 541714

Eurofins Disposable Lab S.A.S. (1)
Technopole Montesquieu 7 Allee Isaac Newton, 33650, Martillac, France
Tel.: (33) 557120732
Pharmaceutical & Cosmetic Product Testing Services
N.A.I.C.S.: 541611

Eurofins Dispositifs au Contact de l'Eau France SAS (1)
Rue Lucien Cuenot Site Saint-Jacques II, BP 51 005, 54521, Maxeville, France
Tel.: (33) 383503617
Laboratory Testing Services
N.A.I.C.S.: 541380

Eurofins Donor & Product Testing, Inc. (1)
6933 S Revere Pkwy, Centennial, CO 80112
Environmental & Food Testing Services
N.A.I.C.S.: 541380

Eurofins Dr. Specht Express GmbH (1)
Am Neulander Gewerbepark 2, D-21079, Hamburg, Germany
Tel.: (49) 40881448500
Scientific & Technical Consulting Services
N.A.I.C.S.: 541690

Eurofins Dr. Specht Express Testing & Inspection GmbH (1)
Am Neulander Gewerbepark 2, 21079, Hamburg, Germany
Tel.: (49) 40881448500
Laboratory Analysis & Inspection Services
N.A.I.C.S.: 541350

Eurofins Dr. Specht International GmbH (1)
Am Neulander Gewerbepark 2, 21079, Hamburg, Germany
Tel.: (49) 40881448450
Laboratory Testing Services
N.A.I.C.S.: 541380

Eurofins E&E CML Limited (1)
Newport Business Park New Port Road, Ellesmere Port, CH65 4LZ, United Kingdom
Tel.: (44) 1515591160
Web Site: https://www.cmlex.com
Certification & Testing Services
N.A.I.C.S.: 541990

Eurofins E&E ETC Limited (1)
Clovelly Road, Caddsdown Industrial Park, Bideford, EX39 3DX, United Kingdom
Tel.: (44) 1237423388
Web Site: http://www.etcal.co.uk
EMC Testing & Calibration Services
N.A.I.C.S.: 541380

Eurofins E&E Hursley Limited (1)
Trafalgar House Trafalgar Close Chandler's Ford, Eastleigh, SO53 4BW, United Kingdom
Tel.: (44) 2380271111

Web Site: http://www.emctesting.co.uk
Laboratory Operator
N.A.I.C.S.: 541380
Andy Coombes (Mng Dir & Dir-Technical)

Eurofins E&E Taiwan, Ltd. (1)
18F No 716 ZhongZheng Rd, Zhonghe Dist, New Taipei City, 235, Taiwan
Tel.: (886) 282261579
Laboratory Testing Services
N.A.I.C.S.: 541380

Eurofins EAC Corporation (1)
5 Daiwa Building 3 Chome-23 Higashiikebukuro, Toshima-ku, Tokyo, 171-0013, Japan
Tel.: (81) 3 3987 2182
Environmental Consulting Services
N.A.I.C.S.: 541620

Eurofins EAG Agroscience, LLC (1)
675 Alfred Nobel Dr, Hercules, CA 94547
Tel.: (510) 741-3000
Pharmaceutical Research & Testing Services
N.A.I.C.S.: 541380

Eurofins EAG Materials Science China Ltd. (1)
101 201 Building 2 177 Jiangkai Road, Minhang District, Shanghai, China
Tel.: (86) 2168796088
Laboratory Testing Services
N.A.I.C.S.: 541380

Eurofins EAG Materials Science Netherlands B.V. (1)
High Tech Campus 11, 5656 AE, Eindhoven, Netherlands
Tel.: (31) 35121789477
Laboratory Testing Services
N.A.I.C.S.: 621511

Eurofins EAG Materials Science Singapore, Pte. Ltd. (1)
65 Chulia St 38-02/03 OCBC Centre, Singapore, 049513, Singapore
Tel.: (65) 82238560
Laboratory Testing Services
N.A.I.C.S.: 541380

Eurofins EAG Materials Science Tokyo Corporation KK (1)
Chiyoda First Building East Building 12F 3-8-1 Nishi-Kanda, Chiyoda-ku, Tokyo, 101-0065, Japan
Tel.: (81) 343303709
Laboratory Testing Services
N.A.I.C.S.: 541380

Eurofins ELS Limited (1)
85 Port Road, Moera Wellington, Lower Hutt, New Zealand
Tel.: (64) 45765016
Laboratory Testing Services
N.A.I.C.S.: 541380

Eurofins EPK Built Environment Testing, LLC (1)
6340 NW 5th Way, Fort Lauderdale, FL 33309
Tel.: (954) 333-8149
Web Site: https://aemlinc.com
Biological Laboratory Testing Services
N.A.I.C.S.: 621511

Eurofins Eag Materials Science Taiwan, Ltd. (1)
5F-2 No 31 Puding Road, Hsinchu, 30047, Taiwan
Tel.: (886) 35632303
Environmental & Pharmaceutical Product Testing Services
N.A.I.C.S.: 541611

Eurofins Earth Consul KK (1)
8-17 Hibari, Imizu, 939-0351, Toyama, Japan
Tel.: (81) 766561180
Pharmaceutical & Consumer Product Analytical Services
N.A.I.C.S.: 541611

Eurofins Eastern Ventures BV (1)
Bergschot 69-71, 4801 DM, Breda, Netherlands
Tel.: (31) 765737373
Venture Capital Management Services
N.A.I.C.S.: 523910

Subsidiary (Non-US):

Eurofins Steins Laboratorium Sp. z.o.o. (2)

Aleja Wojska Polskiego 90A, 82-200, Malbork, Poland
Tel.: (48) 55 272 04 73
Laboratory Testing Services
N.A.I.C.S.: 541380

Eurofins Ecca BTX B.V. (1)
Ambachtsweg 5, 9820, Merelbeke, Belgium
Tel.: (32) 92526444
Food Testing Services
N.A.I.C.S.: 541380

Eurofins Ecca N.V. (1)
Ambachtsweg 3, 9820, Merelbeke, Belgium
Tel.: (32) 92526444
Food Testing Services
N.A.I.C.S.: 541380

Eurofins Ecosur SA (1)
Calle Castillo de Aledo 33-39 Martiun, Pol Ind Base 2000 - San Martin Lorqui, 30564, Murcia, Spain
Tel.: (34) 968676842
Chemical Testing Services
N.A.I.C.S.: 541380

Eurofins Ecotoxicologie France S.A.S. (1)
Site Saint-Jacques II, BP 51 005, 54521, Maxeville, France
Tel.: (33) 383503617
Food Testing Services
N.A.I.C.S.: 541380

Eurofins Eichrom Radioactivite SAS (1)
Campus de Ker Lann Parc de Lormandiere Rue Maryse Bastie-Bat C, 35170, Bruz, France
Tel.: (33) 223501380
Laboratory Testing Services
N.A.I.C.S.: 541380

Eurofins Electric & Electronic Product Testing AG (1)
Luppmenstrasse 3, 8320, Fehraltorf, Switzerland
Tel.: (41) 582203200
Web Site: https://www.eurofins.ch
Laboratory Testing Services
N.A.I.C.S.: 541380

Eurofins Electric & Electronics Finland Oy (1)
Kivimiehentie 4, 02150, Espoo, Finland
Tel.: (358) 406311311
Laboratory Analysis & Inspection Services
N.A.I.C.S.: 541350

Eurofins Electrical & Electronic UK Limited (1)
Caddsdown Industrial Park Clovelly Road, Bideford, EX39 3DX, United Kingdom
Tel.: (44) 1237423388
Web Site: https://www.etcal.co.uk
Electronic Calibration Services
N.A.I.C.S.: 811210

Eurofins Electrical & Electronics France S.A.S. (1)
505 Rue Louis Berton CS 60560, 13594, Aix-en-Provence, France
Tel.: (33) 678930666
Electrical Safety Testing Services
N.A.I.C.S.: 541380

Eurofins Electrical Testing Service (Shenzhen) Co., Ltd. (1)
1st Floor Building 2 Chunu Meisheng Huigu Science and Technology Park, No 83 Dabao Road Bao'an District, Shenzhen, 518000, China
Tel.: (86) 75582911867
Laboratory Testing Services
N.A.I.C.S.: 541380

Eurofins Enviro-Works, Inc. (1)
18949 111 Ave NW, Edmonton, T5S 2X4, AB, Canada
Tel.: (780) 457-4652
Web Site: https://www.enviro-works.com
Laboratory Testing Services
N.A.I.C.S.: 621511

Eurofins Environ-Lab S.R.L. (1)
Via Don Bosco No 3, PV, 27014, Corteolona e Genzone, Italy
Tel.: (39) 0382969696
Web Site: https://www.envirolabsrl.it
Emp.: 50

Environmental & Food Analysis Services
N.A.I.C.S.: 541380

Eurofins Environment Testing Australia Pty Ltd (1)
6 Monterey Road, Dandenong South, 3175, VIC, Australia
Tel.: (61) 385645000
Laboratory Testing Services
N.A.I.C.S.: 541380

Eurofins Environment Testing Estonia OU (1)
Paavli 5-3, 10412, Tallinn, Estonia
Tel.: (372) 58837202
Laboratory Testing Services
N.A.I.C.S.: 541380

Eurofins Environment Testing Finland Oy (1)
Niemenkatu 73, 15140, Lahti, Finland
Tel.: (358) 403567895
Agricultural Testing Services
N.A.I.C.S.: 541380

Eurofins Environment Testing Ireland Limited (1)
Pigeon House Road, Ringsend, Dublin, 4, Ireland
Tel.: (353) 16136003
Environmental & Food Analysis Services
N.A.I.C.S.: 541380

Eurofins Environment Testing NZ Limited (1)
Tel.: (64) 95264551
Laboratory Testing Services
N.A.I.C.S.: 541380

Eurofins Environment Testing Northeast, LLC (1)
646 Camp Ave, North Kingstown, RI 02852
Tel.: (413) 789-9018
Environmental & Cosmetic Product Testing Services
N.A.I.C.S.: 541611

Eurofins Environment Testing Northwest, LLC (1)
5755 8th St E, Tacoma, WA 98424
Tel.: (253) 922-2310
Environmental & Cosmetic Product Testing Services
N.A.I.C.S.: 541611

Eurofins Environment Testing Norway AS (1)
Fabrikkveien 10, Forus Stavanger, NO-4033, Klepp, Norway
Tel.: (47) 94504252
Web Site: https://www.eurofins.no
Emp.: 500
Environmental Testing Services
N.A.I.C.S.: 541380

Eurofins Environment Testing Philadelphia, LLC (1)
702 Electronic Dr, Horsham, PA 19044
Tel.: (215) 355-3900
Environmental & Cosmetic Product Testing Services
N.A.I.C.S.: 541611

Eurofins Environment Testing South Central, LLC (1)
4901 Hawkins, Albuquerque, NM 87109
Tel.: (505) 345-3975
Pharmaceutical & Cosmetic Product Testing Services
N.A.I.C.S.: 541611

Eurofins Environment Testing Southeast, LLC (1)
8021-6 Philips Hwy, Jacksonville, FL 32256
Tel.: (904) 296-3007
Pharmaceutical Research & Testing Services
N.A.I.C.S.: 541380

Eurofins Environment Testing Sweden Holding AB (1)
Sjohagsgatan 3, Box 737, Lidkoping, 531 19, Sweden
Tel.: (46) 104908100
Sales Range: $25-49.9 Million
Emp.: 100
Environmental Testing & Consulting Services
N.A.I.C.S.: 541620

Thomas Kiratsopoulos *(Mng Dir)*

Subsidiary (Domestic):

Eurofins Environment Testing Sweden AB   **(2)**
Sjohagsgatan 3 port 1, SE-531 40, Lidkoping, Sweden
Tel.: (46) 104908110
Web Site: https://www.eurofins.se
Sales Range: $25-49.9 Million
Emp.: 100
Environmental Testing Services
N.A.I.C.S.: 541380

Eurofins Environnement Formation et Conseil S.A.S.   **(1)**
505 Rue Louis Berton Bat 2, 13590, Aix-en-Provence, France
Tel.: (33) 442943598
Environmental & Food Analysis Services
N.A.I.C.S.: 541380

Eurofins Environnement Logistique France SAS   **(1)**
9 rue du Baron Chouard, Monswiller, F-67700, Saverne, France
Tel.: (33) 810122611
Logistic Services
N.A.I.C.S.: 488510

Eurofins Euraceta N.V.   **(1)**
Rue le Marais 15, 4530, Villers-le-Bouillet, Belgium
Tel.: (32) 42599320
Web Site: https://www.euraceta.be
Environmental Analysis Services
N.A.I.C.S.: 541380

Eurofins Evic Product Testing France SAS   **(1)**
122 rue de la Croix de Seguey, 33000, Bordeaux, France
Tel.: (33) 556955995
Clinical Testing Services
N.A.I.C.S.: 541380

Eurofins Evic Product Testing Romania SRL   **(1)**
64-66 Marasesti Boulevard District 4, 040256, Bucharest, Romania
Tel.: (40) 213357090
Web Site: https://www.evic.ro
Laboratory Testing Services
N.A.I.C.S.: 541380

Eurofins Expert Services Oy   **(1)**
Kivimiehentie 4, 02150, Espoo, Finland
Tel.: (358) 406311311
Laboratory Testing Services
N.A.I.C.S.: 541380

Eurofins Expertise Microbiologique France SAS   **(1)**
Rue Lucien Cuenot Site Saint-Jacques II, BP 51 005, 54521, Marseille, France
Tel.: (33) 383503617
Laboratory Testing Services
N.A.I.C.S.: 541380

Eurofins Expertises Environnementales SAS   **(1)**
Rue Lucien Cuenot Site Saint-Jacques II, BP 51 005, 54521, Maxeville, France
Tel.: (33) 383503617
Laboratory Testing Services
N.A.I.C.S.: 541380

Eurofins FQL Ltd.   **(1)**
1-1 Shinogura, Saiwai-ku, Kawasaki, 212-8510, Kanagawa, Japan
Tel.: (81) 443303455
Environmental & Food Analytical Testing Services
N.A.I.C.S.: 541380

Eurofins Food & Agro Testing Sweden AB   **(1)**
Estrids Vag 1, 291 65, Kristianstad, Sweden
Tel.: (46) 10 490 83 00
Web Site: http://www.eurofins.se
Food Product Testing Services
N.A.I.C.S.: 541380

Eurofins Food & Feed Testing Leipzig GmbH   **(1)**
Permoserstrasse 19, 04318, Leipzig, Germany
Tel.: (49) 341649660
Laboratory Analysis Services

N.A.I.C.S.: 621511

Eurofins Food & Feed Testing Norway AS   **(1)**
Mollebakken 40, NO-1538, Moss, Norway
Tel.: (47) 94504161
Laboratory Testing Services
N.A.I.C.S.: 541380

Eurofins Food & Feed Testing Sweden AB   **(1)**
Abelvagen 2 Port 6, 553 02, Jonkoping, Sweden
Tel.: (46) 104908310
Laboratory Testing Services
N.A.I.C.S.: 541380

Eurofins Food & Product Testing Japan KK   **(1)**
Shinjuku Yochomachi Building 10-10 Yochomachi, Shinjuku-ku, Tokyo, 162-0055, Japan
Tel.: (81) 353616217
Laboratory Testing Services
N.A.I.C.S.: 541380

Eurofins Food Analytica Kft.   **(1)**
Henyei Miklos u 5, 5700, Gyula, Hungary
Tel.: (36) 66321016
Laboratory Testing Services
N.A.I.C.S.: 541380

Eurofins Food Assurance Certification US, LLC   **(1)**
2120 Rittenhouse St Ste A, Des Moines, IA 50321
Tel.: (515) 299-6979
Environmental & Food Testing Services
N.A.I.C.S.: 541380

Eurofins Food Assurance Italia Srl   **(1)**
via Borgonuovo 13, Somma Lombardo, VA, Italy
Tel.: (39) 0331259911
Laboratory Testing Services
N.A.I.C.S.: 541380

Eurofins Food Assurance US, LLC   **(1)**
2120 Rittenhouse St Ste A, Des Moines, IA 50321
Tel.: (515) 299-6979
Environmental & Food Testing Services
N.A.I.C.S.: 541380

Eurofins Food Barcelona, S.L.U.   **(1)**
Ctra Santa Creu de Calafell 49b, Sant Boi de Llobregat, 08830, Barcelona, Spain
Tel.: (34) 935527777
Pharmaceutical & Cosmetic Product Testing Services
N.A.I.C.S.: 541611

Eurofins Food Chemistry Testing Des Moines, Inc.   **(1)**
2200 Rittenhouse St 150, Des Moines, IA 50321
Tel.: (515) 265-1461
Lipid & Food Analytical Services
N.A.I.C.S.: 541380

Eurofins Food Chemistry Testing Madison, Inc.   **(1)**
6304 Ronald Reagan Ave, Madison, WI 53704
Laboratory Testing Services
N.A.I.C.S.: 541380

Eurofins Food Control Services GmbH   **(1)**
Am Neulander Gewerbepark 8, 21079, Hamburg, Germany
Tel.: (49) 40492944002
Laboratory Testing Services
N.A.I.C.S.: 621511

Eurofins Food Denmark Holding A/S   **(1)**
Smedeskovvej 38, 8464, Galten, Denmark
Tel.: (45) 70224266
Investment Management Service
N.A.I.C.S.: 523999

Subsidiary (Domestic):

Eurofins Steins Laboratorium A/S   **(2)**
Ladelundvej 85, DK - 6600, Vejen, Denmark
Tel.: (45) 70224286
Web Site: https://www.eurofins.dk

Laboratory Testing Services
N.A.I.C.S.: 541380

Eurofins Food GmbH   **(1)**
Am Neulander Gewerbepark 1, 21079, Hamburg, Germany
Tel.: (49) 40 49 29 47 99
Web Site: http://www.eurofins.de
Laboratory Testing Services
N.A.I.C.S.: 541380

Subsidiary (Domestic):

Eurofins CTC GmbH   **(2)**
Am Neulaender Gewerbepark 1, 21079, Hamburg, Germany
Tel.: (49) 40 49294 600
Web Site: http://www.eurofins.de
Conference & Training Services
N.A.I.C.S.: 611430

Eurofins Fintelmann und Meyer GMP GmbH   **(2)**
Grossmoorbogen 25, 21079, Hamburg, Germany
Tel.: (49) 40 49 29 46 70
Sales Range: $10-24.9 Million
Emp.: 30
Microbiological Testing Services
N.A.I.C.S.: 541380

Eurofins Global Control GmbH   **(2)**
Am Neulander Gewerbepark 8, 21079, Hamburg, Germany
Tel.: (49) 40492943450
Web Site: http://www.global-testing.de
Sales Range: $25-49.9 Million
Emp.: 10
Food Product Testing Services
N.A.I.C.S.: 541380
Gabriel Linder *(Mng Dir)*

Sofia GmbH   **(2)**
Rudower Chaussee 29, 12489, Berlin, Germany
Tel.: (49) 30 677 98560
Web Site: http://www.eurofins.de
Sales Range: $25-49.9 Million
Emp.: 80
Vegetable & Animal Feed Testing Services
N.A.I.C.S.: 541380
Peter Schlusche *(CEO)*

Eurofins Food Integrity Control Services GmbH   **(1)**
Berliner Strasse 2, D-27721, Ritterhude, Germany
Tel.: (49) 42924077200
Laboratory Testing Services
N.A.I.C.S.: 541380

Eurofins Food Integrity Testing UK Limited   **(1)**
Otley Road, Harrogate, HG3 1PY, United Kingdom
Tel.: (44) 1423848864
Laboratory Testing Services
N.A.I.C.S.: 541380

Eurofins Food Safety Solutions BV   **(1)**
Munsterstraat 2, 7418 EV, Deventer, Netherlands
Tel.: (31) 888310330
Laboratory Testing Services
N.A.I.C.S.: 541380

Eurofins Food Safety Solutions Limited   **(1)**
i54 Business Park Valiant Way, Wolverhampton, WV9 5GB, United Kingdom
Tel.: (44) 1902627200
Laboratory Testing Services
N.A.I.C.S.: 541380

Eurofins Food Testing Belgium NV   **(1)**
Venecoweg 5, B-9810, Nazareth, Belgium
Tel.: (32) 50450060
Laboratory Testing Services
N.A.I.C.S.: 541380

Eurofins Food Testing Japan KK Ltd.   **(1)**
Shibukawa 100, Shimizu-Ku, Shizuoka, 424-0053, Japan
Tel.: (81) 543485274
Laboratory Testing Services
N.A.I.C.S.: 541380

Laboratory Testing Services
N.A.I.C.S.: 541380

Eurofins Food Testing Lisboa, Unipessoal, Ltda.   **(1)**
Rua Dos Jasmins No 541, 2890-189, Alcochete, Portugal
Tel.: (351) 212340399
Environmental & Food Analytical Services
N.A.I.C.S.: 541380

Eurofins Food Testing Netherlands Holding BV   **(1)**
Leeuwarderstraatweg 129, 8441 PK, Heerenveen, Netherlands
Tel.: (31) 888310000
Sales Range: $100-124.9 Million
Emp.: 175
Investment Management Service
N.A.I.C.S.: 523999

Subsidiary (Domestic):

C-mark BV   **(2)**
Munsterstraat 2 L, 7418 EV, Deventer, Netherlands
Tel.: (31) 88 831 05 00
Web Site: http://www.c-mark.nl
Emp.: 20
Drinking Water Testing Services
N.A.I.C.S.: 541380

Eurofins Food Netherlands BV   **(2)**
Bijdorpplein 21-23, PO Box 510, 2992 LB, Barendrecht, Netherlands
Tel.: (31) 88 831 04 61
Food Testing Services
N.A.I.C.S.: 541380

Eurofins Food Testing Rotterdam B.V.   **(1)**
Bijdorpplein 21-23, 2992 LB, Barendrecht, Netherlands
Tel.: (31) 180643000
Pharmaceutical & Cosmetic Product Testing Services
N.A.I.C.S.: 541611

Eurofins Food Testing SRL   **(1)**
6 Preciziei Street 6th District, 062203, Bucharest, Romania
Tel.: (40) 314313420
Laboratory Testing Services
N.A.I.C.S.: 541380

Eurofins Food Testing Service (Dalian) Co., Ltd.   **(1)**
Floor 5th No 1 Bld Guangxian Road No 107 High-Tech District, Dalian, China
Tel.: (86) 4000308680
Laboratory Testing Services
N.A.I.C.S.: 541380

Eurofins Food Testing Singapore Pte. Ltd.   **(1)**
61 Science Park Road 05-03/08 The Galen, Singapore, 117525, Singapore
Tel.: (65) 69710890
Laboratory Testing Services
N.A.I.C.S.: 541380

Eurofins Food Testing Slovakia s.r.o.   **(1)**
Komjaticka 73, SK-940 02, Nove Zamky, Slovakia
Tel.: (421) 908810030
Laboratory Testing Services
N.A.I.C.S.: 541380

Eurofins Food Testing Sud GmbH   **(1)**
Ob dem Himmelreich 9, 72074, Tubingen, Germany
Tel.: (49) 40492949000
Pharmaceutical & Cosmetic Product Testing Services
N.A.I.C.S.: 541611

Eurofins Food Testing Taiwan, Ltd.   **(1)**
No 158 Lide Road, Beitou District, Taipei, 112, Taiwan
Tel.: (886) 228987831
Laboratory Testing Services
N.A.I.C.S.: 541380

Eurofins Food Testing Thailand Co. Ltd.   **(1)**
50 Faculty of Science Kasetsart University Ngamwongwan Road, Lad Yao Sub-district Chatuchak District, Bangkok, Thailand
Tel.: (66) 23390699
Laboratory Testing Services

Eurofins Scientific S.E.—(Continued)

N.A.I.C.S.: 541380
Vorrakorn Rangsee (Country Mgr-Sls)

Eurofins Food Testing UK Limited (1)
i54 Business Park Valiant Way, Wolverhampton, WV9 5GB, United Kingdom
Tel.: (44) 1902627200
Laboratory Testing Services
N.A.I.C.S.: 541380

Eurofins Food US Holdings I BV (1)
Bergschot 71, Breda, 4817PA, Netherlands
Tel.: (31) 765737373
Investment Management Service
N.A.I.C.S.: 523940
Elena Logan (Gen Mgr)

Eurofins Food US Holdings II BV (1)
Bergschot 71, 4817PA, Breda, Netherlands
Tel.: (31) 765737373
Investment Management Service
N.A.I.C.S.: 523999

Eurofins Forensic Services Limited (1)
Queens Road, Teddington, TW11 0LY, United Kingdom
Tel.: (44) 2031507150
Laboratory Testing Services
N.A.I.C.S.: 541380

Eurofins Forensics Belgium - Brugge (1)
Lieven Bauwensstraat 6, 8200, Brugge, Belgium
Tel.: (32) 50 31 02 52
Web Site: http://www.eurofins.be
Analytical Laboratory Testing Services
N.A.I.C.S.: 541380

Eurofins France Holding SAS (1)
Rue Pierre Adolphe Bobiere, 44000, Nantes, France
Tel.: (33) 2 5183 2100
Web Site: http://www.eurofins.fr
Holding Company
N.A.I.C.S.: 551112

Subsidiary (Domestic):

ADME Bioanalyses SAS (2)
75 A Avenue de Pascalet, 30310, Vergeze, France
Tel.: (33) 466731773
Web Site:
     http://www.eurofinsadmebioanalyses.com
Sales Range: $25-49.9 Million
Emp.: 75
Research & Development in the Physical Engineering & Life Sciences
N.A.I.C.S.: 541715

Chemtox SAS (2)
3 rue Gruninger CS 60191, 67405, Illkirch-Graffenstaden, Cedex, France
Tel.: (33) 390400540
Web Site: https://www.labochemtox.com
Sales Range: $25-49.9 Million
Emp.: 9
Laboratory Testing Services
N.A.I.C.S.: 541380

Eurofins ADME Bioanalyses SAS (2)
75 A Avenue de Pascalet, F-30310, Vergeze, France
Tel.: (33) 466731773
Web Site: https://www.eurofins.com
Biotechnology Research & Development Services
N.A.I.C.S.: 541714

Eurofins ATS SAS (2)
505 Rue Louis Berton, 13594, Aix-en-Provence, France
Tel.: (33) 442371414
Emp.: 80
Laboratory Testing Services
N.A.I.C.S.: 541380

Eurofins Agroscience Services France SAS (2)
19 Rue Du Verger, Sene, 56000, France
Tel.: (33) 297683499
Sales Range: $25-49.9 Million
Emp.: 1
Agricultural Chemical Research Services
N.A.I.C.S.: 541715
Laurent Emmanuel Migeon (Office Mgr)

Eurofins Agrosciences Services SAS (2)
ZA du Rival, Lafrancaise, 82130, Meauzac, France
Tel.: (33) 5 63 31 64 44
Web Site: http://www.eurofins.com
Sales Range: $25-49.9 Million
Emp.: 15
Environmental Testing Services
N.A.I.C.S.: 541380

Eurofins Air a l'Emission France SAS (2)
557 Route de Noyelles PA du Pommier, 62110, Henin-Beaumont, France
Tel.: (33) 3 21 08 80 20
Bio Analytical Testing Services
N.A.I.C.S.: 541380

Eurofins Analyses pour l'Environnement France SAS (2)
5 rue d'Otterswiller, 67700, Saverne, France
Tel.: (33) 388911911
Laboratory Testing Services
N.A.I.C.S.: 541380

Eurofins Analyses pour le Batiment Ile de France (2)
117 Quai de Valmy, CS 5004, 75484, Paris, Cedex, France (100%)
Tel.: (33) 140370303
Web Site: http://www.eurofins.fr
Sales Range: $25-49.9 Million
Emp.: 17
Testing Laboratories
N.A.I.C.S.: 541380

Eurofins Analytics France SAS (2)
Rue Pierre Adolphe Bobiere, BP 42301, 44323, Nantes, France
Tel.: (33) 251832100
Sales Range: $75-99.9 Million
Emp.: 400
Laboratory Testing Services
N.A.I.C.S.: 541380

Eurofins Ascal Environnement SAS (2)
Parc Europa, 57602, Forbach, France
Tel.: (33) 3 87 83 48 00
Web Site: http://www.eurofins.com
Ground & Waste Water Testing Services
N.A.I.C.S.: 541380

Subsidiary (Domestic):

Eurofins Ascal Batiment Nord SAS (3)
557 Route de Noyelles PA du Pommier, 62110, Henin-Beaumont, France
Tel.: (33) 3 21 13 49 70
Web Site: http://www.eurofins.fr
Asbestos Testing Services
N.A.I.C.S.: 541380

Eurofins Ascal Batiment Sud Est SAS (3)
Route de St Genis, BP 18, 69610, Sainte-Foy-l'Argentiere, France
Tel.: (33) 4 74 72 26 40
Web Site: http://www.eurofins.com
Laboratory Testing Services
N.A.I.C.S.: 541380

Subsidiary (Domestic):

Eurofins Biosciences Cervac Consulting (2)
ZA des Chabauds Nord, 64 Rue Eugene Schneider, F-13320, Marseille, Bouc Bel Air, France (100%)
Tel.: (33) 442943530
Web Site: http://www.eurofins.fr
Sales Range: $25-49.9 Million
Emp.: 17
Management Consulting Services
N.A.I.C.S.: 541618

Eurofins Biosciences SAS (2)
Z I de Courtaboeuf 9 Avenue de Laponie, Les Ulis, 91978, France
Tel.: (33) 1 69 10 88 88
Biotechnology Research & Development Services
N.A.I.C.S.: 541714

Eurofins Cerep SA (2)
Le bois l'Eveque, Celle-Levescault, 86600, Celle l'Evescault, France

Tel.: (33) 549893000
Pharmaceuticals Mfr & Researcher
N.A.I.C.S.: 325412

Subsidiary (Non-US):

Cerep Ltd. (3)
326 Aidisheng Road B 302-1, Zhangjiang High-Tech Park, Shanghai, 201203, China
Tel.: (86) 21 5132 0568
Pharmaceutical Research Services
N.A.I.C.S.: 325412

Subsidiary (US):

Eurofins Panlabs, Inc. (3)
6 Research Park Dr, Saint Charles, MO 63304
Pharmaceutical Developer
N.A.I.C.S.: 325412

Subsidiary (Domestic):

Eurofins Certification SARL (2)
Certification Unit Immeuble Odyssee 2-12 rue du Chemin des Femmes, 91300, Massy, France (100%)
Tel.: (33) 169108891
Sales Range: $25-49.9 Million
Emp.: 80
Testing Laboratories
N.A.I.C.S.: 541380

Eurofins Cervac Sud SAS (2)
Z A des Chabauds Nord 505 Rue Louis Berton, 13594, Aix-en-Provence, Cedex, France (100%)
Tel.: (33) 442943500
Emp.: 100
Testing Laboratories
N.A.I.C.S.: 541380

Eurofins Eaux Residuaires SAS (2)
1 rue du Professeur Calmette, 59046, Lille, France
Tel.: (33) 3 27 86 95 60
Web Site: http://www.eurofins.com
Waste Water Testing Services
N.A.I.C.S.: 541380

Eurofins Environnement & Sante SAS (2)
9 Av de la Laponie, Z A I de Courtaboeuf, 91940, Orleans, France (100%)
Tel.: (33) 169108888
Sales Range: $25-49.9 Million
Emp.: 50
Testing Laboratories
N.A.I.C.S.: 541380

Eurofins Environnement SAS (2)
9 Av de la Laponie, Z A I de Courtaboeuf, 91967, Courtaboeuf, France (100%)
Tel.: (33) 169108888
Web Site: http://www.eurofins.fr
Sales Range: $25-49.9 Million
Emp.: 80
Testing Laboratories
N.A.I.C.S.: 541380
Gilles G. Martin (Chm & CEO)

Eurofins Genomics SAS (2)
Rue Pierre Adolphe Bobiere, 44323, Nantes, France
Tel.: (33) 800903807
Web Site: http://www.eurofins.com
Sales Range: $25-49.9 Million
Emp.: 9
Pharmaceutical Products Research Services
N.A.I.C.S.: 541715

Eurofins Hydrologie France SAS (2)
ZAI de Courtaboeuf 9 Avenue de Laponie, 91978, Les Ulis, France
Tel.: (33) 169108888
Emp.: 75
Waste Treatment Services
N.A.I.C.S.: 221310
Oliver Argaut (CEO)

Eurofins Hygiene des lieux de Travail SAS (2)
5 Rue d Otterswiller, 67700, Saverne, France
Tel.: (33) 3 88 91 19 11
Laboratory Testing Services
N.A.I.C.S.: 541380

Eurofins Hygiene du Batiment Paris SAS (2)

20 Rue Du Kochersberg, 67700, Saverne, France
Tel.: (33) 3 88 91 19 11
Real Estate Manangement Services
N.A.I.C.S.: 531390

Eurofins IPL Environnement SAS (2)
5 Rue d'Otterswiller, Saverne, 67700, France
Tel.: (33) 820 20 05 25
Web Site:
Environmental Consulting Services
N.A.I.C.S.: 541620

Subsidiary (Domestic):

Eurofins IPL Est SAS (3)
Rue Lucien Cuenot - Site Saint Jacques II, BP 51 005, 54521, Maxeville, France
Tel.: (33) 3 83 50 36 00
Waste Treatment Services
N.A.I.C.S.: 221310

Eurofins IPL Ile de France SAS (3)
9 Avenue de Laponie - ZAI de Courtaboeuf, Les Ulis, 91940, France
Tel.: (33) 1 69 10 88 88
Emp.: 170
Water Testing Services
N.A.I.C.S.: 541380

Eurofins IPL Sud SAS (3)
778 rue de la Croix Verte, 34196, Montpellier, France
Tel.: (33) 4 67 84 74 27
Web Site: http://www.eurofins.com
Water Testing Services
N.A.I.C.S.: 541380

IPL Sante Environnement Durable Atlantique SAS (3)
1 Rue du Professeur Vezes, Bordeaux, 33300, France
Tel.: (33) 5 56 01 84 00
Laboratory Testing Services
N.A.I.C.S.: 541380
Proietti Pierre (Gen Mgr)

LCAM SAS (3)
40 Route de Rombas, 57140, Woippy, France
Tel.: (33) 3 87 37 40 60
Web Site: http://www.eurofins.com
Biological Testing Services
N.A.I.C.S.: 541380

Subsidiary (Domestic):

Eurofins Laboratoire Centre SAS (2)
ZAC Les Esses Galerne, 45760, Vennecy, France
Tel.: (33) 238774890
Sales Range: $25-49.9 Million
Emp.: 30
Laboratory Testing Services
N.A.I.C.S.: 541380

Eurofins Laboratoire Nord SAS (2)
ZI Douai Dorignies Rue Maurice Caullery, 59500, Douai, France
Tel.: (33) 327869560
Microbiological Testing Services
N.A.I.C.S.: 541380

Eurofins Laboratoire de Microbiologie Est SAS (2)
16 rue Clement Ader, 68127, Sainte-Croix-en-Plaine, France
Tel.: (33) 3 89 22 27 70
Web Site: http://www.eurofins.fr
Microbiological Testing Services
N.A.I.C.S.: 541380

Eurofins Laboratoire de Pathologie Vegetale SAS (2)
81 Bis Rue Bernard Palissy, 62750, Loos-en-Gohelle, France
Tel.: (33) 321426215
Pathological Testing Laboratory Services
N.A.I.C.S.: 541380

Eurofins Laboratoires de Microbiologie Ouest SAS (2)
11 Rue Pierre Adolphe Bobiere, 44300, Nantes, France
Tel.: (33) 251837979
Food Product Testing Services
N.A.I.C.S.: 541380

Eurofins Lara SA (2)
1 Impasse De Lisieux, 31025, Toulouse, France

Tel.: (33) 5 61 16 15 00
Laboratory Testing Services
N.A.I.C.S.: 541380

Eurofins Lem SAS (2)
20 Rue du Kochersberg, 67700, Saverne,
France
Tel.: (33) 388911911
Web Site: http://www.eurofins.fr
Sales Range: $25-49.9 Million
Emp.: 100
Management Consulting Services
N.A.I.C.S.: 541618

Eurofins MWG Biotech France
S.A.
9 Av de la Laponie, Z A I de Courtaboeuf,
91978, Les Ulis, France (100%)
Tel.: (33) 169108888
Web Site: http://www.mwg-biotech.sa
Sales Range: $25-49.9 Million
Emp.: 80
Testing Laboratories
N.A.I.C.S.: 541380

Eurofins Marketing Research
SAS (2)
5 Rue Cadet, 75009, Paris, France
Tel.: (33) 153349926
Web Site: http://www.eurofins-marketing-
research.com
Sales Range: $25-49.9 Million
Emp.: 60
Marketing Research Service
N.A.I.C.S.: 541910

Eurofins Medinet SAS (2)
48-52 rue de la Gare, BP 11, 78372, Plaisir,
France (100%)
Tel.: (33) 130546000
Web Site: http://www.eurofins-medinet.com
Sales Range: $10-24.9 Million
Emp.: 6
Medical Laboratories
N.A.I.C.S.: 621511

Eurofins NDSC Food France
SAS (2)
Rue Pierre Adolphe Bobierre, Nantes,
44300, France
Tel.: (33) 251832100
Web Site: http://www.eurofins.com
Food Product Testing Services
N.A.I.C.S.: 541380

Eurofins NSC Developpement France
SAS (2)
20 Rue Du Kochersberg, 67700, Saverne,
France (100%)
Tel.: (33) 388911911
Biotechnology Research & Development
Services
N.A.I.C.S.: 541714

Eurofins Optimed Lyon SAS (2)
Centre Hospitalier Lyon Sud Pavillon 40
165 Chemin du Grand Revoyet, 69310,
Pierre-Benite, France
Tel.: (33) 478866526
Web Site: https://www.optimed-
recrutement.com
Biotechnology Research & Development
Services
N.A.I.C.S.: 541714

Eurofins Optimed SAS (2)
1 rue des Essarts, 38610, Gieres, France
Tel.: (33) 438372740
Web Site: https://www.optimed.fr
Sales Range: $25-49.9 Million
Emp.: 80
Clinical Research & Biometry Services
N.A.I.C.S.: 541380

Eurofins Pharma Control SAS (2)
9 Av de la Laponie, Z A I de Courtaboeuf,
Les Ulis, 91940, France (100%)
Tel.: (33) 169108888
Emp.: 100
Testing Laboratories
N.A.I.C.S.: 541380
Luc Leroy *(CEO)*

Eurofins Pharma Quality Control
SAS (2)
16 rue Clement Ader, 68127, Sainte-Croix-
en-Plaine, France
Tel.: (33) 389222770
Pharmaceutical Product Laboratory Testing
Services

N.A.I.C.S.: 541380

Eurofins Scientific AgroGene
SARL (2)
Rue Pierre Adolphe Bobierre, BP 42301,
Nantes, 44323, France (100%)
Tel.: (33) 251832100
Sales Range: $25-49.9 Million
Emp.: 200
Research & Development in the Physical
Engineering & Life Sciences
N.A.I.C.S.: 541715

Eurofins Scientific Analytics SAS (2)
9 Rue Pierre Adolphe Bobierre, Nantes,
44323, France (100%)
Tel.: (33) 251832100
Sales Range: $75-99.9 Million
Emp.: 300
Scientific & Technical Consulting Services
N.A.I.C.S.: 541690

Eurofins Scientific Biosciences
SAS (2)
ZI de Courtaboeuf9 avenue de Laponie,
91978, Les Ulis, France (100%)
Tel.: (33) 169108888
Web Site: http://www.eurofins.fr
Sales Range: $25-49.9 Million
Emp.: 1,000
Testing Laboratories
N.A.I.C.S.: 541380

Eurofins Scientific Test Center
SAS (2)
5 Rue Cadet, 75009, Paris,
France (100%)
Tel.: (33) 153341747
Web Site: http://www.eurofins.com
Sales Range: $25-49.9 Million
Emp.: 20
Testing Laboratories
N.A.I.C.S.: 541380

Eurofins Test Center SAS (2)
64 Rue Eugene Schneider, Z A I de Courta-
boeuf Bouc-Bel, 13320, Toulon,
France (100%)
Tel.: (33) 442943500
Web Site: http://www.eurofins.com
Testing Laboratories
N.A.I.C.S.: 541380

GAB France SARL (2)
58 rue des Ateliers, 67220, Saint-Pierre,
France (100%)
Tel.: (33) 388089943
Web Site: http://www.eurofins.com
Sales Range: $25-49.9 Million
Emp.: 10
Research & Development in the Physical
Engineering & Life Sciences
N.A.I.C.S.: 541715
Francois Vigneau *(Mng Dir)*

LCN SAS (2)
9 Av de la Laponie, Z A I de Courtaboeuf,
91940, Les Ulis, France (100%)
Tel.: (33) 169108888
Web Site: http://www.eurofins.com
Sales Range: $25-49.9 Million
Emp.: 80
Testing Laboratories
N.A.I.C.S.: 541380

Optimed S.A. (2)
1 Rue des Essarts, Gieres, 38610, Gieres,
France (100%)
Tel.: (33) 438372740
Web Site: http://www.optimed.fr
Sales Range: $25-49.9 Million
Emp.: 80
Testing Laboratories
N.A.I.C.S.: 541380

Toxlab SAS (2)
7 Rue Jacques Cartier, 75018, Paris,
France
Tel.: (33) 158592800
Sales Range: $25-49.9 Million
Emp.: 35
Laboratory Testing Services

N.A.I.C.S.: 541380

Eurofins Galys SAS (1)
Rue Pierre Adolphe Bobierre, 44300,
Nantes, France
Tel.: (33) 254558888
Laboratory Testing Services

Eurofins Gelre B.V. (1)
Albert Schweitzerlaan 31, 7334 DZ, Apel-
doorn, Netherlands
Tel.: (31) 555811816
Clinical Diagnostic Centre Operator
N.A.I.C.S.: 621512

Eurofins GeneScan GmbH (1)
Engesser strasse 4, 79108, Freiburg, Ger-
many
Tel.: (49) 76164004010
Emp.: 70
Testing Laboratory
N.A.I.C.S.: 541380

Eurofins GeneScan Technologies
GmbH (1)
Engesserstr 4, 79108, Freiburg, Germany
Tel.: (49) 7615038200
Laboratory Testing Services
N.A.I.C.S.: 541380

Eurofins GeneTech KK (1)
12th Floor East Building Chiyoda First
Building 3 8-1 Nishi-Kanda, Chiyoda-ku,
Tokyo, 101-0065, Japan
Tel.: (81) 364472746
Web Site: https://www.genetech.co.jp
Clinical Research & Testing Services
N.A.I.C.S.: 621512

Eurofins Genoma Group Srl (1)
Via Castel Giubileo 11, 00138, Rome, Italy
Tel.: (39) 068811270
Emp.: 200
Laboratory Testing Services
N.A.I.C.S.: 541380

Eurofins Genome Valley Hyderabad
Resources Private Limited (1)
Sy Nos 101/2 Genome Valley Lalgadi
Malakpet, Rangareddy District, Shamirpet,
500101, Telangana, India
Tel.: (91) 4069030700
Pharmaceutical Research & Testing Ser-
vices
N.A.I.C.S.: 541380

Eurofins Genomics Austria
GmbH (1)
Viehmarktgasse 1B/Buro 2, 1030, Vienna,
Austria
Tel.: (43) 6645266860
Laboratory Testing Services
N.A.I.C.S.: 541380

Eurofins Genomics Blue Heron
LLC (1)
22310 20th Ave SE 100, Bothell, WA 98021
Tel.: (425) 368-5000
Web Site: https://www.blueheronbio.com
Gene Synthesis Research & Development
Services
N.A.I.C.S.: 541714

Eurofins Genomics Engineering,
LLC (1)
12701 Plantside Dr, Louisville, KY 40299
DNA Sequencing & Research Services
N.A.I.C.S.: 541714

Eurofins Genomics Europe Genotyp-
ing A/S (1)
Smedeskovvej 38, 8464, Galten, Denmark
Tel.: (45) 80881262
Laboratory Testing Services
N.A.I.C.S.: 541380

Eurofins Genomics Europe Pharma &
Diagnostics Products & Services
Sanger/PCR GmbH (1)
Jakob-Stadler-Platz 7, 78467, Konstanz,
Germany
Tel.: (49) 7531816068
Food Testing Services
N.A.I.C.S.: 541380

Eurofins Genomics Europe Sequenc-
ing GmbH (1)
Jakob-Stadler-Platz 7, 78467, Konstanz,
Germany

Tel.: (49) 7531816068
Laboratory Testing Services
N.A.I.C.S.: 541380

Eurofins Genomics France
S.A.S. (1)
Rue Pierre Adolphe Bobierre, 44323,
Nantes, France
Tel.: (33) 800903807
Food Testing Services
N.A.I.C.S.: 541380

Eurofins Genomics Germany
GmbH (1)
Anzinger Str 7a, 85560, Ebersberg, Ger-
many
Tel.: (49) 7531816068
Web Site: https://eurofinsgenomics.eu
Genomics Services
N.A.I.C.S.: 541714

Eurofins Genomics India Pvt Ltd (1)
540/1 Doddanakundi Industrial Area 2
Graphite India Road Hoodi, Whitefield, Ben-
galuru, 560048, Karnataka, India
Tel.: (91) 8030982500
Web Site:
https://www.eurofinsgenomics.co.in
Scientific & Technical Consulting Services
N.A.I.C.S.: 541690

Eurofins Genomics KK (1)
3-8-1 Nishikanda, Chiyoda-Ku, Tokyo, 101-
0065, Japan
Tel.: (81) 366310100
Web Site: https://www.eurofinsgenomics.jp
Laboratory Testing Services
N.A.I.C.S.: 541380

Eurofins Genomics Srl (1)
Via Bruno Buozzi 2, vimodrone, I-20090,
Milan, Italy
Tel.: (39) 0225071596
Bio Technology Services
N.A.I.C.S.: 541714

Eurofins Genomics Sweden AB (1)
Frosundaviks alle 15 4th Floor, 16970,
Solna, Sweden
Tel.: (46) 86553609
Laboratory Testing Services
N.A.I.C.S.: 541380

Eurofins Genomics UK Limited (1)
i54 Business Park Valiant Way, Wolver-
hampton, WV9 5GB, United Kingdom
Tel.: (44) 1902627250
Laboratory Testing Services
N.A.I.C.S.: 541380

Eurofins GfA GmbH (1)
Stenzelring 14b, Hamburg, 21107,
Germany (100%)
Tel.: (49) 406970960
Web Site: http://www.eurofins-umwelt.de
Sales Range: $25-49.9 Million
Emp.: 20
Air Testing & Monitoring Services
N.A.I.C.S.: 541990
Gerd Volkmer *(Mng Dir)*

Eurofins Global Central
Laboratory (1)
Bergschot 71, 4817 PA, Breda,
Netherlands (100%)
Tel.: (31) 76 572 72 72
Web Site:
http://www.centrallab.eurofins.com
Testing Laboratories
N.A.I.C.S.: 541380

Eurofins Gynae-Screen Limited (1)
Coombe Women & Infants University Hospi-
tal Dolphin Barn, Dublin, 8, Ireland
Tel.: (353) 14085245
Pharmaceutical & Cosmetic Product Testing
Services
N.A.I.C.S.: 541611

Eurofins HT-Analytik GmbH (1)
Schelsenweg 15, D-41238, Monchenglad-
bach, Germany
Tel.: (49) 21669986780
Laboratory Testing Services
N.A.I.C.S.: 541380

Eurofins Hong Kong Ltd. (1)
Unit F 8th Fl Caliant Industri Ctr St No 2 12
Au Pui Wan, Shaiin, Hong Kong, China
(Hong Kong) (100%)
Tel.: (852) 26363288

Eurofins Scientific S.E.—(Continued)

Web Site: http://www.eurofins.cn
Sales Range: $25-49.9 Million
Emp.: 100
Professional Scientific & Technical Services
N.A.I.C.S.: 541990
Enders Wong *(Mgr-Sls)*

Eurofins Human Factors MD, LLC **(1)**
8049 Corporate Ctr Dr, Charlotte, NC 28226
Tel.: (980) 585-2482
Web Site: https://www.humanfactorsmd.com
Medical Device Mfr & Distr
N.A.I.C.S.: 334510

Eurofins Hydrobiologie France S.A.S. **(1)**
Rue Lucien Cuenot Site Saint Jacques II, 54521, Maxeville, France
Tel.: (33) 637475771
Environmental & Food Analysis Services
N.A.I.C.S.: 541380

Eurofins Hydrologie Centre Est SAS **(1)**
33 avenue du Dr Georges Levy Zone d activite Green Campus, BP 51 005, Batiment 54 Venissieux, 69200, Maxeville, France
Tel.: (33) 477922600
Laboratory Testing Services
N.A.I.C.S.: 541380

Eurofins Hydrologie Est SAS **(1)**
Rue Lucien Cuenot Site Saint-Jacques II, BP 51 005, 54521, Maxeville, France
Tel.: (33) 383503600
Laboratory Testing Services
N.A.I.C.S.: 541380

Eurofins Hydrologie Ile De France SAS **(1)**
2 avenue de Laponie ZAI de Courtaboeuf, 91940, Les Ulis, France
Tel.: (33) 182820485
Laboratory Testing Services
N.A.I.C.S.: 541380

Eurofins Hydrologie Nord SAS **(1)**
Rue Maurice Caullery, ZI Douai Dorignies, 59500, Douai, France
Tel.: (33) 327869587
Laboratory Testing Services
N.A.I.C.S.: 541380

Eurofins Hydrologie Normandie SAS **(1)**
8 rue de Navarre, 14123, Cormelles-le-Royal, France
Tel.: (33) 231827406
Laboratory Testing Services
N.A.I.C.S.: 541380

Eurofins Hydrologie Ouest SAS **(1)**
758 Rue Pierre Landais, 56850, Caudan, France
Tel.: (33) 297808080
Laboratory Testing Services
N.A.I.C.S.: 541380

Eurofins Hydrologie Sud Ouest SAS **(1)**
4 Chemin des Maures, 33170, Gradignan, France
Tel.: (33) 788261003
Laboratory Testing Services
N.A.I.C.S.: 541380

Eurofins Hydrologie Sud SAS **(1)**
75D avenue de Pascalet, 30310, Vergeze, France
Tel.: (33) 466731570
Analytical Testing Services
N.A.I.C.S.: 541380

Eurofins Hygiene Alimentaire Ile-de-France SAS **(1)**
2 avenue de Laponie, ZI de Courtaboeuf, 91978, Les Ulis, France
Tel.: (33) 969370102
Laboratory Testing Services
N.A.I.C.S.: 541380

Eurofins Hygiene Alimentaire Nord-Est SAS **(1)**
40 Route de Rombas, 57140, Woippy, France
Tel.: (33) 969370102
Laboratory Testing Services
N.A.I.C.S.: 541380

Eurofins Hygiene Alimentaire Nord-Ouest SAS **(1)**
Rue Pierre Adolphe Bobierre, BP. 42301, 44300, Nantes, France
Tel.: (33) 969370102
Laboratory Testing Services
N.A.I.C.S.: 541380

Eurofins Hygiene Alimentaire SAS **(1)**
9 rue Pierre Adolphe Bobierre, F-44300, Nantes, France
Tel.: (00) 909070102
Emp.: 250
Laboratory Testing Services
N.A.I.C.S.: 541380

Eurofins Hygiene Alimentaire Sud-Ouest SAS **(1)**
rue Pierre-Adolphe Bobierre, 44300, Nantes, France
Tel.: (33) 969370102
Laboratory Testing Services
N.A.I.C.S.: 541380

Eurofins Hygiene Hospitaliere Nord S.A.S. **(1)**
2 Avenue de Laponie, 91940, Les Ulis, France
Tel.: (33) 169108888
Environmental & Food Analysis Services
N.A.I.C.S.: 541380

Eurofins Hygiene Hospitaliere Ouest S.A.S. **(1)**
3 Rue des Aeronefs, 37210, Parcay-Meslay, France
Tel.: (33) 673908962
Environmental & Food Analysis Services
N.A.I.C.S.: 541380

Eurofins Hygiene Hospitaliere Sud SAS **(1)**
24 Boulevard de la Bougie, 13014, Marseille, France
Tel.: (33) 491828240
Microbiological Testing Services
N.A.I.C.S.: 541380

Eurofins Hygiene Institut Berg GmbH **(1)**
Zieglerstrasse 11a, D-52078, Aachen, Germany
Tel.: (49) 2419908940
Laboratory Testing Services
N.A.I.C.S.: 541380

Eurofins I Verwaltungsgesellschaft GmbH **(1)**
Stenzelring 14 b, 21107, Hamburg, Germany
Tel.: (49) 40 7527090
Business Management Consulting Services
N.A.I.C.S.: 541611

Subsidiary (Domestic):

Institut fur Lebensmittel-, Wasser- und Umweltanalytik Nurnberg GmbH **(2)**
Schweinauer Hauptstrasse 38, Nuremberg, 90441, Germany
Tel.: (49) 911 383860
Laboratory Testing Services
N.A.I.C.S.: 541380
Andreas Mueller *(Mng Dir)*

Eurofins IDmyk SAS **(1)**
Bat 4B 1 rue des vergers, 69760, Limonest, France
Tel.: (33) 437499351
Microbiological Testing Services
N.A.I.C.S.: 541380

Eurofins IESPM S.A.S. **(1)**
Rue Denis Papin- CS 30525, 27 130, Verneuil d'Avre et d'Iton, France
Tel.: (33) 232321990
Web Site: https://www.iespm.fr
Emp.: 80
Oil Analysis & Research Services
N.A.I.C.S.: 541713

Eurofins INLAB GmbH **(1)**
Otto-Hahn-Strasse 15, 44227, Dortmund, Germany
Tel.: (49) 23197425700

Microbiological & Molecular Biological Testing Services
N.A.I.C.S.: 541380

Eurofins IT Infrastructure GSC S.A. **(1)**
Building 7B Level 3 Ultrapark - La Aurora, 40104, Heredia, Costa Rica
Tel.: (506) 41024121
Web Site: https://www.eurofins.cr
Computer Software Services
N.A.I.C.S.: 541511

Eurofins IT Solutions India Pvt Ltd **(1)**
540/1 Doddanakundi Industrial Area 2 Graphite India Road, Hoodi Whitefield, Bengaluru, 560048, Karnataka, India
Tel.: (91) 8067223200
Web Site: https://www.eurofins.in
Emp.: 1,000
Bio Analytical Testing Services
N.A.I.C.S.: 541380

Eurofins Inpac Medizintechnik GmbH **(1)**
Gewerbestrasse 34, 75217, Birkenfeld, Germany
Tel.: (49) 708294570
Web Site: https://www.inpac-medizintechnik.de
Emp.: 150
Cleaning Service
N.A.I.C.S.: 561720

Eurofins Institut Dr. Appelt Hilter GmbH **(1)**
Munsterstrasse 9-11, 49176, Hilter, Germany
Tel.: (49) 5424226370
Laboratory Testing Services
N.A.I.C.S.: 621511

Eurofins Institut Dr. Appelt Leipzig GmbH **(1)**
Taubchenweg 28, 04317, Leipzig, Germany
Tel.: (49) 341649660
Laboratory Testing Services
N.A.I.C.S.: 541380

Eurofins Institut Dr. Rothe GmbH **(1)**
Otto-Hahn-Str 15, 44227, Dortmund, Germany
Tel.: (49) 23197425900
Food Testing Services
N.A.I.C.S.: 541380

Eurofins Institut Jager GmbH **(1)**
Ernst-Simon-Strasse 2-4, D-72072, Tubingen, Germany
Tel.: (49) 707170070
Sales Range: $25-49.9 Million
Emp.: 30
Microbiological Testing Services
N.A.I.C.S.: 541380

Eurofins Institut Nehring GmbH **(1)**
Heesfeld 17, 38112, Braunschweig, Germany
Tel.: (49) 531238990
Laboratory Testing Services
N.A.I.C.S.: 541380

Eurofins Interlab SELAS S.A.S **(1)**
6 Rue Jacques Monod, 81000, Albi, France
Tel.: (33) 563773160
Environmental & Food Analysis Services
N.A.I.C.S.: 541380

Eurofins International Holdings LUX SARL **(1)**
Rue Henri M Schnadt 10 A, 2530, Luxembourg, Luxembourg
Tel.: (352) 2618531
Investment Management Service
N.A.I.C.S.: 523940

Subsidiary (Domestic):

Eurofins Environment Testing LUX Holding SARL **(2)**
Rue Henri M Schnadt 10 A, 2530, Luxembourg, Luxembourg
Tel.: (352) 26185341
Investment Management Service
N.A.I.C.S.: 523940

Subsidiary (Non-US):

Eurofins Environment II DE GmbH **(3)**

Am Neulander Gewerbepark 1, 21079, Hamburg, Germany
Tel.: (49) 40 49294100
Environmental Consulting Services
N.A.I.C.S.: 541620

Eurofins Environment Testing Netherlands Holding BV **(3)**
Bergschot 71, 4817 PA, Breda, Netherlands
Tel.: (31) 765737373
Investment Management Service
N.A.I.C.S.: 523940

Eurofins Environmental Services Ltd **(3)**
28-32 Westway Estate, Acton, London, W3 7XR, United Kingdom
Tel.: (44) 2082 22 60 70
Web Site: http://www.eurofins.co.uk
Environmental Consulting Services
N.A.I.C.S.: 541620

Subsidiary (Domestic):

Eurofins Industrial Testing Lux SARL **(3)**
Val Fleuri 23, 1526, Luxembourg, Luxembourg
Tel.: (352) 26185320
Web Site: https://www.eurofins.com
Emp.: 100
Industrial Testing Services
N.A.I.C.S.: 541380

Subsidiary (Domestic):

Eurofins GSC LUX SARL **(2)**
10A Rue Henri Schnadt, 2530, Luxembourg, Luxembourg
Tel.: (352) 26185341
Laboratory Testing Services
N.A.I.C.S.: 541380

Eurofins Izmir Gida Analiz Laboratuvarlari Limited Sirketi **(1)**
Karacaoglan Mahallesi 6166 Sokak No 27/A Isikkent, Bornova, 35100, Izmir, Turkiye
Tel.: (90) 2324920057
Environmental & Food Analytical Services
N.A.I.C.S.: 541380

Eurofins J3 Resources, Inc. **(1)**
3113 Red Bluff Rd, Pasadena, TX 77503
Tel.: (713) 290-0223
Pharmaceutical Research & Testing Services
N.A.I.C.S.: 541380

Eurofins Japan Analytical Chemistry Consultants Co., Ltd. **(1)**
1-7-3 Funado, Itabashi-Ku, Tokyo, 174-0041, Japan
Tel.: (81) 339678235
Laboratory Testing Services
N.A.I.C.S.: 541380

Eurofins Japan KK **(1)**
Ota Ward Hamashima Miyako, Tokyo, 143-0003, Japan
Tel.: (81) 3 5492 7344
Web Site: http://www.eurofins.co.jp
Laboratory Testing Services
N.A.I.C.S.: 541380

Eurofins KCTL Co., Ltd. **(1)**
52-20 Sinjeong-ro 41 Beon-Gil, Giheung-gu, Yongin, Gyeonggi-do, Korea (South)
Tel.: (82) 313266700
Web Site: https://www.kctl.co.kr
Testing & Safety Certification Services
N.A.I.C.S.: 541611

Eurofins KVI-PLUSZ Kornyezetvedelmi Vizsgalo Iroda Kft. **(1)**
Szallito u 6, 1211, Budapest, Hungary
Tel.: (36) 612612978
Web Site: http://www.kviplusz.hu
Laboratory Testing Services
N.A.I.C.S.: 541380

Eurofins Korea Analytic Service Co., Ltd. **(1)**
13 Sanbon-ro 101beon-gil, Gunpo, 15849, Gyeonggi-do, Korea (South)
Tel.: (82) 313617777
Laboratory Testing Services
N.A.I.C.S.: 541380

Eurofins LCDI SAS **(1)**
2 allee des Tisserands Zone Artisanale de

Jailly, 57535, Marange-Silvange, France
Tel.: (33) 387801180
Laboratory Testing Services
N.A.I.C.S.: 541380

Eurofins LCPL BV   (1)
Visseringlaan 24K, 2288 ER, Rijswijk, Netherlands
Tel.: (31) 882350235
Web Site: https://www.eurofins-nmdl-lcpl.com
Laboratory Testing Services
N.A.I.C.S.: 541380

Eurofins LEA SAS   (1)
24 Boulevard de la Bougie, 13014, Marseille, France
Tel.: (33) 491466135
Laboratory Testing Services
N.A.I.C.S.: 541380

Eurofins LGS Megalab Analisis Veterinarios SLU   (1)
Calle de la Rosa 12 1, 38002, Santa Cruz de Tenerife, Spain
Tel.: (34) 922533680
Web Site: http://www.lgs-analisis.es
Healtcare Services
N.A.I.C.S.: 621999

Eurofins Lab Environment Testing Portugal, Unipessoal Lda.   (1)
Rua do Monte de Alem 62, 4580-733, Sobrosa, Portugal
Tel.: (351) 255102111
Testing Laboratory Services
N.A.I.C.S.: 541380

Eurofins Lab Solution Srl   (1)
Via Tevere 37, Fino Mornasco, 22073, Como, Italy
Tel.: (39) 031881043
Web Site: https://www.lab-solution.it
Laboratory Testing Services
N.A.I.C.S.: 541380

Eurofins Lab Zeeuws-Vlaanderen (LZV) BV   (1)
Zandbergsestraat 1, 4569 TC, Graauw, Netherlands
Tel.: (31) 114383824
Emp.: 90
Testing Laboratory Services
N.A.I.C.S.: 541380

Eurofins Labazur Bretagne SELAS   (1)
2 rue de Rosampont, 22300, Lannion, France
Tel.: (33) 296370056
Microbiological Testing Services
N.A.I.C.S.: 541380

Eurofins Labazur Provence SELAS   (1)
143 Chem du Merlan a la Rose, 13013, Marseille, France
Tel.: (33) 491630630
Microbiological Testing Services
N.A.I.C.S.: 541380

Eurofins Labazur Rhone-Alpes SELAS   (1)
6 avenue de Verdun, 73100, Aix-les-Bains, France
Tel.: (33) 479350434
Microbiological Testing Services
N.A.I.C.S.: 541380

Eurofins Labo Van Poucke BVBA   (1)
Engelse Wandeling 7, 8500, Kortrijk, Belgium
Tel.: (32) 56258401
Laboratory Testing Services
N.A.I.C.S.: 541380

Eurofins Laboratoire Contaminants Sud SAS   (1)
75 chemin de Sommieres, F-30310, Vergeze, France
Tel.: (33) 466731685
Pesticide Testing Services
N.A.I.C.S.: 541380

Eurofins Laboratoire De Bromatologie Ouest Et Bretagne SAS   (1)
46 rue Ernest Renan, 29140, Rosporden, France
Tel.: (33) 298598060

Laboratory Testing Services
N.A.I.C.S.: 541380

Eurofins Laboratoire Dermscan SAS   (1)
114 boulevard du 11 novembre 1918, 69100, Villeurbanne, France
Tel.: (33) 472823656
Web Site: https://www.dermscan.com
Sales Range: $1-9.9 Million
Emp.: 50
Laboratory Testing Services
N.A.I.C.S.: 541380

Eurofins Laboratoire Microbiologie Rhone-Alpes S.A.S.   (1)
33 Av du Dr Georges Levy Batiment 54 Gauche, 69200, Venissieux, France
Tel.: (33) 443860383
French Food Testing & Support Services
N.A.I.C.S.: 541380

Eurofins Laboratoire de Microbiologie Sud SAS   (1)
505 rue Louis Berton, CS 60560, 13594, Aix-en-Provence, Cedex, France
Tel.: (33) 442171306
Microbiological Testing Services
N.A.I.C.S.: 541380

Eurofins Laboratories Ltd.   (1)
Dunham House N cross St, Ashburton Road West Trafford P, Sale, M337HH, United Kingdom   (100%)
Tel.: (44) 1618687600
Web Site: http://www.eurofins.co.uk
Sales Range: $25-49.9 Million
Emp.: 6
Business Support Services
N.A.I.C.S.: 561499

Eurofins Laboratorio Alfalab Internacional, SL   (1)
C/Nunez De Balboa 119, 28006, Madrid, Spain
Tel.: (34) 915622974
Laboratory Testing Services
N.A.I.C.S.: 541380

Eurofins Laboratorio Angel Mendez, SL   (1)
C/Dr Oloriz 15 Sotano Derecha, 18012, Granada, Spain
Tel.: (34) 958173060
Laboratory Testing Services
N.A.I.C.S.: 541380

Eurofins Laboratorio Bernad-Munoz, SL   (1)
C/Zurita 12 1 Oficina 3, 500001, Zaragoza, Spain
Tel.: (34) 976235833
Laboratory Testing Services
N.A.I.C.S.: 541380

Eurofins Laboratorio Calbo, SL   (1)
C/La Puebla 8 Bajo, 34005, Palencia, Spain
Tel.: (34) 979713434
Laboratory Testing Services
N.A.I.C.S.: 541380

Eurofins Laboratorio Clinico Sanitario, SL   (1)
C/Capitan Angosto Y Gomez De Castrillon 30-1 Izq, 28300, Aranjuez, Spain
Tel.: (34) 918754586
Laboratory Testing Services
N.A.I.C.S.: 541380

Eurofins Laboratorio Dr. Valenzuela, SL   (1)
C/Obispo Aguirre 22 Bajo, 27001, Lugo, Spain
Tel.: (34) 982315740
Laboratory Testing Services
N.A.I.C.S.: 541380

Eurofins Laboratorio Dres. Cermeno, SL   (1)
Avenida De Portugal 37, 05001, Avila, Spain
Tel.: (34) 920211804
Laboratory Testing Services
N.A.I.C.S.: 541380

Eurofins Laboratorio Medicantabria SL   (1)
Calle Castilla 10, 39002, Santander, Spain
Tel.: (34) 942318344
Food Products Services

N.A.I.C.S.: 722511

Eurofins Laboratorio Pilar Larraz, SL   (1)
Avenida Bayona 24 1 B, 31011, Pamplona, Spain
Tel.: (34) 948198525
Laboratory Testing Services
N.A.I.C.S.: 541380

Eurofins Laboratorio Prefasi SL   (1)
Av Principe de Asturias ed Europe III Calle Azarbe del Papel 7, Ground Floor 2, 30007, Murcia, Spain
Tel.: (34) 968246630
Web Site: http://www.laboratorioprefasi.es
Medical Laboratory Services
N.A.I.C.S.: 621511

Eurofins Laboratorio Recio, SL   (1)
C/Roma N 5 Local, 45003, Toledo, Spain
Tel.: (34) 925221205
Laboratory Testing Services
N.A.I.C.S.: 541380

Eurofins Laboratorio Sarro SL   (1)
Rambla De Catalunya 120, 08008, Barcelona, Spain
Tel.: (34) 932187091
Laboratory Testing Services
N.A.I.C.S.: 541380

Eurofins Laboratorio Surlab, SL   (1)
C/Rio Guadiana 1, Parla, 28980, Madrid, Spain
Tel.: (34) 916057257
Laboratory Testing Services
N.A.I.C.S.: 541380

Eurofins Laboratorio Virtudes SL   (1)
C/Republica Dominicana 3-Bajo, 45004, Toledo, Spain
Tel.: (34) 925210492
Laboratory Testing Services
N.A.I.C.S.: 541380

Eurofins Laboratorio de Castilla y Leon, SL   (1)
C/Fidel Recio 1, 47002, Valladolid, Spain
Tel.: (34) 983290751
Web Site: http://www.laboratoriosdecastilla.es
Medical Laboratory Services
N.A.I.C.S.: 621511

Eurofins Laborservices GmbH   (1)
Kobelweg 12 1/6, D-86156, Augsburg, Germany
Tel.: (49) 821240920
Emp.: 20
Laboratory Testing Services
N.A.I.C.S.: 541380

Eurofins Labtarna Lietuva UAB   (1)
Kauno g 1A, LT-01314, Vilnius, Lithuania
Tel.: (370) 52130726
Web Site: https://www.eurofins.lt
Laboratory Testing Services
N.A.I.C.S.: 541380

Eurofins Labtium Oy   (1)
Tekniikantie 2, 02150, Espoo, Finland
Tel.: (358) 505742813
Laboratory Testing Services
N.A.I.C.S.: 541380

Eurofins Lamm S.R.L.   (1)
Via Luigi Boccherini 626, Porcari, 55016, Lucca, Italy
Tel.: (39) 0583581491
Web Site: https://www.lammlab.it
Clinical Test & Analysis Services
N.A.I.C.S.: 811210

Eurofins Lanagram SAS   (1)
20 Rue Galibert Pons, 81200, Mazamet, France
Tel.: (33) 563984195
Laboratory Testing Services
N.A.I.C.S.: 541380

Eurofins Lancaster Laboratories Environment Testing, LLC   (1)
2425 New Holland Pike, Lancaster, PA 17601
Tel.: (717) 656-2300
Environmental & Cosmetic Product Testing Services
N.A.I.C.S.: 541611

Eurofins Lebensmittelanalytik Osterreich GmbH   (1)

Palmersstrasse 2, 2351, Wiener Neudorf, Austria
Tel.: (43) 571572000
Laboratory Testing Services
N.A.I.C.S.: 621511

Eurofins LifeCodexx GmbH   (1)
Line-Eid-Strasse 3, 78467, Konstanz, Germany
Tel.: (49) 75319769460
Web Site: http://www.lifecodexx.com
Medical Device Mfr
N.A.I.C.S.: 339112
Marcus Cholewa (Mng Dir)

Eurofins Limed Ltd.   (1)
24th Imber St, Petach Tikva, Israel
Tel.: (972) 586600168
Web Site: https://www.li-med.com
Medical Device Mfr & Distr
N.A.I.C.S.: 334510

Eurofins MGS Laboratories Limited   (1)
Unit 2 Merlin Park Airport Services Road, Portsmouth, PO3 5FU, United Kingdom
Tel.: (44) 2393277990
Microbiological Contract Testing Laboratory Services
N.A.I.C.S.: 541380

Eurofins MITOX FOPSE S.A.R.L.   (1)
Le Pichoy, 32250, Fources, France
Tel.: (33) 562294143
Environmental & Laboratory Testing Services
N.A.I.C.S.: 621511

Eurofins MTS Consumer Product Testing (Hong Kong) Co., Ltd.   (1)
Unit 808 CEO Tower 77 Wing Hong Street, Cheung Sha Wan Kowloon, Hong Kong, China (Hong Kong)
Tel.: (852) 36041328
Textile Product Mfr & Distr
N.A.I.C.S.: 313310

Eurofins MTS Consumer Product Testing (Shanghai) Co., Ltd.   (1)
Building 1 No 105 Guangzhong Rd, Zhuanqiao Town Minhang, Shanghai, 201108, China
Tel.: (86) 2123509600
Food Testing Services
N.A.I.C.S.: 541380

Eurofins MTS Consumer Product Testing Cambodia Ltd.   (1)
No 882 St 598 Phum Savy Pak Sangkat Svay Pak, Khan Russie Keo, Phnom Penh, Cambodia
Tel.: (855) 23900993
Pharmaceutical Research & Testing Services
N.A.I.C.S.: 541380

Eurofins MTS Consumer Product Testing Germany GmbH   (1)
Provinostr 52 Gebaude A 17, 86153, Augsburg, Germany
Tel.: (49) 8215697960
Web Site: https://www.mts-germany.eu
Food & Pharmaceutical Testing Services
N.A.I.C.S.: 541380

Eurofins MTS Consumer Product Testing UK Limited   (1)
118 Lupton Avenue, Leeds, LS9 6ED, United Kingdom
Tel.: (44) 1132488830
Food & Pharmaceutical Testing Services
N.A.I.C.S.: 541380

Eurofins Mas Control SLU   (1)
C/N Diesel 5 Trasera Nave 3 El Chorrilo, Pol Ind La Campana, 38109, Santa Cruz de Tenerife, Spain
Tel.: (34) 922684115
Laboratory Testing Services
N.A.I.C.S.: 541380

Eurofins Maser B.V.   (1)
Auke Vleerstraat 26, 7521 PG, Enschede, Netherlands
Tel.: (31) 534802680
Web Site: https://www.maserengineering.eu
Electronic Component Mfr & Distr
N.A.I.C.S.: 334419

Eurofins Scientific, S.E.—(Continued)

Eurofins Materials Science Netherlands BV (1)
High Tech Campus 11, 5656 AE, Eindhoven, Netherlands
Tel.: (31) 621174227
Medical Device Mfr
N.A.I.C.S.: 339112

Eurofins Mechem Pte. Ltd. (1)
127 Woodlands Industrial Park E5 Woodlands e-Terrace, Singapore, 757500, Singapore
Tel.: (65) 64536038
Laboratory Testing Services
N.A.I.C.S.: 541380

Eurofins Medigenomix Forensik GmbH (1)
Anzinger Strasse 7a, D-85560, Ebersberg, Germany
Tel.: (49) 80928289400
Web Site: https://www.eurofins.de
Laboratory Testing Services
N.A.I.C.S.: 541380

Eurofins Medigenomix GmbH (1)
Anzinger Str 7a, 85560, Ebersberg, Germany (100%)
Tel.: (49) 80928289400
Web Site: http://www.medigenomix.de
Sales Range: $25-49.9 Million
Emp.: 200
Research & Development in the Physical Engineering & Life Sciences
N.A.I.C.S.: 541715

Eurofins Medinet BV (1)
Bergschot 71, PO Box 5510, 4817 PA, Breda, Netherlands (100%)
Tel.: (31) 765727272
Web Site: http://www.eurofins-medinet.com
Sales Range: $75-99.9 Million
Emp.: 251
Research & Development in the Physical Engineering & Life Sciences
N.A.I.C.S.: 541715

Eurofins Medinet Pte. Ltd. (1)
1 International Business Park 01-16 The Synergy, Singapore, 609917, Singapore (100%)
Tel.: (65) 65623858
Web Site: http://www.eurofins.ph
Sales Range: $25-49.9 Million
Emp.: 18
Testing Laboratories
N.A.I.C.S.: 541380

Eurofins Mediscan Laboratories Sdn. Bhd. (1)
No 47 Jalan Rajawali 2, Bandar Puchong Jaya, 47100, Puchong, Selangor Darul Ehsan, Malaysia
Tel.: (60) 380763213
Pharmaceutical Research & Testing Services
N.A.I.C.S.: 541380

Eurofins Medische Microbiologie B.V. (1)
Houtlaan 55, Postbus 9650, 2334 CK, Leiden, Netherlands
Tel.: (31) 715178384
Pharmaceutical & Cosmetic Product Testing Services
N.A.I.C.S.: 541611

Eurofins Megalab SA (1)
C de los Pajaritos 19, Retiro, 28007, Madrid, Spain
Tel.: (34) 914202205
Web Site: https://www.eurofins-megalab.com
Health Fitness Services
N.A.I.C.S.: 713940

Eurofins Metodos Servicios Agricolas, S.L.U. (1)
El Campico, 30860, Puerto de Mazarron, Spain
Tel.: (34) 609477335
Pharmaceutical Research & Testing Services
N.A.I.C.S.: 541380

Eurofins Microbiologie des Eaux Ouest SAS (1)
Rue Pierre-Adolphe Bobierre, 44323,

Nantes, France
Tel.: (33) 251832100
Microbiological Testing Services
N.A.I.C.S.: 541380

Eurofins Microbiology Laboratories Inc. (1)
2200 Rittenhouse St Ste 175, Des Moines, IA 50321
Tel.: (515) 698-5025
Laboratory Testing Services
N.A.I.C.S.: 541380

Eurofins Microscan S.A. (1)
Rue de la Blancherie 17 / CP, 1022, Chavannes-pres-Renens, Switzerland
Tel.: (41) 216918252
Web Site: https://www.microscan.ch
Pharmaceutical & Construction Analysis Services
N.A.I.C.S.: 541380

Eurofins Mikro Kemi AB (1)
Seminariegatan 29, Box 15018, 750 15, Uppsala, Sweden
Tel.: (46) 18 57 22 00
Web Site: http://www.mikrokemi.se
Sales Range: $25-49.9 Million
Emp.: 20
Pharmaceutical Product Testing Services
N.A.I.C.S.: 541380
Tobias Svensson-Mejer (Mgr-Laboratory)

Eurofins Miljo (Galten) (1)
Smedeskovvej 38, Galten, DK 8464, Arhus, Denmark (100%)
Tel.: (45) 70224276
Web Site: http://www.eurofins.dk
Testing Laboratories
N.A.I.C.S.: 541380

Eurofins Miljo A/S (1)
Ladelundvej 85, DK-6600, Vejen, Denmark (100%)
Tel.: (45) 70224266
Web Site: https://www.eurofins.dk
Sales Range: $200-249.9 Million
Emp.: 600
Analytical Laboratory Instrument Mfr
N.A.I.C.S.: 334516

Eurofins Miljo Luft A/S (1)
Smedeskovvej 38, 8464, Galten, Denmark
Tel.: (45) 70224266
Web Site: https://www.eurofinsmiljoluft.com
Laboratory Product Mfr
N.A.I.C.S.: 334516

Eurofins Milk Testing Denmark A/S (1)
Ladelundvej 85, 6600, Vejen, Denmark
Tel.: (45) 70224286
Web Site: https://www.eurofins.dk
Laboratory Testing Services
N.A.I.C.S.: 541380

Eurofins Milk Testing Sweden AB (1)
Kabelvqagen 2, 553 02, Jonkoping, Sweden
Tel.: (46) 104908500
Web Site: https://www.ringfeder-rf.com
Laboratory Testing Services
N.A.I.C.S.: 541380

Eurofins Minerag Kft. (1)
Keselyusi ut 9, 7100, Szekszard, Hungary
Tel.: (36) 74529680
Web Site: https://www.eurofins-agro.com
Soil Testing Services
N.A.I.C.S.: 541380

Eurofins Mitox BV (1)
Science Park 408, 1098 XH, Amsterdam, Netherlands
Tel.: (31) 562294143
Laboratory Testing Services
N.A.I.C.S.: 541380

Eurofins Modern Testing Service Taiwan, Ltd. (1)
649-8 Zhong Zheng Road, Xin Zhuang District, New Taipei City, 242051, Taiwan
Tel.: (886) 229039977
Food Testing Services
N.A.I.C.S.: 541380

Eurofins Modern Testing Services Bangladesh Limited (1)
280 East Narsingahpur, Ashulia Savar, Dhaka, 1341, Bangladesh
Tel.: (880) 1755642001

Textile Product Mfr & Distr
N.A.I.C.S.: 313310

Eurofins Munuera, S.L.U. (1)
C/ Julian Romea Parcela 22-1 Poligono Industrial Oeste, 30169, Murcia, Spain
Tel.: (34) 968898007
Web Site: https://www.laboratoriosmunuera.com
Environmental & Laboratory Testing Services
N.A.I.C.S.: 621511

Eurofins NBLSC Environment Testing Spain, S.L.U. (1)
Camino de la Raya 16, Castello de la Plana, 12006, Castellon de la Plana, Spain
Tel.: (34) 964251072
Pharmaceutical & Cosmetic Product Testing Services
N.A.I.C.S.: 541611

Eurofins NDSC Food Testing Germany GmbH (1)
Neulander Kamp 1a, 21079, Hamburg, Germany
Tel.: (49) 40492949000
Sales Range: $25-49.9 Million
Emp.: 100
Laboratory & Food Testing Services
N.A.I.C.S.: 541380

Subsidiary (Domestic):

Institut Dr. Appelt Hilter GmbH & Co. KG (2)
Munsterstrasse 9-11, 49176, Hilter, Germany
Tel.: (49) 5424 22 637 0
Web Site: http://www.appelt-laboratorien.de
Laboratory Testing Services
N.A.I.C.S.: 541380

Institut Dr. Appelt Thuringen GmbH & CO. KG (2)
Talstrasse 50, 98544, Zella-Mehlis, Germany
Tel.: (49) 3682 89 65 0
Web Site: http://www.appelt-laboratorien.de
Sales Range: $25-49.9 Million
Emp.: 20
Testing Laboratory Services
N.A.I.C.S.: 541380

Eurofins NDSC Umweltanalytik GmbH (1)
Neulander Kamp 1a, D-21079, Hamburg, Germany
Tel.: (49) 2236897125
Laboratory Testing Services
N.A.I.C.S.: 541380

Eurofins NDSM Limited (1)
Unit 1 Eden Business Park Edenhouse Drive, Old Malton, Malton, YO17 6AE, United Kingdom
Tel.: (44) 1653917921
Agro Science Research & Testing Services
N.A.I.C.S.: 541380

Eurofins NM Laboratory Sdn Bhd (1)
78 and 80 Lorong Perda Selatan 1 Bandar Perda, Bukit Mertajam, 14000, Pulau Penang, Malaysia
Tel.: (60) 45388081
Web Site: https://www.eurofins.my
Laboratory Testing Services
N.A.I.C.S.: 541380

Eurofins NSC Denmark A/S (1)
Tel.: (45) 70224266
Web Site: https://www.eurofins.dk
Sales Range: $25-49.9 Million
Emp.: 100
Business Management Consulting Services
N.A.I.C.S.: 541618

Eurofins NSC Finance Germany GmbH (1)
Stenzelring 14 b, Hamburg, 21107, Germany
Tel.: (49) 40 73 44 12 100
Web Site: http://www.eurofins.de
Emp.: 60
Financial Consulting Services
N.A.I.C.S.: 541611
Dietrich Roettger (Gen Mgr)

Eurofins NSC Netherlands BV (1)
Koopvaardijweg 32-34, 4906 CV, Ooster-

hout, Netherlands
Tel.: (31) 765737373
Web Site: http://www.eurofinsmedenet.com
Emp.: 250
Laboratory Testing Services
N.A.I.C.S.: 541380
Dina De Haeck (Mng Dir)

Eurofins NSC UK & Ireland Ltd (1)
Room 139 Woodthorne Wergs Road, Wolverhampton, WV6 8TQ, United Kingdom
Tel.: (44) 1902693215
Laboratory Testing Services
N.A.I.C.S.: 541380

Eurofins Nab Labs Oy (1)
Nuottasaarentie 17 Door K301, FI-90400, Oulu, Finland
Tel.: (358) 404503100
Laboratory Testing Services
N.A.I.C.S.: 541380

Eurofins Nanolab Technologies, Inc. (1)
1708 Mccarthy Blvd, Milpitas, CA 95035
Tel.: (408) 433-3320
Pharmaceutical & Cosmetic Product Testing Services
N.A.I.C.S.: 541611

Eurofins Norsk Matanalyse AS (1)
Nils Hansens Vei 4, 0602, Oslo, Norway
Tel.: (47) 23050500
Web Site: http://www.eurofins.no
Laboratory Testing Services
N.A.I.C.S.: 541380
Christina Haug (Mng Dir)

Eurofins Norsk Miljoanalyse AS (1)
Sandviksvn 110, PO Box 17, Sandviken, Bergen, 5035, Norway
Tel.: (47) 55 54 92 92
Laboratory Testing Services
N.A.I.C.S.: 541380

Eurofins North Malaya Laboratory Sdn Bhd (1)
65 67 and 69 Lebuh Kurau 5 Taman Chai Leng, Perai, 13700, Pulau Penang, Malaysia
Tel.: (60) 43902085
Laboratory Testing Services
N.A.I.C.S.: 541380

Eurofins OBIKS Polska Sp. z.o.o. (1)
Ul Owocowa 8, 40-158, Katowice, Poland
Tel.: (48) 322597036
Web Site: https://www.obiks.pl
Laboratory Testing Services
N.A.I.C.S.: 541380

Eurofins OkoLabor Kft. (1)
Petofi u 45, 5643, Bekescsaba, Hungary
Tel.: (36) 66899055
Biogas Plant Fermentation Testing Services
N.A.I.C.S.: 541380

Eurofins Okometric GmbH (1)
Bernecker Str 17-21, 95448, Bayreuth, Germany
Tel.: (49) 921726330
Web Site: https://www.oekometric.de
Dioxin & Furan Research Services
N.A.I.C.S.: 541714

Eurofins Omegam BV (1)
H J E Wenckebachweg 120, Duivendrecht, 1114 AD, Amsterdam, Netherlands
Tel.: (31) 205976680
Laboratory Testing Services
N.A.I.C.S.: 541380

Eurofins PHAST Development GmbH & Co. KG (1)
Byk-Gulden-Str 2, 78467, Konstanz, Germany
Tel.: (49) 684192420
Food Testing Services
N.A.I.C.S.: 541380

Eurofins PROXY Laboratories BV (1)
Archimedesweg 25, 2333 CM, Leiden, Netherlands
Tel.: (31) 715244080
Pharmaceuticals Product Mfr
N.A.I.C.S.: 325412

Eurofins Panlabs Discovery Services Taiwan, Ltd. (1)

25 Wugong 6th Road, Wugu District, New Taipei City, 24891, Taiwan
Tel.: (886) 277517000
Laboratory Testing Services
N.A.I.C.S.: 541380

Eurofins Pathologie SELAS (1)
2 Impasse des Colonies, 13008, Marseille, France
Tel.: (33) 491373030
Laboratory Testing Services
N.A.I.C.S.: 541380

Eurofins Pegasuslab AB (1)
Rapsgatan 21, 754 50, Uppsala, Sweden
Tel.: (46) 104008260
Laboratory Testing Services
N.A.I.C.S.: 541380

Eurofins Pharma BioAnalytics Services US, Inc. (1)
15 Research Park Dr, Saint Charles, MO 63304
Tel.: (636) 362-7000
Drug Discovery & Drug Development Services
N.A.I.C.S.: 541714

Eurofins Pharma Quality Control Denmark A/S (1)
Smedeskovvej 38, 8464, Galten, Denmark
Tel.: (45) 70224296
Web Site: http://www.eurofins.com
Emp.: 100
Pharmaceuticals Product Mfr
N.A.I.C.S.: 325412

Eurofins Pharma Services India Pvt Ltd (1)
183 1st Floor Gayatri Tech Park PIP 2nd Phase, Whitefield, Bengaluru, 560066, India
Tel.: (91) 8030706666
Web Site: https://www.pharma.eurofins.cn
Pharmaceutical Product Testing Services
N.A.I.C.S.: 541380

Eurofins Pharma US Holdings BV (1)
Bergschot 71, 4817 PA, Breda, Netherlands
Tel.: (31) 765737373
Investment Management Service
N.A.I.C.S.: 523940

Eurofins Phyliae S.A.S. (1)
3005 La Vieille Route, 76190, Valliquerville, France
Tel.: (33) 693285745
Pharmaceutical & Cosmetic Product Testing Services
N.A.I.C.S.: 541611

Eurofins Pivetti Srl (1)
Via San Biagio 76/A, 42024, Castelnovo di Sotto, RE, Italy
Tel.: (39) 0522682371
Laboratory Testing Services
N.A.I.C.S.: 541380

Eurofins Polska Sp. z.o.o. (1)
Aleja Wojska Polskiego 90A, 82-200, Malbork, Poland
Tel.: (48) 552720473
Web Site: https://www.eurofins.pl
Laboratory Testing Services
N.A.I.C.S.: 541380

Eurofins Precision TEM, LLC (1)
3350 Scott Blvd Bldg 36, Santa Clara, CA 95054
Tel.: (408) 980-8898
Semiconductor Device Distr
N.A.I.C.S.: 423690

Eurofins Prelevement pour le Batiment Est SAS (1)
20 rue du Kochersberg, 67700, Saverne, France
Tel.: (33) 785567312
Asbestos Testing Services
N.A.I.C.S.: 541380

Eurofins Prelevement pour le Batiment Ile-de-France SAS (1)
117 quai de Valmy, 75010, Paris, France
Tel.: (33) 140371505
Asbestos Testing Services
N.A.I.C.S.: 541380

Eurofins Prelevement pour le Batiment Sud-Ouest SAS (1)

4 chemin des Maures, 33170, Gradignan, France
Tel.: (33) 67010101
Laboratory Testing Services
N.A.I.C.S.: 541380

Eurofins ProMicro Pty Ltd. (1)
46-48 Banksia Road, Welshpool, 6106, WA, Australia
Tel.: (61) 862534444
Laboratory Testing Services
N.A.I.C.S.: 541380

Eurofins Product Service (Thailand) Co., Ltd (1)
344/2 Soi Soonvijai 4 Rama9 Rd, Bangkapi Huaykwang, Bangkok, 10320, Thailand
Tel.: (66) 27168530
Web Site: https://www.eurofins.co.th
Electrical Product Laboratory Testing Services
N.A.I.C.S.: 541380

Eurofins Product Service GmbH (1)
Storkower Strasse 38C, Reichenwalde, D-15526, Brandenburg, Germany
Tel.: (49) 33631888801
Laboratory Testing Services
N.A.I.C.S.: 541380

Eurofins Product Testing Denmark A/S (1)
Smedeskovvej 38 Port 9, 8464, Galten, Denmark
Tel.: (45) 70224276
Web Site: https://www.eurofins.dk
Laboratory Testing Services
N.A.I.C.S.: 541380

Eurofins Product Testing India Pvt Ltd (1)
Plot No 157 First Floo Udyog Vihar Phase 1, Gurgaon, 122016, Haryana, India
Tel.: (91) 1246250300363
Laboratory Testing Services
N.A.I.C.S.: 541380

Eurofins Product Testing Italy Srl (1)
Via Cuorgne 21, I-10156, Turin, Italy
Tel.: (39) 0112222225
Web Site: https://www.eurofins.it
Laboratory Testing Services
N.A.I.C.S.: 541380

Eurofins Product Testing Japan KK (1)
2-1-13 Sachiura, Kanazawa-ku, Yokohama, 236-0003, Kanagawa, Japan
Tel.: (81) 457803831
Emp.: 15
Environmental & Food Analytical Testing Services
N.A.I.C.S.: 541380

Eurofins Product Testing Service (Shanghai) Co., Ltd (1)
Building 18 No 2168 Chenhang Highway, Minhang District, Shanghai, 201114, China
Tel.: (86) 2161819181
Web Site: https://www.eurofins.cn
Laboratory Testing Services
N.A.I.C.S.: 541380

Eurofins Product Testing Services Ltd (1)
Unit 16 Willan Trading Estate Waverly road, Sale, M33 7AY, Manchester, United Kingdom
Tel.: (44) 1618687600
Sales Range: $25-49.9 Million
Emp.: 5
Laboratory Testing Services
N.A.I.C.S.: 541380

Eurofins Product Testing US Inc. (1)
11822 N Creek Pkwy N Ste 110, Bothell, WA 98011
Laboratory Testing Services
N.A.I.C.S.: 541380
Maria Johnson *(Dir-Global Bus Dev)*

Eurofins Product Testing Verwaltungs GmbH (1)
Grossmoorbogen 25, 21079, Hamburg, Germany
Tel.: (49) 4049294360
Laboratory Testing Services
N.A.I.C.S.: 541380

Subsidiary (Domestic):

Eurofins Consumer Product Testing GmbH (2)

Am Neulander Gewerbepark 4, D-21079, Hamburg, Germany
Tel.: (49) 40492946900
Web Site: https://www.eurofins.com
Emp.: 60
Consumer Product Testing Services
N.A.I.C.S.: 541380

Eurofins Product Testing, Cosmetics & Personal Care Spain, S.L.U. (1)
Ausias March No 148-150, 08013, Barcelona, Spain
Tel.: (34) 935533177
Pharmaceutical & Cosmetic Product Testing Services
N.A.I.C.S.: 541611

Eurofins Professional Scientific Services Belgium NV (1)
Schalienhoevedreef 20 T, B-2800, Mechelen, Belgium
Tel.: (32) 92227759
Laboratory Testing Services
N.A.I.C.S.: 541380

Eurofins Q-Bioanalytic GmbH (1)
Fischkai 1, 27572, Bremerhaven, Germany
Tel.: (49) 4719008210
Web Site: https://www.q-bioanalytic.net
Laboratory Testing Services
N.A.I.C.S.: 541380

Eurofins QKEN KK (1)
411-1 Oumaru, Munakata, 811-3422, Fukuoka, Japan
Tel.: (81) 940378070
Web Site: https://www.nouyaku-bunseki.net
Emp.: 87
Food Product Mfr & Distr
N.A.I.C.S.: 311412

Eurofins QTA Inc. (1)
8900 Beckett Rd, West Chester, OH 45069
Tel.: (513) 842-3999
Laboratory Testing Services
N.A.I.C.S.: 541380

Eurofins Qualitech AG (1)
Almuesenacherstrasse 3, 5506, Magenwil, Switzerland
Tel.: (41) 628896969
Web Site: https://www.qualitech.ch
Food Testing Services
N.A.I.C.S.: 541380

Eurofins Quimico Onubense, S.L.U. (1)
Parque Huelva Empresarial Factoria Comercial Nave 13, 21007, Huelva, Spain
Tel.: (34) 959256486
Agriculture & Environment Analysis Services
N.A.I.C.S.: 541620

Eurofins Radon Testing Sweden AB (1)
Robetsviksgatan 6a, 972 41, Lulea, Sweden
Tel.: (46) 104908480
Web Site: https://radon.eurofins.se
Laboratory Testing Services
N.A.I.C.S.: 541380

Eurofins Radonlab AS (1)
Hoffsveien 13, 0275, Oslo, Norway
Tel.: (47) 21960350
Web Site: https://www.radonshop.no
Laboratory Testing Services
N.A.I.C.S.: 541380

Eurofins Regulatory & Consultancy Services Italy S.R.L. (1)
Via Bruno Buozzi 2, Vimodrone, 20055, Milan, Italy
Tel.: (39) 022507151
Pharmaceutical & Consumer Product Analytical Services
N.A.I.C.S.: 541611

Eurofins Regulatory AG (1)
Weidenweg 15, 4310, Rheinfelden, Switzerland
Tel.: (41) 618362083
Web Site: https://www.eurofins.com
Sales Range: $25-49.9 Million
Emp.: 12
Agricultural Chemical Testing Services
N.A.I.C.S.: 541380

Eurofins Reservoirs Environmental, Inc. (1)

5801 Logan St Ste 100, Denver, CO 80216
Tel.: (303) 964-1986
Environmental & Laboratory Testing Services
N.A.I.C.S.: 621511

Eurofins SAM sensory & marketing Italy Srl (1)
Viale Monza 270, 20128, Milan, Italy
Tel.: (39) 0227007019
Web Site: http://www.samresearch.com
Analytical Laboratory Testing Services
N.A.I.C.S.: 541380
Paolo Manfredi *(Mng Dir)*

Eurofins SEPO Sp. z o.o. (1)
Ul Dworcowa 47, 44-190, Knurow, Poland
Tel.: (48) 322360316
Web Site: https://www.sepo.pl
Environmental Protection Design & Construction Services
N.A.I.C.S.: 238210

Eurofins SOFIA GmbH (1)
Rudower Chaussee 29, 12489, Berlin, Germany
Tel.: (49) 3067798560
Food Testing Services
N.A.I.C.S.: 541380

Eurofins Sac Ky Hai Dang Company Ltd. (1)
Room 319 Vietnam Korean TechFarm Road 8 Tra Noc 2 I P, Phuoc Thoi Ward O Mon District, Can Tho, Vietnam
Tel.: (84) 2871077879
Laboratory Testing Services
N.A.I.C.S.: 541380

Eurofins Salux B.V. (1)
Rooseveltstraat 18, Postbus 16080, 2321 BM, Leiden, Netherlands
Tel.: (31) 715160020
Pharmaceutical & Cosmetic Product Testing Services
N.A.I.C.S.: 541611

Eurofins Sanitas Inspections BV (1)
Zuideinde 68, 2991 LK, Barendrecht, Netherlands
Tel.: (31) 102922940
Laboratory Testing Services
N.A.I.C.S.: 541380

Eurofins Saudi Ajal Laboratories Ltd. (1)
Al Anwar St Building No 2648, Riyadh, 14813, Saudi Arabia
Tel.: (966) 114279999
Web Site: https://www.saudiajal.com
Pharmaceutical & Cosmetic Product Testing Services
N.A.I.C.S.: 541611

Eurofins Scientific (Ireland) Limited (1)
Red Oak North, South County Business Park, Dublin, D18 X4K7, Ireland (100%)
Tel.: (353) 15252555
Testing Laboratories
N.A.I.C.S.: 541380

Subsidiary (Domestic):

Eurofins Food Testing Ireland Limited (2)
Unit D13 North City Business Park North Road, Finglas, Dublin, Ireland
Tel.: (353) 14311306
Laboratory Testing Services
N.A.I.C.S.: 541380

Eurofins Scientific AG (1)
Parkstrasse 10, 5012, Schonenwerd, Switzerland (100%)
Tel.: (41) 628587100
Web Site: https://www.eurofins.ch
Sales Range: $25-49.9 Million
Emp.: 20
Research & Development in the Physical Engineering & Life Sciences
N.A.I.C.S.: 541715
Axel Prauser *(Mng Dir)*

Eurofins Scientific BV (1)
Bergschot 71, PO Box 5510, 4801 DM, Breda, Netherlands (100%)
Tel.: (31) 765737373
Web Site: http://www.eurofins.com

Eurofins Scientific S.E.—(Continued)

Sales Range: $150-199.9 Million
Emp.: 250
Testing Laboratories
N.A.I.C.S.: 541380
Dina Dehaecak (Mgr)

Eurofins Scientific CZ S.r.o. (1)
Schr 41 Nechvilova 1821, CA 14800,
Prague, Czech Republic (100%)
Tel.: (420) 271 911 344
Web Site: http://www.eurofins.com
Testing Laboratories
N.A.I.C.S.: 541380

Eurofins Scientific Finland Oy (1)
Raisionkaari 55, FI-21200, Raisio, Finland
Tel.: (358) 440306500
Laboratory Testing Services
N.A.I.C.S.: 541380

Eurofins Scientific GmbH (1)
Am Neulander Gewerbepark 1, 21079,
Hamburg, Germany (100%)
Tel.: (49) 4049 294360
Web Site: http://www.eurofins.de
Sales Range: $25-49.9 Million
Emp.: 60
Laboratory Testing Services
N.A.I.C.S.: 541380
Markus Brandmeier (Mng Dir)

Subsidiary (Domestic):

**Eurofins Deutsches Institut fur Leb-
ensmitteluntersuchung GmbH** (2)
Neulander Kamp 1, 21079, Hamburg, Ger-
many
Tel.: (49) 40 492 94 0
Web Site: http://www.eurofins.de
Food Product Testing Services
N.A.I.C.S.: 541380
Markuus Brandnear (Mgr)

**Eurofins Dr. Specht Laboratorien
GmbH** (2)
Am Neulander Gewerbepark 2, 21079,
Hamburg, Germany
Tel.: (49) 40881448700
Sales Range: $25-49.9 Million
Emp.: 200
Laboratory Testing Services
N.A.I.C.S.: 541380

Eurofins GfA Lab Service GmbH (2)
Neulander Kamp 1a, 21079, Hamburg, Ger-
many
Tel.: (49) 40492945050
Laboratory Testing Services
N.A.I.C.S.: 541380

Eurofins IT-infrastructure GmbH (2)
Am Neulander Gewerbepark 1, Hamburg,
21079, Germany
Tel.: (49) 4049294360
Information Technology Consulting Services
N.A.I.C.S.: 541512

**Eurofins Information Systems
GmbH** (2)
Neulander Kamp 1a, 21079, Hamburg, Ger-
many
Tel.: (49) 4049294799
Data Processing Services
N.A.I.C.S.: 518210

Eurofins Scientific Inc. (1)
2200 Rittenhouse St Ste 150, Des Moines,
IA 50321-3155
Tel.: (515) 230-8378
Web Site: http://www.eurofins.com
Testing Laboratories
N.A.I.C.S.: 541715

Subsidiary (Domestic):

Advantar Laboratories, Inc. (2)
5451 Oberlin Dr Ste 100, San Diego, CA
92121
Tel.: (858) 228-7788
Web Site: http://www.advantarlabs.com
Sales Range: $1-9.9 Million
Emp.: 70
Analytical Development & Clinical Formula-
tion Laboratory Services
N.A.I.C.S.: 621511
Rich Kenley (Founder & CEO)

**Eurofins Agroscience Services
Inc.** (2)

150 Industrial Park Dr, Forsyth, GA 31029
Tel.: (478) 994-1092
Web Site: http://www.eurofins.com
Sales Range: $25-49.9 Million
Emp.: 60
Laboratory Testing Services
N.A.I.C.S.: 541380

**Eurofins Analytical Testing Center
Inc.** (2)
401 W State St Rm T235B, Jacksonville, FL
32202
Tel.: (904) 359-0947
Web Site: http://www.eurofins.com
Analytical Laboratory Testing Services
N.A.I.C.S.: 541380

Eurofins BioDiagnostics, Inc. (2)
507 Highland Dr, River Falls, WI 54022
Tel.: (715) 426-0246
Web Site: https://www.eurofins-
biodiagnostics.com
Emp.: 120
Seed & Plant-Tissue Testing Services
N.A.I.C.S.: 541380
Farhad Ghavami (Chief Science Officer)

**Eurofins Central Analytical Laborato-
ries Inc.** (2)
2219 Lakeshore Dr Ste 100, New Orleans,
LA 70122
Tel.: (504) 297-3400
Web Site: http://www.centralanalytical.com
Food & Chemical Testing Services
N.A.I.C.S.: 541380
John Reuther (Pres)

Eurofins DQCI (2)
5205 Quincy St, Mounds View, MN 55112
Tel.: (763) 785-0484
Web Site: https://www.dqci.com
Emp.: 50
Dairy Product Laboratory Testing Services
N.A.I.C.S.: 541380

Eurofins GeneScan USA Inc. (2)
2219 Lakeshore Dr Ste 400, New Orleans,
LA 70122 (100%)
Tel.: (504) 297-4330
Web Site: http://www.eurofinsus.com
Sales Range: $25-49.9 Million
Emp.: 20
Testing Laboratories
N.A.I.C.S.: 541380

**Eurofins Lancaster Laboratories,
Inc.** (2)
2425 New Holland Pike, Lancaster, PA
17601 (100%)
Tel.: (717) 656-2300
Web Site: https://www.lancasterlabs.com
Sales Range: $100-124.9 Million
Emp.: 800
Research & Analytical Laboratory Services
N.A.I.C.S.: 541715
Timothy Oostdyk (Pres)

Subsidiary (Domestic):

Eurofins Air Toxics, LLC (3)
180 Blue Ravine Rd Ste B, Folsom, CA
95630
Tel.: (916) 985-1000
Web Site: http://www.airtoxics.com
Laboratory Testing Services
N.A.I.C.S.: 541380

Eurofins CEI, Inc. (3)
730 SE Maynard Rd, Cary, NC 27511
Tel.: (919) 481-1413
Laboratory Testing Services
N.A.I.C.S.: 541380

Eurofins Calscience, LLC (3)
7440 Lincoln Way, Garden Grove, CA
92841
Tel.: (714) 895-5494
Laboratory Testing Services
N.A.I.C.S.: 541380

Eurofins Eaton Analytical, LLC (3)
750 Royal Oaks Dr Ste 100, Monrovia, CA
91016
Tel.: (626) 386-1100
Laboratory Testing Services
N.A.I.C.S.: 541380

Branch (Domestic):

**Eurofins Lancaster Laboratories, Inc.
- Portage** (3)

6859 Quality Way, Portage, MI
49002 (100%)
Tel.: (269) 323-3366
Web Site:
http://www.pharm.lancasterlabs.com
Sales Range: $25-49.9 Million
Emp.: 50
Testing Laboratories
N.A.I.C.S.: 541380

Subsidiary (Domestic):

J3 Resources, Inc. (3)
6110 W 34th St, Houston, TX 77092
Tel.: (713) 290-0221
Web Site: http://www.j3ro00uro0o.com
Emp.: 28
Bio Technology Services
N.A.I.C.S.: 541714
Cathy Poye (Pres)

Subsidiary (Domestic):

Eurofins MWG Operon Inc. (2)
2211 Seminole Dr Ste 201, Huntsville, AL
35805
Tel.: (256) 704-8200
Web Site: http://www.operon.com
Sales Range: $25-49.9 Million
Emp.: 100
Biological Testing Services
N.A.I.C.S.: 541380

Eurofins Medinet Inc. (2)
14100 Park Meadow Dr Ste 110, Chantilly,
VA 20151 (100%)
Tel.: (703) 480-2500
Sales Range: $10-24.9 Million
Emp.: 90
Medical Laboratories
N.A.I.C.S.: 621511

Eurofins NTD, Inc. (2)
80 Ruland Rd Ste 1, Melville, NY 11747
Web Site: http://www.ntdlabs.com
Sales Range: $10-24.9 Million
Emp.: 80
Prenatal Screening Services
N.A.I.C.S.: 541380

**Eurofins Product Safety Labs
Inc.** (2)
2394 Hwy 130, Dayton, NJ
08810-1500 (100%)
Tel.: (732) 438-5100
Web Site: http://www.productsafetylabs.com
Testing Laboratories
N.A.I.C.S.: 541380
Daniel Merkel (Pres)

**Eurofins SF Analytical Laboratories,
Inc.** (2)
2345 S 170th St, New Berlin, WI 53151
Tel.: (262) 754-5300
Web Site: https://www.eurofins.com
Testing Laboratories
N.A.I.C.S.: 541380

Eurofins Scientific Italia Srl (1)
Via Bruno Buozzi 2, 20090, Vimodrone,
Italy
Tel.: (39) 022507151
Sales Range: $25-49.9 Million
Emp.: 100
Laboratory Testing Services
N.A.I.C.S.: 541380

Subsidiary (Domestic):

Eurofins Biolab Srl (2)
Via Bruno Buozzi 2, I-20055, Vimodrone,
Milan, Italy
Tel.: (39) 022507151
Web Site: https://www.biolab.it
Laboratory Testing Services
N.A.I.C.S.: 541380

Eurofins Chemical Control Srl (2)
Via Celdit 2, Madonna dell Olmo, I-12100,
Cuneo, Italy
Tel.: (39) 0171412470
Web Site: https://www.eurofins.it
Sales Range: $10-24.9 Million
Emp.: 50
Chemical Product Research & Development
Services
N.A.I.C.S.: 541715

Eurofins Consulting Italia Srl (2)
Via Sansovino 217, 10151, Turin, Italy
Tel.: (39) 011 22 22 228

Web Site: http://www.eurofins.it
Emp.: 20
Laboratory Testing Services
N.A.I.C.S.: 541380

**Eurofins Environment Testing Italy
Srl** (2)
Via Austria 25B, Padua, 35127, Italy
Tel.: (39) 049 87 01 192
Web Site: http://www.eurofins.it
Emp.: 40
Environmental Testing Services
N.A.I.C.S.: 541380
Franco Piatelli (Gen Mgr)

Eurofins Modulo Uno SpA (2)
Via Cuorgne 21, 10156, Turin, Italy
Tel.: (39) 011 22 22 225
Web Site: http://www.eurofins.it
Sales Range: $25-49.9 Million
Emp.: 100
Testing & Inspection Services
N.A.I.C.S.: 541380

Eurofins Scientific Japan K.K. (1)
Shimouma 4-16-21, Setagaya-ku, Tokyo,
154-0002, Japan (100%)
Tel.: (81) 5055396350
Management Consulting Services
N.A.I.C.S.: 541618

Eurofins Scientific Services S.A. (1)
48 Avenue Herrmann-Debroux, Kraainem,
1160, Brussels, Belgium (100%)
Tel.: (32) 27661620
Web Site: http://www.eurofins.com
Sales Range: $25-49.9 Million
Emp.: 80
Testing Laboratories
N.A.I.C.S.: 541380
Gilles G. Martin (Chm & CEO)

Eurofins Scitec S.A. (1)
Avenue de Provence 18, 1007, Lausanne,
Switzerland
Tel.: (41) 581005393
Web Site: https://www.scitecsa.com
Pharmaceutical & Food Analysis Services
N.A.I.C.S.: 541380

Eurofins Selcia Limited (1)
Fyfield Business & Research Park Fyfield
Road, Ongar, CM5 0GS, Essex, United
Kingdom
Tel.: (44) 1277367000
Web Site: https://www.selcia.com
Drug Product Mfr & Distr
N.A.I.C.S.: 325412

**Eurofins Sensory Consumer & Prod-
uct Research (Shanghai), Ltd.** (1)
Suite 301 No 500 South Xiangyang Road,
Shanghai, 200031, China
Tel.: (86) 2162863878
Laboratory Testing Services
N.A.I.C.S.: 541380

Eurofins Sica AgriQ SL (1)
Bulevar Ciudad de Vicar 789-791, Vicar,
Almeria, Spain
Tel.: (34) 950554362
Laboratory Testing Services
N.A.I.C.S.: 541380

Eurofins Sisthema S.R.L. (1)
Via Giuseppe di Vittorio 70, 20026, Novate
Milanese, MI, Italy
Tel.: (39) 023562759
Pharmaceutical Research & Testing Ser-
vices
N.A.I.C.S.: 541380

**Eurofins Spectrum Analytical,
LLC** (1)
830 Silver St, Agawam, MA 01001
Tel.: (413) 789-9018
Laboratory Testing Services
N.A.I.C.S.: 541380

**Eurofins Spinnovation Analytical
BV** (1)
Kloosterstraat 9 Pivot Park RK, 5349 AB,
Oss, Netherlands
Tel.: (31) 242403400
Laboratory Testing Services
N.A.I.C.S.: 541380

**Eurofins Summit Tsiande Environ-
mental Co., Ltd.** (1)
7F-1 No 210 Gongyequ 38th Rd, Tai-

Chung Industrial Park, Taichung, 40768, Taiwan
Tel.: (886) 423507780
Laboratory Testing Services
N.A.I.C.S.: 541380

Eurofins Taiyo Techno Research KK (1)
Pearl Building 3-76 Takahata, Kanazawa, 921-8001, Ishikawa, Japan
Tel.: (81) 762563918
Web Site: https://www.taiyo.vc
Environmental & Food Analytical Testing Services
N.A.I.C.S.: 541380

Eurofins Technologies Australia Pty Ltd (1)
6 Monterey Road, Dandenong South, 3175, VIC, Australia
Tel.: (61) 385645937
Laboratory Testing Services
N.A.I.C.S.: 541380

Eurofins Technology Service (Guangzhou) Co., Ltd. (1)
201 Building C 48 Nanxiang 3rd Road Science City, Huangpu, Guangzhou, 510663, China
Tel.: (86) 2082180865
Laboratory Testing Services
N.A.I.C.S.: 541380

Eurofins Technology Service (Qingdao) Co., Ltd. (1)
Floor 2 Building 6 No 368 Hedong Road High-tech Zone, Qingdao, 266111, Shandong, China
Tel.: (86) 4000761880
Laboratory Testing Services
N.A.I.C.S.: 541380

Eurofins Technology Service (Suzhou) Ltd. (1)
10 B1 Long Shan Road, 215163, Suzhou, Jiangsu, China (100%)
Tel.: (86) 51268785300
Web Site: http://www.eurofins.cn
Professional Scientific & Technical Services
N.A.I.C.S.: 541990

Eurofins Technology Services (Suzhou) Co., Ltd (1)
No 101 Jialingjiang Road SSTT SND, Suzhou, 215163, Jiangsu, China
Tel.: (86) 4008285088
Web Site: https://www.eurofins.cn
Sales Range: $25-49.9 Million
Emp.: 50
Analytical Testing Services
N.A.I.C.S.: 541380

Eurofins TestOil, Inc. (1)
20338 Progress Dr, Strongsville, OH 44149
Tel.: (216) 251-2510
Web Site: https://www.testoil.com
Oil & Petroleum Product Analytical Testing Services
N.A.I.C.S.: 541380

Eurofins Testing A/S (1)
Smedeskovvej 38 Port 9, 8464, Galten, Denmark (100%)
Tel.: (45) 70224276
Web Site: http://www.eurofins.dk
Sales Range: $200-249.9 Million
Emp.: 800
Analytical Laboratory Instrument Mfr
N.A.I.C.S.: 334516

Eurofins Testing Chile S.A. (1)
Avda Parque Antonio Rabat 6165, Vitacura, 7660118, Santiago, Chile
Tel.: (56) 22400338
Food Testing Services
N.A.I.C.S.: 541380

Eurofins Testing Inspection Certification (Chengdu) Co., Ltd. (1)
F8 Block B2 No 18 Bio-town Middle Road Section Two, Shuangliu District, Chengdu, Sichuan, China
Tel.: (86) 2885820877
Food Testing Services
N.A.I.C.S.: 541380

Eurofins Testing Inspection Certification (Xiamen) Co., Ltd. (1)
No 71 Houxiang Road Building 18 XBB, Xiamen, 361028, Fujian, China

Tel.: (86) 4008538588
Food Testing Services
N.A.I.C.S.: 541380

Eurofins Testing Technology (Shenzhen) Co., Ltd (1)
4/F Building 3 Runheng Dingfeng Industrial Park No 1 Liuxian 3rd Road, Bao'an District, Shenzhen, 518040, China
Tel.: (86) 755 8358 5700
Web Site: http://www.eurofins.hk
Laboratory Testing Services
N.A.I.C.S.: 541380

Eurofins Textile Testing Spain SL (1)
C/German Bernacer 4, 03202, Elche, Alicante, Spain
Tel.: (34) 966602870
Laboratory Testing Services
N.A.I.C.S.: 541380

Eurofins Trialcamp, S.L.U. (1)
Poligono Industrial L Alter Avenida Antic Regne de Valencia N 25, Alcasser Bajo, 46290, Valencia, Spain
Tel.: (34) 962986143
Pharmaceutical Research & Testing Services
N.A.I.C.S.: 541380

Eurofins Tsing Hua Environment Testing Co., Ltd. (1)
No 55 Jhonghe St, Jhubei, 302, Hsinchu, Taiwan
Tel.: (886) 35545022
Laboratory Testing Services
N.A.I.C.S.: 541380

Eurofins Tuketici Urunleri Test Hizmetleri A.S. (1)
Mahmutbey Mah Tasocagi Yolu Cad 2538 Sokak Kisik Plaza No 6 /11-12, Bagcilar, Istanbul, Turkiye
Tel.: (90) 4447362
Laboratory Testing Services
N.A.I.C.S.: 541380

Eurofins Turkey Analiz Hizmetleri Limited Sirketi (1)
Mh Sitma Pinar Sk No 2/1 D 1 Kadikoy, Kozyatagi, 34742, Istanbul, Turkiye
Tel.: (90) 2164644412
Laboratory Testing Services
N.A.I.C.S.: 541380

Eurofins Umwelt Ost GmbH (1)
Lobstedter Strasse 78, D-07749, Jena, Germany
Tel.: (49) 364146490
Web Site: https://www.eurofins-umwelt-ost.de
Scientific & Technical Consulting Services
N.A.I.C.S.: 541690

Eurofins VBM Laboratoriet A/S (1)
Gunnekaer 26, 2610, Rodovre, Denmark
Tel.: (45) 36727000
Web Site: http://www.vbmlab.dk
Laboratory Testing Services
N.A.I.C.S.: 541380

Eurofins VRL, Inc. (1)
6665 S Kenton St Ste 205, Centennial, CO 80111
Medical Testing Laboratory Services
N.A.I.C.S.: 621511

Subsidiary (Domestic):

Evans Analytical Group, Inc. (2)
4747 Executive Dr Ste 700, San Diego, CA 92121
Tel.: (408) 530-3500
Web Site: http://www.eag.com
Surface Analysis & Materials Characterization Laboratories
N.A.I.C.S.: 541380

Subsidiary (Non-US):

EAG Laboratories GmbH (3)
Eiselauer Weg 4 Geb Bld 5, 80981, Ulm, Germany
Tel.: (49) 731 400 693 0
Web Site: http://www.eurofins.com
Pesticide Analysis Services
N.A.I.C.S.: 541380

Subsidiary (Domestic):

Eurofins EAG Easton (3)

8598 Commerce Dr, Easton, MD 21601
Tel.: (410) 822-8600
Web Site: http://www.eag.com
Industrial Chemical Testing Services
N.A.I.C.S.: 541380

Eurofins EAG Hercules (3)
625 Alfred Nobel Dr, Hercules, CA 94547
Tel.: (510) 741-3000
Web Site: http://www.eag.com
Chemical Research & Development Services
N.A.I.C.S.: 541715

Division (Domestic):

Eurofins EAG Princeton (3)
104 Windsor Center Dr Ste 101, East Windsor, NJ 08520
Tel.: (609) 371-4800
Web Site: http://www.eag.com
Testing Laboratories
N.A.I.C.S.: 541380

Eurofins EAG Santa Clara (3)
2710 Walsh Ave, Santa Clara, CA 95051
Tel.: (408) 454-4600
Web Site: http://www.eag.com
Chemical Engineering Services
N.A.I.C.S.: 541330

Subsidiary (Non-US):

Eurofins EAG Shanghai (3)
1F Bldg 4 No 1151 Lianxi Rd Pudong Area, Pudong Area, Shanghai, 201204, China
Tel.: (86) 21 6879 6088
Web Site: http://www.eag.com
Surface Analysis & Materials Characterization Laboratories
N.A.I.C.S.: 541380

Eurofins EAG Singapore (3)
65 Chulia St, Singapore, 049513, Singapore
Tel.: (65) 8223 8560
Web Site: http://www.eurofins.sg
Surface Analysis & Materials Characterization Laboratories
N.A.I.C.S.: 541380

Subsidiary (Domestic):

Eurofins EAG St Louis (3)
2672 Metro Blvd, Maryland Heights, MO 63043
Tel.: (314) 291-6620
Web Site: http://www.eag.com
Testing Laboratory
N.A.I.C.S.: 541380

Division (Domestic):

Eurofins EAG Sunnyvale (3)
810 Kifer Rd, Sunnyvale, CA 94086
Tel.: (408) 530-3500
Web Site: http://www.eag.com
Chemical Testing Laboratory Services
N.A.I.C.S.: 541380

Subsidiary (Non-US):

Eurofins EAG Taiwan (3)
5F-1 No 31 PuDing Road, Hsin-chu, 30072, Taiwan
Tel.: (886) 3 5632303
Web Site: http://www.eag.com
Surface Analysis & Materials Characterization Laboratories
N.A.I.C.S.: 541380

Eurofins EAG Tokyo (3)
7F Sumitomo Bldg Higashi Ikebrukuro 1-10-1, Toshima-ku, Tokyo, 170-0013, Japan
Tel.: (81) 3 5396 0531
Web Site: http://www.eag.com
Surface Analysis & Materials Characterization Laboratories
N.A.I.C.S.: 541380

Eurofins EAG Toulouse (3)
94 Chemin de la Peyrette, Tournefeuille, 31170, France
Tel.: (33) 5 61 73 15 29
Web Site: http://www.eag.com
Surface Analysis & Materials Characterization Laboratories
N.A.I.C.S.: 541380

Subsidiary (Domestic):

MWG Biotech Inc. (2)
2211 Seminole Dr, Huntsville, AL 35805 (100%)
Tel.: (336) 812-9995
Web Site: http://www.mwg-biotech.com
Sales Range: $25-49.9 Million
Emp.: 100
In-Vitro Diagnostic Substance Mfr
N.A.I.C.S.: 325413

My Eye Media, LLC (2)
2211 N Hollywood Way, Burbank, CA 91505
Tel.: (818) 559-7200
Web Site: http://www.myeyemedia.com
Quality Assurance, Technical Analysis & Testing of Digital Motion Picture Content
N.A.I.C.S.: 541519
Michael Kadenacy (Founder & CEO)

Viracor-IBT Laboratories, Inc. (2)
1001 NW Technology Dr, Lees Summit, MO 64086
Tel.: (816) 347-0113
Web Site: http://www.viracor.com
Sales Range: $10-24.9 Million
Emp.: 125
Medical Laboratory
N.A.I.C.S.: 621511
Steven Kleiboeker (VP-R&D)

Eurofins Vetcontrol Kft. (1)
Deli-Bekoto ut 8, 1211, Budapest, Hungary
Tel.: (36) 202489044
Web Site: https://www.vetcontrol.hu
Veterinary Diagnostic Testing Services
N.A.I.C.S.: 541380

Eurofins Viljavuuspalvelu Oy (1)
Graanintie 7, FI-50190, Mikkeli, Finland
Tel.: (358) 15320400
Agricultural Testing Services
N.A.I.C.S.: 541380

Eurofins Villapharma Research SL (1)
Parque Tecnologico de Fuente Alamo Ctra El Estrecho-Lobosillo Km 2 5, Av Azul Fuente Alamo de, 30320, Murcia, Spain
Tel.: (34) 968197524
Laboratory Testing Services
N.A.I.C.S.: 541380

Eurofins Viracor BioPharma Services, Inc. (1)
18000 W 99th St, Lenexa, KS 66219
Web Site: https://www.eurofins-viracorbiopharma.com
Pharmaceutical Research & Development Services
N.A.I.C.S.: 541611

Eurofins Viracor, Inc. (1)
1001 NW Technology Dr, Lees Summit, MO 64086
Web Site: http://www.eurofins-viracor.com
Medical Testing Laboratory Services
N.A.I.C.S.: 621511
Michelle Altrich (Pres)

Eurofins WEJ Contaminants GmbH (1)
Neulander Kamp 1, 21079, Hamburg, Germany
Tel.: (49) 40492942222
Sales Range: $25-49.9 Million
Emp.: 100
Food Testing Services
N.A.I.C.S.: 541380

Eurofins WFC Analytics B.V. (1)
Kolk 27, 4241 TH, Arkel, Netherlands
Tel.: (31) 183629749
Food Safety & Testing Services
N.A.I.C.S.: 541380

Eurofins WFC-Food Safety B.V. (1)
Kolk 27, 4241 TH, Arkel, Netherlands
Tel.: (31) 183629749
Web Site: https://foodconsult.squarespace.com
Food Safety & Testing Services
N.A.I.C.S.: 541380

Eurofins WKS Labservice GmbH (1)
Industriestr 1, 49849, Uelzen, Germany
Tel.: (49) 5945890
Testing Laboratory Services
N.A.I.C.S.: 541380

Eurofins Scientific S.E.—(Continued)

Eurofins Water Testing Sweden AB (1)
Sjohagsgatan 3 port 1, 531 40, Linkoping, Sweden
Tel.: (46) 104908110
Laboratory Testing Services
N.A.I.C.S.: 541380

Eurofins Woosol Co., Ltd. (1)
328 Techno 2-ro, Yuseong-gu, Daejeon, 34036, Korea (South)
Tel.: (82) 429361212
Food Product Testing Services
N.A.I.C.S.: 541380

Eurofins York Limited (1)
Unit 1 Ground Floor Arabesque House Monks Cross Drive, York, YO32 9GW, United Kingdom
Tel.: (44) 3304303456
Web Site: http://www.yorkemc.com
Laboratory Testing Services
N.A.I.C.S.: 541380
Nick Wainwright *(CEO)*

Eurofins ams Laboratories Pty. Ltd. (1)
179 Magowar Road, Girraween, 2145, NSW, Australia
Tel.: (61) 297042300
Food Testing Services
N.A.I.C.S.: 541380

Eurofins avd. Moss (1)
Postboks 3055, Kambo, NO-1506, Moss, Norway (100%)
Tel.: (47) 6 900 5200
Web Site: http://www.eurofins.no
Testing Laboratories
N.A.I.C.S.: 541380

Eurofins bestLab Oy (1)
Myllarinkatu 19, 65100, Vaasa, Finland
Tel.: (358) 105818570
Web Site: https://www.bestlab.fi
Food Testing Services
N.A.I.C.S.: 541380

Eurofins do Brasil Analise de Alimentos Ltda (1)
Rodovia Engenheiro Ermenio de Oliveira Penteado s/n km 57 7, Condominio Industriale Bairro Tombadouro Indaiatuba, Sao Paulo, 13337-300, Brazil (100%)
Tel.: (55) 1921075500
Web Site: http://www.eurofins.com.br
Sales Range: $25-49.9 Million
Emp.: 32
Testing Laboratories
N.A.I.C.S.: 541380

Eurofins prelevement Pour Le batiment France SAS (1)
20 rue du Kochersberg, 67700, Saverne, France
Tel.: (33) 388717845
Asbestos Testing Services
N.A.I.C.S.: 541380

Eurofins prelevement Pour Le batiment Nord SAS (1)
21 rue de l'Albeck, ZI de Petite Synthe, 59640, Dunkerque, France
Tel.: (33) 328282440
Asbestos Testing Services
N.A.I.C.S.: 541380

Eurofins prelevement Pour Le batiment Ouest SAS (1)
7 rue Pierre Adolphe Bobierre, 44300, Nantes, France
Tel.: (33) 789016823
Asbestos Testing Services
N.A.I.C.S.: 541380

Eurofins prelevement Pour Le batiment Sud-Est SAS (1)
2 rue Chanoine Ploton, CS 40265, 42016, Saint-Etienne, France
Tel.: (33) 672979492
Asbestos Testing Services
N.A.I.C.S.: 541380

Eurofins testiranja in raziskave okolja Slovenija d.o.o. (1)
Koroska Cesta 58, 3320, Velenje, Slovenia
Tel.: (386) 3981930
Web Site: https://www.eurofins.si

Environmental & Food Analytical Services
N.A.I.C.S.: 541380

Eurofins water&waste GmbH (1)
Eumigweg 7, 2351, Wiener Neudorf, Austria
Tel.: (43) 571571
Web Site: https://www.eurofins.at
Laboratory Testing Services
N.A.I.C.S.: 541380

Eurofins-GAB GmbH (1)
Eutingerstrasse 24, 75223, Niefern-Oschelbronn, 75223, Germany (100%)
Tel.: (49) 723396270
Web Site: http://www.eurofins-gab.com
Sales Range: $25-49.9 Million
Emp.: 60
Management Consulting Services
N.A.I.C.S.: 541618

Express Microbiology Limited (1)
Unit 22/4 Mill Road Industrial Estate, Linlithgow, EH49 7SF, United Kingdom
Tel.: (44) 1506845405
Web Site:
https://www.expressmicroscience.co.uk
Food & Beverage Mfr
N.A.I.C.S.: 311421

GCL Capacita SA (1)
Parque Antonio Rabat Sur 6165, Vitacura, 7660118, Santiago, Chile
Tel.: (56) 222400659
Food Industry Training Services
N.A.I.C.S.: 611519

GFA GmbH (1)
Von-Drais-Str 18, 55469, Simmern, Germany (100%)
Tel.: (49) 676190530
Web Site: http://www.gf-a.de
Sales Range: $25-49.9 Million
Emp.: 25
Testing Laboratories
N.A.I.C.S.: 541380

Genetic Lab Co., Ltd. (1)
3F Sapporo IT Front Building 196 Kita 9-jo Nishi 15-28, Chuo-ku, Sapporo, 060-0009, Japan
Tel.: (81) 116447301
Emp.: 55
Medical Development & Diagnostic Services
N.A.I.C.S.: 621512

GenoSkan A/S (1)
Niels Pedersens Alle 2, 8830, Viborg, Denmark
Tel.: (45) 24904252
Testing Laboratory Services
N.A.I.C.S.: 541380

Genolytic Diagnostik GmbH (1)
Deutscher Platz 5, 04103, Leipzig, Germany
Tel.: (49) 22129212830
Web Site: https://www.resultan.de
Molecular Biological Diagnostic Services
N.A.I.C.S.: 621512

Gold Standard Diagnosis Frankfurt GmbH (1)
Waldstrasse 23 A6, 63128, Dietzenbach, Germany
Tel.: (49) 6074236980
Pharmaceutical & Cosmetic Product Testing Services
N.A.I.C.S.: 541611

Gold Standard Diagnostics CD Kassel GmbH (1)
Otto-Hahn-Strasse 16, 34123, Kassel, Germany
Tel.: (49) 5614917420
Web Site:
https://icd.goldstandarddiagnostics.com
Allergen Diagnostic Product Distr
N.A.I.C.S.: 423450

Gold Standard Diagnostics Corp, Inc. (1)
2795 2nd St Ste 300, Davis, CA 95618
Web Site: http://www.gsdx.us
Clinical research Laboratory Services
N.A.I.C.S.: 621511

Gold Standard Diagnostics Freiburg GmbH (1)
Engesser Strasse 4, D-79108, Freiburg, Germany
Tel.: (49) 16096739998

Food Testing Services
N.A.I.C.S.: 541380

Gold Standard Diagnostics Horsham, Inc. (1)
124 Railroad Dr, Warminster, PA 18974
Tel.: (215) 357-3911
Web Site:
https://www.goldstandarddiagnostics.us
Diagnostic Medical Device Mfr & Distr
N.A.I.C.S.: 334510

Gold Standard Diagnostics Kassel GmbH (1)
Otto-Hahn-Str 16, 34123, Kassel, Germany
Tel.: (40) 5614017420
Web Site:
https://kassel.goldstandarddiagnostics.com
Diagnostic Test Equipment Mfr & Distr
N.A.I.C.S.: 334510

Gold Standard Diagnostics Shanghai Co., Ltd. (1)
Building 18 No 2168 Chenhang Highway, Minhang District, Shanghai, China
Tel.: (86) 15921514977
Web Site:
https://www.goldstandarddiagnostics.cn
Food Testing Services
N.A.I.C.S.: 541380

Gold Standard Diagnostics Singapore Pte. Ltd. (1)
61 Science Park Road 05-03/08 The Galen Singapore Science Park II, Singapore, 117525, Singapore
Tel.: (65) 69710895
Diagnostic Research & Testing Services
N.A.I.C.S.: 541380

Gold Standard Diagnostics Trieste S.R.L. (1)
Area Science Park Padriciano 99, TS, 34149, Trieste, Italy
Tel.: (39) 0403755341
Veterinary Diagnostic Testing Services
N.A.I.C.S.: 541380

Gynae-Screen Limited (1)
Coombe Women and Infants University Hospital Dolphin's Barn, Dublin, Ireland
Tel.: (353) 14085245
Laboratory Testing Services
N.A.I.C.S.: 541380

INLAB GmbH Institut fur Lebensmittelmikrobiologie (1)
Otto-Hahn-Strasse 15, 44227, Dortmund, Germany
Tel.: (49) 23197425700
Web Site: http://www.inlab-dortmund.de
Sales Range: $25-49.9 Million
Emp.: 20
Microbiological Testing Services
N.A.I.C.S.: 541380

IfB Institut fur Blutgruppenforschung GmbH (1)
Stolberger Str 370, 50933, Cologne, Germany
Tel.: (49) 2212921280
Web Site: https://www.dna-ifb.de
Forensic & Testing Services
N.A.I.C.S.: 541380

Immunolab Clinical Diagnostics GmbH (1)
Herrengraben 1, 21465, Reinbek, Germany
Tel.: (49) 406366540
Web Site: http://www.immunolab-clinical.de
Medical Device Mfr
N.A.I.C.S.: 339112

Immunolab GmbH (1)
Otto-Hahn-Strasse 16, 34123, Kassel, Germany
Tel.: (49) 5614917420
Web Site: http://www.immunolab.de
Medical Device Mfr
N.A.I.C.S.: 339112

Infinity Laboratories Inc. (1)
1585 S Perry St, Castle Rock, CO 80104
Tel.: (303) 730-7330
Web Site: http://www.infinitylaboratories.com
Testing Laboratories
N.A.I.C.S.: 541380
Justin Pate *(VP-Sls & Mktg)*

Subsidiary (Domestic):

Quadrants Scientific, Inc. (2)

10840 Thornmint Rd Ste 113, San Diego, CA 92127
Tel.: (858) 618-4708
Web Site: http://www.quadscience.com
Testing Laboratories
N.A.I.C.S.: 541380
Elizabeth Kind *(Pres)*

Innolab do Brasil Ltda. (1)
Rua Barros Barreto 35, Bonsucesso, Rio de Janeiro, 20221-161, Brazil
Tel.: (55) 21 3509 1750
Web Site: http://www.eurofins.com.br
Sales Range: $25-49.9 Million
Emp.: 80
Laboratory Testing Services
N.A.I.C.S.: 541380

Institut Dr. Rothe GmbH (1)
Otto-Hahn-Str 15, 44227, Dortmund, Germany
Tel.: (49) 23197425900
Web Site: http://www.instro.de
Laboratory Testing Services
N.A.I.C.S.: 541380

Institut Francais Des Empreintes Genetiques S.A.S. (1)
Rue Pierre Adolphe Bobierre, BP 42301, 44323, Nantes, France
Tel.: (33) 272642195
Pharmaceutical & Cosmetic Product Testing Services
N.A.I.C.S.: 541611

Institut Prof. Dr. Jager GmbH (1)
Ernst-Simon-Strasse 2-4, 72072, Tubingen, Germany (100%)
Tel.: (49) 707170070
Web Site: http://www.eurofins.de
Research & Development in the Physical Engineering & Life Sciences
N.A.I.C.S.: 541715

Integrated Petroleum Expertise Company - Servicos em Petroleo Ltda. (1)
Rua Barros Barreto 35, Bonsucesso, Rio de Janeiro, 20221-161, RJ, Brazil
Tel.: (55) 2135091750
Laboratory Testing Services
N.A.I.C.S.: 541380

Labor Tres Laboratorios e Consultoria Tecnica Ltda. (1)
Av Damasceno Vieira N542 - Vila Mascote, Sao Paulo, CEP 04363-040, SP, Brazil
Tel.: (55) 1156782333
Web Site: https://www.labor3.com.br
Microbiological Research Services
N.A.I.C.S.: 541715

Laboratori Cat-Gairin, S.L.U. (1)
C/Figuerola 35, 17001, Girona, Spain
Tel.: (34) 972207225
Pharmaceutical Research & Testing Services
N.A.I.C.S.: 541380

Laboratorio ALAC Ltda. (1)
Rua David Sartori 601, Bairro Alfandega, Garibaldi, 95720-000, RS, Brazil
Tel.: (55) 5433883232
Testing Laboratory Services
N.A.I.C.S.: 541380

Laboratorio Gessyma Galea, S.L. (1)
Ramon y Cajal Etorb 56, 48014, Bilbao, Bizkaia, Spain
Tel.: (34) 944755693
Pharmaceutical Research & Testing Services
N.A.I.C.S.: 541380

Laboratorio Pasteur de Analises Clinicas Ltda. (1)
Av Ana Costa no 424 Gonzaga, Santos, 11060-002, SP, Brazil
Tel.: (55) 13996635129
Web Site: http://www.pasteur.com.br
Laboratory Testing Services
N.A.I.C.S.: 541380

Laboratorio Sao Lucas Ltda. (1)
Av 2 529, Rio Claro, Brazil
Tel.: (55) 1935311380
Web Site:
http://www.laboratoriosaolucas.com.br
Medical Laboratory Services

N.A.I.C.S.: 621511

Laboratorio de Analises Clinicas J. Pinto de Barros, S.A. (1)
Rua do Monte de Alem 62, 4580-733, Sobrosa, Portugal
Tel.: (351) 255102108
Pharmaceutical & Cosmetic Product Testing Services
N.A.I.C.S.: 541611

Laboratorios Montoro Botella SL (1)
Avenida Baleares 31, 46023, Valencia, Spain
Tel.: (34) 963375792
Web Site: http://www.montorobotella.com
Medical Laboratory Services
N.A.I.C.S.: 621511

Laboratorios Vital, S.L.U. (1)
Pol Ind La Negrilla Calle Imprenta 28, 41016, Sevilla, Spain
Tel.: (34) 954534509
Web Site: https://www.laboratoriosvital.com
Laboratory Testing Services
N.A.I.C.S.: 541380

M.A.H. Food Controll Kft. (1)
Deli-bekoto ut 8, 1211, Budapest, Hungary
Tel.: (36) 202979708
Laboratory Testing Services
N.A.I.C.S.: 541380

MET Korea, Ltd. (1)
Suite 2002 2003 Building A Bundang Suji U tower 767 Sinsu-ro, Suji-gu, Yongin, 16827, Gyeonggi-do, Korea (South)
Tel.: (82) 316978202
Laboratory Testing Services
N.A.I.C.S.: 541380

MV Genetix GmbH (1)
Anzinger Str 7a, D-85560, Ebersberg, Germany (100%)
Tel.: (49) 898998920
Web Site: http://www.medigenomix.de
Sales Range: $25-49.9 Million
Emp.: 60
Research & Development in the Physical Engineering & Life Sciences
N.A.I.C.S.: 541715

MWG Biotech AG (1)
Anzinger Strasse 7A, Ebersberg, Augsburg, 85560, Germany (100%)
Tel.: (49) 809282890
Web Site: http://www.eurofinsdna.com
Sales Range: $50-74.9 Million
Emp.: 150
Biological Product Mfr
N.A.I.C.S.: 325414

Subsidiary (Domestic):

Eurofins MWG GmbH (2)
Anzinger Str 7a, 85560, Ebersberg, Germany
Tel.: (49) 8092828977
Web Site: http://www.eurofinsdna.com
Sales Range: $25-49.9 Million
Emp.: 300
Laboratory Testing Services
N.A.I.C.S.: 541380

Eurofins MWG Synthesis GmbH (2)
Anzinger Str 7a, Ebersberg, 85560, Bavaria, Germany
Tel.: (49) 809282890
Chemical Products Mfr
N.A.I.C.S.: 325998
Bruno Poddevin (Mng Dir)

MWG Biotech Pvt Ltd. (1)
No 17 5th Cross Vidya Nagar Opp M/S SKF Bearings Hosur Main Road, 560100, Bengaluru, India (100%)
Tel.: (91) 80 307 06666
Web Site: http://www.eurofinsdna.com
Biological Product Mfr
N.A.I.C.S.: 325414

Medinet International BV (1)
Bergschot 71, PO Box 5510, 4817PA, Breda, Netherlands (100%)
Tel.: (31) 765737373
Web Site: http://www.eurofinsmedinet.com
Sales Range: $25-49.9 Million
Emp.: 250
Research & Development in the Physical Engineering & Life Sciences
N.A.I.C.S.: 541715

Medserv Kft. (1)
Lehel u 59, 1135, Budapest, Hungary
Tel.: (36) 13095018
Pharmaceutical & Cosmetic Product Testing Services
N.A.I.C.S.: 541611

Modern Testing Services (Dongguan) Co., Ltd. (1)
No 76 Liang Ping Lu Xin Jiu Wei Cun, Liaobu, Dongguan, 523400, China
Tel.: (86) 76981120818
Food Testing Services
N.A.I.C.S.: 541380

Modern Testing Services (Hong Kong) Co., Ltd. (1)
Unit 808 CEO Tower 77 Wing Hong Street, Cheung Sha Wan Kowloon, Hong Kong, China (Hong Kong)
Tel.: (852) 36041328
Pharmaceutical & Cosmetic Product Testing Services
N.A.I.C.S.: 541611

Modern Testing Services (India) Private Limited (1)
Khata 275/270/271 Survey 37/1 SD Chambers 2nd & 3rd Floor, Singasandra Village Hosur Main Road, Bengaluru, 560068, Karnataka, India
Tel.: (91) 8025740679
Textile Product Mfr & Distr
N.A.I.C.S.: 313310

Modern Testing Services (Vietnam) Co., Ltd. (1)
Lot II-12 Road 19/5A Tan Binh Industrial Park, Tay Thanh Ward Tan Phu District, Ho Chi Minh City, Vietnam
Tel.: (84) 2862896363
Textile Product Mfr & Distr
N.A.I.C.S.: 313310

Modern Testing Services Lanka Private Limited (1)
Ground Floor No 235/2 Hekitta Road, Wattala, Colombo, Sri Lanka
Tel.: (94) 117633009
Food & Pharmaceutical Testing Services
N.A.I.C.S.: 541380

NDSM Limited (1)
Unit 1 Eden Business Park Edenhouse Drive, Old Malton, Malton, YO17 6AE, United Kingdom
Tel.: (44) 1653917921
Laboratory Testing Services
N.A.I.C.S.: 541380

New Zealand Laboratory Services Ltd (1)
85 Port Road Seaview Lower Hutt, Moera, Wellington, 5045, New Zealand
Tel.: (64) 4 576 5016
Web Site: http://www.eurofins.co.nz
Emp.: 55
Laboratory Testing Services
N.A.I.C.S.: 541380
Rob Deacon (Mng Dir)

NovaTec Immundiagnostica GmbH (1)
Waldstrasse 23 A6, 63128, Dietzenbach, Germany
Tel.: (49) 607448760
Web Site: http://www.novatec-id.com
Pharmaceuticals Product Mfr
N.A.I.C.S.: 325412

Nutrilab, S.L. (1)
Carles Fages de Climent 9, Girona, 17600, Figueres, Spain
Tel.: (34) 972674256
Web Site: https://www.nutrilab.cat
Food Testing Services
N.A.I.C.S.: 541380

OEKOMETRIC GmbH (1)
Bayreuther Institut fur Umweltforschung Bernecker Str 17-21, 95448, Bayreuth, Germany
Tel.: (49) 921726330
Web Site: http://www.oekometric.de
Sales Range: $25-49.9 Million
Emp.: 20
Analytical Testing Services
N.A.I.C.S.: 541380
Horst Rottler (Mng Dir)

P.T. Angler Biochem Lab Ltd. (1)
JL Sawo No17-19 Kel Beringin, Kec Sambikerep, Surabaya, 60218, Indonesia
Tel.: (62) 317456111
Web Site: https://www.anglerlab.co.id
Laboratory Testing Services
N.A.I.C.S.: 621511

Pharmacology Discovery Services Taiwan, Ltd. (1)
25 Wugong 6th Road, Wugu District, New Taipei City, 24891, Taiwan
Tel.: (886) 277517100
Web Site: https://www.pharmacologydiscovery.com
Medical Laboratory Services
N.A.I.C.S.: 621511

Pranatal-Medizin Munchen Frauenarzte und Humangenetiker MVZ GmbH (1)
Friends Tower I Friedenheimer Brucke 19, 80639, Munich, Germany
Tel.: (49) 891307440
Web Site: http://en.praenatal-medizin.de
Pregnancy Care Services
N.A.I.C.S.: 621410

ProMonitoring BV (1)
Mercuriusweg 37, NL 3771, Barneveld, Netherlands (100%)
Tel.: (31) 342400606
Web Site: http://www.promonitoring.nl
Sales Range: $25-49.9 Million
Emp.: 15
Professional Scientific & Technical Services
N.A.I.C.S.: 541990

Product Perceptions Limited (1)
Unit B1 Windsor Place Faraday Road, Crawley, RH10 9TF, West Sussex, United Kingdom
Tel.: (44) 1293558955
Pharmaceutical Research & Testing Services
N.A.I.C.S.: 541380

Proefbedrijf Gewasbescherming De Bredelaar BV (1)
Reethsestraat 17, 6662 PK, Elst, Netherlands
Tel.: (31) 481462379
Crop Safety Research Services
N.A.I.C.S.: 541715

Public Analyst Scientific Services (NI) Ltd (1)
Room 74 4th Floor 16 Donegal Square South, BT1 5JJ, Belfast, United Kingdom - Northern Ireland
Tel.: (44) 28 9032 1691
Web Site: http://www.publicanalystservices.co.uk
Analytical Laboratory Testing Services
N.A.I.C.S.: 541380

Public Analyst Scientific Services Ltd (1)
i54 Business Park Valiant Way, Wolverhampton, WV9 5GB, United Kingdom
Tel.: (44) 1902627200
Web Site: https://www.publicanalystservices.co.uk
Analyst Scientific & Laboratory Testing Services
N.A.I.C.S.: 541380

QualcoDuna Proficiency Testing Hungary Nonprofit Kft. (1)
Anonymus Street 6, 1045, Budapest, Hungary
Tel.: (36) 18723628
Web Site: https://qualcoduna.hu
Proficiency Testing Services
N.A.I.C.S.: 541380

Quasfar M&F S.A. (1)
Calle 46A 82-54 Bodega 10 Parque Industrial San Cayetano 2, 111071, Bogota, Colombia
Tel.: (57) 14470047
Web Site: https://www.quasfar.com.co
Pharmaceutical & Veterinary Product Distr
N.A.I.C.S.: 424210

Repertoire Genesis Co., Ltd. (1)
Saito Bioincubator 402 7-7-15 Saito-Asagi, Ibaraki, 567-0085, Osaka, Japan
Tel.: (81) 726578686

Web Site: https://www.repertoire.co.jp
Diagnostic Support & Development Services
N.A.I.C.S.: 621512

SAM Sensory & Marketing International GmbH (1)
Oetztaler Strasse 1, D-81373, Munich, Germany
Tel.: (49) 897437670
Web Site: https://www.samresearch.com
Medical Product Research Services
N.A.I.C.S.: 541715

SAM Sensory & Marketing Italy S.R.L. (1)
Viale Monza 270, 20128, Milan, Italy
Tel.: (39) 0227007019
Food & Pharmaceutical Testing Services
N.A.I.C.S.: 541380

SAM Sensory International France S.A.S. (1)
46 Rue Armand Carrel, 75019, Paris, France
Tel.: (33) 148246100
Pharmaceutical & Cosmetic Product Testing Services
N.A.I.C.S.: 541611

SNiP Biotech GmbH & Co. KG (1)
Fraunhoferstr 22, Bundesrepublik Planegg, 82152, Martinsried, Germany (100%)
Tel.: (49) 898998920
Sales Range: $25-49.9 Million
Emp.: 60
Professional Scientific & Technical Services
N.A.I.C.S.: 541990

Selcia Limited (1)
Fyfield Business and Research Park Fyfield Road, Ongar, CM5 0GS, Essex, United Kingdom
Tel.: (44) 1277367000
Web Site: http://www.selcia.com
Drug Discovery Services
N.A.I.C.S.: 541714
Clive Cornell (Mng Dir & COO)

Sensory & Marketing Spain, S.L.U. (1)
C/ d Ausias March 148-150, 08013, Barcelona, Spain
Tel.: (34) 935533177
Food & Pharmaceutical Testing Services
N.A.I.C.S.: 541380

Spectro Analytical Labs Ltd. (1)
E-41 Phase II, Okhla Industrial Area, New Delhi, 110020, India
Tel.: (91) 1140522000
Web Site: http://www.spectro.in
Analytical Laboratory Testing Services
N.A.I.C.S.: 541380

Spectro Research Lab Ventures Private Limited (1)
G-3 Bajrangbali Industrial Area Near Panki Site-IV, Kanpur, 208020, Uttar Pradesh, India
Tel.: (91) 9235503984
Electrical & Electronic Testing Services
N.A.I.C.S.: 541380

Spectro SSA Labs Private Limited (1)
Sector 8 MIDC Industrial Area, Rabale, Navi Mumbai, 400701, Maharashtra, India
Tel.: (91) 2227699612
Electrical & Electronic Testing Services
N.A.I.C.S.: 541380

Spincontrol Amerique du Nord, Inc. (1)
550 Sherbrooke St W Suite 2055, Montreal, H3A 1B9, QC, Canada
Tel.: (514) 759-3351
Web Site: https://www.spincontrol.ca
Cosmetic Product Mfr & Distr
N.A.I.C.S.: 325620

Spincontrol S.A.S. (1)
238 Rue Giraudeau, 37000, Tours, France
Tel.: (33) 247376279
Web Site: https://www.spincontrol.fr
Cosmetic Product Testing Services
N.A.I.C.S.: 541611

St. Marien Krankenhaus Lampertheim GmbH (1)

Eurofins Scientific S.E.—(Continued)

Neue Schulstrasse 12, 68623,
Lampertheim, Germany
Tel.: (49) 62065090
Web Site:
https://www.stmarienkrankenhaus.de
Hospital Healthcare Services
N.A.I.C.S.: 621999

Stats Asia Pacific Pte. Ltd. (1)
71 Toh Guan Road East 02-01/02/06 TCH
Techcentre, Singapore, 608598, Singapore
Tel.: (65) 62526686
Web Site: https://www.statsasiapac.com
Environmental & Engineering Consulting
Services
N.A.I.C.S.: 541330

Steripac GmbH (1)
Oberreichenbacher Strasse 15-17, Altburg,
75365, Calw, Germany
Tel.: (49) 705158880
Web Site: https://www.steripac.com
Medical Device Mfr & Distr
N.A.I.C.S.: 334510

Svensk Arbetshygien AB (1)
Vingakersvagen 10, Box 324, 641 23,
Katrineholm, Sweden
Tel.: (46) 15014230
Web Site:
https://www.svenskarbetshygien.se
Environmental Consulting Services
N.A.I.C.S.: 541620

**TA Technology (Shanghai) Co.,
Ltd.** (1)
No 145 Jintang Rd, Tangzhen Industry Park
Pudong, Shanghai, 201201, China
Tel.: (86) 4008893499
Web Site: https://www.ta-shanghai.cn
Food Testing Services
N.A.I.C.S.: 541380

Taiyo Techno Research Ltd. (1)
Pearl Building 3-76 Takabatake, Kanazawa,
921-8001, Toyama, Japan
Tel.: (81) 762563918
Web Site: http://www.taiyo.vc
Laboratory Testing Services
N.A.I.C.S.: 541380

Tecna Srl (1)
Via Statale Sud no 115, 41037, Mirandola,
MO, Italy
Tel.: (39) 053527833
Web Site: http://www.tecnasrl.com
Software Development Services
N.A.I.C.S.: 541511

**Thai Environmental Technic Co.,
Ltd.** (1)
No 1/6 Soi Ramkhamhaeng 145, Saphan
Sung Subdistrict Saphan Sung District,
Bangkok, 10240, Thailand
Tel.: (66) 23737799
Web Site: https://www.tet1995.com
Environmental Quality Testing Services
N.A.I.C.S.: 541380

**The Maastricht Forensic Institute
B.V.** (1)
Oxfordlaan 70, 6229 EV, Maastricht, Neth-
erlands
Tel.: (31) 851051410
Deoxyribonucleic Acid Testing Services
N.A.I.C.S.: 621511

The National Food Lab, Inc. (1)
3755 1st Ave N Ste 500, Plymouth, MN
55441
Tel.: (619) 538-0256
Web Site: https://www.thenfl.com
Food Research & Testing Services
N.A.I.C.S.: 541380

Transplant Genomics, Inc. (1)
175 Crossing Blvd, Framingham, MA 01702
Web Site: https://transplantgenomics.com
Bio Technology Services
N.A.I.C.S.: 541714

Virotech Diagnostics GmbH (1)
Lowenplatz 5, 65428, Russelsheim, Ger-
many
Tel.: (49) 614269090
Web Site:
http://www.virotechdiagnostics.com
Medical Device Mfr
N.A.I.C.S.: 339112

Marcello Salio (Mng Dir)

bioskin GmbH (1)
Messberg 4, 20095, Hamburg, Germany
Tel.: (49) 406068970
Web Site: http://www.bioskincro.com
Dermatological Product Mfr
N.A.I.C.S.: 325412
Walter Wigger-Alberti (CEO)

EUROFLACO COMPIEGNE SARL
7 Ave Louis Barbillon, 60200, Comp-
iegne, France
Tel.: (33) 344382525
Web Site: http://www.alpla.com
Plastics Products
N.A.I.C.S.: 326199

EUROFRAGANCE SLU
Vallsolana Garden Business Park,
C/Cami de Can Camps 17-19 Kibo
Building, 08174, Sant Cugat del
Valles, Catalonia, Spain
Tel.: (34) 93 697 23 61
Web Site:
http://www.eurofragance.com
Year Founded: 1990
Perfume Mfr
N.A.I.C.S.: 456120
Santiago Sabates (Chm & Pres)

Subsidiaries:

Eurofragance, LLC (1)
1349 Old 41 Hwy NW Ste 110, Marietta,
GA 30060-7929
Tel.: (678) 486-7830
Web Site: http://www.fragrancedesign.net
Perfume Mfr & Distr
N.A.I.C.S.: 424210
William Hamilton (Founder)

EUROGAS INTERNATIONAL INC.
Suites 205-207 Dowell House Roe-
buck & Palmetto Streets, Bridgetown,
Barbados
Tel.: (246) 436 7967
Web Site:
http://www.eurogasinternational.com
EI—(CNSX)
Assets: $1,792
Liabilities: $43,370,864
Net Worth: ($43,369,072)
Earnings: ($1,300,042)
Fiscal Year-end: 12/31/20
Oil & Gas Exploration & Mining Ser-
vices
N.A.I.C.S.: 211120
Bruce Sherley (CEO-Acting)

EUROGERM SA
Parc d'activites bois Guillaume 2 rue
Champ Dore, 21850, Saint Apolli-
naire, France
Tel.: (33) 3 80 730 777
Web Site: http://www.eurogerm.com
Year Founded: 1989
ALGEM—(EUR)
Sales Range: $125-149.9 Million
Emp.: 488
Flour Corrector & Bread Making Im-
prover Mfr
N.A.I.C.S.: 311999
Jean-Philippe Girard (Founder &
CEO)

Subsidiaries:

**EUROGERM BRASIL PRODUTOS
ALIMENTICIOS LIMITADA** (1)
Rua Caramuru n 417 conjunto 93, Chacara
Inglesa, Sao Paulo, 04138-001, Brazil
Tel.: (55) 11 2309 5262
Web Site: http://www.eurogerm-brasil.com
Bakery Products Mfr
N.A.I.C.S.: 311812

EUROGERM IBERIA, S.L.U. (1)

Cami dels Sagraments 65 Naves 20-21,
Poligono Industrial Sant Ermengol II Abrera,
08630, Barcelona, Spain
Tel.: (34) 93 770 4910
Web Site: http://www.eurogerm-iberia.com
Bakery Products Mfr
N.A.I.C.S.: 311812

Eurogerm Andina (1)
Jazpampa 309, Callao, Peru
Tel.: (51) 1 5617952
Web Site: http://www.eurogerm-andina.com
Bakery Product Distr
N.A.I.C.S.: 424490

Eurogerm Maroc (1)
22 rue Ibnou Koutia - Lot Att Taoufik - ZI
Oukacha, Ain Sebaa, 20250, Casablanca,
Morocco
Tel.: (212) 522 35 18 71
Web Site: http://www.eurogerm-maroc.com
Bakery Product Distr
N.A.I.C.S.: 424490

Eurogerm Mexico SA De Cv (1)
Calz Las Armas No 40 A Parque Industrial
Las Armas, Tlalnepantla, Mexico
Tel.: (52) 55 53 57 08 30
Web Site: http://www.eurogerm-mexico.com
Bakery Product Distr
N.A.I.C.S.: 424490

Eurogerm Senegal (1)
140 Mousse Diop x Republique, BP 6938,
11524, Dakar, Senegal
Tel.: (221) 33 842 22 78
Web Site: http://www.eurogerm-
senegal.com
Bakery Product Distr
N.A.I.C.S.: 424490

Eurogerm South Africa (Pty) Ltd. (1)
Unit No 5 14 Riverhorse Close, Origin In-
dustrial Park, Durban, 4001, South Africa
Tel.: (27) 318254533
Baking Product Mfr
N.A.I.C.S.: 311812
Pierre-Edouard Molina (Mng Dir)

Problend-Eurogerm LLC (1)
1801 Hicks Rd-Ste H, Rolling Meadows, IL
60008
Tel.: (847) 221-5004
Web Site: http://www.problend-
eurogerm.com
Food Products Mfr
N.A.I.C.S.: 311999
Deborah Hodgson (Acct Mgr-Natl)

EUROGROUP LAMINATIONS S.P.A.
Via Stella Rosa 48, 20021, Baran-
zate, Milano, Italy
Tel.: (39) 02350001   IT
Web Site: https://www.euro-group.it
Year Founded: 1967
EGLA—(ITA)
Rev.: $918,532,269
Assets: $1,037,927,908
Liabilities: $826,806,605
Net Worth: $211,121,304
Earnings: $47,245,845
Emp.: 2,332
Fiscal Year-end: 12/31/22
Software Development Services
N.A.I.C.S.: 541511
Guardala Isidoro (CFO)

Subsidiaries:

CorradaS.p.a. (1)
Via M Buonarroti 8, Lainate, 20020, Milan,
Italy
Tel.: (39) 0235000800
Dyeing Mfr
N.A.I.C.S.: 333514

DS4 S.r.l. (1)
Via Giardini 32, 24066, Pedrengo, BG, Italy
Tel.: (39) 035661140
Web Site: https://www.ds4.it
Industrial Products Mfr
N.A.I.C.S.: 332999

Euro Automation S.r.l. (1)
Via Moriggia 14, 20900, Monza, MB, Italy
Tel.: (39) 0392279617
Emp.: 10

Industrial Automation Services
N.A.I.C.S.: 541330

**EuroMisi High Tech, Jiaxing Co.,
Ltd.** (1)
N 806 Gangshan Road, Economic Develop-
ment Zone, Jiaxing, 314003, Zhejiang,
China
Tel.: (86) 57382339221
Steel Lamination Mfr
N.A.I.C.S.: 331110

Euroslot Tools S.r.l. (1)
Via De Gasperi 10, 20066, Melzo, MI, Italy
Tel.: (39) 0235000500
Stool Lamination Mfr
N.A.I.C.S.: 331110

**Eurotranciatura Mexico S.A. De
C.V.** (1)
Avenida La Noria n 201 - Parque Industrial,
Santa Rosa Jauregui, 76220, Queretaro,
Mexico
Tel.: (52) 4421535300
Steel Lamination Mfr
N.A.I.C.S.: 331110

Eurotranciatura S.p.a. (1)
Via Stella Rosa 48/50-CP 108 Bollate,
20021, Baranzate, MI, Italy
Tel.: (39) 02350001
Steel Lamination Mfr
N.A.I.C.S.: 331110

Eurotranciatura Tunisie S.a.r.l. (1)
Zone Industrielle Zriba, 1052, Zaghouan,
Tunisia
Tel.: (216) 72677823
Steel Lamination Mfr
N.A.I.C.S.: 331110

EUROHAUS LLC
Dame Gruev 5/2, 1000, Skopje, North
Macedonia
Tel.: (389) 2 3217 036
Web Site:
http://www.eurohaus.com.mk
Year Founded: 2008
Securities Brokerage Services
N.A.I.C.S.: 523150
Stefan Stepanoski (Exec Dir)

EUROHERC OSIGURANJE D.D.
Trg Medunarodnog Prijateljstva 20,
Sarajevo, Bosnia & Herzegovina
Tel.: (387) 33755515
Web Site: https://www.euroherc.ba
EHOSR—(SARE)
Rev.: $37,677,922
Assets: $63,583,215
Liabilities: $38,300,750
Net Worth: $25,282,465
Earnings: $5,866,892
Emp.: 358
Fiscal Year-end: 12/31/20
General Insurance Services
N.A.I.C.S.: 524210

EUROHOLD BULGARIA AD
Christopher Columbus Blvd 43, Euro-
hold Business Centre, 1592, Sofia,
1592, Bulgaria
Tel.: (359) 29651651
Web Site: https://www.eurohold.bg
Year Founded: 1995
EUBG—(BUL)
Rev.: $2,433,392,317
Assets: $1,427,894,943
Liabilities: $1,390,562,011
Net Worth: $37,332,932
Earnings: $11,916,082
Emp.: 4,262
Fiscal Year-end: 12/31/22
Holding Company; Financial Ser-
vices, Leasing, Insurance & Car
Sales
N.A.I.C.S.: 551112
Kiril Iwanow Boshov (Chm-Mgmt Bd)

Subsidiaries:

Avto Union AD (1)

Christopher Columbus blvd 43 Eurohold
Business Centre, Sofia, 3594, Bulgaria
Tel.: (359) 2 462 11 88
Web Site: http://www.avto-union.bg
Sales Range: $25-49.9 Million
Emp.: 20
New Car Dealers
N.A.I.C.S.: 441110
Assen Asenov *(CEO)*

Subsidiary (Domestic):

Auto Italia EAD   **(2)**
43 Hristophor Kolumb Blvd 1592, Sofia,
Bulgaria
Tel.: (360) 2 462 11 11
Web Site: http://www.autoitalia.bg
New Car Dealers
N.A.I.C.S.: 441110

Bulvaria Holding EAD   **(2)**
84 Orion Str, Sofia, 1324, Bulgaria
Tel.: (359) 2 926 77 77
Web Site: http://www.bulvaria.bg
Investment Management Service
N.A.I.C.S.: 523940
Asen Asenov *(Mgr)*

Bulvaria Varna EOOD   **(2)**
Yanush Hunyadi St 7, Varna, Bulgaria
Tel.: (359) 700 10799
Financial Investment Services
N.A.I.C.S.: 523999

Daru Car AD   **(2)**
Druzhba 1 2 Ilia Beshkov Str, Sofia, 1592,
Bulgaria
Tel.: (359) 29 60 16 03
Web Site: http://www.darucar.bg
New & Used Car Dealer
N.A.I.C.S.: 441110
Zdravko Kostov *(CEO)*

Gransport Auto EOOD   **(2)**
43 Hristofor Kolumb Blvd, Sofia, 1592, Bul-
garia
Tel.: (359) 2 462 11 60
Web Site: http://www.maserati.bg
New Car Dealers
N.A.I.C.S.: 441110

N Auto Sofia EAD   **(2)**
100 Tsarigradsko Shosse Blvd, 1784, Sofia,
Bulgaria
Tel.: (359) 293760160
Web Site: https://www.sofia.nissan.bg
Sales Range: $25-49.9 Million
Emp.: 24
Car Lending Services
N.A.I.C.S.: 532112
Danail Danailov *(CEO)*

CEZ Razpredelenie Bulgaria AD   **(1)**
330 Tzar Simeon Str, Sofia, 1309,
Bulgaria   **(67%)**
Tel.: (359) 700 10 010
Web Site: http://www.cez-rp.bg
Electric Power Distribution Services
N.A.I.C.S.: 221122

Electrohold Bulgaria EOOD   **(1)**
Tsarigradsko Shose Boulevard 159, Bench-
Mark Business Center Mladost, 1784, Sofia,
Bulgaria
Tel.: (359) 70010010
Web Site: https://electrohold.bg
Solar Electric Power Generation Services
N.A.I.C.S.: 221114

Electrohold Sales AD   **(1)**
Tsarigradsko shose boulevard 159 Bench-
Mark Business Center, Mladost district, PK
1784, Sofia, Bulgaria
Tel.: (359) 70010010
Power Generator Distr
N.A.I.C.S.: 423610

Electrohold Trade EAD   **(1)**
2 Positano Square 7th floor, 1000, Sofia,
Bulgaria
Tel.: (359) 8959123
Web Site: https://electrohold.bg
Solar Electric Power Generation Services
N.A.I.C.S.: 221114

Euro Lease Auto AD   **(1)**
16 GM Dimitrov Blvd, Sofia, 1797, Bulgaria
Tel.: (359) 2 965 15 55
Web Site: http://www.euroleaseauto.bg
Car Lending Services
N.A.I.C.S.: 532112

Euroins Georgia AD   **(1)**
24 Ilo Mosashvili Str, 162, Tbilisi, Georgia
Tel.: (995) 322203333
Web Site: https://euroins.ge
Emp.: 1,600
Insurance Agencies Services
N.A.I.C.S.: 524210

Euroins Insurance Group AD   **(1)**
Christopher Columbus blvd 43 Eurohold
Business Centre, 1592, Sofia,
Bulgaria   **(100%)**
Tel.: (359) 29651500
Web Site: https://www.eig.bg
Sales Range: $50-74.9 Million
Emp.: 25
General Insurance Services
N.A.I.C.S.: 524210

Subsidiary (Non-US):

EUROINS INSURANCE AD
Skopje   **(2)**
Skopi No 12, Skopje, North Macedonia
Tel.: (389) 2 3216 983
Web Site: http://www.euroins.com.mk
General Insurance Services
N.A.I.C.S.: 524298
Janko Georgiev Nikolov *(Member-Mgmt Bd & Exec Dir)*

SC Euroins Romania Insurance Rein-
surance SA   **(2)**
Bucuresti North Road nr 10 Global City
Business Park, O23 Building 4th floor, Vol-
untari, 077190, Ilfov, Romania
Tel.: (40) 21 317 07 11
Web Site: http://www.euroins.ro
General Insurance Services
N.A.I.C.S.: 524201
Iulius Alin Bucsa *(Co-CEO)*

Eurolease Group EAD   **(1)**
Christopher Columbus blvd 43 Fl 10 Avto
Union Centre, Sofia, 1540, Bulgaria
Tel.: (359) 2 9651 651
Web Site: http://www.euroleasegroup.com
Financial Investment Services
N.A.I.C.S.: 523999

IC Euroins-Life EAD   **(1)**
43 Christopher Columbus Blvd, 1592, Sofia,
Bulgaria
Tel.: (359) 70089039
Web Site: https://euroinslife.bg
Insurance Agencies Services
N.A.I.C.S.: 524210

EUROINS INSURANCE PLC
Christopher Columbus blvd 43, 1592,
Sofia, Bulgaria
Tel.: (359) 2 965 1525
Web Site: http://www.euroins.bg
Insurance Services
N.A.I.C.S.: 524298
Joanna Tsoneva *(Chm)*

EUROKAI GMBH & CO. KGAA
Kurt-Eckelmann-Strasse 1, D-21129,
Hamburg, Germany
Tel.: (49) 4074052005
Web Site: https://www.eurokai.de
EUK3—(DEU)
Rev.: $13,098,576
Assets: $1,003,642,786
Liabilities: $346,285,462
Net Worth: $657,357,324
Earnings: $59,759,355
Emp.: 848
Fiscal Year-end: 12/31/23
Holding Company; Terminal Opera-
tions
N.A.I.C.S.: 551112
Cecilia E.M. Eckelmann-Battistello
(Member-Mgmt Bd)

Subsidiaries:

Contship Italia S.p.A.   **(1)**
Via I Maggio 1, 20066, Melzo, MI, Italy
Tel.: (39) 0295529611
Web Site: https://www.contshipitalia.com
Logistic Services
N.A.I.C.S.: 488510

Subsidiary (Domestic):

La Spezia Container Terminal
S.p.A.   **(2)**
Viale S Bartolomeo 20, 19126, La Spezia,
SP, Italy
Tel.: (39) 01875551
Logistic Services
N.A.I.C.S.: 488510

Subsidiary (Domestic):

Salerno Container Terminal
S.p.A.   **(3)**
Via Camillo Sorgente 72 a, Salerno, Italy
Tel.: (39) 0892754899
Web Site:
   http://www.salernocontainerterminal.com
Logistic Services
N.A.I.C.S.: 488510
Giuseppe Lamberti *(Mgr-ICT)*

Terminal Container Ravenna
S.p.A.   **(3)**
Via Classicana 105, 48122, Ravenna, Italy
Tel.: (39) 0544434411
Web Site: http://www.tcravenna.it
Logistic Services
N.A.I.C.S.: 488510
Milena Fico *(Gen Mgr)*

Subsidiary (Domestic):

Sogemar S.p.A.   **(2)**
Via 1 Maggio 1, 20066, Melzo, MI, Italy
Tel.: (39) 02950761
Logistic Services
N.A.I.C.S.: 488510

Subsidiary (Domestic):

Oceanogate Italia S.p.A.   **(3)**
Via I Maggio 1, 20066, Melzo, MI, Italy
Tel.: (39) 02950761
Railroad Transportation Services
N.A.I.C.S.: 488210

EUROLAND CORPORATE SA
17 avenue Georges V, 75008, Paris,
France
Tel.: (33) 144702080
Web Site: https://www.elcorp.com
MLERO—(EUR)
Sales Range: $1-9.9 Million
Financial Support Services
N.A.I.C.S.: 523940
Marc Fiorentino *(Chm & CEO)*

EUROLAND FINANCE SA
17 avenue Georges V Paris 8, Paris,
75008, France
Tel.: (33) 144702080
Web Site: http://www.elcorp.com
Financial Support Services
N.A.I.C.S.: 523940
Marc Fiorentino *(Chm & CEO)*

EUROLEDER FASHION LIM-
ITED
10 Periya Palayathu Amman Koil
Street Bazaar Road, Chromepet,
Chennai, 600044, Tamil Nadu, India
Tel.: (91) 4442157220
Web Site: https://www.euroleder.com
Rev.: $13,151,534
Assets: $8,365,877
Liabilities: $6,450,695
Net Worth: $1,915,181
Earnings: $110,883
Fiscal Year-end: 03/31/18
Garment Mfr & Whsr
N.A.I.C.S.: 315250
Manjunatha Nagendra *(CFO)*

EUROLLS S.P.A.
Via Malignani 14, 33040, Attimis, Italy
Tel.: (39) 0432796511   IT
Web Site: http://www.eurolls.com
Year Founded: 1987
Tube Forming & Wire Production
N.A.I.C.S.: 331222
Renato Railz *(Founder)*

Subsidiaries:

EUROLLS CARBIDE S.r.l.   **(1)**
Viale Industria 41/43, Boffalora Sopra Ti-
cino, 20010, Milan, Italy
Tel.: (39) 02 97259132
Steel Products Mfr
N.A.I.C.S.: 331222

EUROLLS DE MEXICO S. de R.L. de
C.V.   **(1)**
Unidad Nacional No 2020 Fracc Industrial U
Nacional, Santa Catarina, 66350, Nuevo
Leon, Mexico
Tel.: (52) 81 8336 1467
Structured Steel Products Mfr
N.A.I.C.S.: 331221
Alan Tafoya *(Gen Mgr)*

EUROLLS DO BRASIL LTDA   **(1)**
Rua Flor de Novia 980 Gp 04, Sao Paulo,
Brazil
Tel.: (55) 11 4645 3626
Structured Steel Products Mfr
N.A.I.C.S.: 331222

EUROLLS MACHINERY (SHANG-
HAI) CO. LTD.   **(1)**
N 1070 Chenxiang road Nanxiang, Jiading,
Shanghai, 201802, China
Tel.: (86) 21 69177804
Web Site: http://www.eurolls.com.cn
Steel Product Distr
N.A.I.C.S.: 423510

ROLL ENG S.r.l.   **(1)**
Via Divisione Julia 22, Villa Santina, 33029,
Udine, Italy
Tel.: (39) 0433 750533
Structured Steel Products Mfr
N.A.I.C.S.: 331222

Teurema SL   **(1)**
Poligono Txirrita Maleo 10, Errenteria, E
20100, Guipuzcoa, Spain
Tel.: (34) 943341919
Web Site: http://www.teurema.com
Sales Range: $1-9.9 Million
Emp.: 25
Designs & Mfr Equipment for the Wire in-
dustry
N.A.I.C.S.: 333992

EUROLOG CANOLA SOCIMI,
S.A.U.
Calle de Genova 27, 28004, Madrid,
Spain
Tel.: (34) 917698950
Web Site:
   https://www.eurologcanola.com
MLCAN—(EUR)
Rev.: $5,095,163
Assets: $113,521,030
Liabilities: $10,059,443
Net Worth: $103,461,587
Earnings: $4,950,410
Fiscal Year-end: 12/31/23
Real Estate Investment Services
N.A.I.C.S.: 531190
Victor Salamanca Cuevas *(Chm)*

EUROMAX RESOURCES LTD.
10th Floor 595 Howe Street, Vancou-
ver, V6C 2T5, BC, Canada
Tel.: (604) 669-5999   BC
Web Site:
   http://www.euromaxresources.com
EOX—(OTCIQ)
Sales Range: Less than $1 Million
Gold Mining
N.A.I.C.S.: 212220
Patrick William Forward *(COO)*

Subsidiaries:

OMAX International Limited   **(1)**
PO Box 232004, Dubai, United Arab Emir-
ates
Tel.: (971) 522100986
Web Site:
   http://www.omaxinternationalltd.com
Real Estate Property Investment & Devel-
opment Services
N.A.I.C.S.: 531390

Euromax Resources Ltd.—(Continued)

EUROMEDICA SA
Rigillis 16A, 106 74, Athens, Greece
Tel.: (30) 2103686600
Web Site: http://www.euromedica.gr
Health Care Srvices
N.A.I.C.S.: 621610
Georgios Mitrainas *(Chm & CEO)*

EUROMEDIS GROUPE SA
Zi De La Tuillerie, 60290, Clermont, France
Tel.: (33) 33344738360
Web Site: https://www.euromedis.fr
EMG—(EUR)
Sales Range: $75-99.9 Million
Medical Equipment Mfr & Distr
N.A.I.C.S.: 339113
Danielle Roturier *(Chm-Exec Bd)*

EUROMEZZANINE CONSEIL SAS
11 rue Scribe, 75009, Paris, France
Tel.: (33) 153302330
Web Site:
http://www.emzpartners.com
Year Founded: 1999
Sales Range: $900-999.9 Million
Equity Investment Firm
N.A.I.C.S.: 523999
Thierry Raiff *(Chm)*

Subsidiaries:

Ubiqus SAS (1)
1 avenue du General de Gaulle, 92074, Paris, Cedex, La Defense, France
Tel.: (33) 1 44 14 15 16
Web Site: http://www.ubiqus.fr
Language Translation Services
N.A.I.C.S.: 541930
Joanne Bove *(CEO)*

Subsidiary (US):

The Language Works, Inc. (2)
1123 Broadway Ste 201, New York, NY 10010
Tel.: (212) 447-6060
Web Site: http://www.languageworks.com
Translation & Interpretation Services
N.A.I.C.S.: 541930
Kevin Rees *(Pres)*

Ubiqus Reporting, Inc. (2)
22 Cortlandt St Ste 802, New York, NY 10007
Tel.: (212) 346-6666
Web Site: http://www.ubiqus.com
Court Reporting & Stenotype Services; Language Translation Services
N.A.I.C.S.: 561492
Joanne Bove *(CEO)*

Subsidiary (Non-US):

Ubiqus UK Limited (2)
61 Southwark Street, London, SE1 0HL, United Kingdom
Tel.: (44) 207 269 0370
Language Translation Services
N.A.I.C.S.: 541930

EURONA WIRELESS TELE-COM, S.A.
Ctra Hospitalet 11 Nau 4, 09840, Cornella de Llobregat, Barcelona, Spain
Tel.: (34) 902906359
Web Site: http://www.eurona.net
EWT—(MAD)
Sales Range: $1-9.9 Million
Wireless Communication Services
N.A.I.C.S.: 517112
Jaume Sanpera Izoard *(Pres & CEO)*

EURONAV NV
De Gerlachekaai 20, 2000, Antwerp, Belgium
Tel.: (32) 32474411 BE
Web Site: https://cmb.tech
Year Founded: 1989

CMBT—(NYSE)
Rev.: $1,235,127,000
Assets: $3,419,280,000
Liabilities: $1,061,907,000
Net Worth: $2,357,373,000
Earnings: $858,027,000
Emp.: 3,216
Fiscal Year-end: 12/31/23
Freight Transportation Services
N.A.I.C.S.: 488510
Alex Staring *(COO & Member-Mgmt Bd)*

Subsidiaries:

Euronav (UK) Agencies Ltd. (1)
81-99 Kings Road 1st Floor 99 Kings Road, London, SW3 4PA, United Kingdom
Tel.: (44) 2078700400
Shipping Agency Services
N.A.I.C.S.: 488510

Euronav Hong Kong Ltd (1)
Room 2503-05 25th Floor No 39 Gloucester Road, Wanchai, Hong Kong, China (Hong Kong)
Tel.: (852) 28613880
Crude Oil Shipping Services
N.A.I.C.S.: 488330

Euronav Ltd. (1)
25 The Slipway, Port Solent, Portsmouth, PO6 4TR, Hampshire, United Kingdom
Tel.: (44) 2392988806
Web Site: http://www.euronav.co.uk
Emp.: 4
Marine Navigation & Electronic Charting Products Mfr
N.A.I.C.S.: 334511

Euronav Luxembourg SA (1)
20 rue de Hollerich, PO Box 2255, Luxembourg, 1022, Luxembourg
Tel.: (352) 482850
Marine Shipping Services
N.A.I.C.S.: 483111

Euronav MI II Inc. (1)
299 Park Ave 2nd Fl, New York, NY 10171
Tel.: (212) 763-5600
Web Site: http://www.euronav.com
Deep Sea Freight Transportation Services
N.A.I.C.S.: 483111

Subsidiary (Domestic):

Gener8 Maritime Management LLC (2)
299 Park Ave 2nd Fl, New York, NY 10171-0299
Tel.: (212) 763-5698
Web Site: http://www.euronav.com
Crude Oil Transportation Services
N.A.I.C.S.: 486110
David Fillis *(Mgr-Ops)*

Euronav SaS (1)
Les Salorges 1 15 Quai Ernest Renaud, 44104, Nantes, France
Tel.: (33) 228034250
Sales Range: $25-49.9 Million
Emp.: 200
Marine Shipping Services
N.A.I.C.S.: 483111

Euronav Ship Management (Hellas) Ltd (1)
31-33 Athinon Avenue, 10447, Athens, Greece
Tel.: (30) 2104558000
Sales Range: $25-49.9 Million
Emp.: 35
Ship Transportation Services
N.A.I.C.S.: 483111

Euronav Ship Management SaS (1)
15 quai Ernest Renaud CS 20421, 44104, Nantes, Cedex 4, France
Tel.: (33) 228034250
Sales Range: $25-49.9 Million
Emp.: 9
Marine Shipping Services
N.A.I.C.S.: 483111

Euronav Singapore Pte. Ltd. (1)
79 Anson Road 23-06, Singapore, 079906, Singapore
Tel.: (65) 68569880
Shipping Support Services

N.A.I.C.S.: 488510

EURONEXT N.V.
Beursplein 5, NL-1012 JW, Amsterdam, Netherlands
Tel.: (31) 207214444 NI
Web Site: http://www.euronext.com
Year Founded: 2000
ENX—(OTCIQ)
Rev.: $1,591,524,930
Assets: $207,465,261,170
Liabilities: $203,056,297,216
Net Worth: $4,408,963,954
Earnings: $578,906,756
Emp.: 2,259
Fiscal Year-end: 12/31/23
Holding Company; Securities & Commodities Exchange Operator
N.A.I.C.S.: 551112
Vincent van Dessel *(Member-Mgmt Bd)*

Subsidiaries:

Commcise Software Ltd. (1)
11th floor CARGO Building 25 North Colonnade, London, E14 5HS, United Kingdom
Tel.: (44) 2033693699
Web Site: https://commcise.com
Investment Management Service
N.A.I.C.S.: 523940
Amrish Ganatra *(CEO)*

Company Webcast B.V. (1)
Rivium Boulevard 176, 2909 LK, Capelle aan den IJssel, Netherlands
Tel.: (31) 102829500
Web Site:
https://www.companywebcast.com
Internet Publishing Services
N.A.I.C.S.: 513199

Euronext Amsterdam N.V. (1)
Beurstlein No 5, PO Box 19163, 1000 GD, Amsterdam, Netherlands
Tel.: (31) 207214444
Web Site: http://www.euronext.com
Sales Range: $1-4.9 Billion
Emp.: 380
Securities & Commodities Exchange
N.A.I.C.S.: 523210
Simone Huis in't Veld *(CEO)*

Euronext Brussels N.V./S.A. (1)
1 Rue du Marquis bte 1/ Markiesstraat 1, 1000, Brussels, Belgium
Tel.: (32) 26201500
Web Site: http://www.euronext.com
Sales Range: $100-124.9 Million
Emp.: 60
Securities & Commodities Exchange
N.A.I.C.S.: 523210
Vincent van Dessel *(CEO)*

Euronext Lisbon - Sociedad Gestora de Mercados Regulamentados, S.A. (1)
Av da Liberdade 196 Fl 7, Lisbon, 1250-147, Portugal
Tel.: (351) 210600600
Web Site: http://www.euronext.com
Sales Range: $25-49.9 Million
Emp.: 4
Securities & Commodity Exchange Services
N.A.I.C.S.: 523210

Euronext London Limited (1)
10th Floor 110 Cannon Street, 100 St Pauls Churchyard, London, EC4N 6EU, United Kingdom
Tel.: (44) 2070760900
Web Site: http://www.euronext.com
Securities & Commodities Exchange Services
N.A.I.C.S.: 523210
Chris Topple *(CEO & Head-Sls-Global)*

Subsidiary (Domestic):

SmartPool Trading Limited (2)
Juxon House, 100 St Pauls Churchyard, London, EC4M 8BU, United Kingdom
Tel.: (44) 2072806883
Web Site: http://www.tradeonsmartpool.com
Securities & Commodity Exchange Services
N.A.I.C.S.: 523210
Lee Hodgkinson *(CEO)*

Euronext Paris S.A. (1)
14 Place Des Reflets, La Defense, 92054, Paris, Cedex, France
Tel.: (33) 170482400
Web Site: http://www.euronext.com
Sales Range: $1-4.9 Billion
Emp.: 550
Securities & Commodities Exchange
N.A.I.C.S.: 523210

Fish Pool ASA (1)
Fantoftvegen 38, 5072, Bergen, Norway
Tel.: (47) 55706700
Web Site: https://fishpool.eu
Financial Services
N.A.I.C.S.: 523999
Soren Martens *(Mng Dir)*

Interbolsa S.A. (1)
Avenida da Boavista 3433, 4100-138, Porto, Portugal
Tel.: (351) 226158400
Web Site: https://www.interbolsa.pt
Securities Brokerage Services
N.A.I.C.S.: 523150

Nord Pool Finland Oy (1)
Keilasatama 5, 02150, Espoo, Finland
Tel.: (358) 968404800
Electric Utility Services
N.A.I.C.S.: 221111

Nord Pool Holding AS (1)
Tel.: (47) 67109100
Web Site: https://www.nordpoolgroup.com
Electric Utility Services
N.A.I.C.S.: 221111
Tom Darell *(CEO)*

Oslo Bors VPS Holding ASA (1)
Tollbugata 2, PO Box 460, Sentrum, 0105, Oslo, Norway
Tel.: (47) 22341700
Web Site: http://www.osloborsvps.no
Rev.: $119,929,198
Assets: $168,671,843
Liabilities: $112,127,089
Net Worth: $56,544,754
Earnings: $39,786,459
Fiscal Year-end: 12/31/2018
Holding Company; Securities Trading
N.A.I.C.S.: 551112

Subsidiary (Domestic):

Oslo Bors ASA (2)
Tollbugata 2, Box 460, Sentrum, Oslo, 0105, Norway (100%)
Tel.: (47) 22341700
Web Site: http://www.oslobors.no
Sales Range: $350-399.9 Million
Emp.: 100
Stock Exchange Regulator
N.A.I.C.S.: 523210

The Irish Stock Exchange plc (1)
Exchange Buildings Foster Place, Dublin, 2, Ireland
Tel.: (353) 16174200
Web Site: https://www.euronext.com
Stock Exchange
N.A.I.C.S.: 523210
Daryl Byrne *(CEO)*

Subsidiary (Non-US):

European Wholesale Securities Market Limited (2)
Garrison Chapel Castille Place, Valletta, VLT 1063, Malta
Tel.: (356) 21 223178
Web Site: http://www.ewsm.eu
Securities Brokerage Services
N.A.I.C.S.: 523150

iBabs B.V. (1)
Maelsonstraat 28-4, Zwaag, 1624 NP, Hoorn, Netherlands
Tel.: (31) 2039364784
Web Site: https://www.ibabs.com
Software Development Services
N.A.I.C.S.: 541511

EURONICS INTERNATIONAL BV
Transpolis Commerce Center Schiphol Airport, Polarisavenue 83a, 2132 JH, Hoofddorp, Netherlands
Tel.: (31) 23 56851 40

Web Site: http://www.euronics.com
Rev.: $21,378,580,000
Emp.: 50,000
Consumer Electronics Retailer
N.A.I.C.S.: 449210

Subsidiaries:

EURONICS SK a.s. (1)
Farskeho 26, 851 01, Bratislava, Slovakia
Tel.: (421) 2 622 470 00
Web Site: http://www.euronics.sk
Electronic Store Operator
N.A.I.C.S.: 449210

EURONICS Schweiz AG (1)
Zurcherstrasse 310, 8500, Frauenfeld, Switzerland
Tel.: (41) 52 728 00 20
Web Site: http://www.euronics.ch
Electronic Store Operator
N.A.I.C.S.: 449210

Euronics AB (1)
Svetsarvagen 15, Solna, 171 41, Sweden
Tel.: (46) 8 54 55 34 60
Web Site: http://www.euronics.se
Electronic Store Operator
N.A.I.C.S.: 449210

Euronics Austria reg. Genossenschaft
m.b.H. (1)
Georg-Humbhandl-Gasse 7, 2362, Biedermannsdorf, Austria
Tel.: (43) 2236 47 140
Web Site: http://www.redzac.at
Emp.: 16
Consumer Electronics Retailer
N.A.I.C.S.: 449210
Alexander Klaus (Gen Mgr)

Euronics Baltic OU (1)
Taamsaare 134B, 12918, Tallinn, Estonia
Tel.: (372) 651 2222
Web Site: http://www.euronics.ee
Consumer Electronics Retailer
N.A.I.C.S.: 449210

Euronics Belgium cvba (1)
Uilenbaan 90 K3, Wommelgem, 2160, Belgium
Tel.: (32) 3 320 84 77
Web Site: http://www.euronics.be
Electronic Store Operator
N.A.I.C.S.: 449210
M. Hans Carpels (Mng Dir)

Euronics CR a.s. (1)
Zlin nam Prace 2523, Prstne - Kutiky 637, 760 01, Zlin, Czech Republic
Tel.: (420) 577055777
Web Site: http://www.euronics.cz
Emp.: 25
Consumer Electronics Retailer
N.A.I.C.S.: 449210

Euronics Deutschland eG (1)
Berblingerstr 1, 71254, Ditzingen, Germany
Tel.: (49) 71 56 93 30
Web Site: http://www.euronics.de
Emp.: 37
Consumer Electronics Retailer
N.A.I.C.S.: 449210
Benedict Kober (Mng Dir)

Euronics Espana (1)
Madre Vedruna 38, 50008, Zaragoza, Spain
Tel.: (34) 976 226 313
Web Site: http://www.euronics.es
Consumer Electronics Retailer
N.A.I.C.S.: 449210
Javier Manzano (Mng Dir)

Euronics France (1)
Route d Aix Noulette, BP 09, 62143, Paris, France
Tel.: (33) 3 21 72 61 61
Web Site: http://www.euronics.fr
Electronic Store Operator
N.A.I.C.S.: 449210

Euronics Ireland (1)
Unit 4H Six Cross Roads Business Park, Kilbarry, Waterford, X9N2Y, Ireland
Tel.: (353) 15310700
Web Site: http://www.euronics.ie
Emp.: 4
Consumer Electronics Retailer
N.A.I.C.S.: 449210

Euronics Italia S.p.A. (1)

Via Montefeltro 6, 20156, Milan, Italy
Tel.: (39) 02 3070 1721
Web Site: http://www.euronics.it
Electronic Store Operator
N.A.I.C.S.: 449210

Euronics Kft. (1)
Petzval Jozsef u 35-37, 1119, Budapest, Hungary
Tel.: (36) 1 480 1188
Web Site: http://www.euronics.hu
Consumer Electronics Retailer
N.A.I.C.S.: 449210

Euronics Latvia SIA (1)
Ieriku Str 3 Korpus 2B 309, LV-1003, Riga, Latvia
Tel.: (371) 67218560
Web Site: http://www.euronics.lv
Consumer Electronics Retailer
N.A.I.C.S.: 449210

Euronics Norge AS (1)
PO Box 1417, 1602, Fredrikstad, Norway
Tel.: (47) 815 00 635
Web Site: http://www.euronics.no
Consumer Electronics Retailer
N.A.I.C.S.: 449210

Euronics Portugal (1)
Rua do Arquitecto Cassiano Barbosa 112 D
Office Number 7, 112 D Esc 7, 4100-009, Porto, Portugal
Tel.: (351) 22 605 78 20
Web Site: http://www.euronics.pt
Consumer Electronics Retailer
N.A.I.C.S.: 449210

EUROPA APOTHEEK VENLO BV

Dirk Hartogweg 14, 5928 LV, Venlo, Netherlands
Tel.: (31) 77 850 59 00 NI
Web Site: http://www.europa-apotheek.com
Year Founded: 2001
Sales Range: $75-99.9 Million
Emp.: 400
Pharmacy Services
N.A.I.C.S.: 456110
Michael Kohler (CEO)

Subsidiaries:

Europa Apotheek Service Venlo
B.V. (1)
Dirk Hartogweg 14, Venlo, 5928 LV, Netherlands
Tel.: (31) 778505900
Web Site: http://www.europa-apotheek.com
Medical Laboratories
N.A.I.C.S.: 621511

EUROPA GROWTH COMPANY

Baarerstrasse 78, 6300, Zug, Switzerland
Tel.: (41) 727 7500 Ky
Year Founded: 2021
Emp.: 3
Investment Services
N.A.I.C.S.: 523999
Michal Krupinski (CEO)

EUROPA METALS LIMITED

Level 8 99 St Georges Terrace, Perth, 6000, WA, Australia
Tel.: (61) 894864036
Web Site:
  https://www.europametals.com
Year Founded: 2005
EUZ—(AIM)
Assets: $453,968
Liabilities: $80,112
Net Worth: $373,856
Earnings: ($2,256,488)
Emp.: 12
Fiscal Year-end: 06/30/23
Iron Mining & Exploration Services
N.A.I.C.S.: 212210
Laurence Read (Exec Dir)

EUROPA OIL & GAS (HOLDINGS) PLC

30 Newman Street, London, W1T 1PT, United Kingdom
Tel.: (44) 2039686411 UK
Web Site: https://www.europaoil.com
EOG—(AIM)
Rev.: $4,512,123
Assets: $12,360,942
Liabilities: $7,583,400
Net Worth: $4,777,542
Earnings: ($8,569,242)
Fiscal Year-end: 07/31/24
Hydrocarbons Exploration & Production
N.A.I.C.S.: 211130
Phil Greenhalgh (Sec & Dir-Fin)

Subsidiaries:

Europa Oil & Gas Limited (1)
11 Chambers Vineyard, Abingdon, OX14 3PX, Oxfordshire, United Kingdom
Tel.: (44) 1235553266
Sales Range: $50-74.9 Million
Emp.: 4
Oil & Gas Field Exploration Services
N.A.I.C.S.: 213112

EUROPACIFIC METALS INC.

Suite 650-1021 W Hastings Street, Vancouver, V6E 0C3, BC, Canada
Tel.: (604) 655-1420 BC
Web Site:
  https://www.europacificmetals.ca
Year Founded: 2017
AUCCF—(OTCQB)
Assets: $1,318,236
Liabilities: $83,283
Net Worth: $1,234,953
Earnings: $1,329,427
Fiscal Year-end: 12/31/22
Gold Exploration Services
N.A.I.C.S.: 212220
Catalin Kilofliski (Founder)

EUROPACKAGING LTD.

20 Brickfield Road, Yardley, Birmingham, B25 8HE, United Kingdom
Tel.: (44) 1217066181
Web Site:
  http://www.europackaging.co.uk
Year Founded: 1974
Sales Range: $75-99.9 Million
Emp.: 375
Packaging Products Mfr
N.A.I.C.S.: 326199

Subsidiaries:

Euro Packaging Europe (1)
395 rue Paradis, Marseille, 13008, France
Tel.: (33) 491 800 527
Web Site: http://www.europackaging.com
Sales Range: $50-74.9 Million
Emp.: 3
Packaging Product Mfr & Whslr
N.A.I.C.S.: 326199
Alexander Miniere (Dir-Sls)

Europackaging Ltd. - Euro Packaging
Luxury Division (1)
Morgenstrasse 129, 3018, Bern, Switzerland
Tel.: (41) 31 991 8790
Web Site:
  http://www.europackagingluxury.co.uk
Emp.: 10
Packaging Products Mfr
N.A.I.C.S.: 326199
Nicolas Marino (CEO)

EUROPACORP

20 Rue Ampere, 93200, Saint Denis, France
Tel.: (33) 155995000 FR
Web Site:
  https://www.europacorp.com
Year Founded: 1999
ALECP—(EUR)
Rev.: $40,842,086
Assets: $132,888,494
Liabilities: $131,612,689

Net Worth: $1,275,804
Earnings: $68,638
Emp.: 30
Fiscal Year-end: 03/31/23
Film Production & Distribution Services
N.A.I.C.S.: 512110
Luc Besson (Chm & CEO)

EUROPASTRY, S.A.

Pza Xavier Cugat 2 Edificio C Planta 4 in Parc Sant Cugat Nord, 8174, Sant Cugat del Valles, Spain
Tel.: (34) 900118888 ES
Web Site: http://www.europastry.com
Sales Range: $450-499.9 Million
Emp.: 2,500
Frozen Pastry & Bread Dough Mfr & Whslr
N.A.I.C.S.: 311824

Subsidiaries:

Wenner Bread Products, Inc. (1)
33 Rajon Rd, Bayport, NY 11705-1101
Tel.: (631) 563-6262
Web Site: http://www.wenner-bread.com
Sales Range: $25-49.9 Million
Emp.: 425
Commercial Baked Goods & Dough Mfr
N.A.I.C.S.: 311812
Anthony Lupo (Mgr-Production)

EUROPE ONLINE TRADE EAD

ul Kozyak 21a vh A et 1 ofis 2, Sofia, 1407, Bulgaria
Tel.: (359) 887930924
Web Site: http://www.europe-online.trade
EOT—(BUL)
Sales Range: Less than $1 Million
Motor Vehicle Components Distr
N.A.I.C.S.: 423120

EUROPEAN BANK FOR RECONSTRUCTION & DEVELOPMENT

One Exchange Square, London, EC2A 2JN, United Kingdom
Tel.: (44) 2073386000
Web Site: http://www.ebrd.com
Year Founded: 1991
Rev.: $1,581,242,320
Assets: $69,264,460,860
Liabilities: $51,029,780,480
Net Worth: $18,234,680,380
Earnings: $380,752,400
Emp.: 1,591
Fiscal Year-end: 12/31/19
Transition Bank
N.A.I.C.S.: 521110
Alistair Clark (Mng Dir-Environment & Sustainability Dept)

EUROPEAN CANNABIS CORPORATION LIMITED

404 25 Lime Street, Sydney, 2000, NSW, Australia
Tel.: (61) 410622118 AU
Web Site:
  https://www.europeancannabis.com
Holding Company; Cloud-Based Human Resources Software Platform Developer & Publisher
N.A.I.C.S.: 551112

EUROPEAN CENTRAL BANK

Sonnemannstrasse 22, 60314, Frankfurt am Main, Germany
Tel.: (49) 6913440
Web Site: http://www.ecb.europa.eu
Year Founded: 1998
Rev.: $3,007,943,960
Assets: $511,867,848,520
Liabilities: $500,641,252,020
Net Worth: $11,226,596,500
Earnings: $2,649,588,760
Emp.: 3,770

Fiscal Year-end: 12/31/19
Central Banking Institution for the European Union & the Euro Currency
N.A.I.C.S.: 521110
Yves Mersch *(Vice Chm-Supervisory Bd)*

EUROPEAN COLOUR PLC
124 Chriswell Street, London, EC1Y 4YX, United Kingdom
Tel.: (44) 1606892313   UK
Web Site: http://www.ccplc.com
Year Founded: 1900
Sales Range: $25-49.9 Million
Emp.: 199
Specialty Chemical & Pigment Mfr
N.A.I.C.S.: 325998
Steve Smith *(Chm)*

Subsidiaries:

European Colour (Pigments) Limited   **(1)**
Hempshaw Lane, Stockport, SK1 4LG, Cheshire, United Kingdom
Tel.: (44) 1614803891
Sales Range: $25-49.9 Million
Emp.: 5
Pigment Mfr
N.A.I.C.S.: 325130
Max Steinborn *(Mgr-Sls-Central Europe)*

EUROPEAN DIRECTORIES S.A.
Herikerbergweg 88, 1101 CM, Amsterdam, Netherlands
Tel.: (31) 204873688   LU
Web Site:
http://www.europeandirectories.com
Sales Range: $650-699.9 Million
Emp.: 1,500
Publisher of Online & Printed Directories
N.A.I.C.S.: 513140
Masha Kodden *(CMO)*

Subsidiaries:

Youvia B.V.   **(1)**
Herikerbergweg 88, 1101 CM, Amsterdam, Netherlands
Tel.: (31) 20 408 6400
Online Marketing Directory Publisher
N.A.I.C.S.: 513140

EUROPEAN DRINKS S.A.
Strada Libertatii 14-16, PO Box 306, Oradea, Romania
Tel.: (40) 259402400
Web Site:
http://www.europeandrinks.ro
Sales Range: $1-9.9 Million
Emp.: 1,000
Soft Drink & Mineral Water Bottler & Mfr
N.A.I.C.S.: 312111

Subsidiaries:

European Food   **(1)**
Complex Transylvania Str Treatului 1-2, PO Box 306, Oradea, 410020, Romania
Tel.: (40) 259407200
Web Site: http://www.europeanfood.ro
Snack Foods, Cereal, Biscuits & Ketchup
N.A.I.C.S.: 311919
Ioan Micula *(Co-Pres)*

Scandic Distilleries   **(1)**
Complex Transylvania Street Treatului 1-2, PO Box 306, Oradea, 410020, Romania
Tel.: (40) 259407200
Web Site: http://www.scandicdistilleries.ro
Distillery
N.A.I.C.S.: 312140
Ioan Micula *(Co-Founder)*

EUROPEAN ELECTRIC METALS INC.
488 - 1090 West Georgia Street, Vancouver, V6E 3V7, BC, Canada
Tel.: (604) 687-7130   BC
Web Site: https://www.eu-electricmetals.com
Year Founded: 2006
EVX—(OTCIQ)
Assets: $10,612
Liabilities: $1,196,565
Net Worth: ($1,185,954)
Earnings: ($326,356)
Fiscal Year-end: 04/30/21
Metal Exploration Services
N.A.I.C.S.: 213114
Fred Antonio C. Tejada *(CEO)*

EUROPEAN ENERGY LIMITED
Level 2 BGC Centre 28 The Esplanade, Perth, 6000, WA, Australia
Tel.: (61) 8 9486 4422
Web Site:
http://www.europeanenergy.com.au
Oil & Gas Exploration Services
N.A.I.C.S.: 211120
William Paul Brooks *(Chm)*

EUROPEAN ENERGY METALS CORP.
503-905 West Pender, Vancouver, V6C 1L6, BC, Canada
Tel.: (604) 722-9842   BC
Web Site:
https://www.europeanenergy.com
Year Founded: 2021
FIN—(TSXV)
Assets: $608,515
Liabilities: $58,687
Net Worth: $549,828
Earnings: ($322,385)
Fiscal Year-end: 05/31/22
Mineral Exploration Services
N.A.I.C.S.: 212390
Gino DeMichele *(Chm)*

EUROPEAN FERRO METALS LTD.
Suite 700 510 West Hastings Street, Vancouver, V6B 1L8, BC, Canada
Tel.: (604) 787-8875   BC
Year Founded: 2013
Metal Mining
N.A.I.C.S.: 212290
Justin Blanchet *(CFO)*

EUROPEAN FINE WINES LTD.
11-13 Bromley Common, Bromley, BR2 9LS, United Kingdom
Tel.: (44) 203 236 0100
Web Site: http://www.efwines.com
Year Founded: 2005
Sales Range: $25-49.9 Million
Emp.: 55
Wine Distribution Services
N.A.I.C.S.: 424820
Scott Assemakis *(Founder)*

EUROPEAN HEALTHCARE ACQUISITION & GROWTH COMPANY B.V.
Theresienhohe 28, 80338, Munich, Germany
Tel.: (49) 894523240
Web Site: https://www.ehc-company.com
Year Founded: 2021
QXO—(MUN)
Investment Management Service
N.A.I.C.S.: 523999
Thomas Rudolph *(Chief Investment Officer)*

EUROPEAN INSTITUTE OF SCIENCE AB
Ideongatan 1A, 223 70, Lund, Sweden
Tel.: (46) 462862230
Web Site: http://www.euris.org
Year Founded: 1990
Pharmaceuticals Product Mfr
N.A.I.C.S.: 325412
Dario Kriz *(Pres)*

EUROPEAN INVESTMENT BANK
98-100 Boulevard Konrad Adenauer, L-2950, Luxembourg, Luxembourg
Tel.: (352) 43 79 1   BE
Web Site: http://www.eib.org
Year Founded: 1958
Rev.: $105,180,611
Assets: $3,815,901,673
Liabilities: $246,867,538
Net Worth: $3,569,034,135
Earnings: $3,403,255
Emp.: 3,203
Fiscal Year-end: 12/31/19
Investment Bank of the European Union
N.A.I.C.S.: 523150
Christopher Hurst *(Dir Gen)*

Subsidiaries:

European Investment Fund   **(1)**
37 B Avenue JF Kennedy, 2968, Luxembourg, Luxembourg   **(61.9%)**
Tel.: (352) 24851
Web Site: http://www.eif.org
Sales Range: $100-124.9 Million
Emp.: 250
Equity Investments in Venture Capital Funds & Guarantees to Financial Institutions
N.A.I.C.S.: 523999
Maria Leander *(Sec)*

EUROPEAN INVESTOR RELATIONS SA
Rue De Contamines 18, Geneva, 1211, Switzerland
Tel.: (41) 22 591 22 66
Web Site: http://www.voxia.ch
Sales Range: $10-24.9 Million
Emp.: 20
Marketing & Communication Agency
N.A.I.C.S.: 541613
Laurent Ashenden *(Founding Partner)*

EUROPEAN LITHIUM LIMITED
32 Harrogate Street, West Leederville, 6007, WA, Australia
Tel.: (61) 861819792   AU
Web Site:
https://europeanlithium.com
EULIF—(OTCQB)
Rev.: $135,953
Assets: $60,759,079
Liabilities: $574,282
Net Worth: $60,184,798
Earnings: ($9,439,208)
Fiscal Year-end: 06/30/22
Other Nonmetallic Mineral Mining & Quarrying
N.A.I.C.S.: 212390
Dietrich Wanke *(CEO)*

Subsidiaries:

Critical Metals Corp.   **(1)**
Kingston Chambers, Tortola, Virgin Islands (British)   **(83.8%)**
Tel.: (302) 636-5400
Web Site: https://criticalmetalscorp.com
Rev.: $117,660
Assets: $59,351,536
Liabilities: $78,460,334
Net Worth: ($19,108,798)
Earnings: ($147,489,253)
Emp.: 4
Fiscal Year-end: 06/30/2024
Lithium Mining Services
N.A.I.C.S.: 212390
Tony Sage *(Exec Chm)*

Subsidiary (US):

Sizzle Acquisition Corp.   **(2)**
4201 Georgia Ave NW, Washington, DC 20011
Tel.: (202) 846-0300
Web Site: https://www.sizzlespac.com
Rev.: $2,414,031
Assets: $160,643,833
Liabilities: $169,661,921
Net Worth: ($9,018,088)
Earnings: ($253,833)
Emp.: 2
Fiscal Year-end: 12/31/2022
Investment Services
N.A.I.C.S.: 523999

EUROPEAN METAL RECYCLING LIMITED
Sirius House Delta Crescent, Westbrook, Warrington, WA5 7NS, United Kingdom
Tel.: (44) 1925 715 400   UK
Web Site: http://www.emrltd.com
Year Founded: 1994
Sales Range: $1-4.9 Billion
Emp.: 2,300
Holding Company; Recycling Services & Recycled Materials Whslr
N.A.I.C.S.: 551112
Colin Liles *(CEO)*

Subsidiaries:

EMR Ltd   **(1)**
Unit 902 Floor 9 118 Connaught Road West, Hong Kong, China (Hong Kong)
Tel.: (852) 28599818
Metal Recycling Services
N.A.I.C.S.: 423930

European Metal Recycling BV   **(1)**
Amerikahavenweg 3 Westportno 5467, 1045 AA, Amsterdam, Netherlands
Tel.: (31) 206116656
Metal Recycling Services
N.A.I.C.S.: 423930

European Metal Recycling GmbH   **(1)**
Hinterbergstrasse 9, Cham, Zug, Switzerland
Tel.: (41) 417483280
Metal Recycling Services
N.A.I.C.S.: 423930

European Metal Recycling GmbH   **(1)**
Harburger Schlossstrasse 28, Hamburg, 21079, Germany
Tel.: (49) 407309060
Metal Recycling Services
N.A.I.C.S.: 423930

Recycle Metal & Commodities Private Ltd   **(1)**
493 First Floor Sector - 31, Gurgaon, 122 001, Haryana, India
Tel.: (91) 1244267377
Metal Recycling Services
N.A.I.C.S.: 423930

Smith Industries, Inc.   **(1)**
2001 Kenilworth Ave, Capitol Heights, MD 20743   **(50%)**
Tel.: (301) 773-1266
Web Site: http://www.smithindustries.us
Rev.: $21,400,000
Emp.: 2
Holding Company; Scrap Metal Processing, Recycling & Materials Whslr
N.A.I.C.S.: 551112
R. Paul Smith *(Pres)*

Subsidiary (Domestic):

Joseph Smith & Sons, Inc.   **(2)**
2001 Kenilworth Ave, Capitol Heights, MD 20743
Tel.: (301) 773-1266
Web Site: http://www.smithindustries.us
Scrap Metal Processing, Recycling & Materials Whslr
N.A.I.C.S.: 562920
R. Paul Smith *(Pres)*

Southern Recycling, LLC   **(1)**
902 Julia St, New Orleans, LA 70113
Tel.: (504) 636-7200
Web Site: http://www.sorec-emr.com
Rev.: $110,000,000

Emp.: 16
Metal Recycling Services & Materials Whslr
N.A.I.C.S.: 562920
David Farnsworth *(CFO)*

Subsidiary (Domestic):

Auto Shred Recycling, LLC   **(2)**
1000 Myrick St, Pensacola, FL
32505-8061   **(100%)**
Tel.: (850) 432-0977
Web Site: http://www.sorec-emr.com
Sales Range: $25-49.9 Million
Scrap & Waste Materials
N.A.I.C.S.: 423930

Isco Metals & Supply, LLC   **(2)**
10062 S Park Dr, Gulfport, MS 39503
Tel.: (228) 896-7888
Sales Range: $25-49.9 Million
Emp.: 7
Metal Distributor
N.A.I.C.S.: 423930

Resource Recycling, LLC   **(2)**
13130 56th Ct Ste 604, Clearwater, FL
33760
Tel.: (727) 573-2482
Web Site: http://www.resourcerecycling.com
Sales Range: $10-24.9 Million
Ash Processing & Metal Recovery Systems
Developer & Installation Services
N.A.I.C.S.: 333994

SSX, L.C.   **(2)**
6847 Scenic Hwy, Baton Rouge, LA
70807-6254   **(100%)**
Tel.: (225) 355-4453
Web Site: http://www.sorec-emr.com
Metal Recycling & Merchant Whslr
N.A.I.C.S.: 562920
Chip Hunter *(Pres)*

Southern Recycling Sales, LLC   **(2)**
902 Julia St, New Orleans, LA
70113   **(100%)**
Tel.: (504) 636-7200
Web Site: http://www.sorec-emr.com
Rev.: $1,400,000
Emp.: 5
Recycled Metal Materials Whslr
N.A.I.C.S.: 423930
Joel Dupre *(CEO)*

Southern Scrap Recycling Morgan
City, LLC   **(2)**
222 S Railroad St, Morgan City, LA 70380-
6054
Tel.: (985) 384-1960
Web Site: http://www.sorec-emr.com
Sales Range: $10-24.9 Million
Scrap & Waste Materials
N.A.I.C.S.: 423930
Leland Neio *(Gen Mgr)*

EUROPEAN METALS CORP.
131 Bloor Street West Suite 202, To-
ronto, M5S 3L7, ON, Canada
Tel.: (647) 478-1255   ON
Web Site:
   http://www.europeanmetalscorp.com
Year Founded: 1997
MNTCF—(OTCIQ)
Metal Mining & Exploration Services
N.A.I.C.S.: 212290
Vicki Rosenthal *(CEO & CFO)*

**EUROPEAN METALS HOLD-
INGS LIMITED**
Ground Floor 41 Colin Street, West
Perth, 6005, WA, Australia
Tel.: (61) 862452050
Web Site:
   https://www.europeanmet.com
EMH—(AIM)
Rev.: $845,065
Assets: $28,328,237
Liabilities: $899,011
Net Worth: $27,429,227
Earnings: ($5,212,310)
Fiscal Year-end: 06/30/22
Other Metal Ore Mining
N.A.I.C.S.: 212290
Keith Coughlan *(Chm)*

Subsidiaries:

Equamineral SA   **(1)**
621 Route de l Aeroport, BP 282, Pointe
Noire, Congo, Republic of
Tel.: (242) 6654 62 74
Mineral Exploration Services
N.A.I.C.S.: 212290

European Metals UK Limited   **(1)**
3rd Floor Dudley House, London, United
Kingdom
Tel.: (44) 20 3178 8914
Mineral Exploration Services
N.A.I.C.S.: 212290

Subsidiary (Non-US):

Geomet S.R.O   **(2)**
Vajanskeho 2983/25 Svatoplukova 2, 984
01, Lucenec, Slovakia
Tel.: (421) 903492502
Web Site: https://www.geomet.sk
Engineeering Services
N.A.I.C.S.: 541330

**EUROPEAN REAL ESTATE IN-
VESTMENT TRUST LIMITED**
Sarnia House Le Truchot, Saint Peter
Port, GY1 4NA, Guernsey
Tel.: (44) 1481737600   GY
Real Estate Investment Services
N.A.I.C.S.: 531190

**EUROPEAN RELIANCE GEN-
ERAL INSURANCE S.A.**
274 Kifisias Avenue, 152 32, Chalan-
dri, Greece
Tel.: (30) 2106829601
Web Site: http://www.europisti.gr
Rev.: $219,873,192
Assets: $500,161,652
Liabilities: $361,927,410
Net Worth: $138,234,242
Earnings: $19,135,814
Emp.: 1,121
Fiscal Year-end: 12/31/17
Fire, Marine & Casualty Insurance
N.A.I.C.S.: 524126
Nikolaos Chalkiopoulos *(Chm)*

**EUROPEAN RESIDENTIAL
REIT**
11 Church Street Suite 401, Toronto,
M5E 1W1, ON, Canada
Tel.: (416) 354-0167
Web Site: https://www.eresreit.com
EREUF—(OTCIQ)
Rev.: $105,623,137
Assets: $1,901,627,111
Liabilities: $1,430,000,000
Net Worth: $471,627,111
Earnings: $82,935,203
Fiscal Year-end: 12/31/23
Real Estate Investment Services
N.A.I.C.S.: 523991
Mark Kenney *(CEO)*

**EUROPEAN SATELLITE LINK
GMBH**
Hanskampring 4, 22885, Barsbuttel,
Germany
Tel.: (49) 4068 277 0
Web Site: http://www.nsslglobal.com
Sales Range: $25-49.9 Million
Emp.: 170
Supplier of Satellite Communications
Equipment
N.A.I.C.S.: 517410
Henrick Christensen *(CEO & Mng
Dir)*

**EUROPEJSKIE CENTRUM
ODSZKODOWAN S.A.**
M Kolbe 18, 59-220, Legnica, Poland
Tel.: (48) 767239800
Web Site: https://www.euco.pl
Year Founded: 2004

EUC—(WAR)
Rev.: $5,145,071
Assets: $4,628,557
Liabilities: $27,986,026
Net Worth: ($23,357,469)
Earnings: ($1,042,937)
Fiscal Year-end: 12/31/23
Claims Recovery Services
N.A.I.C.S.: 524291
Krzysztof Lewandowski *(CEO)*

EUROPLASMA SA
471 Cantegrit road, BP 23, 40110,
Morcenx, France
Tel.: (33) 556497000
Web Site:
   https://www.europlasma.com
Year Founded: 1992
ALEUP—(EUR)
Sales Range: $10-24.9 Million
Emp.: 217
Torches & Complete Plasma Torch
Waste Treatment Systems
N.A.I.C.S.: 562211
Jean-Eric Petit *(CEO)*

Subsidiaries:

Europe Environment S.A.   **(1)**
1 Rue des Pins, Aspach-le-Haut, 68700,
Thann, Haut-Rhin, France
Tel.: (33) 389374141
Web Site: http://www.europe-
   environnement.com
Sales Range: $25-49.9 Million
Emp.: 100
Environmental Control System Mfr
N.A.I.C.S.: 334512
Pierre Bellmann *(Mng Dir)*

Inertam SAS   **(1)**
471 Route de Cantegrit Est, BP 23, 40110,
Morcenx, Landes, France
Tel.: (33) 558041749
Web Site: http://www.inertam.fr
Sales Range: $10-24.9 Million
Emp.: 42
Asbestos Disposal Services
N.A.I.C.S.: 562910

EUROPRIS ASA
Dikeveien 57, 1661, Rolvsoy, Norway
Tel.: (47) 94050937
Web Site:
   https://www.investor.europris.no
EPR—(OSL)
Rev.: $930,647,752
Assets: $915,439,049
Liabilities: $560,381,140
Net Worth: $355,057,909
Earnings: $89,344,896
Emp.: 2,144
Fiscal Year-end: 12/31/23
Software Development Services
N.A.I.C.S.: 541511
Espen Eldal *(CFO)*

Subsidiaries:

Lunehjem.No AS   **(1)**
Gulliveien 6, 3157, Barkaker, Norway
Tel.: (47) 47246976
Web Site: https://www.lunehjem.no
Interior Design Services
N.A.I.C.S.: 541410

EUROPROJECT LLC
14 Kievskaya str B9, 121059, Mos-
cow, Russia
Tel.: (7) 495 229 42 42
Web Site: http://www.sia-abrasives.ru
Surface Processing & Refinement
Solutions
N.A.I.C.S.: 327910
Sergey Dolgun *(Gen Mgr)*

EUROPTRONIC GROUP LTD.
60 Kaki Bukit Place Eunos Techpark
01-10, Singapore, 415979, Singapore
Tel.: (65) 64472037   SG

Web Site:
   http://www.europtronicgroup.com
Year Founded: 1977
Sales Range: Less than $1 Million
Film Capacitor Mfr
N.A.I.C.S.: 334416
Yoen Har Wong *(Sec)*

Subsidiaries:

Europtronic (HK) Company
Limited   **(1)**
Unit 11A Phase 1 Goodman Shatin Logis-
tics Centre 6 Wong, Chuk Yeung Street Fo-
tan, Sha Tin, New Territories, China (Hong
Kong)
Tel.: (852) 27564786
Electric Component Whslr
N.A.I.C.S.: 423690

Europtronic (Singapore) Pte. Ltd.   **(1)**
60 Kaki Bukit Place Eunos Techpark 0110,
Singapore, 415979, Singapore
Tel.: (65) 63485558
Sales Range: $25-49.9 Million
Emp.: 25
Electronic Components Mfr & Distr
N.A.I.C.S.: 334416
Justin Chien-Hung Huang *(CEO)*

Europtronic (Taiwan) Ind. Corp.   **(1)**
10F-4 No 2 Lane 258 Rueiguang Road,
Neihu District, Taipei, 114, Taiwan
Tel.: (886) 287523118
Sales Range: $25-49.9 Million
Emp.: 20
Electronic Components Mfr
N.A.I.C.S.: 334416
Shih An Huang *(Pres)*

Subsidiary (Domestic):

Housing Technology Corp.   **(2)**
No 8 Lane 646 Po Ai Street, Chupei, Hsin-
chu, 302, Taiwan
Tel.: (886) 35533280
Chip Inductors & Chip Beads Mfr
N.A.I.C.S.: 334413

Europtronic Electronic (Shenzhen)
Co., Ltd.   **(1)**
Block 19 8/F Shatoujiao Free Trade Zone,
Shenzhen, 518081, China
Tel.: (86) 75525260670
Web Site: http://www.europtronic.com
Electronic Components Mfr
N.A.I.C.S.: 334416

Europtronic Green Energy Pte.
Ltd.   **(1)**
60 Kakidukit Place Unit No 01-10 Eunon
Tech Park, Singapore, 415979, Singapore
Tel.: (65) 64472037
Web Site: http://www.europtronicgroup.com
Sales Range: $10-24.9 Million
Emp.: 26
Plantlets Breeding Services
N.A.I.C.S.: 561990
Justin Hoang *(Gen Mgr)*

Europtronic Investment Pte. Ltd.   **(1)**
60 Kaki Bukit Place Eunos Techpark 01-10,
Singapore, 415979, Singapore
Tel.: (65) 64472037
Web Site: http://www.europtronicgroup.com
Emp.: 20
Investment Management Service
N.A.I.C.S.: 523999

UPT Component (S) Pte. Ltd.   **(1)**
60 Kaki Bukit Pl Eunos Techpark 05-10,
Singapore, 415979, Singapore
Tel.: (65) 63485558
Web Site: http://www.europtronic.com
Sales Range: $25-49.9 Million
Emp.: 25
Electronic Components Distr
N.A.I.C.S.: 423690
Mei Theng Leong *(Controller-Fin)*

Subsidiary (Non-US):

UPT Crypson Component (Shanghai)
Co., Ltd.   **(2)**
Room 1301 No 333 Zhao Jia Bang Road,
Shanghai, 200032, China
Tel.: (86) 2164162909
Web Site: http://www.europtronicgroup.com

Europtronic Group Ltd.—(Continued)

Sales Range: $25-49.9 Million
Emp.: 20
Electric Component Whslr
N.A.I.C.S.: 423690
Shih an Huang *(Chm)*

EUROQUARZ GMBH
Sudwall 15, 46282, Dorsten, Germany
Tel.: (49) 236220050
Web Site: http://www.euroquarz.com
Year Founded: 1897
Rev.: $54,648,804
Emp.: 101
Silica Products Distr
N.A.I.C.S.: 424690
Holger Vespermann *(Mgr-Sls)*

Subsidiaries:

SIGRANO Nederland b.v. **(1)**
Koolkoelenweg 40, 6414 XP, Heerlen, Limburg, Netherlands
Tel.: (31) 455636414
Chemical Products Mfr
N.A.I.C.S.: 325199

EUROSCREEN S.A.
Route de Lennik 802, 01070, Brussels, Belgium
Tel.: (32) 71348500
Web Site: http://www.euroscreen.be
Sales Range: $10-24.9 Million
Emp.: 44
Biopharmaceutical Services
N.A.I.C.S.: 325412
Jean Combalbert *(Pres & CEO)*

EUROSEAS LTD.
Messogiou Thallasis 4 & Evropis, 151 24, Maroussi, Greece
Tel.: (30) 2111804005 MH
Web Site: https://www.euroseas.gr
Year Founded: 2005
ESEA—(NASDAQ)
Rev.: $182,694,244
Assets: $328,590,425
Liabilities: $160,435,228
Net Worth: $168,155,197
Earnings: $106,244,916
Emp.: 374
Fiscal Year-end: 12/31/22
Deep Sea Transportation Services
N.A.I.C.S.: 483111
Anastasios Aslidis *(CFO & Treas)*

Subsidiaries:

Eternity Shipping Company **(1)**
Rm 1302 Shun Tak Centre, W Tower Connaught Rd, 168 200, Hong Kong, China (Hong Kong)
Tel.: (852) 25451212
Shipping Services
N.A.I.C.S.: 488510
Jimmy Tse *(Mgr)*

EUROSPAN HOLDINGS BERHAD
1168 Kampung Teluk Sungai Dua Kawasan Perusahaan Sungai Lokan, 13800, Butterworth, Penang, Malaysia
Tel.: (60) 43563727
Web Site:
https://www.eurospan.com.my
EUROSP—(KLS)
Rev.: $7,967,471
Assets: $8,909,850
Liabilities: $1,917,906
Net Worth: $6,991,944
Earnings: ($1,300,395)
Fiscal Year-end: 05/31/23
Home Furnishing Mfr
N.A.I.C.S.: 337121
Kim Teck Lim *(Sec)*

Subsidiaries:

Dynaspan Furniture Sdn. Bhd. **(1)**
2 Lorong Bakau 3 Kawasan Perusahaan Perabot Sungai Baon, 14200, Sungai Bakap, Kedah, Malaysia
Tel.: (60) 45822070
Web Site: http://www.eurospan.com.my
Sales Range: $25-49.9 Million
Emp.: 80
Furniture Mfr
N.A.I.C.S.: 337126
K. P. Andy *(Sr Mgr-Production)*

Eurospan Furniture Sdn. Bhd. **(1)**
1168 Kampung Teluk Kawasan Perusahaan Sungai Lokan, Sungai Dua, 13800, Butterworth, Penang, Malaysia
Tel.: (60) 43563727
Web Site: https://www.eurospan.com.my
Sales Range: $100-124.9 Million
Emp.: 300
Furniture Mfr
N.A.I.C.S.: 333248

EUROSPORTS GLOBAL LIMITED
24 Leng Kee Road 01-03, Singapore, 159096, Singapore
Tel.: (65) 65655995
Web Site:
https://www.eurosportsglobal.com
Year Founded: 1998
5G1—(CAT)
Rev.: $45,115,969
Assets: $30,083,735
Liabilities: $15,720,637
Net Worth: $14,363,097
Earnings: ($3,293,072)
Emp.: 80
Fiscal Year-end: 03/31/23
Luxury Automobile Distr
N.A.I.C.S.: 423110
Melvin Goh *(Chm & CEO)*

Subsidiaries:

deLaCour Asia Pacific Pte. Ltd. **(1)**
6 rue Adhemar Fabri, 1201, Geneva, Switzerland
Tel.: (41) 767741526
Web Site: https://www.delacour.ch
Watch Distr
N.A.I.C.S.: 423940

EUROSTANDARD BANKA AD
Nikola Kljusev no 2, Skopje, 1000, North Macedonia
Tel.: (389) 2 3249 437
Web Site:
http://www.eurostandard.com.mk
Year Founded: 2001
ESB—(MAC)
Sales Range: $1-9.9 Million
Banking Services
N.A.I.C.S.: 522110
Nikolche Petkoski *(Chm & Mgr)*

EUROSTAR INTERNATIONAL LTD
Times House Bravingtons Walk, 5 Bravingtons Walk, London, N1 9AW, United Kingdom
Tel.: (44) 3432186186 UK
Web Site: http://www.eurostar.com
Year Founded: 1994
Sales Range: $450-499.9 Million
Emp.: 1,376
Train Service
N.A.I.C.S.: 482111
James Cheesewright *(CFO)*

EUROTECH S.P.A.
Via Fratelli Solari 3/a, Amaro, 33020, Udine, Italy
Tel.: (39) 0433485411 IT
Web Site: https://www.eurotech.com
Year Founded: 1992
ETH—(ITA)
Rev.: $104,469,588
Assets: $171,671,266

Liabilities: $66,451,043
Net Worth: $105,220,223
Earnings: ($3,441,881)
Emp.: 393
Fiscal Year-end: 12/31/23
Information Technology Research & Development; Computer Hardware & Software
N.A.I.C.S.: 541519
Roberto Siagri *(CEO)*

Subsidiaries:

Advanet Inc. **(1)**
616-4 Tanaka, Kita-ku, Okayama, 700-0951, Japan
Tel.: (81) 862452861
Web Site: https://www.advanet.co.jp
Sales Range: Less than $1 Million
Computer Software Publisher
N.A.I.C.S.: 513210
Ludovico Ciferri *(Mng Dir)*

Chengdu Vantron Technology Inc. **(1)**
Floor 5-6 Building 1 No 9 Wuke Dongsan Road, Wuhou District, Chengdu, Sichuan, China
Tel.: (86) 2885123930
Web Site: http://www.vantrontech.cn
Sales Range: $25-49.9 Million
Computer Software Publisher
N.A.I.C.S.: 513210

Dynatem, Inc. **(1)**
23263 Madero St Ste C, Mission Viejo, CA 92691
Tel.: (949) 855-3235
Web Site: http://www.dynatem.com
Sales Range: $25-49.9 Million
Emp.: 15
Computer Equipment Mfr
N.A.I.C.S.: 334111

EthLab S.R.L. **(1)**
Viale Dante 300, 38056, Pergine Valsugana, Trento, Italy
Tel.: (39) 0461538358
Web Site: https://www.eurotech.com
Sales Range: $25-49.9 Million
Emp.: 10
Computer Related Research & Development Services
N.A.I.C.S.: 541715

Eurotech France S.A.S. **(1)**
33 Ave du Dr Georges Levy Parc du Moulin a Vent, 69693, Venissieux, Cedex, France
Tel.: (33) 472890090
Web Site: http://www.eurotech.com
Sales Range: $25-49.9 Million
Computer Boards Mfr
N.A.I.C.S.: 334118

Eurotech Inc. **(1)**
10260 Old Columbia Rd, Columbia, MD 21046
Tel.: (301) 490-4007
Web Site: http://www.eurotech-inc.com
Sales Range: $25-49.9 Million
Single Board Computer Mfrs
N.A.I.C.S.: 334118
Leann Zawodniak *(CFO)*

Subsidiary (Domestic):

Eurotech Inc. **(2)**
7500 W 161st St, Overland Park, KS 66085
Tel.: (913) 549-1000
Web Site: http://www.eurotech.com
Sales Range: $25-49.9 Million
Emp.: 12
Single Board Computer Mfrs
N.A.I.C.S.: 334118

Eurotech Ltd. **(1)**
3 Clifton Court, Cambridge, CB1 7BN, United Kingdom
Tel.: (44) 1223403410
Web Site: http://www.eurotech.com
Sales Range: $25-49.9 Million
Emp.: 25
Mfr of Industrial Controls Devices
N.A.I.C.S.: 334513

InoNet Computer GmbH **(1)**
Wettersteinstrasse 18, 82024, Taufkirchen, Germany
Tel.: (49) 896660960

Web Site: https://www.inonet.com
Robust & Powerful Industrial Computer Mfr
N.A.I.C.S.: 334112

EUROTEL S.A.
Ul Mysliwska 21, 80-126, Gdansk, Poland
Tel.: (48) 585203819
Web Site: https://www.eurotel.pl
ETL—(WAR)
Rev.: $110,078,252
Assets: $46,919,207
Liabilities: $26,868,648
Net Worth: $20,050,559
Earnings: $4,137,957
Fiscal Year-end: 12/31/23
Telecommunication Servicesb
N.A.I.C.S.: 517810
Krzysztof Jerzy Stepokura *(Chm-Mgmt Bd)*

EUROTERRA BULGARIA AD
1 Vitosha blvd, 1040, Sofia, Bulgaria
Tel.: (359) 29816606
Web Site:
https://www.euroterrabulgaria.bg
EUTR—(BUL)
Sales Range: Less than $1 Million
Real Estate Services
N.A.I.C.S.: 531210
Michail Therianos *(Chm, CEO & Gen Mgr)*

EUROTEX INDUSTRIES & EXPORTS LIMITED
Raheja Chambers 12th Floor 213 Nariman Point, Mumbai, 400021, India
Tel.: (91) 2222041408
Web Site:
https://www.eurotexgroup.in
Year Founded: 1989
521014—(BOM)
Rev.: $4,732,346
Assets: $6,920,509
Liabilities: $7,872,023
Net Worth: ($951,514)
Earnings: ($1,601,241)
Emp.: 100
Fiscal Year-end: 03/31/21
Cotton Yarn Mfr & Distr
N.A.I.C.S.: 313110
Rahul Rawat *(Officer-Compliance & Sec)*

EUROTIN INC.
77 King Street West Suite 700, Toronto, M5K 1G8, ON, Canada
Tel.: (416) 648-1626 ON
Web Site: http://blog.eurotin.ca
Year Founded: 2008
LIM.H—(TSXV)
Assets: $10,565
Liabilities: $1,338,320
Net Worth: ($1,327,754)
Earnings: ($280,543)
Fiscal Year-end: 03/31/21
Metal Mining Services
N.A.I.C.S.: 212290
John Walter Wallen Hick *(Chm)*

EUROVESTECH PLC
17C Curzon Street, London, W1J 5HU, United Kingdom
Tel.: (44) 20 7478 9070 UK
Web Site:
http://www.eurovestech.com
Year Founded: 2000
Sales Range: $10-24.9 Million
Emp.: 71
Venture Capital Investment Services
N.A.I.C.S.: 523999
Richard Philip Bernstein *(CEO)*

Subsidiaries:

Audionamix SA **(1)**
114 Ave de Flandre, 75019, Paris, France
Tel.: (33) 140055511

Web Site: http://www.audionamix.com
Audio Mixing Services
N.A.I.C.S.: 512290
Pierre Leveau *(Chief Scientific Officer)*

EUROVITI S.R.L.
Via per Ospitaletto 159, 25046, Caz-
zago San Martino, BS, Italy
Tel.: (39) 030 775 0520   IT
Web Site: http://www.euroviti.com
Year Founded: 1992
Plastic Screw & Other Fastener Mfr
N.A.I.C.S.: 326199

EUROZ HARTLEYS GROUP LIMITED
Level 37 QV1 250 St Georges Ter-
race, Perth, 6000, WA, Australia
Tel.: (61) 892682888   AU
Web Site: https://eurozhartleys.com
EZL—(ASX)
Rev.: $59,572,987
Assets: $128,739,844
Liabilities: $52,458,487
Net Worth: $76,281,357
Earnings: $3,651,217
Emp.: 185
Fiscal Year-end: 06/30/24
Fund Management Services
N.A.I.C.S.: 523940
Andrew McKenzie *(Exec Chm & Chm)*

Subsidiaries:

Entrust Wealth Management Pty
Ltd   **(1)**
Level 6 141 St Georges Tce, Perth, 6000,
WA, Australia
Tel.: (61) 89 476 3900
Web Site: https://entrustwealth.com.au
Emp.: 20
Investment Management Service
N.A.I.C.S.: 541611
Rebecca Gordon *(Compliance Officer)*

Westoz Funds Management Pty.
Ltd.   **(1)**
Level 18 Alluvion 58 Mounts Bay Road,
Perth, 6000, WA, Australia
Tel.: (61) 89 321 7877
Web Site: https://www.westozfunds.com.au
Sales Range: $50-74.9 Million
Emp.: 2
Investment Fund Management Services
N.A.I.C.S.: 525910
Dermot Woods *(Exec Dir & Mgr-Fund)*

Zero Nominees Pty. Ltd.   **(1)**
St Georges Terrace, PO Box Z5036, Perth,
6831, Western Australia, Australia
Tel.: (61) 894881400
Web Site: http://www.euroz.com.au
Sales Range: $25-49.9 Million
Emp.: 60
Business Consulting Services
N.A.I.C.S.: 541611

EUROZET SP. Z.O.O.
ul Zurawia 8, 00-503, Warsaw, Po-
land
Tel.: (48) 22 583 32 00
Web Site: http://www.eurozet.pl
Radio Station Broadcasting Services
N.A.I.C.S.: 516110

EUSKALTEL SA
Parque Tecnologico Edificio 809, De-
rio, 48160, Spain
Tel.: (34) 944011000
EU4—(BER)
Rev.: $748,405,798
Assets: $3,266,945,181
Liabilities: $2,167,281,856
Net Worth: $1,099,663,325
Earnings: $69,451,477
Fiscal Year-end: 12/31/19
Telecommunication Servicesb
N.A.I.C.S.: 517112
Jose Miguel Garcia Fernandez *(CEO)*

EUSU HOLDINGS CO., LTD.
60 Yeouinaruro, Yeongdeungpo-gu,
Seoul, Korea (South)
Tel.: (82) 267163000
Web Site: https://www.eusu-
holdings.com
Year Founded: 1949
000700—(KRS)
Rev.: $427,684,852
Assets: $402,618,292
Liabilities: $60,788,715
Net Worth: $341,829,577
Earnings: $22,283,371
Emp.: 20
Fiscal Year-end: 12/31/22
Holding Company
N.A.I.C.S.: 551112

Subsidiaries:

CyberLogitec Global Pte. Ltd.   **(1)**
Tel.: (65) 62740576
Logistic Services
N.A.I.C.S.: 488510

CyberLogitec Shanghai Co., Ltd.   **(1)**
Room 513 Dongdaming Road No 1050,
Hongkou, Shanghai, 200082, China
Tel.: (86) 2152004105
Logistic Services
N.A.I.C.S.: 488510

CyberLogitec Spain S.L.U.   **(1)**
Red Logistica de Andalucia Area Bahia de
Algeciras, Edf de Servicios Oficina B006
Area de El Fresno Los Barrios, 11370,
Cadiz, Spain
Tel.: (34) 956688307
Logistic Services
N.A.I.C.S.: 488510

CyberLogitec Vietnam Co., Ltd.   **(1)**
Scetpa Building 19A Cong Hoa Street,
Ward 12 Tan Binh District, Ho Chi Minh
City, Vietnam
Tel.: (84) 2838132967
Logistic Services
N.A.I.C.S.: 488510

Eusu Logistics Co., Ltd.   **(1)**
Web Site: http://www.eusu-logistics.com
Logistic Services
N.A.I.C.S.: 488510

Subsidiary (Non-US):

Eusu Logistics (Hong Kong) Co.,
Ltd.   **(2)**
Rm 1710 17/F Tower 2 Ever Gain Plaza 88
Container Port Road, Kwai Chung, China
(Hong Kong)
Logistic Services
N.A.I.C.S.: 488510

Eusu Logistics (M) Sdn. Bhd.   **(2)**
Lot PT 5038-5041 Jalah Teluk Datuk 28/40,
Off Persiaran Sepang Seksyen 28, 40400,
Shah Alam, Selangor, Malaysia
Tel.: (60) 358798593
Logistic Services
N.A.I.C.S.: 488510

Eusu Logistics (Shanghai) Co.,
Ltd.   **(2)**
Tel.: (86) 2161815600
Logistic Services
N.A.I.C.S.: 488510

Eusu Logistics (Shenzhen) Co.,
Ltd.   **(2)**
Tel.: (86) 75536808123
Logistic Services
N.A.I.C.S.: 488510

Eusu Logistics Japan Co., Ltd.   **(2)**
3F Takata Bldg 1-14-2 Bakurocho Nihon-
bashi, Chuo-Ku, Tokyo, 103-0002, Japan
Tel.: (81) 3666700701
Logistic Services
N.A.I.C.S.: 488510

Eusu Logistics LLC   **(2)**
M-01 Sharaf Building Taiq Bin Ziyad Road,
PO Box 34653, 318-429, Dubai, United
Arab Emirates
Tel.: (971) 43060131
Logistic Services
N.A.I.C.S.: 488510

Eusu Logistics Singapore Pte.
Ltd.   **(2)**
460 Alexandra Road 15-01 PSA Building,
Singapore, 119963, Singapore
Tel.: (65) 62740698
Logistic Services
N.A.I.C.S.: 488510

Eusu Logistics Spain S.A.   **(2)**
Paseo de la Alameda 35-Bis-4 Izq, 46023,
Valencia, Spain
Tel.: (34) 963939700
Logistic Services
N.A.I.C.S.: 488510

Eusu Logistics Thailand Co., Ltd.   **(2)**
3388/39 12th Floor Sirinrat Building Rama 4
Rd Klongton, Khlong Toei, Bangkok, 10110,
Thailand
Tel.: (66) 26856019
Logistic Services
N.A.I.C.S.: 488510

H&H Int'l Logistics (Fujian) Co.,
Ltd.   **(2)**
Unit 31B International Plaza No 8 Lujing
Road, Xiamen, 361000, China
Tel.: (86) 5922260112
Logistic Services
N.A.I.C.S.: 488510

Hanjin Arkas Logistics & Trading
S.A.   **(2)**
Kasap Sokak Arkas Binasi Nr 2, Esentepe,
Istanbul, 34394, Turkiye
Tel.: (90) 2123405025
Logistic Services
N.A.I.C.S.: 488510

NAL Maroc Ltd.   **(2)**
353 Boulevard Mohamed V Espace Idriss
8eme Etage, 20300, Casablanca, Morocco
Tel.: (212) 522248369
Logistic Services
N.A.I.C.S.: 488510

PT. EUSU Logistics Indonesia   **(2)**
Logistic Services
N.A.I.C.S.: 488510

EUTELSAT COMMUNICATIONS SA
70 rue Balard, FR-75015, Paris, Ce-
dex 15, France
Tel.: (33) 153984747
Web Site: http://www.eutelsat.com
ETCMY—(OTCIQ)
Rev.: $1,220,915,174
Assets: $7,997,841,571
Liabilities: $4,682,387,222
Net Worth: $3,315,454,349
Earnings: $354,306,065
Emp.: 1,067
Fiscal Year-end: 06/30/23
Holding Company
N.A.I.C.S.: 517112
Yohann Leroy *(Deputy CEO & CTO)*

Subsidiaries:

Eutelsat Asia Pte. Ltd.   **(1)**
7 Temasek Boulevard 21-04 Suntec Tower
1, Singapore, 038987, Singapore
Tel.: (65) 68082088
Web Site: http://www.eutelsatasia.com
Broadband Services
N.A.I.C.S.: 517810

Eutelsat Communications Finance
S.A.S.   **(1)**
32 boulevard Gallieni, 92130, Issy-les-
Moulineaux, France
Tel.: (33) 153984747
Telecommunication Servicesb
N.A.I.C.S.: 517112

Eutelsat Latin America S.A.   **(1)**
Blvd Costa del Este Calle la Rotonda Piso
35 Finantial Park Tower, Panama, Panama
Tel.: (507) 2322556
Broadband Services
N.A.I.C.S.: 517810

Eutelsat Madeira Lda.   **(1)**
Rua da Alfandega 78 2nd Floor, 9000-059,
Funchal, Portugal
Tel.: (351) 291969900
Broadband Services

N.A.I.C.S.: 517810

Eutelsat Networks LLC   **(1)**
Entrance 3 d 21/5 Kuznetsky Most Street,
Moscow, 107031, Russia
Tel.: (7) 4951500858
Web Site: http://www.eutelsatnetworks.ru
Broadband Services
N.A.I.C.S.: 517810

Eutelsat S.A.   **(1)**
32 boulevard Gallieni, 92130, Issy-les-
Moulineaux, France
Tel.: (33) 153984747
Sales Range: $100-124.9 Million
Emp.: 500
Satellite Telecommunication Services
N.A.I.C.S.: 517810

Subsidiary (US):

Eutelsat America Corp.   **(2)**
1776 I St NW Ste 810, Washington, DC
20006
Tel.: (202) 559-4330
Web Site: https://eutelsatamerica.com
Satellite Telecommunication Sales
N.A.I.C.S.: 517410
Kevin Steen *(Pres)*

Subsidiary (Non-US):

Eutelsat GmbH   **(2)**
Im Mediapark 8A, 50670, Cologne, Ger-
many
Tel.: (49) 2216500450
Web Site: http://www.eutelsat.de
Sales Range: $25-49.9 Million
Emp.: 15
Satellite Communication Services
N.A.I.C.S.: 517410

Eutelsat Polska s.p.z.o.   **(2)**
Ul Panska 81/83, 00-834, Warsaw, Poland
Tel.: (48) 224328030
Web Site: https://www.eutelsat.pl
Sales Range: $25-49.9 Million
Emp.: 4
Satellite Communication Services
N.A.I.C.S.: 517410

Eutelsat Services und Beteiligungen
GmbH   **(2)**
Spichernstrasse 73, Cologne, 50670, Ger-
many
Tel.: (49) 2216500450
Web Site: http://www.eutelsat.de
Emp.: 30
Telecommunication Servicesb
N.A.I.C.S.: 517112
Alessandro Lanfranconi *(Gen Mgr)*

Eutelsat UK Ltd.   **(2)**
North West House 119 Marylebone Rd,
London, NW1 5PU, United Kingdom
Tel.: (44) 2078688873
Web Site: http://www.eutelsat.com
Sales Range: $25-49.9 Million
Emp.: 5
Satellite Communication Services
N.A.I.C.S.: 517410

Subsidiary (Domestic):

Eutelsat VAS S.A.S.   **(2)**
70 Rue Balard, 75015, Paris, France
Tel.: (33) 153984747
Telecommunication Servicesb
N.A.I.C.S.: 517112

Subsidiary (Non-US):

Eutelsat do Brasil SA   **(2)**
Rua Araujo Porto Alegre 36 sala 904, Rio
de Janeiro, CEP 20030-013, Brazil
Tel.: (55) 2125240894
Web Site: http://www.eutelsatamerica.com
Sales Range: $25-49.9 Million
Emp.: 5
Satellite Communication Services
N.A.I.C.S.: 517410
Eloi Stivalletti *(Dir-Mktg & Sls)*

Satelites Mexicanos S.A de C.V.   **(2)**
Avenida Paseo de la Reforma 222 Piso 20
y 21, Colonia Juarez, 06600, Mexico,
Mexico
Tel.: (52) 5526295800
Web Site: http://www.satmex.com.mx
Rev.: $132,856,000
Assets: $821,885,000

EUTELSAT COMMUNICATIONS SA

Eutelsat Communications SA—(Continued)

Liabilities: $484,685,000
Net Worth: $337,200,000
Earnings: ($2,003,000)
Emp.: 172
Fiscal Year-end: 12/31/2013
Satellite Services
N.A.I.C.S.: 517410
Patricio Ernesto Northland (CEO)

Skylogic Mediterraneo S.r.l　　(2)
Via Gianquinto De Gioannis 25 A, 09125,
Cagliari, Italy
Tel.: (39) 070247645
Web Site: http://www.skylogic.it
Television Broadcasting Services
N.A.I.C.S.: 516120

Skylogic S.p.A.　　(2)
Piazza Lagrange 2, 10123, Turin, Italy
Tel.: (39) 0115585400
Web Site: http://www.skylogic.com
Sales Range: $25-49.9 Million
Emp.: 100
Broadband Satellite Communications Services
N.A.I.C.S.: 517410

Eutelsat do Brasil Participatoes
Ltda.　　(1)
Praca XV de Novembro 20 sala 403 Ed
Bolsa de Valores, Rio de Janeiro, 20010-
010, RJ, Brazil
Tel.: (55) 2125240894
Web Site: https://www.eutelsatamericas.com
Broadband Services
N.A.I.C.S.: 517810

EUTILEX CO., LTD.

Suite 408 Gasan digital 1-Ro 58,
Geumcheon-gu, Seoul, 08591, Korea
(South)
Tel.: (82) 220713310
Web Site: https://www.eutilex.com
Year Founded: 2015
263050—(KRS)
Rev.: $165,413
Assets: $80,122,779
Liabilities: $10,427,997
Net Worth: $69,694,783
Earnings: ($26,438,606)
Emp.: 114
Fiscal Year-end: 12/31/22
Biotechnology Research & Development Services
N.A.I.C.S.: 541714
Byoung S. Kwon (Founder & Co-CEO)

EUWAX AG

Boersenstr 4, D-70174, Stuttgart,
Germany
Tel.: (49) 7112229850
Web Site: https://www.euwax-ag.de
Year Founded: 1991
EUX—(DEU)
Assets: $150,458,108
Liabilities: $58,968,981
Net Worth: $91,489,127
Earnings: $7,252,456
Emp.: 93
Fiscal Year-end: 12/31/23
Security Brokerage Services
N.A.I.C.S.: 523150
Alexander Hoeptner (Chm-Mgmt Bd)

EV ADVANCED MATERIAL CO., LTD.

26 Seongseo-ro 35-gol, Dalseo-gu,
Daegu, 42719, Korea (South)
Tel.: (82) 535938560　　KR
Web Site: https://evam.co.kr
Year Founded: 2004
131400—(KRS)
Rev.: $44,539,962
Assets: $92,463,432
Liabilities: $38,054,150
Net Worth: $54,409,281
Earnings: ($8,204,581)
Emp.: 149

Fiscal Year-end: 12/31/22
Printed Circuit Boards Mfr & Distr
N.A.I.C.S.: 334412
Kwon Ik Ki (CFO)

EV DIGITAL INVEST AG

Joachimsthaler Str 12, 10719, Berlin,
Germany
Tel.: (49) 30403691550
Web Site: https://www.ev-digitalinvest.de
Year Founded: 2015
ENGL—(DEU)
Rev.: $4,570,041
Assets: $6,258,969
Liabilities: $1,280,495
Net Worth: $4,978,474
Earnings: ($4,073,297)
Emp.: 50
Fiscal Year-end: 12/31/23
Asset Management Services
N.A.I.C.S.: 523999

EV DYNAMICS (HOLDINGS) LIMITED

46th Floor United Asia Finance Centre333 Lockhart Road, Wanchai,
China (Hong Kong)
Tel.: (852) 21529998　　BM
Web Site:
https://www.evdynamics.com
Year Founded: 1996
0476—(HKG)
Rev.: $6,442,164
Assets: $259,471,001
Liabilities: $25,933,364
Net Worth: $233,537,637
Earnings: ($53,538,437)
Emp.: 89
Fiscal Year-end: 03/31/22
Holding Company; Electric Vehicles,
Batteries & Mining
N.A.I.C.S.: 551112
Ngan Cheung (Chm)

EV NICKEL INC.

150 King St W Suite 200, Toronto,
M5H 1J9, ON, Canada
Tel.: (647) 948-7424　　ON
Web Site: https://www.evnickel.com
Year Founded: 2021
EVNIF—(OTCIQ)
Assets: $1,875,714
Liabilities: $1,130,644
Net Worth: $745,070
Earnings: ($3,903,784)
Fiscal Year-end: 06/30/22
Mineral Mining Services
N.A.I.C.S.: 213115
Sean Samson (Pres)

EV PARKING SERVICE CO., LTD.

50-11 World Cup-ro 14-gil, Mapo-gu,
Seoul, Korea (South)
Tel.: (82) 15335421
Web Site: https://www.evps.co.kr
Year Founded: 2021
419700—(KRS)
Electric Equipment Mfr
N.A.I.C.S.: 333414

EV PRIVATE EQUITY

Kongsgaardbakken 1, 4005, Sta-vanger, Norway
Tel.: (47) 51 84 12 95
Web Site:
http://www.evprivateequity.no
Year Founded: 2002
Holding Company
N.A.I.C.S.: 551112
Kjell Jacobsen (Chm)

Subsidiaries:

Enhanced Well Technologies AS　　(1)
Smalonane 16, 5343, Straume, Norway

Tel.: (47) 56154000
Drilling, Cementing & Safe Enhancement
Technology
N.A.I.C.S.: 213111
Kjetil Lunde (VP-Fin & Bus Support)

Subsidiary (Domestic):

IKM Cleandrill AS　　(2)
Smalonane 5, Trollhaugmyra 15, 5353,
Straume, Norway
Tel.: (47) 958 27 109
Web Site: http://www.ikm.com
Collection Management & Transfer of Drilling Fluid & Cutting Services
N.A.I.C.S.: 213112
Tom Hasler (Mng Dir)

EV RESOURCES LIMITED

311-313 Hay St, Subiaco, 6008, WA,
Australia
Tel.: (61) 864890600
Web Site:
https://www.evresources.com.au
Year Founded: 1985
EVR—(ASX)
Rev.: $7,964
Assets: $4,204,954
Liabilities: $432,457
Net Worth: $3,772,497
Earnings: ($3,519,940)
Fiscal Year-end: 06/30/23
Mineral Mining Services
N.A.I.C.S.: 213115

EV8 TECHNOLOGIES LIMITED

Adelphi 12th Floor 1-11 John Adam
Street, London, WC2N 6HT, United
Kingdom
Tel.: (44) 2074688000
Web Site: https://www.ev8-tech.com
Year Founded: 2018
Software Development Services
N.A.I.C.S.: 541511

EVA PRECISION INDUSTRIAL HOLDINGS LIMITED

Unit 8 6th Floor Greenfield Tower
Concordia Plaza, No 1 Science Museum Road, Kowloon, China (Hong
Kong)
Tel.: (852) 26206488
Web Site: http://www.eva-group.com
0838—(HKG)
Rev.: $799,178,288
Assets: $925,238,430
Liabilities: $563,341,920
Net Worth: $361,896,510
Earnings: $26,267,168
Emp.: 9,434
Fiscal Year-end: 12/31/22
Metal Products Mfr
N.A.I.C.S.: 333517
Yaohua Zhang (CEO)

Subsidiaries:

EVA Precision Industrial (Suzhou)
Limited　　(1)
Yihe Industrial Park No 268 Mayun Road
Suzhou New District, Suzhou, 215129, Jiangsu, China
Tel.: (86) 51289179999
Plastic & Metal Mold Mfr
N.A.I.C.S.: 333511

Okutatu (Macao Commercial Offshore) Limited　　(1)
Rm I 17/F Centro Comercial Cheng Feng,
Macau, China (Macau)
Tel.: (853) 28755785
Metal & Plastic Component Distr
N.A.I.C.S.: 423830

EVADIX SA

160/4 rue de Namur, 1400, Nivelles,
Belgium
Tel.: (32) 69895160
Web Site: http://www.evadix.com
ROCK—(EUR)
Rev.: $250,006,225

Assets: $28,935,419
Liabilities: $12,658,857
Net Worth: $16,276,562
Earnings: ($838,845)
Emp.: 148
Fiscal Year-end: 12/31/22
Commercial Printing & Marketing
Services
N.A.I.C.S.: 323120
Jean-Francois Gosse (Chm)

EVALUE VENTURES AG

Kennedydamm 1, 40476, Dusseldorf,
Germany
Tel.: (49) 2115209940
Web Site:
http://www.evalueventures.de
Emp.: 25
Digital Direct Marketing Services
N.A.I.C.S.: 541860
Erwin Plomp (CEO)

EVANCIA SAS

24 rue du Moulin des Bruyeres,
Courbevoie, 92400, Paris, France
Tel.: (33) 1 41 49 96 50　　FR
Web Site: http://www.babilou.fr
Year Founded: 2003
Child Care Services
N.A.I.C.S.: 624410
Rodolphe Carle (Chm)

Subsidiaries:

Little Sprouts LLC　　(1)
354 Merrimack St, Lawrence, MA 01843
Web Site: http://www.littlesprouts.com
Sales Range: $10-24.9 Million
Emp.: 415
Day Care, Preschool & Kindergarten
N.A.I.C.S.: 624410
Mark Anderegg (CEO)

EVANS ELECTRIC LTD.

430 A Wing 3rd Floor Orchard Mall
Royal Palms Estate Aarey Milk
Colony, Goregaon East, Mumbai,
400065, Maharashtra, India
Tel.: (91) 2235113042
Web Site:
https://www.evanselectric.co.in
Year Founded: 1951
542668—(BOM)
Rev.: $1,043,765
Assets: $1,858,599
Liabilities: $275,892
Net Worth: $1,582,707
Earnings: $112,386
Emp.: 12
Fiscal Year-end: 03/31/22
Electrical Equipment Distr
N.A.I.C.S.: 423440

EVANS MEDICAL PLC.

Plot 6 Abimbola Way Isolo, PMB
1120, Apapa, Lagos, Nigeria
Tel.: (234) 1 7901401
Year Founded: 1954
Pharmaceuticals Mfr
N.A.I.C.S.: 325412
S. A. Edu (Chm)

EVATEC AG

Hauptstrasse 1a, 9477, Trubbach,
Switzerland
Tel.: (41) 814038000
Web Site: http://www.evatecnet.com
Year Founded: 2004
Emp.: 60
Thin Film Deposition & Etch System
Mfr
N.A.I.C.S.: 333248
Andreas Waelti (CEO)

Subsidiaries:

Evatec (Liechtenstein) AG　　(1)
Fohrenweg 16, 9496, Balzers, Liechtenstein
Tel.: (423) 3881910

Web Site: http://www.evatec.li
Industrial Machinery & Equipment Distr
N.A.I.C.S.: 423830

Evatec Europe GmbH (1)
Karl Hammerschmidt Str 34, 85609, As-chheim, Germany
Tel.: (49) 8975505100
Industrial Machinery & Equipment Distr
N.A.I.C.S.: 423830

Evatec Italia S.r.l (1)
Via Villoresi 3 Barbaiana, 20010, Lainate, Italy
Tel.: (39) 0293257447
Industrial Machinery & Equipment Distr
N.A.I.C.S.: 423830

Evatec NA Inc. (1)
150 Dow St, Manchester, NH 03101-1227
Tel.: (603) 669-9656
Web Site: http://www.evatecnet.com
Thin Film Deposition & Etch System Mfr
N.A.I.C.S.: 333248
Carlo Tavernini (VP-Tech)

Evatec Process Systems B.V. (1)
Hoefzijde 4-01, 3961 MX, Wijk bij Duurst-ede, Netherlands
Tel.: (31) 343595470
Web Site: http://www.evatec.nl
Industrial Machinery & Equipment Distr
N.A.I.C.S.: 423830

EVATHERM AG
Hintermattlistrasse 3, 5506, Ma-genwil, Switzerland
Tel.: (41) 62 889 79 00
Web Site: http://www.evatherm.com
Emp.: 30
Evaporation & Crystallization Technol-ogy & Services
N.A.I.C.S.: 333248
Peter Kondorosy (Chm)

Subsidiaries:

EVATHERM GmbH (1)
Dubener Strasse 17, D-06774, Muldestau-see, Germany
Tel.: (49) 342 08 71 295
Evaporation & Crystallization Technology & Services
N.A.I.C.S.: 333248

EVATHERM Kft. (1)
Beregszaszter 16, H-1118, Budapest, Hun-gary
Tel.: (36) 1 246 37 77
Web Site: http://www.evatherm.com
Evaporation & Crystallization Technology & Services
N.A.I.C.S.: 333248

EVAXION BIOTECH A/S
Dr Neergaards Vej 5F, 2970, Horsh-olm, Denmark
Tel.: (45) 53531850   DK
Web Site: https://www.evaxion-biotech.com
Year Founded: 2008
EVAX—(NASDAQ)
Rev.: $2,831,000
Assets: $22,025,000
Liabilities: $13,722,000
Net Worth: $8,303,000
Earnings: ($23,169,000)
Emp.: 63
Fiscal Year-end: 12/31/22
Biotechnology Research & Develop-ment Services
N.A.I.C.S.: 541714
Glenn S. Vraniak (CFO)

EVD BERHAD
No 39 Jalan Putra Mahkota 77B Pu-tra Heights, 47650, Subang Jaya, Selangor, Malaysia
Tel.: (60) 351914390
Web Site: https://evd-berhad.com
Year Founded: 2006
EVD—(KLS)
Rev.: $21,772,488
Assets: $55,240,195

Liabilities: $26,203,851
Net Worth: $29,036,344
Earnings: $1,676,437
Fiscal Year-end: 12/31/22
Software Solutions
N.A.I.C.S.: 513210
Daniel Hui Siong Boo (Co-Founder & Mng Dir)

Subsidiaries:

OS Solutions Sdn. Bhd. (1)
Block E2 7-4 Jalan PJU 1/42A Dataran Prima, Petaling Jaya, 47301, Selangor Darul Ehsan, Malaysia
Tel.: (60) 3 7880 6093
Web Site:
http://www.idimensionsystems.com
Sales Range: $25-49.9 Million
Emp.: 12
Software Development Services
N.A.I.C.S.: 541511
Daniel Boo (Mng Dir)

iDimension MSC Pte Ltd (1)
14 Robinson Road 13-00 Far East Finance Bldg, Singapore, 048545, Singapore
Tel.: (65) 6494 9192
Web Site:
http://www.idimensionsystems.com
Software Development Services
N.A.I.C.S.: 513210
Daniel Boo (Mng Dir)

iDimension MSC Sdn. Bhd. (1)
A-1-02 1st Floor Block A Sme Technopre-neur Centre, 2270 Jalan Usahawan 2, Cy-berjaya, 63000, Selangor, Malaysia
Tel.: (60) 3 7880 5303
Sales Range: $25-49.9 Million
Emp.: 40
Electronic Software Development Services
N.A.I.C.S.: 541511

EVE & CO INCORPORATED
2941 Napperton Drive, Strathroy, N7G 3H8, ON, Canada
Tel.: (416) 922-9096   ON
Web Site: http://www.evecannabis.ca
Year Founded: 2014
EVE—(TSXV)
Rev.: $2,984,837
Assets: $39,457,779
Liabilities: $21,609,028
Net Worth: $17,848,752
Earnings: ($7,677,056)
Fiscal Year-end: 12/31/20
Investment Services
N.A.I.C.S.: 523999
Melinda Rombouts (Pres & CEO)

EVE ENERGY CO., LTD.
38 Huifeng 7th Road, Zhongkai Hi-tech Zone, Huizhou, 516006, Guang-dong, China
Tel.: (86) 7522630809
Web Site: http://www.evebattery.com
Year Founded: 2001
300014—(SSE)
Rev.: $6,754,484,271
Assets: $13,064,263,680
Liabilities: $7,802,125,388
Net Worth: $5,262,138,292
Earnings: $560,779,616
Emp.: 28,000
Fiscal Year-end: 12/31/23
Battery Mfr
N.A.I.C.S.: 335910

Subsidiaries:

EVE Energy Co., Ltd. - Jingmen Factory (1)
68th Jingnan Road, Duodao Hi-tech District, Jingmen, 516006, Hubei, China
Tel.: (86) 7246079699
Lithium Battery Mfr
N.A.I.C.S.: 335910

EVE Energy Co., Ltd. - Xikeng Factory (1)
Eve Ind Park Xikeng Ind Zone, Huihuan Town, Huizhou, 516006, Guangdong, China
Tel.: (86) 7525753325

Lithium Battery Mfr
N.A.I.C.S.: 335910

EVE Energy Co., Ltd. - Zhongkai Factory (1)
38th Huifeng 7 Road, Zhongkai Hi-tech Dis-trict, Huizhou, 516006, Guangdong, China
Tel.: (86) 7522630809
Lithium Battery Mfr
N.A.I.C.S.: 335910

EVE Energy North America Corporation (1)
46 Village Pointe Dr, Powell, OH 43065
Tel.: (614) 389-2552
Web Site: http://www.evebatteryusa.com
Emp.: 6
Lithium Product Mfr
N.A.I.C.S.: 335910
John Wu (Gen Mgr)

EVE Germany GmbH (1)
Taunusstr 42, 80807, Munich, Germany
Tel.: (49) 17680332535
Primary Battery Mfr
N.A.I.C.S.: 335910

EVE Hyperpower Batteries Inc. (1)
No 63 Huitai Industrial Park, Zhongkai High-tech Zone, Huizhou, Guangdong, China
Tel.: (86) 7525790010
Primary Battery Mfr
N.A.I.C.S.: 335910

EVE Innovation Energy Co., Ltd. (1)
No 3 Xinghai Road Fenghua Economic De-velopment Zone, Binhai New District, Ningbo, Zhejiang, China
Tel.: (86) 57459557007
Primary Battery Mfr
N.A.I.C.S.: 335910

EVE HEALTH GROUP LIMITED
Suite 1 245 Churchill Avenue, Subi-aco, 6008, WA, Australia
Tel.: (61) 864655500
Web Site:
https://www.evehealthgroup.com.au
EVE—(ASX)
Rev.: $1,424,794
Assets: $1,684,751
Liabilities: $867,449
Net Worth: $817,302
Earnings: ($1,034,123)
Fiscal Year-end: 06/30/24
Miscellaneous Financial Investment Activities
N.A.I.C.S.: 523999
Gregory Fry (CEO & Mng Dir)

Subsidiaries:

Jenbrook Pty Ltd (1)
1 245 Churchill Avenue, Subiaco, 6008, WA, Australia
Tel.: (61) 64655500
Web Site: https://www.jenbrook.com.au
Tea Tree Farming Services
N.A.I.C.S.: 111998

EVE SLEEP PLC
North Yard 2 Interchange Atri The Stables Market, Chalk, London, NW1 8AH, United Kingdom
Tel.: (44) 8008085766
Web Site: http://www.evesleep.co.uk
EVE—(BER)
Rev.: $31,285,504
Assets: $17,599,789
Liabilities: $6,902,334
Net Worth: $10,697,454
Earnings: ($15,918,797)
Emp.: 51
Fiscal Year-end: 12/31/19
Mattress Mfr
N.A.I.C.S.: 337910
James Sturrock (CEO)

Subsidiaries:

Eve sleep SASU (1)
5 rue des Suisses, 75014, Paris, France
Tel.: (33) 975182875
Web Site: http://www.evematelas.fr
Mattress Retailer

N.A.I.C.S.: 449110

EVEN CONSTRUTORA E IN-CORPORADORA S.A.
Rua Hungria 1 400 - 3 andar, Jardim America, 01455-000, Sao Paulo, Bra-zil
Tel.: (55) 1133773777
Web Site: https://www.even.com.br
Year Founded: 2002
EVEN3—(BRAZ)
Rev.: $531,568,960
Assets: $1,304,701,168
Liabilities: $789,888,612
Net Worth: $514,812,557
Earnings: $61,009,634
Emp.: 2,241
Fiscal Year-end: 12/31/23
Real Estate Development Services
N.A.I.C.S.: 531390
Dany Muszkat (Co-CEO, IR Officer & Member-Exec Bd)

Subsidiaries:

Armadillo Even Empreendimentos Imobiliarios Ltda. (1)
Rua Refinaria Mataripe 365 Vila Antonieta, Sao Paulo, 03477-010, Brazil
Tel.: (55) 11 2722 4010
Real Estate Development Services
N.A.I.C.S.: 531390

Capricornus Even Empreendimentos Imobiliarios Ltda. (1)
Rua Conde de Porto Alegre 1041, Campo Belo, Sao Paulo, 04608-001, Brazil
Tel.: (55) 11 5096 0765
Real Estate Development Services
N.A.I.C.S.: 531390

Cat Even Empreendimentos Imobil-iarios Ltda. (1)
Avenida Otacilio Tomanik 686 - Vila Polo-poli, Sao Paulo, Brazil
Tel.: (55) 11 3733 3079
Real Estate Development Services
N.A.I.C.S.: 531390

Cepheus Even Empreendimentos Imobiliarios Ltda. (1)
Rua Celso de Azevedo Marques 295 - Parque da Mooca, Sao Paulo, 03122-010, Brazil
Tel.: (55) 11 2076 3921
Real Estate Development Services
N.A.I.C.S.: 531390

Chamaeleon Even Empreendimentos Imobiliarios Ltda. (1)
Rua Trajano Reis 777, Jardim das Ver-tentes, Sao Paulo, 05541-030, Brazil
Tel.: (55) 11 3743 9105
Real Estate Development Services
N.A.I.C.S.: 531390

Columba Even Empreendimentos Imobiliarios Ltda. (1)
Rua Gabriele D'Annunzio 1066, Sao Paulo, 04619-000, Brazil
Tel.: (55) 11 5093 2555
Real Estate Development Services
N.A.I.C.S.: 531390

EVEN - SP 47/10 Empreendimentos Imobiliarios Ltda. (1)
Rua Giestas 186 - Vila Bela, Sao Paulo, Brazil
Tel.: (55) 11 2084 8185
Real Estate Development Services
N.A.I.C.S.: 531390

EVEN - SP 59/11 Empreendimentos Imobiliarios Ltda. (1)
Rua Haddock Lobo 117, Sao Paulo, Brazil
Tel.: (55) 11 3257 9580
Real Estate Development Services
N.A.I.C.S.: 531390

Even - SP 35/10 Empreendimentos Imobiliarios Ltda. (1)
Rua Professor Ciridao Buarque 96 - Vila Anglo Brasileira, Sao Paulo, Brazil
Tel.: (55) 11 3672 2514
Real Estate Development Services
N.A.I.C.S.: 531390

Even Construtora e Incorporadora S.A.—(Continued)

Even SP 18/10 Empreendimentos Imobiliarios Ltda. (1)
Rua Coari 170, Sao Paulo, Brazil
Tel.: (55) 11 3862 2453
Real Estate Development Services
N.A.I.C.S.: 531390

Goat Even Empreendimentos Imobiliarios Ltda. (1)
Rua Eugenio de Freitas 371, Sao Paulo, Brazil
Tel.: (55) 11 2901 8317
Real Estate Development Services
N.A.I.C.S.: 631300

Irigny Empreendimentos Imobiliarios S.A. (1)
Rua Arizona 701, Cidade Moncoes, Sao Paulo, 04567-002, Brazil
Tel.: (55) 11 5041 1815
Real Estate Development Services
N.A.I.C.S.: 531390

Lionfish Even Empreendimentos Imobiliarios Ltda. (1)
Rua Amapa 222 Vila Canero, Sao Paulo, 03191-160, Brazil
Tel.: (55) 11 2021 3555
Real Estate Development Services
N.A.I.C.S.: 531390

Melnick Even Desenvolvimento Imobiliario S.A. (1)
Rua Carlos Trein Filho 551, Auxiliadora, Porto Alegre, 90450-120, Brazil
Tel.: (55) 51 3016 9000
Real Estate Development Services
N.A.I.C.S.: 531390

Omicron Even Rio Empreendimentos Imobiliarios Ltda. (1)
Av Das Americas 500, Rio de Janeiro, 22640-100, Brazil
Tel.: (55) 2135649893
Real Estate Development Services
N.A.I.C.S.: 531390

Ophiuchus Even Empreendimentos Imobiliarios Ltda. (1)
Rua Maria Alves Conceicao 181, Sao Jose do Rio Pardo, 15053-635, Brazil
Tel.: (55) 17 3014 2020
Real Estate Development Services
N.A.I.C.S.: 531390

Pisces Even Empreendimentos Imobiliarios Ltda. (1)
Avenida Alberto Ramos 487 Vila Independencia, Sao Paulo, 03222-000, Brazil
Tel.: (55) 11 2218 1818
Real Estate Development Services
N.A.I.C.S.: 531390

Rabbit Even Empreendimentos Imobiliarios Ltda. (1)
Rua Jose Vicente de Barros 1802, Parque Santo Antonio, Taubate, 12061-001, Sao Paulo, Brazil
Tel.: (55) 12 3624 6279
Real Estate Development Services
N.A.I.C.S.: 531390

Snake Even Empreendimentos Imobiliarios Ltda. (1)
Rua Jaci 51, Sao Paulo, Brazil
Tel.: (55) 11 2276 1187
Real Estate Development Services
N.A.I.C.S.: 531390

Terra Vitris Empreendimentos Imobiliarios Ltda. (1)
Rua Funchal 418 Pvm 29 Cj 2901 Sl 5 B Vila Olimpia, Sao Paulo, 04551-060, Brazil
Tel.: (55) 11 5083 0080
Real Estate Development Services
N.A.I.C.S.: 531390

EVENING STANDARD LTD.
2 Derry Street, London, W8 5TT, United Kingdom
Tel.: (44) 2033677000 UK
Web Site: http://www.standard.co.uk
Year Founded: 2008
Newspaper & Magazine Publisher; Television Network Operator
N.A.I.C.S.: 513110

Manish Malhotra *(Grp Mng Dir-Interim & CFO)*

Subsidiaries:

Independent Print Limited (1)
Northcliffe House 2 Derry Street, London, W8 5HF, United Kingdom
Tel.: (44) 2070052000
Web Site: http://www.independent.co.uk
Newspaper Publishers
N.A.I.C.S.: 513110

EVENT HOSPITALITY & ENTERTAINMENT LIMITED
478 George Street, Sydney, 2000, NSW, Australia
Tel.: (61) 293736600 AU
Web Site: http://www.evt.com
Year Founded: 1910
EVT—(ASX)
Rev.: $818,437,497
Assets: $1,743,450,180
Liabilities: $1,099,656,780
Net Worth: $643,793,400
Earnings: $3,215,812
Emp.: 10,000
Fiscal Year-end: 06/30/24
Holding Company; Hospitality & Entertainment Properties Operator
N.A.I.C.S.: 551112
Jane Hastings *(CEO & Mng Dir)*

Subsidiaries:

Event Cinemas Limited (1)
Metro Building Level 3 291-297 Queen St, Auckland, 1010, New Zealand
Tel.: (64) 93692400
Web Site: https://www.eventcinemas.co.nz
Event Cinema Operator
N.A.I.C.S.: 711310

Kosciuszko Thredbo Pty Limited (1)
PO Box 92, Thredbo, 2625, NSW, Australia
Tel.: (61) 264594100
Web Site: http://www.thredbo.com.au
Recreational Event Operator
N.A.I.C.S.: 721214

QT Hotels & Resorts Pty Limited (1)
49 Market Street, Sydney, 3699, VIC, Australia
Tel.: (61) 282620000
Web Site: https://www.qthotels.com
Hotel Operator
N.A.I.C.S.: 721110

Rydges Bankstown Pty Limited (1)
874 Hume Highway Bass Hill, Sydney, 2197, NSW, Australia
Tel.: (61) 287072800
Web Site: https://www.rydges.com
Hotel Operator
N.A.I.C.S.: 721110

Rydges Cronulla Pty Limited (1)
20-26 the Kingsway, Cronulla, 2230, NSW, Australia
Tel.: (61) 295273100
Web Site: https://www.rydges.com
Hotel Operator
N.A.I.C.S.: 721110

Rydges Hobart Hotel Pty Limited (1)
393 Argyle St, Hobart, 7000, TAS, Australia
Tel.: (61) 362311588
Hotel Operator
N.A.I.C.S.: 721110

Rydges Rotorua Hotel Limited (1)
10 Tryon Street Whakarewarewa, Rotorua, 3010, New Zealand
Tel.: (64) 73481189
Web Site: https://www.rydges.com
Hotel Operator
N.A.I.C.S.: 721110

Sunshine Cinemas Pty Limited (1)
29 Sunshine Beach Road Noosa Heads, Shire of Noosa, 4567, QLD, Australia
Tel.: (61) 754475130
Web Site: http://www.noosacinemas.com.au
Event Cinema Operator
N.A.I.C.S.: 711310

The Greater Union Organisation Pty Limited (1)

49 Market St, Sydney, 2000, NSW, Australia
Tel.: (61) 93736655
Web Site: http://www.statetheatre.com.au
Event Cinema Operator
N.A.I.C.S.: 711310

EVENT MARKETING SERVICE GMBH
Geusaugasse 9, A-1030, Vienna, Austria
Tel.: (43) 1 714 88 77 0
Web Site: http://www.ems-entertainment.com
Sales Range: $1-9.9 Million
Emp.: 100
Touring Shows, Exhibits & Event Marketing
N.A.I.C.S.: 711190
Christoph Rahofer *(CEO)*

Subsidiaries:

EMS Entertainment (M) Sdn Bhd (1)
18 Persiaran Damansara Endah, Damasara Heights, 50490, Kuala Lumpur, Malaysia
Tel.: (60) 320950288
Entertainment Services
N.A.I.C.S.: 512131
Christoph Rahofer *(CEO)*

EMS Exhibits Las Vegas, Inc. (1)
3799 Las Vegas Blvd S, Las Vegas, NV 89109
Tel.: (702) 481-2527
Entertainment Services
N.A.I.C.S.: 512131
Christoph Rahofer *(CEO)*

EMS Exhibits Miami, LLC. (1)
5310 N Central Ave Ste A, Tampa, FL 33603
Tel.: (800) 555-1212
Web Site: http://www.ems-exhibitsus.com
Entertainment Services
N.A.I.C.S.: 512131

EMS Exhibits Orlando, LLC. (1)
7220 International Dr, Orlando, FL 32819
Tel.: (407) 226-7220
Entertainment Services
N.A.I.C.S.: 512131
Christoph Rahofer *(CEO)*

EMS Live Entertainment GmbH (1)
Geusaugasse 9/10, 1030, Vienna, Austria
Tel.: (43) 171488770
Web Site: http://www.ems-entertainment.com
Entertainment Services
N.A.I.C.S.: 512131

EVENTA ENTERTAINMENT GROUP LTD.
118 Queens Road, Brighton, BN1 3XG, United Kingdom
Tel.: (44) 1273 225 071
Web Site:
http://www.theeventagroup.com
Year Founded: 2002
Sales Range: $10-24.9 Million
Emp.: 70
Event Organizing Services
N.A.I.C.S.: 711310
Pat Heath *(CTO)*

EVENTIKO INC.
Xinzhong St 3, Dongcheng, Beijing, 100026, China
Tel.: (86) 17026054808 NV
Year Founded: 2020
Rev.: $11,350
Assets: $16,530
Liabilities: $35,015
Net Worth: ($18,485)
Earnings: ($9,936)
Emp.: 1
Fiscal Year-end: 04/30/23
Event Management Services
N.A.I.C.S.: 711310
Zhong Wei *(CEO, Treas & Sec)*

EVER GLORY LOGISTICS PTE. LTD.
119 Neythal Road Block B Level 1, Singapore, 628605, Singapore
Tel.: (65) 69108000 SG
Web Site: http://www.everglory.biz
Year Founded: 1977
Sales Range: $1-9.9 Million
Freight Trucking & Warehousing Services
N.A.I.C.S.: 484121
Jeffrey Tan Tian Hong *(Mng Dir)*

EVER HARVEST GROUP HOLDINGS LIMITED
17/F Excel Centre 483A Castle Peak Road Cheung Sha Wan, Kowloon, China (Hong Kong)
Tel.: (852) 34169178 Ky
Web Site: http://www.xhsl.com.hk
Year Founded: 1993
1549—(HKG)
Rev.: $83,578,545
Assets: $52,674,330
Liabilities: $24,574,605
Net Worth: $28,099,725
Earnings: $3,524,355
Emp.: 203
Fiscal Year-end: 12/31/22
Freight Forwarding Services
N.A.I.C.S.: 488510
Yu Leung Lau *(Founder & Chm)*

EVER HARVEST INTERNATIONAL GROUP INC.
1947 Leslie St, Toronto, M3B 2M3, ON, Canada
TLGN—(OTCIQ)
Rev.: $488,663
Assets: $7,504
Liabilities: $81,473
Net Worth: ($73,969)
Earnings: ($184,466)
Emp.: 5
Fiscal Year-end: 12/31/21
Recycling Machine Mfr
N.A.I.C.S.: 333310
Shawn Dym *(CEO)*

EVER LOTUS ENTERPRISE CO., LTD.
No 89 Yu Ping Road, T'ainan, 70843, Taiwan
Tel.: (886) 62999757
Web Site: http://www.everlotus.com
Year Founded: 1996
Plastic Computerware & Accessories
N.A.I.C.S.: 326199
Jenifer Chang *(CEO)*

EVER REACH GROUP (HOLDINGS) COMPANY LIMITED
No 266 Bayi Road, Weidu District, Xuchang, Henan, China
Tel.: (86) 3742778585 Ky
Web Site:
http://www.everreachgroup.com
Year Founded: 1992
3616—(HKG)
Rev.: $401,792,648
Assets: $1,408,141,238
Liabilities: $1,145,106,472
Net Worth: $263,034,767
Earnings: $10,918,768
Emp.: 755
Fiscal Year-end: 12/31/22
Residential & Commercial Property Development Services
N.A.I.C.S.: 531210
Xiaobing Li *(Chm)*

EVER SUPREME BIO TECHNOLOGY CO., LTD.
7F No 360 Sec 1 Jingmao Rd, Beitun Dist, Taichung, 406040, Taiwan

Tel.: (886) 423252888
Web Site: https://www.ever-supreme.com.tw
Year Founded: 2016
6712—(TPE)
Rev.: $19,620,173
Assets: $61,708,408
Liabilities: $5,673,326
Net Worth: $56,035,081
Earnings: $6,275,646
Fiscal Year-end: 12/31/22
Biotechnological Research & Development Services
N.A.I.C.S.: 541714
Chu-Chi Liu (Chm)

EVER-CLEAR ENVIRONMENTAL ENG CORP.
No 261 Sec 5 Longfu Rd, Xitun District, Taichung, 407, Taiwan
Tel.: (886) 422550168
Web Site: https://www.ever-clear.com.tw
Year Founded: 1999
6624—(TPE)
Rev.: $14,388,206
Assets: $28,310,915
Liabilities: $17,699,246
Net Worth: $10,611,669
Earnings: $766,751
Fiscal Year-end: 12/31/22
Electrical Engineering Services
N.A.I.C.S.: 541330
Chia-Ching Ho (Chm)

EVER-GLORY INTERNATIONAL GROUP INC.
Ever-Glory Commercial Center 509 Chengxin Road, Jiangning Development Zone, Nanjing, Jiangsu, China
Tel.: (86) 2552096831   FL
Web Site:
http://www.everglorygroup.com
Year Founded: 1994
EVK—(NASDAQ)
Rev.: $267,354,000
Assets: $331,726,000
Liabilities: $197,277,000
Net Worth: $134,449,000
Earnings: $3,280,000
Emp.: 4,700
Fiscal Year-end: 12/31/20
Men's, Women's & Children's Casual Wear, Sportswear & Outerwear Mfr
N.A.I.C.S.: 315250
Edward Yihua Kang (Pres, CEO & Chm)

EVER-GOTESCO RESOURCES & HOLDINGS, INC.
12/F Ever Gotesco Corporate Center 1958 C M Recto Ave, Manila, Philippines
Tel.: (63) 7356901
Year Founded: 1994
EVER—(PHI)
Rev.: $209,322
Assets: $67,711,908
Liabilities: $12,175,653
Net Worth: $55,536,256
Earnings: $1,132,350
Fiscal Year-end: 12/31/23
Holding Company
N.A.I.C.S.: 551112
Evelyn C. Go (Treas)

EVERARC HOLDINGS LIMITED
Kingston Chambers, PO Box 173, Road Town, Tortola, Virgin Islands (British)   VG
Web Site:
http://www.everarcholdings.com
Year Founded: 2019
EVRA—(LSE)
Financial Investment Services
N.A.I.C.S.: 523999

Nick Howley (Co-Chm)
Subsidiaries:

Perimeter Solutions LP   **(1)**
8000 Maryland Ave Ste 350, Clayton, MO 63105
Tel.: (314) 396-7343
Web Site: http://www.perimeter-solutions.com
Fire Retardants & Suppressant Gels Mfr
N.A.I.C.S.: 922160
William N. Thorndike Jr. (Co-Chm)

Subsidiary (Domestic):

H&S Transportation Co. Inc.   **(2)**
2608 S Hume Ave, Marshfield, WI 54449   **(100%)**
Tel.: (715) 387-3414
Web Site: http://www.hsmfgco.com
Sales Range: $10-24.9 Million
Emp.: 12
Provider of Transport Services
N.A.I.C.S.: 484121

River City Fabrication, Inc.   **(2)**
2911 Burke St, Jacksonville, FL 32254
Tel.: (904) 389-9888
Specialty Trade Contractors
N.A.I.C.S.: 238990

EVERARDS BREWERY LTD
Castle Acres, Narborough, LE19 1BY, Leicestershire, United Kingdom
Tel.: (44) 1162014100
Web Site: http://www.everards.co.uk
Year Founded: 1849
Sales Range: $25-49.9 Million
Emp.: 110
Brewing Services
N.A.I.C.S.: 312130
Richard Everard (Chm)

EVERBRIGHT GRAND CHINA ASSETS LIMITED
Room 1302 13/F Bank of East Asia Harbour View Centre, 56 Gloucester Road, Wanchai, China (Hong Kong)
Tel.: (852) 28150638   UK
Web Site: http://www.ebgca.com.hk
Year Founded: 2000
3699—(HKG)
Rev.: $7,342,499
Assets: $165,849,044
Liabilities: $30,322,609
Net Worth: $135,526,435
Earnings: $3,096,241
Emp.: 137
Fiscal Year-end: 12/31/22
Property Management Services
N.A.I.C.S.: 531190
Jia Liu (Chm & CEO)

EVERBRIGHT JIABAO CO., LTD.
14-15F Jiabao Building No 1-6 Lane 333 Yima Road, Jiading District, Shanghai, 201821, China
Tel.: (86) 2159524888
Web Site: http://www.jbjt.com
Year Founded: 2000
600622—(SHG)
Sales Range: $300-349.9 Million
Real Estate Development Services
N.A.I.C.S.: 531390
Hongfei Chen (Pres, Exec VP & Dir)

EVERBRITE TECHNOLOGY CO., LTD.
No 140 Lunping, Lunping Vil Guanyin Dist, Taoyuan, 328, Taiwan
Tel.: (886) 34982821
Web Site:
https://www.everbrite.com.tw
Year Founded: 1987
4523—(TPE)
Rev.: $17,421,974
Assets: $46,104,556
Liabilities: $16,801,363

Net Worth: $29,303,192
Earnings: ($2,959,510)
Emp.: 62
Fiscal Year-end: 12/31/22
Electric Equipment Mfr
N.A.I.C.S.: 334419

EVERCHINA INT'L HOLDINGS COMPANY LIMITED
Unit 1506 15th Floor Capital Centre 151 Gloucester Road, Wanchai, China (Hong Kong)
Tel.: (852) 35887111   HK
Web Site:
https://www.everchina202.com.hk
0202—(HKG)
Rev.: $16,392,455
Assets: $404,443,231
Liabilities: $144,617,793
Net Worth: $259,825,438
Earnings: ($17,424,037)
Emp.: 153
Fiscal Year-end: 03/31/21
Holding Company
N.A.I.C.S.: 551112
Zhaobai Jiang (Chm)

EVERDISPLAY OPTRONICS SHANGHAI CO., LTD.
No 1568 Jiugong Road Jinshan Industrial Zone, Shanghai, 201506, China
Tel.: (86) 2160892866
Web Site: http://www.everdisplay.com
Year Founded: 2012
688538—(SHG)
Rev.: $588,399,763
Assets: $4,337,409,815
Liabilities: $2,118,380,458
Net Worth: $2,219,029,357
Earnings: ($224,891,611)
Fiscal Year-end: 12/31/22
Electronic Product Mfr & Distr
N.A.I.C.S.: 334419
Wenbiao Fu (Chm)

EVEREADY EAST AFRICA PLC
Sameer Industrial Park Mombasa Enterprise Road Junction, PO Box 44765, 00100, Nairobi, Kenya
Tel.: (254) 722205469
Web Site: https://eveready.co.ke
Year Founded: 1967
EVRD—(NAI)
Rev.: $127,763
Assets: $165,998
Liabilities: $837,346
Net Worth: ($671,348)
Earnings: ($332,649)
Emp.: 12
Fiscal Year-end: 09/30/23
Alkaline Batteries Mfr
N.A.I.C.S.: 335910
Margaret A. Odhiambo (CEO & Mng Dir)

EVEREADY INDUSTRIES INDIA LTD
2 Rainey Park, Kolkata, 700019, West Bengal, India
Tel.: (91) 3324864961
Web Site:
https://www.evereadyindia.com
531508—(NSE)
Rev.: $171,059,220
Assets: $138,741,507
Liabilities: $105,310,228
Net Worth: $33,431,280
Earnings: ($42,522,562)
Emp.: 2,179
Fiscal Year-end: 03/31/21
Battery, Lantern, Tea & Insect Repellant Mfr
N.A.I.C.S.: 335910
Suvamoy Saha (Mng Dir)

Subsidiaries:

Everfast Rechargeables Limited   **(1)**
Unit B 13Th Floor Success Industrial Building No 17 Sheung Hei Street, San Po Kong, Kowloon, China (Hong Kong)
Tel.: (852) 31523688
Web Site: http://www.everfast.com.hk
Sales Range: $50-74.9 Million
Emp.: 5
Rechargeable Batteries Distr
N.A.I.C.S.: 423610

Idea Power Limited   **(1)**
Room 1009 10/F Block A Hoi Luen Industrial Centre 55 Hoi Yuen Road, Kwun Tong, Kowloon, China (Hong Kong)
Tel.: (852) 27931191
Rechargeable Batteries Mfr & Distr
N.A.I.C.S.: 335910

Industrial - Uniross Batteries (PTY) Ltd.   **(1)**
18 Silverstone Crescent Kyalami Business Park, Kyalami, 1685, South Africa
Tel.: (27) 114661156
Web Site: http://www.uniross.co.za
Sales Range: $25-49.9 Million
Emp.: 20
Batteries Mfr
N.A.I.C.S.: 335910

Uniross SA   **(1)**
ZI de la Madeleine, 77185, Lognes, France
Tel.: (33) 160950040
Web Site: http://www.uniross.com
Electronic Device Battery & Battery Charger Designer, Mfr & Distr
N.A.I.C.S.: 335910

Subsidiary (US):

Uniross Batteries HK Ltd.   **(2)**
10 State St Ste 1c, Woburn, MA 01801-6820
Tel.: (914) 241-9510
Web Site: http://www.uniross.com
Electronic Device Battery & Battery Charger Mfr & Distr
N.A.I.C.S.: 335910

Subsidiary (Domestic):

Uniross Batteries SAS   **(2)**
Zone Industrielle De La Madeleine 27 Rue De La Maison Rouge, Seine Et Marne, Lognes, France
Tel.: (33) 160950040
Web Site: http://www.uniross.com
Rechargeable Batteries Mfr & Distr
N.A.I.C.S.: 335910
Christophe Gurtner (Gen Mgr)

Zhongshan Uniross Industry Co. Limited   **(1)**
39 Middle Industrial Main Road Xiaolan, 528415, Zhongshan, Guangdong, China
Tel.: (86) 76022139808
Web Site: http://www.forseepower.com
Emp.: 200
Rechargeable Batteries Mfr
N.A.I.C.S.: 335910
Fredric Poupeau (Gen Mgr)

EVEREST BANK LIMITED
EBL House Lazimpat, PO Box 13384, Kathmandu, Nepal
Tel.: (977) 14443377   NP
Web Site:
https://www.everestbankltd.com
EBL—(NEP)
Rev.: $117,371,549
Assets: $1,556,045,025
Liabilities: $1,399,304,858
Net Worth: $156,740,168
Earnings: $21,161,610
Emp.: 868
Fiscal Year-end: 07/15/20
Investment Banking Services
N.A.I.C.S.: 523150
Ashutosh Sharma (Asst Gen Mgr)

EVEREST FINANCIAL GROUP LIMITED
Level 35 AMP Centre 50 Bridge St, Sydney, 2000, NSW, Australia

Everest Financial Group Limited—(Continued)

Tel.: (61) 280019100
Web Site: http://www.everest.com.au
Sales Range: $1-9.9 Million
Investment Services
N.A.I.C.S.: 523940
Michael Sutherland (Sec & Gen counsel)

EVEREST GROUP, LTD.

Seon Place-4th Floor 141 Front Street, PO Box HM 845, Hamilton, HM 19, Bermuda
Tel.: (441) 2050006   BM
Web Site:
https://www.everestglobal.com
Year Founded: 1999
EG—(NYSE)
Rev.: $14,587,000,000
Assets: $49,399,000,000
Liabilities: $36,197,000,000
Net Worth: $13,202,000,000
Earnings: $2,517,000,000
Emp.: 2,844
Fiscal Year-end: 12/31/23
Insurance Holding Company
N.A.I.C.S.: 524113
Glen Browne (Head-Accident & Health-Global)

Subsidiaries:

Everest Advisors (UK), Ltd.   (1)
40 Lime Street, London, EC3M 5BS, United Kingdom
Tel.: (44) 2074504282
Sales Range: $50-74.9 Million
Emp.: 30
Direct Property & Casualty Insurance Services
N.A.I.C.S.: 524126
Paul Tester (Chief Underwriting Officer)

Everest Global Services, Inc.   (1)
477 Martinsville Rd, Liberty Corner, NJ 07938-0830
Tel.: (908) 604-3000
Web Site: http://www.everestre.com
Emp.: 500
Direct Property & Casualty Insurance Services
N.A.I.C.S.: 524126
Dawn Lauer (Chief Comm Officer)

Subsidiary (Domestic):

Everest Indemnity Insurance Company   (2)
477 Martinsville Rd, Liberty Corner, NJ 07938   (100%)
Tel.: (908) 604-3000
Web Site: http://www.everestre.com
Sales Range: $150-199.9 Million
Emp.: 450
Provider of Excess & Surplus Lines Insurance Products
N.A.I.C.S.: 524210

Everest National Insurance Company   (2)
477 Martinsville Rd, Liberty Corner, NJ 07938-0830   (100%)
Tel.: (908) 604-3000
Web Site: http://www.everestnational.com
Sales Range: $100-124.9 Million
Emp.: 500
Property & Casualty Insurance Services
N.A.I.C.S.: 524126
Michael Mulray (Chief Underwriting Officer)

Subsidiary (Non-US):

Everest Reinsurance Company   (2)
The Exchange Tower 130 King Street West Suite 2520, PO Box 431, Toronto, M5X 1E3, ON, Canada   (100%)
Tel.: (416) 862-1228
Web Site: http://www.everestre.com
Sales Range: $100-124.9 Million
Emp.: 25
Provider of Property & Casualty Insurance Products
N.A.I.C.S.: 524126

Subsidiary (Domestic):

Everest Reinsurance Company   (2)

100 Everest Way, Warren, NJ 07059   (100%)
Tel.: (908) 604-3000
Web Site: http://www.everestnational.com
Sales Range: $150-199.9 Million
Emp.: 300
Provider of Property & Casualty Insurance & Reinsurance Products
N.A.I.C.S.: 524126

Subsidiary (Domestic):

Everest Denali Insurance Company   (3)
477 Martinsville Rd, Liberty Corner, NJ 07038
Tel.: (908) 604-3000
Fire Insurance Services
N.A.I.C.S.: 524130

Everest National   (3)
300 Vestavia Pkwy Ste 2305, Birmingham, AL 35216   (100%)
Tel.: (205) 795-2070
Web Site: http://www.everestnational.com
Sales Range: $25-49.9 Million
Emp.: 3
Workers Compensation
N.A.I.C.S.: 541611

Subsidiary (Non-US):

Everest Reinsurance Company - Escritorio de Representa cao No Brasil Ltda.   (3)
Av Rio Branco 1 - CJ 1501, Centro, Rio de Janeiro, 20090-907, Brazil
Tel.: (55) 21 2213 0966
Direct Property & Casualty Insurance Services
N.A.I.C.S.: 524126

Subsidiary (Domestic):

Everest Security Insurance Company   (2)
2580 Westside Pkwy Ste 10, Alpharetta, GA 30004-8947   (100%)
Tel.: (678) 942-2300
Web Site: http://www.esicinsurance.com
Sales Range: $25-49.9 Million
Emp.: 35
Direct Property & Casualty Insurance Services
N.A.I.C.S.: 524126

Mt. McKinley Managers, LLC   (2)
477 Martinsville Rd, Liberty Corner, NJ 07938   (99%)
Tel.: (908) 604-3000
Web Site: http://www.everestre.com
Sales Range: $150-199.9 Million
Emp.: 450
Insurance Policy Management Services
N.A.I.C.S.: 524210

Everest Insurance (Ireland), Designated Activity Company   (1)
3rd Floor Huguenot House, 35-38 St Stephen s Green, Dublin, Ireland
Tel.: (353) 14180300
Reinsurance Company Services
N.A.I.C.S.: 524130

Everest Insurance (Ireland), dac   (1)
3rd Floor Huguenot House 35-38 St Stephen s Green, 2, Dublin, D02 NY63, Ireland
Tel.: (353) 14180300
N.A.I.C.S.: 524210

Everest Insurance Company of Canada   (1)
The Exchange Tower 130 King Street West Suite 2620, Toronto, M5X 1C7, ON, Canada
Tel.: (416) 487-3900
Web Site: http://www.everestre.com
Property & Casualty Insurance Services
N.A.I.C.S.: 524126
Darin Scanzano (CEO)

Everest Reinsurance (Bermuda), Ltd.   (1)
Seon Place 4th Floor 141 Front Street, PO Box HM 845, 45 Reid Street 2nd Floor, Hamilton, HM 19, Bermuda   (100%)
Tel.: (441) 2950006
Web Site: https://www.everestglobal.com
Property & Casualty Insurance & Reinsurance Products
N.A.I.C.S.: 524126

Cindy Hooper (Assoc VP)

Everest Reinsurance Company (Ireland), Limited   (1)
3rd Fl Huguenot House 35-38 St, Stephen's Green, Dublin, 2, Ireland
Tel.: (353) 14180300
Emp.: 7
Direct Property & Casualty Insurance Services
N.A.I.C.S.: 524126
Nigel Smith (Gen Mgr)

Everest Reinsurance Holdings, Inc.   (1)
100 Everest Way, Warren, NJ 07059   (100%)
Tel.: (908) 604-3000
Web Site: https://www.everestregroup.com
Rev.: $7,526,000,000
Assets: $27,957,000,000
Liabilities: $22,303,000,000
Net Worth: $5,654,000,000
Earnings: ($445,000,000)
Emp.: 1,933
Fiscal Year-end: 12/31/2022
Reinsurance Services; Holding Company
N.A.I.C.S.: 551112

Subsidiary (Domestic):

Everest Specialty Underwriters, LLC   (2)
461 5th Ave 20th FL, New York, NY 10017-6234
Tel.: (646) 746-1990
Direct Property & Casualty Insurance Services
N.A.I.C.S.: 524126
John Iannotti (Sr VP)

Specialty Insurance Group, Inc.   (2)
111 Congressional Blvd Ste 220, Carmel, IN 46032
Tel.: (317) 853-7050
Web Site:
http://www.specialtyinsurancegroup.com
Emp.: 30
Insurance Management Services
N.A.I.C.S.: 524298
Lowery Robinson (VP)

Subsidiary (Domestic):

SIG Sports, Leisure and Entertainment Risk Purchasing Group, LLC   (3)
111 Congressional Blvd Ste 220, Carmel, IN 46032-5661
Tel.: (317) 853-7050
Insurance Management Services
N.A.I.C.S.: 524298

Mt. Logan Management, Ltd.   (1)
1717 W 6th St Ste 380, Austin, TX 78703
Tel.: (512) 647-6060
Web Site: https://mountlogan.com
N.A.I.C.S.: 525910
Ted Goldthorpe (Chm)

Mt. Logan Re, Ltd.   (1)
Seon Place 4th Floor 141 Front Street, Hamilton, HM 19, Bermuda
Tel.: (441) 2990500
Web Site: https://www.mtloganre.bm
N.A.I.C.S.: 524210
John Modin (Pres)

EVEREST INDUSTRIES LTD

Gat No 152 Lakhmapur Taluka Dindori, Nashik, 422 202, Maharashtra, India
Tel.: (91) 2557250375
Web Site:
https://www.everestind.com
EVERESTIND—(NSE)
Rev.: $190,289,176
Assets: $144,466,167
Liabilities: $70,442,954
Net Worth: $74,023,213
Earnings: $6,017,630
Emp.: 1,420
Fiscal Year-end: 03/31/22
Industrial, Commercial & Residential Construction Requirements Provider
N.A.I.C.S.: 236220

Neeraj Kohli (Compliance Officer, Sec & Head-Legal)

EVEREST KANTO CYLINDER LIMITED

204 Raheja Centre Free Press Journal Marg 214 Nariman Point, Mumbai, 400 021, India
Tel.: (91) 2249268300
Web Site:
https://www.everestkanto.com
Year Founded: 1978
532684—(BOM)
Rev.: $153,460,644
Assets: $164,590,936
Liabilities: $44,755,326
Net Worth: $119,835,609
Earnings: $9,129,345
Emp.: 290
Fiscal Year-end: 03/31/23
Gas Cylinder Mfr
N.A.I.C.S.: 332420
Pushkar Khurana (Chm)

Subsidiaries:

CP Industries Holdings, Inc   (1)
2214 Walnut St, McKeesport, PA 15132-7054
Tel.: (412) 664-6604
Web Site: https://cp-industries.com
Sales Range: $50-74.9 Million
Emp.: 118
Ultra Large Seamless Cylinders Mfr
N.A.I.C.S.: 332313
Dave Treadwell (VP-Technology)

EKC International FZE   (1)
Plot No M 03130 Jebel Ali Free Zone, PO Box 61041, Dubai, United Arab Emirates
Tel.: (971) 48832796
Web Site: https://ekcuae.com
Industrial Gas Mfr
N.A.I.C.S.: 325120
Prem Kumar Khurana (Chm & Mgr Dir)

Medical Engineers (I) Pvt. Ltd.   (1)
B- 69/2, Wazirpur Industrial Area, New Delhi, 110052, India
Tel.: (91) 8048737799
Web Site: http://www.medicalengineers.org
Medical Equipment Supplier
N.A.I.C.S.: 423450

EVEREST ORGANICS LIMITED

Plot No 127 128 Kavuri Hills Lakeview Plaza Lakeview Plaza 1st Floor, Amar Co - OP Society Madhapur, Hyderabad, 500033, India
Tel.: (91) 40040783   In
Web Site:
https://www.everestorganicsltd.com
Year Founded: 1993
524790—(BOM)
Rev.: $24,928,794
Assets: $18,479,097
Liabilities: $12,121,529
Net Worth: $6,357,569
Earnings: $1,872,092
Emp.: 417
Fiscal Year-end: 03/31/21
Pharmaceuticals Product Mfr
N.A.I.C.S.: 325412
K. Ramakrishnam Raju (Chm)

Subsidiaries:

Everest Organics Limited Medak Factory   (1)
Aroor Village Sadashivpet Mandal, Medak District, Medak, Andhra Pradesh, India
Tel.: (91) 8455250113
Pharmaceuticals Product Mfr
N.A.I.C.S.: 325412

EVEREST TEXTILE CO., LTD.

No 256 Minghe Vil, Shanshang Dist, T'ainan, 74342, Taiwan
Tel.: (886) 65782561
Web Site:
https://www.everest.com.tw
Year Founded: 1988

1460—(TAI)
Rev.: $256,340,682
Assets: $403,750,042
Liabilities: $211,859,896
Net Worth: $191,890,146
Earnings: ($39,634,126)
Emp.: 2,365
Fiscal Year-end: 12/31/23
Textile Fabric Mfr
N.A.I.C.S.: 313210
Johnny Shih (Chm)

Subsidiaries:

Everest Textile (HK) Co. Ltd. **(1)**
Room 3006 Laws Commercial Plaza 788
Cheung Sha Wan Road, Cheung Sha Wan,
Kowloon, China (Hong Kong)
Tel.: (852) 023081938
Sales Range: $25-49.9 Million
Emp.: 1
Woven Fabrics Mfr
N.A.I.C.S.: 313220
Carol Chang (Mgr)

Everest Textile (Shanghai), Ltd. **(1)**
31F Bao An Tower No 800 Dongfang Road,
Pudong New Area, Shanghai, 200122,
China
Tel.: (86) 2168751111
Emp.: 517
Fabric Mfr & Distr
N.A.I.C.S.: 313310

Everest Textile Co., Ltd. - Shanghai
Factory **(1)**
No 197 Baisha Road Xinghuo Development
Zone, Fengxian, Shanghai, 201419, China
Tel.: (86) 2157502111
Garments Mfr
N.A.I.C.S.: 315250

Everest Textile Co., Ltd. - Thailand
Factory **(1)**
49 Moo 1 Taladnadwadsoita Road Ban
Muang Subdistrict, Banpong District, Ratch-
aburi, 70110, Thailand
Tel.: (66) 32 354070
Nylon Fabrics Mfr
N.A.I.C.S.: 315120

Everest Textile USA, LLC **(1)**
1331 W Main St, Forest City, NC 28043
Tel.: (828) 245-6755
Yarn Texturizing Mfr
N.A.I.C.S.: 313110

EVERFOCUS ELECTRONICS CO., LTD.
No 134 Ln 235 Baoqiao Rd, Xindian
Dist, New Taipei City, Taiwan
Tel.: (886) 226622338
Web Site: https://www.everfocus.com
5484—(TAI)
Rev.: $12,085,254
Assets: $29,783,739
Liabilities: $10,399,751
Net Worth: $19,383,988
Earnings: ($1,601,655)
Emp.: 615
Fiscal Year-end: 12/31/23
Closed Circuit Camera Mfr
N.A.I.C.S.: 334511

Subsidiaries:

EverFocus Electronics (Beijing) Co.,
Ltd. **(1)**
Room 609 Kemao Mansion Shangdi Xinxi
Road, Haidian District, Beijing, 100085,
China
Tel.: (86) 1062973336
Electronic Products Mfr
N.A.I.C.S.: 334419

EverFocus Electronics AG **(1)**
Albert Einstein Street 1, 46446, Emmerich
am Rhein, Nordrhein-Westfalen, Germany
Tel.: (49) 282293940
Web Site: http://www.everfocus.de
Sales Range: $25-49.9 Million
Emp.: 21
Surveillance Systems Mfr
N.A.I.C.S.: 334511
Detlef Schreiber (Reg Dir-Sls)

EverFocus Electronics Corp. **(1)**
324 W Blueridge Ave, Orange, CA 92865
Tel.: (626) 844-8888
Web Site: http://www.everfocus.com
Sales Range: $25-49.9 Million
Emp.: 45
Surveillance Systems Mfr
N.A.I.C.S.: 334419

EverFocus Japan Corp. **(1)**
4th floor 2-19-9 Iwamotocho, Chiyoda-ku
Tokyo maruei Building, Tokyo, 130-0022,
Japan
Tel.: (81) 358218579
Web Site: http://www.everfocus.co.jp
Sales Range: $25-49.9 Million
Emp.: 7
Surveillance Equipment Mfr & Sales
N.A.I.C.S.: 334511

Everfocus Electronics (India) Private
Ltd. **(1)**
Suite 803 8th Floor Housefin Bhavan C 21
Bandra Kurla Complex, Bandra, Mumbai,
400 051, India
Tel.: (91) 2261288700
Web Site: http://www.everfocus.in
Sales Range: $25-49.9 Million
Emp.: 12
Surveillance Systems Mfr
N.A.I.C.S.: 334511

EVERFUEL A/S
Ost Hogildvej 4A, 7400, Herning,
Denmark
Tel.: (45) 53666999
Web Site: https://www.everfuel.com
Year Founded: 2019
EFUEL—(OSL)
Rev.: $6,678,178
Assets: $119,998,921
Liabilities: $44,142,025
Net Worth: $75,856,896
Earnings: ($29,820,850)
Emp.: 67
Fiscal Year-end: 12/31/23
Hydrogen Fuel Mfr
N.A.I.C.S.: 325120
Jeppe Hjuler Mikkelsen (COO)

EVERGENT INVESTMENTS SA
Bacau street Pictor AmanAman
Street 94 C, 600164, Bacau, Roma-
nia
Tel.: (40) 234576740
Web Site: https://www.evergent.ro
SIF2—(BUC)
Rev.: $19,060,392
Assets: $971,045,079
Liabilities: $501,899,788
Net Worth: $469,145,290
Earnings: ($4,924,345)
Emp.: 34
Fiscal Year-end: 12/31/20
Financial Services
N.A.I.C.S.: 523940
Claudiu Liviu Doros (CEO)

EVERGOLD CORP.
110 Yonge St Suite 1601, Toronto,
M5C 1T4, ON, Canada
Tel.: (613) 622-1916
Web Site:
    https://www.evergoldcorp.ca
EVER—(MUN)
Assets: $574,997
Liabilities: $30,952
Net Worth: $544,044
Earnings: ($1,518,936)
Fiscal Year-end: 12/31/22
Mineral Exploration Services
N.A.I.C.S.: 213115
Andrew J. Mitchell (VP-Exploration)

EVERGRANDE PROPERTY SERVICES GROUP LIMITED
9th Floor Evergrande Center No 78
Huangpu Avenue West, Tianhe District, Guangzhou, 510660, Guangdong, China

Tel.: (86) 2089183923 **Ky**
Web Site:
    https://www.evergrandeservice.com
Year Founded: 1997
6666—(HKG)
Rev.: $1,635,076,429
Assets: $989,667,008
Liabilities: $1,199,121,622
Net Worth: ($209,454,613)
Earnings: $204,720,591
Emp.: 72,076
Fiscal Year-end: 12/31/22
Asset Management Services
N.A.I.C.S.: 529999
Changlong Zhao (Exec Dir)

EVERGREEN BAMBOO INTER-NATIONAL LIMITED
1/F Winner Mansion 691A Nathan
Road, Mong Kok, Kowloon, China
(Hong Kong)
Tel.: (852) 35829570
Web Site:
    http://www.evergreenbamboointl.com
Nutraceutical Product Mfr
N.A.I.C.S.: 325411
Hong Hua Liu (Chm)

EVERGREEN CORPORATION
15-04 The Pinnacle Persiaran La-
goon Bandar Sunway, Petaling Jaya,
Selangor, Malaysia
Tel.: (60) 376102988 **Ky**
Year Founded: 2021
EVGR—(NASDAQ)
Investment Holding Company
N.A.I.C.S.: 551112
Liew Choon Lian (CEO & Chm)

EVERGREEN FIBREBOARD BERHAD
PLO 22 Parit Raja Industrial Estate,
Parit Raja, 80400, Batu Pahat, Johor,
Malaysia
Tel.: (60) 74541933
Web Site:
    https://evergreengroup.com.my
EVERGRN—(KLS)
Rev.: $233,372,745
Assets: $278,024,405
Liabilities: $63,819,736
Net Worth: $214,204,670
Earnings: ($5,520,167)
Emp.: 2,056
Fiscal Year-end: 12/31/22
Wooden Furniture Mfr
N.A.I.C.S.: 321999
Mary Henerietta Kim Neo Lim (Exec
Dir)

Subsidiaries:

Allgreen Timber Products Sdn.
Bhd. **(1)**
Plot 202 Segamat Industrial Area II, 85000,
Segamat, Johor, Malaysia
Tel.: (60) 79279933
Sales Range: $50-74.9 Million
Emp.: 200
Particleboard Mfr
N.A.I.C.S.: 339999

Evergreen Adhesive & Chemicals
Sdn. Bhd. **(1)**
Plo 3 Parit Raja Industrial Estate Parit Raja,
86400, Batu Pahat, Johor, Malaysia
Tel.: (60) 74543122
Web Site:
    http://www.evergreengroup.com.my
Sales Range: $25-49.9 Million
Emp.: 15
Adhesive Mfr
N.A.I.C.S.: 325520

Evergreen Fibreboard (JB) Sdn.
Bhd. **(1)**
Plo 416 Jalan Suasa Kawasan Perindus-
trian Pasir Gudang, 81700, Pasir Gudang,
Johor, Malaysia
Tel.: (60) 72513088

Sales Range: $50-74.9 Million
Emp.: 240
Fibreboard Mfr
N.A.I.C.S.: 339999
Zuhairi Ozir (Mgr)

Evergreen Fibreboard (Nilai) Sdn.
Bhd. **(1)**
Lot 5776 Nilai Industrial Estate, 71800,
Nilai, Negeri Sembilan, Malaysia
Tel.: (60) 67992355
Wood Products Mfr
N.A.I.C.S.: 321219

PT Hijau Lestari Raya
Fibreboard **(1)**
Desa Pematang Palas Kecamatan Banyua-
sin I, Palembang, South Sumatera, Indone-
sia
Tel.: (62) 7117082712
Web Site: http://www.hijaulestari.co.id
Sales Range: $50-74.9 Million
Emp.: 200
Fibreboard Mfr
N.A.I.C.S.: 339999

Siam Fibreboard Company
Limited **(1)**
417 / 112-113 Kanchanavanich Rd, Tumbol
Patong Amphur Haadyai, Songkhla, 90230,
T Patong, Thailand
Tel.: (66) 74291111
Web Site: http://www.siamfibreboard-
    sfm.com
Sales Range: $200-249.9 Million
Emp.: 600
Fibreboard Mfr
N.A.I.C.S.: 322211

EVERGREEN INTERNATIONAL HOLDINGS LIMITED
Room 1305-1307 13/F New East
Ocean Centre 9 Science Museum
Road, Tsim Sha Tsui East, Kowloon,
China (Hong Kong)
Tel.: (852) 27122288
Web Site: http://www.evergreen-
    intl.com
Rev.: $41,366,508
Assets: $179,554,760
Liabilities: $64,008,093
Net Worth: $115,546,667
Earnings: ($16,256,201)
Emp.: 400
Fiscal Year-end: 12/31/18
Menswear Clothing Stores
N.A.I.C.S.: 458110
Yuk Ming Chan (Chm)

EVERGREEN INTERNATIONAL STORAGE & TRANSPORT CORP.
899 Ching Kuo Rd, Taoyuan District,
Taoyuan, Taiwan
Tel.: (886) 33252060
Web Site: https://www.evergreen-
    eitc.com.tw
Year Founded: 1973
2607—(TAI)
Rev.: $536,121,305
Assets: $1,419,863,578
Liabilities: $377,726,857
Net Worth: $1,042,136,721
Earnings: $92,626,047
Emp.: 1,338
Fiscal Year-end: 12/31/23
Transport & Container Yard Services
N.A.I.C.S.: 488999
Yeh Chang (Sr VP-Occupational
Safety & Health Dept)

Subsidiaries:

Evergreen International Logistics
(HK) Ltd. **(1)**
Room1208 12/F Metroplaza Tower Two 223
Hing Fong Road, New Territories, Kwai
Chung, China (Hong Kong)
Tel.: (852) 28541215
Marine & Air Freight Forwarding Services
N.A.I.C.S.: 541614

Evergreen International Storage & Transport Corp.—(Continued)

Evergreen International Logistics (Korea) Co., Ltd. (1)
Unit 1508 Ace Hi-Tech City 3 Building 130 Seonyu-Ro, Yeongdeungpo-gu, Seoul, 07255, Korea (South)
Tel.: (82) 220680567
Marine & Air Freight Forwarding Services
N.A.I.C.S.: 541614

Evergreen Logistics (India) Private Ltd. (1)
Marathon Icon Unit No 708 Opp Peninsula Corporate Park Off, Ganapatrao Kadam Marg Lower Parel, Mumbai, 400013, Maharashtra, India
Tel.: (91) 2268758800
Marine & Air Freight Forwarding Services
N.A.I.C.S.: 541614

Evergreen Logistics Malaysia Sdn. Bhd. (1)
K03-10-05 Tower 3 Uoa Business Park No 1 Jalan Pengaturcara U1/51A, Seksyen U1, 40150, Shah Alam, Selangor, Malaysia
Tel.: (60) 355906777
Freight Forwarding Services
N.A.I.C.S.: 561910

Evergreen Logistics Philippines Corp. (1)
Unit 1814 Cityland Herrera Tower 98 V A Rufino Cor Valero Sts, Salcedo Village, Makati, 1200, Philippines
Tel.: (63) 28400551
Marine & Air Freight Forwarding Services
N.A.I.C.S.: 541614

Evergreen Logistics Vietnam Co., Ltd. (1)
6th Floor 311 Dien Bien Phu, Ward 4 District 3, Ho Chi Minh City, Vietnam
Tel.: (84) 2838181761
Marine & Air Freight Forwarding Services
N.A.I.C.S.: 541614

EVERGREEN LITHIUM LIMITED
Suite 205 9-11 Claremont St, South Yarra, 3141, VIC, Australia
Tel.: (61) 1300288664
Web Site: https://www.evergreenlithium.com
Year Founded: 2022
EG1—(ASX)
Rev.: $103,512
Assets: $11,280,576
Liabilities: $208,119
Net Worth: $11,072,457
Earnings: ($3,619,525)
Fiscal Year-end: 06/30/24
Support Activities for Nonmetallic Minerals (except Fuels) Mining
N.A.I.C.S.: 213115

EVERGREEN MARINE CORPORATION (TAIWAN) LTD.
1-4F No 166 Sec 2 Minsheng E Rd, Zhongshan Dist, Taipei, 104473, Taiwan
Tel.: (886) 225057766   TW
Web Site: https://www.evergreen-marine.com
Year Founded: 1968
2603—(TAI)
Rev.: $8,651,934,622
Assets: $22,881,867,179
Liabilities: $8,161,708,032
Net Worth: $14,720,159,147
Earnings: $1,249,904,668
Emp.: 3,121
Fiscal Year-end: 12/31/23
Transportation Services
N.A.I.C.S.: 488510
Cheng-Yung Chang (Chm)

Subsidiaries:

EVA Airways Corporation (1)
No 376 Sec 1 Hsin-Nan Rd, Luchu Dist, Taoyuan, Taiwan

Tel.: (886) 33515151
Web Site: https://www.evaair.com
Sales Range: $1-4.9 Billion
Emp.: 4,300
Air Transportation
N.A.I.C.S.: 481111
Tsai Ta-Wei (Officer-Fin & Exec VP-Fin Div)

Subsidiary (Domestic):

Evergreen Aviation Technologies Corp. (2)
6 Hang-Zhan S Rd, Tayuan, Tayouan, 337, Taiwan
Tel.: (886) 33519051
Web Site: http://www.egat.com.tw
Sales Range: $250-299.9 Million
Emp.: 3,500
Aircraft Upgrade & Maintenance Services
N.A.I.C.S.: 561990

Evergreen Agency (South Africa) (PTY) Ltd. (1)
No 9B Riley Road, Bedfordview, Johannesburg, 2007, Gauteng, South Africa
Tel.: (27) 112849000
Web Site: http://www.evergreen-shipping.co.za
Emp.: 50
Marine Shipping Services
N.A.I.C.S.: 483111

Evergreen Heavy Industrial Corp (M) Berhad (1)
Lot 139 Jalan Ceasir Phase 2 Free Trade Zone Johor Port Authority, Pasir Gudang, 81700, Johor, Malaysia
Tel.: (60) 72510432
Web Site: http://www.evergreen-heavy.com.my
Sales Range: $100-124.9 Million
Emp.: 400
Cargo Containers Mfr
N.A.I.C.S.: 339999
Zulkarnain Ali (Mgr-HR)

Evergreen Marine (Hong Kong) Limited (1)
22-23 Floor Harcourt House 39 Gloucester Road, Wanchai, China (Hong Kong)
Tel.: (852) 28258211
Shipping Transportation Services
N.A.I.C.S.: 488510

Subsidiary (Non-US):

Evergreeb Shipping Agency (Chile) SPA. (2)
Alcantara 200 Of 501, Las Condes, Santiago, Chile
Tel.: (56) 224286000
Shipping Transportation Services
N.A.I.C.S.: 488510

Evergreeb Shipping Agency (México) S.A. DE C.V. (2)
Av Benjamin Franklin 204 Col Escandon Del Miguel Hidalgo, Mexico, 11800, Mexico
Tel.: (52) 5550917547
Shipping Transportation Services
N.A.I.C.S.: 488510

Evergreen Shipping Agency (Colombia) S.A.S. (1)
Tel.: (57) 17954730
Shipping Transportation Services
N.A.I.C.S.: 488510

Evergreen Shipping Agency (Peru) S.A.C. (2)
Tel.: (51) 16168000
Shipping Transportation Services
N.A.I.C.S.: 488510

Evergreen Shipping Service (Cambodia) Co., Ltd. (2)
Tel.: (855) 23901278
Shipping Transportation Services
N.A.I.C.S.: 488510

Evergreen Marine Corp. (Malaysia) Sdn. Bhd. (1)
Tel.: (60) 378832600
Shipping Transportation Services
N.A.I.C.S.: 488510

Evergreen Shipping (Spain) S.L. (1)
Calle Siete Aguas 11 - Entlo, 46023, Valencia, Spain
Tel.: (34) 960451280

Web Site: https://www.shipmentlink.com
Sales Range: $25-49.9 Million
Emp.: 50
Marine Shipping Services
N.A.I.C.S.: 483111

Evergreen Shipping Agency (Australia) Pty. Ltd. (1)
Level 11 77 Pacific Highway, North Sydney, 2060, NSW, Australia
Tel.: (61) 299365700
Web Site: http://www.evergreen-line.com
Sales Range: $25-49.9 Million
Emp.: 20
Marine Shipping Services
N.A.I.C.S.: 483111

Evergreen Shipping Agency (Deutschland) GmbH (1)
Evergreen Building Amsinckstrasse 55, Hamburg, 20097, Germany
Tel.: (49) 40237080
Web Site: http://www.evergreen-shipping.de
Sales Range: $50-74.9 Million
Emp.: 130
Marine Shipping Services
N.A.I.C.S.: 483111

Evergreen Shipping Agency (India) Pvt. Ltd. (1)
Marathon Nextgen Innova A G-01 Opp Peninsula Corporate Park, Off Ganpatrao Kadam Marg Lower Parel West, Mumbai, 400013, Maharashtra, India
Tel.: (91) 2261657900
Shipping Transportation Services
N.A.I.C.S.: 488510

Evergreen Shipping Agency (Ireland) Ltd. (1)
22 Fitzwilliam Place, Dublin, D02 R820, Leinster, Ireland
Tel.: (353) 16612095
Web Site: http://www.evergreen-line.com
Sales Range: $25-49.9 Million
Emp.: 12
Marine Shipping Services
N.A.I.C.S.: 483111

Evergreen Shipping Agency (Italy) S.p.A. (1)
Scali Cerere 9, 57122, Livorno, Italy
Tel.: (39) 0586413111
Web Site: http://www.shipmentlink.com
Sales Range: $25-49.9 Million
Emp.: 60
Marine Shipping Services
N.A.I.C.S.: 483330

Evergreen Shipping Agency (Korea) Corporation (1)
12F 19 Saemunan-ro 5-Gil, Jongno-gu, Seoul, 03173, Korea (South)
Tel.: (82) 237021800
Shipping Transportation Services
N.A.I.C.S.: 488510

Evergreen Shipping Agency (Netherlands) B.V. (1)
Portcity II - Havennummer 2235 Waalhaven zz 19, Zuid Holland, Rotterdam, 3089 JH, Netherlands
Tel.: (31) 102311000
Web Site: http://www.evergreen-shipping.nl
Sales Range: $50-74.9 Million
Emp.: 120
Marine Shipping Services
N.A.I.C.S.: 483111

Evergreen Shipping Agency (Poland) SP. ZO. O (1)
Ul Chmielna 132/134, 00-805, Warsaw, Poland
Tel.: (48) 226562440
Web Site: http://www.shipmentlink.com
Sales Range: $25-49.9 Million
Emp.: 10
Marine Shipping Services
N.A.I.C.S.: 483111

Evergreen Shipping Agency (Russia) Ltd. (1)
3rd Floor Office 316-b No 1/25 Litera A Kazanskaya Street, Business Centre Atrium, 191186, Saint Petersburg, Russia
Tel.: (7) 8126102889
Web Site: http://www.evergreen-shipping.ru
Shipping Transportation Services
N.A.I.C.S.: 488510

Evergreen Shipping Agency (Singapore) PTE. Ltd. (1)
200 Cantonment Road No 12-01 Southpoint, Singapore, 089763, Singapore
Tel.: (65) 63477188
Web Site: http://www.evergreen-shipping.com.sg
Sales Range: $25-49.9 Million
Emp.: 100
Marine Shipping Services
N.A.I.C.S.: 488330

Evergreen Shipping Agency (Thailand) Co., Ltd. (1)
Green Tower 24-25th Floors 3656/81 Rama Iv Road Klongton, Klongton Klongtoey, Bangkok, 10110, Thailand
Tel.: (66) 22299999
Web Site: http://www.evergreen-shipping.co.th
Marine Shipping Services
N.A.I.C.S.: 488510

Evergreen Shipping Agency (UK) Limited (1)
Evergreen House 160 Euston Road, Greater London, London, NW1 2DX, United Kingdom
Tel.: (44) 2075598241
Web Site: https://www.evergreen-marine.co.uk
Sales Range: $25-49.9 Million
Emp.: 100
Marine Shipping Services
N.A.I.C.S.: 483111

Evergreen Shipping Agency (Vietnam) Corp. (1)
Floor 30th Pearl Plaza 561A Dien Bien Phu Street, Ward 25 Binh Thanh District, Ho Chi Minh City, Vietnam
Tel.: (84) 2835121888
Web Site: https://www.shipmentlink.com
Marine Shipping Services
N.A.I.C.S.: 483111

Evergreen Shipping Agency France S.A. (1)
Tour W 102 Terrasse Boieldieu, Puteaux Hauts-De-Seine, 92800, Paris, France
Tel.: (33) 158580231
Web Site: http://www.evergreen-line.com
Sales Range: $25-49.9 Million
Emp.: 90
Marine Shipping Services
N.A.I.C.S.: 483111

Evergreen Shipping Agency Philippines Corporation (1)
6th Flr BDO Equitable Bank Tower Condominium 8751 Paseo De Roxas St, Makati, Philippines
Tel.: (63) 288860258
Web Site: https://www.evergreen-shipping.com.ph
Cargo Transportation Services
N.A.I.C.S.: 811310

Hemlock Equipment LLC (1)
Pierce County Terminal, Tacoma, WA 98421
Tel.: (253) 896-0189
Construction Equipment Rental Services
N.A.I.C.S.: 238910

P.T. Evergreen Shipping Agency Indonesia (1)
Mega Plaza Building 9th Floors Jl H R Rasuna Said Kav C-3, Jakarta, 12920, Indonesia
Tel.: (62) 215212310
Web Site: http://www.evergreen-line.com
Sales Range: $25-49.9 Million
Emp.: 35
Marine Shipping Services
N.A.I.C.S.: 488330

P.T. Multi Bina Pura International (1)
Jl Raya Cakung Cilincing Km 4 Jakarta Utara, Jakarta, 14260, Indonesia
Tel.: (62) 214406403
Web Site: http://www.mbpi.co.id
Warehousing & Freight Forwarding Services
N.A.I.C.S.: 488510

P.T. Multi Bina Transport (1)
Jl Raya Cakung Cilincing Km 4 Jakarta Utara, Jakarta, 14260, Indonesia
Tel.: (62) 214406405
Freight Forwarding Services

N.A.I.C.S.: 488510

Shenzhen Greentrans Transportation Co., Ltd. (1)
Sanjiaolong Warehouse & Storage Zone Fukang Road, Henggang Town, Shenzhen, 518115, Guangdong, China
Tel.: (86) 75528863245
Freight Forwarding Services
N.A.I.C.S.: 488510

Taiwan Terminal Service Corporation Ltd. (1)
10 Chi Chin 1st Road, Kaohsiung, Taiwan
Tel.: (886) 75718963
Marine Shipping Services
N.A.I.C.S.: 488330

EVERGREEN PRODUCTS GROUP LIMITED
11/F Chiap Luen Industrial Building No 30-32 Kung Yip Street, Kwai Chung, NT, China (Hong Kong)
Tel.: (852) 24275899   Ky
Web Site: https://www.epfhk.com
Year Founded: 1962
1962—(HKG)
Rev.: $140,297,813
Assets: $200,248,058
Liabilities: $87,016,838
Net Worth: $113,231,220
Earnings: $7,434,270
Emp.: 25,536
Fiscal Year-end: 12/31/22
Hair Product Mfr & Distr
N.A.I.C.S.: 339999
Felix Yoe Chong Chang *(Chm, CEO & Exec Dir)*

EVERJOY HEALTH GROUP CO., LTD.
No 1288 Hengnan Road, Minhang District, Shanghai, China
Tel.: (86) 2154339779
Web Site:
  https://www.everjoyhealth.com
Year Founded: 1993
002162—(SSE)
Rev.: $163,233,252
Assets: $349,645,140
Liabilities: $206,854,128
Net Worth: $142,791,012
Earnings: ($39,090,168)
Emp.: 857
Fiscal Year-end: 12/31/22
Holding Company
N.A.I.C.S.: 551112
Li Cixiong *(Chm)*

EVERLANCE CO., LTD.
19/F No 460 Section 4 Hsini Road, Taipei, Hsien, Taiwan
Tel.: (886) 277182918
Rev.: $17,353,474
Assets: $43,316,072
Liabilities: $33,654,187
Net Worth: $9,661,885
Earnings: ($606,314)
Fiscal Year-end: 12/31/19
Trolley System Product Mfr
N.A.I.C.S.: 333922
Yuan-Chi Chao *(Chm & Pres)*

EVERLAND PUBLIC COMPANY LIMITED
223/96 Country Complex Building A 21st Floor Sanphawut Road Bangna, Bangna Tai, Bangkok, 10260, Thailand
Tel.: (66) 23616156   TH
Web Site: https://www.everland.co.th
Year Founded: 1988
EVER—(THA)
Rev.: $48,387,837
Assets: $193,429,801
Liabilities: $127,092,952
Net Worth: $66,336,850
Earnings: ($9,931,920)

Emp.: 620
Fiscal Year-end: 12/31/23
Real Estate Development Services
N.A.I.C.S.: 531390
Kamtorn Udomritthiruj *(VP)*

EVERLIGHT CHEMICAL INDUSTRIAL CO.
5 6F No 77 Sec 2 Dun Hua S Rd, Taipei, 106, Taiwan
Tel.: (886) 227066006
Web Site: https://www.ecic.com.tw
Year Founded: 1972
1711—(TAI)
Rev.: $257,085,703
Assets: $421,881,864
Liabilities: $138,815,881
Net Worth: $283,065,982
Earnings: $3,109,225
Emp.: 1,842
Fiscal Year-end: 12/31/23
Chemicals Mfr
N.A.I.C.S.: 325199
Chien-Hsin Chen *(Chm)*

Subsidiaries:

Anda Semiconductor Technology (Suzhou) Co., Ltd. (1)
D304-2 Science Park No 1355 Jing ji Lake avenue China-Singapore, Suzhou Industrial Park, Suzhou, 215021, China
Tel.: (86) 51262520666
Chemicals Mfr
N.A.I.C.S.: 325199

Elite Foreign Trading Inc. (1)
Mersin Serbest Bolgesi, Mersin, Turkiye
Tel.: (90) 3242377789
Web Site: http://www.eliteboya.com
Emp.: 20
Chemicals Mfr
N.A.I.C.S.: 325199
Ahmet Povan *(Mgr-Fin)*

Ethical (Qingdao) Ltd. (1)
Rm 1601 No 29 shandong Road Galaxy Building, Qingdao, China
Tel.: (86) 53285016051
Chemicals Mfr
N.A.I.C.S.: 325199

Ethical International Trading & Warehousing (Shanghai) Co., Ltd. (1)
Tel.: (86) 2162196954
Chemicals Mfr
N.A.I.C.S.: 325199

Ethical Trading Company (1)
4611 Dovetail Dr Unit 1, Madison, WI 53704
Tel.: (608) 467-6331
Chemicals Mfr
N.A.I.C.S.: 325199

Everlight (Suzhou) Advanced Chemicals Ltd. (1)
No 33 Ping Sheng Rd Suzhou Industrial Park, Suzhou, 215126, China
Tel.: (86) 51262871980
Chemicals Mfr
N.A.I.C.S.: 325199

Everlight Chemical Industrial Co. - Taoyuan 1st Plant (1)
No 271 Zhongshan N Rd Dayuan Dist, Taoyuan, 33759, Taiwan
Tel.: (886) 33868081
Chemicals Mfr
N.A.I.C.S.: 325199

Everlight Chemical Industrial Co. - Taoyuan 2nd Plant (1)
No 12 Gongye 3rd Rd Guanyin Dist, Taoyuan, 32853, Taiwan
Tel.: (886) 34838088
Chemicals Mfr
N.A.I.C.S.: 325199

Everlight Chemical Industrial Co. - Taoyuan 3rd Plant (1)
No 935 and 937 Sec 2 Chenggong Rd Guanyin Dist, Taoyuan, 32849, Taiwan
Tel.: (886) 34837682
Chemicals Mfr
N.A.I.C.S.: 325199

Everlight Chemical Industrial Co. - Taoyuan 4th Plant (1)
No 399 Datan N Rd Guanyin Dist, Taoyuan, 32841, Taiwan
Tel.: (886) 34737366
Chemicals Mfr
N.A.I.C.S.: 325199

Everlight Chemicals (Vietnam) Company Limited (1)
Unit 605 Floor 6 Me Linh Point Tower No 2 Ngo Duc Ke Street, Ben Nghe Ward District 1, Ho Chi Minh City, Vietnam
Tel.: (84) 2835202761
Chemical Product Mfr & Distr
N.A.I.C.S.: 325998

Everlight Europe B.V. (1)
Rivium Boulevard 224, 2909 LK, Capelle aan den IJssel, Netherlands
Tel.: (31) 102380099
Web Site: http://www.ecic.com
Emp.: 20
Chemicals Mfr
N.A.I.C.S.: 325199

Everlight Hong Kong Limited (1)
Rm 1704 17F Tower 2 Metroplaza No 223 Hing Fong Road, Kwai Chung, China (Hong Kong)
Tel.: (852) 226191095
Chemicals Mfr
N.A.I.C.S.: 325199

Everlight Pte. Ltd. (1)
Blk 12 North Bridge Road, Singapore, Singapore
Tel.: (65) 3 158 5444
Web Site: https://everlightpte.com
Chip Connector Distr
N.A.I.C.S.: 423690

Everlight USA, Inc. (1)
10507 Southern Loop Blvd, Pineville, NC 28134
Tel.: (704) 588-1004
Chemicals Mfr
N.A.I.C.S.: 325199

Guangzhou Ethical Trading Company (1)
Rm 409 Regal Business Center No 578 TianHe North Road, Guangzhou, 510630, China
Tel.: (86) 2038497030
Chemicals Mfr
N.A.I.C.S.: 325199

Trend Tone Imaging, Inc. (1)
No 3 Gungyedung 1st Road Hsinchu Science Park, Hsinchu, 30075, Taiwan
Tel.: (886) 35783620
Web Site: https://www.tti-toner.com
Chemicals Mfr
N.A.I.C.S.: 325199

EVERLIGHT ELECTRONICS CO., LTD.
No 6-8 Zhonghua Rd, Shulin Dist, Taipei, 23860, Taiwan
Tel.: (886) 226856688
Web Site: https://www.everlight.com
Year Founded: 1983
2393—(TAI)
Rev.: $583,584,268
Assets: $854,207,169
Liabilities: $235,945,248
Net Worth: $618,261,921
Earnings: $49,337,648
Emp.: 6,400
Fiscal Year-end: 12/31/23
Electronic Products Mfr
N.A.I.C.S.: 334413
Robert Yeh *(Founder, Chm, Pres & Gen Mgr)*

Subsidiaries:

E&E Components (HK) Limited (1)
Unit 613-613A 6F Ocean Centre 5 Canton Road, Tsim Tsa Tsui, Kowloon, China (Hong Kong)
Tel.: (852) 31889701
Web Site: http://www.everlight.com
Light Emitting Diode Distr
N.A.I.C.S.: 423690

Everlight Americas, Inc. (1)
3220 Commander Dr Ste 100, Carrollton, TX 75006
Tel.: (972) 490-4008
Web Site:
  https://www.everlightamericas.com
Sales Range: $25-49.9 Million
Emp.: 20
Lighting Fixture Distr
N.A.I.C.S.: 423610

Subsidiary (Non-US):

Everlight Canada, Inc. (2)
1011 Upper Middle Road, PO Box 86056, Oakville, L7L 0A0, ON, Canada
Tel.: (905) 315-5050
Lighting Fixture Distr
N.A.I.C.S.: 423610

Everlight Electronics (Europe) GmbH (1)
Siemensallee 84 Building 7302 5th floor, 76187, Karlsruhe, Germany
Tel.: (49) 721824473
Web Site: https://www.everlighteurope.com
Sales Range: $25-49.9 Million
Emp.: 30
Electronic Components Distr
N.A.I.C.S.: 449210

Everlight Electronics (Suzhou) Ltd. (1)
Binhe Rd 1388 X2 Creative Block A-608, Suzhou, Jiangsu, China
Tel.: (86) 51268021303
Light Emitting Diode Displays Mfr
N.A.I.C.S.: 334419

Everlight Intelligence Technology Co., Ltd. (1)
5F No 6-8 Zhonghua Rd, Shulin Dist, New Taipei City, 23860, Taiwan
Tel.: (886) 226856688
Web Site: https://www.everlightlighting.com
Light Emitting Diode Light Product Mfr & Distr
N.A.I.C.S.: 335131

Everlight Japan Corporation (1)
7F Mitsuiseimei Kyoto Yamashina Bldg 46-1 Takehanadounomaechou, Yamashina Ku, Kyoto, 607-8085, Japan
Tel.: (81) 755846070
Light Emitting Diode Distr
N.A.I.C.S.: 423690

Everlight Optoelectronics (M) Sdn Bhd (1)
B-04-20 Krystal Point 303 Jalan Sultan Azlan Shah, 11900, Penang, Malaysia
Tel.: (60) 46464233
Sales Range: $25-49.9 Million
Emp.: 2
Electronic Components Distr
N.A.I.C.S.: 449210

Evervision Electronics Co., Ltd. (1)
No 6-8 Zhonghua Rd, Shulin Dist, New Taipei City, Taiwan
Tel.: (886) 282272788
Web Site: https://www.evervisionlcd.com
Electronic Equipment Mfr & Distr
N.A.I.C.S.: 335314

Evlite Electronics Co., Ltd. (1)
Unit 1606-10 Prosperity Place 6 Shing Yip Street, Kwun Tong, Kowloon, China (Hong Kong)
Tel.: (852) 23880602
Web Site: https://en.everlight.com
Sales Range: $25-49.9 Million
Emp.: 50
Light Emitting Diode Components Distr
N.A.I.C.S.: 423690

Guangzhou Yi-Liang Trading Co., Ltd. (1)
No 708 No 88 LiWan North Road, Guangzhou, Guangdong, China
Tel.: (86) 2081947439
Electronic Components Distr
N.A.I.C.S.: 423690

Yi-Liang International Trade (Shanghai) Ltd. (1)
Rm 3F-A1 No 825 Zhao Jiao Babg Rd, Shanghai, 200030, China
Tel.: (86) 2164036237
Electronic Components Distr

Everlight Electronics Co., Ltd.—(Continued)

N.A.I.C.S.: 423690

Zenaro Lighting GmbH (1)
Carl-Friedrich-Gauss-Str 64, 47475, Kamp-Lintfort, Nordrhein-Westfalen, Germany
Tel.: (49) 2842908110
Web Site: http://www.zenarolighting.com
Lighting Fixtures Mfr & Distr
N.A.I.C.S.: 335131

EVERLON FINANCIALS LTD.
67 Regent Chambers Nariman Point, Mumbai, 400 021, India
Tel.: (91) 2222049233
Web Site: https://www.everlon.in
514358—(BOM)
Rev.: $4,664,245
Assets: $1,630,510
Liabilities: $737,099
Net Worth: $893,411
Earnings: $11,325
Emp.: 40
Fiscal Year-end: 03/31/21
Textile Products Mfr
N.A.I.C.S.: 313310
Jitendra K. Vakharia (Mng Dir)

EVERMASTER GROUP BERHAD
Ste 11 05B Level 11 The Gardens S Tower, Mid Valley City Lingkaran Syed Putra, 59200, Kuala Lumpur, Malaysia
Tel.: (60) 322793080
Sales Range: $10-24.9 Million
Timber Plywood Mfr
N.A.I.C.S.: 321215
Ching Chi Tsai (Mng Dir)

EVERMORE CHEMICAL INDUSTRY CO., LTD.
No 7 Gongye S 2nd Road, Nant'ou, 54066, Taiwan
Tel.: (886) 492255356
Web Site: https://www.twemc.com
1735—(TAI)
Rev.: $77,422,804
Assets: $107,840,965
Liabilities: $58,864,415
Net Worth: $48,976,551
Earnings: $2,459,694
Emp.: 362
Fiscal Year-end: 12/31/23
Coagulated Polyurethane Resins Mfr
N.A.I.C.S.: 325211

Subsidiaries:

Chem-Mat Technologies Co., Ltd. (1)
Tel.: (886) 492260316
Web Site: http://www.chem-mat.com.tw
Emp.: 20
Footwear Mfr
N.A.I.C.S.: 316210
Sam Wu (Gen Mgr)

Giant Star Trading Co., Ltd. (1)
8F 3 No 540 Sec 3 Taiwan Blvd Xitun Dist, Taichung, 407, Taiwan
Tel.: (886) 424523357
Footwear Mfr
N.A.I.C.S.: 316210

Pou Chien Chemical Co., Ltd. (1)
Yueyuen Industrial Park Industrial District Huangjiang Town, Dongguan, GuangDong, China
Footwear Mfr
N.A.I.C.S.: 316210

Topco (Shanghai) Co., Ltd. (1)
Room 603 Huawen International Mansion No 999 Zhongshan West Road, Changning Dist, Shanghai, China
Tel.: (86) 2162296859
Footwear Mfr
N.A.I.C.S.: 316210

EVERONN EDUCATION LIMITED
Capital Towers Unit No 203 & 204 II Floor New Door Nos 6/13 & 6/14, High Road Dr MGR Salai, Chennai, 600 034, Tamil Nadu, India
Tel.: (91) 44 2826 5001
Web Site: http://www.everonn.com
Rev.: $4,254,159
Assets: $16,823,325
Liabilities: $158,301,965
Net Worth: ($141,478,640)
Earnings: ($121,974,338)
Emp.: 1,056
Fiscal Year-end: 03/31/16
Education & Training Services
N.A.I.C.S.: 611710
Himansu Sekhar Kabi (CFO)

EVERPIA JOINT STOCK COMPANY
Noi Tyuong Residential Complex Duong Xa, Gia Lam, Hanoi, Vietnam
Tel.: (84) 438276490
Web Site: https://www.everpia.vn
Year Founded: 1993
EVE—(HOSE)
Rev.: $102,167,501
Assets: $145,669,538
Liabilities: $42,885,417
Net Worth: $102,784,120
Earnings: $9,157,483
Emp.: 1,206
Fiscal Year-end: 12/31/22
Bedding & Padding Services
N.A.I.C.S.: 561990
Jae Eun Lee (Chm, CEO & Gen Dir)

Subsidiaries:

Everpia Joint Stock Company - Dong Nai Factory (1)
Lot No 16 Road 10 12 Giang Dien Industrial Zone Tam Phuoc Ward, Bien Hoa, Dong Nai, Vietnam
Tel.: (84) 618869161
Bedding & Padding Services
N.A.I.C.S.: 561990

Everpia Joint Stock Company - Hanoi Factory (1)
Noi Thuong Residential Area, Duong Xa Gia Lam, Hanoi, Vietnam
Tel.: (84) 2438276490
Bedding & Padding Services
N.A.I.C.S.: 561990

Everpia Korea JSC (1)
18-104 Samsung-ro Samsung Building, Kangnam-gu Samsung-dong, Seoul, Korea (South)
Tel.: (82) 1021719284
Web Site: http://www.everpia.com
Finance Services
N.A.I.C.S.: 522320

EVERSAFE RUBBER BERHAD
Lot 94 Portland Avenue, Tasek Industrial Estate, 31400, Ipoh, Perak, Malaysia
Tel.: (60) 52910599 MY
Web Site: https://www.eversafe.com.my
Year Founded: 2015
ESAFE—(KLS)
Rev.: $30,658,981
Assets: $27,694,917
Liabilities: $15,185,508
Net Worth: $12,509,410
Earnings: ($944,826)
Emp.: 211
Fiscal Year-end: 12/31/22
Holding Company
N.A.I.C.S.: 551112
Cheah-Siang Tee (CEO & Mng Dir)

Subsidiaries:

Eversafe Rubber Works Sdn Bhd (1)
Lot 93 Portland Avenue, Tasek Industrial Estate, 31400, Ipoh, Perak, Malaysia
Tel.: (60) 52910599
Web Site: https://www.eversafe.com.my

Rubber Products Mfr
N.A.I.C.S.: 326291

Olympic Retreads (M) Sdn Bhd (1)
6424 Jalan Permatang Pauh, Mak Mandin Industrial Estate, 13400, Butterworth, Penang, Malaysia
Tel.: (60) 43329206
Web Site:
https://www.olympicretreads.com.my
Tiles Mfr
N.A.I.C.S.: 326211

EVERSENDAI CORPORATION BERHAD
Level 5 Menara Mudajaya 12A Jalan PJU 7/3, Mutiara Damansara, 47810, Petaling Jaya, Selangor Darul Ehsan, Malaysia
Tel.: (60) 377103362
Web Site:
https://www.eversendai.com
Year Founded: 1984
SENDAI—(KLS)
Rev.: $275,559,818
Assets: $770,208,615
Liabilities: $583,612,425
Net Worth: $186,596,190
Earnings: ($34,422,300)
Emp.: 15,000
Fiscal Year-end: 12/31/20
Structural Steel Construction & Engineering Services
N.A.I.C.S.: 238120
A. K. Nathan Elumalay (Founder, Chm & Mng Dir-Grp)

Subsidiaries:

Eversendai Construction (S) Pte. Ltd. (1)
237 Alexandra Road 03-13 The Alexcier, Singapore, 159929, Singapore
Tel.: (65) 62270335
Power Plant Construction Services
N.A.I.C.S.: 237130

Eversendai Construction Pvt. Ltd. (1)
Plot No 1-2 The Lords Block-1 5th Floor Thiru-vi-ka Industrial Estate, Jawaharlal Nehru Road Ekkattuthangal Guindy, Chennai, 600 032, India
Tel.: (91) 4440701234
Power Plant Construction Services
N.A.I.C.S.: 237130

Eversendai Constructions (M) Sdn Bhd (1)
Lot 19956 Jalan Industri 3/6 Rawang Integrated Industrial Park, 48000, Rawang, Selangor, Malaysia
Tel.: (60) 360912575
Power Plant Construction Services
N.A.I.C.S.: 237130

Eversendai Engineering FZE (1)
Plot No 2E-04 05 09 10 Hamriyah Free Zone Establishment, PO Box 42531, Sharjah, United Arab Emirates
Tel.: (971) 42673738
Power Plant Construction Services
N.A.I.C.S.: 237130

Eversendai Engineering LLC (1)
29th Floor Vision Tower Al Khaleej Al Tejari Street 1, PO Box 29537, Business Bay, Dubai, United Arab Emirates
Tel.: (971) 44539881
Power Plant Construction Services
N.A.I.C.S.: 237130

Eversendai Engineering Qatar WLL (1)
Building No 190 Street No 8 Zone No 81 New Industrial Area, PO Box 35283, Doha, Qatar
Tel.: (974) 44114378
Power Plant Construction Services
N.A.I.C.S.: 237130

Eversendai Engineering Saudi LLC (1)
Al-Masif Area Al Iman Saudi Bin Aziz Bin Mohammed Road, PO Box 241763, Riyadh, 11692, Saudi Arabia

Tel.: (966) 14944891
Power Plant Construction Services
N.A.I.C.S.: 237130

Eversendai Offshore RMC FZE (1)
RAK Maritime City Free Zone, PO Box 65159, Ras al Khaimah, United Arab Emirates
Tel.: (971) 72689191
Power Plant Construction Services
N.A.I.C.S.: 237130

Eversendai Offshore Sdn Bhd (1)
Lot 19956 Jalan Industri 3/6 Rawang Integrated Industrial Park, Mutiara Damansara, 48000, Rawang, Selangor Darul Ehsan, Malaysia
Tel.: (60) 360912575
Power Plant Construction Services
N.A.I.C.S.: 237130

Eversendai S-Con Engineering Co. Ltd. (1)
Bina Puri Building Bangna Complex 6th Floor No11 Soi Bangna-Trad 25, Kwang/Khed Bangna, Bangkok, 10260, Thailand
Tel.: (66) 27278618
Power Plant Construction Services
N.A.I.C.S.: 237130

Eversendai S-Con Engineering Co. Ltd. - Sanamchaikhed Factory (1)
140 Moo 2 T Khuyaimee A Sanamchaikhed, Chachoengsao, 24160, Thailand
Tel.: (66) 38502707
Power Plant Construction Services
N.A.I.C.S.: 237130

EVERSET SA
11 Rue Mirabeau, FR-38000, Grenoble, France
Tel.: (33) 476840386
MLEVE—(EUR)
Sales Range: Less than $1 Million
Motor Cycle Distr
N.A.I.C.S.: 423110

EVERSHEDS LLP
1 Wood Street, London, EC2V 7WS, United Kingdom
Tel.: (44) 2079194500 UK
Web Site: http://www.eversheds-sutherland.com
Emp.: 930
Law firm
N.A.I.C.S.: 541110
Paul Worth (Partner)

Subsidiaries:

Eversheds Attorneys Ltd. (1)
Fabianinkatu 29 B, Helsinki, 00100, Finland
Tel.: (358) 10 684 1300
Web Site: http://www.eversheds.fi
Law firm
N.A.I.C.S.: 541110
Hanna-Maija Elo (Partner)

Eversheds Sutherland (US) LLP (1)
999 Peachtree St NE Ste 2300, Atlanta, GA 30309-3996
Tel.: (404) 853-8000
Web Site: https://www.eversheds-sutherland.com
Legal Advisory Services
N.A.I.C.S.: 541110
Peter J. Anderson (Partner)

EVERSHINE GROUP HOLDINGS LIMITED
16th Floor Henan Building No 90 and 92 Jaffe Road, Wanchai, China (Hong Kong)
Tel.: (852) 3896 0888 HK
Web Site:
http://www.evershinegroup.com.hk
Year Founded: 1997
Rev.: $441,474
Assets: $39,500,842
Liabilities: $29,140,723
Net Worth: $10,360,119
Earnings: ($11,952,531)
Emp.: 43

Fiscal Year-end: 12/31/19
Holding Company
N.A.I.C.S.: 551112
Alan Tat Chi Hung (Officer-Compliance)

Subsidiaries:

Color-Bridge Printing & Packaging Company Limited (1)
Unit No 03 On 11/F Railway Plaza 39 Chatham Road South, Kowloon, China (Hong Kong)
Tel.: (852) 29470648
Web Site: http://www.color-bridge.com
Printing Services
N.A.I.C.S.: 323111

Plant (Non-US):

Color-Bridge Printing & Packaging Company Limited - Dongguan Color-Bridge Printing & Paper Products Factory (2)
Huaxia Industrial District Qiaotou Town, Dongguan, Guangdong, China
Tel.: (86) 76983346808
Printing Services
N.A.I.C.S.: 323111

EVERSPRING INDUSTRY CO., LTD.
3F No 50 Sec 1 Zhonghua Rd, Tucheng Dist, New Taipei City, 23666, Taiwan
Tel.: (886) 222606868
Web Site: https://www.everspring.com
Year Founded: 1980
2390—(TAI)
Rev.: $21,201,608
Assets: $99,746,620
Liabilities: $15,658,523
Net Worth: $84,088,096
Earnings: ($2,632,068)
Emp.: 73
Fiscal Year-end: 12/31/23
Security System Device Mfr
N.A.I.C.S.: 561621
Nally Chang (Founder & Chm)

Subsidiaries:

Dong-Guan Li Yuan Electronics Co., Ltd. (1)
Xing City Industrial Zone Heng Li Town, Dongguan, 523477, Guangdong, China
Tel.: (86) 76983723988
Security Product Mfr
N.A.I.C.S.: 334290

Dongguan Found Chain IOT Co., Ltd. (1)
No 13 3rd Street Daxi First Road, Qiaotou Town, Dongguan, Guangdong, China
Tel.: (86) 76982367686
Electronic Computer Mfr
N.A.I.C.S.: 334111

Everspring Tech USA, Inc. (1)
3018 N Durfee Ave Unit E, El Monte, CA 91732
Tel.: (626) 698-1898
Electronic Computer Mfr
N.A.I.C.S.: 334111

Phase Electronics Ltd. (1)
Unit B1 Willow Drive Sherwood Business Park, Nottingham, NG15 0DP, United Kingdom
Tel.: (44) 1623758333
Security Product Mfr
N.A.I.C.S.: 334290

EVERSTONE CAPITAL ADVISORS PVT. LTD.
One Indiabulls Centre 16th Floor Tower 2A Senapati Bapat Marg, Elphinstone Road, Mumbai, 400013, India
Tel.: (91) 22 4043 6000
Web Site: http://www.everstonecapital.com
Year Founded: 2006
Rev.: $1,800,000,000
Emp.: 100
Privater Equity Firm
N.A.I.C.S.: 523999
Atul Kapur (Co-Founder & Chief Investment Officer)

Subsidiaries:

Everstone Capital Asia Pte. Ltd. (1)
250 North Bridge Road, 12-03 Raffles City Tower, Singapore, 179101, Singapore
Tel.: (65) 6511 6888
Web Site: http://www.everstonecapital.com
Privater Equity Firm
N.A.I.C.S.: 523999
Atul Kapur (Co-Founder & Mng Partner)

Subsidiary (Non-US):

IL&FS Environmental Infrastructure & Service Limited (2)
2nd & 3rd Floor MM Tower Plot no 8 & 9 Udyog Vihar, Udyog Vihar Phase - IV, Gurgaon, 122001, Haryana, India (97.5%)
Tel.: (91) 1244297200
Web Site: http://www.ilfsenv.com
Environmental Consulting Services
N.A.I.C.S.: 541620
Mahesh Babu (Mng Dir)

Everstone Capital Limited (1)
3rd Floor Raffles Tower 19 Cybercity, Ebene, Mauritius
Tel.: (230) 467 7986
Web Site: http://www.everstonecapital.com
Privater Equity Firm
N.A.I.C.S.: 523999

Harry's Holdings Ltd. (1)
77 High Street 07-09/11 High Street Plaza, Singapore, 179433, Singapore
Tel.: (65) 63370657
Web Site: http://www.harrys.com.sg
Sales Range: $25-49.9 Million
Bars, Restaurants, Night Clubs, Children's Play Centers, Hotel & Catering
N.A.I.C.S.: 722410

Subsidiary (Domestic):

Harry s Esplanade Pte. Ltd. (2)
8 Raffles Ave, 01-05 07 Esplanade Mal, Singapore, 179433, Singapore
Tel.: (65) 6334 0132
Web Site: http://www.harrys.com.sg
Restaurant Operating Services
N.A.I.C.S.: 722511
Kulwant Singh (Mgr-Area Ops)

Harry s International Pte. Ltd (2)
28 Boatquay, High Street Plaza, Singapore, 049818, Singapore
Tel.: (65) 6337 0657
Web Site: http://www.harrys.com.sg
Sales Range: $10-24.9 Million
Emp.: 40
Restaurant Operating Services
N.A.I.C.S.: 722511

EVERTECHNO CO., LTD.
139-1 Sandong-ri Eumbong-myun, Asan, Chungcheongnam-do, Korea (South)
Tel.: (82) 41 580 6600
Web Site: http://www.evertechno.co.kr
Year Founded: 2000
Electronic Components Mfr
N.A.I.C.S.: 334419
Back-Woon Jung (CEO)

EVERTEX FABRINOLOGY LIMITED
9 Rongan Rd, Luzhu Dist, Taoyuan, 33853, Taiwan
Tel.: (886) 225503266
Web Site: https://www.evertex.tw
Year Founded: 1986
1470—(TAI)
Rev.: $21,427,155
Assets: $37,448,084
Liabilities: $5,225,972
Net Worth: $32,222,112

Earnings: $1,613,722
Emp.: 72
Fiscal Year-end: 12/31/23
Fabrics Mfr
N.A.I.C.S.: 313240

EVERTON RESOURCES INC.
5460 Canotek Road Unit 99, Ottawa, K1J 9G9, ON, Canada
Tel.: (613) 241-2332   Ca
Web Site: https://www.evertonresources.com
EVR—(OTCIQ)
Rev.: $34
Assets: $748,507
Liabilities: $362,316
Net Worth: $386,191
Earnings: ($2,234,771)
Fiscal Year-end: 10/31/19
Gold & Other Metal Mining Services
N.A.I.C.S.: 212220
Andre D. Audet (Chm, Pres & CEO)

EVERTOP WIRE CABLE CORPORATION
1F NO 1 Lane 91 Sec 2 Ren-Ai Road, Chung Cheng Dist, Taipei, Taiwan
Tel.: (886) 223218855
Web Site: https://www.evertop.com
1616—(TAI)
Rev.: $134,559,562
Assets: $109,324,598
Liabilities: $47,891,754
Net Worth: $61,432,844
Earnings: $7,381,601
Fiscal Year-end: 12/31/23
Electronic Wire & Power Cords Mfr
N.A.I.C.S.: 332618

Subsidiaries:

Evertop Wire Cable Corporation - Chungli Plant (1)
No 32 Lane 363 Sec 2 Chung-Cheng Road, Chung-li, Taoyuan, 320, Taiwan
Tel.: (886) 34253111
Web Site: http://www.evertop.com
Cables & Power Cords Mfr
N.A.I.C.S.: 331420

EVERTRADE (PTY) LTD.
363 Rivonia Boulevard Euro Centre Building 1St Floor, Johannesburg, 2191, South Africa
Tel.: (27) 11 807 5345
Home Furnishings & Kitchenware Whslr & Distr
N.A.I.C.S.: 423220

EVERTZ MICROSYSTEMS LIMITED
5292 John Lucas Dr, Burlington, L7L 5Z9, ON, Canada
Tel.: (905) 335-3700   Ca
Web Site: https://www.evertz.com
Year Founded: 1966
ET—(TSX)
Rev.: $344,997,996
Assets: $329,323,452
Liabilities: $146,545,295
Net Worth: $182,778,157
Earnings: $56,853,764
Emp.: 1,767
Fiscal Year-end: 04/30/22
Video & Audio Equipment Design & Mfr
N.A.I.C.S.: 334310
Romolo Magarelli (Pres & CEO)

Subsidiaries:

Evertz Microsystems Ltd. (1)
5292 John Lucas Drive, Burlington, L7L 5Z9, ON, Canada (100%)
Tel.: (905) 335-3700
Web Site: http://www.evertz.com
Broadcasting & Communications Equipment Mfr
N.A.I.C.S.: 334310

Evertz UK Limited (1)
100 Berkshire Place Wharfedale Road, Winnersh, RG41 5RD, Berkshire, United Kingdom
Tel.: (44) 118 921 6800
Wireless Communication Equipment Mfr
N.A.I.C.S.: 334220

Quintech Electronics & Communications, Inc. (1)
250 Airport Rd, Indiana, PA 15701
Tel.: (724) 349-1412
Web Site: http://www.quintechelectronics.com
Radio & Television Broadcasting & Wireless Communications Equipment Mfr
N.A.I.C.S.: 334220

Studer Professional Audio GmbH (1)
Althardstrasse 30, Regensdorf, 8105, Switzerland (100%)
Tel.: (41) 448707511
Web Site: http://studer.evertz.com
Mixing Consoles & Routing Equipment Mfr
N.A.I.C.S.: 333120

Subsidiary (Non-US):

Soundcraft Canada (2)
2100 Onesime-Gagnon, Lachine, H8T 3M8, QC, Canada (100%)
Tel.: (514) 780-0808
Web Site: http://www.scmediacanada.com
Mixing Consols & Routing Equipment Mfr
N.A.I.C.S.: 334220
Debra Mullin (Mgr-Credit Dept)

Studer Deutschland GmbH (2)
Rudower Chaussee 3, D 12489, Berlin, Germany (100%)
Tel.: (49) 307239340
Web Site: http://www.studer.evertz.com
Mixing Consoles & Routing Equipment Mfr
N.A.I.C.S.: 334220

EVERYBODY LOVES LANGUAGES CORP.
151 Bloor Street West Suite 609, Toronto, M5S 1S4, ON, Canada
Tel.: (416) 927-7000
Web Site: http://www.lingomedia.com
LM—(OTCIQ)
Rev.: $1,644,395
Assets: $1,874,370
Liabilities: $413,831
Net Worth: $1,460,539
Earnings: $868,627
Emp.: 41
Fiscal Year-end: 12/31/20
Education Training Services
N.A.I.C.S.: 611710
Michael P. Kraft (Founder & Chm)

EVERYBOT, INC.
10th Floor of H Square B/D S Pangyoyeok-ro 231, Bundang-gu, Seongnam, 13494, Gyeonggi-do, Korea (South)
Tel.: (82) 7088010575
Web Site: https://everybot.global
270660—(KRS)
Rev.: $41,875,139
Assets: $68,622,727
Liabilities: $19,447,114
Net Worth: $49,175,613
Earnings: $5,490,034
Fiscal Year-end: 12/31/22
Industrial Machinery Mfr
N.A.I.C.S.: 333248

EVERYDAY NETWORK CO., LTD.
Xindong Rd Longchi St, Liuhe District, Nanjing, 210012, Jiangsu, China
Tel.: (86) 2583203503
Web Site: http://www.house365.com
Year Founded: 2006
300295—(CHIN)
Rev.: $26,728,048
Assets: $195,355,471
Liabilities: $17,981,418
Net Worth: $177,374,053

Everyday Network Co., Ltd.—(Continued)

Earnings: ($12,819,590)
Fiscal Year-end: 12/31/23
Real Estate Support Services
N.A.I.C.S.: 531390
Guanghui Hu (Chm)

EVERYDAY PEOPLE FINAN-CIAL CORP.

Suite 450 11150 Jasper Avenue, Edmonton, T5K 0C7, AB, Canada
Web Site:
https://overydaypoopIofinanoial.com
Year Founded: 2015
EPF—(TSX)
Financial Services
N.A.I.C.S.: 523999
Mayank Mahajan (CFO)

Subsidiaries:

BPO Collections Ltd.   (1)
Marina Quay, Dock Road, Ardrossan, Ayrshire, Scotland, KA22 8DA, United Kingdom
Tel.: (44) 0141375095
Web Site: https://www.bpocollections.co.uk
Credit Management
N.A.I.C.S.: 541618

EVERYMAN MEDIA GROUP PLC

Studio 4 2 Downshire Hill, Hampstead, London, NW3 1NR, United Kingdom
Tel.: (44) 2031450500
Web Site:
https://www.everymancinema.com
EMAN—(AIM)
Rev.: $99,491,290
Assets: $217,018,430
Liabilities: $158,612,724
Net Worth: $58,405,706
Earnings: ($4,423,125)
Emp.: 1,380
Fiscal Year-end: 12/29/22
Movie Theater Owner & Operator
N.A.I.C.S.: 512131
Paul Wise (Chm)

EVERYMATRIX LTD.

St Julians Business Centre Level 3 3 Triq Elija Zammit, Saint Julian's, STJ 3155, Malta
Tel.: (356) 27136414   Mt
Web Site:
http://www.everymatrix.com
Year Founded: 2008
Sales Range: $25-49.9 Million
Emp.: 400
Gaming Industry Software Publisher & Content Hosting Services
N.A.I.C.S.: 513210
Ebbe Groes (Co-Founder & CEO)

Subsidiaries:

Fantasma Games AB   (1)
Frejgatan 32, 113 26, Stockholm, Sweden
Tel.: (46) 766376831
Web Site: https://www.fantasmagames.com
Rev.: $4,707,260
Assets: $4,511,132
Liabilities: $1,520,507
Net Worth: $2,990,624
Earnings: $212,893
Emp.: 36
Fiscal Year-end: 12/31/2023
Software Development Services
N.A.I.C.S.: 541511

EVERYTHING FRESH LTD.

78 Marcus Garvey Dr, Kingston, 11, Jamaica
Tel.: (876) 7589030
Web Site:
https://www.everythingfreshja.com
Year Founded: 1996
EFRESH—(JAM)
Rev.: $20,577,105

Assets: $9,404,863
Liabilities: $6,403,008
Net Worth: $3,001,855
Earnings: $651,554
Emp.: 61
Fiscal Year-end: 12/31/23
Dairy Products Distr
N.A.I.C.S.: 424430
Courtney Lancelot Pullen (Founder & Mng Dir)

EVEXIA LIFECARE LIMITED

illage Tundav, Savli, Vadodara, 391775, Gujarat, India
Tel.: (91) 2652361100
Web Site:
https://www.evexialifecare.com
524444—(BOM)
Rev.: $24,710,431
Assets: $19,560,805
Liabilities: $8,689,140
Net Worth: $10,871,665
Earnings: $175,075
Emp.: 2
Fiscal Year-end: 03/31/21
Petroleum Lubricating Oil Mfr
N.A.I.C.S.: 324191
Jayesh Thakkar (Mng Dir)

EVGEN PHARMA PLC

Suite 24G13 - Block 24 Congleton Road, Alderley Park, Nether Alderley, SK10 4TG, United Kingdom
Tel.: (44) 1625315090
Web Site: https://www.evgen.com
EVG—(AIM)
Rev.: $32,585
Assets: $13,085,705
Liabilities: $558,023
Net Worth: $12,527,682
Earnings: ($3,706,576)
Emp.: 9
Fiscal Year-end: 03/31/22
Pharmaceuticals Mfr
N.A.I.C.S.: 325412
Richard Moulson (CFO)

EVIANA HEALTH CORPORATION, INC.

100 Richmond Street West Suite 414, Toronto, M5H 3K6, ON, Canada
Tel.: (416) 369-9993
Web Site: http://www.eviana.ca
Cannabis Pharmacist Product Distr
N.A.I.C.S.: 456110
Avram Adizes (CEO)

EVIATION AIRCRAFT LTD.

1 Ha'Ofeh Street, Tzoran-Kadima, 6092000, Israel
Tel.: (972) 8 913 7914   Il
Web Site: http://www.eviation.com
Year Founded: 1998
EVTNF—(OTCIQ)
Emp.: 9
Aircraft Mfr
N.A.I.C.S.: 336411
Omer Bar-Yohay (CEO)

EVIIVO LTD.

Commercial House Commercial Street, Sheffield, S1 2AT, United Kingdom
Tel.: (44) 20 8576 5600
Web Site: http://www.eviivo.com
Year Founded: 2004
Sales Range: $10-24.9 Million
Emp.: 80
Hospitality Industry Software Developer
N.A.I.C.S.: 513210
Michele Fitzpatrick (CEO)

EVINCE TEXTILES LTD.

Lotus Kamal Tower One Level 12 57 Joar Sahara C/A Nikunja-2, New Air-

port Road, Dhaka, 1229, Bangladesh
Tel.: (880) 28961552
Web Site:
https://www.evincetextiles.com
Year Founded: 1999
ETL—(CHT)
Rev.: $25,838,186
Assets: $52,095,758
Liabilities: $30,917,143
Net Worth: $21,178,615
Earnings: $128,952
Emp.: 1,500
Fiscal Year-end: 06/30/23
Textile & Apparel Mfr
N.A.I.C.S.: 313310
Abu Kawser Majumder (Mng Dir)

EVION GROUP NL

Suite 3 Ground Floor 28 Ord Street, West Perth, 6005, WA, Australia
Tel.: (61) 861589916   AU
Web Site: https://eviongroup.com
Year Founded: 2016
EVG—(ASX)
Rev.: $399,398
Assets: $6,529,442
Liabilities: $474,675
Net Worth: $6,054,766
Earnings: ($2,144,814)
Fiscal Year-end: 06/30/24
Support Activities for Metal Mining
N.A.I.C.S.: 213114
Thomas Revy (Mng Dir)

EVISO S.P.A.

Corso Luigi Einaudi 3, 12037, Saluzzo, CN, Italy
Tel.: (39) 017544648
Web Site: https://www.eviso.it
Year Founded: 2012
EVISO—(EUR)
Software Development Services
N.A.I.C.S.: 541511
Gianfranco Sorasio (Chm)

EVIXAR INC.

1F Matsui Bldg 1-17-22 Shinkawa, Chuo-ku, Tokyo, 104-0033, Japan
Tel.: (81) 355425855
Web Site: https://www.evixar.com
Year Founded: 2004
4257—(TKS)
Rev.: $1,070,590
Assets: $900,430
Liabilities: $1,722,870
Net Worth: ($822,440)
Earnings: ($900,430)
Fiscal Year-end: 12/31/23
Software Development Services
N.A.I.C.S.: 541511
Jun Takikawa (Pres & CEO)

EVLI PANKKI OYJ

Aleksanterinkatu 19 A 4th floor, PO Box 1081, 00101, Helsinki, Finland
Tel.: (358) 9476690
Web Site: https://www.evli.com
Year Founded: 1985
EVLI—(HEL)
Rev.: $108,892,726
Assets: $395,639,974
Liabilities: $240,880,639
Net Worth: $154,759,335
Earnings: $27,088,280
Emp.: 294
Fiscal Year-end: 12/31/22
Banking Services
N.A.I.C.S.: 522110
Henrik Andersin (Chm)

Subsidiaries:

Aurator Asset Management Ltd.   (1)
Aurakatu 8 3 Floor, PO Box 146, 20101, Turku, Finland
Tel.: (358) 265166630
Web Site: http://www.aurator.fi
Emp.: 7

Asset Management Services
N.A.I.C.S.: 523940
Mikko Paalijarvi (Sr Mgr-Portfolio)

Evli Awards Management Oy   (1)
Aleksanterinkatu 19a 4th Floor, 00100, Helsinki, Finland
Tel.: (358) 9476690
Web Site: http://www.eam.fi
Asset Management Services
N.A.I.C.S.: 523940
Pertti Helaniemi (Mng Dir)

Fellow Finance PLC   (1)
Pursimiehenkatu 4 A, 00150, Helsinki, Finland
Tel.: (358) 757568603
Web Site: https://www.fellowfinance.com
Rev.: $21,660,911
Assets: $337,622,491
Liabilities: $309,388,085
Net Worth: $28,234,405
Earnings: $330,240
Emp.: 78
Fiscal Year-end: 12/31/2023
Commercial Banking Services
N.A.I.C.S.: 522110
Kai Myllyneva (Chm)

EVN AG

EVN Platz, 2344, Maria Enzersdorf, Austria
Tel.: (43) 22362000   AT
Web Site: https://www.evn.at
EVN—(VIE)
Rev.: $4,067,235,053
Assets: $11,867,040,794
Liabilities: $4,890,675,588
Net Worth: $6,976,365,206
Earnings: $628,210,663
Emp.: 7,255
Fiscal Year-end: 09/30/23
Electricity, Natural Gas, Heat, Water & Related Services Distr
N.A.I.C.S.: 221122
Norbert Griesmayr (Vice Chm-Supervisory Bd)

Subsidiaries:

AVN Abfallverwertung Niederosterreich GmbH   (1)
Evn Platz, Maria, 2344, Enzersdorf, Niederosterreich, Austria   (100%)
Tel.: (43) 2236466990
Web Site: https://www.evn-waermekraftwerke.at
Sales Range: $150-199.9 Million
Emp.: 600
Solid Waste Combustors & Incinerators
N.A.I.C.S.: 562213

Allplan GmbH   (1)
Schwindgasse 10, 1040, Vienna, Austria   (50%)
Tel.: (43) 150537070
Web Site: http://www.allplan.at
Sales Range: $25-49.9 Million
Emp.: 45
Engineeering Services
N.A.I.C.S.: 541330

Burgenland Holding AG   (1)
Technologiezentrum Marktstrasse 3, 7000, Eisenstadt, Austria   (73.63%)
Tel.: (43) 223620012473
Web Site: https://www.buho.at
Rev.: $12,320,973
Assets: $94,774,798
Liabilities: $22,611
Net Worth: $94,752,188
Earnings: $12,111,173
Fiscal Year-end: 09/30/2020
Holding Company
N.A.I.C.S.: 551112
Klaus Kohlhuber (Member-Exec Bd)

EVN Bulgaria Elektrorazpredelenie AD   (1)
37 Hristo G Danov street, 4000, Plovdiv, Bulgaria
Tel.: (359) 32 627 804
Web Site: http://www.evn.bg
Sales Range: $200-249.9 Million
Electricity Distribution Services
N.A.I.C.S.: 221122

Klaus Kohlhuber *(Vice Chm-Supervisory Bd)*

EVN Bulgaria Elektrosnabdiavane AD   **(1)**
37 Hristo G Danov street, 4000, Plovdiv, Bulgaria
Tel.: (359) 70017777
Web Site: https://www.evn.bg
Sales Range: $400-449.9 Million
Electricity Distribution Services
N.A.I.C.S.: 221122
Joerg Sollfelner *(Chm-Mgmt Bd)*

EVN Bulgaria Toplofikatsia EAD   **(1)**
37 Hristo G Danov Str, 4000, Plovdiv, Bulgaria
Tel.: (359) 70017777
Web Site: https://www.evn.bg
Heat Power Generation Services
N.A.I.C.S.: 221330

EVN Business Service GmbH   **(1)**
Evn Platz, Maria Enzersdorf, 2344, Niederosterreich, Austria   **(100%)**
Tel.: (43) 22362000
Web Site: http://www.evn.at
Restaurant
N.A.I.C.S.: 722511

EVN Croatia Plin d.o.o   **(1)**
Zagrebacka avenija 104, 10000, Zagreb, Croatia
Web Site: http://www.evn.hr
Sales Range: $75-99.9 Million
Emp.: 2
Natural Gas Distribution Services
N.A.I.C.S.: 221210

EVN Energievertrieb GmbH & Co Kg   **(1)**
Evn Platz, Maria, 2344, Enzersdorf, Niederosterreich, Austria   **(100%)**
Tel.: (43) 22362000
Web Site: http://www.evn.at
Sales Range: $1-4.9 Billion
Emp.: 1,000
Electrical Apparatus & Equipment Wiring Supplies & Related Equipment Merchant Whslr
N.A.I.C.S.: 423610

EVN Finanzservice GmbH   **(1)**
Maria Evn Platz, 2344, Enzersdorf, Niederosterreich, Austria   **(100%)**
Tel.: (43) 22362000
Sales Range: $550-599.9 Million
Emp.: 2,500
Holding Company
N.A.I.C.S.: 551112
Stefan Szyskqwitz *(Gen Mgr)*

EVN Geoinfo GmbH   **(1)**
EVN Platz, 2344, Maria Enzersdorf, Austria
Tel.: (43) 22362000
Web Site: https://www.evn-geoinfo.at
Sales Range: $25-49.9 Million
Emp.: 40
Geographic Information Services
N.A.I.C.S.: 519290

EVN Kraftwerks- und Beteiligungsgesellschaft mbH   **(1)**
Evn Platz, Maria Enzersdorf, 2344, Austria
Tel.: (43) 2236 200 0
Web Site: http://www.evn.at
Sales Range: $1-4.9 Billion
Emp.: 2,500
Eletric Power Generation Services
N.A.I.C.S.: 221118
Peter Layr *(Gen Mgr)*

EVN Macedonia AD   **(1)**
Str Lazar Lichenoski Nr 11, 1000, Skopje, North Macedonia
Tel.: (389) 23205000
Web Site: https://www.evn.mk
Electricity Distribution Services
N.A.I.C.S.: 221122
Jurgen Fleischhacker *(Vice Chm)*

EVN Macedonia Elektrani DOOEL   **(1)**
Tel.: (389) 23205000
Web Site: https://elektrani.evn.mk
Electricity Generation Services
N.A.I.C.S.: 221118
Maximilian Hoyer *(Mgr)*

EVN Macedonia Elektrosnabduvanje DOOEL   **(1)**

Tel.: (389) 23205500
Web Site: https://snabduvanje.evn.mk
Electricity Distribution Services
N.A.I.C.S.: 221122
Aleksandar Mijalkov *(Acct Mgr)*

EVN Netz GmbH   **(1)**
Evn Platz, 2344, Maria Enzersdorf, Austria   **(100%)**
Tel.: (43) 22362010
Web Site: http://www.evn.at
Sales Range: $550-599.9 Million
Emp.: 2,500
Electrical Apparatus & Equipment Wiring Supplies & Related Equipment Merchant Whslr
N.A.I.C.S.: 423610

EVN Projektmanagement GmbH   **(1)**
EVN Platz, 2344, Maria Enzersdorf, Austria
Tel.: (43) 22362000
Eletric Power Generation Services
N.A.I.C.S.: 221118

EVN Trading South East Europe EAD   **(1)**
14 Tsar Osvoboditel blvd, 1000, Sofia, Bulgaria
Tel.: (359) 70013636
Web Site: https://www.evn-trading.com
Sales Range: $75-99.9 Million
Emp.: 12
Electric Power Distribution Services
N.A.I.C.S.: 221122

Subsidiary (Non-US):

EVN Trading d.o.o. Beograd   **(2)**
3 Cincar Jankova, Belgrade, 11000, Serbia
Tel.: (381) 113208900
Electric Power Distribution Services
N.A.I.C.S.: 221122

EVN Umweltholding Und Betriebs-GmbH   **(1)**
Evn Platz, 2344, Enzersdorf, Niederosterreich, Austria   **(100%)**
Tel.: (43) 22362000
Web Site: http://www.evn.at
Sales Range: $25-49.9 Million
Emp.: 90
Marketing Consulting Services
N.A.I.C.S.: 541613

Subsidiary (Domestic):

EVN Umwelt Beteiligungs und Service GmbH   **(2)**
EVN Platz, 23443, Maria Enzersdorf, Austria
Tel.: (43) 22362000
Web Site: http://www.evn.at
Environmental Consulting Services
N.A.I.C.S.: 541620
Uno Makotsvana *(Mng Dir)*

EVN Umwelt Finanz- und Service-GmbH   **(2)**
EVN Platz, 2344, Maria Enzersdorf, Austria
Tel.: (43) 2236 200 0
Web Site: http://www.evn.at
Financial Investment Services
N.A.I.C.S.: 523999
Stefan Szyszkowitz *(Gen Mgr)*

Subsidiary (Non-US):

WTE Wassertechnik GmbH   **(2)**
Ruhrallee 185, 45136, Essen, Germany
Tel.: (49) 2018968571
Web Site: https://www.wte.de
Sales Range: $100-124.9 Million
Emp.: 11
Waste Water Treatment Services
N.A.I.C.S.: 221310

Subsidiary (Non-US):

Storitveno podjetje Lasko d.o.o.   **(3)**
Modric 8, 3270, Lasko, 3270, Slovenia
Tel.: (386) 45885070
Water Treatment Plant Services
N.A.I.C.S.: 221310

UAB WTE Baltic   **(3)**
Inovaciju 3, Biruliskes, 54469, Kaunas, Lithuania
Tel.: (370) 37332681
Web Site: https://www.wte.de

Sales Range: $75-99.9 Million
Emp.: 7
Waste Treatment Services
N.A.I.C.S.: 221310

WTE Projektna druzba Bled d.o.o.   **(3)**
Savska Cesta 23, 4260, Bled, Slovenia
Tel.: (386) 45885070
Web Site: http://www.wte.se
Waste Treatment Services
N.A.I.C.S.: 221310
Bengt Ivo Martens *(Dir)*

WTE Projektna druzba Kranjska Gora d.o.o.   **(3)**
Kolodvorska Ulica 1B, 4280, Kranjska Gora, Slovenia
Tel.: (386) 45885070
Web Site: http://www.wte.se
Emp.: 1
Waste Treatment Services
N.A.I.C.S.: 221310
Bengtivo Martin *(Gen Mgr)*

WTE Wassertechnik (Polska) Sp. z o.o   **(3)**
Ul Ryzowa 45, 02495, Warsaw, Poland
Tel.: (48) 223314650
Web Site: https://www.wte.de
Water Supply Services
N.A.I.C.S.: 221310

EVN Warme GmbH   **(1)**
Evn Platz, 2344, Maria Enzersdorf, Austria
Tel.: (43) 22362000
Web Site: https://www.evn.at
Emp.: 10
Eletric Power Generation Services
N.A.I.C.S.: 221118
Peter Layr *(Mng Dir)*

EVN Wasser GmbH   **(1)**
Evn Platz, 2344, Maria Enzersdorf, Niederosterreich, Austria   **(100%)**
Tel.: (43) 22364460113029
Web Site: http://www.evn.at
Sales Range: $1-4.9 Billion
Emp.: 3,000
Water Supply & Irrigation Systems
N.A.I.C.S.: 221310

Elektrodistribucija DOOEL   **(1)**
Ul Lazar Licenoski no 11, 1000, Skopje, North Macedonia
Tel.: (389) 23205300
Web Site: https://www.elektrodistribucija.mk
Electricity Distribution Services
N.A.I.C.S.: 221122
Sasho Saltirovski *(Mgr)*

Elektrorazpredelenie Yug EAD   **(1)**
37 Hristo G Danov St, 4000, Plovdiv, Bulgaria
Tel.: (359) 70010007
Web Site: https://www.elyug.bg
Electricity Distribution Services
N.A.I.C.S.: 221122

Kabelsignal AG   **(1)**
Sudstadtzentrum 4, 2344, Maria Enzersdorf, Niederosterreich, Austria   **(100%)**
Tel.: (43) 50514
Web Site: http://www.kabsi.at
Sales Range: $25-49.9 Million
Emp.: 70
Radio & Television Broadcasting & Wireless Communications Equipment Mfr
N.A.I.C.S.: 334220

Netz Niederosterreich GmbH   **(1)**
EVN Platz, 2344, Maria Enzersdorf, Austria
Tel.: (43) 22362012070
Web Site: http://www.netz-noe.at
Electricity Distribution Services
N.A.I.C.S.: 221122
Werner Hengst *(Mng Dir)*

gesellschaftRAG-Beteiligungs-Aktiengesellschaft   **(1)**
Schwarzenbergplatz 16, 1015, Vienna, Austria   **(50.03%)**
Tel.: (43) 50724
Web Site: http://www.rag-austria.at
Holding Company; Crude Petroleum & Natural Gas Extraction
N.A.I.C.S.: 551112

Subsidiary (Domestic):

RAG Austria AG   **(2)**

Schwarzenbergplatz 16, Postfach 56, 1015, Vienna, Austria
Tel.: (43) 50724
Web Site: https://www.rag-austria.at
Natural Gas Distribution Services
N.A.I.C.S.: 221210
Markus Mitteregger *(CEO)*

Rohol-Aufsuchungs Aktiengesellschaft   **(2)**
Schwarzenbergplatz 16, Postfach 56, 1015, Vienna, Austria
Tel.: (43) 50724
Web Site: https://www.rag-austria.at
Sales Range: $75-99.9 Million
Emp.: 400
Crude Petroleum & Natural Gas Extraction
N.A.I.C.S.: 211120
Markus Mitteregger *(CEO & Member-Exec Bd)*

Subsidiary (Non-US):

RAG Hungary Kft.   **(3)**
Bocskai ut 134-146 Dorottya Udvar Building D 3rd floor, 1113, Budapest, Hungary
Tel.: (36) 15056800
Web Site: https://www.rag-austria.at
Sales Range: $1-9.9 Million
Emp.: 13
Petroleum Products
N.A.I.C.S.: 324110

Toplak GmbH   **(1)**
Berta von Suttner Strasse 14, Obersdorf, 2120, Wolkersdorf im Weinviertel, Austria   **(50%)**
Tel.: (43) 224521200
Web Site: https://www.toplak.com
Sales Range: $50-74.9 Million
Emp.: 25
Construction Mining & Forestry Machinery & Equipment Rental & Leasing
N.A.I.C.S.: 532412

V&C GmbH   **(1)**
Josef Perger-Str 2 - A-05, Pressbaum, 3031, Austria   **(100%)**
Tel.: (43) 223357771
Web Site: http://www.vc-austria.com
Sales Range: $25-49.9 Million
Emp.: 38
Engineeering Services
N.A.I.C.S.: 541330

WTE Betriebsgesellschaft mbH   **(1)**
Gaensefurth 7-10, 39444, Hecklingen, Germany
Tel.: (49) 392592690
Web Site: http://www.wteb.info
Sales Range: $75-99.9 Million
Emp.: 500
Waste Treatment Services
N.A.I.C.S.: 221310
Bojan Pelivano *(Mng Dir)*

WTE Projektgesellschaft Sud-West Wasser mbH   **(1)**
Ruhrallee 185, 45136, Essen, Germany
Tel.: (49) 2018968500
Sales Range: $75-99.9 Million
Emp.: 10
Waste Treatment Services
N.A.I.C.S.: 221310
Joerg Koering *(Gen Mgr)*

evn naturkraft Beteiligungs- und Betriebs-GmbH   **(1)**
EVN Platz, 2344, Maria Enzersdorf, Austria
Tel.: (43) 2236 200 0
Sales Range: $75-99.9 Million
Emp.: 5
Eletric Power Generation Services
N.A.I.C.S.: 221118

evn naturkraft Erzeugungsgesellschaft m.b.H.   **(1)**
EVN Platz, 2344, Maria Enzersdorf, Austria
Tel.: (43) 22362000
Web Site: https://www.evn-naturkraft.at
Emp.: 60
Hydroelectric Power Generation Services
N.A.I.C.S.: 221111

kabelplus GmbH   **(1)**
Sudstadtzentrum 4, 2344, Maria Enzersdorf, Austria
Tel.: (43) 50514
Web Site: https://www.kabelplus.at
Cable Network Operator Services
N.A.I.C.S.: 517111

EvoAir Holdings Inc.—(Continued)

EVOAIR HOLDINGS INC.
Ul Sveti Kliment Ohridski 27 Apt 8,
8000, Burgas, Bulgaria
Tel.: (359) 884303333   NV
Year Founded: 2017
Liabilities: $53,634
Net Worth: ($53,634)
Earnings: ($61,545)
Emp.: 1
Fiscal Year-end: 08/31/21
Holding Company
N.A.I.C.S.: 551112

EVOC INTELLIGENT TECH-NOLOGY COMPANY LIMITED
EVOC Technology Building 31
Gaoxin Central Avenue 4th, Nanshan
District, Shenzhen, 518057, China
Tel.: (86) 75586255066   CN
Web Site: http://www.evoc.com
Year Founded: 1993
2308—(HKG)
Rev.: $236,638,361
Assets: $1,253,413,155
Liabilities: $824,517,081
Net Worth: $428,896,074
Earnings: $32,256,527
Emp.: 867
Fiscal Year-end: 12/31/20
Advanced Process Automation Prod-uct Mfr
N.A.I.C.S.: 335314
Zhi Chen *(Chm)*

EVOKE PLC
Suite 601/701 Europort Europort
Road, Gibraltar, Gibraltar
Tel.: (350) 20049800   GI
Web Site: https://www.evokeplc.com
Year Founded: 1997
EVOK—(LSE)
Rev.: $2,178,103,128
Assets: $3,497,899,441
Liabilities: $3,396,180,790
Net Worth: $101,718,651
Earnings: ($71,801,401)
Emp.: 6,676
Fiscal Year-end: 12/31/23
Holding Company; Online Gaming
Services
N.A.I.C.S.: 551112
Aviad Kobrine *(CFO)*

Subsidiaries:

Alfabet S.A.S.   (1)
Cra 100 No 11-60 Of 412 Farallones Tower
Holguines, Trade Shopping Center, Cali,
Colombia
Tel.: (57) 3450526
Web Site: https://www.williamhill.co
Online Gambling Site Operator
N.A.I.C.S.: 713290

Sparkware Technologies SRL   (1)
Bucharest Business Garden Building C -
Calea Plevnei 159, Sector 6, Bucharest,
Romania
Tel.: (40) 31 224 1600
Web Site: https://888sparkware.ro
Information Technology & Services
N.A.I.C.S.: 541519

Virtual Marketing Services (UK)
Limited   (1)
20 Thayer st, London, W1U 2DD, United
Kingdom
Tel.: (44) 2074878678
Sales Range: $25-49.9 Million
Emp.: 25
Advertising Services
N.A.I.C.S.: 541810

William Hill Latvia SIA   (1)
Dzirnavu iela 39-8, Riga, LV1010, Latvia
Tel.: (371) 20005811
Web Site: https://www.williamhill.lv
Online Sports Betting & Gaming Services
N.A.I.C.S.: 713290

EVOLEM S.A.
6 Quai Saint Antoine CS 60026,
69289, Lyon, Cedex 02, France
Tel.: (33) 472689800
Web Site: http://www.evolem.com
Year Founded: 1997
Sales Range: $25-49.9 Million
Emp.: 17
Investment Management Service
N.A.I.C.S.: 523940
Bruno Rousset *(Founder, Chm & CEO)*

Subsidiaries:

Chemica S.A.S   (1)
8 rue Poncetton, Saint-Etienne, 42000,
France
Tel.: (33) 477492090
Web Site: http://www.chemica.fr
Textile Heat Transfer Product Mfr
N.A.I.C.S.: 314999

Dufieux Industrie S.A.S.   (1)
4 Rue Monmousseau, 38433, Echirolles,
France
Tel.: (33) 4 76 33 26 10
Web Site: http://www.dufieux-industrie.com
Machine Tools Mfr
N.A.I.C.S.: 333517

EVOLUTION AB
Hamngatan 11, Stockholm, Sweden
Tel.: (46) 084404660
Web Site: https://www.evolution.com
Year Founded: 2006
EVO—(OMX)
Software Development Services
N.A.I.C.S.: 541511
Jacob Kaplan *(CFO)*

Subsidiaries:

Transigo Ltd.   (1)
8 South Ring Business Park Kinsale Road,
Cork, Ireland
Tel.: (353) 214316776
Web Site: https://www.transigo.com
Smart Charging Rack Mfr & Distr
N.A.I.C.S.: 334417

EVOLUTION BLOCKCHAIN GROUP INC.
7458 Allison Place, Chilliwack, V4Z
1Z7, BC, Canada
Tel.: (778) 823-3104   NV
Year Founded: 2014
EVBC—(OTCIQ)
Sales Range: Less than $1 Million
Fabric Technology Developer
N.A.I.C.S.: 314999
Devon Loosdrecht *(Pres, CEO, CFO, Treas & Sec)*

EVOLUTION CAPITAL (UK) LIMITED
48 Dover Street, London, W1S 4FF,
United Kingdom
Tel.: (44) 20 3696 2810   UK
Web Site:
  http://www.evolutioncapital.com
Year Founded: 2003
Corporate Financial Services
N.A.I.C.S.: 523910
Nigel David Cook *(Founder & Mng Dir)*

EVOLUTION ENERGY MINER-ALS LIMITED
Level One 1318 Hay Street, West
Perth, 6005, WA, Australia
Tel.: (61) 892003426   AU
Web Site:
  https://www.evolutionenergy.com.au
Year Founded: 2021
P77—(DEU)
Rev.: $45,248
Assets: $6,638,358
Liabilities: $713,332
Net Worth: $5,925,025

Earnings: ($9,057,696)
Fiscal Year-end: 06/30/23
Mineral Exploration Services
N.A.I.C.S.: 212390
Phil Hoskins *(Mng Dir)*

EVOLUTION HEALTHCARE PTY. LTD.
Gateway Tower Suite 2 Level 16 1
Macquarie Place, Sydney, 2000,
NSW, Australia
Tel.: (61) 2 9247 7688   AU
Web Site:
  http://www.evolutioncare.com.au
Healtcare Services
N.A.I.C.S.: 551112
Benedict Joseph Thynne *(Founder & Mng Dir)*

Subsidiaries:

Acurity Health Group Limited   (1)
30 Florence Street, Wellington, 6021, New
Zealand
Tel.: (64) 4 920 0131
Web Site: http://www.acurity.co.nz
Sales Range: $75-99.9 Million
Emp.: 600
Surgical & Medical Health Care Services
N.A.I.C.S.: 524114
Andrew Savage *(Chm)*

Evolution Healthcare Management
Pty. Ltd.   (1)
Suite 1003 Level 10 - 1 Alfred Street, Syd-ney, 2000, NSW, Australia   (100%)
Tel.: (61) 2 9247 7688
Web Site:
  http://www.evolutionhealthcare.com.au
Hospital Administrative Services
N.A.I.C.S.: 561110
Benedict Thynne *(Founder & CEO)*

Subsidiary (Non-US):

Boulcott Hospital Limited   (2)
666 High Street, Boulcott, Lower Hutt,
5010, Wellington, New Zealand
Tel.: (64) 4 569 7555
Web Site: http://www.boulcotthospital.co.nz
Emp.: 120
Surgical Hospital Operator
N.A.I.C.S.: 622110
Linda Healy *(Mgr-Clinical Nurse)*

Subsidiary (Domestic):

Canberra Private Hospital Pty.
Ltd.   (2)
Equinox Business Park Bldg 2 Level 3 70
Kent Street, Deakin, 2600, ACT, Australia
Tel.: (61) 2 6173 3733
Web Site:
  http://www.canberraprivate.com.au
Hospital Operator
N.A.I.C.S.: 622110
Libby Tuohy *(Dir-Nursing)*

Evolution Hurstville Pty. Ltd.   (2)
31 Dora Street, Hurstville, 2220, NSW, Aus-tralia
Tel.: (61) 2 9598 0000
Web Site: http://www.waratahprivate.com.au
Hospital Operator
N.A.I.C.S.: 622110
Kathryn McKeefry *(Gen Mgr & Dir-Nursing)*

EVOLUTION MINING LIMITED
Level 24 175 Liverpool Street, Syd-ney, 2000, NSW, Australia
Tel.: (61) 296962900   AU
Web Site:
  https://www.evolutionmining.com.au
Year Founded: 2003
EVN—(ASX)
Rev.: $2,147,323,709
Assets: $5,888,649,148
Liabilities: $3,122,759,736
Net Worth: $2,765,889,412
Earnings: $281,963,808
Emp.: 3,101
Fiscal Year-end: 06/30/24
Gold Exploration & Mining
N.A.I.C.S.: 212220

Evan Elstein *(Sec & VP-IT)*

Subsidiaries:

Battle North Gold Corporation   (1)
Suite 830 - 121 King Street West, Toronto,
M5H 3T9, ON, Canada
Tel.: (604) 792-4601
Web Site: http://www.rubiconminerals.com
Sales Range: Less than $1 Million
Gold Exploration Services
N.A.I.C.S.: 212220
Allan Candelario *(Dir-IR & Corp Dev)*

CMOC Mining Services Pty Ltd   (1)
Bogan Rd, Goonumbla, Parkes, 2870, New
South Wales, Australia   (80%)
Tel.: (61) 268613000
Web Site: http://www.northparkes.com
Sales Range: $200-249.9 Million
Emp.: 300
Mining Facility
N.A.I.C.S.: 212390
Hubert Lehman *(Mng Dir)*

Ernest Henry Mining Pty. Ltd.   (1)
Zingari Rd, PO Box 527, Cloncurry, 4824,
QLD, Australia   (100%)
Tel.: (61) 7 4769 4500
Web Site:
  http://www.ernesthenrymining.com.au
Copper & Gold Mining
N.A.I.C.S.: 212230

EVOLUTION TECHNOLOGY RESOURCES, INC.
SS-02-13 and 13A Sky-Pod Square,
Puchong Jaya South, 47100, Pu-chong, Selangor, Malaysia
Tel.: (60) 380823158   DE
Year Founded: 2006
ETKR—(OTCIQ)
Sales Range: Less than $1 Million
Financial Investment Services
N.A.I.C.S.: 523999
Timo Bernd Strattner *(CFO)*

EVOLVA HOLDING SA
Duggingerstrasse 23, CH-4153, Rein-ach, Switzerland
Tel.: (41) 614852000
Web Site: https://www.evolva.com
ELVAF—(OTCEM)
Rev.: $8,539,617
Assets: $189,001,202
Liabilities: $24,688,752
Net Worth: $164,312,450
Earnings: ($33,827,105)
Emp.: 65
Fiscal Year-end: 12/31/20
Biopharmaceutical Developer & Mfr
N.A.I.C.S.: 325412
Oliver Walker *(CEO)*

Subsidiaries:

Evolva A/S   (1)
Bulowsvej 25, 1870, Frederiksberg, Den-mark
Tel.: (45) 35200230
Drug Discovery & Development Services
N.A.I.C.S.: 325412

Evolva Biotech Private Limited   (1)
401-405 Ticel Bio Park Ltd 4th Floor Tara-mani Road, Taramani, Chennai, 600 113,
Tamil Nadu, India
Tel.: (91) 44 4297 1050
Web Site: http://www.evolva.com
Sales Range: $25-49.9 Million
Emp.: 21
Medical Compound Research & Develop-ment Services
N.A.I.C.S.: 541715

EVOLVE EDUCATION GROUP LIMITED
Level 15 16 Kingston Street, Auck-land, 1010, New Zealand
Tel.: (64) 93778700
Web Site:
  https://www.evolveeducation.co.nz
EVO—(NZX)
Early Childhood Educational Services

N.A.I.C.S.: 611110
Chris Scott *(Mng Dir)*

Subsidiaries:

Lollipops Educare (Birkenhead)
Limited   (1)
71 Roseberry Ave, Birkenhead, Auckland,
New Zealand
Tel.: (64) 94196826
Childhood Education Support Services
N.A.I.C.S.: 624410
Joanne MacAskill *(Mgr-Centre)*

EVOLVE IT AUSTRALIA PTY. LTD.
1/476 Canterbury Road, Forest Hill,
3131, VIC, Australia
Tel.: (61) 3 8872 6000
Web Site: http://www.evolveit.com.au
Year Founded: 1993
Sales Range: $1-9.9 Million
IT Services
N.A.I.C.S.: 541519
Nick Moran *(CEO)*

EVOLVING GOLD CORP.
Suite 605-1166 Alberni Street, Vancouver, V6E 3Z3, BC, Canada
Tel.: (604) 685-6375   Ca
Web Site:
http://www.evolvinggold.com
Year Founded: 2003
EVG—(CNSX)
Assets: $127,214
Liabilities: $216,683
Net Worth: ($89,469)
Earnings: ($144,228)
Emp.: 1
Fiscal Year-end: 03/31/21
Gold Mining Services
N.A.I.C.S.: 212220
Charles E. Jenkins *(Acting CEO)*

EVOQ REMEDIES LIMITED
F-12-A First Floor V R Complex Near
Sanathal Cross Road Santhal,
Ahmedabad, 382210, Gujarat, India
Tel.: (91) 7948402525
Web Site:
https://www.evoqremedies.com
Year Founded: 2010
543500—(NSE)
Pharmaceutical Product Mfr & Distr
N.A.I.C.S.: 325412
Bhumishth Narendrabhai Patel *(Mng Dir & Chm)*

EVORA S.A.
R Siqueira Campos 1163 7 andar,
Centro Historico, Porto Alegre,
90010-001, Rio Grande do Sul, Brazil
Tel.: (55) 5132876333   BR
Web Site: http://www.evora.com
Year Founded: 1988
Sales Range: $350-399.9 Million
Emp.: 1,843
Polypropylene Nonwoven Mfr
N.A.I.C.S.: 313230
Eduardo Lubisco Souza *(CFO & IR Officer)*

Subsidiaries:

America Tampas S/A   (1)
Rua Djanir Hausen de Oliveira 585, Venancio Aires, 95800-000, RS, Brazil
Tel.: (55) 51 3793 2322
Web Site: http://www.americatampas.com.br
Sales Range: $25-49.9 Million
Emp.: 150
Plastic Closure Mfr
N.A.I.C.S.: 326199
Gustavo Alvarez *(CEO)*

CROWN Embalagens Metalicas da
Amazonia S.A.   (1)
Rua Jutai 405, Distrito Industrial, Manaus,
69075-130, Amazonas, Brazil
Tel.: (55) 1145291000

Web Site:
http://www.crownembalagens.com.br
Emp.: 15
Metal Tank Mfr
N.A.I.C.S.: 332431
Johan Van Rompaey *(Office Mgr)*

Fitesa Simpsonville, Inc.   (1)
840 SE Main St, Simpsonville, SC 29681-7118
Tel.: (864) 967-5600
Web Site: http://www.fiberweb.com
Nonwoven Fabric Mfr
N.A.I.C.S.: 313230
Hal Singley *(CFO)*

Subsidiary (Non-US):

Fitesa Germany GmbH   (2)
Woltorfer Strasse 124, PO Box 1107,
31201, Peine, Germany
Tel.: (49) 5171408500
Web Site: http://www.fitesa.com
Sales Range: $25-49.9 Million
Emp.: 120
Non-Woven Specialist Fabric Mfr
N.A.I.C.S.: 313230

Fitesa Italia Srl   (2)
Via Bologna 7, IT-20060, Trezzano Rosa,
MI, Italy
Tel.: (39) 02 90 99 91
Web Site: http://www.fitesa.com
Sales Range: $25-49.9 Million
Emp.: 120
Non-Woven Specialist Fabric Mfr
N.A.I.C.S.: 313230

Fitesa Mexico   (2)
Km 60 2 Carretera 57, Queretaro San Luis
Potosi, San Jose Iturbide, 37980, Mexico
Tel.: (52) 419 198 3200
Web Site: http://www.fitesa.com
Nonwoven Fabric Mfr
N.A.I.C.S.: 313230

Fitesa Peru S.A.C.   (2)
ZI Parcelacion Cajamarquilla Av Principal
No 71, Lurigancho, Lima, Peru
Tel.: (51) 1 614 3545
Web Site: http://www.fitesa.com
Nonwoven Fabric Mfr
N.A.I.C.S.: 313230

Fitesa SA   (2)
Rua Paul Zivi 80, Distrito Industrial, Gravatai, 94045-430, RS, Brazil
Tel.: (55) 51 3489 7000
Web Site: http://www.fitesa.com
Nonwoven Fabric Mfr
N.A.I.C.S.: 313230

Fitesa Sweden AB   (2)
Ostra Bravikenvagen 18, PO Box 913,
60119, Norrkoping, Sweden
Tel.: (46) 11 24 44 00
Web Site: http://www.fitesa.com
Emp.: 120
Non-Woven Specialist Fabric Mfr
N.A.I.C.S.: 313230
Anders Fogelberg *(Mgr-Production)*

Subsidiary (Domestic):

Fitesa Washougal, Inc.   (2)
3720 Grant St, Washougal, WA 98671-2807
Tel.: (360) 835-8787
Web Site: http://www.fitesa.com
Sales Range: $25-49.9 Million
Emp.: 113
Non-Woven Specialist Fabric Mfr
N.A.I.C.S.: 313230
Joseph Hisey *(Mgr-Continuous Improvement & Quality)*

EVOTEC SE
Essener Bogen 7, 22419, Hamburg,
Germany
Tel.: (49) 40560810   De
Web Site: https://www.evotec.com
EVO—(NASDAQ)
Rev.: $862,596,313
Assets: $2,486,442,213
Liabilities: $1,250,204,217
Net Worth: $1,236,237,996
Earnings: ($92,629,429)
Emp.: 5,061
Fiscal Year-end: 12/31/23

Pharmaceutical Developer & Mfr
N.A.I.C.S.: 325412
Werner Lanthaler *(CEO & Member-Mgmt Bd)*

Subsidiaries:

Aptuit, LLC   (1)
2 Greenwich Ofc Park, Greenwich, CT
06831
Tel.: (855) 427-8848
Web Site: http://www.aptuit.com
Pharmaceutical Development Services
N.A.I.C.S.: 541715
Henning Steinhagen *(Pres-R&D Ops & Head-Verona Site)*

Subsidiary (Non-US):

Aptuit (Oxford) Limited   (2)
111 Innovation Drive, Abingdon, OX14 4RZ,
Oxfordshire, United Kingdom
Tel.: (44) 123 543 3600
Web Site: http://www.aptuit.com
Pharmaceutical Preparation Mfr
N.A.I.C.S.: 325412

Aptuit (Verona) Srl   (2)
Via Alessandro Fleming 4, 37135, Verona,
Italy
Tel.: (39) 045 821 8111
Web Site: http://www.aptuit.com
Pharmaceutical Preparation Mfr
N.A.I.C.S.: 325412

Laurus Labs Limited   (2)
2nd Floor Serene Chambers Road No 7
Banjara Hills, Hyderabad, 500 034, Telangana, India
Tel.: (91) 4039804333
Web Site: https://www.lauruslabs.com
Rev.: $675,558,975
Assets: $951,137,460
Liabilities: $492,627,135
Net Worth: $458,510,325
Earnings: $113,599,395
Emp.: 5,304
Fiscal Year-end: 03/31/2022
Pharmaceuticals Product Mfr
N.A.I.C.S.: 325412
G. S. R. Anjaneyulu *(Exec VP & Head-Supply Chain Mgmt)*

Cyprotex Limited   (1)
No 24 Mereside Alderley Park, Nether Alderley, Macclesfield, SK10 4TG, Cheshire,
United Kingdom   **(100%)**
Tel.: (44) 162 550 5100
Web Site: https://www.cyprotex.com
Emp.: 200
Pharmaceutical Contract Research Services
N.A.I.C.S.: 541715
Anthony D. Baxter *(CEO)*

Subsidiary (Domestic):

Cyprotex Discovery Limited   (2)
No 24 Mereside Alderley Park, Nether Alderley, Macclesfield, SK10 4TG, Cheshire,
United Kingdom
Tel.: (44) 1625505100
Web Site: https://www.cyprotex.com
Pharmaceutical Contract Research Services
N.A.I.C.S.: 541715

Cyprotex Us   (1)
313 Pleasant St, Watertown, MA 02472
Web Site: https://www.cyprotex.com
Pharmaceuticals Product Mfr
N.A.I.C.S.: 325412

Evotec (India) Private Ltd.   (1)
DIL Complex Ghodbunder Road, Majiwada,
Thane, 400610, Maharashtra, India
Tel.: (91) 22 6623 0900
Sales Range: $50-74.9 Million
Emp.: 160
Pharmaceuticals Product Mfr
N.A.I.C.S.: 325412

Evotec (UK) Ltd.   (1)
Dorothy Crowfoot Hodgkin Campus 114 Innovation Drive, Milton Park, Abingdon,
OX14 4RZ, Oxfordshire, United Kingdom
Tel.: (44) 1235861561
Sales Range: $75-99.9 Million
Emp.: 250
Pharmaceutical Products Distr
N.A.I.C.S.: 424210
Werner Lanthler *(CEO)*

Kinaxo Biotechnologies GmbH   (1)
Am Klopferspitz 19a, Martinsried, 82152,
Planegg, Bavaria, Germany
Tel.: (49) 89 461 3363 0
Web Site: http://www.kinaxo.de
Sales Range: $25-49.9 Million
Emp.: 30
Biotechnology Research & Development
Services
N.A.I.C.S.: 541714
Christoph Schaab *(Dir-Bioinformatics)*

EVPU A.S.
Trencianska 19, 018 51, Nova
Dubnica, Slovakia
Tel.: (421) 424409102
Web Site: http://www.evpu.sk
Year Founded: 1968
Sales Range: $25-49.9 Million
Emp.: 240
Electric Motors Mfr, Researcher &
Developer
N.A.I.C.S.: 336320
Jozef Buday *(Mng Dir)*

Subsidiaries:

EVPU CR s.r.o.   (1)
Ceskoslovenske Armady 383/5, Hradec
Kralove, Czech Republic
Tel.: (420) 495514997
Electrical Equipment Distr
N.A.I.C.S.: 423610

EVPU Defence a.s.   (1)
Jaktare 1781, 686 01, Uherske Hradiste,
Czech Republic
Tel.: (420) 572 557 542
Web Site: http://www.evpudefence.com
Emp.: 50
Surveillance & Monitoring System Mfr
N.A.I.C.S.: 334511

EVRAZ PLC
2 Portman street, London, W1H 6DU,
United Kingdom
Tel.: (44) 2078328990   UK
Web Site: http://www.evraz.com
Year Founded: 2011
EVR—(LSE)
Rev.: $13,486,000,000
Assets: $9,854,000,000
Liabilities: $7,620,000,000
Net Worth: $2,234,000,000
Earnings: $3,107,000,000
Emp.: 71,591
Fiscal Year-end: 12/31/21
Holding Company; Steel Mfr & Distr;
Coal & Iron Ore Mining
N.A.I.C.S.: 551112

Subsidiaries:

AVT-Ural LLC   (1)
2 Sverdlova St, Kachkanar, Sverdlovskaya,
624350, Russia
Tel.: (7) 3434149103
Drilling & Blasting Services
N.A.I.C.S.: 213115

CF&I Steel LP   (1)
2100 S Fwy, Pueblo, CO 81004
Tel.: (719) 561-6000
Steel Products Mfr
N.A.I.C.S.: 331210

EVRAZ Market JSC   (1)
ul Chemical 9, 347913, Taganrog, Rostov,
Russia
Tel.: (7) 8634328696
Web Site: https://evraz.market
Metal Product Distr
N.A.I.C.S.: 423510

Evraz Group S.A.   (1)
46A Avenue JF Kennedy, PO Box 415,
L-1855, Luxembourg, Luxembourg **(100%)**
Tel.: (352) 442078328998
Web Site: http://www.evraz.com
Holding Company
N.A.I.C.S.: 551112

Branch (Non-US):

Evraz LLC   (2)
Belovezhskaya Street 4 Block B, 121353,

Evraz plc—(Continued)

Moscow, Russia **(100%)**
Tel.: (7) 4953631963
Web Site: http://www.evraz.com
Holding Company; Steel Mfg, Iron Ore & Coal Mining
N.A.I.C.S.: 551112

Subsidiary (Non-US):

Evraz Highveld Steel & Vanadium Limited **(3)**
Old Pretoria Road Portion 93 of the farm Schoongezicht, 308 JS, Witbank, Mpumalanga, South Africa **(85.11%)**
Tel.: (27) 13 690 9911
Web Site: http://www.evrazhighveld.co.za
Sales Range: $450-499.9 Million
Emp.: 2,303
Steel & Vanadium Products Mfr
N.A.I.C.S.: 331513
Anre Weststrate (Sec)

Subsidiary (US):

Evraz North America Limited **(3)**
71 S Wacker Dr Ste 1700, Chicago, IL 60606
Tel.: (312) 533-3555
Rev.: $2,748,931,000
Assets: $3,782,647,000
Liabilities: $1,772,387,000
Net Worth: $2,010,260,000
Earnings: ($759,516,000)
Emp.: 4,132
Fiscal Year-end: 12/31/2013
Engineered Steel Products Mfr
N.A.I.C.S.: 331110
Jerry Reed (Chief Comml Officer)

Subsidiary (Domestic):

Colorado & Wyoming Railway Company **(4)**
2100 S Freeway, Pueblo, CO 81004-3406
Tel.: (719) 561-6358
Web Site: https://www.cwrailway.com
Emp.: 100
Short Line Railroad Operator
N.A.I.C.S.: 482112

Evraz Inc. NA **(4)**
71 S Wacker Dr Ste 1700, Chicago, IL 60606
Tel.: (312) 533-3555
Web Site: https://www.evrazna.com
Emp.: 1,400
Steel Products Mfr
N.A.I.C.S.: 331221
Jerry Reed (Chief Comml Officer)

Plant (Domestic):

Evraz Inc. NA - Pueblo **(5)**
2100 S Freeway, Pueblo, CO 81004-3406
Tel.: (719) 561-6000
Web Site: https://www.evraz.com
Seamless Casing & Tubing; Rails; Heat Treated Rails; Reinforcing Bars, Hot Rolled Bars & Wire Rods Mfr
N.A.I.C.S.: 331110

Subsidiary (Non-US):

Evraz Inc. NA Canada **(5)**
100 Armour Road, Regina, S4P 3C7, SK, Canada
Tel.: (306) 924-7700
Web Site: http://www.evrazna.com
Emp.: 600
Steel Production
N.A.I.C.S.: 331513

Plant (Domestic):

Evraz Inc. NA Canada - Camrose **(6)**
5302 39th Street, Camrose, T4V 2N8, AB, Canada
Tel.: (780) 672-3116
Web Site: http://www.evrazna.com
Sales Range: $50-74.9 Million
Emp.: 350
Mfr of Steel Pipe
N.A.I.C.S.: 331210

Joint Venture (Domestic):

Oregon Ferralloy Partners **(5)**

14400 N Rivergate Blvd, Portland, OR 97203 **(60%)**
Tel.: (503) 286-8869
Web Site: https://www.feralloy.com
Flat Rolled Steel Products Processor & Distr
N.A.I.C.S.: 423510

Evraz Nikom A.S. **(1)**
Prazska 900, Mnisek pod Brdy, 252 10, Prague, Czech Republic
Tel.: (420) 318592190
Ferroalloy & Corundum Material Mfr
N.A.I.C.S.: 331110

Evraz North America plc **(1)**
71 S Wacker Dr Ste 1700, Chicago, IL 60606
Tel.: (312) 533-3555
Web Site: https://www.evrazna.com
N.A.I.C.S.: 331110
Skip Herald (Pres)

Evraz Palini e Bertoli S.r.l **(1)**
Via E Fermi 28, San Giorgio di Nogaro, 33058, Udine, Italy
Tel.: (39) 0431623111
Web Site: http://www.evrazpaliniebertoli.it
Emp.: 100
Rolled Steel Plate Mfr
N.A.I.C.S.: 331221
Daniele Peressutti (Mgr-IT)

OJSC EVRAZ Vanady Tula **(1)**
Ul Przheval'skogo 1, 300016, Tula, Russia
Tel.: (7) 4872256900
Vanadium Pentoxide Mfr
N.A.I.C.S.: 325180

EVROFARMA SA

1 km Didimoticho - Orestiada, 68300, Alexandroupoli, Greece
Tel.: (30) 2553020020
Web Site: https://www.evrofarma.gr
Year Founded: 1991
EVROF—(ATH)
Sales Range: Less than $1 Million
Dairy Products Mfr & Distr
N.A.I.C.S.: 311514
Athanasios H. Papazilakis (Chm)

EVROFINANCE MOSNAR-BANK OJSC

29 Novy Arbat St, 121099, Moscow, Russia
Tel.: (7) 4959678182 **RU**
Web Site:
  http://www.evrofinance.com
Commercial Banking Services
N.A.I.C.S.: 522110
Sergey N. Yarosh (Chm-Mgmt Bd & CEO)

EVROPA AD

ul 808 br 8, 1000, Skopje, North Macedonia
Tel.: (389) 23114066
Web Site:
  https://www.evropa.com.mk
Year Founded: 1882
EVRO—(MAC)
Rev.: $15,749,893
Assets: $20,126,774
Liabilities: $2,399,854
Net Worth: $17,726,920
Earnings: $644,923
Fiscal Year-end: 12/31/23
Chocolate Mfr
N.A.I.C.S.: 311351

EVROPEYSKAYA ELEKTROTEKHNICA PJSC

1 Lyotchika Babushkina St Building 3 Floor 2 Space IX Room 23, 129344, Moscow, 129344, Russia
Tel.: (7) 4956603876
Web Site: https://www.euroetpao.ru
Year Founded: 2004
EELT—(MOEX)
Emp.: 350
Electrical Equipment Mfr & Distr
N.A.I.C.S.: 335210

Sergey Dubenok (Chm & Dir-Dev)

EVS BROADCAST EQUIPMENT S.A.

Liege Science Park 13 Rue Bois St Jean, 4102, Seraing, 4102, Belgium
Tel.: (32) 43617000
Web Site: https://www.evs.com
Year Founded: 1994
EVSBY—(OTCIQ)
Rev.: $186,910,209
Assets: $271,504,425
Liabilities: $65,050,723
Net Worth: $206,453,702
Earnings: $39,872,653
Emp.: 622
Fiscal Year-end: 12/31/23
Digital Equipment & Automation Software Designer, Mfr & Marketer
N.A.I.C.S.: 334220
Michel Counson (Mng Dir)

Subsidiaries:

EVS Broadcast Equipment Iberica S.L. **(1)**
12-2C Avenida de Europa, Edificio Monaco Parque Empresarial de la Moraleja, 28108, Alcobendas, Madrid, Spain
Tel.: (34) 914903930
Sales Range: $25-49.9 Million
Emp.: 4
Broadcasting Equipment Mfr
N.A.I.C.S.: 334220

EVS Broadcast Equipment Ltd. **(1)**
Room A 35/F Lee & Man Commercial Center 169 Electric Road, North Point, China (Hong Kong)
Tel.: (852) 29142501
Emp.: 12
Broadcasting Equipment Mfr
N.A.I.C.S.: 334220

EVS Broadcast UK Ltd. **(1)**
13th Floor One Angel Court, London, EC2R 7HJ, Surrey, United Kingdom
Tel.: (44) 1372387250
Sales Range: $50-74.9 Million
Emp.: 27
Broadcasting Equipment Distr
N.A.I.C.S.: 423690

EVS Canada Inc. **(1)**
1200 Avenue Papineau Bureau 240, Montreal, H2K 4R5, QC, Canada
Tel.: (514) 400-9360
Web Site: http://www.evs-global.com
Sales Range: $25-49.9 Million
Emp.: 3
Television Broadcasting Equipment Mfr
N.A.I.C.S.: 334220

EVS Deutschland GmbH **(1)**
Fraunhoferstrasse 7, 85737, Ismaning, Germany
Tel.: (49) 89411194900
Emp.: 14
Broadcast Equipment Mfr
N.A.I.C.S.: 334220
Jamie Gordon Mitchell (Mgr-Office)

EVS France Developpement S.A.R.L. **(1)**
48 Quai Carnot, 92210, Saint-Cloud, Hauts-de-Seine, France
Tel.: (33) 1 41 12 1245
Web Site: http://www.evs-global.com
Television Broadcasting Equipment Mfr
N.A.I.C.S.: 334220

EVS France S.A. **(1)**
62bis Avenue Andre Morizet, 92100, Boulogne-Billancourt, France
Tel.: (33) 146999000
Web Site: http://www.evs.tv
Sales Range: $25-49.9 Million
Emp.: 3
Television Broadcasting Equipment Mfr
N.A.I.C.S.: 334220

EVS Inc. **(1)**
700 US 46 E Fl 3, Fairfield, NJ 07004
Tel.: (324) 361-7014
Web Site: http://www.evs-global.com
Sales Range: $25-49.9 Million
Emp.: 10
Broadcast Equipment Mfr

N.A.I.C.S.: 334220

EVS Italy S.R.L. **(1)**
Via Milano 2, 25126, Brescia, Italy
Tel.: (39) 030296400
Sales Range: $25-49.9 Million
Emp.: 3
Broadcasting Equipment Mfr
N.A.I.C.S.: 334220

Fundamental Acoustic Research (FAR) **(1)**
Poissonrue 43, 4500, Huy, Belgium
Tel.: (32) 85318123
Sales Range: $25-49.9 Million
Emp.: 3
Acoustic Studio Designer & Mfr
N.A.I.C.S.: 512240

XDC S.A. **(1)**
Rue De Mulhouse 36, Liege, 4020, Belgium
Tel.: (32) 43641200
Web Site: http://www.dcinex.com
Sales Range: $1-9.9 Million
Emp.: 80
Digital Cinema Service Company
N.A.I.C.S.: 512199
Georges Garic (Sr VP-Acting)

EVZ LIMITED

Suite 115 838 Collins Street, Melbourne, 3008, VIC, Australia
Tel.: (61) 395455288 **AU**
Web Site: https://www.evz.com.au
EVZ—(ASX)
Rev.: $74,237,380
Assets: $40,015,138
Liabilities: $19,690,713
Net Worth: $20,324,424
Earnings: $965,534
Emp.: 350
Fiscal Year-end: 06/30/23
Engineering Services
N.A.I.C.S.: 541330
Scott Farthing (CEO)

Subsidiaries:

Brockman Engineering Pty Ltd **(1)**
87 St Georges Rd, Norlane, Geelong, 3214, VIC, Australia
Tel.: (61) 35 274 1222
Web Site: https://www.brockmaneng.com.au
Sales Range: $25-49.9 Million
Emp.: 135
Tank Engineering & Steel Fabrication Services
N.A.I.C.S.: 332111

Danum Engineering Pty. Ltd. **(1)**
17 Seaforth Street, North Shore, Geelong, 3214, VIC, Australia
Tel.: (61) 3 5278 4488
Web Site: http://www.danum.com.au
Sales Range: $25-49.9 Million
Emp.: 100
Engineering Services
N.A.I.C.S.: 541330

Syfon Systems Pty Ltd **(1)**
22 Hargreaves Street, Huntingdale, 3166, VIC, Australia
Tel.: (61) 39 542 6000
Web Site: https://www.syfon.com
Sales Range: $25-49.9 Million
Emp.: 70
Roof Drainage Services
N.A.I.C.S.: 238160
Adam Bellgrove (Mng Dir)

TSF Engineering Pty Ltd **(1)**
F41/16 Mars Road, Lane Cove, 2066, NSW, Australia
Tel.: (61) 290025650
Web Site: http://www.tsfeng.com.au
Sales Range: $50-74.9 Million
Emp.: 30
Power Generation Equipments Mfr
N.A.I.C.S.: 221118
Andrew Green (Gen Mgr)

TSF Power Pty Ltd **(1)**
3/74 Glendenning Rd, Glendenning, 2761, NSW, Australia
Tel.: (61) 29 002 5650
Web Site: https://www.tsfpower.com.au
Industrial Machinery Repair Services
N.A.I.C.S.: 811310

EW GROUP GMBH

Hogenbogen 1, 49429, Visbek, Germany
Tel.: (49) 4445950590
Web Site: http://www.ew-group.de
Poultry Breeding Services
N.A.I.C.S.: 112340

Subsidiaries:

Aviagen Limited **(1)**
11 Lothend Rd, Newbridge, EH28 8SZ, Midlothian, United Kingdom
Tel.: (44) 313331056
Web Site: http://www.aviagen.com
Sales Range: $25-49.9 Million
Emp.: 150
Poultry Producer
N.A.I.C.S.: 112390
Ben Thompson (Pres)

Subsidiary (US):

Aviagen Incorporated **(2)**
Cummings Research Park 5015 Bradford Dr NW, Huntsville, AL 35805-1943
Tel.: (256) 890-3800
Web Site: http://www.aviagen.com
Sales Range: $25-49.9 Million
Emp.: 80
Poultry Breeders
N.A.I.C.S.: 112390
Marcelo Silva (Head-Nutrition Svcs-Global)

Subsidiary (Domestic):

Aviagen Inc. **(3)**
Cummings Research Park 920 Explorer Blvd NW, Huntsville, AL 35806
Tel.: (256) 890-3800
Web Site: http://www.en.aviagen.com
Sales Range: $75-99.9 Million
Turkey Breeding & Genetic Research Services
N.A.I.C.S.: 112330
Curt Brammer (VP-Ops)

CWT Farms International, Inc. **(3)**
1180 Airport Industrial Park, Gainesville, GA 30501
Tel.: (770) 532-3181
Sales Range: $10-24.9 Million
Emp.: 30
Egg Production Services
N.A.I.C.S.: 112390
Rickey Smith (Pres)

EWE AKTIENGESELLSCHAFT

Tirpitzstrasse 39, 26122, Oldenburg, Lower Saxony, Germany
Tel.: (49) 441 4805 0   De
Web Site: http://www.ewe.com
Sales Range: $5-14.9 Billion
Emp.: 9,162
Energy Services
N.A.I.C.S.: 221122

Subsidiaries:

BCC Business Communication Company GmbH **(1)**
Heinrich-Nordhoff-Str 69, Wolfsburg, 38440, Germany
Tel.: (49) 5361 2777 0
Web Site: http://www.icyteas.de
Sales Range: $25-49.9 Million
Emp.: 1,000
Information Technology Consulting Services
N.A.I.C.S.: 541512
Norbert Westphal (Gen Mgr)

BTC Bilisim Hizmetleri A.S. **(1)**
Icerenkoy Mah Cayir Cad No 1/4 PARTAS Center Specialty Site 2-12-13, Umraniye, 34752, Istanbul, Turkiye
Tel.: (90) 2165754590
IT Consulting Services
N.A.I.C.S.: 541618
Engin Guler (Mgr-Svc Desk)

BTC Business Technology Consulting AG **(1)**
Escherweg 5, 26121, Oldenburg, Germany
Tel.: (49) 441 36 12 0
Web Site: http://www.btc-ag.com
Rev.: $219,829,561
Emp.: 1,512
Information Technology Consulting Services

N.A.I.C.S.: 541512
Bulent Uzuner (CEO)

BTC Embedded Systems AG **(1)**
Gerhard-Stalling-Strasse 19, 26135, Oldenburg, Germany
Tel.: (49) 4419697380
Web Site: http://www.btc-es.de
Software Development Services
N.A.I.C.S.: 541511
Udo Brockmeyer (CEO)

BTC IT Services GmbH **(1)**
Escherweg 5, 26121, Oldenburg, Germany
Tel.: (49) 441 36 192 0
Web Site: http://www.btc-it-services.com
Information Technology Consulting Services
N.A.I.C.S.: 541512

BTC Software Systems Sp. z o.o. **(1)**
ul Grunwaldzka 184, 60-166, Poznan, Poland
Tel.: (48) 531018780
Web Site: http://www.btc-ag.pl
IT Consulting Services
N.A.I.C.S.: 541618
Patryk Dabrowski (Engr-Software)

BTC Software Technology (Shanghai) Co., Ltd. **(1)**
No 888 MoYu South Road Room 603, Jiading District, Shanghai, China
Tel.: (86) 2169891361
IT Consulting Services
N.A.I.C.S.: 541618

Brekom GmbH **(1)**
At Weser Terminal 1, 28217, Bremen, Germany
Tel.: (49) 42124004444
Web Site: http://www.brekom.de
Communication & Security Services
N.A.I.C.S.: 561621

Bursagaz Bursa Sehirici Dogalgaz Dagitim Ticaret ve Taahhut A.S. **(1)**
Kavaklidere Sk No 15, 16265, Bursa, Turkiye
Tel.: (90) 444 1 133
Natural Gas Distr
N.A.I.C.S.: 221210

Digitalprojekt 1 GmbH **(1)**
Neue Grunstrasse 27, 10179, Berlin, Germany
Tel.: (49) 3056837744
Web Site: http://www.vertragsatlas.de
Digital Data Services
N.A.I.C.S.: 518210

E&D Energie- und Dienstleistungs GmbH & Co. KG **(1)**
Merlostr 10, 50668, Cologne, Germany
Tel.: (49) 221 972242 0
Natural Gas Distr
N.A.I.C.S.: 221210

ENRo Ludwigsfelde Energie GmbH **(1)**
Rudolf-Diesel-Strabe 15 Industriepark, 14974, Ludwigsfelde, Germany
Tel.: (49) 3378 82 30
Web Site: http://www.enro-ludwigsfelde.de
Electric Power, Heat & Natural Gas Distr
N.A.I.C.S.: 221122

EWE Biogas GmbH & Co. KG **(1)**
Isums 45a, Wittmund, 26409, Germany
Tel.: (49) 4462 9199 0
Web Site: http://www.ewe-biogas.de
Emp.: 10
Electric Power Generation Services
N.A.I.C.S.: 221118
Manuela Beyer (Mng Dir)

EWE Direkt GmbH **(1)**
Cloppenburger Strasse 310, 26133, Oldenburg, Germany
Tel.: (49) 44180001202
Web Site: http://www.ewedirekt.de
Energy & Telecommunication Provider Services
N.A.I.C.S.: 237130

EWE ERNEUERBARE ENERGIEN GmbH **(1)**
Donnerschweer Strasse 22-26, 26123, Oldenburg, Germany
Tel.: (49) 44148067101

Web Site: http://www.ewe-erneuerbare.de
Energy Renewable Generation Services
N.A.I.C.S.: 221114
Georg Boie (Mng Dir)

Subsidiary (Domestic):

EWE Offshore Service & Solutions GmbH **(2)**
Donnerschweer Strasse 22-26, 26123, Oldenburg, Germany
Tel.: (49) 44135021151
Web Site: http://www.ewe-oss.de
Offshore Planning & Construction Services
N.A.I.C.S.: 541330
Jan-Dirk Kleine Holthaus (Co-CEO)

EWE Enerji AS **(1)**
Buyukdere Cad No 127 Astoria Tower A Kat 4, 34394, Esentepe, Istanbul, Turkiye
Tel.: (90) 212 336 60 10
Web Site: http://www.eweenerji.com.tr
Sales Range: $75-99.9 Million
Emp.: 15
Natural Gas Distr
N.A.I.C.S.: 221210

EWE Gasspeicher GmbH **(1)**
Moslestrasse 7, 26122, Oldenburg, Germany
Tel.: (49) 441350100
Web Site: http://www.ewe-gasspeicher.de
Natural Gas Storage & Distr
N.A.I.C.S.: 486210
Peter Schmidt (Mng Dir)

EWE IMMoBILIEN GmbH **(1)**
Donnerschweer Str 22, Oldenburg, 26123, Germany
Tel.: (49) 44148050
Web Site: http://www.ewe.de
Emp.: 9,100
Natural Gas Distr
N.A.I.C.S.: 221210
Werner Brinker (CEO)

EWE Polska Sp. z o.o. **(1)**
Ul Grunwaldzka 184, 60-166, Poznan, Poland
Tel.: (48) 801100800
Natural Gas Distribution Services
N.A.I.C.S.: 221210
Daniel Waschow (CEO)

EWE TEL GmbH **(1)**
Cloppenburger Str 310, 26133, Oldenburg, Germany
Tel.: (49) 441 8000 2773
Telecommunication Servicesb
N.A.I.C.S.: 517810

EWE TRADING GmbH **(1)**
Tirpitzstrabe 39, Oldenburg, Germany
Tel.: (49) 441 35095 0
Sales Range: $100-124.9 Million
Emp.: 65
Electric Power & Natural Gas Distr
N.A.I.C.S.: 221122

EWE Urbanisation Dienstleistungs GmbH **(1)**
Am Weser-Terminal 1, 28217, Bremen, Germany
Tel.: (49) 421 696527 0
Web Site: http://www.udg-ewe.de
Sales Range: $25-49.9 Million
Emp.: 1
Residential Building Construction Services
N.A.I.C.S.: 236116
Manuel Braun (Gen Mgr)

EWE VERTRIEB GmbH **(1)**
Donnerschweer Str 22-26, 26123, Oldenburg, Germany
Tel.: (49) 4 41 803 0
Electric Power & Natural Gas Distr
N.A.I.C.S.: 221122

Subsidiary (Domestic):

EWE NETZ GmbH **(2)**
Cloppenburger Str 302, Oldenburg, 26133, Germany
Tel.: (49) 441 4808 0
Web Site: http://www.ewe-netz.de
Energy Infrastructure Network Operator
N.A.I.C.S.: 237130

EWE Wasser GmbH **(1)**
Humphry-Davy-Str 41, 27472, Cuxhaven, Germany

Tel.: (49) 472159260
Web Site: http://www.wasser.ewe.de
Waste Water Management Services
N.A.I.C.S.: 221320
Sonke Duetsch (Mgr-Comml)

EWE energia Sp. z o. o. **(1)**
Ul January 30 67, Miedzyrzecz, 66-300, Gorzow, Poland
Tel.: (48) 801100800
Web Site: http://www.ewe.pl
Natural Gas Distribution Services
N.A.I.C.S.: 221210

Gastransport Nord GmbH **(1)**
Cloppenburger Strasse 363, 26133, Oldenburg, Germany
Tel.: (49) 44120980252
Web Site: http://www.gtg-nord.de
Emp.: 40
Gas Pipeline Transport Services
N.A.I.C.S.: 486210
Kay Borchelt (Mng Dir)

Gemeinschaftskraftwerk Bremen GmbH & Co. KG **(1)**
Theodor-Heuss-Allee 20, 28215, Bremen, Germany
Tel.: (49) 4213592726
Web Site: http://www.gk-bremen.de
Gas & Steam Turbine Power Plant Services
N.A.I.C.S.: 221112

Kayserigaz Kayseri Dogalgaz Dagitim Pazarlama ve Ticaret A.S. **(1)**
Yeni Mahalle Mustafa Kemal Pasa Bulvari 5 Cadde No 61, Kocasinan, 38090, Kayseri, Turkiye
Tel.: (90) 352 207 20 00
Web Site: http://www.kayserigaz.com
Sales Range: $125-149.9 Million
Emp.: 150
Natural Gas Distr
N.A.I.C.S.: 221210

Limon GmbH **(1)**
Grosse Rosenstrasse 21, 34117, Kassel, Germany
Tel.: (49) 5612207040
Web Site: http://www.limon-gmbh.de
Energy Efficiency & Management Services
N.A.I.C.S.: 221118
Mark Junge (Founder & CEO)

NaturWatt GmbH **(1)**
Rummelweg 14, Oldenburg, 26122, Germany
Tel.: (49) 441 350910 0
Web Site: http://www.naturwatt.de
Electric Power Distr
N.A.I.C.S.: 221122

PRo CoNSULT Management- und Systemberatung GmbH **(1)**
Wilhelm-Theodor-Romheld-Strabe 24, 55130, Mainz, Germany
Tel.: (49) 6131 27562 0
Web Site: http://www.proconsult.de
Business Management Consulting Services
N.A.I.C.S.: 541611

SEC Selecta Energy Consulting GmbH **(1)**
Am Hohenstein 3-5, 65779, Kelkheim, Germany
Tel.: (49) 619567360
Web Site: http://www.mysec.de
Emp.: 30
Program Development Services
N.A.I.C.S.: 541511
Andreas Kerker (Mng Dir)

SoCoN Sonar Control Kavernenvermessung GmbH **(1)**
Windmuhlenstrabe 41, Emmerke, 31180, Giesen, Germany
Tel.: (49) 5121 998 19 0
Web Site: http://www.socon.info
Sales Range: $25-49.9 Million
Emp.: 60
Cavern Surveying Services
N.A.I.C.S.: 541360

TEWE Energieversorgungsgesellschaft mbH **(1)**
Hegermuhlenstr 58, Strausberg, 15344, Berlin, Germany
Tel.: (49) 3341382120
Web Site: http://www.tewe-energie.de
Heating System Installation Services

EWE Aktiengesellschaft—(Continued)

N.A.I.C.S.: 238220

best-blu consulting with energy GmbH (1)
In the Blumentrifte 60, 38226, Salzgitter, Germany
Tel.: (49) 5341853930
Web Site: http://www.best-blu.de
IT Management Services
N.A.I.C.S.: 541611

offshore Windpark RIFFGAT GmbH & Co. KG (1)
Tirpitzstrasse 39, 26122, Oldenburg, Germany
Tel.: (49) 44148050
Web Site: http://www.ewe.de
Electric Power Generation & Distri
N.A.I.C.S.: 221118

qbig GmbH (1)
Cloppenburger Strasse 363, 26133, Oldenburg, Germany
Tel.: (49) 4914541920
Web Site: http://www.qbig-calibration.de
Oil & Natural Gas Services
N.A.I.C.S.: 213112
Holger Waden (CEO)

swb Beleuchtung GmbH (1)
Am Gaswerkgraben 2, 28197, Bremen, Germany
Tel.: (49) 4213594541
Waste Disposal Services
N.A.I.C.S.: 562119

swb Entsorgung GmbH & Co. KG (1)
Otavistr 7-9, Bremen, 28237, Germany
Tel.: (49) 421 359 79 333
Emp.: 132
Waste Disposal Services
N.A.I.C.S.: 562211
Christian Walter (Dir-Sls)

swb Erzeugung GmbH & Co. KG (1)
Theodor-Heuss-Allee 20, 28215, Bremen, Germany
Tel.: (49) 421 359 3351
Sales Range: $250-299.9 Million
Emp.: 500
Eletric Power Generation Services
N.A.I.C.S.: 221118

swb Gasumstellung GmbH (1)
Theodor-Heuss-Allee 20, 28215, Bremen, Germany
Tel.: (49) 4213595302
Natural Gas Distribution Services
N.A.I.C.S.: 221210

swb Messung und Abrechnung GmbH (1)
Theodor-Heuss-Allee 20, 28215, Bremen, Germany
Tel.: (49) 421 988 68 0
Web Site: http://www.swb-gruppe.de
Sales Range: $25-49.9 Million
Emp.: 180
Utility Metering Services
N.A.I.C.S.: 561990
Thorsten Koehne (Gen Mgr)

swb Services AG & Co. KG (1)
Theodor-Heuss-Allee 20, 28215, Bremen, Germany
Tel.: (49) 421 359 0
Web Site: http://www.swb-services.de
Sales Range: $25-49.9 Million
Emp.: 180
Energy Consulting Services
N.A.I.C.S.: 541690
Torsten Butt (Head-Electric Energy Sys)

swb Vertrieb Bremen GmbH (1)
Theodor-Heuss-Allee 20, 28215, Bremen, Germany
Tel.: (49) 421 359 3590
Electric Power Distr
N.A.I.C.S.: 221122

swb Vertrieb Bremerhaven GmbH & Co. KG (1)
Schifferstrasse 36 - 40, 27568, Bremerhaven, Germany
Tel.: (49) 471 477 1111
Web Site: http://www.swb.de
Electric Power Distr

N.A.I.C.S.: 221122

wesernetz Bremen GmbH (1)
Theodor-Heuss-Allee 20, 28215, Bremen, Germany
Tel.: (49) 4213591212
Web Site: http://www.wesernetz.de
Natural Gas Distribution Services
N.A.I.C.S.: 221210

wesernetz Bremerhaven GmbH (1)
Rickmersstrabe 90, 27568, Bremerhaven, Germany
Tel.: (49) 471 477 2300
Web Site: http://www.wesernetz.de
Eltric Power Generation Services
N.A.I.C.S.: 221118
Andreas Frostl (CEO)

EWEIN BERHAD

Suite 1-1-2 Menara IJM Land 1 Lebuh Tunku Kudin 3, 11700, Gelugor, Penang, Malaysia
Tel.: (60) 42910036
Web Site:
https://www.eweinberhad.com
EWEIN—(KLS)
Rev.: $9,958,470
Assets: $60,310,372
Liabilities: $7,400,855
Net Worth: $52,909,517
Earnings: ($100,869)
Emp.: 400
Fiscal Year-end: 12/31/22
Holding Company; Precision Sheet Metal Fabricated Parts Mfr
N.A.I.C.S.: 551112
Swee Kheng Ewe (Pres & Mng Dir-Grp)

Subsidiaries:

City of Dreams Penang Sdn. Bhd. (1)
City of Dreams No 1 Jalan Peter Paul Dason, Bandar Seri Tanjung Pinang Tanjung Tokong DTL, 10470, Penang, Malaysia
Tel.: (60) 12 443 8888
Web Site:
https://www.cityofdreamspenang.com.my
Residential Properties Services
N.A.I.C.S.: 531311

Kelpen Resources Sdn Bhd (KRSB) (1)
212 Tkt Perusahaan 4, 13600, Prai, Pulau Pinang, Malaysia
Tel.: (60) 43976584
Sales Range: $25-49.9 Million
Emp.: 100
Investment Management Service
N.A.I.C.S.: 541618

Subsidiary (Domestic):

Kelpen Plastics Technology Sdn. Bhd (2)
Plot 212 Mukim 1 Tingkat Perusahaan 4, Free Industrial Zone, Prai, 13600, Pulau Pinang, Malaysia
Tel.: (60) 43977255
Web Site: http://www.kelpen.com.my
Sales Range: $25-49.9 Million
Metal Products Mfr
N.A.I.C.S.: 332999

Precision Press Industries Sdn Bhd (PPISB) (1)
Plot 318 Tingkat Perusahaan 3 Mk 1 Kawasan, Perindustrian Prai, Perai, 13600, Penang, Malaysia
Tel.: (60) 43992122
Web Site: http://www.tekunasas.com
Sales Range: $25-49.9 Million
Emp.: 10
Metal Stamping Service Provider
N.A.I.C.S.: 332119

Tekun Asas Sdn Bhd (TASB) (1)
Plot 318 Tingkat Perusahaan Tiga Mukim 1 Kawasan Perusahaan Perai, Perusahaan, 13600, Perai, Penang, Malaysia
Tel.: (60) 4 399 2122
Web Site: https://www.tekunasas.com
Sales Range: $100-124.9 Million
Emp.: 300
Metal Products Mfr

N.A.I.C.S.: 332999

Tekun Asas Sdn. Bhd. (1)
Plot 318 Tingkat Perusahaan Tiga Mukim 1 Kawasan Perusahaan, 13600, Perai, Penang, Malaysia
Tel.: (60) 43992122
Web Site: https://www.tekunasas.com
Sheet Metal Work Mfg
N.A.I.C.S.: 332322
Ewe Swee Kheng (Founder)

EWG SLUPSK SP. Z.O.O

Stefana Okrzei 17, Legnica, 59-220, Poland
Tel.: (48) 76 852 28 10
Web Site: http://www.windfarm.pl
Chemical Products Mfr
N.A.I.C.S.: 325998
Waldameer Nazarewicz (Gen Mgr)

EWING PUBLIC RELATIONS, S.R.O.

Classic 7 Business Park Building L Jankovcova 1603 / 47a, Holesovice, 170 00, Prague, Czech Republic
Tel.: (420) 224 828 065 8
Web Site: http://www.ewingpr.cz
Year Founded: 1998
Sales Range: $1-9.9 Million
Emp.: 20
Public Relations Agency
N.A.I.C.S.: 541820
Jiri Hrabovsky (Owner)

EWON COMFORTECH CO., LTD.

8 Cheomdan 1-ro, Yeounmu-eup, Jeongeup, Jeonlabuk-do, Korea (South)
Tel.: (82) 639281000
Web Site:
https://www.ewonseat.co.kr
Year Founded: 1994
088290—(KRS)
Rev.: $36,645,209
Assets: $75,071,082
Liabilities: $37,084,637
Net Worth: $37,986,444
Earnings: ($7,397,396)
Emp.: 74
Fiscal Year-end: 12/31/22
Automobile Seats Mfr
N.A.I.C.S.: 336360
Zin Young Hong (Co-CEO)

Subsidiaries:

Ewon Comfortech Co., Ltd. - Jeongup Factory (1)
8 Cheomdan 1-ro, 56121, Jeongeup, Jeollabuk-do, Korea (South)
Tel.: (82) 639281000
Automotive Car Seat Mfr
N.A.I.C.S.: 336360

Ewon Comfortech Co., Ltd. - Jiangyang Factory (1)
2-2 Hyundai-dong, Jiangyang, Luzhou, Sichuan, China
Tel.: (86) 18080560307
Automotive Car Seat Mfr
N.A.I.C.S.: 336360

Ewon Comfortech Co., Ltd. - Turkey Factory (1)
Hasanaga Organize Sanayi Bolgesi 1 Cadde No 18, Nilufer, 16225, Bursa, Turkiye
Tel.: (90) 2244842627
Automotive Car Seat Mfr
N.A.I.C.S.: 336360

EWORK GROUP AB

Vasagatan 16, 111 21, Stockholm, Sweden
Tel.: (46) 850605500
Web Site:
https://www.eworkgroup.com
EWRK—(OMX)
Rev.: $1,505,149,625

Assets: $449,591,540
Liabilities: $425,159,928
Net Worth: $24,431,613
Earnings: $13,036,706
Emp.: 268
Fiscal Year-end: 12/31/22
IT & Management Consulting Services
N.A.I.C.S.: 541690
Staffan Salen (Chm)

Subsidiaries:

eWork Danmark ApS (1)
Havnegade 39, 1058, Copenhagen, Denmark
Tel.: (45) 88969550
Web Site: http://www.eworknordic.com
Sales Range: $25-49.9 Million
Emp.: 7
Business Consulting Services
N.A.I.C.S.: 541611

eWork Nordic OY (1)
Tekniikantie 4B, 02150, Espoo, Uusimaa, Finland
Tel.: (358) 207870800
Web Site: http://www.eworknordic.com
Sales Range: $25-49.9 Million
Emp.: 10
Business Consulting Services
N.A.I.C.S.: 541611

eWork Norge AS (1)
Ovre Slottsgate 12B, 0157, Oslo, Norway
Tel.: (47) 22403620
Web Site: http://www.ework.no
Sales Range: $25-49.9 Million
Emp.: 10
Business Consulting Services
N.A.I.C.S.: 541611

EX A.D.

Kralja Aleksandra I Karadordevica 33, Kragujevac, Serbia
Tel.: (381) 34 335 222
Year Founded: 1996
MDEX—(BEL)
Sales Range: Less than $1 Million
Retail Store Operator
N.A.I.C.S.: 459999
Dragoljub Milovanovic (Exec Dir)

EXA E&C INC.

Daerung Post Tower 1st 15F Digitalro 288, Guro-Gu, Seoul, Korea (South)
Tel.: (82) 232895100
Web Site: https://www.exaenc.com
Year Founded: 1988
054940—(KRS)
Rev.: $174,923,211
Assets: $116,029,993
Liabilities: $59,711,851
Net Worth: $56,318,143
Earnings: $5,785,422
Emp.: 194
Fiscal Year-end: 12/31/22
Interior Design Services
N.A.I.C.S.: 541410

Subsidiaries:

EXA E&C Inc. - Kimpo Factory (1)
43 Gahyeon-ro, Tongjin-eup, Gimpo, Gyeonggi-do, Korea (South)
Tel.: (82) 7046982406
Glass Products Mfr
N.A.I.C.S.: 327211

Emsonic Co., Ltd (1)
54-8 Cheomdangieop 3-ro, Sandongmyeon, Gumi, Gyeongsangbuk-do, Korea (South)
Tel.: (82) 544764800
Electronic Components Mfr
N.A.I.C.S.: 334419
Cha Kuek Koo (Chm)

EXACT THERAPEUTICS AS

Ostre Aker vei 19, 0581, Oslo, Norway
Tel.: (47) 93022509   NO
Web Site: https://www.exact-tx.com
Year Founded: 2012

EXTX—(OSL)
Rev.: $118,238
Assets: $5,664,047
Liabilities: $1,498,069
Net Worth: $4,165,978
Earnings: ($4,464,594)
Emp.: 12
Fiscal Year-end: 12/31/23
Biotechnology Research & Development Services
N.A.I.C.S.: 541714
Amir Snapir (CMO)

EXALCO FINANCE PLC
Cornerstone Business Centre-Level 4
16th September Square, Mosta, MST
1180, Malta
Tel.: (356) 2 142 4430
Web Site:
   http://www.exalcogroup.com
Year Founded: 1987
EX28A—(MAL)
Rev.: $914,532
Assets: $18,914,004
Liabilities: $18,490,257
Net Worth: $423,748
Earnings: $44,102
Fiscal Year-end: 12/31/21
Building Maintenance Services
N.A.I.C.S.: 562910
Alexander Montanaro (Founder)

EXAMOBILE SA
ul Kustronia 40, 43-300, Bielsko-
Biala, Poland
Tel.: (48) 797121313
Web Site: https://www.examobile.pl
Year Founded: 2011
Software Development Services
N.A.I.C.S.: 541511
Maciek Blasiak (CEO)

EXASOL AG
Neumeyerstr 22-26, 90411, Nuremberg, Germany
Tel.: (49) 911239910
Web Site: https://www.ir.exasol.com
EXL—(DEU)
Rev.: $38,795,322
Assets: $22,081,936
Liabilities: $11,801,665
Net Worth: $10,280,272
Earnings: ($9,066,750)
Emp.: 193
Fiscal Year-end: 12/31/23
Software Development Services
N.A.I.C.S.: 541511
Aaron Auld (Co-CEO & Member-Mgmt Bd)

Subsidiaries:

EXASOL UK Ltd.   (1)
Parkshot House 5 Kew Road, Richmond,
London, TW9 2PR, United Kingdom
Tel.: (44) 2038138310
Database Development Services
N.A.I.C.S.: 518210

Exasol Schweiz AG   (1)
Claridenstrasse 25, 8002, Zurich, Switzerland
Tel.: (41) 435881125
Analytics Database Management Software
Services
N.A.I.C.S.: 518210

EXATEL S.A.
ul Perkuna 47, 04-164, Warsaw, Poland
Tel.: (48) 223406050   PL
Web Site: http://www.exatel.pl
Year Founded: 1993
Data Transmission; IT Services;
Radio-Communications; Mobile &
Fixed Telephony; Line Facilities General Contractor
N.A.I.C.S.: 518210
Nikodem Boncza Tomaszewski (Chm)

EXCALA GROUP
Cra 42 86 25 Autopista Sur, Itagui,
Antioquia, Colombia
Tel.: (57) 6043658888
Web Site: https://grupoexcala.com
Year Founded: 2000
EMPAQUES—(COLO)
Sales Range: Less than $1 Million
Fiber & Plastic Resin Mfr
N.A.I.C.S.: 325211
Pedro Miguel Estrada Londono (Pres)

EXCALIBUR GLOBAL FINANCIAL HOLDINGS LTD.
Room 2512 Cosco Tower 183
Queen's Road Central, Hong Kong,
China (Hong Kong)
Tel.: (852) 25260388
Web Site:
   http://www.excalibur.com.hk
8350—(HKG)
Rev.: $895,305
Assets: $8,431,830
Liabilities: $8,591,970
Net Worth: ($160,140)
Earnings: ($1,624,350)
Emp.: 17
Fiscal Year-end: 12/31/22
Financial Investment Services
N.A.I.C.S.: 523999
Allan Poon (Chm & CEO)

Subsidiaries:

Excalibur Global Financial Group
Ltd.   (1)
Room 2512 Cosco Tower 183 Queens
Road, Central, China (Hong Kong)
Tel.: (852) 25260388
Financial Services
N.A.I.C.S.: 523999
Poon Kwok Wah Allan (CEO & Exec Dir)

EXCEED COMPANY LTD.
Level 12 China Minmetals Tower 79
Chatham Road South, Tsim Sha Tsui,
Kowloon, China (Hong Kong)
Tel.: (852) 39758116   VG
Web Site: http://www.xdlong.cn
Year Founded: 2001
Sales Range: $200-249.9 Million
Emp.: 2,016
Sportswear & Footwear Mfr
N.A.I.C.S.: 315250
Shuipan Lin (Founder, Chm & CEO)

EXCEED WORLD, INC.
1-23-38-8F Esakacho, Suita-shi,
Osaka, 564-0063, Japan
Tel.: (81) 663394177   DE
Year Founded: 2014
EXDW—(OTCIQ)
Rev.: $25,922,721
Assets: $23,283,769
Liabilities: $6,669,826
Net Worth: $16,613,943
Earnings: ($551,747)
Emp.: 41
Fiscal Year-end: 09/30/23
Food Produts & Consumer Goods
Distr
N.A.I.C.S.: 424490
Tomoo Yoshida (Pres, CEO, CFO,
Treas & Sec)

EXCEL CELL ELECTRONIC CO., LTD.
No 20 25 Rd Taichung Industrial
Park, Taichung, 40850, Taiwan
Tel.: (886) 423591253
Web Site: https://www.ece.com.tw
2483—(TAI)
Rev.: $58,747,897
Assets: $137,919,515
Liabilities: $54,950,585
Net Worth: $82,968,930
Earnings: $1,211,158
Fiscal Year-end: 12/31/23

Electronic Components Mfr
N.A.I.C.S.: 334417

Subsidiaries:

Excel Cell Electronic (Suzhou) Co.,
Ltd.   (1)
No 577 Chenyun Road, Xiangcheng Area,
Suzhou, Jiangsu, China
Tel.: (86) 51265767668
Electronic Components Mfr
N.A.I.C.S.: 334419

Excel Cell Electronic (USA)
Corp.   (1)
628 Rte 10 Unit 12, Whippany, NJ 07981
Tel.: (973) 887-8116
Electronic Components Distr
N.A.I.C.S.: 423690

Excel Cell Electronic Anhui Co.,
Ltd.   (1)
No 529 Huzhou Road, Sino Singapore Suzhou Chuzhou High Tech Zone, Chuzhou,
Anhui, China
Tel.: (86) 5503900246
Electronic Components Mfr
N.A.I.C.S.: 334419

Good Sky Relay (Shenzhen) Co.,
Ltd.   (1)
No 27 Fuxin Road, Pingdi Subdistrict Longgang District, Shenzhen, Guangdong, China
Tel.: (86) 75584095566
Electronic Components Mfr
N.A.I.C.S.: 334419

EXCEL DEVELOPMENT BANK LTD.
Mukti Chowk Ward No 4 Birtamode
Municipality, Jhapa, Birtamod, 57203,
Nepal
Tel.: (977) 23543714
Web Site: https://www.edb.com.np
EDBL—(NEP)
Rev.: $9,267,777
Assets: $107,298,258
Liabilities: $95,056,838
Net Worth: $12,241,420
Earnings: $722,827
Emp.: 270
Fiscal Year-end: 07/16/22
Banking Services
N.A.I.C.S.: 522110
Mahendra Kumar Goyal (Chm)

EXCEL INDUSTRIES LIMITED
184-87 S V Road, Jogeshwari West,
Mumbai, 400 102, Maharashtra, India
Tel.: (91) 2266464200
Web Site: https://www.excelind.co.in
EXCELINDUS—(NSE)
Rev.: $103,587,011
Assets: $151,671,866
Liabilities: $35,436,588
Net Worth: $116,235,278
Earnings: $9,703,225
Emp.: 1,015
Fiscal Year-end: 03/31/21
Specialty Chemicals Mfr
N.A.I.C.S.: 325180
Ashwin C. Shroff (Chm & Mng Dir)

EXCEL MARITIME CARRIERS LTD.
c/o 17th Km National Road Athens-
Lamia & Finkos Street, 145 64, Athens, Nea Kifisia, Greece
Tel.: (30) 210 62 09 520   LR
Web Site:
   http://www.excelmaritime.com
Year Founded: 1989
Sales Range: $350-399.9 Million
Emp.: 1,171
Deep Sea Dry Bulk Cargo Carrier
Operator
N.A.I.C.S.: 483111
Pavlos Kanellopoulos (CFO)

Subsidiaries:

Maryville Maritime Inc.   (1)

Isestou 76 19400, Nea Kifisia, Koropi,
19400, Greece   **(100%)**
Tel.: (30) 2106209520
Sales Range: $75-99.9 Million
Emp.: 80
Vessel Manager & Shipping Services
N.A.I.C.S.: 483111
Kostas Koutsoubelis (Gen Mgr)

EXCEL REALTY N INFRA LTD.
31-A Laxmi Industrial Estate New
Link Road, Andheri West, Mumbai,
400053, India
Tel.: (91) 2226394246
Web Site: https://www.excel-infoways.com
EXCEL—(NSE)
Rev.: $1,267,850
Assets: $24,275,377
Liabilities: $779,797
Net Worth: $23,495,580
Earnings: $107,526
Emp.: 9
Fiscal Year-end: 03/31/21
Collections, Telemarketing, Customer
Care & IT Call Center & Outsourcing
Services
N.A.I.C.S.: 561422
Lakhmendra Khurana (Founder, Chm
& Mng Dir)

EXCEL SYSTEM (BEIJING) LIMITED
1305/H North Star Huiyuan Plaza No
8 Beichen East Road, Chaoyang District, Beijing, 100101, China
Tel.: (86) 1084871590
Web Site: http://www.excel.com.hk
Information Technology Services
N.A.I.C.S.: 513210

EXCEL TRANSPORTATION INC.
333 Ongman Road, Prince George,
V2K 4K9, BC, Canada
Tel.: (250) 563-7356
Web Site:
   http://exceltransportation.ca
Truck Transportation Services
N.A.I.C.S.: 484110
Annie Horning (CEO)

EXCELDOR COOPERATIVE AVICOLE
5700 rue J B Michaud Bureau 500,
Levis, G6V 0B1, QC, Canada
Tel.: (418) 830-5600
Web Site: http://www.exceldor.ca
Year Founded: 1945
Sales Range: $100-124.9 Million
Emp.: 800
Poultry Products Supplier
N.A.I.C.S.: 311615
Rene Proulx (Pres & CEO)

Subsidiaries:

Exceldor Cooperative Avicole - Saint-
Anselme Plant   (1)
1000 route Begin, Saint-Anselme, G0R
2N0, QC, Canada
Tel.: (418) 885-4451
Poultry Product Mfr
N.A.I.C.S.: 311615

Exceldor Cooperative Avicole - Saint-
Damase Plant   (1)
125 rue Sainte-Anne, Saint-Damase-de-
L'Islet, J0H 1J0, QC, Canada
Tel.: (450) 797-3331
Poultry Product Mfr
N.A.I.C.S.: 311615

Parrish & Heimbecker, Limited   (1)
201 Portage Avenue Suite 1400, Winnipeg,
R3B 3K6, MB, Canada
Tel.: (204) 956-2030
Web Site:
   http://www.parrishandheimbecker.com
Emp.: 400
Grain Production & Distribution Services

Exceldor Cooperative Avicole—(Continued)

N.A.I.C.S.: 111199
Gordon Ironside *(Mgr-Crop Input)*

Subsidiary (Domestic):

P&H Milling Group (2)
1060 Fountain St North, Cambridge, N3E
0A1, ON, Canada
Tel.: (519) 650-6400
Web Site: http://www.dovergrp.com
Sales Range: $250-299.9 Million
Flour & Food Mix Mfr; Ice Cream Cones,
Disposable Food Containers, Plastic Drink-
ing Straws & Folding Cartons Mfr
N.A.I.C.S.: 311211
Peter M. Downe *(VP-HR)*

Division (Domestic):

Dover Flour Mills Ltd. (3)
140 King St W, PO Box 3368, Cambridge,
N3H 4T3, ON, Canada
Tel.: (519) 653-6267
Web Site: http://www.phmilling.com
Sales Range: $25-49.9 Million
Emp.: 75
Types of Flour & Feed Mfr
N.A.I.C.S.: 311211

Plant (Domestic):

Dover Flour Halifax (4)
730 Marginal Rd, PO Box 2185, Halifax,
B3H 0A1, NS, Canada
Tel.: (902) 429-0622
Web Site: http://www.phmilling.com
Sales Range: $25-49.9 Million
Emp.: 65
Flour, Mixes & Feed Mfr
N.A.I.C.S.: 311211
Stan Thomas *(VP)*

Division (Domestic):

P&H Milling Group (2)
252 14th St, PO Box 219, Hanover, N4N
3C5, ON, Canada
Tel.: (519) 364-3260
Web Site: http://www.newlifemills.com
Sales Range: $75-99.9 Million
Emp.: 250
Livestock Feed & Custom Milled Flours
N.A.I.C.S.: 112112
Dave Park *(Gen Mgr)*

Plant (Domestic):

Parrish & Heimbecker, Limited - P&H
Foods Hanover Processing Plant (2)
478 - 14th Street, Hanover, N4N 1Z9, ON,
Canada
Tel.: (519) 364-1770
Grain Product Mfr
N.A.I.C.S.: 311211
Craig Shaw *(Gen Mgr)*

EXCELFORCE MSC BERHAD

Level 31 MYEG Tower Empire City
No 8 Jalan Damansara PJU 8,
47820, Petaling Jaya, Selangor, Ma-
laysia
Tel.: (60) 377352288   MY
Web Site:
   http://www.excelforce.com.my
Year Founded: 1994
EFORCE—(KLS)
Rev.: $9,180,963
Assets: $22,676,383
Liabilities: $2,169,373
Net Worth: $20,507,010
Earnings: $2,494,025
Emp.: 90
Fiscal Year-end: 06/30/23
Information Technology Consulting
Services
N.A.I.C.S.: 541512
Teck Ban Gan *(Exec Dir)*

Subsidiaries:

Insage (MSC) Sdn Bhd (1)
Level 31 MYEG Tower Empire City No 8
Jalan Damansara PJU 8, 47820, Petaling
Jaya, Selangor Darul Ehsan, Malaysia
Tel.: (60) 377352238
Web Site: https://www.insage.com.my

Investor Relation Services
N.A.I.C.S.: 523999

EXCELLENCE COMMERCIAL PROPERTY & FACILITIES MANAGEMENT GROUP LIMITED

Floor 38A Building 4 Excellence Cen-
tury Center Fuhua 3rd Road, Futian,
Shenzhen, 518000, Guangdong,
China
Tel.: (86) 75582927388   Ky
Web Site: https://www.excepm.com
Year Founded: 1999
6989—(HKG)
Rev.: $543,698,494
Assets: $719,759,360
Liabilities: $214,013,901
Net Worth: $505,745,459
Earnings: $44,770,021
Emp.: 85
Fiscal Year-end: 12/31/23
Property Management Services
N.A.I.C.S.: 531311
Yan Zhang *(Chief HR Officer)*

EXCELLENCE REAL ESTATE GROUP LIMITED

22nd Floor Excellence Mansion 98
Fuhua First Road, Futian Central Dis-
trict, Shenzhen, 518000, Guangdong,
China
Tel.: (86) 75582877000   Ky
Web Site: http://www.excegroup.com
Sales Range: $350-399.9 Million
Emp.: 1,560
Commercial & Residential Real Es-
tate Developer & Manager
N.A.I.C.S.: 236220
Hua Li *(Chm)*

EXCELLENCE SA

Lipa 20A, 95-010, Strykow, Poland
Tel.: (48) 427198112
Web Site: https://www.excellence-
sa.com
Year Founded: 1992
8XY—(DEU)
Beverages Mfr
N.A.I.C.S.: 312111
Dariusz Polinceusz *(Chm)*

EXCELLENT RETAIL BRANDS B.V.

Hoofdveste 10, 3992 DG, Houten,
Netherlands
Tel.: (31) 30 635 6300
Holding Company
N.A.I.C.S.: 551112
Roland Kahn *(Founder & CEO)*

Subsidiaries:

AT B.V. (1)
Diemermere 1, 1112 TA, Diemen, Nether-
lands
Tel.: (31) 205602600
Web Site: http://www.america-today.com
Sales Range: $25-49.9 Million
Emp.: 25
American Label Garments, Footwear & Ac-
cessories for Young People
N.A.I.C.S.: 458110
Gheo Houtmam *(Mng Dir)*

EXCELLERANT, INC.

54 Blvd du Regent, Brussels, 1000,
Belgium
Tel.: (32) 27810118   NV
Web Site: http://www.excellerant.vc
Year Founded: 2019
Assets: $20,745
Liabilities: $26,832
Net Worth: ($6,087)
Earnings: ($26,344)
Emp.: 1
Fiscal Year-end: 09/30/20
Health Care Consulting Services

N.A.I.C.S.: 541611
Marco von Pfetten *(Chm)*

EXCELLERATE HOLDINGS LTD.

3A Summit Rd Hyde Park, Johannes-
burg, South Africa
Tel.: (27) 116998600
Web Site:
   http://www.excellerate.co.za
Sales Range: $100-124.9 Million
Emp.: 8
Investment Holding Company
N.A.I.C.S.: 551112
James Wellsted *(Dir-Fin)*

Subsidiaries:

Ferrengi Household Products (Pty)
Ltd. (1)
772 Sixth St, Wynberg, Johannesburg,
2012, Gauteng, South Africa
Tel.: (27) 118872730
Web Site: http://www.ferrengi.co.za
Sales Range: $50-74.9 Million
Emp.: 60
Kitchen Accessories Mfr & Distr
N.A.I.C.S.: 325612

First Park (Pty) Ltd. (1)
1 Palm Blvd, Umhlanga, 4320, KwaZulu-
Natal, South Africa
Tel.: (27) 315663116
Parking Lot Operation Services
N.A.I.C.S.: 812930

Foodserv Solutions (Pty) Ltd. (1)
No 9 Watkins Street, Denver, Johannes-
burg, 2001, Gauteng, South Africa
Tel.: (27) 116165183
Web Site: http://www.foodserv.co.za
Sales Range: $75-99.9 Million
Food Service Equipment Distr
N.A.I.C.S.: 423440
Athol C. Stewart *(Mng Dir)*

Interpark (South Africa) (Pty) Ltd. (1)
37 Angus Crescent Longmeadow Bus Es-
tate E, Edenvale, 1609, Gauteng, South
Africa
Tel.: (27) 118790200
Web Site: http://www.interpark.co.za
Sales Range: $25-49.9 Million
Parking Lot Operation Services
N.A.I.C.S.: 812930
Kate Wolfaardt *(Mng Dir)*

Levingers Dry Cleaners (Pty)
Ltd. (1)
37 Angus Crescent Longmeadow Bus Es-
tate E, Private Bag x782, Edenvale, 1609,
Gauteng, South Africa
Tel.: (27) 118790270
Web Site: http://www.levingers.co.za
Dry Cleaning Services
N.A.I.C.S.: 812320

EXCELLIANCE MOS CORP.

4F 1 No 22 Taiyuan St, Hsinchu
County, Zhubei, 30288, Taiwan
Tel.: (886) 35600689
Web Site:
   https://www.excelliancemos.com
Year Founded: 2008
5299—(TPE)
Rev.: $72,993,184
Assets: $85,748,335
Liabilities: $29,194,478
Net Worth: $56,553,857
Earnings: $17,813,807
Fiscal Year-end: 12/31/22
Electric Equipment Mfr
N.A.I.C.S.: 335999
Chi-Lung Li *(Chm)*

EXCELLON RESOURCES INC.

10 King Street East Suite 200, To-
ronto, M5C 1C3, ON, Canada
Tel.: (416) 364-1130   BC
Web Site:
   https://www.excellonresources.com
Year Founded: 1987

EXN—(NYSEAMEX)
Rev.: $37,955,000
Assets: $41,560,000
Liabilities: $46,047,000
Net Worth: ($4,487,000)
Earnings: ($57,773,000)
Emp.: 257
Fiscal Year-end: 12/31/21
Silver, Zinc & Lead Mining & Devel-
opment Services
N.A.I.C.S.: 212220
Andre Y. Fortier *(Chm)*

Subsidiaries:

Otis Gold Corp. (1)
580 - 625 Howe Street, Vancouver, V6C
2T6, BC, Canada
Tel.: (604) 683-2507
Web Site: http://www.otisgold.com
Rev.: $857
Assets: $20,677,461
Liabilities: $203,356
Net Worth: $20,474,105
Earnings: ($1,149,460)
Fiscal Year-end: 06/30/2019
Gold Mining Services
N.A.I.C.S.: 212220
Craig T. Lindsay *(Pres & CEO)*

EXCELSIOR BIOPHARMA, INC.

5F No 508 Sec 7 Zhongxiao E Rd,
Nangang Dist, Taipei, 11561, Taiwan
Tel.: (886) 226557568   TW
Web Site:
   https://www.excelsiorgroup.com.tw
Year Founded: 1986
6496—(TPE)
Rev.: $21,003,752
Assets: $53,621,393
Liabilities: $15,868,774
Net Worth: $37,752,619
Earnings: ($1,055,467)
Fiscal Year-end: 12/31/22
Pharmaceutical Product Mfr & Distr
N.A.I.C.S.: 325411
Joseph Chen *(Chm)*

EXCELSIOR CAPITAL ASIA (HK) LIMITED

Hong Kong Advisor Units 1208 Level
12 Core F Cyberport 3, 100 Cyber-
port Road, Hong Kong, China (Hong
Kong)
Tel.: (852) 2230 9800   HK
Web Site:
   http://www.excelsiorcapitalasia.com
Year Founded: 1998
Privater Equity Firm
N.A.I.C.S.: 523999
Gary Lawrence *(Founder & Mng Part-
ner)*

Subsidiaries:

Excelsior Capital Korea Limited (1)
9th Floor 27 Yeouinaru-ro, Yeongdeungpo-
gu, Seoul, 07321, Korea (South)
Tel.: (82) 2 2088 1288
Web Site:
   http://www.excelsiorcapitalasia.com
Privater Equity Firm
N.A.I.C.S.: 523999
Seungki Min *(Partner)*

Office Depot Korea Co., Ltd. (1)
B1 Gangnam Nesville Building, Yoksam-
dong Gangnam-gu, Seoul, 830-841, Korea
(South)
Tel.: (82) 18996800
Web Site: http://www.officedepot.co.kr
Office Supplies Stores Operator & Services
N.A.I.C.S.: 459410

EXCELSIOR CAPITAL LTD.

Level 57 Servcorp 25 Martin Place,
Sydney, 2000, NSW, Australia
Tel.: (61) 292169043   AU
Web Site:
   https://excelsiorcapital.com.au
Year Founded: 1991

ECL—(ASX)
Rev.: $33,786,725
Assets: $81,503,739
Liabilities: $3,458,868
Net Worth: $78,044,871
Earnings: $29,846,421
Emp.: 57
Fiscal Year-end: 06/30/24
Electrical Component Mfr & Distr
N.A.I.C.S.: 334419

EXCELSIOR HOTEL BEO-GRAD
Kneza Milosa 5, 11000, Belgrade, Serbia
Tel.: (381) 11 32 31 381
Web Site:
http://www.hotelexcelsior.co.rs
Hotel & Motel Services
N.A.I.C.S.: 721110

EXCELSIOR MEDICAL CO., LTD.
17F No 880 Zhongzheng Road, Zhonghe Dist, Taipei, 235, Taiwan
Tel.: (886) 222251888
Web Site:
https://www.excelsiormedical.com.tw
Year Founded: 1988
4104—(TAI)
Rev.: $269,250,260
Assets: $591,252,962
Liabilities: $234,375,412
Net Worth: $356,877,550
Earnings: $30,179,207
Emp.: 939
Fiscal Year-end: 12/31/23
Medical Equipment Distr
N.A.I.C.S.: 423450

Subsidiaries:

EG Healthcare, Inc.   (1)
14F Ramon Magsaysay Center 1680 Roxas Blvd, Manila, Philippines
Tel.: (63) 285220365
Web Site: https://www.excelsior.net.ph
Kidney Dialysis Services
N.A.I.C.S.: 621492

Guangzhou Dynamic Inc.   (1)
Room 1315 Renfeng Tower No 490 Tianhe Road, Tianhe District, Guangzhou, 510630, China
Tel.: (86) 2038109308
Web Site: https://www.dynamicinchk.com
Medical Equipment Distr
N.A.I.C.S.: 423450

Medi-Chem Systems Sdn. Bhd.   (1)
5 Lorong Perusahaan 3 Taman Industri Kimpal, 68100, Batu Caves, Selangor, Malaysia
Tel.: (60) 361888811
Hospital Equipment Distr
N.A.I.C.S.: 423450

RTS Excelsior Co., Ltd.   (1)
Chongjheng Road, Zhonghe, Taipei, 880, Taiwan
Tel.: (886) 2 2225 7111
Sales Range: $10-24.9 Million
Emp.: 100
General Medical Services
N.A.I.C.S.: 621491

EXCELSIOR MINING CORP.
Suite 2400 1055 West Georgia Street, Vancouver, V6E 3P3, BC, Canada
Tel.: (604) 723-1433   BC
Web Site:
https://www.excelsiormining.com
Year Founded: 2005
MIN—(TSXV)
Rev.: $602,000
Assets: $128,819,000
Liabilities: $103,337,000
Net Worth: $25,482,000
Earnings: ($23,880,000)
Emp.: 94

Fiscal Year-end: 12/31/19
Copper Mining Services
N.A.I.C.S.: 212230
Stephen Clayton Twyerould (Pres & CEO)

EXCELSIOR UNITED DEVEL-OPMENT COMPANIES LIM-ITED
8th Floor Dias Pier Le Caudan Waterfront, Port Louis, Mauritius
Tel.: (230) 2119430   MU
Web Site: https://eudcos.com
Year Founded: 1974
EUDC—(MAU)
Rev.: $1,225,704
Assets: $46,376,923
Liabilities: $2,404,292
Net Worth: $43,972,631
Earnings: $3,790,483
Emp.: 9
Fiscal Year-end: 06/30/23
Financial Services
N.A.I.C.S.: 523999

EXCEPTIONAL INNOVATION BV
Claude Debussylaan 18, 1082 MD, Amsterdam, Netherlands
Web Site:
http://www.exceptionalinnovate.com
Holding Company
N.A.I.C.S.: 551112
Seale Moorer (Founder & CEO)

Subsidiaries:

Quadriga Worldwide Limited   (1)
Forum 1 Station Road, Theale, RG7 4RA, United Kingdom
Tel.: (44) 1189306030
Web Site: http://www.quadriga.com
Holding Company; Guestroom Technology Services Software & Technologies Developer
N.A.I.C.S.: 551112
John Peacock (Gen Mgr)

Subsidiary (Non-US):

MHT Elektronik Tasarim ve Ticaret A.S.   (2)
Mustafa Kermal Mah 2120 Cad Gozum Is, Merkezi No 5/6 Kat 3 Cankaya, Ankara, 06520, Turkiye
Tel.: (90) 3122194414
Web Site: http://www.mht.com.tr
Enterprise IT & Telecommunications Products & Services
N.A.I.C.S.: 517810
Hamza Durak (Project Mgr)

Subsidiary (Domestic):

Quadriga UK Ltd.   (2)
Forum 1 Station Road, Theale, RG7 4RA, Berks, United Kingdom
Tel.: (44) 1189306030
Web Site: http://www.quadriga.com
Guestroom Technology Services Software & Technologies Developer
N.A.I.C.S.: 513210
John Peacock (Gen Mgr)

EXCHANGE INCOME CORPO-RATION
101-990 Lorimer Blvd, Winnipeg, R3P 0Z9, MB, Canada
Tel.: (204) 982-1857   Ca
Web Site:
https://www.exchangeincomecorp.ca
Year Founded: 2002
0ON—(DEU)
Rev.: $1,886,603,135
Assets: $3,080,743,862
Liabilities: $2,140,262,290
Net Worth: $940,481,572
Earnings: $92,356,462
Fiscal Year-end: 12/31/23
Investment Services
N.A.I.C.S.: 523999

Gary A. Filmon (Chm)

Subsidiaries:

Advanced Window, Inc.   (1)
4635 Wedgewood Blvd Ste 113, Frederick, MD 21703
Tel.: (301) 696-0707
Web Site: http://www.advancedwindow.net
Window & Door Products Mfr
N.A.I.C.S.: 332321
Jason Glatt (Pres)

Bearskin Lake Air Service Ltd.   (1)
1475 W Walsh St, Thunder Bay, P7E 4X6, ON, Canada
Tel.: (807) 577-1141
Web Site: http://www.bearskinairlines.com
Sales Range: $25-49.9 Million
Emp.: 240
Oil Transportation Services
N.A.I.C.S.: 481111

Ben Machine Products Co. Inc.   (1)
1-8065 Huntington Road, Vaughan, L4H 3T9, ON, Canada
Tel.: (905) 856-7707
Web Site: http://www.benmachine.com
Emp.: 125
Sheet Metal Component Mfr & Retailer
N.A.I.C.S.: 332322

Calm Air International Ltd.   (1)
90 Thompson Dr, Thompson, R8N 1Y8, MB, Canada
Tel.: (204) 778-6471
Web Site: http://cargo.calmair.com
Sales Range: $150-199.9 Million
Emp.: 300
Oil Transportation Services
N.A.I.C.S.: 481111

Custom Helicopters Ltd.   (1)
706 South Gate Road St Andrews Airport, Saint Andrews, Charlottetown, R1A 3P8, MB, Canada
Tel.: (204) 338-7953
Web Site: http://www.customheli.com
Helicopter Services
N.A.I.C.S.: 481211

Jasper Tank Ltd   (1)
200-53016 AB-60, Acheson, T7X 5A7, AB, Canada
Tel.: (780) 962-1333
Web Site: http://www.jaspertank.com
Emp.: 25
Trucks Mfr
N.A.I.C.S.: 336211

Subsidiary (US):

Stainless Fabrication, Inc   (2)
4455 W Kearney St, Springfield, MO 65803
Tel.: (417) 865-5696
Web Site: http://www.stainlessfab.com
Sales Range: $50-74.9 Million
Emp.: 150
Stainless Steel Tank Mfr
N.A.I.C.S.: 331110
Claude Mizell (Pres)

Keewatin Air LP   (1)
50 Morberg Way, Winnipeg, R3H 0A4, MB, Canada
Tel.: (204) 888-0100
Web Site: http://www.keewatinair.ca
Emp.: 50
Oil Transportation Services
N.A.I.C.S.: 481111
David White (Pres)

L.V. Control Manufacturing Limited   (1)
660 Golspie Street, Winnipeg, R2K 2V1, MB, Canada
Tel.: (204) 669-3600
Web Site: http://www.lvcontrol.com
Electrical Distribution Equipment Mfr
N.A.I.C.S.: 335311
Brent Murray (Pres & Gen Mgr)

Overlanders Manufacturing LP   (1)
30320 Fraser Hwy, Abbotsford, V4X 1G1, BC, Canada
Tel.: (604) 856-6815
Web Site: http://www.overlanders.com
Fabricated Metal Products Mfr
N.A.I.C.S.: 332312
Randy Lowry (Dir-Sls)

Perimeter Aviation LP   (1)
626 Ferry Road, Winnipeg, R3H 0T7, MB, Canada
Tel.: (204) 786-7031
Web Site: http://www.perimeter.ca
Oil Transportation Services
N.A.I.C.S.: 481111

Provincial Aerospace Ltd.   (1)
St John's International Airport Hangar 1, PO Box 29030, Saint John's, A1A 5B5, NL, Canada
Tel.: (709) 576-1800
Web Site: https://palaerospace.com
Emp.: 800
Airborne & Maritime Surveillance Services
N.A.I.C.S.: 488330

Quest Window Systems Inc.   (1)
6811 Goreway Dr, Mississauga, L4V 1L9, ON, Canada
Tel.: (905) 851-8588
Web Site: http://www.questwindows.com
Unitized Window Mfr
N.A.I.C.S.: 332321
Martin Cash (CEO)

Regional One, Inc.   (1)
6750 NE 4th Ct, Miami, FL 33138
Tel.: (305) 759-0670
Web Site: http://www.regionalone.com
Sales Range: $25-49.9 Million
Aircraft Engines & Parts Distr & Aircraft Leasing Services
N.A.I.C.S.: 423860
Doron Marom (CEO)

Water Blast Manufacturing LP   (1)
3611 - 60 Ave SE, Calgary, T2C 2E5, AB, Canada
Tel.: (403) 717-4280
Web Site: http://www.hotsyab.com
Sales Range: $25-49.9 Million
Emp.: 8
High Pressure Cleaning Equipments & Pumping Systems Mfr
N.A.I.C.S.: 335999

Subsidiary (Domestic):

Water Blast Manufacturing B.C. Ltd.   (2)
20575 Langley Bypass Ste 112, Langley, V3A 5E8, BC, Canada
Tel.: (604) 532-7002
Web Site: http://www.hotsybc.com
Sales Range: $25-49.9 Million
Emp.: 4
Pressure Washers Mfr & Sales
N.A.I.C.S.: 332722

WestTower Communications Ltd.   (1)
9647 45th Ave NW, Edmonton, T6E 5Z8, AB, Canada
Tel.: (780) 789-2375
Web Site: http://www.westower.ca
Communication Tower Construction Services
N.A.I.C.S.: 237130
Nathan Schauerte (Pres & CEO)

EXCITE HOLDINGS CO., LTD.
Daiwa Azabu Terrace 4F 3-20-1, Minamiazabu Minato-ku, Tokyo, Japan
Tel.: (81) 364502729
Web Site: https://www.excite-holdings.co.jp
Year Founded: 2018
5571—(TKS)
Rev.: $50,982,930
Assets: $41,609,950
Liabilities: $17,628,870
Net Worth: $23,981,080
Earnings: $2,644,000
Fiscal Year-end: 03/31/24
Holding Company
N.A.I.C.S.: 551112
Shinichi Saijo (Pres)

EXCITE TECHNOLOGY SER-VICES LIMITED
157 Walker Street, Sydney, 2060, NSW, Australia
Tel.: (61) 284128200   AU
Web Site: http://www.covata.com
Year Founded: 2007

Excite Technology Services Limited—(Continued)

EXT—(ASX)
Rev.: $4,562,933
Assets: $4,397,894
Liabilities: $3,433,857
Net Worth: $964,037
Earnings: ($2,389,841)
Fiscal Year-end: 03/31/23
Holding Company; Information Technology Security Software & Services
N.A.I.C.S.: 551112
Steven Bliim *(Bd of Dirs, CFO, Co-Sec & Exec Dir)*

EXCITON TECHNOLOGY
No 9 Jingyuan Road Ningbo High-tech Zone, Ningbo, 315040, Zhejiang, China
Tel.: (86) 57487908260
Web Site: https://www.excitontech.cn
Year Founded: 2007
300566—(CHIN)
Rev.: $324,416,002
Assets: $557,195,755
Liabilities: $295,017,860
Net Worth: $262,177,894
Earnings: $20,336,571
Fiscal Year-end: 12/31/23
Light Emitting Diode Mfr & Distr
N.A.I.C.S.: 334413
Zhang Yan *(Chm & Gen Mgr)*

EXCLAMATION INVESTMENTS CORP.
1255 Bay St Stu 400, Toronto, M5V 3M6, ON, Canada
Investment Management Service
N.A.I.C.S.: 525990
Marc B. Lavine *(Founder, Chm & CEO)*

EXCLUSIVE CONTRACT SERVICES LIMITED
8-12 Salisbury Square, Hatfield, AL9 5AD, Hertfordshire, United Kingdom
Tel.: (44) 1707264400
Web Site:
http://www.exclusivecontracts.co.uk
Year Founded: 1987
Rev.: $24,320,758
Emp.: 2,500
Commercial Cleaning Services
N.A.I.C.S.: 561720
Debbie Lancaster *(Mng Dir-Retail Div)*

EXCLUSIVE GROUP SASU
20 quai du Point du Jour, 92659, Boulogne, Cedex, France
Tel.: (33) 141315304
Web Site: http://www.exclusive-networks.com
Cyber Security Services
N.A.I.C.S.: 541512
Andy Travers *(Sr VP-Global Sls & Mktg)*

EXCO TECHNOLOGIES LIMITED
130 Spy Court 2nd Floor, Markham, L3R 5H6, ON, Canada
Tel.: (905) 477-3065　　ON
Web Site: https://www.excocorp.com
Year Founded: 1952
XTC—(OTCIQ)
Rev.: $360,764,850
Assets: $336,479,750
Liabilities: $66,547,777
Net Worth: $269,931,972
Earnings: $30,055,198
Emp.: 5,000
Fiscal Year-end: 09/30/21
Casting Technologies, Extrusion Tooling For Automotive & Industrial Markets
N.A.I.C.S.: 333514

Brian A. Robbins *(Chm)*

Subsidiaries:

AFX Industries LLC　　　　**(1)**
1411 3rd St Ste G, Port Huron, MI 48060
Tel.: (810) 966-4650
Web Site: https://www.afxindustries.com
Emp.: 400
Automotive & Apparel Trimmings Supplier
N.A.I.C.S.: 314999

Allper AG　　　　**(1)**
Industriestrasse 12, PO Box 12, 3186, Dudingen, Fribourg, Switzerland
Tel.: (41) 204929000
Web Site: http://www.allper.com
Sales Range: $25-49.9 Million
Emp.: 10
Die Casting Materials Mfr
N.A.I.C.S.: 331523

BE&H Extrusion Dies, Inc.　　　**(1)**
911 Hensley Ln, Wylie, TX 75098
Tel.: (972) 442-3131
Web Site: http://www.etsdies.com
Sales Range: $1-9.9 Million
Emp.: 25
Extrusion Die Mfr
N.A.I.C.S.: 333514

EDCO, Inc.　　　　**(1)**
5244 Enterprise Blvd, Toledo, OH 43612
Tel.: (419) 726-1595
Web Site: https://excoengusa.com
Emp.: 60
Industrial Die Mfr
N.A.I.C.S.: 333514

Exco Automotive Solutions L.P.　**(1)**
1550 W Maple Rd, Troy, MI 48084 **(100%)**
Tel.: (248) 822-8111
Web Site: http://www.excoautomotive.com
Sales Range: $25-49.9 Million
Emp.: 20
Motor Vehicle Interior Trim Component Mfr & Distr
N.A.I.C.S.: 336390
William P. Schroers *(Pres & CEO)*

Exco Engineering　　　　**(1)**
1314 Ringwell Drive, Newmarket, L3Y 9C6, ON, Canada
Tel.: (905) 853-8568
Web Site: http://www.excoeng.com
High-Pressure Die-Casting Die Mfr
N.A.I.C.S.: 333514

Exco Tooling Solutions　　　**(1)**
130 Spy Court, Markham, L3R 5H6, ON, Canada
Tel.: (905) 477-1208
Web Site: http://etsdies.com
Sales Range: $25-49.9 Million
Emp.: 100
Extrusion Die Mfr
N.A.I.C.S.: 333514
Nick Gnatyuk *(VP & Gen Mgr)*

Subsidiary (US):

Exco Extrusion Dies, Inc.　　　**(2)**
56617 N Bay Dr, Chesterfield, MI 48051-3746
Tel.: (586) 749-5400
Emp.: 100
Special Die & Tool, Die Set, Jig & Fixture Mfr
N.A.I.C.S.: 333514
Bonnie Cartwright *(Pres)*

Neocon　　　　**(1)**
35 Akerley Blvd, Dartmouth, B3B 1J7, NS, Canada
Tel.: (902) 468-6663
Automotive Interior Protection & Convenience Products Mfr
N.A.I.C.S.: 326199
Julie Kohl *(VP-Sls)*

Polydesign Systems S.A.R.L.　　**(1)**
Zone Franche Boukhalef Lot 18B, Tangiers, Morocco
Tel.: (212) 539399400
Web Site:
http://www.polydesignsystems.com
Sales Range: $200-249.9 Million
Emp.: 2,000
Automotive Interiors Mfr
N.A.I.C.S.: 336360

EXEBLOCK TECHNOLOGY CORP.
Year Founded: 2015
1DF—(STU)
Rev.: $2,399
Assets: $803,630
Liabilities: $50,802
Net Worth: $752,828
Earnings: ($246,144)
Fiscal Year-end: 08/31/21
Application Software Development Services
N.A.I.C.S.: 541511
Ian Klassen *(CEO)*

EXECUS SPA
Viale Premuda 46, 20129, Milan, Italy
Tel.: (39) 0286882907
Web Site: https://www.execus.com
Year Founded: 2010
EXEC—(EUR)
Management Consulting Services
N.A.I.C.S.: 541618

EXECUTIVE FLIGHT CENTRE FUEL SERVICES LTD.
200 680 Palmer Road NE, Calgary, T2E 7R3, AB, Canada
Tel.: (403) 291-2825
Web Site: https://www.efcaviation.ca
Year Founded: 1946
Rev.: $13,282,870
Emp.: 35
Aviation Services
N.A.I.C.S.: 481219
Dean Buckland *(Pres)*

Subsidiaries:

EFC Developments Ltd.　　　**(1)**
200 680 Palmer Road NE, Calgary, T2E 7R3, AB, Canada
Tel.: (403) 291-8075
Web Site: http://www.efcdev.ca
Real Estate Development Services
N.A.I.C.S.: 531390

EXEDY CORPORATION
1-1-1 Kitamotomiya, Neyagawa, 572-8570, Osaka, Japan
Tel.: (81) 728221183
Web Site: https://www.exedy.com
7278—(TKS)
Rev.: $2,038,114,180
Assets: $2,127,990,350
Liabilities: $584,297,560
Net Worth: $1,543,692,790
Earnings: ($66,252,030)
Emp.: 1,191
Fiscal Year-end: 03/31/24
Drivetrain-Related Products Mfr
N.A.I.C.S.: 336340
Shogo Okamura *(Sr Exec Mng Officer)*

Subsidiaries:

DYNAX America Corporation　　**(1)**
568 East Park Dr, Roanoke, VA 24019
Tel.: (540) 966-6010
Web Site: http://www.dynax-j.com
Sales Range: $100-124.9 Million
Emp.: 360
Automotive Transmission Component Mfr
N.A.I.C.S.: 336350
Tatsuo Kuroda *(Pres)*

DYNAX Corporation　　　　**(1)**
1053-1 Kamiosatsu, Chitose, 066-0077, Hokkaido, Japan
Web Site: http://www.dynax-j.com
Emp.: 1,266
Automotive Parts Mfr & Distr
N.A.I.C.S.: 336390

Dynax Industry (Shanghai) Co., Ltd.　　　　**(1)**
350 Rongxiang Road, Songjiang District, Shanghai, 201613, China
Web Site: http://dxs.dynax-j.com
Emp.: 507
Motor Vehicle Parts Mfr

N.A.I.C.S.: 336390

EXEDY Casting Co., Ltd.　　　**(1)**
112 Haishi, Fukuchiyama, 620-0955, Kyoto, Japan
Tel.: (81) 773221156
Web Site: https://ecc.exedy.com
Sales Range: $25-49.9 Million
Emp.: 67
Automotive Die Casting Parts Mfr
N.A.I.C.S.: 336390

EXEDY Hiroshima Co., Ltd.　　**(1)**
6-11 Taguchi Kenkyu Danchi, Higashi-hiroshima, 739-0038, Hiroshima, Japan
Tel.: (81) 82 425 3434
Web Site: http://www.exedy.com
Sales Range: $25-49.9 Million
Emp.: 100
Automobile Parts Mfr
N.A.I.C.S.: 336390

EXEDY Kyoto Co., Ltd.　　　**(1)**
Web Site: http://www.exedy.com
Sales Range: $25-49.9 Million
Emp.: 40
Automobile Parts Mfr
N.A.I.C.S.: 336390

EXEDY Logistics Co., Ltd.　　**(1)**
1-30-1 Kidamotomiya, Neyagawa, 572-0822, Osaka, Japan
Tel.: (81) 72 822 1462
Sales Range: $25-49.9 Million
Emp.: 127
Logistics Consulting Servies
N.A.I.C.S.: 541614

EXEDY New Zealand Ltd.　　　**(1)**
151 Wairau Road Glenfield, 745, Auckland, New Zealand
Tel.: (64) 94440901
Web Site: http://www.exedy.com
Sales Range: $25-49.9 Million
Emp.: 14
Automotive Clutch Distr
N.A.I.C.S.: 423120

EXEDY Precision Co., Ltd.　　**(1)**
104-1 Joden, Mimasaka, 701-2625, Okayama, Japan
Tel.: (81) 868743501
Web Site: http://www.exedy.com
Sales Range: $50-74.9 Million
Emp.: 109
Automobile Parts Mfr
N.A.I.C.S.: 336390

EXEDY Sun Co., Ltd.　　　　**(1)**
1-16-5 Kidamotomiya, Neyagawa, 572-0822, Osaka, Japan
Tel.: (81) 728221147
Web Site: http://www.exedy.com
Automobile Parts Mfr
N.A.I.C.S.: 336390

EXEDY Trading Co., Ltd.　　　**(1)**
1-1-33 Kidamotomiya, Neyagawa, 572-0822, Osaka, Japan
Tel.: (81) 728247633
Sales Range: $25-49.9 Million
Emp.: 49
Automobile Parts Distr
N.A.I.C.S.: 423120
Yoshihiro Yamamura *(Gen Mgr)*

Exedy (Malaysia) Sdn.Bhd.　　**(1)**
PT 16748 Jalan Permata 1/5, Arab-Malaysian Industrial Park, 71800, Nilai, Negeri Sembilan, Malaysia
Tel.: (60) 67992988
Web Site: https://www.exedy.com.my
Sales Range: $75-99.9 Million
Emp.: 155
Motor Vehicle Supplies & New Parts Whslr
N.A.I.C.S.: 423120
Satoshi Tanaka *(Mng Dir)*

Exedy (Shanghai) Co., Ltd.　　**(1)**
1399 Chengqiao Road, Fengxian District, Shanghai, 201401, China
Tel.: (86) 2167109075
Web Site: http://www.esc.exedy.com
Sales Range: $250-299.9 Million
Emp.: 850
Motor Vehicle Supplies & New Parts Whslr
N.A.I.C.S.: 423120

Exedy (Thailand) Co., Ltd.　　**(1)**
700/316 Moo 6 Bangna-Trad Road, Tumbon Don Hua Roh Amphur Muang, Chon

Buri, 20000, Thailand
Tel.: (66) 38214423
Web Site: http://www.ext.exedy.com
Sales Range: $250-299.9 Million
Emp.: 1,571
Motor Vehicle Supplies & New Parts Whslr
N.A.I.C.S.: 423120
Hideki Kanai *(Pres)*

Exedy America Corporation (1)
2121 Holston Bend Dr, Mascot, TN 37806
Tel.: (865) 932-3700
Automobile Parts Mfr
N.A.I.C.S.: 336390
David Hollomon *(Dir-Acctg & HR)*

Exedy Australia Pty. Ltd. (1)
21 Fiveways Blvd, Keysborough, 3173, VIC,
Australia
Web Site: http://www.exedy.com.au
Sales Range: $25-49.9 Million
Emp.: 100
Motor Vehicle Parts Mfr
N.A.I.C.S.: 336390

Exedy Beijing Co., Ltd. (1)
No 256 2nd Floor C2 District Beijing Fan-
grun Property, Southwest corner of Wu-
fangqiao Wangsiying Township Chaoyang
District, Beijing, 100023, China
Tel.: (86) 1067298437
Automobile Parts Mfr
N.A.I.C.S.: 336390

Exedy Chongqing Co., Ltd. (1)
No 4 Longjing Road, North New Economic
Development Zone, Chongqing, 401122,
China
Tel.: (86) 2367460801
Web Site: http://www.exc.exedy.com
Motor Vehicle Supplies & New Parts Whslr
N.A.I.C.S.: 423120

Exedy Clutch Europe Ltd. (1)
Unit 2 Rokeby Court, Runcorn, WA7 1RW,
Cheshire, United Kingdom
Tel.: (44) 1928571850
Web Site: https://www.exedy.co.uk
Sales Range: $25-49.9 Million
Emp.: 30
Motor Vehicle Parts Mfr
N.A.I.C.S.: 336390

Exedy Clutch India Pvt. Ltd. (1)
Plot No 5-P 9-18 19P 32-38, Narasapura
Industrial Area Appasandra Village, Kolar,
India
Tel.: (91) 9108035061
Automobile Parts Mfr
N.A.I.C.S.: 336390
Vijay Kumar *(Asst Mgr)*

Exedy Corporation - Kawagoe (1)
Plant
1-103-25 Yoshinodai, Kawagoe, 350-0833,
Saitama, Japan
Tel.: (81) 492250601
Sales Range: $50-74.9 Million
Emp.: 138
Automobile Parts Mfr
N.A.I.C.S.: 336390

Exedy Corporation - Ueno (1)
Division
2418 Ota-cho, Iga, 518-0825, Mie, Japan
Tel.: (81) 595238101
Web Site: http://www.exedy.com
Sales Range: $400-449.9 Million
Emp.: 1,974
Automobile Parts Mfr
N.A.I.C.S.: 336390

Exedy DYNAX Shanghai Co., (1)
Ltd.
1399 Chenqiao Road, Fengxian District,
Shanghai, 201401, China
Tel.: (86) 2167109075
Automobile Parts Mfr
N.A.I.C.S.: 336390

Exedy Dynax Europe Ltd. (1)
Szarkalab UT6, 2800, Tatabanya, Hungary
Tel.: (36) 34311117
Web Site: http://www.ede.exedy.com
Sales Range: $25-49.9 Million
Emp.: 35
Manual Clutch Mfr & Assembler
N.A.I.C.S.: 336390

Exedy Dynax Mexico, S.A. De (1)
C.V.

Circuito Progreso 101, Parque Industrial de
Logitica Automotriz Pila Penuelas, 20340,
Aguascalientes, Mexico
Tel.: (52) 4491760000
Automobile Parts Mfr
N.A.I.C.S.: 336390
Mario Luna *(Mgr-HR)*

Exedy Electric Facilities Co., Ltd. (1)
8-6 Hyuga-cho, Moriguchi, Moriguchi, 570-
0023, Osaka, Japan
Tel.: (81) 669973131
Automobile Parts Mfr
N.A.I.C.S.: 336390

Exedy Engineering Asia Co., Ltd. (1)
700/552 Moo 6 Bangna-Trad Road Tumbon
Don Hua Roh Amphur Muang, Chon Buri,
20000, Thailand
Tel.: (66) 38453182
Automobile Parts Mfr
N.A.I.C.S.: 336390

Exedy Friction Material Co.,Ltd. (1)
700/359 Moo 6 Bangna-Trad Road, Tum-
bon Don Hua Roh Amphur Muang, Chon
Buri, 20000, Thailand
Tel.: (66) 38743923
Web Site: http://www.efm.exedy.com
Sales Range: $150-199.9 Million
Emp.: 500
Motor Vehicle Supplies & New Parts Whslr
N.A.I.C.S.: 423120

Exedy Fukushima Co., Ltd. (1)
65 Matsubara Torimiyama Fukushima,
Matsuyama-machi, Kitakata, 966-0901,
Japan
Tel.: (81) 241233100
Automobile Parts Mfr
N.A.I.C.S.: 336390

Exedy Globalparts Corporation (1)
8601 Haggerty Rd, Van Buren Township, MI
48111-1607
Tel.: (734) 397-3333
Web Site: https://www.exedyusa.com
Sales Range: $25-49.9 Million
Emp.: 30
Automobile & Motor Vehicle Whslr
N.A.I.C.S.: 423110
Takeshi Nakano *(Pres)*

Exedy Guangzhou Co., Ltd. (1)
Room3240 Xinguangcong Automobile
Spare Parts Market, No 889 Baiyundadao-
bei Road Baiyun District, Guangzhou,
510800, China
Tel.: (86) 2083581900
Web Site: http://egc.exedy.com
Sales Range: $25-49.9 Million
Emp.: 16
Motor Vehicle Supplies & New Parts Whslr
N.A.I.C.S.: 423120

Exedy Holdings of America
Corporation (1)
8601 Haggerty Rd S, Belleville, MI 48111
Tel.: (734) 397-3333
Web Site: http://www.exedyusa.com
Sales Range: $25-49.9 Million
Emp.: 30
Holding Company; Motor Vehicle Supplies
& New Parts Whslr
N.A.I.C.S.: 551112

Exedy India Ltd. (1)
Plot No L-4 M I D C Industrial Area, Chika-
lthana, Aurangabad, 431 210, Maharashtra,
India
Tel.: (91) 2402484014
Web Site: http://www.exedyindia.in
Sales Range: $50-74.9 Million
Emp.: 10
Motor Vehicle Supplies & New Parts Whslr
N.A.I.C.S.: 423120
Naoki Yoshii *(Pres)*

Plant (Domestic):

Ceekay Daikin Ltd. - Aurangabad
Plant (2)
Plot No L-4 M I D C Industrial Area Chika-
lthana, Aurangabad, 431 210, Maharashtra,
India
Tel.: (91) 24833341
Web Site: http://www.exedyindia.in
Automotive Transmission Clutch Compo-
nent Mfr
N.A.I.C.S.: 336350

Exedy Latin America S.A. (1)
Paitilla Office Tower Building Avenida 8va
South and Calle 56 Este, Office 902 903
904 - San Francisco, Panama, Panama
Tel.: (507) 3957122
Web Site: http://www.exedylatinamerica.com
Automobile Parts Mfr
N.A.I.C.S.: 336390

Exedy Mexico Aftermarket Sales,
S.A. de C.V. (1)
Calle Mineros Exterior 107 Naves Numero
8-D Y 9-D, Colonia Distrito Industrial Ori-
ente El Castillo Kilometro 18, 38107,
Mexico, Guanajuato, Mexico
Tel.: (52) 4424557875
Automobile Parts Mfr
N.A.I.C.S.: 336390

Exedy Middle East FZCO (1)
Warehouse No ZE 05 ZE 06 Near R/ABT
13, PO Box 18199, Jebel Ali Free Zone,
Dubai, United Arab Emirates
Tel.: (971) 48832244
Web Site: https://www.exedy.ae
Emp.: 20
Motor Vehicle Supplies & New Parts Whslr
N.A.I.C.S.: 423120
Yoshio Katayama *(Co-Pres & CEO)*

Exedy Nara Co., Ltd. (1)
68 Nukatabeteramachi, Yamatokoriyama,
Nara, 639-1036, Japan
Tel.: (81) 743566878
Automobile Parts Mfr
N.A.I.C.S.: 336390

Exedy Poipet Co., Ltd. (1)
Techno Park Poi Pet Plotno C005 C010
Sanco Poi Pet SEZ, Phum Phsar Kandal
Sangkat Phsar Kandal Poi Pet city, Phnom
Penh, Banteay Meanchey, Cambodia
Tel.: (855) 89954232
Automobile Parts Mfr
N.A.I.C.S.: 336390

Exedy SB Hyogo Co., Ltd. (1)
3-2-4 Nakanoshima, Kita-ku, Osaka, 530-
0005, Japan
Tel.: (81) 676348017
Automobile Parts Mfr
N.A.I.C.S.: 336390

Exedy Singapore Pte. Ltd. (1)
45 Ubi Road 1 02-01, Singapore, 408696,
Singapore
Tel.: (65) 67491395
Automobile Parts Mfr
N.A.I.C.S.: 336390

Exedy Vietnam Co.,Ltd. (1)
Khai Quang Industrial Zone, Vinh Yen, Vinh
Phuc, Vietnam
Tel.: (84) 2113721252
Web Site: http://www.exedy.com.au
Motor Vehicle Supplies & New Parts Whslr
N.A.I.C.S.: 423120
Toshikazu Boumuki *(Pres)*

Exedy-Dynax America
Corporation (1)
8601 Haggerty Rd S, Belleville, MI 48111
Tel.: (734) 397-6556
Web Site: http://eda.exedy.com
Emp.: 11
Motor Vehicle Supplies & New Parts Whslr
N.A.I.C.S.: 423120

Nippon Retarder System Co.;
Ltd. (1)
1-1-33 Kidamotomiya, Neyagawa, 572-
0822, Osaka, Japan
Tel.: (81) 728200911
Automobile Parts Mfr
N.A.I.C.S.: 336390

P.T. Exedy Motorcycle Indonesia (1)
JI Pulobuaran Raya Kav IIIFF 8-9 Pulo Ga-
dung, 13920, Jakarta, Indonesia
Tel.: (62) 214602581
Motor Vehicle Supplies & New Parts Whslr
N.A.I.C.S.: 423120

PT. Exedy Manufacturing
Indonesia (1)
JI Permata V Lot EE 3 KIIC, Kawasan In-
dustri, Karawang, 41361, Jawa Barat, Indo-
nesia
Tel.: (62) 2189114666
Automobile Parts Mfr

N.A.I.C.S.: 336390

PT. Exedy Prima Indonesia (1)
JI Gardu Induk Pln No 5 Tandes, Margomu-
lyo, Surabaya, 60187, East Java, Indonesia
Tel.: (62) 312977777
Automobile Parts Mfr
N.A.I.C.S.: 336390

Shanghai Dynax Co., Ltd. (1)
1399 Chengqiao Rd, Fengxian District,
Shanghai, 201401, China
Tel.: (86) 2167109075
Web Site: http://www.dxchina.com.cn
Motor Vehicle Supplies & New Parts Whslr
N.A.I.C.S.: 423120

EXEL COMPOSITES OYJ
Makituvantie 5, FI-1510, Vantaa, Finland
Tel.: (358) 207541350
Web Site:
  https://www.exelcomposites.com
Year Founded: 1960
EXL1V—(HEL)
Rev.: $147,839,413
Assets: $122,013,814
Liabilities: $89,221,886
Net Worth: $32,791,927
Earnings: $2,314,915
Emp.: 721
Fiscal Year-end: 12/31/22
Reinforced Composite Tubes & Pro-
files Mfr
N.A.I.C.S.: 322219
Eric Moussiaux *(VP-Tech)*

Subsidiaries:

Exel Composites (Australia) Pty
Ltd (1)
991 Mountain Hwy, Boronia, 3155, VIC,
Australia (100%)
Tel.: (61) 387279600
Web Site: http://www.exelcomposite.com.au
Sales Range: $25-49.9 Million
Emp.: 40
Household Furniture Mfr
N.A.I.C.S.: 337126
Steve Smith *(Gen Mgr)*

Exel Composites GmbH (1)
Industriestrasse-West 8, Kapfenberg, 8605,
Austria (100%)
Tel.: (43) 386233180
Web Site: http://www.exelcomposites.com
Sales Range: $25-49.9 Million
Emp.: 40
All Other Plastics Product Mfr
N.A.I.C.S.: 326199

Exel Composites N.V. (1)
Industriepark De Bruwaan 2, 9700, Oud-
enaarde, Belgium
Tel.: (32) 499923917
Sales Range: $25-49.9 Million
Emp.: 50
Other Nonscheduled Air Transportation
N.A.I.C.S.: 481219

Exel Composites UK Ltd. (1)
Fairoak Lane, Whitehouse Cheshire Run-
corn, Runcorn, WA7 3DU, United
Kingdom (100%)
Tel.: (44) 1928701515
Web Site: http://www.exel.com
Sales Range: $25-49.9 Million
Emp.: 50
All Other Plastics Product Mfr
N.A.I.C.S.: 326199
Richard Thomas *(Mng Dir)*

Exel GmbH (1)
Alte Hunxer Strasse 139, 46562, Voerde,
Germany
Tel.: (49) 2811641210
Web Site: http://www.exelcomposites.com
Sales Range: $25-49.9 Million
Emp.: 30
Other Pressed & Blown Glass & Glassware
Mfr
N.A.I.C.S.: 327212

Exel Sports NA (1)
113 Elm St, Winooski, VT 05454
Tel.: (802) 846-5565
Web Site: http://www.nordicwalker.com

Exel Composites Oyj—(Continued)

Marine Cargo Handling
N.A.I.C.S.: 488320

Exel Sports Sweden AB (1)
Furunasvagen 105, 94152, Pitea,
Sweden (100%)
Tel.: (46) 91166501
Web Site: http://www.intgateway.se
Sales Range: $50-74.9 Million
Emp.: 5
Sporting & Recreational Goods & Supplies
Whslr
N.A.I.C.S.: 423910

Exel USA Inc. (1)
7210 W Paradise Dr, Peoria, AZ
85345 (100%)
Tel.: (623) 487-5076
Hotels & Motels
N.A.I.C.S.: 721110

**Kineco Exel Composites India Private
Limited** (1)
Plot No 41, Pilerne Industrial Estate Bardez,
Goa, 403511, India
Tel.: (91) 9879006592
Web Site: https://www.kinecoexelindia.com
Turbine Mfr
N.A.I.C.S.: 333611

Pacific Composites Pty. Ltd (1)
991 Mountain Highway, Boronia, 3155, VIC,
Australia (100%)
Tel.: (61) 387279600
Web Site: http://www.exelcomposites.com
Sales Range: $25-49.9 Million
Emp.: 25
Broadwoven Fabric Mills
N.A.I.C.S.: 313210
Stephen Smith (Mng Dir)

EXEL INDUSTRIES SA
78 Boulevard Malesherbes, 75008,
Paris, France
Tel.: (33) 171704950   FR
Web Site: https://www.exel-
industries.com
Year Founded: 1987
EXE—(EUR)
Rev.: $901,412,491
Assets: $824,189,948
Liabilities: $437,011,632
Net Worth: $387,178,316
Earnings: $26,366,063
Emp.: 4,080
Fiscal Year-end: 09/30/22
Crop Spraying Equipment Mfr
N.A.I.C.S.: 333111
M. Patrick Ballu (Chm)

Subsidiaries:

Agrifac Machinery BV (1)
Eesveenseweg 15, 8332 JA, Steenwijk,
Netherlands
Tel.: (31) 52 152 7210
Web Site: https://www.agrifac.com
Agriculture Machinery Mfr & Distr
N.A.I.C.S.: 333111

Berthoud Agricole SAS (1)
1 rue de l'Industrie, BP 202, 69220, Le
Plessis-Belleville, France
Tel.: (33) 474065050
Web Site: http://www.berthoud.com
Rev.: $65,126,800
Emp.: 190
Farm Machinery & Equipment Mfr
N.A.I.C.S.: 333111

Subsidiary (Non-US):

Berthoud Sprayers Ltd (2)
G1 Boston Enterprise Centre Venture
House Enterprise Way, Boston, PE21 7TW,
Lincolnshire, United Kingdom
Tel.: (44) 1205726753
Web Site: https://www.berthoud.co.uk
Farm Machinery & Equipment Mfr
N.A.I.C.S.: 333111

CMC SAS (1)
1 Rue Vincent Ballu, 51200, Epernay,
France
Tel.: (33) 32 651 1888
Web Site: https://www.cmc51.fr

Sales Range: $25-49.9 Million
Emp.: 2
Farm Machinery & Equipment Mfr
N.A.I.C.S.: 333111
Joel Thomas (Mgr-Comml)

Capagri SAS (1)
Rue Pasteur, Noyelles-sur-Escaut, 59159,
Hauts-de-Seine, France
Tel.: (33) 327725272
Web Site: https://www.capagri.com
Farm Equipment Distr
N.A.I.C.S.: 423820

Caruelle-Nicolas SAS (1)
2 Rue de l'Industrie, BP 2, 45550, Saint-
Denis-de-l'Hotel, France
Tel.: (33) 238463131
Web Site: http://www.caruelle-nicolas.com
Emp.: 100
Farm Machinery & Equipment Mfr
N.A.I.C.S.: 333111

EXEL gsa SAS (1)
Rue de l'abbaye, BP 424, Villefranche-sur-
Saone, 69400, France
Tel.: (33) 474624848
Web Site: http://www.exelgsa.fr
Sales Range: $50-74.9 Million
Emp.: 130
Spraying Equipment Mfr
N.A.I.C.S.: 333111

FISCHER New SARL (1)
En Bovery A, Case Postale 184, Collombey,
1868, Switzerland
Tel.: (41) 244735080
Web Site: http://www.fischer-sarl.ch
Farm Machinery & Equipment Mfr
N.A.I.C.S.: 333111

Hardi Evrard SA (1)
43 rue du Cuivre, BP 59, 77542, Savigny-
le-Temple, France
Tel.: (33) 164105400
Web Site: http://www.hardi-fr.com
Farm Machinery & Equipment Mfr
N.A.I.C.S.: 333111

Hardi International AS (1)
Helgeshoj Alle 38, 2630, Taastrup, Denmark
Tel.: (45) 4358 8300
Web Site: http://www.hardi-international.com
Sales Range: $150-199.9 Million
Emp.: 65
Crop Spraying Services
N.A.I.C.S.: 115112
Sten Kjelstrup (Pres & CEO)

Subsidiary (Non-US):

Agripower Ltd (2)
3 George Terrace, Auckland, New Zealand
Tel.: (64) 9 634 4632
Web Site: https://www.agripower.co.nz
Farm Machinery & Equipment Mfr
N.A.I.C.S.: 333111

HARDI Australia Pty. Ltd. (2)
534 - 538 Cross Keys Rd, Cavan, 5094,
SA, Australia
Tel.: (61) 883439999
Web Site: https://hardi.com
Farm Machinery & Equipment Mfr
N.A.I.C.S.: 333111

HARDI Crop Protection SA LTD. (2)
11 Rand Road, Blackheath, Cape Town,
8001, Western Cape, South Africa
Tel.: (27) 21 905 2260
Web Site: https://www.hardi.co.za
Sales Range: $25-49.9 Million
Emp.: 11
Agricultural Equipment Distr
N.A.I.C.S.: 423820
Clive Crouse (Mng Dir)

HARDI GmbH (2)
Werksvertretung Osterreich Nr 56, 3662,
Munichreith, Austria
Tel.: (43) 6649232373
Farm Machinery & Equipment Mfr
N.A.I.C.S.: 333111

HARDI INC. (2)
337 Sovereign Rd, London, N6M 1A6, ON,
Canada
Tel.: (519) 659-2771
Web Site: http://www.hardi-us.com
Emp.: 4
Farm Machinery & Equipment Distr

N.A.I.C.S.: 423820

HARDI Kenya Ltd. (2)
PO Box 47409, 00100, Nairobi, Kenya
Tel.: (254) 20 238 4212
Web Site: https://www.hardi.co.ke
Farm Machinery & Equipment Mfr
N.A.I.C.S.: 333111
Robinson Ngano (Mgr-Ops)

Hardi Gmbh (2)
Schaumburger Str 17, 30900, Wedemark,
Germany
Tel.: (49) 51 309 7680
Web Site: https://www.hardi-gmbh.com
Sales Range: $25-49.9 Million
Emp.: 16
Farm Machinery & Equipment Mfr
N.A.I.C.S.: 333111
Karsten Hemmingsen (Gen Mgr)

Hardi Ltd (2)
4 Thorby Avenue, March, PE15 0AZ, Cam-
bridgeshire, United Kingdom
Tel.: (44) 135 466 0552
Web Site: https://www.hardi.co.uk
Sales Range: $25-49.9 Million
Emp.: 3
Spraying Equipment Distr
N.A.I.C.S.: 423820
Peter Wiles (Mgr-Sls)

Subsidiary (US):

Hardi North America Inc (2)
7301 Vine St Ct, Davenport, IA 52806
Tel.: (563) 386-1730
Web Site: https://hardi.com
Farm Machinery & Equipment Mfr
N.A.I.C.S.: 333111

Subsidiary (Non-US):

Svenska Hardi AB (2)
Box 50 444, 202 14, Malmo, Sweden
Tel.: (46) 4 021 0250
Web Site: http://www.svenskahardi.se
Sales Range: $25-49.9 Million
Emp.: 60
Farm Machinery & Equipment Mfr
N.A.I.C.S.: 333111

Holmer Maschinenbau GmbH (1)
Regensburger Strasse 20, Eggmuhl Schier-
ling, 84069, Regensburg, Germany
Tel.: (49) 94 519 3030
Web Site: https://www.holmer-
maschinenbau.com
Emp.: 400
Agricultural Machinery Mfr
N.A.I.C.S.: 333111
Wolfgang Bergmann (CEO & Exec Mgr)

Hozelock Ltd. (1)
Midpoint Park, Birmingham, B76 1AB,
United Kingdom
Tel.: (44) 121 313 1122
Web Site: https://www.hozelock.com
Garden Equipment Mfr & Distr
N.A.I.C.S.: 333112
Simon Tyers (Dir-Pur)

ILEMO HARDI, S.A.U. (1)
N-230 Km 5 6, Segura i Farre parc 712-
713, 25196, Lleida, Spain
Tel.: (34) 973208012
Web Site: https://www.hardi.es
Sales Range: $25-49.9 Million
Emp.: 50
Agricultural Spraying Equipment Mfr
N.A.I.C.S.: 333111
J. M. Goida (Gen Mgr)

Matrot Equipements SAS (1)
116 rue des Pommiers, 60480, Noyers-
Saint-Martin, France
Tel.: (33) 3 44 80 66 33
Web Site: http://www.matrot.fr
Rev.: $38,226,600
Farm Machinery & Equipment Mfr
N.A.I.C.S.: 333111

Matrot UK Ltd (1)
Mill Lane Great Massingham, King's Lynn,
PE32 2HT, Norfolk, United Kingdom
Tel.: (44) 1485520626
Farm Machinery & Equipment Distr
N.A.I.C.S.: 423820

Preciculture SAS (1)
165 rue des Verriers, 51230, Fere-

Champenoise, France
Tel.: (33) 326424051
Web Site: http://www.preciculture.fr
Spraying Equipment Distr
N.A.I.C.S.: 423820

Sames Kremlin SAS (1)
13 chemin de Malacher Inovallee, BP 86,
38243, Meylan, France
Tel.: (33) 476416060
Web Site: https://www.sames.com
Spraying Equipment Distr
N.A.I.C.S.: 423830
Didier Brotons (Gen Mgr)

Subsidiary (Domestic):

Kremlin-Rexson SA (2)
150 Ave de Stalingrad, 93240, Stains,
France
Tel.: (33) 149402525
Web Site: http://www.kremlinrexson-
sames.com
Emp.: 200
Spraying Equipment Distr
N.A.I.C.S.: 423830
Dominique Lagouge (Gen Mgr)

Subsidiary (Domestic):

API Technologies SAS (3)
29 Avenue Ashton Under Lyne, 52000,
Chaumont, France
Tel.: (33) 325011919
Web Site: http://www.api-technologies.com
Farm Machinery & Equipment Mfr
N.A.I.C.S.: 333111

Subsidiary (Non-US):

EXEL Finishing Pvt Ltd (3)
Kothari House Gate No 634 Pune Nagar
Road, Wagholi, Pune, 412207, India
Tel.: (91) 20 30472700
Web Site: http://www.kremlinrexson-
sames.com
Crop Precision Spraying Machine Mfr
N.A.I.C.S.: 333111

EXEL INDUSTRIAL E.P.E. LDTA (3)
Avenida Jose Luis Sereno 1200, 13212-
210, Jundiai, Brazil
Tel.: (55) 11 45 81 63 04
Web Site: http://www.exel-industrial.com.br
Sales Range: $25-49.9 Million
Emp.: 15
Farm Machinery & Equipment Mfr
N.A.I.C.S.: 333111

EXEL INDUSTRIAL E.P.E., S.A. (3)
C/Botanica 49, 8908, L'Hospitalet de Llo-
bregat, Barcelona, Spain
Tel.: (34) 93 264 1540
Web Site: http://www.kremlin-rexson.com
Emp.: 14
Farm Machinery & Equipment Mfr
N.A.I.C.S.: 333111
Marc Oblado (Mgr-Mktg)

**EXEL Lackier- und Beschichtungs-
systeme GmbH** (3)
Moselstrasse 19, 41464, Neuss, Germany
Tel.: (49) 2131 369 22 00
Farm Machinery & Equipment Mfr
N.A.I.C.S.: 333111
Hermann Rothe (Mgr-Sls)

Subsidiary (US):

EXEL NORTH AMERICA INC. (3)
45001 5 Mile Rd, Plymouth, MI 48170
Tel.: (734) 979-0100
Web Site: http://www.exel-na.com
Emp.: 100
Farm Machinery & Equipment Mfr
N.A.I.C.S.: 333111
Regan Murray (CEO)

Subsidiary (Non-US):

EXEL S.A. de C.V. (3)
Moises Saenz 1510 Col Leones, Monterrey,
64600, Nuevo Leon, Mexico
Tel.: (52) 8112571111
Emp.: 3
Farm Machinery & Equipment Mfr
N.A.I.C.S.: 333111
Martin Soria (Dir-Sls)

Exel Industrial Canada Inc. (3)
931 Progress Avenue Unit 7, Scarborough,

M1G 3V5, ON, Canada
Tel.: (416) 431-5017
Web Site: http://www.kremlinrexson-sames.com
Emp.: 15
Farm Machinery & Equipment Mfr
N.A.I.C.S.: 333111

KREMLIN REXSON PTE LTD (3)
German Centre International Business Park
05-109E, Singapore, 609916, Singapore
Tel.: (65) 65628290
Web Site: http://www.kremlinrexson-sames.sg
Sales Range: $25-49.9 Million
Emp.: 5
Spraying Equipment Mfr
N.A.I.C.S.: 811310

KREMLIN REXSON S.p.A (3)
Via F Brunelleschi 16, 20146, Milan, Italy
Tel.: (39) 0248952815
Web Site: http://www.kremlinrexson-sames.it
Spraying Equipment Mfr
N.A.I.C.S.: 333111

Kremlin Rexson Polska Sp. z o.o. (3)
Modlinska 221B, 03120, Warsaw, Poland
Tel.: (48) 22 510 3850
Web Site: http://www.kremlin-rexson.pl
Sales Range: $25-49.9 Million
Emp.: 10
Farm Machinery & Equipment Mfr
N.A.I.C.S.: 333111

Tecnoma Technologies SAS (1)
54 rue Marcel Paul, BP 195, Epernay, 51200, France
Tel.: (33) 326519999
Web Site: http://www.tecnoma.com
Sales Range: $50-74.9 Million
Emp.: 160
Farm Machinery & Equipment Mfr
N.A.I.C.S.: 333111

Tricoflex SA (1)
17 Avenue Jean Juif, 51301, Vitry-le-Francois, France
Tel.: (33) 326736767
Thermoplastic Hoses Mfr & Retailer
N.A.I.C.S.: 326220

Vermorel SRL (1)
3 Strada Pompelor, 100411, Ploiesti, Romania
Tel.: (40) 344104178
Web Site: http://www.vermorel.eu
Farm Machinery & Equipment Mfr
N.A.I.C.S.: 333111
Silvia Dascal (Gen Mgr)

EXELERATE CAPITAL CORP.
43 Vanderhoof Av, Toronto, M4G 2H2, ON, Canada
Tel.: (416) 209-8016   BC
Year Founded: 2018
XCAP.P—(TSXV)
Rev.: $37,136
Assets: $833,380
Liabilities: $29,772
Net Worth: $803,608
Earnings: ($31,609)
Fiscal Year-end: 02/29/24
Business Consulting Services
N.A.I.C.S.: 522299
Mark William Kohler (CEO)

EXELGEN DISCOVERY
Bude-Stratton Business Park, Bude, EX23 8LY, Cornwall, United Kingdom
Tel.: (44) 1288 356500
Web Site: http://www.exelgendiscovery.com
Sales Range: $10-24.9 Million
Emp.: 35
Pharmaceutical & Biotechnology Research & Development
N.A.I.C.S.: 541714

EXELIXIS INVESTMENTS PUBLIC LIMITED
Leoforos Agion Omologiton 15, 1080, Nicosia, Cyprus

Tel.: (357) 22452600
EXIN—(CYP)
Sales Range: Less than $1 Million
Financial Services
N.A.I.C.S.: 523999
Nicos Papageorgiou (Exec Dir)

EXEM CO., LTD.
40 Magokjungang 8-ro 5-gil, Gangseo-gu, Seoul, Korea (South)
Tel.: (82) 262036300
Web Site: https://www.ex-em.com
Year Founded: 2014
205100—(KRS)
Rev.: $42,287,223
Assets: $91,288,905
Liabilities: $13,489,632
Net Worth: $77,799,273
Earnings: $7,365,508
Emp.: 303
Fiscal Year-end: 12/31/22
Software Publishing Services
N.AICS.: 513210
Chongarm Cho (CEO)

Subsidiaries:

EXEM China Co., Ltd. (1)
Suite 1307 No738 Suncome Liauws Plaza Shangcheng Road, Pudong, Shanghai, China
Tel.: (86) 2158359587
Information Technology Services
N.A.I.C.S.: 541511

EXEM Japan Co., Ltd. (1)
Tokyodo Nishikicho Building 4F 3-7 Kanda Nishiki-cho, Chiyoda-ku, Tokyo, 101-0054, Japan
Tel.: (81) 335180771
Information Technology Services
N.A.I.C.S.: 541511

EXEM USA, Inc. (1)
14730 Beach Blvd Ste 208, La Mirada, CA 90638
Tel.: (714) 323-9901
Information Technology Services
N.A.I.C.S.: 541511

EXENT CORP.
Room 6B1-2 Block AB Tianxiagn Building, Futian District, Shenzhen, 517000, Guangdong, China
Tel.: (86) 75583218411   NV
Year Founded: 2017
EXNN—(OTCIQ)
Liabilities: $9,344
Net Worth: ($9,344)
Earnings: ($69,705)
Emp.: 1
Fiscal Year-end: 12/31/20
Drywall Steel Studs Mfr & Distr
N.A.I.C.S.: 333120
Li Deng (Chm, Pres, Treas & Sec)

EXEO GROUP INC.
29-20 Shibuya 3-chome, Shibuya-ku, Tokyo, 150-0002, Japan
Tel.: (81) 357781073
Web Site: https://www.exeo.co.jp
Year Founded: 1954
1951—(TKS)
Rev.: $4,059,167,950
Assets: $3,910,720,570
Liabilities: $1,800,696,200
Net Worth: $2,110,024,370
Earnings: $132,583,380
Emp.: 17,056
Fiscal Year-end: 03/31/24
Telecommunications Equipment Mfr
N.A.I.C.S.: 238210
Hideo Higuchi (Mng Operating Officer & Gen Mgr-Accounts & Fin Div)

Subsidiaries:

C-CUBE Corporation (1)
Tel.: (81) 323328000
Web Site: http://www.c-cube-g.co.jp
Construction Engineering Services
N.A.I.C.S.: 237130

Daiwa Densetsu Corp. (1)
2-5-1 Omachi, Aoba-ku, Sendai, 980-0804, Miyagi, Japan   (56.9%)
Tel.: (81) 222163111
Web Site: https://www.ddk.co.jp
Emp.: 217
Electrical Contractor
N.A.I.C.S.: 238210

DeClout Limited (1)
29 Tai Seng Ave 05-01 Natural Cool Lifestyle Hub, Singapore, 534119, Singapore   (95.04%)
Tel.: (65) 6818 1833
Web Site: http://www.declout.com
Rev.: $204,569,515
Assets: $185,120,507
Liabilities: $91,413,554
Net Worth: $93,706,953
Earnings: ($15,334,205)
Emp.: 628
Fiscal Year-end: 12/31/2017
IT Services & Solutions
N.A.I.C.S.: 541519
Moi Heyang Lin (Sec)

Subsidiary (Non-US):

Corous360 Sdn. Bhd. (2)
Suite 15 2 Level 15 Menara Weld, No 76 Jalan Raja Chulan, 50200, Kuala Lumpur, Malaysia
Tel.: (60) 3 2725 0038
Information Technology Consulting Services
N.A.I.C.S.: 541512

Subsidiary (Domestic):

Procurri Corporation Limited (2)
8 Aljunied Avenue 3, The Pulse, Singapore, 389933, Singapore   (97.34%)
Tel.: (65) 60119700
Web Site: https://www.procurri.com
Rev.: $149,353,935
Assets: $87,042,339
Liabilities: $50,302,204
Net Worth: $36,740,135
Earnings: ($6,414,451)
Emp.: 486
Fiscal Year-end: 12/31/2023
Information Technology Services
N.A.I.C.S.: 423430
Sean Murphy (Chm & CEO-Global)

Subsidiary (Non-US):

Procurri GmbH (3)
Erlanger Str 9, 91083, Baiersdorf, Germany
Tel.: (49) 15150173032
Information Technology & Services
N.A.I.C.S.: 541511

Procurri India Private Limited (3)
1st Floor Tower D RMZ Infinity, Municipal No 3 Old Madras Road, Bengaluru, 560016, India
Tel.: (91) 8067431157
Information Technology & Services
N.A.I.C.S.: 541511
Balasubramanian Rajagopalan (Mgr-Logistics)

Subsidiary (US):

Procurri LLC (3)
5825 Peachtree Corners E, Norcross, GA 30092
Tel.: (770) 817-9049
Emp.: 30
Computer Hardware Sales & Maintenance Services
N.A.I.C.S.: 423430

Subsidiary (Domestic):

Congruity, LLC. (4)
56 Pembroke Woods Dr, Pembroke, MA 02359   (51%)
Tel.: (781) 499-6144
Web Site: http://www.congruity.com
IT Lifecycle Services
N.A.I.C.S.: 541519
Robert Curry (Dir-Maintenance & Svcs)

Subsidiary (Non-US):

Procurri Malaysia Sdn. Bhd. (3)
Unit L3-2 3rd Floor Infinite Centre No 1 Jalan 13/6, 46200, Petaling Jaya, Selangor Darul Ehsan, Malaysia
Tel.: (60) 379588829

Information Technology & Services
N.A.I.C.S.: 541511
Ivan Teng (Sr Acct Mgr)

Procurri S. de R.L. de C.V. (3)
Blvd Diaz Ordaz 130 Piso 10, Col Rincon de Santa Maria, 64650, Monterrey, Nuevo Leon, Mexico
Tel.: (52) 8188518227
Information Technology & Services
N.A.I.C.S.: 541511

Procurri UK Limited (3)
Bankside Park 15 Love Lane, Cirencester, GL7 1YG, Gloucestershire, United Kingdom
Tel.: (44) 1285642222
Web Site: https://www.procurri.com
Computer Equipment Sales & Service
N.A.I.C.S.: 423430
Mathew Jordan (Mng Dir)

EXEO Digital Solutions, Inc. (1)
Sumitomo Fudosan Mita Twin Building East Tower 4-2-8 Shibaura Minato Ward, Tokyo, Japan
Tel.: (81) 354 432 221
Web Site: https://www.exeo-digitalsolutions.co.jp
Digital System Solutions
N.A.I.C.S.: 561499
Yuji Sato (Pres)

Ecos Hokuei Corp. (1)
1-20-3 Atsubetsuminami, Sapporo, Atsubetsu-Ku, Japan   (100%)
Tel.: (81) 118916201
Electrical Contractor
N.A.I.C.S.: 238210

Exeo Asia Co., Ltd. (1)
128/239-240 22nd Floor Phayathai Plaza Building Phayathai Rd, Thung Phayathai, Bangkok, 10400, Thailand
Tel.: (66) 22500165
Web Site: https://www.exeoasia.com
Telecommunication Servicesb
N.A.I.C.S.: 517111

Exeo Sanko Corp. (1)
15-5 Nampeidaicho, Shibuya-Ku, Tokyo, Japan   (89.5%)
Tel.: (81) 334636221
Cellular & Wireless Telecommunications
N.A.I.C.S.: 517112

Exeo Tech Corporation (1)
4-1-23 Heiwajima, Ota-ku, Tokyo, 143-0006, Japan
Tel.: (81) 364042600
Construction Business
N.A.I.C.S.: 236220
Yasuro Otsubo (Pres & CEO)

KANAC Corp. (1)
136 Mitanicho, Takamatsu, 761-0492, Kagawa, Japan   (100%)
Tel.: (81) 878898111
Web Site: https://www.kanac.co.jp
Sales Range: $50-74.9 Million
Emp.: 233
Cellular & Wireless Telecommunications
N.A.I.C.S.: 517112

Leng Aik Engineering Pte. Ltd. (1)
17 Soon Lee Road, Singapore, 628080, Singapore
Tel.: (65) 65154553
Web Site: https://www.lengaik.com
Engineeering Services
N.A.I.C.S.: 541330

MG Exeo Network Inc. (1)
Elizabeth Ave Sta Ana Drive Sun Valley, Paranaque, 1700, Philippines
Tel.: (63) 288898633
Web Site: https://www.mgexeo.com.ph
Emp.: 918
Telecommunication Servicesb
N.A.I.C.S.: 517111

Nippon Dentsu Co., Ltd. (1)
2-21-1 Isoji, Minato-ku, Osaka, 552-0003, Japan
Tel.: (81) 665774111
Web Site: http://www.ndknet.co.jp
Emp.: 871
Telecommunication Network Support Services
N.A.I.C.S.: 541512
Toshio Kami (Chm & Pres)

EXEO Group Inc.—(Continued)

Shinwa Mfg. Co. (1)
3-128 Negishicho, Naka-ku, Yokohama,
231-0836, Kanagawa, Japan (99.9%)
Tel.: (81) 456220567
Mens & Boys Cut & Sew Other Outerwear
Mfr
N.A.I.C.S.: 315250
F. Yoda (Gen Mgr)

Winner Engineering Pte. Ltd. (1)
18 Woodlands Industrial Park E1, Singapore, 757738, Singapore
Tel.: (65) 64818423
Web Site: http://www.wepl.online
Air Conditioning Installation Services
N.A.I.C.S.: 238220

santec Holdings Corporation (1)
Photonics Valley Ohkusa Campus 5823
Ohkusa-Nenjyozaka, Komaki, 485-0802,
Aichi, Japan
Tel.: (81) 568793535
Web Site: https://www.santec.com
Rev.: $124,710,870
Assets: $170,723,080
Liabilities: $53,494,730
Net Worth: $117,228,350
Earnings: $25,455,110
Emp.: 310
Fiscal Year-end: 03/31/2024
Optical Component Mfr
N.A.I.C.S.: 339999
Daikou Tei (Chm, Chief Security Officer &
Exec VP)

vCargo Cloud Pte. Ltd. (1)
2 Tanjong Katong Road 05-01 Paya Lebar
Quarter PLQ 3, Singapore, 437161, Singapore
Tel.: (65) 67796218
Web Site: http://www.vcargocloud.com
Software Services
N.A.I.C.S.: 541511
Desmond Tay (Co-Founder & CEO)

EXERGY21 CO., LTD.
2026-Ho 225 Gasan digital 1-ro,
Geumcheon-gu, Seoul, Korea (South)
Tel.: (82) 25697610
Web Site:
http://www.pharmswell.com
Year Founded: 1999
043090—(KRS)
Rev.: $2,988,670
Assets: $55,911,117
Liabilities: $13,354,813
Net Worth: $42,556,303
Earnings: ($2,573,432)
Emp.: 29
Fiscal Year-end: 12/31/22
Pharmaceuticals Product Mfr
N.A.I.C.S.: 325412
Jang Yunsik (CEO)

EXERION PRECISION TECH-NOLOGY HOLDING B.V.
De Hogenkamp 16, 7071 EC, Ulft,
Netherlands
Tel.: (31) 315689555
Web Site: http://www.exerion.nl
Emp.: 80
Semiconductor & Electronic Component Mfr
N.A.I.C.S.: 334413
Vos Willart (CEO)

Subsidiaries:

Exerion Precision Technology Olomouc, s.r.o. (1)
Lipenska 1170/45, 779 00, Olomouc, Czech
Republic
Tel.: (420) 588490511
Web Site: http://www.exerion.cz
Metal Frame & Electronic Component Mfr
N.A.I.C.S.: 332999

Exerion Precision Technology Ulft NL B.V. (1)
De Hogenkamp 16, Ulft, 7071 EC, Netherlands
Tel.: (31) 315 689 555
Web Site: http://www.exerion.nl

Sales Range: $25-49.9 Million
Emp.: 50
Semiconductor & Electronic Component Mfr
N.A.I.C.S.: 334419

EXETER PRODUCE & STOR-AGE CO. LIMITED
215 Thames Road West, Exeter,
N0M 1S3, ON, Canada
Tel.: (519) 235-0141
Web Site:
http://www.exeterproduce.com
Year Founded: 1951
Rev.: $17,937,709
Emp.: 50
Fresh Fruits & Vegetables Whslr
N.A.I.C.S.: 424480

EXFO INC.
400 Godin Avenue, Quebec, G1M
2K2, QC, Canada
Tel.: (418) 683-0211 Ca
Web Site: http://www.exfo.com
Year Founded: 1985
Rev.: $265,583,000
Assets: $310,654,000
Liabilities: $138,091,000
Net Worth: $172,563,000
Earnings: ($9,540,000)
Emp.: 1,814
Fiscal Year-end: 08/31/20
Fiber-Optic Test, Measurement &
Monitoring Instruments Telecommunications Industries Mfr
N.A.I.C.S.: 334515
Benoit Ringuette (Gen Counsel &
Sec)

Subsidiaries:

EXFO America Inc. (1)
3400 Waterview Pkwy Ste 100, Richardson,
TX 75080
Tel.: (972) 761-9271
Sales Range: $1-9.9 Million
Emp.: 60
Fiber-Optic Test, Measurement & Monitoring
Instruments Mfr
N.A.I.C.S.: 334515

EXFO Asia Pacific PTE Ltd. (1)
100 Beach Road 25-01/03 Shaw Tower,
Singapore, 189702, Singapore
Tel.: (65) 63338241
Web Site: http://www.exfo.com
Sales Range: $25-49.9 Million
Emp.: 10
Mfr of Fiber-Optic Test, Measurement &
Monitoring Instruments for Telecommunications Industry
N.A.I.C.S.: 334515

Subsidiary (Non-US):

**EXFO Electro-Optical Engineering
India Private Ltd.** (2)
Office No 604 Tower S-4 Cybercity Magarpatta, Hadapsar, Pune, 411 013, India
Tel.: (91) 20 66040246
Web Site: http://www.exfo.com
Wireless Telecommunication Services
N.A.I.C.S.: 517112

EXFO Telecom Equipment (Shenzhen) Co. Ltd. (2)
2 3/F Block 10 Yusheng Industrial Park
Side Of Gushu Cross, Shenzhen, China
Tel.: (86) 75529553100
Sales Range: $25-49.9 Million
Telecommunications Equipment Mfr
N.A.I.C.S.: 334290

NetHawk Solutions Pvt. Ltd. (2)
308 3rd Floor Iris Technology Park Sector
48 Sona Road, Gurgaon, 12218, India
Tel.: (91) 9871871633
Web Site: http://www.exfo.com
Emp.: 12
Wireless Telecommunication Services
N.A.I.C.S.: 517112

EXFO Asia Pacific PTE. Ltd. (1)
Room 1207 Office Tower C Global Trade
Center No 36 N 3rd Ring East Rd,

Dongcheng District, Beijing, 100013, PR,
China (100%)
Tel.: (86) 1058257755
Web Site: http://www.exfo.com
Emp.: 34
Sales Distribution of Test & Monitoring Solutions for Network Services
N.A.I.C.S.: 334515

EXFO Asia Pacific Pte. Ltd. (1)
Room 2711 Trade Center No 4028 Jintian
Road, Futian District, Shenzhen, 518035,
PR, China (100%)
Tel.: (86) 75582032300
Web Site: http://www.exfo.com
Sales Distribution of Test & Monitoring Solutions for Network Services & Equipment
Mfrs
N.A.I.C.S.: 334515

EXFO Europe Ltd. (1)
Winchester House School Ln, Chandlers
Ford, Chandlers Ford, SO53 4DG, United
Kingdom
Tel.: (44) 2380 246 800
Web Site: http://www.exfo.com
Sales Range: $25-49.9 Million
Emp.: 30
Mfr of Fiber-Optic Test, Measurement &
Monitoring Instruments for Telecommunications Industry
N.A.I.C.S.: 334515

EXFO Finland Oy (1)
Elektroniikkatie 2, 90590, Oulu, 90590, Finland
Tel.: (358) 403 010 300
Wireless Network Equipment Mfr
N.A.I.C.S.: 334220

EXFO India (1)
7th Floor 701 Building B1, Cerebrum Lt
Park Vadgaontri, Pune, 411 001,
India (100%)
Tel.: (91) 2040186615
Web Site: http://www.exfo.com
Sales Range: $50-74.9 Million
Emp.: 150
Test & Monitoring Solutions for Network
Services
N.A.I.C.S.: 334515

EXFO Japan (1)
4-6-3-202 Akasaka Minato-ku, Tokyo, 107
0052, Japan (100%)
Tel.: (81) 355625344
Web Site: http://www.exfo.com
Test & Monitoring Solutions for Network
Services & Equipment Mfrs
N.A.I.C.S.: 334515

EXFO Navtel Product Group (1)
160 Drumlin Circle, Concord, L4K 3E5, ON,
Canada
Tel.: (905) 738-3741
Web Site: http://www.exfo.com
Sales Range: $25-49.9 Million
Emp.: 47
Network Test Solutions Developer for Mobile & Fixed Network Industries
N.A.I.C.S.: 334515

EXFO Service Assurance Inc. (1)
285 Mill Rd, Chelmsford, MA 01824
Tel.: (978) 367-5600
Sales Range: $25-49.9 Million
Emp.: 50
Telecommunication Network Quality Assurance Solutions
N.A.I.C.S.: 334220
Rick Rigoli (CFO)

NetHawk S.a.r.l (1)
27 rue de Solferino, Boulogne-Billancourt,
92100, France
Tel.: (33) 1 46 08 19 53
Wireless Telecommunication Services
N.A.I.C.S.: 517112

EXGEN RESOURCES INC.
1240 - 1140 West Pender Street,
Vancouver, V6E 4G1, BC, Canada
Tel.: (604) 688-2641 AB
Web Site:
http://www.exgresources.com
EXG—(OTCIQ)
Assets: $704,446
Liabilities: $169,549

Net Worth: $534,897
Earnings: ($221,952)
Fiscal Year-end: 12/31/19
Mineral Exploration Services
N.A.I.C.S.: 213114

EXHICON EVENTS MEDIA SO-LUTIONS LTD.
Plot No 22 Veera Desai Road, Andheri W, Mumbai, 400053, India
Tel.: (91) 18002588103
Web Site:
https://www.exhicongroup.com
Year Founded: 2010
543895—(BOM)
Digital Marketing Services
N.A.I.C.S.: 541810
Abul Fazl (Chief Strategy Officer)

Subsidiaries:

**United Helicharters Private
Limited** (1)
Hangar No C 2 Juhu Civil Aerodrome Vile
Parle West, Mumbai, 400 056,
India (89.99%)
Tel.: (91) 2266701800
Web Site: https://www.uhpl.in
Drilling Services
N.A.I.C.S.: 213111

EXICOM TELE-SYSTEMS LIM-ITED
Plot No. 38, Institutional Area, Sector
32,, Gurugram, 122001, Haryana,
India
Tel.: (91) 1246615200
Web Site: https://www.exicom.in
Year Founded: 1994
EXICOM—(NSE)
Electronics Mfg
N.A.I.C.S.:
Anant Nahata (Mng Dir)

Subsidiaries:

Tritium DCFC Limited (1)
48 Miller Street, Murarrie, 4172, QLD, Australia
Tel.: (61) 731478500
Web Site: https://www.tritiumcharging.com
Rev.: $184,544,000
Assets: $275,176,000
Liabilities: $418,831,000
Net Worth: ($143,655,000)
Earnings: ($121,370,000)
Emp.: 818
Fiscal Year-end: 06/30/2023
Electric Equipment Mfr
N.A.I.C.S.: 335999
David Finn (Founder)

EXICON CO., LTD.
28 Sampyeong-dong DHK Solution
7F Pangyo-ro 255 Beon-gil,
Bundang-gu, Seongnam, 13486,
Gyeonggi-do, Korea (South)
Tel.: (82) 316399200
Web Site: https://www.exicon.co.kr
Year Founded: 2001
092870—(KRS)
Rev.: $69,917,741
Assets: $130,097,108
Liabilities: $19,046,831
Net Worth: $111,050,277
Earnings: $11,667,134
Emp.: 198
Fiscal Year-end: 12/31/22
Semiconductor Devices Mfr
N.A.I.C.S.: 334413
Park Sang-jun (CEO)

EXIDE INDUSTRIES LIMITED
Exide House 59E Chowringhee
Road, Kolkata, 700020, India
Tel.: (91) 3322832118
Web Site:
https://www.exideindustries.com
EXIDEIND—(NSE)
Rev.: $2,097,641,910

Assets: $3,915,790,515
Liabilities: $2,916,816,630
Net Worth: $998,973,885
Earnings: $37,031,085
Emp.: 5,202
Fiscal Year-end: 03/31/21
Storage Batteries Mfr
N.A.I.C.S.: 335910
A. K. Mukherjee *(CFO & Dir-Fin)*

Subsidiaries:

Associated Battery Manufacturers
(Ceylon) Limited   (1)
No 31 Katukurunduwatte Road off Attidiya
Road, Ratmalana, Sri Lanka
Tel.: (94) 112713111
Web Site: http://www.exide.lk
Battery Mfr
N.A.I.C.S.: 335910
Arun Mittal *(Chm)*

Caldyne Automatics Limited   (1)
Plot No Y-21 Block Ep Sector-5 Salt Lake
Electronics Complex, Bidhannagar, Kolkata,
700091, West Bengal, India
Tel.: (91) 3323575851
Web Site:
    http://www.caldyneautomatics.com
Sales Range: $50-74.9 Million
Emp.: 110
High End Industrial Chargers Mfr
N.A.I.C.S.: 335910

Chloride Batteries S E Asia Pte
Limited   (1)
106 Neythal Road, Jurong Town, Singa-
pore, 628594, Singapore
Tel.: (65) 62652444
Web Site: http://www.cbsea.com.sg
Sales Range: $25-49.9 Million
Emp.: 60
Batteries & Chargers Mfr & Distr
N.A.I.C.S.: 335999

Chloride Power Systems & Solutions
Limited   (1)
Plot No Y-21 Block-EP Sector-V Salt Lake
Electronics Complex, Kolkata, 700 091,
India
Tel.: (91) 3323575851
Web Site:
    http://www.chloridepowersystems.co.in
Battery Charger Mfr
N.A.I.C.S.: 335999
A. K. Mukherjee *(Chm)*

Espex Batteries Limited   (1)
Unit 15 Atlantic Trading Estate, Barry, CF63
3RF, Vale of Glamorgan, United Kingdom
Tel.: (44) 2920705453
Web Site: http://www.espexbatteries.co.uk
Sales Range: $25-49.9 Million
Emp.: 11
Power Traction Cells & Battery Charges Mfr
& Distr
N.A.I.C.S.: 335910
Amit Ghosal *(Gen Mgr)*

Exide Life Insurance Company
Limited   (1)
3rd Floor JP Techno Park No 3/1 Millers
Road, Bengaluru, 560 001, India
Tel.: (91) 8041345444
Web Site: http://www.exidelife.in
Financial Investment Services
N.A.I.C.S.: 523999
Rajan Raheja *(Chm)*

ING Vysya Life Insurance Company
Ltd.   (1)
ING Vysya House 5th Floor, 22 M G Road,
560001, Bengaluru, India
Tel.: (91) 805328000
Web Site: http://www.ingvysyalife.com
Insurance Services
N.A.I.C.S.: 524113

Leadage Alloys India Limited   (1)
60 2 Sheethanayakanahalli, Kolar Dist,
Malur, 563130, Karnataka, India
Tel.: (91) 8151 233333
Web Site: http://www.leadage.in
Lead & Lead Alloys Mfr & Supplier
N.A.I.C.S.: 331492

The Standard Batteries Limited   (1)
Rustom Court Opp Podar Hospital Dr A B
Road, Worli, Mumbai, 400 030, India

Tel.: (91) 2224919569
Web Site:
    https://www.standardbatteries.co.in
Rev.: $16,476
Assets: $1,073,027
Liabilities: $143,175
Net Worth: $929,852
Earnings: ($49,577)
Emp.: 5
Fiscal Year-end: 03/31/2021
Battery Mfr
N.A.I.C.S.: 335910
T. R. Swaminathan *(Chm)*

EXILLON ENERGY PLC
Zolotorozhskiy Val Street 32 1, Mos-
cow, 111033, Russia
Tel.: (7) 4959876712   IM
Web Site:
    http://www.exillonenergy.com
Year Founded: 2009
Rev.: $136,819,000
Assets: $725,733,000
Liabilities: $193,866,000
Net Worth: $531,867,000
Earnings: $47,647,000
Emp.: 418
Fiscal Year-end: 12/31/17
Oil & Gas Exploration Services
N.A.I.C.S.: 211120
Viacheslav Nekrasov *(CEO)*

EXIMBANK KAZAKHSTAN JSC
80 Bogenbai Batyr str, 050010, Al-
maty, Kazakhstan
Tel.: (7) 7272663094   KZ
Web Site: http://www.eximbank.kz
Year Founded: 1994
Rev.: $14,359,971
Assets: $186,183,181
Liabilities: $151,100,256
Net Worth: $35,082,924
Earnings: $846,095
Emp.: 311
Fiscal Year-end: 12/31/15
Commercial Banking Services
N.A.I.C.S.: 522110
Dmitry Prihozhan *(Chm-Mgmt Bd &
CEO)*

EXIMO AGRO-MARKETING AG
Jungfernstieg 41, 20354, Hamburg,
Germany
Tel.: (49) 40 34911 0   De
Web Site: http://www.eximo.de
Year Founded: 1976
Sales Range: $300-349.9 Million
Emp.: 30
Milk & Dairy Products Wholesale
Trade Distr
N.A.I.C.S.: 425120
Andreas Dreissig *(Mng Dir-Logistics)*

**EXIR PHARMACEUTICAL
COMPANY**
Second door of Daroupakhsh Fac-
tory, Daropakhsh St 18 kiloometer of
Tehran-Karaj highroad, Tehran, Iran
Tel.: (98) 2144983395
Web Site: http://www.exir.co.ir
Year Founded: 1984
EXIR—(THE)
Sales Range: Less than $1 Million
Emp.: 570
Pharmaceutical Preparation Mfr
N.A.I.C.S.: 325412
Mohsen Kordi *(CEO)*

EXM MANUFACTURING LTD.
870 boul Michele-Bohec, Blainville,
J7C 5E2, QC, Canada
Tel.: (450) 979-4373
Web Site: http://www.exmweb.com
Year Founded: 1975
Sales Range: $10-24.9 Million
Emp.: 30
Cabinetry Mfr
N.A.I.C.S.: 337110

Maurizio Ciocca *(Founder)*

EXMAR N.V.
De Gerlachekaai 20, 2000, Antwerp,
Belgium
Tel.: (32) 32475611
Web Site: https://www.exmar.com
EXM—(EUR)
Rev.: $158,245,000
Assets: $909,767,000
Liabilities: $460,828,000
Net Worth: $448,939,000
Earnings: ($13,202,000)
Emp.: 2,416
Fiscal Year-end: 12/31/19
Deep Sea Freight Transportation
N.A.I.C.S.: 483111
Nicolas Saverys *(Chm)*

Subsidiaries:

Belgibo N.V.   (1)
De Gerlachekaai 20, Antwerp, 2000, Bel-
gium
Tel.: (32) 475811
Web Site: http://www.belgibo.be
Sales Range: $50-74.9 Million
Emp.: 45
Insurance Agencies
N.A.I.C.S.: 524298

Bexco N.V.   (1)
Industriepark Zwaarveld 25, 9220, Hamme,
East Flanders, Belgium
Tel.: (32) 52499370
Web Site: http://www.bexco.be
Sales Range: $25-49.9 Million
Emp.: 120
Rope Mfr & Suppliers
N.A.I.C.S.: 314994
Monique Thienpont *(Mgr-Mktg)*

EXMAR Lux SA   (1)
Jean Pierre Brasseur 6, Luxembourg, 1258,
Luxembourg
Tel.: (352) 2638481
Shipping Agencies
N.A.I.C.S.: 483111
Brijitte Chouly *(Sec)*

EXMAR Marine N.V.   (1)
De Gerlachekaai 20, 2000, Antwerp, Bel-
gium
Tel.: (32) 32475611
Web Site: http://www.exmar.be
Sales Range: $25-49.9 Million
Emp.: 40
Shipping Agencies
N.A.I.C.S.: 483111

EXMAR Shipmanagement N.V.   (1)
De Gerlachekaai 20, 2000, Antwerp, Bel-
gium
Tel.: (32) 32475011
Web Site: http://www.exmar.be
Sales Range: $25-49.9 Million
Emp.: 80
Marine Transportation Services
N.A.I.C.S.: 483111
Marc Nuytemans *(CEO)*

EXMAR Shipping N.V.   (1)
De Gerlachekaai 20, 2000, Antwerp, Bel-
gium
Tel.: (32) 32475611
Web Site: http://www.exmar.be
Marine Transportation Services
N.A.I.C.S.: 483111

Exmar (UK) Shipping Company
Ltd.   (1)
21 Bedford Square, London, WC1B 4PA,
United Kingdom
Tel.: (44) 2078701300
Shipping Management Services
N.A.I.C.S.: 488390

Exmar Energy Partners LP   (1)
Room 3206 32nd Floor Lippo Center Tower
2 No 89, Queensway, Hong Kong, China
(Hong Kong)
Tel.: (852) 2861 9668
Oil & Gas Exploration
N.A.I.C.S.: 211120
Miguel de Potter *(CEO)*

Exmar Hong Kong Ltd.   (1)
N 39 Gloucester Road Room 2503-05 25th

Floor Harcourt House, Wanchai, China
(Hong Kong)
Tel.: (852) 28613880
Shipping Management Services
N.A.I.C.S.: 488390

Exmar Offshore Company   (1)
3700 W Sam Houston Pkwy S Ste 300,
Houston, TX 77042
Tel.: (281) 679-3900
Web Site: http://www.exmaroffshore.com
Sales Range: $25-49.9 Million
Emp.: 65
Construction Management Services
N.A.I.C.S.: 237990

Exmar Offshore Services SA   (1)
25 Boulevard Prince Henri, Luxembourg,
1724, Luxembourg
Tel.: (352) 2638481
Shipping Management Services
N.A.I.C.S.: 488390

Exmar Shipmanagement India, Pvt.
Ltd.   (1)
Shop No 405 406 407 Mint Chambers, 45
47 Mint Rd Fort, Mumbai, 400001, Maha-
rashtra, India
Tel.: (91) 2222640226
Sales Range: $25-49.9 Million
Emp.: 10
Marine Transportation Services
N.A.I.C.S.: 483111

Exmar Shipping USA Inc.   (1)
3700 W Sam Houston Pkwy S Ste 300,
Houston, TX 77042
Tel.: (281) 679-3900
Shipping Management Services
N.A.I.C.S.: 488390

Exmar Singapore Pte. Ltd.   (1)
10 Hoe Chiang Road Keppel Towers 21-03,
Singapore, 089315, Singapore
Tel.: (65) 65760170
Shipping Management Services
N.A.I.C.S.: 488390

Exmar Yachting NV   (1)
De Gerlachekaai 20, 2000, Antwerp, Bel-
gium
Tel.: (32) 32475000
Web Site: http://www.exmaryachting.com
Luxury Motor Yacht & Sailing Yacht Distr
N.A.I.C.S.: 441222
Jill Zwaans *(Mgr-Comml)*

Franship Offshore Lux SA   (1)
Sirraj Road Opposite The Audi Garage,
Tripoli, Libya
Tel.: (218) 217202815
Shipping Management Services
N.A.I.C.S.: 488390

Tecto Cyprus Limited   (1)
15 Navpliou St 2nd Fl, Limassol, 3025, Cy-
prus
Tel.: (357) 25960114
Emp.: 2
Marine Shipping Agencies
N.A.I.C.S.: 488510
Pampos Papas *(Gen Mgr)*

Travel Plus N.V.   (1)
Verviersstraat 2 4, 2000, Antwerp, Belgium
Tel.: (32) 32475800
Web Site: http://www.travelplus.be
Sales Range: $25-49.9 Million
Emp.: 14
Travel Agencies
N.A.I.C.S.: 561510

EXMCEUTICALS INC.
421 7th Avenue S W 30th Floor, Cal-
gary, T2P 4K9, AB, Canada
Tel.: (587) 390-8541   BC
Web Site:
    http://www.exmceuticals.com
Year Founded: 2008
EXM—(DEU)
Rev.: $550
Assets: $979,138
Liabilities: $6,730,293
Net Worth: ($5,751,155)
Earnings: ($7,766,513)
Fiscal Year-end: 06/30/20
Gold Mining Services
N.A.I.C.S.: 212220

EXMCeuticals Inc.—(Continued)

Jonathan Summers *(Chm & CEO)*

EXMOTION CO., LTD.
2-11-1 Osaki, Shinagawa-Ku, Tokyo, 141-0032, Japan
Tel.: (81) 364200019
Web Site:
   https://corporate.exmotion.co.jp
4394—(TKS)
Rev.: $7,834,450
Assets: $12,060,090
Liabilities: $1,049,320
Net Worth: $11,010,770
Earnings: $42,540
Fiscal Year-end: 11/30/23
Security Consulting Services
N.A.I.C.S.: 541690
Hiroyuki Watanabe *(Pres)*

EXO U INC.
9300 Trans Canada Highway Suite 1009, Montreal, H4S 1K5, QC, Canada
Tel.: (514) 613-5775   Ca
Year Founded: 2011
EXO—(TSXV)
Sales Range: Less than $1 Million
Investment Services
N.A.I.C.S.: 523999
Douglas McCollam *(CFO)*

EXOCOBIO INC.
18-cha, Daeryung Techno Town, 19, Gasan digital 1-ro, Geumcheon-gu, Seoul, 08594, Korea (South)
Tel.: (82) 20383915
Web Site: http://www.exocobio.com
Year Founded: 2017
Biotechnology Research
N.A.I.C.S.: 541714
Byong Seung Cho *(CEO)*

Subsidiaries:

Benev Company, Inc.   **(1)**
23263 Madero Ste A, Mission Viejo, CA 92691
Tel.: (949) 768-6146
Web Site: http://www.benev.com
Sales Range: $1-9.9 Million
Emp.: 30
Drugs, Proprietaries, And Sundries
N.A.I.C.S.: 424210
Ethan Min *(Gen Mgr)*

EXOIL LIMITED
Level 21 500 Collins St, Melbourne, 3000, VIC, Australia
Tel.: (61) 38 610 4700
Web Site: http://www.exoil.net
Year Founded: 1979
Sales Range: $1-9.9 Million
Oil & Gas Exploration Services
N.A.I.C.S.: 211120

EXOMA ENERGY LIMITED
Level 7 127 Creek Street, Brisbane, 4000, QLD, Australia
Tel.: (61) 732265600
Web Site: http://www.exoma.net
Sales Range: Less than $1 Million
Emp.: 1
Oil & Gas Exploration Services
N.A.I.C.S.: 211120

EXOPHARM LTD.
Level 17/31 Queen St, Melbourne, 3000, VIC, Australia
Tel.: (61) 391110026
Web Site: http://www.exopharm.com
Year Founded: 2013
EX1—(ASX)
Rev.: $76,412
Assets: $10,430,688
Liabilities: $3,682,272
Net Worth: $6,748,416
Earnings: ($7,726,268)

Emp.: 50
Fiscal Year-end: 06/30/22
Pharmaceuticals Product Mfr
N.A.I.C.S.: 325412
David Parker *(Sec)*

EXOTIC FOOD PUBLIC COMPANY LIMITED
130-132 Sindhorn Tower Tower 2 9th Floor Wireless Rd Lumphini, Pathum Wan, Bangkok, 10330, Thailand
Tel.: (66) 26507779
Web Site:
   https://www.exoticfoodthailand.com
Year Founded: 1999
XO—(THA)
Rev.: $73,968,073
Assets: $64,725,604
Liabilities: $12,072,923
Net Worth: $52,652,681
Earnings: $22,916,864
Emp.: 420
Fiscal Year-end: 12/31/23
Seasoning Products Mfr
N.A.I.C.S.: 311941
Banphot Hongthong *(Chm)*

EXP GLOBAL INC.
56 Queen Street East Suite 301, Brampton, L6V 4M8, ON, Canada
Tel.: (905) 796-3200   IL
Web Site: http://www.exp.com
Year Founded: 1959
Sales Range: $300-349.9 Million
Emp.: 3,000
Building Engineering, Earth & Environmental Engineering, Infrastructure Engineering, Planning & Design, Program Management & Sustainability Services
N.A.I.C.S.: 541330
Vincent Latendresse *(Exec VP-Quebec)*

Subsidiaries:

exp Federal Inc.   **(1)**
205 N Michigan Ave Ste 3800, Chicago, IL 60601
Tel.: (312) 616-7500
Web Site: http://www.expfederal.com
Architectural & Engineering Design, Construction Management Services & Landscape Design
N.A.I.C.S.: 541310
John Samis *(Pres & Gen Mgr)*

exp U.S. Services Inc.   **(1)**
2601 Westhall Ln, Maitland, FL 32751
Tel.: (407) 660-0088
Sales Range: $50-74.9 Million
Architectural & Engineering Services
N.A.I.C.S.: 541310
Richard Poirier *(Principal)*

EXPECT DISTRIBUTION
Unit 2 Premier Point Premier Gate, Staithgate Lane, Bradford, BD6 1DW, West Yorkshire, United Kingdom
Tel.: (44) 1274378220
Web Site:
   http://www.expectdistribution.com
Rev.: $19,107,556
Emp.: 144
Transportation & Warehousing Services
N.A.I.C.S.: 488510
Robert Rushworth *(Mng Dir)*

EXPERIAN PLC
2 Cumberland Place Fenian Street, Dublin, D02 HY05, Ireland
Tel.: (353) 18469100   JE
Web Site:
   https://www.experianplc.com
Year Founded: 1826
EXPN—(LSE)
Rev.: $7,097,000,000
Assets: $11,712,000,000

Liabilities: $7,043,000,000
Net Worth: $4,669,000,000
Earnings: $1,203,000,000
Emp.: 22,261
Fiscal Year-end: 03/31/24
Credit Reporting Services, Decision Analytics & Marketing Support Services
N.A.I.C.S.: 561450
Charles Brown *(Sec)*

Subsidiaries:

Altovision Inc.   **(1)**
Kataho Building Third Floor 2-16-11 Ginza, Chuo-ku, Tokyo, 104-0061, Japan
Tel.: (81) 3 5550 6440
Web Site: http://www.altovision.co.jp
Sales Range: $1-9.9 Million
Marketing Consulting Services
N.A.I.C.S.: 541613

CSH Group (Pty) Ltd   **(1)**
Experian House 3 Neutron Avenue Techno Park, Stellenbosch, 7600, South Africa
Tel.: (27) 218886000
Data Management Services
N.A.I.C.S.: 518210

CSIT Botswana (Pty) Ltd   **(1)**
Plot 54373 Western Commercial Road Unit 2 SFB House Matante Mews, PO Box 794 AAH, Gaborone, Botswana
Tel.: (267) 3117714
Web Site: http://www.experian.co.bw
Information Services
N.A.I.C.S.: 519290

CSIdentity Corporation   **(1)**
1501 S Mopac Expy Ste 200, Austin, TX 78746
Web Site: https://csidprotector.com
Data Security Providers
N.A.I.C.S.: 513210

Clarity Services, Inc.   **(1)**
PO Box 16, Allen, TX 75013
Web Site: https://www.clarityservices.com
Financial Services
N.A.I.C.S.: 523999

Experian (Malaysia) Sdn. Bhd.   **(1)**
Ground Floor Quill 18, Lingkaran Teknokrat 3 Barat, 63000, Cyberjaya, Selangor, Malaysia
Tel.: (60) 383160000
Information Services
N.A.I.C.S.: 519290

Experian (Thailand) Co., Ltd.   **(1)**
1788 Singha Complex 1905 unit 19th Floor New Phetchaburi road, Bang kapi Huai Khwang, Bangkok, 10310, Thailand
Tel.: (66) 20328900
Web Site: http://www.experian.co.th
Information Services
N.A.I.C.S.: 519290

Experian AS   **(1)**
Professor Kohts vei 9, 1366, Lysaker, Norway
Tel.: (47) 81555454
Web Site: http://www.experian.no
Marketing Consulting Services
N.A.I.C.S.: 541613

Experian Asia-Pacific Holdings Pte. Ltd.   **(1)**
10 Kallang Avenue 14-18 Aperia Tower 2, Singapore, 339510, Singapore
Tel.: (65) 65937500
Information Services
N.A.I.C.S.: 519290

Experian Australia Credit Services Pty Ltd   **(1)**
GPO Box 1969, North Sydney, 2060, NSW, Australia
Tel.: (61) 300783684
Web Site: https://www.experian.com.au
N.A.I.C.S.: 518210

Experian Background Data, Inc.   **(1)**
475 Anton Blvd, Costa Mesa, CA 92626
Information Services
N.A.I.C.S.: 519290

Experian Bilgi Hizmetleri Limited Sirketi   **(1)**
River Plaza Buyukdere Cad Bahar Sok No

13 Kat 8, Levent, 34394, Istanbul, Turkiye
Tel.: (90) 2123441515
Web Site: https://www.experian.com.tr
Information Services
N.A.I.C.S.: 519290

Experian Bulgaria EAD   **(1)**
Space Tower Building 86 Tsarigradsko Shosse Blvd, 1784, Sofia, Bulgaria
Tel.: (359) 24620800
Web Site: https://www.experian.bg
Emp.: 1,000
Information Services
N.A.I.C.S.: 519290

Experian Bureau de Credito, S.A.   **(1)**
C/ Principe de Vergara 132 1a, 28002, Madrid, Spain
Tel.: (34) 915300370
Information Services
N.A.I.C.S.: 519290

Experian Credit Information Company of India Private Limited   **(1)**
5th Floor East Wing Tower 3 Equinox Business Park LBS Marg, Kurla West, Mumbai, 400070, India
Tel.: (91) 2268186700
Web Site: https://www.experian.in
Information Services
N.A.I.C.S.: 519290

Experian Credit Service (Beijing) Company Limited   **(1)**
2005B Floor 20 Tower 3 China Central Placern77 Jianguo Road, Chaoyang District, Beijing, 100025, China
Tel.: (86) 1059267800
Web Site: http://www.experian.com.cn
Information Services
N.A.I.C.S.: 519290

Experian Data Quality UK   **(1)**
George West House 2 3 Clapham Common North Side, London, SW4 0QL, United Kingdom
Tel.: (44) 8001977920
Web Site: http://www.edq.com
Data Accuracy & Identity Management Services
N.A.I.C.S.: 519290
Jonathan Hulford-Funnell *(Mng Dir-Global)*

Experian Decision Analytics   **(1)**
Landmark House NG2 Business Pk Experian Way, Nottingham, NG80 1ZZ, United Kingdom
Tel.: (44) 01159410888
Web Site: http://www.experian-da.com
Sales Range: $75-99.9 Million
Emp.: 200
Data Intelligence, Predictive Analytics, Strategy Optimisation & Technical Consulting Services
N.A.I.C.S.: 518210

Subsidiary (Non-US):

Experian Decision Analytics   **(2)**
6 Georgiou Mpakou Street, 11524, Athens, Filothei, Greece
Tel.: (30) 2106930790
Web Site: http://www.experian-da.com
Sales Range: $25-49.9 Million
Emp.: 10
Credit Risk Analysis & Software Development Services
N.A.I.C.S.: 541511

Experian Deutschland Holding GmbH   **(2)**
Circus 2, 20359, Hamburg, Germany
Tel.: (49) 408995000
Web Site: http://www.experian.de
Sales Range: $25-49.9 Million
Emp.: 35
Provider of Decision Support & Outsourcing Services with Information on Consumers, Businesses, Motor Vehicles & Property
N.A.I.C.S.: 333310
David Groom *(Gen Mgr)*

Experian Espana S.L.U.   **(2)**
C/ Principe de Vergara 132 1 Planta, 28002, Madrid, Spain
Tel.: (34) 915300370
Web Site: https://www.experian.es
Credit Risk Analysis & Software Development Services

N.A.I.C.S.: 541511
Lorena Caballero *(Dir-Fin)*

Subsidiary (US):

Experian Scorex US, LLC   **(2)**
5909 Peachtree Dunwoody Rd Ste 1100,
Atlanta, GA 30328
Tel.: (678) 731-1100
Provider of Credit Risk Analysis & Software
Development Services
N.A.I.C.S.: 561499

Subsidiary (Domestic):

Experian Tallyman   **(2)**
3110 Great Western Court Hunts Ground
Road, Aztec W, Bristol, BS34 8HP, United
Kingdom
Tel.: (44) 1454441000
Web Site: http://www.experian-da.com
Sales Range: $10-24.9 Million
Emp.: 80
IT Solutions
N.A.I.C.S.: 334610
Martin Aldridge *(Office Mgr)*

Subsidiary (Non-US):

Experian-Scorex S.r.l. Italia   **(2)**
Viale Dell Esperanto 71, 00144, Rome, Italy
Tel.: (39) 06 59 29 301
Web Site: http://www.experian-scorex.com
Credit Risk Analysis & Software Develop-
ment Services
N.A.I.C.S.: 541511
Elio Vitucci *(CEO-MicroAnalytics)*

Subsidiary (Domestic):

Scorex (UK) Limited   **(2)**
Scorex House 1 Bolton Rd, Bradford, BD1
4AS, United Kingdom
Tel.: (44) 1274762700
Sales Range: $25-49.9 Million
Emp.: 70
Provider of Credit Risk Analysis & Software
Development Services
N.A.I.C.S.: 541511

Subsidiary (Non-US):

Scorex Scandinavia   **(2)**
Glarmestervej 2, DK 8600, Silkeborg, Den-
mark
Tel.: (45) 70100107
Web Site: http://www.experian-scorex.com
Sales Range: $10-24.9 Million
Emp.: 50
Credit Risk Analysis & Software Develop-
ment Services
N.A.I.C.S.: 541511

Subsidiary (US):

The 41st Parameter, Inc.   **(2)**
16260 N 71st St Ste 400, Scottsdale, AZ
85254
Tel.: (480) 776-5500
Web Site: http://www.the41.com
Emp.: 20
Internet Fraud Detection & Prevention Ser-
vices
N.A.I.C.S.: 541511
Elazar Katz *(VP-Enterprise Strategies & Fin
Svcs)*

Experian Finance Holdings
Limited   **(1)**
Newenham House Northern Cross Malahide
Road, Dublin, Ireland
Tel.: (353) 1 846 9100
Investment Management Service
N.A.I.C.S.: 523940

Experian GmbH   **(1)**
Rheinstrasse 99, 76532, Baden-Baden,
Germany
Tel.: (49) 72217793300
Web Site: https://www.experian.de
N.A.I.C.S.: 518210

Experian Holdings Ireland
Limited   **(1)**
Newenham House Northern Cross, Dublin,
Ireland
Tel.: (353) 18469100
Investment Management Service
N.A.I.C.S.: 523940

Experian Information Services (Ma-
laysia) Sdn. Bhd.   **(1)**
Suite 16 02 Level 16 Centrepoint South Mid
Valley City, Lingkaran Syed Putra, 59200,
Kuala Lumpur, Malaysia
Tel.: (60) 326151100
Web Site: https://www.experian.com.my
Information Services
N.A.I.C.S.: 519290

Experian Information Solutions,
Inc.   **(1)**
4400 Easton Cmns Ste 125, Columbus, OH
43219
Tel.: (714) 830-7000
Rev.: $1,030,211,200
Emp.: 1,200
Decision Support & Outsourcing Services
with Information on Consumers, Busi-
nesses, Motor Vehicles & Property
N.A.I.C.S.: 561450

Subsidiary (Domestic):

ConsumerInfo.com, Inc.   **(2)**
C T Corporation System 818 W 7th St, Los
Angeles, CA 90017
Tel.: (949) 567-3800
Credit Reporting Services
N.A.I.C.S.: 561450

Division (Domestic):

Experian Healthcare   **(2)**
720 Cool Springs Blvd Ste 200, Franklin,
TN 37067
Tel.: (615) 661-5657
Web Site: http://www.experian.com
Sales Range: $50-74.9 Million
Emp.: 167
Software Developer for Medical Group Re-
imbursement Services
N.A.I.C.S.: 513210
Tom Stampiglia *(CEO)*

Branch (Domestic):

Experian Information Solutions, Inc. -
Chicago   **(2)**
955 American Ln, Schaumburg, IL 60173-
4983
Tel.: (224) 698-5600
Web Site: http://www.experian.com
Sales Range: $125-149.9 Million
Emp.: 568
Information Services, List Development &
Enhancement, Mail Production, Database
Development & Credit Reports
N.A.I.C.S.: 561450

Subsidiary (Domestic):

Passport Health Communications,
Inc.   **(2)**
720 Cool Springs Blvd, Franklin, TN 37067
Tel.: (615) 661-5657
Web Site: http://www.passporthealth.com
Sales Range: $25-49.9 Million
Emp.: 150
Internet-Based Financial Management Tools
for Healthcare Industry
N.A.I.C.S.: 541511
Seth Rupp *(CTO)*

Joint Venture (Domestic):

VantageScore Solutions, LLC   **(2)**
107 Elm St Ste 907, Stamford, CT 06902
Tel.: (203) 363-0269
Web Site: http://www.vantagescore.com
Sales Range: $10-24.9 Million
Emp.: 15
Consumer Credit Scoring Services
N.A.I.C.S.: 561450
Barrett Burns *(Pres & CEO)*

Experian Investment Holdings
Limited   **(1)**
The Sir John Peace Building Experian Way
NG2 Business Park, Nottingham, NG80
1ZZ, United Kingdom
Tel.: (44) 1159410888
Investment Management Service
N.A.I.C.S.: 523999

Experian Italia S.p.A.   **(1)**
Piazza Indipendenza 11B, 00185, Rome,
Italy
Tel.: (39) 0645486499
Web Site: https://www.experian.it

Information Services
N.A.I.C.S.: 519290

Experian Japan Co., Ltd.   **(1)**
7th Floor Otemachi Park Building 1-1-1,
Otemachi Chiyoda-ku, Tokyo, 100-0004,
Japan
Tel.: (81) 362627600
Information Services
N.A.I.C.S.: 519290

Experian Ltd.   **(1)**
Tel.: (44) 1159410888
Web Site: https://www.experian.co.uk
Sales Range: $350-399.9 Million
Emp.: 1,300
Credit Reporting Services, Decision Analyt-
ics & Marketing Support Services
N.A.I.C.S.: 561450

Subsidiary (Non-US):

CreditInform AS   **(2)**
Karenslyst Alle 6, 0278, Oslo, Norway
Tel.: (47) 81555454
Web Site: http://www.creditinform.no
Sales Range: $25-49.9 Million
Emp.: 80
Credit Reporting Services
N.A.I.C.S.: 561450
Gabor Molnar *(Mng Dir)*

Experian A/S   **(2)**
Lyngbyvej 2, 2100, Copenhagen, Denmark
Tel.: (45) 70100107
Web Site: https://www.experian.dk
Sales Range: $10-24.9 Million
Emp.: 170
Operates as a Credit & Business Informa-
tion Group
N.A.I.C.S.: 522299

Experian Australia Pty. Ltd.   **(2)**
Level 26/2 Southbank Blvd, Southbank,
3004, VIC, Australia
Tel.: (61) 386221600
Web Site: https://www.experian.com.au
Sales Range: $25-49.9 Million
Emp.: 230
Decision Support & Outsourcing Services
with Information on Consumers, Busi-
nesses, Motor Vehicles & Property
N.A.I.C.S.: 333310

Experian Australia Pty. Ltd. - Sydney
Office   **(2)**
Level 20 101 Miller Street, North Sydney,
2060, NSW, Australia
Tel.: (61) 28 907 7200
Web Site: https://www.experian.com.au
Sales Range: $25-49.9 Million
Emp.: 15
Provider of Decision Support & Outsourcing
Services with Information on Consumers,
Businesses, Motor Vehicles & Property
N.A.I.C.S.: 333310

Experian Data Services S.r.l.   **(2)**
Cinecitta 2 Palazzo Experian, Via Quinta-
valle 68, 00173, Rome, Italy
Tel.: (39) 06724221
Web Site: http://www.experian.it
Decision Support & Outsourcing Services
with Information on Consumers, Busi-
nesses, Motor Vehicles & Property
N.A.I.C.S.: 333310

Experian France   **(2)**
19 Boulevard Malesherbes, La Defense,
75008, Paris, Cedex, France
Tel.: (33) 114451001
Web Site: https://www.experian.fr
Sales Range: $25-49.9 Million
Emp.: 250
Risk Management & Marketing Solutions
N.A.I.C.S.: 561499

Experian Hong Kong Ltd.   **(2)**
31/F Tower Two Times Square 1 Matheson
Street, Causeway Bay, China (Hong Kong)
Tel.: (852) 37696499
Web Site: https://www.experian.com.hk
Sales Range: $25-49.9 Million
Emp.: 60
Provider of Decision Support & Outsourcing
Services with Information on Consumers,
Businesses, Motor Vehicles & Property
N.A.I.C.S.: 333310
Ben Elliott *(CEO-Asia Pacific)*

Experian Ireland Ltd.   **(2)**

Lincoln House Lincoln Place, Dublin, D02
VH29, Ireland
Tel.: (353) 15677000
Web Site: https://www.experian.ie
Sales Range: $25-49.9 Million
Emp.: 25
Provider Business & Personal Information
Solutions
N.A.I.C.S.: 517810

Experian Nederland B.V.   **(2)**
Grote Marktstraat 49, Sijthoff City, 2511 BH,
Hague, Netherlands
Tel.: (31) 90039737426
Web Site: https://www.experian.nl
Sales Range: $25-49.9 Million
Emp.: 100
Provider of Decision Support & Outsourcing
Services with Information on Consumers,
Businesses, Motor Vehicles & Property
N.A.I.C.S.: 333310

Experian Singapore Pte. Ltd.   **(2)**
10 Kallang Avenue 05-18 Aperia Tower 2,
Singapore, 339510, Singapore
Tel.: (65) 65937500
Web Site: https://www.experian.com.sg
Sales Range: $10-24.9 Million
Emp.: 50
Credit Reporting Services, Decision Analyt-
ics & Marketing Support Services
N.A.I.C.S.: 561450

Experian South Africa   **(2)**
Experian House Ballyoaks Office Park 35
Ballyclare Drive, Bryanston, Johannesburg,
2021, Gauteng, South Africa
Tel.: (27) 117793400
Web Site: https://www.experian.co.za
Sales Range: $25-49.9 Million
Emp.: 115
Provider of Decision Support & Outsourcing
Services with Information on Consumers,
Businesses, Motor Vehicles & Property
N.A.I.C.S.: 561450
Prabashnie Moodley *(Head-HR)*

Experian Micro Analytics SAM   **(1)**
Athos Palace 2 Rue de la Lujernata, 98000,
Monaco, Monaco
Tel.: (377) 97985454
Information Services
N.A.I.C.S.: 519290

Experian New Zealand Limited   **(1)**
Level 9 4 Williamson Avenue, Grey Lynn,
Auckland, 1021, New Zealand
Tel.: (64) 99274611
Web Site: https://www.experian.co.nz
Information Services
N.A.I.C.S.: 519290

Experian Osterreich GmbH   **(1)**
Strozzigasse 10/14, 1080, Vienna, Austria
Tel.: (43) 152491980
Web Site: http://www.experian.at
Information Services
N.A.I.C.S.: 519290

Experian Peru S.A.C   **(1)**
Av Canaval y Moreyra 480 Piso 19 Edificio
Chocavento, San Isidro, Lima, Peru
Tel.: (51) 15149000
Web Site: https://www.experian.com.pe
Information Services
N.A.I.C.S.: 519290

Experian Polska spolka z ogranic-
zona odpowiedzialnoscia   **(1)**
Metropolitan Complex Plac Pilsudskiego 3,
00-078, Warsaw, Poland
Tel.: (48) 224490119
Web Site: http://www.experian.com.pl
Information Services
N.A.I.C.S.: 519290

Experian Services Chile S.A.   **(1)**
Av Del Valle 515, Huechuraba, Santiago,
Chile
Tel.: (56) 28345000
Web Site: http://www.experian.cl
Information Services
N.A.I.C.S.: 519290

Experian Services Costa Rica,
S.A.   **(1)**
Zona Franca UltraPark II Edificios 3 - 3er
Piso - y 5 - 1er Piso, Heredia, Costa Rica
Tel.: (506) 25622400
N.A.I.C.S.: 518210

Experian plc—(Continued)

Experian Services India Private Limited (1)
5th Floor East Wing Tower 3 Equinox Business Park LBS Marg, Kurla West, Mumbai, 400070, India
Tel.: (91) 2268186700
Information Services
N.A.I.C.S.: 519290

Experian Strategic Solutions SA (1)
Carlos Pellegrini 887 Piso 4, C1009ABK, Buenos Aires, Argentina
Tel.: (54) 1139889702
Wob Sito: http://www.experian.com.ar
Information Services
N.A.I.C.S.: 519290

Experian Tecnología Brasil Ltda (1)
Alameda dos Quinimuras 187-3rd Floor Planalto Paulista, Sao Paulo, 04068-900, Brazil
Tel.: (55) 1133737272
Information Services
N.A.I.C.S.: 519290

Garlik Limited (1)
1-3 Halford Road, Richmond, TW10 6AW, United Kingdom
Tel.: (44) 845 862 2441
Web Site: http://www.garlik.com
Sales Range: $25-49.9 Million
Emp.: 16
Online Security Services
N.A.I.C.S.: 513199
Andy Thomas (Mng Dir)

MCI-Experian Co., Ltd. (1)
10th Floor Shinhan L Tower 358 Samil-daero, Jung-gu, Seoul, Korea (South)
Tel.: (82) 23985400
Web Site: http://www.mciexperian.com
Management Consulting Services
N.A.I.C.S.: 541611

My Health Direct, Inc. (1)
C T Corporation 300 Montvue Rd, Knoxville, TN 37919-5546
Tel.: (714) 830-7000
Women Healthcare Services
N.A.I.C.S.: 621610

Neuro-ID, Inc. (1)
911 Wisconsin Ave Ste 203, Whitefish, MT 59937
Tel.: (406) 552-0745
Web Site: https://www.neuro-id.com
Behavioral Analytics Solutions
N.A.I.C.S.: 518210
Jack Alton (CEO)

PT. Experian Decision Analytics Indonesia (1)
World Trade Centre 3 Lantai 27 Jl Jend Sudirman Kav 29-31, Jakarta, 12920, Indonesia
Tel.: (62) 2150862820
Information Services
N.A.I.C.S.: 519290

Runpath Regulated Services Limited (1)
Runpath Digital Ground and Mezzanine Floors, White Collar Factory 1 Old Street Yard, London, EC1Y 8AF, United Kingdom
Tel.: (44) 2071017979
Web Site: http://www.runpath.com
Financial Management Services
N.A.I.C.S.: 541611

Serasa S.A. (1)
Alameda dos Quinimuras 187 Planalto Paulista, Sao Paulo, 04068-900, SP, Brazil (99.6%)
Tel.: (55) 30047728
Web Site: https://www.serasaexperian.com.br
Sales Range: $800-899.9 Million
Credit Bureaus
N.A.I.C.S.: 561450

Tapad, Inc. (1)
261 Madison Ave 4th Fl, New York, NY 10016
Tel.: (646) 561-6500
Web Site: https://go.tapad.com
Cross-Platform Advertising Technology
N.A.I.C.S.: 513210
Are Traasdahl (Founder)

Techlightenment Limited (1)
3 08 Tea Building 56 Shoreditch High Street, London, E1 6JJ, United Kingdom
Tel.: (44) 20 7033 3567
Web Site: http://www.techlightenment.com
Sales Range: $25-49.9 Million
Emp.: 40
Marketing Consulting Services
N.A.I.C.S.: 541613

Virid Interatividade Digital Ltda (1)
Rua Bandeira Paulista 275 - 12 Andar, Itaim Bibi, Sao Paulo, 04532-010, Brazil
Tel.: (55) 11 3708 4000
Sales Range: $25-49.9 Million
Emp.. 40
Online Marketing Services
N.A.I.C.S.: 541613

EXPERIENCE CO LIMITED
Tel.: (61) 742424900
Web Site:
https://www.experienceco.com
Year Founded: 1999
EXP—(ASX)
Rev.: $84,829,690
Assets: $128,229,451
Liabilities: $42,129,720
Net Worth: $86,099,731
Earnings: ($47,410)
Fiscal Year-end: 06/30/24
Skydiving & Other Related Sports Activities
N.A.I.C.S.: 713990
Bob East (Chm)

Subsidiaries:

Australia Skydive Pty. Ltd. (1)
PO Box 5361, Wollongong, 2500, NSW, Australia
Tel.: (61) 1300585224
Web Site: https://www.skydive.com.au
Skydiving Services
N.A.I.C.S.: 713990

Calypso Reef Charters Pty. Ltd. (1)
44 Wharf Street, Port Douglas, 4877, QLD, Australia
Tel.: (61) 742227465
Web Site:
https://www.calypsoreefcruises.com
Cruise Services
N.A.I.C.S.: 487210

GBR Helicopters Pty. Ltd. (1)
Hangar 10 Bush Pilots Avenue General Aviation, Cairns, 4870, QLD, Australia
Tel.: (61) 740818888
Web Site:
https://www.gbrhelicopters.com.au
Cruise Services
N.A.I.C.S.: 721214

ILB Pty. Ltd. (1)
3/14 Ralph Black Drive, Wollongong, 2500, NSW, Australia
Tel.: (61) 242270000
Web Site: https://www.ilb.com.au
Software Development Services
N.A.I.C.S.: 541511
Kevin Withnall (Owner & Mgr)

Performance Aviation (New Zealand) Limited (1)
4 Lloyd Dunn Ave Wanaka Airport, Wanaka, New Zealand
Tel.: (64) 34438989
Web Site:
https://www.performanceaviation.co.nz
Aircraft Repair Services
N.A.I.C.S.: 811310
Pete McKenna (Mgr-Avionics)

Performance Aviation Australia (1)
Hangar 5 32 Airport Rd, Albion Park Rail, Shellharbour, 2527, NSW, Australia
Tel.: (61) 242314299
Web Site: https://www.aerocentre.com.au
Aircraft Maintenance Services
N.A.I.C.S.: 488190
Cameron Sherrington (Mgr-Quality Safety)

Reef Magic Cruises Pty. Ltd. (1)
Cairns Reef Fleet Terminal 1 Spence Street, Cairns, 4870, QLD, Australia
Tel.: (61) 740311588
Web Site: https://www.reefmagic.com.au

Cruise Services
N.A.I.C.S.: 721214

Skydive Queenstown Limited (1)
35 Shotover Street, Queenstown, New Zealand
Tel.: (64) 34425867
Web Site: https://www.nzoneskydive.co.nz
Emp.: 65
Cruise Services
N.A.I.C.S.: 721214
Ken Stone (Ops Mgr-Parachutes)

Skydive Wanaka Limited (1)
14 Mustang Lane Wanaka Airport, Wanaka, 9382, New Zealand
Tel.: (64) 34437207
Web Site: https://www.skydivewanaka.com
Cruise Services
N.A.I.C.S.: 721214
Clark Scott (Gen Mgr)

EXPERT SYSTEMS HOLDINGS LIMITED
22/F Yen Sheng Centre 64 Hoi Yuen Road Kwun Tong, Kowloon, China (Hong Kong)
Tel.: (852) 21683800   Ky
Web Site:
https://www.expertsystems.com.hk
Year Founded: 1985
8319—(HKG)
Rev.: $87,988,737
Assets: $69,618,503
Liabilities: $47,578,787
Net Worth: $22,039,715
Earnings: $2,174,990
Emp.: 903
Fiscal Year-end: 03/31/22
Information Technology Support Services
N.A.I.C.S.: 541512
Wai Kwok Lau (CEO, Compliance Officer & Exec Dir)

Subsidiaries:

Expert Systems (Macau) Limited (1)
Avenida Do Dr Rodrigo Rodrigues No 600-E Sala 1404, First International Commercial Centre, Macau, China (Macau)
Tel.: (853) 28722078
Web Site:
http://www.expertsystems.com.mo
Information Technology Infrastructure Services
N.A.I.C.S.: 541512

EXPERT.AI S.P.A.
Via Virgilio 48/H Scala 5, 41123, Modena, Italy
Tel.: (39) 059894011
Web Site: https://www.expert.ai
EXSY—(ITA)
Rev.: $43,942,998
Assets: $81,071,371
Liabilities: $62,111,778
Net Worth: $18,959,594
Earnings: ($25,775,441)
Emp.: 311
Fiscal Year-end: 12/31/22
Semantic Analysis Products & Services
N.A.I.C.S.: 513210
Stefano Spaggiari (Co-Founder & Chm)

Subsidiaries:

Expert System USA Inc. (1)
908 King St-Ste 201, Alexandria, VA 22314
Tel.: (703) 567-2255
Web Site: http://www.expertsystem.us
Software Development Services
N.A.I.C.S.: 541511
Louis Andre (CEO)

EXPLICIT FINANCE LIMITED
Office No 305 3rd Floor Sohan Commercial Plaza Opp Shiv Sena Office, Vasai E, Thane, 401210, India
Tel.: (91) 9320478152

Web Site:
https://www.explicitfinance.net
Year Founded: 1994
530571—(BOM)
Rev.: $914,828
Assets: $1,169,963
Liabilities: $56,099
Net Worth: $1,113,864
Emp.: 2
Fiscal Year-end: 03/31/21
Investment Banking & Securities Dealing Services
N.A.I.C.S.: 523150
Avinach Mainkar (Soo)

EXPLOITS DISCOVERY CORP.
131 Roe Avenue, Gander, A1V 1W5, NL, Canada
Tel.: (778) 819-2708
Web Site:
https://www.exploitsdiscovery.com
634—(DEU)
Rev.: $936
Assets: $26,913,137
Liabilities: $1,065,802
Net Worth: $25,847,335
Earnings: ($5,910,342)
Emp.: 10
Fiscal Year-end: 10/31/22
Mineral Exploration Services
N.A.I.C.S.: 213115
Jeff Swinoga (Pres & CEO)

EXPLORANCE, INC.
1470 Peel Street Suite 500, H3A 1T1, Montreal, QC, Canada
Tel.: (514) 938-2111
Web Site: http://www.explorance.com
Year Founded: 2003
Information Technology Services
N.A.I.C.S.: 519290
Samer Saab (CEO)

Subsidiaries:

KnowledgeAdvisors, Inc. (1)
1919 N Lynn St, Arlington, VA 22209
Tel.: (571) 303-3000
Web Site:
http://www.knowledgeadvisors.com
Software Publisher
N.A.I.C.S.: 513210
Sara Chizzo (VP-Sls)

EXPLOREX RESOURCES INC.
Suite 488-625 Howe Street, Vancouver, V6C 2T6, BC, Canada
Tel.: (604) 681-0221   BC
Web Site: http://www.explorex.ca
Year Founded: 2011
RICH—(CNSX)
Rev.: $6,297,110
Assets: $24,665,941
Liabilities: $2,487,854
Net Worth: $22,178,087
Earnings: ($301,998)
Fiscal Year-end: 06/30/20
Mining Company
N.A.I.C.S.: 212390
William E. A. Wishart (Chm)

EXPLOSIVE CO., LTD.
Research Building No 389 Guyuan Road, Yuelu District, Changsha, 410221, Hunan, China
Tel.: (86) 73188936121
Web Site: http://www.hnnlmb.com
Year Founded: 2001
002096—(SSE)
Rev.: $323,511,084
Assets: $496,580,760
Liabilities: $219,911,328
Net Worth: $276,669,432
Earnings: $6,697,080
Fiscal Year-end: 12/31/22
Explosive Material Mfr
N.A.I.C.S.: 325920
Fu Jun (Chm)

EXPO GAS CONTAINERS LTD.
Expo House 150 Sheriff Devji House,
Mumbai, 400 003, India
Tel.: (91) 2261319600
Web Site: https://www.expogas.com
Year Founded: 1982
526614—(BOM)
Rev.: $6,594,601
Assets: $10,243,570
Liabilities: $7,270,266
Net Worth: $2,973,304
Earnings: ($329,760)
Emp.: 59
Fiscal Year-end. 03/31/21
Engineering & Construction Services
N.A.I.C.S.: 541330
Hasanain S. Mewawala *(Mng Dir)*

EXPOBANK LLC
29 Kalanchevskaya Str Bldg 2,
107078, Moscow, Russia
Tel.: (7) 4952311111   RU
Web Site: http://www.expobank.ru
Year Founded: 1994
Retail & Commercial Banking
N.A.I.C.S.: 522110

Subsidiaries:

Expobank CZ a.s.   (1)
Na strzi 2097/63, 140 00, Prague, Czech
Republic
Tel.: (420) 233233233
Web Site: http://www.expobank.cz
Commercial Banking Services
N.A.I.C.S.: 522110
Igor Kim *(Owner & Chm-Supervisory Bd)*

EXPOLANKA HOLDINGS PLC
15A Clifford Avenue 03, Colombo, Sri
Lanka
Tel.: (94) 114659500
Web Site:
https://www.expolanka.com
Year Founded: 1978
EXPO.N0000—(COL)
Rev.: $1,818,850,507
Assets: $735,624,224
Liabilities: $237,542,662
Net Worth: $498,081,562
Earnings: $103,359,271
Emp.: 3,700
Fiscal Year-end: 03/31/23
Logistic & Supply Chain Services
N.A.I.C.S.: 541614
Imdadh Marikar *(CEO)*

Subsidiaries:

AVS Cargo Management Services
Private Limited   (1)
New Door No7A Old Door Nos 2 3 & 4 2nd
Floor, Anjanalaya Building Halls Road
Egmore, Chennai, 600 008, Tamil Nadu,
India
Tel.: (91) 4466010608
Web Site: https://www.avscargo.com
Cargo Services
N.A.I.C.S.: 488510

Airline Cargo Resources FZCO   (1)
Dubai Airport Free Zone, PO Box 94073,
Dubai, United Arab Emirates
Tel.: (971) 7142045164
Web Site: https://www.acrdxb.com
Aviation Services
N.A.I.C.S.: 488190

Complete Transport Systems,
LLC   (1)
22 Lawrence Ln, Lawrence, NY 11559
Tel.: (718) 995-2026
Web Site: https://www.completetrans.net
General Freight Trucking, Local
N.A.I.C.S.: 484110
John Debetta *(Pres)*

EFL Express Private Limited   (1)
No 16 Haddows Road 1st Street, Nungam-
bakkam, Chennai, 600 006, Tamil Nadu,
India
Tel.: (91) 4443900700
Freight Forwarding Services

EFL Global B.V.   (1)
Bedrijvenzone Machelen-Cargo 832, 1830,
Machelen, Belgium
Tel.: (32) 22559090
Freight Forwarding Services
N.A.I.C.S.: 488510

EFL Malaysia Sdn. Bhd.   (1)
D-08-07 Block D Level 8 Sky Park at One
City Jalan USJ 25/1, 47650, Subang Jaya,
Selangor, Malaysia
Tel.: (60) 350223335
Freight Forwarding Services
N.A.I.C.S.: 488510

Expo Freight (Shanghai) Limited   (1)
Room C303-304 Building C No 1038 Jin-
shajiang Road, Putuo Qu, Shanghai,
200062, China
Tel.: (86) 2168866670
Freight Forwarding Services
N.A.I.C.S.: 488510

Expolanka Freight (Private)
Limited   (1)
No 69 Ramyaweera Mawatha Kittampa-
huwa, Colombo, Sri Lanka
Tel.: (94) 114766300
Freight Forwarding Services
N.A.I.C.S.: 484121

Subsidiary (Non-US):

Locher Evers International, Inc.   (2)
456 Humber Pl, Annacis Business Park,
New Westminster, V3M6A5, BC, Canada
Tel.: (604) 523-5100
Web Site: http://www.lei.ca
Sales Range: $500-549.9 Million
Emp.: 175
Logistics Services; Warehousing & Domes-
tic Trucking
N.A.I.C.S.: 484121
Bruno Locher *(Pres)*

Subsidiary (US):

Trans American Customhouse Bro-
kers, Inc.   (2)
2775 Broadway St, Buffalo, NY 14227
Tel.: (716) 896-7800
Web Site: http://www.tacustoms.com
Sales Range: $1-9.9 Million
Emp.: 65
Freight Transportation Arrangement
N.A.I.C.S.: 488510
Mark Magiera *(Mgr)*

IDEA Global LLC   (1)
770 Old Roswell Pl Ste F100, Roswell, GA
30076
Tel.: (404) 996-5297
Web Site: https://ideaglobalc.com
Bookkeeping Services
N.A.I.C.S.: 541219

Pulsar Shipping Agencies (Private)
Limited   (1)
No 23 Palm Grove, 3, Colombo, Sri Lanka
Tel.: (94) 117208951
Web Site: http://www.pulsarshipping.com
Shipping Agency Services
N.A.I.C.S.: 488510

EXPONENT PRIVATE EQUITY
LLP
30 Broadwick Street, London, W1F
8JB, United Kingdom
Tel.: (44) 2078458520   UK
Web Site:
http://www.exponentpe.com
Year Founded: 2004
Privater Equity Firm
N.A.I.C.S.: 523940
Nancy Cruickshank *(Operating Part-
ner)*

Subsidiaries:

Durrants Ltd.   (1)
Discovery House, 28-42 Banner Street,
London, EC1Y 8QE, United Kingdom
Tel.: (44) 2076740200
Web Site: http://www.durrants.co.uk

Sales Range: $75-99.9 Million
Media Planning, Monitoring & Evaluation
Services
N.A.I.C.S.: 541840
John Moore *(Chm)*

Subsidiary (Domestic):

Portfolio Metrica Ltd.   (2)
140 Old Street, London, EC1V 9BJ, United
Kingdom   (100%)
Tel.: (44) 20 7664 0800
Web Site: http://www.gorkana.com
Sales Range: $25-49.9 Million
Emp.: 500
Media Analycic Through Public Relations
Measurement Products, Services & Consul-
tancy
N.A.I.C.S.: 541840
Paul Hender *(Dir-Media Analysis)*

Enva UK Ltd   (1)
Brailwood Road, Bilsthorpe, Newark, NG22
8UA, United Kingdom
Tel.: (44) 1623871964
Web Site: http://enva.com
Water & Hazardous Waste Management
Services
N.A.I.C.S.: 562211
Tom Walsh *(CEO)*

Subsidiary (Non-US):

Rilta Environmental Ltd   (2)
Block 402 Grants Drive Greenogue Busi-
ness Park, Rathcoole, Dublin, Ireland
Tel.: (353) 14018000
Web Site: http://www.enva.com
Waste Management Services
N.A.I.C.S.: 562219
Eftim Ivanoff *(Gen Mgr)*

HSS Hire Group PLC   (1)
Building 2 Mosley Road, Think Park, Man-
chester, M17 1FQ, United Kingdom
Tel.: (44) 2082603343
Web Site: https://www.hsshiregroup.com
Rev.: $444,441,468
Assets: $546,376,183
Liabilities: $313,162,489
Net Worth: $233,213,693
Earnings: $5,397,817
Emp.: 2,037
Fiscal Year-end: 12/30/2023
Commercial Equipment Rental Services
N.A.I.C.S.: 532490
Steve Ashmore *(CEO)*

Leisure Pass Group Limited   (1)
75 Well Street, London, W1T 3QH, United
Kingdom
Tel.: (44) 2075 808 060
Web Site: http://www.leisurepassgroup.com
Tourism Management Services
N.A.I.C.S.: 561591
Amanda Truman *(COO-EMEA)*

SHL Group Limited   (1)
The Pavilion 1 Atwell Place, Thames Ditton,
KT7 0NE, Surrey, United Kingdom
Tel.: (44) 2083358000
Web Site: http://www.shl.com
Workplace Assessment Services
N.A.I.C.S.: 923130
Andy Bradshaw *(CEO)*

Subsidiary (Domestic):

Saville & Holdsworth Limited   (2)
The Pavilion 1 Atwell Place, Thames Ditton,
KT7 0NE, Surrey, United Kingdom
Tel.: (44) 2083358000
Web Site: http://www.shl.com
Holding Company; Human Resource Tech-
nology & Psychometric Science Products &
Services
N.A.I.C.S.: 551112

Subsidiary (Domestic):

SHL (UK) Limited   (3)
The Pavilion 1 Atwell Pl, Thames Ditton,
KT70NE, Surrey, United Kingdom
Tel.: (44) 8700708000
Web Site: http://www.shl.com
Wokplace Assessment Services
N.A.I.C.S.: 923130

Subsidiary (Non-US):

SHL AG   (3)

Schulhausstrasse 41, 8002, Zurich, Switzer-
land
Tel.: (41) 442099020
Web Site: http://www.shl.com
Management Consulting Services
N.A.I.C.S.: 541618

SHL Belgium SA   (3)
Airport Plz Bldg C Kyoto, 1831, Diegem,
Belgium
Tel.: (32) 26634820
Web Site: http://www.cbglobal.com
Employment Placement Agencies
N.A.I.C.S.: 561311
Matti Taipale *(Head-Europe North)*

SHL Danmark A/S   (3)
Tuborg Boulevard 12, DK-2900, Hellerup,
Denmark
Tel.: (45) 80 8877 91
Web Site: http://www.shl.com
Management Consulting Services
N.A.I.C.S.: 541618

SHL France SAS   (3)
3rd Floor 124-126 rue de Provence, Paris,
75008, France
Tel.: (33) 153049444
Web Site: http://www.shl.com
Holding Company
N.A.I.C.S.: 551112

SHL Hong Kong Limited   (3)
Lee Garden Six 16th Floor 111 Leighton
Rd, Causeway Bay, China (Hong Kong)
Tel.: (852) 25771246
Web Site: http://www.shl.com
Management Consulting Services
N.A.I.C.S.: 541618

SHL Nederland BV   (3)
Secoya Building 5e verdieping Papen-
dorpseweg 99, 3528 BJ, Utrecht, Nether-
lands
Tel.: (31) 302329555
Web Site: http://www.shl.com
Management Consulting Services
N.A.I.C.S.: 541618

SHL New Zealand Limited   (3)
Barfoot and Thompson Building Level 10,
34 Shortland Street, Auckland, 1010, New
Zealand
Tel.: (64) 800452214
Guided Missile & Space Vehicle Mfr
N.A.I.C.S.: 336414

Subsidiary (Domestic):

SHL People Solutions Ltd.   (3)
The Pavillion 1 Atwell Place, Thames Dit-
ton, KT7 0NE, Surrey, United Kingdom
Tel.: (44) 2083358000
Management Consulting Services
N.A.I.C.S.: 541618

Subsidiary (Non-US):

SHL Polska sp. z o.o.   (3)
WeWork Mennica Legacy Tower ul Prosta
20, 00-850, Warsaw, Poland
Tel.: (48) 225095020
Web Site: http://www.shl.com.pl
Management Consulting Services
N.A.I.C.S.: 541618

SHL Saville & Holdsworth
(Deutschland) GmbH   (3)
Speicherstrasse 59, Frankfurt am Main,
60327, Germany
Tel.: (49) 699207113
Management Consulting Services
N.A.I.C.S.: 541618

SHL Sverige AB   (3)
Regeringsgatan 59, 11156, Stockholm,
Sweden
Tel.: (46) 200896825
Employment Placement Agencies
N.A.I.C.S.: 561311

Subsidiary (US):

SHL US LLC   (3)
111 Washington Ave S Ste 500, Minneapo-
lis, MN 55401
Tel.: (612) 361-8600
Web Site: https://www.shl.com
Business Improvement & Metrics Technolo-
gies & Services
N.A.I.C.S.: 561499

Exponent Private Equity LLP—(Continued)

Scotts Holdings Limited (1)
1 Archipelago Way, Lyon Way, Frimley,
GU16 7ER, Surrey, United Kingdom
Tel.: (44) 1276 401 300
Web Site: http://www.lovethegarden.com
Holding Company; Lawn & Garden Chemi-
cal Products Mfr & Marketer
N.A.I.C.S.: 551112
Karl Kahofer (CEO)

Subsidiary (Domestic):

**Evergreen Garden Care (UK)
Ltd** (2)
1 Archipelago Way, Lyon Way, Frimley,
GU16 7ER, Surrey, United Kingdom
Tel.: (44) 1276 401 300
Web Site: http://www.lovethegarden.com
Lawn & Garden Services
N.A.I.C.S.: 325314
Steve Fuller (Dir-IT)

Subsidiary (Domestic):

**The Scotts Company (Manufacturing)
Limited** (3)
5th Floor 6 Saint Andrew Street, London,
EC4A 3AE, United Kingdom
Tel.: (44) 1430434301
Lawn & Garden Product Mfr & Marketer
N.A.I.C.S.: 325320

Subsidiary (Non-US):

**Evergreen Garden Care Australia Pty
Ltd.** (2)
Level 2 Bldg E 24-32 Lexington Drive, Bella
Vista, 2153, NSW, Australia
Tel.: (61) 2 8602 9000
Web Site: http://www.scottsaustralia.com.au
Lawn & Garden Products & Services
N.A.I.C.S.: 561730

**Evergreen Garden Care Belgium
bvba** (2)
Voshol 8, 9160, Lokeren, Belgium
Tel.: (32) 9 210 3010
Web Site: http://www.ilovemygarden.be
Lawn & Garden Services
N.A.I.C.S.: 561730

**Evergreen Garden Care Deutschland
GmbH** (2)
Wilhelm-Theodor-Romheld-Strasse 30,
55130, Mainz, Germany
Tel.: (49) 6131 2106 0
Web Site: http://www.liebedeinengarten.de
Lawn & Garden Products Mfr & Distr
N.A.I.C.S.: 325320
Stefan Eha (Mng Dir)

**Evergreen Garden Care France
SAS** (2)
21 Chemin de la Sauvegarde, 69130,
Ecully, France
Tel.: (33) 805371392
Web Site: http://www.lapausejardin.fr
Lawn & Garden Care Products Distr
N.A.I.C.S.: 424690
Karl Kahofer (Pres)

**Evergreen Garden Care Poland Sp. z
o.o.** (2)
Ostrobramska 101A, 04041, Warsaw, Po-
land
Tel.: (48) 224656180
Web Site: http://www.substral.pl
Lawn & Garden Products Sales
N.A.I.C.S.: 561730

Trainline Plc (1)
50 Farringdon Road, London, EC1M 3HE,
United Kingdom
Tel.: (44) 871 244 1545
Web Site: http://www.thetrainline.com
Online Train Ticket Retailer
N.A.I.C.S.: 561599
Clare Gilmartin (CEO)

EXPONENTIAL-E LIMITED
100 Lemen St, London, E1 8EU,
United Kingdom
Tel.: (44) 2070964100
Web Site: http://www.exponential-
e.com
Year Founded: 2002

Sales Range: $25-49.9 Million
Emp.: 300
Computer Network Design Services
N.A.I.C.S.: 541512
Lee Wade (CEO)

**EXPORT DEVELOPMENT
BANK**
Gamhoria Avenue, Khartoum, Sudan
Tel.: (249) 187181230
Web Site: http://www.edbank.sd
Year Founded: 1981
EDBA—(KHAR)
Sales Range: Less than $1 Million
Banking Services
N.A.I.C.S.: 522110
Siddig Adam Abdallah (Chm)

**EXPORT DEVELOPMENT
BANK OF EGYPT**
78 El Tesseen street Fifth Settlement,
Cairo, Egypt
Tel.: (20) 237619006
Web Site: https://ebank.com.eg
Year Founded: 1985
EXPA.CA—(EGX)
Rev.: $173,109,908
Assets: $2,073,144,558
Liabilities: $1,863,005,791
Net Worth: $210,138,766
Earnings: $28,242,474
Emp.: 1,580
Fiscal Year-end: 12/31/22
Commercial Banking Services
N.A.I.C.S.: 522110
Yaser Osama Abdel Sadek (Mgr-
Investment)

**EXPORT DEVELOPMENT
CANADA**
150 Slater Street, Ottawa, K1A 1K3,
ON, Canada
Tel.: (613) 598-2500
Web Site: http://www.edc.ca
Year Founded: 1944
Sales Range: $1-4.9 Billion
Emp.: 1,071
Provider of Loans & Investments for
New Businesses
N.A.I.C.S.: 523940
Fernanda Custodio (Sr Mgr-Brazil)

Subsidiaries:

Export Development Corporation (1)
1 Front Street West 4th Floor, Toronto, M5H
3S5, ON, Canada (100%)
Tel.: (416) 640-7600
Sales Range: $50-74.9 Million
Emp.: 20
Provider of Loans & Investments for New
Businesses
N.A.I.C.S.: 523940

Monarch Industries Limited (1)
51 Burmac Rd, Winnipeg, R2J 4J3, MB,
Canada
Tel.: (204) 786-7921
Web Site:
http://www.monarchindustries.com
Hydraulic Cylinders & Metal Casting Mfr
N.A.I.C.S.: 333517
Roy Cook (Pres & CEO)

**EXPORT IMPORT BANK OF
BANGLADESH LIMITED**
Symphony Plot SE F 9 Road 142
Gulshan Avenue, Dhaka, 1212, Ban-
gladesh
Tel.: (880) 9666716246
Web Site:
https://www.eximbankbd.com
EXIMBANK—(CHT)
Rev.: $132,534,317
Assets: $4,929,381,519
Liabilities: $4,638,693,904
Net Worth: $290,687,615
Earnings: $33,945,187
Emp.: 3,357

Fiscal Year-end: 12/31/22
Commercial Banking Services
N.A.I.C.S.: 522110
Mohammad Nazrul Islam Mazumder
(Chm)

Subsidiaries:

**EXIM Exchange Company (UK)
Limited** (1)
5 Old Montague Street, London, E1 5NL,
United Kingdom
Tel.: (44) 2073772474
Web Site: https://www.eximexchange.co.uk
Money Transmission Services
N.A.I.C.S.: 522390

**EXIM Finance (Hong Kong)
Limited** (1)
Unit 901 9th Floor Carnarvon Plaza No 20
Carnarvon Road, Tsim Sha Tsui, Kowloon,
China (Hong Kong)
Tel.: (852) 26625661
Web Site: https://www.eximfinance.com.hk
Banking Services
N.A.I.C.S.: 522110

EXIM Islami Investment Ltd. (1)
Printer's Building 5th Floor 5 Rajuk Avenue
Motijheel, Dhaka, 1000, Bangladesh
Tel.: (880) 29561604
Banking Services
N.A.I.C.S.: 522110
Nazrul Islam Mazumder (Chm)

**Exim Exchange Company (CANADA)
Ltd.** (1)
Unit-2 3096 Danforth Avenue, Toronto, M1L
1B1, ON, Canada
Tel.: (416) 699-5802
Web Site: http://www.eximexchangeca.com
Sales Range: $50-74.9 Million
Emp.: 2
Foreign Currency Exchange Services
N.A.I.C.S.: 523160

**EXPORT INVESTMENT CO.
LTD.**
PO Box 29086, Tel Aviv, 61290, Is-
rael
Tel.: (972) 35107476
Year Founded: 1963
EXPO—(TAE)
Rev.: $210,144,492
Assets: $6,037,020,765
Liabilities: $5,698,386,981
Net Worth: $338,633,784
Earnings: $34,237,878
Emp.: 224
Fiscal Year-end: 12/31/23
Miscellaneous Financial Investment
Activities
N.A.I.C.S.: 523999
Zalman Shoval (Chm)

**EXPORT PACKERS COMPANY
LIMITED**
107 Walker Dr, Brampton, L6T 5K5,
ON, Canada
Tel.: (905) 792-9700
Web Site:
http://www.exportpackers.com
Year Founded: 1937
Sales Range: $550-599.9 Million
Emp.: 150
Agricultural Commodity Trader; Food
& Poultry Products Whslr
N.A.I.C.S.: 424510
Ira Tytel (Mgr-Sls-Fresh Seafood)

**EXPORT TRADING GROUP
PTE LTD.**
Vivéa Business Park Moka,, 81406,
Mauritius, Mauritius
Tel.: (44) 2032077800
Web Site: https://www.etgworld.com
Year Founded: 1967
Emp.: 1,596
Food & Beverage Services
N.A.I.C.S.: 311999
Mahesh Patel (Chm)

EXPOSOFT SOLUTIONS INC.
7895 Tranmere Drive Suite 221, Mis-
sissauga, L5S 1V9, ON, Canada
Tel.: (905) 672-7001
Web Site: http://www.exposoft.com
Year Founded: 1996
Sales Range: $1-9.9 Million
Emp.: 40
Software Developer & Technical Sup-
port for Event Industry-Conferences,
Trade Shows & Special Events
N.A.I.C.S.: 513210
Bassel Annab (Pres & CEO)

**EXPRES2ION BIOTECHNOLO-
GIES**
Agern Alle 1, 2970, Horsholm, Den-
mark
Tel.: (45) 22221019
Web Site:
https://www.expres2ionbio.com
Year Founded: 2010
Biotechnology Research & Develop-
ment Services
N.A.I.C.S.: 541714
Bent U. Frandsen (CEO)

**EXPRESS CUSTOM TRAILERS
MFG. INC.**
1365 Alberni Highway, Parksville,
V9P 2B9, BC, Canada
Tel.: (250) 248-2218
Web Site:
http://www.expresscustom.com
Year Founded: 1992
Aluminum & Steel Trailers Mfr
N.A.I.C.S.: 333924
Tony Ethier (Pres)

EXPRESS TRANSPORT SA
Str Margaritarului 1, Gorj, Targu Jiu,
Romania
Tel.: (40) 253 244669
Sales Range: $1-9.9 Million
Emp.: 118
Land Transportation Services
N.A.I.C.S.: 485999

EXPRESSBANK OJSC
Yusuf Vazir Chamanzaminli Str 134
C, Baku, AZ1052, Azerbaijan
Tel.: (994) 12132
Web Site: http://www.expressbank.az
Year Founded: 1989
EXBNK—(BAK)
Rev.: $28,139,384
Assets: $257,451,292
Liabilities: $182,050,150
Net Worth: $75,401,142
Earnings: $8,510,212
Emp.: 700
Fiscal Year-end: 12/31/22
Commercial Banking Services
N.A.I.C.S.: 522110
Mehman Memmedov (Chm-Exec Bd)

EXPRESSWAY MOTORS LTD
1554 Haysville Rd, New Hamburg,
N3A 1A3, ON, Canada
Tel.: (519) 662-3900
Web Site:
https://expresswayford.com
Year Founded: 1982
Sales Range: $10-24.9 Million
Emp.: 47
New & Used Car Dealers
N.A.I.C.S.: 441110
Nelda Brenneman (Co-Founder)

EXPRIVIA SPA
Via A Olivetti 11, 70056, Molfetta,
Italy
Tel.: (39) 0803382070
Web Site: https://www.exprivia.it
XPR—(ITA)
Rev.: $224,071,090

Assets: $246,645,325
Liabilities: $141,957,170
Net Worth: $104,688,155
Earnings: $14,523,678
Emp.: 2,505
Fiscal Year-end: 12/31/23
Software Designer & Developer
N.A.I.C.S.: 513210
Domenico Favuzzi *(Chm & CEO)*

Subsidiaries:

Exprivia Projects S.r.l.   **(1)**
Via della Bufalotta 378, 00139, Rome,
Italy   **(100%)**
Tel.: (39) 06870901
Sales Range: $75-99.9 Million
Emp.: 300
Management Consulting Services
N.A.I.C.S.: 541611

GST Gruppo Soluzioni Tecnologiche
S r l   **(1)**
Via Maccani, 5438100, Trento, Italy
Tel.: (39) 0461431333
Web Site: http://www.gsttn.it
Sales Range: $25-49.9 Million
Emp.: 16
Engineering Consultancy Services
N.A.I.C.S.: 541330
Marco Biraghi *(CEO & Gen Mgr)*

EXPRO GROUP HOLDINGS N.V.
Mastenmakersweg 1, 1786 PB, Den
Helder, Netherlands   NI
Web Site: https://www.expro.com
XPRO—(NYSE)
Rev.: $1,512,764,000
Assets: $2,013,007,000
Liabilities: $717,134,000
Net Worth: $1,295,873,000
Earnings: ($23,360,000)
Emp.: 8,000
Fiscal Year-end: 12/31/23
Holding Company; Oil & Gas Tubular
Products Mfr
N.A.I.C.S.: 551112
John Symington *(Chief Compliance
Officer, Gen Counsel, Sec & Sr VP)*

Subsidiaries:

Frank's International AS   **(1)**
Luramyrveien 36, 4313, Sandnes, Norway
Tel.: (47) 51819550
Web Site:
   http://www.franksinternational.com
Engineered Tubular Services
N.A.I.C.S.: 541330

Frank's International C.V.   **(1)**
Prins Bernhardplein 200, 1097 JB, Amster-
dam, Netherlands
Tel.: (31) 205214777
Engineered Tubular Services
N.A.I.C.S.: 541330

Frank's International, LLC   **(1)**
10260 Westheimer Rd St 700, Houston, TX
77042
Tel.: (281) 966-7300
Web Site:
   http://www.franksinternational.com
Emp.: 150
Engineeering Services
N.A.I.C.S.: 541330

Subsidiary (Domestic):

Blackhawk Specialty Tools, LLC   **(2)**
10260 Westheimer Rd Ste 600, Houston,
TX 77042   **(100%)**
Tel.: (713) 466-4200
Web Site: http://www.blackhawkst.com
Site Preparation Contractor
N.A.I.C.S.: 238910
Ron Robichaux *(Co-Founder)*

Franks Eiendom AS   **(1)**
Drobakveien 470, 1449, Drobak, Norway
Tel.: (47) 989085840
Real Estate Agency Services
N.A.I.C.S.: 531110

Integrated Services (Intl) Limited   **(1)**
Hareness Circle Altens Industrial Estate,

Aberdeen, AB12 3LY, Aberdeenshire, United
Kingdom
Tel.: (44) 1224248200
Oil Exploration Services
N.A.I.C.S.: 213112

PT Franks Indonesia   **(1)**
Duta Fatmawati Block D1 / 17 - JI RS Fat-
mawati No 39, Jakarta, 12150, Indonesia
Tel.: (62) 217224437
Oil & Gas Field Services
N.A.I.C.S.: 213112

EXRO TECHNOLOGIES, INC.
12-21 Highfield Circle SE, Calgary,
T2G 5N6, AB, Canada
Tel.: (587) 619-1517
Web Site: https://www.exro.com
EXRO—(TSX)
Rev.: $42,524
Assets: $39,250,571
Liabilities: $1,696,639
Net Worth: $37,553,933
Earnings: ($8,581,184)
Emp.: 26
Fiscal Year-end: 12/31/20
Eletric Power Generation Services
N.A.I.C.S.: 221114
William John Meekison *(CFO)*

EXSCIENTIA PLC
The Schrodinger Building Oxford Sci-
ence Park, Oxford, OX44GE, United
Kingdom
Tel.: (44) 1865818941   UK
Web Site: https://www.exscientia.com
Year Founded: 2012
EXAI—(NASDAQ)
Rev.: $25,345,872
Assets: $644,686,948
Liabilities: $195,651,351
Net Worth: $449,035,597
Earnings: ($184,250,189)
Emp.: 483
Fiscal Year-end: 12/31/23
Biotechnology Research & Develop-
ment Services
N.A.I.C.S.: 541714
David Nicholson *(Chm)*

EXSITEC HOLDING AB
Snickaregatan 40, 58226, Linkoping,
Sweden
Tel.: (46) 103333300
Web Site: https://www.exsitec.se
Year Founded: 2000
EXS—(OMX)
Rev.: $70,365,375
Assets: $75,420,308
Liabilities: $36,548,746
Net Worth: $38,871,561
Earnings: $6,633,136
Emp.: 522
Fiscal Year-end: 12/31/23
Holding Company
N.A.I.C.S.: 551112
Johan Kallblad *(CEO)*

EXSULAR FINANCIAL GROUP INC.
Room 1105 11/F Hip Kwan Commer-
cial Bldg No 38 Pitt St, Yau Ma Tei,
Kowloon, China (Hong Kong)
Tel.: (852) 29803711   CO
Year Founded: 2011
Liabilities: $87,480
Net Worth: ($87,480)
Earnings: ($29,332)
Fiscal Year-end: 12/31/21
Financial Investment Services
N.A.I.C.S.: 523940
Seng Yeap Kok *(Pres, CEO & Sec)*

EXTE - EXTRUDERTECHNIK GMBH
Wasserfuhr 4, PO Box 1220, Wipper-
furth, 51676, Germany
Tel.: (49) 22676870

Web Site: http://www.exte.de
Year Founded: 1959
Rev.: $21,159,996
Emp.: 231
Windows & Door Product Services
N.A.I.C.S.: 449122
Dan Friedl *(Co-Mng Dir)*

EXTENDICARE INC.
3000 Steeles Avenue East Suite 400,
Markham, L3R 4T9, ON, Canada
Tel.: (905) 470-4000
Web Site:
   https://www.extendicare.com
Year Founded: 1968
5XE—(DEU)
Rev.: $1,639,844,965
Assets: $1,049,191,650
Liabilities: $914,010,627
Net Worth: $135,181,022
Earnings: $93,369,290
Emp.: 1,000
Fiscal Year-end: 12/31/22
Long-Term Care Services
N.A.I.C.S.: 623110
Jillian E. Fountain *(VP-Investor Rela-
tions)*

Subsidiaries:

9994165 Canada Inc.   **(1)**
3 Concert Way, Barrie, L4N 0M7, ON,
Canada
Tel.: (705) 812-6485
Retirement Community Services
N.A.I.C.S.: 623311
Karin Rossi *(Gen Mgr)*

Bolton Mills Retirement Community
Inc.   **(1)**
100 Morra Avenue, Bolton, L0J 1C0, ON,
Canada
Tel.: (289) 206-0775
People Living Facility Services
N.A.I.C.S.: 623312
Carmelina Cicuto *(Gen Mgr)*

Cedar Crossing Retirement Commu-
nity Inc.   **(1)**
395 Cedar Street, Simcoe, N3Y 2N4, ON,
Canada
Tel.: (226) 484-6000
People Living Facility Services
N.A.I.C.S.: 623312
Cody Lyons *(Coord-Community Rels)*

Douglas Crossing Retirement Com-
munity Inc.   **(1)**
6 Douglas Road, Uxbridge, L9P 1S9, ON,
Canada
Tel.: (289) 640-1922
People Living Facility Services
N.A.I.C.S.: 623312
Stacey Sellery *(Gen Mgr)*

Empire Crossing Retirement Commu-
nity Inc.   **(1)**
224 Ward Street, Port Hope, L1A 3V6, ON,
Canada
Tel.: (905) 885-9898
People Living Facility Services
N.A.I.C.S.: 623312
Katy Tranter *(Gen Mgr-Interim)*

Extendicare (Canada), Inc.   **(1)**
3000 Steeles Avenue East Suite 400,
Markham, L3R 4T9, ON, Canada
Tel.: (905) 470-4000
Web Site:
   http://www.extendicarecanada.com
Sales Range: $25-49.9 Million
Emp.: 160
Nursing Home Services
N.A.I.C.S.: 623110
Elaine E. Everson *(CFO & VP)*

Extendicare Health Services Inc.   **(1)**
111 W Michigan St, Milwaukee, WI 53203-
2903
Tel.: (414) 908-8000
Web Site: http://www.extendicare.com
Sales Range: $50-74.9 Million
Emp.: 450
Skilled Nursing Services
N.A.I.C.S.: 623110

Subsidiary (Domestic):

Tendercare, Inc.   **(2)**
111 W Michigan St, Milwaukee, WI 53203
Tel.: (414) 908-8000
Web Site: http://www.tendercare.net
Sales Range: $50-74.9 Million
Nursing Care Services
N.A.I.C.S.: 623110

Extendicare, Inc.   **(1)**
3000 Steeles Ave E Ste 700, Markham,
L3R 9W2, ON, Canada   **(100%)**
Tel.: (905) 470-4000
Web Site:
   http://www.extendicarecanada.com
Sales Range: $25-49.9 Million
Emp.: 160
Provider of Nursing Centers, Home Care
Services, Hospital Management & Develop-
ment, Assisted Living & Retirement Centers,
Institutional Pharmacy & Durable Medical
Supply Business
N.A.I.C.S.: 621610

Harvest Retirement Community
Inc.   **(1)**
15 Harvest Ave, Tillsonburg, N4G 4Z6, ON,
Canada
Tel.: (519) 688-0448
People Living Facility Services
N.A.I.C.S.: 623312
Jamie-Lynn Hultema *(Gen Mgr)*

Lynde Creek Manor Retirement Com-
munity Inc.   **(1)**
50 Paul Burns Way, Whitby, L1R 2Y9, ON,
Canada
Tel.: (905) 665-9227
People Living Facility Services
N.A.I.C.S.: 623312
Janelle Williams *(Gen Mgr)*

Riverbend Crossing Retirement Com-
munity Inc.   **(1)**
2235 Heseltine Road, Regina, S4V 2T7,
SK, Canada
Tel.: (306) 347-7773
People Living Facility Services
N.A.I.C.S.: 623312
Michele Glaze *(Coord-Community Rels)*

Stonebridge Crossing Retirement
Community Inc.   **(1)**
102 Wellman Crescent, Saskatoon, S7T
0G3, SK, Canada
Tel.: (306) 974-7990
People Living Facility Services
N.A.I.C.S.: 623312
Linda Dahl *(Coord-Community Rels)*

West Park Crossing Retirement Com-
munity Inc.   **(1)**
1801 Meier Drive, Moose Jaw, S6J 0C3,
SK, Canada
Tel.: (306) 694-4744
People Living Facility Services
N.A.I.C.S.: 623312

Yorkton Crossing Retirement Com-
munity Inc.   **(1)**
348 Morrison Drive, Yorkton, S3N 4G2, SK,
Canada
Tel.: (306) 782-0005
People Living Facility Services
N.A.I.C.S.: 623312
Jan Morrison *(Gen Mgr)*

EXTER B.V.
Gerrit Bolkade 10, 1507 BR, Zaan-
dam, Netherlands
Tel.: (31) 756700041   NI
Web Site:
   http://www.exteraroma.com
Year Founded: 1928
Sales Range: $10-24.9 Million
Emp.: 50
Development, Production & Trade of
Foodstuff Ingredients
N.A.I.C.S.: 325998
Sonja Sikkes *(Mgr-HR)*

EXTERNET TELECOMMUNI-CATIONS SERVICE PROVIDER PUBLIC CO.

EXTERNET Telecommunications Service Provider Public Co.—(Continued)

Szapary ut 18, HU-5000, Szolnok, Hungary
Tel.: (36) 12371860
Web Site: http://www.externet.hu
EXTERNET—(BUD)
Sales Range: $10-24.9 Million
Emp.: 38
Telecommunication Servicesb
N.A.I.C.S.: 517112
Andras Porffy (Vice Chm-Mgmt Bd)

EXTOL COMMERCIAL LIMITED
20 Bhaveshwar Sadan 207, Sion East, Mumbai, 400 022, India
Tel.: (91) 22 32506927
Web Site:
http://www.extolcommercial.com
Assets: $13,323
Liabilities: $15,996
Net Worth: ($2,673)
Earnings: ($6,528)
Fiscal Year-end: 03/31/16
Commercial Trading Services
N.A.I.C.S.: 423990

EXTRACT GROUP LIMITED
61 Maple Street Pomona, Kempton Park, 1619, South Africa
Tel.: (27) 119662000   ZA
Web Site: http://www.eqstra.co.za
Year Founded: 1972
EGL—(JSE)
Rev.: $11,705,804
Assets: $55,813,579
Liabilities: $17,238,523
Net Worth: $38,575,056
Earnings: $17,888,328
Fiscal Year-end: 08/31/22
Holding Company; Construction, Mining & Industrial Equipment & Passenger Vehicle Distr, Leasing & Rental Services
N.A.I.C.S.: 551112
Hendrik Matthys Lindeque (Treas-Grp)

Subsidiaries:

Mutual Construction Company Transvaal (Pty) Limited   (1)
60 Radio Pl Comml, Midrand Industrial Park, Johannesburg, 1685, Gauteng, South Africa
Tel.: (27) 119906600
Web Site: http://www.mccgroup.co.za
Sales Range: $100-124.9 Million
Emp.: 397
Commercial Building Construction Services
N.A.I.C.S.: 236220

Subsidiary (Domestic):

MCC Contracts (Pty) Limited   (2)
60 Radio Pl Comml Midran Industrial Park, Halfway House, Johannesburg, 1683, Gauteng, South Africa
Tel.: (27) 119906600
Sales Range: $100-124.9 Million
Emp.: 200
Contract Mining Services
N.A.I.C.S.: 213114

EXTRACTION (PAKISTAN) LIMITED
Hajiabad Sheikhupura Road, Faisalabad, Pakistan
Tel.: (92) 50537 50569
Chemical Products Mfr
N.A.I.C.S.: 325199

EXTRAWELL PHARMACEUTICAL HOLDINGS LTD.
Suites 2206-08 22/F Devon House Taikoo Place 979 Kings Road, Quarry Bay, China (Hong Kong)
Tel.: (852) 28561918   BM

Web Site:
http://www.extrawell.com.hk
0858—(HKG)
Rev.: $10,163,882
Assets: $150,163,546
Liabilities: $17,405,206
Net Worth: $132,758,340
Earnings: ($15,434,134)
Emp.: 171
Fiscal Year-end: 03/31/21
Pharmaceuticals Product Mfr
N.A.I.C.S.: 551112
Yi Xie (Chm & CEO)

Subsidiaries:

Changchun Extrawell Pharmaceutical Co., Ltd.   (1)
1299 Changchun Economic Development Zone, 130033, Changchun, China   (68%)
Tel.: (86) 4314634271
Web Site: http://www.ccepcd.com
Pharmaceuticals Product Mfr
N.A.I.C.S.: 325412

Extrawell Enterprises Limited   (1)
Rm 09-10 34th Floor China Resources Buildling 26 Harbour Road, Wanchai, China (Hong Kong)
Tel.: (852) 28561918
Web Site: http://www.extrawell.com.hk
Sales Range: $50-74.9 Million
Emp.: 15
Investment Management Service
N.A.I.C.S.: 523999

Extrawell Pharmaceutical (HK) Limited   (1)
Suites 2206-08 22/F Devon House Taikoo Pl 979 King's Rd, Quarry Bay, China (Hong Kong)
Tel.: (852) 28561918
Pharmaceutical Products Distr
N.A.I.C.S.: 424210

Jilin Extrawell Changbaishan Pharmaceutical Co., Ltd.   (1)
Jilin Changchun Economic Development Zone, 940 Shenzhen Street, Changchun, 130033, Jilin, China
Tel.: (86) 43186821498
Web Site: http://www.jycbs.com
Pharmaceuticals Product Mfr
N.A.I.C.S.: 325412

EXTREME CO., LTD.
Metropolitan Plaza Bld 21F 1-11-1 Nishiikebukuro, Toshima-ku, Tokyo, 171-0021, Japan
Tel.: (81) 366738535
Web Site: https://www.e-xtreme.co.jp
Year Founded: 2005
6033—(TKS)
Rev.: $67,534,370
Assets: $56,099,070
Liabilities: $17,622,260
Net Worth: $38,476,810
Earnings: $6,834,740
Emp.: 727
Fiscal Year-end: 03/31/24
Gaming Software
N.A.I.C.S.: 513210
Shohei Sato (Pres & CEO)

Subsidiaries:

Epark Pet Life Inc.   (1)
5F Safety Building 4-16-25 Shibaura, Minato-ku, Tokyo, 108-0023, Japan
Tel.: (81) 335184277
Web Site: https://www.e-petlife.co.jp
Emp.: 50
Pet Care Services
N.A.I.C.S.: 541940

Sakata SAS Co., Ltd.   (1)
1-4-10 Nakamachi Nakamachi Government Building 1F, Sakata, 998-0044, Japan
Tel.: (81) 234231750
Web Site: https://www.sas-sakata.co.jp
Emp.: 13
Application Software Development Services
N.A.I.C.S.: 541511

ex-labo Co., Ltd.   (1)
21F Metropolitan Plaza Building 1-11-1,

Nishi-Ikebukuro Toshima-ku, Tokyo, 171-0021, Japan
Tel.: (81) 359571770
Web Site: https://www.exlabo.co.jp
Software Development Services
N.A.I.C.S.: 541511

Subsidiary (Non-US):

Extreme Vietnam Co., Ltd   (2)
31st Floor Keangnam Hanoi Landmark 72 Lot E6 Pham Hung Street, Me Tri Ward Nam Tu Liem District, Hanoi, Vietnam
Tel.: (84) 2473051525
Web Site: http://extremevn.com.vn
Application Software Development Services
N.A.I.C.S.: 541511
Utsumi Eri (Mgr)

EXXARO RESOURCES LTD.
The conneXXion 263B West Avenue, Centurion, 0163, South Africa
Tel.: (27) 123075000
Web Site: https://www.exxaro.com
EXX—(JSE)
Rev.: $2,107,493,080
Assets: $5,056,828,840
Liabilities: $1,440,303,620
Net Worth: $3,616,525,220
Earnings: $800,725,380
Emp.: 6,797
Fiscal Year-end: 12/31/23
Coal, Metal & Mineral Exploration & Mining Services
N.A.I.C.S.: 212115
Mxolisi Donald Mbuyisa Mgojo (CEO)

Subsidiaries:

Exxaro Base Metals (Pty) Limited   (1)
Cnr Vogelstruis and Plover Street, Springs, 1559, Gauteng, South Africa
Tel.: (27) 118129500
Metal Mining Services
N.A.I.C.S.: 212290

Exxaro Base Metals and Industrial Minerals Holdings (Pty) Limited   (1)
Exxaro Building Rodger Dyson Road, Pretoria, 0183, South Africa
Tel.: (27) 123075000
Metal Mining Services
N.A.I.C.S.: 212290
Sipho Abednego Nkosi (CEO)

Exxaro Coal (Pty) Limited   (1)
1 Roger Dyason St, Pretoria, 0183, South Africa
Tel.: (27) 123075000
Web Site: http://www.exxaro.com
Coal Mining Services
N.A.I.C.S.: 212115

Exxaro Holdings Sands (Pty) Limited   (1)
R34 Melmoth Rd, Empangeni, 3880, South Africa
Tel.: (27) 359027000
Sand Mining Services
N.A.I.C.S.: 212321

Exxaro Insurance Company Limited   (1)
Roger Dyason Road, PO Box 9229, Pretoria, 0001, South Africa
Tel.: (27) 123074550
Web Site: http://www.exxaro.com
Emp.: 200
General Insurance Services
N.A.I.C.S.: 524210

Exxaro International Coal Trading BV   (1)
Strawinskylaan 333b-Tower 3E, Amsterdam, 1077 XX, Netherlands
Tel.: (31) 208804195
Sales Range: $50-74.9 Million
Emp.: 2
Coal Distr
N.A.I.C.S.: 423520
Ian Jennings (Mgr-Fin)

Exxaro International Trading BV   (1)
Strawinskylaan 333b-Tower 3e, Amsterdam, Netherlands
Tel.: (31) 208804195

Iron Products Whslr
N.A.I.C.S.: 423510

Inyanda Coal (Pty) Limited   (1)
Portion 21 284 JS Zaaihoek Road, Witbank, 1034, South Africa
Tel.: (27) 136528534
Sales Range: $50-74.9 Million
Emp.: 100
Coal Mining Services
N.A.I.C.S.: 212115

The Vryheid (Natal) Railway Coal and Iron Company Limited   (1)
PO Box 28, Hlobane, 3145, South Africa
Tel.: (27) 349071258
Sales Range: $50-74.9 Million
Emp.: 20
Coal & Iron Ore Mining Services
N.A.I.C.S.: 212115

EXXARO TILES LIMITED
12th Floor D-Block Ganesh Glory11 Nr BSNL Office Jagatput Chenpur Road, S G Highway, Ahmedabad, 382470, Gujarat, India
Tel.: (91) 8758572121
Web Site:
https://www.exxarotiles.com
Year Founded: 2007
EXXARO—(NSE)
Rev.: $44,589,581
Assets: $55,261,274
Liabilities: $18,843,934
Net Worth: $36,417,340
Earnings: $2,470,827
Emp.: 588
Fiscal Year-end: 03/31/22
Flooring Product Mfr
N.A.I.C.S.: 326199

EXXELLIN GMBH
Rogatzer Strasse 34, 39326, Wolmirstedt, Germany
Tel.: (49) 39201 700500
Web Site: http://www.exxellin.com
Steel Sheet Mfr
N.A.I.C.S.: 331221

EYEBRIGHT MEDICAL TECHNOLOGY BEIJING CO., LTD.
No 9 Xingchang Road, Changping Science & Technology Park Changping, Beijing, 102200, China
Tel.: (86) 1060745730
Web Site:
https://www.ebmedical.com
Year Founded: 2010
688050—(SHG)
Rev.: $81,361,365
Assets: $315,120,275
Liabilities: $45,532,422
Net Worth: $269,587,853
Earnings: $32,670,238
Fiscal Year-end: 12/31/22
Medical Product Mfr & Distr
N.A.I.C.S.: 339112
Jiangbing Xie (Chm & Gen Mgr)

EYECARE PARTNERS LIMITED
PO Box 641, Botany, 1455, NSW, Australia
Tel.: (61) 1300769882
Web Site: http://www.eyeq.com.au
Sales Range: $10-24.9 Million
Emp.: 100
Optical Products Provider
N.A.I.C.S.: 811210
Raymond John Fortescue (Chm & CEO)

Subsidiaries:

EyeQ Optometrists Pty. Ltd.   (1)
Shop 144 Level 1 Karrinyup Shopping Centre Karrinyup Road, Karrinyup, Perth, 6018, WA, Australia
Tel.: (61) 894458870
Web Site: http://www.eyeq.com.au

Sales Range: $10-24.9 Million
Emp.: 15
Optometrist Center Service
N.A.I.C.S.: 621320

Focus Optics Pty. Ltd. (1)
113 Wickham Ter, Brisbane, 4000, Australia
Tel.: (61) 738312900
Web Site: http://www.focusoptics.com.au
Optical Goods Stores & Services
N.A.I.C.S.: 456130

EYEGENE INC.
2F 13 Yangjipyeon 2-ro, Gangseo-gu,
Uiwang, 16000, Gyeonggi-do, Korea
(South)
Tel.: (82) 23221687
Web Site: https://www.eyegene.co.kr
Year Founded: 2006
185490—(KRS)
Rev.: $4,060,079
Assets: $61,652,404
Liabilities: $8,763,370
Net Worth: $52,889,034
Earnings: ($19,906,038)
Emp.: 91
Fiscal Year-end: 12/31/22
Pharmaceuticals Mfr
N.A.I.C.S.: 325412
Rhee Mj (CFO)

EYELOGIC SYSTEMS INC.
Suite 160A 340 Midpark Way SE,
Calgary, T2X IPI, AB, Canada
Tel.: (403) 264-5896 AB
Web Site: http://www.eyelogic.com
Year Founded: 1986
Sales Range: Less than $1 Million
Emp.: 50
Ophthalmic Equipment Mfr
N.A.I.C.S.: 339112
Kristoffer Moen (CFO)

EYEMAXX REAL ESTATE AG
Auhofstrasse 25 Aschaffenburg bei,
63741, Frankfurt, Germany
Tel.: (49) 60213866917 De
Web Site: http://www.eyemaxx.com
Year Founded: 1996
BNT1—(DEU)
Rev.: $9,518,810
Assets: $315,800,520
Liabilities: $243,009,620
Net Worth: $72,790,900
Earnings: $6,943,132
Emp.: 60
Fiscal Year-end: 10/30/19
Real Estate Manangement Services
N.A.I.C.S.: 531210
Michael Mueller (Founder & CEO)

EYESVISION CORP.
17F 556 Gangnam-daero, Gangnam-
gu, Seoul, Korea (South)
Tel.: (82) 263305038
Web Site:
https://www.eyesvision.com
Year Founded: 1992
031310—(KRS)
Rev.: $146,973,734
Assets: $189,086,409
Liabilities: $62,935,470
Net Worth: $126,150,939
Earnings: ($4,135,108)
Emp.: 51
Fiscal Year-end: 12/31/22
Communication Equipment Services
N.A.I.C.S.: 334220
Seung-Hee Suh (Mgr)

EYRIR INVEST HF.
Skolavorousttigur 13, 101, Reykjavík,
Iceland
Tel.: (354) 5250200
Web Site: https://eyrir.is
Emp.: 100
Investment Services
N.A.I.C.S.: 523999

Signy Sif Sigurdardóttir (Mng Dir)

EZ SYSTEMS AS
Hollenderigata 3, 3732, Skien, Nor-
way
Tel.: (47) 35 58 70 20
Web Site: http://www.ez.no
Year Founded: 1999
Sales Range: $10-24.9 Million
Emp.: 85
Software Development Services
N.A.I.C.S.: 513210
Aleksander Farstad (Co-Founder)

Subsidiaries:

eZ Systems China (1)
L24 Tower 3 China Central Place 77 Jian-
guo Road, Chaoyang District, Beijing,
100025, China
Tel.: (86) 10 8587 2237
Web Content Management Software
N.A.I.C.S.: 513210

eZ Systems France (1)
13 Rue Gilibert, Lyon, 69002, France
Tel.: (33) 1 44 93 15 50
Web Site: http://www.ez.no
Emp.: 12
Web Content Management Software
N.A.I.C.S.: 513210

eZ Systems Germany (1)
Bonner Strasse 484, Cologne, 50968, Ger-
many
Tel.: (49) 221 367 4860
Web Site: http://ez.no
Emp.: 10
Web Content Management Software
N.A.I.C.S.: 513210

eZ Systems Italy (1)
Via San Pietro all'Orto 3, 20121, Milan, Italy
Tel.: (39) 02 7631 7631
Web Content Management Software
N.A.I.C.S.: 513210

eZ Systems Japan (1)
Namisho Building 2F 2-3-7 Shinkawa,
Chuo-ku, Tokyo, 104-0033, Japan
Tel.: (81) 3 6327 1514
Emp.: 3
Web Content Management Software
N.A.I.C.S.: 513210
Eijiro Hattori (Gen Mgr)

eZ Systems Nordics (1)
Askergata 1, 0158, Oslo, Norway
Tel.: (47) 35 58 70 20
Web Site: http://www.ez.no
Emp.: 3
Web Content Management Software
N.A.I.C.S.: 513210
Alexandar Fairstad (Gen Mgr)

eZ Systems Polska Sp. z o.o. (1)
Gliwicka 6/5, 40-079, Katowice, Poland
Tel.: (48) 327850550
Software Development Services
N.A.I.C.S.: 541511

eZ Systems Spain (1)
Barcelona Activa c/ Llacuna 162, 08018,
Barcelona, Spain
Tel.: (34) 93 401 98 77
Content Management Software
N.A.I.C.S.: 513210

eZ Systems US Inc. (1)
35 Meadow St Ste 103, Brooklyn, NY
11206
Tel.: (929) 295-0699
Software Development Services
N.A.I.C.S.: 541511

EZAGOO LIMITED
B127 2/F Block B Beijing Pudi Hotel
No 7 South Street of Jianguomen,
Yuelu District, Beijing, 100000, Hu-
nan, China
Tel.: (86) 13975109168 NV
Year Founded: 2018
EZOO—(OTCIQ)
Rev.: $286,054
Assets: $685,235
Liabilities: $2,961,257
Net Worth: ($2,276,022)

Earnings: ($1,253,608)
Emp.: 46
Fiscal Year-end: 12/31/22
Advertising Agency Services
N.A.I.C.S.: 541810

EZAKI GLICO CO., LTD.
4-6-5 Utajima, Nishi-Yodogawa-ku,
Osaka, 555-8502, Japan
Tel.: (81) 664778352
Web Site: https://glico.com
Year Founded: 1922
2206—(TKS)
Rev.: $2,358,063,100
Assets: $2,805,817,870
Liabilities: $940,325,430
Net Worth: $1,865,492,440
Earnings: $100,202,970
Emp.: 5,439
Fiscal Year-end: 12/31/23
Confectionery & Convenience Food
Producer
N.A.I.C.S.: 311340
Katsuhisa Ezaki (Pres & CEO)

Subsidiaries:

Ezaki Glico USA Corporation (1)
18022 Cowan Ste 110, Irvine, CA 92614
Tel.: (949) 251-0144
Confectionery Product Distr
N.A.I.C.S.: 424450

Generale Biscuit Glico France
S.A. (1)
3 rue Saarinen Silic, Rungis, F 94150, Val
De Marne, France
Tel.: (33) 156344000
Dairy Product Whslr
N.A.I.C.S.: 424430

Glico Asia Pacific Pte. Ltd (1)
138 Market Street Capital Green #35-04,
Singapore, 048946, Singapore
Tel.: (65) 6290 9380
Confectionery & Ice Cream Products Mfr &
Distr
N.A.I.C.S.: 311919

Subsidiary (Non-US):

Thai Glico Co., Ltd. (2)
Ploenchit Tower 4th Fl 898 Ploenchit Road,
Pathumwan, Bangkok, 10330,
Thailand (97%)
Tel.: (66) 2 263 0510
Web Site: https://www.glico.com
Sales Range: $50-74.9 Million
Emp.: 100
Confectionery Product Mfr
N.A.I.C.S.: 424450
Ratana Buarawoung (Mgr-Logistics)

Glico Canada Corporation (1)
162 5th Ave W, Vancouver, V5Y 1H7, BC,
Canada
Tel.: (604) 876-7192
Confectionery Product Mfr
N.A.I.C.S.: 424450

ICREO Co., Ltd. (1)
Aqua City 4F 4-16-23 Shibaura Minato-ku,
Tokyo, 108 0023, Japan
Tel.: (81) 337697500
Web Site: http://www.icreo.co.jp
Sales Range: $100-124.9 Million
Emp.: 393
Infant Formula Milk & Health Foods Produc-
tion Services
N.A.I.C.S.: 311514

Kansai Frozen Distribution Co.,
Ltd. (1)
42-8 Minaminokuchi Kaminara, Yawata,
614-8164, Kyoto Prefecture, Japan
Tel.: (81) 759723330
Web Site: http://www.kansai-frozen.co.jp
Frozen Food Mfr & Distr
N.A.I.C.S.: 311520

PT Glico Indonesia (1)
CIBIS Nine 9th Floor Unit A-E JI T B Si-
matupang No 02, Cilandak Timur Pasar
Minggu, Jakarta Selatan, 12560, Indonesia
Tel.: (62) 2150845450
Confectionery Product Distr
N.A.I.C.S.: 424450

TCHO Ventures, Inc. (1)
3100 San Pablo Ave Ste 170, Berkeley, CA
94702
Tel.: (415) 981-0189
Web Site: http://www.tcho.com
Grocery & Related Products Merchant
Whslr
N.A.I.C.S.: 424490
Mag Donaldson (Dir-Mktg)

EZCARETECH CO., LTD.
4FL Kwanghee Bldg 307 Toegye-ro,
Jung-gu, Seoul, Korea (South)
Tel.: (82) 27478640
Web Site:
https://www.ezcaretech.com
Year Founded: 2001
099750—(KRS)
Rev.: $55,622,503
Assets: $45,040,876
Liabilities: $19,078,462
Net Worth: $25,962,414
Earnings: ($7,285,602)
Emp.: 460
Fiscal Year-end: 03/31/23
Information Technology Services
N.A.I.C.S.: 541511
Hiroki Segawa (CEO)

Subsidiaries:

EzCaretech Japan Co., Ltd. (1)
Centennial Aoyama 9FL 2-22-17 Minami-
aoyama, Minato-ku, Tokyo, 107-0062, Ja-
pan
Tel.: (81) 364470222
Electronic Health Record Software Services
N.A.I.C.S.: 541511

Saudi Korean Health Informatics
Company (1)
2601 king Abdullah Ibn Abdul Aziz Rd-al
Quds Unit 256, Riyadh, 13214-8401, Saudi
Arabia
Tel.: (966) 112459689
Web Site: https://www.skhic.com.sa
Health Informatics Services
N.A.I.C.S.: 541611

EZCONN CORPORATION
13F No 27-8 Sec 2 Zhongzheng E
Rd, Tamsui Dist, New Taipei City,
25170, Taiwan
Tel.: (886) 228086333
Web Site: https://www.ezconn.com
6442—(TAI)
Rev.: $85,594,195
Assets: $109,480,914
Liabilities: $42,417,703
Net Worth: $67,063,211
Earnings: $5,495,340
Emp.: 799
Fiscal Year-end: 12/31/23
Broadband, Optical, Radio Frequency
& Interconnect Products
N.A.I.C.S.: 334220

Subsidiaries:

EZconn Czech a.s. (1)
Nachodska 529, 541 01, Porici nad
Sazavou, Czech Republic
Tel.: (420) 778971173
Optical Fibber Component Mfr
N.A.I.C.S.: 335921

Light Master Technology Inc. (1)
Beylikduzu OSB Mustafa Kurdoglu Cad No
38 Beylikduzu, Istanbul, Turkiye
Tel.: (90) 2122954000
Web Site: https://www.lightmaster.com.tr
Financial Investment Services
N.A.I.C.S.: 523999

EZDAN HOLDING GROUP
COMPANY (Q.S.C.)
Ezdan Tower, PO Box 30503, Doha,
Qatar
Tel.: (974) 44332333
Web Site:
https://www.ezdanholding.qa
Year Founded: 1960

Ezdan Holding Group Company (Q.S.C.)—(Continued)
ERES—(QE)
Rev.: $367,125,383
Assets: $13,674,278,010
Liabilities: $4,896,613,284
Net Worth: $8,777,664,725
Earnings: $16,639,264
Fiscal Year-end: 12/31/21
Real Estate Management Services
N.A.I.C.S.: 531390
Khalid Thani Abdullah Al-Thani *(Chm)*

EZEN TECH CO., LTD.
577-6 Chilgoe-dong, Gyeonggi-do, Pyeongtaek, 459050, Korea (South)
Tel.: (82) 31 6609900
Web Site: http://www.ezentech.co.kr
Rev.: $17,130,971
Assets: $56,884,282
Liabilities: $44,601,086
Net Worth: $12,283,196
Earnings: ($8,376,881)
Emp.: 43
Fiscal Year-end: 12/31/18
Automobile Parts & Home Appliance Mfr
N.A.I.C.S.: 336390

EZETOP LTD.
3 Shelbourne Buildings Crampton Avenue Shelbourne Road, Dublin, Ireland
Tel.: (353) 1 630 6300
Web Site: http://www.ezetop.com
Year Founded: 2006
Mobile Phone Services
N.A.I.C.S.: 517112
Mark English *(COO)*

Subsidiaries:

iSend LLC   (1)
765 Harris Turnpike, Middlebury, CT 06762
Tel.: (877) 212-7363
Web Site: http://www.isendonline.com
Sales Range: $100-124.9 Million
Emp.: 20
Global Electronic Payment Network
N.A.I.C.S.: 522320
Steven LaBella *(Founder, Pres & CEO)*

EZFLY INTERNATIONAL TRAVEL AGENT CO., LTD.
2F-1 No 51 Hengyang Road, Zhongzheng District, Taipei, Taiwan
Tel.: (886) 277250800   TW
Web Site: https://www.ezfly.com
Year Founded: 1988
2734—(TPE)
Rev.: $13,618,422
Assets: $24,276,647
Liabilities: $13,798,080
Net Worth: $10,478,567
Earnings: ($1,562,611)
Fiscal Year-end: 12/31/22
Travel Agency Services
N.A.I.C.S.: 561510
Zhou Yunsheng *(Chm)*

EZGO TECHNOLOGIES LTD.
Building A Floor 2 Science and Education Town, Changzhou Institute of Dalian University of Technology Wujin District, Changzhou, 213164, Jiangsu, China
Tel.: (86) 51983683805   VG
Web Site:
https://www.ezgotech.com.cn
Year Founded: 2019
EZGO—(NASDAQ)
Rev.: $23,422,006
Assets: $42,011,670
Liabilities: $9,475,170
Net Worth: $32,536,500
Earnings: ($2,978,673)
Emp.: 115
Fiscal Year-end: 09/30/21

Holding Company
N.A.I.C.S.: 551112
Jingyan Wu *(CFO)*

EZI GMBH
Reiherstrasse 2, 35708, Haiger, Germany
Tel.: (49) 27738350
Web Site: http://www.ezi.de
Rev.: $10,980,024
Emp.: 50
Customs Consulting & Agency Services
N.A.I.C.S.: 541618
Berit Wagener-Gog *(Co-CEO)*

EZION HOLDINGS LIMITED
438B Alexandra Road 05-08/10 Alexandra Technopark, Singapore, 119968, Singapore
Tel.: (65) 63090555
Web Site:
http://www.ezionholdings.com
5ME—(OTCIQ)
Rev.: $66,944,953
Assets: $653,584,685
Liabilities: $1,296,482,131
Net Worth: ($642,897,446)
Earnings: ($455,753,667)
Fiscal Year-end: 12/31/19
Offshore Services
N.A.I.C.S.: 336611
David Leong Ching Poh *(Chief Bus Dev Officer & Head-China & Mexico)*

Subsidiaries:

Teras 336 Pte Ltd   (1)
15 Hoe Chiang Road Tower Fifteen 12-05, Singapore, 089316, Singapore
Tel.: (65) 63090555
Ship Chartering Services
N.A.I.C.S.: 483111

Teras Cargo Transport (America) LLC   (1)
5358 33rd Ave NW Ste 302, Gig Harbor, WA 98335
Tel.: (253) 857-9209
Web Site: http://www.terasamerica.com
Sales Range: $25-49.9 Million
Emp.: 15
Marine Logistics Services
N.A.I.C.S.: 488320
Kathleen Reed *(Acct Mgr)*

Teras Conquest 2 Pte Ltd   (1)
438B Alexandra Road 05-08/10 Alexandra Technopark, Singapore, 119968, Singapore
Tel.: (65) 63090555
Ship Chartering Services
N.A.I.C.S.: 483111

Teras Offshore Pte Ltd   (1)
15 Hoe Chiang Road Tower Fifteen 12-05, Singapore, 39316, Singapore
Tel.: (65) 63090555
Web Site: http://www.terasoffshore.com
Marine Logistics & Support Services
N.A.I.C.S.: 483111
Peter Kon Meng Lee *(Deputy CEO)*

EZRA HOLDINGS LTD.
51 Shipyard Road, Singapore, 628139, Singapore
Tel.: (65) 63498535   SG
Web Site:
http://www.ezraholdings.com
Year Founded: 1992
5DN—(SES)
Sales Range: $800-899.9 Million
Offshore Oil & Gas Operation Support Services
N.A.I.C.S.: 213112
Kian Soo Lee *(Founder & Chm)*

Subsidiaries:

EMAS Offshore Limited   (1)
15 Hoe Chiang Road 28-01 Tower Fifteen, Singapore, 089316, Singapore
Tel.: (65) 6 349 8535
Web Site: http://www.emasoffshore.com

Sales Range: $150-199.9 Million
Offshore Construction Services
N.A.I.C.S.: 211120
Kian Soo Lee *(Chm)*

Subsidiary (Non-US):

EMAS AMC   (2)
Lilleakervn 2A, Oslo, 0283, Norway
Tel.: (47) 2212 7500
Web Site: http://www.emas.com
Marine Engineering & Installation Contractor
N.A.I.C.S.: 541330

London Marine Consultants Limited   (1)
20 St Thomas Street, London, SE1 9RS, United Kingdom
Tel.: (44) 2076210050
Web Site: https://www.londonmarine.co.uk
Marine Construction Services
N.A.I.C.S.: 237990
Richard Martin *(Founder)*

EZTD INC.
6 Yehezkel Koifman Street, 68012, Tel Aviv, Israel
Tel.: (972) 737058000   DE
EZTD—(OTCBB)
Sales Range: $25-49.9 Million
Emp.: 161
Binary Options Online Trading
N.A.I.C.S.: 513199
Shimon Citron *(Founder)*

EZTEC EMPREENDIMENTOS E PARTICIPACOES S.A.
Avenida Republica do Libano 1921 Ibirapuera, Sao Paulo, 04501-003, Brazil
Tel.: (55) 1150568303
Web Site: https://www.eztec.com.br
Year Founded: 1979
EZTC3—(BRAZ)
Rev.: $193,627,567
Assets: $1,050,985,117
Liabilities: $209,909,006
Net Worth: $841,076,111
Earnings: $43,992,062
Fiscal Year-end: 12/31/23
Real Estate Development Services
N.A.I.C.S.: 531390
Ernesto Zarzur *(Chm)*

EZY NET PTE LTD.
3791 Jalan Bukit Merah #06-29 E Centre at redhill, Singapore, 159471, Singapore
Tel.: (65) 6271 7791
Web Site: http://www.ezynet.sg
Electronic Payment Services
N.A.I.C.S.: 522320

Subsidiaries:

Diners Club (Singapore) Pte. Ltd.   (1)
7500-E Beach Road 03-201 The Plaza, Singapore, 199595, Singapore
Tel.: (65) 64160800
Web Site: http://www.dinersclub.com.sg
Sales Range: $100-124.9 Million
Financial Processing & Insurance Services
N.A.I.C.S.: 522320

EZZ LIFE SCIENCE HOLDINGS LIMITED
55/59 Parramatta Rd, Lidcombe, 2141, NSW, Australia
Tel.: (61) 291602305   AU
Web Site: https://www.ezzlife.com.au
Year Founded: 2015
EZZ—(ASX)
Rev.: $24,218,120
Assets: $11,502,002
Liabilities: $1,994,183
Net Worth: $9,507,819
Earnings: $2,366,647
Fiscal Year-end: 06/30/23
Holding Company
N.A.I.C.S.: 551112

Anthony Guarna *(CFO)*

EZZ STEEL CO. S.A.E.
Four Seasons Nile Plaza 1089 Cornich El-Nil, Garden City, Cairo, Egypt
Tel.: (20) 227989800
Web Site: https://www.ezzsteel.com
Year Founded: 1994
AEZD—(LSE)
Rev.: $4,623,899,689
Assets: $3,668,046,619
Liabilities: $3,626,106,742
Net Worth: $41,939,877
Earnings: ($23,182,970)
Fiscal Year-end: 12/31/23
Steel Products Mfr
N.A.I.C.S.: 331110
Hassan Nouh *(Mng Dir)*

Subsidiaries:

Al Ezz Dekheila Steel Co.   (1)
El-Dekheila, Alexandria, Egypt
Tel.: (20) 33082220
Steel Product Mfr & Distr
N.A.I.C.S.: 331210

Al Ezz Dekheila Steel Company Alexandria SAE   (1)
10 Shehab Street Mohandessin, Cairo, Egypt   (54.59%)
Tel.: (20) 233046060
Web Site: http://www.ezzsteel.com
Sales Range: $1-4.9 Billion
Emp.: 2,791
Steel Mfr & Exporter
N.A.I.C.S.: 331110
Farouk Ibrahim *(Chm)*

Al Ezz Flat Steel Company   (1)
5th Floor 10 Shehab Street, Giza, Egypt
Tel.: (20) 233030493
Flat Steel Mfr
N.A.I.C.S.: 331110

Al Ezz Rolling Mills Company   (1)
First Industrial Zone A1, District 2 Al-Sharqia, 10th of Ramadan City, Egypt
Tel.: (20) 554410460
Steel Product Mfr & Distr
N.A.I.C.S.: 331210

EZZ Flat Steel Company   (1)
Northwest Gulf of Suez km 44 Suez/Hurghada Road, Economic Industrial Zone Ain Sokhna, Suez, Egypt
Tel.: (20) 623598361
Steel Product Mfr & Distr
N.A.I.C.S.: 331210

EZZI VISION PTY LTD
13U/175 Lower Gibbes Street, Chatswood, 2067, NSW, Australia
Tel.: (61) 410834175   AU
Web Site:
http://www.ezzivision.com.au
Year Founded: 2000
Glove Box & Thin Film Product Mfr
N.A.I.C.S.: 326199

F & J PRINCE HOLDINGS CORPORATION
5th Floor BDO Towers Paseo formerly Citibank Center Paseo de Roxas, Makati, 8741, Philippines
Tel.: (63) 288927133
Web Site: https://www.fjprince.com
FJP—(PHI)
Rev.: $3,403,691
Assets: $34,039,995
Liabilities: $1,189,201
Net Worth: $32,850,794
Earnings: $1,150,340
Fiscal Year-end: 12/31/23
Investment Services
N.A.I.C.S.: 523940
Johnson U. Co *(VP-Admin)*

F MEC INTERNATIONAL FINANCIAL SERVICES LTD.
IInd Floor Central Bank Building 13-B

Netaji Subhash Marg Daryaganj, Delhi, 110 002, India
Tel.: (91) 1143680407
Web Site:
https://www.fmecinternational.com
Year Founded: 1993
539552—(BOM)
Rev.: $70,863
Assets: $562,685
Liabilities: $108,510
Net Worth: $454,175
Earnings: $6,781
Fiscal Year-end: 03/31/21
Financial Support Services
N.A.I.C.S.: 523999
Manoj Kumar Thakur *(CFO)*

F&B GROUP
15 rue Pasteur, Levallois-Perret, 92300, France
Tel.: (33) 1 4105 5555   FR
Web Site: http://www.naefa.com
Year Founded: 2011
Emp.: 70
Investment Holding Company
N.A.I.C.S.: 551112
Julien Saada *(Partner)*

Subsidiaries:

Maesa SA   (1)
15 rue Pasteur, 92300, Levallois-Perret, France   **(96.2%)**
Tel.: (33) 141055555
Web Site: http://www.maesa.com
Sales Range: $25-49.9 Million
Perfume & Cosmetic Products Mfr & Retailer
N.A.I.C.S.: 325620
Julien Saada *(Pres & CEO)*

Subsidiary (US):

Maesa Home   (2)
10940 Wilshire Blvd Ste 2300, Los Angeles, CA 90024
Tel.: (310) 208-7200
Sales Range: $25-49.9 Million
Emp.: 35
Cosmetics & Beauty Solutions Whslr
N.A.I.C.S.: 424210
Katherine Shanks *(Office Mgr)*

Maesa Inc   (2)
40 Worth St Rm 705, New York, NY 10013-2994
Tel.: (212) 431-6613
Web Site: http://www.maesa.com
Soap & Detergent Mfr
N.A.I.C.S.: 325611
Scott Kestenbaum *(Sr VP)*

Subsidiary (Non-US):

Maesa UK Ltd   (2)
Crown House 143-147 Regent St, London, W1B 4NR, United Kingdom
Tel.: (44) 20 74946101
Soap & Detergent Mfr
N.A.I.C.S.: 325611

F&C INVESTMENT TRUST PLC
Cannon Place 78 Cannon Street, London, EC4N 6AG, United Kingdom
Tel.: (44) 2074645000   UK
Web Site: https://www.fandc.com
Year Founded: 1868
FCIT—(LSE)
Rev.: $737,171,384
Assets: $7,114,876,125
Liabilities: $751,769,463
Net Worth: $6,363,106,662
Earnings: $673,458,037
Fiscal Year-end: 12/31/23
Investment Trust & Management Services
N.A.I.C.S.: 525990

F&D SCENE CHANGES LTD.
2B 803 24th Avenue SE, Calgary, T2G 1P5, AB, Canada
Tel.: (403) 233-7633
Web Site: https://fdscene.com

Year Founded: 1982
Rev.: $12,684,628
Emp.: 120
Prefabricated Design Components Mfr
N.A.I.C.S.: 332311
Joe Kondrat *(Mgr-Bus Dev)*

F&F HOLDINGS CO., LTD.
541 Eonju-ro, Gangnam-gu, Seoul, Korea (South)
Tel.: (82) 25200001
Web Site: https://www.fnf.co.kr
Year Founded: 1972
007700—(KRS)
Rev.: $1,393,497,057
Assets: $2,757,455,847
Liabilities: $541,568,316
Net Worth: $2,215,887,531
Earnings: $101,396,179
Emp.: 44
Fiscal Year-end: 12/31/22
Apparel Mfr & Distr
N.A.I.C.S.: 315990
Chang In Ho *(Mgr)*

F&M CO., LTD.
F&M Building 1-23-38 Esakacho Suita City, Osaka, 564-0063, Japan
Tel.: (81) 663397177
Web Site: https://www.fmltd.co.jp
Year Founded: 1990
4771—(TKS)
Rev.: $98,231,210
Assets: $100,485,220
Liabilities: $23,690,240
Net Worth: $76,794,980
Earnings: $10,635,490
Emp.: 928
Fiscal Year-end: 03/31/24
General Affairs, Administrative Consulting Services, Training, Examination Services & ISO Certification Acquisition Support Services
N.A.I.C.S.: 561499
Ichiro Morinaka *(Founder, Chm & Pres)*

F-TECH INC.
19 Showa-numa Shobu-Cho, Kuki, Saitama, 346-0194, Japan
Tel.: (81) 480855211
Web Site: https://www.ftech.co.jp
Year Founded: 1947
7212—(TKS)
Rev.: $1,974,796,990
Assets: $1,267,612,920
Liabilities: $793,398,300
Net Worth: $474,214,620
Earnings: $11,124,630
Emp.: 9,763
Fiscal Year-end: 03/31/24
Automotive Parts, Related Dies, Machinery & Equipment Mfr & Sales
N.A.I.C.S.: 336390
Yuichi Fukuda *(Pres & CEO)*

Subsidiaries:

DYNA-MIG Mfg. of Stratford Inc.   (1)
275 Wright Blvd, PO Box 1123, Stratford, N5A 7Y1, ON, Canada
Tel.: (519) 272-2188
Web Site: https://www.dynamig.com
Sales Range: $100-124.9 Million
Emp.: 650
Automobile Parts Mfr
N.A.I.C.S.: 336390
Janice Hofmann *(Mgr-HR & Safety)*

F&P America Mfg., Inc.   (1)
2101 Corporate Dr, Troy, OH 45373
Tel.: (937) 339-0212
Web Site: http://www.fandp.com
Sales Range: $200-249.9 Million
Emp.: 600
Automobile Parts Mfr
N.A.I.C.S.: 336390

F&P Georgia Mfg., Inc.   (1)

88 Enterprise Dr, Rome, GA 30161
Tel.: (706) 291-7550
Web Site: http://www.fandpgeorgia.com
Sales Range: $100-124.9 Million
Emp.: 375
Automobile Parts Mfr
N.A.I.C.S.: 336390

F&P Mfg. De Mexico, S.A. De C.V. (1)
Calle Santiago 242, Centro Industrial de Guanajuato Irapuato, 36835, Mexico, Mexico
Tel.: (52) 4621661700
Automobile Parts Mfr
N.A.I.C.S.: 336390

F&P Mfg. Inc.   (1)
1 Nolan Road, PO Box 4000, Tottenham, L0G 1W0, ON, Canada
Tel.: (905) 936-3435
Web Site: https://fandpmfg.com
Sales Range: $200-249.9 Million
Emp.: 600
Automobile Parts Mfr
N.A.I.C.S.: 336390
Andrew Kochanek *(Pres)*

F-Tech Automotive Components Pvt. Ltd.   (1)
14th Floor Tower 5B DLF Epitome Dlf Cyber City Phase 3, Gurgaon, 122002, Haryana, India
Tel.: (91) 1244607777
Automobile Parts Mfr
N.A.I.C.S.: 336390

F-Tech Inc - Kuki Plant   (1)
19 Showa-numa Shobu-Cho, Kuki, Saitama, Japan
Tel.: (81) 480855215
Emp.: 350
Automobile Parts Mfr
N.A.I.C.S.: 336390

F-Tech Inc. - Kameyama Plant   (1)
395-43 Sagiyama Shiraki-cho, 519-0169, Mie, Japan
Tel.: (81) 595 83 2111
Web Site: http://www.ftech.co.jp
Automobile Parts Mfr
N.A.I.C.S.: 336390

F-Tech Inc. - Kameyama Wada Plant   (1)
1370-2 Wada-cho, Kameyama, Mie, Japan
Tel.: (81) 595823321
Precision Machining Tools Mfr
N.A.I.C.S.: 332721

F-Tech Zhongshan Inc.   (1)
No 16 Torch road, Torch Industrial Development Zone, Zhongshan, 528437, Guangdong, China
Tel.: (86) 76085335336
Web Site: http://www.ftech-zs.com.cn
Automobile Parts Mfr
N.A.I.C.S.: 336390

F-tech Philippines Mfg., Inc.   (1)
118 North Science Avenue, Laguna Technopark, Binan, Laguna, Philippines
Sales Range: $200-249.9 Million
Emp.: 530
Automobile Parts Mfr
N.A.I.C.S.: 336390

F.E.G. DE QUERETARO S.A. DE C.V   (1)
Cerrada la Noria No 106 Parque Industrial Queretaro, Santa Rosa Jauregui, 76220, Queretaro, Mexico
Tel.: (52) 4422295100
Web Site: https://www.fegq.mx
Emp.: 250
Stamping Parts Mfr
N.A.I.C.S.: 336370

F.Tech R&D (Guangzhou) Inc.   (1)
Room401 2507 KaichuangAvenue, Huangpu District, Guangzhou, Guangdong, China
Tel.: (86) 2082113255
Automobile Parts Mfr
N.A.I.C.S.: 336390

F.tech Mfg. (Thailand) Ltd.   (1)
99 Moo 3 Tambon Banchang, Amphoe Uthai, Ayutthaya, 13210, Thailand
Tel.: (66) 35746700

Web Site: https://www.ftech-thai.com
Dies & Die Component Mfr
N.A.I.C.S.: 333514

F.tech R&D North America Inc   (1)
1191 Horizon W Ct, Troy, OH 45373
Tel.: (937) 339-2777
Web Site: http://www.ftech.co.jp
Sales Range: $25-49.9 Million
Emp.: 43
Automotive Components Mfr
N.A.I.C.S.: 336320

F.tech R&D Philippines Inc   (1)
F tech Annex Bldg 123 North Science Avenue Laguna Technopark, Binan, 4024, Laguna, Philippines
Tel.: (63) 495440937
Web Site: http://www.frdp.com.ph
Automobile Parts Mfr
N.A.I.C.S.: 336390

F.tech Wuhan Inc.   (1)
No 619 Gexin Avenue, Dongxihu District, Wuhan, Hubei, China
Tel.: (86) 2783068806
Automobile Parts Mfr
N.A.I.C.S.: 336390

Fukuda Engineering Co., Ltd.   (1)
3206-3 Koguki, Kazo, 347-0111, Saitama, Japan
Tel.: (81) 480701171
Dies & Die Component Mfr
N.A.I.C.S.: 333514

Kyushu F-Tech Inc.   (1)
4455 Kuhara, Yamaga, 861-0522, Kumamoto, Japan
Tel.: (81) 968445116
Web Site: https://q-ft.com
Sales Range: $25-49.9 Million
Emp.: 65
Dies & Die Component Mfr
N.A.I.C.S.: 333514

PT. F.Tech Indonesia   (1)
Jl maligi ix lot v-3 Kel Margakaya Kec Telukjambe Barat Kab Prop, Kawasan Industri Kiic, Karawang, 41361, Jawa Barat, Indonesia
Tel.: (62) 2129259980
Automobile Parts Mfr
N.A.I.C.S.: 336390

Reterra Co., Ltd   (1)
2703 Ryojin Thin Ogano-machi, Chichibugun, Saitama, 368-0201, Japan
Tel.: (81) 494623024
Web Site: http://www.reterra.co.jp
Emp.: 279
Automotive Aluminum Die Casting Parts Mfr
N.A.I.C.S.: 336390
Hiroaki Fukushima *(CEO)*

Yantai Fuyan Mould Co., Ltd.   (1)
Room 501 Building C 133-1 Yingchun Street, Laishan, Yantai, China
Tel.: (86) 5352102278
Automobile Parts Mfr
N.A.I.C.S.: 336390

F. MCCLURE & SONS LTD.
55 Ouellette Street, Grand Falls, E3Z 0A6, NB, Canada
Tel.: (506) 473-2024
Web Site:
http://www.mccluretoyota.com
Year Founded: 1973
Rev.: $12,496,887
Emp.: 28
New & Used Car Dealers
N.A.I.C.S.: 441110
Donald McClure *(Co-Owner)*

F. MURPF AG
Industriestrasse West 36, 4614, Hagendorf, Switzerland
Tel.: (41) 62 209 40 00
Web Site: http://www.murpf.ch
Year Founded: 1962
Emp.: 450
Trucking & Logistics Services
N.A.I.C.S.: 484110
Andrea Kyburz-Murpf *(Mgr-Fin & Admin)*

F. Murpf AG—(Continued)

Subsidiaries:

Lineafresca Logistic AG (1)
Industriestrasse West 36, 4614, Hagendorf,
Switzerland
Tel.: (41) 622097090
Web Site: http://www.murpf.ch
Freight Transportation & Logistics Services
for Chilled & Frozen Products
N.A.I.C.S.: 541614

**F. RAMADA INVESTIMENTOS,
SGPS, S.A.**
Rua Manuel Pinto de Azevedo 818,
4100-320, Porto, Portugal
Tel.: (351) 228347100
Web Site:
https://www.ramadainvestimentos.pt
RAM—(EUR)
Rev.: $209,033,137
Assets: $258,170,344
Liabilities: $113,425,636
Net Worth: $144,744,709
Earnings: $21,620,491
Emp.: 482
Fiscal Year-end: 12/31/22
Holding Company; Steel & Storage
Systems
N.A.I.C.S.: 551112
Joao Manuel Matos Borges de Ol-
iveira (Chm)

Subsidiaries:

**F. Ramada, Acos e Industrias,
S.A.** (1)
Apartado 10, 3884-004, Ovar, Portugal
Tel.: (351) 256580400
Web Site: https://www.ramada.pt
Steel Product Distr
N.A.I.C.S.: 423510
Borges de Oliveira (Gen Mgr)

NV STORAX BENELUX SA (1)
Au Fonds Race 17, 4300, Waremme, Bel-
gium
Tel.: (32) 19 33 86 86
Web Site: http://www.storax-ramada.com
Sales Range: $25-49.9 Million
Emp.: 15
Racking Systems Mfr
N.A.I.C.S.: 333248
Philippe Tromme (Gen Mgr)

Planfuro Global, S.A. (1)
Zona Industrial Vieira de Leiria Lt 6, 2430-
600, Leiria, Portugal
Tel.: (351) 24 469 8020
Web Site: https://planfuroglobal.pt
Emp.: 63
Metal Mould Mfr
N.A.I.C.S.: 333511

F.C.C. CO., LTD.
7000-36 Nakagawa Hosoe-cho, Kita-
ku, Hamamatsu, 431-1394, Shizuoka,
Japan
Tel.: (81) 535232400
Web Site: https://www.fcc-net.co.jp
Year Founded: 1939
7296—(TKS)
Rev.: $1,588,270,630
Assets: $1,619,476,440
Liabilities: $386,037,220
Net Worth: $1,233,439,220
Earnings: $80,846,910
Emp.: 7,838
Fiscal Year-end: 03/31/24
Clutch Systems & Facings Mfr for
Cars, Motorcycles & Utility Vehicles;
Plastics Molding & Machining Ser-
vices; Specialized Tools & Dies Mfr
N.A.I.C.S.: 336370
Yoshitaka Saito (Pres)

Subsidiaries:

F.C.C. (Adams), LLC (1)
936 E Parr Rd, Berne, IN 46711 **(100%)**
Tel.: (260) 589-8555
Web Site: http://www.fcc-net.co.jp

Sales Range: $100-124.9 Million
Emp.: 500
Motor Vehicle Parts Mfr
N.A.I.C.S.: 336390

F.C.C. (North Carolina), LLC (1)
18000 Fieldcrest Rd, Laurinburg, NC
28352 **(100%)**
Tel.: (910) 462-4465
Emp.: 400
Automotive Stores
N.A.I.C.S.: 441330
Robert Kendall (Mgr)

F.C.C. (Taiwan) Co., Ltd. (1)
38 Taiyi Road Tukuli. Rende District. Tainan
City, Taiwan
Tel.: (886) 62720722
Web Site: http://www.fcc-net.co.jp
Sales Range: $25-49.9 Million
Emp.: 150
Motorcycle Clutches Mfr & Sales; Owned by
F.C.C. Co., Ltd., by Kwang Yang Motor Co.,
Ltd (KYMCO) & by King Hwa Sin Industrial
Co., Ltd.
N.A.I.C.S.: 336991

F.C.C. (Thailand) Co.,Ltd. (1)
286 Chalong Krung Road Ladkrabang In-
dustrial Estate, Lamplathew Latkrabang,
Bangkok, 10520, Thailand **(58%)**
Tel.: (66) 232604237
Web Site: https://www.fccthai.co.th
Sales Range: $200-249.9 Million
Emp.: 1,000
Automotive Stores
N.A.I.C.S.: 441330

FCC (INDIANA), INC. (1)
555 Industrial Park Rd, Portland, IN 47371
Tel.: (260) 726-8023
Web Site: http://www.fcc-na.com
Emp.: 790
Clutch Assemblies & Component Mfr
N.A.I.C.S.: 336390

FCC (North America) , Inc. (1)
555 Industrial Park Rd, Portland, IN 47371
Tel.: (260) 726-8023
Web Site: http://www.fcc-na.com
Automobile Parts Mfr
N.A.I.C.S.: 336390

FCC (TAIWAN) CO., LTD. (1)
38 Tai Yi Rd, Jenteh Hsiang, T'ainan,
71747, Taiwan
Tel.: (886) 62720722
Web Site: http://www.fcc.com.tw
Clutch Assemblies Mfr
N.A.I.C.S.: 336390

FCC DO BRASIL LTDA. (1)
Rua Mogno 11, Manaus, 69075-170, Ama-
zonas, Brazil
Tel.: (55) 9221260202
Clutch Assemblies Mfr
N.A.I.C.S.: 336390

Flint Co., Ltd. (1)
Web Site: http://www.flint-sk.jp
Emp.: 34
Automobile Parts Mfr
N.A.I.C.S.: 336390
Yoshiaki Ueda (Pres)

Kyushu F.C.C. Co., Ltd. (1)
74-1 Urakawachi, Matsubase-machi Uki-shi,
Kumamoto, 869-0521, Japan **(100%)**
Tel.: (81) 964322323
Emp.: 125
Motor Vehicle Parts Mfr
N.A.I.C.S.: 336390

Tenryu Sangyo Co., Ltd. (1)
1550-1 Takagi, Iwata, 438-0202, Shizuoka,
Japan **(53.55%)**
Tel.: (81) 534211431
Sales Range: $50-74.9 Million
Emp.: 199
Automotive Stores
N.A.I.C.S.: 441330

Tohoku Chemical Industries, Ltd. (1)
1200 Fujita, Nasukarasuyama, 321-0532,
Tochigi, Japan
Tel.: (81) 287882761
Web Site: http://www.tci-web.co.jp
Sales Range: $25-49.9 Million
Emp.: 60
Industrial Chemicals Mfr
N.A.I.C.S.: 325998

Nishimura Masahiko (Auditor)

Subsidiary (Non-US):

**Tohoku Chemical Industries (Viet-
nam), Ltd** (2)
Amata Industrial Zone Lot 211 St 9, Long
Binh Ward, Bien Hoa, Dong Nai, Vietnam
Tel.: (84) 613936014
Chemical Products Mfr
N.A.I.C.S.: 325998

F.E. BORDING A/S
Turbinevej 4-6, Herlev, DK-2730,
Denmark
Tel.: (45) 70115011
Web Site: http://www.bording.dk
Year Founded: 1792
Rev.: $86,556,535
Assets: $62,248,628
Liabilities: $42,533,964
Net Worth: $19,714,664
Earnings: ($4,034,078)
Emp.: 370
Fiscal Year-end: 12/31/19
Marketing Consulting Services
N.A.I.C.S.: 541613
Bernt Johan Therp (Dir-Digital)

F.G. EUROPE S.A.
128 Vouliagmenis Ave Glyfada,
16674, Athens, Greece
Tel.: (30) 210 96 96 500
Web Site: http://www.fgeurope.gr
Year Founded: 1958
Rev.: $89,550,750
Assets: $174,208,367
Liabilities: $139,196,955
Net Worth: $35,011,412
Earnings: $595,915
Emp.: 145
Fiscal Year-end: 12/31/18
Household Product Whslr
N.A.I.C.S.: 423620
Georgios Fidakis (Chm)

**F.H. PAPENMEIER GMBH &
CO. KG**
Talweg 2, 58239, Schwerte, Germany
Tel.: (49) 23042050
Web Site: http://www.papenmeier.de
Year Founded: 1956
Rev.: $15,773,730
Emp.: 102
Engineeering Services
N.A.I.C.S.: 541330

**F.I.L.A. - FABBRICA ITALIANA
LAPIS ED AFFINI S.P.A.**
Via XXV Aprile 5, 20016, Pero, Italy
Tel.: (39) 02381051   IT
Web Site: https://www.fila.it
Year Founded: 2013
FILA—(ITA)
Rev.: $757,024,496
Assets: $1,401,830,844
Liabilities: $994,945,638
Net Worth: $406,885,206
Earnings: $9,975,765
Emp.: 8,070
Fiscal Year-end: 12/31/20
Pens & Pencils Mfr & Distr
N.A.I.C.S.: 339940
Massimo Candela (CEO)

Subsidiaries:

Canson SAS (1)
N 67 rue Louis et Laurent Seguin, CS
70139, 07104, Annonay, Cedex, France
Tel.: (33) 475698800
Web Site: https://fr.canson.com
Stationery Product Mfr
N.A.I.C.S.: 322230

DOMS Industries Pvt. Ltd. (1)
Plot No 117 G I D C 52 Hector Expansion
Area, Umbergaon Dist Valsad, Gujarat, In-
dia
Tel.: (91) 7434888445
Web Site: http://www.domsindia.com

Stationery Product Mfr
N.A.I.C.S.: 322230

Dixon Ticonderoga ART ULC (1)
27 Lorena St, Barrie, L4N 3H5, ON,
Canada
Tel.: (705) 722-6701
Paper Products Mfr
N.A.I.C.S.: 322299

Dixon Ticonderoga Company (1)
615 Crescent Executive Ct Ste 500, Lake
Mary, FL 32746-5007
Tel.: (407) 829-9000
Web Site: https://dixonwriting.com
Writing & Drawing Materials Mfr & Marketer
N.A.I.C.S.: 339940

Subsidiary (Non-US):

Dixon Europe, Ltd. (2)
23 Maxwell Rd, Peterborough, PE2 7JD,
United Kingdom
Tel.: (44) 733371237
Sales Range: $25-49.9 Million
Emp.: 25
Stationary & Office Supplies Whslr
N.A.I.C.S.: 459410

Dixon Stationery Company Ltd. (2)
No 16 Yaoxinzhuang Village Zhangjiawan
Town, Tongzhou, Beijing, 10110-1100,
China
Tel.: (86) 10 61501177
Stationery Product Mfr
N.A.I.C.S.: 322230

Dixon Ticonderoga Inc. (2)
210 Pony Dr Unit 1, Newmarket, L3Y 7B6,
ON, Canada
Tel.: (905) 895-5122
Web Site: http://www.prang.com
Sales Range: $1-9.9 Million
Emp.: 13
Pencils Mfr & Distr
N.A.I.C.S.: 339940
Tim Gomez (CEO)

**Dixon Ticonderoga de Mexico, S.A.
de C.V.** (2)
Autopista Mexico-Queretaro Km 33 5 n 104,
Lecheria, 54940, Tultitlan, Mexico
Tel.: (52) 5558647900
Web Site: http://www.dixon.com.mx
Sales Range: $25-49.9 Million
Emp.: 60
Writing Instruments Mfr
N.A.I.C.S.: 339940
Diego Cespedes Creixell (CEO)

F.I.L.A. Chile Ltda (2)
San Ignacio 300 Bodega C Quilicura,
8710030, Santiago, Chile
Tel.: (56) 2 29289670
Web Site: http://www.giotto.cl
Stationery Product Mfr
N.A.I.C.S.: 322230

FILALYRA GB Ltd. (2)
23 Maxwell Road, Woodston, Peterborough,
PE2 7JD, United Kingdom
Tel.: (44) 1733 371237
Emp.: 5
Stationery Product Mfr
N.A.I.C.S.: 322230
Giovanni Colombo (Mng Dir)

Subsidiary (Domestic):

Pacon Corporation (1)
2525 N Casaloma Dr, Appleton, WI 54912-
7068
Tel.: (920) 830-5050
Web Site: http://www.pacon.com
Paper Products, Educational Aids & Arts &
Crafts Supplies Mfr
N.A.I.C.S.: 322299
Jim Schmitz (Pres & CEO)

Division (Domestic):

Bemiss-Jason (3)
1097 Ehlers Rd, Neenah, WI 54956
Web Site: http://www.bemiss-jason.com
Corrugated Paper Decoration & Display
Products Mfr
N.A.I.C.S.: 322220

Strathmore Artist Papers (3)
1097 Ehlers Rd, Neenah, WI 54956
Tel.: (920) 727-2159

Web Site: http://www.strathmoreartist.com
Fine Paper Product & Envelope Mfr
N.A.I.C.S.: 322120

F.I.L.A. Hispania S.L. (1)
Pol Ind Autopista Sud Passeig Fluvial 4,
08150, Barcelona, Spain (96.77%)
Tel.: (34) 93 573 13 30
Web Site: http://www.filahispania.es
Stationery Product Mfr
N.A.I.C.S.: 322230

FILA Art Products AG (1)
Schwimmbadstrasse 45, CH-5430, Wettingen, Switzerland
Tel.: (41) 564300466
Web Site: https://www.fila.it
Stationery Product Mfr
N.A.I.C.S.: 322230
Francesco Del Prete (CEO)

FILA Hellas S.A. (1)
1/757 Block Anagenniseos Str Evosmos,
PO Box 1069, 57013, Thessaloniki,
Greece (50%)
Tel.: (30) 2310778970
Stationery Product Mfr
N.A.I.C.S.: 322230

**FILA Stationary and Office Equipment
Industry Ltd. Co.** (1)
19 Mayis Mahallesi Esin Sokak - Yazgan Is
Merkezi No 3/ 7, Kadikoy, 34736, Istanbul,
Turkiye (100%)
Tel.: (90) 2163685797
Web Site: https://www.filaturkey.com
Stationery Product Mfr
N.A.I.C.S.: 322230

Fila Iberia S. L. (1)
Av Rabassaires 28 p3, Mollet del Valles,
08100, Barcelona, Spain
Tel.: (34) 935731330
Web Site: http://www.fila.it
Stationery Product Mfr
N.A.I.C.S.: 322230

Fila Polska Sp. z o.o. (1)
ul Radzikowskiego 17, 31-315, Krakow,
Poland
Tel.: (48) 122920806
Web Site: https://filapolska.pl
Artist Paint Distr
N.A.I.C.S.: 424990

Fila SA Pty. Ltd. (1)
Tel.: (27) 871503549
Web Site: https://www.fila.it
Stationery Product Mfr & Distr
N.A.I.C.S.: 322230

**Grupo F.I.L.A.-Dixon, S.A. de
C.V.** (1)
Mexico-Queretaro Highway No 104 Interior
C Lecheria, CP 54940, Tultitlan, Mexico
Tel.: (52) 5558647900
Web Site: https://www.dixon.com.mx
Stationery Product Mfr & Distr
N.A.I.C.S.: 322230

Industria Maimeri S.p.A. (1)
Via G Maimeri 1, Bettolino di Mediglia,
20076, Modigliana, MI, Italy
Tel.: (39) 02906981
Web Site: https://www.maimeri.it
N.A.I.C.S.: 325510

**Johann Froescheis Lyra Bleistift-
Fabrik GmbH & Co. KG** (1)
Willstatterstrasse 54-56, D-90449, Nuremberg, Germany
Tel.: (49) 91168050
Web Site: https://www.fila.it
Emp.: 100
Stationery Product Mfr
N.A.I.C.S.: 322230

Subsidiary (Non-US):

Lyra Asia PTE Ltd. (2)
Singapore Blk 5012 Ang Mo Kio Ave 5
03-05 Techplace II, Singapore, 569876,
Singapore
Tel.: (65) 6482 1198
Web Site: http://www.lyraasia.com
Stationery Product Mfr
N.A.I.C.S.: 322230

Lyra Scandinavia AB (2)
Signalgatan 2, 442 40, Kungalv, Sweden
Tel.: (46) 303 37 37 80

Web Site: http://www.lyra.se
Stationery Product Mfr
N.A.I.C.S.: 322230
Bjorn Cederloo (CEO)

PT. Lyra Akrelux (2)
Tel.: (62) 2145854350
Stationery Product Mfr
N.A.I.C.S.: 322230

Licyn Mercantil Industrial Ltda (1)
Rua Tiguassu 165, Diadema, Sao Paulo,
Brazil
Tel.: (55) 11 4049 2441
Web Site: http://www.utiguti.com.br
Stationery Product Mfr
N.A.I.C.S.: 322230

Omyacolor S.A. (1)
Rue de Marson, 51240, Saint-Germain,
France
Tel.: (33) 3 26 69 26 26
Web Site: http://www.giottofrance.fr
Stationery Product Mfr
N.A.I.C.S.: 322230

F.I.T. INVESTMENT JSC
17 The Giao Street Le Dai Hanh
Ward, Hai Ba Trung District, Hanoi,
Vietnam
Tel.: (84) 4 35430005
Web Site: http://www.fitgroup.com.vn
Investment Services
N.A.I.C.S.: 523999
Nguyet Thi Minh Nguyen (Gen Mgr)

F.P. BOURGAULT INDUSTRIES LTD.
200-5th Ave S St. Brieux,, S0K 3V0,
SK, Canada
Tel.: (800) 878-7714
Web Site: https://www.tillagetools.ca
Year Founded: 1991
Farm Machinery Equipment Mfr &
N.A.I.C.S.: 333111

Subsidiaries:

Herschel Parts, Inc. (1)
1301 N 14th St, Indianola, IA 50125
Web Site: https://www.herschelparts.com
Farm Machinery Equipment Mfr & Distr
N.A.I.C.S.: 333111

F.P.I. FERRARA PROMOZIONE INDUSTRIALE SRL
Via Romolo Gessi 15, 44124, Ferrara, Italy
Tel.: (39) 0532733731
Year Founded: 1946
Sales Range: $125-149.9 Million
Emp.: 300
Mfr of Alloy Wheels for Motor Vehicles & Motorcycles
N.A.I.C.S.: 336390

F.W. NEUKIRCH (GMBH & CO.) KG
Zum Panrepel 37, 28307, Bremen,
Germany
Tel.: (49) 42148940
Web Site: http://www.neukirch.de
Year Founded: 1805
Rev.: $49,987,375
Emp.: 92
Transportation Services
N.A.I.C.S.: 488999

F.W. THORPE PLC
Merse Road, North Moons Moat,
Redditch, B98 9HH, Worcestershire,
United Kingdom
Tel.: (44) 1527583200 UK
Web Site: https://www.fwthorpe.co.uk
Year Founded: 1936
TFW—(LSE)
Rev.: $222,191,607
Assets: $301,942,618
Liabilities: $78,532,609
Net Worth: $223,410,010
Earnings: $30,729,272

Emp.: 900
Fiscal Year-end: 06/30/24
Lighting Products Designer, Mfr &
Distr
N.A.I.C.S.: 335132
Tony Cooper (Dir-Mfg-Thorlux Lighting)

Subsidiaries:

Electrozemper S.A. (1)
Avenida de la Ciencia 3, 13005, Ciudad
Real, Spain
Tel.: (34) 926271837
Web Site: https://www.qzemper.com
Emergency Lighting Mfr
N.A.I.C.S.: 335132

**Famostar Emergency Lighting
B.V.** (1)
Florijnweg 8, 6883 JP, Velp, Netherlands
Tel.: (31) 26 384 6846
Web Site: https://famostar.nl
Electric Lighting Equipment Mfr & Distr
N.A.I.C.S.: 335131

Lightronics B.V. (1)
Spuiweg 19, 5145 NE, Waalwijk, Netherlands
Tel.: (31) 41 656 8600
Web Site: https://www.lightronics.nl
Lighting Equipment Mfr & Distr
N.A.I.C.S.: 335139
Jos Spapens (Mng Dir)

Philip Payne Limited (1)
Thornhill House Thornhill Road, Solihull,
B91 2HB, United Kingdom
Tel.: (44) 121 705 2384
Web Site: https://www.philippayne.co.uk
Sales Range: $25-49.9 Million
Emp.: 18
Illuminated Signs Mfr
N.A.I.C.S.: 339950
David Taylor (Mng Dir)

Portland Lighting Limited (1)
Unit 2 Reedswood Park Road, Regal Drive,
Walsall, WS2 8DQ, United Kingdom
Tel.: (44) 1922 272 1133
Web Site: https://www.portlandlighting.co.uk
Sales Range: $25-49.9 Million
Emp.: 12
Sign Lighting Products Designer & Mfr
N.A.I.C.S.: 335132
David Harrison (Mng Dir)

Solite Europe Ltd (1)
Unit 6 Spark Business Park Hamilton Road,
Stockport, SK1 2AE, Cheshire, United Kingdom
Tel.: (44) 161 320 9999
Web Site: https://www.solite-europe.com
Sales Range: $25-49.9 Million
Emp.: 12
Lighting Equipments & Luminaires Mfr &
Distr
N.A.I.C.S.: 335132
Phil Myers (Mng Dir)

Sugg Lighting Limited (1)
Foundry Lane, Horsham, RH13 5PX, West
Sussex, United Kingdom
Tel.: (44) 1293540111
Web Site: http://www.sugglighting.co.uk
Sales Range: $25-49.9 Million
Emp.: 11
Decorative & Heritage Lightings Mfr
N.A.I.C.S.: 335131

TRT Lighting Limited (1)
Heming Point Claybrook Drive Washford
Ind Est, Redditch, B98 0FH, United Kingdom
Tel.: (44) 152 791 9650
Web Site: https://www.trtlighting.co.uk
Lighting Equipment Mfr & Distr
N.A.I.C.S.: 335139

Thorlux Lighting (1)
Merse Road North Moons Moat, Redditch,
B98 9HH, Worcestershire, United Kingdom
Tel.: (44) 152 758 3200
Web Site: https://thorlux.co.uk
Sales Range: $125-149.9 Million
Emp.: 300
Commercial & Institutional Lighting Products
Mfr
N.A.I.C.S.: 335132

Tony Cooper (Dir-Mfg)

Subsidiary (Domestic):

Compact Lighting Limited (2)
Unit 1 The Nelson Ctr Portfield Rd, Portsmouth, PO3 5SF, Hampshire, United Kingdom
Tel.: (44) 2392652999
Web Site: http://www.thorlux.co.uk
Lighting Systems Mfr & Supplier
N.A.I.C.S.: 335132
Simon Wootton (Mng Dir)

Thorlux Lighting Limited (1)
Unit G6 Riverview Business Park Nangor
Road, Gallanstown, Dublin, D12 FT52, Ireland
Tel.: (353) 1 460 4608
Web Site: https://www.thorlux.ie
Electric Lighting Equipment Mfr & Distr
N.A.I.C.S.: 335131

Zemper France S.A.R.L (1)
189 chemin des Frozieres Charnay les,
71850, Macon, France
Tel.: (33) 385346620
Web Site: https://www.zemper.fr
Emp.: 30
Emergency Light Mfr & Distr
N.A.I.C.S.: 332439

F12..NET, INC.
13555 156 Street NW, Edmonton,
T5V 1R9, AB, Canada
Tel.: (587) 603-5616
Web Site: http://f12.net
Year Founded: 1996
IT Solutions
N.A.I.C.S.: 541519
Alex Webb (CEO)

F2I - FONDI ITALIANI PER LE INFRASTRUTTURE SGR S.P.A.
Via San Prospero 1, 20121, Milan,
Italy
Tel.: (39) 0272179200 IT
Web Site: http://www.f2isgr.it
Year Founded: 2007
Infrastructure Investment & Asset
Management Services
N.A.I.C.S.: 523999
Carlo Michelini (CIO & Gen Mgr)

Subsidiaries:

E.ON Italia S.p.A. (1)
Via Amerigo Vespucci 2, 20124, Milan, Italy
Tel.: (39) 0289448001
Web Site: https://www.eon-italia.com
Emp.: 400
Energy Services Management
N.A.I.C.S.: 221112
Peter Ilyes (CEO)

Subsidiary (Domestic):

**E.ON Climate & Renewables Italia
S.r.l.** (2)
Via Amerigo Vespucci 2, 20124, Milan, Italy
Tel.: (39) 0289448001
Web Site: http://www.eon-italia.com
Eletric Power Generation Services
N.A.I.C.S.: 221118
Roberta Benedetti (Mng Dir)

E.ON Energia S.p.A. (2)
Via dell'Unione 1, 20122, Milan, Italy
Tel.: (39) 0800999777
Web Site: https://www.eon-energia.com
Energy Services
N.A.I.C.S.: 221122
Daniela Leotta (Chief Innovation Officer)

SO.MET. ENERGIA S.r.l. (2)
Sede in Via G Testore 12, 14055, Costigliole d'Asti, Asti, Italy
Tel.: (39) 0141962311
Eletric Power Generation Services
N.A.I.C.S.: 221118

Enel F2i Solare Italia S.p.A. (1)
Via del Brennero 111, 38121, Trento, Italy
Tel.: (39) 04611915800
Photvaltaics & Solar Panels Mfr
N.A.I.C.S.: 221114
Matteo Riccieri (COO)

F2i - Fondi Italiani per le infrastrutture SGR
S.p.A.—(Continued)

Subsidiary (Non-US):

Renovalia Energy, S.A. **(2)**
Calle Maria de Molina 54 9th Floor, 28006,
Madrid, Spain
Tel.: (34) 902 10 42 02
Web Site: http://www.renovalia.com
Renewable Energy Project Development
Services
N.A.I.C.S.: 221118
Jose Manuel Olea Aviles (CFO)

Sorgenia S.p.A **(1)**
Via V Viviani 12, Milan, 20124, Italy
Tel.: (39) 02671941
Web Site: http://www.sorgenia.it
Natural Gas Production Services
N.A.I.C.S.: 213112
Simone Lonostro (Gen Mgr)

F3 URANIUM CORP.
750 - 1620 Dickson Avenue, Kel-
owna, V1Y 9Y2, BC, Canada
Tel.: (778) 484-8030
Web Site: https://f3uranium.com
Year Founded: 2013
FUUF—(OTCQB)
Rev.: $165,838
Assets: $11,982,426
Liabilities: $366,483
Net Worth: $11,615,943
Earnings: ($1,811,570)
Fiscal Year-end: 06/30/19
Uranium Mining
N.A.I.C.S.: 212290
Ross E. McElroy (COO)

F8 ENTERPRISES (HOLDINGS) GROUP LIMITED
Unit 3304 33/F Tower 1 Enterprise
Square 5 38 Wang Chiu Rd Kowloon
Bay, Kowloon, China (Hong Kong)
Tel.: (852) 2 988 8761
Web Site: http://www.f8.com.hk
Year Founded: 2016
8347—(HKG)
Rev.: $46,106,610
Assets: $23,362,534
Liabilities: $11,061,712
Net Worth: $12,300,823
Earnings: ($4,112,785)
Emp.: 28
Fiscal Year-end: 03/31/22
Fuel Product Distr
N.A.I.C.S.: 424720
Chun Man Fong (Founder, Chm & Compliance Officer)

F@N COMMUNICATIONS, INC.
Aoyama Diamond Building 1-1-8
Shibuya, Shibuya-ku, Tokyo, 150-
0002, Japan
Tel.: (81) 357663780
Web Site: https://www.fancs.com
Year Founded: 1999
2461—(TKS)
Rev.: $52,437,640
Assets: $165,750,020
Liabilities: $38,924,100
Net Worth: $126,825,920
Earnings: $8,741,970
Emp.: 440
Fiscal Year-end: 12/31/23
Advertising Services
N.A.I.C.S.: 541810
Yasuyoshi Yanagisawa (Board of Directors & Pres)

FA. ANTON SCHLECKER
Talstrasse 12, D 89579, Ehingen,
Germany
Tel.: (49) 73915840
Web Site: http://www.schlecker.com
Year Founded: 1975
Sales Range: $5-14.9 Billion
Emp.: 52,000

Discount Drug Stores & Internet
Shopping Services
N.A.I.C.S.: 459999
Anton Schlecker (CEO)

FAB FORM INDUSTRIES LTD.
19 1610 Derwent Way, Delta, V3M
6W1, BC, Canada
Tel.: (604) 596-3278
Web Site: https://www.fab-form.com
Year Founded: 1995
FABFF—(OTCIQ)
Rev.: $3,422,733
Assets: $4,428,346
Liabilities: $514,125
Net Worth: $3,914,221
Earnings: $564,277
Fiscal Year-end: 06/30/24
Building Structures Related Services
N.A.I.C.S.: 238190
Joey Fearn (Mgr-Ops)

Subsidiaries:

Fab-Form Industries (1986) Ltd. **(1)**
19 1610 Derwent Way, Delta, V3M 6W1,
BC, Canada
Tel.: (604) 596-3278
Web Site: http://www.fab-form.com
Emp.: 4
Fabricated Concrete Products Mfr
N.A.I.C.S.: 327390

FABASOFT AG
Honauerstrasse 4, 4020, Linz, Austria
Tel.: (43) 7326061620
Web Site: https://www.fabasoft.com
FAA—(DEU)
Rev.: $71,833,616
Assets: $85,607,100
Liabilities: $52,132,647
Net Worth: $33,474,453
Earnings: $9,678,531
Emp.: 386
Fiscal Year-end: 03/31/22
Software Services
N.A.I.C.S.: 541511
Leopold Bauernfeind (Member-Mgmt Bd)

Subsidiaries:

Fabasoft Austria GmbH **(1)**
Honauerstrasse 4, 4020, Linz, Austria
Tel.: (43) 7326061620
Software Development Services
N.A.I.C.S.: 541511

Fabasoft Deutschland GmbH **(1)**
The Squaire 13 Am Flughafen, 60549,
Frankfurt am Main, Germany
Tel.: (49) 6964355150
Software Development Services
N.A.I.C.S.: 541511

KnowledgeFox GmbH **(1)**
Laxenburger Str 2, 1100, Vienna, Austria
Tel.: (43) 158573970
Web Site: https://knowledgefox.net
Software Development Services
N.A.I.C.S.: 541511

Mindbreeze Corporation **(1)**
311 W Monroe St, Chicago, IL 60606
Tel.: (312) 300-6745
Web Site: https://inspire.mindbreeze.com
Cloud Data Migration Services
N.A.I.C.S.: 518210

Mindbreeze GmbH **(1)**
Honauerstrasse 2, 4020, Linz, Austria
Tel.: (43) 732606162620
Web Site: https://inspire.mindbreeze.com
Cloud Data Migration Services
N.A.I.C.S.: 518210

FABBRICA D'ARMI PIETRO BERETTA S.P.A.
Via Pietro Beretta 18, 25063, Gar-
done Val Trompia, Brescia, Italy
Tel.: (39) 03083411
Web Site: http://www.beretta.it
Year Founded: 1526
Sales Range: $350-399.9 Million

Emp.: 2,000
Firearms & Gun Accessories Mfr
N.A.I.C.S.: 332994
Ugo Gussalli Beretta (Pres)

Subsidiaries:

Beretta Holding S.p.A. **(1)**
Via P Beretta 18, 25063, Gardone Val
Trompia, Italy **(100%)**
Tel.: (39) 03083411
Sales Range: $50-74.9 Million
Holding Company
N.A.I.C.S.: 551112

Subsidiary (Domestic):

Benelli Armi S.p.A. **(2)**
Via della Stazione 50, Urbino, 61029, PU,
Italy
Tel.: (39) 07223071
Web Site: http://www.benelli.it
Sales Range: $50-74.9 Million
Emp.: 140
Mfr of Firearms
N.A.I.C.S.: 332994
Mauro Dellacostanza (Mng Dir & Mgr-Sls)

Subsidiary (US):

Benelli U.S.A. Corporation **(3)**
17603 Indian Head Hwy Ste 200, Acco-
keek, MD 20607 **(100%)**
Tel.: (301) 283-6981
Web Site: http://www.benelliusa.com
Sales Range: $25-49.9 Million
Emp.: 66
Mfr & Supplier of Firearms & Accessories
N.A.I.C.S.: 423990
Tom DeBolt (Gen Mgr)

Division (Domestic):

Stoeger Industries **(4)**
17603 Indian Head Hwy, Accokeek, MD
20607
Tel.: (301) 283-6300
Web Site: http://www.stoegerindustries.com
Rev.: $15,000,000
Emp.: 13
Firearms Mfr
N.A.I.C.S.: 332994

Subsidiary (US):

Beretta U.S.A. Corp. **(2)**
17601 Beretta Dr, Accokeek, MD
20607-9515 **(100%)**
Tel.: (301) 283-2191
Web Site: http://www.berettausa.com
Sales Range: $100-124.9 Million
Emp.: 400
Mfr of Firearms
N.A.I.C.S.: 332994
Casey Betzold (Mgr-Intl Sls)

Subsidiary (Non-US):

Sako Ltd. **(2)**
PO Box 149, Riihimaki, 11101,
Finland **(100%)**
Tel.: (358) 108305200
Web Site: http://www.sako.fi
Sales Range: $25-49.9 Million
Emp.: 250
Firearms Mfr
N.A.I.C.S.: 332994
Raimo Karjalainen (Mgr-Factory)

FABEGE AB
Pyramidvagen 7, PO Box 730, SE-
169 56, Solna, Sweden
Tel.: (46) 855514800
Web Site: https://www.fabege.se
FBGGF—(OTCIQ)
Rev.: $390,136,406
Assets: $8,261,361,747
Liabilities: $4,365,556,888
Net Worth: $3,895,804,859
Earnings: ($547,779,309)
Emp.: 226
Fiscal Year-end: 12/31/23
Real Estate Agents & Brokerage Ser-
vices
N.A.I.C.S.: 531210
Fredrik Paulsson (Chm)

Subsidiaries:

Birger Bostad AB **(1)**
Luntmakargatan 18, 11137, Stockholm,
Sweden
Tel.: (46) 86231910
Web Site: https://www.birgerbostad.se
Emp.: 19
Property Development Services
N.A.I.C.S.: 531210

Fastighets AB Tornet **(1)**
Djaknegatan 23, 211 35, Malmo,
Sweden **(82.4%)**
Tel.: (46) 6142680
Web Site: http://www.tornet.se
Sales Range: $75-99.9 Million
Real Estate Properties Purchase & Acquisi-
tion Services
N.A.I.C.S.: 531390

FABER-CASTELL AG
Nurnberger Strasse 2, 90546, Stein,
Germany
Tel.: (49) 91199650   De
Web Site: http://www.faber-
castell.com
Year Founded: 1761
Sales Range: $350-399.9 Million
Emp.: 7,000
Writing Instruments Mfr
N.A.I.C.S.: 339940
Daniel Rogger (Chm)

Subsidiaries:

A.W. Faber-Castell (Aust.) Pty.
Ltd. **(1)**
15 Gibbon Road, PO Box 126, Winston
Hills, Sydney, 2153, NSW, Australia
Tel.: (61) 2 9854 2000
Web Site: http://www.faber-castell.com.au
Emp.: 30
Stationery Product Mfr & Distr
N.A.I.C.S.: 339940
Craig Hopwood (Mgr-Supply Chain)

A.W. Faber-Castell (H.K.) Ltd. **(1)**
Southmark Tower B 11th Floor Flat 1111-
1112 11 Yip Hing Street, Aberdeen, Hong
Kong, China (Hong Kong)
Tel.: (852) 2555 9411
Web Site: http://www.faber-castell.hk
Stationery Product Mfr & Distr
N.A.I.C.S.: 339940

A.W. Faber-Castell (India) Ltd. **(1)**
801 Kamla Executive Park Near Vazir Glass
Works Off, Andheri East, Mumbai, 400059,
India
Tel.: (91) 67729100
Web Site: http://www.faber-castell.in
Stationery Product Mfr & Distr
N.A.I.C.S.: 339940
Anup Rana (Mng Dir)

A.W. Faber-Castell (M) Sdn.
Bhd. **(1)**
No 9 Jalan TP2 Taman Perindustrian Sime
UEP, 47600, Subang Jaya, Selangor, Ma-
laysia
Tel.: (60) 3 8024 6363
Stationery Product Mfr & Distr
N.A.I.C.S.: 339940

A.W. Faber-Castell (NZ) Ltd. **(1)**
Unit 6 23 Springs Road East Tamaki, PO
Box 58574, Botany, 2163, Auckland, New
Zealand
Tel.: (64) 9 274 9155
Web Site: http://www.faber-castell.co.nz
Stationery Product Mfr & Distr
N.A.I.C.S.: 339940

A.W. Faber-Castell (S) Pte. Ltd. **(1)**
18 Tannery Lane 02-01/02 Lian Tong Build-
ing, Singapore, 347780, Singapore
Tel.: (65) 6745 0318
Web Site: http://www.faber-castell.sg
Emp.: 20
Stationery Product Distr
N.A.I.C.S.: 424120
Ivy Ong (Mgr-Sls)

A.W. Faber-Castell Argentina
S.A. **(1)**
Bartolome Hidalgo 1980, Villa Bosch, Bue-
nos Aires, Argentina

Tel.: (54) 11 4751 8888
Web Site: http://www.faber-castell.com.ar
Stationery Product Mfr & Distr
N.A.I.C.S.: 339940

A.W. Faber-Castell Austria Gmbl l (1)
Wienerbergstr 11 Turm A 6 OG Vienna Twin Tower, 1100, Vienna, Austria
Tel.: (43) 1 603 13 54
Stationery Product Distr
N.A.I.C.S.: 424120

A.W. Faber-Castell Colombia Ltda. (1)
Calle 17A No 68-70, Bogota, Colombia
Tel.: (57) 14204084
Stationery Product Distr
N.A.I.C.S.: 424120

A.W. Faber-Castell Ges.m.b.H. (1)
Saag 7, 4090, Engelhartszell an der Donau, Austria
Tel.: (43) 7717 8053 0
Web Site: http://www.faber-castell.at
Stationery Product Mfr
N.A.I.C.S.: 339940

A.W. Faber-Castell Guangzhou Stationery Co., Ltd.
Technological Development Zone 13 Xin Feng Lu Yonghe Economic Zone, 511356, Guangzhou, China
Tel.: (86) 20 8297 7500
Stationery Product Mfr & Distr
N.A.I.C.S.: 339940
Kant Liang (Mgr-Supply Chain)

A.W. Faber-Castell Italia S.r.l. (1)
Via Stromboli 14, 20144, Milan, Italy
Tel.: (39) 02 430 696 01
Web Site: http://www.faber-castell.it
Quality Writing Tool Mfr & Distr
N.A.I.C.S.: 339940

A.W. Faber-Castell Nordic ApS (1)
Tonsbakken 16-18, 2740, Skovlunde, Denmark
Tel.: (45) 70 25 10 77
Web Site: http://www.faber-castell.dk
Stationery Product Mfr & Distr
N.A.I.C.S.: 339940

A.W. Faber-Castell Peruana S.A. (1)
Av La Molina 161 Lima 3 Casilla 1388, Lima, Peru
Tel.: (51) 612 1900
Web Site: http://www.faber-castell.com.pe
Stationery Product Mfr & Distr
N.A.I.C.S.: 339940
Alfonso Orbegoso (Mgr-Quality, R&D & Chemical)

A.W. Faber-Castell S.A. (1)
Rua Cel Jose Augusto de Oliveira Salles 1876, 13570-820, Sao Carlos, Sao Paulo, Brazil
Tel.: (55) 16 3373 1063
Web Site: http://www.faber-castell.com.br
Stationery Product Mfr & Distr
N.A.I.C.S.: 339940

A.W. Faber-Castell S.A.R.L. (1)
Le Centralis 3eme etage 63 av du General Leclerc, 92340, Bourg-la-Reine, France
Tel.: (33) 1 46 15 92 60
Web Site: http://www.faber-castell.fr
Stationery Product Mfr & Distr
N.A.I.C.S.: 339940

A.W. Faber-Castell Schweiz AG (1)
Zurichstr 104, 8134, Adliswil, Switzerland
Tel.: (41) 43 3772050
Web Site: http://www.faber-castell.ch
Stationery Product Mfr
N.A.I.C.S.: 339940

A.W. Faber-Castell USA Inc (1)
9450 Allen Dr, Cleveland, OH 44125
Tel.: (216) 643-4660
Web Site: http://www.fabercastell.com
Sales Range: $25-49.9 Million
Emp.: 60
Pens Producer
N.A.I.C.S.: 339940
Cathy Blankenship (Dir-Sls-Children's Brands)

A.W. Faber-Castell Vertrieb GmbH (1)
Faber-Castell Strasse 17, 95179, Gerolds-

grun, Germany
Tel.: (49) 9288 957 00
Stationery Product Mfr & Distr
N.A.I.C.S.: 339940
Silke Bachmann (Head-Mktg, Art & Graphic)

A.W. Faber-Castell de Mexico SA de CV (1)
Carretera Estatal 431 KM 1 3 4 5 6 7 S Parque Ind B Quintana, 76246, El Marques, Queretaro, Mexico
Tel.: (52) 5 52039535
Web Site: http://www.faber-castell.com.mx
Stationery Product Mfr & Distr
N.A.I.C.S.: 339940
Jimena Freige (Mgr-Mktg)

A.W. Faber-Castell spol. s ro. (1)
U Faberu 1017, 373 41, Hluboka nad Vltavou, Czech Republic
Tel.: (420) 389 822 758
Web Site: http://www.faber-castell.cz
Stationery Product Mfr & Distr
N.A.I.C.S.: 339940
David Sebestik (Gen Mgr)

Faber-Castell Vertrieb GmbH (1)
Nurnberger Strasse 2, 90546, Stein, Germany
Tel.: (49) 91199650
Stationery Product Mfr
N.A.I.C.S.: 339940

Faber-Castell- Chile S.A. (1)
Cordillera 372/Parque Industrial Americo Vespucio Oeste, Santiago, 562, Quilicura, Chile
Tel.: (56) 2 413 35 00
Web Site: http://www.faber-castell.cl
Emp.: 65
Stationery Product Mfr & Distr
N.A.I.C.S.: 339940
Andres Nunez Lathrop (Product Mgr)

LLC Faber-Castell Anadolu (1)
Nagatino i-land Techno Park Pr-kt Andropopova Str 18 bld 7, 115432, Moscow, Russia
Tel.: (7) 4952259634
Stationery Product Distr
N.A.I.C.S.: 424120

PT. Faber-Castell International Indonesia (1)
Jl Raya Narorong Pangkalan 1B Batargebang, Bekasi, 17151, Indonesia
Tel.: (62) 21 825 07 55
Web Site: http://www.faber-castell.co.id
Stationery Product Mfr & Distr
N.A.I.C.S.: 339940
Yohanes Sunardi (Mgr-Factory)

FABINO LIFE SCIENCES LIMITED
B-Wing Shubham Garden Complex Murthal Rd, Sonipat, 131001, Haryana, India
Tel.: (91) 9883900021
Web Site: https://www.fabinolife.com
Year Founded: 2011
543444—(BOM)
Rev.: $417,581
Assets: $307,385
Liabilities: $129,564
Net Worth: $177,821
Earnings: $4,116
Fiscal Year-end: 03/31/21
Pharmaceutical Product Mfr & Distr
N.A.I.C.S.: 325412
Atul Jain (Mng Dir)

FABLED COPPER CORP.
1500 West Georgia Street Suite 480, Vancouver, V6G 2Z6, BC, Canada
Tel.: (604) 684-4535   BC
Web Site:
    https://www.fabledcoppercorp.com
Year Founded: 2016
FBCPF—(OTCIQ)
Rev.: $224,438
Assets: $2,526,207
Liabilities: $546,952
Net Worth: $1,979,256
Earnings: ($2,046,655)

Fiscal Year-end: 12/31/22
Mineral Mining Services
N.A.I.C.S.: 213115
Eric Tsung (CFO)

FABMATICS GMBH
Zur Steinhohe 1, 01109, Dresden, Germany
Tel.: (49) 351652370   De
Web Site: http://www.fabmatics.com
Year Founded: 1991
Emp.: 200
Semiconductor & Equipment Mfr
N.A.I.C.S.: 333248
Andreas Purath (Member-Exec Bd)

Subsidiaries:

Fabmatics GmbH (1)
Manfred-von-Ardenne-Ring 7, 01099, Dresden, Germany
Tel.: (315) 316-1480
Web Site: http://www.fabmatics.com
Emp.: 100
Industrial Machinery Mfr
N.A.I.C.S.: 333248
Heinz Martin Esser (Mng Dir)

FABREL AG
Seestrasse 50, 6052, Hergiswil, Switzerland
Tel.: (41) 41 632 68 58
Holding Company
N.A.I.C.S.: 551112
Hans Muller-Meier (Mng Partner & Pres)

Subsidiaries:

Fabrel Lotos AG (1)
Seestrasse 50, CH 6052, Hergiswil, Switzerland
Tel.: (41) 41 632 68 52
Web Site: http://www.fabrellotos.ch
Sales Range: $25-49.9 Million
Emp.: 100
Privater Equity Firm
N.A.I.C.S.: 523999

Holding (Domestic):

Buss AG (2)
Hohenrainstrasse 10, 4133, Pratteln, Switzerland
Tel.: (41) 618256600
Web Site: http://www.busscorp.com
Sales Range: $50-74.9 Million
Engineering & Machinery for Chemical & Plastic Plant Mfr
N.A.I.C.S.: 333310
Philip Nising (Pres & CEO)

FABRICA DE SCULE RASNOV SA
Str Campului Nr 1, Rasnov, 505400, Brasov, Romania
Tel.: (40) 268257776
Web Site: https://www.fsr.ro
Year Founded: 1919
FACY—(BUC)
Rev.: $1,937,423
Assets: $6,527,203
Liabilities: $925,058
Net Worth: $5,602,145
Earnings: $430,491
Emp.: 37
Fiscal Year-end: 12/31/23
Cutting Tool Mfr
N.A.I.C.S.: 333515

FABRICA DE TECIDOS CARLOS RENAUX S.A.
Av Primeiro de Maio 1283 Centro, CP 10, 88353-901, Brusque, SC, Brazil
Tel.: (55) 47 3351 0922
Web Site: http://www.renaux.com.br
Year Founded: 1892
Apparel Fabric Mfr
N.A.I.C.S.: 315990
Jorge Paulo Krieger Filho (Dir-IR)

FABRIKA BAKARNIH CEVI A.D.
Industrijska zona BB, 19250, Majdanpek, Serbia
Tel.: (381) 30 453 000
Web Site: http://www.fbc-m.com
Year Founded: 1978
FBCM—(BEL)
Sales Range: $75-99.9 Million
Emp.: 317
Copper Tube Mfr
N.A.I.C.S.: 331420
Vladimir Eremeev (Mng Dir)

FABRIKA CEMENTA LUKAVAC D.D.
Lukavackih brigada bb, 75 300, Lukavac, Bosnia & Herzegovina
Tel.: (387) 35552100
Web Site:
    http://www.lukavaccement.ba
Year Founded: 1974
Cement Mfr & Distr
N.A.I.C.S.: 327310

FABRIKA HLEBA I MLEKA A.D.
Naselje Belo Polje bb, 17530, Surdulica, Serbia
Tel.: (381) 17815381
Web Site:
    https://www.hlebsurdulica.com
Year Founded: 1984
FHMS—(BEL)
Rev.: $856,311
Assets: $549,091
Liabilities: $241,202
Net Worth: $307,889
Earnings: ($16,850)
Emp.: 37
Fiscal Year-end: 12/31/21
Bread Product Mfr
N.A.I.C.S.: 311812
Vesna Milovanovic (Exec Dir)

FABRIKA KOZE LAUS A.D.
Karadordeva 386, 78000, Banja Luka, Bosnia & Herzegovina
Tel.: (387) 51212279
Year Founded: 2001
FKLS-R-A—(BANJ)
Sales Range: Less than $1 Million
Emp.: 9
Real Estate Prorperty Leasing Services
N.A.I.C.S.: 531190
Vukan Strbac (Chm-Mgmt Bd)

FABRIKA MAZIVA FAM A.D. KRUSEVAC
Jug Bogdanova 42, 37000, Krusevac, Serbia
Tel.: (381) 37430400
Web Site: https://fam.co.rs
FAMKR—(BEL)
Rev.: $3,802,200
Assets: $8,357,843
Liabilities: $46,716,715
Net Worth: ($38,358,872)
Earnings: ($674,575)
Emp.: 5
Fiscal Year-end: 12/31/23
Lubricant Product Mfr
N.A.I.C.S.: 324191
Igor Jokic (Gen Mgr & Sls Dir)

FABRIKA OPRUGA CACAK A.D.
Vukasina Ignjatovica bb, 32000, Cacak, Serbia
Tel.: (381) 32357164
Web Site: https://www.foc.co.rs
Year Founded: 1979
FOCA—(BEL)
Sales Range: Less than $1 Million
Emp.: 3

Fabrika opruga Cacak A.D.— (Continued)

Spring Product Mfr
N.A.I.C.S.: 332613
Zoran Bogicevic *(Exec Dir)*

FABRIKA STOCNE HRANE JABUKA A.D.
Skrobara Trg Marsala Tita 63,
Pancevo, Serbia
Tel.: (381) 13 2315 212
Web Site: http://www.fsh-jabuka.rs
Year Founded: 1966
Sales Range: $25-49.9 Million
Emp.: 129
Animal Feed Mfr
N.A.I.C.S.: 311119
Goran Radic *(Gen Mgr)*

FABRYKA FARB I LAKIEROW SNIEZKA S.A.
Chlodna 51, 00-867, Warsaw, Maso-
vian, Poland
Tel.: (48) 146811111
Web Site: https://sniezkagroup.com
Year Founded: 1984
SKA—(WAR)
Rev.: $217,930,132
Assets: $208,024,898
Liabilities: $112,967,988
Net Worth: $95,056,910
Earnings: $21,209,604
Emp.: 1,140
Fiscal Year-end: 12/31/23
Paints & Varnishes Mfr
N.A.I.C.S.: 325510
Jaroslaw Wojdyla *(Sec-Supervisory Board)*

Subsidiaries:

Hadrokor sp. z o.o. **(1)**
ul Smocza 19, 87-800, Wloclawek, Poland
Tel.: (48) 544127600
Web Site: http://www.hadrokor.com.pl
Paint & Varnish Mfr
N.A.I.C.S.: 325510

Powder Paints and Varnishes Plant
Ltd. **(1)**
ul Lesna 5, 77-100, Bytow, Pomeranian,
Poland
Tel.: (48) 544127600
Paint & Varnish Mfr
N.A.I.C.S.: 325510

FABRYKA WAGONOW GNIEWCZYNA SA
Gniewczyna 591, 37-203,
Gniewczyna Lancucka, Poland
Tel.: (48) 166488364
Web Site: http://www.gniewczyna.pl
Year Founded: 1982
Sales Range: $10-24.9 Million
Emp.: 750
Railway Repair Services
N.A.I.C.S.: 811210
Wiktor Baj *(Dir-Technical)*

FABRYKI MEBLI FORTE S.A.
Biala 1, 07-300, Ostrow Mazowiecka,
Poland
Tel.: (48) 296442222   PL
Web Site: https://www.forte.com.pl
Year Founded: 1992
FTE—(WAR)
Rev.: $357,747,935
Assets: $387,554,669
Liabilities: $173,257,048
Net Worth: $214,297,621
Earnings: $29,898,401
Emp.: 3,000
Fiscal Year-end: 12/31/21
Furniture Mfr & Distr
N.A.I.C.S.: 337211
Maciej Formanowicz *(Founder, CEO & Member-Mgmt Bd)*

Subsidiaries:

FORTE Furniture Ltd. **(1)**
108 Courtyard Radway Green Business
Park, Crewe, CW2 5PR, United
Kingdom **(100%)**
Tel.: (44) 8453510355
Web Site: http://www.fortefurniture.co.uk
Sales Range: $50-74.9 Million
Emp.: 1
Trade Activities
N.A.I.C.S.: 425120

FORTE Iberia **(1)**
Avenida De Aragon, 46004, Valencia,
Spain **(100%)**
Tel.: (34) 963818970
Web Site: http://www.forteiberia.es
Sales Range: $50-74.9 Million
Emp.: 2
Trade Activities
N.A.I.C.S.: 425120

FORTE Mobilier SARL **(1)**
88 Boulevard de la Villette, 75019, Paris,
France **(100%)**
Tel.: (33) 142402040
Trade Activities
N.A.I.C.S.: 425120

FORTE RUS Ltd. **(1)**
Dobrosielskaja 4-a, 600016, Vladimir, Rus-
sia
Tel.: (7) 0922211701
Furniture
N.A.I.C.S.: 423210

FORTE SK GmbH **(1)**
Sportova 2757, 024 01, Nove Mesto,
Slovakia **(100%)**
Tel.: (421) 414220488
Trade Activities
N.A.I.C.S.: 425120

FORTE UKRAINE, Ltd. **(1)**
Patrisa Lumumby 95, 84-500, Artiomowsk,
Ukraine **(100%)**
Tel.: (380) 627432052
Web Site: http://www.forte.com.pl
Furniture
N.A.I.C.S.: 423210

Meble Polonia, Ltd. **(1)**
Bruckner S 25-43, 51-411, Wroclaw,
Poland **(100%)**
Tel.: (48) 713255078
Web Site: http://www.meblepolonia.pl
Furniture & Interior Design Sales
N.A.I.C.S.: 423210

Mobelvertrieb FORTE GmbH **(1)**
Ketteler 5, D-59929, Brilon,
Germany **(100%)**
Tel.: (49) 296196000
Web Site: http://www.moebel-forte.de
Furniture Trade
N.A.I.C.S.: 423210

FABRYKI SPRZETU I NARZEDZI GORNICZYCH GRUPA KAPITALOWA FASING S.A.
ul Modelarska 11, 40-142, Katowice,
Poland
Tel.: (48) 327350000
Web Site: https://fasing.pl
Year Founded: 1913
FSG—(WAR)
Rev.: $74,487,042
Assets: $80,689,786
Liabilities: $35,880,589
Net Worth: $44,809,197
Earnings: $4,318,598
Fiscal Year-end: 12/31/23
Ornamental & Architectural Metal
Work Manufacturing
N.A.I.C.S.: 332323
Zdzislaw Bik *(Pres & Gen Dir)*

FACB INDUSTRIES INCORPO-RATED BERHAD
Etiqa Twins Tower 1 Level 13 11
Jalan Pinang, 50450, Kuala Lumpur,
Malaysia
Tel.: (60) 321620060

Web Site: https://www.facbi.com
Year Founded: 1979
FACBIND—(KLS)
Rev.: $9,852,434
Assets: $51,095,535
Liabilities: $2,260,961
Net Worth: $48,834,574
Earnings: $1,752,167
Fiscal Year-end: 06/30/23
Stainless & Carbon Steel Mfr
N.A.I.C.S.: 331110
Lip Keong Chen *(Pres)*

Subsidiaries:

Dream Products Sdn. Bhd. **(1)**
Plo 97 Tanjung Agas Industrial Estate,
84007, Muar, Johor, Malaysia
Tel.: (60) 69512900
Web Site: http://www.dreamland.com.my
Sales Range: $25-49.9 Million
Emp.: 30
Bed & Pillow Mfr
N.A.I.C.S.: 337910
Winnie Suah *(Mgr)*

Dreamland Corporation (Malaysia)
Sdn. Bhd. **(1)**
56 Kompleks Selayang Taman Perindus-
trian Selayang Baru Batu 8 1/2, Jalan Ipoh,
68100, Batu Caves, Selangor, Malaysia
Tel.: (60) 361380499
Web Site: https://www.dreamland.com.my
Sales Range: $50-74.9 Million
Emp.: 100
Furniture & Mattresses Whslr
N.A.I.C.S.: 423210

Kanzen Management Sdn. Bhd. **(1)**
Lot 4 Persiaran Perusahaan Section 23, PO
Box 7272, 40300, Shah Alam, Selangor,
Malaysia
Tel.: (60) 355421400
Web Site: http://www.kanzen-tedsu.com
Sales Range: $75-99.9 Million
Emp.: 320
Management & Secretarial Services
N.A.I.C.S.: 115116

FACC AG
Fischerstrasse 9, A-4910, Ried im
Innkreis, Austria
Tel.: (43) 596160
Web Site: https://www.facc.com
FACC—(VIE)
Rev.: $655,058,278
Assets: $705,833,153
Liabilities: $486,233,542
Net Worth: $219,599,611
Earnings: ($1,061,947)
Emp.: 2,919
Fiscal Year-end: 12/31/22
Aircraft Composite Components Mfr
N.A.I.C.S.: 336413
Robert Machtlinger *(Chm-Mgmt Bd & CEO)*

Subsidiaries:

CoLT Pruf und Test GmbH **(1)**
Breitenaich 52, St Martin im Innkreis, 4973,
Ried im Innkreis, Austria
Tel.: (43) 596163000
Web Site: https://www.colt-lab.at
Material Testing Services
N.A.I.C.S.: 541380

FACEDRIVE, INC.
44 East Beaver Creek Rd, Richmond
Hill, L4B 1G6, ON, Canada
Tel.: (289) 452-0164
Web Site: http://www.facedrive.com
Z6N—(DEU)
Rev.: $13,390,123
Assets: $19,408,204
Liabilities: $17,783,000
Net Worth: $1,625,204
Earnings: $691,720
Fiscal Year-end: 12/31/23
Car Rental Services
N.A.I.C.S.: 532111
Sayan Navaratnam *(Chm & CEO)*

FACEPHI BIOMETRIA SA
Perfect Avenue Fountain Palace 6,
3003, Alicante, Spain
Tel.: (34) 965108008
Web Site: https://facephi.com
Year Founded: 2012
ALPHI—(EUR)
Rev.: $27,765,740
Assets: $50,459,776
Liabilities: $28,334,764
Net Worth: $22,125,012
Earnings: ($4,757,199)
Emp.: 264
Fiscal Year-end: 12/31/23
Software Publisher
N.A.I.C.S.: 513210
Javier Mira *(Founder, Chm, Pres & CEO)*

Subsidiaries:

FacePhi APAC, Ltd. **(1)**
511 9-22 Pangyo-ro 255, Bundang, Seong-
nam, 13486, Gyeonggi-do, Korea (South)
Tel.: (82) 316052005
Computer Software Development Services
N.A.I.C.S.: 541511

FACIL CORPORATE BVBA
Geleenlaan 20, 3600, Genk, Belgium
Tel.: (32) 89 41 04 50   BE
Web Site: http://www.facil.be
Holding Company; Fastening Tech-
nology Solutions
N.A.I.C.S.: 551112
Rene Achten *(CEO)*

Subsidiaries:

Facil Europe BVBA **(1)**
Geleenlaan 20, 3600, Genk, Belgium
Tel.: (32) 89 41 04 50
Web Site: http://www.facil.be
Emp.: 100
Fastener Technology Solutions for Automo-
tive Industry
N.A.I.C.S.: 332722
Paul Rijs *(Mng Dir)*

Subsidiary (US):

Facil North America, Inc. **(2)**
2242 Pinnacle Pkwy #100, Twinsburg, OH
44087
Tel.: (330) 487-2500
Mfr & Distr of Automotive Fastening Prod-
ucts
N.A.I.C.S.: 332722
Frank Vaes *(Pres)*

FACILITIES BY ADF PLC
Ground floor 31 Oldfield road Bocam
Park, Bridgend, CF35 5LJ, United
Kingdom
Tel.: (44) 1656725560   UK
Web Site:
https://www.facilitiesbyadf.com
Year Founded: 1992
ADF—(AIM)
Rev.: $39,654,128
Assets: $37,303,711
Liabilities: $2,573,845
Net Worth: $34,729,866
Earnings: $5,821,762
Emp.: 203
Fiscal Year-end: 12/31/22
Commercial Vehicle Leasing Services
N.A.I.C.S.: 532490

Subsidiaries:

CAD Services Ltd. **(1)**
7 Lords Court Cricketers Way, Basildon,
SS13 1SS, United Kingdom
Tel.: (44) 1268242800
Web Site: https://www.cadservices.com
Computer Aided Design Drafting Services
N.A.I.C.S.: 541340

Location One Ltd. **(1)**
Unit 7 New Harbours 75 River Road, Bark-
ing, IG11 0DR, United Kingdom
Tel.: (44) 3330153990
Web Site: https://www.locationone.co.uk

Media Production Services
N.A.I.C.S.: 512110

FACOR ALLOYS LIMITED

Shreeramnagar, Garividi, Vizianaga-
ram, 535101, Andhra Pradesh, India
Tel.: (91) 8952282029   In
Web Site: https://www.facoralloys.in
Year Founded: 2004
532656—(BOM)
Rev.: $39,100,905
Assets: $29,673,928
Liabilities: $8,176,021
Net Worth: $21,497,908
Earnings: $834,614
Emp.: 393
Fiscal Year-end: 03/31/23
Ferro Chrome & Alloys Mfr
N.A.I.C.S.: 331110
M. S. S. Sarma (CEO)

FACT CORPORATION

5614E Burbank Road SE, Calgary,
T2H 1Z4, AB, Canada
Tel.: (403) 693-8004   CO
Web Site: http://www.factfoods.com
Year Founded: 1982
Sales Range: $1-9.9 Million
Emp.: 3
Holding Company; Bake Mixes Whslr
N.A.I.C.S.: 551112
Jacqueline R. Danforth (Pres, CEO &
Treas)

FACT ENTERPRISE LIMITED

C/208 Crystal Plaza Opp Infinity Mall
New Link Road, Andheri - West,
Mumbai, 400 053, Maharashtra, India
Tel.: (91) 22 26732223
Web Site:
   http://www.factmediahouse.com
Sales Range: Less than $1 Million
Real Estate Development Services
N.A.I.C.S.: 531390
Rajiv Rajaram Kashyap (Chm & Mng
Dir)

FACT, INC.

Xinkaicun group 5 Weizigouzhen
Jiutai, Changchun, 130519, Jilin,
China
Tel.: (86) 852 8170 3801   NV
Year Founded: 2017
Assets: $12,237
Liabilities: $664,482
Net Worth: ($652,245)
Earnings: ($1,260,691)
Fiscal Year-end: 01/31/21
Air Infiltration Valve Mfr & Distr
N.A.I.C.S.: 332912
Patricia Trompeter (CEO & CFO)

FACTOR FORMS LTD

8411 McIntyre Road, Edmonton, T6E
6G3, AB, Canada
Tel.: (780) 468-1111
Web Site:
   https://www.factorforms.com
Year Founded: 1971
Rev.: $14,335,392
Emp.: 103
Printing Services
N.A.I.C.S.: 323111
Bryn Dergousoff (Pres)

FACTOR GAS LIQUIDS INC.

840 7th Avenue SW Suite 1260, Cal-
gary, T2P 3G2, AB, Canada
Tel.: (403) 266-8778
Web Site: http://www.factorgas.com
Year Founded: 1995
Sales Range: $10-24.9 Million
Emp.: 10
Liquefied Petroleum Gas Distr
N.A.I.C.S.: 221210
David shaw (Mgr-Bus Dev)

FACTORY CRO BV

Prof Bronkhorstlaan 10 bld 54, 3723
MB, Bilthoven, Netherlands
Tel.: (31) 302292727
Web Site: http://www.factory-cro.com
Year Founded: 1994
Medical Devices & in Vitro Diagnos-
tics Contract Research Services
N.A.I.C.S.: 541714
Dirk Meijer (CEO & Dir-Medical)

Subsidiaries:

Boston Biomedical Associates
LLC   (1)
386 W Main St Ste 7, Northborough, MA
01532
Tel.: (508) 351-8632
Web Site: http://www.boston-
  biomedical.com
Sales Range: $1-9.9 Million
Emp.: 30
Biomedical Regulatory Services
N.A.I.C.S.: 813990
Lauren S. Baker (Pres & CEO)

FAD A.D. GORNJI MILANOVAC

Kneza Aleksandra 210, 32 300,
Gornji Milanovac, Serbia
Tel.: (381) 32 725 255
Web Site: http://www.fad.rs
Emp.: 1,500
Motor Vehicle Steering & Suspension
Component Mfr
N.A.I.C.S.: 336330
Danijela Mojsovski (Mgr-Trade)

FADAP A.D.

Industrijska zona bb, 22408, Vrdnik,
Serbia
Tel.: (381) 22466014
Web Site: http://www.fadap.co.rs
Year Founded: 1989
FADP—(BEL)
Sales Range: Less than $1 Million
Emp.: 39
Farm Machinery Mfr
N.A.I.C.S.: 333111
Nebojsa Veselinovic (Exec Dir)

FADE GIDA YATIRIM SANAYI TICARET A.S.

Cumhuriyet Mah 136/2 Sk No 10/A,
Menemen, 35660, Izmir, Turkiye
Tel.: (90) 2328462271
Web Site: https://www.fadefood.com
Year Founded: 1995
FADE—(IST)
Rev.: $4,102,746
Assets: $17,658,312
Liabilities: $4,581,074
Net Worth: $13,077,238
Earnings: $5,459,378
Fiscal Year-end: 12/31/22
Dehydrated Food Mfr
N.A.I.C.S.: 311423
Haci Ali Demir (Chm)

FAE TECHNOLOGY S.P.A.

Via Cesare Battisti 136, 24025, Gaz-
zaniga, Bergamo, Italy
Tel.: (39) 035738130
Web Site: https://fae.technology
Year Founded: 1990
FAE—(ITA)
Electronic Components Mfr
N.A.I.C.S.: 334419

FAES FARMA, S.A.

Avada Autonomia 10, 48940, Leioa,
Vizcaya, Spain
Tel.: (34) 944818300
Web Site: https://www.faesfarma.com
Year Founded: 1933
FAE—(BAR)
Rev.: $498,032,896
Assets: $856,638,702
Liabilities: $124,384,590

Net Worth: $732,254,112
Earnings: $101,217,574
Emp.: 1,761
Fiscal Year-end: 12/31/23
Pharmaceutical Drug Developer, Mfr
& Sales
N.A.I.C.S.: 325412

Subsidiaries:

Biotecnet I Mas D S.A.   (1)
Cl Alpedrete 24, 28045, Madrid, Spain
Tel.: (34) 914680800
Medical Laboratories
N.A.I.C.S.: 621511
Francisco Quintailla (Mng Dir)

Colpharma, S.R.L.   (1)
Via Am Vicenzi 19 / A, 43124, Parma, Italy
Tel.: (39) 0521272544
Web Site: https://www.colpharma.com
Pharmaceuticals Whslr
N.A.I.C.S.: 424210

Faes Farma Del Ecuador SA   (1)
Av Shyris 860, Quito, Ecuador
Tel.: (593) 900924734
Pharmaceutical Product Mfr & Distr
N.A.I.C.S.: 325412

Hispana Dos S.A.   (1)
Calle Serrano 88, Madrid, Spain
Tel.: (34) 913199800
Web Site: http://www.faes.es
Investment Advice
N.A.I.C.S.: 523940

Iquinosa Farma S.A.   (1)
Cl Alpedrete 24, 28045, Madrid, Spain
Tel.: (34) 914680800
Web Site: http://www.faes.es
Sales Range: $25-49.9 Million
Emp.: 40
Pharmaceutical Preparation Mfr
N.A.I.C.S.: 325412
Francisco Quintailla (Mng Dir)

Laboratorios Veris S.A.   (1)
Via de los Poblados 3, 28045, Madrid,
Spain
Tel.: (34) 914680800
Medical Laboratories
N.A.I.C.S.: 621511

Laboratorios Vitoria S.A.   (1)
Rua Elias Garcia, 26 Venda Nova, 2700,
Amadora, Portugal   (99.83%)
Tel.: (351) 14745333
Web Site: http://www.faes.es
Pharmaceutical Preparation Mfr
N.A.I.C.S.: 325412

Lazlo International SA   (1)
Cl Alpedrete 24, 28045, Madrid, Spain
Tel.: (34) 914680800
Sales Range: $25-49.9 Million
Emp.: 80
Pharmaceutical Preparation Mfr
N.A.I.C.S.: 325412

Olve Farmaceutica Limitada   (1)
R Elias Garcia 28, Amadora,
Portugal   (100%)
Tel.: (351) 214758300
Web Site: http://www.labvictory.pt
Sales Range: $25-49.9 Million
Emp.: 100
Pharmaceutical Preparation Mfr
N.A.I.C.S.: 325412

Veris Farmaceutica Limitada   (1)
R Elias Garcia 28, Amadora,
Portugal   (100%)
Tel.: (351) 214763667
Biological Product (except Diagnostic) Mfr
N.A.I.C.S.: 325414

FAGE DAIRY INDUSTRY S.A.

35 Hermou St, GR 144 52, Metamor-
fosis, Athens, Greece
Tel.: (30) 2102892555   GR
Web Site: http://www.fage.gr
Year Founded: 1989
Sales Range: $500-549.9 Million
Emp.: 1,000
Dairy Products Mfr
N.A.I.C.S.: 311514
John Filippou (Pres)

Subsidiaries:

FAGE Italia S.r.l.   (1)
L.Dvimci No-97, 20090, Trezzano sul
Naviglio, Milan, Italy
Tel.: (39) 0248610311
Web Site: http://www.italia.fage.eu
Sales Range: $50-74.9 Million
Emp.: 10
Dairy Products Distr
N.A.I.C.S.: 424430
Germana Trovato (Key Acct Mgr)

FAGE USA Holdings, Inc.   (1)
1 Opportunity Dr, Johnstown, NY 12095-
3349
Tel.: (518) 762-5912
Dairy Product Mfr & Distr
N.A.I.C.S.: 311514

Subsidiary (Domestic):

FAGE USA Dairy Industry, Inc.   (2)
1 Opportunity Dr Johnstown Industrial Park,
Johnstown, NY 12095
Tel.: (866) 962-5912
Web Site: http://www.fageusa.com
Yoghurt Mfr & Distr
N.A.I.C.S.: 311514

FAGERDALA WORLD FOAMS AB

Odelbergsvagen 11, Gustavsberg,
13482, Sweden
Tel.: (46) 857013200
Sales Range: $350-399.9 Million
Emp.: 20
Offices of Holding Companies
N.A.I.C.S.: 551112
Leif Sparrremo (CFO)

FAGERHULT GROUP AB

Avagen 1, SE-56692, Habo, Sweden
Tel.: (46) 84029019   SE
Web Site:
  https://www.fagerhultgroup.com
FAG—(OMX)
Rev.: $774,546,442
Assets: $1,248,756,638
Liabilities: $604,156,715
Net Worth: $644,599,923
Earnings: $53,977,353
Emp.: 3,812
Fiscal Year-end: 12/31/22
Holding Company; Residential, Com-
mercial & Industrial Lighting Fixture
Mfr & Distr
N.A.I.C.S.: 551112
Frank Augustsson (Mng Dir-Reg &
Head-Bus Area-Premium)

Subsidiaries:

9850-333 Canada Inc.   (1)
Eclairage Delux 1975 Frank-Carrel Ste 205,
Quebec, G1N 2E6, QC, Canada
Tel.: (418) 658-6558
Lighting Product Mfr & Distr
N.A.I.C.S.: 335132

Arlight Aydinlatma A.S.   (1)
Saray Mahallesi 205 Sok No 4/1 Kahra-
mankazan, 06980, Ankara, Turkiye
Tel.: (90) 3128154661
Web Site: https://www.arlight.net
Lighting Product Mfr
N.A.I.C.S.: 335139
Saltuk Erdemli (Mng Dir)

Atelje Lyktan AB   (1)
Fyrvaktaregatan 7, Ahus, 296 35, Kristian-
stad, Sweden
Tel.: (46) 44289800
Web Site: https://www.ateljelyktan.se
Lighting System Mfr
N.A.I.C.S.: 335132
Richard Wegele (Mgr-Norway)

Commtech Commissioning Services
S.A.   (1)
13 Stockholm Street Pol Ind Europolis,
28230, Las Rozas, Spain
Tel.: (34) 916378179
Web Site: http://www.commgt.com
Environmental Commissioning Services

Fagerhult Group AB—(Continued)

N.A.I.C.S.: 541620

Designplan Lighting Ltd (1)
16 Kimpton Park Way, Sutton, SM3 9QS,
Surrey, United Kingdom
Tel.: (44) 2082542020
Web Site: https://www.designplan.co.uk
Emp.: 140
Lighting System Mfr
N.A.I.C.S.: 335132

Eagle Lighting (Australia) Pty Ltd (1)
17-19 Jets Court, Melbourne, 3045, VIC,
Australia
Tel.: (61) 393447444
Web Site: https://www.eaglelighting.com.au
Lighting System Mfr & Distr
N.A.I.C.S.: 335132

Elenco Lighting AB (1)
Almenasvagen 18, 506 32, Boras, Sweden
Tel.: (46) 33 7221500
Lighting System Mfr & Distr
N.A.I.C.S.: 335132

Fagerhult (NZ) Ltd (1)
Level 1 18A Neilpark Drive, East Tamaki,
Auckland, 2013, New Zealand
Tel.: (64) 21 509 248
Web Site: http://www.fagerhult.co.nz
Lighting System Mfr & Distr
N.A.I.C.S.: 335132

Fagerhult AS (1)
Herstedvang 14, 2620, Albertslund, Den-
mark
Tel.: (45) 43553700
Web Site: http://www.fagerhult.com
Lighting System Distr
N.A.I.C.S.: 423220

Fagerhult BV (1)
Lichtschip 19, 3991 CP, Houten, Nether-
lands
Tel.: (31) 306889900
Web Site: https://www.fagerhult.com
Lighting System Distr
N.A.I.C.S.: 423220
Max Barenbrug *(Mng Dir)*

Fagerhult Belysning AS (1)
Strandveien 30, 1366, Lysaker, Norway
Tel.: (47) 22065500
Web Site: https://www.fagerhult.com
Lighting System Distr
N.A.I.C.S.: 423220

Fagerhult France (1)
105 avenue Jean Jaures Batiment B5,
69600, Oullins, France
Tel.: (33) 437226410
Web Site: https://www.fagerhult.com
Lighting System Distr
N.A.I.C.S.: 423220

Fagerhult Lighting Ltd (1)
33-34 Dolben Street, London, SE1 0UQ,
United Kingdom
Tel.: (44) 2074034123
Web Site: https://www.fagerhult.com
Lighting System Mfr & Distr
N.A.I.C.S.: 335132

Fagerhult Lighting Ltd (1)
Unit F1 Calmount Park, Ballymount, Dublin,
D12 PN81, Ireland
Tel.: (353) 314260200
Web Site: https://www.fagerhult.com
Lighting System Distr
N.A.I.C.S.: 335132

**Fagerhult Lighting System (Suzhou)
Co. Ltd.** (1)
No 11 in Genway 12th Workshop 10 Gang-
tian Road, Suzhou Industrial Park, Suzhou,
215021, China
Tel.: (86) 52162838676
Lighting Product Mfr
N.A.I.C.S.: 335139
Emanuel Kantis *(Mng Dir)*

Fagerhult OU (1)
Artelli 10C, EE-10621, Tallinn, Estonia
Tel.: (372) 6507901
Web Site: http://www.fagerhult.com
Lighting System Distr
N.A.I.C.S.: 423220

Fagerhult OY (1)

Mannerheimintie 113, 00280, Helsinki, Fin-
land
Tel.: (358) 97771580
Web Site: https://www.fagerhult.com
Lighting System Distr
N.A.I.C.S.: 423220

Fagerhult S.L. (1)
C/ Bravo Murillo 101 planta 10, 28020, Ma-
drid, Spain
Tel.: (34) 916407246
Lighting System Distr
N.A.I.C.S.: 423220
Javier Marti Blanc *(Project Mgr)*

Fagerhult Sp.z.o.o (1)
Ul Komitetu Obrony Robotnikow 48, 02-146,
Warsaw, Poland
Tel.: (48) 227491250
Web Site: https://www.fagerhult.com
Lighting System Distr
N.A.I.C.S.: 423220

Fagerhult Spb (1)
Children's Lane 5 Office 208, Saint Peters-
burg, Russia
Tel.: (7) 8127110148
Web Site: http://www.fagerhult.com
Lighting System Distr
N.A.I.C.S.: 423220
Dinara Bektashova *(Mng Dir)*

Fagerhult s.r.o. (1)
Tomasikova 23, 821 01, Bratislava, Slovakia
Tel.: (421) 903661566
Web Site: https://www.fagerhult.com
Lighting System Mfr & Distr
N.A.I.C.S.: 335132
Peter Meinl *(CEO)*

Fagerhults Belysning AB (1)
Avagen 1, 566 80, Habo, Sweden
Tel.: (46) 3 610 8500
Web Site: http://www.fagerhult.com
Residential, Commercial & Industrial Light-
ing Fixture Mfr & Distr
N.A.I.C.S.: 335131

Subsidiary (Domestic):

Fagerhult Retail AB (2)
Rinnavagen 12, Bollebygd, 51733, Sweden
Tel.: (46) 3323 6600
Web Site: http://www.fagerhult.se
Commercial Lighting Fixture Mfr & Distr
N.A.I.C.S.: 335132

Fagerhults Belysning Sverige AB (2)
Avagen 1, 566 80, Habo, Sweden
Tel.: (46) 36108500
Web Site: https://www.fagerhult.com
Indoor & Outdoor Residential Light Fixture
Mfr & Distr
N.A.I.C.S.: 335131

Subsidiary (Non-US):

I-Valo Oy (2)
Tehtaantie 3 B, 14500, Iittala,
Finland
Tel.: (358) 105013000 **(100%)**
Web Site: https://i-valo.com
Sales Range: $10-24.9 Million
Industrial Lighting Equipment Mfr
N.A.I.C.S.: 335132
Meike Virtanen Kinnunen *(Mgr-Mktg)*

LED Linear GmbH (1)
Dr-alfred-herrhausen-allee 20, 47228, Duis-
burg, Germany
Tel.: (49) 206594322100
Web Site: https://www.led-linear.de
Lighting Product Mfr
N.A.I.C.S.: 335139
Michael Kramer *(CEO)*

LED Linear UK Ltd. (1)
8 Century Court Tolpits Lane, Watford,
WD18 9RS, Hertfordshire, United Kingdom
Tel.: (44) 1923618300
Lighting Product Mfr
N.A.I.C.S.: 335139
Stuart Knox *(Mng Dir)*

LED Linear USA Inc. (1)
2186 Liberty Dr, Niagara Falls, NY 14304
Tel.: (716) 283-4400
Web Site: https://www.ledlinearusa.com
Lighting Product Mfr
N.A.I.C.S.: 335139
Daniel Montante *(Dir-Fin)*

LTS Licht & Leuchten GmbH (1)
Waldesch 24, 88069, Tettnang, Germany
Tel.: (49) 754293070
Web Site: https://www.lts-light.com
Emp.: 150
Lighting System Mfr
N.A.I.C.S.: 335132

**Lighting Innovations Africa (Pty)
Ltd.** (1)
14A Kramer Road, Kramerville, Johannes-
burg, 2090, South Africa
Tel.: (27) 11 444 1168
Web Site:
     https://www.lightinginnovations.co.za
Emp.: 250
Lighting Equipment Mfr
N.A.I.C.S.: 335139
Melvin Chetty *(Ops Mgr)*

**Shanghai iGuzzini Trading Co.,
Ltd.,** (1)
No 2758 Huan Cheng West Road, Fengx-
ian Industrial Park, Shanghai, 201401,
China
Tel.: (86) 2163411199
Lighting Product Mfr & Distr
N.A.I.C.S.: 335132

Veko Lightsystems GmbH (1)
Philosophenweg 31, 47051, Duisburg,
47051, Germany
Tel.: (49) 20393319347
Web Site: https://www.veko.com
Lighting Product Mfr
N.A.I.C.S.: 335139
Thomas Lehmkuhl *(Sls Mgr)*

**Veko Lightsystems International
B.V.** (1)
Witte Paal 3, 1742 NL, Schagen, Nether-
lands
Tel.: (31) 224273273
Web Site: https://www.veko.com
Emp.: 140
Lighting Product Mfr
N.A.I.C.S.: 335139
Menno Veldboer *(Comml Dir)*

Veko Lightsystems S.L. (1)
Calle Ruisenor 39, Torrelodones, 28250,
Madrid, Spain
Tel.: (34) 910133645
Lighting Product Mfr
N.A.I.C.S.: 335139

WE-EF Helvetica SA (1)
Chemin Malombre 5, 1206, Geneva, Swit-
zerland
Tel.: (41) 227524994
Lighting Product Mfr
N.A.I.C.S.: 335139

WE-EF Leuchten GmbH (1)
Topinger Strasse 16, 29646, Bispingen,
Germany
Tel.: (49) 51949090
Web Site: https://we-ef.com
Lighting Product Mfr
N.A.I.C.S.: 335139
Thomas Mueller *(Head-Sls)*

WE-EF Lighting Co. Ltd. (1)
57 Moo 5 Kingkaew Rd, Bangplee, Samut
Prakan, Thailand
Tel.: (66) 27389610
Lighting Product Mfr
N.A.I.C.S.: 335139

WE-EF Lighting Ltd. (1)
Suite 2c East Bridgford Business Park
Kneeton Road, East Bridgford, Nottingham,
NG13 8PJ, United Kingdom
Tel.: (44) 8448805346
Lighting Product Mfr
N.A.I.C.S.: 335139
Katy Smith *(Mgr-Lighting Design & Mktg)*

WE-EF Lighting Pty. Ltd. (1)
6/13 Downard Street, Braeside, 3195, VIC,
Australia
Tel.: (61) 385870444
Lighting Product Mfr
N.A.I.C.S.: 335139

WE-EF Lighting USA LLC (1)
410-D Keystone Dr, Warrendale, PA 15086
Tel.: (724) 742-0030
Web Site: https://www.we-ef.com
Lighting Product Mfr

N.A.I.C.S.: 335139
Kevin Rose *(VP-Sls & Mktg)*

Waco N.V. (1)
Hundelgemsesteenweg 80, Baaigem, 9890,
Gavere, Belgium
Tel.: (32) 0 362 44 04
Web Site: http://www.waco.be
Emp.: 10
Lighting System Mfr & Distr
N.A.I.C.S.: 335132

Whitecroft Lighting Ltd (1)
Burlington Street, Ashton under Lyne, OL7
0AX, Lancashire, United Kingdom
Tel.: (44) 1613306811
Web Site: https://www.whitecroftlighting.com
Lighting System Mfr & Distr
N.A.I.C.S.: 335132

iGuzzini Lighting USA, Ltd., (1)
105 Madison Ave Ste 302, New York, NY
10016
Tel.: (212) 481-8188
Lighting Product Mfr & Distr
N.A.I.C.S.: 335132

iGuzzini Lighting WLL (1)
Al Amir Street D-Ring Road, 22403, Doha,
Qatar
Tel.: (974) 44419862
Lighting Product Mfr & Distr
N.A.I.C.S.: 335132

iGuzzini Middle East FZE (1)
Dubai Airport Free Zone Authority, Bldg 6EB
Office No 835, Dubai, United Arab Emirates
Tel.: (971) 47017825
Lighting Product Mfr & Distr
N.A.I.C.S.: 335132

iGuzzini S.E.A. Pte. Ltd. (1)
1 Commonwealth Lane 09-10 One Com-
monwealth, Singapore, 149544, Singapore
Tel.: (65) 677910
Lighting Product Mfr & Distr
N.A.I.C.S.: 335132

**iGuzzini illuminazione Schweiz
AG** (1)
Uetlibergstrasse 194, 8045, Zurich, Switzer-
land
Tel.: (41) 444654646
Lighting Product Mfr & Distr
N.A.I.C.S.: 335132

iGuzzini illuminazione UK Ltd. (1)
Astolat Business Park Astolat Way, Off Old
Portsmouth Road, Guildford, GU3 1NE,
United Kingdom
Tel.: (44) 1483468000
Lighting Product Mfr & Distr
N.A.I.C.S.: 335132

FAGRON NV
Fascinatio Boulevard 350, 3065 WB,
Rotterdam, Netherlands
Tel.: (31) 883311288   BE
Web Site: https://www.fagron.com
Year Founded: 1990
FAGR—(EUR)
Rev.: $846,884,866
Assets: $1,111,550,944
Liabilities: $595,349,376
Net Worth: $516,201,568
Earnings: $78,423,667
Emp.: 3,282
Fiscal Year-end: 12/31/23
Holding Company
N.A.I.C.S.: 551112
Constantijn van Rietschoten *(Chief
Comm Officer)*

Subsidiaries:

APPEG SA (1)
Rue de la Sambre 6, 6032, Charleroi, Bel-
gium
Tel.: (32) 71362929
Pharmaceuticals Distr
N.A.I.C.S.: 456110

AnazaoHealth Inc. (1)
5710 Hoover Blvd, Tampa, FL 33634-5339
Tel.: (800) 995-4363
Web Site: http://www.anazaohealth.com
Emp.: 120
Pharmaceutical Mfr & Retailer

N.A.I.C.S.: 325412

ApodanNordic PharmaPackaging A/S **(1)**
Kigkurren 8M, 2300, Copenhagen, Denmark
Tel.: (45) 32971555
Web Site: http://www.apodanpharma.dk
Pharmaceutical Products Distr
N.A.I.C.S.: 424210
Henrik Schosler Hansen *(Gen Mgr)*

Arseus BV **(1)**
Kralingseweg 207-211, 3062, Rotterdam, Netherlands
Tel.: (31) 883311211
Sales Range: $25-49.9 Million
Emp.: 40
Pharmaceuticals Whslr
N.A.I.C.S.: 456110
Gerardus van Jeveren *(CEO)*

Subsidiary (Domestic):

Arseus Dental Nederland B.V. **(2)**
Cartografenweg 18, 5141 MT, Waalwijk, Netherlands
Tel.: (31) 416675000
Web Site: http://www.arseus-dental.nl
Sales Range: $25-49.9 Million
Dental Mfr, Supplier & Distr
N.A.I.C.S.: 339114

Arseus Tec NV **(1)**
Textielstraat 24, Waregem, Belgium
Tel.: (32) 56628866
Pharmaceuticals Mfr
N.A.I.C.S.: 325412

Central de Drogas S.A. de C.V. **(1)**
Camino a la Montana 176, Col Industrial La Perla, 53348, Naucalpan, Mexico, Mexico
Tel.: (52) 5555608111
Web Site: https://www.cedrosa.com.mx
Emp.: 73
Chemical Products Mfr
N.A.I.C.S.: 325998

Curaphar B.V. **(1)**
De Pinckart 54, 5674 CC, Nuenen, Netherlands
Tel.: (31) 408512290
Web Site: https://www.curaphar.com
Innovative Healthcare Services
N.A.I.C.S.: 621491

De Collegiale Bereiding BV **(1)**
Hinmanweg 13 A, 7575 BE, Oldenzaal, Netherlands
Tel.: (31) 541573240
Web Site: http://www.spruyt-hillen.nl
Sales Range: $50-74.9 Million
Emp.: 6
Pharmaceuticals Whslr & Distr
N.A.I.C.S.: 424210

Denteco 2000 SA **(1)**
ZAC du Pre Catelan, Rue Delesalle, La Madeleine, France
Tel.: (33) 320061515
Pharmaceuticals Mfr
N.A.I.C.S.: 325412

Dr Kulich Pharma S.R.O. **(1)**
Pileticka 178/61, 500 03, Hradec Kralove, Czech Republic
Tel.: (420) 323619700
Web Site: https://www.kulich.cz
Pharmaceutical Product Mfr & Whslr
N.A.I.C.S.: 325412

Eurotec Dental GmbH **(1)**
Forumstrasse 12, 4468, Neuss, Germany
Tel.: (49) 21311257872
Web Site: http://www.eurotec-dental.info
Sales Range: $25-49.9 Million
Emp.: 4
Dental Equipment Mfr
N.A.I.C.S.: 339114

Fagron A.S. **(1)**
Holicka 1098/31m, 779 00, Olomouc, Czech Republic
Tel.: (420) 585222590
Web Site: https://shop.fagron.cz
Pharmaceutical Product Mfr & Distr
N.A.I.C.S.: 325412

Fagron Canada Inc. **(1)**
Rue Sainte-Catherine Ou 4150, Montreal, H3Z 2Y5, QC, Canada

Tel.: (813) 391-1893
Pharmaceutical Product Mfr & Distr
N.A.I.C.S.: 325412

Fagron Care Sp. z.o.o. **(1)**
Ul Komandosow 1/1, 32-085, Modlniczka, Poland
Tel.: (48) 123343500
Web Site: https://fagroncare.pl
Pharmaceutical Product Whslr
N.A.I.C.S.: 424210

Fagron Colombia SAS **(1)**
Cra 1 4 - 02 Bodega 15 Parque Industrial K2, Chia, Colombia
Tel.: (57) 17435939
Web Site: http://www.co.fagron.com
Pharmaceuticals Product Mfr
N.A.I.C.S.: 325412

Fagron Group BV **(1)**
Venkelbaan 101, Capelle aan den IJssel, 2908 KE, Netherlands
Tel.: (31) 883311200
Web Site: http://www.fagron.com
Sales Range: $25-49.9 Million
Emp.: 100
Pharmeceutical Raw Material Mfr
N.A.I.C.S.: 325412

Subsidiary (Domestic):

Fagron BV **(2)**
Lichtenauerlaan 182, 3062 ME, Rotterdam, Netherlands
Tel.: (31) 883311288
Web Site: https://www.fagron.nl
Pharmaceuticals Mfr
N.A.I.C.S.: 325412

Subsidiary (Non-US):

Fagron GmbH & Co KG **(2)**
Wilhelm-Bergner-Strasse 11g, 21509, Glinde, Germany
Tel.: (49) 40670675
Web Site: https://fagron.de
Emp.: 40
Pharmaceuticals Mfr
N.A.I.C.S.: 325412

Fagron Iberica SAU **(2)**
C/ De les Cosidores 150, 08226, Terrassa, Barcelona, Spain
Tel.: (34) 937310722
Web Site: https://www.fagron.es
Sales Range: $25-49.9 Million
Emp.: 50
Pharmaceuticals Mfr
N.A.I.C.S.: 325412

Fagron Services BVBA **(2)**
Industrieweg 2, 2850, Boom, Belgium
Tel.: (32) 34440720
Web Site: http://www.fagron.be
Sales Range: $25-49.9 Million
Emp.: 11
Pharmaceuticals Mfr
N.A.I.C.S.: 325412
Marc Lenssens *(Mgr)*

Subsidiary (US):

Fagron, Inc. **(2)**
201 W 5th St Ste 1250, Austin, TX 78701
Tel.: (651) 681-9517
Web Site: https://www.fagron.us
Sales Range: $10-24.9 Million
Emp.: 29
Pharmaceutical Preparation Mfr
N.A.I.C.S.: 325412

Subsidiary (Domestic):

B&B Pharmaceuticals, Inc. **(3)**
17200 E Ohio Dr, Aurora, CO 80017
Tel.: (303) 755-5110
Web Site: http://www.bandbpharmaceuticals.com
Active Pharmaceutical Ingredients Mfr
N.A.I.C.S.: 325412
Matt Johnson *(Pres)*

Fagron Hrvatska d.o.o. **(1)**
Donjozelinska 114, 10382, Donja Zelina, Croatia
Tel.: (385) 12043322
Web Site: https://www.fagron.hr
Pharmacy Retailer
N.A.I.C.S.: 445292

Fagron Nordic A/S **(1)**
Kigkurren 8M, 2300, Copenhagen, Denmark
Tel.: (45) 33278000
Web Site: https://www.fagron.dk
Pharmaceuticals Product Mfr

Fagron SAS **(1)**
2 rue Jean Lantier, 75001, Paris, France
Tel.: (33) 148901729
Web Site: http://www.fagron.fr
Pharmaceutical Product Mfr & Distr
N.A.I.C.S.: 325412

Fagron SH Ltd. **(1)**
Chong Hing Finance Center 288 West Nanjing Road, Shanghai, 200003, China
Tel.: (86) 2163150875
Pharmaceutical Product Mfr & Distr
N.A.I.C.S.: 325412

Fagron South Africa Ltd. **(1)**
55 14th Avenue, Northcliff, Johannesburg, South Africa
Tel.: (27) 116755331
Web Site: https://www.fagron.co.za
Pharmaceuticals Product Mfr
N.A.I.C.S.: 325412

Fagron Sp. z o.o **(1)**
Ul Pasternik 26, 31-354, Krakow, Poland
Tel.: (48) 123343512
Web Site: https://pl.fagron.com
Pharmaceuticals Product Mfr
N.A.I.C.S.: 325412

Fagron UK Ltd **(1)**
Media Exchange 4B Coquet Street, Newcastle upon Tyne, NE1 2QB, United Kingdom
Tel.: (44) 8456522525
Web Site: https://www.fagron.co.uk
Emp.: 10
Pharmaceuticals Mfr & Distr
N.A.I.C.S.: 325412

Florien Fitoativos Ltda **(1)**
Vicente Bellini Road 175 Conceicao, Piracicaba, 13427-225, Brazil
Tel.: (55) 1934291199
Web Site: http://www.florien.com.br
Pharmaceutical Products Distr
N.A.I.C.S.: 424210

Fresenius Kabi Compounding LLC **(1)**
3 Corporate Dr, Lake Zurich, IL 60047
Tel.: (847) 550-2300
Web Site: https://www.fresenius-kabi.com
Emp.: 1,500
Pharmaceuticals Product Mfr
N.A.I.C.S.: 325412

GX Sciences, LLC **(1)**
807 Las Cimas Pkwy Ste 145, Austin, TX 78746
Tel.: (512) 258-5564
Web Site: https://www.gxsciences.com
Medical Laboratory Services
N.A.I.C.S.: 621511
Kendal Stewart *(Founder, Mng Dir & Dir-Medical)*

Gako Deutschland GmbH **(1)**
Am Steinernen Kreuz 24, D-96110, Schesslitz, Germany
Tel.: (49) 891222387200
Web Site: https://www.unguator.com
Pharmaceutical Product Mfr
N.A.I.C.S.: 325412

Galfarm Sp. z o.o. **(1)**
Ul Przemyslowa 12, 30-701, Krakow, Poland
Tel.: (48) 126567100
Web Site: https://www.galfarm.pl
Pharmaceutical Product Retailer
N.A.I.C.S.: 456110

Hader SA **(1)**
Rue Jardiniere 153, 2300, La Chaux-de-Fonds, Switzerland
Tel.: (41) 329259050
Web Site: http://www.hader-swiss.com
Sales Range: $25-49.9 Million
Emp.: 70
Medical Instrument Mfr
N.A.I.C.S.: 339112

Hiperscan GmbH **(1)**

Weisseritzstr 3, 01067, Dresden, Germany
Tel.: (49) 3512124960
Web Site: https://www.hiperscan.com
Emp.: 60
Infrared Spectroscopy Technology Services
N.A.I.C.S.: 541690

Humco Holding Group, Inc. **(1)**
201 W 5th St Ste 1250, Austin, TX 78701
Tel.: (903) 831-7808
Web Site: http://www.humco.com
Over-the-Counter Pharmaceutical Preparations Mfr & Marketer
N.A.I.C.S.: 325412
John O. Trimble *(Chief Scientific Officer & Exec VP)*

Infinity Pharma BV **(1)**
Munsterstraat 4, 7575 ED, Oldenzaal, Netherlands
Tel.: (31) 541585600
Web Site: https://www.infinitypharma.com
Pharmaceutical Product Mfr & Distr
N.A.I.C.S.: 325412

JPG Pharma NV **(1)**
Ondernemersstraat 4, 2500, Lier, Belgium
Tel.: (32) 34800980
Web Site: http://www.jpgpharma.be
Sales Range: $50-74.9 Million
Emp.: 10
Pharmaceuticals Whslr
N.A.I.C.S.: 424210

Letco Medical, LLC **(1)**
460 E Swedesford Rd Ste 2040, Wayne, PA 19087
Tel.: (800) 239-5288
Web Site: http://www.letcomedical.com
Medical Supplies & Equipment Mfr
N.A.I.C.S.: 423830
Steve Bencetic *(Chief Admin Officer)*

Multident GmbH **(1)**
Edewechter Landstrasse 148, 26131, Oldenburg, Germany
Tel.: (49) 44193080
Web Site: http://www.multident.de
Sales Range: $25-49.9 Million
Emp.: 100
Pharmaceuticals Mfr
N.A.I.C.S.: 325412

Nolte GmbH **(1)**
Konrad-Nolte-Strasse 20, 76726, Germersheim, Germany
Tel.: (49) 72 745 1120
Web Site: https://nolte.de
Pharmaceuticals Mfr
N.A.I.C.S.: 325412

Pharmaflore SA **(1)**
Rue Botrieux 7, 7864, Lessines, Belgium
Tel.: (32) 68332105
Web Site: http://www.pharmaflore.be
Sales Range: $25-49.9 Million
Emp.: 15
Medicinal Product Mfr
N.A.I.C.S.: 325412
Failures Elke *(Gen Mgr)*

Spruyt hillen BV **(1)**
Venkelbaan 101, 2908 KE, Capelle aan den IJssel, Netherlands
Tel.: (31) 302814411
Web Site: https://www.spruyt-hillen.nl
Sales Range: $25-49.9 Million
Emp.: 52
Pharmaceuticals Product Mfr
N.A.I.C.S.: 325412

Timm Health Care BV **(1)**
Bosberg 41, 7271 LE, Borculo, Netherlands
Tel.: (31) 545251050
Web Site: http://www.timmhealthcare.nl
Sales Range: $10-24.9 Million
Emp.: 8
Pharmaceutical Drug Mfr
N.A.I.C.S.: 325412

Van Hopplynus Ophtalm SA **(1)**
Rue Colonel Bourg 105, 1030, Brussels, Belgium
Tel.: (32) 27022828
Web Site: http://www.vho.be
Sales Range: $25-49.9 Million
Emp.: 50
Medical Instruments & Apparatus Mfr
N.A.I.C.S.: 339112
Cedrec Veqennear *(Mng Dir)*

Fagron NV—(Continued)

XO CARE The Netherlands BV (1)
Bijsterhuizen 20-18A, 6604 LJ, Wijchen, Netherlands
Tel.: (31) 246778776
Web Site: http://www.xo-care.nl
Dental Equipment Mfr
N.A.I.C.S.: 339114

FAH MAI HOLDINGS, INC.
1000/196 199 3rd Floor Liberty Building, Sukhumvit 55 Road Klongton Neau Wattana, Bangkok, 10110, Thailand
Tel.: (66) 2 107 1047   DE
Web Site:
http://www.fahmaiholdings.com
Year Founded: 2016
Rev.: $23,252
Assets: $421,969
Liabilities: $84,651
Net Worth: $337,318
Earnings: ($570,434)
Emp.: 8
Fiscal Year-end: 12/31/18
Holding Company
N.A.I.C.S.: 551112
Louis Joseph Haseman (Founder, Co-Pres, CEO, CFO & Sec)

FAIFEY INVEST SOCIMI, S.A.
4th Floor Calle Principe de Vergara 112, 28002, Madrid, Spain   ES
Web Site:
https://www.faifeysocimi.com
Year Founded: 2019
MLECE—(EUR)
Rev.: $3,058,242
Assets: $113,241,855
Liabilities: $220,716
Net Worth: $113,021,140
Earnings: $7,956,502
Fiscal Year-end: 12/31/22
Real Estate Investment Services
N.A.I.C.S.: 531190
Jose Ma Ortiz Lopez-Camara (Sec)

FAIR FRIEND GROUP
11066 No 186 Yung Chi Road, Taipei, Taiwan
Tel.: (886) 2 2763 9696
Web Site: http://www.ffg-tw.com
Year Founded: 1979
Industrial Equipment Mfr
N.A.I.C.S.: 333248
Jimmy Chih-Yaung Chu (Chm)

Subsidiaries:

ECOCA INDUSTRIAL CO., LTD. (1)
No 401 28th Road Taichung Industrial Park, Taichung, Taiwan
Tel.: (886) 4 23597666
Web Site: http://www.ecoca.com
Industrial Machinery Mfr
N.A.I.C.S.: 333248

FAIRSKQ (TAIWAN) CO., LTD. (1)
12 Gond 32nd Road, Taichng Industrial Park, Taichung, 407, Taiwan
Tel.: (886) 4 23508208
Web Site: http://www.fairfriend.imb2b.com
Industrial Machine Tool Mfr
N.A.I.C.S.: 333517

FFG Asia-Pacific Ltd. (1)
607 Yangpyeong-ro 149, Yeongdeungpo-gu, Seoul, 150-105, Korea (South)
Tel.: (82) 2 718 7881
Emp.: 1
Industrial Machinery Distr
N.A.I.C.S.: 423830
Norbert Seo (Mng Dir)

FFG Europe Machinery (Beijing) Co., Ltd. (1)
Room 2709 Tower A Third Property Building No 1 Shuguang Xili, Chaoyang District, Beijing, 100028, China
Tel.: (86) 10 5822 2670
Industrial Machinery Distr
N.A.I.C.S.: 423830

FFG Europe S.p.A. (1)
Corso Venezia 16, 20121, Milan, Italy
Tel.: (39) 02 3659 0824
Web Site: http://www.ffgeurope.com
Holding Company; Regional Managing Office
N.A.I.C.S.: 551112

Subsidiary (Domestic):

Jobs Automazione S.p.A. (2)
Via Emilia Parmense 164, 29122, Piacenza, Italy
Tel.: (39) 0523 549 611
Web Site: http://www.jobs.it
Automated Machine Tool Mfr & Distr
N.A.I.C.S.: 333517
Marco Livelli (CEO)

Division (Domestic):

Jobs Automazione S.p.A. - Sachman Division (3)
Via Masaccio 15/A, 42124, Reggio Emilia, Italy
Tel.: (39) 0522 233 311
Automated Machine Tool Mfr & Distr
N.A.I.C.S.: 333517

Subsidiary (Domestic):

Sigma Technology S.r.l. (2)
Via San Giovanni 109, 27029, Vigevano, Italy
Tel.: (39) 0381 3051
Web Site: http://www.sigmaekkon.it
Machine Tool Mfr & Distr
N.A.I.C.S.: 333517

Sky Thrive Rambaudi S.r.l. (2)
Via Acqui 10/B, 10098, Rivoli, TO, Italy
Tel.: (39) 011 957 6254
Web Site: http://www.ffgrambaudi.it
Machine Tool Mfr & Distr
N.A.I.C.S.: 333517

FFG Russia (Russia) Automation Solutions (1)
Office 33 Entrance 2 5th Floor 17 Nauchnyi proezd, 117246, Moscow, Russia
Tel.: (7) 4955106130
Industrial Machinery Distr
N.A.I.C.S.: 423830

FFG Werke GmbH (1)
Stuttgarter Strasse 169, 73066, Uhingen, Germany
Tel.: (49) 71 61 1567 0
Web Site: http://www.ffg-werke.com
Emp.: 700
N.A.I.C.S.: 333248
Luigi Maniglio (Mng Dir)

Fair Friend Enterprise Co., Ltd. (1)
No 133 Gong 1st Road, Taichung Industrial Park, Taichung, Taiwan
Tel.: (886) 4 2359 4075
Web Site: http://www.feeler.com
Machine Tools Mfr & Distr
N.A.I.C.S.: 333517
Yu-Wei Chu (Pres)

Fair Friend Enterprise Group (1)
No 186 Yung Chi Road, Xinyi District, Taipei, 110, Taiwan
Tel.: (886) 2 2763 9696
Web Site: http://www.fairfriend.com.tw
Office Administrative Services
N.A.I.C.S.: 561110

Feeler Hardware Industrial Corporation (1)
No 52-5 Hukun Lane, PO Box 55151, Shinkuang Tsun Min-Chen Village, Nant'ou, Taiwan
Tel.: (886) 492731101
Web Site: http://www.feelerdoors.com.tw
Hardware Mfr
N.A.I.C.S.: 332510

Hangzhou Fair Fine electromechanics Co., Ltd. (1)
No 431 the 14th Street, Xiasha Economy & Technology Development Areas, Hangzhou, China
Tel.: (86) 571 8673 2292
Industrial Machinery Distr
N.A.I.C.S.: 423830

Hangzhou Glory Friend Machinery Technology Co., Ltd. (1)

No 6690 Jiangdong 3 Rd Xiaoshan Jiang-Dong Industry Park, Hangzhou, China
Tel.: (86) 571 8285 6258
Industrial Machinery Distr
N.A.I.C.S.: 423830

Huller Hille GmbH (1)
Steige 61, Mosbach, 74821, Germany
Tel.: (49) 6261 660
Industrial Machinery Distr
N.A.I.C.S.: 423830

Ikegai Corp (1)
920-52 Serizawa, Namegata, Ibaraki, 311-3501, Japan
Tel.: (81) 299 55 3111
Web Site: http://www.ikegai.co.jp
Emp.: 245
Industrial Machinery Mfr & Distr
N.A.I.C.S.: 333248
Zhang Chun Hua (CEO)

Subsidiary (Non-US):

Ikegai (Shanghai) Machinery Company (2)
190 Hua Ning Lu, Min Hang Qu, Shanghai, 200245, China
Tel.: (86) 21 6430 8918
Industrial Machinery Distr
N.A.I.C.S.: 423830

Subsidiary (Domestic):

Ikegai Metal Corp (2)
21-9 Arai-cho, Kawaguchi, 332-0005, Saitama, Japan
Tel.: (81) 48 222 5141
Industrial Mold Mfr & Distr
N.A.I.C.S.: 333511
Yukio Muraki (Pres)

JOBS GmbH (1)
Aindlinger Strasse 3, 86167, Augsburg, Germany
Tel.: (49) 821 5976 630
Industrial Machinery Distr
N.A.I.C.S.: 423830

JOBS Inc. (1)
200 S Alloy Dr, Fenton, MI 48430
Tel.: (810) 714-0522
Industrial Machinery Distr
N.A.I.C.S.: 423830

JOBS PRC (1)
RM 907 Tower A Soho New Town No 88 Jiangguo Road, Chaoyang Dist, 100222, Beijing, China
Tel.: (86) 10 85802526
Industrial Machinery Distr
N.A.I.C.S.: 423830

JOBS Sarl (1)
158 avenue du Presence, 69200, Venissieux, France
Tel.: (33) 4 7278 6982
Industrial Machinery Distr
N.A.I.C.S.: 423830

MAG IAS GmbH (1)
Salacher Strasse 93, 73054, Eislingen, Germany
Tel.: (49) 71 61 805 0
Machine Tool Mfr & Distr
N.A.I.C.S.: 333517
Gerald Weber (Mng Dir)

Shin Nippon Koki Co. Ltd. (1)
500 1 Takao 2 Cho, Minami-ku, Osaka, Japan
Tel.: (81) 722711201
Web Site: http://www.snkc.co.jp
Emp.: 681
Mfr of Machine Tools
N.A.I.C.S.: 333517
Shunka Cho (CEO)

Subsidiary (Domestic):

Communication Science Corporation (2)
Izumikan Sanbancho Bldg 3-8, Chiyoda-ku, Tokyo, 102-0075, Japan
Tel.: (81) 3 5215 0111
Web Site: http://www.kkcsc.co.jp
Industrial Products Mfr
N.A.I.C.S.: 333994

Subsidiary (Non-US):

EMP Fras- und Messtechnik Gmbh (2)

Daimlerstrasse 37, 73037, Goppingen, 73037, Germany
Tel.: (49) 71619991930
Web Site: http://www.emp-milling.de
Machine Tools Importer & Exporter
N.A.I.C.S.: 333517
Murat Hecber (CEO)

Subsidiary (Domestic):

Fuji Honing Industrial Co., Ltd. (2)
Yaesu Dai Building 7th Floor 1 1 1 Kyobashi, Chuo-ku, Tokyo, 104-0031, Japan
Tel.: (81) 3 6225 5870
Web Site: http://www.fujihoning.co.jp
Machine Tools Mfr
N.A.I.C.S.: 333517

KYC Machine Industry Co. Ltd. (2)
AD Bldg 7F 2-3-12 Minami-honmachi, Chuo-ku, Osaka, 541-0054, Japan
Tel.: (81) 6 6268 3100
Web Site: http://www.kyc.co.jp
Construction Machinery Whslr
N.A.I.C.S.: 423830
Masatoshi Naokawa (Pres & CEO)

Subsidiary (Domestic):

IZUTECH Corporation (3)
5th floor Honmachi 2-3-12 Minmihonmachi, Chuo-ku, Osaka, 541-0054, Japan
Tel.: (81) 6 6268 3501
Web Site: http://www.izutech.co.jp
Emp.: 100
Conveyor Mfr
N.A.I.C.S.: 333922
Masatoshi Naokawa (Pres & CEO)

Plant (Domestic):

IZUTECH Corporation - Shinshiro Plant (4)
1-1 Ochiai Arumi, Shinshiro, 441-1317, Aichi, Japan
Tel.: (81) 536 25 1161
Conveyor Mfr
N.A.I.C.S.: 333922

Subsidiary (Non-US):

KMI Services Pte Ltd (3)
41 Sungei Kadut Street 4, Singapore, 729060, Singapore
Tel.: (65) 62659123
Web Site: http://www.kmi.com.sg
Construction Machinery Whslr
N.A.I.C.S.: 423830

KYC Machine Co., Ltd. (3)
11F-9 No 229 Fuxing 2nd Rd, Jhubei, 30271, Hsinchu, Taiwan
Tel.: (886) 3 6675231 2
Web Site: http://www.twkyc.com.tw
Construction Machinery Whslr
N.A.I.C.S.: 423830

Plant (Domestic):

KYC Machine Industry Co. Ltd. Nishiwaki Plant (3)
1339-1 Kamihie-cho, Nishiwaki, 677-0039, Hyogo, Japan
Tel.: (81) 795 25 0700
Construction Machinery Whslr
N.A.I.C.S.: 423830

Subsidiary (Domestic):

KYC Sorimachi Co., Ltd. (3)
3-8-15 Joka, Nagaoka, 940-0021, Niigata, Japan
Tel.: (81) 258 21 2501
Web Site: http://www.kyc.co.jp
Construction Machinery Whslr
N.A.I.C.S.: 423830

Subsidiary (Domestic):

Niigata Machine Techno Co., Ltd. (2)
1300 Okayama, Higashi-ku, Niigata, 950-0821, Japan
Tel.: (81) 25 274 5121
Web Site: http://www.n-mtec.co.jp
Emp.: 338
Industrial Machinery Mfr
N.A.I.C.S.: 333310
Yukio Tamura (Pres & CEO)

Nissin Koki Co., Ltd. (2)

700-1 Toyotomi Toyotomi-cho, Himeji, 679-2123, Hyogo, Japan
Tel.: (81) 79 264 0303
Web Site: http://www.nissin-machine.co.jp
Industrial Machinery & Equipment Mfr
N.A.I.C.S.: 333248

Subsidiary (Non-US):

PT.Japan Engineering
Technology   **(2)**
Jalan Ciledug Raya No 104 RT 013 RW
006 Kel Cipulir Kec, Kebayoran Lama, Jakarta, 12230, Indonesia
Tel.: (62) 21 27081507
Industrial Machinery & Equipment Mfr
N.A.I.C.S.: 333248

Subsidiary (US):

SNK America, Inc.   **(2)**
1150 Feehanville Dr, Mount Prospect, IL
60056
Tel.: (847) 364-0801
Web Site: http://www.snkamerica.com
Machine Tools Sales & Service
N.A.I.C.S.: 423830
Keith Huang *(Pres & CEO)*

SNK America, Inc.   **(2)**
W Coast Branch 2791 Saturn Unit B Brea,
Los Angeles, CA 92821
Tel.: (714) 779-8818
Web Site: http://www.snkamerica.com
Import & Export of Machine Tools
N.A.I.C.S.: 423830

Subsidiary (Non-US):

SNK EG TAIWAN
CORPORATION   **(2)**
2F-1 No 12 Sec 1 Pei-hsin Road, Hsin-tien
Dist, Taipei, Taiwan
Tel.: (886) 2 2915 6765
Industrial Machinery & Equipment Mfr
N.A.I.C.S.: 333248

SNK ENGINEERING KOREA CO,
LTD.   **(2)**
Rm 611 Pyeongchon Digital Empire 16
Heungan-Daero 427 Beon-Gil, Dongan-gu,
Anyang, Gyeonggi, Korea (South)
Tel.: (82) 3180695121 2
Web Site: http://www.snkc.co.jp
Industrial Machinery & Equipment Mfr
N.A.I.C.S.: 333248

SNK GmbH   **(2)**
Daimlerstrasse 18, 73037, Goppingen, Germany
Tel.: (49) 716199919 88
Web Site: http://www.snk-gmbh.de
Import & Export Machine Tools
N.A.I.C.S.: 333517

SNK INDIA PRIVATE LIMITED   **(2)**
1006 & 1007 10th Floor Indraprakash Building 21, Barakhamba Road, New Delhi,
110001, India
Tel.: (91) 1149878960 61
Industrial Machinery & Equipment Mfr
N.A.I.C.S.: 333248

SNK Nanjing Technology
Corporation   **(2)**
Room101 Building3 Zijin Entrepreneur R&D
Center 89 victory road, Jiangning District,
Nanjing, JiangSu, China
Tel.: (86) 25 5212 0211
Industrial Machinery & Equipment Mfr
N.A.I.C.S.: 333248

SNK THAI CO., LTD.   **(2)**
Q DistrictGusto 299/264 Moo14 Soi
Kingkaew37/5 Tambon Rachathewa, Samutprakarn, Samut Prakan, 10540, Thailand
Tel.: (66) 2 327 0601
Industrial Machinery & Equipment Mfr
N.A.I.C.S.: 333248

Subsidiary (Domestic):

Shin Nippon Koki Co. Ltd. -
Misaki   **(2)**
3513-1 Fuke Misaki-cho, Sennan-gun,
Osaka, Japan
Tel.: (81) 724922111
Sales of Machine Tools & Post Sale Services
N.A.I.C.S.: 333517

Taisei koki Co., Ltd.   **(2)**
1-1-3-2700 Umeda, Kita-ku, Osaka, 530-0001, Japan
Tel.: (81) 663447784
Web Site: http://www.taiseikiko.co.jp
Pipe Fitting Mfr
N.A.I.C.S.: 332919
Hiroki Yamauchi *(Dir-Gen Acctg Dept & Pur Div)*

Subsidiary (Non-US):

Y.M.P. (THAILAND) CO., LTD.   **(2)**
Amata Nakorn Industrial Estate 700/153
Moo 1 T Bankao A Panthong, Chon Buri,
20160, Thailand
Tel.: (66) 38 214 051
Web Site: http://www.ymp-t.co.th
Emp.: 380
Industrial Machinery & Equipment Mfr
N.A.I.C.S.: 333248
Masakazu Okamoto *(Pres)*

Subsidiary (Domestic):

Y.M.P.-international Corporation   **(2)**
5th Floor Tanimachi South Building 1-1-14
Izumi-machi, Chuo-ku, Osaka, 540-0019,
Japan
Tel.: (81) 6 6920 0161
Web Site: http://www.ymp-i.co.jp
Information Technology Consulting Services
N.A.I.C.S.: 541512
Hisakazu Yamaguchi *(Chm)*

FAIR OAKS INCOME LIMITED
Sarnia House Le Truchot, PO Box
296, Saint Peter Port, GY1 4NA,
Guernsey   GG
Web Site:
  https://www.fairoaksincome.com
Year Founded: 2014
FAIR—(LSE)
Rev.: $314,897
Assets: $262,940,586
Liabilities: $595,297
Net Worth: $262,345,289
Earnings: ($687,265)
Fiscal Year-end: 12/31/22
Asset Management Services
N.A.I.C.S.: 523999
Professor Claudio Albanese *(Chm)*

FAIRCAP GMBH
Theatiner Str 11 8th Floor, 80333,
Munich, Germany
Tel.: (49) 89 69313211
Web Site: https://en.fair-cap.com
Emp.: 100
Investment Services
N.A.I.C.S.: 523999

Subsidiaries:

NYCO Flexible Packaging GmbH   **(1)**
Solotur St 28, 3422, Kirchberg, Switzerland
Tel.: (41) 344470047
Web Site: http://www.nyco.ch
Sales Range: $25-49.9 Million
Emp.: 180
Flexible Packaging Producers
N.A.I.C.S.: 322220
Bernhard Jaggi *(Mng Dir)*

Overum Industries AB   **(1)**
Bruksgatan 4, 59096, Overum, Sweden
Tel.: (46) 49336100
Web Site: https://overum-industries.com
Agricultural machinery
N.A.I.C.S.: 325320

FAIRCHEM ORGANICS LIMITED
253P 312 Chekhala Sanand Kadi
Highway, Ahmedabad, 400 709, India
Tel.: (91) 2717687900
Web Site: https://www.fairchem.in
FAIRCHEMOR—(NSE)
Rev.: $54,170,243
Assets: $35,299,255
Liabilities: $12,266,996
Net Worth: $23,032,259
Earnings: $5,799,162
Emp.: 200

Fiscal Year-end: 03/31/21
Chemical Products Mfr
N.A.I.C.S.: 325998
Utkarsh Shah *(Chm)*

FAIRCOURT GOLD INCOME CORP.
120 Adelaide Street West Suite 2107,
Toronto, M5H1T1, ON, Canada
Tel.: (416) 364-8989
Web Site:
  http://www.faircourtassetmgt.com
Year Founded: 2007
Rev.: $953,100
Assets: $10,988,084
Liabilities: $1,737,925
Net Worth: $9,250,159
Earnings: ($1,517,663)
Fiscal Year-end: 12/31/18
Financial Investment Services
N.A.I.C.S.: 523999
Charles Taerk *(Pres & CEO)*

FAIRCOURT SPLIT TRUST
150 King St W Suite 306-01, Toronto,
M5H 1J9, ON, Canada
Tel.: (416) 364-8989
Web Site:
  http://www.faircourtassetmgt.com
Year Founded: 2006
Rev.: $1,893,643
Assets: $16,476,848
Liabilities: $11,091,290
Net Worth: $5,385,558
Earnings: $712,445
Fiscal Year-end: 12/31/17
Financial Investment Services
N.A.I.C.S.: 523999
Charles Taerk *(Pres & CEO)*

FAIRFAX FINANCIAL HOLDINGS LIMITED
95 Wellington Street West Ste 800,
Toronto, M5J 2N7, ON, Canada
Tel.: (416) 367-4941   Ca
Web Site: https://www.fairfax.ca
Year Founded: 1985
FFH—(TSX)
Rev.: $26,934,800,000
Assets: $91,985,100,000
Liabilities: $64,284,200,000
Net Worth: $27,700,900,000
Earnings: $5,094,900,000
Emp.: 51,044
Fiscal Year-end: 12/31/23
Holding Company
N.A.I.C.S.: 551112
John Varnell *(VP-Corp Dev)*

Subsidiaries:

9938982 Canada Inc.   **(1)**
100 Domain Dr, Exeter, NH 03833-4801
Tel.: (603) 610-5802
Holding Company
N.A.I.C.S.: 551112
Paul Desmarais III *(Chm)*

Subsidiary (Domestic):

Bauer Hockey, Inc.   **(2)**
100 Domain Dr, Exeter, NH 03833-4801
Tel.: (603) 430-2111
Web Site: http://www.bauer.com
Hockey Equipment Designer, Mfr & Marketer
N.A.I.C.S.: 423910

Combat Sports   **(2)**
6651 S 216th St, Kent, WA 98032
Tel.: (253) 891-8377
Web Site:
  http://www.combatsportsgroup.com
Sporting & Athletic Goods Distr
N.A.I.C.S.: 423910

Easton Baseball/Softball Inc.   **(2)**
3500 Willow Ln, Thousand Oaks, CA 91361
Web Site: https://easton.rawlings.com
Sports Equipment, Sport Bags & Accessories Mfr & Whslr
N.A.I.C.S.: 339920

Subsidiary (Non-US):

Inaria International Inc.   **(2)**
600 Steeprock Dr, Toronto, M6M 4L5, ON,
Canada
Tel.: (416) 766-8825
Web Site: http://www.inariasoccer.com
Sporting & Athletic Goods Whslr
N.A.I.C.S.: 423910

Subsidiary (Domestic):

Maverik Lacrosse   **(2)**
535 W 24th St 5th Fl, New York, NY 10011-1140
Tel.: (800) 537-1702
Web Site: http://www.maveriklacrosse.com
Sporting & Athletic Goods Whslr
N.A.I.C.S.: 423910

APR Energy plc   **(1)**
3600 Port Jacksonville Pkwy, Jacksonville,
FL 32226   **(45%)**
Tel.: (904) 223-8488
Web Site: http://www.aprenergy.com
Sales Range: $450-499.9 Million
Emp.: 270
Holding Company; Temporary & Mobile
Electric Power Generation & Transmission
Services
N.A.I.C.S.: 551112

Subsidiary (Domestic):

APR Energy, LLC   **(2)**
3600 Port Jacksonville Pkwy, Jacksonville,
FL 32226
Tel.: (904) 223-8488
Web Site: http://www.aprenergy.com
Temporary & Mobile Electric Power Generation & Transmission Services
N.A.I.C.S.: 221121
Charles P. Ferry *(Pres)*

ARX Insurance Company   **(1)**
St Illinska 8, 04070, Kiev, Ukraine
Tel.: (380) 443911121
Web Site: http://arx.com.ua
Insurance Services
N.A.I.C.S.: 524210

Advent Capital (Holdings) PLC   **(1)**
2nd Floor 2 Minster Court Mincing Lane,
London, EC3R 7BB, United
Kingdom   **(100%)**
Tel.: (44) 2077438200
Web Site: http://www.adventgroup.co.uk
Sales Range: $200-249.9 Million
Emp.: 65
Insurance & Reinsurance Services
N.A.I.C.S.: 524126
Trevor J. Ambridge *(Chm)*

Allied World Assurance Company
Holdings, Ltd   **(1)**
     (70.89%)
Tel.: (441) 2785400
Web Site: http://www.awac.com
Sales Range: $1-4.9 Billion
Property-Casualty Insurance & Reinsurance
Services
N.A.I.C.S.: 524126
Tom McKevitt *(Exec VP-Reinsurance)*

Subsidiary (US):

Allied World Assurance
Company   **(2)**
311 S Wacker Dr Ste 1100, Chicago, IL
60606
Tel.: (312) 646-7700
Insurance Agencies & Brokerages
N.A.I.C.S.: 524210

Subsidiary (Non-US):

Allied World Assurance Company
(Europe) Designated Activity
Company   **(2)**
3rd Floor Georges Quay Plaza, Georges
Quay, Dublin, 2, Ireland
Tel.: (353) 14361400
Direct Property & Casualty Insurance Carriers
N.A.I.C.S.: 524126

Subsidiary (US):

Allied World Assurance Company
(U.S.) Inc.   **(2)**

Fairfax Financial Holdings Limited—(Continued)

199 Water St 24th Fl, New York, NY 10038
Tel.: (646) 794-0500
Insurance Services
N.A.I.C.S.: 524298

Subsidiary (Domestic):

AW Underwriters Inc. **(3)**
1690 New Britain Ave Ste 101, Farmington,
CT 06032
Tel.: (860) 284-1300
Liability Insurance Underwriting Services
N.A.I.C.S.: 524298

**Allied World Specialty Insurance
Company** **(3)**
1690 New Britain Ave Ste 101, Farmington,
CT 06032
Tel.: (860) 284-1300
Insurance Services
N.A.I.C.S.: 524298

**Allied World Surplus Lines Insurance
Company** **(3)**
425 W Capitol Ave Ste 1800, Little Rock,
AR 72201
Tel.: (646) 794-0500
Professional Liability Insurance Services
N.A.I.C.S.: 524298

Subsidiary (Domestic):

**Allied World Assurance Company,
Ltd** **(2)**
27 Richmond Rd, HM 08, Pembroke, Ber-
muda
Tel.: (441) 2785400
Insurance & Reinsurance Services
N.A.I.C.S.: 524298
Thomas McKevitt (Exec VP)

Subsidiary (Non-US):

**Allied World Assurance Holdings (Ire-
land) Ltd** **(2)**
3rd Floor George s Quay Plaza George s
Quay, Dublin, 2, Ireland
Tel.: (353) 14361400
N.A.I.C.S.: 524298

Subsidiary (US):

**Allied World Assurance Holdings
(U.S.) Inc.** **(2)**
199 Water St 25th Fl, New York, NY 10038
Tel.: (646) 794-0500
N.A.I.C.S.: 524298

Allied World Insurance Company **(2)**
199 Water St 25th Fl, New York, NY 10038
Tel.: (212) 635-5533
Insurance Management Services
N.A.I.C.S.: 524292

**Allied World Reinsurance
Company** **(2)**
199 Water St 25th Fl, New York, NY 10038
Tel.: (212) 635-5533
Property & Casualty Insurance Services
Provider
N.A.I.C.S.: 524126

Subsidiary (Non-US):

**Allied World Syndicate Services (Sin-
gapore) Pte. Ltd.** **(2)**
138 Market Street #03-02 Capita Green,
Singapore, 048946, Singapore
Tel.: (65) 66312500
Casualty Insurance & Reinsurance Services
N.A.I.C.S.: 524210
Yeo Meng Wong (Sr VP & Head-Asia Pa-
cific Treaty Reinsurance Div)

Amynta Agency, Inc. **(1)**
909 3rd Ave 33rd Fl, New York, NY 10022
Tel.: (888) 210-4142
Web Site: http://www.amyntagroup.com
Insurance Services
N.A.I.C.S.: 524298
Robert Giammarco (Chm & CEO)

Subsidiary (Non-US):

Amynta Surety Solutions **(2)**
141 Front St, Hamilton, HM19,
Bermuda **(100%)**
Tel.: (441) 2958201
Web Site: http://www.aspen.bm

Sales Range: $50-74.9 Million
Emp.: 50
Insurance Related Activities
N.A.I.C.S.: 524298

Arbor Memorial Services Inc. **(1)**
2 Jane Street, Toronto, M6S 4W8, ON,
Canada
Tel.: (416) 763-4531
Web Site: https://www.arbormemorial.com
Sales Range: $250-299.9 Million
Emp.: 1,550
Crematories, Funeral Homes & Cemeteries
Operator
N.A.I.C.S.: 812220

Brit Limited **(1)**
The Leadenhall Building 122 Leadenhall
Street, London, EC3V 4AB, United King-
dom
Tel.: (44) 2038570000
Insurance Services
N.A.I.C.S.: 524210

Subsidiary (US):

Ambridge Partners, LLC **(2)**
520 8th Ave 25th Fl, New York, NY 10018
Tel.: (212) 871-5400
Web Site: http://www.ambridgepartners.com
Sales Range: $1-9.9 Million
Emp.: 10
Insurance Agencies & Brokerages
N.A.I.C.S.: 524210
Jesseman Pryor (CEO)

Subsidiary (Domestic):

Brit Group Services Limited **(2)**
55 Bishopsgate 2nd Fl, London, EC2N
3AS, United Kingdom
Tel.: (44) 2079848500
Web Site: http://www.britinsurance.com
Sales Range: $200-249.9 Million
Emp.: 400
Insurance Agencies & Brokerages
N.A.I.C.S.: 524210

Brit Insurance Limited **(2)**
The Leadenhall Building 122 Leadenhall
Street, London, EC3V 4AB, United King-
dom
Tel.: (44) 2038570000
Web Site: https://www.britinsurance.com
Sales Range: $50-74.9 Million
Emp.: 500
Insurance Agencies & Brokerages
N.A.I.C.S.: 524210
Matthew Wilson (CEO)

Brit Syndicates Limited **(2)**
55 Bishopsgate, London, EC2N 3AS,
United Kingdom
Tel.: (44) 2079848700
Web Site: http://www.britinsurance.com
Emp.: 400
Insurance Agencies & Brokerages
N.A.I.C.S.: 524210

Brit UW Limited **(2)**
Leadenhall Building 122 Leadenhall Street,
London, EC3V 4AB, United Kingdom
Tel.: (44) 2079848700
Sales Range: $200-249.9 Million
Emp.: 750
Insurance Agencies & Brokerages
N.A.I.C.S.: 524210

Bryte Insurance Company Ltd. **(2)**
Rosebank Towers 5th Floor 15 Biermann
Avenue, Rosebank, Johannesburg, 2196,
South Africa
Tel.: (27) 110887000
Web Site: https://www.brytesa.com
Insurance Services
N.A.I.C.S.: 524210
Edwyn O'Neill (CEO)

Colonnade Insurance S.A. **(1)**
1 rue Jean Piret, 2350, Luxembourg, Lux-
embourg
Tel.: (352) 281156209
Emp.: 200
Insurance Services
N.A.I.C.S.: 524126
Peter Csakvari (Gen Dir)

Crum & Forster Holdings Corp. **(1)**
305 Madison Ave, Morristown, NJ
07960 **(100%)**

Tel.: (973) 490-6600
Rev.: $1,529,700,000
Earnings: $29,300,000
Emp.: 1,345
Fiscal Year-end: 12/31/2012
Holding Company; Property & Casualty In-
surance Services
N.A.I.C.S.: 551112

Subsidiary (Domestic):

Crum & Forster Insurance **(2)**
160 Water St, New York, NY
10038 **(100%)**
Tel.: (212) 277-1660
Web Site: http://www.cfins.com
Sales Range: $50-74.9 Million
Emp.: 20
Insurance
N.A.I.C.S.: 524126

**Crum & Forster Insurance
Company** **(2)**
305 Madison Ave, Morristown, NJ
07960-6117 **(100%)**
Tel.: (973) 490-6600
Sales Range: $750-799.9 Million
Emp.: 879
Commercial Lines Property & Casualty In-
surance
N.A.I.C.S.: 524210
Marc Adee (Chm & CEO)

Division (Domestic):

Fairmont Specialty **(3)**
11490 Westheimer Ste 300, Houston, TX
77077
Tel.: (713) 954-8100
Insurance Services
N.A.I.C.S.: 524210

Subsidiary (Non-US):

**First Mercury Financial
Corporation** **(2)**
Tel.: (248) 358-4010
Web Site: http://www.firstmercury.com
Sales Range: $300-349.9 Million
Emp.: 349
Insurance Services
N.A.I.C.S.: 524126

Subsidiary (Non-US):

CoverXSpecialty **(3)**
Tel.: (248) 358-4010
Web Site: http://www.coverx.com
Sales Range: $75-99.9 Million
Emp.: 120
Liability Insurance Products
N.A.I.C.S.: 524298

**First Mercury Insurance
Company** **(3)**
(100%)
Tel.: (248) 358-4010
Web Site: http://www.coverx.com
Sales Range: $50-74.9 Million
Emp.: 107
Insurance Services
N.A.I.C.S.: 524126

Subsidiary (Non-US):

Seneca Insurance Company Inc. **(2)**
Tel.: (212) 344-3000
Web Site: http://www.senecainsurance.com
Sales Range: $50-74.9 Million
Emp.: 100
Insurance Services
N.A.I.C.S.: 524126
Jessica Frankovich (Exec VP)

Subsidiary (Domestic):

**The North River Insurance
Company** **(2)**
305 Madison Ave, Morristown, NJ
07962 **(100%)**
Tel.: (973) 490-6600
Web Site: http://www.cfins.com
Sales Range: $300-349.9 Million
Emp.: 600
Insurance Company
N.A.I.C.S.: 524126

**United States Fire Insurance
Company** **(2)**
305 Madison Ave, Morristown, NJ
07960 **(100%)**

Tel.: (973) 490-6600
Web Site: https://www.cfins.com
Sales Range: $300-349.9 Million
Emp.: 600
Fire Insurance
N.A.I.C.S.: 524126

Subsidiary (Domestic):

**Crum & Forster Pet Insurance
Group** **(3)**
1208 Massillon Rd Ste G 200, Akron, OH
44306
Tel.: (234) 231-1830
Pet Insurance Products & Services
N.A.I.C.S.: 524128
Michael Kalman (CIO)

**Eurolife ERB Insurance Group Hold-
ings S.A.** **(1)**
33-35 El Venizelou (Panepistimiou) & Korai
Str, 10564, Athens, Greece **(40%)**
Tel.: (30) 2109303800
Web Site: http://www.eurolife.gr
Holding Company; Insurance Products &
Services
N.A.I.C.S.: 551112

Subsidiary (Domestic):

**Eurolife ERB General Insurance
S.A.** **(2)**
Panepistimiou 33-35 Korai, 10564, Athens,
Greece
Tel.: (30) 2109303800
Web Site: https://www.eurolife.gr
General Insurance Products & Services
N.A.I.C.S.: 524126

**Fairfax Brasil Seguros Corporativos
S.A.** **(1)**
To The Santos 1940 4th Walk, Cerqueira
Cesar, 01418-000, Sao Paulo, Brazil
Tel.: (55) 1130413020
Web Site: https://www.fairfax.com.br
Sales Range: $50-74.9 Million
Emp.: 100
Insurance Management Services
N.A.I.C.S.: 524298

**Fairfax India Holdings
Corporation** **(1)**
95 Wellington Street West Suite 800, To-
ronto, M5J 2N7, ON, Canada **(95.1%)**
Tel.: (416) 367-4755
Web Site: https://www.fairfaxindia.ca
Rev.: $693,539,000
Assets: $3,584,346,000
Liabilities: $681,912,000
Net Worth: $2,902,434,000
Earnings: $494,500,000
Emp.: 9
Fiscal Year-end: 12/31/2021
Investment Holding Company
N.A.I.C.S.: 551112
Vivan Prem Watsa (Founder & Chm)

Fairfirst Insurance Limited **(1)**
Access Towers II 14th Floor 278/4 Union
Place, 02, Colombo, Sri Lanka
Tel.: (94) 112428428
Web Site: https://www.fairfirst.lk
Insurance Services
N.A.I.C.S.: 524210

**Falcon Insurance Company (Hong
Kong) Limited** **(1)**
Suites 307-11 3/F 12 Taikoo Wan Road, 25
Westlands Road, Taikoo Shing, China
(Hong Kong)
Tel.: (852) 22322888
Web Site:
https://www.falconinsurance.com.hk
Sales Range: $50-74.9 Million
Emp.: 100
Insurance Services
N.A.I.C.S.: 524210

Golf Town Limited **(1)**
302-610 Applewood Crescent, Vaughan,
L4K 0E3, ON, Canada
Web Site: http://www.golftown.com
Golf Goods Retailer
N.A.I.C.S.: 459110

Gulf Insurance Group K.S.C.P. **(1)**
KIPCO Tower Floor 40 Khaled Ibn Alwaleed
Street, PO Box 1040, Safat, 13011, Kuwait,
13011, Kuwait **(90.01%)**
Tel.: (965) 1802080

Web Site: https://gulfinsgroup.com
Rev.: $2,702,938,022
Assets: $4,374,545,809
Liabilities: $3,188,894,667
Net Worth: $1,185,651,142
Earnings: $139,903,799
Emp.: 3,800
Fiscal Year-end: 12/31/2022
Insurance & Reinsurance Services
N.A.I.C.S.: 524126
Khaled Saoud Al Hasan *(CEO)*

Subsidiary (Non-US):

Arab Misr Insurance Group   **(2)**
13 Ma ahad Alishteraki St Merryland, Helio-
polis, Cairo, Egypt   **(94.85%)**
Tel.: (20) 24517620
Web Site: http://www.amig.com.eg
Sales Range: $125-149.9 Million
Emp.: 242
Insurance Services
N.A.I.C.S.: 524126
Alaa El Zoheiry *(Mng Dir)*

Arab Orient Insurance Co. Ltd.   **(2)**
Third Circle -Abdul Monem Riad Street, PO
Box 213590, Amman, 11121,
Jordan   **(55%)**
Tel.: (962) 65654550
Web Site: https://www.gig.com.jo
Sales Range: $100-124.9 Million
Emp.: 164
Insurance Services
N.A.I.C.S.: 524298
Ali al-Wazni *(CEO)*

Bahrain Kuwait Insurance Company
B.S.C.   **(2)**
BKIC Tower 2775 road 2835 block 428,
Seef District, Manama, Bahrain **(56.12%)**
Tel.: (973) 17119999
Web Site: https://www.gigbh.com
Rev.: $276,549,694
Assets: $557,078,062
Liabilities: $440,237,659
Net Worth: $116,840,402
Earnings: $13,073,924
Emp.: 177
Fiscal Year-end: 12/31/2022
Property & Casualty, Life & Health Insur-
ance Products & Services
N.A.I.C.S.: 524128
Abdulla Rabia *(Gen Mgr-Kuwait)*

Co-Headquarters (Non-US):

Bahrain Kuwait Insurance Company
B.S.C.   **(3)**
BBK Building 5th and 6th Floors Ahmed
Al-Jaber Street, Al-Sharq, Kuwait
Tel.: (965) 1885511
Web Site: https://www.gigbh.com
Property & Casualty, Life & Health Insur-
ance Products & Services
N.A.I.C.S.: 524128
Abdulla Rabia *(Deputy CEO)*

Subsidiary (Domestic):

Takaful International Company
B.S.C   **(3)**
Building No 680 Road 2811, PO Box 3230,
Seef District, 428, Manama,
Bahrain   **(81.9%)**
Tel.: (973) 17565656
Web Site: https://www.gigtakaful.bh
Rev.: $13,241,180
Assets: $110,322,580
Liabilities: $78,261,534
Net Worth: $32,061,046
Earnings: $4,012,608
Emp.: 105
Fiscal Year-end: 12/31/2023
General Insurance Services
N.A.I.C.S.: 524210
Essam M. Al-Ansari *(CEO)*

Subsidiary (Non-US):

Dar Al Salam Insurance
Company   **(2)**
Sadoun Street District 101 Street 51 Build-
ing 13, Baghdad, Iraq   **(51%)**
Tel.: (964) 7901914772
Web Site: http://www.gulfins.com.kw
Sales Range: Less than $1 Million
Insurance Management Services
N.A.I.C.S.: 524298

Egypt Life Takaful Insurance Com-
pany S.A.E.   **(2)**
The eastern tower Plot 204 - North 90th St,
New Cairo, Egypt
Tel.: (20) 224138700
Web Site: http://www.giglt.com.eg
Fire Insurance Services
N.A.I.C.S.: 524210
Raafat El Salamony *(Chm)*

Egyptian Life Takaful   **(2)**
40 Syria St Mohandessen, Giza,
Egypt   **(59.5%)**
Tel.: (20) 237636641
Fire Insurance Services
N.A.I.C.S.: 524113

Fajr Al-Gulf Insurance & Reinsurance
Company   **(2)**
Olivetti Building Adlieh Square, PO Box
116-5047, Beirut, Lebanon   **(54.7%)**
Tel.: (961) 1511122
Web Site: http://www.fajralgulf.com
Insurance Services
N.A.I.C.S.: 524113

Subsidiary (Domestic):

Gulf Life Insurance Company   **(2)**
Sharq Khaled Bin Alwaleed Street Kitco
Tower Floor 41, PO Box 24518, Kuwait,
13106, Kuwait
Tel.: (965) 22961777
Web Site: http://www.gulfinsurance.com
Sales Range: $50-74.9 Million
Emp.: 79
Fire Insurance Services
N.A.I.C.S.: 524113
Tareq Abdul Wahab Al Sahhaf *(Chm)*

Subsidiary (Non-US):

Gulf Sigorta A.S.   **(2)**
Saray Mah Dr Adnan Buyukdeniz Cad
Akkom Office Park, Cessas Plaza No 4
Floor 4-5 Umraniye, Istanbul,
Turkiye   **(99.22%)**
Tel.: (90) 2164002400
Web Site: https://www.gulfsigorta.com.tr
Property & Casualty Insurance Products &
Services
N.A.I.C.S.: 524126
Ayse Figen Gardet *(Exec VP)*

Syrian Kuwaiti Insurance
Company   **(2)**
King Abd Alazeez Aal Saud St Bldg No 4
Abu Rummaneh, PO Box 5778, Damascus,
Syria   **(53.78%)**
Tel.: (963) 11 9276
Web Site: http://www.gig.com.sy
Sales Range: $100-124.9 Million
Emp.: 111
Insurance Services
N.A.I.C.S.: 524298
Samer Fouad Bakdash *(Gen Mgr)*

Hamblin Watsa Investment Counsel
Ltd.   **(1)**
95 Wellington Street West Suite 802, To-
ronto, M5J 2N7, ON, Canada
Tel.: (416) 366-9544
Web Site: https://www.hwic.ca
Investment Management Service
N.A.I.C.S.: 523940
Vivan Prem Watsa *(VP)*

ICICI Lombard General Insurance
Co. Ltd.   **(1)**
Ground floor- Interface 11 Sixth floor- Inter-
face 16, Office no 601 602 New linking
Road Malad, Mumbai, 400064,
India   **(35%)**
Tel.: (91) 8655222666
Web Site: http://www.icicilombard.com
Insurance Services
N.A.I.C.S.: 524210
Bhargav Dasgupta *(CEO & Mng Dir)*

Kitchen Stuff Plus, Inc.   **(1)**
125 Tycos Drive, Toronto, M6B 1W6, ON,
Canada
Web Site: http://www.kitchenstuffplus.com
House Ware & Home Decor Retailer
N.A.I.C.S.: 449129

La Meridional Compania Argentina de
Seguros S.A.   **(1)**
646 Piso 1, Buenos Aires, C1038AAN, Argentina

Tel.: (54) 1149097450
Web Site:
    http://www.meridionalseguros.com.ar
Property & Casualty Insurance Services
N.A.I.C.S.: 524126

Mosaic Capital Corporation   **(1)**
400 2424 4th Street SW, Calgary, T2S 2T4,
AB, Canada
Tel.: (403) 218-6500
Rev.: $302,485,598
Assets: $233,660,677
Liabilities: $152,500,088
Net Worth: $81,160,589
Earnings: ($8,149,041)
Emp.: 1,150
Fiscal Year-end: 12/31/2019
Investment Services
N.A.I.C.S.: 523999

Subsidiary (Domestic):

BASSI CONSTRUCTION LP   **(2)**
2575 Delzotto Avenue Unit A, Gloucester,
K1T 3V6, ON, Canada
Tel.: (613) 822-6767
Web Site: http://www.bassi.ca
Construction & Remodeling Services
N.A.I.C.S.: 236118
John Bassi *(Co-Pres)*

Northbridge Financial
Corporation   **(1)**
105 Adelaide Street West Suite 700, To-
ronto, M5H 1P9, ON, Canada
Tel.: (416) 350-4400
Web Site: https://www.nbfc.com
Sales Range: $1-4.9 Billion
Emp.: 1,480
Financial Services Holding Company
N.A.I.C.S.: 551111
Silvy Wright *(Pres & CEO)*

Subsidiary (Domestic):

Federated Insurance Company of
Canada   **(2)**
255 Commerce Drive, Winnipeg, R3C 3C9,
MB, Canada
Tel.: (204) 786-6431
Web Site: https://www.federated.ca
Sales Range: $125-149.9 Million
Emp.: 150
Property, Automobile, Liability, Life & Health
Insurance
N.A.I.C.S.: 524128

Northbridge General Insurance
Corporation   **(2)**
105 Adelaide Street West, Toronto, M5H
1P9, ON, Canada   **(100%)**
Tel.: (416) 350-4400
Web Site:
    https://www.northbridgeinsurance.ca
Sales Range: $800-899.9 Million
Emp.: 550
Insurance Services
N.A.I.C.S.: 524126

Subsidiary (Domestic):

Northbridge Commercial Insurance
Corporation   **(3)**
105 Adelaide St W 4th Fl, Toronto,
M5H1P9, ON, Canada
Tel.: (416) 364-7800
Web Site: http://www.nbfc.com
Sales Range: $200-249.9 Million
Emp.: 230
Long-Haul Trucking, Property, Liability &
Automobile Insurance Carrier
N.A.I.C.S.: 524126

Northbridge Indemnity Insurance
Corporation   **(3)**
Suite 1500 595 Burrard Street Tower III,
Vancouver, V7X 1G4, BC, Canada
Tel.: (604) 683-5511
Web Site: http://www.nbfc.com
Sales Range: $125-149.9 Million
Emp.: 200
Property, Casualty, Marine & Energy Insur-
ance Carrier
N.A.I.C.S.: 524126

Subsidiary (US):

Northbridge Indemnity Insurance
Corporation   **(4)**

1700 7th Ave Ste 1850, Seattle, WA 98101-
1397
Tel.: (206) 382-6670
Sales Range: $75-99.9 Million
Emp.: 200
Property, Casualty, Marine & Energy Insur-
ance Carrier
N.A.I.C.S.: 524126

Odyssey Re Holdings Corp.   **(1)**
300 1st Stamford Pl, Stamford, CT
06902   **(100%)**
Tel.: (203) 977-8000
Web Site: http://www.odysseyre.com
Rev.: $2,773,218,000
Assets: $11,217,559,000
Liabilities: $7,538,793,000
Net Worth: $3,678,766,000
Earnings: $282,513,000
Emp.: 721
Fiscal Year-end: 12/31/2012
Reinsurance Services
N.A.I.C.S.: 524130
Philippe E. Mallier *(CEO-Reinsurance Ops-
Latin America)*

Subsidiary (Non-US):

Hudson Insurance Group   **(2)**
                                    (100%)
Tel.: (212) 978-2800
Web Site: http://www.hudsoninsgroup.com
Sales Range: $50-74.9 Million
Emp.: 30
Specialty Insurance Products; Medical Mal-
practice & Fire & Marine Casualty Insur-
ance Services
N.A.I.C.S.: 524126
Mike Cifone *(Officer-Ops & Sr VP)*

Subsidiary (Domestic):

Clearwater Insurance Company   **(3)**
100 William St, New York, NY 10038
Tel.: (212) 978-2800
Web Site:
    http://www.hudsoninsurancecompany.com
Sales Range: $125-149.9 Million
Reinsurance Services
N.A.I.C.S.: 524298

Clearwater Select Insurance
Company   **(3)**
300 1st Stamford Pl 6th Fl, Stamford, CT
06902
Tel.: (203) 977-8000
Web Site: https://greystoneinsuranceco.com
Sales Range: $75-99.9 Million
Reinsurance Services
N.A.I.C.S.: 524130
Andrew A. Barnard *(Chm & CEO)*

Subsidiary (Non-US):

Newline Underwriting Management
Ltd.   **(2)**
1 Fen Court, 3 Minster Court Suite 4, Lon-
don, EC3M 5BN, United Kingdom   **(100%)**
Tel.: (44) 2070901700
Sales Range: $25-49.9 Million
Emp.: 95
Holding Company; Insurance Services
N.A.I.C.S.: 551112

Subsidiary (Domestic):

Odyssey America Reinsurance
Corporation   **(2)**
300 1st Stamford Pl, Stamford, CT
06902-6765   **(100%)**
Tel.: (203) 977-8000
Sales Range: $100-124.9 Million
Emp.: 250
Reinsurance Services
N.A.I.C.S.: 524130

Subsidiary (Non-US):

Odyssey Reinsurance Company   **(2)**
                                    (100%)
Tel.: (305) 722-8401
Web Site: http://www.odysseyre.com
Sales Range: $50-74.9 Million
Emp.: 9
Reinsurance Services
N.A.I.C.S.: 524130
Brian Quinn *(CEO-North America)*

Division (Non-US):

Odyssey Reinsurance EuroAsia
Division   **(2)**

Fairfax Financial Holdings Limited—(Continued)

15 Rue Du 4 Septembre, 75002, Paris, France
Tel.: (33) 149261000
Sales Range: $50-74.9 Million
Emp.: 62
Reinsurance Services
N.A.I.C.S.: 524130

Pethealth Inc. (1)
710 Dorval Drive Suite 400, Oakville, L6K 3V7, ON, Canada
Tel.: (905) 842-2615
Web Site: https://www.pethealthinc.com
Sales Range: $25-49.9 Million
Emp.: 250
Pet Insurance & Recovery Services
N.A.I.C.S.: 524298
Nicole Bennett (CEO)

Subsidiary (US):

PTZ Insurance Agency, Ltd. (2)
3315 Algonquin Rd Ste 310, Rolling Meadows, IL 60008
Emp.: 50
Medical Insurance Services for Animals
N.A.I.C.S.: 524114
Sean Smith (CEO)

Polskie Towarzystwo Reasekuracji Spolka Akcyjna (1)
ul Bytomska 4, 01-612, Warsaw, Poland
Tel.: (48) 228320256
Web Site: https://www.polishre.com
Insurance Management Services
N.A.I.C.S.: 524298
Tomasz Czalbowski (CFO, Member-Mgmt Bd & VP)

Recipe Unlimited Corporation (1)
199 Four Valley Drive, Vaughan, L4K 0B8, ON, Canada (75.7%)
Tel.: (905) 760-2244
Web Site: http://www.recipeunlimited.com
In-Flight Catering, Airport Restaurants, Gift Shops, Multi-Unit Restaurants, Institutional Catering & Food Distribution
N.A.I.C.S.: 722320
Frank Hennessey (CEO)

Subsidiary (Domestic):

Groupe St-Hubert Inc. (2)
1755 Lionel Bertrand Blvd, Boisbriand, J7H 1N8, QC, Canada
Tel.: (514) 385-5555
Web Site: http://www.st-hubert.com
Restaurant Chain Operator
N.A.I.C.S.: 722511
Richard Scofield (Pres & CEO)

Kelseys International, Inc. (2)
6303 Airport Rd, Mississauga, L4V 1R8, ON, Canada (61%)
Tel.: (844) 729-7829
Web Site: http://www.kelseys.ca
Eating Place
N.A.I.C.S.: 722513

Prime Restaurants Inc. (2)
10 Kingsbridge Garden Circle, Mississauga, L5R 3K6, ON, Canada
Tel.: (905) 568-0000
Restaurant Operators
N.A.I.C.S.: 722511

RiverStone Managing Agency Limited (1)
Park Gate 161-163 Preston Road, Brighton, BN1 6AU, East Sussex, United Kingdom
Tel.: (44) 1273562345
Sales Range: $50-74.9 Million
Emp.: 75
Insurance Management Services
N.A.I.C.S.: 524298

Subsidiary (US):

Electric Insurance Company (2)
75 Sam Fonzo Dr, Beverly, MA 01915
Tel.: (978) 921-2080
Web Site: http://www.electricinsurance.com
Sales Range: $450-499.9 Million
Emp.: 510
Insurance Company
N.A.I.C.S.: 524126
Gerard P. McCarthy (Chief Underwriting Officer & Sr VP-Personal Lines Programs)

Singapore Reinsurance Corporation Limited (1)
85 Amoy Street, Singapore, 069904, Singapore (100%)
Web Site: http://www.singre.com.sg
Rev.: $176,498,044
Assets: $654,499,252
Liabilities: $451,926,420
Net Worth: $202,572,832
Earnings: $7,271,325
Emp.: 47
Fiscal Year-end: 12/31/2019
General Reinsurance
N.A.I.C.S.: 524130
Carlene Lay Hoon Lim (Controller-Fin, Investment, Admin & HR)

Subsidiary (Non-US):

SR-China Advisory Services Co Ltd (2)
53 Huangpu Road Unit 1918 The Panorama, Shanghai, 200080, China
Tel.: (86) 2133011088
Sales Range: $50-74.9 Million
Emp.: 1
Reinsurance Services
N.A.I.C.S.: 524130

Subsidiary (Domestic):

Singapore-Re Management Services Pte. Ltd. (2)
85 Amoy Street, Singapore, 069904, Singapore (100%)
Tel.: (65) 63247388
Web Site: http://www.singre.com.sg
Sales Range: $25-49.9 Million
Management & Computer Consulting
N.A.I.C.S.: 541513

Sleep Country Canada Holdings, Inc. (1)
7920 Airport Road, Brampton, L6T 4N8, ON, Canada
Tel.: (289) 748-0206
Web Site: https://www.sleepcountry.ca
Rev.: $706,070,425
Assets: $840,051,367
Liabilities: $516,139,622
Net Worth: $323,911,744
Earnings: $54,017,509
Emp.: 1,696
Fiscal Year-end: 12/31/2023
Holding Company
N.A.I.C.S.: 551112
David Friesema (CEO)

Southbridge Insurance Company (1)
Av Presidente Riesco 5335 15th floor, Las Condes, Santiago, Chile
Tel.: (56) 228268000
Holding Company; Insurance Services
N.A.I.C.S.: 551112

Subsidiary (Non-US):

SBI Seguros Uruguay S.A. (2)
Colonia 999, Montevideo, 11100, Uruguay
Tel.: (598) 29000330
Web Site: https://institucional.sbi.uy
Casualty Insurance Services
N.A.I.C.S.: 524126

SBS Seguros Colombia S.A. (2)
Av 9 101-67 Floor 7, Bogota, Colombia
Tel.: (57) 6013138700
Web Site: https://www.sbseguros.co
Rev.: $137,817,964
Assets: $367,710,117
Liabilities: $332,723,545
Net Worth: $34,986,572
Earnings: ($6,024,952)
Fiscal Year-end: 12/31/2018
Property & Casualty Insurance Services
N.A.I.C.S.: 524126

Southbridge Compania de Seguros Generales S.A. (2)
Tel.: (56) 28268000
Property & Casualty Insurance Services
N.A.I.C.S.: 524126

Sporting Life Inc. (1)
2665 Yonge Street, Toronto, M4P 2J6, Canada (75%)
Tel.: (416) 485-1611
Web Site: http://www.sportinglife.ca
Sales Range: $50-74.9 Million
Emp.: 650
Sporting Goods Store Retailer

N.A.I.C.S.: 459110

TIG Holdings, Inc. (1)
250 Commercial St Ste 5000, Manchester, NH 03101
Tel.: (972) 831-5000
Web Site: http://www.riverstone-group.com
Sales Range: $100-124.9 Million
Emp.: 200
Insurance Holding Company
N.A.I.C.S.: 524126

Subsidiary (Domestic):

TIG Insurance Co. (2)
5205 N O'Connor Blvd, Irving, TX 75039-3707 (100%)
Tel.: (972) 831-5000
Web Site: http://www.tiginsurance.com
Property & Casualty Insurance; Reinsurance, Specialty, Commercial & Personal Insurance; Underwrites Sports, Leisure & Entertainment Events
N.A.I.C.S.: 524126

The Pacific Insurance Berhad (1)
40-01 Q-Sentral 2A Jalan Stesen Sentral 2, Kuala Lumpur Sentral, 50470, Kuala Lumpur, Wilayah Persekutuan, Malaysia
Tel.: (60) 326338999
Web Site:
　https://www.pacificinsurance.com.my
Insurance Services
N.A.I.C.S.: 524210
Khalid Abdol Rahman (Chm)

Thomas Cook (India) Limited (1)
Shop No 324 Dr Dn Road Fort, Mumbai, 400001, India (67.63%)
Tel.: (91) 8879837843
Web Site: http://www.thomascook.in
Rev.: $129,093,510
Assets: $650,225,804
Liabilities: $388,693,715
Net Worth: $261,532,089
Earnings: ($40,294,254)
Emp.: 1,642
Fiscal Year-end: 03/31/2021
Travel Services
N.A.I.C.S.: 561599
Madhavan Menon (Chm & Mng Dir)

Subsidiary (US):

Allied T-Pro Inc. (2)
501 7th Ave Ste 1610, New York, NY 10018
Tel.: (212) 596-1000
Web Site: https://www.alliedtpro.com
Travel Agency; Tour Operating Services
N.A.I.C.S.: 561510
Mark Morello (CEO)

Subsidiary (Non-US):

Asian Trails Ltd. (2)
12th Floor Regent House 183 Rajdamri Road, Lumpini, Bangkok, 10330, Thailand
Tel.: (66) 28202000
Travel Agency
N.A.I.C.S.: 561510
Luzi Matzig (Co-Founder & Chm)

Subsidiary (Non-US):

AT Laos Co., Ltd. (3)
4th Floor Premier Building Sethathirath Road, PO Box 5422, Phiavat Village Sisattanak District, Vientiane, Lao People's Democratic Republic
Tel.: (856) 21263936
Tour Operating Services
N.A.I.C.S.: 561520
Andreas Hofmann (Mng Dir)

Asian Trails Tour Ltd. (3)
635-J Yoma Yeik Thar Pyay Road, Kamayut Township, Yangon, Myanmar
Tel.: (95) 9 4534 11155
Web Site: http://asiantrails.travel
Tour Operating Services
N.A.I.C.S.: 561520
Thomas Carnevale (Mng Dir)

Subsidiary (Non-US):

Australian Tours Management Pty Ltd. (2)
28 Victoria Street Level 1, Melbourne, 3053, VIC, Australia
Tel.: (61) 3 9662 1599
Web Site: http://www.atmtravel.com.au

Travel Agency; Tour Operating Services
N.A.I.C.S.: 561510

Desert Adventures Tourism LLC (2)
3rd Floor Al Barsha Boutique Building, PO Box 25488, Al Barsha 1, Dubai, United Arab Emirates
Tel.: (971) 44504450
Web Site:
　https://www.desertadventures.com
Travel Agency; Tour Operating Services
N.A.I.C.S.: 561510
Peter Payet (CEO)

Gulf Dunes LLC (2)
Al Barsha Boutique Building 3rd Floor, PO Box 124174, Al Barsha 1, Dubai, United Arab Emirates
Tel.: (971) 44504460
Web Site: https://www.gulfdunes.com
Tour Operating Services
N.A.I.C.S.: 561510
Peter Payet (CEO)

Kuoni Travel (China) Ltd. (2)
30/F AXA Tower Landmark East 100 How Ming Street, Kwun Tong, Kowloon, China (Hong Kong)
Tel.: (852) 2956 6888
Web Site: http://www.kuonitravel.com.hk
Travel & Tour Operating Services
N.A.I.C.S.: 561520

Private Safaris (Pty) Ltd. (2)
Unit 114 First Floor Block 2 Northgate Park, Corner Section Street Platinum Drive Paarden Eiland, Cape Town, 7405, South Africa
Tel.: (27) 215282200
Web Site: https://www.privatesafaris.com
Tourism Management Services
N.A.I.C.S.: 561510

Subsidiary (Non-US):

Private Safaris (East Africa) Ltd. (3)
OiLibya Plaza 2nd Floor, PO Box 16913, Muthaiga, 00620, Nairobi, Kenya
Tel.: (254) 203607000
Web Site: https://www.privatesafaris.co.ke
Travel Agency; Tour Operating Services
N.A.I.C.S.: 561510

Private Safaris Namibia (Pty) Ltd. (3)
Suite 320 3rd Floor Office Towers, Regus Business Centre Maerua Mall, Windhoek, Namibia
Tel.: (264) 833307479
Tour Operating Services
N.A.I.C.S.: 561520

Subsidiary (Domestic):

SOTC Travel Services Private Limited (2)
11th Floor Marathon Futurex NM Joshi Marg, Lower Parel, Mumbai, 400 013, India (100%)
Tel.: (91) 2249059100
Web Site: https://www.sotc.in
Travel & Tourism Services
N.A.I.C.S.: 561510
Vishal Suri (Mng Dir)

Subsidiary (Non-US):

Sterling Holiday Resorts (India) Limited (2)
Web Site: http://www.sterlingholidays.com
Sales Range: $10-24.9 Million
Emp.: 1,900
Tourism Services
N.A.I.C.S.: 561599
Vikram Lalvani (CEO & Mng Dir)

Toys "R" Us (Canada) Ltd. (1)
2777 Langstaff Rd, Concord, L4K 4M5, ON, Canada
Tel.: (905) 660-2000
Web Site: http://www.toysrus.ca
Toy Retailer
N.A.I.C.S.: 459120

Wentworth Insurance Company Ltd. (1)
12 Pine Commercial Centre, Saint Michael, BB11103, Barbados
Tel.: (246) 4240865
Web Site: https://wentworth.bb

N.A.I.C.S.: 524298

William Ashley China Corporation (1)
55 Bloor St W, Toronto, M4W 3V1, ON, Canada
Tel.: (416) 964-9111
Web Site: http://www.williamashley.com
Coins & Gift Products Retailer
N.A.I.C.S.: 459420

Zenith National Insurance Corp. (1)
21255 Califa St, Woodland Hills, CA 91367-5005
Tel.: (818) 713-1000
Sales Range: $550-599.9 Million
Emp.: 1,400
Holding Company; Property & Casualty Reinsurance & Workers' Compensation Insurance Services
N.A.I.C.S.: 551112

Subsidiary (Domestic):

Zenith Insurance Company (2)
21255 Califa St, Woodland Hills, CA 91367 **(100%)**
Tel.: (818) 713-1000
Web Site: https://www.thezenith.com
Sales Range: $600-649.9 Million
Emp.: 1,076
Workers' Compensation Underwriting Services
N.A.I.C.S.: 524298
Kari L. Van Gundy (Pres & CEO)

FAIRMILE GOLDTECH INC.
2001 837 W Hastings St, Vancouver, V6C 3N7, BC, Canada
Tel.: (604) 294-1082
Year Founded: 1987
FMGDF—(TSX)
Mineral Exploration Services
N.A.I.C.S.: 213115
Ian R. F. MacCulloch (Pres & CEO)

FAIRPLAY PROPERTIES REIT
51B Cherni Vruh Blvd, 1407, Sofia, 1407, Bulgaria
Tel.: (359) 28199103
Web Site: https://www.fpp.bg
6F3—(BUL)
Rev.: $6,542,299
Assets: $144,930,304
Liabilities: $8,356,233
Net Worth: $136,574,072
Earnings: $1,966,812
Fiscal Year-end: 12/31/19
Real Estate Manangement Services
N.A.I.C.S.: 531311
Manu Todorov Moravenov (CEO)

FAIRPLAY SCHLEPPDAMPFSCHIFFS-REEDEREI RICHARD BORCHARD GMBH
Ludwig-Erhard-Str 22, 20459, Hamburg, Germany
Tel.: (49) 403070680
Web Site: http://www.fairplay-towage.com
Year Founded: 1905
Rev.: $19,989,750
Emp.: 70
Tugboat Operator
N.A.I.C.S.: 488330
Walter Collet (Mng Dir)

Subsidiaries:

Antwerp Towage NV (1)
Tavernierkaai 2 bus 3, 2000, Antwerp, Belgium
Tel.: (32) 32121000
Web Site: http://www.antwerp-towage.com
Ship Management & Barge Towing Services
N.A.I.C.S.: 483211
Robert B. van Hees (Gen Mgr)

FAIRPLAY TOWAGE POLSKA Sp. z.o.o. Sp.k. (1)
Plac Rodla 9, 70-419, Szczecin, Poland
Tel.: (48) 918522720

Logistics Consulting Servies
N.A.I.C.S.: 541614
Mirek Wiater (Mng Dir)

Fairplay Towage B.V. (1)
Terwenakker 42/44, 3011 XS, Rotterdam, Netherlands
Tel.: (31) 104112999
Logistics Consulting Servies
N.A.I.C.S.: 541614
Set Van denB out (Mgr)

Theodor Buschmann GmbH & Co KG (1)
Reiherstieg Deich 53, 21107, Hamburg, Germany
Tel.: (49) 407519830
Web Site: http://www.theodor-buschmann.com
Ship Management & Barge Towing Services
N.A.I.C.S.: 483211
Holger Schwesig (Mng Dir)

FAIRPOINT GROUP PLC
Fairclough House Church Street, Adlington, PR7 4EX, Lancs, United Kingdom
Tel.: (44) 8448261209 UK
Web Site: http://www.fairpoint.co.uk
Year Founded: 1997
Sales Range: $75-99.9 Million
Emp.: 825
Holding Company; Personal & Commercial Support Services
N.A.I.C.S.: 551112
David Terence Digby Harrel (Chm)

Subsidiaries:

Simpson Millar LLP (1)
27 St Paul's Street, Leeds, LS1 2JG, W Yorkshire, United Kingdom
Tel.: (44) 844 858 3200
Web Site: http://www.simpsonmillar.co.uk
Emp.: 300
Law firm
N.A.I.C.S.: 541110
Peter Watson (Mng Dir)

FAIRSTAR RESOURCES LTD.
U3 136 Main Street, Osborne Park, 6017, WA, Australia
Tel.: (61) 892425111
Web Site: http://www.fairstarresources.com
Sales Range: Less than $1 Million
Emp.: 9
Oil & Gas Exploration Services
N.A.I.C.S.: 211120
Kevin J. Robertson (Mng Dir)

FAIRVEST LIMITED
3rd Floor Upper Building 1 Sturdee Avenue, Rosebank, Johannesburg, South Africa
Tel.: (27) 101000076 ZA
Web Site: http://www.arrowheadproperty.co.za
Year Founded: 2011
FTAE—(JSE)
Rev.: $101,444,777
Assets: $667,227,474
Liabilities: $258,145,101
Net Worth: $409,082,373
Earnings: $35,237,698
Emp.: 46
Fiscal Year-end: 09/30/23
Real Estate Development Services
N.A.I.C.S.: 531390
Mark Kaplan (CEO)

Subsidiaries:

Indluplace Properties Limited (1)
3rd Floor 1 Sturdee Avenue parking entrance in Baker Street, Rosebank, South Africa **(56.8%)**
Tel.: (27) 101000076
Web Site: http://www.indluplace.co.za
Rev.: $39,825,350
Assets: $240,473,616
Liabilities: $98,906,552
Net Worth: $141,567,064

Earnings: $762,475
Fiscal Year-end: 09/30/2022
Real Estate Manangement Services
N.A.I.C.S.: 531390
Grant Harris (COO)

FAIRVEST PROPERTY HOLDINGS LIMITED
8th Floor The Terraces 34 Bree Street, Cape Town, 8001, South Africa
Tel.: (27) 212760800 ZA
Web Site: http://www.fairvest.co.za
FVT—(JSE)
Rev.: $33,898,677
Assets: $245,771,138
Liabilities: $75,246,087
Net Worth: $170,525,051
Earnings: $17,788,164
Fiscal Year-end: 06/30/19.
Real Estate Development Services
N.A.I.C.S.: 531390
Darren M. Wilder (CEO)

FAIRVIEW COVE AUTO LTD.
30 Bedford Highway, Halifax, B3M 2J2, NS, Canada
Tel.: (902) 457-1555
Web Site: http://www.atlanticacura.ns.ca
Year Founded: 1987
New & Used Car Dealers
N.A.I.C.S.: 441110
Bruce Hill (Pres)

FAIRWAY FORD SALES LTD.
236 Main Street, Steinbach, R5G 1Y6, MB, Canada
Tel.: (204) 326-3412
Web Site: https://www.fairwayford.ca
Year Founded: 1914
New & Used Car Dealers
N.A.I.C.S.: 441110
Daryl Friesen (Mgr-Sls-New Car)

FAIRWOOD HOLDINGS LIMITED
2/F TRP Commercial Centre, 18 Tanner Road, North Point, China (Hong Kong)
Tel.: (852) 28567111 BM
Web Site: https://www.fairwoodholdings.com
Year Founded: 1972
0052—(HKG)
Rev.: $371,712,879
Assets: $301,460,827
Liabilities: $209,338,667
Net Worth: $92,122,159
Earnings: $5,499,707
Emp.: 5,700
Fiscal Year-end: 03/31/22
Fast Foods Industry
N.A.I.C.S.: 722511
Dennis Hoi Yeung Lo (Chm)

Subsidiaries:

Fairwood Fast Food Limited (1)
2/F TRP Commercial Centre 18 Tanner Road, North Point, China (Hong Kong)
Tel.: (852) 28567217
Web Site: http://ssl.fairwood.com.hk
Restaurant Operators
N.A.I.C.S.: 722511

FAISAL ISLAMIC BANK OF EGYPT
3 26th July St, Cairo, Egypt
Tel.: (20) 37621285
Web Site: http://www.faisalbank.com.eg
Year Founded: 1979
Sales Range: $75-99.9 Million
Emp.: 1,000
Banking Services
N.A.I.C.S.: 522110
Amr Al-Faisal Aal-Saoud (Chm)

FAISAL SPINNING MILLS LIMITED
Umer House Plot 23/1 Sector 23 SM Farooq Road Korangi Industrial Area, Karachi, 74900, Pakistan
Tel.: (92) 2135115177
Web Site: https://www.umergroup.com
FASM—(LAH)
Rev.: $100,725,105
Assets: $73,109,313
Liabilities: $35,213,940
Net Worth: $37,895,374
Earnings: $6,594,829
Emp.: 1,009
Fiscal Year-end: 06/30/19
Yarn Mfr
N.A.I.C.S.: 313110
Anwar Hussain (CFO)

FAITH, INC.
Imon-Meiji-Yasudaseimei bldg 566-1 Toraya-cho Karasumadori-Oike-Sagaru, Nakagyo-ku, Kyoto, 604-8171, Japan
Tel.: (81) 752133933
Web Site: https://www.faith-inc.com
Year Founded: 1992
4295—(TKS)
Rev.: $90,808,180
Assets: $144,778,830
Liabilities: $57,037,690
Net Worth: $87,741,140
Earnings: ($7,244,560)
Emp.: 429
Fiscal Year-end: 03/31/24
Content Delivery & Electronic Money Businesses
N.A.I.C.S.: 522390
Hajime Hirasawa (Pres & CEO)

Subsidiaries:

Brave, Inc. (1)
No 23 Sq 3F Ebisu 1-chome, Shibuya-ku, Tokyo, Japan
Tel.: (81) 3 5789 9800
Digital Content Services
N.A.I.C.S.: 323111

Faith Wonderworks, Inc. (1)
Face Minami Aoyama Building 6-10-12 Minami Aoyama, Minato-ku, Tokyo, 107-0062, Japan
Tel.: (81) 354685400
Web Site: https://www.faith-wonderworks.co.jp
Emp.: 12
Cellular Phone Services
N.A.I.C.S.: 517112

Goody Point, Inc. (1)
Tel.: (81) 752566011
Web Site: http://www.goody.co.jp
Sales Range: $25-49.9 Million
Emp.: 29
Retail Business Service
N.A.I.C.S.: 459999

Nippon Columbia Co., Ltd. (1)
Faith Minami-Aoyama 6-10-12 Minami-Aoyama, Minato-ku, Tokyo, 107-0062, Japan **(50.62%)**
Tel.: (81) 359626990
Web Site: https://columbia.jp
Software Development Services
N.A.I.C.S.: 541511
Hajime Hirasawa (Chm)

Rightsscale, Inc. (1)
Faith Minami Aoyama Minami Aoyama 6-10-12, Minato-ku, Tokyo, 107-0062, Japan
Tel.: (81) 354647633
Web Site: https://www.rightsscale.co.jp
Sales Range: $50-74.9 Million
Emp.: 7
Digital Music Distr
N.A.I.C.S.: 423990
Yuka Kinoshita (Pres & CEO)

FAITHNETWORK CO., LTD.
3-2-1 Sendagaya, Shibuya-Ku, Tokyo, 151-0051, Japan

FaithNetwork Co., Ltd.—(Continued)

Tel.: (81) 364329937
Web Site: https://faithnetwork.co.jp
Year Founded: 2001
3489—(TKS)
Rev.: $147,297,240
Assets: $175,885,490
Liabilities: $126,766,580
Net Worth: $49,118,910
Earnings: $6,233,230
Fiscal Year-end: 03/31/24
Real Estate Development Services
N.A.I.C.S.: 531311
Jiro Hachiya *(Founder, Chm & Pres)*

FAJARBARU BUILDER GROUP BHD.
No 61 63 Jalan SS 6/12 Kelana Jaya,
47301, Petaling Jaya, Selangor Darul
Ehsan, Malaysia
Tel.: (60) 378049698
Web Site:
　https://www.fajarbaru.com.my
Year Founded: 1976
FAJAR—(KLS)
Rev.: $47,419,471
Assets: $121,257,778
Liabilities: $40,156,402
Net Worth: $81,101,376
Earnings: ($3,521,481)
Emp.: 250
Fiscal Year-end: 06/30/23
Property Development Services
N.A.I.C.S.: 531311
Kam Loong Kong *(Dir-Construction-Building)*

Subsidiaries:

Asiahub Trading Sdn. Bhd.　　　(1)
No 61 and 63 Jalan SS 6/12 Kelana Jaya,
47301, Petaling Jaya, Selangor, Malaysia
Tel.: (60) 378049698
Web Site: https://www.asiahubtrading.com
Construction Materials Whslr
N.A.I.C.S.: 423390

Fajarbaru Builder Sdn. Bhd.　　　(1)
No 61 & 63 Jalan SS 6/12, Kelana Jaya,
Petaling Jaya, 47301, Selangor, Malaysia
Tel.: (60) 378049698
Sales Range: $50-74.9 Million
Emp.: 100
Construction Services
N.A.I.C.S.: 237990

FAKOM AD
Bul Aleksandar Makedonski no 18,
1000, Skopje, North Macedonia
Tel.: (389) 25513103
Web Site: https://www.fakom.com.mk
Year Founded: 1960
FAKM—(MAC)
Rev.: $19,415,731
Assets: $25,092,694
Liabilities: $15,830,853
Net Worth: $9,261,842
Earnings: $1,259
Fiscal Year-end: 12/31/23
Metal Work Mfr
N.A.I.C.S.: 332322
Minco Jordanov *(Chm/Chm-Supervisory Bd)*

FAKTOR 3 AG
Kattunbleiche 35, 22041, Hamburg,
Germany
Tel.: (49) 40 67 94 46 53
Web Site: http://www.faktor3.de
Year Founded: 2005
Emp.: 120
Automotive, Consumer Goods,
E-Commerce, Information Technology
N.A.I.C.S.: 541810
Sabine Richter *(Owner)*

FAL GROUP OF COMPANIES
PO Box 6600, Sharjah, United Arab
Emirates

Tel.: (971) 65286666
Web Site: http://www.falgroup.com
Sales Range: $100-124.9 Million
Emp.: 500
Petroleum Products Marketer & Whslr
N.A.I.C.S.: 425120
Abdulla Juma Al Sari *(Chm)*

Subsidiaries:

FAL Energy Co., Ltd.　　　　　(1)
PO Box 6600, Sharjah, United Arab Emirates
Tel.: (971) 65286666
Web Site: http://www.falgroup.com
Marine Lubes & Bunkers Supplier to Ship
Owners & Charterers
N.A.I.C.S.: 424720

FAL Shipping Co., Ltd.　　　　(1)
PO Box 6600, Sharjah, United Arab Emirates
Tel.: (971) 65286666
Sales Range: $25-49.9 Million
Emp.: 70
Owner & Operator of Tanker Vessels
N.A.I.C.S.: 488320

FALABELLA S.A.
Manuel Rodriguez Norte 730, Santiago, Chile
Tel.: (56) 23802000
Web Site: http://www.falabella.com
FALABELLA—(SGO)
Rev.: $10,672,515,837
Assets: $23,001,808,034
Liabilities: $16,369,046,052
Net Worth: $6,632,761,982
Earnings: $135,113,134
Emp.: 102,542
Fiscal Year-end: 12/31/22
Department Store Retailer
N.A.I.C.S.: 455110
Pablo Meza Martinez *(CEO-TI Corp)*

Subsidiaries:

Linio Colombia S.A.S.　　　　(1)
Calle 99 14-49 Piso 9, Bogota, Colombia
Tel.: (57) 14842220
Web Site: http://www.linio.com
Janitorial Services
N.A.I.C.S.: 561790

Mall Plaza Colombia S.A.S.　　(1)
Cra 55 No 98, Barranquilla, Colombia
Tel.: (57) 53858520
Web Site: http://www.mallplaza.co
Shopping Mall Services
N.A.I.C.S.: 531120

Mall Plaza Peru S.A.　　　　　(1)
Av Oscar R Benavides 3866, Callao, 07011,
Peru
Tel.: (51) 15005202
Shopping Mall Services
N.A.I.C.S.: 531120

Plaza Antofagasta S.A.　　　　(1)
Avenida Balmaceda, 2355, Antofagasta,
Chile
Tel.: (56) 6005857000
Web Site:
　http://www.antofagasta.mallplaza.cl
Food Service
N.A.I.C.S.: 561439

Plaza Del Trebol SpA　　　　　(1)
Avenida Jorge Alessandri, 3177, Talcahuano, Chile
Tel.: (56) 6005857000
Web Site: http://www.trebol.mallplaza.cl
Food Service
N.A.I.C.S.: 561439

Plaza Oeste SpA　　　　　　　(1)
Av Americo Vespucio, 1501, Cerrillos, Chile
Tel.: (56) 6005857000
Web Site: http://www.oeste.mallplaza.cl
Food Service
N.A.I.C.S.: 561439

Plaza Tobalaba SpA　　　　　　(1)
Avenida Camilo Henriquez, 3692, Puente
Alto, Chile
Tel.: (56) 6005857000
Web Site: http://www.tobalaba.mallplaza.cl
Food Service

N.A.I.C.S.: 561439

Plaza Vespucio SpA　　　　　　(1)
Avenida Vicuna Mackenna, La Florida,
7110, Santiago, Chile
Tel.: (56) 6005857000
Web Site: http://www.vespucio.mallplaza.ol
Food Service
N.A.I.C.S.: 561439

FALANX CYBER SECURITY LTD
The Blade Abbey Square, Reading,
RG1 3BE, United Kingdom
Tel.: (44) 2078569457　　　VG
Web Site: http://www.falanx.com
FCS—(LSE)
Rev.: $4,398,838
Assets: $10,302,702
Liabilities: $4,902,276
Net Worth: $5,400,426
Earnings: $1,843,554
Emp.: 51
Fiscal Year-end: 03/31/22
Holding Company
N.A.I.C.S.: 551112
Mike D. Read *(CEO)*

FALCK S.P.A.
GE Falck 63, 20099, Milan, Italy
Tel.: (39) 0224331
Web Site: http://www.falck.it
Year Founded: 1906
Sales Range: $200-249.9 Million
Emp.: 296
Renewable Energy Production & Iron
& Steel Mfg
N.A.I.C.S.: 331110
Enrico Falck *(Chm)*

Subsidiaries:

Cambrian Wind Energy Ltd　　　(1)
7 Beaumont Mews West Central, London,
W1G 6EB, United Kingdom
Tel.: (44) 20 7486 5400
Eletric Power Generation Services
N.A.I.C.S.: 221118

Falck Accial-CNS SpA　　　　　(1)
Via Lungo Serio 21, Grassobbio, Bergamo,
24050, Italy
Tel.: (39) 035335668
Iron & Steel Mfr
N.A.I.C.S.: 331110

Falck Renewables S.p.A.　　　　(1)
via Alberto Falck 4-16, 20099, Sesto San
Giovanni, MI, Italy　　　　　　(68.7%)
Tel.: (39) 0224331
Web Site: http://www.falckrenewables.eu
Rev.: $419,380,851
Assets: $2,003,339,951
Liabilities: $1,322,842,464
Net Worth: $680,497,487
Earnings: $54,241,539
Emp.: 498
Fiscal Year-end: 12/31/2019
Renewable Energy Production
N.A.I.C.S.: 221118
Enrico Falck *(Chm)*

Subsidiary (Domestic):

Ambiente 2000 Srl　　　　　　(2)
Via Brasile 2, Roseto degli Abruzzi, 64026,
Teramo, Italy
Tel.: (39) 085 8426953
Web Site: http://www.ambiente2000.eu
Electric Equipment Mfr
N.A.I.C.S.: 335999

Ecosesto SpA　　　　　　　　(2)
Contrada Cancello Magdalone Rende,
Cosenza, 87036, Italy
Tel.: (39) 0984403364
Eletric Power Generation Services
N.A.I.C.S.: 221111

ITLA S.p.A.　　　　　　　　　(1)
Localita IL PIANO, CASOLE D'ELSA,
Siena, 22048, Tuscany, Italy
Tel.: (39) 0577 949007
Web Site: http://www.itla.it
Emp.: 60
Steel Mfrs

N.A.I.C.S.: 331110
Alberto Bartalucci *(Gen Mgr)*

Wysoka Wind Farm Sp. Z.o.o.　　(1)
ul Rubiez 46, 61-612, Poznan, Poland
Tel.: (48) 61 622 69 30
Eletric Power Generation Services
N.A.I.C.S.: 221111

FALCO HOLDINGS CO., LTD.
1-3-7 Uchihiranomachi, Chuo-ku,
Osaka, 540-0037, Japan
Tel.: (81) 752578585
Web Site: https://www.falco-hd.co.jp
Year Founded: 1962
4671—(TKS)
Rev.: $284,276,270
Assets: $240,769,250
Liabilities: $68,737,390
Net Worth: $172,031,860
Earnings: $11,012,260
Emp.: 928
Fiscal Year-end: 03/31/24
Contract Clinical & Genetic Testing
Services
N.A.I.C.S.: 621511
Tadashi Yasuda *(Pres & Pres)*

Subsidiaries:

FALCO Pharmacies, Ltd.　　　　(1)
346 Shimizucho Kawaramachidori Ni-
joagaru, Nakagyo-Ku, Kyoto, 604-0911,
Japan　　　　　　　　　　　　(100%)
Tel.: (81) 752131621
Web Site: http://www.falco-hd.co.jp
Sales Range: $100-124.9 Million
Emp.: 1,600
Pharmaceuticals Dispensing
N.A.I.C.S.: 456110
Kenjiro Hirasaki *(Pres)*

Falco Biosystems Ltd.　　　　　(1)
44-3 Shogoin Rengezocho, Sakyo-ku,
Kyoto, 606-8357, Japan
Tel.: (81) 75 320 4240
Web Site: https://www.falco.co.jp
In-Vitro Diagnostic Drug Mfr
N.A.I.C.S.: 325413
Nobumasa Matsubara *(Pres & CEO)*

Tulip Drug Dispensary Co., Ltd.　(1)
2-21 Shinsakuramachi MKD 9 Toyama
Building 5F, Toyama, 930-0005, Japan
Tel.: (81) 76 441 1331
Web Site: https://www.tulip-tz.co.jp
Pharmaceutical Products Distr
N.A.I.C.S.: 424210
Osamu Abe *(Pres & CEO)*

FALCO RESOURCES LTD.
1100 avenue des Canadiens-de-
Montreal Suite 300, Montreal, H3B
2S2, QC, Canada
Tel.: (514) 905-3162　　　　BC
Web Site: https://www.falcores.com
Year Founded: 2010
FPC—(OTCIQ)
Rev.: $41,561
Assets: $88,083,583
Liabilities: $56,160,534
Net Worth: $31,923,048
Earnings: ($3,011,175)
Fiscal Year-end: 06/30/21
Metal Exploration & Mining Services
N.A.I.C.S.: 212290
Helene Cartier *(VP-Environment & Sustainable Dev)*

FALCO-SOPRON BUTOR KFT.
Banfalvi ut 27, Sopron, 9400, Hungary
Tel.: (36) 209450848
Web Site: http://www.falcosopron.hu
Year Founded: 1961
Sales Range: $10-24.9 Million
Emp.: 100
Office Furnishings Mfr
N.A.I.C.S.: 337214

FALCON ENERGY GROUP LIMITED

10 Raeburn Park 0133B, Singapore,
088702, Singapore
Tel.: (65) 65387177   SG
Web Site:
  https://www.falconenergy.com.sg
Rev.: $44,537,000
Assets: $366,509,000
Liabilities: $269,495,000
Net Worth: $97,014,000
Earnings: ($93,444,000)
Fiscal Year-end: 06/30/18
Offshore Oil & Gas Operation Support Services
N.A.I.C.S.: 213112
Pong Tyea Tan *(Chm & CEO)*

Subsidiaries:

Longzhu Oilfield Services (S) Pte.
Ltd.   (1)
10 Anson Road 14-19/20 International
Plaza, Singapore, 079903, Singapore
Tel.: (65) 62734963
Web Site: http://www.longzhugroup.com
Offshore Logistic Services
N.A.I.C.S.: 488510
Mdm Long *(Chm)*

PT. Bayu Maritim Berkah   (1)
10/F E3B Financial Ave No 20 Plaza Erd
Teda, Tianjin, 300457, China
Tel.: (86) 2266282258
Web Site: http://www.cdstj.com
Oil & Gas Field Exploration Services
N.A.I.C.S.: 213112

FALCON GOLD CORP.
1100-1111 Melville St, Vancouver,
V6E 3V6, BC, Canada
Tel.: (604) 716-0551
Web Site: https://www.falcongold.ca
Year Founded: 2006
3FA—(DEU)
Rev.: $26,526
Assets: $2,075,809
Liabilities: $338,166
Net Worth: $1,737,643
Earnings: ($1,042,568)
Fiscal Year-end: 06/30/22
Mineral Exploration Services
N.A.I.C.S.: 213114
Kenneth Anthony Cawkell *(Sec)*

FALCON MACHINE TOOLS CO. LTD.
No 34 Hsing Kong Road Shang
Kang, Changhua, Shengang, 509004,
Taiwan
Tel.: (886) 47991126
Web Site:
  https://www.chevaliertw.com
Year Founded: 1978
4513—(TPE)
Rev.: $50,356,502
Assets: $77,329,331
Liabilities: $51,660,288
Net Worth: $25,669,043
Earnings: ($718,976)
Fiscal Year-end: 12/31/22
Machine Tool Mfr & Distr
N.A.I.C.S.: 333517
Po-Ming Chang *(Chm)*

Subsidiaries:

Chevalier Machinery Co., Ltd.   (1)
No 58 Huangpujiang Road, High-tech Development Zone, Changshu, China
Tel.: (86) 5128 235 5999
Web Site: https://www.sz-chevalier.com
Surface Grinder Mfr
N.A.I.C.S.: 333517

Chevalier Machinery, Inc.   (1)
9925 Tabor Pl, Santa Fe Springs, CA 90670
Tel.: (562) 903-1929
Web Site: https://www.chevalierusa.com
Rev.: $5,969,100
Emp.: 25
Surface Grinder Mfr
N.A.I.C.S.: 333517
Peter Chang *(CEO)*

FALCON METALS LIMITED
Suite 6 Level 6 350 Collins St, Melbourne, 3000, VIC, Australia
Tel.: (61) 386486684   AU
Web Site:
  https://www.falconmetals.com.au
Year Founded: 2021
FAL—(ASX)
Rev.: $448,352
Assets: $11,760,982
Liabilities: $545,815
Net Worth: $11,215,167
Earnings: ($6,038,992)
Emp.: 4
Fiscal Year-end: 06/30/23
Metal Exploration Services
N.A.I.C.S.: 213114
Pradeep Subramaniam *(CFO)*

FALCON OIL & GAS LTD.
68 Merrion Square South, Dublin, 2,
Ireland
Tel.: (353) 16768702
Web Site:
  http://www.falconoilandgas.com
FOG—(AIM)
Assets: $61,958,000
Liabilities: $15,934,000
Net Worth: $46,024,000
Earnings: ($3,991,000)
Fiscal Year-end: 12/31/22
Oil & Gas Exploration Services
N.A.I.C.S.: 213112
Philip O'Quigley *(CEO)*

FALCON POWER CO., LTD.
6F-5 No 495 Guangfu S Rd, Xinyi
District, Taipei, 110, Taiwan
Tel.: (886) 227200095
Web Site:
  http://www.falconpower.com.tw
1516—(TAI)
Rev.: $27,885,639
Assets: $15,806,762
Liabilities: $1,087,707
Net Worth: $14,719,055
Earnings: $431,701
Fiscal Year-end: 12/31/23
Bicycle Parts, Exercise Products &
Parts Mfr
N.A.I.C.S.: 339920

FALCON SOCIAL APS
Kobmagergade 45, 1150, Copenhagen, Denmark
Tel.: (45) 29 36 75 60
Web Site:
  http://www.falconsocial.com
Year Founded: 2010
Emp.: 200
Social Media Management Software
Developer
N.A.I.C.S.: 513210

FALCON-SOFTWARE COMPANY, INC.
2826 Bryn Maur Road, Victoria, V9B
3T4, BC, Canada
Tel.: (250) 481-1311
Web Site: http://www.falcon-
  software.com
Year Founded: 1993
Sales Range: $1-9.9 Million
Emp.: 20
Software Publisher
N.A.I.C.S.: 513210

FALK BUILDING SYSTEMS BV
Neonstraat 23 Ede, 6718 WX,
Gelderland , Netherlands
Tel.: (31) 318670670
Web Site:
  https://www.falkbouwsystemen.nl
Year Founded: 2007
Emp.: 75

Insulated Metals : Sandwichpanelen,
Gevels, Daken, Prefab, Circulair &
Duurzaam Mfg.
N.A.I.C.S.: 332311

Subsidiaries:

Salzgitter Bauelemente GmbH   (1)
Eisenhuttenstrasse 99, 38239, Salzgitter,
Germany
Tel.: (49) 5341214413
Web Site: http://www.szbe.de
Sales Range: $50-74.9 Million
Emp.: 80
Steel Product Distr
N.A.I.C.S.: 423510

FALKLAND ISLANDS RADIO SERVICE
John Street, FIQQ 1ZZ, Stanley,
Falkland Islands
Tel.: (500) 27277
Web Site: http://www.firs.co.fk
Sales Range: $10-24.9 Million
Emp.: 12
Radio Broadcasting Services
N.A.I.C.S.: 516110
Corina Goss *(Mgr-Station)*

FALLUJAH FOR CONSTRUCTION MATERIALS CO.
Near Al Fallujah Cement Factory Al
Anbar, Fallujah, Iraq
Tel.: (964) 2 4662083
Year Founded: 1989
Construction Materials Distr
N.A.I.C.S.: 423320

FALMAC LIMITED
215 Henderson Road No 03 05 Henderson Industrial Park, Singapore,
159544, Singapore
Tel.: (65) 62654033
Sales Range: $1-9.9 Million
Machinery & Components Mfr
N.A.I.C.S.: 333248
Lock Chee Wong *(Mng Dir)*

Subsidiaries:

Falmac Machinery (Tianjin) Ltd.   (1)
Ninghe Jingji Kaifa Qu, Ninghe County,
Tianjin, 301500, Hebei, China
Tel.: (86) 2269581388
Web Site: http://www.falmac.com
Circular Knitting Machinery Mfr & Distr
N.A.I.C.S.: 333248

Falmac Textile (Tianjin) Ltd.   (1)
7 KuanMing Road Lutai, Tianjin, 301500,
China
Tel.: (86) 22 6958 8173
Textile Mfr
N.A.I.C.S.: 314999

FAM AB
Arsenalsgatan 8C 2nd Floor, PO Box
16066, Stockholm, Sweden
Tel.: (46) 8 50 400 300
Web Site: http://www.fam.se
Holding Company; Asset Management Services
N.A.I.C.S.: 551112
Marcus Wallenberg *(Chm)*

Subsidiaries:

IPCO AB   (1)
2453-B Vastra Verken, 81181, Sandviken,
Sweden
Tel.: (46) 703120300
Web Site: http://www.ipco.com
Steel Belts, Press Plates, Conveyor & Processing Systems Mfr, Distr & Installation
Services
N.A.I.C.S.: 331221
Alexander Pollnow *(Mgr-Technical)*

Unit (Non-US):

IPCO Germany GmbH   (2)
Salierstrasse 35, PO Box 70736, Fellbach,
70736, Germany
Tel.: (49) 71151050

Web Site: http://www.ipco.com
Steel Belts, Press Plates, Conveyor & Processing Systems Distr & Installation Services
N.A.I.C.S.: 423830

Subsidiary (Non-US):

IPCO Process System (Shanghai)
Ltd.   (2)
No 4555 Yin Du Road Xin Zhuang Industry
Park, 201108, Shanghai, China
Tel.: (86) 21 34073700
Web Site: http://www.ipco.com
Steel Belt Distr
N.A.I.C.S.: 423510

Unit (Non-US):

IPCO Process Systems B.V.   (2)
Overemer 8 Industrie Nr 4190, 4824 AH,
Breda, Netherlands
Tel.: (31) 6 1501 5083
Web Site: http://www.ipco.com
Steel Belts, Press Plates, Conveyor & Processing Systems Distr & Installation Services
N.A.I.C.S.: 423830

Subsidiary (Non-US):

IPCO Rus LTD   (2)
Ul Polkovaja 1, 127018, Moscow, Russia
Tel.: (7) 4956898386
Web Site: http://www.ipco.com
Steel Belts, Press Plates, Conveyor & Processing Systems Distr & Installation Services
N.A.I.C.S.: 423830

Subsidiary (US):

IPCO US, LLC   (2)
21 Campus Rd, Totowa, NJ
07512-1201   (100%)
Tel.: (973) 790-1600
Web Site: http://www.ipco.com
Steel Belts, Press Plates, Conveyor & Processing Systems Mfr, Distr & Installation
Services
N.A.I.C.S.: 331221
Robert Stivale *(Pres)*

The Grand Group AB   (1)
Sodra Blasieholmshamnen 8, PO Box 164
24, 103 27, Stockholm, Sweden
Tel.: (46) 8 679 3500
Web Site: http://www.grandhotel.se
Sales Range: $200-249.9 Million
Emp.: 260
Home Management Services
N.A.I.C.S.: 523999

Subsidiary (US):

Grand Hotel - Mackinac Island   (2)
286 Grand Ave, Mackinac Island, MI 49757
Tel.: (906) 847-3331
Web Site: http://www.grandhotel.com
Home Management Services
N.A.I.C.S.: 721110

Subsidiary (Domestic):

New Grand Hotel AB   (2)
Sodra Blasieholmshamnen 8, Stockholm,
11148, Sweden
Tel.: (46) 86793500
Web Site: http://www.grandhotel.se
Sales Range: $25-49.9 Million
Emp.: 200
Hotels & Motels
N.A.I.C.S.: 721110
Marie-Louise Kjellstrom *(Mng Dir)*

FAM GRUPA KAPITALOWA S.A.
Ul Avlcenny 16, 54-611, Wroclaw,
Poland
Tel.: (48) 71 38 39 905
Web Site: http://www.famgk.pl
Fabricated Metal Products Mfr
N.A.I.C.S.: 332312
Pawel Relidzynski *(Chm-Mgmt Bd)*

FAMEGLOW HOLDINGS LTD.
Shop 1 21/F iSQUARE 63 Nathan

Fameglow Holdings Ltd.—(Continued)

Road, Tsim Sha Tsui, Kowloon, China
(Hong Kong)
Tel.: (852) 3 185 7805   **Ky**
Web Site: http://www.fameglow.com
8603—(HKG)
Rev.: $10,583,841
Assets: $31,849,934
Liabilities: $30,313,782
Net Worth: $1,536,152
Earnings: ($3,477,172)
Emp.: 111
Fiscal Year-end: 03/31/21
Beauty Salon Operator
N.A.I.C.S.: 812112
Danny Chun Kwok Yip *(Exec Dir)*

FAMILY ADVERTISING
4-5 Mitchell St, Leith, Edinburgh, EH6
7BD, Scotland, United Kingdom
Tel.: (44) 1315538666
Web Site:
   http://www.familycomms.com
Year Founded: 2002
Sales Range: $10-24.9 Million
Emp.: 15
Advertising, Graphic Design, Outdoor,
Radio, T.V.
N.A.I.C.S.: 541810
Ian Wright *(Mng Dir)*

FAMILY BAKERY SDN. BHD.
No 33 Jalan Meru Indah 20 Taman
Perindustrian Meru Indah, Kelang,
42200, Selangor, Malaysia
Tel.: (60) 333931436   **MY**
Bakery Products Mfr & Distr
N.A.I.C.S.: 311812

FAMILY CARE HOSPITALS LTD.
A - 357 Road No 26 Wagle Industrial
Estate MIDC Thane West, Thane,
400604, India
Tel.: (91) 2225833205
Web Site:
   https://www.familycarehospitals.com
Year Founded: 1994
516110—(BOM)
Rev.: $5,788,969
Assets: $8,910,437
Liabilities: $3,417,997
Net Worth: $5,492,441
Earnings: $630,322
Emp.: 103
Fiscal Year-end: 03/31/23
Dental Imaging Services
N.A.I.C.S.: 621512
Gautam Mohan Deshpande *(Chm & Mng Dir)*

FAMILY MEMORIALS INC.
601 Squier St, Thunder Bay, P7B
4A7, ON, Canada
Tel.: (807) 577-6463
Web Site: http://www.family-
   memorials.ca
Year Founded: 2003
FAM—(TSXV)
Funeral Services
N.A.I.C.S.: 812210
Scott C. Kellaway *(Pres & CEO)*

Subsidiaries:

Barber Monuments Ltd.   (1)
120 Bunting Road, Saint Catharines, L2P
3G5, ON, Canada
Tel.: (905) 684-7913
Monument & Grave Stone Distr
N.A.I.C.S.: 423990

Lons Memorials   (1)
100 Everett Street, Belleville, K8P 3K6, ON,
Canada
Tel.: (613) 968-8897
Web Site: http://www.lonsmemorials.com

Sales Range: $25-49.9 Million
Emp.: 1
Monument Retailer
N.A.I.C.S.: 459999

R.H. Verduyn Granite Co. Ltd.   (1)
69 Aylmer St N, Peterborough, K9J 3J4,
ON, Canada
Tel.: (705) 742-2715
Monument & Grave Stone Distr
N.A.I.C.S.: 423990

Somerville Memorials Ltd.   (1)
7134R Fisher St SE, Calgary, T2H 0W5,
AB, Canada
Tel.: (403) 265-0780
Web Site:
   http://www.somervillememorials.com
Emp.:
Monument & Grave Stone Retailer
N.A.I.C.S.: 459999

FAMILY ZONE CYBER SAFETY LIMITED
945 Wellington Street, West Perth,
6005, WA, Australia
Tel.: (61) 893227600   **AU**
Web Site: http://www.familyzone.com
QOR—(ASX)
Rev.: $66,405,832
Assets: $198,588,430
Liabilities: $106,473,466
Net Worth: $92,114,964
Earnings: ($36,572,002)
Emp.: 500
Fiscal Year-end: 06/30/24
Software Development Services
N.A.I.C.S.: 513210
Tim Levy *(Mng Dir)*

Subsidiaries:

Linewize Limited   (1)
120 Nayland Street Sumner, Christchurch,
8081, New Zealand
Tel.: (64) 36671578
Software Development Services
N.A.I.C.S.: 513210
Scott Noakes *(Gen Mgr)*

Linewize Services Limited   (1)
Level 1 192 St Asaph Street, Christchurch,
8011, New Zealand
Tel.: (64) 36681218
Web Site: http://www.linewize.com
Network Access Management Services
N.A.I.C.S.: 517810

FAMILY, INC.
2-8-15 Higashichiba Chuo-ku, Chiba,
260-0041, Japan
Tel.: (81) 432841111
Web Site:
   http://www.cardealerfamily.co.jp
Sales Range: Less than $1 Million
Car Retailer
N.A.I.C.S.: 441110
Tokuzo Saijo *(Founder & Pres)*

FAMILYTEX (BD) LIMITED
Plot No 47-48 Road No 05 Sector No
4 Chittagong Export Processing
Zone, Chittagong, 4000, Bangladesh
Tel.: (880) 31801056   **BD**
Web Site:
   https://www.familytexbd.com
Year Founded: 2003
FAMILYTEX—(CHT)
Rev.: $7,218,112
Assets: $52,447,921
Liabilities: $5,288,196
Net Worth: $47,159,725
Earnings: ($618,419)
Emp.: 2,000
Fiscal Year-end: 03/30/20
Garments Mfr
N.A.I.C.S.: 315250
Mohammad E. Meraj Mostafa *(Chm)*

FAMOS D.D.
Put Famosa 38, Ilidza, Sarajevo,
71210, Bosnia & Herzegovina

Tel.: (387) 3 351 4252
Web Site: http://www.famos.ba
FAMSR—(SARE)
Rev.: $639,938
Assets: $6,848,644
Liabilities: $157,230
Net Worth: $6,691,414
Earnings: $58,940
Emp.: 12
Fiscal Year-end: 12/31/20
Automobile Mfr
N.A.I.C.S.: 336110

FAMOS GRADNJA D.D.
Kralja Tvrtka bb, 74264, Jelah, Bos-
nia & Herzegovina
Tel.: (387) 3 266 3887
Web Site: http://www.famus-
   gradnja.ba
FMGRRK1—(SARE)
Rev.: $7,467
Assets: $339,898
Liabilities: $10,799
Net Worth: $329,099
Earnings: ($36,406)
Emp.: 1
Fiscal Year-end: 12/31/20
Construction Engineering Services
N.A.I.C.S.: 237990

FAMOS SA
Str Targului Nr 6, Odorheiu Secuiesc,
Harghita, Romania
Tel.: (40) 266218330
Web Site: http://www.famos.ro
Year Founded: 1948
FAMS—(BUC)
Rev.: $9,545,670
Assets: $11,115,875
Liabilities: $9,409,634
Net Worth: $1,706,241
Earnings: $105,225
Emp.: 354
Fiscal Year-end: 12/31/20
Furniture Product Mfr
N.A.I.C.S.: 321999

FAMOUS BRANDS LIMITED
478 James Crescent, PO Box 2884,
Halfway House, Midrand, 1685, Gau-
teng, South Africa
Tel.: (27) 113153000   **ZA**
Web Site:
   https://www.famousbrands.co.za
FMBRY—(OTCIQ)
Rev.: $436,975,767
Assets: $193,474,923
Liabilities: $134,725,054
Net Worth: $58,749,869
Earnings: $26,342,574
Emp.: 3,066
Fiscal Year-end: 02/29/24
Restaurant Franchises & Food Re-
lated Services
N.A.I.C.S.: 722513
Darren Paul Hele *(CEO)*

Subsidiaries:

Cater Chain Foodservices (Pty)
Ltd.   (1)
30 Angus Rd, Johannesburg, 2197, South
Africa
Tel.: (27) 116107300
Restaurant Services
N.A.I.C.S.: 722511

Coffee Contact (Proprietary)
Limited   (1)
58 Dawson St, Brunswick, 3056, VIC, Aus-
tralia
Tel.: (61) 393801111
Web Site: https://www.coffex.com.au
Coffee Product Mfr
N.A.I.C.S.: 311920

Debonairs Pizza (Pty) Ltd.   (1)
PO Box 2884, Halfway House Estate, Jo-
hannesburg, 1685, South Africa
Tel.: (27) 861374992

Web Site: http://www.debonairspizza.co.za
Pizza Restaurant Services
N.A.I.C.S.: 722513

Famous Brands Cheese Company
(Pty) Ltd.   (1)
Cable Road Zone 3, Coega IDZ, Port Eliza-
beth, 6100, South Africa
Tel.: (27) 414050000
Restaurant Services
N.A.I.C.S.: 722511

Famous Brands Coffee Company
(Pty) Ltd.   (1)
154 Edward Avenue, Centurion, South Af-
rica
Tel.: (27) 116515961
Restaurant Services
N.A.I.C.S.: 722511

GBK Restaurants Limited   (1)
1 Lindsey Street, London, EC1A 9HP,
United Kingdom
Tel.: (44) 8454506089
Web Site: http://www.gbkrestaurants.com
Sales Range: $50-74.9 Million
Restaurant Operators
N.A.I.C.S.: 722511

Lamberts Bay Foods (Pty) Ltd.   (1)
Axel St, Lambert's Bay, Western Cape,
South Africa
Tel.: (27) 274328000
Restaurant Operators
N.A.I.C.S.: 722511

Mugg & Bean Franchising (Pty)
Ltd.   (1)
478 James Crescent, Midrand, Gauteng,
South Africa
Tel.: (27) 861627328
Web Site: https://www.muggandbean.co.za
Restaurant Services
N.A.I.C.S.: 722511

Pouyoukas Foods (Proprietary)
Limited   (1)
6 Jacobs Street Chamdor, Trio Plastic Of-
fice Park, Krugersdorp, 1739, Gauteng,
South Africa
Tel.: (27) 11 7625261
Web Site: http://www.pouyoukas.co.za
Food Products Mfr
N.A.I.C.S.: 424490
Peter Bradley *(CEO)*

Steers (Proprietary) Limited   (1)
PO Box 3149, North Parramatta, Sydney,
1750, NSW, Australia
Tel.: (61) 296308482
Web Site: http://www.steers.com.au
Sales Range: $25-49.9 Million
Emp.: 5
Auctioneers & Valuers
N.A.I.C.S.: 561990

FAN MILK LIMITED
1 Dadeban Road North Industrial
Area, PO Box 6460, Accra, Ghana
Tel.: (233) 21224732
Web Site: http://www.fanmilk-gh.net
Year Founded: 1960
FML—(GHA)
Rev.: $53,693,800
Assets: $58,406,000
Liabilities: $37,898,100
Net Worth: $20,507,900
Earnings: ($4,159,600)
Emp.: 355
Fiscal Year-end: 12/31/22
Milk & Dairy Products Mfr & Distr
N.A.I.C.S.: 311511
Charles Mensa *(Chm)*

FANCAMP EXPLORATION LTD.
7290 Gray Avenue, Burnaby, V5J
3Z2, BC, Canada
Tel.: (604) 434-8829
Web Site: https://www.fancamp.ca
FNC—(TSXV)
Sales Range: Less than $1 Million
Mineral Exploration Services
N.A.I.C.S.: 213114
Peter H. Smith *(Founder)*

FANCY WOOD INDUSTRIES PUBLIC COMPANY LIMITED
357 Mu 12 Soi Suksawat 84 Kusang Suksawat Rd, Prasamutjaedee, Samut Prakan, 10290, Thailand
Tel.: (66) 24612100
Web Site:
    https://www.fancywood.in.th
Year Founded: 1970
FANCY—(THA)
Rev.: $3,468,006
Assets: $24,837,696
Liabilities: $835,766
Net Worth: $24,001,930
Earnings: ($206,679)
Fiscal Year-end: 12/31/23
Wood Products Mfr
N.A.I.C.S.: 321999
Darran Yutthawonsuk *(Chm)*

Subsidiaries:

Fancy Asset Company Limited   **(1)**
219 Moo 5 Sai Asia Road, Tha Rong Chang Subdistrict Phunphin District, Surat Thani, 84130, Thailand
Tel.: (66) 25 782 8234
Web Site: https://www.fancyasset.com
Real Estate Services
N.A.I.C.S.: 531210

Fancy Wood Industries Public Company Limited - Suratthani
Factory   **(1)**
219 Mu 5 Asia Highway Tharongchang Punpin, Surat Thani, 84130, Thailand
Tel.: (66) 7725 4121 3
Thin Chipboard Mfr
N.A.I.C.S.: 321219

FANDANGO HOLDINGS PLC
27-28 Eastcastle Street, London, W1W 8DH, United Kingdom   UK
Web Site:
    https://www.fandangoholdings.com
Year Founded: 2016
FHP—(LSE)
Offices of Other Holding Companies
N.A.I.C.S.: 551112
Tim Cottier *(CEO)*

Subsidiaries:

ST Brides Partners Ltd.   **(1)**
Warnford Court 29 Throgmorton Street, London, EC2N 2AT, United Kingdom
Tel.: (44) 2072361177
Web Site:
    https://www.stbridespartners.co.uk
Public Relation & Communication Services
N.A.I.C.S.: 926130

FANDIFI TECHNOLOGY CORP.
Suite 830 1100 Melville Street, Vancouver, V6E 4A6, BC, Canada
Tel.: (604) 256-6990   BC
Web Site: https://www.fandifi.com
Year Founded: 2006
FDMSF—(OTCQB)
Assets: $3,856,325
Liabilities: $109,599
Net Worth: $3,746,726
Earnings: ($2,954,415)
Fiscal Year-end: 01/31/22
Sports Entertainment Company; Mobile Application Investment Services
N.A.I.C.S.: 523999
Tristan Brett *(Founder)*

FANE VALLEY CO-OPERATIVE SOCIETY LTD.
Units 1 2 Glenavy Road Business Park, 20 Glenavy Road, Moira, BT67 0LYT, Moira, United Kingdom
Tel.: (44) 2892610477
Web Site:
    http://www.fanevalleystores.com
Agricultural Food Business
N.A.I.C.S.: 926140
Trevor Lockhart *(CEO)*

Subsidiaries:

Robert Smyth & Sons Limited   **(1)**
Daleside Mill Ballindrait, Lifford, Donegal, Ulster, Ireland
Tel.: (353) 74 9171300
Web Site: http://www.smythfeeds.com
Animal Feeds Mfr & Distr
N.A.I.C.S.: 311119
Ray Wanters *(Gen Mgr)*

FANG BROTHERS KNITTING LTD.
20-24 Kwai Wing Road Kwai Chung, Hong Kong, China (Hong Kong)
Tel.: (852) 24016688
Web Site:
    http://www.fangbrothersknitting.com
Sales Range: $25-49.9 Million
Emp.: 150
Knitted Mfr
N.A.I.C.S.: 315120
Kenneth Fang *(Chm)*

Subsidiaries:

Pringle of Scotland Ltd.   **(1)**
2 Victoria Road, Hawick, TD9 7AH, United Kingdom
Tel.: (44) 1450360260
Web Site: http://www.pringlescotland.com
Sales Range: $25-49.9 Million
Emp.: 25
Knitwear & Clothing
N.A.I.C.S.: 313210
Douglas Fang *(CEO)*

FANG HOLDINGS LTD.
Tower A No 20 Guogongzhuang Middle Street, Fengtai District, Beijing, 100070, China
Tel.: (86) 1056318000   Ky
Web Site: https://www.fang.com
Year Founded: 1999
SFUN—(NYSE)
Rev.: $80,481,000
Assets: $1,208,923,000
Liabilities: $617,119,000
Net Worth: $591,804,000
Earnings: ($75,562,000)
Emp.: 1,503
Fiscal Year-end: 12/31/22
Real Estate Internet Portal
N.A.I.C.S.: 531390
Vincent Tianquan Mo *(Founder & Chm)*

FANGDA CARBON NEW MATERIAL CO., LTD.
No 11 Carbon Road, Honggu Dist, Lanzhou, 730084, Gansu, China
Tel.: (86) 9316239219
Web Site: https://www.fdtsgs.com
600516—(SHG)
Rev.: $746,969,193
Assets: $2,832,610,814
Liabilities: $475,519,061
Net Worth: $2,357,091,753
Earnings: $117,927,436
Fiscal Year-end: 12/31/22
Carbon Product Mfr & Distr
N.A.I.C.S.: 335991
Dang Xijiang *(Chm)*

Subsidiaries:

Chengdu Carbon Material Co., Ltd.   **(1)**
The Open Area South Road 88, Longquanyi District, Chengdu, Sichuan, China
Tel.: (86) 2884860443
Web Site: https://www.cdcarbon.cn
Electronic Equipment Mfr & Distr
N.A.I.C.S.: 335314

Chengdu Rongguang Carbon Co., Ltd.   **(1)**
Ganmei Industrial Park, Meishan, 620000, Sichuan, China
Tel.: (86) 2838088668
Web Site: https://en.cd-ts.cn

Graphite Electrode Mfr
N.A.I.C.S.: 335991

Fushun Carbon Co., Ltd.   **(1)**
47 West Section Heping Road, Wanghua District, Fushun, 113001, Liaoning, China
Tel.: (86) 2456884812
Web Site: https://www.fs-carbon.com
Graphite Electrode Mfr
N.A.I.C.S.: 335991

FANGDA SPECIAL STEEL TECHNOLOGY CO., LTD.
No 511 Yejin Avenue, Qingshanhu District, Nanchang, 330012, Jiangxi, China
Tel.: (86) 79188387625
Web Site: https://www.fangda-specialsteels.com
Year Founded: 1999
600507—(SHG)
Rev.: $3,262,703,975
Assets: $2,436,352,650
Liabilities: $1,208,005,770
Net Worth: $1,228,346,880
Earnings: $130,039,126
Fiscal Year-end: 12/31/22
Iron & Steel Product Mfr & Distr
N.A.I.C.S.: 331110
Zhixin Xu *(Board of Directors & Chm)*

FANGDD NETWORK GROUP LTD.
18/F Unit B2 Kexing Science Park 15 Keyuan Road Technology Park, Nanshan District, Shenzhen, 518057, China
Tel.: (86) 75526998968   Ky
Web Site: https://www.fangdd.com
Year Founded: 2011
DUO—(NASDAQ)
Rev.: $39,454,613
Assets: $106,599,053
Liabilities: $80,084,736
Net Worth: $26,514,317
Earnings: ($12,891,006)
Emp.: 130
Fiscal Year-end: 12/31/23
Holding Company
N.A.I.C.S.: 551112
Duan Yi *(Co-Founder, Chm & Co-CEO)*

FANHUA INC.
60/F Pearl River Tower No 15 West Zhujiang Road, Guangzhou, 510623, Guangdong, China
Tel.: (86) 2083886888   Ky
Web Site:
    https://www.fanhuaholdings.com
Year Founded: 1999
FANH—(NASDAQ)
Rev.: $426,171,081
Assets: $473,344,746
Liabilities: $208,087,524
Net Worth: $265,257,223
Earnings: $15,362,673
Emp.: 5,238
Fiscal Year-end: 12/31/22
Insurance Brokerage Services
N.A.I.C.S.: 524210
Yinan Hu *(Founder, Co-Chm & CEO)*

FANLOGIC INTERACTIVE INC.
Suite 301 1107-17th Avenue SW, Calgary, T2T 0B5, AB, Canada
Tel.: (650) 475-7779   BC
Web Site: http://www.spriza.com
Year Founded: 2007
FLGC—(OTCIQ)
Sales Range: Less than $1 Million
Investment Services
N.A.I.C.S.: 523999
Christopher C. Robbins *(CFO)*

FANSUNITE ENTERTAINMENT, INC.
1080-789 W Pender Street, Vancouver, V6C 1H2, BC, Canada
Tel.: (604) 329-8669
Web Site: http://www.fansunite.com
FUNFF—(OTCQB)
Rev.. $20,167,689
Assets: $57,215,779
Liabilities: $25,463,544
Net Worth: $31,752,235
Earnings: ($45,259,659)
Fiscal Year-end: 12/31/22
Online Betting Services
N.A.I.C.S.: 713290
Scott Burton *(CEO)*

FANTAGIO CORP.
Fantagio Building 248 Yeoksam-ro, Gangnam-gu, Seoul, 06226, Korea (South)
Tel.: (82) 25435564
Web Site: https://www.fantagio.kr
032800—(KRS)
Rev.: $29,666,180
Assets: $60,416,993
Liabilities: $27,531,966
Net Worth: $32,885,027
Earnings: ($14,212,690)
Emp.: 75
Fiscal Year-end: 06/30/23
Tutoring Services
N.A.I.C.S.: 611691

FANTASIA HOLDINGS GROUP CO., LIMITED
Block A Funian Plaza Intersection of Shihua Road and Zijing Road, interchange in Futian Duty-Free Trade Zone, Shenzhen, 518040, Guangdong, China
Tel.: (86) 75583451777
Web Site: http://www.cnfantasia.com
1777—(HKG)
Rev.: $3,333,672,489
Assets: $16,171,347,061
Liabilities: $12,444,721,870
Net Worth: $3,726,625,191
Earnings: $268,319,124
Emp.: 35,965
Fiscal Year-end: 12/31/20
Property Developer & Manager
N.A.I.C.S.: 531390
Jun Pan *(Chm & CEO)*

FANTASISTA CO., LTD.
Akasaka Biz Tower 27F 5-3-1 Akasaka, Minato-Ku, Tokyo, 107-6327, Japan
Tel.: (81) 355727848
Web Site: https://fantasista-tokyo.jp
Year Founded: 1950
1783—(TKS)
Rev.: $61,289,760
Assets: $98,936,400
Liabilities: $52,889,040
Net Worth: $46,047,360
Earnings: $2,018,400
Fiscal Year-end: 09/30/24
Holding Company
N.A.I.C.S.: 551112
So Kanai *(Pres)*

Subsidiaries:

Fairy Forest Co., Ltd.   **(1)**
14th Floor Hibiya Central Building 1-2-9 Nishi-Shimbashi, Minato-ku, Tokyo, 1050003, Japan
Tel.: (81) 355327288
Web Site: https://www.fairyforest.co.jp
Supplement Product Distr
N.A.I.C.S.: 424210

Hundredyears Co., Ltd.   **(1)**
8th floor Maruto Ginza 3rd Building 3-10-5 Ginza, Chuo-ku, Tokyo, Japan
Tel.: (81) 366814024
Web Site: https://hundredyears.jp
Medical Device Mfr & Distr
N.A.I.C.S.: 334413

Fantasista Co., Ltd.—(Continued)

Nanno Construction Co., Ltd. **(1)**
No 3-6 Ikenomiya 2-chome, Hirakata, 573-0005, Japan
Tel.: (81) 728484174
Web Site: https://www.nanno.co.jp
Civil Engineering Services
N.A.I.C.S.: 541330

Nc Max World Co., Ltd. **(1)**
8F Maruto Ginza 3rd Building 3-10-6 Ginza, Chuo-ku, Tokyo, 104-0061, Japan
Tel.: (81) 362606767
Web Site: https://www.ncmaxworld.co.jp
Real Estate Property Management Services
N.A.I.C.S.: 531110

FANUC CORPORATION

3580 Shibokusa Oshino-mura, Minamitsuru-gun, Yamanashi, 401-0597, Japan
Tel.: (81) 555845555
Year Founded: 1956
FUCA—(DEU)
Rev.: $5,256,761,140
Assets: $12,731,104,570
Liabilities: $1,367,192,570
Net Worth: $11,363,912,000
Earnings: $880,180,990
Emp.: 9,432
Fiscal Year-end: 03/31/24
Numerical Control Systems, Laser, Power Motion & Robots Mfr
N.A.I.C.S.: 335314
Yoshiharu Inaba *(Chm)*

Subsidiaries:

Beijing-Fanuc Mechatronics Co., Ltd. **(1)**
No 9 Xinxi Road Shangdi Information Industry Base, Haidian District, Beijing, 100085, China
Tel.: (86) 10 62984743
Web Site: http://www.bj-fanuc.com.cn
Sales Range: $50-74.9 Million
Emp.: 100
Sales & Servicer of Industrial Controls
N.A.I.C.S.: 423830

FANUC Adria d.o.o. **(1)**
Ipavceva 21, 3000, Celje, Slovenia
Tel.: (386) 8 205 6497
Web Site: https://www.fanuc.eu
Automation Product Mfr & Distr
N.A.I.C.S.: 333998

FANUC America Corporation **(1)**
3900 W Hamlin Rd, Rochester Hills, MI 48309-3253
Tel.: (248) 377-7000
Web Site: http://www.fanucamerica.com
Industrial Robotic Automation Distr
N.A.I.C.S.: 423830
Cathy Powell *(Mgr-PR & Comm)*

Division (Domestic):

Fanuc America Corporation - Midwest **(2)**
1800 Lakewood Blvd, Hoffman Estates, IL 60192-5008 **(100%)**
Tel.: (847) 898-5000
Web Site: http://www.fanucamerica.com
CNC & Laser Service
N.A.I.C.S.: 811210

FANUC Automation Israel Ltd. **(1)**
3 Ha'arava Street Beit AiZenberg Airport city, 7019900, Tel Aviv, Israel
Tel.: (972) 399739900
Web Site: http://www.fanuc.eu
Automation Product Mfr & Distr
N.A.I.C.S.: 333998

FANUC Automation Romania S.R.L. **(1)**
Ferma 9 Hala 25, Floresti Jud Cluj, 407280, Cluj-Napoca, Romania
Tel.: (40) 747232682
Web Site: http://www.fanuc.eu
Automation Product Mfr & Distr
N.A.I.C.S.: 333998

FANUC Benelux BV **(1)**
Oude Baan 3F B - red area, 2800, Mechelen, Belgium

Tel.: (32) 15207157
Web Site: http://www.fanuc.eu
Factory Automation Product Mfr & Distr
N.A.I.C.S.: 333998

FANUC Czech s.r.o. **(1)**
K Bllernu vrchu 3142/7, Horni Pocernice
Praha 9, 193 00, Prague, Czech Republic
Tel.: (420) 234072900
Web Site: http://www.fanuc.eu
Automation Product Mfr & Distr
N.A.I.C.S.: 333998

FANUC Europe Corporation, S.A. **(1)**
7 Rue Benedikt Zender, 6468, Echternach, Luxembourg
Tel.: (352) 7277770
Emp.: 250
Industrial Machinery Distr
N.A.I.C.S.: 423830
Marco Ghirardello *(Pres & CEO)*

FANUC FA Bulgaria Ltd. **(1)**
467 Okolovrasten pat, 1588, Sofia, Bulgaria
Tel.: (359) 2 963 33 19
Web Site: http://www.fanuc.eu
Emp.: 10
Robotic Machinery Sales & Maintenance Services
N.A.I.C.S.: 423830

FANUC FA Deutschland GmbH **(1)**
Bernhauser Str 36, 73765, Neuhausen auf den Fildern, Germany
Tel.: (49) 715812820
Web Site: http://www.fanuc.eu
Industrial Machinery Repair & Maintenance Services
N.A.I.C.S.: 811310

FANUC FA France S.A.S. **(1)**
ZAC des Folies 15 rue Leonard de Vinci, 91090, Lisses, France
Tel.: (33) 172073000
Web Site: http://www.fanuc.eu
Industrial Machinery Repair & Maintenance Services
N.A.I.C.S.: 811310

FANUC FA Hungary Kft **(1)**
Torbagy utca 7, 2045, Torokbalint, Hungary
Tel.: (36) 23884200
Web Site: http://www.fanuc.eu
Sales Range: $25-49.9 Million
Emp.: 5
Robotic Machinery Repair & Maintenance Services
N.A.I.C.S.: 811310

FANUC FA Iberia S.A.U. **(1)**
Pl Olaso C/ Olaso n 3, Elgoibar, 20870, Gipuzkoa, Spain
Tel.: (34) 902133535
Web Site: http://www.fanuc.eu
Emp.: 21
Industrial Machinery Repair & Maintenance Services
N.A.I.C.S.: 811310

FANUC FA Nordic AB **(1)**
Hammarbacken 4 B, 191 49, Sollentuna, Sweden
Tel.: (46) 8 505 80 700
Robotic Machine Repair & Maintenance Services
N.A.I.C.S.: 811310
Bob Strujk *(Gen Mgr)*

FANUC FA SATIS VE SERVIS TICARET LTD. **(1)**
Serifali Mahallesi Turgut Ozal Bulvari No 190-192, Umraniye, 34775, Istanbul, Turkiye
Tel.: (90) 4449362
Web Site: http://www.fanuc.co.jp
Sales Range: $25-49.9 Million
Emp.: 15
Industrial Machinery Repair & Maintenance Services
N.A.I.C.S.: 811310

FANUC FA Switzerland GmbH **(1)**
Grenchenstrasse 7, 2504, Biel/Bienne, Switzerland
Tel.: (41) 32 366 63 63
Web Site: http://www.fanuc.eu
Industrial Machinery Repair & Maintenance Services
N.A.I.C.S.: 811310

Peter Baumann *(Pres)*

FANUC FA UK LIMITED **(1)**
Fanuc House 1 Station Approach, Ruislip, HA4 8LF, Middlesex, United Kingdom
Tel.: (44) 1895 6 34 182
Sales Range: $25-49.9 Million
Emp.: 2
Industrial Machinery Distr
N.A.I.C.S.: 333998
Andrew Myhill *(Mng Dir)*

FANUC KOREA SERVICE CORPORATION **(1)**
42 Ungnam-dong, Seongsan-gu, Changwon, Gyeongsangnam-do, Korea (South)
Tel.: (82) 55 282 0122
Robotic Machine Repair & Maintenance Services
N.A.I.C.S.: 811310

FANUC LLC **(1)**
Bolshoi boulevard 7 Innovation Center Skolkovo, 121205, Moscow, Russia
Tel.: (7) 4951181280
Industrial Machinery Mfr & Distr
N.A.I.C.S.: 333248

FANUC Mexico S.A. de C.V. **(1)**
Circuito Aguascalientes Norte 136, Parque Industrial Valle de Aguascalientes, 20358, San Francisco de los Romo, Mexico
Tel.: (52) 4499228000
Web Site: http://www.fanucrobotics.com.mx
Automation Product Mfr & Distr
N.A.I.C.S.: 333998

FANUC Nordic AB **(1)**
Djurhagegatan 10, 20122, Malmo, Sweden
Tel.: (46) 850580700
Web Site: http://www.fanuc.eu
Automation Product Mfr & Distr
N.A.I.C.S.: 333998

FANUC Osterreich GmbH **(1)**
Josef Haas Strasse 9A, Vorchdorf, 4655, Gmunden, Austria
Tel.: (43) 72022762100
Web Site: http://www.fanuc.eu
Automation Product Mfr & Distr
N.A.I.C.S.: 333998

FANUC Polska Sp. z o.o. **(1)**
ul Tadeusza Wendy 2, 52-407, Wroclaw, Poland
Tel.: (48) 71 7766 160
Web Site: http://www.fanuc.eu
Industrial Machinery Repair & Maintenance Services
N.A.I.C.S.: 811310

FANUC ROBOMACHINE EUROPE GmbH **(1)**
Bernhauser Str 22, 73765, Neuhausen auf den Fildern, Germany
Tel.: (49) 7158 187 200
Web Site: http://www.fanucrobomachine.eu
Sales Range: $25-49.9 Million
Emp.: 4
Industrial Automation Machinery Distr
N.A.I.C.S.: 423830
Martin Schopf *(Mgr-Sls)*

FANUC Serbia d.o.o. **(1)**
Kralja Petra I Karadordevica 92a, 22330, Nova Pazova, Serbia
Tel.: (381) 22 215 0324
Web Site: https://www.fanuc.eu
Automation Product Mfr & Distr
N.A.I.C.S.: 333998

FANUC Slovakia s.r.o. **(1)**
Pri Jelsine 3636/ 1, 949 01, Nitra, Slovakia
Tel.: (421) 376300759
Web Site: http://www.fanuc.eu
Automation Product Mfr & Distr
N.A.I.C.S.: 333998

FANUC South America Equipamentos de Automacao e Servicos Ltda. **(1)**
Av Embaixador Macedo Soares 10001 Predio 6 Espaco 1, Condominio e-Business Park Vila Anastacio, Sao Paulo, SP, Brazil
Tel.: (55) 1136190599
Web Site: http://www.fanucamerica.com
Emp.: 1,500
Automation Product Mfr & Distr
N.A.I.C.S.: 333998

FANUC Thai Limited **(1)**

1301 Pattanakam Road, Kwaeng Suanluang Khet Suanluang, Bangkok, 10250, Thailand
Tel.: (66) 27146111
Robot System Services
N.A.I.C.S.: 541618

FANUC Turkey Endustriyel Otomasyon Tic. Ltd. Sti. **(1)**
Serifali Mevkii Barbaros Caddesi Soylesi Sok 23, Umraniye, 34760, Istanbul, Turkiye
Tel.: (90) 4449362
Web Site: http://www.fanuc.eu
Automation Product Mfr & Distr
N.A.I.C.S.: 333998

FANUC Ukraine LLC **(1)**
Stolychne Hwy 100, 03680, Kiev, Ukraine
Tel.: (380) 445315550
Web Site: http://www.fanuc.eu
Automation Product Mfr & Distr
N.A.I.C.S.: 333998

FANUC VIETNAM LIMITED **(1)**
9th Floor Green Power No 35 Ton Duc Thang Street, District 1, Ho Chi Minh City, Vietnam
Tel.: (84) 8 3824 6638
Web Site: http://www.fanuc.com
Sales Range: $25-49.9 Million
Emp.: 8
Robot Machine Repair & Maintenance Services
N.A.I.C.S.: 811310

Fanuc Europe GmbH **(1)**
Bernhauser Str 36, 73765, Neuhausen, Germany **(100%)**
Tel.: (49) 715812820
Web Site: http://www.fanuc.eu
Sales Range: $25-49.9 Million
Emp.: 25
Relay & Industrial Control Manufacturing
N.A.I.C.S.: 335314

Subsidiary (Non-US):

FANUC FA Italia S.r.l. **(2)**
Via Lodi 13, 20020, Lainate, MI, Italy **(100%)**
Tel.: (39) 0236015015
Web Site: http://www.fanucfa.com
Sales Range: $25-49.9 Million
Industrial Automation Controls Servicer
N.A.I.C.S.: 335314

FANUC Iberia S.L.U. **(2)**
Oficina Central P I El Cami Ral Ronda Can Rabada no 23 nave 1, Castelldefels, 08860, Barcelona, Gava, Spain **(100%)**
Tel.: (34) 902133535
Web Site: http://www.fanuc.eu
Emp.: 8
Industrial Control Services
N.A.I.C.S.: 335314

Fanuc Bulgaria Corporation **(2)**
ulitsa Okolovrasten pat 467, 1588, Sofia, Bulgaria **(100%)**
Tel.: (359) 29633319
Web Site: http://www.fanuc.eu
Sales Range: $25-49.9 Million
Emp.: 10
Provider of Industrial Controls
N.A.I.C.S.: 335314
Jordan Todorov *(Pres)*

Fanuc France S.A. **(2)**
ZAC des Folies 15 rue Leonard de Vinci, 91090, Lisses, France **(100%)**
Tel.: (33) 172073000
Web Site: http://www.fanuc.eu
Sales Range: $25-49.9 Million
Emp.: 18
Provider of Industrial Controls
N.A.I.C.S.: 335314

Subsidiary (Domestic):

Fanuc Germany Service GmbH **(2)**
Bernhauser Strasse 22, 73765, Neuhausen, Germany **(100%)**
Tel.: (49) 158187300
Web Site: http://www.fanuc.de
Sales Range: $25-49.9 Million
Provider of Industrial Controls
N.A.I.C.S.: 335314

Subsidiary (Non-US):

Fanuc Robotics Europe S.A. **(2)**

Zn Ind, 6468, Echternach,
Luxembourg　　　　　　**(100%)**
Tel.: (352) 7277771
Web Site: http://www.fanucrobotics.lu
Sales Range: $25-49.9 Million
Emp.: 200
Robot Sales & Services
N.A.I.C.S.: 335314
Olas Gahrals *(Pres & CEO)*

Fanuc Turkey Ltd.　　　　　　**(2)**
Serifali Mevkii Barbaros Caddesi Soylesi
Sok No 23 B Blok 34760, Istanbul, 34760,
Turkiye　　　　　　**(80%)**
Tel.: (90) 2166511408
Sales Range: $25-49.9 Million
Emp.: 11
Relay & Industrial Control Manufacturing
N.A.I.C.S.: 335314

Fanuc U.K. Limited　　　　　　**(2)**
Sapphire Way, Ansty, Coventry, CV7 9DR,
United Kingdom　　　　　　**(100%)**
Tel.: (44) 247 605 3000
Web Site: https://www.fanuc.eu
Sales Range: $25-49.9 Million
Emp.: 18
Provider of Industrial Control Services
N.A.I.C.S.: 335314
Tom Bouchier *(Mng Dir)*

Fanuc India Private Limited　　**(1)**
41-A Electronics City Hosur Road, Benga-
luru, 560 100, Karnataka, India　**(100%)**
Tel.: (91) 8028520057
Web Site: http://www.fanucindia.com
Sales Range: $50-74.9 Million
Emp.: 160
Mfr of CNC; Joint Venture of General Elec-
tric Company (60%) & Fanuc Ltd. (40%)
N.A.I.C.S.: 335999

**Fanuc Mechatronics (Malaysia) Sdn.
Bhd.**　　　　　　**(1)**
No 22 Persiaran Astana / KU 2 Bandar
Bukit Raja, 41050, Klang, Selangor,
Malaysia　　　　　　**(100%)**
Tel.: (60) 330821222
Web Site: http://www.fanuc.com
Sales Range: $1-9.9 Million
Emp.: 20
Laser Robot & Robomachine Services
N.A.I.C.S.: 335314

Fanuc Oceania Pty. Limited　　**(1)**
10 Healey Circuit, Huntingwood, 2148,
NSW, Australia　　　　　　**(100%)**
Tel.: (61) 28 822 4600
Web Site: https://www.fanucoceania.com.au
Sales Range: $25-49.9 Million
Emp.: 13
Equipment & Machinery
N.A.I.C.S.: 333517
Gaby Gahabach *(Mng Dir)*

Fanuc Philippines Corporation　**(1)**
Unit 1 Orient Goldcrest Building 10 Lot 4
Block 1 Phase 7A, Laguna Technopark Inc,
Binan, 4024, Laguna, Philippines　**(100%)**
Tel.: (63) 495460178
Web Site: http://www.fanuc.com
Sales Range: $25-49.9 Million
Emp.: 7
Laser, Robot & Robomachine Services
N.A.I.C.S.: 335314

**Fanuc Robomachine (Shenzhen)
Ltd.**　　　　　　**(1)**
2/F A Wanshan Building 2nd Wenxin Road
Nanshan Commercial Culture, Centre Area,
Shenzhen, 518054, Guangdong, China
Tel.: (86) 75526422423
Web Site: http://www.fanuc.co.jp
Sales Range: $50-74.9 Million
Emp.: 500
Special Industry Machinery
N.A.I.C.S.: 333248
Jhang Wei *(Mgr-Sls)*

Fanuc Singapore Pte. Ltd.　　**(1)**
No 1 Teban Gardens Crescent, Singapore,
608919, Singapore　　　　**(100%)**
Tel.: (65) 6 220 3911
Web Site: https://www.fanuc.com
Sales Range: $25-49.9 Million
Emp.: 20
CNC, Laser, Robot & Robomachine Sales &
Service
N.A.I.C.S.: 335314
E. Rudy *(Mng Dir)*

Fanuc South Africa Pty. Limited　**(1)**
17 Loper Ave Aeroport Industrial Estates,
Isando, Johannesburg, 1619, South
Africa　　　　　　**(100%)**
Tel.: (27) 113923610
Web Site: http://www.fanuc.co.za
Sales Range: $25-49.9 Million
Emp.: 15
Equipment & Machinery
N.A.I.C.S.: 333517

Fanuc Taiwan Limited　　　　**(1)**
Taichung Industrial Park Road 16 10, Taic-
hung Industrial Park, Taichung, 40768,
Taiwan　　　　　　**(100%)**
Tel.: (886) 423591842
Web Site: http://www.fanuctaiwan.com.tw
Sales Range: $25-49.9 Million
Emp.: 80
Provider of Industrial Control Products &
Services
N.A.I.C.S.: 335314

Korea Fanuc Corporation　　　**(1)**
101 Wanam-ro, Seongsan-gu, Changwon,
642-290, Gyeongsangnam, Korea (South)
Tel.: (82) 55 278 1200
Web Site: http://www.fkc.co.kr
Sales Range: $50-74.9 Million
Emp.: 200
Provider of Industrial Control Products &
Services
N.A.I.C.S.: 335314

PT. FANUC INDONESIA　　　　**(1)**
Jl Boulevard Bukit Gading Raya Blok R,
Jakarta, 14240, Indonesia
Tel.: (62) 21 45847285
Sales Range: $25-49.9 Million
Emp.: 30
Robot Machine Repair & Maintenance Ser-
vices
N.A.I.C.S.: 811310
Mince Lauw *(Mgr-Fin)*

**SHANGHAI-FANUC Robotics CO.,
LTD.**　　　　　　**(1)**
No 1500 Fulian Road, Baoshan Area,
Shanghai, 201906, China
Tel.: (86) 2150327700
Web Site: http://www.shanghai-
fanuc.com.cn
Sales Range: $50-74.9 Million
Emp.: 500
Robot System Mfr & Distr
N.A.I.C.S.: 333998

**Shanghai-FANUC Robomachine Co.,
Ltd.**　　　　　　**(1)**
1/F 1st Building No 1500 Fulian Road,
Baoshan, Shanghai, 21906, China
Tel.: (86) 2150327700
Industrial Machinery Distr
N.A.I.C.S.: 423830

**TAIWAN FANUC ROBOTICS
CORPORATION**　　　　　　**(1)**
No 4 17th Road Taichung Industrial Park,
Taichung, Taiwan
Tel.: (886) 4 2359 2827
Web Site: http://www.fanuc.co.jp
Robot System Mfr & Distr
N.A.I.C.S.: 333998

Taiwan FANUC Corporation　　**(1)**
407-68 16 Taichung Industrial Park Road
10, Taichung, Taiwan
Tel.: (886) 423590522
Web Site: http://www.fanuctaiwan.com.tw
Automation Product Mfr & Distr
N.A.I.C.S.: 333998

**Tatung-Fanuc Robotics
Company**　　　　　　**(1)**
22 Sec 3 Chungshan N Rd, Taipei, 104,
Taiwan
Tel.: (886) 225925252
Web Site: http://www.tatungfanuc.com.tw
Sales Range: $200-249.9 Million
Emp.: 1,000
Robot Sales & Services
N.A.I.C.S.: 335314

FAP - KORPORACIJA A.D.
Radnicka bb, 31330, Priboj, Serbia
Tel.: (381) 33 451 331
Web Site: http://www.fap.co.rs
Truck & Bus Mfr

N.A.I.C.S.: 336120

FAR AD
Bunaya 16 et 2 ap 5, Sofia, 1505,
Bulgaria
Tel.: (359) 29434718
Web Site: http://www.farad.bg
FAR—(BUL)
Sales Range: Less than $1 Million
Information Technology Management
Services
N.A.I.C.S.: 541512

FAR CITY MINING LIMITED
Room No 301 302 New East Ocean
Centre, 9 Science Museum Road,
Tsim Sha Tsui, Kowloon, China (Hong
Kong)
Tel.: (852) 27238638　　　　VG
Web Site:
　http://www.farcitymining.com
Year Founded: 2009
Sales Range: Less than $1 Million
Precious & Base Metals Mining &
Exploration Services
N.A.I.C.S.: 212290
Harry Tak Shing Lam *(Chm & CEO)*

**FAR EAST CONSORTIUM IN-
TERNATIONAL LIMITED**
16/F Far East Consortium Building
121 Des Voeux Road, Central, China
(Hong Kong)
Tel.: (852) 2 850 0600
Web Site: http://www.fecil.com.hk
0035—(HKG)
Rev.: $760,419,131
Assets: $7,068,660,678
Liabilities: $4,758,637,648
Net Worth: $2,310,023,029
Earnings: $194,828,933
Emp.: 3,500
Fiscal Year-end: 03/31/22
Property Development & Investment
Services
N.A.I.C.S.: 523999
David Chiu *(Chm & CEO)*

Subsidiaries:

Cosmopolitan Hotel Limited　　**(1)**
387-397 Queens Road East, Wanchai,
China (Hong Kong)　　　　**(100%)**
Tel.: (852) 35521111
Web Site:
　http://www.cosmopolitanhotel.com.hk
Sales Range: $10-24.9 Million
Emp.: 100
Hotels & Motels721110
N.A.I.C.S.: 721110
Anita Chan *(Gen Mgr)*

Dorsett Bukit Bintang Sdn. Bhd.　**(1)**
Dorsett Residences Show Gallery Dorsett
Kuala Lumpur Level 4 172, Jalan Imbi,
55100, Kuala Lumpur, Malaysia
Tel.: (60) 166999070
Web Site:
　http://www.dorsettresidencesbb.com
Hotel Services
N.A.I.C.S.: 721110

**Dorsett Hospitality International (Sin-
gapore) Pte. Limited**　　　　**(1)**
333 New Bridge Road, Singapore, 088765,
Singapore
Tel.: (65) 66788333
Hotel Hospitality Services
N.A.I.C.S.: 721110

**Dorsett Hospitality International
Limited**　　　　　　**(1)**
6th Floor Unicorn Trade Centre 127-131
Des Voeux Road Central, Central, China
(Hong Kong)
Tel.: (852) 3516 8328
Web Site:
　http://www.dorsettinternational.com
Sales Range: $200-249.9 Million
Emp.: 2,700
Hotel Owner & Operator
N.A.I.C.S.: 721110
Winnie Wing Kwan Chiu *(Pres)*

**Dorsett Regency Hotel (M) Sdn.
Bhd.**　　　　　　**(1)**
172 Jalan Imbi, 55100, Kuala Lumpur,
Malaysia　　　　　　**(100%)**
Tel.: (60) 327161000
Web Site: http://www.dorsetthotels.com
Sales Range: $25-49.9 Million
Emp.: 208
Hotels & Motels
N.A.I.C.S.: 721110

**Far East Consortium Holdings (Aus-
tralia) Pty Limited**　　　　**(1)**
Suite 501 Level 5 370 St Kilda Road, Mel-
bourne, 3004, VIC, Australia　**(100%)**
Tel.: (61) 396816988
Web Site: https://www.fareast.net.au
Sales Range: $25-49.9 Million
Emp.: 13
Land Subdivision
N.A.I.C.S.: 237210
Craig Williams *(Exec Dir)*

Far East Consortium Limited　　**(1)**
16th Floor Far East Consortium Bldg, Cen-
tral Area, Central, China (Hong
Kong)　　　　　　**(100%)**
Tel.: (852) 28500600
Real Estate Property Lessors
N.A.I.C.S.: 531190

Far East Vault Limited　　　　**(1)**
Castle Peak Road, Tsuen Wan, China
(Hong Kong)
Tel.: (852) 36232338
Web Site: http://www.fareastvault.com
Vault Services
N.A.I.C.S.: 561622

New China Homes Ltd.　　　　**(1)**
16/F Far East Consortium Building, 121
Des Voeux Road Central, Hong Kong,
China (Hong Kong)　　　　**(75%)**
Tel.: (852) 28500600
Web Site: http://www.fecil.com.hk
Sales Range: $25-49.9 Million
Emp.: 46
Holding Company for Residential Property
Developer
N.A.I.C.S.: 551112
Boswell Cheung *(CFO)*

Ruby Way Limited　　　　　　**(1)**
16th Floor Far East Consortium Bldg, Cen-
tral Area, Central, China (Hong
Kong)　　　　　　**(100%)**
Tel.: (852) 28500600
Real Estate Property Lessors
N.A.I.C.S.: 531190

**Scarborough Development
Limited**　　　　　　**(1)**
Europa House, Scarborough, United
Kingdom　　　　　　**(100%)**
Tel.: (44) 1723850908
Land Subdivision
N.A.I.C.S.: 237210

Tang City Properties Pte Limited.　**(1)**
100A EU Tong Sen Street, Singapore,
059813, Singapore　　　　**(100%)**
Tel.: (65) 63230234
Web Site: http://www.tanggroup.com.sg
Sales Range: $25-49.9 Million
Emp.: 15
Holding Company
N.A.I.C.S.: 551112
Dennis Chiu *(Mng Dir)*

**The Hotel of Lan Kwai Fong
Limited**　　　　　　**(1)**
3 Kau U Fong, Central, China (Hong
Kong)　　　　　　**(100%)**
Tel.: (852) 36500299
Web Site: http://www.dcollection.com
Sales Range: $25-49.9 Million
Emp.: 125
Hotels & Motels
N.A.I.C.S.: 721110

Tomarta Sdn. Bhd.　　　　　　**(1)**
31st Fl Maytower Hotel No 7 Jalan Munshi
Abdullah, Kuala Lumpur, 50100,
Malaysia　　　　　　**(100%)**
Tel.: (60) 326929663
Web Site: http://www.mela.com.my
Real Estate Property Lessors
N.A.I.C.S.: 531190

Top Trend Developments Limited　**(1)**

Far East Consortium International Limited—(Continued)

Unit F1-F, 12/F Phase 1 Hang Fung Industrial Bldg, 2G Hok Yuen St, Hunghom, Kowloon, China (Hong Kong) **(100%)**
Tel.: (052) 04200020
Web Site: http://www.toptrendhk.com
Real Estate Property Lessors
N.A.I.C.S.: 531190

Trans World Corporation **(1)**
545 5th Ave Ste 940, New York, NY 10017
Tel.: (212) 983-3355
Web Site: https://www.transworldhotels.com
Casino & Hotel Operators
N.A.I.C.S.: 721120
Rami S. Ramadan *(Pres & CEO)*

Subsidiary (Non-US):

Trans World Hotels & Entertainment a.s. **(2)**
Ceska Kubice 64, Ceska Kubice, 345 32, Plzen, Czech Republic
Tel.: (420) 379792011
Web Site: https://www.twhe.cz
Casino Operator
N.A.I.C.S.: 721120
Tomas Kment *(Chm-Exec Bd)*

Trans World Hotels Germany GmbH **(2)**
Am Reitpfad 4, Froschhausen, 63500, Seligenstadt, Germany
Tel.: (49) 61828400
Web Site: https://seligenstadt.twhotels.de
Casino & Gaming Services
N.A.I.C.S.: 721120

Trans World Hotels Austria GmbH **(1)**
Am Winterhafen 13, 4020, Linz, Austria
Tel.: (43) 73278990
Web Site: https://linz.twhotels.at
Hotel Services
N.A.I.C.S.: 721110

FAR EAST GROUP LIMITED

51 Ubi Avenue 3, Singapore, 408858, Singapore
Tel.: (65) 62939733
Web Site: https://www.fareastgroup.com.sg
Year Founded: 1953
5TJ—(CAT)
Rev.: $41,198,713
Assets: $81,828,178
Liabilities: $47,563,865
Net Worth: $34,264,313
Earnings: ($5,388,976)
Emp.: 400
Fiscal Year-end: 12/31/20
Refrigeration Equipment Distr
N.A.I.C.S.: 423740
Steven Mun Yew Loh *(CEO)*

Subsidiaries:

Edenkool Pte Ltd **(1)**
112 Lavender Street 01-00 Far East Refrigeration Building, Singapore, 338728, Singapore
Tel.: (65) 6748 9989
Web Site: http://www.fareastgroup.com.sg
Emp.: 3
Air Conditioning Equipment Distr
N.A.I.C.S.: 423730

FE & B Engineering (M) Sdn. Bhd. **(1)**
No 12 Jln Shahbandar 2 Taman Ungku Tun Aminah, Skudai, 81300, Johor Bahru, Malaysia
Tel.: (60) 7 556 1263
Sales Range: $25-49.9 Million
Emp.: 4
Refrigeration Equipment Repair & Maintenance Services
N.A.I.C.S.: 811310
Teo Moi *(Mgr-Sls)*

Far East Enterprises (Johor Bahru) Sdn Bhd **(1)**
No 12 12A Jalan Shah Bandar 2, Taman Ungku Tun Aminah, 81300, Skudai, Johor Bahru, Malaysia

Tel.: (60) 7 556 1221
Web Site: http://www.fareastgroup.com.sg
Refrigeration Cooler & Compressor Distr
N.A.I.C.S.: 423740

Far East Enterprises (Kuala Lumpur) Sdn Bhd **(1)**
1-1 Jalan Kalong Off Jalan Sungai Besi, Kuala Lumpur, 55200, Malaysia
Tel.: (60) 3 9221 3832
Emp.: 20
Refrigeration Cooler & Compressor Distr
N.A.I.C.S.: 423740
Auyong Pengkwan *(Asst Gen Mgr)*

Far East Enterprises (Penang) Sd Bhd **(1)**
60 Lebuh Noordin, 10300, George Town, Pulau Pinang, Malaysia
Tel.: (60) 4 262 0711
Refrigeration Cooler & Compressor Distr
N.A.I.C.S.: 423730

Far East Maju Engineering Works Sdn Bhd **(1)**
Lot 1998/D Jalan Perusahaan 3 Taman Industri Selesa Jaya, 43300, Seri Kembangan, Selangor Darul Ehsan, Malaysia
Tel.: (60) 3 8961 0910
Web Site: http://www.eden.com
Sales Range: $25-49.9 Million
Emp.: 40
Refrigeration Equipment Repair & Maintenance Services
N.A.I.C.S.: 811310

Far East Refrigeration (Kuching) Sdn Bhd **(1)**
Lot 7758 7759 Ground Floor Section 64, Ktld Jalan Datuk Abang Abdul Rahim, 93450, Kuching, Sarawak, Malaysia
Tel.: (60) 8 233 8588
Web Site: http://www.fareastgroup.com.sg
Emp.: 4
Refrigeration Equipment Distr
N.A.I.C.S.: 423740
Ang Kian Boon *(Mgr)*

Far East Refrigeration (M) Sdn. Bhd. **(1)**
No 1-1 Jalan Kalong Off Jalan, Sungei Besi, 55200, Kuala Lumpur, Malaysia
Tel.: (60) 392213832
Refrigeration & Air-Conditioning Product Mfr
N.A.I.C.S.: 333415

Subsidiary (Domestic):

Green Point Compressor Services & Parts Sdn. Bhd. **(1)**
Lot 5 Jln Minlon Utama Off Jln Taming 2, Accession Industrial Park, 43300, Balakong, Selangor, Malaysia
Tel.: (60) 389645016
Automobile Parts Mfr
N.A.I.C.S.: 336390

Far East Refrigeration Limited **(1)**
Room E&F 18/F Wang Cheong Building, 251 Reclamation Street, Mongkok, Kowloon, China (Hong Kong)
Tel.: (852) 2 388 3737
Web Site: http://www.fareastgroup.com.sg
Sales Range: $50-74.9 Million
Emp.: 4
Refrigeration & Air Conditioning Equipment Distr
N.A.I.C.S.: 423740
Pilly Yau *(Branch Mgr)*

Green Point (Singapore) Pte. Ltd. **(1)**
5 Third Lok Yang Road, Singapore, 628000, Singapore
Tel.: (65) 684 116 11
Web Site: http://www.greenpoint.com.sg
Emp.: 3
Industrial Machinery Mfr
N.A.I.C.S.: 333248
Benjamin Ho *(Gen Mgr)*

PT. Far East Refrigeration Indonesia **(1)**
Gedung Jakarta Design Centre Lt 4 SR 26 Jl Gatot Subroto Kav 53 Slipi, Jakarta, 10260, Indonesia
Tel.: (62) 2153690551
Refrigeration & Air-Conditioning Product Mfr
N.A.I.C.S.: 333415

Wira Endratami *(Country Mgr)*

RSP Systems Pte Ltd **(1)**
112 Lavender Street 04-00 Far East Refrigeration Building, Singapore, 338728, Singapore
Tel.: (65) 6297 4880
Emp.: 10
Refrigeration Equipment Supplier
N.A.I.C.S.: 423740
Rhee Chang Shik *(Mng Dir)*

FAR EAST HOLDINGS BER-HAD

Level 23 Menara Zenith Jalan Putra Square 6, 25200, Kuantan, Pahang Darul Makmur, Malaysia
Tel.: (60) 95141936
Web Site: https://www.fehb.com.my
FAREAST—(KLS)
Rev.: $118,058,099
Assets: $370,409,645
Liabilities: $59,043,571
Net Worth: $311,366,074
Earnings: $22,947,281
Emp.: 117
Fiscal Year-end: 12/31/23
Oil Palm Cultivation Services
N.A.I.C.S.: 115112
Asmin Yahya *(Co-Sec & Gen Mgr)*

Subsidiaries:

B.S. Oil Palm Plantations Sdn Bhd **(1)**
Pejabat Pos Bandar Tun Razak, Bandar Tun Abdul Razak, 26900, Pahang Darul Makmur, Malaysia
Tel.: (60) 94530617
Sales Range: $25-49.9 Million
Emp.: 100
Oil Palm Plantation Services
N.A.I.C.S.: 115112
P. Ceechnsua *(Mng Dir)*

Far East Delima Plantations Sdn Bhd **(1)**
Peti Surat 29 Pejabat Pos, PO Box 29, 26800, Kuala Rompin, Pahang, Malaysia
Tel.: (60) 94134093
Web Site: http://www.fehb.com.my
Sales Range: $25-49.9 Million
Emp.: 100
Oil Palm Plantation Services
N.A.I.C.S.: 115112

Kilang Kosfarm Sdn Bhd **(1)**
1101 Blok C Kelana Bussiness Centre 97 Jalan SS 7/2, 47301, Petaling Jaya, Selangor Darul Ehsan, Malaysia
Tel.: (60) 378044036
Sales Range: $25-49.9 Million
Emp.: 30
Oil Palm Plantation Services
N.A.I.C.S.: 311224

Madah Perkasa Sdn Bhd **(1)**
Suite 5 Level 8 Teruntum Complex Jalan Mahkota, PO Box 35, 25000, Kuantan, Pahang, Malaysia
Tel.: (60) 95141936
Sales Range: $25-49.9 Million
Emp.: 100
Oil Palm Plantation Services
N.A.I.C.S.: 111998
Asmin Yahya *(Gen Mgr)*

FAR EAST HOLDINGS INTERNATIONAL LIMITED

Unit 904 9 Floor Wings Building 110-116 Queen's Road, 287299 Queens Road, Central, Sheung Wan, China (Hong Kong)
Tel.: (852) 21108886 **HK**
Web Site: https://www.0036.com.hk
Year Founded: 1973
0036—(HKG)
Sales Range: $1-9.9 Million
Emp.: 93
Investment Holding Company
N.A.I.C.S.: 523999
Cheung Sze Ming *(Sec & Exec Dir)*

FAR EAST HOTELS AND EN-

TERTAINMENT LIMITED
Suite 1902 19th Floor The Suns Group Centre 200 Gloucester Road, Wanchai, China (Hong Kong)
Tel.: (852) 2 744 9110 **HK**
Web Site: http://www.trlcor.com.hk
37—(HKG)
Rev.: $6,409,220
Assets: $50,187,958
Liabilities: $8,222,381
Net Worth: $41,965,577
Earnings: $1,017,781
Emp.: 70
Fiscal Year-end: 03/31/21
Investment Management Service
N.A.I.C.S.: 523940
Derek Chiu *(Chm, CEO & Mng Dir)*

FAR EAST KNITTING & DYEING INDUSTRIES LTD.

House 9B Road 3 Gulshan-1, Dhaka, 1212, Bangladesh
Tel.: (880) 29848508
Web Site: https://www.fareastknit.com
Year Founded: 1994
FEKDIL—(DHA)
Rev.: $60,102,176
Assets: $56,220,592
Liabilities: $17,053,666
Net Worth: $39,166,927
Earnings: $2,918,554
Emp.: 6,043
Fiscal Year-end: 06/30/23
Knit Garment Mfr
N.A.I.C.S.: 313240
Asif Moyeen *(Mng Dir)*

FAR EAST ORCHARD LIMITED

6 Eu Tong Sen Street 04-28 The Central, Singapore, 59817, Singapore
Tel.: (65) 68306599
Web Site: https://www.fareastorchard.com
Year Founded: 1967
O10—(SES)
Rev.: $139,074,453
Assets: $1,980,722,562
Liabilities: $946,207,680
Net Worth: $1,034,514,882
Earnings: $50,034,841
Fiscal Year-end: 12/31/23
Hospitality & Property Investment Services
N.A.I.C.S.: 531311
Arthur Kim Hock Kiong *(CEO-Far East Hospitality)*

FAR EAST ORGANIZATION PTE. LTD.

14 Scotts Road 06-00 Far East Plaza, Singapore, 228213, Singapore
Tel.: (65) 62352411 **SG**
Web Site: http://www.fareast.com.sg
Sales Range: $400-449.9 Million
Emp.: 2,500
Investment Holding Company
N.A.I.C.S.: 551112
Kelvin Ling *(COO)*

Subsidiaries:

Bestcan Food Technological Industrial Sdn Bhd **(1)**
Lot 49494 Batu 3 Jalan Jelapang, 30020, Ipoh, Perak, Malaysia
Tel.: (60) 55260131
Web Site: http://www.yeos.com
Emp.: 133
Food & Beverage Distr
N.A.I.C.S.: 424490
Siva Nandan Sivam *(Gen Mgr)*

Far East Hospitality Trust **(1)**
1 Tanglin Road 05-01 Orchard Rendezvous Hotel, Singapore, 247905, Singapore
Tel.: (65) 68336676
Web Site: https://www.fehtrust.com
Rev.: $80,894,494

Assets: $1,986,256,910
Liabilities: $572,403,999
Net Worth: $1,413,852,911
Earnings: $98,695,751
Fiscal Year-end: 12/31/2023
Real Estate Investment Trust
N.A.I.C.S.: 525990
Kheng Jin Wee *(Chm)*

Orchard Parade Holdings Ltd.   **(1)**
1 Tanglin Rd, Singapore, 247905,
Singapore   **(58.9%)**
Tel.: (65) 67371133
Web Site: http://www.orchardparade.com.sg
Hotel Property Development & Investment;
Investment Holdings; Food & Beverage
N.A.I.C.S.: 551112
Philip Ng Chee Tat *(CEO)*

Yeo Hiap Seng Limited   **(1)**
3 Senoko Way, Singapore, 758057,
Singapore   **(58.27%)**
Tel.: (65) 67522122
Web Site: https://www.yeos.com.sg
Rev.: $252,019,995
Assets: $490,252,973
Liabilities: $68,430,660
Net Worth: $421,822,313
Earnings: $5,079,906
Emp.: 1,717
Fiscal Year-end: 12/31/2023
Holding Company; Bottled Beverage &
Canned Foods Mfr & Distr
N.A.I.C.S.: 551112
Samuel Chee Boon Koh *(CEO)*

Subsidiary (Non-US):

**YHS Hong Kong (2000) Pte
Limited**   **(2)**
8/F Ever Gain Centre 28 On Muk Street,
New Territories, Sha Tin, China (Hong
Kong)
Tel.: (852) 26860288
Web Site: http://www.yeos.com.hk
Food & Beverage Distr
N.A.I.C.S.: 424490
Iris Yu *(Asst VP)*

Subsidiary (US):

YHS Trading (USA) Inc.   **(2)**
755 Epperson Dr, City of Industry, CA
91748
Tel.: (626) 810-8731
Food & Beverage Distr
N.A.I.C.S.: 424490
Cham-Leong Quek *(VP)*

Subsidiary (Non-US):

**Yeo Hiap Seng (Guangzhou) Food &
Beverages Ltd**   **(2)**
288 Chigang Road West, Haizhu,
Guangzhou, 510300, China
Tel.: (86) 2022280888
Food & Beverage Distr
N.A.I.C.S.: 424490
Eddie Tang *(VP)*

**Yeo Hiap Seng (Malaysia)
Berhad**   **(2)**
7 Jalan Tandang, 46050, Petaling Jaya, Se-
langor, Malaysia
Tel.: (60) 377873888
Web Site: http://www.yeos.com.my
Food & Beverage Distr
N.A.I.C.S.: 424490
Ong Chay Seng *(VP-Grp)*

**Yeo Hiap Seng (Sarawak) Sdn
Bhd**   **(2)**
2050 Jalan Swasta Pending Industrial Es-
tate, 93450, Kuching, Sarawak, Malaysia
Tel.: (60) 82487911
Food & Beverage Distr
N.A.I.C.S.: 424490

**FAR EAST SMARTER ENERGY
CO., LTD.**
No 6 Gaocheng Yuandong Avenue,
Yixing, 214257, Jiangsu, China
Tel.: (86) 51087249788
Web Site: http://www.600869.com
Year Founded: 1990
600869—(SHG)
Rev.: $3,043,822,874
Assets: $2,676,733,820

Liabilities: $2,054,151,558
Net Worth: $622,582,263
Earnings: $77,501,249
Fiscal Year-end: 12/31/22
Electrical Component Mfr & Distr
N.A.I.C.S.: 335999
Jiang Xipei *(Chm)*

Subsidiaries:

Anhui Cable Co., Ltd.   **(1)**
No 1 Anlan Avenue, Tianchang, Anhui,
China
Tel.: (86) 5507022056
Web Site: http://www.en.anhuicable.com
Emp.: 620
Electrical Equipment & Component Mfr
N.A.I.C.S.: 335999

Detroit Electric Co., Ltd.   **(1)**
Units 706-707 Enterprise Place Phase One
HK Science Park, Hong Kong, New Territo-
ries, China (Hong Kong)
Tel.: (852) 39968773
Web Site: http://www.detroit-electric-
group.com
Electrical Equipment & Component Mfr
N.A.I.C.S.: 335999

Far East Cable Co., Ltd.   **(1)**
No 8 Far East Avenue, Yixing, 214257, Ji-
angsu, China
Tel.: (86) 51087242500
Electrical Equipment & Component Mfr
N.A.I.C.S.: 335999

**Far East Intergeration Technology
Co., Ltd.**   **(1)**
10/F Rongbao Building No 26 Gulou Wai
Street, Dongcheng District, Beijing, China
Tel.: (86) 1059956888
Web Site: http://www.fe-first.com
Cable Wire Mfr & Distr
N.A.I.C.S.: 335929

**Far East Material Trading Center Co.,
Ltd.**   **(1)**
29 Far East Avenue on the Third Floor, Yix-
ing, 214257, Jiangsu, China
Web Site: http://www.fe-cable.com
Electrical Equipment & Component Mfr
N.A.I.C.S.: 335999

New Far East Cable Co., Ltd.   **(1)**
No 200 Fanxing Avenue, Yixing, Jiangsu,
214257, China
Tel.: (86) 51087248833
Web Site: https://www.newfareast.com.cn
Cable Wire Mfr & Distr
N.A.I.C.S.: 335929

**FAR EAST WIND POWER
CORP.**
Wangzuo Center West Tower Suite
1608 Guanghua Road, Beijing,
100020, China
Tel.: (86) 8621363580
Year Founded: 2008
Wind Energy Services
N.A.I.C.S.: 221115
Xiaobu Liu *(Pres & CEO)*

FAR EASTERN BANK OJSC
Verkhneportovaya Street 27a,
690990, Vladivostok, Russia
Tel.: (7) 4232371371
Web Site: http://www.dvbank.ru
Sales Range: Less than $1 Million
Securities Brokerage Services
N.A.I.C.S.: 523150

**FAR EASTERN SHIPPING
COMPANY OJSC**
Novokuznetskaya St 7/11 Building 1,
115184, Moscow, 115184, Russia
Tel.: (7) 8002344499   **RU**
Web Site: https://www.fesco.ru
Year Founded: 1880
FESH—(MOEX)
Rev.: $1,922,440,547
Assets: $2,355,471,387
Liabilities: $823,601,320
Net Worth: $1,531,870,066
Earnings: $423,050,029

Emp.: 6,549
Fiscal Year-end: 12/31/23
Freight Transportation & Logistics
Services
N.A.I.C.S.: 483111
Hellman Steven *(Chief Restructuring
Officer)*

Subsidiaries:

FESCO Agencies N.A., Inc.   **(1)**
1000 2nd Ave Ste 1310, Seattle, WA 98104
Tel.: (206) 583-0860
Web Site: http://www.fesco-na.com
Sales Range: $1-9.9 Million
Emp.: 5
Deep Sea Freight Transportation Services
N.A.I.C.S.: 483111

FESCO Lines Management Ltd.   **(1)**
248 Queen's Rd E, Wanchai, China (Hong
Kong)
Tel.: (852) 21198651
Freight Transportation Services
N.A.I.C.S.: 488510

FESCO Logistic LLC   **(1)**
Prospekt Mira 39 Building 2 3rd Floor, Mos-
cow, 129110, Russia
Tel.: (7) 4955807061
Freight Transportation Services
N.A.I.C.S.: 488510

Firm Transgarant LLC   **(1)**
              (100%)
Tel.: (7) 4957806002
Web Site: http://www.transgarant.com
Sales Range: $200-249.9 Million
Rail Transportation & Transport Services
N.A.I.C.S.: 482111

VMTP PJSC   **(1)**
Tel.: (7) 88007700070
Web Site: http://www.vmtp.ru
Transport & Logistic Services
N.A.I.C.S.: 541614

**FAR EASTERN UNIVERSITY
INC.**
Nicanor Reyes Street, PO Box 609,
Sampaloc, Manila, 1015, Philippines
Tel.: (63) 287777338
Web Site: https://www.feu.edu.ph
Year Founded: 1928
FEU—(PHI)
Rev.: $86,013,643
Assets: $316,459,663
Liabilities: $68,559,912
Net Worth: $247,899,752
Earnings: $34,589,912
Emp.: 2,556
Fiscal Year-end: 05/31/23
Education Services
N.A.I.C.S.: 611710
Gianna R. Montinola *(Sr VP-Corp
Affairs)*

Subsidiaries:

FEU Alabang, Inc.   **(1)**
Corporate Woods cor South Corporate Av-
enues Woods District, Filinvest City Alabang,
Muntinlupa, 1781, Philippines
Tel.: (63) 282818888
Web Site: http://www.feualabang.edu.ph
Online Education Services
N.A.I.C.S.: 611710

FAR GLORY HOTEL CO., LTD.
No 18 Shanling, Shoufeng Township,
Hua-lien, 97449, Taiwan
Tel.: (886) 38123999
Web Site: https://www.farglory-
hotel.com.tw
2712—(TAI)
Rev.: $16,663,352
Assets: $57,980,365
Liabilities: $19,890,317
Net Worth: $38,090,048
Earnings: $754,057
Emp.: 320
Fiscal Year-end: 12/31/22
Hotel Owner & Operator
N.A.I.C.S.: 721110

Hsien-Te Hung *(Chm)*

FAR LIMITED
Level 4 96-100 Albert Road, South
Melbourne, 3205, VIC, Australia
Tel.: (61) 396927222   **AU**
Web Site: https://www.far.com.au
Year Founded: 1984
FAR—(OTCIQ)
Rev.: $494,000
Assets: $35,470,000
Liabilities: $1,784,000
Net Worth: $33,686,000
Earnings: ($5,188,000)
Emp.: 9
Fiscal Year-end: 12/31/22
Oil & Gas Exploration Services
N.A.I.C.S.: 211120
Claire Newstead-Sinclair *(Sec)*

Subsidiaries:

Flow Energy Limited   **(1)**
Level 7 Exchange Tower 530 Little Collins
St, Melbourne, 3000, Australia
Tel.: (61) 399097609
Sales Range: $150-199.9 Million
Emp.: 6
Oil & Gas Exploration Services
N.A.I.C.S.: 213112

**FARABI PHARMACEUTI-
CAL.CO**
Km 15 Shiraz Road, Isfahan, Iran
Tel.: (98) 3133132000
Web Site:
  https://www.farabipharma.ir
Year Founded: 1993
DFRB1—(THE)
Sales Range: Less than $1 Million
Pharmaceutical Preparation Mfr
N.A.I.C.S.: 325412
Abolfazl Beykihassan *(Mgr-
Pharmacist & Excellence)*

FARADAY COPPER CORP.
2800 - 1055 Dunsmuir Stree, Van-
couver, V7X 1L2, BC, Canada
Tel.: (604) 484-7855   **BC**
Web Site: https://faradaycopper.com
Year Founded: 2014
FDY—(TSX)
Assets: $8,787,536
Liabilities: $571,650
Net Worth: $8,215,886
Earnings: ($4,284,199)
Fiscal Year-end: 12/31/21
Copper Exploration & Mining
N.A.I.C.S.: 213114
J. Gianni Kovacevic *(CEO)*

**FARADAY TECHNOLOGY
CORPORATION**
No 5 Li-Hsin Rd III, Hsinchu Science
Park, Hsin-chu, 30078, Taiwan
Tel.: (886) 35787888
Web Site: https://www.faraday-
tech.com
Year Founded: 1993
3035—(TAI)
Rev.: $391,300,355
Assets: $438,799,846
Liabilities: $116,534,578
Net Worth: $322,265,268
Earnings: $51,057,390
Emp.: 623
Fiscal Year-end: 12/31/23
Semiconductor Component Distr &
Intellectual Property Licensor
N.A.I.C.S.: 423690
Stan Hung *(Chm)*

Subsidiaries:

Artery Technology Company   **(1)**
No 5 Li-Hsin Rd III Hsinchu Science Park,
Hsinchu, 300, Taiwan
Tel.: (886) 35778788
Web Site: http://www.arterytek.com

Faraday Technology Corporation—(Continued)

Microcontroller Product Mfr
N.A.I.C.S.: 334413

Artery Technology Corporation,
Ltd. (1)
10F Kangtianxiinhui Bldg 1 No 60 Kecheng
Rd, Jiulongpo Dist, Chongqing, China
Tel.: (86) 2368688899
Microcontroller Product Mfr
N.A.I.C.S.: 334413

Faraday Technology Corporation (1)
C302 No 1355 JinJiHu Avenue International
Science Technology Park, Suzhou Industrial
Park, Suzhou, 215021, China
Tel.: (86) 51262511089
Semiconductor Product Mfr
N.A.I.C.S.: 334413

Subsidiary (Domestic):

Faraday Technology China
Corporation (2)
Room 1101 Yuanzhong Scientific Research
Building No 1905 Hongmei Rd, Shanghai,
200233, China
Tel.: (86) 2154453398
Semiconductor Product Mfr
N.A.I.C.S.: 334413

Faraday Technology Corporation (1)
2860 Zanker Rd Ste 101, San Jose, CA
95134
Tel.: (408) 522-8888
Web Site: https://www.faraday-tech.com
Sales Range: $1-9.9 Million
Emp.: 40
Semiconductor & Related Device Mfr
N.A.I.C.S.: 334413

Faraday Technology Japan
Corporation (1)
Tokyo Central Place Bldg 3F 22-6 Kabuto-
cho, Nihonbashi Chuo-ku, Tokyo, 103-0026,
Japan
Tel.: (81) 355396471
Semiconductor Product Mfr
N.A.I.C.S.: 334413

Faraday Technology Vietnam Com-
pany Limited (1)
Room 602 6th floor Royal Tower B Royal
Tower Center Building, 235 Nguyen Van Cu
Street Nguyen Cu Trinh ward District 1, Ho
Chi Minh City, Vietnam
Tel.: (84) 2871099939
Semiconductor Product Mfr
N.A.I.C.S.: 334413

Innopower Technology
Corporation (1)
8F No 5 Li-Hsin Rd III Hsinchu Science
Park, Hsinchu, 300, Taiwan
Tel.: (886) 35635228
Web Site: http://www.innopower-tech.com
Semiconductor Product Mfr
N.A.I.C.S.: 334413

FARAN SUGAR MILLS LTD
431E B Block 6 P E C H S off Razi
Road Shahrahe, Karachi, Pakistan
Tel.: (92) 2134322851
Web Site: https://www.faran.com.pk
Year Founded: 1981
FRSM—(KAR)
Rev.: $29,746,821
Assets: $36,301,620
Liabilities: $21,359,980
Net Worth: $14,941,640
Earnings: $2,450,067
Emp.: 588
Fiscal Year-end: 09/30/19
Sugar Processing
N.A.I.C.S.: 311314
Mohammad Omar Amin Bawany
(Chm)

Subsidiaries:

Faran Sugar Mills Ltd - Sindh
Mill (1)
Tando Ebrahim Bawany Shaikh Bhirkio, Dis-
trict Tando Muhammad Khan, Hyderabad,
Sindh, Pakistan
Tel.: (92) 22303594344

Sugar Mfr
N.A.I.C.S.: 311314

**FARASIS ENERGY (GAN-
ZHOU) CO., LTD.**
Jinling West Road, Economic Devel-
opment Zone, Ganzhou, 341000, Ji-
angxi, China
Tel.: (86) 7977329849
Web Site: https://www.farasis.com
Year Founded: 2009
688567—(SHG)
Rev.: $1,626,968,777
Assets: $4,510,655,328
Liabilities: $2,823,529,658
Net Worth: $1,687,125,670
Earnings: ($130,149,228)
Fiscal Year-end: 12/31/22
Energy Distribution Services
N.A.I.C.S.: 221122
Wang Yu (Chm)

FARBANCA S.P.A.
Via Irnerio 43/b, 40126, Bologna, Italy
Tel.: (39) 051 2100811
Web Site: http://www.farbanca.it
Year Founded: 1997
Consumer Lending Services
N.A.I.C.S.: 522291
Bernardelle Giampiero (CEO)

FARBCHEMIE BRAUN KG
Daimlerring 11, 65205, Wiesbaden,
Germany
Tel.: (49) 612291190
Web Site: http://www.farbchemie-
braun.eu
Year Founded: 1930
Rev.: $12,731,862
Emp.: 60
Dyestuff Mfr
N.A.I.C.S.: 325130
Boris Braun (Mng Dir)

Subsidiaries:

TECXO Farben Produktionsgesell-
schaft mbH (1)
Thiuramstr 6, Greppin, Germany
Tel.: (49) 349376302
Dyestuff Mfr
N.A.I.C.S.: 325130

**FARCENT ENTERPRICE CO.,
LTD.**
13F No 230 Section 3 Chengde
Road, Datong District, Taipei, 103,
Taiwan
Tel.: (886) 225922860
Web Site: https://www.farcent.com.tw
1730—(TAI)
Rev.: $85,557,013
Assets: $83,589,519
Liabilities: $19,328,002
Net Worth: $64,261,517
Earnings: $8,492,298
Fiscal Year-end: 12/31/23
Deodorant Mfr & Distr
N.A.I.C.S.: 325620

Subsidiaries:

Farcent Enterprice Co., Ltd. -
Guanyin Factory (1)
13F No 230 Cheng Teh Rd Sec 3, Taipei,
103, Taiwan
Tel.: (886) 34833728
Sales Range: $25-49.9 Million
Emp.: 70
Household Cleaning Product Mfr
N.A.I.C.S.: 335220

**FAREAST FINANCE & INVEST-
MENT LIMITED**
Simple Tree Lighthouse 10th floor
Plot53 Road No 21 BlockB Kemal,
Ataturk Avenue Banani, Dhaka, 1213,
Bangladesh
Tel.: (880) 255033328　　　　BD

Web Site: https://www.ffilbd.com
Year Founded: 2001
FAREASTFIN—(CHT)
Rev.: $961,436
Assets: $106,108,848
Liabilities: $165,166,422
Net Worth: ($59,057,574)
Earnings: ($21,565,826)
Emp.: 27
Fiscal Year-end: 12/31/22
Financial Services
N.A.I.C.S.: 523999
Mohammad Rofiqul Alam (Sr VP &
Head-Ops)

**FAREAST ISLAMI LIFE INSUR-
ANCE CO. LTD.**
Fareast Tower 35 Topkhana Road,
Dhaka, 1000, Bangladesh
Tel.: (880) 9613000123
Web Site:
　　https://www.fareastislamilife.com
Year Founded: 2000
FAREASTLIF—(DHA)
Rev.: $88,833,655
Assets: $388,068,528
Liabilities: $124,440,744
Net Worth: $263,627,784
Earnings: $225,916,361
Emp.: 2,581
Fiscal Year-end: 12/31/20
Investment Management Service
N.A.I.C.S.: 523999
Mohammad Nazrul Islam (Chm & Sr
VP)

Subsidiaries:

Fareast Islami Securities Limited (1)
Fareast Tower level-12 35 Topkhana Road,
Dhaka, 1000, Bangladesh
Tel.: (880) 29562053
Web Site: http://www.fislbd.com
Security Brokerage Services
N.A.I.C.S.: 523150
Nazrul Islam (Chm)

FAREVA SA
80 Ave de la Grande Armee, 75017,
Paris, France
Tel.: (33) 158051110　　　　FR
Web Site: http://www.fareva.com
Year Founded: 1990
Sales Range: $1-4.9 Billion
Emp.: 10,000
Pharmaceutical & Cosmetics Manu-
facturing Services
N.A.I.C.S.: 325412
Bernard Fraisse (Chm)

Subsidiaries:

EXCELLA GmbH (1)
Nurnberger Str 12, D 90537, Feucht, Ger-
many
Tel.: (49) 9128404521
Web Site: http://www.excella-pharma-
source.de
Sales Range: $125-149.9 Million
Emp.: 420
Pharmaceuticals Product Mfr
N.A.I.C.S.: 325412

FAREVA ITUPEVA (1)
Rua Americo Simoes 620, 13 295 000, Sao
Paulo, Brazil
Tel.: (55) 11 45 93 82 00
Pharmaceutical Products Distr
N.A.I.C.S.: 424210

FAREVA LOUVEIRA (1)
Rua Karl Kielblock 1033, 13 290 000, Lou-
veira, Sao Paulo, Brazil
Tel.: (55) 19 3129 18
Pharmaceutical Products Distr
N.A.I.C.S.: 424210

Fareva Holding SA (1)
28 place de la Gare, 1616, Luxembourg,
Luxembourg
Tel.: (352) 261 881 540
Pharmaceutical Products Distr
N.A.I.C.S.: 424210

Fareva Richmond Inc. (1)
2248 Darbytown Rd, Henrico, VA 23231
Tel.: (804) 652-6700
Pharmaceutical Products Distr
N.A.I.C.S.: 424210
Jay Jamison (Dir-Fin)

FARFALLI
Via Selva 21, 33085, Maniago,
Pordenone, Italy
Tel.: (39) 042771271
Web Site: https://www.farfalli.com
Year Founded: 1950
Screw & Bottle Product Mfr
N.A.I.C.S.: 332722

**FARGLORY F T Z INVEST-
MENT HOLDING CO., LTD.**
101 Hangxiang Road, Dayuan Dis-
trict, Taoyuan, Taiwan
Tel.: (886) 33992888
Web Site: https://www.ftz.com.tw
Year Founded: 1991
5607—(TAI)
Rev.: $95,098,299
Assets: $824,028,583
Liabilities: $497,340,476
Net Worth: $326,688,107
Earnings: $29,176,983
Emp.: 656
Fiscal Year-end: 12/31/23
Land & Air Transportation Services
N.A.I.C.S.: 488999
Chen Sung-Tsao (Gen Mgr)

**FARGLORY LAND DEVELOP-
MENT CO., LTD.**
16F No 200 Keelung Rd Sec 1, Tai-
pei, Taiwan
Tel.: (886) 27239999
Web Site: http://www.farglory.com.tw
5522—(TAI)
Rev.: $714,326,079
Assets: $3,143,883,756
Liabilities: $1,657,063,249
Net Worth: $1,486,820,507
Earnings: $121,574,507
Emp.: 280
Fiscal Year-end: 12/31/23
Building & Construction Services
N.A.I.C.S.: 236210
Wen Chia Chao (Chm)

FARITEC HOLDINGS LIMITED
Faritec House 150 Kelvin Drive,
Woodmead, 2148, Sandton, South
Africa
Tel.: (27) 118441000
Web Site: http://www.faritec.co.za
Sales Range: $100-124.9 Million
Emp.: 400
Information Technology Services &
Solutions
N.A.I.C.S.: 541611
Faine Van Rensburg (CEO)

**FARLIM GROUP (MALAYSIA)
BHD**
No 2-8 Bangunan Farlim Jalan PJS
10/32, Taman Sri Subang, 46150,
Petaling Jaya, Selangor Darul Ehsan,
Malaysia
Tel.: (60) 356355533
Web Site: https://www.farlim.com.my
FARLIM—(KLS)
Rev.: $3,346,986
Assets: $31,860,925
Liabilities: $4,885,315
Net Worth: $26,975,610
Earnings: ($1,479,025)
Emp.: 60
Fiscal Year-end: 12/31/23
Property Development & Investment
Services
N.A.I.C.S.: 531312
Mohamed Iqbal Kuppa Pitchai Raw-
ther (Exec Dir)

FARM BOY INC.
1427 Ogilvie Road 2nd Floor, Ottawa, K1J 8M7, ON, Canada
Tel.: (613) 247-1007
Web Site: http://www.farmboy.ca
Year Founded: 1981
Sales Range: $75-99.9 Million
Regional Supermarket Chain
N.A.I.C.S.: 445110
Carolyn Trudel *(Dir-Mktg)*

FARM BUSINESS CONSULTANTS INC.
3015 5 Ave NE 150, Calgary, T2A 6T8, AB, Canada
Tel.: (403) 735-6105
Web Site: https://www.fbc.ca
Year Founded: 1952
Tax Return & Administrative Services
N.A.I.C.S.: 541213
James Gary Ibbotson *(Pres)*

FARM CREDIT CANADA
1800 Hamilton Street, Box 4320, Regina, S4P 4L3, SK, Canada
Tel.: (306) 780-8100
Web Site: http://www.fcc-fac.ca
Rev.: $1,225,853,882
Assets: $36,989,345,512
Liabilities: $30,279,552,375
Net Worth: $6,709,793,138
Earnings: $728,996,562
Emp.: 2,200
Fiscal Year-end: 03/31/22
Agricultural Financial Services
N.A.I.C.S.: 523999
Greg Honey *(Chief HR Officer & Exec VP)*

Subsidiaries:

FCC Ventures **(1)**
1800 Hamilton Street, PO Box 4320, Regina, S4P 4L3, SK, Canada
Tel.: (306) 780-8100
Web Site: http://www.fcc-fac.ca
Sales Range: $350-399.9 Million
Emp.: 600
Venture Capital Services
N.A.I.C.S.: 523999
Michael Hoffort *(Pres & CEO)*

FARM FRESH BERHAD
No 11-1 Jalan Petaling Kawasan Perindustrian Larkin, 80350, Johor Bahru, Johor, Malaysia
Tel.: (60) 72323463   **MY**
Web Site:
https://www.farmfresh.com.my
Year Founded: 2009
FFB—(KLS)
Rev.: $133,267,881
Assets: $224,896,486
Liabilities: $90,314,137
Net Worth: $134,582,348
Earnings: $10,568,100
Emp.: 992
Fiscal Year-end: 03/31/23
Dairy Product Mfr & Distr
N.A.I.C.S.: 311514
Loi Ee *(CEO & Mng Dir)*

FARM LANDS OF AFRICA, INC.
c/o Pearl Capital Partners Ltd. Ground Floor, Suite GFE The Phoenix Brewery, 13 Bramley Road, London, W10 6SP, United Kingdom
Tel.: (44) 2070340035   **NV**
Web Site:
http://www.farmlandsofguinea.com
Year Founded: 2007
FLAF—(OTCIQ)
Sales Range: Less than $1 Million
Farming Technology Services
N.A.I.C.S.: 111998
S. N. Kumar Buddhavarapu *(Chm)*

FARM PRIDE FOODS LTD.
551 Chandler Road, Keysborough, 3173, VIC, Australia
Tel.: (61) 397987077   **AU**
Web Site:
https://www.farmpride.com.au
FRM—(ASX)
Rev.: $64,816,373
Assets: $40,605,636
Liabilities: $38,721,287
Net Worth: $1,884,348
Earnings: ($1,565,839)
Emp.: 240
Fiscal Year-end: 06/30/24
Holding Company; Egg Production & Whslr; Processed Egg Products Mfr & Whslr
N.A.I.C.S.: 551112
Bruce De Lacy *(Sec & Sec)*

FARMACEUTICA REMEDIA S.A.
Deva Bd Nicolae Balcescu nr 2, Hunedoara, Romania
Tel.: (40) 254223260   **RS**
Web Site:
https://corporate.remedia.ro
Year Founded: 1991
RMAH—(BUC)
Rev.: $5,676,549
Assets: $13,908,112
Liabilities: $2,528,607
Net Worth: $11,379,505
Earnings: $941,864
Fiscal Year-end: 12/31/23
Pharmaceuticals Producut Sales
N.A.I.C.S.: 424210
Zoe Chirita *(Mgr)*

Subsidiaries:

Sibmedica SRL **(1)**
Bulevardul Metalurgiei Nr 78, 041836, Bucharest, Romania
Tel.: (40) 213211640
Web Site: https://remediadl.ro
Pharmaceutical Products Distr
N.A.I.C.S.: 424210

FARMACOL S.A.
ul Rzepakowa 2, 40-541, Katowice, Poland
Tel.: (48) 322080600   **PL**
Web Site:
https://www.farmacol.com.pl
Year Founded: 1990
Pharmaceutical Product Whslr
N.A.I.C.S.: 424210
Andrzej Olszewski *(Chm-Supervisory Bd)*

FARMACOOP A.D.
Svetosavska 118 Kac, Backa Palanka, Serbia
Tel.: (381) 216350717
Year Founded: 1989
FRMC—(BEL)
Assets: $261,393
Liabilities: $42,093
Net Worth: $219,299
Earnings: ($6,654)
Fiscal Year-end: 12/31/22
Poultry Services
N.A.I.C.S.: 112340

FARMACOSMO S.P.A.
Via Crispi 51, 80121, Naples, Italy
Web Site:
https://www.farmacosmo.com
Year Founded: 2013
COSMOS—(ITA)
Rev.: $70,004,983
Assets: $41,687,595
Liabilities: $21,411,915
Net Worth: $20,275,680
Earnings: ($2,137,459)
Fiscal Year-end: 12/31/22
Pharmaceutical Products Distr

N.A.I.C.S.: 424210
Fabio De Concilio *(CEO)*

FARMAFORCE LIMITED
Level 9 85 Castlereagh Street, Sydney, 2000, NSW, Australia
Tel.: (61) 282395400
Web Site:
http://www.farmaforce.com.au
FFC—(ASX)
Rev.: $10,714,327
Assets: $4,129,118
Liabilities: $6,355,171
Net Worth: ($2,226,052)
Earnings: ($1,287,242)
Fiscal Year-end: 06/30/20
Health Care Srvices
N.A.I.C.S.: 621999
Clair O'Gorman *(Head-Ops)*

FARMAK JSC
str Kyrylivska 63, 4080, Kiev, Ukraine
Tel.: (380) 444968787
Web Site: https://www.farmak.ua
Year Founded: 1925
FARM—(UKR)
Rev.: $263,638,268
Assets: $295,638,454
Liabilities: $76,403,714
Net Worth: $219,234,740
Earnings: $39,912,445
Fiscal Year-end: 12/31/20
Pharmaceuticals Product Mfr
N.A.I.C.S.: 325412
Filya Zhebrovska *(Chm-Supervisory Bd)*

Subsidiaries:

NORD FARM Sp. z o.o. **(1)**
ul Domaniewska 37 lokal 2 43, 02-672, Warsaw, Poland
Tel.: (48) 512721141
Web Site: http://www.lutidin.pl
Eye Care Service
N.A.I.C.S.: 621320
Krzysztof Masternak *(Product Mgr)*

FARMAX INDIA LIMITED
S No 658 Bowrampet V Quthbullapur, Ranga Reddy Dist, Hyderabad, 500043, India
Tel.: (91) 841 824 2207
Web Site: http://www.farmax.co.in
Rev.: $2,466,191
Assets: $5,000,620
Liabilities: $6,356,491
Net Worth: ($1,355,871)
Earnings: ($1,451,359)
Fiscal Year-end: 03/31/16
Fast Moving Consumer Goods Mfr & Distr
N.A.I.C.S.: 311999

FARMER BUSINESS DEVELOPMENTS PLC
Irish Farm Centre, Bluebell, Dublin, 12, Ireland
Tel.: (353) 1 426 0334   **IE**
Web Site:
http://www.farmerdevelopments.ie
Year Founded: 1988
Rev.: $83,970,199
Assets: $384,311,152
Liabilities: $122,191,086
Net Worth: $262,120,067
Earnings: $7,216,171
Emp.: 682
Fiscal Year-end: 12/31/18
Investment Holding Company
N.A.I.C.S.: 551112
Padraig Walshe *(Chm)*

Subsidiaries:

FBD Property & Leisure Limited **(1)**
FBD House Bluebell, Bluebell, Dublin, 12, Ireland **(100%)**
Tel.: (353) 14554292
Web Site: http://www.fbd.ie

Sales Range: $450-499.9 Million
Emp.: 400
Real Estate Investment & Marketing Services
N.A.I.C.S.: 525990
Andrew Langford *(CEO)*

Subsidiary (Domestic):

FBD Hotels (Ireland) Limited **(2)**
FBD House Naas Road, Bluebell, Dublin, 12, Ireland **(100%)**
Tel.: (353) 14282400
Web Site: http://www.fbdhotels.com
Emp.: 7
Home Management Services
N.A.I.C.S.: 721110

Subsidiary (Non-US):

La Cala Golf Club S.L. **(2)**
Urb La Cala Golf s/n, Mijas Costa, ES-29649, Malaga, Spain **(75%)**
Tel.: (34) 952669016
Web Site: http://www.lacala.com
Sales Range: $75-99.9 Million
Emp.: 180
Golf Resort Operator
N.A.I.C.S.: 713910
Patrick Murphy *(Mng Dir)*

Sunset Beach Club S.A. **(2)**
Avenida del Sol 5, Benalmadena, Malaga, Spain **(100%)**
Tel.: (34) 952579400
Web Site: http://www.sunsetbeachclub.com
Emp.: 100
Hotels & Resort Operator
N.A.I.C.S.: 721110
Mark Wardell *(Gen Mgr)*

FARMER CONSTRUCTION LTD.
360 Harbour Rd, Victoria, V9A 3S1, BC, Canada
Tel.: (250) 388-5121
Web Site: https://www.farmer-ltd.com
Year Founded: 1951
Rev.: $28,830,762
Emp.: 100
Construction Services
N.A.I.C.S.: 236220
Paul Gray *(VP)*

FARMERS COMMERCIAL BANK
SudanAlgasr Street, PO Box 1116, Khartoum, Sudan
Tel.: (249) 183 774960
Web Site: http://www.fcbsudan.com
Year Founded: 1998
Commercial Banking Services
N.A.I.C.S.: 522110

FARMFOODS LTD
7 Greens Road, Blairlinn, Cumbernauld, G67 2TU, United Kingdom
Tel.: (44) 1236456789
Web Site: http://www.farmfoods.co.uk
Sales Range: $750-799.9 Million
Emp.: 3,000
Frozen Food Supplier & Mfr
N.A.I.C.S.: 311412
Gerard Savage *(Dir-Retail)*

FARMINGTONS HOLDING GMBH
Beekebreite 18 20, 49124, Georgsmarienhutte, Germany
Tel.: (49) 54014900
Web Site: http://www.farmingtons-group.com
Sales Range: $75-99.9 Million
Emp.: 300
Motor Vehicle Parts Mfr
N.A.I.C.S.: 336390
Matthias Reckmann *(CEO)*

Subsidiaries:

IndiKar - Individual Karosseriebau GmbH **(1)**
Am Schmelzbach 85, 08112, Wilkau-

Farmingtons Holding GmbH—(Continued)

Hasslau, Germany
Tel.: (49) 375 6068 0
Web Site: http://www.indikar.welp-
  group.com
Vehicle Engineering Services
N.A.I.C.S.: 541330

**pgam Advanced Technologies
Ltd.** (1)
I8 Lake View House Tournament Fields,
Warwick, CV34 6RA, United Kingdom
Tel.: (44) 1926679586
Web Site: http://www.pgam.com
Vehicle Engineering Services
N.A.I.C.S.: 541330
Ken Brown (Mng Dir)

FARMINVESTE SGPS S.A.
Santa Catarina Crossing 8, 1200-403,
Lisbon, Portugal
Tel.: (351) 213400600
Web Site: http://www.farminveste-
sgps.com
MLFMV—(EUR)
Sales Range: $900-999.9 Million
Holding Company
N.A.I.C.S.: 551112
Marcos Andre Alves Teixeira (Sec)

FARMLAND A.D.
Nova Topola bb, 78418, Gradiska,
Bosnia & Herzegovina
Tel.: (387) 51 891 431
Web Site: http://www.farmland.cc
Year Founded: 1892
GOVF—(BANJ)
Sales Range: $10-24.9 Million
Emp.: 119
Milk Production Services
N.A.I.C.S.: 112120
Dragan Vasiljevic (Chm-Mgmt Bd)

FARMMI, INC.
Fl 1 Building No 1 888 Tianning
Street, Liandu, Lishui, 323000, Zheji-
ang, China
Tel.: (86) 571875555801   Ky
Web Site: https://www.farmmi.com
Year Founded: 2015
FAMI—(NASDAQ)
Rev.: $110,364,887
Assets: $174,800,086
Liabilities: $12,824,160
Net Worth: $161,975,926
Earnings: $2,543,813
Emp.: 70
Fiscal Year-end: 09/30/23
Agricultural Product Mfr & Distr
N.A.I.C.S.: 111411
Yefang Zhang (Co-Founder, Chm &
CEO)

FARMS.COM LTD.
52 Royal Rd Unit A Guelph, London,
N1H 1G3, ON, Canada
Tel.: (519) 438-5729
Web Site: http://www.farms.com
Year Founded: 1995
Sales Range: $25-49.9 Million
Emp.: 40
Online Livestock & Agriculture Market
Data
N.A.I.C.S.: 926140
David Gilmour (Chm)

Subsidiaries:

AgCareers.com (1)
PO Box 1736, Clinton, NC 28329
Web Site: http://www.agcareers.com
Online Information Services
N.A.I.C.S.: 519290
Kathryn Doan (Dir-Global Bus Dev)

**Farms.com Risk Management
Inc.** (1)
1531 Airport Rd Ste 101, Ames, IA 50010
Tel.: (877) 438-5729

Web Site:
  http://www.riskmanagement.farms.com
Online Information Services
N.A.I.C.S.: 519290
Maurizio Agostino (Gen Mgr)

PigCI IAMP Inc. (1)
Ames Business Park 1601 Golden Aspen
Dr Unit 109, Ames, IA 50010
Tel.: (774) 242
Web Site: http://www.pigchamp.com
Supplier of Swine Management Information
& Services
N.A.I.C.S.: 541511

eHARVEST (1)
1615 North Routledge Park, London, N6H
5N5, ON, Canada (100%)
Tel.: (519) 438-5729
Web Site: http://www.farms.com
Sales Range: $25-49.9 Million
Emp.: 29
Agricultural Consulting Services
N.A.I.C.S.: 541690
J. Douglas Maus (Pres & CEO)

FARMSCO.
273-4 Gyereuk-ri, Miyang-myeon,
Anseong, Gyeonggi-do, Korea
(South)
Tel.: (82) 262009901
Web Site: http://www.farmsco.com
Year Founded: 1999
036580—(KRS)
Rev.: $1,458,455,723
Assets: $938,174,635
Liabilities: $725,062,383
Net Worth: $213,112,252
Earnings: ($26,321,955)
Emp.: 421
Fiscal Year-end: 12/31/22
Cattle Feed Mfr
N.A.I.C.S.: 112112
Lee Jeong-Gu (Exec Mng Dir)

**FARMSECURE HOLDINGS
(PTY) LTD.**
Avanti South Building 3rd Floor 3
Churchill Close Tygerfalls, Carl
Cronje Drive Tyger Valley, Cape
Town, South Africa
Tel.: (27) 21 974 1950
Web Site:
  http://www.farmsecure.co.za
Emp.: 4,500
Agriculture Product Distr
N.A.I.C.S.: 424590
Jerome Yazbek (CEO)

Subsidiaries:

Kynoch Fertilizers (Pty) Ltd. (1)
Lower Roos Street, 2094, Johannesburg,
South Africa
Tel.: (27) 11 317 2000
Web Site: http://www.kynoch.co.za
Emp.: 65
Fertilizer Mfr & Distr
N.A.I.C.S.: 325311
Gordon Hesom (Mng Dir)

FARMSTORY CO., LTD.
3F 310 Gangnam-daero, Gangnam-
Gu, Seoul, 06253, Korea (South)
Tel.: (82) 25011648
Year Founded: 1991
027510—(KRS)
Rev.: $1,094,087,875
Assets: $748,558,376
Liabilities: $557,277,648
Net Worth: $191,280,728
Earnings: ($5,791,435)
Emp.: 407
Fiscal Year-end: 12/31/22
Animal Feed Mfr
N.A.I.C.S.: 311119
Kim Choong Suk (Exec Dir)

FARON PHARMACEUTICALS
Joukahaisenkatu 6, FI-20520, Turku,
Finland

Tel.: (358) 24695151
Web Site: https://www.faron.com
FARN—(AIM)
Rev.: $866,609
Assets: $12,163,825
Liabilitioc: $24,548,888
Net Worth: ($12,385,064)
Earnings: ($31,005,828)
Emp.: 40
Fiscal Year-end: 12/31/22
Pharmaceutical Manufacture & Sales
N.A.I.C.S.: 325412
Markku Jalkanen (Founder & CEO)

FARR VINTNERS LTD
Commodore House Battersea Reach
Juniper Drive, London, SW18 1TW,
United Kingdom
Tel.: (44) 20 7821 2000
Web Site: http://www.farrvintners.com
Year Founded: 1978
Sales Range: $150-199.9 Million
Wine Whslr
N.A.I.C.S.: 424820
Stephen Browett (Chm)

Subsidiaries:

Farr Vintners Ltd (1)
8/F Redana Centre 25 Yiu Wa Street,
Causeway Bay, China (Hong Kong)
Tel.: (852) 2575 8773
Web Site: http://www.farrhk.com
Emp.: 6
Wine Merchant
N.A.I.C.S.: 424820
Jason Naude (Gen Mgr)

**FARS & KHUZESTAN CEMENT
CO.**
No 4 4th Alley Pakistan St, Tehran,
Iran
Tel.: (98) 2188737115
Web Site: https://office.fkcco.com
Year Founded: 1950
SFKZ—(THE)
Sales Range: Less than $1 Million
Cement Mfr
N.A.I.C.S.: 327310

Subsidiaries:

Bojnourd Cement Co. (1)
No 16 4th Alley Mir Emad St Ostad Mot-
ahary St, Tehran, 15878-43613, Iran
Tel.: (98) 21 88754424
Web Site: http://www.bojnourdcement.com
Emp.: 320
Cement Product Mfr & Distr
N.A.I.C.S.: 327310

Doroud Cement Company (1)
No 69 Siman Khash Building 1st Floor
North Sohravardi St, Andishe 2nd St Quds,
68819-33331, Tehran, Iran
Tel.: (98) 2142147000
Web Site: https://www.dcementco.com
Sales Range: Less than $1 Million
Emp.: 865
Cement Product Mfr & Distr
N.A.I.C.S.: 327310

Farsnov Cement Co. (1)
No 142 Shahid Rajaie Alley Cultural City
13th Station, Shiraz, 175168, Fars, Iran
Tel.: (98) 711 6314955
Web Site: http://www.farsnov.com
Emp.: 271
Cement Mfr
N.A.I.C.S.: 327310

FARS CEMENT COMPANY
The End Of Fakhteh St 10th Km Amir
Kabeer Blvd, Shiraz, 71887 46847,
Fars, Iran
Tel.: (98) 711 8228644
Year Founded: 1940
SFRS—(THE)
Sales Range: Less than $1 Million
Emp.: 228
Cement Mfr
N.A.I.C.S.: 327310

**FARS CHEMICAL INDUSTRIES
COMPANY**
End of Kargar Street Zarghan, En-
trance Blvd Pasdaran 28 km Shiraz
Road, Marvdasht, Fars, Iran
Tel.: (98) 7132622141
Web Site:
  http://www.farschemical.com
Year Founded: 1981
Emp.: 160
Resin Mfr
N.A.I.C.S.: 325211

**FARSIGHT BIOSCIENCE LIM-
ITED**
29 Harley Street, London, W1G 9QR,
United Kingdom
Tel.: (44) 2073771489   UK
Web Site:
  http://farsightbioscience.com
Year Founded: 2005
Pharmaceuticals Product Mfr
N.A.I.C.S.: 325412
Erling Refsum (CEO-British)

**FARSTARCAP INVESTMENT
CORP.**
1199 West Hastings St.,, Vancouver,
V6E 3T5, BC, Canada
Tel.: (604) 313-9940
FRS.P—(TSXV)
Assets: $23,681
Liabilities: $6,830
Net Worth: $16,851
Earnings: ($38,594)
Fiscal Year-end: 09/30/23
Asset Management Services
N.A.I.C.S.: 523940
Konstantine Tsakumis (CEO)

**FAS FINANCE & INVESTMENT
LIMITED**
Suvastu Imam Square 4th and 5th
Floor 65 Gulshan Avenue Gulshan 1,
Dhaka, 1212, Bangladesh
Tel.: (880) 258815841
Web Site: https://www.fasbd.com
Year Founded: 1997
FASFIN—(CHT)
Rev.: $761,706
Assets: $189,158,499
Liabilities: $309,563,439
Net Worth: ($120,404,940)
Earnings: ($66,899,454)
Emp.: 32
Fiscal Year-end: 12/31/22
Financial Services
N.A.I.C.S.: 523999
Md. Munir Hossain (VP & Head-ICC)

Subsidiaries:

FAS Capital Management Ltd. (1)
Suvastu Imam Square 4th 65 Gulshan Av-
enue Gulshan-1, Dhaka, 1212, Bangladesh
Tel.: (880) 288342534
Web Site: https://www.fcmlbd.com
Financial Management Services
N.A.I.C.S.: 541611
Siddiqur Rahman (Chm)

FASHION B AIR S.A.
210 rue Saint Denis, 75002, Paris,
France
Tel.: (33) 145080664
Web Site: https://www.fashion-
belair.com
ALFBA—(EUR)
Sales Range: $1-9.9 Million
Emp.: 86
Women's Clothing Retailer
N.A.I.C.S.: 458110
Eric Sitruk (Chm & CEO)

FASHION BOX S.P.A.
Via Marcoai 1, 31011, Asolo, Italy
Tel.: (39) 04239251

Web Site: http://www.replay.it
Clothing Designer
N.A.I.C.S.: 315250
Matteo Sinigaglia *(Pres)*

Subsidiaries:

Fashion Box Greece S.A.   (1)
90 Kapodistriou St, Nea Ionia, 142 35, Attica, Greece
Tel.: (30) 2102717757
Web Site: http://www.fashionbox.gr
Sales Range: $25-49.9 Million
Emp.: 172
Clothing, Footgear & Related Accessories Importer, Exporter & Producer
N.A.I.C.S.: 315250

FASHION TV HOLDING LTD.
Wasagasse 4, 1090, Vienna, Austria
Tel.: (43) 15131267
Web Site: http://www.ftv.com
Television Programming
N.A.I.C.S.: 516120
Gabriel Lisowski *(Chm-Supervisory Bd)*

FASHY GMBH
Kornwestheimer Strasse 46, D-70825, Korntal-Munchingen, Germany
Tel.: (49) 715092060
Web Site: http://www.fashy.de
Year Founded: 1986
Rev.: $34,209,120
Emp.: 97
Hot Water Bottle Mfr
N.A.I.C.S.: 339999
Volker Kraus *(Co-CEO)*

FASIL A.D.
Svetolika Lazarevica 18, 31230, Arilje, Serbia
Tel.: (381) 313891131
Web Site: https://www.fasil.rs
Year Founded: 1965
FSIL—(BEL)
Sales Range: Less than $1 Million
Emp.: 455
Sliding Bearing Element Mfr
N.A.I.C.S.: 332991
Free Malovic *(Gen Mgr)*

FASMA A.D.
Milosa Savkovica 4-6, Belgrade, Serbia
Tel.: (381) 11 334 3334
Year Founded: 1951
FSMA—(BEL)
Sales Range: Less than $1 Million
Emp.: 1
Valve & Tap Mfr
N.A.I.C.S.: 332913
Radenko Tresac *(Exec Dir)*

FASOO CO.,LTD.
396 World Cup Buk-ro, Mapo-gu, Seoul, 03925, Korea (South)
Tel.: (82) 23009000
Web Site: https://www.fasoo.com
Year Founded: 2000
150900—(KRS)
Rev.: $33,842,964
Assets: $39,622,117
Liabilities: $14,773,734
Net Worth: $24,848,383
Earnings: $3,997,810
Emp.: 216
Fiscal Year-end: 12/31/22
Data & Software Security
N.A.I.C.S.: 513210
Deborah Kish *(Exec VP-Mktg & Res)*

Subsidiaries:

Fasoo USA Inc.   (1)
197 State Route 18 S, East Brunswick, NJ 08816
Tel.: (408) 389-3097
Software Publisher

N.A.I.C.S.: 513210

FAST CASUALWEAR AG
Osterwaldstr 57, 80805, Munich, Germany
Tel.: (49) 406091860
Web Site: http://www.fast-casualwear.com
Sales Range: $100-124.9 Million
Footwear & Apparel Mfr
N.A.I.C.S.: 316210
Wing Chi Chong *(CEO)*

FAST EJENDOM DANMARK A/S
Raadhusvej 13, 2920, Charlottenlund, Denmark
Tel.: (45) 70228030
Web Site:
    https://www.fastejendom.dk
Year Founded: 2005
FED—(CSE)
Rev.: $28,700,207
Assets: $202,967,690
Liabilities: $116,340,380
Net Worth: $86,627,310
Earnings: $16,425,750
Emp.: 7
Fiscal Year-end: 12/31/22
Commercial & Residential Properties Investments
N.A.I.C.S.: 523999
Dorte Keller *(Sec)*

FAST ENERGY HOLDINGS BERHAD
11 Jalan Pasaran 23/5 Seksyen 23, 40300, Shah Alam, Selangor Darul Ehsan, Malaysia
Tel.: (60) 355485112   MY
Web Site:
    https://www.techfast.com.my
FAST—(KLS)
Rev.: $57,577,258
Assets: $29,569,087
Liabilities: $3,233,900
Net Worth: $26,335,188
Earnings: ($950,790)
Emp.: 18
Fiscal Year-end: 12/31/22
Management Services
N.A.I.C.S.: 551114
Tock Ooi Lim *(Chm)*

Subsidiaries:

Fast Assets Sdn. Bhd.   (1)
B2-1-12 Solaris Dutamas No 1 Jalan Dutamas 1, 50480, Kuala Lumpur, Malaysia
Tel.: (60) 364136680
Property Investment Services
N.A.I.C.S.: 921190

Fast Energy Sdn. Bhd.   (1)
No 11 Jalan Pasaran 23/5 Seksyen 23, 40300, Shah Alam, Selangor, Malaysia
Tel.: (60) 355485112
Bunkering Services
N.A.I.C.S.: 541990

Fast Solar Sdn. Bhd.   (1)
B2-1-12 Solaris Dutamas No 1 Jalan Dutamas 1, 50480, Kuala Lumpur, Malaysia
Tel.: (60) 364136680
Solar Energy Services
N.A.I.C.S.: 926130

Fast Technology Sdn. Bhd.   (1)
B2-1-12 Solaris Dutamas No 1 Jalan Dutamas 1, 50480, Kuala Lumpur, Malaysia
Tel.: (60) 364136680
Bunkering Services
N.A.I.C.S.: 541990

FAST FINANCE 24 HOLDING AG
Uhlandstrasse 165/166, 10719, Berlin, Germany
Tel.: (49) 30726212341
Web Site:
    https://www.fastfinance24.com

Year Founded: 2003
FF24—(DEU)
Rev.: $2,023,744
Assets: $41,221,504
Net Worth: $40,789,248
Earnings: $1,837,088
Fiscal Year-end: 12/30/22
Holding Company
N.A.I.C.S.: 551112
Soren Jensen *(Chm)*

FAST FINANCE S.A.
ul Borowska 283B, 50-556, Wroclaw, Poland
Tel.: (48) 717974100
Web Site: https://www.fastfinance.pl
Year Founded: 2004
FFI—(WAR)
Rev.: $462,359
Assets: $654,191
Liabilities: $4,251,784
Net Worth: ($3,597,593)
Earnings: $5,980,554
Emp.: 40
Fiscal Year-end: 12/31/22
Debt Recovery Services
N.A.I.C.S.: 522299
Jacek Longin Daroszewski *(Chm-Mgmt Bd)*

Subsidiaries:

Columbus Factoring Solutions S.A.   (1)
128 Obywatelska St, 94-104, Lodz, Poland
Tel.: (48) 42 689 83 42
Web Site: http://www.cfs.pl
Financial & Security Services
N.A.I.C.S.: 523999

FAST FITNESS JAPAN, INC.
Shinjuku i-LAND WING 6 Chome-3-1 Nishishinjuku, Shinjuku-ku, Tokyo, 160-0023, Japan
Tel.: (81) 62790861
Web Site:
    https://www.fastfitnessjapan.jp
Year Founded: 2010
7092—(TKS)
Rev.: $104,603,250
Assets: $144,084,780
Liabilities: $58,815,780
Net Worth: $85,269,000
Earnings: $14,033,030
Emp.: 255
Fiscal Year-end: 03/31/24
Sports Club Facility Operator
N.A.I.C.S.: 713940
Akira Okuma *(Chm)*

FAST INTERNATIONAL CO.
Block No 156 Garden-West Prnice Hotel, Khartoum, Sudan
Tel.: (249) 183790000   Sd
Web Site:
    http://www.fastinternational-ltd.com
Year Founded: 1991
Emp.: 95
Pharmaceuticals Product Mfr
N.A.I.C.S.: 325412
Tarig Mohy Aldin *(Chm)*

FAST LINE HLDG, INC.
804-750 West Pender Street, Vancouver, V6C 2T7, BC, Canada
Tel.: (604) 569-0799
GFGVF—(OTCIQ)
Sales Range: $550-599.9 Million
Holding Company
N.A.I.C.S.: 551112
Richard Di Biase *(Pres & CEO)*

FAST RETAILING CO., LTD.
107171 Sayama, Yamaguchi, 754-0894, Japan
Tel.: (81) 368650050   JP

Web Site:
    https://www.fastretailing.com
Year Founded: 1963
9983—(TKS)
Rev.: $19,305,859,920
Assets: $22,314,054,300
Liabilities: $9,450,114,420
Net Worth: $12,864,539,880
Earnings: $2,313,833,780
Emp.: 15,081
Fiscal Year-end: 08/31/24
Holding Company; Apparel Mfr; Retail Store Operator
N.A.I.C.S.: 551112
Takeshi Okazaki *(Grp Sr Exec Officer)*

Subsidiaries:

Cabin Co., Ltd.   (1)
4-62-17 Yoyogi 3-15-5 Shinjyoku, Shinjyuju-Ku, Tokyo, 160-0023, Japan   **(93.89%)**
Tel.: (81) 353345091
Web Site: http://www.cabin.co.jp
Women's Clothing Store
N.A.I.C.S.: 458110

Fast Retailing USA, Inc.   (1)
450 W 14th St 7th Fl, New York, NY 10014
Tel.: (212) 221-9037
Web Site: http://www.uniqlo.com
Sales Range: $25-49.9 Million
Emp.: 20
Family Clothing Stores
N.A.I.C.S.: 458110
Rebekka Bay *(Dir-Creative-Research & Design Center)*

G.U. Co., Ltd.   (1)
1-6-7 Ariake, Koto-ku, Tokyo, 135-0063, Japan   **(100%)**
Tel.: (81) 368650101
Web Site: https://www.gu-global.com
Clothing & Furnishings Merchant Whslr
N.A.I.C.S.: 424350

J Brand, Inc.   (1)
1318 E 7th St Ste 260, Los Angeles, CA 90021
Web Site: https://www.jbrandjeans.com
Apparel Product Mfr & Distr
N.A.I.C.S.: 315990
Kazumi Yanai *(CEO)*

Petit Vehicule S.A.   (1)
9 Rue Brea, Paris, France
Tel.: (33) 0143120300
Womens & Girls Cut & Sew Dress Mfr
N.A.I.C.S.: 315250

Theory, LLC   (1)
38 Gansevoort St, New York, NY 10014
Web Site: https://www.theory.com
Apparel Product Mfr & Distr
N.A.I.C.S.: 327910
Kazumi Yanai *(Chm)*

Uniqlo Australia Pty Ltd   (1)
Level 19 Wesley Place 150 Lonsdale Street, Melbourne, 3000, VIC, Australia
Tel.: (61) 386370251
Web Site: https://www.uniqlo.com
N.A.I.C.S.: 458110

Uniqlo Hong Kong, Ltd.   (1)
Hong KongRoom 702-706 7/F Mira Place One 132 Nathan Road, Tsim Sha Tsui, Kowloon, China (Hong Kong)   **(100%)**
Tel.: (852) 23148886
Web Site: https://www.uniqlo.com
Sales Range: $25-49.9 Million
Emp.: 80
Family Clothing Stores
N.A.I.C.S.: 458110

Uniqlo Vietnam Co., Ltd.   (1)
Tel.: (84) 2862846667
Web Site: http://www.uniqlo.com
Men & Women Clothing Mfr
N.A.I.C.S.: 315250

FAST TRUCKING SERVICE LTD .
Fast Ln, PO Box 700, Carnduff, S0C 0S0, SK, Canada
Tel.: (306) 482-3244

Fast Trucking Service Ltd .—(Continued)

Web Site:
http://www.fasttruckingservice.com
Year Founded: 1957
Rev.: $15,823,981
Emp.: 150
Trucking Service
N.A.I.C.S.: 484121
Tony Day *(Pres)*

FAST-AID PRODUCTS LIMITED
24/3 Dryden Road Bilston Glen Industrial Estate, Edinburgh, EH20 9HX, United Kingdom
Tel.: (44) 131 440 3929
Web Site:
http://www.fastaidproducts.com
Sales Range: $25-49.9 Million
Emp.: 15
Medical Equipment Distr
N.A.I.C.S.: 423450

FASTATOR AB
Linnegatan 2, 114 47, Stockholm, Sweden
Tel.: (46) 86606700
Web Site: https://www.fastator.se
Year Founded: 2011
R71—(BER)
Sales Range: Less than $1 Million
Investment Banking Services
N.A.I.C.S.: 523150
Bjorn Rosengren *(Chm)*

FASTEEL INDUSTRIES LTD
19176 21st Avenue, Surrey, V3S 3M3, BC, Canada
Tel.: (604) 542-8881
Web Site:
http://www.fasteelindustries.com
Rev.: $12,540,000
Emp.: 25
Steel Distr & Whslr
N.A.I.C.S.: 331513

FASTER ENTERPRISES LTD
G02 8 Ellingworth Parade, Box Hill, 3128, VIC, Australia
Tel.: (61) 398974540   AU
Web Site:
http://www.fasterenterprises.com.au
Year Founded: 2015
FE8—(ASX)
Rev.: $74,175
Assets: $4,746,348
Liabilities: $3,341,774
Net Worth: $1,404,574
Earnings: ($979,426)
Fiscal Year-end: 06/30/20
Residential Property Development Services
N.A.I.C.S.: 531311

FASTFORMS INC.
251 Massey Road, Guelph, N1K 1B2, ON, Canada
Tel.: (519) 824-4910
Year Founded: 1967
Rev.: $33,221,994
Emp.: 150
Printing Services
N.A.I.C.S.: 323111
Gary Christie *(Pres)*

FASTIGHETS AB BALDER
Parkgatan 49, Po Box 53 121, 411 38, Gothenburg, Sweden
Tel.: (46) 774494949   SE
Web Site: https://www.balder.se
Year Founded: 2005
BALD-B—(OMX)
Rev.: $1,118,697,725
Assets: $23,766,519,617
Liabilities: $14,963,518,690
Net Worth: $8,803,000,927
Earnings: ($721,102,963)

Emp.: 1,145
Fiscal Year-end: 12/31/24
Property Management Services
N.A.I.C.S.: 523999
Christina Rogestam *(Chm)*

Subsidiaries:

Anthon Eiendom AS   (1)
Ovre Vollgt 13, 0158, Oslo, Norway
Tel.: (47) 24145490
Web Site: https://www.anthoneiendom.no
Real Estate Development Services
N.A.I.C.S.: 531390

Balder Germany GmbH   (1)
Alfredstr 98, 45131, Essen, Germany
Tel.: (49) 20184387120
Web Site: https://www.balder-gmbh.de
Emp.: 90
Cleaning Service
N.A.I.C.S.: 561720

FASTIGHETS AB TRIANON
Stenhuggaregatan 2, 211 41, Malmo, Sweden
Tel.: (46) 406113400   SE
Web Site: http://www.trianon.se
Year Founded: 1973
TRIAN.B—(OMX)
Rev.: $74,860,525
Assets: $1,353,028,792
Liabilities: $854,666,761
Net Worth: $498,362,031
Earnings: ($20,459,825)
Emp.: 85
Fiscal Year-end: 12/31/23
Real Estate Services
N.A.I.C.S.: 531390
Mari-Louise Hedbys *(Deputy CEO & CFO)*

Subsidiaries:

Signatur Fastigheter AB   (1)
Stjarnplan 3, 216 18, Limhamn, Sweden   (96.1%)
Tel.: (46) 40 608 82 00
Web Site: http://www.signaturfastigheter.se
Sales Range: Less than $1 Million
Real Estate Services
N.A.I.C.S.: 531390
Dan Astren *(CEO)*

FASTNED B.V.
James Wattstraat 77-79, 1097 DL, Amsterdam, Netherlands
Tel.: (31) 207155316   Nl
Web Site:
https://www.fastnedcharging.com
Year Founded: 2012
FAST—(EUR)
Rev.: $38,827,973
Assets: $340,200,734
Liabilities: $166,830,348
Net Worth: $173,370,386
Earnings: ($23,960,717)
Emp.: 159
Fiscal Year-end: 12/31/22
Eletric Power Generation Services
N.A.I.C.S.: 221111
Michiel Langezaal *(CEO)*

Subsidiaries:

Fastned Deutschland GmbH & Co KG   (1)
Mohrenstrasse 7-9, 50670, Cologne, Germany
Tel.: (49) 22182829613
Electric Charging Station Operator
N.A.I.C.S.: 457120
Maarten Smit *(Mgr-Network Dev)*

Fastned UK Ltd.   (1)
1st Floor 3 Bath Place, London, EC2A 3DR, United Kingdom
Tel.: (44) 2039361703
Electric Charging Station Operator
N.A.I.C.S.: 457120
Mark Ward *(Mgr-Construction)*

FASTPARTNER AB

Sturegatan 38, Stockholm, Sweden
Tel.: (46) 84023460
Web Site: https://www.fastpartner.se
Year Founded: 1987
FPAR—(OMX)
Rev.: $107,009,644
Assets: $3,570,766,248
Liabilities: $2,034,514,410
Net Worth: $1,536,251,838
Earnings: $7,914,430
Emp.: 84
Fiscal Year-end: 12/31/22
Property Management Services
N.A.I.C.S.: 531312
Peter Carlsson *(Chm)*

FASTWIRE PTE. LTD.
Level 9, 77 Pacific Highway, Sydney, NSW, Australia
Tel.: (61) 299290666
Web Site: http://www.fastwire-group.com
Year Founded: 1998
Sales Range: $10-24.9 Million
Emp.: 125
Network Infrastructure & OSS Solutions Provider
N.A.I.C.S.: 517810
Rod Fisher *(Co-Mng Dir)*

FAT MEDIA LTD.
Harpers Mill White Cross Industrial Estate, Lancaster, LA1 4XF, United Kingdom
Tel.: (44) 1524 487 452
Web Site: http://www.fatmedia.co.uk
Year Founded: 2005
Digital Advertising
N.A.I.C.S.: 541810
David Durnford *(CEO)*

Subsidiaries:

Reading Room, Ltd.   (1)
65-66 Frith St, Soho, London, W1D 3JR, United Kingdom
Tel.: (44) 2071732800
Web Site: http://www.readingroom.com
Communications, Digital/Interactive, New Technologies, Planning & Consultation, Strategic Planning/Research
N.A.I.C.S.: 541810
Jamie Griffiths *(Bus Dir)*

FAT PROJECTS ACQUISITION CORP.
27 Bukit Manis Road, Singapore, 099892, Singapore
Tel.: (65) 85902056   Ky
Web Site:
http://www.fatprojectscorp.com
Year Founded: 2021
FATPU—(NASDAQ)
Rev.: $1,752,167
Assets: $116,946,189
Liabilities: $122,515,458
Net Worth: ($5,569,269)
Earnings: ($736,161)
Emp.: 3
Fiscal Year-end: 12/31/22
Investment Services
N.A.I.C.S.: 523999
Tristan Lo *(Chm & CO-CEO)*

FAT PROPHETS GLOBAL CONTRARIAN FUND LTD.
Level 3 22 Market St, Sydney, 2000, NSW, Australia
Tel.: (61) 1300881177
Web Site:
https://www.fatprophets.com.au
Year Founded: 2000
FPC—(ASX)
Rev.: $5,248,397
Assets: $41,431,624
Liabilities: $18,050,214
Net Worth: $23,381,410
Earnings: $2,985,443

Fiscal Year-end: 06/30/24
Investment Services
N.A.I.C.S.: 523999
Angus Geddes *(Founder, CEO & CIO)*

FAT PROPHETS GLOBAL PROPERTY FUND
Level 3 22 Market Street, Sydney, 2000, NSW, Australia
Tel.: (61) 290246700
Web Site:
https://www.fpproperty.com.au
Year Founded: 2000
FPP—(ASX)
Rev.: $1,453,210
Assets: $13,045,806
Liabilities: $472,430
Net Worth: $12,573,376
Earnings: $1,110,571
Fiscal Year-end: 06/30/24
Investment Management Service
N.A.I.C.S.: 525990
Angus Geddes *(Founder, CEO, Partner & CIO)*

FATE S.A.I.C.I.
Av Blanco Encalada 3003, B1644GPK, Victoria, Buenos Aires, Argentina
Tel.: (54) 1147258100   Ar
Web Site: http://www.fate.com.ar
Year Founded: 1940
Emp.: 2,000
Tire Exporter Mfr
N.A.I.C.S.: 326211
Javier S. Madanes Quintanilla *(Pres)*

FATEH INDUSTRIES LIMITED
Plot no 442 Mirpurkhas Road, Hyderabad, Pakistan
Tel.: (92) 3332725577
Web Site: https://fateh1.com
Year Founded: 1986
FIL—(PSX)
Rev.: $57,237
Assets: $244,939
Liabilities: $554,362
Net Worth: ($309,423)
Earnings: ($19,592)
Emp.: 20
Fiscal Year-end: 06/30/23
Textile Products Mfr
N.A.I.C.S.: 314999

FATEH SPORTS WEAR LIMITED
Plot 442 Mirpurkhas Road, Hyderabad, Pakistan
Tel.: (92) 223886263
Web Site: https://fatehsports.com
Year Founded: 1984
FSWL—(PSX)
Assets: $2,135,439
Liabilities: $100,245
Net Worth: $2,035,194
Earnings: $548,967
Emp.: 100
Fiscal Year-end: 06/30/23
Garment & Sports Wear Mfr
N.A.I.C.S.: 315120
Ghous Muhammad Khan *(Sec)*

FATEH TEXTILE MILLS LIMITED
A/4 Hali Rd SITE, PO Box 69, 71000, Hyderabad, Sindh, Pakistan
Tel.: (92) 223880463
Sales Range: $25-49.9 Million
Emp.: 334
Textile, Yarn & Fabrics Mfr
N.A.I.C.S.: 313310

FATES A.D.
Marka Ecimovica Bb, 71350, Sokolac, Bosnia & Herzegovina

Tel.: (387) 57448572
FATS—(BANJ)
Sales Range: Less than $1 Million
Emp.: 46
Carpet & Rug Mfr
N.A.I.C.S.: 014110
Mirko Cvijetic *(Chm-Mgmt Bd)*

FATEX A.D.
Industrijska bb, 16203, Vucje, Serbia
Tel.: (381) 16 885 461
Year Founded: 1989
FATX—(BEL)
Sales Range: Less than $1 Million
Emp.: 13
Farm Machinery Mfr
N.A.I.C.S.: 333111
Stojan Pesic *(Exec Dir)*

FATFISH GROUP LTD.
Level 4 91 William Street, Melbourne, 3000, VIC, Australia
Tel.: (61) 386115353   AU
Web Site: https://www.fatfish.co
FFG—(ASX)
Rev.: $888,166
Assets: $10,447,076
Liabilities: $8,587,924
Net Worth: $1,859,152
Earnings: ($1,694,066)
Fiscal Year-end: 12/31/23
Venture Investment Services
N.A.I.C.S.: 523910
Wah-Yew Chaw *(Fin Mgr)*

Subsidiaries:

Beam Storage Pte Ltd   (1)
Block 71 Ayer Rajah Crescent 06-04/05/06, Singapore, 139951, Singapore
Tel.: (65) 31294445
Web Site: https://www.beamspace.com
Storage Services
N.A.I.C.S.: 493110
Kash Patel *(Co-Founder & CEO)*

FATHOM NICKEL INC.
104 1240 Kensington Road NW, Box 311, Calgary, T2N 3P7, AB, Canada
Tel.: (403) 870-4349   AB
Web Site:
    https://www.fathomnickel.com
Year Founded: 2018
FNICF—(OTCIQ)
Rev.: $29,478
Assets: $13,521,549
Liabilities: $516,155
Net Worth: $13,005,394
Earnings: ($1,517,943)
Emp.: 3
Fiscal Year-end: 12/31/23
Mineral Mining Services
N.A.I.C.S.: 213115
Doug Porter *(CFO)*

FATIMA FERTILIZER COMPANY LIMITED
E-110 Khayaban-e-Jinnah, Lahore, Pakistan
Tel.: (92) 111328462   PK
Web Site: https://www.fatima-group.com
Year Founded: 2003
FATIMA—(PSX)
Rev.: $846,935,473
Assets: $841,377,893
Liabilities: $411,888,089
Net Worth: $429,489,804
Earnings: $82,772,777
Emp.: 2,477
Fiscal Year-end: 12/31/23
Holding Company; Fertilizer Mfr
N.A.I.C.S.: 551112
Fawad Ahmed Mukhtar *(Chm)*

FATTAL HOLDINGS (1998) LTD.
Triangular Building 35th Floor Azrieli

Center, Tel Aviv, Israel
Tel.: (972) 35110000
Web Site: http://www.fattal-hotels.com
FTAL—(TAE)
Rev.: $1,914,203,589
Assets: $7,352,621,794
Liabilities: $6,425,831,368
Net Worth: $926,790,426
Earnings: $12,454,206
Emp.: 17,000
Fiscal Year-end: 12/31/23
Full-Service Restaurants
N.A.I.C.S.: 722511

Subsidiaries:

Fattal Hotels Ltd.   (1)
23rd floor 2 Alon Tower 94 Yigal Alon Street, Tel Aviv, Israel
Tel.: (972) 35110000
Web Site: https://www.fattal-hotels.com
Emp.: 12,000
Hotel & Motel Operator
N.A.I.C.S.: 721110

FAUJI FOODS LIMITED
42 CCA Ex Park View DHA Phase VIII, Lahore, Pakistan
Tel.: (92) 4237136315
Web Site: https://www.faujifoods.com
Year Founded: 2015
FFL—(KAR)
Rev.: $36,996,978
Assets: $78,264,073
Liabilities: $101,949,015
Net Worth: ($23,684,942)
Earnings: ($37,280,757)
Emp.: 842
Fiscal Year-end: 12/31/19
Dairy Products Mfr
N.A.I.C.S.: 112120
Abdul Khaliq Khan *(Exec Dir)*

FAUJI FOUNDATION
68 Tipu Road, Chaklala, Rawalpindi, Pakistan
Tel.: (92) 51 595 1821
Web Site: http://www.fauji.org.pk
Year Founded: 1954
Sales Range: $1-4.9 Billion
Veteran Welfare Services
N.A.I.C.S.: 525120
Nadeem Inayat *(Dir-Investment)*

Subsidiaries:

Askari Bank Ltd.   (1)
AWT Plaza The Mall, PO Box 1084, Rawalpindi, Pakistan   (50.57%)
Tel.: (92) 518092624
Web Site: https://www.askaribank.com.pk
Rev.: $190,241,142
Assets: $5,367,373,094
Liabilities: $5,094,303,035
Net Worth: $273,070,059
Earnings: $45,289,751
Emp.: 7,848
Fiscal Year-end: 12/31/2019
Banking Services
N.A.I.C.S.: 522110
Saleem Anwar *(CFO)*

Subsidiary (Domestic):

Askari Investment Management Limited   (2)
Plot 20-C Khayaban-e-Nishat Phase-VI DHA, Karachi, Pakistan
Tel.: (92) 21 111 246 111
Web Site: http://www.aiml.com.pk
Investment Management Service
N.A.I.C.S.: 523940

Fauji Akbar Portia Marine Terminals Limited   (1)
10 2nd Floor Services Club Extension Bldg, Mereweather Road, Karachi, 75520, Pakistan   (75.31%)
Tel.: (92) 21 3567 8985
Web Site: http://www.fapterminals.com
Grain, Oilseeds & Fertilizer Port Terminal Operator
N.A.I.C.S.: 488310

Hassan Sobuctageen *(COO)*

Fauji Cement Company Limited   (1)
Fauji Tower Block III 68 Tipu Road Chaklala, Rawalpindi, Pakistan   (39.39%)
Tel.: (92) 519280081
Web Site: http://www.fccl.com.pk
Rev.: $336,849,763
Assets: $706,065,058
Liabilities: $347,524,150
Net Worth: $358,540,908
Earnings: $44,168,873
Emp.: 2,226
Fiscal Year-end: 06/30/2022
Cement Mfr
N.A.I.C.S.: 327310
Waqar Ahmed Malik *(Chm)*

Fauji Cereals   (1)
Dhamial Road, PO Box 57, Rawalpindi, Pakistan
Tel.: (92) 51 512 6556
Web Site: http://www.faujicereals.com.pk
Cereal Mfr.
N.A.I.C.S.: 311230
Khalid Mahmud *(Country Mgr)*

Fauji Fertilizer Company Limited   (1)
156 The Mall, Rawalpindi, Pakistan   (44.35%)
Tel.: (92) 518450001
Web Site: http://www.ffc.com.pk
Rev.: $707,223,985
Assets: $1,193,899,905
Liabilities: $803,218,232
Net Worth: $390,681,673
Earnings: $111,629,543
Emp.: 3,457
Fiscal Year-end: 12/31/2019
Fertilizer Producer
N.A.I.C.S.: 325314
Tariq Iqbal Khan *(Co-Chm, CEO & Mng Dir)*

Subsidiary (Domestic):

Fauji Fertilizer Bin Qasim Limited   (2)
FFBL Tower C1/C2 Sector B Jinnah Boulevard Phase II DHA, Islamabad, Pakistan   (51%)
Tel.: (92) 518763325
Web Site: https://www.ffbl.com
Rev.: $430,445,002
Assets: $587,112,704
Liabilities: $543,101,996
Net Worth: $44,010,709
Earnings: ($38,129,598)
Emp.: 950
Fiscal Year-end: 12/31/2019
Granular Urea & Di-Ammonium Phosphate Fertilizer Mfr
N.A.I.C.S.: 325312
Wasim Ejaz *(Head-Internal Audit)*

Plant (Domestic):

Fauji Fertilizer Company Limited - Plant I (Goth Machhi)   (2)
Goth Machhi, Sadiqabad, 64450, Rahim Yar Khan, Pakistan
Tel.: (92) 6857864209
Sales Range: $125-149.9 Million
Emp.: 300
Fertilizer Services
N.A.I.C.S.: 424910
Naveed Ahmed Khan *(Gen Mgr-Products & Ops)*

Fauji Kabirwala Power Company Limited   (1)
17 Km Jhand Road Near Adda Chopperhatta, Kabirwala, Pakistan
Tel.: (92) 65 241 1005
Web Site: http://www.faujipower.com
Power Generation Services
N.A.I.C.S.: 221118

Fauji Oil Terminal & Distribution Company Limited   (1)
Port Bin Qasim, PO Box 9101 PQA, Karachi, 75020, Pakistan   (52%)
Tel.: (92) 21 3472 0003
Web Site: http://www.fotco.com.pk
Petroleum Bulk Terminal Operator & Distr
N.A.I.C.S.: 424710
Shujahat Hussain *(Asst Mgr-Ops & Technical Svcs)*

Foundation Gas   (1)
Services Plaza Shahrahe Quaid-e-Azam, PO Box 422, Rawalpindi, Pakistan

Tel.: (92) 51 556 2470
Web Site: http://www.fauji.org.pk
Liquefied Petroleum Gas Distr
N.A.I.C.S.: 457210

Foundation Securities (Pvt) Limited   (1)
Ground Floor Bahria Complex II MT Khan Road, Karachi, Pakistan   (95%)
Tel.: (92) 21111000375
Web Site: http://www.fs.com.pk
Investment Banking, Securities Brokerage & Dealing Services
N.A.I.C.S.: 523150
Ahmad Zaidi *(CEO & Mng Dir)*

Overseas Employment Services   (1)
Fauji Towers 68 Tipu Road, Chaklala, Rawalpindi, 46000, Pakistan
Tel.: (92) 51 595 1726
Web Site: http://www.faujioes.org.pk
Employment Agency
N.A.I.C.S.: 561311
Arshad Mehmood Bhatti *(Gen Mgr)*

FAVITE INC.
No 197 Sec 2 Huanbei Rd, Hsinchu County, Zhubei, 302047, Taiwan
Tel.: (886) 35545988
Web Site: https://www.favite.com
Year Founded: 2000
3535—(TAI)
Rev.: $14,574,544
Assets: $54,406,126
Liabilities: $18,344,222
Net Worth: $36,061,904
Earnings: ($1,079,205)
Emp.: 86
Fiscal Year-end: 12/31/23
Automatic Optical Inspection (AOI) & Measurement Machines Developer & Mfr
N.A.I.C.S.: 334519

Subsidiaries:

FAVITE Inc.- RFID Division   (1)
No 176 Taihe Road, Zhubei, 30267, Hsinchu, Taiwan
Tel.: (886) 35545988
Web Site: http://www.rfid.favite.com
Antenna Mfr
N.A.I.C.S.: 334220

FAVORIT HOLD AD
Angel Kanchev 25, 1000, Sofia, 1000, Bulgaria
Tel.: (359) 29813468
Web Site: https://www.favhold.com
FAVH—(BUL)
Sales Range: Less than $1 Million
Investment Management Service
N.A.I.C.S.: 523940
Daniel Georgiev Rizov *(Chm-Mgmt Bd & CEO)*

Subsidiaries:

Kotlostroene JSCo   (1)
8 Istoria Slavyanobulgarska blvd Voenna rampa, 1220, Sofia, Bulgaria   (82%)
Tel.: (359) 29315077
Web Site: https://www.kotlostroene.net
Boiler Mfr
N.A.I.C.S.: 339999

FAWCETTS GARAGE (NEWBURY) LIMITED
The Triangle Pinchington Lane, Newbury, RG14 7HT, Berkshire, United Kingdom
Tel.: (44) 163546660
Web Site: http://fawcettsgarage.co.uk
Rev.: $23,408,649
Emp.: 30
New & Used Car Dealers
N.A.I.C.S.: 441110
Tim Day *(Gen Mgr-Sls)*

FAWER AUTOMOTIVE PARTS LIMITED COMPANY

FAWER Automotive Parts Limited Company—(Continued)

No 701 Xuehai Street, Hi-tech Zone, Changchun, 130012, Jilin, China
Tel.: (86) 43185122797
Web Site: http://www.fawer.com.cn
Year Founded: 2007
000030—(SSE)
Rev.: $1,764,901,008
Assets: $2,149,487,496
Liabilities: $988,765,596
Net Worth: $1,160,721,900
Earnings: $70,334,784
Fiscal Year-end: 12/31/22
Automobile Parts Mfr
N.A.I.C.S.: 336110
Hanjie Hu *(Chm)*

Subsidiaries:

Fawer Liaoning Automotive Spring Company Limited　　　**(1)**
No 61 Shengli Road, Liaoyang, Liaoning, China
Tel.: (86) 4192121284
Emp.: 946
Automotive Suspension Spring Mfr
N.A.I.C.S.: 332613

FAYAT SAS
137 rue du Palais Gallien, 33000, Bordeaux, France
Tel.: (33) 5 56 00 21 00
Web Site: http://www.fayat.com
Year Founded: 1957
Holding Company;Construction & Engineering Services
N.A.I.C.S.: 551112
Clement Fayat *(Founder)*

Subsidiaries:

3D Dominique Declercq Distribution　　　**(1)**
Avenue d'Immercourt Zone Industrielle Est, 62000, Arras, France
Tel.: (33) 3 21 22 75 90
Web Site: http://www.3d.fr
Cleaning Equipment Distr
N.A.I.C.S.: 423810

ABCELEC　　　**(1)**
223 rue La Fontaine, 94120, Fontenay-sous-Bois, France
Tel.: (33) 1 53 99 90 90
Web Site: http://www.abcelec.fr
Electrical Security System Mfr
N.A.I.C.S.: 334290

ACML　　　**(1)**
ZI de Chace Rue du Docteur Weys, 49400, Saumur, France
Tel.: (33) 2 41 83 10 40
Web Site: http://www.acml.fayat.com
Steel Products Mfr
N.A.I.C.S.: 331110

ADC BRETAGNE　　　**(1)**
Rue Marcel Beau - CS 70069, 79200, Parthenay, France
Tel.: (33) 5 49 64 48 22
Web Site: http://www.adc-fayat.com
Emp.: 210
Lifting Equipment Mfr
N.A.I.C.S.: 333923
Jean-Claude Fayat *(Pres)*

ADC MEDITERRANEE　　　**(1)**
153 avenue Marechal Leclerc, ZAC des Balarucs, 84510, Caumont, France
Tel.: (33) 6 85 91 46 02
Lifting Equipment Mfr
N.A.I.C.S.: 333923

ADC NORD　　　**(1)**
945 rue du Faubourg d'Esquerchin, 59553, Cuincy, France
Tel.: (33) 3 27 95 95 77
Lifting Equipment Mfr
N.A.I.C.S.: 333923

ADC NORMANDIE　　　**(1)**
Route de Giberville, BP 20370, 14461, Colombelles, France
Tel.: (33) 6 86 05 19 73
Lifting Equipment Mfr

N.A.I.C.S.: 333923

ADC RHONE-ALPES　　　**(1)**
17 rue Jean-Pierre Timbaud, BP 31, 42420, Lorette, France
Tel.: (33) 4 77 73 27 21
Lifting Equipment Mfr
N.A.I.C.S.: 333923

ADC SUD-OUEST　　　**(1)**
14 rue de la Prune d'Ente, 47440, Casseneuil, France
Tel.: (33) 5 53 70 88 59
Lifting Equipment Mfr
N.A.I.C.S.: 333923

ADE TP　　　**(1)**
47 route de Lesparre, 33340, Gaillan-en-Medoc, France
Tel.: (33) 5 56 73 40 96
Civil Engineering Services
N.A.I.C.S.: 541330

ADEN France　　　**(1)**
53 avenue de l'Europe, 95330, Domont, France
Tel.: (33) 1 39 35 49 00
Web Site: http://www.adenfrance-fayat.com
Sewage Treatment Equipment Mfr
N.A.I.C.S.: 333310

AES FAMATEC　　　**(1)**
225 255 avenue de l'Europe, 77240, Vert-Saint-Denis, France
Tel.: (33) 1 64 64 33 70
Web Site: http://www.aes.fayat.com
Construction Machinery Mfr
N.A.I.C.S.: 333120

ATS Asphalttechnik GmbH　　　**(1)**
Unterortstrasse 48, 65760, Eschborn, Germany
Tel.: (49) 6196 59052 0
Web Site: http://www.ats-asphalt.de
Construction Equipment Distr
N.A.I.C.S.: 423810
Claus Horstmann *(Gen Mgr)*

Atlas Copco Dynapac AB　　　**(1)**
Industrivagen 2, Karlskrona, 37123, Sweden
Tel.: (46) 455 30 61 00
Web Site: http://www.dynapac.com
Holding Company; Road Construction & Paving Equipment Mfr & Distr
N.A.I.C.S.: 551112

Subsidiary (Domestic):

Dynapac Compaction Equipment AB　　　**(2)**
Industrivagen 2, Blekinge County, Karlskrona, 371 46, Sweden
Tel.: (46) 4 55 30 61 00
Web Site: http://www.dynapac.com
Construction Equipment Mfr & Distr
N.A.I.C.S.: 333120

Subsidiary (Non-US):

Dynapac France SAS　　　**(2)**
52 Avenue du General de Gaulle, Marlesen-Brie, 77610, Seine-et-Marne, France
Tel.: (33) 1 64 42 59 01
Web Site: http://www.dynapac.com
Compaction & Paving Equipment Mfr
N.A.I.C.S.: 333120

Dynapac GmbH　　　**(2)**
Ammerlander Strasse 93, Wardenburg, 26203, Oldenburg, Germany
Tel.: (49) 4407 972 444
Web Site: http://www.dynapac.com
Compaction & Paving Equipment Mfr
N.A.I.C.S.: 333120

Dynapac do Brasil ind. com Ltda.　　　**(2)**
Av Georg Schaeffler 430 Iporanga, CEP 18087-175, Sorocaba, Sao Paulo, Brazil
Tel.: (55) 15 3412 7591
Web Site: http://dynapac.com
Industrial Machinery Distr
N.A.I.C.S.: 423830

BARBOT CM　　　**(1)**
Les Morinieres, BP 49, 37160, Descartes, France
Tel.: (33) 2 47 59 76 50
Web Site: http://www.barbot.fayat.com
Structured Steel Products Mfr

N.A.I.C.S.: 333923

BARBOT CM MAXILLY　　　**(1)**
BP 2, Maxilly-sur-Saone, France
Tel.: (33) 3 80 47 42 47
Construction Equipment Distr
N.A.I.C.S.: 423810

BCES　　　**(1)**
Akinei Yolu 2 km, Yenikent Sincan, 6935, Ankara, Turkiye
Tel.: (90) 312 254 02 54
Emp.: 200
Lifting Equipment Mfr
N.A.I.C.S.: 333923
Ozgur Guney *(Mgr-Quality Control)*

BEC CONSTRUCTION CHAMPAGNE　　　**(1)**
ZA Les Terres Rouges 6 allee de la Cote-des-Blancs, BP 286, 51208, Epernay, Cedex, France
Tel.: (33) 3 26 51 00 59
Construction Engineering Services
N.A.I.C.S.: 541330

BEC CONSTRUCTION LANGUE-DOC ROUSSILLON　　　**(1)**
1111 avenue Justin-Bec, 34680, Saint-Georges-d'Orques, France
Tel.: (33) 4 67 10 37 50
Construction Engineering Services
N.A.I.C.S.: 541330

BEC CONSTRUCTION PROVENCE　　　**(1)**
25 boulevard de Saint-Marcel CS 70039, 13396, Marseille, Cedex, France
Tel.: (33) 4 91 45 60 80
Construction Engineering Services
N.A.I.C.S.: 541330

BERNARD PAYSAGE & ENVIRONNEMENT　　　**(1)**
97 avenue du Roy, 33440, Ambares, France
Tel.: (33) 5 56 77 78 79
Web Site: http://www.bernard-paysage.fr
Construction Engineering Services
N.A.I.C.S.: 541330

BIANCO　　　**(1)**
La Plaine - Marthod, BP 13, 73401, Ugine, Cedex, France
Tel.: (33) 4 79 37 66 00
Highway & Street Construction Services
N.A.I.C.S.: 237310

BOMA EQUIPMENT　　　**(1)**
700 Castle Peak Road, Room 1003 - 10/F Charm Centre, Kowloon, China (Hong Kong)
Tel.: (852) 27216363
Construction Machinery Mfr
N.A.I.C.S.: 333120

BOMAG GmbH　　　**(1)**
Hellerwald, Boppard, 56154, Germany
Tel.: (49) 67421000
Web Site: http://www.bomag.com
Sales Range: $900-999.9 Million
Emp.: 2,200
Construction Machinery Mfr
N.A.I.C.S.: 333120
Ralf Junker *(Mng Dir)*

Subsidiary (Non-US):

BOMAG (CHINA) Construction Machinery Co., Ltd　　　**(2)**
No 2808 West Huancheng Road, Shanghai Comprehensive Industrial Zone Fengxian, Shanghai, 201401, China
Tel.: (86) 21 3365 5566
Construction Machinery Distr
N.A.I.C.S.: 423810

Subsidiary (US):

BOMAG Americas, Inc.　　　**(2)**
2000 Kentville Rd, Kewanee, IL 61443-1714
Tel.: (309) 853-3571
Web Site: http://www.bomag.com
Sales Range: $25-49.9 Million
Emp.: 125
Construction Machinery Mfr
N.A.I.C.S.: 333120
Dave Dennison *(Product Mgr)*

Subsidiary (Non-US):

BOMAG BRESIL　　　**(2)**

Rua Wallace Barnes, 13054-701, Campinas, Brazil
Tel.: (55) 117 320 09 30
Construction Machinery Mfr
N.A.I.C.S.: 333120

Subsidiary (Domestic).

BOMAG CHEMNITZ　　　**(2)**
Querstrasse 6, 09247, Chemnitz, Germany
Tel.: (49) 372 251 59 0
Construction Machinery Mfr
N.A.I.C.S.: 333120

Subsidiary (Non-US):

BOMAG France S.A.S.　　　**(2)**
2 avenue du General de Gaulle, 91170, Viry, Chatillon, France
Tel.: (33) 1 69 57 86 00
Construction Machinery Distr
N.A.I.C.S.: 423810

BOMAG Italia Srl.　　　**(2)**
Z I Via Mella 6, Desenzano del Garda, 25015, Brescia, Italy
Tel.: (39) 030 9127263
Construction Machinery Distr
N.A.I.C.S.: 423810

BOMAG Marini Latin America　　　**(2)**
Avenida Clemente Cifali 530, Cachoeira, CEP-94935-225, RS, Brazil
Tel.: (55) 51 2125 6677
Web Site: http://www.bomagmarini.com.br
Emp.: 100
Road Paving & Construction Equipment Mfr
N.A.I.C.S.: 333120
Walter Rauen *(CEO)*

BOMAG Maschinenhandelsgesellschaft m.b.H.　　　**(2)**
Porschestrasse 9, 1230, Vienna, Austria
Tel.: (43) 1 69040 0
Construction Machinery Distr
N.A.I.C.S.: 423810

BOMAG Singapore　　　**(2)**
300 Beach Road 18-06, The Concourse, Singapore, 199555, Singapore
Tel.: (65) 6294 1277
Construction Machinery Distr
N.A.I.C.S.: 423810

Bomag (Great Britain) Ltd　　　**(2)**
Sheldon Way Larkfield, Aylesford, ME20 6SE, Kent, United Kingdom
Tel.: (44) 1622 716611
Construction Machinery Distr
N.A.I.C.S.: 423810

Fayat Bomag Polska Sp. z o.o.　　　**(2)**
Ul Szyszkowa 52, 02-285, Warsaw, Poland
Tel.: (48) 22 482 04 00
Web Site: http://www.bsa.bomag.com
Emp.: 15
Construction Machinery Distr
N.A.I.C.S.: 423810
Zbigniew Brinkeh *(Gen Mgr)*

BOMAG PAVING PRODUCTS INC　　　**(1)**
618 Enterprise Dr, Warrensburg, MO 64093
Tel.: (660) 422-4272
Construction Machinery Distr
N.A.I.C.S.: 423810

BP CONSTRUCTION　　　**(1)**
10 avenue Zanaroli, 74600, Seynod, France
Tel.: (33) 4 50 33 99 50
Construction Engineering Services
N.A.I.C.S.: 541330

BREINING Maschinen-und Fahrzeugbau GmbH　　　**(1)**
Uferstrasse 24, 73630, Remshalden, Germany
Tel.: (49) 7151 9771 00
Web Site: http://www.breining.fayat.com
Construction Machinery Mfr
N.A.I.C.S.: 333120

BULBULOGLU VINC SANAYII VE TICARET A.S.　　　**(1)**
Organize Sanayi - Bolgesi Oguz Caddesi N 21, Sincan, 06930, Ankara, Turkiye
Tel.: (90) 312 267 29 29
Web Site: http://www.bvs.com.tr
Lifting Equipment Mfr
N.A.I.C.S.: 333923

CASTEL ALU (1)
Zone Industrielle Le Bosc, BP 9, 32501, Fleurance, Cedex, France
Tel.: (33) 5 62 67 46 06
Web Site: http://www.castelalu.fayat.com
Construction Engineering Services
N.A.I.C.S.: 541330

Subsidiary (Domestic):

CASTEL ALU JARNAC (2)
La Belloire, BP 58, 16200, Jarnac, France
Tel.: (33) 5 46 36 03 02
Construction Engineering Services
N.A.I.C.S.: 541330

CASTEL ET FROMAGET (1)
35 Avenue Clement Fayat, BP 22, 32501, Fleurance, Cedex, France
Tel.: (33) 5 62 67 45 45
Web Site: http://www.casteletfromaget.fr
Construction Engineering Services
N.A.I.C.S.: 541330

Subsidiary (Non-US):

CF Steel Morocco (2)
Space Gate Anfa 3 Rue Bab, Mansour, 20050, Casablanca, Morocco
Tel.: (212) 522 36 54 86
Construction Engineering Services
N.A.I.C.S.: 541330

CASTEL ET FROMAGET ASIA (1)
Park Trade Centre - Unit 61 Investment Drive, Madrigal Business Park Alabang, 1716, Muntinlupa, Philippines
Tel.: (63) 2 84 23 427
Construction Engineering Services
N.A.I.C.S.: 541330

CASTEL ET FROMAGET REUNION (1)
5 rue Luc Donat, Coteaux Moulin Joli, 97419, La Possession, Reunion
Tel.: (262) 2 62 49 62 80
Construction Engineering Services
N.A.I.C.S.: 541330

CHARIGNON (1)
8 chemin des Sarrazines, 26300, Chatuzange-le-Goubet, France
Tel.: (33) 475 47 24 66
Web Site: http://www.charignon.com
Structured Steel Products Mfr
N.A.I.C.S.: 331110

CHARLATTE MANUTENTION (1)
Route du Boutoir, 89210, Brienon-sur-Armancon, France
Tel.: (33) 3 86 43 01 30
Web Site: http://www.charlattemanutention.fayat.com
Emp.: 65
Electric Vehicle Mfr
N.A.I.C.S.: 336110
Bastien Devaux (Dir-Publ)

Subsidiary (US):

CHARLATTE OF AMERICA (2)
600 Mountain Ln, Bluefield, VA 24605
Tel.: (276) 326-1510
Web Site: http://www.charlatteus.com
Automotive Distr
N.A.I.C.S.: 423110

Subsidiary (Non-US):

Charlatte (UK) Limited (2)
14 Huffwood Trading Estate Brookers road, Billingshurst, RH14 9UR, United Kingdom
Tel.: (44) 1403 780533
Automotive Distr
N.A.I.C.S.: 423110

CHARLATTE RESERVOIRS (1)
17 rue Paul Bert, 89400, Migennes, France
Tel.: (33) 3 86 92 30 14
Web Site: http://www.charlatte.com
Industrial Pressure Vessel Mfr
N.A.I.C.S.: 332420
Alain Ansel (Mgr-After Sls & Svc)

CITEPARK (1)
34 rue Charles Piketty, 91170, Viry, Chatillon, France
Tel.: (33) 1 69 12 70 06
Highway & Street Construction Services
N.A.I.C.S.: 237310

COMETE (1)
ZI du Mont Revois, BP 9, 38280, Anthon, France
Tel.: (33) 4 72 46 90 00
Web Site: http://www.comete.fayat.com
Lifting Equipment Mfr
N.A.I.C.S.: 333923

COTEG (1)
219 rue des Marais, 94120, Fontenay-sous-Bois, France
Tel.: (33) 1 41 95 65 00
Web Site: http://www.coteg-sa.fr
Construction Engineering Services
N.A.I.C.S.: 541330

COUTURIER (1)
14 rue du pont de Gres CS 10203, 62213, Carvin, Cedex, France
Tel.: (33) 3 91 83 79 79
Web Site: http://www.couturier.fayat.com
Construction Engineering Services
N.A.I.C.S.: 541330

Compagnie Industrielle des Composants Beton (1)
Rue Anatole France, BP 23, 47190, Aiguillon, France
Tel.: (33) 5 53 79 61 50
Construction Engineering Services
N.A.I.C.S.: 541330

DARRAS ET JOUANIN (1)
2 rue des Sables, 91170, Viry, Chatillon, France
Tel.: (33) 1 69 12 69 16
Construction Engineering Services
N.A.I.C.S.: 541330

DEJEAN-SERVIERES (1)
583 chemin de Lugan Bas, BP 95, Monteils, 82303, Caussade, Cedex, France
Tel.: (33) 5 63 93 10 78
Web Site: http://www.dejean-servieres.fr
Construction Engineering Services
N.A.I.C.S.: 541330

DHENIN (1)
12 avenue Gustave Eiffel, 28630, Gellainville, France
Tel.: (33) 2 37 24 91 36
Web Site: http://www.e-r-s.fr
Construction Engineering Services
N.A.I.C.S.: 541330

ENROBES 34 (1)
31 avenue de Larrieu, 31081, Toulouse, Cedex, France
Tel.: (33) 4 67 46 15 04
Construction Engineering Services
N.A.I.C.S.: 541330

ERS (1)
7 Parc activites de Broceliande, PQ Box 16135, 35761, Saint-Gregoire, Cedex, France
Tel.: (33) 2 99 68 85 00
Web Site: http://www.ers-fayat.fr
Construction Engineering Services
N.A.I.C.S.: 541330

FARECO (1)
131/151 rue du 1er mai, 92752, Nanterre, Cedex, France
Tel.: (33) 1 55 66 22 22
Construction Engineering Services
N.A.I.C.S.: 541330

FAYAT CONSTRUCTION ACHATS INVESTISSEMENTS (1)
3 rue Rene Razel, Christ de Saclay, 91400, Saclay, Cedex, France
Tel.: (33) 1 60 12 86 00
Construction Engineering Services
N.A.I.C.S.: 541330

FAYAT SYSTEME D'INFORMATION (1)
Chemin Richelieu, 33270, Floirac, France
Tel.: (33) 6 56 93 91 11
Construction Engineering Services
N.A.I.C.S.: 541330

FAYAT TP (1)
Avenue du General-de-Gaulle, BP 160, 33502, Libourne, Cedex, France
Tel.: (33) 5 57 55 32 90
Construction Engineering Services
N.A.I.C.S.: 541330

FELIX CONSTRUCTIONS SA (1)

Rte de la Pale 14, 1026, Denges, Switzerland
Tel.: (41) 21 706 31 31
Web Site: http://www.felix-constructions.ch
Construction Engineering Services
N.A.I.C.S.: 541330

FRANKI FONDATION (1)
137 rue du Palais Gallien, 90028, Bordeaux, Cedex, France
Tel.: (33) 556002100
Web Site: http://fayat.com
Construction Engineering Services
N.A.I.C.S.: 541330

Fayat Batiment SAS (1)
Z I 1ere avenue 5455 m, BP 88, 06513, Carros, Cedex, France
Tel.: (33) 4 92 08 40 39
Web Site: http://www.cari.fr
Construction Engineering Services
N.A.I.C.S.: 541330

Division (Domestic):

CARI AQUITAINE (2)
Europarc Bat B 10 7 avenue Leonard de Vinci, 33600, Pessac, France
Tel.: (33) 5 56 36 30 49
Construction Engineering Services
N.A.I.C.S.: 541330

CARI LORRAINE (2)
1 rue Claude Chappe, BP 65210, 57076, Metz, Cedex, France
Tel.: (33) 3 87 15 74 00
Construction Engineering Services
N.A.I.C.S.: 541330

CARI MENUISERIE (2)
136 rue Leon Faucher, BP 2759, 51065, Reims, France
Tel.: (33) 3 26 48 42 43
Construction Engineering Services
N.A.I.C.S.: 541330

CARI PROVENCE (2)
52 rue Emmanuel Eydoux, BP 187, 13322, Marseille, Cedex, France
Tel.: (33) 4 91 46 61 61
Construction Engineering Services
N.A.I.C.S.: 541330

CARI RHONE LYON (2)
52 rue Jean Zay Batiment G, 69800, Saint-Priest-en-Jarez, France
Tel.: (33) 4 37 54 17 70
Construction Engineering Services
N.A.I.C.S.: 541330

IBS (2)
25 avenue Jose Nobre ZI Sud, 13500, Martigues, France
Tel.: (33) 4 42 07 28 40
Construction Engineering Services
N.A.I.C.S.: 541330

Fayat Bomag rus LLC (1)
Klyazma block h 1-g, 141400, Khimki, Moscow, Russia
Tel.: (7) 4952879290
Construction Machinery Distr
N.A.I.C.S.: 423810
Sergey Gulyaev (Project Mgr)

GABRIELLE (1)
1 avenue Raymond Sommer, 31480, Cadours, France
Tel.: (33) 5 61 85 62 27
Construction Engineering Services
N.A.I.C.S.: 541330

GTTP (1)
Lieu dit l'Etang Vignon, BP 8, 37210, Vouvray, France
Tel.: (33) 2 47 52 74 67
Construction Engineering Services
N.A.I.C.S.: 541330

JOSEPH PARIS (1)
7 boulevard du General Koenig, BP 64017, 44040, Nantes, Cedex, France
Tel.: (33) 2 40 38 56 60
Construction Engineering Services
N.A.I.C.S.: 541330

LACHAUX PAYSAGES (1)
Rue des Etangs, 77410, Villevaude, France
Tel.: (33) 1 60 27 66 66
Construction Engineering Services
N.A.I.C.S.: 541330

LAGLASSE & OMHOVERE (1)
Zac Mermoz Le Venturi, 57155, Marly, France
Tel.: (33) 3 87 52 61 83
Web Site: http://www.laglasse-omhovere-fayat.com
Underground Cable Laying Services
N.A.I.C.S.: 237130

LE RESERVOIR (1)
Rue Eugene-Sue Zone Industrielle, BP 1139, 03103, Montlucon, France
Tel.: (33) 4 70 03 47 47
Web Site: http://www.lereservoir.com
Emp.: 18
Metal Tank Mfr
N.A.I.C.S.: 332420
Fausto Mendes (Gen Mgr)

LE RESERVOIR MASSAL (1)
Chemin des Sept Fonts, BP 10026, 34301, Agde, France
Tel.: (33) 4 67 94 79 11
Web Site: http://massal.fayat.com
Pressure Control Equipment Mfr
N.A.I.C.S.: 332911

LN MAURICE (1)
244 rue Roger Espagnet, 33440, Saint-Louis-de-Montferrand, France
Tel.: (33) 5 56 38 78 91
Web Site: http://www.gravieres-maurice.fr
Construction Engineering Services
N.A.I.C.S.: 541330

LRM (1)
71 rue Clement Ader Espace Lunel Littoral, 34403, Lunel, Cedex, France
Tel.: (33) 4 67 83 12 54
Construction Engineering Services
N.A.I.C.S.: 541330

MARINI FAYAT LANGFANG China (1)
No 20 Huaxiang Road, Langfang Economic & Technical Development Zone, Langfang, 065001, Hebei, China
Tel.: (86) 316 6087001
Web Site: http://www.marini-china.com
Asphalt Distr
N.A.I.C.S.: 423320

MARINI INDIA PRIVATE LTD (1)
301 Balazee Mall Opp IIT Gandhinagar, Motera Gandhinagar Highway, Ahmedabad, 380005, India
Tel.: (91) 79 40194999
Web Site: http://www.marini.co.in
Emp.: 100
Asphalt Mfr & Distr
N.A.I.C.S.: 324121
Blessen Varghese (Mng Dir)

MARINI SpA (1)
via Roma 50, 48011, Alfonsine, Ravenna, Italy
Tel.: (39) 0544 88111
Web Site: http://www.marini.fayat.com
Emp.: 400
Asphalt Product Mfr
N.A.I.C.S.: 324121
Luca Camprini (Mng Dir)

Subsidiary (Non-US):

FAYAT MIDDLE EAST FZE (2)
Jafza South FZS1AH03, Jebel Ali Free zone, Dubai, United Arab Emirates
Tel.: (971) 4 8863233
Asphalt Distr
N.A.I.C.S.: 423320

FAYAT RO SRL (2)
Loc Timisoara Str Calea Stan Vidrighin nr 18 Parter - Sad 2, Jud Timis - Confom, 147730, Timisoara, Romania
Tel.: (40) 356 43 94 12
Asphalt Distr
N.A.I.C.S.: 423320

MARINI UK LIMITED (1)
Unit 1 - Burnhouse Industrial Estate, Whitburn, EH47 OLQ, West Lothian, United Kingdom
Tel.: (44) 1416462066
Web Site: http://www.cormac.co.uk
Asphalt Mfr & Distr
N.A.I.C.S.: 324121

MARINI-ERMONT (1)
Rue Jean Pierre Timbaud, BP 1, 42420,

FAYAT SAS—(Continued)

Lorette, France
Tel.: (33) 4 77 73 52 65
Construction Engineering Services
N.A.I.C.S.: 541330

MATHIEU (1)
85 rue Sebastien Choulette, PO Box 32,
54202, Toul, Cedex, France
Tel.: (33) 3 83 65 22 22
Web Site: http://www.mathieu.fayat.com
Road Maintenance Equipment Mfr & Distr
N.A.I.C.S.: 333120

MULTIPHONE (1)
10 rue Perier, BP 126, 92124, Montrouge,
Cedex, France
Tel.: (33) 1 46 12 02 02
Telecommunication Servicesb
N.A.I.C.S.: 517111

Marini Makina A.S. (1)
1 OSB kirim Hanligi Cad No 1, Sincan,
06935, Ankara, Türkiye
Tel.: (90) 312 386 33 22
Web Site: http://www.marini.com.tr
Emp.: 150
Asphalt Machinery Mfr
N.A.I.C.S.: 333120
Can Gecit (Mgr-Sls)

**NORD FRANCE
CONSTRUCTIONS** (1)
2 rue Simon Vollant CS 80027, 59831,
Lambersart, Cedex, France
Tel.: (33) 3 20 17 61 00
Web Site: http://www.nfc.fr
Construction Engineering Services
N.A.I.C.S.: 541330

**NORD FRANCE CONSTRUCTIONS
COMPIEGNE** (1)
14 rue du Fonds Pernant, 60200, Comp-
iegne, Cedex, France
Tel.: (33) 3 44 86 46 58
Construction Engineering Services
N.A.I.C.S.: 541330

PTC (1)
56 Rue de Neuilly, 93136, Noisy-le-Sec,
France
Tel.: (33) 1 49 42 72 95
Web Site: http://www.ptc.fayat.com
Construction Machinery Mfr
N.A.I.C.S.: 333120
Didier Maubert (Mgr-Sls-Export)

Subsidiary (Non-US):

PTC ERS SA de CV (2)
Calle Pioneros del Cooperativismo n 205,
Col Mexico Nuevo, Ciudad Lopez Mateos,
52966, Estado de Mexico, Mexico
Tel.: (52) 55 16 68 11 50
Construction Machinery Distr
N.A.I.C.S.: 423810

Subsidiary (US):

PTC USA (2)
2000 Kentville Rd, Kewanee, IL 61443
Tel.: (309) 852-6267
Construction Machinery Distr
N.A.I.C.S.: 423810

Subsidiary (Non-US):

**Ptc Piling Equipment (Far East) Pte
Ltd** (2)
N 3 Tuas Avenue 16, 638926, Singapore,
Singapore
Tel.: (65) 68617977
Construction Machinery Distr
N.A.I.C.S.: 423810

PTC OCEAN INDIEN (1)
3 bis Avenue Piton Batard, ZA Cambaie,
97460, Saint-Paul, Reunion
Tel.: (262) 2 62 42 39 39
Construction Machinery Mfr
N.A.I.C.S.: 333120

RAZEL-BEC S.A.S. (1)
3 Rue Rene Razel, Christ de Saclay,
91892, Orsay, Cedex, France
Tel.: (33) 169856985
Web Site: http://www.razel-bec.com
Sales Range: $1-4.9 Billion
Emp.: 6,000
Civil Engineering Construction Services

N.A.I.C.S.: 237990
Laurent Fayat (Chm)

Subsidiary (Non-US):

RAZEL ALGERIE SARL (2)
15 rue Poirson, El-Biar, 16030, Algiers, Al-
geria
Tel.: (213) 21 92 97 04
Construction Engineering Services
N.A.I.C.S.: 541330

RAZEL ANGOLA (2)
Street Cafaco 1 1 B, District Kinaxixi, Lu-
anda, Angola
Tel.: (244) 921 54 60 98
Construction Engineering Services
N.A.I.C.S.: 541330

RAZEL CAMEROUN (2)
637 rue de l independance, BP 11306, Im-
meuble Stamatiades, Yaounde, Cameroon
Tel.: (237) 222 03 06
Construction Engineering Services
N.A.I.C.S.: 541330

RAZEL GUINEE EQUATORIALE (2)
BP 1071, Caracolas, Malabo, Equatorial
Guinea
Tel.: (240) 333 09 91 45
Construction Engineering Services
N.A.I.C.S.: 541330

RAZEL MALAISIE (2)
First floor lot 432 section 54 KTLD Travilion,
Commercial center Jalan Petanak, 93100,
Kuching, Sarawak, Malaysia
Tel.: (60) 82628968
Construction Engineering Services
N.A.I.C.S.: 541330

RAZEL MAURITANIE (2)
Ilot K Extension - Secteur 1 Villa n 184, BP
5124, Nouakchott, Mauritania
Tel.: (222) 45 24 07 06
Construction Engineering Services
N.A.I.C.S.: 541330

RAZEL NIGER (2)
Rue du Grand Hotel porte 194 quartier ter-
minus, BP 854, Niamey, Niger
Tel.: (227) 20 73 68 13
Construction Engineering Services
N.A.I.C.S.: 541330

RAZEL-BEC COTE-D'AZUR (2)
Avenue Jamot Immeuble harmonie - Entree
H 9eme etage, BP2486, Abidjan, Cote
d'Ivoire
Tel.: (225) 20 21 08 59
Construction Engineering Services
N.A.I.C.S.: 541330

RESERVOIRS X. PAUCHARD (1)
1 boulevard de l'industrie, BP 63, 71402,
Autun, Cedex, France
Tel.: (33) 3 85 86 53 33
Web Site:
   http://www.reservoirspauchard.com
Boiler Mfr
N.A.I.C.S.: 333414

SAE (1)
14 Zone Industrielle, 37500, Saint-Benoit-la-
Foret, France
Tel.: (33) 2 47 58 00 31
Web Site: http://www.sae.fayat.com
Construction Machinery Mfr
N.A.I.C.S.: 333120

SAPB (1)
1035 Chemin des Grands Marais, 05230,
La Batie-Neuve, France
Tel.: (33) 4 92 50 30 01
Construction Engineering Services
N.A.I.C.S.: 541330

SAREC TOULOUSE (1)
29 chemin de la Salvetat, 31770, Colom-
iers, France
Tel.: (33) 5 61 30 27 98
Construction Engineering Services
N.A.I.C.S.: 541330

SATELEC (1)
24 avenue du General de Gaulle, 91178,
Viry, Cedex, Chatillon, France
Tel.: (33) 1 69 56 56 56
Underground Cable Laying Services
N.A.I.C.S.: 237130
Daniel Duminy (Pres)

SECMAIR (1)
Rue des Freres Lumiere, BP 10042, 53230,
Cosse-le-Vivien, France
Tel.: (33) 2 43 98 27 76
Web Site: http://www.secmair.fayat.com
Construction Machinery Mfr
N.A.I.C.S.: 333120

SEFI FONTEC (1)
14 / 3 Mohamed Baddar St Of Nasr St El
Laselky Division, New Maadi Maadi, Cairo,
Egypt
Tel.: (20) 2 251 609 21
Web Site: http://www.sefi-fontec.com
Construction Engineering Services
N.A.I.C.S.: 541330
Hemmat Abdelkader (Mgr-Fin & Admin)

SINGLANDE (1)
BP Catoy, 47450, Colayrac-Saint-Cirq,
France
Tel.: (33) 5 53 87 57 25
Construction Engineering Services
N.A.I.C.S.: 541330

SIRFIA (1)
12 rue Saint Marie, 07100, Annonay,
France
Tel.: (33) 4 75 67 07 45
Construction Engineering Services
N.A.I.C.S.: 541330

SODECLIM (1)
56 rue Louis Auroux, 94120, Fontenay-
sous-Bois, France
Tel.: (33) 1 48 80 43 76
Construction Engineering Services
N.A.I.C.S.: 541330

SOLS ET FONDATIONS (1)
920 rue Saint-Gabriel, 45200, Amilly,
France
Tel.: (33) 2 38 89 32 00
Web Site:
   http://www.solsetfondations.fayat.com
Construction Engineering Services
N.A.I.C.S.: 541330

SOMATRA (1)
Brezegoux, 47510, Foulayronnes, France
Tel.: (33) 5 53 67 81 35
Construction Engineering Services
N.A.I.C.S.: 541330

SOMIFA (1)
91 Rue Nuyens Batiment D, 33100, Bor-
deaux, France
Tel.: (33) 5 56 40 68 50
Construction Engineering Services
N.A.I.C.S.: 541330

Scarab Sweepers Limited (1)
Pattenden Lane, Marden, Tonbridge, TN12
9QD, Kent, United Kingdom
Tel.: (44) 1622 831006
Web Site: http://www.scarab-sweepers.com
Road Maintenance Equipment Mfr
N.A.I.C.S.: 333120
David Cassingham (Mng Dir)

Transport Tertiaire Industrie SAS (1)
122 rue Vaillant Couturie, BP 47, 93136,
Noisy-le-Sec, Cedex, France
Tel.: (33) 1 41 83 87 90
Construction Engineering Services
N.A.I.C.S.: 541330

**VIGNOBLES CLEMENT FAYAT ST
EMILION** (1)
Chateau La Dominique, 33330, Saint-
Emilion, France
Tel.: (33) 5 57 51 31 36
Web Site: http://www.vignobles-fayat.com
Wine Mfr
N.A.I.C.S.: 312130

**FAYE CLACK COMMUNICA-
TIONS INC.**
108A Royal York road, Toronto, M8V
2V1, ON, Canada
Tel.: (416) 255-6879
Web Site: http://www.fayeclack.com
Year Founded: 1975
Sales Range: $1-9.9 Million
Emp.: 50
Food Beverage & Consumer Product
Advertising
N.A.I.C.S.: 541810

Virginia Zimm (Pres)

**FAYENCERIES DE SARREGU-
EMINES DIGOIN VITRY-LE-
FRANCOIS SA**
5 Rue du Helder, 75009, Paris,
France
Tel.: (33) 153245348
Web Site: https://www.fsdv.fr
FAYE—(EUR)
Sales Range: $1-9.9 Million
Ceramic Products Mfr
N.A.I.C.S.: 327120
Alain-Jean Candelier (CEO)

FAYOLLE ET FILS
30 rue de l'Egalite CS 30009, 95230,
Soisy-sous-Montmorency, France
Tel.: (33) 1 34 28 40 40
Web Site: http://www.fayolleetfils.fr
Year Founded: 1920
Construction Services
N.A.I.C.S.: 236220
Bruno Fayolle (Dir Gen)

Subsidiaries:

Fayolle Canada Inc. (1)
1655 De Beauharnois Street West, Mont-
real, H4N 1J6, QC, Canada
Tel.: (514) 381-6970
Web Site: http://www.fayolle.ca
Sales Range: $500-549.9 Million
Emp.: 400
Construction Services
N.A.I.C.S.: 236220
Bruno Fayolle (Pres & CEO)

Unit (Domestic):

MC Group (2)
1655 rue De Beauharnois Ouest, Montreal,
H4N 1J6, QC, Canada
Tel.: (514) 341-9899
Web Site: http://www.mcgroup.ca
Emp.: 60
Construction Services
N.A.I.C.S.: 236220
Alain Guvin (Pres)

Subsidiary (Domestic):

Magil Construction (3)
1655 rue De Beauharnois Ouest, Montreal,
H4N 1J6, QC, Canada
Tel.: (514) 341-9899
Web Site: http://www.magil.com
Emp.: 200
Construction Services
N.A.I.C.S.: 236220

**McKay-Cocker Construction
Limited** (3)
1665 Oxford St E, London, N5Y 5R9, ON,
Canada
Tel.: (519) 451-5270
Web Site: http://www.mckaycocker.com
Construction Services
N.A.I.C.S.: 236220
Robert Skinner (Pres)

**Task Construction Management
Inc.** (3)
4405 Canada Way, Burnaby, V5G 1J3, BC,
Canada
Tel.: (604) 565-5476
Web Site: http://www.taskcm.com
Construction Services
N.A.I.C.S.: 236220
Antonio Niro (Pres)

FAZAL CLOTH MILLS LIMITED
59/3 Abdali Road, Multan, Pakistan
Tel.: (92) 6145790010
Web Site: https://www.fazalcloth.com
Year Founded: 1966
FZCM—(PSX)
Rev.: $279,515,200
Assets: $387,717,160
Liabilities: $227,101,120
Net Worth: $160,616,039
Earnings: $2,108,478
Emp.: 6,927
Fiscal Year-end: 06/30/23

Textile Products Mfr
N.A.I.C.S.: 314999

FAZE THREE LIMITED

Survey No 380/1 Khanvel Silvassa
Road Village Dapada, Worli, Mumbai,
396 191, Dadra And Nagar Have,
India
Tel.: (91) 2602699323
Web Site: https://www.fazethree.com
530079—(BOM)
Rev.: $44,597,280
Assets: $48,666,345
Liabilities: $17,799,600
Net Worth: $30,866,745
Earnings: $3,402,945
Fiscal Year-end: 03/31/21
Home Furnishings Store
N.A.I.C.S.: 423220
Ajay Anand *(Chm, Chm, CEO, CEO,*
Mng Dir & Mng Dir)

Subsidiaries:

Faze Three Autofab Limited   **(1)**
63-64 C Wing Mitttal Court, Nriman Point,
Mumbai, 400 021, India
Tel.: (91) 226 242 1313
Web Site: http://fazethreeautofab.com
Rev.: $18,408,390
Assets: $16,425,045
Liabilities: $11,422,320
Net Worth: $5,002,725
Earnings: $1,516,515
Fiscal Year-end: 03/31/2021
Automotive Fabric Mfr
N.A.I.C.S.: 332999
Ajay Anand *(Founder, Chm & Mng Dir)*

Faze Three Limited - Works II   **(1)**
380/1 Khanvel Silvassa Road, Dapada, Sil-
vassa, 396 230, India
Tel.: (91) 260 2699323
Home Furnishing Mfr
N.A.I.C.S.: 314120

FAZERLES AD-SILISTRA

Western Industrial Zone, 7500, Silis-
tra, Bulgaria
Tel.: (359) 86819206
Web Site: https://www.fazerles.com
Year Founded: 1993
FZLS—(BUL)
Sales Range: Less than $1 Million
Wood Products Mfr
N.A.I.C.S.: 321999
Milko Kesarovski *(Exec Dir)*

FBC HOLDINGS LIMITED

6th Floor FBC Centre 45 Nelson
Mandela Avenue, PO Box 1227, Ha-
rare, Zimbabwe
Tel.: (263) 242783204
Web Site: https://www.fbc.co.zw
Year Founded: 1997
FBC—(ZIM)
Rev.: $1,267,767,519
Assets: $9,377,982,621
Liabilities: $7,427,503,670
Net Worth: $1,950,478,951
Earnings: $904,634,137
Emp.: 588
Fiscal Year-end: 12/31/23
Financial Services
N.A.I.C.S.: 524130
Webster Rusere *(Exec Dir)*

Subsidiaries:

FBC Bank Limited   **(1)**
6th Floor FBC Centre 45 Nelson Mandela
Avenue, PO Box 1227, Harare, Zimbabwe
Tel.: (263) 242700312
Web Site: http://www.fbc.co.zw
Emp.: 750
Commercial Banking Services
N.A.I.C.S.: 522110

FBC Building Society   **(1)**
FBC House 2nd Floor 113 Leopold
Takawira, Harare, Zimbabwe
Tel.: (263) 242756817
Web Site: http://www.fbc.co.zw

Mortgage Banking Services
N.A.I.C.S.: 522310

FBC Insurance Company (Private)
Limited   **(1)**
Eagle House 105 Jason Moyo Avenue/4TH
Street, Harare, Zimbabwe
Tel.: (263) 24 270 8212
Insurance Services
N.A.I.C.S.: 524210
Musa Bako *(Mng Dir)*

FBC Reinsurance Limited   **(1)**
4th Floor FBC Centre 45 Nelson Mandela
Avenue, PO Box 4282, Harare, Zimbabwe
Tel.: (263) 4 797783
Web Site: http://www.fbc.co.zw
Reinsurance Services
N.A.I.C.S.: 524130
Kleto Chiketsani *(Mng Dir)*

FBC Securities (Private) Limited   **(1)**
2nd Floor Bank Chambers 76 Samora Ma-
chel Av, Harare, Zimbabwe
Tel.: (263) 24 279 7775
Insurance Services
N.A.I.C.S.: 524210
Benson Gasura *(Mng Dir)*

Microplan Financial Services (Private)
Limited   **(1)**
4th Floor FBC House 113 Leopold
Takawira, Harare, Zimbabwe
Tel.: (263) 24 277 2745
Insurance Services
N.A.I.C.S.: 524210
Patrick Mangwendeza *(Mng Dir)*

FBD HOLDINGS PLC

FBD House Bluebell, Dublin, 12, Ire-
land
Tel.: (353) 17617617   IE
Web Site: https://www.fbdgroup.com
Year Founded: 1960
EG7I—(LSE)
Rev.: $442,682,415
Assets: $1,509,078,265
Liabilities: $979,263,716
Net Worth: $529,814,549
Earnings: $76,764,544
Emp.: 950
Fiscal Year-end: 12/31/23
Holding Company; Property & Casu-
alty Insurance Products & Services;
Hospitality Properties Investment &
Development
N.A.I.C.S.: 551112
John O'Grady *(CFO)*

Subsidiaries:

FBD Insurance plc   **(1)**
FBD House, Bluebell, Dublin, D12 Y0HE,
Ireland   **(100%)**
Tel.: (353) 17617617
Web Site: http://www.fbd.ie
Sales Range: $50-74.9 Million
Emp.: 900
Automotive, Home & Property Insurance
Carrier
N.A.I.C.S.: 524298

FBD Life & Pensions Limited   **(1)**
FBD House Bluebell, Dublin, 12, Ireland
Tel.: (353) 17617617
Web Site: http://www.fbd.ie
General Insurance Services
N.A.I.C.S.: 524210

FBN HOLDINGS PLC

Samuel Asabia House 35 Marina, PO
Box 5216, Lagos, Nigeria
Tel.: (234) 9052000
Web Site:
   https://www.fbnholdings.com
Year Founded: 1894
FBNH—(NIGE)
Rev.: $408,542,624
Assets: $7,829,599,035
Liabilities: $7,092,553,609
Net Worth: $737,045,426
Earnings: $100,794,973
Emp.: 7,957
Fiscal Year-end: 12/31/22

Bank Holding Company; Banking
Services
N.A.I.C.S.: 551111
Obafemi Adedamola Otudeko *(Chm)*

Subsidiaries:

FBN (Merchant Bankers) Limited   **(1)**
9/11 Macarthy Street, Onikan, Lagos,
Nigeria   **(60%)**
Tel.: (234) 1 2600800
Merchant Banking Services
N.A.I.C.S.: 523150

FBN Bank (UK) Ltd   **(1)**
28 Finsbury Circus, London, EC2M 7DT,
United Kingdom   **(100%)**
Tel.: (44) 207 920 4920
Web Site: https://www.fbnbank.co.uk
Emp.: 170
Banking Services
N.A.I.C.S.: 522110
Paul Cardoen *(CEO)*

FBN Capital Ltd.   **(1)**
16 Keffi Street Off Awolowo Road, Ikoyi
South West, Lagos, Nigeria
Tel.: (234) 12707180
Web Site: http://www.fbncapital.com
Investment Banking Services
N.A.I.C.S.: 523150

FBN Insurance Brokers Limited   **(1)**
9/11 Macarthy Street, Onikan, Lagos, Nige-
ria
Tel.: (234) 12703380
Web Site:
   https://www.fbninsurancebrokers.com
Insurance Brokerage Services
N.A.I.C.S.: 524210
Olumide Ibidapo *(CEO & Mng Dir)*

FBN Mortgages Ltd.   **(1)**
124 Awolowo way Ikoyi, PO Box 9875,
South West Ikoyi, Lagos, Nigeria
Tel.: (234) 8127433340
Web Site: http://www.fbnmortgages.com
Mortgage Banking Services
N.A.I.C.S.: 522292

First Funds Ltd.   **(1)**
90 Awolowo Road, Ikoyi, Lagos, Nigeria
Tel.: (234) 12793910
Web Site: http://www.firstfunds.com.ng
Emp.: 10
Private Equity & Venture Capital Funds
Mangement Services
N.A.I.C.S.: 523910
Margaret Baale *(CFO)*

First Pension Custodian Ltd.   **(1)**
6 Maduike Street Off Raymond Njoku
Street, Ikoyi, Lagos, Nigeria
Tel.: (234) 12777800
Web Site:
   http://www.firstpensioncustodian.com
Sales Range: $25-49.9 Million
Emp.: 100
Custodial Services
N.A.I.C.S.: 561720
Mallam Umar Yahaya *(Chm)*

Subsidiary (Domestic):

Access Pension Fund Custodian
Limited   **(2)**
18 Ahmadu Bello Way, Victoria Island, La-
gos, Nigeria
Tel.: (234) 12713680
Web Site: http://www.accesspfc.com
Pension Custodial Services
N.A.I.C.S.: 525110
Idu Okwuosa *(CEO & Mng Dir)*

First Registrars Nigeria Limited   **(1)**
     (100%)
Tel.: (234) 1 270 1078
Web Site:
   https://www.firstregistrarsnigeria.com
Financial Services
N.A.I.C.S.: 525990

International Commercial Bank
Limited   **(1)**
Meridian House Ring Road Central, Private
Mail Bag No 16, Accra North, Accra, Ghana
Tel.: (233) 30 2236 136
Commercial Banking Services
N.A.I.C.S.: 522110

FBS GLOBAL LIMITED

74 Tagore Lane 02-00 Sindo Indus-
trial Estate, Singapore, 787498, Sin-
gapore
Tel.: (65) 62857781   Ky
Web Site:
   https://www.fbsglobal.com.sg
Year Founded: 2022
FBGL—(NASDAQ)
Rev.: $16,519,213
Assets: $13,836,642
Liabilities: $9,978,040
Net Worth: $3,858,603
Earnings: $3,548
Emp.: 98
Fiscal Year-end: 12/31/23
Construction Engineering Services
N.A.I.C.S.: 541330

FBV CONSTRUCTION JSC

G1 Sunview 2 building Cay Keo
street, Tam Phu Ward Thu Duc Dis-
trict, Ho Chi Minh City, Vietnam
Tel.: (84) 2837292966
Web Site: http://www.fbv.vn
Year Founded: 2017
Construction Design Services
N.A.I.C.S.: 541310

FCF CO., LTD.

No 8 Min Chuan 2nd Road 28th
Floor, Chien Chen District, Kaohsi-
ung, Taiwan
Tel.: (886) 7 339 1636
Web Site: http://www.fcf.com.tw
Tuna & Other Marine Products Mar-
keter
N.A.I.C.S.: 424460
Max Chou *(Pres)*

Subsidiaries:

Bumble Bee Foods LLC   **(1)**
280 10th ave, San Diego, CA 92101
Tel.: (858) 715-4000
Web Site: http://www.bumblebee.com
Sales Range: $900-999.9 Million
Canned Tuna, Salmon, Oysters, Pet Food,
Frozen Shrimp & Other Seafoods Mfr
N.A.I.C.S.: 311710
Dave Melbourne *(Sr VP-Mktg)*

Subsidiary (Domestic):

Bumble Bee Puerto Rico   **(2)**
3075 Carr 64, Mayaguez, PR 00681-6031
Tel.: (787) 834-3450
Web Site: http://www.bumblebee.com
Sales Range: $25-49.9 Million
Canned Tuna & Other Seafoods Mfr
N.A.I.C.S.: 311710

Bumble Bee Seafoods LLC   **(2)**
13100 Arctic Cir, Santa Fe Springs, CA
90670-5508
Tel.: (562) 483-7474
Web Site: http://www.bumblebee.com
Sales Range: $25-49.9 Million
Canned Tuna & Other Seafoods Mfr
N.A.I.C.S.: 311710
Angel Rodriguez *(Mgr-Ops)*

FCMB GROUP PLC

Primrose Towers 17A Tinubu Street,
Lagos, Lagos, Nigeria
Tel.: (234) 12793030
Web Site: https://www.fcmb.com
Year Founded: 1982
FCMB—(NIGE)
Rev.: $496,624,808
Assets: $4,571,705,878
Liabilities: $4,021,879,266
Net Worth: $549,826,613
Earnings: $47,504,131
Emp.: 3,893
Fiscal Year-end: 12/31/19
Financial Services
N.A.I.C.S.: 921130
Adam Nuru *(Mng Dir)*

FCMB Group Plc—(Continued)

Subsidiaries:

CSL Capital (UK) Limited (1)
43-44 New Bond Street, London, W1S 2SA, United Kingdom
Tel.: (44) 2081871220
Web Site: https://www.cslcapitaluk.com
Financial Brokerage Services
N.A.I.C.S.: 523999

CSL Stockbrokers Limited (1)
4th Floor First City Plaza Marina, PO Box 9117, Lagos, Nigeria
Tel.: (234) 127139204
Web Site: https://www.cslstockbrokers.com
Financial Investment Services
N.A.I.C.S.: 523999
Oluwatoyin Ashiru (Chm)

Credit Direct Limited (1)
48/50 Isaac John Street, Ikeja GRA, Lagos, Nigeria
Tel.: (234) 14482225
Web Site: https://www.creditdirect.ng
Credit Financial Services
N.A.I.C.S.: 522299
Chukwuma Nwanze (Exec Dir)

FCMB Asset Management Limited (1)
5th Floor First City Plaza 44 Marina, PO Box 9117, Lagos, Nigeria
Tel.: (234) 9085502406
Web Site: https://www.fcmbassetmanagement.com
Investment Services
N.A.I.C.S.: 523940

FCMB Bank (UK) Limited (1)
81 Gracechurch Street, London, EC3V 0AU, United Kingdom
Tel.: (44) 2072201000
Web Site: https://www.fcmbuk.com
Banking Services
N.A.I.C.S.: 522110
Frank Le Roex (Chm)

FCMB Capital Markets Limited (1)
First City Plaza 44 Marina, Lagos, Nigeria
Tel.: (234) 14485420
Web Site: https://www.fcmbcapitalmarketsng.com
Financial Security Services
N.A.I.C.S.: 523999
Otunba M. O. Balogun (Chm)

FCMB Microfinance Bank Limited (1)
10 Moshood Abiola Way Challenge, Ibadan, Nigeria
Tel.: (234) 8034842241
Web Site: http://www.fcmbmfb.ng
Financial Security Services
N.A.I.C.S.: 523999
Yemisi Edun (Chm)

FCMB Pensions Limited (1)
Plot 207 Zakaria Maimalari Street Cadastral Zone AO, Central Business District, Abuja, Nigeria
Tel.: (234) 8059580002
Web Site: https://www.fcmbpensions.com
Pension Fund Services
N.A.I.C.S.: 525110
Ladi Balogun (Chm)

FCMB Trustees Limited (1)
2nd Floor Promise Tower 17A Tinubu Street, Lagos, Nigeria
Tel.: (234) 12902721
Web Site: https://www.fcmbtrustees.com
Mutual Fund Services
N.A.I.C.S.: 525910
Samuel Adesanmi (Mng Dir)

First City Monument Bank Limited (1)
Primrose Tower 17A Tinubu Street Marina, Lagos, Nigeria
Tel.: (234) 12793030
Web Site: https://www.fcmb.com
Investment Banking & Financial Services
N.A.I.C.S.: 523150

FCR IMMOBILIEN AG
Tel.: (49) 89413249600   De

Web Site: https://www.fcr-immobilien.de
Year Founded: 1985
FC9—(MUN)
Rev.: $62,512,158
Assets: $196,167,188
Liabilities: $357,819,460
Net Worth: $138,348,027
Earnings: $9,603,669
Emp.: 68
Fiscal Year-end: 12/31/23
Real Estate Manangement Services
N.A.I.C.S.: 531210
Falk Raudies (Member-Mgmt Bd)

FCS SOFTWARE SOLUTIONS LTD
Plot No - 83 NSEZ Noida Dadri Road Phase - 2 Gautam Budh Nagar, Noida, 201305, Uttar Pradesh, India
Tel.: (91) 1204635920
Web Site: https://www.fcsltd.com
Year Founded: 1993
FCSSOFT—(NSE)
Rev.: $4,451,795
Assets: $46,684,851
Liabilities: $3,664,133
Net Worth: $43,020,718
Earnings: $175,025
Emp.: 256
Fiscal Year-end: 03/31/23
Information Technology Services
N.A.I.C.S.: 541511
Anil Kumar Sharma (CFO)

FCW HOLDINGS BERHAD
29th Floor Menara JKG No 282 Jalan Raja Laut, 50350, Kuala Lumpur, Malaysia
Tel.: (60) 327758199
Web Site: https://www.fcw.com.my
FCW—(KLS)
Rev.: $7,143,098
Assets: $52,505,640
Liabilities: $1,561,230
Net Worth: $50,944,410
Earnings: $5,964,503
Fiscal Year-end: 06/30/22
Property Rental & Leasing Services
N.A.I.C.S.: 531311
Poh Wah Loh (Sec)

Subsidiaries:

Coscolab Sdn. Bhd. (1)
No 1 Jalan Taming 2, Kawasan Perindustrian Taming Jaya, 43300, Seri Kembangan, Selangor, Malaysia (100%)
Tel.: (60) 38 961 8169
Web Site: https://www.coscolab.com
Sales Range: $25-49.9 Million
Emp.: 80
Skin Care Product Mfr
N.A.I.C.S.: 339999

FD TECHNOLOGIES PLC
Brian Conlon House 3 Canal Quay, Newry, BT35 6BP, Co Down, United Kingdom
Tel.: (44) 2830252242
Web Site:
https://www.fdtechnologies.com
Year Founded: 1996
GYO—(EUR)
Rev.: $357,708,984
Assets: $478,099,374
Liabilities: $216,685,323
Net Worth: $261,414,051
Earnings: $8,726,066
Emp.: 2,766
Fiscal Year-end: 02/28/22
Software & Information Technology Services
N.A.I.C.S.: 513210
Patrick Gerald Brazel (Chief Comml Officer)

Subsidiaries:

First Derivatives (Hong Kong) Limited (1)

Level 66 The Center 99 Queens Road, Central, China (Hong Kong)
Tel.: (852) 39653181
Financial Consulting Services
N.A.I.C.S.: 541611

First Derivatives (Ireland) Limited (1)
6th Floor Block A 1 George's Quay Plaza, Dublin, D02 Y098, Ireland
Tel.: (353) 16307700
Financial Consulting Services
N.A.I.C.S.: 541611

First Derivatives Canada Inc. (1)
31 Lakeshore Rd East Suite 201, Mississauga, L5G 4V5, ON, Canada
Tel.: (905) 278-9444
Web Site:
http://solutions.firstderivatives.com
Software Development Services
N.A.I.C.S.: 541511

First Derivatives Japan Co. Limited (1)
20F Shin-Marunouchi Center Building 1-6-2, Marunouchi Chiyoda-ku, Tokyo, 100-0005, Japan
Tel.: (81) 366349799
Financial Consulting Services
N.A.I.C.S.: 541611

First Derivatives Pte Limited (1)
One Raffles Quay North Tower 30-03, Singapore, 048583, Singapore
Tel.: (65) 65921960
Financial Consulting Services
N.A.I.C.S.: 541611

First Derivatives Pty Limited (1)
Rose Pk House 30 Kensington Rd, Rose Park, 5067, SA, Australia
Tel.: (61) 883644242
Sales Range: $25-49.9 Million
Emp.: 1
Software Support Services
N.A.I.C.S.: 541511

Kx Systems, Inc. (1)
530 Lytton Ave Ste 2, Palo Alto, CA 94301-1541
Tel.: (203) 283-4495
Web Site: http://www.kx.com
Memory Computing, Streaming Analytics & Operational Intelligence Services
N.A.I.C.S.: 518210
Janet Lustgarten (CEO)

Market Resource Partners LLC (1)
1650 Arch St Ste 2210, Philadelphia, PA 19103
Tel.: (215) 587-8800
Web Site: http://www.mepfd.com
Rev.: $6,600,000
Emp.: 100
Collateral, Email, Event Planning & Marketing, Exhibit/Trade Shows, High Technology, Market Research, Web (Banner Ads, Popups, etc.)
N.A.I.C.S.: 541810
John Butler (COO)

Reference Data Factory LLC (1)
14 Vervalen St, Closter, NJ 07624
Tel.: (201) 633-5745
Web Site:
http://www.referencedatafactory.com
Financial Management Consulting Services
N.A.I.C.S.: 541611

FDB GROUP
Vallensbaek Torvevej 9, DK 2620, Albertslund, Denmark
Tel.: (45) 39470000
Web Site: http://www.fdb.dk
Year Founded: 1893
Sales Range: $150-199.9 Million
Emp.: 55
Cooperative Food Retailing Services
N.A.I.C.S.: 445298
Lasse Bolander (Pres)

Subsidiaries:

Coop Danmark A/S (1)
Roskildevej 65, 2620, Albertslund, Denmark (100%)
Tel.: (45) 43864386
Web Site: http://www.coop.dk
All Other General Merchandise Stores

N.A.I.C.S.: 455219

Joint Venture (Domestic):

Coop Trading A/S (2)
Helgeshoj Alle 57, Hoje Taastrup, 2620, Denmark
Tel.: (45) 8853 0000
Web Site: http://www.cooptrading.com
Internordic Procurement of Branded Products
N.A.I.C.S.: 455219
Per Bank (Chm)

Subsidiary (Domestic):

Fakta A/S (2)
Hjulmagervej 12, 7100, Vejle, Denmark
Tel.: (45) 76414300
Web Site: http://www.fakta.dk
Sales Range: $25-49.9 Million
Supermarkets & Other Grocery except Convenience Stores
N.A.I.C.S.: 445110
Michael Christensen (Mng Dir)

Subsidiary (Domestic):

Dansk Vinimport Vejle ApS (3)
Hjulmagervej 12, 7100, Vejle, Denmark
Tel.: (45) 76414300
Supermarkets & Other Grocery except Convenience Stores
N.A.I.C.S.: 445110

Irma A/S (1)
Roskilde Vej 65, 2620, Albertslund, Denmark (100%)
Tel.: (45) 43863822
Web Site: http://www.irma.dk
Sales Range: $400-449.9 Million
Supermarkets & Other Grocery except Convenience Stores
N.A.I.C.S.: 445110

FDC INTERNATIONAL HOTELS CORPORATION
6F No 66 Wugong Rd Xinzhuang Dist, New Taipei City, Taiwan
Tel.: (886) 229986788
Web Site: https://www.fdc-i.com
Year Founded: 2012
2748—(TAI)
Rev.: $77,150,983
Assets: $162,920,756
Liabilities: $70,269,431
Net Worth: $92,651,326
Earnings: $9,260,342
Emp.: 591
Fiscal Year-end: 12/31/23
Hotel & Restaurant Management Services
N.A.I.C.S.: 721110

FDC LTD
B-8 MIDC Area, Aurangabad Dist, Waluj, 431 136, Maharashtra, India
Tel.: (91) 2402554407
Web Site: https://www.fdcindia.com
531599—(BOM)
Rev.: $195,226,259
Assets: $267,025,832
Liabilities: $30,340,060
Net Worth: $236,685,772
Earnings: $41,113,704
Emp.: 5,519
Fiscal Year-end: 03/31/21
Health Care Products Mfr
N.A.I.C.S.: 325412
Mohan A. Chandavarkar (Co-Mng Dir)

Subsidiaries:

FDC International Limited (1)
Unit 6 Fulcrum 1 Solent Way Solent Business Park, Whiteley, Fareham, PO15 7FE, Hampshire, United Kingdom
Tel.: (44) 1489565222
Web Site: http://www.fdcindia.com
Sales Range: $25-49.9 Million
Emp.: 2
Ophthalmic Product Mfr
N.A.I.C.S.: 326199

Fair Deal Corporation Pharmaceutical SA (Pty.) Limited (1)
Willows Office Park Farm Roadt, The Willows, Pretoria, South Africa
Tel.: (27) 832519018
Pharmaceutical Mfr & Distr
N.A.I.C.S.: 325412

FDG ELECTRIC VEHICLES LIMITED
Room 3001-3005 30th Floor China Resources Building, 26 Harbour Road, Wanchai, China (Hong Kong)
Tel.: (852) 3104 2803   BM
Web Site: http://www.fdgev.com
Rev.: $44,131,069
Assets: $940,498,907
Liabilities: $1,008,874,732
Net Worth: ($68,375,824)
Earnings: ($384,012,352)
Emp.: 1,738
Fiscal Year-end: 03/31/19
Holding Company; Electric Vehicles & Battery Products Mfr
N.A.I.C.S.: 551112

Subsidiaries:

FDG Kinetic Limited (1)
Rooms 3001-3005 30th Floor China Resources Building 26 Harbour Road, Wanchai, China (Hong Kong)   **(89.54%)**
Tel.: (852) 39098910
Web Site: http://www.fdgkinetic.com
Rev.: $5,390,267
Assets: $70,816,574
Liabilities: $64,327,503
Net Worth: $6,489,071
Earnings: ($45,896,045)
Emp.: 9
Fiscal Year-end: 03/31/2020
Investment Management Service
N.A.I.C.S.: 523940
Jaime Che (CEO)

Infast Brokerage Limited (1)
18/F 8 Lyndhurst Terrace, Central, China (Hong Kong)
Tel.: (852) 28531818
Web Site: http://www.infast.hk
Securities Brokerage Services
N.A.I.C.S.: 523150

FDM GROUP (HOLDINGS) PLC
Cottons Centre Cottons Lane, London, SE1 2QG, United Kingdom
Tel.: (44) 2030568240   UK
Web Site: https://www.fdmgroup.com
Year Founded: 1991
FDM—(LSE)
Rev.: $397,448,865
Assets: $156,862,035
Liabilities: $56,647,635
Net Worth: $100,214,400
Earnings: $42,049,095
Fiscal Year-end: 12/31/22
Human Resource Consulting Services
N.A.I.C.S.: 541612
Rod Flavell (CEO)

Subsidiaries:

FDM Astra Ireland Limited (1)
3 Dublin Landings North Wall Quay, Dublin, 1, Ireland
Tel.: (353) 2030568240
Consulting Recruitment & Training Provider Services
N.A.I.C.S.: 541612

FDM Group Australia Pty Ltd. (1)
Level 21 Tower Three International Towers 300 Barangaroo Avenue, Sydney, 2000, NSW, Australia
Tel.: (61) 481470766
Consulting Recruitment & Training Provider Services
N.A.I.C.S.: 541612

FDM Group Canada Inc. (1)
130 Adelaide St West Suite 2100, Toronto, M5H 3P5, ON, Canada
Tel.: (647) 560-9730

Consulting Recruitment & Training Provider Services
N.A.I.C.S.: 541612

FDM Group HK Limited (1)
6/F The Annex Central Plaza 18 Harbour Road, Admiralty, Hong Kong, China (Hong Kong)
Tel.: (852) 37093752
Consulting Recruitment & Training Provider Services
N.A.I.C.S.: 541612

FDM Group NV (1)
Rue Medori 99, Laeken, 1020, Brussels, Belgium
Tel.: (32) 2030568240
Consulting Recruitment & Training Provider Services
N.A.I.C.S.: 541612

FDM Singapore Consulting Pte Limited (1)
77 Robinson Road 13-00 Robinson 77, Singapore, 068896, Singapore
Tel.: (65) 69091570
Consulting Recruitment & Training Provider Services
N.A.I.C.S.: 541612

FDM South Africa (Pty) Limited (1)
9 Kinross Street South, Germiston, 1401, South Africa
Tel.: (27) 2030568240
Consulting Recruitment & Training Provider Services
N.A.I.C.S.: 541612

FDM Switzerland GmbH (1)
Lavaterstrasse 40, 8002, Zurich, 8002, Switzerland
Tel.: (41) 442857557
Consulting Recruitment & Training Provider Services
N.A.I.C.S.: 541612

FDM Technology (Shanghai) Co. Limited (1)
C33 22/F Jing'an Kerry Centre Office Tower 3 1228 Middle Yan An Road, Jing An, Shanghai, 200040, China
Tel.: (86) 2131063383
Consulting Recruitment & Training Provider Services
N.A.I.C.S.: 541612

FE (INDIA) LIMITED
W-19 Greater Kailash Part II, New Delhi, 110020, India
Tel.: (91) 11 4732 9900
Web Site: http://www.fegroup.co.in
Year Founded: 1994
Sales Range: $150-199.9 Million
Agricultural Product Whslr
N.A.I.C.S.: 423820
Praveen Kumar Chowdhary (CFO)

FE BATTERY METALS CORP.
700 West Georgia Street 25th Floor, Vancouver, V7Y 1B3, BC, Canada
Tel.: (604) 375-6005   BC
Web Site:
  https://www.febatterymetals.com
FEMFF—(OTCQB)
Rev.: $124
Assets: $6,868,135
Liabilities: $480,927
Net Worth: $6,387,208
Earnings: ($4,901,435)
Fiscal Year-end: 03/31/24
Other Metal Ore Mining
N.A.I.C.S.: 212290
Gurminder Sangha (Pres & CEO)

FE INVESTMENTS LIMITED
Level 15 Chorus House 66 Wyndham St, Auckland, New Zealand
Tel.: (64) 9 359 9445   AU
Web Site: http://www.fei.co.nz
Year Founded: 2003
Rev.: $9,279,195
Assets: $48,977,788
Liabilities: $40,985,950
Net Worth: $7,991,838

Earnings: ($10,362,762)
Fiscal Year-end: 06/30/18
Investment Holding Company
N.A.I.C.S.: 551112

Subsidiaries:

WolfStrike Distributors Ltd. (1)
72 Anzac Street, Takapuna, 0622, Auckland, New Zealand
Tel.: (64) 9 280 3347
Web Site: http://www.wolfstrike.co.nz
Electronic Product Distr
N.A.I.C.S.: 423690
Ian Bailey (Mng Dir)

WolfStrike Distributors Pty Limited (1)
Level 57 MLC Centre 19-29 Martin Place, Sydney, 2000, NSW, Australia
Tel.: (61) 2 8011 1806
Web Site: http://www.wolfstrike.net
Electronic Product Distr
N.A.I.C.S.: 423690

FEARLESS FILMS, INC.
467 Edgeley Blvd Unit 2, Concord, L4K 4E9, ON, Canada
Tel.: (416) 665-7297
Web Site: http://www.fearlessent.com
FERL—(OTCIQ)
Assets: $379,087
Liabilities: $1,005,933
Net Worth: ($626,846)
Earnings: ($1,242,555)
Fiscal Year-end: 12/31/21
Film Production & Distribution
N.A.I.C.S.: 512110
Victor Altomare (Founder, Chm, Pres, CEO & Interim CFO)

FEATURE INTEGRATION TECHNOLOGY, INC.
3F-7 No 36 Tai Yuen St, Tai Yuen Hi-Tech Industrial Park Bldg J, Chupei, 302, Hsinchu, Taiwan
Tel.: (886) 35600168
Web Site: https://www.fintek.com.tw
Year Founded: 2002
4951—(TPE)
Rev.: $13,361,162
Assets: $31,430,883
Liabilities: $3,903,561
Net Worth: $27,527,322
Earnings: $3,676,019
Fiscal Year-end: 12/31/23
Semiconductor Mfr
N.A.I.C.S.: 334413
Shen-Pao Chen (Chm)

FEB D.D. SARAJEVO
Mula Mustafe Baseskije 11, 71000, Sarajevo, Bosnia & Herzegovina
Tel.: (387) 3 321 5802
Web Site: http://www.feb.ba
FEBSR—(SARE)
Rev.: $466,778
Assets: $187,629
Liabilities: $38,582
Net Worth: $149,047
Earnings: $5,091
Emp.: 14
Fiscal Year-end: 12/31/20
Accounting & Auditing Services
N.A.I.C.S.: 541219

FECON CORPORATION
15th Floor CEO Tower Lot HH2-1 Urban Me Tri Ha Pham Hung Street, Ward Me Tri Nam Tu Liem District, Hanoi, Vietnam
Tel.: (84) 2462690481
Web Site: https://www.fecon.com.vn
Year Founded: 2004
FCN—(HOSE)
Rev.: $118,638,160
Assets: $353,555,781
Liabilities: $215,049,951
Net Worth: $138,505,830

Earnings: ($1,734,067)
Emp.: 1,151
Fiscal Year-end: 12/31/23
Mining Services
N.A.I.C.S.: 212311
Pham Viet Khoa (Chm)

FECTO GROUP OF COMPANIES
1st Floor Panorama Centre-2 Raja Ghazanfar Ali Khan Road, Saddar, Karachi, 75530, Pakistan
Tel.: (92) 2135682178
Web Site: http://www.fecto.com
Sales Range: $350-399.9 Million
Emp.: 1,500
Holding Company
N.A.I.C.S.: 551112
Munawar Ali Fecto (CEO & Mng Dir)

Subsidiaries:

Baba Farid Sugar Mills Limited (1)
2-D-1 Gulberg III, Lahore, Pakistan
Tel.: (92) 4235771066
Web Site: https://www.bfsml.com
Rev.: $16,135,459
Assets: $17,466,112
Liabilities: $7,302,124
Net Worth: $10,163,988
Earnings: $322,121
Emp.: 87
Fiscal Year-end: 09/30/2023
Sugar Mills
N.A.I.C.S.: 311314
Qaiser Shamim Khan (Chm)

Fecto Cement Limited (1)
Plot 60-C Khayaban-e-Shahbaz Phase VI Defence Housing Authority, Karachi, 75500, Pakistan
Tel.: (92) 2135248921
Web Site: https://fectogroup.com
Rev.: $31,234,189
Assets: $26,357,038
Liabilities: $13,417,697
Net Worth: $12,939,341
Earnings: ($479,349)
Emp.: 336
Fiscal Year-end: 06/30/2023
Cement Mfr
N.A.I.C.S.: 327310
Abdul Samad (CFO)

Fecto Orient (Pvt.) Ltd. (1)
1st Floor Panorama Centre-2, Raja Ghazanfar Ali Khan Road, Karachi, Pakistan
Tel.: (92) 215662991
Web Site: http://www.fecto.com
Clearing, Forwarding & Indenting; Imports & Clearance
N.A.I.C.S.: 561990

Fecto Sugar Mills Ltd. (1)
1st Floor Panorama Centre-2, Raja Ghazanfar Ali Khan Road, Karachi, 75530, Pakistan
Tel.: (92) 215682178
Web Site: http://www.fecto.com
Sales Range: $10-24.9 Million
Emp.: 1,338
Sugar Mfr
N.A.I.C.S.: 311314

FEDDERS ELECTRIC AND ENGINEERING LIMITED
159 Okhla Phase-3, New Delhi, 110020, India
Tel.: (91) 1140627200
Web Site:
  http://www.fedderslloyd.com
Sales Range: $150-199.9 Million
Emp.: 562
Air-Conditioning Equipment & Structured Steel Products Mfr
N.A.I.C.S.: 333415

Subsidiaries:

Luvata Czech S.R.O. (1)
Vrazska 143 Radotin, 15300, Prague, 5, Czech Republic
Tel.: (420) 257 811 129
Air Conditioning Equipment Mfr
N.A.I.C.S.: 333415

Fedders Electric and Engineering
Limited—(Continued)

PSL Engineering Pvt. Ltd. (1)
Plot No 30 Sectyor C Maneri Industrial
Area, Tehsil-Niwas District Mandla, Jabal-
pur, MP, India
Tel.: (91) 7643 233228
Air Conditioning Equipment Mfr
N.A.I.C.S.: 333415

FEDERAL CORPORATION

No 369 Huanxi Rd, Guanyin Dist,
Taoyuan, 328, Taiwan
Tel.: (886) 4522156
Web Site: https://www.federaltire.com
Year Founded: 1954
2102—(TAI)
Rev.: $15,644,788
Assets: $450,485,447
Liabilities: $215,369,101
Net Worth: $235,116,345
Earnings: ($56,551,847)
Fiscal Year-end: 12/31/20
Automobile Tires Mfr & Distr
N.A.I.C.S.: 326211
Shu-Jam Ma (Chm)

Subsidiaries:

Federal Tire (Jiangxi) Co., Ltd. (1)
No 639 Shanghai Road, Nanchang,
330029, Jiangxi, China
Tel.: (86) 7918310138
Tiles Mfr
N.A.I.C.S.: 326211

FEDERAL INSURANCE COM-PANY LIMITED

Navana DH Tower 6th Floor 6 Pan-
thapath, Dhaka, 1215, Bangladesh
Tel.: (880) 22337405455
Web Site:
　https://www.federalinsubd.com
Year Founded: 1987
FEDERALINS—(DHA)
Rev.: $2,206,627
Assets: $17,393,176
Liabilities: $7,660,861
Net Worth: $9,732,315
Earnings: $1,487,199
Emp.: 459
Fiscal Year-end: 12/31/20
General Insurance Services
N.A.I.C.S.: 524210
Elias Siddiquee (Vice Chm)

FEDERAL INTERNATIONAL (2000) LTD

12 Chin Bee Drive, Singapore,
619868, Singapore
Tel.: (65) 67478118
Web Site: https://www.federal-
int.com.sg
BDU—(SES)
Rev.: $38,099,674
Assets: $70,940,695
Liabilities: $22,738,014
Net Worth: $48,202,681
Earnings: ($1,011,134)
Emp.: 133
Fiscal Year-end: 12/31/23
Drilling Services
N.A.I.C.S.: 213111
Maggie Koh (Exec Dir)

Subsidiaries:

Alton International (S) Pte Ltd (1)
12 Chin Bee Drive, Singapore, 619868,
Singapore
Tel.: (65) 67478118
Web Site: https://federal-int.com.sg
Sales Range: $25-49.9 Million
Emp.: 30
Oilfield Equipments & Supplies Distr
N.A.I.C.S.: 423440

Subsidiary (Domestic):

Geo Link Nusantara Pte Ltd (2)

No 12 Chin Bee Drive, Singapore, 619868,
Singapore
Tel.: (65) 68618586
Web Site: http://www.alton.com.sg
Sales Range: $25-49.9 Million
Oil & Gas Field Engineering Services
N.A.I.C.S.: 213112

**Eastern Jason Fabrication Services
Pte Ltd** (1)
12 Chin Bee Drive, Singapore, 619868,
Singapore
Tel.: (65) 67478118
Web Site: https://federal-int.com.sg
Sales Range: $25-49.9 Million
Emp.: 20
Vessel Chartering Services
N.A.I.C.S.: 561990
Koh Kian Kiong (CEO)

Federal Capital Pte Ltd (1)
47/49 Genting Road, Singapore, 349489,
Singapore
Tel.: (65) 67478118
Emp.: 20
Investment Management Service
N.A.I.C.S.: 523999
Sandra Lee (Gen Mgr)

Federal Energi Pte Ltd (1)
47/49 Genting Road, Singapore, 349489,
Singapore
Tel.: (65) 67478118
Emp.: 100
Electric Power Distribution Services
N.A.I.C.S.: 221122
Tina Ng (Mgr-HR)

**Federal Environmental & Energy Pte.
Ltd.** (1)
12 Chin Bee Drive, Singapore, 619868,
Singapore
Tel.: (65) 6 745 6566
Web Site: http://www.sgfee.com
Environmental & Energy Consulting Ser-
vices
N.A.I.C.S.: 541620

Subsidiary (Non-US):

**FEE Investment Management & Con-
sultancy (Shanghai) Co., Ltd.** (2)
Unit I Floor 6 GreenLand S & T Building
201 Ning Xia Road, Shanghai, China
Tel.: (86) 2152358336
Web Site: http://www.federal.com.sg
Sales Range: $50-74.9 Million
Emp.: 20
Investment Management Service
N.A.I.C.S.: 523999

Federal Fire Engineering Pte Ltd (1)
12 Chin Bee Drive, Singapore, 619868,
Singapore
Tel.: (65) 6 862 5180
Web Site: https://federal-int.com.sg
Sales Range: $50-74.9 Million
Emp.: 10
Fire Prevention Systems Installation Ser-
vices
N.A.I.C.S.: 922160

**Federal Hardware Engineering Co
Pte Ltd** (1)
12 Chin Bee Drive, Singapore, 619868,
Singapore
Tel.: (65) 6 747 8118
Web Site: http://www.federal.com.sg
Industrial Engineering Services
N.A.I.C.S.: 541330

Subsidiary (Non-US):

**Federal International (Shanghai) Co.,
Ltd.** (2)
Unit I Floor 6 GreenLand S & T Building
201 Ning Xia Road, Shanghai, 200063,
China
Tel.: (86) 2152358336
Web Site: http://www.federal.com.sg
Emp.: 20
Steel Pipe Distr
N.A.I.C.S.: 423510

PT Fedsin Rekayasa Pratama (2)
South Quarter Tower A 16th Floor Unit H R
A Kartini Kav 8, Jakarta, 12430, Indonesia
Tel.: (62) 217507884
Web Site: https://federal-int.com.sg
Hardware Whslr

N.A.I.C.S.: 423710

**Federal IESE Environmental Technol-
ogy (Shanghai) Co., Ltd.** (1)
Unit I Floor 6 GreenLand S & T Building
201 Ning Xia Road, Shanghai, 200063,
China
Tel.: (86) 2152358336
Sales Range: $75-99.9 Million
Emp.: 20
Waste Water Treatment Services
N.A.I.C.S.: 221310
George Deng (CEO)

**Federal Offshore Services Pte
Ltd** (1)
47/49 Genting Road, Singapore, 349489,
Singapore
Tel.: (65) 67478118
Sales Range: $25-49.9 Million
Emp.: 70
Vessel Chartering Services
N.A.I.C.S.: 483111
Sandra Lee (Gen Mgr)

**Federal Resources Services Pte
Ltd** (1)
47/49 Genting Road, Singapore, 349489,
Singapore
Tel.: (65) 67478118
Web Site: http://www.federal.com.sg
Emp.: 50
Industrial Construction & Engineering Ser-
vices
N.A.I.C.S.: 541330

KVC (UK) Ltd (1)
6 Beardmore Way, Clydebank Industrial Es-
tate, Clydebank, G81 4HT, Dunbartonshire,
United Kingdom
Tel.: (44) 141 435 7640
Web Site: https://kvc-uk.com
Sales Range: $25-49.9 Million
Emp.: 12
Ball Valve Mfr
N.A.I.C.S.: 332911

PT Federal International (1)
Ariobimo Sentral Building 11th Floor JI HR
Rasuna Said X2 Kav 5, Jakarta, 12950,
Indonesia
Tel.: (62) 21 5296 4767
Sales Range: $50-74.9 Million
Emp.: 40
Investment Management Service
N.A.I.C.S.: 523999

PT Geo Link Nusantara (1)
Menara Global Building 15th Floor Jalan
Jendral Gatot Subroto Kav 27, Jakarta Se-
latan, Jakarta, 12950, Indonesia
Tel.: (62) 21 5279788
Web Site: http://www.geo-ln.com
Sales Range: $100-124.9 Million
Emp.: 150
Oil & Gas Field Engineering Services
N.A.I.C.S.: 211120
Eka Taufik Syah Putera (Chm)

PT. Mega Federal Energy (1)
Wisma 46 Kota BNI Lt 29 Jalan Jend
Sudirman Kav 1, Central Jakarta, Jakarta,
10220, Indonesia
Tel.: (62) 21 571 9543
Web Site: http://www.federal.com.sg
Electric Power Distribution Services
N.A.I.C.S.: 221122

FEDERAL INTERNATIONAL HOLDINGS BERHAD

Level P1 Menara Choy Fook On No
1B Jalan Yong Shook Lin, 46050,
Petaling Jaya, Malaysia
Tel.: (60) 392128008
Web Site: https://www.fihb.my
Year Founded: 1962
FIHB—(KLS)
Rev.: $24,337,289
Assets: $41,095,361
Liabilities: $11,619,774
Net Worth: $29,475,587
Earnings: $3,186,830
Emp.: 8
Fiscal Year-end: 06/30/23
Furniture Mfr
N.A.I.C.S.: 337122
Chooi Peng Mak (Co-Sec)

Subsidiaries:

**Federal Furniture (1982) Sdn
Bhd** (1)
Lot 104 Jalan 1 Kompleks Perabut Olak
Lempit, Kuala Langat, 42700, Banting, Se-
langor, Malaysia
Tel.: (60) 331491257
Web Site: https://www.ff1982.com.my
Emp.: 31
Furniture Mfr
N.A.I.C.S.: 337127
Victor Ng (COO)

Federal Furniture (M) Sdn Bhd (1)
Lot 104 Jalan 1 Kompleks Perabut Olak
Lempit, Kuala Langat, Banting, 42700, Se-
langor, Malaysia
Tel.: (60) 331491154
Web Site: http://www.ff1982.com.my
Sales Range: $25-49.9 Million
Emp.: 21
Furniture & Furnishing Products Whslr
N.A.I.C.S.: 423210

**Federal Furniture Industries Sdn
Bhd** (1)
No 8 Koi Kinrara Jalan Pipit, Bukit Tandang,
47100, Puchong, Selangor, Malaysia
Tel.: (60) 38 070 9200
Web Site: https://www.ffi.com.my
Sales Range: $25-49.9 Million
Emp.: 35
Interior Design Services
N.A.I.C.S.: 541410
S. K. Choy (Chief Dev Officer-Kitchen Proj-
ect)

**Federal Furniture Lifestyle Sdn
Bhd** (1)
53 Jalan Puteri 2/1 Bandar Puteri Puchong,
47100, Puchong, Selangor,
Malaysia　　　　(100%)
Tel.: (60) 377258899
Interior Design & Furnishing Services
N.A.I.C.S.: 541410
James Shii (COO)

FEDERAL WHITE CEMENT, LTD.

355151 35th Line, PO Box 1609,
Woodstock, N4S 0A8, ON, Canada
Tel.: (519) 485-5410
Web Site:
　http://www.federalwhitecement.com
Year Founded: 1979
Rev.: $18,342,178
Emp.: 100
Cement Mfr
N.A.I.C.S.: 327310

FEDERATED CO-OPERATIVES LIMITED

401 22nd Street East, PO Box 1050,
Saskatoon, S7K 3M9, SK, Canada
Tel.: (306) 244-3311
Web Site:
　http://www.coopconnection.ca
Sales Range: $5-14.9 Billion
Retail Cooperative
N.A.I.C.S.: 813990
Tony Van Burgsteden (VP-Fin)

Subsidiaries:

**Consumers' Co-operative Refineries
Limited** (1)
9th Avenue North, Box 260, Regina, S4P
3A1, SK, Canada
Tel.: (306) 721-5353
Web Site: http://www.ccrl-fcl.ca
Emp.: 1,000
Petroleum Distr
N.A.I.C.S.: 424720

FCL Enterprises Ltd. (1)
10909 92 St Ss 1, High Level, T0H 1Z0,
AB, Canada
Tel.: (780) 926-8837
Food Store Operator
N.A.I.C.S.: 445131

FCL Ventures Ltd. (1)
13232170 Street, Edmonton, T5V 1M7, AB,
Canada
Tel.: (780) 447-8556

Investment Management Service
N.A.I.C.S.: 523940

Federated Co-operatives Limited - Calgary Feed Plant (1)
1020 26th Street NW, Calgary, T2A 2M4, AB, Canada
Tel.: (403) 531-6656
Animal Feed Mfr
N.A.I.C.S.: 311119

Federated Co-operatives Limited - Edmonton Feed Plant (1)
1818 121st Avenue NE, Edmonton, T6S 1B1, AB, Canada
Tel.: (780) 472-6767
Animal Feed Mfr
N.A.I.C.S.: 311119
Bevon Raycraft (Plant Mgr)

Federated Co-operatives Limited - Moosomin Feed Plant (1)
806 Park Avenue, Box 859, Moosomin, S0G 3N0, SK, Canada
Tel.: (306) 435-3331
Animal Feed Mfr
N.A.I.C.S.: 311119

Federated Co-operatives Limited - Saskatoon Feed Plant (1)
201 105th Street E, Saskatoon, S7N 1Z4, SK, Canada
Tel.: (306) 477-6464
Animal Feed Mfr
N.A.I.C.S.: 311119

Interprovincial Cooperative Limited (1)
945 Marion Street, Winnipeg, R2J 0K7, MB, Canada
Tel.: (204) 233-3461
Web Site: https://www.ipco.ca
Agricultural Chemicals Mfr & Whslr
N.A.I.C.S.: 325320

The Grocery People Ltd. (1)
13232 170th Street, Edmonton, T5V 1M7, AB, Canada
Tel.: (780) 447-5700
Web Site: https://www.tgp.crs
Food Product Whslr
N.A.I.C.S.: 424420
Felicia Morin (Mgr-Sls)

FEDERATION ASSET MANAGEMENT PTY. LTD.
Suite 30 04 Chifley Tower 2 Chifley Square, Sydney, 2000, NSW, Australia
Tel.: (61) 2 8650 4500
Web Site:
  http://www.federationam.com
Private Equity Fund
N.A.I.C.S.: 551112
Cameron Brownjohn (CEO)

FEDERATION INTERNATIONALE DE FOOTBALL ASSOCIATION
FIFA-Strasse 20, PO Box 8044, Zurich, Switzerland
Tel.: (41) 432227777
Web Site: http://www.fifa.com
Year Founded: 1904
Sales Range: $700-749.9 Million
Emp.: 300
Professional Soccer Organization
N.A.I.C.S.: 813990
Gianni Infantino (Co-Pres)

Subsidiaries:

Early Warning System GmbH (1)
Streulistrasse 19, 8032, Zurich, Switzerland
Tel.: (41) 44 388 81 60
Web Site: http://www.fifa-ews.com
Sport Betting Monitoring Services
N.A.I.C.S.: 561990

FIFA Ticketing AG (1)
Aurorastrasse 100, 8032, Zurich, Switzerland
Tel.: (41) 43 222 77 77
Web Site: http://www.fifa.com
Sport Event Ticketing Services
N.A.I.C.S.: 561599

Falk Eller (Sr Mgr-Ticketing Sys)

FIFA Transfer Matching System GmbH (1)
Zollikerstrasse 226, 8008, Zurich, Switzerland
Tel.: (41) 43 222 5400
Web Site: http://www.fifatms.com
Soccer Player Transfer Services
N.A.I.C.S.: 711211
Mark Goddard (Gen Mgr)

FEDERMANN ENTERPRISES, LTD.
99 Hayarkon St, Tel Aviv, 63432, Israel
Tel.: (972) 35202555
Web Site: http://www.federmann-ent.com
Sales Range: $300-349.9 Million
Emp.: 7
Defense Electronic & Technology Investment Services
N.A.I.C.S.: 551112
Michael Federmann (Chm & CEO)

Subsidiaries:

Freiberger Compound Materials GmbH (1)
Am Junger Loewe Schacht 5, 09599, Freiberg, Saxony, Germany (87%)
Tel.: (49) 37312800
Web Site: http://www.freiberger.com
Sales Range: $50-74.9 Million
Compound Semiconductor Substrates Mfr
N.A.I.C.S.: 334413
Stefan Schneidewind (CEO)

Subsidiary (Non-US):

Freiberger Compound Materials Taiwan Ltd. (2)
No 66 Jiaqin S Rd, Jhubei, 30268, Hsinchu, Taiwan
Tel.: (886) 3 6570 165
N.A.I.C.S.: 334413
Joe Chou (Gen Mgr)

Subsidiary (US):

Freiberger Compound Materials USA, Inc. (2)
7071 Corporate Way Ste 203, Dayton, OH 45459
Tel.: (937) 291-2899
Web Site: http://www.freiberger.com
Sales Range: $25-49.9 Million
Emp.: 2
Semiconductor Mfr
N.A.I.C.S.: 334413

Subsidiary (Non-US):

K1 Solution, Inc. (2)
Room 904, E&C Venture Dream Tower 3rd, Seoul, 152-719, Guro-Dong, Korea (South)
Tel.: (82) 28382866
Compound Semiconductor Substrates Mfr
N.A.I.C.S.: 334413

Topco Scientific (Shanghai) Co., Ltd. (2)
Rm 606 No 333, Zhao Jia Ban, Shanghai, 200032, ROC, China
Tel.: (86) 2164220458
Compound Semiconductor Substrates Mfr
N.A.I.C.S.: 334413

FEDNAV LIMITED
1000 De La Gauchetiere Street West Suite 3500, Montreal, H3B 4W5, QC, Canada
Tel.: (514) 878-6500
Web Site: http://www.fednav.com
Year Founded: 1944
Sales Range: $450-499.9 Million
Emp.: 170
International Shipping Services
N.A.I.C.S.: 483111
Paul Pathy (Pres & CEO)

Subsidiaries:

Fednav (Belgium) N.V. (1)

Sneeuwbeslaan 14, Wilrijk, Antwerp, 2610, Belgium
Tel.: (32) 3 821 1300
Web Site: http://www.fednav.com
Deep Sea Freight Transportation Services
N.A.I.C.S.: 483111

Fednav (Hamburg) GmbH (1)
Katharinenstrasse 4, Hamburg, 20457, Germany
Tel.: (49) 40 3787 9900
Deep Sea Freight Transportation Services
N.A.I.C.S.: 483111

Fednav Asia Ltd. (1)
Toranomon 1-chome Mori Bldg 6F 1-19-5 Toranomon, Minato-ku, Tokyo, 105-0001, Japan
Tel.: (81) 3 3507 0360
Deep Sea Freight Transportation Services
N.A.I.C.S.: 483111

Fednav Brasil Agencia Maritima Ltda (1)
Rua da Assembleia 10 / sala 1707, Rio de Janeiro, 20011-010, Brazil
Tel.: (55) 21 2132 8466
Deep Sea Freight Transportation Services
N.A.I.C.S.: 483111

Fednav Europe Limited (1)
88 York Street, London, W1H 1QT, United Kingdom
Tel.: (44) 20 7831 0616
Deep Sea Freight Transportation Services
N.A.I.C.S.: 483111

Fednav International Ltd. (1)
1st Floor The Atrium Haggatt Hall, PO Box 1108, Saint Michael, BB11063, Barbados
Tel.: (246) 427 8527
Deep Sea Freight Transportation Services
N.A.I.C.S.: 483111

Fednav Singapore Pte. Ltd. (1)
30 Cecil Street 10-03/04 Prudential Tower, 049712, Singapore, Singapore
Tel.: (65) 6372 8989
Web Site: http://www.fednav.com
Emp.: 10
Deep Sea Freight Transportation Services
N.A.I.C.S.: 483111
Jon Mann (Mng Dir)

FEDRIGONI SPA
Piazzale Lodi 3, 20137, Milan, Italy
Tel.: (39) 02467101
Web Site: http://www.fedrigoni.com
Year Founded: 1888
Paper Products Mfr
N.A.I.C.S.: 424110
Marco Nespolo (CEO)

Subsidiaries:

Acucote Inc. (1)
910 E Elm St, Graham, NC 27253
Tel.: (336) 578-1800
Web Site: http://www.acucote.com
Sales Range: $25-49.9 Million
Emp.: 125
Adhesive Backing Products Mfr
N.A.I.C.S.: 322220
Brenda Seel (Controller)

Mohawk Fine Papers, Inc. (1)
465 Saratoga St, Cohoes, NY 12047
Tel.: (518) 237-1740
Web Site: http://www.mohawkpaper.com
Coated Texts & Printing Papers Mfr
N.A.I.C.S.: 322220
F. Joseph O'Connor (Sr VP & Mgr-Natl Acct-West)

Subsidiary (Domestic):

Crane & Co., Inc. (2)
1466 Curran Hwy, North Adams, MA 01247
Tel.: (413) 684-2600
Web Site: http://www.crane.com
Specialty Cotton & Nonwoven Paper & Stationery Products Mfr; Personal & Commercial Print Services
N.A.I.C.S.: 322120

FEDRUS INTERNATIONAL NV
Schoonmansveld 48, 2870, Puurs, Belgium

Tel.: (32) 475 44 17 40   BE
Web Site:
  http://www.fedrusinternational.be
Sales Range: $550-599.9 Million
Emp.: 1,300
Roofing & Building Facade Materials Distr
N.A.I.C.S.: 423330
Mark Vandecruys (Owner)

Subsidiaries:

Umicore Building Products France s.a.s. (1)
Les Mercuriales Tour de Ponant 40 rue Jean Jaures, 93170, Bagnolet, France
Tel.: (33) 1 4972 4242
Web Site: http://www.vmzinc.com
Rolled Zinc Building Products Mfr & Marketer
N.A.I.C.S.: 331491

Subsidiary (Non-US):

Umicore Building Products Hungary kft. (2)
Kagylo u 4-6 Pf 101, Budakeszi, H-2092, Hungary
Tel.: (36) 23452452
Web Site: http://www.vmzinc.hu
Building Materials Distr
N.A.I.C.S.: 444180

Umicore Building Products Iberica S.L. (2)
C/ Juan Gris 4-6a planta, 08014, Barcelona, Spain
Tel.: (34) 93 298 88 80
Web Site: http://www.vmzinc.es
Building Materials Distr
N.A.I.C.S.: 444180

Umicore Building Products Italia s.r.l. (2)
Via Riccardo Lombardi 19/16, 20153, Milan, Italy
Tel.: (39) 0247998223
Web Site: http://www.vmzinc.it
Building Materials Distr
N.A.I.C.S.: 444180
Giulio Paoli (Mng Dir)

Subsidiary (US):

Umicore Building Products USA Inc. (2)
3600 Glenwood Ave Ste 250, Raleigh, NC 27612
Tel.: (984) 212-5471
Web Site: http://www.vmzinc-us.com
Zinc Products Mfr
N.A.I.C.S.: 325180

FEED ONE CO., LTD.
2-23-2 Tsuruyacho, Yokohama, 221-0835, Kanagawa, Japan
Tel.: (81) 453112300
Web Site: https://www.feed-one.co.jp
2060—(TKS)
Rev.: $2,074,713,750
Assets: $866,161,180
Liabilities: $530,003,020
Net Worth: $336,158,160
Earnings: $33,605,240
Emp.: 902
Fiscal Year-end: 03/31/24
Holding Company; Formula Feed, Livestock & Fisheries
N.A.I.C.S.: 551112
Takashi Yamauchi (Pres & CEO)

FEEDBACK PLC
Health Foundry Canterbury House 1 Royal Street South Bank, London, SE1 7LL, United Kingdom
Tel.: (44) 203 997 7634   UK
Web Site: http://www.fbkmed.com
Year Founded: 1958
FDBK—(AIM)
Rev.: $390,229
Assets: $7,903,883
Liabilities: $750,587
Net Worth: $7,153,296
Earnings: ($2,198,845)

Feedback plc—(Continued)

Emp.: 18
Fiscal Year-end: 05/31/21
Medical Imaging Products
N.A.I.C.S.: 339112
Alastair James Riddell (Chm)

Subsidiaries:

Feedback Medical Limited   **(1)**
Canterbury House 1 Royal Street South
Bank, London, SE1 7LL, United Kingdom
Tel.: (44) 2039977634
Medical Imaging Services
N.A.I.C.S.: 621512

FEEDFORCE GROUP, INC.
3F Lattice Aoyama Square 1-2-6 Mi-
namiaoyama, Minato-ku, Tokyo, 107-
0062, Japan
Tel.: (81) 358467016
Web Site: https://feedforcegroup.jp
Year Founded: 2006
7068—(TKS)
Rev.: $26,204,163
Assets: $47,036,670
Liabilities: $27,941,857
Net Worth: $19,094,813
Earnings: $740,007
Emp.: 63
Fiscal Year-end: 05/31/23
Digital Marketing Services
N.A.I.C.S.: 541870
Koji Tsukada (Founder & Pres)

**FEEI CHERNG DEVELOP
TECHNOLOGY CO., LTD.**
11F 2NO248 Section 2 Yonghua
Road, Anping Dist, Tainan City, Tai-
wan
Tel.: (886) 2995586
Web Site: https://www.fce.com.tw
3313—(TPE)
Rev.: $278,961
Assets: $56,368,039
Liabilities: $24,803,458
Net Worth: $31,564,581
Earnings: ($5,421,505)
Fiscal Year-end: 12/31/22
Electrical Component Mfr & Distr
N.A.I.C.S.: 335999
Ching-Tsung Yang (Chm & Pres)

FEELGOOD SVENSKA AB
Linnegatan 87 A, Stockholm, 115 23,
Sweden
Tel.: (46) 8 54581000
Web Site: http://www.feelgood.se
FEEL—(OMX)
Rev.: $83,181,067
Assets: $51,422,309
Liabilities: $30,729,926
Net Worth: $20,692,384
Earnings: $2,727,477
Emp.: 599
Fiscal Year-end: 12/31/19
Health Care Srvices
N.A.I.C.S.: 621999
Joachim Morath (CEO)

FEELUX CO., LTD.
235-48 Gwangjeok-Ro Gwangjeok-
Myeon, Yangju, Gyeonggi-Do, Korea
(South)
Tel.: (82) 70 7780 8200   **KR**
Web Site: http://www.feelux.com
Year Founded: 1984
Lighting Products & Electronic Com-
ponents Mfr
N.A.I.C.S.: 335132
Won Hwan Ahn (CEO)

Subsidiaries:

FEELUX Lighting Co., Ltd.   **(1)**
235-48 Gwangjeok-ro Gwangjeok-Myeon,
Yangju, Gyeonggi-Do, Korea (South)
Tel.: (82) 70 7780 8200

Web Site: http://www.feelux.com
Rev.: $105,287,355
Assets: $180,289,374
Liabilities: $92,193,822
Net Worth: $88,095,552
Earnings: $3,502,667
Emp.: 150
Fiscal Year-end: 12/31/2017
Electronic Components Mfr
N.A.I.C.S.: 335311

Subsidiary (US):

FEELUX Lighting, Inc.   **(2)**
3000 northwood parkway ste165, Norcross,
GA 30071
Tel.: (678) 668-7005
Web Site: http://www.feeluxlighting.com
Emp.: 12
Lighting Product Distr
N.A.I.C.S.: 423610
Peter Christopher Augusta (Dir-Ops-North
America)

FEERUM S.A.
ul Okrzei 6, 59-225, Chojnow, Poland
Tel.: (48) 768196738
Web Site: https://www.feerum.pl
Year Founded: 2002
FEE—(WAR)
Rev.: $16,075,203
Assets: $38,686,738
Liabilities: $9,315,295
Net Worth: $29,371,443
Earnings: ($179,624)
Fiscal Year-end: 12/31/23
Grain Elevators & Other Agricultural
Equipment Mfr
N.A.I.C.S.: 333111
Magdalena Labudzka-Janusz (Super-
visory Bd of Dirs & Chm-Supervisory
Bd)

**FEHA LASERTEC HALLE
GMBH**
Brachwitzer Str 16, 06118, Bitterfeld-
Wolfen, Germany
Tel.: (49) 34552570
Web Site: http://www.feha-laser.de
Rev.: $12,414,600
Emp.: 42
Water Equipment Mfr
N.A.I.C.S.: 333310
Ekkehard-Torsten Henze (Gen Mgr)

FEIHE INTERNATIONAL, INC.
Star City International Building 10
Jiuxianqiao Road C-16th Floor, Cha-
oyang District, Beijing, 100016, China
Tel.: (86) 10 6431 9357   **UT**
Web Site: http://ady.feihe.com
Sales Range: $250-299.9 Million
Emp.: 1,932
Dairy Products Mfr
N.A.I.C.S.: 311514
You-Bin Leng (Chm, Pres, CEO &
Gen Mgr)

Subsidiaries:

Heilongjiang Feihe Dairy Co.,
Limited   **(1)**
Star City Intl Bldg 10 Jiuxianqiao Rd C-16th
Fl, Chaoyang, Beijing, 100016, China
Tel.: (86) 1084574688
Sales Range: $250-299.9 Million
Emp.: 1,000
Dairy Products Mfr
N.A.I.C.S.: 424430

**FEILONG AUTO COMPO-
NENTS CO., LTD.**
Industrial Avenue, Xixia County,
Henan, 474500, China
Tel.: (86) 37769697329
Web Site: https://www.flacc.com
Year Founded: 1952
002536—(SSE)
Rev.: $457,424,604
Assets: $616,569,408
Liabilities: $294,272,784

Net Worth: $322,296,624
Earnings: $11,811,852
Emp.: 4,800
Fiscal Year-end: 12/31/22
Water Pump Mfr
N.A.I.O.G.: 333914
Yaozhi Sun (Chm)

**FEINKOST DITTMANN REICH-
OLD FEINKOST GMBH**
August Horch Strasse 4-8, D-65582,
Diez, Germany
Tel.: (49) 64329550
Web Site: http://www.feinkost-
dittmann.de
Year Founded: 1901
Rev.: $137,655,515
Emp.: 282
Gourmet Products Mfr
N.A.I.C.S.: 311999
Thorsten Reichold (Mng Dir)

**FEINMECHANIK MICHAEL
DECKEL GMBH & CO. KG.**
Am Oferl 17 19, Weilheim, 82362,
Germany
Tel.: (49) 8816880
Web Site: http://www.michael-
deckel.de
Year Founded: 1950
Rev.: $12,000,000
Emp.: 100
Tool Grinding Machines Design & Mfr
N.A.I.C.S.: 333517
Martin Fack Mann (Mng Dir)

**FEISHANG ANTHRACITE RE-
SOURCES LIMITED**
Room 2205 22/F Shun Tak Centre
West Tower 200 Connaught Road,
Central, China (Hong Kong)
Tel.: (852) 28589860
Web Site:
http://www.fsanthracite.com
1738—(HKG)
Rev.: $225,088,859
Assets: $465,808,450
Liabilities: $542,724,343
Net Worth: ($76,915,894)
Earnings: $14,185,454
Emp.: 1,742
Fiscal Year-end: 12/31/22
Anthracite Coal Mining & Production
N.A.I.C.S.: 212115
Weibing Han (Chm & CEO)

Subsidiaries:

Haitong Unitrust International Leasing
Corporation   **(1)**
10F Celebrity Mansion No 300 East Nanjing
Road Huangpu Distri, Shanghai, 200001,
China
Tel.: (86) 2161355345
Equipment Rental Services
N.A.I.C.S.: 532490

**FEITIAN TECHNOLOGIES CO.,
LTD.**
Tower B Huizhi Mansion No 9
Xueqing Road, Haidian District, Bei-
jing, 100085, China
Tel.: (86) 1062304466
Web Site: https://www.ftsafe.com
300386—(CHIN)
Rev.: $121,822,272
Assets: $265,329,324
Liabilities: $24,255,504
Net Worth: $241,073,820
Earnings: ($16,986,996)
Emp.: 1,000
Fiscal Year-end: 12/31/22
Information Security Products Mfr &
Services
N.A.I.C.S.: 541512
Yu Huang (Founder)

Subsidiaries:

FEITIAN Technologies US,Inc.   **(1)**
4677 Old Ironsides Dr Ste 312, Santa
Clara, CA 95054
Tel.: (408) 352-5553
Data Processing Services
N.A.I.C.S.: 518210
Tom Barber (Dir-Bus Dev)

**FEIYANG INTERNATIONAL
HOLDINGS GROUP LIMITED**
1-140 30 Dashani Street, Haishu Dis-
trict, Ningbo, Zhejiang, China   **Ky**
Year Founded: 2018
1901—(HKG)
Rev.: $73,978,594
Assets: $78,489,560
Liabilities: $67,388,541
Net Worth: $11,101,019
Earnings: ($1,601,268)
Emp.: 257
Fiscal Year-end: 12/31/23
Holding Company
N.A.I.C.S.: 551112
Binfeng He (Founder)

Subsidiaries:

DS Wellness & Health Management
Limited   **(1)**
25 / F 8 Lam Chak Street, Kowloon Bay,
China (Hong Kong)
Tel.: (852) 22678904
Web Site: https://www.fyskbuy.com
Health Care Treatment Services
N.A.I.C.S.: 621498

**FEIYU TECHNOLOGY INTER-
NATIONAL COMPANY LTD.**
Floor 2 Block 2 14 Wanghai Road,
Ruanjian Yuan Two Siming, Xiamen,
Fujian, China
Tel.: (86) 5922208755
Web Site: http://www.feiyuhk.com
1022—(HKG)
Rev.: $26,889,268
Assets: $87,842,243
Liabilities: $23,749,222
Net Worth: $64,093,021
Earnings: ($3,419,582)
Emp.: 365
Fiscal Year-end: 12/31/22
Video Game Publisher
N.A.I.C.S.: 513210
Jianjun Yao (Chm & CEO)

FELDER GMBH
Im Lipperfeld 11, Oberhausen, 46047,
Germany
Tel.: (49) 208850350
Web Site: http://www.felder.de
Year Founded: 1979
Rev.: $19,311,600
Emp.: 96
Soldering Flux Mfr
N.A.I.C.S.: 325998

FELISSIMO CORPORATION
7-1 Shinkocho, Chuo-ku, Hyogo, Ja-
pan
Tel.: (81) 783255555
Web Site: http://www.felissimo.co.jp
Year Founded: 2002
3396—(TKS)
Rev.: $209,913,630
Assets: $206,063,760
Liabilities: $71,757,890
Net Worth: $134,305,870
Earnings: ($6,083,220)
Emp.: 717
Fiscal Year-end: 02/29/24
Mail Order Sales Operator
N.A.I.C.S.: 458110
Kazuhiko Yazaki (Pres & CEO)

FELIX GLOBAL CORP.
100 University Ave., Toronto, M5J
1V6, ON, Canada

Tel.: (416) 512-7244
Web Site: http://www.felixglobal.com
Year Founded: 1986
Career Transition Services
N.A.I.C.S.: 561312
Jim Graham *(CEO)*

FELIX GOLD LIMITED
L1 371 Queen St, Brisbane, 4000,
QLD, Australia
Tel.: (61) 730547108   AU
Web Site:
https://felixgold.investorportal.com
Year Founded: 2020
FXG—(ASX)
Assets: $12,284,290
Liabilities: $87,078
Net Worth: $12,197,212
Earnings: ($1,449,827)
Fiscal Year-end: 06/30/23
Gold Exploration Services
N.A.I.C.S.: 212220
Anthony Reilly *(CEO)*

**FELIX GROUP HOLDINGS LIM-
ITED**
24 Macquarie St, Teneriffe, 4005,
QLD, Australia
Tel.: (61) 1300010527   AU
Web Site: https://www.felix.net
Year Founded: 2012
FLX—(ASX)
Rev.: $3,462,575
Assets: $3,857,087
Liabilities: $3,170,824
Net Worth: $686,263
Earnings: ($3,993,410)
Fiscal Year-end: 06/30/23
Holding Company
N.A.I.C.S.: 551112
Michael Peter Davis *(CEO)*

FELIX INDUSTRIES LIMITED
208 Devshruti Complex Mithakhali
Crossroad Ellisbridge, Ahmedabad,
380006, Gujarat, India
Tel.: (91) 7926463658
Web Site:
https://www.felixindustries.co
FELIX—(NSE)
Rev.: $2,330,460
Assets: $2,915,221
Liabilities: $972,496
Net Worth: $1,942,725
Earnings: $140,315
Emp.: 121
Fiscal Year-end: 03/31/23
Waste Water Treatment Services
N.A.I.C.S.: 221320
Ritesh Vinaybhai Patel *(Founder &
Mng Dir)*

**FELIX KOCH OFFENBACH
COULEUR UND KARAMEL
GMBH**
Lindenstrasse 70, 63071, Offenbach,
Germany
Tel.: (49) 699854200
Web Site: https://www.koch-felix.com
Year Founded: 1904
Sales Range: $25-49.9 Million
Sugar Products Mfr
N.A.I.C.S.: 311313
Felix Koch *(Mng Dir)*

**FELIX SCHOELLER HOLDING
GMBH & CO. KG**
Burg Gretesch, 49086, Osnabruck,
Germany
Tel.: (49) 54138000
Web Site: http://www.felix-
schoeller.com
Year Founded: 1895
Sales Range: $150-199.9 Million
Emp.: 2,270
Holding Company

N.A.I.C.S.: 551112
Matthias Baumgartner *(VP & Head-
SIs)*

Subsidiaries:

Felix Schoeller North America   (1)
179 County Rte 2A, New York, NY 13142
Tel.: (315) 298-5133
Paper Mfr & Distr
N.A.I.C.S.: 322120

Felix Schoeller Supply Chain Tech-
nologies GmbH & Co. KG   (1)
Burg Gretesch, 49086, Osnabruck, Ger-
many
Tel.: (49) 541 3800 0
Web Site: http://www.felix-schoeller-sct.com
Paper Mfr & Distr
N.A.I.C.S.: 322120

Felix Schoeller jr Shanghai   (1)
Room 1111-1112 11F Pos Plaza No 1600
Century Avenue Pu Dong New Area,
Shanghai, 200122, China
Tel.: (86) 21 5820 5877
Web Site: http://www.felix-schoeller.com
Paper Mfr & Distr
N.A.I.C.S.: 322120

Schoeller India Industries Pvt.
Ltd.   (1)
Plot No E 141 Additional Patalganga MIDC
Village - Karade Khurd Taluka, Panvel, 410
206, Maharashtra, India
Tel.: (91) 2192674400
Web Site: http://www.felix-schoeller-
india.com
Specialty Paper Mfr
N.A.I.C.S.: 322120
Rajan Vaswani *(CEO & Mng Dir)*

Schoeller Technocell GmbH & Co.
KG   (1)
Katja Opitz, PO Box 3667, 49026, Osn-
abruck, Germany
Tel.: (49) 541 3800 0
Paper Mfr & Distr
N.A.I.C.S.: 322120

Technocell Dekor Shanghai   (1)
11F POS Plaza Room 1111-1112 1600 Century Avenue Pudong New Area, Shanghai,
200122, China
Tel.: (86) 21 5820 5877
Paper Mfr & Distr
N.A.I.C.S.: 322120

Technocell Dekor USA   (1)
179 County Rte 2A, Pulaski, NY 13142
Tel.: (315) 298-8300
Web Site: http://www.technocell.com
Emp.: 6
Paper Mfr & Distr
N.A.I.C.S.: 322120
Richard Paterson - Jones *(Pres)*

Technocell Inc.   (1)
3075 rue Bernier, Drummondville, J2C 6Y4,
QC, Canada
Tel.: (819) 475-0066
Paper Mfr
N.A.I.C.S.: 322120

Winbon Schoeller New Materials Co.,
Ltd.   (1)
No 38 Jinxing Road, Industrial Area
Longyou, Quzhou, 324400, Zhejiang, China
Tel.: (86) 5707669988
Emp.: 1,069
Specialty Paper Mfr
N.A.I.C.S.: 322120
Stefan Tubbesing *(Dir-Quality Sys)*

FELLAZO CORP.
T2-L8-3 Level 8 IOI City Tower Two,
Lebuh IRC IOI Resort City, 62502,
Putrajaya, 62502, Malaysia
Tel.: (60) 179989889   NV
Web Site: https://www.fellazo.com
Year Founded: 2014
FLLZ—(OTCIQ)
Rev.: $17,143
Assets: $4,233
Liabilities: $328,466
Net Worth: ($324,233)
Earnings: ($55,661)
Fiscal Year-end: 08/31/22

Commercial Printing Services
N.A.I.C.S.: 323113
Antheny Kit Chuan Yap *(Chm, Pres,
CEO, CFO, Treas & Sec)*

FELLAZO INC.
568 Jinshan West Road Jinshan
Building East Unit 1903, Yongkang,
321300, Zhejiang, China
Tel.: (86) 57989265975   Ky
Year Founded: 2018
FLLCU—(NASDAQ)
Emp.: 3
Investment Services
N.A.I.C.S.: 523999

FELLESKJOPET AGRI SA
PO Box 469, Sentrum, 0105, Oslo,
Norway
Tel.: (47) 2286 1000   NO
Web Site: http://www.felleskjopet.no
Year Founded: 1896
Agricultural Cooperative
N.A.I.C.S.: 813910
John Arne Ulvan *(CEO)*

Subsidiaries:

Granngarden AB   (1)
Vhttenvksver 47, 205 03, Malmo, Sweden
Tel.: (46) 771222444
Web Site: http://www.granngarden.se
Garden Supplies Distr
N.A.I.C.S.: 444240

FELLFAB LIMITED
2343 Barton St E, Hamilton, L8E
5V8, ON, Canada
Tel.: (905) 560-9230
Web Site: http://www.fellfab.com
Year Founded: 1952
Sales Range: $10-24.9 Million
Emp.: 130
Textile Products Mfr
N.A.I.C.S.: 313310

Subsidiaries:

FELLFAB Corporation   (1)
200 Tradeport Dr Ste 100, Atlanta, GA
30354
Tel.: (404) 363-8905
Furniture Mfr
N.A.I.C.S.: 337127
Chris Potter *(Program Mgr)*

FEMTO TECHNOLOGIES INC.
2264 East 11th Avenue, Vancouver,
V5Z 1N6, BC, Canada
Tel.: (604) 833-6820   BC
Web Site: https://www.cannasoft-
crm.com
Year Founded: 2019
BCAN—(NASDAQ)
Rev.: $837,812
Assets: $37,227,793
Liabilities: $471,852
Net Worth: $36,755,941
Earnings: ($1,241,854)
Emp.: 8
Fiscal Year-end: 12/31/22
Software Development Services
N.A.I.C.S.: 541511
Yftah Ben Yaackov *(CEO)*

FEMTOBIOMED INC.
D-510 700 Pangyo-ro, Bundang-gu,
Seongnam, 13516, Gyeonggi-do, Ko-
rea (South)
Tel.: (82) 316288158
Web Site:
https://www.femtobiomed.com
Year Founded: 2011
327610—(KRS)
Antibiotic Drug Distr
N.A.I.C.S.: 424210

FENALU GESTAO DE INVESTI-

**MENTOS E PARTICIPACOES
SA**
Rua dos bem lembrados 141 Ma-
nique, 2645-471, Alcabideche, Portu-
gal
Tel.: (351) 214457830
Web Site: http://www.fenalugip.pt
Real Estate Rental Services
N.A.I.C.S.: 531110
Alain Luis Bonte *(Chm & CEO)*

FENBI LTD.
1-6/F Building 103 No 10 Courtyard
Jiuxianqiao North Road, Chaoyang
District, Beijing, China
Tel.: (86) 1057035160   Ky
Web Site: https://www.fenbi.com
Year Founded: 2020
2469—(HKG)
Rev.: $430,585,827
Assets: $250,270,986
Liabilities: $1,914,579,726
Net Worth: ($1,664,308,739)
Earnings: ($319,802,434)
Emp.: 7,440
Fiscal Year-end: 12/31/22
Educational Support Services
N.A.I.C.S.: 611710
Haiyan Sheng *(VP)*

FENBO HOLDINGS LIMITED
Unit J 19/F World Tech Centre 95
How Ming Street, Kwun Tong, Kow-
loon, China (Hong Kong)
Tel.: (852) 23433328   Ky
Web Site: https://www.fenbo.com
Year Founded: 1993
FEBO—(NASDAQ)
Rev.: $15,265,320
Assets: $10,191,840
Liabilities: $5,596,230
Net Worth: $4,595,610
Earnings: $1,103,258
Emp.: 4
Fiscal Year-end: 12/31/22
Holding Company
N.A.I.C.S.: 551112

FENDX TECHNOLOGIES, INC.
2010 Winston Park Drive 2nd Floor,
Oakville, L6H 5R7, ON, Canada   BC
Web Site: https://www.fendxtech.com
Year Founded: 2020
FNDX—(CNSX)
Software Development Services
N.A.I.C.S.: 541511
Andrea Mulder *(COO)*

**FENERBAHCE FUTBOL
ANONIM SIRKETI**
Fenerbahce Sukru Saracoglu Stad
Maraton Girisi, Kzltoprak Kadikoy,
Istanbul, Turkiye
Tel.: (90) 2165421907
Web Site:
https://www.fenerbahce.org
FENER—(IST)
Rev.: $61,064,176
Assets: $232,957,233
Liabilities: $260,559,269
Net Worth: ($27,602,036)
Earnings: $20,492,158
Fiscal Year-end: 06/30/23
Broadcasting Services
N.A.I.C.S.: 516210
Ali Yildirim Koc *(Chm)*

FENG CHING METAL CORP.
30F- 4 No 38 Xinguang Rd, Lingya
Dist, Kaohsiung, 802, Taiwan
Tel.: (886) 72693339
Web Site: https://www.fcm.com.tw
Year Founded: 1983
2061—(TPE)
Rev.: $28,993,184
Assets: $36,053,466

Feng Ching Metal Corp.—(Continued)

Liabilities: $20,476,409
Net Worth: $15,577,057
Earnings: ($2,281,868)
Fiscal Year-end: 12/31/22
Copper Wire Mfr & Distr
N.A.I.C.S.: 331420
Fu-Te Chen *(Chm & Pres)*

Subsidiaries:

Boluo Feng Ching Magnet Wire
Manufacturing Co., Ltd. **(1)**
Liucunxiaozu Road, Liucun Village Longhua
Town Boluo County, Huizhou, Guangdong,
China
Tel.: (86) 7526398421
Magnet Wire Mfr & Distr
N.A.I.C.S.: 331318

FENG HSIN STEEL CO., LTD.
No 998 Sec 1 Jiahou Rd, Houli Dist,
Taichung, 421, Taiwan
Tel.: (886) 425565101
Web Site:
  https://www.fenghsin.com.tw
Year Founded: 1969
2015—(TAI)
Rev.: $1,140,718,195
Assets: $884,507,112
Liabilities: $167,373,910
Net Worth: $717,133,202
Earnings: $77,683,734
Emp.: 970
Fiscal Year-end: 12/31/23
Iron & Steel Product Mfr
N.A.I.C.S.: 331110

FENG TAY ENTERPRISES CO., LTD.
No 52 Kegong 8th Rd, Douliu, 640,
Yunlin, Taiwan
Tel.: (886) 55379100
Web Site: https://www.fengtay.com
9910—(TAI)
Rev.: $2,804,776,505
Assets: $1,656,264,792
Liabilities: $836,917,199
Net Worth: $819,347,593
Earnings: $178,094,012
Emp.: 136,169
Fiscal Year-end: 12/31/23
Athletic Shoe Mfr
N.A.I.C.S.: 316210
Richard Chien-Hung Wang *(Chm)*

Subsidiaries:

Great Eastern Industries Limited **(1)**
Unit No3 on 10th Floor Century Centre Nos
44-46 Hung To Road, Kowloon, China
(Hong Kong)
Tel.: (852) 26159188
Web Site: https://www.greatchinaind.com
Packaging Product Mfr & Distr
N.A.I.C.S.: 333993

P.T. Feng Tay Indonesia
Enterprises **(1)**
Jl Raya Banjaran Km 14 6, Bandung,
40376, West Java, Indonesia
Tel.: (62) 225940688
Sport Shoe Mfr
N.A.I.C.S.: 316210

FENGATE CAPITAL MANAGEMENT LTD.
499 King Street East, Hamilton, L8N
1E1, ON, Canada
Tel.: (905) 524-2985
Web Site:
  http://www.fengatecapital.com
Year Founded: 1974
Rev.: $10,781,174
Emp.: 100
Property Management Services
N.A.I.C.S.: 531311
Marco Di Carlantonio *(Mng Partner)*

FENGRAIN LTD.

Hook Lane, Wimblington, PE15 0QN,
Cambs, United Kingdom
Tel.: (44) 1354740691 UK
Web Site: http://www.fengrain.co.uk
Sales Range: $125-149.9 Million
Emp.: 30
Crop Testing Services
N.A.I.C.S.: 541380
Paul Wilkinson *(Chm)*

FENGXING CO., LTD.
Fengxing Hill, Ningguo, 242300, Anhui, China
Tel.: (86) 5634150397
Web Site: https://www.fengxing.com
Year Founded: 1997
002760—(SSE)
Rev.: $114,583,248
Assets: $249,158,052
Liabilities: $110,514,456
Net Worth: $138,643,596
Earnings: $8,780,616
Fiscal Year-end: 12/31/22
Industrial Machinery Mfr
N.A.I.C.S.: 333248

FENIE BROSSETTE
Sidi Hajjaj Oued Hassar, Casablanca,
Mediouna, Morocco
Tel.: (212) 529022869
Web Site:
  https://www.feniebrossette.ma
FBR—(CAS)
Sales Range: Less than $1 Million
Professional Equipment Distr
N.A.I.C.S.: 423490
Tarafa Marouane *(Chm & Mng Dir)*

FENIX ENTERTAINMENT S.P.A.
Piazzale delle Belle Arti 6, 00196,
Rome, Italy
Tel.: (39) 0677610950
Web Site: https://www.fenixent.com
Year Founded: 2016
FNX—(EUR)
Entertainment Broadcasting Services
N.A.I.C.S.: 516120
Andrea Musso *(CEO)*

FENIX OUTDOOR INTERNATIONAL AG
Weidstrasse 1a, 6300, Baar, Zug,
Switzerland
Tel.: (41) 660266200
Web Site:
  https://www.fenixoutdoor.com
FOI.B—(OMX)
Rev.: $828,086,985
Assets: $820,402,914
Liabilities: $359,846,561
Net Worth: $460,556,353
Earnings: $35,290,871
Emp.: 2,972
Fiscal Year-end: 12/31/23
Clothing Apparel Mfr & Distr
N.A.I.C.S.: 315990
Thomas Lindberg *(CFO)*

Subsidiaries:

Bus Sport AG **(1)**
Schingasse 4A, 9470, Buchs, Switzerland
Tel.: (41) 817500330
Web Site: https://www.bussport.ch
Sporting Goods Distr
N.A.I.C.S.: 459110

Fenix Outdoor AB **(1)**
Tel.: (46) 660266200
Clothing Retailer
N.A.I.C.S.: 458110

Fenix Outdoor Austria Italy
GmbH **(1)**
Valiergasse 60 / Top 0-05, 6020, Innsbruck,
Austria
Tel.: (43) 512793418
Clothing Retailer
N.A.I.C.S.: 458110
Gerhard Liebl *(Mgr-Country)*

Fenix Outdoor Danmark ApS **(1)**
Norddigesvej 4, 8240, Risskov, Denmark
Tel.: (45) 86202075
Clothing Retailer
N.A.I.C.S.: 458110
Kasper Holmboe *(Mgr-Country)*

Fenix Outdoor Finland Oy **(1)**
Mikkolantie 1 A, 00640, Helsinki, Finland
Tel.: (358) 98771133
Clothing Retailer
N.A.I.C.S.: 458110
Jouni Rajala *(Mgr-Country)*

Fenix Outdoor Logistics B.V. **(1)**
Koningsbeltsweg 12, 1329 AG, Almere,
Netherlands
Tel.: (31) 365359401
Web Site: https://fenixoutdoorlogistics.com
Emp.: 125
Clothing Retailer
N.A.I.C.S.: 458110

Subsidiary (Non-US):

Fenix Outdoor Logistics GmbH **(2)**
Am Alten Flugplatz 5, 19288, Ludwigslust,
Germany
Tel.: (49) 38746200100
Web Site:
  https://www.fenixoutdoorlogistics.de
Emp.: 125
Clothing Retailer
N.A.I.C.S.: 458110

Fenix Outdoor Norge A/S **(1)**
Storgata 56, 2609, Lillehammer, Norway
Tel.: (47) 61246900
Web Site: https://www.fjallraven.no
Clothing Retailer
N.A.I.C.S.: 458110

Fenix Outdoor s.r.o **(1)**
V Oblouku 226, 252 43, Pruhonice, Czech
Republic
Tel.: (420) 230234329
Clothing Retailer
N.A.I.C.S.: 458110

Fjallraven GmbH **(1)**
Wiesenfeldstrasse 7, 85256, Vierkirchen,
Germany
Tel.: (49) 813980230
Clothing Retailer
N.A.I.C.S.: 458110

Fjallraven International AB **(1)**
Tel.: (46) 660266200
Clothing Retailer
N.A.I.C.S.: 458110

Fjallraven USA LLC **(1)**
1795 Dogwood St Ste400, Louisville, CO
80027
Clothing Retailer
N.A.I.C.S.: 458110

Friluftsland A/S **(1)**
Frederiksborggade 52 2 sal, 1360, Copenhagen, Denmark
Tel.: (45) 33145150
Web Site: https://www.friluftsland.dk
Sporting Goods Distr
N.A.I.C.S.: 459110

Naturkompaniet AB **(1)**
Tel.: (46) 8200342
Web Site: https://www.naturkompaniet.se
Clothing Retailer
N.A.I.C.S.: 458110

Subsidiary (Domestic):

Utebutiken I Umea AB **(2)**
Storgatan 38, Umea, Sweden
Tel.: (46) 90120220
Web Site: http://www.utebutiken.se
Clothing Retailer
N.A.I.C.S.: 458110

Partioaitta Oy **(1)**
Nuijamiestentie 5 C, 00400, Helsinki, Finland
Tel.: (358) 207760719
Web Site: https://www.partioaitta.fi
Sporting Goods Distr
N.A.I.C.S.: 459110
Nina Ehrnrooth *(CEO)*

RR Canada Inc. **(1)**
51 B Caldari Road Unit 10, Vaughan, L4K
4G3, ON, Canada

Tel.: (905) 761-0762
Web Site: https://www.rrcanadainc.com
Hydraulic Equipment Distr
N.A.I.C.S.: 423830

Royal Robbins, LLC **(1)**
675 Sutter St, San Francisco, CA 94102
Web Site: https://www.royalrobbins.com
Apparel Retailer
N.A.I.C.S.: 458110

Tierra Products AB **(1)**
PO Box 209, 891 25, Ornskoldsvik, Sweden
Tel.: (46) 660266200
Clothing Retailer
N.A.I.C.S.: 458110

FENIX RESOURCES LIMITED
Level 33 Mia Yellagonga Tower 3 1
Spring Street, Perth, 6000, WA, Australia
Tel.: (61) 862850456
Web Site:
  https://www.fenixresources.com.au
FEX—(ASX)
Rev.: $173,079,085
Assets: $178,135,217
Liabilities: $67,063,968
Net Worth: $111,071,249
Earnings: $22,460,616
Emp.: 114
Fiscal Year-end: 06/30/24
Iron, Copper, Lead, Zinc, Gold, Nickel
& Uranium Exploration & Mining Services
N.A.I.C.S.: 212210
Matthew Foy *(Sec)*

FENNIA GROUP
Kyllikinportti 2, Helsinki, 00017, Finland
Tel.: (358) 105031 FI
Web Site:
  http://www.vuosikertomus.fennia.fi
Non-life & Life Insurance & Asset
Management Services
N.A.I.C.S.: 524298
Alexander Schoschkoff *(Mng Dir)*

Subsidiaries:

Folksam Skadeforsakring AB **(1)**
Maraholmskajen 3, Helsinki, 00180,
Finland **(100%)**
Tel.: (358) 10808180
Fire Insurance Services
N.A.I.C.S.: 524113

FENOPLAST LIMITED
306 - 308 Chenoy Trade Centre
Parklane, Secunderabad, 500003,
Telangana, India
Tel.: (91) 4027840322
Web Site: http://www.fenoplast.com
Year Founded: 1975
Rev.: $26,702,844
Assets: $21,781,714
Liabilities: $17,154,727
Net Worth: $4,626,987
Earnings: $96,049
Emp.: 286
Fiscal Year-end: 03/31/19
PVC Leather Cloth Mfr
N.A.I.C.S.: 316990
V. B. V. R. Ratnaji *(CFO)*

FENPLAST
160 Industry Blvd, Candiac, J5R 1J3,
QC, Canada
Tel.: (514) 990-0012
Web Site: http://www.fenplast.com
Year Founded: 1989
Rev.: $13,038,400
Emp.: 300
Door & Window Mfr
N.A.I.C.S.: 332321
Jean Marchand *(Pres)*

FENWAL CONTROLS OF JAPAN,LTD.

1-5-10 Iidabashi, Chiyoda-Ku, Tokyo,
102-0072, Japan
Tel.: (81) 332373561
Web Site: https://www.fenwal.co.jp
Year Founded: 1961
0870—(TK3)
Rev.: $89,341,090
Assets: $135,241,750
Liabilities: $45,340,550
Net Worth: $89,901,200
Earnings: $2,729,650
Emp.: 255
Fiscal Year-end: 12/31/23
Medicinal Product Mfr
N.A.I.C.S.: 339112
Hitoshi Tahara *(Pres)*

FENWICK LTD.
39 Northumberland Street, Newcastle
upon Tyne, NE99 1AR, United King-
dom
Tel.: (44) 1912325100
Web Site: http://www.fenwick.co.uk
Year Founded: 1897
Sales Range: $550-599.9 Million
Emp.: 3,000
Departmental Store Operator
N.A.I.C.S.: 455110
Robbie Feather *(CEO)*

Subsidiaries:

Fenwick Ltd.   **(1)**
31-39 Northumberland Street, Newcastle,
NE99 1AR, Surrey, United Kingdom
Tel.: (44) 1912325100
Web Site: http://www.fenwick.co.uk
Sales Range: $200-249.9 Million
Emp.: 900
Departmental Store Operator
N.A.I.C.S.: 455110
David Quinn *(Mng Dir)*

**FEPA TEKSTIL SANAYI VE
PAZARLAMA A.S.**
Tesvikiye Bostan Sok Ayda Apt No 11
D 2, Nisantasi, 34365, Istanbul, Tur-
kiye
Tel.: (90) 2122594354   TR
Real Estate Development Services
N.A.I.C.S.: 531390

FEPER SA
8 Dimitrie Pompeiu Bd, 020337, Bu-
charest, Romania
Tel.: (40) 212420275
Web Site: https://www.feper.ro
Year Founded: 1975
FEP—(BUC)
Rev.: $16,662,480
Assets: $27,793,048
Liabilities: $2,201,424
Net Worth: $25,591,624
Earnings: ($140,070)
Emp.: 234
Fiscal Year-end: 12/31/23
Metal Equipment Mfr
N.A.I.C.S.: 332322
Paula Dumitrescu *(CFO)*

**FERATEL MEDIA TECHNOLO-
GIES AG**
Maria-Theresien-Strasse 8, 6020,
Innsbruck, Austria
Tel.: (43) 51272800   AT
Web Site: http://www.feratel.at
Year Founded: 1978
Sales Range: $25-49.9 Million
Emp.: 74
Tourism Information System Services
N.A.I.C.S.: 519290
Ferdinand Hager *(Member-Mgmt Bd
& Mgr)*

Subsidiaries:

Feratel Espana SL   **(1)**
Calle Muntaner numero 438 5 1, 08006,
Barcelona, Spain   **(100%)**

Tel.: (34) 620840321
Web Site: http://www.feratel.com
Tourism Information System Services
N.A.I.C.S.: 519290

Feratel Media Technologies B.V.   **(1)**
Aak 17, NL-9408, Assen,
Netherlands   **(100%)**
Tel.: (31) 16470775
Web Site: http://www.feratelbenelux.be
Tourism Information System Services
N.A.I.C.S.: 519290

Feratel Media Technologies
GmbH   **(1)**
Conradin-Kreutzer-Strasse 21, 88602, Mer-
zenich, Germany   **(100%)**
Tel.: (49) 757592100
Web Site: http://www.feratel.de
Tourism Information System Services
N.A.I.C.S.: 519290

Feratel Schweiz AG   **(1)**
Riedstrasse 1, 6343, Rotkreuz,
Switzerland   **(100%)**
Tel.: (41) 417995050
Web Site: http://www.feratel.com
Sales Range: $25-49.9 Million
Emp.: 9
Tourism Information Services
N.A.I.C.S.: 519290

Sitour Ceska republika s.r.o.   **(1)**
U Cikanky 158/2, 155 00, Prague, Czech
Republic
Tel.: (420) 257 219 900
Web Site: http://www.sitour.cz
Tourism Information Services
N.A.I.C.S.: 561591
Pavlina Jurdikova *(Mgr)*

Sitour Japan KK   **(1)**
Kioicho Hills 1F 3-32 Kioichi, Chiyoda-Ku,
Tokyo, 102-0094, Japan
Tel.: (81) 3 5210 5091
Web Site: http://www.sitour.jp
Tourism Information Services
N.A.I.C.S.: 561591

Sitour Marketing GmbH   **(1)**
Bundesstrasse 2b, 6063, Innsbruck, Austria
Tel.: (43) 512 24805 0
Web Site: http://www.sitour.at
Ski Advertising Services
N.A.I.C.S.: 541890
Peter Buglas *(Mgr-Sls)*

Sitour spol. s r.o.   **(1)**
T Vansovej 10, 974 01, Banska Bystrica,
Slovakia
Tel.: (421) 48 41 42 197
Web Site: http://www.sitoursk.sk
Advertising Services
N.A.I.C.S.: 541890

feratel development center
EOOD   **(1)**
Johan Ekzarh Str 7, 1421, Sofia, Bulgaria
Tel.: (359) 2 816 5831
Web Site: http://www.feratel.bg
Tourism Information Services
N.A.I.C.S.: 561591

sitour Italia S.r.l.   **(1)**
Via Dolomiti 26/28, 39040, Montagna, Italy
Tel.: (39) 0471 81 90 44
Web Site: http://www.sitour.it
Ski Advertising Services
N.A.I.C.S.: 541890

sitour USA   **(1)**
195 Hurley Ave, Kingston, NY 12401
Tel.: (845) 331-9000
Web Site: http://www.sitourusa.com
Advertising Services
N.A.I.C.S.: 541890
David Cutler *(CEO)*

FERAUD SARL
2 rue de Bassano, 75116, Paris,
France
Tel.: (33) 149524400   FR
Web Site: http://www.feraud.com
Clothing Designer & Mfr
N.A.I.C.S.: 458110
Elisabeth Baur *(Dir Gen)*

Subsidiaries:

Louis Feraud Inc.   **(1)**

570 7th Ave, New York, NY 10018
Tel.: (212) 840-8220
Rev.: $31,000,000
Emp.: 21
Designer Clothing Mfr
N.A.I.C.S.: 424350

FERAX CAPITAL AG
Hausener Weg 29, 60489, Frankfurt
am Main, Germany
Tel.: (49) 6978808806
Web Site: https://en.lodgyslife.com
Year Founded: 2020
Investment Management Service
N.A.I.C.S.: 525990
Sascha Magsamen *(CEO)*

FERD AS
Strandveien 50, PO Box 34, Lysaker,
1366, Norway
Tel.: (47) 67108000   NO
Web Site: http://www.ferd.no
Year Founded: 1778
Sales Range: $450-499.9 Million
Emp.: 2,375
Holding Company
N.A.I.C.S.: 551112
John Giverholt *(Co-CEO)*

Subsidiaries:

Aibel AS   **(1)**
Vestre Svanholmen 14, 4068, Stavanger,
Norway   **(50%)**
Tel.: (47) 85270000
Web Site: http://www.aibel.com
Sales Range: $1-4.9 Billion
Emp.: 1,500
Oil & Gas Production Facilities Support
Services
N.A.I.C.S.: 213112
Mads Andersen *(Pres & CEO)*

Elopak A/S   **(1)**
Industriveien 30, PO Box 24, 3431, Spikke-
stad, Norway   **(100%)**
Tel.: (47) 31271000
Web Site: http://www.elopak.com
Sales Range: Less than $1 Million
Emp.: 160
Mfr Food Packaging Systems
N.A.I.C.S.: 322219
Thomas Kormendi *(CEO-Global)*

Subsidiary (Non-US):

Elocoat b.v.   **(2)**
Osloweg 1, 4538 BM, Terneuzen, Nether-
lands
Tel.: (31) 115682000
Web Site: http://www.elopak.com
Sales Range: $25-49.9 Million
Emp.: 98
Packaging Solutions
N.A.I.C.S.: 561910
Erik Voet *(Dir-Coating)*

Elopak   **(2)**
Koubkova 13 228, Prague, 12000, Czech
Republic   **(100%)**
Tel.: (420) 222520666
Web Site: http://www.elopak.com
Sales Range: $25-49.9 Million
Emp.: 10
Packaging Solutions
N.A.I.C.S.: 561910
Josef Horky *(Mgr-Mktg)*

Elopak AB   **(2)**
Hogastensgatan 19, Helsingborg, 25005,
Sweden   **(50%)**
Tel.: (46) 424505300
Web Site: http://www.elopak.se
Sales Range: $10-24.9 Million
Emp.: 50
Packaging Solutions
N.A.I.C.S.: 561910

Elopak B.V.   **(2)**
Calle Severo Ochoa 3, 28232, Madrid,
Spain
Tel.: (34) 917104494
Packaging Solutions
N.A.I.C.S.: 561910

Elopak Denmark AS   **(2)**
Hovmarken 8, 8520, Lystrup, Denmark

Tel.: (45) 87435100
Web Site: http://www.elopak.com
Sales Range: $25-49.9 Million
Emp.: 200
Tobacco Manufacturing & Packaging Solu-
tions
N.A.I.C.S.: 312230
Henorak Jensen *(Mng Dir)*

Elopak France B.V.   **(2)**
27 29 Ave Rene Duguay Trouin, ZA De La
Grande Ile, F 78960, Voisins-le-Bretonneux,
France   **(100%)**
Tel.: (33) 130649200
Web Site: http://www.elopak.com
Sales Range: $25-49.9 Million
Emp.: 21
Packaging Solutions
N.A.I.C.S.: 561910

Elopak Ges.m.b.H   **(2)**
Johannroithner St 131, 4050, Traun,
Austria   **(100%)**
Tel.: (43) 7229794990
Web Site: http://www.elopak.com
Emp.: 20
Packaging Solutions
N.A.I.C.S.: 561910
Johammis Gaispiuer *(Gen Mgr)*

Elopak GmbH   **(2)**
Brunckstr 22, PO Box 1280, 67346, Speyer,
Germany   **(100%)**
Tel.: (49) 62326390
Web Site: http://www.elopak.com
Sales Range: $150-199.9 Million
Emp.: 220
Packaging Solution Services
N.A.I.C.S.: 561910
Thomas Hener *(Mgr)*

Elopak Hungary   **(2)**
Montevideo u 3/B, Budapest, 1037, Hun-
gary
Tel.: (36) 13467390
Web Site: http://www.elopak.com
Sales Range: $25-49.9 Million
Emp.: 6
Packaging Solutions
N.A.I.C.S.: 561910
Gabor Peszterícz *(Mgr)*

Elopak Ltd.   **(2)**
Unit 67 Broomhill Rd, Tallaght, Dublin, 24,
Ireland   **(100%)**
Tel.: (353) 14521111
Web Site: http://www.elopak.com
Sales Range: $25-49.9 Million
Emp.: 5
Packaging Solutions
N.A.I.C.S.: 561910

Elopak Malaysia Sdn Bhd   **(2)**
38-1 Jalan Tun Sambanthan 3, Kuala Lum-
pur, 50470, Malaysia   **(100%)**
Tel.: (60) 322747495
Web Site: http://www.elopak.com
Sales Range: $25-49.9 Million
Emp.: 10
Packaging Solutions
N.A.I.C.S.: 561910
Fione Foong *(Gen Mgr)*

Elopak Obeikan Ltd.   **(2)**
Second Indl City, PO Box 369, Riyadh,
11383, Central Region, Saudi
Arabia   **(49%)**
Tel.: (966) 14983392
Web Site: http://www.elopak.com
Sales Range: $10-24.9 Million
Packaging Solutions
N.A.I.C.S.: 561910

Elopak Oy   **(2)**
Pajalantie 21-23, 04400, Jarvenpaa, Fin-
land
Tel.: (358) 94155510
Web Site: http://www.elopak.fi
Sales Range: $25-49.9 Million
Emp.: 60
Packaging Solutions
N.A.I.C.S.: 561910

Elopak S.A.   **(2)**
Ul Dunska 3, 05 152, Czosnow,
Poland   **(100%)**
Tel.: (48) 227859000
Web Site: http://www.elopak.com
Sales Range: $10-24.9 Million
Emp.: 30
Packaging Solutions

Ferd AS—(Continued)

N.A.I.C.S.: 561910

Elopak S.p.A. (2)
Via Sirtori 13 B, Passirana Di Rho, 20017,
Milan, Italy
Tel.: (39) 029320831
Web Site: http://www.elopak.com
Sales Range: $25-49.9 Million
Emp.: 19
Packaging Solutions
N.A.I.C.S.: 561910

Elopak Systems AG (2)
Cherstrasse 4, 8152, Glattbrugg, Switzer-
land
Tel.: (41) 448096363
Web Site: http://www.elopak.com
Packaging Solutions
N.A.I.C.S.: 561910
Petter H. Haug (Gen Mgr)

Elopak UK Ltd. (2)
Rutherford Close, Meadway, Stevenage,
SG1 2PR, Herts, United Kingdom (100%)
Tel.: (44) 1438847400
Web Site: http://www.elopak.com
Sales Range: $25-49.9 Million
Emp.: 5
Packaging Solutions
N.A.I.C.S.: 561910

Elopak Ukraine (2)
12 Gorodetskogo Str Ste 30, 1001, Kiev,
Ukraine (100%)
Tel.: (380) 442302423
Web Site: http://www.elopak.com
Sales Range: $25-49.9 Million
Emp.: 10
Packaging Solutions
N.A.I.C.S.: 561910
Anya Yavorskaya (Mgr-Mktg)

Elopak b.v. (2)
Mr F J Haarmanweg 44, Terneuzen, 4538
AS, Netherlands (100%)
Tel.: (31) 115682000
Web Site: http://www.elopak.com
Sales Range: $75-99.9 Million
Packaging Solutions
N.A.I.C.S.: 561910
Reynard Dreesman (Plant Mgr)

Elopak b.v. (2)
Rua Fonte de Maio, 9, Edificio Espaco,
Piso 1-D, 2780-596, Paco d'Arcos, Portugal
Tel.: (351) 214409750
Web Site: http://www.elopak.com
Packaging Solutions
N.A.I.C.S.: 561910

Subsidiary (US):

Elopak, Inc. (2)
30000 S Hill Rd, New Hudson, MI 48165
Tel.: (248) 486-4600
Web Site: http://www.elopak.com
Sales Range: $50-74.9 Million
Sanitary Containers Mfr
N.A.I.C.S.: 322291

Subsidiary (Non-US):

Envases Elopak S.A. De C.V. (2)
Calz Lazaro Cardenas Y Valle Del Guadi-
ana, Parque Industrial Lagunero, Gomez
Palacio, 35078, Mexico (100%)
Tel.: (52) 8717500000
Web Site: http://www.elopak.com
Sales Range: $75-99.9 Million
Packaging Solutions
N.A.I.C.S.: 561910
Jesus Holguin (Gen Mgr)

Unifill S.p.A. (2)
Via Viazza 82, 41030, San Prospero, Italy
Tel.: (39) 053549041
Web Site: http://www.unfill.com
Tobacco Manufacturing & Packaging Solu-
tions
N.A.I.C.S.: 312230

ZAO Elopak (2)
Ul Usacheva 35 build 1, 119048, Moscow,
Russia
Tel.: (7) 4956265490
Web Site: http://www.elopak.com
Emp.: 25
Packaging Solutions & Tobacco Manufactur-
ing

N.A.I.C.S.: 561910

Elopak AS - Market Unit (1)
Industrieveien 30, PO Box 24, 3431, Spikke-
stad, Norway
Tel.: (47) 31271000
Financial Investment Services
N.A.I.C.S.: 523940

Elopak EQS GmbH (1)
Hanns-Martin-Schleyer-Strasse 17, 41199,
Monchengladbach, Germany
Tel.: (49) 216694570
Financial Investment Services
N.A.I.C.S.: 523940

Elopak Israel AS (1)
Italy building Euro Park, Yakum, Israel
Tel.: (972) 99524555
Financial Investment Services
N.A.I.C.S.: 523940
Ron Rotem (Mgr-Market)

**Elopak Production Services GmbH &
Co KG** (1)
Abtsbrede 129, 33098, Paderborn, Ger-
many
Tel.: (49) 5251205740
Web Site: http://www.elopak.com
Financial Investment Services
N.A.I.C.S.: 523940

Elopak South Africa (Pty) Ltd. (1)
Cnr Commando and Price Street Ext Indus-
tria West 2093, PO Box 6167, 2000, Johan-
nesburg, South Africa
Tel.: (27) 112495200
Financial Investment Services
N.A.I.C.S.: 523940

Elopak d.o.o. (1)
Batajniaki drum 23, Zemun, 11080, Bel-
grade, Serbia
Tel.: (381) 113160922
Financial Investment Services
N.A.I.C.S.: 523940
Ilija Djenic (Gen Mgr & Plant Mgr)

Ferd Investment Group (1)
Strandveien 50, PO Box 34, 1324, Lysaker,
Norway (100%)
Tel.: (47) 67108000
Web Site: http://www.ferd.com
Sales Range: $50-74.9 Million
Emp.: 42
Provider of Financial Investment Services
N.A.I.C.S.: 523940

Subsidiary (Domestic):

Ferd Eiendom (2)
Joh H Andersens Vei 5, PO Box 6086, Et-
terstad, Oslo, 6086, Norway (100%)
Tel.: (47) 22666400
Web Site: http://www.if.no
Sales Range: $50-74.9 Million
Emp.: 8
Provider of Financial Investment Services
N.A.I.C.S.: 523940

Ferd Invest (2)
Strandveien 50, PO Box 34, 1366, Lysaker,
Norway (100%)
Tel.: (47) 67108000
Web Site: http://www.ferd.no
Provider of Financial Investment Services
N.A.I.C.S.: 523940

Ferd Private Equity (2)
Strandveien 50, PO Box 34, 34, Lysaker,
Norway (100%)
Tel.: (47) 67108000
Web Site: http://www.ferd.no
Sales Range: $25-49.9 Million
Equity & Investment Services
N.A.I.C.S.: 523940
John Giverholt (CEO)

Subsidiary (Non-US):

Norse Crown Co. (M) Sdn Bhd (2)
26-5 & 26-6 Menara Permata Damans, 685
Jalan Damansara, 60000, Kuala Lumpur,
Malaysia (20%)
Tel.: (60) 3 7492 2377
Web Site: http://www.norse-crown.com.my
Sales Range: $1-9.9 Million
Emp.: 15
Financial Investment Services
N.A.I.C.S.: 523940
Kanagasingam Kulasingam (Mng Dir)

Ferd Seafoods (1)
Sct Cathrine vej 31, DK 9800, Hjorring,
Denmark (100%)
Tel.: (45) 98902000
Web Site: http://www.ferdseafood.dk
Sales Range: $150-199.9 Million
Emp.: 600
Mfr of Processed Fish Products
N.A.I.C.S.: 311710

Interwell AS (1)
Kvernevik Ring 177, Stavanger, 4048, Nor-
way
Tel.: (47) 400 04 399
Web Site: http://www.interwell.com
Financial Investment Services
N.A.I.C.S.: 523940

Subsidiary (Non-US):

Interwell Australia Pty Ltd (2)
58 Tulloch Way Canning Vale, Perth, 6155,
WA, Australia
Tel.: (61) 425830720
Financial Investment Services
N.A.I.C.S.: 523940

Interwell LLC (2)
Al-Roya Building Floor 2 Office 26, PO Box
2096, Al Qurum, 130, Muscat, Oman
Tel.: (968) 93201678
Financial Investment Services
N.A.I.C.S.: 523940

**Interwell Qatar Petroleum Technology
Co. W.L.L.** (2)
5th Floor Toyota Tower, PO Box 16069,
Doha, Qatar
Tel.: (974) 33549834
Financial Investment Services
N.A.I.C.S.: 523940

**Interwell Saudi Arabia Gas & Oil
Technologies L.L.C** (2)
PO Box 402, Al Khobar, Saudi Arabia
Tel.: (966) 555883656
Financial Investment Services
N.A.I.C.S.: 523940

Interwell UK Ltd (2)
2 Links Place, Aberdeen, AB11 5DY, United
Kingdom
Tel.: (44) 1224577200
Financial Investment Services
N.A.I.C.S.: 523940
Graham Masson (Mgr-Sls)

Subsidiary (US):

Interwell US LLC (2)
6832 Bourgeois Rd, Houston, TX 77066
Tel.: (832) 461-1500
Financial Investment Services
N.A.I.C.S.: 523940
Paul Yerby (Pres)

Mestergruppen AS (1)
Nils Hansens vei 2, Oslo, Norway
Tel.: (47) 23377500
Web Site: http://www.mestergruppen.no
Financial Investment Services
N.A.I.C.S.: 523940

Mintra Holding AS (1)
Inger Bang Lunds vei 16, 5059, Bergen,
Norway
Tel.: (47) 55986300
Web Site: https://www.mintra.com
Rev: $28,892,444
Assets: $122,722,873
Liabilities: $30,596,118
Net Worth: $92,126,755
Earnings: $6,336,267
Emp.: 130
Fiscal Year-end: 12/31/2022
Holding Company
N.A.I.C.S.: 551112
Gareth Gilbert (COO)

Subsidiary (Non-US):

Mintra Ltd. (2)
Offshore House Claymore Drive, Aberdeen,
AB23 8GD, United Kingdom
Tel.: (44) 1224651340
Online Education Services
N.A.I.C.S.: 611710

Subsidiary (Domestic):

Mintra Trainingportal AS (2)

Fjosangerveien 50D, 5059, Bergen, Norway
Tel.: (47) 55986300
Web Site:
https://www.mintratrainingportal.com
Online Education Services
N.A.I.C.S.: 611710

Subsidiary (Non-US):

Safebridge Cyprus Ltd. (2)
359 28th October Street World Trade Centre Floor 2 Office 217, 3107, Limassol, Cyprus
Tel.: (357) 25001490
Online Education Services
N.A.I.C.S.: 611710

Safebridge GmbH (2)
Raboisen 38, 20095, Hamburg, Germany
Tel.: (49) 4055565790
Web Site: https://www.safebridge.net
Online Education Services
N.A.I.C.S.: 611710

Norse Crown Co. (M) Sdn. Bhd. (1)
38 Jalan Tun Sambanthan 3, Brickfields,
50740, Kuala Lumpur, Malaysia (20%)
Tel.: (60) 322749077
Web Site: http://www.norse-crown.com.my
Sales Range: $25-49.9 Million
Emp.: 15
Provider of Electrosurgery & Laparoscopy
Services
N.A.I.C.S.: 339113

Overseas Commodex Corp. (1)
109 S Main St, Rocky Mount, NC 27801
Tel.: (252) 937-6044
Exports Tobacco
N.A.I.C.S.: 424590

Servi Cylinderservice AS (1)
Kvithyllveien 193, 7100, Rissa, Norway
Tel.: (47) 73850500
Financial Investment Services
N.A.I.C.S.: 523940
Per Johan Fenstad (Mgr-Pur)

Servi Group AS (1)
Rasmus Solbergs vei 1, PO Box 3230, Ski,
1400, Norway
Tel.: (47) 64979797
Web Site: http://www.servi.no
Sales Range: $125-149.9 Million
Emp.: 105
Pneumatic, Hydraulic & Mechanical Equip-
ment & Components Mfr
N.A.I.C.S.: 333995
Bjorn Arne Gundersen (CEO)

Servi Hydranor AS (1)
Midtunheia 20, 5224, Bergen, Norway
Tel.: (47) 55108220
Web Site: http://www.servi.no
Financial Investment Services
N.A.I.C.S.: 523940

Servi Ulsteinvik AS (1)
Brendehaugen 24, 6065, Ulsteinvik, Norway
Tel.: (47) 70318550
Financial Investment Services
N.A.I.C.S.: 523940

Swix Sport AS (1)
Servicebox, N 2626, Lillehammer,
Norway (100%)
Tel.: (47) 61222100
Web Site: http://www.swixsport.no
Sales Range: $25-49.9 Million
Emp.: 104
Mfr, Developer & Marketer of Sports & Rec-
reational Products
N.A.I.C.S.: 339920
Cecilie Torgunrud (Mgr-Mktg)

Subsidiary (Non-US):

Swix Sport Japan K.K. (2)
3-2-2 Kanda Ogawamachi, Chiyoda-ku, To-
kyo, 101 0052, Japan (70%)
Tel.: (81) 3 5282 3755
Web Site: http://www.swix.co.jp
Sales Range: $25-49.9 Million
Emp.: 10
Marketer of Sports & Recreational Products
N.A.I.C.S.: 423910

Holding (US):

Swix Sport USA Inc. (2)

60 Newark St, Haverhill, MA
01887-4491 **(100%)**
Tel.: (978) 657-4820
Web Site: http://www.swixsport.com
Sales Range: $10-24.9 Million
Emp.: 20
Develops Manufactures & Markets Sports &
Recreational Products
N.A.I.C.S.: 423910
Steve Poulin *(Pres)*

FERD CORP.
Via Amerigo Vespucci 19 Int 6,
30173, Venice, Italy
Tel.: (39) 0418520009 NV
Web Site: http://www.ferdcorp.com
Year Founded: 2016
Sales Range: Less than $1 Million
Emp.: 1
Artificial Fabric Flowers Mfr
N.A.I.C.S.: 339999
Leonid Skupchenko *(Pres, CEO,
CFO, Treas & Sec)*

FERDINAND GROSS GMBH &
CO. KG
Daimlerstrasse 8, 70771, Leinfelden-
Echterdingen, Germany
Tel.: (49) 71116040
Web Site: http://www.schrauben-
gross.com
Year Founded: 1864
Rev.: $85,104,975
Emp.: 230
Warehousing & Logistic Services
N.A.I.C.S.: 493110
Gerald Hering *(Co-Mng Dir)*

Subsidiaries:

Ferdinand Gross Czech, s.r.o. **(1)**
Ve Svahu 482/5, Podoli, 147 00, Prague,
Czech Republic
Tel.: (420) 236163666
Web Site: http://www.schrauben-gross.cz
Fastener Mfr
N.A.I.C.S.: 332722

Ferdinand Gross Hungary Kft. **(1)**
Szarkalab u 3, 2800, Tatabanya, Hungary
Tel.: (36) 14257523
Web Site: http://www.schrauben-gross.hu
Fastener Mfr
N.A.I.C.S.: 332722

Ferdinand Gross Polska Sp z
o.o. **(1)**
Ul Bierutowska 81 Bud A, 51-317, Wroclaw,
Poland
Tel.: (48) 713376660
Web Site: http://www.schrauben-gross.pl
Fastener Mfr
N.A.I.C.S.: 332722

Ferdinand Gross Romania
S.R.L. **(1)**
Calea Timisorii Nr 212/2, 310229, Arad,
Romania
Tel.: (40) 357435926
Web Site: http://www.schrauben-gross.ro
Fastener Mfr
N.A.I.C.S.: 332722

FERDINAND KREUTZER SA-
BAMUHLE GMBH
Burgbernheimer Str 11, 90431,
Nuremberg, Germany
Tel.: (49) 911324720
Web Site: http://www.sabamuehle.de
Year Founded: 1869
Rev.: $16,845,122
Emp.: 40
Food & Pharmaceutical Ingredients
Mfr
N.A.I.C.S.: 311942
Brigitte Kranzle *(Co-Mng Dir)*

FERDINAND LUSCH GMBH &
CO. KG
Im Brocke 11, D-33649, Bielefeld,
Germany
Tel.: (49) 52194170

Web Site: http://www.ferdinand-
lusch.de
Year Founded: 1945
Rev.: $18,127,200
Emp.: 132
Furniture Mfr
N.A.I.C.S.: 337121
Katharina Lusch *(Co-Mng Dir)*

FERFINA S.P.A.
Via Salaria n 1039, 00138, Rome,
Italy
Tel.: (39) 06883341 IT
Sales Range: $800-899.9 Million
Emp.: 4,000
Holding Company
N.A.I.C.S.: 551112

Subsidiaries:

Societe Italiana per Condotte d'Acqua
S.p.A. **(1)**
Via Salaria 1039, 00138, Rome, Italy
Tel.: (39) 06883341
Web Site: http://www.condotte.com
Water Supply Services
N.A.I.C.S.: 221310
Dutio Astaldi *(Pres)*

Subsidiary (US):

Condotte America Inc. **(2)**
10790 NW 127th St, Medley, FL 33178
Tel.: (305) 670-7585
Web Site: http://www.condotteamerica.com
Sales Range: $25-49.9 Million
Emp.: 50
Provider of Bridge Construction Services
N.A.I.C.S.: 237310
Andres G. Mendoza *(Pres)*

FERGO AISA, S.A.
Muntaner 340 Pral, 08021, Barce-
lona, Spain
Tel.: (34) 93 2419197
Web Site: http://www.fergoaisa.com
Sales Range: $25-49.9 Million
Real Estate Services; Property Devel-
oper & Manager
N.A.I.C.S.: 531390
Carlos Fernandez Gomez *(Pres &
CEO)*

FERGUSON PLC
1020 Eskdale Road, Winnersh Tri-
angle, Wokingham, RG41 5TS,
Berks, United Kingdom
Tel.: (44) 1189273800 JE
Web Site:
https://www.corporate.ferguson.com
Year Founded: 1986
FERG—(NYSE)
Rev.: $29,734,000,000
Assets: $15,994,000,000
Liabilities: $10,957,000,000
Net Worth: $5,037,000,000
Earnings: $1,889,000,000
Emp.: 35,000
Fiscal Year-end: 07/31/23
Holding Company; Heating & Plumb-
ing Supplies, Materials & Services
N.A.I.C.S.: 551112
Kevin M. Murphy *(CEO)*

Subsidiaries:

AMRE Supply Canada Inc. **(1)**
3780 98 Street, Edmonton, T6E 6B4, AB,
Canada
Web Site: https://www.amresupply.com
Household Appliance Distr
N.A.I.C.S.: 423620

Airefco Inc. **(1)**
18755 SW Teton Ave, Tualatin, OR 97062-
8848
Tel.: (503) 692-3210
Web Site: https://www.airefco.com
Sales Range: $10-24.9 Million
Emp.: 200
Warm Air Heating & Air Conditioning Con-
tractors
N.A.I.C.S.: 423730

J. K. Hussa *(Pres & CEO)*

Andrews Lighting & Hardware
Gallery **(1)**
3244 NW 23rd St, Oklahoma City, OK
73107 **(100%)**
Tel.: (405) 943-5785
Web Site: http://www.andrewslighting.com
Sales Range: $1-9.9 Million
Emp.: 20
Retails & Wholesales Light Fixtures
N.A.I.C.S.: 449129

Bruce Supply Corp. **(1)**
8805 18th Ave, Brooklyn, NY 11214-4601
Tel.: (718) 259-4900
Web Site:
http://www.brucesupplyplumbing.com
Sales Range: $1-4.9 Billion
Emp.: 750,000
Plumbing Fixtures, Equipment & Supplies
N.A.I.C.S.: 423720
Sanjiv Patel *(CEO)*

Cal-Steam, Inc. **(1)**
1595 Crocker Ave, Hayward, CA 94544
Tel.: (510) 512-7700
Web Site: https://www.calsteam.com
Sales Range: $150-199.9 Million
Emp.: 75
Plumbing Fixtures, Equipment & Supplies
Distr
N.A.I.C.S.: 423720
Jim Bresnahan *(Pres)*

Comptoir des Fers et Metaux SA
(CFM) **(1)**
5 Rue G Kroll, 2204, Luxembourg,
Luxembourg **(100%)**
Tel.: (352) 4995206
Web Site: http://www.cfm.lu
Rev.: $64,580,064
Emp.: 110
Distr of Plumbing & Heating Supplies
N.A.I.C.S.: 423720

Continental Product Engineering
Limited **(1)**
Prospect House Little Money Road Loddon
Business Park, Loddon, Norwich, NR14
6JD, Norfolk, United Kingdom
Tel.: (44) 1508522400
Web Site: http://www.continental-uk.com
Natural Gas Producer
N.A.I.C.S.: 221210

Ferguson Enterprises, LLC **(1)**
751 Lakefront Commons, Newport News,
VA 23606
Tel.: (757) 874-7795
Sales Range: $1-4.9 Billion
Emp.: 17,500
Industrial Plumbing & Heating Supplies &
Equipment Whslr
N.A.I.C.S.: 423720
Kevin M. Murphy *(Grp CEO)*

Subsidiary (Domestic):

Bruce-Rogers Company **(2)**
601 Wheeler Ave, Fort Smith, AR 72901-
4421
Tel.: (479) 782-7901
Web Site: http://www.brcco.com
Warm Air Heating & Air-Conditioning Equip-
ment Supplies Merchant Whslr
N.A.I.C.S.: 423730

Subsidiary (Non-US):

Davidson Pipe Company Inc. **(2)**
Tel.: (718) 439-6300
Web Site: http://www.davidsonpipe.com
Sales Range: $125-149.9 Million
Emp.: 200
Industrial Supplies
N.A.I.C.S.: 551112

Subsidiary (Non-US):

Davidson Pipe Supply Co. Inc. **(3)**
Tel.: (718) 439-6300
Web Site: http://www.davidsonpipe.com
Sales Range: $50-74.9 Million
Emp.: 80
Mfr & Service of Metal Products
N.A.I.C.S.: 551112

Monotube Pile Corporation **(3)**
Tel.: (330) 454-6111
Web Site: http://www.monotube.com

Sales Range: $25-49.9 Million
Steel Pole Mfr
N.A.I.C.S.: 331110

Subsidiary (Domestic):

Energy & Process Corp. **(2)**
2146 B Flintstone Dr, Tucker, GA 30084-
5008
Sales Range: $25-49.9 Million
Emp.: 40
Whslr of Pipe Valves & Fittings
N.A.I.C.S.: 423840
Mark Capallo *(Chm)*

Branch (Domestic):

Ferguson Enterprises **(2)**
1095 S Rock Blvd, Reno, NV 89502
Tel.: (775) 353-3800
Web Site: https://www.ferguson.com
Sales Range: $25-49.9 Million
Emp.: 40
Plumbing Fittings & Supplies Distr
N.A.I.C.S.: 423720

Subsidiary (Domestic):

Ferguson Enterprises Midwest,
Inc. **(2)**
2055 S State St, Ann Arbor, MI 48104
Tel.: (734) 663-9335
Web Site: http://www.ferguson.com
Sales Range: $50-74.9 Million
Emp.: 150
Holding Company; Plumbing Fixtures,
Equipment & Supply Services
N.A.I.C.S.: 551112

Branch (Domestic):

Ferguson Enterprises, Inc. **(2)**
2121 N Columbia Blvd, Portland, OR 97217
Tel.: (503) 283-3333
Web Site: https://www.ferguson.com
Sales Range: $550-599.9 Million
Emp.: 1,600
Distribution of Plumbing & Heating Supplies
& Equipment
N.A.I.C.S.: 423720

Ferguson Enterprises, Inc. **(2)**
3688 W Orange Grove Rd, Tucson, AZ
85741 **(51%)**
Tel.: (520) 575-7350
Web Site: http://www.ferguson.com
Emp.: 50
Distr of Plumbing Accessories
N.A.I.C.S.: 423720

Ferguson Enterprises, Inc. **(2)**
4100 W Marginal Way SW, Seattle, WA
98106
Tel.: (206) 767-7700
Web Site: http://www.ferguson.com
Rev.: $52,000,000
Emp.: 112
Valves & Fittings Sales
N.A.I.C.S.: 423830

Ferguson Enterprises, Inc. **(2)**
884 S Rohlwing Rd, Addison, IL 60101
Tel.: (630) 495-2620
Web Site: http://www.ferguson.com
Sales Range: $75-99.9 Million
Emp.: 200
Plumbing & Hydronic Heating Supplies
N.A.I.C.S.: 423720
Bill Brundage *(CFO)*

Subsidiary (Domestic):

Ferguson Fire & Fabrication, Inc. **(2)**
2750 S Towne Ave, Pomona, CA 91766
Tel.: (909) 517-3085
Web Site: http://www.fergusonfire.com
Emp.: 50
Fire Protection Systems Distr & Pipe Fabri-
cation Services
N.A.I.C.S.: 332996

Ferguson Heating & Cooling **(2)**
8220 Ferguson Ave, Sacramento, CA 95828
Tel.: (916) 210-7993
Web Site: http://www.ferguson.com
Sales Range: $50-74.9 Million
Emp.: 15
Warm Air Heating & Air Conditioning
N.A.I.C.S.: 423730

Ferguson plc—(Continued)

Ferguson Lyon Conklin & Company Inc. (2)
7030 Troy Hills Dr Ste 700, Elkridge, MD 21075
Tel.: (757) 874-7795
Web Site: http://www.ferguson.com
Sales Range: $75-99.9 Million
Emp.: 130
Whslr of Sheet Metal, Roofing, Heating & Air Conditioning Supplies
N.A.I.C.S.: 423730

Ferguson Valves & Automation Co. (2)
4120 NE Columbia Blvd, Portland, OR 97211
Tel.: (503) 287-8383
Web Site: http://www.fnwvalve.com
Sales Range: $25-49.9 Million
Emp.: 25
Mfr of Valves
N.A.I.C.S.: 444180

Ferguson Waterworks (2)
8008 E Sligh Ave, Tampa, FL 33610-9513 (100%)
Tel.: (813) 627-1240
Sales Range: $25-49.9 Million
Emp.: 20
Holding Company
N.A.I.C.S.: 423720

Subsidiary (Domestic):

Louisiana Utilities Supply Company (3)
2056 Sorrel Ave, Baton Rouge, LA 70802
Tel.: (225) 383-8916
Web Site: http://www.ferguson.com
Sales Range: $50-74.9 Million
Emp.: 25
Wholesale Municipal Water Works Supplies
N.A.I.C.S.: 423510

Subsidiary (Domestic):

Ferguson Waterworks (2)
3726 Bishop Ln, Louisville, KY 40218-2904
Tel.: (502) 459-9974
Sales Range: $25-49.9 Million
Emp.: 20
Distr of Water Works Products
N.A.I.C.S.: 423720

Ferguson Waterworks (2)
11909 Tech Center Ct, Poway, CA 92064
Tel.: (858) 391-3700
Web Site: http://www.ferguson.com
Sales Range: $25-49.9 Million
Emp.: 40
Valves & Fittings Supplier
N.A.I.C.S.: 423720

Grand Junction Concrete Pipe Co. (2)
2868 I-70 Business Loop, Grand Junction, CO 81501
Tel.: (970) 243-4604
Web Site: http://www.gjpipe.com
Concrete Pipe & Other Products Mfr
N.A.I.C.S.: 327332
Lane Bybee (Pres)

Lincoln Products (2)
18825 E San Jose Ave, Industry, CA 91748 (100%)
Tel.: (626) 964-2395
Distr of Plumbing Products
N.A.I.C.S.: 423720
Mike Aucoin (Pres)

Matera Paper Company, Inc. (2)
835 N W W White Rd, San Antonio, TX 78219
Industrial & Personal Service Paper
N.A.I.C.S.: 424130
Brice Cheek (Acct Mgr)

Plumbing Specialties & Supplies, Inc. (2)
925 Kokea St, Honolulu, HI 96817-4528 (100%)
Tel.: (808) 832-7474
Web Site: http://www.bestplumbingonline.com
Sales Range: $25-49.9 Million
Emp.: 35
Distr of Plumbing Supplies

Heatmerchants (1)
Unit 2 Moydrum Road, Co Westmeath, Athlone, N37 K5W4, Ireland (100%)
Tel.: (353) 90 649 1056
Web Site: https://www.heatmerchants.ie
Sales Range: $150-199.9 Million
Emp.: 420
Plumbing & Heating Supplies
N.A.I.C.S.: 423720

James Electric Motor Services Ltd. (1)
4020-8th Street SE, Calgary, T2G 3A7, AB, Canada
Tel.: (403) 252-5477
Web Site: https://www.jameselectric.ca
Emp.: 55
Pump & Motor Repair Services
N.A.I.C.S.: 811310

James Martin Signature Vanities, LLC (1)
3575 Moreau Ct Ste 220, South Bend, IN 46628
Tel.: (512) 795-4171
Web Site: https://jamesmartinfurniture.com
N.A.I.C.S.: 337121

Kennedy Culvert & Supply Company (1)
8000 Midlantic Dr Ste 200N, Mount Laurel, NJ 08054
Tel.: (856) 813-5000
Sales Range: $50-74.9 Million
Emp.: 150
Water, Storm, Sanitary Sewer & Erosion Control Products Distr
N.A.I.C.S.: 423990
James Lynn (Controller)

Lawrence Plumbing Supply Co. (1)
31 SW 57th Ave, Miami, FL 33144
Tel.: (305) 266-1571
Web Site: http://www.lpsco.com
Sales Range: $50-74.9 Million
Emp.: 4
Plumbing & Hydronic Heating Supplies
N.A.I.C.S.: 423720

Manzardo SpA (1)
via G di Vittorio 1B, 39100, Bolzano, Italy
Tel.: (39) 0471567511
Web Site: http://www.manzardo.it
Plumbing & Heating Supplies
N.A.I.C.S.: 423720

Old Dominion Supply, Inc. (1)
6945 San Tomas Rd Ste I-Q, Elkridge, MD 21075
Tel.: (410) 796-1284
Web Site: http://www.olddominionsupply.com
Metals Service Center
N.A.I.C.S.: 423510
William Vermillion (Pres)

Power Equipment Direct Inc. (1)
969 Veterans Pkwy Ste C, Bolingbrook, IL 60490
Web Site: https://www.powerequipmentdirect.com
N.A.I.C.S.: 423610

S.G. Torrice Co., Inc. (1)
80 Industrial Way, Wilmington, MA 01887
Tel.: (978) 657-7779
Web Site: http://www.sgtorrice.com
Sales Range: $10-24.9 Million
Emp.: 44
Warm Air Heating & Air Conditioning
N.A.I.C.S.: 423730
Stephen Torrice (Pres)

S.W. Anderson Sales Corp. (1)
63 Daniel St, Farmingdale, NY 11735
Tel.: (631) 293-4000
Web Site: http://www.swanderson.com
Warm Air Heating & Air Conditioning
N.A.I.C.S.: 423730

Safe Step Walk In Tub, LLC (1)
520 Royal Pkwy Ste 100, Nashville, TN 37214
Web Site: http://www.safesteptub.com
Bath Tub Retailer
N.A.I.C.S.: 449129

The Plumbing Source, Inc. (1)
840 Moowaa St, Honolulu, HI 96817

Tel.: (808) 845-3881
Web Site: http://www.ferguson.com
Plumbing & Heating Equipment & Supplies (Hydronics) Merchant Whslr
N.A.I.C.S.: 423720

Thomson Brothers Limited (1)
Mylord Crescent Camperdown Industrial Estate, Killingworth, Newcastle upon Tyne, NE125UJ, United Kingdom
Tel.: (44) 1912160397
Plumbing & Heating Equipment Distr
N.A.I.C.S.: 423720
Douglas Neill (Mng Dir)

Wasco Groothandelsgroep Central Verwarming BV (1)
Leigraaf 54 Twello, 7391 AL, Zwolle, Netherlands (100%)
Tel.: (31) 571279777
Web Site: http://www.wasco.nl
Sales Range: $150-199.9 Million
Emp.: 500
Distr of Heating Equipment & Supplies
N.A.I.C.S.: 423720

William Wilson Ltd. (1)
5-7 Wardpark Place Wardpark South, Cumbernauld, G67 3XH, Dunbartonshire, United Kingdom
Tel.: (44) 8000213038
Web Site: https://www.williamwilson.co.uk
N.A.I.C.S.: 423390

Wolseley (Schweiz) AG (1)
Tobler Haustechnik Ag, 8902, Urdorf, Switzerland
Tel.: (41) 0447355000
Web Site: http://www.haustechnikdk.ch
Sales Range: $250-299.9 Million
Emp.: 720
Plumbing & Heating Equipment & Supplies (Hydronics) Merchant Wholesalers
N.A.I.C.S.: 423720

Wolseley Austria AG (1)
Hugo Mischek Strase 6, 1110, Vienna, Austria
Tel.: (43) 01760600
Plumbing & Heating Equipment & Supplies (Hydronics) Merchant Wholesalers
N.A.I.C.S.: 423720

Wolseley Canada Inc. (1)
880 Laurentian Drive, Burlington, L7N 3V6, ON, Canada
Tel.: (905) 335-7373
Web Site: https://www.wolseleyinc.ca
Sales Range: $25-49.9 Million
Emp.: 15
Plumbing & Heating Equipment & Supplies (Hydronics) Merchant Wholesalers
N.A.I.C.S.: 332913

Wolseley Central and Eastern Europe AG (1)
Dammstrasse 19, Zug, 6300, Switzerland
Tel.: (41) 417232230
Building Materials Distr
N.A.I.C.S.: 423390

Wolseley France SAS (1)
Immeuble Le Jean Monnet 11 Place des Vosges, La Defense, 92400, Courbevoie, France
Tel.: (33) 141925087
Sanitaryware Distr
N.A.I.C.S.: 423720

Wolseley HVAC R Group (1)
4075 Industrial Blvd, Laval, H7 L6E3, QC, Canada (100%)
Tel.: (450) 628-5777
Web Site: http://www.wolseley.com
Sales Range: $25-49.9 Million
Emp.: 100
Refrigeration, Heating, Cooling & Ventilation
N.A.I.C.S.: 333415

Wolseley Holdings Canada Inc. (1)
880 Laurentian Drive, Burlington, L7N 3V6, ON, Canada
Tel.: (905) 335-7373
Web Site: http://www.wolseleyinc.ca
Sales Range: $75-99.9 Million
Emp.: 200
Offices of Bank Holding Companies
N.A.I.C.S.: 551111

Wolseley Holdings Denmark A/S (1)

Gladsaxe Mollevej 5, 2860, Soborg, Denmark
Tel.: (45) 39559700
Web Site: http://www.dtgroup.dk
Sales Range: $50-74.9 Million
Emp.: 4
Investment Management Service
N.A.I.C.S.: 523999

Subsidiary (Domestic):

Electro-Oil International A/S (2)
Gl Landevej 2, 2600, Glostrup, Denmark (100%)
Tel.: (45) 43441800
Web Site: https://electro-energy.dk
Sales Range: $25-49.9 Million
Emp.: 25
Supplier of Oil-Fired Heating Equipment
N.A.I.C.S.: 423720

Wolseley Industrial Products Group Inc (1)
3 Kerr Crescent, Guelph, N1H 6H9, ON, Canada
Tel.: (519) 885-6500
Sales Range: $50-74.9 Million
Emp.: 5
Plumbing & Heating Equipment & Supplies (Hydronics) Merchant Wholesalers
N.A.I.C.S.: 423720

Wolseley Overseas Ltd. (1)
Po Box 18, Droitwich, United Kingdom
Tel.: (44) 1905794444
Offices of Other Holding Companies
N.A.I.C.S.: 551112

Wolseley UK Ltd. (1)
Boroughbridge Rd, PO Box 21, Ripon, HG4 1SL, North Yorkshire, United Kingdom
Tel.: (44) 1765690690
Web Site: https://www.wolseley.co.uk
Sales Range: $1-4.9 Billion
Emp.: 400
Plumbing & Heating Supplies
N.A.I.C.S.: 423720

FERIA DE OSORNO S.A.
Cochrane 460, Osorno, Chile
Tel.: (56) 642269100
Web Site: https://www.fossa.cl
Year Founded: 1945
FERIAOSOR—(SGO)
Sales Range: Less than $1 Million
Meat Product Distr
N.A.I.C.S.: 311613
Maria Gracia Cariola Cubillos (Chm & Pres)

FERING D.D.
Zlatnih Ljiljana 24, 75320, Gracanica, Bosnia & Herzegovina
Tel.: (387) 35 704 950
Web Site: http://www.fering.com.ba
Year Founded: 1955
Sales Range: Less than $1 Million
Emp.: 117
Crane Mfr
N.A.I.C.S.: 333923
Tuholjak Nihad (Gen Dir)

FERMAT GROUP, A.S.
Prumyslova 11, 102 00, Prague, Czech Republic
Tel.: (420) 277 009 603
Web Site: http://www.fermatmachinery.com
Year Founded: 1990
Emp.: 530
Industrial Machinery Mfr
N.A.I.C.S.: 333517
Jan Ferenc (Co-Owner)

Subsidiaries:

FERMAT CZ. s.r.o. (1)
Rm 602 Summit Center 1088 West Yan an Road, Shanghai, 200052, China
Tel.: (86) 2162101163
Machine Tools Mfr
N.A.I.C.S.: 333517
Jiri Ferenc (Mgr-Sls)

FERMAT Machinery Pvt. Ltd. (1)

No 487 J T Plaza 2nd Floor 1st A Cross Road K H B Colony 5th Block, Koramangala, Bengaluru, 560095, Karnataka, India
Tel.: (91) 8041668329
Machine Tools Mfr
N.A.I.C.S.: 333517
Sonia Nautiyal *(Mgr-Fin, HR & Admin)*

HMB, spol. s r.o. (1)
Chabarovska 19, 460 06, Liberec, Czech Republic
Tel.: (420) 482360460
Web Site: http://www.hmb.cz
Machine Tools Mfr
N.A.I.C.S.: 333517
Antonin Kropacek *(CEO)*

Lucas Precision LLC (1)
13020 Saint Clair Ave, Cleveland, OH 44108
Tel.: (216) 451-5588
Web Site: http://www.lucasprecision.com
Sales Range: $1-9.9 Million
Emp.: 25
Industrial Equipment Distribution, Repair & Maintenance Services
N.A.I.C.S.: 811310
Paul Mandelbaum *(CEO)*

PRESSL, spol. s r.o. (1)
Madlonova 21, Rokycany, 337 01, Czech Republic
Tel.: (420) 371740611
Web Site: http://www.pressl.cz
Machine Tools Mfr
N.A.I.C.S.: 333517
Jan Rebec *(Exec Dir)*

FERMENTA BIOTECH LIMITED
A -1501 Thane One DIL Complex Ghodbunder Road, Majiwada, Thane, 400610, Maharashtra, India
Tel.: (91) 2267980888
Web Site: https://www.fermentabiotech.com
Year Founded: 1951
506414—(BOM)
Rev.: $55,507,943
Assets: $96,484,001
Liabilities: $45,780,817
Net Worth: $50,703,184
Earnings: $2,055,772
Emp.: 604
Fiscal Year-end: 03/31/22
Organic Chemical Mfr
N.A.I.C.S.: 325199
Krishna Datla *(Vice Chm)*

Subsidiaries:

Fermenta USA LLC (1)
3524 NE Stallings Dr Ste 300, Nacogdoches, TX 75965
Web Site: https://fermentausa.com
Animal Nutrition Product Mfr & Distr
N.A.I.C.S.: 311119

FERMENTALG SA
4 rue Riviere, 33500, Libourne, France
Tel.: (33) 557250220
Web Site: https://www.fermentalg.com
Year Founded: 2009
FALG—(EUR)
Sales Range: Less than $1 Million
Chemicals Mfr
N.A.I.C.S.: 325998
Philippe Lavielle *(CEO)*

FERMOB SA
Parc Actival, 01140, Thoissey, France
Tel.: (33) 4 2730 0123   FR
Web Site: http://www.fermob.com
Outdoor Metal Furniture Mfr & Whslr
N.A.I.C.S.: 337126
Bernard Reybier *(Chm & Dir Gen)*

Subsidiaries:

Rodet SAS (1)
Combbrune, 26140, Anneyron, France
Tel.: (33) 4 7531 6666
Web Site: http://www.rodet.net

Sales Range: $10-24.9 Million
Commercial & Institutional Furniture Mfr & Whslr
N.A.I.C.S.: 337127
Sylvie Suchier *(Mgr-Mktg & Comm)*

FERNANDES CO., LTD.
2-14-26 Shimoochiai, Tokyo, 161-0033, Japan
Tel.: (81) 359966469
Web Site: http://www.fernandes.co.jp
Year Founded: 1969
Sales Range: $10-24.9 Million
Emp.: 20
Guitar Mfr & Sales
N.A.I.C.S.: 339992
Masaki Kamei *(COO & Exec VP)*

FERNBROOK HOMES
2220 Hwy 7 West Unit 5, Concord, L4K 1W7, ON, Canada
Tel.: (416) 667-0447
Web Site: http://www.fernbrookhomes.com
Rev.: $20,692,898
Emp.: 110
Residential Construction Services
N.A.I.C.S.: 236116
Bessie Poon *(Controller)*

FERNLEA FLOWERS LTD.
1211 Hwy 3, Delhi, N4B 2W6, ON, Canada
Tel.: (519) 582-3060
Web Site: http://www.fernlea.com
Year Founded: 1939
Sales Range: $25-49.9 Million
Emp.: 150
Flower Nurseries
N.A.I.C.S.: 113210
Jim McDonald *(CFO)*

Subsidiaries:

Fernlea Nursery Inc. (1)
1625 SE Darling St, Stuart, FL 34997
Tel.: (772) 287-0847
Web Site: http://www.ferlea.com
Rev.: $11,000,000
Emp.: 120
Nursery Stock
N.A.I.C.S.: 424930

FEROELEKTRO D.D.
Marsala Tita 28, 71000, Sarajevo, Bosnia & Herzegovina
Tel.: (387) 3 320 5711
FRESR—(SARE)
Rev.: $336,830
Assets: $14,835,280
Liabilities: $10,089,967
Net Worth: $4,745,312
Earnings: ($308,250)
Emp.: 25
Fiscal Year-end: 12/31/20
Domestic & Foreign Trading Services
N.A.I.C.S.: 238990

FERONIA INC.
Suite 1800 181 Bay Street, Toronto, M5J 2T9, ON, Canada
Tel.: (443) 713-1833   ON
Web Site: http://www.feronia.com
Year Founded: 2005
FRN—(TSXV)
Rev.: $29,654,359
Assets: $52,945,336
Liabilities: $93,824,506
Net Worth: ($40,879,170)
Earnings: ($91,173,211)
Emp.: 3,807
Fiscal Year-end: 12/31/19
Agricultural Services Including Soybean Farming & Processing
N.A.I.C.S.: 111110
Larry Seruma *(Chm)*

Subsidiaries:

Feronia Incorporated Services Limited (1)
No 1 King Street, London, EC2V 8AU, United Kingdom
Tel.: (44) 2037131830
Palm Oil Distr
N.A.I.C.S.: 424590

FEROZSONS LABORATORIES LIMITED
197-A The Mall, Rawalpindi, 42000, Pakistan
Tel.: (92) 514252150
Web Site: https://www.ferozsons-labs.com
Year Founded: 1954
FEROZ—(PSX)
Rev.: $55,139,308
Assets: $74,261,154
Liabilities: $25,249,294
Net Worth: $49,011,860
Earnings: $8,001,333
Emp.: 1,127
Fiscal Year-end: 06/30/21
Pharmaceuticals Product Mfr
N.A.I.C.S.: 325412
Akhter Khalid Waheed *(Chm)*

Subsidiaries:

BF Biosciences Limited (1)
5-KM Sundar Raiwind Road, Lahore, Pakistan
Tel.: (92) 4236026700
Web Site: https://bfbio.com
Biopharmaceutical Product Mfr & Distr
N.A.I.C.S.: 325412

FERPAL INFRASTRUCTURE LTD.
171 Fenmar Drive, Toronto, M9L 1M7, ON, Canada
Tel.: (416) 742-3713
Web Site: http://www.ferpalinfrastructure.com
Year Founded: 1986
Rev.: $22,309,087
Emp.: 115
Safe Drinking Water Solution & Water Pipeline Construction Services
N.A.I.C.S.: 237110
David O'Sullivan *(Pres)*

Subsidiaries:

FER-PAL Construction USA LLC. (1)
26187 Northline Rd, Taylor, MI 48180
Tel.: (734) 946-2034
Water Pipeline Construction Services
N.A.I.C.S.: 237110

FERRARELLE S.P.A.
Via Porta Pinciana 4, 179, Rome, Italy
Tel.: (39) 06780541
Web Site: http://www.ferrarelle.it
Sales Range: $200-249.9 Million
Emp.: 613
Bottled Water Mfr
N.A.I.C.S.: 312112
Carlo Pontecorvo *(Pres)*

Subsidiaries:

FERRARELLE USA (1)
Shore Pointe One Selleck St, Norwalk, CT 06855
Tel.: (866) 999-8490
Web Site: http://www.ferrarelle.org
Mineral Water Distr
N.A.I.C.S.: 424490

FERRARI N.V.
Via Abetone Inferiore n 4, I-41053, Maranello, MO, Italy
Tel.: (39) 0536949111   NL
Web Site: https://www.ferrari.com
Year Founded: 2015

RACE—(NYSE)
Rev.: $6,443,067,127
Assets: $8,689,091,302
Liabilities: $5,375,232,031
Net Worth: $3,313,859,270
Earnings: $1,351,228,146
Emp.: 4,988
Fiscal Year-end: 12/31/23
Holding Company; Automobile Mfr
N.A.I.C.S.: 551112
Michele Antoniazzi *(Chief HR Officer)*

Subsidiaries:

Ferrari S.p.A. (1)
Via Abetone Inferiore No 4, 41053, Maranello, MO, Italy (100%)
Tel.: (39) 0536949111
Sales Range: $1-4.9 Billion
Emp.: 2,870
Sports Cars Mfr & Whslr
N.A.I.C.S.: 336110

Subsidiary (Domestic):

Ferrari Financial Services S.p.A. (2)
Via Abetone Inferiore 4, 41053, Maranello, MO, Italy (100%)
Web Site: http://auto.ferrari.com
Luxury Sports Car Sales Financing Services
N.A.I.C.S.: 522220

Subsidiary (Non-US):

Ferrari Japan KK (2)
Roppongi Hills Mori Tower 37F 6-10-1 Roppongi, Minato-Ku, Tokyo, 106-6137, Japan
Tel.: (81) 368906200
Automotive Distr
N.A.I.C.S.: 423110

Ferrari Management Consulting (Shanghai) Co., Ltd. (2)
No 708 Beijing W Rd, Jing'An Dist, Shanghai, 200041, China
Tel.: (86) 2161201001
Business Management Consulting Services
N.A.I.C.S.: 541611

Subsidiary (US):

Ferrari North America, Inc. (2)
250 Sylvan Ave, Englewood Cliffs, NJ 07632-2500
Tel.: (201) 816-2600
Web Site: http://www.ferrariusa.com
Rev.: $70,000,000
Emp.: 75
Sports Cars Importer & Distr
N.A.I.C.S.: 423110
Edwin Fenech *(Pres & CEO)*

Subsidiary (Non-US):

Ferrari North Europe Limited (2)
275 Leigh Road, Slough, SL1 4HF, Berks, United Kingdom
Tel.: (44) 1753 878700
Web Site: http://www.ferrari.com
Sales Range: $25-49.9 Million
Emp.: 20
New & Used Car Dealer
N.A.I.C.S.: 441110

Ferrari South West Europe S.A.R.L. (2)
49 Avenue Georges Pompidou, 92593, Levallois-Perret, France
Tel.: (33) 149645454
Car Mfr & Distr
N.A.I.C.S.: 336110

FERRARI S.A.
BP 54, 38352, La Tour-du-Pin, France
Tel.: (33) 474974133
Web Site: http://www.ferrari.com
Year Founded: 1960
Sales Range: $50-74.9 Million
Emp.: 250
Textile Mfr
N.A.I.C.S.: 314999
Sebastien Ferrari *(Chm)*

Subsidiaries:

Serge Ferrari AG (1)

Ferrari S.A.—(Continued)

Wasterkingerweg 2, CH 8193, Eglisau, Switzerland
Tel.: (41) 448682626
Web Site: http://en.sergeferrari.com
Sales Range: $25-49.9 Million
Emp.: 100
Fabric Coating Mfr
N.A.I.C.S.: 314999
Niklaus Zemp (Gen Mgr)

FERRELL BUILDER'S SUPPLY LTD.
1549 Rymal Road East, Hamilton, L8W 3N2, ON, Canada
Tel.: (905) 387-1948
Web Site: http://www.ferrellbrick.com
Year Founded: 1971
Rev.: $18,606,219
Emp.: 80
Building Material Supplier
N.A.I.C.S.: 444180

FERRERO INTERNATIONAL S.A.
Findel Business Center Complexe B Rue de Treves, Findel, 2632, Luxembourg, Luxembourg
Tel.: (352) 349 7111　　　　LU
Web Site: http://www.ferrero.com
Rev.: $15,107,352,000
Fiscal Year-end: 08/31/20
Holding Company; Confectionery Products Mfr, Whslr & Retailer
N.A.I.C.S.: 551112
Giovanni Ferrero (Chm)

Subsidiaries:

Ferrero S.p.A.　　　　　　　　　(1)
Piazzale Pietro Ferrero 1, 12051, Alba, CN, Italy
Tel.: (39) 0173295111
Sales Range: $15-24.9 Billion
Chocolate Confectionery Mfr, Whslr & Retailer
N.A.I.C.S.: 311351

Subsidiary (Non-US):

Ferrero Ardennes S.A.　　　　　(2)
Rue Pietro Ferrero 5, 6700, Arlon, Belgium
Tel.: (32) 63 211211
Web Site: http://www.ferrero.be
Food Products Mfr
N.A.I.C.S.: 311351
Etienne Thomas (Head-Supply Chain)

Ferrero Argentina S.A.　　　　　(2)
Edison 2659 Tower 2 Floor 3, San Isidro, 1640, Buenos Aires, Argentina
Tel.: (54) 11 40144400
Web Site: http://www.ferrero.com.ar
Chocolate Product Coconut Almond Mfr & Distr
N.A.I.C.S.: 311351

Plant (Domestic):

Ferrero Argentina S.A. - Pastora Plant　　　　　　　　　　　　(3)
Ruta Provincial 6 Km 180 100, Partido de Exaltacion de la Cr, Los Cardales, Argentina
Tel.: (54) 2 304 497300
Food Products Mfr
N.A.I.C.S.: 311999

Subsidiary (Non-US):

Ferrero Asia Limited　　　　　　(2)
7F-9 National Enterprise Center 188 Nanking East Road Section 5, Taipei, Taiwan
Tel.: (886) 2 27473883
Food Products Mfr
N.A.I.C.S.: 311999
Rick Chi (Pres)

Ferrero Asia Ltd　　　　　　　　(2)
1302 13 F 5 Mabang-ro 10 gil, Seocho-gu, Seoul, 137-943, Korea (South)
Tel.: (82) 2 5895710
Web Site: http://www.ferrero
N.A.I.C.S.: 311999

Ferrero Asia Ltd (Singapore)　　(2)

79 Science Park Drive 03-06/08 Cintech IV Science Park 1, Singapore, 118264, Singapore
Tel.: (65) 65944750
Food Products Mfr
N.A.I.C.S.: 311999

Ferrero B.V.　　　　　　　　　　(2)
Westbroek 58 4822 ZW, Breda, Netherlands
Tel.: (31) 76 548 26 60
Web Site: http://www.ferrero.com
Food Products Mfr
N.A.I.C.S.: 311999

Ferrero Canada Ltd.　　　　　　(2)
1 Ferrero Boulevard, Brantford, N3V 1G3, ON, Canada
Tel.: (519) 756-6205
Food Products Mfr
N.A.I.C.S.: 311999

Ferrero Ceska S.r.o.　　　　　　(2)
Karla Englise 6/3201, 150 00, Prague, Czech Republic
Tel.: (420) 225 020 111
Web Site: http://www.ferrero.cz
Food Products Mfr
N.A.I.C.S.: 311999

Ferrero D.o.o.　　　　　　　　　(2)
Radnicka cesta 39, 10000, Zagreb, Croatia
Tel.: (385) 1 2355000
Food Products Mfr
N.A.I.C.S.: 311999

Ferrero De Mexico S.A. de C.V. e　　　　　　　　　　　　　(2)
Avenida Mariano Otero 2510, Colonia Jardines del Bosque, 44520, Guadalajara, Jalisco, Mexico
Tel.: (52) 33 3121 3242
Food Products Mfr
N.A.I.C.S.: 311999

Ferrero Del Ecuador S.A　　　　(2)
Calle Josefa Lozano Interseccion Av Oswaldo Guayasamin, Tumbaco, Quito, Ecuador
Tel.: (593) 2 2984500
Food Products Mfr
N.A.I.C.S.: 311999

Ferrero Deutschland G.m.b.h　　(2)
Hainer Weg 120, 60599, Frankfurt am Main, Germany
Tel.: (49) 69 68050
Web Site: http://www.ferrero.de
Food Products Mfr
N.A.I.C.S.: 311999

Ferrero FSC Luxembourg S.A.　(2)
Findel Business Center Complexe B Rue de Treves, Findel, Luxembourg, 2632, Luxembourg
Tel.: (352) 3497111
Food Products Mfr
N.A.I.C.S.: 311999

Ferrero France S.A.　　　　　　(2)
18 Rue Jacques Monod, CS 90058, 76136, Mont-Saint-Aignau, France
Tel.: (33) 235 883600
Web Site: http://www.ferrero.fr
Food Products Mfr
N.A.I.C.S.: 311999

Ferrero Iberica S.A.　　　　　　(2)
WTC Almeda Park Placa de la Pau s/n Edificio 2 Planta3a, Cornella de Llobregat, 08940, Barcelona, Spain
Tel.: (34) 93 4798600
Food Products Mfr
N.A.I.C.S.: 311999
Philippe Steyaert (Gen Mgr)

Ferrero India Private Limited　　(2)
Unit 201-202 Pentagon Tower 1, Magarpatta Hadapsar, Pune, 411 028, India
Tel.: (91) 20 66804100
Food Products Mfr
N.A.I.C.S.: 311999

Ferrero Ireland Limited　　　　　(2)
Kinsale Road, Cork, Ireland
Tel.: (353) 21 4917600
Food Products Mfr
N.A.I.C.S.: 311999

Ferrero Ithemba RSA (Pty) Ltd　(2)
Ground Floor Block C 204 Rivonia Road

Morningside, 2057, Johannesburg, Sandton, South Africa
Tel.: (27) 11 230 5500
Food Products Mfr
N.A.I.C.S.: 311999

Ferrero Japan Ltd　　　　　　　(2)
Kowa Hiroo Bldg 2F 5-2-32, Minami-Azabu, Tokyo, 106-0047, Japan
Tel.: (81) 3 5420 3200
Food Products Mfr
N.A.I.C.S.: 311999

Ferrero LADM　　　　　　　　　(2)
Avenida 7 N 156-68 Piso 24 Edificio North Point III, Bogota, Colombia
Tel.: (57) 1 649 9200
Food Products Mfr
N.A.I.C.S.: 311999

Ferrero Lanka (Pvt) Ltd　　　　(2)
No101 Vinayalankara Mawatha, Colombo, Sri Lanka
Tel.: (94) 11 2596612
Food Products Mfr
N.A.I.C.S.: 311999

Ferrero Magyarorszag Kft.　　　(2)
Vaci ut 76, Budapest, 1133, Hungary
Tel.: (36) 1 238 91 00
Web Site: http://www.ferrero.com
Food Products Mfr
N.A.I.C.S.: 311999
Tizeano Giraudo (Gen Mgr)

Ferrero Osterreich Handels G. m.b.H.　　　　　　　　　　　(2)
Rheinstrasse 12, 35260, Stadtallendorf, Germany
Tel.: (49) 64 28790
Food Products Mfr
N.A.I.C.S.: 311999

Ferrero Polska Sp. z.o.o.　　　　(2)
Ul Szkolna 6 K/Grojca, 05-622, Belsk Duzy, Poland
Tel.: (48) 48 6610600
Food Products Mfr
N.A.I.C.S.: 311999

Subsidiary (Domestic):

Ferrero Pubbliregia S.r.l.　　　　(2)
Via Legnanino 1, 10023, Chieri, Italy
Tel.: (39) 011 8152111
Food Products Mfr
N.A.I.C.S.: 311999

Subsidiary (Non-US):

Ferrero Romania S.R.L.　　　　　(2)
Piata Presei Libere nr 3-5 City Gate Turnul Sud etaj 14 sector 1, Bucharest, 1012178, Romania
Tel.: (40) 215282200
Food Products Mfr
N.A.I.C.S.: 311999

Ferrero Russia CJSC　　　　　　(2)
2nd Brestskaya st 8, 125057, Moscow, Russia
Tel.: (7) 4959612400
Food Products Mfr
N.A.I.C.S.: 311999

Ferrero S.p.A Greece Single-partner Limited Liability Company　　　(2)
Artemidos 3, Athens, 15225, Greece
Tel.: (30) 2106849232
Web Site: http://www.ferrero.gr
Food Products Mfr
N.A.I.C.S.: 311999

Plant (Domestic):

Ferrero S.p.A. - Angelo dei Lombardi Factory　　　　　　　　　　　(2)
Localita Porrara, Sant Angelo dei Lombardi, 83054, Avellino, Italy
Tel.: (39) 0827 201111
Food Products Mfr
N.A.I.C.S.: 311999

Ferrero S.p.A. - Balvano Factory　(2)
Localita San Potito, 85050, Potenza, Balvano, Italy
Tel.: (39) 0971 996111
Food Products Mfr
N.A.I.C.S.: 311999

Ferrero S.p.A. - Pozzuolo Martesana Factory　　　　　　　　　　　(2)
Via Pietro Ferrero 5, Pozzuolo Martesana, Milan, Italy
Tel.: (39) 02 952561
Food Products Mfr
N.A.I.C.S.: 311999

Subsidiary (Non-US):

Ferrero Scandinavia A/B　　　　(2)
Hjalmaregatan 3, 211 18, Malmo, Sweden
Tel.: (46) 40 109800
Food Products Mfr
N.A.I.C.S.: 311999

Ferrero Schweiz A.G.　　　　　　(2)
Baarerstrasse 82, 6300, Zug, Switzerland
Tel.: (41) 41 7116630
Web Site: http://www.ferrero.com
Emp.: 27
Food Products Mfr
N.A.I.C.S.: 311999

Ferrero Trading (Shanghai) Company, Ltd　　　　　　　　　　　　　(2)
F Floor 9 LJZ Fund Tower 1528 Century Avenue, Shanghai, 200135, China
Tel.: (86) 21 2035 9300
Food Products Mfr
N.A.I.C.S.: 311999

Ferrero Trading Dubai　　　　　　(2)
Dubai Media City Al Thuraya Tower 1 10th F Office n 1004, PO Box 502238, Dubai, United Arab Emirates
Tel.: (971) 4 3612741
Food Products Mfr
N.A.I.C.S.: 311999

Ferrero Turkiye Cikolata Ve Tarim Urunleri Sanayi Ve Dis Ticaret A.S.　　　　　　　　　　　　　(2)
Balmumcu Mah Gazi Umur Pasa Sokak No 27, 34349, Istanbul, Turkiye
Tel.: (90) 212 2156222
Web Site: http://www.ferrero.com.tr
Emp.: 60
Food Products Mfr
N.A.I.C.S.: 311999
Azmi Gumusluoglu (Country Mgr)

Subsidiary (US):

Ferrero U.S.A., Inc.　　　　　　(2)
7 Sylvan Way 4th Fl, Parsippany, NJ 07054　　　　　　　　　　　(100%)
Tel.: (732) 584-4700
Web Site: http://www.ferrerousa.com
Candy & Confectionery Products Mfr
N.A.I.C.S.: 424450
Alanna Y. Cotton (Chief Bus Officer/Pres-North America)

Subsidiary (Domestic):

Fannie May Confections Brands, Inc.　　　　　　　　　　　　(3)
5353 Lauby Rd, North Canton, OH 44720
Tel.: (312) 453-0010
Web Site: http://www.fanniemay.com
Holding Company; Confectionery & Specialty Food Products Mfr
N.A.I.C.S.: 551112

Subsidiary (Domestic):

Harry London Candies, Inc.　　　(4)
5353 Lauby Rd, Canton, OH 44720
Tel.: (330) 494-0833
Web Site: http://www.fanniemay.com
Chocolate & Other Confections
N.A.I.C.S.: 311352

Subsidiary (Domestic):

The Ferrara Candy Company　　　(3)
404 W Harrison St Ste 650, Chicago, IL 60607
Tel.: (708) 366-0500
Web Site: http://www.ferrarausa.com
Confectionery & Cookie Mfr & Whslr
N.A.I.C.S.: 311351
Marco Capurso (CEO)

Group (Domestic):

Kellogg Co. - Cookies & Snacks Business　　　　　　　　　　　(4)
500 Weaver Rd, Florence, KY 41042-2902

Tel.: (859) 371-0015
Sales Range: $75-99.9 Million
Emp.: 160
Cookies, Pie Crusts & Fruit-Flavored
Snacks Mfr
N.A.I.C.S.: 311821

Subsidiary (Domestic):

Famous Amos Chocolate Chip
Cookie Co., LLC   (5)
1 Kellogg Sq, Battle Creek, MI 49017-3534
Tel.: (269) 961-2000
Web Site: http://www.famous-amos.com
Cookie Mfr
N.A.I.C.S.: 311821

Mother's Cookie Company,
L.L.C.   (5)
2287 Ralph Ave, Louisville, KY 40216
Tel.: (502) 448-1730
Food Supplement Store Operator
N.A.I.C.S.: 456191

Murray Biscuit Company, L.L.C.   (5)
1550 Marvin Griffin Rd, Augusta, GA 30906
Tel.: (706) 798-8600
Emp.: 1,000
Cookie Mfr
N.A.I.C.S.: 311821

Stretch Island Fruit Sales L.L.C.   (5)
16371 E State Route 3, Allyn, WA 98524-
9728
Tel.: (360) 275-6050
Snack Food Mfr
N.A.I.C.S.: 311919

Subsidiary (Non-US):

Ferrero UK Ltd.   (2)
Building 7 Hatters Lane, Croxley Green
Business Park, Watford, WD18 8PA, United
Kingdom
Tel.: (44) 1923 690300
Food Products Mfr
N.A.I.C.S.: 311999

Subsidiary (Domestic):

Thorntons Ltd.   (3)
Thornton Park, Somercotes, Alfreton, DE55
4XJ, Derbyshire, United Kingdom
Tel.: (44) 3451211911
Web Site: http://www.thorntons.co.uk
Chocolates Mfr & Retailer
N.A.I.C.S.: 311352
Barry Bloomer (CEO)

Subsidiary (Non-US):

Ferrero Ukraine LLC   (2)
12 Amosova Street Building 1, Kiev, 03680,
Ukraine
Tel.: (380) 44 247 19 35
Food Products Mfr
N.A.I.C.S.: 311999

Ferrero do Brasil Industria Doceira E
Alimentar Ltda   (2)
Rua Benjamin Lins n 790 - Batel, Curitiba,
80420-100, Parana, Brazil
Tel.: (55) 41 21095000
Food Products Mfr
N.A.I.C.S.: 311999

Kelsen Group A/S   (2)
Bredgade 27, 8766, Norre Snede, Denmark
Tel.: (45) 7211 0110
Web Site: http://www.kelsen.com
Butter Cookies Mfr & Distr
N.A.I.C.S.: 311821

Subsidiary (Non-US):

Kelsen South Africa (Pty) Ltd.   (3)
Unit 109 Block 2 Northgate Park 20 Section
Street Paarden Eiland, Cape Town, 7420,
South Africa
Tel.: (27) 215520499
Cookie Whslr
N.A.I.C.S.: 424490
Oliver Hugo (Dir-Mktg)

Subsidiary (US):

Kelsen, Inc.   (3)
40 Marcus Dr Ste 101, Melville, NY 11747
Tel.: (631) 694-8080
Web Site: http://www.kelsen.com

Sales Range: $25-49.9 Million
Butter Cookie Whslr
N.A.I.C.S.: 424490

FERREXPO PLC
55 St James s Street, London, SW1A
1LA, United Kingdom
Tel.: (44) 2073898300   UK
Web Site: https://www.ferrexpo.com
FEEXF—(OTCIQ)
Rev.: $1,248,490,000
Assets: $1,354,700,000
Liabilities: $104,450,000
Net Worth: $1,250,250,000
Earnings: $219,440,000
Fiscal Year-end: 12/31/22
Iron Ore Mining
N.A.I.C.S.: 212210
Viktor Lotous (Chm-Mgmt Bd-FPM &
Gen Dir-FPM)

Subsidiaries:

Ferrexpo AG   (1)
Bahnhofstrasse 13, 6340, Baar, Switzerland
Tel.: (41) 41 769 3660
Web Site: https://www.ferrexpo.com
Iron Ore Pellets Production & Sales Ser-
vices
N.A.I.C.S.: 212210

Ferrexpo Belanovo Mining LLC   (1)
16 Budivelnykiv Street, Horishni Plavni, Pol-
tava, 39802, Ukraine
Tel.: (380) 53 487 4311
Web Site:
    https://www.ferrexpobelanovomine.com
Iron Ore Mining Services
N.A.I.C.S.: 212210
Yuriy Khimich (Gen Dir)

Ferrexpo Middle East FZE   (1)
Office A2207 Jafza One Jebel Ali Free
Zone, PO Box 18341, Dubai, United Arab
Emirates
Tel.: (971) 48833074
Iron Ore Mining Services
N.A.I.C.S.: 212210

Ferrexpo Singapore Pte Ltd   (1)
1 Fullerton Road One Fullerton 02-01, Sin-
gapore, 049213, Singapore
Tel.: (65) 64083899
Iron Ore Mining Services
N.A.I.C.S.: 212210

First-DDSG Logistics Holding
GmbH   (1)
Handelskai 348, 1020, Vienna, Austria
Tel.: (43) 172 5000
Web Site: https://www.ddsg-holding.com
Fleet Maintenance & Logistic Services
N.A.I.C.S.: 488510
Viatcheslav Vdovitchenko (Mng Dir)

FERRING HOLDING SA
Ch de la Vergognausaz 50, 1162,
Saint Prex, Switzerland
Tel.: (41) 583010000
Web Site: http://www.ferring.com
Year Founded: 1954
Sales Range: $900-999.9 Million
Emp.: 2,700
Holding Company; Pharmaceutical
Mfr
N.A.I.C.S.: 551112
Michel L. Pettigrew (COO)

Subsidiaries:

FERRING (IRELAND) LTD.   (1)
United Drug House Magna Magna
Business Park Citywest Road, Dublin,
D24XKE5, Ireland
Tel.: (353) 1 463 7355
Web Site: http://www.ferring.com
Emp.: 7
Biopharmaceutical Product Mfr
N.A.I.C.S.: 325412
Sean Davis (Gen Mgr)

FERRING AG   (1)
Baarermatte Eingang Sud, 6340, Baar,
Switzerland
Tel.: (41) 41 768 96 96
Web Site: http://www.ferring.ch

Pharmaceuticals Product Mfr
N.A.I.C.S.: 325412
Claudia Zerobin Kleist (Mgr-Medical &
Regulatory Affairs)

FERRING ARZNEIMITTEL
GESMBH   (1)
Fabrikstrasse 7, 24103, Kiel, Germany
Tel.: (49) 431 58 52 0
Web Site: http://www.ferring.de
Pharmaceuticals Product Mfr
N.A.I.C.S.: 325412
Michael Gedamke (Mgr-Medical)

FERRING ARZNEIMITTEL
GMBH   (1)
Vienna Twin Tower Turm West 10 OG Wie-
nerbergstrasse 11, 1100, Vienna, Austria
Tel.: (43) 1 60808 0
Web Site: http://www.ferring.at
Pharmaceuticals Product Mfr
N.A.I.C.S.: 325412

FERRING CONTROLLED THERA-
PEUTICS LTD   (1)
1 Redwood Place Peel Park Campus, East
Kilbride, G74 5PB, United Kingdom
Tel.: (44) 1355 239166
Pharmaceuticals Product Mfr
N.A.I.C.S.: 325412
Eleanor Campbell (Mgr-HR & Admin)

FERRING GALENISCHES LABOR
AG   (1)
Gewerbestrassse 18, 4123, Allschwil,
Basel-Landschaft, Switzerland
Tel.: (41) 61 486 4000
Pharmaceuticals Product Mfr
N.A.I.C.S.: 325412

FERRING GMBH   (1)
Wittland 11, 24109, Kiel, Germany
Tel.: (49) 431 5852 100
Pharmaceuticals Product Mfr
N.A.I.C.S.: 325412
Astrid Claus (Mgr-Production Tech Svc &
Validation)

FERRING HELLAS PHARMACEUTI-
CALS E.P.E.   (1)
3 Gyzi Street Marousi, 15125, Athens,
Greece
Tel.: (30) 210 6 843 449
Web Site: http://www.ferring.gr
Pharmaceuticals Product Mfr
N.A.I.C.S.: 325412
Stavros Papaevangelou (Gen Mgr)

FERRING HUNGARY PHARMACEU-
TICAL TRADING CO LTD   (1)
Tomori Utca 34, 1138, Budapest, Hungary
Tel.: (36) 1 236 3800
Pharmaceuticals Product Mfr
N.A.I.C.S.: 325412

FERRING ILAC SANAYI VE TI-
CARET LTD STI   (1)
Buyukdere Caddesi Nurol Plaza No 255 A
Blok Kat 13 Maslak, Sisli, 34398, Istanbul,
Turkiye
Tel.: (90) 212 335 62 00
Web Site: http://www.ferring.com.tr
Pharmaceuticals Product Mfr
N.A.I.C.S.: 325412

FERRING INC.   (1)
200 Yorkland Boulevard Suite 500, Toronto,
M2J 5C1, ON, Canada
Tel.: (416) 490-0121
Web Site: http://www.ferring.ca
Emp.: 90
Pharmaceuticals Product Mfr
N.A.I.C.S.: 325412

FERRING INTERNATIONAL
PHARMA-SCIENCE CENTRE
(CHINA) CO. LTD.   (1)
Suite 1102-2 Tower A No 28 Jianguomennei
Street Minsheng Financial, Centre
Dongcheng District, Beijing, China
Tel.: (86) 10 8529 5318
Web Site: http://www.ferring.com.cn
Pharmaceuticals Product Mfr
N.A.I.C.S.: 325412
Wanmei Wang (Gen Mgr & Sr Dir-Legal)

FERRING LAAKKEET OY   (1)
Keilaranta 10, 2150, Espoo, Finland
Tel.: (358) 207 401 440
Web Site: http://www.ferringlaakkeet.fi

Pharmaceuticals Product Mfr
N.A.I.C.S.: 325412
Marjukka Suomela (Gen Mgr)

FERRING LAEGEMIDLER A/S   (1)
Kay Fiskers Plads 11, 2300, Copenhagen,
Denmark
Tel.: (45) 88 16 88 17
Emp.: 500
Pharmaceuticals Product Mfr
N.A.I.C.S.: 325412
Elizabeth Weis (Gen Mgr)

FERRING LAKEMEDEL AB   (1)
Sodergatan 26 3TR, Box 4041, 211 34,
Malmo, Sweden
Tel.: (46) 40 691 69 00
Web Site: http://www.ferring.se
Pharmaceuticals Product Mfr
N.A.I.C.S.: 325412

FERRING LECIVA AS   (1)
K Rybniku 475, 252 42, Jesenice, Czech
Republic
Tel.: (420) 241 041 111
Web Site: http://www.ferring.cz
Pharmaceuticals Product Mfr
N.A.I.C.S.: 325412
Vadim Lukasevic (Mgr-Supply Chain)

FERRING LEGEMIDLER AS   (1)
Nydalsveien 36B, 0484, Oslo, Norway
Tel.: (47) 22 02 08 80
Pharmaceuticals Product Mfr
N.A.I.C.S.: 325412

FERRING NV   (1)
Capucienenlaan 93c, Aalst, 9300, Belgium
Tel.: (32) 53 72 92 00
Web Site: http://www.ferring.be
Pharmaceuticals Product Mfr
N.A.I.C.S.: 325412
Vera Lamberts (Mgr-Bus Unit)

FERRING PHARMACEUTICALS
(ASIA) CO. LTD.   (1)
23/F GC Tower 1088 Yuanshen Road, Pu-
dong New District, Shanghai, 200122,
China
Tel.: (86) 21 3852 9666
Web Site: http://www.ferring.com.cn
Pharmaceuticals Product Mfr
N.A.I.C.S.: 325412
Lars Peter Brunse (Chief Production Officer,
Member-Exec Bd & Exec VP)

FERRING PHARMACEUTICALS CO.
LTD.   (1)
27/Fl Unit 278 Thai Cc Tower 889 South
Sathorn Road Yannawa Sathorn, Bangkok,
10120, Thailand
Tel.: (66) 2 673 9784
Pharmaceuticals Product Mfr
N.A.I.C.S.: 325412
Sophie Opdyke (VP/Gen Mgr-Oncology-US)

FERRING PHARMACEUTICALS KO-
REA CO., LTD.   (1)
14th Floor AD Culture Center Olympic-ro
35-137, Songpa-gu, Seoul, 138-921, Korea
(South)
Tel.: (82) 2 534 2761
Web Site: http://www.ferring.co.kr
Pharmaceuticals Product Mfr
N.A.I.C.S.: 325412
Dominic Whang (Mng Dir & Dir-
Representative)

FERRING PHARMACEUTICALS
LLC   (1)
Kosmodamianskaya Nab 52 Bld 4, 115054,
Moscow, Russia
Tel.: (7) 4952870343
Web Site: http://www.ferring.ru
Emp.: 40
Pharmaceuticals Product Mfr
N.A.I.C.S.: 325412
Letozchemko Kerel (Gen Mgr)

FERRING PHARMACEUTICALS
LTD.   (1)
Units 1 - 12 25/Fl No 1 Hung To Road
Ngau Tau Kok, Kowloon, China (Hong
Kong)
Tel.: (852) 2622 8000
Web Site: http://www.ferring.com.hk
Emp.: 170
Pharmaceuticals Product Mfr
N.A.I.C.S.: 325412

Ferring Holding SA—(Continued)

**FERRING PHARMACEUTICALS PO-
LAND SP. Z O.O.**   **(1)**
Ul Szamocka 8, 01-748, Warsaw, Poland
Tel.: (48) 22 2460680
Web Site: http://www.ferring.pl
Emp.: 20
Pharmaceuticals Product Mfr
N.A.I.C.S.: 325412
Lukasz Swiech *(Product Mgr)*

**FERRING PHARMACEUTICALS PTE
LTD.**   **(1)**
20 Sin Ming Lane 03-63, Midview City, Sin-
gapore, Singapore
Tel.: (65) 6 746 2096
Pharmaceuticals Product Mfr
N.A.I.C.S.: 325412

**FERRING PHARMACEUTICALS PTY
LTD**   **(1)**
Suite 2 Level 1 Building 1 Pymble Corpo-
rate Centre 20 Bridge Street, PO Box 315,
Pymble, 2073, NSW, Australia
Tel.: (61) 2 9497 2300
Web Site: http://www.ferring.com.au
Pharmaceuticals Product Mfr
N.A.I.C.S.: 325412
Carmen Langley *(Mgr-Compliance)*

**FERRING PHARMACEUTICALS PVT
LTD**   **(1)**
International Pharmascience Center Plot No
B-57 Off Road No 31, Wagle Industrial Es-
tate, Thane, 400604, Maharastra, India
Tel.: (91) 22 66222800
Pharmaceuticals Product Mfr
N.A.I.C.S.: 325412
Ashok Alate *(Exec Chm)*

**FERRING PHARMACEUTICALS RO-
MANIA S.R.L.**   **(1)**
Str Coriolan Brediceanu nr 10 City Business
Center Cladirea C et 6, 300011, Timisoara,
Romania
Tel.: (40) 356 113 270
Web Site: http://www.ferring.ro
Pharmaceuticals Product Mfr
N.A.I.C.S.: 325412
Mihaela Scurtu-Martin *(Mgr-Medical)*

**FERRING PHARMACEUTICALS
SA**   **(1)**
Gospodar Jevremova 47/v, 11000, Bel-
grade, Serbia
Tel.: (381) 11 404 88 00
Pharmaceuticals Product Mfr
N.A.I.C.S.: 325412
Canga Milosavljevic *(Office Mgr)*

**FERRING PORTUGUESA PRODU-
TOS FARMACEUTICOS SOCIE-
DADE UNIPESSOAL, LDA.**   **(1)**
Rua Alexandre Herculano Edificio 1-6 Piso,
2795-240, Linda-a-Velha, Portugal
Tel.: (351) 21 940 51 90
Web Site: http://www.ferring.pt
Pharmaceuticals Product Mfr
N.A.I.C.S.: 325412

**FERRING PRODUCTOS FARMA-
CEUTICOS SPA**   **(1)**
Presidente Riesco 5711 Oficina 803, Las
Condes, 7561114, Santiago, Chile
Tel.: (56) 2 2706 30 60
Web Site: http://www.ferring.cl
Pharmaceuticals Product Mfr
N.A.I.C.S.: 325412

FERRING PTY LTD   **(1)**
Route 21 Corporate Park 6 Regency Drive
Irene Ext 30, Irene, Centurion, 0157, Gau-
teng, South Africa
Tel.: (27) 12 345 6358
Web Site: http://www.ferring.co.za
Pharmaceuticals Product Mfr
N.A.I.C.S.: 325412

**FERRING RESEARCH INSTITUTE
INC.**   **(1)**
4245 Sorrento Valley Blvd, San Diego, CA
92121
Tel.: (858) 657-1400
Web Site: http://www.ferring-research.com
Emp.: 70
Commercial Physical Research, Nsk
N.A.I.C.S.: 541715
Paul Acosta *(Dir-HR & Admin)*

FERRING S.A.S.   **(1)**
7 rue Jean-Baptiste Clement, 94250, Gen-
tilly, France
Tel.: (33) 1 49 08 91 23
Web Site: http://www.ferring.fr
Pharmaceuticals Product Mfr
N.A.I.C.S.: 325412

FERRING SA DE CV   **(1)**
Av Nemesio Diez Riega Mza 2 Lote 15 No
15 Col Parque, Industrial Cerrillo II, Lerma,
Mexico, Mexico
Tel.: (52) 55 11058860
Web Site: http://www.ferring.com.mx
Pharmaceuticals Product Mfr
N.A.I.C.S.: 325412
Elvira Serrato *(Dir-Fin)*

FERRING SAU   **(1)**
C/Gobelas 11, 28023, Madrid, Spain
Tel.: (34) 91 799 47 80
Web Site: http://www.ferring.es
Emp.: 40
Pharmaceuticals Product Mfr
N.A.I.C.S.: 325412
Rafael Mendoza Feliu *(Mgr-Bus Unit)*

FERRING SDN BHD   **(1)**
21-6 Block B Jaya One No 72-A Jalan Uni-
versiti, 46200, Petaling Jaya, Selangor
Darul Ehsan, Malaysia
Tel.: (60) 3 7960 3032
Pharmaceuticals Product Mfr
N.A.I.C.S.: 325412
Shameena Nathesan *(Supvr-Sls)*

FERRING SLOVAKIA S.R.O.   **(1)**
BC Aruba Galvaniho 7/D, 821 04, Brati-
slava, Slovakia
Tel.: (421) 2 5441 6010
Web Site: http://www.ferring.sk
Pharmaceuticals Product Mfr
N.A.I.C.S.: 325412

FERRING SPA   **(1)**
Via Senigallia 18/2, 20161, Milan, Italy
Tel.: (39) 026400011
Web Site: http://www.ferring.it
Pharmaceuticals Product Mfr
N.A.I.C.S.: 325412
Massimo Bertolotti *(Dir-Fin)*

**FERRING THERAPEUTICS PRIVATE
LTD.**   **(1)**
K-28/1 Additional MIDC Anand Nagar, Am-
barnath, 421506, India
Tel.: (91) 226776 4700
Pharmaceuticals Product Mfr
N.A.I.C.S.: 325412

Ferring BV   **(1)**
Polaris Avenue 130, Hoofddorp, 2132JX,
Netherlands
Tel.: (31) 235680390
Pharmaceutical Preparations & Research
N.A.I.C.S.: 325412

Subsidiary (Non-US):

**Bio-Technology General (Israel)
Ltd.**   **(2)**
Be'er Tuvia Industrial Zone Caesarea Indus-
trial Park, PO Box 3551, Kiryat Malachi,
83104, Israel
Tel.: (972) 46309500
Web Site: http://www.ferring.com
Sales Range: $50-74.9 Million
Emp.: 237
Mfr & Developer of Recombinant Products
for the Human Healthcare Industry
N.A.I.C.S.: 325412

Ferring International Center SA   **(1)**
CH de la Vergognausaz 50, 1162, Saint
Prex, Switzerland
Tel.: (41) 583010000
Web Site: http://www.ferring.com
Emp.: 700
Pharmaceutical Preparations & Research
N.A.I.C.S.: 325412
Klaus Dugi *(Chief Medical Officer & Exec
VP)*

**Ferring International Pharmascience
Center U.S.**   **(1)**
100 Interpace Pkwy, Parsippany, NJ 07054
Tel.: (973) 796-1600
Pharmaceuticals Product Mfr
N.A.I.C.S.: 325412

**Ferring Pharmaceutical (China) Com-
pany Limited**   **(1)**
No 6 Hui Ling Lu Ferring Road National
Health Technology Park, Zhongshan,
Guangdong, China
Tel.; (86) 760 8858 7800
Pharmaceuticals Product Mfr
N.A.I.C.S.: 325412
Brady Zhao *(Dir-Medical Science)*

**LABORATORIOS FERRING
LTDA**   **(1)**
Praca Sao Marcos 624 Alto De Pinheiros -
Vila Ida, 05455-050, Sao Paulo, Brazil
Tel.: (55) 11 3024 7500
Web Site: http://www.ferring.com.br
Pharmaceuticals Product Mfr
N.A.I.C.S.: 325412

LABORATORIOS FERRING SA   **(1)**
Avenida Del Libertador 350, B1638BEP,
Buenos Aires, Vicente Lopez, Argentina
Tel.: (54) 11 45 85 89 00
Web Site: http://www.ferring.com.ar
Pharmaceuticals Product Mfr
N.A.I.C.S.: 325412

FERRO S.A.
ul Przemyslowa 7, 32-050, Skawina,
Poland
Tel.: (48) 122562100
Web Site:
  https://www.ferrocompany.com
FRO—(WAR)
Rev.: $204,069,867
Assets: $195,349,847
Liabilities: $79,512,195
Net Worth: $115,837,652
Earnings: $17,119,156
Emp.: 110
Fiscal Year-end: 12/31/23
Sanitary & Installation Fittings; Heat-
ing Equipment
N.A.I.C.S.: 332919
Artur Bialon *(VP)*

**FERRO-ALLOY RESOURCES
LIMITED**
Noble House Les Baissieres, Saint
Peter Port, GY1 2UE, Guernsey
Tel.: (44) 1481740335   GY
Web Site: https://www.ferro-alloy.com
Year Founded: 2000
FAR—(LSE)
Rev.: $6,271,000
Assets: $18,955,000
Liabilities: $3,542,000
Net Worth: $15,413,000
Earnings: ($4,286,000)
Emp.: 200
Fiscal Year-end: 12/31/22
Mineral Mining Services
N.A.I.C.S.: 212390
Nicholas John Bridgen *(CEO)*

FERROAMP ELEKTRONIK AB
Domnarvsgatan 16, Spanga, 163 53,
Stockholm, Sweden
Tel.: (46) 868433390
Web Site: https://ferroamp.com
Year Founded: 2010
FNM—(OMX)
Rev.: $35,266,147
Assets: $36,381,957
Liabilities: $11,407,271
Net Worth: $24,974,686
Earnings: ($10,625,013)
Emp.: 74
Fiscal Year-end: 12/31/23
Other Electronic Component Manu-
facturing
N.A.I.C.S.: 334419

FERRONORDIC AB
Nybrogatan 6, SE114 34, Stockholm,
Sweden
Tel.: (46) 850907280   SE
Web Site:
  https://www.ferronordic.com

Year Founded: 2010
FNM—(OMX)
Rev.: $184,794,927
Assets: $301,310,330
Liabilities: $125,881,593
Net Worth: $175,428,737
Earnings: $41,211,236
Emp.: 457
Fiscal Year-end: 12/31/22
Construction Machinery & Trucks
Distr
N.A.I.C.S.: 423810
Per-Olof Eriksson *(Co-Chm)*

Subsidiaries:

Ferronordic GmbH   **(1)**
Rowentastrasse 8, 63071, Offenbach, Ger-
many
Tel.: (49) 6980086250
Web Site: https://ferronordic.de
Construction Equipment Distr
N.A.I.C.S.: 423810

Ferronordic Kazakhstan LLP   **(1)**
Suyunbaya str 157/1, Almaty, Kazakhstan
Tel.: (7) 7273394919
Web Site: https://ferronordic.kz
Construction Equipment Distr
N.A.I.C.S.: 423810

Ferronordic Machines LLC   **(1)**
Business Center Country Park Panfilova str
21/1, 141407, Khimki, Moscow, Russia
Tel.: (7) 4956639237
Web Site: http://www.ferronordic.com
Construction Equipment Distr
N.A.I.C.S.: 423810

Rudd Equipment Company Inc.   **(1)**
4344 Poplar Level Rd, Louisville, KY
40213-1841
Tel.: (502) 456-4050
Web Site: http://www.ruddequipment.com
Rev.: $175,000,000
Emp.: 370
Construction & Mining Machinery
N.A.I.C.S.: 423810

**FERROTEC (AN HUI) TECH-
NOLOGY DEVELOPMENT CO.,
LTD.**
No 18 Nanhai Road Jinqiao Develop-
ment Zone, Shunan Town Yian Dis-
trict, Tongling, 244151, Anhui, China
Tel.: (86) 5625316888
Web Site: https://www.ftvas.com
Year Founded: 2017
301297—(CHIN)
Rev.: $87,575,904
Assets: $244,430,784
Liabilities: $53,182,116
Net Worth: $191,248,668
Earnings: $12,366,432
Fiscal Year-end: 12/31/22
Electronic Component Mfr & Distr
N.A.I.C.S.: 334419
Xianhan He *(Chm)*

**FERROTEC HOLDINGS COR-
PORATION**
2-3-4 Nihonbashi Plaza Building 5F,
Chuo-ku, Tokyo, 103-0027, Japan
Tel.: (81) 332818808   JP
Web Site: https://www.ferrotec.co.jp
Year Founded: 1980
6890—(TKS)
Rev.: $1,470,262,300
Assets: $3,371,271,860
Liabilities: $1,532,594,600
Net Worth: $1,838,677,260
Earnings: $100,167,940
Emp.: 14,192
Fiscal Year-end: 03/31/24
Vacuum Seals, Ceramics, Quartz,
Silicon Crystal, Thermo Modules, Fer-
rofluid & Electronic Device Mfr
N.A.I.C.S.: 339991
Akira Yamamura *(Pres)*

Subsidiaries:

ALIONTEK CORPORATION   **(1)**

2-37-1 Miharashi Hill, Yamagata, 990-2317, Japan
Tel.: (81) 236891560
Web Site: https://www.aliontek.co.jp
Semiconductor Equipment Mfr & Sales
N.A.I.C.S.: 334413
Hiroyuki Yamakawa *(Pres)*

Advanced Quartz Material (Hangzhou) Co., Ltd. **(1)**
668 Binkang Road, Binjiang District, Hangzhou, 310051, Zhejiang, China **(100%)**
Tel.: (86) 571 86698292
Web Site: http://www.ferrotec.com.cn
Quartz Product Mfr
N.A.I.C.S.: 334419

Asahi Seisakusho Co., Ltd. **(1)**
Kyoeki Building 7F 1-13-8 Sengen-cho, Nishi, Yokohama, 220-0072, Kanagawa, Japan
Tel.: (81) 45 620 3156
Industrial Automation Equipments Mfr
N.A.I.C.S.: 333248
Takahiro Sugimoto *(Pres)*

FERROTEC CORPORATION SINGAPORE PTE LTD **(1)**
1 Tai Seng Avenue Block A 02-11 Tai Seng Exchange, Singapore, 536464, Singapore
Tel.: (65) 6562337733
Web Site: https://www.ferrotec.com.sg
Sales Range: $25-49.9 Million
Emp.: 6
Semiconductor Equipment Mfr
N.A.I.C.S.: 334413

Ferrotec (USA) Corporation **(1)**
33 Constitution Dr, Bedford, NH 03110 **(100%)**
Tel.: (603) 472-6800
Web Site: https://www.ferrotec.com
Sales Range: $25-49.9 Million
Emp.: 90
Thermal Modules, Vacuum Feedthroughs, E-Beam Guns & Ferrofluids Mfr & Sales
N.A.I.C.S.: 339991
Eiji Miyanaga *(Pres)*

Subsidiary (Domestic):

Meivac, Inc. **(2)**
5830 Hellyer Ave, San Jose, CA 95138
Tel.: (408) 362-1000
Web Site: http://www.meivac.com
Sales Range: $1-9.9 Million
Emp.: 30
Sputtering Deposition For Magnetic Heads/Disk Drives
N.A.I.C.S.: 334413
David Meidinger *(Founder & CEO)*

Ferrotec AMC Malaysia Sdn. Bhd. **(1)**
A502 5th Floor West Wing Wisma Consplant 2 No 7 Jalan SS16/1, 47500, Subang Jaya, Selangor, Malaysia
Tel.: (60) 35 638 1688
Web Site: https://ferrotec.com.my
Semiconductor Equipment Distr
N.A.I.C.S.: 423690

Ferrotec Alion Corporation **(1)**
2-37-4 Miharashi No Oka, Yamagata, 990-2317, Japan
Tel.: (81) 23 676 8880
Quartz Product Mfr
N.A.I.C.S.: 327991
Kiyoshi Maekawa *(Pres)*

Ferrotec Ceramics Corporation **(1)**
2-3-4 Nihonbashi, Chuo-ku, Tokyo, 103-0027, Japan
Tel.: (81) 335160800
Web Site: http://www.ft-ceramics.co.jp
Sales Range: $50-74.9 Million
Semiconductor Ceramic Products Mfr & Sales
N.A.I.C.S.: 334413
Shiro Tsuda *(Pres)*

Ferrotec GmbH **(1)**
Seerosenstrasse 1, 72669, Unterensingen, Germany **(100%)**
Tel.: (49) 702292700
Web Site: http://www.ferrotec.com
Sales Range: $25-49.9 Million
Emp.: 50

Environmental Seals, Fluid Bearings & Thermal Solutions
N.A.I.C.S.: 325998

Ferrotec Korea Corporation **(1)**
610 Building B 40 Imi-ro Poil-dong Indeokwon IT Valley, Uiwang, 16066, Gyeonggi, Korea (South)
Tel.: (82) 31 423 6420
Web Site: https://www.ferrotec.co.kr
Electronic Components Mfr
N.A.I.C.S.: 334419

Ferrotec Material Technologies Corporation **(1)**
5th Floor Nihonbashi Plaza Building 2-3-4, Nihonbashi Chuo-ku, Tokyo, 103-0027, Japan
Tel.: (81) 33 516 0800
Web Site: https://ft-mt.co.jp
Emp.: 400
Semiconductor Equipment Related Product Mfr
N.A.I.C.S.: 333242
Tatsuya Noguchi *(Pres)*

Ferrotec Power Semiconductor (Japan) Corp. **(1)**
2-3-4 Nihonbashi Nihonbashi Plaza Building, Chuo-ku, Tokyo, 103-0027, Japan
Tel.: (81) 33 516 0800
Web Site: https://www.ftpowersemi.co.jp
Emp.: 7
Semiconductor Equipment Related Product Mfr
N.A.I.C.S.: 333242
Taku Hamaguchi *(Pres & CEO)*

Ferrotec Power Semiconductor GmbH **(1)**
Seerosenstrasse 1, 72669, Unterensingen, Germany
Tel.: (49) 70 229 2700
Electronic Components Mfr
N.A.I.C.S.: 334419

Ferrotec S.R.L. **(1)**
Centro Direzionale Colleoni Palazzo Cassiopea 3 Via Paracelso 26, 20864, Agrate Brianza, MB, Italy
Tel.: (39) 039 890 1579
Web Site: https://www.ferrotec-global.com
Essential Device Mfr
N.A.I.C.S.: 339999

Ferrotec Semiconductor Material Corporation **(1)**
Nihonbashi Plaza BLDG 2-3-4, Nihonbashi Chuo-Ku, Tokyo, 103-0027, Japan
Tel.: (81) 33 510 7077
Electronic Components Mfr
N.A.I.C.S.: 334419

Ferrotec Silicon Corporation **(1)**
Nihonbashi Plaza Building 2-3-4 Nihonbashi, Chuo-ku, Tokyo, 103-0027, Japan
Tel.: (81) 352995001
Web Site: https://sifusion.co.jp
Sales Range: $25-49.9 Million
Emp.: 2
Semiconductor Product Mfr
N.A.I.C.S.: 334413

Ferrotec Taiwan Co., Ltd. **(1)**
1 4th Floor No 25 Puding Road, East District, Hsinchu, 30072, Taiwan
Tel.: (886) 36662369
Web Site: https://www.ferrotec.com.tw
Sales Range: $25-49.9 Million
Emp.: 10
Semiconductor Devices Mfr
N.A.I.C.S.: 334413

Ferrotec-Nord Corporation **(1)**
Peschany Carier 3, 109383, Moscow, Russia
Tel.: (7) 4993565389
Web Site: https://www.ferrotec-nord.com
Thermoelectric Modules Mfr
N.A.I.C.S.: 335999

HANGZHOU DAHE THERMO-MAGNETICS CO., LTD. (FTH) **(1)**
777 Binkang Road Binjiang District, Hangzhou, 310053, Zhejiang, China
Tel.: (86) 571 866 99985
Web Site: http://www.ferrotec.com.cn
Ferrofluidic, Thermoelectric & Precision Machining Technologies
N.A.I.C.S.: 333248

HANGZHOU DAHE THERMO-MAGNETICS CO., LTD. - Quartz Division **(1)**
668/777 Binkang Road, Binjiang District, Hangzhou, 310053, Zhejiang, China
Tel.: (86) 57186698292
Sales Range: $200-249.9 Million
Quartz Crucible Mfr
N.A.I.C.S.: 334419

HANGZHOU DAHE THERMO-MAGNETICS CO., LTD. - TE Division **(1)**
15F Block C 70 Caobao Road, Shanghai, 200235, China
Tel.: (86) 2164325027
Web Site: http://www.ferrotec.com.cn
Thermoelectric Products Mfr
N.A.I.C.S.: 335999

HANGZHOU DAHE THERMO-MAGNETICS CO., LTD. - VF Division **(1)**
777 Binkang Road, Binjiang District, Hangzhou, 310053, Zhejiang, China
Tel.: (86) 571 86699985
Web Site: http://www.ferrotec.com.cn
Ferrofluidic Seals Mfr
N.A.I.C.S.: 332999

HANGZHOU WAGEN PRECISION TOOLING CO., LTD. **(1)**
No 488 Shenban Road Gongshu Section, Hangzhou, 310022, Zhejiang, China
Tel.: (86) 571 88132960
Web Site: http://www.ferrotec.com
Sales Range: $50-74.9 Million
Precision Tool Mfr
N.A.I.C.S.: 333517
Dai Ming *(Gen Mgr)*

Hangzhou Semiconductor Wafer Co., Ltd. **(1)**
888 Dongken Road, Qiantang New District, Hangzhou, Zeijiang, China
Tel.: (86) 5718 213 8188
Web Site: https://ferrotec-silicon.com
Semiconductor Silicon Wafer Mfr
N.A.I.C.S.: 334413
He Xianhan *(CEO)*

Integrated Materials, Inc. **(1)**
3945 Freedom Cir Ste 450, Santa Clara, CA 95054
Tel.: (408) 437-7591
Semiconductor Mfr
N.A.I.C.S.: 334413

Ohizumi Mfg. Co., Ltd. **(1)**
1-11-4 Shinsayama, Sayama, Saitama, 350-1387, Japan **(51%)**
Tel.: (81) 429539211
Web Site: http://www.ohizumi-mfg.jp
Rev.: $115,022,590
Assets: $109,862,269
Liabilities: $76,199,876
Net Worth: $33,662,394
Earnings: $4,138,442
Emp.: 1,588
Fiscal Year-end: 03/31/2022
Thermistors & Temperature Sensors Mfr
N.A.I.C.S.: 334513
Hidetsune Goto *(Co-Pres)*

Subsidiary (Domestic):

Hakkoda Denshi Co., Ltd. **(2)**
237-14 Aza-Senzaimori Oaza-Sanbongi, Towada, 034-0001, Aomori, Japan
Tel.: (81) 176229393
Electronic Components Mfr
N.A.I.C.S.: 334413

Subsidiary (Non-US):

OHIZUMI MFG (THAILAND) CO., LTD. **(2)**
700/735 700/853 Moo 1, Tambol Phanthong Amphur, Phan Thong, 20160, Chonburi, Thailand
Tel.: (66) 38185588
Electronic Component Mfr & Distr
N.A.I.C.S.: 334413

Plant (Domestic):

Ohizumi MFG Co., Ltd. - Towada Plant **(2)**
1 Aza-Satonosawa Oaza-Sanbongi,

Towada, 034-0001, Aomori, Japan
Tel.: (81) 176235336
Electronic Components Mfr
N.A.I.C.S.: 334413

Subsidiary (Domestic):

Sensor Kogyo Co., Ltd. **(2)**
1-19-35 Higashino, Towada, 034-0004, Aomori, Japan
Tel.: (81) 176241666
Electronic Components Mfr
N.A.I.C.S.: 334413

Plant (Domestic):

Sensor Kogyo Co., Ltd. - Hachinohe Plant **(3)**
21-1 Aza-Deguchitaira Oaza-Niida, Hachinohe, 031-0813, Aomori, Japan
Tel.: (81) 178252002
Electronic Components Mfr
N.A.I.C.S.: 334413

Sensor Kogyo Co.,Ltd. - Gonohe Plant **(3)**
25-7 Atagoushiro Gonohemachi, Sannohe, Aomori, 039-1536, Japan
Tel.: (81) 178626222
Electronic Components Mfr
N.A.I.C.S.: 334413

Shanghai Hanhong Precision Machinery Co., Ltd. **(1)**
188 ShanLian Road BaoShan Vrban Industrial Garden, Shanghai, 200444, China
Tel.: (86) 2136162928
Web Site: http://www.hanhong.sh.cn
Precision Tool Mfr
N.A.I.C.S.: 333517

Shanghai Shenhe Thermo-Magnetics Co., Ltd. - PV Material Division **(1)**
181 Shanlian Road Baoshan City Industrial Park, Shanghai, 200444, China
Tel.: (86) 2136161010
Semiconductor Devices Mfr
N.A.I.C.S.: 334413

Shanghai Shenhe Thermo-Magnetics Co., Ltd. - Silicon Material Division **(1)**
No 181 Shanlian Road Baoshan Urban Industrial Park, Shanghai, 200444, China
Tel.: (86) 2136160798
Web Site: http://www.ferrotec.com.cn
Semiconductor Devices Mfr
N.A.I.C.S.: 334413
Xian Han He *(Pres)*

Shanghai Shenhe Thermo-Magnetics Co., Ltd. - TE Division **(1)**
No 181 Shanlian Rd Baoshan Urban Industrial Park, Shanghai, 200444, China
Tel.: (86) 21 36160564
Web Site: http://www.ferrotec.sh.cn
Sales Range: $400-449.9 Million
Thermoelectric Components Mfr
N.A.I.C.S.: 335999
Xian Han He *(Mgr-Factory)*

Toyo Knife Company, Ltd **(1)**
34-11 Tomiya Aza Hiwatashi, Tomiya-machi Kurokawa-gun, Miyagi, Japan **(91.05%)**
Tel.: (81) 223588911
Web Site: http://www.toyoknife.co.jp
Rev.: $50,190,800
Assets: $66,162,800
Liabilities: $42,233,840
Net Worth: $23,928,960
Earnings: $4,559,280
Emp.: 204
Fiscal Year-end: 03/31/2022
Knife Mfr
N.A.I.C.S.: 333515
Yoshiaki Seino *(Pres & Chm)*

FERROVIA CENTRO-ATLANTICA S.A.

R Sapucai 383-Floresta, Belo Horizonte, 30150-050, Minas Gerais, Brazil
Tel.: (55) 3132794900
VSPT3—(BRAZ)
Sales Range: Less than $1 Million
Transportation & Logistics Services
N.A.I.C.S.: 541614

Ferrovia Centro-Atlantica S.A.—(Continued)

Marcello Magistrini Spinelli *(Chm & CEO)*

FERROVIAL S.A.
Principe de Vergara 135, 28002, Madrid, Spain
Tel.: (34) 915862500　　　ES
Web Site: https://www.ferrovial.com
Year Founded: 1952
FER—(MAD)
Rev.: $7,791,954,560
Assets: $28,406,734,720
Liabilities: $23,706,260,240
Net Worth: $4,700,474,480
Earnings: ($503,578,400)
Emp.: 80,119
Fiscal Year-end: 12/31/20
Transport Infrastructure Design, Construction, Management, Administration & Maintenance Services
N.A.I.C.S.: 488999
Rafael del Pino Calvo-Sotelo *(Chm)*

Subsidiaries:

Amey TPT Limited　　　　　　**(1)**
3rd Floor 10 Furnival Street, London, EC4A
1AB, United Kingdom
Tel.: (44) 2079212930
Web Site: http://www.tpt.amey.co.uk
Consulting Services
N.A.I.C.S.: 541618
Stephen Ames *(Comml Dir)*

Budimex Bau GmbH　　　　　　**(1)**
An d Wuhlheide 232B 1 OG, 12459, Berlin,
Germany
Tel.: (49) 3080907046
Web Site: https://budimex-bau.de
N.A.I.C.S.: 541330
Jacek Zwiech *(Chm)*

California Rail Builders, LLC　　　**(1)**
400 N F St, Wasco, CA 93280
Tel.: (661) 438-3440
Web Site:
http://www.californiarailbuilders.com
Rail Services
N.A.I.C.S.: 488210
Israel Valencia *(Coord-Procurement)*

Cintra Infraestructuras, S.A.U.　　**(1)**
Plaza Manuel Gomez Moreno 2, 28020,
Madrid, Spain　　　　　　**(100%)**
Tel.: (34) 914185600
Web Site: http://www.Cintra.es
Sales Range: $1-4.9 Billion
Emp.: 4,456
Toll Road Operation
N.A.I.C.S.: 488490

Ditecpesa, S.A.　　　　　　**(1)**
C/ Charles Darwin 4, 28806, Alcala de
Henares, Madrid, Spain
Tel.: (34) 918796930
N.A.I.C.S.: 324121

FBSerwis Dolny Slask Sp. z o.o　　**(1)**
Scinawka Dolna 86, 57-410, Scinawka
Srednia, Poland
Tel.: (48) 746629050
Biological Waste Treatment Services
N.A.I.C.S.: 562211

FBSerwis Kamiensk Sp. z o.o.　　**(1)**
Ul Wielunska 50, Kamiensk, 97-360, Lodz,
Poland
Tel.: (48) 887803432
Biological Waste Treatment Services
N.A.I.C.S.: 562211

FBSerwis Karpatia Sp. z o.o.　　**(1)**
Ul Odlegla 8, 33-100, Tarnow, Poland
Tel.: (48) 146263540
Biological Waste Treatment Services
N.A.I.C.S.: 562211

FBSerwis Odbior Sp. z o.o.　　　**(1)**
Ul Siedmiogrodzka 9, 01-204, Warsaw,
Poland
Tel.: (48) 226236380
Biological Waste Treatment Services
N.A.I.C.S.: 562211

FBSerwis SA　　　　　　　**(1)**

Ul Siedmiogrodzka 9, 01-204, Warsaw,
Poland
Tel.: (48) 226236380
Web Site: http://www.fbserwis.pl
Biological Waste Treatment Services
N.A.I.C.S.: 562211

FBSerwis Wroclaw Sp. z o.o.　　**(1)**
Ul Atramentowa 10, Kobierzyce, 55-040,
Bielany Wroclawskie, Poland
Tel.: (48) 713287036
Biological Waste Treatment Services
N.A.I.C.S.: 562211

Ferrovial Aeropuertos S.A.　　**(1)**
Caleruega 102 104 Planta 9 Edificio Ofipi-
nar, 28033, Madrid, Spain
Tel.: (34) 917686600
Sales Range: $25-49.9 Million
Emp.: 50
Airport Operator
N.A.I.C.S.: 488119

Holding (Non-US):

Heathrow Airport Holdings
Limited　　　　　　　**(2)**
The Compass Centre Nelson Road, London
Heathrow Airport, Hounslow, TW6 2GW,
Mddx, United Kingdom　　**(49.99%)**
Tel.: (44) 844 335 1801
Web Site: http://www.heathrowairport.com
Sales Range: $1-4.9 Billion
Assets: $23,148,724,770
Liabilities: $21,813,438,420
Net Worth: $1,335,286,350
Earnings: ($180,545,760)
Emp.: 6,714
Airport Operator
N.A.I.C.S.: 488119
Carol Hui *(Gen Counsel & Sec)*

Subsidiary (Domestic):

Aberdeen Airport Ltd.　　　**(3)**
Aberdeen International Airport, Dyce, Aber-
deen, AB21 7DU, United Kingdom
Tel.: (44) 344 481 6666
Web Site: https://www.aberdeenairport.com
Emp.: 85
Airport
N.A.I.C.S.: 488119

Glasgow Airport Ltd.　　　　**(3)**
St Andrews Drive, Paisley, PA3 2SW, Ren-
frewshire, United Kingdom
Tel.: (44) 344 481 5555
Web Site: https://www.glasgowairport.com
Sales Range: $125-149.9 Million
Emp.: 500
Airport
N.A.I.C.S.: 488119
Francois Bourienne *(Dir-Comml)*

Subsidiary (Non-US):

Heathrow Airport Ltd.　　　**(3)**
Tel.: (44) 844 335 1801
Web Site: https://www.heathrow.com
Sales Range: $1-4.9 Billion
Emp.: 4,500
Airport Operator
N.A.I.C.S.: 488119

Subsidiary (Domestic):

Southampton International　　**(3)**
Wide Lane, Southampton, SO18 2NL,
United Kingdom
Tel.: (44) 344 481 7777
Web Site:
https://www.southamptonairport.com
Sales Range: $25-49.9 Million
Emp.: 213
Airport Operations
N.A.I.C.S.: 488119
Steve Szalay *(Dir-Ops)*

Ferrovial Construccion, S.A.　　**(1)**
C Ribera del Loira 42 Puerta de las Na-
ciones Business Park, 28042, Madrid,
Spain
Tel.: (34) 913008500
Transportation Infrastructure Construction
Services
N.A.I.C.S.: 237310

Ferrovial Construction　　　**(1)**
C/ Ribera del Loira 42 Parque Empresarial
Puerta de las Naciones, 28042, Madrid,
Spain

Tel.: (34) 913008500
Sales Range: $1-4.9 Billion
Emp.: 13,870
Infrastructure Construction Services
N.A.I.C.S.: 237990
Ignacio Gaston *(CEO)*

Subsidiary (Domestic):

Cadagua S.A.　　　　　　**(2)**
Gran Via 45 7th and 8th, 48011, Bilbao,
Spain
Tel.: (34) 944817300
Web Site: http://www.cadagua.es
Sales Range: $200-249.9 Million
Emp.: 440
Water Treatment Plant Construction Ser-
vices
N.A.I.C.S.: 237110

Subsidiary (US):

Ferrovial Agroman US Corp.　　**(2)**
9600 Great Hills Trl Ste 200 E, Austin, TX
78759
Tel.: (512) 637-8587
Web Site: http://www.fauscorp.com
Sales Range: $25-49.9 Million
Emp.: 45
Construction Services
N.A.I.C.S.: 237990
Ignacio Vivancos *(Mng Dir)*

Webber LLC　　　　　　**(2)**
14333 Chrisman Rd, Houston, TX 77039
Tel.: (832) 850-2745
Web Site: http://www.wwebber.com
Sales Range: $550-599.9 Million
Emp.: 2,000
Infrastructure Construction Services
N.A.I.C.S.: 237990
Mitchell J. Beckman *(Chief HR Officer & Dir-HR)*

Ferrovial Construction Canada
Inc.　　　　　　　　**(1)**
2680 Skymark Avenue Suite 520, Missis-
sauga, L4W 5L6, ON, Canada
Tel.: (905) 366-3663
Transportation Infrastructure Construction
Services
N.A.I.C.S.: 237310

Ferrovial Construction Texas,
LLC　　　　　　　　**(1)**
9600 Great Hills Trl Ste 200E, Austin, TX
78759
Tel.: (512) 637-8587
Transportation Infrastructure Construction
Services
N.A.I.C.S.: 237310

Ferrovial Corporacion, S.A.　　**(1)**
C Principe de Vergara 135, 28002, Madrid,
Spain
Tel.: (34) 915862500
Transportation Infrastructure Construction
Services
N.A.I.C.S.: 237310

Subsidiary (Non-US):

Budimex S.A.　　　　　　**(2)**
ul Siedmiogrodzka 9, 01-204, Warsaw,
Poland　　　　　　　**(59%)**
Tel.: (48) 226236000
Web Site: https://www.budimex.pl
Rev.: $2,490,222,301
Assets: $2,138,780,736
Liabilities: $1,739,822,912
Net Worth: $398,957,824
Earnings: $189,549,034
Emp.: 5,076
Fiscal Year-end: 12/31/2023
Construction Services
N.A.I.C.S.: 237990
Henryk Urbanski *(Member-Mgmt Bd)*

Ferrovial Servicios Chile SPA　　**(1)**
Avenida Del Valle Sur 577 Office 402, Hue-
churaba, Santiago, Chile
Tel.: (56) 232849300
Web Site: http://www.ferrovialservicios.cl
Transportation Infrastructure Construction
Services
N.A.I.C.S.: 237310

Ferrovial Servicios S.A.　　　**(1)**
C/Quintanavides 21 Parque Via Norte - Edi-
ficio 5, 28050, Madrid, Spain　　**(99.88%)**
Tel.: (34) 913388300

Web Site: https://www.ferrovial.com
Sales Range: $15-24.9 Billion
Business Support Services
N.A.I.C.S.: 561499

Subsidiary (Non-US):

Amey UK plc　　　　　　**(2)**
The Sherard Building Edmund Halley Road,
Oxford, OX4 4DQ, United
Kingdom　　　　　　　**(100%)**
Tel.: (44) 1865713100
Web Site: http://www.amey.co.uk
Rev.: $3,658,439,519
Assets: $2,776,514,354
Liabilities: $2,036,308,370
Net Worth: $740,205,984
Earnings: $144,986,631
Emp.: 10,964
Fiscal Year-end: 12/31/2014
Infrastructure Maintenance & Support Ser-
vices
N.A.I.C.S.: 488999
Andrew Nelson *(CFO)*

Subsidiary (Domestic):

Amey Infrastructure Services
Ltd.　　　　　　　　**(3)**
Sutton Courtenay, Abingdon, OX14 4PP,
Oxfordshire, United Kingdom　**(100%)**
Tel.: (44) 1235848811
Web Site: http://www.amey.co.uk
Sales Range: $1-4.9 Billion
Emp.: 9,000
Public & Private Infrastructure Services
N.A.I.C.S.: 488490

Subsidiary (Domestic):

Amey Rail Ltd.　　　　　　**(4)**
1 Redcliff Street, Bristol, BS1 6QZ, United
Kingdom　　　　　　　**(100%)**
Tel.: (44) 1179348836
Web Site: http://www.amey.co.uk
Sales Range: $25-49.9 Million
Emp.: 70
Railway Systems Services
N.A.I.C.S.: 485112
Nicola Hindle *(Mng Dir-Consulting & Rail)*

Subsidiary (Domestic):

Ferroser　　　　　　　**(2)**
C Serrano Galvache 56 Edificio Madrono,
28033, Madrid, Spain
Tel.: (34) 913388300
Web Site: http://www.ferroser.com
Sales Range: $800-899.9 Million
Infrastructure Maintenance Services
N.A.I.C.S.: 561210

Ferrovial Servicos, S.A.　　　**(1)**
Av Almirante Gago Coutinho 144, 1700-
033, Lisbon, Portugal
Tel.: (351) 218459390
Web Site: http://www.ferrovialservicos.pt
Facility Services
N.A.I.C.S.: 561210

I-77 Mobility Partners LLC　　**(1)**
8015 W WT Harris Blvd, Charlotte, NC
28216
Tel.: (980) 337-2400
Web Site: https://www.i77express.com
N.A.I.C.S.: 532411

Inagra, S.A.　　　　　　**(1)**
Plaza de los Campos 4, 18009, Granada,
Spain
Tel.: (34) 958229107
Web Site: http://www.inagra.es
Street Cleaning & Waste Collection Ser-
vices
N.A.I.C.S.: 562998

Subsidiary (US):

Cintra Developments, LLC　　**(2)**
9600 Great Hills Trl Ste 250E, Austin, TX
78759
Tel.: (512) 637-8545
Sales Range: $25-49.9 Million
Emp.: 40
Transportation Services
N.A.I.C.S.: 488999
Nicalos Ruvio *(Pres)*

Mostostal Krakow S.A.　　　**(1)**
Ujastek 7 Street, 30-969, Krakow, Poland
Tel.: (48) 126802525

Web Site: http://www.mostostal.com.pl
Construction Services
N.A.I.C.S.: 236220
Jacek Lech *(Chm)*

NTE Mobility Partners LLC **(1)**
9001 Airport Fwy Ste 600, North Richland
Hills, TX 76180
Tel.: (682) 334-5470
Transportation Infrastructure Construction
Services
N.A.I.C.S.: 237310
Robert Hinkle *(Dir-Corp Affairs)*

**Nationwide Distribution Services
Ltd.** **(1)**
Unit B Great Central Way, Rugby, CV21
3XH, Warwickshire, United Kingdom
Tel.: (44) 1788821400
Web Site: https://nds.limited
Emp.: 80
Cable Installation & Civil Work Services
N.A.I.C.S.: 238210

Southern Crushed Concrete LLC **(1)**
1725 Hughes Landing Ste 1200, The
Woodlands, TX 77380
Tel.: (281) 907-8600
Web Site: http://www.scctx.com
Recycled Concrete Product Mfr
N.A.I.C.S.: 327320
Wayne Webber *(Founder)*

Steel Ingenieria, S.A. **(1)**
Francisco Astaburuaga 9477, 9130547, Lo
Espejo, Chile
Tel.: (56) 933735564
Web Site: https://www.steelchileingenieria.cl
N.A.I.C.S.: 332999

Vialivre, S.A. **(1)**
Av da Republica n 32 3 Esq, 1050-193, Lis-
bon, Portugal
Tel.: (351) 252004460
Web Site: http://www.vialivre.pt
Toll Collection Services
N.A.I.C.S.: 488490

Wondo Mobility, S.L.U. **(1)**
C Principe de Vergara 135, 28002, Madrid,
Spain
Tel.: (34) 900998705
Web Site: http://www.wondo.es
Mobile Application Services
N.A.I.C.S.: 541511

FERROVIE DELLO STATO ITALIANE S.P.A.

Piazza della Croce Rossa 1, 00161,
Rome, Italy
Tel.: (39) 06 44101 IT
Web Site: http://www.fsitaliane.it
Rev.: $13,814,695,620
Assets: $82,946,507,010
Liabilities: $35,253,895,380
Net Worth: $47,692,611,630
Earnings: $617,646,600
Emp.: 82,944
Fiscal Year-end: 12/31/18
Holding Company; Railway Transpor-
tation Services
N.A.I.C.S.: 551112
Giovanni Conti *(Chief Risk Officer)*

Subsidiaries:

**Anas International Enterprise
S.p.A.** **(1)**
Via Giovanni Giolitti 2, 00185, Rome, Italy
Tel.: (39) 06 444 6101
Web Site:
https://www.anasinternational.com
Engineeeing Services
N.A.I.C.S.: 541330

Ataf Gestioni S.r.l. **(1)**
Viale dei Mille 115, 50131, Florence, Italy
Tel.: (39) 0555 6501
Transportation Services
N.A.I.C.S.: 485999
Bonora Stefano *(CEO)*

**Berchtesgardener Land Bahn
GmbH** **(1)**
Hermann-Lons-Strasse 4, 83395, Freilass-
ing, Germany
Tel.: (49) 180 123 1236
Web Site: https://www.blb.info

Rail Transportation Services
N.A.I.C.S.: 488210

Blu Jet S.r.l. **(1)**
Via Calabria 1, 98122, Messina, ME, Italy
Tel.: (39) 03423255869
Web Site: https://www.blujetlines.it
Transportation Services
N.A.I.C.S.: 485999

Bluferries S.r.l. **(1)**
Via Calabria 1, 98122, Messina, ME, Italy
Tel.: (39) 090 678 6626
Web Site: https://www.bluferries.it
Transportation Services
N.A.I.C.S.: 485999

Busitalia Campania S.p.A. **(1)**
Via Santi Martiri Salernitani SNC interno
Stazione FS, 84123, Salerno, Italy
Tel.: (39) 089 984 7508
Transportation Services
N.A.I.C.S.: 485999
Sergio Paglicci *(Chm)*

Busitalia Rail Service S.r.l. **(1)**
Piazza della Croce Rossa 1, 00161, Rome,
Italy
Tel.: (39) 064 410 5471
Rail Transportation Services
N.A.I.C.S.: 488210

Busitalia Veneto S.p.A. **(1)**
Via del Pescarotto 25/27, 35131, Padova,
Italy
Tel.: (39) 049 820 6811
Transportation Services
N.A.I.C.S.: 485999
Sabrina Lai *(Chm)*

Cremonesi Workshop S.r.l. **(1)**
Via Cefalonia 70, 25124, Brescia, Italy
Tel.: (39) 03 022 1166
Web Site: https://www.crew.it
Architecture & Planning Services
N.A.I.C.S.: 541310

Die Landerbahn CZ s.r.o. **(1)**
Husova 400, 440 01, Louny, Czech Repub-
lic
Tel.: (420) 47 847 9202
Web Site: https://www.laenderbahn.cz
Rail Transportation Services
N.A.I.C.S.: 488210

Erixx GmbH **(1)**
Biermannstrasse 33, 29221, Celle, Ger-
many
Tel.: (49) 519 196 9440
Web Site: https://www.erixx.de
Rail Transportation Services
N.A.I.C.S.: 488210
Jost Knebel *(Mng Dir)*

FS Sistemi Urbani S.r.l. **(1)**
Piazza della Croce Rossa 1, 00161, Rome,
Italy
Tel.: (39) 064 410 5070
Web Site: https://www.fssistemiurbani.it
Railway Supporting Services
N.A.I.C.S.: 488210

Ferservizi S.p.A. **(1)**
Piazza della Croce Rossa 1, 00161, Rome,
Italy **(100%)**
Tel.: (39) 06 44105 592
Web Site: http://www.ferservizi.it
Office Administrative, Facility & Technology
Support Services
N.A.I.C.S.: 561499
Francesco Rossi *(CEO & Gen Mgr)*

Grandi Stazioni S.p.A. **(1)**
Via G Giolitti 34, 00185, Rome,
Italy **(59.99%)**
Tel.: (39) 06 478 411
Web Site: http://www.grandistazioni.it
Railway Station Redevelopment, Enhance-
ment & Management Services
N.A.I.C.S.: 561210
Silvio Gizzi *(CEO & Gen Mgr)*

Infrarail Firenze S.r.l. **(1)**
Via Circondaria 32-34, 50127, Florence,
Italy
Tel.: (39) 0559 0781
Web Site: https://www.ifrfirenze.it
Railway Bypass Construction Services
N.A.I.C.S.: 237310
Sandro Starace *(Mgr-Human Resources)*

Italcertifer S.p.A. **(1)**
Piazza della Stazione 45, 50123, Florence,
Italy
Tel.: (39) 055 298 8811
Web Site: https://www.italcertifer.com
Rail Transportation Services
N.A.I.C.S.: 488210
Rosario Gaetano *(Pres)*

Italferr S.p.A. **(1)**
Via Vito Giuseppe Galati 71, 00155, Rome,
Italy **(100%)**
Tel.: (39) 0649752109
Web Site: http://www.italferr.it
Railway Industry Engineering Services
N.A.I.C.S.: 541330
Andrea Nardinocchi *(Mgr-Technical)*

Mercitalia Intermodal S.p.A. **(1)**
Via Valtellina 5/7, 20159, Milan, Italy
Tel.: (39) 0266 8951
Web Site: https://www.mercitaliaintermodal.it
Transportation Services
N.A.I.C.S.: 485999
Francesco Parlato *(Pres)*

**Mercitalia Shunting & Terminal
S.r.l.** **(1)**
Via Angelo Scarsellini 119-17 Piano-Torre
B, 16149, Genoa, Italy
Tel.: (39) 01 064 8541
Web Site:
https://mercitaliashuntingandterminal.it
Railway Maintenance Services
N.A.I.C.S.: 488210

**Metronom Eisenbahngesellschaft
mbH** **(1)**
St-Viti-Str 15, 29525, Uelzen, Germany
Tel.: (49) 58 197 1640
Web Site: https://www.der-metronom.com
Rail Transportation Services
N.A.I.C.S.: 488210
Lorenz Kasch *(Mng Dir)*

**Quadrilatero Marche-Umbria
S.p.A.** **(1)**
Via Monzambano 10, 00185, Rome, Italy
Tel.: (39) 068 456 0531
Web Site: https://www.quadrilaterospa.it
Road Construction Services
N.A.I.C.S.: 237310

**Rete Ferroviaria Italiana - RFI
S.p.A.** **(1)**
Piazza della Croce Rossa 1, 00161, Rome,
Italy **(100%)**
Tel.: (39) 06 442 49390
Web Site: http://www.rfi.it
Railway Infrastructure Management Ser-
vices
N.A.I.C.S.: 488210
Maurizio Gentile *(CEO & Gen Mgr)*

Rom Rail S.r.l. **(1)**
Str Pechea Nr 10-12 Et 2 Ap 10 Sector 1,
013982, Bucharest, Romania
Tel.: (40) 21 319 1613
Web Site: https://www.romrail.ro
Rail Transportation Services
N.A.I.C.S.: 488210

Savit S.r.l. **(1)**
Bruno Capponi 102, 05100, Terni, TR, Italy
Tel.: (39) 074 461 1120
Web Site: https://savitnet.com
Transportation Services
N.A.I.C.S.: 485999

Sippel-Travel GmbH **(1)**
Anna-Birle-Strasse 5b, 55252, Mainz-
Kastel, Germany
Tel.: (49) 61 229 1240
Transportation Services
N.A.I.C.S.: 485999

TX Logistik A/S **(1)**
Istedvej 11, 6330, Padborg, Denmark
Tel.: (45) 7 367 0620
Logistic Services
N.A.I.C.S.: 484110

TX Logistik AB **(1)**
Springpostgranden 3, 25220, Helsingborg,
Sweden
Tel.: (46) 42 600 5010
Logistic Services
N.A.I.C.S.: 484110

TX Logistik GmbH **(1)**

Hofackerstrasse 1, 4132, Muttenz, Switzer-
land
Tel.: (41) 61 501 1030
Logistic Services
N.A.I.C.S.: 484110

TX Logistik Transalpine GmbH **(1)**
Concorde Business Park 1/E2, 2320,
Schwechat, Austria
Tel.: (43) 17 072 3250
Logistic Services
N.A.I.C.S.: 484110

Terminal Alptransit S.r.l. **(1)**
Via Valtellina 5/7, 20159, Milan, Italy
Tel.: (39) 0266 8951
Freight Transportation Services
N.A.I.C.S.: 488510

Thello SAS **(1)**
Tour de Lyon 185 Rue de Bercy, 75012,
Paris, France
Tel.: (33) 18 382 0000
Web Site: https://www.thello.com
Rail Transportation Services
N.A.I.C.S.: 488210

TrainOSE SA **(1)**
41 Syggrou Av and 13 Petmeza Str, 11743,
Athens, Greece
Tel.: (30) 213 012 1121
Web Site: https://www.trainose.gr
Transportation Services
N.A.I.C.S.: 485999
Dario Lo Bosco *(Chm)*

Trenitalia S.p.A. **(1)**
Piazza della Croce Rossa 1, 00161, Rome,
Italy **(100%)**
Tel.: (39) 06 68475475
Web Site: http://www.trenitalia.com
Commuter & Freight Railway Operator
N.A.I.C.S.: 485112
Barbara Morgante *(CEO)*

Subsidiary (Non-US):

Trenitalia c2c Limited **(2)**
2nd Floor Cutlers Court 115 Houndsditch,
London, EC3A 7BR, United
Kingdom **(100%)**
Tel.: (44) 345 744 4422
Web Site: http://www.c2c-online.co.uk
Train Service
N.A.I.C.S.: 482111

Trenitalia TPER Scarl **(1)**
Via del Lazzaretto 16, 40131, Bologna, Italy
Tel.: (39) 084 015 1152
Web Site: https://trenitaliatper.force.com
Rail Transportation Services
N.A.I.C.S.: 488210

Verkehrstriebe Bils GmbH **(1)**
Haberkamp 2-6 Albersloh, Sendenhorst,
48324, Warendorf, Germany
Tel.: (49) 253 5890
Web Site: https://www.bils.de
Transportation Services
N.A.I.C.S.: 485999

Vlexx GmbH **(1)**
Mombacher Strasse 36, 55122, Mainz, Ger-
many
Tel.: (49) 6131 610 1211
Web Site: https://www.vlexx.de
Rail Transportation Services
N.A.I.C.S.: 488210

**sei mobil Verkehrsgesellschaft
mbH** **(1)**
Am neue Baum 20, 59229, Ahlen, Germany
Tel.: (49) 253 5890
Web Site: https://www.seimobil.net
Transportation Services
N.A.I.C.S.: 485999

FERRUM S.A.

ul Porcelanowa 11, 40-246, Katowice,
Poland
Tel.: (48) 327304799
Web Site: https://www.ferrum.com.pl
Year Founded: 1874
FER—(WAR)
Rev.: $159,818,597
Assets: $120,145,071
Liabilities: $87,838,668
Net Worth: $32,306,402
Earnings: ($87,907)

Ferrum S.A.—(Continued)

Emp.: 300
Fiscal Year-end: 12/31/23
Steel Pole Mfr
N.A.I.C.S.: 331210
Grzegorz Kowalik (Vice Chm-Mgmt Bd-Fin & Restructuring)

FERSPED A.D.
Ul Makedonija 11a, 1000, Skopje, North Macedonia
Tel.: (389) 23149444
Web Site:
   https://www.fersped.com.mk
Year Founded: 1968
FERS—(MAC)
Rev.: $83,661,671
Assets: $49,274,530
Liabilities: $6,182,648
Net Worth: $43,091,882
Earnings: $2,762,824
Fiscal Year-end: 12/31/23
Holding Company; Transportation & Logistics Services
N.A.I.C.S.: 488510
Shterjo Nakov (Chm)

Subsidiaries:

Fertrade d.o.o. (1)
Kralja Milutina 55, 11 000, Belgrade, Serbia
Tel.: (381) 113618664
Web Site: http://www.fersped.com.mk
Freight Transportation Arrangement
N.A.I.C.S.: 488510

Hoteli-Metropol AD (1)
Naselba Dolno Konjsko bb, 6000, Ohrid, North Macedonia
Tel.: (389) 46203001
Web Site:
   https://www.metropol-ohrid.com.mk
Rev.: $3,790,252
Assets: $11,259,940
Liabilities: $1,540,825
Net Worth: $9,719,115
Earnings: $681,946
Fiscal Year-end: 12/31/2019
Home Management Services
N.A.I.C.S.: 721110

FERTEK, INC.
3000 Francis Hughes, Laval, H7L 3J5, QC, Canada
Tel.: (450) 663-8700
Web Site: http://www.numesh.com
Sales Range: $200-249.9 Million
Emp.: 150
Mfr of Steel Wire & Mesh Products
N.A.I.C.S.: 332618
Yvan Despres (VP)

Subsidiaries:

Numesh, Inc. (1)
3000 Av Francis-Hughes, Laval, H7L 3J5, QC, Canada (100%)
Tel.: (450) 663-8700
Web Site: https://www.numesh.com
Sales Range: $50-74.9 Million
Emp.: 110
Mfr of Wire, Pipe, Mine & Construction Welded Mesh Products
N.A.I.C.S.: 332618
Jean-Francois Thibault (VP)

FERTIGAMA, S.L.
Plaza Felisa Munarriz 2 Entreplanta-Oficina B, Navarre, 31005, Pamplona, Spain
Tel.: (34) 948238833   ES
Web Site: http://www.fertigama.es
Chemicals Mfr
N.A.I.C.S.: 325180

Subsidiaries:

SLIR, S.L. (1)
Ctra Figarol, 31310, Carcastillo, Navarre, Spain
Tel.: (34) 948 399 017
Web Site: http://www.slir.es
Organic Fertilizer Mfr

N.A.I.C.S.: 325311

FERTOZ LTD.
Level 5 126 Phillip Street, Sydney, 2000, NSW, Australia
Tel.: (61) 280721400
Web Site: http://www.fertoz.com
Year Founded: 2010
FTZ—(ASX)
Rev.: $1,897,598
Assets: $8,478,631
Liabilities: $1,165,248
Net Worth: $7,313,383
Earnings: ($3,048,224)
Emp.: 1,500
Fiscal Year-end: 12/31/23
Fertilizer Mfr
N.A.I.C.S.: 325312
Patrick L. Avery (Chm & Exec Dir)

FERUS INC.
Suite 120 401 9th Avenue SW, Calgary, T2P 3C5, AB, Canada
Tel.: (403) 517-8777
Web Site: http://www.ferus.ca
Year Founded: 2001
Rev.: $181,801,890
Emp.: 95
Energy Service Provider
N.A.I.C.S.: 541620
Chad Porter (COO)

Subsidiaries:

Eagle LNG Partners LLC (1)
Chasewood Technology Park 20445 State Hwy 249 Ste 250, Houston, TX 77070
Tel.: (844) 253-2453
Web Site: http://www.eaglelng.com
Gas Mfr
N.A.I.C.S.: 325120
Dario Alvarez (Mgr-PR)

Ferus Inc. - Dawson Creek N2 Plant (1)
2600 92nd Ave, Dawson Creek, V1G 0G2, BC, Canada
Tel.: (250) 782-9331
Gas Mfr
N.A.I.C.S.: 325120

Ferus Inc. - Joffre N2 Plant (1)
LSD-NE-25-38-26W4 38432 RR 25-5, PO Box 549, Joffre, T4L 2N2, AB, Canada
Tel.: (403) 885-3250
Gas Mfr
N.A.I.C.S.: 325120

Ferus Inc. - Utah CO2 Plant (1)
801 S 13000, Price, UT 84501
Tel.: (435) 888-5242
Gas Mfr
N.A.I.C.S.: 325120

FERVENT SYNERGIES LIMITED
B-7/8 Satyam Shopping Center MG Road, Ghatkopar East, Mumbai, 400077, Maharashtra, India
Tel.: (91) 2225017801   In
Web Site:
   https://www.ferventsynergies.com
Year Founded: 2009
533896—(BOM)
Rev.: $555,099
Assets: $5,209,939
Liabilities: $28,308
Net Worth: $5,181,632
Earnings: $27,612
Fiscal Year-end: 03/31/23
Pharmaceutical Product Mfr & Whslr
N.A.I.C.S.: 325412
Vijay Pravinchandra Thakkar (Chm)

FERVI SPA
Via Del Commercio 81, 41058, Vignola, Modena, Italy
Tel.: (39) 059767172
Web Site: https://www.fervi.com
FVI—(ITA)
Sales Range: Less than $1 Million

Industrial Equipment Mfr
N.A.I.C.S.: 334513
Roberto Tunioli (Pres & CEO)

FESCO GROUP CO., LTD.
Block B Shidong International Building Yard No 18 Guangqu Road, Chaoyang District, Beijing, 100022, China
Tel.: (86) 1067771218
Web Site: http://www.bjcx.com.cn
Year Founded: 1992
600861—(SHG)
Rev.: $67,917,110
Assets: $393,181,439
Liabilities: $98,853,941
Net Worth: $294,327,498
Earnings: ($30,210,359)
Emp.: 1,092
Fiscal Year-end: 12/31/22
Supermarket Store Operator
N.A.I.C.S.: 445110

FESTA HOLDING PLC
48 Vladislav Varnenchik Blvd Shop Exemplary House Fl 2, 9000, Varna, Bulgaria
Tel.: (359) 52669100
Web Site: http://www.festa.bg
Year Founded: 1991
Holding Company
N.A.I.C.S.: 551112
Petia Slavova (Chm)

Subsidiaries:

Investbank AD (1)
83 A Bulgaria Blvd, 1404, Sofia, Bulgaria (78.72%)
Tel.: (359) 29807722
Web Site: http://www.ibank.bg
Sales Range: $1-9.9 Million
Banking Services
N.A.I.C.S.: 522110

FESTARIA HOLDINGS CO., LTD.
Yubinbango 153 0061Nakameguro chome No 6 No 20, Meguro-ku, Tokyo, 153-0061, Japan
Tel.: (81) 357689969   JP
Web Site: http://www.festaria.co.jp
Year Founded: 1920
2736—(TKS)
Rev.: $84,448,320
Assets: $68,757,040
Liabilities: $58,970,560
Net Worth: $9,786,480
Earnings: $1,239,040
Fiscal Year-end: 08/31/21
Jewelry Product Whslr
N.A.I.C.S.: 423940

Subsidiaries:

D&Q Jewellery Co., Ltd. (1)
No 9-Cat Bi, Hai An, Haiphong, Vietnam
Tel.: (84) 313558034
Web Site: http://www.dqjewellery.vn
Jewelry Retailer
N.A.I.C.S.: 458310

FESTI HF
Dalvegur 10-14, 201, Kopavogur, Iceland
Tel.: (354) 4401200
Web Site: https://www.festi.is
Year Founded: 2007
FESTI—(ICE)
Rev.: $995,842,713
Assets: $701,886,493
Liabilities: $439,919,237
Net Worth: $261,967,256
Earnings: $25,129,294
Emp.: 2,259
Fiscal Year-end: 12/31/23
Service Centers, Self-Service Stations, Garages & Corporate Stores Operator
N.A.I.C.S.: 457110
Hinrik Orn Bjarnason (COO)

Subsidiaries:

Bakkinn voruhotel ehf. (1)
Skarfagardar 2, 104, Reykjavik, Iceland
Tel.: (354) 5227900
Web Site: https://bakkinn.is
Packaging & Labelling Product Distr
N.A.I.C.S.: 423840

ELKO ehf. (1)
Dalvegur 10-14, 200, Kopavogur, Iceland
Tel.: (354) 5610003280
Electronic Home Appliances Distr
N.A.I.C.S.: 423620

N1 ehf. (1)
Dalvegur 10-14, 201, Kopavogur, Iceland
Tel.: (354) 4401000
Web Site: https://www.n1.is
Oil & Gas Distr
N.A.I.C.S.: 424720

Oliudreifing ehf. (1)
Holmaslod 8-10, 101, Reykjavik, Iceland
Tel.: (354) 5509900
Web Site: https://www.odr.is
Emp.: 130
Oil & Fuel Equipment Distr
N.A.I.C.S.: 424720

FESTO AG & CO. KG
Ruiter Strasse 82, 73734, Esslingen, Germany
Tel.: (49) 7113470   De
Web Site: http://www.festo.com
Year Founded: 1925
Sales Range: $1-4.9 Billion
Emp.: 12,000
Automation Technology & Pneumatic Components & Systems Mfr
N.A.I.C.S.: 333922
Wilfried Stoll (Chm-Supervisory Bd)

Subsidiaries:

Dp Festo (1)
Borissoglebskaja 11, U04070, Kiev, Ukraine (100%)
Tel.: (380) 442392433
Web Site: http://www.festo.com.ua
Automation Technology & Pneumatic Components & Systems
N.A.I.C.S.: 334513

Festo (China) Ltd. (1)
1156 Yunqiao Rd Jin Qiao Export Processing Zone, Shanghai, 201206, China (100%)
Tel.: (86) 2160815100
Web Site: http://www.festo.com.cn
Emp.: 400
Automation Technology & Pneumatic Components & Systems
N.A.I.C.S.: 334513
J. J. Chen (Gen Mgr)

Festo (Pty.) Ltd. (1)
22-26 Electron Ave, PO Box 255, Isando, 1600, South Africa (100%)
Tel.: (27) 119715500
Web Site: http://www.festo.co.za
Sales Range: $50-74.9 Million
Emp.: 150
Automation Technology & Pneumatic Components & Systems
N.A.I.C.S.: 334512
Richard Teagre (Mng Dir)

Festo - Automacao, Unipessoal, Lda. (1)
Rua Manuel Pinto de Azevedo 567 Apartado 8013, 4109-016, Porto, Portugal
Tel.: (351) 22 615 61 50
Automotive Pneumatic Product Distr
N.A.I.C.S.: 423830

Festo A/S (1)
Islevdalvej 180, 2610, Rodovre, Denmark (100%)
Tel.: (45) 70211090
Web Site: http://www.festo.dk
Sales Range: $10-24.9 Million
Emp.: 40
Automation Technology, Pneumatic Component & System Mfr
N.A.I.C.S.: 334513
Tobias Liden (Mng Dir)

Festo AB (1)

Stillmansgatan 1, PO Box 21038, Malmo,
21225, Sweden **(100%)**
Tel.: (46) 40383800
Web Site: http://www.festo.se
Sales Range: $25-49.9 Million
Emp.: 70
Automation Technology & Pneumatic Com-
ponents & Systems
N.A.I.C.S.: 334512
Tobias Liden *(Mng Dir)*

Festo AG **(1)**
Moosmati Strasse 24, CH 8953, Zurich,
Switzerland **(100%)**
Tel.: (41) 17445544
Web Site: http://www.festo.ch
Sales Range: $25-49.9 Million
Emp.: 100
N.A.I.C.S.: 335314

Festo AS **(1)**
Ole Deviks vei 2, N 0666, Oslo,
Norway **(100%)**
Tel.: (47) 22728950
Web Site: http://www.festo.no
Sales Range: $25-49.9 Million
Emp.: 16
Automation Technology & Pneumatic Com-
ponents & Systems
N.A.I.C.S.: 334512

Festo Automation Ltd. **(1)**
Motorways Centre Ground Floor Block C
Alausa, Ikeja, Lagos, Nigeria
Tel.: (234) 1 794 78 20
Automotive Pneumatic Product Distr
N.A.I.C.S.: 423830

Festo B.V. **(1)**
Schieweg 62, 2627 AN, Delft,
Netherlands **(100%)**
Tel.: (31) 0152518899
Web Site: http://www.festo.nl
Sales Range: $50-74.9 Million
Emp.: 140
Automation Technology & Pneumatic Com-
ponents & Systems
N.A.I.C.S.: 334512
Thomas Pahrson *(Mng Dir)*

Festo Belgium N.V./S.A. **(1)**
Rue Colonel Bourgstraat 101, 1030, Brus-
sels, Belgium **(100%)**
Tel.: (32) 27023211
Web Site: http://www.festo.be
Sales Range: $25-49.9 Million
Emp.: 65
Automation Technology & Pneumatic Com-
ponents & Systems
N.A.I.C.S.: 334513
Go Verstraeten *(Asst Gen Mgr)*

Festo Brasil Ltda. **(1)**
Rua Giuseppe Crespi 76, Jardim Santa
Emilia, BR 04183 080, Sao Paulo, SP,
Brazil **(100%)**
Tel.: (55) 11 5013 1600
Web Site: http://www.festo.com.br
Sales Range: $25-49.9 Million
Emp.: 500
Automation Technology & Pneumatic Com-
ponents & Systems
N.A.I.C.S.: 334513

Festo Bulgaria EOOD **(1)**
9 Hristofor Kolumb Blvd, 1592, Sofia,
Bulgaria **(100%)**
Tel.: (359) 29600712
Web Site: http://www.festo.bg
Sales Range: $1-9.9 Million
Emp.: 20
Automation Technology & Pneumatic Com-
ponents & Systems
N.A.I.C.S.: 334513
Sherbert Pfeifer *(Gen Mgr)*

Festo C.A. **(1)**
Avda 23 Esquina Calle 71, PO Box 22 62,
Maracaibo, 4002, Venezuela **(100%)**
Tel.: (58) 2617590944
Web Site: http://www.festo.com
Automation Technology & Pneumatic Com-
ponents & Systems
N.A.I.C.S.: 334513

Festo Chile SA **(1)**
Americo Uaesvucio 760, Santiago,
6500151, Chile **(100%)**
Tel.: (56) 26902800
Web Site: http://www.festo.cl

Sales Range: $25-49.9 Million
Emp.: 50
Automation Technology & Pneumatic Com-
ponents & Systems
N.A.I.C.S.: 334513

Festo Co., Ltd. **(1)**
9 Kung 8th Rd Linkou 2nd Industrial Zone,
Taipei, 244, Taiwan **(100%)**
Tel.: (886) 226019281
Web Site: http://www.festo.com.tw
Sales Range: $25-49.9 Million
Emp.: 82
Automation Technology & Pneumatic Com-
ponents & Systems
N.A.I.C.S.: 334512

Festo Controls Pvt. Ltd. **(1)**
237B Bommasandra Industrial Area, Banga-
lore Hosur Highway, Bengaluru, 560 099,
India **(100%)**
Tel.: (91) 8022894100
Web Site: http://www.festo.com
Sales Range: $100-124.9 Million
Emp.: 300
Automation Technology & Pneumatic Com-
ponents & Systems
N.A.I.C.S.: 334513

Festo Corporation **(1)**
395 Moreland Rd, Hauppauge, NY
11788-3947 **(100%)**
Tel.: (631) 435-0800
Web Site: http://www.festo-usa.com
Sales Range: $150-199.9 Million
Emp.: 406
Mfr of Pneumatic Components & Systems;
Electronic Controller & Control Technology
Training Systems
N.A.I.C.S.: 423840
Bill Sicari *(Gen Mgr)*

Festo Didactic Inc. **(1)**
607 Industrial Way W, Eatontown, NJ
07724
Tel.: (732) 938-2000
Web Site: http://www.labvolt.com
Sales Range: $10-24.9 Million
Emp.: 110
Electrical Supplies & Equipment
N.A.I.C.S.: 333310
Daniel Rodriguez *(Exec VP-Sls & Mktg)*

Subsidiary (Non-US):

Festo Didactic Ltd. **(2)**
675 Rue du Carbone, Quebec, G2N 2K7,
QC, Canada
Tel.: (418) 849-1000
Web Site: http://www.labvolt.com
Electrical Supplies & Equipment
N.A.I.C.S.: 333310

Festo E.U.R.L. **(1)**
8 rue du Clos Sainte Catherine, Bry-sur-
Marne, 94360, Paris, France **(100%)**
Tel.: (33) 14882 6500
Web Site: http://www.festo.com
Emp.: 150
Automation Technology Services
N.A.I.C.S.: 811310

Festo GmbH **(1)**
Lincerstrasse 227, Vienna, A 1141,
Austria **(100%)**
Tel.: (43) 1910750
Web Site: http://www.festo.at
Sales Range: $25-49.9 Million
Emp.: 80
Automation Technology & Pneumatic Com-
ponents & Systems
N.A.I.C.S.: 334513
Festo Pfeiffer *(Mng Dir)*

Festo Inc. **(1)**
Km 18 W Service Rd S Super Hwy, 1700
Paranaque City, 1700, Manila,
Philippines **(100%)**
Tel.: (63) 27766888
Web Site: http://www.festo.com
Sales Range: $25-49.9 Million
Emp.: 50
Automation Technology & Pneumatic Com-
ponents & Systems
N.A.I.C.S.: 334512

Festo Inc. **(1)**
5300 Explorer Dr, Mississauga, L4W 5G4,
ON, Canada **(100%)**
Tel.: (905) 614-4600

Web Site: https://www.festo.com
Sales Range: $50-74.9 Million
Emp.: 100
Pneumatic Parts Distr
N.A.I.C.S.: 423830

Festo Israel Ltd **(1)**
Ha atzma ut Road 48, PO Box 1076, Ye-
hud, 56100, Israel
Tel.: (972) 3 632 22 66
Automotive Pneumatic Product Distr
N.A.I.C.S.: 423820

Festo K.K. **(1)**
1 26 10 Hayabuchi, Tsuzuki Ku, Yokohama,
224 0025, Japan **(100%)**
Tel.: (81) 455935610
Web Site: http://www.festo.jp
Sales Range: $25-49.9 Million
Emp.: 50
Automation Technology & Pneumatic Com-
ponents & Systems
N.A.I.C.S.: 334512

Festo Kft. **(1)**
Csillaghegei St 32-34, Budapest, 1037,
Hungary
Tel.: (36) 14365111
Web Site: http://www.festo.hu
Sales Range: $25-49.9 Million
Emp.: 15
Automation Technology & Pneumatic Com-
ponents & Systems
N.A.I.C.S.: 334513
Martom Szovenyilux *(Mgr)*

Festo Korea Co. Ltd. **(1)**
470 1 Kasan Dong, Kumchun Ku, Seoul,
153 803, Korea (South) **(100%)**
Tel.: (82) 28507114
Web Site: http://www.festo.co.kr
Emp.: 100
Automation Technology & Pneumatic Com-
ponents & Systems
N.A.I.C.S.: 334512

Festo Limited **(1)**
20 Fisher Crescent, Mount Wellington,
Auckland, 1060, New Zealand **(100%)**
Tel.: (64) 95741094
Web Site: http://www.festo.co.nz
Sales Range: $1-9.9 Million
Emp.: 12
Automation Technology & Pneumatic Com-
ponents & Systems
N.A.I.C.S.: 334512
Chris Mathiason *(Gen Mgr)*

Festo Limited **(1)**
Technology House 1 Fleetwood Park, Bar-
ley Way, Fleet, GU51 2QX, Hants, United
Kingdom **(100%)**
Tel.: (44) 1252 775 001
Web Site: http://www.festo.co.uk
Sales Range: $25-49.9 Million
Emp.: 17
Automation Technology & Pneumatic Com-
ponents & Systems
N.A.I.C.S.: 334513
Eliza Rawlings *(Mng Dir)*

Festo Limited **(1)**
Unit C & D 7th Floor Leroy Plaza 15,
Chueng Shun Street, Kowloon, China
(Hong Kong) **(100%)**
Tel.: (852) 27438379
Web Site: http://www.festo.com
Automation Technology & Pneumatic Com-
ponents & Systems
N.A.I.C.S.: 334513

Festo Limited **(1)**
Unit 5 Sandyford Park Sandyford Industrial
Est, Dublin, 18, Ireland **(100%)**
Tel.: (353) 12954955
Web Site: http://www.festo.ie
Sales Range: $25-49.9 Million
Emp.: 16
Automation Technology & Pneumatic Com-
ponent Mfr
N.A.I.C.S.: 334513

Festo Ltd. **(1)**
1250 Viranuvat Building 6th-7th Fl Bangna-
Trad Road Soi 34, Bangna, Bangkok,
10260, Thailand **(100%)**
Tel.: (66) 27853700
Web Site: http://www.festo.co.th
Sales Range: $25-49.9 Million
Emp.: 100

Automation Technology & Pneumatic Components & Systems
N.A.I.C.S.: 334513

Festo Ltd. **(1)**
Tatoiou 92, PC 144 52, Metamorfosis,
Greece **(100%)**
Tel.: (30) 21034129004
Web Site: http://www.festo.gr
Sales Range: $25-49.9 Million
Emp.: 20
Automation Technology & Pneumatic Com-
ponents & Systems
N.A.I.C.S.: 334513
Dimtleos Pakou Lieriss *(Mng Dir)*

Festo Ltda. **(1)**
Avda Eldorado No 98 43, Bogota,
Colombia **(100%)**
Tel.: (57) 14048088
Web Site: http://www.festo.com.co
Sales Range: $25-49.9 Million
Emp.: 63
Automation Technology & Pneumatic Com-
ponents & Systems
N.A.I.C.S.: 334513

Festo OY **(1)**
Makituvantle 9, PO Box 86, 1511, Vantaa,
Finland **(100%)**
Tel.: (358) 9870651
Web Site: http://www.festo.fi
Sales Range: $25-49.9 Million
Emp.: 10
Automation Technology & Pneumatic Com-
ponents & Systems
N.A.I.C.S.: 334513
Pekka Parikka *(Mng Dir)*

Festo OY AB Eesti Filiaal **(1)**
Tammsaare 118 B, Tallinn, 12918,
Estonia **(100%)**
Tel.: (372) 6661560
Web Site: http://www.festo.ee
Sales Range: Less than $1 Million
Emp.: 6
Automation Technology & Pneumatic Com-
ponents & Systems
N.A.I.C.S.: 334513
Frog Kaljas *(Mgr-Sls)*

Festo Pneumatic S.A. **(1)**
Zaylan 3 Tequesquinahuac, Tlalnepantla,
54020, Mexico, Mexico **(100%)**
Tel.: (52) 5553216600
Web Site: http://www.festo.com.mx
Sales Range: $50-74.9 Million
Emp.: 250
Automation Technology & Pneumatic Com-
ponents & Systems
N.A.I.C.S.: 334512
Bernd Schribir *(Mng Dir)*

Festo Pneumatic S.A. **(1)**
Avenida De La Gran Via 159, L'Hospitalet
de Llobregat, 8908, Barcelona,
Spain **(100%)**
Tel.: (34) 932616400
Web Site: http://www.festo.es
Automation Technology & Pneumatic Com-
ponents & Systems
N.A.I.C.S.: 334512

Festo Pneumatic S.K. **(1)**
6th Street 16th Avenue Km 8 Special Karaj
Rd Ste 2, PO Box 15815-1485, Tehran,
1389793761, Iran
Tel.: (98) 2144522409
Web Site: http://www.festo.com
Automation Technology & Pneumatic Com-
ponents & System Service
N.A.I.C.S.: 334513

Festo Pte. Ltd. **(1)**
6 Kian Teck Way, Singapore, 628754,
Singapore **(100%)**
Tel.: (65) 62640152
Web Site: http://www.festo.com.sg
Sales Range: $25-49.9 Million
Emp.: 130
Automation Technology & Pneumatic Com-
ponents & Systems
N.A.I.C.S.: 334512
Christian Burdin *(Mng Dir)*

Festo Pty. Ltd. **(1)**
179 187 Browns Rd, PO Box 261, Noble
Park, 3174, VIC, Australia **(100%)**
Tel.: (61) 397959555
Web Site: http://www.festo.com.au

Festo AG & Co, KG—(Continued)

Sales Range: $25-49.9 Million
Emp.: 85
Automation Technology & Pneumatic Components & Systems
N.A.I.C.S.: 334513
Steve Williams *(Mng Dir)*

Festo S.A. (1)
Edison 2392, 1640, Martinez, Buenos Aires, Argentina (100%)
Tel.: (54) 8104443127
Web Site: http://www.festo.com.ar
Sales Range: $25-49.9 Million
Emp.: 80
Automation Technology & Pneumatic Components & Systems
N.A.I.C.S.: 334513

Festo S.I.A. (1)
Gunara Astras 8b, 1082, Riga, Latvia (100%)
Tel.: (371) 67577864
Web Site: http://www.festo.com
Sales Range: $25-49.9 Million
Emp.: 10
Automation Technology & Pneumatic Component & System Mfr
N.A.I.C.S.: 334512

Festo S.R.L. (1)
Sf Constantin No 17, RO-70751, Bucharest, Romania
Tel.: (40) 213102983
Web Site: http://www.festo.ro
Sales Range: $25-49.9 Million
Emp.: 22
Automation Technology & Pneumatic Components & Systems
N.A.I.C.S.: 334512
Radu Alexandru *(Gen Mgr)*

Festo S.R.L. (1)
Calle Amador Merino Reyna 480 San Isidro, Lima, Peru
Tel.: (51) 1 219 69 60
Automotive Pneumatic Product Distr
N.A.I.C.S.: 423830

Festo S.p.A. (1)
Via Enrico Fermi 36 38, Assago, 20090, Milan, Italy (100%)
Tel.: (39) 02457881
Web Site: http://www.festo.it
Sales Range: $50-74.9 Million
Emp.: 150
Automation Technology & Pneumatic Components & Systems
N.A.I.C.S.: 334513
Giampiero Bighiani *(Gen Mgr)*

Festo San. ve Tic A.S. (1)
Tuzla Memerciler Organize Sanayi Bolgesi 6 18, TR 34956, Istanbul, Turkiye (100%)
Tel.: (90) 2165850085
Web Site: http://www.festo.com.tr
Sales Range: $50-74.9 Million
Emp.: 110
Automation Technology & Pneumatic Components & System Mfr
N.A.I.C.S.: 334513

Festo Sdn. Bhd. (1)
10 Persiaran Industria Bangar Sri Damasra, Wilayah Persekutuan, Kuala Lumpur, 52200, Malaysia (100%)
Tel.: (60) 362728122
Web Site: http://www.festo.com.my
Sales Range: $1-9.9 Million
Emp.: 80
Automation Technology & Pneumatic Components & Systems
N.A.I.C.S.: 334512

Festo Sp.z.o.o. (1)
Janki k/Warsawy ul. Mszczonowska 7, Raszyn, PL-05090, Raszyn, Poland
Tel.: (48) 227204166
Web Site: http://www.festo.pl
Automation Technology & Pneumatic Components & Systems
N.A.I.C.S.: 334512

Festo Spol. s.r.o. (1)
Modranska 543/76, 147 00, Prague, Czech Republic (100%)
Tel.: (420) 261099611
Web Site: http://www.festo.cz
Sales Range: $25-49.9 Million
Emp.: 50

Automation Technology & Pneumatic Components & Systems
N.A.I.C.S.: 334513

Festo U.A.B. (1)
Partizanu 63M, Kaunas, 50306, Lithuania
Tel.: (370) 37321314
Web Site: http://www.festo.lt
Sales Range: $25-49.9 Million
Emp.: 210
Automation Technology & Pneumatic Components & Systems
N.A.I.C.S.: 334513
Pektta Parika *(Gen Mgr)*

Festo d.o.o. (1)
Nova Cesta 181, 10 000, Zagreb, Croatia (100%)
Tel.: (385) 6191969
Web Site: http://www.festo.com
Sales Range: $25-49.9 Million
Emp.: 11
Automation Technology & Pneumatic Components & Systems
N.A.I.C.S.: 334513
Bogdan Opaskar *(Dir)*

Festo d.o.o. Ljubljana (1)
IC Trzin Blatnica 8, Trzin, 1236, Ljubljana, Slovenia (100%)
Tel.: (386) 15302100
Web Site: http://www.festo.si
Sales Range: $25-49.9 Million
Emp.: 15
Automation Technology & Pneumatic Components & Systems
N.A.I.C.S.: 334512

Festo spol. s.r.o. (1)
Gavlovicova ul 1, 831 03, Bratislava, Slovakia (100%)
Tel.: (421) 249104910
Web Site: http://www.festo.sk
Sales Range: $25-49.9 Million
Emp.: 22
Automation Technology & Pneumatic Components & Systems
N.A.I.C.S.: 334512
Meroslao Jaroline *(Mng Dir)*

Festo, s.r.o. (1)
Modranska 543/76, 147 00, Prague, Czech Republic
Tel.: (420) 261 099 611
Web Site: http://www.festo.cz
Automotive Pneumatic Product Distr
N.A.I.C.S.: 423830

OOO Festo-RF (1)
Mitschurinskij Prospect 49, 119607, Moscow, Russia
Tel.: (7) 4957373487
Web Site: http://www.festo.ru
Automation Technology & Pneumatic Components & Systems
N.A.I.C.S.: 334512

PT. Festo (1)
JL Sultan Iskandar Muda No. 68, Arteri Pondok Indah, Jakarta, 12240, Indonesia (100%)
Tel.: (62) 27507900
Web Site: http://www.festo.co.id
Sales Range: $1-9.9 Million
Emp.: 100
Automation Technology & Pneumatic Components & Systems
N.A.I.C.S.: 334513

FETIM B.V.
Kopraweg 1, PO Box 770, 1047 BP, Amsterdam, Netherlands
Tel.: (31) 20 58 05 333
Web Site: http://www.fetimgroup.com
Year Founded: 1919
Emp.: 300
Building Material & Supply Whslr
N.A.I.C.S.: 423490
Mike Jones *(Mng Dir-UK)*

Subsidiaries:

Aqualux Products Holdings Ltd. (1)
Universal Point Steelmans Road, Wednesbury, WS10 9UZ, West Midlands, United Kingdom
Tel.: (44) 8702416131
Web Site: http://www.aqualux.co.uk

Sales Range: $75-99.9 Million
Emp.: 150
Shower Enclosures & Bath Screens Distr
N.A.I.C.S.: 423220

Holding (Domestic):

Aqualux Products Ltd. (2)
Universal Point Steelmans Rd, Off Park Ln, Wednesbury, WS10 9UZ, West Midlands, United Kingdom
Tel.: (44) 8702416131
Web Site: http://www.aqualux.co.uk
Shower Enclosure & Bath Screens Distr
N.A.I.C.S.: 423220

FEV GMBH
Neuenhofstrasse 181, 52078, Aachen, Germany
Tel.: (49) 241 5689 0
Web Site: http://www.fev.com
Sales Range: $400-449.9 Million
Engineeering Services
N.A.I.C.S.: 541330
Stefan Pischinger *(Pres & CEO)*

Subsidiaries:

Comgraph Co., Ltd. (1)
662/47-48 Rama III Bangpongpang, Yan Nawa, Bangkok, 10120, Thailand
Tel.: (66) 22930211
Web Site: http://www.comgraph.co.th
Software Development Services
N.A.I.C.S.: 541511
Wacharin Thaisawasdi *(Product Mgr)*

FEV America Latina Ltda. (1)
Mario Covas 641 Rua B 161, Bairro Macuco, 13279-411, Valinhos, Brazil
Tel.: (55) 1935157178
Engineering Consulting Services
N.A.I.C.S.: 541330

FEV China Co., Ltd. (1)
No 35 Xinda Street Qixianling High Tech Zone, 116023, Dalian, China
Tel.: (86) 41184821688
Emp.: 160
Engineering Consulting Services
N.A.I.C.S.: 541330
Rolf Weinowski *(Chm)*

FEV France S.A.S. (1)
17/20 Esplanade Charles De Gaulle, 92000, Nanterre, France
Tel.: (33) 141209080
Engineering Consulting Services
N.A.I.C.S.: 541330
Olivier Mayeux *(Acct Mgr)*

FEV India Private Limited (1)
10th floor Iit Madras Research Park Kanagam road, Tharamani, 600 113, Chennai, India
Tel.: (91) 8754428794
Engineering Consulting Services
N.A.I.C.S.: 541330
Ajith Prasad B *(Sr Mgr)*

FEV India Pvt. Ltd. (1)
Technical Center Pune A-21, Talegaon Dabhade, Pune, 410 507, India
Tel.: (91) 2114666000
Emp.: 200
Engineering Consulting Services
N.A.I.C.S.: 541330
Neeraj Kumar Gupta *(Sr Mgr-HR)*

FEV Italia s.r.l (1)
Corso Susa 299A, 10098, Rivoli, Italy
Tel.: (39) 0119550358
Engineering Consulting Services
N.A.I.C.S.: 541330

FEV Japan Co., Ltd. (1)
1008 Burex Kojimachi 3-5-2 Kojimachi, Tokyo, 102-0083, Japan
Tel.: (81) 332220711
Engineering Consulting Services
N.A.I.C.S.: 541330

FEV Korea Ltd. (1)
215 Trapalace Building 10-1 Sunae-dong, Bundang-gu, Seongnam, 463-873, Gyeonggi, Korea (South)
Tel.: (82) 317816510
Engineering Consulting Services
N.A.I.C.S.: 541330
Dongchan Jeon *(Pres & CEO)*

FEV Polska Sp. z o.o. (1)
ul Bosakow 5a, 31-476, Krakow, Poland
Tel.: (48) 124462100
Engineering Consulting Services
N.A.I.C.S.: 541330

FEV Sverige AB (1)
Stena Center 1A, 412 92, Gothenburg, Sweden
Tel.: (46) 31155888
Engineering Consulting Services
N.A.I.C.S.: 541330
Peter Sjostedt *(Mng Dir)*

FEV TR Otomotiv ve Enerji Arastirma ve Muhendislik Ltd. Sti. (1)
Itu Ayazaga Kampusu Ari Teknokent Ari-1 Binasi Ofis No 4, Maslak, Istanbul, Turkiye
Tel.: (90) 2122760686
Engineering Consulting Services
N.A.I.C.S.: 541330

FEV UK Ltd. (1)
Discovery Way, Binley, Coventry, CV3 2NT, United Kingdom
Tel.: (44) 1223655465
Engineering Consulting Services
N.A.I.C.S.: 541330
Stephen Jones *(Mng Dir)*

FEV, Inc. (1)
554 Glenmeade Ln, Auburn Hills, MI 48326
Tel.: (248) 373-6000
Engineeering Services
N.A.I.C.S.: 541330
John Zelasko *(Dir-Bus Dev)*

Subsidiary (Domestic):

DGE Inc. (2)
4554 Glenmeade Lane, Auburn Hills, MI 48326
Tel.: (248) 293-1300
Web Site: http://www.dgeinc.net
Sales Range: $1-9.9 Million
Emp.: 40
Electrical Engineering & Design Services for Automotive Industry
N.A.I.C.S.: 541330
Chris Price *(Mgr-IT)*

Felicity Scientific Co., Ltd. (1)
10FL No 168 Cheng-San Road Section 1 Yung-Ho 234, Taipei, Taiwan
Tel.: (886) 6289230066
Engineering Consulting Services
N.A.I.C.S.: 541330

Fev Iberia sl (1)
Block Sur - 2a Planta Muelle de, 08039, Barcelona, Spain
Tel.: (34) 933443200
Engineering Consulting Services
N.A.I.C.S.: 541330

FEVERTREE DRINKS PLC
186-188 Shepherds Bush Road, London, W6 7NL, United Kingdom
Tel.: (44) 2073494922   UK
Web Site: https://www.fever-tree.com
FEVR—(AIM)
Rev.: $434,612,472
Assets: $393,335,016
Liabilities: $91,391,063
Net Worth: $301,943,954
Earnings: $31,431,457
Emp.: 300
Fiscal Year-end: 12/31/22
Holding Company; Specialty Mixer Soft Drink Mfr
N.A.I.C.S.: 551112
William Ronald *(Chm)*

Subsidiaries:

Fevertree Limited (1)
186-188 Shepherds Bush Road, London, W6 7NL, United Kingdom
Tel.: (44) 2073494922
Web Site: https://fever-tree.com
Specialty Mixer Soft Drink Mfr
N.A.I.C.S.: 312111

Fevertree USA Inc. (1)
37 W 26th St The Penthouse, New York, NY 10010
Tel.: (347) 735-5437
Web Site: https://fever-tree.com

Soft Drink Mfr & Distr
N.A.I.C.S.: 312111

GDP Global Drinks Partnership GmbH (1)
Marienstr 17, 80331, Munich, Germany
Tel.: (49) 8924887470
Web Site: https://www.gdp-drinks.de
Soft Drink Mfr & Distr
N.A.I.C.S.: 312111

Powell & Mahoney LLC (1)
39 Norman St, Salem, MA 01970
Tel.: (978) 745-4332
Web Site:
   https://www.powellandmahoney.com
Premium Mixer Drink Distr
N.A.I.C.S.: 424490

FEXCO HOLDINGS

Fexco Centre Iveragh Road, Killorg-
lin, Kerry, Ireland
Tel.: (353) 66 9761258   IE
Web Site: http://www.fexco.com
Year Founded: 1981
Sales Range: $350-399.9 Million
Emp.: 2,300
Global Payments Services
N.A.I.C.S.: 921130
Brian McCarthy *(Founder & Chm)*

Subsidiaries:

FEXCO Asset Finance (1)
Ely Place, Dublin, 2, Ireland
Tel.: (353) 637 3000
Web Site: http://www.fexcoassetfinance.com
Sales Range: $50-74.9 Million
Emp.: 23
Leasing & Sales Financing Services
N.A.I.C.S.: 522220

FEXCO Financial Services (1)
Iveragh Road, Killorglin, V93WN9T, Kerry,
Ireland
Tel.: (353) 66 9761258
Financial Management Services
N.A.I.C.S.: 523999

Subsidiary (Non-US):

**FEXCO Business Consulting (Shang-
hai) Ltd** (2)
Silver Centre 1388 Shaan Xi North Road,
Shanghai, 200060, China
Tel.: (86) 21 6149 8047
Financial Management Services
N.A.I.C.S.: 523999

FEXCO DCC Solutions FZ-LLC (2)
PO Box 500591, Dubai, United Arab Emir-
ates
Tel.: (971) 44 348 037
Financial Management Services
N.A.I.C.S.: 523999

FEXCO Ltd (2)
15 Galena Road, Hammersmith, London,
W6 0LT, United Kingdom
Tel.: (44) 208 846 2400
Financial Management Services
N.A.I.C.S.: 523999
Ross P. Burnside *(Head-Agency Svcs &
Bus Support)*

FEXCO Pacific New Zealand (2)
Level 2 Tower One Stanway Business Park
646-648 Great South Rd, Ellerslie, Auck-
land, 1547, New Zealand
Tel.: (64) 9 582 0092
Web Site: http://www.fexcopacific.co.nz
Financial Management Services
N.A.I.C.S.: 523999
Richard Cronin *(Mgr-Sls-Southern)*

Goodbody Corporate Finance (1)
Ballsbridge Park, Ballsbridge, Dublin, Ire-
land
Tel.: (353) 1 667 0400
Web Site: http://www.goodbody.ie
Financial Management Services
N.A.I.C.S.: 523999
Brian O'Kelly *(Mng Dir)*

FEY LAMELLENRINGE GMBH & CO. KG

Josef-Fey-Str 2, 86343, Konigsbrunn,
Germany

Tel.: (49) 823196180
Web Site: http://www.fey-
   lamellenringe.de
Year Founded: 1946
Sales Range: $25-49.9 Million
Laminar Ring Mfr
N.A.I.C.S.: 336310
Elke Fey *(Gen Mgr)*

Subsidiaries:

**Fey Lamelove Krouzky Prodeje
S.R.O.** (1)
Legionarska 266, 664 34, Kurim, Czech
Republic
Tel.: (420) 547216221
Web Site: http://www.fey.cz
Laminar Ring Mfr
N.A.I.C.S.: 333310
Vladimir Bednar *(Mng Dir)*

FFI HOLDINGS LIMITED

23 Knock Place, PO Box 3029, Jan-
dakot, 6164, WA, Australia
Tel.: (61) 894174088   AU
Web Site:
   https://www.ffiholdings.com.au
FFI—(ASX)
Rev.: $35,431,080
Assets: $42,181,289
Liabilities: $12,358,536
Net Worth: $29,822,752
Earnings: $1,160,355
Fiscal Year-end: 06/30/24
Food Product Mfr & Distr
N.A.I.C.S.: 311812
Rodney G. Moonen *(Chm)*

FFP SA

66 avenue Charles de Gaulle CS,
60049, Neuilly-sur-Seine, Cedex,
France
Tel.: (33) 184138720
Web Site: http://www.groupe-ffp.fr
Year Founded: 1929
PEUG—(EUR)
Rev.: $299,094,823
Assets: $9,804,890,166
Liabilities: $2,135,176,068
Net Worth: $7,669,714,098
Earnings: $225,746,771
Emp.: 32
Fiscal Year-end: 12/31/23
Portfolio Investment Services
N.A.I.C.S.: 523940
Robert Peugeot *(Chm & CEO)*

FFRI SECURITY, INC.

2F Shin-Tokyo Building 3-3-1
Marunouchi, Chiyoda-ku, Tokyo, 100-
0005, Japan
Tel.: (81) 362771811
Web Site: https://www.ffri.jp
Year Founded: 2007
3692—(TKS)
Rev.: $16,168,060
Assets: $22,348,410
Liabilities: $7,932,000
Net Worth: $14,416,410
Earnings: $2,855,520
Fiscal Year-end: 03/31/24
Security Software
N.A.I.C.S.: 513210
Yuji Ukai *(Founder, Pres & CEO)*

FGP LTD.

9 Wallace Street Fort, Mumbai,
400001, Maharashtra, India
Tel.: (91) 2222070273
Web Site: https://www.fgpltd.in
Rev.: $235,508
Assets: $630,511
Liabilities: $26,851
Net Worth: $603,660
Earnings: $59,596
Emp.: 3
Fiscal Year-end: 03/31/19
Fiber Glass Products Mfr

N.A.I.C.S.: 327215
Manish Tiwary *(Sec & Fin Mgr)*

FGV HOLDINGS BHD

Wisma FGV Jalan Raja Laut, 50350,
Kuala Lumpur, Malaysia
Tel.: (60) 327890000   MY
Web Site:
   https://www.fgvholdings.com
FGV—(KLS)
Rev.: $5,409,850,370
Assets: $3,832,936,720
Liabilities: $2,164,220,317
Net Worth: $1,668,716,402
Earnings: $268,486,984
Emp.: 16,812
Fiscal Year-end: 12/31/22
Investment Holding Company
N.A.I.C.S.: 551112
Azhar Abdul Hamid *(Chm)*

Subsidiaries:

Delima Oil Products Sdn. Bhd. (1)
Level 3A Wisma FGV Jalan Raja Laut,
50350, Kuala Lumpur, Malaysia
Tel.: (60) 327890000
Web Site: https://www.fgvdelima.com
Palm Oil Mfr
N.A.I.C.S.: 311225

FGV Agri Services Sdn. Bhd. (1)
Level 9 West Wisma FGV Jalan Raja Laut,
50350, Kuala Lumpur, Malaysia
Tel.: (60) 32 789 1000
Web Site: https://www.fgvagri.com
Palm Oil Mfr
N.A.I.C.S.: 311225
Romzi Ishak *(CEO)*

**FGV Agro Fresh Technology Sdn.
Bhd.** (1)
9A Lorong Ara Kiri 1 Lucky Garden, Bang-
sar, 59100, Kuala Lumpur, Malaysia
Tel.: (60) 361270725
Web Site: http://www.gogopasar.com
Dairy Farm Services
N.A.I.C.S.: 112120

FGV Dairy Farm Sdn. Bhd. (1)
63 & 65 Jalan PJU 1A/42 Ara Damansara
Taman Putra Damai, 47301, Petaling Jaya,
Malaysia
Tel.: (60) 1700811700
Web Site: https://www.fgvdairyfarm.com
Dairy Farm Services
N.A.I.C.S.: 112120
Zakaria Abd Rahman *(COO)*

FGV Johor Bulkers Sdn. Bhd. (1)
Lorong Sawit Satu Johor Port Area, 81700,
Pasir Gudang, Johor, Malaysia
Tel.: (60) 72511830
Web Site: http://www.fjb.com.my
Bulk Storage Services
N.A.I.C.S.: 493190

FGV Johore Bulkers Sdn. Bhd. (1)
Lorong Sawit Satu Johor Port Area, 81700,
Pasir Gudang, Johor, Malaysia
Tel.: (60) 72511830
Web Site: https://fjb.com.my
Bulk Storage Services
N.A.I.C.S.: 493190

FGV Prodata Systems Sdn. Bhd. (1)
Level 19 East Wisma FGV Jalan Raja Laut,
50350, Kuala Lumpur, Malaysia
Tel.: (60) 327890900
Web Site: https://fgvprodata.com.my
IT Services
N.A.I.C.S.: 541519
Muhamad Nasran Md Daud *(COO & Head-
Bus Ops)*

**FGV Security Services Sdn.
Bhd.** (1)
Level 10 East Wisma FGV Jalan Raja Laut,
50350, Kuala Lumpur, Malaysia
Tel.: (60) 327890999
Web Site: https://www.fgvsecurity.com.my
Security & Patrol Services
N.A.I.C.S.: 561612

**FGV Transport Services Sdn.
Bhd.** (1)
Level 6 East Wisma FGV Jalan Raja Laut,
50350, Kuala Lumpur, Malaysia

Tel.: (60) 327891155
Web Site: https://www.fgvtransport.com
Supply Chain & Logistics Services
N.A.I.C.S.: 484110
Jamaluddin Jaafar *(Gen Mgr-Bus Dev &
Support)*

FGV USA Properties, Inc (1)
285 Columbus Ave, Boston, MA 02116
Tel.: (857) 233-2917
Property Management Services
N.A.I.C.S.: 531311

Subsidiary (Domestic):

**Fore River Transportation
Corporation** (2)
145 E Howard St, Quincy, MA 02169
Tel.: (617) 773-7770
Railroad Management Services
N.A.I.C.S.: 926120

**Twin Rivers Technologies Holdings,
Inc.** (2)
780 Washington St, Quincy, MA 02169
Tel.: (617) 472-9200
Holding Company
N.A.I.C.S.: 551112

**Felda Global Ventures Perlis Sdn
Bhd** (1)
23 Jalan Kilang Gula Chuping Beseri,
02400, Kangar, Perlis, Malaysia
Tel.: (60) 4 944 1002
Holding Company
N.A.I.C.S.: 551112

Felda Holdings Bhd. (1)
Level 42 Menara Felda Platinum Park, No
11 Persiaran KLCC, 50088, Kuala Lumpur,
Malaysia   **(49%)**
Tel.: (60) 328590000
Web Site: http://www.feldaglobal.com
Sales Range: $5-14.9 Billion
Emp.: 19,000
Holding Company; Agricultural Products
Farming, Processing & Whslr
N.A.I.C.S.: 551112
Mohammed Isa Abdul Samad *(Chm)*

Felda Properties Sdn. Bhd. (1)
Balai Felda Tingkat 2 Jalan Gurney Satu,
54000, Kuala Lumpur, Malaysia
Tel.: (60) 326988211
Property Development Services
N.A.I.C.S.: 531390

Felda Travel Sdn. Bhd. (1)
Level 7E Wisma FGV Jalan Raja Laut,
50350, Kuala Lumpur, Malaysia
Tel.: (60) 327891133
Web Site: https://www.feldatravel.com.my
Travel Agency Services
N.A.I.C.S.: 561510

MSM Logistics Sdn. Bhd. (1)
Level 44 Menara Felda Platinum Park No
11 Persiaran KLCC, 50088, Kuala Lumpur,
Malaysia
Tel.: (60) 32 181 5018
Web Site: https://www.msmsugar.com
Logistic Services
N.A.I.C.S.: 484110

MSM Malaysia Holdings Berhad (1)
Level 44 Menara Felda Platinum Park, No
11 Persiaran KLCC, 50088, Kuala Lumpur,
Malaysia   **(51%)**
Tel.: (60) 321815018
Web Site: https://www.msmsugar.com
Rev.: $543,065,608
Assets: $595,088,466
Liabilities: $274,507,090
Net Worth: $320,581,376
Earnings: ($37,822,646)
Emp.: 1,038
Fiscal Year-end: 12/31/2022
Holding Company; Cane Sugar Mfr
N.A.I.C.S.: 551112
Shuang Yen Koo *(Sec)*

Subsidiary (Domestic):

**Malayan Sugar Manufacturing Com-
pany Berhad** (2)
Levell 44 Menara Felda Platinum Park, No
11 Persiaran KLCC, 50088, Kuala Lumpur,
Malaysia
Tel.: (60) 3 2181 4818
Web Site: http://www.msm.com.my

FGV Holdings Bhd—(Continued)

Cane Sugar Mfr
N.A.I.C.S.: 311314
Awab Abod (Pres & CEO)

MSM Perlis Sdn. Bhd. (1)
Mukim Chuping, Chuping, 2500, Kangar,
Perlis, Malaysia
Tel.: (60) 49441301
Web Site: https://www.msmsugar.com
Sugar Mfr
N.A.I.C.S.: 311314

MSM Prai Berhad (1)
Level 44 Menara Felda Platinum Park No
11, Persiaran KLCC, 50088, Kuala Lumpur,
Malaysia
Tel.: (60) 32 181 4818
Web Site: https://www.msmsugar.com
Sugar Mfr
N.A.I.C.S.: 311314

**MSM Trading International
DMCC** (1)
No Unit 404 and 405 Jumeirah Bay X3
Cluster X, Jumeirah Lakes Tower JLT,
Dubai, United Arab Emirates
Tel.: (971) 4 557 4635
Web Site: https://www.msmsugar.com
Raw Sugar Mfr
N.A.I.C.S.: 311314

**Pontian United Plantations
Berhad** (1)
KM52 off Jalan Sandakan, PO Box 60525,
91114, Lahad Datu, Sabah, Malaysia
Tel.: (60) 89565620
Web Site: http://www.pontianunited.com
Palm Oil Mfr
N.A.I.C.S.: 311225

FHB MORTGAGE BANK PUB-LIC LIMITED COMPANY
Ulloi ut 48, 1082, Budapest, Hungary
Tel.: (36) 14529100
Web Site: http://www.fhb.hu
Sales Range: $25-49.9 Million
Emp.: 811
Mortgage Banking Services
N.A.I.C.S.: 522292
Jozsef Vida (Chm)

Subsidiaries:

FHB Life Annuity Ltd. (1)
Ulloi St 48, 1082, Budapest, Hungary
Tel.: (36) 14529100
Banking Services
N.A.I.C.S.: 522110

FHB Real Estate Leasing Ltd. (1)
Rumbach Sebestyen utca 15, 1075, Buda-
pest, Hungary
Tel.: (36) 1 461 6040
Web Site: http://www.fhb.hu
Sales Range: $50-74.9 Million
Emp.: 20
Real Estate Lending Services
N.A.I.C.S.: 531110

FHB Real Estate Ltd. (1)
Ulloi ut 48, 1082, Budapest, Hungary
Tel.: (36) 14528527
Web Site: http://www.fhbingatlan.hu
Mortgage Banking Services
N.A.I.C.S.: 522292

FHB Services Ltd (1)
Ulloi Street 48, 1082, Budapest, Hungary
Tel.: (36) 14529100
Sales Range: $200-249.9 Million
Emp.: 500
Banking Services
N.A.I.C.S.: 522110
Gyula Kobli (Gen Mgr)

FHL I. KIRIAKIDIS MARBLE -GRANITE SA
Industrial Park of Prosotsani, 66200,
Drama, Greece
Tel.: (30) 25220 23514
Web Site: http://www.fhl.gr
Year Founded: 1991
KYRM—(ATH)
Sales Range: $50-74.9 Million
Emp.: 247

Marble & Granite Quarrying Services
N.A.I.C.S.: 212313
Kiriakidis Ilias (Pres & Mng Dir)

Subsidiaries:

MARMI BIANCHI SRL (1)
Viale da Verrazzano 11/G, 54036, Carrara,
Italy
Tel.: (39) 039 338 691 079 5
Marble & Granite Quarrying Services
N.A.I.C.S.: 212313

FIACAO TEC SAO JOSE S.A.
R Jose Prenassi 04, 36200026, Bar-
bacena, Minas Gerais, Brazil
Tel.: (55) 8132331288
Apparel Store Operator
N.A.I.C.S.: 315990

FIAMM S.P.A.
Via Le Europa 63, I 36075, Montec-
chio Maggiore, Vichensa, Italy
Tel.: (39) 0444709311   IT
Web Site:
http://www.fiammgroup.com
Year Founded: 1942
Sales Range: $650-699.9 Million
Emp.: 3,600
Automotive, Industrial & Consumer
Batteries & Automobile Horns Mfr
N.A.I.C.S.: 335910

Subsidiaries:

**FABBRICA Italiana Accumulatori Mo-
tocarri Montecchio Iberica S.A.** (1)
Calle Esteban Terradas 6-Pl Nuestra Se-
nora de Butarque, 28914, Leganes, Spain
Tel.: (34) 91 488 0247
Battery Mfr & Distr
N.A.I.C.S.: 335910

FIAMM Automotive Czech A.S. (1)
Nadrazni 84, 29362, Mlada Boleslav, Czech
Republic
Tel.: (420) 326714373
Automotive Parts & Accessory Mfr
N.A.I.C.S.: 336330

FIAMM Autotech Co., Ltd (1)
Han Nan road 458 Shamao, Hannan,
430090, Wuhan, Hubey, China
Tel.: (86) 2784736816
Automotive Parts & Accessory Mfr
N.A.I.C.S.: 336330
Li Xiangmei (Mgr-Pur & Supply Chain)

FIAMM Energy LLC (1)
1 FIAMM Way, Waynesboro, GA 30830
Tel.: (706) 437-3220
Automotive Parts & Accessory Mfr
N.A.I.C.S.: 336330

FIAMM France Sarl (1)
12 Rue Augustin Fresnel, 78410, Aubergen-
ville, France
Tel.: (33) 139297701
Automotive Parts & Accessory Mfr
N.A.I.C.S.: 336330

FIAMM Latin America Ltda. (1)
Av Piraporinha 121 CEP, 09891-0000, Sao
Bernardo do Campo, Brazil
Tel.: (55) 1137376137
Automotive Parts & Accessory Mfr
N.A.I.C.S.: 336330

FIAMM Slovakia s.r.o (1)
Turna nad Bodvou, 04402, Bratislava, Slo-
vakia
Tel.: (421) 554662834
Automotive Parts & Accessory Mfr
N.A.I.C.S.: 336330

FIAMM Sonick S.A. (1)
Via Laveggio 15, 6855, Stabio, Switzerland
Tel.: (41) 916415511
Automotive Parts & Accessory Mfr
N.A.I.C.S.: 336330

Fiamm Asia Pacific Pte Ltd. (1)
24 Jurong Port Road 02-04 CWT Distripark,
Singapore, 619097, Singapore
Tel.: (65) 68676152
Automotive Parts & Accessory Mfr
N.A.I.C.S.: 336330

**Fiamm Energy Technology (France)
S.a.r.l.** (1)
2 bis rue Dupont de l'Eure, 75020, Paris,
France
Tel.: (33) 17 590 9045
Battery Mfr & Distr
N.A.I.C.S.: 335910

**Fiamm Energy Technology (USA)
LLC** (1)
770 Mills Rd, Waynesboro, GA 30830
Tel.: (706) 437-3220
Battery Mfr & Distr
N.A.I.C.S.: 335910

**Fiamm Energy Technology (Wuhan)
Co., Ltd** (1)
Xingsheng Road 157, Shamao Town Han-
nan District, Wuhan, 430090, Hubei, China
Tel.: (86) 1398 611 2137
Battery Mfr & Distr
N.A.I.C.S.: 335910

**Fiamm Energy Technology
S.p.A.** (1)
Viale Europa 75, 36075, Montecchio Mag-
giore, VI, Italy
Tel.: (39) 044 470 9311
Web Site: https://www.fiamm.com
Battery Mfr & Distr
N.A.I.C.S.: 335910

Fiamm Malaysia Sdn. Bhd. (1)
No 13 Jalan TS 6/8 Taman Industri Subang,
Subang Jaya, 47510, Kuala Lumpur, Malay-
sia
Tel.: (60) 35 631 2022
Battery Mfr & Distr
N.A.I.C.S.: 335910

Fiamm S.p.A. - Avezzano Plant (1)
Via Volta Alessandro 9, 67051, Avezzano,
Italy
Tel.: (39) 086349841
Automotive Battery Mfr
N.A.I.C.S.: 336320

Fiamm Technologies Inc. (1)
1550 Leeson Ave, Cadillac, MI
49601-8975   **(100%)**
Tel.: (231) 775-2900
Web Site: http://www.fiamm.com
Sales Range: $50-74.9 Million
Emp.: 175
Mfr of Automobile Horns
N.A.I.C.S.: 336320
Michael Fewless (Mgr-IT-United States)

Fiamm UK Limited (1)
12a Ridings Park Eastern Way Hawks
Green, Cannock, WS11 7FJ, United King-
dom
Tel.: (44) 154 345 6977
Battery Mfr & Distr
N.A.I.C.S.: 335910

Fiamm-GS S.p.A. (1)
Viale Europa 63, 36075, Montecchio Mag-
giore, Italy
Tel.: (39) 0444709350
Batteries Mfr
N.A.I.C.S.: 335910

FIAMMA HOLDINGS BERHAD
Wisma Fiamma No 20 Jalan 7A/62
Bandar Manjalara, 52200, Kuala
Lumpur, Malaysia
Tel.: (60) 362798888   MY
Web Site:
https://www.fiamma.com.my
Year Founded: 1979
FIAMMA—(KLS)
Rev.: $102,887,619
Assets: $194,048,889
Liabilities: $47,306,032
Net Worth: $146,742,857
Earnings: $16,095,450
Emp.: 296
Fiscal Year-end: 12/31/23
Holding Company; Consumer Appli-
ances, Sanitaryware, Cabinets, Bath-
room Fittings & Healthcare Products
Distr
N.A.I.C.S.: 551112
Yit Chan Tai (Co-Sec)

Subsidiaries:

Active Edge Sdn Bhd (1)
No 20 Jalan 7A/62A Bandar, Manjalara,
52200, Kuala Lumpur, Malaysia
Tel.: (60) 362798708
Web Site: https://eastparc.com.my
Property Investment Services
N.A.I.C.S.: 531390

Enex-Dynamic Sdn. Bhd. (1)
3-2 Wisma Fiamma No 20 Jalan 7A/62A,
Bandar Manjalara, 52200, Kuala Lumpur,
Malaysia
Tel.: (60) 362798787
Web Site: http://www.e-enex.com
Sales Range: $75-99.9 Million
Emp.: 7
Water Supply Services
N.A.I.C.S.: 221310

FHB Management Sdn. Bhd. (1)
Level 9 Wisma Fiamma Lot 44653 Jalan
7A/62A, Bandar Manjalara, 52200, Kuala
Lumpur, Malaysia
Tel.: (60) 362798888
Sales Range: $75-99.9 Million
Emp.: 200
Property Management Services
N.A.I.C.S.: 531311
Lim Choo Hong (CEO)

Fiamma Properties Sdn Bhd (1)
Level 10 Wisma Fiamma No 20 Jalan
7A/62A, Bandar Manjalara, 52200, Kuala
Lumpur, Malaysia
Tel.: (60) 36 279 8708
Web Site:
https://www.fiammaproperty.com.my
Electrical Home Appliances Distr
N.A.I.C.S.: 423620

Fiamma Trading Sdn. Bhd. (1)
Wisma Fiamma No 20 Jalan 7A/62A Ban-
dar Manjalara, 52200, Kuala Lumpur, Ma-
laysia
Tel.: (60) 362798943
Web Site: http://www.fmtrd.com.my
Sales Range: $75-99.9 Million
Emp.: 200
Consumer Electrical Equipments Distr
N.A.I.C.S.: 423620

Fimaco Sdn. Bhd. (1)
8-2 Wisma Fiamma No 20 Jalan 7A/62A,
Bandar Manjalara, 52200, Kuala Lumpur,
Malaysia
Tel.: (60) 36 279 8888
Web Site:
https://www.faberappliances.com.my
Sales Range: $75-99.9 Million
Emp.: 200
Consumer Electrical Equipments Distr
N.A.I.C.S.: 423620

**Kingston Medical Supplies (Pte.)
Ltd.** (1)
35 Tannery Road 11-01 Tannery Block,
Ruby Industrial Complex, Singapore,
347740, Singapore
Tel.: (65) 6 745 3922
Web Site: https://kingsmed.com.sg
Sales Range: $25-49.9 Million
Emp.: 30
Medical Instrument Distr
N.A.I.C.S.: 423450

Kinsmedic Sdn. Bhd. (1)
9-2 Wisma Fiamma No 20 Jalan 7A/62A,
Bandar Manjalara, 52200, Kuala Lumpur,
Malaysia
Tel.: (60) 125136848
Sales Range: $25-49.9 Million
Emp.: 30
Medical Instruments & Healthcare Products
Distr
N.A.I.C.S.: 423450

Oaksvilla Sdn. Bhd. (1)
PTD 5490 Jalan Remia Taman Kota Jaya,
81900, Kota Tinggi, Johor, Malaysia
Tel.: (60) 78822716
Emp.: 5
Property Development Services
N.A.I.C.S.: 531390
Ho Hong Seng (Mgr)

Uniphoenix Jaya Sdn. Bhd. (1)
PTD 5490 Jalan Remia Taman Kota Jaya,
81900, Kota Tinggi, Johor, Malaysia

Tel.: (60) 78822716
Property Development Services
N.A.I.C.S.: 531390
Ho Hong Seng *(Mgr-Fin)*

FIATC MUTUA DE SEGUROS Y DE REASEGUROS APF
Avenida Diagonal 648, 08017, Barcelona, Spain
Tel.: (34) 900567567   ES
Web Site: http://www.fiatc.es
Year Founded: 1930
Insurance Services
N.A.I.C.S.: 524126
Joan Castells Trius *(Chm & CEO)*

Subsidiaries:

Inverfiatc S.A.   **(1)**
Caravel La Nina 12 Bajos, Barcelona, 08017, Spain
Tel.: (34) 93 2805 107
Web Site: http://www.inverfiatc.com
Financial Investment Services
N.A.I.C.S.: 523999
Joan Castells Trius *(Chm & CEO)*

FIBA HOLDING A.S.
Buyukdere Cad 1 Levent Plz No 173/A, Levent, 34330, Istanbul, Turkiye
Tel.: (90) 2123391900
Web Site:
  http://www.fibaholding.com.tr
Year Founded: 1987
Sales Range: $1-4.9 Billion
Emp.: 10,972
Holding Company
N.A.I.C.S.: 551112
Husnu M. Ozyegin *(Founder & Chm)*

Subsidiaries:

Anadolu Japan Turizm A.S.   **(1)**
Bayildim Cad No 2 Macka Besiktas, Istanbul, Turkiye
Tel.: (90) 212 326 11 00
Emp.: 371
Hotel Operator
N.A.I.C.S.: 721110

Anchor Retail Investments N.V.   **(1)**
Strawinskylaan 1265 World Trade Center D Tower Level 12, Amsterdam, Netherlands
Tel.: (31) 20 820 11 20
Holding Company
N.A.I.C.S.: 551112

Holding (Non-US):

Anchor Grup S.A.   **(2)**
Anchor Plaza Office Building 26Z Timisoara Blvd, 6th District, Bucharest, 61331, Romania
Tel.: (40) 214078402
Web Site: http://www.anchorgrup.ro
Emp.: 123
Real Estate Development Services
N.A.I.C.S.: 531210
Affan Yildirim *(Gen Mgr)*

Credit Europe Group N.V.   **(1)**
Karspeldreef 6a, Amsterdam, Netherlands   **(95%)**
Tel.: (31) 203576410
Web Site: http://www.crediteurope.nl
Holding Company
N.A.I.C.S.: 551112

Subsidiary (Domestic):

Credit Europe Bank N.V.   **(2)**
Karspeldreef 6A, 1101, Amsterdam, Netherlands
Tel.: (31) 203576300
Web Site: http://www.crediteuropebank.na
Sales Range: $1-4.9 Billion
Emp.: 5,242
Commericial Banking
N.A.I.C.S.: 522110
Murag Basbay *(CEO)*

Subsidiary (Non-US):

Credit Europe Bank (Dubai) Ltd.   **(3)**
Currency House Office Building 1 Level 7

Unit 7, Al Fattan Area DIFC, Dubai, United Arab Emirates
Tel.: (971) 44387100
Web Site: http://www.crediteuropebank.com
Sales Range: $50-74.9 Million
Emp.: 19
Commericial Banking
N.A.I.C.S.: 522110
Cenk Atmaca *(CEO)*

Credit Europe Bank (Romania) S.A.   **(3)**
Anchor plaza Building B section 26Z Timisoara boulevard 6th District, 061331, Bucharest, Romania
Tel.: (40) 214064607
Web Site: http://www.crediteurope.ro
Sales Range: $700-749.9 Million
Emp.: 1,200
Commericial Banking
N.A.I.C.S.: 522110
Husnu Ozyegin *(Owner)*

Credit Europe Bank (Suisse) S.A.   **(3)**
12 rue du Mont-Blanc, 1201, Geneva, Switzerland
Tel.: (41) 228391919
Web Site: http://www.crediteurope.ch
Sales Range: $50-74.9 Million
Emp.: 40
Commericial Banking
N.A.I.C.S.: 522110
Iale Kosenovlu *(Mng Dir)*

Credit Europe Bank Ltd.   **(3)**
Cosmodamianskaya Nab 52-3, 11305, Moscow, Russia
Tel.: (7) 4957757757
Web Site: http://www.crediteurope.ru
Sales Range: $1-4.9 Billion
Emp.: 2,747
Commericial Banking
N.A.I.C.S.: 522110
Husnu M. Ozyegin *(Chm)*

Holding (Non-US):

Credit Europe Leasing LLC   **(3)**
Diamond Hall Olimpiskiy Prospekt 14, 129090, Moscow, Russia
Tel.: (7) 495 725 56 56
Web Site: http://www.crediteuropeleasing.ru
Emp.: 28
Vehicle Leasing Services
N.A.I.C.S.: 532112
Jeyhun Nasibov *(CFO)*

Credit Europe Leasing LLC   **(3)**
77A Chervonoarmiyska Street, 1601, Kiev, Ukraine
Tel.: (380) 44 499 44 00
Emp.: 3
Vehicle Leasing Services
N.A.I.C.S.: 532112
Oleksandr Gashenko *(Mgr)*

Subsidiary (Non-US):

PJSC Credit Europe Bank   **(3)**
77-A Chervonoarmiyaska Str, 3150, Kiev, Ukraine   **(100%)**
Tel.: (380) 443906733
Web Site: http://www.crediteurope.com.ua
Commericial Banking
N.A.I.C.S.: 522110

Fiba Air Hava Tasimacilik ve Hizmetleri A.S.   **(1)**
Buyukdere Cad 1 Levent Plaza A Blok No 173 Kat 8, 34330, Istanbul, Levent, Turkiye
Tel.: (90) 212 339 19 00
Emp.: 16
Vehicle Leasing Services
N.A.I.C.S.: 532112

Fiba Emeklilik ve Hayat A.S.   **(1)**
Sarikanarya Sokak Yolbulan Plaza B Blok K 5 Kozyatagi, Istanbul, Kadikoy, Turkiye
Tel.: (90) 216 665 28 00
Web Site: http://www.fibaemeklilik.com.tr
General Insurance Services
N.A.I.C.S.: 524113
Husnu Mustafa Ozyegin *(Chm)*

Fiba Faktoring A.S.   **(1)**
Buyukdere Cad 1 Levent Plaza A Blok No 173, Istanbul, Levent, Turkiye
Tel.: (90) 212 385 14 00
Web Site: http://www.fibafaktoring.com.tr

Emp.: 116
Financial Investment Services
N.A.I.C.S.: 523940
Sukru Alp Oztekbas *(Exec VP-Mktg, Sls & Treasury)*

Fiba Portfoy Yonetimi A.S.   **(1)**
Sarikanarya Sokak Yolbulan Plaza B Blok No 16/11, Kozyatagi Kadikoy, Istanbul, Besiktas, Turkiye
Tel.: (90) 2123817290
Web Site: https://fibaportfoy.com.tr
Emp.: 5
Holding Company
N.A.I.C.S.: 551112
Hakan Avci *(Gen Mgr)*

Fina Enerji Holding A.S.   **(1)**
Kisikli Cad Sarkuysan Ak Is Merkezi No 4 A Blok Kat 1, 34662, Istanbul, Altunizade-Uskudar, Turkiye
Tel.: (90) 216 554 54 00
Web Site: http://www.finaenerji.com.tr
Emp.: 189
Electric Power Distribution Services
N.A.I.C.S.: 221122
Oytun Kutay *(Gen Mgr)*

Genc Magazalari A.S.   **(1)**
Sarikanarya Sok Yolbulan Plaza B Blok No 16 Kat 6, Kozyatagi, 34742, Istanbul, Erenkoy, Turkiye
Tel.: (90) 216 571 00 00
Emp.: 63
Apparel Distr
N.A.I.C.S.: 458110
Gurol Ciragoz *(COO)*

Girisim Varlik Yonetimi A.S.   **(1)**
Merkez Mah Cendere Cad No 22 Ofishane Binasi, 34406, Istanbul, Kagithane, Turkiye
Tel.: (90) 212 381 24 00
Web Site: http://www.girisimvarlik.com.tr
Emp.: 256
Asset Management Services
N.A.I.C.S.: 531390
Hasan Tengiz *(Gen Mgr)*

FIBABANKA A.S.
Esentepe Mah Buyukdere Cad No 129, Sisli, 34394, Istanbul, Turkiye
Tel.: (90) 2123818282
Web Site:
  http://www.fibabanka.com.tr
Year Founded: 1987
FBBNK—(IST)
Rev.: $201,455,236
Assets: $2,291,482,016
Liabilities: $2,088,190,267
Net Worth: $203,291,748
Earnings: $84,032,339
Emp.: 1,979
Fiscal Year-end: 12/31/22
Banking Services
N.A.I.C.S.: 522110
Husnu M. Ozyegin *(Chm)*

Subsidiaries:

Finberg Arastirma Gelistirme Danismanlik Yatirim Hizmetleri A.S.   **(1)**
Ahi Evran Cad No 6 Kolektif House, Maslak, Istanbul, Turkiye
Tel.: (90) 2123813537
Web Site: http://www.finberg.com.tr
N.A.I.C.S.: 523999
Omer Mert *(Chm)*

Subsidiary (Domestic):

Birlesik Odeme Hizmetleri A.S.   **(2)**
Maya Akar Center Esentepe Mah Buyukdere Cad No 100-102 B Blok Kat 3, Sisli, 34394, Istanbul, Turkiye
Tel.: (90) 2122415459
Web Site: http://www.birlesikodeme.com
Electronic Fund Services
N.A.I.C.S.: 522320
Burak Elgin *(Exec VP)*

Bizim Hesap A.S.   **(2)**
Business Istanbul B-Blok Kat 14, Kadikoy, Istanbul, Turkiye
Tel.: (90) 2167060660
Web Site: http://www.bizimhesap.com
E-collection Integration Services
N.A.I.C.S.: 541512

FIBAM COMPANHIA INDUSTRIAL
Av Humberto de Alencar Castelo Branco 39, 9850300, Sao Bernardo do Campo, SP, Brazil
Tel.: (55) 11 2139 5300
Web Site: http://www.fibam.com.br
Year Founded: 1951
Sales Range: $25-49.9 Million
Emp.: 386
Metal Fastener Mfr & Whslr
N.A.I.C.S.: 339993
Paolo Paperini *(Chm & CEO)*

FIBEMI NV
Rokin 55, 1012 KK, Amsterdam, Netherlands
Tel.: (31) 20 527 9111
Investment Services
N.A.I.C.S.: 523999

Subsidiaries:

Duvel Moortgat NV   **(1)**
Breendonkdorp 58, 2870, Puurs, Belgium
Tel.: (32) 3 860 94 00
Web Site: http://www.duvelmoortgat.be
Emp.: 773
Beers & Malt Liquors Mfrs
N.A.I.C.S.: 312120
Michel Moortgat *(CEO)*

Subsidiary (US):

Boulevard Brewing Co.   **(2)**
2501 SW Blvd, Kansas City, MO 64108
Tel.: (816) 474-7095
Web Site: http://www.boulevard.com
Sales Range: $10-24.9 Million
Emp.: 125
Beer Mfr & Distr
N.A.I.C.S.: 312120
John McDonald *(Founder)*

Subsidiary (Domestic):

Brasserie d'Achouffe nv   **(2)**
Rue du Village 32, Achouffe, 6666, Houffalize, Belgium   **(100%)**
Tel.: (32) 61 28 81 47
Web Site: http://www.achouffe.be
Sales Range: $10-24.9 Million
Emp.: 36
Brewery
N.A.I.C.S.: 312120

Subsidiary (US):

Brouwerij Belame Ltd   **(2)**
656 County Hwy 33, Cooperstown, NY 13326-9248   **(100%)**
Tel.: (607) 544-1800
Web Site: http://www.ommegang.com
Brewery Mfr
N.A.I.C.S.: 312120

Subsidiary (Domestic):

Brouwerij De Koninck nv   **(2)**
Mechelsesteenweg 291, 2018, Antwerp, Belgium   **(100%)**
Tel.: (32) 3218 4048
Web Site: http://www.dekoninck.be
Brewery
N.A.I.C.S.: 312120

Subsidiary (Non-US):

Duvel Moortgat France sarl   **(2)**
540 Allee des Hetres, 69760, Limonest, France   **(100%)**
Tel.: (33) 437 59 82 30
Web Site: http://www.duvelmoortgat.be
Emp.: 15
Beer & Ale Whslr
N.A.I.C.S.: 424810

Duvel Moortgat Shanghai Ltd   **(2)**
322 Jiaozhou Road, Shanghai, 200030, China   **(100%)**
Tel.: (86) 21 62 55 79 19
Beer & Ale Importer, Distr & Whslr
N.A.I.C.S.: 424810

Duvel Moortgat UK Ltd   **(2)**
134 Curtain Road, Shoreditch, London, EC2A 3AR, United Kingdom   **(100%)**
Tel.: (44) 20 77 29 72 16

Fibemi NV—(Continued)

Web Site: http://www.duvelmoortgat.be
Beer & Ale Whslr
N.A.I.C.S.: 424810

Subsidiary (US):

Duvel Moortgat USA, Ltd. (100%)
21 Railroad Ave Ste 32, Cooperstown, NY 13326
Tel.: (607) 544-1800
Web Site: http://www.duvelmoortgatusa.com
Sales Range: $25-49.9 Million
Emp.: 25
Sales & Distribution of Beer & Ale
N.A.I.C.S.: 424810
Simon Thorpe (Pres & CEO)

Firestone Walker, LLC (2)
620 McMurry Rd, Buellton, CA 93427
Tel.: (805) 686-1557
Sales Range: $1-9.9 Million
Emp.: 25
Breweries
N.A.I.C.S.: 312120
Adam Firestone (Principal)

FIBER INTERMEDIATE PRODUCTS COMPANY
45th Km of Isfahan Mobarakeh Road, PO Box 81655-569, Isfahan, Iran
Tel.: (98) 335 5528229
Web Site: http://www.fipcoiran.com
Year Founded: 1992
Emp.: 354
Chemical Products Mfr
N.A.I.C.S.: 325199

FIBERHOME TECHNOLOGIES GROUP
No 6 Gaoxinsilu East Lake High-Tech Development Zone, Hongshan District, Wuhan, 430205, Hubei, China
Tel.: (86) 2787693885
Web Site: https://www.fiberhome.com
Year Founded: 1974
600498—(SHG)
Rev.: $4,340,867,628
Assets: $5,411,849,822
Liabilities: $3,513,397,048
Net Worth: $1,898,452,773
Earnings: $56,973,379
Fiscal Year-end: 12/31/22
Information Technology Services
N.A.I.C.S.: 541512
Jun Zeng (Chm)

Subsidiaries:

Wuhan Hongxin Communication Technologies Co., Ltd. (1)
5 Dongxin Rd East Lake High-Tech Developing Zone, Wuhan, 430073, Hubei, China
Tel.: (86) 27 87693786
Web Site: http://www.hxct.com
Emp.: 3,600
Wireless Telecommunication Services
N.A.I.C.S.: 517112
Scott Huang (Engr-Thermal)

FIBERLABS INC.
KDDI Research Building 2-1-15 Ohara, Fujimino, 356-8502, Saitama, Japan
Tel.: (81) 492787829
Web Site: http://www.fiberlabs.com
Year Founded: 2000
Sales Range: $25-49.9 Million
Emp.: 14
Optical Fiber Communication Equipment & Optical Fiber Mfr
N.A.I.C.S.: 335921
Yoshinori Mimura (Pres)

FIBERLINKS TEXTILES INC.
4747 Cote Vertu Ouest, Saint Laurent, H4S 1C9, QC, Canada
Tel.: (514) 694-9440
Web Site: http://fiberlinks.com
Textile Product Mfr & Distr
N.A.I.C.S.: 314999

Wilhelm Dres (Co-Founder & Exec VP)

Subsidiaries:

Priva Inc. (1)
815C Tecumseh, Pointe-Claire, H9R 4B1, QC, Canada
Tel.: (514) 356-8881
Web Site: http://www.fiberlinkstextiles.com
Sales Range: $10-24.9 Million
Emp.: 20
Waterproof Textile Products Mfr
N.A.I.C.S.: 314120

FIBERWEB (INDIA) LTD.
Airport Road Kadaiya Village, Nani Daman, Daman, 396210, Daman & Diu, India
Tel.: (91) 2602220766
Web Site: https://fiberwebindia.com
Year Founded: 1985
507910—(BOM)
Rev.: $14,828,240
Assets: $25,781,113
Liabilities: $1,867,968
Net Worth: $23,913,145
Earnings: $1,961,740
Emp.: 133
Fiscal Year-end: 03/31/21
Spunbonded Fabrics Mfr
N.A.I.C.S.: 313230
G. Ravindran (Deputy Pres-Ops)

FIBI HOLDINGS LTD.
42 Rothschild Blvd, Tel Aviv, 6688310, Israel
Tel.: (972) 35196111
Web Site: https://www.fibi.co.il
Year Founded: 1972
FIBIH—(TAE)
Rev.: $1,346,727
Assets: $60,084,594
Liabilities: $58,500,624
Net Worth: $1,583,971
Earnings: $283,878
Fiscal Year-end: 12/31/23
Bank Holding Company
N.A.I.C.S.: 551112
Smadar Barber-Tsaddik (CEO-First International Bank of Israel Ltd)

Subsidiaries:

Bank Otsar Hahayal Ltd. (1)
11 Menachem Begin Rd, Ramat Gan, 5268104, Israel
Tel.: (972) 37556000
Web Site: http://www.bankotsar.co.il
Rev.: $189,472,260
Assets: $5,498,771,920
Liabilities: $5,178,881,970
Net Worth: $319,889,950
Earnings: $22,181,860
Fiscal Year-end: 12/31/2016
Commercial Banking Services
N.A.I.C.S.: 522110

First International Bank of Israel Ltd. (1)
42 Rothschild Blvd, Tel Aviv, 6688310, Israel (54.33%)
Tel.: (972) 35196111
Web Site: http://www.fibi.co.il
Rev.: $3,177,786,937
Assets: $61,221,991,031
Liabilities: $57,728,138,344
Net Worth: $3,493,852,687
Earnings: $593,728,406
Emp.: 3,628
Fiscal Year-end: 12/31/2023
Commericial Banking
N.A.I.C.S.: 522110
Yael Ronen (Exec VP)

Subsidiary (Domestic):

Bank Massad Ltd. (2)
80 Rothschild Boulevard, PO Box 2639, Tel Aviv, 61025, Israel (51%)
Tel.: (972) 35641333
Web Site: http://www.bankmassad.co.il

Sales Range: $100-124.9 Million
Emp.: 241
Commercial Banking Services
N.A.I.C.S.: 522110

Bank Otsar Ha-Hayal Ltd. (2)
11 Menachem Begin St, 52521, Ramat Gan, Israel (68%)
Tel.: (972) 37556005
Web Site: http://www.bankotsar.co.il
Sales Range: $50-74.9 Million
Emp.: 782
Commercial Banking Services
N.A.I.C.S.: 522110
Baruch Granot (CFO)

Bank Poaley Agudat Israel Ltd. (2)
9 Ahad Ha Am Street, Tel Aviv, 65251, Israel (68.68%)
Tel.: (972) 35196650
Web Site: http://www.pagi.co.il
Sales Range: $25-49.9 Million
Emp.: 50
Commercial Banking Services
N.A.I.C.S.: 522110

Modus Selective Investment Management & Advice Ltd. (2)
17 Yitzhak Sadeh Street, 67211, Tel Aviv, Israel (50%)
Tel.: (972) 036241166
Sales Range: $50-74.9 Million
Emp.: 25
Investment Management Service
N.A.I.C.S.: 523940

The First International & Co.-Underwriting and Investment Ltd. (2)
38 Rothschild Blvd, Tel Aviv, Israel (75%)
Tel.: (972) 35115730
Commericial Banking
N.A.I.C.S.: 522110

UBank Ltd. (2)
38 Rothschild Blvd, Tel Aviv, 66883, Israel (100%)
Tel.: (972) 3 564 5630
Web Site: http://www.u-bank.net
Sales Range: $150-199.9 Million
Emp.: 260
Commericial Banking
N.A.I.C.S.: 522110
Amir Masor (Mgr-Tel Aviv Branch)

Ubank Trust Company Ltd. (1)
38 Rotschild Blvd, Tel Aviv, 66888307, Jaffa, Israel
Tel.: (972) 35645205
Commercial Banking Services
N.A.I.C.S.: 522110
Kfir Naaman (Mgr)

FIBOCOM WIRELESS, INC.
Floor 10 14th Tower A Building 6, Shenzhen International Innovation Valley Dashi 1st Rd Nanshan District, Shenzhen, 518055, Guangdong, China
Tel.: (86) 75526733555
Web Site: https://www.fibocom.com
Year Founded: 1999
300638—(CHIN)
Rev.: $792,757,368
Assets: $898,446,276
Liabilities: $557,598,600
Net Worth: $340,847,676
Earnings: $51,170,184
Fiscal Year-end: 12/31/22
Communication Equipment Mfr & Distr
N.A.I.C.S.: 334220

FIBON BERHAD
12A Jalan 20 Taman Sri Kluang, Kluang, 86000, Johor, Malaysia
Tel.: (60) 77736918
Web Site: https://www.fibon.com.my
FIBON—(KLS)
Rev.: $4,118,730
Assets: $12,935,238
Liabilities: $579,259
Net Worth: $12,355,979
Earnings: $1,033,651
Fiscal Year-end: 05/31/23

Polymer Matrix Fiber Composite Materials Mfr
N.A.I.C.S.: 325998
Fok Seng Pang (Mng Dir)

Subsidiaries:

Fibon Australia Pty Ltd (1)
Fiber Composite Materials Mfr
N.A.I.C.S.: 325220

Fibon Capital Sdn. Bhd. (1)
12A Jalan 20 Taman Sri Kluang, 86000, Kluang, Johor, Malaysia
Tel.: (60) 77736918
Web Site: https://fiboncapital.com.my
Investment Fund Services
N.A.I.C.S.: 523940

Fibon Electric (M) Sdn. Bhd. (1)
12A Jalan 20 Taman Sri Kluang, 86000, Kluang, Johor, Malaysia
Tel.: (60) 77728000
Electric Equipment Mfr
N.A.I.C.S.: 335311

Fibon UK Limited (1)
4 Parkside Court Greenhough Road, Lichfield, WS13 7AU, Staffordshire, United Kingdom
Tel.: (44) 154 330 4167
Web Site: http://www.fibon.co.uk
Emp.: 2
Electrical Insulator Mfr
N.A.I.C.S.: 327110

Hexa Analisa Sdn. Bhd. (1)
12A Jalan 20 Taman Sri Kluang, 86000, Keluang, Johor, Malaysia
Tel.: (60) 77736918
Electronic Components Mfr
N.A.I.C.S.: 334419

FIBRA DANHOS
Monte Pelvoux 220 Lomas Virreyes, Miguel Hidalgo, 11000, Mexico, Mexico
Tel.: (52) 5552840030
Web Site: https://www.fibradanhos.com.mx
Year Founded: 1976
Real Estate Manangement Services
N.A.I.C.S.: 531390
Salvador Daniel Kabbaz Zaga (CEO)

FIBRA HD SERVICIOS SC
Av Santa Fe 498 piso 3 Lomas de Santa Fe Cuajimalpa de, 05348, Morelos, Mexico
Tel.: (52) 5575880250
Web Site: https://www.fibrahd.com.mx
Real Estate Investment Services
N.A.I.C.S.: 531190

FIBRA INN
Av Ricardo Margain Zozaya No 605 1st Floor, San Pedro Garza Garcia, Mexico, 66267, Nuevo Leon, Mexico
Tel.: (52) 8150000200
Web Site: http://www.fibrainn.mx
FINN—(MEX)
Sales Range: Less than $1 Million
Hotel & Resort Operator
N.A.I.C.S.: 721110
Miguel Aliaga Gargollo (CFO)

FIBRA MACQUARIE
Pedregal 24 Piso 21 Torre Virreyes Lomas-Virreyes Molino del Rey, 11040, Mexico, Mexico
Tel.: (52) 5591877700
Web Site: https://www.fibramacquarie.com
Year Founded: 2012
FIBRAMQ—(MEX)
Emp.: 89
Real Estate Manangement Services
N.A.I.C.S.: 531390
Juan Monroy (CEO)

FIBRA PROLOGIS

Paseo de los Tamarindos 90 Torre 2
Piso 22, Bosques de las Lomas,
05120, Mexico, 05120, Mexico
Tel.: (52) 5511052900
Web Site:
   https://www.fibraprologis.com
Year Founded: 2013
FIBRAPL—(MEX)
Sales Range: Less than $1 Million
Real Estate Manangement Services
N.A.I.C.S.: 531390
Hector Ibarzabal *(Mng Dir)*

FIBRA SHOP PORTAFOLIOS INMOBILIARIOS SAPI DE CV

Juan Salvador Agraz No 40 Piso Del-
egacion Cuajimalpa, Colonia Sante
Fe, 5109, Mexico, 5109, Mexico
Tel.: (52) 5552921160
Web Site: https://fibrashop.mx
FSHOP—(MEX)
Sales Range: Less than $1 Million
Real Estate Manangement Services
N.A.I.C.S.: 531390
Salvador Cayon Caballos *(Chm & CEO)*

FIBRA UNO ADMINISTRACION SA DE CV

Antonio Dovali Jaime No 70 11th
Floor Tower B, Samara Santa Fe,
01219, Mexico, Mexico
Tel.: (52) 5541707070
Web Site: https://funo.mx
Year Founded: 2011
FUNO—(MEX)
Rev.: $1,573,643,726
Assets: $20,450,627,770
Liabilities: $8,688,605,679
Net Worth: $11,762,022,091
Earnings: $1,107,827,051
Emp.: 1,066
Fiscal Year-end: 12/31/23
Real Estate Investment
N.A.I.C.S.: 523999
Andre El-Mann *(Co-CEO)*

FIBRAHOTEL

Av Santa Fe 481 Piso 7, 5348, Colo-
nia, Mexico
Tel.: (52) 5552928050
Web Site: https://www.fibrahotel.com
FIHO—(MEX)
Rev.: $307,826,858
Assets: $1,040,862,272
Liabilities: $297,716,912
Net Worth: $743,145,360
Earnings: $32,968,657
Emp.: 33
Fiscal Year-end: 12/31/23
Hotel & Restaurant Operator
N.A.I.C.S.: 721110

FIBRE-CROWN MANUFAC-TURING, INC.

4025 McConnell Drive, Burnaby, V5A
3A7, BC, Canada
Tel.: (604) 433-6955
Web Site: https://fibrecrown.com
Year Founded: 1998
FBR.H—(TSXV)
Rev.: $51,987
Assets: $706,653
Liabilities: $19,774
Net Worth: $686,878
Earnings: $6,647
Fiscal Year-end: 12/31/23
Timber Molding Mfr
N.A.I.C.S.: 337212

FIBRECHEM TECHNOLOGIES LIMITED

Industrial Area of Donghaibincheng
Fengze District, Quanzhou, China
Tel.: (86) 5952908288   BM
Fibre Material Mfr & Distr

N.A.I.C.S.: 325220
Peirong Zheng *(CFO)*

FIBREGEN PLC

31 Harley St, London, W1G 9QS,
United Kingdom
Tel.: (44) 2075807576
Web Site: http://www.fibregen.co.uk
Sales Range: $10-24.9 Million
Operator of Biomass-to-Energy Facili-
ties
N.A.I.C.S.: 221118

FIBRELITE COMPOSITES LIM-ITED.

Snaygill Industrial Estate Keighley
Road, Skipton, BD23 2QR, North
Yorkshire, United Kingdom
Tel.: (44) 1756799773
Web Site: http://www.fibrelite.com
Year Founded: 1980
Rev.: $18,339,817
Emp.: 97
Manhole Cover Mfr
N.A.I.C.S.: 331511
David Holmes *(Dir-Technical)*

Subsidiaries:

Fibrelite Australia   **(1)**
17/720 MacArthur Avenue Central,
Pinkenba, 4008, QLD, Australia
Tel.: (61) 747880519
Manhole Cover Distr
N.A.I.C.S.: 423510

FIBRESOURCES CORP.

1090 Homer Street Suite 320, Van-
couver, V6B 2W9, BC, Canada
Tel.: (604) 669-0699
Bioresource Information Development
Services
N.A.I.C.S.: 519290

FIBROLAN LTD.

2 Carmel Street, Yoqne'am Illit,
20692, Israel
Tel.: (972) 4 9591717
Web Site: http://www.fibrolan.com
Year Founded: 1996
Sales Range: $1-9.9 Million
Communication Equipment Mfr
N.A.I.C.S.: 334290
Shamir Stein *(CEO)*

FIC GLOBAL, INC

1 9F No 300 Yang Guang St, Neihu,
Taipei, 114, Taiwan
Tel.: (886) 287518751
Web Site: http://www.ficg.com.tw
Year Founded: 2004
3701—(TAI)
Rev.: $434,396,007
Assets: $386,828,234
Liabilities: $149,800,380
Net Worth: $237,027,853
Earnings: $20,495,339
Emp.: 5,485
Fiscal Year-end: 12/31/23
Information Technology Services
N.A.I.C.S.: 519290
Chien Leo Ming Tz *(Chm & Gen Mgr)*

Subsidiaries:

3CEMS Group - Fremont Branch   **(1)**
5020 Brandin Ct, Fremont, CA 94538
Tel.: (510) 252-8870
Electronic Component Mfr & Distr
N.A.I.C.S.: 334419

Amertek Computer (Shenzhen) Co.
Ltd.   **(1)**
Bldg 30 No 2015 Shatoujiao Free Trade
Zone Shenyan Road, Shenzhen, China
Tel.: (86) 75566850888
Electronic Components Mfr
N.A.I.C.S.: 334419

Broad Technology (Guangzhou)
Inc.   **(1)**

No 18 Baoying Dadao Guangzhou Free
Trade Zone, Guangzhou, China
Tel.: (86) 2082224900
Electronic Components Mfr
N.A.I.C.S.: 334419

Broad Technology Incorporated   **(1)**
Suite 1-2 11F No 1071 Chung Cheng Rd,
Taoyuan, 330, Taiwan
Tel.: (886) 33265380
Electronic Component Mfr & Distr
N.A.I.C.S.: 334419

Broadteam Electronics (Guangzhou)
Inc.   **(1)**
No 9 Kangda Road Dongcheng Section
Yunpu Industrial District, Guangzhou, China
Tel.: (86) 2082059033
Electronic Component Mfr & Distr
N.A.I.C.S.: 334419

ComServe Network Netherlands
B.V.   **(1)**
Crude Kampweg 11, 5222 AT, 's-
Hertogenbosch, Netherlands
Tel.: (31) 736273300
Web Site: http://www.comservegroup.com
Consumer Products Distr
N.A.I.C.S.: 423620

Danriver Technology (Guangzhou)
Inc.   **(1)**
No 16 Baoying Dadao Guangzhou Free
Trade Zone, Guangzhou, China
Tel.: (86) 2082219590
Electronic Component Mfr & Distr
N.A.I.C.S.: 334419

Delton Technology (Guangzhou)
Inc.   **(1)**
No 18-20 Baoying Nan Rd Guangzhou Free
Trade Zone, Guangzhou, China
Tel.: (86) 2082210736
Electronic Component Mfr & Distr
N.A.I.C.S.: 334419

First International Computer, Inc   **(1)**
8F No 300 Yang Guang St, Neihu, Taipei,
114, Taiwan
Tel.: (886) 287518751
Web Site: http://www.fic.com.tw
Engineeering Services
N.A.I.C.S.: 523940

Prime Foundation Inc.   **(1)**
Suite 1-4 11F No 1071 Chung Cheng Rd,
Taoyuan, 330, Taiwan
Tel.: (886) 33170818
Electronic Component Mfr & Distr
N.A.I.C.S.: 334419

Prime Technology (Guangzhou)
Inc.   **(1)**
No 19 Baoying Nan Rd Guangzhou Free
Trade Zone, Guangzhou, China
Tel.: (86) 2082217620
Electronic Components Mfr
N.A.I.C.S.: 334419

Ubiqconn Technology Inc.   **(1)**
4F No 300 Yangguang St, Neihu District,
Taipei, 11491, Taiwan
Tel.: (886) 287516008
Web Site: http://www.ubiqconn.com
Electronic Product Mfr & Distr
N.A.I.C.S.: 334118

FICHA, INC.

3-1-1 Higashi-Ikebukuro, Toshima-Ku,
Tokyo, 170-6019, Japan
Tel.: (81) 369070312
Web Site: https://www.ficha.jp
Year Founded: 2005
4052—(TKS)
Rev.: $3,072,680
Assets: $4,776,960
Liabilities: $242,580
Net Worth: $4,534,380
Earnings: ($43,540)
Fiscal Year-end: 06/30/24
Software Development Services
N.A.I.C.S.: 541511
Kenichiro Waki *(Pres & CEO)*

FICHOU SAS

Z I Kergonan 20 Rue Gustave Zede,
29200, Brest, Finistere, France

Tel.: (33) 298424242
Rev.: $20,200,000
Emp.: 117
Motor Vehicle Supplies & New Parts
N.A.I.C.S.: 423120
Jean-Luc Aridon *(Dir)*

FICODIS INC.

465 Saint John Suite 1001, Montreal,
H2Y 2R6, QC, Canada
Tel.: (514) 360-4007
Web Site: http://ficodis.ca
Year Founded: 2010
Multi-specialized Industrial Supply
Distr
N.A.I.C.S.: 423840
Christophe Bevillard *(Pres)*

Subsidiaries:

Berliss Bearing Co.   **(1)**
664 West Mount Pleasant Ave, Livingston,
NJ 07039
Tel.: (973) 992-4242
Web Site: http://www.berliss.com
Rev.: $6,666,666
Emp.: 70
Ball & Roller Bearing Mfr
N.A.I.C.S.: 332991
John Rubinstein *(Pres)*

Blue Point Tool & Supply Co,
Inc.   **(1)**
41 Keyland Ct Ste B, Bohemia, NY 11716
Tel.: (631) 567-8844
Web Site: https://bluepointtool.com
Industrial Supplies, Nsk
N.A.I.C.S.: 423840
David Monheit *(Founder)*

Reliable Bearing Co. Ltd.   **(1)**
955 Meyerside Drive, Mississauga, L5T
1P9, ON, Canada
Tel.: (905) 670-1055
Web Site: https://reliablebearing.com
Bearings & Power Transmission Products
Distr
N.A.I.C.S.: 423840
Carl Faria *(Owner)*

FICONT INDUSTRY BEIJING CO., LTD.

No 8 Cuiyuan Road, Wuqing Devel-
opment Zone, Tianjin, China
Tel.: (86) 1061518677
Web Site: https://www.3sindustry.com
Year Founded: 2005
605305—(SHG)
Rev.: $112,235,704
Assets: $351,559,522
Liabilities: $47,852,349
Net Worth: $303,707,173
Earnings: $21,780,168
Emp.: 900
Fiscal Year-end: 12/31/22
Wind Turbine Mfr
N.A.I.C.S.: 333611
Zhixin Liu *(Chm & Gen Mgr)*

FIDEA HOLDINGS CO. LTD.

3-1-24 Chuo, Aoba-ku, Sendai, 980-
0021, Miyagi, Japan
Tel.: (81) 222908800
Web Site: https://www.fidea.co.jp
Year Founded: 2009
8713—(TKS)
Rev.: $330,129,840
Assets: $20,230,989,040
Liabilities: $19,663,692,400
Net Worth: $567,296,640
Earnings: $247,875
Fiscal Year-end: 03/31/24
Bank Holding Company
N.A.I.C.S.: 551111
Satoru Nishibori *(Chm)*

Subsidiaries:

The Hokuto Bank, Ltd.   **(1)**
3-1-41 Nakadori, Akita, 010-0001, Japan
Tel.: (81) 18 833 4211
Web Site: http://www.hokutobank.co.jp
Emp.: 790

FIDEA Holdings Co. Ltd.—(Continued)

Banking Services
N.A.I.C.S.: 522110
Eikichi Saito *(Pres)*

The Shonai Bank, Ltd.   **(1)**
1-9-7 Honcho, Tsuruoka, 997-8611, Yamagata, Japan
Tel.: (81) 235 22 5211
Web Site: http://www.shonai.co.jp
Emp.: 838
Banking Services
N.A.I.C.S.: 522110
Masashi Ueno *(Pres)*

FIDEICOMISO DE CREDITO BANCO GENERAL COSTA RICA
Torre Banco General 18th Floor Street Aqilino Guard 5th B South Avenue, PO Box 0816-00843, Panama, Panama
Tel.: (507) 303 800
Commercial Banking Services
N.A.I.C.S.: 522110

FIDEICOMISO ENA NORTE
HSBC Plaza Building 47th Street East, Aquilino De La Guardia Flat No 5, Panama, Panama
Tel.: (507) 206 8480
ENAN—(PAN)
Sales Range: Less than $1 Million
Financial Services
N.A.I.C.S.: 523999

FIDEICOMISO ENA SUR
Tower of the Americas Tower B 14th Floor Streets, PO Box 0834-00555, Coronado & Punta Punta Darien Boulevard Punta Pacifica Panama, Panama, Panama
Tel.: (507) 210 5900
Year Founded: 2011
Financial Administration Services
N.A.I.C.S.: 523999

FIDELIS INSURANCE HOLDINGS LIMITED
Wellesley House South 90 Pitts Bay Road, Pembroke, HM 08, Bermuda
Tel.: (441) 2792500   BM
Web Site:
  https://www.fidelisinsurance.com
Year Founded: 2014
FIHL—(NYSE)
Holding Company; Property & Casualty Insurance Products & Services
N.A.I.C.S.: 551112

FIDELITAS INDUSTRIEHOLDING GMBH
August Pfander Strasse 18, 72622, Nurtingen, Germany
Tel.: (49) 497022243808
Web Site: http://www.fidelitas-industrieholding.de
Year Founded: 2014
Privater Equity Firm
N.A.I.C.S.: 523999

Subsidiaries:

ERNI Electronic Solutions GmbH   **(1)**
Zillenhardtstr 35, Gewerbegebiet Voralb Eschenbach, 73037, Goppingen, Germany
Tel.: (49) 7161 38997 0
Web Site: http://www.erni-es.com
Electronic Product Mfr & Distr
N.A.I.C.S.: 334417

FIDELITY ASIAN VALUES PLC
Beech Gate Millfield Lane, Lower Kingswood, Tadworth, KT20 6RP, Surrey, United Kingdom
Tel.: (44) 1737836347   UK
Year Founded: 1996

FAS—(LSE)
Rev.: $22,251,011
Assets: $502,699,696
Liabilities: $7,232,053
Net Worth: $495,467,643
Earnings: $14,730,636
Fiscal Year-end: 07/31/24
Investment Management Service
N.A.I.C.S.: 523999
Kate Bolsover *(Chm)*

FIDELITY BANK PLC.
Fidelity Place 2 Kofo Abayomi Street, Victoria Island, Lagos, Nigeria
Tel.: (234) 14485252   NG
Web Site: http://www.fidelitybank.ng
FIDELITYBK—(NIGE)
Rev.: $249,483,712
Assets: $2,952,656,200
Liabilities: $2,719,967,579
Net Worth: $232,688,621
Earnings: $34,585,008
Emp.: 3,038
Fiscal Year-end: 12/31/22
Retail & Commercial Banking Services
N.A.I.C.S.: 522110
Aku P. Odinkemelu *(Exec Dir-Comml & Consumer Banking-South)*

Subsidiaries:

Algorithm Media Limited   **(1)**
22 Idowu Taylor Street, Victoria Island, Lagos, Nigeria
Tel.: (234) 907 028 9102
Web Site: https://www.algorithmmedia.com
Media Consultancy Services
N.A.I.C.S.: 541890
Rajesh Jha *(Mng Dir)*

FIDELITY EMERGING MARKETS LIMITED
21 Grosvenor Place, Belgravia, London, SW1X 7HU, United Kingdom
Tel.: (44) 2072017200
FEML—(LSE)
Rev.: $40,601,000
Assets: $830,823,000
Liabilities: $34,089,000
Net Worth: $796,734,000
Earnings: $14,549,000
Fiscal Year-end: 06/30/23
Investment Management Service
N.A.I.C.S.: 525990
Andrew Graham Elder *(Mgr-Fund)*

FIDELITY EUROPEAN TRUST PLC
Beech Gate Millfield Lane, Lower Kingswood, Tadworth, KT20 6RP, United Kingdom
Tel.: (44) 1732777377
FEV—(LSE)
Assets: $1,676,435,145
Liabilities: $13,020,645
Net Worth: $1,663,414,500
Earnings: ($68,620,365)
Fiscal Year-end: 12/31/22
Investment Management Service
N.A.I.C.S.: 525990
Vivian Bazalgette *(Chm)*

FIDELITY JAPAN TRUST PLC
Beech Gate Millfield Lane, Lower Kingswood, Tadworth, KT20 6RP, Surrey, United Kingdom
Tel.: (44) 1732361144   UK
Web Site: https://www.fidelity.co.uk
FJV—(LSE)
Assets: $286,622,820
Liabilities: $1,915,155
Net Worth: $284,707,665
Earnings: ($91,542,000)
Fiscal Year-end: 12/31/22
Miscellaneous Financial Investment Activities
N.A.I.C.S.: 523999

David Robins *(Chm)*

FIDELITY LIFE ASSURANCE LIMITED
7th Floor Fidelity House 66 Julius Nyerere Way, Harare, Zimbabwe
Tel.: (263) 4 750927 34
Web Site: http://www.fidelitylife.co.zw
Year Founded: 1936
FIDL—(ZIM)
Sales Range: Less than $1 Million
Emp.: 129
Funeral Services
N.A.I.C.S.: 812210
Fungayi Ruwende *(Chm)*

Subsidiaries:

Fidelity Life Asset Management Company (Private) Limited   **(1)**
2nd Floor Fidelity House 66 Julius Nyerere Way, Harare, Zimbabwe
Tel.: (263) 24275092734
Funeral Services
N.A.I.C.S.: 812210

Fidelity Life Financial Services (Private) Limited   **(1)**
4th Floor Fidelity House 66 Julius Nyerere Way, Harare, Zimbabwe
Tel.: (263) 24275092734
Funeral Services
N.A.I.C.S.: 812210

FIDELITY MINERALS CORP.
1201 - 1166 Alberni Street, Vancouver, V6E 3Z3, BC, Canada
Tel.: (604) 671-1353   ON
Web Site:
  https://www.fidelityminerals.com
Year Founded: 2017
FMN—(TSXV)
Assets: $4,304,040
Liabilities: $186,810
Net Worth: $4,117,230
Earnings: ($629,965)
Fiscal Year-end: 07/31/21
Mineral Exploration Services
N.A.I.C.S.: 213114
Anthony Balic *(CFO)*

FIDELITY SECURITY GROUP (PTY) LTD.
104C Mimosa St, Helderkruin, Roodepoort, 1724, South Africa
Tel.: (27) 117639000   ZA
Web Site:
  http://www.fidelitysecurity.co.za
Year Founded: 1957
Holding Company; Security Guard & Surveillance Services
N.A.I.C.S.: 551112
Wahl J. Bartmann *(CEO)*

Subsidiaries:

Fidelity ADT (Pty) Ltd   **(1)**
1 Charles Crescent Eastgate Ext 4, Sandton, 2146, South Africa
Tel.: (27) 86 01 00 911
Web Site: http://www.adt.co.za
Alarm System Sales & Installation Services
N.A.I.C.S.: 423610

Fidelity Security Services (Pty) Ltd.   **(1)**
104 D Mimosa Street, Helderkruin, Roodepoort, 1724, South Africa
Tel.: (27) 11 763 9000
Web Site: http://www.fidelitysecurity.co.za
Security Guard & Surveillance Services
N.A.I.C.S.: 561612

FIDELITY SPECIAL VALUES PLC
25 Cannon Street, London, EC4M 5TA, United Kingdom
Tel.: (44) 1732777377
Financial Investment Services
N.A.I.C.S.: 523999
Lord Howard Flight *(Mgr-Fund)*

FIDELIUM GMBH
Sendlinger Strasse 10, 80331, Munich, Germany
Tel.: (49) 89 55289490
Web Site: http://www.fidelium-partners.com
Year Founded: 2017
Privater Equity Firm
N.A.I.C.S.: 523940
Dominik Beck *(Founder & Mng Partner)*

FIDELIX CO., LTD.
6F Hunus Bldg 93 Baekhyeon-ro, Bundang-gu, Seongnam, 13595, Gyeonggi-do, Korea (South)
Tel.: (82) 317853500
Web Site: https://www.fidelix.co.kr
Year Founded: 2000
032580—(KRS)
Rev.: $55,652,815
Assets: $44,307,451
Liabilities: $6,673,611
Net Worth: $37,633,840
Earnings: $6,325,185
Emp.: 70
Fiscal Year-end: 12/31/22
Semiconductor Mfr
N.A.I.C.S.: 334413
YingXia Xie *(Co-CEO)*

FIDIA S.P.A.
C so Lombardia 11, 10099, San Mauro Torinese, TO, Italy
Tel.: (39) 0112227111   IT
Web Site: https://www.fidia.it
FDA—(ITA)
Rev.: $18,897,674
Assets: $33,420,640
Liabilities: $26,259,085
Net Worth: $7,161,554
Earnings: $2,161
Emp.: 197
Fiscal Year-end: 12/31/22
Mfr & Marketer of Electronic Components & Software for Industrial Sector
N.A.I.C.S.: 334419
Giuseppe Morfino *(Pres & Mng Dir)*

Subsidiaries:

Beijing Fidia Machinery & Electronics Co., Ltd.   **(1)**
Room 1509 15/F Tower A TYG Center Mansion C2 North Road, East Third Ring Road Chaoyang District, Beijing, 100027, China
Tel.: (86) 106 460 5813
Mailing Machine Mfr
N.A.I.C.S.: 333248

FIDIA Co.   **(1)**
3098 Research Dr, Rochester Hills, MI 48309
Tel.: (248) 680-0700
Web Site: http://www.fidia.com
Sales Range: $25-49.9 Million
Emp.: 20
Mfr & Marketer of Electronic Components & Software for Industrial Sector
N.A.I.C.S.: 335314

FIDIA Co.   **(1)**
24 C No 1076 Jiangning Rd, Putuo Dist, Shanghai, 200060, China
Tel.: (86) 2152521635
Web Site: http://www.fidia.com.cn
Mfr & Marketer of Electronic Components & Software for Industrial Sector
N.A.I.C.S.: 334419

FIDIA Do BRASIL Ltda.   **(1)**
Salifara Maluci 4236 Mooca, Sao Paulo, 3194010, Brazil   **(100%)**
Tel.: (55) 69657600
Web Site: http://www.fidia.com.br
Sales Range: $25-49.9 Million
Emp.: 50
Mfr & Marketer of Electronic Components & Software for Industrial Sector
N.A.I.C.S.: 334419

FIDIA GmbH   **(1)**
Robert-Bosch-Strasse 18, Sprendlingen,

63303, Dreieich, Germany **(100%)**
Tel.: (49) 61034858700
Web Site: http://www.fidia.de
Sales Range: $25-49.9 Million
Emp.: 20
Mfr & Marketer of Electronic Components &
Software for Industrial Sector
N.A.I.C.S.: 334419

FIDIA Iberica S.A. **(1)**
Laida Bidea Edificio 208 Parque Tecno-
logico, 48170, Zamudio, Bizkaia,
Spain **(100%)**
Tel.: (34) 944209820
Sales Range: $1-9.9 Million
Emp.: 12
Electronic Components & Software for In-
dustrial Sector
N.A.I.C.S.: 334419

FIDIA Machinery & Electronics Co.
Ltd. **(1)**
Room 1509 15/F Tower A TYG Center Man-
sion, C2 North Road East Third Ring Road
Chaoyang District, Beijing, 100027, China
Tel.: (86) 1064605813
Web Site: http://www.fidia.co.cn
Sales Range: $25-49.9 Million
Emp.: 20
Mfr & Marketer of Electronic Components &
Software for Industrial Sector
N.A.I.C.S.: 334419

FIDIA S.a.r.l. **(1)**
47 bis Avenue de l'Europe, 77313, Marne-
la-Vallee, Cedex 2, France **(100%)**
Tel.: (33) 164616824
Web Site: http://www.fidia.fr
Sales Range: $25-49.9 Million
Emp.: 50
Mfr & Marketer of Electronic Components &
Software for Industrial Sector
N.A.I.C.S.: 334419

FIDIA do Brasil Comercio de Equipa-
mentos Ltda. **(1)**
Av Padre Anchieta 161 Jordanopolis, Sao
Bernardo do Campo, 09891-420, Sao
Paulo, Brazil
Tel.: (55) 113 996 2925
Mailing Machine Mfr
N.A.I.C.S.: 333248

OOO FIDIA **(1)**
Sushovskiy Val Dom 5 Str 2 Office 411,
127018, Moscow, Russia
Tel.: (7) 4999730461
Web Site: http://www.fidia.com
Mfr & Marketer of Electronic Components &
Software for Industrial Sector
N.A.I.C.S.: 334419

Shenyang FIDIA NC & Machine Co.,
Ltd. **(1)**
No 1 17 Jia Kaifa Rd, Shenyang Economic
& Technological Development Zone, She-
nyang, 110141, China
Tel.: (86) 242 519 1218
Mailing Machine Mfr
N.A.I.C.S.: 333248

Sitra Automazione Srl **(1)**
Via De Pretis 1 E, 15100, Alessandria,
Italy **(100%)**
Tel.: (39) 0131248090
Web Site: http://www.fidia.it
Sales Range: $1-9.9 Million
Emp.: 20
Mfr & Marketer of Electronic Components &
Software for Industrial Sector
N.A.I.C.S.: 334419

**FIDITOUR JOINT STOCK COM-
PANY**
129 Nguyen Hue Street, District 1,
Ho Chi Minh City, Vietnam
Tel.: (84) 839141414
Web Site: http://www.fiditour.vn
Year Founded: 1989
FDT—(HNX)
Rev.: $23,295,176
Assets: $20,604,391
Liabilities: $11,685,279
Net Worth: $8,919,113
Earnings: $1,157,759
Emp.: 350
Fiscal Year-end: 12/31/19

Travel & Tour Operating Services
N.A.I.C.S.: 561510

FIDSON HEALTHCARE PLC
268 Ikorodu Road, PO Box 7210,
Obanikoro Shomolu, Lagos, Nigeria
Tel.: (234) 3429102
Web Site: https://www.fidson.com
Year Founded: 1995
FIDSON—(NIGE)
Rev.: $30,077,308
Assets: $31,814,663
Liabilities: $19,291,047
Net Worth: $12,523,615
Earnings: $3,099,326
Emp.: 397
Fiscal Year-end: 12/31/22
Pharmaceuticals Product Mfr
N.A.I.C.S.: 325412
Fidelis Ayebae *(CEO & Mng Dir)*

FIDUCIAL
41 Rue du Capitaine Guynemer,
92400, Courbevoie, France
Tel.: (33) 472207600
Web Site: http://www.fiducial.fr
Year Founded: 1970
Sales Range: $1-4.9 Billion
Emp.: 15,000
Management Consulting Services
N.A.I.C.S.: 541611
Christian Latouche *(Founder & Chm)*

Subsidiaries:

Fiducial Expertise S.A. **(1)**
Avenue Louise 148, 1050, Brussels, Bel-
gium
Tel.: (32) 26498016
Web Site: http://www.fiducial.be
Sales Range: $25-49.9 Million
Emp.: 8
Accounting & Tax Services
N.A.I.C.S.: 541219
Christian Latouche *(Pres & CEO)*

Fiducial SA **(1)**
Boulevard Emile Jaques-Dalcroze 5 3Ieme
Etage, Geneva, 1204, Switzerland
Tel.: (41) 223466272
Web Site: http://www.fiducial.com
Sales Range: $25-49.9 Million
Emp.: 8
Accounting & Tax Services
N.A.I.C.S.: 541219

Fiducial, Inc. **(1)**
10100 Old Columbia Rd, Columbia, MD
21046 **(100%)**
Tel.: (410) 910-5885
Web Site: http://www.fiducial.com
Sales Range: $25-49.9 Million
Emp.: 80
Accounting Services
N.A.I.C.S.: 561110
Bill Morice *(Dir-Field Ops)*

Subsidiary (Domestic):

Fiducial, Inc. **(2)**
55E59th St 9th Fl, New York, NY 10022
Tel.: (212) 207-4700
Web Site: http://www.fiducial.com
Sales Range: $75-99.9 Million
Accounting Services
N.A.I.C.S.: 541219
Christian Latouche *(CEO)*

**FIDUCIAL OFFICE SOLUTIONS
SA**
38 rue Sergent Michel Berthet, BP
414, 69009, Lyon, Cedex 09, France
Tel.: (33) 472207878
Web Site: https://www.fiducial-office-
solutions.fr
SACI—(EUR)
Sales Range: $200-249.9 Million
Furniture Distr
N.A.I.C.S.: 424120
Jean-Claude Carquillat *(Chm & CEO)*

FIDUCIAL REAL ESTATE SA
41 rue du Capitaine Guynemer, FR-

92400, Paris, France
Tel.: (33) 472207600 　　FR
Web Site: http://www.fiducial-real-
estate.fr
Year Founded: 1955
ORIA—(EUR)
Sales Range: $75-99.9 Million
Emp.: 97
Real Estate Support Services
N.A.I.C.S.: 531390
Bertrand Cote *(Chm)*

FIDUCIAN GROUP LIMITED
Level 4 60 Carrington Street, Sydney,
2000, NSW, Australia
Tel.: (61) 282984600
Web Site:
https://www.fiducian.com.au
FID—(ASX)
Rev.: $52,952,724
Assets: $47,678,953
Liabilities: $11,211,271
Net Worth: $36,467,681
Earnings: $10,042,735
Emp.: 100
Fiscal Year-end: 06/30/24
Holding Company; Portfolio Manage-
ment & Investment Advisory Services
N.A.I.C.S.: 551112
Inderjit Singh *(Founder & Chm)*

Subsidiaries:

Fiducian Portfolio Services
Limited **(1)**
Level 4 1 York Street, Sydney, 2000, NSW,
Australia
Tel.: (61) 282984600
Web Site: http://www.fiducian.com.au
Sales Range: $10-24.9 Million
Portfolio Management & Investment Advi-
sory Services
N.A.I.C.S.: 523940

Subsidiary (Domestic):

Fiducian Business Services Pty.
Ltd. **(2)**
Level 4 1 York St, PO Box 4175, Sydney,
2000, NSW, Australia
Tel.: (61) 282984600
Web Site: http://www.fiducianbpo.com.au
Emp.: 2
Business Management Services
N.A.I.C.S.: 541618
Alan Dunne *(Mgr-IT)*

Fiducian Financial Services Pty.
Ltd. **(2)**
Level 4 1 York St, PO Box 4175, Sydney,
2001, NSW, Australia
Tel.: (61) 282984600
Web Site: http://www.fiducianfs.com.au
Emp.: 30
Financial Planning Services
N.A.I.C.S.: 523999

FIEBIG & SCHILLINGS GMBH
Dillberg 24, 97828, Marktheidenfeld,
Germany
Tel.: (49) 939160090
Web Site: http://www.fiebig-
schillings.de
Year Founded: 1977
Sales Range: $10-24.9 Million
Bookbinding Products Mfr
N.A.I.C.S.: 333248
Siegfried Fiebig *(Founder)*

FIEBIG+TEAM GMBH
Strahlenberger Weg 26, 60599,
Frankfurt am Main, Germany
Tel.: (49) 696050160
Web Site: http://fiebig.com
Rev.: $13,794,000
Emp.: 51
Communication Solutions & Services
N.A.I.C.S.: 517810
Walter Fiebig *(Mng Dir)*

FIELD DAY INC.

171 E Liberty St Ste 320, Toronto,
M6K 3P6, ON, Canada
Tel.: (416) 408-4446
Web Site: http://www.fieldday.com
Year Founded: 1989
Sales Range: $10-24.9 Million
Emp.: 10
N.A.I.C.S.: 541810
Andrew Arntfield *(Pres-Strategic Plng)*

**FIELD FISHER WATERHOUSE
LLP**
Riverbank House 2 Swan Lane, Lon-
don, EC4R 3TT, United Kingdom
Tel.: (44) 20 7861 4000
Web Site: http://www.ffw.com
Emp.: 167
Law firm
N.A.I.C.S.: 541110
Jon Fife *(Partner)*

Subsidiaries:

Fieldfisher Ryser **(1)**
1408-09 Shanghai Times Square 93 Huai
Hai Road Middle, Shanghai, 200021, China
Tel.: (86) 2151086331
Legal Serivces
N.A.I.C.S.: 541110

**FIELD SOLUTIONS HOLDINGS
LIMITED**
38/23 Narabang Way, Belrose, 2085,
NSW, Australia
Tel.: (61) 1300000488 　　AU
Web Site: https://www.fieldsolutions-
group.com
FSG—(ASX)
Rev.: $32,787,607
Assets: $47,363,527
Liabilities: $15,602,931
Net Worth: $31,760,596
Earnings: $1,017,390
Fiscal Year-end: 06/30/22
Holding Company; Internet Services
N.A.I.C.S.: 551112
Kenneth Carr *(Chm)*

**FIELD SYSTEMS DESIGNS
HOLDINGS PLC**
Blackbrook House The Dorking Busi-
ness Park Station Road, Dorking,
RH4 1HJ, Surrey, United Kingdom
Tel.: (44) 1306880800
Web Site: https://www.fsdl.co.uk
Automobile Parts Mfr
N.A.I.C.S.: 336390
Bruce D. Smith *(Sec)*

FIELDWAY GROUP LIMITED
Unit 12 Block E Paramount Business
Park, Liverpool, L36 6AW, England,
United Kingdom
Tel.: (44) 1514809909
Web Site: https://fieldway.co.uk
Emp.: 100
Fire Safety & Electrical Service Con-
tractor
N.A.I.C.S.: 238210

Subsidiaries:

Intumescent Protective Coatings
Limited **(1)**
2 Jupiter Ct Orion Bus Park, North Shields,
NE29 7SN, Tyne & Wear, United Kingdom
Tel.: (44) 1912728225
Web Site: http://www.ipcl.co.uk
Sales Range: $50-74.9 Million
Emp.: 100
Fire Protection Services
N.A.I.C.S.: 922160
Chris Arnott *(Sec)*

FIELMANN GROUP AG
Weidestrasse 118 A, 22083, Ham-
burg, Germany
Tel.: (49) 40270760
Web Site: https://www.fielmann.de

Fielmann Group AG—(Continued)

Year Founded: 1972
FIE—(DEU)
Rev.: $2,173,608,340
Assets: $2,192,892,948
Liabilities: $1,235,120,143
Net Worth: $957,772,805
Earnings: $140,897,967
Emp.: 23,412
Fiscal Year-end: 12/31/23
Optical Products Mfr & Sales
N.A.I.C.S.: 333310
Mark K. Binz *(Chm-Supervisory Bd)*

Subsidiaries:

Baur Optik
Geschaftsfuhrungs-AG   **(1)**
Reichsstrasse 15, 86609, Donauworth, Germany
Tel.: (49) 906 18 00
Web Site: http://www.bauroptik.de
Optical Product Retailer
N.A.I.C.S.: 456130

Baur Optik GmbH Rain   **(1)**
Hauptstrasse 57, Rain am Lech, 86641, Donauworth, Germany
Tel.: (49) 909090900
Eyewear Product Mfr
N.A.I.C.S.: 339115

Betriebsgesellschaft Pfortnerhaus
mbH   **(1)**
Schloss 0, Plon, 24306, Germany
Tel.: (49) 4522 7446460
Optical Product Mfr & Distr
N.A.I.C.S.: 333310

Born Brillen Optik GmbH & Co.
OHG   **(1)**
O4 5 Planken, 68161, Mannheim, Germany
Tel.: (49) 621129010
Web Site: http://www.born-brillen-optik.de
Eyewear Product Mfr
N.A.I.C.S.: 339115

Brillen Muller GmbH & Co. OHG **(1)**
Burgstrasse 61, 54516, Wittlich, Germany
Tel.: (49) 657191640
Web Site: http://www.brillen-mueller.com
Eyewear Product Mfr
N.A.I.C.S.: 339115

Brillen-Bunzel GmbH   **(1)**
Neuer Markt 3, 76275, Ettlingen, Germany
Tel.: (49) 72 43 1 66 03
Web Site: http://www.brillen-bunzel.de
Optical Product Retailer
N.A.I.C.S.: 456130

FFN Holding AG   **(1)**
Schutzenstrasse 32, Langenthal, Bern, 4900, Switzerland
Tel.: (41) 629220963
Optical Product Retailer
N.A.I.C.S.: 456130

Fielmann AG & Co. Bad Cannstatt
OHG   **(1)**
Marktstr 45, Stuttgart, 70372, Baden-Wurttemberg, Germany
Tel.: (49) 40270760
Optical Product Retailer
N.A.I.C.S.: 456130

Fielmann AG & Co. Barbarossaplatz
OHG   **(1)**
Barbarossaplatz 4, 50674, Cologne, Germany
Tel.: (49) 221 211117
Optical Product Retailer
N.A.I.C.S.: 456130

Fielmann AG & Co. Barmen
OHG   **(1)**
Werth 8, Wuppertal, 42275, Nordrhein-Westfalen, Germany
Tel.: (49) 202 592131
Optical Product Retailer
N.A.I.C.S.: 456130

Fielmann AG & Co. Bergedorf
OHG   **(1)**
Sachsentor 21, Hamburg, 21029, Germany
Tel.: (49) 407211145
Optical Product Retailer
N.A.I.C.S.: 456130

Fielmann AG & Co. Berlin-Hellersdorf
OHG   **(1)**
Janusz-Korczak-Str 4 Zentrum Helle Mitte, 12627, Berlin, Germany
Tel.: (49) 3099401893
Eyewear Product Mfr
N.A.I.C.S.: 339115

Fielmann AG & Co. Billstedt KG   **(1)**
Billstedter Platz 39 k, Hamburg, 22111, Germany
Tel.: (49) 40 7331717
Optical Product Retailer
N.A.I.C.S.: 456130

Fielmann AG & Co. Bonn-Bad
Godesberg OHG   **(1)**
Theaterplatz 6, 53177, Bonn, Germany
Tel.: (49) 228 3680186
Web Site: http://www.fielmann.de
Emp.: 21
Optical Product Retailer
N.A.I.C.S.: 456130
Axel Eilers *(Mgr)*

Fielmann AG & Co. Bornheim
KG   **(1)**
Berger Strasse 171, 60385, Frankfurt am Main, Germany
Tel.: (49) 69 4691230
Optical Product Retailer
N.A.I.C.S.: 456130

Fielmann AG & Co. Brackwede
KG   **(1)**
Hauptstrasse 78, 33647, Berlin, Germany
Tel.: (49) 521164730
Eyewear Product Mfr
N.A.I.C.S.: 339115

Fielmann AG & Co. Bramfeld KG **(1)**
Bramfelder Chaussee 296, Hamburg, 22177, Germany
Tel.: (49) 40 6428090
Optical Product Retailer
N.A.I.C.S.: 456130

Fielmann AG & Co. Buer OHG   **(1)**
Hochstr 5, Gelsenkirchen, 45894, Germany
Tel.: (49) 209379181
Web Site: http://www.fielmann.com
Emp.: 15
Optical Product Distr
N.A.I.C.S.: 456130

Fielmann AG & Co. Chorweiler
KG   **(1)**
Weideestrasse St 118, Hamburg, 22083, Nordrhein-Westfalen, Germany
Tel.: (49) 40270760
Optical Product Retailer
N.A.I.C.S.: 456130

Fielmann AG & Co. City Galerie
OHG   **(1)**
Willy-Brandt-Platz 1 City-Galerie, 86153, Augsburg, Germany
Tel.: (49) 8215670660
Eyewear Product Mfr
N.A.I.C.S.: 339115

Fielmann AG & Co. City-Arkaden
KG   **(1)**
Alte Freiheit 9 City-Arkaden, 42103, Wuppertal, Germany
Tel.: (49) 2029464810
Eyewear Product Mfr
N.A.I.C.S.: 339115

Fielmann AG & Co. Derendorf
OHG   **(1)**
Nordstr 45, Dusseldorf, 40477, Nordrhein-Westfalen, Germany
Tel.: (49) 211499410
Optical Product Distr
N.A.I.C.S.: 423460

Fielmann AG & Co. Dresden Altstadt
OHG   **(1)**
Webergasse 1, Dresden, 01067, Sachsen, Germany
Tel.: (49) 351 4968042
Optical Product Retailer
N.A.I.C.S.: 456130

Fielmann AG & Co. Dresden
Neustadt OHG   **(1)**
Bautzner Str 27, 01099, Dresden, Germany
Tel.: (49) 351 8045493
Optical Product Retailer

N.A.I.C.S.: 456130

Fielmann AG & Co. EKZ Hamburger
Strabe KG   **(1)**
Hamburger Strasse 19-47 Hamburger Meile, 22083, Hamburg, Germany
Tel.: (49) 4020769780
Eyewear Product Mfr
N.A.I.C.S.: 339115

Fielmann AG & Co. EKZ Hamburger
Strasse KG   **(1)**
Hamburger Str 23, Hamburg, 22083, Germany
Tel.: (49) 40 20769780
Optical Product Distr
N.A.I.C.S.: 423460

Fielmann AG & Co. EKZ Milaneo
OHG   **(1)**
Mailander Platz 7 Milaneo, 70173, Stuttgart, Germany
Tel.: (49) 7115853250
Eyewear Product Mfr
N.A.I.C.S.: 339115

Fielmann AG & Co. EKZ Westpark
OHG   **(1)**
Am Westpark 6 Westpark, 85057, Ingolstadt, Germany
Tel.: (49) 841 1428180
Web Site: http://www.fielmann.de
Optical Product Retailer
N.A.I.C.S.: 456130

Fielmann AG & Co. Ebertplatz
KG   **(1)**
Neusser Str 3, 50670, Cologne, Germany
Tel.: (49) 221134101
Eyewear Product Mfr
N.A.I.C.S.: 339115

Fielmann AG & Co. Eimsbuttel
OHG   **(1)**
Osterstr 120, 20255, Hamburg, Germany
Tel.: (49) 404903930
Optical Product Retailer
N.A.I.C.S.: 456130

Fielmann AG & Co. Elberfeld
OHG   **(1)**
Willy-Brandt-Platz 1, 42105, Wuppertal, Germany
Tel.: (49) 202442995
Eyewear Product Mfr
N.A.I.C.S.: 339115

Fielmann AG & Co. Eppendorf
KG   **(1)**
Eppendorfer Landstrasse 77, 20249, Hamburg, Germany
Tel.: (49) 4054803920
Emp.: 9
Optical Product Retailer
N.A.I.C.S.: 456130

Fielmann AG & Co. Ernst-August-
Galerie KG   **(1)**
Ernst August Platz 2, Hannover, 30159, Niedersachsen, Germany
Tel.: (49) 511 12313860
Optical Product Retailer
N.A.I.C.S.: 456130

Fielmann AG & Co. Essen-
Ruttenscheid OHG   **(1)**
Ruttenscheider Strasse 82, 45130, Essen, Germany
Tel.: (49) 201 8777366
Optical Product Retailer
N.A.I.C.S.: 456130

Fielmann AG & Co. Essen-Steele
OHG   **(1)**
Hansastrasse 34, 45276, Essen, Germany
Tel.: (49) 201 851451
Optical Product Retailer
N.A.I.C.S.: 456130

Fielmann AG & Co. Forum Mittelrhein
OHG   **(1)**
Zentralplatz 2 Forum Mittelrhein, 56068, Koblenz, Germany
Tel.: (49) 2619144200
Eyewear Product Mfr
N.A.I.C.S.: 339115

Fielmann AG & Co. Friedrichshagen
OHG   **(1)**
Bolschestr 114, 12587, Berlin, Germany

Tel.: (49) 306418868
Eyewear Product Mfr
N.A.I.C.S.: 339115

Fielmann AG & Co. Friedrichshain
OHG   **(1)**
Frankfurter Allee 7 l - 77, 10247, Berlin, Germany
Tel.: (49) 3042812031
Eyewear Product Mfr
N.A.I.C.S.: 339115

Fielmann AG & Co. Friedrichstrasse
OHG   **(1)**
Friedrichstr 57-59, Dusseldorf, 40217, Nordrhein-Westfalen, Germany
Tel.: (49) 211374169
Optical Product Retailer
N.A.I.C.S.: 456130

Fielmann AG & Co. Gesundbrunnen-
Center KG   **(1)**
Badstrasse 4 Gesundbrunnen-Center, 13357, Berlin, Germany
Tel.: (49) 3049301130
Eyewear Product Mfr
N.A.I.C.S.: 339115

Fielmann AG & Co. Glacis-Galerie
OHG   **(1)**
Bahnhofstrasse 1/2 Glacis-Galerie, 89231, Neu-Ulm, Germany
Tel.: (49) 7312060430
Eyewear Product Mfr
N.A.I.C.S.: 339115

Fielmann AG & Co. Gropius Passa-
gen OHG   **(1)**
Johannisthaler Chaussee 317 Gropius Passagen, 12351, Berlin, Germany
Tel.: (49) 3067066970
Eyewear Product Mfr
N.A.I.C.S.: 339115

Fielmann AG & Co. Haidhausen
OHG   **(1)**
Weissenburger Str 21, Munich, 81667, Germany
Tel.: (49) 89485372
Optical Product Retailer
N.A.I.C.S.: 456130

Fielmann AG & Co. Hamborn
KG   **(1)**
Jagerstr 72, 47166, Duisburg, Germany
Tel.: (49) 203400181
Optical Product Retailer
N.A.I.C.S.: 456130

Fielmann AG & Co. Harburg Sand
OHG   **(1)**
Sand 35, 21073, Hamburg, Germany
Tel.: (49) 40777689
Eyewear Product Mfr
N.A.I.C.S.: 339115

Fielmann AG & Co. Hessen-Center
OHG   **(1)**
Borsigallee 26 Hessen-Center, 60388, Frankfurt am Main, Germany
Tel.: (49) 6109504100
Eyewear Product Mfr
N.A.I.C.S.: 339115

Fielmann AG & Co. Hiltrup OHG   **(1)**
Bodelschwingstrasse 15, 48165, Munster, Germany
Tel.: (49) 2501 6061
Optical Product Retailer
N.A.I.C.S.: 456130

Fielmann AG & Co. Hochst OHG   **(1)**
Konigsteiner Str 1, 65929, Frankfurt am Main, Hessen, Germany
Tel.: (49) 69311157
Optical Product Retailer
N.A.I.C.S.: 456130

Fielmann AG & Co. Jahnplatz
KG   **(1)**
Oberntorwall 25, 33602, Berlin, Germany
Tel.: (49) 521173089
Eyewear Product Mfr
N.A.I.C.S.: 339115

Fielmann AG & Co. KG   **(1)**
Marktplatz 53, Bayern, Lauf an der Pegnitz, 91207, Germany
Tel.: (49) 9123980860
Optical Product Distr

N.A.I.C.S.: 423460

Fielmann AG & Co. Kaufpark KG (1)
Dohnaer Strasse 246, 01239, Dresden, Germany
Tel.: (49) 351 2593340
Optical Product Distr
N.A.I.C.S.: 456130

Fielmann AG & Co. Klosterstrasse OHG (1)
Klosterstr 53, 48143, Munster, Nordrhein-Westfalen, Germany
Tel.: (49) 25147629
Optical Product Retailer
N.A.I.C.S.: 456130

Fielmann AG & Co. Kontaktlinsen-Service KG (1)
An den Flugzeughallen 3, 14712, Rathenow, Germany
Tel.: (49) 22233444
Web Site: http://www.kontaktlinsen.fielmann.de
Eyewear Product Mfr
N.A.I.C.S.: 339115

Fielmann AG & Co. Kreuzberg KG (1)
Kottbusser Damm 32, 10967, Berlin, Germany
Tel.: (49) 306923381
Eyewear Product Mfr
N.A.I.C.S.: 339115

Fielmann AG & Co. Leipziger Strasse OHG (1)
Leipziger Strasse 2, 60487, Frankfurt am Main, Germany
Tel.: (49) 6924795011
Eyewear Product Mfr
N.A.I.C.S.: 339115

Fielmann AG & Co. Leopoldstrasse OHG (1)
Leopoldstrasse 46, 80802, Munich, Germany
Tel.: (49) 89391604
Eyewear Product Mfr
N.A.I.C.S.: 339115

Fielmann AG & Co. Linden-Center KG (1)
Prerower Platz 1 Linden-Center, 13051, Berlin, Germany
Tel.: (49) 3092403090
Eyewear Product Mfr
N.A.I.C.S.: 339115

Fielmann AG & Co. Lister Meile OHG (1)
Lister Meile 72, 30161, Hannover, Germany
Tel.: (49) 511 392121
Optical Product Retailer
N.A.I.C.S.: 456130

Fielmann AG & Co. Markisches Zentrum KGB (1)
Wilhelmsruher Damm 136 Markisches Zentrum, 13439, Berlin, Germany
Tel.: (49) 3040728260
Eyewear Product Mfr
N.A.I.C.S.: 339115

Fielmann AG & Co. Marzahn OHG (1)
Marzahner Promenade 1 a Eastgate, 12679, Berlin, Germany
Tel.: (49) 309339178
Eyewear Product Mfr
N.A.I.C.S.: 339115

Fielmann AG & Co. Moabit KG (1)
Turmstrasse 44, 10551, Berlin, Germany
Tel.: (49) 303956426
Eyewear Product Mfr
N.A.I.C.S.: 339115

Fielmann AG & Co. Neukolln KG (1)
Karl-Marx-Strasse 151, 12043, Berlin, Germany
Tel.: (49) 306885168
Eyewear Product Mfr
N.A.I.C.S.: 339115

Fielmann AG & Co. Neumarkt KG (1)
Hochstr 65, Krefeld, 47798, Nordrhein-Westfalen, Germany
Tel.: (49) 215121642

Optical Product Retailer
N.A.I.C.S.: 456130

Fielmann AG & Co. Nordstadt OHG (1)
Engelbosteler Damm 66, 30167, Hannover, Germany
Tel.: (49) 511 7000333
Web Site: http://www.fielmann.de
Emp.: 15
Optical Product Retailer
N.A.I.C.S.: 456130
Marco Froese *(Gen Mgr)*

Fielmann AG & Co. Nurnberg Lorenz OHG (1)
Breite Gasse 64-66, Bayern, Nuremberg, 90402, Germany
Tel.: (49) 911227160
Optical Product Retailer
N.A.I.C.S.: 456130

Fielmann AG & Co. Nurnberg-Langwasser OHG (1)
Glogauer Strasse 30-38, 90473, Nuremberg, Germany
Tel.: (49) 911 808212
Optical Product Retailer
N.A.I.C.S.: 456130

Fielmann AG & Co. Nurnberg-Sud KG (1)
Breitscheidstr 5 Bayern, Nuremberg, 90459, Germany
Tel.: (49) 911436057
Web Site: http://www.fielmann.com
Optical Product Retailer
N.A.I.C.S.: 456130

Fielmann AG & Co. OHG (1)
Leipziger Strasse 102, 06108, Halle, Germany
Tel.: (49) 3452025683
Eyewear Product Mfr
N.A.I.C.S.: 339115

Fielmann AG & Co. OHG Sterkrade (1)
Bahnhofstr 40, Oberhausen, 46145, Germany
Tel.: (49) 208666408
Optical Product Retailer
N.A.I.C.S.: 456130

Fielmann AG & Co. Oberhausen OHG (1)
Marktstr 94, 46045, Oberhausen, Germany
Tel.: (49) 208 26727
Optical Product Retailer
N.A.I.C.S.: 456130

Fielmann AG & Co. Oberkassel OHG (1)
Luegallee 107, 40545, Dusseldorf, Germany
Tel.: (49) 211 570242
Web Site: http://www.fielmann.de
Optical Product Retailer
N.A.I.C.S.: 456130

Fielmann AG & Co. Obernstrasse OHG (1)
Obernstrasse 32, 28195, Berlin, Germany
Tel.: (49) 421320585
Eyewear Product Mfr
N.A.I.C.S.: 339115

Fielmann AG & Co. Ochsenzoll OHG (1)
Langenhorner Chaussee 692, 22419, Hamburg, Germany
Tel.: (49) 40 5278464
Optical Product Retailer
N.A.I.C.S.: 456130

Fielmann AG & Co. Othmarschen OHG (1)
Waitzstrasse 12, 22607, Hamburg, Germany
Tel.: (49) 40892652
Eyewear Product Mfr
N.A.I.C.S.: 339115

Fielmann AG & Co. Ottensen OHG (1)
Ottenser Hauptstrasse 10, 22765, Hamburg, Germany
Tel.: (49) 40 39 33 53
Optical Product Retailer
N.A.I.C.S.: 456130

Fielmann AG & Co. Pankow OHG (1)
Breite Strasse 15, 13187, Berlin, Germany
Tel.: (49) 304857483
Eyewear Product Mfr
N.A.I.C.S.: 339115

Fielmann AG & Co. Pasing OHG (1)
Pasinger Bahnhofsplatz 5, Munich, 81241, Germany
Tel.: (49) 89 89620966
Optical Product Retailer
N.A.I.C.S.: 456130

Fielmann AG & Co. Paunsdorf-Center OHG (1)
Paunsdorfer Allee 1, 04329, Leipzig, Germany
Tel.: (49) 341 2512243
Web Site: http://www.fielmann.com
Emp.: 35
Optical Product Retailer
N.A.I.C.S.: 456130

Fielmann AG & Co. Pferdemarkt OHG (1)
Pferdemarkt 16, 18273, Rostock, Germany
Tel.: (49) 3843682000
Eyewear Product Mfr
N.A.I.C.S.: 339115

Fielmann AG & Co. Prenzlauer Berg OHG (1)
Schonhauser Allee 70 c, 10437, Berlin, Germany
Tel.: (49) 304469365
Eyewear Product Mfr
N.A.I.C.S.: 339115

Fielmann AG & Co. Rahlstedt OHG (1)
Schweriner Str 7, 22143, Hamburg, Germany
Tel.: (49) 406777028
Eyewear Product Mfr
N.A.I.C.S.: 339115

Fielmann AG & Co. Rathaus OHG (1)
Jungfernstieg 40, 20354, Hamburg, Germany
Tel.: (49) 403005060
Eyewear Product Mfr
N.A.I.C.S.: 339115

Fielmann AG & Co. Rethelstrasse OHG (1)
Rethelstr 174, 40237, Dusseldorf, Germany
Tel.: (49) 211 661443
Optical Product Retailer
N.A.I.C.S.: 456130

Fielmann AG & Co. Rhein-Galerie KG (1)
Im Zollhof 4 Rhein Galerie, 67061, Ludwigshafen, Germany
Tel.: (49) 6215914660
Eyewear Product Mfr
N.A.I.C.S.: 339115

Fielmann AG & Co. RheinRuhrZentrum OHG (1)
Humboldtring 13, 45472, Mulheim an der Ruhr, Germany
Tel.: (49) 2088826700
Optical Product Retailer
N.A.I.C.S.: 456130

Fielmann AG & Co. Rheydt oHG (1)
Marktstrasse 27, 41236, Monchengladbach, Germany
Tel.: (49) 2166 48294
Optical Product Mfr & Distr
N.A.I.C.S.: 333310

Fielmann AG & Co. Riem Arcaden KG (1)
Willy-Brandt-Platz 5, Riem Arcaden, 81829, Munich, Germany
Tel.: (49) 8942001890
Web Site: http://www.fielmann.de
Optical Product Distr
N.A.I.C.S.: 423460
Gunther Fielmann *(Gen Mgr)*

Fielmann AG & Co. Roland-Center KG (1)
Alter Dorfweg 30-50, 28259, Bremen, Germany

Tel.: (49) 421 89 83 00 0
Optical Product Retailer
N.A.I.C.S.: 456130

Fielmann AG & Co. Rossmarkt OHG (1)
Rossmarkt 15, 60311, Frankfurt am Main, Germany
Tel.: (49) 69295043
Web Site: http://www.fielmann.de
Optical Product Retailer
N.A.I.C.S.: 456130

Fielmann AG & Co. Schildergasse OHG (1)
Schildergasse 78-82, 50667, Cologne, Germany
Tel.: (49) 2212725340
Optical Product Retailer
N.A.I.C.S.: 456130

Fielmann AG & Co. Schloss-Arkaden KG (1)
Platz am Ritterbrunnen 1, 38100, Braunschweig, Germany
Tel.: (49) 531 1206650
Optical Product Retailer
N.A.I.C.S.: 456130

Fielmann AG & Co. Schoneweide OHG (1)
Bruckenstrasse 4, 12439, Berlin, Germany
Tel.: (49) 306310931
Eyewear Product Mfr
N.A.I.C.S.: 339115

Fielmann AG & Co. Schwarzer Bar OHG (1)
Blumenauer Str 1-7, 30449, Hannover, Germany
Tel.: (49) 511 45 14 45
Optical Product Retailer
N.A.I.C.S.: 456130

Fielmann AG & Co. Schwenningen KG (1)
In der Muslen 35, 78054, Villingen-Schwenningen, Germany
Tel.: (49) 7720 99333 0
Web Site: http://www.fielmann.de
Optical Product Retailer
N.A.I.C.S.: 456130

Fielmann AG & Co. Spandau OHG (1)
Breite Strasse 22, 13597, Berlin, Germany
Tel.: (49) 3035302800
Eyewear Product Mfr
N.A.I.C.S.: 339115

Fielmann AG & Co. Steglitz OHG (1)
Schlossstrasse 28, 12163, Berlin, Germany
Tel.: (49) 3079702950
Eyewear Product Mfr
N.A.I.C.S.: 339115

Fielmann AG & Co. Stern Center OHG (1)
Mercedesstrasse 12, 71063, Sindelfingen, Germany
Tel.: (49) 7031 81731 0
Optical Product Retailer
N.A.I.C.S.: 456130

Fielmann AG & Co. Sudenburg OHG (1)
Halberstadter Str 100, Magdeburg, 39112, Sachsen-Anhalt, Germany
Tel.: (49) 391 6229045
Optical Product Retailer
N.A.I.C.S.: 456130

Fielmann AG & Co. Tal KG (1)
Tal 23, Bayern, Munich, 80331, Germany
Tel.: (49) 40270760
Optical Product Retailer
N.A.I.C.S.: 456130

Fielmann AG & Co. Tempelhof OHG (1)
Tempelhofer Damm 182/184, 12099, Berlin, Germany
Tel.: (49) 307526047
Eyewear Product Mfr
N.A.I.C.S.: 339115

Fielmann AG & Co. Thuringen-Park OHG (1)
Nordhauser Str 73, 99091, Erfurt, Germany

Fielmann Group AG—(Continued)
Tel.: (49) 361 5559870
Optical Product Retailer
N.A.I.C.S.: 456130

Fielmann AG & Co. Treptow KG (1)
Baumschulenstrasse 18, 12437, Berlin,
Germany
Tel.: (49) 305328382
Eyewear Product Mfr
N.A.I.C.S.: 339115

**Fielmann AG & Co. Vegesack
OHG** (1)
Gerhard-Rohlfs-Str 73, Bremen, 28757,
Germany
Tel.: (49) 42166108586
Emp.: 15
Optical Product Retailer
N.A.I.C.S.: 456130

**Fielmann AG & Co. Venloer Strasse
OHG** (1)
Venloer Str 369, Cologne, 50823, Germany
Tel.: (49) 221 515928
Optical Product Mfr & Distr
N.A.I.C.S.: 333310

**Fielmann AG & Co. Vita-Center
KG** (1)
Wladimir-Sagorski-Str 22, 09122, Chemnitz,
Germany
Tel.: (49) 371 2781650
Emp.: 13
Optical Product Retailer
N.A.I.C.S.: 456130
Rosemari Sehueert *(Gen Mgr)*

**Fielmann AG & Co. Volksdorf
OHG** (1)
Weisse Rose 10, 22359, Hamburg, Germany
Tel.: (49) 40 6038850
Optical Product Retailer
N.A.I.C.S.: 456130

**Fielmann AG & Co. Wandsbek
OHG** (1)
Wandsbeker Marktstrasse 57, 22041, Hamburg, Germany
Tel.: (49) 406522233
Eyewear Product Mfr
N.A.I.C.S.: 339115

**Fielmann AG & Co. Wattenscheid
KG** (1)
Oststrasse 36, 44866, Bochum, Germany
Tel.: (49) 2327 15900
Optical Product Retailer
N.A.I.C.S.: 456130

**Fielmann AG & Co. Weissensee
KG** (1)
Berliner Allee 85, 13088, Berlin, Germany
Tel.: (49) 30929019660
Eyewear Product Mfr
N.A.I.C.S.: 339115

**Fielmann AG & Co. Weserpark
OHG** (1)
Hans-Bredow-Strasse 19 Weserpark,
28307, Bremen, Germany
Tel.: (49) 421488091
Eyewear Product Mfr
N.A.I.C.S.: 339115

Fielmann AG & Co. Westend KG (1)
Reichsstrasse 104, 14052, Berlin, Germany
Tel.: (49) 303062099
Eyewear Product Mfr
N.A.I.C.S.: 339115

**Fielmann AG & Co. Westliche Kaiser-
strasse KG** (1)
Kaiserstr 163, 76133, Karlsruhe, Germany
Tel.: (49) 721 5704590
Optical Product Retailer
N.A.I.C.S.: 456130

**Fielmann AG & Co. Wilmersdorf
KG** (1)
Wilmersdorfer Strasse 57, 10627, Berlin,
Germany
Tel.: (49) 3031519130
Eyewear Product Mfr
N.A.I.C.S.: 339115

Fielmann AG & Co. Zentrum KG (1)

Limbecker Strasse 74, 45127, Essen, Germany
Tel.: (49) 2018277660
Eyewear Product Mfr
N.A.I.C.S.: 339115

**Fielmann AG & Co. am Hauptmarkt
OHG** (1)
Hauptmarkt 10, 90403, Nuremberg, Germany
Tel.: (49) 911223902
Eyewear Product Mfr
N.A.I.C.S.: 339115

**Fielmann AG & Co. am Kugelbrunnen
KG** (1)
Adalbertstr 45-47, Aachen, 52062,
Nordrhein-Westfalen, Germany
Tel.: (49) 2411606920
Optical Product Retailer
N.A.I.C.S.: 456130

**Fielmann AG & Co. am Markt
OHG** (1)
Markt 17, Leipzig, 04109, Saxony, Germany
Tel.: (49) 341 9605281
Optical Product Retailer
N.A.I.C.S.: 456130

Fielmann AG & Co. im Alexa KG (1)
Grunerstrasse 20 Alexa, 10179, Berlin, Germany
Tel.: (49) 3027878890
Eyewear Product Mfr
N.A.I.C.S.: 339115

**Fielmann AG & Co. im Alsterta-
lEinkaufszentrum OHG** (1)
Heegbarg 31 Alstertal-Einkaufszentrum
AEZ, 22391, Hamburg, Germany
Tel.: (49) 406020065
Eyewear Product Mfr
N.A.I.C.S.: 339115

**Fielmann AG & Co. im Centrum
OHG** (1)
Schadowstr 63, Bayern, Dusseldorf, 40212,
Germany
Tel.: (49) 211 133077
Optical Product Mfr & Distr
N.A.I.C.S.: 333310
Esther Eckert *(Gen Mgr)*

**Fielmann AG & Co. im Donau-
Einkaufszentrum KG** (1)
Weichser Weg 5, Bayern, Regensburg,
93059, Germany
Tel.: (49) 94146453430
Optical Product Retailer
N.A.I.C.S.: 456130

**Fielmann AG & Co. im ElbeE-
inkaufszentrum OHG** (1)
Osdorfer Landstrasse 131 Elbe-
Einkaufszentrum EEZ, 22609, Hamburg,
Germany
Tel.: (49) 4087972910
Eyewear Product Mfr
N.A.I.C.S.: 339115

**Fielmann AG & Co. oHG An der
Rothenburg** (1)
Rothenburg 43/44, 48143, Munster, Germany
Tel.: (49) 251 58420
Optical Product Retailer
N.A.I.C.S.: 456130

**Fielmann AG & Co. oHG
Bremen-Neustadt** (1)
Pappelstr 131, Bremen, 28199, Germany
Tel.: (49) 40270760
Web Site: http://www.fielmann.com
Optical Product Retailer
N.A.I.C.S.: 456130

**Fielmann AG & Co. oHG
City-Galerie** (1)
Willy-Brandt-Platz 1, Augsburg, 86153, Germany
Tel.: (49) 40270760
Optical Product Distr
N.A.I.C.S.: 423460

Fielmann AG & Co. oHG Kalk (1)
Kalker Hauptstr 55, Cologne, 51103,
Nordrhein-Westfalen, Germany
Tel.: (49) 2214602320
Optical Product Retailer
N.A.I.C.S.: 456130

Manuel Kampmann *(Gen Mgr)*

**Fielmann AG & Co. oHG
Kavalierstrasse** (1)
Kavalierstr 49, Dessau, 06844, Sachsen-
Anhalt, Germany
Tel.: (49) 3408507760
Optical Product Retailer
N.A.I.C.S.: 456130

**Fielmann AG & Co. oHG
Ludwigsplatz** (1)
Ludwigsplatz 1a, 64283, Darmstadt, Germany
Tel.: (49) 6151 396890
Optical Product Mfr & Distr
N.A.I.C.S.: 333310

**Fielmann AG & Co. oHG Munchen
OEZ** (1)
Hanauer Strasse 68 Olympia Einkaufszentrum OEZ, 80993, Munich, Germany
Tel.: (49) 891434720
Eyewear Product Mfr
N.A.I.C.S.: 339115

**Fielmann AG & Co. oHG Munchen
PEP** (1)
Ollenhauerstr 6, Bayern, Munich, 81737,
Germany
Tel.: (49) 8963849883
Optical Product Retailer
N.A.I.C.S.: 456130

**Fielmann AG & Co. oHG
Niendorf** (1)
Tibarg 19v, 22459, Hamburg, Germany
Tel.: (49) 40 581195
Optical Product Retailer
N.A.I.C.S.: 456130

**Fielmann AG & Co. oHG
Schnelsen** (1)
Frohmestr 46, Hamburg, 22457, Germany
Tel.: (49) 405591911
Optical Product Mfr & Distr
N.A.I.C.S.: 333310

**Fielmann AG & Co. oHG
Sendling** (1)
Plinganserstr 51, Bayern, Munich, 81369,
Germany
Tel.: (49) 8976757510
Optical Product Retailer
N.A.I.C.S.: 456130
Patrik Opacak *(Gen Mgr)*

**Fielmann AG & Co. oHG
Wellingdorf** (1)
Schonberger Strasse 84, 24148, Kiel, Germany
Tel.: (49) 431 728404
Web Site: http://www.fielmann.de
Emp.: 35
Optical Product Retailer
N.A.I.C.S.: 456130

Fielmann AG - Varel (1)
Hindenburgstr 4, Varel, 26316, Germany
Tel.: (49) 4451 8 22 77
Optical Product Mfr & Distr
N.A.I.C.S.: 333310

**Fielmann Akademie schloss Plon,
gemeinnutzige Bildungsstatte der Au-
genoptik GmbH** (1)
Schloss, 24306, Plon, Germany
Tel.: (49) 4522 8010
Web Site: http://www.fielmann-
akademie.com
Optician Training Services
N.A.I.C.S.: 611310

**Fielmann Augenoptik AG & Co. Halle-
Neustadt OHG** (1)
Neustadter Passage 16, Halle, 06122,
Sachsen-Anhalt, Germany
Tel.: (49) 3458070410
Optical Product Retailer
N.A.I.C.S.: 456130

**Fielmann Augenoptik AG & Co.
OHG** (1)
Hauptstr 33, Bitburg, 54634, Germany
Tel.: (49) 6561 94640 0
Optical Product Retailer
N.A.I.C.S.: 456130

Fielmann Augenoptik Ag (1)
Hauptstrasse 33, 54634, Bitburg, Germany

Tel.: (49) 6561946400
Web Site: http://www.fielmann.de
Emp.: 600
Ophthalmic Goods Mfr
N.A.I.C.S.: 339115

**Fielmann Augenoptik im Centrum AG
& Co. oHG** (1)
Bahnhofstrasse 48, 58452, Witten, Germany
Tel.: (49) 230227274
Web Site: http://www.fielmann.de
Optical Product Mfr & Distr
N.A.I.C.S.: 333310

Fielmann B.V. (1)
Picassopassage 74, 7811 DP, Emmen,
Netherlands
Tel.: (31) 591 670850
Web Site: http://www.fielmann.nl
Optical Product Retailer
N.A.I.C.S.: 456130

Fielmann Finanzservice GmbH (1)
Weidestr 118a, Hamburg, 22083, Germany
Tel.: (49) 40270760
Optical Product Retailer
N.A.I.C.S.: 456130

Fielmann Gmbh (1)
Europastrasse 1, 5020, Salzburg, Austria
Tel.: (43) 662420835
Web Site: http://www.fielmann.com
Sales Range: $25-49.9 Million
Emp.: 30
Ophthalmic Goods Mfr
N.A.I.C.S.: 339115

Fielmann Holding B.V. (1)
Dr Poelsstraat 63 C, Oldenzaal, 7572 ZV,
Netherlands
Tel.: (31) 541581050
Emp.: 4
Optical Product Retailer
N.A.I.C.S.: 456130
Gunther Fielmann *(Gen Mgr)*

**Fielmann Modebrillen Rathenow AG
& Co. KG** (1)
Muhlendamm 4, 14712, Rathenow, Germany
Tel.: (49) 3385594100
Eyewear Product Mfr
N.A.I.C.S.: 339115

**Fielmann Schloss Plon Hotel- und
Catering GmbH** (1)
Castle Area 1, 24306, Plon, Germany
Tel.: (49) 45227446460
Web Site: http://www.pfortnerhaus-schloss-
ploen.de
Food Restaurant Services
N.A.I.C.S.: 722511

Fielmann Schweiz AG (1)
Weber Treuhand Ag St Gallen, Sankt Gal-
lenkappel, 9008, Switzerland
Tel.: (41) 712208920
Optical Product Retailer
N.A.I.C.S.: 456130

Fielmann Ventures GmbH (1)
Weidestrasse 118a, 22083, Hamburg, Germany
Tel.: (49) 40270763090
Web Site: http://www.fielmann-ventures.com
Emp.: 1,000
Fashionable Eyewear Product Mfr
N.A.I.C.S.: 339115
Michael Ahrens *(Mng Dir)*

**Fielmann-optic Fielmann GmbH &
Co. KG** (1)
Hauptstr 7, 40597, Dusseldorf, Germany
Tel.: (49) 211 712447
Optical Product Retailer
N.A.I.C.S.: 456130

**Groeneveld Brillen en Contactlenzen
B.V.** (1)
Slaak 120, 3061 CZ, Rotterdam, Netherlands
Tel.: (31) 10 411 23 44
Web Site: http://www.groeneveldbrillen.nl
Optical Product Mfr & Distr
N.A.I.C.S.: 333310

**HID Hamburger Immobiliendienste
GmbH** (1)
Weberstr 3, Hamburg, Germany

Tel.: (49) 40 275969
Optical Product Retailer
N.A.I.C.S.: 456130

Hofland Optiek B.V. **(1)**
St Plechelmusplein 13, 7571 EG, Olden-
zaal, Netherlands
Tel.: (31) 541 514177
Web Site: http://www.hoflandoptiek.nl
Optical Product Mfr & Distr
N.A.I.C.S.: 333310

Lochte-Optik GmbH **(1)**
Matthiasstr 17, 48431, Rheine, Germany
Tel.: (49) 5971 2108
Optical Product Retailer
N.A.I.C.S.: 456130

OTR Oberflachentechnik GmbH **(1)**
Muhlendamm 4, 14712, Rathenow, Ger-
many
Tel.: (49) 3385 594 275
Web Site: http://www.otr-gmbh.de
Electroplating Material Mfr
N.A.I.C.S.: 332813

Optik Hess GmbH **(1)**
Hauptstrasse 165, 79576, Weil am Rhein,
Germany
Tel.: (49) 7621 7 11 99
Web Site: http://www.optikhess.de
Optical Product Retailer
N.A.I.C.S.: 456130

Optik Hess GmbH & Co. KG **(1)**
Dellbrucker Hauptstrasse 103, 51069, Co-
logne, Germany
Tel.: (49) 221 68 58 69
Web Site: http://www.optik-hess.de
Emp.: 6
Optical Product Mfr & Distr
N.A.I.C.S.: 333310

Optik Horger GmbH & Co. OHG **(1)**
Unterboihinger Str 16, 73240, Wendlingen
am Neckar, Germany
Tel.: (49) 70247493
Web Site: http://www.hoerger-optik.de
Eyewear Product Mfr
N.A.I.C.S.: 339115

**Optik Kapernick GmbH & Co.
KG** **(1)**
Langgasse 10, 65183, Wiesbaden, Ger-
many
Tel.: (49) 611 30 18 94
Web Site: http://www.optik-kaepernick.de
Emp.: 15
Optical Product Retailer
N.A.I.C.S.: 456130

**Optik Kluttermann Verwaltungs
GmbH** **(1)**
Schenkelstrasse 23, 52349, Duren, Ger-
many
Tel.: (49) 2421 14224
Optical Product Retailer
N.A.I.C.S.: 456130

**Optik Schuppin GmbH & Co.
OHG** **(1)**
Stuttgarter Strasse 103, 70469, Stuttgart,
Germany
Tel.: (49) 711817275
Web Site: http://www.optik-schuppin.de
Eyewear Product Mfr
N.A.I.C.S.: 339115

Optik Simon GmbH **(1)**
Breite Strasse 54, 50667, Cologne, Ger-
many
Tel.: (49) 221 925860 0
Web Site: http://www.optiksimon.de
Optical Product Retailer
N.A.I.C.S.: 456130

Optiker Carl GmbH **(1)**
Eppendorfer Landstrasse 11, 20249, Ham-
burg, Germany
Tel.: (49) 40 460994 0
Web Site: http://www.optiker-carl.de
Emp.: 30
Optical Product Mfr & Distr
N.A.I.C.S.: 333310

Pro-optik Ag **(1)**
Steinenvorstadt 62, 4051, Basel, Switzer-
land
Tel.: (41) 612818145
Web Site: http://www.pro-optik.info
Ophthalmic Goods Mfr

N.A.I.C.S.: 339115

Rathenower Optik GmbH **(1)**
An den Flugzeughallen 3, 14712, Rath-
enow, Germany
Tel.: (49) 33854972085
Web Site: http://www.optikrathenow.de
Optical Product Mfr & Distr
N.A.I.C.S.: 333310
Karsten Lange *(CIO)*

**Rathenower Optische Werke
Gmbh** **(1)**
An Den Flugzeughallen 3, Rathenow,
14712, Brandenburg, Germany
Tel.: (49) 33854972085
Web Site: http://www.fielmann.de
Sales Range: $200-249.9 Million
Emp.: 900
Ophthalmic Goods Mfr
N.A.I.C.S.: 339115

Rokku Designstudio GmbH **(1)**
Schrammsweg 11, 20249, Hamburg, Ger-
many
Tel.: (49) 4057009830
Web Site: http://www.rokku-design.com
Eyewear Product Mfr
N.A.I.C.S.: 339115

SVS Vision, Inc **(1)**
118 CASS Ave., Mt. Clemens, MI 48043
Web Site: http://www.svsvision.com
Optical Goods Stores
N.A.I.C.S.: 456130
Susie Messer *(Dir-Labor Rels)*

**Stadt Optik Fielmann Langenthal
AG** **(1)**
Marktgasse 17, Langenthal, 4900, Switzer-
land
Tel.: (41) 62 923 9910
Optical Product Retailer
N.A.I.C.S.: 456130

**fielmann Farmsen Fielmann GmbH &
Co. KG** **(1)**
Berner Heerweg 173/175 EKT Farmsen,
22159, Hamburg, Germany
Tel.: (49) 406430572
Eyewear Product Mfr
N.A.I.C.S.: 339115

FIEM INDUSTRIES LTD.

D -5 Mansarover Garden, New Delhi,
110015, India
Tel.: (91) 1125101002
Web Site:
https://www.fiemindustries.com
Year Founded: 1989
532768—(BOM)
Rev.: $222,871,926
Assets: $126,254,397
Liabilities: $34,993,034
Net Worth: $91,261,363
Earnings: $16,765,398
Emp.: 2,478
Fiscal Year-end: 03/31/23
Automotive Component Mfr & Distr
N.A.I.C.S.: 336390
J. K. Jain *(Chm & Mng Dir)*

FIERA CAPITAL CORPORA-
TION

1981 McGill College Avenue Suite
1500, Montreal, H3A 0H5, QC,
Canada
Tel.: (514) 954-3300
Web Site:
https://www.fieracapital.com
FSZ—(DEU)
Rev.: $503,389,968
Assets: $981,998,227
Liabilities: $725,751,644
Net Worth: $256,246,583
Earnings: $23,285,809
Emp.: 856
Fiscal Year-end: 12/31/22
Investment Management Service
N.A.I.C.S.: 523999
Jean-Guy Desjardins *(Co-Founder &
Chm)*

Subsidiaries:

Augean PLC **(1)**
4 Rudgate Court Walton, Wetherby, LS23
7BF, Yorkshire, United Kingdom
Tel.: (44) 1937 844980
Web Site: http://www.augeanplc.com
Holding Company; Hazardous Waste Man-
agement Services
N.A.I.C.S.: 551112
Gene Wilson *(Dir-Environmental Planning)*

Subsidiary (Domestic):

Augean North Limited **(2)**
4 Rudgate Court, Walton, Wetherby, LS23
7BF, United Kingdom
Tel.: (44) 1937 846 681
Web Site: http://www.augeanplc.com
Hazardous Waste Landfill Operator
N.A.I.C.S.: 562212

**Augean North Sea Services
Limited** **(2)**
Yard B Blackdog Industrial Estate, Bridge
Of Don, Aberdeen, AB23 8BT, United King-
dom
Tel.: (44) 122 471 9200
Web Site: http://www.augeanplc.com
Emp.: 100
Offshore Oil & Gas Waste Management
Services
N.A.I.C.S.: 562112
Simon Gibb *(Mng Dir)*

Augean South Limited **(2)**
4 Rudgate Court, Walton, Wetherby, LS23
7BF, W Yorkshire, United Kingdom
Tel.: (44) 1937 846 681
Web Site: http://www.augeanplc.com
Sales Range: $25-49.9 Million
Emp.: 200
Hazardous Waste Landfill Operator
N.A.I.C.S.: 562212

Augean Treatment Limited **(2)**
4 Rudgate Court, Walton, Wetherby, LS23
7BF, W Yorkshire, United Kingdom
Tel.: (44) 1937 844 980
Web Site: http://www.augeanplc.com
Sales Range: $25-49.9 Million
Hazardous Waste Treatment Services
N.A.I.C.S.: 562211

Future Industrial Services Ltd **(2)**
Image Business Park Acornfield Rd Knows-
ley Ind Park, Liverpool, L33 7UF, United
Kingdom
Tel.: (44) 1512033222
Web Site: http://www.futureindustrial.com
Waste Management Services
N.A.I.C.S.: 562219
David Lusher *(CEO)*

Bel Air Investment Advisors LLC **(1)**
1999 Avenue of the Stars Ste 3200, Los
Angeles, CA 90067
Tel.: (310) 229-1500
Web Site: https://www.belair-llc.com
Sales Range: $200-249.9 Million
Emp.: 200
Investment Advisor
N.A.I.C.S.: 523940
Todd M. Morgan *(Chm)*

Canadian High Yield Focus Fund **(1)**
1 Adelaide Street East Suite 600, Toronto,
M5C 2V9, ON, Canada
Tel.: (416) 955-4929
Web Site: http://www.fieracapital.com
Closed-End Investment Fund
N.A.I.C.S.: 525990

Charlemagne Capital Limited **(1)**
39 St James's Street, London, SW1A 1JD,
United Kingdom **(100%)**
Tel.: (44) 2075182100
Web Site:
http://www.charlemagnecapital.com
Investment Management Service
N.A.I.C.S.: 523999
Jayne Sutcliffe *(Pres & CEO)*

Subsidiary (Non-US):

**Charlemagne Capital (IOM)
Limited** **(2)**
Saint Mary's Court 20 Hill Street, Douglas,
IM1 1EU, Isle of Man
Tel.: (44) 1624640200

Investment Management Service
N.A.I.C.S.: 523940

Clearwater Capital Partners LLC **(1)**
Suite 3205 No 9 Queens Road Central,
Hong Kong, China (Hong Kong)
Tel.: (852) 3713 4800
Web Site:
http://www.clearwatercapitalpartners.com
Privater Equity Firm
N.A.I.C.S.: 523999
Amit Gupta *(Co-Founder & Partner)*

**Fiera Capital (Asia) Hong Kong
Limited** **(1)**
Suite 3205 No 9 Queen's Road Central,
Chai Wan, China (Hong Kong)
Tel.: (852) 37134800
Web Site: https://hk.fieracapital.com
Asset Management Services
N.A.I.C.S.: 523940

Fiera Capital (Germany) GmbH **(1)**
Walther-von-Cronberg-Platz 13, 60594,
Frankfurt, Germany
Tel.: (49) 6992020750
Investment Management Service
N.A.I.C.S.: 523940

Fiera Capital (Iom) Limited **(1)**
St Mary's Court 20 Hill Street, Douglas, IM1
1EU, Isle of Man
Tel.: (44) 1624640200
Investment Management Service
N.A.I.C.S.: 523940

Fiera Capital (Uk) Limited **(1)**
3rd Floor Queensberry House 3 Old Burl-
ington Street, London, W1S 3AE, United
Kingdom
Tel.: (44) 2075182100
Web Site: https://uk.fieracapital.com
Asset Management Services
N.A.I.C.S.: 523940

Fiera Capital Inc. **(1)**
375 Park Ave 8th Fl, New York, NY 10152
Tel.: (212) 300-1600
Investment Management Service
N.A.I.C.S.: 523940

Fiera Infrastructure Inc. **(1)**
200 Bay Street Suite 3800 South Tower,
Toronto, M5J 2J1, ON, Canada
Tel.: (416) 646-2707
Web Site:
https://www.fierainfrastructure.com
Investment Management Service
N.A.I.C.S.: 523940

Fiera Properties Limited **(1)**
1 Adelaide Street East Suite 2410, Toronto,
M5C 2V9, ON, Canada
Web Site: http://www.fieraproperties.com
Real Estate Investment Services
N.A.I.C.S.: 531390
Peter Cuthbert *(Pres)*

Subsidiary (Non-US):

Palmer Capital Partners Limited **(2)**
Time & Life Building 1 Bruton Street, May-
fair, London, W1J 6TL, United
Kingdom **(80%)**
Tel.: (44) 20 7409 5500
Web Site: http://www.palmercapital.co.uk
Real Estate Investment Management &
Venture Capital Investment Services
N.A.I.C.S.: 531390
Ray Palmer *(Founder & Chm)*

Subsidiary (Domestic):

**Invista Real Estate Investment Man-
agement Holdings Limited** **(3)**
Exchequer Court 33 St Mary Axe, London,
EC3A 8AA, United Kingdom
Tel.: (44) 2071539300
Sales Range: $50-74.9 Million
Emp.: 37
Real Estate Fund Management Services
N.A.I.C.S.: 525910

Subsidiary (Domestic):

**Invista Real Estate Investment Man-
agement Limited** **(4)**
Exchequer Ct, 33 St Mary Axe, London,
EC3A 8AA, United Kingdom
Tel.: (44) 2071539300

FIERA CAPITAL CORPORATION

Fiera Capital Corporation—(Continued)

Sales Range: $25-49.9 Million
Emp.: 36
Real Estate Fund Management Services
N.A.I.C.S.: 531390

Subsidiary (Non-US):

Palmer Capital Czech Republic, s.r.o. (3)
Politickych veznu 912/10, Prague, 110 00, Czech Republic
Tel.: (420) 284 086 400
Web Site: http://www.palmercapital.cz
Property Management Services
N.A.I.C.S.: 531312
Martin Krejci (Head-Fin Control)

Palmer Capital Nederland N.V. (3)
Parkweg 4, 7411 SH, Deventer, Netherlands
Tel.: (31) 570665860
Web Site: http://www.palmercapital.nl
Emp.: 10
Financial Investment
N.A.I.C.S.: 523999
Guy Barker (Mng Dir)

Holding (Non-US):

Biotika, a.s. (4)
Priboj 566, 97613, Slovenska Lupca, Slovakia
Tel.: (421) 484368111
Web Site: https://www.biotika.sk
Sales Range: $75-99.9 Million
Emp.: 426
Pharmaceuticals Mfr
N.A.I.C.S.: 325412
Miroslava Vargova (Dir-Personnel & Gen Office Mgr)

Holding (Domestic):

Palmer Capital Fondsenbeheer B.V. (4)
Parkweg 4, 7411 SH, Deventer, Netherlands
Tel.: (31) 5706658060
Financial Investments & Funds Management
N.A.I.C.S.: 523999

Integrated Asset Management Corp. (1)
70 University Avenue Suite 1200, Toronto, M5J 2M4, ON, Canada
Tel.: (416) 360-7667
Web Site: http://www.iamgroup.ca
Rev.: $14,281,702
Assets: $20,228,817
Liabilities: $5,072,605
Net Worth: $15,156,211
Earnings: $2,885,654
Fiscal Year-end: 09/30/2018
Asset Management Services
N.A.I.C.S.: 523999
Victor Koloshuk (Co-Founder & Chm)

Subsidiary (Domestic):

IAM Real Estate Group (2)
70 University Avenue Suite 1200, Toronto, M5J 2M4, ON, Canada (100%)
Tel.: (416) 864-0040
Web Site: http://www.iamgroup.ca
Sales Range: $50-74.9 Million
Emp.: 15
Real Estate Investment
N.A.I.C.S.: 523999
David Warkentin (Sr VP-Investments)

Integrated Private Debt Corp. (2)
70 University Ave Ste 1200, Toronto, M5J 2M4, ON, Canada
Tel.: (416) 360-7667
Web Site: http://www.iamgroup.ca
Real Estate Manangement Services
N.A.I.C.S.: 531210

Samson Capital Advisors LLC (1)
375 Park Ave 8th Fl, New York, NY 10152
Tel.: (212) 300-1600
Web Site: http://www.fieracapital.com
Financial Investment Activities
N.A.I.C.S.: 523999
Benjamin Stephen Thompson (Founder & Principal)

Strategic Income Allocation Fund (1)

1 Adelaide Street East Suite 600, Toronto, M5C 2V9, ON, Canada
Tel.: (416) 640-4959
Web Site: http://www.fieracapital.com
Closed-End Investment Fund
N.A.I.C.S.: 525990

Wilkinson O'Grady & Co., Inc. (1)
499 Park Ave 7th Fl, New York, NY 10022
Tel.: (212) 644-5252
Web Site: http://www.wilkinsonogrady.com
Emp.: 28
Investment Advisory & Portfolio Management Services
N.A.I.C.S.: 523940
Judith M. Lickson (VP-Ops)

FIERA FOODS COMPANY
50 Marmora St, Toronto, M9M 2X5, ON, Canada
Tel.: (416) 746-1010
Web Site: http://www.fierafoods.com
Year Founded: 1987
Rev.: $43,800,000
Emp.: 350
Bakery Products Mfr
N.A.I.C.S.: 311812
Boris Serebryany (Pres & CEO)

FIERA MILANO SPA
Piazzale Carlo Magno 1, 20149, Milan, Italy
Tel.: (39) 0249971 IT
Web Site: https://www.fieramilano.it
Year Founded: 1920
FM—(ITA)
Rev.: $313,311,624
Assets: $832,906,502
Liabilities: $669,057,291
Net Worth: $163,849,211
Earnings: $31,978,143
Emp.: 713
Fiscal Year-end: 12/31/23
Value Added Services
N.A.I.C.S.: 561990
Carlo Bonomi (Co-Chm)

Subsidiaries:

CIPA Fiera Milano Publicacoes e Eventos Ltda. (1)
Avenida Angelica n 2491 Conjunto 204, Bairro Consolacao, Sao Paulo, 01227-200, Brazil
Tel.: (55) 1155854355
Web Site: http://www.fieramilano.com.br
Event Management Services
N.A.I.C.S.: 561920

Fiera Milano Congressi SpA (1)
Piazzale Carlo Magno 1, 20149, Milan, Italy
Tel.: (39) 0249977134
Web Site: https://www.fieramilanocongressi.it
Event Management Services
N.A.I.C.S.: 561920

Fiera Milano Exhibitions Africa Pty. Ltd. (1)
4th Floor Brewster Building - 77 Hout Street City Center, Cape Town, 8000, South Africa
Tel.: (27) 217022280
Web Site: https://www.fieramilano.co.za
Event Management Services
N.A.I.C.S.: 561920

Mico DMC S.r.l. (1)
Piazzale Carlo Magno 1, 20149, Milan, Italy
Tel.: (39) 0249976275
Web Site: https://www.micodmc.it
Interior Design Services
N.A.I.C.S.: 541410

FIERA YMG CAPITAL INC.
1981 McGill College Ste 1500, Montreal, H3A 3M8, QC, Canada
Tel.: (514) 954-3300
Web Site: http://www.fieracapital.com
Year Founded: 2003
Sales Range: $25-49.9 Million
Emp.: 200
Investment Services
N.A.I.C.S.: 523999
Sylvain Brosseau (Pres & COO)

FIERATEX S.A.
Nea Santa, 54500, Kilkis, Greece
Tel.: (30) 2341075500
Web Site: https://www.fieratex.gr
Year Founded: 1988
FIER—(ATH)
Emp.: 176
Knitt & Fabric Mills
N.A.I.C.S.: 313240
Dimitrios Anezoulaki (Vice Chm)

Subsidiaries:

MINERVA S.A. (1)
6th klm Thessaloniki, Oraiokastro, 564 29, Thessaloniki, Greece
Tel.: (30) 2310683110
Web Site: http://www.minerva.gr
Emp.: 250
Clothing Apparel Mfr
N.A.I.C.S.: 315250
Elaine Philip (Mng Dir)

FIFTH AVENUE AUTO HAUS LTD.
1120 Meridian Road NE, Calgary, T2A 2N9, AB, Canada
Tel.: (403) 273-2500
Web Site: http://www.fifthavenuevw.com
Sales Range: $10-24.9 Million
Emp.: 40
New & Used Car Dealer
N.A.I.C.S.: 441110
Carl Cress (Mgr-Svc)

FIFTH ELEMENT RESOURCES LIMITED
C/- SRK Consulting Unit 1 Balbu Close, Beresfield, 2322, NSW, Australia
Tel.: (61) 2 4922 2100
Web Site: http://www.fifthelement.com
Copper & Gold Exploration
N.A.I.C.S.: 212230
Yang Zhang (Chm & CEO)

FIFTH RING LTD
St Marys Court 47-49 Huntly Street, Aberdeen, AB10 1TH, United Kingdom
Tel.: (44) 1224 626288
Web Site: http://www.fifthring.com
Year Founded: 1991
Sales Range: $10-24.9 Million
Emp.: 80
Advertising Services
N.A.I.C.S.: 541810
Ian Ord (Founder, Mng Dir & Dir-Bus Dev)

Subsidiaries:

Fifth Ring Inc. (1)
5151 San Felipe Ste 1399, Houston, TX 77056
Tel.: (281) 404-4313
Web Site: http://www.fifthring.com
Emp.: 7
Advetising Agency
N.A.I.C.S.: 541810
Ed Davis (Gen Mgr)

Fifth Ring LLC (1)
Suite 701-703 The Fairmont Dubai Sheikh Zayed Road, PO Box 126593, Dubai, United Arab Emirates
Tel.: (971) 4 372 0100
Web Site: http://www.fifthring.ae
Emp.: 15
Advetising Agency
N.A.I.C.S.: 541810
Yoshio Minomiya (Dir-Bus Dev)

FIFTH WHEEL TRUCK STOPS
40 Chisholm Drive, Milton, L9T 3G9, ON, Canada
Tel.: (905) 878-8446
Web Site: http://www.5thwheel.com
Rev.: $197,401,015

Emp.: 400
Truck Fuel Supplier
N.A.I.C.S.: 457210
Bruce Rankin (Pres)

FIGARO COFFEE GROUP INCORPORATED
116 East Main Avenue Phase V-Sez Laguna Technopark, Binan, Laguna, Philippines
Tel.: (63) 286714232
Web Site: https://www.figaro.ph
Year Founded: 1993
FCG—(PHI)
Rev.: $76,342,318
Assets: $57,445,326
Liabilities: $9,267,095
Net Worth: $48,178,232
Earnings: $8,242,818
Fiscal Year-end: 06/30/23
Restaurant Operators
N.A.I.C.S.: 722511

FIGEAC-AERO SA
Zone Industrielle de l'Aiguille, 46100, Figeac, France
Tel.: (33) 565345252
Web Site: https://www.figeac-aero.com
FGA—(EUR)
Rev.: $368,607,814
Assets: $757,558,817
Liabilities: $682,064,537
Net Worth: $75,494,280
Earnings: ($19,527,304)
Emp.: 2,588
Fiscal Year-end: 03/31/23
Aeronautical Subassemblies Designer & Mfr
N.A.I.C.S.: 334511
Joel Malleviale (CFO-Grp)

Subsidiaries:

Ateliers Tofer SAS (1)
ZI de Bogues, Escalquens, 31750, Toulouse, France
Tel.: (33) 534667260
Web Site: http://www.tofer.fr
Aerospace Equipment Mfr
N.A.I.C.S.: 336413
Benjamin Thomas (Mng Dir)

Auvergne Aeronautique SAS (1)
1 rue Touria Chaoui, 63510, Aulnat, France
Tel.: (33) 473604141
Web Site: http://www.auvergneaero.com
Sales Range: $50-74.9 Million
Emp.: 705
Aircraft Components & Equipment Mfr
N.A.I.C.S.: 336413

FGA North America Inc. (1)
9313 39th St, Wichita, KS 67226
Tel.: (316) 634-2500
Aerospace Equipment Mfr
N.A.I.C.S.: 336413

Figeac Aero Auxerre SASU (1)
15 Rue de la Plaine des Isles, 89000, Auxerre, France
Tel.: (33) 373401501
Aerospace Equipment Mfr
N.A.I.C.S.: 336413

Figeac Aero North America, Inc (1)
9313 39th St, Wichita, KS 67226
Tel.: (316) 634-2500
Sales Range: $10-24.9 Million
Emp.: 40
Engineeering Services
N.A.I.C.S.: 541330

M.T.I. SAS (1)
Route de Hutting, Kalhausen, 57412, Sarreguemines, France
Tel.: (33) 387263980
Web Site: https://www.mtisas.fr
Emp.: 10
Electrical Repair & Maintenance Services
N.A.I.C.S.: 811114

MECABRIVE IND. SAS (1)
1 Impasse Langevin, 19100, Brive-la-Gaillarde, France

Tel.: (33) 555927500
Emp.: 150
Aerospace Equipment Distr
N.A.I.C.S.: 423860

SN Auvergne Aeronautique SAS (1)
Aeroport de Clermont-Ferrand 1 Rue Touria
Chaoui, 63510, Aulnat, France
Tel.: (33) 473604141
Emp.: 600
Aerospace Equipment Mfr
N.A.I.C.S.: 336413

Tofer Europe Solutions SRL (1)
Str Piatra Craiului nr 7 Hala 10, Parc Indus-
trial DIBO Sat Negoiesti jud Prahova,
107086, Brazii, Romania
Tel.: (40) 318243070
Aerospace Equipment Mfr
N.A.I.C.S.: 336413

FIGENE CAPITAL SA
Ul Nowogrodzka 6a lok 35, 00-513,
Warsaw, Poland
Tel.: (48) 515942686
Web Site: https://www.figene.pl
Year Founded: 1991
20X—(DEU)
Electricity Distribution Services
N.A.I.C.S.: 237990

Subsidiaries:

Figene Energia Sp. z o.o. (1)
Ul Nowogrodzka 6A lok 13, 00-513, War-
saw, Poland
Tel.: (48) 221006130
Web Site: https://figene-energia.pl
Electricity Distribution Services
N.A.I.C.S.: 237990

Hagart Sp. z o.o. (1)
Ul Cyklamenow 9, 04-798, Warsaw, Poland
Tel.: (48) 223535276
Web Site: https://hadart.pl
Architecture & Planning Services
N.A.I.C.S.: 541310

Proreta Sp. z o.o. (1)
Ateities pl 28, 52181, Kaunas, Lithuania
Tel.: (370) 37393444
Web Site: https://proreta.eu
Truck Parts Mfr & Distr
N.A.I.C.S.: 336390

FIGTREE HOLDINGS LIMITED
8 Jalan Kilang Barat 03-01 Central
Link, Singapore, 159351, Singapore
Tel.: (65) 62789722
Web Site:
https://www.figtreeasia.com
5F4—(CAT)
Rev.: $31,574,856
Assets: $50,241,857
Liabilities: $25,417,358
Net Worth: $24,824,499
Earnings: ($6,194,564)
Fiscal Year-end: 12/31/22
Commercial & Industrial Building
Construction & Development
N.A.I.C.S.: 236220
Danny Siaw *(Chm & Mng Dir)*

Subsidiaries:

**Figtree Projects (Shanghai) Co.,
Ltd.** (1)
Room 403 Building 10 Hai Shanghai New
City 990 Dalian Road, Yangpu District,
Shanghai, 200092, China
Tel.: (86) 2151287228
Commercial & Building Construction Ser-
vices
N.A.I.C.S.: 236220

FIH ERHVERVSBANK A/S
Sundkrogsgade 7, 2100, Copenha-
gen, Denmark
Tel.: (45) 72225000   DK
Web Site: http://www.fih.com
Year Founded: 1958
Sales Range: $100-124.9 Million
Emp.: 233
Banking Services
N.A.I.C.S.: 522110

Henrik Sjogreen *(CEO)*

FIH GROUP PLC
Kenburgh Court 133-137 South
Street, Bishop's Stortford, CM23
3HX, Hampshire, United Kingdom
Tel.: (44) 1279461630   UK
Web Site: https://www.fihplc.com
Year Founded: 1852
FIH—(AIM)
Rev.: $66,220,783
Assets: $102,360,718
Liabilities: $45,455,783
Net Worth: $56,904,935
Earnings: $2,486,751
Fiscal Year-end: 03/31/24
Holding Company: General Trading,
Logistics & Storage Service
N.A.I.C.S.: 551112
John Foster *(CEO)*

Subsidiaries:

**Falkland Islands Shipping
Limited** (1)
Crozier Place, Stanley, FIQQ 1ZZ, Falkland
Islands
Tel.: (500) 27629
Web Site:
  https://www.falklandislandshipping.com
Bespoke Shipping Services
N.A.I.C.S.: 492110

Gosport Ferry Limited (1)
South Street, Gosport, PO12 1EP, Hamp-
shire, United Kingdom
Tel.: (44) 2392524551
Web Site: http://www.gosportferry.co.uk
Sales Range: $25-49.9 Million
Emp.: 45
Ferry Passenger Transportation Services
N.A.I.C.S.: 483114
John L. Foster *(Mng Dir)*

Momart Limited (1)
Exchange Tower 6th Floor 2 Harbour Ex-
change Square, London, E14 9GE, United
Kingdom
Tel.: (44) 2074263000
Web Site: http://www.momart.co.uk
Sales Range: $50-74.9 Million
Emp.: 130
Fine Arts & Antiquities Handling Services
N.A.I.C.S.: 488991

**Portsea Harbour Company
Limited** (1)
First Station S St, Gosport, PO12 1EP,
Hampshire, United Kingdom
Tel.: (44) 2392524551
Web Site: http://www.gosportferry.co.uk
Sales Range: $25-49.9 Million
Emp.: 40
Ferry Passenger Transportation Services
N.A.I.C.S.: 483114
John L. Foster *(Mng Dir)*

**The Falkland Islands Company
Limited** (1)
Kenburgh Court 133-137 South Street,
Bishop's Stortford, CM23 3HX, Hertford-
shire, United Kingdom
Tel.: (44) 1279461630
Web Site: http://www.the-falkland-islands-
  co.com
Sales Range: $25-49.9 Million
Emp.: 7
Retail Store Operation Services
N.A.I.C.S.: 445110
Kevin Ironside *(Mng Dir)*

FIHUMIN-GESELLSCHAFT
M.B.H.
Georg Sasse Str 43, Ammersbek,
22949, Germany
Tel.: (49) 406056710
Web Site: http://www.fihumin.de
Year Founded: 1935
Sales Range: $50-74.9 Million
Emp.: 9
Pet Food Product Mfr
N.A.I.C.S.: 311111
Dirk Jungclaussen *(Mng Dir)*

FIJI NATIONAL PROVIDENT
FUND
Provident Plaza 2 33 Ellery Street,
Private Mail Bag, Suva, Fiji
Tel.: (679) 330 7811   FJ
Web Site: http://www.myfnpf.com.fj
Year Founded: 1966
Sales Range: $350-399.9 Million
Superannuation Pension Fund
N.A.I.C.S.: 525110
Ajith Kodagoda *(Chm)*

Subsidiaries:

**Amalgamated Telecom Holdings
Limited** (1)
2nd Flr Harbour Front Building Rodwell
Road, GPO Box 11643, Suva, Fiji   (58%)
Tel.: (679) 330 8700
Web Site: http://www.ath.com.fj
Rev.: $310,992,671
Assets: $713,527,246
Liabilities: $411,207,268
Net Worth: $302,319,979
Earnings: $27,113,207
Emp.: 1,002
Fiscal Year-end: 03/31/2022
Telecommunications & Information Services
N.A.I.C.S.: 517111
Ajith Kodagoda *(Chm)*

Subsidiary (US):

AST Telecom, LLC (2)
478 Laufou Shopping Ctr, Pago Pago, AS
96799
Tel.: (684) 699-2759
Web Site: http://www.bluesky.as
Telecommunication Servicesb
N.A.I.C.S.: 517111

Subsidiary (Non-US):

BlueSky Samoa Ltd. (3)
Chief Post Office Beach Road, Apia, Samoa
(Western)   (75%)
Tel.: (685) 67788
Web Site: http://www.blueskysamoa.ws
Telecommunication Servicesb
N.A.I.C.S.: 517111

Subsidiary (Non-US):

Telecom Cook Islands Limited (4)
Avarua, PO Box 106, Rarotonga, Cook
Islands   (60%)
Tel.: (682) 29680
Web Site: http://www.telecom.co.ck
Telecommunication Servicesb
N.A.I.C.S.: 517111

Subsidiary (Domestic):

ATH Call Centre Limited (2)
Garden City Raiwai, PO Box 5040, Rai-
waqa, Suva, Fiji   (100%)
Tel.: (679) 679 3310 333
Call Center Services
N.A.I.C.S.: 517810

Subsidiary (Non-US):

**Amalgamated Telecom Holdings Kiri-
bati Limited** (2)
Main Street, PO Box 72, Bairiki, Tarawa,
Kiribati
Tel.: (686) 20700
Web Site: http://www.athkl.com.ki
Sales Range: $25-49.9 Million
Emp.: 150
Telecommunication Servicesb
N.A.I.C.S.: 517111

Subsidiary (Domestic):

Fiji Directories Limited (2)
Levels 3&4 Telecom New Wing Building,
PO Box 16059, Suva, Fiji   (100%)
Tel.: (679) 3311 000
Web Site: http://fdl.com.fj
Telephone Directory Services
N.A.I.C.S.: 513140
Sitla Chandra *(CEO)*

**Pacific Emerging Technologies
Limited** (2)
Level 4 General Post Office Building Ed-
ward Street, PO Box U43 USP, Suva,
Fiji   (100%)

Tel.: (679) 331 0025
Technology Services
N.A.I.C.S.: 561499
Patricia Gock *(Sec)*

Telecom Fiji Ltd. (2)
Edward Street, Ganilau House, Suva,
FJ696, Fiji   (100%)
Tel.: (679) 3304019
Web Site: http://www.telecomfiji.com.fj
Sales Range: $50-74.9 Million
Emp.: 200
Telecommunications
N.A.I.C.S.: 517810
Samuela Vadei *(Sec)*

Subsidiary (Domestic):

Internet Services Fiji Limited (3)
Garden City Raiwai, PO Box 13779, Suva,
Fiji
Tel.: (679) 3300 100
Web Site: http://www.connect.com.fj
Internet Services
N.A.I.C.S.: 517810

Transtel Limited (3)
5th Floor Telecom New Wing Guilding Ed-
ward Street, Private Mail Bag, Suva, Fiji
Tel.: (679) 3210 528
Web Site: http://www.transtel.com.fj
Telecommunication Servicesb
N.A.I.C.S.: 517810

Xceed Pasifika Limited (3)
1 Carpenter St, Garden City Raiwai, Suva,
Fiji
Tel.: (679) 3216000
Web Site: http://www.xceed.com
Sales Range: $25-49.9 Million
Emp.: 8
Telecommunications
N.A.I.C.S.: 517810
Joseph Naua *(Mgr-Cable)*

Subsidiary (Non-US):

Telecom Vanuatu Limited (2)
Telecom House, Father Walter Lini High-
way, Port-Vila, Vanuatu   (100%)
Tel.: (678) 22185
Web Site: http://www.tvl.vu
Telecommunication Servicesb
N.A.I.C.S.: 517810
Divik Deo *(CEO)*

Subsidiary (Domestic):

Vodafone Fiji Ltd. (2)
168 Princess Rd Tamavua, Suva,
Fiji   (51%)
Tel.: (679) 3312000
Web Site: http://www.vodafone.com.fj
Sales Range: $50-74.9 Million
Emp.: 106
Cellular Communications Services
N.A.I.C.S.: 517112
Ajith Kodagoda *(Chm)*

**Fiji International Telecommunications
Limited** (1)
151 Riffle Range Vatuwaqa Communication
Centre, Vatuwaqa, Suva, Fiji
Tel.: (679) 3312933
Web Site: http://www.fintel.com.fj
Telecommunication Servicesb
N.A.I.C.S.: 517111
George Samisoni *(CEO)*

Home Finance Company Limited (1)
Ground Floor 371 Victoria Parade, PO Box
161, Suva, Fiji
Tel.: (679) 3316555
Web Site: http://www.hfc.com.fj
Commercial Banking Services
N.A.I.C.S.: 522110
Tom Ricketts *(Chm)*

Natadola Bay Resort Limited (1)
Private Mail Bag 0381, Nadi Airport, Nadi,
Fiji
Tel.: (679) 6721001
Web Site: http://www.natadola.com
Resort Management Services
N.A.I.C.S.: 721110

FIJIAN HOLDINGS LIMITED
Level 7 Ra Marama 91 Gordon
Street, PO Box 2110, Government
Buildings, Suva, Fiji

FIJIAN HOLDINGS LIMITED

Fijian Holdings Limited—(Continued)

Tel.: (679) 3305017
Web Site:
http://www.fijianholdings.com.fj
Year Founded: 1984
FHL—(SPSE)
Rev.: $153,935,044
Assets: $288,941,025
Liabilities: $145,692,764
Net Worth: $143,248,261
Earnings: $22,354,114
Emp.: 1,600
Fiscal Year-end: 06/30/23
Holding Company
N.A.I.C.S.: 551112
Abilash Ram (CEO-Acting)

Subsidiaries:

Blue Lagoon Cruises Holdings Pte
Limited   (1)
South Sea Cruises, PO Box PD052, Dena-
rau, Nadi, Fiji
Tel.: (679) 9995512
Web Site:
https://www.bluelagooncruises.com
Ship Cruising Services
N.A.I.C.S.: 483112

FHL Properties Pte Limited   (1)
Suite 2A FHLP Building 41 Gladstone
Road, Suva, Fiji
Tel.: (679) 3303506
Web Site: https://fhlproperties.com.fj
Investment Management Service
N.A.I.C.S.: 541611
Catherine Grey (Gen Mgr)

Fiji Television Limited   (1)
78 Brown Street, PO Box 2442, Suva, Fiji
Tel.: (679) 3305100
Web Site: http://www.fijione.tv
Rev.: $2,504,274
Assets: $4,932,474
Liabilities: $1,947,239
Net Worth: $2,985,235
Earnings: $186,955
Fiscal Year-end: 06/30/2023
Television Broadcasting Services
N.A.I.C.S.: 516120
Ajai Punja (Mng Dir-Blue Gas)

Merchant Finance Pte Limited   (1)
Level 1 Ra Marama House 91 Gordon
Street, PO Box 14213, Suva, Fiji
Tel.: (679) 331 4955
Web Site: https://merchantfinance.com.fj
Merchant Finance Services
N.A.I.C.S.: 522320

Pacific Cement Pte Limited   (1)
Qoya Forest Reserve, GPO Box 1165,
Lami, Suva, Fiji
Tel.: (679) 336 1133
Web Site: https://pacificcement.com
Cement Product Mfr & Distr
N.A.I.C.S.: 327310

RB Patel Group Limited   (1)
RB Patel CentrePoint Building, Ratu Dovi
Road Laucala Beach Estate, Nasinu, Fiji
Tel.: (679) 3391899
Web Site: http://www.rbpatel.com.fj
Rev.: $73,306,133
Assets: $49,800,006
Liabilities: $22,221,326
Net Worth: $27,578,680
Earnings: $5,983,988
Emp.: 748
Fiscal Year-end: 06/30/2023
Supermarket Operator
N.A.I.C.S.: 445110

Serendib Investments Pte
Limited   (1)
8 Viria East Road Vatuwaqa, GPO Box 98,
Suva, Fiji
Tel.: (679) 3385999
Web Site: https://www.serendib.com.fj
Stationery Product Distr
N.A.I.C.S.: 424120

FIJICARE INSURANCE LIM-
ITED
Level 9- 343-359 FNPF Place, PO

Box 15808, Victoria Parade, Suva,
Fiji
Tel.: (679) 330 2717
Web Site: http://www.fijicare.com.fj
Year Founded: 1993
FIL—(SPSE)
Rev.: $15,780,993
Assets: $24,363,955
Liabilities: $13,721,531
Net Worth: $10,642,424
Earnings: $2,950,465
Fiscal Year-end: 12/31/21
Insurance Services
N.A.I.C.S.: 524298
Peter J. McPherson (Mng Dir)

FILA HOLDINGS CORPORA-
TION
9F 10F 35 Bomun-ro, Seongbuk-gu,
Seoul, 02873, Korea (South)
Tel.: (82) 215336400
Web Site:
https://www.filaholdings.com
Year Founded: 1911
081660—(KRS)
Rev.: $3,238,082,347
Assets: $3,698,321,657
Liabilities: $1,723,631,579
Net Worth: $1,974,690,078
Earnings: $358,606,126
Emp.: 49
Fiscal Year-end: 12/31/22
Sportswear & Footwear Retailer &
Distr
N.A.I.C.S.: 458110
Yoon-Soo Yoon (Chm)

Subsidiaries:

Acushnet Holdings Corp.   (1)
333 Bridge St, Fairhaven, MA
02719   (53.1%)
Tel.: (508) 979-2000
Web Site:
https://www.acushnetholdingscorp.com
Rev.: $2,270,336,000
Assets: $2,193,807,000
Liabilities: $1,217,104,000
Net Worth: $976,703,000
Earnings: $199,278,000
Emp.: 7,300
Fiscal Year-end: 12/31/2022
Golf Product Mfr & Distr
N.A.I.C.S.: 339920
Mary Lou Bohn (Pres-Titleist Golf Balls)

Subsidiary (Domestic):

Acushnet Company   (2)
333 Bridge St, Fairhaven, MA 02719-4905
Tel.: (508) 979-2000
Web Site:
http://www.acushnetholdingscorp.com
Golfing Equipment & Accessories Mfr
N.A.I.C.S.: 339920
Walter R. Uihlein (Pres & CEO)

Subsidiary (Non-US):

Acushnet Canada Inc.   (3)
500 Harry Walker Parkway North, East
Gwillimbury, Newmarket, L9N 0M9, ON,
Canada
Tel.: (905) 898-7575
Web Site: https://www.titleist.ca
Golfing Equipment & Accessories Mfr
N.A.I.C.S.: 339920

Acushnet Europe Ltd.   (3)
Caxton Road, Saint Ives, PE27 3LU, Cam-
bridgeshire, United Kingdom
Tel.: (44) 800363672
Web Site: http://www.titleist.co.uk
Golfing Equipment & Accessories Mfr
N.A.I.C.S.: 339920
Jeromy Tomlinson (VP)

Acushnet GmbH   (3)
Richard-Klinger-Str 11, 65510, Idstein, Ger-
many
Tel.: (49) 61265503319
Web Site: https://www.titleist.de
Golfing Equipment & Accessories Mfr
N.A.I.C.S.: 339920
Peltzer Nikolaus (Mng Dir)

Acushnet Korea Co., Ltd.   (3)
651 Seolleung-ro, Gangnam-gu, Seoul,
6100, Korea (South)
Tel.: (82) 230143800
Web Site: https://www.titleist.co.kr
Golf Equipments & Accessories Mfr
N.A.I.C.S.: 339920

Acushnet Nederland B.V.   (3)
Heibloemweg 3, 5704, Helmond, Nether-
lands
Tel.: (31) 492505050
Web Site: http://www.titleist.co.uk
Golfing Equipment & Accessories Mfr
N.A.I.C.S.: 339920

Acushnet Sverige AB   (3)
Boplatsgatan 2C, 21376, Malmo, Sweden
Tel.: (46) 20027080
Web Site: https://www.titleist.se
Golfing Equipment & Accessories Mfr
N.A.I.C.S.: 339920

Fila Argentina S.A.   (1)
Guatemala 5125, B1667JNA, Buenos Aires,
Argentina
Tel.: (54) 3327518437
Web Site: https://filagroup.com.ar
Sales Range: $25-49.9 Million
Emp.: 40
Sporting & Athletic Goods Mfr
N.A.I.C.S.: 339920

Fila Canada, Inc.   (1)
6085 Belgrave Rd, Mississauga, L5R 4E6,
ON, Canada
Tel.: (905) 361-2405
Web Site: http://www.fila.com
Sales Range: $25-49.9 Million
Emp.: 25
Sporting & Athletic Goods Mfr
N.A.I.C.S.: 339920

Fila Europe S.p.A   (1)
Siasra pampuri no9 A, 20141, Milano, Italy
Tel.: (39) 0252823200
Web Site: http://www.filacorsocono.com
Sales Range: $25-49.9 Million
Emp.: 9
Sporting & Athletic Goods Mfr
N.A.I.C.S.: 339920

Subsidiary (Non-US):

Fila France S.A.   (2)
2 Bd Montmartre, 75009, Paris, France
Tel.: (33) 1 4523 2966
Web Site: http://www.fila.eu
Sales Range: $25-49.9 Million
Sporting & Athletic Goods Mfr
N.A.I.C.S.: 339920

Fila Sport (Hong Kong) Limited (1)
12th Floor Tower 3 China Hong Kong City,
33 Canton Road, Tsimshatsui, Kowloon,
China (Hong Kong)
Tel.: (852) 221706100
Athletic Clothing & Accessories Mfr
N.A.I.C.S.: 339920

Fila Sport Taiwan Ltd.   (1)
7th Floor No 130 Sec 2 Chung Teh Road,
Taichung, 406, Taiwan
Tel.: (886) 422325855
Web Site: http://www.fila.com.th
Sales Range: $50-74.9 Million
Emp.: 113
Sporting & Athletic Goods Sales
N.A.I.C.S.: 458210

Fila UK Limited   (1)
Unit 5 & 6 Colonial Business Park, Colonial
Way, Watford, WD24 4PR, Herts, United
Kingdom
Tel.: (44) 1923475600
Web Site: http://www.fila.co.uk
Sales Range: $25-49.9 Million
Emp.: 15
Sporting & Athletic Goods
N.A.I.C.S.: 339920

Fila USA, Inc.   (1)
930 Ridgebrook Rd Ste 200, Sparks, MD
21152-3000
Tel.: (410) 773-3000
Web Site: https://www.fila.com
Sales Range: $650-699.9 Million
Apparel & Athletic Footwear Distr & Mfr
N.A.I.C.S.: 424340

FILAMENT HEALTH CORP.

4475 Wayburne Drive Unit 210,
Burnaby, V5G 4X4, BC, Canada
Tel.: (604) 500-2407   BC
Web Site: https://www.filament.health
Year Founded: 2021
FLHLF—(OTCQB)
Rev.: $271,917
Assets: $3,536,530
Liabilities: $1,154,312
Net Worth: $2,382,218
Earnings: ($12,283,983)
Emp.: 11
Fiscal Year-end: 12/31/22
Pharmaceuticals Product Mfr
N.A.I.C.S.: 325412
Andry Tjahyana (VP)

FILATEX FASHIONS LIMITED

D No 1-80-40-SP-58-65 Shilpa
Homes Layout Gachibowli Seri Lin-
gampally, K V Rangareddy, Hydera-
bad, Telangana, India
Tel.: (91) 4066748931
Web Site:
https://www.filatexfashions.co.in
532022—(BOM)
Rev.: $20,112,763
Assets: $28,092,704
Liabilities: $18,140,579
Net Worth: $9,952,125
Earnings: $1,428,535
Emp.: 90
Fiscal Year-end: 03/31/23
Textile Product Mfr & Whslr
N.A.I.C.S.: 314910
Prabhat Sethia (Mng Dir)

FILATEX INDIA LTD.

43 Community Centre New Friends
Colony, New Delhi, 110025, India
Tel.: (91) 1126312503
Web Site: https://www.filatex.com
FILATEX—(NSE)
Rev.: $305,296,910
Assets: $246,567,321
Liabilities: $142,490,712
Net Worth: $104,076,609
Earnings: $22,636,232
Emp.: 2,349
Fiscal Year-end: 03/31/21
Polypropylene Yarn Mfr
N.A.I.C.S.: 313110
Madhu Sudhan Bhageria (Chm & Co-
Mng Dir)

FILINVEST DEVELOPMENT
CORPORATION
6th Floor The Beaufort, Building 5th
Corner 23rd Street Metro Manila,
Bonifacio Global City, Taguig, 1634,
Philippines
Tel.: (63) 277983977
Web Site:
https://www.filinvestgroup.com
Year Founded: 1955
FDC—(PHI)
Rev.: $1,308,465,226
Assets: $13,927,184,669
Liabilities: $10,576,077,782
Net Worth: $3,351,106,886
Earnings: $184,823,538
Emp.: 11,514
Fiscal Year-end: 12/31/21
Holding Company; Real Estate De-
velopment, Banking, Leasing, Finan-
cial & Sugar Business
N.A.I.C.S.: 551112
Lourdes Josephine Gotianun Yap
(Pres & CEO)

Subsidiaries:

Chroma Hospitality, Inc.   (1)
8/F Vector Two Building Northgate Cyberzone Filinvest Corporate City, Alabang,
Muntinlupa, Philippines
Tel.: (63) 2 846 0278

Web Site:
https://www.chromahospitality.com
Home Management Services
N.A.I.C.S.: 721110
Dave Romano (Mgr-Talent Dev)

Cyberzone Properties Inc. (1)
FAI Administration Bldg, Alabang-Zapote
Road Filinvest, 1781, Muntinlupa,
Philippines (100%)
Tel.: (63) 2 807 6729
Web Site: http://www.northgate-
cyberzone.com
Sales Range: $1-4.9 Billion
Emp.: 6,000
Miscellaneous Financial Investment Activities
N.A.I.C.S.: 523999

East West Banking Corporation (1)
The Beaufort 5th Avenue corner 23rd Street
Bonifacio Global City, Taguig, 1634,
Philippines (100%)
Tel.: (63) 288881700
Web Site: https://www.eastwestbanker.com
Rev.: $502,557,357
Assets: $7,497,580,701
Liabilities: $6,411,575,648
Net Worth: $1,086,005,053
Earnings: $82,299,692
Emp.: 7,242
Fiscal Year-end: 12/31/2022
Commericial Banking
N.A.I.C.S.: 522110
Jonathan T. Gotianun (Chm)

FDC Utilities, Inc. (1)
Unit D 11th Floor Cyber Sigma Lawton Avenue, McKinley West Fort Bonifacio,
Taguig, 1630, Philippines
Tel.: (63) 28 575 1600
Web Site: https://www.fdcutilities.com
Power Generation Services
N.A.I.C.S.: 221111
Juan Eugenio L. Roxas (Pres & CEO)

Filinvest Alabang Inc. (1)
23F Axis Tower One Northgate Cyberzone
Filinvest City, Alabang, Muntinlupa, 1781,
Philippines
Tel.: (63) 8 846 0278
Web Site: https://www.filinvestcity.com
Residential Property Managers
N.A.I.C.S.: 531311

Filinvest Land Inc. (1)
79 Epifanio de los Santos Ave, Mandaluyong, 1550, Philippines
Tel.: (63) 279188188
Web Site: https://www.filinvestland.com
Rev.: $350,819,248
Assets: $4,019,049,445
Liabilities: $2,151,412,786
Net Worth: $1,867,636,659
Earnings: $89,548,742
Fiscal Year-end: 12/31/2021
Real Estate Services
N.A.I.C.S.: 531390
Lourdes Josephine Gotianun Yap (Pres &
CEO)

Filinvest Supermall Inc. (1)
Filinvest Corporate City Alabang, Muntinlupa, Philippines (100%)
Tel.: (63) 28503517
Web Site: http://www.festivalsupermall.com
Sales Range: $75-99.9 Million
Emp.: 123
Nonresidential Buildings Lessors
N.A.I.C.S.: 531120

H.B. Fuller (Phils.) Inc. (1)
11 Gyro St LISP 1 Bo Diezmo, Cabuyao,
4025, Laguna, Philippines
Tel.: (63) 49 554 8440
Sales Range: $25-49.9 Million
Emp.: 44
Adhesive Mfr
N.A.I.C.S.: 325520

FILIPINO FUND, INC.
Units 1210-1212 12/F PSE Tower 5th
Avenue corner 28th Street, Bonifacio
Global City, Taguig, Philippines
Tel.: (63) 88987522
Web Site:
https://www.filipinofund.com.ph
Year Founded: 1991

FFI—(PHI)
Rev.: $204,339
Assets: $4,318,482
Liabilities: $45,245
Net Worth: $4,273,236
Earnings: $91,284
Fiscal Year-end: 12/31/21
Financial Services
N.A.I.C.S.: 525990
Bernardo M. Villegas (Chm)

FILIPPA K AB
Soder Malar Strang 65 Level 9,
Stockholm, 100 64, Sweden
Tel.: (46) 86157000
Web Site: http://www.filippa-k.se
Year Founded: 1993
Rev.: $44,247,000
Emp.: 120
Men's & Women's Clothing Mfr &
Retailer
N.A.I.C.S.: 315250
Filippa Knutsson (Founder)

FILLING & PACKING MATERIALS MANUFACTURING COMPANY
New Industrial city Phase 3, PO Box
8762, Riyadh, 11492, Saudi Arabia
Tel.: (966) 112652299
Web Site: https://www.fipco.com.sa
Year Founded: 1991
2180—(SAU)
Rev.: $63,473,371
Assets: $76,459,027
Liabilities: $38,139,562
Net Worth: $38,319,464
Earnings: $3,197,224
Emp.: 1,000
Fiscal Year-end: 12/31/23
Plastic Packaging Product Mfr &
Whslr
N.A.I.C.S.: 325211
Faisal Mohammed Al Harbi (Vice
Chm & Mng Dir)

FILMON.COM PLC
111 Wardour Street, London, W1F
0UH, United Kingdom
Tel.: (44) 2077342819
Web Site: http://www.filmon.com
Emp.: 7
Online Media Services
N.A.I.C.S.: 516210
Alki David (Founder, Chm & CEO)

Subsidiaries:

FilmOn Networks USA (1)
301 N Canon Dr Ste 208, Beverly Hills, CA
90210
Tel.: (877) 733-1830
Media Streaming Services
N.A.I.C.S.: 518210
Brandon Howe (VP-Production)

FILMS AT 59
59 Cotham Hill, Clifton, Bristol, BS6
6JR, United Kingdom
Tel.: (44) 1179064300
Web Site: http://www.filmsat59.com
Year Founded: 1990
Rev.: $12,371,486
Emp.: 103
Equipment Hire & Post Production
Services
N.A.I.C.S.: 512240
Gina Fucci (Mng Dir)

FILO CORP.
Suite 2800 Four Bentall Centre 1055
Dunsmuir Street, Vancouver, V7X
1L2, BC, Canada
Tel.: (604) 689-7842
Web Site: https://www.filo-
mining.com
FLMMF—(NASDAQ)
Assets: $23,984,705

Liabilities: $5,525,111
Net Worth: $18,459,594
Earnings: ($25,360,899)
Emp.: 75
Fiscal Year-end: 12/31/21
Metal Exploration Services
N.A.I.C.S.: 213114
Adam Lundin (CEO)

FILSYN CORPORATION
Unit 8 5B Pearlbank Centre 146
Valero Street, Makati, 1227, Philippines
Tel.: (63) 27523383
Web Site: http://www.filsyncorp.com
Year Founded: 1968
Sales Range: Less than $1 Million
Polyester Fiber Mfr
N.A.I.C.S.: 313110
Apolinario L. Posio (Sr VP-Acctg, Auditor & Cheif Compliance Officer)

FILTER VISION PUBLIC COMPANY LIMITED
95 Soi Ram Intra 117 Ram Intra
Road, Min Buri Subdistrict Min Buri
District, Bangkok, 10510, Thailand
Tel.: (66) 25182722
Web Site:
https://www.filtervision.co.th
Year Founded: 1995
FVC—(THA)
Rev.: $28,338,981
Assets: $34,041,632
Liabilities: $16,970,460
Net Worth: $17,071,172
Earnings: $2,640,706
Fiscal Year-end: 12/31/23
Water Filter Equipment
N.A.I.C.S.: 213114
Wijit Techakasem (Chm & Mng Dir)

FILTISAC SA
Autoroute d Abobo, BP 3962, 1, Abidjan, Cote d'Ivoire
Tel.: (225) 20304600
Web Site: https://www.filtisac.com
Year Founded: 1965
FTSC—(BRVM)
Sales Range: Less than $1 Million
Industrial Equipment Mfr
N.A.I.C.S.: 333248

FILTRA CONSULTANTS & ENGINEERS LTD.
W-27 T-Block MIDC Bhosari Haveli,
Goregaon E, Pune, 411026, Maharashtra, India
Tel.: (91) 8446294002
Web Site: https://www.filtra.in
539098—(BOM)
Rev.: $10,908,651
Assets: $3,965,865
Liabilities: $1,549,152
Net Worth: $2,416,714
Earnings: $412,829
Emp.: 67
Fiscal Year-end: 03/31/23
Water Treatment Equipment Distr
N.A.I.C.S.: 423830
Ketan Khant (Chm & Mng Dir)

FILTRATION LAB INC.
193 Rang de L Eglise, Saint Ligouri,
J0K 2X0, QC, Canada
Tel.: (450) 754-4222
Web Site: http://www.filtrationlab.com
Year Founded: 1987
Rev.: $11,042,009
Emp.: 110
Filtration Products Mfr
N.A.I.C.S.: 334513
Claude Bedard (Pres)

FILTRON ENGINEERS LIMITED
6 Filtron House Sinhagad Road, Sita-

bag Colony, Pune, 411030, Maharashtra, India
Tel.: (91) 020 24338642 In
Web Site: http://www.filtronindia.com
Year Founded: 1982
Food Product Machinery Mfr
N.A.I.C.S.: 333241

FILTRONIC PLC
Filtronic House 3 Airport West Lancaster Way, Yeadon, Leeds, LS19
7ZA, West Yorkshire, United Kingdom
Tel.: (44) 1132200000 UK
Web Site: https://www.filtronic.com
Year Founded: 1994
FTC—(AIM)
Rev.: $32,100,543
Assets: $31,898,574
Liabilities: $13,191,140
Net Worth: $18,707,434
Earnings: $3,963,653
Fiscal Year-end: 05/31/24
Designer & Mfr of Radio Frequency
Electronics
N.A.I.C.S.: 334220
Maura Moynihan (Sec & Gen Counsel)

Subsidiaries:

Filtronic (Suzhou) Telecommunication
Products Co. Ltd. (1)
33 Huoju Rd, Suzhou, 215009, Jiangsu,
China
Tel.: (86) 51268081636
Web Site: http://www.filtronic.com.cn
Mfr of Equipment for Wireless Communications
N.A.I.C.S.: 334220

Filtronic Broadband Ltd. (1)
Heighington Lane Business Park, Newton
Aycliffe, DL5 6JW, United
Kingdom (100%)
Tel.: (44) 1325 301 111
Web Site: http://www.filtronic.co.uk
Sales Range: $50-74.9 Million
Mfr of RF Subsystems for Wireless Communication Systems
N.A.I.C.S.: 334220

Filtronic Wireless Ltd. (1)
31901 Comtek Ln, Salisbury, MD 21804-
1788
Tel.: (410) 341-7802
Sales Range: $125-149.9 Million
Mfr of RF Filters & Subsystems for Wireless
Communication Systems
N.A.I.C.S.: 334419

Branch (Domestic):

Filtronic Wireless Ltd. (2)
39 Depot St, Merrimack, NH 03054
Tel.: (410) 202-8811
Web Site: http://www.filtronic.co.uk
Research & Development of RF Filters &
Subsystems for Wireless Communication
Systems
N.A.I.C.S.: 334419

FIMA CORPORATION BERHAD
Suite 4 1 Level 4 Block C Plaza Damansara, 45 Jalan Medan Setia 1
Bukit Damansara, 50490, Kuala Lumpur, Malaysia
Tel.: (60) 320921211
Web Site: https://www.fimacorp.com
Year Founded: 1974
FIMACOR—(KLS)
Rev.: $62,627,937
Assets: $152,069,630
Liabilities: $25,029,418
Net Worth: $127,040,212
Earnings: $8,253,122
Emp.: 1,710
Fiscal Year-end: 03/31/23
Property Management Services
N.A.I.C.S.: 531312
Roslan Hamir (Mng Dir)

Subsidiaries:

Fima Technology Sdn. Bhd. (1)

Fima Corporation Berhad—(Continued)

Suite 4 1 Level 4 Block C Plaza Damansara
No 45 Jalan Medan Setia 1, Bukit Daman-
sara, 50490, Kuala Lumpur, Malaysia
Tel.: (60) 320921211
Web Site: http://www.fimatechnology.com
Engineeering Services
N.A.I.C.S.: 541330
Nazri Talib (Head-Engrg)

PT Nunukan Jaya Lestari   (1)
Tel.: (62) 55624551
Security Printer Services
N.A.I.C.S.: 561990

Security Printers (M) Sdn. Bhd.   (1)
No 1 Jalan Chan Sow Lin, 55200, Kuala
Lumpur, Malaysia
Tel.: (60) 392222511
Security Printer Services
N.A.I.C.S.: 561990

FIMA GLOBAL INVEST D.O.O
Medimurska 28, 42000, Varazdin,
Croatia
Tel.: (385) 42660900
Web Site: http://www.fgi.hr
Financial & Investment Services
N.A.I.C.S.: 523999
Goran Dobrojevic (Pres)

FIMALAC S.A.
97 rue de Lille, 75007, Paris, France
Tel.: (33) 47536150   FR
Web Site: http://www.fimalac.com
Business-To-Business Services
N.A.I.C.S.: 561499

Subsidiaries:

West World Media LLC   (1)
63 Copps Hill Rd Ste 74, Ridgefield, CT
06877-4051
Tel.: (203) 438-8389
Web Site: http://www.westworldmedia.com
Emp.: 80
Movie Showtime Listings Via Internet
N.A.I.C.S.: 519290
Jordan Marker (Editor-Media Guide)

FIMARO INVEST SA
B-Dul Constantin Brancusi Nr 133
Etaj 2, Cluj-Napoca, Romania
Tel.: (40) 264 406080
Sales Range: Less than $1 Million
Building Construction Services
N.A.I.C.S.: 236115

FIMBANK P.L.C.
Mercury Tower The Exchange Finan-
cial and Business Centre, Elia Zam-
mit Street St Julians, Valletta, STJ
3155, Malta
Tel.: (356) 21322100   Mt
Web Site: http://www.fimbank.com
Year Founded: 1994
Rev.: $50,531,699
Assets: $1,893,030,224
Liabilities: $1,612,017,622
Net Worth: $281,012,602
Earnings: $4,530,103
Emp.: 346
Fiscal Year-end: 12/31/19
Banking Services
N.A.I.C.S.: 522110
Simon Lay (Deputy CEO & CEO-
Forfaiting-London)

Subsidiaries:

FIM Business Solutions Limited   (1)
Mercury Tower The Exchange Financial and
Bussiness Center, San Giljan, STJ 3155,
Malta
Tel.: (356) 21322100
Web Site: http://www.fimbs.net
Financial Advisory Services
N.A.I.C.S.: 523940

FIM Property Investment Limited   (1)
7th Floor The Plaza Commercial Centre
Bisazza Street, Sliema, SLM 1640, Malta
Tel.: (356) 21322100

Sales Range: $75-99.9 Million
Emp.: 160
Property Management Services
N.A.I.C.S.: 531312

London Forfaiting Company Ltd   (1)
15-18 Austin Friars, London, EC2N 2HE,
United Kingdom   (100%)
Tel.: (44) 2073971510
Web Site: http://www.forfaiting.com
Sales Range: $1-9.9 Million
Emp.: 11
International Trade Finance Services; For-
faiting Services; Short-Term Financing for
Exporters
N.A.I.C.S.: 522299
Simon Lay (CEO)

Subsidiary (Non-US):

London Forfaiting A Paris SA   (2)
260 Blvd Saint Germain, F 75007, Paris,
France
Tel.: (33) 140626190
Sales Range: $50-74.9 Million
Emp.: 35
Provider of Forfaiting Services; Short-Term
Financing for Exporters
N.A.I.C.S.: 523910

Subsidiary (US):

London Forfaiting Americas Inc.   (2)
444 Madison Ave Ste 36A, New York, NY
10022
Tel.: (212) 377-2012
Web Site: http://www.forfaiting.com
Sales Range: $75-99.9 Million
Emp.: 3
Trade Financial Services
N.A.I.C.S.: 522299
Gregory Bernardi (Pres)

Subsidiary (Non-US):

London Forfaiting Deutschland
GmbH   (2)
Niederrheinstrasse 23, D 40474, Dussel-
dorf, Germany
Tel.: (49) 2114303040
Provider of Forfaiting Services; Short-Term
Financing for Exporters
N.A.I.C.S.: 523910

London Forfaiting Polska Sp.
Z.O.O   (2)
Ilmet Bldg U1 Jana Pawla II 15, PL 00 828,
Warsaw, Poland
Tel.: (48) 226977277
Sales Range: $50-74.9 Million
Emp.: 35
Provider of Forfaiting Services; Short-Term
Financing for Exporters
N.A.I.C.S.: 523910

London Forfaiting do Brasil Ltda   (2)
Av das Nacoes Unidas 14171 - 15 andar,
Rochavera Corporate Towers - Torre B
Marble Tower, Sao Paulo, 04794-000, Brazil
Tel.: (55) 1135682111
Web Site: http://www.forfaiting.com
International Trade Financing
N.A.I.C.S.: 522299
Alexandre T. Ozzetti (Mng Dir)

Menafactors Limited   (1)
Office 3 And 4 Level 1 The Gate Village 06,
PO Box 506554, Dubai, United Arab Emir-
ates
Tel.: (971) 4 4242660
Web Site: http://www.menafactors.com
Sales Range: $50-74.9 Million
Emp.: 25
Financial Advisory Services
N.A.I.C.S.: 523940
Veene Mankar (Chm)

FIMOPART GROUP
20 rue de Saint-Petersbourg, 75008,
Paris, France
Tel.: (33) 231717000
Web Site: http://www.fimopart.com
Sales Range: $125-149.9 Million
Emp.: 1,600
Holding Company
N.A.I.C.S.: 551112

Subsidiaries:

Airborne   (1)

Quartier Beaudesert, 33702, Merignac,
France   (100%)
Tel.: (33) 558719820
Web Site: http://www.airborne.fr
Sales Range: $1-9.9 Million
Emp.: 30
Designer & Mfr of Office Furniture
N.A.I.C.S.: 337211

FIN MILE LOGISTICS LIMITED
8a St Leonard's Rd, London, NW10
6ST, United Kingdom
Tel.: (44) 2035761701   UK
Web Site: https://finmile.co
Year Founded: 2022
Transportation, Logistics & Supply
Chain Services
N.A.I.C.S.: 541614
Rich Pleeth (Founder & CEO)

Subsidiaries:

Urb-it AB   (1)
Birger Jarlsgatan 57A, 113 56, Stockholm,
Sweden
Tel.: (46) 103300322
Web Site: http://www.urb-it.com
Rev.: $1,533,325
Assets: $13,575,296
Liabilities: $6,034,414
Net Worth: $7,540,882
Earnings: ($7,927,875)
Emp.: 150
Fiscal Year-end: 12/31/2020
Logistics & Supply Chain Services
N.A.I.C.S.: 541614
Kevin Kviblad (CEO)

FIN RESOURCES LIMITED
Level 1 35 Richardson Street, West
Perth, 6005, WA, Australia
Tel.: (61) 861170453   AU
Web Site:
    https://www.finresources.com.au
Year Founded: 1985
FIN—(ASX)
Rev.: $62,684
Assets: $2,284,028
Liabilities: $492,813
Net Worth: $1,791,215
Earnings: ($2,407,906)
Fiscal Year-end: 06/30/24
Mineral Exploration Services
N.A.I.C.S.: 212220
Aaron Bertolatti (Sec)

FIN.PART S.P.A.
Foro Buonaparte 51, 20121, Milan,
Italy
Tel.: (39) 02 725501
Sales Range: $300-349.9 Million
Emp.: 1,570
Apparels Mfr
N.A.I.C.S.: 315990

FINACCEL PTE LTD.
80 Amoy Street #03-02 Attic Floor,
Singapore, 069899, Singapore
Tel.: (65) 68172710   SG
Web Site: https://finaccel.co
Year Founded: 2015
Financial Technology Company
N.A.I.C.S.: 541511
Akshay Garg (Co-Founder & CEO)

Subsidiaries:

PT Finaccel Teknologi Indonesia   (1)
Dipo Tower Level M Jalan Jenderal Gatot
Subroto Kav 51-52 RW7, Central Jakarta,
10260, Indonesia
Tel.: (62) 212 205 5677
Web Site: https://finaccel.co
Emp.: 100
Financial Technology Company
N.A.I.C.S.: 541511

Subsidiary (Domestic):

PT Krom Bank Indonesia Tbk   (2)
Jl Ir H Juanda No 137, Kecamatan Cob-
long, Bandung, 40132, Indonesia
Tel.: (62) 2150996920

Web Site: https://krom.id
Rev.: $6,576,043
Assets: $100,886,399
Liabilities: $30,257,618
Net Worth: $70,628,781
Earnings: $2,462,291
Emp.: 89
Fiscal Year-end: 12/31/2020
Bank Holding Company
N.A.I.C.S.: 551111
Laniwati Tjandra (Pres)

**FINALYSIS CREDIT & GUAR-
ANTEE CO. LTD.**
17 Damji Shamji Complex Kurla
West, Mumbai, 400070, Maharashtra,
India
Tel.: (91) 22 25158000
Web Site: http://www.finalysis.in
Year Founded: 1988
Sales Range: Less than $1 Million
Financial Lending Services
N.A.I.C.S.: 522220

**FINAM INVESTMENT COM-
PANY JSC**
7/2 Nastas Inskiy Per, 127006, Mos-
cow, Russia
Tel.: (7) 4951346346
Web Site: http://www.finam.ru
Sales Range: Less than $1 Million
Investment Advisory Services
N.A.I.C.S.: 523940

FINANCE HOUSE P.J.S.C.
FH Cube 842 Hazza Bin Zayed The
First St Al Nahyan Zone 1, PO Box
7878, Abu Dhabi, United Arab Emir-
ates
Tel.: (971) 26194000
Web Site:
    https://www.financehouse.ae
Year Founded: 2004
FH—(ABU)
Rev.: $60,104,002
Assets: $752,932,751
Liabilities: $572,718,757
Net Worth: $180,213,994
Earnings: $4,031,854
Fiscal Year-end: 12/31/23
Investment & Financial Services
N.A.I.C.S.: 523999
Mohammed Abdulla Jumaa Alqubaisi
(Chm)

Subsidiaries:

Benyan Development Co. L.L.C.   (1)
102 Arab Tower Hamdan Street, PO Box
60711, Abu Dhabi, 60711, United Arab
Emirates
Tel.: (971) 26724322
Web Site: http://www.benyan.ae
Emp.: 40
Construction Engineering Services
N.A.I.C.S.: 541330
Adnir Eninovic (Gen Mgr)

Emirates National Electromechanical
L.L.C.   (1)
Arab Tower Hamdan Street, PO Box 60711,
Abu Dhabi, 60711, United Arab Emirates
Tel.: (971) 2 6711141
Web Site: http://www.ene-llc.com
Electromechanical Engineering Services
N.A.I.C.S.: 541330
Haffan Younis (Gen Mgr)

FH Capital Limited   (1)
The Gate Level 14, PO Box 74777, Dubai,
United Arab Emirates
Tel.: (971) 43394674
Sales Range: $50-74.9 Million
Emp.: 5
Investment & Asset Management Services
N.A.I.C.S.: 523999

FINANCIA CREDIT, S.A.
Spain Via & Calle Elvira Mendez PH
Delta 5th Floor Office 501, Panama,
Panama
Tel.: (507) 214 6221

Web Site:
http://www.financiacredit.com
Year Founded: 2008
FCRE—(PAN)
Sales Range: Less than $1 Million
Renting Services
N.A.I.C.S.: 522291

FINANCIAL & ENERGY EX-CHANGE LIMITED
Level 1 7 Bridge Street, Sydney, 2000, NSW, Australia
Tel.: (61) 280245200   AU
Wob Sito: http://www.fox.oom.au
Year Founded: 2006
Sales Range: $25-49.9 Million
Emp.: 30
Holding Company; Derivatives & Commodity Exchanges
N.A.I.C.S.: 551112
Brian Price *(Chm)*

Subsidiaries:

Mercari Pty. Ltd.   (1)
Level 1 7 Bridge St, Sydney, 2000, NSW, Australia   **(100%)**
Tel.: (61) 280245200
Web Site: http://www.mercari.com.au
Sales Range: $50-74.9 Million
Emp.: 5
Interest Rate & Foreign Exchange Derivatives Exchange
N.A.I.C.S.: 523210

FINANCIAL COMPANY REAL-INVEST.KZ JSC
st. Amangeldy 59a, 4th floor, 050012, Almaty, Kazakhstan
Tel.: (7) 7272676426
Web Site: http://www.realinvest.kz
REAL—(KAZ)
Sales Range: Less than $1 Million
Financial Services
N.A.I.C.S.: 525990
Elena Vasilieva *(CEO)*

FINANCIAL GROUP FUTURE PJSC
2 Tsvetnoy Boulevard floor 4, Moscow, 127051, Russia
Tel.: (7) 4955454049   RU
Web Site: http://www.futurefg.ru
Year Founded: 1996
FTRE—(RUS)
Investment Management Service
N.A.I.C.S.: 523940
Dmitry Mints *(Chm)*

FINANCIAL INDEX AUSTRALIA PTY LTD.
Level 17 181 William Street, Melbourne, 3000, VIC, Australia
Tel.: (61) 3 9292 0101
Web Site:
http://www.findex.com.au.com
Year Founded: 1987
Retail Financial Planning, Accounting & Wealth Management Services
N.A.I.C.S.: 523940
Spiro Paule *(CEO)*

Subsidiaries:

Crowe Horwath Australasia Ltd.   (1)
Level 17 181 William Street, Melbourne, 3000, VIC, Australia
Tel.: (61) 3 9258 6700
Web Site: http://www.crowehorwath.com.au
Sales Range: $300-349.9 Million
Emp.: 2,622
Accounting, Audit, Tax, Business & Financial Services
N.A.I.C.S.: 541211
Spiro Paule *(CEO)*

Subsidiary (Domestic):

Analysis-one   (2)
Level 16 120 Edward St, Brisbane, 4000, QLD, Australia

Tel.: (61) 7 3233 3555
Web Site: http://www.analysis-one.com
Business Management Consulting Services
N.A.I.C.S.: 541611

Subsidiary (Non-US):

Crowe Horwath (NZ) Ltd   (2)
Level 29 188 Quay Street, Auckland, 1010, New Zealand
Tel.: (64) 93034586
Web Site: http://www.crowehorwath.co.nz
Financial Advisory Services
N.A.I.C.S.: 523940
Glen Gernhoefer *(Principal)*

Subsldlary (Domestlc):

Prescott Securities Limited   (2)
245 Fullarton Road, Eastwood, 5063, SA, Australia
Tel.: (61) 883721300
Web Site:
http://www.prescottsecurities.com.au
Financial Advisory Services
N.A.I.C.S.: 523940
Malcolm Caire *(Mgr-Adviser Svcs)*

Subsidiary (Non-US):

TEO Training Limited   (2)
PO Box 193, Dunedin, 9054, New Zealand
Tel.: (64) 34677000
Web Site: http://www.teo.co.nz
Emp.: 2
Professional Training Services
N.A.I.C.S.: 611430
Kim Kingsley *(Mgr)*

FINANCIAL PARTNERS GROUP CO., LTD.
JP TOWER 29th Floor 2-7-2 Marunouchi, Chiyoda-ku, Tokyo, 100-7029, Japan
Tel.: (81) 352885692
Web Site: https://www.fpg.jp
Year Founded: 2001
7148—(TKS)
Rev.: $750,155,760
Assets: $1,605,108,240
Liabilities: $1,233,938,400
Net Worth: $371,169,840
Earnings: $142,380,720
Emp.: 355
Fiscal Year-end: 09/30/24
Leasing Services
N.A.I.C.S.: 522310
Hisanaga Tanimura *(Founder, CEO & Exec Officer)*

Subsidiaries:

FPG Amentum Limited   (1)
4th Floor Mespil Court Mespil Road, Dublin, Ireland
Tel.: (353) 1 639 8111
Web Site: https://www.fpg-amentum.aero
Aircraft Lesser Services
N.A.I.C.S.: 532411
Martin Bouzaima *(CEO)*

FINANCIAL SERVICES COMPANY SAOG
Building no 1480 - Way no 3518, PO Box 2777, 112, Ruwi, Oman
Tel.: (968) 24825600
Web Site: https://www.fscoman.net
Year Founded: 1989
FSCI—(MUS)
Rev.: $834,796
Assets: $13,352,978
Liabilities: $5,384,023
Net Worth: $7,968,955
Earnings: ($805,478)
Emp.: 20
Fiscal Year-end: 12/31/23
Financial Investment Services
N.A.I.C.S.: 523999

FINANCIAL STREET HOLDING CO., LTD.
Block D Financial Street Apartment

No 7 Jinchengfang Stree, Xicheng, Beijing, 100033, China
Tel.: 1066573088
Web Site: https://www.jrjkg.com.cn
Year Founded: 1995
000402—(SSE)
Rev.: $2,879,011,512
Assets: $21,487,360,752
Liabilities: $15,531,473,412
Net Worth: $5,955,887,340
Earnings: $118,828,944
Fiscal Year-end: 12/31/22
Holding Company
N.A.I.C.S.: 551112
Yang Yang *(Chm)*

FINANCIAL STREET PROP-ERTY COMPANY LIMITED
Office Building T2 Xihuan Plaza Xizhimen Outer Street, Xicheng District, Beijing, China
Tel.: (86) 1066218966   Ky
Web Site: https://www.jrjlife.com
Year Founded: 1994
1502—(HKG)
Property Management Services
N.A.I.C.S.: 531311
Lv Bin *(Deputy Gen Mgr)*

FINANCIERA CONFIANZA S.A.A
441 Calle Las Begonias, San Isidro, Lima, 15046, Peru
Tel.: (51) 2089000
Web Site: https://confianza.pe
FCONFIC1—(LIM)
Sales Range: Less than $1 Million
Financial Services
N.A.I.C.S.: 522320

FINANCIERA EFECTIVA SA
Jiron Santorin N 167 Urbanizacion el Vivero Santiago de Surco, Lima, Peru
Tel.: (51) 16412412
Web Site:
https://www.efectiva.com.pe
EFECTIC1—(LIM)
Rev.: $440,920,303
Assets: $601,633,876
Liabilities: $443,494,184
Net Worth: $158,139,692
Earnings: $2,597,900
Fiscal Year-end: 12/31/23
Financial Banking Services
N.A.I.C.S.: 522110
Manuel Emilio Tudela Gubbins *(Chm)*

FINANCIERA FAMILIAR, S.A.
Calle 42 & Avenida Cuba Bella Vista, Panama, Panama
Tel.: (507) 800 3432
Web Site:
http://www.financierafamiliar.com
Year Founded: 1988
FFAM—(PAN)
Sales Range: Less than $1 Million
Renting Services
N.A.I.C.S.: 522291
Richard Kilborn *(Pres)*

FINANCIERA INDEPENDEN-CIA, S.A.B. DE C.V., SOFOM, E.N.R.
Extension of the reforma walk No 600-420, Pena Blanca Sante Fe, 01210, Mexico, Mexico
Tel.: (52) 5552290200
Web Site:
https://www.independencia.com.mx
Year Founded: 1993
FINDEP—(MEX)
Rev.: $283,621,872
Assets: $621,913,675
Liabilities: $308,968,621
Net Worth: $312,945,053
Earnings: $41,833,199

Emp.: 4,473
Fiscal Year-end: 12/31/23
Investment Management Service
N.A.I.C.S.: 523940
Jose Maria Cid Michavila *(CFO)*

FINANCIERA QAPAQ S.A.
Av Faustino Sanchez Carrion No 455, Magdalena del Mar, Lima, Peru
Tel.: (51) 2054320
Web Site: http://www.qapaq.pe
Year Founded: 2009
QAPAQC1—(LIM)
Sales Range: Less than $1 Million
Financial Services
N.A.I.C.S.: 523999
Hector Gonzalo Martinez Figueroa *(Chm)*

FINANCIERE DE L'ODET
31-32 quai de Dion-Boutonx, 92811, Puteaux, Cedex, France
Tel.: (33) 146964433
Web Site: http://www.financiere-odet.fr
ODET—(EUR)
Sales Range: $25-49.9 Billion
Emp.: 81,003
Holding Company; Logistics Services; Plastic Products Mfr; Media Services
N.A.I.C.S.: 551112
Vincent Claude Henri Bollore *(Chm)*

Subsidiaries:

Alraine Shipping Agencies Ltd.   (1)
28 Burma Road Apapa, Lagos, Nigeria
Tel.: (234) 14600340
Transport & Logistic Services
N.A.I.C.S.: 541614
Fidelia Aluku *(Mgr-Customer Svcs)*

Ami (Tanzania) Ltd.   (1)
Nelson Mandela Road Plot 27 -1/2/3 Tabata, Dar es Salaam, Tanzania
Tel.: (255) 222401016
Transport & Logistic Services
N.A.I.C.S.: 541614

Ascens Services SAS   (1)
Abidjan Marcory Zone 4, BP 54, Abidjan, Cote d'Ivoire
Tel.: (225) 21356735
Web Site: http://www.ascens-services.talent-soft.com
Information Technology Services
N.A.I.C.S.: 541512

Automatic Control Systems Inc.   (1)
45 Rockefeller Plz Ste 2000, New York, NY 10111
Automatic Entrance Control Equipment Distr
N.A.I.C.S.: 423610

Automatic Systems (Belgium) SA   (1)
5 Avenue Mercator, 1300, Wavre, Belgium
Tel.: (32) 10230211
Electric Equipment Mfr
N.A.I.C.S.: 335312

Automatic Systems Equipment UK Ltd.   (1)
Units 3 and 10 Adams House Northampton Science Park Kings Park Rd, Northampton, NN3 6LG, United Kingdom
Tel.: (44) 1604654210
Electric Equipment Mfr
N.A.I.C.S.: 335312

Automatic Systems Espanola SA   (1)
Calle de la Torre de Don Miguel 23, 28031, Madrid, Spain
Tel.: (34) 916590766
Electric Equipment Mfr
N.A.I.C.S.: 335312

Benin Terminal S.A.   (1)
Zone Portuaire Boulevard de France Rue 230 Ilot 2287, Parcelle A Quartier Zongo Ehuru, Cotonou, Benin
Tel.: (229) 21368300
Transport & Logistic Services
N.A.I.C.S.: 541614

Blue Point London Ltd.   (1)

Financiere de L'Odet—(Continued)

5 Cavendish Square, London, W1G 0PG, United Kingdom
Tel.: (44) 2030568989
Web Site: http://www.sourcelondon.net
Electric Vehicle Charging Services
N.A.I.C.S.: 457120
Jean-Christophe Court (COO)

Bluecity UK Ltd. (1)
5 Cavendish Square, London, W1G 0PG, United Kingdom
Tel.: (44) 3454040506
Web Site: http://www.blue-city.co.uk
Automobile Vehicle Distr
N.A.I.C.S.: 423110
Frederic Le Ballois (Gen Mgr)

Bluecub SAS (1)
23 rue du Professeur Victor Pauchet, 92420, Vaucresson, France
Tel.: (33) 556393939
Web Site: http://www.bluecub.eu
Automobile Vehicle Distr
N.A.I.C.S.: 423110

Bluelib SAS (1)
23 rue du Professeur Victor Pauchet, 92420, Vaucresson, France
Tel.: (33) 185151599
Web Site: http://www.bluelib.fr
Electric Vehicle Charging Services
N.A.I.C.S.: 457120

Bluely SAS (1)
23 rue du Professeur Victor Pauchet, 92420, Vaucresson, France
Tel.: (33) 472696969
Web Site: http://www.bluely.eu
Electric Vehicle Charging Services
N.A.I.C.S.: 457120

Bluetorino Srl (1)
Via Giuseppe Giacosa 38, 10125, Turin, Italy
Tel.: (39) 0115790030
Web Site: http://www.bluetorino.eu
Automotive Repair Services
N.A.I.C.S.: 811111

Bollore Africa Logistics (SL) Ltd. (1)
Deep Water Quay, Cline Town, Freetown, Sierra Leone
Tel.: (232) 76608226
Transport & Logistic Services
N.A.I.C.S.: 541614

Bollore Africa Logistics Angola Limitada (1)
Estrada de Cacuaco No 288, Luanda, Angola
Tel.: (244) 222015730
Transport & Logistic Services
N.A.I.C.S.: 541614
Jean Claude Junin (Mng Dir)

Bollore Africa Logistics Maroc SA (1)
43 Avenue Khalid Bnou Loualid Ain Sebaa, Casablanca, 20250, Morocco
Tel.: (212) 522351990
Transport & Logistic Services
N.A.I.C.S.: 541614

Bollore Logistics (Cambodia) Ltd. (1)
42 Street 222 Sangkat Boeung Raing, Phnom Penh, Cambodia
Tel.: (855) 23427955
Transport & Logistic Services
N.A.I.C.S.: 541614
Socheat Teav (Mgr-HR & Admin)

Bollore Logistics (Shanghai) Co. Ltd. (1)
No 389 Huajing Road Wai Gao Qiao Free Trade Zone, Shanghai, 200131, China
Tel.: (86) 2150482000
Transport & Logistic Services
N.A.I.C.S.: 541614
Flavien Mao (Acct Mgr)

Bollore Logistics Argentina SA (1)
San Jeronimo 167 Floor 5 Of A, X5000IYG, Cordoba, Argentina
Tel.: (54) 3514741195
Transport & Logistic Services
N.A.I.C.S.: 541614

Bollore Logistics Asia-Pacific Corporate Pte. Ltd. (1)

1 Magazine Road 06-03 Central Mall, Singapore, 059567, Singapore
Tel.: (65) 64168385
Web Site:
N.A.I.C.S.: 541614
Nora Wong (Reg Mgr-Acct)

Bollore Logistics Australia Pty. Ltd. (1)
Unit 14 and 15 2-12 Beauchamp Road, Botany Bay Industrial Estate, Banksmeadow, 2019, NSW, Australia
Tel.: (61) 283363900
Transport & Logistic Services
N.A.I.C.S.: 541614
Liam Butler (Ops Mgr)

Bollore Logistics Belgium NV (1)
Rijnkaai 37, 2000, Antwerp, Belgium
Tel.: (32) 32345590
Transport & Logistic Services
N.A.I.C.S.: 541614
Dirk Jacobs (CEO)

Bollore Logistics Brazil Ltda (1)
Rua Do Rocio 313-7 andar-Vila Olimpia, 04552-904, Sao Paulo, Brazil
Tel.: (55) 1138978422
Transport & Logistic Services
N.A.I.C.S.: 541614

Bollore Logistics Canada Inc. (1)
3400 Douglas B Floreani, Ville Saint Laurent, H4S 1V2, QC, Canada
Tel.: (514) 956-7870
Transport & Logistic Services
N.A.I.C.S.: 541614
Patrick Lafrance (CEO)

Bollore Logistics Chile SA (1)
Almirante Pastene 333 Piso 9-Providencia, 7500506, Santiago, Chile
Tel.: (56) 24984400
Transport & Logistic Services
N.A.I.C.S.: 541614
Jorge Barros (Mng Dir)

Bollore Logistics China Co. Ltd. (1)
24th Floor East Building New Hualian Mansion 755 Middle Huaihai Road, Shanghai, 200020, China
Tel.: (86) 2133950600
Transport & Logistic Services
N.A.I.C.S.: 541614

Bollore Logistics Czech Republic s.r.o. (1)
Fugnerovo nabr 2506, 760 01, Zlin, Czech Republic
Tel.: (420) 577220723
Transport & Logistic Services
N.A.I.C.S.: 541614

Bollore Logistics Germany GmbH (1)
CargoCity Sued-Geb 571, 60549, Frankfurt, Germany
Tel.: (49) 69697155100
Transport & Logistic Services
N.A.I.C.S.: 541614
Thomas Kuhn (COO)

Bollore Logistics Guadeloupe SAS (1)
Zone Franche Cee Batiment C Z I de Jarry, 97122, La Baie Mahault, Guadeloupe
Tel.: (590) 590268589
Transport & Logistic Services
N.A.I.C.S.: 541614

Bollore Logistics Hong Kong Ltd. (1)
5/F Magnet Place Tower 1 77-81 Container Port Road, Kwai Chung, New Territories, China (Hong Kong)
Tel.: (852) 27652000
Transport & Logistic Services
N.A.I.C.S.: 541614
Joey Lam (Acct Mgr)

Bollore Logistics India Ltd. (1)
Kankaria Court 5th Floor 7 Kyd Street, Kolkata, 700016, West Bengal, India
Tel.: (91) 3366800700
Transport & Logistic Services
N.A.I.C.S.: 541614
Biswajit Das (Mgr-Sea Freight)

Bollore Logistics Japan KK (1)
Higashi-Yaesu City Bldg 5th Floor 3-14-2 Hatchobori, Chuo-ku, Tokyo, 104-0032, Japan

Tel.: (81) 355417339
Transport & Logistic Services
N.A.I.C.S.: 541614

Bollore Logistics Korea Co. Ltd. (1)
Room 102 Kunshin 2nd New building 16 Samgaero, Mapo-gu, 04173, Seoul, Korea (South)
Tel.: (82) 267199100
Transport & Logistic Services
N.A.I.C.S.: 541614
Yoon-Ju Cho (Mng Dir)

Bollore Logistics Lao Ltd. (1)
House 069/Unit 04 Ban Watnak, PO Box 2289, Sissattanak District, Vientiane, Lao People's Democratic Republic
Tel.: (856) 21315262
Transport & Logistic Services
N.A.I.C.S.: 541614
Eric Delgrange (Gen Mgr)

Bollore Logistics Luxembourg SA (1)
Offices F 2040 New Cargo Centre Luxembourg Airport, 1360, Luxembourg, Luxembourg
Tel.: (352) 348999
Transport & Logistic Services
N.A.I.C.S.: 541614
Astrid Vanier (Acct Mgr-Global)

Bollore Logistics Martinique SAS (1)
ZIP de la Pointe des Grives, 97200, Fort-de-France, Martinique
Tel.: (596) 596603232
Transport & Logistic Services
N.A.I.C.S.: 541614

Bollore Logistics Mayotte SARL (1)
ZI Vallee III, 97690, Longoni, Mayotte, France
Tel.: (33) 269640990
Transport & Logistic Services
N.A.I.C.S.: 541614

Bollore Logistics Mexico, SA de CV (1)
Lago Victoria 74 Piso 8 Colonia Granada, 11520, Mexico, Mexico
Tel.: (52) 5543347000
Transport & Logistic Services
N.A.I.C.S.: 541614
Kai Schmersahl (CEO)

Bollore Logistics Netherlands BV (1)
Breguetlaan 67, 1438 BD, Oude Meer, Netherlands
Tel.: (31) 206588900
Transport & Logistic Services
N.A.I.C.S.: 541614
Jolanda Verbruggen-Gnirrep (Mgr-HR)

Bollore Logistics New Zealand Ltd. (1)
7 Landing Drive Airport Oaks, Mangere, Auckland, New Zealand
Tel.: (64) 92753223
Transport & Logistic Services
N.A.I.C.S.: 541614
Michael Peterson (Country Mgr)

Bollore Logistics Norway AS (1)
Drammensveien 167, 0277, Oslo, Norway
Tel.: (47) 21953030
Transport & Logistic Services
N.A.I.C.S.: 541614

Bollore Logistics Nouvelle-Caledonie SA (1)
ZI Ducos 18 rue Fernand Forest, BP 1425, 98845, Noumea, New Caledonia
Tel.: (687) 283243
Transport & Logistic Services
N.A.I.C.S.: 541614
Pauline Delathiere (Mgr-Customer Svc)

Bollore Logistics Poland sp. z.o.o. (1)
ul Janka Wisniewskiego 31, 81-156, Gdynia, Poland
Tel.: (48) 58623747
Transport & Logistic Services
N.A.I.C.S.: 541614

Bollore Logistics Polynesie SAS (1)
Zone 7 Aeroport, BP 20359, 98713, Papeete, French Polynesia
Tel.: (689) 40866269
Web Site: http://www.bollore-logistics-polynesie.com
Transport & Logistic Services

N.A.I.C.S.: 541614

Bollore Logistics Portugal Lda (1)
Azinhaga dos Lameiros CPL Edificio 9, 1600-485, Lisbon, Portugal
Tel.: (351) 217102900
Transport & Logistic Services
N.A.I.C.S.: 541614

Bollore Logistics Reunion SAS (1)
ZAC Ravine a Marquet 3 Rue Gustave Eiffe, 97419, La Possession, Reunion
Tel.: (262) 262220040
Transport & Logistic Services
N.A.I.C.S.: 541614

Bollore Logistics Singapore Pte. Ltd. (1)
101 ALPS Ave 03-01, Singapore, 498793, Singapore
Tel.: (65) 64168333
Transport & Logistic Services
N.A.I.C.S.: 541614
Kelvin Lai (Mgr-Customer Svc)

Bollore Logistics Taiwan Ltd. (1)
Pa-Teh Road Sec 4 Lane 768 9FL No 18 Alley 1, Taipei, 115, Taiwan
Tel.: (886) 227823360
Transport & Logistic Services
N.A.I.C.S.: 541614
Alexandre Pezant (Gen Sls Mgr)

Bollore Logistics Tanger Med SA (1)
Quartier Gueznaya Route Sidi Kacem Boukhalef, 90000, Tangiers, Morocco
Tel.: (212) 539393989
Transport & Logistic Services
N.A.I.C.S.: 541614

Bollore Logistics UK Ltd. (1)
Unit 1 Skyline Great South West Road Heathrow, London, TW14 8NT, United Kingdom
Tel.: (44) 2038977800
Transport & Logistic Services
N.A.I.C.S.: 541614
Tom Walsh (Comml Dir)

Bollore Logistics Vietnam Co. Ltd. (1)
Etown 2 Building 6th Floor 364 Cong Hoa Street, Tan Binh District, Ho Chi Minh City, Vietnam
Tel.: (84) 2838120602
Transport & Logistic Services
N.A.I.C.S.: 541614
Dung Vuong (Mgr-HR & Admin)

Bollore Media Regie SA (1)
31-32 Quai de Dion Bouton, 92800, Puteaux, France
Tel.: (33) 146964841
Web Site: http://www.bolloremediaregie.com
Media Advertising Services
N.A.I.C.S.: 541810

Bollore S.A. (1)
Bollore Tower 31-32 quai de Dion Bouton, 92811, Puteaux, Cedex, France
Tel.: (33) 146964433
Web Site: https://www.bollore.com
Rev.: $22,313,727,606
Assets: $54,060,220,160
Liabilities: $22,733,110,296
Net Worth: $31,327,109,864
Earnings: $2,930,606,518
Emp.: 74,325
Fiscal Year-end: 12/31/2022
Holding Company
N.A.I.C.S.: 551112
Cedric de Bailliencourt (Vice Chm)

Division (Domestic):

A.M. Productions (2)
14 chemin de la Litte, 92397, Villeneuve-la-Garenne, France
Tel.: (33) 141473636
Web Site: http://www.amprod.com
Sales Range: $10-24.9 Million
Emp.: 20
Business Support Services
N.A.I.C.S.: 561499

Subsidiary (Domestic):

Blue Solutions S.A. (2)
Tour Bollore 31-32, quai de Dion-Bouton, 92811, Puteaux, Cedex, France (96.6%)
Tel.: (33) 146964433

Web Site: http://www.blue-solutions.com
Rev.: $43,703,072
Earnings: ($38,167,129)
Emp.: 423
Fiscal Year-end: 12/31/2018
Lithium Battery Mfr & Distr
N.A.I.C.S.: 335910

Division (Domestic):

Bollore Energie (2)
Tour Bollore 31-32 Quai de Dion Bouton,
92811, Puteaux, Cedex, France
Tel.: (33) 146964433
Web Site: http://www.bollore-energy.com
Sales Range: $25-49.9 Million
Emp.: 55
Logistics & Fuel Distribution Services
N.A.I.C.S.: 488510

Bollore Intermedia (2)
31-32 quai de Dion-Bouton, 92811, Pu-
teaux, Cedex, France
Tel.: (33) 146963128
Advertising Services
N.A.I.C.S.: 541810

Bollore Plastic Film Division (2)
Odet Ergue Gaberic, 29556, Quimper, Ce-
dex, France
Tel.: (33) 298667200
Web Site: http://www.bollorefilms.com
Plastics Films Mfr
N.A.I.C.S.: 326199

Direct Matin plus (2)
31-32 quai de Dion-Bouton, 92800, Pu-
teaux, France
Tel.: (33) 146963100
Web Site: http://directmatin.directmedia.fr
Sales Range: $150-199.9 Million
Emp.: 800
Newspaper Publishers
N.A.I.C.S.: 513110

IER (2)
3 Rue Salomon de Rothschild, BP 320,
92150, Suresnes, Cedex, France
Tel.: (33) 141386000
Web Site: http://www.ier.com
Sales Range: $150-199.9 Million
Emp.: 800
Ticket Machines & Terminals for Boarding
Control & Secure Automated Processing of
Passengers & Baggage
N.A.I.C.S.: 333310

Subsidiary (Domestic):

**SAS des Domaines de la Bastide et
de la Croix** (2)
Boulevard de Taberin, La Croix Valmer,
France
Tel.: (33) 494950175
Web Site: http://www.domainedelacroix.com
Sales Range: $25-49.9 Million
Emp.: 20
Wine Producer & Sales
N.A.I.C.S.: 312130

Division (Domestic):

SDV International Logistics (2)
Tour Bollore 31-32 quai de Dion Bouton,
Puteaux, 92811, France
Tel.: (33) 146964433
Web Site: http://www.sdv.com
Sales Range: $1-4.9 Billion
Emp.: 15,000
Transportation & Logistics Services
N.A.I.C.S.: 541614

Subsidiary (US):

SDV (USA) Inc. (3)
15010 132nd Ave, Jamaica, NY 11434
Tel.: (718) 525-8100
Web Site: http://www.sdvusa.com
Rev.: $117,644,232
Emp.: 150
Foreign Freight Forwarding
N.A.I.C.S.: 488510

**Bollore Transport & Logistics (SL)
Ltd.** (1)
Deep Water Quay, PO Box 569, Cline
Town, Freetown, Sierra Leone
Tel.: (232) 76608226
Transport & Logistic Services
N.A.I.C.S.: 541614

**Bollore Transport & Logistics Bo-
tswana (Pty) Ltd.** (1)
Plot 5625 Lejara Road, Broadhurst Indus-
trial, Gaborone, Botswana
Tel.: (267) 3951961
Transport & Logistic Services
N.A.I.C.S.: 541614

**Bollore Transport & Logistics Burundi
SA** (1)
BP 1306, Bujumbura, Burundi
Tel.: (257) 22224849
Transport & Logistic Services
N.A.I.C.S.: 541614
Jimbere Carmel *(Mgr-Customer Ops)*

**Bollore Transport & Logistics Camer-
oun SA** (1)
BP 4057, Douala, Cameroon
Tel.: (237) 33501212
Transport & Logistic Services
N.A.I.C.S.: 541614

**Bollore Transport & Logistics Cen-
trafrique SA** (1)
BP 32, Bangui, Central African Republic
Tel.: (236) 21614822
Transport & Logistic Services
N.A.I.C.S.: 541614

**Bollore Transport & Logistics Congo
SA** (1)
Avenue de Loango, Pointe Noire, Congo,
Republic of
Tel.: (242) 57750701
Transport & Logistic Services
N.A.I.C.S.: 541614
Katelijne Verschaeren *(Mgr-Comml)*

**Bollore Transport & Logistics Cote
d'Ivoire SA** (1)
1 Avenue Christiani 01, Treichville, Abidjan,
Cote d'Ivoire
Tel.: (225) 21220420
Transport & Logistic Services
N.A.I.C.S.: 541614
Thibault Motte *(Mgr-Logistics & Export)*

**Bollore Transport & Logistics Gambia
Ltd.** (1)
PO Box 257, Banjul, Gambia
Tel.: (220) 4227518
Transport & Logistic Services
N.A.I.C.S.: 541614

**Bollore Transport & Logistics Guinee
SA** (1)
BP 2011, Conakry, Guinea
Tel.: (224) 622356400
Transport & Logistic Services
N.A.I.C.S.: 541614

**Bollore Transport & Logistics Kenya
Ltd.** (1)
PO Box 46586-00100, Nairobi, 100, Kenya
Tel.: (254) 206421000
Transport & Logistic Services
N.A.I.C.S.: 541614

**Bollore Transport & Logistics Lekki
FZE** (1)
Lekki Free Trade Zone Ibeju Lekki Akodo,
Tiye Town, Lagos, Nigeria
Tel.: (234) 8090493964
Transport & Logistic Services
N.A.I.C.S.: 541614

**Bollore Transport & Logistics
Madagascar** (1)
BP 411, Toamasina, 501, Madagascar
Tel.: (261) 205347109
Transport & Logistic Services
N.A.I.C.S.: 541614

**Bollore Transport & Logistics Malawi
Ltd.** (1)
PO Box 838, Blantyre, Malawi
Tel.: (265) 1871555
Transport & Logistic Services
N.A.I.C.S.: 541614

**Bollore Transport & Logistics
Mali** (1)
BP 2454, Bamako, Mali
Tel.: (223) 44976500
Transport & Logistic Services
N.A.I.C.S.: 541614

**Bollore Transport & Logistics Maroc
SA** (1)
43 Avenue Khalid Bnou Loualid Ain Sebaa,
20250, Casablanca, Morocco
Tel.: (212) 522351990
Transport & Logistic Services
N.A.I.C.S.: 541614

**Bollore Transport & Logistics Mocam-
bique SA** (1)
PO Box 72, Beira, Mozambique
Tel.: (258) 23324001
Transport & Logistic Services
N.A.I.C.S.: 541614

**Bollore Transport & Logistics Namibia
Proprietary Ltd.** (1)
Pro Industrial Park, Windhoek, Namibia
Tel.: (264) 61223230
Transport & Logistic Services
N.A.I.C.S.: 541614

**Bollore Transport & Logistics Nigeria
Ltd.** (1)
26 Creek Road Apapa, PO Box 265, Lagos,
Nigeria
Tel.: (234) 146005414
Transport & Logistic Services
N.A.I.C.S.: 541614

**Bollore Transport & Logistics RDC
SA** (1)
Quartier Kingabwa, Kinshasa, Congo,
Democratic Republic of
Tel.: (243) 815563445
Transport & Logistic Services
N.A.I.C.S.: 541614

**Bollore Transport & Logistics Rwanda
Ltd.** (1)
PO Box 1338, Gasabo District, Kigali,
Rwanda
Tel.: (250) 252575584
Transport & Logistic Services
N.A.I.C.S.: 541614

**Bollore Transport & Logistics South
Africa (Pty.) Ltd.** (1)
24 Covora Street Jet Park, 1469, Boksburg,
South Africa
Tel.: (27) 113985000
Transport & Logistic Services
N.A.I.C.S.: 541614

**Bollore Transport & Logistics Tanza-
nia Ltd.** (1)
PO Box 9041, Dar es Salaam, Tanzania
Tel.: (255) 222401016
Transport & Logistic Services
N.A.I.C.S.: 541614

**Bollore Transport & Logistics Togo
Co., Ltd.** (1)
BP 34, Lome, Togo
Tel.: (228) 22275878
Transport & Logistic Services
N.A.I.C.S.: 541614

**Bollore Transport & Logistics Tunisie
SA** (1)
Zone Portuaire Route du Port, 2040,
Rades, Tunisia
Tel.: (216) 71449651
Transport & Logistic Services
N.A.I.C.S.: 541614

**Bollore Transport & Logistics Uganda
Ltd.** (1)
PO Box 5501, Kampala, Uganda
Tel.: (256) 414336000
Transport & Logistic Services
N.A.I.C.S.: 541614

**Bollore Transport & Logistics Zambia
Ltd.** (1)
PO Box 30131, Heavy Industrial Area,
10101, Lusaka, Zambia
Tel.: (260) 211246191
Transport & Logistic Services
N.A.I.C.S.: 541614

**Bollore Transport & Logistics Zimba-
bwe (Private) Ltd.** (1)
PO Box HG 89, Harare, Zimbabwe
Tel.: (263) 4335534
Transport & Logistic Services
N.A.I.C.S.: 541614

**Bollore Transport Logistics Corporate
SAS** (1)
Tour Bollore 31-32 Quai de Dion Bouton,
Puteaux, 92811, France

Tel.: (33) 146964433
Transport & Logistic Services
N.A.I.C.S.: 541614

**Bollore Transport Logistics Spain
SA** (1)
Av Aragon 30-5 A Edificio Europa, Valencia,
46021, Spain
Tel.: (34) 963939850
Transport & Logistic Services
N.A.I.C.S.: 541614

**Burkina Logistics & Mining Services
SA** (1)
01 BP 379, Ouagadougou, Burkina Faso
Tel.: (226) 50493000
Transport & Logistic Services
N.A.I.C.S.: 488510

CICA SA (1)
Hochbergerstrasse 60a, 4057, Basel, Swit-
zerland
Tel.: (41) 616388500
Web Site: http://www.cica.ch
Oil & Energy Whslr
N.A.I.C.S.: 424720
S. Villiger *(CEO)*

Calpam Mineralol GmbH (1)
Schillerstrasse 98, 63741, Aschaffenburg,
Germany
Tel.: (49) 602140260
Web Site: http://www.calpam.com
Petroleum Product Distr
N.A.I.C.S.: 424720

**Cherbourg Maritime Voyages
SARL** (1)
Zone portuaire des Mielles, Tourlaville,
50110, France
Tel.: (33) 234000000
Transport & Logistic Services
N.A.I.C.S.: 541614

DME Almy SA (1)
Boulevard Henri Martel, Avion, 62210,
France
Tel.: (33) 321282009
Transport & Logistic Services
N.A.I.C.S.: 541614

Deutsche Calpam GmbH (1)
Grosse Elbstrasse 141 a, 22767Hamburg,
Hamburg, Germany
Tel.: (49) 403068620
Web Site: http://www.calpam-hamburg.de
Petroleum Product Distr
N.A.I.C.S.: 424720
Stefan Facklam *(Mng Dir)*

EUSU Logistics Spain SA (1)
Paseo de la Alameda 35-Bis-4 Izq, 46023,
Valencia, Spain
Tel.: (34) 963939700
Transport & Logistic Services
N.A.I.C.S.: 541614

**East Africa Commercial & Shipping
Co., Ltd.** (1)
Changamwe Roundabout Changamwe,
Mombasa, 80107, Kenya
Tel.: (254) 413434395
Transport & Logistic Services
N.A.I.C.S.: 541614

Hello Fioul SA (1)
31-32 Quai de Dion Bouton, 92800, Pu-
teaux, France
Tel.: (33) 969392404
Web Site: http://www.hello-fioul.fr
Petroleum Product Distr
N.A.I.C.S.: 424720

Lome Multipurpose Terminal SA (1)
Zone Portuaire, BP 34, Lome, Togo
Tel.: (228) 307085000
Transport & Logistic Services
N.A.I.C.S.: 541614

Niger Terminal SA (1)
Rue de la Libye, Niamey, Nigeria
Tel.: (234) 20732201
Transport & Logistic Services
N.A.I.C.S.: 541614

**Owendo Container Terminal
SARL** (1)
Zone portuaire d Owendo, Libreville, Gabon
Tel.: (241) 1704718
Transport & Logistic Services
N.A.I.C.S.: 541614

Financiere de L'Odet—(Continued)

PT Bollore Logistics Indonesia (1)
Soewarna Business Park Unit E8 Block B
Lot 7-8, Soekarno-Hatta Intl Airport, 19110,
Jakarta, Indonesia
Tel.: (62) 2155911717
Transport & Logistic Services
N.A.I.C.S.: 541614

Saga Gabon SA (1)
Zone Portuaire Oprag, Port-Gentil, Gabon
Tel.: (241) 551553
Transport & Logistic Services
N.A.I.C.S.: 541614

Saga Reunion SA (1)
Z A C Ravine a Marquet 3 Rue Gustave
Eiffel, La Possession, 97419, Reunion
Tel.: (262) 262220170
Transport & Logistic Services
N.A.I.C.S.: 541614

Scanship (Ghana) Ltd. (1)
Commercial Warehouse Road Main Harbour Area, Tema, Ghana
Tel.: (233) 303000000
Transport & Logistic Services
N.A.I.C.S.: 541614

**Societe de Manutention du Terminal
a Conteneurs de Cotonou** (1)
Zone Portuaire Boulevard de France Rue
230 Ilot 2287, Parcelle A Quartier Zongo
Ehuru, Cotonou, Benin
Tel.: (229) 21368300
Transport & Logistic Services
N.A.I.C.S.: 541614

Socopao RDC SA (1)
4200 Av Gen Bobozo Adruma Quartier
Kingabwa, Kinshasa, Congo, Democratic
Republic of
Tel.: (243) 815563445
Transport & Logistic Services
N.A.I.C.S.: 541614

Tema Conteneur Terminal Ltd. (1)
Western Gate Main Harbour Area, Tema,
Ghana
Tel.: (233) 303212340
Transport & Logistic Services
N.A.I.C.S.: 541614

Timor Port SA (1)
Rua Jose Maria Marques, Dili, Timor-Leste
Tel.: (670) 3322818
Transport & Logistic Services
N.A.I.C.S.: 541614

FINANCIERE DE TUBIZE SA
Allee De La Recherche 60, 1070,
Brussels, Belgium
Tel.: (32) 477452713
Web Site: https://www.financiere-
tubize.be
TUB—(EUR)
Rev.: $103,377,100
Assets: $2,119,709,075
Liabilities: $136,494,262
Net Worth: $1,983,214,813
Earnings: $97,307,945
Fiscal Year-end: 12/31/23
Investment Management Service
N.A.I.C.S.: 523940
Francois Tesch (Chm)

FINANCIERE HOCHE BAINS-
LES-BAINS SA
10 place Vendome, 75001, Paris,
France
Tel.: (33) 41217288838
MLHBB—(EUR)
Sales Range: Less than $1 Million
Financial Investment Services
N.A.I.C.S.: 523940

FINANCIERE IMMOBILIERE
ETANG BERRE MEDIT SA
Lou Soulei 5 Avenue Draio del Mar,
13620, Carry-le-Rouet, France
Tel.: (33) 442447575
BERR—(EUR)
Sales Range: $1-9.9 Million
Mobile Home Rental Services

N.A.I.C.S.: 459930
Marie-Catherine Sulitzer (Chm, CEO
& Dir-IR)

FINANCIERE LR SARL
24 rue Emile Menier, Paris, 75116,
France
Tel.: (33) 17856991
Private Investment Firm
N.A.I.C.S.: 523999
Lionel Rozenberg (Owner)

FINANCIERE MARJOS SA
58 avenue de Wagram, 75017, Paris,
France
Tel.: (33) 146946286
Web Site: https://www.financiere-
marjos.com
FINM—(EUR)
Sales Range: Less than $1 Million
Children Apparel Mfr
N.A.I.C.S.: 315250
Lalou Elie Haioun (Chm & CEO)

FINANCIERE MONCEY SA
Tour Bollore 31-32 quai de Dion Bouton, 92800, Puteaux, Cedex, France
Tel.: (33) 146964433
Web Site: https://www.financiere-
moncey.fr
MONC—(EUR)
Sales Range: Less than $1 Million
Holding Company
N.A.I.C.S.: 551112
Francois Laroze (CEO)

FINANCIERE PINAULT SCA
12 rue Francois 1er, 75008, Paris,
France
Tel.: (33) 1.4411.2020   FR
Web Site:
    http://www.groupeartemis.com
Year Founded: 1992
Sales Range: $15-24.9 Billion
Holding Company
N.A.I.C.S.: 551112
Patricia Marie Marguerite Barbizet
(CEO)

Subsidiaries:

ACHP plc (1)
1 Royal Exchange Avenue Suite 306, London, EC3V 3LT, United Kingdom (66.5%)
Tel.: (44) 2074644194
Web Site: http://www.ach-plc.com
Holding Company; Insurance Consulting &
Outsourcing Services
N.A.I.C.S.: 551112
Gilles Erulin (CEO)

Subsidiary (Domestic):

Pro Insurance Solutions Limited (2)
Floor 6 Walsingham House 35 Seething
Lane, London, EC3N 4AH, United Kingdom
Tel.: (44) 2070688000
Web Site: http://www.pro-global.com
Sales Range: $150-199.9 Million
Emp.: 300
Insurance Consulting & Outsourcing Services
N.A.I.C.S.: 541611
Simon Byrne (CFO)

Artemis S.A. (1)
12 rue Francois 1ER, Paris, 75008, France
Tel.: (33) 1.4411.2020
Web Site: http://www.groupeartemis.com
Investment Holding Company
N.A.I.C.S.: 551112

Holding (Domestic):

Capi France (2)
L'Aeroplane - Bat C - ZAC de l'aeroport 99,
34470, Perols, France
Tel.: (33) 4 67 92 46 77
Web Site: http://www.capifrance.fr
Real Estate Consulting Service
N.A.I.C.S.: 531210

L'Agefi (2)

8 Rue Du Sentier, 75002, Paris, Cedex,
France
Tel.: (33) 176410308
Web Site: http://www.agefi.fr
Financial Management Services
N.A.I.C.S.: 541611

Le Point (2)
Redaction 74 avenue du Maine, 75014,
Paris, France
Tel.: (33) 1 44 10 10 10
Web Site: http://www.lepoint.fr
Magazine Publisher
N.A.I.C.S.: 513120

Christie's International plc (1)
8 King Street, Saint James's, London,
SW1Y 6QT, United Kingdom (100%)
Tel.: (44) 2078399060
Web Site: http://www.christies.com
Sales Range: $800-899.9 Million
Emp.: 1,517
Holding Company; Auction Houses
N.A.I.C.S.: 551112
Catherine Manson (Global Head-Comm)

Subsidiary (Domestic):

**C.I. Property & Investments
Limited** (2)
8 King Street, Saint James's, London,
SW1Y 6QT, United Kingdom (100%)
Tel.: (44) 2078399060
Web Site: http://www.christies.com
Property Management Services
N.A.I.C.S.: 531312

**Christie Manson & Woods
Limited** (2)
8 King Street, St James, London, SW1Y
6QT, United Kingdom (100%)
Tel.: (44) 2078399060
Web Site: http://www.christies.com
Sales Range: $25-49.9 Million
Emp.: 100
Art Auctioneers
N.A.I.C.S.: 561990

Subsidiary (Domestic):

Christie's South Kensington Ltd. (3)
85 Old Brompton Rd, London, SW7 3LD,
United Kingdom (100%)
Tel.: (44) 2079306074
Web Site: http://www.christies.com
Sales Range: $25-49.9 Million
Emp.: 80
Art Auctioneers
N.A.I.C.S.: 561990

Subsidiary (Non-US):

Christie's (International) S.A. (2)
8 Pl De La Taconnerie, Geneva, 1204,
Switzerland (100%)
Tel.: (41) 223191766
Web Site: http://www.christies.com
Sales Range: $10-24.9 Million
Emp.: 40
Art Auctioneers
N.A.I.C.S.: 561990
Francois Curiel (Chm-Europe)

Branch (Non-US):

**Christie's (International) S.A. - filiale
Italiana, Rome** (3)
Palazzo Massimo Lancellotti Piazza Navona
114, Rome, 00186, Italy
Tel.: (39) 0066863333
Web Site: http://www.christies.com
Sales Range: $10-24.9 Million
Art Auctioneers
N.A.I.C.S.: 561499

Subsidiary (Non-US):

Christie's (Israel) Ltd. (2)
Asia House 4 Weizman St Fl 4, Tel Aviv,
64239, Israel (100%)
Tel.: (972) 36950695
Web Site: http://www.christie.com
Sales Range: $25-49.9 Million
Emp.: 4
Art Auctioneers
N.A.I.C.S.: 561990
Mary Gilben (Chm)

Christie's Amsterdam B.V. (2)
Cornelius Schuystraat 57, Amsterdam, 1071
JG, Netherlands (100%)
Tel.: (31) 205755255

Web Site: http://www.christie.com
Sales Range: $25-49.9 Million
Emp.: 60
Art Auctioneers
Jop Ubbens (Chm)

Christie's Australia Pty. Ltd. (2)
287 New S Head Rd, Edgecliff, 2027, NSW,
Australia (100%)
Tel.: (61) 293261422
Art Auctioneers
N.A.I.C.S.: 561499

Christie's Hong Kong Ltd. (2)
22 Fl Alexandra House 18 Chater Rd Central, Hong Kong, China (Hong
Kong) (100%)
Tel.: (852) 25215396
Web Site: http://www.christies.com
Sales Range: $25-49.9 Million
Emp.: 100
Art Auctioneers
N.A.I.C.S.: 561499
Francois Curiel (Pres)

Subsidiary (US):

Christie's Inc. (2)
20 Rockefeller Plz, New York, NY
10020-1902 (100%)
Tel.: (212) 636-2000
Web Site: http://www.christies.com
Sales Range: $200-249.9 Million
Emp.: 550
Art Auctioneers
N.A.I.C.S.: 455219
Stephen Lash (Chm)

Subsidiary (Non-US):

**Christie's International Singapore Pte.
Ltd.** (2)
501 Orchard Road 1903 Wheelock Place,
22 Scotts Road, Singapore, 238880,
Singapore (100%)
Tel.: (65) 62353828
Web Site: http://www.christies.com
Sales Range: $25-49.9 Million
Emp.: 9
Art Auctioneers
N.A.I.C.S.: 561499
Wen Li Tang (Mng Dir)

Christie's Monaco S.A.M. (2)
4 Avenue des Citronniers Le Mirabel,
98000, Monte Carlo, Monaco (100%)
Tel.: (377) 97971100
Sales Range: $25-49.9 Million
Emp.: 2
Art Auctioneer Services
N.A.I.C.S.: 561499
Nancy Gotta (Gen Mgr)

Subsidiary (Domestic):

Christie's Scotland Limited (2)
5 Wemyss Pl, Edinburgh, EH3 6DH, United
Kingdom (100%)
Tel.: (44) 312254756
Web Site: http://www.christies.com
Sales Range: $25-49.9 Million
Emp.: 5
Art Auctioneers
N.A.I.C.S.: 561499

Subsidiary (Non-US):

Christie's Zurich S.A. (2)
Steinwiesplatz, CH 8032, Zurich,
Switzerland (100%)
Tel.: (41) 442681010
Sales Range: $25-49.9 Million
Emp.: 10
Art Auctioneers
N.A.I.C.S.: 561499

**New California Life Holdings,
Inc.** (1)
1105 N Market St 13th Fl, Wilmington, DE
19801-1216 (67%)
Tel.: (302) 427-2073
Sales Range: $300-349.9 Million
Emp.: 550
Holding Company; Life Insurance & Annuity
Product Administration Services
N.A.I.C.S.: 551112

Subsidiary (Domestic):

**Aurora National Life Assurance
Company** (2)

27201 Tourney Rd Ste 225, Valencia, CA 91355-1804
Tel.: (661) 253-1688
Web Site: http://www.auroralife.com
Life Insurance & Annuity Product Administration Services
N.A.I.C.S.: 524292

Tawa Associates Ltd. **(1)**
Walsingham House 35 Seething Lane, London, EC3N 4AH, United Kingdom
Tel.: (44) 20 3713 2081
Web Site: http://www.tawa.net
Holding Company; Reinsurance Products & Services
N.A.I.C.S.: 551112
Gilles Erulin *(CEO)*

Affiliate (Domestic):

CX Reinsurance Company
Limited **(2)**
Floor 6 Walsingham House 35 Seething Lane, London, EC3N 4AH, United Kingdom **(49.95%)**
Tel.: (44) 2070688000
Web Site: http://www.cxre.com
Reinsurance Products & Services
N.A.I.C.S.: 524130

Joint Venture (US):

Lincoln General Insurance
Company **(2)**
3501 Concord Rd, York, PA 17402-8607 **(51%)**
Tel.: (717) 757-0000
Web Site: http://www.lincolngeneral.com
Property & Casualty Insurance Products & Services
N.A.I.C.S.: 524126
Frank Amodeo *(COO)*

Subsidiary (Domestic):

Tawa Management Ltd. **(2)**
Walsingham House 35 Seething Lane, London, EC3N 4AH, United Kingdom
Tel.: (44) 20 3713 2081
Reinsurance Policy Administration Services
N.A.I.C.S.: 524298
Gilles Erulin *(CEO)*

FINANCIERE QUICK S.A.S.
50 avenue du President Wilson, Parc des Portes de Paris-Bat 123, 93214, La Plaine Saint-Denis, France
Tel.: (33) 1 4951 6464 FR
Web Site: http://groupe.quick.fr
Sales Range: $1-4.9 Billion
Emp.: 19,000
Holding Company; Fast Food Restaurants Owner, Operator & Franchisor
N.A.I.C.S.: 551112
Cedric Dugardin *(Chm-Mgmt Bd & CEO)*

FINANCIERE SNOP DUNOIS SA
Avenue d'Auvergne, 43100, Brioude, France
Tel.: (33) 471504131 FR
Web Site: http://www.snop.fr
Stamping, Roll Forming, Assembly, Automotive Parts & Tools Mfr
N.A.I.C.S.: 811198
Valerie Troubetzkoy *(Dir-Publication)*

Subsidiaries:

Tower Automotive Holdings Europe
B.V. **(1)**
Oude Utrechtseweg 16, 3743 KN, Baarn, Netherlands
Tel.: (31) 355488710
Holding Company
N.A.I.C.S.: 551112

Subsidiary (Non-US):

Tower Automotive Belgium
B.V.B.A. **(2)**
Belgicastraat 5, 9042, Gent, Belgium
Tel.: (32) 92505010
Engineered Structural Metal Component Mfr
N.A.I.C.S.: 332312

Tower Automotive Holding GmbH **(2)**
De-Gasperi-Str 8 Reg Bez Koln Nordrhein Westfalen, 51469, Bergisch Gladbach, Germany
Tel.: (49) 22021030
Web Site: http://www.towerautomotive.com
Sales Range: $25-49.9 Million
Emp.: 150
Automotive Metal Stampings & Tools Mfr
N.A.I.C.S.: 336370

Subsidiary (Domestic):

MT Stahl Handelsgesellschaft
GmbH **(3)**
Am Neumarkt 7, 41564, Kaarst, Germany
Tel.: (49) 2131661900
Web Site: http://www.mt-stahl.de
Motor Vehicle Metal Stamping Services
N.A.I.C.S.: 336370
Andrew Mutz *(Head-Fin)*

Tower Automotive Auslandsbeteiligungen GmbH **(3)**
De-Gasperi-Str 8, 51469, Bergisch Gladbach, Nordrhein-Westfalen, Germany
Tel.: (49) 22021030
Sales Range: $10-24.9 Million
Emp.: 50
Engineered Structural Metal Component Mfr
N.A.I.C.S.: 332312

Tower Automotive Presswerk Zwickau
GmbH **(3)**
Kopernikusstrasse 60, Zwickau, 08056, Germany
Tel.: (49) 37544800
Web Site: http://www.towerautomotive.com
Sales Range: $25-49.9 Million
Automotive Metal Stampings & Tools Mfr
N.A.I.C.S.: 336370

Tower Automotive Umformtechnick
GmbH **(3)**
Waldbitze 20, 53567, Buchholz, Germany
Tel.: (49) 268397840
Web Site: http://www.towerinternational.com
Sales Range: $25-49.9 Million
Emp.: 80
Automotive Metal Stampings & Tools Mfr
N.A.I.C.S.: 336370

Subsidiary (Non-US):

Tower Automotive Polska Sp.
zo.o. **(2)**
Ul Oswiecimska 122 E, 45-641, Opole, Poland
Tel.: (48) 774020200
Web Site: http://www.towerinternational.com
Sales Range: $25-49.9 Million
Automotive Metal Stampings & Tools Mfr
N.A.I.C.S.: 336370

Tower Automotive S.A. **(2)**
Tovarenska 13, 901 01, Malacky, Slovakia
Tel.: (421) 347968325
Automotive Metal Stampings & Tools Mfr
N.A.I.C.S.: 336370

Tower Automotive Spain SL **(2)**
Constitucion 1 Planta 5 A Oficina 3 A, PO Box 2, 8960, Sant Just Desvern, Barcelona, Spain
Tel.: (34) 934700620
Web Site: http://www.towerautomotive.com
Sales Range: $10-24.9 Million
Emp.: 3
Automotive Metal Stampings & Tools Mfr
N.A.I.C.S.: 336370

Tower Italia S.r.l. **(2)**
SS 79 Via Appia Km 191 600, 81052, Pignataro Maggiore, Caserta, Italy
Tel.: (39) 0823503620
Engineered Structural Metal Component Mfr
N.A.I.C.S.: 332312

Subsidiary (Domestic):

Tower Automotive Melfi, S.r.l. **(3)**
85025 Area Industriale S Nicola, Potenza, 85025, Melfi, Italy
Tel.: (39) 0972763211
Web Site: http://www.towerautomotive.com
Sales Range: $25-49.9 Million
Emp.: 120
Automotive Metal Stampings & Tools Mfr
N.A.I.C.S.: 336370

Tower Automotive S.r.L. **(3)**
Via Torino 21 Pianezza, 10044, Turin, Italy
Tel.: (39) 0119990111
Web Site: http://www.towerautomotive.com
Automotive Metal Stampings & Tools Mfr
N.A.I.C.S.: 336370

Tower Automotive Sud S.r.l. **(3)**
Strada Statale 7 Via Appia Km 191600, 81052, Pignataro Maggiore, Italy
Tel.: (39) 0823871666
Web Site: http://www.towerautomotive.com
Automotive Metal Stampings & Tools Mfr
N.A.I.C.S.: 336370

FINANCIERE SYZ & CO SA
Baarerstrasse 112, CH-6302, Zug, Switzerland
Tel.: (41) 41 767 2593 CH
Web Site: http://www.syzgroup.com
Year Founded: 1996
Rev.: $13,466,656
Assets: $2,580,287,291
Liabilities: $2,288,574,512
Net Worth: $291,712,779
Earnings: $2,608,979
Emp.: 389
Fiscal Year-end: 12/31/18
Financial Holding Company
N.A.I.C.S.: 551111
Eric Max Charles Syz *(CEO-Grp)*

Subsidiaries:

Banque SYZ SA **(1)**
Quai des Bergues 1, 1201, Geneva, Switzerland
Tel.: (41) 58 799 1000
Web Site: http://www.syzgroup.com
Private Banking
N.A.I.C.S.: 523150
Eric Max Charles Syz *(CEO)*

SYZ Asset Management (Suisse)
SA **(1)**
Rue du Rhone 30, Case Postale 5015, 1211, Geneva, Switzerland
Tel.: (41) 58 799 1800
Web Site: http://www.syzgroup.com
Asset Management Services
N.A.I.C.S.: 523940
Florent Guy-Ducrot *(Head-Bus Dev)*

Sinwa Australia Pty Limited **(1)**
39 Jessie Lee Street, Henderson, 6166, WA, Australia
Tel.: (61) 894947500
Logistic Services
N.A.I.C.S.: 541614

Windsor Marine Pte. Ltd. **(1)**
28 Joo Koon Circle, Singapore, 629057, Singapore
Tel.: (65) 63491930
Web Site: http://www.windsormarine.com.sg
Marine Equipment & Accessory Whslr
N.A.I.C.S.: 423860

FINANSIA SYRUS SECURITIES PUBLIC COMPANY LIMITED
999/9 The Offices at Centralworld 18th Floor Rama 1 Rd Pathumwan, Bangkok, 10330, Thailand
Tel.: (66) 26589001
Web Site: http://www.fnsyrus.com
FSS—(THA)
Rev.: $58,213,496
Assets: $198,151,904
Liabilities: $117,145,517
Net Worth: $81,006,386
Earnings: $2,734,086
Fiscal Year-end: 12/31/20
Securities Brokerage Services
N.A.I.C.S.: 523150
Chatchaval Jiaravanon *(Chm)*

FINANSINOS S/A - CREDITO FINANCIAMENTO E INVESTIMENTO
R Bento Goncalves 2575, 93510001, Novo Hamburgo, RS, Brazil
Tel.: (55) 51 3594 2488 BR

Web Site:
http://www.finansinos.com.br
Year Founded: 1962
FNCN3—(BRAZ)
Emp.: 24
Financial Services
N.A.I.C.S.: 523999
Roberto Cardoso *(Dir-IR)*

FINANTEC CO., LTD.
4F Annex Kabutocho Kaisei Bldg 13-1 Kabutocho Nihonbashi, Chuo-ku, Tokyo, 103-0026, Japan
Tel.: (81) 345006880
Web Site: http://www.finantec-net.com
Year Founded: 1998
Sales Range: $10-24.9 Million
Emp.: 25
Business Information Publishing Services
N.A.I.C.S.: 519290
Masaki Kai *(CEO)*

Subsidiaries:

Tokyo IPO **(1)**
2F Akasaka Long Beach Building 21-20 Akasaka 3-chome, Minto-ku, Tokyo, Japan
Tel.: (81) 335605469
Web Site: http://www.tokyoipo.com
Business Information Publisher
N.A.I.C.S.: 513140

FINANZA.TECH S.P.A. SB
Via Santa Maria Fulcorina 19, 20123, Milan, Italy
Tel.: (39) 0287167578
Web Site: https://www.finanza.tech
Year Founded: 2012
FTC—(EUR)
Management Consulting Services
N.A.I.C.S.: 541618
Nicola Occhinegro *(Founder)*

FINANZAS E INVERSIONES VALENCIANAS S.A.
Calle Caballeros n20, 46001, Valencia, 46001, Spain
Tel.: (34) 963923466
Web Site:
https://www.finanzasinversiones.com
Year Founded: 1974
Financial Investment Services
N.A.I.C.S.: 523999
Agnes Borel Lemonnier *(Chm)*

FINARTE SPA
Via Brera 8, 20121, Milan, Italy
Tel.: (39) 02 36569100 IT
Web Site: http://www.finarte.it
Year Founded: 1959
Sales Range: $10-24.9 Million
Emp.: 56
Auction Services
N.A.I.C.S.: 459999
Fabio Massimo Bertolo *(CEO)*

FINASUCRE S.A.
Rue de la Gare 36, BE-1040, Brussels, Belgium
Tel.: (32) 26611911
Web Site: http://www.finasucre.com
Year Founded: 1929
Rev.: $384,719,485
Assets: $871,323,209
Liabilities: $166,721,118
Net Worth: $704,602,091
Earnings: $125,542,390
Emp.: 2,330
Fiscal Year-end: 03/31/19
Sugar Refining
N.A.I.C.S.: 311314
Olivier Lippens *(Mng Dir)*

Subsidiaries:

Bundaberg Sugar Group Ltd. **(1)**

FINASUCRE S.A.

Finasucre S.A.—(Continued)

147 Wharf St, Spring Hill, 4000, QLD,
Australia   **(100%)**
Tel.: (61) 7 3835 8400
Web Site: http://www.bundysugar.com.au
Holding Company; Sugar Production; Engineering Services
N.A.I.C.S.: 551112

Subsidiary (Domestic):

Bundaberg Sugar Ltd.   **(2)**
147 Wharf Street, Spring Hill, 4000, QLD,
Australia   **(100%)**
Tel.: (61) 7 3835 8400
Web Site: http://www.bundysugar.com.au
Sales Range: $25-49.9 Million
Emp.: 60
Sugar Production
N.A.I.C.S.: 311314

Bundaberg Walkers Engineering
Ltd.   **(2)**
4 Gavin Street, PO Box 12, Bundaberg,
4670, QLD, Australia   **(100%)**
Tel.: (61) 741508700
Web Site:
   http://www.bundabergwalkers.com.au
Sales Range: $25-49.9 Million
Emp.: 100
Industrial Engineering, Manufacturing & Installation Services
N.A.I.C.S.: 541330
Ray Hatt (CEO)

Finasucre Holdings (Australia) Pty
Ltd   **(1)**
21 Magura St, Enoggera, Queensland,
Australia   **(100%)**
Tel.: (61) 733358300
Holding Company
N.A.I.C.S.: 551112

Finasucre Investments (Australia) Pty
Ltd   **(1)**
21 Magura Street, 4051, Enoggera, Queensland, Australia   **(100%)**
Tel.: (61) 733358300
Holding Company
N.A.I.C.S.: 551112

Galactic S.A.   **(1)**
Place d Escanaffles 23, Escanaffles, 7760,
Brussels, Belgium   **(55%)**
Tel.: (32) 69454921
Web Site: http://www.lactic.com
Sales Range: $25-49.9 Million
Emp.: 350
Beet Sugar Mfr
N.A.I.C.S.: 311313

Joint Venture (Non-US):

Anhui COFCO Biochemical & Galactic Lactic Acid Co., Ltd.   **(2)**
Grain 1st Avenue, Bengbu, 233010, Anhui,
China
Tel.: (86) 552 2081 288
Web Site: http://www.bglactic.com.cn
Emp.: 130
Lactic Acid Mfr & Whslr
N.A.I.C.S.: 325199

Subsidiary (Non-US):

B&G Japan Co., Ltd.   **(3)**
15-19 Kami-osaki 2-chome, Shinagawa-ku,
Tokyo, 141-0021, Japan
Tel.: (81) 3 6459 3646
Web Site: http://www.b-gjapan.com
Biochemical Distr
N.A.I.C.S.: 424910

Subsidiary (Non-US):

Galactic Bioquimicos Ltda.   **(2)**
Batel Business Center Av Batel n 1230 Cj
405 Torre BBC, Curitiba, 820420090, Brazil
Tel.: (55) 41 3042 7113
Web Site: http://www.lactic.com
Lactic Acid & Lactate Distr
N.A.I.C.S.: 424690

Subsidiary (US):

Galactic Inc   **(2)**
2700 W Silver Spring Dr, Milwaukee, WI
53209
Tel.: (414) 462-1990
Web Site: http://www.lactic.com

Emp.: 10
Wheat Farming
N.A.I.C.S.: 111140

Iscal Sugar S.A./N.V.   **(1)**
Chaussee de la Sucrerie 1, Fontenoy,
7643, Tournai, Belgium   **(100%)**
Tel.: (32) 69871711
Web Site: http://www.iscalsugar.com
Sales Range: $25-49.9 Million
Emp.: 100
Beet Sugar Mfr
N.A.I.C.S.: 311313

Subsidiary (Non-US):

Iscal Sugar B.V.   **(2)**
Zuiveringweg 14, 8243 PZ, Lelystad, Netherlands
Tel.: (31) 320 254 344
Web Site: http://www.iscalsugar.nl
Emp.: 40
Sugar Product Mfr & Distr
N.A.I.C.S.: 311314

Northern Land Holdings Ltd   **(1)**
4 Gavin St, Bundaberg, 4670, QLD,
Australia   **(100%)**
Tel.: (61) 741508500
Web Site: http://www.bundysugar.com.au
Cane Sugar Refining
N.A.I.C.S.: 311314
Richard Peterson (Gen Mgr-Fin & Acctg)

Queensland Urban Projects Pty
Ltd   **(1)**
21 Magura St, Enoggera, Queensland,
Australia   **(100%)**
Tel.: (61) 741508502
Investment Advice
N.A.I.C.S.: 523940

FINATIS SA

103 rue La Boetie, 75008, Paris,
France
Tel.: (33) 144711400
Web Site: https://www.finatis.fr
FNTS—(EUR)
Sales Range: $25-49.9 Billion
Emp.: 152,964
Holding Company; Real Estate Management & Retail Services
N.A.I.C.S.: 551112

Subsidiaries:

Fonciere Euris   **(1)**
83 Rue du Faubourg Sainte Honore, Paris,
75008, France   **(89.2%)**
Tel.: (33) 0144711400
Web Site: http://www.fonciere-euris.fr
Rev.: $29,666,199,552
Emp.: 124,226
Supermarkets, Hypermarkets & Other Retail
Distribution Outlets Operator; Land & Real
Estate Management Services
N.A.I.C.S.: 531390

Subsidiary (Domestic):

Carpinienne de Participations SA   **(2)**
103 Rue la Boetie, 75008, Paris, France
Tel.: (33) 144711400
Web Site: http://www.carpinienne-de-participations.fr
Sales Range: Less than $1 Million
Real Estate Support Services
N.A.I.C.S.: 531390
Didier Leveque (Chm & CEO)

Rallye S.A.   **(2)**
83 Rue Du Faubourg Saint Honore, 75008,
Paris, France
Tel.: (33) 144711373
Web Site: http://www.rallye.fr
Rev.: $36,703,000,216
Assets: $35,257,932,225
Liabilities: $31,091,085,690
Net Worth: $4,166,846,536
Earnings: ($274,120,440)
Emp.: 208,000
Fiscal Year-end: 12/31/2022
Holding Company; Food & Specialized
Sporting Goods Retailer
N.A.I.C.S.: 551112
Jean-Charles Henri Naouri (Chm)

Subsidiary (Domestic):

Casino Guichard-Perrachon SA   **(3)**

1 Cours Antoine Guichard, CS 50306,
42008, Saint Etienne, Cedex 1, France
Tel.: (33) 477453131
Web Site: https://www.groupe-casino.fr
Rev.: $39,930,082,400
Assets: $37,482,200,080
Liabilities: $29,967,827,760
Net Worth: $7,514,372,320
Earnings: ($1,088,220,640)
Emp.: 202,955
Fiscal Year-end: 12/31/2020
Hypermarkets, Supermarkets, Restaurants,
Convenience Stores & Discount Stores
Owner & Operator
N.A.I.C.S.: 445110
Jean-Charles Henri Naouri (Chm & CEO)

Subsidiary (Domestic):

Casino Cafeteria SAS   **(4)**
1 Esplanade de France, BP 306, Saint Etienne, 42008, France
Tel.: (33) 477453228
Web Site: http://www.casino-cafeteria.fr
Emp.: 1,800
Self Service Restaurants
N.A.I.C.S.: 722513
Weidmann Boris (Mgr)

Casino Vacances SNC   **(4)**
67 Rue De Richelieu, 75002, Paris, France
Tel.: (33) 53454300
Web Site: http://www.casinovacances.fr
Sales Range: $10-24.9 Million
Emp.: 20
Travel Agent & Operator
N.A.I.C.S.: 561510

Subsidiary (Non-US):

Cnova N.V.   **(4)**
Strawinskylaan 3051, 1077 ZX, Amsterdam,
Netherlands   **(98.8%)**
Tel.: (31) 203012240
Web Site: https://www.cnova.com
Rev.: $1,834,845,672
Assets: $1,131,339,305
Liabilities: $1,537,245,845
Net Worth: ($405,906,540)
Earnings: ($135,519,102)
Emp.: 2
Fiscal Year-end: 12/31/2022
Holding Company; E-Commerce Services
N.A.I.C.S.: 551112
Jean-Yves Haagen (Chm)

Subsidiary (Domestic):

Easydis   **(4)**
Estiknae Efrant 306, 42008, Rond Pt Auguste Colonna, 42160, Saint-Etienne,
France
Tel.: (33) 477020400
Web Site: http://www.easydis.com
Sales Range: $10-24.9 Million
Emp.: 50
General Warehousing & Storage
N.A.I.C.S.: 493110

Monoprix S.A.   **(4)**
204 Rond Pt Du Pont De Sevres, Tour Vendome, 92216, Boulogne-Billancourt,
France   **(100%)**
Tel.: (33) 155208809
Web Site: http://www.monoprix.fr
Sales Range: $1-4.9 Billion
Emp.: 18,000
Supermarket Retailer
N.A.I.C.S.: 455219
Stephane Maquaire (Deputy CEO)

Subsidiary (Domestic):

Groupe GO Sport SA   **(3)**
17 Avenue de la Falaise, 38360, Sassenage, France
Tel.: (33) 476282020
Web Site: http://www.groupegosport.com
Sales Range: $75-99.9 Million
Emp.: 5,029
Sporting Goods & Leisure Wear Distr
N.A.I.C.S.: 423910

FINAXO ENVIRONNEMENT SA

12 allee des Missions, 51170,
Fismes, France
Tel.: (33) 326480147
Web Site: http://www.finaxo.fr
MLFXO—(EUR)

Sales Range: Less than $1 Million
Water Treatment Equipment Mfr
N.A.I.C.S.: 333310
Pascal Colignon (Chm & Mng Dir)

FINBAR GROUP LIMITED

Level 6 181 Adelaide Terrace, Perth,
6004, WA, Australia
Tel.: (61) 862113300
Web Site: https://www.finbar.com.au
FRI—(ASX)
Rev.: $129,770,299
Assets: $470,442,039
Liabilities: $299,168,669
Net Worth: $171,273,370
Earnings: $11,086,405
Emp.: 28
Fiscal Year-end: 06/30/24
Property Investment & Development
Services
N.A.I.C.S.: 531390
Darren John Pateman (Mng Dir)

Subsidiaries:

Finbar To Rent Pty. Ltd.   **(1)**
Level 4 181 Adelaide Terrace, East Perth,
Perth, 6004, WA, Australia
Tel.: (61) 862113388
Web Site: http://www.finbartorent.com.au
Property Rental Services
N.A.I.C.S.: 531110
Meg Hunt (Mgr-Property)

FINBOND GROUP LIMITED

Rigel Office Park 446 Rigel Ave
South Erasmusrand, Pretoria, 0181,
South Africa
Tel.: (27) 124607288   **ZA**
Web Site:
   http://www.finbondlimited.co.za
Year Founded: 2001
FGL—(JSE)
Rev.: $44,740,306
Assets: $232,997,906
Liabilities: $187,689,474
Net Worth: $45,308,433
Earnings: ($73,848)
Emp.: 2,210
Fiscal Year-end: 02/29/24
Financial Services
N.A.I.C.S.: 523999
Willem van Aardt (CEO)

Subsidiaries:

America's Financial Choice, LLC   **(1)**
1100 Jorie Blvd Ste 207, Oak Brook, IL
60523
Web Site: http://www.afchoice.com
Financial Services
N.A.I.C.S.: 523999

Bondexcel (Pty) Ltd   **(1)**
Blakes Maphanga Building 271 Kent Ave,
Randburg, Gauteng, South Africa
Tel.: (27) 117814445
Financial Management Services
N.A.I.C.S.: 523999

Finbond Group International
Limited   **(1)**
Tower Road 170, Sliema, SLM1603, Malta
Tel.: (356) 20107207
Financial Services
N.A.I.C.S.: 523999

Finbond Group North America,
LLC   **(1)**
875 North Michigan Ave Ste 3100, Chicago,
IL 60611
Tel.: (312) 794-7848
Financial Services
N.A.I.C.S.: 523999

TV Profile, LLC   **(1)**
352 Louisiana 3161, Cut Off, LA
70345   **(100%)**
Web Site:
   https://www.americancashadvance.net
Consumer Lending
N.A.I.C.S.: 522291

FINCANNA CAPITAL CORP.

Suite 550 - 800 West Pender Street,
Vancouver, V6C 2V6, BC, Canada
Tel.: (778) 327-5799   BC
Web Site:
  http://www.fincannacapital.com
Year Founded: 2011
FNNZF—(OTCQB)
Rev.: $111,023
Assets: $5,004,164
Liabilities: $5,284,513
Net Worth: ($280,350)
Earnings: ($8,830,977)
Fiscal Year-end: 04/30/21
Pharmaceutical Preparation Mfr; Cannabis Mfr
N.A.I.C.S.: 325412
Robert Scott *(CFO)*

FINCANTIERI S.P.A.

Via Genova 1, 34121, Trieste, Italy
Tel.: (39) 0403193111   IT
Web Site: https://www.fincantieri.com
Year Founded: 1959
FCT—(ITA)
Rev.: $8,351,512,454
Assets: $11,154,303,320
Liabilities: $10,129,660,067
Net Worth: $1,024,643,253
Earnings: $26,794,056
Emp.: 20,000
Fiscal Year-end: 12/31/21
Ship Building, Repair & Maintenance
Services; Marine & Industrial Diesel
Engine Mfr
N.A.I.C.S.: 336611
Giuseppe Bono *(CEO)*

Subsidiaries:

Centro per gli Studi di Tecnica Navale
Cetena S.p.A.   **(1)**
Via Ippolito d Aste 5, 16121, Genoa,
Italy   **(71.1%)**
Tel.: (39) 0105995460
Web Site: https://www.cetena.it
Sales Range: $25-49.9 Million
Emp.: 75
Naval & Maritime Research & Consultancy
Services
N.A.I.C.S.: 541715

Fincantieri (Shanghai) Trading Co.
Ltd.   **(1)**
Room 803b Building a No 1518 Minsheng
Road, Shanghai, China
Tel.: (86) 13817638352
Engineering Design & Development Services
N.A.I.C.S.: 541330

Fincantieri Infrastructure S.p.A   **(1)**
Via del Lavoro 1, Valeggio sul Mincio,
37067, Verona, Italy
Tel.: (39) 0454648511
Fabricated Metal Mfr
N.A.I.C.S.: 332312

Fincantieri Infrastructure S.p.A.   **(1)**
Via del Lavoro 1, Valeggio sul Mincio,
37067, Verona, Italy
Tel.: (39) 0454648511
Fabricated Metal Mfr
N.A.I.C.S.: 332312

Fincantieri Infrastrutture Sociali
S.p.A.   **(1)**
Via G del Pian dei Carpini 1, 50127, Firenze, Italy
Tel.: (39) 055799271
Construction Services
N.A.I.C.S.: 237990

Fincantieri Marine Group Holdings
Inc.   **(1)**
1600 Ely St, Marinette, WI 54143-2434
Tel.: (715) 735-9341
Web Site: http://www.usfincantieri.com
Emp.: 2,000
Holding Company; Owned 87.34% by Fincantieri - Cantieri Navali Italiani S.p.A. &
12.66% by Lockheed Martin Corporation
N.A.I.C.S.: 551112
Gary Roughead *(Chm)*

Holding (Domestic):

Fincantieri Marine Group, LLC   **(2)**
1600 Ely St, Marinette, WI 54143   **(100%)**
Tel.: (715) 735-9341
Web Site:
  https://www.fincantierimarinegroup.com
Sales Range: $300-349.9 Million
Emp.: 1,500
Ship Building & Repairing Services
N.A.I.C.S.: 336611

Subsidiary (Domestic):

Bay Shipbuilding Co.   **(3)**
605 N 3rd Ave, Sturgeon Bay, WI
54235-0830   **(100%)**
Tel.: (920) 743-5524
Web Site:
  http://www.fincantierimarinegroup.com
Sales Range: $150-199.9 Million
Emp.: 675
Ship Building & Repairing Services
N.A.I.C.S.: 336611
Todd Thayse *(VP & Gen Mgr)*

Cleveland Ship Repair Company   **(3)**
1847 Columbus Rd, Cleveland, OH
44113   **(100%)**
Tel.: (216) 621-9111
Web Site:
  http://www.fincantierimarinegroup.com
Sales Range: $25-49.9 Million
Emp.: 8
Ship Repairing Services
N.A.I.C.S.: 336611

Marinette Marine Corporation   **(3)**
1600 Ely St, Marinette, WI
54143-2434   **(100%)**
Tel.: (715) 735-9341
Web Site: http://www.marinettemarine.com
Sales Range: $150-199.9 Million
Emp.: 950
Ship Building & Repairing Services
N.A.I.C.S.: 336611

Fincantieri Marine Repair LLC   **(1)**
2060 E Adams St, Jacksonville, FL 32202
Web Site: https://fincantierimarinerepair.com
Machine Repair Services
N.A.I.C.S.: 713930

Fincantieri Marine Systems LLC   **(1)**
800-C Principal Ct, Chesapeake, VA 23320
Tel.: (757) 548-6000
Web Site:
  https://fincantierimarinesystems.com
Machine Repair Services
N.A.I.C.S.: 713930

Fincantieri Marine Systems North
America Inc.   **(1)**
800-C Principal Ct, Chesapeake, VA
23320   **(100%)**
Tel.: (757) 548-6000
Web Site:
  https://www.fincantierimarinesystems.com
Sales Range: $50-74.9 Million
Emp.: 30
Integrated Marine Vessel Systems & Components Whslr & Support Services
N.A.I.C.S.: 423860

Fincantieri Oil & Gas S.p.A   **(1)**
Via Genova 1, Trieste, Italy
Tel.: (39) 0403192473
Oil & Gas Sector Services
N.A.I.C.S.: 213111

Ids Australasia Pty. Ltd.   **(1)**
Unit 1 39 Navigator Place, Hendra, 4011,
QLD, Australia
Tel.: (61) 732055524
Ship Building Mfr
N.A.I.C.S.: 336611

Ids Ingegneria Dei Sistemi (uk)
Ltd.   **(1)**
3 Gloster Court Whittle Avenue Segensworth West, Fareham, PO155SH, Hampshire, United Kingdom
Tel.: (44) 1489885807
Engineeering Services
N.A.I.C.S.: 541330

Ids Ingegneria Dei Sistemi S.p.A.   **(1)**
Via Enrica Calabresi 24, 56121, Pisa, Italy
Tel.: (39) 05031241
Web Site: https://www.idscorporation.com

Emp.: 200
Information Technology Services
N.A.I.C.S.: 541511

Ids Korea Co. Ltd.   **(1)**
Daejeon IT Venture Town Room 308 35
Techno 9-ro, Yuseong-gu, Daejeon, 34027,
Korea (South)
Tel.: (82) 429321555
Ship Building Mfr
N.A.I.C.S.: 336611

Ids North America Ltd.   **(1)**
260 Hearst Way Unit 402, Kanata, K2L3H1,
ON, Canada
Tel.: (613) 591-0500
Engineering Services
N.A.I.C.S.: 541330

Isotta Fraschini Motori S.p.A.   **(1)**
V le F de Blasio Z I, 70132, Bari,
Italy   **(100%)**
Tel.: (39) 0805345000
Web Site: https://www.isottafraschini.it
Marine & Industrial Diesel Engine Designer,
Mfr & Distr
N.A.I.C.S.: 333618

Issel Nord S.r.l.   **(1)**
Via Trieste 4, 19020, Follo, SP, Italy
Tel.: (39) 0187941414
Web Site: http://www.isselnord.it
Integrated Logistics Engineering Services
N.A.I.C.S.: 541614

Marine Interiors S.p.A.   **(1)**
Tel.: (39) 0481757211
Web Site: https://www.marineinteriors.com
Emp.: 370
Ship Interior Services
N.A.I.C.S.: 541410

Orizzonte Sistemi Navali S.p.A.   **(1)**
Viale Brigata Bisagno 45 R, 16129, Genoa,
Italy   **(51%)**
Tel.: (39) 0109817111
Web Site: https://www.orizzontesn.it
Contract Naval Vessel Design & Engineering Services
N.A.I.C.S.: 541490

Rob Int S.R.L.   **(1)**
Via Venezia 46 Follo, 19020, La Spezia,
Italy
Tel.: (39) 0187939836
Ship Building Mfr
N.A.I.C.S.: 336611

Seastema S.p.A.   **(1)**
Viale Brigate Partigiane 92R, 16129,
Genoa, Italy
Tel.: (39) 0109863600
Web Site: http://www.seastema.it
Automation System Services
N.A.I.C.S.: 541512

Sof S.p.A.   **(1)**
Via G del Pian dei Carpini 1, 50127, Firenze, Italy
Tel.: (39) 0554249307
Medical Equipment Maintenance Services
N.A.I.C.S.: 811210

Vard Electro Brazil (instalacoes Eletricas) Ltda.   **(1)**
Rua Sete de Maio 11, Centro, Niteroi,
24030-058, RJ, Brazil
Tel.: (55) 2136285082
Ship Building Mfr
N.A.I.C.S.: 336611

Vard Holdings Limited   **(1)**
Skansekaia 2, 6002, Alesund,
Norway   **(95.99%)**
Tel.: (47) 70 21 06 00
Web Site: http://www.vard.com
Sales Range: $1-4.9 Billion
Emp.: 9,172
Ship Designer & Builder
N.A.I.C.S.: 336611

Subsidiary (Non-US):

Vard Group AS   **(2)**
Tel.: (47) 70210600
Web Site: https://www.vard.com
Emp.: 8,000
Holding Company
N.A.I.C.S.: 551112

Subsidiary (Non-US):

Seaonics AS   **(3)**

Tel.: (47) 71391600
Subsea Construction & Deck Handling Services
N.A.I.C.S.: 237990

Subsidiary (Domestic):

Vard Accommodation AS   **(3)**
Skansekaia 2, 6002, Alesund, Norway
Tel.: (47) 7021 0600
Web Site: http://www.vard.com
Emp.: 60
Marine Vessel Heating, Air Conditioning &
Insulation Services
N.A.I.C.S.: 333415

Subsidiary (Non-US):

Vard Accommodtion Tulcea SRL   **(4)**
22 Ing Dumitru Ivanov Street, 820 242, Tulcea, Romania
Tel.: (40) 240534918
Web Site: http://www.vard.com
Emp.: 41
Marine Vessel Heating, Air Conditioning &
Insulation Services
N.A.I.C.S.: 333415
Valentina Munteana *(Mng Dir)*

Subsidiary (Non-US):

Vard Aqua Chile SA   **(3)**
Avenida Diego Portales 2000 Oficina 33,
Puerto Montt, Chile
Tel.: (56) 652290305
Engineering Consultancy Services
N.A.I.C.S.: 541330
Jorge Enrique Flores *(Mgr-Sls)*

Vard Aqua Scotland Ltd.   **(3)**
Kilmory Industrial Estate Argyll, Lochgilphead, PA318RR, United Kingdom
Tel.: (44) 1546603989
Engineering Consultancy Services
N.A.I.C.S.: 541330
Lorraine Campbell *(Gen Mgr)*

Subsidiary (Domestic):

Vard Aqua Sunndal AS   **(3)**
Industrivegen 3, 6600, Sunndalsora, Norway
Tel.: (47) 48022600
Engineering Consultancy Services
N.A.I.C.S.: 541330
Svein Arve Tronsgard *(Mgr-Sls & Mktg)*

Subsidiary (Non-US):

Vard Braila SA   **(3)**
Celuozei Street 1A, RO-810282, Braila,
Romania
Tel.: (40) 239 607 000
Ship Building Services
N.A.I.C.S.: 336611
Alina Puia *(Gen Dir)*

Subsidiary (Domestic):

Vard Brattvaag AS   **(3)**
Strandgata 74, 6270, Brattvag, Norway
Tel.: (47) 70210600
Ship Building & Repairing
N.A.I.C.S.: 336611

Vard Brevik Holding AS   **(3)**
Stromtangvn 21, NO-3950, Brevik, Norway
Tel.: (47) 3551 8700
Business Support Services
N.A.I.C.S.: 561499
Joshua Overby *(Gen Mgr)*

Vard Design AS   **(3)**
Skansekaia 2, NO-6002, Alesund, Norway
Tel.: (47) 70210600
Ship Building Design Services
N.A.I.C.S.: 541490

Subsidiary (Non-US):

Vard Design Liburna Ltd.   **(4)**
Fiorella La Guardie 13, 51000, Rijeka,
Croatia
Tel.: (385) 913281769
Design & Engineering Services
N.A.I.C.S.: 541330

Subsidiary (Domestic):

Vard Electro AS   **(3)**
Tennfjordvegen 113, 6264, Tennfjord, Norway

Fincantieri S.p.A.—(Continued)

Tel.: (47) 70210600
Emp.: 800
Electrical Engineering Services
N.A.I.C.S.: 237990

Subsidiary (Non-US):

Vard Electrical Installation and Engineering (India) Private Limited (4)
3-B 3rd Floor KG Oxford Business Centre
39/4609 Sreekandath Road, Ravipuram Ernakulam, Kochi, 682 016, India
Tel.: (91) 4842355430
Electrical Engineering Services
N.A.I.C.S.: 237990

Vard Electro Braila SRL (4)
Celuozei Street 1A, RO-810282, Braila, Romania
Tel.: (40) 239 607 336
Emp.: 130
Electrical Engineering Services
N.A.I.C.S.: 237990
Adrian Talaba (Mgr)

Vard Electro Brazil Ltda. (4)
Rua Jose Figueiredo 5 Centro, 24030-055, Niteroi, RJ, Brazil
Tel.: (55) 21 3628 5087
Electrical Engineering Services
N.A.I.C.S.: 237990

Vard Electro Tulcea SRL (4)
22 Ing Dumitru Ivanov Street, Electrical Section, 820242, Tulcea, Romania
Tel.: (40) 240534026
Web Site: http://www.vard.com
Emp.: 300
Electrical Engineering Services
N.A.I.C.S.: 237990
Adriane Talaba (Gen Mgr)

Subsidiary (Domestic):

Vard Engineering Brevik AS (3)
Stromtangvn 19, 3950, Brevik, Norway
Tel.: (47) 35518700
Design & Engineering Services
N.A.I.C.S.: 541330

Subsidiary (Non-US):

Vard Marine Inc. (3)
2930 Virtual Way Suite 180, Vancouver, V5M 0A5, BC, Canada
Tel.: (604) 216-3360
Web Site: https://www.vardmarine.com
Naval Architectural & Marine Engineering Services & Designer
N.A.I.C.S.: 336611
Mark Cook (COO & VP)

Vard Niteroi SA (3)
Praca Alcides Pereira, 1 Parte Ilha da Conceicao, Niteroi, CEP 24050-350, RJ, Brazil
Tel.: (55) 212 7189 90
Ship Building Services
N.A.I.C.S.: 336611

Subsidiary (Domestic):

Vard Offshore Brevik AS (3)
Industrivn 12, Porsgrunn, 3940, Norway
Tel.: (47) 3593 2025
Web Site: http://www.vard.com
Emp.: 55
Business Support Services
N.A.I.C.S.: 561499
Andre Solum (Gen Mgr)

Vard Piping AS (3)
Johangarden Naeringspark, NO-6270, Tennfjord, Norway
Tel.: (47) 7021 0600
Pipe Producer & Pipe Installation Services
N.A.I.C.S.: 332996

Subsidiary (Non-US):

Vard Piping Tulcea SRL (4)
22 ing Dumitru Ivanov Street, RO-820 242, Tulcea, Romania
Tel.: (40) 240 506 234
Pipe Producer & Pipe Installation Services
N.A.I.C.S.: 332996

Subsidiary (Non-US):

Vard Promar SA (3)
AE Zona Industrial Portuaria ZIP, Ilha de

Tatuoca SN, Ipojuca, CEP 55 590-000, PE, Brazil
Tel.: (55) 8135612500
Emp.: 30
Ship Building Services
N.A.I.C.S.: 336611

Vard Singapore Pte. Ltd. (3)
Tel.: (65) 68360813
Business Support Services
N.A.I.C.S.: 561499

Vard Tulcea SA (3)
22 ing Dumitru Ivanov Street, 820242, Tulcea, Romania
Tel.: (40) 240534026
Ship Building Services
N.A.I.C.S.: 336611

Vard Vung Tau Ltd. (3)
No 6 Dong Xuyen IP Rach Dua Ward, VN-76999, Vung Tau, Ba Ria - Vung Tau, Vietnam
Tel.: (84) 643615600
Emp.: 900
Ship Building Services
N.A.I.C.S.: 336611

Vard Marine Gdansk Sp. Z o.o. (1)
Ul Chrzanowskiego 11, 80278, Gdansk, Poland
Tel.: (48) 734432444
Ship Building Mfr
N.A.I.C.S.: 336611

FINCAS ANZIZU SL
Gran Via 631 1, 08010, Barcelona, Spain
Tel.: (34) 932702552
Web Site:
http://www.fincasanzizu.com
Year Founded: 1904
Property Management & Consultancy Services
N.A.I.C.S.: 531390
Josep Maria de Anzizu Furest (Chm & Partner)

FINCERA INC.
27F Kai Yuan Tower No 5 East Main Street, Shijiazhuang, 050011, Hebei, China
Tel.: (86) 31183827688   Ky
Web Site: https://www.fincera.net
Year Founded: 2007
YUANF—(OTCIQ)
Sales Range: $150-199.9 Million
Web-Based Financing & eCommerce Services
N.A.I.C.S.: 561499
Xiu Wen (VP-Product)

FINCH CAPITAL PARTNERS B.V
Concertgebouwplein 9, 1071 LL, Amsterdam, Netherlands
Web Site: http://www.finchcapital.com
Private Equity
N.A.I.C.S.: 523999
Radboud Vlaar (Mng Partner)

Subsidiaries:

Nomu Pay (1)
7/8 Wilton Terrace 4th Floor, Dublin, 0002, Ireland
Web Site: http://www.nomupay.com
Payment Services
N.A.I.C.S.: 525990
Peter Burridge (CEO)

Subsidiary (Non-US):

Wirecard Payment Solutions Malaysia Sdn. Bhd. (2)
Lot No 19-01 Level 19 Menara 2 Menara Kembar Bank, Rakyat No 33 Jalan Rakyat, 50470, Kuala Lumpur, Malaysia
Tel.: (60) 364195271
Online Payment & Processing Services
N.A.I.C.S.: 522320
Gunendran Rajanayagam (Product Mgr-Ops)

FINCHAIN CAPITAL PARTNERS AG
Girardet House Konigsallee 27, 40212, Dusseldorf, Germany
Tel.: (49) 21123855195
Web Site:
https://www.finchaincapital.com
Year Founded: 2011
U1DA—(DEU)
Investment Management Service
N.A.I.C.S.: 523999
Roland Pfaus (CEO)

FINCRAFT CAPITAL JSC
97 Samal-2 Microdistrict, Medeu district, Almaty, 050051, Kazakhstan
Tel.: (7) 272505412
JSCP—(KAZ)
Assets: $805,699,170
Liabilities: $6,958,260
Net Worth: $798,740,910
Earnings: ($29,764,440)
Fiscal Year-end: 12/31/19
Financial Investment Services
N.A.I.C.S.: 523940

FINCRAFT GROUP LLP
F 53 77/2 Al-Farabi Ave, Almaty, 050040, Kazakhstan
Tel.: (7) 272505412
NCOM—(KAZ)
Assets: $663,503,838
Liabilities: $302,632,812
Net Worth: $360,871,026
Earnings: ($412,955,196)
Fiscal Year-end: 12/31/21
Financial Investment Services
N.A.I.C.S.: 523940

FINCRAFT INVESTMENT HOUSE JSC
Al-Farabi Ave 77/2 MK Esentai Apartments Block B 20-floor apt 20A, Almaty, 050040, Kazakhstan
Tel.: (7) 273550102
Web Site: http://www.fincraft.kz
Year Founded: 1997
IDFC—(KAZ)
Rev.: $54,298,752
Assets: $94,433,058
Liabilities: $54,298,752
Net Worth: $40,134,305
Earnings: $995,860
Fiscal Year-end: 12/31/20
Investment Management Service
N.A.I.C.S.: 523940
Rashid Amirov (Chm)

FINCRAFT RESOURCES JSC
Dostyk Avenue building 300/26, A25D7Y5, Almaty, Kazakhstan
Tel.: (7) 7272777111   KZ
Web Site:
https://www.fincraftresources.kz
Year Founded: 2001
SATC—(KAZ)
Assets: $48,831,423
Liabilities: $14,794,832
Net Worth: $34,036,591
Earnings: ($1,486,681)
Emp.: 6
Fiscal Year-end: 12/31/23
Holding Company; Natural Resource Management & Production Services; Construction & Mechanical Engineering Services; Transportation Services
N.A.I.C.S.: 551112
Kenges Khamituly Rakishev (Chm)

Subsidiaries:

SAT & Co. Holding A.S. (1)
Cumhuriyet Mah 1992 Sok E-5 Mevkii Vetro City Residence No 16, Kat 10 No 209 Beylikduzu, Istanbul, Turkiye   (100%)
Tel.: (90) 212 624 60 06
Web Site: http://www.satcoholding.com.tr

Holding Company; Chrome Ore Mining Services
N.A.I.C.S.: 551112
Samatbek Tokhanov (Gen Dir)

FINDER ENERGY HOLDINGS LIMITED
Suite 1 Level 4 South Shore Centre
85 South Perth Esplanade, South Perth, 6151, WA, Australia
Tel.: (61) 893270100   AU
Web Site:
https://www.finderenergy.com
Year Founded: 2004
FDR—(ASX)
Rev.: $1,736,242
Assets: $6,577,525
Liabilities: $6,422,326
Net Worth: $155,199
Earnings: ($1,619,112)
Fiscal Year-end: 06/30/23
Holding Company
N.A.I.C.S.: 551112
Damon Neaves (CEO)

FINDERS RESOURCES LIMITED
Level 1 25 Colin Street, West Perth, 6005, WA, Australia
Tel.: (61) 8 6555 3996   AU
Web Site:
http://www.findersresources.com
Rev.: $163,516,557
Assets: $226,015,855
Liabilities: $122,280,929
Net Worth: $103,734,926
Earnings: $43,965,782
Emp.: 489
Fiscal Year-end: 12/31/17
Copper Producer
N.A.I.C.S.: 212230

Subsidiaries:

P.T. Batutua Tembaga Raya (1)
Jl Jend Gatot Subroto Kav 32-34 Patra Ofc Tower Lt 9 Ruang 93, Kuningan Timur Setia Budi, Jakarta, 12950, Indonesia
Tel.: (62) 2152900051
Web Site: http://www.batutua.com
Sales Range: $50-74.9 Million
Emp.: 20
Metal Mining & Exploration Services
N.A.I.C.S.: 213114
Dean Stuart (Pres)

FINDEV INC.
200 Bay Street Suite 3800, Royal Bank Plaza South Tower, Toronto, M5J 2Z4, ON, Canada
Tel.: (647) 789-5188   ON
Web Site: https://www.findev.ca
Year Founded: 2004
FDI—(TSXV)
Sales Range: Less than $1 Million
Investment Services
N.A.I.C.S.: 523999
Sruli Weinreb (CEO)

FINDEX INC.
4-9-6 Sanbancho, Matsuyama, 7900003, Ehime, Japan
Tel.: (81) 899473388
Web Site: https://www.findex.co.jp
Year Founded: 1985
3649—(TKS)
Rev.: $36,804,190
Assets: $42,072,060
Liabilities: $7,721,010
Net Worth: $34,351,050
Earnings: $7,508,310
Emp.: 298
Fiscal Year-end: 12/31/23
Medical Software Publisher
N.A.I.C.S.: 513210

FINDOS INVESTOR GMBH
Gisela strasse 12, D-80802, Munich, Germany

Tel.: (49) 8920000950   De
Web Site: http://www.findos.eu
Sales Range: $25-49.9 Million
Emp.: 5
Privater Equity Firm
N.A.I.C.S.: 523999
Hans H. Freudenberg (Co-Founder &
Partner)

Subsidiaries:

Maier Sports GmbH & Co. KG   (1)
Nurtinger Strasse 27, 73257, Kongen, Germany
Tel.: (49) 7024 8000 0
Web Site: http://www.maier-sports.de
Sales Range: $25-49.9 Million
Emp.: 100
Outdoor Apparel Mfr
N.A.I.C.S.: 339920
Gerhard Meier (Mng Dir)

FINE BESTEEL CO., LTD.
A 259-33 Changmil-ro, Changnyeong-gun, Changnyeong,
Gyeongsangnam-do, Korea (South)
Tel.: (82) 552592000
Web Site:
    https://www.finebesteel.com
Year Founded: 2007
133820—(KRS)
Rev.: $107,076,442
Assets: $137,770,772
Liabilities: $77,743,063
Net Worth: $60,027,709
Earnings: ($1,993,419)
Emp.: 173
Fiscal Year-end: 12/31/22
Structural Steel Products Mfr
N.A.I.C.S.: 331513
Inho Jung (CEO)

FINE BLANKING & TOOL CO., LTD.
No 3 Kon Eighth Rd, Chuang Hine
Industrial Park Hsen-Kang, Chang-Hua, Taiwan
Tel.: (886) 47990118
4535—(TPE)
Rev.: $98,217,960
Assets: $103,555,920
Liabilities: $17,043,210
Net Worth: $86,512,710
Earnings: $9,582,528
Fiscal Year-end: 12/31/22
Vehicle Parts Mfr & Distr
N.A.I.C.S.: 336390
Chung-Yi Wu (Chm)

FINE FOODS & PHARMACEU-TICALS N.T.M. S.P.A.
Via Berlino 39, Zingonia-Verdellino,
24040, Bergamo, Italy
Tel.: (39) 0354821382
Web Site: https://www.finefoods.it
Year Founded: 1984
FF—(ITA)
Rev.: $279,177,600
Assets: $266,653,988
Liabilities: $126,517,916
Net Worth: $140,136,072
Earnings: ($3,887,955)
Emp.: 753
Fiscal Year-end: 12/31/23
Pharmaceuticals Product Mfr
N.A.I.C.S.: 325412
Marco Francesco Eigenmann (Pres &
Co-CEO)

Subsidiaries:

Euro Cosmetic S.p.A.   (1)
Via Dei Dossi 16, Trenzano, 25030, Brescia, Italy
Tel.: (39) 0309974760
Web Site: https://www.eurocosmetic.it
Emp.: 115
Cosmetic Product Mfr & Distr
N.A.I.C.S.: 339910

Pharmatek PMC S.R.L.   (1)
Piazza Delle Industrie 3, 26010, Cremosano, CR, Italy
Tel.: (39) 0373290228
Web Site: https://pharmatek-pmc.it
Medical Instrument Mfr
N.A.I.C.S.: 339112

FINE FOODS LIMITED
New Market City Complex Level-6
44/1 Rahim Square Newmarket,
Dhaka, 1205, Bangladesh
Tel.: (880) 1926766469
Web Site:
    https://finefoodslimited.com
FINEFOODS—(CHT)
Rev.: $562,034
Assets: $1,412,149
Liabilities: $67,061
Net Worth: $1,345,088
Earnings: $8,377
Fiscal Year-end: 06/30/23
Fish Production & Whslr
N.A.I.C.S.: 424460
Nazrul Islam (CEO & Mng Dir)

FINE METAL TECHNOLOGIES PUBLIC COMPANY LIMITED
183 Regent House Building 14th
Floor Rajadamri Road, Kaweng Lum-pini Pathumwan District, Bangkok,
10330, Thailand
Tel.: (66) 22560641
Web Site: https://www.fmt.co.th
Year Founded: 1988
FMT—(THA)
Rev.: $197,365,133
Assets: $81,515,119
Liabilities: $33,346,372
Net Worth: $48,168,747
Earnings: $2,815,714
Emp.: 580
Fiscal Year-end: 12/31/23
Copper Tube Products Mfr & Distr
N.A.I.C.S.: 331420

FINE ORGANICS INDUSTRIES LTD.
Fine House Anandji Street Off M G
Road, Ghatkopar East, Mumbai,
400077, India
Tel.: (91) 2221025000
Web Site:
    https://www.fineorganics.com
Year Founded: 1970
541557—(BOM)
Rev.: $370,149,080
Assets: $216,606,151
Liabilities: $31,815,203
Net Worth: $184,790,948
Earnings: $74,108,543
Emp.: 825
Fiscal Year-end: 03/31/23
Organic Additive Mfr
N.A.I.C.S.: 325998
Prakash Damodar Kamat (Chm)

FINE SEMITECH CORP.
15 23 Dongtansandan 6-gil, Dongtan-myeon, Hwaseong, 445 811,
Gyeonggi-do, Korea (South)
Tel.: (82) 313712400
Web Site: https://www.fstc.co.kr
Year Founded: 1987
036810—(KRS)
Rev.: $171,342,820
Assets: $302,780,771
Liabilities: $114,287,864
Net Worth: $188,492,907
Earnings: $33,805,407
Emp.: 590
Fiscal Year-end: 12/31/22
Semiconductor Material & Equipment
Mfr
N.A.I.C.S.: 334413

FINE SINTER CO., LTD.

1189-11 Nishinohora Akechi-cho, Ka-sugai, 480-0303, Aichi, Japan
Tel.: (81) 568884355
Web Site: https://www.fine-sinter.com
Year Founded: 1950
5994—(TKS)
Rev.: $280,197,900
Assets: $331,795,560
Liabilities: $209,477,510
Net Worth: $122,318,050
Earnings: ($3,919,730)
Emp.: 2,123
Fiscal Year-end: 03/31/24
Powder Metallurgy Product Mfr
N.A.I.C.S.: 332117
Yoichi Inoue (Pres)

Subsidiaries:

American Fine Sinter Co., Ltd.   (1)
957 N Maule Rd, Tiffin, OH 44883
Tel.: (419) 443-8880
Web Site: https://www.afsus.com
Powder Metallurgy Product Mfr
N.A.I.C.S.: 332117
Ryan Mcbride (Gen Mgr)

Fine Sinter Co., Ltd. - Kasugai
Plant   (1)
438 Daisenji-cho, Kasugai, 486-0812, Aichi,
Japan
Tel.: (81) 568816258
Powder Metallurgy Product Mfr
N.A.I.C.S.: 332117

Fine Sinter Co., Ltd. - Kawagoe
Plant   (1)
10-3 1-Chome Minamidai, Kawagoe, 350-1165, Saitama, Japan
Tel.: (81) 49 242 3131
Web Site: https://www.fine-sinter.com
Hydraulic Pumps Mfr
N.A.I.C.S.: 333996

Fine Sinter Co., Ltd. - Shiga
Plant   (1)
10-2 Kanotono Aisho-cho, Echi-gun, Shiga,
529-1204, Japan
Tel.: (81) 74 937 2511
Web Site: https://www.fine-sinter.com
Powder Metallurgy Product Mfr
N.A.I.C.S.: 332117

Fine Sinter Co., Ltd. - Tamagawa
Plant   (1)
91 Tamagawa Tokigawa-cho, Hiki-gun, Saitama, 355-0342, Japan
Tel.: (81) 493651122
Powder Metallurgy Product Mfr
N.A.I.C.S.: 332117

Fine Sinter Co., Ltd. - Yamashina
Plant   (1)
5-1 Kitsunezuka Kurisuno, Yamashina-ku,
Kyoto, 607-8201, Japan
Tel.: (81) 75 581 3111
Powder Metallurgy Product Mfr
N.A.I.C.S.: 332117

Fine Sinter Sanshin Co., Ltd.   (1)
442-1 Tomori Kawashima-cho, Hiki, 350-0166, Saitama, Japan
Tel.: (81) 492971266
Powder Metallurgy Product Mfr
N.A.I.C.S.: 332117

Fine Sinter Tohoku Co., Ltd.   (1)
65 Matsunagane Iwayado, Esashi-ku,
Oshu, Iwate, Japan
Tel.: (81) 197357171
Powder Metallurgy Product Mfr
N.A.I.C.S.: 332117

PT. Fine Sinter Indonesia   (1)
Kawasan Industri Mitra Karawang Jl Mitra
Raya II Blok E No 6, Desa Parungmulya
Kec Ciampel, Karawang, 41361, Indonesia
Tel.: (62) 2678631720
Web Site: https://www.fine-sinter.com
Powder Metallurgy Product Mfr
N.A.I.C.S.: 332117
Toshihiro Nakashima (Pres)

Precision Sintered Products (Wuxi)
Co., Ltd.   (1)
No 86 Xinmei Road New District, Wuxi,
214028, Jiangsu, China
Tel.: (86) 510 8532 2101

Powder Metallurgy Product Mfr
N.A.I.C.S.: 332117

Thai Fine Sinter Co., Ltd.   (1)
Easter Seaboard Industrial Estate Rayong
32 Moo, 4 T Pluak-Daeng A Pluak Daeng,
Rayong, 21140, Thailand
Tel.: (66) 33212091
Powder Metallurgy Product Mfr
N.A.I.C.S.: 332117

FINE SOUNDS S.P.A.
c/o Sonus faber Via Antonio Meucci
10, Arcugnano, 36057, Italy
Tel.: (39) 0444 288 788   IT
Web Site: http://www.sonusfaber.com
Sales Range: $50-74.9 Million
Emp.: 250
Holding Company; Music Equipment
Mfr & Distr
N.A.I.C.S.: 551112
Mauro Grange (CEO)

Subsidiaries:

Audio Research Corporation   (1)
3900 Annapolis Ln N, Plymouth, MN 55447-5447
Tel.: (763) 577-9700
Web Site: http://www.audioresearch.com
Sales Range: $1-9.9 Million
Emp.: 50
Amplifier Electronic Crossovers & Audio Related Product Designer & Mfr
N.A.I.C.S.: 334310

Unit (Domestic):

Wadia Digital   (2)
2 Chambers St, Binghamton, NY 13903
Tel.: (607) 723-3539
Web Site: http://www.wadia.com
Digital Audio Technoloies Developer & Mfr
N.A.I.C.S.: 334310
John W. Schaffer (Pres)

Fine Sounds Asia Limited   (1)
RM 901 1 Duddell Street, Central, China
(Hong Kong)
Tel.: (852) 2359 3600
Web Site: http://www.finesoundsasia.com
Audio Equipment Distr
N.A.I.C.S.: 423620

McIntosh Laboratory, Inc.   (1)
2 Chambers St, Binghamton, NY 13903-2699
Tel.: (607) 723-3512
Web Site: http://www.mcintoshlabs.com
Sales Range: $25-49.9 Million
Emp.: 130
Home & Mobile Audio Equipment Mfr &
Distr
N.A.I.C.S.: 334310
Charles Randall (Pres & CEO)

Sonus faber S.p.A.   (1)
Via A Meucci 10, 36057, Arcugnano, VI,
Italy
Tel.: (39) 0444 288 788
Web Site: http://www.sonusfaber.com
Audio Equipment Mfr & Distr
N.A.I.C.S.: 334310
Mauro Grange (CEO)

Vertical Cubed   (1)
2431 5th St, Berkeley, CA 94710
Tel.: (510) 843-4500
Web Site: http://www.sumikoaudio.net
Sales Range: $1-9.9 Million
Emp.: 10
Audio Equipment Distr
N.A.I.C.S.: 423620
John Hunter (Pres)

FINE-LINE CIRCUITS LIMITED
145 SDF-V SEEPZ-SEZ, Andheri E,
Mumbai, 400096, Maharashtra, India
Tel.: (91) 2228290244
Web Site:
    https://www.finelineindia.com
Year Founded: 1990
517264—(BOM)
Rev.: $3,105,757
Assets: $2,045,862
Liabilities: $1,024,555
Net Worth: $1,021,307

Fine-Line Circuits Limited—(Continued)

Earnings: $7,221
Emp.: 141
Fiscal Year-end: 03/31/21
Printed Circuit Board Mfr
N.A.I.C.S.: 334412
Bhagwandas T. Doshi (Chm)

FINEDIGITAL INC.
7th floor Fine Venture Bldg 41
Seongnamdaero 925 beongil,
Bundang-gu, Seongnam, 463-828,
Gyeonggi, Korea (South)
Tel.: (82) 317888800
Web Site: https://www.finedigital.com
Year Founded: 1992
038950—(KRS)
Rev.: $69,874,289
Assets: $80,619,357
Liabilities: $9,691,942
Net Worth: $70,927,415
Earnings: ($1,406,410)
Fiscal Year-end: 12/31/22
Telecommunication & Broadcasting
Devices Mfr
N.A.I.C.S.: 334220

FINEDNC. CO., LTD.
169 Yeonamsan-ro, Eumbong-myeon,
Asan, 31413, Chungcheongnam-do,
Korea (South)
Tel.: (82) 415389000
Web Site: https://www.finednc.com
Year Founded: 1992
049120—(KRS)
Rev.: $44,712,967
Assets: $82,258,333
Liabilities: $61,465,596
Net Worth: $20,792,737
Earnings: ($19,412,178)
Emp.: 131
Fiscal Year-end: 12/31/22
Electronic Components Mfr
N.A.I.C.S.: 334419
Sung-Chun Hong (Pres & CEO)

FINELAND LIVING SERVICES GROUP LIMITED
Fineland Plaza No 28 Tiyu East
Road, Tianhe District, Guangzhou,
China
Tel.: (86) 2022825536　　　　　　Ky
Web Site:
　　http://www.finelandassets.com
Year Founded: 1997
9978—(HKG)
Rev.: $71,877,078
Assets: $80,566,855
Liabilities: $47,220,872
Net Worth: $33,345,983
Earnings: $4,452,365
Emp.: 2,004
Fiscal Year-end: 12/31/22
Real Estate Management Services
N.A.I.C.S.: 531210
Haiming Rong (CEO)

FINEMAT APPLIED MATERIALS CO., LTD.
No 36 Gongye 1st Road, Annan District, Tainan City, 70955, Taiwan
Tel.: (886) 66016388
Web Site: https://www.fine-mat.com
6698—(TAI)
Rev.: $39,102,898
Assets: $97,384,110
Liabilities: $39,852,078
Net Worth: $57,532,033
Earnings: $710,033
Fiscal Year-end: 12/31/22
Electronic Components Mfr
N.A.I.C.S.: 334419
Chin-Hsiao Chao (Chm)

FINEOS CORP. LTD.
Fineos House East Point Business

Park, Dublin, 3, Ireland
Tel.: (353) 16399700
Web Site: http://www.fineos.com
Year Founded: 1993
Rev.: $48,300,000
Emp.: 250
Software Development Services
N.A.I.C.S.: 541511
Michael Kelly (CEO)

FINEOTEX CHEMICAL LTD.
42 43 Manorama Chambers SV Rd,
Bandra West, Mumbai, 400 050, India
Tel.: (91) 2226559174
Web Site: https://www.fineotex.com
Year Founded: 1979
533333—(BOM)
Rev.: $62,861,963
Assets: $50,680,283
Liabilities: $8,036,473
Net Worth: $42,643,810
Earnings: $10,737,342
Emp.: 103
Fiscal Year-end: 03/31/23
Chemicals Mfr
N.A.I.C.S.: 325998
Surendrakumar Tibrewala (Chm & Mng Dir)

FINEPART SWEDEN AB
Rinnavagen 6, 51733, Bollebygd,
Sweden
Tel.: (46) 33284145
Web Site: https://www.finepart.com
Year Founded: 2012
Waterjet Cutting Machinery Mfr
N.A.I.C.S.: 333517
Lars Magnus Darvall (CEO)

FINERS STEPHENS INNOCENT LLP
179 Great Portland Street, London,
W1W 5LS, United Kingdom
Web Site:
　　http://www.howardkennedyfsi.com
Law firm
N.A.I.C.S.: 541110

FINESSE HOME LIVING
4210 Gateway Boulevard, Edmonton,
T6J 7K1, AB, Canada
Tel.: (780) 444-7100
Web Site:
　　https://www.finessehomeliving.com
Year Founded: 1983
Rev.: $24,605,421
Emp.: 170
Furniture Retailer
N.A.I.C.S.: 449110
Soraida Shamey (Controller)

FINET GROUP LIMITED
30/F Fortis Building 77-79 Gloucester
Road, Wanchai, China (Hong Kong)
Tel.: (852) 21103690　　　　　　BM
Web Site: https://www.finet.hk
Year Founded: 1998
8317—(HKG)
Rev.: $1,838,481
Assets: $8,789,987
Liabilities: $4,373,196
Net Worth: $4,416,791
Earnings: ($1,112,066)
Emp.: 79
Fiscal Year-end: 03/31/22
Financial Information Services
N.A.I.C.S.: 523940
Yuk Yee Lo (Chm & Compliance Officer)

Subsidiaries:

Finet Holdings Limited　　　　　　(1)
30/F Fortis Tower 77-79 Gloucester Road,
Wanchai, China (Hong Kong)
Tel.: (852) 21537275
Web Site: https://ir.finet.hk

Financial Services
N.A.I.C.S.: 523940

Finet Securities Limited　　　　　　(1)
30 / F Fortis Building 77-79 Gloucester
Road, Wanchai, China (Hong Kong)
Tel.: (852) 28698800
Web Site: https://www.finetsecurities.com
Investment Advisory Services
N.A.I.C.S.: 523940

FINETECHNIX CO., LTD.
38 Deokcheon-Ro, Manan-Gu, Anyang, 430-817, Gyeonggi-do, Korea (South)
Tel.: (82) 234567890
Web Site:
　　https://www.finetechnix.com
Year Founded: 2009
106240—(KRS)
Rev.: $39,469,099
Assets: $125,445,070
Liabilities: $45,491,815
Net Worth: $79,953,255
Earnings: $192,232,840
Emp.: 106
Fiscal Year-end: 12/31/22
Light Emitting Diode Mfr
N.A.I.C.S.: 334413
Geunwoo Kim (CEO)

Subsidiaries:

Fine DNC Co., Ltd.　　　　　　(1)
11-2 Wonnam-ri, Eumbong-myun, Asan,
31423, Choongcheongnam-do, Korea
(South)
Tel.: (82) 415389000
Electronic Components Mfr
N.A.I.C.S.: 334419

FINETEK CO., LTD
202 38 Mapo-daero, Mapo-gu, Seoul,
Korea (South)
Tel.: (82) 27117900
Web Site: https://www.ifinetek.com
Year Founded: 2008
131760—(KRS)
Rev.: $62,442,532
Assets: $59,583,907
Liabilities: $33,066,113
Net Worth: $26,517,795
Earnings: $4,535,782
Emp.: 105
Fiscal Year-end: 12/31/22
Display Component Mfr & Distr
N.A.I.C.S.: 334419

FINETEX ENE, INC.
23-1 Hyoryeong-ro, Seocho-gu,
Seoul, Korea (South)
Tel.: (82) 2 3489 3300
Web Site:
　　http://www.enesystem.co.kr
Year Founded: 1997
Rev.: $64,391,892
Assets: $109,683,504
Liabilities: $36,577,715
Net Worth: $73,105,789
Earnings: ($7,972,254)
Emp.: 80
Fiscal Year-end: 12/31/17
Energy Storage System Mfr
N.A.I.C.S.: 237130
Kim Yong-Won (CEO)

Subsidiaries:

Finetex EnE, Inc. - Hwasung
Plant　　　　　　(1)
25-5 Juseok-ro, Hwaseong, Gyeonggi-do,
Korea (South)
Tel.: (82) 31 356 8530
Eletric Power Generation Services
N.A.I.C.S.: 221118

Finetex EnE, Inc. - Rosario Plant　(1)
Block 8 Lot 5 Phase I PEZA, Rosario, 4106,
Cavite, Philippines
Tel.: (63) 46 437 1100
Timber Product Mfr
N.A.I.C.S.: 313310

FINEX CAPITAL MANAGEMENT LLP
4th Floor 39 Dover Street, London,
W1S 4NN, United Kingdom
Tel.: (44) 20 7663 3300
Web Site: http://www.finxcapital.com
Asset Management & Investment
Services
N.A.I.C.S.: 523999
Simon Luhr (Mng Partner)

FINEX KREDIT OJSC
S Rustam Str 11, Baku, Azerbaijan
Tel.: (994) 124405615
Web Site: http://www.finexkredit.az
Year Founded: 2013
FNEX—(BAK)
Sales Range: Less than $1 Million
Commercial Banking Services
N.A.I.C.S.: 522110
Rashad Gasimov (Chm)

FINEXIA FINANCIAL GROUP LTD.
Tel.: (61) 1300886103　　　　　　AU
FNX—(ASX)
Rev.: $7,595,267
Assets: $75,346,727
Liabilities: $64,531,895
Net Worth: $10,814,832
Earnings: $47,069
Fiscal Year-end: 06/30/24
Asset Management Services
N.A.I.C.S.: 531390
Neil Sheather (CEO)

Subsidiaries:

Yieldreport Pty Ltd　　　　　　(1)
Level 7 7 Macquarie Place, Sydney, 2000,
NSW, Australia
Tel.: (61) 28 114 2222
Web Site: https://www.yieldreport.com.au
Online News Portal Services
N.A.I.C.S.: 513110
Matt Wilson (Publr)

FINEXT VAGYONKEZELO NYILVANOSAN MUKODO RESZVENYTARSASAG
Futo Utca 47-53 VII Emelet, 1082,
Budapest, Hungary
Tel.: (36) 12662181
Web Site: https://www.finextnyrt.hu
Year Founded: 2009
FINEXT—(BUD)
Rev.: $37,483
Assets: $393,755
Liabilities: $197,565
Net Worth: $196,190
Earnings: ($4,056)
Fiscal Year-end: 12/31/23
Financial Investment Services
N.A.I.C.S.: 523999
Ezer Rezso (Chm-Mgmt Bd)

FINGEN S.P.A.
Piazza Strozzi 1, 50123, Florence,
Italy
Tel.: (39) 055266041　　　　　　IT
Web Site: http://www.fingen.it
Year Founded: 1979
Sales Range: $10-24.9 Million
Emp.: 50
Fashion, Retail & Real Estate Services
N.A.I.C.S.: 459999
Marcello Fratini (VP)

Subsidiaries:

Jeanswear Services Far East
Ltd.　　　　　　(1)
1201 Peninsula Square 18 Sung On Street,
Hung Hom, Hong Kong, China (Hong Kong)
Tel.: (852) 23651330
Web Site: http://www.jws.hk
Garments Mfr
N.A.I.C.S.: 315250

Tie Rack Retail Group Limited **(1)**
Capital Interchange Way, London, TW8
0EX, Middlesex, United Kingdom **(100%)**
Tel.: (44) 2082302333
Web Site: http://www.tie-rack.co.uk
Mens' & Womens' Ties & Scarves; Store
Franchiser; Photographic & Printing Services
N.A.I.C.S.: 315990

Subsidiary (Non-US):

Tie Rack France SAS **(2)**
32 Rue du Gros Horloge, 76000, Rouen,
France **(100%)**
Tel.: (33) 9 53 71 04 35
Web Site: http://www.tie-rack.fr
Mens' & Womens' Ties & Scarves; Store
Franchiser; Photographic & Printing Services
N.A.I.C.S.: 315990
Yann Billard (Dir-Natl Ops)

Tie Rack Limited **(2)**
Ste 501 5F Chunags Tower, 30-32 Connaught Road, Central, China (Hong Kong)
Tel.: (852) 34813119
Mens' & Womens' Ties & Scarves; Store
Franchiser; Photographic & Printing Services
N.A.I.C.S.: 315990

FINGER INC.
43F Fki Tower 24 Yeouido-Daero,
Yeongdeungpo-Gu, Seoul, 07320,
Korea (South)
Tel.: (82) 15449350
Web Site: https://www.finger.co.kr
Year Founded: 2000
163730—(KRS)
Rev.: $69,108,492
Assets: $47,051,044
Liabilities: $12,217,842
Net Worth: $34,833,201
Earnings: $1,470,227
Emp.: 255
Fiscal Year-end: 12/31/22
Software Development Services
N.A.I.C.S.: 541511
Hyeok Jang (CTO)

FINGERPRINT CARDS AB
Kungsgatan 20, SE-411 19, Gothenburg, Sweden
Tel.: (46) 101720000
Web Site:
https://www.fingerprints.com
FING.B—(OMX)
Rev.: $153,295,856
Assets: $192,288,208
Liabilities: $47,879,776
Net Worth: $144,408,432
Earnings: ($41,604,864)
Emp.: 240
Fiscal Year-end: 12/31/20
Fingerprint Cards Developer
N.A.I.C.S.: 561621
Pontus Jagemalm (CTO)

FINGERTANGO, INC.
3rd Floor Huixin Building No 1132
Zhongshan Avenue, Tianhe District,
Guangzhou, China
Tel.: (86) 2083939219 **Ky**
Web Site: http://www.fingertango.com
6860—(HKG)
Rev.: $116,884,404
Assets: $148,298,764
Liabilities: $39,094,240
Net Worth: $109,204,524
Earnings: ($19,565,302)
Emp.: 361
Fiscal Year-end: 12/31/22
Mobile Application Development Services
N.A.I.C.S.: 541511
Jie Liu (Co-Founder, Chm & CEO)

FININVEST S.P.A.
Via Paleocapa 3, 20121, Milan, Italy

Tel.: (39) 0285411 **IT**
Web Site: http://www.fininvest.it
Year Founded: 1961
Sales Range: $5-14.9 Billion
Emp.: 17,009
Investment Holding Company
N.A.I.C.S.: 551112
Marina Berlusconi (Chm)

Subsidiaries:

Arnoldo Mondadori Editore
S.p.A. **(1)**
via Bianca di Savoia 12, 20122, Milan,
Italy **(53.3%)**
Tel.: (39) 0275421
Web Site: https://www.mondadori.com
Sales Range: $1-9.9 Million
Book, Magazine & Newspaper Publisher,
Marketer & Distr
N.A.I.C.S.: 513120
Marina Berlusconi (Mng Dir)

Subsidiary (Domestic):

Cemit Interactive Media S.p.A. **(2)**
Via Toscana 9, I-10099, San Mauro Torinese, TO, Italy
Tel.: (39) 0122 27411
Web Site: http://www.cemit.it
Marketing, Database Management & Consulting Services
N.A.I.C.S.: 541618

Giulio Einaudi Editore S.p.A. **(2)**
Via M Biancamano 2, 10121, Turin, Italy
Tel.: (39) 01156561
Web Site: http://www.einaudi.it
Sales Range: $25-49.9 Million
Book Publishers
N.A.I.C.S.: 513130

Affiliate (Domestic):

Mach 2 Libri S.p.A. **(2)**
Via Galileo Galilei 1, 20068, Milan, Peschiera Borromeo, Italy **(100%)**
Tel.: (39) 02 5539041
Web Site: http://www.mach2.it
Book Publishers
N.A.I.C.S.: 513130

Subsidiary (Domestic):

Mondadori Electa S.p.A. **(2)**
Via Trentacoste 7, I 20134, Milan,
Italy **(100%)**
Tel.: (39) 02215631
Web Site: http://www.electaweb.it
Sales Range: $50-74.9 Million
Emp.: 150
Book Publishers
N.A.I.C.S.: 513130

Subsidiary (US):

Rizzoli International Publications,
Inc. **(3)**
300 Park Ave S 4th Fl, New York, NY
10010-5313
Tel.: (212) 387-3400
Web Site: https://www.rizzoliusa.com
Sales Range: $50-74.9 Million
Emp.: 100
Publisher of Books
N.A.I.C.S.: 424920
Marco Ausenda (Pres & CEO)

Subsidiary (Domestic):

Mondadori Franchising S.p.A. **(2)**
Strada Statale Marecchia 51A, 47827 Villa
Verucchio, Rimini, 47900, Italy
Tel.: (39) 0541679911
Web Site: http://www.libreriemondadori.com
Sales Range: $25-49.9 Million
Emp.: 100
Book Marketer & Distr
N.A.I.C.S.: 513130
Mario Maiocchi (Gen Mgr)

Mondadori Scienza S.p.A. **(2)**
Via Battistotti Sassi 11/A, 20133, Milan, Italy
Tel.: (39) 02762101
Web Site: http://www.focus.it
Magazine Publisher
N.A.I.C.S.: 513120
Roberto De Melgazzi (CEO)

Joint Venture (Domestic):

Mondolibri S.p.A. **(2)**
Via Lampedusa 13, 20141, Milan, Italy
Tel.: (39) 02844011
Web Site: http://www.mondolibri.it
Sales Range: $50-74.9 Million
Emp.: 130
Book Publisher, Marketer & Distr; Owned
50% by Bertelsmann AG & 50% by Fininvest S.p.A.
N.A.I.C.S.: 513130

Subsidiary (Domestic):

Rizzoli Libri S.p.A. **(2)**
Via Bianca di Savoia 12, 20122, Milan,
Italy **(99.99%)**
Tel.: (39) 0275421
Web Site: http://www.rizzolilibri.it
Periodical Publishers
N.A.I.C.S.: 513120

Sperling & Kupfer Editori S.p.A. **(2)**
Corso Como 15, 20154, Milano,
Italy **(100%)**
Tel.: (39) 0221721
Web Site: http://www.sperling.it
Sales Range: $25-49.9 Million
Emp.: 40
Book Publishers
N.A.I.C.S.: 513130

Teatro Manzoni SpA **(1)**
Via Manzoni 42, 20121, Milan, Italy
Tel.: (39) 027636901
Web Site: http://www.teatromanzoni.it
Emp.: 50
Theater Operator
N.A.I.C.S.: 512131
Alessandro Arnone (Gen Mgr)

FINLAY MINERALS LTD.
615 - 800 West Pender Street, Vancouver, V6C 2V6, BC, Canada
Tel.: (604) 684-3099
Web Site:
https://www.finlayminerals.com
Year Founded: 1999
FYMNF—(OTCQB)
Rev.: $12,835
Assets: $8,994,632
Liabilities: $1,307,584
Net Worth: $7,687,048
Earnings: ($297,740)
Emp.: 4
Fiscal Year-end: 12/31/23
Metal Exploration Services
N.A.I.C.S.: 213114
Robert F. Brown (Pres & CEO)

FINLOGIC S.P.A.
Via Galileo Ferraris 125 IT, 20021,
Bollate, Italy
Tel.: (39) 0296741014
Web Site: http://www.finlogic.it
FNL—(ITA)
Packaging Product Mfr & Distr
N.A.I.C.S.: 333993

FINMAC LUMBER LTD.
945 Elgin Avenue, Winnipeg, R3E
1B3, MB, Canada
Tel.: (204) 786-7694
Web Site:
https://www.finmaclumber.com
Year Founded: 1967
Rev.: $18,585,147
Emp.: 50
Lumber Whslr
N.A.I.C.S.: 423310
Bruce McGregor (Comptroller)

FINMATICA S.P.A.
Via Pietro Marone 22, 25124, Brescia, Italy
Tel.: (39) 030294860
Web Site:
http://www.fallimentofinmatica.com
Sales Range: $100-124.9 Million
Emp.: 846

Software Applications Designer &
Developer
N.A.I.C.S.: 334610
Marco Bettini (Mgr)

FINNAIR PLC
Tietotie 9, PO Box 15, 01053, Vantaa, Finland
Tel.: (358) 600 081881 **UK**
Web Site:
http://www.finnairgroup.com
Year Founded: 1923
Rev.: $3,076,583,624
Assets: $3,458,341,606
Liabilities: $2,241,675,204
Net Worth: $1,216,666,402
Earnings: $202,917,484
Emp.: 5,526
Fiscal Year-end: 12/31/17
Holding Company; Scheduled Passenger & Cargo Air Transportation
Services
N.A.I.C.S.: 551112
Sami Sarelius (Member-Exec Bd,
Gen Counsel & Sr VP)

Subsidiaries:

Finnair Business Services Ou **(1)**
Tahe 4, Tartu, 51010, Estonia
Tel.: (372) 7440313
Web Site:
https://businessservices.finnair.com
Business Support Services
N.A.I.C.S.: 561499

Finnair Oyj **(1)**
Tietotie 11 A, Helsinki-Vantaa Airport, FI-
01053, Vantaa, Finland **(100%)**
Tel.: (358) 981881
Web Site: http://www.finnair.fi
Sales Range: $1-4.9 Billion
Scheduled Passenger & Freight Air Transportation Services
N.A.I.C.S.: 481111
Jouko Karvinen (Chm)

Subsidiary (Domestic):

Amadeus Finland Oy **(2)**
Itamerenkatu 1, PO Box 278, FIN 00180,
Helsinki, Finland **(95%)**
Tel.: (358) 107737900
Sales Range: $10-24.9 Million
Emp.: 40
Scheduled Passenger & Cargo Air Transportation Services
N.A.I.C.S.: 481111

Area Travel Agency Ltd. **(2)**
Mannerheimintie 102, FIN 00251, Helsinki,
Finland **(100%)**
Tel.: (358) 9818383
Web Site: http://www.area.fi
Sales Range: $100-124.9 Million
Emp.: 350
N.A.I.C.S.: 481111

Subsidiary (Non-US):

Aurinko Ou **(2)**
Parnu Rd 10, 10148, Tallinn, Estonia
Tel.: (372) 64 09053
Sales Range: $25-49.9 Million
Emp.: 11
Tour Operating Services
N.A.I.C.S.: 561520

Back Office Services Estonia OU **(2)**
Vallikraavi 2, 51003, Tartu, Estonia
Tel.: (372) 7440309
Sales Range: $25-49.9 Million
Emp.: 100
Office Administrative Services
N.A.I.C.S.: 561110

Subsidiary (Domestic):

FTS Financial Services Oy **(2)**
Tietotie 11, 01053, Vantaa, Finland
Tel.: (358) 9 81881
Financial Management Services
N.A.I.C.S.: 523999

Finland Travel Bureau Ltd. **(2)**
Tietotie 9, FIN 00100, Vantaa, Finland
Tel.: (358) 108261

Finnair Plc—(Continued)

Web Site: http://www.smt.fi
Sales Range: $125-149.9 Million
Emp.: 620
Promoter & Provider of Information of Tourism
N.A.I.C.S.: 561510

Subsidiary (Non-US):

Estravel AS (3)
Suur Karja 15, Tallinn, 10140,
Estonia (70%)
Tel.: (372) 6266200
Web Site: http://www.estravel.ee
Sales Range: $50-74.9 Million
Emp.: 150
N.A.I.C.S.: 481111
Anne Samlik (Mng Dir & Member-Mgmt Bd)

Subsidiary (Domestic):

Finnair Aircraft Finance Oy (2)
Tietotie 11 A, PO Box 15, 01053, Vantaa,
Finland
Tel.: (358) 98 1881
Web Site: http://www.finnairgroup.com
Aircraft Procurement & Leasing Services
N.A.I.C.S.: 532411

Finnair Cargo Oy (2)
Rahtitie 1, 1530, Vantaa, Finland
Tel.: (358) 9 818 81
Web Site: http://www.finnaircargo.com
Sales Range: $50-74.9 Million
Emp.: 18
Air Freight Transportation Services
N.A.I.C.S.: 488510
Lars-Erik Lehtoranta (Sr Mgr-Ground Handling Agreements)

Subsidiary (Domestic):

Finnair Cargo Terminal Operations Oy (3)
Rahtitie 1, 1530, Vantaa, Finland
Tel.: (358) 981 8501
Sales Range: $125-149.9 Million
Air Freight Terminal Services
N.A.I.C.S.: 488119
Karel Navratil (Gen Mgr)

Subsidiary (Domestic):

Finnair Facilities Management Oy (2)
Tietotie 11 A, PO Box 200, Vantaa, 1053,
Finland
Tel.: (358) 9 818 81
Facility Management Services
N.A.I.C.S.: 561210

Finnair Flight Academy Oy (2)
Helsinki Airport Pyhtaankorventie 11-13,
01530, Vantaa, Finland
Tel.: (358) 9 818 4046
Web Site:
http://www.finnairflightacademy.com
Sales Range: $10-24.9 Million
Emp.: 40
Airline Training Services
N.A.I.C.S.: 611512
Merja Alhola (Head-Sls)

Representative Office (US):

Finnair Oyj-New York (2)
150 E 42nd St, New York, NY 10017
Tel.: (212) 499-9000
Web Site: http://www.finnair.com
Sales Range: $25-49.9 Million
Emp.: 4
International Airline Services
N.A.I.C.S.: 481111

Subsidiary (Domestic):

Finnair Technical Services Oy (2)
Helsinki Airport Teknikontie 5, 01530, Vantaa, Finland
Tel.: (358) 9 818 2400
Web Site:
http://www.finnairtechnicalservices.com
Sales Range: $350-399.9 Million
Emp.: 1,600
Aircraft Technical Consulting Services
N.A.I.C.S.: 541690

Finnair Travel Services Oy (2)
Tieto Tie 11, PO Box 275, FIN 00101, Hel-

sinki, Finland (100%)
Tel.: (358) 981881
Web Site: http://www.finnair.fi
Sales Range: $100-124.9 Million
Emp.: 400
N.A.I.C.S.: 481111

Mikkelin Matkatoimisto Oy (2)
Porrassalmenkatu 23, FIN 50100, Mikkeli,
Finland (100%)
Tel.: (358) 15321100
Sales Range: $1-9.9 Million
N.A.I.C.S.: 481111

Oy Aurinkomatkat-Suntours Ltd. Ab (2)
Pohjoinen Rautatiekatu 25, PO Box 287,
FIN 00100, Helsinki, Finland (99%)
Tel.: (358) 10446441
Web Site: http://www.aurinkomatkat.fi
Sales Range: $50-74.9 Million
Emp.: 160
Tour Operator
N.A.I.C.S.: 481111
Timo Kousa (Gen Mgr)

FINNING INTERNATIONAL INC.

Suite 300-565 Great Northern Way,
Vancouver, V5T 0H8, BC, Canada
Tel.: (604) 691-6444 BC
Web Site: https://www.finning.com
Year Founded: 1933
FTT—(TSX)
Rev.: $4,847,006,880
Assets: $4,269,684,240
Liabilities: $2,543,974,560
Net Worth: $1,725,709,680
Earnings: $181,488,960
Emp.: 13,188
Fiscal Year-end: 12/31/20
Holding Company; Construction & Mining Equipment Sales, Rental & Maintenance Services
N.A.I.C.S.: 551112
Kevin Parkes (Pres-Canada)

Subsidiaries:

4Refuel Canada LP (1)
Suite 215 9440-202nd Street, Langley, V1M
4A6, BC, Canada
Web Site: http://www.4refuel.com
On-Site Fuel Delivery Services
N.A.I.C.S.: 457210

Finning (Ireland) Limited (1)
Unit A Aerodrome Business Park, Collegeland Rathcoole, Dublin, D24 WC04, Leinster, Ireland
Tel.: (353) 12574000
Caterpillar Machinery & Equipment Distr
N.A.I.C.S.: 423830

Finning (UK) Ltd. (1)
Watling St, Cannock, WS11 1SL, Staffs,
United Kingdom (100%)
Tel.: (44) 1543 461 461
Web Site: http://www.finning.com
Sales Range: $150-199.9 Million
Emp.: 450
Construction & Mining Equipment Sales, Rental & Maintenance Services
N.A.I.C.S.: 423810
Kevin Parkes (Mng Dir-UK & Ireland)

Finning Argentina S.A. (1)
Camino Boulogne Bancalari 2955, Victoria,
1644, Buenos Aires, Argentina
Tel.: (54) 1147258800
Web Site: http://www.finning.com.ar
Construction & Mining Equipment Sales, Rental & Maintenance Services
N.A.I.C.S.: 423810

Subsidiary (Domestic):

Finning Soluciones Mineras S.A. (2)
Camino Boulogne Bancalari 2955, 1644,
San Fernando, Buenos Aires, Argentina
Tel.: (54) 1147258800
Mining Equipment Sales, Rental & Maintenance Services
N.A.I.C.S.: 423810

Finning Bolivia S.A. (1)
Av Banzer y Quinto Anillo Km 3 5 al Norte,
Santa Cruz, Andres Ibanez, Bolivia
Tel.: (591) 33144100

Web Site: http://www.finning.com.bo
Construction & Mining Equipment Sales, Rental & Maintenance Services
N.A.I.C.S.: 423810

Finning Canada Inc. (1)
16901 109th Ave, Edmonton, T5P 4P6, AB,
Canada
Tel.: (780) 930-4900
Web Site: http://www.finning.com
Emp.: 3,000
Construction & Mining Equipment Sales, Rental & Maintenance Services
N.A.I.C.S.: 423810
Kevin Parkes (Pres)

Finning Chile S.A. (1)
Av Los Jardines 924 Huechuraba, Santiago,
Chile
Tel.: (56) 229277000
Web Site: http://www.finning.cl
Sales Range: $300-349.9 Million
Emp.: 927
Construction & Mining Equipment Sales, Rental & Maintenance Services
N.A.I.C.S.: 423810

Finning Uruguay S.A. (1)
Juan Burghi 2646 Ruta 1 Y Camino Cibils,
12800, Montevideo, Uruguay
Tel.: (598) 23130131
Web Site: http://www.finning.com.uy
Construction & Mining Equipment Sales, Rental & Maintenance Services
N.A.I.C.S.: 423810

OEM Remanufacturing Company Inc. (1)
13315-156 Street, Edmonton, T5V 1V2, AB,
Canada
Tel.: (780) 468-6220
Web Site: http://www.oemreman.com
Engine Mfr
N.A.I.C.S.: 336310

FINNMIRROR OY

Peiltie 15, 38200, Sastamala, Finland
Tel.: (358) 351161 FI
Web Site: http://www.finnmirror.fi
Year Founded: 1923
Sales Range: $50-74.9 Million
Emp.: 105
Mirrors, Storage Units & Bathroom Fixtures Mfr
N.A.I.C.S.: 327215
Pala Aleksi (Mng Dir)

FINO PAYMENTS BANK LIMITED

Mindspace Juinagar Plot No Gen
2/1/F Tower 1 8th Floor, TTC Industrial Area MIDC Shirwane Juinagar,
Navi Mumbai, 400706, India
Tel.: (91) 2271047000
Web Site: https://www.finobank.com
Year Founded: 2017
543386—(BOM)
Rev.: $107,975,186
Assets: $137,904,776
Liabilities: $131,819,606
Net Worth: $6,085,170
Earnings: $2,794,742
Fiscal Year-end: 03/31/21
Banking Services
N.A.I.C.S.: 522110
Rishi Gupta (CEO & Mng Dir)

FINOLEX GROUP

26-27 Mumbai-Pune Road, Pimpri,
Pune, 411 018, India
Tel.: (91) 20 2747 5963
Web Site: http://www.finolex.com
Year Founded: 1958
Holding Company
N.A.I.C.S.: 551112
Deepak Chhabria (Chm)

Subsidiaries:

Finolex Cables Ltd. (1)
26-27 Mumbai-Pune Road, Pimpri, Pune,
411 018, India
Tel.: (91) 2027475963

Web Site: http://www.finolex.com
Rev.: $388,356,150
Assets: $530,393,955
Liabilities: $64,313,340
Net Worth: $466,080,615
Earnings: $62,989,290
Emp.: 1,649
Fiscal Year-end: 03/31/2021
Electrical & Communication Cable Mfr
N.A.I.C.S.: 335929
D. K. Chhabria (Chm)

Finolex Industries Ltd. (1)
Gat No 399 Village Urse Taluka-Maval,
Pune, 410506, Maharashtra, India
Tel.: (91) 2114237251
Web Site: http://www.finolexpipes.com
Rev.: $482,441,505
Assets: $586,114,620
Liabilities: $157,646,580
Net Worth: $428,468,040
Earnings: $100,708,335
Emp.: 1,377
Fiscal Year-end: 03/31/2021
Plastic Tank Mfr
N.A.I.C.S.: 326122
Prakash P. Chhabria (Chm)

FINOTEK CO., LTD.

3F 1 Yangjaecheon-ro 9-gil, Seocho-gu, Seoul, 137-863, Korea (South)
Tel.: (82) 2 5223558
Web Site: http://www.finotek.co.kr
Year Founded: 2008
Rev.: $13,840,840
Assets: $13,729,900
Liabilities: $12,083,000
Net Worth: $1,646,900
Earnings: $1,493,820
Fiscal Year-end: 12/31/19
Financial Digital Services
N.A.I.C.S.: 541512
Henry Kim (CEO)

FINPROJECT S.P.A.

Via San Gabriele 96, 62010, Morrovalle, MC, Italy
Tel.: (39) 0733 8671 IT
Web Site: http://www.finproject.com
Year Founded: 1965
Polyolefin Compound Products Mfr
N.A.I.C.S.: 325991
Euro Vecchiola (Co-Founder & Pres)

Subsidiaries:

Padanaplast S.r.l. (1)
Strada Paganina 3, 43010, Roccabianca,
Parma, Italy
Tel.: (39) 05 21 52 91
Web Site: http://www.padanaplast.com
Polymer Compound Mfr
N.A.I.C.S.: 325998
Caterina Bocchia (Mgr-R&D & Technical)

FINSETA PLC

14-18 Copthall Avenue, London,
EC2R 7DJ, United Kingdom
Tel.: (44) 2039714750 UK
Web Site: https://finseta.com
Year Founded: 2010
FIN—(LSE)
Rev.: $12,284,192
Assets: $8,588,536
Liabilities: $6,480,917
Net Worth: $2,107,619
Earnings: $2,716,554
Emp.: 34
Fiscal Year-end: 12/31/23
Computer System Design Services
N.A.I.C.S.: 541512

FINSHORE MANAGEMENT SERVICES LTD.

Sikkim Commerce House 5th Floor
Room 505, 4/1 Middleton Street, Kolkata, 700 071, India
Tel.: (91) 33 22895101
Web Site:
http://www.finshoregroup.com
Year Founded: 2011

Financial Advisory & Management
Services
N.A.I.C.S.: 525990
Alok Chaturvedi *(Mng Dir)*

FINSOFT FINANCIAL INVEST-MENT HOLDINGS LIMITED

Unit Nos 1209-10 12/F Prosperity
Millennia Plaza No 663 Kings Road,
North Point, Hong Kong, China (Hong
Kong)
Tel.: (852) 26169933   Ky
Web Site: http://www.finsoftcorp.com
Year Founded: 2012
8018—(HKG)
Rev.: $7,754,933
Assets: $13,212,315
Liabilities: $5,115,683
Net Worth: $8,096,633
Earnings: ($3,514,665)
Emp.: 74
Fiscal Year-end: 12/31/22
Financial Software Development Ser-
vices
N.A.I.C.S.: 541511
Ting Lin *(Exec Dir)*

Subsidiaries:

Well In Technology Development
Limited   (1)
Unit 811 8/F New Kowloon Plaza 38 Tai
Kok Tsui Road, Kowloon, China (Hong
Kong)
Tel.: (852) 39761300
Mobile Application Development Services
N.A.I.C.S.: 541511

FINTAXI, SEC

6850 boulevard Louis-H Lafontaine
211, Anjou, H1M 2T2, QC, Canada
Tel.: (514) 353-2757
Year Founded: 2003
Rev.: $19,849,917
Emp.: 8
Taxi Financing Services
N.A.I.C.S.: 485310
Josee Patry *(VP)*

FINTEC GLOBAL BERHAD

10th Floor Menara Hap Seng No 1 &
3 Jalan P Ramlee, 50250, Kuala
Lumpur, Malaysia
Tel.: (60) 323824288   MY
Web Site: https://www.fintec.global
Year Founded: 2007
FINTEC—(KLS)
Rev.: $4,714,973
Assets: $51,939,014
Liabilities: $7,156,580
Net Worth: $44,782,433
Earnings: ($6,879,062)
Emp.: 22
Fiscal Year-end: 06/30/23
Investment Holding Company
N.A.I.C.S.: 551112
Sik Eek Tan *(Exec Dir)*

Subsidiaries:

Gro Asia Agritechnology Sdn.
Bhd.   (1)
67 And 68 Jalan Waja 2 Taman Industri
Waja, 9000, Kulim, Malaysia
Tel.: (60) 44026350
Web Site: https://gro.asia
Emp.: 250
Agriculture & Farming Technology Develop-
ment Services
N.A.I.C.S.: 541714

Platinum Energy Sdn. Bhd.   (1)
1st Fl S Wing Block Syed Kechik Found
Bldg, Jalan Kapas Bangsar, 59100, Kuala
Lumpur, Malaysia
Tel.: (60) 3 2095 1080
Biodiesel Mfr
N.A.I.C.S.: 457210

Subsidiary (Domestic):

Ganz Biofuels Sdn. Bhd.   (2)

Jalan Usaha 9, Melaka, 75450, Melaka,
Malaysia
Tel.: (60) 6 2323118
Biodiesel Mfr
N.A.I.C.S.: 457210

FINTECH ASIA LTD.

Les Echelons Court Les Echelons,
Saint Peter Port, GY1 1AR, Guernsey
Tel.: (44) 1481211000   UK
Web Site:
https://www.fintechasialtd.com
Year Founded: 2021
FINA—(LSE)
Rev.: $12,307
Assets: $415,069
Liabilities: $2,589,344
Net Worth: ($2,174,275)
Earnings: ($4,329,627)
Fiscal Year-end: 12/31/23
Investment Management Service
N.A.I.C.S.: 523999
Oliver Stuart Fox *(Chm & CEO)*

FINTECH CHAIN LIMITED

1701 Block B2 No 15 Keyuan Road
KeXing Science Park, Nanshan Dis-
trict, Shenzhen, 518000, Guangdong,
China
Tel.: (86) 7552554680
Web Site: http://www.ttg.hk
Year Founded: 2010
FTC—(ASX)
Rev.: $9,874,016
Assets: $7,719,915
Liabilities: $7,988,279
Net Worth: ($268,364)
Earnings: $174,761
Emp.: 156
Fiscal Year-end: 03/31/22
Software & Information Services; Mo-
bile Coupon Applications
N.A.I.C.S.: 513210
John Xiong *(Co-Chm & CEO)*

Subsidiaries:

Jiangxi Tao-taogu E-commerce Co.,
Limited   (1)
Rm 3603 36/F 1 Serviced Apartment No59
North Yanjiang Road, Donghu District, Nan-
chang, 330000, Jiangxi, China
Tel.: (86) 79187870107
Electronic Financial Payment Services
N.A.I.C.S.: 522320

FINTECH GLOBAL INCORPO-RATED

Meguro Central Square 15th Floor
3-1-1 Kamiosaki, Shinagawa-ku, To-
kyo, 141-0021, Japan
Tel.: (81) 5058643978
Web Site: https://www.fgi.co.jp
Year Founded: 1994
8789—(TKS)
Rev.: $65,951,180
Assets: $135,582,070
Liabilities: $68,985,700
Net Worth: $66,596,370
Earnings: $11,365,270
Fiscal Year-end: 09/30/23
Investment Banking Services
N.A.I.C.S.: 523150
Nobumitsu Tamai *(Pres, CEO &
Head-Investment Banking Bus Div)*

Subsidiaries:

FinTech Asset Management
Incorporated   (1)
Meguro Central Square 15Th Floor 3-1-1
Kamiosaki, Shinagawa-ku, Tokyo, 141-
0021, Japan
Tel.: (81) 36 456 4640
Web Site: https://www.fgiam.co.jp
Asset Management Services
N.A.I.C.S.: 541611
Naoko Yoshioka *(Pres)*

Geoplan Namtech Inc.   (1)
4-2-7 Kojimachi Kojimachi Mid Square 8F,

Chiyoda-ku, Tokyo, 102-0083, Japan
Tel.: (81) 36 868 8685
Web Site: https://www.geoplan.co.jp
Emp.: 20
Telecommunication Servicesb
N.A.I.C.S.: 517810
Tsunehiko Nishizawa *(CEO)*

Public Management Consulting
Corporation   (1)
15th floor of Meguro Central Square 3-1-1
Kamiosaki, Shinagawa, Tokyo, 141-0021,
Japan
Tel.: (81) 36 456 4660
Web Site: https://public.ac
Management Consulting Services
N.A.I.C.S.: 541618
Harugo Washimoto *(Pres & CEO)*

SGI-Aviation Services B.V.   (1)
Margriet Toren Haaksbergweg 75 6th Floor,
1101 BR, Amsterdam, Netherlands
Tel.: (31) 20 880 4222
Web Site: https://www.sgiaviation.com
Aircraft Technical Advisory Services
N.A.I.C.S.: 541690
Paolo Lironi *(CEO)*

FINTECH SCION LIMITED

Portman House 2 Portman Street,
London, W1H 6DU, United Kingdom
Tel.: (44) 2039825041   NV
Web Site:
https://www.fintechcashier.com
Year Founded: 2013
HWGC—(OTCIQ)
Rev.: $3,084,279
Assets: $63,825,261
Liabilities: $4,943,467
Net Worth: $58,881,794
Earnings: $5,918,970
Emp.: 50
Fiscal Year-end: 12/31/22
Holding Company
N.A.I.C.S.: 551112
Lim Chun Hoo *(CFO)*

FINTECH SELECT LTD.

100 King Street West Unit T201A,
Toronto, N7M 6A9, ON, Canada
Tel.: (905) 752-0352   ON
Web Site:
https://www.fintechselect.com
Z1S1—(DEU)
Rev.: $2,823,507
Assets: $410,170
Liabilities: $991,499
Net Worth: ($581,329)
Earnings: $243,194
Fiscal Year-end: 12/31/23
Telecommunication Servicesb
N.A.I.C.S.: 517810
Mohammad Abuleil *(Pres & CEO)*

FINTEL ENERGIA GROUP S.P.A.

Via E Fermi 19, 62010, Pollenza,
Italy
Tel.: (39) 0733 201170   IT
Web Site: http://www.fintel.bz
Electricity & Natural Gas Distr
N.A.I.C.S.: 221122
Tiziano Giovannetti *(CEO)*

Subsidiaries:

Energogreen Renewables S.r.l.   (1)
Via Enrico Fermi 19, 62010, Pollenza, Mac-
erata, Italy
Tel.: (39) 0733201681
Web Site: http://www.energogreen.com
Sales Range: $25-49.9 Million
Emp.: 3
Renewable Energy Consulting Services
N.A.I.C.S.: 541690
Fedealea Aoanzato *(Dir-Mktg)*

Fintel Energija a.d   (1)
Masarikova 5 21 sprat, 11000, Belgrade,
Serbia
Tel.: (381) 114418531
Web Site: https://www.fintelenergija.rs
Rev.: $20,024,557

Assets: $130,056,258
Liabilities: $111,896,042
Net Worth: $18,160,216
Earnings: $6,417,618
Fiscal Year-end: 12/31/2022
Electric Power Distribution Services
N.A.I.C.S.: 221115
Milan Novakovic *(CFO)*

FINTEL PLC

Fintel House St Andrews Road, Hud-
dersfield, HD1 6NA, United Kingdom
Tel.: (44) 1484439100
Web Site:
https://www.simplybizgroup.co.uk
Year Founded: 2002
SBIZ—(LSE)
Rev.: $82,329,132
Assets: $174,718,236
Liabilities: $83,666,964
Net Worth: $91,051,272
Earnings: $11,319,108
Fiscal Year-end: 12/31/19
Financial Consulting Services
N.A.I.C.S.: 541611

Subsidiaries:

Threesixty Services LLP   (1)
The Royals Altrincham Road, Manchester,
M22 4BJ, United Kingdom
Tel.: (44) 3707360360
Web Site:
https://www.threesixtyservices.co.uk
Financial Advice & Discretionary Manage-
ment Firm Services
N.A.I.C.S.: 523940

FINVOLUTION GROUP

Building G1 No 999 Dangui Road,
Pudong New District, Shanghai,
201203, China
Tel.: (86) 2131186888   Ky
Web Site: https://ir.finvgroup.com
Year Founded: 2007
FINV—(NYSE)
Rev.: $1,705,871,242
Assets: $3,276,075,794
Liabilities: $1,369,455,635
Net Worth: $1,906,620,160
Earnings: $347,232,386
Emp.: 4,144
Fiscal Year-end: 12/31/22
Online Financial Transaction Process-
ing Services
N.A.I.C.S.: 522320
Tiezheng Li *(Co-Founder, Vice Chm
& Chief Strategy Officer)*

FINZSOFT SOLUTIONS LIM-ITED

11 Britomart Place 37 Galway Street,
Britomart, 1010, Auckland, New Zea-
land
Tel.: (64) 95716800
Web Site: http://www.finzsoft.com
FIN—(NZX)
Rev.: $8,361,890
Assets: $8,258,490
Liabilities: $5,092,684
Net Worth: $3,165,806
Earnings: $44,628
Emp.: 90
Fiscal Year-end: 06/30/19
Software Development & Mainte-
nance Services
N.A.I.C.S.: 541511
Andrew Holliday *(Mng Dir)*

FIOR FAMILIE GMBH

Hegelstr 6, 40667, Meerbusch, Ger-
many
Tel.: (49) 17623974496
Web Site: https://fiorhome.de
Frozen Food Mfr & Distr
N.A.I.C.S.: 311412

FIORE EXPLORATION LTD.

Suite 3123-595 Burrard Street, PO

Fiore Exploration Ltd.—(Continued)

Box 49139, Three Bentall Centre,
Vancouver, V7X 1JI, BC, Canada
Tel.: (604) 609-6110   BC
Web Site: http://fioreexploration.com
Year Founded: 1988
Rev.: $32,748
Assets: $18,615,401
Liabilities: $242,965
Net Worth: $18,372,436
Earnings: ($3,241,318)
Fiscal Year-end: 01/31/17
Metal Mining
N.A.I.C.S.: 212290

FIORE GOLD LTD.
Suite 1410 120 Adelaide St West,
Toronto, M5H 1T1, ON, Canada
Tel.: (416) 639-1426
Web Site: http://www.fioregold.com
2FO—(BER)
Rev.: $53,742,000
Assets: $56,156,000
Liabilities: $16,837,000
Net Worth: $39,319,000
Earnings: $2,422,000
Fiscal Year-end: 09/30/19
Gold Mining Exploration Services
N.A.I.C.S.: 212220
Tim Warman (CEO)

FIPLASTO SA
Alsina 756, 1087, Buenos Aires,
1087, Argentina
Tel.: (54) 3407423000
Web Site: https://www.fiplasto.com.ar
FIPL—(BUE)
Sales Range: Less than $1 Million
Wood Material Mfr
N.A.I.C.S.: 321999
Guillermo Viegener (Chm)

FIPP S.A.
55 rue Pierre Charron, 75008, Paris,
France
Tel.: (33) 156524500
Web Site: https://www.f-i-p-p.com
FIPP—(EUR)
Sales Range: $1-9.9 Million
Asset Management Services
N.A.I.C.S.: 531390
Richard Lonsdale-Hands (Chm &
CEO)

FIRAN TECHNOLOGY GROUP CORPORATION
250 Finchdene Square, Toronto, M1X
1A5, ON, Canada
Tel.: (416) 299-4000   Ca
Web Site: https://www.ftgcorp.com
Year Founded: 1983
FTGFF—(OTCIQ)
Rev.: $70,111,063
Assets: $65,512,821
Liabilities: $26,950,328
Net Worth: $38,562,493
Earnings: $600,791
Emp.: 462
Fiscal Year-end: 11/30/22
Designer & Mfr of Custom-Made
Printed Circuit Boards & Recreational
Vehicles
N.A.I.C.S.: 334412
Hardeep Heer (CTO & VP-Engrg)

Subsidiaries:

FLYHT Aerospace Solutions Ltd. (1)
500 1212 - 31 Avenue NE, Calgary, T2E
7S8, AB, Canada
Tel.: (403) 250-9956
Web Site: https://www.flyht.com
Rev.: $16,201,018
Assets: $11,276,750
Liabilities: $7,007,870
Net Worth: $4,268,879
Earnings: ($571,355)
Emp.: 50

Fiscal Year-end: 12/31/2019
Aerospace Products Developer, Mfr & Tes-
ter
N.A.I.C.S.: 334511
Alana Forbes (CFO)

Subsidiary (US):

FLYHT Inc (2)
34 Brooks Rd, Sudbury, MA 01776-3406
Tel.: (978) 440-7803
Sales Range: $25-49.9 Million
Emp.: 5
Aviation Software Development Services
N.A.I.C.S.: 541511
Richard Hayden (Pres)

FTG Aerospace Inc. (1)
10 Commander Blvd, Toronto, M1S 3T2,
ON, Canada
Tel.: (416) 438-6076
Web Site: http://www.firantechnology.com
Sales Range: $25-49.9 Million
Emp.: 20
Mfr of Lighting Display Panels, Bezels, Key-
boards & Indicators for Aerospace Industry
N.A.I.C.S.: 336413
Randy Drake (Dir-Ops)

Subsidiary (US):

Airco Industries, Inc. (2)
5600 Blue Mound Rd, Fort Worth, TX
76131
Tel.: (817) 332-3806
Web Site: http://www.photo-etch.com
Emp.: 90
Aircraft Parts & Auxiliary Equipment Mfr
N.A.I.C.S.: 336413
Michael Tebrinke (Gen Mgr)

FTG Circuits - Chatsworth (1)
20750 Marilla St, Chatsworth, CA 91311
Tel.: (818) 407-4024
Web Site: http://www.ftgcorp.com
Emp.: 100
Printed Circuit Board Mfr
N.A.I.C.S.: 334412

FTG Circuits - Toronto (1)
250 Finchdene Square, Toronto, M1X 1A5,
ON, Canada
Tel.: (416) 299-4000
Sales Range: $50-74.9 Million
Emp.: 150
Printed Circuit Board Mfr
N.A.I.C.S.: 334412

FTG Circuits Fredericksburg Inc. (1)
1026 Warrenton Rd, Fredericksburg, VA
22406
Tel.: (540) 752-5511
Web Site: https://www.ftgcorp.com
Bare Printed Circuit Board Mfr
N.A.I.C.S.: 334412

Holaday Circuits, Inc. (1)
11126 Bren Rd W, Minnetonka, MN 55343-
9074
Tel.: (952) 933-3303
Web Site: http://www.holaday.com
Bare Printed Circuit Board Mfr
N.A.I.C.S.: 334412
Marshall Lewis (Pres & CEO)

IMI Inc. (1)
140 Hilldale Ave, Haverhill, MA 01832-3830
Tel.: (978) 373-9190
Web Site: http://www.imipcb.com
Bare Printed Circuit Board Mfr
N.A.I.C.S.: 334412
Pete Beaulieu (Pres)

FIRE & FLOWER HOLDINGS CORP.
Suite 400 Centre 1045241 Calgary
Trail NW, Edmonton, T6H 5G8, AB,
Canada
Web Site:
    http://www.fireandflower.com
FAF—(OTCIQ)
Rev.: $137,289,358
Assets: $174,354,566
Liabilities: $83,851,029
Net Worth: $90,503,538
Earnings: ($49,746,750)
Emp.: 398
Fiscal Year-end: 01/29/22

Healtcare Services
N.A.I.C.S.: 423450
John Chou (CFO)

Subsidiaries:

Friendly Stranger Holdings Corp. (1)
237 Queen St W, Toronto, M5V 1Z4, ON,
Canada
Tel.: (647) 374-5670
Web Site: https://friendlystranger.com
Cannabis Retailer
N.A.I.C.S.: 459991

PGED Corp. (1)
3000 Lawrence St, Denver, CO 80205
Web Site: https://potguide.com
Consumer Product Delivery Services
N.A.I.C.S.: 492110

Pineapple Express Delivery Inc. (1)
1150 Northside Rd Unit 12 & 13, Burlington,
L7M 1A5, ON, Canada
Tel.: (905) 745-5508
Web Site:
   https://pineappleexpressdelivery.com
Transportation Delivery Services
N.A.I.C.S.: 492110

FIRE EATER A/S
Volundsvej 17, 3400, Hillerod, Den-
mark
Tel.: (45) 70222769   DK
Web Site: http://www.fire-eater.com
Year Founded: 1974
Sales Range: $25-49.9 Million
Commercial & Industrial Fire Preven-
tion & Extinguishing Equipment Mfr &
Whslr
N.A.I.C.S.: 339999
Kristian Petersen (Mgr-Sls-Global)

Subsidiaries:

Fire Eater Hungaria Kft. (1)
Teleki U 57/C, 1184, Budapest, Hungary
Tel.: (36) 14020535
Web Site: http://www.fire-eater.com
Commercial & Industrial Fire Prevention &
Extinguishing Equipment Whslr
N.A.I.C.S.: 423990

Fire Eater Norge AS (1)
Tangen 16, 4070, Randaberg, Norway
Tel.: (47) 5141 9710
Web Site: http://www.fire-eater.com
Commercial & Industrial Fire Prevention &
Extinguishing Equipment Whslr
N.A.I.C.S.: 423990

Fire Eater Poland Sp. z oo (1)
Ul Zielona 52, 05-500, Piaseczno, Poland
Tel.: (48) 222 442 200
Fire Extinguisher Mfr & Distr
N.A.I.C.S.: 339999

Fire Eater Spain (1)
C / Vilamari 86-88 bajos, 08015, Barcelona,
Spain
Tel.: (34) 93 531 57 57
Fire Extinguisher Mfr & Distr
N.A.I.C.S.: 339999

Fire Eater spol. s.r.o. (1)
Modranska 11, 143 00, Prague, 4, Czech
Republic
Tel.: (420) 241773897
Web Site: http://www.fire-eater.com
Emp.: 2
Commercial & Industrial Fire Prevention &
Extinguishing Equipment Whslr
N.A.I.C.S.: 423990
Stanislav Musil (Mgr)

FIRE RIVER GOLD CORP.
1305 Welch St unit 115, Vancouver,
V7P 1B3, BC, Canada
Tel.: (604) 449-2026   BC
Web Site: https://yumybear.com
Year Founded: 1997
FVGCF—(OTCIQ)
Assets: $64,807
Liabilities: $822,003
Net Worth: ($757,196)
Earnings: ($147,924)
Fiscal Year-end: 10/31/19

Gold & Base Metals Exploration &
Mining Services
N.A.I.C.S.: 212220
Anthony K. Jackson (CEO)

FIRE ROCK HOLDINGS LIM-ITED
9th Floor Block 1 Chongwen Garden
Nanshan IPark, 3370 Liuxian Avenue
Nanshan District, Shenzhen, Guang-
dong, China
Tel.: (86) 75586111004   Ky
Web Site: http://www.firerock.hk
1909—(HKG)
Rev.: $79,805,613
Assets: $117,072,630
Liabilities: $11,617,499
Net Worth: $105,455,130
Earnings: $52,844,018
Emp.: 216
Fiscal Year-end: 12/31/20
Online Game Development Services
N.A.I.C.S.: 541511
Yong Huang (CEO)

FIREANGEL SAFETY TECH-NOLOGY GROUP PLC
Vanguard Centre, Coventry, CV4
7EZ, United Kingdom
Tel.: (44) 2477717700
Web Site:
    https://www.fireangeltech.com
Year Founded: 1998
FA—(AIM)
Rev.: $59,022,804
Assets: $46,267,024
Liabilities: $18,816,641
Net Worth: $27,450,383
Earnings: ($4,453,322)
Emp.: 153
Fiscal Year-end: 12/31/21
Other Communications Equipment
Manufacturing
N.A.I.C.S.: 334290
Mike Stilwell (Grp Dir-Fin)

Subsidiaries:

FireAngel Safety Technology
Limited (1)
Sir William Lyons Rd Vanguard Centre,
Coventry, CV4 7EZ, United Kingdom
Tel.: (44) 3300945830
Web Site: http://www.fireangel.co.uk
Security Alarm Distr
N.A.I.C.S.: 423610
Nick Rutter (Chief Product Officer)

FIREBIRD METALS LIMITED
Unit 38 460 Stirling Highway, Pepper-
mint Grove, Perth, 6011, WA, Austra-
lia
Tel.: (61) 62459818
Web Site:
    https://www.firebirdmetals.com.au
Year Founded: 2016
FRB—(ASX)
Rev.: $211,457
Assets: $4,383,445
Liabilities: $217,396
Net Worth: $4,166,049
Earnings: ($620,807)
Fiscal Year-end: 06/30/23
Metal Exploration Services
N.A.I.C.S.: 213114
Alex Neuling (Sec)

FIREBRICK PHARMA LIMITED
Level 10 440 Collins St, Melbourne,
3000, VIC, Australia
Tel.: (61) 1300301874   AU
Web Site:
    https://www.firebrickpharma.com
Year Founded: 2012
FRE—(ASX)
Rev.: $40,749
Assets: $1,944,617
Liabilities: $330,210

Net Worth: $1,614,407
Earnings: ($4,435,073)
Fiscal Year-end: 06/30/23
Pharmaceutical Product Mfr & Distr
N.A.I.C.S.: 325412
Peter Molloy (Chm)

FIREFINCH LIMITED

Tel.: (61) 861497977
Web Site:
https://www.firefinchltd.com
FFX—(ASX)
Rev.: $364,909
Assets: $109,986,566
Liabilities: $24,272,493
Net Worth: $85,714,073
Earnings: $275,797,437
Fiscal Year-end: 12/31/22
Mineral Exploration Services
N.A.I.C.S.: 212220
Eric Hughes (CFO & Sec)

FIREFLY BOOKS

50 Staples Avenue Unit 1, Richmond
Hill, L4B 0A7, ON, Canada
Tel.: (416) 499-8412
Web Site:
http://www.fireflybooks.com
Year Founded: 1977
Rev.: $25,568,578
Emp.: 60
Book Sellers & Publisher
N.A.I.C.S.: 513130

FIREFLY POINT OF VIEW LTD.

Milton House 33a Milton Road,
Hampton, London, United Kingdom
Tel.: (44))20 8746 2991   UK
Web Site: http://www.f-pov.com
Year Founded: 2019
Interior & Lighting Consultant
N.A.I.C.S.: 541410
Bernie Tan-Hayes (CEO)

Subsidiaries:

Firefly Lighting Design Ltd.   (1)
Milton House 33a Milton Road, Hampton,
TW12 2LL, Mddx, United Kingdom
Tel.: (44) 20 8746 2991
Web Site:
http://www.fireflylightingdesign.com
Lighting Designs & Consultancy
N.A.I.C.S.: 335132
Peter Robert Veale (Principal)

Subsidiary (Non-US):

Point of View Design Pty Limited   (2)
Level 3 207 Clarence Street, Sydney, 2000,
NSW, Australia
Tel.: (61) 298186355
Web Site: http://www.pov.com.au
Lighting Design Consulting Services
N.A.I.C.S.: 541490
Mark Elliot Iald (Principal)

FIREFOX GOLD CORP.

Suite 650 - 1021 West Hastings St,
Vancouver, V6E 0C3, BC, Canada
Tel.: (778) 938-1994
Web Site:
https://www.firefoxgold.com
Year Founded: 2017
FFOXF—(OTCQB)
Rev.: $26,493
Assets: $1,645,107
Liabilities: $194,252
Net Worth: $1,450,855
Earnings: ($2,645,845)
Fiscal Year-end: 12/31/22
Metal Exploration Services
N.A.I.C.S.: 213114
Janice Craig (Sec)

FIRERING STRATEGIC MINER-ALS PLC

Immeuble Arc-en-ciel 2eme Etage
Coin Av Chardy et Boulevard, boite
postale numero 3121, Lagunaire Pla-

teau, 01, Abidjan, Cote d'Ivoire
Tel.: (225) 2520004600
Web Site: https://www.fireringplc.com
Year Founded: 2019
FRG—(AIM)
Assets: $6,776,067
Liabilities: $1,769,755
Net Worth: $5,006,312
Earnings: ($227,215)
Fiscal Year-end: 12/31/22
Mineral Mining Services
N.A.I.C.S.: 212390

FIRESTONE DIAMONDS PLC

The Triangle 5-17 Hammersmith
Grove, London, W6 0LG, United
Kingdom
Tel.: (44) 2087417810
Web Site:
http://www.firestonediamonds.com
Sales Range: Less than $1 Million
Emp.: 61
Diamond Mining & Exploration
N.A.I.C.S.: 212390
Paul Bosma (CEO)

Subsidiaries:

Asam Resources SA (Proprietary)
Limited   (1)
Metropolitan Ctr Coen Steytler Ave, PO Box
8399, Foreshore, 8001, Cape Town, West-
ern Cape, South Africa   **(100%)**
Tel.: (27) 214466040
Diamond Exploration & Mining Services
N.A.I.C.S.: 212390

Liqhobong Mining Development Co-
.(Proprietary) Limited   (1)
32 Erwee St, PO Box 87, 9730, Ficksburg,
South Africa
Tel.: (27) 519334495
Web Site: http://www.goldenmile.co.za
Sales Range: $50-74.9 Million
Emp.: 10
Diamond Mining Services
N.A.I.C.S.: 212390
Tes Sourie (Mgr)

FIRESTONE VENTURES INC.

36 Toronto St Ste 1050, Toronto,
M5C 2C5, ON, Canada
Tel.: (416) 583-1430   BC
Web Site:
https://www.firestoneventures.com
Year Founded: 1987
FSVEF—(OTCEM)
Assets: $434,555
Liabilities: $546,488
Net Worth: ($111,933)
Earnings: ($110,427)
Fiscal Year-end: 03/31/23
Mineral Exploration Services
N.A.I.C.S.: 213114
Keith Michael Barron (Pres & CEO)

FIRETAIL RESOURCES LIM-ITED

T2 64-68 Hay Street, Subiaco, 6008,
WA, Australia
Tel.: (61) 893222338   AU
Web Site:
https://www.firetailresources.com.au
Year Founded: 2021
FTL—(ASX)
Rev.: $108,230
Assets: $9,495,775
Liabilities: $375,607
Net Worth: $9,120,168
Earnings: ($552,336)
Fiscal Year-end: 06/30/23
Exploration & Mining Services
N.A.I.C.S.: 213115
Brett Grosvenor (Chm)

FIRETRADE ENGINEERING PCL

No 1198/5 Rama 9 Road, Phatthana-

kan Subdistrict Suan Luang District,
Bangkok, 10250, Thailand
Tel.: (66) 2026047092
Web Site: https://www.firetrade.co.th
Year Founded: 1999
FTE—(THA)
Rev.: $33,422,381
Assets: $34,521,533
Liabilities: $9,807,698
Net Worth: $24,713,836
Earnings: $3,435,858
Fiscal Year-end: 12/31/23
Fire Protection Equipments Distr
N.A.I.C.S.: 423850
Pornsak Limboonyaprasert (Chm)

Subsidiaries:

Fire Inspector Company Limited   (1)
1198/5 Rama IX Road, Phatthanakan Suan
Luang, Bangkok, 10250, Thailand
Tel.: (66) 2 026 0493
Web Site: https://www.fire-inspector.com
Fire Suppression Services
N.A.I.C.S.: 922160
Krisada Lehavanich (Sls Mgr)

FIREWEED ZINC LTD.

Suite 1020 800 Pender Street, Van-
couver, V6C 2V6, BC, Canada
Tel.: (604) 646-8360
Web Site: https://fireweedmetals.com
FWEDF—(OTCQB)
Rev.: $226,156
Assets: $40,342,724
Liabilities: $4,026,653
Net Worth: $36,316,071
Earnings: ($9,998,819)
Fiscal Year-end: 12/31/22
Mineral Exploration Services
N.A.I.C.S.: 213114
Pamela O'Hara (VP-Sustainability)

FIRICH ENTERPRISES CO., LTD.

10F No 75 Sec 1 Sin Tai Wu Rd,
Sijhih Dist, New Taipei City, 221, Tai-
wan
Tel.: (886) 226981446
Web Site: http://www.fecpos.com
Year Founded: 1995
Sales Range: $25-49.9 Million
Emp.: 320
Point-of-Sale Systems & Equipment
Mfr
N.A.I.C.S.: 334118
Bill Hsu (Pres & Gen Mgr)

Subsidiaries:

Firich Korea Co., Ltd.   (1)
Room 901 Byeoksan Digital Valley 6th 219
Gasan digital 1-ro, Geumcheon-gu, Seoul,
153-704, Korea (South)
Tel.: (82) 215667031
Computer Peripheral Equipment Distr
N.A.I.C.S.: 423430
Kwon Charlie (Gen Mgr)

Firich USA Inc.   (1)
41668 Christy St, Fremont, CA 94538
Tel.: (510) 683-9188
Computer Peripheral Equipment Distr
N.A.I.C.S.: 423430

Tiga Gaming, Inc.   (1)
Building11 No 75 Sec 1 Hsintai, Hsichih
Dist, New Taipei City, 221, Taiwan
Tel.: (886) 226982786
Computer Peripheral Equipment Distr
N.A.I.C.S.: 423430
Hsu Ming-Che (Chm)

FIRM CAPITAL APARTMENT REAL ESTATE INVESTMENT TRUST

163 Cartwright Avenue, Toronto, M6A
1V5, ON, Canada
Tel.: (416) 635-0221
Web Site:
https://www.firmcapital.com
Year Founded: 1988

FCA.UN—(TSXV)
Rev.: $12,074,882
Assets: $124,404,400
Liabilities: $70,992,807
Net Worth: $53,411,593
Earnings: ($8,709,932)
Fiscal Year-end: 12/31/23
Real Estate Investment Services
N.A.I.C.S.: 531210
Eli Dadouch (Vice Chm)

FIRM CAPITAL MORTGAGE INVESTMENT CORPORATION

163 Cartwright Avenue, Toronto, M6A
1V5, ON, Canada
Tel.: (416) 635-0221
Web Site:
https://www.firmcapital.com
Year Founded: 2010
FC—(TSX)
Rev.: $34,558,234
Assets: $436,414,353
Liabilities: $167,820,250
Net Worth: $268,594,103
Earnings: $20,615,795
Emp.: 1
Fiscal Year-end: 12/31/20
Financial Investment Services
N.A.I.C.S.: 523999
Eli Dadouch (Pres & CEO)

FIRM CAPITAL PROPERTY TRUST

163 Cartwright Avenue, Toronto, M6A
1V5, ON, Canada
Tel.: (416) 635-0221
Web Site:
https://www.firmcapital.com
Year Founded: 2007
FCD.UN—(TSXV)
Rev.: $43,425,274
Assets: $481,294,398
Liabilities: $261,032,533
Net Worth: $220,261,864
Earnings: $11,604,486
Emp.: 1
Fiscal Year-end: 12/31/23
Real Estate Investment Trust
N.A.I.C.S.: 531390
Sandy Poklar (CFO)

FIRMCO LTD.

Firmin House 127 129 Stanley Road,
Ilford, IG1 1RQ, United Kingdom
Tel.: (44) 2085145544
Web Site: http://www.firmco.co.uk
Sales Range: $10-24.9 Million
Emp.: 33
Refurbishment Services
N.A.I.C.S.: 238390
Feargal McEneaney (Mng Dir)

FIRMENICH INTERNATIONAL SA

Rue de la Bergère 7, 1242, Satigny,
Switzerland
Tel.: (41) 227802211   CH
Web Site: https://www.firmenich.com
Year Founded: 1895
Emp.: 11,000
Holding Company; Fragrances & Fla-
vorings Mfr
N.A.I.C.S.: 551112
Patrick Firmenich (Chm)

Subsidiaries:

DRT Pinova Inc.   (1)
2801 Cook St, Brunswick, GA 31520
Tel.: (912) 265-3550
Web Site: https://www.pinovasolutions.com
Polyterpene Resin Product Mfr & Distr
N.A.I.C.S.: 325211

DRT-Anthea Aroma Chemicals Private Limited   (1)
502/503 5th Floor Sigma IT Park Rabale

Firmenich International SA—(Continued)

MIDC, Navi Mumbai, 400701, Maharashtra, India
Tel.: (91) 704 558 7328
Web Site: https://www.anthea-aromatics.in
Fragrance Chemical Mfr
N.A.I.C.S.: 325620
Vincent Paul *(Founder & Chm)*

Firmenich & Cia. Ltda (1)
Rod Raposo Tavares Km 26 150, Caixa Postal 25, Cotia, 06707000, Sao Paulo, Brazil (100%)
Tel.: (55) 1146178800
Sales Range: $125-149.9 Million
Emp.: 300
Mfr of Flavors, Perfumes & Chemicals
N.A.I.C.S.: 325620

Firmenich & Cie. S.A.S. (1)
41 Rue De Villiers, 92523, Paris, Neuilly Su Seine, France (100%)
Tel.: (33) 40887342
Web Site: http://www.firmenich.com
Sales Range: $50-74.9 Million
Emp.: 250
Sales & Research & Development of Perfumes
N.A.I.C.S.: 325620

Firmenich (Philippines), Inc. (1)
2nd Fl Utrc 3 2289 Vonchinoroces Extn Ave, PO Box 4853, Makati, 1200, Manila, Philippines (100%)
Tel.: (63) 28120711
Sales Range: $25-49.9 Million
Emp.: 20
Mfr of Perfumes, Flavors & Chemicals
N.A.I.C.S.: 325620
Cynthia Macapugay *(Gen Mgr)*

Firmenich (Pty.) Ltd. (1)
Half Way House, Pvt Bag X113, Midrand, 1685, Gauteng, South Africa (100%)
Tel.: (27) 116530700
Web Site: http://www.firmenich.com
Sales Range: $25-49.9 Million
Emp.: 35
Mfr & Sales of Perfumes
N.A.I.C.S.: 325620
Andre Ferreira *(Mng Dir)*

Firmenich (Thailand) Ltd. (1)
12/F Vanit Building II 1126/2 New Petchburi Road, Makkasan Rajthavee, Bangkok, 10400, Thailand
Tel.: (66) 2 022 4220
Perfume Ingredient Mfr & Distr
N.A.I.C.S.: 325620

Firmenich Aromatics (China) Co. Ltd. (1)
No 3901 Jin Du Road, Xinzhuang Industry Park Minhang, Shanghai, 201108, China
Tel.: (86) 2133238000
Perfume Ingredient Mfr & Distr
N.A.I.C.S.: 325620

Firmenich Aromatics (India) Pvt Ltd. (1)
Novell House 13th Road, MIDC Andheri East, Mumbai, 400 093, India (100%)
Tel.: (91) 2266400564
Web Site: http://www.firmenich.com
Sales Range: $25-49.9 Million
Emp.: 100
Mfr of Perfumes, Flavors & Chemicals
N.A.I.C.S.: 325620
Satish Rao *(Chm & Mng Dir)*

Firmenich Aromatics (Shanghai) Co. (1)
No 3901 Jin Du Rd Xinzhuang Industry Park, Shanghai, 201108, China (100%)
Tel.: (86) 2154428000
Web Site: http://www.firmenich.com
Sales Range: $25-49.9 Million
Emp.: 10
Mfr of Perfumes, Flavors & Chemicals
N.A.I.C.S.: 325620

Firmenich Aromatics (Zhangjiagang) Co., Ltd. (1)
No 1328 Gangfeng Road, Jiangsu Yangtze River International Chemical Industry Park, Zhangjiagang, 315633, Jiangsu, China
Tel.: (86) 5128 883 6500
Perfume Ingredient Mfr & Distr
N.A.I.C.S.: 325620

Firmenich Aromatics Production (India) Pvt. Ltd. (1)
9th Floor Arena Space CTS 20 New Shyam Nagar Road, Off JVLR Behind Majas BEST Depot Jogeshwari East, Mumbai, 400 060, India
Tel.: (91) 2266196000
Perfume Ingredient Mfr & Distr
N.A.I.C.S.: 325620

Firmenich Asia Pte. Ltd. (1)
10 Tuas W Rd, Singapore, 638377, Singapore (100%)
Tel.: (65) 63472888
Sales Range: $50-74.9 Million
Emp.: 200
Mfr of Perfumes, Flavors & Chemicals
N.A.I.C.S.: 325620
Matthew Furner *(Mng Dir)*

Firmenich Belgium S.A. (1)
Avenue Jean Etienne Lenoir 9, Louvain-la-Neuve, 1348, Belgium
Tel.: (32) 10453445
Flavoring Agent Mfr
N.A.I.C.S.: 311930

Firmenich Bjorge Biomarin AS (1)
Bjorge, Ellingsoy, 6057, Alesund, Norway
Tel.: (47) 70115300
Cosmetic & Toilet Product Whslr
N.A.I.C.S.: 424210

Firmenich Co Ltd (1)
Bum Ah Building 5th floor Yangjae-Dong, Seocho-Ku, Seoul, 137-889, Korea (South)
Tel.: (82) 25775026
Cosmetic & Toilet Product Whslr
N.A.I.C.S.: 424210

Firmenich Denmark ApS (1)
Agro Food Park 13, Arhus, Denmark
Tel.: (45) 89413700
Cosmetic & Toilet Product Whslr
N.A.I.C.S.: 424210

Firmenich Dis Tic. Ltd. STI (1)
Ayazmadere Caddesi Aksit Plaza No 12 Kat 9 Fl, Fulya, 34349, Istanbul, Turkiye (100%)
Tel.: (90) 2123274212
Web Site: http://www.firmenich.com
Sales Range: $25-49.9 Million
Emp.: 25
Fragrance & Flavors Research
N.A.I.C.S.: 541380
Dilek Arlas *(Gen Mgr)*

Firmenich FZ-LLC (1)
Dubiotech Park Nucleotide Complex - Office 122, PO Box 502648, Dubai, United Arab Emirates
Tel.: (971) 43636900
Cosmetic & Toilet Product Whslr
N.A.I.C.S.: 424210

Firmenich Ges.m.b.H. (1)
Dresdner Strasse 89, 1200, Vienna, Austria (100%)
Tel.: (43) 12705453
Sales Range: $25-49.9 Million
Emp.: 36
Sales of Perfumes
N.A.I.C.S.: 325620

Firmenich GmbH (1)
Alfred Nobel Str 46 56, 50169, Kerpen, Germany (100%)
Tel.: (49) 223769010
Web Site: http://www.firmenich.com
Sales Range: $50-74.9 Million
Emp.: 100
Distr of Perfumes & Aromas
N.A.I.C.S.: 424210

Firmenich Grasse SAS (1)
Parc Industriel Les Bois de Grasse, PO Box 92113, 06131, Grasse, France
Tel.: (33) 493708080
Cosmetic & Toilet Product Whslr
N.A.I.C.S.: 424210

Firmenich Incorporated (1)
250 Plainsboro Rd, Plainsboro, NJ 08536
Tel.: (609) 452-1000
Web Site: http://www.firmenich.com
Fragrances & Flavorings Mfr
N.A.I.C.S.: 325620

Subsidiary (Domestic):

Agilex Flavors & Fragrances, Inc. (2)

140 Centennial Ave, Piscataway, NJ 08854-3908
Tel.: (800) 542-7662
Web Site: https://www.agilexfragrances.com
Fragrance Mfr
N.A.I.C.S.: 325620

Essex Laboratories Inc. (2)
115 Klein Rd, Chehalis, WA 98532-8426
Tel.: (360) 740-1770
Web Site: http://www.essexlabs.com
Sales Range: $10-24.9 Million
Emp.: 8
Essential Oil Mfr
N.A.I.C.S.: 311942
Mark Morlan *(Founder & CFO)*

Plant (Domestic):

Firmenich (2)
424 S Atchison St, Anaheim, CA 92805
Tel.: (714) 535-2871
Web Site: http://www.firmenich.com
Powdered Citru Juice & Fragrance Mfr
N.A.I.C.S.: 325199
Michael Westerfield *(Mgr-Mfg)*

Firmenich (2)
100 N Vly St, New Ulm, MN 56073-1601
Tel.: (507) 354-4188
Web Site: http://www.firmenich.com
Sales Range: $25-49.9 Million
Emp.: 80
Mfr of Industrial Foods
N.A.I.C.S.: 311513
Donna Wheaton *(Coord-Domestic Shipment)*

Unit (Domestic):

Firmenich International Fine Fragrance Center (2)
625 Madison Ave 17th Fl, New York, NY 10022-3213
Tel.: (212) 489-4800
Web Site: http://www.firmenich.com
Sales Range: $50-74.9 Million
Emp.: 80
Perfumes & Fragrances Mfr
N.A.I.C.S.: 424690
Carole Dumont *(Sr Mgr-Fragrance Dev)*

Subsidiary (Domestic):

Natural Flavors, Inc. (2)
268 Doremus Ave, Newark, NJ 07105
Tel.: (973) 589-1230
Web Site: http://www.firmenich.com
Flavoring Extracts And Syrups, Nec
N.A.I.C.S.: 311942

Senomyx, Inc. (2)
4767 Nexus Centre Dr, San Diego, CA 92121 (100%)
Tel.: (858) 646-8300
Web Site: http://www.senomyx.com
Sales Range: $25-49.9 Million
Flavor & Fragrance Development Services
N.A.I.C.S.: 541715
Douglas J. Lucht *(VP-Fin)*

Firmenich LLC (1)
Entrance 5 building B 31 Shabolovka Street, 115162, Moscow, Russia
Tel.: (7) 4959810500
Cosmetic & Toilet Product Whslr
N.A.I.C.S.: 424210

Firmenich LLC (1)
1B Salutnaya St Office 144, 04111, Kiev, Ukraine
Tel.: (380) 444004157
Cosmetic & Toilet Product Whslr
N.A.I.C.S.: 424210

Firmenich Limited (1)
73 Kenneth Rd, Balgowlah, 2093, NSW, Australia (100%)
Tel.: (61) 299079344
Web Site: http://www.firmenich.com
Sales Range: $25-49.9 Million
Emp.: 30
Mfr of Perfumes & Flavors
N.A.I.C.S.: 325620

Firmenich Productions S.A.S. (1)
766 Rd Firmenich, PO Box 23, 40260, Castets, France (100%)
Tel.: (33) 558550255

Sales Range: $25-49.9 Million
Emp.: 34
Mfr of Aroma Chemicals
N.A.I.C.S.: 325199
Marc Ciano *(Mng Dir)*

Firmenich S.A. (1)
Avenida El Dorado No 98-43, Interior 3, Bogota, DC, Colombia (100%)
Tel.: (57) 14254343
Web Site: http://www.firmenich.com
Sales Range: $50-74.9 Million
Emp.: 120
Mfr of Perfumes, Flavors & Chemicals
N.A.I.C.S.: 325620

Firmenich S.A. (1)
Avda De Madrid 213, 8014, Barcelona, Spain (100%)
Tel.: (34) 934905808
Sales Range: $25-49.9 Million
Emp.: 20
Mfr & Sales of Perfumes
N.A.I.C.S.: 325620

Firmenich S.A.I.C. y F. (1)
Colectora Panamericana Este 25 201, Don Torcuato, Buenos Aires, 1611, Argentina (85%)
Tel.: (54) 1147485200
Web Site: http://www.firmenich.com
Sales Range: $25-49.9 Million
Emp.: 50
Mfr & Sales of Perfumes & Flavors
N.A.I.C.S.: 325620

Firmenich S.p.A. (1)
Via Fortezza 7, Milan, 20126, Italy (100%)
Tel.: (39) 02270731
Web Site: http://www.firmenich.com
Sales Range: $25-49.9 Million
Emp.: 25
Sales of Perfumes
N.A.I.C.S.: 456120

Firmenich Sp.z o.o (1)
Ul Chrzanowska 10, Grodzisk Mazowiecki, 5825, Poland (100%)
Tel.: (48) 227552611
Web Site: http://www.firmenich.com
Sales Range: $25-49.9 Million
Emp.: 15
Mfr & Sales of Perfumes
N.A.I.C.S.: 325620
Tomasz Bielak *(Gen Mgr)*

Firmenich UK Ltd. (1)
Hayes Road, Southall, UB2 5NN, Middlesex, United Kingdom (100%)
Tel.: (44) 2088436111
Web Site: http://www.firmenich.com
Sales Range: $50-74.9 Million
Emp.: 120
Research & Development of Flavors & Perfumes
N.A.I.C.S.: 325620

Firmenich UK Ltd. (1)
Dalton Airfield Industrial Est, YO73HE, Thirsk, North Yorkshire, United Kingdom (100%)
Tel.: (44) 845576400
Web Site: http://www.firmenich.com
Sales Range: $25-49.9 Million
Emp.: 50
Research & Development of Flavors & Perfumes
N.A.I.C.S.: 325620

Firmenich Vietnam LLC (1)
11th Floor Unit 4 Green Power Building 35 Ton Duc Thang Street, District 1, Ho Chi Minh City, Vietnam
Tel.: (84) 822205390
Cosmetic & Toilet Product Whslr
N.A.I.C.S.: 424210

Firmenich Wellingborough (UK) Ltd (1)
Denington Road Dennington Industrial Estate, Wellingborough, NN8 2QJ, Northamptonshire, United Kingdom
Tel.: (44) 1933304200
Cosmetic & Toilet Product Whslr
N.A.I.C.S.: 424210

Firmenich de Mexico S.A. de C.V. (1)
Jose Vasconcelos No 105 Floors 7 and 8 Col Hipodromo Condesa, Delegacion Benito

Juarez, 06100, Mexico, Cuauhtemoc,
Mexico   **(100%)**
Tel.: (52) 5553402000
Sales Range: $25-49.9 Million
Emp.: 50
Mfr of Perfumes & Flavors
N.A.I.C.S.: 325620

Kunming Firmenich Aromatics Co.
Ltd.   **(1)**
Guo Jia Ao Jin Ma Si, East Suburb, Kun-
ming, 650216, China   **(100%)**
Tel.: (86) 8713808286
Web Site: http://www.firmenich.com
Sales Range: $50-74.9 Million
Emp.: 119
Mfr of Aromas
N.A.I.C.S.: 325199

Les Derives Resiniques Et Terpe-
niques SA   **(1)**
30 rue Gambetta, PO Box 206, 40105, Dax,
Cedex, France
Tel.: (33) 5 58 56 62 00
Web Site: http://www.drt.fr
Resin Mfr
N.A.I.C.S.: 325211
Laurent Labatut *(Pres & CEO)*

Subsidiary (Domestic):

ACTION PIN SA   **(2)**
Z I de Cazalieu CS 60030, 40260, Castets,
France
Tel.: (33) 558550700
Web Site: http://www.action-pin.fr
Chemical Products Mfr
N.A.I.C.S.: 325199

Subsidiary (Non-US):

DCI-Brazil   **(2)**
Rua Padre Ildefonso Penalba 187 - Todos
os Santos, Rio de Janeiro, 20775 020, Bra-
zil
Tel.: (55) 2132782844
Web Site: http://www.dci.com.br
Chemical Products Distr
N.A.I.C.S.: 424690

Subsidiary (US):

DRT America, Inc.   **(2)**
24 Cathedral Pl Ste 409, Saint Augustine,
FL 32084
Tel.: (904) 819-7188
Chemical Products Distr
N.A.I.C.S.: 424690

Subsidiary (Non-US):

DRT Specialty Chemicals (Wuxi) Co.,
Ltd.   **(2)**
Land Plot B31E 100 Mei Yu Road, Wuxi
National High New Tech, Wuxi, 214028,
China
Tel.: (86) 51088556768
Chemical Products Distr
N.A.I.C.S.: 424690

Subsidiary (Domestic):

Granel SA   **(2)**
166 Chemin Du Bouscat, Lesperon, 40260,
France
Tel.: (33) 558566200
Chemical Products Distr
N.A.I.C.S.: 424690

Societe Bearnaise de Synthese
S.A.S.   **(2)**
23 Rue Bossuet, BP 181, 91160,
Longjumeau, Essonne, France
Tel.: (33) 169097785
Web Site: http://www.pcas.com
Sales Range: $1-9.9 Million
Emp.: 12
Pharmaceutical Chemicals Mfr
N.A.I.C.S.: 325998
Christian Moretti *(Mgr)*

Nihon Firmenich K.K.   **(1)**
Kowa-Kawasaki Nishiguchi Bldg 66-2
Horikawacho, Saiwai-ku, Kawasaki, 212-
0013, Kanagawa, Japan   **(100%)**
Tel.: (81) 445436111
Web Site: http://www.firmenich.com
Sales Range: $50-74.9 Million
Emp.: 70
Perfumes, Flavors & Chemicals Mfr

N.A.I.C.S.: 325620

Branch (Domestic):

Nihon Firmenich K.K. - Osaka
Branch   **(2)**
3 floor Wakasugi Grand Bldg, Tenjinbashi
2-5-25 Kita Ku, Osaka, 530 0041, Japan
Tel.: (81) 663534061
Web Site: http://www.firmenich.com
Sales Range: $25-49.9 Million
Mfr of Perfumes, Flavors & Chemicals
N.A.I.C.S.: 325620

PT Firmenich Aromatics
Indonesia   **(1)**
Jl Maligi VIII Lot S-1 Kawasan Industri KIIC,
Telukjambe-Karawang Barat, Karawang,
41361, Jawa Barat, Indonesia
Tel.: (62) 2678631801
Cosmetic & Toilet Product Whslr
N.A.I.C.S.: 424210
Rachmat Suyatno *(Mgr-Supply Chain Proj-
ect)*

PT Firmenich Indonesia   **(1)**
Jl Tanah Abang II No 78, Jakarta, 10150,
Indonesia   **(100%)**
Tel.: (62) 213863977
Sales Range: $25-49.9 Million
Emp.: 80
Mfr of Perfumes, Flavors & Chemicals
N.A.I.C.S.: 325620
Dixy Olyviardy *(Gen Mgr)*

Suzhou Firmenich Aromatics Co.
Ltd.   **(1)**
No 3901 Jin Du Rd Xinzhuang Industrial
Park, Shanghai, 201108, Jiangsu,
China   **(100%)**
Tel.: (86) 2154428000
Web Site: http://www.firmenich.com
Sales Range: $25-49.9 Million
Emp.: 20
Mfr of Aromas
N.A.I.C.S.: 325199

FIROUZA ENGINEERING COM-
PANY
9th Km Karaj Makhsous Road,
1399617911, Tehran, Iran
Tel.: (98) 21 445224156
Web Site:
http://www.firouzacranes.com
Year Founded: 1967
Emp.: 300
Crane Mfr
N.A.I.C.S.: 333923
Ghasem Ebrahimi Majd *(Mng Dir)*

FIRST ABACUS FINANCIAL
HOLDINGS CORPORATION
Unit 2904A East Tower, Philippine
Stock Exchange Centre Exchange
Road Ortigas Center, Pasig, 1600,
Philippines
Tel.: (63) 286678900
Web Site:
https://www.firstabacusfinancial.com
Year Founded: 1994
FAF—(PHI)
Rev.: $9,269,043
Assets: $135,767,096
Liabilities: $118,722,774
Net Worth: $17,044,322
Earnings: ($2,920,454)
Emp.: 75
Fiscal Year-end: 12/31/20
Holding Company
N.A.I.C.S.: 551112
Paulino S. Soo *(Chm & CEO)*

FIRST ABU DHABI BANK
P.J.S.C.
Al Qurm - Business Park, PO Box
6316, Abu Dhabi, United Arab Emir-
ates
Tel.: (971) 26811511   AE
Web Site: https://www.bankfab.com
Year Founded: 1968
FAB—(ABU)
Rev.: $7,689,084,096

Assets: $302,157,269,059
Liabilities: $270,840,592,914
Net Worth: $31,316,676,145
Earnings: $3,653,498,614
Emp.: 6,765
Fiscal Year-end: 12/31/22
Commercial Banking Services
N.A.I.C.S.: 522110
James Burdett *(CFO)*

Subsidiaries:

Abu Dhabi National Islamic Finance
Pvt. JSC   **(1)**
Golden Beach tower Building Corniche
Street, PO Box 40057, Abu Dhabi, United
Arab Emirates   **(100%)**
Tel.: (971) 24104444
Islamic Banking Services
N.A.I.C.S.: 522110

Abu Dhabi National Leasing LLC   **(1)**
One NBAD Tower 17th Floor Sheikh Khalifa
Street, PO Box 4, Abu Dhabi, United Arab
Emirates   **(100%)**
Tel.: (971) 26112000
Web Site: http://www.adnl.ae
Sales Range: $50-74.9 Million
Emp.: 25
Financial Lending Services
N.A.I.C.S.: 522220
Yousef Abdulla *(Mng Dir)*

Abu Dhabi National Properties
PrJC   **(1)**
Muroor Road Street 4 Opposite Madinat
Zayed Shopping Centre, PO Box 3520, Abu
Dhabi, United Arab Emirates   **(100%)**
Tel.: (971) 2 659 4888
Web Site: http://www.nbad.com
Property Management Services
N.A.I.C.S.: 531210

FAB Private Bank (Suisse) SA   **(1)**
Quai de l'Ile 5, PO Box 5055, 1211, Ge-
neva, Switzerland
Tel.: (41) 227075000
Banking Services
N.A.I.C.S.: 522110

FAB Properties   **(1)**
Unite 1A Building 14 Gate 7/4, PO Box
488178, Dubai, United Arab Emirates
Tel.: (971) 43710129
Web Site: http://www.fabproperties.ae
Real Estate Manangement Services
N.A.I.C.S.: 531390
Jasim Al Ali *(CEO)*

First Abu Dhabi Bank Misr S.A.E   **(1)**
Al Salam Axis New Cairo 1, 4391044,
Cairo, Egypt
Tel.: (20) 16555
Web Site: https://www.fabmisr.com.eg
Retail & Commercial Banking
N.A.I.C.S.: 522110

First Abu Dhabi Bank USA N.V.   **(1)**
1430 K St NW Ste 400, Washington, DC
20005
Tel.: (202) 842-7900
N.A.I.C.S.: 522110

Mismak Properties Co. LLC   **(1)**
FAB Business Park Office AL Qurm area
right behind Khalifa Park, PO Box 94453,
the Ministry of Labour and diagonally
across ADNOC Ground floor, Abu Dhabi,
United Arab Emirates
Tel.: (971) 26354444
Web Site: https://www.mismak.ae
Real Estate Services
N.A.I.C.S.: 531390
Jasim Al Ali *(CEO)*

NBAD Americas N.V.   **(1)**
1430 K St Nw Ste 400, Washington, DC
20005   **(100%)**
Tel.: (202) 842-7900
Sales Range: $50-74.9 Million
Emp.: 22
Banking Services
N.A.I.C.S.: 522299
Nagy S. Kolta *(Exec VP)*

NBAD Private Bank (Suisse) SA   **(1)**
Quai de l Ile 5, PO Box 5055, 1211, Ge-
neva, Switzerland   **(100%)**
Tel.: (41) 227075000

Web Site: http://www.nbadsuisse.ch
Private Banking Services
N.A.I.C.S.: 523150
Tony Zeiger *(Head-Investment Grp)*

NBAD Securities LLC   **(1)**
Corniche Road HH Sheikh Sultan Building,
Abu Dhabi, United Arab Emirates **(100%)**
Tel.: (971) 26161600
Web Site: http://www.nbadsecurities.com
Securities Brokerage & Dealing Services
N.A.I.C.S.: 523150
Mohammad Ali Yasin *(Mng Dir)*

FIRST ADVISORY GROUP LIM-
ITED
Wuhrstrasse 6, PO Box 86, Vaduz,
9490, Liechtenstein
Tel.: (423) 236 3000   LI
Web Site:
http://www.firstadvisorygroup.com
Sales Range: $100-124.9 Million
Emp.: 200
Financial Consulting Services
N.A.I.C.S.: 523991
Angelika Moosleithner *(Owner &
Member-Mgmt Bd)*

FIRST AL NOOR MODARABA
96-A Sindhi Muslim Housing Society,
Karachi, 7440, Pakistan
Tel.: (92) 2134558268
Web Site: https://www.fanm.co
Year Founded: 1992
FANM—(PSX)
Rev.: $127,051
Assets: $954,291
Liabilities: $41,509
Net Worth: $912,782
Earnings: $1,923
Emp.: 9
Fiscal Year-end: 06/30/23
Financial Services
N.A.I.C.S.: 523999
Zainuddin Aziz *(CEO)*

FIRST ALUMINIUM NIGERIA
PLC
2 Akilo Street, Ogba Ikeja, Lagos,
Nigeria
Tel.: (234) 1 342 8302   NG
Web Site: http://www.fanplc.com
Year Founded: 1991
Rev.: $25,816,395
Assets: $27,182,631
Liabilities: $12,984,606
Net Worth: $14,198,025
Earnings: $577,308
Emp.: 222
Fiscal Year-end: 12/31/17
Aluminium Products Mfr
N.A.I.C.S.: 331313
Callistus N. Udalor *(Exec Dir)*

FIRST AMERICAN SCIENTIFIC
CORP.
30758 South Fraser Way #201, Ab-
botsford, V2T 6L4, BC, Canada
Tel.: (604) 850-8959   NV
Web Site: http://www.fasc.net
Year Founded: 1995
Sales Range: Less than $1 Million
Kinetic Disintegration System Devel-
oper & Marketer
N.A.I.C.S.: 562219
John Brian Nichols *(Pres, CEO,
Treas & Sec)*

FIRST AMERICAN URANIUM
INC.
1240-890 W Pender St, Vancouver,
V6C 1H2, BC, Canada
Tel.: (604) 683-3995   BC
Web Site:
https://firstamericanuranium.com
Year Founded: 2020
PROP—(CNSX)
Assets: $143,325

First American Uranium Inc.—(Continued)

Liabilities: $127,234
Net Worth: $16,091
Earnings: ($183,620)
Fiscal Year-end: 12/31/21
Mineral Exploration Services
N.A.I.C.S.: 212220
Mike England (CEO)

FIRST ANGUILLA TRUST COMPANY LIMITED

Mitchell House, PO Box 174, The Valley, Anguilla
Tel.: (264) 4988800
Web Site:
   http://www.firstanguilla.com
Sales Range: $25-49.9 Million
Emp.: 14
Offshore Financial Services
N.A.I.C.S.: 525990
John Dyrud (Chm, Mng Dir & Legal Counsel)

FIRST ASIA HOLDINGS LIMITED

Suite 823-825 8/F Ocean Center Harbour City 5 Canton Road, Tsim Sha Tsui, Kowloon, China (Hong Kong)
Tel.: (852) 31523168
Web Site:
   http://www.firstasiaholdings.com
Sales Range: $1-9.9 Million
Emp.: 8
Property Development & Management Services
N.A.I.C.S.: 531390
Luk Lai Ching (Chm, Pres & CEO)

Subsidiaries:

First Asia Properties (M) SdnBhd **(1)**
No 31-07-07 Lebuh Nipah 5, Bayan Lepas, 11940, Penang, Malaysia
Tel.: (60) 4 237 0836
Property Development & Management Services
N.A.I.C.S.: 531390
Max Shangkar (Mgr)

PT. First Asia Indonesia **(1)**
The Room Wisma BNI 46 Jl Jend Sudirman kav 1 1 08, Jakarta, 10220, Indonesia
Tel.: (62) 21 574 5555
Property Development & Management Services
N.A.I.C.S.: 531390

FIRST ASSET INVESTMENT MANAGEMENT INC.

95 Wellington Street West Suite 1400, Toronto, M5J 2N7, ON, Canada
Tel.: (416) 642-1289   Ca
Web Site: http://www.firstasset.com
Sales Range: $50-74.9 Million
Emp.: 20
Investment & Asset Management Services
N.A.I.C.S.: 523940
Lee Goldman (Sr VP & Portfolio Mgr)

Subsidiaries:

JFT Strategies Fund **(1)**
2 Queen Street East 20 Floor, Toronto, M5C 3G7, ON, Canada
Tel.: (416) 640-1289
Web Site: http://www.firstasset.com
Rev.: $12,084,670
Assets: $185,307,457
Liabilities: $43,495,476
Net Worth: $141,811,981
Earnings: $5,720,169
Fiscal Year-end: 12/31/2019
Closed-End Investment Fund
N.A.I.C.S.: 525990

FIRST ATLANTIC NICKEL CORP

Suite 1890 1075 West Georgia Street, Vancouver, V6E 3C9, BC, Canada
Tel.: (604) 687-2038   BC
Web Site: http://www.arcpacific.ca
Year Founded: 2011
ACPRF—(OTCIQ)
Assets: $1,134,879
Liabilities: $489,492
Net Worth: $645,387
Earnings: ($1,897,928)
Fiscal Year-end: 01/31/23
Metal Mining
N.A.I.C.S.: 212290
Jim Henning (CFO)

FIRST AU LIMITED

Level 1 123 Whitehorse Road, PO Box 82, Balwyn, 3103, VIC, Australia
Tel.: (61) 398170700   AU
Web Site: https://www.firstau.com
FAU—(ASX)
Rev.: $152,013
Assets: $1,892,891
Liabilities: $144,272
Net Worth: $1,748,619
Earnings: ($1,252,586)
Fiscal Year-end: 12/31/23
Investment Management Service
N.A.I.C.S.: 523940
Ryan Skeen (CEO & Mng Dir)

FIRST BAKING CO., LTD.

3-6-1 Ogawahigashi-cho, Kodaira, 187-8611, Tokyo, Japan
Tel.: (81) 423480211
Web Site:
   https://www.daiichipan.co.jp
Year Founded: 1947
2215—(TKS)
Rev.: $187,473,780
Assets: $125,705,700
Liabilities: $81,669,710
Net Worth: $44,035,990
Earnings: $3,360,660
Emp.: 298
Fiscal Year-end: 12/31/23
Confectionery Product Mfr & Distr
N.A.I.C.S.: 311351
Masanori Hosokai (Pres)

FIRST BROTHERS CO., LTD.

25F Marunouchi Building 2-4-1 Marunouchi Chiyoda-ku, Tokyo, 100-6325, Japan
Web Site:
   http://www.firstbrothers.com
3454—(TKS)
Rev.: $157,880,120
Assets: $637,674,600
Liabilities: $464,487,170
Net Worth: $173,187,430
Earnings: $22,588,740
Emp.: 184
Fiscal Year-end: 11/30/23
Real Estate Investment & Asset Management
N.A.I.C.S.: 531390
Tomoki Yoshihara (Exec Dir)

Subsidiaries:

First Brothers Asset Management Co., Ltd. **(1)**
25F Marunouchi Building 2-4-1 Marunouchi, Chiyoda-ku, Tokyo, 100-6325, Japan
Tel.: (81) 352195380
Web Site: https://www.firstbrothers.com
Asset Management Services
N.A.I.C.S.: 523940

First Brothers Capital Co., Ltd. **(1)**
25F Marunouchi Building 2-4-1 Marunouchi, Chiyoda-ku, Tokyo, 100-6325, Japan
Tel.: (81) 352195390
Web Site: https://www.firstbrothers.com
Investment Services
N.A.I.C.S.: 523999

First Brothers Development Co., Ltd. **(1)**

25F Marunouchi Building 2-4-1 Marunouchi, Chiyoda-ku, Tokyo, 100-6325, Japan
Tel.: (81) 352195585
Web Site: https://www.firstbrothers.com
Infrastructure Development Services
N.A.I.C.S.: 541330

Higashinihon Fudosan Co., Ltd. **(1)**
Higashinihon Fudosan Hirosaki Building 13-1 Kitakawarakecho, Hirosaki, 036-8012, Aomori Prefecture, Japan
Tel.: (81) 172350055
Web Site: https://www.firstbrothers.com
Real Estate Development Services
N.A.I.C.S.: 531390

The Fuji Facility Service, Inc. **(1)**
6F Nagahori Community Building 2-5-8 Minamisenba, Chuo-ku, Osaka, 542-0081, Japan
Tel.: (81) 661252123
Web Site: https://www.fujifs.jp
Emp.: 47
Security Services
N.A.I.C.S.: 561612

FIRST CANADIAN MANAGEMENT CORPORATION

Metrotower II 1050 - 4720 Kingsway, Burnaby, V5H 4N2, BC, Canada
Tel.: (604) 689-2467
Web Site: https://www.fcmc.ca
Investment Services
N.A.I.C.S.: 523999

Subsidiaries:

Lakeview Hotel Investment Corp. **(1)**
600 - 185 Carlton Street, Suite 600, Winnipeg, R3C 3J1, MB, Canada
Tel.: (204) 947-1161
Web Site: http://www.lakeviewhotels.com
Rev.: $10,908,046
Assets: $22,276,416
Liabilities: $42,333,291
Net Worth: ($20,056,875)
Earnings: $6,992,246
Fiscal Year-end: 12/31/2019
Investment Management Service
N.A.I.C.S.: 523940
Greg McCartney (Dir-Sls)

Subsidiary (Domestic):

1323785 Alberta Ltd. **(2)**
2622-39th Ave NE, Calgary, T1Y 7J9, AB, Canada
Tel.: (403) 735-3230
Web Site: http://www.lakeviewhotels.com
Investment Management Service
N.A.I.C.S.: 523940

FIRST CAPITAL CHINA CORPORATION

Room 1131 Xian KeJi Dian Building, Ba Gua Si Road, Futian District, Shenzhen, 518029, China
Tel.: (86) 775 23990959   DE
Year Founded: 1994
Investment Services
N.A.I.C.S.: 523999
Te Xiao Li (Chm, Pres & CFO)

FIRST CAPITAL HOLDINGS PLC

No 02 Deal Place, 300, Colombo, Sri Lanka
Tel.: (94) 112639898
Web Site: https://firstcapital.lk
Year Founded: 1982
CFVF—(COL)
Rev.: $47,591,438
Assets: $221,784,192
Liabilities: $199,545,142
Net Worth: $22,239,050
Earnings: $8,812,170
Emp.: 91
Fiscal Year-end: 03/31/23
Investment Management Service
N.A.I.C.S.: 523940
Dinesh Schaffter (Mng Dir)

FIRST CAPITAL S.P.A.

Viale Luigi Majno 17/A, 20122, Milan, Italy
Tel.: (39) 0276390184   IT
Web Site: https://www.firstcapital.it
FIC—(ITA)
Sales Range: Less than $1 Million
Investment Services
N.A.I.C.S.: 523999
Renzo Torchiani (Partner)

FIRST CAPITAL SECURITIES CO., LTD.

16th Floor Investment Bank Building, No 115 Fuhua 1st Road Futian Street Futian District, Shenzhen, 518046, China
Tel.: (86) 75523838868
Web Site:
   https://www.firstcapital.com.cn
Year Founded: 1998
002797—(SSE)
Rev.: $366,634,944
Assets: $6,712,088,760
Liabilities: $4,569,483,672
Net Worth: $2,142,605,088
Earnings: $56,273,724
Fiscal Year-end: 12/31/22
Investment Banking Services
N.A.I.C.S.: 523150
Fang Wang (Pres)

FIRST CAPITAL SECURITIES CORPORATION LIMITED

2nd & 3rd Floor Pace Mall Fortress Stadium, Lahore, Pakistan
Tel.: (92) 4236623245
Web Site: https://www.fcil.com.pk
Year Founded: 1994
FCSC—(LAH)
Rev.: $1,559,922
Assets: $36,362,139
Liabilities: $27,255,291
Net Worth: $9,106,848
Earnings: ($1,942,241)
Emp.: 8
Fiscal Year-end: 06/30/20
Investment Services
N.A.I.C.S.: 523999
Nadeem Hussain (Chm-FCMF)

Subsidiaries:

First Capital Equities Limited **(1)**
4th Floor Lakson Square Building No 1, Sarwar Shaheed Road, Karachi, Pakistan   **(67.27%)**
Tel.: (92) 21111226226
Web Site: https://www.firstcapital.com.pk
Rev.: $7,709
Assets: $4,860,201
Liabilities: $3,655,875
Net Worth: $1,204,325
Earnings: ($61,843)
Fiscal Year-end: 06/30/2023
Brokerage Services
N.A.I.C.S.: 523150
Mian Ehsan Ul Haq (CEO)

Lanka Securities Pvt. Ltd. **(1)**
228/1 Galle Road, 04, Colombo, Sri Lanka
Tel.: (94) 114706757
Web Site: https://www.lsl.lk
Securities Trading & Brokerage Services; Owned by First Capital Securities Corporation & Bank of Ceylon
N.A.I.C.S.: 523150

FIRST CHINA PHARMACEUTICAL GROUP, INC.

Room 1301 13th Floor CRE Building, 303 Hennessy Road, Wanchai, China (Hong Kong)
Tel.: (852) 2138 1668   NV
Web Site:
   http://www.firstchinapharma.com
Sales Range: $25-49.9 Million
Pharmaceuticals Distr
N.A.I.C.S.: 424210
Zhen Jiang Wang (Chm & CEO)

FIRST CHOICE PRODUCTS INC.
2076 Townline Road Suite 6, Abbotsford, V2T 6E5, BC, Canada
Tel.: (604) 853-2655 **AB**
Year Founded: 1989
Sales Range: $1-9.9 Million
Investment Company; Innovative Product Mfr
N.A.I.C.S.: 523999
David Martens *(Mgr-Products Div)*

FIRST CLASS METALS PLC
Suite 10 Freckleton Business Centre Freckleton Road, Blackburn, BB2 2AL, United Kingdom
Tel.: (44) 7488362641 **UK**
Web Site:
https://www.firstclassmetalsplc.com
Year Founded: 2021
FCM—(LSE)
Mineral Exploration Services
N.A.I.C.S.: 213115
James Knowles *(Chm)*

FIRST COPPER TECHNOLOGY CO., LTD.
No 170 Chung Cheng 4th Rd, Chien Chin Dist, Kaohsiung, Taiwan
Tel.: (886) 72814161
Web Site: https://www.fcht.com.tw
Year Founded: 1989
2009—(TAI)
Rev.: $86,534,841
Assets: $259,530,452
Liabilities: $63,976,583
Net Worth: $195,553,869
Earnings: ($310,474)
Emp.: 243
Fiscal Year-end: 12/31/23
Copper & Copper Alloy Strips Mfr
N.A.I.C.S.: 331420
Mao-Yang Hung *(Gen Mgr)*

FIRST CREDIT FINANCE GROUP LIMITED
21/F Fung House 1920 Connaught Road, Central, China (Hong Kong)
Tel.: (852) 2710 8918 **Ky**
Web Site:
http://www.firstcredit.com.hk
Year Founded: 2009
Sales Range: $10-24.9 Million
Holding Company
N.A.I.C.S.: 551112

FIRST DAWOOD PROPERTIES LIMITED
19th Floor Saima Trade Towers B II Chundrigar Road, Karachi, 74000, Pakistan
Tel.: (92) 2132270182
Web Site: https://firstdawood.com
Year Founded: 1994
FDIBL—(PSX)
Rev.: $120,954
Assets: $3,170,841
Liabilities: $1,157,318
Net Worth: $2,013,522
Earnings: $52,185
Emp.: 5
Fiscal Year-end: 06/30/23
Investment Banking Services
N.A.I.C.S.: 523150
Christopher John Aitken Andrew *(Chm)*

FIRST EFFORT INVESTMENTS LTD.
90 Morton Avenue East, Brantford, N3R 7J7, ON, Canada
Tel.: (519) 759-6411
Web Site:
http://www.campuscrew.com
Year Founded: 1979
Sales Range: $50-74.9 Million

Business Consultants
N.A.I.C.S.: 561499
Jim Turnoull *(VP)*

FIRST EIE SA
Chemin de la Vuarpilliere 29, 1260, Nyon, Switzerland
Tel.: (41) 223070630
Web Site: http://www.FirstEIE.com
Year Founded: 1979
Industrial Machinery Mfr
N.A.I.C.S.: 333248
Gregory Stoeckli *(CEO)*

FIRST ELITE CAPITAL MODARABA
50-A Garden Block New, Garden Town, Lahore, Pakistan
Tel.: (92) 4235442735
Web Site: https://www.fecm.com.pk
Year Founded: 1980
FECM—(PSX)
Rev.: $122,326
Assets: $586,025
Liabilities: $253,107
Net Worth: $332,918
Earnings: ($25,402)
Emp.: 13
Fiscal Year-end: 06/30/23
Financial Investment Services
N.A.I.C.S.: 523999
Muneeb Ahmed Dar *(Chm)*

Subsidiaries:

Indus Surveyors (Pvt.) Ltd. **(1)**
Office No 111 1st floor Siddiq Trade center 72-main Gulberg, Lahore, Pakistan
Tel.: (92) 42578173136
Web Site: https://www.indus.net.pk
Engineering Consulting Services
N.A.I.C.S.: 541330

FIRST FIDELITY LEASING MODARABA
93 B-1Canal Park Gulberg-II, Lahore, Pakistan
Tel.: (92) 423571346164
Web Site:
https://www.fidelitymodaraba.com
FFLM—(PSX)
Rev.: $149,201
Assets: $2,324,966
Liabilities: $254,285
Net Worth: $2,070,682
Earnings: ($18,054)
Emp.: 13
Fiscal Year-end: 06/30/21
Asset Management Services
N.A.I.C.S.: 523940
Wasim ul-Haq Osmani *(CEO)*

FIRST FINANCE CO.
King Abdullah 2nd st Building no 172, PO Box 144596, Khalda, Amman, 11814, Jordan
Tel.: (962) 65506740
Web Site: https://www.ffc.jo
Year Founded: 2006
FFCO—(AMM)
Rev.: $4,605,418
Assets: $72,701,020
Liabilities: $5,607,748
Net Worth: $67,093,273
Earnings: $1,608,345
Emp.: 67
Fiscal Year-end: 12/31/23
Financial Services
N.A.I.C.S.: 523999

FIRST FINANCE LIMITED
Jahangir Tower 3rd Floor 10 Kawran Bazar C/A, Dhaka, 1215, Bangladesh
Tel.: (880) 29145487 **BD**
Web Site: http://www.first-lease.com.bd
Year Founded: 1993
FIRSTFIN—(DHA)

Sales Range: $1-9.9 Million
Financial Services
N.A.I.C.S.: 525990
Faruk Ahmed Chowdhury *(Chm)*

FIRST FINANCIAL HOLDING CO., LTD.
18F 30 Sec 1 Chung King S Rd, Taipei, 100, Taiwan
Tel.: (886) 223111111
Web Site:
https://www.firstholding.com.tw
Year Founded: 2003
1FINH (LUX)
Rev.: $3,252,561,642
Assets: $138,492,646,656
Liabilities: $130,724,632,461
Net Worth: $7,768,014,195
Earnings: $702,279,367
Emp.: 9,924
Fiscal Year-end: 12/31/23
Holding Company
N.A.I.C.S.: 551112
Chien-Hao Lin *(Pres)*

Subsidiaries:

FCB International Leasing Co., Ltd. **(1)**
Room 1008 Jianwu Building 188 Wangdun Road, Suzhou Industrial Park, Jiangsu, China
Tel.: (86) 51262963678
Rental & Leasing Services
N.A.I.C.S.: 522220

First Capital Management Inc. **(1)**
Web Site: http://www.fcmi.com.tw
Capital Management Services
N.A.I.C.S.: 523940

First Commercial Bank (U.S.A.) **(1)**
200 E Main St, Alhambra, CA 91801 **(100%)**
Tel.: (626) 300-6000
Web Site: http://www.bankfcb.com
Sales Range: $50-74.9 Million
Commericial Banking
N.A.I.C.S.: 522110
Terry Ju *(CFO)*

First Commercial Bank Ltd. **(1)**
30 Chung King South Road Sec 1, Taipei, 100, Taiwan
Tel.: (886) 223481111
Web Site: http://www.firstbank.com.tw
Sales Range: $1-4.9 Billion
Commercial Banking Services
N.A.I.C.S.: 522110

Subsidiary (Domestic):

FCB Leasing Co., Ltd **(2)**
94 Chung Hsiao East Road Sec 6, Taipei, Taiwan
Tel.: (886) 2 3343 7099
Financial Lending Services
N.A.I.C.S.: 522220

First Financial Assets Management Co., Ltd. **(1)**
7F 94 Jhong Siao East Rd Sec 2, Taipei, 100, Taiwan
Tel.: (886) 233437000
Web Site: http://www.firstfinancial.com
Sales Range: $50-74.9 Million
Emp.: 80
Financial Assets Management Services
N.A.I.C.S.: 523999

First Financial Leasing (Chengdu) Ltd. **(1)**
No 04 05 18th Floor No 7 Xinguanghua Street, Jinjiang District, Chengdu, Sichuan, China
Tel.: (86) 2886587521
Rental & Leasing Services
N.A.I.C.S.: 522220

First Financial Management Consulting Co., Ltd. **(1)**
9th Floor 30 Chung King South Road Sec 1, Taipei, Taiwan **(100%)**
Tel.: (886) 223484982
Web Site: http://www.fhc.com.tw
Management Consulting Services
N.A.I.C.S.: 541618

First Life Insurance Co., Ltd. **(1)**
13F No 456 Section 4 Xinyi Road, Taipei, Taiwan
Tel.: (886) 800001110
Web Site: https://www.firstlife.com.tw
Insurance Services
N.A.I.C.S.: 524210

First Property and Casualty Insurance Agency Co., Ltd. **(1)**
9th Floor 30 Chung King South Road Sec 1, Taipei, 100, Taiwan **(100%)**
Tel.: (886) 223484277
Web Site: http://www.firstholding.com.tw
Direct Property & Casualty Insurance Carriers
N.A.I.C.S.: 524126

First Securities Inc. **(1)**
4th Floor No 22 Section 1 Chang'an East Road, Taipei, 104, Jhongshan District, Taiwan **(100%)**
Tel.: (886) 225636262
Web Site: https://www.firstsec.com.tw
Investment Banking & Securities Dealing
N.A.I.C.S.: 523150

Subsidiary (Non-US):

First Worldsec Securities Limited **(2)**
room 1003 10 / F Infinitus Plaza 199 Des Voeux Road Central, Hong Kong, China (Hong Kong)
Tel.: (852) 28677288
Web Site: http://www.firstworldsec.com.hk
Securities Brokerage Services
N.A.I.C.S.: 523150

First Securities Investment Trust Co., Ltd **(1)**
7F 6 Min Chuan E Road Sec 3, Taipei, 104, Taiwan
Tel.: (886) 2 2504 1000
Web Site: http://www.firstholding.com.tw
Investment Management Service
N.A.I.C.S.: 523940

First Taisec Securities Inc. **(1)**
4th Floor 6th Floor 7th Floor 27 An Ho Rd, Sec 1, Taipei, Taiwan **(100%)**
Tel.: (886) 227413434
Web Site: http://www.ffhc.com.tw
Investment Banking & Securities Dealing
N.A.I.C.S.: 523150

First Venture Capital Co., Ltd. **(1)**
9F 30 Chung King S Rd Sec 1, Taipei, 100, Taiwan **(100%)**
Tel.: (886) 223484981
Web Site: http://www.firstholding.com.tw
Sales Range: $50-74.9 Million
Emp.: 7
Financial Investment Activities
N.A.I.C.S.: 523999

FIRST FORTUNE INTERNATIONAL COMPANY LIMITED
No.194, Pantinwun U Shwe Bin Street Industrial Zone Part 1, Township 113, Dagon Myothit East, Yangon, Myanmar
Tel.: (95) 9954218873
Web Site: http://www.hgmetal.com
Year Founded: 2019
Steel Fabrication Mfg.
N.A.I.C.S.: 332312

FIRST GEN CORPORATION
6/F Rockwell Business Center Tower 3, Ortigas Avenue, Pasig, 1604, Philippines
Tel.: (63) 234496400 **PH**
Web Site:
https://www.firstgen.com.ph
Year Founded: 1998
FSGCY—(OTCQB)
Rev.: $2,474,748,000
Assets: $6,126,657,000
Liabilities: $2,825,531,000
Net Worth: $3,301,126,000
Earnings: $449,333,000
Emp.: 2,333
Fiscal Year-end: 12/31/23
Power Generation & Distr
N.A.I.C.S.: 221122

First Gen Corporation—(Continued)

Aloysius L. Santos *(VP)*

Subsidiaries:

Bac-Man Geothermal Inc. **(1)**
One Corporate Center, Pasig, 1605, Manila, Philippines
Tel.: (63) 26677332
Eletric Power Generation Services
N.A.I.C.S.: 221111

EDC Wind Energy Holdings, Inc. **(1)**
36th & 42nd Floor One Corporate Center Building Julia Vargas Avenue, Corner Meralco Avenue Ortigas, Pasig, 1005, Manila, Philippines
Tel.: (63) 2 755 2332
Eletric Power Generation Services
N.A.I.C.S.: 221111

Energy Development Corporation Peru S.A.C. **(1)**
Av Manuel Olguin 335 Oficina 1301 Edificio Link Tower, Santiago de Surco, Lima, Peru
Tel.: (51) 513120111
Web Site: http://www.edc.com.pe
Electric Power Distribution Services
N.A.I.C.S.: 221122

FG Bukidnon Power Corporation - Bukidnon Plant **(1)**
Damilag, Manolo Fortich, 8705, Bukidnon, Philippines
Tel.: (63) 24496593
Eletric Power Generation Services
N.A.I.C.S.: 221111

First Gas Power Corporation - Batangas Plant **(1)**
Sta Rita, Batangas, Philippines
Tel.: (63) 437239526
Web Site: http://www.firstgen.com.ph
Eletric Power Generation Services
N.A.I.C.S.: 221111

First Gen Hydro Power Corporation - Pantabangan Plant **(1)**
Barangay West Poblacion, Pantabangan, 3124, Nueva Ecija, Philippines
Tel.: (63) 6324496520
Eletric Power Generation Services
N.A.I.C.S.: 221111

FIRST GLOBAL DATA LIMITED
555 Richmond Street West Suite 918, Toronto, M5V 3B1, ON, Canada
Tel.: (416) 504-3813   **ON**
Web Site:
http://www.firstglobaldata.com
Year Founded: 2011
Assets: $6,885,513
Liabilities: $12,993,375
Net Worth: ($6,107,862)
Earnings: ($684,834)
Fiscal Year-end: 12/31/16
Financial Transaction Services
N.A.I.C.S.: 522320
Andre Itwaru *(Chm, Pres & CEO)*

FIRST GRAPHENE LIMITED
1 Sepia Close, Henderson, 6166, WA, Australia
Tel.: (61) 1300660448   **AU**
Web Site:
https://www.firstgraphene.net
Year Founded: 1920
M11—(DEU)
Rev.: $554,203
Assets: $11,813,694
Liabilities: $5,392,929
Net Worth: $6,420,765
Earnings: ($3,856,317)
Emp.: 21
Fiscal Year-end: 06/30/22
Graphite Mining
N.A.I.C.S.: 212290
Michael Bell *(CEO & Mng Dir)*

Subsidiaries:

2D Fluidics Pty Ltd **(1)**
1 Sepia Close, Henderson, 6166, WA, Australia

Tel.: (61) 1300660448
Web Site: https://www.2dfluidics.com
Fluidic Device Mfr
N.A.I.C.S.: 334514

First Graphene (UK) Ltd. **(1)**
The University of Manchester Sackville Street, Graphene Engineering and Innovation Centre, Manchester, M13 9PL, United Kingdom
Tel.: (44) 1618262350
Graphite Product Mfr
N.A.I.C.S.: 335991

FIRST GROWTH HOLDINGS LTD.
Unit 235, 4388 Still Creek Drive, Vancouver, V5C 6C6, BC, Canada
Tel.: (778) 588-5626   **BC**
Year Founded: 2011
Investment Services
N.A.I.C.S.: 523999
Ting Zhao *(CEO)*

FIRST HEARTLAND CAPITAL JSC
45 Khadzhi Mukan Street, 050059, Almaty, Kazakhstan
Tel.: (7) 7272581506
Web Site:
http://www.firstheartlandcapital.com
Asset Management Company
N.A.I.C.S.: 523999
Yevgeniy Pan *(Chm)*

Subsidiaries:

First Heartland Securities JSC **(1)**
Republic of Kazakhstan ul Khadzhi Mukan 45, 050059, Almaty, Kazakhstan
Tel.: (7) 7273901395
Brokerage Company
N.A.I.C.S.: 523999
Yevgenly Pan *(Chm)*

Subsidiary (Domestic):

First Heartland Jusan Bank JSC **(2)**
24 Syganak St, Nur-Sultan, 010000, Kazakhstan
Tel.: (7) 7172587711
Web Site: http://www.tsb.kz
Banking Services
N.A.I.C.S.: 522110
Galym Ordabayev *(Deputy Chm-Mgmt Bd)*

FIRST HEARTLAND JUSAN INVEST JSC
24 Syganak st, Nur-Sultan, 010000, Kazakhstan
Tel.: (7) 172644000
Web Site: http://www.jysaninvest.kz
Year Founded: 2004
FHJI—(KAZ)
Rev.: $1,267,835
Assets: $20,840,227
Liabilities: $5,979,791
Net Worth: $14,860,429
Earnings: $1,210,541
Emp.: 50
Fiscal Year-end: 12/31/20
Financial Investment Services
N.A.I.C.S.: 523940
Nurdaulet Aidossov *(CEO)*

FIRST HELIUM INC.
550 800 West Pender St, Vancouver, V6C 2V6, BC, Canada
Tel.: (778) 327-5799   **BC**
Web Site:
https://www.firsthelium.com
Year Founded: 2016
FHELF—(OTCQX)
Rev.: $4,289,405
Assets: $12,731,329
Liabilities: $2,077,611
Net Worth: $10,653,719
Earnings: ($5,171,949)
Fiscal Year-end: 03/31/23
Mineral Mining Services
N.A.I.C.S.: 213115

David L. Safton *(VP)*

FIRST HI-TEC ENTERPRISE CO., LTD.
No 3 Lane 43 Xingbang Rd, Taoyuan, 33068, Taiwan
Tel.: (886) 33767800
Web Site: https://www.fht.com.tw
Year Founded: 1988
5439—(TPE)
Rev.: $100,821,624
Assets: $119,552,043
Liabilities: $45,655,911
Not Worth: $73,806,132
Earnings: $11,576,306
Emp.: 706
Fiscal Year-end: 12/31/22
Printed Circuit Board Mfr
N.A.I.C.S.: 334412
Ching-Shan Chang *(Chm & Gen Mgr)*

FIRST HIGH-SCHOOL EDUCATION GROUP CO., LTD.
No 1 Tiyuan Road, Xishan District, Kunming, 650228, Yunnan, China
Tel.: (86) 87165155502   **Ky**
Web Site: https://ir.diyi.top
Year Founded: 2018
FHSEY—(OTCIQ)
Rev.: $36,864,477
Assets: $137,298,405
Liabilities: $115,775,781
Net Worth: $21,522,624
Earnings: ($9,781,098)
Emp.: 2,194
Fiscal Year-end: 12/31/23
Holding Company
N.A.I.C.S.: 551112
Shaowei Zhang *(Chm & CEO)*

FIRST HOTEL COMPANY LTD.
63 NanJing E Rd Sec 2, Taipei, Taiwan
Tel.: (886) 25418234
Web Site:
https://www.firsthoteltaipei.com
2706—(TAI)
Rev.: $11,226,528
Assets: $373,621,883
Liabilities: $49,840,771
Net Worth: $323,781,112
Earnings: $9,833,382
Fiscal Year-end: 12/31/23
Hotel Operator
N.A.I.C.S.: 721120
A S Ku *(Chm)*

FIRST HOTELS AB
Humlegardsgatan 22, 114 46, Stockholm, Sweden   **SE**
Web Site:
https://www.firsthotelsab.com
HOTEL—(OMX)
Rev.: $50,370
Assets: $20,359,085
Liabilities: $6,121,550
Net Worth: $14,237,535
Earnings: ($10,330,116)
Emp.: 9
Fiscal Year-end: 12/31/19
Hotel Management
N.A.I.C.S.: 721110
Thomas Gillespie *(CEO)*

FIRST HYDROGEN CORP.
755 Burrard Street Suite 440, Vancouver, V6Z 1X6, BC, Canada
Web Site: https://firsthydrogen.com
FIT—(DEU)
Rev.: $119,405
Assets: $3,163,136
Liabilities: $2,350,541
Net Worth: $812,595
Earnings: ($10,231,908)
Fiscal Year-end: 03/31/23
Commercial Machinery Mfr

N.A.I.C.S.: 333310
Nader Vatanchi *(CEO)*

FIRST IDAHO RESOURCES INC.
1873 12th Avenue West, Vancouver, V6J 2E7, BC, Canada
Tel.: (778) 899-0259   **Ca**
Web Site:
http://www.firstidahoresources.com
Rev.: $48
Assets: $232,438
Liabilities: $322,451
Net Worth: ($90,013)
Earnings: ($42,456)
Fiscal Year-end: 12/31/17
Metal Mining Services
N.A.I.C.S.: 212390
Li Hongjie *(CEO)*

FIRST INSURANCE CO.
King Abdullah II Street Khalda - Dabouq Circle Building no 95, PO Box 189, Amman, 11822, Jordan
Tel.: (962) 65777555
Web Site:
https://www.solidarity.com.jo
Year Founded: 2007
FINS—(AMM)
Rev.: $65,396,115
Assets: $85,664,671
Liabilities: $38,988,298
Net Worth: $46,676,374
Earnings: $3,220,417
Emp.: 165
Fiscal Year-end: 12/31/19
Insurance Services
N.A.I.C.S.: 524298
Ashraf Bseisu *(Chm)*

Subsidiaries:

Solidarity Bahrain B.S.C. **(1)**
Seef Mall Gate 10, Seef, Bahrain
Tel.: (973) 77911114
Web Site: https://www.solidarity.com.bh
Motor & Car Insurance Services
N.A.I.C.S.: 524298

FIRST INTERNATIONAL COMPUTER, INC.
No 300 Yang Guang St, Neihu, Taipei, 114, Taiwan
Tel.: (886) 287518751
Web Site: http://www.fic.com.tw
Year Founded: 1980
Sales Range: $1-4.9 Billion
Emp.: 1,250
Design & Mfr Computer Product & Electronic Components
N.A.I.C.S.: 334111
Frank Yang *(Project Mgr)*

FIRST INVESTEC MODARABA
406 4th Floor Trade Center I I Chundrigar Road, Karachi, Pakistan
Tel.: (92) 32211325
Financial Services
N.A.I.C.S.: 523999

FIRST INVESTMENT BANK AD
37 Dragan Tsankov Blvd, 1797, Sofia, Bulgaria
Tel.: (359) 28171100   **BG**
Web Site: https://www.fibank.bg
FIB—(BUL)
Rev.: $189,017,217
Assets: $7,448,947,136
Liabilities: $6,676,614,060
Net Worth: $772,333,076
Earnings: $54,072,398
Emp.: 2,990
Fiscal Year-end: 12/31/22
Banking Services
N.A.I.C.S.: 522110
Maya Lubenova Georgieva *(Deputy Chm-Supervisory Bd)*

Subsidiaries:

FI Health Insurance AD   **(1)**
2 Prof Alexander Fol St entr B 2nd Floor,
1700, Sofia, Bulgaria
Tel.: (359) 24456664
Web Site: http://www.fihealth.bg
Health Insurance Services
N.A.I.C.S.: 524114

**First Investment Bank Albania
Sh.a**   **(1)**
Blvd Deshmoret e Kombit, Twin Towers Nr
2 Kati 14/15, 1019, Tirana, Albania
Tel.: (355) 42276702
Web Site: http://www.fibank.al
Sales Range: $50-74.9 Million
Emp.: 40
Banking Services
N.A.I.C.S.: 521110
Bozhidar Todorov *(CEO)*

MyFin EAD   **(1)**
37 Dragan Tsankov Blvd, 1715, Sofia, Bulgaria
Tel.: (359) 70016429
Web Site: http://www.myfin.bg
Electronic Payment Processing Services
N.A.I.C.S.: 522320

FIRST INVESTMENT COMPANY K.S.C.C.

Al Hamra Tower Floor 68 Sharq, PO
Box 20230, Kuwait, 13063, Kuwait
Tel.: (965) 1804050
Web Site: https://www.fic.com.kw
ALOLA—(KUW)
Rev.: $13,879,931
Assets: $271,635,393
Liabilities: $182,224,034
Net Worth: $89,411,359
Earnings: ($72,614,196)
Emp.: 39
Fiscal Year-end: 12/31/22
Investment & Financial Services
N.A.I.C.S.: 523999
Bader Mohammed Al Qattan *(Chm)*

Subsidiaries:

**Gulf Bussiness Forms Company
W.L.L.**   **(1)**
Block 2 Plot 1 - Pepsi Cola Str, PO Box
26524, Subhan Industrial Area Safat, Kuwait, 13126, Kuwait
Tel.: (965) 24760331
Web Site: http://www.gulforms.com
Printing Products Mfr
N.A.I.C.S.: 333248

Masadar Energy Company for General Trading W.L.L.   **(1)**
Jibla Block 9 Abdulla al Mubarak st A14
Building Office 701, PO Box 314, Safat, Kuwait, 13004, Kuwait
Tel.: (965) 22469006
Web Site: http://www.masdar.com.kw
Trading Services
N.A.I.C.S.: 425120

FIRST ISRAEL MEZZANINE INVESTORS LTD.

Electra Tower 98 Yigal Alon Street,
Tel Aviv, 6789141, Israel
Tel.: (972) 3 565 2244   II
Web Site: http://www.fimi.co.il
Year Founded: 1996
Rev.: $3,000,000,000
Privater Equity Firm
N.A.I.C.S.: 523999
Ishay Davidi *(Founder & CEO)*

Subsidiaries:

Ashot Ashkelon Industries Ltd.   **(1)**
1 Ezra Yessodi St, PO B 21, Ashkelon,
7810001, Israel   **(85%)**
Tel.: (972) 86721511
Web Site: https://www.ashot.co.il
Rev.: $90,255,835
Assets: $188,024,586
Liabilities: $78,439,286
Net Worth: $109,585,300
Earnings: $9,002,625
Fiscal Year-end: 12/31/2023

Aircraft Engine & Engine Parts Manufacturing
N.A.I.C.S.: 336412

Subsidiary (US):

Reliance Gear Ltd.   **(2)**
616 Lamont Rd, Elmhurst, IL 60126
Tel.: (630) 543-6640
Web Site: http://www.reliancegear.com
Precision Gear Mfr
N.A.I.C.S.: 333612

E&M Computing Ltd.   **(1)**
6 Hahilazon St, Ramat Gan, 52522,
Israel   **(62.5%)**
Tel.: (972) 35766999
Web Site: https://www.emet.co.il
Rev.: $393,393,556
Assets: $242,101,391
Liabilities: $191,714,046
Net Worth: $50,387,346
Earnings: $8,338,168
Emp.: 1,400
Fiscal Year-end: 12/31/2023
Computer System Design Services
N.A.I.C.S.: 541512

TAT Technologies Ltd.   **(1)**
4 Habonim St, PO Box 143, Bnei Ayish,
Kiryat Gat, 8258204, Israel   **(53.8%)**
Tel.: (972) 88628500
Web Site: https://www.tat-technologies.com
Rev.: $84,556,000
Assets: $126,651,000
Liabilities: $51,081,000
Net Worth: $75,570,000
Earnings: ($1,562,000)
Emp.: 471
Fiscal Year-end: 12/31/2022
Aircraft Heat-Transfer Equipment & Component Parts Mfr
N.A.I.C.S.: 336412
Yair Raz *(Exec VP-Strategy-Global)*

Subsidiary (US):

Limco-Piedmont Inc.   **(2)**
5304 S Lawton Ave, Tulsa, OK
74107-9428   **(100%)**
Tel.: (918) 445-4300
Sales Range: $50-74.9 Million
Emp.: 170
Aviation Parts Mfr
N.A.I.C.S.: 336413
Mary Dowdy *(CFO)*

Subsidiary (Domestic):

Limco Airepair Inc.   **(3)**
5304 S Lawton Ave, Tulsa, OK
74107   **(100%)**
Tel.: (918) 445-4300
Web Site: http://www.limcoairepair.com
Aircraft Heat Transfer Manufacturing & Repair
N.A.I.C.S.: 336413
Yair Raz *(Pres)*

Piedmont Aviation Component Services LLC   **(3)**
1031 E Mountain St Bldg 320, Kernersville,
NC 27284   **(100%)**
Tel.: (336) 776-6300
Web Site: http://www.piedmontaviation.com
Aircraft Components Maintenance & Overhaul Services
N.A.I.C.S.: 336413
David Tennant *(Dir-Quality)*

Subsidiary (Domestic):

Turbochrome Ltd.   **(2)**
4 Ha-Bonim Street, South District, Kiryat
Gat, 82000, Israel   **(100%)**
Tel.: (972) 86603001
Web Site: http://www.turbochrome.com
Jet Engine & Turbine Components Mfr &
Repair Services
N.A.I.C.S.: 336412
Robert Iancu *(Chief Engr & Dir-QA)*

FIRST ISRAEL TURNAROUND ENTERPRISE

37 Mencham Begin Rd 29th Fl, Tel
Aviv, 67137, Israel
Tel.: (972) 36086838
Web Site: http://www.fiteinv.com
Year Founded: 2004

Sales Range: $25-49.9 Million
Emp.: 10
Privater Equity Firm
N.A.I.C.S.: 523999
Amiram Boehm *(CEO & Mng Partner)*

Subsidiaries:

Global Wire Ltd.   **(1)**
PO Box 56, Tel Aviv, 61000, Israel
Tel.: (972) 39269200
Mfr of Non-Ferrous Wires & Conductors
N.A.I.C.S.: 332618

FIRST JORDAN INVESTMENT COMPANY PLC

Al Rabyah Abdullah bin Rawaha st
building Nom 4, PO Box 17532, Amman, 11195, Jordan
Tel.: (962) 65562130
Web Site:
  http://www.firstjordan.com.jo
Year Founded: 2006
FRST—(AMM)
Rev.: $870,950
Assets: $84,104,797
Liabilities: $13,926,666
Net Worth: $70,178,130
Earnings: ($7,004,963)
Emp.: 11
Fiscal Year-end: 12/31/20
Commercial Investment Services
N.A.I.C.S.: 523999

FIRST JUKEN CO., LTD.

5-6-9 Higashi-Naniwa-cho, Amagasaki, 660-0892, Hyogo, Japan
Tel.: (81) 648685388
Web Site: https://www.f-juken.co.jp
Year Founded: 1999
8917—(TKS)
Rev.: $307,514,570
Assets: $373,458,660
Liabilities: $96,686,330
Net Worth: $276,772,330
Earnings: $12,414,590
Fiscal Year-end: 10/31/23
Building Construction Services
N.A.I.C.S.: 236115

FIRST LITHIUM MINERALS CORP.

77 King Street West Suite, PO Box
95, Toronto, M5K 1G8, ON, Canada
Tel.: (416) 402-2428   ON
Web Site: https://www.firstlithium.ca
Year Founded: 2017
PGPXF—(OTCIQ)
Assets: $3,905,598
Liabilities: $151,198
Net Worth: $3,754,400
Earnings: ($2,977,785)
Fiscal Year-end: 12/31/22
Mineral Exploration Services
N.A.I.C.S.: 213115
Aldo Moreno *(VP)*

FIRST MAJESTIC SILVER CORP.

1800 - 925 West Georgia Street,
Vancouver, V6C 3L2, BC, Canada
Tel.: (604) 688-3033   BC
Web Site:
  https://www.firstmajestic.com
Year Founded: 1998
AG—(NYSE)
Rev.: $624,221,000
Assets: $2,110,009,000
Liabilities: $698,711,000
Net Worth: $1,411,298,000
Earnings: ($114,276,000)
Emp.: 4,634
Fiscal Year-end: 12/31/22
Silver Exploration & Mining
N.A.I.C.S.: 212220
Douglas Penrose *(Chm)*

FIRST METRO INVESTMENT CORPORATION

45th Floor GT Tower International,
6813 Ayala Ave cor H V Dela Costa
St, Makati, 1227, Philippines
Tel.: (63) 288587900
Web Site:
  http://www.firstmetro.com.ph
Rev.: $34,371,122
Assets: $701,302,673
Liabilities: $408,694,756
Net Worth: $292,607,917
Earnings: $7,999,826
Emp.: 143
Fiscal Year-end: 12/31/19
Investment Banking Services
N.A.I.C.S.: 523150
Francisco C. Sebastian *(Chm)*

Subsidiaries:

**First Metro Asset Management,
Inc.**   **(1)**
18th Floor PS Bank Center 777 Paseo de
Roxas Ave cor, Sedeno St Salcedo Village,
Makati, 1226, Philippines
Tel.: (63) 288912860
Web Site: http://fami.com.ph
Investment Advisory Services
N.A.I.C.S.: 523940

Multi-Currency FX Corp.   **(1)**
5th Floor Metrobank Plaza Sen Gil Puyat
Avenue, Makati, 1200, Philippines
Tel.: (63) 28989863
Foreign Currency Exchange Services
N.A.I.C.S.: 523160

SBC Properties, Inc.   **(1)**
Lyceum of the Philippines 109 LP Leviste
St, Makati, 1227, Philippines
Tel.: (63) 2 840 5751
Investment Banking Services
N.A.I.C.S.: 523150

FIRST MICROFINANCE LAGHUBITTA BITTIYA SANSTHA LTD.

Kathmandu-30, PO Box 24800, Kathmandu, Nepal
Tel.: (977) 14525361
Web Site: https://www.fmdb.com.np
Year Founded: 2010
FMDBL—(NEP)
Rev.: $10,852,714
Assets: $69,239,644
Liabilities: $57,233,265
Net Worth: $12,006,379
Earnings: $1,502,008
Fiscal Year-end: 07/16/23
Commercial Banking Services
N.A.I.C.S.: 522110
Surendra Raj Regmi *(Chm)*

FIRST MINING GOLD CORP.

Suite 2070 - 1188 West Georgia
Street, Vancouver, V6E 4A2, BC,
Canada
Tel.: (604) 688-3033   BC
Web Site:
  https://www.firstmininggold.com
Year Founded: 2005
FMG—(DEU)
Rev.: $206,522
Assets: $208,816,347
Liabilities: $30,714,660
Net Worth: $178,101,688
Earnings: ($12,734,736)
Emp.: 33
Fiscal Year-end: 12/31/22
Mineral Mining Assets Holding Company
N.A.I.C.S.: 551112
Keith N. Neumeyer *(Chm)*

FIRST MUTUAL HOLDINGS LIMITED

ReNaissance Park Borrowdale Road,
PO Box BW178, Harare, Zimbabwe
Tel.: (263) 4886000

First Mutual Holdings Limited—(Continued)

FML—(ZIM)
Rev.: $21,186,046
Assets: $42,767,089
Liabilities: $24,817,321
Net Worth: $17,949,768
Earnings: $6,474,790
Emp.: 536
Fiscal Year-end: 12/31/20
Financial & Investment Services
N.A.I.C.S.: 523940
Douglas Hoto *(CEO)*

FIRST MUTUAL PROPERTIES LIMITED
First Floor First Mutual Park 100 Borrowdale Road, PO Box MP37, Mount Pleasant, Harare, Zimbabwe
Tel.: (263) 2428861214　　ZW
Web Site:
　https://firstmutualproperties.com
Year Founded: 2007
FMP—(ZIM)
Rev.: $113,104,004
Assets: $3,049,238,116
Liabilities: $3,046,400,621
Net Worth: $2,837,495
Earnings: $1,530,623,526
Emp.: 34
Fiscal Year-end: 12/31/23
Commercial & Retail Properties Maintenance Services
N.A.I.C.S.: 236220
Elisha Moyo *(Chm)*

FIRST NATIONAL ENERGY CORPORATION
44 Greystone Crescent, Georgetown, L7G 1G9, ON, Canada
Tel.: (416) 918-6987　　NV
Web Site:
　http://www.firstnationalenergy.com
FNEC—(OTCIQ)
Assets: $77,000
Liabilities: $826,000
Net Worth: ($749,000)
Earnings: ($48,000)
Fiscal Year-end: 12/31/19
Wind Energy Generation
N.A.I.C.S.: 221118
Peter Wanner *(CFO)*

Subsidiaries:

Pavana Power Corporation　　**(1)**
2000 Webber St Ste 3113, Sarasota, FL 34238
Tel.: (416) 918-6987
Web Site: http://www.pavanapower.com
Wind Power
N.A.I.C.S.: 221118

FIRST NATIONAL EQUITIES LIMITED
Room No 1007 10th Floor New Stock Exchange Building, Karachi, Pakistan
Tel.: (92) 2132472119
Web Site: https://www.fnetrade.com
FNEL—(PSX)
Rev.: $74,287
Assets: $6,642,995
Liabilities: $2,362,620
Net Worth: $4,280,375
Earnings: ($314,761)
Emp.: 22
Fiscal Year-end: 06/30/23
Stock Brokerage Services
N.A.I.C.S.: 523150
Shahzad Akbar *(Chm)*

FIRST NATIONAL FINANCIAL CORPORATION
16 York Street Suite 1900, Toronto, M5J 0E6, ON, Canada
Tel.: (416) 593-1100
Web Site: https://www.firstnational.ca
Year Founded: 2011

FN—(TSX)
Rev.: $655,218,953
Assets: $30,891,084,902
Liabilities: $30,444,558,695
Net Worth: $446,526,206
Earnings: $148,812,342
Emp.: 1,211
Fiscal Year-end: 12/31/20
Financial Services
N.A.I.C.S.: 522310
Stephen Smith *(Co-Founder, Chm & CEO)*

Subsidiaries:

First National Asset Management Inc.　　**(1)**
120 N Lake St Ste 1220, Chicago, IL 60602
Tel.: (312) 683-0800
Web Site: https://firstnationalassets.com
Financial Services
N.A.I.C.S.: 523999

FIRST NATIONAL MORTGAGE INVESTMENT FUND
36 Toronto Street Suite 710, Toronto, M5C 2C5, ON, Canada
Tel.: (416) 364-9188　　ON
Year Founded: 2012
Sales Range: $1-9.9 Million
Investment Services
N.A.I.C.S.: 523999
Richard G. Stone *(Pres & CEO)*

FIRST NATIONS BANK OF CANADA
300 224 4th Avenue South, Saskatoon, S7K 5M5, SK, Canada
Tel.: (306) 955-6739
Web Site: http://www.fnbc.ca
Year Founded: 1996
Rev.: $17,308,198
Assets: $514,371,371
Liabilities: $480,759,734
Net Worth: $33,611,637
Earnings: $2,014,877
Fiscal Year-end: 10/31/19
Commericial Banking
N.A.I.C.S.: 522110
Keith G. Martell *(CEO)*

FIRST NZ CAPITAL LIMITED
Level 39 ANZ Centre 23-29 Albert Street, Auckland, 1010, New Zealand
Tel.: (64) 9 302 5500
Web Site:
　http://www.firstnzcapital.co.nz
Investment Banking & Securities Broking Services
N.A.I.C.S.: 523150
James Lee *(CEO & Mng Dir)*

FIRST PACIFIC COMPANY LIMITED
24/F Two Exchange Square 8 Connaught Place, Central, China (Hong Kong)
Tel.: (852) 28424388　　HK
Web Site: https://www.firstpacific.com
Year Founded: 1981
0142—(OTCIQ)
Rev.: $10,304,900,000
Assets: $25,491,800,000
Liabilities: $15,126,000,000
Net Worth: $10,365,800,000
Earnings: $1,049,600,000
Emp.: 101,203
Fiscal Year-end: 12/31/22
Holding Company; Telecommunication Services; Property Development Services; Food Manufacturing
N.A.I.C.S.: 551112
Albert F. del Rosario *(Chm)*

Subsidiaries:

Infrontier Ltd.　　**(1)**
Ste 1203 05 The Broadway, 54 62 Lockhart

Rd, Wanchai, Hong Kong, China (Hong Kong)　　**(100%)**
Tel.: (852) 21110789
Web Site: http://www.infrontier.com
N.A.I.C.S.: 517111

PT Darya-Varia Laboratoria Tbk　**(1)**
South Quarter Tower C 18th -19th Floor Jl R A Kartini Kav 8, Jakarta, 12430, Indonesia　　**(89.5%)**
Tel.: (62) 212 276 8000
Web Site: https://www.darya-varia.com
Emp.: 1,497
Mfr & Marketer of Pharmaceutical, Sterile & Soft Gelatine Capsule
N.A.I.C.S.: 325412
Marlia Hayati Goestam *(Chm)*

PT Indofood Sukses Makmur Tbk.　　**(1)**
Sudirman Plaza Indofood Tower 27th Floor, Jl Jend Sudirman Kav 76-78, Jakarta, 12910, Indonesia　　**(50.1%)**
Tel.: (62) 2157958822
Web Site: https://www.indofood.com
Rev.: $7,254,032,498
Assets: $12,117,021,928
Liabilities: $5,592,831,906
Net Worth: $6,524,190,022
Earnings: $746,403,021
Emp.: 81,367
Fiscal Year-end: 12/31/2023
Food Mfr, Processor, Marketer & Distr
N.A.I.C.S.: 311423
Anthoni Salim *(Chm)*

Subsidiary (Non-US):

Indofood Agri Resources Ltd.　　**(2)**
8 Eu Tong Sen Street 16-96/97 The Central, Singapore, 059818, Singapore**(74.5%)**
Tel.: (65) 65572389
Web Site: https://www.indofoodagri.com
Oil Palm Seed Breeding, Cultivation, Milling, Refining, Branding & Marketing
N.A.I.C.S.: 111191
Suaimi Suriady *(Head-Edible Oils & Fats Div)*

Subsidiary (Domestic):

PT Salim Ivomas Pratama Tbk　　**(2)**
Sudirman Plaza Indofood Tower Lt 11 Jl Jend Sudirman Kav 76-78, Jakarta, 12910, Indonesia
Tel.: (62) 2157958822
Web Site: https://www.simp.co.id
Rev.: $1,039,211,636
Assets: $2,273,702,074
Liabilities: $863,145,204
Net Worth: $1,410,556,870
Earnings: $60,184,963
Emp.: 32,738
Fiscal Year-end: 12/31/2023
Palm Oil Mfr & Distr
N.A.I.C.S.: 311225
Mark Julian Wakeford *(Chm)*

PacificLight Power Pte. Ltd.　　**(1)**
8 Jurong Town Hall Road 12-01/06 The JTC Summit, Singapore, 609434, Singapore
Tel.: (65) 62661188
Web Site: https://www.pacificlight.com.sg
Electricity Power Generate Services
N.A.I.C.S.: 221118
Tat Ming Yu *(CEO)*

FIRST PARAMOUNT MODARABA
Suite No 107-108 PECHS Community Office Complex Block No 2 PECHS, Shahrah e Quaideen Road, Karachi, Pakistan
Tel.: (92) 21 34381037
Web Site: http://www.fpm.com.pk
Rev.: $1,411,392
Assets: $3,007,120
Liabilities: $1,618,822
Net Worth: $1,388,298
Earnings: $77,828
Emp.: 21
Fiscal Year-end: 06/30/19
Banking Services
N.A.I.C.S.: 522110
Wajih Hassan *(CEO)*

FIRST PERSON LTD.

1840 444-5th Ave SW, Calgary, T2P 2T8, AB, Canada
Tel.: (587) 577-9261　　Ca
Year Founded: 2021
Emp.: 1
Holding Company
N.A.I.C.S.: 551112
Cory J. Rosenberg *(Pres, CEO & Chm)*

FIRST PROPERTY GROUP PLC
32 St James Street, London, SW1A 1HD, United Kingdom
Tel.: (44) 2073400270
Web Site: https://www.fprop.com
FPO—(LSE)
Rev.: $9,910,376
Assets: $95,601,745
Liabilities: $44,024,236
Net Worth: $51,667,508
Earnings: ($5,528,907)
Emp.: 51
Fiscal Year-end: 03/31/24
Property Trading Services
N.A.I.C.S.: 531312
George R. W. Digby *(Sec & Dir-Fin)*

Subsidiaries:

First Property Asset Management Ltd.　　**(1)**
32 St James's Street, London, SW1A 1HD, United Kingdom
Tel.: (44) 2073400270
Web Site: http://www.fprop.com
Sales Range: $50-74.9 Million
Emp.: 10
Property Asset Management Services
N.A.I.C.S.: 525920

First Property Asset Management Romania SRL　　**(1)**
50-52 Strada Buzesti, 11015, Bucharest, Romania
N.A.I.C.S.: 533999
Bader Mohammed *(Chm)*

First Property Poland Sp. z o.o.　**(1)**
Plac Bankowy 2, 00-095, Warsaw, Poland
Tel.: (48) 22 331 7676
Real Estate Services
N.A.I.C.S.: 531210

First Property Romania SRL　　**(1)**
50-52 Strada Buzesti, 11015, Bucharest, Romania
Tel.: (40) 72 316 3074
Real Estate Services
N.A.I.C.S.: 531210
Przemyslaw Kiszka *(Mng Dir)*

FIRST PRUDENTIAL MODARABA
3 rd Floor Horizon Vista Plot No Commercial 10 Block-4 Clifton, Sarwar Shaheed Road Opposite Press Club, Karachi, Pakistan
Tel.: (92) 3537427374　　PK
Web Site:
　https://www.firstprudential.com
Year Founded: 1989
PMI—(PSX)
Rev.: $642,265
Assets: $3,626,898
Liabilities: $996,339
Net Worth: $2,630,559
Earnings: $354,518
Emp.: 15
Fiscal Year-end: 06/30/23
Financial Services
N.A.I.C.S.: 523999
Aftab Afroz Mahmoodi *(CFO)*

FIRST PUNJAB MODARABA
Office No 100 3rd Floor National Tower 28-Egerton Road, Lahore, 54000, Pakistan
Tel.: (92) 4236305131　　PK
Web Site:
　https://www.punjabmodaraba.com.pk
Year Founded: 1992
FPJM—(PSX)
Rev.: $827,658
Assets: $7,448,630
Liabilities: $7,435,375

Net Worth: $13,255
Earnings: ($322,253)
Emp.: 55
Fiscal Year-end: 12/31/22
Business Support Services
N.A.I.C.S.: 561499
Khalid Siddiq Tirmizey *(Chm)*

Subsidiaries:

Punjab Capital Securities (Private)
Limited   **(1)**
Office 319 3rd Floor Pakistan Stock Exchange Building, 19-Khayaban-e-Aiwan-e-Iqbal Garhi Shahu, Lahore, 54000, Punjab, Pakistan
Tel.: (92) 4236311051
Web Site: https://www.punjabcapital.com.pk
Equity Brokerage Services
N.A.I.C.S.: 523150
Asif Riaz *(Chm)*

FIRST QUANTUM MINERALS LTD.

1133 Melville Street Suite 3500 The Stack, PO Box 49314, Vancouver, V6E 4E5, BC, Canada
Tel.: (416) 361-6400   BC
Web Site: https://www.first-quantum.com
Year Founded: 1996
FM—(LSE)
Rev.: $4,067,000,000
Assets: $24,747,000,000
Liabilities: $14,085,000,000
Net Worth: $10,662,000,000
Earnings: ($51,000,000)
Emp.: 20,000
Fiscal Year-end: 12/31/19
Copper, Nickel, Gold, Zinc & Platinum Exploration, Development & Mining
N.A.I.C.S.: 212290
Juliet Wall *(Gen Mgr-Fin)*

Subsidiaries:

Cayeli Bakir Isletmeleri A.S   **(1)**
Cayeli, Rize, Turkiye   **(100%)**
Tel.: (90) 4645441544
Web Site: http://www.cayelibakir.com
Sales Range: $150-199.9 Million
Emp.: 500
Copper Ore & Nickel Ore Mining
N.A.I.C.S.: 212230

Cobre Las Cruces S.A.   **(1)**
3410 KM 4 100, Gerena, 41860, Seville, Spain
Tel.: (34) 955783475
Web Site: http://www.cobrelascruces.com
Emp.: 200
Copper Exploration Services
N.A.I.C.S.: 221118
Sean Whittome *(Mng Dir)*

FQM Australia Holdings Pty Ltd   **(1)**
L 1 24 Outram St, West Perth, 6005, Western Australia, Australia
Tel.: (61) 893460100
Precious Metal Mining Services
N.A.I.C.S.: 212230

Subsidiary (Domestic):

FQM Australia Nickel Pty Ltd   **(2)**
L 1 24 Outram Street, West Perth, Perth, 6005, WA, Australia
Tel.: (61) 893460100
Sales Range: $150-199.9 Million
Emp.: 500
Nickel Ore Mining Services
N.A.I.C.S.: 212230
Philip Pascall *(CEO)*

Subsidiary (Domestic):

Ravensthorpe Nickel Operations Pty. Ltd.   **(3)**
PO Box 100, Ravensthorpe, 6346, WA, Australia
Tel.: (61) 898382000
Nickel Ore Mining Services
N.A.I.C.S.: 212230
Rudi Badenhorst *(Mng Dir)*

FQML Scandinavia Inc.   **(1)**

543 Granville St 8th Fl, Vancouver, V6C 1X8, BC, Canada
Tel.: (604) 688-6577
Web Site: http://www.firstquantumminerals.com
Sales Range: $50-74.9 Million
Emp.: 2
Metal Mining Services
N.A.I.C.S.: 213114
Philip Pascall *(CEO)*

First Quantum (UK) Ltd.   **(1)**
1st Fl Mill House, Mill Bay Ln, Horsham, RH12 1SS, United Kingdom
Tel.: (44) 1403273484
Web Site: http://www.first-quantum.com
Sales Range: $75-99.9 Million
Emp.: 3
Mineral Exploration & Mining Services; Copper, Gold & Sulphuric Acid Production
N.A.I.C.S.: 212230

First Quantum Minerals (Australia) Pty Limited   **(1)**
Level 1 24 Outram St, Perth, 6005, WA, Australia
Tel.: (61) 892265777
Web Site: http://www.firstquantum.com
Sales Range: $50-74.9 Million
Emp.: 40
Mineral Exploration & Mining Services; Copper, Gold & Sulphuric Acid Production
N.A.I.C.S.: 212230

Minera Panama S.A.   **(1)**
Torre De Las Americas Torre A Piso 21, Punta Pacifica, Panama, Panama
Tel.: (507) 2945700
Web Site: http://www.cobrepanama.com
Copper Mining Services
N.A.I.C.S.: 212230

Ok Tedi Mining Limited   **(1)**
1 Dakon Road, Western Province, 332, Tabubil, Papua New Guinea
Tel.: (675) 6493000
Web Site: https://oktedi.com
Sales Range: $550-599.9 Million
Emp.: 2,000
N.A.I.C.S.: 212230

Pyhasalmi Mine Oy   **(1)**
Pl 51, 86801, Pyhasalmi, Finland   **(100%)**
Tel.: (358) 87696111
Web Site: http://www.inmetmining.com
Sales Range: $75-99.9 Million
Emp.: 250
Crushed & Broken Stone Mining
N.A.I.C.S.: 212319

FIRST REAL ESTATE INVESTMENT TRUST

333 Orchard Road 33-02 Hilton, Singapore, 238867, Singapore
Tel.: (65) 64350168
Web Site: https://www.first-reit.com
FESNF—(OTCIQ)
Rev.: $60,109,956
Assets: $758,675,393
Liabilities: $408,391,962
Net Worth: $350,283,431
Earnings: ($266,058,978)
Fiscal Year-end: 12/31/20
Real Estate Investment Trust
N.A.I.C.S.: 525990
Victor Tan Kok Mian *(CEO)*

FIRST RESOURCES LIMITED

7 Temasek Boulevard 24-01 Suntec Tower One, Singapore, 38987, Singapore
Tel.: (65) 66020200
Web Site: https://www.first-resources.com
Year Founded: 1992
FSRCY—(OTCIQ)
Rev.: $1,225,428,000
Assets: $1,832,725,000
Liabilities: $433,810,000
Net Worth: $1,398,915,000
Earnings: $339,120,000
Emp.: 22,267
Fiscal Year-end: 12/31/22
Oil Palm Cultivation Services

N.A.I.C.S.: 311224
Ming Seong Lim *(Chm)*

Subsidiaries:

PT Muriniwood Indah Industry   **(1)**
Jalan Jend Sudirman No 395, Pekanbaru, 28116, Riau, Indonesia
Tel.: (62) 76132888
Oil Palm Plantation Services
N.A.I.C.S.: 115112

PT Surya Intisari Raya   **(1)**
Wisma 777th Floor Jalan Letjen S Parman Kav 77, Jakarta, 11410, Indonesia
Tel.: (62) 2153670888
Oil Palm Plantation Services
N.A.I.C.S.: 115112

FIRST SECURITY ISLAMI BANK LIMITED

Rangs RD Center Block SE F Plot 03 Gulshan Avenue Gulshan1, Dhaka, 1212, Bangladesh
Tel.: (880) 255045700
Web Site: https://fsibplc.com
FIRSTSBANK—(CHT)
Rev.: $368,553,305
Assets: $5,623,037,290
Liabilities: $5,416,334,122
Net Worth: $206,703,167
Earnings: $27,013,617
Emp.: 5,406
Fiscal Year-end: 12/31/22
Commercial Banking Services
N.A.I.C.S.: 522110
Mohammad Saiful Alam *(Chm)*

Subsidiaries:

First Security Islami Capital & Investment Limited   **(1)**
12th Floor Al-Amin Center 25/A Dilkusha C/A, Dhaka, 1000, Bangladesh
Tel.: (880) 2223380794
Web Site: https://www.fsicibd.com
Banking Services
N.A.I.C.S.: 522110
Mohammad Saiful Alam *(Chm)*

FIRST SHANGHAI INVESTMENTS LIMITED

19th Floor Wing On Group Building 71 Des Voeux Road, Central, China (Hong Kong)
Tel.: (852) 25222101
Web Site: https://www.firstshanghai.com.hk
0227—(HKG)
Rev.: $43,628,333
Assets: $752,345,753
Liabilities: $448,894,095
Net Worth: $303,451,658
Earnings: ($7,502,610)
Emp.: 566
Fiscal Year-end: 12/31/22
Fund Management Services
N.A.I.C.S.: 523940
Wai Kin Yeung *(CFO & Sec)*

Subsidiaries:

Crimson Pharmaceutical (Shanghai) Company Limited   **(1)**
328 Bibo Rd Block C 4th Fl Zhang Jiang Hi-Tech Park, Shanghai, 201203, China
Tel.: (86) 2150805146
Drugs Mfr & Sales
N.A.I.C.S.: 325412

First Shanghai Capital Limited   **(1)**
19th Fl Wing On House 71 Des Voeux Rd, Central, China (Hong Kong)
Tel.: (852) 25222101
Web Site: http://www.mystockhk.com
Investment Advisory Services
N.A.I.C.S.: 523940

First Shanghai Direct Investments Limited   **(1)**
Rm 1903 19 F Wing On House 71 Des Voeux Rd, Central, China (Hong Kong)
Tel.: (852) 25222101
Web Site: http://www.mystockhk.com

Emp.: 120
Investment Management Service
N.A.I.C.S.: 523940

First Shanghai Finance Limited   **(1)**
Rm 1903 19 F Wing On House 71 Des Voeux Rd, Central, China (Hong Kong)
Tel.: (852) 25222101
Emp.: 120
Securities Brokerage Services
N.A.I.C.S.: 523150
Hong Qiu *(Chm & CEO)*

First Shanghai Financial Holding Limited   **(1)**
19th Fl Wing On House 71 Des Voeux Rd. Central, China (Hong Kong)
Tel.: (852) 25222101
Web Site: http://www.firstshanghai.com.hk
Brokerage & Investment Banking Services
N.A.I.C.S.: 523150

First Shanghai Futures Limited   **(1)**
19th Floor Wing On House 71 Des Voeux Rd, Central, China (Hong Kong)
Tel.: (852) 25222101
Web Site: http://www.firstshanghai.com.hk
Emp.: 120
Futures Brokerage Services
N.A.I.C.S.: 523160

First Shanghai Management Services Limited   **(1)**
Rm 1903 19 F Wing On House 71 Des Voeux Rd, Central, China (Hong Kong)
Tel.: (852) 25222101
Web Site: http://www.mystockhk.com
Sales Range: $25-49.9 Million
Emp.: 100
Secretarial Services
N.A.I.C.S.: 561410

First Shanghai Nominees Limited   **(1)**
Rm 1903 19 F Wing On House 71 Des Voeux Rd, Central, China (Hong Kong)
Tel.: (852) 25222101
Web Site: http://www.mystock.com
Office Administrative Services
N.A.I.C.S.: 561110

First Shanghai Properties Limited   **(1)**
Rm 1903 19 F Wing On Hse 71 Des Voeux Rd, Central, China (Hong Kong)
Tel.: (852) 25222101
Web Site: http://www.firstshanghai.com.hk
Emp.: 120
Property Investment & Development Services
N.A.I.C.S.: 531210

First Shanghai Securities Limited   **(1)**
19th Fl Wing On House 71 Des Voeux Rd, Central, China (Hong Kong)
Tel.: (852) 25222101
Web Site: http://www.firstshanghai.com.hk
Emp.: 100
Securities Brokerage Services
N.A.I.C.S.: 523150

First eFinance Limited   **(1)**
19th Fl Wing On House 71 Des Voeux Rd, Central, China (Hong Kong)
Tel.: (852) 25222101
Online Financial Transaction Processing Services
N.A.I.C.S.: 523910

IVF Centre (Hong Kong) Limited   **(1)**
Room 1322-1325 13th Floor Ocean Centre Harbour City 5 Canton Road, Tsim Sha Tsui, Kowloon, China (Hong Kong)
Tel.: (852) 34683168
Clinical Services
N.A.I.C.S.: 621399

International Medical Centre (Hong Kong) Limited   **(1)**
22 Des Voeux Road Central, MTR Central Station Exit C, Hong Kong, China (Hong Kong)
Tel.: (852) 28782988
Web Site: http://www.imchk.hk
Health Care Srvices
N.A.I.C.S.: 622110
Ben Lam *(Mgr-Fin)*

World Trade Capital Group Limited   **(1)**
19/F Wing On House No 71 Des Voeux

First Shanghai Investments Limited—(Continued)

Road Central, Central, China (Hong Kong)
Tel.: (852) 25222101
Web Site: http://www.wtcapital.com.hk
Financial Services
N.A.I.C.S.: 523940

FIRST SHIP LEASE TRUST
7 Temasek Boulevard 12-10 Suntec
Tower One, Singapore, 38987, Singapore
Tel.: (65) 68363000   SG
Web Site:
https://www.firstshipleasetrust.com
D8DU—(SES)
Rev.: $8,510,000
Assets: $65,734,000
Liabilities: $10,922,000
Net Worth: $54,812,000
Earnings: $3,670,000
Emp.: 109
Fiscal Year-end: 12/31/23
Investment Management Service
N.A.I.C.S.: 531120
Roger Woods (CEO)

FIRST SPONSOR GROUP LIMITED
63 Market Street 06-03 Bank of Singapore Centre, Singapore, 048942,
Singapore
Tel.: (65) 6436 4920
Property Development & Investment
N.A.I.C.S.: 525990
Teck Pheng Neo (CEO)

FIRST STAGE CORPORATION
22nd Floor Meiji Yasuda Life Osaka
Umeda Building 3-3-20 Umeda, Kita-Ku, Osaka, 530-0001, Japan
Tel.: (81) 663471106
Web Site: https://www.1st-stage.co.jp
Year Founded: 2007
2985—(TKS)
Real Estate Investment Services
N.A.I.C.S.: 531190
Hideki Nakano (Founder & CEO)

FIRST STEAMSHIP CO., LTD.
14 F No 237 Fu Hsing South Rd Section 2, Taipei, Taiwan
Tel.: (886) 227069911
Web Site:
https://www.firsteam.com.tw
2601—(TAI)
Rev.: $179,924,876
Assets: $1,156,641,867
Liabilities: $798,662,680
Net Worth: $357,979,188
Earnings: ($82,815,230)
Fiscal Year-end: 12/31/23
Ship Chartering Services
N.A.I.C.S.: 483111
Jerry Kuo (Chm & Pres)

Subsidiaries:

First Steamship S.A.   (1)
14th Fl No 237 Fuhsing S Rd Sec 2, Taipei,
Taiwan
Tel.: (886) 227069911
Transportation Agency Services
N.A.I.C.S.: 541614

Mariner Capital Ltd.   (1)
37 Triq Censu Tabone, Saint Julian's, Malta
Tel.: (356) 22470100
Web Site: http://www.mariner.com.mt
Transportation Agency Services
N.A.I.C.S.: 541614

Morgan Finance Ltd.   (1)
Level 29 Riverside Centre 123 Eagle Street,
PO Box 202, Brisbane, 4000, QLD, Australia
Tel.: (61) 733344888
Web Site: http://www.morgans.com.au
Emp.: 950
Stock Brokerage Services
N.A.I.C.S.: 523150

FIRST TAKAFUL INSURANCE COMPANY K.S.C.C.
Alqibla-Abdullah Almubarak St Souq
Alsafat Building First Fl-Office 4, PO
Box 5713, Safat, Kuwait, 13058, Kuwait
Tel.: (965) 1880055
Web Site:
https://www.firsttakaful.com
FTI—(KUW)
Rev.: $1,162,982
Assets: $43,184,705
Liabilities: $13,141,532
Net Worth: $30,043,173
Earnings: $456,547
Emp.: 83
Fiscal Year-end: 12/31/22
Insurance Services
N.A.I.C.S.: 524126
Hussain Ali Mohammed Al-Attal (CEO & Mng Dir)

FIRST TELLURIUM CORP.
Suite 381 - 1440 Garden Place,
Delta, V4M 3Z2, BC, Canada
Tel.: (604) 916-7259
Web Site: https://firsttellurium.com
Year Founded: 2004
FTEL—(CNSX)
Assets: $1,277,897
Liabilities: $410,470
Net Worth: $867,426
Earnings: ($1,479,595)
Fiscal Year-end: 07/31/23
Mineral Exploration Services
N.A.I.C.S.: 213114
Tony Fogarassy (Chm)

FIRST TIN PLC
First Floor 47-48 Piccadilly, London,
W1J 0DT, United Kingdom
Tel.: (44) 2073895010   UK
Web Site: https://www.firsttin.com
Year Founded: 2012
1SN—(LSE)
Assets: $55,022,954
Liabilities: $2,278,841
Net Worth: $52,744,113
Earnings: ($4,093,595)
Emp.: 27
Fiscal Year-end: 12/31/22
Mining Services
N.A.I.C.S.: 212290
Thomas Buenger (CEO)

Subsidiaries:

Saxore Bergbau GmbH   (1)
Platz der Oktoberopfer 1 A, 09599,
Freiberg, Germany
Tel.: (49) 37317758160
Web Site: https://www.saxorebergbau.com
Small Scale Metal Mining Services
N.A.I.C.S.: 541330

FIRST TRACTOR COMPANY LIMITED
154 Jianshe Road, Luoyang, 471004,
Henan, China
Tel.: (86) 37964967038   CN
Web Site: https://www.first-tractor.com.cn
Year Founded: 1955
FIRRF—(OTCIQ)
Rev.: $1,763,954,754
Assets: $1,823,254,379
Liabilities: $911,051,585
Net Worth: $912,202,794
Earnings: $95,619,560
Emp.: 7,145
Fiscal Year-end: 12/31/22
Tractor Mfr
N.A.I.C.S.: 333112
Li Xiaoyu (Chm)

FIRST WINNER INDUSTRIES LIMITED

605 Business Classic Chincholi
Bunder Road, Malad West, Mumbai,
400064, India
Tel.: (91) 2228802255
Web Site: http://www.firstwinnerind.in
Year Founded: 2003
Rev.: $31,084
Assets: $63,147,618
Liabilities: $51,627,891
Net Worth: $11,519,727
Earnings: $3,389,105
Emp.: 3
Fiscal Year-end: 03/31/17
Textile Products Mfr
N.A.I.C.S.: 314999

Subsidiaries:

First Winner Lifestyle Ltd.   (1)
605 Business Classic Chincholi Bunder
Road Malad West, Mumbai, 400064, Maharashtra, India
Tel.: (91) 2228802255
Web Site: http://www.firstwinnerind.com
Sales Range: $25-49.9 Million
Emp.: 44
Textile Products Mfr
N.A.I.C.S.: 314999
Indra Kumar Patodia (Gen Mgr)

Ramshyam Textile industries Ltd.   (1)
605 6th Floor Business Classic CTS No
10-A Chincholi Bunder Road, Malad West,
Mumbai, 400064, India
Tel.: (91) 22 2880 2255
Textile Products Mfr
N.A.I.C.S.: 314999

FIRST-CORPORATION INC.
8F Fujisawa Building 43016 Ogikubo,
Suginami-ku, Tokyo, 167-0051, Japan
Tel.: (81) 353479103
Web Site: https://www.1st-corp.com
Year Founded: 2011
1430—(TKS)
Rev.: $188,285,850
Assets: $156,769,370
Liabilities: $100,795,890
Net Worth: $55,973,480
Earnings: $6,239,840
Emp.: 80
Fiscal Year-end: 05/31/24
Condominium Construction Services
N.A.I.C.S.: 236116
Toshiaki Nakamura (Pres)

FIRSTCAUTION SA
Avenue Edouard-Rod 4, 1260, Nyon,
Switzerland
Tel.: (41) 840787878
Web Site: https://www.firstcaution.ch
Year Founded: 2008
MLFIR—(EUR)
Sales Range: $10-24.9 Million
Insurance Services
N.A.I.C.S.: 524298
Celine Frey (CEO)

FIRSTEC CO., LTD.
485 Nammyeon-ro, Seongsan-gu,
642050, Changwon, 642050,
Gyeongsangnam-do, Korea (South)
Tel.: (82) 552824131
Web Site:
https://www.firsteccom.co.kr
Year Founded: 1975
010820—(KRS)
Rev.: $122,838,494
Assets: $162,074,730
Liabilities: $118,614,828
Net Worth: $43,459,902
Earnings: $1,376,134
Emp.: 375
Fiscal Year-end: 12/31/22
Aerospace & Defense Product Mfr
N.A.I.C.S.: 332992
Kyeong Seok Son (CEO)

FIRSTFARMS A/S

Majsmarken 1, 7190, Billund, Denmark
Tel.: (45) 75868787
Web Site: https://www.firstfarms.dk
Year Founded: 2005
FFARMS—(CSE)
Rev.: $51,603,523
Assets: $188,502,512
Liabilities: $108,694,963
Net Worth: $79,807,548
Earnings: $4,092,746
Emp.: 334
Fiscal Year-end: 12/31/20
Farm Products Mfr
N.A.I.C.S.: 339999
Henrik Hougaard (Chm)

Subsidiaries:

FirstFarms Agra M. s.r.o.   (1)
Yinohredok 5741, 901 01, Malacky, Slovakia
Tel.: (421) 347722021
Milk Mfr
N.A.I.C.S.: 112120

FirstFarms Slovakiet ApS   (1)
Majsmarken 1, 7190, Billund, Ribe, Denmark
Tel.: (45) 75868787
Web Site: http://www.firstfarms.com
Emp.: 5
Milk Mfr
N.A.I.C.S.: 112120

FIRSTGROUP PLC
395 King Street, Aberdeen, AB24
5RP, United Kingdom
Tel.: (44) 1224650100   UK
Web Site:
https://www.firstgroupplc.com
Year Founded: 1995
FGROY—(OTCIQ)
Rev.: $5,904,759,000
Assets: $5,471,619,160
Liabilities: $4,539,275,720
Net Worth: $932,343,440
Earnings: $118,343,540
Emp.: 30,000
Fiscal Year-end: 03/25/23
Train & Bus Service Operator
N.A.I.C.S.: 485113
Rachael Borthwick (Dir-Corp Svcs)

Subsidiaries:

CentreWest London Buses
Limited   (1)
B Block 3rd Floor Macmillan House Paddington Station, London, W12 1TY, United
Kingdom
Tel.: (44) 20 7298 7300
Bus Transit Services
N.A.I.C.S.: 485210

First Aberdeen Limited   (1)
395 King Street, Aberdeen, AB24 5RP,
United Kingdom
Tel.: (44) 1224 650000
Web Site: http://www.firstgroup.com
Sales Range: $125-149.9 Million
Emp.: 500
Passenger Bus Transportation Services
N.A.I.C.S.: 485999

First Beeline Buses Limited   (1)
Coldborough House Market St, Bracknell,
RG12 1JA, Berkshire, United Kingdom
Tel.: (44) 1344 782222
Web Site: http://www.firstgroup.com
Sales Range: $125-149.9 Million
Emp.: 300
Passenger Bus Transportation Services
N.A.I.C.S.: 485999

First Bristol Limited   (1)
First Enterprise House Eastern Road, Bristol, BS5 0DZ, United Kingdom
Tel.: (44) 1179 558211
Web Site: http://www.firstgroup.com
Sales Range: $450-499.9 Million
Emp.: 2,000
Passenger Bus Transportation Services
N.A.I.C.S.: 485999
Alan Parrett (Gen Mgr)

First Capital Connect Limited (1)
50 Eastbourne Terrace, Paddington, London, W2 6LG, United Kingdom
Tel.: (44) 8450264700
Web Site:
http://www.firstcapitalconnect.co.uk
Commuter Rail Services
N.A.I.C.S.: 485112

First Capital North Limited (1)
Macmillan House Paddington Station, London, W2 1TY, United Kingdom
Tel.: (44) 20 7298 7300
Local Passenger Transportation Services
N.A.I.C.S.: 485999

First Devon & Cornwall Limited (1)
The Ride, Plymouth, PL9 7JT, Devon, United Kingdom
Tel.: (44) 8456001420
Web Site: http://www.firstgroup.com
Passenger Bus Transportation Services
N.A.I.C.S.: 485999
Marc Reddy (Mng Dir)

First Eastern Counties Buses Limited (1)
6 Dogs Head Street, Ipswich, IP4 1AD, Suffolk, United Kingdom
Tel.: (44) 1473 253734
Web Site: http://www.firstgroup.com
Local Passenger Transportation Services
N.A.I.C.S.: 485999

First Glasgow (No. 1) Limited (1)
197 Victoria Rd, Glasgow, G42 7AD, United Kingdom
Tel.: (44) 141 423 6600
Sales Range: $1-4.9 Billion
Emp.: 2,800
Passenger Bus & Coach Operating Services
N.A.I.C.S.: 485999
Ronnie Park (Mng Dir)

First Glasgow (No. 2) Limited (1)
197 Victoria Road, Glasgow, G42 7AD, United Kingdom
Tel.: (44) 1414 236600
Web Site: http://www.firstgroup.com
Sales Range: $1-4.9 Billion
Emp.: 2,800
Passenger Bus Operating Services
N.A.I.C.S.: 485999
Ronnie Park (Mng Dir)

First Greater Western Limited (1)
Milford House 1 Milford Street, Swindon, SN1 1HL, United Kingdom
Tel.: (44) 3457000125
Web Site: http://www.gwr.com
Travel & Tour Operating Services
N.A.I.C.S.: 561599
Mark Hopwood (Mng Dir)

First Manchester Limited (1)
Wallshaw Street, Oldham, OL1 3TR, Lancs, United Kingdom
Tel.: (44) 161 627 2929
Web Site: http://www.firstgroup.com
Sales Range: $450-499.9 Million
Emp.: 2,329
Local Bus Chartering Services
N.A.I.C.S.: 485510
Dave Alexander (Mng Dir-North Reg)

First Midland Red Buses Limited (1)
Island Drive, Kidderminster, DY10 1EZ, Worcestershire, United Kingdom
Tel.: (44) 156268267
Web Site: http://www.firstgroup.com
Bus & Coach Chartering Services
N.A.I.C.S.: 485510

First Potteries Limited (1)
Dividy Road, Stoke-on-Trent, ST3 5YY, United Kingdom
Tel.: (44) 870 850 0868
Bus & Coach Chartering Services
N.A.I.C.S.: 485510
Nigel Barrett (Reg Mng Dir)

First ScotRail Limited (1)
Atrium court, 50 waterloo street, Glasgow, G2 6HQ, Scotland, United Kingdom (100%)
Tel.: (44) 8456015929
Web Site: http://www.scotrail.co.uk
Sales Range: $1-4.9 Billion
Emp.: 3,000
Train Service

N.A.I.C.S.: 482111
Jacqueline Taggart (Dir-Customer Svcs)

First Scotland East Limited (1)
Carmuirs House 300 Stirling Road, Larbert, FK5 3NJ, Stirlingshire, United Kingdom
Tel.: (44) 8708727271
Sales Range: $450-499.9 Million
Emp.: 1,200
Passenger Bus Transportation Services
N.A.I.C.S.: 485999
Paul Thomas (Mng Dir)

First Somerset & Avon Limited (1)
Priory Rd, Wells, BA5 1SZ, Somerset, United Kingdom
Tel.: (44) 1749677774
Passenger Coach & Bus Operating Services
N.A.I.C.S.: 485999

First South Yorkshire Limited (1)
Midland Road, Rotherham, S61 1TF, United Kingdom
Tel.: (44) 1709566000
Web Site: http://www.firstgroup.com
Sales Range: $450-499.9 Million
Emp.: 1,600
Passenger Bus & Coach Operating Services
N.A.I.C.S.: 485999
Dave Alexander (Mng Dir-North Reg)

First TransPennine Express Limited (1)
8th Floor The Point 37 North Wharf Road, London, W2 1AF, United Kingdom
Tel.: (44) 345 600 1671
Web Site: https://www.tpexpress.co.uk
Railway Transportation Services
N.A.I.C.S.: 482111
Matthew Golton (Mng Dir)

First Travel Solutions Limited (1)
Unit 5 Petre Court Petre Road Clayton Business Park, Clayton Le Moors, Accrington, BB5 5HY, United Kingdom
Tel.: (44) 345 528 0270
Web Site:
https://www.firsttravelsolutions.com
Travel Agency Services
N.A.I.C.S.: 561510
Andy Scholey (Mng Dir)

First West Yorkshire Limited (1)
Hunslet Park Donisthorpe Street, Leeds, LS10 1PL, West Yorkshire, United Kingdom
Tel.: (44) 845 604 5460
Web Site: http://www.firstgroup.com
Sales Range: $1-4.9 Billion
Emp.: 3,500
Passenger Bus & Coach Operating Services
N.A.I.C.S.: 485999
Dave Alexander (Mng Dir-North Reg)

FirstGroup America Inc. (1)
600 Vine St Ste 1400, Cincinnati, OH 45202
Tel.: (513) 241-2200
Web Site: http://www.firstgroupamerica.com
Sales Range: $700-749.9 Million
Emp.: 100,000
Bus Operator; Vehicle Maintenance Services
N.A.I.C.S.: 485410
Kevin Middleton (Exec VP-Engrg)

Subsidiary (Domestic):

First Student Inc. (2)
600 Vine St Ste 1400, Cincinnati, OH 45202
Tel.: (513) 241-2200
Web Site: https://firststudentinc.com
Sales Range: $100-124.9 Million
Emp.: 400
School Bus Transportation
N.A.I.C.S.: 485410
Danny Cozort (Mgr-Fleet Sls-Western)

Branch (Domestic):

First Student (3)
487 Industrial Dr, Naperville, IL 60563
Tel.: (630) 369-4237
Web Site: http://www.firststudentinc.com
Sales Range: $50-74.9 Million
Emp.: 250
Local Transportation Services

N.A.I.C.S.: 485410

First Student (3)
6951 State St, South Holland, IL 60473
Tel.: (708) 210-2200
Sales Range: $25-49.9 Million
Emp.: 100
School Bus Transportation
N.A.I.C.S.: 485410
Julie Gonzales (Branch Mgr)

Subsidiary (Non-US):

First Student Canada (3)
1111 International Blvd Ste 700, Burlington, L7L 6W1, ON, Canada
Tel.: (289) 288-4359
Sales Range: $25-49.9 Million
Emp.: 70
School Bus Transportation Services
N.A.I.C.S.: 485410

FirstBus Canada (3)
140 4th Avenue East, Regina, S4N 4Z4, SK, Canada
Tel.: (306) 721-4499
Web Site: http://www.firstbuscanada.com
Sales Range: $50-74.9 Million
Emp.: 200
School Bus Transportation
N.A.I.C.S.: 485410
Greg Logel (Mng Dir)

Subsidiary (Domestic):

First Vehicle Services (2)
600 Vine St Ste 1400, Cincinnati, OH 45202
Tel.: (513) 684-8853
Web Site:
http://www.firstvehicleservices.com
Transportation Maintenance & Management Solutions
N.A.I.C.S.: 811114
Dale Domish (Sr VP)

Hull Trains Company Limited (1)
4th Floor Europa House 184 Ferensway, Hull, HU1 3UT, United Kingdom
Tel.: (44) 3450710222
Web Site: http://www.hulltrains.co.uk
Emp.: 100
Rail Transportation Services
N.A.I.C.S.: 488210
Louise Cheeseman (Mng Dir)

Northampton Transport Limited (1)
Bus Depot Saint James Road, Northampton, NN5 5JD, Northamptonshire, United Kingdom
Tel.: (44) 1604 751 431
Sales Range: $25-49.9 Million
Emp.: 90
Passenger Bus Operating Services
N.A.I.C.S.: 485999

Tram Operations Limited (1)
Tramlink Depot Coomber Way, Croydon, CRO 4TQ, United Kingdom
Tel.: (44) 208 665 9695
Web Site:
https://www.tramoperationsltd.com
Public Transportation Services
N.A.I.C.S.: 485113

Transit Management of Volusia, Inc. (1)
950 Big Tree Rd, South Daytona, FL 32119-8815
Tel.: (386) 756-7496
Web Site: https://www.votran.org
Public Transportation Services
N.A.I.C.S.: 485113
Kelvin Miller (Gen Mgr)

Transportation Claims Limited (1)
57-75 Kings Road, Reading, RG1 3AB, United Kingdom
Tel.: (44) 870 162 9002
Web Site:
https://www.transportationclaims.co.uk
Public Transportation Services
N.A.I.C.S.: 485113

FIRSTINVISION GESMBH
Jesserniggstrasse 11, 9020, Klagenfurt am Worthesee, Austria
Tel.: (43) 46330401010
Software Publisher
N.A.I.C.S.: 513210

FIRSTLINK INVESTMENTS CORPORATION LIMITED
1 Phillip Street 08-01, Singapore, 048692, Singapore
Tel.: (65) 6448 6211
Web Site:
http://www.firstlinkcorp.com.sg
Sales Range: Less than $1 Million
Emp.: 10
Investment Holding Company
N.A.I.C.S.: 551112
Yew Kong Ling (Chm & Mng Dir)

FIRSTLOGIC INC.
5F Sumitomo Real Estate Hatchobori Building 3-3-5 Hatchobor, Chuo-ku, Tokyo, 104-0032, Japan
Tel.: (81) 368334576
Web Site: https://www.firstlogic.co.jp
6037—(TKS)
Sales Range: $1-9.9 Million
Emp.: 20
Online Real Estate Services
N.A.I.C.S.: 531390
Naohiro Sakaguchi (Pres)

FIRSTMAC HOLDINGS LTD.
Riverside Centre 123 Eagle, Street Level 40, Brisbane, QLD, Australia
Tel.: (61) 13 12 20
Holding Company
N.A.I.C.S.: 551112

FIRSTOBJECT TECHNOLOGIES LTD.
302 The Bureau Chambers Above State Bank of India, Chembur, Mumbai, 400071, Maharashtra, India
Tel.: (91) 2225272510
Web Site:
http://www.firstobjectindia.com
Year Founded: 2000
532379—(BOM)
Rev.: $281,400
Assets: $1,472,235
Liabilities: $195,388
Net Worth: $1,276,847
Earnings: ($23,091)
Emp.: 2,914
Fiscal Year-end: 03/31/24
Software Development Services
N.A.I.C.S.: 541511
Sriram Kumar (Mng Dir)

FIRSTRAND LIMITED
4 Merchant Place Corner Fredman Drive & Rivonia Road, Sandton, 2196, South Africa
Tel.: (27) 112821808
Web Site: https://www.firstrand.co.za
Year Founded: 1998
FSR—(JSE)
Rev.: $8,021,630,985
Assets: $121,336,832,877
Liabilities: $110,897,295,071
Net Worth: $10,439,537,807
Earnings: $2,044,381,542
Emp.: 39,561
Fiscal Year-end: 06/30/23
Holding Company
N.A.I.C.S.: 551112
Sam Moss (Head-IR)

Subsidiaries:

FNB Lesotho Limited (1)
Corner Kingsway and Parliament Road, Maseru, Lesotho
Tel.: (266) 22241000
Web Site: https://www.fnb.co.ls
Banking Services
N.A.I.C.S.: 522110

FNB Zambia Limited (1)
Acacia Office Park Cnr Thabo Mbeki and Great East Roads, Lusaka, Zambia
Tel.: (260) 211366800
Web Site: https://www.fnbzambia.co.zm
Banking Services

FirstRand Limited—(Continued)

N.A.I.C.S.: 522110

FirstRand Bank Limited (1)
6th Floor First Place Corner Simmonds &
Pritchard Streets, Bank City, Johannesburg,
2001, Gauteng, South Africa (100%)
Tel.: (27) 113691088
Web Site: http://www.fnb.co.za
Financial Holding Company Services
N.A.I.C.S.: 551111
Rakhesh Bhoola (Head-Learning and Dev)

Subsidiary (Domestic):

First National Bank (2)
Simmonds and Pritchard Streets, Johannesburg, 2000, Gauteng, South Africa
Tel.: (27) 113691088
Web Site: http://www.fnb.co.za
Sales Range: $1-4.9 Billion
Emp.: 8,000
Banking Services
N.A.I.C.S.: 522110
Leonard Haynes (CEO)

FirstRand Bank Holdings Limited (2)
4 Merchant Pl, 1 Fredman Dr, Sandton,
2196, Gauteng, South Africa (100%)
Tel.: (27) 112828000
Web Site: http://www.rmb.co.za
Sales Range: $25-49.9 Million
Emp.: 2,948
Bank
N.A.I.C.S.: 551111

Subsidiary (Non-US):

First National Bank of Botswana (3)
Plot 54362 First Place, PO Box 1552, Central Business District, Gaborone, Botswana
Tel.: (267) 3706000
Web Site: http://www.fnbbotswana.co.bw
Rev.: $142,305,919
Assets: $2,192,682,190
Liabilities: $1,920,813,163
Net Worth: $271,869,027
Earnings: $81,394,494
Emp.: 1,600
Fiscal Year-end: 06/30/2023
Banking Services
N.A.I.C.S.: 522110
Steven Lefentse Bogatsu (CEO)

Representative Office (Non-US):

FirstRand Bank Limited - India (2)
101 103A and First floor 103B First International Financial Centre, C-54 and C-55 G
Block Near CBI office Bandra-Kurla complex, Bandra, 400 051, India
Tel.: (91) 2266258600
Web Site: https://www.firstrand.co.in
Emp.: 200
Financial Management Services
N.A.I.C.S.: 523999
Pritish Mohanty (Head-Risk)

Subsidiary (Domestic):

FirstRand EMA Holdings Limited (2)
Cnr Fredman Dr And Rivonia Rd, Sandton,
2196, Gauteng, South Africa
Tel.: (27) 112824000
Web Site: http://www.rmb.co.za
Sales Range: $350-399.9 Million
Emp.: 1,000
Financial Management Services
N.A.I.C.S.: 523999

Subsidiary (Non-US):

**First National Bank of Zambia
Limited** (3)
Stand Number 22768 Acacia Office Park
Cnr Thabo Mbeki Great East Roads, Lusaka, Zambia
Tel.: (260) 211366800
Web Site: https://www.fnbzambia.co.zm
Commercial Banking Services
N.A.I.C.S.: 522110
Ackim L. Chalwe (Co-CFO)

FirstRand Namibia Ltd. (3)
130 Independence Avenue c/o Fidel Castro,
Box 285, Windhoek, Namibia
Tel.: (264) 612992222
Web Site: https://www.fnbnamibia.com.na
Rev.: $142,401,261
Assets: $3,080,804,698

Liabilities: $2,764,748,756
Net Worth: $316,055,942
Earnings: $82,454,288
Emp.: 2,319
Fiscal Year-end: 06/30/2023
Holding Company
N.A.I.C.S.: 551112
Sarel Jacobus Van Zyl (CEO)

Subsidiary (Domestic):

**Firstrand Finance Company
Limited** (2)
Merchant Place Cnr of Rivonia Road and
Fredman Drive, Sandown, Sandton, 2146,
Gauteng, South Africa
Tel.: (27) 112821808
Web Site: http://www.firstrand.com
Financial Management Services
N.A.I.C.S.: 523999

Rand Merchant Bank (2)
1 Merchant Place Cnr Fredman Drive and
Rivonia Road, Sandton, Johannesburg,
2196, South Africa (100%)
Tel.: (27) 112828000
Web Site: http://www.rmb.co.za
Sales Range: $350-399.9 Million
Emp.: 800
Banking Services
N.A.I.C.S.: 522110
Martin Oberholster (Chief Investment Officer)

Subsidiary (Domestic):

**RMB Asset Management (Pty)
Limited** (3)
7 Merchant Place Fredman Drive, Sandton,
2196, South Africa
Tel.: (27) 115051000
Web Site: http://www.rmbam.com
Investment Management Service
N.A.I.C.S.: 523999

Subsidiary (Non-US):

RMB Australia Ltd. (3)
Suite 15 Level 14 309 Kent Street, Sydney,
2000, NSW, Australia (100%)
Tel.: (61) 299948002
Web Site: http://www.rmb.com.au
Sales Range: $50-74.9 Million
Emp.: 16
Investment Bank
N.A.I.C.S.: 523150

Subsidiary (Domestic):

RMB Corvest (Pty) Ltd. (3)
8 Melville Road, Illovo, 2196, South Africa
Tel.: (27) 113808300
Web Site: https://www.rmbcorvest.co.za
Privater Equity Firm
N.A.I.C.S.: 523999
Neil Page (Founder)

Subsidiary (Non-US):

RMB Financial Services Limited (3)
Jutland Hall Steamboat Quay, Limerick,
Ireland
Tel.: (353) 61468575
Sales Range: $50-74.9 Million
Emp.: 3
Insurance Services
N.A.I.C.S.: 524210
Patrick Liston (Mng Dir)

Subsidiary (Domestic):

**RMB Private Equity Holdings (Pty)
Ltd** (3)
No 5 Merchant Place 9 Fredman Drive,
Sandton, 2196, South Africa
Tel.: (27) 113035000
Web Site: http://www.rmbprivatebank.com
Sales Range: $50-74.9 Million
Emp.: 100
Financial Management Services
N.A.I.C.S.: 523999

Holding (Domestic):

Denny Mushrooms (Pty) Limited (4)
The Oval, Wanderers Building, Bryanston,
2128, Gauteng, South Africa
Tel.: (27) 861 888 182
Sales Range: $100-124.9 Million
Mushroom Farming & Sales
N.A.I.C.S.: 111411

Carla Renard (Mgr-IT)

Subsidiary (Domestic):

**RMB Structured Insurance
Limited** (3)
Fourth Fl 2 Merchant Pl 1 Fredman Dr,
Sandton, 2196, Gauteng, South Africa
Tel.: (27) 116857600
Web Site: http://www.rmbsi.co.za
Sales Range: $50-74.9 Million
Emp.: 27
Insurance Underwriting Services
N.A.I.C.S.: 524113
Gustavo Arroyo (CEO)

Subsidiary (Non-US):

**RMB Structured Insurance Limited
PCC** (4)
Ste 114 3rd Fl Medine Mews, Chaussee,
Port Louis, 11328, Mauritius
Tel.: (230) 2111395
Sales Range: $25-49.9 Million
Emp.: 2
General Insurance Services
N.A.I.C.S.: 524210
Dario Adolphe (Mgr)

MineRP (1)
Ground Floor 267 West Avenue, Centurion,
0157, South Africa
Tel.: (27) 879803100
Web Site: http://www.minerp.com
Sales Range: $150-199.9 Million
Emp.: 200
Mining Management Software Solutions
N.A.I.C.S.: 541511

Subsidiary (Non-US):

**GIJIMAAST Americas
Incorporated** (2)
432 Westmount Ave Unit AB, Sudbury, P3A
5Z8, ON, Canada
Tel.: (705) 525-4774
Web Site: http://www.gijimaast.ca
Sales Range: $25-49.9 Million
Emp.: 10
Mining Software Consulting Services
N.A.I.C.S.: 541511

GijimaAst (Pty) Limited (3)
2 44 Denis St, Subiaco, 6008, WA, Australia
Tel.: (61) 863801719
Sales Range: $25-49.9 Million
Emp.: 6
Mining Software Consulting Services
N.A.I.C.S.: 541512

NewBucks Operations Pty., Ltd. (1)
10th Fl 30 Diagonal Street cnr Kerk Street,
FNB Place BankCity, Sandton, 2000, Johannesburg, South Africa
Tel.: (27) 113775061
Web Site: https://www.ebucks.com
Sales Range: $25-49.9 Million
Emp.: 200
Rewards Program Solutions
N.A.I.C.S.: 561499
Johan Moolman (CEO)

OUTsurance Limited (1)
1241 Embankment Rd Zwartkop Ext 7,
Centurion, Gauteng, South Africa
Tel.: (27) 126886800
Web Site: https://www.outsurance.co.za
Sales Range: $700-749.9 Million
Emp.: 2,500
General Insurance Services
N.A.I.C.S.: 524210
Micky Maharaj (COO-Shared Svcs)

Pemba Capital Partners Pty. Ltd. (1)
Level 45 Gateway 1 Macquarie Place, Sydney, 2000, NSW, Australia
Tel.: (61) 292566300
Web Site: https://pemba.com.au
Emp.: 100
Investment Management Service
N.A.I.C.S.: 523940
Magnus Hildingsson (Mng Dir)

Subsidiary (Domestic):

MSL Solutions Limited (2)
Level 1 307 Queen Street, Brisbane, 4000,
QLD, Australia
Tel.: (61) 735123510

Web Site: https://www.mslsolutions.com
Rev.: $18,918,763
Assets: $28,126,835
Liabilities: $16,290,732
Net Worth: $11,836,103
Earnings: $678,844
Fiscal Year-end: 06/30/2021
Holding Company; Software Development
Services
N.A.I.C.S.: 551112
Patrick Howard (CEO)

Subsidiary (Non-US):

GolfBox A/S (3)
Sensommervej 34 F, 8600, Silkeborg, Denmark
Tel.: (45) 21734000
Web Site: https://www.golfbox.net
Software Development Services
N.A.I.C.S.: 541511

MSL Verteda Limited (3)
Steam Mill Business Centre Suite A3 Steam
Mill Street, Chester, CH3 5AN, Cheshire,
United Kingdom
Tel.: (44) 1925401310
Web Site: http://www.verteda.com
Computer System Design Services
N.A.I.C.S.: 541512

Subsidiary (Domestic):

OrderMate Pty Ltd. (3)
59 Fennell St, Port Melbourne, 3207, VIC,
Australia
Tel.: (61) 1300667067
Web Site: https://www.ordermate.com.au
Advanced Table Management Services
N.A.I.C.S.: 492210

Rockit Pty. Ltd. (3)
66-68 Sackville Street, Collingwood, 3066,
VIC, Australia
Tel.: (61) 394156320
Web Site: https://rockit.au
Software Development Services
N.A.I.C.S.: 541511
Nik Devidas (Mng Dir)

Rentworks Africa (Pty) Ltd (1)
RentWorks Place Turnberry Office Park 48
Grosvenor Road, PO Box 69320, Bryanston, 2021, Johannesburg, South Africa
Tel.: (27) 115499000
Web Site: http://www.rentworks.co.za
Sales Range: $50-74.9 Million
Emp.: 55
Venture Capital Services
N.A.I.C.S.: 523910
Kuben Rayan (CEO)

WesBank (1)
Enterprise Road, Fairland, Randburg, 2170,
South Africa
Tel.: (27) 861937265
Web Site: https://www.wesbank.co.za
Vehicle Financing Services
N.A.I.C.S.: 921130

**FIRSTSERVICE CORPORA-
TION**
1255 Bay Street Suite 600, Toronto,
M5R 2A9, ON, Canada
Tel.: (416) 960-9566   ON
Web Site:
    https://www.firstservice.com
Year Founded: 1989
FSV—(NASDAQ)
Rev.: $4,334,548,000
Assets: $3,625,743,000
Liabilities: $2,601,597,000
Net Worth: $1,024,146,000
Earnings: $100,391,000
Emp.: 29,000
Fiscal Year-end: 12/31/23
Holding Company; Property Management Services
N.A.I.C.S.: 551112
Charlie E. Chase (Pres/CEO-
FirstService Brands)

Subsidiaries:

American Pool Enterprises Inc. (1)
11515 Cronridge Dr Ste Q, Owings Mills,
MD 21117 (96.4%)

Tel.: (443) 471-1190
Web Site: http://www.americanpool.com
Swimming Pool Management, Maintenance,
Construction & Recreational Facility Man-
agement Services
N.A.I.C.S.: 541611
Mitchell B. Friedlander *(CEO)*

Century Fire Protection, LLC   **(1)**
2450 Satellite Blvd, Duluth, GA 30096-0096
Tel.: (770) 945-2330
Web Site: http://www.centuryfp.com
Fire Protection Systems Mfr & Installation
Services
N.A.I.C.S.: 333998
Richard Deeb *(Co-Pres)*

Subsidiary (Domestic):

Advanced Fire & Security, Inc.   **(2)**
2701 Gateway Dr, Pompano Beach, FL
33069
Web Site: https://www.advfireonline.com
Security System Services
N.A.I.C.S.: 561621
Eric Rode *(Pres)*

**Advantage Fire Sprinkler Co.,
Inc.**   **(2)**
2300 E Fork Alcovy Rd, Dacula, GA 30019
Tel.: (770) 822-9550
Web Site: http://www.advantagefire.com
Emp.: 100
Plumbing, Heating & Air-Conditioning Con-
tractors
N.A.I.C.S.: 238220
Andy Cheatham *(Co-Founder & CEO)*

**Condominium Concepts Manage-
ment, LLC**   **(1)**
3400 Peachtree Rd NE Ste 1700, Atlanta,
GA 30326
Tel.: (678) 624-9453
Property Management & Residential Build-
ings Leasing
N.A.I.C.S.: 531110

FS Brands, Inc.   **(1)**
1140 Bay Street Suite 4000, Toronto, M5S
2B4, ON, Canada   **(95.7%)**
Tel.: (866) 366-0420
Web Site: http://www.fsvbrands.com
Holding Company; Contract Services Fran-
chisor
N.A.I.C.S.: 551112
Charlie E. Chase *(Pres & CEO)*

Subsidiary (US):

California Closet Company, Inc.   **(2)**
1414 Harbour Way S Ste 1750, Richmond,
CA 94804
Tel.: (510) 763-2033
Web Site: https://www.californiaclosets.com
Contract Custom Closet & Cabinetry Ser-
vices Franchisor
N.A.I.C.S.: 449129
Kenneth Martin *(Dir-IT)*

CertaPro Painters, Ltd.   **(2)**
2621 Van Buren Ave Ste 550A, Audubon,
PA 19403
Web Site: https://www.certapro.com
Contract Painting & Wall Covering Services
Franchisor
N.A.I.C.S.: 533110
Michael Stone *(Pres & CEO)*

**Floor Coverings International,
Ltd.**   **(2)**
5390 Triangle Pkwy Ste 125, Norcross, GA
30092
Tel.: (770) 874-7600
Web Site:
  https://www.floorcoveringinternational.com
Contract Flooring Services Franchisor
N.A.I.C.S.: 533110
Thomas W. Wood *(Pres & CEO)*

Paul Davis Restoration, Inc.   **(2)**
7251 Salisbury Rd Ste 6, Jacksonville, FL
32256
Web Site: https://pauldavis.com
Property Damage Mitigation, Reconstruction
& Remodeling Services Franchisor
N.A.I.C.S.: 533110
Barry Floyd *(CFO)*

Subsidiary (Domestic):

Telelink Services Inc.   **(2)**

700 Richmond Street, London, N6A 5C7,
ON, Canada
Tel.: (519) 439-9247
Web Site: http://www.tlscv.com
Multi-Channel Customer Care Call Center
Services
N.A.I.C.S.: 561421
Laurie Dietz *(Pres & CEO)*

FS Brands, Inc.   **(1)**
2621 Van Buren Ave Ste 550A, Audubon,
PA 19403
Web Site: https://www.fsvbrands.com
Property Management Services
N.A.I.C.S.: 531311
Charlie Chase *(Pres & CEO)*

FirstOnSite Restoration Ltd.   **(1)**
Greater Toronto Area 110 Matheson Blvd W
Suite 210, Mississauga, L5R 4G7, ON,
Canada
Tel.: (905) 696-2900
Web Site: https://firstonsite.ca
Property Restoration & Reconstruction Ser-
vices
N.A.I.C.S.: 531311
Jeff Johnson *(CEO)*

Subsidiary (US):

Drypatrol, LLC   **(2)**
8772 Thomas Rd, Middletown, OH 45042-
1200
Tel.: (513) 705-9730
Web Site: http://www.drypatrol.com
Professional, Scientific & Technical Services
N.A.I.C.S.: 541990
Derron Oakley *(Pres)*

**Insurance Restoration Specialists,
Inc.**   **(2)**
30 Abeel Rd, Monroe Township, NJ 08831
Tel.: (609) 409-5666
New Single-Family Housing Construction
(except Operative Builders)
N.A.I.C.S.: 236115
Leo DiFonzo *(Mgr-Sls)*

Moore Restoration, Inc.   **(2)**
3610 Shelby St, Indianapolis, IN 46227
Tel.: (317) 791-3862
Web Site: http://www.moorerestoration.com
Rev.: $1,700,000
Emp.: 13
Residential Remodeler
N.A.I.C.S.: 236118
Kenny Cochran *(Pres)*

ProConstruction LLC   **(2)**
511 Wynnehurst Rd, Pensacola, FL 32503
Tel.: (850) 225-5354
Web Site: http://www.completedki.com
Sales Range: $10-24.9 Million
Construction Services
N.A.I.C.S.: 236220
Shaun Carpentier *(Pres)*

FirstService Residential, Inc.   **(1)**
1855 Griffin Rd Ste A-330, Dania Beach, FL
33004   **(100%)**
Tel.: (954) 926-2921
Web Site: http://www.fsresidential.com
Residential Property Management
N.A.I.C.S.: 531311
Gene Gomberg *(Chm)*

Subsidiary (Domestic):

**Citiscape Property Management
Group, LLC.**   **(2)**
3450 3rd St Ste 1A, San Francisco, CA
94124-1444
Tel.: (415) 401-2000
Web Site: https://www.citiscapesf.com
Sales Range: $1-9.9 Million
Emp.: 96
Real Estate Services
N.A.I.C.S.: 531210
Robert Simms *(Sr Partner)*

Subsidiary (Non-US):

**Crossbridge Condominium Services
Ltd.**   **(2)**
111 Gordon Baker Road Suite 700, North
York, M2H 3R1, ON, Canada
Tel.: (416) 510-8700
Web Site:
  http://www.crossbridgecondominiums.com

Condominium Property Management Ser-
vices
N.A.I.C.S.: 531311
John M. Oakes *(Chm)*

Subsidiary (Domestic):

**FirstService Residential Florida,
Inc.**   **(2)**
2950 N 28th Ter, Hollywood, FL
33020   **(100%)**
Tel.: (954) 925-8200
Residential Property Management Services
N.A.I.C.S.: 531210
Paula Allen *(VP-HR)*

**FirstService Residential, Nevada,
LLC**   **(2)**
8290 Arville St, Las Vegas, NV 89139
Tel.: (702) 515-5077
Web Site: http://www.fsresidential.com
Community Management & Consulting Ser-
vices
N.A.I.C.S.: 541618
Chris Wood *(VP-Bus Dev-West Reg)*

Rizzetta & Company, Inc.   **(2)**
3434 Colwell Ave Ste 200, Tampa, FL
33614
Tel.: (813) 933-5571
Web Site: http://www.rizzetta.com
Sales Range: $1-9.9 Million
Emp.: 82
Real Estate Management Consulting Ser-
vices
N.A.I.C.S.: 541611
William Rizzetta *(Founder & Pres)*

Tudor Realty Services Corp.   **(2)**
250 Park Ave S, New York, NY 10003
Tel.: (212) 557-3600
Web Site: https://tudorrealty.com
Sales Range: $1-9.9 Million
Emp.: 40
Real Estate Agent/Manager
N.A.I.C.S.: 531210
Howard J. Lazuras *(Principal & Gen Coun-
sel)*

Maxons Restorations, Inc.   **(1)**
280 Madison Ave, New York, NY 10016
Tel.: (212) 447-6767
Web Site: http://www.maxons.com
Sales Range: $1-9.9 Million
Emp.: 50
Repair Services, Nec, Nsk
N.A.I.C.S.: 238990
Damon Gersh *(Pres & CEO)*

Midboro Management, Inc.   **(1)**
333 7th Av 5th Fl, New York, NY 10001
Tel.: (212) 877-8500
Web Site: http://www.midboro.com
Sales Range: $1-9.9 Million
Emp.: 25
Operator of Apartment Buildings
N.A.I.C.S.: 531110
Michael Jay Wolfe *(Pres)*

Roofing Corp of America, LLC   **(1)**
270 Carpenter Dr NE Ste 225, Atlanta, GA
30328
Tel.: (404) 941-9131
Web Site: https://www.roofingcorp.com
Roofing Contractors
N.A.I.C.S.: 238160
Randy Korach *(CEO)*

Subsidiary (Domestic):

**Crowther Roofing & Sheet Metal of
Florida, Inc.**   **(2)**
2543 Rockfill Rd, Fort Myers, FL 33916
Tel.: (239) 337-1300
Web Site: http://www.crowther.net
Sales Range: $10-24.9 Million
Emp.: 325
Roofing & HVAC Contractor
N.A.I.C.S.: 238160
Lee Scott Crowther *(CEO)*

**Front Range Roofing Systems,
LLC**   **(2)**
222 13th Ave, Greeley, CO 80631
Tel.: (970) 353-2322
Web Site: http://www.frontrangeroofing.com
Roofing Contractors
N.A.I.C.S.: 238160
Michael Trotter *(Pres)*

Watermark Restoration Inc.   **(1)**
3656 Cahaba Beach Rd, Birmingham, AL
35242
Web Site: http://www.watermarkrestinc.com
Commercial Property Water & Fire Restora-
tion & Renovation Services
N.A.I.C.S.: 221310
Mark VanDyke *(Branch Mgr)*

FIRSTSOURCE SOLUTIONS LIMITED

5th Floor Paradigm B Wing Mind-
space Link Road Malad West, Mum-
bai, 400 064, India
Tel.: (91) 2266660888
Web Site:
  https://www.firstsource.com
Year Founded: 2001
FSL—(NSE)
Rev.: $221,506,194
Assets: $375,123,977
Liabilities: $58,467,864
Net Worth: $316,656,113
Earnings: $52,905,899
Emp.: 16,045
Fiscal Year-end: 03/31/22
Business Process Management Ser-
vices
N.A.I.C.S.: 561499
Dinesh Jain *(Pres & CFO)*

Subsidiaries:

Firstsource Advantage LLC   **(1)**
205 Bryant Woods S, Buffalo, NY 14228-
3609
Tel.: (716) 564-4400
Web Site:
  http://www.firstsourceadvantagellc.com
Emp.: 500
Business Process Outsourcing Services
N.A.I.C.S.: 541611
Dana Lojacono-Latona *(Mgr-Payroll)*

Division (Domestic):

Firstsource Advantage LLC   **(2)**
1232 W State Rd 2, La Porte, IN 46350
Tel.: (219) 326-7754
Emp.: 60
Business Process Outsourcing Services
N.A.I.C.S.: 541611
Arjun Mitra *(Pres)*

MedAssist, Inc.   **(1)**
1661 Lyndon Farm Ct, Louisville, KY 40223
Tel.: (502) 499-0855
Web Site:
  http://www.medassistsolutions.com
Emp.: 150
Healthcare Revenue Cycle Management
Services
N.A.I.C.S.: 541219
Derek Kung *(Gen Counsel & Sr VP)*

**Twin Medical Transaction Services,
Inc**   **(1)**
5590 S Fort Apache Rd, Las Vegas, NV
89148
Tel.: (702) 307-8687
Business Process Outsourcing Services
N.A.I.C.S.: 541611

FIS INFORMATIONSSYSTEME UND CONSULTING GMBH

Rothleiner Weg 1, 97506, Schwein-
furt, Germany
Tel.: (49) 972391880
Web Site: http://www.fis-gmbh.de
Year Founded: 1992
Rev.: $41,922,683
Emp.: 300
Software Maintenance Services
N.A.I.C.S.: 541511
Frank Schongarth *(Mng Dir)*

Subsidiaries:

**FIS Application Service Providing und
IT-Outsourcing GmbH**   **(1)**
Rothleiner Weg 4, 97506, Berlin, Germany
Tel.: (49) 97239188500
Software Development Services
N.A.I.C.S.: 541511

FIS Informationssysteme und Consulting GmbH—(Continued)

FIS Information Systems Inc. (1)
520 White Plains Rd Ste 500, Tarrytown, NY 10591
Tel.: (914) 366-7590
Software Development Services
N.A.I.C.S.: 541511

FIS Information Systems UK Limited (1)
One Central Park Northampton Road, Manchester, M40 5BP, United Kingdom
Tel.: (44) 1619186765
Software Development Services
N.A.I.C.S.: 541511

FISCHER AG PRAZISIONSSPINDELN
Ernst Fischer-Weg 5, PO Box 31, 3360, Herzogenbuchsee, Switzerland
Tel.: (41) 629562222
Web Site:
http://www.fischerspindle.com
Sales Range: $25-49.9 Million
Emp.: 400
High-Performance Spindle Mfr for Machine Tools
N.A.I.C.S.: 333517
Daniel Schmid (CEO)

Subsidiaries:

Fischer Precise USA, Inc. (1)
3715 Blue River Ave, Racine, WI 53405-4131
Tel.: (262) 632-6173
Web Site: http://www.fischerspindle.com
Sales Range: $25-49.9 Million
Emp.: 40
High Speed Spindle Systems for Precision Milling, Drilling & Grinding Applications
N.A.I.C.S.: 332216
Rick Mauldin (Treas)

FISCHER CHEMIC LIMITED
104 First Floor Raghuleela Mega Mall Behind Poisar Depot, Kandivali West, Mumbai, 400067, Maharashtra, India
Tel.: (91) 8655550209
Web Site:
http://www.fischerchemic.com
Year Founded: 1993
524743—(BOM)
Rev.: $22,523
Assets: $34,619
Liabilities: $34,194
Net Worth: $425
Earnings: $19,194
Fiscal Year-end: 03/31/21
Laboratory Chemicals Whslr
N.A.I.C.S.: 424690
Ravi Egurla (CFO)

FISCHERAPPELT AG
Waterloohain 5, 22769, Hamburg, Germany
Tel.: (49) 408996990
Web Site:
http://www.fischerappelt.com
Year Founded: 1986
Digital Marketing, Creative Campaigning & Design
N.A.I.C.S.: 541613
Dino Buscher (Mng Partner)

Subsidiaries:

Philipp und Keuntje GmbH (1)
Bei St Annen 2, 20457, Hamburg, Germany
Tel.: (49) 402800700
Web Site: http://www.philippundkeuntje.de
Marketing & Advertising
N.A.I.C.S.: 541810

FISCHERWERKE GMBH & CO. KG
Weinhalde 14-18, Waldachtal, 72178, Germany
Tel.: (49) 7443120
Web Site: http://www.fischer.de

Sales Range: $800-899.9 Million
Emp.: 3,900
Holding Company
N.A.I.C.S.: 551112
Klaus Fischer (CEO)

Subsidiaries:

OOO fischer Befestigungssysteme Rus (1)
I Dokukina 16/1 Building 1, 129226, Moscow, Russia
Tel.: (7) 4952230334
Building Hardware Distr
N.A.I.C.S.: 423710

fischer (Taicang) fixings Co. Ltd. (1)
Shanghai Rep Office Rm 1503-1504 No 68 Chifeng Road, 200092, Shanghai, China
Tel.: (86) 2151001668
Building Hardware Distr
N.A.I.C.S.: 423710

fischer Argentina s.a. (1)
Armenia 3044, Munro Ra-PCIA, B1605CDT, Buenos Aires, Argentina
Tel.: (54) 1147622778
Web Site: http://www.fischer.com.ar
Building Hardware Distr
N.A.I.C.S.: 423710

fischer Benelux B.V. (1)
Amsterdamsestraatweg 45 B/C, 1411 AX, Naarden, Netherlands
Tel.: (31) 356956666
Building Hardware Distr
N.A.I.C.S.: 423710

fischer Cobemabel snc (1)
Schalienhoevedreef 20 D, 2800, Mechelen, Belgium
Tel.: (32) 15284700
Building Hardware Distr
N.A.I.C.S.: 423710

fischer Consulting GmbH (1)
Weinhalde 14-18, Waldachtal, 72178, Germany
Tel.: (49) 7443 12 0
Web Site: http://www.fischer.de
Emp.: 20
Management Consulting Services
N.A.I.C.S.: 541618
Poris Katic (Gen Mgr)

fischer FZE (1)
Jebel Ali Free Zone, PO Box 261738, Dubai, United Arab Emirates
Tel.: (971) 48837477
Building Hardware Distr
N.A.I.C.S.: 423710
Jayanta Mukherjee (Mng Dir)

fischer Finland Oy (1)
Suomalaistentie 7 B, 02270, Espoo, Finland
Tel.: (358) 207414660
Building Hardware Distr
N.A.I.C.S.: 423710

fischer Hellas Emporiki EPE (1)
Nat Road Athens-Lamia 17th & Roupel 6, Kifissia, Athens, Greece
Tel.: (30) 2102838167
Building Hardware Distr
N.A.I.C.S.: 423710

fischer Hungaria Bt. (1)
Szeremi ut 7/b, 1117, Budapest, Hungary
Tel.: (36) 13479755
Building Hardware Distr
N.A.I.C.S.: 423710

fischer Iberica S.A.U. (1)
Klaus Fischer 1 Mont roig del Camp, 43300, Tarragona, Spain
Tel.: (34) 977838711
Building Hardware Distr
N.A.I.C.S.: 423710

fischer Innovative Solutions Co. LTD. (1)
38 40 Chaleom Prakiat Ratchankan-Thi 9 Road, 10250, Bangkok, Thailand
Tel.: (66) 274737512
Building Hardware Distr
N.A.I.C.S.: 423710

fischer Japan K.K. (1)
3-4-15 Kudan Minami, Chiyoda-ku, Tokyo, 102-0074, Japan
Tel.: (81) 332634491

Building Hardware Distr
N.A.I.C.S.: 423710

fischer Korea Co., Ltd (1)
131 Kasan Digital-1Ro, Geumcheon, 153-803, Seoul, Korea (South)
Tel.: (82) 15448955
Building Hardware Distr
N.A.I.C.S.: 423710
Gin W. Kang (Pres)

fischer Metal Sanayi Ve Ticaret Ltd Sti (1)
Yeni yol Sokak ETAP Is Merkezi A Blok No 16/9, Hasanpasa Kadikoy, Istanbul, Turkiye
Tel.: (90) 2163260066
Building Hardware Distr
N.A.I.C.S.: 423710

fischer Norge AS (1)
Oluf Onsumsvei 9, Oslo, 0680, Norway
Tel.: (47) 23242710
Building Hardware Distr
N.A.I.C.S.: 423710
Nils Harald Rusek (Mgr-Sls)

fischer S. A. S. (1)
12 rue Livio, PO Box 10182, 67022, Strasbourg, Cedex, France
Tel.: (33) 388391867
Building Hardware Distr
N.A.I.C.S.: 423710

fischer S.K. s.r.o. (1)
Nova RoznavskA 134 A, 831 04, Bratislava, Slovakia
Tel.: (421) 249206046
Building Hardware Distr
N.A.I.C.S.: 423710

fischer Sistemas de Fijacion, S.A. de C.V. (1)
Blvd Manuel Avila Camacho 3130-400B Col Valle Dorado, Tlalnepantla, Estado de, Mexico
Tel.: (52) 5555720883
Building Hardware Distr
N.A.I.C.S.: 423710

fischer Sverige AB (1)
Tenngatan 4, 602 23, Norrkoping, Sweden
Tel.: (46) 11314452
Building Hardware Distr
N.A.I.C.S.: 423710

fischer a/s (1)
Sandvadsvej 17 A, Koge, Denmark
Tel.: (45) 46320220
Web Site: http://www.fischerdanmark.dk
Building Hardware Distr
N.A.I.C.S.: 423710

fischer automotive systems GmbH & Co. KG (1)
Industriestrasse 103, 72160, Horb am Neckar, Germany
Tel.: (49) 74 43 12 55 00
Web Site: http://www.fischer.de
Motor Vehicle Interior Component Mfr
N.A.I.C.S.: 336360
Andreas Gerecke (Pres)

Subsidiary (US):

fischer America Inc. (2)
1084 Doris Rd, Auburn Hills, MI 48326
Tel.: (248) 276-1940
Web Site: http://www.fischerus.com
Sales Range: $25-49.9 Million
Emp.: 170
Motor Vehicle Interior Component Mfr
N.A.I.C.S.: 336360

fischer brasil Industria e Comercio Ltda. (1)
Estrada do Dende 300 Ilha do, Governador, 21920-001, Rio de Janeiro, Brazil
Tel.: (55) 2124678796
Building Hardware Distr
N.A.I.C.S.: 423710

fischer fixings LLC (1)
850 S Jupiter Rd, Garland, TX 75042
Tel.: (845) 504-5098
Building Hardware Distr
N.A.I.C.S.: 423710

fischer fixings UK Ltd. (1)
Hithercroft Industrial Estate, Wallingford, OX10 9AT, Oxfordshire, United Kingdom
Tel.: (44) 1491827900

Building Hardware Distr
N.A.I.C.S.: 423710

fischer international s.r.o. (1)
Jarosova 1, 83103, Bratislava, Slovakia
Tel.: (421) 10254777419
Surgical & Medical Product Distr
N.A.I.C.S.: 423450

fischer international s.r.o. (1)
Prumyslova 1833, 25001, Brandys nad Labem, Czech Republic
Tel.: (420) 326904601
Building Hardware Distr
N.A.I.C.S.: 423710

fischer italia S.R.L (1)
Corso Stati Uniti 25, Casella Postale 391, 35127, Padua, Italy
Tel.: (39) 0498063111
Building Hardware Distr
N.A.I.C.S.: 423710

fischer systems Asia Pte. Ltd. (1)
150 Kampong Ampat 04-03 KA Centre, Singapore, 368324, Singapore
Tel.: (65) 62852207
Building Hardware Distr
N.A.I.C.S.: 423710

fischerpolska Sp.z o.o (1)
ul Albatrosow 2, 30-716, Krakow, Poland
Tel.: (48) 122900880
Building Hardware Distr
N.A.I.C.S.: 423710
Marek Smoleniec (Mgr-Export)

fischertechnik GmbH (1)
Weinhalde 14-18, 72178, Waldachtal, Germany
Tel.: (49) 7443 12 0
Web Site: http://www.fischertechnik.de
Toy Mfr
N.A.I.C.S.: 339930

fischerwerke Portugal, Lda. (1)
Av Casal da Serra N 7 R/C, 2625-085, Povoa de Santa Iria, Portugal
Tel.: (351) 219537450
Building Hardware Distr
N.A.I.C.S.: 423710

FISHBURN HEDGES
77 Kingsway, London, WC2B 6SR, United Kingdom
Tel.: (44) 20 7839 4321
Year Founded: 1991
Emp.: 170
N.A.I.C.S.: 541820
Fiona Thorne (CEO)

Subsidiaries:

Seventy Seven PR (1)
77 Kingsway, London, WC2B 6SR, United Kingdom
Tel.: (44) 207 492 0977
Sales Range: $75-99.9 Million
Emp.: 20
N.A.I.C.S.: 541820
Alan Twigg (Joint Mng Partner)

FISHER & PAYKEL HEALTHCARE CORPORATION LIMITED
15 Maurice Paykel Place, East Tamaki, Auckland, 2013, New Zealand
Tel.: (64) 95740100
Web Site: https://www.fphcare.com
Year Founded: 1934
FPH—(NZX)
Rev.: $1,417,292,800
Assets: $1,491,925,000
Liabilities: $398,397,900
Net Worth: $1,093,527,100
Earnings: $376,899,800
Emp.: 6,897
Fiscal Year-end: 03/31/21
Medical Device Mfr
N.A.I.C.S.: 339112
Lewis G. Gradon (CEO & Mng Dir)

Subsidiaries:

Fisher & Paykel Healthcare (Guangzhou) Limited (1)

301 G12 31 Kefeng Lu, Guangzhou Science City Guangzhou Economic Technological Development, Guangzhou, 510663, China
Tel.: (86) 2032053486
Emp.: 30
Medical Device Mfr
N.A.I.C.S.: 339112

Fisher & Paykel Healthcare AB (1)
Svetsarvagen 15 2tr, 17141, Solna, Sweden
Tel.: (46) 856476680
Sales Range: $25-49.9 Million
Emp.: 8
Medical Device Mfr
N.A.I.C.S.: 339112

Fisher & Paykel Healthcare Asia Limited (1)
10F -1 No 61 and 10F No 69 Jhozih Street, Neihu, Taipei, 114, Taiwan
Tel.: (886) 287511739
Investment Management Service
N.A.I.C.S.: 523999

Fisher & Paykel Healthcare GmbH & Co. KG (1)
Wiesenstrasse 49, 73614, Schorndorf, Germany
Tel.: (49) 7181985990
Medical Device Mfr
N.A.I.C.S.: 339112

Fisher & Paykel Healthcare Inc. (1)
17400 Laguna Canyon Rd Ste 300, Irvine, CA 92618
Tel.: (949) 453-4000
Web Site: http://www.fphcare.com
Sales Range: $25-49.9 Million
Emp.: 80
Medical Device Mfr
N.A.I.C.S.: 339112

Fisher & Paykel Healthcare India Private Limited (1)
Brigade Opus 3rd Floor Unit No 302B 303 Kodigehalli Gate, Hebbal, Bengaluru, 560092, India
Tel.: (91) 8023096400
Healthcare Devices Distr
N.A.I.C.S.: 423450
Thekkanathu Paily Bastin (Gen Mgr)

Fisher & Paykel Healthcare K.K. (1)
4-8-2 Hacchobori, Chuo-ku, Tokyo, 104-0032, Japan
Tel.: (81) 351177110
Sales Range: $25-49.9 Million
Emp.: 38
Medical Device Mfr
N.A.I.C.S.: 339112

Fisher & Paykel Healthcare Limited (1)
Unit 16 Cordwallis Park Clivemont Road, Maidenhead, SL6 7BU, Berkshire, United Kingdom
Tel.: (44) 1628626136
Sales Range: $25-49.9 Million
Emp.: 50
Medical Device Mfr
N.A.I.C.S.: 339112
Jillneson Nelson (Gen Mgr)

Fisher & Paykel Healthcare Limited (1)
339 1 HIG A Sector 2nd Stage Extension, Yelahanka New Town, Bengaluru, 560064, India
Tel.: (91) 8041236041
Sales Range: $25-49.9 Million
Emp.: 50
Medical Device Mfr
N.A.I.C.S.: 339112
D. B. Bastin (Gen Mgr)

Fisher & Paykel Healthcare Limited (1)
Unit 802-5 Delta House 3 On Yiu Street Siu Lek Yuen Shatin, Sha Tin, New Territories, China (Hong Kong)
Tel.: (852) 21160032
Medical Equipment Mfr
N.A.I.C.S.: 334510

Fisher & Paykel Healthcare Limited (1)
2045 Blvd Dagenais O Ste 180, Laval, H7L 5V1, QC, Canada

Tel.: (949) 453-4000
Medical Equipment Distr
N.A.I.C.S.: 423450

Fisher & Paykel Healthcare Properties Limited (1)
15 Maurice Paykel Place, East Tamaki, Auckland, 2013, New Zealand
Tel.: (64) 95740100
Web Site: http://www.fphcare.com
Sales Range: $450-499.9 Million
Emp.: 2,000
Health Care Products Mfr
N.A.I.C.S.: 325412

Fisher & Paykel Healthcare Pty. Limited (1)
19-31 King Street, PO Box 167, Nunawading, Melbourne, 3131, VIC, Australia
Tel.: (61) 398714900
Sales Range: $25-49.9 Million
Emp.: 25
Medical Device Mfr
N.A.I.C.S.: 339112
David Boyle (Dir-Ops)

Fisher & Paykel Healthcare S.A. de C.V. (1)
Pacifico Industrial Center No 13 Av Todos los Santos 12831, Parque Industrial Pacifico, 22643, Tijuana, Baja California, Mexico
Tel.: (52) 6642313450
Medical Device Mfr
N.A.I.C.S.: 339112

Fisher & Paykel Healthcare SAS (1)
10 Avenue du Quebec - Batiment F5, BP 512, Villebon-Sur-Yvette, 91946, Courtaboeuf, Cedex, France
Tel.: (33) 164465201
Sales Range: $25-49.9 Million
Emp.: 100
Medical Device Mfr
N.A.I.C.S.: 339112

Fisher & Paykel Holdings GmbH (1)
Wiesenstr 49, 73614, Schorndorf, Germany
Tel.: (49) 7181985990
Investment Management Service
N.A.I.C.S.: 523999

Fisher & Paykel do Brasil Ltda (1)
277 Sampaio Viana 2nd Floor Offices 21 and 22, Sao Paulo, 04004-000, Brazil
Tel.: (55) 1125487002
Marketing Consulting Services
N.A.I.C.S.: 541613

Fisher Paykel Saglik Urunleri Ticaret Limited Sirketi (1)
Ostim Mahallesi 1249 Cadde No 6, Yenimahalle, 06374, Ankara, Turkiye
Tel.: (90) 3123543412
Medical Device Mfr
N.A.I.C.S.: 339112

Limited Liability Company Fisher & Paykel Healthcare (1)
Tel.: (7) 4957822150
Medical Device Mfr
N.A.I.C.S.: 339112

FISHER GRAHAM LIMITED
Level 4 91 William Street, Melbourne, 3000, VIC, Australia
Tel.: (61) 3 96467606
Web Site:
http://www.fishergraham.com.au
Sales Range: Less than $1 Million
Emp.: 3
Investment Services
N.A.I.C.S.: 523940
John Lawson Walker (Sec & Exec Dir)

FISHERMAN'S MARKET INTERNATIONAL INC.
607 Bedford Highway, Halifax, B3M 2L6, NS, Canada
Tel.: (902) 443-3474
Web Site:
http://www.fishermansmarket.ca
Year Founded: 1948
Rev.: $26,889,270
Emp.: 100

Seafood Supplier & Whslr
N.A.I.C.S.: 311710
JR Ewing (VP)

FISHERS STORES CONSOLIDATED PTY. LTD.
100 106 Commercial St, Merbein, Mildura, 3505, Victoria, Australia
Tel.: (61) 350218300
Web Site: http://www.fishers.com.au
Sales Range: $50-74.9 Million
Emp.: 600
Supermarket Services
N.A.I.C.S.: 445110
Alan Fisher (Mng Dir)

FISKARHEDENVILLAN AB
Bygatan 35, 784 34, Borlange, Sweden
Tel.: (46) 243 79 42 42
Web Site:
http://www.fiskarhedenvillan.se
Year Founded: 1993
Sales Range: $50-74.9 Million
Emp.: 6
Residential Housing Construction
N.A.I.C.S.: 236115
Gunnar Jonsson (CEO)

FISKARS OYJ ABP
Hameentie 135A, PO Box 130, FI-00561, Helsinki, Finland
Tel.: (358) 2043910   FI
Web Site:
https://www.fiskarsgroup.com
Year Founded: 1649
FSKRS—(HEL)
Rev.: $1,221,095,344
Assets: $1,527,824,998
Liabilities: $671,692,028
Net Worth: $856,132,970
Earnings: $58,680,664
Emp.: 6,984
Fiscal Year-end: 12/31/19
Cutlery, Garden Equipment, Hand Tool & Housewares Mfr
N.A.I.C.S.: 332216
Jyri Luomakoski (Vice Chm)

Subsidiaries:

Fiskars Americas Holding Oy Ab (1)
Hameentie 135, 560, Helsinki, Finland
Tel.: (358) 2043910
Investment Management Service
N.A.I.C.S.: 523999
Kari Kauniskangas (Pres)

Subsidiary (Non-US):

Fiskars (Thailand) Co., Limited (2)
349 SJ Infinite One Business Complex Unit 2201-2203 22nd floor, Vibhavadi - Rangsit Rd Chompol Jatuchak, Bangkok, 10900, Thailand
Tel.: (66) 26552214
Web Site: http://www.fiskars.com
Household Glass Product Mfr
N.A.I.C.S.: 327215

Fiskars Australia Pty. Limited (2)
39-41 Fennell Street, Port Melbourne, 3207, VIC, Australia
Tel.: (61) 86452400
Garden Equipment Mfr
N.A.I.C.S.: 333111

Fiskars Brands Germany GmbH (1)
Ost Strasse 23, Herford, 32051, Germany
Tel.: (49) 52219350
Web Site: http://www.fiskars.de
Sales Range: $50-74.9 Million
Emp.: 130
Manufacturers of Aluminum Boats
N.A.I.C.S.: 333923

Fiskars Brands Hungary Ltd. (1)
Fehervari 50-52-Dexagon Irodahaz, 1117, Budapest, Hungary (100%)
Tel.: (36) 14530945
Web Site: http://www.fiskars.hu

Sales Range: $25-49.9 Million
Emp.: 11
N.A.I.C.S.: 441222

Fiskars Brands Italy S.R.L. (1)
Via Provinciale 15, I 23862, Civate, LC, Italy (100%)
Tel.: (39) 0341215111
Web Site: http://www.fiskars.it
Sales Range: $75-99.9 Million
Emp.: 150
Consumer Products Sales
N.A.I.C.S.: 423990
Francesco Chinaglia (Gen Mgr)

Fiskars Brands Oy AB (1)
Ruukintie 22, PO Box 10330, 10330, Billnas, Finland (100%)
Tel.: (358) 447828877
Web Site: http://www.fiskars.com
Emp.: 500
N.A.I.C.S.: 441222

Fiskars Brands Pty. Ltd. (1)
39-41 Fennell St, Port Melbourne, 3207, VIC, Australia (100%)
Tel.: (61) 86452400
Web Site: http://www.fiskars.com.au
Sales Range: $25-49.9 Million
Emp.: 20
Consumer Products Sales
N.A.I.C.S.: 423990

Fiskars Brands, Inc. (1)
7800 Discovery Dr, Middleton, WI 53562 (100%)
Tel.: (608) 259-1649
Web Site: http://www.fiskars.com
Sales Range: $50-74.9 Million
Emp.: 250
Scissors, Cutlery, Sporting Goods & Garden Shears Mfr
N.A.I.C.S.: 332215

Subsidiary (Domestic):

EnviroWorks, Inc. (2)
3000 Orange Ave, Apopka, FL 32703-3347
Tel.: (407) 889-5533
Web Site: http://www.enviroworks.com
N.A.I.C.S.: 441222

Unit (Domestic):

Fiskars Brands, Inc. - Gerber Gear (2)
14200 SW 72nd Ave, Portland, OR 97224
Tel.: (503) 639-6161
Web Site: http://www.fiskarsgroup.com
Mfr of Sportsmens Knives, Multi Function Tools & Outdoor Recreational Products
N.A.I.C.S.: 332215
Rob Kass (Pres)

Fiskars Brands, Inc. - Nelson (2)
1 Sprinkler Ln, Peoria, IL 61615
Tel.: (309) 690-2200
Web Site: http://www.lrnelson.com
Lawn & Garden Hose, Sprinkler Systems & Related Products Mfr & Whslr
N.A.I.C.S.: 326220

Division (Domestic):

Fiskars Garden & Outdoor Living (2)
780 Carolina St, Sauk City, WI 53583-1369 (100%)
Tel.: (608) 643-2380
Web Site: http://www.fiskars.com
Consumer Gardening & Landscaping Tools Mfr
N.A.I.C.S.: 423820

Fiskars Outdoor Leisure Products (2)
3000 Orange Ave, Apopka, FL 32703-3347
Tel.: (407) 889-5533
Web Site: http://www.fiskars.com
Sales Range: $50-74.9 Million
Emp.: 200
N.A.I.C.S.: 441222

Fiskars Canada Inc. (1)
675 Cochrane Drive East Toer 6th Floor, 675 Cochrane Drive, Markham, L3R 0B8, ON, Canada (100%)
Tel.: (905) 940-8460
Web Site: http://www.fiskars.com
Sales Range: $25-49.9 Million
Emp.: 12
Distr of Scissors

Fiskars Oyj Abp—(Continued)

N.A.I.C.S.: 332215

Fiskars Commercial (Shanghai) Co., Ltd. **(1)**
Room 2705 Raffles City No 268 Middle Xizang Rd, Huangpu District, Shanghai, 200001, China
Tel.: (86) 2163597733
Home Interior Design Services
N.A.I.C.S.: 541410

Fiskars Consumer Goods (Shanghai) Co., Ltd. **(1)**
Room 1204 Central Plaza 227 North Huang Pi Road, Huang Pu District, Shanghai, 200003, China
Tel.: (86) 2163597733
Ceramic Glass Product Distr
N.A.I.C.S.: 444180

Fiskars Danmark A/S **(1)**
Smedeland 46, 2600, Silkeborg, Denmark **(100%)**
Tel.: (45) 38144888
Web Site: http://www.fiskars.dk
Sales Range: $25-49.9 Million
Emp.: 65
Manufacturers of Consumer Products & Aluminum Boats
N.A.I.C.S.: 333923

Fiskars Estonia AS **(1)**
Parnu Mnt 154, 11317, Tallinn, Estonia
Tel.: (372) 6500749
Web Site: http://www.fiskarsgroup.com
Sales Range: $50-74.9 Million
Emp.: 4
Household Utensils & Appliance Distr
N.A.I.C.S.: 423220

Fiskars Europe Holding Oy Ab
Hameentie 135, Helsinki, 00561, Finland
Tel.: (358) 20 43 910
Investment Management Service
N.A.I.C.S.: 523999
Kari Kauniskangas *(Mng Dir)*

Subsidiary (Non-US):

Excalibur Management Consulting (Shanghai) Co., Ltd. **(2)**
21st Floor Middle East Building 1219 Zhenguang Road, Putou District, Shanghai, 200333, China
Tel.: (86) 21 626 516 87
Web Site: http://www.fiskarsgroup.com
Sales Range: $10-24.9 Million
Emp.: 5
Business Management Consulting Services
N.A.I.C.S.: 541611

Fiskars Denmark A/S **(2)**
Vestre Ringvej 45, PO Box 360, 8600, Silkeborg, Denmark
Tel.: (45) 8720 1100
Sales Range: $25-49.9 Million
Emp.: 80
Gardening Equipment Mfr & Distr
N.A.I.C.S.: 333112
Lars Tantrup *(Gen Mgr)*

Subsidiary (Non-US):

Fiskars Hong Kong Ltd. **(3)**
Room 1402 14/F OfficePlus Wan Chai No303 Hennesy Road, Wanchai, China (Hong Kong)
Tel.: (852) 28336393
Garden Equipment Mfr
N.A.I.C.S.: 333111

Subsidiary (Non-US):

Waterford Wedgwood Doulton Commercial (Shanghai) Ltd. **(4)**
Room 1204 Central Plaza 227 North Huang Pi Road, Huang Pu District, Shanghai, 200003, China
Tel.: (86) 2163597733
Garden Equipment Mfr
N.A.I.C.S.: 333111

Subsidiary (Domestic):

Fiskars Finland Oy AB **(2)**
Hameentie 135 A, PO Box 130, 00561, Helsinki, Finland
Tel.: (358) 2043910
Garden Equipment Mfr

N.A.I.C.S.: 333111
Tiina Pekola *(Mgr-Mktg)*

Subsidiary (Non-US):

Fiskars Benelux B.V. **(3)**
Weena 324, 3012 NJ, Rotterdam, Netherlands
Tel.: (31) 103161900
Web Site: https://www.fiskars.nl
Garden Equipment Mfr
N.A.I.C.S.: 333111

Subsidiary (Non-US):

Fiskars Italy S.r.l. **(2)**
Via Paracelso 24, 20864, Agrate Brianza, MB, Italy
Tel.: (39) 0395787501
Web Site: https://www.fiskarspromozioni.it
Garden Machinery Mfr & Distr
N.A.I.C.S.: 333112

Fiskars Norway AS **(2)**
Lorenfaret 1C, 0585, Oslo, Norway
Tel.: (47) 23006440
Web Site: https://www.fiskars.no
Sales Range: $25-49.9 Million
Emp.: 35
Home & Garden Tool Distr
N.A.I.C.S.: 423820
Bernhard Spidso *(Gen Mgr)*

Fiskars Poland Sp. z.o.o. **(2)**
Biuro Handlowe Ul Marywilska 22, 03-228, Warsaw, Poland
Tel.: (48) 22 676 0400
Sales Range: $25-49.9 Million
Emp.: 15
Gardening Equipment Mfr & Distr
N.A.I.C.S.: 333112

Fiskars Spain S.L. **(2)**
Isabel Colbrand 6 5a Planta, 28050, Madrid, Spain
Tel.: (34) 91 344 67 03
Emp.: 3
Household Kitchen Tool Distr
N.A.I.C.S.: 423710
Jose Luis Gallego *(Gen Mgr)*

Fiskars UK Limited **(2)**
17th Floor Mclaren Building 46 The Priory Queensway, Birmingham, B4 7LR, United Kingdom **(100%)**
Tel.: (44) 1217960444
Emp.: 50
Garden Equipment Mfr
N.A.I.C.S.: 333111

ZAO Fiskars Brands Rus **(2)**
Office 5 1 Building 93A Obvodniy Canal, 191119, Saint Petersburg, Russia
Tel.: (7) 812 320 4323
Web Site: http://www.fiskarsgroup.com
Sales Range: $50-74.9 Million
Emp.: 100
Household Tools Distr
N.A.I.C.S.: 423710

Fiskars France S.A.R.L. **(1)**
Immeuble le Pelican Air Park South Paris 3 Avenue Jeanne Garnerin, 91320, Wissous, France **(100%)**
Tel.: (33) 169751515
Web Site: http://www.fiskars.com
Sales Range: $25-49.9 Million
Emp.: 50
Manufacturers of Aluminum Boats
N.A.I.C.S.: 333923

Fiskars Living US, LLC **(1)**
1330 Campus Pkwy, Wall, NJ 07719-1454
Tel.: (732) 938-5800
Home Interior Design Services
N.A.I.C.S.: 541410

Fiskars Norge A/S **(1)**
Nydalen, 0402, Oslo, Norway **(100%)**
Tel.: (47) 23006440
Web Site: http://www.fiskars.no
Sales Range: $1-9.9 Million
Emp.: 40
Manufacturers of Consumer Products & Aluminum Boats
N.A.I.C.S.: 333923

Fiskars Oyj Abp - Arabia porcelain Factory **(1)**
Hameentie 135, PO Box 130, 561, Helsinki, Finland

Tel.: (358) 204 39 10
Web Site: http://www.fiskarsgroup.com
Sales Range: $50-74.9 Million
Emp.: 150
Porcelain Electrical Products Mfr
N.A.I.C.S.: 327110

Fiskars Oyj Abp - Iittala glass Factory **(1)**
Hameentie 135 Sa, 00560, Helsinki, Finland
Tel.: (358) 204 39 10
Glass Products Mfr
N.A.I.C.S.: 327215

Fiskars Oyj Abp - Nuutajarvi glass Factory **(1)**
Hameentie 135a, 561, Helsinki, Finland
Tel.: (358) 204 39 10
Glass Products Mfr
N.A.I.C.S.: 327215

Fiskars Poland Ltd. **(1)**
Komitetu Obrony Robotnikow 45B, 02-146, Warsaw, Poland
Tel.: (48) 226760400
Sales Range: $50-74.9 Million
Emp.: 250
Boat Mfr
N.A.I.C.S.: 441222

Fiskars Polska Sp. z o.o. **(1)**
ul Komitetu Obrony Robotnikow 45B Budynek Zephirus, 02-146, Warsaw, Poland
Tel.: (48) 223108500
Web Site: https://www.fiskars.pl
Steel Products Mfr
N.A.I.C.S.: 332111

Fiskars Polska Sp. z.o.o. **(1)**
Fehervari 50-52, Dexagon Irodahaz, 1117, Budapest, Hungary
Tel.: (36) 14530945
Home Interior Design Services
N.A.I.C.S.: 541410

Fiskars Real Estate **(1)**
Fiskarsintie 336, 10470, Fiskars, Finland **(100%)**
Tel.: (358) 192777504
Web Site: http://www.fiskarsgroup.com
Sales Range: $1-9.9 Million
Emp.: 20
Boat Distr
N.A.I.C.S.: 441222

Fiskars Services Oy Ab **(1)**
Hameentie 135 A, 561, Helsinki, Finland
Tel.: (358) 20 43 910
Web Site: http://www.fiskarsgroup.com
Financial & Accounting Services
N.A.I.C.S.: 541219

Fiskars Sweden AB **(1)**
Kungsbroplan 3, 11227, Stockholm, Sweden **(100%)**
Tel.: (46) 42361100
Web Site: http://www.fiskars.se
Sales Range: $25-49.9 Million
Emp.: 30
Consumer Products Sales
N.A.I.C.S.: 423990

Iittala Group Oy Ab **(1)**
Hameentie 135, PO Box 130, 561, Helsinki, Finland
Tel.: (358) 204 3910
Web Site: http://www.iittala.com
Sales Range: $75-99.9 Million
Emp.: 120
Household Glass Utensils Mfr & Distr
N.A.I.C.S.: 327215

Inha Works Ltd. **(1)**
Saarikylantie 21, FIN 63700, Ahtari, Finland **(100%)**
Tel.: (358) 65355111
Web Site: http://www.inha.fi
Sales Range: $25-49.9 Million
Emp.: 40
Mfr of Aluminum Motor Boats, Special-Purpose Radiators for Bathrooms & Other Humid Rooms & Rail Fasteners & Fitting Components
N.A.I.C.S.: 336612

PT Doulton **(1)**
JL Raya Serang KM29 9 Desa Gembong, Balaraja, Tangerang, 15610, Banten, Indonesia
Tel.: (62) 215951329

Garden Equipment Mfr
N.A.I.C.S.: 333111

Richard Sankey & Son Ltd. **(1)**
Bennerley Rd, Bulwell, Nottingham, NG6 8PE, United Kingdom **(100%)**
Tel.: (44) 1159 277335
Web Site: http://www.rsankey.com
Sales Range: $25-49.9 Million
Emp.: 75
Mfr of Garden Products
N.A.I.C.S.: 333112

Royal Copenhagen A/S **(1)**
Smedeland 17, DK-2600, Glostrup, Denmark **(100%)**
Tel.: (45) 38144848
Web Site: http://www.corporateroyalcopenhagen.com
Sales Range: $100-124.9 Million
Emp.: 90
Retail Sales of Porcelain, Silver & Glass
N.A.I.C.S.: 327110

Unit (Domestic):

Royal Copenhagen Flagship Store **(2)**
Amagertorv 6, 1160, Copenhagen, Denmark
Tel.: (45) 33137181
Web Site: http://www.royalcopenhagen.com
Sales Range: $50-74.9 Million
Retail Sales of Glassware
N.A.I.C.S.: 327211

Royal Copenhagen Korea Ltd. **(1)**
3rd floor Media Center Building 58-9 Nonhyeon-dong, Gangnam-gu, 135-815, Seoul, Korea (South)
Tel.: (82) 27492002
Web Site: https://www.royalcopenhagen.co.kr
Ceramic Glass Product Distr
N.A.I.C.S.: 444180

Steklarna Rogaska d.o.o. **(1)**
Talcev Street 1, 3250, Rogaska Slatina, Slovenia
Tel.: (386) 38180170
Web Site: https://www.steklarna-rogaska.si
Garden Equipment Mfr
N.A.I.C.S.: 333111

WWRD Ireland Limited **(1)**
House of Waterford The Mall, Waterford, Ireland
Tel.: (353) 51317000
Web Site: https://www.waterfordvisitorcentre.com
Garden Equipment Mfr
N.A.I.C.S.: 333111

WWRD United Kingdom Limited **(1)**
Wedgwood Drive Barlaston, Stoke-on-Trent, ST12 9ER, Staffs, United Kingdom
Tel.: (44) 1782204141
Web Site: http://www.wwrd.com
Holding Company; Regional Managing Office
N.A.I.C.S.: 551112
Ralf Kuhn *(Exec VP-Ops)*

Subsidiary (Non-US):

WWRD Australia Pty Limited **(2)**
100 Holbeche Road, Arndell Park, 2148, NSW, Australia
Tel.: (61) 2 8665 8200
Web Site: http://www.wwrd.com.au
Fine China, Casual Tableware, Crystal, Glassware & Ceramic Ornaments Distr
N.A.I.C.S.: 423220

Subsidiary (US):

WWRD US, LLC **(2)**
PO Box 1454, Wall, NJ 07719-1454
Tel.: (732) 938-5800
Web Site: http://www.waterford.com
Holding Company; Regional Managing Office
N.A.I.C.S.: 551112
Michael Craig *(Pres)*

Werga-Tools GmbH **(1)**
Oststrasse 23, D 32051, Herford, Germany **(100%)**
Tel.: (49) 522176360
Web Site: http://www.fiskars.de
Sales Range: $50-74.9 Million
Emp.: 130

Manufacturers of Consumer Products & Aluminum Boats
N.A.I.C.S.: 333923
Jan Wigg *(Dir)*

ZAO Baltic Tool (1)
Obvodniy Canal 93A of 5/1, RUS-191119, Saint Petersburg, Russia
Tel.: (7) 8125670901
N.A.I.C.S.: 441222

iittala BV (1)
Hoevestein 19, PO Box 474, Oosterhout, 4903 SE, Netherlands
Tel.: (31) 162488188
Web Site: http://www.iittala.com
Sales Range: $25-49.9 Million
Emp.: 20
Household Glassware Distr
N.A.I.C.S.: 423220

iittala BVBA (1)
Korte Gasthuisstraat 24, 2000, Antwerp, Belgium
Tel.: (32) 3 213 2517
Web Site: http://www.iittala.com
Sales Range: $25-49.9 Million
Emp.: 7
Household Appliance Retailer
N.A.I.C.S.: 449210

iittala GmbH (1)
Ober der Muhle 6, 42699, Solingen, Germany
Tel.: (49) 212546960
Web Site: https://www.iittala.com
Glass Products Distr
N.A.I.C.S.: 424310

FISKEBY INTERNATIONAL HOLDING AB
Fiskeby Road 1, PO Box 1, Norrkoping, 602 10, Sweden
Tel.: (46) 11155700 SE
Web Site: http://www.fiskeby.com
Year Founded: 2007
Emp.: 300
Holding Company; Packaging Board Mfr
N.A.I.C.S.: 551112
Torbjorn Hansen *(Mng Dir)*

Subsidiaries:

Fiskeby Board AB (1)
Fiskebyvagen 100, PO Box 1, 601 02, Norrkoping, Sweden (100%)
Tel.: (46) 1115 5700
Web Site: http://www.fiskeby.com
Sales Range: $75-99.9 Million
Packaging Board Mfr
N.A.I.C.S.: 322130
Torbjorn Hansen *(CEO)*

FISSION URANIUM CORP.
700 1620 Dickson Ave, Kelowna, V1Y 9Y2, BC, Canada
Tel.: (250) 868-8140 Ca
Web Site:
  https://www.fissionuranium.com
Year Founded: 2013
FCU—(OTCIQ)
Rev.: $212,296
Assets: $246,961,516
Liabilities: $568,420
Net Worth: $246,393,096
Earnings: ($4,132,111)
Emp.: 16
Fiscal Year-end: 12/31/19
Uranium Exploration
N.A.I.C.S.: 212290
Ross E. McElroy *(Pres & CEO)*

FIT BIOTECH OY
Biokatu 8, 33520, Tampere, Finland
Tel.: (358) 3 3138 7000
Web Site: http://www.fitbiotech.com
FITBIO—(HEL)
Sales Range: Less than $1 Million
Emp.: 12
Biopharmaceutical Mfr
N.A.I.C.S.: 325412

Kalevi Reijonen *(Chief Medical Officer & Sr VP)*

FIT BOXX HOLDINGS LIMITED
13/F Le Diamant 703 Nathan Road, Mongkok, Kowloon, China (Hong Kong)
Tel.: (852) 2944 6856 Ky
Web Site: http://www.fitboxx.com
Year Founded: 2009
Sales Range: $25-49.9 Million
Emp.: 110
Holding Company
N.A.I.C.S.: 551112
Yiu Kwong Chan *(Chm & CEO)*

FIT CO., LTD.
2-501 Hanasakidai, Moriyama-ku, Nagoya, 463-0808, Aichi, Japan
Tel.: (81) 527390671
Web Site: https://www.fit-finishing.co.jp
Year Founded: 2009
1436—(TKS)
Rev.: $63,958,360
Assets: $80,126,420
Liabilities: $46,858,290
Net Worth: $33,268,130
Earnings: $2,181,300
Emp.: 69
Fiscal Year-end: 04/30/24
Housing Construction Services
N.A.I.C.S.: 236116

FITAIHI HOLDING GROUP
Al Madinah Al Munawarah Al-Sharafeyah, Jeddah, 22234, Saudi Arabia
Tel.: (966) 122604200
Web Site: https://www.fitaihi.com.sa
Year Founded: 1907
4180—(SAU)
Rev.: $14,223,899
Assets: $129,359,994
Liabilities: $6,633,802
Net Worth: $122,726,192
Earnings: ($4,597,930)
Emp.: 160
Fiscal Year-end: 12/31/22
Jewelry & Clothing Mfr & Whslr
N.A.I.C.S.: 339910
Ahmed Hassan Fitaihi *(Chm)*

FITELL CORPORATION
23-25 Mangrove Lane, Sydney, Taren Point, 2229, NSW, Australia
Tel.: (61) 295245266 Ky
Web Site: https://www.fitellcorp.com
Year Founded: 2007
FTEL—(NASDAQ)
Rev.: $4,466,775
Assets: $11,478,290
Liabilities: $2,469,418
Net Worth: $9,008,872
Earnings: ($9,312,145)
Emp.: 15
Fiscal Year-end: 06/30/24
Fitness Equipment Retailer
N.A.I.C.S.: 423910
Jamarson Kong *(CFO)*

FITGENES AUSTRALIA PTY LTD.
Level 8 110 Eagle Street, PO Box 3120, Mentone, 3194, VIC, Australia
Tel.: (61) 1300348436
Web Site: http://www.fitgenes.com
Emp.: 500
Energy Medicine & Wellness Products & Services
N.A.I.C.S.: 713940
Carrie Hillyard *(Chm)*

Subsidiaries:

Atos Wellness Pte Ltd (1)
213 Kaki Bukit Avenue 1 Shun Li Industrial

Park, Singapore, 416041, Singapore
Tel.: (65) 6289 3000
Web Site: http://www.atoswellness.com.sg
Sales Range: $10-24.9 Million
Emp.: 40
Spa Management Services
N.A.I.C.S.: 721110
Ananda Rajah *(Founder)*

Subsidiary (Domestic):

Atos Consumer Products Pte Ltd (2)
1 Tannery Rd 9-01, Singapore, 347719, Singapore
Tel.: (65) 62893000
Web Site: http://www.atos.com.sg
Emp.: 100
Spa Management Services
N.A.I.C.S.: 721110

Body Contours Pte ltd (1)
1 Tannery Rd 04-06, Singapore, 347719, Singapore
Tel.: (65) 62203415
Web Site: http://www.bodycontours.com.sg
Sales Range: $10-24.9 Million
Emp.: 30
Spa Management Services
N.A.I.C.S.: 721110
Richard Chow *(Gen Mgr)*

Inner Harmony Pte Ltd (1)
2 Handy Rd 03-08, Singapore, 347719, Singapore
Tel.: (65) 67349959
Web Site: http://www.innerharmony.com.sg
Spa Management Services
N.A.I.C.S.: 721110

FITIPOWER INTEGRATED TECHNOLOGY, INC.
3F No 6-8 Du Sing Rd, East District, Hsinchu, 300, Taiwan
Tel.: (886) 35788618
Web Site: https://www.fitipower.com
Year Founded: 1995
4961—(TAI)
Rev.: $532,604,709
Assets: $813,377,810
Liabilities: $120,207,098
Net Worth: $693,170,712
Earnings: $77,412,568
Emp.: 829
Fiscal Year-end: 12/31/23
Electronic Components Mfr
N.A.I.C.S.: 334419
Yung-Chieh Lin *(Chm & CEO)*

Subsidiaries:

Jadard Technology Limited (1)
22F No 1-146 Zhonghua Rd, Yongkang Dist, Tainan City, China
Tel.: (86) 63127999
Computer Design Services
N.A.I.C.S.: 541512

FITTERS DIVERSIFIED BERHAD
No 1 Jalan Tembaga SD 5/2 Bandar Sri Damansara, 52200, Kuala Lumpur, Malaysia
Tel.: (60) 362767155
Web Site: https://fittersgroup.com
FITTERS—(KLS)
Rev.: $87,812,063
Assets: $106,747,090
Liabilities: $43,585,185
Net Worth: $63,161,905
Earnings: ($14,629,630)
Emp.: 15
Fiscal Year-end: 03/31/23
Fire Safety Materials & Equipment
N.A.I.C.S.: 332919
Hooi Yin Goh *(Exec Dir)*

Subsidiaries:

FITTERS (Ipoh) Sdn Bhd (1)
13 & 13A Jalan Dato Haji Megat Khas Taman Bandaraya Utama, 31400, Ipoh, Perak, Malaysia
Tel.: (60) 55477622

Sales Range: $50-74.9 Million
Emp.: 7
Fire Safety Equipment Distr
N.A.I.C.S.: 423490

FITTERS (S) Pte Ltd. (1)
83 Genting Lane 06-01, Singapore, 349568, Singapore
Tel.: (65) 267441171
Fire Safety Material & Equipment Distr
N.A.I.C.S.: 423990

FITTERS (Sarawak) Sdn Bhd (1)
28 Ground Floor Wisma Koperkasa Jalan Simpang Tiga, 93300, Kuching, Sarawak, Malaysia
Tel.: (60) 82250221
Sales Range: $50-74.9 Million
Emp.: 5
Safety Materials & Equipment Distr
N.A.I.C.S.: 423450

FITTERS Marketing Sdn Bhd (1)
Wisma Fitters No 1 Jalan Tembaga SD 5/2, Bandar Sri Damansara, 52200, Kuala Lumpur, Malaysia
Tel.: (60) 361576199
Door & Builing Materials Distr
N.A.I.C.S.: 444180

FITTERS Sdn Bhd (1)
No 1 Wisma Fitters Jalan Tembaga Sd 5/2, Bandar Sri Damansara, 52200, Kuala Lumpur, Malaysia
Tel.: (60) 362767155
Fire Safety Materials & Equipment Mfr
N.A.I.C.S.: 339999
Wong Swee Yee *(Mng Dir)*

Future NRG Sdn Bhd (1)
Wisma Fitters No 1 Jalan Tembaga SD 5/2, Bandar Sri Damansara, 52200, Kuala Lumpur, Wilayah Persekutuan, Malaysia
Tel.: (60) 362772200
Web Site: https://www.futurenrg.net
Sales Range: $25-49.9 Million
Emp.: 200
Renewable Energy Development Services
N.A.I.C.S.: 561990

Master Pyroserve Sdn Bhd (1)
Bangunan Fitters Lot 2221 Kampung Jaya Industrial Area Sungai Buloh, 47000, Kuala Lumpur, Wilayah Persekutuan, Malaysia
Tel.: (60) 361576199
Sales Range: $25-49.9 Million
Emp.: 40
Fire Alarm & Communication Systems Mfr
N.A.I.C.S.: 334220

Molecor (SEA) Sdn. Bhd. (1)
No 10 Jalan Gebeng 2/13 Kawasan Perindustrian, Gebeng, 26080, Kuantan, Pahang Darul Makmur, Malaysia
Tel.: (60) 95834920
Web Site: https://www.molecorsea.com
Pipe Mfr & Distr
N.A.I.C.S.: 332996

FITZROY RIVER CORPORATION LTD
79 Careniup Avenue, Perth, 6018, WA, Australia
Tel.: (61) 892435164 AU
Web Site:
  https://www.fitzroyriver.net.au
FZR—(ASX)
Rev.: $989,222
Assets: $5,911,348
Liabilities: $27,504
Net Worth: $5,883,844
Earnings: $652,038
Fiscal Year-end: 06/30/22
Investment Holding Company
N.A.I.C.S.: 551112
Brendon Chan *(Sec)*

Subsidiaries:

Royalco Resources Limited (1)
Suite 6 02 Level 6 28 O Connell Street, Sydney, 2000, NSW, Australia (100%)
Tel.: (61) 290488856
Web Site: http://www.royalco.com.au
Rev.: $627,716
Assets: $6,838,003
Liabilities: $77,824
Net Worth: $6,760,179

Fitzroy River Corporation Ltd—(Continued)

Earnings: ($329,111)
Emp.: 7
Fiscal Year-end: 06/30/2018
Copper & Gold Mining & Exploration Services
N.A.I.C.S.: 212230
Justin Clyne *(Sec)*

FIVE BROKERS CAPITAL JSC

77/2 office 6D Al-Farabi ave, Bostandyk district, Almaty, 050000, Kazakhstan
Tel.: (7) 273908312
FIVE—(KAZ)
Assets: $598,531
Liabilities: $204,128
Net Worth: $394,403
Earnings: $13,752
Fiscal Year-end: 12/31/22
Securities Brokerage Services
N.A.I.C.S.: 523150

FIVE BY FIVE

4 Grosvenor Sq, Southampton, SO15 2BE, United Kingdom
Tel.: (44) 23 8082 8525
Web Site:
http://www.fivebyfivedigital.com
Emp.: 150
N.A.I.C.S.: 541810
Mark Scott *(Mng Dir)*

FIVE CORE EXIM LIMITED

WZ-15B/1 Room No 203/204 Uggersain Market Ashok Nagar, New Delhi, 110018, India
Tel.: (91) 7042292838
Web Site:
http://www.fivecoreexim.com
Year Founded: 1994
Rev.: $652,841
Assets: $1,953,523
Liabilities: $788,555
Net Worth: $1,164,968
Earnings: $230,682
Emp.: 3
Fiscal Year-end: 03/31/18
Holding Company; Information Technology Products & Services
N.A.I.C.S.: 551112
Surinder Kaur Kalra *(Chm)*

FIVE X TRADECOM LIMITED

B1/A, Utkarsh Co-op Housing Society M A Road Andheri West, Mumbai, 400072, Maharashtra, India
Tel.: (91) 2226204220
Web Site:
http://www.fivexfinance.com
Year Founded: 2010
536751—(BOM)
Rev.: $26,016
Assets: $2,310,603
Liabilities: $6,713
Net Worth: $2,303,890
Earnings: $149
Emp.: 5
Fiscal Year-end: 03/31/21
Financial Services
N.A.I.C.S.: 523999
Vijayshree Krishnat Desai *(Mng Dir & CFO)*

FIVE-STAR BUSINESS FINANCE LIMITED

New No 27 Old No 4 Taylors Road Kilpauk, Chennai, 600010, India
Tel.: (91) 4446106200
Web Site:
https://www.fivestargroup.in
Year Founded: 1984
543663—(BOM)
Rev.: $182,345,003
Assets: $1,043,441,988
Liabilities: $523,145,279
Net Worth: $520,296,709

Earnings: $72,357,305
Emp.: 7,347
Fiscal Year-end: 03/31/23
Investment Management Service
N.A.I.C.S.: 523999

FIVERR INTERNATIONAL LTD.

8 Eliezer Kaplan St, Tel Aviv, 6473409, Israel
Tel.: (972) 722280910
Web Site: https://www.fiverr.com
Year Founded: 2010
FVRR—(NYSE)
Rev.: $361,075,000
Assets: $1,023,604,000
Liabilities: $667,830,000
Net Worth: $355,774,000
Earnings: $3,681,000
Emp.: 775
Fiscal Year-end: 12/31/23
Online Shopping Services
N.A.I.C.S.: 459999
Micha Kaufman *(Founder, Chm & CEO)*

FIVES, SOCIETE ANONYME

3 Rue Drouot, 75009, Paris, France
Tel.: (33) 145237575   FR
Web Site: http://www.fivesgroup.com
Year Founded: 1812
Rev.: $2,238,476,955
Assets: $1,854,263,068
Liabilities: $1,403,751,229
Net Worth: $450,511,839
Earnings: ($25,300,997)
Emp.: 8,400
Fiscal Year-end: 12/31/19
Industrial Equipment Mfr & Industrial Engineering Services
N.A.I.C.S.: 541330
Martin Duverne *(Deputy CEO)*

Subsidiaries:

Cinetic Automation   (1)
23400 Halsted Rd, Farmington, MI 48335-2840
Tel.: (248) 477-0800
Web Site: http://www.cineticusa.com
Sales Range: $50-74.9 Million
Emp.: 220
Mfr of Automated Assembly Machines
N.A.I.C.S.: 333519
Jeff Jugan *(Mgr-Mktg)*

Subsidiary (Domestic):

Cinetic Landis Ltd.   (2)
16778 Halfway Blvd, Hagerstown, MD 21740
Tel.: (301) 797-3400
Web Site: http://www.fivesgroup.com
Sales Range: $25-49.9 Million
Emp.: 130
Precision Grinding Machines
N.A.I.C.S.: 333998

Gardner Abrasives   (2)
481 Gardner St, South Beloit, IL 61080
Tel.: (815) 389-2251
Web Site: http://www.gardnerabrasives.com
Sales Range: $50-74.9 Million
Emp.: 100
Abrasive Wheel Mfr
N.A.I.C.S.: 522130

Cinetic Giustina s.r.l.   (1)
Corso Lombardia 79 ZI Pescarito, San Mauro Torinese, 10099, Torino, Italy
Tel.: (39) 0112228611
Sales Range: $25-49.9 Million
Emp.: 60
Grinding Machine Mfr
N.A.I.C.S.: 333517
Paolo Poletti *(Pres)*

Cinetic Sorting Corp.   (1)
500 E Burnett Ave, Louisville, KY 40217-1120   (100%)
Tel.: (502) 636-1414
Web Site: http://www.sorting.com
Sales Range: $25-49.9 Million
Emp.: 100
Sorting & Material Handling System Mfr

N.A.I.C.S.: 333922
Ray Horine *(Acct Mgr)*

Fives DMS   (1)
1 Rue du Mont-de-Templemars Z I Lille Seclin, BP 30219, 59472, Seclin, Cedex, France   (100%)
Tel.: (33) 320493500
Web Site: http://www.fivesgroup.com
Sales Range: $50-74.9 Million
Emp.: 150
Rolling Mills & Allied Equipment for Ferrous & Nonferrous Metals, Hot Strip Downcoilers, Computerized Hydraulic Mill Automatic Gauge Control Systems, Mill Modernization of Existing Facilities
N.A.I.C.S.: 333519
Benoeit Caracge *(Gen Mgr)*

Fives Fletcher Limited   (1)
33 Brunel Parkway, Pride Park, Derby, DE24 8HR, United Kingdom   (100%)
Tel.: (44) 1332636000
Web Site: http://www.fivesgroup.com
Sales Range: $10-24.9 Million
Emp.: 33
Sugar Processing Machinery Mfr
N.A.I.C.S.: 311314

Fives Machining Systems, Inc.   (1)
1338 Cox Ave, Erlanger, KY 41018
Tel.: (859) 534-4600
Web Site: http://www.fivesmsi.com
Sales Range: $400-449.9 Million
Metal Cutting Machines & Automated Systems for Automotive/Commercial Vehicle Industry
N.A.I.C.S.: 333517

Plant (Domestic):

Fives Machining Systems, Inc. - Fond du Lac   (2)
142 Doty St, Fond Du Lac, WI 54935-3331
Tel.: (920) 921-9400
Web Site: http://www.fivesmsi.com
Machine Tools & Factory Automation Equipment Mfr & Services
N.A.I.C.S.: 333517

Unit (Domestic):

Fives Machining Systems, Inc. - Global Services, Chatsworth   (2)
20701 Plummer St, Chatsworth, CA 91311-5002
Tel.: (818) 407-1400
Web Site: http://www.fivesmsi.com
Sales Range: $25-49.9 Million
Emp.: 6
Machine Tool Rebuild, Retrofit & Maintenance Services
N.A.I.C.S.: 541990
Bill Wier *(Mgr-HR)*

Plant (Domestic):

Fives Machining Systems, Inc. - Hebron   (2)
2200 Litton Ln, Hebron, KY 41048
Tel.: (859) 534-4600
Web Site: http://www.fivesmsi.com
Sales Range: $200-249.9 Million
Machine Tools Mfr
N.A.I.C.S.: 333517

Fives North American Combustion, Inc.   (1)
4455 E 71st St, Cleveland, OH 44105-5600
Tel.: (216) 271-6000
Web Site: http://www.namfg.com
Sales Range: $125-149.9 Million
Mfr of Industrial Furnace Components & Edge Guide Materials; Electrical & General Engineering
N.A.I.C.S.: 333414

FIX AUTO CANADA, INC.

99 Emilien-Marcoux Suite 101, Blainville, J7C 0B4, QC, Canada
Tel.: (450) 433-1414
Web Site: http://www.fixauto.com
Automotive Repair Shops
N.A.I.C.S.: 811198
Carl Brabander *(VP-Mktg-Global)*

FIX PRICE GROUP PLC

155 Archiepiskopou Makariou III Pro-

teas House, 3026, Limassol, Cyprus
Tel.: (357) 96450403   VG
Web Site: https://fix-price.com
Year Founded: 2007
FIXP—(AIM)
Rev.: $3,409,468,320
Assets: $1,387,959,280
Liabilities: $1,028,560,520
Net Worth: $359,398,760
Earnings: $262,927,080
Fiscal Year-end: 12/31/22
Apparel Product Distr
N.A.I.C.S.: 455219
Dmitry Kirsanov *(CEO)*

FIXINOX SA

1Ere Rue N 8, 6040, Charleroi, Belgium
Tel.: (32) 71810526
Web Site: http://www.fixinox.com
Sales Range: $1-9.9 Million
Emp.: 24
Rustproof Metal Fixation Systems Mfr & Distr
N.A.I.C.S.: 332999
Hugues Wauters *(Mng Dir)*

FIXIT AG

Schachen 416, 5113, Holderbank, Switzerland
Tel.: (41) 628875300
Web Site: https://www.fixit.ch
Year Founded: 1896
Emp.: 200
Construction Material Mfr & Distr
N.A.I.C.S.: 333120

FIXSTARS CORPORATION

Tamachi Station Tower N 28 Floor 311 Shibaura, Minato-ku, Tokyo, 141-0032, Japan
Tel.: (81) 364200751
Web Site: https://www.fixstars.com
3687—(TKS)
Rev.: $49,899,420
Assets: $58,010,380
Liabilities: $16,711,130
Net Worth: $41,299,250
Earnings: $10,259,230
Emp.: 320
Fiscal Year-end: 09/30/23
Software Developer
N.A.I.C.S.: 513210
Satoshi Miki *(CEO)*

Subsidiaries:

Fixstars Solutions Inc.   (1)
100 Progress Ste 130, Irvine, CA 92618
Tel.: (949) 393-8810
Web Site: https://us.fixstars.com
Software Development Services
N.A.I.C.S.: 541511
Akihiro Asahara *(CEO)*

Oscar Technology Corporation   (1)
Tamachi Station Tower N 28th Floor 3-1-1 Shibaura, Minato-ku, Tokyo, 108-0023, Japan
Tel.: (81) 36 420 0762
Web Site: https://www.oscartech.jp
Software Licensing Services
N.A.I.C.S.: 541511
Satoshi Miki *(CEO)*

FIYTA PRECISION TECHNOLOGY CO., LTD.

20th Floor Fiyta Technology Building Gaoxin South 1st Road, Nanshan District, Shenzhen, 518057, Guangdong, China
Tel.: (86) 75586013360
Web Site: https://www.fiytagroup.com
000026—(SSE)
Rev.: $611,315,640
Assets: $578,046,456
Liabilities: $137,693,088
Net Worth: $440,353,368
Earnings: $37,441,872

Fiscal Year-end: 12/31/22
Watch Part & Accessory Mfr
N.A.I.C.S.: 334519
Yongfeng Huang *(Chm)*

FJ BENJAMIN HOLDINGS LTD.

1 Jalan Kilang Timor Pacific Tech
Centre 07-01/02, Singapore, 159303,
Singapore
Tel.: (65) 67370155   SG
Web Site:
  https://www.fjbenjamin.com
Year Founded: 1959
F10—(CAT)
Rev.: $64,063,727
Assets: $61,942,942
Liabilities: $31,933,309
Net Worth: $30,009,633
Earnings: $2,606,891
Emp.: 1,662
Fiscal Year-end: 06/30/23
Fashion Apparel, Timepieces & Home
Fashions Retailer & Distr; Leather
Accessories Designer & Licensor
N.A.I.C.S.: 315990
Frank Benjamin *(Founder & CEO)*

Subsidiaries:

Benmark Pte. Ltd.   **(1)**
141 Kaki Bukit Avenue 1 Shun Li Industrial
Park, FJ Benjamin Bldg, Singapore,
416005, Singapore   **(100%)**
Tel.: (65) 6 842 6880
Web Site: https://www.benmark.com.sg
Sales Range: $150-199.9 Million
Emp.: 500
Retailer & Distributor of Home Furnishings
N.A.I.C.S.: 423220

F J Benjamin (Taiwan) Ltd   **(1)**
5F No 260 Tun Hwa North Road, Taipei,
Taiwan
Tel.: (886) 2 2719 3880
Fashion Apparels Retailer
N.A.I.C.S.: 458110

F J Benjamin Concepts Pte Ltd   **(1)**
1 Jalan Kilang Timor Pacific Tech Centre
07-01/02, Singapore, 159303, Singapore
Tel.: (65) 67370155
Web Site: http://www.fjbenjamin.com
Sales Range: $1-4.9 Billion
Emp.: 8,200
Fashion Apparels Retailer
N.A.I.C.S.: 458110

F J Benjamin Fashions (U.S.)
Inc   **(1)**
601 W 26th St Ste 1745, New York, NY
10001
Tel.: (212) 206-8264
Web Site: http://www.fjbenjamin.com
Sales Range: $25-49.9 Million
Emp.: 7
Fashion Apparels Retailer
N.A.I.C.S.: 458110

F J Benjamin Luxury Timepieces
Sdn. Bhd   **(1)**
12th Floor KH Tower, 50250, Kuala Lumpur,
Malaysia
Tel.: (60) 32 056 6888
Web Site: https://www.fjbenjamin.com
Sales Range: $25-49.9 Million
Emp.: 100
Fashion Apparels Retailer
N.A.I.C.S.: 458110

F J Benjamin Trading HK Ltd   **(1)**
Island Place Tower Room 2308, 510 Kings
Road, North Point, China (Hong
Kong)   **(100%)**
Tel.: (852) 25062666
Web Site: http://www.fjbenjamin.com
Sales Range: $25-49.9 Million
Emp.: 40
N.A.I.C.S.: 315990

F. J. B. Investment Pte Ltd   **(1)**
10 Science Park Road 04-01 The Alpha,
Singapore, 117684, Singapore
Tel.: (65) 67370155
Investment Management Service
N.A.I.C.S.: 523999

Subsidiary (Domestic):

F J Benjamin (Singapore) Pte
Ltd   **(2)**
1 Jalan Kilang Timor Pacific Tech Centre
07-01/02, Singapore, 159303, Singapore
Tel.: (65) 67370155
Web Site: https://www.fjbenjamin.com
Sales Range: $25-49.9 Million
Emp.: 100
Fashion Apparels Retailer
N.A.I.C.S.: 458110

F J Benjamin (M) Sdn. Bhd.   **(1)**
12th Floor KH Tower No 8 Lorong P Ram-
lee, 50250, Kuala Lumpur,
Malaysia   **(100%)**
Tel.: (60) 320566888
Web Site: https://www.fjbenjamin.com
Sales Range: $25-49.9 Million
Emp.: 100
Fashion Apparel, Timepieces & Home Fash-
ions Retailer & Distr; Leather Accessories
Designer & Licensor
N.A.I.C.S.: 316990

Subsidiary (Domestic):

F J Benjamin Lifestyle Sdn. Bhd   **(2)**
12th Floor KH Tower, No 8 Lorong P Ram-
lee, 50250, Kuala Lumpur, Malaysia
Tel.: (60) 32 056 6888
Web Site: https://www.fjbenjamin.com
Sales Range: $25-49.9 Million
Emp.: 100
Fashion Apparels Retailer
N.A.I.C.S.: 458110

F J Benjamin Fashions (HK) Ltd.   **(1)**
Island Place Tower Room 2308, 510 Kings
Road, North Point, China (Hong
Kong)   **(100%)**
Tel.: (852) 25062666
Web Site: http://www.fjbenjamin.com
Sales Range: $25-49.9 Million
Emp.: 30
Fashion Retailer
N.A.I.C.S.: 458310

F J Benjamin Fashions (Singapore)
Pte. Ltd.   **(1)**
1 Jalan Kilang Timor Pacific Tech Centre
07-01/02, Singapore, 159303,
Singapore   **(100%)**
Tel.: (65) 6 737 0155
Web Site: https://www.fjbenjamin.com
Sales Range: $25-49.9 Million
Emp.: 200
Retail Fashion Mfr
N.A.I.C.S.: 316990

F J Benjamin Singapore Pte. Ltd.   **(1)**
1 Jalan Kilang Timor Pacific Tech Centre
07-01/02, Singapore, 159303,
Singapore   **(100%)**
Tel.: (65) 67370155
Web Site: https://www.fjbenjamin.com
Importer & Distributor of Timepieces
N.A.I.C.S.: 458310

Fashion Dynamics Singapore Pte
Ltd.   **(1)**
1 Jalan Kilang Timor 07-01/02 Pacific Tech
Centre, Singapore, 159303, Singapore
Tel.: (65) 67370155
Fashion Wear & Accessory Distr
N.A.I.C.S.: 424350

Peppo Fashions Group Company
Lmd   **(1)**
193/30 Floor 7B Lake Rajada Office Com-
plex, 193 30 Rajadapisek Rd, Bangkok,
810010, Klongtoey, Thailand
Tel.: (66) 26619599
Web Site: http://www.peppofashions.com
Sales Range: $125-149.9 Million
Emp.: 300
N.A.I.C.S.: 315990

FJ NEXT HOLDINGS CO., LTD.

Shinjuku Island Tower 11th floor 6-5-1
Nishi-Shinjuku, Shinjuku-ku, Tokyo,
163-1311, Japan
Tel.: (81) 367335100
Web Site: https://www.fjnext.com
Year Founded: 1980
8935—(TKS)
Rev.: $663,677,050

Assets: $629,807,410
Liabilities: $180,122,500
Net Worth: $449,684,910
Earnings: $42,654,330
Fiscal Year-end: 03/31/24
Real Estate Manangement Services
N.A.I.C.S.: 531390
Yukiharu Hida *(Chm, Pres & CEO)*

Subsidiaries:

FJ Community Co., Ltd.   **(1)**
Shinjuku Island Tower 3F 6-5-1 Nishishin-
juku, Shinjuku-ku, Tokyo, Japan
Tel.: (81) 367358890
Web Site: https://www.fjcommunity.com
Real Estate Brokerage Services
N.A.I.C.S.: 531210

FJARDE AP-FONDEN

Jakobsbergsgatan 16, Box 3069, 103
61, Stockholm, Sweden
Tel.: (46) 8 787 75 00
Web Site: http://www.ap4.se
Rev.: $75,467,000,000
Assets: $422,633,000,000
Liabilities: $4,605,000,000
Net Worth: $418,028,000,000
Earnings: $75,236,000,000
Emp.: 53
Fiscal Year-end: 12/31/19
Investment & Funding Services
N.A.I.C.S.: 523999
Niklas Ekvall *(CEO)*

Subsidiaries:

Polhem Infra AB   **(1)**
Norrlandsgatan 12, Stockholm, Sweden
Tel.: (46) 738 00 67 25
Web Site: http://www.polheminfra.se
Privater Equity Firm
N.A.I.C.S.: 523999
Mikael Lundin *(CEO & VP)*

Subsidiary (Domestic):

Telia Carrier AB   **(2)**
Stjarntorget 1, 169 94, Solna, Sweden
Tel.: (46) 850455000
Web Site: http://www.teliasoneraic.com
Sales Range: $25-49.9 Million
Mobile Network Services
N.A.I.C.S.: 517112
Staffan Gojeryd *(CEO)*

FJARSKIPTI HF.

Skutuvogi 2, 104, Reykjavik, Iceland
Tel.: (354) 5999000
Web Site: http://www.vodafone.is
Sales Range: $125-149.9 Million
Emp.: 400
Mobile Telecommunications & Inter-
net Services
N.A.I.C.S.: 517112
Gestur G. Gestsson *(CTO)*

FJORDLAND EXPLORATION INC.

Suite 1100 1111 Melville Street, Van-
couver, V6E 3V6, BC, Canada
Tel.: (604) 688-3415
Web Site:
  https://www.fjordlandex.com
Year Founded: 1996
FEXXF—(OTCIQ)
Assets: $3,166,757
Liabilities: $67,400
Net Worth: $3,099,357
Earnings: ($435,565)
Fiscal Year-end: 12/31/23
Mineral Exploration Services
N.A.I.C.S.: 213114
Richard C. Atkinson *(Chm)*

FKL AD TEMERIN

Industrijska zona bb, 21235, Temerin,
Serbia
Tel.: (381) 21 6841 100
Web Site: http://www.fkl-serbia.com
Year Founded: 1961

Emp.: 603
Rolling Bearing Mfr
N.A.I.C.S.: 332991

FL ENTERTAINMENT N.V.

5 Rue Francois 1er, 75008, Paris,
France
Tel.: (33) 144952300
Web Site: https://group.banijay.com
Year Founded: 1994
BNJ—(EUR)
Rev.: $4,766,088,973
Assets: $6,328,513,082
Liabilities: $6,269,786,953
Net Worth: $58,726,129
Earnings: $81,245,171
Emp.: 4,551
Fiscal Year-end: 12/31/23
Entertainment Broadcasting Services
N.A.I.C.S.: 516120
Francois Riahi *(CEO)*

FLAGS UNLIMITED

364 St Vincent Street, Barrie, L4M
4A5, ON, Canada
Tel.: (705) 739-4100
Web Site:
  http://www.flagsunlimited.com
Year Founded: 1966
Rev.: $10,694,229
Emp.: 60
Flags & Banners Mfr
N.A.I.C.S.: 455219
Dennis Brown *(Pres & CEO)*

FLAGSHIP GLOBAL CORPO-RATION

50 Hill Crescent Worcester Park,
London, United Kingdom
Tel.: (44) 2089492259   NV
Year Founded: 2007
FGCN—(OTCIQ)
Emp.: 1
Medical Instrument Mfr
N.A.I.C.S.: 339112
Stephen Moscicki *(Chm & CEO)*

FLAGSHIP INVESTMENTS LIM-ITED

Level 12 Corporate Centre One 2
Corporate Court, Bundall, 4217, QLD,
Australia
Tel.: (61) 755741457
Web Site:
  https://www.flagshipinvestments.com
FSI—(ASX)
Rev.: $1,415,153
Assets: $52,678,627
Liabilities: $14,658,747
Net Worth: $38,019,880
Earnings: $1,972,173
Fiscal Year-end: 06/30/22
Investment Services
N.A.I.C.S.: 523999
Emmanuel C. Pohl *(Mng Dir)*

FLAKK HOLDING AS

Korsegata 8, 6002, Alesund, Norway
Tel.: (47) 7011 6430   NO
Web Site: http://www.flakk.no
Year Founded: 2006
Investment Holding Company
N.A.I.C.S.: 551112
Knut Trygve Flakk *(Mng Dir)*

Subsidiaries:

62NORD AS   **(1)**
Skansekaia, 6002, Alesund, Norway
Tel.: (47) 70 11 44 30
Web Site: http://www.62.no
Emp.: 8
Outdoor Recreational Services
N.A.I.C.S.: 713990
Ann Kristin Ytrevik *(Mgr-Mktg)*

Devold of Norway AS   **(1)**
Molvaersvegen 12, 6030, Langevag, Norway

Flakk Holding AS—(Continued)

Tel.: (47) 70 19 77 00
Web Site: http://www.devold.no
Apparel Mfr & Distr
N.A.I.C.S.: 315990
Cathrine Stange (CEO)

Flakk International AS   (1)
Korsegata 8, PO Box 836, Sentrum, 6001,
Alesund, Norway   (100%)
Tel.: (47) 7011 6430
Web Site: http://www.flakk.no
Equity Investment Firm
N.A.I.C.S.: 523999

H-Produkter AS   (1)
Stette, 6260, Skodje, Norway
Tel.: (47) 70 21 74 00
Web Site: http://www.hprodukter.no
Window & Door Mfr
N.A.I.C.S.: 321911

Isolaft AS   (1)
Eidsvika, 6264, Tennfjord, Norway
Tel.: (47) 70 30 08 08
Web Site: http://www.isolaft.no
Prefabricated Modular Buildings Mfr
N.A.I.C.S.: 321992
Jan Erik Nybo (Mgr-Production)

NORD Helikopter AS   (1)
Alesund Lufthavn, Vigra, 6040, Rorvik, Nor-
way
Tel.: (47) 95 89 79 00
Web Site: http://www.nordhelikopter.no
Aircraft Charter Services
N.A.I.C.S.: 481212
Jorund Kile (CEO & Mgr-Technical & Ac-
countable)

FLAME TREE GROUP HOLD-INGS LTD.

Off Enterprise Road Opposite Road
A, Industrial Area, Nairobi, Kenya
Tel.: (254) 2080706037
Web Site:
https://www.flametreegroup.com
Year Founded: 1989
FTGH—(NAI)
Rev.: $28,455,734
Assets: $25,575,775
Liabilities: $17,220,600
Net Worth: $8,355,176
Earnings: ($476,001)
Emp.: 967
Fiscal Year-end: 12/31/23
Plastic Tank & Plastic Product Mfr
N.A.I.C.S.: 326199
George Theobald (Chm)

Subsidiaries:

Chirag Africa Limited   (1)
PO Box 26393, 00500, Nairobi, Kenya
Tel.: (254) 729356346
Web Site: https://www.chirag.co.ke
Crisp & Snack Mfr
N.A.I.C.S.: 311919

Cirrus International FZC   (1)
PO Box 191573, Dubai, United Arab Emir-
ates
Tel.: (971) 503264282
Web Site: http://www.cirrusfzc.com
Plastic Product Distr
N.A.I.C.S.: 424610

Roto Moulders Limited   (1)
Enterprise Road, PO Box 26393, Industrial
Area, 00504, Nairobi, Kenya
Tel.: (254) 798441100
Web Site: https://www.rotomoulders.com
Water Tank Mfr
N.A.I.C.S.: 332420

FLAMINGO THERAPEUTICS BV

Gaston Geenslaan 3, Leuven , 3001,
Belgium
Tel.: (32) 16852641
Web Site: https://flamingtx.com
Biotechnology Research
N.A.I.C.S.: 541714
Mike Garrett (COO)

FLAMURA SA

Str Linariei 90 S4, Bucharest, Roma-
nia
Tel.: (40) 21 3371703
Sales Range: $1-9.9 Million
Emp.: 1
Weaving Services
N.A.I.C.S.: 313210

FLANAGAN FOODSERVICE, INC.

100 Sasaga Drive, Kitchener, N2C
2G7, ON, Canada
Tel.: (519) 748-0878
Web Site: http://www.flanagan.ca
Family Owned Food Distr
N.A.I.C.S.: 445298
Dan Flanagan (CEO)

Subsidiaries:

Summit Food Service Distributors,
Inc.   (1)
580 Industrial Road, London, N5V 1V1, ON,
Canada
Tel.: (519) 453-3410
Web Site: http://www.summitfoods.ca
Sales Range: $50-74.9 Million
Wholesale Food Distr
N.A.I.C.S.: 424490

FLAP KONGRE TOPLANTI HIZMETLERI OTOMOTIV VE TURIZM A.S.

Podgoritsa Caddesi No 1 Birlik, Can-
kaya, Ankara, Turkiye
Tel.: (90) 3124540000
Web Site: https://www.flaptour.com.tr
Year Founded: 1993
FLAP—(IST)
Tour Operator
N.A.I.C.S.: 561520
Gokhan Saygi (Chm & Mgr)

FLAROS S.A.

Str Ion Minulescu nr 67-93 sector 3,
Bucharest, Romania
Tel.: (40) 213215720
Web Site: http://www.flaros.com
FLAO—(BUC)
Rev.: $1,530,240
Assets: $25,543,703
Liabilities: $478,340
Net Worth: $25,065,363
Earnings: $397,811
Emp.: 16
Fiscal Year-end: 12/31/23
Footwear Mfr
N.A.I.C.S.: 316210

FLASHAPP INC.

2 Infirmary street, Leeds, LS1 2JP,
United Kingdom
Tel.: (44) 7441913734
Web Site: http://www.flashapp.pro
Year Founded: 2018
Mobile Application Development Ser-
vices
N.A.I.C.S.: 541511
Vladimir Novakovic (Pres, CEO,
CFO, Treas & Sec)

FLASKAMP AG

Klosterstrasse 64, 10179, Berlin, Ger-
many
Tel.: (49) 30 4600 6260
Web Site: http://www.flaskamp.de
Year Founded: 1970
Rev.: $39,452,742
Emp.: 35
Communications, Direct Marketing,
Event Marketing, High Technology,
Public Relations
N.A.I.C.S.: 541810
Antonius Flaskamp (Pres & CEO)

FLASR, INC.

El Dorado, Panama, 0819-11689,
Panama
Tel.: (507) 4073741407
Year Founded: 2013
Translation Services
N.A.I.C.S.: 541930
Maria Del Pilar Jaen (Pres , Sec &
Treas)

FLAT GLASS GROUP CO., LTD.

No 1999 Yunhe Road, Xiuzhou Dis-
trict, Jiaxing, Zhejiang, China
Tel.: (86) 57382703000   CN
Web Site:
https://www.flatgroup.com.cn
Year Founded: 1998
6865—(HKG)
Rev.: $2,170,702,389
Assets: $4,546,393,854
Liabilities: $2,576,238,265
Net Worth: $1,970,155,589
Earnings: $298,038,372
Emp.: 7,693
Fiscal Year-end: 12/31/22
Photovoltaic Glass Mfr & Distr
N.A.I.C.S.: 335999

Subsidiaries:

Shanghai Flat Glass Co., Ltd.   (1)
No 59 Yuanting Road, Dazhong Industrial
Park Anting Town Jiading District, Shanghai,
China
Tel.: (86) 2169576758
Glass Product Mfr & Distr
N.A.I.C.S.: 327211

Zhejiang Flat Glass Co., Ltd.   (1)
No 655 Yunhe Road, Xiuzhou District, Jiax-
ing, Zhejiang, China
Tel.: (86) 57382790204
Glass Product Mfr & Distr
N.A.I.C.S.: 327211

Zhejiang Jiafu Glass Co., Ltd.   (1)
No 999 Hongfu Road, Honhe Town, Jiaxing,
Zhejiang, China
Tel.: (86) 57383365666
Glass Product Mfr & Distr
N.A.I.C.S.: 327211

FLATEXDEGIRO AG

Rotfeder-Ring 7, D-60327, Frankfurt
am Main, Germany
Tel.: (49) 694500010
Web Site: https://flatexdegiro.com
FTK—(MUN)
Rev.: $431,315,125
Assets: $5,011,602,916
Liabilities: $4,268,014,007
Net Worth: $743,588,909
Earnings: $79,324,098
Emp.: 1,285
Fiscal Year-end: 12/31/23
Securities Brokerage & Investment
Services
N.A.I.C.S.: 523150
Frank Niehage (Chm-Mgmt Bd &
CEO)

Subsidiaries:

Factoring.plus.GmbH   (1)
Martin-Luther-Ring 13, 04109, Leipzig, Ger-
many
Tel.: (49) 3411492040
Web Site: http://www.factoring-plus.de
Financial Services
N.A.I.C.S.: 327910

Subsidiary (Domestic):

Financial.service.plus GmbH   (2)
Martin-Luther-Ring 13, 04109, Leipzig, Ger-
many
Tel.: (49) 34135525960
Web Site: http://www.financial-service-
plus.de
Financial Services
N.A.I.C.S.: 541611
Robert Bahrmann (Mng Dir)

Flatex Bank AG   (1)

Rotfeder-Ring 7, 60327, Frankfurt, Germany
Tel.: (49) 69506041910
Web Site: http://www.flatex-bank.com
Financial Banking Services
N.A.I.C.S.: 522110
Frank Niehage (CEO)

Xervices GmbH   (1)
Allee 8, 47877, Willich, Germany
Tel.: (49) 693650550
Web Site: http://www.xervices.de
Software Product Services
N.A.I.C.S.: 541511
Pascal Beaud (Mng Dir)

FLATWORLD ACQUISITION CORP.

Palm Grove House Road Town, Tor-
tola, VG1110, Virgin Islands (British)
Tel.: (284) 5456127   VG
Year Founded: 2010
Liabilities: $740,102
Net Worth: ($740,102)
Earnings: ($105,400)
Emp.: 4
Fiscal Year-end: 12/31/18
Investment Services
N.A.I.C.S.: 523999
Gilbert H. Lamphere (Chm)

FLAVORITE FOODS LIMITED

128 Boundary Road, PO Box 597,
San Juan, Port of Spain, Trinidad &
Tobago
Tel.: (868) 638 2236   TT
Web Site:
http://www.flavoritefoodstt.com
Sales Range: $10-24.9 Million
Emp.: 298
Food Products Mfr
N.A.I.C.S.: 311520
Godfrey Bain (Chm)

FLAVUS BETEILIGUNGEN AG

Otto-Brenner-Str. 17, 21337,
Luneburg, Germany
Tel.: (49) 4131 2244200
Web Site: http://www.flavus-
beteiligungen.de
Management Holding Company
N.A.I.C.S.: 551112

FLC GROUP JOINT STOCK COMPANY

5th Floor FLC Landmark Tower Le
Duc Tho road, Tu Liem, Hanoi, Viet-
nam
Tel.: (84) 4 3771 1111
Web Site: http://www.flc.vn
Year Founded: 2008
Real Estate Development Services
N.A.I.C.S.: 531390
Trinh Van Quyet (Chm-Mgmt Bd)

FLEET CANADA INC.

1011 Gilmore Rd, Fort Erie, L2A 5M4,
ON, Canada
Tel.: (905) 871-2100
Web Site: http://www.fleet.ca
Year Founded: 2006
Sales Range: $50-74.9 Million
Emp.: 100
Aerospace Components; Metal to
Metal Bonding & Conventional Con-
struction & Composite Bonding
N.A.I.C.S.: 336413

FLEETPARTNERS GROUP LIMITED

Level 6 601 Pacific Highway, St
Leonards, Sydney, 2065, NSW, Aus-
tralia
Tel.: (61) 289737272   AU
Web Site:
https://investors.fleetpartners.com.au
Year Founded: 2008

FPR—(ASX)
Rev.: $460,986,309
Assets: $1,530,702,949
Liabilities: $1,097,705,197
Net Worth: $432,997,752
Earnings: $55,187,658
Emp.: 445
Fiscal Year-end: 09/30/23
Holding Company; Vehicle Fleet Management & Leasing Services
N.A.I.C.S.: 551112
Damien Berrell *(CEO, Mng Dir & CFO)*

Subsidiaries:

Fleet Partners Pty. Ltd. **(1)**
L3 40 River Blvd, Richmond, 3121, VIC, Australia
Tel.: (61) 384165300
Web Site: https://www.fleetpartners.com.au
Sales Range: $300-349.9 Million
Emp.: 200
Passenger & Commercial Vehicle Leasing & Fleet Management Services
N.A.I.C.S.: 532112

FLEETPRO RIVER LTD.
Nauenstrasse 63A, Basel, 4002, Switzerland
Tel.: (41) 61 205 15 30   CH
Web Site: http://www.fleetpro-psm.com
Year Founded: 1999
Ocean-Going Passenger Ships, Technical & Hotel Services
N.A.I.C.S.: 541611
Robert Straubhaar *(Vice Chm & CEO)*

FLEETWOOD LIMITED
Level 2 464 Hay St, Subiaco, 6008, WA, Australia
Tel.: (61) 893233300
Web Site:
      https://www.fleetwoodlimited.com
FWD—(ASX)
Rev.: $278,015,490
Assets: $167,324,385
Liabilities: $56,987,179
Net Worth: $110,337,206
Earnings: $2,530,716
Emp.: 650
Fiscal Year-end: 06/30/24
Tent Trailers Mfr
N.A.I.C.S.: 336214
Bradley Denison *(CEO & Mng Dir)*

Subsidiaries:

Camec (NZ) Limited **(1)**
44 Montgomerie Road, Mangere, Auckland, 2022, New Zealand
Tel.: (64) 92572419
Web Site: https://www.camec.co.nz
Household Appliance Whslr
N.A.I.C.S.: 423620

Camec Pty Ltd **(1)**
47-63 Remington Drive, Dandenong, 3175, VIC, Australia
Tel.: (61) 1300422632
Web Site: https://www.camec.com.au
Sales Range: $25-49.9 Million
Emp.: 100
Recreational & Marine Vehicles Equipment Mfr & Supplier
N.A.I.C.S.: 336999

Coromal Caravans Pty Ltd **(1)**
25 Harrison Rd, Forrestfield, Perth, 6058, WA, Australia
Tel.: (61) 893520900
Web Site: http://www.coromal.com.au
Emp.: 200
Caravan Mfr
N.A.I.C.S.: 336110
Bradley van Hemert *(CEO)*

Fleetwood Pty Ltd **(1)**
1202 Abernethy Road Perth Airport, High Wycombe, Perth, 6105, WA, Australia
Tel.: (61) 892817500
Web Site: https://www.fleetwood.com.au

Sales Range: $25-49.9 Million
Emp.: 650
Transportable Homes Construction Services
N.A.I.C.S.: 321991
Andrew Wackett *(CFO)*

Northern RV Pty. Ltd. **(1)**
29 - 33 Freight Drive, Somerton, 3062, VIC, Australia
Tel.: (61) 393575151
Web Site: https://www.northernrv.com.au
Caravan & Motorhome Services
N.A.I.C.S.: 541219

FLEISCHHACKER GMBH & CO. KG
An der Silberkuhle 18, 58239, Schwerte, Germany
Tel.: (49) 23049310   De
Web Site:
      http://www.fleischhacker.biz
Year Founded: 1970
Sales Range: $25-49.9 Million
Medical Equipment Distr
N.A.I.C.S.: 423450
Lutz Fleischhacker *(Pres)*

FLERIE AB
Skeppsbron 16 111 30, 11130, Stockholm, Sweden
Tel.: (46) 761310127
Web Site: https://www.flerie.com
INDEX—(OMX)
Rev.: $4,485,187
Assets: $32,906,797
Liabilities: $1,626,064
Net Worth: $31,280,733
Earnings: ($9,397,379)
Emp.: 6
Fiscal Year-end: 12/31/22
Biotechnology Research & Development Services
N.A.I.C.S.: 541714
Peter Zerhouni *(CEO)*

FLETCHER BUILDING LIMITED
810 Great South Road, Penrose, Auckland, 1061, New Zealand
Tel.: (64) 95259000
Web Site:
      https://www.fletcherbuilding.com
FCREY—(OTCIQ)
Rev.: $5,065,191,388
Assets: $5,431,220,096
Liabilities: $3,232,057,416
Net Worth: $2,199,162,679
Earnings: $151,913,876
Emp.: 14,900
Fiscal Year-end: 06/30/23
Commercial Construction, Civil & Mechanical Engineering Building Products Mfr & Distr
N.A.I.C.S.: 444180
Dean Fradgley *(CEO-Australia)*

Subsidiaries:

AHI Roofing Limited **(1)**
90-104 Felton Matthew Ave, PO Box 18071, Auckland, 1072, New Zealand **(100%)**
Tel.: (64) 99789010
Web Site: http://www.gerardroof.co.nz
Sales Range: $50-74.9 Million
Emp.: 180
Roofing Siding & Sheet Metal Contractors
N.A.I.C.S.: 238160
Caz Johnson *(Gen Mgr)*

Subsidiary (Non-US):

AHI Roofing (Malaysia) SDN BHD **(2)**
75-3 Jln USJ 21/10, 47630, Subang Jaya, Selangor, Malaysia
Tel.: (60) 380119039
Emp.: 140
Building Roofing Material Mfr & Distr
N.A.I.C.S.: 332322
Idrose Harun *(Mgr-Ops)*

AHI Roofing Gyarto Es Kereskedelmi Korlatolt Felelossegu Tarasag **(2)**

Fehervari Ut 28/14, Varpalota, 8100, Hungary
Tel.: (36) 88552800
Building Roofing Material Whslr
N.A.I.C.S.: 423330

Amatek Industries Pty Limited **(1)**
Level 4 68 Waterloo Road, Macquarie Park, 2113, NSW, Australia
Tel.: (61) 299283500
Building Material & Concrete Mfr
N.A.I.C.S.: 327320
Mark Adamson *(CEO)*

Approach Signs Limited **(1)**
Ruahine St, PO Box 207, Paraparaumu, 5254, New Zealand
Tel.: (64) 42982981
Web Site: https://www.approachsigns.co.nz
Traffic Equipment Distr
N.A.I.C.S.: 423860

Australian Construction Products Pty Limited **(1)**
Tel.: (61) 28 708 4400
Web Site: https://www.acprod.com.au
Emp.: 3
Steel Civil Road System Mfr & Distr
N.A.I.C.S.: 331210
Zalman Paris *(Gen Mgr)*

Australian Fibre Glass Pty Limited **(1)**
2/ 16 Amberley Crs, Dandenong, 3175, VIC, Australia
Tel.: (61) 397921227
Fiber Glass Mfr
N.A.I.C.S.: 327212
Peter Giret *(CEO)*

Building Choices Limited **(1)**
2-20 Mandeville St, Riccarton, 8011, Canterbury, New Zealand
Tel.: (64) 33482039
Web Site: http://www.placemakers.co.nz
Sales Range: $75-99.9 Million
Emp.: 190
Hardware Parts Distr
N.A.I.C.S.: 423710
Katherine Freeman-Greene *(Mgr-Ops)*

Cemac (Hong Kong) Limited **(1)**
Room 1203 Core45 43 Tsun Yip Street, Kwun Tong, Hong Kong, China (Hong Kong) **(100%)**
Tel.: (852) 28115253
Sales Range: $10-24.9 Million
Emp.: 40
Business Support Services
N.A.I.C.S.: 561499
Chi Wing Shum *(Mgr)*

Crane Distribution Properties Limited **(1)**
Level 1 64 Cook Street, Auckland, 1010, New Zealand
Tel.: (64) 33381009
Web Site: http://www.mico.co.nz
Emp.: 5
Industrial Crane Distr
N.A.I.C.S.: 423830
Mark Adamson *(Office Mgr)*

Crane Group Limited **(1)**
Level 14 15 Blue Street, North Sydney, 2060, NSW, Australia
Tel.: (61) 289233000
Web Site: http://www.crane.com.au
Sales Range: $1-4.9 Billion
Emp.: 4,353
Plastic Pipeline Systems & Nonferrous Metal Products Mfr; Plumbing & Electrical Supplies Mfr
N.A.I.C.S.: 326191

Division (Domestic):

Austral Wright Metals **(2)**
183-139 Cowpasture Rd, Wetherill Park, 2164, NSW, Australia **(100%)**
Tel.: (61) 298270790
Sales Range: $25-49.9 Million
Emp.: 50
Nonferrous Metals & Metal Products Distr
N.A.I.C.S.: 423510
Alex Gouch *(Mgr-Technical)*

Crane Copper Tube **(2)**
2115 Castlereagh Road, Penrith, 2750, NSW, Australia **(100%)**

Tel.: (61) 247205300
Web Site: http://www.cranecopper.com.au
Sales Range: $25-49.9 Million
Emp.: 170
Copper Tube Mfr
N.A.I.C.S.: 331420

Crane Enfield Metals Pty Limited **(2)**
2115 Castlereagh Road, Penrith, 2750, NSW, Australia
Tel.: (61) 247205300
Web Site: http://www.cranecopper.com.au
Emp.: 12
Aluminium Tube & Metal Products Mfr
N.A.I.C.S.: 331318

Iplex Pipelines Australia Pty Ltd **(2)**
Fujitsu Centre Level 14, Locked Bag 2125, 15 Blue Street, North Sydney, 2060, NSW, Australia **(100%)**
Tel.: (61) 1300047539
Web Site: https://www.iplex.com.au
Sales Range: $200-249.9 Million
Emp.: 1,000
Pipe & Pipe Fittings Mfr & Distr
N.A.I.C.S.: 332996

Subsidiary (Domestic):

Northern Iron and Brass Foundry Pty. Ltd. **(3)**
22 Meyer Avenue, Wangan, Innisfail, 4871, QLD, Australia
Tel.: (61) 740640500
Sales Range: $25-49.9 Million
Emp.: 10
Iron Product Mfr
N.A.I.C.S.: 331511
Joe Vecchio *(Gen Mgr)*

Subsidiary (Non-US):

Iplex Pipelines NZ Limited **(2)**
67 Malden Street, Roslyn, Palmerston North, 4414, New Zealand **(100%)**
Tel.: (64) 63582004
Sales Range: $50-74.9 Million
Emp.: 110
Plastic Pipes & Pipe Fittings Mfr & Distr
N.A.I.C.S.: 332996
Craig Mangos *(Gen Mgr)*

Division (Domestic):

Tradelink Plumbing Centres **(2)**
1051 Nudgee Road, Banyo, Brisbane, 4014, QLD, Australia **(100%)**
Tel.: (61) 732609777
Web Site: https://tradelink.com.au
Sales Range: $1-4.9 Billion
Emp.: 200
Plumbing Supplies for Bathrooms, Kitchens & Laundries
N.A.I.C.S.: 423720
David Kelly *(Office Mgr)*

Crevet Pipelines Pty Ltd **(1)**
Cnr Southpine and Johnstone Rd, Brendale, 4500, Brisbane, QLD, Australia
Tel.: (61) 738819290
Web Site: http://www.crevet.com.au
Sales Range: $75-99.9 Million
Emp.: 200
Building Pipe Mfr & Distr
N.A.I.C.S.: 423390
Bill Volkman *(Mgr-Distr)*

DVS Limited **(1)**
17a Piermark Drive Rosedale, North Shore City, Auckland, 0632, New Zealand
Tel.: (64) 9 414 2755
Web Site: http://www.dvs.co.nz
Home Ventilation Services
N.A.I.C.S.: 561790
Jason Bezuidenhout *(Mgr-Sls-Scotland)*

Decra Roofing Systems Inc. **(1)**
1230 Railroad St, Corona, CA 92882 **(100%)**
Tel.: (951) 272-8180
Sheet Metal Work Mfg
N.A.I.C.S.: 332322

FBHS (Aust) Pty Limited **(1)**
33-83 Quarry Road, Erskine Park, 2759, NSW, Australia
Tel.: (61) 246468200
Web Site:
      https://www.fairdinkumbuilds.com.au
Steel Roll Mfr & Distr
N.A.I.C.S.: 331221

Fletcher Building Limited—(Continued)

Fletcher Aluminium (1)
30-32 Bowden Rpad, Mount Wellington, Auckland, 1060, New Zealand (100%)
Tel.: (64) 9 574 1500
Web Site:
http://www.fletcheraluminium.co.nz
Sales Range: $1-4.9 Billion
Emp.: 240
Designs, Develops & Manufactures Premium Aluminum Extrusions for Industries
N.A.I.C.S.: 331318
Mark Adamson *(CEO & Mng Dir)*

Fletcher Building Australia (1)
1051 Nudgee Road, Locked Bag 7013, Banyo, Brisbane, 4014, QLD, Australia
Tel.: (61) 283112588
Web Site: https://fletcherbuilding.com
Sales Range: $25-49.9 Million
Emp.: 30
Mfr of Concrete Products
N.A.I.C.S.: 327390
Steven Baker *(Gen Mgr-Pipeline Products)*

Fletcher Building Holdings Limited (1)
810 Great South Road, Penrose, Auckland, 1061, New Zealand (100%)
Tel.: (64) 95259000
Web Site: https://www.fletcherbuilding.co.nz
Holding Company
N.A.I.C.S.: 551112

Fletcher Building Netherlands B.V. (1)
Schouwburgplein 30-34, 3012CL, Rotterdam, Zuid-Holland, Netherlands
Tel.: (31) 102245333
Construction Engineering Services
N.A.I.C.S.: 541330

Fletcher Building Nominees Limited (1)
810 Great South Road Penrose, Auckland, 1061, New Zealand
Tel.: (64) 95259000
Web Site: http://www.fletcherbuilding.com
Sales Range: $25-49.9 Million
Emp.: 7
Civil Engineering Construction Services
N.A.I.C.S.: 237990
Ljubisa Vucinic *(CEO)*

Fletcher Building Products Limited (1)
810 Great South Road, 810 Great S Rd, Penrose, 1061, New Zealand (100%)
Tel.: (64) 95259000
Emp.: 800
Building Material Dealers
N.A.I.C.S.: 444180

Fletcher Concrete and Infrastructure Limited (1)
165 The Strand, Parnell, Auckland, 1010, New Zealand (100%)
Tel.: (64) 93034755
Web Site: https://www.firth.co.nz
Concrete Contractor
N.A.I.C.S.: 238110
Mark Adamson *(CEO-Infrastructure)*

Fletcher Construction (Solomon Islands) Limited (1)
Ranadi Industrial Estate, PO Box 836, Honiara, Solomon Islands
Tel.: (677) 30556
Construction Services
N.A.I.C.S.: 236220
Richard Simpson *(Reg Mgr)*

Fletcher Construction Australia Pty Limited (1)
L 11 Tower B Zenith Centre 821 Pacific Hwy, Chatswood, 2067, NSW, Australia
Tel.: (61) 299283500
Construction Materials Mfr
N.A.I.C.S.: 327331

Fletcher Construction Buildings Limited (1)
812 Great South Road, Penrose, Auckland, 1061, New Zealand
Tel.: (64) 95799979
Construction Services
N.A.I.C.S.: 236220
Gary Walker *(Gen Mgr-Buildings)*

Fletcher Construction Company (Fiji) Limited (1)
Wailada Industrial Estate, PO Box 3070, Lami, Suva, 679, Fiji
Tel.: (679) 3361511
Web Site:
http://www.fletcherconstruction.com.nz
Emp.: 63
Construction Engineering Services
N.A.I.C.S.: 541330
John Mathews *(Gen Mgr)*

Fletcher Insulation Pty. Limited (1)
161 Arthur Street, Homebush, 2140, NSW, Australia
Tel.: (61) 1300654444
Web Site: https://www.insulation.com.au
Sales Range: $150-199.9 Million
Emp.: 120
Insulation Material Distr
N.A.I.C.S.: 423330

Subsidiary (Domestic):

Baron Insulation Pty Ltd (2)
76 Naxos Way, Keysborough, 3173, VIC, Australia
Tel.: (61) 397764006
Emp.: 24
Insulation Material Mfr
N.A.I.C.S.: 327993
Darren Davies *(Gen Mgr)*

Fletcher Morobe Construction Pty Limited (1)
Saraga St Six Mile, PO Box 848, Port Moresby, Papua New Guinea (100%)
Tel.: (675) 3253144
Web Site:
http://www.fletcherconstruction.com.pg
Sales Range: $900-999.9 Million
Emp.: 700
Heavy & Civil Engineering Construction
N.A.I.C.S.: 237990
Keith Fletcher *(Gen Mgr)*

Fletcher Pacific Steel (Fiji) Limited (1)
Leonidas St, Walu Bay, Suva, Fiji
Tel.: (679) 331 4500
Emp.: 50
Steel Products Mfr & Distr
N.A.I.C.S.: 331110
Christopher Mclaughlin *(Gen Mgr)*

Fletcher Residential Limited (1)
810 Great South Road, Private Bag 99922, Auckland, 1061, New Zealand (100%)
Tel.: (64) 95259555
Web Site: https://www.fletcherliving.co.nz
Sales Range: $25-49.9 Million
Emp.: 45
New Housing Operative Builders
N.A.I.C.S.: 236117
Mark Adamson *(CEO)*

Fletcher Steel Limited (1)
Private Bag 92114, Auckland, 1142, New Zealand (100%)
Tel.: (64) 95259000
Web Site: https://www.fletchersteel.co.nz
Sales Range: $50-74.9 Million
Emp.: 250
Iron & Steel Mills
N.A.I.C.S.: 331110
Craig Dixon *(Gen Mgr)*

Fletcher Wood Panels (Australia) Pty Limited (1)
Level 11 Tower B Zenith Centre 821 Pacific Hwy, Chatswood, 2067, NSW, Australia
Tel.: (61) 289860900
Web Site:
http://www.fletcherbuilding.com.au
Wood Panel & Plastic Sheet Mfr
N.A.I.C.S.: 321999

Forman Group Limited (1)
27B Smales Rd, PO Box 12349, East Tamaki Penrose, Auckland, 1642, New Zealand (100%)
Tel.: (64) 92764000
Web Site: http://www.forman.co.nz
Sales Range: $50-74.9 Million
Emp.: 10
Holding Company
N.A.I.C.S.: 551112

Subsidiary (Domestic):

Forman Building Systems Limited (2)

27B Smales Rd, East Tamaki, Auckland, 2013, New Zealand
Tel.: (64) 92764000
Web Site: https://www.forman.co.nz
Emp.: 30
Ceiling & Interior Wall System Distr
N.A.I.C.S.: 424950
Mike Budd *(Mgr-Natl Sls & Mktg)*

Subsidiary (Non-US):

Forman Building Systems Pty Limited (2)
28 Biloela St, Villawood, 2163, NSW, Australia
Tel.: (61) 2 9728 3088
Sales Range: $50-74.9 Million
Emp.: 6
Construction Equipment Distr
N.A.I.C.S.: 423320
Mark Jarmey *(Gen Mgr)*

Subsidiary (Domestic):

Forman Insulation Limited (2)
27 Smales Road, East Tamaki, Auckland, 1060, New Zealand
Tel.: (64) 92764000
Web Site: http://www.forman.co.nz
Insulation System Installation Services
N.A.I.C.S.: 238310

Forman Manufacturing Limited (2)
95 Hugo Johnstone Drive, Penrose, Auckland, 1061, New Zealand
Tel.: (64) 95793881
Plastic Foam Product Mfr
N.A.I.C.S.: 326140

G. E. Crane N.Z. Holdings Ltd (1)
50 Hazelddean Road, Christchurch, New Zealand
Tel.: (64) 33381009
Electrical Equipment Distr
N.A.I.C.S.: 423610

Gatic Pty Limited (1)
169 Philip Highway, Elizabeth, 5112, SA, Australia
Tel.: (61) 1300047539
Web Site: https://www.gatic.com.au
Steel Frames & Grill Mfr
N.A.I.C.S.: 331210
Bill Volkman *(Mgr-Distr)*

Hedges Building Supplies Limited (1)
Canada Street, 3792, Morrinsville, New Zealand
Tel.: (64) 78895142
Sales Range: $25-49.9 Million
Emp.: 12
Building Materials Whslr
N.A.I.C.S.: 423390

Higgins Group Holdings Limited (1)
124 Keith Street, Roslyn, Palmerston North, 4414, New Zealand
Tel.: (64) 63571026
Web Site: https://www.higgins.co.nz
Civil Construction Services
N.A.I.C.S.: 237990

Home & Dry Limited (1)
15 Jarden Mile, Ngauranga, Wellington, 6035, New Zealand
Tel.: (64) 508 466363
Web Site: http://www.homeanddry.co.nz
Sales Range: $25-49.9 Million
Emp.: 15
Housing Ventilation Services
N.A.I.C.S.: 561790
Kerry Shannon *(Mgr-Bus Unit)*

Insulation Solutions Holdings Pty Limited (1)
161 Arthur Street, Homebush, 2140, NSW, Australia
Tel.: (61) 297529268
Web Site: http://www.insulation.com.au
Investment Management Service
N.A.I.C.S.: 523999

John Cockburn Building Supplies Limited (1)
115 Alford Forest Road, Ashburton, 7700, New Zealand
Tel.: (64) 33089099
Sales Range: $25-49.9 Million
Emp.: 14
Construction Materials Whslr

N.A.I.C.S.: 423320
John Cockburn *(Gen Mgr)*

Kenna Building Supplies Limited (1)
Cnr Semple St Titahi Bay Rd, Porirua, 5022, New Zealand
Tel.: (64) 42379189
Web Site: http://www.placemakers.co.nz
Emp.: 25
Building Materials Whslr
N.A.I.C.S.: 423390
Boyd Kenna *(Gen Mgr)*

Kevin Jarvis Building Supplies Limited (1)
53 Molesworth Street, New Plymouth, 4601, New Zealand
Tel.: (64) 67575789
Sales Range: $25-49.9 Million
Emp.: 40
Construction Materials Distr
N.A.I.C.S.: 423390

Key Plastics Pty. Ltd. (1)
110 Airds Road, Minto, 2566, NSW, Australia
Tel.: (61) 2 9603 0300
Web Site: http://www.keyplastics.com.au
Plastic Plumbing Equipment Mfr
N.A.I.C.S.: 326122

Kingston Bridge Engineering Pty Limited (1)
125 Sheffield Road, Welshpool, 6106, WA, Australia
Tel.: (61) 894589022
Web Site: http://www.kingstonbridge.com.au
Polyethylene Pipe Mfr
N.A.I.C.S.: 332996
Ben Harrison *(Mgr-Mfg)*

Laminex (Australia) Pty. Ltd. (1)
90-94 Tram Road, Doncaster, 3108, VIC, Australia
Tel.: (61) 398484811
Web Site: http://www.laminex.com.au
Sales Range: $50-74.9 Million
Emp.: 130
Building Materials Mfr
N.A.I.C.S.: 326199

Laminex Group Pty Limited (1)
130 Sharps Rd, MelbourneAirport Business-Center, Melbourne, 3045, VIC, Australia
Tel.: (61) 132136
Web Site: https://www.laminex.com.au
Emp.: 140
Decorative Surface Material Mfr & Distr
N.A.I.C.S.: 423390
Graham Andrew *(Gen Mgr-Mfg)*

Laminex US Holdings Pty Limited (1)
L11 821 Pacific Hwy, Chatswood, 2067, NSW, Australia
Tel.: (61) 299283500
Investment Management Service
N.A.I.C.S.: 523999

New Zealand Ceiling & Drywall Supplies Limited (1)
129 Sunnybrae Rd, Glenfield, North Shore, 0610, New Zealand
Tel.: (64) 94435006
Sales Range: $50-74.9 Million
Emp.: 5
Building Materials Whslr
N.A.I.C.S.: 423390
Shane Borrell *(Gen Mgr)*

Oliveri Solutions Pty Limited (1)
51 Naweena Road, Regency Park, Adelaide, 5010, SA, Australia
Tel.: (61) 883486444
Web Site: https://www.oliveri.com.au
Sink Mfr & Distr
N.A.I.C.S.: 326191

Phoenix Aluminium 2011 Limited (1)
78 Ellice Road Wairau Valley, PO Box 100-134, North Shore, Auckland, 745, New Zealand
Tel.: (64) 9 477 4090
Web Site: http://www.phoenixnz.co.nz
Sales Range: $25-49.9 Million
Emp.: 2
Fabricated Aluminium Door & Window Mfr
N.A.I.C.S.: 332999
Steve Cowan *(Mgr-Sls)*

PlaceMakers Limited (1)
810 Great South Road, Penrose, Auckland, 1741, New Zealand (50.1%)
Tel.: (64) 95259000
Web Site: http://www.placemakers.co.nz
Sales Range: $50-74.9 Million
Emp.: 100
Holding Company; Home Centers Operator & Franchisor
N.A.I.C.S.: 551112
Dean Fradgley (CEO)

Subsidiary (Domestic):

Fletcher Distribution Limited (2)
810 Great South Road, Penrose, Auckland, 1061, New Zealand (100%)
Tel.: (64) 95259000
Sales Range: $25-49.9 Million
Emp.: 120
Home Centers Operator & Franchisor
N.A.I.C.S.: 444110
Angela Percy (Gen Mgr-Mktg)

Polymer Fusion Education Pty Ltd (1)
125 Sheffield Rd, Welshpool, 6106, WA, Australia
Tel.: (61) 892589444
Engineering Services
N.A.I.C.S.: 541330

Raylight Aluminium Limited (1)
20 Pilkington Way, Wigram, Christchurch, 8042, New Zealand
Tel.: (64) 33665637
Web Site: https://www.raylight.co.nz
Aluminum Sheet Mfr
N.A.I.C.S.: 331315

Rolleston Building Supplies Limited (1)
Matthews Avenue, 410, Kaitaia, New Zealand
Tel.: (64) 94080630
Sales Range: $25-49.9 Million
Emp.: 12
Building Materials Whslr
N.A.I.C.S.: 423390

Servicios Formica de Mexico SA DE CV (1)
Miguel Aleman 55 Buenos Aires, Cuauhtemoc, Mexico, 6780, Mexico
Tel.: (52) 5555303135
Sales Range: $25-49.9 Million
Emp.: 4
Building Materials Whslr
N.A.I.C.S.: 423390

Shanghai Formica Decorative Material Co. Ltd (1)
1701 International Corporate City 3000 Zhongshan North Rd Putuo, Shanghai, 200052, China
Tel.: (86) 2122113668
Web Site: http://www.formica.com.cn
Building Decorative Material Mfr & Distr
N.A.I.C.S.: 326199

Shed Boss NZ Limited (1)
3 Blenheim St, Upper Hutt, Wellington, 5018, New Zealand
Tel.: (64) 45278350
Web Site: http://www.shedboss.co.nz
Emp.: 1
Commercial Building Construction Services
N.A.I.C.S.: 236220
Phil Kirk (Mgr)

Steven Marshall Building Supplies Limited (1)
3 Link Drv, Glenfield, 1310, New Zealand
Tel.: (64) 94445155
Web Site: http://www.placemakers.co.nz
Sales Range: $25-49.9 Million
Emp.: 5
Building Materials Whslr
N.A.I.C.S.: 423390
Steve Marshall (Gen Mgr)

Stramit Corporation Pty Limited (1)
L 11 Tower B Zenith Center 821 Pacific Highway, Chatswood, 2067, NSW, Australia (100%)
Tel.: (61) 299283600
Web Site: http://www.stramit.com.au
Sales Range: $25-49.9 Million
Emp.: 50
Fabricated Structural Metal Mfr

N.A.I.C.S.: 332312
Andrea Pidcock (Gen MGr)

Stramit Pty Limited (1)
L 11 Tower B Zenith Centre 821 Pacific Hwy, Chatswood, 2067, NSW, Australia
Tel.: (61) 299283600
Web Site: http://www.stramit.com.au
Sales Range: $25-49.9 Million
Emp.: 90
Construction Engineering Services
N.A.I.C.S.: 236220
Jonathan Blanchard (Gen Mgr)

Sullivan & Armstrong Building Supplies Limited (1)
17 Clark Street, 640, New Lynn, Auckland, New Zealand
Tel.: (64) 98250088
Building Materials Whslr
N.A.I.C.S.: 423390
John Sullivan (Gen Mgr)

Surface Materials Iki Oy (1)
C/O Formical Iki Oy, 35990, Kolho, Finland
Tel.: (358) 3580001
Construction Materials Distr
N.A.I.C.S.: 423390

Tasman Building Products Pty Limited (1)
Level 4 68 Waterloo Road, Macquarie Park, 2113, NSW, Australia
Tel.: (61) 299283500
Web Site: http://www.fletcherbuilding.com
Emp.: 50
Metal Building Materials Mfr
N.A.I.C.S.: 332311
Mark Adamson (CEO)

Tasman Insulation New Zealand Limited (1)
9-15 Holloway Place, PO Box 12-069, Auckland, 1061, New Zealand (100%)
Tel.: (64) 800746522
Web Site: https://www.pinkbatts.co.nz
Sales Range: $25-49.9 Million
Emp.: 100
Drywall Plastering Acoustical & Insulation Contractors
N.A.I.C.S.: 238310
David Thomas (Gen Mgr)

Tasman Sinkware Pty Limited (1) (100%)
Tel.: (61) 883486444
Sales Range: $25-49.9 Million
Emp.: 50
Enameled Iron & Metal Sanitary Ware Mfr
N.A.I.C.S.: 332999

Ted Harper Building Supplies Limited (1)
1 Te Kumi Rd, Te Kuiti, 3910, New Zealand
Tel.: (64) 78788149
Building Materials Whslr
N.A.I.C.S.: 423390

Terry Mellsop Building Supplies Limited (1)
53 Corunna Bay, PO Box 3440, Napier, 4110, New Zealand
Tel.: (64) 68435816
Emp.: 19
Construction Materials Whslr
N.A.I.C.S.: 423320
Andrew Milne (Mng Dir)

The Fletcher Construction Company Limited (1)
Level 2 Fletcher House Tahi 810 Great South Road, Penrose, Auckland, 1061, New Zealand (100%)
Tel.: (64) 95259000
Web Site: https://www.fletcherconstruction.co.nz
Heavy & Civil Engineering Construction
N.A.I.C.S.: 237990
Graham Darlow (CEO-Construction Grp)

The O'Brien Group Limited (1)
8 Gow Street, PO Box 91, Mosgiel, Dunedin, 9024, New Zealand
Tel.: (64) 34899487
Web Site: https://www.obrien-group.co.nz
Sales Range: $50-74.9 Million
Emp.: 12
Kitchen Ware Accessories Mfr
N.A.I.C.S.: 337110

Tradelink Pty Ltd (1)
Support Centre 1051 Nudgee Road, Locked bag 71, Virginia, 4014, QLD, Australia
Tel.: (61) 732609777
Web Site: https://trade.tradelink.com.au
Plumbing Product Mfr & Distr
N.A.I.C.S.: 326191

Winstone Wallboards Limited (1)
37 Felix Street, PO Box 12256, Onehunga, Auckland, 1061, New Zealand (100%)
Tel.: (64) 96330100
Sales Range: $50-74.9 Million
Emp.: 120
Gypsum Product Mfr
N.A.I.C.S.: 327420
David Thomas (Gen Mgr)

ee-Fit Pty Limited (1)
600 Woodstock Ave, Rooty Hill, 2766, NSW, Australia
Tel.: (61) 1800433348
Web Site: http://www.eefit.com.au
Insulation & Building Wrap Services
N.A.I.C.S.: 238310

FLETCHER KING PLC
19-20 Great Pulteney Street, MAYFAIR, London, W1F 9NF, United Kingdom
Tel.: (44) 2074938400   UK
Web Site:
    https://www.fletcherking.co.uk
FLK—(AIM)
Rev.: $3,822,588
Assets: $6,838,461
Liabilities: $1,650,663
Net Worth: $5,187,798
Earnings: $285,453
Fiscal Year-end: 04/30/23
Property Investment Fund & Asset Management Services
N.A.I.C.S.: 531390
David J. R. Fletcher (Partner & Chm)

Subsidiaries:

Fletcher King Services Limited (1)
61 Conduit Street Mayfair, London, W1S 2GB, United Kingdom
Tel.: (44) 2074938400
Web Site: http://www.fletcherking.co.uk
Emp.: 20
Real Estate Agencies & Valuers
N.A.I.C.S.: 531210
Richard E. Goode (Mng Dir)

FLEURY MICHON SA
La Gare, 85700, Pouzauges, France
Tel.: (33) 251663232
Web Site: https://www.fleurymichon.fr
Year Founded: 1905
ALFLE—(EUR)
Sales Range: $900-999.9 Million
Packaged Meat Products Producer & Sales
N.A.I.C.S.: 424470
Billy Salha (CEO)

Subsidiaries:

Fleury Michon Logistique (1)
Route De La Gare, Pouzauges, 85700, Vendee, France
Tel.: (33) 251663188
Convenience Foods Mfr
N.A.I.C.S.: 311412

FLEURY S.A.
Av Santo Amaro 4584, Jabaquara, Sao Paulo, 04701-200, SP, Brazil
Tel.: (55) 31790822
Web Site: https://www.fleury.com.br
Year Founded: 1926
FLRY3—(BRAZ)
Rev.: $1,333,508,497
Assets: $2,386,392,163
Liabilities: $1,333,106,230
Net Worth: $1,053,285,932
Earnings: $86,722,926
Fiscal Year-end: 12/31/23
Healtcare Services
N.A.I.C.S.: 621999

Subsidiaries:

Instituto Hermes Pardini S.A. (1)
Rua dos Aimores 66 9 andar Funcionarios, Belo Horizonte, 30140-070, Minas Gerais, Brazil
Tel.: (55) 3132286200
Web Site: https://www.hermespardini.com.br
Health Care Diagnostic Services
N.A.I.C.S.: 621511

FLEWWELLING INSURANCE BROKERS LIMITED
320 North Queen St Suite 132, Toronto, M9C 5K4, ON, Canada
Tel.: (416) 622-8713
Web Site: http://www.flewwelling.com
Rev.: $13,526,900
Emp.: 29
Insurance Agency & Brokerage Services
N.A.I.C.S.: 524210
Robert Flewwelling (Pres)

FLEX EQUIPOS DE DESCANSO SA
Calle Rio Almanzora 2 Getafe, 28906, Madrid, Spain
Tel.: (34) 916918689
Web Site: http://www.flex.es
Year Founded: 1912
Sales Range: $25-49.9 Million
Emp.: 200
Quilt, Pillow, Bed & Orthopedic Shape Mattress Mfr & Distr
N.A.I.C.S.: 337910
Julia Sanchez (Deputy Gen Dir & Dir-Comml)

Subsidiaries:

Vi-Spring Ltd. (1)
Ernesettle Lane, Ernesettle, Plymouth, PL5 2TT, Devon, United Kingdom
Tel.: (44) 1752366311
Web Site: http://www.vispring.co.uk
Sales Range: $25-49.9 Million
Emp.: 250
Bed & Mattress Mfr
N.A.I.C.S.: 337121
Jim Gerety (Mng Dir)

Subsidiary (US):

E.S. Kluft & Co. (2)
11096 Jersey Blvd Ste 101, Rancho Cucamonga, CA 91730 (51%)
Tel.: (909) 373-4211
Web Site: http://www.kluftmattress.com
Sales Range: $25-49.9 Million
Emp.: 17
Mattresses & Box Springs Mfr
N.A.I.C.S.: 337910
Laurent Boilly (VP-Intl Sls)

FLEX LNG LTD.
Par-La-Ville Place 14 Par-La-Ville Road, Hamilton, HM08, Bermuda
Tel.: (441) 2956935   VG
Web Site: https://www.flexlng.com
FLNG—(NYSE)
Rev.: $347,917,000
Assets: $2,679,512,000
Liabilities: $1,772,422,000
Net Worth: $907,090,000
Earnings: $188,042,000
Emp.: 9
Fiscal Year-end: 12/31/22
LNG Carrier Services
N.A.I.C.S.: 483111
David McManus (Chm)

FLEX LTD.
2 Changi South Lane, Singapore, 486123, Singapore
Tel.: (65) 68769899   SG
Web Site: https://www.flex.com
Year Founded: 1969
FLEX—(NASDAQ)
Rev.: $26,415,000,000
Assets: $18,257,000,000

Flex Ltd.—(Continued)

Liabilities: $12,932,000,000
Net Worth: $5,325,000,000
Earnings: $1,245,000,000
Emp.: 148,115
Fiscal Year-end: 03/31/24
Logistical & Engineering Services &
Electronics Mfr
N.A.I.C.S.: 335999
Scott Offer *(Exec VP & Gen Counsel)*

Subsidiaries:

AGM Automotive, LLC (1)
1708 Northwood Dr, Troy, MI 48084
Tel.: (248) 776-0600
Web Site: http://agmautomotive.com
Interior & Exterior Lighting Mfr
N.A.I.C.S.: 335132

Anord Mardix (Ireland) Ltd. (1)
Tel.: (353) 429320500
Web Site: http://www.anordmardix.com
Switchgear Mfr
N.A.I.C.S.: 335313
James Peacock *(CEO)*

Subsidiary (Non-US):

Anord Mardix (UK) Limited (2)
Castle Mills Aynam Road, Kendal, LA9
7DE, Cumbria, United Kingdom
Tel.: (44) 1539720161
Switchgear Mfr
N.A.I.C.S.: 335313
Dean Bradshaw *(VP-Sls-EMEA)*

**Fit Instituto De Tecnologia Da
Amazonia** (1)
Tel.: (55) 1540090606
Web Site: http://www.fit-tecnologia.org.br
Information Technology Services
N.A.I.C.S.: 541512

Flex Lighting Solutions, Inc. (1)
6201 America Center Dr, San Jose, CA
95002
Tel.: (913) 851-3000
Electronic Product Distr
N.A.I.C.S.: 423690
Mark Stranczek *(Sr Product Mgr)*

FlexMedical Slovakia s.r.o. (1)
Hlavna 1409/48, Vrable, 95201, Slovakia
Tel.: (421) 372852918
Electronic Equipment Distr
N.A.I.C.S.: 423690

FlexPower India Private Limited (1)
Plot No 3 Phase 2 Sipcot Industrial Park,
Sriperumbudur, Kanchipuram, 602106,
Tamil Nadu, India
Tel.: (91) 4467105000
Web Site: http://www.flextronics.com
Electronic Components Mfr
N.A.I.C.S.: 334419

Flextronics (Israel) Ltd (1)
Tel.: (972) 46448200
Electronic Components Mfr
N.A.I.C.S.: 334419

Flextronics (Malaysia) Sdn. Bhd. (1)
PLO 226 Jalan Cyber 1 Kawasan Perindus-
trian Senai III, 81400, Senai, Johore, Malay-
sia
Tel.: (60) 75995695
Plastic Mfr
N.A.I.C.S.: 325211

**Flextronics (Nanjing) Technology Co.,
Ltd.** (1)
99 Zhuangpai Rd Jiangning Economic &
Technological Development Zone, Nanjing,
211100, Jiangsu, China
Tel.: (86) 2552122288
Electronic Components Mfr
N.A.I.C.S.: 334419

Flextronics (Shanghai) Co., Ltd. (1)
Tel.: (86) 2139158318
Electronic Components Mfr
N.A.I.C.S.: 334419

Flextronics Australia Pty Ltd (1)
359-361 City Rd Southbank, Melbourne,
3006, VIC, Australia
Tel.: (61) 133539
Electronic Product Distr

N.A.I.C.S.: 423690

Flextronics Automotive Inc (1)
213 Harry Walker Pky S, Newmarket, L3Y
8T3, ON, Canada
Tel.: (800) 668-5649
Electronic Components Mfr
N.A.I.C.S.: 334419

Flextronics Automotive USA, Inc. (1)
2120 Austin Ave, Rochester Hills, MI 48309
Tel.: (248) 853-5724
Emp.: 2,000
Electronic Product Distr
N.A.I.C.S.: 423690

**Flextronics Canada Design Services,
Inc.** (1)
1280 Carin Rd, Kanata, K2K 2C1, ON,
Canada
Tel.: (613) 895-2050
Web Site: http://www.flextronics.com
Sales Range: $25-49.9 Million
Emp.: 144
Mechanical Engineering Services
N.A.I.C.S.: 541330

**Flextronics Computing (Suzhou) Co.
Ltd.** (1)
No 1 Guanpu Road Guoxiang Street Wu-
zhong District, Suzhou, China
Tel.: (86) 51267868800
Web Site: http://www.flextronics.com
Electronic Components Mfr
N.A.I.C.S.: 334419

Flextronics Design Korea Ltd. (1)
5/F B/D 104 Sk Ventium 522 Dangjeong-
Dong, Kunpo, 431060, Korea (South)
Tel.: (82) 314500000
Electric Equipment Mfr
N.A.I.C.S.: 335999

Flextronics Design Srl (1)
Via Borgazzi 27, 20052, Monza, Italy
Tel.: (39) 0392098610
Web Site: http://www.flextronics.com
Design Services
N.A.I.C.S.: 541330

Flextronics Design, s.r.o. (1)
Turanka 1222/115, 627 00, Brno, Czech
Republic
Tel.: (420) 545426555
Web Site: http://www.flextronics.cz
Sales Range: $25-49.9 Million
Emp.: 65
Electronic Component Developer & Mfr
N.A.I.C.S.: 334111

Flextronics EMS Canada Inc. (1)
21 Richardson Side Rd, Kanata, K2K 2C1,
ON, Canada
Tel.: (613) 271-4382
Engineeering Services
N.A.I.C.S.: 541330

**Flextronics Electronics (Mauritius)
Limited** (1)
Alexander House 35, Ebene, 72001, Mauri-
tius
Tel.: (230) 4030800
Electronic Components Distr
N.A.I.C.S.: 423690

**Flextronics Electronics Technology
(Suzhou) Co., Ltd.** (1)
No 9 Suqian Road Suzhou Industrial Park,
Suzhou, 215021, Jiangsu, China
Tel.: (86) 51267612300
Printed Circuit Board Mfr
N.A.I.C.S.: 334418

**Flextronics Enclosure (Zhuhai) Co.,
Ltd** (1)
Xinqing Science & Technology Industrial
Park, Zhuhai, 519180, Guangdong, China
Tel.: (86) 7565181186
Electric Equipment Mfr
N.A.I.C.S.: 335999

**Flextronics Enclosures (Hong Kong)
Ltd.** (1)
17 & 18/F Nina Twr Twr II 8 Yeung Uk Rd,
Tsuen Wan, New Territories, China (Hong
Kong)
Tel.: (852) 22761800
Web Site: http://www.flextronics.com
Electronic Components Mfr
N.A.I.C.S.: 334419

**Flextronics Germany Holding
GmbH** (1)
Heinz-Nixdorf-Ring 1, 33106, Paderborn,
Germany
Tel.: (49) 52511800
Investment Management Service
N.A.I.C.S.: 523940

**Flextronics Global Enclosures (Singa-
pore) Pte. Ltd.** (1)
31 Joo Koon Circle, Jurong, 629108, Singa-
pore
Tel.: (65) 68616218
Electronics Design, Engineering & Logistics
Services
N.A.I.C.S.: 334419

**Flextronics Global Services (Man-
chester) Limited** (1)
Stretton Green Distribution Centre Langford
Way, Appleton, Warrington, WA4 4TQ,
Cheshire, United Kingdom
Tel.: (44) 1925 260 700
Web Site: http://www.flextronics.com
Sales Range: $100-124.9 Million
Emp.: 220
Computer Peripheral Equipment Mfr
N.A.I.C.S.: 334118

**Flextronics Global Services Canada
Inc.** (1)
213 Harry Walker Parkway South, Newmar-
ket, L3Y 8T3, ON, Canada
Tel.: (905) 952-1000
Web Site: http://www.flextronics.com
Rev.: $16,627,500
Emp.: 400
Electronic Components Mfr
N.A.I.C.S.: 334419

Flextronics Group Sweden AB (1)
Rombvagen 4 Karlskrona, PO Box 532, 371
23, Lyckeby, Sweden
Tel.: (46) 45554400
Sales Range: $100-124.9 Million
Emp.: 400
Electronic Components Mfr
N.A.I.C.S.: 334419

Flextronics Holding GmbH (1)
Tel.: (43) 16024100
Web Site: http://www.flextronics.com
Emp.: 40
Investment Management Service
N.A.I.C.S.: 523999

**Flextronics Holdings Mexico, S.A. de
C.V.** (1)
Carretera Base Aerea 5850, La Mora,
45136, Guadalajara, Jalisco, Mexico
Tel.: (52) 3338183200
Financial Management Services
N.A.I.C.S.: 523999

Flextronics International (1)
3 Tian Fu Road Tong Fu Yu Industrial Park,
Fu Yong Town Bao An District, Shenzhen,
518103, China
Tel.: (86) 755 7314188
Electronic Components & Printed Circuit
Boards Mfr
N.A.I.C.S.: 334419

Flextronics International (1)
No 9 Suqian Road, Suzhou Industrial Park,
Suzhou, 215021, China
Tel.: (86) 51267612300
Electronic Components Mfr
N.A.I.C.S.: 334419

Flextronics International (UK) Ltd (1)
West Avenue, Paisley, PA1 2FB, United
Kingdom
Tel.: (44) 141 849 5600
Web Site: http://www.flextronics.com
Electric Equipment Mfr
N.A.I.C.S.: 335999

Flextronics International AB (1)
Fridhemsvagen 15, 372 22, Ronneby, Ble-
kinge, Sweden
Tel.: (46) 45554400
Sales Range: $100-124.9 Million
Emp.: 400
Electronic Components Mfr
N.A.I.C.S.: 334419

**Flextronics International Cork
B.V.** (1)
Kilbarry Industrial Park Dublin Hill Black-

pool, Cork, Ireland
Tel.: (353) 214300530
Web Site: http://www.flextronics.com
Sales Range: $100-124.9 Million
Emp.: 400
Electronic Components Mfr
N.A.I.C.S.: 334419

**Flextronics International Denmark
A/S** (1)
Hjortevej 4, Skive, DK-7800, Denmark
Tel.: (45) 96143000
Web Site: http://www.flextronics.com
Sales Range: $100-124.9 Million
Emp.: 400
Electronic Components Mfr
N.A.I.C.S.: 334419

Flextronics International GmbH (1)
Office Park 4 Top A 54 55 Vienna Airport,
1300, Vienna, Austria (100%)
Tel.: (43) 16024100
Sales Range: $25-49.9 Million
Emp.: 60
Engineering, Electronics Manufacturing &
Logistical Services to Telecommunications,
Networking, Computer, Consumer & Medi-
cal Electronics Industries
N.A.I.C.S.: 541330
Erwin Brunner *(Mng Dir)*

Subsidiary (Domestic):

Flextronics International (2)
Friesacher Strasse 3, 9330, Althofen,
Austria (100%)
Tel.: (43) 42622644126
Design Services
N.A.I.C.S.: 541330

**Flextronics International Japan Co.,
Ltd.** (1)
Tel.: (81) 335176900
Electronic Equipment Repair & Maintenance
Services
N.A.I.C.S.: 811310

Flextronics International Kft (1)
Ikervari Ut 42, 9600, Sarvar, Ikervari,
Hungary (100%)
Tel.: (36) 95533000
Web Site: http://www.flex.com
Sales Range: $1-9.9 Million
Emp.: 2,800
Plastic Mfr
N.A.I.C.S.: 325211

Plant (Domestic):

Flextronics International Kft (2)
Posta Ut 63, H 8900, Zalaegerszeg,
Hungary (100%)
Tel.: (36) 92508000
Web Site: http://www.flextronics.com
Sales Range: $1-4.9 Billion
Emp.: 6,000
Plastic Mfr
N.A.I.C.S.: 325211

Flextronics International Kft. (2)
Munkas utca 28, 8660, Tab, Hungary
Tel.: (36) 84526000
Web Site: http://www.flextronics.com
Sales Range: $1-4.9 Billion
Emp.: 2,500
Communication Equipment Mfr
N.A.I.C.S.: 811210

Flextronics International Kft. (2)
Hangar Utca 5 37, 1183, Budapest, Hun-
gary
Tel.: (36) 12963100
Web Site: http://www.flextronics.com
Sales Range: $200-249.9 Million
Emp.: 1,000
Electronic Components Contract Manufac-
turing
N.A.I.C.S.: 334419

**Flextronics International Ltd. - Asia
Pacific Regional Headquarters** (1)
8th Floor Hale Weal Industrial Building
22-28 Tai Chung Road, Tsuen Wan, NT,
China (Hong Kong)
Tel.: (852) 24899813
Web Site: http://www.flextronics.com
Sales Range: $25-49.9 Million
Emp.: 120
Provider of Engineering, Electronics Manu-
facturing & Logistical Services to Telecom-
munications, Networking, Computer, Con-
sumer & Medical Electronics Industries

N.A.I.C.S.: 541330

Flextronics International Poland Sp z.o.o. (1)
Malinowska 28, 83-100, Tczew, Poland
Tel.: (48) 587777000
Sales Range: $1-4.9 Billion
Emp.: 3,000
Electronic Components Distr
N.A.I.C.S.: 423690

Flextronics International Sweden AB (1)
Rombvagen 4 Verko, SE 371 23, Karlskrona, Sweden (100%)
Tel.: (46) 45554400
Web Site: http://www.flextronics.se
Sales Range: $75-99.9 Million
Emp.: 450
Engineering, Electronics Manufacturing & Logistical Services to Telecommunications, Networking, Computer, Consumer & Medical Electronics Industries
N.A.I.C.S.: 541330

Subsidiary (Domestic):

Flextronics Network Services Sweden AB (2)
Odenskogsvagen 27 29, PO Box 370, 831 25, Ostersund, Sweden
Tel.: (46) 063169000
Web Site: http://www.flextronics.se
Sales Range: $25-49.9 Million
Emp.: 15
Electronic Components Developer & Mfr
N.A.I.C.S.: 334419

Flextronics International Taiwan Ltd. (1)
5f 6 Chung Hsing Rd Se, Wuku Hsiang, Taipei, 24872, Taiwan
Tel.: (886) 289771888
Web Site:
http://www.flextronics365.sharepoint.com
Emp.: 300
Electronic Components Mfr
N.A.I.C.S.: 334419

Flextronics International USA, Inc. (1)
6201 America Ctr Dr, San Jose, CA 95002 (100%)
Tel.: (408) 576-7000
Sales Range: $400-449.9 Million
Emp.: 2,000
Engineering, Electronics Manufacturing & Logistical Services to Telecommunications Networking Computer, Consumer & Medical Electronics Industries
N.A.I.C.S.: 334412

Subsidiary (Domestic):

Advance Mold & Manufacturing Inc. (2)
71 Utopia Rd, Manchester, CT 06042
Tel.: (860) 432-5887
Web Site: http://www.advancemold.com
Electric Equipment Mfr
N.A.I.C.S.: 334416

Farm Design, Inc. (2)
12 Silver Lake Rd, Hollis, NH 03049
Tel.: (603) 402-5500
Web Site: https://www.farmpd.com
Sales Range: $1-9.9 Million
Emp.: 50
Medical Devices Designer & Mfr
N.A.I.C.S.: 339112
Robert W. Dumas (Dir-Bus Dev)

FlexMedical Disposables (2)
700 Bent Branch Dr, Irving, TX 75063
Tel.: (817) 877-4343
Sales Range: $250-299.9 Million
Emp.: 20
Single-Use Medical Device Distr
N.A.I.C.S.: 423450

Unit (Domestic):

FlexMedical Disposables (3)
5950 Nancy Rdg Dr, San Diego, CA 92121
Tel.: (858) 457-1988
Sales Range: $10-24.9 Million
Single-Use Medical Device Distr
N.A.I.C.S.: 423450

FlexMedical Disposables (3)

3161 Sweeten Creek Rd, Asheville, NC 28803
Tel.: (828) 684-1618
Sales Range: $25-49.9 Million
Single-Use Medical Product Distr
N.A.I.C.S.: 423450

Subsidiary (Domestic):

Flextron Global Services (2)
4400 Commerce Crossing Dr, Louisville, KY 40229
Tel.: (502) 810-2280
Web Site: http://www.flextronics.com
Rev.: $3,900,000
Emp.: 1,500
Electronic Equipment Repair Services
N.A.I.C.S.: 811210

Flextronics America, LLC (2)
6800 Solectron Dr, Charlotte, NC 28262
Tel.: (704) 509-8700
Sales Range: $100-124.9 Million
Emp.: 400
Electronic Components Mfr
N.A.I.C.S.: 334419
John Mainey (Gen Mgr)

Subsidiary (Non-US):

Flextronics Brasil Ltda. (2)
Rod Gov Dr Adhemar Pereira de Barros 323, Jaguariuna, Sao Paulo, 13820-000, Brazil
Tel.: (55) 1938379000
Sales Range: $350-399.9 Million
Emp.: 1,200
Electronic Components Contract Manufacturing
N.A.I.C.S.: 334419

Subsidiary (Domestic):

Flextronics International PA, Inc. (2)
637 Gibraltar Ct, Milpitas, CA 95035
Tel.: (408) 577-2444
Printed Circuit Board Mfr
N.A.I.C.S.: 334412

Subsidiary (Non-US):

Flextronics International Technologia Ltda. (2)
Rodovia Km 128 7A Tanquinho, Sao Paulo, SP 340, Brazil (100%)
Tel.: (55) 19 96480327
Web Site: http://www.flextronics.com
Sales Range: $150-199.9 Million
Emp.: 1,000
Design, Manufacturing, Distribution & Aftermarket Services
N.A.I.C.S.: 541330

Plant (Domestic):

Flextronics International USA Inc. (2)
6800 Solectron Dr, Charlotte, NC 28262
Tel.: (704) 598-3300
Web Site: http://www.flextronics.com
Sales Range: $350-399.9 Million
Emp.: 2,000
Electronics Repair & Manufacturing Services
N.A.I.C.S.: 334419

Flextronics International USA Inc. (2)
600 Shiloh Rd, Plano, TX 75074
Tel.: (469) 229-1000
Web Site: http://www.flextronics.com
Sales Range: $75-99.9 Million
Emp.: 400
Semiconductor Design Services
N.A.I.C.S.: 334412

Flextronics International USA Inc. (2)
1000 Technology Dr, West Columbia, SC 29170
Tel.: (803) 936-5200
Web Site: http://www.flextronics.com
Sales Range: $100-124.9 Million
Emp.: 450
Mfr of Electronic Circuits
N.A.I.C.S.: 334419

Flextronics International USA Inc. - Austin (2)
12455 Research Blvd, Austin, TX 78759

Tel.: (512) 425-4100
Web Site: http://www.flextronics.com
Electric Equipment Mfr
N.A.I.C.S.: 334419

Subsidiary (Non-US):

Flextronics Manufacturing Juarez, S.A. de C.V. (2)
Bulevar Independencia 4240 Lote Bravo Juarez, Fraccionamiento Lote Bravo, 32695, Chihuahua, Mexico
Tel.: (52) 6562952078
Electronic Components Manufacturing
N.A.I.C.S.: 334419

Flextronics Manufacturing Mexico, S.A. de C.V. (2)
Libramiento Carretera a la Base Aerea 5850-4 La Mora Jardin Real, 45136, Zapopan, Mexico (100%)
Tel.: (52) 3338183200
Sales Range: $200-249.9 Million
Telephone Apparatus
N.A.I.C.S.: 334210

Flextronics Manufacturing Mexico, S.A. de C.V. (2)
Carretera A La Base Aerea 5850-4 La Morea Jardin Real Zapopan, Jalisco, 45136, Mexico
Tel.: (52) 3338183200
Web Site: http://www.flextronic.com
Electronic Components Mfr
N.A.I.C.S.: 334419

Subsidiary (Domestic):

Flextronics Semiconductor, Inc. (2)
2241 Lundy Ave Bldg 2, San Jose, CA 95131
Tel.: (408) 576-7000
Semiconductor Devices Mfr
N.A.I.C.S.: 334413

Flextronics Systems Texas Ltd. (2)
10900 Cash Rd, Stafford, TX 77477 (100%)
Tel.: (281) 295-3200
Web Site: http://www.flextronics.com
Sales Range: $10-24.9 Million
Emp.: 150
Contract Manufacturer Specializing in the Production of Electrical & Fiber Optic Cable Assemblies, Electrical & Mechanical Subsystems & Cable-Intensive Mechanical Enclosures
N.A.I.C.S.: 334419

Multek Flexible Circuits, Inc. (2)
1150 Sheldahl Rd, Northfield, MN 55057-9444
Tel.: (507) 663-8000
Web Site: http://www.multek.com
Sales Range: $75-99.9 Million
Emp.: 450
Flexible Electronic Component Mfr
N.A.I.C.S.: 334419

Vista Point Technologies, Inc. (2)
3054 Fite Cir Ste 101, Sacramento, CA 95827
Tel.: (408) 576-7000
Sales Range: $75-99.9 Million
Emp.: 3,200
Computer Monitor, Camera Module, Power Supply & Electronic Component Developer & Mfr
N.A.I.C.S.: 334419

Branch (Non-US):

Vista Point Technologies, Inc. (3)
Ste 8018 8th Fl Tower 1 China Hong Kong Ct, 33 Canton Rd Tsin Sha Tsui, Kowloon, China (Hong Kong)
Tel.: (852) 26102120
Mfr of Turnkey Assemblies & LCD Products
N.A.I.C.S.: 334220

Vista Point Technologies, Inc. (3)
No 102 Li Jia Rd Henggang Street Office, Longgang District, Shenzhen, 518115, China
Tel.: (86) 75561266888
Web Site: http://www.vptech.com
Mfr of Turnkey Assemblies
N.A.I.C.S.: 334220

Flextronics Italy S.P.A (1)
Strada Statale 234 1/3, Somaglia, 26867,

Lodi, Italy
Tel.: (39) 0377926611
Call Center Operating Services
N.A.I.C.S.: 561421

Flextronics Japan K.K. (1)
Meguro Suda Building 6th Floor, 3 9 1 Meguro Meguro ku, Tokyo, 153 0063, Japan
Tel.: (81) 357947310
Web Site: http://flextronics.com
Electronic Components Mfr
N.A.I.C.S.: 334419

Subsidiary (Domestic):

Flextronics Digital Design Japan, Ltd. (2)
23 11 Naka Ohshio Chino shi, Nagano, 391 0293, Japan
Tel.: (81) 266 82 2000
Web Site: http://www.secinfo.com
Electronic Component Developer & Mfr
N.A.I.C.S.: 334111

Flextronics Laval S.N.C. (1)
Centre D Affaires Technopolis BA Rue Albert Einstein, PO Box 1215, Laval, 53810, France
Tel.: (33) 243674000
Communication Equipment Mfr
N.A.I.C.S.: 334290

Flextronics Logistics B.V. (1)
Nobelstraat 10-14, Oostrum, 5807 GA, Netherlands
Tel.: (31) 478518000
Web Site: http://www.flextronics.com
Sales Range: $75-99.9 Million
Emp.: 450
Logistics Consulting Servies
N.A.I.C.S.: 541614

Flextronics Logistics Poland SP. z.o.o. (1)
Al Ofiar Terroryzmu 11 wrzesnia nr 17, 92-410, Lodz, Poland
Tel.: (48) 422096100
Logistics Consulting Servies
N.A.I.C.S.: 541614

Flextronics Manufacturing (H.K.) Ltd. (1)
17 & 18/F Nina Twr Twr II 8 Yeung Uk Rd, Tsuen Wan, New Territories, China (Hong Kong)
Tel.: (852) 22761800
Web Site: http://www.flextronics.com
Printed Circuit Board Mfr
N.A.I.C.S.: 334418

Flextronics Manufacturing (Penang) Sdn. Bhd. (1)
Plot 13 Phase 4, Prai Industrial Estate, Penang, 13600, Prai, Malaysia
Tel.: (60) 45075600
Web Site: http://www.flextronics.com
Sales Range: $1-4.9 Billion
Emp.: 10,000
Electronic Components Mfr
N.A.I.C.S.: 334419

Flextronics Manufacturing (Singapore) Pte. Ltd. (1)
2 Changi South Lane, Singapore, 486123, Singapore
Tel.: (65) 68769893
Web Site: http://www.flextronics.com
Sales Range: $200-249.9 Million
Emp.: 12,797
Electronic Components Mfr
N.A.I.C.S.: 334419

Flextronics Manufacturing (Zhuhai) Co., Ltd. (1)
No 168 Zhufeng Ave Xinqing Science & Technology Industrial Park, Zhuhai, 519180, Guangdong, China
Tel.: (86) 7565188560
Communication Equipment Mfr
N.A.I.C.S.: 334290

Flextronics ODM Netherlands NV (1)
Nobelstraat 10-14, 5807 GA, Oostrum, Netherlands
Tel.: (31) 478518000
Investment Management Service
N.A.I.C.S.: 523999

Flextronics Plastic Technology (ShenZhen) Ltd. (1)

Flex Ltd.—(Continued)

Yangbei Jixiang Industrial Zone Huangtian Community Xixiang St, Shenzhen, 518128, Guangdong, China
Tel.: (86) 75581468888
Plastic Materials Mfr
N.A.I.C.S.: 326199

Flextronics Plastics (Zhuhai) Co., Ltd (1)
Xinqing Technology Industrial Zone Jing An Town, Doumen District, Zhuhai, 519100, Guangdong, China
Tel.: (86) 7565186147
Electrical Component Mfr
N.A.I.C.S.: 335999

Flextronics Plastics, S.A. de C.V. (1)
Carretera A Base Aerea 5850 Km 5 La Mora, Zapopan, 45100, Mexico
Tel.: (52) 3338183200
Plastics Product Mfr
N.A.I.C.S.: 326199

Flextronics Romania SRL (1)
DN6 km 5 7, 300000, Timisoara, 300668, Romania
Tel.: (40) 256303500
Electronic Components Mfr
N.A.I.C.S.: 334419

Flextronics S.R.L (1)
Via Professor Don A Dalla Torre 6/a, Ponte di Piave, 31047, Italy
Tel.: (39) 0422202611
Web Site: http://www.flextronics.com
Sales Range: $50-74.9 Million
Emp.: 150
Plastic Injection Mold Mfr
N.A.I.C.S.: 326199

Flextronics Sales & Marketing North Asia (L) Ltd. (1)
Jalan Merdeka, 87000, Labuan, Sabah, Malaysia
Tel.: (60) 87453119
Sales Range: $50-74.9 Million
Emp.: 8
Electric Component Whslr
N.A.I.C.S.: 423690
Fiona Chin (Mgr-Fin)

Flextronics Servicios Guadalajara, S.A. de C.V. (1)
Carretera Base Aerea 5850, La Mora, Guadalajara, Jalisco, Mexico
Tel.: (52) 3338183200
Electronic Components Mfr
N.A.I.C.S.: 334419

Flextronics Special Business Solutions
Solectronstrasse 2, 71083, Herrenberg, Germany
Tel.: (49) 70329980
Web Site: http://www.sbs.flextronics.com
Sales Range: $50-74.9 Million
Emp.: 250
Electronic Component Development & Logistics Services
N.A.I.C.S.: 334419

Flextronics Technologies (India) Pvt Ltd. (1)
Plot 3 Pase II Sipcot Industrial Park Sandavellur C Village, Sriperumbudur, Kanchipuram, 602 106, Tamilnadu, India
Tel.: (91) 44 6710 5000
Web Site: http://www.flextronics.com
Emp.: 3,000
Electronic Components Mfr
N.A.I.C.S.: 334419

Flextronics Technologies Mexico, S.de R.L. de C.V. (1)
Calle Prol Lopez Mateos 2915, La Tijera, 45640, Tlajomulco de Zuniga, Mexico
Tel.: (52) 3337704200
Electric Equipment Mfr
N.A.I.C.S.: 335999

Flextronics Technology (Penang) Sdn. Bhd. (1)
Plot 13 Phase 4 Prai Industrial Estate, Perai Pulau, Penang, 13600, Malaysia
Tel.: (60) 45075600
Web Site: http://www.flextronics.com
Sales Range: $1-4.9 Billion
Emp.: 8,000
Electronics Manufacturing Services

N.A.I.C.S.: 334419

Flextronics Technology (Shanghai) Co., Ltd.
Zone 1c No 77 Yongsheng Road Malu Town, Jiading District, Shanghai, 201808, China
Tel.: (86) 2139158000
Electronic Components Mfr
N.A.I.C.S.: 334419

Flextronics Technology (ShenZhen) Co., Ltd.
Building C9-11 No 2 Industrial Park Xixiang Town, Bao An District, Shenzhen, 518126, Guangdong, China
Tel.: (86) 75527497333
Electronic Components Mfr
N.A.I.C.S.: 334419

Flextronics Technology (Shenzhen) Co., Ltd.
C9 Bldg 2nd Industrial ZoneXixiang Town Baoan District, Shenzhen, 518126, China
Tel.: (86) 75527497333
Web Site: http://www.flextronics.com
Sales Range: $25-49.9 Million
Emp.: 100
Enclosure Systems & Design Services
N.A.I.C.S.: 334111

Flextronics Technology Sdn Bhd (1)
Plot 56 Taman Perindustrian Bukit, 14100, Bukit Minyak, Penang, Malaysia
Tel.: (60) 04 384 7448
Web Site: http://www.flextronics.com
Sales Range: $450-499.9 Million
Emp.: 1,496
Design & Engineering of Plastics
N.A.I.C.S.: 325211

Frog Design S.R.L (1)
Via Gattamelata 34, 20149, Milan, Italy
Tel.: (39) 0289825900
Design Engineering Services
N.A.I.C.S.: 541330

Grolleau SAS (1)
Tel.: (33) 241758822
Web Site: http://www.grolleau.fr
Electronic Enclosure Mfr
N.A.I.C.S.: 334419

Irumold, S.L.U. (1)
Poligono Industrial Arazuri-Orkoien Calle C N 1, 31160, Orkoien, Spain
Tel.: (34) 948286006
Web Site: https://www.irumold.com
Electronic Product Distr
N.A.I.C.S.: 423690

Masa da Amazonia Ltda. (1)
Av Solimoes 805-Distrito Industrial, 69075-200, Manaus, AM, Brazil
Tel.: (55) 9236178200
Web Site:
http://www.masadaamazonia.com.br
Sales Range: $400-449.9 Million
Emp.: 1,500
Electronic Components Mfr
N.A.I.C.S.: 334419

Multek Brazil Ltda (1)
Avenida Giovanni Gronchi 6899 - Vila Andrade, 05724-005, Sao Paulo, Brazil
Tel.: (55) 11 3205 8300
Web Site: http://www.multek.com
Printed Circuit Board Mfr
N.A.I.C.S.: 334418

Multek Display (Hong Kong) Limited (1)
17/F Nina Twr Ii 8 Yeung Uk Rd, Tsuen Wan, New Territories, China (Hong Kong)
Tel.: (852) 22761000
Electronic Components Mfr
N.A.I.C.S.: 334419

Multek Hong Kong Limited (1)
17th Floor Tower II Nina Tower 8 Yeung Uk Road, Tsuen Wan, New Territories, China (Hong Kong)
Tel.: (852) 2276 1000
Printed Circuit Board Mfr
N.A.I.C.S.: 334418

NEXTracker Australia Pty. Ltd. (1)
39 East Esplanade Suite 303 / 304, Manly, 2095, NSW, Australia
Tel.: (61) 284597515
N.A.I.C.S.: 541690

Nextracker Mexico, S. De R.I. De C.v. (1)
Av Paseo de la Reforma 483 STE 1503 Col Cuauhtemoc, 06600, Mexico, Mexico
Tel.: (52) 5573162151
N.A.I.C.S.: 541690

PT Flextronics Technology Indonesia (1)
Jalan Rambutan Lot 515 Batamindo Industrial Park, Batam, 29433, Indonesia
Tel.: (62) 770 612660
Web Site: http://www.flextronics.com
Electronic Components Mfr
N.A.I.C.S.: 334419

Power Systems Technologies Far East Limited (1)
17 & 18/F Nina Twr Twr Ii 8 Yeung Uk Rd, Tsuen Wan, New Territories, China (Hong Kong)
Tel.: (852) 22761800
Electric Equipment Mfr
N.A.I.C.S.: 335999

Qingdao Victory Plastic Co., Ltd (1)
Qingdao E&T Development Zone, Qingdao, 266000, Shandong, China
Tel.: (86) 159 69890625
Plastic Goods Mfr
N.A.I.C.S.: 326199

RIWISA AG, Kunststoffwerke Hagglingen (1)
Kunststoffwerke Sonnhalde, 5607, Bremgarten, Switzerland
Tel.: (41) 566169393
Web Site: http://www.riwisa.ch
Electric Equipment Mfr
N.A.I.C.S.: 334416

Sonderborg Vaerktojsfabrik A/S (1)
Elholm 6, DK-6400, Sonderborg, Denmark
Tel.: (45) 74428242
Web Site: http://www.sv.dk
Injection Molding Tool Distr
N.A.I.C.S.: 424210
Jens Dominic (Gen Mgr)

Sonderborg Vrktojsfabrik A/S (1)
Elholm 6, 6400, Sonderborg, Denmark
Tel.: (45) 74428242
Web Site: https://www.sv.dk
Emp.: 40
Electric Equipment Mfr
N.A.I.C.S.: 334416
Jens Dominic (Gen Mgr)

Vista Point Technologies (Malaysia) Sdn. Bhd. (1)
No 7 Jalan Keluli 1 Kawasan Perindustrian Bukit Raja Seksyen 7, Shah Alam, 40000, Selangor, Malaysia
Tel.: (60) 333615000
Electronic Components Mfr
N.A.I.C.S.: 334419

FLEX RESORTS & REAL ESTATE COMPANY K.S.C.
Bnied Algar-Block 2 Istqlal Street, Kuwait, Kuwait
Tel.: (965) 22522566
Web Site: http://www.flexq8.com
Year Founded: 1992
Fitness & Recreational Center Operator
N.A.I.C.S.: 713940
Mohamed Salam (Head-Ops & Sls)

FLEXDEAL SIMFE S.A.
Rua Dr Francisco Torres n 78, 4750-160, Barcelos, Portugal
Tel.: (351) 707913780
Web Site: https://www.flexdeal.pt
FLEXD—(EUR)
Sales Range: Less than $1 Million
Investment Management Service
N.A.I.C.S.: 523940
Alberto Jorge da Silva Amaral (Chm & CEO)

FLEXIBLE INDUSTRIAL PACKAGES CO. SAOC
Plot no 225/226 Road no 21, PO Box

60, Rusayl Industrial Estate, 124, Muscat, Oman
Tel.: (968) 24446121
Web Site: http://www.fipco.net
Year Founded: 1999
Sales Range: $1-9.9 Million
Emp.: 85
Packaging Products Mfr
N.A.I.C.S.: 326112
Vinay Bhardwaj (CEO)

FLEXIBLE PACKAGING HOLDING B.V.
Nesland 5 F, 1382 MZ, Weesp, Notherlands
Tel.: (31) 294 43 0036
Web Site:
http://www.flexiblepackaging.nl
Holding Company; Printing & Packaging
N.A.I.C.S.: 551112
Esther de Bruijn (Controller)

FLEXIBLE SOLUTIONS INTERNATIONAL, INC.
6001 54 Ave, Taber, T1G 1X4, AB, Canada
Tel.: (403) 223-2995   NV
Web Site:
https://www.flexiblesolutions.com
FSI—(NYSEAMEX)
Rev.: $45,840,469
Assets: $51,587,192
Liabilities: $16,348,222
Net Worth: $35,238,970
Earnings: $7,713,229
Emp.: 42
Fiscal Year-end: 12/31/22
Water & Energy Conservation Chemicals & Products Developer, Mfr & Marketer
N.A.I.C.S.: 325998
Daniel B. O'Brien (Pres & CEO)

Subsidiaries:

Flexible Solutions, Ltd. (1)
920 Unit 206, Victoria, V8T 1Z8, BC, Canada
Tel.: (250) 477-9969
Web Site: http://www.flexiblesolutions.com
Sales Range: $50-74.9 Million
Emp.: 5
Basic Inorganic Chemical Mfr
N.A.I.C.S.: 325180
Daniel B. O'Brien (Founder)

NanoChem Solutions Inc. (1)
6502 S Archer Rd, Bedford Park, IL 60501
Tel.: (708) 563-9200
Web Site:
http://www.nanochemsolutions.com
Sales Range: $25-49.9 Million
Emp.: 7
Biodegradable Water-Soluble Polymers for Industrial & Consumer Applications
N.A.I.C.S.: 325998

WaterSavr Global Solutions Inc. (1)
920 Hillside Avenue Unit 206, Victoria, V8T 1Z8, BC, Canada
Tel.: (250) 477-9969
Sales Range: $25-49.9 Million
Emp.: 5
Basic Inorganic Chemical Mfr
N.A.I.C.S.: 325180
Daniel O'Brien (CEO)

FLEXICARE (GROUP) LIMITED
Cynon Valley Business Park, Mountain Ash, Cynon Valley, CF45 4ER, United Kingdom
Tel.: (44) 1443474647   UK
Web Site: https://flexicare.com
Holding Company; Medical Devices Mfr
N.A.I.C.S.: 551112

Subsidiaries:

Flexicare Medical Ltd. (1)
Cynon Valley Business Park, Mountain Ash,

CF45 4ER, United Kingdom
Tel.: (44) 1443474647
Medical Device Mfr
N.A.I.C.S.: 339112

Subsidiary (US):

Allied Medical, LLC   (2)
1720 Sublette Ave, St. Louis, MO 63110
Tel.: (800) 444-3940
Web Site: https://alliedmedicalllc.com
Medicinal Product Mfr
N.A.I.C.S.: 339112

Subsidiary (Non-US):

Medisize B.V.   (2)
Edisonstraat 1, 2181 AB, Hillegom, Netherlands
Tel.: (31) 88 77 44 555
Web Site: http://www.medisize.com
Medical Devices, Drug Delivery Systems & Personal Care Products Mfr
N.A.I.C.S.: 339113
Rob de Vroet *(Mng Dir)*

Subsidiary (Non-US):

Medisize Italia Srl   (3)
Vialle del'Umanesimo 303, 00144, Rome, Italy
Tel.: (39) 065935621
Web Site: http://www.medisize.com
Medical Devices, Drug Delivery Systems & Personal Care Products Sales
N.A.I.C.S.: 423450
Gualtiero Piana *(Country Mgr)*

Medisize Oy   (3)
Ensolantie 10, FI 80710, Lehmo, Finland
Tel.: (358) 102892400
Medical Devices, Drug Delivery Systems & Personal Care Products Mfr
N.A.I.C.S.: 339112

Medisize Schweiz AG   (3)
Hakabstrasse 5, Nurensdorf, 8309, Switzerland
Tel.: (41) 448383939
Emp.: 100
Medical Devices, Drug Delivery Systems & Personal Care Products Mfr
N.A.I.C.S.: 339112
Jurg Wiedler *(Mng Dir)*

FLEXIROAM LIMITED

Suite 6 4 Riseley Street, Applecross, 6153, WA, Australia
Tel.: (61) 863892688   AU
Web Site: https://www.flexiroam.com
Year Founded: 2011
FRX—(ASX)
Rev.: $1,844,935
Assets: $4,736,063
Liabilities: $5,484,039
Net Worth: ($747,976)
Earnings: $1,999,769
Fiscal Year-end: 06/30/23
Mobile Roaming Services
N.A.I.C.S.: 517810
Steve Picton *(Exec Chm & CEO)*

FLEXITUFF VENTURES INTERNATIONAL LIMITED

C 41-50 SEZ SectorIII, Dist Dhar, Pithampur, 454 775, Madhya Pradesh, India
Tel.: (91) 7292401681
Web Site: https://www.flexituff.com
Year Founded: 1993
FLEXITUFF—(NSE)
Rev.: $128,388,215
Assets: $148,029,200
Liabilities: $128,118,354
Net Worth: $19,910,846
Earnings: ($7,879,463)
Emp.: 8,488
Fiscal Year-end: 03/31/21
Flexible Intermediate Bulk Containers
N.A.I.C.S.: 561910
Anirudh Chittaranjan Sonpal *(Chm)*

Subsidiaries:

Flexituff Technology International Limited   (1)

Plot No-76 First Floor Phase 3, Okhla Industrial Estate, New Delhi, India
Tel.: (91) 1140375900
Plastics Bag Mfr
N.A.I.C.S.: 326111

Nanofil Technologies Pvt. Ltd.   (1)
Mahuakhedaganj, Kashipur, 244713, Uttarkhand, India
Tel.: (91) 9540895061
Web Site: http://www.nanofil.in
Emp.: 1,500
Polymer Compound Mfr
N.A.I.C.S.: 325998

FLEXIUM INTERCONNECT, INC.

No 1 Shangfa 5th Rd Hofa Industrial Park, Daliao Dist, Kaohsiung, 831, Taiwan
Tel.: (886) 77871008
Web Site: https://www.flexium.com.tw
6269—(TAI)
Rev.: $1,070,305,136
Assets: $1,317,780,976
Liabilities: $432,942,788
Net Worth: $884,838,189
Earnings: $67,226,624
Emp.: 5,606
Fiscal Year-end: 12/31/23
Flexible Printed Circuit Board Mfr
N.A.I.C.S.: 334412
Ming-Chih Cheng *(Chm)*

Subsidiaries:

Flexium Interconnect America, LLC   (1)
4020 Moorpark Ave Ste 111, San Jose, CA 95117
Tel.: (408) 838-2234
Marketing Services
N.A.I.C.S.: 541613

Flexium Interconnect, Inc - Kunshan Plant   (1)
No 1399 Hanpu Road, Kunshan, 215300, Jiangsu, China
Tel.: (86) 512 57775599
Printed Circuit Board Mfr
N.A.I.C.S.: 334412

FLEXO PRODUCTS LIMITED

4777 Kent Ave, Niagara Falls, L2H 1J5, ON, Canada
Tel.: (905) 354-2723
Web Site:
  http://www.flexoproducts.com
Year Founded: 1918
Rev.: $13,355,955
Emp.: 75
Sanitation Suppliers & Industrial Equipments Whslr
N.A.I.C.S.: 423830
Stephen Parker *(Pres & CEO)*

FLEXOPACK S.A.

Ifestou 36 Thesi Tzima, Koropi, 19400, Greece
Tel.: (30) 2106680000
Web Site: https://www.flexopack.com
FLEXO—(ATH)
Rev.: $162,974,315
Assets: $189,962,227
Liabilities: $75,016,188
Net Worth: $114,946,039
Earnings: $15,219,081
Emp.: 496
Fiscal Year-end: 12/31/22
Flexible Plastic Films Mfr
N.A.I.C.S.: 326112
Asimina Ginosati *(Exec Dir)*

Subsidiaries:

FLEXOPACK Plastics S.A.   (1)
Thesi Tzima Attica, PO Box 136, Tzima, 194 00, Koropi, Greece
Tel.: (30) 2106680000
Web Site: http://www.flexopack.com
Plastic Packaging Products Mfr
N.A.I.C.S.: 326199

Subsidiary (Non-US):

FESCOPACK Sp.zo.o   (2)
Tragamin 17, 82 200, Malbork, Pomorskie, Poland
Tel.: (48) 552733738
Web Site: http://www.fesco.pl
Sales Range: $25-49.9 Million
Emp.: 21
Frozen Foods Distributors & Packaging Mfr
N.A.I.C.S.: 311412
Maciej Bujalski *(Gen Mgr)*

Flexopack Denmark ApS   (1)
Svogerslev Hovedgade 7, 4000, Roskilde, Denmark
Tel.: (45) 43901383
Web Site: https://www.flexopack.dk
Packaging Machinery Distr
N.A.I.C.S.: 423830

Flexopack Polska Sp. z o.o.   (1)
Tragamin 17, 82-200, Malbork, Poland
Tel.: (48) 552720048
Plastic Packaging Materials Mfr
N.A.I.C.S.: 326112

Flexopack Pty Ltd   (1)
17 Dixon Street, Yatala, 4207, QLD, Australia
Tel.: (61) 733862999
Plastics Product Mfr
N.A.I.C.S.: 326199

FLEXOS S.A.

35 Square de Meeus, 1000, Brussels, Belgium
Tel.: (32) 87293770
Web Site: http://www.flexos.com
FLEX—(EUR)
Sales Range: Less than $1 Million
Emp.: 50
IT Services
N.A.I.C.S.: 541519

Subsidiaries:

FleXos France   (1)
27 Ave de l'Opera, 75001, Paris, France
Tel.: (33) 170385468
Web Site: http://www.flexos.com
Network Installation & Maintenance Services
N.A.I.C.S.: 541512

FLEXQUBE AB

Neongatan 8, 431 53, Molndal, Sweden
Tel.: (46) 727111477
Web Site: https://www.flexqube.com
FLEXQ—(OMX)
Rev.: $19,162,663
Assets: $14,395,928
Liabilities: $7,902,161
Net Worth: $6,493,767
Earnings: ($662,002)
Emp.: 58
Fiscal Year-end: 12/31/22
Logistic & Supply Chain Services
N.A.I.C.S.: 541614
Anders Fogelberg *(CEO)*

Subsidiaries:

FlexQube Europe AB   (1)
Neongatan 8, 431 53, Molndal, Sweden
Tel.: (46) 727111477
Industrial Component Mfr
N.A.I.C.S.: 336999

FlexQube GmbH   (1)
Feldbergstrasse 27-29, 61440, Oberursel, Germany
Tel.: (49) 1602436305
Material Handling Cart Mfr
N.A.I.C.S.: 336999
Jan Brettmann *(Sls Mgr)*

FlexQube Inc.   (1)
317 Tucapau Rd, Duncan, SC 29334
Tel.: (864) 274-0444
Industrial Component Mfr
N.A.I.C.S.: 336999

FLEXWORK PROPERTIES LTD.

The Toronto Star Building 1 Yonge Street Suite 1801, Toronto, M5E 1W7, ON, Canada
Tel.: (416) 820-4107
Gold Mining Services
N.A.I.C.S.: 212220

FLI INTERNATIONAL LIMITED

Six Cross Roads Business Park, Carriganard, Waterford, Ireland
Tel.: (353) 51 353190
Web Site: http://www.fli-group.com
Year Founded: 1989
Sales Range: $75-99.9 Million
Emp.: 140
Environmental Services
N.A.I.C.S.: 541620
Michael Flynn *(Chm)*

Subsidiaries:

FLI Energy Limited   (1)
Regent House Wolsely Road, Kempston, MK42 7JY, Bedfordshire, United Kingdom   (100%)
Tel.: (44) 845 6886065
Web Site: http://www.fli-energy.com
Sales Range: $25-49.9 Million
Emp.: 40
Anaerobic Digestion Plant Engineering Services
N.A.I.C.S.: 333248
Declan McGrath *(Mng Dir)*

FLI France SAS   (1)
21 rue Christophe Plantin Z A La Haute Limougere, 37230, Fondettes, France
Tel.: (33) 247428282
Web Site: http://www.flifrance.com
Environmental Consulting Services
N.A.I.C.S.: 541620
Michael Flynn *(Chm)*

FLI Water Limited   (1)
Regent House Wolseley Road, Kempston, Bedford, MK42 7JY, United Kingdom
Tel.: (44) 1234 852900
Web Site: http://www.fliwater.com
Water Utility Engineering Services
N.A.I.C.S.: 541330
Ian Martin *(Dir-Sls)*

VertaseFLI Limited   (1)
Number One Middle Bridge Business Park Bristol Road, Portishead, Bristol, BS20 6PN, United Kingdom
Tel.: (44) 1275397600
Web Site: http://www.vertasefli.co.uk
Civil Engineering & Construction Services
N.A.I.C.S.: 541330
Trevor Snell *(Mng Dir)*

FLIGHT CENTRE TRAVEL GROUP LIMITED

275 Grey Street, Southpoint, Brisbane, 4101, QLD, Australia
Tel.: (61) 730830033   AU
Web Site: https://www.fctgl.com
Year Founded: 1987
FLT—(ASX)
Rev.: $1,810,061,424
Assets: $2,814,023,092
Liabilities: $2,010,602,289
Net Worth: $803,420,803
Earnings: $92,918,669
Emp.: 12,514
Fiscal Year-end: 06/30/24
Holding Company; Business & Leisure Travel Agency Operator
N.A.I.C.S.: 551112
Graham F. Turner *(CEO & Mng Dir-Global)*

Subsidiaries:

American International Travel Limited   (1)
7/F Island Place Tower 510 King's Road, North Point, China (Hong Kong)
Tel.: (852) 28302828
Web Site: http://www.fcmtravel.com
Sales Range: $25-49.9 Million
Emp.: 60
Air Travel Management Services

Flight Centre Travel Group Limited—(Continued)
N.A.I.C.S.: 561510

Australian OpCo Pty. Ltd. (1)
Level 4 545 Queen Street, Brisbane, 4000,
QLD, Australia **(100%)**
Tel.: (61) 731707979
Web Site: http://www.fcmtravel.com
Business Travel Agencies Operator
N.A.I.C.S.: 561599

Subsidiary (Non-US):

FCm Travel Solutions (L.L.C) (2)
Level 20 Sidra Tower Al Soufah, PO Box
22092, 22092, Dubai, United Arab
Emirates **(49%)**
Tel.: (971) 42456000
Web Site: http://www.fcmtravel.com
Business Travel Agencies Operator
N.A.I.C.S.: 561599

FCm Travel Solutions Singapore Pte.
Ltd. (2)
7500A Beach Rd 05-323 The Plz, Singa-
pore, 199591, Singapore **(100%)**
Tel.: (65) 65930376
Web Site: http://www.sg.fcm.travel
Sales Range: $25-49.9 Million
Emp.: 55
Business Travel Agencies Operator
N.A.I.C.S.: 561599
Bertrand Saillet (Mng Dir-Asia)

Group (US):

FCm Travel Solutions USA (2)
105 W Madison St Ste 2000, Chicago, IL
60602
Tel.: (312) 215-0874
Web Site: http://www.us.fcm.travel
Sales Range: $75-99.9 Million
Emp.: 430
Business Travel Agencies Operator
N.A.I.C.S.: 561599
Jo Greenfield (Gen Mgr-UK)

Casto Travel US, LLC (1)
2560 N 1st St Ste 150, San Jose, CA
95131
Tel.: (800) 832-3445
Travel Management Services
N.A.I.C.S.: 561599

FCm Travel Solutions (India) Private
Limited (1)
JC-43 Khirki Extension Malviya Nagar, New
Delhi, 110 017, India
Tel.: (91) 1142536666
Web Site: http://in.fcm.travel
Travel Management Services
N.A.I.C.S.: 561599

Flight Centre (UK) Limited (1)
320 Chiswick High Road, London, W4 5TA,
United Kingdom
Tel.: (44) 2030567993
Web Site: https://www.flightcentre.co.uk
Sales Range: $650-699.9 Million
Emp.: 3,000
Travel Management Services
N.A.I.C.S.: 561510
Robert Pyla (Mgr)

Flight Centre Technology Pty.
Ltd. (1)
12 157 Ann St, Brisbane, 4000, QLD,
Australia **(100%)**
Tel.: (61) 731707979
Flight Ticket Booking Services
N.A.I.C.S.: 561599

Flight Centre USA Holding Corp. (1)
5 Paragon Dr Ste 200 Montvale, Montvale,
NJ 07645 **(100%)**
Tel.: (201) 934-3500
Web Site:
http://www.flightcentertravelgroup.com
Holding Company; Regional managing Of-
fice
N.A.I.C.S.: 551112
Dean W. Smith (Pres)

Subsidiary (Domestic):

FC USA Inc. (2)
5 Paragon Dr Ste 200, Montvale, NJ
07645 **(100%)**
Tel.: (201) 934-3848
Web Site: https://www.libertytravel.com

Subsidiary
Street Suite 1801, Toronto,
ON, Canada
Tel.: [...]
Emp.: 400
Travel Agencies & Services
N.A.I.C.S.: 561510
Dean W. Smith (Pres)

Subsidiary (Domestic):

Garber's Travel Service, Inc. (3)
27 Boylston St, Chestnut Hill, MA 02467
Tel.: (617) 739-2200
Web Site: http://www.garbertravel.com
Business & Leisure Travel Services
N.A.I.C.S.: 561510
Debbie Lee Nashed (Mgr-Ops-Chestnut
Hill)

Ignite Travel Group (1)
Level 1 Suite 127a The Oasis Shopping
Centre Victoria Avenue, PO Box 361,
Broadbeach, 4218, QLD, Australia **(100%)**
Tel.: (61) 755558888
Web Site: http://www.ignitetravel.com
Travel Support Services
N.A.I.C.S.: 561510
Randall Deer (Founder)

Moneywise Global Pty. Ltd. (1)
Level 3 545 Queen St, Brisbane, 4000,
QLD, Australia **(100%)**
Tel.: (61) 731707518
Web Site: http://www.moneywiseglobal.com
Emp.: 18
Financial Management Consulting Services
N.A.I.C.S.: 541611
Chris Herdman (Head-Advice)

Scott Dunn Limited (1)
7th Floor, 1 Butterwick, London, W6 8DL,
United Kingdom
Tel.: (44) 2086825099
Web Site: http://www.scottdunn.com
Travel Agency
N.A.I.C.S.: 561510
Andrew Dunn (Founder & Pres-Global)

Subsidiary (US):

Scott Dunn USA (2)
420 N Cedros Ave Ste 102, Solana Beach,
CA 92075
Tel.: (858) 523-9000
Web Site: https://www.scottdunn.com
Travel Agencies
N.A.I.C.S.: 561510
John Spence (Pres)

FLIGHT SOLUTIONS CO., LTD.
3F Ebisu MF Bldg 4-6-1 Ebisu,
Shibuya-ku, Tokyo, 150-0013, Japan
Tel.: (81) 334406100
Web Site: https://www.flight.co.jp
Year Founded: 1988
3753—(TKS)
Rev.: $21,204,880
Assets: $10,952,770
Liabilities: $7,965,050
Net Worth: $2,987,720
Earnings: ($694,050)
Emp.: 111
Fiscal Year-end: 03/31/24
Holding Company
N.A.I.C.S.: 551112
Keiichiro Katayama (Founder, Chm,
Pres & CEO)

FLINDERS EXPLORATION LIM-
ITED
58 Beulah Rd, Norwood, 5067, SA,
Australia
Tel.: (61) 881327980
Web Site:
http://www.fexploration.com
Sales Range: $25-49.9 Million
Emp.: 1
Diamond Mining Services
N.A.I.C.S.: 212311
David Tucker (Mng Dir)

FLINDERS MINES LIMITED
45 Ventnor Avenue, West Perth,
6005, WA, Australia
Tel.: (61) 893894483   AU

Web Site:
http://www.flindersmines.com
RHK—(ASX)
Rev.: $130,876
Assets: $63,077,591
Liabilities: $2,298,344
Net Worth: $60,779,247
Earnings: ($6,475,694)
Emp.: 100
Fiscal Year-end: 06/30/24
Iron Ore Exploration & Development
N.A.I.C.S.: 212210
Neil Frederick Warburton (Chm)

FLINDERS PORTS PTY LTD
296 St Vincent St, Port Adelaide,
5015, SA, Australia
Tel.: (61) 884470611   AU
Web Site:
http://www.flindersports.com.au
Sales Range: $25-49.9 Million
Emp.: 165
Port, Land & Shipping Infrastructure
Management
N.A.I.C.S.: 488330
Vincent Tremaine (CEO)

FLINT CORP.
Bow Valley Square 2 Suite 3500 205
5th Avenue SW, Calgary, T2P 2V7,
AB, Canada
Tel.: (587) 318-0997   ON
Web Site: https://flintcorp.com
NWPIF—(OTCIQ)
Rev.: $495,166,164
Assets: $163,583,156
Liabilities: $205,217,452
Net Worth: ($41,634,296)
Earnings: ($9,736,517)
Emp.: 3,200
Fiscal Year-end: 12/31/23
Holding Company
N.A.I.C.S.: 551112
Neil Wotton (COO)

Subsidiaries:

ClearStream Contracting LP (1)
202 - 427 Gregoire Drive, Fort McMurray,
T9H 4K7, AB, Canada
Tel.: (780) 791-2258
Industrial Building Construction Services
N.A.I.C.S.: 236210
Clayton MacEachern (District Mgr)

ClearStream Wear Technologies
LP (1)
11 Liberty Road, Sherwood Park, T8H 2V2,
AB, Canada
Tel.: (780) 410-1950
Web Site: http://www.clearstreamenergy.ca
Industrial Building Construction Services
N.A.I.C.S.: 236210

ClearWater Energy Services LP (1)
355 MacKenzie Blvd, Fort McMurray, T9H
5E2, AB, Canada
Tel.: (780) 743-2171
Web Site: http://www.clearstreamenergy.ca
Industrial Building Construction Services
N.A.I.C.S.: 236210

FLINT INT'L SERVICES, INC.
2300 Steeles Avenue West 120, Con-
cord, L4K 5X6, ON, Canada   VG
Web Site: https://www.flintls.com
Sales Range: Less than $1 Million
Emp.: 3
Online Education Services
N.A.I.C.S.: 611710
Russell Hiebert (Pres, Sec & Treas)

FLITE HOCKEY
3400 Ridgeway Drive Unit 2, Missis-
sauga, ON, Canada
Tel.: (905) 828-6030
Web Site: http://www.flitehockey.com
Year Founded: 1993
Rev.: $32,984,982
Emp.: 310
Sports Equipment Mfr

N.A.I.C.S.: 339920
Gerry McSorley (Founder & Pres)

FLITTO INC.
6F 20 Yeongdong-daero 96-gil,
Gangnam-gu, Seoul, 06173, Korea
(South)
Tel.: (82) 25120142
Web Site: https://www.flitto.com
Year Founded: 2012
300080—(KRS)
Rev.: $10,461,448
Assets: $18,996,831
Liabilities: $9,799,458
Net Worth: $9,197,373
Earnings: ($4,501,004)
Emp.: 136
Fiscal Year-end: 12/31/22
Translation Services
N.A.I.C.S.: 541930
Simon Lee (Co-Founder & CEO)

FLIVA APS
Jens Baggesens Vej 47, 8200, Arhus,
Denmark
Tel.: (45) 45 8827 6727
Web Site: http://fliva.com
Year Founded: 2014
Multimedia & Advertising Services
N.A.I.C.S.: 541870
Carsten Hjorth Pedersen (Co-
Founder & CEO)

FLIXMOBILITY GMBH
Friedenheimer Brucke 16, Munich,
80639, Germany
Tel.: (49) 30 300137300
Web Site:
http://www.global.flixbus.com
Year Founded: 2013
Intercity Bus Services
N.A.I.C.S.: 485113
Jochen Engert (Co-Founder & Co-
CEO)

Subsidiaries:

Greyhound Lines, Inc. (1)
PO Box 660362, Dallas, TX 75266-0362
Tel.: (214) 849-8100
Web Site: https://www.greyhound.com
Bus Charters & Tours, Package Express,
Regular Route Passenger Service, Travel
Services & Sightseeing
N.A.I.C.S.: 485119
Dave Leach (Pres & CEO)

Subsidiary (Non-US):

Greyhound Canada Transportation
Corp. (2)
81 Bay St, Toronto, M5J 2X8, ON, Canada
Tel.: (403) 260-0877
Web Site: http://www.greyhound.ca
Sales Range: $450-499.9 Million
Emp.: 2,500
Commercial Passenger Carrier & Charter
Transportation
N.A.I.C.S.: 485210
Stuart Kendrick (Sr VP)

FLJ GROUP LIMITED
Room 1610 No 917 East Longhua
Road, Huangpu District, Shanghai,
200023, China
Tel.: (86) 2164179625   Ky
Year Founded: 2012
FLJ—(NASDAQ)
Assets: $614,791,538
Liabilities: $5,233,095,983
Net Worth: ($4,618,304,445)
Earnings: ($511,863,320)
Emp.: 19
Fiscal Year-end: 09/30/23
Holding Company
N.A.I.C.S.: 551112
Gang Xie (CTO)

FLO S.P.A.
Frazione Ghiara Sabbioni 33 A,

43012, Fontanellato, Parma, Italy
Tel.: (39) 0521 823 111　　　　　IT
Web Site: http://www.flo.eu
Year Founded: 1973
Plastic & Paper Cup Mfr
N.A.I.C.S.: 326199
Antonio Simonazzi *(Founder)*

Subsidiaries:

F. Bender Limited　　　　　　　(1)
Gresford Industrial Park Chester Road, Wrexham, LL12 8LX, United Kingdom
Tel.: (44) 1978 855 661
Web Site: http://www.benders.co.uk
Sanitary Food & Beverage Containers & Service Products Mfr
N.A.I.C.S.: 322219
Andrew Cunliffe *(Mng Dir)*

Flo Deutschland Gmbh　　　　　(1)
Linprunstrasse 49, 80335, Munich, Germany
Tel.: (49) 88 49 54 4
Plastics Product Mfr
N.A.I.C.S.: 322219

Flo Vending　　　　　　　　　(1)
Rue Henri Becquerel 14, 93275, Paris, France
Tel.: (33) 149361626
Plastics Product Mfr
N.A.I.C.S.: 322219

Nupik Internacional SL　　　　　(1)
Pintor Goya 1-7, Poligono Industrial Sureste, 08213, Polinya, Spain
Tel.: (34) 937 284 000
Web Site: http://www.nupik.es
Disposable Plastic Cup, Plate, Cutlery & Container Mfr
N.A.I.C.S.: 326199

Subsidiary (Non-US):

NUPIK FRANCE Eurl.　　　　　(2)
5 rue Fourrier, 89000, Auxerre, France
Tel.: (33) 386 406 692
Web Site: http://www.nupik.es
Disposable Plastic Cup, Plate, Cutlery & Container Distr
N.A.I.C.S.: 424610

Nupik-flo UK Ltd　　　　　　　(1)
6 Cantelupe Mews Cantelupe Road, East Grinstead, RH19 3BG, West Sussex, United Kingdom
Tel.: (44) 1342 317688
Web Site: http://www.nupik-flo.co.uk
Plastic Product Mfr & Distr
N.A.I.C.S.: 326199

FLO-LINE HYDRAULICS PTE LTD.
47 Joo Koon Circle, Singapore, 629067, Singapore
Tel.: (65) 6863 2022　　　　SG
Web Site: http://www.floline.com.sg
Year Founded: 1987
Sales Range: $10-24.9 Million
Emp.: 160
Hydraulic Components Distr
N.A.I.C.S.: 423830
K. I. Chia *(Exec Dir)*

FLOATEL INTERNATIONAL LTD.
Lilla Badhusgatan 2, Gothenburg, 411 21, Sweden
Tel.: (46) 313520700　　　　BM
Web Site: http://www.floatel.se
Year Founded: 2006
Sales Range: $25-49.9 Million
Emp.: 65
Holding Company; Offshore Floatel Fleet Owner & Operator
N.A.I.C.S.: 551112
Peter Jacobsson *(CEO)*

Subsidiaries:

Floatel International AB　　　　(1)
Lilla Badhusgatan 2, Gothenburg, 431 53, Sweden　　　　　　　(100%)
Tel.: (46) 313520700
Web Site: http://www.floatel.se

Offshore Floatel Fleet Operator
N.A.I.C.S.: 483112
Peter Jacobsson *(CEO)*

FLOBAL CORPORATION
Tatsuno Nishihonmachi Building 1-15-10 Nishihonmachi, Nishi-ku, Osaka, 550-0005, Japan
Tel.: (81) 664652680
Web Site: https://www.flobal.jp
Year Founded: 1910
7132—(TKS)
Rev.: $45,056,280
Assets: $27,016,560
Liabilities: $11,249,730
Net Worth: $15,766,830
Earnings: $430,200
Fiscal Year-end: 03/31/23
Hardware Product Mfr & Distr
N.A.I.C.S.: 332510

FLODOR S.A.S.
ZA du Pre de la Dame Jeanne Route de Survilliers, F-60128, Plailly, France
Tel.: (33) 3 445 41930　　　　FR
Web Site: http://www.flodor.fr
Year Founded: 1958
Sales Range: $10-24.9 Million
Snack Chip Mfr & Distr
N.A.I.C.S.: 311919
Alberto Vitaloni *(Chm & Pres)*

FLOFORM COUNTERTOPS
125 Hamelin Street, Winnipeg, R3T 3Z1, MB, Canada
Tel.: (204) 453-0639
Web Site: http://www.floform.com
Rev.: $13,911,192
Emp.: 160
N.A.I.C.S.: 337110
Ted Sherritt *(CEO)*

FLOMIC GLOBAL LOGISTICS LTD.
205 Enterprise Centre Off Nehru Road Beside Orchid Hotel, Vile Parle East, Mumbai, 400 093, Maharashtra, India
Tel.: (91) 2267312345　　　　In
Web Site:
　　https://www.flomicgroup.com
Year Founded: 1981
504380—(BOM)
Rev.: $50,953,804
Assets: $17,338,301
Liabilities: $12,344,236
Net Worth: $4,994,065
Earnings: $1,136,982
Fiscal Year-end: 03/31/23
Securities Brokerage Services
N.A.I.C.S.: 523150
Satyaprakash S. Pathak *(CFO)*

FLOOIDCX CORP.
1282 A Cornwall Road, Oakville, L6J 7W5, ON, Canada　　　　NV
Web Site: http://www.flooidcx.com
Year Founded: 2014
FLCX—(OTCIQ)
Rev.: $53,710
Assets: $20,515
Liabilities: $5,037,472
Net Worth: ($5,016,957)
Earnings: ($838,833)
Emp.: 2
Fiscal Year-end: 02/28/22
Social Marketing Services
N.A.I.C.S.: 541519
Aditya Kelagar *(Co-Founder)*

FLOORS MY HOME LIMITED
74 Newtown Row, Birmingham, B6 4HA, United Kingdom
Tel.: (44) 1213590234
Year Founded: 1999
Sales Range: $100-124.9 Million

Emp.: 590
Wood Flooring Retailer
N.A.I.C.S.: 449121
Robert Hodges *(Mng Dir)*

FLORA CORPORATION LIMITED
H No14-8-346/1B Ground Floor Jummerat Bazar, Hyderabad, 500012, Telangana, India
Tel.: (91) 4027638111
Web Site:
　　https://www.floracorporation.com
Year Founded: 1900
Rev.: $17,024,217
Assets: $5,429,361
Liabilities: $4,801,018
Net Worth: $628,343
Earnings: $35,664
Fiscal Year-end: 03/31/18
Fish Farming Services
N.A.I.C.S.: 114111
Rajesh Gandhi *(CFO)*

FLORA GROWTH CORP.
65 Queen Street W Suite 800, Toronto, M5H 2M5, ON, Canada
Tel.: (416) 861-2267　　　　Ca
Web Site: http://www.floragrowth.ca
Year Founded: 2019
FLGC—(NASDAQ)
Rev.: $37,171,000
Assets: $80,987,000
Liabilities: $24,575,000
Net Worth: $56,412,000
Earnings: ($52,629,000)
Emp.: 337
Fiscal Year-end: 12/31/22
Cannabis Product Mfr
N.A.I.C.S.: 325412
Kevin Taylor *(Chm)*

FLORA MANUFACTURING & DISTRIBUTING LTD.
7400 Fraser Park Drive, Burnaby, V5J 5B9, BC, Canada
Tel.: (604) 436-6000
Web Site:
　　https://www.florahealth.com
Year Founded: 1965
Sales Range: $10-24.9 Million
Emp.: 125
Herbal Remedies Mfr & Distr
N.A.I.C.S.: 325411
Thomas Greither *(Owner & Pres)*

Subsidiaries:

Flora Inc.　　　　　　　　　(1)
805 E Badger Rd, Lynden, WA 98264
Tel.: (360) 354-2110
Web Site: http://www.florahealth.com
Herbal Remedies Mfr & Distr
N.A.I.C.S.: 325411
Thomas Greither *(Pres)*

FLORA TEXTILES LIMITED
23 Bharathi Park Road, Coimbatore, 641 043, Tamil Nadu, India
Tel.: (91) 4222447395
Web Site: https://www.floratextiles.in
Year Founded: 1993
530705—(BOM)
Rev.: $51,346
Assets: $84,942
Liabilities: $1,581,743
Net Worth: ($1,496,802)
Earnings: ($79,379)
Fiscal Year-end: 03/31/23
Woven Fabric Mfr & Distr
N.A.I.C.S.: 313210
Nidhi Gupta *(Mng Dir)*

FLORENTAISE SA
Le Grand Patis, Saint-Mars-du-Desert, 44850, Nort-sur-Erdre, France
Tel.: (33) 240774444

Web Site: https://www.florentaise.fr
Year Founded: 1973
ALFLO—(EUR)
Nutrition Product Distr
N.A.I.C.S.: 456191
Jean-Pascal Chupin *(Chm)*

FLORIDA ICE AND FARM CO. S.A.
Calle 12 Ave 4 y 6, Postal 2046-3000, Heredia, San Jose, 2044300, Costa Rica
Tel.: (506) 24376700
Web Site: http://www.florida.co.cr
Sales Range: $200-249.9 Million
Emp.: 2,400
Holding Company; Beer, Bottled Water & Fruit Juice & Malt Beverages Distr; Real Estate Management & Tourism Services; Investment Services
N.A.I.C.S.: 551112
Ramon Mendiola Sanchez *(Dir Gen)*

Subsidiaries:

Alimentos Kern de Guatemala, S.A.　　　　　　　　　　　(1)
CA-9 Norte Ruta Al Atlantico 9-60, Zona 17, 1018, Guatemala, Guatemala
Tel.: (502) 2323 7100
Web Site: http://www.alikerns.com
Sales Range: $1-9.9 Million
Emp.: 700
Nectar & Fruit Juice, Vegetable & Tomato Products Mfr
N.A.I.C.S.: 311421
Ricardo Santico *(CEO)*

North American Breweries, Inc.　(1)
445 Saint Paul St, Rochester, NY 14605-1726
Tel.: (585) 546-1030
Web Site: http://www.nabreweries.com
Sales Range: $250-299.9 Million
Emp.: 450
Holding Company; Breweries & Alcoholic Beverage Distr
N.A.I.C.S.: 551112
Peter Bodenham *(VP-Mktg)*

Subsidiary (Domestic):

Dundee Brewing Co.　　　　　(2)
25 Cataract St, Rochester, NY 14605
Tel.: (585) 263-9200
Web Site: http://www.dundeebeer.com
Alcoholic Beverage Distr
N.A.I.C.S.: 424810

Genesee Brewing Company　　(2)
445 Saint Paul St, Rochester, NY 14605-1726
Tel.: (585) 546-1030
Web Site: http://www.nabreweries.com
Sales Range: $100-124.9 Million
Emp.: 400
Brewery & Beer Distr
N.A.I.C.S.: 312120
James Barber *(VP-Matl)*

Independent Brewers United, Inc.　　　　　　　　　　　(2)
431 Pine St Ste G 14, Burlington, VT 05401
Tel.: (802) 658-2739
Web Site: http://www.nabreweries.com
Holding Company
N.A.I.C.S.: 551112
Rich Lozyniak *(Pres & CEO)*

Subsidiary (Domestic):

Magic Hat Brewing Co. & Performing Arts Center Inc.　　　　　(3)
5 Bartlett Bay Rd, South Burlington, VT 05403
Tel.: (802) 658-2739
Web Site: http://www.magichat.net
Sales Range: $10-24.9 Million
Emp.: 70
Brewery
N.A.I.C.S.: 312120
Kris Sirchio *(CEO)*

Subsidiary (Domestic):

Pyramid Breweries Inc.　　　　(4)

Florida Ice and Farm Co. S.A.—(Continued)

91 S Royal Brougham Way, Seattle, WA
98134-1219
Tel.: (206) 682-8322
Web Site: http://www.pyramidbrew.com
Sales Range: $25-49.9 Million
Ales, Lagers & Soda Mfr; Restaurant Operator
N.A.I.C.S.: 312120
Teresa Morgan *(Gen Mgr-Pyramid Alehouse)*

Subsidiary (Domestic):

**Pyramid Gilman Street Property,
LLC** (5)
901 Gilman St, Berkeley, CA 94710
Tel.: (510) 528-9880
Web Site: http://www.pyramidbrew.com
Sales Range: $10-24.9 Million
Emp.: 136
Malt Mfr & Restaurant Owners
N.A.I.C.S.: 311213

Subsidiary (Domestic):

Labatt USA LLC (2)
50 Fountain Plz Ste 900, Buffalo, NY 14202
Tel.: (716) 604-1050
Web Site: http://www.labattus.com
Sales Range: $25-49.9 Million
Emp.: 250
Beer Importer & Distr
N.A.I.C.S.: 424810
Lisa Texido *(Brand Mgr)*

FLORIDIENNE SA

Dreve Richelle 161 Building P, Box 4,
B-1410, Waterloo, Belgium
Tel.: (32) 23530028
Web Site: https://www.floridienne.be
Year Founded: 1898
FLOB—(EUR)
Rev.: $567,146,557
Assets: $656,293,978
Liabilities: $421,584,287
Net Worth: $234,709,691
Earnings: $12,989,424
Emp.: 3,000
Fiscal Year-end: 12/31/22
Holding Company; Non-Ferrous Metal
Salts Mfr & Marketer; Agrofoods; Life-
Sciences
N.A.I.C.S.: 551112
Gaetan Waucquez *(CEO & Mng Dir-
Chemical Div)*
Subsidiaries:

Biobest S.A. (1)
Ilse Velden 18, 2260, Waterloo, Belgium
Tel.: (32) 14257980
Web Site: http://www.biobestgroup.com
Emp.: 1,700
Biological Control Services
N.A.I.C.S.: 561710

Subsidiary (US):

Bioworks, Inc. (2)
345 Woodcliff Dr, Fairport, NY 14450
Tel.: (585) 641-0581
Web Site: http://www.bioworksinc.com
Rev.: $2,600,000
Emp.: 20
Fiscal Year-end: 12/31/2006
Mfg Agricultural Chemicals
N.A.I.C.S.: 325320
William Foster *(CEO)*

Delka S.A. (1)
Rue de Battice 22B, 4800, Petit-Rechain,
Belgium
Tel.: (32) 87766338
Web Site: https://www.delka.be
Food Service
N.A.I.C.S.: 722310

Florago SA (1)
Dreve Richelle 161 4 Bldg P, 1410, Waterloo, Belgium
Tel.: (32) 23530028
Web Site: http://www.floridienne.be
Sales Range: $25-49.9 Million
Emp.: 3
Food Production & Marketing Services
N.A.I.C.S.: 541611

Subsidiary (Non-US):

Francaise De Gastronomie (2)
2 Allee Helsinki, CA80072 Schiltigheim,
Strasbourg, 67013, Cedex, France
Tel.: (33) 388593060
Web Site: http://www.francaise-de-
gastronomie.fr
Emp.: 20
Holding Company
N.A.I.C.S.: 551112

Larzul SA (2)
Rue Henri Lautredou, Finistere, 29720,
Plonéour-Lanvern, France
Tel.: (33) 298826868
Web Site: http://www.groupe-larzul.com
Specialty Foods
N.A.I.C.S.: 311999

Florinvest SA (1)
Drege Richelle 161 Bldg P, PO Box 4, Waterloo, 1410, Belgium
Tel.: (32) 23530028
Sales Range: $50-74.9 Million
Emp.: 10
Investment Services
N.A.I.C.S.: 523999
Christian Van Osselaer *(CEO)*

Subsidiary (Domestic):

Chemcom SA (2)
Route de Lennik 802, 1070, Brussels, Belgium
Tel.: (32) 25290011
Web Site: https://www.chemcom.be
Sales Range: $25-49.9 Million
Biopharmaceutical Services
N.A.I.C.S.: 325412

H-Phar SA (2)
Chaussee de Bruxelles, 141 Jumet, 6040,
Brussels, Belgium
Tel.: (32) 10417078
Web Site: http://www.h-phar.com
Sales Range: $25-49.9 Million
Emp.: 7
Clinical Research & Development
N.A.I.C.S.: 541715
Michel Vandevelde *(Dir-Medical)*

IKA GmbH & CO.KG (1)
ChemiePark Bitterfeld Wolfen, Filmstrasse
4, Wolfen, 06766, Germany
Tel.: (49) 34946961
Web Site: http://www.ika-wolsen.de
Sales Range: $25-49.9 Million
Emp.: 77
Chemical Production
N.A.I.C.S.: 325180

KIMFLOR AS (1)
Yazibasi Mah Yazibasi-izmir Cad No 23,
Torbali, 35875, Izmir, Turkiye
Tel.: (90) 2328539066
Web Site: https://www.kimflor.com
Sales Range: $25-49.9 Million
Emp.: 50
Lead-Based Products
N.A.I.C.S.: 325180

Kamapim Ltd. (1)
Papua New Guinea, Madang, Papua New
Guinea
Tel.: (675) 71339811
Web Site: http://www.kamapim.com
Agricultural Services
N.A.I.C.S.: 115116

Karras S.A. (1)
Avenue de Lambusart 11, B-6220, Fleurus,
Belgium
Tel.: (32) 71822625
Web Site: http://karrasgroup.be
Food Products Mfr
N.A.I.C.S.: 311999

Pomarom S.R.L. (1)
Str Liverzil 41, 510170, Alba Iulia, Romania
Tel.: (40) 258911000
Business Information Services
N.A.I.C.S.: 519290

Sidech S.A. (1)
Rue de la Station 7, B 1495, Tilly, Belgium
Tel.: (32) 71988821
Component Metal Production
N.A.I.C.S.: 332117
Laurent Raskin *(CEO)*

Simon Dutriaux S.A.S. (1)
ZA du bois Rigault Rue gustave Eiffel, BP
34, 62880, Vendin-le-Vieil, France
Tel.: (33) 321142480
Web Site: https://www.simon-dutriaux.com
Chemicals Mfr
N.A.I.C.S.: 325199

Societe Nouvelle d'Affinage des
Metaux - SNAM S.A.S. (1)
Avenue Jean Jaures, BP 4, 12110, Viviez,
France
Tel.: (33) 565437730
Web Site: http://www.snam.com
Chemical Production & Recovery
N.A.I.C.S.: 325180

Subsidiary (Domestic):

Euro Bat Tri (2)
Rue de la Garenne BP 735, Saint-Quentin-
Fallavier, F-88297, France
Tel.: (33) 474945014
Web Site: http://www.snam.com
Chemical Recovery
N.A.I.C.S.: 325180

Sotecna S.A. (1)
Dreve Richelle 161/4 Bat P, 1410, Waterloo, Belgium
Tel.: (32) 23530028
Web Site: https://sotecna.be
Essential Oil Mfr
N.A.I.C.S.: 325199

UAB Camargo (1)
Pakalne str 7, Bezdonys, LT-15201, Vilnius,
Lithuania
Tel.: (370) 852696493
Food Service
N.A.I.C.S.: 722310

Vera Chimie Developpements
S.A.S. (1)
35 rue de la Garenne, BP 70734, 38070,
Saint-Quentin-Fallavier, France
Tel.: (33) 474948210
Web Site: https://www.vcd-floridienne.com
Chemicals Mfr
N.A.I.C.S.: 325199

FLORIM CERAMICHE S.P.A.

Via Canaletto 24, 41042, Fiorano-
Modenese, Modena, Italy
Tel.: (39) 0536840111 IT
Web Site: http://www.florim.it
Sales Range: $400-449.9 Million
Emp.: 1,058
Ceramic Wall & Floor Tile Mfr
N.A.I.C.S.: 327120
Claudio Lucchese *(Pres & CEO)*

Subsidiaries:

Florim USA, Inc. (1)
300 International Blvd, Clarksville, TN (87%)
37040
Tel.: (931) 645-5100
Web Site: http://www.florimusa.com
Sales Range: $50-74.9 Million
Emp.: 200
Mfr of Ceramic Floor & Wall Tiles
N.A.I.C.S.: 327120
Andrea Croxatto *(Mgr-IT)*

FLORIN MINING INVESTMENT COMPANY LIMITED

10 Murray Street, Hamilton, 2303,
NSW, Australia
Tel.: (61) 249202877
Web Site: https://www.florin.com.au
FMI—(NSXA)
Sales Range: Less than $1 Million
Investment Services
N.A.I.C.S.: 523999
Steven Shane Pritchard *(Chm)*

FLORINT B.V.

Schellingweg 17 C, Zaandam, 1507
DR, Netherlands
Tel.: (31) 20 797 0100
Web Site:
http://www.florintcapital.com
FLO—(LUX)
Sales Range: Less than $1 Million

Investment Management Service
N.A.I.C.S.: 523999

FLORISTS SUPPLY LTD.

35 Airport Road, Winnipeg, R3H 0V5,
MB, Canada
Tel.: (204) 632-1210
Web Site:
https://www.floristssupply.com
Year Founded: 1935
Rev.: $10,534,386
Emp.: 69
Floral importer & Mfr
N.A.I.C.S.: 424930
Laurie Nesbitt *(Pres)*

FLOUR MILLS C. SARANTO-POULOS S.A.

3 Dimokratias St, 18756, Keratsini,
Greece
Tel.: (30) 2104009696
Web Site:
https://www.ksarantopoulos.gr
Year Founded: 1935
KYSA—(ATH)
Sales Range: Less than $1 Million
Emp.: 58
Flour Product Mfr
N.A.I.C.S.: 311824
Konstantinos Theodoros Sarantopou-
los *(Chm, Pres & CEO)*

FLOUR MILLS KEPENOS S.A.

Vi Pe Patron Patra, 25018, Patras,
Greece
Tel.: (30) 2610241940
Web Site: https://www.kepenos.gr
Year Founded: 1952
KEPEN—(ATH)
Sales Range: Less than $1 Million
Emp.: 122
Production of Flour & Flour Products
N.A.I.C.S.: 311211
Kepenos Dimitrios Georgios *(Chm &
CEO)*

FLOUR MILLS OF FIJI LIMITED

Leonidas Street, Walu Bay, Suva, Fiji
Tel.: (679) 3301188
Web Site: http://www.fmf.com.fj
Year Founded: 1973
Sales Range: $50-74.9 Million
Emp.: 900
Flour Milling Services
N.A.I.C.S.: 311211
Hari Punja *(Founder & Chm)*

Subsidiaries:

The Rice Company of Fiji
Limited (1)
Leonidas Street, PO Box 977, Walu Bay,
Suva, Fiji
Tel.: (679) 3301188
Web Site: http://www.fmf.com.fj
Rev.: $18,836,457
Assets: $9,356,640
Liabilities: $3,155,656
Net Worth: $6,200,984
Earnings: $1,289,379
Fiscal Year-end: 06/30/2023
Rice Product Whslr
N.A.I.C.S.: 424490
Ram Bajekal *(Mng Dir)*

FLOUR MILLS OF NIGERIA PLC.

1 Golden Penny Place Wharf Road,
Apapa, Lagos, Nigeria
Tel.: (234) 7056891000 NG
Web Site: https://www.fmnplc.com
Year Founded: 1960
FLOURMILL—(NIGE)
Rev.: $1,696,213,787
Assets: $1,104,740,912
Liabilities: $931,792,851
Net Worth: $172,948,061
Earnings: $2,623,826

Emp.: 5,404
Fiscal Year-end: 03/31/24
Flour Product Mfr
N.A.I.C.S.: 311211
Emmanuel A. Ukpabi *(Vice Chm)*

Subsidiaries:

Apapa Bulk Terminal Limited **(1)**
ABTL Admin Building Terminal A and B
Apapa Port, Lagos, Nigeria
Tel.: (234) 9082991423
Web Site: http://apapabulk.com
Terminal Services
N.A.I.C.S.: 488310

Golden Fertilizer Company
Limited **(1)**
1 Golden Penny Place Wharf Road, Apapa,
Lagos, Nigeria
Tel.: (234) 8188700257
Web Site: https://www.goldenagriinputs.com
Edible Oil Mfr
N.A.I.C.S.: 311225

Golden Noodles Nigeria Limited **(1)**
47 Eric Moore Road Iganmu, PMB 12845,
Lagos, 101001, Nigeria
Tel.: (234) 8032204667
Flour Mfr
N.A.I.C.S.: 333241

Golden Sugar Company Limited **(1)**
2 Old Dock Road Apapa, Lagos, Nigeria
Tel.: (234) 7056891000
Web Site: http://goldensugarng.com
Sugar Products Mfr
N.A.I.C.S.: 311314

Nigeria Eagle Flour Mills Limited **(1)**
Eagle Flour Road, Lagos - Ibadan Express
Toll Point, Ibadan, Oyo, Nigeria
Tel.: (234) 8055891106
Web Site: http://eagleflour.com
Flour Product Mfr & Distr
N.A.I.C.S.: 311211

Nigerian Eagle Flour Mills
Limited **(1)**
Eagle Flour Road Lagos-Ibadan Express
Toll Point, Ibadan, Oyo, Nigeria
Tel.: (234) 8055891106
Web Site: https://www.eagleflour.com
Emp.: 220
Flour Milling Services
N.A.I.C.S.: 561730

Northern Nigeria Flour Mills Plc **(1)**
15 Maimalari Road, Bompai Industrial Es-
tate, Kano, Nigeria
Tel.: (234) 8033345177
Flour Product Mfr & Distr
N.A.I.C.S.: 311211

Premier Feed Mills Company
Limited **(1)**
No 1 Eagle flour road, Ibadan, Oyo, Nigeria
Tel.: (234) 9087504822
Web Site: https://premierfeedsltd.com
Animal Food Distr
N.A.I.C.S.: 423820

Premium Edible Oil Products
Limited **(1)**
Alomaja Junction off Ibadan-Ijebu Ode
Road, Idi-Ayunre, Ibadan, Oyo, Nigeria
Tel.: (234) 8171111102
Web Site: https://www.peopltd.com
Edible Oil Mfr
N.A.I.C.S.: 311225

Thai Farm International Limited **(1)**
3rd Floor FMN House Golden Penny Place
Apapa, Lagos, Nigeria
Tel.: (234) 7045124227
Web Site: http://www.tfinigeria.com
Cassava Flour Mfr
N.A.I.C.S.: 311211
Louw Burger *(CEO & Mng Dir)*

FLOVAL EQUIPMENT LTD.
250 Rayette Road Unit 1, Concord,
L4K 2G6, ON, Canada
Tel.: (905) 669-4500
Web Site: http://www.floval.com
Year Founded: 1976
Sales Range: $10-24.9 Million
Emp.: 20

Valving Instrumentation & Process
Control Equipment Mfr
N.A.I.C.S.: 423830

FLOW CAPITAL CORP.
1 Adelaide Street East Suite 3002,
PO Box 171, Toronto, M5C 2V9, ON,
Canada
Tel.: (416) 777-0383   BC
Web Site: https://flowcap.com
Year Founded: 1993
FW—(TSX)
Rev.: $8,156,792
Assets: $34,434,427
Liabilities: $16,170,534
Net Worth: $18,263,893
Earnings: $4,378,636
Emp.: 7
Fiscal Year-end: 12/31/21
Investment Fund Management Ser-
vices
N.A.I.C.S.: 523940
Vernon Lobo *(Chm)*

FLOW METALS CORP.
1111 Melville Street 11th Floor, Van-
couver, V6E 3V6, BC, Canada
Tel.: (604) 725-1857
Web Site:
    https://www.flowmetals.com
FWM—(CNSX)
Rev.: $351
Assets: $572,827
Liabilities: $215,694
Net Worth: $357,133
Earnings: ($271,797)
Fiscal Year-end: 07/31/23
Mining Services
N.A.I.C.S.: 212290

FLOW TRADERS NV
Jacob Bontiusplaats 9, 1018 LL, Am-
sterdam, 1018 LL, Netherlands
Tel.: (31) 207996799
Web Site:
    https://www.flowtraders.com
Year Founded: 2004
FLOW—(EUR)
Rev.: $495,006,475
Assets: $11,984,338,442
Liabilities: $11,329,994,604
Net Worth: $654,343,838
Earnings: $136,873,516
Emp.: 660
Fiscal Year-end: 12/31/22
Financial Trading Services
N.A.I.C.S.: 522299

Subsidiaries:

Flow Traders Asia Pte. Ltd. **(1)**
32-03 Guoco Tower 1 Wallich St, Singa-
pore, 078881, Singapore
Tel.: (65) 64171070
Liquidity Services
N.A.I.C.S.: 522320

Flow Traders Hong Kong Ltd. **(1)**
Room 2803 Hysan Place500 Hennessy
Road, Causeway Bay, China (Hong Kong)
Tel.: (852) 2 593 3000
Financial Services
N.A.I.C.S.: 523999

Flow Traders Technologies SRL **(1)**
96B Republicii Street, 400489, Cluj-Napoca,
Romania
Tel.: (40) 264599414
Liquidity Services
N.A.I.C.S.: 522320

Flow Traders U.S. LLC **(1)**
1114 Ave of the Americas 4th Fl, New York,
NY 10036
Tel.: (917) 210-5000
Liquidity Services
N.A.I.C.S.: 522320

**FLOWER KING ECO-
ENGINEERING INC.**

No 88 South Second Ring Road,
Danyang, 212300, Jiangsu, China
Tel.: (86) 4009280555
Web Site:
    https://www.flowersking.com
Year Founded: 2003
603007—(SHG)
Rev.: $27,483,890
Assets: $347,437,238
Liabilities: $308,032,307
Net Worth: $39,404,931
Earnings: ($32,009,417)
Fiscal Year-end: 12/31/22
Landscaping Services
N.A.I.C.S.: 561730
Weitao He *(Chm & Gen Mgr)*

FLOWER ONE HOLDINGS INC.
20 Richmond Street East Suite 600,
Toronto, M5C 2R9, ON, Canada
Tel.: (416) 913-9642   BC
Web Site: http://www.flowerone.com
Year Founded: 2007
FONE—(OTCIQ)
Rev.: $34,243,122
Assets: $130,201,697
Liabilities: $142,068,379
Net Worth: ($11,866,682)
Earnings: ($117,470,004)
Emp.: 90
Fiscal Year-end: 12/31/20
Investment Services
N.A.I.C.S.: 523999
Kellen O'Keefe *(Pres & CEO)*

FLOWGROUP PLC
Felaw Maltings 48 Felaw Street, Ips-
wich, IP2 8PN, United Kingdom
Tel.: (44) 20 3137 4466
Web Site: http://flowgroup.uk.com
Rev.: $123,869,437
Assets: $38,664,376
Liabilities: $57,152,763
Net Worth: ($18,488,387)
Earnings: ($55,966,678)
Emp.: 296
Fiscal Year-end: 12/31/16
Alternative Energy Products Develop-
ment
N.A.I.C.S.: 237130

**FLOWING CLOUD TECHNOL-
OGY LTD.**
Hop 8 Jingyuan Art Center
Guangqulu No 3, Chaoyang District,
Beijing, China   Ky
Web Site:
    https://www.flowingcloud.com
Year Founded: 2008
6610—(HKG)
Rev.: $172,342,019
Assets: $238,324,380
Liabilities: $37,251,052
Net Worth: $201,073,327
Earnings: $36,543,947
Emp.: 142
Fiscal Year-end: 12/31/23
Information Technology Services
N.A.I.C.S.: 541512
Lei Wang *(Chm)*

**FLOWTECH FLUIDPOWER
PLC**
Bollin House Bollin Walk, Wilmslow,
SK9 1DP, United Kingdom
Tel.: (44) 169552759
Web Site:
    https://www.flowtechfluidpower.com
Year Founded: 1983
FLO—(AIM)
Rev.: $144,869,982
Assets: $164,611,209
Liabilities: $61,936,380
Net Worth: $102,674,830
Earnings: ($7,891,946)
Emp.: 595

Fiscal Year-end: 12/31/22
Fluid Power Products Mfr
N.A.I.C.S.: 333996
Bryce Brooks *(CEO)*

Subsidiaries:

Derek Lane & Co Limited **(1)**
Unit 9 International House Battle Road,
Heathfield Industrial Estate Newton Abbot,
Devon, TQ12 6RY, United Kingdom
Tel.: (44) 162 683 1400
Web Site: https://www.dereklane.co.uk
Hydraulic Component Distr
N.A.I.C.S.: 423830

Flowtechnology Benelux B.V. **(1)**
Hamburgweg 3, 7418 ES, Deventer, Neth-
erlands
Tel.: (31) 570820000
Web Site:
    https://www.flowtechnologybenelux.nl
Hydraulic & Industrial Component Mfr
N.A.I.C.S.: 333996

Fluidpower Group Services UK
Limited **(1)**
Unit 6 A Millshaw Park Industrial Estate
Millshaw, Leeds, LS11 0LX, West Yorkshire,
United Kingdom
Tel.: (44) 3452160088
Web Site: https://fpg-services.com
Hydraulic Equipment Mfr
N.A.I.C.S.: 333995

Group HES Limited **(1)**
Dowco House Innsworth Technology Park,
Innsworth Lane, Gloucester, GL3 1DL,
United Kingdom
Tel.: (44) 145 273 0774
Web Site: https://www.grouphes.com
Hydraulic Component & System Distr
N.A.I.C.S.: 423830
Christopher Way *(Mng Dir)*

Hi-Power Limited **(1)**
Ballincolly Industrial Park, Ballincolly Dublin
Hill, Cork, T23 CP03, Ireland
Tel.: (353) 21 430 1742
Web Site: https://www.hipower.ie
Engineering Component Mfr
N.A.I.C.S.: 336390

Hydraulics & Transmissions
Limited **(1)**
Lingen Road, Ludlow, SY8 1XD, Shrop-
shire, United Kingdom
Tel.: (44) 158 487 3012
Web Site: https://www.htluk.co.uk
Engineering Component Mfr
N.A.I.C.S.: 336390

Hydroflex-Hydraulics BV **(1)**
Willem Beukelszstraat 1, 3261 LV, Oud-
Beijerland, Netherlands
Tel.: (31) 186620777
Web Site: https://www.hydroflex.nl
Hydraulic Component Distr
N.A.I.C.S.: 423830

Hydroflex-Hydraulics Belgium NV **(1)**
Brusselsesteenweg 36, 1860, Meise, Bel-
gium
Tel.: (32) 22674114
Hydraulic Component Distr
N.A.I.C.S.: 423830

Hydroflex-Hydraulics Rotterdam
BV **(1)**
Geyssendorfferweg 63, 3088 GJ, Rotter-
dam, Netherlands
Tel.: (31) 102839000
Hydraulic Component Distr
N.A.I.C.S.: 423830

Nelson Hydraulics Limited **(1)**
Unit H1/H2 Knockmore Industrial Estate
Moira Road, Co Antrim, Lisburn, BT28 2EJ,
United Kingdom
Tel.: (44) 2892662781
Web Site: https://www.nelsonhydraulics.co.uk
Hydraulic Equipment Mfr
N.A.I.C.S.: 333996

FLOYD PCL
No 31/4 Village No 2 Soi Wat Som
Kliang Kanchanaphisek Road, Bang
Mae Nang Subdistrict Bang Yai Dis-
trict, Nonthaburi, 11140, Thailand

Floyd PCL—(Continued)

Tel.: (66) 21916258
Web Site: https://www.floyd.co.th
Year Founded: 2014
FLOYD—(THA)
Rev.: $11,753,855
Assets: $16,071,639
Liabilities: $2,690,332
Net Worth: $13,381,307
Earnings: $610,404
Fiscal Year-end: 12/31/23
Mechanical & Electrical Construction Services
N.A.I.C.S.: 541330
Ayuth Jayant *(Chm)*

FLSMIDTH & CO. A/S

Vigerslev Alle 77, Copenhagen, 2500, Valby, Denmark
Tel.: (45) 36181000   DK
Web Site: https://www.flsmidth.com
Year Founded: 1882
FLS—(CSE)
Rev.: $2,902,095,670
Assets: $3,805,358,710
Liabilities: $2,093,912,950
Net Worth: $1,711,445,760
Earnings: $58,929,990
Emp.: 10,117
Fiscal Year-end: 12/31/21
Cement & Non Metallic Mineral Product Mfr
N.A.I.C.S.: 327310
Vagn Ove Sorensen *(Chm)*

Subsidiaries:

FFE Invest A/S   (1)
Vigerslev Alle 77, 2500, Valby, Denmark
Tel.: (45) 36183600
Web Site: http://www.flsmidth.com
Sales Range: $350-399.9 Million
Emp.: 160
Engineering Consulting Services
N.A.I.C.S.: 541330

FLS Global Finance A/S   (1)
Vigerslev Alle 77, 2500, Valby, Denmark   (100%)
Tel.: (45) 36181800
Web Site: http://www.flsmidth.com
Sales Range: $400-449.9 Million
Provider of Financial Services
N.A.I.C.S.: 518210

FLS Japan Ltd.   (1)
2-4-11 Sannomiya, Chuo-ku, Kobe, 6500021, Japan   (100%)
Tel.: (81) 783273811
Sales Range: $25-49.9 Million
Emp.: 81
Concrete Production Machinery Mfr
N.A.I.C.S.: 333120
Aramaki Hideki *(Pres)*

FLS Maroc S.A.   (1)
Lotissement La Colline Immeuble California Garden, Batiment A Sidi Maarouf, 20270, Casablanca, Morocco
Tel.: (212) 661770499
Cement & Non Metallic Mineral Product Mfr
N.A.I.C.S.: 327310

FLS Plast A/S   (1)
Vigerslev Alle 77, 2500, Valby, Denmark
Tel.: (45) 36181000
Web Site: http://www.flsmidth.com
Sales Range: $350-399.9 Million
Emp.: 160
Engineering Consulting Services
N.A.I.C.S.: 541330

FLS Real Estate A/S   (1)
Vigerslev Alle 77, 2500, Valby, Denmark   (100%)
Tel.: (45) 36181800
Web Site: http://www.flsmith.com
Sales Range: $1-4.9 Billion
Emp.: 1,500
Real Estate Services
N.A.I.C.S.: 531210

FLS US Holdings, Inc.   (1)
2040 Ave C, Bethlehem, PA 18017-2118
Tel.: (610) 264-6011

Cement Making Machinery Mfr
N.A.I.C.S.: 333248

Subsidiary (Domestic):

FLSmidth Inc.   (2)
2040 Ave C, Bethlehem, PA 18017-2118   (100%)
Tel.: (610) 264-6011
Web Site: http://www.flsmidth.com
Rev.: $208,828,000
Emp.: 1,160
Holding Company; Bulk Material Handling Equipment Mfr & Services
N.A.I.C.S.: 551112
Brenda Kaplan *(Mgr-Adv)*

Subsidiary (Domestic):

Fuller Company   (3)
2040 Ave C, Bethlehem, PA 18017-2188
Tel.: (610) 264-6011
Cleaning Products Mfr & Whslr
N.A.I.C.S.: 325612

FLSmidth (Beijing) Ltd.   (1)
03 05 10th Floor Guanjie Tower No 9 Sun Palace Middle Road, Chaoyang District, Beijing, 100028, China
Tel.: (86) 1084689100
Cement & Non Metallic Mineral Product Mfr
N.A.I.C.S.: 327310

FLSmidth (Thailand) Co., Ltd.   (1)
141 Major Tower 7th Floor Unit 703-704 Soi Sukhumvit 63 Ekamai, Sukhumvit Road Klongton Nuea Wattana, Bangkok, 10110, Thailand
Tel.: (66) 23927747
Cement & Non Metallic Mineral Product Mfr
N.A.I.C.S.: 327310

FLSmidth A/S   (1)
Vigerslev Alle 77, Copenhagen, 2500, Valby, Denmark   (100%)
Tel.: (45) 36181000
Web Site: https://www.flsmidth.com
Emp.: 1,500
Engineeering Services
N.A.I.C.S.: 541330

Subsidiary (Non-US):

FLSmidth (Jersey) Limited   (2)
1-13 New Street, PO Box 719, Saint Helier, Je40QA, Jersey
Tel.: (44) 1534 729074
Web Site: http://www.flsjersey.com
Human Resource Consulting Services
N.A.I.C.S.: 541612
Bjarne Moltke Hansen *(Chm)*

FLSmidth (Private) Ltd.   (2)
PAKLAND Business Center Office no 14 1st Floor Markaz I-8, Islamabad, 44000, Pakistan
Tel.: (92) 514861792
Sales Range: $25-49.9 Million
Emp.: 5
Construction Machinery Mfr
N.A.I.C.S.: 333120
Abdul Razzaq *(Gen Mgr)*

FLSmidth (UK) Limited   (2)
Wemco House 9 Mitchell Court Castle Mound Way, Central Park, Rugby, CV23 0UY, Warwickshire, United Kingdom
Tel.: (44) 1788555777
Sales Range: $25-49.9 Million
Emp.: 4
Construction Machinery Mfr
N.A.I.C.S.: 333120
Marco Fossataro *(Mng Dir)*

FLSmidth Krebs GmbH   (2)
Neuberg Str 1, 7100, Neusiedl am See, Austria
Tel.: (43) 216733450
Sales Range: $25-49.9 Million
Emp.: 35
Construction Machinery Mfr
N.A.I.C.S.: 333120
Roman van Ommen *(Mng Dir)*

FLSmidth MAAG Gear AG   (2)
Lagerhausstrasse 11, PO Box 8401, 8401, Winterthur, Switzerland
Tel.: (41) 522603500
Sales Range: $25-49.9 Million
Emp.: 10
Gear Unit Mfr

N.A.I.C.S.: 333612
Yasuhiro Haba *(Gen Mgr)*

Subsidiary (Non-US):

FLSmidth MAAG Gear S.p.A   (3)
Via Rubattino 94/A, 20134, Milan, Italy
Tel.: (39) 0226922058
Sales Range: $25-49.9 Million
Emp.: 39
Construction Machinery Mfr
N.A.I.C.S.: 333120
Marco Dergamaschi *(CEO)*

FLSmidth MAAG Gear Sp. z o.o.   (3)
ul Stoczniowa 2, 82-300, Elblag, Poland
Tel.: (48) 558811111
Sales Range: $50-74.9 Million
Construction Machinery Mfr
N.A.I.C.S.: 333120
Wlodzimierz Zajac *(Pres)*

Subsidiary (Non-US):

FLSmidth Milano S.R.L.   (2)
Via R Rubattino 94/A, 20134, Milan, Italy
Tel.: (39) 0295 6888
Web Site: https://www.flsmidth.com
Sales Range: $25-49.9 Million
Emp.: 3
Construction Machinery Mfr
N.A.I.C.S.: 333120

FLSmidth Mongolia   (2)
402 4th Floor Blue Sky Tower Peace Avenue-17, CPO Box-2759, 1st micro district Sukhbaatar district, Ulaanbaatar, 14240, Mongolia
Tel.: (976) 70108082
Emp.: 1
Construction Machinery Mfr
N.A.I.C.S.: 333120

Subsidiary (Domestic):

FLSmidth Rusland Holding A/S   (2)
Vigerslev Alle 77, 2500, Valby, Denmark
Tel.: (45) 36181000
Emp.: 1,500
Construction Machinery Mfr
N.A.I.C.S.: 333120
Thomas Schulz *(CEO)*

Subsidiary (Non-US):

FLSmidth Rus OOO   (3)
4th floor bld 23 Novoslobodskaya street, Meyerhold Business Center, 127055, Moscow, Russia
Tel.: (7) 4956412778
Emp.: 55
Cement Industry Machinery Distr
N.A.I.C.S.: 423830

Subsidiary (Non-US):

FLSmidth S.A.   (2)
Edificio F L Smidth Carretera de La Coruna Km 17 8, Las Rozas, 28231, Madrid, Spain
Tel.: (34) 916349000
Sales Range: $25-49.9 Million
Emp.: 25
Construction Machinery Mfr
N.A.I.C.S.: 333120
Ignacio Puertas *(Gen Mgr)*

FLSmidth SARL   (2)
22 rue Pierre Mendes France, 77200, Torcy, France   (100%)
Tel.: (33) 160171263
Web Site: http://www.flsmidth.com
Sales Range: $25-49.9 Million
Emp.: 11
Supplier of Equipment, Systems & Processes for Mineral & Processing Industry
N.A.I.C.S.: 423830

FLSmidth Sp. z.o.o.   (2)
ul Stoczniowa 2, 82300, Elblag, Poland
Tel.: (48) 55 237 8994
Construction Machinery Mfr
N.A.I.C.S.: 333120

FLSmidth Ventomatic SpA   (2)
Via G Marconi 20, 24030, Valbrembo, Italy
Tel.: (39) 035483111
Web Site: https://www.flsmidth.com
Emp.: 160
Industrial Machinery Mfr & Whslr
N.A.I.C.S.: 333248
Ferrandico Francesco *(CEO & Mng Dir)*

PT FLSmidth Indonesia   (2)
Wisma GKBI 21st Floor Suite 2101 Jalan Jendral Sudirman Kav 28, Jakarta, 10210, Indonesia
Tel.: (62) 21 251 2738
Web Site: http://www.flsmidth.com
Emp.: 50
Cement Industry Machinery Distr
N.A.I.C.S.: 423830

FLSmidth A/S (Jordan) Ltd.   (1)
Jabal Amman Third Circle Middle East Insurance Building First Floor, Amman, Jordan
Tel.: (962) 30932153
Cement & Non Metallic Mineral Product Mfr
N.A.I.C.S.: 327310

FLSmidth Caucasus Limited Liability Company   (1)
Khanjyan 19, Yerevan, 0010, Armenia
Tel.: (374) 10510881
Cement & Non Metallic Mineral Product Mfr
N.A.I.C.S.: 327310

FLSmidth Co., Ltd.   (1)
3rd Floor Quy Hanh Building 165 Ba Trieu Str, Le Dai Hanh Ward Hai Ba Trung District, Hanoi, Vietnam
Tel.: (84) 2439749456
Cement & Non Metallic Mineral Product Mfr
N.A.I.C.S.: 327310

FLSmidth GmbH   (1)
Neubergstrasse 1, 7100, Neusiedl am See, Austria
Tel.: (43) 21673345
Web Site: http://www.flsmidth.com
Sales Range: $50-74.9 Million
Emp.: 6
Industrial Machinery Distr
N.A.I.C.S.: 423830

FLSmidth Hamburg GmbH   (1)
Haderslebener Strasse 7, 25421, Pinneberg, Germany
Tel.: (49) 41017880
Web Site: http://www.flsmidth.com
Sales Range: $50-74.9 Million
Emp.: 80
Industrial Machinery Whslr
N.A.I.C.S.: 423830

FLSmidth Industrial Solutions (Canada) Inc.   (1)
Westmount Corporate Campus Building 3 4838 Richard Road SW Suite 400, Calgary, T3E 6L1, AB, Canada
Tel.: (403) 910-1000
Web Site: https://umatac.ca
Mining Engineering & Equipment Services
N.A.I.C.S.: 541330

FLSmidth Industrial Solutions Makine Sanayi Ve Ticaret A.S.   (1)
Mustafa Kemal Mahallesi Dumlupinar Bulvari No 266, Tepe Prime B-Blok No 17 Cankaya, Ankara, Turkiye
Tel.: (90) 3122878546
Industrial Equipment Mfr & Distr
N.A.I.C.S.: 334513

FLSmidth Krebs Chile Limitada   (1)
Fresia 2132, Comuna De Conchale, Santiago, Chile
Tel.: (56) 2463 8300
Web Site: http://www.flsmidth.com
Pumps, Valves & Customized Manifold Systems Mfr
N.A.I.C.S.: 333914

FLSmidth Ltda.   (1)
Rua Jose Dolles 264 - Jardim Clarice I, Votorantim, 18110-650, Sao Paulo, Brazil
Tel.: (55) 1535009000
Cement & Non Metallic Mineral Product Mfr
N.A.I.C.S.: 327310

FLSmidth Minerals A/S   (1)
Vigerslev Alle 77, 2500, Valby, Denmark
Tel.: (45) 36183600
Web Site: http://www.flsmidthminerals.com
Sales Range: $25-49.9 Million
Emp.: 50
Mineral Processing Equipment Mfr
N.A.I.C.S.: 423810

Subsidiary (Domestic):

FLSmidth Airtech   (2)

Vigerslevalle 77, 2500, Valby, Denmark **(100%)**
Tel.: (45) 36181100
Web Site: http://www.flsmdth.com
Emp.: 1,200
Flue Gas Cleaning Systems Svcs
N.A.I.C.S.: 213112

Subsidiary (Domestic):

Pedershaab A/S **(3)**
Saltumvej 25, 9700, Bronderslev, Denmark **(100%)**
Tel.: (45) 96454000
Web Site: http://www.pedershaab.com
Sales Range: $25-49.9 Million
Emp.: 100
Concrete Production Machinery Mfr
N.A.I.C.S.: 333120
Carsten S. Nielsen *(CFO & Mng Dir)*

Subsidiary (Non-US):

PUK Ltd. **(4)**
Unit 5 Gamma, Orchard Industrial Estate Toddington Cheltenham, Stratford-upon-Avon, GL54 5EB, Gloucestershire, United Kingdom **(100%)**
Tel.: (44) 178 972 1655
Web Site: https://www.pukservices.co.uk
Sales Range: $25-49.9 Million
Emp.: 4
Precast Concrete Mfr
N.A.I.C.S.: 238120

Subsidiary (Non-US):

FLSmidth Dorr-Oliver Eimco GmbH **(2)**
Am Klingenweg 4a, 65396, Walluf, Germany
Tel.: (49) 6123975300
Sales Range: $25-49.9 Million
Emp.: 50
Pulp & Paper Equipment
N.A.I.C.S.: 423830

FLSmidth Minerals Ltd. **(2)**
174 West St South, Orillia, L3V 6L4, ON, Canada **(100%)**
Tel.: (705) 325-6181
Web Site: http://www.flsmidth.com
Sales Range: $25-49.9 Million
Mineral Processing Equipment Mfr
N.A.I.C.S.: 423810

FLSmidth S.A. **(2)**
Av El Bosque Norte 500 Piso 9, Las Condes, Santiago, 7550092, Chile **(100%)**
Tel.: (56) 22 290 0000
Web Site: https://www.flsmidth.com
Cement & Minerals Equipment Whslr
N.A.I.C.S.: 423830

FLSmidth Minerals Holding ApS **(1)**
Vigerslev Alle 77, 2500, Valby, Denmark
Tel.: (45) 36181100
Web Site: http://www.flsmidth.com
Emp.: 1,500
Investment Management Service
N.A.I.C.S.: 523999

Subsidiary (Non-US):

FLSmidth S.A. **(2)**
Av El Bosque Norte 500 Piso 9, Las Condes, Santiago, Chile
Tel.: (56) 22 290 0000
Web Site: https://www.flsmidth.com
Emp.: 50
Cement Industry Machinery Distr
N.A.I.C.S.: 423830

FLSmidth S.A. de C.V. **(2)**
San Alberto 406 Residencial Santa Barbara, San Pedro, 66260, Garza Garcia, Nuevo Leon, Mexico
Tel.: (52) 8111783322
Web Site: https://www.flsmidth.com
Industrial Equipment Distr
N.A.I.C.S.: 423830

FLSmidth Philippines, Inc. **(1)**
Unit 2001 Taipan Place F Ortigas Jr Road Ortigas Center, Pasig, 1605, Manila, Philippines
Tel.: (63) 26879251
Cement & Non Metallic Mineral Product Mfr
N.A.I.C.S.: 327310

FLSmidth Private Limited **(1)**

FLSmidth House 34 Egatoor Kelambakkam, Chennai, 603103, Tamil Nadu, India
Tel.: (91) 4447481000
Web Site: http://www.flsmidth.com
Industrial Machinery Equipment Mfr
N.A.I.C.S.: 423830

Subsidiary (Domestic):

Transweigh India Ltd. **(2)**
124 ABCD Govt Indl Estate Charkop Kandivli W, Mumbai, 400 067, India
Tel.: (91) 22 6772 6000
Industrial Weighing Equipment Mfr
N.A.I.C.S.: 423830

FLSmidth Pty. Ltd. **(1)**
Lake View House, PO Box 5221, Constantia Park 14 Ave, Roodepoort, 1715, Johanssberg, South Africa **(100%)**
Tel.: (27) 116792593
Sales Range: Less than $1 Million
Emp.: 3
Supplier of Equipment; Systems & Processes for Mineral & Processing Industries
N.A.I.C.S.: 423830

Subsidiary (Domestic):

FLSmidth Buffalo (Pty.) Ltd. **(2)**
40 Nobel Rd, Witbank, 1034, South Africa
Tel.: (27) 136998900
Web Site: http://www.flsmidth.com
Mining Equipment Mfr
N.A.I.C.S.: 333131

FLSmidth Krebs Africa (Pty.) Ltd. **(2)**
Chariot Street Stormill Extension 10, Roodepoort, Johannesburg, 1724, South Africa
Tel.: (27) 11 474 8875
Industrial Pump & Gate Valve Mfr
N.A.I.C.S.: 333914
Brad Moralee *(Gen Mgr)*

FLSmidth Roymec (Pty.) Ltd. **(2)**
Constantia Blvd Constantia Kloof 1719, PO Box 5073, Weltevreden Park, 1715, Roodepoort, Gauteng, South Africa
Tel.: (27) 102104000
Material Handling Equipment Distr
N.A.I.C.S.: 423830

Subsidiary (Non-US):

FLSmidth (Pty.) Ltd. **(3)**
PO Box 401805, Gaborone, Botswana
Tel.: (267) 102104000
Mineral Mining Services
N.A.I.C.S.: 212390

Subsidiary (Non-US):

FLSmidth Mozambique Limitada **(4)**
Bairro Bagamoio Rua Beliluana, Parcela 128 Zona Industrial EN7 Parque Empresarial da Tri-M Moatize, Tete, Mozambique
Tel.: (258) 731212900
Cement & Non Metallic Mineral Product Mfr
N.A.I.C.S.: 327310

FLSmidth Pty. Ltd. **(1)**
11 Kullara, Beresfield, 2322, NSW, Australia
Web Site: https://www.flsmidth.com
Industrial Machinery Mfr
N.A.I.C.S.: 423830

Subsidiary (Domestic):

FLSmidth ABON Pty. Ltd. **(2)**
6 Rosella Street McDougalls Hill, Singleton, 2330, NSW, Australia
Tel.: (61) 265712542
Web Site: http://www.flsmidth.com
Emp.: 10
Cement Industry Machinery Distr
N.A.I.C.S.: 423830

FLSmidth Dorr-Oliver Eimco Pty Limited **(2)**
5 Comserv Close, Gosford, 2250, NSW, Australia
Tel.: (61) 2 43204700
Sales Range: $25-49.9 Million
Emp.: 60
Industrial Machinery Equipment Mfr
N.A.I.C.S.: 423830

FLSmidth Krebs Australia Pty. Ltd. **(2)**

---

51 Days Road, Coomera, 4209, QLD, Australia
Tel.: (61) 7 5519 5700
Web Site: http://www.flsmidth.com
Sales Range: $25-49.9 Million
Emp.: 50
Cement Industrial Machinery Distr
N.A.I.C.S.: 423830

Ludowici Limited **(2)**
67 Randle Road, PO Box 116, Pinkenba, 4008, QLD, Australia
Tel.: (61) 731212900
Web Site: http://www.flsmidth.com
Sales Range: $200-249.9 Million
Emp.: 500
Designs, Manufactures & Markets Mineral Processing Equipment for Mining Industry
N.A.I.C.S.: 333131

Subsidiary (Non-US):

Ludowici (Beijing) Co., Ltd **(3)**
7th Fl Tower A Penguin Intl Financial Ctr 123 Xin yuan S Rd, Xicheng District, Beijing, 100027, China
Tel.: (86) 106 852 1036
Web Site: http://www.flsmidth.com
Sales Range: $25-49.9 Million
Emp.: 10
Industrial Equipment Mfr
N.A.I.C.S.: 326220

Subsidiary (Domestic):

Ludowici Australia Pty Ltd. **(3)**
67 Randle Rd, Pinkenba, 4008, QLD, Australia **(100%)**
Tel.: (61) 732924444
Sales Range: $100-124.9 Million
Emp.: 400
Industrial Machinery Mfr
N.A.I.C.S.: 333248
David Ricketts *(Gen Mgr-Global Bus Dev)*

Subsidiary (Domestic):

Ludowici Packaging Australia Pty Limited **(4)**
67 Randle Road, Pinkenba, Brisbane, 4008, QLD, Australia
Tel.: (61) 731212900
Web Site: http://www.flsmidth.com
Sales Range: $100-124.9 Million
Emp.: 500
Packaging Materials Mfr
N.A.I.C.S.: 322130

Rojan Advanced Ceramics Pty Ltd **(4)**
55 Alacrity Pl, PO Box 7126, Henderson, 6166, WA, Australia
Tel.: (61) 894371155
Web Site: http://www.rojan.com.au
Sales Range: $25-49.9 Million
Emp.: 30
Industrial Ceramic Products Mfr & Distr
N.A.I.C.S.: 327120

Subsidiary (Non-US):

Ludowici India Private Limited **(3)**
Ganesh Towers New 104 Old 90 Dr Radhakrishnan Salai, Mylapore, Chennai, 600004, Tamil Nadu, India
Tel.: (91) 44 4221 5900
Sales Range: $25-49.9 Million
Emp.: 20
Mineral Processing Equipments Mfr & Distr
N.A.I.C.S.: 333998

Subsidiary (Domestic):

Ludowici Mining Process India PVT Limited **(4)**
Ganesh Towers New 104 Old 90 Dr Radhakrishnan Salai, Mylapore, Chennai, 600004, Tamil Nadu, India
Tel.: (91) 44 44000510
Mineral Processing Equipments Mfr & Distr
N.A.I.C.S.: 333998

Subsidiary (US):

Ludowici LLC **(3)**
Rte 10 S Phico, Chapmanville, WV 25508
Tel.: (304) 855-7880
Sales Range: $25-49.9 Million
Emp.: 100
Mining Equipment Mfr

N.A.I.C.S.: 333998
Ed Vickers *(Gen Mgr)*

Ludowici Screens LLC **(3)**
785 Lithia Rd, Wytheville, VA 24382-5129
Tel.: (276) 228-6781
Mining Equipment Mfr
N.A.I.C.S.: 333998

Subsidiary (Domestic):

Ludowici Technologies Pty Ltd **(3)**
67 Randle Road, Pinkenba, Brisbane, 4008, QLD, Australia
Tel.: (61) 731212900
Industrial Equipment Mfr
N.A.I.C.S.: 326220

FLSmidth Qingdao Ltd. **(1)**
No 8 Taisu Road, Beiguan Industrial Park, Jiaozhou, 266309, Shandong, China
Tel.: (86) 53285266700
Cement & Non Metallic Mineral Product Mfr
N.A.I.C.S.: 327310

FLSmidth S.A.C. **(1)**
Av Juan de Arona No 151 Oficina 801 I - Torre - I, San Isidro, Peru
Tel.: (51) 1 708 0500
Web Site: https://www.flsmidth.com
Cement Industry Machinery Distr
N.A.I.C.S.: 423830

FLSmidth SAS **(1)**
Calle 77B 59-61 Office 906, Barranquilla, Colombia
Tel.: (57) 53015341
Cement & Non Metallic Mineral Product Mfr
N.A.I.C.S.: 327310

FLSmidth Shanghai Ltd. **(1)**
Building 935-3 Xinsiping Road, Situan Town Fengxian District, Shanghai, 201413, China
Tel.: (86) 2157542777
Web Site: http://www.flsmidth.com
Mineral Industry Machinery Distr
N.A.I.C.S.: 423810

FLSmidth Spol. s.r.o. **(1)**
Ripska 4A, 62700, Brno, Czech Republic
Tel.: (420) 548425111
Cement & Non Metallic Mineral Product Mfr
N.A.I.C.S.: 423830

FLSmidth Wiesbaden GmbH **(1)**
Am Klingenweg 4a, 65396, Walluf, Germany
Tel.: (49) 6123975300
Sales Range: $25-49.9 Million
Emp.: 4
Industrial Machinery Distr
N.A.I.C.S.: 423830

FLSmidth Wuppertal GmbH **(1)**
In Der Fleute 53, Postfach 24 02 28, Wuppertal, 42389, Germany
Tel.: (49) 202262840
Web Site: http://www.flsmidth.com
Sales Range: $50-74.9 Million
Emp.: 60
Construction Material Machinery Mfr
N.A.I.C.S.: 423390

Subsidiary (Domestic):

Pfaff Maschinenbau GmbH **(2)**
Industriegebiet Augustenhohe 10, Harzgerode, 6493, Germany
Tel.: (49) 3948472030
Machine Tools Mfr
N.A.I.C.S.: 333517

Morse Rubber, LLC **(1)**
3588 Main St, Keokuk, IA 52632-2632
Web Site: http://www.morserubber.com
Plastics Product Mfr
N.A.I.C.S.: 326199
Pat Boyd *(Pres)*

NL Supervision Company Tunisia SARL **(1)**
B 2-3 Immeuble Lac De Constance Rue Du Lac De Constance 1053, Les Berges Du Lac, 1053, Tunis, Tunisia
Tel.: (216) 71169400
Cement & Non Metallic Mineral Product Mfr
N.A.I.C.S.: 327310

NLSupervision Company Angola, Ltda. **(1)**
R 10 Maio 191 20 Andar, Sumbe, Kwanza

FLSmidth & Co. A/S—(Continued)

Sul, Angola
Tel.: (244) 942694221
Cement & Non Metallic Mineral Product Mfr
N.A.I.C.S.: 327310
Antonio Mario (Mgr-HR)

NI Supervision Company A/S (1)
B 2-3 Lake Constance Building Rue du lac
de Constance, Les Berges Du Lac, 1053,
Tunis, Tunisia
Tel.: (216) 71169400
Cement Distr
N.A.I.C.S.: 423830

**Oresund Unloader Design Bureau
AB** (1)
Karjeksgatan 1, 211 45, Malmo, Sweden
Tel.: (46) 40 690 33 00
Industrial Machinery Mfr
N.A.I.C.S.: 333248

Pfister Holding GmbH (1)
Statzlinger Str 70, 86068, Augsburg, Germany
Tel.: (49) 82179490.
Web Site: http://www.pfister.de
Investment Management Service
N.A.I.C.S.: 523999

Subsidiary (Domestic):

FLSmidth Pfister GmbH (2)
Am mittleren moos 53, 86167, Augsburg,
Germany
Tel.: (49) 82179490
Web Site: https://pfister.flsmidth.com
Industrial Machinery Mfr
N.A.I.C.S.: 333248

SK Stok (1)
Erik Stoks Alle 4, 5550, Langeskov,
Denmark (100%)
Tel.: (45) 7 220 0700
Web Site: https://www.stok.dk
Sales Range: $25-49.9 Million
Emp.: 50
Develops, Manufactures & Distributes Packaging Materials for Industrial & Agricultural
Use
N.A.I.C.S.: 333993
Martin Fredefen (Mng Dir)

SLS Corporation (1)
511 N Washington Ave, Marshall, TX 75670
Tel.: (408) 852-0067
Web Site: http://www.slscorp.com
Software & Hardware Product Design Services
N.A.I.C.S.: 541512

Subsidiary (Domestic):

FLSmidth USA Inc. (2)
2040 Ave C, Bethlehem, PA 18017
Tel.: (610) 264-6011
Web Site: http://www.flsmidth.com
Industrial Machinery Maintenance Services
N.A.I.C.S.: 811310

Subsidiary (Domestic):

Excel Foundry & Machine Inc. (3)
14463 Wagonseller Rd, Pekin, IL 61555-
0400
Tel.: (309) 347-6155
Web Site: http://www.excelfoundry.com
Sales Range: $75-99.9 Million
Emp.: 300
Industrial Machinery Mfr
N.A.I.C.S.: 333248
Doug Parsons (Gen Mgr)

FLSmidth Boise, Inc. (3)
2471 S Titanium Pl, Meridian, ID 83642
Tel.: (208) 342-2653
Web Site: http://www.flsmidth.com
Industrial Machinery Mfr
N.A.I.C.S.: 333248

FLSmidth Minerals Inc. (3)
2040 Avenue C, Bethlehem, PA 18017
Tel.: (610) 264-6900
Web Site: http://www.flsmidthminerals.com
Sales Range: $25-49.9 Million
Emp.: 100
Mineral Processing Equipment Mfr
N.A.I.C.S.: 423810

Subsidiary (Domestic):

**FLSmidth Conveyor Engineering,
Inc.** (4)

2471 S Titianium Pl, Meridian, ID 83642
Tel.: (208) 342-2653
Web Site:
http://www.conveyorengineering.com
Sales Range: $10-24.9 Million
Emp.: 30
Bulk Material Handling Systems Mfr
N.A.I.C.S.: 333248

FLSmidth Krebs Inc. (4)
5505 W Gillette Rd, Tucson, AZ 85743
Tel.: (520) 744-8200
Web Site: http://www.krebs.com
Sales Range: $75-99.9 Million
Hydrocyclones & Solid/Liquid Separation
Equipment & Slurry Pump Developer & Mfr
N.A.I.C.S.: 333248

Subsidiary (Non-US):

FLSmidth Krebs (Beijing) Ltd. (5)
7F Tower A No 1-3 Xinyung South Road,
Chaoyang District, 100027, Beijing, China
Tel.: (86) 10 8468 9100
Sales Range: $25-49.9 Million
Emp.: 10
Hydroclone Mfr
N.A.I.C.S.: 333248

Subsidiary (Domestic):

FLSmidth Salt Lake City, Inc. (4)
7158 S FLSmidth Dr, Midvale, UT 84047-
5559
Tel.: (801) 871-7000
Web Site: https://www.flsmidth.com
Sales Range: $50-74.9 Million
Liquid/Solid Separation Equipment & Process Technology Supplier
N.A.I.C.S.: 333310

Subsidiary (Domestic):

FLSmidth Spokane, Inc. (3)
605 E Holland Ave, Spokane, WA 99218
Tel.: (509) 467-0770
Web Site: http://www.flsmidth.com
Sales Range: $25-49.9 Million
Emp.: 130
Custom Mining Machinery Mfr
N.A.I.C.S.: 333131

Fuller International Inc. (3)
1718 Potrero Ave Ste A, El Monte, CA
91733-3041
Tel.: (626) 279-9287
Construction Engineering Services
N.A.I.C.S.: 237990

Phillips Kiln Services Ltd. (3)
2607 Dakota Ave, South Sioux City, NE
68776
Tel.: (402) 494-6837
Web Site: http://www.kiln.com
Sales Range: $50-74.9 Million
Emp.: 190
Industrial Maintenance Repair Service
N.A.I.C.S.: 811210

Saudi FLSmidth Co. (1)
Office No 401 fourth floor Al Zarah Tower
building, Al Alyaa Neighborhood, Al Khobar,
Saudi Arabia
Tel.: (966) 545590000
Cement & Non Metallic Mineral Product Mfr
N.A.I.C.S.: 327310

Subsidiary (Non-US):

FLSmidth Pfister Ltda. (2)
Rua Vigario J J Rodrigues 905 -cj 51,
30201-490, Jundiai, Sao Paulo, Brazil
Tel.: (55) 11 45266744
Web Site: http://www.flsmidth.com
Sales Range: $25-49.9 Million
Emp.: 4
Industrial Equipment Distr
N.A.I.C.S.: 423830

Subsidiary (US):

FLSmidth Pfister, Inc. (2)
2158 Ave C Ste 201, Bethlehem, PA 18017-
2148
Tel.: (610) 264-5110
Web Site: http://www.flsmidth.com
Industrial Machinery Mfr
N.A.I.C.S.: 333248

Smith & Co. (1)
Vigerslev Alle 77, 2500, Valby, Denmark

Tel.: (45) 36 18 10 00
Web Site: http://www.flsmidth.com
Sales Range: $400-449.9 Million
Emp.: 1,500
Construction Machinery Mfr
N.A.I.C.S.: 333120

Union Cement Corporation (1)
7th Fl Two World Sq McKinley Hill, Taguig,
1634, Bonifacio, Philippines (100%)
Tel.: (63) 24593333
Sales Range: $600-649.9 Million
Emp.: 1,300
Hydraulic Cement Mfr
N.A.I.C.S.: 327332

**Yantai Ludowıci Mineral Processing
Equipment Limited** (1)
Yantai Economic Development Zone 298
Huanghe Road, Yantai, Shandong, China
Tel.: (86) 535 216 5280
Sales Range: $25-49.9 Million
Emp.: 50
Mining Equipment Distr
N.A.I.C.S.: 423830

FLUGGER GROUP A/S
Islevdalvej 151, 2610, Rodovre, Denmark
Tel.: (45) 70151505
Web Site: https://www.flugger.com
Year Founded: 1783
FLUG.B—(OMX)
Rev.: $383,218,259
Assets: $367,364,936
Liabilities: $217,572,164
Net Worth: $149,792,772
Earnings: $1,231,422
Emp.: 1,873
Fiscal Year-end: 04/30/22
Surface Treatment Paint & Other
Product Mfr
N.A.I.C.S.: 325510
Carl F. S. Trock (Chm)

Subsidiaries:

Flugger Denmark A/S (1)
Islevdalvej 151, 2610, Rodovre, Denmark
Tel.: (45) 70150515
Web Site: https://www.flugger.dk
Paint Product Mfr & Distr
N.A.I.C.S.: 325510

Flugger Iceland ehf. (1)
Storhofoa 44, 110, Reykjavik, Iceland
Tel.: (354) 5674400
Web Site: https://www.flugger.is
Paint Product Mfr & Distr
N.A.I.C.S.: 325510

Flugger Norway AS (1)
Waldemar Thranesgt 84 B, 0175, Oslo,
Norway
Tel.: (47) 23302190
Web Site: https://www.flugger.no
Paint Product Mfr & Distr
N.A.I.C.S.: 325510

Flugger Poland sp. z o.o. (1)
Ul Rakietowa 20A, 80-298, Gdansk, Poland
Tel.: (48) 583402800
Web Site: https://shop.flugger.pl
Paint Product Mfr & Distr
N.A.I.C.S.: 325510

Flugger Sweden AB (1)
Hallaslattsvagen 10, SE-517 33, Bollebygd,
Sweden
Tel.: (46) 337002300
Paint Product Mfr & Distr
N.A.I.C.S.: 325510

PP Professional Paint A/S (1)
Islevdalvej 185, 2610, Rodovre, Denmark
Tel.: (45) 44541689
Web Site: http://www.pp-
professionalpaint.dk
Wall Paint Mfr
N.A.I.C.S.: 325510

Stiwex - Flugger Sweden AB (1)
Junegatan 3-5, SE-564 22, Bankeryd, Sweden
Tel.: (46) 337002600
Paint Product Mfr & Distr
N.A.I.C.S.: 325510

Stiwex SRL (1)
Junegatan 3-5, Box 63, 564 22, Bankeryd,
Sweden
Tel.: (46) 337002600
Wall Paint Mfr
N.A.I.C.S.: 325510

Unicell Nordic A/S (1)
Islevdalvej 151, 2610, Rodovre, Denmark
Tel.: (45) 70158800
Wall Paint Mfr
N.A.I.C.S.: 325510

FLUGHAFEN WIEN AKTIENG-ESELLSCHAFT
Wien-Flughafen, Postfach 1, A-1300,
Vienna, Austria
Tel.: (43) 170070 **AT**
Web Site:
https://www.viennaairport.com
Year Founded: 1938
FLU—(VIE)
Rev.: $975,763,246
Assets: $2,576,394,822
Liabilities: $1,029,970,406
Net Worth: $1,546,424,417
Earnings: $196,760,186
Emp.: 5,767
Fiscal Year-end: 12/31/19
Airport Operator
N.A.I.C.S.: 488119
Rita Heiss (Member-Mgmt Bd-Fin &
Acctg)

Subsidiaries:

**City Air Terminal Betriebsgesellschaft
m.b.H.** (1)
PO Box 1, 1300, Vienna, Austria (50.1%)
Tel.: (43) 125250
Web Site: https://www.cityairporttrain.com
Airport Operations
N.A.I.C.S.: 488119
Michael Forstner (Mng Dir)

Flughafen Parken GmbH (1)
Terminalstr Mitte 18, Flughafen, 85356, Munich, Germany
Tel.: (49) 8997592999
Web Site: https://park.aero
Airport Parking Services
N.A.I.C.S.: 488119

Flughafen Wien Immobilienverw-ertungsgesellschaft m.b.H (1)
Flughafen, 1300, Vienna, Austria (100%)
Tel.: (43) 170070
Web Site: https://www.viennaairport.com
Real Estate Property Lessors
N.A.I.C.S.: 531190

**GetService-Flughafen-Sicherheits-
und Servicedienst GmbH** (1)
PO Box 177, A-1300, Vienna, Austria
Tel.: (43) 1700726834
Web Site: https://www.get-service.at
Airport Cleaning Services
N.A.I.C.S.: 488119

**Letisko Kosice - Airport Kosice,
A.S.** (1)
Letisko Kosice, 556832123, Kosice,
Slovakia (66%)
Tel.: (421) 556832123
Web Site: http://www.airportkosice.sk
Sales Range: $50-74.9 Million
Emp.: 172
Airport Operations
N.A.I.C.S.: 488119

Malta International Airport Plc (1)
Malta International Airport, Luqa, 4000,
LQA, Malta (48.4%)
Tel.: (356) 2 124 9600
Web Site: http://www.maltairport.com
Rev.: $58,259,147
Assets: $298,037,392
Liabilities: $136,196,408
Net Worth: $161,840,984
Earnings: $8,565,689
Emp.: 310
Fiscal Year-end: 12/31/2021
Airport Operations
N.A.I.C.S.: 488119
Alan Borg (CEO)

Mazur Parkplatz GmbH (1)

Hainburger Bundesstrasse 143, 2320,
Schwechat, Austria
Tel.: (43) 170070
Web Site: https://www.mazur-parken.at
Car Parking Services
N.A.I.C.S.: 812930
Susanne Schlagenhaufen *(Mng Dir)*

**Sky Parks Business Center
Limited** **(1)**
Malta International Airport, Luqa, LQA 4000,
Malta
Tel.: (356) 21257722
Web Site:
https://www.skyparksbusiness.com
Property Management Services
N.A.I.C.S.: 531311

**Vienna Aircraft Handling Gesellschaft
m.b.H.** **(1)**
Niki Lauda Allee Object 140, Flughafen,
1300, Vienna, Austria **(100%)**
Tel.: (43) 1700722345
Web Site: https://www.viennaairport-fbo.com
Sales Range: $25-49.9 Million
Emp.: 70
Law firm
N.A.I.C.S.: 541199
Alexandra Schellhorn *(Mng Dir-)*

**Vienna Airport Health Center
GmbH** **(1)**
Object 682 Office Park 3 Building 2 4th
Floor Airport, PO Box 1, 1300, Vienna, Aus-
tria
Tel.: (43) 1700724900
Web Site:
https://www.healthcenterairport.com
Medical Care Services
N.A.I.C.S.: 621498
Christian Steyrer *(Mng Dir)*

Vienna Airport Technik GmbH **(1)**
Object 420 Airport, Postfach 1, A-1300, Vi-
enna, Austria
Tel.: (43) 1700725400
Web Site: https://www.viennaairport-
technik.com
Electrical Engineering Maintenance Ser-
vices
N.A.I.C.S.: 541330
Thomas Briza *(Mng Dir)*

**Vienna International Airport Security
Services Ges.m.b.H.** **(1)**
Obj 115, Postfach 177, A-1300, Vienna,
Austria **(100%)**
Tel.: (43) 1700726815
Web Site: https://www.vias.at
Sales Range: $200-249.9 Million
Emp.: 1,200
Airport Operations
N.A.I.C.S.: 488119
Franz Spitzer *(Mng Dir & Member-Mgmt
Bd)*

FLUGHAFEN ZURICH AG

PO Box 8058, PO Box 8058, Zurich,
Switzerland
Tel.: (41) 438162211 **CH**
Web Site: https://www.flughafen-
zuerich.ch
Year Founded: 2000
FHZN—(SWX)
Rev.: $1,246,096,100
Assets: $4,730,179,905
Liabilities: $2,187,613,906
Net Worth: $2,542,565,999
Earnings: $318,334,858
Emp.: 1,909
Fiscal Year-end: 12/31/19
Aviation Services
N.A.I.C.S.: 488119
Andreas Schmid *(Chm)*

Subsidiaries:

A-port S.A. **(1)**
AV Vitacura 2736 Piso 21, CP 7550597,
Las Condes, Santiago, Chile
Tel.: (56) 223629840
Web Site: https://www.aport.cl
Airport Parking Services
N.A.I.C.S.: 812930

Unique Betriebssysteme AG **(1)**

Flughafen, Kloten, 8058, Zurich, Switzer-
land
Tel.: (41) 438162211
Web Site: http://www.Flughafen-zurich.ch
Emp.: 180
Airport Operation Services
N.A.I.C.S.: 488119

FLUICELL AB

Flojelbergsgatan 8C, 431 37, Moln-
dal, Sweden
Tel.: (46) 762083354
Web Site: https://www.fluicell.com
Year Founded: 2012
FLUI—(OMX)
Rev.: $304,401
Assets: $2,975,639
Liabilities: $779,267
Net Worth: $2,196,372
Earnings: ($2,024,034)
Emp.: 20
Fiscal Year-end: 12/31/22
Biotechnology Research & Develop-
ment Services
N.A.I.C.S.: 541714
Stefan Tilk *(Chm)*

FLUID UTVA A.D.

Utve zlatokrile 9, Pancevo, Serbia
Tel.: (381) 13342399
Year Founded: 1999
FLUT—(BEL)
Sales Range: Less than $1 Million
Emp.: 44
Trucks Mfr
N.A.I.C.S.: 333924
Mazibrada Zdravko *(Exec Dir)*

FLUIDATA LTD.

2 More London, London, SE1 2AP,
United Kingdom
Tel.: (44) 845 868 7848
Web Site: http://www.fluidata.co.uk
Year Founded: 2004
Sales Range: $10-24.9 Million
Emp.: 47
Wired Telecommunication Services
N.A.I.C.S.: 517111
Piers Daniell *(Mng Dir)*

FLUIDOIL LIMITED

24 West 4th Avenue, Vancouver, V5Y
1G3, BC, Canada
Tel.: (604) 897-0132 **BC**
Year Founded: 2006
Sales Range: $25-49.9 Million
Mineral Exploration Services
N.A.I.C.S.: 213114
Simon Anderson *(CFO)*

Subsidiaries:

FluidOil Limited **(1)**
Eastlands II London Road, Basingstoke,
RG21 4AW, United Kingdom
Tel.: (44) 20 7043 0720
Web Site: http://www.fluidoilcorp.com
Viscositor Heavy Oil Upgrading Technolo-
gies Developer, Mfr & Whslr
N.A.I.C.S.: 333248
Charles Parker *(CEO)*

FLUIDOMAT LTD.

7C-8J I S Gajra Industrial Area-1 AB
Road, Dewas, 455001, MP, India
Tel.: (91) 7314281333
Web Site: https://www.fluidomat.com
522017—(BOM)
Rev.: $7,067,338
Assets: $8,527,516
Liabilities: $1,224,059
Net Worth: $7,303,457
Earnings: $1,564,983
Emp.: 182
Fiscal Year-end: 03/31/24
Industrial Machinery Mfr
N.A.I.C.S.: 333248
Ashok Jain *(Chm & Mng Dir)*

Subsidiaries:

Fluidomat UK Private Limited **(1)**
6th Floor 9 Appold Street, London, EC2A
2AP, United Kingdom
Tel.: (44) 9981122008
Automotive Fluid Coupling Product Mfr
N.A.I.C.S.: 332912

FLUIDRA SA

Av Alcalde Barnils 69, 8174, Sant
Cugat del Valles, Barcelona, Spain
Tel.: (34) 937243900
Web Site: https://www.fluidra.com
Year Founded: 1969
FDR—(BAR)
Rev.: $2,324,350,370
Assets: $3,871,772,823
Liabilities: $2,131,438,349
Net Worth: $1,740,334,474
Earnings: $128,988,851
Emp.: 6,259
Fiscal Year-end: 12/31/23
Water Conservation Treatment Solu-
tions
N.A.I.C.S.: 221310
Eloy Planes Corts *(Chm & Pres)*

Subsidiaries:

ASTRALPOOL CHINA **(1)**
Block E18/F JinXuan Building No 238 East
NanDan Road, Xuhui District, Shanghai,
200030, China
Tel.: (86) 21 63910575
Web Site: http://www.astralpool.com
Swimming Pool Equipments Distr
N.A.I.C.S.: 423910

**ATH Aplicaciones Tecnicas Hidrauli-
cas S.L.** **(1)**
Joan Torruella i Urpina 31, 08758, Cervello,
Barcelona, Spain
Tel.: (34) 936 802 222
Web Site: http://www.ath.es
Sales Range: $25-49.9 Million
Emp.: 45
Water Purifiers Rental Services
N.A.I.C.S.: 532289

Accent Graphic S.L. **(1)**
Obradors 14 Pol Ind Santiga, 08130, Santa
Perpetua de Mogoda, Barcelona, Spain
Tel.: (34) 937183480
Web Site: http://www.accentgraphic.es
Sales Range: $25-49.9 Million
Emp.: 20
Graphic Designing Services
N.A.I.C.S.: 541430

Astral Piscine S.A.S **(1)**
Avenue Maurice Bellonte, 66000, Perpig-
nan, Pyrenees-Orientales, France
Tel.: (33) 468520684
Web Site: http://www.astralpool.fr
Swimming Pool Equipments Distr
N.A.I.C.S.: 423910

AstralPool Chile Ltd **(1)**
El Conquistador del Monte 4731, Hue-
churaba, Santiago, Chile
Tel.: (56) 27400620
Web Site: http://www.astralpool.cl
Swimming Pool Equipments Distr
N.A.I.C.S.: 423910

AstralPool S.A. **(1)**
Avda Francesc Macia 60 Planta 20, 08208,
Sabadell, Barcelona, Spain
Tel.: (34) 937136344
Web Site: http://www.fluidra.com
Sales Range: $25-49.9 Million
Emp.: 70
Swimming Pool Design & Construction Ser-
vices
N.A.I.C.S.: 238990

Subsidiary (Non-US):

**Astral - bazenove prislusenstvi,
s.r.o.** **(2)**
Doubravice 86, 251 70, Dobrejovice, Czech
Republic
Tel.: (420) 323638206
Web Site: https://www.astralpool.cz
Emp.: 9
Swimming Pool Equipment Whslr

N.A.I.C.S.: 423910
Zuzana Rihva *(Dir-Fin)*

Subsidiary (Domestic):

Astral Export, S.A. **(2)**
c/Mogoda 75 Pl Can Salvatella, 08210, Bar-
bera del Valles, Barcelona, Spain
Tel.: (34) 937136344
Web Site: http://www.astralexport.com
Swimming Pool Equipments Distr
N.A.I.C.S.: 423910
Gilles Monier *(Gen Mgr-Sls)*

Subsidiary (Non-US):

Astral India Private Ltd **(2)**
Sofian Chambers 2nd floor 33/34 Mount
Road, Guindy, Chennai, 600 085, Tamil
Nadu, India
Tel.: (91) 442447472141
Web Site: http://www.astralpool.com
Sales Range: $25-49.9 Million
Emp.: 40
Swimming Pool Equipments Distr
N.A.I.C.S.: 423910

Astral Italia Spa **(2)**
Via Trebocche 7 E, 25081, Bedizzole, Bres-
cia, Italy
Tel.: (39) 0306870441
Web Site: http://www.astralpool.com
Swimming Pool Equipments Distr
N.A.I.C.S.: 423910

Astral Marazul **(2)**
Estrada Nacional N 249 4, 2785-035, Sao
Domingos de Rana, Portugal
Tel.: (351) 214444720
Sales Range: $25-49.9 Million
Emp.: 25
Swimming Pool Equipments Distr
N.A.I.C.S.: 423910

Astral Nigeria Ltd **(2)**
58 Akanbi Onitiri Close Off Eric Moore, Su-
rulere, Lagos, Nigeria
Tel.: (234) 17740709
Web Site: http://www.astralpoolnigeria.com
Swimming Pool Equipments Distr
N.A.I.C.S.: 423910

Astral Pool Australia Pty Limited **(2)**
111 Indian Drive, Keysborough, 3174, VIC,
Australia
Tel.: (61) 395542200
Web Site: http://www.astralpool.com.au
Sales Range: $25-49.9 Million
Swimming Pool & Spa Equipments Mfr &
Distr
N.A.I.C.S.: 333310

Astral Pool Hellas SA **(2)**
Lakko Katsari, Aspropyrgos, Athens, 19300,
Greece
Tel.: (30) 2105594527
Web Site: http://www.fluibra.gr
Sales Range: $25-49.9 Million
Emp.: 15
Swimming Pool Equipments Distr
N.A.I.C.S.: 423910

**Astral Pool Swimming Pool Equip-
ment (Shanghai) Ltd., Co** **(2)**
Room 1008 Block B Honghui International
Plaza 1602 West Zhongshan Road, Xuhui
District, Shanghai, China
Tel.: (86) 2163910575
Web Site: http://www.astralpool.cn
Swimming Pool Equipments Distr
N.A.I.C.S.: 423910

Astral SNG **(2)**
16-2 Krasnoproletarskaya str, Moscow,
Russia
Tel.: (7) 4956454551
Web Site: http://www.astralpool.ru
Swimming Pool Equipments Distr
N.A.I.C.S.: 423910

Astral Scandinavia A/S **(2)**
Kometvej 28, 6230, Rodekro, Denmark
Tel.: (45) 74693999
Web Site: http://www.fluidra.dk
Swimming Pool Equipments Distr
N.A.I.C.S.: 423910

Astral Sweden AB **(2)**
Ekenleden 11 A, 428 36, Kallered, Vaster-
gotland, Sweden
Tel.: (46) 31994100

Fluidra SA—(Continued)

Web Site: http://www.astralpool.se
Sales Range: $25-49.9 Million
Emp.: 7
Swimming Pool Equipments Distr
N.A.I.C.S.: 423910

Astral UK LTD   **(2)**
Unit 30-32 Palmerston Dr, Newgate Lane,
Fareham, PO14 1DJ, Hampshire, United
Kingdom
Tel.: (44) 1329 514000
Web Site: http://www.astralpool.co.uk
Sales Range: $25-49.9 Million
Emp.: 25
Swimming Pool Equipments Distr
N.A.I.C.S.: 423910

AstralPool Cyprus Ltd   **(2)**
Matheou and Matheou Street No 5, Ayios
Athanasios Industrial Area, 4101, Limassol,
4101, Cyprus
Tel.: (357) 25754424
Web Site: http://www.astralpool.com.cy
Sales Range: $25-49.9 Million
Emp.: 6
Swimming Pool Equipments Distr
N.A.I.C.S.: 423910
Nicos Xenis (Gen Mgr)

AstralPool Switzerland S.A.   **(2)**
Via Industria 10, 6930, Bedano, Ticino,
Switzerland
Tel.: (41) 919354080
Web Site: http://www.it.astralpool.ch
Sales Range: $25-49.9 Million
Emp.: 7
Swimming Pool Equipments Distr
N.A.I.C.S.: 423910

AstralPool Thailand Co., Ltd   **(2)**
110/4 Moo 13, Racha Thewa Subdistrict
Bang Phli District, Bang Phli, 10540, Samut
Prakan, Thailand
Tel.: (66) 73894204
Web Site: https://www.fluidra.co.th
Sales Range: $25-49.9 Million
Emp.: 35
Swimming Pool Equipments Distr
N.A.I.C.S.: 423910

Fluidra Magyarorszag KFT   **(2)**
Leshegy utca 4/a, 2310, Szigetszentmiklos,
Pest, Hungary
Tel.: (36) 706848999
Web Site: https://www.astralpool.hu
Sales Range: $25-49.9 Million
Emp.: 14
Swimming Pool Equipments Distr
N.A.I.C.S.: 423910

Fluidra Polska Sp.z o.o.   **(2)**
Al Armii Krajowej 61, 50-541, Wroclaw,
Lower Silesian, Poland
Tel.: (48) 713604930
Web Site: https://www.astralpool.pl
Sales Range: $25-49.9 Million
Emp.: 18
Swimming Pool Equipments Distr
N.A.I.C.S.: 423910
Dominik Witkowski (Gen Dir)

**Schwimmbad-Sauna-Ausstattungs-
Grosshandels GesmbH**
Untersbergstrasse 10, 5082, Grodig, Austria
Tel.: (43) 624677000
Web Site: http://www.ssa.co.at
Swimming Pool Equipments Distr
N.A.I.C.S.: 423910
Helmut Brabenetz (Mgr)

Astramatic S.A.U.   **(1)**
Pl Ramassar C Barcelones 15, 08520, Les
Franqueses del Valles, Barcelona, Spain
Tel.: (34) 938616047
Web Site: http://www.astramatic.com
Sales Range: $25-49.9 Million
Emp.: 20
Water Treatment Plant Construction Ser-
vices
N.A.I.C.S.: 237110

Auric Pool, S.A.   **(1)**
C des Ametllers N 6, 08213, Polinya, Bar-
celona, Spain
Tel.: (34) 937133718
Web Site: http://www.auricpool.com
Sales Range: $25-49.9 Million
Emp.: 35
Management Services

N.A.I.C.S.: 551112
Carles Franquesa (Gen Mgr)

Subsidiary (Non-US):

**Europeenne de Couverture Automa-
tiques,. S.A.R.L.**   **(2)**
105 Henry Potez-Zac Torremila, 66000,
Perpignan, France
Tel.: (33) 468617530
Web Site: http://www.eca-interpool.com
Sales Range: $25-49.9 Million
Swimming Pool Equipments Mfr
N.A.I.C.S.: 339999

Subsidiary (Domestic):

I.D. Electroquimica, S.L.   **(2)**
Poligono Ind Las Atalayas calle Dracma 19,
03114, Alicante, Spain
Tel.: (34) 965101979
Web Site: https://www.idegis.es
Sales Range: $25-49.9 Million
Emp.: 10
Water Treatment Devices Mfr
N.A.I.C.S.: 333310
Gaspar Cano Sanchez (Gen Dir)

Metalast S.A.   **(2)**
Passeig de Sanllehi 25, 08213, Polinya,
Barcelona, Spain
Tel.: (34) 937131855
Web Site: http://www.fluidra.com
Sales Range: $25-49.9 Million
Swimming Pool Equipments Mfr
N.A.I.C.S.: 333310

Poltank, S.A.U.   **(2)**
Poligono Industrial Pla de Poliger Sud Sec-
tor I, 17854, Sant Jaume de Llierca, Girona,
Spain
Tel.: (34) 972287070
Web Site: https://www.poltank.com
Sales Range: $25-49.9 Million
Emp.: 270
Filters & Accessories Mfr
N.A.I.C.S.: 333998

Prelast, S.A.   **(2)**
Pol Ind Pla De Cisteller S N, 17857, Barce-
lona, Spain
Tel.: (34) 972 29 00 79
Web Site: http://www.prelast.net
Sales Range: $25-49.9 Million
Emp.: 11
Rubber Joints Mfr
N.A.I.C.S.: 326291

Talleres Del Agua SL   **(2)**
Poligono Ind de Barros parcela 5, 39400,
Los Corrales de Buelna, Cantabria, Spain
Tel.: (34) 942842072
Web Site: http://www.talleresdelagua.com
Sales Range: $25-49.9 Million
Swimming Pool Equipments Mfr & Distr
N.A.I.C.S.: 333414

Togama S.A.   **(2)**
Ctra Villarreal Onda-Km 6-Apdo 176,
12540, Villarreal, Castellon, Spain
Tel.: (34) 964626512
Web Site: http://www.togamamosaic.com
Sales Range: $25-49.9 Million
Emp.: 70
Mosaic Tiles Mfr
N.A.I.C.S.: 327120

Cepex S.A.U.   **(1)**
Av Ramon Ciurans 40 Pol Ind Congost P6,
08530, La Garriga, Barcelona, Spain
Tel.: (34) 938704208
Web Site: https://www.cepex.com
Mfr of Plastic Valves, Fittings & Fluid Han-
dling Devices
N.A.I.C.S.: 332912

Subsidiary (Non-US):

Cepex France S.A.S.   **(2)**
Avenue G Guignard ZI Boe, BP 100,
47553, Boe, Lot-et-Garonne, France
Tel.: (33) 5 53 48 14 26
Sales Range: $1-4.9 Billion
Emp.: 3,000
Fittings & Valves Distr
N.A.I.C.S.: 423720

Cepex GmbH   **(2)**
Neue Strasse 10, 31032, Betheln, Lower
Saxony, Germany
Tel.: (49) 5182908152

Web Site: http://www.cepex.de
Fittings & Valves Distr
N.A.I.C.S.: 423720

Cepex Portugal, Lda   **(2)**
Qta da Marquesa Herdade da Qta da Torre
Armazem n1 - Fraccao n4, Quinta do Anjo,
2950-678, Palmela, Portugal
Tel.: (351) 212108190
Web Site: http://www.cepex.pt
Fittings & Valves Distr
N.A.I.C.S.: 423720

Cepex S.r.l.   **(2)**
Via Trebocche 7 E, 25081, Bedizzole, Bres-
cia, Italy
Tel.: (39) 0306871281
Web Site: http://www.cepex.it
Fittings & Valves Distr
N.A.I.C.S.: 423720

Plant (Domestic):

Cepex, S.A.U. (Granollers)   **(2)**
Lluis Companys 51-53, 08400, Granollers,
Barcelona, Spain
Tel.: (34) 938604930
Web Site: http://www.cepex.es
Fittings & Valves Mfr
N.A.I.C.S.: 332912

Cepex, S.A.U. (La Garriga)   **(2)**
Av Ramon Ciurans 40 - Pol Ind Congost -
Parcel a 6, 08530, La Garriga, Barcelona,
Spain
Tel.: (34) 938704208
Emp.: 200
Fittings & Valves Mfr
N.A.I.C.S.: 332912

**Cepex, S.A.U. (Sant Jaume de
Llierca)**   **(2)**
Pol Ind Pla de Poliger Sud - Sector 1 S N,
17854, Sant Jaume de Llierca, Girona,
Spain
Tel.: (34) 972287893
Fittings & Valves Mfr
N.A.I.C.S.: 332912

Certikin Iberica S.L.U   **(1)**
Sanllehy Walk 23, 08389, Polinya, Barce-
lona, Spain
Tel.: (34) 902020342
Web Site: http://www.certikin.com
Sales Range: $25-49.9 Million
Emp.: 20
Swimming Pool Equipments Mfr & Distr
N.A.I.C.S.: 339999
Jaume Alberola (Mgr)

Certikin International Ltd.   **(1)**
Witan Park Avenue 2 Station Lane Indus-
trial Estate, Witney, OX28 4FJ, Oxfordshire,
United Kingdom
Tel.: (44) 1993778855
Web Site: http://www.certikin.co.uk
Sales Range: $50-74.9 Million
Emp.: 200
Swimming Pool Equipments Mfr & Distr
N.A.I.C.S.: 333310

Subsidiary (Non-US):

**Certikin Swimming Pool Products In-
dia PVT Ltd.**   **(2)**
7A Dyvasandra Industrial Area 3rd Cross,
Singayanapalaya, Bengaluru, 560 048, Kar-
nataka, India
Tel.: (91) 80 4094 3024
Sales Range: $25-49.9 Million
Emp.: 8
Swimming Pool Equipments Distr
N.A.I.C.S.: 423910

Certikin Italia SpA   **(1)**
Via Gavardina 96/98/100, 25010, Calcinato,
Brescia, Italy
Tel.: (39) 0309980088
Web Site: http://www.certikin.com
Sales Range: $25-49.9 Million
Emp.: 17
Swimming Pool Equipments Mfr & Distr
N.A.I.C.S.: 339999

Certikin Portugal SA   **(1)**
Estrada Nacional 249 Km 4 Zona Industrial
Cabra Figa Lote 15, 2635-047, Rio de
Mouro, Portugal
Tel.: (351) 219154690
Web Site: http://www.certikin.com

Sales Range: $25-49.9 Million
Emp.: 30
Swimming Pool Equipments Distr
N.A.I.C.S.: 423910

**FLUIDRA SOUTH AFRICA (PTY)
LTD.**   **(1)**
35 Reedbuck Crescent Corporate Park
South, Randjesfontein, Midrand, 1683, Gau-
teng, South Africa
Tel.: (27) 82 800 9810
Sales Range: $50-74.9 Million
Emp.: 6
Swimming Pool Equipments Distr
N.A.I.C.S.: 423910

INQUIDE ITALIA SRL   **(1)**
Via Traversa Gabardina 36-44, 25081, Be-
dizzole, Brescia, Italy
Tel.: (39) 0306871641
Sales Range: $50-74.9 Million
Emp.: 7
Swimming Pool Chemicals & Equipments
Distr
N.A.I.C.S.: 424690

**Industrias Mecanicas Lago,
S.A.U**   **(1)**
Pol Industrial La Rasa C/Muntanya S/N,
17481, Sant Julia de Ramis, Girona, Spain
Tel.: (34) 972170058
Web Site: http://www.imlago.com
Emp.: 20
Swimming Pool Pumps & Accessories Mfr
N.A.I.C.S.: 333996

MEIP INTERNATIONAL, S.L.   **(1)**
Paseo Sanllehy 25, 08213, Polinya, Barce-
lona, Spain
Tel.: (34) 937149502
Web Site: http://www.meipinter.com
Sales Range: $25-49.9 Million
Emp.: 10
Water Treatment Devices Mfr
N.A.I.C.S.: 333310

POOL SUPPLIER, S.L.   **(1)**
Calle Pintor Velazquez 10, 08213, Polinya,
Barcelona, Spain
Tel.: (34) 937136344
Sales Range: $50-74.9 Million
Emp.: 7
Swimming Pool Equipment
N.A.I.C.S.: 423910
Manuel Marzo Laoz (Gen Mgr)

Sacopa, S.A.U.   **(1)**
Pol Ind Poliger Sud - Sector 1 s/n, 17854,
Sant Jaume de Llierca, Girona, Spain
Tel.: (34) 972287272
Web Site: https://www.sacopamedical.com
Sales Range: $50-74.9 Million
Emp.: 120
Thermoplastic Injection Parts & Compo-
nents Mfr
N.A.I.C.S.: 326199

Tracelogistics, S.A.   **(1)**
Pol Ind Puigtio Carrer B, 17412, Macanet
de la Selva, Girona, Spain
Tel.: (34) 972879300
Web Site: http://www.tracelogistics.net
Sales Range: $25-49.9 Million
Emp.: 100
Logistics Distribution Services
N.A.I.C.S.: 541614

FLUITRONICS GMBH
Europark Fichtenhain B2, Krefeld,
47807, Germany
Tel.: (49) 2151 4589 0   **De**
Web Site: http://www.fluitronics.com
Sales Range: $10-24.9 Million
Emp.: 79
Hydraulic Equipment & Components
Mfr & Distr
N.A.I.C.S.: 333995
Christoph Kempermann (Mng Dir)

**FLUKE TRANSPORTATION
GROUP**
450 Sherman Avenue N 2nd Floor,
Hamilton, L8L 8J6, ON, Canada
Tel.: (905) 578-0677
Web Site: http://www.fluke.ca

Year Founded: 1920
Rev.: $16,380,429
Emp.: 200
Freight Movement & Warehousing Services
N.A.I.C.S.: 484110
Ron Foxcroft *(Chm, Pres & CEO)*

FLUOGUIDE A/S
Ole Maaloes Vej 3, 2200, Copenhagen, Denmark
Tel.: (45) 31226660
Web Site: https://www.fluoguide.com
Year Founded: 2010
FLUO—(OMX)
Rev.: $61,206
Assets: $4,284,267
Liabilities: $2,443,750
Net Worth: $1,840,517
Earnings: ($5,552,951)
Emp.: 8
Fiscal Year-end: 12/31/23
Biotechnology Research & Development Services
N.A.I.C.S.: 541714
Grethe Norskov Rasmussen *(Chief Dev Officer)*

FLUROTECH LTD.
601 246 Stewart Green SW, Calgary, T3H 3C8, AB, Canada
Web Site: https://www.flurotech.com
FLURF—(OTCEM)
Assets: $171,968
Liabilities: $308,152
Net Worth: ($136,184)
Earnings: ($80,562)
Fiscal Year-end: 12/31/23
Laboratory Testing Services
N.A.I.C.S.: 541380
Danny Dalla Longa *(Founder)*

FLUTTER ENTERTAINMENT PLC
Belfield Office Park Beech Hill Road, Clonskeagh, Dublin, Ireland
Tel.: (353) 19051000   IE
Web Site: https://www.flutter.com
Year Founded: 1988
FLUT—(NYSE)
Rev.: $11,790,000,000
Assets: $24,635,000,000
Liabilities: $14,419,000,000
Net Worth: $10,216,000,000
Earnings: ($1,211,000,000)
Emp.: 23,009
Fiscal Year-end: 12/31/23
Gambling Machine Opertors
N.A.I.C.S.: 551112
Edward Traynor *(Gen Counsel & Sec)*

Subsidiaries:

Aviator LLC   **(1)**
26 May Square 1, Tbilisi, Georgia
Tel.: (995) 322711010
Web Site: http://www.adjarabet.com
Gambling Portal Services
N.A.I.C.S.: 713290

Betfair Group Limited   **(1)**
Waterfront Hammersmith Embankment Chancellors Road, London, W6 9HP, United Kingdom
Tel.: (44) 208 834 8000
Holding Company; Online Gambling Products & Services
N.A.I.C.S.: 551112

Subsidiary (Domestic):

Betfair Limited   **(2)**
Waterfront Hammersmith Embankment Chancellors Road, London, W6 9HP, United Kingdom
Tel.: (44) 208 834 8000
Web Site: http://corporate.betfair.com
Online Gambling Services
N.A.I.C.S.: 713290

Subsidiary (Non-US):

Betfair Holding (Malta) Limited   **(3)**
Betfair Triq Il-Kappillan Mifsud, Santa Vennera, SVR 1851, Malta
Tel.: (356) 8448717000
Web Site: http://www.betfair.com
Holding Company
N.A.I.C.S.: 551112

Subsidiary (Domestic):

Blue Square Ltd.   **(3)**
1st Floor Park House 16 Finsbury Circus, London, EC2M 7DJ, United Kingdom
Tel.: (44) 20 7688 6210
Web Site: http://www.bluesq.com
Sales Range: $50-74.9 Million
Emp.: 150
Interactive Betting Services
N.A.I.C.S.: 713290

Subsidiary (US):

ODS Technologies LP   **(3)**
19545 N W Von Neumann Dr Ste 210, Beaverton, OR 97006
Tel.: (888) 752-9884
Online Gambling Services
N.A.I.C.S.: 541511

FanDuel Inc.   **(1)**
300 Park Ave S 14th Fl, New York, NY 10010   **(57.8%)**
Tel.: (917) 525-4538
Web Site: http://www.fanduel.com
Online & Mobile Fantasy Sports Gaming Platform Operator
N.A.I.C.S.: 518210
Tom Griffiths *(Founder & Chief Product Officer)*

Subsidiary (Domestic):

numberFire, Inc.   **(2)**
300 Park Ave S 14th Fl, New York, NY 10010
Tel.: (215) 264-5806
Web Site: http://www.numberfire.com
Software Publisher
N.A.I.C.S.: 513210
Nik Bonaddio *(Founder & CEO)*

Power Leisure Bookmakers Ltd.   **(1)**
Crowne House 56-58 Southwark St, London, SE1 1UN, United Kingdom
Tel.: (44) 2070899700
Web Site: http://www.paddypower.com
Sales Range: $25-49.9 Million
Emp.: 30
Book Publishers
N.A.I.C.S.: 513130

Sisal S.p.A.   **(1)**
Via Ugo Bassi 6, Milan, Italy
Tel.: (39) 028868971
Web Site: https://www.sisal.com
N.A.I.C.S.: 713290

Sportsbet Pty Limited   **(1)**
L 17/367 Collins St, Melbourne, 3000, VIC, Australia
Tel.: (61) 879808700
Web Site: http://www.sportsbet.com.au
Online Gambling Services
N.A.I.C.S.: 713290
Barni Evans *(CEO)*

The Stars Group Inc.   **(1)**
200 Bay Street South Tower Suite 3205, Toronto, M5J 2J3, ON, Canada
Tel.: (437) 371-5742
Web Site: http://www.starsgroup.com
Rev.: $2,528,448,000
Assets: $11,275,782,000
Liabilities: $6,756,339,000
Net Worth: $4,519,443,000
Earnings: $61,862,000
Emp.: 4,591
Fiscal Year-end: 12/31/2019
Holding Company; Casino Game & Online Gaming Platform Developer & Services
N.A.I.C.S.: 551112
Rafael Ashkenazi *(CEO)*

Subsidiary (Non-US):

Amaya (International) Ltd.   **(2)**
The Emporium Level 4 Saint Louis Street, MSD 1421, Msida, Malta
Tel.: (356) 21373778

Sales Range: $25-49.9 Million
Emp.: 10
Online Software Gaming Services
N.A.I.C.S.: 541511

Subsidiary (US):

Cadillac Jack, Inc.   **(2)**
2450 Satellite Blvd, Duluth, GA 30096
Tel.: (770) 908-2094
Web Site: http://www.cadillacjack.com
Sales Range: $75-99.9 Million
Emp.: 350
Gaming Machinery Mfr
N.A.I.C.S.: 333310

Diamond Game Enterprises, Inc.   **(2)**
9340 Penfield Ave, Chatsworth, CA 91311
Tel.: (818) 727-1690
Web Site: https://www.diamondgame.com
Sales Range: $1-9.9 Million
Emp.: 35
Gaming Products Developer & Mfr
N.A.I.C.S.: 339999
Bill Breslo *(Pres)*

Subsidiary (Non-US):

Rational Group Limited   **(2)**
Douglas Bay Complex King Edward Road, Onchan, IM3 1DZ, Isle of Man
Tel.: (44) 1624 632 060
Web Site: http://www.rationalgroup.com
Sales Range: $1-4.9 Billion
Emp.: 1,700
Holding Company; Poker Websites Developer & Operator
N.A.I.C.S.: 551112

Subsidiary (Domestic):

Rational Entertainment Enterprises Limited   **(3)**
Douglas Bay Complex King Edward Road, Onchan, IM3 1DZ, Isle of Man
Tel.: (44) 1624 632 060
Web Site: http://www.rationalgroup.com
Poker Websites Developer & Operator
N.A.I.C.S.: 713290

Tombola International Malta Plc   **(1)**
Soho Savoy Gardens J Block Rue D Argens, Gzira, GZR1362, Malta
Tel.: (356) 203699099
Web Site: https://www.tombola.nl
Gaming & Entertainment Services
N.A.I.C.S.: 541219

FLUXTEK INTERNATIONAL CORP.
No 21 Jingjian Road, Ping-tung, 90093, Taiwan
Tel.: (886) 87558557
Web Site: https://www.fluxtek.com
Year Founded: 2000
7443—(TPE)
Rev.: $18,070,145
Assets: $19,198,142
Liabilities: $11,128,813
Net Worth: $8,069,328
Earnings: $66,058
Fiscal Year-end: 12/31/23
Water Purification Equipment Mfr
N.A.I.C.S.: 333310
Yen-Tsun Lai *(Chm & Pres)*

FLY SRL
Via delle Fosse, 29 Loria, 31037, Veneto, Italy
Tel.: (39) 0423492107
Web Site: https://flysrl.com
Furniture & Home Furnishings Mfg
N.A.I.C.S.: 337127

Subsidiaries:

Carraro S.p.A.   **(1)**
Via Olmo 37, Campodarsego, 35011, Padua, Italy
Tel.: (39) 0499219111
Web Site: https://www.carraro.com
Rev.: $587,931,467
Assets: $977,036,670
Net Worth: $77,643,192
Earnings: ($3,710,513)
Emp.: 738

Fiscal Year-end: 12/31/2020
Axles, Gears, Transmissions & Related Components Mfr for Cars, Earth-Moving Equipment, Forklifts, Tractors & Other Industrial Vehicles
N.A.I.C.S.: 333612
Enrico Carraro *(Chm)*

Subsidiary (Domestic):

A.E. Srl   **(2)**
Via Nazionale Sannitica 35, Benevento, Italy
Tel.: (39) 0824903081
Sales Range: $25-49.9 Million
Emp.: 36
Motor Vehicle Parts Whslr
N.A.I.C.S.: 423140

Subsidiary (Non-US):

Carraro Argentina S.A.   **(2)**
Valentin Gomez 577, Haedo, 1706, Buenos Aires, Argentina
Tel.: (54) 1144897200
Web Site: http://www.carraro.com
Sales Range: $100-124.9 Million
Emp.: 354
Speed Changer Industrial High-Speed Drive & Gear Mfr
N.A.I.C.S.: 333612
Antonio Minchio *(Mng Dir)*

Carraro China Drive System Co., Ltd.   **(2)**
No 11 Road, Qingda Industrial Park Jihongtan Subdistrict Chengyang District, Qingdao, 266111, Shandong, China
Tel.: (86) 53266963000
Transmission System & Gear Mfr
N.A.I.C.S.: 333612

Carraro Drive Tech Do Brasil Inc.   **(2)**
Rua Gilberto De Zorzi n 380 Bairro Forqueta, Caxias do Sul, 95115-730, Rio Grande do Sul, Brazil
Tel.: (55) 5432209350
Transmission System & Gear Mfr
N.A.I.C.S.: 333612

Carraro India Ltd.   **(2)**
B2/2 MIDC Ind. Area Ranjangaon, Pune, 412210, India   **(100%)**
Tel.: (91) 2138662666
Web Site: http://www.carraro.com
Machine Tool (Metal Forming Types) Mfr
N.A.I.C.S.: 333517

Subsidiary (US):

Carraro North America Inc.   **(2)**
2505 International Pkwy, Virginia Beach, VA 23452-7821
Tel.: (757) 689-3725
Web Site: http://www.carraro.com
Motor Vehicle Steering & Suspension Components (except Spring) Mfr
N.A.I.C.S.: 336330

Subsidiary (Non-US):

Carraro Qingdao Ltd.   **(2)**
The West of Kun Lun Shan Road, 262555, Qingdao, Shandong, China
Tel.: (86) 53286721991
All Other Motor Vehicle Parts Mfr
N.A.I.C.S.: 336390

Carraro Technologies India Pvt. Ltd.   **(2)**
501-A and B 5th Floor Gamma 1 Building Gigaspace, Viman Nagar, Pune, 411014, India
Tel.: (91) 2066216700
Transmission System & Gear Mfr
N.A.I.C.S.: 333612
Ravindra Ingale *(Asst Mgr)*

Subsidiary (Domestic):

Driveservice Srl   **(2)**
Contrada Mortella 64, Poggiofiorito, 66030, Chieti, Italy
Tel.: (39) 0871938111
Transmission System & Gear Mfr
N.A.I.C.S.: 333612

Subsidiary (Non-US):

Fabryca Osi Napedowych S.A.   **(2)**

FLY Srl—(Continued)

Ul Krasickiego 63/71, Radomsko, Radom, Poland **(100%)**
Tel.: (48) 446821471
Sales Range: $100-124.9 Million
Emp.: 300
All Other Motor Vehicle Parts Mfr
N.A.I.C.S.: 336390
Ciupa Iwona *(Pres)*

Subsidiary (Domestic):

SIAP S.p.A. **(2)**
Via Monfalcone 4, 33085, Maniago, Italy **(73.8%)**
Tel.: (39) 0427706911
Web Site: http://www.siapgears.com
Sales Range: $150-199.9 Million
Emp.: 340
Gear Assembly Mfr
N.A.I.C.S.: 333612

Subsidiary (Domestic):

TQT S.r.l. **(3)**
Via Monfalcone 4, 33085, Maniago, Italy **(100%)**
Tel.: (39) 0427706911
Web Site: http://www.carraro.com
Sales Range: $75-99.9 Million
All Other Professional Scientific & Technical Services
N.A.I.C.S.: 541990
Paolo Decol *(Mgr)*

Subsidiary (Domestic):

Trenton S.p.A. **(2)**
Via Matilde Di Canossa 21, Frassinoro, Modena, Italy
Tel.: (39) 0536971711
Sales Range: $50-74.9 Million
Emp.: 52
Industrial Supplies Whslr
N.A.I.C.S.: 423840

FLY VICTOR LTD.
522 Fulham Road, London, SW6 5NR, United Kingdom
Tel.: (44) 203 1315 150 **UK**
Web Site: http://www.flyvictor.com
Private Passenger Air Transportation Chartering Services
N.A.I.C.S.: 481211
Alex Sozonoff *(Chm)*

Subsidiaries:

YoungJets, LLC **(1)**
403 E Gutierrez St, Santa Barbara, CA 93101
Tel.: (805) 966-9336
Web Site: http://www.youngjets.com
Small Air Transportation Chartering Services
N.A.I.C.S.: 481211
David Young *(Founder & CEO)*

FLYING A PETROLEUM LTD.
#142 757 West Hastings Street, Vancouver, V6C 1A1, BC, Canada
Tel.: (604) 809-4799
Year Founded: 1986
Oil & Gas Exploration Services
N.A.I.C.S.: 213112
Ke Feng Yuan *(CFO)*

FLYING CEMENT COMPANY LIMITED
4 Sarwar Colony Sarwar Road, Lahore, 54600, Pakistan
Tel.: (92) 426674301
Web Site:
 https://www.flyingcement.com
Year Founded: 1992
FLYNG—(KAR)
Rev.: $34,620,329
Assets: $96,711,309
Liabilities: $37,607,217
Net Worth: $59,104,092
Earnings: $1,022,162
Emp.: 383
Fiscal Year-end: 06/30/19
Cement Mfr

N.A.I.C.S.: 325520
Momin Qamar *(Exec Dir)*

Subsidiaries:

Flying Paper Industries Ltd. **(1)**
103 Fazal Road St John Park, Lahore, 54600, Pakistan
Tel.: (92) 4266743015
Web Site: https://www.flyingpaper.com.pk
Emp.: 700
Kraft Paper Mfr
N.A.I.C.S.: 322120

FLYING EAGLE PU TECHNICAL CORP.
Long Shan Development Area, Han Jiang Town, Shishi, Fujian, China
Tel.: (86) 59588680828 **OK**
Web Site: http://www.china-wintop.com
Sales Range: $25-49.9 Million
Emp.: 516
Synthetic Polyurethane Leather Mfr
N.A.I.C.S.: 316990
Kang Han Ang *(Chm & Pres)*

FLYING FINANCIAL SERVICE HOLDINGS LIMITED
18/F Block 1-C Shenzhen Software Industry Base Nanshan, Shenzhen, China
Tel.: (86) 7553 698 8000, **Ky**
Web Site:
 http://www.flyingfinancial.hk
Rev.: $3,021,454
Assets: $60,466,625
Liabilities: $14,242,708
Net Worth: $46,223,917
Earnings: ($72,061,864)
Emp.: 90
Fiscal Year-end: 12/31/20
Financial Management Services
N.A.I.C.S.: 523940
Weijing Zheng *(Founder, Chm, CEO & Compliance Officer)*

FLYING GARDEN CO., LTD.
3-4-18 Hongo-cho, Oyama, 323-0026, Tochigi, Japan
Tel.: (81) 285304129
Web Site: https://www.fgarden.co.jp
Year Founded: 1981
33170—(TKS)
Sales Range: Less than $1 Million
Restaurant Services
N.A.I.C.S.: 722511
Takashi Nozawa *(Pres & CEO)*

FLYING MONKEY CAPITAL CORP.
Suite 2300 - 1066 West Hastings Street, Vancouver, V6E 3X2, BC, Canada
Tel.: (604) 684-4535 **BC**
Year Founded: 2014
Assets: $162,398
Liabilities: $18,956
Net Worth: $143,442
Earnings: ($62,426)
Fiscal Year-end: 12/31/17
Financial Investment Services
N.A.I.C.S.: 523999
Peter J. Hawley *(Pres & CEO)*

FLYING SPARK LTD.
Yitzhak Modai St, Rehovot, 7608804, Israel
Tel.: (972) 86339556
Web Site:
 https://www.flyingspark.com
Year Founded: 2015
FLYS—(TAE)
Rev.: $4,338
Assets: $7,814,110
Liabilities: $2,993,601
Net Worth: $4,820,509
Earnings: ($3,111,816)

Fiscal Year-end: 06/30/23
Food Mfr
N.A.I.C.S.: 311999
Eran Gronich *(CEO)*

FLYING TECHNOLOGY CO., LTD.
No 8 Feihong Road, Liangxi District, Wuxi, 214024, China
Tel.: (86) 51081003265
Web Site: https://www.wxflying.com
603488—(SHG)
Rev.: $70,080,365
Assets: $167,352,742
Liabilities: $29,212,677
Net Worth: $138,140,065
Earnings: $5,825,421
Emp.: 500
Fiscal Year-end: 12/31/22
Elevator Equipment Mfr & Distr
N.A.I.C.S.: 333921
Jin Peirong *(Chm & Pres)*

FLYKE INTERNATIONAL HOLDINGS LTD.
Shell Street No 9-23 Show Center 12 Building D Room, No 6-8 Harbour Road, North Point, China (Hong Kong)
Tel.: (852) 28063282 **Ky**
Web Site: http://www.chinaflyke.com
Year Founded: 1998
Sales Range: $150-199.9 Million
Sport Shoes & Apparel Mfr & Sales
N.A.I.C.S.: 459110
Wenjian Lin *(Chm & CEO)*

FLYNN CANADA LTD.
6435 Northwest Drive, Mississauga, L4V 1K2, ON, Canada
Tel.: (905) 671-3971
Web Site: http://www.flynn.ca
Year Founded: 1978
Rev.: $250,800,000
Emp.: 2,000
Contracting Services
N.A.I.C.S.: 238990
Doug Flynn *(CEO)*

FLYNN GOLD LIMITED
Level 4 96-100 Albert Rd, South Melbourne, 3205, VIC, Australia
Tel.: (61) 396927222 **AU**
Web Site:
 https://www.flynngold.com.au
Year Founded: 2020
FG1—(ASX)
Rev.: $72,735
Assets: $2,737,007
Liabilities: $495,728
Net Worth: $2,241,279
Earnings: ($3,623,751)
Fiscal Year-end: 06/30/23
Gold Exploration Services
N.A.I.C.S.: 212220
Mathew Watkins *(Sec)*

FLYTECH TECHNOLOGY CO., LTD.
No 168 Singai Road, Neihu District, Taipei, 11494, Taiwan
Tel.: (886) 287914988
Web Site: https://www.flytech.com
6206—(TAI)
Rev.: $114,079,135
Assets: $184,214,879
Liabilities: $30,368,324
Net Worth: $153,846,556
Earnings: $15,458,648
Emp.: 423
Fiscal Year-end: 12/31/23
Notebook Computers Mfr
N.A.I.C.S.: 334111
Thomas Tai Seng Lam *(Chm)*

Subsidiaries:

Flytech Electronic (Shanghai) Co., Ltd. **(1)**
3rd Floor Building 39 No 333 Qinjiang Road Caohejing Development Zone, Shanghai, 200233, China
Tel.: (86) 2154261555
Web Site: https://www.flytech.com.cn
Computers Equipment Mfr & Distr
N.A.I.C.S.: 334118

Flytech Technology (U.S.A.) Inc. **(1)**
271 E Brokaw Rd, San Jose, CA 95112
Tel.: (510) 257-5180
Web Site: https://www.flytech.com
Sales Range: $50-74.9 Million
Emp.: 10
Personal Computer Distr
N.A.I.C.S.: 423430

Flytech Technology (U.S.A.) Inc. **(1)**
271 E Brokaw Rd, San Jose, CA 95112
Tel.: (510) 257-5180
Web Site: https://www.flytech.com
Sales Range: $25-49.9 Million
Emp.: 8
Notebook Computers Mfr
N.A.I.C.S.: 334111

Flytech Technology Co., Ltd. - Taipei Factory **(1)**
No 34 Wucyuan 3rd Road, Wugu Township, Taipei, 248, Taiwan
Tel.: (886) 222982696
Sales Range: $100-124.9 Million
Emp.: 300
Personal Computer Mfr
N.A.I.C.S.: 334118

Flytech Technology Hong Kong Ltd.
Room 01 6/F Block A Tonic Industrial Centre 26 Kai Cheung Road, Kowloon Bay, Kowloon Bay, China (Hong Kong)
Tel.: (852) 3 525 5800
Web Site: https://www.kioskhk.com
Sales Range: $25-49.9 Million
Emp.: 10
Personal Computer Mfr
N.A.I.C.S.: 334111

Inefi Incorporation **(1)**
2F No 268 Xinhu 3rd Rd, Neihu Dist, Taipei, 114065, Taiwan
Tel.: (886) 227905399
Web Site: https://www.inefi.com
Software Development Services
N.A.I.C.S.: 541511

Poindus Systems Corp. **(1)**
5th Floor No 59 Lane 77 Xing'ai Road, Neihu District, Taipei, 114, Taiwan
Tel.: (886) 27 721 4688
Web Site: https://www.poindus.com
Computer Peripheral Equipment Mfr
N.A.I.C.S.: 334118

FLYTXT
Plot 2 7A Leela Info Prk Tecno Prk, Trivandrum, Kerala, 695581, India
Tel.: (91) 4712700101
Web Site: http://www.flytxt.com
Sales Range: $25-49.9 Million
Emp.: 110
Technology Services to Mobile Operators & Mobile Marketers
N.A.I.C.S.: 541890
Vinod Vasudevan *(CEO)*

FM GLOBAL LOGISTICS HOLDINGS BERHAD
Lot 37 Lebuh Sultan Mohamad 1 Kawasan Perindustrian, Bandar Sultan Suleiman, 42000, Port Klang, Selangor, Malaysia
Tel.: (60) 331761111
Web Site:
 https://www.fmgloballogistics.com
FM—(KLS)
Rev.: $200,711,323
Assets: $145,827,090
Liabilities: $60,214,180
Net Worth: $85,612,910
Earnings: $9,979,259

Emp.: 1,651
Fiscal Year-end: 06/30/23
Freight Services
N.A.I.C.S.: 483111
Hooi Mooi Lim *(Co-Sec)*

Subsidiaries:

**Advance International Freight Sdn.
Bhd.** **(1)**
Lot 37 Lebuh Sultan Mohamad 1 Kawasan Perindustrian, Bandar Sultan Suleiman, 42000, Port Klang, Selangor, Malaysia
Tel.: (60) 331768001
Web Site: http://www.fmgloballogistics.com
Sales Range: $25-49.9 Million
Emp.: 75
Freight Forwarding Services
N.A.I.C.S.: 488510
Yang Heng Lam *(Mgr)*

**FM Global Consolidation Services
Private Limited** **(1)**
Sakar IX 4th Floor B-411 OPP Gold City Cinema Ashram road, Ahmedabad, 380009, India
Tel.: (91) 73495025
Integrated Logistics Services
N.A.I.C.S.: 541614

**FM Global Logistics (Ipoh) Sdn.
Bhd.** **(1)**
No 1B 2nd Floor Persiaran Greentown 9 Greentown Business Centre, 30450, Ipoh, Perak, Malaysia
Tel.: (60) 52421600
Web Site: http://www.fmgloballogistics.com
Sales Range: $25-49.9 Million
Emp.: 20
Freight Forwarding Services
N.A.I.C.S.: 488510
James Tan *(Mgr-Bus Dev)*

**FM Global Logistics (M) Sdn.
Bhd.** **(1)**
Lot 37 Lebuh Sultan Mohamad 1, Kawasan Perindustrian Bandar Sultan Suleiman, 42000, Port Klang, Selangor, Malaysia
Tel.: (60) 331761111
Freight Forwarding Services
N.A.I.C.S.: 488510
Chong Keat Chew *(Mng Dir)*

**FM Global Logistics (M) Sdn.
Bhd.** **(1)**
No 1-2 Jalan PPMP 1 Pusat Perniagaan Malim Permai Hang Tuah Jaya, Malim, 75250, Melaka, Malaysia
Tel.: (60) 63368888
Web Site: http://www.fmmalaysia.com.my
Sales Range: $25-49.9 Million
Emp.: 7
Freight Forwarding Services
N.A.I.C.S.: 488510
Chong Keat Chew *(Mng Dir)*

FM Global Logistics Pty Ltd. **(1)**
Tel.: (61) 893142004
Web Site:
 http://www.fmgloballogistics.com.au
Sales Range: $25-49.9 Million
Emp.: 12
Freight Forwarding Services
N.A.I.C.S.: 488510

**FM Multimodal Services Sdn.
Bhd.** **(1)**
Lot 37B Lebuh Sultan Muhamad 1, Kawasan Perindustrian Bandar Sultan Sulaiman, 42000, Port Klang, Malaysia
Tel.: (60) 331766888
Web Site: https://www.fmmultimodal.com.my
Emp.: 1,200
Air Freight Services
N.A.I.C.S.: 481112

**FM-Hellmann Worldwide Logistics
Sdn. Bhd.** **(1)**
Web Site: http://www.fmmalaysia.com.my
Sales Range: $25-49.9 Million
Emp.: 40
Freight Forwarding Services
N.A.I.C.S.: 488510

**Freight Management (Penang) Sdn.
Bhd.** **(1)**
No 4453 & 4454 Jalan Bagan Luar, 12000, Butterworth, Penang, Malaysia
Tel.: (60) 43314358

Web Site: http://www.fmmalaysia.com.my
Sales Range: $25-49.9 Million
Emp.: 50
Freight Forwarding Services
N.A.I.C.S.: 488510

Icon Freight Services Co. Ltd. **(1)**
731/6 Ratchadapisek Road, Bangpongpang Yannawa, Bangkok, 10120, Thailand
Tel.: (66) 26836352
Web Site: http://www.fmmalaysia.com.my
Sales Range: $25-49.9 Million
Emp.: 20
Freight Forwarding Services
N.A.I.C.S.: 488510

Integrated SCM Co., Ltd. **(1)**
9/53 Unit 2B14 Moo 5 Phaholyotin Road, Klongnueng, Pathumthani, 12120, Thailand
Tel.: (66) 25161022
Packaging Machinery Distr
N.A.I.C.S.: 423840

PT. FM Global Logistics **(1)**
Rukan Artha Gading Niaga Blok H No 11 Jl Bulevar Artha Gading, Kelapa Gading, 14240, Jakarta Utara, Indonesia
Tel.: (62) 2145856727
Air Freight Services
N.A.I.C.S.: 481112

FM MATTSSON MORA GROUP AB
Ostnorsvagen 95, 792 27, Mora, Sweden
Tel.: (46) 250596000
Web Site: https://www.fmm-
 mora.com
1FS0—(BER)
Rev.: $183,471,039
Assets: $168,316,254
Liabilities: $71,540,654
Net Worth: $96,775,600
Earnings: $13,944,333
Emp.: 568
Fiscal Year-end: 12/31/23
Faucet & Accessory Mfr
N.A.I.C.S.: 332913
Fredrik Skarp *(Pres & CEO)*

Subsidiaries:

**FM Mattsson Mora Group Belgie
NV** **(1)**
Pegasuslaan 5, 1831, Diegem, Belgium
Tel.: (32) 25233060
Mixer Tap Mfr & Retailer
N.A.I.C.S.: 332913

**FM Mattsson Mora Group Nederland
BV** **(1)**
Plesmanstraat 4, 3833 LA, Leusden, Netherlands
Tel.: (31) 854018780
Web Site: http://www.damixa.nl
Bath Ware Product Whslr
N.A.I.C.S.: 423710

**FM Mattsson Mora Group Norge
AS** **(1)**
Stromsveien 200, 0668, Oslo, Norway
Tel.: (47) 22091900
Bath Ware Product Whslr
N.A.I.C.S.: 423710

Hotbath Srl **(1)**
Via Marco Polo 135/D, 55049, Viareggio, LU, Italy
Tel.: (39) 05841783742
Web Site: http://www.hotbath.it
Bath Ware Product Distr
N.A.I.C.S.: 423710

FMBCAPITAL HOLDINGS PLC
2nd Floor GFin Building Cybercity, 72201, Ebene, 72201, Mauritius
Tel.: (230) 6592000
Web Site:
 https://fmbcapitalgroup.com
Year Founded: 1995
FMBCH—(MALA)
Rev.: $148,247,857
Assets: $1,393,564,105
Liabilities: $1,196,681,639
Net Worth: $196,882,466

Earnings: $61,194,804
Emp.: 1,913
Fiscal Year-end: 12/31/22
Bank Holding Company
N.A.I.C.S.: 551111
Mahendra Gursahani *(Mng Dir-Interim)*

Subsidiaries:

First Capital Bank Plc **(1)**
Livingstone Towers 21 Glyn Jones Road, P/Bag 122, Blantyre, Malawi **(100%)**
Tel.: (265) 1 821955
Web Site: http://firstcapitalbank.co.mw
Emp.: 850
Full Service Commercial Bank
N.A.I.C.S.: 522110
Hitesh Anadkat *(Chm)*

Subsidiary (Non-US):

First Capital Bank Limited **(2)**
Barclay House, PO Box 1279, Corner 1st St & Jason Moyo Ave, Harare, Zimbabwe **(67.68%)**
Tel.: (263) 242250579
Web Site: http://firstcapitalbank.co.zw
Banking Services
N.A.I.C.S.: 522110
Ciaran McSharry *(Mng Dir)*

FMCG BUSINESS PARTNER AB
Svetsarvagen 15 2 tr, 171 41, Solna, Sweden
Tel.: (46) 8557 790 50
Web Site: http://www.ancrona.se
Sales Range: $25-49.9 Million
Emp.: 15
Privater Equity Firm
N.A.I.C.S.: 523999
Peter Nordwall *(CEO)*

Subsidiaries:

Ancrona AB **(1)**
Svetsarv. 15, 17141, Solna, Sweden **(100%)**
Tel.: (46) 855779050
Web Site: http://www.ancrona.se
Sales Range: $10-24.9 Million
Emp.: 100
Other Grocery & Related Products Whslr
N.A.I.C.S.: 424490
Sophie Ramsten *(Mgr-Mktg & Bus Dev)*

Subsidiary (Non-US):

Castus A/S **(2)**
Unionsvej 4, 4600, Koge, Denmark
Tel.: (45) 5630 3600
Web Site: http://www.castus.dk
Grocery Product Distr
N.A.I.C.S.: 424410

Subsidiary (Domestic):

Graveleijs produkter AB **(2)**
Ostra Tullgatan 20, 824 52, Hudiksvall, Gavleborg, Sweden
Tel.: (46) 650 31585
Web Site: http://www.graveleij.se
Grocery Product Distr
N.A.I.C.S.: 424410

Rootfruit Scandinavia AB **(2)**
Industrigatan 23, Box 1, 312 21, Laholm, Sweden
Tel.: (46) 430 134 40
Web Site: http://www.rootfruit.se
Food Product Mfr & Distr
N.A.I.C.S.: 311821
Hans Jacobsson *(Gen Mgr)*

FMR RESOURCES LIMITED
Level 5 126 Phillip St, Sydney, 2000, NSW, Australia
Tel.: (61) 893888290 AU
Web Site:
 https://fmrresources.com.au
Year Founded: 2003
FMR—(ASX)
Rev.: $18,732
Assets: $3,612,366
Liabilities: $3,291,596

Net Worth: $320,770
Earnings: ($359,417)
Fiscal Year-end: 06/30/24
Investment Services
N.A.I.C.S.: 523999

FMS ENTERPRISES MIGUN LTD.
Imber 27, Petach Tikva, 61180, Israel
Tel.: (972) 39223206
Web Site: https://fms.co.il
Year Founded: 1986
FBRT—(TAE)
Rev.: $113,418,000
Assets: $166,468,000
Liabilities: $17,941,000
Net Worth: $148,527,000
Earnings: $37,706,000
Emp.: 100
Fiscal Year-end: 12/31/23
All Other Miscellaneous Fabricated Metal Product Manufacturing
N.A.I.C.S.: 332999

FMS WERTMANAGEMENT AOR
Prinzregentenstrasse 56, 80538, Munich, Germany
Tel.: (49) 89 954 7627 0
Web Site: http://www.fms-wm.de
Holding Company
N.A.I.C.S.: 551112
Michael Kemmer *(Chm-Supervisory Bd)*

Subsidiaries:

DEPFA BANK plc **(1)**
Block 5 Irish Life Centre, Lower Abbey Street, Dublin, D01 P767, Ireland
Tel.: (353) 17922222
Web Site: http://www.depfa.com
Banking Services
N.A.I.C.S.: 522110
Fiona Flannery *(CEO & Exec Dir)*

Subsidiary (Domestic):

DEPFA ACS Bank plc **(2)**
1 Commons Street, Dublin, 1, Ireland
Tel.: (353) 17922222
Sales Range: $100-124.9 Million
Emp.: 20
Commercial Banking Services
N.A.I.C.S.: 522110

Subsidiary (Non-US):

DEPFA Finance N.V. **(2)**
De Entree 99-197, Amsterdam, 1101 HE, Netherlands
Tel.: (31) 205554603
Commercial Banking Services
N.A.I.C.S.: 522110

FN FACTORY OUTLET PCL
991 FN Building Rama 9 Road, Suan Luang Subdistrict Suan Luang District, Bangkok, 10250, Thailand
Tel.: (66) 23004951
Web Site: https://www.fnoutlet.com
Year Founded: 2015
FN—(THA)
Rev.: $13,226,882
Assets: $36,224,899
Liabilities: $5,846,276
Net Worth: $30,378,624
Earnings: ($7,031,762)
Emp.: 315
Fiscal Year-end: 12/31/23
Apparel & Textile Product Mfr
N.A.I.C.S.: 314999
Benyiam Songwatana *(CEO)*

FNC ENTERTAINMENT CO., LTD.
111 Cheongdam-dong, Gangnam-gu, Seoul, Korea (South)
Tel.: (82) 25175426
Web Site: https://www.fncent.com
Year Founded: 2006

FNC Entertainment Co., Ltd.—(Continued)

173940—(KRS)
Rev.: $50,458,224
Assets: $73,351,589
Liabilities: $39,289,757
Net Worth: $34,061,832
Earnings: ($13,494,720)
Emp.: 177
Fiscal Year-end: 12/31/22
Music Recordings, Concert Promotions, Film Production
N.A.I.C.S.: 512250
Seo Kyesang (Dir)

FNG GROUP NV
Bautersemstraat 68, 2800, Mechelen, Belgium
Tel.: (32) 15293444
Web Site: http://www.fng.eu
Children's Clothing Mfr & Distr
N.A.I.C.S.: 424350

FNGUIDE INC.
FnGuide Building 61 Magokjungang 2-ro, Gangseo-gu, Seoul, 07805, Korea (South)
Tel.: (82) 27697700
Web Site: https://corp.fnguide.com
Year Founded: 2000
Financial Market Data
N.A.I.C.S.: 519290
Lee Chul-Soon (CEO)

FNM S.P.A.
Piazzale Cadorna 14, 20123, Milan, Italy
Tel.: (39) 0285111   IT
Web Site: http://www.fnmgroup.it
FNM—(ITA)
Sales Range: $300-349.9 Million
Emp.: 2,800
Holding Company; Regional Commuter Transportation & Infrastructure Engineering Services
N.A.I.C.S.: 551112
Norberto Achille (Chm)

Subsidiaries:

LeNORD S.R.L.   (1)
Ple Cadorna 14, Milan, 20123, Italy
Tel.: (39) 0285114382
Web Site: http://www.lenord.it
Railway Transport Services
N.A.I.C.S.: 482111

NordCom S.p.A.   (1)
Paleocapa St 6, Milan, 20121, Italy   (58%)
Tel.: (39) 02721511
Web Site: http://www.nord-com.it
System Integration Services
N.A.I.C.S.: 541512

FNS HOLDINGS PUBLIC COMPANY LIMITED
TISCO Tower 20/F 48/45 North Sathorn Road, Bangkok, 10500, Thailand
Tel.: (66) 26973800
Web Site: https://www.finansa.com
Year Founded: 1991
FNS—(THA)
Rev.: $75,753,045
Assets: $708,579,870
Liabilities: $497,514,162
Net Worth: $211,065,708
Earnings: $10,538,038
Emp.: 970
Fiscal Year-end: 12/31/23
Investment Banking & Financial Management Services
N.A.I.C.S.: 523150
Vorasit Pokachaiyapat (Mng Dir)

Subsidiaries:

Finansa Credit Ltd.   (1)
TISCO Tower 12A/F, 48 North Sathorn Road, Bangkok, 10500, Thailand

Earnings: $5,161,740
Emp.: 1,513
Fiscal Year-end: 12/31/22
Credit Services
N.A.I.C.S.: 522299

Finansa Fund Management Ltd.   (1)
TISCO Tower 16F, 48 N Sathorn Rd, Bangkok, 10500, Thailand
Tel.: (66) 26973700
Web Site: http://www.finansa.com
Emp.: 10
Investment Fund Management Services
N.A.I.C.S.: 523999

Finansa Securities Ltd.   (1)
TISCO Tower 20/F 48/45 North Sathorn Road, Bangkok, 10500, Thailand
Tel.: (66) 2 697 3800
Web Site: https://www.finansa.com
Financial Investment Services
N.A.I.C.S.: 523940

FNS TECH CO.,LTD
19 4sandan 2-gil Jiksan-eup, Seobukgu, Cheonan, Chungcheongnam-do, Korea (South)
Tel.: (82) 415844460
Web Site: https://www.fnstech.com
Year Founded: 2002
083500—(KRS)
Rev.: $51,881,417
Assets: $70,845,018
Liabilities: $21,767,420
Net Worth: $49,077,598
Earnings: $3,106,031
Emp.: 156
Fiscal Year-end: 12/31/22
Electronic Equipment Mfr & Distr
N.A.I.C.S.: 334413
Sang Jae Yang (Co-CEO)

FNZ GROUP LTD.
Level 7 256 Lambton Quay, Wellington, 6011, New Zealand
Tel.: (64) 48039400   NZ
Web Site: http://www.fnz.com
Investment Services
N.A.I.C.S.: 523940
Alastair Conway (CEO)

FOBI AI INC.
541 Howe St Suite 2F, Vancouver, V6C 2C2, BC, Canada
Web Site: https://www.fobi.ai
Year Founded: 2017
FOBIF—(OTCQB)
Rev.: $123,247
Assets: $9,138,864
Liabilities: $765,265
Net Worth: $8,373,599
Earnings: ($8,680,635)
Fiscal Year-end: 06/30/21
Information Technology Services
N.A.I.C.S.: 541512
Rob Anson (CEO)

FOCALTECH SYSTEMS CO., LTD.
4F No 6 Dusing First Road Hsinchu Science Park, Hsinchu, 30078, Taiwan
Tel.: (886) 36661660
Web Site: http://www.focaltech-systems.com
Year Founded: 2005
Holding Company; Mobile Electronic Integrated Circuit Products Mfr & Whslr
N.A.I.C.S.: 551112
Genda Hu (Chm)

FOCE INDIA LIMITED
4 Kingstone Shastri nagar Lokhandwala Complex Andheri West, Mumbai, 400053, Maharashtra, India
Tel.: (91) 9820053986   In
Web Site: https://www.foceindia.com
Year Founded: 2001
FOCE—(NSE)
Rev.: $6,928,565

Assets: $103,662,994
Liabilities: $97,852,371
Net Worth: $5,810,623
Earnings: $1,019,351
Emp.: 8
Fiscal Year-end: 03/31/23
Watch Product Mfr
N.A.I.C.S.: 334519

FOCI FIBER OPTIC COMMUNICATIONS, INC.
No 18 Prosperity Rd II, Science-Based Industrial Park, Hsinchu, 300, Taiwan
Tel.: (886) 35770099
Web Site: https://www.foci.com.tw
Year Founded: 1995
3363—(TPE)
Rev.: $50,672,514
Assets: $72,773,286
Liabilities: $18,026,483
Net Worth: $54,746,803
Earnings: $1,470,187
Fiscal Year-end: 12/31/22
Fiber Optic Electrical Equipment Mfr
N.A.I.C.S.: 335921

Subsidiaries:

Jiangxi FOCI Fiber Optic Communication, Inc.   (1)
601 of No 3 Jv Neng Rd, Hi-tech Development Zone, Yingtan, 335000, Jiangxi, China
Tel.: (86) 7016689969
Optical Isolator Mfr
N.A.I.C.S.: 335921

Shanghai FOCI Fiber Optic Communication Equipments, Inc.   (1)
No 8 Qiu Jing Rd Jiu Ting Economic Development Zone, SongJiang, Shanghai, 201615, China
Tel.: (86) 2157632828
Optical Isolator Mfr
N.A.I.C.S.: 335921

Shanghai FOCI Fiber Optic Communications, Inc.   (1)
No 8 Qiu Jing Rd Jiu Ting Economic Development Zone, SongJiang, Shanghai, 201615, China
Tel.: (86) 2157632828
Optical Glass Mfr & Distr
N.A.I.C.S.: 334610

Zhongshan FOCI Fiber Optic Communications, Inc.   (1)
301 of 3rd floor 4th Floor and 502 of 5th Floor No 18-2 ZhiYe Rd, Torch Hi-tech Industrial Development Zone, Zhongshan, 528436, Guangdong, China
Tel.: (86) 76088588600
Optical Isolator Mfr
N.A.I.C.S.: 335921

FOCKE & CO. (GMBH & CO.) VERPACKUNGSMASCHINEN
Siemensstrasse 10, Aller, 27283, Verden, Germany
Tel.: (49) 42318910
Web Site: http://www.focke.com
Year Founded: 1955
Sales Range: $100-124.9 Million
Emp.: 1,000
Packaging Machinery Mfr
N.A.I.C.S.: 333993
Thomas Hafker (Mng Dir)

Subsidiaries:

FQPAC Maschinenbau GmbH   (1)
Industriestrasse 17, 26676, Barssel, Germany
Tel.: (49) 4499820
Emp.: 300
Packaging Machinery Mfr
N.A.I.C.S.: 333993

Focke & Co. (UK) Ltd.   (1)
Courtenay Works Monument Way, Woking, GU21 5LY, Surrey, United Kingdom
Tel.: (44) 1483 756094
Emp.: 21
Industrial Supplies Whslr

N.A.I.C.S.: 423840

Focke & Co., Inc.   (1)
5730 Millstream Rd, Whitsett, NC 27377-9789   (100%)
Tel.: (336) 449-7200
Web Site: http://www.focke.biz
Sales Range: $25-49.9 Million
Emp.: 70
Marketing & Sale of Packaging Machinery
N.A.I.C.S.: 333993
Johann Betschart (VP-Sls)

Focke (Hong Kong) Ltd.   (1)
Unit B 7th Floor Shell Industrial Building 12 Lee Chung Street, Chai Wan, China (Hong Kong)
Tel.: (852) 2897 6260
Web Site: http://www.focke.com
Emp.: 20
Industrial Supplies Whslr
N.A.I.C.S.: 423840
Peta Pang (Gen Mgr)

Focke (Singapore) PTE LTD   (1)
No 25 International Business Park 01-18/21 German Centre, Singapore, 609916, Singapore
Tel.: (65) 6468 9227
Emp.: 30
Industrial Supplies Whslr
N.A.I.C.S.: 423840

Focke do Brasil Ltda.   (1)
Av Carlos Gomes 141 7 Andar/Conj 707 Bairro Auxilladora, Porto Alegre, 90480-003, Brazil
Tel.: (55) 51 3328 6551
Emp.: 9
Industrial Machinery Maintenance Services
N.A.I.C.S.: 811310

H.-H. Focke GmbH & Co. KG   (1)
Auguste-Viktoria-Allee 15, 13403, Berlin, Germany
Tel.: (49) 30 41 00 6
Emp.: 350
Packaging Machinery Mfr
N.A.I.C.S.: 333993

LCC FOCKE SERVICE ST.-PB   (1)
Zastavskaya 22 Office 903, 196084, Saint Petersburg, Russia
Tel.: (7) 8123133080
Emp.: 20
Industrial Supplies Whslr
N.A.I.C.S.: 423840
Andreas Bohne (Gen Dir)

FOCUS (DIY) GROUP LTD.
Gawsworth House Westmere Dr, Crewe, CW1 6XB, United Kingdom
Tel.: (44) 1270501555
Year Founded: 1987
Sales Range: $550-599.9 Million
Emp.: 4,000
Holding Company; Chain of DIY Stores
N.A.I.C.S.: 444140
Andrew Unitt (Dir-Fin)

FOCUS 4U LTD.
Europa House, Southwick Square, Southwick, BN42 4FJ, West Sussex, United Kingdom
Tel.: (44) 8454505225
Web Site: http://www.Focus4U.co.uk
Year Founded: 2003
Sales Range: $10-24.9 Million
Emp.: 70
Corporate Telecommunications Services
N.A.I.C.S.: 517810
Chris Goodman (Dir-Sls)

Subsidiaries:

Focus Digital Media   (1)
46-50 Southwick Sqaure, Brighton, BN42 4FJ, United Kingdom
Tel.: (44) 330 024 2007
Web Site: http://www.focus-dm.co.uk
Web Development Services
N.A.I.C.S.: 541511
Chris Pellatt (Dir-Technical)

FOCUS BUSINESS SOLUTION LTD.

703 Rajhans Complex Nr Nirmal Hospital Ring Road, Surat, 395002, India
Tel.: (91) 2614002823
Web Site: https://www.focusbsl.com
543312—(BOM)
Rev.: $1,557,956
Assets: $538,366
Liabilities: $231,284
Net Worth: $307,082
Earnings: $14,663
Fiscal Year-end: 03/31/21
Software Development Services
N.A.I.C.S.: 541511
Mohamed Yaseen Nathani *(Chm & Mng Dir)*

FOCUS DIGITAL MEDIA LIMITED

Europa House Southwick Square, Southwick, BN42 4FJ, W Sussex, United Kingdom
Tel.: (44) 844 692 8000　　UK
Web Site: http://www.focus-grp.co.uk
Year Founded: 2003
Sales Range: $25-49.9 Million
Emp.: 150
Wireless Telecommunication Services
N.A.I.C.S.: 517112
Ralph Gilbert *(Mng Dir)*

FOCUS DYNAMICS GROUP BERHAD

Lot 12 1 12th Floor Menara Lien Hoe No 8 Persiaran Tropicana, Tropicana Golf & Country Resort, 47410, Petaling Jaya, Selangor, Malaysia
Tel.: (60) 378037333　　MY
Web Site:
　https://www.focusdynamics.com.my
Year Founded: 2002
FOCUS—(KLS)
Rev.: $12,748,571
Assets: $49,501,587
Liabilities: $14,665,608
Net Worth: $34,835,979
Earnings: ($15,657,778)
Emp.: 83
Fiscal Year-end: 06/30/22
Engineeering Services
N.A.I.C.S.: 541330
Tay Ben Seng *(Exec Dir)*

Subsidiaries:

Lavo Gallery Sdn. Bhd.　　(1)
Taman Perindustrian Jaya 12 14 & 16 Jalan TPJ 10, 47200, Petaling Jaya, Malaysia
Tel.: (60) 378450896
Control Systems Mfr
N.A.I.C.S.: 334512

FOCUS GRAPHITE INC.

945 Princess Street, Box 116, Kingston, K7L 0E9, ON, Canada
Tel.: (613) 241-4040　　Ca
Web Site:
　https://www.focusgraphite.com
FMS—(TSXV)
Rev.: $16,261
Assets: $22,467,800
Liabilities: $5,060,600
Net Worth: $17,407,200
Earnings: ($4,386,235)
Fiscal Year-end: 09/30/20
Metal Mining Services
N.A.I.C.S.: 212290
Marc Roy *(Pres & CEO)*

FOCUS H&S CO., LTD.

Focus Bldg 16-17 LS-ro 91beon-gil, Dongan-gu, Anyang, 14119, Gyeonggi-do, Korea (South)
Tel.: (82) 316893380
Web Site: https://www.focushns.com
Year Founded: 2012

331380—(KRS)
Rev.: $47,266,829
Assets: $28,818,716
Liabilities: $12,806,521
Net Worth: $16,012,195
Earnings: $2,059,330
Emp.: 89
Fiscal Year-end: 12/31/22
Camera Mfr & Distr
N.A.I.C.S.: 334419
Kim Dae Jung *(CEO)*

FOCUS HOME INTERACTIVE SAS

11 rue Cambrai Batiment 28, Parc de Flandre Le Beauvaisis, Paris, 75019, France
Tel.: (33) 157422082
ALPUL—(EUR)
Rev.: $211,476,308
Assets: $334,609,419
Liabilities: $175,542,419
Net Worth: $159,067,000
Earnings: $11,179,360
Emp.: 590
Fiscal Year-end: 03/31/23
Video Game Publishing Services
N.A.I.C.S.: 449210
Deborah Bellange *(CFO)*

FOCUS HOTMELT COMPANY LTD.

No 97 Chuangqiang Road Ningxi Street, Zengcheng District, Guangzhou, 511335, Guangdong, China
Tel.: (86) 2082469190
Web Site:
　https://www.focushotmelt.com
Year Founded: 2012
301283—(CHIN)
Rev.: $189,643,896
Assets: $235,782,144
Liabilities: $37,250,928
Net Worth: $198,531,216
Earnings: $12,255,516
Fiscal Year-end: 12/31/22
Adhesive Product Mfr & Distr
N.A.I.C.S.: 325520
Kirk Liu *(VP)*

FOCUS INDUSTRIAL RESOURCES LIMITED

104 Mukand House Commercial Complex, Azadpur, Delhi, 110033, India
Tel.: (91) 011 47039000　　In
Web Site: http://www.focuslimited.in
Year Founded: 1985
Rev.: $262,547
Assets: $4,057,101
Liabilities: $669,203
Net Worth: $3,387,897
Earnings: $1,820
Emp.: 6
Fiscal Year-end: 03/31/18
Financial Lending Services
N.A.I.C.S.: 522291
Punit Seth *(CFO)*

FOCUS LIGHTING & FIXTURES LIMITED

1007-1010 Corporate Avenue Sonawala Crosslane Goregoan East, Mumbai, 400063, India
Tel.: (91) 2226865671
Web Site:
　https://www.pluslighttech.com
FOCUS—(NSE)
Industry Machinery Mfr
N.A.I.C.S.: 333248
Amit Vinod Sheth *(Mng Dir)*

Subsidiaries:

Focus Lighting & Fixtures Pte. Ltd.　　(1)

30 Cecil Street 19-08 Prudential Tower, Singapore, 049712, Singapore
Tel.: (65) 9 723 7900
Focus Lighting Equipment Mfr
N.A.I.C.S.: 335139

Focus Lighting Corp.　　(1)
221 W 116th St, New York, NY 10026
Tel.: (212) 865-1565
Web Site: http://www.focuslighting.com
Electronic Parts & Equipment Merchant Whslr
N.A.I.C.S.: 541490
Dan Nichols *(Project Mgr)*

Plus Light Tech FZE　　(1)
Block D1-19 Free Zone gate -1 AL Bustan, Ajman, United Arab Emirates
Tel.: (971) 55 325 3121
Focus Lighting Equipment Mfr
N.A.I.C.S.: 335139

FOCUS LIGHTINGS TECH CO., LTD.

Rooms 01-05 32F Zhongxin Building No 15 Yueliangwan Road, Suzhou Industrial Park, Suzhou, 215123, Jiangsu, China
Tel.: (86) 51282258385
Web Site:
　https://www.focuslightings.com
Year Founded: 2010
300708—(CHIN)
Rev.: $349,438,244
Assets: $667,592,900
Liabilities: $261,495,955
Net Worth: $406,096,945
Earnings: $17,064,485
Fiscal Year-end: 12/31/23
Electronic Parts Mfr & Distr
N.A.I.C.S.: 334413
Pan Huarong *(Chm & Gen Mgr)*

FOCUS LUMBER BERHAD

Mile 3 Jalan Masak Kampung Ulu Patikang, Locked Bag No 13, SM-88, 89009, Keningau, Sabah, Malaysia
Tel.: (60) 87335457
Web Site:
　https://www.focuslumber.com.my
Year Founded: 1989
FLBHD—(KLS)
Rev.: $28,533,241
Assets: $41,784,892
Liabilities: $1,456,239
Net Worth: $40,328,652
Earnings: $5,856,023
Emp.: 557
Fiscal Year-end: 12/31/22
Plywood & Veneer Mfr & Sales
N.A.I.C.S.: 321212
Hao Wen Lin *(Mng Dir)*

FOCUS MEDIA HOLDING LIMITED

Unit 2001 The Centrium 60 Wyndham Street, Central, China (Hong Kong)
Tel.: (852) 3752 8009　　Ky
Web Site: http://www.focusmedia.cn
Year Founded: 2003
Sales Range: $900-999.9 Million
Emp.: 6,700
Holding Company; Media Advertising Services
N.A.I.C.S.: 551112
Jason Nanchun Jiang *(Chm & CEO)*

Subsidiaries:

Focus Media Information Technology Co., Ltd.　　(1)
28th Floor Mega World Trade Center No 369 Jiangsu Road, Changning District, Shanghai, 200050, China
Tel.: (86) 2122165288
Web Site: https://www.focusmedia.cn
Rev.: $1,671,282,976
Assets: $3,420,286,773
Liabilities: $887,320,334
Net Worth: $2,532,966,439

Earnings: $677,725,079
Fiscal Year-end: 12/31/2023
Holding Company; LCD Flat Panel Display Mfr
N.A.I.C.S.: 551112
Jason Nanchun Jiang *(Founder, Chm & CEO)*

Subsidiary (Domestic):

Focus Media Technology (Shangahi) Co., Ltd.　　(2)
28-30F Zhao Feng World Trade Bldg 369 Jiangsu Road, Changning District, Shanghai, 200050, China
Tel.: (86) 21 3212 4661
LCD Flat Panel Display Mfr
N.A.I.C.S.: 334118

FOCUS MINERALS LIMITED

Tel.: (61) 892157888　　AU
Web Site:
　https://www.focusminerals.com.au
FML—(ASX)
Rev.: $22,532,442
Assets: $168,102,371
Liabilities: $105,014,258
Net Worth: $63,088,113
Earnings: ($1,905,177)
Fiscal Year-end: 12/31/23
Gold, Nickel & Other Base Metal Mining & Exploration
N.A.I.C.S.: 212220
Zaiqian Zhang *(CFO & Sec)*

Subsidiaries:

Crescent Gold Limited　　(1)
Level 2 159 Adelaide Terrace East, Perth, 6008, WA, Australia　　**(81.75%)**
Tel.: (61) 863807100
Sales Range: $50-74.9 Million
Emp.: 20
Gold Ore Mining
N.A.I.C.S.: 212220

Focus Operations Pty Ltd　　(1)
Three Mile Hill Great Eastern Hwy PMB 3, Coolgardie, 6429, WA, Australia
Tel.: (61) 890220222
Sales Range: $50-74.9 Million
Emp.: 80
Potash Soda & Borate Mining Services
N.A.I.C.S.: 212390

FOCUS POINT HOLDINGS BERHAD

Unit 1 3 5 and 7 Jalan PJU 1/37 Dataran Prima, 47301, Petaling Jaya, Selangor, Malaysia
Tel.: (60) 378805520
Web Site: https://www.focus-point.com.my
FOCUSP—(KLS)
Rev.: $39,503,970
Assets: $47,574,450
Liabilities: $30,668,715
Net Worth: $16,905,735
Earnings: $2,632,658
Emp.: 703
Fiscal Year-end: 12/31/20
Eye Care Centers
N.A.I.C.S.: 621498
Choon Liang Liaw *(Pres & CEO)*

Subsidiaries:

Excelview Laser Eye Centre Sdn Bhd　　(1)
S-068 S-069 2nd Floor Mid Valley Megamall, 58000, Kuala Lumpur, Malaysia
Tel.: (60) 32 287 3797
Web Site: https://www.excelview.com
Laser Eye Surgery Services
N.A.I.C.S.: 621498

Focus Point Vision Care Group Sdn. Bhd.　　(1)
Unit 1 3 5 7 Jalan PJU 1/37, Dataran Prima, 47301, Petaling Jaya, Selangor, Malaysia
Tel.: (60) 378805520
Web Site: https://www.focus-point.com

Focus Point Holdings Berhad—(Continued)

Sales Range: $100-124.9 Million
Emp.: 500
Optical Retail Stores Management & Operation Services
N.A.I.C.S.: 456130

Multiple Reward Sdn Bhd (1)
No 3 Jalan Teknologi 3/5A Kota Damansara, 47810, Petaling Jaya, Selangor, Malaysia
Tel.: (60) 361402430
Web Site: https://www.komugi.com.my
Bakery Retailer
N.A.I.C.S.: 311811

FOCUS SUITES SOLUTIONS & SERVICES LIMITED
2nd Floor Kalpak Arcade No 46/17 Church Street, Bengaluru, 560 001, Karnataka, India
Tel.: (91) 02226540725
Web Site: http://www.focus-suites.com
Rev.: $4,297,841
Assets: $5,202,857
Liabilities: $857,745
Net Worth: $4,345,112
Earnings: $503,387
Emp.: 8
Fiscal Year-end: 03/31/19
Business Development Services
N.A.I.C.S.: 541720
Soniya Singh (Mng Dir)

FOCUS SYSTEMS CORPORATION
Focus Gotanda Building 2-7-8 Higashigotanda, Shinagawa-Ku, Tokyo, 141-0022, Japan
Tel.: (81) 354217777
Web Site: https://www.focus-s.com
Year Founded: 1977
46620—(TKS)
Rev.: $227,334,800
Assets: $172,381,440
Liabilities: $65,291,600
Net Worth: $107,089,840
Earnings: $9,922,000
Emp.: 1,237
Fiscal Year-end: 03/31/21
Software Development Services
N.A.I.C.S.: 513210
Keiichi Mori (Pres)

FOCUS TECHNOLOGY CO., LTD.
No 7 Lijing Road, Jiangbei New Area, Nanjing, 210032, Jiangsu, China
Tel.: (86) 2566677777
Web Site: https://www.focuschina.com
Year Founded: 1996
002315—(SSE)
Rev.: $207,070,344
Assets: $499,477,212
Liabilities: $181,200,240
Net Worth: $318,276,972
Earnings: $42,176,160
Fiscal Year-end: 12/31/22
Information Technology & Software Development Services
N.A.I.C.S.: 541512
Shen Jinhua (Chm & Pres)

Subsidiaries:

inQbrands, Inc. (1)
1150 S Milliken Ave, Ontario, CA 91761
Tel.: (909) 390-7788
Web Site: https://www.inqbrands.com
Marketing Consulting Services
N.A.I.C.S.: 541613
John Shen (Chm)

FOCUSED MONEY SOLUTIONS INC.
Suite 410 800 6th Avenue Southwest, Calgary, T2P 3G3, AB, Canada

Tel.: (403) 229-4420
Life Settlement Services
N.A.I.C.S.: 525990
Victor DeLaet (Pres & CEO)

FOCUSED PHOTONICS (HANGZHOU), INC.
459 Qianmo Road, Binjiang District, Hangzhou, 310052, Zhejiang, China
Tel.: (86) 57185012111
Web Site: https://www.fpi-inc.com
Year Founded: 2002
300203—(CHIN)
Rev.: $484,467,040
Assets: $1,444,346,748
Liabilities: $946,113,480
Net Worth: $498,233,268
Earnings: ($52,624,728)
Emp.: 6,000
Fiscal Year-end: 12/31/22
Air Quality, Sewage & Surface Water Quality Monitoring Equipment Mfr
N.A.I.C.S.: 333413
Gu Haitao (Chm)

Subsidiaries:

ANPLE Laboratory Technologies (Shanghai) Inc. (1)
Room 507 HaiWen Building No 50 Lane 2897 XieTu Rd, Shanghai, 200030, China
Tel.: (86) 2164684886
Web Site: https://anpelsci.com
Emp.: 500
Laboratory Consumable Product Mfr
N.A.I.C.S.: 334516

ARUN Technology Ltd. (1)
Unit 16 The Brunel Centre Newton Road, Crawley, RH10 9TU, West Sussex, United Kingdom
Tel.: (44) 129 351 3123
Web Site: https://aruntechnology.co.uk
Laboratory Equipment Mfr & Distr
N.A.I.C.S.: 334516

Beijing New Biolink Technology Development Co., Ltd. (1)
Floor 9th No 5 Building Air City, Liqiao Town Shunyi District, Beijing, 101304, China
Tel.: (86) 1081466559
Sewage Treatment Facility Services
N.A.I.C.S.: 221320

Beijing Titan Instrument Co., Ltd. (1)
Floor 3-4 Building M6 No 1 Jiuxianqiao East Road, Chaoyang District, Beijing, 100015, China
Tel.: (86) 4000688800
Web Site: https://www.bjtitanco.com
Laboratory Instrument Mfr
N.A.I.C.S.: 334516

Synspec B.V. (1)
Zernike Campus De Deimten 1, 9747 AV, Groningen, Netherlands
Tel.: (31) 505266454
Testing Laboratory Services
N.A.I.C.S.: 541380
Titia Meuwese (Founder)

Systea S.p.A. (1)
Via Fratta Rotonda Vado Largo 2/A, 03012, Anagni, Italy
Tel.: (39) 077 577 6058
Web Site: https://www.systea.it
Chemicals Mfr
N.A.I.C.S.: 325199

Wuxi Cas Photonics Co., Ltd. (1)
Building C No 200 Linghu Street, Wuxi, China
Tel.: (86) 5108 857 0961
Web Site: https://www.cas-pe.com
Advanced Technology Services
N.A.I.C.S.: 811210

FOCUSLIGHT TECHNOLOGIES INC.
56 Zhangba 6th Rd, High-Tech Zone, Xi;An, 710077, Shaanxi, China
Tel.: (86) 2989560050
Web Site: https://www.focuslight.com
High Power Diode Lasers & Micro Optics Developer & Mfr

N.A.I.C.S.: 334419
Xingsheng Liu (Chm & CEO)

Subsidiaries:

Focuslight Switzerland SA (1)
Rouges-Terres 61, 2068, Neuchatel, Switzerland
Tel.: (41) 763469838
Web Site: http://www.suss-microoptics.com
Sales Range: $25-49.9 Million
Emp.: 20
Memory Chip & Electronic Products Mfr
N.A.I.C.S.: 334418
Reinhard Voelkel (CEO)

FOCUSRITE PLC
Hillbottom Road, High Wycombe, HP12 4HJ, Buckinghamshire, United Kingdom
Tel.: (44) 1494462246
Web Site: https://www.focusriteplc.com
Year Founded: 2014
TUNE—(AIM)
Rev.: $200,353,428
Assets: $256,508,505
Liabilities: $109,946,661
Net Worth: $146,561,844
Earnings: $3,298,779
Fiscal Year-end: 08/31/24
Audio Equipment Mfr
N.A.I.C.S.: 334310
Phil Dudderidge (Founder & Chm)

Subsidiaries:

ADAM Audio GmbH (1)
Rudower Chaussee 50, 12489, Berlin, Germany
Tel.: (49) 308 630 0970
Web Site: https://www.adam-audio.com
Loudspeaker Mfr & Distr
N.A.I.C.S.: 334310
Christian Hellinger (Mng Dir)

ADAM Audio USA, Inc. (1)
2937 Berry Hill Dr, Nashville, TN 37211
Tel.: (615) 983-6213
Loudspeaker Mfr & Distr
N.A.I.C.S.: 334310

Focusrite Audio Engineering Ltd. (1)
Artisan Hillbottom Road, High Wycombe, HP12 4HJ, Bucks, United Kingdom
Tel.: (44) 1494462246
Web Site: https://focusrite.com
Sales Range: $25-49.9 Million
Emp.: 85
Musical Instrument Mfr
N.A.I.C.S.: 339992
Damian Hawley (Dir-Global Mktg & Sls)

Subsidiary (Non-US):

Focusrite Novation Deutschland (2)
Postfach 1465, 74604, Ohringen, Germany
Tel.: (49) 7941699925400
Web Site: http://www.focusrite.de
Musical Instrument Distr
N.A.I.C.S.: 423990

Martin Audio Ltd. (1)
Century Point Halifax Rd, Cressex Bus Pk, High Wycombe, HP12 3SL, Buckinghamshire, United Kingdom
Tel.: (44) 1494535312
Web Site: http://www.martin-audio.com
Loudspeaker Mfr
N.A.I.C.S.: 334310
James King (Dir-Mktg)

Martin Audio US, LLC (1)
909 N Pacific Coast Hwy Ste 270, El Segundo, CA 90245
Tel.: (323) 381-5310
Web Site: https://martin-audio.com
Loudspeaker Mfr & Distr
N.A.I.C.S.: 334310

Sequential LLC (1)
1527 Stockton St 3rd Fl, San Francisco, CA 94133
Tel.: (415) 830-6393
Web Site: https://www.sequential.com
Musical Instrument Mfr & Distr
N.A.I.C.S.: 339992

FOGA SYSTEM INTERNATIONAL AB
Mogolsvagen 8, 555 93, Jonkoping, Sweden
Tel.: (46) 362906690
Web Site: http://www.fogasystem.com
Year Founded: 1971
Sales Range: $25-49.9 Million
Emp.: 6
Aluminum Profile System Office & Shop Fitting Screen Wall Glass Showcase & Exhibition Stand Mfr
N.A.I.C.S.: 337215
David Norburg (CEO)

Subsidiaries:

Aluscand AB (1)
Stromfallsvagen 34, 135 49, Tyreso, Sweden
Tel.: (46) 8770 88 80
Metal Door Mfr
N.A.I.C.S.: 332321

Display Ways Ltd. (1)
15 Te Puni Street Petone Lower Hutt, PO Box 39165, Wellington, 5012, New Zealand
Tel.: (64) 45760990
Web Site: http://www.displayways.co.nz
Sales Range: $25-49.9 Million
Emp.: 20
N.A.I.C.S.: 337215
Martin McDonald (CEO)

Eurofoga S.L. (1)
Daniel De Olmo Parcela 6, Poligono Argales, E 47008, Valladolid, Spain
Tel.: (34) 983235307
Web Site: http://www.eurofoga.es
Aluminum Profile Systems Mfr for Office & Shop Fittings, Screen Walls, Glass Showcases & Exhibition Stands
N.A.I.C.S.: 337215

FOGA SYSTEMS AUSTRALIA PTY LTD
Unit 7 no 34 Technology, Warana, 4575, QLD, Australia (1)
Tel.: (61) 7 5493 4949
Metal Door Mfr
N.A.I.C.S.: 332321

Foga Benelux B.V. (1)
PO Box 2051, NL-5001 CB, Tilburg, Netherlands
Tel.: (31) 134556915
N.A.I.C.S.: 337215

Foga Interijere d.o.o. (1)
Sljemenska 2, 10290, Zagreb, Croatia
Tel.: (385) 13351558
Web Site: http://www.officefoga.com
Sales Range: $25-49.9 Million
Emp.: 4
Showcase, Partition, Shelving & Locker Mfr
N.A.I.C.S.: 337215

Foga Polen Sp. z o.o. (1)
Wala Chynowska 107, PL-03-650, Chynow, Poland
Tel.: (48) 486614276
Web Site: http://www.pogasystems.com
N.A.I.C.S.: 337215

Foga System Corporation (1)
3 1 2 Azabudai, Minato-Ku, Tokyo, 106 0041, Japan
Tel.: (81) 335051341
Web Site: http://www.foga.co.jp
Sales Range: $25-49.9 Million
N.A.I.C.S.: 337215

Foga System Ethiopia (1)
Kebele 18 House No 010/B Kirkos Kifle Ketema, Addis Ababa, Ethiopia
Tel.: (251) 11 6626190
Metal Door Mfr
N.A.I.C.S.: 332321

Foga System France S.a.r.L. (1)
15, rue du Gen, Vandenberg, F-67140, Paris, Barr, France
Tel.: (33) 388080008
Web Site: http://www.foga.se
N.A.I.C.S.: 337215

Foga System GmbH (1)

Schongauer Strasse 25, 04328, Leipzig, Germany
Tel.: (49) 3412519266
N.A.I.C.S.: 337215

Foga System Scandinavia AB (1)
Stromfallsvagen 34, SE 135 49, Stockholm, Tyreso, Sweden
Tel.: (46) 87708880
Web Site: http://www.foga.se
Sales Range: $25-49.9 Million
Commercial Furniture Mfr
N.A.I.C.S.: 337215

Hungseo Industrial Co., Ltd. (1)
Hwajin Bldg 738 25 Yuksam Dong, Seoul, Korea (South)
Tel.: (82) 25624441
Web Site: http://www.hsint.com
Sales Range: $25-49.9 Million
Emp.: 30
N.A.I.C.S.: 337215
Changwhan Lee (Gen Mgr)

KATEKS SISUSTUS (1)
Punane 58, 13619, Tallinn, Estonia
Tel.: (372) 6053173
Web Site: http://www.kateks.ee
Metal Door Mfr
N.A.I.C.S.: 332321
Valdo Rose (Mng Dir)

Norking Aluminium Ltd. (1)
L K H Estate Tickhill Rd, Doncaster, DN4 8QG, United Kingdom
Tel.: (44) 302855907
Sales Range: $25-49.9 Million
N.A.I.C.S.: 337215
Graeme Gibson (Mng Dir)

Outwater Plastic Industries, Inc. (1)
24 River Rd, Bogota, NJ 07603
Tel.: (201) 498-8750
Web Site: http://www.outwater.com
Sales Range: $75-99.9 Million
Hardware & Decorative Trim Plastic Moldings
N.A.I.C.S.: 423710
Joey Shimm (VP-Mktg & Adv)

SCENOGRAFIE S.R.O (1)
Cernokostelecka 90, 100 00, Prague, Czech Republic
Tel.: (420) 777619090
Web Site: http://www.scenografie.cz
Metal Door Mfr
N.A.I.C.S.: 332321

FOGS D.D. SARAJEVO

Ul Vrbanjusa br 25, 71000, Sarajevo, Bosnia & Herzegovina
Tel.: (387) 3 344 1280
Year Founded: 1946
FOGSRK6—(SARE)
Rev.: $1,816,043
Assets: $4,812,221
Liabilities: $4,433,284
Net Worth: $378,937
Earnings: ($305,238)
Emp.: 131
Fiscal Year-end: 12/31/20
Shoe Mfr
N.A.I.C.S.: 316990

FOKUS MINING CORPORATION

147 Quebec Avenue, Rouyn-Noranda, J9X 6M8, QC, Canada
Tel.: (819) 762-0609   Ca
Web Site:
   https://www.fokusmining.com
Year Founded: 1985
F7E1—(MUN)
Rev.: $8,359
Assets: $6,987,865
Liabilities: $185,696
Net Worth: $6,802,169
Earnings: ($932,979)
Fiscal Year-end: 12/31/23
Gold Mining & Exploration Services
N.A.I.C.S.: 212220
Jean Rainville (Pres & CEO)

FOLIATEAM SASU

4 Passage Dartois Bidot, Paris, 94101, France
Tel.: (33) 1 55 12 55 12
Computer Softwares Mfr
N.A.I.C.S.: 513210
Dominique Bayon (Pres)

FOLIUM GROUP LTD

Kingsbury Business Park Kingsbury Road, Minworth, Birmingham, B76 9DL, West Midlands, United Kingdom
Tel.: (44) 1213522000
Web Site: http://www.folium.co.uk
Sales Range: $10-24.9 Million
Emp.: 64
Printing Services
N.A.I.C.S.: 323111
John Steed (Chm)

FOLKSAM OMSESIDIG SAK-FORSAKRING

Bohusgatan 14, 106 60, Stockholm, Sweden
Tel.: (46) 771950950   SE
Web Site: http://www.folksam.se
Year Founded: 1908
Emp.: 4,000
Insurance & Investment Products & Services
N.A.I.C.S.: 524298
AnnKristine Wuopio-Mogestedt (Sr VP & Head-Claims)

Subsidiaries:

Folksam omsesidig livforsakring (1)
Bohusgatan 14, 106 60, Stockholm, Sweden
Tel.: (46) 771 960 960
Web Site: http://www.folksam.se
Life Insurance Products & Services
N.A.I.C.S.: 524113

Forenade Liv Gruppforsakring AB (1)
Ostgotagatan 90, 106 60, Stockholm, Sweden
Tel.: (46) 87004080
Web Site: http://www.forenadeliv.se
Fire Insurance Services
N.A.I.C.S.: 524113

Fortum Distribution AB (1)
Hangovagen 19, 115 77, Stockholm, Sweden (17.5%)
Tel.: (46) 8 671 70 00
Electric Power Distr
N.A.I.C.S.: 221122

KPA Pensionsforsakring AB (1)
Ostgotagatan 90, Stockholm, 106 85, Sweden
Tel.: (46) 8 6650400
Fire Insurance Services
N.A.I.C.S.: 524113

SalusAnsvar AB (1)
Tullvaktsvagen 11, Stockholm, 115 56, Sweden
Tel.: (46) 855545000
Web Site: http://www.salusansvar.se
Sales Range: $100-124.9 Million
Emp.: 180
Commercial Banking Services
N.A.I.C.S.: 522110
Anna Karyn Laurell (Gen Mgr)

FOLKUP DEVELOPMENT INC.

Unit 17-18 23/F Metropole Square, 2 On Yiu Street, Sha Tin, New Territories, China (Hong Kong)
Tel.: (852) 3487 6330   NV
Year Founded: 2016
Rev.: $2,593,376
Assets: $3,582,437
Liabilities: $5,139,803
Net Worth: ($1,557,366)
Earnings: ($901,521)
Emp.: 30
Fiscal Year-end: 12/31/20
Eco-Transportation Leasing Services
N.A.I.C.S.: 532112
Hak Yiu Ng (Chm, Pres & Treas)

FOLLI FOLLIE S.A.

23rd km Athens-Lamia Highway, 145 65, Athens, Greece
Tel.: (30) 210 6241 000   GR
Web Site: http://www.ffgroup.com
Year Founded: 1979
FFGRP—(OTCIQ)
Sales Range: $150-199.9 Billion
Emp.: 4,800
Holding Company; Duty Free Merchandise Retailer
N.A.I.C.S.: 551112
Dimitrios Koutsolioutsos (Chm)

Subsidiaries:

Attica Department Stores S.A. (1)
9 Panepistimious Street, 10671, Athens, Greece
Tel.: (30) 2111802600
Web Site: http://www.atticadps.gr
Discount Department Stores Operation Services
N.A.I.C.S.: 455110

Elmec Romania SRL (1)
Strada Progresului Nr 134-138 Sector Nr 5, 050693, Bucharest, Romania
Tel.: (40) 214117086
Web Site: http://www.elmecromania.ro
Sales Range: $150-199.9 Million
Sports & Fashion Articles Retailer
N.A.I.C.S.: 423910
Cristian Beznoska (CEO)

Factory Outlet Airport S.A. (1)
Airport Commerce Park, 190 01, Spata, East Attica, Greece
Tel.: (30) 2103541800
Web Site: http://www.factoryoutlet.gr
Sales Range: $1-4.9 Billion
Discount Department Stores Operation Services
N.A.I.C.S.: 455110
Miltos Galanis (Gen Mgr)

Factory Outlet S.A. (1)
Athinon Ave 76 Peiraios, 185 47, Piraeus, Greece
Tel.: (30) 2104833928
Web Site: http://www.factory.gr
Apparel & Accessory Stores Operation Services
N.A.I.C.S.: 458110

Folli Follie Hong Kong Ltd. (1)
18 F The Centrium 60 Wyndham Street, Central, China (Hong Kong)
Tel.: (852) 24012332
Web Site: http://www.follifollie.com.hk
Watches & Jewelry Whslr
N.A.I.C.S.: 423940

Folli Follie Japan, Ltd. (1)
6-6-9 Roppongi Roppongi Piramide 4F, Minato-ku, Tokyo, 160-0032, Japan
Tel.: (81) 334780429
Web Site: http://www.follifollie.co.jp
Watches & Jewelry Retailer
N.A.I.C.S.: 458310

Folli Follie Korea Ltd. (1)
3F Bosung Building 666-4 Sin-Sa Dong, Seoul, Korea (South)
Tel.: (82) 25447474
Web Site: http://www.follifollie.co.kr
Watches & Jewelry Whslr
N.A.I.C.S.: 423940

Folli Follie Malaysia Ltd. (1)
Suite 02-02A 2nd Floor Menara Keck Seng 203 Jalan Bukit Bintang, 55100, Kuala Lumpur, Malaysia
Tel.: (60) 323810851
Emp.: 10
Watches & Jewelry Whslr
N.A.I.C.S.: 423940

Folli Follie Poland Sp. z o.o. (1)
Ul Konstruktorska 6, 02-673, Warsaw, Poland
Tel.: (48) 22 6220866
Watches & Jewelry Whslr
N.A.I.C.S.: 423940

Folli Follie Singapore Ltd. (1)
491B River Valley Road 14-03A Valley Point, Singapore, 248373, Singapore
Tel.: (65) 6 737 4473

Web Site: http://www.follifollie.com.sg
Sales Range: $25-49.9 Million
Emp.: 16
Watches & Jewelry Whslr
N.A.I.C.S.: 423940
Christin Chan (Country Mgr)

Folli Follie Spain S.A. (1)
A/alcala 265 Edizio 2 Planta 3, Madrid, 28027, Spain
Tel.: (34) 917810763
Web Site: http://www.wfollifollie.es
Sales Range: $50-74.9 Million
Emp.: 100
Watches, Jewelry & Fashion Accessories Distr
N.A.I.C.S.: 423940
Andres Aguilar (Mgr)

Folli Follie Taiwan Ltd. (1)
15F-1 163 Keelung Road Section 1, 11070, Taipei, Taiwan
Tel.: (886) 2 2767 5988
Watches & Jewelry Whslr
N.A.I.C.S.: 423940
Wei Shen (Gen Mgr)

Folli Follie Thailand Ltd. (1)
Room 2928 Level 29 The Offices At Central World 999/9 Rama 1 Road, Pathumwan, 10330, Bangkok, Thailand
Tel.: (66) 2207 23 88
Sales Range: $25-49.9 Million
Emp.: 17
Watches & Jewelry Whslr
N.A.I.C.S.: 423940

Folli Follie UK Ltd. (1)
124 Regent Street, London, W1B 5SB, United Kingdom
Tel.: (44) 2072879912
Web Site: http://www.follifollie.co.uk
Women Jewelry & Watches Retailer
N.A.I.C.S.: 458310

Hellenic Distributions S.A. (1)
23rd Klm Athinons-Lamias, 145 65, Agios Stefanos, Attikis, Greece
Tel.: (30) 2106269400
Sales Range: $75-99.9 Million
Emp.: 200
Watches & Jewelry Distr
N.A.I.C.S.: 423940
Georgios Velentzas (Mng Dir)

Links (London) Limited (1)
Francis House Francis St, London, SW8 9AZ, United Kingdom
Tel.: (44) 844 477 0909
Web Site: http://www.linksoflondon.com
Jewelry Mfr & Retailer
N.A.I.C.S.: 339910

Subsidiary (Domestic):

Links of London (International) Ltd. (2)
28 Ludgate Hill, London, EC4M 7DR, United Kingdom
Tel.: (44) 20 7236 5564
Women Jewelry & Watches Distr
N.A.I.C.S.: 423940

Subsidiary (US):

Links of London, Inc. (2)
369 lexington 64, New York, NY 10016
Tel.: (212) 588-0660
Web Site: http://www.linksoflondon.com
Sales Range: $25-49.9 Million
Emp.: 25
Watches & Jewelry Whslr
N.A.I.C.S.: 423940

Planaco SA (1)
Kavouropetra, Aegina, 18010, Greece
Tel.: (30) 2297029040
Web Site: http://www.planaco.gr
Sales Range: $25-49.9 Million
Emp.: 25
Yacht Repair & Maintenance Services
N.A.I.C.S.: 336611
Stelios Tsoukalas (Gen Mgr)

FOMENTO DE CONSTRUCCIONES Y CONTRATAS, S.A.

Avda Camino de Santiago 40, 28050, Madrid, Spain
Tel.: (34) 913595400   ES

Fomento de Construcciones y Contratas, S.A.—(Continued)

Web Site: https://www.fcc.es
Year Founded: 1900
FCC—(MAD)
Rev.: $7,028,500,048
Assets: $14,081,276,420
Liabilities: $11,311,012,667
Net Worth: $2,770,263,754
Earnings: $298,671,141
Emp.: 58,432
Fiscal Year-end: 12/31/19
Construction & Infrastructure Mainte-
nance Services
N.A.I.C.S.: 237990
Francisco Vicent Chulia *(Sec)*

Subsidiaries:

.A.S.A. Abfall Service AG **(1)**
Hans-Hruschka-Gasse 9, 2325, Himberg,
Austria **(100%)**
Tel.: (43) 22358550
Web Site: http://www.asa-group.com
Sales Range: $350-399.9 Million
Emp.: 700
Municipal, Industrial, Commercial & Retail
Waste Management
N.A.I.C.S.: 924110

Subsidiary (Domestic):

.A.S.A. Abfall Service Halbenrain
GmbH **(2)**
Hans-Hruschka-Gasse 9, 2325, Himberg,
Austria **(100%)**
Tel.: (43) 22358550
Web Site: http://www.asa-group.com
Sales Range: $250-299.9 Million
Emp.: 80
Waste Management Services
N.A.I.C.S.: 924110

.A.S.A. Abfall Service Neunkirchen
GmbH **(2)**
Schloglmuhl 5 Gloggnitz, A-2640, Ne-
unkirchen, Austria **(100%)**
Tel.: (43) 266245230
Web Site: http://www.asa.at
Sales Range: $25-49.9 Million
Emp.: 22
Waste Management Services
N.A.I.C.S.: 562998

Subsidiary (Non-US):

.A.S.A. Areal spol. s.r.o **(2)**
Dablicka 791/89, Prague, 18200, Czech
Republic
Tel.: (420) 283061301
Web Site: http://www.prague-asa.cz
Sales Range: $50-74.9 Million
Emp.: 80
Waste Management Services
N.A.I.C.S.: 924110

Subsidiary (Domestic):

A.S.A. Abfall Service Wiener
Neustadt GmbH **(2)**
Neunkirchner Strasse 119, A-2700, Wiener
Neustadt, Austria **(100%)**
Tel.: (43) 2622872150
Web Site: http://www.asa.at
Sales Range: $25-49.9 Million
Emp.: 12
Hazardous Waste Disposal Services
N.A.I.C.S.: 562112

Abfallwirtschaftszentrum Mostviertel
GmbH **(2)**
Sudlandstrasse 3, A-3300, Amstetten,
Austria **(100%)**
Tel.: (43) 747263083
Web Site: http://www.asa.at
Sales Range: $10-24.9 Million
Emp.: 34
Waste Management Services
N.A.I.C.S.: 562998

Entsorga Entsorgungs GmbH Nfg
KG **(2)**
Hohenbergenstrasse 41, 9121, Volkermarkt,
Austria
Tel.: (43) 42324116
Web Site: http://www.fcc-group.eu
Landfill Management

N.A.I.C.S.: 562212

A.S.A. Hodmezovasarhely Koztlsz-
tasagl Kft **(1)**
Nagysziget tanya 18 Earlier Maroslelei Str
01957/I, 6800, Hodmezovasarhely, Hungary
Tel.: (36) 62535780
Waste Management Services
N.A.I.C.S.: 562998
Ferenc Csengeri *(Head-Plant)*

ASMJ s.r.o. **(1)**
Hruskove Dvory 117, 586 01, Jihlava,
Czech Republic
Tel.: (420) 567220701
Waste Management Services
N.A.I.C.S.: 562998

Acque di Caltanissetta, S.p.A. **(1)**
Corso Vittorio Emanuele 61, Caltanissetta,
93100, Palermo, Italy
Tel.: (39) 093423478
Web Site: https://www.caltaqua.it
Non Alcoholic Beverage Mfr
N.A.I.C.S.: 312111
Massimo Guadagnuolo *(Mgr-IT)*

Aguas Y Servicios De La Costa
Tropical De Granada, A.I.E. **(1)**
Plaza Javier de Burgos 5, Motril, 18600,
Granada, Spain
Tel.: (34) 958607300
Web Site: http://www.aguasyservicios.es
Water Supply Services
N.A.I.C.S.: 221310

Aigues de Vallirana, S.A. **(1)**
Aigues de Vallirana Conca de Tremps 14,
8759, Barcelona, Spain
Tel.: (34) 900813281
Water Utility Services
N.A.I.C.S.: 221310

Aquafundalia - Agua Do Fundao,
S.A. **(1)**
Praca da Republica n 12, 7350-126, Elvas,
Portugal
Tel.: (351) 2686392012
Web Site: http://www.aquaelvas.pt
Water Utility Services
N.A.I.C.S.: 221310

Aqualia Czech, S.L. **(1)**
Rua dos Restauradores Lote A e B r/c Loja
A, Fundao, 6230-496, Castelo Branco, Por-
tugal
Tel.: (351) 275771482
Web Site: http://www.aquafundalia.pt
Water Utility Services
N.A.I.C.S.: 221310

Aqualia Gestion Integral del Agua
S.A. **(1)**
C/Ulises 18, 28043, Madrid, Spain
Tel.: (34) 917036463
Web Site: http://www.aqualia.es
Sales Range: $150-199.9 Million
Emp.: 300
Water Utilities Management
N.A.I.C.S.: 924110

Aqualia Infraestructuras Montenegro
(AIM) d.o.o. **(1)**
Aleksandra Vukovica bb, Zidovici Pljevlja,
84210, Podgorica, Montenegro
Tel.: (382) 628725558
Water Utility Services
N.A.I.C.S.: 221310

Aqualia Infraestructuras d.o.o. **(1)**
Koce Kapetana 32-sprat 3 Stan 9, 11000,
Belgrade, Serbia
Tel.: (381) 69178506
Water Utility Services
N.A.I.C.S.: 221310

Aqualia Infraestructuras d.o.o. **(1)**
Dr Ante Starcevica, 88000, Mostar, Bosnia
& Herzegovina
Tel.: (387) 63433678
Water Utility Services
N.A.I.C.S.: 221310

Aqualia Mexico, S.A. de C.V. **(1)**
Avda 5 de Febrero N 1351 Corporativo Em-
presalia Edif Roble Of 304, Colonia Carrillo
Puerto, 76138, Queretaro, Mexico
Tel.: (52) 4424275900
Water Utility Services
N.A.I.C.S.: 221310

Aquamaior - Aguas de Campo Maior,
S.A. **(1)**
Rua de Sao Joao n 2A, Campo Maior,
7370-202, Portalegre, Portugal
Tel.: (351) 268689309
Web Site: http://www.aquamaior.pt
Water Utility Services
N.A.I.C.S.: 221310

Cementos Portland Valderrivas,
S.A. **(1)**
Paseo de la Castellana 216 16th floor,
28046, Madrid, Spain **(79.08%)**
Tel.: (34) 913960100
Web Site: https://www.valderrivas.es
Sales Range: $1-4.9 Billion
Emp.: 1,083
Cement & Concrete Producer
N.A.I.C.S.: 327310

Subsidiary (US):

CDN-USA, Inc. **(2)**
57 Atlantic Pl, South Portland, ME
04106 **(100%)**
Tel.: (207) 774-6355
Sales Range: $50-74.9 Million
Emp.: 240
Concrete & Cement
N.A.I.C.S.: 327320
Ray DeGrass *(Plant Mgr)*

Dragon Alfa Cement Limited **(1)**
The Cement Terminal Sharpness Docks
Sharpness, Gloucester, GL13 9UX, United
Kingdom
Tel.: (44) 1453811587
Web Site: http://www.dragonalfacement.com
Cement Mfr
N.A.I.C.S.: 327310
Michael Marler *(Gen Mgr)*

Dragon Portland Limited **(1)**
Britannia Building Portland Port, Portland,
Dorset, DT5 1PP, United Kingdom
Tel.: (44) 1453811587
Web Site: https://www.dragonportland.co.uk
Cement Mfr
N.A.I.C.S.: 327310

Ecodeal-Gestao Integral de Residuos
Industriais, S.A. **(1)**
Eco-parque do Relvao Rua Pinhal do
Duque Carregueira, Chamusca, 2140-671,
Santarem, Portugal
Tel.: (351) 249749030
Web Site: http://www.ecodeal.pt
Hazardous Waste Management Services
N.A.I.C.S.: 562112

FCC Ambito, S.A. **(1)**
Avda Camino de Santiago n 40, 28050, Ma-
drid, Spain
Tel.: (34) 917573924
Web Site: http://www.fccambito.com
Hazardous Waste Management Services
N.A.I.C.S.: 562112

FCC BEC s.r.o. **(1)**
Prosmycka 88/2, 410 02, Lovosice, Czech
Republic
Tel.: (420) 416724111
Waste Management Services
N.A.I.C.S.: 562998
Ivo Micek *(Mng Dir)*

FCC Bratislava s.r.o. **(1)**
Lamacska cesta 3/B, 841 04, Bratislava,
Slovakia
Tel.: (421) 25563929
Waste Management Services
N.A.I.C.S.: 562998

FCC Bulgaria E.O.O.D. **(1)**
3A Nikolay Haitov Str, 1113, Sofia, Bulgaria
Tel.: (359) 29712197
Waste Management Services
N.A.I.C.S.: 562998

FCC Ceska Republika s.r.o. **(1)**
Dablicka 791/89, Dablice, 182 00, Prague,
Czech Republic
Tel.: (420) 283061301
Waste Management Services
N.A.I.C.S.: 562998

FCC Ceske Budejovice s.r.o. **(1)**
Dolni ulice 876/1, 370 04, Ceske Budejov-
ice, Czech Republic
Tel.: (420) 387004601

Waste Management Services
N.A.I.C.S.: 562998
Radim Kolar *(Reg Sls Mgr)*

FCC Construccion Chile, SPA **(1)**
Avenida Vitacura 2771 Office 403, Las Con-
des, Santiago, Chile
Tel.: (56) 225772700
Web Site: https://www.fccco.com
Construction Services
N.A.I.C.S.: 236220
Carlos Loscertales *(Mgr-Country)*

FCC Construccion Costa Rica,
S.A. **(1)**
75 m Norte Hotel San Jose Palacio Edificio
FCC, Uruca, 11415-1000, San Jose, Costa
Rica
Tel.: (506) 22427500
Web Site: https://www.fccco.com
Construction Services
N.A.I.C.S.: 236220
Antonio Vivero *(Mgr-Country)*

FCC Construccion Peru, S.A.C. **(1)**
Av Javier Prado Este 560 Office 2301, San
Isidro, 15046, Lima, Peru
Tel.: (51) 15125100
Web Site: https://www.fccco.com
Construction Services
N.A.I.C.S.: 236220

FCC Construction Inc. **(1)**
1101 Brickell Ave Ste N1601 N, Miami, FL
33131
Tel.: (305) 372-2536
Construction Services
N.A.I.C.S.: 236220

FCC Construction Ireland DAC **(1)**
Fitzwilliam Business Centre 77 Sir John
Rogersons Quay, Dublin, Ireland
Tel.: (353) 16401955
Construction Services
N.A.I.C.S.: 236220

FCC Construgoes do Brasil Ltda. **(1)**
Avenida Clavasio Alves da Silva 67 Sala 9
Vila Siqueira, 02722 030, Sao Paulo, Brazil
Tel.: (55) 1126991481
Construction Services
N.A.I.C.S.: 236220

FCC Dacice s.r.o. **(1)**
Pivovarska 1204, 584 01, Ledec nad
Sazavou, Czech Republic
Tel.: (420) 384420493
Waste Management Services
N.A.I.C.S.: 562998

FCC EKO Polska sp. z.o.o. **(1)**
ul Lecha 10, 41-800, Zabrze, Poland
Tel.: (48) 323763450
Waste Management Services
N.A.I.C.S.: 562998

FCC EKO d.o.o. **(1)**
Bulevar kralja Aleksandra 79, 11120, Bel-
grade, Serbia
Tel.: (381) 116555617
Web Site: https://www.fcc-group.eu
Waste Management Services
N.A.I.C.S.: 562998
Amir Mujezinovic *(Country Mgr)*

FCC EKO-Radomsko sp. z.o.o. **(1)**
ul Narutowicza 5b, 97-500, Radomsko, Po-
land
Tel.: (48) 446832531
Hazardous Waste Management Services
N.A.I.C.S.: 562112
Anna Ozga *(Mgr-Sewage Treatment Plant &*
Waste Disposal Installation)

FCC Environment (Lincolnshire)
Ltd. **(1)**
Paving Way Off Whisby Road, North Hyke-
ham, Lincoln, LN6 3QW, Lincolnshire,
United Kingdom
Tel.: (44) 1522814315
Web Site:
http://www.lincolnshire.fccenvironment.com
Environmental Consultancy Services
N.A.I.C.S.: 541620

FCC Environment (UK) Limited **(1)**
3 Sidings Court White Rose Way,
Northampton Business Park, Doncaster,
DN4 5NU, Yorkshire, United
Kingdom **(100%)**
Tel.: (44) 3447369990

Web Site: https://www.fccenvironment.co.uk
Sales Range: $200-249.9 Million
Emp.: 2,400
Waste Collection, Management & Recycling Services
N.A.I.C.S.: 562998

Subsidiary (Domestic):

FCC Recycling (UK) Limited **(2)**
3 Sidings Court White Rose Way,
Northampton Business Park, Doncaster,
DN4 5NU, United Kingdom **(100%)**
Tel.: (44) 3447369990
Web Site: https://www.fccenvironment.co.uk
Emp.: 60
Recycling Services
N.A.I.C.S.: 562920
Paul Taylor (CEO)

FCC Waste Services (UK)
Limited **(2)**
Ground Floor West 900 Pavilion Drive,
Northampton Business Park, Northampton,
NN4 7RG, United Kingdom **(100%)**
Tel.: (44) 1604826200
Web Site: http://www.fccenvironment.co.uk
Sales Range: $25-49.9 Million
Emp.: 150
Waste Processing & Disposal Services
N.A.I.C.S.: 562998

Affiliate (Domestic):

Mercia Waste Management Ltd. **(2)**
The Marina Kings Road, Evesham, WR11
3XZ, Worcestershire, United Kingdom
Tel.: (44) 1386443376
Web Site: http://www.severnwaste.com
Sales Range: $50-74.9 Million
Emp.: 100
Waste Management Services
N.A.I.C.S.: 924110

Severn Waste Services Limited **(2)**
The Marina Kings Road, Evesham, WR11
3XZ, Worcs, United Kingdom
Tel.: (44) 1386 443 376
Web Site: http://www.severnwaste.com
Emp.: 12
Solid Waste Management Services
N.A.I.C.S.: 924110

FCC Environment Portugal, S.A. **(1)**
Rua do Outeiro n 915 1st Right Maia Industrial Zone Sector II, 4470-208, Maia, Portugal
Tel.: (351) 226199490
Web Site: https://www.fccenvironment.pt
Hazardous Waste Management Services
N.A.I.C.S.: 562112

FCC Environment Romania
S.R.L. **(1)**
Centura Nord OP 8 CP 147, 310580, Arad,
310580, Romania
Tel.: (40) 357130920
Web Site: https://www.fcc-group.eu
Waste Management Services
N.A.I.C.S.: 562998
Constantin Ristin (Mgr-Landfill)

FCC Freistadt Abfall Service
GmbH **(1)**
Hans-Hruschka-Gasse 9, A-2325, Himberg,
Austria
Tel.: (43) 22358550
Web Site: https://www.fcc-group.eu
Waste Management Services
N.A.I.C.S.: 562998
Thomas Roitmeier (Mgr-Ops & Sls)

FCC HP s.r.o. **(1)**
28 Rijna 875, 285 04, Uhlirske Janovica,
Czech Republic
Tel.: (420) 327543093
Waste Management Services
N.A.I.C.S.: 562998
Libor Lunacek (Reg Sls Mgr)

FCC Halbenrain Abfall Service GmbH
& Co. Nfg KG **(1)**
Halbenrain 147, 8492, Halbenrain, Austria
Tel.: (43) 347632600
Waste Management Services
N.A.I.C.S.: 562998
Georg Kraxner (Acct Mgr-Austria)

FCC Inmobilien Holding GmbH **(1)**

Wolfentalstrasse 29, 88400, Biberach, Germany
Tel.: (49) 73515790
Web Site: http://www.eqos-energie.com
Electrical Generation & Transmission Services
N.A.I.C.S.: 221121

FCC Liberec s.r.o. **(1)**
Mydlarska 105/10, 460 10, Liberec, Czech
Republic
Tel.: (420) 485213020
Waste Management Services
N.A.I.C.S.: 562998
Petr Grof (Mng Dir)

FCC Lublienec sp. z.o.o. **(1)**
ul Przemyslowa 5, 42-700, Lubliniec, Poland
Tel.: (48) 343531302
Waste Management Services
N.A.I.C.S.: 562998
Marek Knabel (Chm & Mng Dir)

FCC Magyarorzag Kft **(1)**
Korosi ut 53, 2360, Gyal, Hungary
Tel.: (36) 29540250
Waste Management Services
N.A.I.C.S.: 562998
Tibor Szekely (Dir-Comml)

FCC Mostviertel Abfall Service
GmbH **(1)**
Clemens-Holzmeister-Strasse 2, 3300, Amstetten, Austria
Tel.: (43) 747263083
Waste Management Services
N.A.I.C.S.: 562998
Max Schmidhofer (Sls Mgr)

FCC Neratovice s.r.o. **(1)**
Ke Spolane 655, 277 11, Neratovice, Czech
Republic
Tel.: (420) 315682544
Waste Management Services
N.A.I.C.S.: 562998
Jindrich Suchan (Reg Mgr-Ops)

FCC Neunkirchen Abfall Service
GmbH **(1)**
Schloglmuhl 5, Payerbach, 2640, Neunkirchen, Austria
Tel.: (43) 266245230
Waste Management Services
N.A.I.C.S.: 562998
Florian Pratscher (Mgr-Sls)

FCC Regios AS **(1)**
Uholicky 215, Velke Prilepy, 252 64,
Prague, Czech Republic
Tel.: (420) 220930524
Waste Management Services
N.A.I.C.S.: 562998
Libor Lunacek (Chm)

FCC Slovensko s.r.o. **(1)**
Lamacska cesta 3/B, 841 04, Bratislava,
Slovakia
Tel.: (421) 250206811
Waste Management Services
N.A.I.C.S.: 562998

FCC Tarnobrzeg.sp. z.o.o. **(1)**
ul Strefowa 8, 39-400, Tarnobrzeg, Poland
Tel.: (48) 158232379
Waste Management Services
N.A.I.C.S.: 562998

FCC Textil2Use GmbH **(1)**
Hans-Hruschka-Gasse 9, 2325, Himberg,
Austria
Tel.: (43) 3162927913138
Waste Management Services
N.A.I.C.S.: 562998
Georg Kraxner (Mgr)

FCC Trnava s.r.o. **(1)**
Priemyselna 5, 917 01, Trnava, Slovakia
Tel.: (421) 333240600
Waste Management Services
N.A.I.C.S.: 562998

FCC Uhy s.r.o. **(1)**
Uhy, 273 24, Velvary, Czech Republic
Tel.: (420) 315739000
Waste Management Services
N.A.I.C.S.: 562998

FCC Unanov s.r.o. **(1)**
Unanov 385, Unanov, 671 31, Znojmo,
Czech Republic

Tel.: (420) 515265459
Waste Management Services
N.A.I.C.S.: 562998

FCC Vrbak d.o.o. **(1)**
Ratnika solunskog Fronta bb, 34220,
Lapovo, Serbia
Tel.: (381) 34850350
Waste Management Services
N.A.I.C.S.: 562998

FCC Zabcice s.r.o. **(1)**
Oulehly 450, Zabcice, 664 63, Brno, Czech
Republic
Tel.: (420) 547234087
Waste Management Services
N.A.I.C.S.: 562998

FCC Zabovresky s.r.o. **(1)**
Korejska 3082/4, 616 00, Brno, Czech Republic
Tel.: (420) 541211888
Waste Management Services
N.A.I.C.S.: 562998
Martin Grepl (Reg Mgr-Ops)

FCC Zisterdorf Abfall Service
GmbH **(1)**
Am Ziegelwerk 4, 2225, Zisterdorf, Austria
Tel.: (43) 253280470
Waste Management Services
N.A.I.C.S.: 562998
Wolfgang Heimbucher (Sls Mgr-East &
West)

FCC Zohor.s.r.o. **(1)**
Bratislavska 18, Zohor, 900 51, Malacky,
Slovakia
Tel.: (421) 903576261
Waste Management Services
N.A.I.C.S.: 562998

Fomento de Construcciones y Contratas Canada Ltd. **(1)**
4789 Yonge Street Suite 804, Toronto, M2N
0G3, ON, Canada
Tel.: (416) 613-9104
Construction Services
N.A.I.C.S.: 236220
Enrique Marijuan (Mgr-Country)

Houston Waste Solutions, LLC **(1)**
6418 Chippewa Blvd, Houston, TX 77086-3804
Tel.: (281) 999-0030
Web Site:
   http://www.houstonwastesolutions.com
Hazardous Waste Treatment & Disposal
N.A.I.C.S.: 562211
Doug Card (Owner)

Kent Enviropower Limited **(1)**
20/20 Business Park Laverstoke Road, Allington, Maidstone, ME16 0LE, Kent, United
Kingdom
Tel.: (44) 8447369990
Web Site: http://www.fccenvironment.co.uk
Hazardous Waste Management Services
N.A.I.C.S.: 562112

Manipulacion y Recuperacion
Marepa, S.A. **(1)**
Avda San Martin de Valdeiglesias 22,
28922, Alcorcon, Madrid, Spain
Tel.: (34) 4881642
Web Site: http://www.marepa.es
Tape Distr
N.A.I.C.S.: 424110

Mantenimiento de Infraestructuras,
S.A. **(1)**
c/ Federico Salmon 13-2 Planta, 28016,
Madrid, Spain
Tel.: (34) 913439000
Web Site: https://www.matinsa.es
Construction Services
N.A.I.C.S.: 236220

Megaplas Italia, S.p.A. **(1)**
Via Piemonte 1, 10071, Borgaro, TO, Italy
Tel.: (39) 0114701906
Web Site: http://www.eshopmegaplas.com
Industrial Machinery Mfr
N.A.I.C.S.: 333248

Megaplas, S.A. **(1)**
C/Hilanderas 4-14-La Poveda, 28500, Arganda del Rey, Madrid, Spain
Tel.: (34) 918760652
Web Site: http://www.megaplas.com
Sign Board Mfr

N.A.I.C.S.: 339950

Miejskie Przedsiebiorstwo Gospodarki
Komunalnej sp. z.o.o. **(1)**
ul Lecha 10, 41-800, Zabrze, Poland
Tel.: (48) 322717281
Waste Management Services
N.A.I.C.S.: 562998
Pawel Szewczyk (CEO)

Obsed A.S. **(1)**
Frydecka 740, Hrabova, 739 32, Ostrava,
Czech Republic
Tel.: (420) 596614555
Web Site: http://www.obsed.cz
Waste Water Treatment Services
N.A.I.C.S.: 221320

Prefabricados Delta, S.A. **(1)**
Calle Federico Salmon N 13, CP 28016,
Madrid, Spain
Tel.: (34) 915300047
Web Site:
   http://www.prefabricadosdelta.com
Fabricated Metal Mfr
N.A.I.C.S.: 332313

Quail Spol. s.r.o. **(1)**
Dolni ulice 876/1, 370 04, Ceske Budejovice, Czech Republic
Tel.: (420) 387004616
Waste Management Services
N.A.I.C.S.: 562998
Pavel Czinege (Mng Dir)

Ramalho Rosa Cobetar Sociedade
De Construcoes, S.A. **(1)**
Rua Padre Americo No 2 A-Escritorio 5,
1600-548, Lisbon, Portugal
Tel.: (351) 214147500
Construction Services
N.A.I.C.S.: 236220
Bernardo Teixeira (Mgr-Country)

Sistemas y Vehiculos de Alta Tecnologia, S.A. **(1)**
C/ Federico Salmon 13, 28016, Madrid,
Spain
Tel.: (34) 914013001
Web Site: https://www.svat.es
Sanitation & Utility Vehicle Mfr
N.A.I.C.S.: 325612

Vodotech, Spol. s.r.o. **(1)**
Jaselska 220/47, 747 07, Opava, Czech
Republic
Tel.: (420) 553712205
Web Site: https://www.vodotech.cz
Water Utility Services
N.A.I.C.S.: 221310

FOMENTO ECONOMICO MEXICANO, S.A.B. DE C.V.

General Anaya No 601 Pte, Colonia
Bella Vista, Monterrey, 64410, Nuevo
Leon, Mexico
Tel.: (52) 8183286000 **MX**
Web Site: http://www.femsa.com
Year Founded: 1986
FMX—(NYSE)
Rev.: $42,436,679,429
Assets: $48,666,916,285
Liabilities: $25,816,614,931
Net Worth: $22,850,301,354
Earnings: $4,630,645,103
Emp.: 392,932
Fiscal Year-end: 12/31/23
Beverage Mfg Services
N.A.I.C.S.: 312111
Alfonso Garza Garza (CEO-Strategic
Businesses)

Subsidiaries:

Coca-Cola FEMSA, S.A.B. de
C.V. **(1)**
Calle Mario Pani No 100 Santa Fe Cuajimalpa, Cuajimalpa de Morelos, 05348,
Mexico, DF, Mexico **(53.7%)**
Tel.: (52) 5515195000
Web Site: https://www.coca-colafemsa.com
Rev.: $11,398,219,800
Assets: $13,974,808,650
Liabilities: $7,345,402,130
Net Worth: $6,629,406,520
Earnings: $986,599,020
Emp.: 80,445

Fomento Economico Mexicano, S.A.B. de
C.V.—(Continued)

Fiscal Year-end: 12/31/2022
Holding Company; Soft Drinks Bottler &
Distr
N.A.I.C.S.: 551112
John Anthony Santa Maria Otazua (CEO)

Subsidiary (Domestic):

Jugos del Valle, S.A.B. de C.V.   **(2)**
Avenida Ejercito Nacional 904 Piso 15, Col
Palmas Polanco Seccion Miguel Hidalgo,
CP 11560, Mexico, DF, Mexico   **(50%)**
Tel.: (52) 55 25816500
Web Site: http://www.jvalle.com.mx
Sales Range: $650-699.9 Million
Juices & Fruit Beverages Mfr
N.A.I.C.S.: 311411

FEMSA Comercio, S.A. de C.V.   **(1)**
Gen Anaya 601 Pte, Colonia Bella Vista,
Monterrey, 64410, Nuevo Leon, Mexico
Tel.: (52) 8183286000
Web Site: http://www.femsa.com
Sales Range: $1-4.9 Billion
Emp.: 7,806
Convenience Store Operator
N.A.I.C.S.: 445131

Valora Holding AG   **(1)**
Hofackerstrasse 40, 4132, Muttenz,
Switzerland   **(97.77%)**
Tel.: (41) 614672020
Web Site: http://www.valora.com
Rev.: $1,922,308,937
Assets: $2,769,890,253
Liabilities: $1,994,097,342
Net Worth: $775,792,911
Earnings: ($7,023,579)
Emp.: 3,578
Fiscal Year-end: 12/31/2020
Holding Company; Newsstands & Conve-
nience Stores Operator; Newspapers &
Magazines Distr; Food & Non-Food Prod-
ucts Distr
N.A.I.C.S.: 551112
Michael Mueller (CEO)

Subsidiary (Non-US):

BackWerk AT GmbH   **(2)**
Josefplatz 12 Top 122, 2500, Baden, Aus-
tria
Tel.: (43) 2252252145
Web Site: https://back-werk.at
Bakery Product Distr
N.A.I.C.S.: 445291

BackWerk NL B.V.   **(2)**
Oude Utrechtseweg 20, 3743 KN, Baarn,
Netherlands
Tel.: (31) 352210001
Web Site: https://www.back-werk.nl
Bakery Product Distr
N.A.I.C.S.: 445291

Brezelbackerei Ditsch GmbH   **(2)**
Robert-Bosch-Strasse 44, 55129, Mainz,
Germany
Tel.: (49) 613199570
Pretzel Product Mfr
N.A.I.C.S.: 311919
Sebastian Gooding (Mng Dir)

Subsidiary (Domestic):

Brezelkonig AG   **(2)**
Neuenkirchstrasse 91, 6020, Em-
menbrucke, Switzerland
Tel.: (41) 412896464
Web Site: https://brezelkoenig.ch
Bakery Product Distr
N.A.I.C.S.: 424490

Subsidiary (US):

Ditsch USA LLC   **(2)**
311 Northland Blvd, Cincinnati, OH 45246
Tel.: (513) 782-8888
Pretzel Product Mfr
N.A.I.C.S.: 311919
Gary Gottenbusch (Mng Dir)

Subsidiary (Domestic):

K Kiosk AG   **(2)**
Hofackerstrasse 40, 4132, Muttenz, Swit-
zerland
Tel.: (41) 614672020
Web Site: https://www.kkiosk.ch

Grocery Product Services
N.A.I.C.S.: 445110

Subsidiary (Non-US):

Kaumy s.r.o.   **(2)**
Jerlochovice 156, 742 45, Fulnek,
Moravian-Silesian, Czech Republic
Tel.: (420) 556740801
Emp.: 20
Confectionery Product Distr
N.A.I.C.S.: 424450

Oy Valora Trade Finland AB   **(2)**
Tel.: (358) 207411220
Web Site: http://www.valoratrade.fi
Sales Range: $25-49.9 Million
Emp.: 54
Food & Retail Goods Wholesale Trade Distr
N.A.I.C.S.: 425120
Riku Lahdensuo (Mng Dir)

Valora Holding Finance Ltd.   **(2)**
24 Smith Street, PO Box 51, Saint Peter
Port, GY1 4BB, Guernsey
Tel.: (44) 1481714481
Investment Management Service
N.A.I.C.S.: 523940

Valora Holding Germany GmbH   **(2)**
Danziger Strasse 35a, 20099, Hamburg,
Germany
Tel.: (49) 402801560
Holding Company
N.A.I.C.S.: 551112

Valora Luxembourg S.a.r.l.   **(2)**
Web Site: http://www.valoraretail.lu
Retail Stores Operator & Products Distr
N.A.I.C.S.: 459210

Subsidiary (Domestic):

Valora Management AG   **(2)**
Hofackerstrasse 40, 4132, Muttenz, Basel-
Land, Switzerland
Tel.: (41) 587894406
Web Site: https://www.valora.com
Fast Moving Consumer Goods Distr
N.A.I.C.S.: 423990

Valora Schweiz AG   **(2)**
Hofackerstrasse 40, 4132, Muttenz, Swit-
zerland
Tel.: (41) 614672020
Web Site: http://www.valora.ch
Sales Range: $25-49.9 Million
Emp.: 15
Confectionery Product Distr
N.A.I.C.S.: 424450

Subsidiary (Non-US):

Valora Trade Denmark A/S   **(2)**
Transformervej 16, 2730, Herlev, Denmark
Tel.: (45) 44575859
Web Site: http://www.valoratrade.dk
Rev.: $673,245,000
Emp.: 450
Fast Moving Consumer Goods Distr
N.A.I.C.S.: 424990

Valora Trade Norway AS   **(2)**
Jon Leiras Vei 10, 3440, Royken, Buskerud,
Norway
Tel.: (47) 31292770
Web Site: http://www.valoratrade.no
Sales Range: $25-49.9 Million
Emp.: 40
Confectionery Product Whslr
N.A.I.C.S.: 424450

Valora Trade Sweden AB   **(2)**
Lofstroms Alle 5, PO Box 10034, Sundby-
berg, 172 66, Stockholm, Sweden
Tel.: (46) 87251400
Web Site: https://www.conaxesstrade.se
Rev.: $673,245,000
Emp.: 150
Confectionery Product Distr
N.A.I.C.S.: 424450

**FOMENTO RESORTS & HO-
TELS LTD**
Cidade de Goa Vainguinim Beach
Dona Paula, Goa, 403004, India
Tel.: (91) 832 2454545
Web Site: http://www.frhl.in
Rev.: $9,795,611
Assets: $64,026,178

Liabilities: $48,670,032
Net Worth: $15,356,147
Earnings: $1,316,369
Emp.: 177
Fiscal Year-end: 03/31/19
Home Management Services
N.A.I.C.S.: 721110
Anju Timblo (CEO & Mng Dir)

FON SE
Harju maakond Kesklinna linnaosa
Tornimae tn 5, Tornimae, 10145, Tal-
linn, Estonia
Tel.: (372) 243673132
Web Site: https://www.fon-sa.pl
Year Founded: 2001
FON—(WAR)
Rev.: $473,478
Assets: $7,392,890
Liabilities: $6,413
Net Worth: $7,386,477
Earnings: $580,358
Fiscal Year-end: 06/30/23
Eletric Power Generation Services
N.A.I.C.S.: 221118
Damian Patrowicz (Chm & CEO)

FON WIRELESS LTD.
25 Farrington St, London, EC4A 4AB,
United Kingdom
Tel.: (44) 34912917600
Web Site: http://www.fon.com
Year Founded: 2005
WiFi Provider
N.A.I.C.S.: 517121
Alexander Puregger (CEO)

**FONCIERE 7 INVESTISSE-
MENT SA**
55 rue Pierre Charron, 75008, Paris,
France
Tel.: (33) 156524500
Web Site:
   https://www.fonciere7investisse.fr
LEBL—(EUR)
Sales Range: Less than $1 Million
Real Estate Support Services
N.A.I.C.S.: 531390
Nicolas Boucheron (Chm & Pres)

FONCIERE ATLAND SA
40 Avenue George V, 75008, Paris,
France
Tel.: (33) 140722020
Web Site: http://www.fonciere-
atland.fr
FATL—(EUR)
Sales Range: $200-249.9 Million
Real Estate Development & Invest-
ment Services
N.A.I.C.S.: 531390
Georges Rocchietta (Chm & CEO)

Subsidiaries:

Atland Voisin SAS   **(1)**
15 Place Grangier, 21000, Dijon, France
Tel.: (33) 380599090
Web Site: http://www.atland-voisin.com
Real Estate Rental Services
N.A.I.C.S.: 531110

Fundimmo SAS   **(1)**
154 Boulevard Haussmann, 75008, Paris,
France
Tel.: (33) 170390870
Web Site: http://www.fundimmo.com
Real Estate Advisory Services
N.A.I.C.S.: 531390

SARL FONCIERE ATLAND
REIM   **(1)**
10 Ave George V, 75008, Paris, France
Tel.: (33) 140722020
Web Site: http://www.fonciere-atland.fr
Emp.: 27
Real Estate Property Management Services
N.A.I.C.S.: 531390
Georges Rocchietta (Gen Mgr)

SNC FONCIERE ATLAND
VALORISATION   **(1)**
10 Ave George V, 75008, Paris, France
Tel.: (33) 140722020
Web Site: http://www.atland.sa
Emp.: 27
Real Estate Lending Services
N.A.I.C.S.: 531390

FONCIERE INEA SA
7 rue du Fosse Blanc, 92230, Genn-
evilliers, France
Tel.: (33) 142866440   **FR**
Web Site: https://www.fonciere-
inea.com
Year Founded: 1998
INEA—(EUR)
Rev.: $58,621,507
Assets: $1,053,683,895
Liabilities: $538,972,268
Net Worth: $514,711,627
Earnings: $61,551,171
Emp.: 4
Fiscal Year-end: 12/31/21
Real Estate Support Services
N.A.I.C.S.: 531390
Philippe Rosio (Chm, CEO & Dir-IR)

FONCIERE PARIS NORD SA
15 rue de la Banque, 75002, Paris,
France
Tel.: (33) 1 5652 4500
Web Site: http://www.fonciere-
parisnord.com
FPN—(EUR)
Sales Range: Less than $1 Million
Real Estate Support Services
N.A.I.C.S.: 531390
Richard Lonsdale-Hands (Chm &
CEO)

FONCIERE R-PARIS SCA
5 rue de Tilsitt, 75008, Paris, France
Tel.: (33) 142442454
Real Estate Support Services
N.A.I.C.S.: 531390
Bruno Ledoux (Gen Mgr)

FONCIERE VINDI SA
3 Avenue Hoche, 75008, Paris,
France
Tel.: (33) 156795115
Web Site:
   https://www.foncierevindi.com
Year Founded: 2007
MLVIN—(EUR)
Sales Range: $1-9.9 Million
Real Estate Manangement Services
N.A.I.C.S.: 531390
Sandrine Choukroun (Chm & CEO)

FONCIERE VOLTA SA
3 avenue Hoche, 75008, Paris,
France
Tel.: (33) 156795110
Web Site:
   https://www.foncierevolta.com
SPEL—(EUR)
Sales Range: $1-9.9 Million
Residential Real Estate Management
Services
N.A.I.C.S.: 531311
Raphael Aboulkheir (Chm & CEO)

**FONDACTION, LE FONDS DE
DEVELOPPEMENT DE LA
CONFEDERATION DES SYNDI-
CATS NATIONAUX POUR LA
COOPERATION ET L'EMPLOI**
2175 boulevard De Maisonneuve Est
bureau 103, Montreal, H2K 4S3, QC,
Canada
Tel.: (514) 525-5505   **QC**
Web Site: http://www.fondaction.com
Year Founded: 1996
Sales Range: $25-49.9 Million

Retirement Fund Manager
N.A.I.C.S.: 524292
Jacques Letourneau *(Chm)*

Subsidiaries:

Atis Group Inc. **(1)**
1111 St Charles Street West Suite 952 East
Tower, Longueuil, J4K 5G4, QC, Canada
Tel.: (450) 928-0101
Web Site: http://www.atisgroup.ca
Emp.: 1,400
Doors & Windows Developer, Mfr, Distr &
Installer
N.A.I.C.S.: 332321
Claude Boucher *(Sr Dir-Sls)*

FONDATIONS CAPITAL SA

5 rue Guillaume Kroll, L-1882, Lux-
embourg, Luxembourg
Tel.: (352) 48 18 28 1
Web Site:
http://www.fondationscapital.com
Year Founded: 2007
Privater Equity Firm
N.A.I.C.S.: 523999
Xavier Marin *(Co-Founder & Partner)*

Subsidiaries:

Buffet Group China **(1)**
Room 206 No 2 2nd Floor Complex, Build-
ing No 9 Hai Ying Roard Science Park, Bei-
jing, China
Tel.: (86) 159 1051 7174
Musical Instrument Distr
N.A.I.C.S.: 423990

Buffet Group Distribution Germany
GmbH **(1)**
Gewebepark 31-33, 8258, Markneukirchen,
Germany
Tel.: (49) 37422 4079 0
Musical Instrument Distr
N.A.I.C.S.: 423990

Buffet Group Japan **(1)**
8-17 Tokyo-4-koto-ku, Tokyo, 135-0016,
Japan
Tel.: (81) 3 5632 5511
Musical Instrument Distr
N.A.I.C.S.: 423990

Fondations Capital Services France
SA **(1)**
24-32 rue Jean Goujon, 75008, Paris,
France
Tel.: (33) 1 55 35 55 00
Web Site: http://www.fondationscapital.com
Privater Equity Firm
N.A.I.C.S.: 523999

Holding (Domestic):

Buffet Crampon Holdings SAS **(2)**
5 rue Maurice Berteaux, 78711, Mantes-la-
Ville, France
Tel.: (33) 1 3098 5130
Web Site: http://www.buffet-group.com
Sales Range: $150-199.9 Million
Emp.: 300
Holding Company; Musical Instrument Mfr &
Distr
N.A.I.C.S.: 551112
Antoine Beaussant *(CEO)*

Subsidiary (Non-US):

Buffet Crampon Deutschland
GmbH **(3)**
Gewerbepark 52, 08258, Markneukirchen,
08258, Germany
Tel.: (49) 374224079
Web Site:
http://www.buffetcrampongroup.com
Musical Instruments Mfr & Sales
N.A.I.C.S.: 339992

Subsidiary (Domestic):

Buffet Crampon S.A.S. **(3)**
5 rue Maurice Berteaux, 78711, Mantes-la-
Ville, France
Tel.: (33) 130985130
Web Site: http://wwwbuffet-crampon.com
Musical Instruments Mfr & Distr
N.A.I.C.S.: 339992
Antoine Beaussant *(CEO)*

Subsidiary (US):

Buffet Group USA, Inc. **(3)**
7255 Salisbury Rd Ste4, Jacksonville, FL
32256
Tel.: (904) 821-0234
Web Site: http://www.buffet-crampon.com
Emp.: 30
Musical Instrument Whslr
N.A.I.C.S.: 423990
Francois Kloc *(Pres & CEO)*

Sepur **(1)**
ZA du Pont Cailloux-Route des Nourrices,
78850, Thiverval-Grignon, France
Tel.: (33) 1 30 79 20 00
Web Site: http://www.sepur.com
Emp.: 2,050
Waste Management Services
N.A.I.C.S.: 562111

FONDAZIONE CASSA DI RISPARMIO DI TORINO

Via XX Settembre 31, Torino, 10121,
Italy
Tel.: (39) 0115065100
Web Site:
https://www.fondazionecrt.it
Emp.: 100
Non Profit Organization
N.A.I.C.S.: 813319

FONDERIE GIROUD INDUST-RIE SAS

Chemin de Renevier RN 90, PO Box
39, 38530, Barraux, France
Tel.: (33) 476971236
Web Site:
http://www.giroudfonderie.com
Sales Range: $1-9.9 Million
Emp.: 70
Industry Castings Mfr
N.A.I.C.S.: 331511
Patrick Collin *(CEO)*

FONDIA OYJ

Aleksanterinkatu 11 Entrance at Kluu-
vikatu 6 A, 100, Helsinki, Finland
Tel.: (358) 207205400
Web Site: https://www.fondia.com
Year Founded: 2004
FONDIA—(HEL)
Emp.: 160
Legal Department Services
N.A.I.C.S.: 541199
Mari Aulio *(Mgr-Mktg)*

FONDINVEST CAPITAL

33 rue de la Baume, 75008, Paris,
France
Tel.: (33) 158364800
Web Site: http://www.fondinvest.com
Year Founded: 1994
Rev.: $2,642,780,000
Emp.: 12
Private Equity Funds Management
Services
N.A.I.C.S.: 523940
Charles Soulignac *(Founder, Chm & CEO)*

FONDO DE VALORES INMO-BILIARIOS S.A.C.A.

Venezuela Avenue El Saman Building
Ground Floor, El Rosal Urbanization,
Caracas, Venezuela
Tel.: (58) 2129059198
Web Site: https://www.fvi.com.ve
Year Founded: 1992
FVI.A—(BVC)
Sales Range: $25-49.9 Million
Real Estate Investment Services
N.A.I.C.S.: 525990

FONDS DE CONSOLIDATION ET DE DEVELOPPEMENT DES ENTREPRISES

59 rue La Boetie, 75008, Paris,
France
Tel.: (33) 1 80 40 04 65
Web Site: http://www.fonds-fcde.fr
Year Founded: 2009
Privater Equity Firm
N.A.I.C.S.: 523999
Julien di Marco *(Partner)*

Subsidiaries:

Babcock Wanson SA **(1)**
106-110 rue du Lt Petit-Le-Roy, Chevilly-
Larue, 94 669, Paris, Cedex, France
Tel.: (33) 149784400
Web Site: http://www.babcock-wanson.com
Emp.: 680
Industrial Machinery Mfr
N.A.I.C.S.: 333248
Cyril Fournier Montgieux *(CEO)*

Plant (Domestic):

Babcock Wanson SA - Manufacturing
Facility **(2)**
7 boulevard Alfred Parent, BP 52, 47600,
Nerac, France
Tel.: (33) 5 53 65 19 00
Web Site: http://www.babcock-wanson.fr
Steam Boiler & Generator Mfr
N.A.I.C.S.: 332410

FONDS DE SOLIDARITE DES TRAVAILLEURS DU QUEBEC

CP 1000 Succ Chabanel, Montreal,
H2N 0B5, QC, Canada
Tel.: (514) 383-3663
Web Site: http://www.fondsftq.com
Year Founded: 1983
Sales Range: $250-299.9 Million
Emp.: 450
Economic Development Services
N.A.I.C.S.: 926110
Gaetan Morin *(Pres & CEO)*

Subsidiaries:

Atis Group Inc. **(1)**
1111 St Charles Street West Suite 952 East
Tower, Longueuil, J4K 5G4, QC, Canada
Tel.: (450) 928-0101
Web Site: http://www.atisgroup.ca
Emp.: 1,400
Doors & Windows Developer, Mfr, Distr &
Installer
N.A.I.C.S.: 332321
Claude Boucher *(Sr Dir-Sls)*

Partner One Software Inc. **(1)**
505 Maisonneuve W 400, Montreal, H3A
3C2, QC, Canada
Tel.: (514) 856-5643
Web Site: https://www.partnerone.com
Privater Equity Firm
N.A.I.C.S.: 523999

Subsidiary (Non-US):

Assima PLC **(2)**
Portsoken House 155-157 Minories, Lon-
don, EC3N 1LJ, United Kingdom
Tel.: (44) 2033283280
Web Site: http://www.assima.net
Rev.: $23,515,645
Assets: $27,345,107
Liabilities: $14,872,618
Net Worth: $12,472,489
Earnings: ($2,595,098)
Emp.: 157
Fiscal Year-end: 12/31/2017
Software Developer & Distr
N.A.I.C.S.: 513210
Tony D. Coates *(Chief Alliance Officer)*

Subsidiary (Non-US):

Assima A/S **(3)**
Stokkerup Strandvejen 724, 2930, Gentofte,
Denmark
Tel.: (45) 5128 0000
Web Site: http://www.assima.net
Computer Software Development Services
N.A.I.C.S.: 541511

Assima Canada, Inc. **(3)**
2070 rue Jules Leger, Saint-Bruno, J3V
5M5, QC, Canada
Tel.: (678) 971-2008

Web Site: http://www.assima.net
Software Developer & Distr
N.A.I.C.S.: 513210
Frederick Sengas *(Mng Dir)*

Assima France SAS **(3)**
38-48 rue Victor Hugo, 92300, Levallois-
Perret, France
Tel.: (33) 1 47 30 71 30
Computer Software Development Services
N.A.I.C.S.: 541511

Assima Software Espafia, S.L. **(3)**
Paseo de la Castellana 141, 28046, Madrid,
Spain
Tel.: (34) 91 572 6589
Computer Software Development Services
N.A.I.C.S.: 541511

Assima Switzerland SA **(3)**
Rue du Simplon 37, 1006, Lausanne, Swit-
zerland
Tel.: (41) 21 612 03 79
Computer Software Development Services
N.A.I.C.S.: 541511

Subsidiary (US):

Assima, Inc. **(3)**
3330 Cumberland Blvd Ste 975, Atlanta,
GA 30339
Tel.: (877) 927-7462
Software Developer & Distr
N.A.I.C.S.: 513210
Jay Kuhlman *(COO & Exec VP)*

Subsidiary (Non-US):

Olas Software Training and Develop-
ment Limited **(3)**
Unit 206 Q House Furze Rd, Sandyford,
Dublin, Ireland
Tel.: (353) 1 2790020
Web Site: http://www.olas.ie
Computer Software Development Services
N.A.I.C.S.: 541511
Ailish O'Connor *(Mng Dir)*

Subsidiary (US):

Fidelis Cybersecurity Solutions,
Inc. **(2)**
4500 E W Hwy Ste 400, Bethesda, MD
20814
Tel.: (301) 652-7190
Web Site: http://www.fidelissecurity.com
Custom Computer Programming Services
N.A.I.C.S.: 541511
Mike Buratowski *(Sr VP-Cybersecurity
Svcs)*

Subsidiary (Domestic):

CloudPassage Inc. **(3)**
44 Tehama St Ste 412, San Francisco, CA
94105
Tel.: (415) 886-3020
Web Site: http://www.cloudpassage.com
Software Publisher
N.A.I.C.S.: 513210
Kent Erickson *(VP-Ops)*

FONDS NATIONAL D'INVESTISSEMENT

168 Avenue Hassiba - ben Bouali, El
Hamma, Algiers, Algeria
Tel.: (213) 2028 4094
Web Site: http://www.fni.dz
Investment Fund
N.A.I.C.S.: 525990
Ahcene Haddad *(Chm)*

Subsidiaries:

Orascom Telecom Algerie SpA **(1)**
Rue Mouloud Feraoun, Lot 8A Dar El-
Beida, Algiers, Algeria **(51%)**
Tel.: (213) 770857777
Web Site: http://www.djezzy.com
Emp.: 4,000
Cellular & Wireless Telecommunications
N.A.I.C.S.: 517112
Waleed El-Sonbaty *(CIO)*

FONE4 COMMUNICATIONS (INDIA) LIMITED

Ashna Arcade Vyloppilly Road, Tham-
manam PO, Kochi, 682032, India

Fone4 Communications (India) Limited—(Continued)

Tel.: (91) 8606777777   In
Web Site: https://www.fone4.in
Year Founded: 2014
543521—(BOM)
Rev.: $7,091,052
Assets: $5,707,638
Liabilities: $4,518,614
Net Worth: $1,189,024
Earnings: $105,487
Emp.: 43
Fiscal Year-end: 03/31/22
E-Commerce Site Operator
N.A.I.C.S.: 459999

FONET BILGI TEKNOLOJILERI AS

Kizilirmak Neighborhood 1445 Street No 2B/1 The Parogon Tower, Cankaya, Ankara, Turkiye
Tel.: (90) 3124385919
Web Site:
   https://www.fonetyazilim.com
Year Founded: 1997
FONET—(IST)
Rev.: $3,958,806
Assets: $8,776,954
Liabilities: $3,002,612
Net Worth: $5,774,342
Earnings: $1,740,976
Emp.: 499
Fiscal Year-end: 12/31/22
Information Technology Services
N.A.I.C.S.: 541512
Abdulkerim Gazen (Chm)

FONEX DATA SYSTEMS INC.

5400 Ch St-Francois, Saint Laurent, H4S 1P6, QC, Canada
Tel.: (514) 333-6639
Web Site: http://www.fonex.com
Year Founded: 1989
Rev.: $18,870,477
Emp.: 50
Telecommunication Equipment Services
N.A.I.C.S.: 517810
Pasquale Di Pierro (Founder & Pres)

Subsidiaries:

FONEX SAS   (1)
17 rue Gutenberg Zone de la butte, 91620, Nozay, France
Tel.: (33) 169807049
Web Site: http://www.fonex.com
Telecommunication Equipment Distr
N.A.I.C.S.: 423690

FONFUN CORPORATION

JMF Building Sasazuka 01 6th floor 2-1-6 Sasazuka, Shibuya-Ku, Tokyo, 151-0073, Japan
Tel.: (81) 353651511
Web Site: https://www.fonfun.co.jp
Year Founded: 1997
2323—(TKS)
Rev.: $4,816,900
Assets: $7,784,050
Liabilities: $3,306,900
Net Worth: $4,477,150
Earnings: $302,000
Emp.: 80
Fiscal Year-end: 03/31/23
Internet Services
N.A.I.C.S.: 519290

FONG CHIEN CONSTRUCTION CO., LTD.

25F-1 No 501 Section 2 Taiwan Avenue, Taichung, Taiwan
Tel.: (886) 423262593
Web Site: https://www.fong-chien.com.tw
Year Founded: 1984
5523—(TPE)
Rev.: $6,798,737
Assets: $193,562,330

Liabilities: $105,078,854
Net Worth: $88,483,476
Earnings: $14,699,559
Fiscal Year-end: 12/31/22
Real Estate Brokerage Services
N.A.I.C.S.: 531210

FONIX MOBILE PLC

23 Heddon Street, London, W1B 4BQ, United Kingdom
Tel.: (44) 2081147000   UK
Web Site: https://www.fonix.com
Year Founded: 2006
FNX—(AIM)
Rev.: $81,943,954
Assets: $73,232,770
Liabilities: $61,382,227
Net Worth: $11,850,543
Earnings: $11,104,519
Emp.: 43
Fiscal Year-end: 06/30/23
Information Technology Services
N.A.I.C.S.: 541512

FONTANA LUIGI S.P.A.

Via Fontana 9, 20837, Veduggio, MB, Italy
Tel.: (39) 03629891
Web Site:
   http://www.gruppofontana.it
Year Founded: 1952
Engineered Fastener Solutions
N.A.I.C.S.: 332722
Giuseppe Fontana (CEO)

Subsidiaries:

Acument Global Technologies Inc.   (1)
6125 Eighteen Mile Rd, Sterling Heights, MI 48314-4205
Tel.: (248) 813-6300
Web Site: http://www.acument.com
Sales Range: $1-4.9 Billion
Emp.: 2,300
Mechanical Fastener Mfr
N.A.I.C.S.: 332722
Thomas Goral (Mgr-Bus Dev)

Subsidiary (Domestic):

Saturn Fasteners Inc.   (2)
425 S Varney St, Burbank, CA 91502
Tel.: (818) 846-7145
Web Site: http://www.saturnfasteners.com
Sales Range: $10-24.9 Million
Emp.: 100
Aerospace Fastener Developer & Mfr
N.A.I.C.S.: 332510

FONTANA FASTENERS INC.   (1)
3595 W State Rd, Frankfort, IN 46041-6708
Tel.: (765) 654-0477
Logistics Consulting Servies
N.A.I.C.S.: 541614

Fontana America Inc.   (1)
1861 Hicks Rd Ste A, Rolling Meadows, IL 60008
Tel.: (847) 221-5773
Rev.: $10,000,000
Emp.: 16
Fastener Distr
N.A.I.C.S.: 423840

Fontana Fasteners De Mexico S.A. C.V.   (1)
Diagonal 19 Poniente N 3102 Oficina 202 Colonia El Vergel Cp, 72400, Mexico, Mexico
Tel.: (52) 2222305090
Logistics Consulting Servies
N.A.I.C.S.: 541614

Fontana Fasteners Deutschland GmbH   (1)
Heinrich - Hertz Strasse 54-56, Erkrath, 40699, Dusseldorf, Germany
Tel.: (49) 211250080
Logistics Consulting Servies
N.A.I.C.S.: 541614
Wolfgang Friesel (Acct Mgr)

Fontana Fasteners Do Brasil Industria e Comercio de Fixadores

Ltda   (1)
Av Lavandisca 360 - unidade 71, Moema, Sao Paulo, 04515-010, Brazil
Tel.: (55) 1150517620
Logistics Consulting Servies
N.A.I.C.S.: 541614

Fontana Fasteners France S.A.S.   (1)
Rue Des Petits Champs - Z I des Perriers, BP 82, 78501, Sartrouville, France
Tel.: (33) 139578662
Logistics Consulting Servies
N.A.I.C.S.: 541614

Fontana Fasteners India Private Ltd   (1)
14/4 Mathura Road, Faridabad, 121 003, India
Tel.: (91) 1294282600
Logistics Consulting Servies
N.A.I.C.S.: 541614
Surepet Chadha (Mgr-Sls)

Fontana Fasteners Italia S.p.A.   (1)
Via Del Lavoro 14, Grisignano di Zocco, 36040, Vicenza, Italy
Tel.: (39) 0714405911
Web Site: http://www.fontanafasteners.it
Logistics Consulting Servies
N.A.I.C.S.: 541614
Mario Zago (Mgr-Pur)

Fontana Fasteners Poland Sp. z.o.o.   (1)
Ul Melgiewska 7/9, 20-952, Lublin, Poland
Tel.: (48) 817491831
Logistics Consulting Servies
N.A.I.C.S.: 541614

Fontana Fasteners S.A.   (1)
Pol Industrial Ampliacion - Ca n'Estella c/Galileu 2y4, 08635, Sant Esteve Sesrovires, Spain
Tel.: (34) 937715890
Logistics Consulting Servies
N.A.I.C.S.: 541614

Fontana Fasteners Srl   (1)
Str Zizinului 111, 500407, Brasov, Romania
Tel.: (40) 268332204
Logistics Consulting Servies
N.A.I.C.S.: 541614

Fontana Fasteners UK Ltd   (1)
Unit 3 Charles Street, Great Bridge, West Bromwich, B70 0AZ, United Kingdom
Tel.: (44) 1215778333
Logistics Consulting Servies
N.A.I.C.S.: 541614

FONTERELLI GMBH & CO KGAA

Waldhornstr 6, Munich, 80997, Germany
Tel.: (49) 4989009119
Web Site: https://www.fonterelli.de
FTRK—(BER)
Sales Range: Less than $1 Million
Investment Management Service
N.A.I.C.S.: 525990
Andreas Beyer (Mng Dir)

FONTERRA CO-OPERATIVE GROUP LTD.

109 Fanshawe Street, Auckland, 1010, New Zealand
Tel.: (64) 93749000
Web Site: https://www.fonterra.com
Year Founded: 2001
FCG—(NZX)
Sales Range: $5-14.9 Billion
Fluid Milk Manufacturing
N.A.I.C.S.: 311511
John Monaghan (Chm)

Subsidiaries:

Fonterra (Japan) Ltd.   (1)
25th Floor Taiyo Life Shinagawa Building 2-16-2 Konan, Minato-Ku, Tokyo, 108-0075, Japan
Tel.: (81) 367371800   (50%)
Web Site: http://www.fonterra.com

Sales Range: $600-649.9 Million
Emp.: 60
Dairy Products Production
N.A.I.C.S.: 424430

Fonterra (USA) Inc.   (1)
8700 W Bryn Mawr Ave Ste 500N, Chicago, IL 60631
Tel.: (847) 928-1600
Dairy Product Whslr
N.A.I.C.S.: 424430
Mark Piper (Pres)

Joint Venture (Domestic):

DairiConcepts, L.P.   (2)
3253 E Chestnut Expy, Springfield, MO 65802-2584
Tel.: (417) 829-3400
Web Site: http://www.dairiconcepts.com
Sales Range: $50-74.9 Million
Emp.: 500
Mfr of Cheese & Dairy Powders
N.A.I.C.S.: 311513

Fonterra Brands (Malaysia) Sdn Bhd   (1)
No 23 Jalan Delima 1/1 Subang Hi-Tech Industrial Park Batu Tiga, 40300, Shah Alam, Selangor, Malaysia
Tel.: (60) 358851888
Web Site: https://www.fonterra.com
Milk Product Mfr
N.A.I.C.S.: 311511

Fonterra Brands (Middle East) LLC   (1)
Floor 19 API Trio Tower Sheikh Zayed Road, PO Box 54730, Al Quoz Industrial Area, 53680, Dubai, United Arab Emirates   (49%)
Tel.: (971) 8002741000
Web Site: http://www.fonterra.com
Sales Range: $25-49.9 Million
Emp.: 60
Milk Production
N.A.I.C.S.: 112120

Fonterra Brands (New Zealand) Limited   (1)
109 Fanshawe Street, Private Bag 92032, Auckland, 1010, New Zealand   (100%)
Tel.: (64) 93749000
Dairy Products
N.A.I.C.S.: 424430
Chelet Tanjuactco (Brand Mgr-Anchor Milk)

Fonterra Brands Indonesia, PT   (1)
Prudential Center 19th Floor Kota Kasablanka Jl Casablanca Kav 88, Jakarta, 12870, Indonesia
Tel.: (62) 218281881
Milk Product Mfr
N.A.I.C.S.: 311511

Fonterra Brands Lanka (Private) Limited   (1)
No 100 Delgoda Road, 11650, Biyagama, Sri Lanka
Tel.: (94) 112488032
Dairy Products Distr
N.A.I.C.S.: 424430

Mainland Products Limited   (1)
109 Fanshawe Street, Auckland, 1010, New Zealand   (100%)
Tel.: (64) 93749000
Web Site: http://www.fonterra.com
Rev.: $31,298,400
Emp.: 100
Dairy Products
N.A.I.C.S.: 311514

Saudi New Zealand Milk Products Company Limited   (1)
PO Box 7493, Dammam, 31462, Saudi Arabia   (100%)
Tel.: (966) 38122200
Web Site: http://www.fonterra.com
Emp.: 190
Processed Cheese & Powdered Milk Mfr
N.A.I.C.S.: 311513

FONUA LTD.

Unit 2 77 Furze Road Sandyford Industrial Estate, Dublin, Ireland
Tel.: (353) 12149223
N.A.I.C.S.: 488510

FOOD & LIFE COMPANIES LTD.
1-22-2 Esaka, Suita, Osaka, Japan
Tel.: (81) 663681001
Web Site: https://food-and-life.co.jp
Year Founded: 2015
3563—(TKS)
Rev.: $2,139,386,230
Assets: $2,492,978,710
Liabilities: $1,977,826,400
Net Worth: $515,152,310
Earnings: $56,003,910
Emp.: 7,134
Fiscal Year-end: 09/30/23
Restaurant Management Services
N.A.I.C.S.: 722511
Koichi Mizutome *(Pres & CEO)*

Subsidiaries:

Sushiro Korea, Inc. **(1)**
18th Floor Gongdeok Building 11
Saechang-ro, Mapo-gu, Seoul, Korea
(South)
Tel.: (82) 234617715
Web Site: https://www.sushiro.co.kr
Restaurant Operators
N.A.I.C.S.: 722511

FOOD AND DRINKS PUBLIC COMPANY LIMITED
15th Floor Regent House Bldg 183
Rajdamri Rd, Lumpini Patumwan,
Bangkok, 10330, Thailand
Tel.: (66) 22535232 TH
Web Site:
https://www.foodanddrinks.co.th
Year Founded: 1985
F&D—(THA)
Rev.: $21,884,141
Assets: $47,179,838
Liabilities: $10,611,403
Net Worth: $36,568,435
Earnings: $1,491,308
Emp.: 534
Fiscal Year-end: 12/31/23
Frozen Food Mfr & Distr
N.A.I.C.S.: 311412

FOOD EMPIRE HOLDINGS LIMITED
31 Harrison Road 08-01 Food Empire
Building, Singapore, 369649, Singa-
pore
Tel.: (65) 66226900
Web Site:
https://www.foodempire.com
F03—(SES)
Rev.: $425,715,000
Assets: $402,905,000
Liabilities: $108,412,000
Net Worth: $294,493,000
Earnings: $56,464,000
Emp.: 3,620
Fiscal Year-end: 12/31/23
Food & Beverage Mfr & Marketer
N.A.I.C.S.: 425120
Wang Cheow Tan *(Founder & Chm)*

Subsidiaries:

FES (Vietnam) Co. Ltd **(1)**
(100%)
Sales Range: $25-49.9 Million
Emp.: 200
Coffee & Tea Mfr
N.A.I.C.S.: 311920

FES Industries Pte Ltd **(1)**
10 Chin Bee Dr, 619859, Singapore,
Singapore **(100%)**
Tel.: (65) 62689806
Sales Range: $25-49.9 Million
Roasted Nuts & Peanut Butter Mfr
N.A.I.C.S.: 311911

FES Industries Sdn Bhd **(1)**
No 7 Jln Bistari 4, Taman Industri Jaya, Jo-
hor, 81300, Malaysia **(100%)**
Tel.: (60) 75127710

Sales Range: $10-24.9 Million
Emp.: 80
Mfr & Processing of Instant Food & Bever-
ages
N.A.I.C.S.: 722515

Foodaworld Marketing Pte Ltd **(1)**
Pymonenka M vul 13 A-C 39, Office 23 5A
Bldg, 4050, Kiev, Ukraine **(100%)**
Tel.: (380) 444942555
Web Site: http://www.maccoffee.com.ua
Sales Range: $25-49.9 Million
Emp.: 14
Coffee & Tea Mfr
N.A.I.C.S.: 311920
Maurice Yeo *(Mng Dir)*

Future Corporation Pte Ltd **(1)**
31 Harrison Road H08-01, Singapore,
369649, Singapore
Tel.: (65) 67448911
Web Site: http://www.futurecorp.com
Food Products Mfr & Slaes
N.A.I.C.S.: 311911
Tan Wang Cheow *(Gen Mgr)*

Future Enterprises Pte Ltd **(1)**
31 Harrison Rd Unit 08-01, Singapore,
369649, Singapore **(100%)**
Tel.: (65) 67448911
Web Site: http://www.foodempire.com
Sales Range: $25-49.9 Million
Emp.: 70
Chocolate & Confectionery Mfr from Cacao
Beans
N.A.I.C.S.: 311351
Tan Wang Chow *(CEO)*

Subsidiary (Non-US):

Empire Distribution (Europe) Spolka
Z Ograniczona
Odpowiedzialnoscia **(2)**
Krolowej Marysienki 9/4a, Warsaw, 02-954,
Masovian, Poland
Tel.: (48) 227420550
Sales Range: $25-49.9 Million
Emp.: 3
Beverage Products Mfr & Distr
N.A.I.C.S.: 311930

**MAHLE Aftermarket Deutschland
GmbH (1)**
Duerrheimerstrasse 49A, 78166, Donaue-
schingen, Germany
Tel.: (49) 7718965324200
Automotive Electronic Parts Mfr & Distr
N.A.I.C.S.: 336320

MAHLE Argentina S.A. (1)
Ruta Panamericana Km 37 5 Centro, Indus-
trial Garin Lote 9A Calle Haendel y Cul de
Sac, 1619, Garin, Argentina
Tel.: (54) 3327414200
Engine Parts Mfr & Distr
N.A.I.C.S.: 336310

**MAHLE Componente de Motor
SRL (1)**
Calea Aradului DN69 Km 6 6, 300645, Timi-
soara, Timis, Romania
Tel.: (40) 256265630
Automotive Parts Mfr & Distr
N.A.I.C.S.: 336390

**MAHLE Engine Components
(Chongqing) Co., Ltd. (1)**
No 125 Hanyu Road, Yubei District,
Chongqing, 401 120, China
Tel.: (86) 2367837700
Engine Parts Mfr & Distr
N.A.I.C.S.: 336310

**MAHLE Engine Components (Nan-
jing) Co., Ltd. (1)**
No 65-1 Taifeng Road, Pukou District, Nan-
jing, 210 032, China
Tel.: (86) 2558690800
Engine Parts Mfr & Distr
N.A.I.C.S.: 336310

**MAHLE Engine Components (Thai-
land) Co., Ltd. (1)**
9/1-2 SOI Serithai 56 Serithai Road, 10230,
Bangkok, 10230, Thailand
Tel.: (66) 5170035
Engine Parts Mfr & Distr
N.A.I.C.S.: 336310

**MAHLE Engine Components (Ying-
kou) Co., Ltd. (1)**

No 49 Daqing Road, Zhan Qian District,
Yingkou, 115 004, Liaoning, China
Tel.: (86) 4173508090
Engine Parts Mfr & Distr
N.A.I.C.S.: 336310

**MAHLE Engineering Services India
Private Limited (1)**
City Survey Number 4270 One Elpro Park
1st, Pune, 411 033, Maharashtra, India
Tel.: (91) 66145432
Automobile Parts Distr
N.A.I.C.S.: 423120

**MAHLE Filter Systems North
America, Inc. (1)**
906 Butler Dr, Murfreesboro, TN 37127
Tel.: (615) 895-5572
Engine Parts Mfr & Distr
N.A.I.C.S.: 336310

**MAHLE Filter Systems Philippines
Corporation (1)**
Lot 5 6 7 Block 8 EPZA Drive, First Cavite
Industrial Estate Brgy Langkaan, Dasmari-
nas, 4126, Cavite, Philippines
Tel.: (63) 464020771
Engine Parts Mfr & Distr
N.A.I.C.S.: 336310

**MAHLE Guangzhou Filter Systems
Co., Ltd. (1)**
East Dongfeng Road, Guangzhou, 510800,
China
Tel.: (86) 236871402
Engine Parts Mfr & Distr
N.A.I.C.S.: 336310

**MAHLE Industria e Comercio
Ltda. (1)**
Rod Engenheiro Joao Tosello, Limeira-Mogi
Mirim S/N KM 96 - Bloco A -Jardim Nova,
Limeira, 13486-264, Brazil
Tel.: (55) 1934047700
Web Site: https://www.br.mahle.com
Automobile Parts Distr
N.A.I.C.S.: 423120

MAHLE International GmbH (1)
Pragstr 26 - 46, 70376, Stuttgart, Germany
Tel.: (49) 7115010
Engine Parts Mfr & Distr
N.A.I.C.S.: 336310

MAHLE Powertrain GmbH (1)
Wamslerstrasse 5, 81829, Munich, Ger-
many
Tel.: (49) 899629150
Engine Parts Mfr & Distr
N.A.I.C.S.: 336310

**MAHLE Shanghai Filter Systems Co.,
Ltd. (1)**
No 1199 Huan Cheng Bei Road, Fengxian,
Shanghai, 201 401, China
Tel.: (86) 2151365716
Engine Parts Mfr & Distr
N.A.I.C.S.: 336310

**MAHLE Siam Filter Systems Co.,
Ltd. (1)**
67 Moo 11 Soi King Kaew 33 King Kaew
Road, Racha Thewa Bang Phli, 10540,
Samut Prakan, 10540, Thailand
Tel.: (66) 27389030
Engine Parts Mfr & Distr
N.A.I.C.S.: 336310

**MAHLE Trading (Shanghai) Co.,
Ltd. (1)**
No 1168 Century Avenue Room 1202 Tower
A Oriental Financial Plaza, Pudong District,
Shanghai, 200120, China
Tel.: (86) 2120690800
Engine Parts Mfr & Distr
N.A.I.C.S.: 336310

Positive Food Ventures Private
Limited **(1)**
56 FF NRI Complex GK 4, New Delhi,
110019, India
Tel.: (91) 1140078711
Web Site: http://www.drinkbrewhouse.com
Brewhouse Ice Tea Product Mfr
N.A.I.C.S.: 312113

Tea Avenue (Private) Limited **(1)**
55 Barnes Place, Colombo, Sri Lanka
Tel.: (94) 112669944
Web Site: http://www.tea-avenue.com

Online Food Services
N.A.I.C.S.: 722310

Tea House LLP **(1)**
13a Taugul/Mamyr, MicroDistrict, 050052,
Almaty, Kazakhstan
Tel.: (7) 7272936551
Web Site: https://en.teahouse.kz
Tea Product Mfr & Distr
N.A.I.C.S.: 311920

FOOD PLANET, INC.
6F CJ Building 2-7-4 Nishishimbashi,
Minato-ku, Tokyo, 105-0003, Japan
Tel.: (81) 3 45778701
Year Founded: 1986
Sales Range: Less than $1 Million
Holding Company
N.A.I.C.S.: 551112
Masahiko Tando *(Pres)*

FOODCO HOLDING CO P.J.S.C
Port Zayed Mina, PO Box 2378, Abu
Dhabi, United Arab Emirates
Tel.: (971) 26731000
Web Site: https://hilyholding.com
Year Founded: 2006
Rev.: $79,398,023
Assets: $239,084,345
Liabilities: $110,004,558
Net Worth: $129,079,787
Earnings: $14,357,667
Emp.: 500
Fiscal Year-end: 12/31/16
Meat Product Distr
N.A.I.C.S.: 424470
Ahmed Ali Al Dhahry *(Chm)*

FOODNAMOO INC.
15F 396 World Cup Buk-Ro, Mapo-
Gu, Seoul, Korea (South)
Tel.: (82) 231528088
Web Site: http://www.foodnamoo.com
Year Founded: 2013
290720—(KRS)
Rev.: $166,594,121
Assets: $81,251,356
Liabilities: $44,532,825
Net Worth: $36,718,532
Earnings: ($2,534,969)
Emp.: 222
Fiscal Year-end: 12/31/22
Packaged Food Product Mfr
N.A.I.C.S.: 333241
Sang-Phil Park *(Gen Mgr)*

FOODS & INNS LTD.
3rd Floor Hamilton House 8 JN Here-
dia Marg Ballard Estate, Mumbai, 400
001, India
Tel.: (91) 2222613102
Web Site:
https://www.foodsandinns.com
507552—(BOM)
Rev.: $52,065,291
Assets: $58,338,953
Liabilities: $33,431,539
Net Worth: $24,907,414
Earnings: $536,486
Emp.: 374
Fiscal Year-end: 03/31/21
Fruit Pulp Mfr
N.A.I.C.S.: 311411
Moloy Saha *(CEO)*

Subsidiaries:

Kusum Spices Private Limited **(1)**
Kusum House T-II Cama Estate Goregaon-
East, Mumbai, 400063, Maharashtra, India
Tel.: (91) 2226851595
Web Site: https://kusumspices.com
Emp.: 50
Chili & Pepper Powder Mfr
N.A.I.C.S.: 311942

FOODTASTIC INC.
9300 Trans Canada Rte Ste 310,
Saint Laurent, Quebec, Canada

Foodtastic Inc.—(Continued)

Tel.: (514) 856-5555
Web Site: https://foodtastic.ca
Year Founded: 2016
Restaurant Franchise
N.A.I.C.S.: 722513
Peter Mammas (Pres & CEO)

Subsidiaries:

Freshii, Inc.　　　　　　　　　　(1)
1055 Yonge Street Unit 101, Toronto, M4W
2K9, ON, Canada
Tel.: (416) 458-1635
Web Site: https://www.freshii.com
Rev.: $18,634,456
Assets: $44,960,478
Liabilities: $20,911,887
Net Worth: $24,048,591
Earnings: ($7,878,123)
Emp.: 57
Fiscal Year-end: 12/26/2021
Restaurant Operators
N.A.I.C.S.: 722511
Matthew Corrin (Founder & CEO)

FOODWELL CORPORATION

1093 Bangchon-dong, Dong-gu,
Daegu, Korea (South)
Tel.: (82) 539803100
Web Site: http://www.foodwell.com
Year Founded: 1968
005670—(KRS)
Rev.: $141,076,070
Assets: $160,916,146
Liabilities: $80,445,693
Net Worth: $80,470,453
Earnings: $3,331,744
Emp.: 176
Fiscal Year-end: 12/31/22
Fruit Product Mfr
N.A.I.C.S.: 311423

Subsidiaries:

Foodwell Corporation - Daegu Fac-
tory 1　　　　　　　　　　　　(1)
1093 Bangchon-dong, Dong-gu, Daegu,
Korea (South)
Tel.: (82) 53 980 3100
Fruit Product Mfr
N.A.I.C.S.: 311423

Foodwell Corporation - Daegu Fac-
tory 2　　　　　　　　　　　　(1)
358-80 Galsan-dong, Dalseo-gu, Daegu,
Korea (South)
Tel.: (82) 53 580 2500
Food Products Mfr
N.A.I.C.S.: 311423

Qingdao Foodwell Corporation　(1)
Haibin 12 Road Economic development
zone, Jiaonan, Qingdao, China
Tel.: (86) 532 8813 9151
Fruit Product Mfr
N.A.I.C.S.: 311423
Kim Sung III (Gen Mgr)

FOOSUNG CO., LTD.

427-9 Rohha-ri, Paltan-myun, Hwa-
sun, 445-909, Korea (South)
Tel.: (82) 31 495 7243　　　　　KR
Web Site: http://www.foosung.com
Year Founded: 2006
Specialty Industrial Gas Mfr
N.A.I.C.S.: 325120
Keun Soo Kim (CEO)

Subsidiaries:

Foosung HDS Co., Ltd.　　　　(1)
113-8 Samsung-dong, Kangnam-gu, Seoul,
Korea (South)
Tel.: (82) 25544108
Web Site: http://www.fsc.co.kr
Chemical, Metal & Mineral Wholesale Trade
Agency
N.A.I.C.S.: 425120

Foosung Industrial Co., Ltd.　　(1)
755-2 Byungam, Sengkuk, Umsong,
Choongbuk, Korea (South)
Tel.: (82) 43 878 4054
Web Site: http://www.fic.co.kr

Plastic Injection Molding Mfr
N.A.I.C.S.: 326199
Ki Soo Kim (CEO)

Foosung Industrial Co., Ltd. - Eum-
sung Factory　　　　　　　　(1)
1524-4 Eumsung Road, Saengguk-Myeon,
Seoul, 369 841, Chungbuk, Korea (South)
Tel.: (82) 43 878 4054
Plastics Product Mfr
N.A.I.C.S.: 326199

Foosung Precision Ind. Co., Ltd. -
Beijing Factory　　　　　　　(1)
No 50 Seotong Road Miyun industrial De-
velopment C, Beijing, China
Tel.: (86) 10 6102 7192 4
Automobile Parts Mfr
N.A.I.C.S.: 336390

Foosung Precision Ind. Co., Ltd. -
Gajae-ri Factory　　　　　　(1)
584-1 Gajae-ri Paltan-myeon, Hwaseong,
Gyunggi, Korea (South)
Tel.: (82) 31 654 4200
Automobile Parts Mfr
N.A.I.C.S.: 336390

Foosung Precision Ind. Co., Ltd. -
Munmak Factory　　　　　　(1)
5-17 Bankye-ri Munmak-eup, Wonju,
Kangwon, Korea (South)
Tel.: (82) 33 731 7481
Automobile Parts Mfr
N.A.I.C.S.: 336390

Foosung Precision Ind. Co., Ltd. -
Ningbo FPI Factory　　　　　(1)
2-301 Dong fang ming zhu APT Ci xi si,
Ningbo, Zhe jiang, China
Tel.: (86) 574 6390 2200
Automobile Parts Mfr
N.A.I.C.S.: 336390

Foosung Precision Ind. Co., Ltd. -
Suzhou Factory　　　　　　(1)
No 58 Lijiang Road, Gaoxin, Suzhou, China
Tel.: (86) 512 6547 3718
Automobile Parts Mfr
N.A.I.C.S.: 336390

Foosung Precision Industry Co.,
Ltd.　　　　　　　　　　　(1)
427-9 Noha-ri, Paltan-myeon, Hwaseong,
Gyeunggi-do, Korea (South)
Tel.: (82) 5 777 2 555
Web Site: http://www.fpi.co.kr
Aluminum Products, Automotive Compo-
nents & Fluoropolymer Lining Systems Mfr
N.A.I.C.S.: 331318

Foosungtech Co., Ltd.　　　　(1)
989-3 Gosaek-dong, Gwonseon-gu, Suwon,
441-813, Gyeonggi-do, Korea (South)
Tel.: (82) 312059270
Web Site: http://wwwfoosungtech.co.kr
Sales Range: $50-74.9 Million
Emp.: 230
Electronic Connector Mfr
N.A.I.C.S.: 334417

FOOTWAY GROUP AB

Victoria Tower floor 32 Nolsogatan 3,
Stockholm, 164 40, Kista, Sweden
Tel.: (46) 20121211
Web Site: https://www.footway.com
FOOT-B—(OMX)
Rev.: $132,932,912
Assets: $167,542,592
Liabilities: $89,911,920
Net Worth: $77,630,672
Earnings: ($2,514,848)
Emp.: 48
Fiscal Year-end: 12/31/20
Shoe Store Retailer
N.A.I.C.S.: 458210
Daniel Muhlbach (Mng Dir)

Subsidiaries:

Sportamore AB　　　　　　　(1)
Gustavslundsvagen 151 E, 167 51, Bro-
mma, Sweden
Tel.: (46) 8 50007500
Web Site: http://www.sportamore.se
Online Sports & Fashion Products
N.A.I.C.S.: 459110

FOPE S.R.L.

Via Zampieri 31, 36100, Vicenza,
Italy
Tel.: (39) 0444286911
Web Site: http://www.fope.com
Year Founded: 1929
Sales Range: $10-24.9 Million
Emp.: 35
Jewelry Mfr
N.A.I.C.S.: 339910
Umberto Cazzola (Pres)

Subsidiaries:

Beijing Fope Jewellry & Arts, Ltd　(1)
Rm 2005 No 109 Bldg, Huizhongbeili Cha-
oyong Dist, 100029, Beijing, China
Tel.: (86) 1064861618
Jewelers Material & Lapidary Work Mfr
N.A.I.C.S.: 339910

FORACO INTERNATIONAL S.A.

26 Plage de L Estaque, 13016, Mar-
seille, France
Tel.: (33) 496151360　　　　　FR
Web Site: https://www.foraco.com
Year Founded: 1961
3F3—(DEU)
Rev.: $370,093,000
Assets: $279,729,000
Liabilities: $181,670,000
Net Worth: $98,059,000
Earnings: $33,916,000
Emp.: 2,756
Fiscal Year-end: 12/31/23
Other Nonmetallic Mineral Mining &
Quarrying
N.A.I.C.S.: 212390
Daniel Simoncini (Chm & CEO)

Subsidiaries:

Foraco Argentina SA　　　　(1)
Carril Rodriguez Pena 4581, Coquimbito
Maipu, M5522CKY, Mendoza, Argentina
Tel.: (54) 92615320160
Mineral Drilling Services
N.A.I.C.S.: 213115

Foraco Burkina Faso SA　　　(1)
Rue Zuug Sliga 549 ZAD, BP 4611, Ouaga-
dougou, Burkina Faso
Tel.: (226) 50370010
Mineral Drilling Services
N.A.I.C.S.: 213115

Foraco CI S.A.　　　　　　　(1)
19 rue Thomas Edison 11, BP 592, 11, Abi-
djan, Cote d'Ivoire
Tel.: (225) 2721353013
Mineral Drilling Services
N.A.I.C.S.: 213115
Denis Simonin (Mgr)

Foraco Canada Ltd.　　　　　(1)
151 Yonge Street Suite 1160, Toronto, M5C
2W7, ON, Canada
Tel.: (647) 351-5483
Mineral Drilling Services
N.A.I.C.S.: 213115
Rob Steadman (VP-HR)

Foraco Chile SA　　　　　　(1)
Avenida Bernardo O higgind Loteo 154,
Parque Industrial Los Libertadores, Colina,
Santiago, Chile
Tel.: (56) 227148500
Mineral Drilling Services
N.A.I.C.S.: 213115

Foraco Ghana Ltd.　　　　　(1)
Dodowa Road, PO Box 1899, Adenta Mam-
probi, Accra, Ghana
Tel.: (233) 21280173
Mineral Drilling Services
N.A.I.C.S.: 213115

Foraco Guinee Sarl　　　　　(1)
BP 436, Quartier Miniere, Conakry, Guinea
Tel.: (224) 30422188
Mineral Drilling Services
N.A.I.C.S.: 213115

Foraco Niger S.A.　　　　　(1)
Avenue de I Afrique Route de Saga, BP

2879, Niamey, Niger
Tel.: (227) 20739098
Mineral Drilling Services
N.A.I.C.S.: 213115

Foraco Pacifique SASU　　　(1)
5 rue Saint Pierre Cedex, BP 27010,
98863, Noumea, New Caledonia
Tel.: (687) 236400
Mineral Drilling Services
N.A.I.C.S.: 213115

Foraco Sahel Sarl　　　　　(1)
Magnambougou Plateau, BP 2330, Ba-
mako, Mali
Tel.: (223) 20205224
Mineral Drilling Services
N.A.I.C.S.: 213115

Foraco Singapore Pte. Ltd.　(1)
18 Robinson Road Level 02-03, Singapore,
048547, Singapore
Tel.: (65) 69557812
Mineral Drilling Services
N.A.I.C.S.: 213115

FORAFRIC GLOBAL PLC

Madison Building Queensway, Mid-
town, GX11 1AA, Gibraltar, Gibraltar
Tel.: (350) 20072505　　　　　GI
Web Site: https://www.forafric.com
Year Founded: 1943
AFRI—(NASDAQ)
Rev.: $289,772,000
Assets: $307,164,000
Liabilities: $262,209,000
Net Worth: $44,955,000
Earnings: ($19,128,000)
Emp.: 750
Fiscal Year-end: 12/31/22
Mineral Mining Services
N.A.I.C.S.: 213115
Julien Benitah (CFO)

FORAJ SONDE CRAIOVA

4 A Fratii Buzesti St, Craiova, Roma-
nia
Tel.: (40) 251415866
Web Site:
　　https://www.craiovadrilling.ro
FOSB—(BUC)
Rev.: $29,015,478
Assets: $27,779,350
Liabilities: $3,842,262
Net Worth: $23,937,088
Earnings: $2,105,052
Emp.: 298
Fiscal Year-end: 12/31/22
Drilling Services
N.A.I.C.S.: 213111

FORAN ENERGY GROUP CO., LTD.

No 25 Jihua 5th Road, Chancheng
District, Foshan, 528000, Guang-
dong, China
Tel.: (86) 75783036288
Web Site: http://www.fsgas.com
Year Founded: 1993
002911—(SSE)
Rev.: $2,656,803,240
Assets: $2,076,760,296
Liabilities: $1,174,097,808
Net Worth: $902,662,488
Earnings: $91,998,504
Fiscal Year-end: 12/31/22
Pipeline Transportation Services
N.A.I.C.S.: 237120
Yin Xiang (Chm)

FORAN MINING CORPORA-TION

904-409 Granville St, Vancouver,
V6C 1T2, BC, Canada
Tel.: (604) 488-0008
Web Site:
　　https://www.foranmining.com
Year Founded: 1989
FOM—(TSXV)
Rev.: $3,009,892

Assets: $409,642,075
Liabilities: $63,752,926
Net Worth: $345,889,149
Earnings: ($10,286,944)
Emp.: 109
Fiscal Year-end: 12/31/23
Gold Mining Services
N.A.I.C.S.: 212220
Darren Morcombe *(Chm & CEO-Interim)*

FORBES MOTORS INCORPO-RATED
165 Weber St S, Waterloo, N2J 4A6, ON, Canada
Tel.: (519) 742-4463
Web Site: http://www.forbesauto.com
Year Founded: 1948
Sales Range: $25-49.9 Million
New & Used Car Dealers
N.A.I.C.S.: 441110
Chris Maunsell *(Mgr-Svc)*

FORBES TRAVEL INTERNA-TIONAL LTD.
700-900 West Hastings Street, Vancouver, V6C 1E5, BC, Canada
Tel.: (604) 689-0461
Web Site: https://www.forbes-travel.com
Year Founded: 1986
Sales Range: $10-24.9 Million
Travel Agency
N.A.I.C.S.: 561599
Cheryl Green *(Partner)*

FORBES-HEWLETT TRANS-PORT INC.
156 Glidden Road, Brampton, L6W 3L2, ON, Canada
Tel.: (905) 455-2211
Web Site:
http://www.forbeshewlett.com
Year Founded: 1985
Rev.: $21,725,687
Emp.: 150
Truckload Services
N.A.I.C.S.: 484122
George V. Stott *(Founder)*

FORBIDDEN FOODS LIMITED
Level 5 126 Phillip Street, Sydney, 2000, NSW, Australia
Tel.: (61) 1300288664   AU
Web Site:
https://www.forbiddenfoods.com.au
Year Founded: 2010
FFF—(ASX)
Rev.: $2,434,160
Assets: $1,728,873
Liabilities: $571,700
Net Worth: $1,157,172
Earnings: ($3,622,512)
Fiscal Year-end: 06/30/23
Food Products Distr
N.A.I.C.S.: 445298
Jade Mcgillivray *(Sec)*

Subsidiaries:

Blue Dinosaur Pty. Ltd.   **(1)**
13/277-289 Middleborough Rd, Box Hill, 3128, VIC, Australia
Tel.: (61) 1300778061
Web Site: https://bluedinosaur.com.au
Snack Food Mfr & Whslr
N.A.I.C.S.: 311919

FORBION CAPITAL PART-NERS MANAGEMENT HOLD-ING BV
Gooimeer 2-35, 1411 TC, Naarden, Netherlands
Tel.: (31) 35 699 30 00
Web Site: http://www.forbion.com
Sales Range: $100-124.9 Million
Emp.: 12

Investment Holding Company
N.A.I.C.S.: 551112
Sander Slootweg *(Mng Partner)*

Subsidiaries:

Cardoz AB   **(1)**
Kornhamnstorg 53, SE 111 27, Stockholm, Sweden
Tel.: (46) 8 566 30 174
Web Site: http://www.cardoz.com
Pharmaceuticals Mfr
N.A.I.C.S.: 325412
Carl-Johan Dalsgaard *(CEO)*

Forbion Capital Partners Germany GmbH   **(1)**
Maximilanstrasse 36, 80539, Munich, Germany
Tel.: (49) 89 41 61 61 95 0
Financial Investment Services
N.A.I.C.S.: 523940
Holger Reithinger *(Gen Partner)*

FORBO HOLDING LTD.
Lindenstrasse 8, PO Box 1339, CH-6341, Baar, Switzerland
Tel.: (41) 587872525   CH
Web Site: https://www.forbo.com
Year Founded: 1928
FBOHF—(OTCIQ)
Rev.: $1,396,719,759
Assets: $1,071,309,727
Liabilities: $413,239,840
Net Worth: $658,069,886
Earnings: $121,583,076
Emp.: 5,190
Fiscal Year-end: 12/31/23
Floor Coverings, Adhesives & Belting Mfr & Supplier
N.A.I.C.S.: 326199
Michael Pieper *(Vice Chm)*

Subsidiaries:

Biuro Forbo Flooring Poland   **(1)**
Ul Wolsztynska 2, Poznan, 60-361, Poland   **(99%)**
Tel.: (48) 618621382
Web Site: http://www.forbo.flooring.pl
Sales Range: $25-49.9 Million
Emp.: 15
N.A.I.C.S.: 314110
Jakub Kuszewski *(Country Mgr)*

Enia Carpets Netherlands B.V.   **(1)**
Parallelweg 14, 5051 HG, Goirle, Netherlands   **(100%)**
Tel.: (31) 135309999
Web Site: http://www.iniacarpets.nl
Sales Range: $50-74.9 Million
Emp.: 150
Sales of Textile Floor Coverings
N.A.I.C.S.: 449121
Hans Vamdenberg *(Mng Dir)*

Forbo America Inc.   **(1)**
1105 N Market St, Wilmington, DE 19801-1216
Tel.: (302) 427-2139
Holding Company
N.A.I.C.S.: 551112

Subsidiary (Domestic):

Forbo Flooring, Inc.   **(2)**
8 Maplewood Dr Humboldt Industrial Park, Hazleton, PA 18202   **(100%)**
Tel.: (570) 459-0771
Web Site: http://www.forboflooringna.com
Sales Range: $25-49.9 Million
Emp.: 25
Vinyl & Linoleum Floor Coverings Mfr
N.A.I.C.S.: 326199
Dennis Paul Darragh *(VP)*

Forbo Siegling LLC   **(2)**
12201 Vanstory Dr, Huntersville, NC 28078
Tel.: (704) 948-0800
Web Site: http://www.forbo-siegling.com
Sales Range: $50-74.9 Million
Flat Belts, Conveyor & Processing Belts Mfr
N.A.I.C.S.: 326220

Division (Domestic):

Transtex Belting   **(3)**

10125 S Tryon St, Charlotte, NC 28273-6509
Tel.: (704) 334-5353
Sales Range: $25-49.9 Million
Emp.: 40
Lightweight PVC Conveyor Belt Mfr
N.A.I.C.S.: 333922

Forbo Contel Handelsges. m.b.H.   **(1)**
Handelskai 52, Vienna, 1200, Austria   **(100%)**
Tel.: (43) 330920105
Web Site: http://www.forbo.com
Sales Range: $25-49.9 Million
Emp.: 15
Sales of Linoleum, Vinyl & Textile Floor Coverings & Wall Coverings
N.A.I.C.S.: 449121

Forbo Erfurt GmbH   **(1)**
August-Robling-Strasse 2, 99091, Erfurt, Germany   **(100%)**
Tel.: (49) 361730410
Web Site: http://www.erfurt.forbo.com
Sales Range: $25-49.9 Million
Coatings & Adhesives Mfr & Sales
N.A.I.C.S.: 325520

Forbo Eurocol BV   **(1)**
Industrieweg 1-2, Postbus 130, 1520 AC, Wormerveer, Netherlands   **(100%)**
Tel.: (31) 756271600
Web Site: http://www.forbo.com
Sales Range: $50-74.9 Million
Emp.: 160
Adhesives, Grout Materials & Levelling Compounds
N.A.I.C.S.: 325520

Forbo Finanz AG   **(1)**
Lindenstrasse 8, PO Box 1041, CH 6341, Baar, Switzerland   **(100%)**
Tel.: (41) 58 787 25 25
Financial Services
N.A.I.C.S.: 525990

Forbo Floorcoverings Pty. Ltd.   **(1)**
23 Ormsby Place, Wetherill Park, 2164, NSW, Australia   **(100%)**
Tel.: (61) 298280200
Web Site: http://www.forbo.com.au
Sales Range: $25-49.9 Million
Sales of Flooring
N.A.I.C.S.: 449121

Forbo Flooring B.V.   **(1)**
Industrieweg 12, Postbus 13, 1566 JP, Assendelft, Netherlands   **(100%)**
Tel.: (31) 75 647 7477
Web Site: https://www.forbo.com
Sales Range: $25-49.9 Million
Emp.: 80
Carpet & Rug Mills
N.A.I.C.S.: 314110
Tom Kuijper *(Mng Dir)*

Forbo Flooring GmbH   **(1)**
Steubenstrasse 27, 33100, Paderborn, Germany
Tel.: (49) 52 511 8030
Web Site: https://www.forbo.com
Sales Range: $50-74.9 Million
Sales of Vinyl Floor Coverings
N.A.I.C.S.: 449121
Martin Thewes *(Mng Dir)*

Forbo Flooring UK Ltd.   **(1)**
Den Road, PO Box 1, Kirkcaldy, KY1 2ER, Fife, United Kingdom   **(100%)**
Tel.: (44) 177 374 4121
Web Site: https://www.forbo.com
Sales Range: $100-124.9 Million
Mfr & Sales of Linoleum, Vinyl & Textile Floor Coverings; Sale of Coatings & Adhesives
N.A.I.C.S.: 449121
Angus Fotheringhame *(Gen Mgr)*

Division (Domestic):

Forbo Flooring UK Ltd.   **(2)**
High Holborn Road, Ripley, DE5 3NT, Derbyshire, United Kingdom
Tel.: (44) 1773744121
Web Site: http://www.forbo.com
Sales Range: $25-49.9 Million
Flocked & Tufted Floor Coverings Mfr
N.A.I.C.S.: 449121
Brent Greenway *(Dir-Ops)*

Forbo Flooring UK Ltd.   **(2)**
Unit 92 Seedlee Road, Walton Summit, Preston, PR5 8AE, United Kingdom   **(100%)**
Tel.: (44) 8708550500
Web Site: http://www.forbo-flooring.co.uk
Carpet & Rug Mills
N.A.I.C.S.: 314110

Forbo Floring Oy AB   **(1)**
Heikkilainkapu No-2, 210, Helsinki, Finland   **(100%)**
Tel.: (358) 986230300
Web Site: http://www.forbo.fi
Sales Range: $25-49.9 Million
Sales of Flooring
N.A.I.C.S.: 449121
Markus Lilius *(CEO)*

Forbo Giubiasco SA   **(1)**
Via Industrie 16, 6512, Giubiasco, Gicino, Switzerland   **(100%)**
Tel.: (41) 918500111
Web Site: http://www.forbo-flooring.ch
Sales Range: $25-49.9 Million
Emp.: 100
PVC Floor Covering Mfr; Tile Flooring Mfr
N.A.I.C.S.: 238330
Guidowte Bruno *(Mng Dir)*

Forbo International Hong Kong Ltd.   **(1)**
805A 8/F Tsim Sha Tsui Centre 66 Mody Road, Tsim Sha Tsui, Kowloon, China (Hong Kong)
Tel.: (852) 37685017
Floor Covering Mfr & Distr
N.A.I.C.S.: 326199

Forbo International SA   **(1)**
Lindenstrasse 8, PO Box 1041, CH 6341, Baar, Switzerland   **(100%)**
Tel.: (41) 587872525
Holding Company
N.A.I.C.S.: 551112

Forbo Ireland Ltd.   **(1)**
Unit 2 Deansgrange Business Park, Deansgrange, Dublin, Ireland   **(100%)**
Tel.: (353) 1 289 8898
Web Site: https://www.forbo-flooring.ie.com
Sales Range: $25-49.9 Million
Emp.: 7
Sales of Linoleum, Vinyl & Textile Floor Coverings
N.A.I.C.S.: 449121
Paul Carney *(Mng Dir)*

Forbo Linoleum   **(1)**
Noordkustlaan 18, Groot-Bijgaarden, 1702, Belgium   **(100%)**
Tel.: (32) 24670660
Web Site: http://www.forbo.be
Sales Range: $25-49.9 Million
Emp.: 25
Sales of Linoleum, Vinyl & Textile Floor Coverings, Wall Coverings, Coatings, Adhesives
N.A.I.C.S.: 449121

Forbo Linoleum A/S   **(1)**
Produktionsvej 14, 2600, Glostrup, Denmark   **(100%)**
Tel.: (45) 44928500
Web Site: http://www.forbo.dk
Sales Range: $25-49.9 Million
Emp.: 15
Sales of Flooring
N.A.I.C.S.: 449121
Jens Christian Holm Iversen *(Gen Mgr)*

Forbo Linoleum A/S   **(1)**
Hagalokka 7 1483, Vettre, 1392, Asker, Norway   **(100%)**
Tel.: (47) 66771200
Web Site: http://www.forbo.no
Sales Range: $25-49.9 Million
Emp.: 30
Sales of Flooring
N.A.I.C.S.: 449121
Mortem Aarhus *(Mng Dir)*

Forbo Linoleum, Inc.   **(1)**
111 Westmore Drive, Toronto, M9V 3Y6, ON, Canada   **(100%)**
Tel.: (416) 661-2351
Web Site: http://www.forboflooringna.com
Sales Range: $25-49.9 Million
Sales of Floor Coverings
N.A.I.C.S.: 449121

Forbo Holding Ltd.—(Continued)

Forbo Linolium B.V. (1)
Industrieweg 12, 1566JP, Assendelft,
Netherlands (100%)
Tel.: (31) 756477477
Web Site: http://www.forbo-flooring.com
Sales Range: $200-249.9 Million
Emp.: 700
Mfr & Sales of Linoleum, Vinyl & Textile
Floor Coverings, Coatings, Adhesives
N.A.I.C.S.: 326199
Tom Kaiser (Exec VP)

Subsidiary (Non-US):

Forbo s.r.o. (2)
Novodvorska 994, 142 00, Prague, Praha,
Czech Republic (100%)
Tel.: (420) 239043011
Web Site: http://www.forbo.cz
Sales Range: $25-49.9 Million
Holding Company
N.A.I.C.S.: 551112

Forbo Management SA (1)
Lindenstrasse 8, 6340, Baar, Switzerland
Tel.: (41) 587872536
Floor Covering Mfr & Distr
N.A.I.C.S.: 326199

Forbo Padloburkolatok Kft. (1)
Megyeri 8, 1117, Budapest, Hungary
Tel.: (36) 0623444005
Web Site: http://www.forbo.com
Sales of Flooring
N.A.I.C.S.: 449121

Forbo Parquet AB (1)
Fabriksgatan 12, Tibro, 54350,
Sweden (100%)
Tel.: (46) 50443920
Web Site: http://www.forboparquet.com
Sales Range: $50-74.9 Million
Emp.: 150
Mfr of Floors
N.A.I.C.S.: 326199
Neil Ringborg (Gen Mgr)

Forbo Pavimentos SA (1)
Pasaje Bofill 13-15, 08013, Barcelona,
Spain (100%)
Tel.: (34) 932090793
Web Site: http://www.forbo-linoleum.es
Sales Range: $25-49.9 Million
Sales of Linoleum, Vinyl & Textile Floor
Coverings
N.A.I.C.S.: 449121

Forbo Resilienti S.r.l. (1)
Centro Commerciale San Felice Lotto 2 Int
5, Segrate, 20090, Milan, Italy
Tel.: (39) 027531488
Web Site: http://www.forbo.com
Linoleum, Vinyl & Textile Floor Coverings &
Wall Coverings Sales
N.A.I.C.S.: 449121

Forbo Sarlino SA (1)
63 rue Gosset, B P 62717, 51055, Reims,
Cedex, France (100%)
Tel.: (33) 326773030
Web Site: http://www.sarlino.forbo.com
Sales Range: $125-149.9 Million
Mfr & Sales of Vinyl & Textile Floor Cover-
ings & Wall Coverings; Sales of Linoleum,
Coatings & Adhesives
N.A.I.C.S.: 326199

Division (Domestic):

Forbo Flooring (2)
Parc Industriel Ouest, 37110, Chateau-
Renalt, France (100%)
Tel.: (33) 247298500
Sales Range: $25-49.9 Million
Emp.: 60
Carpet & Rug Mills
N.A.I.C.S.: 314110
Selepp Pisen (Gen Mgr)

**Forbo Siegling (Thailand) Co.
Ltd.** (1)
777/27 Soi Project TIP6 Moo9, Bang Pla
Bang Plee, Samut Prakan, 10540, Thailand
Tel.: (66) 21300286
Conveyor Belt Mfr & Distr
N.A.I.C.S.: 333922

Forbo Siegling GmbH (1)
Lilienthalstrasse 6 8, PO Box 5346, 30179,

Hannover, Germany (100%)
Tel.: (49) 51167040
Web Site: http://www.forbo-siegling.com
Sales Range: $125-149.9 Million
Flooring, Movement & Bonding Systems Mfr
N.A.I.C.S.: 325520

Subsidiary (Non-US):

Forbo Siegling (Shenyang) (2)
Shenyang Economic and Technological De-
velopment Zone, No 5 Mo Chou Hu St,
Shenyang, 110141, Liaoning,
China (100%)
Tel.: (86) 2425813813
Web Site: http://www.forbo.com
Sales Range: $25-49.9 Million
N.A.I.C.S.: 314110

**Forbo Siegling (Shenyang) Belting
Co. Ltd** (2)
Shenyang Economic and Technological De-
velopment Zone, No 5 Mo Chou Hu Street,
Shenyang, 110141, China (100%)
Tel.: (86) 2425813813
Web Site: http://www.forbo.com
Sales Range: $25-49.9 Million
Emp.: 113
N.A.I.C.S.: 314110

Forbo Siegling Austria GmbH (2)
Oswald-Redlich-Strasse 1, 1210, Vienna,
Austria (100%)
Tel.: (43) 12596516
Web Site: http://www.forbo-siegling.at
Sales Range: $1-9.9 Million
Emp.: 17
Conveyor, Processing, Modular, Timing,
Folder & Carrier Machine Belt Mfr
N.A.I.C.S.: 326220

Forbo Siegling Canada Corp. (2)
3220 Orlando Dr, Mississauga, L4V 1R5,
ON, Canada (100%)
Tel.: (905) 677-9983
Web Site: http://www.forbo.com
Sales Range: $25-49.9 Million
Emp.: 30
Industrial Belt Supplier
N.A.I.C.S.: 326220

Forbo Siegling France S.A.S. (2)
184 Rue De La Mitterie, 59461, Lomme,
Cedex, France (70%)
Tel.: (33) 320170280
Web Site: http://www.forbo-siegling.com
Sales Range: $25-49.9 Million
Composites Mfr
N.A.I.C.S.: 424610

Forbo Siegling Iberica S.A. (2)
Avda La Ferreria 74, 08110, Montcada, Bar-
celona, Spain
Tel.: (34) 935644253
Web Site: http://www.forbo-siegling.es
Sales Range: $25-49.9 Million
Emp.: 35
Sales of Coatings & Adhesives for Flooring
Products
N.A.I.C.S.: 424690

Forbo Siegling Japan Limited (2)
Osaki CN Bldg 5-10-10 Osaki, Shinagawa-
ku, Tokyo, 141-0032, Japan (100%)
Tel.: (81) 35 740 2350
Web Site: https://www.forbo.com
Emp.: 186
Mfr & Sales of Coatings & Adhesives
N.A.I.C.S.: 325520
Mamoru Sato (Pres)

Forbo Siegling Svenska AB (2)
Bangardsvagen 10, Box 140, 428 22,
Kallered, Sweden (100%)
Tel.: (46) 31997050
Web Site: http://www.forbo-siegling.se
Sales Range: $25-49.9 Million
Emp.: 30
Sales of Coatings & Adhesives
N.A.I.C.S.: 424690

Siegling (Schweiz) AG (2)
Kapellenstrasse 2, 4323, Wallbach,
Switzerland (100%)
Tel.: (41) 618656250
Web Site: https://www.forbo.com
Sales Range: $10-24.9 Million
Emp.: 120
Mfr & Sale of Coatings & Adhesives
N.A.I.C.S.: 325520

Siegling Brasil Ltda. (2)
Av Prof Vernon Krieble 500 Bairro Industrial
Itaqui, Itapevi, 06696-070, Brazil (100%)
Tel.: (55) 1141437704
Web Site: https://www.forbo.com
Sales Range: $50-74.9 Million
Emp.: 180
Mfr & Sales of Coatings & Adhesives
N.A.I.C.S.: 325520

Siegling Danmark A/S (2)
Kirkebjerg Parkvej 34, 2605, Brondby,
Denmark (100%)
Tel.: (45) 43431033
Web Site: http://www.forbo-siegling.dk
Sales Range: $25-49.9 Million
Emp.: 24
Sales of Coatings & Adhesives
N.A.I.C.S.: 424690

Siegling Italia S.p.a. (2)
Via Sondrio 4, 20037, Paderno Dugnano,
MI, Italy (100%)
Tel.: (39) 029100231
Web Site: https://www.forbo.com
Sales Range: $25-49.9 Million
Emp.: 60
Sales of Coatings & Adhesives
N.A.I.C.S.: 424690

Siegling Mexico S.A. de C.V. (2)
Sor Juana Ines De La Cruz No 54 Col In-
dustrial San Lorenzo, 54033, Tlalnepantla,
Mexico (100%)
Tel.: (52) 5512536200
Web Site: https://www.forbo.com
Sales Range: $1-9.9 Million
Emp.: 70
Mfr & Sales of Coatings & Adhesives
N.A.I.C.S.: 325520

Siegling Nederland B.V. (2)
Van Rensselaerweg 1, Postbus 129, 6956
AV, Spankeren, Netherlands
Tel.: (31) 313491111
Web Site: http://www.forbo.com
Sales Range: $25-49.9 Million
Emp.: 55
N.A.I.C.S.: 314110
Dietrich Brehm (CEO)

Forbo Tapijt B.V. (1)
, Postbus 56, 5050AB, Goirle, Netherlands
Tel.: (31) 13 5349035
Web Site: http://www.forbo.com
Mfr & Sale of Flooring
N.A.I.C.S.: 449121

Forbo UK Ltd. (1)
Den Road, PO Box 1, Kirkcaldy, KY1 2SB,
Fife, United Kingdom (100%)
Tel.: (44) 1773740688
Web Site: http://www.forbo-flooring.co.uk
Sales Range: $75-99.9 Million
Emp.: 160
Holding Company
N.A.I.C.S.: 551112
Angus Fotheringhame (Gen Mgr)

Forbo-Nairn Ltd. (1)
PO Box 1, Kirkcaldy, KY1 2SB, Fife, United
Kingdom
Tel.: (44) 1592643777
Floor Covering Mfr & Distr
N.A.I.C.S.: 326199

Forbo-Novilon B.V. (1)
De Holwert 12, 7741 KC, Coevorden,
Netherlands (100%)
Tel.: (31) 52 459 6868
Web Site: http://www.forbo.com
Sales Range: $50-74.9 Million
Mfr & Sale of Vinyl Floor Coverings
N.A.I.C.S.: 449121
D Glance (Mng Dir)

Nairn Floors Benelux B.V. (1)
PO Box 1, Kirkcaldy, KY1 2SB, Fife, United
Kingdom
Tel.: (44) 592643777
Web Site: http://www.forbo-flooring.co.uk
Sales of Flooring
N.A.I.C.S.: 449121
Angus Fotherinhame (Gen Mgr)

Novilon Ltd. (1)
PO Box 1, Kirkcaldy, KY1 2SB, United
Kingdom
Tel.: (44) 592643777
Web Site: http://www.forbo.com

Sales of Vinyl Floor Coverings
N.A.I.C.S.: 449121

**FORCE COMMODITIES LIM-
ITED**
Unit 48 First Floor 1008 Wellington
Street, West Perth, 6005, WA, Aus-
tralia
Tel.: (61) 86270 4694
Web Site:
   http://forcecommodities.com.au
Rev.: $237,222
Assets: $8,231,695
Liabilities: $121,354
Net Worth: $8,110,340
Earnings: ($3,630,304)
Fiscal Year-end: 12/31/17
Gold Mining Services
N.A.I.C.S.: 212220
Simon Pooley (CEO)

**FORCE MOS TECHNOLOGY
CO., LTD.**
24F No 555 Siyuan Road, Xinzhuang
District, New Taipei City, 242, Taiwan
Tel.: (886) 289769223
Web Site: https://www.force-mos.com
Year Founded: 2006
4923—(TAI)
Electronic Product Distr
N.A.I.C.S.: 449210
Dover Chung (Pres)

FORCE MOTORS LIMITED
Mumbai Pune Road Akurdi, Pune,
411035, India
Tel.: (91) 2027476381
Web Site:
   https://www.forcemotors.com
FORCEMOT—(NSE)
Rev.: $274,785,420
Assets: $441,918,750
Liabilities: $190,795,605
Net Worth: $251,123,145
Earnings: ($16,863,210)
Emp.: 4,737
Fiscal Year-end: 03/31/21
Light Commercial Vehicles, Utility Ve-
hicles, Three Wheelers, Agricultural
Tractors & Heavy Commercial Ve-
hicles Mfr
N.A.I.C.S.: 336110
Abhaykumar N. Firodia (Chm)

FORCECON TECH. CO., LTD.
2F No 31 Xintai Rd, Zhubei, Hsinchu,
Taiwan
Tel.: (886) 35512035
Web Site: https://www.forcecon.com
Year Founded: 1997
3483—(TPE)
Rev.: $232,044,743
Assets: $228,651,878
Liabilities: $118,687,803
Net Worth: $109,964,075
Earnings: $15,592,596
Fiscal Year-end: 12/31/22
Thermal Module Mfr
N.A.I.C.S.: 334513
Chen-Chi Jao (Chm & Pres)

FORCS CO., LTD.
646 Nonhyeon-ro, Gangnam-gu,
Seoul, 06106, Korea (South)
Tel.: (82) 261888200
Web Site: https://www.forcs.com
Year Founded: 1995
189690—(KRS)
Rev.: $25,600,486
Assets: $56,986,195
Liabilities: $2,553,959
Net Worth: $54,432,235
Earnings: $4,014,813
Emp.: 177
Fiscal Year-end: 06/30/23
Software Publisher
N.A.I.C.S.: 513210

Mikyung Park *(Co-Founder, Co-Pres & Co-CEO)*

FORD & SLATER LEICESTER
Hazel Drive, Leicester, LE3 2JG, United Kingdom
Tel.: (44) 1162632900
Web Site:
http://www.fordandslater.co.uk
Year Founded: 1929
Sales Range: $125-149.9 Million
Emp.: 360
Commercial Vehicle Sales
N.A.I.C.S.: 441227
Ali Drummond *(Gen Mgr-Sls)*

FORD GLORY INTERNA-TIONAL LIMITED
19/F Ford Glory Plaza 37-39 Wing Hong Street, Cheung Sha Wan, Kowloon, China (Hong Kong)
Tel.: (852) 24846688
Web Site:
http://www.fordglory.com.hk
Year Founded: 1996
Sales Range: $25-49.9 Million
Emp.: 61
Apparels Mfr
N.A.I.C.S.: 315210

Subsidiaries:

Ford Glory (Cambodia) Manufacturing Ltd.   (1)
North Bridge Street, Sangkat Steung Meanchey, Phnom Penh, Cambodia
Tel.: (855) 23424102
Apparels Mfr
N.A.I.C.S.: 315250

Jerash Garments and Fashions Manufacturing Co. Ltd.   (1)
Al-Tajamouat Industrial Estate, PO Box 22, Sahab, Amman, 11636, Jordan
Tel.: (962) 775757135
Apparels Mfr
N.A.I.C.S.: 315250

Jiangmen VA Manufacturing Ltd.   (1)
Jin Feng Industrial District, Luo Keng Town Xinhui, Jiangmen, Guangdong, China
Tel.: (86) 750 6462341
Apparels Mfr
N.A.I.C.S.: 315250

PT. V-Apparel Semarang   (1)
JL Coaster 8 Block B03, 04 05 A06 Tanjung Emas Export Processing Zone, Semarang, Indonesia
Tel.: (62) 24 3553327
Apparels Mfr
N.A.I.C.S.: 315250

FOREBRIGHT CAPITAL MAN-AGEMENT LTD.
Suite 3720 Jardine House 1 Connaught Place, Central, Hong Kong, China (Hong Kong)
Tel.: (852) 25982598   HK
Web Site:
http://www.forebrightcapital.com
Year Founded: 2014
Investment Fund Management Services
N.A.I.C.S.: 523940
Kevin Song *(Partner)*

Subsidiaries:

FNOF Precious Honour Limited   (1)
Suite 3720 Jardine House 1 Connaught Place, Central, China (Hong Kong)
Tel.: (852) 2598 2598
Investment Services
N.A.I.C.S.: 523999

Subsidiary (Non-US):

O2Micro International Ltd.   (2)
Grand Pavilion Commercial Centre West Bay Road, PO Box 32331, Georgetown, KY1-1209, Grand Cayman, Cayman Islands
Tel.: (345) 9451110

Web Site: http://www.o2micro.com
Rev.: $101,096,000
Assets: $118,342,000
Liabilities: $18,858,000
Net Worth: $99,484,000
Earnings: $12,113,000
Emp.: 315
Fiscal Year-end: 12/31/2021
Power Management & Security Components & Systems Developer
N.A.I.C.S.: 334413
Sterling Du *(Chm & CEO)*

Subsidiary (Non-US):

O2Micro (China) Co., Ltd   (3)
2 B Zhang Jiang Mansion No 560 songtao Road, Shanghai, 201203, China
Tel.: (86) 2150271133
Web Site: http://www.o2micro.com
Integrated Circuits Mfr
N.A.I.C.S.: 334413

Jinpan International (USA) Ltd.   (1)
390 Veterans Blvd, Carlstadt, NJ 07072   (100%)
Tel.: (201) 460-8778
Web Site: http://www.jstusa.net
Vacuum Cast Resin Transformers Service
N.A.I.C.S.: 811210
Richard Wolff *(VP-Bus Dev)*

FOREIGN CURRENCY DIRECT PLC
Spaces, Building 1 Chalfont Park, Chalfont St. Peter, Gerrards Cross, London, SL9 0BG, Bucks, United Kingdom
Tel.: (44) 1494725353
Web Site:
http://www.currencies.co.uk
Year Founded: 2000
Foreign Currency Exchange Services
N.A.I.C.S.: 523210
Richard Gompels *(CTO)*

Subsidiaries:

EarthportFX Limited   (1)
140 Aldersgate Street, London, EC1A 4HY, United Kingdom
Tel.: (44) 2075940550
Web Site: http://www.earthport-fx.com
Foreign Exchange Financial transaction Processing Services
N.A.I.C.S.: 522320
Eric Peacock *(Chm)*

FOREIGN TRADE DEVELOP-MENT & INVESTMENT COR-PORATION
28 Phung Khac Khoan Street Da Kao Ward, District 1, Ho Chi Minh City, Vietnam
Tel.: (84) 838221043
Web Site: http://www.fidecovn.com
FDC—(HOSE)
Rev.: $773,365
Assets: $27,576,066
Liabilities: $9,214,009
Net Worth: $18,362,057
Earnings: $29,870
Fiscal Year-end: 12/31/23
Real Estate Development Services
N.A.I.C.S.: 531390

FORELAND FABRICTECH HOLDINGS LIMITED
The Second Processing Zone Dongshi Town, Jinjiang, 362271, Fujian, China
Tel.: (86) 59585585508
Web Site:
http://www.fulianknitting.com
Sales Range: $10-24.9 Million
Broadwoven Fabric Mfr
N.A.I.C.S.: 313210

Subsidiaries:

Fulian Knitting Co., Ltd   (1)
Second Processing Zone, Dongshi Town Jinjiang, Fuzhou, Fujian, China

Tel.: (86) 595 85585508
Web Site: http://fulianknitting.cn
Sales Range: $100-124.9 Million
Emp.: 400
Fabric Product Mfr
N.A.I.C.S.: 313240

FOREMAN CAPITAL B.V.
WTC Amsterdam Tower H 24th Floor Zuidplein 202, 1077 XV, Amsterdam, Netherlands
Tel.: (31) 20 470 6944   NI
Web Site:
http://www.foremancapital.nl
Equity Investment Firm
N.A.I.C.S.: 523999
Arent Foch *(Co-Founder & Partner)*

FOREMOST CLEAN ENERGY LTD.
250 - 750 West Pender Street, Vancouver, V6C 2T7, BC, Canada
Tel.: (833) 327-7377   BC
Web Site:
https://foremostcleanenergy.com
Year Founded: 2005
FMST—(NASDAQ)
Rev.: $961
Assets: $12,134,554
Liabilities: $2,477,754
Net Worth: $9,656,800
Earnings: ($3,269,369)
Emp.: 2
Fiscal Year-end: 03/31/24
Iron Ore Mining
N.A.I.C.S.: 212210
Leon Frank Anderson *(Founder)*

FOREMOST INCOME FUND
6614 50th Avenue, Lloydminster, T9V 2W8, AB, Canada
Tel.: (780) 875-6161   Ca
Web Site: https://www.foremost.ca
Year Founded: 2005
Rev.: $114,875,533
Assets: $123,176,857
Liabilities: $16,640,144
Net Worth: $106,536,713
Earnings: $358,898
Emp.: 258
Fiscal Year-end: 12/31/19
Open-End Mutual Fund; Oil & Gas, Mining, Water Well & Construction Equipment Mfr & Distr
N.A.I.C.S.: 525910
Jackie Schenn *(CFO & VP-Fin)*

Subsidiaries:

Foremost Industries LP   (1)
1225 64th Avenue NE, Calgary, T2E 8P9, AB, Canada
Tel.: (403) 295-5800
Industrial, Mining & Construction Equipment Designer, Mfr & Whslr
N.A.I.C.S.: 423810
Jackie Schenn *(VP-Fin)*

Foremost Universal LP   (1)
450-630 6th Avenue SW, Calgary, T2P 0S8, AB, Canada
Tel.: (403) 266-4556
Energy Industry Tank, Vacuum & Compression Equipment Designer, Mfr & Whslr
N.A.I.C.S.: 333132
Jackie Schenn *(VP-Fin)*

FORENINGEN AP PENSION F.M.B.A.
Ostbanegade 135, 2100, Copenhagen, O, Denmark
Tel.: (45) 39165000
Web Site: https://appension.dk
Year Founded: 1919
Holding Company
N.A.I.C.S.: 551112

Subsidiaries:

AP Pension
livsforsikringsaktieselskab   (1)

Ostbanegade 135, 2100, Copenhagen, O, Denmark
Tel.: (45) 3 916 5000
Web Site: http://www.appension.dk
Fire Insurance Services
N.A.I.C.S.: 524113
Bo Normann Rasmussen *(Mgr-Admin & Member-Exec Bd)*

Skandia A/S   (1)
AKy Fiskers Pl 9, 2300, Copenhagen, Denmark
Tel.: (45) 70121213
Web Site: http://www.skandia.dk
Insurance Services
N.A.I.C.S.: 524298

FORESEE PHARMACEUTI-CALS CO., LTD.
9F-2 No 19-3 Sanchong Rd, Nangang Dist, Taipei, 115, Taiwan
Tel.: (886) 277500188
Web Site:
https://www.foreseepharma.com
6576—(TPE)
Rev.: $9,427,071
Assets: $40,772,066
Liabilities: $12,301,348
Net Worth: $28,470,719
Earnings: ($14,777,788)
Emp.: 52
Fiscal Year-end: 12/31/22
Pharmaceuticals Product Mfr
N.A.I.C.S.: 325412
Bien Chien *(Chm)*

FORESIGHT ENTERPRISE VCT PLC
The Shard 32 London Bridge Street, London, SE1 9SG, United Kingdom
Tel.: (44) 2079312100
FTF—(LSE)
Rev.: $33,165,602
Assets: $179,676,198
Liabilities: $175,123
Net Worth: $179,501,075
Earnings: $29,070,418
Fiscal Year-end: 12/31/21
Investment Fund Management Services
N.A.I.C.S.: 523940

FORESIGHT GROUP HOLD-INGS LIMITED
Ground Floor Dorey Court Admiral Park, Saint Peter Port , GY1 2HT, Guernsey
Tel.: (44) 20 3667 8100
Web Site: https://www.fsg-investors.com
Emp.: 251
Infrastructure & Private Equity Investment Services
N.A.I.C.S.: 523999
Bernard Fairman *(Chm)*

Subsidiaries:

Infrastructure Capital Group Ltd. (1)
Level 15 14 Martin Place, Sydney, 2000, NSW, Australia
Tel.: (61) 2 8071 1202
Web Site:
http://www.infrastructurecapital.com.au
Infrastructure Investment Management Services
N.A.I.C.S.: 523999
Andrew Pickering *(Chief Investment Officer & Portfolio Mgr-EIT)*

Subsidiary (Domestic):

Stadium Australia Group Ltd.   (2)
Level 3 Members' Stand Edwin Flack Avenue, Sydney Olympic Park, Sydney, 2127, NSW, Australia
Tel.: (61) 287652000
Web Site: http://www.anzstadium.com.au
Sales Range: $25-49.9 Million
Emp.: 2,500
Venue Operation & Entertainment Services
N.A.I.C.S.: 711310

Foresight Group Holdings Limited—(Continued)

John Clarke (Chm)

FORESIGHT GROUP LLP
The Shard 32 London Bridge Street, London, SE1 9SG, United Kingdom
Tel.: (44) 20 3667 8100
Web Site:
http://www.foresightgroup.eu
Year Founded: 1984
Holding Company
N.A.I.C.S.: 551112
Bernard Fairman (Chm)

FORESIGHT SOLAR & TECHNOLOGY VCT PLC
The Shard 32 London Bridge Street, London, SE1 9SG, United Kingdom
Tel.: (44) 2036678100
Web Site:
http://www.foresightgroup.com
FTSV—(LSE)
Rev.: $23,986,839
Assets: $46,820,974
Liabilities: $663,925
Net Worth: $46,157,049
Earnings: ($1,135,054)
Fiscal Year-end: 03/31/21
Investment Management Service
N.A.I.C.S.: 523940
David Alan Hurst-Brown (Mgr-Fund)

FORESIGHT SOLAR FUND LIMITED
The Shard 32 London Bridge Street, London, SE1 9SG, United Kingdom
Tel.: (44) 2036678100
Web Site:
https://fsfl.foresightgroup.eu
Year Founded: 2013
FSFL—(LSE)
Rev.: $202,403,466
Assets: $958,674,567
Liabilities: $666,847
Net Worth: $958,007,721
Earnings: $191,946,268
Fiscal Year-end: 12/31/22
Investment Management Service
N.A.I.C.S.: 523999
Alexander Ohlsson (Chm)

Subsidiaries:

Misson Solar Limited **(1)**
16 Langbury Lane, Ferring, Worthing, BN12 6PU, United Kingdom
Tel.: (44) 3334040179
Web Site: https://www.missonsolar.co.uk
Solar Cells Mfr & Distr
N.A.I.C.S.: 334413

FORESIGHT VCT PLC
The Shard 32 London Bridge Street, London, SE1 9SG, United Kingdom
Tel.: (44) 2036678100
Web Site:
https://www.foresightenterprise.com
Year Founded: 1998
FTV—(LSE)
Rev.: $1,911,670
Assets: $181,091,336
Liabilities: $180,577
Net Worth: $180,910,759
Earnings: $29,295,524
Emp.: 268
Fiscal Year-end: 12/31/21
Investment Management Service
N.A.I.C.S.: 523999
Margaret Littlejohns (Chm)

Subsidiaries:

Foresight Group CI Limited **(1)**
1st Floor Royal Chambers St Julian s Avenue, PO Box 650, Saint Peter Port, GY1 3JX, Guernsey
Tel.: (44) 749300
Company Financial Services
N.A.I.C.S.: 522320

Foresight Group Iberia SL **(1)**
C/ Jose Abascal 56, 28003, Madrid, Spain
Tel.: (34) 919269230
Company Financial Services
N.A.I.C.S.: 522320

FOREST AGRI SERVICES LTD.
7 Enterprise Dr, Forest, N0N 1J0, ON, Canada
Tel.: (519) 786-2763
Web Site:
http://www.forestagriservices.com
Year Founded: 1996
Agricultural Produts Supplier
N.A.I.C.S.: 926140
Everett Moons (Gen Mgr & Grain Trader)

FOREST ENTERPRISES AUSTRALIA LIMITED
23 Paterson Street, Launceston, 7250, TAS, Australia
Tel.: (61) 300229266
Web Site: http://www.fealtd.com
Sales Range: $75-99.9 Million
Emp.: 15
Forestry & Forest Products Company
N.A.I.C.S.: 115310
Tony Cannon (Exec Dir)

Subsidiaries:

FEA Plantations Limited **(1)**
23 Paterson St, Launceston, 7250, TAS, Australia
Tel.: (61) 363347811
Sales Range: $25-49.9 Million
Forestry Services
N.A.I.C.S.: 115310

FOREST PACKAGING GROUP CO., LTD.
No 460 Daxi North Road, Daxi Town, Wenling, 317525, Zhejiang, China
Tel.: (86) 57686336000
Web Site:
http://www.forestpacking.com
Year Founded: 1998
605500—(SHG)
Rev.: $379,274,342
Assets: $386,496,195
Liabilities: $35,782,863
Net Worth: $350,713,331
Earnings: $19,745,673
Emp.: 1,800
Fiscal Year-end: 12/31/22
Paper Packaging Product Mfr
N.A.I.C.S.: 322220
Kevin Pan (Sls Mgr)

FOREST SUPPORT SERVICES PLC
Forest House Broad Quay Road Felnex Industrial Estate, Newport, NP19 4PN, Gwent, United Kingdom
Tel.: (44) 1633284700
Web Site:
http://www.forestservices.co.uk
Sales Range: $1-9.9 Million
Emp.: 180
Traffic Management Services
N.A.I.C.S.: 541611
Ross Williams (Mng Dir)

Subsidiaries:

Forest Traffic Services Limited **(1)**
Forest House Broad Quay Road Felnex Industrial Estate, Newport, NP19 4PN, Gwent, United Kingdom
Tel.: (44) 1633284700
Web Site:
http://www.forestsupportservices.co.uk
Emp.: 70
Traffic Management & Administration Services
N.A.I.C.S.: 488490
Ross Williams (Mng Dir)

FOREST WATER ENVIRON-

MENTAL ENGINEERING CO., LTD.
3F No 99 Jilin Road Zhongshan District, Taipei, 104, Taiwan
Tel.: (886) 221002195
Web Site: https://www.mfw.com.tw
8473—(TAI)
Rev.: $120,333,525
Assets: $504,788,071
Liabilities: $260,877,717
Net Worth: $243,910,354
Earnings: $5,311,128
Fiscal Year-end: 12/31/23
Water Treatment Operator
N.A.I.C.S.: 221310
Yaqing Huang (Head-Fin)

FORESTAL CHOLGUAN S.A.
Avenida El Golf Piso 14, Las Condes, Santiago, Chile
Tel.: (56) 716395097
Forest Products Mfr
N.A.I.C.S.: 321912
Juan Pablo Pacheco Gilabert (CEO)

FORESTAL, CONSTRUCTORA Y COMERCIAL DEL PACIFICO SUR S.A.
Av Apoquindo 3846 piso 20, PO Box 1263, Las Condes, Santiago, Chile
Tel.: (56) 224216000
Web Site: https://www.pasur.cl
Year Founded: 1954
PASUR—(SGO)
Rev.: $12,508
Assets: $2,539,837
Liabilities: $210,011
Net Worth: $2,329,827
Earnings: $152,651
Emp.: 44
Fiscal Year-end: 12/31/23
Real Estate Development Services
N.A.I.C.S.: 531110
Fernando Carriel Araya (CEO)

FORESTIERE EQUATORIALE SA
Immeuble Bollore Avenue Christiani Treichville, BP 37, 2360, Abidjan, Cote d'Ivoire
Tel.: (225) 146964785
Web Site: https://www.forestiere-equatoriale.com
FORE—(EUR)
Sales Range: Less than $1 Million
Rail Transportation Support Services
N.A.I.C.S.: 488210
Martine Studer (Pres & CEO)

FOREVER ENTERTAINMENT S.A.
al Zwyciestwa 96/98, 81-451, Gdynia, Poland
Tel.: (48) 587282343
Web Site: https://www.forever-entertainment.com
Year Founded: 2010
8FE—(DEU)
Software Development Services
N.A.I.C.S.: 541511
Zbigniew Debicki (Pres)

FOREZ BENNES
Z I Champdieu, 42603, Montbrison, CEDEX, France
Tel.: (33) 477966969
Web Site: http://www.forez-bennes.com
Motor Vehicles & Car Bodies
N.A.I.C.S.: 336110

FORFARMERS GROUP B.V
Kwinkweerd 12, 7241 CW, Lochem, Netherlands
Tel.: (31) 573 28 88 00

Web Site:
http://www.forfarmersgroup.eu
Sales Range: $5-14.9 Billion
Emp.: 2,325
Animal Food Product Mfr
N.A.I.C.S.: 311119
Jan N. Potijk (Chief Comml Officer)

Subsidiaries:

ForFarmers BM GmbH **(1)**
Am Wuhlwinkel 1, Gerdshagen, 16928, Brandenburg, Germany
Tel.: (49) 3398650220
Web Site: http://www.forfarmers.de
Animal Feed Whslr
N.A.I.C.S.: 424910

ForFarmers Beelitz GmbH **(1)**
Am Zollhaus 7, 14547, Beelitz, Germany
Tel.: (49) 332046332100
Animal Feed Whslr
N.A.I.C.S.: 424910

ForFarmers Belgium B.V.B.A. **(1)**
Zuidkaai 6, 8770, Ingelmunster, Belgium
Tel.: (32) 51335760
Web Site: http://www.forfarmers.be
Animal Feed Whslr
N.A.I.C.S.: 424910
Daniel Maenhout (Mgr-Production, Logistics & Quality)

ForFarmers DML B.V. **(1)**
Sluisstraat 24, 7491 GA, Delden, Netherlands
Tel.: (31) 573288080
Web Site: http://www.forfarmersdml.nl
Animal Feed Whslr
N.A.I.C.S.: 424910

ForFarmers Hamburg GmbH & Co. KG **(1)**
Pollhornweg 25, 21107, Hamburg, Germany
Tel.: (49) 4075270523
Web Site: http://www.forfarmers.de
Animal Feed Whslr
N.A.I.C.S.: 424910

ForFarmers Hendrix B.V. **(1)**
Roald Amundsenstraat 6, 7825 AT, Emmen, Netherlands
Tel.: (31) 591642222
Web Site: http://www.forfarmers.nl
Animal Feed Whslr
N.A.I.C.S.: 424910

ForFarmers Langforden GmbH **(1)**
Industriestrasse 7, Langforden, 49377, Vechta, Germany
Tel.: (49) 44478080
Web Site: http://www.forfarmers.de
Animal Feed Whslr
N.A.I.C.S.: 424910

ForFarmers Thesing Mischfutter GmbH & Co. KG **(1)**
Deichstrasse 11, Haffen, 46459, Rees, Germany
Tel.: (49) 285741100
Animal Feed Whslr
N.A.I.C.S.: 424910

ForFarmers UK Ltd. **(1)**
Olympia Mills Barlby Road, Selby, YO8 5AF, United Kingdom
Tel.: (44) 3306781080
Web Site: http://www.forfarmers.co.uk
Animal Feed Whslr
N.A.I.C.S.: 424910
Keith Greyson (Mgr-Credit)

Leafield Feeds Ltd. **(1)**
Blind Lane East Ardsley, Wakefield, WF3 2LB, United Kingdom
Tel.: (44) 1924820500
Web Site: http://www.leafieldfeeds.co.uk
Animal Feed Whslr
N.A.I.C.S.: 424910
Paul Evans (Mgr-Bus Dev)

Pavo Pferdenahrung GmbH **(1)**
Wiesenstr 38, 47574, Goch, Germany
Tel.: (49) 2823417535
Web Site: http://www.pavo.net
Animal Feed Whslr
N.A.I.C.S.: 424910

Reudink B.V. **(1)**

Kwinkweerd 5, 7241CW, Lochem, Netherlands
Tel.: (31) 8007383465
Web Site: http://www.reudink-bio.eu
Animal Feed Whslr
N.A.I.C.S.: 424910

Stimulan B.V. (1)
Veerstraat 38, 5831 JN, Boxmeer, Netherlands
Tel.: (31) 485589408
Web Site: http://www.pavo.nl
Animal Feed Whslr
N.A.I.C.S.: 424910
Anton Baarslag (Gen Mgr)

Wheyfeed Ltd. (1)
Hill Farm Brook Lane Stanton on the Wolds, Nottingham, NG12 5SE, United Kingdom
Tel.: (44) 1159377374
Web Site: http://www.wheyfeed.co.uk
Animal Feed Whslr
N.A.I.C.S.: 424910
Liz Shilton (Gen Mgr)

FORGAME HOLDINGS LIMITED

Room 1106 Block A Phase I Innovation Technology Plaza, Tianan Digital City Chegongmiao Futian, Shenzhen, China
Tel.: (86) 75583669395
Web Site: http://www.forgame.com
Year Founded: 2009
0484—(HKG)
Rev.: $16,021,886
Assets: $101,651,987
Liabilities: $11,345,724
Net Worth: $90,306,263
Earnings: ($2,823,023)
Emp.: 39
Fiscal Year-end: 12/31/22
Web-Based & Mobile Game Developer & Publisher
N.A.I.C.S.: 513210
Dongfeng Wang (Founder)

Subsidiaries:

Netcloud (Hong Kong) Technology Limited (1)
Room B 2/F 109-115 Wo Yi Hop Road, Evergreen Industrial Building, Kwai Chung, New Territories, China (Hong Kong)
Tel.: (852) 22395939
Web Site: https://www.netcloud.com.hk
Data Processing Services
N.A.I.C.S.: 518210

FORGE MEDIA GROUP LIMITED

Suite 6 Level 1 317-319 New North Rd, Kingsland, Auckland, 1021, New Zealand
Tel.: (64) 093020447 NZ
Web Site: http://www.forge.co.nz
Graphic Design, Print Production, CD Reproduction & Packaging & Various Advertising Related Services
N.A.I.C.S.: 541430
Janine Martin (Mgr-Fin)

FORGES DE NIAUX

Lieu Dit Niaux, 9400, Ariege, France
Tel.: (33) 561657100
Web Site:
http://www.forgesdeniaux.com
Rev.: $21,300,000
Emp.: 132
Farm Mach & Equipment
N.A.I.C.S.: 333111
Pascal Fournent (Mgr-Pur)

FORGES TARDIEU LTD

31 Nicolay Road, Port Louis, Mauritius
Tel.: (230) 2065200
Web Site:
http://www.forgestardieu.com
Year Founded: 1931

FORT—(MAU)
Sales Range: $10-24.9 Million
Emp.: 200
Mechanical Engineering Services
N.A.I.C.S.: 541330
Hubert Raffray (CEO)

Subsidiaries:

Electrical & Control Specialists Ltd (1)
31 Nicolay Road, PO Box 20, Port Louis, Mauritius
Tel.: (230) 206 5280
Web Site: http://www.ecs.mu
Emp.: 20
Electrical Engineering Services
N.A.I.C.S.: 541330
Christophe Desvaux de Marigny (Gen Mgr)

Fotaflex Ltd. (1)
31 Nicolay Road, Port Louis, Mauritius
Tel.: (230) 2065260
Emp.: 12
Gasket & Sealing Device Mfr
N.A.I.C.S.: 339991
Hubert Refaey (Gen Mgr)

TARDIEU TECHNICAL SUPPORT LTD. (1)
31 Nicolay Road, PO Box 20, Port Louis, Mauritius
Tel.: (230) 2065270
Web Site: http://www.forgestardieu.com
Boiler Repair & Maintenance Services
N.A.I.C.S.: 811310

FORIND AVIO ELETTRONICA S.P.A.

Via Nicolo Copernico 20, Cassina de' Pecchi, 20060, Milan, Italy
Tel.: (39) 0295343080
Web Site: http://www.forind.it
Year Founded: 1968
Sales Range: $1-9.9 Million
Emp.: 20
Electrical Apparate & Equipment Distr
N.A.I.C.S.: 423610
Roberto Lechiancole (Pres)

FORIS AG

Kurt-Schumacher-Str 18 - 20, 53113, Bonn, Germany
Tel.: (49) 2289575050 De
Web Site: https://www.foris.com
Year Founded: 1996
FRS—(DEU)
Rev.: $25,455,242
Assets: $24,351,372
Liabilities: $7,550,471
Net Worth: $16,800,901
Earnings: $1,203,218
Emp.: 33
Fiscal Year-end: 12/31/23
Financial Services
N.A.I.C.S.: 523940
Christian Rollmann (Chm-Supervisory Bd)

FORISE INTERNATIONAL LTD.

15 Scotts 15 Scotts Road 04-08 Suite 22, Singapore, 228218, Singapore
Tel.: (65) 67169780
Web Site: https://forise-international.com
Year Founded: 2008
8A1—(SES)
Rev.: $421,116
Assets: $1,127,774
Liabilities: $215,103
Net Worth: $912,671
Earnings: $16,663
Emp.: 4
Fiscal Year-end: 12/31/23
Financial Advisory Services
N.A.I.C.S.: 523940

Subsidiaries:

Prisma Technologies Pte Ltd (1)
80 Raffles Place UOB Plaza 2 11-20, Singapore, 048624, Singapore

Tel.: (65) 96409690
Web Site: https://www.prismatech.sg
Information Technology Services
N.A.I.C.S.: 541511
Shreeram Iyer (CEO)

FORLAGSHUSET VIGMOSTAD & BJORKE AS

Kanalveien 51, 5068, Bergen, Norway
Tel.: (47) 5538 8800 NO
Web Site:
http://www.vigmostadbjorke.no
Year Founded: 1992
Book Publisher & Retailer
N.A.I.C.S.: 513130
Arno Vigmostad (Publr)

FORLIFE CO., LTD.

11411 Okurayama, Kohoku-Ku, Yokohama, 222-0037, Japan
Tel.: (81) 455473432
Web Site: https://www.forlifeand.com
3477—(TKS)
Sales Range: Less than $1 Million
Residential Real Estate Management Services
N.A.I.C.S.: 531311
Kenji Okumoto (Pres & CEO)

FORLINK SOFTWARE CORPORATION, INC.

9/F Shenzhou Mansion No 31 Zhong-GuanCun South Street, Haidian District, Beijing, 100081, China
Tel.: (86) 10 6811 8866 NV
Web Site: http://www.forlink.com
Year Founded: 1993
Sales Range: $1-9.9 Million
Emp.: 203
Software Publisher
N.A.I.C.S.: 513210
Yi He (Chm & CEO)

Subsidiaries:

Nanning Bulk Commodities Exchange Corporation Limited (1)
7th Floor Building B Xijiang Mansion NO 100 Minzu Road, Nanning, China
Tel.: (86) 7712260598
Web Site: http://www.nnbce.com
Warehousing & Logistics Services
N.A.I.C.S.: 493110

FORM BIO CO., LTD.

FB tower 10 Seocheon-ro 127beon-gil, Giheung-gu, Yongin, Gyeonggi-do, Korea (South)
Tel.: (82) 318955252
Web Site: https://www.frombio-company.co.kr
Year Founded: 2006
377220—(KRS)
Rev.: $76,186,414
Assets: $71,962,624
Liabilities: $5,223,740
Net Worth: $66,738,884
Earnings: $1,010,917
Emp.: 126
Fiscal Year-end: 12/31/22
Diet Food Product Distr
N.A.I.C.S.: 424420
Shim Tae Jin (CEO)

FORM700 PTY. LTD.

68 - 76 Drake Boulevard, Altona, 3018, VIC, Australia
Tel.: (61) 383317100
Web Site:
http://www.form700.com.au
Year Founded: 2001
Building Construction Services
N.A.I.C.S.: 236115
Craig Head (CFO)

FORMAPHARM ENGINEERING GROUP D.O.O.

Carlija Caplina 36, 11000, Belgrade, Serbia
Tel.: (381) 113291876
Web Site: http://www.formapharm.net
Year Founded: 1994
Sales Range: $10-24.9 Million
Emp.: 110
Engineering Service for Pharmaceutical Industry Services
N.A.I.C.S.: 541330
Slavoljub Korcakoski (Dir-Beograd)

Subsidiaries:

FormaPharm Engineering Group (1)
Koroleva 6D, 249030, Obninsk, Kaluga Oblast, Russia
Tel.: (7) 4843941458
Engineeering Services
N.A.I.C.S.: 541330

FORMAT WERK GMBH & CO. KG

Wallackstrasse 3, 4623, Gunskirchen, Austria
Tel.: (43) 724676610
Web Site: http://www.formatwerk.com
Year Founded: 1976
Sales Range: $10-24.9 Million
Emp.: 100
School & Office Stationery Mfr & Supplier
N.A.I.C.S.: 322230
Reinhard Zehetner (Mgr-Sls-Austria)

FORMATION GROUP PLC

Oakwood House, London, E2 7SY, United Kingdom
Tel.: (44) 2079207590
Web Site:
http://www.formationgroupplc.com
FRM—(AQSE)
Rev.: $46,595,902
Assets: $38,891,563
Liabilities: $11,448,956
Net Worth: $27,442,607
Earnings: $1,282,745
Emp.: 12
Fiscal Year-end: 08/31/19
Construction Services
N.A.I.C.S.: 236115
Noel O'Carroll (Dir-Property Mgmt Svcs)

Subsidiaries:

Formation Architectural Design Limited (1)
Oakwood House 414-422 Hackney Road, London, E2 7SY, United Kingdom
Tel.: (44) 2079207591
Web Site:
http://www.formationdesignandbuild.com
Emp.: 20
Architectural Design Services
N.A.I.C.S.: 541310
Noel O'Carroll (Mng Dir)

Formation Asset Management Limited (1)
9 -13 Manchester Rd, Wilmslow, SK9 1BQ, Cheshire, United Kingdom
Tel.: (44) 1625418160
Web Site:
http://www.formationassetmanagement.com
Sales Range: $50-74.9 Million
Emp.: 10
Asset Management Services
N.A.I.C.S.: 531390

Formation Design & Build Limited (1)
Oakwood House, 414-422 Hackney Road, London, E2 7SY, United Kingdom
Tel.: (44) 2079207590
Web Site:
http://www.formationdesignandbuild.com
Sales Range: $50-74.9 Million
Emp.: 20
Property Management Services
N.A.I.C.S.: 531312
Noel O. Carroll (Mng Dir)

Formation Group PLC—(Continued)

Formation Sports Capital Limited (1)
2 Hollins House 329 Hale Rd, Hale Barns,
WA15 8TS, United Kingdom
Tel.: (44) 16 1980 1210
Sales Range: $50-74.9 Million
Emp.: 20
Corporate Finance & Broking Services
N.A.I.C.S.: 522291

**Formation Wealth Solutions
Limited** (1)
2 Hollins House 329 Hale Rd, Hale Barns,
WA15 8TS, Cheshire, United Kingdom
Tel.: (44) 162 553 6411
Web Site: http://www.formationwealth.com
Investment Services
N.A.I.C.S.: 523940

**James Grant Sports
Management** (1)
3233 M St NW, Washington, DC 20007
Tel.: (202) 333-3661
Sales Range: $25-49.9 Million
Emp.: 5
Sports Management Services
N.A.I.C.S.: 711310
Brendan Fitzgerald (Dir-Mktg)

**FORMET CELIK KAPI SANAYI
VE TICARET AS**
Organize Sanayi Bolgesi 9 Cad No
18, 38070, Kayseri, Türkiye
Tel.: (90) 3523213708
Web Site:
https://www.formetcelikkapi.com.tr
FORMT—(IST)
Rev.: $16,384,242
Assets: $44,854,659
Liabilities: $13,590,891
Net Worth: $31,263,769
Earnings: ($3,526,721)
Fiscal Year-end: 12/31/23
Window & Door Mfr
N.A.I.C.S.: 332321
Mustafa Sezen (Chm & Pres)

FORMETAL, INC.
229-7 Mujangsaneop-ro, Jigok-
myeon, Seosan, Chungcheongnam-
do, Korea (South)
Tel.: (82) 416706200
Web Site: https://www.formetal.co.kr
Year Founded: 1969
119500—(KRS)
Rev.: $53,382,846
Assets: $51,500,434
Liabilities: $14,499,740
Net Worth: $37,000,694
Earnings: $1,324,259
Emp.: 123
Fiscal Year-end: 12/31/22
Metal Forging Services
N.A.I.C.S.: 332111

FORMEX WATCH S.A.
Wasserstrasse 42, 2502, Biel/Bienne,
Switzerland
Tel.: (41) 323332455
Web Site:
http://www.formexwatch.com
Year Founded: 1999
Sales Range: Less than $1 Million
Emp.: 5
Watch Mfr & Distr
N.A.I.C.S.: 334519
Hans Peter Gradel (Gen Mgr)

Subsidiaries:

Formex Watch USA (1)
87 Main St, Peapack, NJ 07977
Tel.: (908) 781-9555
Web Site: http://www.formexwatch.com
Watch Mfr
N.A.I.C.S.: 334519

FORMGLAS PRODUCTS LTD.
181 Regina Rd, Woodbridge, L4L
8M3, ON, Canada

Tel.: (416) 635-8030
Web Site: http://www.formglas.com
Year Founded: 1961
Rev.: $32,700,000
Emp.: 300
Glass Products Mfr & Supplier
N.A.I.C.S.: 327215
John Chettleburgh (Pres)

Subsidiaries:

Formglas Japan Ltd. (1)
1-10-4 Shinjuku, Shinjuku-Ku, Tokyo, 160-
0000, Japan
Tel.: (81) 332258397
Glass Product Distr
N.A.I.C.S.: 423390

**FORMICA CAPITAL HOLDING
AB**
Rosenlundsgatan 3, Gothenburg,
Sweden
Tel.: (46) 709266655
Web Site:
https://www.formicacapital.se
Private Equity
N.A.I.C.S.: 523940

Subsidiaries:

CR Group Nordic AB (1)
Hovslagargatan 5b, 111 48, Blasieholmen,
Stockholm, Sweden
Tel.: (46) 85511024
Web Site: https://cr.se
Cybersecurity
N.A.I.C.S.: 513210
Bjorn Weigel (CEO)

Formica Capital AB (1)
Rosenlundsgatan 3, Gothenburg, Sweden
Tel.: (46) 70926 66 55
Web Site: http://www.formicacapital.se
Investment Services
N.A.I.C.S.: 523999
Olof Cato (CEO)

Subsidiary (Domestic):

Cybercom Group AB (2)
Sveavagen 20, SE-11157, Stockholm,
Sweden (51%)
Tel.: (46) 857864600
Web Site: http://www.cybercom.com
Sales Range: $150-199.9 Million
Emp.: 1,290
IT Consulting Services
N.A.I.C.S.: 541690
Hampus Ericsson (Chm)

Subsidiary (Non-US):

Cybercom Finland (3)
Pakkahuoneenaukio 2 A, PO Box 13,
33201, Tampere, Finland
Tel.: (358) 104364000
Web Site: http://www.cybercom.com
Information Technology Consulting Services
N.A.I.C.S.: 541512
Vel-Matti Nurminen (Head)

Cybercom Poland sp.zo.o. (3)
Hrubieszowska 2, 01-209, Warsaw, Poland
Tel.: (48) 223552170
Web Site: http://www.cybercom.com
Information Technology Consulting Services
N.A.I.C.S.: 541512
Marcin Siech (Head)

Subsidiary (Domestic):

Cybercom Sweden - Gothenburg (3)
Lindholmspiren 3A, 417 56, Gothenburg,
Sweden
Tel.: (46) 317448000
Web Site: http://www.cybercom.com
Information Technology Consulting Services
N.A.I.C.S.: 541512

FORMO MOTORS
1550 Main St E, PO Box 1900, Swan
River, R0L 1Z0, MB, Canada
Tel.: (204) 734-4577
Web Site:
https://www.formomotors.com
Year Founded: 1964
Rev.: $11,051,669

Emp.: 25
New & Used Car Dealer
N.A.I.C.S.: 441110
Tracy Coulthart (Office Mgr)

FORMOPLAST PLC
Industrial zone South, 6600,
Kardjhali, Bulgaria
Tel.: (359) 36162612
Web Site:
https://www.formoplastbg.com
FORM—(BUL)
Sales Range: Less than $1 Million
Mould Design Mfr
N.A.I.C.S.: 339999
Nasm Hickmet Aliosman (CEO)

**FORMOSA ADVANCED TECH-
NOLOGIES CO., LTD.**
NO 329 Henan St, Douliu, 640, Yun-
lin, Taiwan
Tel.: (886) 55574888
Web Site: https://www.fatc.com.tw
Year Founded: 1990
8131—(TAI)
Rev.: $250,125,698
Assets: $433,743,337
Liabilities: $47,620,980
Net Worth: $386,122,357
Earnings: $17,339,186
Emp.: 2,349
Fiscal Year-end: 12/31/23
Integrated Circuit (IC) Assembly &
Testing Services
N.A.I.C.S.: 334418
Wen-Yuan Wong (Chm)

**FORMOSA ELECTRONIC IN-
DUSTRIES INC.**
5th Floor No 8 Lane 130 Minquan
Road, Xindian District, Taipei, Taiwan
Tel.: (886) 222188888
Web Site: https://www.feii.com.tw
8171—(TPE)
Rev.: $29,911,736
Assets: $79,287,743
Liabilities: $27,229,895
Net Worth: $52,057,848
Earnings: ($1,234,638)
Fiscal Year-end: 12/31/23
Electric Equipment Mfr
N.A.I.C.S.: 334419
Tsu-Yu Wu (Chm)

**FORMOSA INTERNATIONAL
HOTELS CORP.**
1-20F 3 Lane39 Chung Shan N Rd
Sec 2, Taipei, Taiwan
Tel.: (886) 225238000
Web Site:
http://www.regenttaipei.com
2707—(TAI)
Rev.: $221,231,621
Assets: $347,663,187
Liabilities: $185,855,155
Net Worth: $161,808,032
Earnings: $49,925,535
Fiscal Year-end: 12/31/23
Home Management Services
N.A.I.C.S.: 561110
Pan Sy-Lian (Chm)

Subsidiaries:

Just Sleep Hualien Zhongzheng Co.,
Ltd. (1)
No 396 Zhongzheng Rd, Hua-lien, 97041,
Taiwan
Tel.: (886) 38900069
Home Management Services
N.A.I.C.S.: 721110

Just Sleep Kaohsiung Station Co.,
Ltd. (1)
No 280 Zhongshan 1st Rd, Xinxing, Kaohsi-
ung, 800, Taiwan
Tel.: (886) 79733588
Home Management Services
N.A.I.C.S.: 721110

Just Sleep Kaohsiung Zhongzheng
Co., Ltd. (1)
No 134 Zhongzheng 1st Rd, Kaohsiung,
80284, Taiwan
Tel.: (886) 79723568
Home Management Services
N.A.I.C.S.: 721110

Just Sleep Osaka Shinsaibashi Co.,
Ltd. (1)
2-chome-9-15 Minamisemba, Chuo Ward,
Osaka, 542-0081, Japan
Tel.: (81) 662513666
Home Management Services
N.A.I.C.S.: 721110

Just Sleep Tainan Hushan Co.,
Ltd. (1)
No 300 Sec 2 Wenhua Rd, Rende, Tainan
City, 717015, Taiwan
Tel.: (886) 62660568
Home Management Services
N.A.I.C.S.: 721110

Just Sleep Taipei NTU Co., Ltd. (1)
No 83 Section 4 Roosevelt Rd, Da'an Dis-
trict, Taipei, 106, Taiwan
Tel.: (886) 277355088
Home Management Services
N.A.I.C.S.: 721110

Just Sleep Taipei Sanchong Co.,
Ltd. (1)
No 107-1 Sec 4 Sanhe Rd, Sanchong, New
Taipei City, 24152, Taiwan
Tel.: (886) 222806111
Home Management Services
N.A.I.C.S.: 721110

Just Sleep Taipei Ximending Co.,
Ltd. (1)
No 41 Section 1 Zhonghua Road,
Zhongzheng District, Taipei, 100, Taiwan
Tel.: (886) 223709000
Home Management Services
N.A.I.C.S.: 721110

Just Sleep Yilan Jiaoxi Co., Ltd. (1)
No 8 Ln 24 Deyang Rd, Jiaoxi, Yilan, Tai-
wan
Tel.: (886) 39102000
Home Management Services
N.A.I.C.S.: 721110

Regent Berlin GmbH (1)
Charlottenstrasse 49, 10117, Berlin, Ger-
many
Tel.: (49) 3020338
Web Site: http://www.regenthotels.com
Sales Range: $25-49.9 Million
Emp.: 200
Home Management Services
N.A.I.C.S.: 561110

Regent Taipei Co., Ltd. (1)
104 No 3 Lane 39 Section 2 Zhongshan
North Road, Zhongshan, Taipei, Taiwan
Tel.: (886) 225238000
Web Site: https://www.regenttaiwan.com
Home Management Services
N.A.I.C.S.: 721110

Silks Club Co., Ltd. (1)
No 199 Zhongshan 2nd Rd, Qianzhen, Ka-
ohsiung, Taiwan
Tel.: (886) 79730189
Web Site: https://silks-club.com
Home Management Services
N.A.I.C.S.: 721110

Silks Place Tainan Co., Ltd. (1)
No 1 He Yi Rd, West Central Dist, Tainan
City, 700, Taiwan
Tel.: (886) 62136290
Web Site: https://tainan.silksplace.com
Home Management Services
N.A.I.C.S.: 721110

Silks Place Taroko Co., Ltd. (1)
No 18 Tianxiang Road, Xiulin, Hua-lien,
972, Taiwan
Tel.: (886) 38691155
Web Site: https://taroko.silksplace.com
Home Management Services
N.A.I.C.S.: 721110

Silks Place Yilan Co., Ltd. (1)
36 Minquan Rd Sec 2, Yilan, Taiwan
Tel.: (886) 39351000

Web Site: https://www.silksplace-
yilan.com.tw
Home Management Services
N.A.I.C.S.: 721110

Wellspring by Silks Co., Ltd. **(1)**
No 67 Wenquan Rd, Jiaoxi, Yilan, 262, Tai-
wan
Tel.: (886) 277355005
Web Site: https://www.silksspring.com
Home Management Services
N.A.I.C.S.: 721110

FORMOSA LABORATORIES, INC.

Front door No36, Louchu, Taoyuan,
33842, Taiwan
Tel.: (886) 33240895
Web Site:
https://www.formosalab.com
4746—(TAI)
Rev.: $142,596,155
Assets: $445,933,173
Liabilities: $177,441,702
Net Worth: $268,491,471
Earnings: ($1,708,983)
Emp.: 896
Fiscal Year-end: 12/31/23
Medical Laboratory Services
N.A.I.C.S.: 621511
C. Y. Cheng *(Chm & Pres)*

Subsidiaries:

Formosa Pharmaceuticals, Inc. **(1)**
5F-10 No 237 Sec 2 Fuxing S Rd Da an
Dist, Taipei, 105, Taiwan
Tel.: (886) 227557659
Web Site: http://www.formosapharma.com
Pharmaceuticals Product Mfr
N.A.I.C.S.: 325411

TaiRx, Inc. **(1)**
6F-1 No 66 San-Chung Rd, Nankang Dist,
Taipei, 115602, Taiwan
Tel.: (886) 226535007
Web Site: https://www.trx.com.tw
Rev.: $166,192
Assets: $27,265,312
Liabilities: $1,982,570
Net Worth: $25,282,742
Earnings: ($6,942,444)
Fiscal Year-end: 12/31/2023
Pharmaceuticals Product Mfr
N.A.I.C.S.: 325412
Du-Shieng Chien *(Chm, Pres & CEO)*

FORMOSA OILSEED PRO-CESSING CO., LTD.

3F No 150 Sec 2 Nanjing East Rd,
Zhongshan Dist, Taipei, 104, Taiwan
Tel.: (886) 225073121
Web Site: https://www.fopco.com.tw
1225—(TAI)
Rev.: $477,142,563
Assets: $285,180,080
Liabilities: $156,563,943
Net Worth: $128,616,137
Earnings: $13,381,797
Emp.: 419
Fiscal Year-end: 12/31/23
Food Products Mfr
N.A.I.C.S.: 311999

FORMOSA OPTICAL TECH-NOLOGY CO., LTD.

16th Floor No 97 Section 1, Xintai 5th
Road, Taipei, Taiwan
Tel.: (886) 800251257
Web Site: https://www.formosa-
optical.com.tw
Year Founded: 1976
5312—(TPE)
Rev.: $103,113,404
Assets: $198,493,731
Liabilities: $117,234,781
Net Worth: $81,258,950
Earnings: $5,320,983
Fiscal Year-end: 12/31/22
Eye Glass Mfr & Distr
N.A.I.C.S.: 339115

Kuo-Chou Tsai *(Chm)*

FORMOSA PETROCHEMICAL CORPORATION

No 1-1 Taisu Industrial Park, Mailiao
Township, Yun-lin, 638, Taiwan
Tel.: (886) 56812345
Web Site: https://www.fpcc.com.tw
Year Founded: 1992
6505—(TAI)
Rev.: $22,055,616,936
Assets: $16,317,990,332
Liabilities: $3,449,935,011
Net Worth: $12,868,055,320
Earnings: $1,755,873,283
Emp.: 5,289
Fiscal Year-end: 12/31/21
Natural Gas Distribution Services
N.A.I.C.S.: 221210
Keh-Yen Lin *(Exec VP)*

Subsidiaries:

Formosa Chemicals & Fibre
Corporation **(1)**
Building A2 No 380 Section 6 Nanjing East
Road, Neihu District, Taipei, 114030, Taiwan
Tel.: (886) 227122211
Web Site: https://en.fcfc.com.tw
Rev.: $9,009,691,341
Assets: $18,916,852,624
Liabilities: $4,850,606,167
Net Worth: $14,066,246,457
Earnings: $766,665,429
Emp.: 4,955
Fiscal Year-end: 12/31/2020
Chemical Product Mfr & Distr
N.A.I.C.S.: 325998
Wen Yuan Wong *(Chm)*

Subsidiary (Domestic):

Formosa Taffeta Corp. **(2)**
317 Shuliou RD, Douliu, 640, Taiwan
Tel.: (886) 55573966
Web Site: https://www.ftc.com.tw
Emp.: 3,000
Broadwoven Fabric Mills
N.A.I.C.S.: 313210

Formosa Oil (Asia Pacific)
Corporation **(1)**
4 FL 201 Tung Hwa N Rd, Taipei, 10508,
Taiwan
Tel.: (886) 227122211
Sales Range: $550-599.9 Million
Emp.: 1,600
Oil Product Retailer
N.A.I.C.S.: 424720
Sandy R.Y. Wang *(Chm)*

Mailiao Harbor Administration
Corporation **(1)**
1-1 Fromosa Plastic Group Industrial Zone,
Mailiao, Yun-lin, 63800, Taiwan
Tel.: (886) 227122211
Web Site: http://www.mlharbor.com.tw
Harbor Administration Services
N.A.I.C.S.: 488310
Wilfred Tsao Wang Wang *(Chm)*

Simosa Oil Corporation **(1)**
No 10-8 Formosa Plastic Group Industrial
Zone, Mailiao, Yun-lin, Taiwan
Tel.: (886) 56812618
Asphalt Production & Sales
N.A.I.C.S.: 324121

Yi-Chi Construction Corporation **(1)**
2F 201-24 Tung Hwa North Road, Taipei,
Taiwan
Tel.: (886) 227122211
Construction Services
N.A.I.C.S.: 236220

FORMOSA PLASTICS CORPO-RATION

Floor 8 11 Building A1 No 380 Sec-
tion 6 Nanjing East Road, Neihu Dis-
trict, Taipei, Taiwan
Tel.: (886) 227122211
Web Site: https://www.fpc.com.tw
Year Founded: 1954
1301—(TAI)
Rev.: $6,226,394,553

Assets: $16,594,389,394
Liabilities: $5,733,615,077
Net Worth: $10,860,774,318
Earnings: $229,425,288
Emp.: 3,000
Fiscal Year-end: 12/31/23
Plastics Product Mfr
N.A.I.C.S.: 326199
Jason Lin *(Chm & Pres)*

Subsidiaries:

FUJIAN Fuxin Special Steel Co.,
Ltd. **(1)**
No 1 Longchi Blvd Longchi Industrial Area,
Taiwanese Investment Zone, Zhangzhou,
Fujian, China
Tel.: (86) 5966057000
Web Site: https://www.fjfss.com.cn
N.A.I.C.S.: 331110

Formosa Asahi Spandex Co.,
Ltd. **(1)**
Rm 386 12F Tun Hwa N road, Taipei, Tai-
wan
Tel.: (886) 227122211
Web Site: http://www.formosa.com
Sales Range: $25-49.9 Million
Emp.: 12
Elastic Products Mfr; Owned 50% by For-
mosa Plastics Corporation & 50% by Asahi
Kasei Corporation
N.A.I.C.S.: 326199

Formosa Daikin Advanced Chemicals
Co., Ltd. **(1)**
105 Room 445 10th Floor 201 Tun Hwa
North Road, Taipei, Taiwan
Tel.: (886) 227122211
Web Site: http://www.fdac.com.tw
Semiconductor Chemical Product Mfr
N.A.I.C.S.: 333242

Plant (Domestic):

Formosa Daikin Advanced Chemicals
Co., Ltd. - Kaohsiung Ren-Wu
Plant **(2)**
814 100 Shui Guan Road, Ren-Wu Town-
ship, Kaohsiung, Taiwan
Tel.: (886) 73711411
Semiconductor Chemical Product Mfr
N.A.I.C.S.: 333242

Formosa Heavy Industries Corp. **(1)**
Tel.: (886) 227178148
Web Site: http://www.fhi.com.tw
Emp.: 1,397
Heavy Industrial Machinery Mfr
N.A.I.C.S.: 333248

Subsidiary (Non-US):

FHI (Ningbo) Co., Ltd. **(2)**
FPG Ningbo Industrial Park, Beilun, Ningbo,
315807, China
Tel.: (86) 57486025060
Construction & Mining Machinery Equip-
ment Mfr
N.A.I.C.S.: 333120

Plant (Domestic):

Formosa Heavy Industries Corp. -
Jen-Wu Plant **(2)**
100 Swei-Kuan Road, Jenwu, Kaohsiung,
Taiwan
Tel.: (886) 73711411
Construction & Mining Machinery Equip-
ment Mfr
N.A.I.C.S.: 333120

Formosa Heavy Industries Corp. -
Mai-Liao Plant **(2)**
3 Formosa Industrial Park, Mailiao Yunlin,
Taichung, Taiwan
Tel.: (886) 568160212
Construction & Mining Machinery Equip-
ment Mfr
N.A.I.C.S.: 333120

Formosa Petrochemical Transporta-
tion Corporation **(1)**
4F 201 Tung-Hwa N Rd, Songshan Dist,
Taipei, Yun Lin, Taiwan **(100%)**
Tel.: (886) 227122211
Web Site: http://www.fpcc.com.tw
Sales Range: $50-74.9 Million
Emp.: 200

Crude Oil Refining & Petroleum & Petrochemical Products Mfr
N.A.I.C.S.: 325110

Formosa Plasma Display
Corporation **(1)**
201 Tung Hwa North Road, Taipei,
Taiwan **(77.5%)**
Tel.: (886) 227122211
Web Site: http://www.fpg.com.tw
Sales Range: $100-124.9 Million
Emp.: 500
Flat Panel Mfr
N.A.I.C.S.: 333248

Formosa Plastics Corporation - Car-
bide Division **(1)**
Rm 309 Fl 4 No 201 Tung Hwa N Road,
Taipei, Taiwan
Tel.: (886) 2 7122211
Plastic Materials Mfr
N.A.I.C.S.: 326199

Formosa Plastics Corporation -
Chemicals Division **(1)**
Rm 215 Fl 4 No 201 Tung Hwa N Road,
Taipei, 10508, Taiwan
Tel.: (886) 2 27122211
Specialty Chemicals Mfr
N.A.I.C.S.: 325998

Formosa Plastics Corporation -
Linyuan Plant **(1)**
1-1 Hsin-Hwa 1st Road Lin-Yuan Village,
Kaohsiung, Taiwan
Tel.: (886) 7 6419911
Plastics Product Mfr
N.A.I.C.S.: 326199

Formosa Plastics Corporation - Plas-
tics Division **(1)**
Rm 06 Fl 4 No 201 Tung Hwa North Road,
Taipei, 10508, Taiwan
Tel.: (886) 2 27122211
Plastic Materials Mfr
N.A.I.C.S.: 326199
Sunny Jian *(Dir-Sls)*

Formosa Plastics Corporation - Poly-
olefin Division **(1)**
Rm 215 Fl 4 No 201 Tung Hwa N Road,
Taipei, 105, Taiwan
Tel.: (886) 5 6811180
Chemical Products Mfr
N.A.I.C.S.: 325180

Formosa Plastics Corporation - Polypropylene Division **(1)**
8F 201 Tung-Hwa North Road, Taipei, Taiwan
Tel.: (886) 2 27122211
Chemical Products Mfr
N.A.I.C.S.: 325180

Formosa Plastics Corporation - Tairy-
lan Division **(1)**
Fl 201 Tung Hua North Road, Taipei, 105,
Taiwan
Tel.: (886) 2 27178135
Web Site: http://www.fpc.com.tw
Emp.: 500
Plastics Product Mfr
N.A.I.C.S.: 326199

Formosa Plastics Corporation,
U.S.A. **(1)**
9 Peach Tree Hill Rd, Livingston, NJ
07039-5702 **(100%)**
Tel.: (973) 992-2090
Web Site: http://www.fpcusa.com
Sales Range: $1-4.9 Billion
Emp.: 2,900
Plastics Product Mfr
N.A.I.C.S.: 325211

Subsidiary (Domestic):

Formosa Hydrocarbons Company,
Inc. **(2)**
103 Fannin Rd, Point Comfort, TX 77978
Tel.: (361) 987-7000
Web Site: http://www.fpcusa.com
Sales Range: $25-49.9 Million
Emp.: 40
Petroleum Products
N.A.I.C.S.: 324199

Branch (Domestic):

Formosa Plastics Corporation,
Delaware **(2)**

Formosa Plastics Corporation—(Continued)

780 Schoolhouse Rd PO Box 320, Delaware City, DE 19706
Tel.: (302) 836-2200
Web Site: http://www.fpcusa.com
Sales Range: $50-74.9 Million
Emp.: 130
Plastics & Resins Mfr
N.A.I.C.S.: 326199

Formosa Plastics Corporation, Louisiana (2)
Gulf States Rd, Baton Rouge, LA 70805
Tel.: (225) 356-3341
Web Site: http://www.fpcusa.com
Sales Range: $50-74.9 Million
Emp.: 220
Plastics & Resins Mfr
N.A.I.C.S.: 326199

Formosa Plastics Corporation, Texas (2)
201 Formosa Dr, Point Comfort, TX 77978
Tel.: (361) 987-7000
Web Site: http://www.fpcusa.com
Sales Range: $50-74.9 Million
Emp.: 1,500
Plastics & Resins Mfr
N.A.I.C.S.: 326199

Subsidiary (Domestic):

Lavaca Pipe Line Company (2)
103 Fannin Rd, Point Comfort, TX 77978
Tel.: (361) 987-8900
Web Site: http://www.fpcusa.com
Sales Range: $50-74.9 Million
Emp.: 42
Natural Gas Distr
N.A.I.C.S.: 221210

Neumin Production Company (2)
103 Fannin Rd, Point Comfort, TX 77978
Tel.: (361) 987-8900
Web Site: http://www.fpcusa.com
Sales Range: $25-49.9 Million
Emp.: 45
Crude Petroleum & Natural Gas Production Services
N.A.I.C.S.: 324110

Mai-Liao Power Corporation (1)
No 1-1 Formosa Industrial Park, MaiLiao, Yun-lin, 63861, Taiwan
Tel.: (886) 5681 2345
Web Site: www.mlmpc.com.tw
Sales Range: $250-299.9 Million
Emp.: 378
Power Generation
N.A.I.C.S.: 221122

Mailiao Power Corp. (1)
No 1-1 Formosa Plastics Industrial Park, Zhongxing Village Mailiao Township, Taichung, Yunlin, Taiwan
Tel.: (886) 56812345
Web Site: https://www.mlmpc.com.tw
Power Generation Equipment Distr
N.A.I.C.S.: 423610

Nan Ya Plastics Corporation (1)
7F No 380-A1 Sec 6 Nanjing E Rd, Neihu Dist, Taipei, 114030, Taiwan
Tel.: (886) 227122211
Web Site: https://www.npc.com.tw
Rev.: $8,121,669,137
Assets: $20,277,270,831
Liabilities: $8,487,130,476
Net Worth: $11,790,140,356
Earnings: $253,573,680
Emp.: 11,370
Fiscal Year-end: 12/31/2023
Plastics Product Mfr
N.A.I.C.S.: 326199
Wilfred Tsao Wang Wang (Mng Dir)

Nan Ya Printed Circuit Board Corporation (1)
No 338 Sec 1 NanKan Road, Luchu Dist, Taoyuan, Taiwan
Tel.: (886) 33223751
Web Site: https://www.nanyapcb.com.tw
Rev.: $1,381,751,411
Assets: $2,303,458,005
Liabilities: $736,764,713
Net Worth: $1,566,693,292
Earnings: $190,215,140
Emp.: 6,484
Fiscal Year-end: 12/31/2023

Printed Circuit Board Mfr & Distr
N.A.I.C.S.: 334419
Andy Tang (Pres)

FORMOSA PROSONIC INDUSTRIES BERHAD
2 Jalan Sultan Mohamed 1 Bandar Sultan Suleiman, Taiwanese Industrial Park, 42000, Port Klang, Selangor, Malaysia
Tel.: (60) 331762700
Web Site: https://staging.thewonderpillars.com
Year Founded: 1989
FPI—(KLS)
Rev.: $208,257,773
Assets: $138,447,284
Liabilities: $34,695,305
Net Worth: $103,751,979
Earnings: $22,423,666
Emp.: 2,672
Fiscal Year-end: 12/31/22
Speaker Systems Mfr
N.A.I.C.S.: 334310
Hooi Mooi Lim (Co-Sec)

Subsidiaries:

Acoustic Energy Limited (1)
16 Bridge Road, Cirencester, GL7 1NJ, Gloucestershire, United Kingdom
Tel.: (44) 1285654432
Web Site: http://www.acoustic-energy.co.uk
Sales Range: $25-49.9 Million
Emp.: 10
Loudspeaker Mfr
N.A.I.C.S.: 334310
Adrian Dykes (Sls Mgr-UK)

Formosa Prosonic Japan Co. Ltd. (1)
11 Kandakon-Yacho Iwata Building 8F, Chiyoda-ku, Tokyo, 101-0035, Japan
Tel.: (81) 352983887
Web Site: http://www.fp-japan.co.jp
Sales Range: $25-49.9 Million
Emp.: 10
Acoustical Equipments Mfr & Distr
N.A.I.C.S.: 335999

Formosa Prosonic Manufacturing Sdn. Bhd. (1)
No 2 Jalan 1 Bandar Sultan Suleiman Taiwanese Industrial Park, 42000, Port Klang, Selangor, Malaysia
Tel.: (60) 331762700
Web Site: http://www.fp-group.com
Emp.: 2,000
Plastic Component Mfr
N.A.I.C.S.: 326191
Shih Chao-Yuan (Mng Dir)

Formosa Prosonic Technics Sdn. Bhd. (1)
2 Jalan Sultan Mohamed 1 Bandar Sultan Suleiman, Taiwanese Industrial Park, 42000, Port Klang, Selangor, Malaysia (100%)
Tel.: (60) 331762700
Web Site: https://www.fp-group.com
Speakers & Mold Plastics Mfr
N.A.I.C.S.: 334310

FORMOSA TAFFETA CO., LTD.
3F 388 Sec 6 Nanjing East Rd, Neihu Dist, Taipei, Taiwan
Tel.: (886) 287701688
Web Site: https://www.ftc.com.tw
Year Founded: 1973
1434—(TAI)
Rev.: $932,061,478
Assets: $2,343,594,601
Liabilities: $566,166,629
Net Worth: $1,777,427,972
Earnings: $14,537,885
Emp.: 2,384
Fiscal Year-end: 12/31/23
Textile Industry Services
N.A.I.C.S.: 314999
Ming-Chang Lee (Pres & Gen Mgr)

Subsidiaries:

Formosa Taffeta (Changshu) Co., Ltd. (1)

15 Peng-Hu Rd Dongnan Street, Changshu, 215500, Jiangsu, China
Tel.: (86) 51252835191
Textile Products Mfr
N.A.I.C.S.: 314999

Formosa Taffeta Dong Nai Co., Ltd. (1)
Nhon Trach 3 Ind Zone, Hiep Phuoc Town Nhon Trach Dist, Nhon Trach, Dong Nai, Vietnam
Tel.: (84) 2513560255
Textile Products Mfr
N.A.I.C.S.: 314999

Schoeller Asia Co., Ltd. (1)
Room 1606 Tower 6 China Hong Kong City 33 Canton RD, Tsimshatsui, Kowloon, China (Hong Kong)
Tel.: (852) 27353558
Fabric Product Distr
N.A.I.C.S.: 424310

FORMOSAN RUBBER GROUP INC.
1 Chao Feng Rd San Ho Tsun, Lung Tan Hsian, Taoyuan, Taiwan
Tel.: (886) 34893456
Web Site: https://www.frg.com.tw
Year Founded: 1952
2107—(TAI)
Rev.: $44,465,743
Assets: $467,145,213
Liabilities: $61,563,881
Net Worth: $405,581,331
Earnings: $16,968,409
Emp.: 125
Fiscal Year-end: 12/31/23
Plastic & Rubber Product Mfr
N.A.I.C.S.: 326199
Richard Teng (Sls Mgr & Mgr-Sls)

Subsidiaries:

Formosan Rubber Group Inc. - Taoyuan Plant (1)
1 Chao Feng Rd San Ho Tsun, Longtan, Taoyuan, Taiwan
Tel.: (886) 34893456
Rubber Products Mfr
N.A.I.C.S.: 326299

FORMOSAN UNION CHEMICAL CORP.
14F No 206 Sec 2 Nanking E Road, Taipei, Taiwan
Tel.: (886) 225071234
Web Site: https://www.fucc.com.tw
Year Founded: 1973
1709—(TAI)
Rev.: $308,456,543
Assets: $395,406,669
Liabilities: $125,455,766
Net Worth: $269,950,904
Earnings: $13,464,240
Fiscal Year-end: 12/31/23
Alkyl Benzene Mfr
N.A.I.C.S.: 324110
Shen-Tsai Hwang (Chm)

Subsidiaries:

Great Victory Chemical Industry Co., Ltd. (1)
14F-1 No 206 Sec 2 Nanjing E Rd, Zhongshan Dist, Taipei, 104, Taiwan
Tel.: (886) 225033131
Web Site: https://www.grevic.com.tw
Chemical Products Distr
N.A.I.C.S.: 423490

Hershey Engineering Company, Ltd. (1)
12 Yuanshan Rd Donghai Village Fanlian Hsiang Pingdong, Hsien, Taiwan
Tel.: (886) 88667692
Chemical Compound Raw Material Mfr
N.A.I.C.S.: 325411

Hershey Environmental Technology Co., Ltd. (1)
No 12 Yongxiang Road, Donghai Village Pingtung County, Fang-liao, Taiwan
Tel.: (886) 67692

Web Site: https://www.hersheypn.com.tw
Petrochemical Mfr & Distr
N.A.I.C.S.: 325110

Soft Chemical Corp. (1)
110 Ngo Quyen Street, Haiphong, Vietnam
Tel.: (84) 313837122
Chemical Products Distr
N.A.I.C.S.: 423490

United Performance Materials Corp. (1)
13F-5 No 206 Sec 2 Nan King E Rd, Taipei, Taiwan
Tel.: (886) 225072887
Web Site: https://www.upmresin.com
Chemical Compound Raw Material Mfr
N.A.I.C.S.: 325411

FORMOUS CORP.
Asanbay Microdistrict 23-10, 720060, Bishkek, Kyrgyzstan
Tel.: (996) 777026772   NV
Year Founded: 2013
Workwear Distr
N.A.I.C.S.: 424350
Nurzada Kermalieva (Pres, CEO, CFO, Principal Acctg Officer, Treas & Sec)

FORMPIPE SOFTWARE AB
Sveavagen 168, SE-104 35, Stockholm, Sweden
Tel.: (46) 855529060
Web Site: http://www.formpipe.com
Year Founded: 1997
FPIP—(OMX)
Rev.: $45,435,200
Assets: $73,294,651
Liabilities: $31,894,312
Net Worth: $41,400,339
Earnings: $820,385
Emp.: 283
Fiscal Year-end: 12/31/22
Enterprise Content Management Software
N.A.I.C.S.: 513210
Christian Sundin (CEO)

Subsidiaries:

FormPipe Software Copenhagen A/S (1)
Park Alla 290, Brondby, 2605, Copenhagen, Denmark
Tel.: (45) 43660210
Sales Range: $25-49.9 Million
Emp.: 14
Business Management Software Development Services
N.A.I.C.S.: 541511
Thomas A. Porta (CEO)

Formpipe Inc. (1)
1200 US Hwy 22 E Ste 2000, Bridgewater, NJ 08807
Tel.: (908) 200-7937
Software Development Services
N.A.I.C.S.: 541511

FORMSCAN LIMITED
Second Floor Park House, Kidwells Park Drive, Maidenhead, SL6 8AQ, United Kingdom
Tel.: (44) 8445617276
Document Management Solutions
N.A.I.C.S.: 513210
Chris Haden (CEO)

FORMULA FORD
940 Kingston Road, Pickering, L1V 1B3, ON, Canada
Tel.: (905) 839-6666
Web Site: http://www.formulafordlincoln.com
Year Founded: 1984
Rev.: $21,562,348
Emp.: 45
New & Used Car Dealers
N.A.I.C.S.: 441110
Joe Chapman (Mgr-Fleet)

FORMULA HONDA

2240 Markham Road, Scarborough,
M1B 2W4, ON, Canada
Tel.: (416) 754-4555
Web Site:
   http://www.formulahonda.com
Year Founded: 1987
Rev.: $22,817,200
Emp.: 50
New & Used Car Dealers
N.A.I.C.S.: 441110
Nial Boatswain *(Gen Mgr)*

FORMULA TELECOM SOLUTIONS LIMITED

5 Haplada Street, PO Box 50116, Or
Yehuda, 6021805, Israel
Tel.: (972) 99526500   II
Web Site: http://www.fts-soft.com
Year Founded: 1997
Sales Range: $10-24.9 Million
Emp.: 500
Business Control, Billing & CRM So-
lutions & Services
N.A.I.C.S.: 513210
Avi Kachlon *(CEO)*

Subsidiaries:

F.T.S- Formula Telecom Solutions
Bulgaria   (1)
23 Vladaiska Str, Sofia, 1606, Bulgaria
Tel.: (359) 2 952 3929
Web Site: http://www.fts-soft.com
Emp.: 5
Telecom Management Solutions Provider
N.A.I.C.S.: 517810
Yehuda Benny *(Mng Dir)*

F.T.S. Global Limited   (1)
Ground Fl Meersig 2 Constantia Blvd, Con-
stantia Kloof, 1710, Johannesburg, South
Africa
Tel.: (27) 11 322 4200
Telecom Management Solutions Provider
N.A.I.C.S.: 517810

Formula Telecom Limited   (1)
Bld 7A 25 Entrance 4 Ofc 3, Staroprovsky
Line, Moscow, 125130, Russia
Tel.: (7) 4956481008
Telecom Management Solutions Provider
N.A.I.C.S.: 517810

FORMYCON AG

Fraunhoferstrasse 15, 82152, Martin-
sried, Planegg, Germany
Tel.: (49) 89864667100
Web Site: https://www.formycon.com
Year Founded: 1999
FYB—(STU)
Rev.: $85,770,699
Assets: $982,841,693
Liabilities: $427,871,051
Net Worth: $554,970,642
Earnings: $83,673,346
Emp.: 230
Fiscal Year-end: 12/31/23
Innovative Pharmaceutical Formula-
tions Mfr
N.A.I.C.S.: 325412
Olaf Stiller *(Chm-Supervisory Bd)*

FORO-MAREE S.A.

123 quai du Midi, Port Chef de Baie,
17045, La Rochelle, Cedex 1, France
Tel.: (33) 546411900   FR
Web Site: http://www.foromaree.com
Sales Range: $1-9.9 Million
Emp.: 58
Fish & Seafood Distr
N.A.I.C.S.: 424460
Bernard Rivasseau *(Dir Gen & Sls
Mgr)*

FORRESTANIA RESOURCES LIMITED

Suite 2 38 Colin Street, West Perth,
6005, WA, Australia
Tel.: (61) 863910113

Web Site:
   https://www.forrestaniaresource.com
Year Founded: 2021
FRS—(ASX)
Rev.: $4,834
Assets: $6,621,772
Liabilities: $525,168
Net Worth: $6,096,604
Earnings: ($1,077,398)
Emp.: 116
Fiscal Year-end: 06/30/23
Exploration & Mining Services
N.A.I.C.S.: 213115
John Hannaford *(Chm)*

FORSEE POWER SAS

1 Boulevard Hippolyte Marques,
94200, Ivry-sur-Seine, France
Tel.: (33) 158916900   FR
Web Site:
   https://www.forseepower.com
Year Founded: 2007
FORSE—(EUR)
Rev.: $184,802,504
Assets: $202,287,934
Liabilities: $138,357,436
Net Worth: $63,930,499
Earnings: ($30,176,991)
Emp.: 702
Fiscal Year-end: 12/31/23
Battery Mfr
N.A.I.C.S.: 335910
Remi Fuste *(VP-Aftermarket & Cus-
tomer Satisfaction)*

FORSIDE CO., LTD.

8F ETS Muromachi Building 3-3-1
Muromachi Nihonbashi, Chuo-ku, To-
kyo, 103-0022, Japan
Tel.: (81) 362621056
Web Site: https://www.forside.co.jp
Year Founded: 2000
2330—(TKS)
Rev.: $34,152,530
Assets: $31,536,320
Liabilities: $20,369,570
Net Worth: $11,166,750
Earnings: $801,170
Emp.: 60
Fiscal Year-end: 12/31/23
Ring Tones & Display Wallpaper for
Mobile Phones
N.A.I.C.S.: 334290

FORSTA AP-FONDEN

Regeringsgatan 28, Box 16294, 103
25, Stockholm, Sweden
Tel.: (46) 8 566 202 00
Web Site: http://www.ap1.se
Rev.: $5,235,897,520
Assets: $39,446,812,090
Liabilities: $248,420,060
Net Worth: $39,198,392,030
Earnings: $5,210,283,890
Emp.: 65
Fiscal Year-end: 12/31/19
Investment & Funding Services
N.A.I.C.S.: 523999
Kristin Magnusson Bernard *(CEO)*

Subsidiaries:

Polhem Infra AB   (1)
Norrlandsgatan 12, Stockholm, Sweden
Tel.: (46) 738 00 67 25
Web Site: http://www.polheminfra.se
Privater Equity Firm
N.A.I.C.S.: 523999
Mikael Lundin *(CEO & VP)*

Subsidiary (Domestic):

Telia Carrier AB   (2)
Stjarntorget 1, 169 94, Solna, Sweden
Tel.: (46) 850455000
Web Site: http://www.teliasoneraic.com
Sales Range: $25-49.9 Million
Mobile Network Services
N.A.I.C.S.: 517112
Staffan Gojeryd *(CEO)*

FORSTER SWISS HOME AG

Egnacherstrasse 37, 9320, Arbon,
Switzerland
Tel.: (41) 714474645   CH
Web Site: http://www.forster-home.ch
Prefabricated Kitchen Installation
Services
N.A.I.C.S.: 332999
Felix Bodmer *(CFO)*

FORSYS METALS CORP.

20 Adelaide Street East Suite 200,
PO Box 909, Toronto, M5C 2T6, ON,
Canada
Tel.: (416) 818-4035
Web Site:
   https://www.forsysmetals.com
FSY—(TSX)
Assets: $19,450,736
Liabilities: $61,674
Net Worth: $19,389,062
Earnings: ($3,020,805)
Emp.: 4
Fiscal Year-end: 12/31/21
Uranium Exploration & Mining Ser-
vices
N.A.I.C.S.: 212290
Martin R. Rowley *(Chm)*

FORSYTH HOLDINGS, INC.

6789 Airport Road, Mississauga, L4V
1N2, ON, Canada
Tel.: (905) 362-1400
Web Site: http://www.forsythshirt.com
Year Founded: 1903
Rev.: $70,000,000
Emp.: 600
Apparel Mfr & Supplier
N.A.I.C.S.: 315990
Harris R. Hester *(CEO)*

FORSYTHE LUBRICATION ASSOCIATES LIMITED

120 Chatham St, Hamilton, L8P 2B5,
ON, Canada
Tel.: (905) 525-7192
Web Site:
   http://www.forsythelubrication.ca
Year Founded: 1911
Rev.: $10,839,876
Emp.: 25
Lubricant Mfr
N.A.I.C.S.: 324191
Lynne Adamson *(Mgr-Pur)*

FORT CITY CHRYSLER SALES LTD.

8424 Alaska Road, Fort Saint John,
V1J 5L6, BC, Canada
Tel.: (250) 787-5220
Web Site:
   http://www.fortcitychrysler.ca
Year Founded: 1997
Rev.: $12,954,798
Emp.: 28
New & Used Car Dealers
N.A.I.C.S.: 441110

FORT PNEUS

795 Route De St Gervasy, 30129,
Nimes, France
Tel.: (33) 4034403000
Web Site: http://www.fortpneus.com
Rev.: $20,500,000
Emp.: 27
Motor Vehicle Supplies & New Parts
N.A.I.C.S.: 423120
Andre Cohen *(Dir-Fin)*

FORT ST. JAMES NICKEL CORP.

Suite 888-888 Dunsmuir St, Vancouver, V6C 3K4, BC, Canada
Tel.: (604) 488-3900
Web Site:
   http://www.fortstjamesnickel.com

FTJ—(TSXV)

Assets: $3,423
Liabilities: $1,169,970
Net Worth: ($1,166,547)
Earnings: ($287,022)
Fiscal Year-end: 04/30/24
Nickel Exploration & Mining
N.A.I.C.S.: 212230
Nicolette Keith *(CFO)*

FORTACO ZRT.

Sportpalya utca 1, 5100, Jaszbereny,
Hungary
Tel.: (36) 57815000
Emp.: 40
Construction Engineering Services
N.A.I.C.S.: 541330
Johan Cannaerts *(Mng Dir)*

FORTE MINERALS CORP.

1005-409 Granville St, Vancouver,
V6C 1T2, BC, Canada
Tel.: (604) 983-8847   BC
Web Site:
   https://www.forteminerals.com
Year Founded: 2011
CUAU—(CNSX)
Rev.: $2,055
Assets: $1,094,685
Liabilities: $150,783
Net Worth: $943,902
Earnings: ($400,446)
Fiscal Year-end: 12/31/21
Mineral Exploration Services
N.A.I.C.S.: 212220
Samantha Shorter *(CFO)*

FORTEBANK JSC

Dostyk str 8/1, Yesil district, 010017,
Astana, Kazakhstan
Tel.: (7) 172599999
Web Site: https://forte.kz
Year Founded: 1993
ASBN—(KAZ)
Rev.: $812,757,353
Assets: $7,132,911,505
Liabilities: $6,190,514,484
Net Worth: $942,397,021
Earnings: $255,299,766
Fiscal Year-end: 12/31/23
Commercial Banking Services
N.A.I.C.S.: 522110
Pirmatov Bekzhan *(Chm & CEO)*

Subsidiaries:

ForteLeasing JSC   (1)
7a 59A Amangeldi str, Almaly district,
050012, Almaty, Kazakhstan
Tel.: (7) 273442888
Assets: $44,558,350
Liabilities: $29,379,209
Net Worth: $15,179,142
Earnings: $3,157,136
Emp.: 35
Fiscal Year-end: 12/31/2023
Sales Financing Services
N.A.I.C.S.: 522220
Rakhmanov Talap *(CEO & Gen Dir)*

OUSA-F LLP   (1)
Kunaev 32, Almaty, Kazakhstan
Tel.: (7) 7273440336
Web Site: http://www.ousa-f.kz
Asset Management Services
N.A.I.C.S.: 523940

FORTEC ELEKTRONIK AG

Augsburger Str 2b, 82110, Germer-
ing, Germany
Tel.: (49) 898944500
Web Site: https://www.fortecag.de
Year Founded: 1984
FEV—(DEU)
Rev.: $101,470,393
Assets: $84,585,496
Liabilities: $22,574,023
Net Worth: $62,011,473
Earnings: $5,689,126
Emp.: 243

FORTEC Elektronik AG—(Continued)

Fiscal Year-end: 06/30/24
Industrial Electronic Component Mfr
N.A.I.C.S.: 334419
Sandra Maile *(Chm-Mgmt Bd & CEO)*

Subsidiaries:

AUTRONIC Steuer- und Regeltechnik
GmbH **(1)**
Siemensstr 17, 74343, Sachsenheim, Germany
Tel.: (49) 7147240
Web Site: https://www.autronic.de
Electronic Component Mfr & Distr
N.A.I.C.S.: 334419

Aushang.online GmbH **(1)**
Augsburger Str 2b, 82110, Germering, Germany
Tel.: (49) 898943630
Web Site: https://aushang.online
Software Development Services
N.A.I.C.S.: 541511

Emtron Electronic GmbH **(1)**
Lise-Meitner-Str 3, 64560, Riedstadt, Germany
Tel.: (49) 615882850
Web Site: https://www.emtron.de
Electronic Component Mfr & Distr
N.A.I.C.S.: 334419

FORTEC Switzerland AG **(1)**
Bahnhofstrasse 3, 5436, Wurenlos, Switzerland
Tel.: (41) 447446111
Web Site: https://www.fortec.ch
Electronic Components Mfr
N.A.I.C.S.: 334419

FORTEC TECHNOLOGY UK
LIMITED **(1)**
Osprey House 1 Osprey Court Hinchingbrooke Business Park, Huntingdon, PE29 6FN, Cambridgeshire, United Kingdom
Tel.: (44) 1480411600
Web Site: https://www.fortec.uk
Electronic Components Mfr
N.A.I.C.S.: 334419

ROTEC Technology GmbH **(1)**
Gutenbergstr 15, 76437, Rastatt, Germany
Tel.: (49) 722210080
Web Site: http://www.rotec.de
Electronic Components Mfr
N.A.I.C.S.: 334419

FORTENOVA GROUP D.D.

Ulica Marijana Cavica 1, 10000, Zagreb, Croatia
Tel.: (385) 3851489411
Web Site: https://fortenova.hr
Year Founded: 2019
Emp.: 45,237
Food & Beverage Services
N.A.I.C.S.: 445298

Subsidiaries:

Poslovni sistem Mercator, d.d. **(1)**
Dunajska cesta 107, 1113, Ljubljana, Slovenia
Tel.: (386) 15601000
Web Site: https://www.mercatorgroup.si
Rev.: $2,395,088,257
Assets: $2,244,051,618
Liabilities: $1,752,462,195
Net Worth: $491,589,424
Earnings: $5,225,267
Emp.: 19,963
Fiscal Year-end: 12/31/2019
Consumer Goods Whslr & Retailer
N.A.I.C.S.: 459999

Subsidiary (Non-US):

Investment International,
d.o.o.e.l. **(2)**
PO Box 456, Skopje, North Macedonia
Tel.: (389) 23290233
Web Site: https://www.investment.mk
Sales Range: $25-49.9 Million
Emp.: 1
Consumer Goods Retailer
N.A.I.C.S.: 455219

Mercator - H, d.o.o. **(2)**

Hrvatske Bratske Zajednice 1, 10410,
Velika Gorica, Croatia
Tel.: (385) 16572000
Sales Range: $450-499.9 Million
Emp.: 2,484
General Stores
N.A.I.C.S.: 455219

Mercator - Mex, d.o.o. **(2)**
Put Radomira Ivanovica br 2, 81000,
Podgorica, Montenegro
Tel.: (382) 81442403
Sales Range: $125-149.9 Million
Emp.: 272
Consumer Goods Retailer
N.A.I.C.S.: 455219

Mercator BH d.o.o. **(2)**
Lozionicka br 16, 71000, Sarajevo, Bosnia
& Herzegovina
Tel.: (387) 33552861139
Sales Range: $550-599.9 Million
Emp.: 1,045
Consumer Goods Retailer
N.A.I.C.S.: 423620

Mercator Makedonija d.o.o.e.l. **(2)**
Temerinski put 50, 21000, Novi Sad, Serbia
Tel.: (381) 214888400
Web Site: https://www.mercator.rs
Consumer Goods Retailer
N.A.I.C.S.: 455219
Ivan Karadzic *(Exec Dir)*

Subsidiary (Domestic):

Mercator-Emba d.d. **(2)**
Trzaska cesta 2c, Logatec, 1370, Slovenia
Tel.: (386) 17598400
Web Site: https://www.mercator-emba.si
Sales Range: $25-49.9 Million
Emp.: 116
Chocolate & Sugar Confectioneries Mfr
N.A.I.C.S.: 311351
Mladen Mladenic *(Gen Mgr)*

Subsidiary (Non-US):

Mercator-S, d.o.o. **(2)**
Autoput za Zagreb 11a, 11070, Beograd,
Serbia
Tel.: (381) 800101202
Web Site: https://www.mercator.rs
Sales Range: $125-149.9 Million
Emp.: 480
Consumer Goods Retailer
N.A.I.C.S.: 455219

Subsidiary (Domestic):

Pekarna Grosuplje, d.d. **(2)**
Gasilska cesta 2, 1290, Grosuplje, Slovenia
Tel.: (386) 17866900
Web Site: https://www.mercator.com
Sales Range: $25-49.9 Million
Emp.: 190
Banking Services
N.A.I.C.S.: 311812
Alenka Zavrl Mozetic *(Mng Dir)*

FORTEQ GROUP

Ipsachstrasse 14, 2560, Nidau, Switzerland
Tel.: (41) 323327332
Web Site: http://www.forteq-group.com
Year Founded: 2005
Sales Range: $25-49.9 Million
Emp.: 700
Plastic Mfr
N.A.I.C.S.: 326199
Lucie Toscani *(CEO)*

Subsidiaries:

forteq Czech s.r.o. **(1)**
Kopisty 1, Most, 43401, Czech Republic
Tel.: (420) 476 203 862
Plastic Product Distr
N.A.I.C.S.: 424610
Tomas Karasek *(Mgr-Logistics & Pur)*

forteq Derendingen AG **(1)**
Gewerbestrasse 4, Derendingen, CH 4552,
Bern, Switzerland
Tel.: (41) 326815123
Sales Range: $50-74.9 Million
Emp.: 30
Automotive Plastics Mfr

N.A.I.C.S.: 326199

forteq Italy S.p.A. **(1)**
Piazza Milano 10, Ciserano Zingonia, IT
24040, Bergamo, BG, Italy
Tel.: (39) 0354182011
Web Site: http://www.forteq.ch
Sales Range: $50-74.9 Million
Emp.: 70
Plastic Mfr
N.A.I.C.S.: 326199

forteq Netherlands BV **(1)**
Lange Dreef 15F, NL 4131 NJ, Vianen,
Netherlands
Tel.: (31) 347376767
Web Site: http://www.forteq.nl
Sales Range: $75-99.9 Million
Emp.: 5
Plastic & Chemical Engineering
N.A.I.C.S.: 326199

forteq North America, Inc. **(1)**
150 Park Center Dr, West Henrietta, NY
14586-9688
Tel.: (585) 427-9410
Web Site: http://www.forteq-group.com
Sales Range: $50-74.9 Million
Emp.: 80
Plastic Mfr
N.A.I.C.S.: 326199
Joe Beonocore *(Gen Mgr)*

forteq Suzhou Ltd. **(1)**
No 4 Building Huayitianhe Estate Suhong
Zhong Road, Suzhou Industrial Park, Suzhou, 215021, China
Tel.: (86) 512 6258 0069
Plastic Product Distr
N.A.I.C.S.: 424610
Ivory Cai *(Key Acct Mgr)*

forteq UK Ltd. **(1)**
Tandem Industrial Estate, Huddersfield,
HD5 0QR, United Kingdom
Tel.: (44) 1484424384
Web Site: http://www.forteq-group.com
Sales Range: $10-24.9 Million
Emp.: 85
Plastic Mfr
N.A.I.C.S.: 326199
Paul Wallis *(Mng Dir)*

FORTESCUE LTD

Level 2 87 Adelaide Terrace, Perth,
6004, WA, Australia
Tel.: (61) 862188888 **AU**
Web Site: https://fortescue.com
Year Founded: 2003
FSUGY—(ASX)
Rev.: $18,220,000,000
Assets: $30,060,000,000
Liabilities: $10,529,000,000
Net Worth: $19,531,000,000
Earnings: $5,664,000,000
Emp.: 13,065
Fiscal Year-end: 06/30/24
Mineral Mining Services
N.A.I.C.S.: 212290
Andrew Forrest *(Chm)*

Subsidiaries:

Chichester Metals Pty Limited **(1)**
Level 2 87 Adelaide Terrace, East Perth,
Perth, 6004, WA, Australia
Tel.: (61) 862188888
Iron Ore Mining Services
N.A.I.C.S.: 212210

The Pilbara Infrastructure Pty
Limited **(1)**
Level 2 87 Adelaide Terrace, Perth, 6004,
WA, Australia
Tel.: (61) 862188888
Web Site: http://www.fmgl.com.au
Iron Ore Mining Services
N.A.I.C.S.: 212210
Andrew Forrest *(Chm)*

FORTH CORPORATION PUBLIC COMPANY LIMITED

1053/1 Phaholyothin Road,
Phayathai, Bangkok, 10400, Thailand
Tel.: (66) 22656700 **TH**
Web Site: https://en.forth.co.th

Year Founded: 1989
FORTH—(THA)
Rev.: $286,664,912
Assets: $324,685,920
Liabilities: $228,885,431
Net Worth: $95,800,488
Earnings: $23,541,950
Emp.: 3,202
Fiscal Year-end: 12/31/23
Telecommunications Equipment Mfr
N.A.I.C.S.: 334290
Sanit Vorapanya *(Chm)*

Subsidiaries:

Forth Corporation Public Company
Limited - FORTH FACTORY **(1)**
77 Moo 11Phuttamonton 5 Road, Raikhing
Sampran District, Nakhon Pathom, 73210,
Thailand
Tel.: (66) 2 811 7921
Electronic Components Mfr
N.A.I.C.S.: 334419

Genius Traffic System Company
Limited **(1)**
226/27-29 Phaholyothin Road Samsennai,
Phayathai, Bangkok, 10400, Thailand
Tel.: (66) 26152440
Web Site: https://www.gets.co.th
Traffic Control Equipment Mfr
N.A.I.C.S.: 334511

FORTH SMART SERVICE PUBLIC COMPANY LIMITED

256 Phaholyothin Road Samsen Nai,
Phaya Thai, Bangkok, 10400, Thailand
Tel.: (66) 22781777
Web Site: https://www.boonterm.com
FSMART—(THA)
Rev.: $65,832,347
Assets: $79,907,804
Liabilities: $45,714,540
Net Worth: $34,193,264
Earnings: $8,741,309
Emp.: 287
Fiscal Year-end: 12/31/23
Pre-Paid Mobile Phones & Online
Games
N.A.I.C.S.: 525990
Pichit Nimkul *(Chm)*

Subsidiaries:

Forth Smart Capital Co., Ltd. **(1)**
256 Phaholyothin Road, Samsennai
Phayathai, Bangkok, 10400, Thailand
Tel.: (66) 22781777
Web Site: https://www.boonterm.com
Personal Loan Services
N.A.I.C.S.: 522390

FORTH WINES LTD

Crawford Place Milnathort, Kinross,
KY13 9XF, United Kingdom
Tel.: (44) 1577866000
Web Site: http://www.forthwines.com
Year Founded: 1963
Rev.: $36,390,377
Emp.: 55
Wine Distr
N.A.I.C.S.: 424820
Tom Clarkson *(Mgr-Sls-Scotland)*

FORTIANA HOLDINGS LTD

36 Ayias Elenis Street 4th Floor Office Flat 403, Galaxias Commercial
Center, 1061, Nicosia, Cyprus
Web Site:
http://www.fortianaholdings.com
Privater Equity Firm
N.A.I.C.S.: 551112
Vladislav Sviblov *(CEO)*

Subsidiaries:

Highland Gold Mining Limited **(1)**
26 New Street, Saint Helier, JE2 3RA,
Channel Islands, Jersey
Tel.: (44) 1534 814202
Web Site: http://www.highlandgold.com

Gold Mining & Production Services
N.A.I.C.S.: 212220
Vladislav Sviblov *(Chm & CEO)*

FORTIFY RESOURCES INC.
1210 1066 West Hastings Street,
Vancouver, V6E 3X1, BC, Canada
Tel.: (604) 668-5820   BC
Year Founded: 2011
Metal Mining
N.A.I.C.S.: 212290

FORTINO CAPITAL PARTNERS
Belgicastraat 3, BE-1930, Zaventem,
Belgium
Tel.: (32) 26691050
Web Site:
   https://www.fortinocapital.com
Year Founded: 2013
Holding Company
N.A.I.C.S.: 523999
Lyzette Martens *(Office Mgr)*

Subsidiaries:

Bonitasoft, S.A.   **(1)**
32 rue Gustave Eiffel, 38000, Grenoble,
France
Tel.: (33) 4 76 49 40 66
Web Site: http://www.bonitasoft.com
Business Process Management Software
Developer
N.A.I.C.S.: 513210
Charles Souillard *(Co-Founder, COO, CTO
& VP-Engrg)*

FORTIS HEALTHCARE LIMITED
Tower A Unitech Business Park
Block-F, South City 1 Sector-41, Gurgaon, 122001, Haryana, India
Tel.: (91) 1244921033   In
Web Site:
   https://www.fortishealthcare.com
Year Founded: 1996
532843—(BOM)
Rev.: $784,185,429
Assets: $1,622,268,198
Liabilities: $665,641,404
Net Worth: $956,626,794
Earnings: $107,827,547
Emp.: 2,861
Fiscal Year-end: 03/31/22
Hospital Owner & Operator
N.A.I.C.S.: 622110
Ashutosh Raghuvanshi *(CEO)*

Subsidiaries:

Escorts Heart Institute and Research
Centre Limited   **(1)**
Okhla Road, New Delhi, 110 025, India
Tel.: (91) 1147135000
Web Site: https://www.fortisescorts.in
Sales Range: $800-899.9 Million
Emp.: 5,500
Health Care Srvices
N.A.I.C.S.: 621491

Subsidiary (Domestic):

Escorts Heart and Super Speciality
Institute Limited   **(2)**
Majitha-Verka Bypass Rd, Amritsar, 143
004, Punjab, India
Tel.: (91) 1832573900
Web Site: http://www.ehirc.com
Health Care Srvices
N.A.I.C.S.: 621491

Escorts Hospital and Research Centre Limited   **(1)**
Neelam Bata Road Opp Neelam Cinema, N
I T, Faridabad, 121 001, Haryana, India
Tel.: (91) 1297116000
Web Site: http://www.fortishealthcare.com
Sales Range: $10-24.9 Million
Emp.: 55
Health Care Srvices
N.A.I.C.S.: 621491

Fortis La Femme Limited   **(1)**
S - 549 Greater Kailash - I, New Delhi,
110048, India

Tel.: (91) 1140579400
Web Site: http://www.fortishealthcare.com
Women Medical Care Services
N.A.I.C.S.: 621111

Fortis Malar Hospitals Limited   **(1)**
52 First Main Road Gandhi Nagar, Adyar,
Chennai, 600 020, India   **(63.17%)**
Tel.: (91) 4442892222
Web Site:
   https://www.fortismalarhospital.com
Rev.: $12,772,128
Assets: $21,964,625
Liabilities: $11,026,675
Net Worth: $10,937,950
Earnings: ($1,129,333)
Emp.: 445
Fiscal Year-end: 03/31/2022
Hospital Management Services
N.A.I.C.S.: 622110
C. Kalyanraman Nageswaran *(Exec Dir)*

Super Religare Laboratories International FZ LLC   **(1)**
Unit 1007-08 Block A 1018-19 Block E Al
Razi Building, Dubai Healthcare City, Dubai,
505143, United Arab Emirates
Tel.: (971) 4 4483 100
Web Site: http://www.srldiagnostics.ae
Medical Laboratories Chain
N.A.I.C.S.: 621511
Mayur Sabhani *(Head-Ops)*

FORTIS INC.
Fortis Place Suite 1100 5 Springdale
Street, Saint John's, A1B 3T2, NL,
Canada
Tel.: (709) 737-2800   NL
Web Site: https://www.fortisinc.com
Year Founded: 1987
FTS—(NYSE)
Rev.: $7,390,981,440
Assets: $45,105,482,520
Liabilities: $28,743,314,040
Net Worth: $16,362,168,480
Earnings: $1,099,103,400
Emp.: 9,095
Fiscal Year-end: 12/31/21
Holding Company; Utilities Investments
N.A.I.C.S.: 551112
David Gerard Hutchens *(Pres &
CEO)*

Subsidiaries:

Belize Electric Company Limited   **(1)**
No 1 Caracol Street, PO Box 87, San Ignacio, Belize
Tel.: (501) 8243016
Electric Power Distr.
N.A.I.C.S.: 221122

CH Energy Group, Inc.   **(1)**
284 South Ave, Poughkeepsie, NY 12601-4839
Tel.: (845) 452-2000
Web Site: https://www.chenergygroup.com
Rev.: $924,719,000
Assets: $1,784,949,000
Liabilities: $1,266,632,000
Net Worth: $518,317,000
Earnings: $39,847,000
Emp.: 1,235
Fiscal Year-end: 12/31/2012
Holding Company for Electricity, Natural
Gas, Propane, Fuel Oil & Petroleum Products
N.A.I.C.S.: 551112
Christopher M. Capone *(CFO & Exec VP)*

Subsidiary (Domestic):

Central Hudson Enterprises
Corporation   **(2)**
284 South Ave, Poughkeepsie, NY 12601-4838
Tel.: (845) 485-5770
Web Site: http://www.centralhudson.com
Fuel Distribution Services
N.A.I.C.S.: 457210

Central Hudson Gas & Electric
Corporation   **(2)**
284 South Ave, Poughkeepsie, NY
12601-4839   **(100%)**

Tel.: (845) 452-2000
Rev.: $644,515,000
Assets: $1,660,367,000
Liabilities: $1,190,706,000
Net Worth: $469,661,000
Earnings: $47,170,000
Emp.: 869
Fiscal Year-end: 12/31/2012
Public Electric & Gas Utility
N.A.I.C.S.: 221122
Denise Doring VanBuren *(VP-PR)*

Caribbean Utilities Company,
Ltd.   **(1)**
457 North Sound Road, PO Box 38,
Georgetown, KY1-1101, Grand Cayman,
Cayman Islands
Tel.: (345) 9495200
Web Site: https://www.cuc-cayman.com
Rev.: $287,225,000
Assets: $777,807,000
Liabilities: $453,065,000
Net Worth: $324,742,000
Earnings: $38,660,000
Emp.: 263
Fiscal Year-end: 12/31/2023
Support Activities for Oil & Gas Operations
N.A.I.C.S.: 213112
David E. Ritch *(Chm)*

Fortis Belize Limited   **(1)**
Mile 71 5 George Price Highway, PO Box
87, Cayo District, Belize, Belize
Tel.: (501) 8243016
Web Site: https://www.fortisbelize.com
Hydroelectric Power Generation Distr
N.A.I.C.S.: 423610

Fortis Properties Brunswick Square
Ltd.   **(1)**
39 King St, Saint John, E2L 4W3, NB,
Canada   **(100%)**
Tel.: (506) 658-1000
Web Site: http://www.fortisproperties.com
Sales Range: $50-74.9 Million
Emp.: 13
Brunswick Square Retail/Office/Hotel Complex; Joint Venture of Aliant & Fortis Properties Corporation
N.A.I.C.S.: 531120
Cathy Lifford *(Mgr-Client Svcs)*

Fortis Properties Corporation   **(1)**
139 Water St Ste 1201, Saint John's, A1B
3T2, NL, Canada   **(100%)**
Tel.: (709) 737-2800
Web Site: http://www.fortisproperties.com
Sales Range: $25-49.9 Million
Emp.: 45
Holding Company for Shopping Centers &
Hotels
N.A.I.C.S.: 551112
Nora M. Duke *(Pres & CEO)*

FortisAlberta Inc.   **(1)**
320 - 17 Avenue SW, Calgary, T2S 2V1,
AB, Canada
Web Site: http://www.fortisalberta.com
Electric Power Distr
N.A.I.C.S.: 221122
Janine Sullivan *(Pres & CEO)*

FortisBC Holdings Inc.   **(1)**
1111 West Georgia Street 10th Floor, Vancouver, V6E 4M3, BC, Canada
Tel.: (604) 443-6500
Web Site: http://www.fortisbc.com
Sales Range: $450-499.9 Million
Emp.: 1,366
Holding Company; Natural Gas & Electricity
Distribution Services
N.A.I.C.S.: 551112
Tracy Medve *(Chm)*

Subsidiary (Domestic):

FortisBC Energy Inc.   **(2)**
16705 Fraser Highway, Surrey, V4N 0E8,
BC, Canada
Tel.: (604) 576-7000
Web Site: http://www.fortisbc.com
Natural Gas Transmission & Distribution
N.A.I.C.S.: 221210

FortisBC Inc.   **(2)**
Suite 100 1975 Springfield Road, Kelowna,
V1Y 7V7, BC, Canada
Tel.: (250) 368-0690
Web Site: http://www.fortisbc.com
Electric Power Distribution Services

N.A.I.C.S.: 221122
Roger Dall'Antonia *(Pres & CEO)*

FortisOntario Inc   **(1)**
1130 Bertie Street, PO Box 1218, Fort Erie,
L2A 5Y2, ON, Canada
Tel.: (905) 871-0330
Web Site: http://www.fortisontario.com
Sales Range: $100-124.9 Million
Emp.: 100
Hydroelectric Power Generation & Distribution Services
N.A.I.C.S.: 221111
Glen King *(CFO & VP-Fin)*

Subsidiary (Domestic):

Algoma Power Inc.   **(2)**
2 Sackville Rd Ste A, Sault Sainte Marie,
P6B 6J6, ON, Canada
Tel.: (705) 256-3850
Web Site: http://www.algomapower.com
Electric Power Distribution Services
N.A.I.C.S.: 221122

Canadian Niagara Power Inc.   **(2)**
1130 Bertie St, PO Box 1218, Fort Erie,
L2A 5Y2, ON, Canada
Tel.: (905) 871-0330
Web Site: http://www.cnpower.com
Sales Range: $75-99.9 Million
Emp.: 100
Electric Power Distribution Services
N.A.I.C.S.: 221122
Kristine Carmichael *(Dir-Corp & Customer
Svcs)*

Division (Domestic):

Canadian Niagara Power Inc. - Eastern Ontario Power Division   **(3)**
PO Box 1179, Cornwall, K6H 5V3, ON,
Canada
Tel.: (613) 382-2118
Web Site:
   http://www.easternontariopower.com
Electric Power Distribution Services
N.A.I.C.S.: 221122

Subsidiary (Domestic):

Cornwall Electric Inc.   **(2)**
1001 Sydney St, Cornwall, K6H 3K1, ON,
Canada
Tel.: (613) 932-0123
Web Site: http://www.cornwallelectric.com
Emp.: 50
Electric Power Distribution Services
N.A.I.C.S.: 221122

FortisTCI Limited   **(1)**
1030 Leeward Highway, PO Box 132, Providenciales, Turks & Caicos Islands
Tel.: (649) 9464313
Web Site: https://www.fortistci.com
Emp.: 170
Electric Power Distr
N.A.I.C.S.: 221122
Ruth Forbes *(Pres & CEO)*

ITC Holdings Corp.   **(1)**
27175 Energy Way, Novi, MI
48377   **(80.1%)**
Tel.: (248) 946-3000
Web Site: https://www.itc-holdings.com
Rev.: $1,466,000,000
Assets: $12,131,000,000
Liabilities: $9,459,000,000
Net Worth: $2,672,000,000
Earnings: $442,000,000
Emp.: 726
Fiscal Year-end: 12/31/2022
Holding Company; Electric Power Transmission Services
N.A.I.C.S.: 551112
Christine Mason Soneral *(Chief Compliance
Officer, Gen Counsel, Sec & Sr VP)*

Subsidiary (Domestic):

International Transmission
Company   **(2)**
27175 Energy Way, Novi, MI
48377   **(100%)**
Tel.: (248) 946-3000
Web Site: http://www.itc-holdings.com
Electric Power Transmission Services
N.A.I.C.S.: 221121

Subsidiary (Domestic):

ITC Grid Development, LLC   **(3)**

Fortis Inc.—(Continued)

27175 Energy Way, Novi, MI 48377
Tel.: (248) 946-3000
Web Site: http://www.itc-holdings.com
Energy Transmission Venture Acquisition &
Development Services
N.A.I.C.S.: 221121
Terry S. Harvill (Pres)

ITC Midwest LLC (3)
123 5th St SE, Cedar Rapids, IA 52401
Tel.: (319) 297-6700
Electric Power Transmission Services
N.A.I.C.S.: 221121
Dusky Terry (Pres)

Subsidiary (Domestic):

Michigan Electric Transmission Company, LLC (2)
27175 Energy Way, Novi, MI
48377 (100%)
Tel.: (248) 946-3000
Web Site: http://www.itc-holdings.com
Electric Power Transmission Services
N.A.I.C.S.: 221121

Maritime Electric Company Limited (1)
180 Kent Street, Charlottetown, C1A 7N2,
PE, Canada
Tel.: (902) 629-3799
Web Site: https://www.maritimeelectric.com
Sales Range: $75-99.9 Million
Emp.: 100
Electric Power Distribution Services
N.A.I.C.S.: 221122
John D. Gaudet (Pres & CEO)

Subsidiary (Domestic):

Newfoundland Power Inc. (1)
Tel.: (709) 737-5600
Web Site:
https://www.newfoundlandpower.com
Sales Range: $300-349.9 Million
Emp.: 600
Electric Power Distr
N.A.I.C.S.: 221122
Ken Bennett (Chm)

Subsidiary (Domestic):

UNS Energy Corporation (1)
88 E Broadway Blvd, Tucson, AZ 85702
Tel.: (520) 571-4000
Web Site: http://www.uns.com
Holding Company; Electric Power Generation & Distribution
N.A.I.C.S.: 551112
David Gerard Hutchens (Co-Pres & CEO)

Subsidiary (Domestic):

Tucson Electric Power Company (2)
88 E Broadway Blvd, Tucson, AZ 85701
Tel.: (520) 571-4000
Web Site: https://www.tep.com
Rev.: $1,808,082,000
Assets: $6,689,781,000
Liabilities: $1,919,136,000
Net Worth: $4,770,645,000
Earnings: $217,425,000
Emp.: 1,675
Fiscal Year-end: 12/31/2022
Electric Power Distribution & Generation
Services
N.A.I.C.S.: 221122
Todd C. Hixon (Gen Counsel, Sec & Sr VP)

Subsidiary (Domestic):

Southwest Energy Solutions, Inc. (3)
3901 E Irvington Rd, Tucson, AZ 85714
Tel.: (520) 571-4000
Electric Power Distr
N.A.I.C.S.: 221122
David G. Hutchens (Pres & CEO)

Subsidiary (Domestic):

UniSource Energy Services, Inc. (2)
PO Box 711, Tucson, AZ 85702-0711
Tel.: (877) 837-4968
Web Site: http://www.uesaz.com
Electric Power Distr
N.A.I.C.S.: 221122
David Gerard Hutchens (Pres & CEO)

Subsidiary (Domestic):

UNS Electric, Inc. (3)
PO Box 80079, Prescott, AZ 86304-8079
Tel.: (928) 681-8966

Web Site: http://www.uesaz.com
Electric Power Distr
N.A.I.C.S.: 221122

UNS Gas, Inc. (3)
PO Box 80078, Prescott, AZ 86304-8078
Tel.: (877) 837-4968
Web Site: http://www.uesaz.com
Natural Gas Distr
N.A.I.C.S.: 221210

FORTISSIMO CAPITAL MANAGEMENT LTD.

14 Hamelacha Street Park Afek,
Rosh Ha'Ayin, 48091, Israel
Tel.: (972) 3 915 7400 II
Web Site: http://www.ffcapital.com
Privater Equity Firm
N.A.I.C.S.: 523999
Yuval Cohen (Founder & Mng
Partner-Investments)

Subsidiaries:

Phoenicia Ltd. (1)
Industrial Zone Zipporit, PO Box 703, Nazareth Illit, Israel
Tel.: (972) 46410200
Web Site: http://www.phoenicia-ltd.com
Emp.: 270
Glass Product Mfr & Distr
N.A.I.C.S.: 327215

Priority Software Ltd (1)
12 Haamal St, Rosh Ha'Ayin, 4809245,
Israel
Tel.: (972) 3 9251000
Web Site: http://www.priority-software.com
Software Development Services
N.A.I.C.S.: 541511
Andres Richter (CEO)

Salt of The Earth Ltd. (1)
1 Melach Haaretz Street, Atlit, 3035001,
Israel
Tel.: (972) 4 954 9555
Web Site: http://www.saltoftheearthltd.com
Salt Production
N.A.I.C.S.: 212390
Revital Ben Shachar (Mgr-Global Mktg)

Tuttnauer Ltd. (1)
Har Tuv B Industrial Zone, Beit Shemesh,
99000, Israel
Tel.: (972) 2 990 4600
Web Site: http://www.tuttnauer.com
Autoclave & Plasma Sterilizers Mfr & Whslr
N.A.I.C.S.: 339113
Ran Tuttnauer (CEO)

Subsidiary (US):

Tuttnauer U.S.A. Co., Ltd. (2)
25 Power Dr, Hauppauge, NY 11788
Tel.: (631) 737-4850
Web Site: http://www.tuttnauerusa.com
Autoclave & Plasma Sterilizers Whslr
N.A.I.C.S.: 423450
Ran Tuttnauer (CEO)

FORTISSIMO FILM SALES

Van Diemenstraat 134, 1013 CN, Amsterdam, Netherlands
Tel.: (31) 202159310
Web Site:
http://www.fortissimofilms.com
Year Founded: 1991
Sales Range: $25-49.9 Million
Emp.: 18
Independent Film Producer, Marketer,
Promoter, Sale & Distr
N.A.I.C.S.: 512110
Michael J. Werner (Chm)

Subsidiaries:

Fortissimo Film Sales (1)
Unit A 264 CKK Commercial Center 289
2295, Hennessy Road, Wanchai, China
(Hong Kong)
Tel.: (852) 23118081
Web Site: http://www.fortissimofilms.com
Sales Range: $25-49.9 Million
Emp.: 10
Independent Film Sales & Distr
N.A.I.C.S.: 512120
Michael J. Werner (Chm)

FORTNOX AB

Bollgatan 3b, PO Box 427, 351 06,
Vaxjo, Sweden
Tel.: (46) 470785000
Web Site: https://www.fortnox.se
Year Founded: 2001
FNOX—(OMX)
Emp.: 886
Software Development Services
N.A.I.C.S.: 541511
Nils Carlsson (CEO)

FORTRESS GLOBAL ENTERPRISES INC.

2nd Floor 157 Chadwick Court, North
Vancouver, V7M 3K2, BC, Canada
Tel.: (604) 904-2328 BC
Web Site: https://www.fortressge.com
Year Founded: 2006
Rev.: $136,292,107
Assets: $253,837,040
Liabilities: $180,659,514
Net Worth: $73,177,526
Earnings: ($23,586,975)
Emp.: 337
Fiscal Year-end: 12/31/18
Banknotes, Passport Papers, Visa
Papers, Non-Woven Wallpaper Based
Products, Graphic & Technical Papers Producer
N.A.I.C.S.: 322120
Kurt Loewen (CFO)

FORTRESS MINERALS LIMITED

9-1 Jalan PJS 8/18 Dataran Mentari,
46150, Petaling Jaya, Selangor, Malaysia
Tel.: (60) 378000113 SG
Web Site: https://www.fortress.sg
Year Founded: 2017
OAJ—(SES)
Rev.: $53,932,963
Assets: $97,220,983
Liabilities: $24,974,391
Net Worth: $72,246,592
Earnings: $10,038,006
Emp.: 400
Fiscal Year-end: 02/29/24
Mineral Exploration & Mining Services
N.A.I.C.S.: 212210
Yew Fei Chee (CEO)

FORTRESS REIT LIMITED

Tel.: (27) 112822800 ZA
Web Site:
https://www.fortressfund.co.za
FFA—(JSE)
Rev.: $243,475,409
Assets: $2,976,620,727
Liabilities: $1,306,691,635
Net Worth: $1,669,929,093
Earnings: $241,404,913
Fiscal Year-end: 06/30/24
Real Estate Investment Trust
N.A.I.C.S.: 525990
Mark Walter Stevens (CEO & Mng
Dir)

FORTUM OYJ

Keilaniemente 2-4 CD building, PO
Box 100, FI-00048, Espoo, Finland
Tel.: (358) 104511 FI
Web Site: https://www.fortum.com
Year Founded: 1996
FORTUM—(HEL)
Rev.: $7,408,102,441
Assets: $20,685,506,129
Liabilities: $11,303,675,904
Net Worth: $9,381,830,225
Earnings: $1,672,370,019
Emp.: 5,225
Fiscal Year-end: 12/31/23

Generation, Distribution & Sale of
Electricity & Heat & Operation &
Maintenance of Power Plants
N.A.I.C.S.: 221113
Ingela Ulfves (VP-IR & Fin Comm)

Subsidiaries:

AS Anne Soojus (1)
Turu 18, 51014, Tartu, Estonia
Tel.: (372) 7337100
Electric Power Distr
N.A.I.C.S.: 221122

AS Fortum Tartu (1)
Turu 18, 51014, Tartu, Estonia
Tel.: (372) 7337100
Web Site: http://www.fortumtartu.ee
Electricity Production Services
N.A.I.C.S.: 221114

AS Tartu Joujaam (1)
Lohkva Kula, Luunja Vald, 62207, Tartu,
Estonia
Tel.: (372) 5056904
Peat Mining Services
N.A.I.C.S.: 212390

AS Tartu Keskkatlamaja (1)
Turu 18, 51014, Tartu, Estonia
Tel.: (372) 7337100
Customer Service Management Services
N.A.I.C.S.: 541613

Barry Danmark ApS (1)
Bragesgade 8b, 2200, Copenhagen, Denmark
Tel.: (45) 89884454
Web Site: https://barry.energy
Electric Power Distr
N.A.I.C.S.: 221122

Ekopartnerit Turku Oy (1)
Ravurinkatu 40, 20380, Turku, Finland
Tel.: (358) 107551557
Web Site: http://www.ekopartnerit.fi
Waste Management Services
N.A.I.C.S.: 562998

Estonia AS Fortum (1)
Bellows 2B, 11415, Tallinn, Estonia
Tel.: (372) 4477210
Web Site: http://www.fortum.ee
Energy Supplier
N.A.I.C.S.: 221122

FB Generation Services B.V. (1)
Claudius Prinsenlaan 128, 4818 CL, Breda,
Netherlands
Tel.: (31) 765244656
Electric Power Generation Services
N.A.I.C.S.: 221118

Fortum BCS Oy (1)
OyKeilaniementie 1, 2150, Espoo, Finland
Tel.: (358) 104 511
Electric Power Distribution Services
N.A.I.C.S.: 221122

Fortum Charge & Drive India Private Limited (1)
The Oberoi Centre Building 11 Level 6 DLF
Cyber City Phase II, Gurgaon, 122002,
India
Tel.: (91) 1244418800
Electric Vehicle Charging Services
N.A.I.C.S.: 926130

Fortum Corporation (1)
10 Presnenskaya Emb Tower B 14th Fl 15
th floor, 123317, Moscow, Russia
Tel.: (7) 495 7884588
Sales Range: $75-99.9 Million
Emp.: 10
Heat Power Generation & Distribution Services
N.A.I.C.S.: 221330
Alexander Chuvaev (Gen Dir)

Fortum Eesti AS (1)
Suur-Joe 52, 80042, Parnu, Estonia
Tel.: (372) 4477222
Web Site: http://www.fortum.ee
Sales Range: $75-99.9 Million
Emp.: 5
Electric Power Generation & Distribution
Services
N.A.I.C.S.: 221118

Fortum Energy LLC (1)
Business Centre Arena Hall Prospekt Do-

brolyubova 16 A 2 4 Floor, 197198, Saint
Petersburg, Russia
Tel.: (7) 812 3367600
Sales Range: $75-99.9 Million
Emp.: 5
Heat Generation & Distribution Services
N.A.I.C.S.: 221330

Fortum FNW Oy (1)
Karhumäenkatu 2, 55120, Imatra, Finland
Tel.: (358) 5 683 55
Electric Power Distribution Services
N.A.I.C.S.: 221122

Fortum Forvaltning AS (1)
BA 2 Centre Bygdoy Alle 2, 0101, Oslo,
Norway
Tel.: (47) 22432990
Heat Supplying Services
N.A.I.C.S.: 221330

Fortum France S.N.C (1)
Paris La Defense Tour Egee 9/11 Allee de
l'Arche, Paris La Defense, 92671, Courbev-
oie, France
Tel.: (33) 170923814
Hydroelectric Power Generation Services
N.A.I.C.S.: 221111

Fortum Heat Naantali Oy (1)
Naantali Power Plant Satamatie 16, 21100,
Naantali, Finland
Tel.: (358) 10 45 42111
Sales Range: $75-99.9 Million
Emp.: 10
Eletric Power Generation Services
N.A.I.C.S.: 221118
Ari Anttila (Mgr-Power Plant)

Fortum India Private Limited (1)
The Oberoi Centre Building No 11 Level 6
DLF Cyber City Complex, Phase 2, Gur-
gaon, 122002, Haryana, India
Tel.: (91) 1244418800
Web Site: https://www.fortum.in
Emp.: 75
Electric Power Distr
N.A.I.C.S.: 221122
Manoj Gupta (VP-Solar)

Fortum Invest LLC (1)
20-B Brodokalmakski Trakt, Chelyabinsk,
454077, Russia
Tel.: (7) 3512596010
Web Site: http://www.fortum.com
Investment Management Service
N.A.I.C.S.: 523999

Fortum Latvia SIA (1)
Rupniecibas Iela 73A, Jelgava, LV-3008,
Latvia
Tel.: (371) 63083381
Electric Power Distr
N.A.I.C.S.: 221122

**Fortum Marketing & Sales Polska
S.A.** (1)
Heweliusza 9, 80-890, Gdansk, Poland
Tel.: (48) 122100000
Electric Power Distr
N.A.I.C.S.: 221122

Fortum Markets AS (1)
Askekroken 11, 0277, Oslo, Norway
Tel.: (47) 21496910
Web Site: http://www.fortum.no
Electricity Production Services
N.A.I.C.S.: 221114

Fortum Markets Oy (1)
Keilaniementie 1, 2150, Espoo,
Finland (100%)
Tel.: (358) 104511
Web Site: http://www.fortum.com
Sales Range: $350-399.9 Million
Emp.: 1,000
Distribution of Petroleum & Natural Gas En-
ergy Solutions
N.A.I.C.S.: 211120

Fortum Meter Lease SNC (1)
46A Ave J F Kennedy, 1855, Luxembourg,
Luxembourg
Tel.: (352) 427 1711
Web Site: http://www.tmf-group.com
Eletric Power Generation Services
N.A.I.C.S.: 221118

**Fortum Network Wroclaw Sp. z
o.o.** (1)

Antoni Slonimskiego 1A, 50-304, Wroclaw,
Poland
Tel.: (48) 785054301
Web Site: http://www.przetargi.fortum.pl
Electric Power Distr
N.A.I.C.S.: 221122
Jozef Augustynow (Mgr-Product Dev & Digi-
talization)

Fortum Nordic AB (1)
Jagmastargatan 2, 115 77, Stockholm,
Sweden
Tel.: (46) 86717000
Web Site: http://www.fortum.se
Emp.: 200
Eletric Power Generation Services
N.A.I.C.S.: 221118

Fortum Nuclear Services Oy (1)
Keilaniementie 1, 2150, Espoo, Finland
Tel.: (358) 104511
Web Site: http://www.fortum.com
Nuclear Power Generation Services
N.A.I.C.S.: 221113

Fortum O&M (UK) Ltd (1)
Grangemouth CHP Plant Utilities Control
Building Boness Road, PO Box 30, Wolver-
ton Mill, Grangemouth, FK3 9XQ, United
Kingdom
Tel.: (44) 1324477636
Web Site: http://www.fortum.com
Sales Range: $50-74.9 Million
Emp.: 10
Crude Petroleum Extraction Services
N.A.I.C.S.: 211120

Fortum Oslo Varme AS (1)
Askekroken 11, 277, Oslo, Norway
Tel.: (47) 22435980
Nuclear Electric Power Generation Services
N.A.I.C.S.: 221113

Fortum Oy (1)
Keilanitmentie 1, 02150, Espoo, Finland
Tel.: (358) 104511
Web Site: http://www.fortum.com
Sales Range: $1-4.9 Billion
Emp.: 3,000
N.A.I.C.S.: 211120

Fortum Petroleum A/S (1)
Strandveien 50, N-1366, Lysaker, Norway
Tel.: (47) 6758 0520
Crude Oil & Gas Production Activities
N.A.I.C.S.: 211120

Fortum Polska Sp. z.o.o. (1)
Ul Postepu 13, 02 676, Warsaw, Poland
Tel.: (48) 225437300
Sales Range: $50-74.9 Million
Emp.: 25
N.A.I.C.S.: 211120

Subsidiary (Domestic):

Fortum Bytom SA (2)
Ul Elektrownia 18, 41-908, Bytom, Poland
Tel.: (48) 32 283 41 00
Heat Generation Services
N.A.I.C.S.: 221330

Fortum Markets Polska S.A. (2)
ul Serdeczna 8, Wysogotowo Tarnowo
Podgorne, 62-081, Przezmierowo,
Poland (100%)
Tel.: (48) 12 210 00 00
Web Site: http://fortum.pl
Natural Gas & Electric Power Distr
N.A.I.C.S.: 221210

Fortum Plock Sp. z.o.o. (2)
ul Harc A Gradowskiego 3a, 09-402, Plock,
Poland
Tel.: (48) 24 36 60 451
Web Site: http://www.fortum.com
Heat Generation Services
N.A.I.C.S.: 221330

Fortum Zabrze SA (2)
ul Wolnosci 416, 41-800, Zabrze, Poland
Tel.: (48) 32271 52 41
Electric Power Generation & Distribution
Services
N.A.I.C.S.: 221118

Fortum Power and Heat Oy (1)
Keilalahdentie 2-4 CD building, 02150, Es-
poo, Finland
Tel.: (358) 104511
Web Site: http://www.fortum

Sales Range: $700-749.9 Million
Emp.: 5,000
Provider of Energy Services, Power & Heat
N.A.I.C.S.: 541690

Subsidiary (Non-US):

AS Fortum Power & Heat (2)
Riga International Airport, Marupes Pagasts,
LV 1053, Riga, Lettland, Latvia
Tel.: (371) 63023446
Sales Range: Less than $1 Million
Emp.: 3
Electric Power Distr
N.A.I.C.S.: 221122

Fortum Power & Heat AB (2)
Jagmaster Gatam No 2, 11577, Stockholm,
Sweden (100%)
Tel.: (46) 86717000
Web Site: http://www.fortum.se
Sales Range: $300-349.9 Million
Emp.: 1,000
N.A.I.C.S.: 211120

Subsidiary (Domestic):

**AB Fortum Varme Holding samagt
med Stockholms stad** (3)
Lidingovagen 115, 115 77, Stockholm, Swe-
den
Tel.: (46) 8 671 70 00
Investment Management Service
N.A.I.C.S.: 523999
Per Langer (Gen Mgr)

Branch (Domestic):

Fortum Power and Heat Oy (2)
Valvomontie 2A, FI-55100, Imatra, Finland
Tel.: (358) 10 45 46111
Web Site: http://www.fortum.fi
Sales Range: $50-74.9 Million
Emp.: 33
Power & Heat Generation Services
N.A.I.C.S.: 221122

Subsidiary (Non-US):

**Fortum Power and Heat Polska Sp.
z.o.o** (2)
ul Antoniego Slonimskiego 1A, 50-304,
Wroclaw, Poland
Tel.: (48) 713405550
Web Site: http://www.fortum.com
Heat Generation & Distribution Services
N.A.I.C.S.: 221330

IVO Energi AB (2)
Biblioteksgatan 29, 2 tr, PO Box 5186,
S-102 44, Stockholm, Sweden
Tel.: (46) 84403700
N.A.I.C.S.: 211120

**Fortum Service Deutschland
GmbH** (1)
Trianelstr 1, 59071, Hamm, Germany
Tel.: (49) 23883010830
Web Site: http://www.fortum.de
Electric Power Distr
N.A.I.C.S.: 221122

Fortum Service Oy (1)
Keilaniementie 2-4 CD building, 00048, Es-
poo, Finland (100%)
Tel.: (358) 104511
Web Site: http://www.fortum.fi
Sales Range: $10-24.9 Million
Emp.: 300
N.A.I.C.S.: 211120

Subsidiary (Domestic):

Johtotec Oy (2)
Rajatorpantie 8 Vantaa, 00048, Fortum,
Finland (100%)
Tel.: (358) 403112222
Web Site: http://www.fortum.com
Crude Petroleum & Natural Gas
N.A.I.C.S.: 211120

Subsidiary (Non-US):

Montivo Kft (2)
MOL RT 1 Sz Ipartelep, 47, 18 Epulet,
2443, Szazhalombatta, Hungary (51%)
Tel.: (36) 23551312
Web Site: http://www.fortum.com
Sales Range: $1-9.9 Million
Emp.: 80
N.A.I.C.S.: 211120

Fortum Small Hydro Holding Oy (1)
Keilaniementie 2-4, 2150, Espoo, Finland
Tel.: (358) 10 4511
Web Site: http://www.fortum.com
Sales Range: $350-399.9 Million
Emp.: 100
Investment Management Service
N.A.I.C.S.: 523999

Fortum Sverige AB (1)
Jagmastargatan 2, 115 77, Stockholm,
Sweden
Tel.: (46) 86717000
Electric Power Distr
N.A.I.C.S.: 221122

Fortum Sweden AB (1)
Jagmastargatan 2, 115 77, Stockholm,
Sweden
Tel.: (46) 8 6717100
Web Site: http://www.fortum.com
Emp.: 500
Electric Power Distribution Services
N.A.I.C.S.: 221122

Subsidiary (Domestic):

**AB Fortum Varme samagt med
Stockholms stad** (2)
Jagmastargatan 2, 11577, Stockholm, Swe-
den
Tel.: (46) 8 671 70 00
Web Site: http://www.fortum.com
Emp.: 500
Eletric Power Generation Services
N.A.I.C.S.: 221118

Fortum 1 AB (2)
Lidingovagen 115, Stockholm, 115 41, Swe-
den
Tel.: (46) 86717100
Eletric Power Generation Services
N.A.I.C.S.: 221118

Fortum AMCO AB (2)
Lidingovagen 115, Stockholm, 115 41, Swe-
den
Tel.: (46) 86717100
Eletric Power Generation Services
N.A.I.C.S.: 221118

Fortum Generation AB (2)
Jamtlandsg 6, Sveg, 842 32, Harjedalen,
Sweden
Tel.: (46) 680 215 00
Eletric Power Generation Services
N.A.I.C.S.: 221118

Fortum Markets AB (2)
Hangovagen 19, 115 77, Stockholm, Swe-
den
Tel.: (46) 86717000
Electric Power Distribution Services
N.A.I.C.S.: 221122

Fortum Produktionsnat AB (2)
Lidingovagen 115, 115 77, Stockholm, Swe-
den
Tel.: (46) 86717000
Web Site: http://www.fortum.se
Emp.: 500
Eletric Power Generation Services
N.A.I.C.S.: 221118
Per Langer (Gen Mgr)

Stockholm Gas AB (2)
Rasundavagen 12, Solna, 169 67, Sweden
Tel.: (46) 771 41 0100
Web Site: http://www.stockholmgas.se
Natural Gas Distribution Services
N.A.I.C.S.: 221210

**Fortum Waste Solutions Norway
AS** (1)
Avd Kirkegata 3, 4006, Stavanger, Norway
Tel.: (47) 90601224
Electric Power Distr
N.A.I.C.S.: 221122

Fortum Waste Solutions Oy (1)
Kuulojankatu 1, 11120, Riihimaki, Finland
Tel.: (358) 107551000
Electric Power Distr
N.A.I.C.S.: 221122

Gota Energi AB (1)
Box 3218, 400 10, Gothenburg, Sweden
Tel.: (46) 20231500
Web Site: http://www.gotaenergi.se
Electric Power Distr
N.A.I.C.S.: 221122

Fortum Oyj—(Continued)

Hafslund Energi AB (1)
Hornsbruksgatan 28 Plan 10, 117 34,
Stockholm, Sweden
Tel.: (46) 101808606
Web Site: http://www.hafslundstrom.no
Electric Power Distr
N.A.I.C.S.: 221122

Kotimaan Energia Oy (1)
Keilalahdentie 2-4, 02150, Espoo, Finland
Tel.: (358) 931581632
Web Site: http://www.kotimaanenergia.fi
Electric Power Distr
N.A.I.C.S.: 221122

Linjebygg Offshore AS (1)
Grandfjaera 32, 6415, Molde,
Norway (100%)
Tel.: (47) 97507000
Web Site: http://www.lbo.no
Sales Range: $50-74.9 Million
Emp.: 45
N.A.I.C.S.: 211120

Mantynummen Lampo Oy (1)
Laurinkatu 48 B, 8100, Lohja, Finland
Tel.: (358) 50 047 1312
Eletric Power Generation Services
N.A.I.C.S.: 221118

Mitt Hjem Norge AS (1)
Kongensgate 10, 3210, Sandefjord, Norway
Tel.: (47) 33458011
Web Site: http://www.mitthjem.as
Furniture Distr
N.A.I.C.S.: 449110

NAPS Systems Oy (1)
Ruosilankuja 4, 00390, Helsinki,
Finland (100%)
Tel.: (358) 207545666
Web Site: http://www.napssolar.com
Sales Range: $50-74.9 Million
Emp.: 30
Solar Power/Wind Power; Joint Venture Between Fortune (69%) & 3i (31%)
N.A.I.C.S.: 221118
Timo Laakso (CEO)

Subsidiary (Non-US):

NAPS Norway A/S (2)
PO Box 12, N-1369, Stabekk, Norway
Tel.: (47) 67105730
N.A.I.C.S.: 211120

NAPS United Kingdom (2)
PO Box 83, Abingdon, OX 14 2TB, Oxon,
United Kingdom (100%)
Tel.: (44) 1235529749
Web Site: http://www.napssystems.com
Sales Range: $50-74.9 Million
Emp.: 1
N.A.I.C.S.: 211120

NCT Middle East (1)
Plot MO 249 Jebel Ali Free Zone, PO Box
170171, Dubai, United Arab
Emirates (100%)
Tel.: (971) 48817771
Web Site: https://www.nctww.com
Sales Range: $50-74.9 Million
Emp.: 32
N.A.I.C.S.: 211120
Jeroen Leenen (CEO & Mng Dir)

PAO Fortum (1)
10 Presnenskaya emb 10 Tower B, 123317,
Moscow, Russia
Tel.: (7) 4957884588
Electric Power Distr
N.A.I.C.S.: 221122

SIA Fortum Jelgava (1)
Pasta iela 47 4 stavs, Jelgava, 3001, Latvia
Tel.: (371) 63023446
Web Site: http://www.fortum.lv
Electric Power Generation & Heat Distribution Services
N.A.I.C.S.: 221118

**Solar One Energy Private
Limited** (1)
Plot no 2 Patel nagar Behind Hotel Golden
Eagle Ajmer Road, Jaipur, 302034, Rajasthan, India
Tel.: (91) 8047635242
Web Site: https://www.solaroneenergy.in
Emp.: 25

Solar Energy Power Generation Services
N.A.I.C.S.: 221114

UAB Fortum Ekosiluma (1)
J Jasinskao 16B, 01112, Vilnius, Lithuania
Tel.: (370) 5 2430044
Web Site: http://www.fortum.lt
Sales Range: $50-74.9 Million
Emp.: 8
Bio Fuel Distr
N.A.I.C.S.: 424720
Rimantas Tenene (Gen Mgr)

UAB Fortum Heat Lietuva (1)
J Jasinskio G 16B, 03163, Vilnius, Lithuania
Tel.: (370) 5 243 0043
Web Site: http://www.fortum.lt
Sales Range: $75-99.9 Million
Emp.: 8
Heat Distribution Services
N.A.I.C.S.: 221330

UAB Fortum Klaipeda (1)
Kretainio G 3 LT, 94100, Klaipeda, Lithuania
Tel.: (370) 46493402
Sales Range: $50-74.9 Million
Emp.: 34
Heat Generation Services
N.A.I.C.S.: 221330
Uozas Doniela (Gen Mgr)

UAB Joniskio Energija (1)
Baznycios g 4, LT-84139, Joniskis, Lithuania
Tel.: (370) 42652293
Web Site: http://www.fortum.lt
Electric Power Distr
N.A.I.C.S.: 221122

UAB Neste Lietuva (1)
P Luksio str 32, LT-08222, Vilnius, Lithuania
Tel.: (370) 52123389
Sales Range: $50-74.9 Million
Emp.: 10
Crude Petroleum Extraction
N.A.I.C.S.: 211120

Uniper SE (1)
Holzstrasse 6, 40221, Dusseldorf,
Germany (73.4%)
Tel.: (49) 211732750
Web Site: https://www.uniper.energy
Rev.: $296,072,739,046
Assets: $131,099,719,404
Liabilities: $126,327,433,628
Net Worth: $4,772,285,776
Earnings: ($20,638,894,885)
Emp.: 6,832
Fiscal Year-end: 12/31/2022
Energy Generation Services
N.A.I.C.S.: 221122
Carlo Beck (Mgr-IR)

Subsidiary (Domestic):

**Energie-Pensions-Management
GmbH** (2)
Tresckowstrasse 5, 30457, Hannover, Germany
Tel.: (49) 5114392722
Web Site: http://www.epm.gmbh
Pension Scheme Services
N.A.I.C.S.: 525110

**Gemeinschaftskraftwerk Irsching
GmbH** (2)
Paarstrasse 30, Vohburg an der Donau,
85088, Pfaffenhofen, Germany
Tel.: (49) 8457750
Electricity & Natural Gas Distr
N.A.I.C.S.: 221118
Marina Haastert (Mng Dir)

Hydropower Evolutions GmbH (2)
Luitpoldstrasse 27, 84034, Landshut, Germany
Tel.: (49) 87196617200
Web Site: http://www.hydropower-
evolutions.com
Emp.: 14,000
Eletric Power Generation Services
N.A.I.C.S.: 221118
Klaus Engels (Mng Dir)

Liqvis GmbH (2)
Huttropstrasse 60, 45138, Essen, Germany
Tel.: (49) 201319377055
Web Site: https://www.liqvis.com
Eletric Power Generation Services
N.A.I.C.S.: 221118

Maik Rensing (Sr Mgr-Sls)

Rhein-Main-Donau AG (2)
Luitpoldstrasse 27, 84034, Landshut,
Germany (77.49%)
Tel.: (49) 87196617401
Web Site: http://www.rmd.de
Sales Range: $100-124.9 Million
Emp.: 150
Operator of Canals & Hydroelectric Power
Stations
N.A.I.C.S.: 221111
Bernhard Fischer (Chm)

Subsidiary (Domestic):

**Mittlere Donau Kraftwerke
Aktiengesellschaft** (3)
Blutenburgstr 20, 80636, Munich, Bayern,
Germany
Tel.: (49) 89 992220
Web Site: http://www.rnd.de
Emp.: 15
Eletric Power Generation Services
N.A.I.C.S.: 221118
Allen Carlson (Gen Mgr)

Subsidiary (Non-US):

Sydkraft AB (2)
Hans Michelsensgatan 2, 211 20, Malmo,
Sweden
Tel.: (46) 771765765
Eletric Power Generation Services
N.A.I.C.S.: 221118
Dahlroth Malin (Dir-Fin)

Sydkraft Forsakring AB (2)
Pulpetgatan 20, 215 37, Malmo, Sweden
Tel.: (46) 771765765
N.A.I.C.S.: 524126

Sydkraft Hydropower AB (2)
Nya Hamngatan 12, 851 24, Sundsvall,
Sweden
Tel.: (46) 771765765
Eletric Power Generation Services
N.A.I.C.S.: 221118

Sydkraft Nuclear Power AB (2)
Pulpetgatan 20, 215 37, Malmo, Sweden
Tel.: (46) 771765765
N.A.I.C.S.: 221113

Sydkraft Thermal Power AB (2)
Flintrenduratan 19 B, 211 24, Malmo, Sweden
Tel.: (46) 771765765
Eletric Power Generation Services
N.A.I.C.S.: 221118

Subsidiary (Domestic):

Uniper Anlagenservice GmbH (2)
Bergmannsgluckstr 41 - 43, 45896, Gelsenkirchen, Germany
Tel.: (49) 2096018432
Web Site:
http://www.anlagenservice.uniper.energy
Eletric Power Generation Services
N.A.I.C.S.: 221118
Michael J. Frank (Mng Dir)

Subsidiary (Non-US):

Uniper Belgium N.V. (2)
Jan Frans Willemsstraat 200, 1800, Vilvoorde, Belgium
Tel.: (32) 27433333
Web Site: http://www.uniper.be
Eletric Power Generation Services
N.A.I.C.S.: 221118

Uniper Benelux N.V. (2)
Capelseweg 400, 3068 AX, Rotterdam,
Netherlands
Tel.: (31) 102895711
N.A.I.C.S.: 221118

Subsidiary (Domestic):

Uniper Energy Sales GmbH (2)
Holzstrasse 6, 40221, Dusseldorf, Germany
Tel.: (49) 211732750
Web Site: http://www.uniper-sales.com
Energy Equipment Retailer
N.A.I.C.S.: 444230

Subsidiary (Non-US):

**Uniper Energy Southern Africa (Pty)
Ltd.** (2)

9th Floor Convention Towers Heerengracht
Street Foreshore, Cape Town, 8001, South
Africa
Tel.: (27) 212005980
Eletric Power Generation Services
N.A.I.C.S.: 221118
Harald Schaaf (CEO)

Uniper Technologies B.V. (2)
Capelseweg 400, 3068 AX, Rotterdam,
Netherlands
Tel.: (31) 102895534
Energy Generation Services
N.A.I.C.S.: 221122

Subsidiary (Domestic):

Uniper Technologies GmbH (2)
Alexander-von-Humboldt Strasse 1, 45896,
Gelsenkirchen, Germany
Tel.: (49) 20960110
Energy Generation Services
N.A.I.C.S.: 221122

Subsidiary (Non-US):

Uniper Technologies Limited (2)
Technology Centre Ratcliffe-on-Soar, Nottingham, NG11 0EE, United Kingdom
Tel.: (44) 1159362192
Energy Generation Services
N.A.I.C.S.: 221122

Subsidiary (Domestic):

Uniper Warme GmbH (2)
Bergmannsgluckstrasse 40, 45896, Gelsenkirchen, Germany
Tel.: (49) 2096015071
Web Site: https://www.uniper.energy
N.A.I.C.S.: 221210
Nikola Feldmann (Mng Dir)

Subsidiary (Non-US):

Unipro PJSC (2)
Energostroiteley Street Building 23 Building
34, Khanty-Mansi Autonomous Okrug - Yugra, Surgut, 628406, Russia
Tel.: (7) 4955453838
Web Site: https://www.unipro.energy
Rev.: $1,187,101,860
Assets: $1,716,728,008
Liabilities: $253,171,169
Net Worth: $1,463,556,839
Earnings: $110,896,557
Emp.: 4,348
Fiscal Year-end: 12/31/2021
Electric Power Generation & Distribution
Services
N.A.I.C.S.: 221118
Maxim Shirokov (Chm-Mgmt Bd & CEO)

FORTUNA MINING CORP.
200 Burrard Street Suite 650, Vancouver, V6C 3L6, BC, Canada
Tel.: (604) 484-4085 BC
Web Site: https://fortunamining.com
Year Founded: 1990
FSM—(NYSE)
Rev.: $681,491,000
Assets: $1,876,224,000
Liabilities: $587,528,000
Net Worth: $1,288,696,000
Earnings: ($135,906,000)
Emp.: 2,440
Fiscal Year-end: 12/31/22
Silver & Other Precious Metal Ore
Exploration & Mining Services
N.A.I.C.S.: 212220
Mario D. Szotlender (Co-Founder)

Subsidiaries:

Chesser Resources Limited (1)
Suite 3 Level 7 100 Edward St, Brisbane,
4000, QLD, Australia
Tel.: (61) 738542387
Web Site:
http://www.chesserresources.com.au
Rev.: $13,459
Assets: $15,977,437
Liabilities: $431,294
Net Worth: $15,546,143
Earnings: ($2,103,821)
Fiscal Year-end: 06/30/2021
Minerals Exploration
N.A.I.C.S.: 213115

Stephen Kelly *(CFO & Sec)*

Subsidiary (Non-US):

Chesser Arama ve Madencilik Limited Sirketi (2)
Sehit Ersan Cad No 4/17, Cankaya, Ankara, Turkiye
Tel.: (90) 3124666042
Web Site: http://www.chesserresources.com
Sales Range: $50-74.9 Million
Emp.: 6
Copper Ore Mining Services
N.A.I.C.S.: 212230

Compania Minera Cuzcatlan S.A. (1)
Carretera 175 Oaxaca-Huatulco, San Jose del Progreso, 68050, Oaxaca, Mexico
Tel.: (52) 9515020010
Web Site: https://mineracuzcatlan.com
Sales Range: $100-124.9 Million
Emp.: 160
Gold & Silver Exploration Services
N.A.I.C.S.: 213115

Mansfield Minera S.A. (1)
Piso 2 Av Reyes Catolicos, 1224, Salta, Argentina
Tel.: (54) 387 398 0904
Mining Services
N.A.I.C.S.: 212290

Minera Bateas S.A.C. (1)
Ave Los Libertadores No 757, San Isidro, Lima, Peru
Tel.: (51) 16166060
Metal Exploration Services
N.A.I.C.S.: 213114

Roxgold Inc. (1)
360 Bay Street Suite 500, Toronto, M5H 2V6, ON, Canada
Tel.: (416) 203-6401
Web Site: http://www.roxgold.com
Rev.: $181,978,000
Assets: $291,683,000
Liabilities: $110,252,000
Net Worth: $181,431,000
Earnings: $5,663,000
Emp.: 460
Fiscal Year-end: 12/31/2019
Gold Exploration Services
N.A.I.C.S.: 212220
Eric Pick *(VP-Corp Dev)*

Roxgold Sango S.A. (1)
Deux Plateaux Vallons 6th tranche Rue des jardins, BP 1967, Seguela, Abidjan, Cote d'Ivoire
Tel.: (225) 272 259 9874
Mining Services
N.A.I.C.S.: 212290

FORTUNA SAZKOVA KANCELAR, A.S.
Vodickova 30, 110 00, Prague, Czech Republic
Tel.: (420) 267218111
Web Site: http://www.ifortuna.eu
Year Founded: 1990
Sales Range: $50-74.9 Million
Emp.: 1,700
Gambling & Other Amusement Operations
N.A.I.C.S.: 713290
Martin Stefunko *(CEO)*

FORTUNE ASIA GROUP LTD
Suite 525 377 Kent Street, Sydney, 2000, NSW, Australia
Tel.: (61) 2 80245932   AU
Web Site: http://www.ergau.com
Year Founded: 2012
Assets: $2,158,207
Liabilities: $517,029
Net Worth: $1,641,178
Earnings: ($268,663)
Fiscal Year-end: 12/31/18
Copper & Gold Mining
N.A.I.C.S.: 212230
Zhang Meilan *(CFO)*

FORTUNE ELECTRIC CO., LTD.

No 10 Jilin Rd, Zhongli Dist, Taoyuan, 32063, Taiwan
Tel.: (886) 34526111
Web Site: https://www.fortune.com.tw
Year Founded: 1969
1519—(TAI)
Rev.: $454,551,799
Assets: $498,602,552
Liabilities: $298,053,391
Net Worth: $200,549,160
Earnings: $83,775,954
Emp.: 720
Fiscal Year-end: 12/31/23
Electronic Products Mfr
N.A.I.C.S.: 423610
H. L. Hsu *(Founder)*

Subsidiaries:

Fortune Electric (Wuhan) Ltd. (1)
No 2832 Dong Si Who Avenue, Wuhan, 430040, China
Tel.: (86) 278 324 0089
Web Site: https://www.whfortune.com.cn
Oil-Immersed Power Transformer System Mfr
N.A.I.C.S.: 335311

Fortune Electric America Inc. (1)
3525 Lomita Blvd Ste 100, Torrance, CA 90505
Power Generation Services
N.A.I.C.S.: 221118

Fortune Electric Co., Ltd. - North American Division (1)
1965 Shenango Valley Fwy, Hermitage, PA 16148
Tel.: (724) 346-2722
Web Site: http://www.fortune.com.tw
Sales Range: $25-49.9 Million
Emp.: 7
Switchgear & Transformers Distr
N.A.I.C.S.: 423690

Fortune Electric Co., Ltd. - Power Division (1)
No 33 Chin Chian Road Section 2 Kuan Yin Industrial Zone, Taoyuan, 328, Taiwan
Tel.: (886) 34836155
Sales Range: $50-74.9 Million
Emp.: 200
Power Transformer Mfr
N.A.I.C.S.: 335311

Fortune Electric Co., Ltd. - Switchgear Division (1)
No 55 Chung Cheng Road, Kuan Yin, Taoyuan, 32843, ROC, Taiwan
Tel.: (886) 34736957
Web Site: http://www.fortune.com.tw
Switchgear Mfr
N.A.I.C.S.: 335313

Fortune Electric Extra High Voltage Co., Ltd. (1)
No 500 Nanheng 1st Rd, Wuqi Dist, Taichung, 435, Taiwan
Tel.: (886) 426578118
Engineeering Services
N.A.I.C.S.: 541330

FORTUNE FOUNTAIN (BEIJING) HOLDING GROUP CO., LTD.
33/F Silver Tower No 2 East Third Ring North Road, Chaoyang District, Beijing, 100027, China
Tel.: (86) 10 5780 7801   CN
Web Site:
http://www.fortunefountaincap.com
Year Founded: 2011
Sales Range: Less than $1 Million
Holding Company; Financial & Investment Services
N.A.I.C.S.: 551112

Subsidiaries:

Baccarat SA (1)
20 rue des Cristalleries, 54120, Baccarat, France   (100%)
Tel.: (33) 140221414
Web Site: http://www.baccarat.fr
Crystal Designer Mfr & Distr

N.A.I.C.S.: 334419
Herve Martin *(Dir-Publication)*

Holding (US):

Baccarat, Inc. (2)
36 Mayfield Ave, Edison, NJ 08837-3821
Tel.: (732) 225-9600
Web Site: http://us.baccarat.com
Home Furnishings Importer & Distr
N.A.I.C.S.: 449129

Beijing Gainfull Wealth Investment Management Co., Ltd. (1)
Room 1916 19th Floor Nanyin Bldg No 2 Eastern 3rd Ring North, Chaoyang District, Beijing, 100027, China
Tel.: (86) 10 5676 3260
Web Site: http://www.gainfullcapital.com
Wealth Management Services
N.A.I.C.S.: 523940
Qiwen Cao *(Gen Mgr)*

Subsidiary (Domestic):

Shanghai Fujin Investment Management Co., Ltd. (2)
33rd Floor Future Assets Bldg No 166 Lujiazui Ring Road, Pudong New District, Shanghai, 200210, China
Tel.: (86) 21 6106 0800
Web Site: http://www.gainfullcapital.com
Wealth management Services
N.A.I.C.S.: 523940
Wenyue Yang *(Gen Mgr)*

FORTUNE GRAPHITE INC.
260 Queens Quay West Suite 3104, Toronto, M5J 2N3, ON, Canada
Tel.: (416) 367-8240
Web Site:
http://www.fortunegraphite.com
Mineral Mining Services
N.A.I.C.S.: 212290
Claus G. J. Wagner-Bartak *(Pres & CEO)*

FORTUNE INFORMATION SYSTEMS CORP.
No 25 Ln 78 Xing ai Rd Neihu Dist, Taipei, 11494, Taiwan
Tel.: (886) 227935566
Web Site: https://www.fis.com.tw
2468—(TAI)
Rev.: $76,469,829
Assets: $66,013,209
Liabilities: $25,671,113
Net Worth: $40,342,096
Earnings: $2,563,131
Emp.: 366
Fiscal Year-end: 12/31/23
Notebook Computers Mfr
N.A.I.C.S.: 334111
Yu-Hua Tang *(Pres)*

Subsidiaries:

Fortune Information System International Co., Ltd. (1)
Room 1804 Westlands Centre 20 Westlands Road, Quarry Bay, Hong Kong, China (Hong Kong)
Tel.: (852) 28119662
Web Site: https://www.fis.com.hk
Sales Range: $25-49.9 Million
Emp.: 20
Scanners & Cameras Distr
N.A.I.C.S.: 449210

Fortune Technology System Corp. (1)
4F No 25 Lane 78 Xingai Road, Neihu District, Taipei, 11494, Taiwan
Tel.: (886) 287920088
Web Site: https://ftsc.com.tw
Information Technology Services
N.A.I.C.S.: 541519

SBAS (HK) Ltd. (1)
Unit 1804 Westlands Centre 20 Westlands Road, Quarry Bay, China (Hong Kong)
Tel.: (852) 28119662
Web Site: https://www.spss.com.hk
Software Development Services
N.A.I.C.S.: 541511

Shanghai WorldTrend Integrated Technologies Inc. (1)
12F No 6555 Hu-Ming Road, Ming-Shin District, Shanghai, 201100, China
Tel.: (86) 2164146050
Web Site: http://www.fis.com.cn
Computer Peripheral Equipment Distr
N.A.I.C.S.: 423430

FORTUNE INTERNATIONAL LIMITED
Community Centre G-4, Naraina Vihar, New Delhi, 110 028, India
Tel.: (91) 1125774212   In
Web Site:
http://www.fortuneinternational.in
Year Founded: 1981
530213—(BOM)
Rev.: $1,870
Assets: $4,141,418
Liabilities: $55,728
Net Worth: $4,085,690
Earnings: ($53,138)
Fiscal Year-end: 03/31/23
Security Brokerage Services
N.A.I.C.S.: 523150
Nivedan Bharadwaj *(Mng Dir)*

FORTUNE JOY INTERNATIONAL ACQUISITION CORP.
1503 Zhongzhou Building Jintian Road, Futian District, Shenzhen, Guangdong, China
Tel.: (86) 75583207846   Ky
Year Founded: 2021
Investment Services
N.A.I.C.S.: 523999
Long Chen *(Chm & CEO)*

FORTUNE MANAGEMENT INC.
c/o FORTUNE Services AG Bahnhofstrasse 10, PO Box 324, 6301, Zug, Switzerland
Tel.: (41) 417271040
Web Site: http://www.fortune-management.com
Year Founded: 1977
Sales Range: $1-9.9 Million
Investment Management Service
N.A.I.C.S.: 523999
Rene Mueller *(CEO & Member-Mgmt Bd)*

FORTUNE MINERALS LIMITED
617 Wellington Street, London, N6A 3R6, ON, Canada
Tel.: (519) 858-8188   ON
Web Site:
https://www.fortuneminerals.com
Year Founded: 1988
FTMDF—(OTCQB)
Rev.: $32,257
Assets: $58,780,890
Liabilities: $8,453,349
Net Worth: $50,327,541
Earnings: ($2,061,552)
Emp.: 6
Fiscal Year-end: 12/31/19
Metal Mining & Exploration
N.A.I.C.S.: 212290
Robin Ellis Goad *(Pres & CEO)*

Subsidiaries:

Fortune Coal Limited (1)
148 Fullarton St Ste 1600, London, N6A 5P3, ON, Canada
Tel.: (519) 858-8188
Web Site: http://www.fortuneminerals.com
Sales Range: $50-74.9 Million
Emp.: 20
Coal Mining Services
N.A.I.C.S.: 212115

Fortune Minerals NWT Inc. (1)
148 Fullarton St Ste 1600, London, N6A 5P3, ON, Canada
Tel.: (519) 858-8188
Web Site: http://www.fortuneminerals.com

Fortune Minerals Limited—(Continued)

Sales Range: $50-74.9 Million
Emp.: 20
Mineral Mining Services
N.A.I.C.S.: 212390

FORTUNE NG FUNG FOOD (HEBEI) CO., LTD.
No 963 Jingyu Street Yanjiao High-tech Park, Langfang, 065201, Hebei, China
Tel.: (86) 1061595607
Web Site: http://www.fucheng.net
Year Founded: 1998
600965—(SHG)
Rev.: $150,774,254
Assets: $349,231,367
Liabilities: $46,511,656
Net Worth: $302,719,711
Earnings: $15,066,450
Emp.: 2,399
Fiscal Year-end: 12/31/22
Beef Cattle Raising & Slaughtering Process
N.A.I.C.S.: 311611
Liang Li (Chm & Gen Mgr)

FORTUNE OIL LIMITED
Nova South 4th Floor 160 Victoria Street, London, SW1E 5LB, United Kingdom
Tel.: (44) 2079734200   UK
Web Site: http://www.fortune-oil.com
Sales Range: $600-649.9 Million
Emp.: 568
Oil & Gas Distr
N.A.I.C.S.: 213112
Daniel Tat Jung Chiu (Chm)

FORTUNE ORIENTAL COMPANY LIMITED
No 6 Ln 54 ZhongSheng Rd, Xindian Dist, Taipei, 231, Taiwan
Tel.: (886) 289112000
Web Site: https://www.focl.com.tw
2491—(TAI)
Rev.: $6,296,641
Assets: $47,403,609
Liabilities: $6,080,611
Net Worth: $41,322,998
Earnings: $1,964,093
Fiscal Year-end: 12/31/23
Storage Disc Mfr & Distr
N.A.I.C.S.: 334112
Bihua Chen (Chm & Gen Mgr)

Subsidiaries:

Chip Goal Electronics Corp.   (1)
10F-8 No 81 Shueili Rd, Hsinchu, 300, Taiwan
Tel.: (886) 35169219
Web Site: https://www.chipgoal.com
Ambient Light Sensor Mfr & Distr
N.A.I.C.S.: 335131

SL LINK CO.,Ltd.   (1)
12F No 287 Sec 2 Kwang-Fu Rd, East Dist, Hsinchu, 30071, Taiwan
Tel.: (886) 35163636
Web Site: https://www.sl-link.com.tw
Semiconductor Device Mfr & Distr
N.A.I.C.S.: 334413

Toll Microelectronics Co., Ltd.   (1)
No 72 Second Sci-Tech Road, B201 zero One Plaza Software Park High-tech Zone, Xi'an, China
Tel.: (86) 2987684439
Web Site: https://en.toll-semi.com
Electronic Device Mfr & Distr
N.A.I.C.S.: 334111

FORTUNE PARTS INDUSTRY PUBLIC COMPANY LIMITED
11/22 Moo 20 Nimitmai Road, Lamlukka, Pathumthani, 12150, Thailand
Tel.: (66) 29934971

Web Site:
https://www.fpiautoparts.com
Year Founded: 1991
FPI—(THA)
Rev.: $73,359,304
Assets: $103,570,103
Liabilities: $36,981,876
Net Worth: $66,588,226
Earnings: $10,918,906
Emp.: 495
Fiscal Year-end: 12/31/23
Automotive Parts Mfr & Distr
N.A.I.C.S.: 336390
Raweewan Mathong (Pres)

Subsidiaries:

Fpi Auto Parts India Private
Limited   (1)
Kh No 673 674 676 677 678 673/2274,, Vill Gugal kota Shahjahanpur Dist, Neemrana, 301706, Rajasthan, India
Tel.: (91) 9818149603
Web Site: https://india.fpiautoparts.com
Automotive Components Mfr
N.A.I.C.S.: 332119

FORTUNE REAL ESTATE INVESTMENT TRUST
5 Temasek Boulevard 12-01 Suntec Tower Five, Singapore, 038985, Singapore
Tel.: (65) 68359232   SG
Web Site: https://www.fortunereit.com
Year Founded: 2003
0778—(HKG)
Rev.: $228,623,703
Assets: $5,057,965,718
Liabilities: $1,463,252,685
Net Worth: $3,594,713,033
Earnings: ($123,604,817)
Emp.: 574
Fiscal Year-end: 12/31/23
Investment Holding Company
N.A.I.C.S.: 551114
Justina Yu Chiu (CEO)

FORTUNE SECURITIES CORPORATION
CR 3 Building 4 Floor 109 Tonciendit District 7, Ho Chi Minh City, Vietnam
Tel.: (84) 854135479
Web Site: http://www.phs.vn
Year Founded: 2006
Emp.: 50
Investment Banking & Securities Brokerage Services
N.A.I.C.S.: 523150
Albert K. Ting (Chm)

FORTUNE SHOES LTD.
Moon Island Suite C-3 Plot 34 36 Road 08 Block E Niketon Gulshan-1, Dhaka, 1212, Bangladesh
Tel.: (880) 29851132
Web Site:
https://www.fortuneshoesbd.com
Year Founded: 2010
FORTUNE—(DHA)
Rev.: $19,777,626
Assets: $32,904,869
Liabilities: $5,942,998
Net Worth: $26,961,870
Earnings: $4,339,528
Emp.: 1,830
Fiscal Year-end: 06/30/22
Footwear Product Mfr
N.A.I.C.S.: 316210
Mizanur Rahman (Chm)

FORTUNE SUN (CHINA) HOLDINGS LIMITED
16/F Sun Life Tower The Gateway Harbour City 21 Canton Road, Tsim Sha Tsui, Kowloon, China (Hong Kong)
Tel.: (852) 28937866

Web Site: http://www.fortune-sun.com
0352—(HKG)
Rev.: $1,674,270
Assets: $5,153,803
Liabilities: $2,290,907
Net Worth: $2,862,896
Earnings: ($2,001,964)
Emp.: 80
Fiscal Year-end: 12/31/22
Property Consultancy & Agency Services Provider
N.A.I.C.S.: 525920
Chien Ju Lin (Co-Founder)

Subsidiaries:

Shanghai Fu Yang Property Consultant Co., Limited   (1)
9/F Oriental Building 1500 Century Avenue, Pudong New Area, Shanghai, 200120, China
Tel.: (86) 2168419699
Web Site: http://www.fortune-sun.com
Emp.: 100
Real Estate Consulting Service
N.A.I.C.S.: 531210
Yungang Wu (Reg Gen Mgr)

FORTUNE VACATION TRAVEL LTD.
21-2-6-1 JinHaiHua YuanDongYuan, XiGangQu, Dalian, 116000, LiaoNing, China
Tel.: (86) 13050500108   NV
Year Founded: 2010
Travel Services
N.A.I.C.S.: 561599
Zhihua Zhang (Pres, Treas & Sec)

FORTUNE VALLEY TREASURES, INC.
13th Floor Building B1 Wisdom Plaza Qiaoxiang Road, Nanshan District, Shenzhen, 518000, Guangdong, China
Tel.: (86) 75586961405   NV
Web Site: https://www.fvti.show
Year Founded: 2014
FVTI—(OTCIQ)
Rev.: $9,234,079
Assets: $9,287,942
Liabilities: $2,788,033
Net Worth: $6,499,909
Earnings: ($1,942,723)
Emp.: 63
Fiscal Year-end: 12/31/22
Data Processing Services
N.A.I.C.S.: 518210
Hongwei Ye (Gen Mgr-Supply Chain)

FORTUS SA
Blv Poitiers 10, Iasi, 700671, Romania
Tel.: (40) 232 222023
Web Site: http://www.fortus-iasi.ro
Sales Range: $1-9.9 Million
Emp.: 664
Metallurgy Product Mfr
N.A.I.C.S.: 332117
Gheorghe Chisca (Exec Dir)

FORU WORLDWIDE INC.
10/F Unit A Jinyu Jiahua Mansion No 9 Shangdi 3rd Street, Haidian District, Beijing, 100085, China
Tel.: (86) 10 8266 5652   Ky
Year Founded: 2014
FOYO—(NASDAQ)
Rev.: $546,334,910
Assets: $236,629,321
Liabilities: $468,003,233
Net Worth: ($231,373,912)
Earnings: ($17,554,649)
Emp.: 644
Fiscal Year-end: 12/31/20
Freight Transportation Services
N.A.I.C.S.: 488510

Dandan Shan (Founder, Chm & CEO)

FORUCOM REIT
Stefan Peshev 87, 5400, Sevlievo, 5400, Bulgaria
Tel.: (359) 675660661
Web Site: https://www.forucom-imoti.com
FFI—(BUL)
Sales Range: Less than $1 Million
Real Estate Investment Services
N.A.I.C.S.: 531210

FORUM - PLASMAN A.D.
Trg Slobode 2, Novi Sad, Serbia
Tel.: (381) 21 639 8079
Year Founded: 1990
Sales Range: Less than $1 Million
Grocery Store Operator
N.A.I.C.S.: 445110

FORUM ENERGY METALS CORP.
Suite 615 800 West Pender Street, Vancouver, V6C 2V6, BC, Canada
Tel.: (604) 630-1585   BC
Web Site:
https://www.forumenergymetals.com
Year Founded: 1987
FDCFF—(OTCQB)
Rev.: $33,234
Assets: $2,604,334
Liabilities: $960,691
Net Worth: $1,643,643
Earnings: ($4,051,192)
Emp.: 2
Fiscal Year-end: 11/30/23
Uranium Exploration & Development Services
N.A.I.C.S.: 212290
Richard J. Mazur (Pres & CEO)

FORUM ENGINEERING, INC.
Okura Prestige Tower 15F 2-10-4 Toranomon, Minato-ku, Tokyo, 105-0001, Japan
Tel.: (81) 335605505
Web Site: https://www.forumeng.co.jp
Year Founded: 1981
7088—(TKS)
Rev.: $206,754,190
Assets: $118,437,980
Liabilities: $30,597,690
Net Worth: $87,840,290
Earnings: $13,477,790
Emp.: 4,662
Fiscal Year-end: 03/31/24
Staffing Services
N.A.I.C.S.: 561311
Masahiro Takeuchi (Mng Dir)

FORUM PACIFIC INC.
35th Floor One Corporate Center Julia Vargas Ave, Corner Meralco Ave Ortigas Center, Pasig, 1605, Philippines
Tel.: (63) 27067888
Web Site:
https://www.forumpacific.com
Year Founded: 1993
FPI—(PHI)
Rev.: $104,104
Assets: $6,181,536
Liabilities: $147,000
Net Worth: $6,034,536
Earnings: $46,353
Fiscal Year-end: 12/31/23
Petroleum Product Mfr
N.A.I.C.S.: 324199

FORUS S.A.
Avda Departamental N 01053 La Florida, Santiago, Chile
Tel.: (56) 229233000
Web Site: https://www.forus.cl

Year Founded: 1980
Online Shopping Services
N.A.I.C.S.: 339113
Seabstian Swett *(CEO)*

FORVAL CORPORATION
14F Aoyama Oval Bldg 5-52-2 Jingu-
mae, Shibuya-ku, Tokyo, 150-0001,
Japan
Tel.: (81) 334981541
Web Site: https://www.forval.co.jp
Year Founded: 1980
8275—(TKS)
Rev.: $498,858,800
Assets: $314,580,640
Liabilities: $175,459,680
Net Worth: $139,120,960
Earnings: $17,772,480
Emp.: 1,966
Fiscal Year-end: 03/31/22
Telecommunications Equipment De-
velopment & Sales
N.A.I.C.S.: 517810
Tatsuya Yuki *(Mng Dir)*

Subsidiaries:

Busica Ltd.   **(1)**
4-25-7 Taito TX Satake Building 5F, Taito-
ku, Tokyo, 110-0016, Japan
Tel.: (81) 35 812 4361
Web Site: https://www.busica.co.jp
Industry Machinery Mfr
N.A.I.C.S.: 333248

Forval Telecom, Inc.   **(1)**
HitotsubashiSI Bldg 2F 3-26 Kanda-
Nishikicho, Chiyoda-ku, Tokyo, 101-0054,
Japan
Tel.: (81) 332331301
Web Site: http://www.forvaltel.co.jp
Rev.: $152,790,150
Assets: $68,076,390
Liabilities: $48,748,750
Net Worth: $19,327,640
Earnings: $4,957,500
Emp.: 291
Fiscal Year-end: 03/31/2024
Telecommunication Carrier Services
N.A.I.C.S.: 517111

FORVAL REALSTRAIGHT INC.
3-23-2 Kanda Jinbocho, Chiyoda-ku,
Tokyo, 101 0051, Japan
Tel.: (81) 368261500
Web Site:
https://www.realstraight.co.jp
Year Founded: 1995
94230—(TKS)
Rev.: $16,959,360
Assets: $6,776,000
Liabilities: $3,097,600
Net Worth: $3,678,400
Earnings: $590,480
Fiscal Year-end: 03/31/20
Consulting Services
N.A.I.C.S.: 541618
Koji Yoshida *(Pres & Chm)*

FORVIA SE
23-27 Avenue des Champs Pierreux,
92000, Nanterre, Cedex, France
Tel.: (33) 172367000
Web Site: https://www.faurecia.com
Year Founded: 1997
FURCF—(OTCIQ)
Rev.: $19,898,008,438
Assets: $19,222,172,928
Liabilities: $14,225,581,580
Net Worth: $4,996,591,348
Earnings: $744,370,942
Emp.: 115,496
Fiscal Year-end: 12/31/19
Car Seats, Interior Systems, Front
End Modules & Exhaust Systems Mfr
N.A.I.C.S.: 336390
Christophe Schmitt *(Exec VP-Ops)*

Subsidiaries:

Clarion Co., Ltd.   **(1)**

7-2 Shintoshin, Chuo-ku, Saitama, 330-
0081, Japan   **(63.77%)**
Tel.: (81) 486013700
Web Site: http://www.clarion.com
Sales Range: $1-4.9 Billion
Holding Company; Motor Vehicle Audio,
Navigation System & Other Electronics
Products Mfr
N.A.I.C.S.: 334310
Hidetoshi Kawamoto *(Chm)*

Subsidiary (Non-US):

Clarion (G.B.) Ltd.   **(2)**
Unit 1 Marshall Rd Hill Mead, Swindon,
SN5 5YU, United Kingdom   **(100%)**
Tel.: (44) 1793870400
Web Site: http://www.clarion.co.uk
Sales Range: $25-49.9 Million
Emp.: 43
Mfr of In-Vehicle Infotainment Technologies
& Safety Systems
N.A.I.C.S.: 334310

Clarion (HK) Industries Co., Ltd   **(2)**
Rm 12 7th Fl Tower 1 Harbour Ctr, 1 Hok
Cheung St Hung Horn, Kowloon, China
(Hong Kong)   **(100%)**
Tel.: (852) 23031395
Web Site: http://www.clarion.com.hk
Sales Range: $25-49.9 Million
Emp.: 100
N.A.I.C.S.: 334310

Clarion (Malaysia) Sdn. Bhd.   **(2)**
Phase 3 Free Industrial Zone, 11900,
Bayan Lepas, Pinang, Malaysia   **(45%)**
Tel.: (60) 46148400
Web Site: http://www.clarion.com.my
Sales Range: $75-99.9 Million
Emp.: 500
Mfr of In-Vehicle Infotainment Technologies
& Safety Systems
N.A.I.C.S.: 334310
Khoo Khayseang *(Dir-Ops)*

Clarion (Taiwan) Manufacturing Co.,
Ltd.   **(2)**
5F #69-8 Sec 2 Chung Tsun East Road,
Tamsui, Taipei, Hsien, Taiwan
Tel.: (886) 228091333
Web Site: http://clarion.com
Mfr of In-Vehicle Infotainment Technologies
& Safety Systems
N.A.I.C.S.: 334310

Clarion Asia Pte. Ltd.   **(2)**
Performance Ctr, 315 Alexandra Rd 04 03,
Singapore, 159944, Singapore   **(100%)**
Tel.: (65) 64755233
Web Site: http://www.clarion.com.sg
Sales Range: $25-49.9 Million
Emp.: 12
Mfr of In-Vehicle Infotainment Technologies
& Safety Systems
N.A.I.C.S.: 334310

Clarion Australia Pty. Ltd.   **(2)**
2/11-13 Lakewood Blvd, Braeside, 3195,
VIC, Australia   **(100%)**
Tel.: (61) 385581115
Web Site: http://www.clarion.com.au
Sales Range: $25-49.9 Million
Emp.: 30
Mfr of In-Vehicle Infotainment Technologies
& Safety Systems
N.A.I.C.S.: 334310
Kenichiro Yashida *(Mng Dir)*

Clarion Canada, Inc.   **(2)**
2239 Winston Pk Dr, Oakville, L6H 5R1,
ON, Canada   **(100%)**
Tel.: (905) 829-4600
Web Site: http://www.clarion.com
Sales Range: $25-49.9 Million
Emp.: 30
Mfr of Car Radios
N.A.I.C.S.: 517112
Hiro Murakami *(Pres)*

Subsidiary (US):

Clarion Corporation of America   **(2)**
661 W Redondo Beach Blvd, Gardena, CA
90247
Tel.: (310) 327-9100
Web Site: http://www.clarion.com
Rev.: $4,100,000
Emp.: 250

Mfr of Car Stereos, Radios, Citizens Band
Radios, Accessories, Cellular Phones &
Video Monitors for Vehicles
N.A.I.C.S.: 423620
Allen H. Gharapetian *(VP-Mktg)*

Branch (Domestic):

Clarion Corp.   **(3)**
4000 Monroe Rd, Charlotte, NC 28205-
7706
Tel.: (704) 331-7000
Web Site: http://www.clarion.com
Sales Range: $450-499.9 Million
Emp.: 400
N.A.I.C.S.: 325412
Ken Golder *(Pres & CEO)*

Subsidiary (Non-US):

Clarion Europa GmbH   **(2)**
Hessenring 19-21, 64546, Morfelden,
64546, Walldorf, Germany
Tel.: (49) 61059770
Web Site: http://www.clarion-europa.com
Sales Range: $25-49.9 Million
Emp.: 30
Audio Electronics Distr
N.A.I.C.S.: 423690
Dieter Koch *(Mgr)*

Clarion Europe S.A.S.   **(2)**
Le Pre a Varois, Route de Pompey, 54670,
Custines, France   **(100%)**
Tel.: (33) 383494400
Web Site: http://www.clarion.com
Sales Range: $25-49.9 Million
Emp.: 100
Car Video, Video & Navigation System Mfr
& Whslr
N.A.I.C.S.: 334310
Gilles Bailly *(Mng Dir)*

Clarion Hungary Electronics Kft   **(2)**
Jaszberenyi Ut 116, H 2760, Nagykata,
Hungary
Tel.: (36) 29641100
N.A.I.C.S.: 334310

Subsidiary (US):

Clarion Manufacturing Corporation of
America   **(2)**
237 Beaver Rd, Walton, KY
41094-8231   **(100%)**
Tel.: (859) 485-6600
Web Site: http://www.clarion.com
Sales Range: $25-49.9 Million
Emp.: 65
N.A.I.C.S.: 334310
Jeff Lehnheart *(VP-Ops)*

Clarion Sales Corporation   **(2)**
661 W Redondo Beach Blvd, Gardena, CA
90247-4201
Tel.: (310) 327-9100
Web Site: http://www.clarion.com
Distribution of Car Stereos
N.A.I.C.S.: 423620

Subsidiary (Non-US):

Dongguan Clarion Orient Electronics
Co., Ltd.   **(2)**
Junda Industrial Zone Dongkeng Industrial
Road, Dongkeng Town, Dongguan, 523455,
Guangdong, China   **(100%)**
Tel.: (86) 769 3385 611
Web Site: http://www.clarion.com
Sales Range: $700-749.9 Million
Emp.: 2,600
N.A.I.C.S.: 334310

Electronica Clarion, S.A. de C.V.   **(2)**
Camino a Santa Teresa 1257, Col del Jar-
dines del Pedregal, Mexico, CP 01900, DF,
Mexico
Tel.: (52) 5554812400
Web Site: http://www.clarion.com
Sales Range: $25-49.9 Million
Emp.: 20
Electric Equipment Mfr
N.A.I.C.S.: 334310

Plant (Domestic):

Electronica Clarion, S.A. de C.V.   **(3)**
Av 3 Calle 9 Zona Industrial, 76800, San
Juan del Rio, Queretaro, Mexico   **(100%)**
Tel.: (52) 4272718800

Sales Range: $25-49.9 Million
Emp.: 15
Electric Equipment Mfr
N.A.I.C.S.: 334310
Gilberto Figueroa *(Gen Mgr)*

Subsidiary (US):

Ungo Security Corporation   **(2)**
26427 Research Rd, Hayward, CA 94545
Tel.: (310) 327-9100
N.A.I.C.S.: 334310

Subsidiary (Non-US):

Xiamen Clarion Electrical Enterprise
Co., Ltd.   **(2)**
40 Guanri Road 6 F Stage II Software Park
Cheng Dong Industrial Area, Dong-An Dis-
trict, Xiamen, 361008, Fujian, China
Tel.: (86) 592 217 7000
Web Site: http://www.clarion.com
Sales Range: $400-449.9 Million
Emp.: 1,031
Cassette Mechanisms & Compact Disc
Mechanisms Mfr
N.A.I.C.S.: 334310

Componentes de Vehiculos de Gali-
cia S.A.   **(1)**
Poligono Industrial Las Gandaras Parcela
101 Atios, E 36400, Porrino, Pontevedra,
Spain
Tel.: (34) 986344003
Web Site: http://www.juropuopopo.com
Sales Range: $25-49.9 Million
Emp.: 72
Automotive Products
N.A.I.C.S.: 336340
Oscar Muniz *(Mng Dir)*

EMCON Technologies Hungary Hold-
ings Kft   **(1)**
Ipar U 2, 5123, Jaszarokszallas, Hungary
Tel.: (36) 5753 15 00
Investment Management Service
N.A.I.C.S.: 523999

Faurecia (Changchun) Automotive
Systems Co., Ltd   **(1)**
No 3946 Guanggu Ave, Changchun,
130000, China
Tel.: (86) 43185550027
Motor Vehicle Parts Mfr
N.A.I.C.S.: 336390

Faurecia (Guangzhou) Automotive
Systems Co., Ltd   **(1)**
North Workshop Checheng Avenue Auto
City, Huadu District, Guangzhou, 510800,
China
Tel.: (86) 2028611099
Automotive Seating Component Mfr
N.A.I.C.S.: 336360

Faurecia (Qingdao) Exhaust Systems
Co, Ltd   **(1)**
No 72 Huanghe W Rd Economic Technol-
ogy Development Zone, Qingdao, 266510,
China
Tel.: (86) 53286838000
Automotive Exhaust System Mfr
N.A.I.C.S.: 336390

Faurecia (Shanghai) Automotive Sys-
tems Co., Ltd   **(1)**
No 58 Yuanting Road Anting Town, Jiading
District, Shanghai, 201805, China
Tel.: (86) 2169576576
Automotive Seating Parts Mfr
N.A.I.C.S.: 336360

Faurecia (Shanghai) Management
Company, Ltd   **(1)**
3/F Building 91 No 1122 Qinzhou North
Road Caohejing, Xinxing, Shanghai,
200233, China
Tel.: (86) 2134014588
Automotive Seat Mfr
N.A.I.C.S.: 336360

Faurecia (Wuhan) Automotive Seat-
ing Co., Ltd   **(1)**
No 17 Chuangye No 3 Road, Wuhan,
430101, China
Tel.: (86) 2784470266
Automotive Seating Component Mfr
N.A.I.C.S.: 336360

FORVIA SE—(Continued)

Faurecia (Wuhu) Exhaust Systems Co, Ltd **(1)**
No 6 Industrial Workshop Shili Venture Park
Jiujiang Economic, Wuhu, 241000, China
Tel.: (86) 5535968129
Automotive Exhaust System Mfr
N.A.I.C.S.: 336390

Faurecia (Wuxi) Seating Components Co., Ltd **(1)**
No 86 Meiyu Road Meicun Town, Binhu
District, Wuxi, 214112, China
Tel.: (86) 51088159688
Automotive Seating Component Mfr
N.A.I.C.S.: 336360

Faurecia - Assentos de Automovel, Limitada **(1)**
Rua Comendador Rainho 44 Aptdo 61,
3700-233, Sao Joao da Madeira, Portugal
Tel.: (351) 256 83 92 00
Motor Vehicle Parts Distr
N.A.I.C.S.: 423120

Faurecia - Sistemas de Escape Portugal, Lda **(1)**
Estrada Do Aeroporto, Braganca, 5301902,
Portugal
Tel.: (351) 273 31 00 25
Web Site: http://www.faurecia.com
Emp.: 600
Automobile Parts Mfr
N.A.I.C.S.: 336390
Paolo Rivello *(Mng Dir)*

Faurecia AST Luxembourg S.A. **(1)**
Op Der Sang 14, Eselborn, Clervaux, 9779,
Luxembourg
Tel.: (352) 9490901
Web Site: http://www.faurecia.com
Sales Range: $25-49.9 Million
Emp.: 110
Automobile Parts Distr
N.A.I.C.S.: 423120
Gianluigi Carnevale *(Mng Dir)*

Faurecia Abgastechnik GmbH **(1)**
Biberbachstr 9, Augsburg, 86154, Germany
Tel.: (49) 82141030
Exhaust System Mfr
N.A.I.C.S.: 336390

Faurecia Asientos para Automovil Espana, S.A. **(1)**
Calle Resina 18, Madrid, 28021, Spain
Tel.: (34) 917 23 39 20
Automobile Parts Mfr
N.A.I.C.S.: 336390

Faurecia Automotive Espana, S.L. **(1)**
Calle Marie Curie 19-Ofic A7, Rivas-
Vaciamadrid, Madrid, 28521, Spain
Tel.: (34) 912 98 24 00
Automobile Parts Mfr
N.A.I.C.S.: 336390

Faurecia Automotive Espania **(1)**
Carretera Villaviciosa Pinto Km 21 1,
28947, Fuenlabrada, Spain **(100%)**
Tel.: (34) 916498200
Web Site: http://www.faurecia.com
Sales Range: $25-49.9 Million
Emp.: 134
Automotive Products
N.A.I.C.S.: 336340

Faurecia Automotive Espania **(1)**
Poligono La Estacion, 47104, Olmedo, Vall-
adolid, Spain **(100%)**
Tel.: (34) 983601820
Web Site: http://www.faurecia.com
Sales Range: $25-49.9 Million
Emp.: 140
Automotive Products
N.A.I.C.S.: 336340

Faurecia Automotive Espania **(1)**
Poligono Industrial San Cipriaon de Vinas
Calle 5, 32005, Orense, Galice,
Spain **(100%)**
Tel.: (34) 98 838 3736
Web Site: http://www.faurecia.com
Automotive Interior Systems Production
N.A.I.C.S.: 336340

Faurecia Automotive Exteriors Espana, S.A. **(1)**

Faurecia Automotive GmbH **(1)**
Carretera Corella S/N, 31500, Tudela,
Spain
Tel.: (34) 948 41 24 44
Automobile Parts Mfr
N.A.I.C.S.: 336390

Faurecia Automotive GmbH **(1)**
Nordsehler Strasse 38, 31655, Stadthagen,
Germany
Tel.: (49) 57217020
Web Site: http://www.faurecia.de
Motor Vehicle Seating Mfr
N.A.I.C.S.: 336360

Faurecia Automotive Industrie **(1)**
Zone Industrielle, PO Box 27, 8210, Mou-
zon, France **(100%)**
Tel.: (33) 324278686
Web Site: http://www.faurecia.com
Sales Range: $75-99.9 Million
Emp.: 400
Automotive Products
N.A.I.C.S.: 336340

Faurecia Automotive Industrie **(1)**
16 Rue Colbert, PO Box 35, Marckolsheim,
67390, France
Tel.: (33) 388583100
Web Site: http://www.faurecia.com
Automotive Products
N.A.I.C.S.: 336340

Faurecia Automotive Industrie **(1)**
12 Rue Cocherel, 27000, Evreux,
France **(100%)**
Tel.: (33) 232398000
Web Site: http://www.faurecia.com
Automotive Products
N.A.I.C.S.: 336340

Faurecia Automotive Seating B.V. **(1)**
Kleibergweg 7, Sittard, 6136 KL, Nether-
lands
Tel.: (31) 464207878
Sales Range: $25-49.9 Million
Emp.: 200
Automotive Seating Component Mfr
N.A.I.C.S.: 336360
Armand Crutzen *(Gen Mgr)*

Faurecia Autositze GmbH **(1)**
Nordsehler Strasse 38, 31655, Stadthagen,
Germany
Tel.: (49) 57217020
Web Site: http://www.faurecia.de
Automotive Seating Parts Mfr
N.A.I.C.S.: 336360

Faurecia Bloc Avant **(1)**
2 Rue Hennape, 92000, Nanterre, France
Tel.: (33) 381376000
Automobile Mfr
N.A.I.C.S.: 336110

Faurecia Emissions Control Technologies Development (Shanghai) Company Ltd **(1)**
No 1099 Yuangong Road Anting Town, Ji-
ading District, Shanghai, 201805, China
Tel.: (86) 2160822988
Emp.: 700
Exhaust System & Emission Control Equip-
ment Mfr
N.A.I.C.S.: 336390
Frank Yao *(Gen Mgr)*

Faurecia Emissions Control Technologies, (Chongqing) Co., Ltd **(1)**
No 5 Workshop Puluosi Logistics Park No 9
Liren St North New, Chongqing, 401120,
China
Tel.: (86) 2388502766
Web Site: http://www.faurecia.com
Emp.: 10
Automotive Emission Control System Mfr
N.A.I.C.S.: 336390
Paul Hellyer *(Gen Mgr)*

Faurecia Emissions Control Technologies, (Shanghai) Co., Ltd **(1)**
No 1099 Yuangong Road Anting Town, Ji-
ading District, Shanghai, 201805, China
Tel.: (86) 2160822988
Automotive Emission Control System Mfr
N.A.I.C.S.: 336390

Faurecia Emissions Control Technologies, Cordoba SA **(1)**
Ruta Nacional N 9 Km 695, Ferreyra, Cor-

doba, 5123, Argentina
Tel.: (54) 3514972431
Automotive Emission Control System Mfr
N.A.I.C.S.: 336390

Faurecia Emissions Control Technologies, Finnentrop GmbH **(1)**
Uferstr 6, Finnentrop, 57413, Germany
Tel.: (49) 27215170
Automotive Emission Control System Mfr
N.A.I.C.S.: 336390

Faurecia Emissions Control Technologies, Germany GmbH **(1)**
Biberbachstrasse 9, Augsburg, 86154, Ger-
many
Tel.: (49) 821 4103 237
Automobile Exhaust & Emission Control
System Mfr
N.A.I.C.S.: 336390

Faurecia Emissions Control Technologies, Mlada Boleslav, s.r.o **(1)**
Plazy 104, Mlada Boleslav, 29301, Czech
Republic
Tel.: (420) 326370670
Sales Range: $25-49.9 Million
Emp.: 6
Automotive Emission Control System Mfr
N.A.I.C.S.: 336390
Roman Budik *(Gen Mgr)*

Faurecia Emissions Control Technologies, Netherlands B.V. **(1)**
Keulsebaan 507, Roermond, 6045 GG,
Netherlands
Tel.: (31) 475884242
Web Site: http://www.faurecia.com
Emp.: 500
Automotive Emission Control System Mfr
N.A.I.C.S.: 336390
D. Stoll *(Mgr)*

Faurecia Emissions Control Technologies, Novaferra GmbH **(1)**
Biberbachstr 9, Augsburg, 86154, Germany
Tel.: (49) 82141030
Automotive Emission Control System Mfr
N.A.I.C.S.: 336390

Faurecia Emissions Control Technologies, Pampelona, S.L. **(1)**
Carretera Echauri 13, Orkoien, 31160,
Spain
Tel.: (34) 948327500
Automotive Emission Control System Mfr
N.A.I.C.S.: 336390

Faurecia Exhaust Mexicana, S.A. de C.V. **(1)**
Blvd Henry Ford No 53 Parque Ind Dynat-
ech Sur, Hermosillo, 83296, Sonora, Mexico
Tel.: (52) 6621081100
Web Site: http://www.faurecia.com
Emp.: 475
Automotive Exhaust System Distr
N.A.I.C.S.: 423120
Jose Forte *(Plant Mgr)*

Faurecia Exhaust Systems South Africa Ltd **(1)**
Cnr Henry Ford & Nicoll Road Neave Indus-
trial Township, Port Elizabeth, 6001, East-
ern Cape, South Africa
Tel.: (27) 414510936
Web Site: http://www.faurecia.com
Emp.: 20
Automotive Exhaust System Mfr
N.A.I.C.S.: 336390
Carlos Cabrera *(Plant Mgr)*

Faurecia Fotele Samochodowe Sp. Zo.o **(1)**
Ul Spoldzielcza 4, Grojec, 05-600, Poland
Tel.: (48) 48 665 01 13
Automotive Seat Mfr
N.A.I.C.S.: 336360

Faurecia Grojec R&D Center Sp. Zo.o **(1)**
Ul Mariana Jachimowicza 3, Walbrzych,
Poland
Tel.: (48) 486650113
Automotive Research & Development Ser-
vices
N.A.I.C.S.: 541715

Faurecia Industrie **(1)**
Industrieleen 198, 1070, Brussels,
Belgium **(100%)**

Tel.: (32) 23310613
Web Site: http://www.faurecia.com
Sales Range: $25-49.9 Million
Emp.: 20
Automotive Products
N.A.I.C.S.: 336340

Faurecia Industrie N.V. **(1)**
Mai Zetterlingstraat 70, 9042, Gent,
Belgium **(100%)**
Tel.: (32) 92189510
Web Site: http://www.faurecia.com
Sales Range: $25-49.9 Million
Emp.: 92
Automotive Products
N.A.I.C.S.: 336340

Faurecia Industries S.A.S. **(1)**
2 Rue Hennape, Nanterre, 92000, France
Tel.: (33) 172367000
Automotive Electric Parts Distr
N.A.I.C.S.: 423690

Faurecia Innenraum Systeme GmbH **(1)**
Woltorfer Strasse 76 A, 31224, Peine,
31224, Germany **(100%)**
Tel.: (49) 51719930
Web Site: http://www.faurecia.com
Sales Range: $50-74.9 Million
Emp.: 150
Automotive Products
N.A.I.C.S.: 424690

Faurecia Interieur Industrie **(1)**
Route de Pontoise, PO Box 70 409, 60114,
Meru, France
Tel.: (33) 344525000
Web Site: http://www.faurecia.com
Sales Range: $150-199.9 Million
Emp.: 700
Automotive Interior & Exterior Parts
N.A.I.C.S.: 441330

Faurecia Interieur Industrie **(1)**
Blvd De Malling, F 62260, Auchel,
France **(100%)**
Tel.: (33) 321644900
Web Site: http://www.faurecia.com
Sales Range: $100-124.9 Million
Emp.: 500
Automotive Products
N.A.I.C.S.: 326199

Faurecia Interieur Industrie **(1)**
Parc Dactivites, 88470, Saint Michel-sur-
Meurthe, France **(100%)**
Tel.: (33) 329534000
Web Site: http://www.faurecia.com
Sales Range: $150-199.9 Million
Emp.: 600
Automotive Products
N.A.I.C.S.: 336340

Faurecia Interieur Industrie **(1)**
Rue de La Fosse, BP 10, Marles Les
Mines, 62540, Auchel, France
Tel.: (33) 321529700
Web Site: http://www.faurecia.com
Sales Range: $25-49.9 Million
Emp.: 100
Automotive Products
N.A.I.C.S.: 424690

Faurecia Interior Systems **(1)**
Pol Ind Ermengol C Progres 18 20, Abrera,
8630, Spain **(100%)**
Tel.: (34) 937733700
Web Site: http://www.faurecia.com
Sales Range: $75-99.9 Million
Emp.: 315
Automotive Products
N.A.I.C.S.: 336340
Enrique Lopez *(Mng Dir)*

Faurecia Interior Systems Bohemia s.r.o. **(1)**
Plazy 100 Central Bohemian Region, Mlada
Boleslav, Bohemia, Czech Republic
Tel.: (420) 326 370 111
Web Site: http://www.faurecia.com
Sales Range: $150-199.9 Million
Emp.: 800
Automobile Panel Mfr
N.A.I.C.S.: 336390
Laurent Fasan *(Gen Mgr)*

Faurecia Interior Systems Espana, S.A. **(1)**
Poligono Ind As Gandaras - Parcela 205,

36400, Porrino, Spain
Tel.: (34) 986 34 40 36
Automotive Exterior Parts Mfr
N.A.I.C.S.: 336390

Faurecia Interior Systems Salc Es-
pana, S.L.   **(1)**
344 Nacional Iii, 46930, Cuart de Poblet,
Spain
Tel.: (34) 961 96 00 00
Automobile Parts Distr
N.A.I.C.S.: 423120

Faurecia Interior Systems South Af-
rica (Pty) Ltd   **(1)**
Nelson Mandela Bay Area Erf 205 Jagt
Vlakte, Uitenhage, 6229, Eastern Cape,
South Africa
Tel.: (27) 419954900
Web Site: http://www.faurecia.com
Emp.: 117
Automobile Parts Mfr
N.A.I.C.S.: 336390
Jan Krutzfeld (Gen Mgr)

Faurecia Interior Systems Thailand
Co., Ltd.   **(1)**
300/67 Moo 1, Pluak Daeng, Rayong,
21140, Thailand
Tel.: (66) 389543435
Automotive Door Panel Distr
N.A.I.C.S.: 423120

Faurecia Japan K.K.   **(1)**
6-113 Aioicho Sakuragichoan Bldg 10f,
Naka-Ku, Yokohama, 231-0012, Kanagawa,
Japan
Tel.: (81) 453456700
Motor Vehicle Parts Mfr
N.A.I.C.S.: 336390
Eric Schonenberger (Pres)

Faurecia Kunststoffe Automobilsys-
teme GmbH   **(1)**
Dieselstr 24, Gaimersheim, 85080, Ger-
many
Tel.: (49) 84583480
Automobile Parts Mfr
N.A.I.C.S.: 336390

Faurecia Netherlands Holding
B.V.   **(1)**
Kleibergweg 7, Sittard, 6136 KL, Nether-
lands
Tel.: (31) 464207878
Investment Management Service
N.A.I.C.S.: 523999

Faurecia Portugal   **(1)**
Parque Industrial Autoeuropa Quinta Da
Marquesa I CCI 10207, 2950-678, Palmela,
Portugal   **(80%)**
Tel.: (351) 212135100
Web Site: http://www.faurecia.com
Automotive Products
N.A.I.C.S.: 336340

Faurecia Systemes
d'Echappement   **(1)**
2 Rue Hennape, 92000, Nanterre, France
Tel.: (33) 172367000
Automobile Parts Mfr
N.A.I.C.S.: 336390

Faurecia USA Holdings, Inc.   **(1)**
2500 Executive Hills Blvd, Auburn Hills, MI
48326   **(100%)**
Tel.: (248) 409-3500
Web Site: http://www.faurecia.com
Sales Range: $75-99.9 Million
Emp.: 350
Automotive Products
N.A.I.C.S.: 541330
Eelco Spoelder (Exec VP-Grp Ops)

Subsidiary (Domestic):

Faurecia Automotive Seating, Inc **(2)**
2800 High Meadow Circle, Auburn Hills, MI
48236
Tel.: (248) 288-1000
Automobile Seating Mfr
N.A.I.C.S.: 336360

Faurecia Emissions Control
Technologies   **(2)**
543 Matzinger Rd, Toledo, OH
43612   **(100%)**
Tel.: (419) 727-5000
Web Site: http://www.faurecia.com

Sales Range: $50-74.9 Million
Emp.: 230
Motor Vehicle Exhaust System Mfr
N.A.I.C.S.: 336390

Subsidiary (Domestic):

Faurecia Emissions Control Technolo-
gies Spartanburg, Inc.   **(3)**
2651 New Cut Rd, Spartanburg, SC 29303
Tel.: (864) 574-2222
Sales Range: $75-99.9 Million
Emp.: 205
Motor Vehicle Exhaust System Mfr
N.A.I.C.S.: 336390

Faurecia Emissions Control Technolo-
gies USA LLC   **(3)**
950 W Rd 450 S, Columbus, IN 47201
Tel.: (812) 341-2000
Motor Vehicle Exhaust System Mfr
N.A.I.C.S.: 336390

Subsidiary (Domestic):

Faurecia Exhaust Systems, Inc.   **(2)**
543 Matzinger Rd, Toledo, OH 43612
Tel.: (419) 727-5000
Automotive Exhaust System Mfr
N.A.I.C.S.: 336390

Faurecia Interior Systems   **(2)**
101 International Blvd, Fountain Inn, SC
29644-7033   **(100%)**
Tel.: (864) 862-1900
Web Site: http://www.faurecia.com
Automotive Products
N.A.I.C.S.: 423120
Jean-Michel Renaudie (Exec VP)

Financiere Faurecia   **(1)**
2 Rue Hennape, 92000, Nanterre, France
Tel.: (33) 1 72 36 70 00
Sales Range: $50-74.9 Million
Emp.: 20
Automobile Parts Distr
N.A.I.C.S.: 423120

SAI Automotive Allibert S.A.   **(1)**
Poligono Industrial De Las Mercedes,
Campezo 4, 28022, Madrid, Spain **(100%)**
Tel.: (34) 917482401
Web Site: http://www.saurecia.com
Automotive Products
N.A.I.C.S.: 336340

SAI Automotive Fradley Ltd.   **(1)**
Common Ln Fradley Business Park, Lich-
field, WS13 8NQ, Staffordshire, United
Kingdom   **(100%)**
Tel.: (44) 1543445200
Web Site: http://www.faurecia.com
Emp.: 485
Automotive Products
N.A.I.C.S.: 424690
Yannick Mace (Plant Mgr)

SAI Automotive Washington Ltd.   **(1)**
Staithes Rd Pattinson South Industrial Es-
tate, District 8 Tyne & Wear, Washington,
NE38 8NW, United Kingdom   **(100%)**
Tel.: (44) 1914197900
Web Site: http://www.faurecia.com
Sales Range: $25-49.9 Million
Emp.: 200
Automotive Products
N.A.I.C.S.: 336340
Julie Heads (Plant Mgr)

SAI Automotive do Brasil Ltda.   **(1)**
Rua Joao Zarpelon 1000 Costeira, 83015
210, San Jose, Dos Pinhais PR,
Brazil   **(100%)**
Tel.: (55) 4140098700
Web Site: http://www.faurecia.com
Sales Range: $75-99.9 Million
Emp.: 300
Automotive Products
N.A.I.C.S.: 336340

FORWARD FASHION INTER-
NATIONAL HOLDINGS COM-
PANY LIMITED
Suite 1204 12/F Tower 6 The Gate-
way Harbour City, Tsim Sha Tsui,
Kowloon, China (Hong Kong)
Tel.: (852) 37552800   **Ky**

Web Site: http://www.forward-
fashion.com
Year Founded: 2005
2528—(HKG)
Rev.: $122,387,250
Assets: $116,083,905
Liabilities: $85,282,073
Net Worth: $30,801,833
Earnings: ($4,654,388)
Emp.: 1,080
Fiscal Year-end: 12/31/22
Holding Company
N.A.I.C.S.: 551112
Wing Ting Fan (Chm)

FORWARD GRAPHIC ENTER-
PRISE CO., LTD.
65 Chung-Shan Road, Tucheng City
Hsien, Taipei, Taiwan
Tel.: (886) 222673777
Web Site: http://www.forward-
net.com.tw
8906—(TPE)
Rev.: $7,153,113
Assets: $39,088,797
Liabilities: $27,883,282
Net Worth: $11,205,515
Earnings: ($156,427)
Fiscal Year-end: 12/31/22
Commercial Printing Product Mfr
N.A.I.C.S.: 323111
Tsung-Han Hsieh (Chm & Pres)

FORWARD INTERNET GROUP
LTD.
Floor 2 Centro 3 19 Mandela Street
Camden Town, London, NW1 0DU,
United Kingdom
Tel.: (44) 20 7121 1199
Web Site: http://www.forward.co.uk
Year Founded: 2004
Sales Range: $200-249.9 Million
Emp.: 218
Financial Investment Services
N.A.I.C.S.: 523999
Rob Murphy (CFO)

Subsidiaries:

Forward Dimension Capital 1
LLP   **(1)**
44 Great Marlborough Street Floor 1, Lon-
don, W1F 7JL, United Kingdom
Tel.: (44) 2030210658
Web Site: http://www.forwarddimension.com
Financial Management Consulting Services
N.A.I.C.S.: 541611
Louise Bale (Dir-Tax & Acct)

FORWARD PHARMA A/S
Ostergade 24A 1st Floor, 1100, Co-
penhagen, Denmark
Tel.: (45) 3 344 4242   **DK**
Web Site: http://www.forward-
pharma.com
Year Founded: 2005
FWP—(NASDAQ)
Assets: $79,714,000
Liabilities: $1,070,000
Net Worth: $78,644,000
Earnings: ($6,449,000)
Emp.: 4
Fiscal Year-end: 12/31/20
Biopharmaceutical Mfr
N.A.I.C.S.: 325412
Florian Schonharting (Founder &
Chm)

Subsidiaries:

Forward Pharma USA, LLC   **(1)**
7 Skyline Dr, Hawthorne, NY 10532
Tel.: (914) 752-3542
Pharmaceuticals Product Mfr
N.A.I.C.S.: 325412

FORWARD WATER TECH-
NOLOGIES CORP

1086 Modeland Road, Sarnia, N7S
6L2, ON, Canada
Tel.: (519) 333-5888
Web Site:
https://www.forwardwater.com
Year Founded: 2012
FWTC—(TSXV)
Rev.: $52,490
Assets: $1,171,174
Liabilities: $1,351,862
Net Worth: ($180,688)
Earnings: ($1,622,608)
Fiscal Year-end: 03/31/24
Renewables & Environment
N.A.I.C.S.: 562998

Subsidiaries:

Fraser Mackenzie Accelerator
Corp.   **(1)**
116 Eastbourne Avenue, Toronto, M5P 2G3,
ON, Canada
Tel.: (416) 955-4777
Web Site: https://fmmc.ca
Private Equity
N.A.I.C.S.: 523999

FORYOU CORPORATION
NO 1 North Shangxia Road Dongji-
ang High-tech Industry Park, Foryou
Industrial Park Area A, Huizhou,
516005, Guangdong, China
Tel.: (86) 7522556666
Web Site:
https://www.foryougroup.com
Year Founded: 1993
002906—(SSE)
Rev.: $791,565,372
Assets: $982,378,800
Liabilities: $390,435,552
Net Worth: $591,943,248
Earnings: $53,416,584
Fiscal Year-end: 12/31/22
Electronic Component Mfr & Distr
N.A.I.C.S.: 334419
Ganrong Zou (Chm & Pres)

Subsidiaries:

Foryou General Electronics Co.,
Ltd.   **(1)**
Foryou Industrial Park No 1 North Shangxia
Road, Dongjiang Hi-tech Industry Park, Hu-
izhou, 516006, Guangdong, China
Tel.: (86) 7522616150
Web Site: https://en.foryouge.com
Electronic Components Mfr
N.A.I.C.S.: 334419

Huizhou Foryou Industries Co.,
Ltd.   **(1)**
Building 5 Zone B Huayang Industrial Park
No 1 Shangxia North Road, Dongjiang
High-tech Development Zone, Huizhou,
China
Tel.: (86) 7525302888
Automobile Mfr
N.A.I.C.S.: 336320

FORZA LITHIUM CORP.
9285-203B Street, Langley, V1M 2L9,
BC, Canada
Tel.: (604) 290-6152   **BC**
Web Site:
https://www.forzalithium.com
Year Founded: 2022
PGR—(CNSX)
Assets: $87,633
Liabilities: $20,680
Net Worth: $66,953
Earnings: ($421,784)
Fiscal Year-end: 10/31/23
Mineral Mining Services
N.A.I.C.S.: 213115
Michele Pillon (CFO)

FORZA PETROLEUM LIMITED
3400 First Canadian Centre 350 7
Avenue Southwest, Calgary, T2P
3N9, AB, Canada
Tel.: (403) 261-5350

Forza Petroleum Limited—(Continued)

Web Site:
https://www.forzapetroleum.com
Year Founded: 2010
FORZ—(TSX)
Rev.: $150,496,000
Assets: $768,254,000
Liabilities: $209,202,000
Net Worth: $559,052,000
Earnings: ($59,199,000)
Emp.: 171
Fiscal Year-end: 12/31/19
Oil & Gas Exploration Services
N.A.I.C.S.: 211120
Kevin McPhee (Gen Counsel & Sec)

Subsidiaries:

Forza Petroleum Services S.A. **(1)**
Route de Pre-Bois 14, Cointrin, 1216, Geneva, Switzerland
Tel.: (41) 587029300
Oil & Gas Exploration Services
N.A.I.C.S.: 213111

OP Hawler Kurdistan Limited **(1)**
1st Floor Global Business Center Gulan Street Kurdistan Region, Erbil, Iraq
Tel.: (964) 662572003
Oil & Gas Exploration Services
N.A.I.C.S.: 211120
Siamand Karim (Branch Mgr)

Oryx Petroleum Services SA **(1)**
Rue Michel-Servet 12, 1206, Geneva, Switzerland
Tel.: (41) 587029300
Oil & Gas Exploration Services
N.A.I.C.S.: 211120

FOS CAPITAL LIMITED
3B / 41 Rose Street, Richmond, 3121, VIC, Australia
Tel.: (61) 1300241087 **AU**
Web Site:
https://www.foscapital.com.au
Year Founded: 2019
FOS—(ASX)
Rev.: $11,162,740
Assets: $8,882,058
Liabilities: $2,826,522
Net Worth: $6,055,536
Earnings: $380,740
Emp.: 55
Fiscal Year-end: 06/30/23
Investment Management Service
N.A.I.C.S.: 523999
Con Scrinis (Mng Dir)

FOS S.P.A.
Via E Melen 77 Ed A 6th floor, 16152, Genoa, Italy
Tel.: (39) 0108906000
Web Site: https://www.gruppofos.it
Year Founded: 1999
Software Development Services
N.A.I.C.S.: 541511
Brunello Botte (Pres)

Subsidiaries:

Esacontrol Srl **(1)**
Via Fiorenzo Semini 28 A/B/C, 16163, Genoa, Italy
Tel.: (39) 010723041
Web Site: http://www.esacontrol.it
Electric Equipment Mfr
N.A.I.C.S.: 335999

Fos Green Tech Srl **(1)**
Via G Colombo 20-13, 16124, Genoa, Italy
Tel.: (39) 0104076998
Information Technology Services
N.A.I.C.S.: 541519

Sesmat Srl **(1)**
Strada Statale ss7 Appia 32, 82018, San Giorgio, BN, Italy
Tel.: (39) 0104076998
Information Technology Services
N.A.I.C.S.: 541519

T&G SRL **(1)**
Via alla Porta degli Archi 3/11, 16121,

Genoa, Italy
Tel.: (39) 0104076998
Information Technology Services
N.A.I.C.S.: 541519

FOSECO INDIA LIMITED
Gat Nos 922 and 923 Sanaswadi, Shirur Taluka, Pune, 412208, Maharashtra, India
Tel.: (91) 2137668100
Web Site:
https://www.fosecoindia.com
Year Founded: 1932
500150—(BOM)
Rev.: $35,129,585
Assets: $35,910,284
Liabilities: $10,978,954
Net Worth: $24,931,329
Earnings: $2,107,123
Emp.: 203
Fiscal Year-end: 12/31/20
Metallurgical Additive & Consumable Mfr & Distr
N.A.I.C.S.: 325998
Sanjay Mathur (CEO)

FOSFATOS DEL PACIFICO SA
150 La Colonia Street Urb El Vivero, Santiago de Surco, Lima, Peru
Tel.: (51) 3176000
Year Founded: 2009
Metallic & Non-Metallic Mining Services
N.A.I.C.S.: 213114

FOSHAN ELECTRICAL & LIGHTING CO., LTD.
No 64 Fenjiang Road North, Chancheng District, Foshan, 528042, Guangdong, China
Tel.: (86) 75782810239
Web Site: https://www.chinafsl.com
Year Founded: 1958
000541—(SSE)
Rev.: $1,229,899,788
Assets: $2,146,303,224
Liabilities: $938,814,084
Net Worth: $1,207,489,140
Earnings: $32,346,756
Emp.: 10,000
Fiscal Year-end: 12/31/22
Electric Light Product Mfr
N.A.I.C.S.: 335139
Joe Wu (Reg Dir-FSL Intl Brand Dept)

FOSHAN GOLDEN MILKY WAY INTELLIGENT EQUIPMENT CO., LTD.
No 6 Baoyun Road, Sanshui District, Foshan, 528100, China
Tel.: (86) 75787323386
Web Site: https://www.goldenyh.com
Year Founded: 2002
300619—(CHIN)
Rev.: $317,172,411
Assets: $648,646,941
Liabilities: $406,598,681
Net Worth: $242,048,260
Earnings: $13,199,617
Fiscal Year-end: 12/31/23
Conveying Equipment Mfr & Distr
N.A.I.C.S.: 333922
Zhang Qifa (Chm & Gen Mgr)

Subsidiaries:

Jiangxi Andeli High Tech Co., Ltd. **(1)**
No 53 59 Dongyang Avenue, Anyi Industrial Park Anyi County, Nanchang, Jiangxi, China
Tel.: (86) 79183389225
Web Site: https://www.jxandeli.com
Resin Product Mfr
N.A.I.C.S.: 325211

FOSHAN HAITIAN FLAVOUR-

ING & FOOD COMPANY LTD.
16 Wensha Road, Chancheng District, Foshan, 528000, China
Tel.: (86) 82810925
Web Site: https://www.haitian-food.com
603288—(SHG)
Rev.: $3,595,595,071
Assets: $4,781,908,296
Liabilities: $1,007,327,389
Net Worth: $3,774,580,908
Earnings: $870,159,453
Fiscal Year-end: 12/31/22
Food Seasoning & Flavouring Product Mfr
N.A.I.C.S.: 311942
Kang Pang (Chm & Pres)

FOSHAN HUAXIN PACKAGING CO., LTD.
19F Jinghua Building No 18 Jihua Road 5th Road, Foshan, 528000, Guangdong, China
Tel.: (86) 7578 398 1729
Web Site: http://www.fshxp.com
200986—(SSE)
Rev.: $562,473,153
Assets: $800,163,684
Liabilities: $294,318,063
Net Worth: $505,845,621
Earnings: $5,108,670
Fiscal Year-end: 12/31/19
Paper Products Mfr
N.A.I.C.S.: 322120
Xiangdong Ji (Vice Chm & Gen Mgr)

FOSHAN NATIONSTAR OPTO-ELECTRONICS CO., LTD.
No 18 South Huabao Road, Chancheng District, Foshan, 528000, Guangdong, China
Tel.: (86) 75782100230
Web Site: https://www.nationstar.com
Year Founded: 1969
002449—(SSE)
Rev.: $502,616,556
Assets: $923,805,324
Liabilities: $396,808,308
Net Worth: $526,997,016
Earnings: $17,036,136
Emp.: 700
Fiscal Year-end: 12/31/22
Semiconductor Optoelectronic Devices & LED Applied Products Mfr
N.A.I.C.S.: 334413
Li Cheng (Pres-White Led Div & Dir-R&D Center)

Subsidiaries:

Foshan Nationstar Optoelectronics Co., Ltd. - LED Lighting Division **(1)**
N0 18 South Hua Bao Road, Chan Cheng District, Foshan, 528000, Guangdong, China
Tel.: (86) 75782100226
Sales Range: $400-449.9 Million
Light Emitting Diode Mfr
N.A.I.C.S.: 334413

FOSHAN YOWANT TECHNOLOGY CO., LTD.
No 2 Qingan Road, Guicheng Subdistrict Nanhai District, Foshan, 528200, Guangdong, China
Tel.: (86) 75786256351
Web Site: https://www.st-sat.com
Year Founded: 2002
002291—(SSE)
Rev.: $547,641,432
Assets: $949,975,884
Liabilities: $215,658,612
Net Worth: $734,317,272
Earnings: ($37,218,636)
Fiscal Year-end: 12/31/22
Footwear Mfr
N.A.I.C.S.: 316210
Rudong Xie (Chm & Gen Mgr)

FOSRICH CO., LTD.
77-79 Molynes Rd, Kingston, Jamaica
Tel.: (876) 9375099
Web Site: https://www.fosrich.com
Year Founded: 1993
FOSRICH—(JAM)
Rev.: $13,156,019
Assets: $17,187,725
Liabilities: $6,027,830
Net Worth: $11,159,895
Earnings: $872,326
Fiscal Year-end: 12/31/20
Electrical Products Distr
N.A.I.C.S.: 423610
Cecil Foster (Mng Dir)

FOSS A/S
Foss Alle 1, PO Box 260, 3400, Hillerod, Denmark
Tel.: (45) 70103370
Web Site: http://www.foss.dk
Year Founded: 1956
Sales Range: $300-349.9 Million
Emp.: 1,237
Measuring & Controlling Devices Mfr
N.A.I.C.S.: 334519
Peter Foss (Chm)

Subsidiaries:

FOSS India Pvt. Ltd. **(1)**
Central Camera Building 195 D N Road Fort, Mumbai, 400 001, India
Tel.: (91) 22 4022 6222
Web Site: http://www.foss-analytical.co.in
Agriculture Analytical Instrument Distr
N.A.I.C.S.: 423820

Foss (Beijing) Science, Technology & Trading Co. **(1)**
Rm 1105 Science & Technology Tower No 11 zhong Guan Cun South Street, Beijing, 100081, China
Tel.: (86) 10 68467239
Agriculture Analytical Instrument Distr
N.A.I.C.S.: 423820
Alan Wang (Reg Mgr)

Foss Analytical A/S **(1)**
Foss Alle 1, 3400, Hillerod, Denmark **(100%)**
Tel.: (45) 70103370
Web Site: http://www.foss.dk
Sales Range: $200-249.9 Million
Emp.: 550
Analytical Instrument Mfr
N.A.I.C.S.: 334516

Foss Belgium B.V **(1)**
Robert Schumanplein 6/5, 1040, Brussels, Belgium **(100%)**
Tel.: (32) 16448421
Web Site: http://www.foss.dk
Sales Range: $25-49.9 Million
Emp.: 16
Measuring & Controlling Devices Mfr
N.A.I.C.S.: 334519

Foss Benelux B.V. **(1)**
Panoven 68, 3401 RB, IJsselstein, Netherlands **(100%)**
Tel.: (31) 334519033
Web Site: http://www.2.foss.dk
Sales Range: $50-74.9 Million
Emp.: 15
Measuring & Controlling Device Mfr
N.A.I.C.S.: 334519

Foss Espana S.A. **(1)**
Avenida Josep Tarradellas 8-10, 08029, Barcelona, Spain **(100%)**
Tel.: (34) 934949940
Web Site: http://www.foss.es
Sales Range: $25-49.9 Million
Emp.: 15
Measuring & Controlling Devices Mfr
N.A.I.C.S.: 334519
Miguel Martinez (Mng Dir)

Foss France S.A.S. **(1)**
35 Rue des Peupliers, 92752, Nanterre, Cedex, France **(100%)**
Tel.: (33) 146491919
Web Site: http://www.fossanalytics.com

Sales Range: $25-49.9 Million
Emp.: 46
Measuring & Controlling Device Mfr
N.A.I.C.S.: 334519

Foss GmbH (1)
Haferweg 26, 22769, Hamburg,
Germany (100%)
Tel.: (49) 4085399790
Web Site: http://www.fossanalytics.com
Sales Range: $25-49.9 Million
Emp.: 52
Measuring & Controlling Device Mfr
N.A.I.C.S.: 334519

Foss Italia S.p.A. (1)
Corso Stati Uniti 1/77, Padua, 35127,
Italy (100%)
Tel.: (39) 0498287211
Web Site: http://www.foss.it
Sales Range: $25-49.9 Million
Emp.: 32
Measuring & Controlling Devices Mfr
N.A.I.C.S.: 334519
Michela Martini (CFO)

Foss Japan Ltd. (1)
Toyo 2414, Kohto Ku, Tokyo, 1350016,
Japan (100%)
Tel.: (81) 356653821
Web Site: http://www.foss.co.jp
Sales Range: $25-49.9 Million
Emp.: 35
Sales of Analytical Instruments
N.A.I.C.S.: 334516
Klaus Jatop (Mng Dir)

Foss Korea Ltd. (1)
3rd Fl KVMA Bldg 272 5 Swohyun Dong
Pudang Ku Sungham Si, Kyung Gi De,
Seoul, 463824, Korea (South) (100%)
Tel.: (82) 317099591
Sales Range: $25-49.9 Million
Emp.: 16
Analytical Instruments
N.A.I.C.S.: 334516

Foss North America, Inc. (1)
8091 Wallace Rd, Eden Prairie, MN
55344-3677 (100%)
Tel.: (952) 974-9892
Web Site: http://www.foss.us
Sales Range: $50-74.9 Million
Emp.: 76
Develops & Produces Analytical Solutions
for Measuring Food Quality
N.A.I.C.S.: 423490

Foss Pacific (NZ) Ltd. (1)
47 Albert St, Cambridge, New
Zealand (100%)
Tel.: (64) 95741416
Web Site: http://www.foss.com.au
Sales Range: $25-49.9 Million
Emp.: 6
Analytical Instruments
N.A.I.C.S.: 334516
Campbell McCracken (Mgr-Sls)

Foss Pacific Pty. Ltd. (1)
5 3-4 Anzed Court, Mulgrave, 3170, VIC,
Australia (100%)
Tel.: (61) 298886788
Web Site: http://www.fossanalytics.com
Sales Range: $25-49.9 Million
Emp.: 40
Analytical Instruments
N.A.I.C.S.: 334516

Foss UK Ltd. (1)
730 Birchwood Blvd, Birchwood, War-
rington, WA3 7QY, Cheshire, United
Kingdom (100%)
Tel.: (44) 1925287700
Web Site: http://www.foss.co.uk
Sales Range: $25-49.9 Million
Emp.: 25
Measuring & Controlling Devices Mfr
N.A.I.C.S.: 334519
Henry Hanson (Mgr)

Ibsen Photonics A/S (1)
Ryttermarken 15-21, Farum, 3520, Den-
mark
Tel.: (45) 44347000
Web Site: http://www.ibsen.com
Sales Range: $1-9.9 Million
Emp.: 37
Transmission Diffraction Grating Compo-
nents & Grating-Based Spectrometer Mod-
ules Developer & Mfr

N.A.I.C.S.: 333310
Kim Vejlby Hansen (Chm)

Lattec I/S (1)
Slangerupgade 69, PO Box 260, Hillerod,
3400, Denmark
Tel.: (45) 7010 3390
Agriculture Analytical Instrument Distr
N.A.I.C.S.: 423820
Steen Thranow (Mgr-R&D Sys)

FOSSE MASTER ISSUER PLC
35 Great St Helens, London, EC3A
6AP, United Kingdom
Tel.: (44) 1632439925
Sales Range: $150-199.9 Million
Financial Support Services
N.A.I.C.S.: 523999
Jennifer Jones (Sec)

FOSTER + PARTNERS LTD.
Riverside 22 Hester Road, London,
SW11 4AN, United Kingdom
Tel.: (44) 2077380455　　　　UK
Web Site:
　http://www.fosterandpartners.com
Year Founded: 1967
Sales Range: $200-249.9 Million
Emp.: 1,163
Architectural Services
N.A.I.C.S.: 541310
Norman Foster (Founder & Chm)

Subsidiaries:

Foster And Partners (Hong Kong),
Limited (1)
3001 Tower 2 Lippo Centre 89 Queensway,
Hong Kong, China (Hong Kong)
Tel.: (852) 29896288
Construction Engineering Services
N.A.I.C.S.: 541330
Michael Gentz (Partner)

FOSTER DENOVO LIMITED
8 Eastcheap 1st Floor, London,
EC3M 1AE, United Kingdom
Tel.: (44) 20 7469 2800
Web Site:
　http://www.fosterdenovo.com
Year Founded: 2005
Financial Advisors
N.A.I.C.S.: 523940
Roger Brosch (CEO)

Subsidiaries:

Thomson Directories Ltd. (1)
25 Templer Avenue, Farnborough, GU14
6FE, United Kingdom
Tel.: (44) 3330145045
Web Site: http://www.thomsonlocal.com
Online Local Business Directory Publisher
N.A.I.C.S.: 513140
Alex Davis (Mgr-Bus Dev)

FOSTER ELECTRIC CO., LTD.
1-1-109 Tsutsujigaoka, Akishima, To-
kyo, 196-8550, Japan
Tel.: (81) 425462311　　　　JP
Web Site: https://www.foster.co.jp
Year Founded: 1949
6794—(TKS)
Rev.: $809,374,670
Assets: $679,157,670
Liabilities: $254,009,080
Net Worth: $425,148,590
Earnings: $15,229,440
Emp.: 16,022
Fiscal Year-end: 03/31/24
Electronic Equipment, Audio & Video
Components Mfr
N.A.I.C.S.: 334310
Hiromi Yoshizawa (CEO)

Subsidiaries:

ESTec Corporation (1)
22 Yusan-dong Yusangongdan 9-gil, Yangsan, 50592, Gyeongsangnamdo, Korea
(South)
Tel.: (82) 553702200

Web Site: https://www.estec.co.kr
Rev.: $359,300,010
Assets: $195,152,665
Liabilities: $88,164,219
Net Worth: $106,988,446
Earnings: $7,314,389
Emp.: 332
Fiscal Year-end: 12/31/2022
Audio Equipment Mfr
N.A.I.C.S.: 334310
Oh In Young (CEO)

FSK (Thailand) Co., Ltd. (1)
31/2 Moo 2 Banmoh, Phromburi, Sing Buri,
16120, Thailand
Tel.: (66) 36598111
Web Site: http://www.fsk-thailand.com
Voice Coil Bobbin Mfr
N.A.I.C.S.: 334416

Foster Business Service Ltd. (1)
1-1-109 Tsutsujigaoka 3rd Floor, Akishima,
196-8550, Japan
Tel.: (81) 425462446
Logistic Services
N.A.I.C.S.: 541614

Foster Electric (Bac Ninh) Co.,
Ltd. (1)
No 1 Street 11 VSIP Bac Ninh, Phu Chan
Ward Tu Son Town, Bac Ninh, Vietnam
Tel.: (84) 2223765868
Electronic Products Mfr
N.A.I.C.S.: 335999

Foster Electric (Da Nang) Co.,
Ltd. (1)
Street 1 Hoa Cam Industrial Zone, Hoa Tho
Tay Ward Cam Le District, Da Nang, Viet-
nam
Tel.: (84) 2363675965
Web Site: http://www.foster.co.jp
Radio Headphones Mfr
N.A.I.C.S.: 334310

Foster Electric (Europe) GmbH (1)
Gotenstrasse 21, 20097, Hamburg,
Germany (100%)
Tel.: (49) 40239120
Web Site: https://www.foster.de
Sales Range: $25-49.9 Million
Emp.: 23
Marketing & Sales of Sound Systems
N.A.I.C.S.: 449210
Marc Ohlmeier (Mng Dir)

Foster Electric (Nanning) Co.,
Ltd. (1)
No 8 Keyuan East 11 Road, Nanning New
and High - Tech Industrial Development
Zone, Nanning, 530007, Guangxi, China
Tel.: (86) 7713810114
Mobile Audio Product Mfr
N.A.I.C.S.: 334310

Foster Electric (Quang Ngai) Co.,
Ltd. (1)
Lot C5-2 Street 5, Tinh Phong Industrial
Zone Tinh Phong Commune Son Tinh Dis-
trict, Quang Ngai, Vietnam
Tel.: (84) 2553688868
Mobile Audio Product Mfr
N.A.I.C.S.: 334310

Foster Electric (Singapore) Pte.
Ltd. (1)
190 Middle Road 16-01 Fortune Centre,
Singapore, 188979, Singapore (100%)
Tel.: (65) 67478811
Web Site: http://www.foster.co.jp
Sales Range: $25-49.9 Million
Emp.: 60
Mfr of Sound Systems
N.A.I.C.S.: 334310

Foster Electric (Thailand) Co.,
Ltd. (1)
2/35 Floor 8th Bangna Complex Office
Tower Soi Bangna-Trad 25, Bangna-Nuea
Bangna, Bangkok, 10260, Thailand
Tel.: (66) 23992113
Speaker Distr
N.A.I.C.S.: 423620

Foster Electric (Thilawa) Co.,
Ltd. (1)
Lot No B-3 Zone A, Thilawa Special Eco-
nomic Zone, Yangon, Myanmar
Tel.: (95) 12309036
Speaker Mfr

N.A.I.C.S.: 334310

Foster Electric (U.S.A.), Inc. (1)
1000 E State Pkwy Ste G, Schaumburg, IL
60173-4592 (100%)
Tel.: (847) 310-8200
Web Site: http://www.foster-electric.com
Sales Range: $25-49.9 Million
Emp.: 11
Mfr of Loudspeakers & Sound Equipment
N.A.I.C.S.: 334310

Division (Domestic):

Foster Electric (U.S.A.), Inc. (2)
28338 Constellation Rd Unit 910, Valencia,
CA 91355 (100%)
Tel.: (661) 295-2200
Web Site: http://www.foster-electric.com
Sales Range: $25-49.9 Million
Sales of Audio Equipment
N.A.I.C.S.: 423690
Yasuo Higashi (Pres)

Foster Electric (Vietnam) Co.,
Ltd. (1)
Web Site: http://www.foster.co.jp
Radio Headphones Mfr
N.A.I.C.S.: 334310

Subsidiary (Domestic):

Foster Electric (Vietnam) Co., Ltd. -
Vietnam Factory 2 (2)
No 20 Vsip II Street 5 Vietnam Singapore
Industrial Park II, Hoa Phu ward, Thu Dau
Mot, Binh Duong, Vietnam
Tel.: (84) 6503635050
Radio Headphones Mfr
N.A.I.C.S.: 334310

Foster Electric Co., (Guangzhou)
Ltd. (1)
Jiu Shui Keng Cun Da Long Jie Panyu Qu,
Guangzhou, 511450, Guangdong, China
Tel.: (86) 2034569181
Electronic Components Mfr
N.A.I.C.S.: 334419

Foster Electric Co., (Heyuan)
Ltd. (1)
66 Xing Ye Road Hi-Tech Development
Zone, Heyuan, Guangdong, China
Tel.: (86) 7623601125
Telecommunications Equipment Mfr
N.A.I.C.S.: 334310

Foster Electric Co., (Hong Kong)
Ltd. (1)
Block D 12th Floor Kaiser Estate 41 Man
Yue Street, Hung Hom, Kowloon, China
(Hong Kong) (100%)
Tel.: (852) 23626233
Web Site: http://www.foster.co.jp
Sales Range: $25-49.9 Million
Emp.: 50
Sales & Distribution of Audio & Sound
Equipment
N.A.I.C.S.: 423690

Foster Electric Co., (Taiwan) Ltd. (1)
12F-2 No 83 Sec 1 Nankan Rd, Luzhu Dist,
Taoyuan, 338207, Taiwan (100%)
Tel.: (886) 32123334
Sales Range: $100-124.9 Million
Emp.: 300
Loudspeaker Mfr
N.A.I.C.S.: 334310

Foster Electric IPO (Thailand)
Ltd. (1)
2/35 Floor 8th Bangna Complex Office
Tower Soi Bangna-Trad 25, Bangna-Nuea
Bangna, Bangkok, 10260, Samut Prakan,
Thailand
Tel.: (66) 23992113
Web Site: http://www.foster.co.jp
Sales Range: $25-49.9 Million
Emp.: 5
Loudspeaker Mfr
N.A.I.C.S.: 334310

Foster Electric Penang Sdn.
Bhd. (1)
Unit 18-34-A1 Gurney Tower Persiaran Gur-
ney, 10250, Penang, Malaysia
Tel.: (60) 43715051
Electrical Equipment Mfr & Distr
N.A.I.C.S.: 335999

Foster Electric Co., Ltd.—(Continued)

Foster Electronics Limited (1)
1-1-109 Tsutsujigaoka 4th Floor, Akishima
City, Tokyo, 196-8550, Japan
Tel.: (81) 425456118
Electronic Equipment Whslr
N.A.I.C.S.: 423690

Fostex Co., Ltd. (1)
1-109 Tsutsujigaoka, Akishima City, Tokyo,
196-8550, Japan
Tel.: (81) 425456111
Web Site: https://www.fostex.jp
Sales Range: $25-49.9 Million
Emp.: 30
Sales & Distribution of Audio & Sound
Equipment
N.A.I.C.S.: 423690

**Guangzhou Panyu Jiu Shui Keng
Foster Electric Factory** (1)
Jiu Shui Keng Cun Da Long Jie, Panyu Qu,
Guangzhou, 511450, Guangdong, China
Tel.: (86) 2084621172
Web Site: http://www.foster.co.jp
Telecommunications Equipment Mfr
N.A.I.C.S.: 334310

P.T. Foster Electric Indonesia (1)
Kawasan Industri Batamindo Block, 3 Jalan
Beringin Mukakuning, Batam, 29433,
Indonesia (100%)
Tel.: (62) 770611635
Sales Range: $550-599.9 Million
Emp.: 1,800
Sales & Distribution of Audio & Sound
Equipment
N.A.I.C.S.: 423690

**FOSTERVILLE SOUTH EXPLO-
RATION LTD.**
488-1090 West Georgia St, Vancou-
ver, V6E 3V7, BC, Canada
Tel.: (604) 229-9445
Web Site:
  http://www.fostervillesouth.com
FSXLF—(OTCQX)
Rev.: $390,158
Assets: $15,682,505
Liabilities: $354,901
Net Worth: $15,327,604
Earnings: ($3,331,321)
Emp.: 3
Fiscal Year-end: 12/31/23
Mineral Exploration Services
N.A.I.C.S.: 213115
Bryan Slusarchuk (Pres & CEO)

**FOSUN INTERNATIONAL LIM-
ITED**
Room 808 Industrial and Commercial
Bank of China Tower 3 Garden Road,
Central, China (Hong Kong)
Tel.: (852) 25093228
Web Site: https://en.fosun.com
Year Founded: 1992
656—(OTCIQ)
Rev.: $24,284,644,855
Assets: $113,971,264,953
Liabilities: $86,330,894,024
Net Worth: $27,640,370,929
Earnings: $638,695,171
Emp.: 108,000
Fiscal Year-end: 12/31/22
Investment Holding Company; Phar-
maceutical Products & Iron & Steel
Mfr & Sales
N.A.I.C.S.: 551112
Guangchang Guo (Founder & Co-
Chm)

Subsidiaries:

**Cares - Companhia de Seguros,
S.A.** (1)
Av Jose Malhoa 13-7, 1070-157, Lisbon,
Portugal
Tel.: (351) 21 440 50 81
Web Site: http://www.cares.pt
Commercial Banking Services
N.A.I.C.S.: 522110

Club Mediterranee SAS (1)
11 rue de Cambrai, 75957, Paris, Cedex
19, France (62.6%)
Tel.: (33) 153353553
Web Site: http://www.clubmed.com
Vacation Villages, Holiday Residences &
Tourist Hotels Owner & Operator
N.A.I.C.S.: 561599
Michel Wolfovski (Deputy CEO & CFO)

Subsidiary (Non-US):

**Club Med Australia & New
Zealand** (2)
227 Elizabeth Street Level 6, Sydney, 2001,
NSW, Australia
Tel.: (61) 2 9265 0500
Web Site: http://www.clubmed.com.au
Sales Range: $10-24.9 Million
Emp.: 89
Holiday Resorts Management Services
N.A.I.C.S.: 721110

Club Med Brasil SA (2)
Rua Lauro Muller 116 Sala 4201 Torre do
Rio Sul Botafogo, Rio de Janeiro, CEP
22290-160, RJ, Brazil
Tel.: (55) 2121234500
Web Site: http://www.Clubmed.com
Emp.: 150
Travel & Tourism Operating Services
N.A.I.C.S.: 561599

Club Med Ferias (2)
Rua Andrade Corvo 33B, Lisbon, 1050-008,
Portugal
Tel.: (351) 21 330 9696
Web Site: http://www.clubmed.pt
Travel & Tourism Operation Services
N.A.I.C.S.: 561599

Subsidiary (US):

**Club Med Management Services
Inc** (2)
6505 Blue Lagoon Dr Ste 225, Miami, FL
33126
Tel.: (305) 925-9168
Web Site: http://www.clubmed.us
Sales Range: $25-49.9 Million
Emp.: 80
Travel & Tourism Operation Services
N.A.I.C.S.: 561599

Subsidiary (Non-US):

Club Med Sales Canada Inc. (2)
3500 Boulevard De Maisonneuve Ouest
Tour 2 Place Alexis Nihon Ste 1500, Mon-
treal, H3Z 3C1, QC, Canada
Tel.: (514) 937-1428
Web Site: http://en.clubmedagents.ca
Travel & Tourism Operation Services
N.A.I.C.S.: 561599
Jacinda Lowry (Dir-Sls)

Subsidiary (US):

Club Med Sales, Inc. (2)
6505 Blue Lagoon Dr Ste 225, Miami, FL
33126 (100%)
Tel.: (305) 925-9168
Web Site: http://www.clubmed.us
Sales Range: $25-49.9 Million
Emp.: 100
Tour Operator Services
N.A.I.G.S.: 561510

Division (Domestic):

Club Med (3)
2151 E Broadway Rd Ste 204, Tempe, AZ
85282
Tel.: (480) 948-9190
Web Site: http://www.clubmed.com
Sales Range: $10-24.9 Million
Emp.: 75
Reservation Center & Ticket Sales
N.A.I.C.S.: 721110
Lori De Montmorency (Mgr-Bus Dev-
Meetings & Events)

Subsidiary (Non-US):

Club Med Vacances (Taiwan) Ltd (2)
Room A 7/F 101 Nanjing East Road Sec
104, Taipei, Taiwan
Tel.: (886) 2 2511 6611
Web Site: http://www.clubmed.com.tw
Travel & Tourism Operation Services

N.A.I.C.S.: 561599

**Club Med Viagens Unipessoal,
Lda** (2)
Rua Andrade Corvo 33 B, Lisbon, 1050-
008, Portugal
Tel.: (351) 213309696
Web Site: http://www.clubmed.pt
Sales Range: $25-49.9 Million
Emp.: 6
Tour Operating Services
N.A.I.C.S.: 561599

Subsidiary (Domestic):

**Club Med Villas et Chalets
Holding** (2)
11 Rue De Cambrai, 75957, Paris, France
Tel.: (33) 153353553
Web Site: http://www.clubmed.fr
Emp.: 700
Travel, Tourism Operations & Investment
Services
N.A.I.C.S.: 561599

Subsidiary (Domestic):

Club Med Villas et Chalets (3)
11 Rue De Cambrai, 75957, Paris, Cedex
19, France
Tel.: (33) 15 335 3553
Web Site: http://www.clubmed.fr
Travel, Tourism Operations & Investment
Services
N.A.I.C.S.: 561599

Subsidiary (Non-US):

Club Mediterranee Hellas S.A. (2)
4 Dimokritou Street, Kolonaki, 10671, Ath-
ens, Greece
Tel.: (30) 2103610207
Web Site: http://www.clubmed.net
Sales Range: $75-99.9 Million
Emp.: 500
Tour Operator
N.A.I.C.S.: 561520
Olivier Marque (Gen Mgr)

Club Mediterranee Holland BV (2)
Stadhouderskade 13, Amsterdam, 1054 ES,
Netherlands
Tel.: (31) 206070607
Web Site: http://www.clubmed.nl
Emp.: 10
Travel & Tourism Operation Services
N.A.I.C.S.: 561599

**Club Mediterranee Hong Kong
Ltd** (2)
Unit B 26/F Fortis Tower 77-79 Gloucester
Road, Wanchai, China (Hong Kong)
Tel.: (852) 3111 9388
Web Site: http://www.clubmed.com.hk
Travel & Tourism Operation Services
N.A.I.C.S.: 561599

Club Mediterranee Italia S.p.A. (2)
Via del Governo Vecchio 5/6, 00186, Rome,
Italy (100%)
Tel.: (39) 02 4149 4393
Web Site: http://www.clubmed.it
Resort, Spa & Tourism Accommodations
N.A.I.C.S.: 721199

Club Mediterranee K.K. (2)
Azabu Green Terrace 6F 3-20-1 Minami
Azabu, Minato-ku, Tokyo, 106 0047,
Japan (100%)
Tel.: (81) 3 5792 7627
Web Site: http://www.clubmed.co.jp
Sales Range: $25-49.9 Million
Emp.: 66
Tour Operator
N.A.I.C.S.: 561510

Club Mediterranee S.A. Belge (2)
523 Avenue Louise, 1050, Brussels,
Belgium (99.6%)
Tel.: (32) 70660660
Web Site: http://www.clubmed.be
Travel Agency
N.A.I.C.S.: 561510

**Club Mediterranee Services India Pri-
vate Ltd** (2)
2 B-118 WeWork Raheja Platinum Sag
Baug Road Off Andheri-Kurla Road, Marol
Andheri East, Mumbai, 400 059, Mahah-
rashtra, India

Tel.: (91) 225 097 2544
Web Site: https://www.clubmed.asia
Travel & Tourism Operation Services
N.A.I.C.S.: 561599

Club Mediterranee Suisse (2)
5 rue Francois Versonnex, CH-1207, Ge-
neva, Switzerland
Tel.: (41) 844855966
Web Site: http://www.clubmed.ch
Sales Range: $25-49.9 Million
Emp.: 20
Travel & Tourism Operation Services
N.A.I.C.S.: 561599
Fabio Calo (CEO)

Club Mediterranee U.K. Ltd. (2)
2nd floor Connect House 133-137 Alexan-
dra Road, Wimbledon, London, SW19 7JY,
United Kingdom (100%)
Tel.: (44) 8453676767
Web Site: http://www.clubmed.co.uk
Sales Range: $10-24.9 Million
Emp.: 30
Resort & Vacation Packages
N.A.I.C.S.: 721199

Subsidiary (US):

Holiday Village of Sandpiper Inc. (2)
4500 SE Pine Valley St, Port Saint Lucie,
FL 34952
Tel.: (772) 398-5100
Web Site: http://www.clubmed.us
Emp.: 200
Travel & Tourism Operation Services
N.A.I.C.S.: 561599
Henri Giscard D'Estaing (Pres)

Subsidiary (Non-US):

Vacances (Pty) Ltd (2)
Offices 212 - 214 2nd Floor Design Quarter
Cnr, William Nicol & Leslie Ave, Sandton,
2191, Gauteng, South Africa
Tel.: (27) 118402600
Web Site: http://www.clubmed.co.za
Emp.: 40
Travel & Tourism Operation Services
N.A.I.C.S.: 561599

FFT GmbH & Co. KGaA (1)
Schleyerstrasse 1, 36041, Fulda, Germany
Tel.: (49) 661 2926 0
Web Site: http://www.fft.de
Sales Range: $900-999.9 Million
Emp.: 2,601
Holding Company; Automotive Manufactur-
ing Machinery Mfr & Whslr
N.A.I.C.S.: 551112
Manfred Hahl (CEO)

Subsidiary (Domestic):

**FFT Produktionssysteme GmbH &
Co. KG** (2)
Industriepark Fulda West Schleyerstrasse 1,
36041, Fulda, Germany
Tel.: (49) 661 2926 0
Web Site: http://www.fft.de
Emp.: 800
Automotive Manufacturing Machinery Mfr &
Whslr
N.A.I.C.S.: 333248
Angela Huther (Head-HR)

Subsidiary (Non-US):

**FFT Espana Tecnologias de Automo-
cion S.A.** (3)
Area VIII del P G O U de Silla Avda de L
Amet 40-42, 46460, Silla, Spain
Tel.: (34) 96 121 9750
Construction Engineering Services
N.A.I.C.S.: 541330
Reinhard Volzing (Mng Dir)

FFT Mexico S.A. de C.V. (3)
Calle L Numero 3 Parque Industrial Puebla,
2000, Puebla, Mexico
Tel.: (52) 222 223 2200
Construction Engineering Services
N.A.I.C.S.: 541330
Enrico Stoelzner (Mng Dir)

**FFT Production Systems (Shanghai)
Co., Ltd.** (3)
No 388 Yuanda Rd, Anting Jiading District,
Shanghai, 201805, China
Tel.: (86) 216 916 9555

Web Site: http://www.fft.de
Emp.: 357
Construction Engineering Services
N.A.I.C.S.: 541330
Changhong Zhang *(CEO & Mng Dir)*

FFT Production Systems S.R.L. **(3)**
Str Traian No 223, 115100, Campulung,
Romania
Tel.: (40) 248 507 402
Construction Engineering Services
N.A.I.C.S.: 541330
Peter Walper *(Mng Dir)*

Subsidiary (US):

FFT Production Systems, Inc. **(3)**
1097 Highway 101 S Ste D-3, Greer, SC
29651
Tel.: (864) 469-7789
Construction Engineering Services
N.A.I.C.S.: 541330
Enrico Stolzner *(Mng Dir)*

**Fidelidade - Companhia de Seguros
SA** **(1)**
Largo Do Calhariz 30, 1249-001, Lisbon,
Portugal
Tel.: (351) 217948800
Web Site: https://www.fidelidade.pt
Insurance
N.A.I.C.S.: 524128

Subsidiary (Domestic):

Luz Saude, S.A. **(2)**
Rua Carlos Alberto da Mota Pinto Edificio
Amoreiras Square 17-9, 1070-313, Lisbon,
Portugal **(96.1%)**
Tel.: (351) 213138260
Web Site: https://www.luzsaude.pt
Rev.: $579,643,626
Assets: $789,651,343
Liabilities: $507,702,051
Net Worth: $281,949,292
Earnings: $20,680,659
Emp.: 12,492
Fiscal Year-end: 12/31/2017
Holding Company; Hospital, Out-Patient
Clinic & Senior Care Facility Operator &
Healthcare Services
N.A.I.C.S.: 551112
Jorge Manuel Batista Magalhaes Correia
(Chm)

Subsidiary (Domestic):

**Cliria - Hospital Privado de Aveiro,
S.A.** **(3)**
Rua do Brasil 21, 3800-009, Aveiro, Portu-
gal
Tel.: (351) 234400700
Web Site: https://www.hospitaldaluz.pt
Sales Range: $200-249.9 Million
Emp.: 249
Health Care Hospital Operating Services
N.A.I.C.S.: 622110
Paula Teixeira Menoita *(Dir-Nursing)*

**Espirito Santo - Unidades de Saude
e de Apoio a Terceira Idade,
S.A.** **(3)**
Rua Carlos Alberto Da Mota Pinto 17 9Fl,
1070-313, Lisbon, Portugal **(100%)**
Tel.: (351) 213138260
Sales Range: $10-24.9 Million
Emp.: 7
Hospital Management Services
N.A.I.C.S.: 622110
Isabel Vaz *(CEO)*

**Esumedica - Prestacao de Cuidados
medicos, S.A.** **(3)**
Rua Rodrigues Sampaio 103 2nd Floor,
1150-005, Lisbon, Portugal
Tel.: (351) 213503615
Web Site: http://www.esumedica.pt
Emp.: 5
Health Care Srvices
N.A.I.C.S.: 621610
Ernie Delfos *(Gen Mgr)*

**HOSPOR - Hospitais Portugueses,
S.A.** **(3)**
Rua Dom Manuel I 183, 4490-592, Povoa
de Varzim, Portugal
Tel.: (351) 25 269 0900
Web Site: https://www.hospitaldaluz.pt
Sales Range: $100-124.9 Million
Emp.: 100
Health Care Hospital Operating Services

N.A.I.C.S.: 622110
Sergio Viana *(Gen Dir)*

Hospital da Arrabida - Gaia, S.A. **(3)**
Praceta Henrique Moreira 150, 4400-346,
Vila Nova de Gaia, Portugal **(100%)**
Tel.: (351) 22 377 6800
Web Site: https://www.hospitaldaluz.pt
Hospital Management Services
N.A.I.C.S.: 622110
Manuel Krug de Noronha *(Dir-Gen Mgmt)*

Hospital da Luz, S.A. **(3)**
Avenida Lusiada 100, 1500-650, Lisbon,
Portugal **(100%)**
Tel.: (351) 21 710 4400
Web Site: https://www.hospitaldaluz.pt
Hospital Management Services
N.A.I.C.S.: 622110
Rita Ferreira *(Dir-Production Mgmt I)*

**RML - Residencia Medicalizada de
Ioures, SGPS, S.A.** **(3)**
Rua Carlos Alberto Da Mota Pinto 17 90,
Lisbon, 1070-313, Portugal **(75%)**
Tel.: (351) 213138260
Financial Management Services
N.A.I.C.S.: 523999

**Sociedade Gestora do Hospital de
Ioures, S.A.** **(3)**
Avenida Carlos Teixeira 3, Loures, 2670-
000, Portugal
Tel.: (351) 219847200
Web Site: http://www.hbeatrizangelo.pt
Hospital Management Services
N.A.I.C.S.: 622110
Artur Vas *(Member-Exec Bd-Admin)*

**Surgicare - Unidades de Saude,
S.A.** **(3)**
Rua Carlos Alberto Da Mota Pinto 17 9th
Flr, Lisbon, 1070-313, Portugal
Tel.: (351) 213138260
Emp.: 100
Health Practitioner Services
N.A.I.C.S.: 621399

**Vila Lusitano - Unidades de Saude,
S.A.** **(3)**
Rua Carlos Alberto Mota Pinto 17 90, 1070-
313, Lisbon, Portugal **(100%)**
Tel.: (351) 213138260
Emp.: 3
Hospital Management Services
N.A.I.C.S.: 622110
Vishaal Gupta *(Gen Mgr)*

Fosun Tourism Group. **(1)**
Tower S1 Bund Finance Center 600 Zhong-
shan No 2 Road East, Shanghai, 210010,
China
Tel.: (86) 2123156762
Web Site: http://www.fosunholiday.com
Rev.: $1,934,390,484
Assets: $5,325,373,966
Liabilities: $4,955,967,947
Net Worth: $369,406,019
Earnings: ($74,663,456)
Emp.: 14,070
Fiscal Year-end: 12/31/2022
Club & Resort Operator
N.A.I.C.S.: 721110
Jiannong Qian *(Chm)*

**Frankfurter Lebensversicherung
AG** **(1)**
Norsk-Data-Strasse 3, 61352, Bad Hom-
burg, Germany
Tel.: (49) 61725957000
Web Site: http://www.flgruppe.de
Third-Party Life Insurance Asset Manage-
ment Services
N.A.I.C.S.: 524292
Bernd Neumann *(Member-Mgmt Bd)*

Gland Pharma Limited **(1)**
Survey No 143-148 150 151 Near Gandi-
maisamma X Roads D P Pally, Dundigal
Gandimaisamma Mandal Medchal-Malkajgiri
District, Hyderabad, 500 043, Telangana,
India
Tel.: (91) 4030510999
Web Site: http://www.glandpharma.com
Pharmaceuticals Mfr.
N.A.I.C.S.: 325412
P. V. N. Raju *(Founder & Chm)*

Hainan Mining Co., Ltd. **(1)**

Building 8801 Walker Park Hainan Ecologi-
cal Software Park, High-tech Industrial
Demonstration Zone Chengmai County
Laocheng, Luoyang, 571927, Hainan, China
Tel.: (86) 89867482025
Web Site: https://www.hnmining.com
Rev.: $678,114,001
Assets: $1,677,158,126
Liabilities: $641,887,965
Net Worth: $1,035,270,162
Earnings: $86,355,702
Fiscal Year-end: 12/31/2022
Iron Ore Mining Services
N.A.I.C.S.: 212210

**Hauck & Aufhauser Privatbankiers
AG** **(1)**
Kaiserstrasse 24, 60311, Frankfurt, Ger-
many
Tel.: (49) 6921610
Web Site: http://www.hauck-aufhaeuser.com
Rev.: $26,735,333
Assets: $6,558,760,994
Liabilities: $6,329,161,192
Net Worth: $229,599,802
Earnings: $4,508,287
Emp.: 697
Fiscal Year-end: 12/31/2018
Bank Holding Company; Private Banking
Services
N.A.I.C.S.: 551111
Michael O. Bentlage *(Chm-Mgmt Bd)*

Subsidiary (Non-US):

**Hauck & Aufhauser (Schweiz)
AG** **(2)**
Talstrasse 58, 8001, Zurich, Switzerland
Tel.: (41) 44 220 11 22
Web Site: http://www.hauck-aufhaeuser.com
Asset Management Services
N.A.I.C.S.: 531390
Remy Schraner *(Chief Investment Officer)*

**Hauck & Aufhauser Fund Platforms
S.A.** **(2)**
1c rue Gabriel Lippmann, 5365, Munsbach,
Luxembourg
Tel.: (352) 4513141
Commercial Banking Services
N.A.I.C.S.: 522110

**Hauck & Aufhauser Investment Ge-
sellschaft S.A.** **(2)**
1c rue Gabriel Lippmann, 5365, Munsbach,
Luxembourg
Tel.: (352) 45 13 14 500
Web Site: http://www.hauck-aufhaeuser.com
Emp.: 350
Investment Management Service
N.A.I.C.S.: 523999
Achim Welschoff *(Mng Dir)*

**Oppenheim Pramerica Asset Man-
agement S.a r.l.** **(2)**
À 2 Boulevard Konrad Adenauer, 1115, Lux-
embourg, Luxembourg
Tel.: (352) 221522610
Web Site: http://www.oppenheim.lu
Sales Range: $50-74.9 Million
Emp.: 150
Open-End Investment Funds
N.A.I.C.S.: 525910

**Hauck Aufhauser Lampe Privatbank
AG** **(1)**
Kaiserstrasse 24, 60311, Frankfurt am
Main, Germany
Tel.: (49) 6921610
Web Site: https://www.hal-privatbank.com
Investment Banking Services
N.A.I.C.S.: 523150

Jeanne Lanvin SAS **(1)**
15 rue du Faubourg Saint-Honore, 75 008,
Paris, France **(65.6%)**
Tel.: (33) 1 44 71 31 25
Web Site: http://www.lanvin.com
Womenswear, Menswear, Kidswear & Ac-
cessories Retailer
N.A.I.C.S.: 458110
Jean-Philippe Hecquet *(CEO)*

Subsidiary (Non-US):

Lanvin Asia Pacific Ltd. **(2)**
Units M7-10 M/F New Henry House 10 Ice
House St, 18 Queens Road, Central, China
(Hong Kong)
Tel.: (852) 29681288

Web Site: http://www.lanvin.com
Clothing & Other Accessories Retailer
N.A.I.C.S.: 458110

Subsidiary (US):

Lanvin Inc. **(2)**
815 Madison Ave, New York, NY 10065-
5003
Tel.: (646) 613-9542
Web Site: http://www.lanvin.com
Clothing & Furnishings Whslr
N.A.I.C.S.: 424350
Ryan Petz *(Dir-PR)*

Subsidiary (Non-US):

Lanvin Japan K.K. **(2)**
7-9-17 Ginza Chuo-Ku, 104-0061, Tokyo,
Japan
Tel.: (81) 332892788
Web Site: http://www.lanvin.com
Clothing & Other Apparel Whslr
N.A.I.C.S.: 423990

Lanvin Group Holdings Limited **(1)**
4F 168 Jiujiang Road Carlowitz & Co,
Huangpu District, Shanghai, 200001,
China **(64.9%)**
Tel.: (86) 13636579351
Web Site: https://www.lanvin-group.com
Rev.: $379,307,533
Assets: $866,536,831
Liabilities: $509,332,704
Net Worth: $357,204,126
Earnings: ($93,901,404)
Emp.: 3,392
Fiscal Year-end: 12/31/2021
Holding Company
N.A.I.C.S.: 551112

Subsidiary (Non-US):

Arpege SAS **(2)**
13 Rue Du Faubourg Montmartre, 75009,
Paris, France
Tel.: (33) 969321921
Web Site: https://arpege.fr
Software Development Services
N.A.I.C.S.: 541511

Subsidiary (US):

L1 Bal Harbour LLC **(2)**
655 - 96th St, Bal Harbour, FL 33154
Tel.: (305) 677-0263
Web Site: https://www.balharbourflorida.com
Home Management Services
N.A.I.C.S.: 721110

L8 South Coast Plaza LLC **(2)**
3333 Bristol St, Costa Mesa, CA 92626
Web Site: https://www.southcoastplaza.com
Shopping Centre Services
N.A.I.C.S.: 531120

Subsidiary (Non-US):

**Primavera Capital Acquisition
Corporation** **(2)**
41/F Gloucester Tower 15 Queens Road,
Central, China (Hong Kong)
Tel.: (852) 37675100
Web Site:
https://www.primavera-capital.com
Rev.: $24,335,174
Assets: $415,120,730
Liabilities: $452,013,698
Net Worth: ($36,892,968)
Earnings: $20,879,042
Emp.: 2
Fiscal Year-end: 12/31/2021
Investment Services
N.A.I.C.S.: 523999

Raffaele Caruso S.p.A. **(2)**
Via Croce Rossa 2, 43019, Soragna, Italy
Tel.: (39) 0524512711
Web Site: https://carusomenswear.com
Clothing Fabric Mfr
N.A.I.C.S.: 314999

**Meadowbrook Insurance Group,
Inc.** **(1)**
26255 American Dr, Southfield, MI 48034-
6112
Tel.: (248) 358-1100
Web Site: http://www.meadowbrook.com
Sales Range: $800-899.9 Million
Holding Company; Insurance Products &
Services

Fosun International Limited—(Continued)
N.A.I.C.S.: 551112
Roger S. Walleck *(Exec VP)*

Subsidiary (Domestic):

Century Insurance Group (2)
550 Polaris Pkwy Ste 300, Westerville, OH 43082
Tel.: (614) 895-2000
Web Site: https://www.centurysurety.com
General Life & Property Insurance Services
N.A.I.C.S.: 524126
Jeff Weichman *(Principal)*

Commercial Carriers Insurance Agency, Inc. (2)
4 Centerpointe Dr Ste 300, La Palma, CA 90623
Tel.: (562) 404-4900
Web Site: https://www.cciainsurance.com
Emp.: 11
Commercial Insurance Services
N.A.I.C.S.: 524210

Florida Preferred Administrators, Inc. (2)
6000 Cattleridge Dr Ste 300, Sarasota, FL 34232-6064
Tel.: (941) 955-2133
Web Site:
  https://www.meadowbrookagency.com
Property & Casualty Insurance Services
N.A.I.C.S.: 524126

Interline Insurance Services, Inc. (2)
4 Centerpointe Dr Ste 300, La Palma, CA 90623
Tel.: (562) 404-0315
Web Site:
  https://www.interlineinsurance.com
Emp.: 1,000
General Insurance Services
N.A.I.C.S.: 524210

Liberty Premium Finance, Inc. (2)
4 Centerpointe Dr Ste 300, La Palma, CA 90623
Tel.: (562) 926-3522
Web Site: https://www.libertypf.com
Insurance Premium Financing Services
N.A.I.C.S.: 522291

Mackinaw Administrators, LLC (2)
PO Box 489, Brighton, MI 48116
Web Site:
  http://www.mackinawadministrators.com
Third-Party General Workers' Compensation & Liability Administration Services
N.A.I.C.S.: 541611
Stephen Flechsig *(Pres)*

Meadowbrook Insurance Agency Florida (2)
6000 Cattleridge Dr Ste 101, Sarasota, FL 34232-6064
Tel.: (941) 955-2133
Web Site:
  http://www.meadowbrookagencyfl.com
Insurance Services
N.A.I.C.S.: 524126
Dean Clemons *(Pres)*

Meadowbrook Insurance, Inc. (2)
2500 Fairlane Dr Ste 100, Montgomery, AL 36116-0047
Tel.: (334) 954-7200
Web Site: http://www.meadowbrook.com
Property & Casualty Insurance Services
N.A.I.C.S.: 524126

Meadowbrook, Inc. (2)
10100 W Charleston Blvd Ste 200, Las Vegas, NV 89135
Tel.: (702) 360-4292
Web Site: http://www.meadowbrook.com
General Insurance Services
N.A.I.C.S.: 524210

Multicare - Seguros de Saude, S.A. (1)
R Alexandre Herculano 53, 1269-152, Lisbon, Portugal
Tel.: (351) 217948880
Web Site: http://www.multicare.pt
Commercial Banking Services
N.A.I.C.S.: 522110

Paref SA (1)

153 Boulevard Haussmann, 75008, Paris, France **(71.37%)**
Tel.: (33) 33140298686
Web Site: https://www.paref.com
Sales Range: $50-74.9 Million
Real Estate Manangement Services
N.A.I.C.S.: 531210
Antoine Castro *(CEO)*

Peak Reinsurance Company Limited (1)
Room 6501-06 The Center 99 Queen's Road, Central, China (Hong Kong)
Tel.: (852) 3 509 6666
Web Site: https://www.peak-re.com
Insurance Services
N.A.I.C.S.: 524210
Li Tao *(Chm)*

Roc Oil Company Limited (1)
Level 11 20 Hunter Street, Sydney, 2000, NSW, Australia
Tel.: (61) 272092400
Web Site: http://www.rocoil.com.au
Rev.: $170,097,000
Emp.: 150
Fiscal Year-end: 12/31/2018
Oil & Gas Exploration
N.A.I.C.S.: 211120
Yuanlin Jiang *(CEO)*

Subsidiary (Non-US):

Roc Oil (Bohai) Company (2)
Room 502 Hyundai Motor Tower 38 Xiaoyun Road, Chaoyang District, Beijing, 100027, China
Tel.: (86) 105 611 7888
Web Site: http://www.rocoil.com.au
Oil & Gas Exploration Services
N.A.I.C.S.: 211120

Subsidiary (Domestic):

Roc Oil (WA) Pty Limited (2)
Suite 2 Ground Floor 100 Havelock Street, West Perth, 6005, WA, Australia
Tel.: (61) 8 9219 7111
Web Site: http://www.rocoil.com.au
Oil & Gas Exploration Services
N.A.I.C.S.: 211120

Subsidiary (Non-US):

Roc Oil Malaysia (Holding) Sdn Bhd (2)
Level 12 Menara Darussalam No 12 Jalan Pinang, 50450, Kuala Lumpur, Malaysia
Tel.: (60) 32 787 2200
Web Site: http://www.rocoil.com.au
Oil & Gas Exploration Services
N.A.I.C.S.: 211120

Shanghai Forte Land Co., Ltd. (1)
5-7 F Fosun Business Building 2 Fu Xing Rd, Shanghai, 200010, China
Tel.: (86) 2163320055
Web Site: https://www.forte.com.cn
Sales Range: $1-4.9 Billion
Emp.: 1,477
Property Development & Investment Services
N.A.I.C.S.: 531390
Wei Fan *(Exec Dir)*

Shanghai Fosun Capital Investment Management Co., Ltd. (1)
No 600 East Zhongshan No 2 Road, Huangpu District Shanghai Bund Financial Center S1, Shanghai, 200010, China
Tel.: (86) 2163325858
Web Site: https://www.fosuncapital.com
Private Equity Fund Management Services
N.A.I.C.S.: 523999

Shine Star (Hubei) Biological Engineering Co., Ltd. (1)
No 666 Chanling Avenue, Douhudi Town Gong An, Jingzhou, 434300, Hubei, China
Tel.: (86) 7165209888
Web Site: https://www.shine-star.com.cn
Biological Product Mfr
N.A.I.C.S.: 325412

St. Hubert SAS (1)
13-15 rue du Pont des Halles, 94150, Rungis, Cedex, France
Tel.: (33) 969326600
Web Site: https://www.sthubert.fr
Food Spreads Mfr & Marketer

N.A.I.C.S.: 311999
Patrick Cahuzac *(CEO)*

Wolford AG (1)
Wolffordstrasse 1, 6900, Bregenz, Austria **(58.05%)**
Tel.: (43) 820899915
Web Site: https://company.wolford.com
Rev.: $135,456,508
Assets: $138,697,388
Liabilities: $159,259,659
Net Worth: ($20,562,271)
Earnings: ($37,628,966)
Emp.: 1,106
Fiscal Year-end: 12/31/2022
Women's Undergarments, Hosiery & Swimwear Mfr
N.A.I.C.S.: 315250
Junyang Shao *(Chm-Supervisory Bd)*

Subsidiary (Non-US):

Wolford (Schweiz) AG (2)
Thurgauerstrasse 117, Glattpark, 8152, Opfikon, Switzerland
Tel.: (41) 448101616
Web Site: http://www.wolfordshop.ch
Tights, Stockings, Leggings, Apparel, Lingerie & Shapewear Mfr
N.A.I.C.S.: 424310

Subsidiary (US):

Wolford America, Inc. (2)
330 7th Ave Ste 1702, New York, NY 10001
Tel.: (212) 453-5556
Web Site: http://www.wolford.com
Childrens & Infants Clothing & Accessories Whslr
N.A.I.C.S.: 424350

Subsidiary (Non-US):

Wolford Belgium N.V (2)
Britselei 23, Antwerp, 2000, Belgium
Tel.: (32) 34513930
Web Site: http://www.wolford.com
Leggings, Tights & Other Apparel Mfr
N.A.I.C.S.: 315990

Wolford Canada Inc. (2)
753 Burrard St, Vancouver, V6Z 1X6, BC, Canada
Tel.: (604) 647-0201
Web Site: http://www.wolfordshop.net
Luxe Hosiery & Lingerie Retailer
N.A.I.C.S.: 315250

Wolford Deutschland GmbH (2)
Widenmayerstrasse 42, 80538, Munich, Germany **(100%)**
Tel.: (49) 89290520
Web Site: http://www.wolfordshop.de
Luxe Hosiery & Lingerie Retailer
N.A.I.C.S.: 315250

Wolford Espana, S.L. (2)
Alcala 85 8, 28009, Madrid, Spain **(100%)**
Tel.: (34) 902887075
Web Site: http://www.wolfordshop.es
Luxe Hosiery & Lingerie Retailer
N.A.I.C.S.: 315250

Wolford Italia S.R.L. (2)
Corso Venezia 8, 20121, Milan, Italy
Tel.: (39) 027 639 1088
Web Site: http://www.wolford.it
Luxe Hosiery & Lingerie Retailer
N.A.I.C.S.: 315250

Wolford London Ltd. (2)
20 Bedford Square Office 10 & 11, London, WC1B 3HH, United Kingdom
Tel.: (44) 8002798279
Web Site: http://www.wolford.com
Luxe Hosiery & Lingerie Retailer
N.A.I.C.S.: 315250

Wolford Nederland B.V. (2)
Pieter Cornelisz Hooftstraat 17a, 1071 BL, Amsterdam, Netherlands
Tel.: (31) 9009909908
Web Site: http://www.wolfordshop.nl
Luxe Hosiery & Lingerie Retailer
N.A.I.C.S.: 315250

Wolford Paris S.A.R.L. (2)
8 rue des Quatre fils, 75003, Paris, France **(100%)**
Tel.: (33) 148043492
Web Site: http://www.wolford.com

Luxury Hosiery & Lingerie Retailer
N.A.I.C.S.: 315250

Wolford Scandinavia Aps (2)
Amagertorv 29 A 3 Sal, 1160, Copenhagen, Denmark **(100%)**
Tel.: (45) 33149560
Web Site: http://www.wolfordshop.dk
Luxe Hosiery & Lingerie Retailer
N.A.I.C.S.: 315250

Wolverhampton Wanderers Football Club (1986) Limited (1)
Molineux Stadium Waterloo Road, Wolverhampton, WV1 4QR, W Midlands, United Kingdom
Tel.: (44) 3712221877
Web Site: http://www.wolves.co.uk
Professional Soccer Club
N.A.I.C.S.: 711211

FOTEX HOLDING SE
272 rue de Neudorf, L-2222, Luxembourg, Luxembourg
Tel.: (352) 28992826
Web Site: http://fotex.lu
FOTEX—(LUX)
Rev.: $37,512,400
Assets: $281,182,041
Liabilities: $97,376,576
Net Worth: $183,805,465
Earnings: $13,773,116
Emp.: 132
Fiscal Year-end: 12/31/20
Financial Investment Services
N.A.I.C.S.: 523940
Gabor Varszegi *(Chm)*

Subsidiaries:

Ajka Crystal Glass Factory Ltd. (1)
Alkotmany Street 4, Ajka, 8400, Veszprem, Hungary
Tel.: (36) 88510521
Web Site: http://www.ajka-crystal.hu
Crystal Products Mfr & Distr
N.A.I.C.S.: 339999

Ajka Crystal USA (1)
Eszter Varszegi Chancy 7157 Obelisco Cir, Carlsbad, CA 92009
Tel.: (888) 512-2552
Web Site: http://www.ajka-crystal.hu
Crystal Products Distr
N.A.I.C.S.: 423220

Balaton Butor Kft. (1)
Hazgyari ut 4, 8200, Veszprem, Hungary
Tel.: (36) 88425866
Web Site: http://www.balaton-butor.hu
Furniture Mfr
N.A.I.C.S.: 337211

Fotex Netherlands B.V. (1)
Sarphatikade 13, 1017 WV, Amsterdam, Netherlands
Tel.: (31) 206102151
Property Management Services
N.A.I.C.S.: 531312

Fotexnet kft. (1)
Fotex Plaza Palatinus utca 1, 1025, Budapest, Hungary
Tel.: (36) 14873600
Web Site: https://www.fotexnet.info
Business Management Services
N.A.I.C.S.: 541611

Hungaroton Records Kft. (1)
Rottenbiller utca 47, 1071, Budapest, Hungary
Tel.: (36) 1 8881200
Web Site: http://www.hungaroton.hu
Music Records Distr
N.A.I.C.S.: 449210

Primo Zrt. (1)
Reitter Ferenc Utca 39-49, 1135, Budapest, Hungary
Tel.: (36) 1350 24 11
Men's Clothing Retailer
N.A.I.C.S.: 458110

Sigma Kft. (1)
Tel.: (36) 14873720
Web Site: https://www.sigma-property.com
Sales Range: $50-74.9 Million
Property Management & Consulting Services

N.A.I.C.S.: 531210

FOTONATION LIMITED
Cliona Building One Parkmore East
Business Park, Galway, Ballybrit,
Ireland
Tel.: (353) 91477000   IE
Web Site: http://www.fotonation.com
Year Founded: 1997
Emp.: 30
Embedded Image Processing
N.A.I.C.S.: 334419
Petronel Bigioi *(Sr VP-Engrg & Gen Mgr)*

FOUAD ALGHANIM & SONS GROUP OF COMPANIES
Al Hamra Business Tower 31st Floor
Al Shuhada St, PO Box 2118, Safat,
13022, Kuwait, Kuwait
Tel.: (965) 22212051
Web Site:
http://www.falghanimgroup.com
Year Founded: 1965
Sales Range: $350-399.9 Million
Emp.: 20,000
Holding & Trading Company Civil
Power & Electro-mechanical & Oil &
Gas Aviation & Airlines Investment
Industrial Healthcare Businesses &
Shipping Services
N.A.I.C.S.: 551112
Fouad M. T. Alghanim *(Chm)*

Subsidiaries:

Ahgar International Co.   (1)
PO Box 2485, Shuwaikh Industrial Safat,
13025, Kuwait, Kuwait
Tel.: (965) 24824016
Web Site: https://www.aic-kw.com
Information Technology Services
N.A.I.C.S.: 541511

Al Musaha Al Mushtaraka Co.   (1)
Block-1 Street-1 Al-Ghazzali Street,
Shuwaikh Industrial Area, 900003, Kuwait,
Kuwait
Tel.: (965) 24824010
Polystyrene Thermal Insulation Mfr
N.A.I.C.S.: 326140

Al-Ahlia Integrated General Trading &
Contracting Co. W.L.L   (1)
Block 3 Safat, PO Box 22240, Kuwait,
13083, Kuwait
Tel.: (965) 22254530
Web Site: https://ahliainteg.net
Electrical Contracting Services
N.A.I.C.S.: 238210

Al-Ghanaem Industrial Company   (1)
St MA4 Plot 6, Shuaiba, Kuwait, Kuwait
Tel.: (965) 23261982
Industrial Mineral Distr
N.A.I.C.S.: 423520

Alghanim Group of Shipping & Trans-
port W.L.L.   (1)
Alfour St Bldg Abdul Mahson Marzook, PO
Box 20842, Safat, Kuwait, 13069,
Kuwait   (100%)
Tel.: (965) 2421701
Web Site: http://www.alghanimgroup.com
Sales Range: $25-49.9 Million
Emp.: 56
Provider of Transportation Services
N.A.I.C.S.: 488210

Alghanim International for Rental
Equipment Co. W.L.L   (1)
Zina St Al-Hayat Complex Mezzanine Floor
Souk Al-Dakhili, PO Box 30, Shuwaikh In-
dustrial Area, 15251, Kuwait, Kuwait
Tel.: (965) 24919903
Equipment Rental Services
N.A.I.C.S.: 532490

Energy International for Petroleum
Projects KCSC   (1)
Awqaf Complex No 11 First Fl Tower 12
Mubarak An Kabeer St Sharq, Safat,
13052, Kuwait, Kuwait   (50%)
Tel.: (965) 2437729
Web Site: http://www.eippc.com

Sales Range: $150-199.9 Million
Emp.: 20
Distr of Petroleum Products
N.A.I.C.S.: 424720

Fouad Alghanim & Sons Automotive
Co.   (1)
Street No 11 Pepsi Cola Street Block No 11
Building No 56A, PO Box 29329, Safat, Ku-
wait, 13154, Kuwait
Tel.: (965) 1811118
Web Site: http://www.faa.com.kw
Automobile Dealers
N.A.I.C.S.: 423110

Kuwait Continental Hotel Co.   (1)
Bneid Algar, PO Box 21047, Safat, Kuwait,
13071, Kuwait
Tel.: (965) 22527300
Web Site: http://www.kcontl.net
Hotel & Restaurant Operator
N.A.I.C.S.: 721110

Kuwait Network Electronic Technol-
ogy Company W.L.L   (1)
31st Floor Al Hamra Tower AL Shuhada
Street, Sharq, Kuwait, Kuwait
Tel.: (965) 22212051
Web Site: http://www.knetco.com.kw
Telecom Construction Contracting Services
N.A.I.C.S.: 237130

Masaha Heavy Equipment Co.   (1)
349 St, PO Box 2485, Ahmadi, Kuwait,
60000, Kuwait
Tel.: (965) 22021290
Web Site: https://www.masahaglobal.com
Heavy Equipment Distr
N.A.I.C.S.: 423810

Riham General Trading & Contr. Co.
W.L.L   (1)
PO Box 2118, Safat, 13022, Kuwait, Kuwait
Tel.: (965) 22633631
Web Site: https://rihamco.com
Construction Product Distr
N.A.I.C.S.: 423390

Tube Clean GmbH   (1)
Untere Bahnhofstrasse 25, 8340, Hinwil,
Switzerland
Tel.: (41) 43 843 10 90
Web Site: http://www.compritubeclean.com
Industrial Nozzle & Projectile Mfr
N.A.I.C.S.: 326199

United Aluminum & Metal Coating
Co. W.L.L   (1)
PO Box 1696, Safat, 13017, Kuwait, Kuwait
Tel.: (965) 24554710
Web Site: https://www.uamcco.com
Engineering Services
N.A.I.C.S.: 541330

FOUNDER HOLDINGS LIMITED
Unit 1408 14th Floor Cable TV Tower,
9 Hoi Shing Road, Tsuen Wan, New
Territories, China (Hong Kong)
Tel.: (852) 26114111   BM
Web Site: https://www.irasia.com
Year Founded: 1992
FOU1—(DEU)
Rev.: $122,378,877
Assets: $189,621,839
Liabilities: $55,422,700
Net Worth: $134,199,139
Earnings: $4,441,193
Emp.: 1,088
Fiscal Year-end: 12/31/22
Software Development Services
N.A.I.C.S.: 541511
Jin Zuo *(Exec Dir)*

FOUNDER SECURITIES CO., LTD.
Room 3701 3717 Bldg 4 & 5 Huayu-
anhua Center No 36 Section 2, Xi-
angjiang Middle Rd Tianxin District,
Changsha, Hunan, China
Tel.: (86) 73185832367
Web Site: https://www.foundersc.com
Year Founded: 1994
601901—(SHG)
Rev.: $999,472,149

Assets: $31,230,808,474
Liabilities: $24,759,590,656
Net Worth: $6,471,217,818
Earnings: $302,204,247
Fiscal Year-end: 12/31/23
Security Brokerage Services
N.A.I.C.S.: 523150

FOUNDER TECHNOLOGY GROUP CORP.
Block K 9F Huamin Hanzun Interna-
tional Building, No 726 Yanan West
Road Changning District, Beijing,
200050, China
Tel.: (86) 2158400030
Web Site:
https://www.foundertech.com
Year Founded: 1985
600601—(SHG)
Rev.: $686,372,469
Assets: $809,367,741
Liabilities: $324,721,360
Net Worth: $484,646,381
Earnings: ($59,465,367)
Emp.: 6,955
Fiscal Year-end: 12/31/22
Computer & Computer Peripheral
Equipment Mfr & Sales
N.A.I.C.S.: 334118
Jian Liu *(Chm)*

Subsidiaries:

Founder International Co., Ltd.   (1)
Founder International Building Creative In-
dustrial Park, No 328 Xinghu Road Suzhou
Industrial Park, Suzhou, 215123, Jiangsu,
China
Tel.: (86) 512 86665500
Web Site:
http://www.founderinternational.com
Software Development Services
N.A.I.C.S.: 513210

Subsidiary (Domestic):

Founder International (Beijing) Co.,
Ltd.   (2)
5th Floor Founder International Building No
52 Beisihuan West Road, Haidian District,
Beijing, 100080, China
Tel.: (86) 1082343333
Software Development Services
N.A.I.C.S.: 513210

Founder International (Changchun)
Co., Ltd.   (2)
Room 312 Floor 3 No 987 Yanan Avenue,
Chaoyang District, Changchun, China
Tel.: (86) 43189156253
Software Development Services
N.A.I.C.S.: 513210

Founder International (Guangzhou)
Co., Ltd.   (2)
Room 502 No 299 Jingtai Building
Guangzhou Avenue Middle Road, Yuexiou
District, Guangzhou, 510600, China
Tel.: (86) 2028829213
Software Development Services
N.A.I.C.S.: 513210

Founder International (Jiangsu) Co.,
Ltd.   (2)
4f/5f Building 2 No 2 Binjiang West Road,
Rm 506 Jiangyin Software Park, Jiangyin,
214433, Jiangsu, China
Tel.: (86) 51086023366
Software Development Services
N.A.I.C.S.: 513210

Founder International (Wuhan) Co.,
Ltd.   (2)
Floor 10-11 Multi-purpose Building Hongfu-
tianmei Square, No 938 Xiongchu Avenue,
Wuhan, 430070, Hubei, China
Tel.: (86) 2759597100
Software Development Services
N.A.I.C.S.: 513210

FOUNDER'S CONSULTANTS HOLDINGS, INC.
Hakata Station East 3-6-18, Hakata
Ward, Fukuoka, 812-0013, Japan

Tel.: (81) 924128300
Web Site: https://www.fchd.jp
Year Founded: 2017
6542—(TKS)
Rev.: $53,031,720
Assets: $57,746,480
Liabilities: $10,916,100
Net Worth: $46,830,380
Earnings: $4,167,400
Emp.: 413
Fiscal Year-end: 06/30/24
Business Management Services
N.A.I.C.S.: 561110

Subsidiaries:

Earth System Science Co., Ltd.   (1)
1-23-1 Shinjuku Marune Building 7th Floor,
Shinjuku-ku, Tokyo, 160-0022, Japan
Tel.: (81) 333571761
Web Site: http://www.ess-jpn.co.jp
Construction Consultancy Services
N.A.I.C.S.: 541618

Ecoplan Co., Ltd.   (1)
Yubinbango 808-0146 Wakamatsu Taka-
sunishi, Kitakyushu, 808-0146, Japan
Tel.: (81) 937415189
Web Site: http://www.ecoplan.jp
Emp.: 15
Software Services
N.A.I.C.S.: 541511

Fukuyama Business Network Co.,
Ltd.   (1)
3-6-18 Hakataekihigashi, Hakata-ku, Fu-
kuoka, Japan
Tel.: (81) 92 471 1437
Web Site: https://www.f-bn.jp
Business Consulting Services
N.A.I.C.S.: 541611
Tadashi Wakabayashi *(Pres)*

Kankyou Bousai Co., Ltd.   (1)
1-57 Ayu-cho, Tokushima, 770-0046, Japan
Tel.: (81) 886320111
Web Site: http://www.kankyobousai.jp
Environment & Disaster Prevention Ser-
vices
N.A.I.C.S.: 562910

Social Value Incubation Lab Co.,
Ltd.   (1)
2-3-2 Koraku, Bunkyo-ku, Tokyo, 112-0004,
Japan
Tel.: (81) 358446249
Construction Consultancy Services
N.A.I.C.S.: 541618

FOUNDING CONSTRUCTION DEVELOPMENT CO., LTD.
3F No 294 Section 1 Dunhua South
Road, Daan District, Taipei, Taiwan
Tel.: (886) 227025887
Web Site:
https://www.founding.com.tw
Year Founded: 1991
5533—(TAI)
Rev.: $123,085,708
Assets: $388,137,923
Liabilities: $73,773,306
Net Worth: $314,364,617
Earnings: $29,089,995
Emp.: 241
Fiscal Year-end: 12/31/23
Residential & Commercial Buildings
Construction, Development, Sales &
Leasing
N.A.I.C.S.: 236116
Hsin-Hsiung Liu *(Co-Chm)*

FOUNDPAC GROUP BERHAD
Plot 35 Hilir Sungai Keluang 2 Bayan
Lepas Industrial Estate, Non-Free
Industrial Zone Phase IV Bayan
Lepas, 11900, Penang, Malaysia
Tel.: (60) 46309336   MY
Web Site: https://www.foundpac.com
Year Founded: 1965
FPGROUP—(KLS)
Rev.: $15,319,153
Assets: $25,931,460
Liabilities: $3,031,550

FoundPac Group Berhad—(Continued)

Net Worth: $22,899,910
Earnings: $1,501,148
Emp.: 388
Fiscal Year-end: 06/30/23
Investment Holding Services
N.A.I.C.S.: 551112
Ong Choon Heng *(CEO)*

Subsidiaries:

FP Stencil Sdn. Bhd. **(1)**
No 8 Lintang Beringin 1 Off Jalan, Permatang Damar Laut, 11960, Bayan Lepas, Malaysia
Tel.: (60) 46266233
Web Site: https://fpstencil.com
Cutting Machinery Mfr & Distr
N.A.I.C.S.: 333517

Plea Sdn. Bhd. **(1)**
Building 2 Plot 35 Hilir Sungai Keluang 2, Industrial Estate Non-Free Industrial Zone Phase IV Bayan Lepas, 11900, Bayan Lepas, Malaysia
Tel.: (60) 125970872
Web Site: https://plea.my
Tracking Device Distr
N.A.I.C.S.: 423610

Sin Yen Technologies Sdn. Bhd. **(1)**
3 Solok Beringin 1, Batu Maung, 11960, Bayan Lepas, Malaysia
Tel.: (60) 46261682
Web Site: https://www.sinyen.com
Coil Winding Machine Mfr & Distr
N.A.I.C.S.: 333519

FOUNDRY FUEL PRODUCTS LTD.

7 C Acharya Jagdish Chandra Bose Road P S Shakespeare Sarani, Kolkata, 700 017, India
Tel.: (91) 22268441
Web Site:
   https://www.foundryfuel.co.in
Year Founded: 1964
513579—(BOM)
Assets: $13,333
Liabilities: $102,704
Net Worth: ($89,371)
Earnings: ($26,269)
Fiscal Year-end: 03/31/23
Metallurgical Coke Mfr
N.A.I.C.S.: 331110
Devendra Kumar Agarwalla *(Exec Dir)*

FOUNTAIN ASSET CORP.

99 Scollard St, Toronto, M5R 1G4, ON, Canada
Tel.: (416) 456-7019   Ca
Web Site:
   https://fountainassetcorp.com
Year Founded: 2005
FA—(TSXV)
Rev.: $19,804
Assets: $5,131,572
Liabilities: $103,120
Net Worth: $5,028,452
Earnings: ($3,972,101)
Fiscal Year-end: 12/31/23
Investment Services
N.A.I.C.S.: 523150
Paul A. Kelly *(Chm)*

FOUNTAIN FROZEN LTD .

Salters Way Cromwell Road, Wisbech, PE14 0SH, Cambridgeshire, United Kingdom
Tel.: (44) 1945 581 424
Web Site:
   http://www.fountainfrozen.co.uk
Food Products Distr
N.A.I.C.S.: 424420

FOUNTAIN S.A.

17 Avenue de l'artisanat, Braine L'alleud, 1420, Brussels, Belgium
Tel.: (32) 23890810

Web Site: https://www.fountain.eu
Year Founded: 1972
FOU—(EUR)
Sales Range: $100-124.9 Million
Hot Beverage Dispenser Mfr
N.A.I.C.S.: 333310
Eric Dienst *(CFO)*

FOUNTAIN SET (HOLDINGS) LIMITED

Block A 6/F Eastern Sea Industrial Building, 29-39 Kwai Cheong Road, Kwai Chung, New Territories, China (Hong Kong)
Tel.: (852) 24851881
Web Site: https://www.fshl.com
0420—(HKG)
Rev.: $771,839,738
Assets: $643,462,538
Liabilities: $206,932,245
Net Worth: $436,530,293
Earnings: ($11,878,410)
Emp.: 5,900
Fiscal Year-end: 12/31/22
Investment Holding Services
N.A.I.C.S.: 523940
Gordon Yen *(Vice Chm)*

Subsidiaries:

Dongguan Shatin Lake Side Textiles Printing & Dyeing Co., Ltd. **(1)**
Lake Side Industrial Park Shatian Environmental Industrial Estate, Shatian Town, Dongguan, 523999, Guangdong, China
Tel.: (86) 76988866583
Emp.: 2,800
Printed Fabric Mfr
N.A.I.C.S.: 313310

Folktune Limited **(1)**
Rm A 7 F Eastern Sea Indl Bldg 29-39 Kwai Cheong Rd, 48-56 Tai Lin Pai Rd, Kwai Chung, New Territories, China (Hong Kong)
Tel.: (852) 24851881
Web Site: http://www.fshl.com
Sales Range: $150-199.9 Million
Emp.: 300
Fabric & Yarn Sales
N.A.I.C.S.: 424310
Chung Fong Ha *(Chm)*

Fountain Set (Europe) Limited **(1)**
1st Floor 68 Great Eastern Street, London, EC2A 3JT, Shoreditch, United Kingdom
Tel.: (44) 2076165922
Fabrics Mfr
N.A.I.C.S.: 314999

Fountain Set Limited **(1)**
Block A 6/F Eastern Sea Industrial Building 29-39 Kwai Cheong Road, Kwai Chung, New Territories, China (Hong Kong)
Tel.: (852) 24251010
Knitted Fabrics & Garments Supplier
N.A.I.C.S.: 424310

Goldlink Thread Limited **(1)**
Block A 6/F Eastern Sea Industrial Building 29-39 Kwai Cheong Road, Kwai Chung, New Territories, China (Hong Kong)
Tel.: (852) 24101010
Web Site: http://www.fshl.com
Sales Range: $25-49.9 Million
Emp.: 100
Sewing Thread Mfr & Sales
N.A.I.C.S.: 313110

Highscene Limited **(1)**
Block A 6/F Eastern Sea Industrial Building 29-39 Kwai Cheong Road, Kwai Chung, New Territories, China (Hong Kong)
Tel.: (852) 3 478 6388
Web Site: http://www.fshl.com
Yarn Mfr
N.A.I.C.S.: 313110

Hiway Textiles Limited **(1)**
6/F Eastern Sea Industrial Building 29-39 Kwai Cheong Road, Kwai Chung, New Territories, China (Hong Kong)
Tel.: (852) 3 478 6668
Web Site: http://www.hiwaytextiles.com
Sales Range: $100-124.9 Million
Emp.: 300
Children Wear Garments Mfr

N.A.I.C.S.: 315210
Jiangyin Fuhui Textiles Limited **(1)**
9 Xiao Shan Road, Jiangyin, 214434, Jiangsu, China
Tel.: (86) 51086406888
Emp.: 3,300
Knitted Fabric Mfr
N.A.I.C.S.: 313240

Jiangyin Jintian Machinery Limited **(1)**
99 Eastern Binjiang Rd, Jiangyin, 214434, Jiangsu, China
Tel.: (86) 51086193999
Web Site: http://www.jtm-machinery.com
Sales Range: $100-124.9 Million
Emp.: 300
Textile Machinery Mfr
N.A.I.C.S.: 333248

Kaiping Hui Hua Textiles Limited **(1)**
22 GangKou Rd, Kaiping, 529300, Guangdong, China
Tel.: (86) 7502291832
Yarns Mfr & Sales
N.A.I.C.S.: 313110

Lake Side Printing Factory Limited **(1)**
Unit A2 on 5/F Unit A1 on 7/F Eastern Sea Industrial Building 29-39, Kwai Cheong Road, Kwai Chung, New Territories, China (Hong Kong)
Tel.: (852) 24851881
Web Site: http://www.fshl.com
Emp.: 300
Knitted Fabric Mfr
N.A.I.C.S.: 313240

Ningbo Young Top Garments Co., Ltd **(1)**
No 66-68 Dan Xia Road, Xiangshan Industrial Development Xiangshan, Ningbo, 315700, Zhejiang, China
Tel.: (86) 57465781178
Garments Mfr & Sales
N.A.I.C.S.: 315210

Ocean Lanka (Private) Limited **(1)**
Biyagama Export Processing Zone Block B, Walgama, Malwana, Western Province, Sri Lanka
Tel.: (94) 11 482 7100
Web Site: https://www.oceanlanka.com
Weft Knitted Fabrics Mfr
N.A.I.C.S.: 313240

P.T. Sandang Mutiara Cemerlang **(1)**
JL Warung Bongkok Desa Sukadanau, Cibitung-Bekasi, Jakarta, Indonesia
Tel.: (62) 2189107383
Fabrics Mfr
N.A.I.C.S.: 314999

Prosperlink (Macao Commercial Offshore) Limited **(1)**
Avenida Da Praia Grande No 599 Edificio Comercial Rodrigues 5th Floor, Unit B, Macau, China (Macau)
Tel.: (853) 83943000
Knitted Fabric Mfr
N.A.I.C.S.: 313240

Prosperlink (Macau Commercial Offshore) Limited **(1)**
Avenida Da Praia Grande No 599 Edificio Comml Rodrigues, 5th Fl Unit B, Macau, China (Macau)
Tel.: (853) 83943000
Yarn Dyestuffs Mfr & Sales
N.A.I.C.S.: 313110

Shanghai Fuhui Textiles Trading Co., Ltd. **(1)**
1st Floor Tower A President Enterprises Building, Song Hong Road No 568 West Tian Shan Road, Shanghai, China
Tel.: (86) 2152174998
Fabrics Mfr
N.A.I.C.S.: 314999

Shenzhen Faun Textiles Limited **(1)**
49 F Block A United Plz Caitian Rd, Futian, Shenzhen, 518026, Guangdong, China
Tel.: (86) 75582966188
Fabrics & Dyed Yarn Sales
N.A.I.C.S.: 424310

Suqian Young Top Garments Co. Ltd. **(1)**

Building No 5 - No 6 Zone A, Standard Facility in Technical Economic Development Area, Suqian, 223800, JiangSu, China
Tel.: (86) 52784567766
Fabrics Mfr
N.A.I.C.S.: 314999

Triumph Luck Limited **(1)**
Unit 06B 37/F Cable TV Tower 9 Hoi Shing Rd, Tsuen Wan, New Territories, China (Hong Kong)
Tel.: (852) 24220000
Knit Wear & Casual Wear Mfr
N.A.I.C.S.: 315120

Yancheng Fuhui Textiles Limited **(1)**
No 38 Huang Shan South Road Economic Development Zone, Yancheng, 224045, Jiangsu, China
Tel.: (86) 5156 866 3888
Web Site: http://www.fshl.com
Sales Range: $150-199.9 Million
Emp.: 1,000
Knitted Fabrics, Dyeing & Finishing Mfr
N.A.I.C.S.: 313240

FOUNTAIN TIRE CORP.

1006 103A Street SW Suite 301, Edmonton, T6W 2P6, AB, Canada
Tel.: (780) 464-3700
Web Site:
   https://www.fountaintire.com
Year Founded: 1956
Emp.: 150
Tire Distr
N.A.I.C.S.: 441340
Brent Hesje *(CEO)*

FOUNTAINE PAJOT SA

Zone Industrielle, 17290, Aigrefeuille-d'Aunis, France
Tel.: (33) 546357040
Web Site: https://www.fountaine-pajot.com
Year Founded: 1976
ALFPC—(EUR)
Sales Range: Less than $1 Million
Cruising Catamaran Mfr
N.A.I.C.S.: 336612
Jean-Francois Fountaine *(Co-Founder)*

FOUNTAINVEST PARTNERS (ASIA) LIMITED

Suite 705-8 ICBC Tower 3 Garden Road, Central, China (Hong Kong)
Tel.: (852) 39723900   HK
Web Site:
   http://www.fountainvest.com
Year Founded: 2007
Rev.: $100,000,000,000
Emp.: 50
Privater Equity Firm
N.A.I.C.S.: 523999
Terry Hu *(Founder & Co-Pres)*

FOUR COMMUNICATIONS GROUP PLC

20 St Thomas Street, London, SE1 9BF, United Kingdom
Tel.: (44) 2036974200   UK
Web Site:
   http://www.fourcommunications.com
Year Founded: 2001
Sales Range: $50-74.9 Million
Emp.: 150
Holding Company; Advertising Agencies
N.A.I.C.S.: 551112
Nan Williams *(Grp CEO)*

Subsidiaries:

Four Communications plc **(1)**
20 St Thomas Street, London, SE1 9BF, United Kingdom
Tel.: (44) 2036974200
Web Site:
   http://www.fourcommunications.com
Advertising Agency Services
N.A.I.C.S.: 541810

Einir Williams *(Mng Dir)*

FOUR MARKETING LTD.
20 Garrett Street London, London,
United Kingdom
Tel.: (44) 2076083100
Web Site:
http://www.fourmarketing.com
Fashion Industry Services
N.A.I.C.S.: 458110
Charles Perez *(Sec)*

Subsidiaries:

Agent Provocateur Limited **(1)**
154 Clerkenwell Road, London, EC1R 5AB,
United Kingdom
Tel.: (44) 20 7923 5200
Web Site: http://www.agentprovocateur.com
Lingerie Whslr
N.A.I.C.S.: 424350
Michelle Ryan *(CEO)*

FOUR NINES GOLD INC/CA
1000 - 409 Granville St, Vancouver,
V6C 1T2, BC, Canada
Tel.: (604) 602-0001
Web Site:
https://www.fourninesgold.ca
FNAU—(CNSX)
Assets: $634,491
Liabilities: $165,048
Net Worth: $469,443
Earnings: ($385,524)
Fiscal Year-end: 01/31/24
Mineral Exploration Services
N.A.I.C.S.: 213115
Charles Ross *(CEO)*

FOUR SEAS MERCANTILE HOLDINGS LIMITED
21/F Manhattan Place No 23 Wang
Tai Road, Kowloon Bay, China (Hong
Kong)
Tel.: (852) 2 799 9777   HK
Web Site:
http://www.fourseasgroup.com.hk
Year Founded: 1971
0374—(HKG)
Rev.: $610,072,304
Assets: $432,372,044
Liabilities: $255,580,577
Net Worth: $176,791,467
Earnings: $2,555,352
Emp.: 2,800
Fiscal Year-end: 03/31/22
Snack Food Mfr
N.A.I.C.S.: 311919
Stephen Tak Fung Tai *(Chm)*

Subsidiaries:

Cowboy Food Company Limited **(1)**
Block A 13/F and A3 12/F Yee Lim Indus-
trial Centre, 2-28 Kwai Lok Street, Kwai
Chung, China (Hong Kong)
Tel.: (852) 26143418
Food Mfr
N.A.I.C.S.: 311999

Four Seas (Hebei) Food Company
Limited **(1)**
Malanyu, Zunhua, Hebei, 064206, China
Tel.: (86) 3156944768
Food Mfr
N.A.I.C.S.: 311999

Four Seas (Suzhou) Food Co.,
Ltd. **(1)**
26 Hong feng Road, Suzhou Industrial
Park, Suzhou, 215021, Jiangsu, China
Tel.: (86) 51267619618
Food Mfr
N.A.I.C.S.: 311999

Four Seas Confectionery (Shenzhen)
Co., Ltd. **(1)**
75 Xin Guang Road Xiti Zhen Nanshan,
Shenzhen, 518055, Guangdong, China
Tel.: (86) 755 2662 3297
Confectionery Mfr
N.A.I.C.S.: 311340

Ginbis Four Seas Foods (Shantou)
Company Limited **(1)**
Shengping Industry Area Daxue Road,
Shantou, 515021, Guangdong, China
Tel.: (86) 754 8254 1380
Web Site: http://fourseasgroup.com.hk
Emp.: 100
Biscuit Mfr
N.A.I.C.S.: 311919
Takashi Miyamoto *(Owner)*

J.P. Inglis Company Limited **(1)**
21/F Manhattan Place, No 23 Wang Tai
Road, Kowloon Bay, China (Hong Kong)
Tel.: (852) 22195000
Food Mfr
N.A.I.C.S.: 311999

Kanro Four Seas Foods (Shantou)
Company Limited **(1)**
Yuepu Industrial Park South, Shantou,
515021, Guangdong, China
Tel.: (86) 7548108811
Web Site: http://www.fourseasgroup.com.hk
Snack Food Mfr
N.A.I.C.S.: 311919

Li Fook (Qingdao) Foods Company
Limited **(1)**
Xixiaoshui Village, Cheng Yang District,
Qingdao, 266107, Shandong, China
Tel.: (86) 532 8787 1645
Web Site: http://www.fourseasgroup.com.hk
Snack Food Mfr
N.A.I.C.S.: 311919

Murray Catering Company
Limited **(1)**
No 18 Tin Hau Road, Nan Fung Industrial
City Block 5, Tuen Mun, NT, China (Hong
Kong)
Tel.: (852) 24548993
Web Site: https://www.murray.com.hk
Catering Services
N.A.I.C.S.: 722320

New Kondo Trading Company
Limited **(1)**
21/F Manhattan Place 23 Wang Tai Road,
Kowloon Bay, China (Hong Kong)
Tel.: (852) 22195200
Web Site: https://www.newkondo.com.hk
Emp.: 60
Food Distr
N.A.I.C.S.: 424490

Nico Four Seas (Shantou) Company
Limited **(1)**
Yuepu Industrial Park South, Shantou,
515021, Guangdong, China
Tel.: (86) 7548115519
Web Site: http://www.fourseasgroup.com.hk
Snack Food Mfr
N.A.I.C.S.: 311919

Shenzhen Matchless Food Co.,
Ltd **(1)**
Building 1 Hebei Industrial District 1
Zhongxing Road Buji, Shenzhen, 518129,
Guangdong, China
Tel.: (86) 755 8471 5282
Sales Range: $25-49.9 Million
Emp.: 20
Snack Food Mfr
N.A.I.C.S.: 311919
Ling Chiu Hui *(Gen Mgr)*

Tsun Fat (Hui Zhou) Biscuit Factory
Limited **(1)**
Long Hu Industrial District, Shui Kou, Hu-
izhou, 516005, Guangdong, China
Tel.: (86) 752 231 8637
Web Site: http://www.fourseasgroup.com.hk
Sales Range: $100-124.9 Million
Emp.: 400
Snack Food Mfr
N.A.I.C.S.: 311919

FOUR SEASONS EDUCATION (CAYMAN) INC.
Room 1301 Zi an Building 309
Yuyuan Road, Jingan Disctrict,
Shanghai, 200040, China
Tel.: (86) 2163176177   Ky
Web Site: https://www.ir.sijiedu.com
Year Founded: 2007

FEDU—(NYSE)
Rev.: $17,261,569
Assets: $92,766,229
Liabilities: $20,367,400
Net Worth: $72,398,830
Earnings: $381,847
Emp.: 190
Fiscal Year-end: 02/29/24
Educational Support Services
N.A.I.C.S.: 611710
Peiqing Tian *(Founder & Chm)*

FOUR WAY DISTRIBUTORS LTD.
11415 120st, Edmonton, T5G 2Y3,
AB, Canada
Tel.: (780) 453-1005
Web Site:
http://www.fourwaydistributors.ca
Rev.: $10,575,760
Emp.: 27
Food Products Mfr
N.A.I.C.S.: 311999
Blaine Munro *(VP-Sls)*

FOURACE INDUSTRIES GROUP HOLDINGS LIMITED
Unit No 07 11/F Manhattan Centre 8
Kwai Cheong Road, Kwai Chung
New Territories, Hong Kong, China
(Hong Kong)
Tel.: (852) 24876976   Ky
Web Site: https://www.fourace.com
Year Founded: 1988
1455—(HKG)
Rev.: $61,057,842
Assets: $60,624,985
Liabilities: $13,575,274
Net Worth: $47,049,711
Earnings: $7,702,815
Emp.: 778
Fiscal Year-end: 03/31/22
Holding Company
N.A.I.C.S.: 551112
Kai Ming Tsang *(CFO)*

FOURLANE FORD SALES LTD.
4412 - 50th Street, Innisfail, T4G
1P7, AB, Canada
Tel.: (403) 227-3311
Web Site:
http://www.fourlaneford.com
Year Founded: 1993
New & Used Car Dealers
N.A.I.C.S.: 441110
Jeff Denham *(Dealer Principal & Gen
Mgr)*

FOURLIS HOLDINGS S.A.
18-20 Sorou Str Building A, Marousi,
GR-15125, Athens, Greece
Tel.: (30) 2106293000
Web Site: https://www.fourlis.gr
Year Founded: 1950
FOYRK—(ATH)
Rev.: $541,095,403
Assets: $811,679,258
Liabilities: $594,664,364
Net Worth: $217,014,893
Earnings: $21,329,592
Emp.: 2,511
Fiscal Year-end: 12/31/22
Fixed Assets & Real Estate Manage-
ment Services
N.A.I.C.S.: 531390
Lida Fourlis *(Dir-Corp Social Respon-
sibility)*

Subsidiaries:

FOURLIS TRADE AEBE **(1)**
Sorou 1820 151 25 Maroussi, Neo psy-
chiko, 154 51, Athens, Greece
Tel.: (30) 2106293000
Sales Range: $25-49.9 Million
Emp.: 50
Consumer Electronics Distr
N.A.I.C.S.: 423620

GENCO BULGARIA LTD **(1)**
82 Boulevard Dondukov, 1504, Sofia, Bul-
garia
Tel.: (359) 29849858
Sales Range: $25-49.9 Million
Emp.: 50
Sporting Goods Mfr
N.A.I.C.S.: 339920

GENCO TRADE SRL **(1)**
Strada Biharia Nr 67-77 Cladirea Metav
Businsess Park, Sector 1, 013981, Bucha-
rest, Romania
Tel.: (40) 212011180
Web Site: https://www.entersport.ro
Sales Range: $150 100.0 Million
Emp.: 350
Sporting Goods Distr
N.A.I.C.S.: 423910
Antoniu Nituleasa *(Gen Mgr)*

Housemarket SA **(1)**
Building 501 Commerial Park of A I A El
Venizelos, Paiania, 19019, Athens, Greece
Tel.: (30) 2106293000
Web Site: https://www.housemarket.gr
Home Furnishings Retailer
N.A.I.C.S.: 449210
Dafni Fourli *(Chm)*

INTERSPORT ATHLETICS AE **(1)**
60 Varis Ave, Vari, 16672, Athens, Greece
Tel.: (30) 2102806000
Web Site: http://www.intersport.gr
Sales Range: $50-74.9 Million
Emp.: 60
Sporting Goods Distr
N.A.I.C.S.: 423910

Intersport Athletics (Cyprus) Ltd. **(1)**
Evagorou 20, 1065, Nicosia, Cyprus
Tel.: (357) 22410140
Web Site: https://www.intersport.com.cy
Sports Apparel Retailer
N.A.I.C.S.: 458110

FOURTH DIMENSION SOLU-TIONS LIMITED
Bungalow No BP-13 Top Floor West
Patel Nagar, New Delhi, 110008, In-
dia
Tel.: (91) 7926566588   In
Web Site: http://www.fdsindia.co.in
Year Founded: 2011
FOURTHDIM—(NSE)
Rev.: $2,574,738
Assets: $20,395,072
Liabilities: $397,518
Net Worth: $19,997,554
Earnings: $538,781
Fiscal Year-end: 03/31/23
Technical Support Services
N.A.I.C.S.: 561499
Rajesh Thakur *(Mng Dir)*

FOURTH GENERATION INFOR-MATION SYSTEMS LIMITED
Flat no 301 SAAI PRIYA apart H No
6366376301 Jaffer Ali Bagh, Soma-
jiguda, Hyderabad, 82, India
Tel.: (91) 4023376096
Web Site: https://www.fgisindia.com
532403—(BOM)
Assets: $160,713
Liabilities: $208,996
Net Worth: ($48,283)
Earnings: ($18,751)
Fiscal Year-end: 03/31/23
Hardware & Software Development &
Consulting Services
N.A.I.C.S.: 541511
C. N. Somasekhar Reddy *(Mng Dir)*

FOV FABRICS AB
Norrby Langgatan 45, Boras, 504 35,
Sweden
Tel.: (46) 33206300
Web Site: http://www.fov.se
Year Founded: 1960
Sales Range: $25-49.9 Million
Emp.: 125
Woven Fabrics Mfr

FOV Fabrics AB—(Continued)
N.A.I.C.S.: 313210
Mats Lundgren *(Mng Dir & Mgr-Mktg)*

FOWLER HYUNDAI LTD.
3900 Victoria Avenue West, Brandon,
R7B 3X3, MB, Canada
Tel.: (204) 727-1461
Web Site:
　http://www.fowlerhyundai.ca
Year Founded: 1982
Sales Range: $10-24.9 Million
Emp.: 32
Car Dealer
N.A.I.C.S.: 441110
David Lee *(Mgr-Sls)*

FOX MARBLE HOLDINGS PLC
160 Camden High St, London, NW1
0NE, United Kingdom
Tel.: (44) 207 380 0999　　　　UK
Web Site: http://www.foxmarble.net
Year Founded: 2011
FOX—(AIM)
Sales Range: $1-9.9 Million
Emp.: 83
Marble Quarrying
N.A.I.C.S.: 212319
Christopher Gilbert *(CEO)*

FOX RIVER RESOURCES CORPORATION
141 Adelaide Street West Suite 301,
Toronto, M5H 1L5, ON, Canada
Tel.: (416) 972-9222
Year Founded: 2015
FOX—(CNSX)
Rev.: $39,826
Assets: $1,344,276
Liabilities: $284,798
Net Worth: $1,059,478
Earnings: ($1,067,883)
Fiscal Year-end: 10/31/23
Nonmetallic Mineral Mining Services
N.A.I.C.S.: 213115
Stephen Case *(Pres)*

FOX WIRE LIMITED
Sheephouse Wood, Stocksbridge,
S36 4GS, Sheffield, United Kingdom
Tel.: (44) 1142884207　　　　　UK
Web Site: http://www.foxwire.co.uk
Year Founded: 1846
Sales Range: $10-24.9 Million
Emp.: 50
Stainless Steel & Nickel Alloy Wire
Mfr
N.A.I.C.S.: 332618
Oliver Baker *(Owner)*

FOX-WIZEL LTD.
Hermon Street Airport-City, PO Box
76, Ben-Gurion Airport, Lod,
7019900, Israel
Tel.: (972) 39051740
Web Site: http://www.fox.co.il
Year Founded: 1995
FOX—(TAE)
Rev.: $1,487,559,584
Assets: $2,128,902,301
Liabilities: $1,502,744,554
Net Worth: $626,157,747
Earnings: $57,622,875
Emp.: 12,000
Fiscal Year-end: 12/31/23
Apparel Accessories & Other Apparel
Manufacturing
N.A.I.C.S.: 315990
Avraham Zeldman *(Chm)*

Subsidiaries:

Fox Group Canada Ltd.　　　　　(1)
200 Fairbank Avenue, Toronto, M6B 1G1,
ON, Canada
Tel.: (647) 499-4988
Women Accessories Mfr & Distr

N.A.I.C.S.: 315990

FOXTONS GROUP PLC
Building One Chiswick Park 566
Chiswick High Road, London, W4
5BE, United Kingdom
Tel.: (44) 2078936000
Web Site:
　https://www.foxtonsgroup.co.uk
Year Founded: 1981
FOXT—(OTCIQ)
Rev.: $177,129,513
Assets: $285,504,923
Liabilities: $130,660,187
Net Worth: $154,844,736
Earnings: $11,521,081
Emp.: 1,201
Fiscal Year-end: 12/31/22
Offices of Real Estate Agents & Brokers
N.A.I.C.S.: 531210
Nicholas Budden *(CEO)*

FOYER S.A.
12 rue Leon Laval, L-3372, Leudelange, Luxembourg
Tel.: (352) 437 437
Web Site: http://www.foyer.lu
Year Founded: 1922
Sales Range: $5-14.9 Billion
Emp.: 583
General Insurance Services
N.A.I.C.S.: 524298
Francois Tesch *(Chm)*

Subsidiaries:

CapitalatWork Foyer Group S.A.　(1)
Kroonlaan 153, 1050, Brussels, Belgium
Tel.: (32) 2 673 77 11
Web Site: http://www.capitalatwork.com
Emp.: 35
Real Estate Manangement Services
N.A.I.C.S.: 531390
Michel Tilmant *(Exec Dir)*

WEALINS S.A.　　　　　　　　　(1)
12 rue Leon Laval, 3372, Leudelange,
Luxembourg　　　　　　　　(100%)
Tel.: (352) 437435200
Web Site: http://www.iwi.lu
Fire Insurance Services
N.A.I.C.S.: 524113

FOYLE FOOD GROUP LTD.
Lisahally Campsie County, Londonderry, BT47 6TJ, Northern Ireland, United Kingdom
Tel.: (44) 2871 860691
Web Site:
　http://www.foylefoodgroup.com
Year Founded: 1976
Sales Range: $350-399.9 Million
Emp.: 704
Meat Product Whslr
N.A.I.C.S.: 424470
Ursula O'Neill *(Mgr-Group Technical)*

Subsidiaries:

Foyle Bio-Energy　　　　　　　(1)
Lisahally, Campsie, Londonderry, BT47
6TJ, Ireland
Tel.: (353) 2871861120
Food Products Distr
N.A.I.C.S.: 424490

Foyle Ingredients　　　　　　　(1)
52 Doogary Road, Omagh, Tyrone, BT79
0BQ, Ireland
Tel.: (353) 2882243201
Food Products Distr
N.A.I.C.S.: 424490

FP CORPORATION
1-13-15 Akebonocho, Fukuyama,
721-8607, Hiroshima, Japan
Tel.: (81) 849531145
Web Site: https://www.fpco.jp
Year Founded: 1962
7947—(TKS)
Rev.: $1,468,081,000

Assets: $1,973,613,800
Liabilities: $1,009,584,960
Net Worth: $964,028,840
Earnings: $77,495,640
Emp.: 984
Fiscal Year-end: 03/31/24
Foamed Polystyrene & Other Synthetic Resin Containers Mfr & Sales
N.A.I.C.S.: 322220
Morimasa Sato *(Pres)*

Subsidiaries:

Cook Labo Co., Ltd.　　　　　　(1)
Oak Tower 6-8-1 Nishi-Shinjuku, Shinjuku-
Ku, Tokyo, 160-0023, Japan
Tel.: (81) 353257502
Food Containers Mfr
N.A.I.C.S.: 322299

Ducks Co.　　　　　　　　　　(1)
1108-1 Nodagou Togitsu-chou, Nishisonogi-
gun, Nagasaki, 851-2104, Japan
Tel.: (81) 9 5882 0439
Plastic Food Containers Mfr
N.A.I.C.S.: 322219

FP CHUPA Corp.　　　　　　　(1)
6-8-1 Nishi-Shinjuku Shinjuku Oak Tower
35F, Shinjuku-Ku, Tokyo, 163-6035, Japan
Tel.: (81) 353392270
Web Site: http://www.chupa.co.jp
Sales Range: $50-74.9 Million
Emp.: 130
Disposable Food Containers Mfr
N.A.I.C.S.: 322219

FP Corporation - Fukuyama
Plant　　　　　　　　　　　(1)
1-13-15 Akebonocho, Fukuyama, 721-8607,
Hiroshima, Japan
Tel.: (81) 849531145
Web Site: https://www.fpco.jp
Emp.: 692
Disposable Food Containers Mfr
N.A.I.C.S.: 322219
Morimasa Sato *(Pres)*

FP Corporation - Hokkaido Plant　(1)
Sakaemachi Building 15-1-1 Kita 42 Johi-
gashi, Higashi-ku, Sapporo, 007-0842, Hok-
kaido, Japan
Tel.: (81) 117952246
Web Site: http://www.fpcorp.co.jp
Sales Range: $125-149.9 Million
Emp.: 300
Plastic Food Containers Mfr
N.A.I.C.S.: 322219

FP Trading Co., Ltd.　　　　　(1)
1-13-13 Akebonocho, Fukuyama, 721-0952,
Hiroshima, Japan
Tel.: (81) 849547717
Sales Range: $50-74.9 Million
Emp.: 5
Plastic Food Containers Distr
N.A.I.C.S.: 424610

FPCO ALRight Co. Ltd.　　　　(1)
2918-46 Mobira, Kasaoka, 714-0062,
Okayama, Japan
Tel.: (81) 8 6566 3000
Web Site: http://www.e-alright.com
Emp.: 138
Plastic Containers & Cardboard Mfr & Whslr
N.A.I.C.S.: 326112
Hashiguchi Saiwaizo *(Pres)*

FPCO Ai Pack Co.　　　　　　(1)
511 5 Aza Murahigashi Nanba Wanouchi
cho, Anpachi-gun, Gifu, 503-0231, Japan
Tel.: (81) 584682041
Disposable Food Containers Mfr
N.A.I.C.S.: 322219

FPCO Chubu Co.　　　　　　　(1)
157-1 Shimoogure Wanouchicho, Ampachi-
Gun, Gifu, 503-0205, Japan
Tel.: (81) 584692985
Sales Range: $50-74.9 Million
Emp.: 200
Disposable Food Containers Mfr
N.A.I.C.S.: 322219

FPCO Dia Foods Co., Ltd.　　　(1)
22nd Floor Daibiru Main Building 3-6-32
Nakanoshima, Kita-ku, Osaka, 530-0005,
Japan
Tel.: (81) 64412474

Web Site: https://fp-diafoods.jp
Emp.: 36
Plastic Food Containers Mfr
N.A.I.C.S.: 322219

FPCO Engineering, Ltd.　　　　(1)
1-12-15 Akebono-cho, Fukuyama-shi, Hiro-
shima, 721-8607, Japan
Web Site:
Engineering & Manufacturing Services
N.A.I.C.S.: 541330

FPCO Fukuyama Co.　　　　　(1)
1-13-15 Akebono-cho, Fukuyama, 721-
8607, Hiroshima, Japan
Tel.: (81) 849531145
Web Site: http://www.fpco.jp
Plastic Food Containers Mfr
N.A.I.C.S.: 326140

FPCO International Package Co.,
Ltd.　　　　　　　　　　　(1)
6-6-1 Tendai, Inage-ku, Chiba, 263-0016,
Japan
Tel.: (81) 432531321
Web Site: https://fp-interpack.jp
Emp.: 240
Food Container Whslr
N.A.I.C.S.: 424130

FPCO Ishida Co., Ltd.　　　　　(1)
5-4-10 Shoko Center, Nishi-ku, Hiroshima,
733-0833, Japan
Tel.: (81) 822777055
Web Site: https://fp-ishida.jp
Emp.: 32
Food Container Whslr
N.A.I.C.S.: 424130

FPCO Kasaoka Co.　　　　　　(1)
100-1 Mochinoe, Kasaoka, 714-0066,
Okayama, Japan
Tel.: (81) 865665060
Plastic Food Containers Mfr
N.A.I.C.S.: 322219

FPCO Minoshima Co.　　　　　(1)
95-6 Minooki-cho, Fukuyama, 721-0956,
Hiroshima, Japan
Tel.: (81) 849538849
Plastic Food Containers Mfr
N.A.I.C.S.: 322219

FPCO Saga Co, Ltd.　　　　　(1)
1830-1 Ishinari, Yoshinogaricho Kanzaki-
Gun, Saga, Japan
Tel.: (81) 952527877
Web Site: http://www.fpco.jp
Sales Range: $25-49.9 Million
Emp.: 80
Plastics Product Mfr
N.A.I.C.S.: 326199

FPCO Shimodate, Ltd.　　　　　(1)
411 Nishiyamada, Chikusei, 308-0867, Iba-
raki, Japan
Tel.: (81) 296232545
Disposable Food Containers Mfr
N.A.I.C.S.: 322219

FPCO Ueda Co.　　　　　　　(1)
4-18-10 Higashifukuhara, Yonago, 683-
0802, Tottori, Japan
Tel.: (81) 859330751
Web Site: https://p-ueda.co.jp
Emp.: 38
Food Container Whslr
N.A.I.C.S.: 424130

FPCO Yamagata, Ltd.　　　　　(1)
162 Chuokogyodanchi, Sagae, 991-0061,
Yamagata, Japan
Tel.: (81) 237853600
Sales Range: $125-149.9 Million
Emp.: 300
Disposable Food Containers Mfr
N.A.I.C.S.: 326140
Jo Masaaki *(Gen Mgr)*

I-Logic Co., Ltd.　　　　　　　(1)
Shinjuku Oak Tower 36F 6-8-1 Nishishin-
juku, Shinjuku-ku, Tokyo, 160-0023, Japan
Tel.: (81) 353257750
Logistics & Distribution Services
N.A.I.C.S.: 541614

Teika-Precision Co.　　　　　　(1)
8-12 Ikurashiroyama Miyamae-cho, Kameoka, 621-0241, Kyoto, Japan
Tel.: (81) 771265115
Web Site: https://www.teika-precision.co.jp

Emp.: 21
Injection Molded Plastic Products Mfr
N.A.I.C.S.: 326199
Ikuta Yukinobu *(Pres)*

FP NEWSPAPERS INC.

650 West Georgia Street Suite 2900,
PO Box 11583, Vancouver, V6B 4N8,
BC, Canada
Tel.: (604) 681-8817　　　　　Ca
Web Site:
　　https://www.fpnewspapers.com
Year Founded: 2002
FP—(TSXV)
Rev.: $6,796
Assets: $3,959,073
Liabilities: $261,270
Net Worth: $3,697,803
Earnings: ($2,431,473)
Fiscal Year-end: 12/30/23
Newspaper Publisher & Distr
N.A.I.C.S.: 513110

Subsidiaries:

FP Canadian Newspapers Limited
Partnership　　　　　　　　　　(1)
1355 Mountain Ave, Winnipeg, R2X 3B6,
MB, Canada
Tel.: (204) 697-7000
Web Site: http://www.fpnewspapers.com
Newspaper Publishers
N.A.I.C.S.: 513110

FPM AGROMEHANIKA A.D.

Dorda Simeonovica 25, 19370, Bolje-
vac, Serbia
Tel.: (381) 30463531
Web Site: https://www.fpm.rs
Year Founded: 1961
Sales Range: $1-9.9 Million
Emp.: 233
Agricultural Machinery Mfr
N.A.I.C.S.: 333111
Rajic Branislav *(CEO & Gen Dir)*

FPS FOOD PROCESSING SYS-TEMS B.V.

Burgemeester G.J.F. Tijdemanstraat
13, 2631 RE, Pijnacker, Netherlands
Tel.: (31) 153107757
Web Site: http://www.fpsholding.nl
Holding Company
N.A.I.C.S.: 551112
J. J. Gras *(CEO)*

Subsidiaries:

AWETA Holding B.V.　　　　　　(1)
Burgemeester Winkellaan 3, 2631 HG,
Nootdorp, Netherlands
Tel.: (31) 886688000
Web Site: http://www.aweta.nl
Sales Range: $75-99.9 Million
Emp.: 120
Holding Company
N.A.I.C.S.: 551112
Rin Alleblas *(Mgr-Mktg)*

Subsidiary (US):

AWETA -Autoline, Inc,　　　　　(2)
621 West J St, Yakima, WA 98902
Tel.: (509) 248-8200
Web Site: http://www.aweta.com
Sales Range: $25-49.9 Million
Emp.: 100
Food Grading & Packing Equipment
N.A.I.C.S.: 333111

Subsidiary (Non-US):

AWETA FRANCE S.A.S.　　　　(2)
Chemin du Cou, Lagnes, 84800, Avignon,
France
Tel.: (33) 490882166
Web Site: http://www.aweta.com
Sales Range: $25-49.9 Million
Emp.: 6
Food Handling Sales, Engineering & Ser-
vices
N.A.I.C.S.: 311999

Subsidiary (Domestic):

AWETA G&P　　　　　　　　　(2)
Burgemeester Winkellaan 3, 2631 HG,
Nootdorp, Netherlands
Tel.: (31) 8 866 88 000
Web Site: http://www.aweta.nl
Sales Range: $50-74.9 Million
Emp.: 120
Commercial Machinery
N.A.I.C.S.: 333310

Subsidiary (Non-US):

AWETA Sistemi S.p.A.　　　　(2)
Via Adriano Olivetti 79, 47522, Cesena,
Italy
Tel.: (39) 0547316900
Web Site: http://www.aweta.nl
Sales Range: $25-49.9 Million
Emp.: 60
Food Handling Equipment Mfr
N.A.I.C.S.: 333311
Marco Pozzi *(Gen Mgr)*

Diamond Automations Inc.　　(1)
23400 Haggerty Rd, Farmington Hills, MI
48335
Tel.: (248) 476-7100
Web Site: http://www.dma-group.com
Sales Range: $50-74.9 Million
Emp.: 120
Egg Grading & Packing Equipment
N.A.I.C.S.: 333111

Jamesway Incubator Company
Inc.　　　　　　　　　　　　　(1)
30 High Ridge Court, Cambridge, N1R 7L3,
ON, Canada
Tel.: (519) 624-4646
Web Site: https://www.jamesway.com
Sales Range: $25-49.9 Million
Emp.: 80
Farm Machinery Equipment & Incubators
Mfr
N.A.I.C.S.: 333111
Jesus Campa *(Sls Dir-Latin America &
Spain)*

MOBA B.V.　　　　　　　　　(1)
Statyonsweg 117, Stationsweg 117, Bar-
neveld, 3771FP, Netherlands
Tel.: (31) 342455655
Web Site: http://www.moba.nl
Sales Range: $125-149.9 Million
Emp.: 200
Egg Grading Packing & Peripheral Equip-
men Mfr
N.A.I.C.S.: 333111
Michiel Peters *(Mng Dir)*

OvoPro　　　　　　　　　　　(1)
23400 Haggerty Rd, Farmington Hills, MI
48335
Tel.: (248) 476-3876
Web Site: http://www.ovopro.com
Sales Range: $50-74.9 Million
Emp.: 120
Egg Processing
N.A.I.C.S.: 112310

Petersime N.V.　　　　　　　(1)
Centrumstraat 125, Zulte, 9870, Belgium
Tel.: (32) 93889611
Web Site: http://www.petersime.com
Sales Range: $50-74.9 Million
Emp.: 150
Poultry Machinery
N.A.I.C.S.: 333111
Stef Vanneste *(CEO)*

FPT CORPORATION

FPT Tower 10 Pham Van Bach Street
Dich Vong Ward, Cau Giay District,
Hanoi, Vietnam
Tel.: (84) 2473007300
Web Site: https://www.fpt.com.vn
FPT—(HOSE)
Rev.: $5,261,790,100
Assets: $6,028,282,800
Liabilities: $3,034,981,700
Net Worth: $2,993,301,100
Earnings: $646,519,000
Emp.: 42,408
Fiscal Year-end: 12/31/23
Software Development Services
N.A.I.C.S.: 541511

Gia Binh Truong *(Chm)*

Subsidiaries:

Cardinal Peak, LLC　　　　　(1)
2569 Park Ln Ste 102, Lafayette, CO
80026
Tel.: (303) 665-3962
Web Site: http://www.cardinalpeak.com
Sales Range: $1-9.9 Million
Emp.: 14
Custom Product Development Contract En-
gineering Consulting
N.A.I.C.S.: 541618

Cyradar Joint Stock Company
Ltd.　　　　　　　　　　　　　(1)
9th Floor FPT Tower 10 Pham Van Bach
street, Cau Giay District, Hanoi, Vietnam
Tel.: (84) 2473006066
Web Site: https://www.cyradar.com
Cyber Security Services
N.A.I.C.S.: 541512

FPT Asia Pacific Pte. Ltd.　　(1)
8 Kallang Avenue 12-09 Aperia Tower 1,
Singapore, 339509, Singapore
Tel.: (65) 63384353
Information Technology Services
N.A.I.C.S.: 541519

FPT Australasia Pty., Ltd.　　(1)
Level 39 2 Park Street, Sydney, 2000,
NSW, Australia
Tel.: (61) 417238103
Information Technology & Software Devel-
opment Services
N.A.I.C.S.: 541512

FPT Canada Co., Ltd.　　　　(1)
242 Rue de Bayeux, Boucherville, J4B 7T9,
QC, Canada
Tel.: (514) 566-5658
Software Development Services
N.A.I.C.S.: 541511

FPT Company for Information Tech-
nology WLL　　　　　　　　　(1)
Anas Bin Malik, Al Malqa, Riyadh, 13521,
Saudi Arabia
Tel.: (966) 547661425
Software Development Services
N.A.I.C.S.: 541511

FPT Deutschland GmbH　　　(1)
Am Thyssenhaus 1-3 Haus 3, 45128, Es-
sen, Germany
Tel.: (49) 20149039350
Software Development Services
N.A.I.C.S.: 541511

FPT Digital Retail Joint Stock
Company　　　　　　　　　　(1)
263 Khanh Hoi quan 4 Tp, Ho Chi Minh
City, Vietnam
Tel.: (84) 8 7302 6666
Computer Hardware Retailer
N.A.I.C.S.: 449210

FPT Education Company Limited　(1)
FPT Cau Giay Building Block B2, Cau Giay
District, Hanoi, Vietnam
Tel.: (84) 473007300
Educational Support Services
N.A.I.C.S.: 611710

FPT India Private Limited　　(1)
11th Floor D - Block ILabs Centre Plot No
18, Software Units Layout Madhapur,
Hyderabad, 500081, India
Tel.: (91) 4040201313
Software Development Services
N.A.I.C.S.: 541511

FPT Informatics Services Company
Limited　　　　　　　　　　　(1)
198 Thai Thinh Street, Dong Da District,
Hanoi, Vietnam
Tel.: (84) 4 3514 9232
Information Technology Consulting Services
N.A.I.C.S.: 541512

FPT Information System Company
Limited　　　　　　　　　　　(1)
22nd Floor Keangnam Landmark Tower E6
Pham Hung Road, Hanoi, Vietnam
Tel.: (84) 2435626000
Web Site: http://www.fpt-is.com
Software Development Services
N.A.I.C.S.: 541511

FPT Japan Holdings Co., Ltd.　(1)
6th Floor Kdx Hamamatsucho Place 1-7-6
Shibakoen, Minato-ku, Tokyo, 105-0011,
Japan
Tel.: (81) 366346868
Web Site: https://fptsoftware.jp
Emp.: 3,500
Information Technology & Software Devel-
opment Services
N.A.I.C.S.: 541512

FPT Online Services Joint Stock
Company　　　　　　　　　　(1)
153 Nguyen Dinh Chieu Phuong 6 Quan 3,
Ho Chi Minh City, Vietnam
Tel.: (84) 8 7300 9999
Web Site: http://www.fptonline.net
Online Entertainment Services
N.A.I.C.S.: 516210
Tran Thi Thu Trang *(Exec VP)*

FPT SERVICE Co., Ltd　　　(1)
So 25 ngo 68 duong Cau Giay, Quan Cau
Giay, Hanoi, Vietnam
Tel.: (84) 4 73000911
Web Site: http://www.ftpservice.com
Information Technology Consulting Services
N.A.I.C.S.: 541512

FPT Semiconductor Joint Stock
Company　　　　　　　　　　(1)
FPT Tower No 10 Pham Van Bach Street,
Dich Vong Ward Cau Giay District, Hanoi,
Vietnam
Tel.: (84) 2437689048
Web Site: https://fpt-semiconductor.com
Electronic Components Mfr
N.A.I.C.S.: 334419

FPT Slovakia s.r.o.　　　　　(1)
Juzna Trieda 6, 040 01, Kosice, Slovakia
Tel.: (421) 905250798
Web Site: https://www.fpt.sk
Emp.: 400
Information Technology Services
N.A.I.C.S.: 541519

FPT Smart Cloud Company
Limited　　　　　　　　　　　(1)
No 9 Pham Van Bach Street, Dich Vong
WardCau Giay District, Hanoi, Vietnam
Tel.: (84) 1900638399
Web Site: http://fptcloud.com
Software Development Services
N.A.I.C.S.: 541511

FPT Software Central Region Com-
pany Limited　　　　　　　　(1)
FPT Complex Building Nam Ky Khoi Nghia
Street, Hoa Hai Ward Ngu Hanh Son Dis-
tric, Da Nang, Vietnam
Tel.: (84) 2363958555
Software Development Services
N.A.I.C.S.: 541511

FPT Software Company Limited　(1)
FPT Cau Giay Building Duy Tan Street,
Dich Vong Hau Ward Cau Giay District, Ha-
noi, Vietnam
Tel.: (84) 2437689048
Web Site: http://www.fpt-software.com
Emp.: 3,000
Software Development Services
N.A.I.C.S.: 541511
Bui Hoang Tung *(Chief Strategy Officer &
Sr VP)*

FPT Software Europe S.A.R.L.　(1)
8 Terrasse Bellini, 92800, Puteaux, France
Tel.: (33) 180874812
Information Technology & Software Devel-
opment Services
N.A.I.C.S.: 541512

FPT Software Ho Chi Minh Company
Limited　　　　　　　　　　　(1)
600 Nguyen Van Cu Street, An Binh Ward
Ninh Kieu District, Can Tho, Vietnam
Tel.: (84) 2923907979
Software Development Services
N.A.I.C.S.: 541511

FPT Software Hue Co., Ltd.　(1)
8th Floor HCC Building 28 Ly Thuong Kiet
Street, Vinh Ninh Ward, Hue, Thua Thien
Hue, Vietnam
Tel.: (84) 2473079999
Information Technology & Software Devel-
opment Services
N.A.I.C.S.: 541512

FPT Corporation—(Continued)

FPT Software Japan Co., Ltd. (1)
Kdx Hamamatsucho Place 6th Floor 1-7-6
Shibakoen Reception 5th Floor, Minato-ku,
Tokyo, Japan
Tel.: (81) 366346868
Emp.: 1,070
Information Technology & Software Devel-
opment Services
N.A.I.C.S.: 541512

FPT Software Korea Co., Ltd. (1)
7th Floor Sewoo Building 115
Yeouigongwon-ro, Yeongdeungpo-gu,
Seoul, Korea (South)
Tel.: (82) 25676650
Web Site: https://fptsoftware.kr
Emp.: 30,000
Information Technology Services
N.A.I.C.S.: 541519

**FPT Software Malaysia Sdn.
Bhd.** (1)
Lot 21-04 Level 21 Menara Hap Seng 2
Plaza Hap Seng 1 Jalan P Ramlee, 50250,
Kuala Lumpur, Malaysia
Tel.: (60) 320220333
Emp.: 300
Software Development Services
N.A.I.C.S.: 541511

FPT Software Philippines Corp. (1)
Ground Floor eBloc Tower 3 Geonzon
Street Cebu IT Park Lahug, Cebu, 6000,
Philippines
Tel.: (63) 324106857
Emp.: 300
Software Development Services
N.A.I.C.S.: 541511

**FPT Software Solutions Asia Pacific
Pte. Ltd.** (1)
Aperia Tower 8 Kallang Avenue 12-09, Sin-
gapore, 339509, Singapore
Tel.: (65) 63384353
Information Technology Services
N.A.I.C.S.: 541519

**FPT Software United Kingdom
Ltd.** (1)
60 Cannon Street, London, EC4N 6NP,
United Kingdom
Tel.: (44) 2045098064
Information Technology & Software Devel-
opment Services
N.A.I.C.S.: 541512

FPT Taiwan Co., Ltd. (1)
3F-3 No 189 Sec 2 Keelung Rd, Xinyi Dis-
trict, Taipei, 110, Taiwan
Tel.: (886) 227320741
Software Development Services
N.A.I.C.S.: 541511

FPT Technology DMCC (1)
1405 Fortune Tower Jumeirah Lakes Tow-
ers, Dubai, United Arab Emirates
Tel.: (971) 45776725
Software Development Services
N.A.I.C.S.: 541511

**FPT Telecom Joint Stock
Company** (1)
FPT Building Duy Tan street, Cau Giay Dis-
trict, Hanoi, Vietnam
Tel.: (84) 4 7300 2222
Web Site: http://www.fpt.net
Sales Range: $400-449.9 Million
Emp.: 2,300
Internet & Telecommunication Services
N.A.I.C.S.: 517810
Truong Dinh Anh (Chm)

FPT University Co. Ltd. (1)
Hoa Lac High-Tech Park - Km29 Thang
Long Avenue, Thach That, Hanoi, Vietnam
Tel.: (84) 2473001866
Web Site: https://hanoi.fpt.edu.vn
University Services
N.A.I.C.S.: 611310

Guangxi FPT Software Co., Ltd. (1)
Room 2823 28th Floor Building 1 Wuxiang
Hangyang Mall No 401, Wuxiang Avenue
Liangqing District, Nanning, Guangxi, China
Tel.: (86) 17321291512
Software Development Services
N.A.I.C.S.: 541511

Intellinet Consulting, LLC (1)

2 Concourse Pkwy Ste 100, Atlanta, GA
30066 **(90%)**
Tel.: (404) 442-8000
Web Site: https://www.intellinet.com
Managment Consulting & Technology Ser-
vices
N.A.I.C.S.: 541611

P.T. FPT Software Indonesia (1)
Treasury Tower SCBD 18th Floor Unit A
District 8, Jl Jendral Sudirman No 52-53
Senayan, Jakarta, 12190, Indonesia
Tel.: (62) 2150106360
Software Development Services
N.A.I.C.S.: 541511

FPX NICKEL CORP.
Suite 320-1155 West Pender Street,
Vancouver, V6E 2P4, BC, Canada
Tel.: (604) 681-8600　　　　　　　AB
Web Site: https://www.fpxnickel.com
Year Founded: 1995
FPX—(TSXV)
Rev.: $15,681
Assets: $8,820,722
Liabilities: $6,289,269
Net Worth: $2,531,453
Earnings: ($953,160)
Emp.: 1
Fiscal Year-end: 12/31/19
Mineral Exploration Services
N.A.I.C.S.: 213114
Peter M. D. Bradshaw (Chm)

FR. KAISER GMBH
Bahnhofstrasse 35, 71332, Waiblin-
gen, Germany
Tel.: (49) 715117150
Web Site: http://www.fr-kaiser.com
Year Founded: 1889
Rev.: $21,712,182
Emp.: 117
Candy Mfr
N.A.I.C.S.: 311351
Thomas Updike (Mng Dir)

**FR. LURSSEN WERFT GMBH
& CO. KG**
Zum Alten Speicher 11, 28759,
Bremen, Germany
Tel.: (49) 42166040
Web Site: http://www.lurssen.com
Ship & Yacht Building Mfr
N.A.I.C.S.: 336611
Peter Lurben (Mng Dir)

Subsidiaries:

Blohm + Voss B.V & Co. KG (1)
Hermann-Blohm-Strasse 3, 20457, Ham-
burg, Germany
Tel.: (49) 4031190
Web Site: http://www.blohmvoss.com
Ship Builder
N.A.I.C.S.: 336611
Dieter Dehlke (Mng Dir)

FRACTAL GAMING GROUP AB
Victor Hasselblads gata 16A, 421 31,
Vastra Frolunda, Sweden
Tel.: (46) 313807100
Web Site:
　　https://www.fractalgaminggroup.se
Year Founded: 2010
FRACTL—(OMX)
Rev.: $73,259,715
Assets: $55,924,115
Liabilities: $21,503,648
Net Worth: $34,420,467
Earnings: $8,396,415
Emp.: 92
Fiscal Year-end: 12/31/23
Computer Equipment Mfr
N.A.I.C.S.: 334111
Alexander Ernryd (CMO)

**FRACTURECODE CORPORA-
TION APS**
Amager Strandvej 390 2 etage, 2770,
Kastrup, Denmark

Tel.: (45) 88960150
Web Site:
　　http://www.fracturecode.com
Year Founded: 2001
Sales Range: $10-24.9 Million
Emp.: 20
Product Authentication, Identification
& Tracking Solutions
N.A.I.C.S.: 513210
Jacob Juul Rasmussen (Mng Dir)

FRAGBITE GROUP AB
Linnegatan 51, 114 58, Stockholm,
Sweden
Tel.: (46) 852027782
Web Site:
　　https://www.fragbitegroup.com
Year Founded: 2015
FRAG—(OMX)
Rev.: $24,908,352
Assets: $92,212,107
Liabilities: $14,997,986
Net Worth: $77,214,120
Earnings: ($4,977,943)
Emp.: 130
Fiscal Year-end: 12/31/23
Software Development Services
N.A.I.C.S.: 541511
Marcus Teilman (Pres)

**FRAGOL BETEILIGUNGS
GMBH + CO.KG**
Solinger Str 16, 45481, Mulheim an
der Ruhr, Germany
Tel.: (49) 208300020
Web Site: http://www.fragol.de
Year Founded: 1962
Sales Range: $25-49.9 Million
Emp.: 20
Mineral & Lubricating Oil Mfr
N.A.I.C.S.: 324191
Heinel Miske (Pres)

FRAGRANCE GROUP LIMITED
456 Alexandra Road 26 01 Fragrance
Empire Building, Singapore, 119962,
Singapore
Tel.: (65) 63466888
Web Site:
　　http://www.fragrancegroup.com.sg
Rev.: $121,729,280
Assets: $2,338,544,241
Liabilities: $1,307,370,960
Net Worth: $1,031,173,281
Earnings: $58,910,254
Fiscal Year-end: 12/31/19
Holding Company; Property Invest-
ment & Development Services
N.A.I.C.S.: 551112
Periakaruppan Aravindan (Deputy
CEO)

Subsidiaries:

AF Global Limited (1)
Aspial One 55 Ubi Avenue 3 04-01, Singa-
pore, 408864, Singapore
Tel.: (65) 62662222
Web Site: http://www.afgl.com.sg
Rev.: $12,401,960
Assets: $236,016,484
Liabilities: $41,485,442
Net Worth: $194,531,042
Earnings: ($467,887)
Fiscal Year-end: 12/31/2022
Holding Company; Hospitality & Investment
Services
N.A.I.C.S.: 551112
Yue Kai Chay (CEO)

Subsidiary (Non-US):

**Cityview Apartments and Commercial
Centre Limited** (2)
12 Mac Dinh Chi Street, Da Kao Ward Dis-
trict 1, Ho Chi Minh City, Vietnam
Tel.: (84) 838221111
Web Site: http://www.cityview.com.vn
Apartment Building Rental Services
N.A.I.C.S.: 531110

**Gateway Enterprise Company
Limited** (2)
Souphanouvang Avenue, PO Box 4793,
Sikottabong District, Vientiane, Lao Peo-
ple's Democratic Republic
Tel.: (856) 21 250 888
Property Management Services
N.A.I.C.S.: 531312

L.C. (London) Ltd (2)
100 Cromewell Road, London, SW7 4ER,
United Kingdom
Tel.: (44) 2073722222
Web Site: http://www.lcdgi.com
Home Management Services
N.A.I.C.S.: 561110

Subsidiary (Domestic):

L.C. Logistics Pte Ltd (2)
55 Ubi Avenue 1 #06-11 Ubi 55 Building,
Singapore, 408935, Singapore
Tel.: (65) 62662222
Web Site: http://www.lcdgi.com
Real Estate Property Development Services
N.A.I.C.S.: 531210

LCD (Indochina) Pte Ltd (2)
55 Ubi Avenue 1 #06-11 Ubi 55 Building,
Singapore, 408935, Singapore
Tel.: (65) 62662222
Web Site: http://www.lcdgi.com
Property Management Services
N.A.I.C.S.: 531311

LCD (Vietnam) Pte Ltd (2)
55 Ubi Avenue 1 #06-11 Ubi 55 Building,
Singapore, 408935, Singapore
Tel.: (65) 62662222
Web Site: http://www.lcdgi.com
Investment Management Service
N.A.I.C.S.: 523940

**LCD Property Management Pte
Ltd** (2)
55 Ubi Avenue 1 #06-11 Ubi 55 Building,
Singapore, 408935, Singapore
Tel.: (65) 6266 2222
Web Site: http://www.lcdgi.com
Property Management Services
N.A.I.C.S.: 531311

ZONE X Leisure Pte Ltd (2)
Terminal 3 65 Airport Boulevard B2-23, Sin-
gapore, 819663, Singapore
Tel.: (65) 69081013
Web Site: http://www.zonex.com.sg
Gaming Centers Operation Services
N.A.I.C.S.: 713120

**Fragrance Hotel Management Pte
Ltd** (1)
168 Changi Road Unit 04-01 Fragrance
Building, Singapore, 419730, Singapore
Tel.: (65) 63456116
Web Site: http://www.fragrancehotel.com
Sales Range: $25-49.9 Million
Emp.: 120
Home Management Services
N.A.I.C.S.: 721110

Fragrance Land Pte Ltd (1)
101 Joo Chiat Road 01-01 Fragrance Cen-
tre, Singapore, Singapore
Tel.: (65) 63466888
Residential Property Development Services
N.A.I.C.S.: 531390

**FRAGRANT PROSPERITY
HOLDINGS LIMITED**
Offshore Incorporations Centre, PO
Box 957, Road Town, Tortola, Virgin
Islands (British)
Tel.: (284) 2086170071　　　　　VG
Web Site:
　　http://www.fragrantprosperity.com
Year Founded: 2016
FPP—(LSE)
Assets: $727,499
Liabilities: $403,070
Net Worth: $324,429
Earnings: ($300,154)
Emp.: 4
Fiscal Year-end: 03/31/21
Investment Management Service
N.A.I.C.S.: 523940
Craig Marshak (Chm)

FRAMATEQ S.A.S.
16 Avenue de Rome, BP 32043, Vitrapole, 13845, Vitrolles, Cedex, France
Tel.: (33) 4 4277 0313   FR
Web Site: http://www.framateq.fr
Sales Range: $10-24.9 Million
Emp.: 30
Construction & Mining Equipment Distr
N.A.I.C.S.: 423810
Herve Louvion *(Pres)*

FRAMESI S.P.A.
Strada Statale dei Giovi 135, Paderno Dugnano, 20037, Milan, Italy
Tel.: (39) 0299040441   IT
Web Site: https://www.framesi.it
Year Founded: 1945
Professional Hair Care Products Mfr & Salon Consultancy Services
N.A.I.C.S.: 325620
Fabio Franchina *(Pres)*

Subsidiaries:

Framesi USA, Inc.   (1)
17 Ave Ste A, Leetsdale, PA 15056-1304
Tel.: (412) 269-2950
Web Site: http://www.framesiglamour.com
Sales Range: $25-49.9 Million
Emp.: 20
Hair Care Products Distr
N.A.I.C.S.: 424210
Dennis Katawczik *(Pres)*

FRAMOS GMBH
Mehlbeerenstr 2, 82024, Taufkirchen, Germany
Tel.: (49) 897106670
Web Site: http://www.framos.com
Year Founded: 1981
Rev.: $13,794,000
Emp.: 18
Image Processing Technology Support Services
N.A.I.C.S.: 561990
Bernd Franz *(Mng Dir)*

Subsidiaries:

FRAMOS Electronics Ltd.   (1)
The Coliseum BC Riverside Way, Camberley, GU15 3YL, Surrey, United Kingdom
Tel.: (44) 1276404140
Image Processing Services
N.A.I.C.S.: 323120

FRAMOS France SA   (1)
40 Rue Des vignobles, Chatou, 78400, Paris, France
Tel.: (33) 139520782
Image Processing Services
N.A.I.C.S.: 323120

FRAMOS Italia Srl   (1)
Centro Direzionale Colleoni Pal Taurus Ing 2 Via Colleoni 3, 20864, Agrate Brianza, Italy
Tel.: (39) 0396899635
Image Processing Services
N.A.I.C.S.: 323120

FRAMOS Technologies Inc.   (1)
2733 Lancaster Road Suite 210, Ottawa, K1B 0A9, ON, Canada
Tel.: (613) 686-1152
Image Processing Services
N.A.I.C.S.: 323120

FRANBO LINES CORP.
3F No 31 Haibian Rd, Lingya District, Kaohsiung, 802609, Taiwan
Tel.: (886) 79697988
Web Site: https://www.franbo.com.tw
Year Founded: 1988
2641—(TPE)
Rev.: $45,866,523
Assets: $250,517,212
Liabilities: $83,652,784
Net Worth: $166,864,428
Earnings: $40,018,479
Fiscal Year-end: 12/31/22

Transport Services
N.A.I.C.S.: 485999
B. C. Tsai *(Chm)*

FRANCE BED HOLDINGS CO. LTD.
6-22-1 Nishi-Shinjuku, Shinjuku-ku, Tokyo, Japan
Tel.: (81) 367415501
Web Site: https://www.francebed-hd.co.jp
7840—(TKS)
Rev.: $390,988,110
Assets: $453,280,750
Liabilities: $200,706,040
Net Worth: $252,574,710
Earnings: $20,715,740
Emp.: 59
Fiscal Year-end: 03/31/24
Beds & Furniture Mfr
N.A.I.C.S.: 321912
Shigeru Ikeda *(Pres, CEO & Chm)*

Subsidiaries:

France Bed Medical Service Co., Ltd.   (1)
2F 4-1-16 Roppongi, Minato-ku, Tokyo, 106-0032, Japan
Tel.: (81) 35 549 2937
Web Site: https://www.francebed.co.jp
Emp.: 1,402
Medical Equipment Distr
N.A.I.C.S.: 423450
Shigeru Ikeda *(Pres & CEO)*

Francebed Co., Ltd.   (1)
5th Fl Shinjuku Square Tower 6-22-1, Nishi-shinjuku Shinjuku-ku, Tokyo, 163-1105, Japan
Tel.: (81) 367415555
Web Site: http://www.francebed.co.jp
Sales Range: $400-449.9 Million
Emp.: 1,402
Bed Linen Whslr & Mfr
N.A.I.C.S.: 313210
Shigeru Ikeda *(Pres & CEO)*

Subsidiary (Domestic):

Francebed Sales Co., Ltd.   (2)
1-2-1 Kikunodai 2nd floor, Chofu, 182-0007, Tokyo, Japan
Tel.: (81) 424430421
Web Site: http://www.bed.co.jp
Sales Range: $25-49.9 Million
Emp.: 90
Furnitures Mfr & Whslr
N.A.I.C.S.: 337215

Tokyo Bed Co., Ltd.   (2)
4-1-16 Roppongi, Minato-ku, 106-0032, Tokyo, Japan
Tel.: (81) 335838521
Web Site: http://www.tokyo-bed.co.jp
Sales Range: $25-49.9 Million
Emp.: 66
Bedroom Furnitures Mfr & Whslr
N.A.I.C.S.: 337122
Kazumi Ikeda *(Pres)*

Kashidasu Co., Ltd.   (1)
6-22-1 Nishi-Shinjuku Shinjuku Square Tower 5th Floor, Shinjuku-ku, Tokyo, 163-1105, Japan
Tel.: (81) 36 894 7162
Web Site: https://www.kashidasu.co.jp
Medical Equipment Distr
N.A.I.C.S.: 423450

FRANCE GALVA SA
ZI La Sauniere, BP 70, 89600, Saint Florentin, France
Tel.: (33) 386438201
Sales Range: $50-74.9 Million
Emp.: 200
Galvanizing Steel Parts Mfr
N.A.I.C.S.: 331210

FRANCE TOURISME IMMOBILIER SA
Hotel Le Totem les Pres de Flaine, 74300, Thyez, France
Tel.: (33) 142979900

Web Site:
https://www.francetourisme.fr
Year Founded: 2013
MLFTI—(EUR)
Sales Range: Less than $1 Million
Jewelry Mfr & Distr
N.A.I.C.S.: 339910

FRANCESCO PARISI S.P.A.
Viale Miramare 5, 34135, Trieste, Italy
Tel.: (39) 0404193111   IT
Web Site:
http://www.francescoparisi.com
Year Founded: 1807
Sales Range: $50-74.9 Million
Emp.: 500
International Shipping & Freight Forwarding
N.A.I.C.S.: 488510

Subsidiaries:

Francesco Parisi GmbH   (1)
Prinzregentenstrasse 83, 81675, Munich, Germany   **(100%)**
Tel.: (49) 899038951
Web Site: http://www.francescoparisi.com
Sales Range: $25-49.9 Million
Emp.: 10
International Rail & Truck Transports, Air & Sea Shipments
N.A.I.C.S.: 483211

Branch (Domestic):

Francesco Parisi GmbH - Cologne   (2)
Friesenwall 53, Cologne, 50672, Germany
Tel.: (49) 2212570231
Web Site: http://www.frenchescoparisi.com
Sales Range: $25-49.9 Million
Emp.: 4
International Rail & Truck Transports, Air & Sea Shipments
N.A.I.C.S.: 483211

Francesco Parisi S.a.g.l.   (1)
Via Soldini 13, PO Box 1547, 6830, Chiasso, Ticino, Switzerland   **(100%)**
Tel.: (41) 916837585
Web Site: http://www.parisi-ch.ch
Sales Range: $25-49.9 Million
Emp.: 10
International Rail & Truck Transports, Air & Sea Shipments
N.A.I.C.S.: 483211
Francesco Parisi *(Pres)*

Francesco Parisi S.p.A. - Fernetti   (1)
Autoporto Doganale, I 34016, Fernetti, TS, Italy
Tel.: (39) 0402176901
Sales Range: $25-49.9 Million
Emp.: 100
International Rail & Truck Transports, Air & Sea Shipments, Storage & Distribution
N.A.I.C.S.: 493190

Francesco Parisi S.p.A. - Genoa   (1)
Via Bruzzo 7, 16162, Genoa, GE, Italy
Tel.: (39) 0107411352
Web Site: http://www.francescoparisi.com
Sales Range: $25-49.9 Million
Emp.: 20
International Rail & Truck Transports, Air & Sea Shipments, Storage & Distribution
N.A.I.C.S.: 493190

Francesco Parisi S.p.A. - Gorizia   (1)
Stazione Confinaria di San Andrea, PO Box 33, Gorizia, 34170, GO, Italy
Tel.: (39) 0481521966
Web Site: http://www.francescoparisi.com
International Rail & Truck Transport Air & Sea Shipment Storage & Distr
N.A.I.C.S.: 493190

Francesco Parisi S.p.A. - Livorno   (1)
Via delle Cateratte 110, 57122, Livorno, LI, Italy
Tel.: (39) 0404193111
Web Site: http://www.francescoparisi.com
Sales Range: $25-49.9 Million
Emp.: 60

International Rail & Truck Transports, Air & Sea Shipments, Storage & Distribution
N.A.I.C.S.: 493190

Francesco Parisi S.p.A. - Milano   (1)
Via Londra 46/48/50 Loc Milano Oltre I, Milan, 20090, Italy
Tel.: (39) 0292393311
Web Site: http://www.francescoparisi.com
Sales Range: $25-49.9 Million
Emp.: 25
International Rail & Truck Transports, Air & Sea Shipments, Storage & Distribution
N.A.I.C.S.: 493190
Francesco Parisi *(Pres)*

Francesco Parisi S.p.A. - Monfalcone   (1)
Via delle Terme Romane 5, Monfalcone, 34074, TS, Italy
Tel.: (39) 048140539
Web Site: http://www.francescoparisi.com
International Rail & Truck Transports, Air & Sea Shipments
N.A.I.C.S.: 483211

Francesco Parisi S.p.A. - Pontebba   (1)
Autoporto Doganale di San Leopoldo, PO Box 59, 32030, Pontebba, Italy
Tel.: (39) 042890271
Web Site: http://www.francescoparisi.com
Sales Range: $25-49.9 Million
Emp.: 3
International Rail & Truck Transports, Air & Sea Shipments
N.A.I.C.S.: 483211
Francesco Parisi *(Gen Mgr)*

Francesco Parisi S.p.A. - Ronchi dei Legionari   (1)
Aeroporto Friuli Venezia Giulia, 34077, Ronchi dei Legionari, GO, Italy
Tel.: (39) 0481474913
International Rail & Truck Transports, Air & Sea Shipments
N.A.I.C.S.: 483211

Francesco Parisi S.p.A. - Sedico   (1)
Agenzia Doganale Via Segusini 8, 32030, Sedico, BL, Italy
Tel.: (39) 0043783627
Web Site: http://www.francescoparisi.com
Sales Range: $25-49.9 Million
Emp.: 30
International Rail & Truck Transports, Air & Sea Shipments
N.A.I.C.S.: 483211

Francesco Parisi S.p.A. - Venezia-Mestre   (1)
Via Torino 65, Venezia-Mestre, I-30172, Venice, VE, Italy
Tel.: (39) 0412907511
Sales Range: $25-49.9 Million
Emp.: 25
International Rail & Truck Transportation & Air & Sea Shipments
N.A.I.C.S.: 483211
Francesco Parisi *(Mgr)*

Parisi Grand Smooth Logistics Ltd.   (1)
Unit G & H 9th Floor Dragon Ind Building 93 King Lam Street, Lai Chi Kok, Kowloon, China (Hong Kong)
Tel.: (852) 2851 0530
Web Site: http://www.pgs-log.com
Logistics Consulting Servies
N.A.I.C.S.: 541614
Helmut Horvath *(Dir-Sls & Mktg)*

FRANCESOIR GROUPE SA
25 C Rue de Ponthieu, 75008, Paris, France
Tel.: (33) 145692990
Web Site: https://groupe.francesoir.fr
Year Founded: 2016
MLFSG—(EUR)
Sales Range: Less than $1 Million
Information Technology Services
N.A.I.C.S.: 541512
Xavier Azalbert *(Chm & CEO)*

FRANCHETTI S.P.A.
Vi Piazzale della Vittoria 7, 36071, Arzignano, Italy

Franchetti S.p.A.—(Continued)

Tel.: (39) 0444671443
Web Site: https://www.franchetti.tech
Year Founded: 2013
FCH—(ITA)
Rev.: $7,749,335
Assets: $14,186,827
Liabilities: $6,953,882
Net Worth: $7,232,945
Earnings: $1,372,341
Emp.: 22
Fiscal Year-end: 12/31/23
Software Development Services
N.A.I.C.S.: 541511

FRANCHISE BANCORP INC.
294 Walker Drive Unit 2, Brampton,
L6T 4Z2, ON, Canada
Tel.: (905) 790-9023
Web Site:
　　http://www.franchisebancorp.com
Year Founded: 1995
Holding Company; Retail Chain Franchisor
N.A.I.C.S.: 551112
James Walker *(Exec Dir)*

Subsidiaries:

Franchise Bancorp Consulting
Ltd.　　　　　　　　　　　　　　**(1)**
294 Walker Drive Unit 2, Brampton, L6T
4Z2, ON, Canada　　　　　　**(100%)**
Tel.: (905) 790-9023
Franchise Marketing & Sales Consulting
N.A.I.C.S.: 541613

Global Pet Food Stores Inc.　　**(1)**
294 Walker Drive Unit 2, Brampton, L6T
4Z2, ON, Canada　　　　　　　**(68%)**
Tel.: (905) 790-9023
Web Site: http://www.globalpetfoods.com
Pet Food Stores Franchisor & Operator
N.A.I.C.S.: 533110
James Walker *(Pres)*

Subsidiary (Domestic):

Global Pet Foods Distribution
Ltd.　　　　　　　　　　　　　　**(2)**
Main St Ctr 110-400 Main St N, Airdrie, T4B
2N1, AB, Canada　　　　　　**(100%)**
Tel.: (905) 790-9023
Sea Food Products Distr
N.A.I.C.S.: 424490

Living Lighting Inc.　　　　　　**(1)**
547 Steeles Avenue E Unit 2E - 1, Brampton, L6W 4S2, ON, Canada
Tel.: (905) 230-8600
Web Site: http://www.livinglighting.com
Sales Range: $25-49.9 Million
Lighting Store Franchisor & Operator Service
N.A.I.C.S.: 533110

FRANCHISE BRANDS PLC
Ashwood Court Springwood Close,
Tytherington Business Park, Macclesfield, SK10 2XF, United Kingdom
Tel.: (44) 1625507910
Web Site:
　　https://www.franchisebrands.co.uk
Year Founded: 2008
FRAN—(AIM)
Rev.: $125,160,313
Assets: $167,177,480
Liabilities: $37,109,316
Net Worth: $130,068,165
Earnings: $10,464,529
Emp.: 414
Fiscal Year-end: 12/31/22
Holding Company; Multi-Brand Franchisors
N.A.I.C.S.: 551112
Stephen Hemsley *(Co-Founder & Chm)*

Subsidiaries:

Filta Group Holdings plc　　　　**(1)**
The Locks Hillmorton, Rugby, CV21 4PP,
United Kingdom

Tel.: (44) 1788550100
Web Site: http://www.filtaplc.com
Sales Range: $25-49.9 Million
Emp.: 68
Holding Company Services
N.A.I.C.S.: 551112
Jason Charles Sayers *(CEO)*

Subsidiary (Domestic):

Environmental Biotech Limited　　**(2)**
Court Langley House Bates Road, Maldon,
CM9 5FA, Essex, United Kingdom
Tel.: (44) 8443358417
Environmental Engineering Services
N.A.I.C.S.: 562910

Subsidiary (Non-US):

Filta Environmental Canada
Limited　　　　　　　　　　　　**(2)**
180 Dundas St W Suite 1200, Toronto,
M5G 1Z8, ON, Canada
Tel.: (407) 996-5550
Web Site: http://www.filta.ca
Waste Management Services
N.A.I.C.S.: 562998

Filta Europe B.V.　　　　　　　**(2)**
Maasstraat 1a, NL-7071 VR, Ulft, Netherlands
Tel.: (31) 315237991
Web Site: https://www.filtafry.eu
Environmental Engineering Services
N.A.I.C.S.: 562910

FiltaFry Deutschland GmbH　　　**(2)**
Pliniusstrasse 8, 48488, Emsburen, Germany
Tel.: (49) 59039689110
Web Site: https://www.filtafry.de
Waste Management Services
N.A.I.C.S.: 562998
Jos van Aalst *(Mng Dir)*

Subsidiary (US):

The Filta Group Incorporated　　**(2)**
7075 Kingspointe Pkwy Ste 1, Orlando, FL
32819
Tel.: (407) 996-5550
Web Site: https://www.gofilta.com
Waste Management Services
N.A.I.C.S.: 562998

Subsidiary (Domestic):

The Filta Group Limited　　　　　**(2)**
The Locks, Hillmorton, Rugby, CV21 4PP,
Warwickshire, United Kingdom
Tel.: (44) 1788550100
Web Site: https://www.filta.co.uk
Waste Management Services
N.A.I.C.S.: 562998

Metro Rod Limited　　　　　　　**(1)**
Ashwood Court Tytherington Business Park,
Macclesfield, SK10 2XF, Cheshire, United
Kingdom
Tel.: (44) 800668800
Web Site: https://www.metrorod.co.uk
Drainage Clearance & Maintenance Services
N.A.I.C.S.: 561790

The Handyman Van Limited　　　**(1)**
Ashwood Court Tytherington Business Park,
Macclesfield, SK10 2XF, United Kingdom
Tel.: (44) 8002851433
Web Site:
　　https://www.thehandymanvan.co.uk
Plumbing & Carpentry Services
N.A.I.C.S.: 238220

Willow Pumps Limited　　　　　**(1)**
Hall Rd, Aylesford, ME20 7QZ, United Kingdom
Tel.: (44) 1634201111
Web Site: https://www.willowpumps.co.uk
Water Pump Installation Services
N.A.I.C.S.: 237110
Ian Lawrence *(Mng Dir)*

FRANCHISE CONCEPTS LIMITED
Caslon Court, PO Box 522, Pitronnerie Road, Saint Peter Port, Guernsey
Tel.: (44) 1481 713425

Web Site:
　　http://www.franchiseconcepts.co.uk
Franchising Services
N.A.I.C.S.: 561499

Subsidiaries:

Sumo Services Ltd　　　　　　　**(1)**
Unit 8 Hayward Business Center, New
Lane, Havant, PO9 2NL, Hampshire, United
Kingdom
Tel.: (44) 845 456 1104
Web Site: https://www.sumoservices.com
Emp.: 20
Utility Mark Out Services
N.A.I.C.S.: 541330

FRANCHISE ENTERTAINMENT GROUP PTY LTD.
Suite 5 Level 9 1 Rider Blvd, PO Box
3531, Rhodes, 2138, NSW, Australia
Tel.: (61) 2 8833 2100
Web Site:
　　http://www.videoezy.com.au
Year Founded: 1983
Video Tapes & Disc Rental Stores
Franchisor
N.A.I.C.S.: 532282
Paul Uniake *(Mng Dir)*

Subsidiaries:

Blockbuster Australia Pty. Ltd.　**(1)**
Level 1 1-5 Errol Street, North Melbourne,
3051, VIC, Australia
Tel.: (61) 393211600
Web Site: http://www.blockbuster.com.au
Sales Range: $10-24.9 Million
Emp.: 30
Video Tape & Disc Rental Services
N.A.I.C.S.: 532282

FRANCO-NEVADA CORPORATION
199 Bay Street Ste 2000, PO Box
285, Commerce Court Postal Station,
Toronto, M5L 1G9, ON, Canada
Tel.: (416) 306-6300
Web Site: https://www.franco-nevada.com
Year Founded: 1986
FNV—(NYSE)
Rev.: $1,219,000,000
Assets: $5,994,100,000
Liabilities: $225,000,000
Net Worth: $5,769,100,000
Earnings: ($466,400,000)
Emp.: 40
Fiscal Year-end: 12/31/23
Gold Exploration & Mining Services
N.A.I.C.S.: 212220
Sandip Rana *(CFO)*

Subsidiaries:

Franco-Nevada (Barbados)
Corporation　　　　　　　　　　**(1)**
Ground Floor Balmoral Hall Balmoral Gap,
Hastings, Christ Church, BB14034, Barbados
Tel.: (246) 434 8200
Mining Services
N.A.I.C.S.: 212290
John Blanchette *(Pres)*

Franco-Nevada Australia Pty.
Ltd.　　　　　　　　　　　　　　**(1)**
Unit 5/9 McDonald St W, Osborne Park,
6017, WA, Australia
Tel.: (61) 863133934
Gold Ore Mining Services
N.A.I.C.S.: 212220

Franco-Nevada U.S. Corporation　**(1)**
1745 Shea Ctr Dr Ste 400, Highlands
Ranch, CO 80129
Tel.: (720) 344-4986
Web Site: https://www.franco-nevada.com
Gold Ore Mining Services
N.A.I.C.S.: 212220

FRANCOIS-CHARLES OBERTHUR FIDUCIAIRE S.A.

50 Quai Michelet, 92300, Levallois-Perret, France
Tel.: (33) 155467200
Web Site: http://www.Oberthur.com
Year Founded: 1984
Sales Range: $1-4.9 Billion
Emp.: 6,800
Holding Company
N.A.I.C.S.: 551112
Jean-Pierre Savare *(Chm)*

Subsidiaries:

Oberthur Cash Protection S.A.　　**(1)**
3 Bis rue du docteur Quignard, BP 67907,
21079, Dijon, France　　　　　**(91%)**
Tel.: (33) 380604300
Web Site: http://www.oberthurcp.com
Cash-In-Transit Technology
N.A.I.C.S.: 561621

Oberthur Fiduciaire SAS　　　　**(1)**
102 boulevard Malesherbes, F-75017,
Paris, France
Tel.: (33) 147646400
Sales Range: $200-249.9 Million
Emp.: 900
Banknote, Passport & Other High Security
Identity Document Printing Services
N.A.I.C.S.: 323111

Subsidiary (Non-US):

Oberthur Fiduciaire (UK) Limited　**(2)**
2 Duke Street St James, London, SW1Y
6BN, United Kingdom
Tel.: (44) 203 002 8750
Web Site: http://www.oberthur-fiduciaire.com
Emp.: 6
Security Printing Services
N.A.I.C.S.: 323113
Charlotte Lafont-Machin *(Mgr-Group Comm)*

FRANCOTYP-POSTALIA HOLDING AG
Prenzlauer Promenade 28, 13089,
Berlin, Germany
Tel.: (49) 30220660410
Web Site: https://www.fp-francotyp.com
Year Founded: 1923
FPH—(MUN)
Rev.: $266,948,882
Assets: $194,435,662
Liabilities: $156,506,689
Net Worth: $37,928,973
Earnings: $11,535,441
Emp.: 1,025
Fiscal Year-end: 12/31/23
Business Support Services
N.A.I.C.S.: 561499
Carsten Lind *(CEO)*

Subsidiaries:

Azolver Danmark Aps　　　　　**(1)**
Marielundvej 46C st, 2730, Herlev, Denmark
Tel.: (45) 70221223
Web Site: https://azolver.dk
Technical Research & Development Services
N.A.I.C.S.: 541990

Azolver Italy S.r.l.　　　　　　　**(1)**
Palazzo Andromeda B1 Via Paracelso 16,
20864, Agrate Brianza, Italy
Tel.: (39) 0989951
Web Site: https://azolver.it
Information Technology Services
N.A.I.C.S.: 541519

Azolver Norge AS　　　　　　　**(1)**
Robsrudskogen 15, 1470, Lorenskog, Norway
Tel.: (47) 23339300
Web Site: https://azolver.no
Technical Research & Development Services
N.A.I.C.S.: 541990

Azolver Suomi OY　　　　　　　**(1)**
Italahdenkatu 22A, 00210, Helsinki, Finland
Tel.: (358) 96824060
Web Site: https://azolver.fi

Technical Research & Development Services
N.A.I.C.S.: 541990

Azolver Svenska AS   (1)
Voltavagen 17, 168 69, Bromma, Sweden
Tel.: (46) 87341700
Web Site: https://azolver.se
Investment Management Service
N.A.I.C.S.: 523940

Azolver Switzerland AG   (1)
Steigstrasse 26, 8406, Winterthur, Switzerland
Tel.: (41) 523545757
Web Site: https://azolver.ch
Technical Research & Development Services
N.A.I.C.S.: 541990

FP Digital Business Solutions GmbH   (1)
Griesbergstr 8, 31162, Bad Salzdetfurth, Germany
Tel.: (49) 5063277440
Web Site: https://www.fp-dbs.com
Digital Signature Services
N.A.I.C.S.: 561990

FP InovoLabs GmbH   (1)
Prenzlauer Promenade 28, 13089, Berlin, Germany
Tel.: (49) 30220660601
Web Site: https://www.inovolabs.com
Electronic & Mechatronic Product Mfr
N.A.I.C.S.: 334419

FP NeoMonitor GmbH   (1)
Prenzlauer Promenade 28, 13089, Berlin, Germany
Tel.: (49) 30220660838
Web Site: https://www.neomonitor.de
Software Development Services
N.A.I.C.S.: 541511

Francotyp Postalia Canada Inc.   (1)
82 Corstate Avenue, Concord, L4K 4X2, ON, Canada
Tel.: (905) 761-6554
Web Site: http://www.francotyp.ca
Mailing Machine Mfr
N.A.I.C.S.: 333248

Francotyp-Postalia GmbH   (1)
Triftweg 21-26, 16547, Birkenwerder, Germany
Tel.: (49) 33035250
Web Site: http://www.francotyp.com
Sales Range: $200-249.9 Million
Mail Processing Machines Mfr
N.A.I.C.S.: 333310
Rudiger Andreas Gunther *(CEO)*

Subsidiary (Non-US):

FP Finance B.V.   (2)
Meidoornkade 22, 3992 AE, Houten, Netherlands
Tel.: (31) 302271624
Web Site: http://www.fpfinance.nl
Financial Advice Services
N.A.I.C.S.: 523940

Francotyp-Postalia France SAS   (2)
14 rue d'Arras, 92000, Nanterre, France
Tel.: (33) 156301090
Web Site: http://www.fp-francotyp.fr
Franking Machine Mfr
N.A.I.C.S.: 333310

Francotyp-Postalia GmbH   (2)
Doerenkampgasse 7, 1100, Vienna, Austria
Tel.: (43) 1680690
Web Site: http://www.fp-francotyp.at
Mail Processing Services
N.A.I.C.S.: 491110

Francotyp-Postalia Ltd.   (2)
74 Powder Mill Ln Questor, Dartford, DA1 1EF, Kent, United Kingdom
Tel.: (44) 3442252233
Web Site: http://www.fpmailing.co.uk
Franking Machine Mfr
N.A.I.C.S.: 333310

Francotyp-Postalia NV   (2)
Quellinstraat 49, 2018, Antwerp, Belgium
Tel.: (32) 27206128
Web Site: http://www.francotyp.be
Franking Machine Mfr
N.A.I.C.S.: 333310

Francotyp-Postalia Sverige AB   (2)
Voltavagen 17, 168 69, Bromma, Sweden
Tel.: (46) 104843000
Web Site: http://www.francotyp.se
Franking Machine Mfr
N.A.I.C.S.: 333310

Italiana Audion S.R.L.   (2)
via Giuseppe Prina 15, 20154, Milan, Italy
Tel.: (39) 0289546086
Web Site: http://www.fp-francotyp.it
Mailing Machine Mfr
N.A.I.C.S.: 333248

Ruys Handelsvereniging B.V   (2)
Koraalrood 37, 2718 SB, Zoetermeer, Netherlands
Tel.: (31) 887897111
Web Site: http://www.fp-ruys.nl
Franking Machine Mfr
N.A.I.C.S.: 333310

Francotyp-Postalia, Inc.   (1)
140 N Mitchell Ct Ste 200, Addison, IL 60101
Web Site: https://www.fp-usa.com
Mailing Machine Mfr
N.A.I.C.S.: 333248

Freesort GmbH   (1)
Karl-Benz-Strasse 10, 40764, Langenfeld, Germany
Tel.: (49) 21733347703
Web Site: https://www.freesort.de
Mailbox Services
N.A.I.C.S.: 561431

Subsidiary (Domestic):

Internet Access GmbH lilibit Berlin Gesellschaft fur Kommunikation und Digitaltechnik   (2)
Albert-Einstein-Strasse 14, 12489, Berlin, Germany
Tel.: (49) 303644400
Franking Machine Mfr
N.A.I.C.S.: 333310

Hefter Systemform GmbH   (1)
Am Muhlbach 6, 83209, Prien am Chiemsee, Germany
Tel.: (49) 8051939200
Web Site: https://www.hefter-systemform.com
Printing Machinery Mfr & Distr
N.A.I.C.S.: 333248

FRANCOUDI & STEPHANOU LTD.

The Maritime Center 141 Omonia Avenue, PO Box 51490, 3506, Limassol, Cyprus
Tel.: (357) 25867000
Web Site: http://www.francoudi-stephanou.com
Year Founded: 1895
Sales Range: $700-749.9 Million
Emp.: 1,500
Holding Company; Shipping, Trading, Insurance, Travel, Hotels, Telecommunications & IT Services
N.A.I.C.S.: 551112

Subsidiaries:

Aeolos Limited   (1)
6 Zenas Kanther Street, CY-1065, Nicosia, Cyprus
Tel.: (357) 22881222
Web Site: http://www.aeolos.com
Sales Range: $25-49.9 Million
Emp.: 200
Travel Services
N.A.I.C.S.: 561510

Division (Domestic):

Bookcyprus.com   (2)
Zenas Kanther 6, CY-1065, Nicosia, Cyprus
Tel.: (357) 22881222
Web Site: http://www.bookcyprus.com
Online Travel Services
N.A.I.C.S.: 561510

Subsidiary (Domestic):

Interyachting   (2)
42 Iapetou Street, PO Box 54292, Limas-
sol, 3722, Cyprus
Tel.: (357) 25811900
Web Site: http://www.interyachting.com
Sales Range: $50-74.9 Million
Emp.: 4
Charter & Leisure Cruise Operations; Yacht & Yacht Equipment Sales
N.A.I.C.S.: 487210
Nicolas Epiphaniou *(Mng Dir)*

BeluggaWeb Ltd.   (1)
12 Zenas Kanther Str Office 501, 1065, Nicosia, Cyprus
Tel.: (357) 22 10 10 90
Web Site: http://www.belugga.com
Emp.: 30
Software Development Services
N.A.I.C.S.: 541511
Sotos Stephanou *(CEO)*

FRANGI S.P.A

Via Volta 5, 22029, Ugiatte, Italy
Tel.: (39) 031809233
Web Site: http://www.frangi.it
Sales Range: $25-49.9 Million
Emp.: 160
Woven Fabrics Mfr
N.A.I.C.S.: 313220
Angelo Frangi *(Pres)*

FRANK H DALE LTD.

Mill Street, Leominster, HR6 8EF, United Kingdom
Tel.: (44) 1568612212
Web Site: http://www.fhdale.co.uk
Year Founded: 1932
Rev.: $37,128,960
Emp.: 75
Steelworks Mfr
N.A.I.C.S.: 332312
Steve Curl *(Dir-Ops)*

FRANK HENRY EQUIPMENT (1987) LTD.

9810 - 60th Ave, Edmonton, T6E 0C5, AB, Canada
Tel.: (780) 434-8778   AB
Web Site: https://www.frank-henry.com
Sales Range: $1-9.9 Million
Oil & Gas Field Equipment Mfr & Whslr
N.A.I.C.S.: 333132
Nancy Snyder *(Gen Mgr)*

FRANK KEY GROUP LIMITED

Mansfield Road, Daybrook, Nottingham, NG5 6BL, United Kingdom
Tel.: (44) 115 9 208 208   UK
Web Site: http://www.frank-key.co.uk
Year Founded: 1907
Emp.: 100
Timber & Building Materials Whslr
N.A.I.C.S.: 444180
Neil Lunn *(Mgr)*

Subsidiaries:

Banson Tool Hire Limited   (1)
125 Pellon Lane, Halifax, HX1 5QN, West Yorkshire, United Kingdom
Tel.: (44) 1422254789
Web Site: http://www.toolhirebatley.co.uk
Machine Tool Mfr & Distr
N.A.I.C.S.: 333517

C Bancroft Ltd.   (1)
Worth Way, Keighley, BD21 5AJ, United Kingdom
Tel.: (44) 8707050070
Web Site: http://www.cbancroft.com
Furniture Distr
N.A.I.C.S.: 423210

Frank Key (Nottingham) Limited   (1)
Mansfield Road, Daybrook, Nottingham, NG5 6BL, United Kingdom
Tel.: (44) 115 9 208 208
Timber & Building Materials Whslr
N.A.I.C.S.: 444180

Subsidiary (Domestic):

The Builders Centre (Sheffield) Limited   (2)
Nunnery Drive, Sheffield, S2 1TA, South Yorkshire, United Kingdom
Tel.: (44) 114 272 4001
Web Site: http://www.frank-key.co.uk
Building & Plumbing Products Whslr
N.A.I.C.S.: 444180
Perry Eyre *(Mng Dir)*

FRANKFURTER ALLGEMEINE ZEITUNG GMBH

Tel.: (49) 6975910
Web Site: http://www.faz.net
Sales Range: $600-649.9 Million
Publisher of Newspapers
N.A.I.C.S.: 513110
Thomas Lindner *(Chm & Mng Dir)*

Subsidiaries:

FAZ 93.6 Berlin   (1)
Kurfurstendamm 207-208, Berlin, 10719, Germany
Tel.: (49) 30884844
Web Site: http://www.104.6rtl.com
Sales Range: $25-49.9 Million
Emp.: 20
Radio Broadcasting
N.A.I.C.S.: 516110

FRANKFURTER SPARKASSE

Neue Mainzer Str 47-53, 60311, Frankfurt am Main, Germany
Tel.: (49) 6926410
Web Site: http://www.frankfurter-sparkasse.de
Year Founded: 1822
Commercial Banking Services
N.A.I.C.S.: 522110
Robert Restani *(Chm-Mgmt Bd)*

Subsidiaries:

1822 Corpus Immobilien-Vermittlung GmbH   (1)
Neue Mainzer Strasse 53, 60311, Frankfurt am Main, Hessen, Germany   (85%)
Tel.: (49) 69979080
Sales Range: $50-74.9 Million
Emp.: 19
Bank
N.A.I.C.S.: 522180

1822 Direkt   (1)
Borsigallee 19, 60388, Frankfurt, Germany   (100%)
Tel.: (49) 69941700
Web Site: http://www.1822direkt.de
Sales Range: $100-124.9 Million
Emp.: 250
Online Bank
N.A.I.C.S.: 522180

Frankfurter Bankgesellschaft   (1)
Neue Mainzer Strasse 47-53, 60311, Frankfurt am Main, Germany   (47.5%)
Tel.: (49) 69156860
Web Site: http://www.frabank.de
Sales Range: $50-74.9 Million
Emp.: 14
Bank
N.A.I.C.S.: 522180
Herbert Hans Gruntker *(Chm)*

I & K Systeme GmbH   (1)
Obere Haingasse 2, D-61203, Reichelsheim, Germany   (33.3%)
Software for Banks
N.A.I.C.S.: 334610

Versicherungsservice der Frankfurter Sparkasse GmbH   (1)
Schaefergasse 33, D 60313, Frankfurt am Main, Germany   (100%)
Tel.: (49) 699291060
Sales Range: $50-74.9 Million
Emp.: 20
Bank
N.A.I.C.S.: 522180

FRANKL & KIRCHNER GMBH & CO KG

Frankl & Kirchner GmbH & Co KG—(Continued)

Scheffelstrasse 73, Schwetzingen, 68723, Germany
Tel.: (49) 62022020
Web Site: http://www.efka.net
Rev.: $54,975,987
Emp.: 230
Electronic Controls Mfr
N.A.I.C.S.: 336320
Lotte Wiest *(Mng Dir)*

FRANKLIN INDUSTRIES LIMITED

708 Scarlet Business Hub Opp Ankur School Nr Mahalaxmi Panch Rasta, Paldi, Ahmedabad, 380007, India
Tel.: (91) 7949258973
Web Site:
https://www.franklinindustries.in
Year Founded: 1983
540190—(BOM)
Rev.: $2,460,565
Assets: $1,177,241
Liabilities: $686,365
Net Worth: $490,876
Earnings: $25,694
Fiscal Year-end: 03/31/23
Real Estate Manangement Services
N.A.I.C.S.: 531210
Alpesh Maheshbhai Gupta *(Chm & Mng Dir)*

FRANKLIN LEASING & FINANCE LIMITED

Unit/Shop No 205 Second Floor Aggarwal City Mall Road No 44 Pitampura, Delhi, 110 034, India
Tel.: (91) 1142351486
Web Site:
https://www.franklinleasing.in
Year Founded: 1992
539839—(BOM)
Rev.: $1,411,749
Assets: $16,530,249
Liabilities: $12,059,899
Net Worth: $4,470,350
Earnings: $18,424
Fiscal Year-end: 03/31/23
Consumer Lending Services
N.A.I.C.S.: 522291
Shanu Jain *(Officer-Compliance & Sec)*

FRANSABANK SAL

Fransabank Center Hamra Str 1st Floor, PO Box 110393, Beirut, Lebanon
Tel.: (961) 1340180
Web Site: http://www.fransabank.com
Year Founded: 1921
Sales Range: $250-299.9 Million
Emp.: 1,300
Banking Services
N.A.I.C.S.: 522110
Adnan Kassar *(Chm)*

Subsidiaries:

Fransa Invest Bank SAL **(1)**
PO Box 110393, Beirut, Lebanon
Tel.: (961) 1340188
Web Site: http://www.fransabank.com
Sales Range: $50-74.9 Million
Emp.: 15
Financial Investment Banking
N.A.I.C.S.: 523999

Fransabank (France) SA **(1)**
104 Avenue des Champs-Elysees, Paris, 75008, France
Tel.: (33) 153768400
Web Site: http://www.fransabank.com
Sales Range: $50-74.9 Million
Emp.: 20
Banking Services
N.A.I.C.S.: 522110

Fransabank El Djazair SPA **(1)**
45B Lot Petite Provence Sidi Yahia, Hydra, Algeria

Tel.: (213) 21 48 00 29
Web Site: http://www.fransabank.dz
Banking Services
N.A.I.C.S.: 522110
Nadim Kassar *(Chm)*

Fransabank OJSC **(1)**
95A Nezavisimosti ave, Minsk, 220012, Belarus
Tel.: (375) 17 389 36 36
Web Site: http://www.fransabank.by
Banking Services
N.A.I.C.S.: 522110
Aleksandr Ignatov *(Chm)*

Fransabank SAL **(1)**
100 m Str Facing Kurdistan Mall, Erbil, Iraq
Tel.: (964) 771 822 9164
Banking Services
N.A.I.C.S.: 522110

Fransabank Syria SA **(1)**
Abou Remmaneh Al Mahdi Ben Barakeh Str Al Otaki Bldg, Damascus, Syria **(55.67%)**
Tel.: (963) 11 2321008
Web Site: http://fransabank.sy
Sales Range: Less than $1 Million
Commercial Banking Services
N.A.I.C.S.: 522110
Nadim Moujaes *(Gen Mgr)*

Lebanese Leasing Company SAL **(1)**
9th Floor Fransabank Center Hamra Street Hamra Sector, PO Box 110393, Beirut, 110144, Lebanon
Tel.: (961) 1340188
Web Site: http://wwwfransabank.com
Sales Range: $50-74.9 Million
Emp.: 9
Lease Financing
N.A.I.C.S.: 523999

Societe Generale Fonciere SAL **(1)**
PO Box 110393, Beirut, Lebanon
Tel.: (961) 1 340188
Real Estate Property Management & Leasing
N.A.I.C.S.: 531390

FRANZ HANIEL & CIE. GMBH

Franz-Haniel-Platz 1, 47119, Duisburg, Germany
Tel.: (49) 2038060
Web Site: http://www.haniel.de
Year Founded: 1756
Rev.: $5,098,722,580
Assets: $7,036,080,380
Liabilities: $3,275,590,500
Net Worth: $3,760,489,880
Earnings: $145,581,800
Emp.: 19,302
Fiscal Year-end: 12/31/19
Holding Company: Pharmaceutical Distr, Brick Mfr; Washroom & Workwear Rental, Stainless Steel Recycling & Trading, Environmental Cleanup Services & Mail Order Businesses
N.A.I.C.S.: 551112
Florian Funck *(Member-Mgmt Bd)*

Subsidiaries:

Bekaert Textiles N.V. **(1)**
Deerlijkseweg 22, 8790, Waregem, Belgium
Tel.: (32) 56624111
Web Site: http://www.bekaerttextiles.com
Mattress Ticking & Mattress Textile Mfr
N.A.I.C.S.: 313210
Dirk Vandeplancke *(CEO)*

Subsidiary (Non-US):

Bekaert (Australia) Pty. Ltd. **(2)**
195 Abbotts Road, Dandenong South, 3175, VIC, Australia
Tel.: (61) 397991202
Web Site: http://www.bekaertdeslee.com
Mattress Ticking & Mattress Textile Mfr
N.A.I.C.S.: 337910

Subsidiary (US):

Bekaert Textiles USA, Inc. **(2)**
240 Business Park Dr, Winston Salem, NC 27107

Tel.: (336) 747-4900
Web Site: http://www.bekaerttextiles.com
Textile Products Mfr
N.A.I.C.S.: 314999

CWS-boco International GmbH **(1)**
Franz-Haniel-Platz 6-8, 47119, Duisburg, Germany **(100%)**
Tel.: (49) 2038060
Web Site: http://www.cws-boco.com
Sales Range: $1-4.9 Billion
Emp.: 50
Washroom Hygiene & Textile Services
N.A.I.C.S.: 812332
Carsten Bettermann *(Co-Chief Divisional Officer & Member-Mgmt Bd)*

Subsidiary (Non-US):

CWS Nederland B.V. **(2)**
The Beverspijken 16, 5221 ED, Den Bosch, Netherlands
Tel.: (31) 736338480
Web Site: http://www.cws.com
Janitorial Services
N.A.I.C.S.: 561720
Cathy Backer *(Acct Mgr-Major Field Sls)*

CWS-boco BeLux N.V. **(2)**
Lichterveld 16 Puurs, Antwerp, 2870, Belgium
Tel.: (32) 33262032
Web Site: http://www.cws-boco.be
Janitorial Services
N.A.I.C.S.: 561720
Gino Verbelen *(Mgr-Mktg)*

CWS-boco Bulgaria EOOD **(2)**
108 Besarabiya str 3rd floor office 1, Krasno Selo Distr, Sofia, 1618, Bulgaria
Tel.: (359) 24835222
Web Site: http://www.cws-boco.bg
Janitorial Services
N.A.I.C.S.: 561720

CWS-boco Ceska republika s.r.o. **(2)**
V Piskovne 2058, 193 00, Kralupy nad Vltavou, Czech Republic
Tel.: (420) 315743211
Web Site: http://www.cws.com
Janitorial Services
N.A.I.C.S.: 561720
Ajoy Chatterjee *(Reg Mng Dir)*

Subsidiary (Domestic):

CWS-boco Deutschland GmbH **(2)**
Dreieich Plaza 1A, 63303, Dreieich, Germany
Tel.: (49) 61033093333
Web Site: http://www.cws.com
Janitorial Services
N.A.I.C.S.: 561720

Subsidiary (Non-US):

CWS-boco Hungary Kft. **(2)**
Repuloteri Ut 2/A, 1112, Budapest, Hungary
Tel.: (36) 13233333
Web Site: http://www.cws.com
Janitorial Services
N.A.I.C.S.: 561720

CWS-boco Ireland Limited **(2)**
Unit 34 Fonthill Business Park, Fonthill, Dublin, Ireland
Tel.: (353) 1 460 6000
Web Site: http://www.cws-boco.ie
Emp.: 370
Surgical Supplies Distr
N.A.I.C.S.: 423450
Clement Higgins *(Member-Mgmt Bd)*

CWS-boco Italia S.p.A **(2)**
Via della Levata 24, 20084, Milan, Lacchiarella, Italy
Tel.: (39) 02 905881
Web Site: http://www.cws-boco.it
Janitorial Services
N.A.I.C.S.: 561720
Antonio Carbonelli *(Head-Pur & Mktg)*

CWS-boco Osterreich Gesellschaft m.b.H. **(2)**
IZ No Sud Str 15 Obj M 42, 2355, Wiener Neudorf, Austria
Tel.: (43) 223667030
Web Site: http://www.cws.com
Janitorial Services
N.A.I.C.S.: 561720

CWS-boco Polska Sp. z o.o. **(2)**
Rokicinska 156 b, 92-124, Lodz, Poland
Tel.: (48) 426839741
Web Site: http://www.cws-boco.pl
Janitorial Services
N.A.I.C.S.: 561720

CWS-boco ROMANIA S.R.L. **(2)**
Strada Emil Racovita numarul 13, Voluntari, 77190, Judet Ilfov, Romania
Tel.: (40) 21 410 03 30
Web Site: http://www.cws.ro
Emp.: 10
Janitorial Services
N.A.I.C.S.: 561720
Emilian Marinescu *(Gen Mgr)*

CWS-boco Slovensko, s. r. o. **(2)**
Bojnicka 10, 831 04, Bratislava, Slovakia
Tel.: (421) 33 73 51 329
Web Site: http://www.cws-eshop.sk
Emp.: 100
Janitorial Services
N.A.I.C.S.: 561720

CWS-boco Suisse SA **(2)**
Industriestrasse 20, 8152, Glattbrugg, Switzerland
Tel.: (41) 44 809 37 77
Web Site: http://www.cws-boco.ch
Janitorial Services
N.A.I.C.S.: 561720
Dirk Goyvaerts *(Head-IT)*

CWS-boco Sweden AB **(2)**
Fyrgatan 2, 195 61, Arlandastad, Sweden
Tel.: (46) 852022500
Web Site: http://www.cws.com
Janitorial Services
N.A.I.C.S.: 561720

CWS-boco d.o.o. **(2)**
Kovinskal ul 4, 10000, Zagreb, Croatia
Tel.: (385) 1 29 21 086
Web Site: http://www.cws.com
Janitorial Services
N.A.I.C.S.: 561720

CWS-boco higienski sistemi in vzdrzevanje d.o.o. **(2)**
Cesta 24 Junija 23, Crnuce, 1231, Ljubljana, Slovenia
Tel.: (386) 1 530 25 80
Web Site: http://www.cws-boco.si
Janitorial Services
N.A.I.C.S.: 561720

Subsidiary (Domestic):

Haniel Textile Service GmbH **(2)**
Franz Haniel Platz 1, 47119, Duisburg, Germany **(100%)**
Tel.: (49) 2038060
Web Site: http://www.haniel.de
Sales Range: $25-49.9 Million
Emp.: 60
Washroom Service & Supplies; Workwear Rental Service
N.A.I.C.S.: 561720

ELG Haniel GmbH **(1)**
Kremerskamp 16, Duisburg, 47138, Germany **(100%)**
Tel.: (49) 20345010
Web Site: http://www.elg.de
Sales Range: $50-74.9 Million
Emp.: 120
Recycling of Raw Materials for the Stainless Steel Industry; International Trading of Metals & Alloys
N.A.I.C.S.: 331210
Norbert Spaeker *(Chm)*

Subsidiary (Non-US):

ELG Canada, Inc. **(2)**
4375 Corporate Dr, Burlington, L7L 5P7, ON, Canada
Tel.: (905) 335-6337
Emp.: 12
Metal Recycling Services
N.A.I.C.S.: 562920
Andre Langlois *(VP-Ops & Trading)*

ELG Carbon Fibre Ltd. **(2)**
Cannon Business Park Darkhouse Lane, Coseley, WV14 8XQ, West Midlands, United Kingdom
Tel.: (44) 1902 406010
Web Site: http://www.elgcf.com
Metal Recycling Services

N.A.I.C.S.: 562920

ELG Haniel Metals Ltd **(2)**
Templeborough Works Sheffield Road,
Sheffield, S9 1RT, United Kingdom
Tel.: (44) 114 2443333
Web Site: http://www.elg.co.uk
Metal Recycling Services
N.A.I.C.S.: 562920

Division (Domestic):

ELG Carrs Stainless Steels **(3)**
Wadsley Bridge, Sheffield, S6 1LL, United
Kingdom
Tel.: (44) 114 2855866
Web Site: http://www.elgcarrs.co.uk
Emp.: 70
Steel Product Mfr & Distr
N.A.I.C.S.: 331513
Nick Buxton *(Dir-Comml)*

Subsidiary (Non-US):

ELG India Private Limited **(2)**
608 Sixth Floor Srishti Plaza Off Saki Vihar
Road, Powai, Mumbai, 400 072, India
Tel.: (91) 22.4015 1525
Metal Recycling Services
N.A.I.C.S.: 562920

ELG Legima Spol. S.r.o. **(2)**
Videnska 116, 619 00, Brno, Czech Repub-
lic
Tel.: (420) 547 212 313
Web Site: http://www.elg-legima.cz
Metal Recycling Services
N.A.I.C.S.: 562920
Pavel Jelinek *(Dir)*

ELG Metals Taiwan Corporation **(2)**
No 1 Ln 33 Zhunan Rd, Renwu, Kaohsiung,
00814, Taiwan
Tel.: (886) 7 9635588
Metal Recycling Services
N.A.I.C.S.: 562920

ELG Metals, Inc. **(2)**
11F No 8 Ming Cheng 4th Rd, Gushan Dis-
trict, Kaohsiung, 00804, Taiwan
Tel.: (886) 7 5225656
Metal Recycling Services
N.A.I.C.S.: 562920

Subsidiary (US):

ELG Metals, Inc. **(2)**
369 River Rd, McKeesport, PA 15132
Tel.: (412) 672-9200
Metal Recycling Services
N.A.I.C.S.: 562920
Simon Merrills *(Pres & CEO)*

Division (Domestic):

**ELG Metals, Inc. - Southern
Division** **(3)**
15135 Jacintoport Blvd, Houston, TX 77015
Tel.: (281) 457-2100
Web Site: http://www.elg.de
Metal Recycling Services
N.A.I.C.S.: 562920
Andres Montes *(Gen Mgr)*

**ELG Metals, Inc. - West Coast
Division** **(3)**
9400 Rayo Ave, South Gate, CA 90280
Tel.: (323) 569-3545
Metal Recycling Services
N.A.I.C.S.: 562920
Terry Brown *(COO & Exec VP)*

Subsidiary (Non-US):

**ELG Recycling Processors Pty
Ltd** **(2)**
170 Northbourne Road, Campbellfield, Mel-
bourne, 3061, VIC, Australia
Tel.: (61) 3 93053535
Metal Recycling Services
N.A.I.C.S.: 562920
James Smillie *(Gen Mgr)*

Subsidiary (US):

ELG Utica Alloys (Hartford), Inc. **(2)**
239 W Service Rd, Hartford, CT 06120
Tel.: (860) 522-3123
Metal Recycling Services
N.A.I.C.S.: 562920

Subsidiary (Non-US):

ELG Utica Alloys Ltd **(2)**
Hawke Street Brightside, Sheffield, S9 2SU,
United Kingdom
Tel.: (44) 1142618495
Metal Recycling Services
N.A.I.C.S.: 562920

Haniel Reederei Holding GmbH **(1)**
Franz Haniel Platz 6 8, Duisburg, 47119,
Germany **(100%)**
Tel.: (49) 2038060
Web Site: http://www.xella.com
Sales Range: $200-249.9 Million
Emp.: 537
Inland Shipping; Industrial Logistics
N.A.I.C.S.: 483211
Jan Buckemden *(Chm)*

Microndean Ireland Ltd. **(1)**
Spiddal Industrial Estate, Spiddal, County
Galway, Ireland
Tel.: (353) 91 553066
Janitorial Services
N.A.I.C.S.: 561720
Clement Higgins *(Mng Dir)*

Rovema GmbH **(1)**
Industriestrasse 1, 35463, Fernwald, Ger-
many
Tel.: (49) 641 409 0
Web Site: http://www.rovema.de
Packaging Machines & Systems Mfr
N.A.I.C.S.: 333993
Jens Torkel *(CEO)*

TAKKT AG **(1)**
Presselstrasse 12, 70191, Stuttgart,
Germany **(70.4%)**
Tel.: (49) 711346580
Web Site: https://www.takkt.de
Rev.: $1,368,820,877
Assets: $1,111,398,393
Liabilities: $401,974,260
Net Worth: $709,424,133
Earnings: $27,100,008
Emp.: 2,435
Fiscal Year-end: 12/31/2023
Business-to-Business Mail Order Services
for Office, Plant & Warehouse Equipment
Mfr
N.A.I.C.S.: 459410
Florian Funck *(Chm-Supervisory Bd)*

Subsidiary (Non-US):

**Avenue Industrial Supply Co.
Ltd.** **(2)**
331 Alden Rd, Markham, L3R 3L4, ON,
Canada **(100%)**
Tel.: (905) 946-8174
Sales Range: $25-49.9 Million
Emp.: 70
Industrial Product Distr
N.A.I.C.S.: 424690

Subsidiary (US):

C&H Distributors, LLC **(2)**
770 S 70th St, Milwaukee, WI 53214
Tel.: (414) 443-1700
Web Site: http://www.chdist.com
Sales Range: $75-99.9 Million
Emp.: 200
Distr of Industrial Supplies
N.A.I.C.S.: 423830
David McKeon *(Pres)*

Subsidiary (Non-US):

Davenport Paper Co Limited **(2)**
Davpack Charlton House Riverside Park
East Service Road Raynesway, Derby,
DE21 7BF, United Kingdom
Tel.: (44) 1332 821200
Web Site: http://www.davpack.co.uk
Cardboard Box Mfr & Distr
N.A.I.C.S.: 322220

Subsidiary (US):

Hubert Company **(2)**
9555 Dry Fork Rd, Harrison, OH 45030-
1906
Tel.: (513) 367-8600
Web Site: http://www.hubert.com
Sales Range: $75-99.9 Million
Food Service Equipment & Supply Distr
N.A.I.C.S.: 423440

Subsidiary (Domestic):

Kaiser & Kraft Europa **(2)**
Presselstr 12, 70191, Stuttgart,
Germany **(100%)**
Tel.: (49) 711346560
Web Site: http://www.kaiserkraft.de
Sales Range: $100-124.9 Million
Emp.: 300
Transportation & Storage of Office Equip-
ment Distr
N.A.I.C.S.: 488210

Subsidiary (Domestic):

Gaerner GmbH **(3)**
Ruhrorter Str 195, 47119, Duisburg,
Germany **(100%)**
Tel.: (49) 20380940
Web Site: http://www.gaerner.de
Sales Range: $25-49.9 Million
Emp.: 50
Office Equipment Distr
N.A.I.C.S.: 459410
Astrid Voss *(Mng Dir)*

Subsidiary (US):

George Patton Associates, Inc. **(3)**
55 Broadcommon Rd, Bristol, RI 02809
Tel.: (401) 247-0333
Sales Range: $10-24.9 Million
Emp.: 85
Sign Mfr
N.A.I.C.S.: 339950
Zachary Zullick *(Dir-E-commerce Strategy)*

Subsidiary (Non-US):

Gerdmans Inrednigar AB **(3)**
Vargvagen 2, 285 39, Markaryd,
Sweden **(100%)**
Tel.: (46) 43374080
Web Site: http://www.gerdmans.se
Emp.: 50
Distr of Industrial & Office Equipment
N.A.I.C.S.: 459410
Anders Magnusson *(CEO)*

KWESTO
Praga Del Nicka 12, 17000, Prague, Czech
Republic
Tel.: (420) 266793734
Web Site: http://www.kwesto.cz
Sales Range: $25-49.9 Million
Emp.: 30
Distr of Office Equipment
N.A.I.C.S.: 459410

Subsidiary (Domestic):

Kaiser & Kraft GmbH **(3)**
Presselstr 12, 70191, Stuttgart,
Germany **(100%)**
Tel.: (49) 711346560
Web Site: http://www.kaiserkraft.de
Sales Range: $125-149.9 Million
Emp.: 300
Transportation & Storage of Office Equip-
ment Distr
N.A.I.C.S.: 488210

Subsidiary (US):

National Business Furniture Inc. **(2)**
770 S 70th St, Milwaukee, WI 53214
Tel.: (414) 276-8511
Web Site:
http://www.nationalbusinessfurniture.com
Sales Range: $100-124.9 Million
Emp.: 150
Business Furniture Whslr
N.A.I.C.S.: 423210
Kent Anderson *(COO)*

Division (Domestic):

Alfax Wholesale Furniture Inc. **(3)**
13901 Midway Rd Ste 102-428, Farmers
Branch, TX 75244
Tel.: (800) 221-5710
Web Site: http://www.alfaxfurniture.com
Sales Range: $50-74.9 Million
Emp.: 7
Furniture & Furnishings Mfr
N.A.I.C.S.: 423210

Dallas Midwest Company **(3)**
4100 Alpha Rd Ste 111, Dallas, TX 75244
Tel.: (972) 866-0101
Web Site: http://www.dallasmidwest.com

Sales Range: $50-74.9 Million
Emp.: 9
Furniture for Schools, Churches & Organi-
zations
N.A.I.C.S.: 449110

National Business Furniture Inc **(3)**
770 S 70th St, Milwaukee, WI 53214
Tel.: (414) 276-8511
Web Site:
http://www.nationalbusinessfurniture.com
Sales Range: $50-74.9 Million
Emp.: 120
Online Retailer of Office Furniture
N.A.I.C.S.: 449110

OfficeFurniture.com **(3)**
735 N Water St Ste 440, Milwaukee, WI
53202
Tel.: (414) 276-8511
Web Site: http://www.officefurniture.com
Sales Range: $25-49.9 Million
Emp.: 50
Office Furniture
N.A.I.C.S.: 449110

Subsidiary (US):

Post-Up Stand, Inc. **(2)**
5461 Dunham Rd, Maple Heights, OH
44137-3644
Web Site: http://www.postupstand.com
Custom Banner Stand Display & Promo-
tional Sign Mfr
N.A.I.C.S.: 339950
Alon Weiner *(Co-Founder)*

FRANZ REINKEMEIER GMBH
Westerwieher Strasse 198, Rietberg,
33397, Germany
Tel.: (49) 52449210
Web Site: http://www.reinkemeier-
rietberg.de
Year Founded: 1971
Rev.: $55,176,000
Emp.: 180
Interior Design Products Distr
N.A.I.C.S.: 423220
Heinrich Reinkemeier *(Mng Dir)*

**FRANZ SUTER GMBH-
PUMPEN UND SYSTEME**
Schurmattstrasse 9, 5643, Sins, Swit-
zerland
Tel.: (41) 7871760
Web Site: http://www.suterpumpen.ch
Pumps Mfr
N.A.I.C.S.: 333914

FRAPORT AG
Frankfurt Airport Services Worldwide,
60547, Frankfurt, Germany
Tel.: (49) 18063724636   De
Web Site: https://www.fraport.com
FPRUF—(OTCIQ)
Rev.: $2,657,688,487
Assets: $15,491,003,424
Liabilities: $11,952,974,944
Net Worth: $3,538,028,480
Earnings: $363,285,131
Emp.: 7,040
Fiscal Year-end: 12/31/23
Airport Retailing & Real Estate Ser-
vices
N.A.I.C.S.: 488119
Matthias Zieschang *(Member-Exec
Bd & Exec Dir-Controlling & Fin)*

Subsidiaries:

**ASG Airport Service Gesellschaft
mbH** **(1)**
Hauspostkasten 149, 60549, Frankfurt am
Main, Germany **(49%)**
Tel.: (49) 6969036031
Web Site: http://www.asg-airport.de
Airport Services
N.A.I.C.S.: 488119

Aerodrom Ljubljana, LLC **(1)**
Zg Brnik 130a, Brnik-aerodrom, 4210, Lju-
bljana, Slovenia
Tel.: (386) 42061000
Web Site: http://www.lju-airport.si

Fraport AG—(Continued)

Airport Operator
N.A.I.C.S.: 481111
Zmago Skobir (Mng Dir)

AirIT Airport IT Services Hahn AG (1)
Building 663 Hahn Airport, 55483, Lautzenhausen, Germany (100%)
Tel.: (49) 6543507302
Web Site: http://www.airit.de
Sales Range: $50-74.9 Million
Emp.: 15
Airport Information & Communications Infrastructure Operations & Planning
N.A.I.C.S.: 488119

AirIT Services AG (1)
Gebaude 663, Hahn-Flughafen, 55483, Lautzenhausen, Germany
Tel.: (49) 654 350 7304
Web Site: https://www.airit.de
Sales Range: $25-49.9 Million
Emp.: 12
Information Technology Consulting Services
N.A.I.C.S.: 541512

AirITSystems Hannover GmbH (1)
Benkendorffstrasse 6, 30855, Langenhagen, Germany (50%)
Tel.: (49) 511 977 4000
Web Site: https://www.airitsystems.com
Sales Range: $25-49.9 Million
Emp.: 200
IT Services & Solutions
N.A.I.C.S.: 541511

Airmail Center Frankfurt GmbH (1)
Airport Frankfurt/Main Gate 3 Building 189, PO Box 750164, Gate 3 Building 189, 60549, Frankfurt am Main, Germany (40%)
Tel.: (49) 6969077000
Web Site: https://www.airmail-center.de
Sales Range: $10-24.9 Million
Emp.: 38
Airmail Handling Services
N.A.I.C.S.: 561431

Airport Assekuranz Vermittlungs-GmbH (1)
Siemensstrasse 6, 63263, Neu-Isenburg, Germany (100%)
Tel.: (49) 6969060180
Web Site: http://www.fraport.com
Sales Range: $50-74.9 Million
Emp.: 15
Insurance Services
N.A.I.C.S.: 524298
Hans-Joerg Schill (Mng Dir)

Airport Cater Service GmbH (1)
Frankfurt Airport Building 101, 60547, Frankfurt am Main, Germany (100%)
Tel.: (49) 6969066002
Catering Services
N.A.I.C.S.: 722320

Cairo Airport Company (1)
Oruba Road, Heliopolis, Cairo, Egypt
Tel.: (20) 2 696 6300
Web Site: https://www.cairo-airport.com
Sales Range: $1-4.9 Billion
Emp.: 4,000
Airport Management Services
N.A.I.C.S.: 488119
Mohamed Saeed Mahrous (Chm)

Energy Air GmbH (1)
Flughafen Frankfurt-Main Terminal 2 Geb 152, 60549, Frankfurt am Main, Germany (100%)
Tel.: (49) 6 906 6700
Web Site: https://www.energy-air.de
Sales Range: $75-99.9 Million
Emp.: 3
Power, Remote Heat, Remote Cooling & Energy Supplier
N.A.I.C.S.: 221122

FPS Frankfurt Passenger Services GmbH (1)
Building 201A HBK 259, 60549, Frankfurt am Main, Germany
Tel.: (49) 69 690 28933
Passenger Air Transportation Services
N.A.I.C.S.: 488190

Flughafen Saarbruecken GmbH (1)

Balthasar-Goldstein-Strasse, 66131, Saarbrucken, Germany (51%)
Tel.: (49) 6893830
Web Site: http://www.flughafen-saarbruecken.de
Airport Operations
N.A.I.C.S.: 488119

FraCareServices GmbH (1)
Hugo-Eckener-Ring FAC1 HBK 41, FAC1 HBK 41, 60549, Frankfurt, Germany (51%)
Tel.: (49) 6969069106
Web Site: https://www.fracareservices.com
Sales Range: $200-249.9 Million
Emp.: 600
Airport Services for the Handicapped
N.A.I.C.S.: 488119

FraSec Fraport Security Services GmbH (1)
Hugo-Eckener-Ring, 60549, Frankfurt am Main, Germany
Tel.: (49) 6969025200
Web Site: http://www.frasec.de
Emp.: 3,000
Security System Services
N.A.I.C.S.: 561621

Frankfurter Kanalreinigungsgesellschaft mbH (1)
Professor-Staudinger Strasse Gebaude 700, 65451, Kelsterbach, Germany
Tel.: (49) 6 182 5979
Web Site: https://www.kanal-service.de
Sewer Cleaning & Disposal Services
N.A.I.C.S.: 562998

Fraport Cleveland Inc. (1)
Cleveland Hopkins International Airport Concourse B 5300 Riverside Dr, Cleveland, OH 44135
Tel.: (216) 265-0700
Food & Beverage Retailer
N.A.I.C.S.: 445298

Fraport IC Ictas Havaliman Yer Hizmetleri AS (1)
Antalya Havalimani 1, DisHatlarTerminali, 7230, Antalya, Turkiye (51%)
Tel.: (90) 2423303600
Web Site: http://www.icfairport.com
Airport Ground Handling Services
N.A.I.C.S.: 488119
Melih Dipova (Mgr-Ops)

Fraport Immobilienservice und -entwicklungs GmbH & Co. KG (1)
Schieferstein 8, 65439, Florsheim, Germany (100%)
Tel.: (49) 6145598661
Sales Range: $50-74.9 Million
Emp.: 9
Real Estate Development Services
N.A.I.C.S.: 531390

Fraport Malta Business Services Ltd. (1)
Mayfair Complex Saint George's Bay, San Giljan, STJ 3311, Malta
Tel.: (356) 21384088
Aviation Terminal Services
N.A.I.C.S.: 488190

Fraport Objekt Monchhof GmbH (1)
Schieferstein 8, 65439, Florsheim, Germany
Tel.: (49) 614559860
Sales Range: $25-49.9 Million
Emp.: 10
Airport Management Services
N.A.I.C.S.: 488119

Fraport Pittsburgh Inc. (1)
Pittsburgh International Airport, Pittsburgh, PA 15231-0318
Tel.: (412) 472-5180
Food & Beverage Retailer
N.A.I.C.S.: 445298

Fraport Real Estate 162 163 GmbH & Co. KG (1)
Schieferstein 8, Florsheim, 65439, Germany
Tel.: (49) 614559860
Web Site: http://www.fraport.com
Sales Range: $50-74.9 Million
Emp.: 1
Real Estate Management Services
N.A.I.C.S.: 531390

Fraport Real Estate Verwaltungs GmbH (1)

Schieferstein 8, Florsheim, 65439, Hessen, Germany
Tel.: (49) 6145598661
Web Site: http://www.fraport.de
Real Estate Management Services
N.A.I.C.S.: 531390

Fraport Saudi Arabia Ltd. (1)
PO Box 12115, Riyadh, 11473, Saudi Arabia (100%)
Tel.: (966) 12200842
Web Site: http://www.fraport.com
Sales Range: $25-49.9 Million
Emp.: 6
Airport Management & Development Services
N.A.I.C.S.: 488119

Fraport Security Services GmbH (1)
Hugo-Eckener-Ring FAC 1 D 6, 60549, Frankfurt am Main, Germany (100%)
Tel.: (49) 6969030153
Web Site: http://www.frasec.de
Sales Range: $650-699.9 Million
Emp.: 7,000
Airport Security Services
N.A.I.C.S.: 561612
Claudia Uhe (Chm)

Fraport Slovenija d.o.o (1)
Zgornji Brnik 130a, 4210, Brnik, Slovenia
Tel.: (386) 42061000
Web Site: https://www.fraport-slovenija.si
Cargo Management Services
N.A.I.C.S.: 488510

Fraport Twin Star Airport Management AD (1)
Varna Airport, 9000, Varna, 9000, Bulgaria
Tel.: (359) 56870201
Web Site: https://www.fraport-bulgaria.com
Sales Range: $200-249.9 Million
Emp.: 590
Airport Operation Services
N.A.I.C.S.: 488119
Dimitar Kostadinov (Dir-Airport)

GCS Gesellschaft fur Cleaning Service mbH & Co. Airport Frankfurt/Main KG (1)
Main KG Gate 3 Building 170, 60547, Frankfurt am Main, Germany
Tel.: (49) 6969020721
Web Site: http://www.gcs-cleaning.de
Emp.: 700
Cleaning & Logistic Services
N.A.I.C.S.: 561720

Lima Airport Partners S.R.L. (1)
Via Expresa Elmer Faucett s/n, 07031, Callao, Peru (80.01%)
Tel.: (51) 15173500
Web Site: https://www.lima-airport.com
Airport Operation Services
N.A.I.C.S.: 488119

MMK Metalurji Sanayi Ticaret Ve Liman Isletmeciligi Anonim Sirketi (1)
Barbaros Mah Cigdem Sok No 1 Section 58 and 59 Pk, Atasehir, 34746, Istanbul, Turkiye
Tel.: (90) 2166883289
Web Site: https://mmkturkey.com.tr
Steel Product Mfr & Distr
N.A.I.C.S.: 331110

Media Frankfurt GmbH (1)
Unterschweinstiege 2-14, 60549, Frankfurt, Germany (51%)
Tel.: (49) 69697080
Web Site: https://www.media-frankfurt.de
Sales Range: $25-49.9 Million
Emp.: 40
Airport Advertising Displays Marketer
N.A.I.C.S.: 488119

Medical Airport Service GmbH (1)
Hessenring 13A, 64546, Morfelden-Walldorf, Germany (50%)
Tel.: (49) 6105 341 3130
Web Site: https://www.medical-airport-service.de
Environmental, Medical & Business Support Services
N.A.I.C.S.: 561499
Udo Sicker (Mng Dir)

N*ICE Aircraft Service & Supports GmbH (1)
Cargo City South Building 640, 60549,

Frankfurt am Main, Germany (52%)
Tel.: (49) 696 902 1596
Web Site: https://nice-services.de
De-Icing Services
N.A.I.C.S.: 488119

Perishable Center GmbH + Co. Betriebs KG (1)
Airport Frankfurt Main Gate 26 Building 454, Building 454 Gate 26, 60549, Frankfurt am Main, Germany
Tel.: (49) 6969502233
Web Site: https://www.pcf-frankfurt.de
Sales Range: $50-74.9 Million
Emp.: 120
Perishable Cargo Handling Services
N.A.I.C.S.: 488119

Shanghai Frankfurt Airport Consulting Services Co., Ltd. (SFACS) (1)
Room 23C T1 Jiahui Plaza No 2601 Xie Tu Rd, Xuhui District, Shanghai, 200030, China (50%)
Tel.: (86) 2164263017
Web Site: https://www.sfacs.cn
Sales Range: $25-49.9 Million
Emp.: 2
Airport Management Training & Consulting Services
N.A.I.C.S.: 541611

Tradeport Frankfurt GmbH (1)
Frankfurt Airport, Cargo City South Building 532, 60549, Frankfurt am Main, Germany
Tel.: (49) 969070652
Web Site: http://www.tradeport-logistics.com
Sales Range: $25-49.9 Million
Emp.: 40
Cargo & Logistics Services
N.A.I.C.S.: 488119

Tradeport Hong Kong Ltd. (1)
Unit 8 2M Tradeport Logistics Centre 21 Chun Yue Road, Hong Kong International Airport Lantau, Hong Kong, China (Hong Kong)
Tel.: (852) 2 286 1388
Web Site: https://www.tradeport-logistics.com
Sales Range: $10-24.9 Million
Emp.: 50
Avionics Logistics Services
N.A.I.C.S.: 561499

Zentrum fur integrierte Verkehrssysteme GmbH (1)
Robert-Bosch-Strasse 7, 64293, Darmstadt, Germany
Tel.: (49) 615 127 0280
Web Site: https://www.ziv.de
Airport Management Services
N.A.I.C.S.: 488119
Joerg Dreiling (Head-IT)

operational services GmbH & Co. KG (1)
Frankfurt Airport Center Gebaude 234 HBK25, 60549, Frankfurt am Main, Germany (50%)
Tel.: (49) 6968 970 2710
Web Site: https://www.operational-services.de
Sales Range: $100-124.9 Million
Emp.: 400
Airport Information & Communication Services
N.A.I.C.S.: 519290
Frank Oidtmann (Mng Dir)

FRAPPA
132 Rue De Soras, 7430, Davezieux, Ardeche, France
Tel.: (33) 475334643
Web Site: http://wwfrappa.com
Rev.: $24,200,000
Emp.: 87
Motor Vehicles & Car Bodies
N.A.I.C.S.: 336110
Julien Torre-Frappa (Pres)

FRAS-LE S.A.
Rodovia RS 122 Km 66 n 10 945 Bairro Forqueta, 95115-550, Caxias do Sul, 95115-550, RS, Brazil
Tel.: (55) 5432391000
Web Site: https://www.fras-le.com

Year Founded: 1954
FRAS3—(BRAZ)
Rev.: $605,755,512
Assets: $699,308,002
Liabilities: $366,615,710
Net Worth: $332,692,292
Earnings: $69,489,639
Emp.: 4,631
Fiscal Year-end: 12/31/23
Brake System Mfr
N.A.I.C.S.: 336340
David Abramo Randon (Chm)

Subsidiaries:

Autoparts Armetal S.A.   (1)
Marcos Sastre 2300, Ricardo Rojas Tigre,
Buenos Aires, Argentina
Tel.: (54) 1147366800
Web Site: http://www.armetal.com.ar
Auto Parts Distr
N.A.I.C.S.: 423120

FRAS-LE AFRICA AUTOMOTIVE
(PTY) LTD.   (1)
Regent Hill office Park Block C Office 7A
Cnr Leslie & Turley Rds, Lonehill, 2062,
Johannesburg, South Africa
Tel.: (27) 11 702 8340
Brake System Distr
N.A.I.C.S.: 423120

FRAS-LE ANDINA COMERCIO Y
REPRESENTACIONES LTDA.   (1)
Calle Andres de Fuenzalida 69 Oficina 701,
Providencia, Santiago, Chile
Tel.: (56) 2 334 9349
Brake System Distr
N.A.I.C.S.: 423120

FRAS-LE ARGENTINA S.A.   (1)
Colectora Oeste de Panamericana N 194,
Garin - Partido de, B1619, Escobar, Bue-
nos Aires, Argentina
Tel.: (54) 1147366873
Brake System Distr
N.A.I.C.S.: 423120
Rafael Rombaldi (Mgr-Ops)

FRAS-LE EUROPE HANDELSGE-
SELLSCHAFT MBH   (1)
Ludwig-Erhard-Strasse 8, 45891, Gelsen-
kirchen, Germany
Tel.: (49) 209 386 240
Brake System Distr
N.A.I.C.S.: 423120

FRAS-LE FRICTION MATERIALS
(PINGHU) CO., LTD   (1)
Pinghu Manufacturing Facility No 2088 Xin
Ming Road, Economic Development Zone
Zheijang Prov, Pinghu, 314200, Zhejiang,
China
Tel.: (86) 57385290700
Brake System Distr
N.A.I.C.S.: 423120

FRAS-LE MEXICO, S. DE R.L. DE
C.V.   (1)
Avenida Homero 1804 INT 504 Colonia
Chapultepec Morales, Delegacion Miguel
Hidalgo, 11570, Mexico, Mexico
Tel.: (52) 5555241896
Web Site: http://www.frasle.com.br
Emp.: 3
Brake System Distr
N.A.I.C.S.: 423120
Gustavo Louvatel (Coord-Expo)

FRAS-LE MIDDLE EAST   (1)
Lob 13 1st Floor No 28, PO Box 261416,
Jebel Ali Free Zone, Dubai, United Arab
Emirates
Tel.: (971) 4 8810344
Brake System Distr
N.A.I.C.S.: 423120

FRAS-LE NORTH AMERICA
INC.   (1)
103 Echlin Blvd, Prattville, AL 36067
Tel.: (334) 358-5775
Web Site: https://www.fras-le.com
Brake System Distr
N.A.I.C.S.: 423120

Fras-le S.A. - ALABAMA
FACILITY   (1)
103 Echlin Blvd, Prattville, AL 36067

Tel.: (334) 358-5775
Web Site: http://www.fras-le.com
Emp.: 75
Vehicle Brake System Mfr
N.A.I.C.S.: 336340

FRASER & COMPANY LIMITED
Shop No 75 Bldg No 75 B Wing
Evershine Helio CHS LTD EMP,
Thakur Village Kandivali E, Mumbai,
400 101, India
Tel.: (91) 9324089432   In
Web Site:
   https://www.fraserindia.co.in
Year Founded: 1917
539032—(BOM)
Rev.: $1,535,682
Assets: $1,623,083
Liabilities: $664,218
Net Worth: $958,865
Earnings: $41,024
Fiscal Year-end: 03/31/23
Export & Import Services
N.A.I.C.S.: 522299
Shanky Handa (Compliance Officer &
Sec)

FRASER FORD SALES LTD.
815 King St W, Oshawa, L1J 2L4,
ON, Canada
Tel.: (905) 576-1800
Web Site: http://www.fraserford.ca
Year Founded: 1996
Rev.: $19,466,485
Emp.: 69
New & Used Car Dealers
N.A.I.C.S.: 441110

FRASER RIVER PILE &
DREDGE (GP) INC.
1830 River Drive, New Westminster,
V3M 2A8, BC, Canada
Tel.: (604) 522-7971
Web Site: https://www.frpd.com
Year Founded: 1911
Marine Construction & Dredging Con-
tractor
N.A.I.C.S.: 488320
Mike Bevan-Pritchard (VP-Major Proj-
ects & Bus Dev)

FRASERS GROUP PLC
Unit A Brook Park East, Shirebrook,
Mansfield, NG20 8RY, United King-
dom
Tel.: (44) 3442459200   UK
Web Site: http://www.frasers.group
Year Founded: 1982
FRAS—(OTCIQ)
Rev.: $4,922,142,316
Assets: $5,139,105,972
Liabilities: $3,494,907,052
Net Worth: $1,644,198,920
Earnings: ($105,902,160)
Emp.: 26,496
Fiscal Year-end: 04/25/21
Sportswear Retailer
N.A.I.C.S.: 423910
Mike Ashley (Founder)

Subsidiaries:

18 Montrose Retail Limited   (1)
6-8 Stable Street, King's Cross, London,
N1C 4AB, United Kingdom
Tel.: (44) 2038055451
Web Site: http://www.18montrose.com
Men & Women Clothing Distr
N.A.I.C.S.: 458110

Brands & Fashion NV   (1)
Leopoldstraat 79, 2800, Mechelen, Belgium
Tel.: (32) 15446585
Socks Mfr & Distr
N.A.I.C.S.: 315120

Eastern Outfitters, Inc.   (1)
4819 Richlands Hwy, Jacksonville, NC
28540
Tel.: (910) 347-4868

Web Site: http://www.easternoutfitter.com
Sales Range: $1-9.9 Million
Sporting Goods Retailer
N.A.I.C.S.: 459110
Jonathon King (Owner)

Everlast Worldwide, Inc.   (1)
1900 HWY DD, Moberly, MO 65270
Tel.: (212) 239-0990
Web Site: https://www.everlast.com
Sales Range: $50-74.9 Million
Emp.: 140
Boxing Equipment Designer, Marketer, Re-
tailer & Mfr
N.A.I.C.S.: 339920

GAME Digital plc   (1)
Unity House Telford Road, Basingstoke,
RG21 6YJ, Hants, United Kingdom
Tel.: (44) 1256 78 4000
Web Site: http://www.gamedigitalplc.com
Sales Range: $900-999.9 Million
Videogame Retailer
N.A.I.C.S.: 459120
Martyn Gibbs (CEO)

Representative Office (Non-US):

GAME Digital plc - Spain Office   (2)
Calle Virgilio 9 Ciudad de la Imagen, Pozu-
elo de Alarcon, 28223, Madrid, Spain
Tel.: (34) 902 222 055
Web Site: http://www.gamedigitalplc.com
Videogame Retailer
N.A.I.C.S.: 459120
Pablo Crespo (Dir Gen)

HK Sports & Golf Aktiebolag   (1)
Eskilstorpsvagen 7, 269 96, Bastad, Swe-
den
Tel.: (46) 43170045
Web Site: https://www.hkab.se
Outdoor Sports Product Distr
N.A.I.C.S.: 459110

House of Fraser (Stores) Limited   (1)
Granite House 31 Stockwell St, Glasgow,
G1 4RZ, United Kingdom
Tel.: (44) 3456021073
Web Site: http://www.houseoffraser.co.uk
Department Stores
N.A.I.C.S.: 455110
Alex Williamson (CEO)

International Brand Management
Limited   (1)
Unit A Brook Park East Meadow Lane,
Marylebone, Shirebrook, NG20 8RY, United
Kingdom
Tel.: (44) 3442459200
Web Site: https://www.ibml.co.uk
Sports Product Distr
N.A.I.C.S.: 423910

Jack Wills Ltd.   (1)
Unit 4 Ockham Drive, Greenford, UB6 0FD,
Mddx, United Kingdom
Tel.: (44) 845 262 5225
Web Site: http://www.jackwills.com
Sales Range: $25-49.9 Million
Emp.: 1,870
Fashion Design Services
N.A.I.C.S.: 541490
Peter Williams (Founder & CEO)

Mountain Sports USA LLC   (1)
2025 W Pioneer Pkwy, Arlington, TX 76013
Tel.: (817) 461-4503
Web Site: https://www.mountainsports.com
Mountain Sports Product Retailer
N.A.I.C.S.: 459110

MySale Group Plc   (1)
3/120 Old Pittwater Road, Brookvale, 2100,
NSW, Australia   (71.3%)
Tel.: (61) 289990407
Web Site: http://www.mysalegroup.com
Rev.: $90,328,438
Assets: $39,952,211
Liabilities: $22,555,101
Net Worth: $17,397,110
Earnings: ($6,472,773)
Emp.: 122
Fiscal Year-end: 06/30/2021
Online Retailer
N.A.I.C.S.: 455219
Carl Jackson (Chm)

SIA Sportland   (1)
A Deglava Street 50, Riga, LV-1035, Latvia
Tel.: (371) 29393040

Web Site: https://www.sportland.com
Sports & Leisure Goods Distr
N.A.I.C.S.: 459110

Sportland Eestie A.S.   (1)
Parnu mnt 144 V floor, 11317, Tallinn, Esto-
nia
Tel.: (372) 6548434
Web Site: https://www.sportland.ee
Sports & Leisure Goods Distr
N.A.I.C.S.: 459110

Sports Direct MST Sdn. Bhd.   (1)
Lot 68 Jalan Beliong 15/11 Off Jalan Utas
15/7 Seksyen 15, 40200, Shah Alam, Ma-
laysia
Tel.: (60) 122642291
Web Site: http://www.my.sportsdirect.com
Sports & Leisure Goods Distr
N.A.I.C.S.: 459110

Sports Direct Spain, S.L.U.   (1)
Travesia Jardines Reales Nr 7 Parque
Comm Puerto Venecia, 50021, Zaragoza,
Spain
Tel.: (34) 876502601
Web Site: https://www.sportsdirect.com
Sports & Leisure Goods Distr
N.A.I.C.S.: 459110

Sportsdirect.com Fitness Limited   (1)
Unit A Brook Park East, Shirebrook, NG20
8RY, United Kingdom
Tel.: (44) 3442459275
Web Site:
   https://www.sportsdirectfitness.com
Fitness Training Services
N.A.I.C.S.: 812990

Studio Retail Group plc   (1)
Church Bridge House Henry Street, Ac-
crington, BB5 4EE, United Kingdom
Tel.: (44) 1613033465
Web Site: http://www.studioretail.group
Rev.: $590,464,282
Assets: $663,202,773
Liabilities: $560,856,482
Net Worth: $102,346,291
Earnings: $11,886,839
Emp.: 1,903
Fiscal Year-end: 03/27/2020
Greeting Cards, Gift Wrap, Crepe Paper,
Stationery; Catalogue Sales; Retail Gift
Shops
N.A.I.C.S.: 459420
Mark Ashcroft (Sec)

Table Tennis Pro Europe Ltd.   (1)
Unit A Brook Park East Meadow Lane,
Shirebrook, NG20 8RY, United Kingdom
Tel.: (44) 1623745476
Web Site: https://www.sportsdirect.com
Table Tennis Equipment Retailer
N.A.I.C.S.: 459110

Tri Yeovil UK Limited   (1)
76 Lyde Road, Yeovil, BA21 5DW, Somer-
set, United Kingdom
Tel.: (44) 1935414142
Web Site: http://www.triuk.com
Bicycles Distr
N.A.I.C.S.: 423910

UAB Sportland LT   (1)
Seimyniskiu str 3 Lithuania V floor, LT-
09312, Vilnius, Lithuania
Tel.: (370) 52501050
Web Site: https://www.sportland.lt
Sports Goods Distr
N.A.I.C.S.: 459110

Zaparoh S.p. z o.o.   (1)
Ul Zernicka 22 Point Park Hall 6 NR 6,
Robakowo, 62-023, Gadki, Poland
Tel.: (48) 612220080
Web Site: https://www.zaparoh.com
Emp.: 270
Upholstered Furniture Mfr & Distr
N.A.I.C.S.: 337121

**FRASERS PROPERTY LIM-
ITED**
438 Alexandra Road 21-00 Alexandra
Point, Singapore, 119958, Singapore
Tel.: (65) 62764882   SG
Web Site:
   https://www.frasersproperty.com
Year Founded: 1963

Frasers Property Limited—(Continued)

FSRPF—(OTCIQ)
Rev.: $2,924,835,865
Assets: $29,478,588,366
Liabilities: $15,992,176,362
Net Worth: $13,486,412,004
Earnings: $218,426,825
Emp.: 6,800
Fiscal Year-end: 09/30/23
Real Estate Development Services
N.A.I.C.S.: 531390
Panote Sirivadhanabhakdi *(Grp CEO)*

Subsidiaries:

FCL Centrepoint Pte Ltd (1)
Alexandra Point 21-00 438 Alexandra Road,
Singapore, 119958, Singapore
Tel.: (65) 62764882
Property Management Services
N.A.I.C.S.: 531312

FCL Property Investments Pte Ltd (1)
Alexandra Point Suite 21-00 438 Alexandra
Road, Singapore, 119958, Singapore
Tel.: (65) 67364688
Property Management Services
N.A.I.C.S.: 531311

FRASERS LOGISTICS & INDUS-TRIAL TRUST (1)
438 Alexandra Road 21-00 Alexandra Point,
Singapore, 119958, Singapore
Tel.: (65) 62764882
Web Site:
http://www.fraserslogisticstrust.com
Trust Management Services
N.A.I.C.S.: 523940
Robert Wallace *(CEO)*

Subsidiary (Domestic):

Frasers Commercial Trust (2)
438 Alexandra Road No 21-00 Alexandra
Point, Singapore, 119958, Singapore
Tel.: (65) 62764882
Web Site: http://www.frasersproperty.com
Rev.: $90,293,320
Assets: $1,631,463,690
Liabilities: $561,825,744
Net Worth: $1,069,637,946
Earnings: $107,034,334
Emp.: 20
Fiscal Year-end: 09/30/2019
Real Estate Investment Management Ser-vices
N.A.I.C.S.: 531120
Catherine Yeo *(Sec)*

Fraser Residence Orchard Pte Ltd (1)
31 Paterson Road, Singapore, 238522,
Singapore
Tel.: (65) 67310888
Web Site: https://www.frasershospitality.com
Emp.: 30
Property Management Services
N.A.I.C.S.: 531311
Choe Peng Sum *(CEO)*

Fraser Suite Sydney (1)
488 Kent Street, Sydney, 2000, NSW, Aus-tralia
Tel.: (61) 28 823 8888
Web Site:
http://sydney.frasershospitality.com
Property Management Services
N.A.I.C.S.: 531312
Benjamin Nesbitt *(Gen Mgr)*

Frasers Centrepoint Property Man-agement Services Pte Ltd (1)
1 Sengkang Square 04-20 Compass Point
Sengkang, Singapore, 545078, Singapore
Tel.: (65) 68812707
Property Management Services
N.A.I.C.S.: 531312
Sharon Tan *(Mng Dir)*

Frasers City Quarter Pty Limited (1)
L 11. 488 Kent St, Sydney, 2000, NSW,
Australia
Tel.: (61) 288238800
Property Management Services
N.A.I.C.S.: 531312

Frasers Hospitality Pte. Ltd. (1)

438 Alexandra Road Alexandra Point Level
14 & 15, Singapore, 119958, Singapore
Tel.: (65) 8003727377
Web Site: https://www.frasershospitality.com
Hospitality Services
N.A.I.C.S.: 622110
Choe Peng Sum *(CEO)*

Subsidiary (Non-US):

Frasers Hospitality (UK) Limited (2)
3rd Floor 95 Cromwell Road, London, SW7
4DL, United Kingdom
Tel.: (44) 2073415595
Web Site: http://www.frasershospitality.com
Sales Range: $50-74.9 Million
Emp.: 20
Real Estate Management Services
N.A.I.C.S.: 531390

Frasers Hospitality Japan Kabushiki Kaisha (2)
1-17-11 Nambanaka, Naniwa-Ku, Osaka,
556-0011, Japan
Tel.: (81) 666357111
Web Site: http://osaka.frasershospitality.com
Sales Range: $10-24.9 Million
Emp.: 20
Residential Operating Services
N.A.I.C.S.: 721310

Subsidiary (Domestic):

Frasers Hospitality Management Pte Ltd (2)
419B River Valley Road 08-03 Valley Point
Downtown, Singapore, 248373, Singapore
Tel.: (65) 62700800
Web Site: http://www.frasershospitality.com
Hospitality Management Consulting Ser-vices
N.A.I.C.S.: 541618
Tonya Khong *(Gen Mgr)*

Frasers Hospitality Trust (1)
(22%)
Tel.: (65) 63490421
Hospitality Real Estate & Business Invest-ment Trust
N.A.I.C.S.: 525990
Chin Fen Eu *(CEO)*

Frasers Property (Europe) Holdings Pte Ltd (1)
438 Alexandra Road 21-00 Alexandra Point,
Singapore, 119958, Singapore
Tel.: (65) 62764882
Web Site:
http://www.fraserscentrepointmalls.com
Financial Management Services
N.A.I.C.S.: 523999
Jorg Schroder *(Chief Investment Officer)*

Frasers Property (Thailand) Public Company Limited (1)
No 944 Mitrtown Office Tower 20th Floor
Rama 4 Road, Wangmai Subdistrict Pa-thumwan District, Bangkok, 10330,
Thailand (58.57%)
Tel.: (66) 24830000
Web Site: https://www.frasersproperty.co.th
Rev.: $490,701,690
Assets: $2,798,651,358
Liabilities: $1,716,146,786
Net Worth: $1,082,504,572
Earnings: $54,313,820
Emp.: 1,365
Fiscal Year-end: 09/30/2023
Turnkey Factory Leasing Services
N.A.I.C.S.: 561499
Somsak Chaiyaporn *(Gen Mgr)*

Subsidiary (Domestic):

ECO Industrial Services Company Limited (2)
49/32 Moo 5 Laemchabang Industrial Es-tate Tungsukhla, Si Racha, 20230, Chon
Buri, Thailand (100%)
Tel.: (66) 2 6796565
Industrial Machinery Equipment Mfr
N.A.I.C.S.: 333248

Frasers Property Industrial (Thailand) Company Limited (2)
No 944 Mitrtown Office Tower 22nd- 23rd
Floor Rama 4 Road, Wangmai Subdistrict
Pathumwan District, Bangkok, 10330,
Thailand (100%)
Tel.: (66) 2 483 0000

Web Site:
https://www.industrial.frasersproperty.co.th
Ready-built Warehouses Developer
N.A.I.C.S.: 493110

Golden Land Property Development Public Company Limited (2)
20th Floor Mitrtown Office Tower 944 Rama
4 Road, Wangmai Pathumwan, Bangkok,
10330, Thailand (94.5%)
Tel.: (66) 27646200
Web Site: http://www.goldenland.co.th
Rev.: $433,300,544
Assets: $1,638,147,579
Liabilities: $944,161,418
Net Worth: $693,986,161
Earnings: $55,977,267
Emp.: 598
Fiscal Year-end: 09/30/2022
Real Estate Management Services
N.A.I.C.S.: 531390
Wanchai Sarathulthat *(Chm)*

Frasers Property (UK) Limited (1)
95 Cromwell Road, London, SW7 4DL,
United Kingdom
Tel.: (44) 2072449889
Web Site: https://www.frasersproperty.com
Property Management Services
N.A.I.C.S.: 531311
Ilaria del Beato *(CEO)*

Subsidiary (Domestic):

Frasers Property Developments Ltd (2)
95 Cromwell Road, London, SW7 4DL,
United Kingdom
Tel.: (44) 2072449889
Web Site: http://www.frasersproperty.com
Emp.: 10
Property Management Services
N.A.I.C.S.: 531311
Simon Lear *(Mgr)*

Frasers Property AHL Limited (1)
Level 2 Building C 1 Homebush Bay Drive,
Rhodes, 2138, NSW, Australia
Tel.: (61) 29 767 2000
Web Site:
https://www.frasersproperty.com.au
Emp.: 190
Real Estate Investment Trust
N.A.I.C.S.: 525990

Subsidiary (Domestic):

Frasers Property (APG) Pty. Limited (1)
Level 2 Building C 1 Homebush Bay Drive,
Rhodes, 2138, NSW, Australia
Tel.: (61) 29 767 2000
Web Site:
https://www.frasersproperty.com.au
Real Estate Management Services
N.A.I.C.S.: 531390

Frasers Property Australia Pty Limited (2)
Level 2 Building C 1 Homebush Bay Drive,
Rhodes, 2138, NSW, Australia
Tel.: (61) 29 767 2000
Web Site:
https://www.frasersproperty.com.au
Real Estate Investment, Development &
Management Services
N.A.I.C.S.: 531390
Rodney Vaughan Fehring *(CEO)*

Subsidiary (Non-US):

Australand HK Company Limited (3)
Office 2001 20/F The World Trade Centre
280 Gloucester Road, Causeway Bay,
Hong Kong, China (Hong Kong)
Tel.: (852) 28109210
Real Estate Management Services
N.A.I.C.S.: 531390

Subsidiary (Domestic):

Australand Wholesale Holdings Limited (3)
L 3 1c Homebush Bay Dr, Rhodes, 2138,
NSW, Australia
Tel.: (61) 297672000
Web Site: http://www.australand.com.au
Emp.: 200
Real Estate Management Services
N.A.I.C.S.: 531390

Frasers Property Management Aus-tralia Pty Limited (1)
L 11 488 Kent St, Sydney, 2000, NSW,
Australia
Tel.: (61) 288238800
Property Management Services
N.A.I.C.S.: 531312

Frasers Town Hall Pty Ltd (1)
L 11 488 Kent St, Sydney, 2000, NSW,
Australia
Tel.: (61) 288238800
Web Site: http://www.fraserstown.com
Property Development Services
N.A.I.C.S.: 531312

River Valley Apartments Pte Ltd (1)
491A River Valley Road, Singapore,
248372, Singapore
Tel.: (65) 67375800
Real Estate Management Services
N.A.I.C.S.: 531390
Peng Sum Choe *(CEO)*

River Valley Shopping Centre Pte Ltd (1)
Alexandra Point 438 Alexandra Road, Sin-gapore, 119958, Singapore
Tel.: (65) 67375523
Sales Range: $25-49.9 Million
Emp.: 36
Property Management Services
N.A.I.C.S.: 531311
Jonathan Koh *(Gen Mgr)*

River Valley Tower Pte Ltd (1)
491b River Valley Road, Singapore,
248371, Singapore
Tel.: (65) 67375523
Property Management Services
N.A.I.C.S.: 531311

Riverside Property Pte Ltd (1)
11 Unity Street, Singapore, 237995, Singa-pore
Tel.: (65) 67364800
Web Site: http://www.singapore-place.frasershospitality.com
Property Development Services
N.A.I.C.S.: 531390
Tonya Khong *(Gen Mgr)*

Vision Huaqing (Beijing) Development Co., Ltd (1)
Unit 408 Level 4 Sohu com Plaza Building
9 No 1 Zhongguancun East Road, Haidian
District, Beijing, 100084, China
Tel.: (86) 10 6279 0008
Property Management Services
N.A.I.C.S.: 531312

FRASERS PROPERTY THAI-LAND INDUSTRIAL FREE-HOLD & LEASEHOLD REIT
944 Mitrtown Office Tower 22nd-23rd Floor Rama 4 Road, Wangmai
Subdistrict Pathumwan District, Bang-kok, 10330, Thailand
Tel.: (66) 805805005
Web Site: https://www.ftreit.co.th
Year Founded: 2014
FTREIT—(THA)
Rev.: $103,927,991
Assets: $1,386,032,831
Liabilities: $457,393,638
Net Worth: $928,639,194
Earnings: $68,573,067
Fiscal Year-end: 09/30/23
Real Estate Investment Trust Ser-vices
N.A.I.C.S.: 523991
Threekwan Bunnag *(Chm)*

FRATELLI DE CECCO DI FIL-IPPO FARA SAN MARTINO S.P.A.
Via F De Cecco, 66015, Fara San
Martino, Chieti, Italy
Tel.: (39) 08729861 IT
Web Site: http://www.dececco.com
Year Founded: 1886
Sales Range: $300-349.9 Million
Emp.: 300
Pasta Mfr

N.A.I.C.S.: 311824
Filippo Antonio De Cecco *(Chm)*

Subsidiaries:

De Cecco Deutschland GMBH **(1)**
Zollhof 4 - Grand Bateau, 40221, Dusseldorf, Germany
Tel.: (49) 2113018570
Web Site: http://www.dececco.de
Food Products Distr
N.A.I.C.S.: 424490
Manuela Filici *(Mgr-Natl Key Acct)*

De Cecco France SARL **(1)**
Zac Bois Chaland 10 Rue Du Bois Chaland, Lisses, 91029, Evry, France
Tel.: (33) 160788662
Food Products Distr
N.A.I.C.S.: 424490

De Cecco U.K. Ltd **(1)**
The Old School House Station Street, Kibworth Beauchamp, Leicester, LE8 0LN, United Kingdom
Tel.: (44) 116 2790022
Food Products Distr
N.A.I.C.S.: 424490

FRATELLO TRADE JSC BANJA LUKA

Ramici bb, 78 000, Banja Luka, Bosnia & Herzegovina
Tel.: (387) 51394180
Web Site: https://www.fratello-trade.com
Year Founded: 1999
FRTL—(BANJ)
Sales Range: $1-9.9 Million
Emp.: 70
Fresh & Frozen Seafood Distr
N.A.I.C.S.: 311710
Matej Penca *(Chm-Mgmt Bd & Pres)*

Subsidiaries:

Fratello Trade d.o.o. **(1)**
Ul Milutina Milankovica Br 23, 11070, Novi Beograd, Serbia
Tel.: (381) 113011979
Seafood Distr
N.A.I.C.S.: 424460

FRAUENTHAL HOLDING AG

Rooseveltplatz 10, A-1090, Vienna, Austria
Tel.: (43) 15054206   AT
Web Site: https://www.frauenthal.at
Year Founded: 1921
FKA—(VIE)
Rev.: $1,193,250,911
Assets: $556,846,230
Liabilities: $344,855,944
Net Worth: $211,990,286
Earnings: $15,894,690
Emp.: 2,862
Fiscal Year-end: 12/31/23
Motor Vehicle Parts Mfr; Plumbing & Heating Fixture Distr
N.A.I.C.S.: 336390
Erika Hochrieser *(CFO & Member-Exec Bd)*

Subsidiaries:

Frauenthal Automotive Components GmbH **(1)**
Rooseveltplatz 10, 1090, Vienna, Austria
Tel.: (43) 15054206
Sales Range: $50-74.9 Million
Emp.: 200
Motor Vehicle Body Mfr
N.A.I.C.S.: 336211

Subsidiary (Non-US):

Frauenthal Automotive Administration GmbH **(2)**
Lindweg 25, Elterlein, Germany **(100%)**
Tel.: (49) 373 4966 20
Web Site: http://www.frauenthal-automotive.com
Holding Company
N.A.I.C.S.: 551112

Subsidiary (Domestic):

Frauenthal Automotive Elterlein GmbH **(3)**
Scheibenbergerstrasse 45, 09481, Elterlein, Germany **(100%)**
Tel.: (49) 373 4966 20
Web Site: http://www.frauenthal-automotive.com
Emp.: 200
Motor Vehicle Components Mfr & Distr
N.A.I.C.S.: 336390

Subsidiary (Domestic):

Frauenthal Automotive Saxony GmbH **(4)**
Scheibenbergerstrasse 45, 09481, Elterlein, Germany **(100%)**
Tel.: (49) 373 4966 215
Web Site: http://www.frauenthal-automotive.com
Holding Company
N.A.I.C.S.: 551112

Subsidiary (Non-US):

Frauenthal Automotive Azambuja, Unipessoal, Lda. **(2)**
Vale do Cardal Apartado 2, 2054-909, Azambuja, Portugal **(100%)**
Tel.: (351) 263 409 500
Web Site: http://www.frauenthal-automotive.com
Sales Range: $50-74.9 Million
Motor Vehicle Components Mfr & Distr
N.A.I.C.S.: 336390
Catarina Batista *(Mgr)*

Frauenthal Gnotec China Co. Ltd. **(1)**
358 Xinsheng Road, Huaqiao, Kunshan, 215332, China
Tel.: (86) 5123 668 7020
Auto Parts Mfr
N.A.I.C.S.: 336390

Frauenthal Gnotec Slovakia s.r.o. **(1)**
Podzavoz 2824, 02201, Cadca, Slovakia
Tel.: (421) 41 370 0111
Web Site: https://www.gnotec.com
Auto Parts Mfr
N.A.I.C.S.: 336390

Frauenthal Ost Beteiligungs-GmbH **(1)**
Gamserstrasse 38, Frauenthal, 8523, Vienna, Austria **(100%)**
Tel.: (43) 346220000
Web Site: http://www.frauenthal.net
Sales Range: $25-49.9 Million
Emp.: 9
Industrial Ceramics Mfr
N.A.I.C.S.: 327120

Frauenthal Powertrain Management GmbH & Co. KG **(1)**
In den Hofwiesen 13, 58840, Plettenberg, Germany
Tel.: (49) 2 391 8140
Web Site: http://frauenthal-powertrain.com
Motor Vehicle Parts Mfr
N.A.I.C.S.: 336310
Marc Schneider *(CEO)*

OAG AG **(1)**
Schemmerlstrasse 66 70, A 1110, Vienna, Austria **(100%)**
Tel.: (43) 50406 61099
Web Site: http://www.oeag.at
Plumbing & Heating Supplies
N.A.I.C.S.: 423720
Alexander Schmeikal *(Mng Dir)*

FRAUNHOFER-GESELLSCHAFT ZUR FORDERUNG DER ANGEWANDTEN FORSCHUNG E.V.

Hansastrasse 27C, 80686, Munich, Germany
Tel.: (49) 8912050
Web Site: https://www.fraunhofer.de
Year Founded: 1949
Rev.: $2,447,243,890,010
Assets: $5,359,845,599,448
Liabilities: $1,149,035,950,067

Net Worth: $4,210,809,649,381
Earnings: $120,275,461
Fiscal Year-end: 12/31/23
Application-Oriented Research Services
N.A.I.C.S.: 541715
Holger Hanselka *(Pres)*

Subsidiaries:

Fraunhofer Austria Research GmbH **(1)**
Theresianumgasse 7, 1040, Vienna, Austria
Tel.: (43) 15046906
Web Site: http://www.fraunhofer.at
Emp.: 50
Logistics Consulting Servies
N.A.I.C.S.: 541614

Fraunhofer Italia Research Konsortialgesellschaft mbH **(1)**
Via Macello 57, 39100, Bolzano, Italy
Tel.: (39) 04711966900
Web Site: http://www.fraunhofer.it
Engineering Research & Development Services
N.A.I.C.S.: 541715
Dominik Matt *(Editor)*

Fraunhofer UK Research Ltd. **(1)**
Level 5 Technology and Innovation Centre 99 George Street, Glasgow, G1 1RD, United Kingdom
Tel.: (44) 1415484667
Web Site: http://www.fraunhofer.co.uk
Industrial Research & Development Services
N.A.I.C.S.: 541715
Simon Andrews *(Exec Dir)*

Fraunhofer USA, Inc. **(1)**
44792 Helm St, Plymouth, MI 48170
Tel.: (734) 354-9700
Web Site: http://www.fraunhofer.org
Emp.: 200
Application-Oriented Research Services
N.A.I.C.S.: 541715
Erin Simmonds *(Treas)*

FRAZEL GROUP SDN. BHD.

06 01-03 Vida Bukit Ceylon, 1D Jalan Ceylon, Kuala Lumpur, 50200, Malaysia
Tel.: (60) 327333388
Web Site: https://frazelgroup.com
Real Estate Services
N.A.I.C.S.: 531390

FREAKOUT HOLDINGS, INC.

Roppongi Hills Cross Point 6-3-1 Roppongi, Chiyoda-ku, Tokyo, 106-0032, Japan
Tel.: (81) 367211740
Web Site: https://www.fout.co.jp
Year Founded: 2010
6094—(TKS)
Rev.: $216,982,360
Assets: $318,241,740
Liabilities: $174,222,570
Net Worth: $144,019,170
Earnings: $55,798,300
Emp.: 1,054
Fiscal Year-end: 09/30/23
Marketing Research & Consulting
N.A.I.C.S.: 541910
Yuzuru Honda *(Founder & CEO-Global)*

Subsidiaries:

Dot GF Co., Ltd. **(1)**
54 BB Building 16 Fl Room 1609 Sukhumvit 21 Rd, Klongtoey NuaWatlana, Bangkok, 10110, Thailand
Tel.: (66) 226 064 0405
Web Site: https://dotgf.net
Design Services
N.A.I.C.S.: 541430

FreakOut (Thailand) Co., Ltd. **(1)**
No 496-502 Amarin Tower 9th Floor Unit No 22 1 Ploenchit Road Lumpini, Pathumwan, Bangkok, 10330, Thailand
Tel.: (66) 21634354
Web Site: http://th.foutap.com

Digital Advertising Services
N.A.I.C.S.: 541810
Kenichi Sato *(CEO)*

FreakOut Taiwan Co., Ltd. **(1)**
20F No 57 Section 2 Dunhua South Road, Da'an District, Taipei, 10681, Taiwan
Tel.: (886) 227070712
Web Site: http://tw.foutap.com
Digital Advertising Services
N.A.I.C.S.: 541810
Ken Yamane *(CEO)*

Intimate Merger, Inc. **(1)**
3-5-27 Roppongi, Minato-Ku, Tokyo, 106-0032, Japan
Tel.: (81) 357977997
Web Site: https://www.corp.intimatemerger.com
Rev.: $21,142,380
Assets: $14,839,370
Liabilities: $3,984,580
Net Worth: $10,854,790
Earnings: $709,000
Fiscal Year-end: 09/30/2023
Digital Marketing Services
N.A.I.C.S.: 541870
Ryoji Yanashima *(Founder & Pres)*

PT Gema Teknologi Cahaya Gemilang **(1)**
Podomoro City Ruko GSA 8DH Jl Letjen S Parman RT 15/RW 5 Tj Duren Sel, Kota Jakarta Barat Daerah Khusus Ibukota, Jakarta, 11460, Indonesia
Tel.: (62) 215 698 7023
Web Site: https://www.thriveagency.id
Advertising Agency Services
N.A.I.C.S.: 541810

PT. FreakOut dewina Indonesia **(1)**
RDTX Tower 28 Floor Kav E4 Jl Prof DR Satrio No 6 East Kuningan, RT 5/RW 2 Kuningan East Kuningan, South Jakarta, 12870, Jakarta, Indonesia
Tel.: (62) 2157991362
Web Site: https://freakout.net
Digital Advertising Services
N.A.I.C.S.: 541810
Tomohiro Yasukura *(CEO)*

Playwire, LLC **(1)**
4855 Technology Way Ste 501, Boca Raton, FL 33431 **(75%)**
Tel.: (954) 418-0779
Web Site: http://www.playwire.com
Sales Range: $25-49.9 Million
Emp.: 104
Advertising Services
N.A.I.C.S.: 541810
Anthony Berrena *(Chief Revenue Officer)*

UUUM Co., Ltd. **(1)**
28th Fl Midtown Tower 9-7-1 Akasaka, Minato-ku, Tokyo, 107-6228, Japan **(100%)**
Tel.: (81) 354147259
Web Site: https://www.uuum.co.jp
Rev.: $152,540,469
Assets: $68,965,973
Liabilities: $46,997,027
Net Worth: $21,968,946
Earnings: ($6,957,384)
Emp.: 476
Fiscal Year-end: 05/31/2023
Internet Entertainment Site Publisher
N.A.I.C.S.: 516210
Kazuki Kamada *(Pres & CEO)*

FRED GROENESTEGE CONSTRUCTION LIMITED

4892 Line 42 Perth County R R 1, Sebringville, N0K 1X0, ON, Canada
Tel.: (519) 393-6579
Web Site: http://www.fgc.ca
Year Founded: 1978
Sales Range: $10-24.9 Million
Agricultural Construction Services
N.A.I.C.S.: 236220

FRED. OLSEN & CO.

Fred Olsens Gate 2, 0152, Oslo, Norway
Tel.: (47) 22341000   NO
Web Site: https://www.fredolsen.com
Year Founded: 1848
Holding Company

Fred. Olsen & Co.—(Continued)

N.A.I.C.S.: 551112
Annette S. Olsen (CEO & Mng Dir)

Subsidiaries:

Bonheur ASA (1)
Fred Olsens Gate 2, N-0152, Oslo,
Norway (52.09%)
Tel.: (47) 22341000
Rev.: $1,056,068,262
Assets: $2,009,296,047
Liabilities: $1,366,751,616
Net Worth: $642,544,430
Earnings: $157,218,456
Emp.: 5,709
Fiscal Year-end: 12/31/2022
Holding Company; Shipping, Energy &
Travel Industries Products & Services
N.A.I.C.S.: 551112
Thomas Fredrik Olsen (Chm)

Subsidiary (Domestic):

First Olsen AS (2)
PO Box 581, Sentrum, 0106, Oslo, Norway
Tel.: (47) 22341180
Marine Shipping Services
N.A.I.C.S.: 488510

Ganger Rolf ASA (2)
Fred Olsens gate 2, 0152, Oslo, Norway
Tel.: (47) 22341000
Web Site: http://www.ganger-rolf.no
Sales Range: $50-74.9 Million
Emp.: 150
Holding Company; Shipping Services, Off-
shore Drilling & Media Operations
N.A.I.C.S.: 551112
Anette S. Olsen (Mng Dir)

Affiliate (Non-US):

Fred. Olsen Cruise Lines Ltd. (3)
Fred Olsen House 42 White House Road,
Ipswich, IP1 5LL, Suffolk, United
Kingdom (50%)
Tel.: (44) 1473742424
Web Site: http://www.fredolsencruise.com
Sales Range: $50-74.9 Million
Emp.: 200
Cruise Line Services
N.A.I.C.S.: 483112
Peter Deer (Mng Dir)

Affiliate (Domestic):

**Fred. Olsen Fly og Luftmateriell
AS** (3)
Prinsensgate 2B, 0152, Oslo,
Norway (50%)
Tel.: (47) 22341388
Web Site: http://www.fredolsen.no
Sales Range: $50-74.9 Million
Emp.: 3
Aircraft Parts Distr
N.A.I.C.S.: 423860

Fred. Olsen Marine Services AS (3)
Prinsens Gate 2b, 0512, Oslo,
Norway (50%)
Tel.: (47) 22341100
Web Site: http://www.fredolsen-marine.com
Marine Support Services
N.A.I.C.S.: 488320
Parlirek Gurrik (Gen Mgr)

Fred. Olsen Renewables AS (3)
Fred Olsens Gate 2, 0152, Oslo,
Norway (50%)
Tel.: (47) 22 34 10 00
Web Site: http://www.fredolsen.com
Eletric Power Generation Services
N.A.I.C.S.: 221118

Subsidiary (Non-US):

Fred. Olsen Renewables Ltd. (4)
64-65 Vincent Square, London, SW1P 2NU,
United Kingdom
Tel.: (44) 2079310975
Sales Range: $50-74.9 Million
Emp.: 6
Energy Renewable Services
N.A.I.C.S.: 221118
Jeremy Dowler (Sec)

Affiliate (Domestic):

Fred. Olsen Travel AS (3)

Fred Olsens gate 2, 0152, Oslo,
Norway (50%)
Tel.: (47) 22341111
Web Site: http://www.fredolsentravel.com
Sales Range: $25-49.9 Million
Emp.: 15
Travel & Tour Operating Agency Service
N.A.I.C.S.: 561520

NHST Media Group AS (3)
Christian Krohgs Gate 16, PO Box 1182,
Sentrum, 0107, Oslo, Norway (27.97%)
Tel.: (47) 2200 1000
Web Site: http://www.nhst.no
Business News Publication
N.A.I.C.S.: 513110
Erik Must (Vice Chm)

Subsidiary (Domestic):

Dagens Naeringsliv AS (4)
Christian Krogh 16, PO Box 1182, Sentrum,
Oslo, 0186, Norway
Tel.: (47) 22001000
Web Site: http://www.dn.no
Sales Range: $100-124.9 Million
Emp.: 480
Business Newspaper
N.A.I.C.S.: 513110

Branch (Domestic):

Dagens Naeringsliv-Bergen (5)
Christian Krohgs Gate 16, 0186, Oslo,
Norway (100%)
Tel.: (47) 22001000
Web Site: http://www.dn.no
Sales Range: $25-49.9 Million
Emp.: 3
Newspaper Publishers
N.A.I.C.S.: 513110

Dagens Naeringsliv-Kristiansand (5)
Tordenskioldsgate 9, 4612, Kristiansand,
Norway (100%)
Tel.: (47) 38071300
Web Site: http://www.dn.no
Sales Range: $25-49.9 Million
Emp.: 1
N.A.I.C.S.: 513110

Dagens Naeringsliv-Lillehammer (5)
Christian Krohgs gate 16, 0186, Oslo,
Norway (100%)
Tel.: (47) 22001000
Web Site: http://www.dn.no
Sales Range: $100-124.9 Million
Emp.: 400
N.A.I.C.S.: 513110

Dagens Naeringsliv-Stavanger (5)
Nygaten 24, 4006, Stavanger,
Norway (100%)
Tel.: (47) 51511010
Web Site: http://www.dn.no
Sales Range: $25-49.9 Million
Emp.: 2
N.A.I.C.S.: 513110

**Dagens
Naeringsliv-Telemark/Vestfold** (5)
Christian Krohgs Gate 16, 0186, Oslo, Nor-
way (100%)
Tel.: (47) 22001000
Web Site: http://www.dn.no
Sales Range: $100-124.9 Million
Emp.: 400
N.A.I.C.S.: 513110

Dagens Naeringsliv-Tromso (5)
PO Box 773, 9258, Tromso,
Norway (100%)
Tel.: (47) 77665660
Web Site: http://www.dn.no
Sales Range: $100-124.9 Million
Emp.: 400
N.A.I.C.S.: 513110

Dagens Naeringsliv-Trondheim (5)
Fjordgata 82, 7011, Trondheim,
Norway (100%)
Tel.: (47) 73808920
Web Site: http://www.dn.no
Sales Range: Less than $1 Million
Emp.: 9
N.A.I.C.S.: 513110

Subsidiary (Domestic):

IntraFish Media AS (4)
Sandbrogaten 5-7, 5003, Bergen, Norway

Tel.: (47) 55213300
Web Site: http://www.intrafish.no
Seafood News Provider
N.A.I.C.S.: 513110
Pal Korneliussen (Dir-Admin & Publr)

Subsidiary (Non-US):

Mynewsdesk AB (4)
Rosenlundsgaten 40, 11853, Stockholm,
Sweden
Tel.: (46) 8 50 900 201
Web Site: http://www.mynewsdesk.com
Public Relations Services
N.A.I.C.S.: 541820
Peter Inqman (CEO)

Subsidiary (Non-US):

Mynewsdesk AS (5)
Christian Krohgs Gate 16, PO Box 1182,
Sentrum, 0107, Oslo, Norway
Tel.: (47) 2200 1019
Web Site: http://www.mynewsdesk.com
Emp.: 19
Public Relations Services
N.A.I.C.S.: 541820
Henriette Sveen (Country Mgr)

Mynewsdesk ApS (5)
Vesterbrogade 149 bygning 6 3 sal, 1620,
Copenhagen, Denmark
Tel.: (45) 3812 3630
Web Site: http://www.mynewsdesk.com
Emp.: 12
Public Relations Services
N.A.I.C.S.: 541820
Martin Karlsson (Country Mgr)

Mynewsdesk GmbH (5)
Ritterstrasse 12-14, 10969, Berlin, Germany
Tel.: (49) 341 35 05 87 77
Web Site: http://www.mynewsdesk.com
Emp.: 30
Public Relations Services
N.A.I.C.S.: 541820
Benjamin Kopcke (Dir-Customer Svc & Acct
Mgmt)

Subsidiary (Domestic):

ddp direct GmbH (6)
Thomasiusstrasse 31, D-04109, Leipzig,
Germany
Tel.: (49) 341 350 587 0
Web Site: http://www.ddpdirect.de
Multimedia Management Services
N.A.I.C.S.: 518210
Jurgen Kopelke (Mng Dir)

Subsidiary (Non-US):

Mynewsdesk Ltd. (5)
Nexus Place, 25 Farringdon Street, London,
EC4A 4AB, United Kingdom
Tel.: (44) 20 7029 5785
Public Relations Services
N.A.I.C.S.: 541820
Adam Cranfield (Head-Mktg)

Mynewsdesk Oy (5)
Vilhonvuorenkatu 11C, 00500, Helsinki,
Finland
Tel.: (358) 9 4250 550
Web Site: http://www.mynewsdesk.com
Public Relations Services
N.A.I.C.S.: 541820
Juhani Levola (Pres)

Branch (Domestic):

Mynewsdesk- Gothenburg (5)
Kungsgatan 23, 411 19, Gothenburg, Swe-
den
Tel.: (46) 31 352 65 00
Web Site: http://www.mynewsdesk.com
Public Relations Services
N.A.I.C.S.: 541820
Carl Jacobsson (Country Mgr)

Mynewsdesk- Malmo (5)
Stora Varvsgatan 6A, 211 19, Malmo, Swe-
den
Tel.: (46) 40 608 4700
Web Site: http://www.mynewsdesk.com
Public Relations Services
N.A.I.C.S.: 541820
Jontan Jansson (Mgr-Community & Con-
tent)

Mynewsdesk- Umea (5)

Storgatan 50, 903 26, Umea, Sweden
Tel.: (46) 706 157 190
Web Site: http://www.mynewsdesk.com
Public Relations Services
N.A.I.C.S.: 541820
Mike Rooseboom (Mgr-Product Mktg)

Subsidiary (Domestic):

Tradewinds A/S (4)
Christian Krohgs gate 16, PO Box 1182,
Sentrum, Oslo, 0107, Norway (100%)
Tel.: (47) 22001200
Web Site: http://www.tradewinds.no
Sales Range: $25-49.9 Million
Emp.: 50
English Language Newspaper
N.A.I.C.S.: 513110
Hege Hansen (Dir-Mktg)

Branch (Non-US):

Tradewinds-Athens (5)
Michalakopoulou 29, GR-115 28, Athens,
Greece
Tel.: (30) 2107245541
Web Site: http://www.tradewinds.no
English Language Newspaper
N.A.I.C.S.: 513110

Tradewinds-Italy (5)
Via Lungo Entella 91, 16043, Chiavari, Italy
Tel.: (39) 03478250375
English Language Newspaper
N.A.I.C.S.: 513110

Tradewinds-London (5)
25 Farringdon St 11th Floor, London, EC4A
4AB, United Kingdom
Tel.: (44) 2078422720
Web Site: http://www.tradewindnews.com
Sales Range: $25-49.9 Million
Emp.: 35
N.A.I.C.S.: 513110

Tradewinds-New Delhi (5)
A9 3 FI GDIDL Northex Twr Netaji Subhash
Pl, New Delhi, 110 070, India
Tel.: (91) 981 8252096
Web Site: http://www.tradewindservices.com
Emp.: 7
English Language Newspaper
N.A.I.C.S.: 513110
Pinaki Routray (Mgr)

Subsidiary (Domestic):

Upstream AS (4)
PO Box 1182, Sentrum, 0107, Oslo,
Norway (100%)
Tel.: (47) 22001300
Web Site: http://www.upstreamonline.com
Sales Range: $25-49.9 Million
Emp.: 13
English Language Newspaper
N.A.I.C.S.: 513110
Sidsel Norvik (Mgr-Mktg)

Branch (US):

Upstream Houston (5)
2 Memorial Plz 820 Gessner Ste 775,
Houston, TX 77024
Tel.: (713) 626-3113
Web Site: http://www.upstreamonline.com
Sales Range: $25-49.9 Million
English Language Newspaper Publisher
N.A.I.C.S.: 513120
Greg Klausmeyer (VP-Sls-Americas)

Branch (Non-US):

Upstream London (5)
International Press Ctr 5 FI, 76 Shoe Ln,
London, EC4A 3JB, United
Kingdom (100%)
Tel.: (44) 2078422738
Web Site: http://www.upstreamonline.com
Sales Range: $25-49.9 Million
Emp.: 6
English Language Newspaper
N.A.I.C.S.: 513110

Upstream Singapore (5)
20 Upper Circular Road 04-04, The River-
walk, Singapore, 058416,
Singapore (100%)
Tel.: (65) 65570600
Web Site: http://www.upstreamonline.com

Sales Range: $25-49.9 Million
Emp.: 10
English Language Newspaper
N.A.I.C.S.: 513110
Leonerd Steornes *(Mng Dir)*

Subsidiary (Domestic):

Knock Tankers Ltd.   (2)
Strandgaten 5, PO Box 743, Sentrum,
0106, Oslo, Norway
Tel.: (47) 22341200
Web Site: http://www.fotl.no
Commercial Chartering Services
N.A.I.C.S.: 488510

Oceanlink Ltd.   (2)
c/o Oceanlink Management AS Tollbugata,
PO Box 581, Vika, 0121, Oslo, Norway
Tel.: (47) 22838983
Web Site: http://www.oceanlink.no
Marine Shipping Services
N.A.I.C.S.: 483111

FREDONIA MINING INC.
82 Richmond St Est, Toronto, M5C
1P1, ON, Canada
Tel.: (416) 361-0737   AB
Web Site:
   https://www.fredoniamanage.com
Year Founded: 2012
FRED—(TSXV)
Assets: $424,332
Liabilities: $571,644
Net Worth: ($147,312)
Earnings: ($2,677,836)
Fiscal Year-end: 09/30/23
Investment Services
N.A.I.C.S.: 523999
Ricardo Auriemma *(Pres)*

FREDUN PHARMACEUTICALS LTD.
11th Floor Tower A Urmi Estate 95
Ganpatrao Kadam Marg, Lower
Parel, Mumbai, 400 031, India
Tel.: (91) 2240318111
Web Site:
   https://www.fredungroup.com
539730—(BOM)
Rev.: $18,467,074
Assets: $22,060,923
Liabilities: $16,181,838
Net Worth: $5,879,085
Earnings: $275,002
Emp.: 267
Fiscal Year-end: 03/31/21
Pharmaceuticals Product Mfr
N.A.I.C.S.: 325412
Daulat N. Medhora *(Chm & Co-Mng Dir)*

FREE RUNNING BUILDINGS LTD.
Advanced Manufacturing Park Tech-
nology Centre, Rotherham, S60
5WG, United Kingdom
Tel.: (44) 7521945444
Web Site:
   https://freerunningbuildings.com
Renewable Energy Services
N.A.I.C.S.: 221210

FREEBIT CO., LTD.
E-Space Tower 3-6 Maruyamacho,
Shibuya-ku, Tokyo, Japan
Tel.: (81) 354590522
Web Site: https://www.freebit.com
Year Founded: 2000
3843—(TKS)
Rev.: $350,574,570
Assets: $252,389,630
Liabilities: $151,944,070
Net Worth: $100,445,560
Earnings: $23,571,260
Emp.: 884
Fiscal Year-end: 04/30/24
Internet-Related Services
N.A.I.C.S.: 517810

Atsuki Ishida *(Co-Pres, Co-CEO & Co-CTO)*
Subsidiaries:

Bekkoame Internet Inc.   (1)
Bekkoame Asakusa Building 1-3-8 Koma-
gata, Taito-ku, Tokyo, 111-0043, Japan
Tel.: (81) 354590271
Hosting Services
N.A.I.C.S.: 541511

Craid Inc.   (1)
8F E Space Tower 3-6 Maruyama-cho,
Shibuya-ku, Tokyo, 150-0044, Japan
Tel.: (81) 357285880
Media Development Services
N.A.I.C.S.: 541840

Fanside Inc.   (1)
3-6 Maruyama-cho E Space Tower 8F,
Shibuya-ku, Tokyo, 150-0044, Japan
Tel.: (81) 357285841
Web Site: https://www.fanside.co.jp
Internet Services
N.A.I.C.S.: 518210
Yu Sekine *(CEO)*

For it Inc.   (1)
9F E-Space Tower 3-6 Maruyamacho,
Shibuya-ku, Tokyo, 150-0044, Japan
Tel.: (81) 357285865
Emp.: 149
Media Services
N.A.I.C.S.: 541840
Takeharu Yoshizawa *(CEO)*

Full Speed Inc.   (1)
8F E Space Tower 3-6 Maruyama-cho,
Shibuya-ku, Tokyo, 150-0044,
Japan   (86.68%)
Tel.: (81) 35 728 4460
Web Site: http://www.fullspeed.co.jp
Rev.: $146,042,160
Assets: $80,760,240
Liabilities: $33,028,160
Net Worth: $47,732,080
Earnings: $3,910,720
Emp.: 302
Fiscal Year-end: 04/30/2022
Web Consulting & Search Engine Optimiza-
tion Services
N.A.I.C.S.: 541690
Nobuaki Tanaka *(Chm)*

Giga Tech Co., Ltd.   (1)
3F Daiichi Minamisakura Building 2-21-2
Nishi-Shinbashi, Minato-ku, Tokyo, 105-
0003, Japan
Tel.: (81) 364160853
Emp.: 77
Construction Services
N.A.I.C.S.: 236220

LinkAd Inc.   (1)
8th floor E Space Tower 3-6 Maruyamacho,
Shibuya-ku, Tokyo, 150-0044, Japan
Tel.: (81) 354577749
Web Site: https://www.link-ad.co.jp
Web Advertising Services
N.A.I.C.S.: 541890

FREED OF LONDON LTD.
62-64 Well Street, London, E9 7PX,
United Kingdom
Tel.: (44) 2085104700
Web Site:
   http://www.freedoflondon.com
Year Founded: 1929
Sales Range: $10-24.9 Million
Emp.: 300
Ballet Shoes
N.A.I.C.S.: 316210
Mark Redhead *(Mng Dir)*
Subsidiaries:

Freed of London Ltd.   (1)
21-01 44th Ave, Long Island City, NY 11101
Tel.: (718) 729-7061
Web Site: http://www.freedusa.com
Ballet Shoes
N.A.I.C.S.: 458210
Julienne Viola *(Gen Mgr)*

Freed of London U.S.   (1)
21-01 43rd Ave, Long Island City, NY 11101
Tel.: (718) 729-7061
Web Site: http://www.freedusa.com

Gift Novelty & Souvenir Stores
N.A.I.C.S.: 459420
Julienne Viola *(Gen Mgr)*

FREEDOM ENERGY INC.
Suite 315 837 Hastings Street West,
Vancouver, V6C 3N6, BC, Canada
Tel.: (604) 638-3946   BC
Year Founded: 2005
Rev.: $19,524
Assets: $83,883
Liabilities: $718,840
Net Worth: ($634,956)
Earnings: ($914,420)
Fiscal Year-end: 03/31/18
Coal Exploration Services
N.A.I.C.S.: 212114
George W. Heard *(Pres & CEO)*

FREEDOM FINANCE JSC
Business Center Esentai Tower 3rd
and 7th floors, Al-Farabi Avenue 77/7,
Almaty, Kazakhstan
Tel.: (7) 7273557555
Web Site: https://www.almaty-ffin.kz
FFIN—(KAZ)
Assets: $5,767,145,942
Liabilities: $5,245,117,912
Net Worth: $522,028,030
Earnings: $124,635,549
Fiscal Year-end: 12/31/23
Investment Management Service
N.A.I.C.S.: 523940
Sergey Lukyanov *(Chm-Mgmt Bd & CEO)*

FREEDOM FORD SALES LTD
7505 75 Street, Edmonton, T6C 4H8,
AB, Canada
Tel.: (780) 462-7575
Web Site: http://www.freedomford.ca
Year Founded: 1971
Rev.: $57,905,337
Emp.: 115
New & Used Car Dealers
N.A.I.C.S.: 441110
Chris Welt *(Mgr-Parts)*

FREEDOM GROUP LIMITED
Level 3, North Ryde, 2113, NSW,
Australia
Tel.: (61) 298829000
Web Site:
   http://www.freedom.com.au
Sales Range: $75-99.9 Million
Emp.: 200
Furniture & Housewares Retailer &
Importer
N.A.I.C.S.: 423210
Subsidiaries:

Steinhoff Asia Pacific Limited   (1)
PO Box 227, Marayong, 2148, NSW, Aus-
tralia
Tel.: (61) 1300135588
Web Site: http://www.freedom.com.au
Furniture & Housewares Retailer & Importer
N.A.I.C.S.: 423210
Michael Ford *(Grp CEO)*

FREEDOM HOLDING CORP.
Almaty 77/7 Al-Farabi ave 7 floor,
50040, Almaty, Kazakhstan
Tel.: (7) 7273111064   NV
Web Site:
   https://www.freedomholding.com
Year Founded: 1981
FRHC—(NASDAQ)
Rev.: $1,635,080,000
Assets: $8,301,930,000
Liabilities: $7,134,972,000
Net Worth: $1,166,958,000
Earnings: $374,952,000
Emp.: 6,132
Fiscal Year-end: 03/31/24
Holding Company; Financial Services
N.A.I.C.S.: 551112

Jason M. Kerr *(Chief Legal Officer)*

FREEDOM RESOURCES HOLDINGS CORP.
39/F PBCOM Tower, 6795 Ayala Ave,
Makati, 1228, Philippines
Tel.: (63) 2 856 88 88
Web Site: http://www.dtsi.com.ph
Sales Range: $75-99.9 Million
Emp.: 200
Holding Company
N.A.I.C.S.: 551112
Miguel C. Garcia *(Pres & CEO)*

FREEE K.K.
21F Art Village Osaki Central Tower
1-2-2 Osaki, Shinagawa-ku, Tokyo,
141-0031, Japan
Tel.: (81) 366834887   JP
Web Site: https://www.freee.co.jp
Year Founded: 2012
FREKF—(OTCIQ)
Rev.: $66,745,923
Assets: $173,255,680
Liabilities: $39,143,423
Net Worth: $134,112,257
Earnings: ($28,778,495)
Fiscal Year-end: 06/30/20
Software Development Services
N.A.I.C.S.: 541511
Masayuki Ogata *(COO)*

FREEGOLD VENTURES LIMITED
Suite 888 - 700 West Georgia Street,
PO Box 10351, Vancouver, V7Y 1G5,
BC, Canada
Tel.: (604) 662-7307
Web Site:
   https://www.freegoldventures.com
FVL—(TSXV)
Rev.: $66,039
Assets: $77,400,293
Liabilities: $926,866
Net Worth: $76,473,427
Earnings: ($802,960)
Emp.: 4
Fiscal Year-end: 12/31/22
Gold Exploration Services
N.A.I.C.S.: 212220
Kristina Walcott *(Pres & CEO)*

FREEHILL MINING LTD.
Level 24 570 Bourke St, Melbourne,
3000, VIC, Australia
Tel.: (61) 386585976
Web Site:
   https://www.freehillmining.com
FHS—(ASX)
Assets: $17,510,413
Liabilities: $126,466
Net Worth: $17,383,947
Earnings: ($1,238,547)
Fiscal Year-end: 06/30/22
Support Activities for Metal Mining
N.A.I.C.S.: 213114
Peter Hinner *(CEO)*

FREEHOLD ROYALTIES LTD.
1000 517-10th Avenue SW, Calgary,
T2R 0A8, AB, Canada
Tel.: (403) 221-0802   AB
Web Site:
   https://www.freeholdroyalties.com
Year Founded: 1996
1FH—(DEU)
Rev.: $314,575,000
Assets: $1,118,423,000
Liabilities: $194,660,000
Net Worth: $923,763,000
Earnings: $131,904,000
Emp.: 105
Fiscal Year-end: 12/31/23
Oil & Gas Exploration Services
N.A.I.C.S.: 211120
Thomas J. Mullane *(Pres & Co-CEO)*

Freehold Royalties Ltd.—(Continued)

Subsidiaries:

Freehold Resources Ltd. **(1)**
517 10 Ave SW Suite 1000, Calgary,
T2R0A8, AB, Canada
Tel.: (403) 221-0802
Web Site: http://www.freehold.com
Sales Range: $25-49.9 Million
Emp.: 125
Petroleum Refineries
N.A.I.C.S.: 324110

Inplay Oil Corp. **(1)**
2000 - 350 7th Avenue SW, Calgary, T2P
3N9, AB, Canada
Tel.: (587) 955-9570
Web Site: https://www.inplayoil.com
Rev.: $32,804,130
Assets: $165,088,460
Liabilities: $129,321,836
Net Worth: $35,766,624
Earnings: ($88,107,414)
Emp.: 25
Fiscal Year-end: 12/31/2020
Oil & Gas Exploration Services
N.A.I.C.S.: 213112
Gordon Reese *(VP-Bus Dev)*

Rife Resources Ltd **(1)**
144 4 AveSWSte400, Calgary, T2P-3N4,
AB, Canada
Tel.: (403) 221-0800
Web Site: http://www.rife.com
Emp.: 67
Oil Production & Supplier
N.A.I.C.S.: 333132

FREELANCE.COM SA

Paroi Nord de la Grande Arche 1
Parvis de la Defense, 92044, Paris,
France
Tel.: (33) 155621234
Web Site: http://www.freelance.com
Year Founded: 1995
ALFRE—(EUR)
Sales Range: $350-399.9 Million
Online Job Portal Services
N.A.I.C.S.: 513140
Sylvestre Blavet *(CEO)*

FREELANCER LTD.

Level 37 Grosvenor Place 225
George Street, Sydney, 2000, NSW,
Australia
Tel.: (61) 285992700
Web Site: http://www.freelancer.com
FLNCF—(OTCQX)
Rev.: $36,328,588
Assets: $60,407,329
Liabilities: $42,135,413
Net Worth: $18,271,916
Earnings: $128,738
Emp.: 318
Fiscal Year-end: 12/31/23
Freelance Outsourcing Services
N.A.I.C.S.: 561311
Robert Matthew Barrie *(Chm & CEO)*

Subsidiaries:

Escrow.Com, Inc. **(1)**
180 Montgomery St Ste 650, San Fran-
cisco, CA 94104
Tel.: (415) 801-2270
Collects, Holds & Disburses Funds for Buy-
ers & Sellers on Internet Transactions
N.A.I.C.S.: 525990
Jackson Elsegood *(Gen Mgr)*

Freemarket (Switzerland) GmbH **(1)**
Friedbergweg 9, 9500, Wil, Sankt Gallen,
Switzerland
Tel.: (41) 719443463
Freelance Outsourcing Services
N.A.I.C.S.: 561311

vWorker.com **(1)**
14310 N Dale Mabry Hwy Ste 280, Tampa,
FL 33618
Tel.: (813) 908-9029
Web Site: http://www.vworker.com
Sales Range: $10-24.9 Million
Software Publisher
N.A.I.C.S.: 513210

Ian Ippolito *(Founder)*

FREELAND S.R.L

Via Verrazzano 4 6 8, Fucecchio,
50054, Florence, Italy
Tel.: (39) 0571244337 　　IT
Web Site: http://www.freeland.it
Sport Shoe Mfr & Distr
N.A.I.C.S.: 316210

FREEMAN GOLD CORP.

555 Burrard Street, PO Box 272,
Vancouver, V7X 1M8, BC, Canada
Tel.: (604) 687-7130
Web Site:
　　https://www.freemangoldcorp.com
FMANF—(OTCQX)
Rev.: $53,653
Assets: $23,448,674
Liabilities: $1,447,158
Net Worth: $22,001,516
Earnings: $568,279
Fiscal Year-end: 11/30/22
Mineral Exploration Services
N.A.I.C.S.: 213115
Dean Besserer *(VP-Exploration)*

FREEMS CORPORATION

14 Samjak-ro 178 Beon-gil, Ojeong-
gu, Bucheon, Gyunggido, Korea
(South)
Tel.: (82) 326791477
Web Site: https://www.freems.co.kr
Year Founded: 1989
053160—(KRS)
Rev.: $22,727,412
Assets: $48,742,446
Liabilities: $4,491,243
Net Worth: $44,251,203
Earnings: $1,026,056
Emp.: 88
Fiscal Year-end: 12/31/22
Industrial Equipment Mfr
N.A.I.C.S.: 333998
Do-Sik Joo *(Chm)*

FREENET AG

Hollerstrasse 126, 24782, Budelsdorf,
Germany
Tel.: (49) 4331691000 　　De
Web Site: https://freenet.ag
FRTAY—(OTCIQ)
Rev.: $2,900,197,651
Assets: $3,769,605,663
Liabilities: $2,179,370,541
Net Worth: $1,590,235,122
Earnings: $170,658,302
Emp.: 3,686
Fiscal Year-end: 12/31/23
Holding Company; Telecommunica-
tions Services
N.A.I.C.S.: 551112
Knut Mackeprang *(Vice Chm-
Supervisory Bd)*

Subsidiaries:

01024 Telefondienste GmbH **(1)**
Deelbogenkamp 4, 22297, Hamburg, Ger-
many
Tel.: (49) 40348584410
Web Site: http://www.01024-
telefondienste.de
Telecommunication Servicesb
N.A.I.C.S.: 517810

01050.com GmbH **(1)**
Deelbogenkamp 4c, 22297, Hamburg, Ger-
many
Tel.: (49) 40348584410
Web Site: http://www.01050.com
Telecommunication Servicesb
N.A.I.C.S.: 517810

Debitel AG **(1)**
Gropiusplatz 10, 70563, Stuttgart, Vaihin-
gen, Germany
Tel.: (49) 7117217000
Web Site: http://www.debitel.de

Sales Range: $1-4.9 Billion
Emp.: 200
Mobile Telecommunications Services
N.A.I.C.S.: 517112

Subsidiary (Domestic):

Talkline GmbH **(2)**
Talkline Platz 1, 25337, Elmshorn,
Germany **(100%)**
Tel.: (49) 41214100
Web Site: http://www.talkline.de
Sales Range: $1-4.9 Billion
Mobile Telecommunications Services
N.A.I.C.S.: 517112

callmoblle GmbH **(2)**
Hollerstrasse 126, 24782, Hamburg, Ger-
many
Tel.: (49) 348585110
Web Site: http://www.callmobile.de
Sales Range: $50-74.9 Million
Mobile Telecommunications Services
N.A.I.C.S.: 517112

Exaring AG **(1)**
Leopoldstrasse 236, 80807, Munich, Ger-
many
Tel.: (49) 8921546240
Web Site: http://www.exaring.de
Digital Entertainment Services
N.A.I.C.S.: 541810
Christoph Bellmer *(Founder & CEO)*

Field Service Deutschland FSD
GmbH **(1)**
Erna-Scheffler-Strasse 1, 51103, Cologne,
Germany
Tel.: (49) 22171015000
Web Site: https://field-service-
deutschland.de
Technical Research & Development Ser-
vices
N.A.I.C.S.: 541990

Freenet Energy GmbH **(1)**
Kaiserin-Augusta-Allee 104, 10553, Berlin,
Germany
Tel.: (49) 3031991200
Web Site: http://www.freenet-energy.de
Energy Distribution Services
N.A.I.C.S.: 221122

Ilove GmbH **(1)**
Karl-Liebknecht-Strasse 32, 10178, Berlin,
Germany
Tel.: (49) 3032500112
Web Site: http://www.ilove.de
Social Dating Community Services
N.A.I.C.S.: 624190

NEXT ID GmbH **(1)**
Konrad-Zuse-Platz 5, 53227, Bonn,
Germany **(100%)**
Tel.: (49) 800 444 54 56
Web Site: http://www.next-id.de
Sales Range: $25-49.9 Million
Emp.: 55
Interactive Telecommunications Services
N.A.I.C.S.: 517810
Bernd Schneider *(Mng Dir)*

Synergy Networks GmbH **(1)**
Unterberg 13, 06108, Halle, Germany
Tel.: (49) 3459639780
Web Site: https://www.synergy-networks.de
Analysis & Consulting Services
N.A.I.C.S.: 541618

The Cloud Networks Germany
GmbH **(1)**
Leuchtenbergring 3, 81677, Munich, Ger-
many
Tel.: (49) 894194220
Web Site: http://www.thecloud.eu
Cloud Management Services
N.A.I.C.S.: 518210

Vene International GmbH **(1)**
Karl-Liebknecht-Strasse 32, 10178, Berlin,
Germany
Tel.: (49) 30695380
Web Site: http://www.vene.io
Digital Content Creation & Advertising Ser-
vices
N.A.I.C.S.: 541810
Christoph Vilanek *(Mng Dir)*

Vitrado GmbH **(1)**
Deelbogenkamp 4, 22297, Hamburg, Germany

Tel.: (49) 40348584499
Web Site: https://www.vitrado.de
Marketing Services
N.A.I.C.S.: 541613

air2mp3 GmbH **(1)**
Haid-und-neu-str 7, Karlsruhe, 76131, Ger-
many
Tel.: (49) 72166338849
Software Development Services
N.A.I.C.S.: 541511

debitel Konzernfinanzierungs
Gmbh **(1)**
Gropiusplatz 10, Stuttgart, 70563, Germany
Tel.: (49) 7117217000
Telecommunication Servicesb
N.A.I.C.S.: 517810

freeXmedia GmbH **(1)**
Deelbogenkamp 4c, 22297, Hamburg, Ger-
many
Tel.: (49) 40 513 06 650
Web Site: http://www.freexmedia.de
Marketing Consulting Services
N.A.I.C.S.: 541613

freenet Cityline GmbH **(1)**
Am Germaniahafen 1-7, 24143, Kiel, Ger-
many
Tel.: (49) 4319020500
Software Development Services
N.A.I.C.S.: 541511

freenet Datenkommunikations
GmbH **(1)**
Deelbogenkamp 4, 22297, Hamburg,
Germany **(100%)**
Tel.: (49) 21153087100
Web Site: https://www.freenet-business.de
Emp.: 400
Commercial Telecommunications Services
N.A.I.C.S.: 517810

freenet Direkt GmbH **(1)**
Deelbogenkamp 4 C, 22297, Hamburg,
Germany
Tel.: (49) 40513060
Telecommunication Servicesb
N.A.I.C.S.: 517810
Christoph Vilanek *(CEO)*

mobilcom Communicationstechnik
GmbH **(1)**
Hollerstrasse 126, 24782, Budelsdorf,
Germany **(100%)**
Tel.: (49) 40555541441
Web Site: http://www.freenet-group.de
Sales Range: $1-4.9 Billion
Telecommunications & Internet Services
N.A.I.C.S.: 517112

mobilcom-debitel GmbH **(1)**
Hollerstrasse 126, 24782, Budelsdorf, Ger-
many
Tel.: (49) 40555541441
Web Site: http://www.mobilcom-debitel.de
Telecommunication Servicesb
N.A.I.C.S.: 517810

Subsidiary (Domestic):

Gravis Computervertriebsgesellschaf
mbH **(2)**
Ernst-Reuter-Platz 8, 10587, Berlin, Ger-
many
Tel.: (49) 3039022222
Web Site: http://www.gravis.de
Electronic Product Distr
N.A.I.C.S.: 449210

Klarmobil GmbH **(2)**
Hollerstrasse 126, Buedelsdorf, 24782,
Rendsburg, Germany
Tel.: (49) 40348585300
Web Site: https://www.klarmobil.de
Mobile Phone Retailer
N.A.I.C.S.: 449210

Media Broadcast GmbH **(2)**
Erna-Scheffler-Strasse 1, 51103, Cologne,
Germany
Tel.: (49) 22171015000
Web Site: https://www.media-broadcast.com
Broadcasting Services
N.A.I.C.S.: 516120

Motion TM Vertriebs GmbH **(2)**
Langbaurghstrasse 14, 53842, Troisdorf,
Germany
Tel.: (49) 22412545110

Web Site: http://www.motion-tm.de
Mobile & Telecommunication Services
N.A.I.C.S.: 517112

new directions GmbH (1)
Piechlerstrasse 3-5, Neusass, 86356, Hamburg, Germany
Tel.: (49) 8215437000
Web Site: http://www.newdirection.de
Emp.: 20
Individual Software Development Services
N.A.I.C.S.: 541511
Alina Weber (Project Mgr)

FREEPORT RESOURCES INC.
Suite 250 750 West Pender St, Vancouver, V6C 2T7, BC, Canada
Tel.: (236) 334-1660   Ca
Web Site:
  https://www.freeportresources.com
Year Founded: 1981
FEERF—(OTCQB)
Assets: $2,604,094
Liabilities: $101,862
Net Worth: $2,502,231
Earnings: ($6,920,421)
Fiscal Year-end: 01/31/21
Mineral Exploration Services
N.A.I.C.S.: 213114
Gord Friesen (Pres & CEO)

FREESEAS INC.
20 Amerikis Street, 10671, Athens, Greece
Tel.: (30) 2107297015   MH
Web Site: http://www.freeseas.gr
Year Founded: 2004
FREEF—(OTCBB)
Shipping Services
N.A.I.C.S.: 488510
Ion G. Varouxakis (Founder, Chm, Pres & CEO)

FREESIA MACROSS CORPORATION
17 Kanda Higashimatsushitacho, Chiyoda-ku, Tokyo, 101-0042, Japan
Tel.: (81) 366351830
Web Site:
  https://www.freesiamacross-extruder.com
Year Founded: 1947
6343—(TKS)
Rev.: $44,419,200
Assets: $201,459,580
Liabilities: $85,857,290
Net Worth: $115,602,290
Earnings: $4,342,770
Emp.: 460
Fiscal Year-end: 03/31/24
Extruding Machinery Mfr
N.A.I.C.S.: 333517
Beji Sasaki (Chm)

Subsidiaries:

Freesia House Co., Ltd. (1)
Freesia Group Head Office Building 17 Kanda Higashi Matsushita-cho, Chiyoda-ku, Tokyo, 101-0042, Japan
Tel.: (81) 366351788
Web Site: https://www.freesia.co.jp
Construction Services
N.A.I.C.S.: 236220

Freesia Trading Co., Ltd. (1)
17-5F Kanda Higashisushitacho, Chiyoda-ku, Tokyo, 101-0042, Japan
Tel.: (81) 366351833
Web Site: https://www.freesia-net.co.jp
Civil Engineering Services
N.A.I.C.S.: 541330

Kouei Industry Co., Ltd. (1)
2060-5 Shimoizumi Kuboizumi-cho, Saga, 849-0903, Iwate, Japan
Tel.: (81) 952718111
Web Site: https://www.kouei-k.co.jp
Sheet Metal Mfr
N.A.I.C.S.: 332322

Maekawa Construction Co., Ltd. (1)
3-9-8 Yokokawa, Sumida-ku, Tokyo, 130-

0003, Japan
Tel.: (81) 336240431
Web Site: https://www.maeken.co.jp
Highway Construction Material Mfr
N.A.I.C.S.: 333120

Picoi Co., Ltd. (1)
1-8-1 Takashi, Chuo-ku, Niigata, 950-0926, Japan
Tel.: (81) 366351782
Web Site: https://www.picoi.co.jp
Emp.: 399
Building Maintenance Services
N.A.I.C.S.: 561790

FREETECH ROAD RECYCLING TECHNOLOGY (HOLDINGS) LIMITED
29/F Chinachem Century Tower 178 Glouchester Road, Wanchai, China (Hong Kong)
Tel.: (852) 23309600   KY
Web Site: https://www.freetech-holdings.hk
Year Founded: 1993
6888—(HKG)
Rev.: $65,231,423
Assets: $170,884,170
Liabilities: $60,748,905
Net Worth: $110,135,265
Earnings: $5,643,278
Emp.: 489
Fiscal Year-end: 12/31/21
Asphalt Paving
N.A.I.C.S.: 324121
Wai Pan Sze (Founder, Founder, Chm, Chm, CEO & Exec Dir)

FREETRAILER GROUP A/S
Gladsaxe Mollevej 67-69, 2860, Soborg, Denmark
Tel.: (45) 88537700
Web Site: https://freetrailer.com
Year Founded: 2005
Commercial Vehicle Rental Services
N.A.I.C.S.: 532120
Allan Sonderskov Darre (CEO)

FREEWON CHINA CO., LTD.
No 168 Yuxi West Road, Qiandeng Town, Kunshan, 215341, Jiangsu, China
Tel.: (86) 51282609999
Web Site:
  https://www.freewon.com.cn
Year Founded: 2006
688678—(SHG)
Rev.: $130,128,841
Assets: $322,766,992
Liabilities: $116,295,201
Net Worth: $206,471,791
Earnings: $22,737,738
Fiscal Year-end: 12/31/22
Metal Parts Mfr & Distr
N.A.I.C.S.: 332119
Huijun Xu (Chm & Gen Mgr)

FREEWORLD TRADING LTD.
21 Annandale Street, Edinburgh, EH7 4AW, United Kingdom
Tel.: (44) 131 557 5600
Web Site: http://www.freeworld-trading.co.uk
Year Founded: 1991
Sales Range: $100-124.9 Million
Emp.: 19
Food Products Mfr
N.A.I.C.S.: 311423
Minoo Das (Co-Owner)

FREIGHTLINER MANITOBA LTD.
2058 Logan Ave, Winnipeg, R2R 0H9, MB, Canada
Tel.: (204) 694-3000
Web Site:
  http://www.freightliner.mb.ca

Year Founded: 1990
Rev.: $35,189,925
Emp.: 101
New & Used Trucks Dealers
N.A.I.C.S.: 484220
Ken Talbot (Pres)

FREIGHTLINER OF RED DEER INC
8046 Edgar Industrial Cres, Red Deer, T4P 3R3, AB, Canada
Tel.: (403) 309-8225
Web Site:
  http://www.freightlinerofreddeer.com
Year Founded: 1993
Rev.: $20,998,171
Emp.: 45
New & Used Truck Dealers
N.A.I.C.S.: 484220
Don Patterson (Pres & Mgr-Sls)

FREIGHTOS LIMITED
Technology Park Building 2 1 Derech Agudat Sport HaPo'el, Jerusalem, 9695102, Israel   Ky
Web Site: https://www.freightos.com
Year Founded: 2012
CRGO—(NASDAQ)
Rev.: $19,085,000
Assets: $41,806,000
Liabilities: $20,146,000
Net Worth: $21,660,000
Earnings: ($24,701,000)
Emp.: 358
Fiscal Year-end: 12/31/22
Freight Transportation Services
N.A.I.C.S.: 483111
Eytan Buchman (CMO)

FREIGHTWAYS GROUP LIMITED
32 Botha Road, Penrose, DX CX10120, New Zealand
Tel.: (64) 95719670
Web Site:
  https://www.freightways.co.nz
Year Founded: 1964
FRW—(NZX)
Rev.: $670,825,359
Assets: $823,346,890
Liabilities: $538,297,847
Net Worth: $285,049,043
Earnings: $45,034,091
Emp.: 450
Fiscal Year-end: 06/30/23
Courier Service
N.A.I.C.S.: 492110
Mark Verbiest (Chm)

Subsidiaries:

Air Freight NZ Limited (1)
Freightways House Ground Floor 32 Botha Road, Penrose, 1061, Auckland, New Zealand
Tel.: (64) 92566534
Web Site: http://www.airfreightnz.co.nz
Emp.: 400
Air Freight Transportation Services
N.A.I.C.S.: 481212
Dean Bracewell (Gen Mgr)

Big Chill Distribution Limited (1)
Tel.: (64) 92727440
Web Site: https://www.bigchill.co.nz
Freight Trucking Services
N.A.I.C.S.: 484110
Jason Wolferstan (Mgr-Natl Transport & Logistics)

Castle Parcels - Christchurch (1)
20 Syd Bradley Road, Dakota Park, Christchurch, New Zealand
Tel.: (64) 3 345 6830
Web Site: https://www.castleparcels.co.nz
Sales Range: $25-49.9 Million
Emp.: 80
Courier Service
N.A.I.C.S.: 492110

Castle Parcels - Wellington (1)

9 Glover Street, Ngauranga, Wellington, 6007, New Zealand   (100%)
Tel.: (64) 4 472 3666
Web Site: https://www.castleparcels.co.nz
Sales Range: $25-49.9 Million
Emp.: 60
Courier Service
N.A.I.C.S.: 492110
Michael Claydon (Gen Mgr)

Castle Parcels Limited (1)
163 Station Road, Penrose, Auckland, 1061, New Zealand   (100%)
Tel.: (64) 95255500
Web Site: https://www.castleparcels.co.nz
Sales Range: $10-24.9 Million
Emp.: 50
Transportion Services
N.A.I.C.S.: 492110
Neil Wilson (Gen Mgr)

DX Mail (1)
20 Fairfax Avenue, DX Box CR59901, Penrose, Auckland, 1061, New Zealand
Tel.: (64) 95263150
Sales Range: $75-99.9 Million
Emp.: 300
Business Mail Services
N.A.I.C.S.: 561439

Databank Technologies Pty Limited (1)
PO Box 251, Alexandria, 1435, NSW, Australia
Tel.: (61) 2 9305 9500
Web Site: http://www.databank.com.au
Data Storage Services
N.A.I.C.S.: 561439

Freightways Information Services Limited (1)
32 Botha Rd, Penrose, Auckland, 1061, New Zealand
Tel.: (64) 95719650
Web Site: https://www.freightways.co.nz
Information Technology Consultancy Services
N.A.I.C.S.: 541512
Richard Mitchel-Lowe (Gen Mgr)

Kiwi Express (1)
Ground Floor Freightways House 32 Botha Road, Penrose, Auckland, New Zealand
Tel.: (64) 95894100
Sales Range: $10-24.9 Million
Emp.: 50
Courier Service
N.A.I.C.S.: 492110
Keenan Brett (Mgr-Ops)

Messenger Services Limited (1)
32 Botha Road, Penrose, Auckland, 1061, New Zealand   (100%)
Tel.: (64) 95263670
Web Site: https://www.sub60.co.nz
Sales Range: $25-49.9 Million
Emp.: 150
Courier Service
N.A.I.C.S.: 492110
Aaron Stubbing (Gen Mgr)

NOW Couriers Limited (1)
161 Station Road, Penrose, Auckland, 1061, New Zealand
Tel.: (64) 95269170
Web Site: https://nowcouriers.co.nz
Courier Service
N.A.I.C.S.: 492110

New Zealand Couriers Limited (1)
32 Botha Road, Auckland, 1061, New Zealand   (100%)
Tel.: (64) 95263100
Web Site: https://nzcextras.co.nz
Sales Range: $25-49.9 Million
Emp.: 200
Courier Service
N.A.I.C.S.: 492110
Steve Well (Gen Mgr)

Subsidiary (Domestic):

Fieldair Holdings Limited (2)
Palmerston North International Airport, Palmerston North, 4414, New Zealand
Tel.: (64) 63571149
Web Site: https://freightways.co.nz
Sales Range: $25-49.9 Million
Emp.: 60
Aviation Engineering Services

FREIGHTWAYS GROUP LIMITED

Freightways Group Limited—(Continued)

N.A.I.C.S.: 541330
Charles Giliam *(Gen Mgr)*

Online Security Services Limited **(1)**
33 Botha Road, Penrose, Auckland, 1061,
New Zealand
Tel.: (64) 95804360
Web Site: https://timg.co.nz
Sales Range: $10-24.9 Million
Emp.: 50
Document Storage Services
N.A.I.C.S.: 561439
Rob Herriott *(Mgr-Sls)*

Post Haste Limited **(1)**
32 Botha Road, Penrose, Auckland, 1061,
New Zealand **(100%)**
Tel.: (64) 95252060
Web Site: https://www.posthaste.co.nz
Sales Range: $25-49.9 Million
Emp.: 250
Courier Service
N.A.I.C.S.: 492110
Warwick Mitchell *(Mgr-Sls)*

SUB60 **(1)**
32 Botha Road, Penrose, Auckland, 1061,
New Zealand
Tel.: (64) 95263680
Web Site: https://www.sub60.co.nz
Sales Range: $10-24.9 Million
Emp.: 100
Courier Service
N.A.I.C.S.: 492110
Aaron Stubbing *(Gen Mgr)*

Security Express Ltd **(1)**
401 Hutt Road, PO Box 30462, Lower Hutt,
5010, New Zealand
Tel.: (64) 45879011
Sales Range: $25-49.9 Million
Emp.: 4
Courier Service
N.A.I.C.S.: 492110
Jodie Richards *(Branch Mgr)*

**The Information Management Group
(NZ) Limited** **(1)**
33 Botha Road, Penrose, Auckland, 1061,
New Zealand
Tel.: (64) 95804360
Web Site: https://timg.co.nz
Digital Services
N.A.I.C.S.: 518210
Ahmed Zaky *(Partner-)*

**The Information Management Group
Pty Limited** **(1)**
PO Box 21, Enfield, Sydney, 2136, NSW,
Australia
Tel.: (61) 293059596
Web Site: https://www.timg.com
Digital Services
N.A.I.C.S.: 518210

FREJA EID GROUP AB

Vasagatan 40, 111 20, Stockholm,
Sweden
Tel.: (46) 87230900
Web Site: https://www.verisec.com
Year Founded: 2002
FREJA—(OMX)
Rev.: $2,755,533
Assets: $5,605,665
Liabilities: $3,605,983
Net Worth: $1,999,682
Earnings: ($3,630,335)
Emp.: 31
Fiscal Year-end: 12/31/22
IT Security Products
N.A.I.C.S.: 561621

Subsidiaries:

VERISEC APAC Pty. Ltd. **(1)**
Level 10 68 Pitt Street, Sydney, 2000,
NSW, Australia
Tel.: (61) 419803132
Financial Transaction Processing Services
N.A.I.C.S.: 522320

VERISEC Technology D.O.O. **(1)**
Vojvode Stepe 78, Belgrade, Serbia
Tel.: (381) 668554500
Financial Transaction Processing Services
N.A.I.C.S.: 522320

Verisec Latam S.A. de C.V. **(1)**
Av Insurgentes Sur 1647 -Floor 1-Office
102, Colonia San Jose Insurgentes Delega-
cion Benito Juarez, 03900, Mexico, Mexico
Tel.: (52) 15511545151
Financial Transaction Processing Services
N.A.I.C.S.: 522320

FREMMAN CAPITAL LIMITED

11 Grosvenor Place,, London, SW1
X7HH, United Kingdom
Tel.: (44) 2074584626
Web Site: https://fremman.com
Year Founded: 2020
Private Equity
N.A.I.C.S.: 523940

FREMONT GOLD LTD.

Suite 1500 - 409 Granville Street,
Vancouver, V6C 1T2, BC, Canada
Tel.: (604) 676-5664 **BC**
Web Site:
https://www.fremontgold.net
Year Founded: 2007
FR20—(DEU)
Assets: $2,457,506
Liabilities: $327,368
Net Worth: $2,130,138
Earnings: ($737,442)
Fiscal Year-end: 03/31/23
Uranium Exploration Services
N.A.I.C.S.: 212290
Dennis Moore *(Founder & Pres)*

FRENCH CONNECTION GROUP PLC

First Floor Centro 1 39 Plender
Street, London, NW1 0DT, United
Kingdom
Tel.: (44) 2070367200 **UK**
Web Site:
http://www.frenchconnection.com
Year Founded: 1984
FCCN—(LSE)
Rev.: $157,260,840
Assets: $103,616,400
Liabilities: $65,448,840
Net Worth: $38,167,560
Earnings: ($10,230,480)
Emp.: 1,092
Fiscal Year-end: 01/31/20
Holding Company; Men's & Women's
Apparel Designer, Whslr & Retailer
N.A.I.C.S.: 551112
Stephen Marks *(Founder)*

Subsidiaries:

**French Connection (London)
Limited** **(1)**
3rd Floor Matrix Beta Matrix Business Park,
Swansea, SA6 8RE, United Kingdom
Tel.: (44) 1792 784 150
Web Site: http://www.frenchconnection.com
Online Clothing Retailer
N.A.I.C.S.: 458110

French Connection Group, Inc. **(1)**
14 E 60th St Frnt 2, New York, NY 10022
Tel.: (212) 421-7720
Web Site: http://usa.frenchconnection.com
Clothing Accessories Stores
N.A.I.C.S.: 458110

Subsidiary (Domestic):

**French Connection Holdings,
Inc.** **(2)**
512 Fashion Ave, New York, NY 10018
Tel.: (212) 768-3479
Web Site: http://usa.frenchconnection.com
Holding Company
N.A.I.C.S.: 551112

French Connection Limited **(1)**
99-103 Long Acre Covent Garden, London,
WC2E 9NR, United Kingdom
Tel.: (44) 2073796560
Web Site: http://www.frenchconnection.com
Men's & Women's Apparel Designer &
Whslr
N.A.I.C.S.: 541490

Stephen Marks *(Founder, Chm & Mng Dir)*

PreTex Textilhandels GmbH **(1)**
Honor St 76-78, 50672, Cologne, Germany
Tel.: (49) 2212572851
Fashion Clothing Dlrs
N.A.I.C.S.: 541490

FRENCKEN GROUP LIMITED

9 Raffles Place 26-01 Republic
Plaza, Singapore, 048619, Singapore
Tel.: (65) 62363333 **SG**
Web Site:
https://www.frenckengroup.com
E28—(SES)
Rev.: $562,644,096
Assets: $556,908,278
Liabilities: $249,949,254
Net Worth: $306,959,024
Earnings: $24,226,312
Emp.: 3,700
Fiscal Year-end: 12/31/23
Electronic Equipment Products Mfr &
Distr
N.A.I.C.S.: 425120
Dennis Au *(Pres)*

Subsidiaries:

Avimac Pte. Ltd. **(1)**
2 Seletar Aerospace Link, Singapore,
797570, Singapore
Tel.: (65) 62620033
Web Site: https://www.avimacsg.com
Aerospace Products Mfr
N.A.I.C.S.: 336413

ETLA Limited **(1)**
1 Changi North Street 2, Singapore,
498808, Singapore
Tel.: (65) 65466466
Web Site: http://www.etla.com.sg
Emp.: 300
Precision Machinery & Tools Mfr
N.A.I.C.S.: 332216

ETLA Technology (M) Sdn.Bhd. **(1)**
Lot 3 Jalan P 1A Bangi Industrial Estate,
43650, Bandar Baru Bangi, Selangor, Ma-
laysia
Tel.: (60) 389110222
Web Site: http://www.frenckengroup.com
Sales Range: $100-124.9 Million
Emp.: 300
Precision Machinery Mfr
N.A.I.C.S.: 333248
Martin Low *(Gen Mgr)*

ETLA Technology (Wuxi) Co.,Ltd. **(1)**
No 9 Xi Xing North Road Wuxi -Singapore
Industrial Park, Wuxi, 214028, Jiangsu,
China
Tel.: (86) 51085280851
Web Site: http://www.etla.com.sg
Emp.: 300
Precision Machinery Mfr & Distr
N.A.I.C.S.: 333517

Frencken Engineering B.V. **(1)**
Hurksestraat 16, 5652 AJ, Eindhoven, Neth-
erlands
Tel.: (31) 402507507
Engineering Services
N.A.I.C.S.: 541330

Frencken Europe B.V. **(1)**
Hurksestraat 16, 5652 AJ, Eindhoven, Neth-
erlands
Tel.: (31) 402507507
Engineering Services
N.A.I.C.S.: 541330

Subsidiary (US):

Frencken America Inc. **(2)**
22924 E Appleway Ave, Liberty Lake, WA
99019
Tel.: (886) 5099249779
Engineering Services
N.A.I.C.S.: 541330

**Frencken Mechatronics (M) Sdn
Bhd** **(1)**
Lot 3 Jalan P/1A Bangi Industrial Estate,
43650, Bandar Baru Bangi, Selangor Darul
Ehsan, Malaysia
Tel.: (60) 38 911 0222
Web Site: http://www.frenckengroup.com

Sales Range: $125-149.9 Million
Emp.: 300
Precision Mechanical Equipments Mfr
N.A.I.C.S.: 332216

Frencken Mechatronics B.V. **(1)**
Tel.: (31) 40 250 7507
Web Site: http://www.frenckengroup.com
Sales Range: $50-74.9 Million
Emp.: 250
Industrial Equipment Mfr
N.A.I.C.S.: 333515

**Frencken Technical Projects Assem-
bly B.V.** **(1)**
Hurksestraat 16, 5652 AJ, Eindhoven, Neth-
erlands
Tel.: (31) 402507507
Web Site: http://www.frencken.nl
Sales Range: $50-74.9 Million
Emp.: 250
Industrial Tools Mfr
N.A.I.C.S.: 333515
Henk Tappel *(Mng Dir)*

Juken Technology Limited **(1)**
33 Loyang Way, Singapore, 508731, Singa-
pore
Tel.: (65) 6565423033
Web Site: http://www.jukentech.com
Sales Range: $50-74.9 Million
Moulded Plastic Components Mfr
N.A.I.C.S.: 326199
Tateiwa Iwao *(Gen Mgr-Thailand)*

Subsidiary (Non-US):

Juken (H.K.) Co., Limited **(2)**
Unit 1603-1604 CFC Tower 28 Mody Road,
Tsim Sha Tsui, Kowloon, China (Hong
Kong)
Tel.: (852) 27508212
Web Site: http://www.jukentech.com
Precision Plastic Products Mfr
N.A.I.C.S.: 326199

Juken (Thailand) Co., Ltd. **(2)**
24/3 Moo 4 Bangna-Trad Road KM35
Bangpleenoi Naklua, Amphur Bangbor,
Samut Prakan, 10560, Thailand
Tel.: (66) 27087477
Web Site: http://www.jukenthai.com
Injection Molded Plastic Products Mfr
N.A.I.C.S.: 326121

Juken (Zhuhai) Co., Ltd. **(2)**
Block 11 Zone 1 Hengli Industrial Park Nan-
shui, Nanshui Town, Zhuhai, 519050,
Guangdong, China
Tel.: (86) 7567233371
Web Site: http://www.jukentech.com
Emp.: 420
Precision Engineered Plastic Products Mfr
N.A.I.C.S.: 326121

Plant (Non-US):

**Juken Engineering Technology Sdn
Bhd - Johor Bahru Factory** **(2)**
No 18 Jalan Masyhur 1, Taman Perindus-
trian Cemerlang, 81800, Ulu Tiram, Johor,
Malaysia
Tel.: (60) 7 863 7568
Web Site: http://www.jukentech.com
Sales Range: $50-74.9 Million
Emp.: 158
Precision Engineered Plastic Products Mfr
N.A.I.C.S.: 326199

**Juken Engineering Technology Sdn
Bhd - Kuala Lumpur Factory** **(2)**
Lot 10 11 & 12 Jalan BRP 9/1C Bukit Rah-
man Putra Industrial Park, Sungai Buloh,
47000, Selangor, Malaysia
Tel.: (60) 361562386
Web Site: http://www.jukentech.com
Sales Range: $50-74.9 Million
Emp.: 200
Precision Engineered Plastic Products Mfr
N.A.I.C.S.: 326199

Subsidiary (Domestic):

**Juken Mecplas Technology Pte
Ltd** **(2)**
33 Loyang Way, Singapore, 508731, Singa-
pore
Tel.: (65) 65423033
Web Site: http://www.jukentech.com

Sales Range: $25-49.9 Million
Emp.: 80
Injection Molded Plastic Products Mfr
N.A.I.C.S.: 326199
David Wong *(Mng Dir)*

Subsidiary (Domestic):

Zelor Technology Pte Ltd (3)
33 Loyang Way, Singapore, 508731, Singapore
Tel.: (65) 6542 3033
Sales Range: $25-49.9 Million
Emp.: 20
Product Validation Services
N.A.I.C.S.: 561990

Subsidiary (Non-US):

Juken Micro-Air (Tianjin) Technology Co., Ltd. (2)
No 8 Shuang Chen Zhong Lu Bei Chen Economy Development District, Tianjin, 300400, China
Tel.: (86) 22 2697 2287
Injection Molded Plastic Products Mfr
N.A.I.C.S.: 326121

Juken Swiss Technology AG (2)
Bundengasse 22, 2540, Grenchen, Solothurn, Switzerland
Tel.: (41) 32 461 4040
Web Site: http://www.jukenswisstech.com
Sales Range: $25-49.9 Million
Emp.: 10
Stepper Motor & Car Clocks Mfr
N.A.I.C.S.: 333612

Juken Uniproducts Pvt Ltd (2)
C-14 Sector-57, Noida, 201 307, Uttar Pradesh, India
Tel.: (91) 120 258 1231
Injection Molded Plastic Parts Mfr
N.A.I.C.S.: 326121

PT Juken Technology Indonesia (2)
EJIP Industrial Park Plot 1F-3C, Cikarang Selatan, Bekasi, 17550, West Java, Indonesia
Tel.: (62) 21 897 0202
Web Site: http://www.jukentech.com
Precision Engineered Plastic Products Mfr
N.A.I.C.S.: 326199

Machinefabriek Gebrs.Frencken B.V. (1)
Hurksestraat 16, 5652 AJ, Eindhoven, Netherlands
Tel.: (31) 402507507
Web Site: http://www.frencken.nl
Precision Machinery Parts Mfr
N.A.I.C.S.: 333515

Micro-Air (Tianjin) Technology Co., Ltd. (1)
No 8 Shuang Chen Zhong Lu, Bei Chen Economy Development District, Tianjin, 300400, China
Tel.: (86) 222 697 2287
Web Site: http://www.micro-airtech.com.sg
Vacuum Coating Mfr
N.A.I.C.S.: 332812

NTZ International Holding B.V. (1)
Sydneystraat 60, 3047 BP, Rotterdam, Netherlands
Tel.: (31) 102383818
Engineering Services
N.A.I.C.S.: 541330

Optiwa B.V. (1)
Tel.: (31) 77 476 9900
Web Site: http://www.optiwa.nl
Sales Range: $25-49.9 Million
Emp.: 80
Precision Mechanical Parts Mfr
N.A.I.C.S.: 332216

Penchem Technologies Sdn. Bhd. (1)
1015 Jalan Perindustrian Bukit Minyak 7, Kawasan Perindustrian Bukit Minyak Mk 13, 14100, Penang, Malaysia
Tel.: (60) 45015973
Web Site: https://www.penchem.com
Electronic Products Mfr
N.A.I.C.S.: 334419

Precico Group Sdn Bhd (1)
Plot 410 Lorong Perusahaan 8B Prai Industrial Estate, 13600, Perai, Penang, Malaysia

Tel.: (60) 43883077
Web Site: http://www.frenckengroup.com
Sales Range: $200-249.9 Million
Emp.: 1,000
Electronic Components Mfr
N.A.I.C.S.: 334418
Guetim Lee *(Mgr-HR)*

US Motion, Inc. (1)
22924 E Appleway Ave, Liberty Lake, WA 99019
Tel.: (509) 924-9779
Web Site: http://www.usmotion.com
Sales Range: $10-24.9 Million
Emp.: 50
Miscellaneous General Purpose Machinery Mfr
N.A.I.C.S.: 333998

FRENDY ENERGY S.P.A.
Foro Buonaparte, 31-20121, Milan, Italy
Tel.: (39) 05415440964
Web Site:
https://frendyenergy.edison.it
Year Founded: 2006
FDE—(ITA)
Sales Range: Less than $1 Million
Eletric Power Generation Services
N.A.I.C.S.: 221111
Marco Stangalino *(Chm)*

FRENKEL TOPPING GROUP PLC
Manchester Office Frenkel House 15 Carolina Way Salford, Manchester, M50 2ZY, United Kingdom
Tel.: (44) 1618868000   UK
Web Site:
https://frenkeltoppinggroup.co.uk
FEN—(LSE)
Rev.: $31,368,200
Assets: $67,082,826
Liabilities: $16,472,229
Net Worth: $50,610,597
Earnings: $2,334,219
Emp.: 206
Fiscal Year-end: 12/31/22
Holding Company; Financial Advisory Services
N.A.I.C.S.: 551112
Richard C. Fraser *(CEO & Sec)*

Subsidiaries:

A&M Bacon Limited (1)
3 Regent Terrace, Doncaster, DN12EE, South Yorkshire, United Kingdom
Tel.: (44) 1733350880
Web Site: https://www.aandmbacon.co.uk
Law Firm Services
N.A.I.C.S.: 541110

Ascencia Investment Management Limited (1)
Frenkel House 15 Carolina Way, Salford, M50 2ZY, Manchester, United Kingdom
Tel.: (44) 1618868000
Web Site: https://www.ascenciaim.co.uk
Financial Services
N.A.I.C.S.: 523999
Richard Fraser *(CEO)*

Bidwell Henderson Costs Consultants Limited (1)
1 Lea Bank Broadmeadows, South Normanton, Alfreton, DE553LH, Derbyshire, United Kingdom
Tel.: (44) 3333441654
Web Site:
https://www.bidwellhenderson.co.uk
Law Firm Services
N.A.I.C.S.: 541110

Frenkel Topping Limited (1)
Frenkel House 15 Carolina Way, Salford, Manchester, M50 2ZY, United Kingdom
Tel.: (44) 1618868000
Web Site: https://www.frenkeltopping.co.uk
Sales Range: $50-74.9 Million
Emp.: 35
Financial Advisory Services
N.A.I.C.S.: 523940

Keystone Case Management Limited (1)
Frenkel House 15 Carolina Way, Salford, M502ZY, United Kingdom
Tel.: (44) 2037937424
Web Site:
https://www.keystonemanagement.co.uk
Law Firm Services
N.A.I.C.S.: 541110

N-Able Services Limited (1)
Egerton House 2 Tower Road, Birkenhead, CH411FN, United Kingdom
Tel.: (44) 1513346066
Web Site: https://www.nableservices.co.uk
Law Firm Services
N.A.I.C.S.: 541110

Partners in Costs Limited (1)
Robson House 4 Regent Terrace, Doncaster, DN12EE, United Kingdom
Tel.: (44) 3458727678
Web Site: https://www.pic.legal
Law Firm Services
N.A.I.C.S.: 541110

Somek & Associates Limited (1)
9 Chess Business Park Moor Road, Chesham, HP51SD, United Kingdom
Tel.: (44) 1494792711
Web Site: https://www.somek.com
Emp.: 200
Law Firm Services
N.A.I.C.S.: 541110

FREQUENCY TELECOM
Unit 44 Barwell Business Park Leatherhead Road, Chessington, KT9 2NY, Surrey, United Kingdom
Tel.: (44) 20 8397 2222
Web Site:
http://www.frequencytelecom.com
Year Founded: 2002
Sales Range: $25-49.9 Million
Emp.: 60
Mobile Accessory Distr
N.A.I.C.S.: 423690
Gareth Limpenny *(Mng Dir)*

FREQUENTIS AG
Innovationsstrasse 1, 1100, Vienna, Austria
Tel.: (43) 1811500
Web Site: https://www.frequentis.com
Year Founded: 1947
FQT—(DEU)
Rev.: $471,893,386
Assets: $409,613,041
Liabilities: $240,202,112
Net Worth: $169,410,929
Earnings: $20,333,285
Emp.: 2,341
Fiscal Year-end: 12/31/23
Voice Communication Software Development Services
N.A.I.C.S.: 513210
Norbert Haslacher *(Chm-Exec Bd & CEO)*

Subsidiaries:

CNS-Solutions & Support GmbH (1)
Gutheil-Schoder-Gasse 8-12, 1100, Vienna, Austria
Tel.: (43) 1811500
Web Site: https://www.cns-solutions.net
Software Development Services
N.A.I.C.S.: 541511
Stefan Ringsmuth *(Fin Dir-ICM Bus)*

ELARA Leitstellentechnik GmbH (1)
Schloss-Rahe-Strasse 19A, 52072, Aachen, Germany
Tel.: (49) 2415662660
Software Development Services
N.A.I.C.S.: 541511

Frequentis Deutschland GmbH (1)
Ohmstrasse 12, 63225, Langen, Germany
Tel.: (49) 6103300860
Software Development Services
N.A.I.C.S.: 541511

Frequentis Orthogon GmbH (1)

Hastedter Osterdeich 222, 28207, Bremen, Germany
Tel.: (49) 421201220
Software Development Services
N.A.I.C.S.: 541511

Frequentis USA Inc. (1)
8661 Robert Fulton Dr Ste 100, Columbia, MD 21046
Tel.: (301) 657-8001
Software Development Services
N.A.I.C.S.: 541511

Regola S.r.l. (1)
Corso Turati 15/H, 10128, Turin, Italy
Tel.: (39) 0115187029
Web Site: https://en.regola.it
Software Development Services
N.A.I.C.S.: 541511

FRERE-BOURGEOIS
Rue De La Blanche Borne 12, Loverval, 6280, Belgium
Tel.: (32) 71606060
Sales Range: $10-24.9 Million
Emp.: 10
Public Relations
N.A.I.C.S.: 541820
Gilles Samyn *(Mng Dir)*

Subsidiaries:

ERBE SA (1)
Rue De La Blanche Borne 12, 6280, Loverval, Belgium   **(53%)**
Tel.: (32) 71606060
Web Site: http://www.cnp.be
Emp.: 20
Holding Company
N.A.I.C.S.: 551112

Subsidiary (Domestic):

Compagnie Nationale a Portefeuille S.A. (2)
Rue de la Blanche Borne 12, 6280, Loverval, Belgium
Tel.: (32) 71606060
Web Site: http://www.cnp.be
Holding Company
N.A.I.C.S.: 551112

Subsidiary (Non-US):

Agesca Nederland NV (3)
Veerkade 5, 3016 DE, Rotterdam, Netherlands   **(100%)**
Tel.: (31) 102183703
Holding Company
N.A.I.C.S.: 551112
Patricia Ottervanger *(Acct Mgr)*

Joint Venture (Domestic):

Parjointco N.V. (4)
Veerkade 5, Rotterdam, 3016DE, Netherlands
Tel.: (31) 4139154
Holding Company; Joint Venture Between Power Financial Europe BV & Agesca Netherland NV
N.A.I.C.S.: 551112

Holding (Non-US):

Pargesa Holding S.A. (5)
11 Grand-Rue, CH-1204, Geneva, Switzerland
Tel.: (41) 228177777
Web Site: http://www.pargesa.ch
Rev.: $5,770,980,992
Assets: $35,020,798,912
Liabilities: $11,115,023,488
Net Worth: $23,905,775,424
Earnings: $866,543,040
Emp.: 94,000
Fiscal Year-end: 12/31/2019
Holding Company
N.A.I.C.S.: 551112
Gerald Frere *(Deputy Chm & Deputy Chm)*

Subsidiary (Non-US):

Entremont S.A. (3)
25 Faubourg des Balmettes, PO Box 50029, 74001, Annecy, Cedex, France   **(75%)**
Tel.: (33) 9 69 32 09 91
Web Site: http://www.entremont.com
Producer of Cheese

Frere-Bourgeois—(Continued)

N.A.I.C.S.: 311513
Olivier Brys (Dir-HR)

Joint Venture (Domestic):

TRASYS S.A (3)
Tarhulpsestaanveg No C 1660, B 1200,
Hoeilaart, Belgium
Tel.: (32) 27737111
Web Site: http://www.trasys.be
Sales Range: $200-249.9 Million
Emp.: 600
IT & Software Business Support Services
N.A.I.C.S.: 541511

Subsidiary (Domestic):

TRASYS Charleroi (4)
Terhulp Sesteenwg 6C, 1560, Hoeilaart,
Belgium
Tel.: (32) 71378211
Web Site: http://www.trasys.be
Sales Range: $50-74.9 Million
Emp.: 130
IT & Software Business Support Services
N.A.I.C.S.: 541511

Subsidiary (Non-US):

TRASYS Greece (4)
3 Arkadias St, Athens, 11526, Attica,
Greece
Tel.: (30) 2107769800
Web Site: http://www.trasys.gr
Sales Range: $25-49.9 Million
Emp.: 30
IT & Software Business Support Services
N.A.I.C.S.: 541511

TRASYS Luxembourg (4)
Route d'Arlon 283, 8011, Strassen, Luxem-
bourg
Tel.: (352) 2611101
Web Site:
http://www.trasysinternational.com
Sales Range: $25-49.9 Million
Emp.: 43
IT & Software Business Support Services
N.A.I.C.S.: 541511

FRESCA GROUP LIMITED
The Fresh Produce Centre Transfesa
Road, Paddock Wood, TN12 6UT,
Kent, United Kingdom
Tel.: (44) 1892 831280
Web Site:
http://www.frescagroup.co.uk
Year Founded: 1874
Sales Range: $450-499.9 Million
Emp.: 848
Fruit & Vegetable Whslr
N.A.I.C.S.: 424480
Christopher Mack (Chm)

Subsidiaries:

DGM Growers Ltd (1)
Oak House Holbeach Bank, Spalding, PE12
8BB, Lincolnshire, United Kingdom
Tel.: (44) 1406422615
Web Site: http://www.dgmgrowers.co.uk
Vegetable Farming Services
N.A.I.C.S.: 111219

Primafruit Ltd (1)
Enterprise Way Vale Business Park, Eve-
sham, WR11 1GT, Worcestershire, United
Kingdom
Tel.: (44) 1386425000
Web Site: http://www.primafruit.co.uk
Fresh Fruit Distr
N.A.I.C.S.: 424480
Johan van Deventer (Dir-Ops)

Wallings Nursery Ltd (1)
38 Harwich Rd, Lawford, Manningtree,
CO11 2LS, Essex, United Kingdom
Tel.: (44) 1206230728
Web Site: http://www.wallingsnursery.com
Strawberry Farming Services
N.A.I.C.S.: 111333

**FRESE & WOLFF WERBE-
AGENTUR GMBH**
Donnerschweer Strasse 79, 26123,
Oldenburg, Germany

Tel.: (49) 44180020   De
Web Site: http://www.frese-wolff.de
Year Founded: 1976
Sales Range: $25-49.9 Million
Emp.: 45
N.A.I.C.S.: 541810
Hans E. Wolff (Owner & CEO)

**FRESENIUS MEDICAL CARE
AG**
ElseKronerStr 1, 61352, Bad Hom-
burg, Germany
Tel.: (49) 61726092525   De
Web Site:
https://www.freseniusmedical.com
Year Founded: 1996
FMS—(NYSE)
Rev.: $23,825,420,400
Assets: $43,914,632,979
Liabilities: $24,939,333,364
Net Worth: $18,975,299,615
Earnings: $827,102,957
Emp.: 128,044
Fiscal Year-end: 12/31/22
Holding Company; Dialysis Products
& Services
N.A.I.C.S.: 551112
Dieter Schenk (Chm-Supervisory Bd)

Subsidiaries:

**ET Software Developments
GmbH** (1)
Im Schuhmachergewann 15, 69123, Heidel-
berg, Germany
Tel.: (49) 62249879861
Web Site: https://www.indication.com
Software Development Services
N.A.I.C.S.: 541511

FMC (Schweiz) AG (1)
Aawasserstrasse 2, 6370, Oberdorf, CH,
Switzerland
Tel.: (41) 416195050
Web Site:
https://www.freseniusmedicalcare.ch
Health Care Srvices
N.A.I.C.S.: 621610

FMC (Shanghai) Co., Ltd. (1)
Room 4601 Tower 2 Ganghui Center 3
Hongqiao Road, Shanghai, 200030, China
Tel.: (86) 2161152800
Health Care Srvices
N.A.I.C.S.: 621610
Liming Zhang (Sr Mgr)

FMC (U.K.) Ltd. (1)
Nunn Brook Road, Huthwaite, NG17 2HU,
Nottinghamshire, United Kingdom
Tel.: (44) 1623445100
Health Care Srvices
N.A.I.C.S.: 621610
Tim Wheeldon (Mng Dir)

FMC Colombia S.A. (1)
Cra 7 Nro 156-10 Piso 26, Bogota, Colom-
bia
Tel.: (57) 12941400
Web Site:
https://www.freseniusmedicalcare.com.co
Medical Care Services
N.A.I.C.S.: 622110

FMC Dializis Center Kft. (1)
Szepvolgyi Ut 35-37, Budapest, 1037, Hun-
gary
Tel.: (36) 14392244
Web Site: http://www.fresenius.hu
Dialysis Center Operator
N.A.I.C.S.: 621492

FMC Espana, S.A.U. (1)
Ronda de Poniente 8 Planta baja, 28760,
Tres Cantos, Madrid, Spain
Tel.: (34) 913276650
Web Site:
https://www.freseniusmedicalcare.es
Health Care Srvices
N.A.I.C.S.: 621610

FMC Holdings, Inc. (1)
Paseo Del Norte 5300 Guadalajara Tech-
nology Park, 45010, Zapopan, Jalisco,
Mexico
Tel.: (52) 3335404200

Web Site: http://www.fmc-mexico.com
Health Care Srvices
N.A.I.C.S.: 621610
Oscar Acosta Ramirez (Gen Mgr)

FMC Hong Kong Ltd. (1)
15th Floor 88 Gloucester Road, Wanchai,
China (Hong Kong)
Tel.: (852) 28982883
Web Site:
https://www.freseniusmedicalcare.hk
Health Care Srvices
N.A.I.C.S.: 621610
Thorsten Bruce (Gen Mgr)

FMC Japan K.K. (1)
92-7 Oaza Minage, Tobu Industrial Park,
Buzen, 828-0045, Fukuoka, Japan
Tel.: (81) 979648510
Web Site: https://www.fresenius.co.jp
Emp.: 210
Health Care Srvices
N.A.I.C.S.: 621610

FMC Ltd. (1)
402 Moo 4 Banpoo Industrial Estate Ban-
poo, Mueang Samutprakarn, Samut Prakan,
10280, Thailand
Tel.: (66) 992877344
Health Care Srvices
N.A.I.C.S.: 621610
Natthavut Kandthong (Project Mgr)

FMC Ltda. (1)
Av das Americas 3443 block 04 2nd floor,
Barra da Tijuca, Rio de Janeiro, 22631-003,
RJ, Brazil
Tel.: (55) 2121792400
Web Site:
https://www.freseniusmedicalcare.com.br
Health Care Srvices
N.A.I.C.S.: 621610

FMC Portugal, S.A. (1)
Rua Joaquim Alves de Sousa Moreira 268,
4470-573, Maia, Portugal
Tel.: (351) 229438280
Rev.: $122,889,270
Emp.: 200
Medical Equipment Distr
N.A.I.C.S.: 423450

FMC Romania S.r.l. (1)
Sos Bucharest-Ploiesti no 19-21 Baneasa
Business Center, Floor 3 Sector 1, Bucha-
rest, 013682, Romania
Tel.: (40) 212334268
Web Site:
http://www.freseniusmedicalcare.ro
Health Care Srvices
N.A.I.C.S.: 621610

FMC Suomi Oy (1)
Valimotie 13 B b, 00380, Helsinki, Finland
Tel.: (358) 9561650
Web Site:
https://www.freseniusmedicalcare.fi
Health Care Srvices
N.A.I.C.S.: 621610

FMC Vietnam LLC (1)
Mezzanine and 2nd Floor PLS Building 366
Nguyen Trai, Ward 08 District 5, Ho Chi
Minh City, Vietnam
Tel.: (84) 2838662828
Health Care Srvices
N.A.I.C.S.: 621610
Phuc Lam (Mgr-Supply Chain-Operations)

FMC del Peru S.A. (1)
Avenida Javier Prado Oeste 2442-Interior
901 Urb, Orrantia Magdalena del Mar, 17,
Lima, Peru
Tel.: (51) 13497520
Health Care Srvices
N.A.I.C.S.: 621610
Daniel Guerra (CFO)

**Fresenius Medical Care (Ireland)
Limited** (1)
Unit 3b Fingal Bay Business Park, Balbrig-
gan, Ireland
Tel.: (353) 18413030
Health Care Srvices
N.A.I.C.S.: 621999

**Fresenius Medical Care (Schweiz)
AG** (1)
Aawasserstrasse 2, 6370, Oberdorf, Swit-
zerland
Tel.: (41) 416195050

Web Site:
https://www.freseniusmedicalcare.ch
Emp.: 50
Medical Instrument Mfr & Distr
N.A.I.C.S.: 334510

**Fresenius Medical Care (Shanghai)
Co., Ltd.** (1)
Rm 4601 Suite 2 Ganghui Center No 3
Hongqiao Road, Xuhui Dis, Shanghai,
200030, China
Tel.: (86) 2161152800
Dialysis & Health Care Services
N.A.I.C.S.: 621492

Subsidiary (Domestic):

FMC (Jiangsu) Co. Ltd. (2)
Gu-li Industry Park Gu-Li Zhen, Changshu,
215533, Jiangsu, China
Tel.: (86) 512 5230 5630
Web Site: http://www.fresenius.com
Health Care Srvices
N.A.I.C.S.: 621999

**Fresenius Medical Care (U.K.)
Ltd.** (1)
Nunn Brook Road, Huthwaite Sutton-in-
Ashfield, Kirkby in Ashfield, NG17 2HU,
Nottinghamshire, United Kingdom
Web Site:
http://www.freseniusmedicalcare.co.uk
Sales Range: $50-74.9 Million
Emp.: 25
Dialysis Equipment Mfr & Distr
N.A.I.C.S.: 334510

Subsidiary (Domestic):

**Fresenius Medical Care Renal Ser-
vices Ltd** (2)
Facet Road, Kings Norton, Birmingham,
B38 9PT, Birminghamshire, United
Kingdom
Tel.: (44) 1214864290
Sales Range: $25-49.9 Million
Emp.: 2
Medical Equipment Rental Services
N.A.I.C.S.: 532490

**Fresenius Medical Care Argentina
S.A.** (1)
Arenales 707 3rd floor, C1061AAA, Buenos
Aires, Argentina
Tel.: (54) 1141301000
Web Site:
https://www.freseniusmedicalcare.com.ar
Dialysis Treatment Services
N.A.I.C.S.: 621492

**Fresenius Medical Care Australia
PTY Ltd.** (1)
Level 17 61 Lavender Street Milsons Point,
Sydney, NSW, Australia
Tel.: (61) 2 9466 8000
Web Site:
http://www.freseniusmedicalcare.com.au
Sales Range: $25-49.9 Million
Emp.: 60
Dialysis Equipment Mfr
N.A.I.C.S.: 334510

Division (Domestic):

**Fresenius Medical Care Australia
PTY Ltd. - NephroCare Australia
Division** (2)
Level 17 61 Lavender Street, Milsons Point,
Sydney, 2061, NSW, Australia
Tel.: (61) 294668009
Web Site: http://www.fmc-au.com
Dialysis Equipment Distr
N.A.I.C.S.: 423450

**Fresenius Medical Care Austria
GmbH** (1)
Lundenburgergasse 5, 1210, Vienna, Aus-
tria
Tel.: (43) 12923501
Web Site:
https://www.freseniusmedicalcare.at
Sales Range: $25-49.9 Million
Emp.: 32
Medical & Surgical Equipment Distr
N.A.I.C.S.: 423450

**Fresenius Medical Care BH
d.o.o.** (1)
Zmaja Od Bosne 7-7a, Sarajevo, 71000,
Bosnia & Herzegovina

Tel.: (387) 33559181
Dialysis Treatment Services
N.A.I.C.S.: 621492

Fresenius Medical Care Belgium
N.V.   **(1)**
Boomsesteenweg 939, Wilrijk, 2610, Ant-
werp, Belgium
Tel.: (32) 3238258620
Medical & Surgical Equipment Distr
N.A.I.C.S.: 423450

Fresenius Medical Care CR,
s.r.o.   **(1)**
Evropska 423/178, 160 00, Prague, Czech
Republic
Tel.: (420) 273037900
Web Site:
  https://www.freseniusmedicalcare.cz
Hospital & Medical Supplies Distr
N.A.I.C.S.: 423450

Subsidiary (Non-US):

FMC Magyarorszag Egeszsegugyi
Korlatolt Felelossegu Tarsasag   **(2)**
Szepvolgyi Ut 35-37, Budapest, 1037, Hun-
gary
Tel.: (36) 14392244
Dialysis Center Operator
N.A.I.C.S.: 621492
Attila Berkes *(Gen Mgr)*

Subsidiary (Domestic):

Fresenius Medical Care - DS,
s.r.o.   **(2)**
Evropska 423/178, 160 00, Prague, 6,
Czech Republic
Tel.: (420) 273037900
Web Site: https://www.nephrocare.cz
Medical Supplies Distr
N.A.I.C.S.: 423450
David Prokes *(CEO)*

Fresenius Medical Care Colombia
S.A.   **(1)**
Cra 7 No 1 5 6 - 1 0 Floor 2 6, Bogota,
Colombia
Tel.: (57) 12941400
Web Site:
  https://www.freseniusmedicalcare.com.co
Dialysis Center Operator
N.A.I.C.S.: 621492

Fresenius Medical Care Danmark
A/S   **(1)**
Oldenburg Alle 1, 2630, Taastrup, Denmark
Tel.: (45) 43226100
Web Site:
  https://www.freseniusmedicalcare.dk
Medical Supplies Distr
N.A.I.C.S.: 423450

Fresenius Medical Care Deutschland
GmbH   **(1)**
Frankfurter Str 6-8, St Wendel, Tholey,
66606, Germany
Tel.: (49) 61726090
Web Site: http://www.fmc-ag.com
Sales Range: $400-449.9 Million
Emp.: 1,600
Medicinal Product Mfr
N.A.I.C.S.: 339112

Fresenius Medical Care Deutschland
GmbH   **(1)**
Hafenstrasse 9, 97424, Schweinfurt, Ger-
many
Tel.: (49) 97216780
Sales Range: $200-249.9 Million
Emp.: 1,200
Medicinal Product Mfr
N.A.I.C.S.: 339112

Fresenius Medical Care Groupe
France S.A.S.   **(1)**
Parc Medicis - 47 avenue des Pepinieres,
94832, Fresnes, Cedex, France
Tel.: (33) 149847800
Web Site:
  https://www.freseniusmedicalcare.fr
Medical & Surgical Equipment Distr
N.A.I.C.S.: 423450

Subsidiary (Domestic):

FMC SMAD S.A.S.   **(2)**
ZI de la Ponchonniere 112 Route des glan-

tiers, BP 0106, Savigny, 69591, L'Arbresle,
France
Tel.: (33) 474016000
Web Site: https://www.fmc-smad.com
Sales Range: $75-99.9 Million
Emp.: 40
Medical Instrument Mfr
N.A.I.C.S.: 334510

Fresenius Medical Care Hong Kong
Limited   **(1)**
15th Floor 88 Gloucester Road, Wanchai,
China (Hong Kong)
Tel.: (852) 28982883
Web Site:
  https://www.freseniusmedicalcare.hk
Emp.: 30
Medical & Surgical Equipment Distr
N.A.I.C.S.: 423450
Thorsten Bruce *(Gen Mgr)*

Subsidiary (Domestic):

Biocare Technology Company
Limited   **(2)**
Rm 5101-5123 51/F Sun Hung Kai Ctr 30
Harbour Rd, Wanchai, China (Hong Kong)
Tel.: (852) 28982883
Sales Range: $25-49.9 Million
Emp.: 35
Pharmaceuticals Product Mfr
N.A.I.C.S.: 325412

Fresenius Medical Care India Private
Limited   **(1)**
Ground Floor SAS Tower Medicity Sec-38,
Gurgaon, 122 001, Haryana, India
Tel.: (91) 1246642500
Web Site:
  https://www.freseniusmedicalcare.co.in
Sales Range: $50-74.9 Million
Emp.: 100
Medical & Dialysis Therapy Apparatus Distr
N.A.I.C.S.: 423450
Dhruv Chaturvedi *(Mng Dir)*

Fresenius Medical Care Italia
S.p.A.   **(1)**
Via Crema 8, 26020, Palazzo Pignano, CR,
Italy
Tel.: (39) 03739741
Web Site:
  https://www.freseniusmedicalcare.it
Medical & Surgical Equipment Mfr & Distr
N.A.I.C.S.: 339112

Subsidiary (Domestic):

SIS-TER S.p.A.   **(2)**
Via Crema 8, 26020, Palazzo Pignano, Cre-
mona, Italy
Tel.: (39) 03739771
Sales Range: $25-49.9 Million
Emp.: 250
Medical Application Tubing Set Mfr
N.A.I.C.S.: 339112

Fresenius Medical Care Korea
Ltd.   **(1)**
Yeouido-dong FKI Tower 14th floor Yeoui-
daero, Yeongdeungpo-gu, Seoul, 07320 24,
Korea (South)
Tel.: (82) 221468800
Web Site:
  https://www.freseniusmedicalcare.kr
Sales Range: $50-74.9 Million
Emp.: 200
Medical Device Mfr
N.A.I.C.S.: 339112

Fresenius Medical Care Lebanon
s.a.r.L.   **(1)**
6th Floor Justinien Bldg Street Kantari Sector, Beirut, Lebanon
Tel.: (961) 1744841
Dialysis Instrument Distr
N.A.I.C.S.: 423450

Fresenius Medical Care Ltda.   **(1)**
Rua Roque Gonzales 128, Itapecerica da
Serra, 06855-690, Sao Paulo, Brazil
Tel.: (55) 1121838900
Medical Equipment Mfr & Distr
N.A.I.C.S.: 339112

Fresenius Medical Care Malaysia
Sdn. Bhd.   **(1)**
Second Floor Axis Technology Centre Lot
13 Jalan 51A/225, 46100, Petaling Jaya,
Selangor, Malaysia

Sales Range: $50-74.9 Million
Emp.: 10
Dialysis Machine Supplies Distr
N.A.I.C.S.: 423450

Fresenius Medical Care Maroc
S.A.   **(1)**
33 Bd Moulay Youssef, 20060, Casablanca,
Morocco
Tel.: (212) 522491991
Web Site: https://www.fmcmaroc.com
Dialysis Operator
N.A.I.C.S.: 621492

Fresenius Medical Care Mexico
S.A.   **(1)**
Paseo Del Norte 5300 Guadalajara Tech-
nology Park, 45010, Zapopan, Jalisco,
Mexico
Tel.: (52) 3335404200
Medical Equipment Mfr & Distr
N.A.I.C.S.: 339112

Fresenius Medical Care Nederland
B.V.   **(1)**
Reitscheweg 5, 5232 BX, 's-
Hertogenbosch, Netherlands
Tel.: (31) 88 1223344
Web Site: http://www.fmc.nl
Emp.: 45
Medical Instrument Mfr
N.A.I.C.S.: 334510

Fresenius Medical Care North
America   **(1)**
920 Winter St, Waltham, MA 02451-1457
Tel.: (781) 699-9000
Web Site: https://www.fmcna.com
Sales Range: $250-299.9 Million
Emp.: 1,135
Mfr & Marketer of Artificial Kidney Supplies
& Treatment Centers, Respiratory Therapy
Products Distribution, Infusion Therapy Ser-
vices & Products
N.A.I.C.S.: 621492
Chris Churchill *(Sr VP-Corporate Strategy-
Innovation)*

Fresenius Medical Care Philippines,
Inc.   **(1)**
18F Aeon Centre Alabang-Zapote Road Cor
North Bridgeway Ave, Filinvest Corporate
City Alabang, Muntinlupa, 1781, Philippines
Tel.: (63) 28919575
Web Site:
  https://www.freseniusmedicalcare.ph
Dialysis Treatment & Medical Equipment
Distr
N.A.I.C.S.: 423450

Subsidiary (Domestic):

FMC Renalcare Corp.   **(2)**
2257 Don Chino Roces Avenue Extention,
Makati, 1231, Philippines
Tel.: (63) 28132520
Dialysis Treatment Services
N.A.I.C.S.: 621492
Elena Lam *(Bus Dir)*

Fresenius Medical Care Polska
S.A.   **(1)**
ul Krzywa 13, 60-118, Poznan, Poland
Tel.: (48) 618392600
Pharmaceuticals Product Mfr
N.A.I.C.S.: 325412

Fresenius Medical Care Romania
Srl   **(1)**
Soseaua Bucuresti-Ploiesti no 19-21 Ba-
neasa Business Center floor 3, Sector 1,
Bucharest, Romania
Tel.: (40) 212334268
Dialysis Equipment Distr
N.A.I.C.S.: 423450

Fresenius Medical Care Singapore
Pte. Ltd.   **(1)**
Centennial Tower No3 Temasek Ave #14-03
Centennial Tower, Singapore, 39190, Singa-
pore
Tel.: (65) 67340303
Sales Range: $10-24.9 Million
Emp.: 20
Dialysis Center Operator
N.A.I.C.S.: 621492
Millie Ng *(Mng Dir)*

Fresenius Medical Care Slovenija
d.o.o.   **(1)**

Dobrava 14, 3214, Zrece, Slovenia
Tel.: (386) 37571140
Web Site: https://www.nefrodial.si
Dialysis Center Operator
N.A.I.C.S.: 621492

Subsidiary (Domestic):

NEFRODIAL d.o.o.   **(2)**
Leskovska 29, Krsko, Slovenia
Tel.: (386) 74904250
Emp.: 21
Dialysis Center Operator
N.A.I.C.S.: 621492

Fresenius Medical Care Slovensko,
spol. s.r.o.   **(1)**
Teplicka 99, 921 01, Piestany, Slovakia
Tel.: (421) 337915211
Web Site: http://www.nephrocare.com
Emp.: 25
Dialysis Center Operator
N.A.I.C.S.: 621492

Fresenius Medical Care South Africa
(PTY.) Ltd.   **(1)**
31A Lake Road Longmeadow Business Es-
tate, Edenvale, 1609, South Africa
Tel.: (27) 11 457 9300
Web Site: http://www.nephrocare.co.za
Dialysis Equipment Mfr & Distr
N.A.I.C.S.: 334510

Fresenius Medical Care Sverige
AB   **(1)**
Djupdalsvagen 1, Box 548, 192 05, Sollen-
tuna, Sweden
Tel.: (46) 859477610
Web Site:
  https://www.freseniusmedicalcare.se
Dialysis Center Operator
N.A.I.C.S.: 621492

Fresenius Medical Care Taiwan Co.,
Ltd.   **(1)**
11F-1 51 Jilung Rd Sec 2 Shinyi Chiu, Tai-
pei, Taiwan
Tel.: (886) 227398800
Dialysis Equipment Distr
N.A.I.C.S.: 423450

Subsidiary (Domestic):

Jiate Excelsior Co., Ltd.   **(2)**
16F 6 No 880 Jhongjheng Rd 235,
Zhonghe, Taipei, '23586, Taiwan
Tel.: (886) 423059335
Dialysis Treatment Services
N.A.I.C.S.: 621492

Fresenius Medical Care Ukraine
LLC   **(1)**
str Boryspilska 9 2nd floor, 02099, Kiev,
Ukraine
Tel.: (380) 443695602
Web Site:
  https://www.freseniusmedicalcare.ua
Dialysis Center Operator
N.A.I.C.S.: 621492

Fresenius Medical Care de Venezu-
ela C.A.   **(1)**
Av Libertador Con Calle Cantaura Qta Con-
cepcion, Los Caobos, Caracas, Venezuela
Tel.: (58) 2127315597
Web Site: http://www.fmc-ag.com.ve
Dialysis Center Operating Services
N.A.I.C.S.: 621492

Fresenius Medical Care del Peru
S.A.   **(1)**
Avenida Javier Prado Oeste 2442 -Interior
901 Urb, Orrantia Magdalena Del Mar, 17,
Lima, Peru
Tel.: (51) 13497520
Web Site:
  https://www.freseniusmedicalcare.pe
Dialysis Treatment Services & Equipment
Distr
N.A.I.C.S.: 621492

Fresenius Medikal Hizmetler A.S. **(1)**
Ruzgarlibahce Mah Cumhuriyet Cad Haso-
glu Plaza No 39 Floor 7, Kavacik, 34805,
Istanbul, Turkiye
Tel.: (90) 2123357200
Web Site:
  https://www.freseniusmedicalcare.com.tr
Medical Equipment Distr
N.A.I.C.S.: 423450

Fresenius Medical Care AG—(Continued)

JSC Fresenius SP   (1)
St Gross d 35, Moscow, 115054, Russia
Tel.: (7) 4957896454
Kidney Disease Treatment Services
N.A.I.C.S.: 621492

MVZ Gelsenkirchen-Buer GmbH (1)
Ludwig-Erhard Str 10, Erle, 45891, Gelsenkirchen, Germany
Tel.: (49) 20993350
Web Site: https://www.nephrocare-gelsenkirchen.de
Kidney Disease Treatment Services
N.A.I.C.S.: 621492

Manadialisis S.A.   (1)
Av 6 Calle 16 Y 17, Manta, Ecuador
Tel.: (593) 52625080
Dialysis Equipment Distr
N.A.I.C.S.: 423450

National Medical Care of Spain, S.A.   (1)
Ronda De Poniente 8 Tres Cantos, Madrid, 28760, Spain
Tel.: (34) 913276650
Kidney Dialysis Center Operator
N.A.I.C.S.: 621492

NephroCare (Thailand) Co., Ltd. (1)
62 Lang Suan Rd, Bangkok, 10330, Thailand
Tel.: (66) 26505355
Medical Care Services
N.A.I.C.S.: 622110

NephroCare Portugal S.A.   (1)
Rua Professor Salazar de Sousa Lote 12, 1750-233, Lisbon, Portugal
Tel.: (351) 217501100
Health Care Srvices
N.A.I.C.S.: 621999

Nephrocare Ahrensburg GmbH (1)
Hagener Allee 5, 22926, Ahrensburg, Germany
Tel.: (49) 4102824414
Web Site: https://www.dialyse-ahrensburg.de
Kidney Disease Treatment Services
N.A.I.C.S.: 621492

Nephrocare Berlin-Weissensee GmbH   (1)
An der Industriebahn 28-29, 13088, Berlin, Germany
Tel.: (49) 309238302
Web Site: https://www.nephrocare-berlin-weissensee.de
Kidney Disease Treatment Services
N.A.I.C.S.: 621492

Nephrocare Betzdorf GmbH (1)
Im Hofergarten 1, 57518, Betzdorf, Germany
Tel.: (49) 27413014
Web Site: https://www.nephrocare-betzdorf.de
Kidney Disease Treatment Services
N.A.I.C.S.: 621492

Nephrocare Bielefeld GmbH (1)
Eckendorfer Strasse 91-93, 33609, Bielefeld, Germany
Tel.: (49) 5211360430
Web Site: https://www.nephrocare-bielefeld.de
Kidney Disease Treatment Services
N.A.I.C.S.: 621492

Nephrocare Buchholz GmbH (1)
Dibberser Muhlenweg 1, 21244, Buchholz, Germany
Tel.: (49) 4181360340
Web Site: https://www.nephrocare-buchholz.de
Kidney Disease Treatment Services
N.A.I.C.S.: 621492

Nephrocare Daun GmbH (1)
Freiherr-vom-Stein-Strasse 5, 54550, Daun, Germany
Tel.: (49) 659295050
Web Site: https://www.nephrocare-daun.de
Kidney Disease Treatment Services
N.A.I.C.S.: 621492

Nephrocare Deutschland GmbH (1)
Else-Kroner-Strasse 1, 61352, Bad Homburg, Germany
Tel.: (49) 61726095785
Web Site: https://www.nephrocare.de
Kidney Disease Treatment Services
N.A.I.C.S.: 621492

Nephrocare Dobeln GmbH (1)
Grimmaische Strasse 23, 04720, Dobeln, Germany
Tel.: (49) 343166550
Web Site: https://www.nephrocare-doebeln.de
Kidney Disease Treatment Services
N.A.I.C.S.: 621492

Nephrocare Dortmund GmbH (1)
Karl-Harr-Strasse 1, 44263, Dortmund, Germany
Tel.: (49) 2312865870
Web Site: https://www.nephrocare-dortmund.de
Kidney Disease Treatment Services
N.A.I.C.S.: 621492

Nephrocare Friedberg GmbH (1)
Max-Hogg-Strasse 8, 86316, Friedberg, Germany
Tel.: (49) 821269940
Web Site: https://www.nephrocare-friedberg.de
Kidney Disease Treatment Services
N.A.I.C.S.: 621492

Nephrocare Grevenbroich GmbH (1)
Von-Weth-Strasse 5, 41515, Grevenbroich, Germany
Tel.: (49) 21817828
Web Site: https://www.nephrocare-grevenbroich.de
Kidney Disease Treatment Services
N.A.I.C.S.: 621492

Nephrocare Hagen GmbH (1)
Mittelstrasse 22, Rathausgalerie, 58095, Hagen, Germany
Tel.: (49) 233136750
Web Site: https://www.nephrocare-hagen.de
Kidney Disease Treatment Services
N.A.I.C.S.: 621492

Nephrocare Hamburg-Altona GmbH   (1)
Morkenstrasse 47, 22767, Hamburg, Germany
Tel.: (49) 4041306330
Web Site: https://www.nephrocare-hamburg-altona.de
Kidney Disease Treatment Services
N.A.I.C.S.: 621492

Nephrocare Hamburg-Barmbek GmbH   (1)
Hebebrandstrasse 6, 22297, Hamburg, Germany
Tel.: (49) 4061186010
Web Site: https://www.nephrocare-hamburg-barmbek.de
Kidney Disease Treatment Services
N.A.I.C.S.: 621492

Nephrocare Hamburg-Suderelbe GmbH   (1)
Schwarzenbergstrasse 29, 21073, Hamburg, Germany
Tel.: (49) 407661320
Web Site: https://www.nephrocare-hamburg-suederelbe.de
Medical Care Services
N.A.I.C.S.: 622110

Nephrocare Ingolstadt GmbH (1)
Kipfenberger Strasse 133, 85055, Ingolstadt, Germany
Tel.: (49) 841370080
Web Site: https://www.nephrocare-ingolstadt.de
Kidney Disease Treatment Services
N.A.I.C.S.: 621492

Nephrocare Kaufering GmbH (1)
Viktor-Frankl-Strasse 13, 86916, Kaufering, Germany
Tel.: (49) 819165686
Web Site: https://www.nephrocare-kaufering.de
Kidney Disease Treatment Services
N.A.I.C.S.: 621492

Nephrocare Krefeld GmbH (1)
Diessemer Bruch 79, 47805, Krefeld, Germany
Tel.: (49) 2151843950
Web Site: https://www.nephrocare-krefeld.de
Kidney Disease Treatment Services
N.A.I.C.S.: 621492

Nephrocare Lahr GmbH (1)
Klostenstr 17/1, Schwarzwald, 77933, Lahr, Germany
Tel.: (49) 7821923780
Web Site: https://www.nephrocare-lahr.de
Kidney Disease Treatment Services
N.A.I.C.S.: 621492

Nephrocare Leverkusen GmbH (1)
Am Gesundheitspark 4, 51375, Leverkusen, Germany
Tel.: (49) 214830580
Web Site: https://www.nephrocare-leverkusen.de
Kidney Disease Treatment Services
N.A.I.C.S.: 621492

Nephrocare Ludwigshafen GmbH   (1)
Altriper Strasse 27-31, Mundenheim, 67065, Ludwigshafen, Germany
Tel.: (49) 6215297000
Web Site: https://www.nephrocare-ludwigshafen.de
Kidney Disease Treatment Services
N.A.I.C.S.: 621492

Nephrocare MVZ Aalen GmbH (1)
Im Kalblesrain 2, 73430, Aalen, Germany
Tel.: (49) 7361551900
Web Site: https://www.nephrocare-aalen.de
Kidney Disease Treatment Services
N.A.I.C.S.: 621492

Nephrocare Mettmann GmbH (1)
Gartenstrasse 4-8, 40822, Mettmann, Germany
Tel.: (49) 2104979960
Web Site: https://www.dialyse-mettmann.de
Emp.: 99
Kidney Disease Treatment Services
N.A.I.C.S.: 621492

Nephrocare Muhlhausen GmbH (1)
Martinistrasse 23, 99974, Muhlhausen, Germany
Tel.: (49) 360183550
Web Site: https://www.nephrocare-muehlhausen.de
Kidney Disease Treatment Services
N.A.I.C.S.: 621492

Nephrocare Munchen-Ost GmbH (1)
Medical care centre Rosenkavalierplatz 5, Bogenhausen, 81925, Munich, Germany
Tel.: (49) 894522380
Web Site: https://www.nierenzentrum24.de
Health & Medical Care Services
N.A.I.C.S.: 524114

Nephrocare Munster GmbH (1)
Hohenzollernring 70, 48145, Munster, Germany
Tel.: (49) 251981270
Web Site: https://www.nephrocare-muenster.de
Medical Care Services
N.A.I.C.S.: 622110

Nephrocare Oberhausen GmbH (1)
Blumenthalstrasse 53-55, 46045, Oberhausen, Germany
Tel.: (49) 208200181
Web Site: https://www.nephrocare-oberhausen.de
Kidney Disease Treatment Services
N.A.I.C.S.: 621492

Nephrocare Papenburg GmbH (1)
Hauptkanal rechts 75 b, 26871, Papenburg, Germany
Tel.: (49) 6192240
Web Site: https://www.nephrocare-papenburg.de
Kidney Disease Treatment Services
N.A.I.C.S.: 621492

Nephrocare Pirmasens GmbH (1)
Dr Robert Schelp Square 1, 66953, Pirmasens, Germany
Tel.: (49) 633127050
Web Site: https://www.nephrocare-pirmasens.de
Kidney Disease Treatment Services
N.A.I.C.S.: 621492

Nephrocare Puttlingen GmbH (1)
In der Humes 31, 66346, Puttlingen, Germany
Tel.: (49) 6898690200
Web Site: https://www.nephrocare-puettlingen.de
Kidney Disease Treatment Services
N.A.I.C.S.: 621492

Nephrocare Recklinghausen GmbH   (1)
Rontgenstrasse 33, 45661, Recklinghausen, Germany
Tel.: (49) 2361653370
Web Site: https://www.nephrocare-rooklinghauoon.de
Kidney Disease Treatment Services
N.A.I.C.S.: 621492

Nephrocare Rostock GmbH (1)
Nobelstrasse 53, 18059, Rostock, Germany
Tel.: (49) 381405020
Web Site: https://www.nephrocare-rostock.de
Medical Health Services
N.A.I.C.S.: 621491

Nephrocare Salzgitter GmbH (1)
Kattowitzer Strasse 191 b, 38226, Salzgitter, Germany
Tel.: (49) 534186300
Web Site: https://www.nephrocare-salzgitter.de
Kidney Disease Treatment Services
N.A.I.C.S.: 621492

Nephrocare Schrobenhausen GmbH   (1)
Georg-Alber-Str 3 c, 86529, Schrobenhausen, Germany
Tel.: (49) 8252881490
Web Site: https://www.nephrocare-schrobenhausen.de
Kidney Disease Treatment Services
N.A.I.C.S.: 621492

Nephrocare Schwandorf-Regenstauf GmbH   (1)
Marktplatz 32 Breite Strasse 12, 92421, Schwandorf, Germany
Tel.: (49) 943171520
Medical Health Services
N.A.I.C.S.: 621491

Nephrocare Wetzlar GmbH (1)
Otto-Wels-Strasse 39, Hermannstein, 35586, Wetzlar, Germany
Tel.: (49) 64412043620
Web Site: https://www.nephrocare-wetzlar.de
Kidney Disease Treatment Services
N.A.I.C.S.: 621492

Nephrocare Witten GmbH (1)
Pferdebachstrasse 16, 58455, Witten, Germany
Tel.: (49) 23021522
Web Site: https://www.nephrocare-witten.de
Kidney Disease Treatment Services
N.A.I.C.S.: 621492

Nephrologisch-Internistische Versorgung Ingolstadt GmbH   (1)
Neuburger Strasse 54, 85049, Ingolstadt, Germany
Tel.: (49) 841126040
Web Site: https://www.dialysezentrumingolstadt.de
Kidney Disease Treatment Services
N.A.I.C.S.: 621492

NxStage Medical, Inc.   (1)
350 Merrimack St, Lawrence, MA 01843
Tel.: (978) 687-4700
Web Site: https://www.nxstage.com
End-Stage Renal Disease & Kidney Failure
Medical Device Developer, Mfr & Marketer
N.A.I.C.S.: 334517
Jeffrey H. Burbank *(Founder)*

Subsidiary (Domestic):

NKC Boca Raton, LLC   (2)
350 Merrimack St, Lawrence, MA 01843
Medical Device Mfr & Distr
N.A.I.C.S.: 339113

NxStage Boston North, LLC   (2)
350 Merrimack St, Lawrence, MA 01843-1748

Tel.: (978) 687-4700
Medical Device Mfr & Distr
N.A.I.C.S.: 339113

NxStage Kidney Care, Inc. (2)
12065 Montgomery Rd, Cincinnati, OH
45249
Tel.: (513) 712-1300
Web Site:
http://www.nxstagekidneycare.com
Dialysis Center Operator
N.A.I.C.S.: 621492

NxStage Oak Brook, LLC (2)
1600 16th St W Ste 13, Oak Brook, IL
60523-1302
Tel.: (630) 475-4340
Web Site:
http://www.nxstagekidneycare.com
Medical Device Mfr & Distr
N.A.I.C.S.: 339113

NxStage Orlando North, LLC (2)
174 State Rd 436 D102, Casselberry, FL
32707
Tel.: (407) 754-0338
Web Site:
http://www.nxstagekidneycare.com
Medical Device Mfr & Distr
N.A.I.C.S.: 339113

**OU Fresenius Medical Care
Estonia** (1)
Vaksali 17, 50410, Tartu, Estonia
Tel.: (372) 64 64 144
Web Site: http://www.fresenius.ee
Health Care Srvices
N.A.I.C.S.: 621999

PT FMC Indonesia (1)
Tempo Scan Tower 20th Floor Jl HR Ra-
suna Said Kav 3-4, Jakarta, 12950, Indone-
sia
Tel.: (62) 2129346200
Web Site: http://www.fmc-id.com
Health Care Srvices
N.A.I.C.S.: 621610

ZAO Fresenius SP (1)
20 K 1 Pilyugina Akademika Ul, Moscow,
117630, Russia
Tel.: (7) 4959362344
Health Care Srvices
N.A.I.C.S.: 621999

**Zentrum fur Nieren- und Hoch-
druckkrankheiten Bensheim
GmbH** (1)
Berliner Ring 153, 64625, Bensheim, Ger-
many
Tel.: (49) 625198610
Web Site: https://www.nephrocare-
bensheim.de
Kidney Disease Treatment Services
N.A.I.C.S.: 621492

FRESENIUS SE & CO. KGAA

Else-Kroner-Str 1, 61352, Bad Hom-
burg, Germany
Tel.: (49) 61726080
Web Site: https://www.fresenius.com
Year Founded: 1912
FRE—(DEU)
Rev.: $46,083,564,800
Assets: $88,386,606,880
Liabilities: $52,413,913,760
Net Worth: $35,972,693,120
Earnings: $2,232,940,320
Emp.: 316,078
Fiscal Year-end: 12/31/21
Healtcare Services
N.A.I.C.S.: 551112
Michael Diekmann (Deputy Chm-
Supervisory Bd)

Subsidiaries:

Allgau Resort GmbH (1)
Sebastian-Kneipp-Allee 7, 87730, Bad
Gronenbach, Germany
Tel.: (49) 8334 534 6500
Web Site: https://www.allgaeu-resort.de
Resort Services
N.A.I.C.S.: 721110

Almeda, A.S. (1)
Alsova 462, 277 11, Neratovice, Czech Republic

Tel.: (420) 31 563 7111
Web Site: https://www.nemocnice-
neratovice.cz
Healthcare Sector Services
N.A.I.C.S.: 621999

**Api Betriebs Gemeinnutzige
GmbH** (1)
Mackgasse 7-11, 1230, Vienna, Austria
Tel.: (43) 188010
Web Site: https://www.api.or.at
Rehabilitation Center Services
N.A.I.C.S.: 623220
Benedikt Wildner (Head-Bus Organization)

Avensys UK Ltd. (1)
Frederick Road, Hoo Farm Industrial Estate,
Kidderminster, DY11 7RA, Worcestershire,
United Kingdom
Tel.: (44) 156 274 5858
Web Site:
https://www.avensysmedical.co.uk
Bio-Medical Engineering Equipment Ser-
vices
N.A.I.C.S.: 541715
Robert Strange (CEO)

**Blumauerplatz Beteiligungs-Holding
GmbH** (1)
Rudolfstrasse 53, 4040, Linz, Austria
Tel.: (43) 732700991
Health Care Srvices
N.A.I.C.S.: 541330

Calea Ltd. (1)
2785 Skymark Avenue Unit 2, Mississauga,
L4W 4Y3, ON, Canada (100%)
Tel.: (905) 624-1234
Web Site: https://www.calea.ca
Emp.: 280
Home Health Care
N.A.I.C.S.: 621610

**Centrum Le Cby Pohyboveho
Aparatu, s.r.o.** (1)
Sokolovska 304, 190 61, Prague, Czech
Republic
Tel.: (420) 26 600 6318
Web Site: https://www.clpa-mediterra.cz
General Hospital Services
N.A.I.C.S.: 622110

Fenwal, Inc. (1)
Three Corporate Dr, Lake Zurich, IL 60047
Tel.: (847) 550-2300
Web Site: http://www.fenwalinc.com
Sales Range: $500-549.9 Million
Emp.: 3,500
Manual & Automated Blood Collection &
Processing Products Mfr
N.A.I.C.S.: 334516
Michael Johnson (CFO)

Fresenius Kabi (China) Co., Ltd. (1)
16th Floor Guanjie Building No 1 Building,
No 16 Sungonggong Middle Road Chaoy-
ang District, Beijing, China
Tel.: (86) 1059096800
Healthcare Sector Services
N.A.I.C.S.: 621999

**Fresenius Kabi (Singapore) Pte.
Ltd.** (1)
238A Thomson Road 23-01 Novena Square
Tower A, Singapore, 307684, Singapore
Tel.: (65) 68372552
Healthcare Sector Services
N.A.I.C.S.: 621999

Fresenius Kabi (Thailand) Ltd. (1)
93/1 GPF Witthayu Tower Building B, 10th
Floor Room 1001-1003 Wireless Road
Lumpini Pathum Wan, Bangkok, 10330,
Thailand
Tel.: (66) 20219800
Healthcare Sector Services
N.A.I.C.S.: 621999

Fresenius Kabi AG (1)
Else Kroener Strasse 1, 61352, Bad Hom-
burg, Germany (100%)
Tel.: (49) 61726860
Web Site: http://www.fresenius-kabi.com
Sales Range: $5-14.9 Billion
Emp.: 25,000
Specialty Pharmaceuticals, Infusion &
Transfusion Technology & Ambulatory Care
N.A.I.C.S.: 325412

Subsidiary (US):

APP Pharmaceuticals, Inc. (2)

3 Corporate Dr, Lake Zurich, IL 60047
Tel.: (847) 969-2700
Web Site: http://www.fresenius-kabi.us
Sales Range: $600-649.9 Million
Emp.: 1,375
Injectable Pharmaceutical Products Mfr
N.A.I.C.S.: 325412
Bernhard Hampl (Chm)

Subsidiary (Non-US):

**Beijing Fresenius Pharmaceutical
Co., Ltd.** (2)
16F GrandyVic Building No 16 Taiyanggong
Mid Street, Chaoyang District, Beijing,
100028, China
Tel.: (86) 1059096999
Web Site: http://www.fresenius-kabi.com
Pharmaceuticals
N.A.I.C.S.: 325412

Fresenius HemoCare Italia S.r.l (2)
Via Santi 293, 37063, Modena, Italy
Tel.: (39) 0535 45411
Web Site: http://www.fresenius-kabi.com
Sales Range: $50-74.9 Million
Emp.: 170
Pharmaceuticals
N.A.I.C.S.: 325412

**Fresenius HemoCare Netherlands
B.V.** (2)
Runde ZZ 41, Emmer-Compascuum, Em-
men, 7881HM, Netherlands
Tel.: (31) 591355700
Web Site: http://www.freseniuskabi.com
Sales Range: $200-249.9 Million
Emp.: 600
Medical Products
N.A.I.C.S.: 423450

Subsidiary (Domestic):

**Fresenius Hemocare Deutschland
GmbH** (2)
Else-Kroner-Strasse 1, 61352, Bad Hom-
burg, Germany
Tel.: (49) 61726860
Web Site: http://www.fresenius.com
Sales Range: $400-449.9 Million
Emp.: 5,000
Pharmaceuticals
N.A.I.C.S.: 325412

Subsidiary (Non-US):

Fresenius Kabi (Schweiz) AG (2)
Am Mattenhof 4, 6010, Kriens, Switzerland
Tel.: (41) 41 552 7000
Web Site: https://www.fresenius-kabi.com
Sales Range: $25-49.9 Million
Emp.: 50
Pharmaceuticals
N.A.I.C.S.: 325412

Fresenius Kabi AB (2)
Rapsgatan 7, 751 74, Uppsala, Sweden
Tel.: (46) 1 864 4000
Web Site: https://www.fresenius-kabi.com
Emp.: 1,100
Pharmaceuticals
N.A.I.C.S.: 325412

Fresenius Kabi Argentina SA (2)
Av Cabildo 2677 Piso 10, C1428AAU, Bue-
nos Aires, Argentina
Tel.: (54) 1147894000
Web Site: http://www.fresenius-kabi.com.ar
Pharmaceuticals
N.A.I.C.S.: 325412

**Fresenius Kabi Asia-Pacific
Limited** (2)
Room 5001-27 50/F Sun Hung Kai Centre
30 Harbour Road, Wanchai, China (Hong
Kong)
Tel.: (852) 2 152 1300
Web Site: http://www.fresenius-kabi.com
Pharmaceuticals Product Mfr
N.A.I.C.S.: 325412

Fresenius Kabi Austria GmbH (2)
Hafnerstrasse 36, 8055, Graz, Austria
Tel.: (43) 316 2490
Web Site: http://www.fresenius-kabi.com
Sales Range: $100-124.9 Million
Emp.: 500
Pharmaceuticals
N.A.I.C.S.: 325412

Fresenius Kabi Brazil Ltda. (2)
Av Marginal Projetada 1652 G1, Tambore,
06464-200, Barueri, Sao Paulo, Brazil
Tel.: (55) 1125041400
Web Site: http://www.fresenius-kabi.com
Pharmaceuticals
N.A.I.C.S.: 325412

Fresenius Kabi Canada Ltd. (2)
165 Galaxy Blvd Suite 100, Toronto, M9W
0C8, ON, Canada
Tel.: (905) 770-3711
Web Site: https://www.fresenius-kabi.com
Emp.: 100
Injectable Pharmaceuticals Mfr
N.A.I.C.S.: 424210

Subsidiary (Domestic):

**Fresenius Kabi Deutschland
GmbH** (2)
Else-Kroner-Strasse 1, 61352, Bad Hom-
burg, Germany (100%)
Tel.: (49) 6 172 6860
Web Site: https://www.fresenius-kabi.com
Sales Range: $50-74.9 Million
Emp.: 200
Patient-infusions for Parenteral Nutrition
N.A.I.C.S.: 325412

Subsidiary (Non-US):

Fresenius Kabi Espana S.A. (2)
Marina 16-18, Torre Mapfre-Vila Olimpica,
08005, Barcelona, Spain
Tel.: (34) 932256565
Web Site: http://www.fresenius-kabi.com
Pharmaceuticals
N.A.I.C.S.: 325412

Fresenius Kabi France S.A.S. (2)
5 place du Marivel, 92316, Sevres, Cedex,
France
Tel.: (33) 14 114 2600
Web Site: http://www.fresenius-kabi.fr
Sales Range: $200-249.9 Million
Emp.: 600
Pharmaceuticals
N.A.I.C.S.: 325412

Fresenius Kabi Italia S.r.l. (2)
Via Camagre 41, Isola della Scala, 37063,
Verona, Italy
Tel.: (39) 045 664 9311
Web Site: http://www.fresenius-kabi.com
Pharmaceuticals
N.A.I.C.S.: 325412

Fresenius Kabi Korea Ltd. (2)
17th floor IT Venture Tower East Building
135 Jung-daero, Songpa-Gu, Seoul, 138-
950, Korea (South)
Tel.: (82) 23 484 0900
Web Site: http://www.fresenius-kabi.co.kr
Sales Range: $25-49.9 Million
Emp.: 100
Pharmaceuticals
N.A.I.C.S.: 325412
Noah Park (Pres & CEO)

Fresenius Kabi Ltd. (2)
Cestrian Court Eastgate Way, Manor Park,
Runcorn, WA7 1NT, United Kingdom
Tel.: (44) 192 853 3533
Web Site: http://www.fresenius-kabi.com
Pharmaceuticals
N.A.I.C.S.: 325412

**Fresenius Kabi Mexico S.A. de
C.V.** (2)
Paseo del Norte 5300A Guadalajara Tech-
nology Park, Carrtera a Nogales Km 125,
45010, Zapopan, Jalisco, Mexico
Tel.: (52) 3335407800
Web Site: http://www.fresenius-kabi.com
Pharmaceuticals
N.A.I.C.S.: 325412

Fresenius Kabi Norge A.S. (2)
Tel.: (47) 2 258 8000
Web Site: http://www.fresenius-kabi.com
Sales Range: $25-49.9 Million
Emp.: 14
Pharmaceuticals
N.A.I.C.S.: 325412

Fresenius Kabi Oncology Limited (2)
Plot No 11 Sector 32, Echelon Institutional
Area, Gurgaon, 122001, Haryana, India
Tel.: (91) 124 488 5000

Fresenius SE & Co. KGaA—(Continued)

Web Site: https://www.fresenius-kabi-
oncology.com
Sales Range: $75-99.9 Million
Emp.: 400
Cancer Pharmaceuticals Researcher Mfr
N.A.I.C.S.: 325412
Rakesh Bhargava (Chm)

Fresenius Kabi Polska Sp z.o.o. **(2)**
Al Jerozolimskie 134, 02-305, Warsaw, Po-
land
Tel.: (48) 22 345 6789
Web Site: http://www.fresenius-kabi.com
Sales Range: $25-49.9 Million
Emp.: 90
Pharmaceuticals
N.A.I.C.S.: 325412
Maciej Chmielowski (Mng Dir)

Fresenius Kabi South Africa (Pty)
Ltd. **(2)**
Tel.: (27) 11 545 0000
Web Site: https://www.fresenius-kabi.com
Sales Range: $50-74.9 Million
Emp.: 203
Pharmaceuticals
N.A.I.C.S.: 325412

Labesfal Laboratorios Almiro S.A **(2)**
Zona Industrial do Lagedo, Santiago de
Besteiros, 3465-157, Tondela, Campo de
Besteiros, Portugal
Tel.: (351) 232831100
Web Site: http://www.labesfalgenericos.pt
Sales Range: $100-124.9 Million
Emp.: 400
Pharmaceuticals
N.A.I.C.S.: 325412

Pharmatel Fresenius Kabi Pty
Ltd. **(2)**
6/6-18 Bridge Street, Hornsby, 2077, NSW,
Australia
Tel.: (61) 294722222
Web Site: http://www.pfk.com.au
Pharmaceuticals
N.A.I.C.S.: 325412

Joint Venture (Non-US):

Sino-Swed Pharmaceutical Corp.,
Ltd. **(2)**
Unit 1801-1805 China Resources Building,
No 8 Jianguomenbei Avenue, Beijing,
100005, China
Tel.: (86) 1065189090
Web Site: http://www.sspc.com.cn
Sales Range: $250-299.9 Million
Emp.: 1,000
Parenteral Nutrition, Enteral Nutrition & Ap-
plication Device Mfr; Owned 51% by Frese-
nius SE & 49% by China National Pharma-
ceutical Group Corporation (SINOPHARM)
N.A.I.C.S.: 325411

Fresenius Kabi Australia Pty
Limited **(1)**
PO Box 580, North Ryde, 1670, NSW, Aus-
tralia
Tel.: (61) 293915555
Healthcare Sector Services
N.A.I.C.S.: 621999

Fresenius Kabi Bidiphar JSC **(1)**
19th Floor Habourview 35 35 Hue Hue, Dis-
trict 1, Ho Chi Minh City, Vietnam
Tel.: (84) 2839142541
Healthcare Sector Services
N.A.I.C.S.: 621999

Fresenius Kabi Brasil Ltda. **(1)**
Marginal Projected Avenue 1652 Tambore
Farm, Barueri, 06460-200, Brazil
Tel.: (55) 1125041400
Healthcare Sector Services
N.A.I.C.S.: 621999

Fresenius Kabi Bulgaria EOOD **(1)**
1 Alexander Zhendov Str Fl 6 ap 37, 1113,
Sofia, Bulgaria
Tel.: (359) 29710263
Web Site: https://www.fresenius-kabi.com
Healthcare Sector Services
N.A.I.C.S.: 621999

Fresenius Kabi Chile Ltda. **(1)**
Carlos Fernadez Concha 244, San Joaquin,
Santiago, Chile

Tel.: (56) 224627000
Healthcare Sector Services
N.A.I.C.S.: 621999

Fresenius Kabi Colombia S.A.S. **(1)**
Carrera 7 155 C - 20 Floor 40 E North
Point Tower, Bogota, Colombia
Tel.: (57) 15717560404
Web Site: https://www.fresenius-kabi.com
Healthcare Sector Services
N.A.I.C.S.: 621999

Fresenius Kabi Danmark A / S **(1)**
Islands Brygge 57, 2300, Copenhagen,
Denmark
Tel.: (45) 33181600
Web Site: https://www.fresenius-kabi.com
Healthcare Sector Services
N.A.I.C.S.: 621999

Fresenius Kabi Hong Kong
Limited **(1)**
5001-5027 50/F Sun Hung Kai Center 30
Harbour Road, Wanchai, China (Hong
Kong)
Tel.: (852) 21761912
Healthcare Sector Services
N.A.I.C.S.: 621999

Fresenius Kabi Hungary Kft. **(1)**
Szepvolgyi ut 6 3rd Floor, 1025, Budapest,
Hungary
Tel.: (36) 612508371
Healthcare Sector Services
N.A.I.C.S.: 621999

Fresenius Kabi Ilac San. ve Tic. Ltd.
Sti. **(1)**
Eski Buyukdere Cad Guney Plaza K 2,
Maslak, 34398, Istanbul, Türkiye
Tel.: (90) 2123655656
Healthcare Sector Services
N.A.I.C.S.: 621999

Fresenius Kabi India Pvt. Ltd. **(1)**
Fifth Floor A Wing Ashoka Plaza Pune-
Nagar Road Survey No 32/2, Vadgaon
Sheri Viman Nagar, Pune, 411 014, India
Tel.: (91) 20266347017
Healthcare Sector Services
N.A.I.C.S.: 621999

Fresenius Kabi Japan K.K. **(1)**
3-13-1 Toranomon Toranomon 40MT Build-
ing 3F, Minato-ku, Tokyo, 105-0001, Japan
Tel.: (81) 364357614
Healthcare Sector Services
N.A.I.C.S.: 621999

Fresenius Kabi Logistik GmbH **(1)**
Freseniusstrasse 1, 61169, Friedberg, Ger-
many
Tel.: (49) 61726866205
Medical Transfusion Services
N.A.I.C.S.: 524114

Fresenius Kabi Malaysia Sdn.
Bhd. **(1)**
3-1 and 3-2 Axis Technology Centre Lot 13
Jalan 51A/225, 46100, Petaling Jaya, Se-
langor, Malaysia
Tel.: (60) 379572929
Healthcare Sector Services
N.A.I.C.S.: 621999

Fresenius Kabi MedTech Services
GmbH **(1)**
Am Neuen Berg 8, 63755, Alzenau, Ger-
many
Tel.: (49) 602397220
Marine Surveyor Services
N.A.I.C.S.: 541990

Fresenius Kabi NV/SA **(1)**
Brandekensweg 9, 2627, Schelle, Belgium
Tel.: (32) 38807300
Web Site: https://www.fresenius-kabi.com
Healthcare Sector Services
N.A.I.C.S.: 621999

Fresenius Kabi Nederland B.V. **(1)**
Amersfoortseweg 10e, 3712 BC, Huissen,
Netherlands
Tel.: (31) 306985270
Healthcare Sector Services
N.A.I.C.S.: 621999

Fresenius Kabi New Zealand
Limited **(1)**
60 Pavilion Drive, Mangere, Auckland,
2022, New Zealand

Tel.: (64) 99252721
Web Site: https://www.fresenius-kabi.com
Healthcare Sector Services
N.A.I.C.S.: 621999

Fresenius Kabi Norway AS **(1)**
Gjerdrums vei 10A, 0484, Oslo, Norway
Tel.: (47) 22588000
Web Site: https://www.fresenius-kabi.com
Healthcare Sector Services
N.A.I.C.S.: 621999

Fresenius Kabi Pharma Portugal,
Lda. **(1)**
Av Forte 3 - Building Sweden IV - Floor 3,
2794-039, Carnaxide, Portugal
Tel.: (351) 214241280
Healthcare Sector Services
N.A.I.C.S.: 621999

Fresenius Kabi Philippines, Inc. **(1)**
Units A and B 18th Floor Aeon Center,
North Bridgeway Avenue Corner Alabang-
Zapote Road Alabang, Muntinlupa, 1781,
Philippines
Tel.: (63) 28896492
Healthcare Sector Services
N.A.I.C.S.: 621999

Fresenius Kabi S.A. **(1)**
Stand 7 Growthpoint Park 2 Tonetti Street,
Midrand, 1682, South Africa
Tel.: (27) 11545007234
Healthcare Sector Services
N.A.I.C.S.: 621999

Fresenius Kabi Scientific Office
Egypt, Lda. **(1)**
9 Ebad El Rahman Street Plot 1142
Sheraton Heliopolis Area, Cairo, Egypt
Tel.: (20) 222676634
Healthcare Sector Services
N.A.I.C.S.: 621999

Fresenius Kabi USA, LLC **(1)**
3 Corporate Dr, Lake Zurich, IL 60047
Tel.: (847) 550-2300
Web Site: https://www.fresenius-kabi.com
N.A.I.C.S.: 325412

Fresenius Kabi d.o.o. **(1)**
Mechanical Road 20, 10000, Zagreb, Croa-
tia
Tel.: (385) 12333242
Healthcare Sector Services
N.A.I.C.S.: 621999

Fresenius Kabi s.r.o. **(1)**
Na strzi 1702/65, Nusle, 140 00, Prague,
Czech Republic
Tel.: (420) 225270111
Web Site: https://www.fresenius-kabi.com
Healthcare Sector Services
N.A.I.C.S.: 621999

Fresenius Netcare GmbH **(1)**
Else-Kroner-Str 1, 61352, Bad Homburg,
Germany
Tel.: (49) 6172 608 0
Web Site: http://www.fresenius-netcare.com
Sales Range: $75-99.9 Million
Emp.: 500
IT Services
N.A.I.C.S.: 541512
Jurgen Gotz (Member-Mgmt Bd)

Fresenius Vial S.A.S. **(1)**
Le Grand Chemin, 38590, Brezins, France
Tel.: (33) 47 667 1111
Web Site: http://www.fresenius-kabi.com
Sales Range: $125-149.9 Million
Emp.: 300
Pharmaceuticals
N.A.I.C.S.: 325412

Gmundnerberg Holding GmbH **(1)**
Hartlgasse 4, Bad Sauerbrunn, 7202, Mat-
tersburg, Austria
Tel.: (43) 26253000
Project & Provide Services
N.A.I.C.S.: 541330

H.C. Hospital Consulting S.p.A **(1)**
Via di Scolivigne 60/1-Localita Grassina,
50012, Bagno a Ripoli, FI, Italy
Tel.: (39) 05 564 9851
Web Site: https://www.hospital-consulting.it
Project & Provide Services
N.A.I.C.S.: 541330

HELIOS Kliniken GmbH **(1)**

Friedrichstr 136, 10117, Berlin, Germany
Tel.: (49) 30 521 3210
Web Site: https://www.helios-gesundheit.de
Sales Range: $1-4.9 Billion
Emp.: 32,000
Pharmaceuticals
N.A.I.C.S.: 325412

Subsidiary (Domestic):

Amper Kliniken AG **(2)**
Krankenhausstrasse 15, 85221, Dachau,
Germany
Tel.: (49) 813 1760
Web Site: http://www.amperkliniken.de
Sales Range: $300-349.9 Million
Emp.: 1,200
General Medical & Surgical Hospitals
N.A.I.C.S.: 561499
Uwe Schmid (Mng Dir)

Aukamm Klinik fur operative Rheu-
matologie und orthopadie GmbH **(2)**
Leibnizstrasse 21, 65191, Wiesbaden, Ger-
many
Tel.: (49) 611 5720
Sales Range: $10-24.9 Million
Emp.: 70
General Medical & Surgical Hospitals
N.A.I.C.S.: 622110

Fachkrankenhaus fur Psychiatrie und
Neurologie Hildburghausen
GmbH **(2)**
Eisfelder Strasse 41, 98646, Hild-
burghausen, Germany
Tel.: (49) 3 685 7760
General Medical & Surgical Hospitals
N.A.I.C.S.: 622110

Frankenwaldklinik Kronach
GmbH **(2)**
Friesener Strasse 41, 96317, Kronach, Ger-
many
Tel.: (49) 926 1590
Web Site: https://www.frankenwaldklinik.de
Sales Range: $100-124.9 Million
Emp.: 570
Specialty Hospitals
N.A.I.C.S.: 622310

HELIOS Klinik Wesermarsch
GmbH **(2)**
Mildred-Scheel-Str 1, 26954, Nordenham,
Germany
Tel.: (49) 473136900
Web Site: https://www.helios-gesundheit.de
General Hospitality Services
N.A.I.C.S.: 622110

HELIOS Klinikum Pforzheim
GmbH **(2)**
Chancellor Street 2-6, 75175, Pforzheim,
Germany
Tel.: (49) 72319690
Web Site: https://www.helios-gesundheit.de
Sales Range: $200-249.9 Million
Emp.: 1,190
General Medical & Surgical Hospitals
N.A.I.C.S.: 622110

HELIOS Klinikum Pirna GmbH **(2)**
Struppener Strasse 13, 1796, Pirna, Ger-
many
Tel.: (49) 350171180
Web Site: https://www.helios-gesundheit.de
Emp.: 800
Health Care Srvices
N.A.I.C.S.: 621999

HELIOS Klinikum Warburg
GmbH **(2)**
Huffertstrasse 50, 34414, Warburg, Ger-
many
Tel.: (49) 5641910
Web Site: https://www.helios-gesundheit.de
General Hospitality Services
N.A.I.C.S.: 622110
Thomas Hoffmann (Gen Mgr)

HELIOS Weisseritztal-Kliniken
GmbH **(2)**
Burgerstrasse 7, 1705, Freital, Germany
Tel.: (49) 35164660
Web Site: https://www.helios-gesundheit.de
General Hospitality Services
N.A.I.C.S.: 622110

Herzzentrum Leipzig Gmbh **(2)**

Strumpellstrasse 39, 04289, Leipzig, Germany
Tel.: (49) 3418650
Web Site: http://www.rhoen-klinikum-ag.com
General Medical & Surgical Hospitals
N.A.I.C.S.: 622110

KDI Klinikservice GmbH **(2)**
Krankenhausstrasse 15, 85221, Dachau, Germany
Tel.: (49) 813176540
Health Care Clinical Services
N.A.I.C.S.: 621498

Klinik Hildesheimer Land GmbH **(2)**
An Der Peesel 6, 31162, Bad Salzdetfurth, Germany
Tel.: (49) 50634701
Sales Range: $25-49.9 Million
Emp.: 19
Health Care Srvices
N.A.I.C.S.: 621999
Erk Scheel *(Gen Mgr)*

Klinik Kipfenberg GmbH **(2)**
Kindinger Strasse 13, 85110, Kipfenberg, Germany
Tel.: (49) 84651750
Web Site: http://www.neurologie-kipfenberg.de
Sales Range: $50-74.9 Million
Emp.: 550
General Medical & Surgical Hospitals
N.A.I.C.S.: 327910
Rainer Meinhardt *(Gen Mgr)*

Klinik fur Herzchirurgie Karlsruhe GmbH **(2)**
Franz-Lust-Strasse 30, 76185, Karlsruhe, Germany
Tel.: (49) 72197380
Web Site: http://www.herzchirurgie-karlsruhe.de
Sales Range: $125-149.9 Million
Emp.: 300
General Medical & Surgical Hospitals
N.A.I.C.S.: 327910
Ulrike Vogg *(Mng Dir)*

Kliniken Herzberg und Osterode GmbH **(2)**
Dr - Frossel-Allee, 37412, Herzberg, Germany
Tel.: (49) 5 521 8660
General Medical & Surgical Hospitals
N.A.I.C.S.: 622110

Kliniken Miltenberg-Erlenbach GmbH **(2)**
Krankenhausstrasse 45, Erlenbach a Main, 63906, Erlenbach, Germany
Tel.: (49) 9 372 7000
General Medical & Surgical Hospitals
N.A.I.C.S.: 926130

Kliniken Munchen Pasing und Perlach GmbH **(2)**
Steinerweg 5, 81241, Munich, Germany
Tel.: (49) 8988920
Web Site: http://www.rhoen-klinikum-ag.com
Sales Range: $150-199.9 Million
Emp.: 1,000
General Medical & Surgical Hospitals
N.A.I.C.S.: 562998

Klinikum Gifhorn GmbH **(2)**
Campus 6, 38518, Gifhorn, Germany
Tel.: (49) 5371870
Web Site: https://www.helios-gesundheit.de
Sales Range: $100-124.9 Million
Emp.: 800
Health Care Srvices
N.A.I.C.S.: 621999
Dieter Kaffke *(Gen Mgr)*

Klinikum Hildesheim GmbH **(2)**
Weinberg 1, 31134, Hildesheim, Germany
Tel.: (49) 512 1890
Web Site: http://www.stk-hildesheim.de
Sales Range: $200-249.9 Million
Emp.: 1,000
General Medical & Surgical Hospitals
N.A.I.C.S.: 327910

Klinikum Meinigen GmbH **(2)**
Bergstrasse 3, 98617, Meiningen, Germany
Tel.: (49) 369 3900
Web Site: http://www.klinikum-meiningen.de
General Medical & Surgical Hospitals
N.A.I.C.S.: 622110

Klinikum Salzgitter GmbH **(2)**
Kattowitzer Strasse 191, 38226, Salzgitter, Germany
Tel.: (49) 5 341 8350
General Medical & Surgical Hospitals
N.A.I.C.S.: 622110

Klinikum Uelzen GmbH **(2)**
Hagenskamp 34, 29525, Uelzen, Germany
Tel.: (49) 581830
Web Site: https://www.helios-gesundheit.de
Hospital Management Services
N.A.I.C.S.: 622110
Franz Caesar *(Gen Mgr)*

Krankenhaus Kothen GmbH **(2)**
Hallesche Strasse 29, 06366, Kothen, Germany
Tel.: (49) 3496520
General Hospitality Services
N.A.I.C.S.: 622110

Krankenhaus St. Barbara Attendorn GmbH **(2)**
Hohler Weg 9, 57439, Attendorn, Germany
Tel.: (49) 2722600
General Medical & Surgical Hospitals
N.A.I.C.S.: 622110

MVZ Management GmbH Attendorn **(2)**
Hohler Weg 9, 57439, Attendorn, Germany
Tel.: (49) 2722 3920
Medical Care Services
N.A.I.C.S.: 621999

MVZ Management GmbH Baden-Wurttemberg **(2)**
Kanzlerstr 2-6, Pforzheim, 75175, Germany
Tel.: (49) 7231 9690
Web Site: http://www.Klinikum-Pforzheim.de
Emp.: 5
General Hospitality Services
N.A.I.C.S.: 622110
Koji Tanabe *(Gen Mgr)*

MVZ Management GmbH Sud **(2)**
Salzburger Leite 1, 97616, Bad Neustadt an der Saale, Germany
Tel.: (49) 9771 650
Medical Care Services
N.A.I.C.S.: 621999
Robert Kortic *(Gen Mgr)*

St. Elisabeth-Krankenhaus GmbH **(2)**
Kissinger Strasse 150, 97688, Bad Kissingen, Germany
Tel.: (49) 9718050
Web Site: http://www.elisabeth-online.de
Sales Range: $50-74.9 Million
Emp.: 300
General Medical & Surgical Hospitals
N.A.I.C.S.: 622110

Stadtisches Krankenhaus Wittingen GmbH **(2)**
Gustav-Dobberkau-Strasse 5, 29378, Wittingen, Germany
Tel.: (49) 5831220
Web Site: http://www.krankenhaus-wittingen.de
Sales Range: $25-49.9 Million
Emp.: 20
General Medical & Surgical Hospitals
N.A.I.C.S.: 327910
Franz Caesar *(Gen Mgr)*

Stiftung Deutsche Klinik fur Diagnostik GmbH **(2)**
Aukammallee 33, Wiesbaden, 65191, Germany
Tel.: (49) 6115770
Web Site: http://www.dkd-wiesbaden.de
Sales Range: $50-74.9 Million
Emp.: 500
General Medical & Surgical Hospitals
N.A.I.C.S.: 622110
Garissen Beate *(Gen Mgr)*

VAMED Leben am Rosenberg Kronach GmbH **(2)**
Friesener Str 41, 96317, Kronach, Germany
Tel.: (49) 9261596701
Sales Range: $10-24.9 Million
Emp.: 25
Nursing Home Operating Services
N.A.I.C.S.: 621610
Robert Kordic *(Gen Mgr)*

Heilbad Sauerbrunn Betriebsgesellschaft m.b.H. **(1)**
Hartiggasse 4, Bad Sauerbrunn, 7202, Mattersburg, Austria
Tel.: (43) 2625 300 8100
Web Site: https://www.heilbad-sauerbrunn.at
Restaurant Services
N.A.I.C.S.: 722511

Helios Agnes-Karll Krankenhaus GmbH **(1)**
Am Hochkamp 21, 23611, Bad Schwartau, Germany
Tel.: (49) 45120070
Surgical Therapy Medical Operator
N.A.I.C.S.: 622110

Helios Aukamm-Klinik Wiesbaden GmbH **(1)**
Leibnizstrasse 21, 65191, Wiesbaden, Germany
Tel.: (49) 6115720
Health & Medical Care Services
N.A.I.C.S.: 524114

Helios Bordeklinik GmbH **(1)**
Kreiskrankenhaus 4, 39387, Oschersleben, Germany
Tel.: (49) 39499350
Health & Medical Care Services
N.A.I.C.S.: 524114

Helios Fachklinik Vogelsang-Gommern GmbH **(1)**
Sophie-von-Boetticher-Strasse 1, Vogelsang, 39245, Gommern, Germany
Tel.: (49) 3920060
Health & Medical Care Services
N.A.I.C.S.: 524114

Helios Fachkliniken Hildburghausen GmbH **(1)**
Eisfelder Strasse 41, 98646, Hildburghausen, Germany
Tel.: (49) 36857760
Surgical Therapy Medical Operator
N.A.I.C.S.: 622110

Helios Frankenwaldklinik Kronach GmbH **(1)**
Friesener Strasse 41, 96317, Kronach, Germany
Tel.: (49) 9261590
Surgical Therapy Medical Operator
N.A.I.C.S.: 622110

Helios Hanseklinikum Stralsund GmbH **(1)**
Grosse Parower Strasse 47-53, 18435, Stralsund, Germany
Tel.: (49) 3831350
Surgical Therapy Medical Operator
N.A.I.C.S.: 622110

Helios Health GmbH **(1)**
Friedrichstrasse 136, 10117, Berlin, Germany
Tel.: (49) 305213210
Web Site: https://www.helios-health.com
Emp.: 120
Health Care System Consulting Services
N.A.I.C.S.: 524114

Helios Klinik Bad Berleburg GmbH **(1)**
An der Gontardslust 7, Bad Berleburg, 57319, Siegen, Germany
Tel.: (49) 27518020
Rehabilitation Center Services
N.A.I.C.S.: 623220

Helios Klinik Bad Ems GmbH **(1)**
Viktoriaallee 27, 56130, Bad Ems, Germany
Tel.: (49) 26039780
Rehabilitation Center Services
N.A.I.C.S.: 623220

Helios Klinik Blankenhain GmbH **(1)**
Wirthstrasse 5, 99444, Blankenhain, Germany
Tel.: (49) 3645950
Health Care System Consulting Services
N.A.I.C.S.: 524114

Helios Klinik Bleicherode GmbH **(1)**
Barbarastrasse 11, 99752, Bleicherode, Germany
Tel.: (49) 36338650
Orthopaedics & Spinal Surgery Services
N.A.I.C.S.: 622110

Helios Klinik Herzberg/Osterode GmbH **(1)**
Dr -Frossel-Allee 1, 37412, Herzberg am Harz, Germany
Tel.: (49) 55218660
Vascular Surgery Services
N.A.I.C.S.: 541940

Helios Klinik Jerichower Land GmbH **(1)**
August-Bebel-Strasse 55a, 39288, Burg, Germany
Tel.: (49) 3921960
Emp.: 400
Surgery Medical Education Services
N.A.I.C.S.: 622110

Helios Klinik Kothen GmbH **(1)**
Hallesche Strasse 29, 6366, Kothen, Germany
Tel.: (49) 3496520
Emp.: 430
Surgical Therapy Medical Operator
N.A.I.C.S.: 622110

Helios Klinik Leezen GmbH **(1)**
Wittgensteiner Platz 1, 19067, Leezen, Germany
Tel.: (49) 3866600
Emp.: 500
Neurological Surgery Services
N.A.I.C.S.: 622310

Helios Klinik Leisnig GmbH **(1)**
Colditzer Strasse 48, 04703, Leisnig, Germany
Tel.: (49) 3432180
Emp.: 80
Wound Patients Care Services
N.A.I.C.S.: 622310

Helios Klinik Lengerich GmbH **(1)**
Martin-Luther-Strasse 49, 49525, Lengerich, Germany
Tel.: (49) 54818010
Surgical Therapy Medical Operator
N.A.I.C.S.: 622110

Helios Klinik Rottweil GmbH **(1)**
Krankenhausstrasse 30, 78628, Rottweil, Germany
Tel.: (49) 7414760
Surgical Therapy Medical Operator
N.A.I.C.S.: 622110

Helios Klinik Schkeuditz GmbH **(1)**
Leipziger Strasse 45, 04435, Schkeuditz, Germany
Tel.: (49) 34204800
Health Care System Consulting Services
N.A.I.C.S.: 524114

Helios Klinik Schleswig GmbH **(1)**
St Jurgener Str 1-3, 24837, Schleswig, Germany
Tel.: (49) 46218120
Medical Education Training Services
N.A.I.C.S.: 622110

Helios Klinik Wipperfurth GmbH **(1)**
Alte Kolner Strasse 9, 51688, Wipperfurth, Germany
Tel.: (49) 22678890
Medical Education Training Services
N.A.I.C.S.: 622110

Helios Klinik Zerbst/Anhalt GmbH **(1)**
Friedrich-Naumann-Strasse 53, 39261, Zerbst, Germany
Tel.: (49) 39237390
Health & Medical Care Services
N.A.I.C.S.: 524114

Helios Kliniken Breisgau Hochschwarzwald GmbH **(1)**
Heliosweg 79, 79379, Mullheim, Germany
Tel.: (49) 7667840
Pharmaceutical Mfr & Distr
N.A.I.C.S.: 325412

Helios Kliniken Mansfeld-Sudharz GmbH **(1)**
Am Beinschuh 2a, 06526, Sangerhausen, Germany
Tel.: (49) 3464660
Medical Education Training Services
N.A.I.C.S.: 622110

Helios Kliniken Mittelweser GmbH **(1)**

Fresenius SE & Co. KGaA—(Continued)

Ziegelkampstr 39, 31582, Nienburg, Germany
Tel.: (49) 502192100
Hospital Services
N.A.I.C.S.: 622110

Helios Klinikum Aue GmbH (1)
Gartenstrasse 6, 08280, Aue, Germany
Tel.: (49) 3771580
Medical Education Training Services
N.A.I.C.S.: 622110

Helios Klinikum Bad Saarow GmbH (1)
Pleskower Strasse 33, 15526, Bad Saarow, Germany
Tel.: (49) 3363170
Medical Education Training Services
N.A.I.C.S.: 622110

Helios Klinikum Berlin-Buch GmbH (1)
Schwanebecker Chaussee 50, 13125, Berlin, Germany
Tel.: (49) 3094010
Health & Medical Care Services
N.A.I.C.S.: 524114

Helios Klinikum Erfurt GmbH (1)
Nordhauser Strasse 74, 99089, Erfurt, Germany
Tel.: (49) 3617810
Medical Education Services
N.A.I.C.S.: 622110

Helios Klinikum Gifhorn GmbH (1)
Campus 6, 38518, Gifhorn, Germany
Tel.: (49) 5371870
Medical Education Services
N.A.I.C.S.: 622110

Helios Klinikum Gotha GmbH (1)
Heliosstrasse 1, 99867, Gotha, Germany
Tel.: (49) 36212200
Health Care System Consulting Services
N.A.I.C.S.: 524114

Helios Klinikum Hildesheim GmbH (1)
Senator-Braun-Allee 33, 31135, Hildesheim, Germany
Tel.: (49) 5121890
Emp.: 1,500
Health Care System Consulting Services
N.A.I.C.S.: 524114

Helios Klinikum Meiningen GmbH (1)
Bergstrasse 3, 98617, Meiningen, Germany
Tel.: (49) 3693900
Medical Education Services
N.A.I.C.S.: 622110

Helios Klinikum Schwelm GmbH (1)
Dr -Moeller-Strasse 15, 58332, Schwelm, Germany
Tel.: (49) 2336480
Health Care System Consulting Services
N.A.I.C.S.: 524114

Helios Klinikum Siegburg GmbH (1)
Ringstrasse 49, 53721, Siegburg, Germany
Tel.: (49) 2241180
Surgical Therapy Medical Operator
N.A.I.C.S.: 622110

Helios Klinikum Uelzen GmbH (1)
Hagenskamp 34, 29525, Uelzen, Germany
Tel.: (49) 581830
Surgical Therapy Medical Operator
N.A.I.C.S.: 622110

Helios Park-Klinikum Leipzig GmbH (1)
Strumpellstrasse 41, 04289, Leipzig, Germany
Tel.: (49) 3418640
Health Care System Consulting Services
N.A.I.C.S.: 524114

Helios Rehakliniken Bad Berleburg GmbH (1)
Am Schlosspark 11, Bad Berleburg, 57319, Siegen, Germany
Tel.: (49) 27518810000
Rehabilitation Center Services
N.A.I.C.S.: 623220

Helios Spital Uberlingen GmbH (1)
Harlenweg 1, 88662, Uberlingen, Germany
Tel.: (49) 755194770
Health Care System Consulting Services
N.A.I.C.S.: 524114

Helios St. Elisabeth Klinik Oberhausen GmbH (1)
Josefstrasse 3, 46045, Oberhausen, Germany
Tel.: (49) 20885080
Health Care System Consulting Services
N.A.I.C.S.: 524114

Helios St. Elisabeth-Krankenhaus Bad Kissingen GmbH (1)
Kissinger Str 150, 97688. Bad Kissingen, Germany
Tel.: (49) 9718050
Health Care System Consulting Services
N.A.I.C.S.: 524114

Helios St. Marienberg Klinik Helmstedt GmbH (1)
Conringstrasse 26, 38350, Helmstedt, Germany
Tel.: (49) 5351140
Emp.: 600
Visceral & Orthopaedic Surgery Services
N.A.I.C.S.: 622110

Helios Versorgungszentren GmbH (1)
Bahnhofstrasse 7, Ohrdruf, 99885, Gotha, Germany
Tel.: (49) 3624307289
Hospital Services
N.A.I.C.S.: 622110

Helios Vogtland-Klinikum Plauen GmbH (1)
Rontgenstrasse 2, 08529, Plauen, Germany
Tel.: (49) 3741490
Emp.: 1,100
Vascular Surgery Services
N.A.I.C.S.: 541940

Hermed Ingenieria Clinica Espana, S.L. (1)
Calle Pedro Teixeira n 8 Planta 6, 28020, Madrid, Spain
Tel.: (34) 91 037 5370
Web Site: https://www.hermed.es
Medical Technical Services
N.A.I.C.S.: 621999

Hermed Medizintechnik Schweiz AG (1)
Eichwiesstrasse 20, Jona, 8645, Rapperswil, Switzerland
Tel.: (41) 55 536 4747
Web Site: https://www.hermed.ch
Medical Technical Services
N.A.I.C.S.: 621999

Hermed Medrott Medical B.V. (1)
Langeweg 7 A-F, 3233 LM, Oosterhout, Netherlands
Tel.: (31) 18 141 9390
Web Site: https://www.hermedmedrott.nl
Medical Technical Services
N.A.I.C.S.: 621999

Hermed Medrott Medical BVBA (1)
Brandekensweg 9, 2627, Schelle, Belgium
Tel.: (32) 3 320 1850
Web Site: https://www.hermedmedrott.nl
Medical Technical Services
N.A.I.C.S.: 621999

Hermed Technische Beratungs GmbH (1)
Robert-Bosch-Strasse 6, 67292, Kirchheimbolanden, Germany
Tel.: (49) 63 524 0160
Web Site: https://www.hermed.de
Emp.: 500
Medical Technical Services
N.A.I.C.S.: 621999

Hospitalia International GmbH (1)
Siemensstrasse 6, 61352, Bad Homburg, Germany
Tel.: (49) 617 288 6800
Web Site: https://www.hospitalia.com
Project & Provide Services
N.A.I.C.S.: 541330
Johannes Fischer (Mng Dir)

Instruclean GmbH (1)
Tenderweg 4, 45141, Essen, Germany
Tel.: (49) 2018 907 7510
Web Site: https://www.instruclean.de
General Hospital Services
N.A.I.C.S.: 622110

Klinikum Erfurt Bewachungs GmbH (1)
Nordhauser Strasse 74, 99089, Erfurt, Germany
Tel.: (49) 3617810
Security Services
N.A.I.C.S.: 561612

Kneipp-Hof Dussnang AG (1)
Kurhausstrasse 34, Dussnang, 8374, Munchwilen, Switzerland
Tel.: (41) 719786363
Health Care Srvices
N.A.I.C.S.: 541330

LVB Lawog-Vamed Bauplanungs- und Errichtungs-GmbH (1)
Rudolfstrasse 53, 4040, Linz, Austria
Tel.: (43) 732700991
Health Care Services
N.A.I.C.S.: 541330

MVZ Campus Gifhorn GmbH (1)
Campus 6, 38518, Gifhorn, Germany
Tel.: (49) 5371871717
Web Site: https://www.mvz-campus-gifhorn.de
Hospital Services
N.A.I.C.S.: 622110

Medi1one Medical Gmbh (1)
Steinbeisstrasse 15, 70736, Fellbach, Germany
Tel.: (49) 711490940
Web Site: https://shop.medi1one.de
Emp.: 50
Injection Mfr & Distr
N.A.I.C.S.: 336310

Mediterra - Sedlcany, s.r.o. (1)
Tyrsova 161, 264 01, Sedlcany, Czech Republic
Tel.: (420) 31 884 1500
Web Site: https://www.nemocnice-sedlcany.cz
Health Care Srvices
N.A.I.C.S.: 621999

Mediterra s.r.o. (1)
Skretova 490/12, Vinohrady, 120 00, Prague, Czech Republic
Tel.: (420) 234094203
Health Care Srvices
N.A.I.C.S.: 541330

Mednet s.r.o. (1)
Skretova 12, 120 00, Prague, Czech Republic
Tel.: (420) 234094222
Health Care Srvices
N.A.I.C.S.: 541330

Melnicka Zdravotni, A.S. (1)
Prazska 528, 276 01, Melnik, Czech Republic
Tel.: (420) 315639101
Health Care Srvices
N.A.I.C.S.: 541330

Nemocnice sv. Zdislavy, A.S. (1)
Mostiste 93, 594 01, Velke Mezirici, Czech Republic
Tel.: (420) 566512311
Web Site: https://www.nemocnice-mostiste.cz
Health Care Srvices
N.A.I.C.S.: 541330

Neurologisches Therapiezentrum Gmundnerberg GmbH (1)
Gmundnerberg 82, 4813, Altmunster, Austria
Tel.: (43) 76 128 8000
Web Site: https://www.ntgb.at
Rehabilitation Center Services
N.A.I.C.S.: 623220

Neurologisches Therapiezentrum Kapfenberg GmbH (1)
Anton-Buchalka-Strasse 1, 8605, Kapfenberg, Austria
Tel.: (43) 3 862 2900
Web Site: https://www.ntk.at
General Hospital Services
N.A.I.C.S.: 622110

Niederosterreichische Facility Management GmbH (1)
Neunkirchnerstrasse 38, 2700, Wiener Neustadt, Austria
Tel.: (43) 160127661
Health Care Services
N.A.I.C.S.: 541330

OOO Vamed (1)
Novoslobodskaya str 23 5th Floor Office 536, 127055, Moscow, Russia
Tel.: (7) 4957879017
Health Care Srvices
N.A.I.C.S.: 541330

Ostsee Resort Damp GmbH (1)
Seeuferweg 10, Ostseebad Damp, 24351, Rendsburg, Germany
Tel.: (49) 43 528 0666
Web Site: https://www.ostsee-resort-dampland.de
Resort Services
N.A.I.C.S.: 721110

PKS Privatklinik Salzburg GmbH & Co KG (1)
Sinnhubstrasse 2, 5020, Salzburg, Austria
Tel.: (43) 662 829 0330
Web Site: https://www.privatkliniksalzburg.at
General Hospital Services
N.A.I.C.S.: 622110

Prinsamed - Projectos Internacionais De Saude Unipessoal Lda. (1)
Rua Fernando Palha No 52-Sala 301, 1950-132, Lisbon, Portugal
Tel.: (351) 217505000
Health Care Srvices
N.A.I.C.S.: 541330

Reha Seewis AG (1)
Schlossstrasse 1, 7212, Davos, Switzerland
Tel.: (41) 813075252
Web Site: http://www.rehaseewis.ch
Rehabilitation Center Services
N.A.I.C.S.: 623220

Rehabilitationsklinik im Montafon Betriebs-GmbH (1)
Wagenweg 4a, 6780, Schruns, Austria
Tel.: (43) 555 6205
Web Site: https://www.rehaklinik-montafon.at
Emp.: 140
Rehabilitation Center Services
N.A.I.C.S.: 623220

Rehabilitationszentrum Kitzbuhel Betriebs-GmbH (1)
Hornweg 32, 6370, Kitzbuhel, Austria
Tel.: (43) 535 667 0670
Web Site: https://www.reha-kitz.at
Emp.: 95
Rehabilitation Center Services
N.A.I.C.S.: 623220

Rehabilitationszentrum Oberndorf Betriebs-GmbH & Co KG (1)
Paracelsusstrasse 37a, Oberndorf, 5110, Salzburg, Austria
Tel.: (43) 627 240 7400
Web Site: https://www.reha-oberndorf.at
Emp.: 88
Rehabilitation Center Services
N.A.I.C.S.: 623220

Rehabilitationszentrum St. Veit im Pongau Betriebs-GmbH (1)
St Veiter Strasse 48, 5621, Sankt Veit an der Glan, Austria
Tel.: (43) 676831271912
Health Care Services
N.A.I.C.S.: 541330

Rehaklinik Dussnang AG (1)
Kurhausstrasse 34, Dussnang, 8374, Fischingen, Switzerland
Tel.: (41) 71 978 6363
Web Site: https://www.rehaklinik-dussnang.ch
Physical Therapy Services
N.A.I.C.S.: 621340

Rehaklinik Wien Baumgarten Betriebs-GmbH (1)
Reizenpfenninggasse 1, 1140, Vienna, Austria
Tel.: (43) 141500
Web Site: https://www.rehawienbaumgarten.at

Emp.: 140
Rehabilitation Center Services
N.A.I.C.S.: 623220

Rehaklinik Zihlschlacht AG (1)
Hauptstrasse 2, Zihlschlacht, 8588, Weinfelden, Switzerland
Tel.: (41) 71 424 3366
Web Site: https://www.rehaklinik-zihlschlacht.ch
Emp.: 580
Rehabilitation Center Services
N.A.I.C.S.: 623220

Rehazentrum Harburg GmbH (1)
Sand 18- 22, 21073, Hamburg, Germany
Tel.: (49) 407665506
Rehabilitation Center Services
N.A.I.C.S.: 623220

Rehazentrum Lubeck GmbH (1)
Konrad-Adenauer-Strasse 4, 23558, Lübeck, Germany
Tel.: (49) 451399390
Rehabilitation Center Services
N.A.I.C.S.: 623220

Rehazentrum Norderstedt GmbH (1)
Stettiner Str 16, 22850, Norderstedt, Germany
Tel.: (49) 405233028
Rehabilitation Center Services
N.A.I.C.S.: 623220

SC Fresenius Kabi Romania SRL (1)
Str Henri Coanda no 2, Ghimbav, Brasov, 507075, Romania
Tel.: (40) 268406260
Healthcare Sector Services
N.A.I.C.S.: 621999

Temamed Medizintechnische Dienstleistungs GmbH (1)
Robert-Bosch-Str 6, 67292, Kirchheimbolanden, Germany
Tel.: (49) 635 270 5980
Web Site: https://www.temamed.de
Independent Medical Technology Product Mfr
N.A.I.C.S.: 339112

Therme Seewinkel Betriebsgesellschaft m.b.H. (1)
Im Seewinkel 1, Frauenkirchen, 7132, Neusiedl am See, Austria
Tel.: (43) 217220500
Project & Provide Services
N.A.I.C.S.: 541330

Tov Vamed Ukraine (1)
11-B Igorivska Str Floor 3, 04070, Kiev, Ukraine
Tel.: (380) 444955060
Health Care Srvices
N.A.I.C.S.: 541330

VAMED AG (1)
Sterngasse 5, 1230, Vienna, Austria
Tel.: (43) 160 1270
Web Site: https://www.vamed.com
Sales Range: $900-999.9 Million
Emp.: 3,724
Public Health Facilities Management, Construction & Development
N.A.I.C.S.: 236220
Ernst Wastler *(Chm-Exec Bd & CEO)*

Subsidiary (Non-US):

Nemocnice Tanvald, s.r.o. (2)
Nemocnicni 287, 468 41, Tanvald, Czech Republic
Tel.: (420) 48 336 7311
Web Site: https://www.nemocnice-tanvald.cz
General Hospital Operator
N.A.I.C.S.: 622110

Subsidiary (Domestic):

Seniorenzentrum St. Corona am Schopfl Betriebsgesellschaft m.b.H. (2)
St Corona am Schopfl 110, 2572, Sankt Corona am Schopfl, Austria
Tel.: (43) 2 673 8291
Web Site: https://www.pflegehotel.at
Living Care Services
N.A.I.C.S.: 623312

VAMED Engineering GmbH & Co KG (2)
Sterngasse 5, 1230, Vienna, Austria
Tel.: (43) 1601270
Web Site: https://www.vamed.com
Sales Range: $25-49.9 Million
Emp.: 150
Architecture & Other Engineering Services
N.A.I.C.S.: 541310
Andrea Raffaseder *(Mng Dir)*

VAMED Estate Development & Engineering GmbH & CO KG (2)
Sterngasse 5, Vienna, 1230, Austria
Tel.: (43) 1601270
Sales Range: $150-199.9 Million
Emp.: 400
Hospitals & Other Health Facilities Real Estate
N.A.I.C.S.: 531390
Erich Ennsbrunner *(Co-Mng Dir)*

VAMED Management und Service GmbH & Co KG (2)
Sterngasse 5, 1230, Vienna, Austria
Tel.: (43) 160 1270
Web Site: https://www.vamed.com
Public Health Facilities Management
N.A.I.C.S.: 561210

VAMED-KMB (2)
Spitalgasse 23, 1090, Vienna, Austria
Tel.: (43) 14040090000
Web Site: http://www.vamed.com
Facilities Technical Systems Management
N.A.I.C.S.: 561790
Christian Krebs *(Mng Dir)*

Subsidiary (Non-US):

Vamed Healthcare Services Sdn. Bhd. (2)
Suites 10 4 and 10 5 10th Floor Menara Tan and Tan No 207, Jalan Tun Razak, 50400, Kuala Lumpur, Malaysia
Tel.: (60) 327812000
Health Care Srvices
N.A.I.C.S.: 541330

Vamed Nederland B.V. (2)
Orteliuslaan 897, 3528 BE, Utrecht, Netherlands
Tel.: (31) 30 303 9944
Web Site: https://www.vamed.nl
Health Care Srvices
N.A.I.C.S.: 541330

Vamed CZ s.r.o. (1)
U Malvazinky 177/7, 150 00, Prague, Czech Republic
Tel.: (420) 234094203
Health Care Srvices
N.A.I.C.S.: 541330

Vamed Engineering Nicaragua, Sociedad Anonima (1)
Rotonda Jean Paul Genie 400 Mts Al Oeste Centro Premier Segundo Piso, Modulo C-201/3, Managua, Nicaragua
Tel.: (505) 22232130
N.A.I.C.S.: 524114

Vamed Gesundheit Holding Deutschland GmbH (1)
Seeuferweg 10, Damp, 24351, Rendsburg, Germany
Tel.: (49) 435 280 1155
Web Site: https://www.vamed-gesundheit.de
Rehabilitation Center Services
N.A.I.C.S.: 623220

Vamed Health Project GmbH (1)
Am Bahnhof Westend 9-11, 14059, Berlin, Germany
Tel.: (49) 302462690
N.A.I.C.S.: 524114
Robert Posthumus *(Mng Dir)*

Vamed Health Projects CZ s.r.o. (1)
Skretova 12 Praha 2, 120 00, Prague, Czech Republic
Tel.: (420) 234094217
Health Care Srvices
N.A.I.C.S.: 541330

Vamed Health Projects Malaysia Sdn. Bhd. (1)
10 4 & 10 5 10th Floor Menara Tan and Tan No 207 Jalan Tun Razak, 50400, Kuala Lumpur, Malaysia

Tel.: (60) 327812000
N.A.I.C.S.: 524114

Vamed Health Projects UK Limited (1)
Barley Mow Centre Studio 7-1st Floor, London, W4 4PH, United Kingdom
Tel.: (44) 2078989907
Health Srvices
N.A.I.C.S.: 541330

Vamed Healthcare Co. Ltd. (1)
1503 GrandyVic Building No 16 Taiyanggong Mid Street, Chaoyang District, Beijing, 100028, China
Tel.: (86) 1058530501
Health Care Srvices
N.A.I.C.S.: 541330

Vamed Healthcare Services Sa (Pty) Ltd. (1)
3rd Floor Assupol Building Summit Place 221 Garsfontein Road, Menlyn, Pretoria, 0181, South Africa
Tel.: (27) 123462749
N.A.I.C.S.: 524114
Lliam Solomons *(Officer-Training)*

Vamed International Hospital Management & Consulting (Beijing) Co., Ltd. (1)
1503 GrandyVic Building No 16 Taiyanggong Mid Street, Chaoyang District, Beijing, 100028, China
Tel.: (86) 1058257490
Health Care Srvices
N.A.I.C.S.: 541330

Vamed Mediterra, A.S. (1)
Skretova 490/12 Panorama Business Centrum, 120 00, Prague, 2, Czech Republic
Tel.: (420) 234094222
Web Site: https://www.vamed-mediterra.cz
N.A.I.C.S.: 524114

Vamed Medizintechnik GmbH (1)
Lazarettgasse 20, 1090, Vienna, Austria
Tel.: (43) 1404880
Health Care Srvices
N.A.I.C.S.: 541330

Vamed Polska Sp. z o.o. (1)
ul Pryzmaty 4A, 02-226, Warsaw, Poland
Tel.: (48) 223109755
Health Care Srvices
N.A.I.C.S.: 541330

Vamed Projets Hospitaliers Internationaux France S.A.S (1)
Tour Ciel 20ter Rue de Bezons, 92400, Courbevoie, France
Tel.: (33) 170841000
Health Care Srvices
N.A.I.C.S.: 541330

Vamed Romania S.r.l. (1)
111 Street Barbu Vacarescu, 2nd District, Bucharest, Romania
Tel.: (40) 372734533
Health Care Srvices
N.A.I.C.S.: 541330

Vamed Service- Und Beteiligungsges mbH (1)
Schicklerstrasse 5-7, 10179, Berlin, Germany
Tel.: (49) 30246269440
Healthcare Sector Services
N.A.I.C.S.: 621999

Vamed Standortentwicklung Und Engineering GmbH (1)
Sterngasse 5, 1230, Vienna, Austria
Tel.: (43) 1601270
Project & Provide Services
N.A.I.C.S.: 541330

Vamed Turkey Muhendislik Insaat Taahhut Medikal Saglik Hizmetleri Limited Sirketi (1)
Unyversyteler Mhallesy 1598 Cadde Bylkent Plaza 3 A Blok Kat 5 No 45, 6 690, Ankara, Turkiye
Tel.: (90) 5492646114
Health Care Srvices
N.A.I.C.S.: 541330

Vamed UKK Projektgesellschaft m.b.H. (1)

Schicklerstrasse 5-7, 10179, Berlin, Germany
Tel.: (49) 302462690
Healthcare Sector Services
N.A.I.C.S.: 621999

Vamed-Hungaria Health Care Ltd. (1)
Vamhaz korut 13, 1093, Budapest, Hungary
Tel.: (36) 14550496
Health Care Srvices
N.A.I.C.S.: 541330

FRESH EXPRESS DELIVERY HOLDINGS GROUP CO., LTD.
Unit D 12/F Seabright Plaza 9-23 Shell Street, North Point, China (Hong Kong)
Tel.: (852) 31059966   Ky
Web Site:
http://www.freshexpressdelivery.com
Rev.: $26,924,629
Assets: $116,012,787
Liabilities: $14,429,812
Net Worth: $101,582,975
Earnings: ($14,438,681)
Emp.: 59
Fiscal Year-end: 03/31/19
Holding Company
N.A.I.C.S.: 551112
Junfeng Pan *(Chm)*

FRESH2 GROUP LTD.
801 Bixing Street, Bihu County, Lishui, 323006, Zhejiang, China
Tel.: (86) 57820516666   VG
Web Site: http://www.anpacbio.com
Year Founded: 2010
FRES—(NASDAQ)
Rev.: $2,755,635
Assets: $10,339,990
Liabilities: $10,138,059
Net Worth: $201,931
Earnings: ($18,185,261)
Emp.: 89
Fiscal Year-end: 12/31/21
Biotechnology Research & Development Services
N.A.I.C.S.: 541714

FRESHBAKED PR LTD
House Three The Maltings E Tyndall St, Cardiff, CF24 5EA, South Glamorgan, United Kingdom
Tel.: (44) 2920491491
Web Site:
http://www.freshbaked.co.uk
Year Founded: 2008
Emp.: 70
Public Relations
N.A.I.C.S.: 541820
Jonathan Hollins *(Mng Dir)*

FRESHLOCAL SOLUTIONS INC.
595 Burrard Street Suite 1703, Vancouver, V7X 1L7, BC, Canada
Tel.: (604) 488-5427   Ca
Year Founded: 2018
LOCL—(TSX)
Rev.: $103,857,057
Assets: $44,767,538
Liabilities: $44,329,461
Net Worth: $438,077
Earnings: ($30,630,956)
Emp.: 950
Fiscal Year-end: 10/02/21
Business Consulting Services
N.A.I.C.S.: 522299

FRESHWATER TECHNOLOGY
130-132 Tooley St, London, SE1 2TU, United Kingdom
Tel.: (44) 1794 521 156
Web Site:
http://www.freshwatertechnology.com
Sales Range: $10-24.9 Million

Freshwater Technology—(Continued)

Emp.: 100
Public Relations
N.A.I.C.S.: 541820
Sarah Clarke *(Sr Mgr-Acct)*

FRESHWATER UK PLC
Raglan House Cardiff Gate Business Park, Cardiff, CF23 8BA, United Kingdom
Tel.: (44) 2920 304050   **UK**
Web Site: http://www.freshwater-uk.com
Sales Range: $1-9.9 Million
Emp.: 71
Public Relations & Marketing Services
N.A.I.C.S.: 541820
John M. Underwood *(CEO)*

Subsidiaries:

Freshwater Consumer Limited (1)
Boundary House 91 Charterhouse Street, London, EC1M 6HR, United Kingdom
Tel.: (44) 2070671597
Public Relations Services
N.A.I.C.S.: 541820
Steve Howell *(CEO)*

Freshwater Healthcare Limited (1)
130-132 Tooley St, London, SE1 2TU, United Kingdom
Tel.: (44) 2077871930
Public Relations Services
N.A.I.C.S.: 541820

Freshwater Scotland Limited (1)
Unit 1-2 Skypark 14 Elliot Pl, Glasgow, G3 8EP, Scotland, United Kingdom
Tel.: (44) 1412294050
Public Relations Services
N.A.I.C.S.: 541820

Freshwater Southern Limited (1)
Centre Gate Colston Ave, Bristol, BS1 4TR, United Kingdom
Tel.: (44) 1173178135
Public Relations Services
N.A.I.C.S.: 541820

Freshwater Technology Limited (1)
1 Horsefair Mews, London, SO51 8JG, Hampshire, United Kingdom
Tel.: (44) 2077871931
Public Relations Services
N.A.I.C.S.: 541820

Lynx PR (1)
The Rookery, Leeds, West Yorkshire, United Kingdom
Tel.: (44) 1132393535
Public Relations Services
N.A.I.C.S.: 541820

Profile Plus (UK) Ltd. (1)
78 The Shore, Edinburgh, EH6 6RG, Scotland, United Kingdom
Tel.: (44) 1315546111
Web Site: http://www.profileplus.co.uk
Advertising Agencies, Direct Marketing, Electronic Media, Event Marketing, Exhibit/Trade Shows, Public Relations, Publicity/Promotions, Sales Promotion, Strategic Planning/Research
N.A.I.C.S.: 541820

Waterfront Conference Company Limited (1)
8-12 New Bridge St, London, EC4V 6AL, United Kingdom
Tel.: (44) 2077871210
Web Site: http://www.thewaterfront.co.uk
Conference Management Services
N.A.I.C.S.: 512290
Nicholas Finney *(Mng Dir)*

FRESNILLO PLC
No 549 Calzada Legaria Torre 2, Colonia 10 de abril Delegacion Miguel Hidalgo, 11250, Mexico, Mexico
Tel.: (52) 5552793000   **MX**
Web Site:
https://www.fresnilloplc.com
Year Founded: 2008

FNLPF—(OTCIQ)
Rev.: $2,705,086,000
Assets: $5,737,606,000
Liabilities: $1,670,409,000
Net Worth: $4,067,197,000
Earnings: $288,300,000
Emp.: 7,260
Fiscal Year-end: 12/31/23
Silver & Gold Mining Services
N.A.I.C.S.: 212220
Mario Arreguin *(CFO)*

Subsidiaries:

Minera Fresnillo, S A de C V (1)
Prol Av No 451, Mexico, Mexico
Tel.: (52) 4939839000
Silver Lead & Zinc Ores Mfr
N.A.I.C.S.: 212230

FREUDENBERG SE
Hoehnerweg 2-4, D-69469, Weinheim, Germany
Tel.: (49) 6201800   **De**
Web Site:
https://www.freudenberg.com
Year Founded: 1849
Rev.: $13,139,198,589
Assets: $14,835,191,524
Liabilities: $6,516,282,151
Net Worth: $8,318,909,373
Earnings: $917,099,018
Emp.: 52,241
Fiscal Year-end: 12/31/23
Holding Company; Sealing Products, Vibration Control Components, Nonwoven Textile Products, Household Products & Specialty Chemicals Mfr
N.A.I.C.S.: 551112
Mohsen M. Sohi *(CEO & Member-Mgmt Bd)*

Subsidiaries:

ALUCON s.r.o. (1)
Dolni Nova Ves 131, Lazne Belohrad, 507 81, Prague, Czech Republic
Tel.: (420) 493760511
Web Site: http://www.alucon.cz
Household Product Distr
N.A.I.C.S.: 423220
Edita Arabaszova *(Plant Mgr)*

APEC (Asia) Limited (1)
Block 2 Beiguang Industrial Park LiangBai Road E Gong Ling, PingHu Town, Shenzhen, 518111, Guangdong, China
Tel.: (86) 75584012502
Medical Device Mfr
N.A.I.C.S.: 334510

Aquabio Ltd. (1)
Unit 10 Ball Mill Top Business Park, Hallow, Worcester, WR2 6LS, United Kingdom
Tel.: (44) 1905641966
Web Site: http://www.aquabio.co.uk
Waste Water Treatment Services
N.A.I.C.S.: 221320

Auto Suppliers Limited (1)
Edwin Avenue Hoo Farm Industrial Estate, Kidderminster, DY11 7RA, Worcestershire, United Kingdom
Tel.: (44) 1562865577
Web Site: http://www.autosuppliers.co.uk
Emp.: 15
Industrial Equipment Distr
N.A.I.C.S.: 423830
Steve Lammas *(Mgr-Warehouse)*

Blacktech Otomotiv Sanayi ve Ticaret A.S. (1)
Yeni Yalova Blv No 493, Osmangazi, Turkiye
Tel.: (90) 2245247801
Industrial Machinery Distr
N.A.I.C.S.: 423830

Cambus Teoranta Ltd. (1)
Baile an TSagairt, Spiddal Industrial Estate Spiddal Co, Galway, H91 TRF6, Ireland
Tel.: (353) 91504633
Web Site: http://www.cambusmedical.com
Medical Equipment Mfr
N.A.I.C.S.: 339112

Capol (U.K.) Limited (1)
Unit 10 Pennine Business Park Longbow Close, Huddersfield, HD2 1GQ, United Kingdom
Tel.: (44) 1513428900
Web Site: http://www.capol.de
Confectionery Product Distr
N.A.I.C.S.: 424450

Capol GmbH (1)
Otto-Hahn-Strasse 10, 25337, Elmshorn, Germany
Tel.: (49) 4121 4774 0
Web Site: http://www.capol.de
Emp.: 50
Confectionery Product Distr
N.A.I.C.S.: 424450
Bernd Strack *(CFO & Member-Mgmt Bd)*

Subsidiary (US):

Capol LLC (2)
707 Lake Cook Rd Ste 320, Deerfield, IL 60015
Web Site: http://www.capol.de
Emp.: 8
Confectionery Product Distr
N.A.I.C.S.: 424450
Michael Gordon *(VP)*

Changchun NOK-Freudenberg Oilseal Co., Ltd. (1)
No 323 Xinghuo Road Qianjin Street, Changchun, 130012, China
Tel.: (86) 43185170180
Industrial Machinery Distr
N.A.I.C.S.: 423830

Chem-Trend (Deutschland) GmbH (1)
Ganghoferstr 47, Gernlinden, 82216, Maisach, Germany
Tel.: (49) 81424171196
House Ware & Automobile Parts Mfr
N.A.I.C.S.: 332215
Siegfried Schweikert *(Mgr-Customer Svc)*

Chem-Trend (Shanghai) Trading Co. Ltd. (1)
No 88 Tuo Qing Road Qingpu Industrial Zone, Shanghai, China
Tel.: (86) 2169225900
Chemical Products Distr
N.A.I.C.S.: 424690

Chem-Trend Australia Pty Ltd (1)
1st Floor 3 Brand Drive, Thomastown, 3074, VIC, Australia
Tel.: (61) 394647577
Web Site: http://www.chemtrend.com
Chemical Products Distr
N.A.I.C.S.: 424690
Victor Pilati *(Gen Mgr)*

Chem-Trend Chemicals Co. Pvt. Ltd. (1)
3rd Floor Silver Jubilee Block 3rd Cross Mission Road, Bengaluru, 560 027, India
Tel.: (91) 8066901300
Web Site: http://www.chemtrend.com
Chemical Products Distr
N.A.I.C.S.: 424690
A. Gerard Lourduraj *(Dir-Sls)*

Chem-Trend Comercial, S.A. de C.V. (1)
Avenida de la Montana 109 Parque Industrial, Santa Rosa Jauregui, 76220, Queretaro, Mexico
Tel.: (52) 4421019100
Chemical Products Distr
N.A.I.C.S.: 424690

Chem-Trend France S.A.S.U. (1)
Immeuble Saint Exupery Aeroparc - 2 rue des Herons, 67960, Entzheim, France
Tel.: (33) 388664166
Chemical Products Distr
N.A.I.C.S.: 424690
Yannick Friess *(Mgr-Sls-Polyurethane)*

Chem-Trend Holding LP (1)
1445 McPherson Park Dr, Howell, MI 48843-3947
Tel.: (517) 546-4520
Holding Company
N.A.I.C.S.: 551112

Chem-Trend Industria e Comercio de Produtos Quimicos Ltda. (1)

Rua Antonio Felamingo 529, Valinhos, 13279-452, Sao Paulo, Brazil
Tel.: (55) 1938818200
Chemical Products Distr
N.A.I.C.S.: 424690

Chem-Trend Italy del Dr. Gian Franco Colori S.a.s. (1)
Via Monferrato 57 Sesto Ulteriano, 20098, San Giuliano Milanese, Milan, Italy
Tel.: (39) 02988141
Chemical Products Distr
N.A.I.C.S.: 424690

Chem-Trend Japan K.K. (1)
Kobe Harborland Center Building 16F 1-3-3 Higashikawasaki-cho, Chuo-ku, Kobe, 650-0044, Japan
Tel.: (81) 783619700
Chemical Products Mfr
N.A.I.C.S.: 325998

Chem-Trend Korea Ltd. (1)
306-2 Gusu-ri Miyang-myeon, Anseong, Gyeonggi-do, Korea (South)
Tel.: (82) 316774471
Web Site: http://www.chem-trend.com
Chemical Products Distr
N.A.I.C.S.: 424690

Chem-Trend Polska sp. z o.o. (1)
ul Pilotow 19, Kobylnica, Janikowo, 62-006, Poland
Tel.: (48) 616464855
Chemical Products Distr
N.A.I.C.S.: 424690

Chem-Trend Romania s.r.l. (1)
Strada Autogarii 1 Office 1 Etaj 1, 550135, Sibiu, Romania
Tel.: (40) 377702134
Chemical Products Mfr
N.A.I.C.S.: 325998

Chem-Trend Singapore Pte. Ltd. (1)
1 Kim Seng Promenade 13-06 Great World City East Tower, Singapore, 237994, Singapore
Tel.: (65) 67360113
Chemical Products Distr
N.A.I.C.S.: 424690
S. M. Woo *(Dir-Sls)*

Chem-Trend Trading (Thailand) Co. Ltd. (1)
88 Dr Gerhard Link Building 12th Floor Krungthepkritha Road Huamark, Bang Kapi, Bangkok, 10240, Thailand
Tel.: (66) 27316557
Chemical Products Distr
N.A.I.C.S.: 424690
Wisit Swatesuttipun *(Mgr-Sls & Technical Svc-Tire)*

Chem-Trend Vietnam Company Limited (1)
7th Floor 157 Vo Thi Sau Street, Ward 6 District 3, Ho Chi Minh City, Vietnam
Tel.: (84) 838209851
Chemical Products Distr
N.A.I.C.S.: 424690
Hai Dang *(Mgr-Sls-Thermoplastic & Polyurethane)*

Chemlease Japan K.K. (1)
7-5-25 Kamisawatori, Hyogo-Ku, Kobe, 652-0046, Japan
Tel.: (81) 785793332
Chemical Products Distr
N.A.I.C.S.: 424690

Corcos Industriale S.p.A. (1)
Corso Torino 332, 10064, Pinerolo, Italy (100%)
Tel.: (39) 0121392222
Web Site: http://www.corcos.it
Sales Range: $200-249.9 Million
Emp.: 550
Mfr of Rubber Products
N.A.I.C.S.: 326299

Corteco China Co. Ltd. (1)
Room 3505 35/F Tower B Center Plaza No 161 Lin He Xi Road, Tianhe District, Guangzhou, 510620, China
Tel.: (86) 2038324968
Web Site: http://www.corteco-china.cn
Industrial Machinery Distr
N.A.I.C.S.: 423830
Deng Jade *(Mgr-Supply Chain)*

Corteco GmbH (1)
Badener Str 4, 69493, Hirschberg, Germany
(100%)
Tel.: (49) 6201259640
Web Site: http://www.corteco.com
Sales Range: $10-24.9 Million
Emp.: 24
Sales, Warehousing & Packaging of Automotive Spare Parts
N.A.I.C.S.: 493190
Thomas Mettke (Member-Mgmt Bd)

Branch (US):

Corteco USA (2)
11617 State Route 13, Milan, OH 44846-9725
Tel.: (419) 499-2502
Web Site: http://www.corteco.com
Automotive Sealing Systems, Vibration Control & Service Parts Distr
N.A.I.C.S.: 423120

Subsidiary (Non-US):

Corteco s.r.l. (2)
Corso Torino 420, 10064, Pinerolo, Italy (100%)
Tel.: (39) 0121369269
Web Site: http://www.corteco.com
Sales of Metal Automotive Parts
N.A.I.C.S.: 423120

Corteco Ltd. (1)
Unit 6 Wycliffe Industrial Park, Lutterworth, LE17 4HG, Leicestershire, United Kingdom
Tel.: (44) 1455550000
Automobile Component Distr
N.A.I.C.S.: 423120
Martin Jones (Gen Mgr)

Corteco SAS (1)
Z A La Couture, 87140, Nantiat, France
Tel.: (33) 555536800
Automobile Component Distr
N.A.I.C.S.: 423120
Eric Burban (Gen Mgr)

Dichtomatik Vertriebsgesellschaft fur technische Dichtungen mbH (1)
Albert-Schweitzer-Ring 1, 22 045, Hamburg, Germany
Tel.: (49) 40 669 89 0
Web Site: http://www.dichtomatik.de
Industrial Product Distr
N.A.I.C.S.: 423840
Alexander Rozman (Mng Dir)

Subsidiary (Non-US):

Dichtomatik (China) Co., Ltd. (2)
No 314 Shenxia Rd, Jiading District, Shanghai, 201818, China
Tel.: (86) 2160822178
Seal Distr
N.A.I.C.S.: 423840

Dichtomatik A.B. (2)
Hjalmar Brantingsvag 25, Box 142, 261 22, Landskrona, Sweden
Tel.: (46) 418449800
Web Site: http://www.dichtomatik.se
Emp.: 8
Seal Distr
N.A.I.C.S.: 423840
Andreas Bildtse (CEO)

Subsidiary (US):

Dichtomatik Americas, LP (2)
1087 Park Pl, Shakopee, MN 55379
Tel.: (800) 328-2840
Web Site: http://www.dichtomatik.us
Seal Distr
N.A.I.C.S.: 423840

Subsidiary (Non-US):

Dichtomatik B.V. (2)
Benjamin Franklinstraat 6, 8013 NC, Zwolle, Netherlands
Tel.: (31) 384601606
Web Site: http://www.dichtomatik.nu
Seal Distr
N.A.I.C.S.: 423840
Gerrit Knopert (Mgr-Comml)

Dichtomatik Canada, Inc. (2)
3900 14th Ave 2, Markham, L3R 4R3, ON, Canada
Tel.: (905) 470-2266

Web Site: http://www.dichtomatik.ca
Seal Distr
N.A.I.C.S.: 423840

Dichtomatik Handelsgesellschaft mbH (2)
Rautenweg 17, 1220, Vienna, Austria
Tel.: (43) 125935410
Web Site: http://www.dichtomatik.at
Seal Distr
N.A.I.C.S.: 423840

Dichtomatik Kft. (2)
Vegyesz u 17-25, Budapest, 1116, Hungary
Tel.: (36) 18026400
Web Site: http://www.dichtomatik.com
Seal Distr
N.A.I.C.S.: 423840

Dichtomatik Ltd. (2)
Donington House Riverside Road Pride Park, Derby, DE24 8HX, United Kingdom
Tel.: (44) 1332524400
Emp.: 23
Seal Distr
N.A.I.C.S.: 423840
David Cook (Gen Mgr)

Dichtomatik S.A.S (2)
Espace entreprise de Macon Loche, 71000, Loches, France
Tel.: (33) 385270280
Seal Distr
N.A.I.C.S.: 423840

Dichtomatik S.a.s. di Externa Italia S.r.l. (2)
6/A Via Delle Fabbriche, 16158, Genoa, Italy
Tel.: (39) 01061275
Seal Distr
N.A.I.C.S.: 423840

Dichtomatik s.r.l. (1)
Via delle Fabbriche 6/A, Voltri, 16158, Genoa, Italy
Tel.: (39) 0106127503
Web Site: http://www.it.dichtomatik.com
Sales Range: $25-49.9 Million
Emp.: 15
Sales of Platic Products
N.A.I.C.S.: 423840

E.D. Oates Pty. Ltd. (1)
13-21 Maygar Boulevard, Broadmeadows, 3047, VIC, Australia
Tel.: (61) 393556900
Web Site: http://www.oates.com.au
Cleaning Products Supplier
N.A.I.C.S.: 424690

EagleBurgmann Germany GmbH & Co. KG (1)
Aeussere Sauerlacher Strasse 6-10, PO Box 1240, 82515, Wolfratshausen, Germany
Tel.: (49) 8171230
Web Site: http://www.burgmann.com
Sales Range: $350-399.9 Million
Emp.: 1,000
Mechanical Seals, Packings, Gaskets, Expansion Joints & Sealing Systems Mfr
N.A.I.C.S.: 339991
Jochen Strasser (Mng Dir)

Subsidiary (Non-US):

Burgmann Dalian Co., Ltd. (2)
No 86 Liaohe East Road DD Port, Dalian, 116620, China
Tel.: (86) 41187581000
Web Site: http://www.eagleburgman.cn
Sales Range: $25-49.9 Million
Emp.: 185
Mechanical Seals & Packings Mfr
N.A.I.C.S.: 339991

Subsidiary (Domestic):

Burgmann Industries Holding GmbH (2)
Aussere Sauerlacher Str 6-10, 82515, Wolfratshausen, Germany
Tel.: (49) 8171230
Holding Company
N.A.I.C.S.: 551012

Burgmann Packings GmbH (2)
Haupstrasse 145, D-74638, Waldenburg, Germany
Tel.: (49) 79 42 94 0

Packing & Sealing Materials Mfr
N.A.I.C.S.: 488991

Subsidiary (Non-US):

Burgmann Sealing Materials Co., Ltd. Cixi (2)
No 787 817 Ciyong Rd, Hushan Town, Nanjing, 315302, China (100%)
Tel.: (86) 57463826241
Web Site: http://www.burgmannpackings.cn
Sealing Material Mfr
N.A.I.C.S.: 339991

Burgmann Shanghai Co., Ltd. (2)
No 127-8 Wenjing Road, Minghang, Shanghai, 200245, China
Tel.: (86) 2164620550
Web Site: http://www.eagleburgmann.cn
Sales Range: $25-49.9 Million
Emp.: 100
Mechanical Seals & Packings Mfr & Sls
N.A.I.C.S.: 339991

Compentek Oy (2)
Sulantie 22, 04300, Tuusula, Finland
Tel.: (358) 400300200
Web Site: http://www.compentek.fi
Expansion Joints & Sales of Heat Resistent Fabrics & Yarns Mfr & Sls
N.A.I.C.S.: 332312
Pasi Virintie (Mng Dir)

EagleBurgmann (Malaysia) SDN BHD (2)
No 7 Lorong SS 13 6B off Jalan SS13 6, Subang Jaya Indus Est, Petaling Jaya, 47500, Selangor darul Ehsan, Malaysia
Tel.: (60) 356348624
Web Site: http://www.eagleburgmann.com
Sales Range: $25-49.9 Million
Emp.: 50
Sealing Technologies Mfr & Sls
N.A.I.C.S.: 339991
Chan Homlim (Mgr-Fin)

EagleBurgmann (Switzerland) AG (2)
Hofstrasse 21, Hoeri, 8181, Zurich, Switzerland
Tel.: (41) 448723930
Web Site: http://www.eagleburgmann.ch
Sales Range: $25-49.9 Million
Emp.: 11
Mechanical Seals & Packings Mfr & Sls
N.A.I.C.S.: 339991

EagleBurgmann (Thailand) Co., Ltd. (2)
13/2 Klongnamhu Road T Nernphra Muang, Rayong, 21150, Thailand
Tel.: (66) 38694422
Web Site: http://www.goburgmann.com
Sales Range: $1-9.9 Million
Emp.: 65
Mechanical Seals & Packings Mfr & Sls
N.A.I.C.S.: 339991
Utpal Chowdhury (Mng Dir)

EagleBurgmann (Wuxi) Co. Ltd. (2)
Changjiang South Road No 28-51, Wuxi, 214028, Wuxi, Jiangsu, China
Tel.: (86) 51085346107
Sales Range: $25-49.9 Million
Emp.: 100
Automotive Mechanical & Electrical Repair & Maintenance
N.A.I.C.S.: 811114

Joint Venture (Non-US):

EagleBurgmann Australasia Pty. Ltd. (2)
16 Stennett Road, Ingleburn, Sydney, 2565, NSW, Australia
Tel.: (61) 29 605 0600
Web Site:
https://www.eagleburgmann.com.au
Emp.: 38
Mechanical Seals & Packing Mfr & Sales
N.A.I.C.S.: 339991

Branch (Domestic):

EagleBurgmann Australasia Pty. Ltd. - Melbourne (3)
19 Inglewood Drive, Thomastown, Melbourne, 3074, VIC, Australia
Tel.: (61) 39 464 6344

Web Site:
https://www.eagleburgmann.com.au
Mechanical Seals Mfr
N.A.I.C.S.: 333991

Subsidiary (Non-US):

EagleBurgmann Austria GmbH (2)
Vogelweider 44A, 5020, Salzburg, Austria
Tel.: (43) 662825701
Web Site: http://www.burgmann.com
Sales Range: $25-49.9 Million
Emp.: 12
Mechanical Seals & Packings Mfr
N.A.I.C.S.: 339991

EagleBurgmann BT S.p.A. (2)
Via A Meucci 58, 36057, Arcugnano, Vicenza, Italy
Tel.: (39) 0444288977
Web Site: http://www.btburgmann.com
Emp.: 70
Steel Mfrs
N.A.I.C.S.: 339991
Alessandro Bedin (Mgr-R&D)

EagleBurgmann Belgium BVBA (2)
Zagerijstraat 11, Sint-Job-int-Goor, 2960, Antwerp, Belgium
Tel.: (32) 36339944
Web Site: http://www.eagleburgmann.be
Sales Range: $25-49.9 Million
Emp.: 16
Mechanical Seals & Packings Sls
N.A.I.C.S.: 339991

EagleBurgmann Bredan s.r.o. (2)
Na Drahach 1364, Zbraslav, 156 00, Prague, 5, Czech Republic
Tel.: (420) 241021811
Web Site: http://www.ke-burgmann.cz
Sales Range: $1-9.9 Million
Emp.: 80
Mechanical Seals & Packings Mfr
N.A.I.C.S.: 339991

EagleBurgmann Canada Inc. (2)
3524-78th Ave NW, Edmonton, T6B 2X9, AB, Canada
Tel.: (780) 434-4928
Web Site: http://www.eagleburgmann.com
Gasket & Sealing Device Mfr
N.A.I.C.S.: 339991

EagleBurgmann Colombia, S.A.S. (2)
Cr 13 A - 86 A - 74 oficina 302, Bogota, Colombia
Tel.: (57) 17029116
Seal Distr
N.A.I.C.S.: 423840
German Rivera (Engr-Sls & Svc)

EagleBurgmann Czech s.r.o. (2)
Na Drahach 1364, Zbraslav, 156 00, Prague, Czech Republic
Tel.: (420) 257920505
Web Site: http://www.eagleburgmann.cz
Emp.: 19
Mechanical Seal & Coupling Mfr
N.A.I.C.S.: 332996
Petr Karasek (Gen Mgr)

EagleBurgmann Endustriyel Sizdirmalik Sanayi ve Ticaret Ltd. Sti. (2)
Melek Aras Bulvari Tuna Cad No 8, Tuzla, 34956, Istanbul, Turkiye
Tel.: (90) 2165930293
Web Site: http://www.eagleburgmann.com.tr
Sales Range: $10-24.9 Million
Emp.: 75
Mechanical Seals & Packings Mfr & Sls
N.A.I.C.S.: 339991

Subsidiary (Domestic):

EagleBurgmann Espey GmbH (2)
Thomas-Edison-Strasse 19, 47445, Moers, Germany
Tel.: (49) 2841998270
Web Site: http://www.eagleburgmann-espey.com
Emp.: 90
Steel Mfrs
N.A.I.C.S.: 339991

Subsidiary (Non-US):

EagleBurgmann France S.A.S. (2)
BP 96, 106 108 Rte De Cormeilles, F 78505, Sartrouville, France

Freudenberg SE—(Continued)

Tel.: (33) 00130865020
Web Site: http://www.burgmann.com
Sales Range: $25-49.9 Million
Emp.: 45
Mechanical Seals & Packings Sls
N.A.I.C.S.: 339991

EagleBurgmann Hungaria Kft. (2)
Lejtoe utca 6, 1124, Budapest, Hungary
Tel.: (36) 13198132
Gasket & Sealing Device Mfr
N.A.I.C.S.: 339991

EagleBurgmann Iberica S. A. (2)
Avda de Quitapesares 40, Madrid, 28670,
Villaviciosa de Odon, Spain
Tel.: (34) 916166601
Web Site: http://www.burgmaniberica.com
Sales Range: $25-49.9 Million
Emp.: 20
Mechanical Seals Mfr
N.A.I.C.S.: 339991
Rafael Jimenez (Gen Mgr)

Joint Venture (Non-US):

EagleBurgmann India Pvt. Ltd. (2)
Gazebo House 52 Gulmohar Road Opp
Cross Road No 7, JVPD Scheme Vile Parle
W, Mumbai, 400 049, India
Tel.: (91) 226 702 1489
Web Site: https://www.eagleburgmann.co.in
Sales Range: $50-74.9 Million
Emp.: 20
Mechanical Seals & Packings Mfr & Sls
N.A.I.C.S.: 339991

Subsidiary (Domestic):

EagleBurgmann India Pvt. Ltd. (3)
Door No 10-50-18/17 Flat No 1/7 First Floor
Siripuram Towers, Siripuram VIP Road, Vi-
sakhapatnam, 530 003, India
Tel.: (91) 8912755703
Mechanical Sealing Device Mfr
N.A.I.C.S.: 339991
Punkaj Dash (VP)

Subsidiary (US):

EagleBurgmann Industries LP (2)
10035 Brookriver Dr, Houston, TX 77040-
3193
Tel.: (713) 939-9515
Web Site: http://www.eagleburgmann.us
Mechanical Seals, Gaskets, Expansion
Joints & Ball Valves Distr
N.A.I.C.S.: 423840

Subsidiary (Non-US):

**EagleBurgmann Industries
Russia** (2)
Nizhny Novgorod Region Zavolzhje St The
Train 1 Building 45, Moscow, 606524, Rus-
sia
Tel.: (7) 83161 300 78
Web Site: http://www.eagleburgmann.ru
Sales Range: $25-49.9 Million
Emp.: 45
Mechanical Seals & Packings Mfr
N.A.I.C.S.: 339991
Stephan Fittkau (Mng Dir)

**EagleBurgmann Industries UK
LP** (2)
Tournament Fields 3 Wilton Drive, Warwick,
CV34 6RG, United Kingdom
Tel.: (44) 1926417600
Web Site: http://eagleburgmann.co.uk
Sales Range: $125-149.9 Million
Emp.: 40
Mechanical Seals & Packings Mfr & Sls
N.A.I.C.S.: 339991

EagleBurgmann Italia s.r.l. (2)
Via Martiri della Liberazione 12, 23875, Vi-
mercate, Osnago, Italy
Tel.: (39) 0399522501
Web Site: http://www.burgman.it
Sales Range: $25-49.9 Million
Emp.: 20
Sales of Mechanical Seals & Packings
N.A.I.C.S.: 339991
Alessandro Pizzi (Mng Dir)

Joint Venture (Non-US):

EagleBurgmann Japan Co., Ltd. (2)

514 Nakagawashin, Gosen, Niigata, 959-
1693, Japan
Tel.: (81) 25 047 1111
Web Site: https://www.eagleburgmann.jp
Sales Range: $200-249.9 Million
Emp.: 800
Metal Valve & Pipe Fitting Mfr
N.A.I.C.S.: 332919
Takafumi Tsuchiya (Pres)

Subsidiary (Non-US):

EagleBurgmann KE A/S (2)
Park Alle 34, 6600, Vejen, Denmark
Tel.: (45) 75361811
Web Site: http://www.eagleburgmann-ej.com
Rev.: $50,907,465
Emp.: 100
Mechanical Seal Packing & Expansion Distr
N.A.I.C.S.: 423840
Thorbjorn Hoyer (CEO)

EagleBurgmann KE Pte. Ltd. (2)
No 3 Tuas Drive 1 Level 2, Singapore,
638670, Singapore
Tel.: (65) 62618581
Web Site: http://www.eagleburgmann-ej.com
Sales Range: $1-9.9 Million
Emp.: 20
Mechanical Seals & Packings Mfr & Sls
N.A.I.C.S.: 339991

EagleBurgmann KE Pvt. Ltd. (2)
Survey No 109/2A-1B Old GNT Road,
Karanodai Sholavaram, Chennai, 600 067,
India
Tel.: (91) 4430882700
Web Site: http://www.eagleburgmann.co.in
Steel Mfrs
N.A.I.C.S.: 339991
Ajay Nair (Sr Mgr-Sls-Asia Pacific)

EagleBurgmann Korea Ltd. (2)
541 Suwolam Ri Seotan Myon Pyongtaik
Si, Kyongki, 451-850, Korea (South)
Tel.: (82) 313754095
Web Site: http://www.burgmannkorea.co.kr
Sales Range: $1-9.9 Million
Emp.: 30
Mechanical Seals, Packings & Expansion
Joints Mfr & Sls
N.A.I.C.S.: 339991

**EagleBurgmann Mexico S.A. de
C.V.** (2)
Calzada De Guadelupe Num 350 6 Col El
Cerrito, Cuautitlan Izcalli, Mexico, CP
54720, Mexico
Tel.: (52) 5558721841
Web Site:
http://www.eagleburgman.com.mx
Sales Range: $25-49.9 Million
Emp.: 128
Mechanical Seals & Packings Mfr & Sls
N.A.I.C.S.: 339991

**EagleBurgmann Middle East
FZE** (2)
Jebel Ali Free Zone Section RA08 Building
CC06, PO Box 61310, Jebel Ali, Dubai,
United Arab Emirates
Tel.: (971) 48838841
Web Site: http://www.eagleburgmann.ae
Sales Range: $1-9.9 Million
Emp.: 30
Steel Mfrs
N.A.I.C.S.: 339991

**EagleBurgmann Netherlands
B.V.** (2)
Koningsschot 9, 3905 PP, Veenendaal,
Netherlands
Tel.: (31) 318542000
Web Site: http://www.eagleburgmann.nl
Sales Range: $25-49.9 Million
Emp.: 21
Mechanical Seals & Packings Sls
N.A.I.C.S.: 339991

Joint Venture (Non-US):

**EagleBurgmann New Zealand,
Ltd.** (2)
47 William Pickering Drive, PO Box 300-
858, North Shore City Albany, Auckland,
752, New Zealand
Tel.: (64) 94485001
Sales Range: $25-49.9 Million
Emp.: 45
Mechanical Seals Mfr

N.A.I.C.S.: 339991
John Hill (Gen Mgr)

Subsidiary (Non-US):

EagleBurgmann Norway A/S (2)
Industriveien 25 D, PO Box 143, 2021,
Skedsmokorset, Norway
Tel.: (47) 64837550
Web Site: http://www.eagleburgmann.no
Sales Range: $25-49.9 Million
Emp.: 21
Mechanical Seals, Expansion Joints &
Packings Mfr
N.A.I.C.S.: 339991

**EagleBurgmann Nova Magnetics
Ltd.** (2)
1 Research Drive, Dartmouth, B2Y 4M9,
NS, Canada
Tel.: (902) 465-6625
Web Site: https://www.novamagnetics.ca
Blower Mfr
N.A.I.C.S.: 333111

EagleBurgmann OOO (2)
Godovikova Str 9 Building 3, 129085, Mos-
cow, Russia
Tel.: (7) 4957212981
Web Site: http://www.eagleburgmann.ru
Sales Range: $25-49.9 Million
Emp.: 30
Mechanical Sealing Device Mfr
N.A.I.C.S.: 339991
Eberharz Grizner (Mng Dir)

EagleBurgmann Philippines Inc. (2)
No 9769 National Rd Maduya, Carmona
Cavite, Cavite, 4116, Philippines
Tel.: (63) 464301426
Web Site: http://www.burgmann.com
Sales Range: $25-49.9 Million
Emp.: 33
Mechanical Seals & Packings Mfr & Sls
N.A.I.C.S.: 339991
Ananvit Homchan (Mng Dir)

**EagleBurgmann Poland sp. z
o.o.** (2)
Al Jerozolimskie 200, 02-486, Warsaw, Po-
land
Tel.: (48) 225351600
Web Site: http://www.eagleburgmann.pl
Emp.: 50
Seal Distr
N.A.I.C.S.: 423840
Andreas Raps (CEO & Gen Mgr)

**EagleBurgmann Production Center
Judenburg GmbH** (2)
Gruenhueblgasse 8, 8750, Judenburg, Aus-
tria
Tel.: (43) 35728279
Steel Mfrs
N.A.I.C.S.: 339991
Felix Hagemann (Mng Dir & Gen Mgr)

**EagleBurgmann Production Center
S.A. de C.V.** (2)
Av 5 de Febrero 1702 Zona Industrial
Benito, Ciudad Juarez, 76120, Mexico
Tel.: (52) 4420000011
Seal Distr
N.A.I.C.S.: 423840

EagleBurgmann RO SRL (2)
Bdul Iuliu Maniu Nr 7 Cladirea E Parter
Hala 3 Sector 6, 061072, Bucharest, Roma-
nia
Tel.: (40) 31 425 0909
Mechanical Sealing Device Mfr
N.A.I.C.S.: 339991

**EagleBurgmann Saudi Arabia Co.
Ltd.** (2)
Al Fayhaa Industrial Area Aziziyah Road,
PO Box 77148, 31952, Al Khobar, Saudi
Arabia
Tel.: (966) 138906111
Web Site: http://www.eagleburgmann.sa
Seal Distr
N.A.I.C.S.: 423840
Tanveer Shaikh (Mgr-Svc)

**EagleBurgmann Seals South Africa
(Pty) Ltd.** (2)
No 1 Brunton Circle Sandersville South, PO
Box 1210, Edenvale, 1610, Gauteng, South
Africa
Tel.: (27) 114579000

Web Site: http://www.eagleburgmann.co.za
Sales Range: $25-49.9 Million
Emp.: 128
Seals, Packing Components, Fabric & Metal
Expansion Joints Mfr
N.A.I.C.S.: 339991
Peter Leresche (Mng Dir)

**EagleBurgmann Singapore Pte.
Ltd** (2)
15 Kwong Min Road, Singapore, 628718,
Singapore
Tel.: (65) 64813439
Industrial Machinery Mfr
N.A.I.C.S.: 333248

EagleBurgmann Sweden AB (2)
Svaermaregatan 3, 603 61, Norrkoping,
Sweden
Tel.: (46) 011140005
Web Site: http://www.burgman.com
Sales Range: $25-49.9 Million
Emp.: 30
Mechanical Seals & Packings Mfr & Sls
N.A.I.C.S.: 339991

Branch (Domestic):

EagleBurgmann Sweden AB (3)
Arbetsledarvagen 12, 85753, Sundsvall,
Sweden
Tel.: (46) 60645090
Gasket & Sealing Component Mfr
N.A.I.C.S.: 339991

Subsidiary (Non-US):

**EagleBurgmann Taiwan
Corporation** (2)
No 134 Hsi Lin Road Yenchao, Kaohsiung,
Taiwan
Tel.: (886) 76164401
Sales Range: $100-124.9 Million
Emp.: 300
Adhesive Mfr
N.A.I.C.S.: 325520

**EagleBurgmann Vietnam Company
Ltd.** (2)
343 Pham Ngu Lao Street 6th Floor Suite
6C International Plaza, Pham Ngu Lao
Ward District 1, Ho Chi Minh City, Vietnam
Tel.: (84) 8 6291 5648
Sales Range: $25-49.9 Million
Emp.: 12
Industrial Machinery Mfr
N.A.I.C.S.: 333248

**EagleBurgmann de Venezuela,
C.A.** (2)
Calle 6 con Calle 9 Edif Fant piso 2, Zona
Industrial La Urbina, Caracas, 1070, Ven-
ezuela
Tel.: (58) 2122421548
Sales Range: $25-49.9 Million
Emp.: 30
Mechanical Seals & Packings Mfr
N.A.I.C.S.: 339991

**EagleBurgmann do Brasil Vedacoes
Industrias Ltda.** (2)
Av Santa Izabel 1721 Barao Geraldo, PO
Box 6560, 13084-643, Campinas, Sao
Paulo, Brazil
Tel.: (55) 1931145600
Web Site:
http://www.eagleburgmann.com.br
Sales Range: $25-49.9 Million
Emp.: 110
Mechanical Seal & Packaging Mfr
N.A.I.C.S.: 339991

Joint Venture (Non-US):

P.T. EagleBurgmann Indonesia (2)
Kawasan East Jakarta Industrial Park EJIP
Plot 7G-4, Cikarang Selatan, 17530,
Bekasi, 17530, Jawa Barat, Indonesia
Tel.: (62) 218975728
Web Site: https://www.eagleburgmann.co.id
Sales Range: $50-74.9 Million
Emp.: 125
Mechanical Seals & Packings Mfr & Sls
N.A.I.C.S.: 339991

EagleBurgmann KE, Inc. (1)
Expansion Joint Solutions 10038 Marathon
Pkwy, Lakeside, CA 92040
Tel.: (619) 562-6083
Seal Distr

N.A.I.C.S.: 423840
Kathy Tyson *(Coord-Mktg)*

Elefanten Portuguesa Lda. Industria de Calcado **(1)**
Alameda Da Bela Vesta, 4415939, Seixe-zelo, Portugal **(100%)**
Tel.: (351) 227471160
Mfr of Shoes
N.A.I.C.S.: 316210

Externa Handels- und Beteiligungsge-sellschaft mbh **(1)**
Hoehnerweg 2 4, 69469, Weinheim, Germany **(100%)**
Tel.: (49) 6201800
Web Site: http://www.freudenberg.com
Rubber Products Mfr
N.A.I.C.S.: 326299

FHP Export GmbH **(1)**
Im Technologiepark 19, Baden-Wurttemberg, 69469, Weinheim, Germany **(100%)**
Tel.: (49) 280887706
Web Site: http://www.fhpexport.diytrade.com
Sales Range: $25-49.9 Million
Emp.: 30
Industrial Products
N.A.I.C.S.: 333310

FHP Hellas S.A. **(1)**
36 Acharnon Str, 14564, Kifissia, Greece
Tel.: (30) 2106236352
Emp.: 35
Industrial Machinery Distr
N.A.I.C.S.: 423830
George Lioutas *(Gen Mgr)*

FHP Holding GmbH **(1)**
Im Technologiepark 19, 69469, Weinheim, Germany **(100%)**
Tel.: (49) 6201800
Holding Company
N.A.I.C.S.: 551112

FHP Vileda S.A. **(1)**
4 Avenue Laurent Cely 4e Etage - Hall D, 92600, Asnieres, Cedex, France **(100%)**
Tel.: (33) 141322232
Web Site: http://www.vileda.com
Sales Range: $10-24.9 Million
Emp.: 25
Sales of Household Cleaning Products (Non-Chemcal)
N.A.I.C.S.: 424690

FHP Vileda S.C.S. **(1)**
Avenue Andre Ernst 3b, 4800, Verviers, Belgium
Tel.: (32) 87322154
Cleaning Equipment Distr
N.A.I.C.S.: 423810

FHP Vileda Sp. z.o.o. **(1)**
Ul Pulawska 182, 02-670, Warsaw, Poland **(100%)**
Tel.: (48) 422794445
Web Site: http://www.vileda.pl
Sales Range: $25-49.9 Million
Emp.: 20
Sales of Rubber Products
N.A.I.C.S.: 424990

FHP di R. Freudenberg S.A.S. **(1)**
Via dei Valtorta 48, 20127, Milan, Italy **(100%)**
Tel.: (39) 022886466
Web Site: http://www.freudenberg.com
Sales Range: $25-49.9 Million
Emp.: 40
Mechanical Household Cleaning Products & Laundry Care Products Distr
N.A.I.C.S.: 423990

Freudenberg & Co. Ltd. Partnership **(1)**
Weinheim, 69465, Weinheim, Germany **(100%)**
Tel.: (49) 6201800
Web Site: http://www.freudenberg.com
Sales Range: $25-49.9 Million
Emp.: 50
Mfr of Rubber, Plastics Processing; Nonwovens Production; Flooring
N.A.I.C.S.: 326299

Freudenberg & Vilene Filter (Thailand) Co. Ltd. **(1)**
700 427 Moo 7 Tambol Dou Hua Roh,

Amata Nakorn Industrial Estate, Amphur Muang, 20000, Chon Buri, Thailand
Tel.: (66) 384532145
Web Site: http://th.freudenberg-filter.com
Filter Mfr
N.A.I.C.S.: 333413
Oratai Penput *(Sls Mgr-Turbomachinery)*

Freudenberg Anlagen-und Werkzeugtechnik KG **(1)**
Dr Werner Freyberg Strasse 7, Laudenbach, 69514, Germany **(100%)**
Tel.: (49) 6201806345
Web Site: http://www.fft.com
Emp.: 70
Mfr of Industrial Machinery
N.A.I.C.S.: 333248
Manfred Cech *(Mgr)*

Freudenberg Austria GmbH **(1)**
Sparchner Strasse 23, Kufstein, 6330, Tirol, Austria
Tel.: (43) 537269100
Industrial Machinery Distr
N.A.I.C.S.: 423830

Freudenberg Beteiligungsgesellschaft mbH **(1)**
Hoehnerweg 2-4, 69469, Weinheim, Germany **(100%)**
Tel.: (49) 6201800
Web Site: http://www.freudenberg.com
Mfr of Rubber
N.A.I.C.S.: 326299

Freudenberg Chemical Specialities SE & Co. KG **(1)**
Geisenhausenerstrasse 7, 81379, Munich, Germany **(100%)**
Tel.: (49) 8978760
Web Site: http://www.fcs-muenchen.com
Sales Range: $750-799.9 Million
Emp.: 2,400
Holding Company; Lubricants & Other Specialty Chemical Products Mfr
N.A.I.C.S.: 551112
Hanno D. Wentzler *(Chm, Pres & CEO)*

Division (US):

Chem-Trend Limited Partnership **(2)**
1445 McPherson Park Dr, Howell, MI 48843-3947 **(100%)**
Tel.: (517) 546-4520
Web Site: http://www.chemtrend.com
Sales Range: $125-149.9 Million
Emp.: 340
Mold Releases Mfr for the Plastic & Rubber Industries; Die Lubricants, Quench Compounds, Plunger Lubricants, Tire Releasants Mfr
N.A.I.C.S.: 324191
Carl Posluszny *(CFO & Exec VP)*

Subsidiary (Non-US):

Chem-Trend (Deutchland) GmbH **(3)**
Ganghofer Strasse 47, Maisach, 82216, Germany **(100%)**
Tel.: (49) 81424170
Web Site: http://www.chemtrends.com
Sales Range: $25-49.9 Million
Emp.: 60
Mfr of Lubricants
N.A.I.C.S.: 324191
Peter Schatzler *(Mng Dir)*

Subsidiary (Domestic):

Kluber Lubrication Deutschland SE & Co. KG **(2)**
Geisenhausenerstrasse 7, PO Box 70 10 47, 81379, Munich, Germany
Tel.: (49) 897876200
Web Site: http://www.klueber.com
Emp.: 2,040
Lubricant Mfr & Distr
N.A.I.C.S.: 325998

Subsidiary (Non-US):

Kluber Lubricacion Mexicana S.A. de C.V. **(3)**
Parque Industrial Queretaro Av La montana 109 Km 28 5 Carr Qro -S L P, Santa Rosa Jauregui, 76220, Queretaro, Mexico
Tel.: (52) 4422295700
Lubricant Distr
N.A.I.C.S.: 424720

Kluber Lubrication (Korea) Ltd. **(3)**
83 Uisadang-daero, Seoul, 07325, Yeongdeungpo-gu, Korea (South) **(50%)**
Tel.: (82) 27825151
Web Site: http://www.klueber.co.kr
Sales Range: $25-49.9 Million
Emp.: 75
Mfr of Lubricants
N.A.I.C.S.: 324191
Kichung Eum *(Gen Mgr)*

Kluber Lubrication (Malaysia) Sdn. Bhd. **(3)**
No 17 Jalan PJU 3/49 Sunway Damansara Technology Park, 47810, Petaling Jaya, Selangor, Malaysia
Tel.: (60) 378034954
Lubricant Distr
N.A.I.C.S.: 424720
Lawrence Hng *(Sr Acct Mgr-Heavy Industry)*

Kluber Lubrication (Pty.) Ltd. **(3)**
12 C Barium, PO Box 11461, Randhart, Alberton, 1449, South Africa **(100%)**
Tel.: (27) 119082457
Web Site: http://www.klueber.com
Sales Range: $25-49.9 Million
Emp.: 14
Sales of Lubricants.
N.A.I.C.S.: 424690
Hennie C. Aucamp *(Mng Dir)*

Kluber Lubrication (Shanghai) Co., Ltd. **(3)**
No 88 Tuo Qing Road Qingpu Industry Zone, Shanghai, 201700, China
Tel.: (86) 2169225666
Lubricant Distr
N.A.I.C.S.: 424720
Wei Xu *(Project Mgr)*

Kluber Lubrication A.S. **(3)**
Literbuen 9, 2740, Skovlunde, Denmark **(100%)**
Tel.: (45) 70234277
Web Site: http://www.klueber.com
Sales Range: $50-74.9 Million
Emp.: 7
Sales of Lubricants.
N.A.I.C.S.: 424690

Kluber Lubrication AG (Schweiz) **(3)**
Thurgauerstrasse 39, PO Box 8727, 8050, Zurich, Switzerland **(100%)**
Tel.: (41) 443086969
Web Site: http://www.klueber.com
Sales Range: $1-9.9 Million
Emp.: 14
Lubricant Mfr
N.A.I.C.S.: 424690

Kluber Lubrication Argentina S.A. **(3)**
Martin J Haedo 4301/63, Florida, Buenos Aires, 1602, Argentina **(100%)**
Tel.: (54) 1147091400
Web Site: http://www.klueber.com
Sales Range: $25-49.9 Million
Emp.: 30
Rubber Mfr
N.A.I.C.S.: 326299
Diego Miguel *(Gen Mgr)*

Kluber Lubrication Australia Pty. Ltd. **(3)**
3 Brand Dr, PO Box 4, Thomastown, 3074, VIC, Australia **(100%)**
Tel.: (61) 394647577
Web Site: http://www.kluber.com.au
Sales Range: $25-49.9 Million
Emp.: 20
Sales of Lubricants.
N.A.I.C.S.: 424690
Kevin Seeley *(Mng Dir)*

Kluber Lubrication Austria GmbH **(3)**
Franz-W Schererstrasse 32, PO Box 84, Salzburg, 5020, Austria **(100%)**
Tel.: (43) 6624527050
Web Site: http://www.klueber.com
Sales Range: $25-49.9 Million
Emp.: 50
Lubrication Mfr
N.A.I.C.S.: 324191
Marcus Murmann *(Gen Mgr)*

Kluber Lubrication Belgium Netherlands S.A. **(3)**
Rue Cardinal Mercier 100, 7711, Dottignies, Belgium
Tel.: (32) 56483311

Web Site: http://www.kluber.com
Emp.: 10
Lubricant Mfr & Distr
N.A.I.C.S.: 325998
Thomas Berger *(Gen Mgr)*

Kluber Lubrication Benelux S.A. **(3)**
Rue Cardinal Mercier 100, 7711, Dottignies, Belgium **(100%)**
Tel.: (32) 56483333
Web Site: http://www.klueber.com
Sales Range: $25-49.9 Million
Emp.: 139
Mfr of Lubricants
N.A.I.C.S.: 324191

Kluber Lubrication CZ, s.r.o. **(3)**
Bohunicka 133/50, 619 00, Brno, Czech Republic
Tel.: (420) 544526200
Lubricant Distr
N.A.I.C.S.: 424720

Kluber Lubrication Chile Ltda. **(3)**
Av Edo Frei Montalva 9950 Modulo B1 - Cargo Park, Quilicura, Santiago, Chile
Tel.: (56) 27471188
Lubricant Distr
N.A.I.C.S.: 424720

Kluber Lubrication China Ltd. **(3)**
Room 1012 Shatin Galleria 18-24 Shan Mei Street, Fotan, Sha Tin, NT, China (Hong Kong) **(100%)**
Tel.: (852) 26920191
Web Site: http://www.klueber.com
Sales Range: $50-74.9 Million
Emp.: 8
Sales of Lubricants.
N.A.I.C.S.: 424690

Kluber Lubrication France S.A.S. **(3)**
14 16 Allee Eugene Ducretet, 26014, Valence, Cedex, France **(100%)**
Tel.: (33) 475448436
Web Site: http://www.klueber.com
Sales Range: $25-49.9 Million
Emp.: 25
Sales of Lubricants.
N.A.I.C.S.: 424690

Kluber Lubrication GmbH Iberica S.en C. **(3)**
Carretera C-17 KM 15 5, Parets del Valles, 08150, Barcelona, Spain **(100%)**
Tel.: (34) 902435500
Web Site: http://www.klueber.com
Emp.: 100
Mfr of Lubricants
N.A.I.C.S.: 324191
Jose Maria Torrens *(Gen Dir-Fin & Admin)*

Kluber Lubrication Great Britain Ltd. **(3)**
Longbow Close Pennine Business Park, Huddersfield, HD2 1GQ, United Kingdom
Tel.: (44) 1422205115
Web Site: http://www.klueber.com
Sales Range: $25-49.9 Million
Emp.: 25
Lubricants Whslr
N.A.I.C.S.: 424690

Kluber Lubrication India Pvt. Ltd. **(3)**
III Floor Silver Jubilee Block III Cross Mission Road, Bengaluru, 560 027, Karnataka, India
Tel.: (91) 8066901200
Lubricant Distr
N.A.I.C.S.: 424720
Ganesh Raj *(Mgr-IT)*

Plant (Domestic):

Kluber Lubrication India Pvt. Ltd. - Mysore Factory **(4)**
347-A Hebbal Industrial Area, Mysore, 570 016, India
Tel.: (91) 8213941041
Lubricant Mfr
N.A.I.C.S.: 325998

Subsidiary (Non-US):

Kluber Lubrication Italia S.A.S. **(3)**
Via Monferrato 57, Sesto Ulteriano San Giuliano M, 20098, San Giuliano Milanese, Milan, Italy **(100%)**
Tel.: (39) 02982131
Web Site: http://www.klueber.com

Freudenberg SE—(Continued)

Sales Range: $25-49.9 Million
Emp.: 55
Mfr of Lubrication
N.A.I.C.S.: 324191

Kluber Lubrication Lubrificantes Especiais Ltda. & Cia. (3)
Rua Sao Paulo 345, Distrito Industrial de Alphaville, 06465-902, Barueri, Sao Paulo, Brazil (100%)
Tel.: (55) 1135559000
Web Site: http://www.klueber.com
Sales Range: $25-49.9 Million
Emp.: 100
Mfr of Lubricants
N.A.I.C.S.: 324191
Enrique Garcia (CEO-South America & Australia)

Kluber Lubrication Mexicana S.A. De C.V. (3)
Parque Industrial Queretaro Av La Montana 109 km 28 5 carr Qro SLP, Santa Rosa Jauregui, 76220, Queretaro, Mexico (100%)
Tel.: (52) 4422295700
Web Site: http://www.klueber.com
Sales Range: $1-9.9 Million
Emp.: 52
Mfr of Lubricants
N.A.I.C.S.: 324191

Subsidiary (Domestic):

Kluber Lubrication Munchen SE & Co. KG (3)
Geisenhausenerstrasse 7, 81379, Munich, Germany (100%)
Tel.: (49) 8978760
Web Site: http://www.kluber.com
Sales Range: $400-449.9 Million
Emp.: 1,500
Lubricant Mfr
N.A.I.C.S.: 324191
Claus Langgartner (Member-Mgmt Bd)

Subsidiary (Non-US):

Kluber Lubrication Nordic A/S (3)
Literbuen 9, 2740, Skovlunde, Denmark
Tel.: (45) 70234277
Lubricant Mfr
N.A.I.C.S.: 424720

Subsidiary (US):

Kluber Lubrication North America LP (3)
32 Industrial Dr, Londonderry, NH 03053-7438 (100%)
Tel.: (603) 647-4104
Web Site: http://www.kluberna.com
Sales Range: $25-49.9 Million
Emp.: 70
Lubricant Mfr
N.A.I.C.S.: 324191
Ron Person (Dir-Bus Dev-Oil & Gas)

Subsidiary (Domestic):

KL Texas L.P. (4)
9010 County Rd 2120, Tyler, TX 75707
Tel.: (903) 534-8021
Web Site: http://www.klsummit.com
Lubricant Mfr
N.A.I.C.S.: 325998

Subsidiary (Non-US):

Kluber Lubrication OOO (3)
Ave Andropova d 18 building 6 Office 5-12, 115432, Moscow, Russia
Tel.: (7) 4994180033
Web Site: http://www.klueber.com
Lubricant Distr
N.A.I.C.S.: 424720

Kluber Lubrication Polska Sp. z o.o. (3)
ul Wierzbiecice 44a, 61-558, Poznan, Poland
Tel.: (48) 618700790
Lubricant Distr
N.A.I.C.S.: 424720
Grzegorz Topolewski (Mgr-Logistics)

Kluber Lubrication South East Asia Pte. Ltd. (3)

25 International Business Park 04-25/26 German Centre, Singapore, 609916, Singapore (100%)
Tel.: (65) 65629470
Web Site: http://www.klueber.com
Sales Range: $25-49.9 Million
Emp.: 7
Sales of Lubricants
N.A.I.C.S.: 324191

Kluber Lubrication Yaglama Urunleri Sanayi Ve Ticaret A.S. (3)
Organize Sanayi Bolgesi Karaagac Mah 10 Sok No 7 PK 56, Kapakli, 59500, Tekirdag, Turkiye (100%)
Tel.: (90) 2827581530
Web Site: http://www.klueber.com
Sales Range: $25-49.9 Million
Emp.: 42
Mfr of Lubricants
N.A.I.C.S.: 324191

Joint Venture (Non-US):

NOK-Kluber Co., Ltd. (3)
1-12-15 Shiba Daimon, Minato-ku, Tokyo, 105-0122, Japan (49%)
Tel.: (81) 293427319
Web Site: https://www.nokklueber.co.jp
Sales Range: $25-49.9 Million
Emp.: 115
Lubricant Mfr
N.A.I.C.S.: 324191

Freudenberg Dichtungs- und Schwingungstechnik GmbH & Co. KG (1)
Hohnerweg 2-4, 69465, Weinheim, Germany (100%)
Tel.: (49) 6201806666
Web Site: http://www.freudenberg-ds.com
Sales Range: $1-4.9 Billion
Emp.: 6,000
Rubber Seals Mfr
N.A.I.C.S.: 339991
Arman Barimani (Member-Mgmt Bd)

Freudenberg Espana S.A. (1)
Ctra C-17 Km 15 Pol Ind Can Volart, Parets del Valles, 08150, Barcelona, Spain (100%)
Tel.: (34) 935656200
Web Site: http://www.freudenberg.com
Sales Range: $50-74.9 Million
Emp.: 200
Rubber Products Mfr
N.A.I.C.S.: 326299

Freudenberg Espana S.A., Telas sin Tejer S.en (1)
Ctra C 17 15 km, Parets Del Valles, 08150, Barcelona, Spain (100%)
Tel.: (34) 935656200
Web Site: http://www.freudenberg.nw.com
Sales Range: $25-49.9 Million
Emp.: 200
Mfr of Nonwoven Interlinings
N.A.I.C.S.: 313230
Peter Schaefer (Gen Mgr)

Freudenberg Evolon S.A.S.U. (1)
20 rue Ampere, 68000, Colmar, France
Tel.: (33) 389206479
Web Site: http://www.evolon.com
Fabrics Mfr
N.A.I.C.S.: 314999
Ulrich Jahn (Dir-Publi)

Freudenberg Evolon s.a.r.l. (1)
20 Rue Ampere, 68027, Colmars, Cedex, France (100%)
Tel.: (33) 3892064
Web Site: http://www.freudenberg.com
Sales Range: $25-49.9 Million
Emp.: 45
Mfr of Nonwovens
N.A.I.C.S.: 313230

Freudenberg Far Eastern Spunweb Comp. Ltd. (1)
38 Lun Din, Shi Hai Village Tayuan, Taoyuan, 33751, Taiwan (60.18%)
Tel.: (886) 33841188
Web Site: http://www.freudenberg.com
Sales Range: $25-49.9 Million
Emp.: 100
Mfr of Nonwoven Products
N.A.I.C.S.: 313230
Lingow Ming (Pres)

Freudenberg Filtration Technologies (Aust) Pty. Ltd. (1)

69 Malcolm Rd, Braeside, 3195, VIC, Australia
Tel.: (61) 85879900
Web Site: http://www.freudenberg-filter.com.au
Filtration Device Mfr & Distr
N.A.I.C.S.: 336390

Freudenberg Filtration Technologies (Pty) Ltd. (1)
48 Koornhof Road Meadowdale Ext 1, Germiston, South Africa
Tel.: (27) 119294500
Web Site: http://www.freudenberg-filter.co.za
Filtration Device Mfr & Distr
N.A.I.C.S.: 336390

Freudenberg Filtration Technologies Finland Oy (1)
Lisenssikatu 11A, 21100, Naantali, Finland
Tel.: (358) 290091970
Web Site: http://www.freudenberg-filter.fi
Filtration Device Distr
N.A.I.C.S.: 423120

Freudenberg Filtration Technologies Inc. (1)
649 Wilton Grove Road, London, N6N 1N7, ON, Canada
Tel.: (519) 686-9888
Natural Gas Distr
N.A.I.C.S.: 221210

Freudenberg Filtration Technologies India Private Limited (1)
837/2 Pune-Nagar Road Nr Hotel Dawat Sanaswadi, Taluka Shirur, Pune, 412208, India
Tel.: (91) 2030082012
Filtration Device Distr
N.A.I.C.S.: 423120
Ashok Pandey (Gen Mgr)

Freudenberg Filtration Technologies LP (1)
2975 Pembroke Rd, Hopkinsville, KY 42240
Tel.: (270) 887-5115
Web Site: http://www.freudenberg-filter.us
Filtration Device Distr
N.A.I.C.S.: 423120

Freudenberg Filtration Technologies OOO (1)
pos Zhdanovsky Pridorozhnaya street 11 room 8, 607684, Kstovo, Russia
Tel.: (7) 9108981467
Web Site: http://www.freudenberg-filter.ru
Filtration Device Distr
N.A.I.C.S.: 423120

Freudenberg Filtration Technologies SAS (1)
3 Avenue du Quebec, 91140, Villebon-sur-Yvette, Cedex, France
Tel.: (33) 169183838
Web Site: http://www.freudenberg-filter.fr
Filtration Device Distr
N.A.I.C.S.: 423120
Philippe Clement (Prés)

Freudenberg Filtration Technologies SE & Co. KG (1)
Hohnerweg 2-4, Weinheim, 69465, Germany
Tel.: (49) 6201 80 6264
Web Site: http://www.freudenberg-filter.com
Filtration Services
N.A.I.C.S.: 333413
Andreas Kreuter (CEO)

Subsidiary (US):

Protect Plus Air, LLC (2)
420 3rd Ave NW Ste A, Hickory, NC 28601-4984
Tel.: (813) 250-9247
Web Site: http://www.protectplusair.com
General Purpose Machinery Manufacturing
N.A.I.C.S.: 333998
John R. Genter (Dir-Sls)

Freudenberg Filtration Technologies Slovensko, s.r.o. (1)
Potvorice 260, 916 25, Potvorice, Slovakia
Tel.: (421) 327461307
Filtration Device Distr
N.A.I.C.S.: 423120
Radovan Malec (Mgr-CIP)

Freudenberg Filtration Technologies UK Limited (1)

Riverside Mills Saddleworth Road, Elland, HX5 0RY, Halifax, United Kingdom
Tel.: (44) 1270655575
Web Site: http://uk.freudenberg-filter.com
Filtration Device Distr
N.A.I.C.S.: 423120
Kevin Jones (Mgr-Technical Support)

Freudenberg Gospodinjski Proizvodi d.o.o. (1)
Limbuska cesta 2, 2341, Limbus, Slovenia
Tel.: (386) 24294910
Web Site: http://www.vileda.si
Fabrics Mfr
N.A.I.C.S.: 314999

Freudenberg Gygli AG (1)
Chamerstrasse 170, 6300, Zug, Switzerland
Tel.: (41) 417413941
Apparels Mfr
N.A.I.C.S.: 315250

Freudenberg Haztartasi Cikkek Kereskedelmi BT (1)
Retkoz u 5, 1118, Budapest, Hungary
Tel.: (36) 12792060
Cleaning Equipment Distr
N.A.I.C.S.: 423850

Freudenberg Home & Cleaning Solutions Iberica, S.L.U. (1)
Carrer Can Gurri 1A Pol Ind Can Volart, 08150, Parets del Valles, Barcelona, Spain
Tel.: (34) 934624800
Advanced Material Whslr
N.A.I.C.S.: 423390

Freudenberg Home & Cleaning Solutions s.r.o. (1)
Na Kralovce 4, 101 00, Prague, Czech Republic
Tel.: (420) 271011011
Web Site: http://shop.vileda.cz
Household Goods Distr
N.A.I.C.S.: 423620
Jiri Krofta (Sls Dir)

Freudenberg Household Products (Suzhou) Co., Ltd. (1)
1720 Bin He Road, Suzhou, 215011, China
Tel.: (86) 51268243327
Household Product Distr
N.A.I.C.S.: 423220

Freudenberg Household Products (Taiwan) Co., Ltd. (1)
4F-6 No 496 Bannan Rd, Zhonghe Distr, 23556, New Taipei City, Taiwan
Tel.: (886) 232347266
Household Product Distr
N.A.I.C.S.: 423220

Freudenberg Household Products AB (1)
Hospitalsgatan 70, PO Box 608, Norrkoping, 602 28, Sweden (100%)
Tel.: (46) 11197900
Web Site: http://www.freudenberg.com
Sales Range: $50-74.9 Million
Emp.: 105
Mfr of Rubber Products
N.A.I.C.S.: 326299
Peter Lehnhardt (Gen Mgr)

Freudenberg Household Products AS (1)
Industriveien 25 inngang B, PO Box 220, 2021, Skedsmokorset, Norway
Tel.: (47) 63872666
Web Site: http://www.vileda.no
Cleaning Equipment Distr
N.A.I.C.S.: 423810

Freudenberg Household Products B.V. (1)
Industriepark KleefseWaard Westervoortsedijk 73, Postbus 9600, 6827 AV, Arnhem, Netherlands (100%)
Tel.: (31) 263665558
Web Site: http://www.freudenberg.com
Sales Range: $25-49.9 Million
Emp.: 20
Mfr of Synthetic Chamois Products
N.A.I.C.S.: 316110

Freudenberg Household Products Evici Kullanim Araclari Sanayi ve Ticaret A.S. (1)
Aksel is Merkezi A Blok 35-1 Kisikli Caddesi

Altunizade, Uskudar, Istanbul, Turkiye
Tel.: (90) 2165549913
Household Product Distr
N.A.I.C.S.: 423220

Freudenberg Household Products Inc. (1)
666 Blvd St Martin West, Laval, H7M 3J4, QC, Canada
Tel.: (450) 975-4535
Cleaning Equipment Distr
N.A.I.C.S.: 423810

Freudenberg Household Products LP (1)
Vileda House 2 Chichester Street, Rochdale, OL16 2AX, United Kingdom
Tel.: (44) 1706759597
Cleaning Equipment Distr
N.A.I.C.S.: 423810

Freudenberg Household Products LP (1)
Vileda House 2 Chichester Street, Rochdale, OL16 2AX, United Kingdom
Tel.: (44) 1706759597
Cleaning Equipment Distr
N.A.I.C.S.: 423810

Freudenberg Household Products LP (1)
2188 Diehl Rd, Aurora, IL 60502-8775 **(100%)**
Tel.: (708) 452-4100
Web Site: http://www.ocedar.com
Sales Range: $25-49.9 Million
Emp.: 45
Mop Sponge Mop & Refill Broom & Dust Mop Mfr
N.A.I.C.S.: 339994
Tim Molek *(Gen Mgr)*

Freudenberg Household Products LP (1)
2 Chichester Street, Rochdale, OL16 2AX, Lancashire, United Kingdom **(100%)**
Tel.: (44) 3457697356
Web Site: http://www.vileda.com
Sales Range: $25-49.9 Million
Emp.: 45
Sales of Rubber Products
N.A.I.C.S.: 424990
Mark Lockwood *(Controller-Fin)*

Freudenberg Household Products Ltd. (1)
Unit 902 9/F Yua Hwa International Building 1 Kowloon Park Drive, Tsim Sha Tsui, Hong Kong, China (Hong Kong)
Tel.: (852) 27383700
Cleaning Equipment Distr.
N.A.I.C.S.: 423810

Freudenberg Household Products Oy AB (1)
Elimaenkatu 32, Box 1055, 00521, Helsinki, Finland **(100%)**
Tel.: (358) 92777220
Web Site: http://www.freudenberg.com
Mfr of Rubber Products
N.A.I.C.S.: 326299

Freudenberg IT (Suzhou) Co., Ltd. (1)
Unit A 1-2 5/F Sicence Plaza 1355 Jin Ji Hu Avenue, International Science Park, Suzhou, 215021, China
Tel.: (86) 51262621988
Information Technology Consulting Services
N.A.I.C.S.: 541512
Horst Reichardt *(Chm)*

Freudenberg IT LP (1)
430 Davis Dr Ste 180, Morrisville, NC 27560
Tel.: (866) 705-6385
Information Technology Consulting Services
N.A.I.C.S.: 541512

Freudenberg Iberica S.A. (1)
Zona Franca Sector B, Calle C 18-22, 08040, Barcelona, Spain **(100%)**
Tel.: (34) 932618610
Web Site: http://www.freudenbergespana.es
Sales Range: $75-99.9 Million
Emp.: 160
N.A.I.C.S.: 314910

Freudenberg Iberica S.A., S.en C. (1)
Pol. Ind. Can Volart Calle Gurri 1, Apartat de Correus 77, 08150, Parets del Valles, Spain
Tel.: (34) 935731011
Web Site: http://www.simrit.com
Sales Range: $50-74.9 Million
Emp.: 150
Mfr of Rubber Products
N.A.I.C.S.: 326299

Freudenberg Joints Elastomeres SAS (1)
Zone Industrielle Les Nouvelles Franchises, Langres, 52206, France
Tel.: (33) 325878071
Steel Mfrs
N.A.I.C.S.: 339991

Freudenberg Medical Europe GmbH (1)
Liebigstr 2-8, 67661, Kaiserslautern, Germany
Tel.: (49) 63153417600
Web Site: http://www.freudenbergmedical.de
Medical Equipment Mfr
N.A.I.C.S.: 339112

Freudenberg Medical srl. (1)
Zona Franca Coyol/Calle 4 Ave 0 Edificio B13 4, Alajuela, Costa Rica
Tel.: (506) 24331126
Medical Equipment Mfr
N.A.I.C.S.: 339112
Alexander Unfried *(Gen Mgr)*

Freudenberg NH Co. Ltd. (1)
2-2-5 Hanakawado, Taito-ku, Tokyo, 111-0033, Japan **(60%)**
Tel.: (81) 3 3842 8276
Web Site: http://www.freudenberg.com
Sales of Rubber Products
N.A.I.C.S.: 424690

Freudenberg Nao-Tecidos Ltda. & Cia. (1)
Ave Pres Humberto Alencar Castelo Branco 2735, 12321-150, Sao Paulo, Brazil **(100%)**
Tel.: (55) 123534222
Web Site: http://www.freudenberg.com
Mfr of Rubber Products
N.A.I.C.S.: 326299

Freudenberg Nao-Tecidos Ltda. & Cia. (1)
Av Presidente Humberto Alencar Castelo Branco 2735 - Rio Abaixo, 12321-150, Jacarei, SP, Brazil **(100%)**
Tel.: (55) 1221277500
Sales Range: $25-49.9 Million
Emp.: 200
Mfr of Nonwovens
N.A.I.C.S.: 313230

Freudenberg Nonwovens (Pty.) Ltd. (1)
46 Industria Ring Road Parow Industria, PO Box 3903, Cape Town, 7493, South Africa **(100%)**
Tel.: (27) 219333501
Web Site: http://www.freudenberg.com
Sales Range: $25-49.9 Million
Emp.: 100
Mfr of Nonwoven Interlinings
N.A.I.C.S.: 313230
Joseph Engelbrecht *(Mgr-Procurement)*

Freudenberg Nonwovens India Pvt. Ltd. (1)
No 104 Poonamallee High Road Velapanchavadi, 600 077, Chennai, India
Tel.: (91) 4432522477
Web Site: http://www.freudenberg.in
Emp.: 70
Fabrics Mfr
N.A.I.C.S.: 313230
G. Sivasailam *(Mng Dir)*

Freudenberg Nonwovens LP (1)
Dorcan 200 Murdock Road Dorcan Industrial Estate, Swindon, SN3 5HY, United Kingdom
Tel.: (44) 1793511160
Fabric Distr
N.A.I.C.S.: 424310
Tracey Hobbs *(Mgr-Operational Excellence)*

Freudenberg Nonwovens LP Vilene Interlinings (1)
Lowfields Business Park, Elland, HX5 5DX,

W Yorkshire, United Kingdom
Tel.: (44) 422327900
Web Site: http://www.vilene.com
Sales Range: $25-49.9 Million
Emp.: 75
Mfr of Nonwoven Interlinings
N.A.I.C.S.: 313230

Freudenberg Nonwovens Limited Partnership (1)
3500 Industrial Dr Eno Industrial Park, Durham, NC 27704 **(100%)**
Tel.: (919) 620-3900
Web Site: http://www.freudenberg.de
Sales Range: $125-149.9 Million
Emp.: 25
Nonwoven Textiles for Apparel, Industry & Air Filtration, Home Decorating Crafts, Full Range of Interlinings, Non-Woven, Woven & Knit
N.A.I.C.S.: 313230

Plant (Domestic):

Freudenberg Nonwovens Tuft Division (2)
3500 Industrial Dr, Durham, NC 27704-0910 **(100%)**
Tel.: (919) 471-2582
Web Site: http://www.freudenberg.com
Sales Range: $25-49.9 Million
Mfr of Spunbonded Nonwovens
N.A.I.C.S.: 313230
Dieter Hutter *(VP-Fin)*

Freudenberg Nonwovens Romania S.R.L. (1)
Str Turnului Nr 5, 500152, Brasov, Romania
Tel.: (40) 268401757
Web Site: http://www.freudenberg-nw.ro
Fabric Distr
N.A.I.C.S.: 424310
Francu Andreea *(Gen Mgr)*

Freudenberg North America Limited Partnership (1)
RR 104 Ragged Mtn Hwy, Bristol, NH 03222 **(100%)**
Tel.: (603) 744-2281
Web Site: http://www.fngp.com
Sales Range: $150-199.9 Million
Emp.: 280
Mfr of Rubber
N.A.I.C.S.: 326291
Bob Evans *(Pres)*

Freudenberg Oil & Gas Canada Inc. (1)
708 19th Avenue, Nisku, T9E 7W1, AB, Canada
Tel.: (780) 955-7500
Seal Distr
N.A.I.C.S.: 423840

Freudenberg Oil & Gas Pte. Ltd. (1)
30 Loyang Way 02-22 23 24, Singapore, 508769, Singapore
Tel.: (65) 65426933
Seal Distr
N.A.I.C.S.: 423840

Freudenberg Oil & Gas Technologies AS (1)
C O Lunds GT 24, PO Box 2176, 3003, Drammen, Norway
Tel.: (47) 32209300
Seal Distr
N.A.I.C.S.: 423840

Freudenberg Oil & Gas Technologies Ltd. (1)
Unit 4 Christchurch Road, Port Talbot, SA12 7BZ, United Kingdom
Tel.: (44) 1639822555
Seal Distr
N.A.I.C.S.: 423840
Dave Holmwood *(Reg Dir-Comml & Bus Dev-EU & Middle East)*

Freudenberg Oil & Gas Technologies Sdn. Bhd. (1)
No 17 Jalan P4/6 Bandar Teknologi Kajang, 43500, Semenyih, Selangor, Malaysia
Tel.: (60) 387233689
Seal Distr
N.A.I.C.S.: 423840
Azmi Mastuki *(Mgr-Ops)*

Freudenberg Oil & Gas UK Ltd. (1)

Harlaw Centre, Aberdeen, AB21 0GN, United Kingdom
Tel.: (44) 1224729580
Seal Distr
N.A.I.C.S.: 423840

Freudenberg Oil & Gas, LLC (1)
19500 State Hwy 249 Ste 440, Houston, TX 77070
Tel.: (281) 233-1400
Steel Mfrs
N.A.I.C.S.: 339991

Freudenberg Performance Materials Apparel SE & Co. KG (1)
Putterstrasse 22, 58636, Iserlohn, Germany
Tel.: (49) 2371966205
House Ware & Automobile Parts Mfr
N.A.I.C.S.: 332215

Freudenberg Performance Materials Holding SE & Co. KG (1)
Hohnerweg 2-4, 69465, Weinheim, Germany
Tel.: (49) 6201803229
House Ware & Automobile Parts Mfr
N.A.I.C.S.: 332215
John McNabb *(CTO)*

Freudenberg Performance Materials LP (1)
3500 Industrial Dr, Durham, NC 27704
Tel.: (919) 479-7212
Fabric Distr
N.A.I.C.S.: 424310
Markus Platz *(VP-Fin)*

Freudenberg Performance Materials Logistics SE & Co. KG (1)
Hohnerweg 2-4 Bau 360, 69465, Weinheim, Germany
Tel.: (49) 6201805799
House Ware & Automobile Parts Mfr
N.A.I.C.S.: 332215

Freudenberg Politex Ltd. (1)
Suite 24 D-G International Shipping & Finance Building No 720, Pudong Avenue, Shanghai, 200120, China
Tel.: (86) 2150367835
Roofing Product Distr
N.A.I.C.S.: 423310

Freudenberg Politex OOO (1)
Zheleznodorozhnaya str 1 bld 45, Zavolzhie, 606524, Nizhniy Novgorod, Russia
Tel.: (7) 8316121212
Roofing Product Distr
N.A.I.C.S.: 423310

Freudenberg Politex Sp. z o.o. (1)
Przybyszewskiego 176/178, 93-120, Lodz, Poland
Tel.: (48) 426767717
Roofing Product Distr
N.A.I.C.S.: 423310

Freudenberg Potreby pro domacnost, k.s. (1)
Na Kralovce 4, 101 00, Prague, Czech Republic
Tel.: (420) 271011011
Cleaning Equipment Distr
N.A.I.C.S.: 423810
Klaus Peter Meier *(CEO)*

Freudenberg Productos del Hogar Ltda. (1)
San Ignacio 500, Santiago, Chile
Tel.: (56) 225941900
Industrial Machinery Distr
N.A.I.C.S.: 423830

Freudenberg Productos del Hogar, S.A. de C.V. (1)
Insurgentes Sur 670 5to Piso Col Del Valle, 03100, Mexico, Mexico
Tel.: (52) 18000138800
Cleaning Equipment Distr
N.A.I.C.S.: 423810

Freudenberg Pty. Ltd. (1)
3 Brand Dr, PO Box 4, Thomastown, 3074, VIC, Australia **(100%)**
Tel.: (61) 394641022
Web Site: http://www.kluber.com.au
Sales Range: $50-74.9 Million
Emp.: 8
Sales of Rubber Products
N.A.I.C.S.: 424690

Freudenberg SE—(Continued)

Norman Moore *(Mng Dir)*

Freudenberg Real Estate GmbH **(1)**
Hohnerweg 2-4, 69465, Weinheim, Germany
Tel.: (49) 6201800
Real Estate Services
N.A.I.C.S.: 531390
Frank Schmitt *(CFO)*

Freudenberg S.A.S. **(1)**
170 Rue Branly ZI Sud B P 2062, 71020, Macon, Cedex, France **(100%)**
Tel.: (33) 385293000
Web Site: http://www.treudenberg.com
Sales Range: $25-49.9 Million
Emp.: 90
Mfr of Rubber Seals
N.A.I.C.S.: 326299

Freudenberg S.p.A. **(1)**
Via dei Valtorta 48, 20127, Milan, Italy
Tel.: (39) 022886466
Web Site: http://www.freudenberg.com
Sales Range: $25-49.9 Million
Emp.: 50
Mfr of Nonwoven Interlinings
N.A.I.C.S.: 313230

Freudenberg Schwab Vibration Control AG **(1)**
Soodstrasse 57, 8134, Adliswil, Switzerland
Tel.: (41) 447111717
Rubber Products Mfr
N.A.I.C.S.: 326291

Freudenberg Sealing Technologies **(1)**
Box 11004, Bromma, 16111, Sweden **(100%)**
Tel.: (46) 883 81 63
Web Site: http://www.fst.com
Sales Range: $25-49.9 Million
Emp.: 40
Mfr of Rubber Seals & other Rubber Products
N.A.I.C.S.: 326299

Freudenberg Sealing Technologies AG **(1)**
Thurgauerstrasse 39, 8050, Zurich, Switzerland
Tel.: (41) 443064422
Web Site: http://switzerland.fst.com
Sealing Components Mfr
N.A.I.C.S.: 339991
Guido Bruggemann *(Mng Dir)*

Freudenberg Sealing Technologies GmbH & Co. KG **(1)**
Hohnerweg 2-4, D-69469, Weinheim, Germany
Tel.: (49) 6201 80 66 66
Web Site: http://www.fst.com
Sealing Technologies & Automotive Engineering Sevices
N.A.I.C.S.: 339991
Claus Moehlenkamp *(CEO & Member-Mgmt Bd)*

Subsidiary (US):

Xalt Energy, LLC **(2)**
2700 S Saginaw Rd, Midland, MI 48640 **(50.1%)**
Tel.: (989) 486-8501
Web Site: http://www.xaltenergy.com
Storage Battery Mfr
N.A.I.C.S.: 335910
Jeff Michalski *(Pres & CEO)*

Freudenberg Sealing Technologies S.a.s. di Externa Italia S.r.l.u. **(1)**
Via Ferrua 4, Zona Industriale Porporata, 10064, Pinerolo, Italy
Tel.: (39) 0121392222
House Ware & Automobile Parts Mfr
N.A.I.C.S.: 332215
Gaetano Iezzi *(Mng Dir)*

Freudenberg Sealing Technologies SAS **(1)**
246 Route des Allogneraies, Charnay les Macon, 71850, Bourgogne, France
Tel.: (33) 385293000
Sealing Equipment Mfr & Whslr
N.A.I.C.S.: 339991

Freudenberg Sealing Technologies, S.L.U. **(1)**
Carrer Gurri 1 Poligono Can Volart, 08150, Parets del Valles, Spain
Tel.: (34) 935738700
Advanced Material Whslr
N.A.I.C.S.: 423390

Freudenberg Simmerringe Kft. **(1)**
Heliport repter, 6000, Kecskemet, Hungary
Tel.: (36) 76501890
Industrial Machinery Distr
N.A.I.C.S.: 423830

Freudenberg Simrit A/S **(1)**
Morteveien 6, PO Box 10, 1483, Skytta, Norway **(100%)**
Tel.: (47) 67067810
Web Site: http://www.simrit.com
Sales Range: $25-49.9 Million
Emp.: 12
Sales of Rubber Seals
N.A.I.C.S.: 424690

Freudenberg Simrit AG **(1)**
Thurgauer Strasse 39, Zurich, 8050, Switzerland **(100%)**
Tel.: (41) 443064422
Web Site: http://www.simrit.ch
Sales Range: $25-49.9 Million
Emp.: 25
Mfr of Rubber Seals
N.A.I.C.S.: 326299

Freudenberg Simrit B.V. **(1)**
Energiestraat 5, 1411 AC, Naarden, Netherlands **(100%)**
Tel.: (31) 356941049
Web Site: http://www.simrit.com
Sales Range: $25-49.9 Million
Emp.: 13
Sales of Rubber Seals
N.A.I.C.S.: 424690

Freudenberg Simrit Kufstein Ges.m.b.H. & Co. KG **(1)**
Untere Sparchen Str 43, 6332, Kufstein, Austria **(100%)**
Tel.: (43) 537269100
Web Site: http://www.simrit.de
Sales Range: $25-49.9 Million
Emp.: 320
Sales of Rubber Seals
N.A.I.C.S.: 424690

Freudenberg Simrit Polska Sp. z o.o. **(1)**
ulica Rzymska 4, 03-976, Warsaw, Poland
Tel.: (48) 228335897
Rubber Product Distr
N.A.I.C.S.: 423840

Freudenberg Simrit SAS **(1)**
170 Rue Branly, 71020, Macon, France **(100%)**
Tel.: (33) 385293000
Web Site: http://www.fst.com
Sales Range: $50-74.9 Million
Emp.: 70
Sealing Technology
N.A.I.C.S.: 339991

Freudenberg Spunweb Japan Company, Ltd. **(1)**
Crystafive 9F 2-5-12 Minami Senba, Chuo-Ku, Osaka, 542-0081, Japan
Tel.: (81) 647053880
Web Site: http://www.freudenberg-pm.com
Emp.: 9
Roofing Product Distr
N.A.I.C.S.: 423310
Jumpei Jofuku *(Mng Dir)*

Freudenberg Technical Products LP **(1)**
Silverfox Way New York Industrial Estate, North Shields, NE27 0QH, Tyne & Wear, United Kingdom **(100%)**
Tel.: (44) 1912269200
Web Site: http://www.freudenberg.com
Sales Range: $50-74.9 Million
Emp.: 250
Mfr of Rubber Products
N.A.I.C.S.: 326299

Freudenberg Telas sin Tejer S.A. **(1)**
Calle 94 No 193, Bellazagala, 1651, San Martin, Buenos Aires, Argentina **(100%)**
Tel.: (54) 1147538833
Web Site: http://www.freudenberg.com

Sales Range: $25-49.9 Million
Emp.: 100
Mfr of Rubber Products & Nonwoven Interlinings
N.A.I.C.S.: 326299

Freudenberg Telas sin Tejer S.A. de C.V. **(1)**
Calz Camarones 577 - Col Santa Maria, Mexico, 53370, CP, Mexico
Tel.: (52) 55513977
Web Site: http://www.vilene.com
Mfr of Nonwoven Interlinings
N.A.I.C.S.: 313230

Freudenberg Textile Technologies, S.A. **(1)**
33 calle 27-01 Zona 12 Bodega 6 Zofracsa, 10012, Guatemala, Guatemala
Tel.: (502) 24700909
Fabric Distr
N.A.I.C.S.: 424310

Freudenberg Uchiyama Europe S.A.S. **(1)**
ZI Les Nouvelles Franchises, 52206, Langres, Cedex, France
Tel.: (33) 325878080
Web Site: http://www.freudenberg.com
Sales Range: $50-74.9 Million
Emp.: 130
Mfr of Rubber Products
N.A.I.C.S.: 326299

Freudenberg Versicherungsvermittlungs-GmbH **(1)**
Hohner Weg 2 4, 69469, Weinheim, Germany **(100%)**
Tel.: (49) 6201800
Web Site: http://www.freudenberg.com
Mfr of Rubber
N.A.I.C.S.: 326299

Freudenberg Vertrieb Einlagestoffe KG **(1)**
Hohnerweg 2 4, Weinheim, 69469, Germany **(100%)**
Tel.: (49) 6201800
Web Site: http://www.freudenberg.de
Mfr of Nonwoven Interlinings
N.A.I.C.S.: 313230
Monika Werline *(Sec)*

Freudenberg Vilene Nonwovens Taiwan Company Ltd. **(1)**
No 40 Min Fu Rd Sector 2, Yang Mei, Taoyuan, 326, Taiwan
Tel.: (886) 34781261
Sales Range: $25-49.9 Million
Emp.: 100
Mfr of Nonwoven Interlinings
N.A.I.C.S.: 313230

Freudenberg Vilene Sp. z.o.o. **(1)**
Ulica Switezianki 16, 91-496, Lodz, Poland **(100%)**
Tel.: (48) 426500511
Web Site: http://www.freudenberg-pm.com
Sales Range: $25-49.9 Million
Emp.: 11
Mfr of Nonwoven Interlinings
N.A.I.C.S.: 313230
Jolanta Stacherek *(Pres)*

Freudenberg Vilene Tela San. Ve Tic. A.S. **(1)**
Yenibosna Merkez Mah Ali Duran Sok No 3 1, Bahcelievler, Istanbul, 34418, Turkiye **(100%)**
Tel.: (90) 2122828300
Web Site: http://www.vilene.com.tr.
Sales Range: $25-49.9 Million
Emp.: 15
Software Solutions & IT Services
N.A.I.C.S.: 513210

Freudenberg-NOK General Partnership **(1)**
47690 E Anchor Ct, Plymouth, MI 48170-2400 **(75%)**
Tel.: (734) 451-0020
Web Site: http://www.freudenberg-nok.com
Sales Range: $1-4.9 Billion
Emp.: 250
Elastomeric Seals, Custom Molded Products & Vibration Control Technologies Mfr
N.A.I.C.S.: 339991
Tom Faust *(VP-Continuous Improvement)*

Plant (Domestic):

Freudenberg NOK **(2)**

450 Pleasant St, Bristol, NH 03222-0501
Tel.: (603) 744-2281
Web Site: http://www.fngp.com
Sales Range: $150-199.9 Million
Appliance Face, Radial Shaft, Engine Valve Stem Seals, Strut Seals, Oil & Water Pump Seal Caliper Boots
N.A.I.C.S.: 522130
Zean Laughy *(Gen Mgr)*

Freudenberg NOK **(2)**
50 Ammon Dr, Manchester, NH 03103-3308
Tel.: (603) 669-4050
Web Site: http://www.freudenberg-nok.com
Sales Range: $75-99.9 Million
Sealing Technologies Mfr
N.A.I.C.S.: 339991

Freudenberg NOK **(2)**
821 S Lk Rd, Scottsburg, IN 47170-6837
Tel.: (812) 752-4232
Web Site: http://www.freudenberg.com
Mfr of Solid Injection Molded Polyurethane Products & Suspension Parts for Automotive Applications
N.A.I.C.S.: 326291

Freudenberg NOK **(2)**
1618 Lukken Industrial Dr W, Lagrange, GA 30240-5704
Tel.: (706) 884-6111
Web Site: http://www.freudenberg-nok.com
Sales Range: $50-74.9 Million
Emp.: 200
Mfr of Rubber Moulded Products for the Automotive Industry
N.A.I.C.S.: 339991
Scott Thompson *(Mgr-Lean Sys)*

Freudenberg NOK **(2)**
131 Verner Ave, Newport, TN 37821-8133
Tel.: (423) 623-2366
Web Site: http://www.corteco-usa.com
Sales Range: $25-49.9 Million
Emp.: 37
Mfr of Automotive Engine Gaskets
N.A.I.C.S.: 339991

Freudenberg NOK **(2)**
1275 Archer Dr, Troy, OH 45373
Tel.: (937) 335-3306
Web Site: http://www.freudenberg-nok.com
Sales Range: $50-74.9 Million
Emp.: 150
Square Cut Seal Rings, Banded Pistons & Various Components For General Industry
N.A.I.C.S.: 326199
Gary Clyburn *(Plant Mgr)*

Freudenberg NOK-Rubber Products **(2)**
1700 Miller Ave, Shelbyville, IN 46176-3114
Tel.: (317) 421-3400
Sales Range: $50-74.9 Million
Emp.: 142
Rocker Cover, Electrical Sealing & Extrusion Gaskets; Electrical Connectors; Brake Parts & Transmission Seals
N.A.I.C.S.: 339991

Freudenberg NOK-Rubber Products **(2)**
487 W Main St, Morristown, IN 46161-9745
Tel.: (765) 763-7246
Sales Range: $25-49.9 Million
Emp.: 215
Mfr of Brake Components, Steering Linkage Components, Electrical Connectors, Oil Seals & Filler Tube Seals & Transmission Seals
N.A.I.C.S.: 339991

Freudenberg NOK-Sealant Products **(2)**
1 Nok Dr, Cleveland, GA 30528
Tel.: (706) 865-1665
Web Site: http://www.freudenberg-nok.com
Sales Range: $125-149.9 Million
Mfr of Oil Seals, Valve Stem Seals, Boots & Dust Covers & Seal Rings
N.A.I.C.S.: 324110
Gary Vanwambeke *(Exec Dir)*

Subsidiary (Non-US):

Freudenberg-NOK Inc. **(2)**
65 Spruce Street, Tillsonburg, N4G 5C4, ON, Canada
Tel.: (519) 842-6451
Web Site: http://www.freudenberg-nok.com

Sales Range: $50-74.9 Million
Emp.: 200
Mfr of Silicone Seals
N.A.I.C.S.: 325212
Ped Mansion *(Dir-Mktg)*

Freudenberg-NOK de Mexico   **(2)**
km 1 Carretera Cuautla Las Estacas,
62740, Cuautla, Morelos, Mexico
Tel.: (52) 7353522821
Web Site: http://www.freudenberg-nok.com
Sales Range: $10-24.9 Million
Emp.: 250
Mfr of Oil Seals, Valve Stem Seals, Molded
Rubber Products, Polyurethane O-Rings,
Engine Mounts
N.A.I.C.S.: 339991

**Freudenberg-NOK de Queretaro, S.A.
de C.V.**   **(2)**
Circuito El Marques Norte No 14, El
Marques, 76240, Queretaro, Mexico
Tel.: (52) 4421533270
Automobile Parts Distr
N.A.I.C.S.: 423120

**Freudenberg-NOK-Componentes Bra-
sil Ltda.**   **(2)**
Av Piraporinha 411 - Vila Oriental, 09950-
902, Diadema, Sao Paulo, Brazil
Tel.: (55) 1140728000
Seal Distr
N.A.I.C.S.: 423840
George Rugitsky *(Country Mgr)*

Hanns Glass GmbH & Co. KG   **(1)**
Altenburger Str 7, 04610, Meuselwitz, Ger-
many
Tel.: (49) 34484660
Web Site: http://www.hanns-glass.de
Car Floor Mat Mfr
N.A.I.C.S.: 326299
Alexander Kasper *(Dir-Plant Paderborn)*

Hansel Textil Interlining GmbH   **(1)**
Putterstr 22, 58636, Iserlohn, Germany
Tel.: (49) 2371966200
Textile Products Distr
N.A.I.C.S.: 424310

Hansel Textilrom srl   **(1)**
Str Serbanescu Alex Cpt 16 Bucuresti-
Sector 1, Bucharest, Romania
Tel.: (40) 212322176
Clothing Apparel Distr
N.A.I.C.S.: 458110

Helix Medical LLC   **(1)**
1110 Mark Ave, Carpinteria, CA 93013
Tel.: (805) 684-3304
Web Site: http://www.helixmedical.com
Sales Range: $50-74.9 Million
Emp.: 700
Plastic Medical Device & Component Mfr
N.A.I.C.S.: 339113
Jorg Schneewind *(Pres & CEO)*

Unit (Domestic):

**Helix Medical LLC - Baldwin
Park**   **(2)**
5050 Rivergrade Rd, Baldwin Park, CA
91706
Tel.: (626) 814-9684
Sales Range: $1-9.9 Million
Emp.: 100
Plastic Medical Device & Component Mfr
N.A.I.C.S.: 339113
Graham Lynggard *(VP-Ops)*

Division (Domestic):

InHealth Technologies   **(2)**
1110 Mark Ave, Carpinteria, CA 93013
Tel.: (805) 684-3304
Voice Restoration Products Mfr
N.A.I.C.S.: 334510

Subsidiary (Domestic):

**MedVenture Technology
Corporation**   **(2)**
2301 Centennial Blvd, Jeffersonville, IN
47130
Tel.: (812) 280-2400
Web Site: http://www.medventure.com
Sales Range: $75-99.9 Million
Emp.: 260
Medical Device Mfr
N.A.I.C.S.: 339112

Japan Lutravil Company Ltd.   **(1)**
Honmachi Takeda Bldg 3 1 29 Kyutaro-
machi, Chu Ku, Osaka, 541 0056,
Japan   **(100%)**
Tel.: (81) 662431560
Sales Range: $25-49.9 Million
Emp.: 12
Printing
N.A.I.C.S.: 323111

Japan Vilene Company, Ltd.   **(1)**
Hama-rikyu Mitsui Bldg 6-4 Tsukiji
5-Chome, Chuo-ku, Tokyo, 104-8423,
Japan   **(75%)**
Tel.: (81) 345461111
Web Site: http://www.vilene.oo.jp
Rev.: $622,940,880
Emp.: 2,148
Fiscal Year-end: 03/31/2017
Nonwoven Fabric Products Mfr & Distr
N.A.I.C.S.: 313230
Satoshi Kawamura *(Pres, CEO & Officer)*

**Jump Distributors (Thailand) Co
Ltd**   **(1)**
No 90 Moo 5 Ampur La-Harn, Bang Bua
Thong, Nonthaburi, 11110, Thailand
Tel.: (66) 29833693
Cleaning Equipment Distr
N.A.I.C.S.: 423810
M. Korakoch *(Mgr-Mktg)*

**Jump International Trading (Shang-
hai) Co.Ltd**   **(1)**
Room 523 Fl 5 Zong He Lou No 500 Bing
Ke Rd Waigaoqiao Free Trade Zone,
Shanghai, 200042, China
Tel.: (86) 52370323
Industrial Machinery Distr
N.A.I.C.S.: 423830

KE-Burgmann UK Ltd.   **(1)**
Units 2-4 First Avenue Radnor Park Ind Est,
Congleton, CW12 4XJ, Cheshire, United
Kingdom
Tel.: (44) 1260291289
Seal Distr
N.A.I.C.S.: 423840
Stephen Machin *(Product Mgr-Metallic &
Rubber)*

Kaul GmbH   **(1)**
Industriestrasse 23, 53359, Rheinbach,
Germany
Tel.: (49) 2226928911
Web Site: http://www.kaul-gmbh.de
Automotive Repair & Maintenance Services
N.A.I.C.S.: 811111

**Klueber Lubrication Romania
s.r.l.**   **(1)**
Strada Autogarii 1 Office 1 Etaj 1, 550135,
Sibiu, Romania
Tel.: (40) 742357095
Chemical Products Mfr
N.A.I.C.S.: 325998

Lederer GmbH   **(1)**
Katzbachstr 4, 58256, Ennepetal, Germany
Tel.: (49) 233383090
Web Site: http://www.lederer-online.com
Fastener Mfr
N.A.I.C.S.: 332722
Peter Henke *(Dir-Sls)*

Low & Bonar PLC   **(1)**
One Connaught Place, London, W2 2ET,
United Kingdom
Tel.: (44) 2075353180
Rev.: $416,170,680
Assets: $378,003,120
Liabilities: $263,238,120
Net Worth: $114,765,000
Earnings: ($81,843,840)
Fiscal Year-end: 11/30/2019
Specialty Materials & Plastics Products Mfr
& Distr
N.A.I.C.S.: 326199
Alex Xu *(Dir-Colbond-APAC)*

Subsidiary (Domestic):

**Anglo-Danish Fibre Industries
Ltd**   **(2)**
Unit 28 Bergen Way, Sutton Fields Indus
Estate, Hull, HU70YQ, United
Kingdom   **(100%)**
Tel.: (44) 1482863777
Web Site: http://www.adfil.co.uk
Emp.: 100

Fabric Coating Mills
N.A.I.C.S.: 313320

Subsidiary (Non-US):

Bonar GmbH & Co. KG   **(2)**
Glanzstoffstrasse 1, Obernburg, 63784,
Hessen, Germany   **(100%)**
Tel.: (49) 6022812020
Nonwoven Fabric Mills
N.A.I.C.S.: 313230

Subsidiary (Domestic):

Bonar Yarns & Fabrics Limited   **(2)**
Caldrum Works, St Salvador St, Dundee,
DD3 7EU, United Kingdom   **(100%)**
Tel.: (44) 1382227346
Web Site: http://www.bonaryarns.eu
Sales Range: $25-49.9 Million
Emp.: 150
Fabric Coating Mills
N.A.I.C.S.: 313320

Subsidiary (Non-US):

Colbond (Nederland) BVArnhem   **(2)**
Westervoortsedijk 73, Arnhem, 6827 AV,
Netherlands
Tel.: (31) 263662203
Textile Products Mfr
N.A.I.C.S.: 314999

Colbond BV   **(2)**
Westervoortsedijk 73, PO Box 9600, 6827
AF, Arnhem, Netherlands   **(100%)**
Tel.: (31) 263662677
Web Site: http://www.colbond.com
Sales Range: $25-49.9 Million
Emp.: 200
Fabric Coating Mills
N.A.I.C.S.: 313320

Colbond Geosynthetics SARL   **(2)**
153 blvd Anatole, Saint-Denis La Plaine Ce-
dex, 93521, Paris, France   **(100%)**
Tel.: (33) 149462430
Web Site: http://www.colbond-
geosynthetics.fr
Sales Range: $25-49.9 Million
Emp.: 6
Nonwoven Fabric Mills
N.A.I.C.S.: 313230
Alain Herault *(Dir-Tech)*

Colbond GmbH and Co. KG   **(2)**
Glanzstoffstr 1, 63784, Obernburg am Main,
Germany
Tel.: (49) 6022 812020
Web Site: http://www.colbond-
geosynthetics.de
Geosynthetics Products Mfr
N.A.I.C.S.: 325998

Colbond Holding BV   **(2)**
Westervoortsedijk 73, PO Box 9600, 6800,
Arnhem, Netherlands   **(100%)**
Tel.: (31) 263662677
Web Site: http://www.colbond.com
Sales Range: $75-99.9 Million
Emp.: 200
Holding Company
N.A.I.C.S.: 551112

Colbond Investments BV   **(2)**
Westervoortsedijk 73, PO Box 9600, 6827,
Arnhem, Netherlands   **(100%)**
Tel.: (31) 263662677
Web Site: http://www.colbond.com
Sales Range: $75-99.9 Million
Emp.: 200
Holding Company
N.A.I.C.S.: 551112

Low And Bonar (Nederland) BV   **(2)**
Duinkerken 20 A, Krommenie,
Netherlands   **(100%)**
Tel.: (31) 570608123
Trusts Estates & Agency Accounts
N.A.I.C.S.: 525920

Mehler Technologies GmbH   **(2)**
Rheinstrasse 11, 41836, Huckelhoven, Ger-
many
Tel.: (49) 24334590
Web Site: http://www.mehler-
texnologies.com
Sales Range: $150-199.9 Million
Emp.: 600
Coated Fabric Mfr
N.A.I.C.S.: 313320

Subsidiary (US):

Mehler Texnologies Inc   **(3)**
220 B Cabell St, Martinsville, VA 24112
Tel.: (276) 638-1007
Web Site: http://www.mehler-
texnologies.com
Sales Range: $25-49.9 Million
Emp.: 6
Fabric Coating Services
N.A.I.C.S.: 313320

Subsidiary (Domestic):

**Mehler Texnologies Logistics
GmbH**   **(3)**
Edelzeller Strasse 44, Fulda, 36043, Ger-
many
Tel.: (49) 24334590
Web Site: http://www.mehler-
texnologies.com
Sales Range: $25-49.9 Million
Emp.: 200
Textile Products Mfr
N.A.I.C.S.: 314999

Subsidiary (Non-US):

Mehler Texnologies Ltd.   **(3)**
Office 008 Kingfisher Business Centre Fu-
tures Park Bacup, Rossendale, OL13 0BB,
United Kingdom
Tel.: (44) 1706 877087
Web Site: http://www.mehler-
texnologies.com
Coated Fabric Mfr
N.A.I.C.S.: 313320

Mehler Texnologies S.I.A   **(3)**
Maskavas Iela 418, 1082, Riga, Latvia
Tel.: (371) 67269322
Coated Fabric Mfr
N.A.I.C.S.: 313320

Mehler Texnologies S.R.L   **(3)**
Str Linia de Centura Nr 2 D2, 077175, Ste-
fanestii de Jos, Romania
Tel.: (40) 21 369 57 51
Web Site: http://www.mehler-
texnologies.com
Sales Range: $25-49.9 Million
Emp.: 7
Coated Fabric Products Mfr
N.A.I.C.S.: 313320
Voicu Cristina *(Dir-Economic)*

Mehler Texnologies S.p.A   **(3)**
Via Enrico Fermi 52, 20019, Settimo Mila-
nese, Italy
Tel.: (39) 023286171
Web Site: http://www.mehler-
texnologies.com
Coated Fabric Mfr
N.A.I.C.S.: 313210

Mehler Texnologies s.a.r.l.   **(3)**
Batiment A1 3 Chemin des Cytises,
Francheville, 69340, France
Tel.: (33) 472661000
Web Site: http://www.mehler-
texnologies.com
Sales Range: $25-49.9 Million
Emp.: 4
Fabric Coating Services
N.A.I.C.S.: 313320

Mehler Texnologies s.r.o   **(3)**
Karla Capka 1085, 512 51, Lomnice nad
Popelkou, Czech Republic
Tel.: (420) 481 641 302
Web Site: http://www.mehler-texnologies.cz
Sales Range: $25-49.9 Million
Emp.: 180
Coated Fabric Mfr
N.A.I.C.S.: 313320

**Merkel Freudenberg Fluidtechnic
GmbH**   **(1)**
Industriestrasse 64, Hamburg, 21107,
Germany   **(100%)**
Tel.: (49) 40753060
Web Site: http://www.freudenberg.com
Sales Range: $100-124.9 Million
Emp.: 400
Packaging Machinery Mfr
N.A.I.C.S.: 333993
Bernt Koch *(Chm)*

**Merkel NOK-Freudenberg Co.
Ltd.**   **(1)**

Freudenberg SE—(Continued)

Foreign Industry Park Building A25 No 105
Shanghai East Road, Taicang, 215400,
China
Tel.: (86) 51253578253
Steel Mfrs
N.A.I.C.S.: 339991
Xiaohui Zhang *(Mgr-Pur)*

Ningbo E&J Brushes Co Ltd. (1)
Qiming Rd Yinzhou Boulevard, Yinzhou Dis-
trict, Ningbo, 315100, Zhejiang, China
Tel.: (86) 57488381566
Cleaning Equipment Distr
N.A.I.C.S.: 423810

OKS Spezialschmierstoffe GmbH (1)
Ganghoferstrasse 47, 82216, Maisach, Ger-
many
Tel.: (49) 81423051500
Web Site: http://www.oks-germany.com
Lubricant Mfr & Distr
N.A.I.C.S.: 325998
Hanno D. Wentzler *(Member-Mgmt Bd)*

OOO SurTec (1)
Andropova 18/6, 117639, Moscow, Russia
Tel.: (7) 4956320213
Web Site: http://www.surtec.com
Emp.: 3
Chemical Products Distr
N.A.I.C.S.: 424690

Oshitari Laboratory, Inc. (1)
755-1 Shimohirose, Sayama, 350-1322,
Saitama, Japan
Tel.: (81) 429302070
Web Site: http://www.oshitari.co.jp
Emp.: 120
Clean Room Equipment Mfr & Whslr
N.A.I.C.S.: 339113
Shuzo Kikuchi *(Pres)*

**PTFE Compounds Germany
GmbH** (1)
On Schiens 4, 39221, Bordeland, Saxony-
Anhalt, Germany
Tel.: (49) 3929728882
Chemical Products Distr
N.A.I.C.S.: 424690

**Politex S.a.s. di Freudenberg Politex
s.r.l.** (1)
Strada Provinciale Novedratese 17/a, Nove-
drate, 22060, Como, Italy
Tel.: (39) 031793111
Web Site: http://www.politex.com
Roofing Product Mfr & Distr
N.A.I.C.S.: 326299
Gabriele D'Alessandro *(Mgr-Site)*

Precision Rubber Sealings s.r.l. (1)
Viale Monza 38, 20127, Milan,
Italy (100%)
Tel.: (39) 0228861
Sales Range: $1-9.9 Million
Emp.: 40
Mfr of Rubber Products
N.A.I.C.S.: 326299

Procal GmbH (1)
Hoehnerweg 2-4, 69469, Weinheim,
Germany (100%)
Web Site: http://www.freudenberg.com
Mfr of Rubber
N.A.I.C.S.: 326299

SF GmbH (1)
Gewerbestr 11, Grunkraut-Gullen, 88287,
Ravensburg, Germany
Tel.: (49) 75176924360
Web Site: http://www.sf-gmbh.de
Screening Machine Mfr
N.A.I.C.S.: 333120
Robert Amann *(Mng Dir)*

ST Iberica Lda. (1)
Rui Costa Zona Industrial de Albergaria
Parque Empresarial Vista, Alegre - Ar-
mazem 3, 3580-184, Albergaria-a-Velha,
Portugal
Tel.: (351) 234527351
Chemical Products Distr
N.A.I.C.S.: 424690

**Sigma Freudenberg NOK PVT.
Ltd.** (1)
Village-Basma Tehsil & Distt, Mohali,
140601, Punjab, India
Tel.: (91) 1762 665400

Web Site: http://www.sfnindia.com
Seal Mfr & Distr
N.A.I.C.S.: 339991
Sanjib Das *(CEO)*

Plant (Domestic):

**Sigma Freudenberg NOK PVT. Ltd. -
2 Plant** (2)
B-70 Industrial Area Phase-VII Sector-73,
Mohali, 160055, Punjab, India
Tel.: (91) 1726629100
Steel Mfrs
N.A.I.C.S.: 339991

Simrax BV (1)
Hopelerweg 250, PO Box 649, 6468 XX,
Kerkrade, Netherlands (100%)
Tel.: (31) 455469222
Web Site: http://www.simrax.com
Sales Range: $50-74.9 Million
Emp.: 60
Mfr of Seals for Automotive Industry
N.A.I.C.S.: 336340

Simrit Distribution et CIE (1)
170 Rue Branly, 71020, Macon, Cedex,
France (100%)
Tel.: (33) 385293000
Web Site: http://www.fst.com
Sales Range: $25-49.9 Million
Emp.: 50
Sales of Rubber Products
N.A.I.C.S.: 424690
Sylvain Loizeau *(Office Mgr)*

**Simrit Service Center Denmark
EagleBurgmann KE A/S** (1)
Industrisvinget 1, 6600, Vejen,
Denmark (100%)
Tel.: (45) 75364988
Web Site: http://www.eagleburgmann.dk
Sales Range: $25-49.9 Million
Emp.: 11
Sales of Rubber Seals
N.A.I.C.S.: 339991

Subsidiary (US):

Tetralene, Inc. (2)
879 Wakefield St, Houston, TX 77018
Tel.: (713) 695-4011
Web Site: http://www.gulfstargroup.com
Specialized Custom Sealing Components
Mfr
N.A.I.C.S.: 326199

SurTec International GmbH (1)
Neuhofstr 9, 64625, Bensheim, Germany
Tel.: (49) 62518622200
Web Site: http://www.surtec.com
Chemical Product Mfr & Distr
N.A.I.C.S.: 325998

Subsidiary (Non-US):

SurTec Adria d.o.o. (2)
Dunajska 156, 1000, Ljubljana, Slovenia
Tel.: (386) 59355210
Chemical Products Distr
N.A.I.C.S.: 424690

SurTec Benelux B.V. (2)
Molenweg 17A, 5953 JR, Reuver, Nether-
lands
Tel.: (31) 773081590
Chemical Products Distr
N.A.I.C.S.: 424690

SurTec CR s.r.o. (2)
Nadrazni 148, Vrane nad Vltavou, 25246,
Prague, Czech Republic
Tel.: (420) 257760037
Chemical Products Distr
N.A.I.C.S.: 424690

SurTec Cacak d.o.o. (2)
Preljinska Baluga bb, 32212, Cacak, Serbia
Tel.: (381) 325381569
Chemical Products Distr
N.A.I.C.S.: 424690
Dragan Belic *(Mgr-Mktg & Sls)*

SurTec Chemicals India Pvt. Ltd. (2)
Gat No 318 Pune - Nagar Road, Lonikand
Haveli, 412216, Pune, India
Tel.: (91) 2066785801
Chemical Products Distr
N.A.I.C.S.: 424690

Subsidiary (Domestic):

SurTec Deutschland GmbH (2)
SurTec-Str 2, 64673, Zwingenberg, Ger-
many
Tel.: (49) 6251171700
Chemical Products Distr
N.A.I.C.S.: 424690

Subsidiary (Non-US):

SurTec France S.A.S. (2)
Centre de Gros Larrieu 19 Rue Gaston Ev-
rard, 31094, Toulouse, Cedex, France
Tel.: (33) 561076126
Chemical Products Distr
N.A.I.C.S.: 424690

SurTec Korea Co., Ltd. (2)
21-22 Gongdan-ro 474beon-gil, Seongsan-
gu, 642-315, Changwon, Gyeongsangnam-
do, Korea (South)
Tel.: (82) 552646083
Chemical Products Distr
N.A.I.C.S.: 424690

SurTec MMC Japan KK (2)
Shinkawa Ohara Bldg 7F 1-27-8 Shinkawa,
Chuo-ku, Tokyo, 104-0033, Japan
Tel.: (81) 335376888
Web Site: http://www.surtec.com
Chemical Products Distr
N.A.I.C.S.: 424690

**SurTec Metal Surface Treatment
Technology Co. Ltd.** (2)
No 70 Hongtai 5 Road, Xiaoshan District,
Hangzhou, 311232, Zhejiang, China
Tel.: (86) 57182696469
Web Site: http://www.surtec.com
Emp.: 80
Chemical Products Distr
N.A.I.C.S.: 424690
Qiaohong Wang *(Mgr-Mktg)*

SurTec Polska Sp. z o.o. (2)
Swojczcka 38, 51-501, Wroclaw, Poland
Tel.: (48) 713408280
Chemical Products Distr
N.A.I.C.S.: 424690

**SurTec Produkte und Systeme fur die
Oberflachenbehandlung
GesmbH** (2)
Industriestrasse 9/Top3 3, 2353, Guntram-
sdorf, Austria
Tel.: (43) 223690390
Chemical Products Distr
N.A.I.C.S.: 424690

SurTec Romania s.r.l. (2)
Strada Traian 63, 500332, Brasov, Romania
Tel.: (40) 268314971
Web Site: http://www.surtec.com
Chemical Products Distr
N.A.I.C.S.: 424690
Radu Dumitrescu *(Mgr)*

SurTec SK s.r.o. (2)
Horny Ohaj 299, 95201, Vrable, Slovakia
Tel.: (421) 377834001
Chemical Products Distr
N.A.I.C.S.: 424690
Martin Hornak *(Mng Dir)*

SurTec Scandinavia ApS (2)
Rytterskolevej 10, 7000, Fredericia, Den-
mark
Tel.: (45) 75563412
Chemical Products Distr
N.A.I.C.S.: 424690

SurTec South Africa Pty. Ltd. (2)
Unit 1 Gamma Park 67 Regency Drive
Route 21 Corporate Park, Centurion, Irene,
South Africa
Tel.: (27) 124500860
Chemical Products Distr
N.A.I.C.S.: 424690

SurTec Viet Nam Co., Ltd. (2)
157 Vo Thi Sau Street, Ward 6 District 3,
700000, Ho Chi Minh City, Vietnam
Tel.: (84) 838207685
Chemical Products Distr
N.A.I.C.S.: 424690

SurTec d.o.o. (2)
Jurja Sizgorica 20, 21000, Split, Croatia
Tel.: (385) 21373699
Chemical Products Distr

N.A.I.C.S.: 424690

SurTec do Brasil Ltda. (2)
Alcir Bertozzo Rua Antonio Felamingo 575,
13279-452, Valinhos, SP, Brazil
Tel.: (55) 1938818010
Web Site: http://www.surtec.com.br
Chemical Products Distr
N.A.I.C.S.: 424690

Subsidiary (US):

SurTec, Inc. (2)
1880 N MacArthur Dr, Tracy, CA 95376
Tel.: (209) 820-3700
Web Site: http://www.surtecsystem.com
Chemical Product Mfr & Distr
N.A.I.C.S.: 325998
David Swindle *(Mgr-Sls)*

**Tianjin VIAM Automotive Products
Co., Ltd.** (1)
No 19 Saida 2 North Road Xiqing Economic
Developing-area, Tianjin, 300385, China
Tel.: (86) 223979798
Web Site: http://www.tjviam.com
Natural Gas Distr
N.A.I.C.S.: 221210

Tobul Accumulator Incorporated (1)
61 Innovation Dr, Bamberg, SC 29003
Tel.: (803) 245-2400
Web Site: http://www.fst.com
Emp.: 120
Hydraulic Accumulators Mfr
N.A.I.C.S.: 332313

Trasfotex s.r.l. (1)
Via Nochette 26, Quaregna, 13854, Biella,
Italy
Tel.: (39) 015922873
Industrial Equipment Distr
N.A.I.C.S.: 423830

**Trelleborg Automotive Toluca SA de
CV** (1)
Carretera Toluca-Naucalpan Km 528 Calle
3-108, Toluca, 50200, Estado de, Mexico
Tel.: (52) 7222620200
Rubber Products Mfr
N.A.I.C.S.: 326291

TrelleborgVibracoustic (1)
1496 Gerber St, Ligonier, IN 46767-2422
Tel.: (260) 894-7448
Web Site: http://www.tbvc.com
Sales Range: $25-49.9 Million
Emp.: 100
Conventional Engine Mounts, Hydromounts,
Crank Shaft Dampers Mfr
N.A.I.C.S.: 336390
Stefan Eck *(CFO)*

VC UK LP (1)
Gilmorton Rd, Lutterworth, LE17 4HG, Leic-
estershire, United Kingdom
Tel.: (44) 1455261227
Web Site: http://www.freudenberg.com
Provider of Management Services
N.A.I.C.S.: 541611

VIAM Manufacturing, Inc. (1)
87 Park Tower Dr, Manchester, TN 37355
Tel.: (931) 461-2300
Web Site: http://www.viammfg.com
Motor Vehicle Parts Mfr
N.A.I.C.S.: 336390

VIS Co., Ltd. (1)
7 Kita-tone, Koga, 306-0213, Ibaraki, Japan
Tel.: (81) 280921521
Business Support Services
N.A.I.C.S.: 561499

Vector Group Inc. (1)
1550 Larimer St Ste 111, Denver, CO
80202
Tel.: (800) 566-0877
Web Site: http://www.vectorgroupinc.com
Management Consulting Services
N.A.I.C.S.: 541611

Subsidiary (Non-US):

Vector Consultants Limited (2)
12th Floor The Broadgate Tower20 Primrose Street, London, EC2A 2EW, United
Kingdom
Tel.: (44) 8456586617
Web Site: http://www.vector-
consultants.com

Management Consulting Services
N.A.I.C.S.: 541611
Alan Stevens *(CEO)*

Subsidiary (Domestic):

Vector Data Services, Inc. (2)
1 Tower Bridge Ste 1111 100 Front St, West
Conshohocken, PA 19428
Tel.: (610) 341-9451
Web Site: http://www.vds450.com
Management Consulting Services
N.A.I.C.S.: 541611

Vestpak AS (1)
Luramyrveien 13, 4313, Sandnes, Norway
Tel.: (47) 51636300
Web Site: http://www.vestpak.no
Emp.: 51
Gaskets Mfr
N.A.I.C.S.: 339991
Leif Jarle Grodeland *(Mgr-Sls)*

Vibracoustic AG (1)
Europaplatz 4, 64293, Darmstadt, Germany
Tel.: (49) 615139640
Web Site: http://www.vibracoustic.com
Automotive Products Mfr
N.A.I.C.S.: 339991
Frank Mueller *(CEO)*

Vibracoustic CV Air Springs
GmbH (1)
Lubeckertordamm 1-3, Hamburg, Germany
Tel.: (49) 4041340
Automobile Parts Distr
N.A.I.C.S.: 423120

Vibracoustic Japan KK (1)
DSM Shin-Yokohama Bldg 8F 2-6-3, Shin-
Yokohama Kohoku-ku, Yokohama, 222-
0033, Kanagawa, Japan
Tel.: (81) 454780736
Automotive Products Mfr
N.A.I.C.S.: 339991
Yutaka Ogawa *(Sls Mgr)*

Vibracoustic Nantes SAS (1)
1 Rue du Tertre ZI Nantes, 44474, Carque-
fou, Cedex, France
Tel.: (33) 240686391
Emp.: 250
Motor Mount Mfr
N.A.I.C.S.: 332510
Uday Shinde *(Project Mgr)*

Vibracoustic North America LP (1)
47690 E Anchor Ct, Plymouth, MI 48170-
2455
Tel.: (734) 354-5406
Measuring Equipment Mfr
N.A.I.C.S.: 334519

Vibracoustic de Mexico S.A. de
C.V. (1)
Blvd Aeropuerto Miguel Aleman Zona Indus-
trial Lerma, 52200, Lerma, Mexico
Tel.: (52) 7225481361
Emp.: 200
Automobile Parts Distr
N.A.I.C.S.: 423120
Dagoberto Sanchez *(VP)*

Vibracoustic do Brasil Industria e Co-
mercio de Artefatos de Borracha
Ltda. (1)
Av Arcenio Riemma 1415 Distrito Industrial
Bairro do Una, Taubate, 12072-250, Brazil
Tel.: (55) 1236012100
Automobile Parts Distr
N.A.I.C.S.: 423120

Vileda GmbH (1)
Im Technologiepark 19, 69469, Weinheim,
Germany **(100%)**
Tel.: (49) 620180871000
Web Site: http://www.vileda.de
Sanitation Goods Mfr
N.A.I.C.S.: 325612

Vilene Create Co., Ltd. (1)
Hama-rikyu Mitsui Bldg 6-4 Tsukiji
5-Chome, Chuo-ku, Tokyo, 104-0045, Ja-
pan
Tel.: (81) 345461188
Nonwoven Product Whslr
N.A.I.C.S.: 424310

Wuxi NOK-Freudenberg Oilseal Co.,
Ltd. (1)
No 280 fengwei Rd xishan Economic, Wuxi,

214101, China
Tel.: (86) 51088709302
Automobile Parts Mfr
N.A.I.C.S.: 336390

FREUND CORPORATION

Freung Bldg 6-25-13 Nishishinjuku,
Shinjuku-ku, Tokyo, 160-0023, Japan
Tel.: (81) 368900750
Web Site: http://www.freund.co.jp
Year Founded: 1964
6312—(TKS)
Rev.: $162,391,188
Assets: $182,850,753
Liabilities: $76,331,823
Net Worth: $106,518,931
Earnings: $5,423,783
Emp.: 468
Fiscal Year-end: 02/29/24
Granulation & Coating Equipment
Developer, Mfr & Sales
N.A.I.C.S.: 325510
Takashi Honda *(Exec Officer)*

Subsidiaries:

Cos.Mec s.r.l. (1)
via Aldo Moro 17/19, Paderno Dugnano,
20037, Milan, Italy
Tel.: (39) 029 108 0107
Web Site: https://www.cosmec-it.com
Powder & Granulate Handling Equipment
Mfr
N.A.I.C.S.: 333998

Freund Pharmatec, Ltd. (1)
Unit 1, IDA Business & Technology Park,
Srah, Tullamore, Ireland
Tel.: (353) 57 932 3534
Emp.: 11
Biopharmaceutical Research & Develop-
ment Services
N.A.I.C.S.: 541715
Frank Nolan *(Mgr-Ops)*

Freund-Chineway Pharmaceutical
Technology Center Co., Ltd. (1)
Unit 506 910 Quyang Road, Shanghai,
China
Tel.: (86) 216 531 2825
Pharmaceutical Products Distr
N.A.I.C.S.: 424210

Freund-Turbo Corporation (1)
1-2-10 Uchikawa, Yokosuka, 239-0836, Ka-
nagawa, Japan
Tel.: (81) 46 836 4900
Web Site: https://www.freund-turbo.co.jp
Emp.: 59
Grinding Machine Mfr
N.A.I.C.S.: 333517
Iwao Fusejima *(Chm)*

Freund-Vector Corporation (1)
675 44th St, Marion, IA 52302
Tel.: (319) 377-8263
Web Site: https://www.freund-vector.com
Sales Range: $25-49.9 Million
Processing Equipment Mfr
N.A.I.C.S.: 334290
Masaaki Kubota *(Pres)*

Parle FREUND Machinery Private
Limited (1)
Shripal Industrial Estate Bldg No 3 Behind
Varun Industries Waliv Road, Vasai East,
Thane, 401208, Maharashtra, India
Tel.: (91) 848 491 1031
Granulating Equipment Mfr & Distr
N.A.I.C.S.: 333998

FREY S.A.

1 rue Rene Cassin, 51430, Reims,
Cedex, France
Tel.: (33) 351005050 FR
Web Site: https://www.frey.fr
Year Founded: 1983
FREY—(EUR)
Rev.: $163,947,456
Assets: $2,646,084,557
Liabilities: $1,413,677,006
Net Worth: $1,232,407,551
Earnings: $27,365,051
Emp.: 84
Fiscal Year-end: 12/31/23

Commercial Real Estate Investor, De-
veloper & Property Manager
N.A.I.C.S.: 531390
Antoine Frey *(Chm)*

Subsidiaries:

Albufeira Retail Park Lda. (1)
Lugar da Tavagueira, Albufeira, 8200-425,
Faro, Portugal
Tel.: (351) 289561285
Web Site:
https://www.albufeiraretailpark.com
All Grocery Product Retailer
N.A.I.C.S.: 455219
Sandrine Pires *(Mgr-Center)*

Algarve Shopping - Centro Comer-
cial, SA (1)
Caminho dos Alamos 2389, Lanka Com-
mercial and Industrial Park of the Algarve
Guia, 8200-425, Guia, Portugal
Tel.: (351) 289105500
Web Site: https://www.algarveshopping.pt
All Grocery Product Retailer
N.A.I.C.S.: 455219
Carla Martins *(Mgr)*

Frey Invest S.L. (1)
Calle de la Selva 12, 08820, El Prat de Llo-
bregat, Spain
Tel.: (34) 933794238
Web Site: http://www.freyinvest.com
Sales Range: $50-74.9 Million
Emp.: 4
Property Management Services
N.A.I.C.S.: 531311

FREYR BATTERY SA

22-24 Boulevard Royal, 2449, Lux-
embourg, Luxembourg
Tel.: (352) 4661113721 LU
Web Site:
https://www.freyrbattery.com
Year Founded: 2018
FREY—(NYSE)
Rev.: $70,559,000
Assets: $732,185,000
Liabilities: $97,469,000
Net Worth: $634,716,000
Earnings: ($73,096,000)
Emp.: 263
Fiscal Year-end: 12/31/23
Battery Mfr
N.A.I.C.S.: 335910
Tom Einar Jensen *(Co-Founder &
Exec Chm)*

FRIASKOG AB

Lovtorpsvagen 3, Jarpen, 837 31,
Are, Sweden
Tel.: (46) 647 61 10 90
Web Site: http://www.friaskog.se
Forestry Services
N.A.I.C.S.: 113110
Tobias Jonsson *(Mng Dir)*

Subsidiaries:

Norske Skog Jamtland AB (1)
Moviksvagen 14, Trangsviken, 83047,
Krokom, Sweden
Tel.: (46) 640683090
Web Site: http://www.norskeskog.se
Paper Products Mfr
N.A.I.C.S.: 322120
Bertil Johansson *(Mgr)*

FRIDENSON LOGISTIC SER-
VICES LTD.

25 Yekuteal Baharav St, PO Box
10441, Haifa, 26113, Israel
Tel.: (972) 722642600
Web Site: https://www.fridenson.co.il
Year Founded: 1975
FRDN—(TAE)
Rev.: $130,891,281
Assets: $91,920,982
Liabilities: $44,706,450
Net Worth: $47,214,532
Earnings: $2,016,853
Emp.: 450
Fiscal Year-end: 12/31/23

Freight Transportation Arrangement
N.A.I.C.S.: 488510
David Fridenson *(CEO)*

Subsidiaries:

Fridenson Air & Ocean Ltd. (1)
31 Hametzuda St, Azor, 5819001, Israel
Tel.: (972) 722642222
Land Transport Services
N.A.I.C.S.: 561910

FRIEDHELM LOH STIFTUNG &
CO. KG

Rudolf-Loh-Strasse 1, 35708, Haiger,
Germany
Tel.: (49) 2773 924 0
Web Site: http://www.friedhelm-loh-
group.com
Year Founded: 1961
Sales Range: $1-4.9 Billion
Emp.: 11,500
Electrical Equipments Mfr & Whslr
N.A.I.C.S.: 335311
Friedhelm Loh *(Owner & CEO)*

Subsidiaries:

Cideon Holding GmbH & Co. KG (1)
Tzschirnerstrasse 5a, 02625, Bautzen, Ger-
many
Tel.: (49) 359137440
Web Site: http://www.cideon.com
Information Technology Consulting Services
N.A.I.C.S.: 551112

Eplan Software & Service GmbH &
Co. KG (1)
An der alten Ziegelei 2, 40789, Monheim
am Rhein, Germany
Tel.: (49) 217339640
Web Site: http://www.eplan.de
Information Technology Consulting Services
N.A.I.C.S.: 541690

German Edge Cloud GmbH &
Co.KG (1)
Dusseldorfer Strasse 40a, 65760, Es-
chborn, Germany
Tel.: (49) 692474718277
Web Site: http://www.oncite.io
Cloud Infrastructure & Data Analysis Plat-
form Services
N.A.I.C.S.: 518210
Sebastian Ritz *(Mng Dir)*

Kiesling Maschinentechnik
GmbH (1)
Mainstrasse 20, 63128, Dietzenbach, Ger-
many
Tel.: (49) 607482900
Web Site: http://www.kiesling.net
Information Technology Consulting Services
N.A.I.C.S.: 541690

LKH Kunststoffwerk Heiligenroth
GmbH & Co. KG (1)
Auf der Birke 2, 56412, Heiligenroth, Ger-
many
Tel.: (49) 2602999420
Web Site: http://www.lkh-kunststoff.de
Information Technology Consulting Services
N.A.I.C.S.: 541690

Loh Services GmbH & Co. KG (1)
Rudolf-Loh-Strasse 1, 35708, Haiger, Ger-
many
Tel.: (49) 27739240
Information Technology Consulting Services
N.A.I.C.S.: 541690

Rittal GmbH & Co. KG (1)
Auf dem Stuetzelberg, 35745, Herborn,
Germany
Tel.: (49) 27725050
Web Site: http://www.rittal.com
Information Technology Consulting Services
N.A.I.C.S.: 541690
Koen Wolfcarius *(Exec VP-North & South
America)*

Stahlo Stahlservice GmbH & Co.
KG (1)
Kasseler Strasse 27, 35683, Dillenburg,
Germany
Tel.: (49) 27713020
Web Site: http://www.stahlo.de
Information Technology Consulting Services

Friedhelm Loh Stiftung & Co. KG—(Continued)

N.A.I.C.S.: 541690

iNNOVO Cloud GmbH (1)
Dusseldorfer Strasse 40a, 65760, Es-
chborn, Germany
Tel.: (49) 6924747180
Web Site: http://www.innovo-cloud.de
Information Technology Services
N.A.I.C.S.: 541511

FRIEDL BUSINESS INFORMA-TION LIMITED
26H Aihe Building 629 Lingling Road,
Shanghai, 200030, China
Tel.: (86) 2164863668
Web Site: http://www.friedlnet.com
Year Founded: 1995
Business Information on Chinese
Companies
N.A.I.C.S.: 513130
Roland Berger (Partner)

FRIEDRICH BOYSEN GMBH & CO. KG
Friedrich Boysen Strasse 14-17, Al-
tensteig, 72213, Germany
Tel.: (49) 74 53 20 0
Web Site: http://www.boysen-
online.de
Sales Range: $800-899.9 Million
Emp.: 1,600
Motor Vehicle Exhaust System Mfr
N.A.I.C.S.: 336390
Rolf Geisel (Pres)

FRIENDLY CORPORATION
3-12-1 Teragawa, Daito, 574-0014,
Osaka, Japan
Tel.: (81) 728742747
Web Site: https://www.friendly-
co.com
Year Founded: 1947
8209—(TKS)
Sales Range: $75-99.9 Million
Restaurant Operators
N.A.I.C.S.: 722511
Tetsuya Ono (Pres)

FRIENDTIMES, INC.
Building 18 Scientific Park of Suhua
No 208 Tongyuan Road, Suzhou In-
dustrial Park, Suzhou, Jiangsu, China
Tel.: (86) 51267671973   Ky
Web Site: http://www.friendtimes.net
Year Founded: 2010
6820—(HKG)
Rev.: $214,024,496
Assets: $226,490,472
Liabilities: $16,318,832
Net Worth: $210,171,640
Earnings: $3,525,584
Emp.: 1,201
Fiscal Year-end: 12/31/22
Software Development Services
N.A.I.C.S.: 541511
Xiaohuang Jiang (Chm & CEO)

FRIGATE AS
Valnu iela 19-1D, Riga, LV-1050, Lat-
via
Tel.: (371) 67969869
Web Site: https://www.frigate.eu
Year Founded: 2015
FRGTE—(RSE)
Sales Range: Less than $1 Million
Asset Management Services
N.A.I.C.S.: 523940
Dmitry Solovyev (Chm)

Subsidiaries:

Frigate Luxembourg S.A. (1)
Haaptstrooss 1, 9806, Hosingen, Luxem-
bourg
Tel.: (352) 28480880
Asset Management Services
N.A.I.C.S.: 523940

Frigate Pay UAB (1)
Forum Palace Konstitucijos ave 26, Vilnius,
Lithuania
Tel.: (370) 69927709
Asset Management Services
N.A.I.C.S.: 523940

Frigate SA (1)
Rue des Bains 33, 1205, Geneva, Switzer-
land
Tel.: (41) 225510155
Web Site: http://www.frigate.ch
Asset Management Services
N.A.I.C.S.: 523940

FRIGO-PAK GIDA MADDELERI SANAYI VE TICARET A.S.
Comert Sk Yapi Kredi Plaza Sitesi B
Blok No 1B, Levent Mah ic Kapi No
23 Besiktas, 34330, Istanbul, Türkiye
Tel.: (90) 8505600110
Web Site: https://www.frigo-
pak.com.tr
Year Founded: 1984
FRIGO—(IST)
Rev.: $25,565,010
Assets: $32,846,748
Liabilities: $13,952,698
Net Worth: $18,894,050
Earnings: ($1,782,614)
Fiscal Year-end: 12/31/23
Soft Drinks Mfr
N.A.I.C.S.: 312111
Alistair Baran Blake (Chm & Gen
Mgr)

FRIGOGLASS S.A.I.C.
15 A Metaxa Str, Kifissia, 145 64,
Greece
Tel.: (30) 2106165700   GR
Web Site: http://www.frigoglass.com
Year Founded: 1993
FRIGO—(ATH)
Assets: $468,965,033
Liabilities: $600,244,982
Net Worth: ($131,279,948)
Earnings: ($28,339,089)
Emp.: 2,931
Fiscal Year-end: 12/31/22
Refrigeration & Other Glass Products
Mfr
N.A.I.C.S.: 333415
Nikos Mamoulis (CEO)

Subsidiaries:

3P Frigoglass Romania SRL (1)
Calea Chisinaului Nr 47A, 700719, Iasi,
Romania
Tel.: (40) 232231583
Injection Molding & Printing Machine Whslr
N.A.I.C.S.: 423840

Frigoglass (Guangzhou) Ice Cold
Equipment Co., Ltd. (1)
23 Yongsheng Road Getdd, Yonghe Indus-
trial District, Guangzhou, 511356, China
Tel.: (86) 2032225818
Commercial & Industrial Equipment Mfr
N.A.I.C.S.: 333248

Frigoglass East Africa Ltd. (1)
A-7 Ashray Industrial Park 25 Kampala
Road Off Enterprise Road, 50896-00200,
Nairobi, Kenya
Tel.: (254) 20237917123
Commercial & Industrial Equipment Mfr
N.A.I.C.S.: 333248

Frigoglass Eurasia LLC (1)
Altufievskoe Shosse K2 Business-Center
Altyfievsky 5th Floor, Office 507, 127566,
Moscow, Russia
Tel.: (7) 4956406164
Commercial & Industrial Equipment Mfr
N.A.I.C.S.: 333248

Frigoglass GmbH (1)
Memeler Strasse 30, 42781, Haan, Ger-
many
Tel.: (49) 2129373200
Commercial & Industrial Equipment Mfr
N.A.I.C.S.: 333248

Frigoglass India Pvt. Ltd. (1)
IMT Manesar Sector 3 Plot 26 A, 122 050,
Gurgaon, India
Tel.: (91) 1244320800
Commercial & Industrial Equipment Mfr
N.A.I.C.S.: 333248
Deepak Chitkara (CFO & Mgr-Fin)

Frigoglass Nordic AS (1)
Bredmyra 10 Kampenes Industriomrade,
PO Box 21, Borgenhaugen, 1740, Sarps-
borg, Norway
Tel.: (47) 69111800
Commercial & Industrial Equipment Mfr
N.A.I.C.S.: 333248

Frigoglass South Africa Ltd. (1)
16 Walton Road, Aeroton, 2013, Johannes-
burg, South Africa
Tel.: (27) 112483000
Commercial & Industrial Equipment Mfr
N.A.I.C.S.: 333248

Frigoglass Sp. z o.o (1)
Sloneczna 16, Kolonia, Lesznowola, 05-
506, Poland
Tel.: (48) 227114600
Commercial & Industrial Equipment Mfr
N.A.I.C.S.: 333248

Frigoglass West Africa Limited (1)
A G Leventis Building Iddo House Iddo
Street 15, Lagos, Nigeria
Tel.: (234) 17746265
Commercial & Industrial Equipment Mfr
N.A.I.C.S.: 333248
Ezenwa Amakoh (Mgr-Field Svc)

PT Frigoglass Indonesia (1)
Jl Jababeka VI Block P No 1, Cikarang,
17530, Bekasi, Indonesia
Tel.: (62) 2128649500
Commercial & Industrial Equipment Mfr
N.A.I.C.S.: 333248
Uyunul Mardiah (Deputy Mgr-Fin)

Scandinavian Appliances A.S (1)
Bredmyra 10, Borgenhaugen, 1739, Sarps-
borg, Norway
Tel.: (47) 8 156 9117
Web Site: https://en.norcool.com
Refrigerator Equipment Mfr
N.A.I.C.S.: 335220

FRIGOSPED GMBH
Salzer Str 1, Ransbach-Baumbach,
56235, Germany
Tel.: (49) 26239800
Web Site: http://www.frigosped.de
Year Founded: 1981
Rev.: $120,395,033
Emp.: 200
Logistics & Warehousing Services
N.A.I.C.S.: 488999
Reinhardt H. Narten (Mng Dir)

Subsidiaries:

FRIGOLOGISTICS CONSULTING
LIMITED (1)
Frigosped House 1 Blackburn Road,
Rotherham, S61 2DW, South Yorkshire,
United Kingdom
Tel.: (44) 1909517321
Web Site: http://www.frigologistics.co.uk
Logistics Consulting Servies
N.A.I.C.S.: 541614
Keith Hampshire (Mng Dir)

Frigoconsult S.L. (1)
Apartado Correos 33, 46760, Tavernes de
la Valldigna, Spain
Tel.: (34) 962824029
Logistics Consulting Servies
N.A.I.C.S.: 541614
Reiner Kuhlen (Mng Dir)

FRIHEDEN INVEST A/S
Hosterkobvej 65, Horsholm, Denmark
Tel.: (45) 45 94 66 12
Private Investment Firm
N.A.I.C.S.: 523999

Subsidiaries:

IC Group A/S (1)
Adelgade 12D, 1304, Copenhagen,
Denmark (55%)

Tel.: (45) 32667788
Web Site: http://www.icgroup.net
Rev.: $395,388,670
Assets: $200,355,190
Liabilities: $96,366,100
Net Worth: $103,989,090
Earnings: $13,232,360
Emp.: 1,186
Fiscal Year-end: 06/30/2017
Fashion Apparel Mfr & Distr
N.A.I.C.S.: 315250
Niels Martinsen (Founder)

Subsidiary (Domestic):

By Malene Birger A/S (2)
Rahbeks Alle 21, 1801, Frederiksberg, Den-
mark
Tel.: (45) 3326 9620
Web Site: http://www.bymalenebirger.com
Apparel Mfr & Distr
N.A.I.C.S.: 315990
Trine Sveindal (Dir-Intl Wholesale)

Designers Remix A/S (2)
Pilestraede 10 1st Floor, 1112, Copenha-
gen, Denmark
Tel.: (45) 33 18 88 99
Web Site: http://www.designersremix.com
Apparel Mfr & Distr
N.A.I.C.S.: 315990
Charlotte Eskildsen (Co-Founder & Creative
Dir)

Subsidiary (Non-US):

IC Companys (Shanghai) Ltd. (2)
Long Cao Road No 222 Building 4 Level 2,
Shanghai, China
Tel.: (86) 21 64517866
Emp.: 40
Apparel Retailer
N.A.I.C.S.: 458110

IC Companys Canada Inc. (2)
265 Boulevard Lebeau, Ville Saint Laurent,
H4N 3H8, QC, Canada
Tel.: (514) 334-1265
Apparel Retailer
N.A.I.C.S.: 458110

IC Companys Finland Oy (2)
Veneentekijantie 8, 00210, Helsinki, Finland
Tel.: (358) 96962120
Apparel Retailer
N.A.I.C.S.: 458110

IC Companys France SARL (2)
910 Avenue Andre Lasquin, Sallanches,
74700, France
Tel.: (33) 45 078 5870
Apparel Retailer
N.A.I.C.S.: 458110

IC Companys Hong Kong Ltd. (2)
13/F Yau Lee Centre 15 Hoi Yuen Road,
Kwun Tong, Kowloon, China (Hong Kong)
Tel.: (852) 27638300
Apparel Retailer
N.A.I.C.S.: 458110

IC Companys Hungary Kft. (2)
Ati-Sziget Ipari Park, 2313, Szigetszentmik-
los, Hungary
Tel.: (36) 24 444230
Apparel Retailer
N.A.I.C.S.: 458110

IC Companys Nederland B.V. (2)
Lange Dreef 11-A, 4131 NJ, Vianen, Neth-
erlands
Tel.: (31) 347 327000
Apparel Retailer
N.A.I.C.S.: 458110

IC Companys Poland Sp. Z o.o. (2)
Domaniewska 42, 02-672, Warsaw, Poland
Tel.: (48) 22 322 9700
Web Site: http://www.iccompanys.pl
Apparel Mfr & Distr
N.A.I.C.S.: 315990

IC Companys Romania SRL (2)
9-9A Pompei Dimitrie Blvd, Bucharest, Ro-
mania
Tel.: (40) 21 204 8210
Apparel Retailer
N.A.I.C.S.: 458110

Tiger of Sweden AB (2)
Torsgatan 4, 111 23, Stockholm, Sweden
Tel.: (46) 8 546 310 00

Web Site: http://www.tigerofsweden.com
Apparel Mfr & Distr
N.A.I.C.S.: 315990
Per Hakans *(Dir-PR & License)*

Vingaker Factory Outlet AB **(2)**
Widengrensvagen 1, 643 30, Vingaker,
Sweden
Tel.: (46) 151750075
Web Site: http://www.vfo.se
Apparel Mfr & Distr
N.A.I.C.S.: 315990

FRINGE81 CO., LTD.
4th fl Dogenzaka Shibuya-ku, Tokyo,
150-0043, Japan
Tel.: (81) 364161290 **JP**
Web Site: http://www.fringe81.com
Year Founded: 2003
Sales Range: $10-24.9 Million
Content Linked Advertising Services
N.A.I.C.S.: 541890
Yuguru Tanaka *(Pres)*

FRIOSUR PESQUERA SA
Jose Maria Caro 300, Santiago, Cha-
cabuco, Chile
Tel.: (56) 67 67 6200
Seafood Mfr
N.A.I.C.S.: 311710
Rodrigo Allimant *(Mgr-Sls)*

Subsidiaries:

Europacifico Alimentos Del Mar
SI **(1)**
Pol Ind Ugaldeguren-I, Pabellon P-6-II,
48160, Derio, Bizkaia, Spain **(60%)**
Tel.: (34) 944544680
Sales Range: $25-49.9 Million
Emp.: 19
Other Marine Fishing
N.A.I.C.S.: 112511

FRISO BOUWGROEP B.V.
Pieter Zeemanstraat 9, PO Box 49,
8600 AA, Sneek, Netherlands
Tel.: (31) 88 429 00 00 **NI**
Web Site:
http://www.frisobouwgroep.nl
Year Founded: 1946
Renovation, Industrial Construction &
Project Development Services
N.A.I.C.S.: 236210

Subsidiaries:

Bouwborg B.V. **(1)**
Osloweg 125, 9723 BK, Groningen, Nether-
lands
Tel.: (31) 50 59 25 500
Web Site: http://www.frisobouwgroep.nl
Industrial Building Construction
N.A.I.C.S.: 236210

**FRISTAM PUMPEN F. STAMP
GMBH & CO. KG**
Kurt-A-Korber-Chaussee 55, 21033,
Hamburg, Germany
Tel.: (49) 40725560
Web Site: http://www.fristam.de
Sales Range: $550-599.9 Million
Emp.: 3,000
Mfr of Stainless Steel Pumps
N.A.I.C.S.: 333914
Wolfgang Stamp *(Mng Dir)*

Subsidiaries:

FRISTAM Pumps (UK) Limited
Partnership **(1)**
Unit 11 Apex Business Park, Hailsham,
East Sussex, United Kingdom
Tel.: (44) 1323 849 84 9
Stainless Steel Pump Distr
N.A.I.C.S.: 423830
Charlotte Payne *(Coord-Mktg)*

Fristam B.V. **(1)**
Claude Debussylaan 18, 1082 MD, Amster-
dam, Netherlands
Tel.: (31) 88 0071 700
Stainless Steel Pump Distr
N.A.I.C.S.: 423830

Fristam Iberica S.L. **(1)**
Avda de la Argentina 132, 33213, Gijon,
Spain
Tel.: (34) 984 047 382
Web Site: http://www.fristam.es
Stainless Steel Pump Distr
N.A.I.C.S.: 423830

Fristam Polska Sp.z.o.o. **(1)**
Ul Belgradzka 4 m 56, 02-793, Warsaw,
Poland
Tel.: (48) 22 852 02 04
Web Site: http://www.fristam.com.pl
Emp.: 2
Stainless Steel Pump Distr
N.A.I.C.S.: 423830
Andrzej Gliwiak *(Mgr)*

Fristam Pumpen, OOO **(1)**
6 b Artuchinoy Str, 109390, Moscow, Rus-
sia
Tel.: (7) 4991790710
Stainless Steel Pump Distr
N.A.I.C.S.: 423830

Fristam Pumper A/S **(1)**
Kobenhavnsvej 4, 4000, Roskilde, Denmark
Tel.: (45) 98 46 26 33
Stainless Steel Pump Distr
N.A.I.C.S.: 423830

Fristam Pumps (I) Pvt Ltd **(1)**
J-340 Bhosari M I D C Industrial Area,
Pune, 411 026, India
Tel.: (91) 20 271 30 751
Web Site: http://www.fristamindia.in
Emp.: 20
Stainless Steel Pump Distr
N.A.I.C.S.: 423830
Mayur Shinde *(Gen Dir)*

Fristam Pumps (Taicang) Co.,
Ltd. **(1)**
No 9 Xingye South Road Economic Devel-
opment Zone, Taicang, 215400, Jiangsu,
China
Tel.: (86) 512 53378625
N.A.I.C.S.: 423830

Fristam Pumps Japan Co., Ltd. **(1)**
5-11-7 Matue, Edogawa-Ku, Tokyo, 132-
0025, Japan
Tel.: (81) 3 5661 8702
Stainless Steel Pump Distr
N.A.I.C.S.: 423830

Fristam Pumps Ltd. **(1)**
21 Mark Edward Drive Half Moon Bay,
Auckland, New Zealand
Tel.: (64) 9 534 12 30
Stainless Steel Pump Distr
N.A.I.C.S.: 423830

Fristam Pumps South East Asia Pte.
Ltd **(1)**
2 Changi Business Park Ave 1 Level 2, Sin-
gapore, 486015, Singapore
Tel.: (65) 6764 4082
Stainless Steel Pump Distr
N.A.I.C.S.: 423830

Fristam Pumps USA, Limited
Partnership **(1)**
2410 Parview Rd, Middleton, WI 53562
Tel.: (608) 831-5001
Web Site: http://www.fristam.com
Pump Equipment Mfr
N.A.I.C.S.: 333914
Duane Ehlke *(VP-Ops)*

PT Fristindo Jaya Pump **(1)**
Komplek Pergudangan Karawaci Blok A/20
RT 010 RW 001, Biong Curug, Tangerang,
Indonesia
Tel.: (62) 21 59 123 21
Web Site: http://www.fristindo.com
Stainless Steel Pump Distr
N.A.I.C.S.: 423830
Irwan Setianto *(Engr-Sls)*

Pompes Fristam S.N.C. **(1)**
ZAC du Prieure Ouest 15 Avenue Christian
Doppler, 77700, Bailly-Romainvilliers,
France
Tel.: (33) 1 60 42 86 10
Web Site: http://www.fristam.de
Emp.: 5
Stainless Steel Pump Distr
N.A.I.C.S.: 423830
Wolfgang Stamp *(Gen Mgr)*

FRITZ BERGER GMBH
Fritz-Berger-Str 1, 92318, Neumarkt,
Germany
Tel.: (49) 91813300
Web Site: http://www.fritz-berger.de
Year Founded: 1958
Sales Range: $50-74.9 Million
Emp.: 240
Camping Sport Equipment & Leisure
Good Whslr
N.A.I.C.S.: 423910
Maurice Perske *(Mng Dir)*

FRITZ EGGER GMBH & CO.
Weiberndorf 20 St Johann, 6380, Ti-
rol, Austria
Tel.: (43) 800888111
Web Site: http://www.egger.com
Year Founded: 1961
Chipboard, MDF, OSB Boards,
Coated Boards, Postformed & Soft-
formed Elements, Components, Lami-
nates, Edges & Laminated Flooring
Products Mfr
N.A.I.C.S.: 322220
Walter Scheigl *(Gen Mgr)*

Subsidiaries:

Carlo Cappellari Italia S.r.l. **(1)**
Via Nazionale 11, 33010, Tavagnacco, Italy
Tel.: (39) 0432478521
Business Services
N.A.I.C.S.: 561499

EGGER AUSTRALASIA PTY
LIMITED **(1)**
PO Box 697, Carlton, 3053, VIC, Australia
Tel.: (61) 448200013
Furniture Distr
N.A.I.C.S.: 423210

EGGER Baltic UAB **(1)**
Zygio g 91 61, 08234, Vilnius, Lithuania
Tel.: (370) 52190003
Furniture Distr
N.A.I.C.S.: 423210

EGGER Beschichtungswerk Marien-
mUnster GmbH & Co. KG **(1)**
Gewerbegebiet 4, Vorden, 37696, Marien-
munster, Germany
Tel.: (49) 527698940
Furniture Distr
N.A.I.C.S.: 423210

EGGER Beschichtungswerk Marien-
mUnster GmbH & Co. KG - Bevern
Plant **(1)**
Fluttenweg 10, 37639, Bevern, Germany
Tel.: (49) 52769894250
Furniture Distr
N.A.I.C.S.: 423210

EGGER CZ s.r.o. **(1)**
Cechova 498, 50002, Hradec Kralove,
Czech Republic
Tel.: (420) 495531531
Furniture Distr
N.A.I.C.S.: 423210

EGGER Holzwerkstoffe Brilon GmbH
& Co. KG **(1)**
Daimlerstrasse 34-40, 32257, Bunde, Ger-
many
Tel.: (49) 522368662710
Furniture Distr
N.A.I.C.S.: 423210

Subsidiary (Non-US):

Masisa Argentina S.A. **(2)**
Bolsa de Comercio de Buenos Aires Av Le-
andro N Alem 356, C1003AAQ, Buenos
Aires, Argentina
Tel.: (54) 1155506000
Reconstituted Wood Product Mfr
N.A.I.C.S.: 321219

EGGER Holzwerkstoffe Schweiz
GmbH **(1)**
Rosenstrasse 2, Postfach 1350, 6011,
Kriens, Switzerland
Tel.: (41) 413495000
Furniture Distr
N.A.I.C.S.: 423210

EGGER Holzwerkstoffe Wismar
GmbH & Co. KG **(1)**
Am Haffeld 1, 23970, Wismar, Germany
Tel.: (49) 38413010
Furniture Distr
N.A.I.C.S.: 423210

EGGER Kunststoffe GmbH & Co.
KG **(1)**
Im Weilandmoor 2, 38518, Gifhorn, Ger-
many
Tel.: (49) 53718650
Furniture Distr
N.A.I.C.S.: 423210

EGGER ORMAN URUNLERI
A.S. **(1)**
GEPOSB 12 Cad No 12, 41400, Gebze,
Kocaeli, Turkiye
Tel.: (90) 2627513600
Furniture Distr
N.A.I.C.S.: 423210
Kamil Sumlu *(Mgr-Sls)*

EGGER Polska Sp. z o.o. **(1)**
ul sw Michala 43, 61-119, Poznan, Poland
Tel.: (48) 616503601
Furniture Distr
N.A.I.C.S.: 423210
Magdalena Serafinowicz *(Office Mgr-Sls)*

EGGER Productos de Madera
Limitada **(1)**
San Francisco de Asis 150 Oficina 403, Vi-
tacura, 7650747, Santiago, Chile
Tel.: (56) 222438583
Furniture Distr
N.A.I.C.S.: 423210

EGGER RS DOO **(1)**
Karadordeva 55/9, 11300, Smederevo, Ser-
bia
Tel.: (381) 112150538
Furniture Distr
N.A.I.C.S.: 423210

EGGER Retail Products France
S.A.S. **(1)**
60 Rue Blaise Pascal Batiment C, CS
41001, 37010, Tours, Cedex, France
Tel.: (33) 247701250
Furniture Distr
N.A.I.C.S.: 423210

Egger (UK) Limited **(1)**
Anick Grange Rd, Hexham, NE46 4JS, Nor-
thumberland, United Kingdom
Tel.: (44) 1434602191
Web Site: http://www.egger.co.uk
Sales Range: $250-299.9 Million
Emp.: 700
Construction Materials Whslr
N.A.I.C.S.: 423990
Bob Livesey *(Mgr)*

Egger Barony Ltd. **(1)**
Barony Road, Auchinleck, Glasgow,
KA182LL, United Kingdom
Tel.: (44) 1290426026
Paperboard Mills
N.A.I.C.S.: 322130

Egger Benelux GCV **(1)**
Limnanderdreef 44, Zulte, 9870, Belgium
Tel.: (32) 93886441
Sales Range: $25-49.9 Million
Emp.: 15
Lumber Plywood Millwork & Wood Panel
Whslr
N.A.I.C.S.: 423310

Egger Retail Products GmbH & Co.
KG **(1)**
Im Kissen 19, 59929, Brilon, Germany
Tel.: (49) 29617700
Furniture Distr
N.A.I.C.S.: 423210
Ralf Lorber *(Mng Dir)*

Egger Romania SRL **(1)**
Maresal Alexandru Averescu Nr 15 B/C Cla-
direa Triumph et 2 Sector 1, 011454, Bu-
charest, Romania
Tel.: (40) 372438000
Web Site: http://www.egger.com
Sales Range: $150-199.9 Million
Emp.: 500
Durable Goods Whslr
N.A.I.C.S.: 423990
Leonard Curcumelis *(Dir-Fin)*

Fritz Egger GmbH & Co.—(Continued)

Egger Scandinavia ApS (1)
Jernbanegade 5A, Tistrup, Ribe, 6862,
Denmark
Tel.: (45) 75291000
Web Site: http://www.egger.com
Sales Range: $50-74.9 Million
Emp.: 7
Construction Materials Whslr
N.A.I.C.S.: 423390
Neels Sunesen (Mng Dir)

Egger Turkiye Ltd. (1)
Keresteciler Sit 11 Blok No 1 Kat 5, 34306,
Istanbul, Turkiye
Tel.: (90) 2126705115
Web Site: http://www.egger.com
Sales Range: $25-49.9 Million
Emp.: 50
Reconstituted Wood Product Mfr
N.A.I.C.S.: 321219

Egger-Rol SA (1)
Ave d Albret, BP 1 Rion-des-Landes, 40371,
Lyon, France
Tel.: (33) 558568181
Web Site: http://www.egger.com
Sales Range: $125-149.9 Million
Emp.: 450
Wood Products Mfr
N.A.I.C.S.: 321999
Cotte Philippe (Gen Mgr)

Fritz EGGER AG (1)
Ikeda building 2nd floor 1-9-5 Ginza, Chuo,
Tokyo, 104-0061, Japan
Tel.: (81) 362286470
Furniture Distr
N.A.I.C.S.: 423210

Fritz EGGER GmbH Hungary (1)
Fo utca 14-18, 1011, Budapest, Hungary
Tel.: (36) 308641917
Furniture Distr
N.A.I.C.S.: 423210

**Fritz Egger GmbH & Co. - EGGER
Panneaux & Decors** (1)
ZI Blanchifontaine, 88700, Rambervillers,
France
Tel.: (33) 329680101
Furniture Distr
N.A.I.C.S.: 423210

IOOO EGGER Drevplit (1)
Nekrasova Str 114 room 72, 220040, Minsk,
Belarus
Tel.: (375) 172878377
Furniture Distr
N.A.I.C.S.: 423210

**OOO EGGER Drevprodukt
Shuya** (1)
Jushnoje Chaussee 1, 155908, Shuya,
Russia
Tel.: (7) 4935139000
Furniture Distr
N.A.I.C.S.: 423210

**OOO Egger Drevprodukt
Gagarin** (1)
Ezhvinsky proezd 1, Gagarin, 215010,
Smolensk, Oblast, Russia
Tel.: (7) 4813579300
Furniture Distr
N.A.I.C.S.: 423210

Roma Plastik A.S. (1)
GEPOSB, 41400, Gebze, Kocaeli, Turkiye
Tel.: (90) 2627513050
Furniture Distr
N.A.I.C.S.: 423210

**TOV EGGER
HOLZWERKSTOFFE** (1)
vul E Chavdar 7 office 4, 02140, Kiev,
Ukraine
Tel.: (380) 445771677
Furniture Distr
N.A.I.C.S.: 423210

FRITZ LANGE GMBH
Sudfeldstrasse 3, 31832, Springe,
Germany
Tel.: (49) 50419950
Web Site: http://www.fritz-lange.de
Year Founded: 1955
Rev.: $26,208,600

Emp.: 130
Number Plates & Road Signs Mfr
N.A.I.C.S.: 331315
Folker Lange (Deputy Dir)

FRITZ MASSONG GMBH
Schiessgartenweg 8a, 67227, Fran-
kenthal, Germany
Tel.: (49) 62333650
Web Site: http://www.massong.com
Year Founded: 1921
Rev.: $34,759,776
Emp.: 75
Fire Extinguishers & Equipment Sup-
plier
N.A.I.C.S.: 423830
Dieter Massong (Owner)

FRITZ NOLS AG
Bleichstrasse 2-4, D-60313, Frank-
furt, Germany
Tel.: (49) 0 69 260 28 605 De
Web Site: http://www.fritznols.com
Year Founded: 1975
FNG—(DEU)
Sales Range: Less than $1 Million
Capital Market Consulting Services
N.A.I.C.S.: 523910
Arnd Christofer Frohne (Member-
Mgmt Bd)

FRITZ PLANUNG GMBH
Am Schonblick 1, 72574, Bad Urach,
Germany
Tel.: (49) 712515000
Web Site: http://www.fritz-planung.de
Year Founded: 1951
Rev.: $11,986,986
Emp.: 95
Construction Services
N.A.I.C.S.: 237990
Karl Schmitt (Mng Dir)

FRITZ STEPHAN GMBH
Kirchstrasse 19, Montabaur, 56410,
Germany
Tel.: (49) 643991250
Web Site: http://www.stephan-
gmbh.com
Year Founded: 1974
Rev.: $26,970,657
Emp.: 115
Medical Device Mfr
N.A.I.C.S.: 334510
Georg Mainusch (CEO & Co-Mng
Dir)

FRITZY TECH INC.
120 High Road East Finchley, Lon-
don, N2 9ED, United Kingdom
Tel.: (44) 3152741520 DE
Year Founded: 2014
FRFR—(OTCIQ)
Liabilities: $241,473
Net Worth: ($241,473)
Earnings: ($68,463)
Fiscal Year-end: 06/30/22
Residential & Commercial Property
Rental & Sales
N.A.I.C.S.: 531210
Hooi Chee Voon (Pres, CEO, CFO,
Treas & Sec)

FRIULCHEM SPA
Cia Lodovica Ariosto 6, 20145, Milan,
Italy
Tel.: (39) 0236591450
Web Site: https://www.friulchem.com
FCM—(ITA)
Sales Range: Less than $1 Million
Biotechnology Research & Develop-
ment Services
N.A.I.C.S.: 541714
Disma Giovanni Mazzola (CEO &
Officer-IR)

FRNT FINANCIAL INC.
49 Wellington St E, Toronto, M5E
1C9, ON, Canada
Tel.: (437) 253-3747 ON
Web Site: https://www.frnt.io
Year Founded: 2018
FRFLF—(OTCQB)
Rev.: $218,561
Assets: $6,444,938
Liabilities: $573,663
Net Worth: $5,871,275
Earnings: ($2,034,259)
Fiscal Year-end: 06/30/22
Investment Management Service
N.A.I.C.S.: 523999
David Washburn (Pres)

**FROCH ENTERPRISE CO.,
LTD.**
No 122 Industrial Road, Touliu, 640,
Yun-Lin, Taiwan
Tel.: (886) 55571669
Web Site: https://www.froch.com
Year Founded: 1970
2030—(TAI)
Rev.: $420,448,625
Assets: $388,416,317
Liabilities: $230,787,623
Net Worth: $157,628,693
Earnings: $1,666,176
Emp.: 268
Fiscal Year-end: 12/31/23
Steel Pole Mfr
N.A.I.C.S.: 339992
P. Y. Chang (Chm)

FROEHLICH BAU AG
Mittelhoefer Strasse 11-13, Hessen,
34587, Germany
Tel.: (49) 56625010
Building Construction Services
N.A.I.C.S.: 236220

FRONTAGE INC.
Maison Blg 1-18-17, Minato-ku, To-
kyo, 105-0003, Japan
Tel.: (81) 3 3596 0300 JP
Web Site: http://www.frontage.jp
Year Founded: 2002
Rev.: $406,646,400
Emp.: 230
Brand Development
N.A.I.C.S.: 541810
Takashi Tachibana (Pres)

FRONTEO, INC.
Meisan Takahama Building 2-12-23
Kounan, Minato-ku, Tokyo, 108-0075,
Japan
Tel.: (81) 354636344 JP
Web Site: https://www.fronteo.com
Year Founded: 2003
FTEO—(NASDAQ)
Rev.: $105,821,760
Assets: $114,466,000
Liabilities: $52,126,800
Net Worth: $62,339,200
Earnings: $12,661,440
Emp.: 387
Fiscal Year-end: 03/31/22
Electronic Data Discovery & Digital
Forensic Investigations Services
N.A.I.C.S.: 518210
Yoshikatsu Shirai (Chief Client Tech
Officer)

Subsidiaries:

Evolve Discovery LLC (1)
611 Mission St 4th Fl, San Francisco, CA
94105
Tel.: (415) 398-8600
Web Site: http://www.evolvediscovery.com
Litigation Consulting Services
N.A.I.C.S.: 541199
Andrew F. Jimenez (Pres & CEO)

Fronteo Korea, Inc. (1)
10F ARC Place 142 Teheran-ro, Gangnam-

gu, Seoul, 06236, Korea (South)
Tel.: (82) 2 350 3000
Web Site: https://korea.fronteo.com
E-Discovery & International Litigation Sup-
port Services
N.A.I.C.S.: 541199

PCF Fronteo Inc. (1)
2 Konan 12-23 Meishan Takahama Build-
ing, Minato-ku, Tokyo, 108-0075, Japan
Tel.: (81) 35 463 8333
Information Technology Services
N.A.I.C.S.: 541511

TechLaw Solutions, Inc. (1)
3675 Concorde Pkwy Ste 1000, Chantilly,
VA 20151
Tel.: (703) 817-0366
Web Site: http://www.techlawsolutions.com
Sales Range: $10-24.9 Million
Emp.: 35
Corporation, Government Agencies & Law
Firm Consulting Services
N.A.I.C.S.: 541611
Andrew F. Jimenez (CEO)

UBIC North America, Inc. Hong
Kong (1)
9 F CLI Bldg 13 Hennessy Rd, Hong Kong,
Wanchai, China (Hong Kong)
Tel.: (852) 21594276
Web Site: http://www.ubicna.com
Sales Range: $25-49.9 Million
Emp.: 10
Forensic Examiners
N.A.I.C.S.: 541380

UBIC North America, Inc. South
Korea (1)
Woolim Lions Vly C Dong 1509, 371 28
Gasan Dong, Seoul, 153 786, Geumchun
gu, Korea (South)
Tel.: (82) 220263362
Web Site: http://www.ubicna.com
Sales Range: $25-49.9 Million
Emp.: 2
Forensic Examiners
N.A.I.C.S.: 541380

**FRONTERA ENERGY CORPO-
RATION**
333 Bay Street Suite 1100, Toronto,
M5H 2R2, ON, Canada
Tel.: (416) 362-7735 BC
Web Site:
https://www.fronteraenergy.ca
Year Founded: 1996
3PY3—(DEU)
Rev.: $1,185,552,000
Assets: $3,016,280,000
Liabilities: $1,182,287,000
Net Worth: $1,833,993,000
Earnings: $192,756,000
Emp.: 767
Fiscal Year-end: 12/31/23
Crude Oil & Natural Gas Exploration,
Extraction & Production
N.A.I.C.S.: 211120
Gabriel de Alba (Chm)

Subsidiaries:

Pacific Rubiales Energy Corp. (1)
Calle 110 No 9 - 25 Piso 14, Bogota, Co-
lombia
Tel.: (57) 15112000
Web Site: http://www.fronteraenergy.ca
Oil & Gas Exploration Services
N.A.I.C.S.: 213112
Murry Provost (Pres)

Sociedad Portuaria Puerto Bahia
S.A. (1)
Calle 110 9-25 Piso 12, Bogota, Colombia
Tel.: (57) 12561033
Web Site: http://www.puertobahia.com.co
General Cargo Terminal Services
N.A.I.C.S.: 488320

**FRONTIER BIOTECHNOLO-
GIES, INC.**
11F Building E-2 Lvdi Zhichuang,
Dongshan Subdistrict Jiangning, Nan-
jing, 211199, Jiangsu, China
Tel.: (86) 2569648375

Web Site:
https://www.frontierbiotech.com
Year Founded: 2013
688221—(SHG)
Rev.: $11,897,552
Assets: $338,484,632
Liabilities: $103,813,136
Net Worth: $234,671,496
Earnings: ($50,089,680)
Fiscal Year-end: 12/31/22
Pharmaceutical Product Mfr & Distr
N.A.I.C.S.: 325412
Xie Dong *(Founder & Chm)*

FRONTIER CAPITAL LIMITED
Office No 7 2nd Floor Readymoney
Terrace 167 Dr A B Road Worli, Pen-
insula Techno Park Off Bandra Kurla
Complex LBS Marg, Mumbai,
400018, India
Tel.: (91) 9819731915
Web Site:
https://www.frontiercapital.in
Rev.: $5,425
Assets: $2,595,323
Liabilities: $2,688,008
Net Worth: ($92,685)
Earnings: ($1,328,184)
Fiscal Year-end: 03/31/19
Financial Support Services
N.A.I.C.S.: 523999
Aniket Naresh Prabhu *(CFO, Officer-
Compliance & Sec)*

FRONTIER CERAMICS LIM-
ITED
29-Industrial Estate Jamrud Road,
Peshawar, Pakistan
Tel.: (92) 91589147079
Web Site: https://www.forte.com.pk
Ceramic Tile Mfr
N.A.I.C.S.: 327120
Omer Khalid *(CEO)*

FRONTIER CHRYSLER LTD
3046 Hwy 16 East, Smithers, V0J
2N0, BC, Canada
Tel.: (250) 847-4266
Web Site:
http://www.frontierchrysler.com
Year Founded: 1958
Rev.: $12,496,887
Emp.: 28
New & Used Car Dealers
N.A.I.C.S.: 441110
Jo Anne Maxwell *(Bus Mgr)*

FRONTIER DEVELOPMENTS
PLC
26 Science Park Milton Road, Cam-
bridge, CB4 0FP, United Kingdom
Tel.: (44) 1223394300
Web Site: https://www.frontier.co.uk
Year Founded: 1994
FDEV—(AIM)
Rev.: $123,128,911
Assets: $219,298,934
Liabilities: $65,667,486
Net Worth: $153,631,449
Earnings: $29,269,728
Emp.: 584
Fiscal Year-end: 05/31/21
Game Developer
N.A.I.C.S.: 513210
David Braben *(Founder & CEO)*

Subsidiaries:

Frontier Developments Inc.   **(1)**
1190 Barrington St Suite 301, Halifax, B3H
2R4, NS, Canada
Tel.: (902) 405-7065
Game Publisher
N.A.I.C.S.: 513210

FRONTIER DIAMONDS LTD.
566 Elizabeth Street Level 1, Melbourne, 3000, VIC, Australia

Tel.: (61) 393472409
Mineral Exploration Services
N.A.I.C.S.: 213114
Jacques Cilliers *(Mgr-Comml & Mktg)*

FRONTIER DIGITAL VEN-
TURES LIMITED
Level 7 330 Collins Street, Mel-
bourne, 3000, VIC, Australia
Tel.: (61) 386899997   AU
Web Site: https://www.frontierdv.com
Year Founded: 2014
FDV—(ASX)
Rev.: $46,266,254
Assets: $101,406,448
Liabilities: $16,313,940
Net Worth: $85,092,509
Earnings: ($7,272,509)
Fiscal Year-end: 12/31/23
Online Financial Services
N.A.I.C.S.: 523940
Anthony Klok *(Chm)*

Subsidiaries:

Le Rouge AB   **(1)**
Brunnsgrand 2-4, 111 30, Stockholm, Swe-
den
Tel.: (46) 73 573 1632
Web Site: https://lerouge.se
Restaurant Operators
N.A.I.C.S.: 722511

Meqasa Limited   **(1)**
23 Kofi Annan Ave, North Legon, Accra,
Ghana
Tel.: (233) 506866060
Online Property Portal Services
N.A.I.C.S.: 519290

Rebbiz Co Ltd   **(1)**
No 150 Mya Nandar Street, Thaketa Town-
ship, Yangon, Myanmar
Tel.: (95) 996 769 9990
Web Site: https://www.carsdb.com
Online Car Portal Operator
N.A.I.C.S.: 519290
Wai Phyo Kyaw *(COO)*

FRONTIER ENERGY LIMITED
Level 20 140 St Georges Terrace,
Perth, 6000, WA, Australia
Tel.: (61) 892003428   AU
Web Site: https://frontierhe.com
FHE—(ASX)
Rev.: $199,475
Assets: $60,677,253
Liabilities: $3,841,103
Net Worth: $56,836,149
Earnings: $1,411,879
Fiscal Year-end: 12/31/23
Copper, Gold & Nickel Mining Ser-
vices
N.A.I.C.S.: 212230
Grant Davey *(Exec Chm & Exec Dir)*

FRONTIER INTERNATIONAL,
INC.
Shibuya East NBF Shibuya East 335
Shibuya, Shibuya-ku, Tokyo, 150-
0002, Japan
Tel.: (81) 357783500
Web Site: https://www.frontier-i.co.jp
Year Founded: 1990
7050—(TKS)
Rev.: $112,632,970
Assets: $73,432,441
Liabilities: $20,607,863
Net Worth: $52,824,579
Earnings: $8,602,577
Fiscal Year-end: 04/30/23
Digital Marketing Services
N.A.I.C.S.: 541870
Yasuhiro Kawamura *(Pres)*

Subsidiaries:

Frontier Direct Inc.   **(1)**
2F NBF Shibuya East 3-3-5 Shibuya,
Shibuya-ku, Tokyo, 150-0002, Japan
Tel.: (81) 357783939
Web Site: https://www.frontier-di.co.jp

Emp.: 504
Advertising Agency Services
N.A.I.C.S.: 541810

PT. Frontier International
Indonesia   **(1)**
Cityloft Sudirman 9th Floor Unit 27 Jl KH
Mas Mansyur Kav 121, Jakarta Pusat,
10220, Indonesia
Tel.: (62) 2129912861
Emp.: 8
Film Production Services
N.A.I.C.S.: 512110
Sozo Tsunekazu *(CEO)*

FRONTIER IP GROUP PLC
93 George Street, Edinburgh, EH2
3ES, United Kingdom
Tel.: (44) 1312401251   UK
Web Site: https://www.frontierip.co.uk
Year Founded: 2007
FIPP—(AIM)
Rev.: $459,466
Assets: $57,110,382
Liabilities: $558,810
Net Worth: $56,551,572
Earnings: ($4,023,432)
Emp.: 16
Fiscal Year-end: 06/30/23
Intellectual Property Owner
N.A.I.C.S.: 533110
Jackie McKay *(COO)*

Subsidiaries:

FIP Portugal, Unipessoal, Lda.   **(1)**
Rua Joao Frederico Ludovice 22A Loja,
1500-357, Lisbon, Portugal
Tel.: (351) 913700775
Intellectual Property Commercialization Ser-
vices
N.A.I.C.S.: 533110

FRONTIER LITHIUM INC.
2614 Belisle Drive Val Caron, Sud-
bury, P3N 1B3, ON, Canada
Tel.: (705) 897-7622
Web Site:
https://www.frontierlithium.com
Year Founded: 1995
LITOF—(OTCQX)
Assets: $19,265,992
Liabilities: $1,024,787
Net Worth: $18,241,205
Earnings: ($8,566,748)
Fiscal Year-end: 03/31/22
Lithium Exploration Services
N.A.I.C.S.: 212390
Reginald F. Walker *(Chm)*

FRONTIER MANAGEMENT
INC.
Sumitomo Fudosan Roppongi Grand
Tower 41F 3-2-1 Roppongi, Minato,
Tokyo, 106-6241, Japan
Tel.: (81) 368625180
Web Site: https://www.frontier-
mgmt.com
Year Founded: 2007
7038—(TKS)
Rev.: $71,077,250
Assets: $77,096,660
Liabilities: $28,728,680
Net Worth: $48,367,980
Earnings: $5,530,200
Emp.: 428
Fiscal Year-end: 12/31/23
Management Consulting Services
N.A.I.C.S.: 541618

Subsidiaries:

Frontier Capital Inc.   **(1)**
43rd floor Sumitomo Fudosan Roppongi
Grand Tower 3-2-1 Roppongi, Minato-ku,
Tokyo, Japan
Tel.: (81) 368625225
Web Site: https://frontier-cptl.com
Emp.: 23
Financial Investment Services
N.A.I.C.S.: 523999

Frontier Management (Shanghai)
Inc.   **(1)**
Unit 2019 20/F HKRI Centre One HKRI Tai-
koo Hui 288 Shimen 1st Road, Jingan Dis-
trict, Shanghai, 200041, China
Tel.: (86) 2180286038
Web Site: https://www.frontier-mgmt.com
Management Consulting Services
N.A.I.C.S.: 541618

FRONTIER MINING LTD.
15 Al Farabi Ave Nurly Tau Business
Centre Block 4V Office 1906, Almaty,
050010, Kazakhstan
Tel.: (7) 7273111544
Web Site:
http://www.frontiermining.kz
Sales Range: $1-9.9 Million
Emp.: 451
Gold & Copper Mining Services
N.A.I.C.S.: 212220
Yerbulat A. Tastanov *(Exec Dir)*

FRONTIER OIL CORPORATION
4th Floor Zaragoza Building 102
Gamboa Street, Legaspi Village,
Makati, 1229, Philippines
Tel.: (63) 2 4785854
Web Site:
http://www.frontieroilcorp.com
Year Founded: 2011
Oil Exploration
N.A.I.C.S.: 211120
Astrolito Del Castillo *(Chm)*

FRONTIER PHARMA LIMITED
Kemp House 160 City Road, London,
EC1V 2NX, United Kingdom
Tel.: (44) 207 1297 410   UK
Web Site:
http://www.frontierpharma.co.uk
Investment Services
N.A.I.C.S.: 523999
M. Levent Selamoglu *(Pres)*

Subsidiaries:

Zdravlje AD   **(1)**
Vlajkova 199, 16000, Leskovac, Serbia
Tel.: (381) 16202000
Pharmaceuticals Mfr
N.A.I.C.S.: 325412
Bojan Jovic *(Gen Dir)*

FRONTIER RARE EARTHS
LIMITED
1 Avenue de la Gare, 1611, Luxem-
bourg, Luxembourg
Tel.: (352) 24873637
Web Site:
http://www.frontierrareearths.com
Sales Range: Less than $1 Million
Emp.: 21
Metal Mining Services
N.A.I.C.S.: 212290
Philip Kenny *(Chm)*

Subsidiaries:

Yolani Minerals (Proprietary) Ltd.   **(1)**
111 Loop St, Cape Town, 8001, Western
Cape, South Africa
Tel.: (27) 214242505
Web Site: http://www.yolaniminerals.co.za
Sales Range: $50-74.9 Million
Mineral Exploration & Mining Services
N.A.I.C.S.: 212390

FRONTIER REAL ESTATE IN-
VESTMENT CORPORATION
Kojun Building 6th Floor 6-8-7 Ginza,
Chuo-ku, Tokyo, 104-0061, Japan
Tel.: (81) 332890440
Web Site: https://www.frontier-
reit.co.jp
Year Founded: 2004
8964—(TKS)
Sales Range: $75-99.9 Million
Real Estate Investment Services
N.A.I.C.S.: 523999

Frontier Real Estate Investment Corporation—(Continued)

Toshihide Ichikawa *(Exec Dir)*

FRONTIER SERVICES GROUP LIMITED

Suite 3902 39/F Far East Finance Centre 16 Harcourt Road, Admiralty, Hong Kong, China (Hong Kong)
Tel.: (852) 37661077
Web Site: http://www.fsgroup.com
500—(OTCIQ)
Rev.: $123,231,050
Assets: $139,486,498
Liabilities: $79,346,812
Net Worth: $60,139,686
Earnings: ($3,354,761)
Emp.: 651
Fiscal Year-end: 12/31/22
Aviation & Logistics Services
N.A.I.C.S.: 481219
Erik Prince *(Deputy Chm)*

Subsidiaries:

Phoenix Aviation Limited (1)
Langata Rd, PO Box 49493-00100, Wilson Airport, Nairobi, Kenya
Tel.: (254) 204945540
Aviation Services
N.A.I.C.S.: 488119

Telequote Data International Limited (1)
Rm 1405 14/F Admiralty Ctr Twr 2 Admiralty, Hong Kong, China (Hong Kong)
Tel.: (852) 25046888
Web Site: http://www.tq.net
Online Financial Information Provider
N.A.I.C.S.: 519290

Transit Freight Forwarding Proprietary Limited (1)
150 / 151 Culverwell Park Houtbaai Street Elandshaven Ext 4, 1401, Germiston, Gauteng, South Africa
Tel.: (27) 119078808
Web Site: http://www.transitco.co.za
Freight Forwarding Services
N.A.I.C.S.: 488510
Robbie Forbes *(CEO)*

FRONTIER SPRINGS LTD.

Km 25/4 Kalpi Road Rania Kanpur Dehat, Kanpur, 209304, Uttar Pradesh, India
Tel.: (91) 5111240212
Web Site:
https://www.frontiersprings.co.in
522195—(BOM)
Rev.: $10,638,265
Assets: $11,382,527
Liabilities: $3,254,027
Net Worth: $8,128,500
Earnings: $1,064,197
Emp.: 174
Fiscal Year-end: 03/31/21
Hot Coil Springs Mfr & Distr
N.A.I.C.S.: 332613
Kundan Lal Bhatia *(Chm & Mng Dir)*

FRONTIER TRANSPORT HOLDINGS LIMITED

103 Bofors Circle Industria, Epping, 7460, South Africa
Tel.: (27) 215078800
Web Site: http://www.hplr.co.za
FTH—(JSE)
Rev.: $30,553,258
Assets: $158,655,901
Liabilities: $62,188,711
Net Worth: $96,467,190
Earnings: $17,519,895
Fiscal Year-end: 03/31/22
Transportation & Logistic Consulting Services
N.A.I.C.S.: 541614
Francois Meyer *(CEO)*

Subsidiaries:

Eljosa Travel & Tours Proprietary Limited (1)
9 Kiaat Road, Kraaifontein Industria, Cape Town, 7570, South Africa
Tel.: (27) 219825249
Web Site: http://www.eljosa.co.za
Travel & Tour Services
N.A.I.C.S.: 561510
Lorrine Fouche *(COO)*

FRONTKEN CORPORATION BERHAD

Level 6 Uptown 5 Tower DNo 5 Jalan SS21/39, Damansara 1 No 9 Jalan 16/11 Off Jalan Damansara, 47400, Petaling Jaya, Selangor, Malaysia
Tel.: (60) 376251381
Web Site: https://www.frontken.com
FRONTKN—(KLS)
Rev.: $109,456,629
Assets: $170,544,030
Liabilities: $46,115,956
Net Worth: $124,428,074
Earnings: $28,606,887
Emp.: 1,320
Fiscal Year-end: 12/31/22
Welding Services
N.A.I.C.S.: 811310
Wai Pin Ng *(Chm & CEO)*

Subsidiaries:

Ares Green Technology Corporation (1)
No 17 Bade Road, Xinying District, T'ainan, Taiwan
Tel.: (886) 6 653 3966
Web Site: https://www.aresgreen.com.tw
Semiconductor & Optoelectronic Product Mfr
N.A.I.C.S.: 334413

Frontken (East Malaysia) Sdn. Bhd. - Kuching Plant (1)
Lot 1030 Section 66 KTLD Jalan Kisar Pending Industrial Estate, 93450, Kuching, Sarawak, Malaysia
Tel.: (60) 82481286
Sales Range: $25-49.9 Million
Emp.: 40
Spray Coating Services
N.A.I.C.S.: 332812
Voon Kianpeng *(Mgr-Sls)*

Frontken (Johor) Sdn. Bhd. (1)
No 7 Jalan Dato' Yunus Utama Taman Perindustrian Dato' Yunus Sulaiman, Lima Kedai, 81120, Gelang Patah, Johor Darul Takzim, Malaysia
Tel.: (60) 75101701
Web Site: http://www.frontken.com
Spray Coating Services
N.A.I.C.S.: 332812

Frontken (Singapore) Pte. Ltd. (1)
156A Gul Circle, Singapore, 629614, Singapore
Tel.: (65) 68634500
Sales Range: $125-149.9 Million
Emp.: 180
Spray Coating Services
N.A.I.C.S.: 325510

Plant (Domestic):

Frontken (Singapore) Pte. Ltd. - Jurong Plant 1 (2)
156A Gul Circle, Singapore, 629614, Singapore
Tel.: (65) 6 863 4500
Web Site: https://www.frontken.com
Sales Range: $75-99.9 Million
Spray Coating Services
N.A.I.C.S.: 332812

Frontken (Singapore) Pte. Ltd. - Jurong Plant 2 (2)
15 Gul Drive, 629466, Singapore, Singapore
Tel.: (65) 68631411
Spray Coating Services
N.A.I.C.S.: 325510

Subsidiary (Non-US):

Frontken (Thailand) Co. Ltd. (2)

3 Moo 6 Putthamonthon VII Road Homkred, Sam Phran, 73110, Nakornpathom, Thailand (100%)
Tel.: (66) 34220838
Web Site: http://www.frontken.com
Spray Coating Services
N.A.I.C.S.: 332812

Frontken Malaysia Sdn. Bhd. - Kulim Plant (1)
Lot 1923 Jalan Hi-Tech 2/3 1, Kulim Hi-Tech Industrial Park, Kulim, Kedah, Malaysia
Tel.: (60) 44036168
Sales Range: $50-74.9 Million
Emp.: 200
Spray Coating Services
N.A.I.C.S.: 332812

Frontken Malaysia Sdn. Bhd. - Shah Alam Plant (1)
Lot 2-46 Jalan Subang Utama 7, Taman Perindustrian Subang Utama Section 22, 40300, Shah Alam, Selangor Darul Ehsan, Malaysia
Tel.: (60) 35 191 5007
Web Site: http://www.frontken.com
Sales Range: $25-49.9 Million
Emp.: 28
Spray Coating Services
N.A.I.C.S.: 332812

Frontken Philippines Inc (1)
Lot C3-9 Carmelray Industrial Park II, Calamba, 4027, Laguna, Philippines
Tel.: (63) 495080049
Web Site: http://www.ph.frontken.com
Sales Range: $25-49.9 Million
Emp.: 88
Spray Coating & Mechanical Engineering Services
N.A.I.C.S.: 332812

PT Frontken Indonesia (1)
Jl Raya Serang Km 13 Rt 003/RW 002 Kp Cirewed Suka Damai Cikupa, Tangerang, 15710, Banten, Indonesia
Tel.: (62) 2159405390
Sales Range: $25-49.9 Million
Emp.: 13
Spraying & Coating Services
N.A.I.C.S.: 332812

FRONTLINE CARRIER SYSTEMS INC.

2788 Portland Drive, Oakville, L6H 6R4, ON, Canada
Tel.: (905) 822-6177
Web Site: http://www.frontline-carrier.com
Year Founded: 1989
Rev.: $10,234,704
Emp.: 23
Transportation Services
N.A.I.C.S.: 488999
Mike Mallon *(Mgr-Ops)*

FRONTLINE GOLD CORPORATION

372 Bay St Suite 301, Toronto, M5H 2W9, ON, Canada
Tel.: (416) 681-9090   Ca
Web Site:
https://www.frontlinegold.com
Year Founded: 2008
FGC—(TSXV)
Assets: $830,888
Liabilities: $1,703,508
Net Worth: ($872,620)
Earnings: $773,087
Fiscal Year-end: 12/31/20
Investment Services
N.A.I.C.S.: 523999
Walter C. Henry *(Pres & CEO)*

FRONTLINE PLC

Par-la-Ville Place 14 Par-la-Ville Road, Hamilton, HM 08, Bermuda
Tel.: (441) 2956935
Web Site: https://www.frontlineplc.cy
FRO—(NYSE)
Rev.: $1,438,248,000
Assets: $4,768,443,000
Liabilities: $2,508,544,000

Net Worth: $2,259,899,000
Earnings: $475,537,000
Emp.: 78
Fiscal Year-end: 12/31/22
Shipping Services; Oil Tankers
N.A.I.C.S.: 483111
Ola Lorentzon *(Chm)*

Subsidiaries:

Frontline Corporate Services Limited (1)
183 St Vincent Street, Glasgow, G2 5QD, United Kingdom
Tel.: (44) 141 471 4260
Shipping Services
N.A.I.C.S.: 492110

Frontline Management (Bermuda) Ltd. (1)
Par-la-Ville Place 14 Par-la-Ville Road, PO Box HM 1593, Hamilton, HM 08, Bermuda
Tel.: (441) 2956935
Crude Oil Seaborne Transportation Services
N.A.I.C.S.: 211120

Frontline Management AS (1)
Bryggegata 3, PO Box 1327 VIKA, 0250, Oslo, Norway (100%)
Tel.: (47) 23114000
Web Site: http://www.frontline.com
Sales Range: $25-49.9 Million
Emp.: 25
Shipping Support Services
N.A.I.C.S.: 483111
Inger Marie Klemp *(CFO)*

Frontline Shipping Singapore Pte Ltd (1)
1 Wallich Street Guoco Tower 14-02, Singapore, 078881, Singapore
Tel.: (65) 6 296 5518
Shipping Services
N.A.I.C.S.: 483111

SFL Corporation Ltd. (1)
Par-la-Ville Place 14 Par-la-Ville Road, Hamilton, HM 08, Bermuda
Tel.: (441) 2959500
Web Site: https://www.sflcorp.com
Rev.: $752,286,000
Assets: $3,731,389,000
Liabilities: $2,691,992,000
Net Worth: $1,039,397,000
Earnings: $83,937,000
Emp.: 21
Fiscal Year-end: 12/31/2023
Oil Tanker Fleet Operator
N.A.I.C.S.: 483111
Ole B. Hjertaker *(CEO)*

FRONTLINE SECURITIES LTD.

M-6 M-Block Market Greater Kailash Part-II, New Delhi, 110048, India
Tel.: (91) 11 2921 2331
Web Site: http://www.fslindia.com
Year Founded: 1995
Rev.: $2,016,685
Assets: $7,400,616
Liabilities: $326,791
Net Worth: $7,073,825
Earnings: $1,550,414
Emp.: 6
Fiscal Year-end: 03/31/18
Financial Services
N.A.I.C.S.: 523940
Rakesh Kumar Jain *(Chm)*

FROSTA AG

Am Lunedeich 116, D 27572, Bremerhaven, Germany
Tel.: (49) 47197360
Web Site: https://www.frosta-ag.com
Year Founded: 1905
NLM—(MUN)
Rev.: $705,902,788
Assets: $478,351,026
Liabilities: $222,054,489
Net Worth: $256,296,537
Earnings: $37,586,774
Emp.: 1,665
Fiscal Year-end: 12/31/23
Frozen Food Mfr
N.A.I.C.S.: 311412

Dirk Ahlers *(Chm-Supervisory Bd)*

Subsidiaries:

Copack France S.a.r.l.   (1)
36 rue L'ancienne Mairie, 92100, Boulogne-Billancourt, France
Tel.: (33) 146948460
Frozen Food Mfr
N.A.I.C.S.: 311412

Copack Tiefkuhlkost-Produktions GmbH   (1)
Am Lunedeich 116, 27572, Bremerhaven, Germany
Tel.: (49) 4719736190
Web Site: https://www.copack.eu
Frozen Food Mfr
N.A.I.C.S.: 311412

ELBTAL Tiefkuhlkost Vertriebs GmbH   (1)
Messaer Strasse 3-5, 01623, Lommatzsch, Germany
Tel.: (49) 471 97 36 117
Frozen Food Distr
N.A.I.C.S.: 424420

FRoSTA CR s.r.o.   (1)
U Nikolajky 833/5, 155 00, Prague, Czech Republic
Tel.: (420) 485236067
Web Site: https://www.frosta.cz
Frozen Food Distr
N.A.I.C.S.: 424420

FRoSTA Foodservice GmbH   (1)
Am Lunedeich 116, 27572, Bremerhaven, Germany
Tel.: (49) 4719736441
Web Site: https://www.frostafoodservice.de
Frozen Food Mfr
N.A.I.C.S.: 311412

FRoSTA France S.a.r.l.   (1)
140 rue Gallieni, 92100, Boulogne-Billancourt, France
Tel.: (33) 1 46948460
Frozen Food Distr
N.A.I.C.S.: 424420

FRoSTA Hungary Kft.   (1)
Szent Tamas u 1, 2500, Esztergom, Hungary
Tel.: (36) 33500300
Web Site: https://www.frosta.hu
Frozen Food Distr
N.A.I.C.S.: 424420

FRoSTA Italia s.r.l.   (1)
Via Ennio Quirino Visconti 103 Int 8, 00193, Rome, Italy
Tel.: (39) 06 68 7 17 49
Frozen Food Distr
N.A.I.C.S.: 424420

FRoSTA Romania S.R.L.   (1)
2 Ciresilor Street, Jud Ilfov, Mogosoaia, Romania
Tel.: (40) 722366555
Frozen Food Mfr
N.A.I.C.S.: 311412

FRoSTA Sp. z o.o.   (1)
ul Witebska 63, 85-778, Bydgoszcz, Poland
Tel.: (48) 523606700
Web Site: https://www.frosta.pl
Emp.: 600
Frozen Food Distr
N.A.I.C.S.: 424420

FRoSTA Tiefkuhlkost GmbH   (1)
Mendelssohnstrasse 15D, 22761, Hamburg, Germany
Tel.: (49) 408541400
Web Site: http://www.frosta.de
Frozen Food Distr
N.A.I.C.S.: 424420

FRoSTA Tiefkuhlkost GmbH u. I.   (1)
Wiener Str 89-91, 2500, Baden, Austria
Tel.: (43) 2252 8 29 23
Web Site: http://www.frosta.at
Frozen Food Distr
N.A.I.C.S.: 424420

Rheintal Tiefkuhlkost Zweigniederlassung der FRoSTA AG   (1)
Industriestrasse 4, 67240, Bobenheim-Roxheim, Germany
Tel.: (49) 62 39 807 0

Frozen Food Distr
N.A.I.C.S.: 424420

Tiko Vertriebsgesellschaft mbH   (1)
Am Lunedeich 116, 27572, Bremerhaven, Germany
Tel.: (49) 4719736190
Frozen Food Mfr
N.A.I.C.S.: 311412

FRP ADVISORY GROUP PLC

110 Cannon Street, London, EC4N 6EU, United Kingdom
Tel.: (44) 2030054000   UK
Web Site:
    https://www.frpadvisory.com
Year Founded: 2010
FRP—(AIM)
Rev.: $129,195,204
Assets: $126,907,446
Liabilities: $66,464,467
Net Worth: $60,442,979
Earnings: $16,171,803
Emp.: 467
Fiscal Year-end: 04/30/22
Advertising Agencies
N.A.I.C.S.: 541810

FRS GMBH & CO. KG

Norderhofenden 19-20, 24937, Flensburg, Germany
Tel.: (49) 461864670
Web Site: http://www.frs.de
Year Founded: 1991
Emp.: 2,000
Passenger Ferry Operations
N.A.I.C.S.: 483212
Christian Baumberger *(Mng Dir)*

Subsidiaries:

Albanian Ferry Terminal Operator SHPK   (1)
Administration Building L1 Porti Detar Detar Terminali I Trageteve, Durres, Albania
Tel.: (355) 52223208
Web Site: http://www.afto.al
Port Agency Services
N.A.I.C.S.: 488510
Erneta Kulla *(Head-Admin)*

Clipper Navigation, Inc.   (1)
2701 Alaskan Way Pier 69, Seattle, WA 98121
Tel.: (206) 443-2560
Web Site: http://www.clippervacations.com
Excursion Boat Transportation & Tour Services
N.A.I.C.S.: 487210
David Gudgel *(CEO)*

Subsidiary (Non-US):

Clipper Navigation Ltd.   (2)
254 Belleville St, Victoria, V8V 1W9, BC, Canada
Tel.: (250) 382-8100
Passenger Transportation Services
N.A.I.C.S.: 483112

Subsidiary (Domestic):

Mosquito Fleet, LLC   (2)
21 NE Old Belfair Hwy, Belfair, WA 98528
Tel.: (360) 275-9100
Passenger Transportation Services
N.A.I.C.S.: 483112

FRS Helgoline GmbH & Co. KG   (1)
Norderhofenden 19-20, 24937, Flensburg, Germany
Tel.: (49) 46186444
Web Site: http://www.helgoline.de
Offshore Logistic Services
N.A.I.C.S.: 488510
Birte Dettmers *(Mng Dir)*

FRS Offshore GmbH & Co. KG   (1)
Norderhofenden 19-20, 24937, Flensburg, Germany
Tel.: (49) 4618640
Web Site: http://www.fwol.de
Offshore Logistic Services
N.A.I.C.S.: 488510
Frank Wiebe *(Ops Mgr)*

FRS Ship Management Ltd.   (1)

256 Makarios Avenue C4 Eftapaton Court, 3105, Limassol, Cyprus
Tel.: (357) 25105357
Web Site: http://www.frs-shipmanagement.eu
Cost Management Services
N.A.I.C.S.: 488310
Lazaros Charalambous *(Mng Dir)*

Forde Reederei Seetouristik Iberia S.L.U.   (1)
C/La Linea de la Concepcion 3, Tarifa, 11380, Cadiz, Spain
Tel.: (34) 956681830
Web Site: http://www.frs.es
Passenger Transportation Services
N.A.I.C.S.: 488510

Reederei Hiddensee GmbH   (1)
Fahrstrasse 16, 18439, Stralsund, Germany
Tel.: (49) 383126810
Web Site: http://www.reederei-hiddensee.de
Shipping Reservation Services
N.A.I.C.S.: 561599
Gotz Becker *(Mng Dir)*

Romo-Sylt Linie GmbH & Co. KG   (1)
Am Fahranleger 3, 25992, List, Germany
Tel.: (49) 461864601
Web Site: http://www.syltfaehre.de
Shipping Reservation Services
N.A.I.C.S.: 561599
Birte Dettmers *(Mng Dir)*

Weisse Flotte GmbH   (1)
Fahrstrasse 16, 18439, Stralsund, Germany
Tel.: (49) 383126810
Web Site: http://www.weisse-flotte.de
Canal Passenger Transportation Services
N.A.I.C.S.: 483212

FRTEK CO., LTD.

30 Obongsandan 1-ro, Donghan-gu, Uiwang, 14055, Gyeonggi-do, Korea (South)
Tel.: (82) 314701515
Web Site: https://www.frtek.co.kr
Year Founded: 2000
073540—(KRS)
Rev.: $14,303,387
Assets: $86,460,158
Liabilities: $43,392,014
Net Worth: $43,068,144
Earnings: $6,177,438
Emp.: 40
Fiscal Year-end: 12/31/22
Repeater Mfr
N.A.I.C.S.: 334210
Milla Woo *(Pres & Co-CEO)*

Subsidiaries:

FRTek Japan Inc.   (1)
Telecommunication Servicesb
N.A.I.C.S.: 517810

FRUIT FORMULATIONS PRIVATE LIMITED

206 Konark Icon Mundhwa - Kharadi Rd, Hadapsar, Pune, 411028, India
Tel.: (91) 2067482500   In
Web Site: https://in.agrana.com
Food & Beverage Mfr
N.A.I.C.S.: 311999
Nikhil Kapoor *(CEO)*

FRUITION VENTURES LIMITED

1301 Padma Tower-1 Rajendra Place, Delhi, 10008, India
Tel.: (91) 1125710171
Web Site: https://fruitionventure.com
Year Founded: 1960
538568—(BOM)
Sales Range: Less than $1 Million
Security Brokerage Services
N.A.I.C.S.: 523150
Sanhit Jain *(Mng Dir)*

FRUTAFRUTA, INC.

Agroforestry Bldg 28 3-2 Kudankita, Chiyoda-ku, Tokyo, 102-0073, Japan
Tel.: (81) 120265726

Web Site: https://frutafrutastore.com
Year Founded: 2000
2586—(TKS)
Sales Range: $10-24.9 Million
Emp.: 40
Fruits & Fruit Juices Distr
N.A.I.C.S.: 424480

FRUTICOLA VICONTO S.A.

Fundo Quinta Maipo S/N Buin, Commune, Santiago, Chile
Tel.: (56) 27076554
Web Site: https://www.viconto.cl
Year Founded: 1986
VICONTO—(SGO)
Sales Range: Less than $1 Million
Fruit & Vegetable Farming Services
N.A.I.C.S.: 111219
Javier Angel Figueroa Guilisasti *(CEO)*

FRUTTAGEL S.C.P.A.

Via Nullo Baldini 26, 48011, Alfonsine, RA, Italy
Tel.: (39) 0544866511   IT
Web Site: http://www.fruttagel.it
Year Founded: 1994
Sales Range: $150-199.9 Million
Emp.: 700
Frozen Fruit, Vegetables & Beverages
N.A.I.C.S.: 311411
Vincenzo Alberti *(Pres)*

Subsidiaries:

Fruttagel Scrl - Larino plant   (1)
Via Statale Sannitica 87, Piane di Larino, Larino, 86035, Campobasso, Italy
Tel.: (39) 0874 82091
Sales Range: $25-49.9 Million
Emp.: 14
Frozen Vegetable Production Services
N.A.I.C.S.: 111219

FS DEVELOPMENT INVESTMENT HOLDINGS

Room 901 Building W2 Oriental Plaza No 1 East Changan Avenue, Dongcheng District, Beijing, 100005, China
Tel.: (86) 1058116070
Web Site:
    http://www.spearhead.com.cn
Year Founded: 2003
300071—(CHIN)
Rev.: $170,441,388
Assets: $164,891,376
Liabilities: $138,035,664
Net Worth: $26,855,712
Earnings: $4,095,468
Fiscal Year-end: 12/31/22
Marketing Services
N.A.I.C.S.: 541613
Chen Yongliang *(Chm & Gen Mgr)*

Subsidiaries:

Smaato Inc.   (1)
240 Stockton St 9th Fl, San Francisco, CA 94108
Tel.: (650) 286-1198
Web Site: http://www.smaato.com
Emp.: 500
Mobile App Monetization & Mobile Advertising Services
N.A.I.C.S.: 541890
Ragnar Kruse *(Co-Founder)*

FS HOLDING AD

Benkovska 4 Street 2nd floor, 2600, Kyustendil, Bulgaria
Tel.: (359) 70151149
Web Site: https://www.fs-holding.free.bg
Year Founded: 1996
HFSI—(BUL)
Sales Range: Less than $1 Million
Holding Company
N.A.I.C.S.: 551112

FS Holding AD—(Continued)

FSA GROUP LIMITED
Level 3 70 Phillip Street, Sydney, 2000, NSW, Australia
Tel.: (61) 89855565
Web Site:
https://www.fsagroup.com.au
FSA—(ASX)
Rev.: $34,792,024
Assets: $579,020,084
Liabilities: $512,061,915
Net Worth: $66,958,169
Earnings: $5,892,242
Emp.: 96
Fiscal Year-end: 06/30/24
Debt Solutions & Lending Services
N.A.I.C.S.: 523940
Deborah Southon (Exec Dir)

Subsidiaries:

Aravanis Insolvency Pty Ltd **(1)**
Level 3 70 Phillip Street, Sydney, 2000, NSW, Australia
Tel.: (61) 1300369108
Web Site: http://www.aravanis.com.au
Emp.: 33
Business Management Services
N.A.I.C.S.: 541611

EBP Money Pty. Ltd. **(1)**
Locked Bag 29, Australia Square, Sydney, 1215, NSW, Australia
Tel.: (61) 1300706000
Web Site: https://www.ebpmoney.com.au
Car & Household Loan Services
N.A.I.C.S.: 522310

FSBM HOLDINGS BERHAD
L3-02/L5-01 KYM Tower 8 Jalan PJU 7/6 PJU 7, Mutiara Damansara, 47800, Petaling Jaya, Selangor, Malaysia
Tel.: (60) 376229377
Web Site: https://www.fsbm.com.my
Year Founded: 1984
FSBM—(KLS)
Computer Products Services
N.A.I.C.S.: 541715
Tan Yen Wan (Exec Dir)

Subsidiaries:

Asialink Technology Development Limited **(1)**
Unit 301-306 Bldg 14 8 Science Park West Ave, Sha Tin, Fo Tan, China (Hong Kong)
Tel.: (852) 28114228
Web Site: http://www.asialink.com.hk
Telecommunication & Networking Services
N.A.I.C.S.: 517810

FSBM CTech Sdn. Bhd. **(1)**
503 Block A Phileo Damansara 1 9 Jalan 16/11 Off Jalan Damansara, Petaling Jaya, Selangor, Selangor, Malaysia
Tel.: (60) 378432312
Software Development Services
N.A.I.C.S.: 541511

FSBM Mes Elite Sdn. Bhd. **(1)**
A-2-6 Glomac Damansara No 699, Jalan Damansara, 60000, Kuala Lumpur, Malaysia
Tel.: (60) 379322313
Web Site: https://fsbmmes.com
Information & Technology Services
N.A.I.C.S.: 519290

FSBM Net Media Sdn. Bhd. **(1)**
306 & 506 Block A Phileo Damansara 1 No 9 Jalan 16/11, Off Jalan Damansara, 46350, Petaling Jaya, Selangor Darul Ehsan, Malaysia
Tel.: (60) 379606080
Communication & Networking Services
N.A.I.C.S.: 517111

Televas Holdings Sdn. Bhd. **(1)**
40-2 Jalan PJU 7/16 Mutiara Damansara, 47800, Petaling Jaya, Selangor Darul Ehsan, Malaysia
Tel.: (60) 377295244
Web Site: http://www.televas.com.my

Sales Range: $50-74.9 Million
Emp.: 10
Telecommunication Equipment Distr
N.A.I.C.S.: 423690
Tan Hock San (Chm)

Unos Sdn. Bhd. **(1)**
306 Block A Phileo Damansara 1 No 9 Jalan 16/11 Off Jalan Damansara, Petaling Jaya, 46350, Selangor, Malaysia
Tel.: (60) 378432288
Web Site: http://www.myunos.com
Sales Range: $50-74.9 Million
Emp.: 200
Telecommunication & Networking Services
N.A.I.C.S.: 517810

FSD PHARMA INC.
55 University Ave Suite 1003, Toronto, M5J 2H7, ON, Canada
Tel.: (416) 854-8884   ON
Web Site:
https://www.fsdpharma.com
Year Founded: 1998
HUGE—(NASDAQ)
Rev.: $367,735
Assets: $38,410,656
Liabilities: $7,868,436
Net Worth: $30,542,220
Earnings: ($23,606,828)
Emp.: 17
Fiscal Year-end: 12/31/22
Investment Services
N.A.I.C.S.: 523999
Anthony Durkacz (Co-Founder & Co-Exec Chm)

Subsidiaries:

Prismic Pharmaceuticals, Inc. **(1)**
Hayden Corporate Ctr 8283 N Hayden Rd, Scottsdale, AZ 85258
Tel.: (480) 422-1813
Pharmaceuticals Mfr
N.A.I.C.S.: 325412

FSE SERVICES GROUP LIMITED
8/F Chevalier Commercial Centre 8 Wang Hoi Road, Kowloon Bay, Kowloon, China (Hong Kong)
Tel.: (852) 27334188   Ky
Web Site:
http://www.fseservices.com.hk
0331—(HKG)
Rev.: $898,595,276
Assets: $464,238,230
Liabilities: $407,903,119
Net Worth: $56,335,111
Earnings: $64,993,538
Emp.: 20,004
Fiscal Year-end: 06/30/22
Holding Company
N.A.I.C.S.: 551112
Rocky Lock Kee Poon (CEO)

Subsidiaries:

Extensive Trading Company Limited **(1)**
Units 1712 17/F Chevalier Commercial Centre 8 Wang Hoi Road, Kowloon Bay, Kowloon, China (Hong Kong)
Tel.: (852) 28891681
Web Site: https://www.fseng.hk
Building Materials Distr
N.A.I.C.S.: 423390

Far East Engineering Services Limited **(1)**
Units 816-819 8/F Chevalier Commercial Centre 8 Wang Hoi Road, Kowloon Bay, Kowloon, China (Hong Kong)
Tel.: (852) 28987331
Web Site: https://www.fseng.com.hk
Engineeering Services
N.A.I.C.S.: 541330

Far East Technical Services (Macao) Limited **(1)**
Avenida Do Nordeste No 196 A Edif Tong Wa San Chun Bloco 12 R/C, Macau, China (Macau)
Tel.: (853) 28760020

Engineeering Services
N.A.I.C.S.: 541330

Hong Kong Island Landscape Company Limited **(1)**
Unit 1714 17/F Chevalier Commercial Centre 8 Wan Hoi Road, Kowloon Bay, China (Hong Kong)
Tel.: (852) 23698367
Web Site: https://www.hkil.com.hk
Landscape Project Services
N.A.I.C.S.: 561730

Kiu Lok Properties (International) Limited **(1)**
Leasing / Sale Department Management Office, 11/F Convention Plaza Apartments 1 Harbour Road, Wanchai, China (Hong Kong)
Tel.: (852) 28297079
Web Site: https://cpa-hk.com.hk
Property Management Services
N.A.I.C.S.: 531311

Kiu Lok Service Management Company Limited **(1)**
Rm 1108 Office Tower Convention Plaza No 1 Harbour Road, Wanchai, China (Hong Kong)
Tel.: (852) 28027966
Web Site: http://www.klsm.com.hk
Engineeering Services
N.A.I.C.S.: 541330

Majestic Engineering (Macao) Company Limited **(1)**
Rua do Almirante Costa Cabral No 17-17A R/C, Macau, China (Macau)
Tel.: (853) 28330033
Engineeering Services
N.A.I.C.S.: 541330

Majestic Engineering Company Limited **(1)**
Units 1707-11 1716-18 17/F Chevalier Commercial Centre 8, Wang Hoi Road Kowloon Bay, Kowloon, China (Hong Kong)
Tel.: (852) 22351881
Web Site: https://www.fseng.com.hk
Engineeering Services
N.A.I.C.S.: 541330

Nova Insurance Consultants Limited **(1)**
Unit 1608 16/F Chevalier Commercial Centre 8 Wang Hoi Road, Kowloon Bay, China (Hong Kong)
Tel.: (852) 28454373
Web Site: https://www.nova-insure.com
Insurance Services
N.A.I.C.S.: 524298

Perfect Event Services Limited **(1)**
Unit 1 7/F 1 Wang Tung Street, Kai Fuk Industrial Centre, Kowloon Bay, China (Hong Kong)
Tel.: (852) 27070222
Web Site: https://www.perfectevent.com.hk
Facility Management Services
N.A.I.C.S.: 541513

Young's Engineering Company Limited **(1)**
Units 1701-6 17/F Chevalier Commercial Centre 8 Wang Hoi Road, Kowloon Bay, Kowloon, China (Hong Kong)
Tel.: (852) 22350900
Web Site: https://www.fseng.com.hk
Air Conditioning Contracting Services
N.A.I.C.S.: 238220

FSI ENERGY GROUP INC.
4535 8A Street Northeast, Calgary, T2E 4J6, AB, Canada
Tel.: (403) 571-4225   AB
Web Site: http://www.fsigroup.ca
Year Founded: 2000
Sales Range: $10-24.9 Million
Filtration & Filtration-Related Products
N.A.I.C.S.: 333248
Richard A. Ball (Pres & CEO)

Subsidiaries:

FSI International Services Ltd. **(1)**
4535 - 8A Street NE, Calgary, P2E 4J6, AB, Canada

Tel.: (403) 571-4230
Web Site: http://www.fsigroup.ca
Filtration Products
N.A.I.C.S.: 333248

FSILON HOME BUILDING MATERIALS CO., LTD.
No 5888 Wuyuan Avenue Wuyuan Street, Haiyan County, Jiaxing, 314300, Zhejiang, China
Tel.: (86) 57389051928
Web Site: http://www.fsilon.com
Year Founded: 2007
605318—(SHG)
Rev.: $95,844,383
Assets: $169,223,460
Liabilities: $59,147,445
Net Worth: $110,076,015
Earnings: $1,583,796
Fiscal Year-end: 12/31/22
Building Material Mfr & Distr
N.A.I.C.S.: 327120
Zhenghua Shen (Chm, Interim Sec & Gen Mgr)

FSM HOLDINGS LIMITED
12 Tuas Link 1, Singapore, 638595, Singapore
Tel.: (65) 68636663   Ky
Web Site: http://www.fsmtech.com
Year Founded: 1992
1721—(HKG)
Rev.: $12,172,234
Assets: $41,797,319
Liabilities: $15,960,766
Net Worth: $25,836,552
Earnings: ($3,693,100)
Emp.: 207
Fiscal Year-end: 12/31/23
Holding Company
N.A.I.C.S.: 551112
Thet Li (Chm)

Subsidiaries:

Fine Sheetmetal Technologies Pte. Ltd. **(1)**
12 Tuas Link 1, Singapore, 638595, Singapore
Tel.: (65) 68636663
Sheet Metal Fabricator Mfr & Distr
N.A.I.C.S.: 332322

FSN CAPITAL PARTNERS AS
Dronning Mauds Gate 11, 0250, Oslo, Norway
Tel.: (47) 24147300
Web Site: http://www.fsncapital.com
Year Founded: 1999
Investment Management Service
N.A.I.C.S.: 523940
Morten Welo (COO-IR & Partner)

Subsidiaries:

Aura Light International AB **(1)**
Vretenvagen 2, 171 54, Solna, Sweden
Tel.: (46) 8 564 881 40
Web Site: http://www.auralight.com
Electronic Components Mfr
N.A.I.C.S.: 335132
Anders Svensson (CFO)

Subsidiary (Non-US):

Aura Light A/S **(2)**
Ulvenveien 92A, 511, Oslo, Norway
Tel.: (47) 228 839 00
Web Site: http://www.auralight.no
Emp.: 16
Electrical Equipment Distr
N.A.I.C.S.: 423610
Fredrik Sventelius (VP-Sls & Reg Mgr)

Subsidiary (Domestic):

Aura Light AB **(2)**
Fonstergatan 17, 598 40, Vimmerby, Sweden
Tel.: (46) 20323030
Web Site: http://www.auralight.com
Electric Equipment Mfr
N.A.I.C.S.: 335132

Subsidiary (Non-US):

Aura Light ApS   (2)
Ved Vesterport 6 5 sal, 1612, Copenhagen,
Denmark
Tel.: (45) 272 183 09
Web Site: http://www.auralight.dk
Electrical Equipment Distr
N.A.I.C.S.: 423610
Benjamin Bak *(Mgr-Sls)*

Aura Light France Sarl   (2)
55 rue Traversiere, 75012, Paris, France
Tel.: (33) 1 75 77 95 35
Web Site: http://www.auralight.fr
Electronic Components Distr
N.A.I.C.S.: 423610

Aura Light GmbH   (2)
Alter Teichweg 15, 22081, Hamburg, Ger-
many
Tel.: (49) 40 756 634 0
Web Site: http://www.auralight.de
Electrical Equipment Distr
N.A.I.C.S.: 423610

Aura Light Greece   (2)
40 Agiou Konstantinou Str Aithrio Commer-
cial Center, Maroussi, 151 24, Athens,
Greece
Tel.: (30) 210 6198040
Web Site: http://www.auralight.gr
Electrical Equipment Distr
N.A.I.C.S.: 423610

Aura Light Italy S.r.l.   (2)
Viale Roma 9a, 40024, Rome, Italy
Tel.: (39) 051 948 150
Web Site: http://www.auralight.it
Electrical Equipment Distr
N.A.I.C.S.: 423610

Aura Light Oy   (2)
Juurakkotie 6, 03100, Nummela, Finland
Tel.: (358) 9 855 3640
Web Site: http://www.auralight.fi
Electrical Equipment Distr
N.A.I.C.S.: 423610

Aura Light Portugal Unipessoal,
LDA   (2)
Av 29 de Agosto N 268 B, Terrugem, 2705-
869, Sintra, Portugal
Tel.: (351) 210 999 344
Web Site: http://www.auralight.pt
Electronic Components Distr
N.A.I.C.S.: 423610

Aura Light Spain, S.L.U.   (2)
Valencia 304 pral 1a, 08009, Barcelona,
Spain
Tel.: (34) 93 272 69 49
Web Site: http://www.auralight.es
Electrical Equipment Distr
N.A.I.C.S.: 423610

Aura Light Trading (Shanghai) Co.,
Ltd   (2)
Rm 6-A3 Building 1 No 825 Zhaojiabang
Rd, Xuhui District, Shanghai, 200032, China
Tel.: (86) 21 3313 0891
Web Site: http://www.auralight.com
Electrical Equipment Distr
N.A.I.C.S.: 423610
Ruodic Xu *(Acct Mgr)*

Subsidiary (US):

Aura Light USA Inc   (2)
150 N Michigan Ave Ste 1950, Chicago, IL
60601
Tel.: (312) 890-1660
Web Site: http://www.auralight.us
Electronic Components Distr
N.A.I.C.S.: 423610

Subsidiary (Non-US):

Aura Long Life Lamps Ltd.   (2)
Waterloo House Waterloo Road Ketley
Business Park, Ketley, Telford, TF1 5JD,
Shropshire, United Kingdom
Tel.: (44) 1952 200181
Web Site: http://www.aura-light.co.uk
Electronic Components Distr
N.A.I.C.S.: 423610

Auralight Polska Sp. z o.o.   (2)
ul Dworcowa 17, 05-500, Piaseczno, Po-
land
Tel.: (48) 22 736 73 00

Web Site: http://www.auralight.pl
Emp.: 15
Electronic Components Distr
N.A.I.C.S.: 423610
Michal Wziatek *(Acct Mgr)*

EET Europarts A/S   (1)
Bregnerodvej 133 D, 3460, Birkerod, Den-
mark
Tel.: (45) 45 82 19 19
Web Site: http://www.eeteuroparts.dk
Electronic Components Distr
N.A.I.C.S.: 423690
Mikael Thulin *(Mng Dir)*

Subsidiary (Non-US):

EET Europarts (Pty) Ltd   (2)
35 Angus Crescent Longmeadow Business
Park, East Modderfontein, 1609, Johannes-
burg, South Africa
Tel.: (27) 11 608 1069
Web Site: http://www.eeteuroparts.co.za
Emp.: 21
Electronic Components Distr
N.A.I.C.S.: 423690
Clive Maher *(Mng Dir)*

EET Europarts AB   (2)
Planiavagen 17, Box 4124, 131 04, Nacka,
Sweden
Tel.: (46) 8 507 510 00
Web Site: http://www.eeteuroparts.se
Electronic Components Distr
N.A.I.C.S.: 423690
Christine Bejas *(Acct Mgr)*

EET Europarts AS   (2)
Olaf Helsetsvei 6, 0694, Oslo, Norway
Tel.: (47) 22 91 95 00
Web Site: http://www.no.eetgroup.com
Electronic Components Distr
N.A.I.C.S.: 423690
Bjorn Berg *(Mng Dir)*

EET Europarts B.V.   (2)
Proostwetering 107 D, 3543 AC, Utrecht,
Netherlands
Tel.: (31) 30 2192040
Web Site: http://www.eeteuroparts.nl
Electronic Components Distr
N.A.I.C.S.: 423690
Barteld Casteleijn *(Mng Dir)*

EET Europarts BV   (2)
Excelsiorlaan 18, 1930, Zaventem, Belgium
Tel.: (32) 2 88 88 901
Web Site: http://www.eeteuroparts.be
Emp.: 3
Electronic Components Distr
N.A.I.C.S.: 423690
Barteld Casteleijn *(Mng Dir)*

EET Europarts EGYPT   (2)
5 Masadk Street, Dokki, Giza, Egypt
Tel.: (20) 2 37628973
Web Site: http://www.eeteuroparts.com.eg
Electronic Components Distr
N.A.I.C.S.: 423690
Mahmoud Maarek *(Mng Dir)*

EET Europarts GmbH   (2)
Bosch 80a, 6331, Hunenberg, Switzerland
Tel.: (41) 41 785 13 13
Web Site: http://www.eeteuroparts.ch
Electronic Components Distr
N.A.I.C.S.: 423690
Ronald Potthoff *(Mng Dir)*

EET Europarts GmbH   (2)
IZ NO-Sud Strasse 2 Obj M7 A-2351, Wie-
ner Neudorf, Austria
Tel.: (43) 2236 374 014
Web Site: http://www.eeteuroparts.at
Electronic Components Distr
N.A.I.C.S.: 423690
Werner Heinreichsberger *(Mng Dir)*

EET Europarts GmbH   (2)
Agnes-Pockels-Str 16, 40721, Hilden, Ger-
many
Tel.: (49) 2 11 75 84 67 0
Web Site: http://www.eeteuroparts.de
Electronic Components Distr
N.A.I.C.S.: 423690
Andreas Solbach *(Acct Mgr)*

EET Europarts Ltd   (2)
Unit 4 Phoenix Works Cornwall Road, Pin-
ner, HA5 4UH, Middlesex, United Kingdom
Tel.: (44) 208 421 0101

Web Site: http://www.eeteuroparts.co.uk
Emp.: 20
Electronic Components Distr
N.A.I.C.S.: 423690
Maureen Hill *(Mgr-Customer Svcs)*

EET Europarts Oy   (2)
Spektri Business Park Toimisto, Espoo,
Finland
Tel.: (358) 9 47 850 900
Web Site: http://www.eeteuroparts.fi
Electronic Components Distr
N.A.I.C.S.: 423690
Berndt Fyhr *(Mng Dir)*

EET Europarts S.A.   (2)
Calle Aragoneses 15, 28108, Alcobendas,
Madrid, Spain
Tel.: (34) 902 902 377
Web Site: http://www.eeteuroparts.es
Electronic Components Distr
N.A.I.C.S.: 423690
Miguel Cervera *(Mng Dir)*

EET Europarts Sp. z o.o.   (2)
ul Rakietowa 22, 80-298, Gdansk, Poland
Tel.: (48) 583200660
Web Site: http://www.eeteuroparts.pl
Electronic Components Distr
N.A.I.C.S.: 423690

EET Europarts s.r.l.   (2)
Sede legale P za Conciliazione 5, 20123,
Milan, Italy
Tel.: (39) 02 49 82 756
Web Site: http://www.eeteuroparts.it
Electronic Components Distr
N.A.I.C.S.: 423690
Matteo Vaccaro *(Mng Dir)*

EET Europarts s.r.o.   (2)
Cercanska 640/30, 140 00, Prague, Czech
Republic
Tel.: (420) 226 259 750
Web Site: http://www.eeteuroparts.cz
Emp.: 10
Electronic Components Distr
N.A.I.C.S.: 423690
Jan Bartos *(Mng Dir)*

EET France SAS   (2)
20 Blv Deruelle - Bat C - Etage 9, 69003,
Lyon, France
Tel.: (33) 4 78 14 05 55
Web Site: http://www.eeteuroparts.fr
Electronic Components Distr
N.A.I.C.S.: 423690
Florent Berge *(Mng Dir)*

EET Portugal   (2)
Nao tem atendimento ao publico, Lisbon,
Portugal
Tel.: (351) 308 802 467
Web Site: http://www.eeteuroparts.pt
Electronic Components Distr
N.A.I.C.S.: 423690
Jose Matos Alves *(Mng Dir)*

Fibo-Trespo AS   (1)
Industriveien 2, 4580, Lyngdal, Norway
Tel.: (47) 38 13 71 00
Web Site: http://www.fibo-trespo.no
Interior Design & Furnishing Services
N.A.I.C.S.: 541410
Arvid Thompsen *(Product Mgr)*

Gram Equipment A/S   (1)
Nordager 2-6, 6000, Kolding, Denmark
Tel.: (45) 73201700
Web Site: http://www.gram-equipment.com
Ice Cream Production Machinery Mfr
N.A.I.C.S.: 333241

Subsidiary (US):

Gram Equipment of America Inc.   (2)
1 S Gold Dr, Hamilton, NJ 08691
Tel.: (609) 981-7610
Web Site: http://www.gram-equipment.com
Ice Cream Production Machinery Mfr
N.A.I.C.S.: 333241

Green Landscaping AB   (1)
Jagershillgatan 14, 213 75, Malmo, Sweden
Tel.: (46) 10 499 70 00
Web Site: http://www.greenlandscaping.se
Emp.: 600
Landscaping Services
N.A.I.C.S.: 561730
Johan Nordstrom *(CEO)*

Kjell & Company   (1)
PO Box 50435, 202 14, Malmo, Sweden
Tel.: (46) 10 680 25 00
Web Site: http://www.kjell.com
Electronic Components Distr
N.A.I.C.S.: 423690
Bjarne Mumm *(Chm)*

Lagkagehuset A/S   (1)
Amerikavej 21, 1756, Copenhagen, Den-
mark
Tel.: (45) 72 14 47 00
Web Site: http://www.lagkagehuset.dk
Bakery Products Mfr
N.A.I.C.S.: 311812
Jesper Friis *(CEO)*

Norman ASA   (1)
Strandveien 37, Lysaker, 1324, Norway
Tel.: (47) 67 10 97 00
Web Site: http://www.norman.com
Sales Range: $25-49.9 Million
Content Security Solutions
N.A.I.C.S.: 513210

Pm Retail AS   (1)
Kartverksvei 6, 3511, Honefoss, Norway
Tel.: (47) 32 11 52 00
Web Site: http://www.pm.no
Apparel Distr
N.A.I.C.S.: 458110
Dag J. Opedal *(Chm)*

Praktiska Sverige AB   (1)
Vikingsgatan 4, 411 04, Gothenburg, Swe-
den
Tel.: (46) 87944200
Web Site: https://www.praktiska.se
Educational Support Services
N.A.I.C.S.: 611710

Praktiska Sverige AB   (1)
Vikingsgatan 4, 411 04, Gothenburg, Swe-
den
Tel.: (46) 87944200
Web Site: https://www.praktiska.se
Educational Support Services
N.A.I.C.S.: 611710

Praktiska Sverige AB   (1)
Vikingsgatan 4, 411 04, Gothenburg, Swe-
den
Tel.: (46) 87944200
Web Site: https://www.praktiska.se
Educational Support Services
N.A.I.C.S.: 611710

Praktiska Sverige AB   (1)
Vikingsgatan 4, 411 04, Gothenburg, Swe-
den
Tel.: (46) 87944200
Web Site: https://www.praktiska.se
Educational Support Services
N.A.I.C.S.: 611710

Rameder Anhangerkupplungen und
Autoteile GmbH   (1)
Am Eichberg Flauer 1, Munschwitz, 07338,
Leutenberg, Germany
Tel.: (49) 36734 35 487
Web Site: http://www.kupplung.de
Automotive Carrier Systems & Products
Distr
N.A.I.C.S.: 441330
Dirk Scholer *(Mng Dir)*

Skamol A/S   (1)
Ostergade 58-60, Mors, 7900, Nykobing,
Denmark
Tel.: (45) 9772 1533
Web Site: http://www.skamol.com
Insulating Brick Mfr
N.A.I.C.S.: 327120
Arne Bech Hald *(Mgr-Supply Chain)*

Plant (Domestic):

Skamol A/S - Calcium Silicate
Plant   (2)
Fur Landevej 118, 7870, Roslev, Denmark
Tel.: (45) 9759 6011
Insulating Brick Mfr
N.A.I.C.S.: 327120

Skamol A/S - Moler brick plant   (2)
Blegagervej 3, 7884, Copenhagen, Den-
mark
Tel.: (45) 9759 3355
Insulating Brick Mfr
N.A.I.C.S.: 327120

FSN CAPITAL PARTNERS AS

FSN Capital Partners AS—(Continued)

Skamol A/S - Vermiculite Plant **(2)**
Fasanvej 7, Rodding Spottrup, 7860, Copenhagen, Denmark
Tel.: (45) 4194 6374
Insulating Brick Mfr
N.A.I.C.S.: 327120

Subsidiary (US):

Skamol Americas, Inc. **(2)**
1701 South Blvd, Charlotte, NC 28203
Tel.: (704) 454-1015
Insulating Brick Distr
N.A.I.C.S.: 423840

Subsidiary (Non-US):

Skamol RUS LLC **(2)**
Chernyshevskogo St 5 Inza, Ulyanovsk, Russia
Tel.: (7) 8422 444918
Web Site: http://www.skamol.ru
Insulating Brick Distr
N.A.I.C.S.: 423840
Sergei Scherbakov *(CFO)*

FSN E-COMMERCE VENTURES LIMITED

104 Vasan Udyog Bhavan Tulsi Pipe Road Sun Mill Compound Lower Parel, Mumbai, 400013, Maharashtra, India
Tel.: (91) 2266149616
543384—(BOM)
Personal Care Product Retailer
N.A.I.C.S.: 456120
Falguni Nayar *(Chm, CEO & Mng Dir)*

FSP TECHNOLOGY INC.

No 22 Jianguo E Rd, Taoyuan Dist, Taoyuan, 330, Taiwan
Tel.: (886) 33759888
Web Site: https://www.fsp-group.com
3015—(TAI)
Rev.: $431,001,030
Assets: $667,870,801
Liabilities: $188,155,197
Net Worth: $479,715,604
Earnings: $20,919,061
Emp.: 5,175
Fiscal Year-end: 12/31/23
Adapters Mfr
N.A.I.C.S.: 332993

Subsidiaries:

3Y Power Technology (TAIWAN) Inc. **(1)**
2nd Fr No 576 Sec 1 Minsheng N Rd, Gueishan, Taoyuan, 333, Taiwan
Tel.: (886) 33214556
Web Site: https://www.3ypower.com
Electronic Equipment Whslr
N.A.I.C.S.: 423620

Crown Joy International Ltd. **(1)**
RM 609 6/F Block A Proficient IND CTR 6 Wang Kwun Road, Kowloon Bay, Kowloon, China (Hong Kong)
Tel.: (852) 23313613
Web Site: http://www.crownjoy.com.hk
Sales Range: $25-49.9 Million
Emp.: 10
Electronic Components Mfr & Distr
N.A.I.C.S.: 334416

FSP (GB) Ltd. **(1)**
Unit 8 Curo Park, Frogmore, Saint Albans, AL2 2DD, Hertfordshire, United Kingdom
Tel.: (44) 1727873888
Web Site: http://www.fspgroup.co.uk
Emp.: 15
Power Supplies Distr
N.A.I.C.S.: 221118

FSP Group USA Corp. **(1)**
14284 Albers Way, Chino, CA 91710
Tel.: (909) 606-0960
Web Site: https://www.fspgroupusa.com
Electrical Equipment Mfr & Distr
N.A.I.C.S.: 334419

FSP North America, Inc. **(1)**
33 Musick, Irvine, CA 92618
Tel.: (949) 305-6703
Web Site: http://www.fspna.com
Electronic Components Distr
N.A.I.C.S.: 423690

FSP Technology Inc. **(1)**
Room S-Z 19 F Building A Fortune Plaza 7002 Shen Nan Rd, Shenzhen, Guangdong, China
Tel.: (86) 75582879118
Web Site: http://www.fsp-group.com.tw
Electronic Components Mfr
N.A.I.C.S.: 334419

FSP Technology Korea Co., Ltd. **(1)**
707 IKP 300-6 Yeomgok-dong, Seocho-ku, Seoul, 137-170, Korea (South)
Tel.: (82) 5 6424130
Web Site: http://www.fsp-group.co.kr
Electronic Component & Peripherals Distr
N.A.I.C.S.: 425120

FSP Technology USA Inc. **(1)**
8831 Research Dr Ste 200, Irvine, CA 92618
Tel.: (949) 877-3699
Electrical Equipment Mfr & Distr
N.A.I.C.S.: 334419

Shenzhen Zhong Han Science & Tech. Co., Ltd. **(1)**
Room L-R 19/F Building A Fortune Plaza 7060 Shen Nan Road, Shenzhen, Guangdong, China
Tel.: (86) 75582933191
Web Site: http://www.fspgroup.co.uk
Electronic Components Distr
N.A.I.C.S.: 334419

Shenzhen Zhonghan Technology Co., Ltd. **(1)**
Building A Hangcheng High-tech Industrial Park Huafeng Zhigu, Hangcheng Street Baoan District, Shenzhen, China
Tel.: (86) 75523305693
Web Site: https://www.zhi-test.com
Inspection & Certification Services
N.A.I.C.S.: 541380

Yuli Electronic Co., Ltd. **(1)**
17F No 461 Hongcao Rd Caohejing Software Building, Shanghai, China
Tel.: (86) 2154262808
Web Site: http://www.fsp-group.com.tw
Electronic Components Distr
N.A.I.C.S.: 423690

FSPG HI-TECH CO., LTD.

No 7 Qinggong 3 Road, Chancheng District, Foshan, 528000, China
Tel.: (86) 13923112257
Web Site: https://www.fspg.com.cn
Year Founded: 1988
000973—(SSE)
Rev.: $369,970,848
Assets: $637,164,684
Liabilities: $179,330,535
Net Worth: $457,826,148
Earnings: $19,151,964
Emp.: 4,000
Fiscal Year-end: 12/31/22
Plastics Product Mfr
N.A.I.C.S.: 326199
Tang Qiang *(Chm)*

FSPORT AB

Jarnvagsgatan 9, 252 24, Helsingborg, Sweden
Web Site: https://www.fsportgroup.se
Year Founded: 2013
77H—(DEU)
Software Development Services
N.A.I.C.S.: 541511
Naim Messo *(Chm)*

FSW COATINGS LIMITED

Virginia, Cavan, Ireland
Tel.: (353) 498547209 **IE**
Web Site: http://www.fleetwood.ie
Year Founded: 1971
Paint & Coating Mfr
N.A.I.C.S.: 325510
Conor Doyle *(Gen Mgr)*

FSW SECURITY PRODUCTS LTD.

Unit 1 Paradise Works Eden Str, Coventry, CV6 5HE, Westmidland, United Kingdom
Tel.: (44) 2476667624 **UK**
Web Site:
http://www.fswsecurity.co.uk
Sales Range: $25-49.9 Million
Emp.: 5
Security & Fire Shutters, Doors, Gates & Other Fabricated Metal Products Mfr
N.A.I.C.S.: 332321

FTA FOOD SOLUTIONS PTY LTD

41 45 Slough Rd Altona, Melbourne, 3018, VIC, Australia
Tel.: (61) 383980500
Web Site:
http://www.ftafoodsolutions.com.au
Year Founded: 1993
Sales Range: $50-74.9 Million
Emp.: 35
Food Service Contractor, Supplier & Other Industry Related Services
N.A.I.C.S.: 722310
Robert Burgess *(Gen Mgr)*

FTGROUP CO LTD.

Jowa-Suitengu Bldg 2-13-6 Nihonbashi Kakigara-cho, Chuo-ku, Tokyo, 103-0014, Japan
Tel.: (81) 358472777
Web Site: http://www.ftcom.co.jp
Year Founded: 1985
2763—(TKS)
Rev.: $241,132,800
Assets: $218,672,020
Liabilities: $62,167,050
Net Worth: $156,504,970
Earnings: $34,927,240
Emp.: 1,564
Fiscal Year-end: 03/31/24
Holding Company; Whslr of Information & Communication Equipment & Software Services
N.A.I.C.S.: 551112
Makoto Kuroyanagi *(Chm)*

Subsidiaries:

Entre Preneur Co., Ltd. **(1)**
Takara Building 6F 1-6-4 Taito, Taito-ku, Tokyo, 108-0023, Japan
Tel.: (81) 367311900
Web Site: https://www.entre-preneur.co.jp
Investment Management Service
N.A.I.C.S.: 523940

Gistar Innovation Inc. **(1)**
4th floor Ochanomizu Anun Building 2-2 Kanda Surugadai, Chiyoda-ku, Tokyo, 101-0062, Japan
Tel.: (81) 36 627 3220
Web Site: https://www.gistar-i.co.jp
Web Marketing Business Services
N.A.I.C.S.: 541613
Nobuhiko Ando *(Pres)*

IFNet Inc. **(1)**
2-2 Kanda Surugadai Ochanomizu Anun Building 4F, Chiyoda-ku, Tokyo, 101-0062, Japan
Tel.: (81) 36 627 3211
Web Site: https://www.if-n.co.jp
Voice Transmission Services
N.A.I.C.S.: 517810
Takanari Moriya *(Pres)*

Japan TSS, Inc. **(1)**
2-13-6 Nihonbashi Kakigaracho, Chuo-ku, Tokyo, 103-0014, Japan
Tel.: (81) 35 847 2731
Web Site: https://www.japan-tss.co.jp
Electrical Equipment Distr
N.A.I.C.S.: 423610

SunDex Co., Ltd. **(1)**
2-13-6 Nihonbashi Kakigaracho EDGE Suitengu, Chuo-ku, Tokyo, 103-0014, Japan
Tel.: (81) 35 847 2722
Web Site: https://www.sundex.co.jp
Outsourcing Business Services
N.A.I.C.S.: 561990

FTI FOODTECH INTERNATIONAL INC.

156 Abbeywood Trail, Toronto, M3B 3B7, ON, Canada
Tel.: (416) 444-1058 **BC**
Web Site: https://www.fti-foodtech.com
Year Founded: 1987
FTI—(TSXV)
Rev.: $53,186
Assets: $322,480
Liabilities: $268,830
Net Worth: $53,650
Earnings: ($14,649)
Fiscal Year-end: 03/31/24
Food Products & Technologies Licenser
N.A.I.C.S.: 533110
William A. Hullah *(Founder, Pres & CEO)*

FTL VENTURES CORP.

Unit 2801 Bank of America Tower, 12 Harcourt Road, Central, China (Hong Kong)
Tel.: (852) 2615 1107 **NV**
Web Site:
http://www.ftlventurescorp.com
Year Founded: 2011
Film Production & Distribution
N.A.I.C.S.: 512110
Edmund Kam Cheong Leong *(Chm, Pres, CEO, CFO, Treas & Sec)*

FTN COCOA PROCESSORS PLC

Plot 5 Block 77 Basheer Shittu Avenue, Magodo GRA, Lagos, Nigeria
Tel.: (234) 17409651
Web Site:
https://www.ftncocoa.com.ng
Year Founded: 1991
FTNCOCOA—(NIGE)
Rev.: $138,693
Assets: $16,227,097
Liabilities: $19,693,716
Net Worth: ($3,466,620)
Earnings: ($961,549)
Emp.: 63
Fiscal Year-end: 12/31/22
Soybean & Other Oilseed Processing
N.A.I.C.S.: 311224
S. O. Oguntimehin *(Chm)*

FU BURG INDUSTRIAL CO., LTD.

2F-3 NO 130 sec 2 Zhong-Xiao E Road, Taipei, 10053, Taiwan
Tel.: (886) 223560429
Web Site: https://www.fuburg.com
Year Founded: 1977
8929—(TPE)
Rev.: $22,301,629
Assets: $37,674,358
Liabilities: $11,600,632
Net Worth: $26,073,727
Earnings: ($2,351,781)
Emp.: 196
Fiscal Year-end: 12/31/22
Baby Diaper & Sanitary Napkin Mfr
N.A.I.C.S.: 322291

FU CHUN SHIN MACHINERY MANUFACTURE CO., LTD.

269 Baodong Rd Pitou Vil, Guanmiao Dist, Tainan City, Taiwan
Tel.: (886) 65950688
Web Site: https://www.fcs.com.tw
Year Founded: 1974
6603—(TPE)
Rev.: $143,989,119

Assets: $218,962,668
Liabilities: $142,287,153
Net Worth: $76,675,515
Earnings: $5,314,605
Fiscal Year-end: 12/31/22
Plastics Product Mfr
N.A.I.C.S.: 326199
Po-Hsun Wang *(Chm)*

FU LOGITEC CO., LTD.
3-2-25 Musashino, Akishima City,
196-0021, Tokyo, Japan
Tel.: (81) 81425192255
Web Site: http://www.foster.co.jp
Sales Range: $25-49.9 Million
Emp.: 50
Provider of Transportation Services
for Audio & Sound Equipment
N.A.I.C.S.: 334310

FU SHEK FINANCIAL HOLD-INGS LIMITED
Room 2705-6 27/F Tower One Lippo
Centre 89 Queensway, Admiralty,
Hong Kong, China (Hong Kong)
Tel.: (852) 2 525 3666   Ky
Web Site:
   http://www.hkfsfinance.com
Year Founded: 2001
2263—(HKG)
Rev.: $5,139,466
Assets: $69,433,803
Liabilities: $27,237,480
Net Worth: $42,196,323
Earnings: $1,378,538
Emp.: 17
Fiscal Year-end: 03/31/21
Holding Company
N.A.I.C.S.: 551112
Stephen Lee Keng *(Chm)*

Subsidiaries:

Sinomax Securities Limited   (1)
Flat 2705-06 27/F Tower One Lippo Centre
89, Queensway, Hong Kong, China (Hong
Kong)
Tel.: (852) 25253666
Web Site: http://www.sinomaxsec.com.hk
Financial Services
N.A.I.C.S.: 523999

FU SHOU YUAN INTERNA-TIONAL GROUP LIMITED
Room 1306 Charity Building No 88
Cao Xi Road North, Xuhui District,
Shanghai, 200030, China
Tel.: (86) 2154255151
Web Site: http://www.fsygroup.com
1448—(HKG)
Rev.: $304,896,290
Assets: $1,097,351,096
Liabilities: $238,944,935
Net Worth: $858,406,162
Earnings: $113,826,352
Emp.: 2,401
Fiscal Year-end: 12/31/22
Cemetaries & Funeral Facilities
N.A.I.C.S.: 812220
Xiaojiang Bai *(Chm)*

FU YU CORPORATION LIM-ITED
8 Tuas Drive 1, Singapore, 638675,
Singapore
Tel.: (65) 65787393   SG
Web Site: https://www.fuyucorp.com
Year Founded: 1978
F13—(SES)
Rev.: $144,195,259
Assets: $133,446,944
Liabilities: $29,347,118
Net Worth: $104,099,826
Earnings: ($7,659,623)
Emp.: 1,352
Fiscal Year-end: 12/31/23
Precision Molds & Injection Plastic
Molds Mfr

N.A.I.C.S.: 326199
Lay Kheng Tan *(Dir-HR)*

Subsidiaries:

Classic Advantage Sdn Bhd   (1)
No 21 Jalan Teknologi 4 Taman Teknologi,
81400, Senai, Johor, Malaysia   **(62.69%)**
Sales Range: $125-149.9 Million
Emp.: 400
Plastics Product Mfr
N.A.I.C.S.: 326199

Fu Hao Manufacturing (M) Sdn
Bhd   (1)
Plot 562 Mukim 1 Jalan Perusahaan Baru 1
Perai III, Perai Industrial Estate, 13600, Pe-
rai, Penang, Malaysia   **(62.69%)**
Tel.: (60) 43980500
Sales Range: $50-74.9 Million
Emp.: 200
Plastics Product Mfr
N.A.I.C.S.: 326199

Fu Yu Moulding & Tooling
(Chongqing) Co., Ltd.   (1)
Block 2 and Block3 No 18 Shigui Road,
Jieshi Town Banan District, Chongqing,
401346, China
Tel.: (86) 2361219988
Industrial Mold Mfr
N.A.I.C.S.: 333511

Fu Yu Moulding & Tooling (Dong-
guan) Co., Ltd.   (1)
Jing Fu Road, Xin Cheng Industry Area
Heng Li Town, Dongguan, 523477, Guang-
dong, China   **(100%)**
Tel.: (86) 76989821818
Web Site: http://www.fuyu.com
Emp.: 600
Plastics Product Mfr
N.A.I.C.S.: 326199

Fu Yu Moulding & Tooling (Shanghai)
Co., Ltd.   (1)
No 888 Xin Ling Road Waigaoqiao Free
Trade Zone, Shanghai, 200131, China
Tel.: (86) 2150461225
Plastics Product Mfr
N.A.I.C.S.: 326199

Fu Yu Moulding & Tooling (Suzhou)
Co., Ltd.   (1)
No 89 Xing Nan Road, Wu Zhong Eco-
nomic Development Zone, Suzhou, 215128,
Jiangsu, China   **(100%)**
Tel.: (86) 51265621838
Precision Molds & Injection Plastic Molds
Mfr
N.A.I.C.S.: 326199

Subsidiary (Domestic):

Fu Yu Moulding & Tooling (Wujiang)
Co., Ltd   (2)
No 2288 Jiang Xing East Road Wujiand
Economic Dev Zone, Wujiang, 215200, Ji-
angsu, China   **(100%)**
Tel.: (86) 512 6300 5959
Web Site: http://www.fuyucorp.com
Plastics Product Mfr
N.A.I.C.S.: 326199

Fu Yu Moulding & Tooling (Zhuhai)
Co., Ltd.   (1)
No 89 Xing Nan Road, WuZhong Economic
Development Zone, Suzhou, 215128, Ji-
angsu, China
Tel.: (86) 51265621838
Industrial Mold Mfr
N.A.I.C.S.: 333511

LCTH Corporation Bhd   (1)
No 21 Jalan Teknologi 4, Taman Teknologi
Johor, 81400, Senai, Johor,
Malaysia   **(62.69%)**
Tel.: (60) 75999980
Web Site: http://www.lcth.com.my
Sales Range: $150-199.9 Million
Emp.: 300
Management Services
N.A.I.C.S.: 562998

NanoTechnology Manufacturing Pte.
Ltd.   (1)
8 Tuas Dr 1, Singapore, 638675,
Singapore   **(100%)**
Tel.: (65) 67552280

Web Site:
   http://www.nanotechnology.com.sg
Sales Range: $25-49.9 Million
Emp.: 50
Special Die & Tool Die Set Jig & Fixture Mfr
N.A.I.C.S.: 333514

Qingdao Fu Qiang Electronics Co.,
Ltd.   (1)
No 1 Haier Road Haier Information Industry
Park T Building, Hi Tech Industrial Zone,
Qingdao, 266101, China
Tel.: (86) 53288609988
Electronics
N.A.I.C.S.: 449210

SolidMicron Technologies Pte
Ltd   (1)
No 2 Serangoon North Avenue 5 #03-00,
554911, Singapore   **(100%)**
Tel.: (65) 64831281
Web Site: http://www.solidmicrontech.com
Sales Range: $25-49.9 Million
Emp.: 30
Bare Printed Circuit Board Mfr
N.A.I.C.S.: 334412

FU YU PROPERTY CO., LTD.
16F-3 No 238 Shihjheng N 2nd Rd,
Situn Dist, Taichung, 40756, Taiwan
Tel.: (886) 422585357
Web Site: https://www.fuyu-
property.com.tw
4907—(TPE)
Building Construction Services
N.A.I.C.S.: 236220
Shih-Hsin Chang *(Chm)*

FU-CHIAN TIRE CO., LTD.
No 285 Sec 2 Liu-Qiao Rd, Chang-
Hua County, Yuanlin, Taiwan
Tel.: (886) 48323161
Web Site: http://www.fuchian.com.tw
Year Founded: 1965
5102—(TPE)
Rev.: $25,115,372
Assets: $56,550,609
Liabilities: $18,772,316
Net Worth: $37,778,292
Earnings: $2,264,102
Fiscal Year-end: 12/31/21
Tiles Mfr
N.A.I.C.S.: 326211
Tsai Wen-Shun *(Chm & CEO)*

FU-WANG CERAMIC LIMITED
Pearl Trade Centre 2nd Floor, Cha
90/3 Pragati Sarani North Badda,
Dhaka, 1212, Bangladesh
Tel.: (880) 2222297544
Web Site:
   https://www.fuwangceramic.com
Year Founded: 1995
FUWANGCER—(CHT)
Rev.: $8,313,133
Assets: $84,743,593
Liabilities: $69,941,689
Net Worth: $14,801,904
Earnings: $328,384
Emp.: 451
Fiscal Year-end: 06/30/23
Ceramic Products Mfr
N.A.I.C.S.: 327110
Anisur Rahman *(Head-Internal Audit
& Compliance)*

FU-WANG FOODS LTD.
House 55 Road 17 Banani C/A,
Dhaka, 1213, Bangladesh
Tel.: (880) 58815476
Web Site:
   https://www.fuwangfoodsltd.com
Year Founded: 1997
FUWANGFOOD—(DHA)
Rev.: $13,241,008
Assets: $13,878,309
Liabilities: $9,794,888
Net Worth: $4,083,421
Earnings: ($2,908,714)
Emp.: 949

Fiscal Year-end: 06/30/22
Food Beverage Product Mfr
N.A.I.C.S.: 311999
Abdul Quader *(Chm)*

FUAN PHARMACEUTICAL (GROUP) CO., LTD.
NO 2 Huangyang Road, Yubei Dis-
trict, Chongqing, 401121, China
Tel.: (86) 2361213011
Web Site: https://www.fapharm.com
Year Founded: 2004
300194—(CHIN)
Rev.: $340,012,296
Assets: $825,268,392
Liabilities: $271,184,004
Net Worth: $554,084,388
Earnings: $28,727,244
Emp.: 1,240
Fiscal Year-end: 12/31/22
Pharmaceuticals Mfr
N.A.I.C.S.: 325412
Wang Tianxiang *(Chm-Grp)*

FUBON FINANCIAL HOLDING CO. LTD.
B1F No 169 Sec 4 Ren'ai Rd, Da'an
Dist, Taipei, Taiwan
Tel.: (886) 87516665
Web Site: https://www.fubon.com
Year Founded: 1951
2881—(TAI)
Rev.: $16,949,321,443
Assets: $328,825,180,938
Liabilities: $301,195,016,885
Net Worth: $27,630,164,054
Earnings: $3,235,862,551
Emp.: 25,870
Fiscal Year-end: 12/31/20
Holding Company; Financial Invest-
ment & Management Services
N.A.I.C.S.: 551112
Richard M. Tsai *(Chm)*

Subsidiaries:

Fu Sheng Insurance Agency Co.,
Ltd.   (1)
5F No 9 Shangyang Road, Zhongzheng
Dist, Taipei, Taiwan
Tel.: (886) 800706688
Life & General Insurance Financial Services
N.A.I.C.S.: 524210

Fubon Asset Management Co.,
Ltd.   (1)
8F 108 Dunhua S Road Sec 1, Da'an Dis-
trict, Taipei, Taiwan   **(100%)**
Tel.: (886) 800070388
Web Site: http://www.fubon.com
Security Brokers & Dealers
N.A.I.C.S.: 523150

Fubon Bank (Hong Kong)
Limited   (1)
Fubon Bank Building 38 Des Voeux Road,
Central, China (Hong Kong)
Tel.: (852) 28426222
Web Site: http://www.fubonbank.com.hk
Rev.: $413,808,031
Assets: $14,305,725,872
Liabilities: $12,424,882,259
Net Worth: $1,880,843,613
Earnings: $77,189,691
Emp.: 899
Fiscal Year-end: 12/31/2019
Commercial Bank
N.A.I.C.S.: 522110
Richard Ming Hsing Tsai *(Vice Chm)*

Fubon Direct Marketing Consulting
Co., Ltd   (1)
17F No 9 Shangyang Road, Zhongzheng
Dist, Taipei, Taiwan
Tel.: (886) 22 370 5199
Web Site: https://www.fubon.com
Emp.: 400
Insurance Management Services
N.A.I.C.S.: 524298

Fubon Futures Co., Ltd   (1)
21F 3F 3F-1 No 9 Xiangyang Road,
Zhongzheng Dist, Taipei, 10046, Taiwan

Fubon Financial Holding Co. Ltd.—(Continued)

Tel.: (886) 22 388 2626
Web Site: https://www.fubon.com
Sales Range: $50-74.9 Million
Emp.: 80
Financial Management Services
N.A.I.C.S.: 523999

Fubon Insurance (Vietnam) Co., Ltd　(1)
10&11F Discovery Complex Tower 302 Cau Giay Street, Dich Vong Ward Cau Giay Dist, Hanoi, Vietnam
Tel.: (84) 246 282 7888
Web Site: https://www.fubonlife.com.vn
Sales Range: $50-74.9 Million
Emp.: 80
General Insurance Services
N.A.I.C.S.: 524210

Fubon Insurance Co., Ltd.　(1)
237 Chien Kuo S Rd Sec 1, Taipei, 10657, Taiwan
Tel.: (886) 227067890
Insurance Management Services
N.A.I.C.S.: 524298

Fubon Life Assurance Co., Ltd.　(1)
14F 108 Tun Hua South Road Sec 1, Taipei, 10548, Taiwan
Tel.: (886) 287716699
Life Insurance Carrier
N.A.I.C.S.: 524113
Richard M. Tsai (Chm)

Fubon Life Insurance (Hong Kong) Company Limited　(1)
Suites 701-705 7/F 12 Taikoo Wan Road, Taikoo Shing, Hong Kong, China (Hong Kong)
Tel.: (852) 25160133
Web Site: https://www.fubonlife.com.hk
Fire Insurance Services
N.A.I.C.S.: 524113

Fubon Life Insurance Co., Ltd　(1)
13th Floor AB Tower 76 Le Lai Street Ben Thanh Ward, District 1, Ho Chi Minh City, Vietnam
Tel.: (84) 8 62586666
Insurance Management Services
N.A.I.C.S.: 524298

Fubon Life Insurance Company Hong Kong Limited　(1)
9F Two Harbour Front 22 Tai Fung Street, Hong Kong, China (Hong Kong)
Tel.: (852) 23067981
Sales Range: $50-74.9 Million
Emp.: 30
Insurance Agents, Brokers & Service
N.A.I.C.S.: 524210

Fubon Multimedia Technology Co., Ltd.　(1)
2f 71 Chou Tzu St, Taipei, 11493, Taiwan
Tel.: (886) 221626688
Online Shopping Services
N.A.I.C.S.: 425120

Fubon Securities Co., Ltd.　(1)
3rd and 4th Floor No 169 Section 4 Renai Road, Daan District, Taipei, Taiwan
Tel.: (886) 28 178 3018
Web Site: https://www.fubon.com
Sales Range: $50-74.9 Million
Emp.: 16
Security Brokers & Dealers
N.A.I.C.S.: 523150

Fubon Securities USA LLC　(1)
3452 E Foothill Blvd Ste100, Pasadena, CA 91107-3142
Tel.: (626) 792-1388
Sales Range: Less than $1 Million
Emp.: 10
Security Brokers & Dealers
N.A.I.C.S.: 523150

Jih Sun Financial Holdings Co., Ltd.　(1)
10/F 85 Section 2 East Nanching Road, Taipei, Taiwan　(53.84%)
Tel.: (886) 225673688
Web Site: http://www.jsun.com.tw
Financial Consulting Services
N.A.I.C.S.: 541611
Ching-Tang Huang (Chm)

Subsidiary (Domestic):

JihSun Securities Co., Ltd.　(2)

3rd and 4th Floor No 111 Section 2 Nanjing East Road, Taipei, Taiwan
Tel.: (886) 22 515 7527
Web Site: https://www.jihsun.com.tw
Security Services
N.A.I.C.S.: 561612

Subsidiary (Domestic):

JihSun Futures Co., Ltd.　(3)
4F No 111 Sec 2 Nanjing E Rd, Zhongshan Dist, Taipei, Taiwan
Tel.: (886) 22 504 2088
Web Site: http://www.jsmarket.jihsun.com.tw
Trading Services
N.A.I.C.S.: 425120

Taipei Fubon Commercial Bank Co., Ltd.　(1)
2nd Fl 169 Jen Ai Road Section 4, Taipei, 10686, Taiwan
Tel.: (886) 227716699
Web Site: http://www.fubon.com
Sales Range: $700-749.9 Million
Emp.: 1,500
National Commercial Banks
N.A.I.C.S.: 522110

FUCHS SE

Einsteinstrasse 11, 68169, Mannheim, Germany
Tel.: (49) 62138020　De
Web Site: https://www.fuchs.com
Year Founded: 1931
FPE—(MUN)
Rev.: $3,821,497,949
Assets: $2,614,936,326
Liabilities: $668,033,671
Net Worth: $1,946,902,655
Earnings: $305,417,656
Emp.: 6,272
Fiscal Year-end: 12/31/23
Mineral Oils, Mineral Oil Products, Lubricating Oils, Hydraulic Oils & Gear Oils Mfr
N.A.I.C.S.: 324191
Stefan R. Fuchs (Chm-Exec Bd)

Subsidiaries:

Alhamrani-Fuchs Petroleum Saudi Arabia Ltd.　(1)
Tahlia St, PO Box 7103, Jeddah, 21462, Saudi Arabia
Tel.: (966) 26635666
Web Site: http://www.fuchs.com.sa
Sales Range: $75-99.9 Million
Emp.: 75
Mfr of Lubricants
N.A.I.C.S.: 324191

Bremer & Leguil GmbH　(1)
Am Burgacker 30 42, 47051, Duisburg, Germany　(100%)
Tel.: (49) 20399230
Web Site: https://www.bremer-leguil.de
Emp.: 40
Mfr of Mineral & Lubricating Oils
N.A.I.C.S.: 324191

FUCHS CORPORATION　(1)
17050 Lathrop Ave, Harvey, IL 60426
Tel.: (708) 333-8900
Web Site: http://www.fuchsus.com
Lubricant Mfr
N.A.I.C.S.: 324191

FUCHS DO BRASIL S.A　(1)
Via de Acesso Joao de Goes No 1 110 Fazenda Itaquiti, Belval, Barueri, 06422-150, Sao Paulo, Brazil
Tel.: (55) 1147892311
Web Site: http://www.fuchs.com
Emp.: 100
Lubricant Mfr
N.A.I.C.S.: 324191
Antonio Olivera (Mng Dir)

FUCHS FINANZSERVICE GMBH　(1)
Friesenheimer Strasse 17, 68169, Mannheim, Germany
Tel.: (49) 62138021132
Web Site: http://www.fuchs-europe.de
Lubricant Mfr & Distr
N.A.I.C.S.: 324191

FUCHS LUBRICANTS BENELUX N.V. / S.A　(1)
Heideveld 54, 1654, Huizingen, Belgium
Tel.: (32) 23631927
Web Site: https://www.fuchs.com
Emp.: 57
Lubricant Mfr
N.A.I.C.S.: 324191
Robins Eddi (Gen Mgr)

FUCHS LUBRIFICANTI S.P.A　(1)
Via Riva 16, 14021, Buttigliera, Italy
Tel.: (39) 0119922811
Web Site: https://www.fuchs.com
Emp.: 10
Lubricant Mfr
N.A.I.C.S.: 324191

FUCHS LUBRITECH S.A.S　(1)
1 Route d'Ungersheim Z I, BP 07, Ensisheim, 68190, France
Tel.: (33) 3 89 83 67 50
Web Site: http://www.fuchs-lubritech.fr
Emp.: 20
Lubricant Mfr
N.A.I.C.S.: 324191

FUCHS MAK DOOEL　(1)
St Praska No 23, 1000, Skopje, North Macedonia
Tel.: (389) 23090309
Web Site: http://www.fuchs.com.mk
Emp.: 4
Lubricant Distr
N.A.I.C.S.: 424720
Goran Kormusoski (Mng Dir)

FUCHS MAZIVA LSL D.O.O　(1)
Cesta krskih zrtev 135C, 8270, Brezice, Slovenia
Tel.: (386) 74991030
Web Site: https://www.fuchs.com
Emp.: 9
Lubricant Mfr
N.A.I.C.S.: 324191

FUCHS OIL CORP. (SK), spol. s ro　(1)
Sturova 51, 977-01, Brezno, Slovakia　(100%)
Tel.: (421) 482858750
Web Site: http://www.fuchs.com
Mineral & Lubricating Oils Distr
N.A.I.C.S.: 324191
Miroslav Kolencik (Mng Dir)

FUCHS OIL HUNGARIA KFT　(1)
Gyar U 2, 2040, Budaors, Hungary
Tel.: (36) 23428924
Web Site: https://www.fuchs.com
Lubricant Mfr
N.A.I.C.S.: 324191

FUCHS PETROLEUM S.A.R.L.　(1)
Moussa Center Safra Highway Keserwan, PO Box 10, Jounieh, Keserwan, Lebanon
Tel.: (961) 9 853071 2
Web Site: http://www.fuchs.com.lb
Lubricant Mfr
N.A.I.C.S.: 324191

FUCHS SMORJMEDEL SVERIGE AB　(1)
Garnisonsgatan 25A, 25466, Helsingborg, Sweden
Tel.: (46) 42256690
Web Site: http://www.fuchs-oil.se
Sales Range: $25-49.9 Million
Emp.: 5
Lubricant Distr
N.A.I.C.S.: 324199

Fuchs Argentina S.A.　(1)
Belgrano 2551, El Talar - Bs As, B1618AUS, Buenos Aires, Argentina　(100%)
Tel.: (54) 1147361850
Web Site: https://www.fuchs.com
Sales Range: $25-49.9 Million
Emp.: 40
Mfr of Mineral & Lubricating Oils
N.A.I.C.S.: 324191

Fuchs Austria Schmiermittel Ges. mbH　(1)
Braumuhlweg 13, PO Box 82, A 5101, Bergheim, Salzburg, Austria　(70%)
Tel.: (43) 662450035
Web Site: http://www.fuchs-austria.at

Sales Range: $25-49.9 Million
Emp.: 25
Mfr of Mineral & Lubricating Oils
N.A.I.C.S.: 324191

Fuchs Belgium N.V.　(1)
Industriezone Heideveld 54, 1654, Huizingen, Belgium　(100%)
Tel.: (32) 23631939
Web Site: http://www.fuchs.com
Sales Range: $25-49.9 Million
Emp.: 70
Mfr of Mineral & Lubricating Oils
N.A.I.C.S.: 324191
Addy Robens (Mng Dir & Dir-Sls)

Fuchs Brasil S.A.　(1)
Via Joao De Goes Km 1 214, BR CEP 06612 00, Jandira, Brazil　(61%)
Tel.: (55) 147892311
Sales Range: $10-24.9 Million
Emp.: 65
Mfr of Lubricants
N.A.I.C.S.: 324191

Fuchs Europe Schmierstoffe GmbH & Co. KG　(1)
Friesenheimer Strasse 15, 68169, Mannheim, Baden Wuerteert, Germany　(100%)
Tel.: (49) 62137010
Web Site: http://www.fuchseurope.de
Sales Range: $250-299.9 Million
Emp.: 500
Mfr of Mineral & Lubricating Oils
N.A.I.C.S.: 324191

Division (Domestic):

FUCHS EUROPE SCHMIERSTOFFE GMBH - Export Division　(2)
Friesenheimer Strasse 19, 68169, Mannheim, Germany
Tel.: (49) 621 3701 0
Web Site: http://www.fuchs-europe.de
Lubricant Mfr
N.A.I.C.S.: 324191

Plant (Domestic):

FUCHS EUROPE SCHMIERSTOFFE GMBH - Kiel Plant　(2)
Neuenrade 2, 24113, Kiel, Germany
Tel.: (49) 431 661 13 0
Lubricant Mfr
N.A.I.C.S.: 324191

Fuchs Hellas S.A.　(1)
2-4 Mesogeion Avenue, Athens Tower, 11527, Athens, Greece　(95.9%)
Tel.: (30) 2106712646
Web Site: https://www.fuchs.com
Sales Range: $25-49.9 Million
Emp.: 10
Mfr of Mineral & Lubricating Oils
N.A.I.C.S.: 324191

Fuchs Lubricantes S.A.　(1)
Calle Ferralla 27 Poligono Industrial San Vicente, Castellbisbal, 08755, Barcelona, Spain　(100%)
Tel.: (34) 935475859
Web Site: https://www.fuchs.com
Sales Range: $25-49.9 Million
Emp.: 150
Lubricant Mfr
N.A.I.C.S.: 324191

Fuchs Lubricantes S.A.　(1)
Avda. de los Olmos, 1, Edificio A - 102, Parque Empresarial INBISA, E-01013, Vitoria, Spain　(100%)
Tel.: (34) 945128096
Web Site: http://www.fuchs.es
Mineral Oils Mfr
N.A.I.C.S.: 212390

Fuchs Lubricants (S.A.) (Pty.) Ltd.　(1)
7 and 8 Diesel Road, Isando, 1600, South Africa　(100%)
Tel.: (27) 11 565 9600
Web Site: http://www.fuchs.com
Sales Range: $1-9.9 Million
Emp.: 100
Mfr of Mineral & Lubricating Oils
N.A.I.C.S.: 324191

Fuchs Lubricants (UK) PLC　(1)
New Century Street, Hanley, Stoke-on-

Trent, ST1 5HU, Staffordshire, United
Kingdom   **(100%)**
Tel.: (44) 1782203700
Web Site: https://www.fuchs.com
Emp.: 350
Holding Company-UK
N.A.I.C.S.: 551112
Richard Halhead *(Mng Dir)*

Subsidiary (Domestic):

B & N Base Oils Ltd.   **(2)**
St Anns House King St, Knutsford, WA16
6PD, Cheshire, United Kingdom   **(100%)**
Tel.: (44) 1565633365
Web Site: http://www.b-nbaseoils.co.uk
Sales Range: $25-49.9 Million
Emp.: 2
Mfr of Lubricants
N.A.I.C.S.: 324191

Fuchs Lubritech (UK) Ltd.   **(2)**
New Century Street Hanley, Stoke-on-Trent,
ST1 5HU, United Kingdom
Tel.: (44) 1782200700
Web Site: http://www.fuchs-lubritech.co.uk
Mineral & Lubricating Oils Mfr
N.A.I.C.S.: 324191
Richard Halhead *(Mng Dir)*

Fuchs Lubricants - Asia Pacific Re-
gional Headquarters   **(1)**
13A Tech Park Crescent, Tuas Tech Park,
Singapore, 637843, Singapore
Tel.: (65) 6558 8133
Emp.: 40
Regional Managing Office; Lubricant Mfr &
Distr
N.A.I.C.S.: 551114

Subsidiary (Non-US):

Fuchs Australia Pty. Ltd.   **(2)**
49 McIntyre Road, PO Box 146, Sunshine,
3020, VIC, Australia   **(100%)**
Tel.: (61) 393006400
Web Site: http://www.fuchs.com
Sales Range: $25-49.9 Million
Emp.: 70
Holding Company; Mineral & Lubricating
Oils Mfr & Distr
N.A.I.C.S.: 551112

Subsidiary (Domestic):

Fuchs Lubricants (Australasia) Pty.
Ltd.   **(3)**
49 McIntyre Road, PO Box 146, Sunshine,
3020, VIC, Australia
Tel.: (61) 393006400
Web Site: https://www.fuchs.com
Emp.: 150
Lubricant Mfr & Distr
N.A.I.C.S.: 324191

Subsidiary (Non-US):

Fuchs Japan Ltd.   **(2)**
Toranomon Waiko Bldg 5F 5 12 1 Tora-
nomon, Minato-ku, Tokyo, 105-0001, Japan
Tel.: (81) 334368303
Web Site: https://www.fuchs.com
Lubricant Mfr
N.A.I.C.S.: 324191

Plant (Domestic):

Fuchs Japan Ltd. - Chiba
Factory   **(3)**
245-2 Kawarago, Shiroi, 270-1403, Chiba-
ken, Japan
Tel.: (81) 47 497 0039
Web Site: http://www.fuchs.co.jp
Lubricant Mfr
N.A.I.C.S.: 324191

Fuchs Japan Ltd. - Iga Ueno
Factory   **(3)**
408-3 Aza Saburodani Ouchi, Iga, 518-
0034, Mie-ken, Japan
Tel.: (81) 595 20 1114
Web Site: http://www.fuchs.co.jp
Emp.: 15
Lubricant Mfr
N.A.I.C.S.: 324191

Subsidiary (Non-US):

Fuchs Lubricants (China) Ltd.   **(2)**
No 888 Jiaxiu Road, High Technology Development Zone Nanxiang Jiading District,

Shanghai, 201802, China   **(100%)**
Tel.: (86) 2139122000
Web Site: https://www.fuchs.com
Emp.: 400
Mfr of Mineral & Lubricating Oils
N.A.I.C.S.: 324191

Fuchs Lubricants (India) Pvt. Ltd. (2)
Sarjan Plaza 2nd Floor 100 Dr Annie Be-
sant Road, Worli, Mumbai, 400 018,
India   **(100%)**
Tel.: (91) 2266255900
Web Site: https://www.fuchs.com
Sales Range: $25-49.9 Million
Emp.: 94
Lubricants Mfr & Whslr
N.A.I.C.S.: 324191
Kersi Hilloo *(Mng Dir)*

Fuchs Lubricants (Korea) Ltd.   **(2)**
14F KPX Building 137, Mapo-daero Mapo-
gu, Seoul, 4143, Korea (South)   **(100%)**
Tel.: (82) 226725832
Web Site: https://www.fuchs.com
Sales Range: $25-49.9 Million
Emp.: 47
Mfr of Mineral & Lubricating Oils
N.A.I.C.S.: 324191

Plant (Domestic):

Fuchs Lubricants (Korea) Ltd. - Ulsan
Plant   **(2)**
288-3 Koyeon-ri Ungchon-myeon, Ulju-gun,
Ulsan, 689-871, Korea (South)
Tel.: (82) 5 988 4648
Sales Range: $25-49.9 Million
Emp.: 17
Lubricant Mfr
N.A.I.C.S.: 324191

Subsidiary (Non-US):

Fuchs Lubricants (Thailand) Co.,
Ltd.   **(2)**
252 SPE Tower Building 11th Floor Phaho-
nyothin Road, Samsen Nai Subdistrict.
Phaya Thai District, Bangkok, 10400, Thai-
land
Tel.: (66) 2615016875
Web Site: https://www.fuchs.com
Sales Range: $25-49.9 Million
Emp.: 35
Lubricant Distr
N.A.I.C.S.: 424720

Fuchs Lubricants (Yingkou) Ltd.   **(2)**
No 10 Jiachen Street, Xishi District, Ying-
kou, 115000, Liaoning, China   **(100%)**
Tel.: (86) 4173360000
Sales Range: $10-24.9 Million
Emp.: 100
Mfr of Lubricating Oils
N.A.I.C.S.: 324191

Subsidiary (Domestic):

Fuchs Lubricants Pte. Ltd.   **(2)**
13A Tuas Tech Park Crescent Tuas Tech
Park, Singapore, 637843, Singapore
Tel.: (65) 65588133
Web Site: https://www.fuchs.com
Lubricant Mfr
N.A.I.C.S.: 324191

Subsidiary (Non-US):

Fuchs Lubricants Taiwan Corp.   **(2)**
6F-5 No 369 Fuxing N Rd, Songshan Dist,
Taipei, 105001, Taiwan   **(100%)**
Tel.: (886) 227177776
Web Site: https://www.fuchs.com
Emp.: 10
Mfr of Mineral Oils
N.A.I.C.S.: 324191

Subsidiary (Non-US):

Fuchs Lubricants (Hong Kong)
Ltd.   **(3)**
Flat R 11 F Block III, Camel Paint Bldg, 60
Hoi Yuen Rd, Kwun Tong, Kowloon, China
(Hong Kong)   **(100%)**
Tel.: (852) 24179770
Web Site: http://www.fuchs.com.hk
Sales Range: Less than $1 Million
Mfr of Mineral Oils
N.A.I.C.S.: 212390

Subsidiary (Non-US):

Fuchs Petrolube (Malaysia) Sdn.
Bhd.   **(2)**

28 Jalan Modal 23/2 Section 23 Kawasan
MIEL 8, 40300, Shah Alam, Selangor Darul
Ehsan, Malaysia
Tel.: (60) 3 5548 8100
Web Site: http://www.fuchs.com.my
Lubricant Distr
N.A.I.C.S.: 424720

PT Fuchs Indonesia   **(2)**
Jababeka Industrial Estate Jalan Jababeka
VI SFB Block J 6 KL, Bekasi, 17530, West
Java, Indonesia
Tel.: (62) 218934960
Web Site: https://www.fuchs.com
Lubricant Mfr
N.A.I.C.S.: 324101

Fuchs Lubricants Co.   **(1)**
17050 Lathrop Ave, Harvey, IL
60426-6035   **(100%)**
Tel.: (708) 333-8900
Web Site: https://www.fuchs.com
Sales Range: $100-124.9 Million
Emp.: 359
Automotive & Industrial Lubricants & Spe-
cialty Chemicals
N.A.I.C.S.: 324191
Keith Brewer *(CEO)*

Division (Domestic):

FUCHS LUBRICANTS CO. - FUCHS
LUBRITECH USA Division   **(2)**
17050 Lathrop Ave, Harvey, IL 60426
Tel.: (708) 333-8900
Lubricant Mfr
N.A.I.C.S.: 324191

FUCHS LUBRICANTS CO. - Mining
Division   **(2)**
801 E Roy Furman Hwy, Waynesburg, PA
15370
Tel.: (724) 627-3200
Web Site: http://www.fuchslubricants.com
Sales Range: $25-49.9 Million
Emp.: 9
Lubricant Mfr
N.A.I.C.S.: 324199

Subsidiary (Non-US):

Fuchs Lubricants Canada Ltd.   **(2)**
405 Dobbie Dr, PO Box 909, Cambridge,
N1T 1S8, ON, Canada   **(100%)**
Tel.: (519) 622-2040
Web Site: https://www.fuchs.com
Sales Range: $25-49.9 Million
Emp.: 27
Industrial Lubricants Mfr
N.A.I.C.S.: 324191

Division (Domestic):

Fuchs Lubricants-Kansas City
Division   **(2)**
2140 S 88th St, Kansas City, KS
66111-1756   **(100%)**
Tel.: (913) 422-4022
Web Site: http://www.fuchs.com
Sales Range: $25-49.9 Million
Emp.: 50
Lubricant Mfr
N.A.I.C.S.: 324191
David Clark *(Pres)*

Fuchs Lubrifiant France S.A.   **(1)**
1 Rue Lavoisier, 92000, Nanterre,
France   **(89.55%)**
Tel.: (33) 141374200
Web Site: https://www.fuchs.com
Sales Range: $25-49.9 Million
Emp.: 700
Mfr of Lubricating Oils
N.A.I.C.S.: 324191

Fuchs Lubrificantes, Unip. Lda.   **(1)**
Zona Industrial Maia 1 - Sector VII
Travessa Eng Nobre da Costa, Moreira,
4470-435, Maia, Portugal   **(100%)**
Tel.: (351) 229479360
Web Site: https://www.fuchs.com
Industrial Lubricants Mfr
N.A.I.C.S.: 324191

Fuchs Lubritech GmbH   **(1)**
Wernerheisenberg Str 1, 67661, Kaiserslau-
tern, Waelaebach, Germany   **(100%)**
Tel.: (49) 63749245
Web Site: http://www.fuchslubritech.com

Sales Range: $50-74.9 Million
Emp.: 250
Mfr of Mineral & Lubricating Oils
N.A.I.C.S.: 324191

Plant (Domestic):

FUCHS LUBRITECH GMBH - Dohna
Plant   **(2)**
Braugasse 1, 1809, Dohna, Germany
Tel.: (49) 3529564630
Lubricant Mfr
N.A.I.C.S.: 324191

FUCHS LUBRITECH GMBH - FLT
Oberflachentechnik Plant   **(2)**
Konigsberger Strasse 2a, 85386, Eching,
Germany
Tel.: (49) 89 327 10 5
Lubricant Mfr
N.A.I.C.S.: 324191
Markus Heck *(Gen Mgr)*

Division (Domestic):

FUCHS LUBRITECH GmbH - MOLY-
PAUL DIVISION   **(2)**
Kleinhulsen 9, 40721, Hilden, Germany
Tel.: (49) 2103 2873 0
Web Site: http://www.kspaul.de
Lubricant Mfr
N.A.I.C.S.: 324191
Bernhard Biehl *(Chm & Mng Dir)*

Fuchs Maziva D.O.O.   **(1)**
I Krmica 8, Domaslovec, 10430, Samobor,
Croatia   **(100%)**
Tel.: (385) 13380526
Web Site: https://www.fuchs.com
Sales Range: $25-49.9 Million
Emp.: 27
Mfr of Mineral & Lubricating Oils
N.A.I.C.S.: 324191

Fuchs Oil Corporation (CZ) Spol. s
r.o.   **(1)**
Technicka 2539, Otice No 40, 251 01,
Prague, Czech Republic   **(100%)**
Tel.: (420) 323637793
Web Site: https://www.fuchs.com
Sales Range: $25-49.9 Million
Emp.: 32
Mfr of Mineral & Lubricating Oils
N.A.I.C.S.: 324191

Fuchs Oil Corporation (PL) SP. Z
O.O.   **(1)**
Ul Kujawska 102, 44 101, Gliwice,
Poland   **(100%)**
Tel.: (48) 324012200
Web Site: https://www.fuchs.com
Sales Range: $50-74.9 Million
Emp.: 500
Mfr of Mineral & Lubricating Oils
N.A.I.C.S.: 324191

Fuchs Oil Finland Oy   **(1)**
Ayritie 8D, 01510, Vantaa, Finland   **(100%)**
Tel.: (358) 207459660
Web Site: https://www.fuchs.com
Sales Range: $25-49.9 Million
Emp.: 6
Mineral & Lubricating Oils Mfr
N.A.I.C.S.: 324191

Fuchs Oil Middle East Ltd.   **(1)**
PO Box 7955, Sharjah, United Arab Emir-
ates
Tel.: (971) 65572210
Lubricant Mfr
N.A.I.C.S.: 324191

Fuchs Petrolub AG   **(1)**
Friesenheimer Strasse 17, Baden Weurtten-
berg, 68169, Mannheim, Germany **(100%)**
Tel.: (49) 62138020
Web Site: http://www.fuchs-oil.de
Emp.: 450
Mfr of Mineral & Lubricating Oils
N.A.I.C.S.: 324191

Fuchs Petrolub AG - CASSIDA
Division   **(1)**
Heideveld 54, 1654, Huizingen, Belgium
Tel.: (32) 2 363 19 33
Lubricant Mfr
N.A.I.C.S.: 324191

Fuchs Petrolub AG - HEIN DE
WINDT Division   **(1)**

FUCHS SE

FUCHS SE—(Continued)

Heideveld 54, 1654, Huizingen, Belgium
Tel.: (32) 2 363 19 38
Web Site: http://www.fuchsbenelux.com
Sales Range: $25-49.9 Million
Emp.: 6
Lubricant Mfr
N.A.I.C.S.: 324191

Fuchs Petrolub AG - PACIFIC DIVISION (1)
19829 - 99A Ave, Langley, V1M 3G4, BC, Canada
Tel.: (604) 888-1552
Web Site: http://www.fuchs.com
Sales Range: $25-49.9 Million
Emp.: 20
Lubricant Mfr
N.A.I.C.S.: 324191

Fuchs Wisura GmbH (1)
Am Gaswerk 2-10, 28197, Bremen, Germany (85%)
Tel.: (49) 421549030
Web Site: http://www.fuchs-wisura.de
Sales Range: $25-49.9 Million
Emp.: 40
Mfr of Mineral & Lubricating Oils
N.A.I.C.S.: 324191

Hein de Windt B.V. (1)
Fabriekstraat 14, PO Box 91, NL-7000 AB, Doetinchem, Netherlands (100%)
Tel.: (31) 4 33 42 54
Holding Company
N.A.I.C.S.: 551112

JV FUCHS MAST YLA UKRAINA (1)
Shevchenko Str 327-A, PO Box 8250, L'viv, Ukraine
Tel.: (380) 32 235 08 14
Web Site: http://www.fuchs-oil.com.ua
Sales Range: $25-49.9 Million
Emp.: 3
Lubricant Distr
N.A.I.C.S.: 424720

LUBRICANTES FUCHS DE MEXICO S.A. DE C.V. (1)
Acceso C No 101 Parque Industrial Jurica, 76120, Queretaro, Qro, Mexico
Tel.: (52) 4422389100
Web Site: https://www.fuchs.com
Lubricant Mfr
N.A.I.C.S.: 324199

Makoto-Fuchs K.K. (1)
1488 Hatakeda 8 Chome, Oji Cho Kitakatsuragi Gun, Nara, 636 0021, Japan (50%)
Tel.: (81) 745731121
Sales Range: $25-49.9 Million
Emp.: 100
Mfr of Mineral & Lubricating Oils
N.A.I.C.S.: 324191
Seiji Ikeda (Mng Dir)

Motorex AG Langenthal (1)
Bern Zurich Strasse 31, 4901, Langenthal, Switzerland (50%)
Tel.: (41) 629197575
Web Site: http://www.motorex.com
Emp.: 250
Mineral & Lubricating Oils Mfr
N.A.I.C.S.: 324191

Nye Lubricants, Inc. (1)
12 Howland Rd, Fairhaven, MA 02719-3453
Tel.: (508) 996-6721
Web Site: https://www.nyelubricants.com
Petroleum Lubricating Oil & Grease Mfr
N.A.I.C.S.: 324191
Derek J. Rogers (Treas)

OOO FUCHS OIL (1)
Leningradsky Prospekt 36/11, Moscow, 125167, Russia
Tel.: (7) 4952800213
Web Site: https://www.fuchs-oil.ru
Emp.: 6
Lubricant Mfr
N.A.I.C.S.: 324191
Mikhail Zlotski (Gen Mgr)

PROMOTORA FUCHS S.A. DE C.V. (1)
Manzana 1 Acceso C No 101 Parque In-

dustrial Jurica, Queretaro, 76120, Mexico
Tel.: (52) 4422389100
Lubricant Mfr
N.A.I.C.S.: 324191

Parafluid GmbH (1)
Schlossstrasse 8c, 22041, Hamburg, Germany
Tel.: (49) 40637040
Web Site: http://www.parafluid.eu
Pharmaceutical & Cosmetic Product Distr
N.A.I.C.S.: 424210

Parafluid Mineraloelgesellschaft mbH (1)
Ueberseering 9, D 22297, Hamburg, Germany (100%)
Tel.: (49) 406370400
Web Site: http://www.parafluid.de
Sales Range: $25-49.9 Million
Emp.: 100
Mfr of Mineral & Lubricating Oils
N.A.I.C.S.: 324191

Ravensberger Schmierstoffvertrieb GmbH (1)
Jollenbecker Str 2, 33824, Werther, Germany (100%)
Tel.: (49) 52 039 7190
Web Site: https://www.ravenol.de
Sales Range: $50-74.9 Million
Emp.: 53
Mfr of Mineral & Lubricating Oils
N.A.I.C.S.: 324191
Paul Becher (Mng Dir)

Statoil Fuel & Retail ASA (1)
Schweigaards gate 16, 107, Oslo, Norway
Tel.: (47) 22962000
Web Site: http://www.statoilfuelretail.com
Road Transportation Fuel Retailer
N.A.I.C.S.: 424720
Alain Bouchard (Chm)

Subsidiary (Non-US):

Circle K Sverige AB (2)
Torkel Knutssonsgatan 24, 118 49, Stockholm, Sweden (100%)
Tel.: (46) 8 429 6000
Web Site: http://www.circlek.se
Fuel Distr & Gas Service Station Operator
N.A.I.C.S.: 457120
Christina Andersson (Sr Dir-Fin & Control)

Ultrachem Inc. (1)
900 Centerpoint Blvd, New Castle, DE 19720
Tel.: (302) 325-9880
Web Site: https://www.ultracheminc.com
Sales Range: $1-9.9 Million
All Other Miscellaneous Chemical Product & Preparation Mfr
N.A.I.C.S.: 325998
James Fath (Mgr-Midwest Territory)

Wisura GmbH (1)
Am Gaswerk 2-10, 28197, Bremen, Germany
Tel.: (49) 421549030
Web Site: http://www.wisura.de
Sales Range: $25-49.9 Million
Emp.: 3
Lubricant Distr
N.A.I.C.S.: 424720

FUCHS-GEWURZE GMBH

Industriestrasse 25, 49201, Dissen, Germany
Tel.: (49) 54213090
Web Site: http://www.fuchs.de
Year Founded: 1969
Sales Range: $75-99.9 Million
Emp.: 450
Spices Mfr
N.A.I.C.S.: 311942
Nils Meyer-Pries (Mng Dir)

Subsidiaries:

Fuchs North America. (1)
3800 Hampstead Mexico Rd, Hampstead, MD 21074
Tel.: (410) 363-1700
Web Site: http://www.fuchsna.com
Sales Range: $25-49.9 Million
Emp.: 100

Dry Mustard Spice Seasoning & Capsicum Producer & Mfr
N.A.I.C.S.: 311942
Christopher Rodski (CFO)

FUDA ALLOY MATERIALS CO., LTD.

No 518 Binhai 4th Road Economic and Technological Development Zone, Wenzhou Economic & Technological Development Zone, Wenzhou, 325025, China
Tel.: (86) 57755888712
Web Site: http://www.china-fuda.com
Year Founded: 1994
603045—(SHG)
Rev.: $307,869,204
Assets: $263,880,073
Liabilities: $137,612,232
Net Worth: $126,267,841
Earnings: $4,179,694
Fiscal Year-end: 12/31/22
Electrical Product Mfr & Distr
N.A.I.C.S.: 335999
Wang Dawu (Chm & Gen Mgr)

Subsidiaries:

Zhejiang Fudar Alloy Materials Technology Co., Ltd. (1)
No 308 Binhai 5th Road, Longwan District, Wenzhou, 325025, Zhejiang, China
Tel.: (86) 57785809999
Web Site: https://www.fudar.com
Electrical Product Mfr & Distr
N.A.I.C.S.: 335999

FUDA FAUCET WORKS, INC.

Ge Jia Ba Hua Ting, Yiyang, 334400, Jiangxi, China
Tel.: (86) 793 5887178 DE
Web Site: http://www.jxfuda.com
Year Founded: 1995
Sales Range: $25-49.9 Million
Emp.: 405
Brass Faucets, Spouts & Fittings Mfr
N.A.I.C.S.: 332913
Yiting Wu (Chm & CEO)

FUDO TETRA CORPORATION

7-2 Nihonbashi-koami-chou, Chuo-ku, Tokyo, 103-0016, Japan
Tel.: (81) 356448500
Web Site: https://www.fudotetra.co.jp
Year Founded: 1947
1813—(TKS)
Rev.: $449,129,670
Assets: $365,182,670
Liabilities: $145,274,580
Net Worth: $219,908,090
Earnings: $13,279,490
Emp.: 850
Fiscal Year-end: 03/31/24
Geo Engineering Services
N.A.I.C.S.: 541330
Hisanori Hamano (Mng Exec Officer & Gen Mgr-Kyushu Branch)

Subsidiaries:

Fudo Construction Inc. (1)
1720 S Amphlett Blvd Ste225, San Mateo, CA 94402
Tel.: (650) 350-1120
Civil Engineering Construction Services
N.A.I.C.S.: 237990

FUELPOSITIVE CORPORATION

99 Northland Rd unit B, Waterloo, N2V 1Y8, ON, Canada
Tel.: (416) 535-8395
Web Site: https://uelpositive.com
ZM7A—(DEU)
Rev.: $20,933
Assets: $20,495,691
Liabilities: $608,066
Net Worth: $19,887,625
Earnings: ($9,909,524)
Fiscal Year-end: 09/30/23

Engineeering Services
N.A.I.C.S.: 541330
Ian Clifford (Founder & CEO)

Subsidiaries:

ZENN Motor Company Limited (1)
85 Scarsdale Rd Suite 100, North York, M3B 2R2, ON, Canada
Tel.: (416) 535-8395
Automobile Parts Mfr
N.A.I.C.S.: 336390

ZMC America, Inc. (1)
160 Greentree Dr Ste 100, Dover, DE 19904-7620
Tel.: (877) 817-7034
Automotive Products Mfr
N.A.I.C.S.: 336110

FUER INTERNATIONAL, INC.

Neiwei Road, Fulaerji District, Qiqihar, 161041, Heiloingjiang, China
Tel.: (86) 452 6969150 NV
Web Site: http://www.fuergroup.com
Year Founded: 1984
Sales Range: $25-49.9 Million
Emp.: 217
Holding Company; Feed & Fertilizers
N.A.I.C.S.: 551112
Zhang Li (CEO)

FUERST DAY LAWSON INDIA PRIVATE LIMITED

45 Milestone Naurangpur Sector 78, Gurgaon, 122001, Delhi, India
Tel.: (91) 1242378550
Food & Beverage Ingredient Distr
N.A.I.C.S.: 424480

FUFENG GROUP LIMITED

West of Huaihai Road, Junan, 276600, Shandong, China
Tel.: (86) 4008520546
Web Site: http://www.fufeng-group.com
546—(DEU)
Rev.: $2,314,048,635
Assets: $2,784,527,234
Liabilities: $1,156,554,520
Net Worth: $1,627,972,714
Earnings: $162,736,611
Emp.: 13,900
Fiscal Year-end: 12/31/19
Biochemical Products Mfr
N.A.I.C.S.: 325199
Xuechun Li (Founder & Chm)

Subsidiaries:

Baoji Fufeng Biotechnologies Co., Ltd. (1)
No 18 Hi-tech 10th Rd East Side of High-tech Development Area, Baoji, 721013, Shaanxi, China
Tel.: (86) 917 6735788
Biochemical Product Mfr & Distr
N.A.I.C.S.: 325199
Wang Shan (Mgr)

Fufeng (Singapore) Pte. Ltd (1)
80 Marine Parade Rd, Singapore, 449269, Singapore
Tel.: (65) 6346 3468
Biochemical Product Distr
N.A.I.C.S.: 424690

HuLunbeier North East Fufeng Biotechnologies Co., Ltd. (1)
Kaichuang Street Zhalantun Lingdong Industrial Development Area, Hulunbuir, 162650, Inner Mongolia, China
Tel.: (86) 470 3265566
Biochemical Product Mfr & Distr
N.A.I.C.S.: 325199

Jiangsu Shenhua Pharmaceutical Co., Ltd. (1)
No 188 Shenhua Road, Jinhua, 211600, Jiangsu, China
Tel.: (86) 4006131818
Web Site: http://www.shenhuapharm.com
Pharmaceutical Product Mfr & Distr
N.A.I.C.S.: 325412

Neimenggu Fufeng Biotechnologies Co., Ltd. **(1)**
Jing er Road ADM Committee Industrial Economic Development Zone, Jinchuan District, Hohhot, 010070, Inner Mongolia, China
Tel.: (86) 471 5661161
Biochemical Product Mfr & Distr
N.A.I.C.S.: 325199

Shandong Fufeng Fermentation Co., Ltd. **(1)**
No 386 Tianqiao Road, Junan, 276600, Shandong, China
Tel.: (86) 539 7212351
Biochemical Product Mfr & Distr
N.A.I.C.S.: 325199

Xinjiang Fufeng Biotechnologies Co., Ltd. **(1)**
Ganquanpu Industrial Park Economic & Technological Development Area, Toutunhe District, Urumqi, 830026, Xinjiang, China
Tel.: (86) 991 6550303
Biochemical Product Mfr & Distr
N.A.I.C.S.: 325199

FUGRO GEOTECHNIQUE
Parc Des Peupliers 27 Rue Des Peupliers, 92000, Nanterre, Hauts De Seine, France
Tel.: (33) 155691770
Web Site: http://www.fugro.fr
Rev.: $23,400,000
Emp.: 175
Engineeering Services
N.A.I.C.S.: 541330
Peter Berger *(Dir-Personnel)*

FUGRO N.V.
Tel.: (31) 703111422 NI
Web Site: https://www.fugro.com
Year Founded: 1961
FUR—(EUR)
Rev.: $2,414,572,249
Assets: $2,650,110,388
Liabilities: $1,211,554,256
Net Worth: $1,438,556,132
Earnings: $284,132,907
Emp.: 10,220
Fiscal Year-end: 12/31/23
Geophysical Surveying & Mapping Services
N.A.I.C.S.: 541360
Mark R. F. Heine *(Chm-Mgmt Bd & CEO)*

Subsidiaries:

Electro Magnetic Marine Exploration Technologies (EMMET) ZAO **(1)**
Wjatskaja Str 35 Building 4 Business Centre Wjatka 3 Floor, 127015, Moscow, Russia
Tel.: (7) 495 984 28 79
Web Site: http://www.emmetech.ru
Electrical Exploration Equipment Mfr
N.A.I.C.S.: 335999
Andrej V. Tulupov *(CEO)*

Fugro (Canada), Inc. **(1)**
25 Pippy Place, Saint John, A1B 3X2, NL, Canada
Tel.: (705) 726-4252
Geophysical Surveying & Mapping Services
N.A.I.C.S.: 541360

Fugro (USA), Inc. **(1)**
6100 Hillcroft St, Houston, TX 77081-1009 **(100%)**
Tel.: (713) 346-4050
Web Site: http://www.fugro.com
Sales Range: $200-249.9 Million
Emp.: 400
Geotechnical Engineering, Marine Geosciences, Construction Services & Surveying
N.A.I.C.S.: 213112

Subsidiary (Domestic):

Fugro Chance, Inc. **(2)**
6100 Hillcroft, Houston, TX 77081
Tel.: (713) 346-3700
Web Site: http://www.fugro-usa.com

Sales Range: $25-49.9 Million
Emp.: 25
Mfr of Energy Electronics Instrumentation
N.A.I.C.S.: 541330
Wade Jumonville *(VP-Contracts)*

Fugro Consultants, Inc. **(2)**
6100 Hillcroft Ave, Houston, TX 77081
Tel.: (713) 369-5400
Web Site: http://www.fugroconsultants.com
Sales Range: $150-199.9 Million
Geotechnical Engineering Services
N.A.I.C.S.: 541330
Daniel Kershner *(Mgr-Bus Dev)*

Subsidiary (Domestic):

Fugro William Lettis & Associates, Inc. **(3)**
1777 Botelho Dr 262, Walnut Creek, CA 94596-5132
Tel.: (925) 256-6070
Web Site: http://www.lettis.com
Geological Engineering Services
N.A.I.C.S.: 541330
Bill Lettis *(Pres)*

Subsidiary (Domestic):

Fugro Consultants, Inc. **(2)**
1000 Broadway, Oakland, CA 95607 **(100%)**
Tel.: (510) 268-0461
Web Site: http://www.fugroconsultants.com
Sales Range: $1-9.9 Million
Emp.: 45
Civil Engineering, Geotechnical Engineering & Environmental Engineering
N.A.I.C.S.: 541330

Fugro EarthData, Inc. **(2)**
7320 Executive Way, Frederick, MD 21704
Tel.: (301) 948-8550
Web Site: http://www.fugro.com
Sales Range: $25-49.9 Million
Emp.: 150
Remote Sensing, Mapping & GIS Services
N.A.I.C.S.: 541370
Debbie Simerlink *(Mgr-Reg Airborne Ops)*

Unit (Domestic):

Fugro EarthData, Inc. - Aviation **(3)**
18227 Airpark Rd, Hagerstown, MD 21742
Tel.: (301) 733-1176
Web Site: http://www.earthdata.com
Sales Range: $25-49.9 Million
Emp.: 20
Mapping & Imaging Operations
N.A.I.C.S.: 541370

Subsidiary (Domestic):

Fugro GeoConsulting, Inc. **(2)**
6100 Hillcroft Ave, Houston, TX 77081
Tel.: (713) 369-5896
Web Site: http://www.fugrogeoconsulting.com
Sales Range: $25-49.9 Million
Emp.: 100
Geophysical Engineering Services
N.A.I.C.S.: 541330

Fugro GeoServices, Inc. **(2)**
6100 Hillcroft Ave, Houston, TX 77081
Tel.: (713) 369-5800
Web Site: http://www.fgsi.fugro.com
Sales Range: $25-49.9 Million
Emp.: 5
Marine Geophysical Surveying Services
N.A.I.C.S.: 541360

Fugro Multi Client Services, Inc. **(2)**
6100 Hillcroft 77081, Houston, TX 77274
Tel.: (713) 369-5859
Web Site: http://www.fugromulticlient.com
Sales Range: $25-49.9 Million
Emp.: 12
Geophysical Surveying & Mapping Services
N.A.I.C.S.: 541360

Fugro Pelagros, Inc **(2)**
3574 Ruffin Rd, San Diego, CA 92123-2597
Tel.: (858) 292-8922
Sales Range: $25-49.9 Million
Emp.: 60
Marine Surveying Services
N.A.I.C.S.: 541360

Fugro Roadware, Inc. **(2)**
3104 Northside Ave, Richmond, VA 23228

Tel.: (804) 264-2982
Web Site: http://www.roadware.com
Sales Range: $25-49.9 Million
Emp.: 100
Infrastructure Management & Data Collection Services
N.A.I.C.S.: 518210

Fugro-GEOS, Inc. **(2)**
6100 Hillcroft 77081, Houston, TX 77274
Tel.: (713) 346-3600
Web Site: http://www.geos.com
Emp.: 35
Geophysical Surveying Services
N.A.I.C.S.: 541360
Rob Smith *(Pres)*

Fugro-ImpROV, Inc. **(2)**
8715 Fallbrook Dr, Houston, TX 77064-3318
Tel.: (832) 912-9009
Remote Intervention Tool Mfr & Distr
N.A.I.C.S.: 333248

John Chance Land Surveys, Inc. **(2)**
200 Dulles Dr, Lafayette, LA 70506
Tel.: (337) 237-1300
Web Site: http://www.jchance.com
Geospatial Mapping Services
N.A.I.C.S.: 541370
Carlos Femmer *(Pres)*

LoadTest, Inc. **(2)**
2631-D NW 41st St, Gainesville, FL 32606
Tel.: (352) 339-7700
Web Site: http://www.loadtest.com
Sales Range: $25-49.9 Million
Emp.: 20
Deep Foundation Testing Services
N.A.I.C.S.: 238990

Fugro Aerial Mapping A/S **(1)**
Naverland 2 10, Hoje Taastrup, 2600, Glostrup, Denmark
Tel.: (45) 8888 8211
Web Site: http://www.fugrogeospatier.com
Emp.: 1
Geophysical Survey & Mapping Services
N.A.I.C.S.: 541360
Doron Sima *(Mgr)*

Fugro Airborne Surveys, Corp. **(1)**
2505 Meadowvale Boulevard, Mississauga, L5N 5S2, ON, Canada
Tel.: (905) 812-0212
Sales Range: $25-49.9 Million
Emp.: 6
Geophysical Surveying Services
N.A.I.C.S.: 541360
Greg Paleolog *(Gen Mgr)*

Fugro Albania sh.p.k. **(1)**
Rr Bilal Sina Pallati Salillari Shakalla 3, Tirana, 1000, Albania
Tel.: (355) 44500195
Geotechnical & Survey Services
N.A.I.C.S.: 541360

Fugro Alluvial Offshore Ltd. **(1)**
Morton Peto Road Gapton Hall Industrial Estate, Great Yarmouth, NR31 OLT, United Kingdom
Tel.: (44) 1493 440320
Web Site: http://www.alluvial.co.uk
Sales Range: $25-49.9 Million
Emp.: 100
Geophysical Surveying & Mapping Services
N.A.I.C.S.: 541360

Fugro Aperio Ltd. **(1)**
Focal Point Newmarket Road, Bottisham, Cambridge, CB25 9BD, United Kingdom
Tel.: (44) 8706008050
Web Site: http://www.fugro-aperio.com
Rev.: $3,144,480
Emp.: 4
Geophysical Survey & Investigation Services
N.A.I.C.S.: 541360

Fugro Austria GmbH **(1)**
Einodstrasse 13, 8600, Bruck an der Mur, Austria
Tel.: (43) 3862 34300 11
Web Site: http://www.fugro.at
Sales Range: $25-49.9 Million
Emp.: 18
Geophysical Surveying & Mapping Services
N.A.I.C.S.: 541360

Fugro BKS Ltd. **(1)**

Killeague House Unit 17 Sandel Village Centre Knocklynn Road, Coleraine, BT52 1WW, United Kingdom
Tel.: (44) 2870352311
Web Site: http://www.fugro-bks.com
Sales Range: $25-49.9 Million
Emp.: 4
Spatial Data & Mapping Services
N.A.I.C.S.: 541370

Fugro BTW Ltd. **(1)**
477 Devon Street, Strandon, New Plymouth, 4312, New Zealand
Tel.: (64) 67695040
Sales Range: $25-49.9 Million
Emp.: 15
Geophysical Surveying & Mapping Services
N.A.I.C.S.: 541360

Fugro Belgique/Belgie S.A./N.V. **(1)**
De Broquevillelaan 12, Brussels, 1150, Belgium
Tel.: (32) 27760310
Web Site: http://www.fugro.be
Geophysical Surveying Services
N.A.I.C.S.: 541360

Fugro Belgium SRL **(1)**
Rue du Bosquet 9, 1348, Louvain-la-Neuve, Belgium
Tel.: (32) 10488200
Geotechnical & Survey Services
N.A.I.C.S.: 541360

Fugro Brasil Levantamentos Ltda. **(1)**
Rua do Geologo n 76 ZEN -Zona Especial de Negocios, Rio das Ostras, 28899-012, RJ, Brazil
Tel.: (55) 2233217700
Emp.: 11,009
Geotechnical & Survey Services
N.A.I.C.S.: 541360

Fugro Brasil Ltda. **(1)**
Rua do Geologo 76 Zona Especial de Negocios, Rio das Ostras, 28899-012, RJ, Brazil
Tel.: (55) 2233217700
Web Site: http://www.fugro.com.br
Sales Range: $350-399.9 Million
Emp.: 1,000
Oil & Gas Exploration Services
N.A.I.C.S.: 213112

Fugro Cameroun SA **(1)**
Route Base Navale Youpwe Douala Port, B P 1883, Douala, Cameroon
Tel.: (237) 233429755
Geotechnical Drilling Oil & Gas Services
N.A.I.C.S.: 213112

Fugro Certification Services Ltd. **(1)**
Fugro Development Centre 5 Lok Yi Street Tai Lam, Tai Lam New Territories, Tuen Mun, New Territory, China (Hong Kong)
Tel.: (852) 2452 7127
Web Site: http://www.fugrocertification.com
Sales Range: $25-49.9 Million
Emp.: 3
Geo Technical Data Collection & Interpretation Services
N.A.I.C.S.: 518210
Arthur Cheng *(Mgr-Bus Dev)*

Fugro Chile S.A. **(1)**
Los Militares 5890 Ofic 803, 7561283, Las Condes, Chile
Tel.: (56) 26235151
Laboratory Testing Services
N.A.I.C.S.: 541380

Fugro Consult GmbH **(1)**
Wolfener Str 36 Aufgang V, 12681, Berlin, Germany
Tel.: (49) 30936510
Web Site: http://www.fugro.de
Sales Range: $25-49.9 Million
Emp.: 150
Geophysical Surveying Services
N.A.I.C.S.: 541360
Geologe Wolfgang Muller *(Mgr-Bus Admin-Single Procuration)*

Fugro Consult Kft. **(1)**
Kelenfoldi Utca 2, Budapest, 1115, Hungary
Tel.: (36) 1 382 0042
Web Site: http://www.fugro.hu
Sales Range: $25-49.9 Million
Emp.: 35
Engineeering Services

Fugro N.V.—(Continued)

N.A.I.C.S.: 541330
Jozsef Pusztai *(Mng Dir)*

Fugro EMU Ltd. (1)
Heriot-Watt University Research Park
South, Edinburgh, EH14 4AP, United Kingdom
Tel.: (44) 131 449 5030
Web Site: http://www.fugro.com
Sales Range: $25-49.9 Million
Emp.: 25
Environmental Consultancy Services
N.A.I.C.S.: 541620

Fugro Eco Consult GmbH (1)
Zone Industrielle, 5366, Munsbach, Luxembourg
Tel.: (352) 358541
Web Site: http://www.fugro.lu
Geotechnical & Survey Services
N.A.I.C.S.: 541360

Fugro Finance AG (1)
Bahnhofstrasse 29, Zug, 6300, Switzerland
Tel.: (41) 417280808
Web Site: http://www.fugro.com
Financial Management Services
N.A.I.C.S.: 523999

Fugro France S.A.S. (1)
Le Carillon 5-6 Esplanade Charles de
Gaulle, 92000, Nanterre, France
Tel.: (33) 147855050
Web Site: http://www.fugro.com
Sales Range: $25-49.9 Million
Emp.: 150
Engineeering Services
N.A.I.C.S.: 541330

Fugro Gabon SARL (1)
Rue Pierre Auguste Avaro, B P 557, Port-
Gentil, Gabon
Tel.: (241) 7355984
Geotechnical Drilling Oil & Gas Services
N.A.I.C.S.: 213112

Fugro GeoConsulting Ltd. (1)
Fugro House Hithercroft Road, Wallingford,
OX10 9RB, Oxfordshire, United Kingdom
Tel.: (44) 1491 820800
Web Site: http://www.fugro.com
Emp.: 400
Geophysical Consulting Services
N.A.I.C.S.: 541690

Fugro GeoServices Ltd. (1)
101 1108 53rd Av NE, Calgary, T2E 6N9,
AB, Canada
Tel.: (403) 234-9018
Web Site: http://www.fugro.ca
Sales Range: $350-399.9 Million
Emp.: 15
Geophysical Surveying & Mapping Services
N.A.I.C.S.: 541360

Fugro GeoSurveys, Inc. (1)
25 Pippy Place, Saint John's, A1B 3X2, NL,
Canada
Tel.: (709) 726-4252
Geological Seismic Surveying Services
N.A.I.C.S.: 541360
Mike Cole *(Gen Mgr)*

Fugro Geodetic AG (1)
49 Route de Meyrin Co 252, 1211, Geneva,
Switzerland
Tel.: (41) 225934544
Web Site: http://www.fugro.ch
Emp.: 7
Geophysical Surveying & Mapping Services
N.A.I.C.S.: 541360

Fugro Geodetic Ltd. (1)
30-E Mohammad Ali Cooperative Housing
Society Miran Mohammad Shah Road, Karachi, 75350, Pakistan
Tel.: (92) 21 3454 6611
Web Site: http://www.fugro.com.pk
Sales Range: $50-74.9 Million
Emp.: 80
Oil & Gas Industry Surveying Services
N.A.I.C.S.: 213112

Fugro Geoid S.A.S. (1)
12 Rue des Frares Lumiare, Jacou, 34830,
France
Tel.: (33) 4 67 59 26 44
Web Site: http://www.geoid.fr
Emp.: 47

Oil & Gas Mining Services
N.A.I.C.S.: 213112

Fugro Geolab Nor AS (1)
Hornebergveien, PO Box 5740, 7437,
Trondheim, Norway
Tel.: (47) 73 96 40 00
Geochemical Consulting Services
N.A.I.C.S.: 541690

Fugro Geoservices Limited (1)
14 Scotts Avenue Sunbury Upon Thames,
Middlesex, TW16 7HZ, United Kingdom
Tel.: (44) 1932784807
Web Site: http://www.fugroseacore.com
Sales Range: $50-74.9 Million
Emp.: 500
Overwater Drilling Engineering Services
N.A.I.C.S.: 237990

Fugro Geotech (Pvt) Ltd. (1)
Plot No 51 Sector 6, Sanpada, Navi Mumbai, 400705, India
Tel.: (91) 22 6516 8662
Sales Range: $25-49.9 Million
Emp.: 12
Geotechnical Engineering Services
N.A.I.C.S.: 541330
Santanu Moitra *(Gen Mgr)*

**Fugro Geotechnical Services
Ltd.** (1)
Units 8-10 10/F Worldwide Industrial Centre
43-47 Shan Mei Street, Fo Tan New Territories, Hong Kong, China (Hong Kong)
Tel.: (852) 26971126
Web Site: http://www.fugro.com.hk
Geophysical Surveying Services
N.A.I.C.S.: 541360

Fugro Geotechnics AS (1)
Hoffsveien 1C, 0275, Oslo, Norway
Tel.: (47) 22 13 46 00
Web Site: http://www.fugro.no
Geophysical Surveying Services
N.A.I.C.S.: 541360

Fugro Geotechnics Vietnam LLC (1)
No 31 Street O D2-16 My Giang 2 Phu My
Hung, Tan Phong Ward District 7, Ho Chi
Minh City, Vietnam
Tel.: (84) 8 54138228
Web Site: http://www.fugro.com.vn
Sales Range: $25-49.9 Million
Emp.: 4
Geophysical Surveying & Consulting Services
N.A.I.C.S.: 541360

Fugro Germany Land GmbH (1)
Wolfener Strasse 36 U, D-12681, Berlin,
Germany
Tel.: (49) 30936510
Geotechnical & Survey Services
N.A.I.C.S.: 541360

Fugro Germany Marine GmbH (1)
Fahrenheitstrasse 7, D-28359, Bremen,
Germany
Tel.: (49) 4214088850
Geotechnical & Survey Services
N.A.I.C.S.: 541360

Fugro Ghana Limited (1)
3rd Floor AWO Plaza 15th Street OSU, Accra, Ghana
Tel.: (233) 3939448
Geotechnical & Subsea Services
N.A.I.C.S.: 541330

Fugro Holding Belgium N.V. (1)
Rue du Bosquet 9, 1348, Louvain-la-Neuve,
Belgium
Tel.: (32) 10488200
Oil & Gas Exploration Services
N.A.I.C.S.: 211120

Fugro Holding France S.A.S. (1)
Work & Share 3-5 Boulevard des Bouvets,
92000, Nanterre, France
Tel.: (33) 155691770
Geotechnical & Survey Services
N.A.I.C.S.: 541360

Fugro Holdings (Hong Kong) Ltd. (1)
7/F Guardian House 32 Oi Kwan Road,
Wanchai, China (Hong Kong)
Tel.: (852) 25779023
Sales Range: $100-124.9 Million
Emp.: 16
Investment Management Service

N.A.I.C.S.: 523999
Lewis Chueng *(Mng Dir)*

Fugro Holdings (NZ) Ltd. (1)
477 Devon Street East, Strandon, New
Plymouth, New Zealand
Tel.: (64) 67695040
Surveying Services
N.A.I.C.S.: 541370

Fugro Holdings (UK) Ltd. (1)
Fugro House, Wallingford, OX10 9RB, Oxfordshire, United Kingdom
Tel.: (44) 8704021500
Web Site: http://www.fugro.com
Emp.: 400
Investment Management Service
N.A.I.C.S.: 523999

Fugro Hong Kong, Ltd. (1)
1 Kwai On Road, 32 Oi Kwan Rd, Kwai
Chung, New Territories, China (Hong
Kong) **(100%)**
Tel.: (852) 25779023
Web Site: http://www.fugro.com.hk
Sales Range: $25-49.9 Million
Emp.: 150
Geotechnical, Surveys, Subsea & Geoscience Services
N.A.I.C.S.: 541330

Fugro In Situ Geotecnia Ltda. (1)
R Apucarana 895 Emiliano Perneta, Pinhais, 83324-450, PR, Brazil
Tel.: (55) 4133451424
Geotechnical & Survey Services
N.A.I.C.S.: 541360

Fugro Interra S.A. (1)
Av Americo Vespucio 2880 13th Fl, Conchali, Chile
Tel.: (56) 2 623 51 51
Web Site: http://www.interra.cl
Sales Range: $25-49.9 Million
Emp.: 10
Geophysical Surveying Services
N.A.I.C.S.: 541360
Mario Scaletta *(Gen Mgr)*

Fugro Italy S.p.A. (1)
Viale Charles Lenormant 268, 00126,
Roma, Italy
Tel.: (39) 065219291
Surveying Services
N.A.I.C.S.: 541370

Fugro Jacques Geosurveys, Inc. (1)
131 Ilsley Ave Ste B, Dartmouth, B3B 1T1,
NS, Canada **(100%)**
Tel.: (902) 468-1130
Web Site: http://www.fugro.com
Sales Range: $50-74.9 Million
Emp.: 40
Marine Geomatics & Offshore Survey
N.A.I.C.S.: 211120

Fugro Japan Co., Ltd. (1)
Nippon Life Hamamatsucho Crea Tower
16F 2-3-1 Hamamatsucho, Minato-ku, Tokyo, 105-0013, Japan
Tel.: (81) 368091345
Web Site: http://www.fugro.co.jp
Geotechnical Engineering Services
N.A.I.C.S.: 541330
Sumio Yamano *(Mng Dir)*

Fugro LADS Corporation Pty Ltd. (1)
7 Valetta Rd, Kidman Park, Adelaide, 5025,
SA, Australia
Tel.: (61) 8 8161 4169
Web Site: http://www.fugrolads.com
Sales Range: $25-49.9 Million
Emp.: 5
Surveying Equipment Mfr
N.A.I.C.S.: 334519

Fugro Loadtest Ltd. (1)
14 Scotts Avenue, Sunbury-on-Thames,
TW16 7HZ, United Kingdom
Tel.: (44) 1932784807
Web Site: http://www.loadtest.co.uk
Sales Range: $25-49.9 Million
Emp.: 13
Deep Foundation Load Testing Services
N.A.I.C.S.: 238390

Fugro Ltd. (1)
Fugro House Hithercroft Road, Wallingford,
OX10 9RB, Herts, United Kingdom
Tel.: (44) 1491820700

Sales Range: $75-99.9 Million
Emp.: 300
Geotechnical, Surveys, Subsea & Geoscience Services
N.A.I.C.S.: 541330

Fugro Malaysia (1)
11th Fl Wisma Genting, 50250, Kuala Lumpur, Malaysia
Tel.: (60) 321262433
Web Site: http://www.fugro.com
Sales Range: $25-49.9 Million
Emp.: 86
Geotechnical Services to Oil, Gas, Mining &
Construction Industries
N.A.I.C.S.: 541330

Fugro Malaysia Land Sdn Bhd (1)
G-32 Jalan 4/8, Bandar Puteri, 47100, Puchong, Selangor, Malaysia
Tel.: (60) 380630299
Geotechnical & Survey Services
N.A.I.C.S.: 541360

Fugro Mauritius Ltd. (1)
1st Floor Palmcourt Building 90 St Jean
Road, Quatre Bornes, Mauritius
Tel.: (230) 4671677
Geotechnical & Survey Services
N.A.I.C.S.: 541360

Fugro Mexico S.A. de C.V. (1)
Calle 5 Sur Manzana Q Lote 10, Puerto
Industrial Pesquero Laguna Azul, 24140,
Ciudad del Carmen, Campeche, Mexico
Tel.: (52) 9383811970
Geotechnical & Survey Services
N.A.I.C.S.: 541360

**Fugro Middle East & Partners
LLC** (1)
Near Holiday Inn Ghala Al Madinah Area,
PO Box 1334, 112, Muscat, Oman
Tel.: (968) 2 4502320
Web Site: http://www.fugrome.com
Sales Range: $25-49.9 Million
Emp.: 16
Geophysical Surveying & Mapping Services
N.A.I.C.S.: 541360

Fugro Middle East B.V. (1)
Al Quoz Industrial Area 2, PO Box 2863,
2863, Dubai, 2863, United Arab
Emirates **(100%)**
Tel.: (971) 43474060
Sales Range: $25-49.9 Million
Emp.: 100
Geotechnical, Surveys, Subsea & Geoscience Services
N.A.I.C.S.: 541330

Subsidiary (Non-US):

Fugro Peninsular (2)
PO Box 47167, Doha, Qatar
Tel.: (974) 4323879
Web Site: http://www.fugrome.com
Sales Range: $25-49.9 Million
Emp.: 80
Engineeering Services
N.A.I.C.S.: 541330

Furgo-Suhaimi Ltd. (2)
PO Box 2165, Dammam, 31451, Saudi
Arabia **(100%)**
Tel.: (966) 38574200
Web Site: http://www.furgo-suhaimi.com
Sales Range: $25-49.9 Million
Geotechnical, Surveys, Subsea & Geoscience Services
N.A.I.C.S.: 541330

Fugro Mozambique Lda. (1)
Rua dos Governadores n 1301 Porta 61
Sommerschield 1, Maputo, Mozambique
Tel.: (258) 21485410
Construction Material Testing Services
N.A.I.C.S.: 541380

**Fugro Multi Client Services Pty
Ltd.** (1)
69 Outram Street, West Perth, Perth, 6005,
WA, Australia
Tel.: (61) 8 9321 4400
Web Site: http://www.fugromcs.com.au
Sales Range: $25-49.9 Million
Emp.: 14
Seismic Data Processing Services
N.A.I.C.S.: 518210

Fugro Nederland B.V. (1)

Veurse Achterweg 10, 2264 SG, Leidschen-
dam, 2264 SG, Netherlands
Tel.: (31) 703111422
Geophysical Surveying & Mapping Services
N.A.I.C.S.: 541360

Subsidiary (Domestic):

Fugro Aerial Mapping B.V. (2)
Dillenburgsingel 69, 2263 HW, Leidschen-
dam, Netherlands
Tel.: (31) 703170700
Web Site: http://www.flimap.nl
Sales Range: $25-49.9 Million
Emp.: 19
Geophysical Surveying & Mapping Services
N.A.I.C.S.: 541360

Fugro C.I.S. B.V. (2)
Veurse Achterweg 10, Leidschendam, 2264
SG, Netherlands
Tel.: (31) 703111422
Web Site: http://www.fugro.com
Geophysical Mapping Services
N.A.I.C.S.: 541360

Fugro GeoServices B.V. (2)
Veurse Achterweg 10, Postbus 63, 2260
AB, Leidschendam, Netherlands
Tel.: (31) 70 311 1333
Web Site: http://www.fugro.com
Emp.: 30
Geophysical Surveying & Mapping Services
N.A.I.C.S.: 541360

Fugro Intersite B.V. (2)
Dillenburgsingel 69, 2263 HW, Leidschen-
dam, Netherlands
Tel.: (31) 703111888
Sales Range: $25-49.9 Million
Emp.: 65
Engineeering Services
N.A.I.C.S.: 541330
Arnold Jongsma (Gen Mgr)

Fugro Marine Services B.V. (2)
Dillenburgsingel 69, Leidschendam, 2263
HW, Netherlands
Tel.: (31) 703119100
Web Site: http://www.fugro.nl
Sales Range: $25-49.9 Million
Emp.: 80
Marine Vessel Management Services
N.A.I.C.S.: 488330

Fugro NL Land B.V. (2)
Veurse Achterweg 10, 2264 SG, Leidschen-
dam, Netherlands
Tel.: (31) 703111422
Geophysical Survey & Positioning Services
N.A.I.C.S.: 541360
Mark Heine (CEO)

Fugro Netherlands Marine BV (2)
Prismastraat 4, 2631 RT, Nootdorp, Nether-
lands
Tel.: (31) 703111444
Sales Range: $25-49.9 Million
Emp.: 200
Engineeering Services
N.A.I.C.S.: 541330
Martin Galavazi (Gen Mgr)

Fugro Survey B.V. (2)
Veurse Achterweg 12, 2264 SG, Leidschen-
dam, Netherlands
Tel.: (31) 703111800
Web Site: http://www.fugro-africa.com
Sales Range: $25-49.9 Million
Emp.: 70
Geophysical Surveying & Mapping Services
N.A.I.C.S.: 541360

Fugro Vastgoed B.V. (2)
Veurse Achterweg 10, Leidschendam, 2264
SG, Netherlands
Tel.: (31) 703111422
Sales Range: $25-49.9 Million
Emp.: 7
Engineeering Services
N.A.I.C.S.: 541330
K. S. Wester (Gen Mgr)

Fugro-Elbocon B.V. (2)
Veurse Achterweg 10, Leidschendam, 2264
SG, Netherlands
Tel.: (31) 703111422
Engineeering Services
N.A.I.C.S.: 541330

Fugro-Inpark B.V. (2)

Dillenburgsingel 69, PO Box 3000, 2260
DA, Leidschendam, Netherlands
Tel.: (31) 703170700
Engineeering Services
N.A.I.C.S.: 541330
Pim Voogd (Project Mgr)

Inpark Detacheringen B.V. (2)
Veurse Achterweg 10, Leidschendam, 2264
SG, Netherlands
Tel.: (31) 70 3111422
Web Site: http://www.fugro.com
Sales Range: $150-199.9 Million
Emp.: 900
Construction Engineering Services
N.A.I.C.S.: 541330

Fugro New Zealand Ltd. (1)
477 Devon Street East, Strandon, New
Plymouth, New Zealand
Tel.: (64) 67695040
Geotechnical & Survey Services
N.A.I.C.S.: 541360

Fugro Nigeria Limited (1)
Fugro Avenue 91Odani Road Off PH-Eleme
Expressway Elelenwo PMB 053, Port Har-
court, Nigeria
Tel.: (234) 84 774175
Web Site: http://www.fugro-prodec.com
Geophysical Surveying Services
N.A.I.C.S.: 541360

Fugro Nigeria Ltd. (1)
Fugro Avenue 91 Odani Road Off PH-
Eleme Expressway Elelenwo PMB 053,
Port Harcourt, Nigeria
Tel.: (234) 84 774175
Web Site: http://www.fugro-prodec.com
Sales Range: $50-74.9 Million
Emp.: 106
Environmental Consulting & Laboratory
Services
N.A.I.C.S.: 541620

Fugro Norway AS (1)
Karenslyst Allee 2, N-0278, Oslo, Norway
Tel.: (47) 22134600
Web Site: http://www.fugro.no
Geotechnical Surveying Services
N.A.I.C.S.: 541360

Fugro OSAE GmbH (1)
Fahrenheitstrasse 7, 28359, Bremen, Ger-
many
Tel.: (49) 4214088850
Web Site: http://www.fugro-osae.de
Sales Range: $10-24.9 Million
Emp.: 40
Hydrographic Surveying Services
N.A.I.C.S.: 541360

Fugro Oceanor AS (1)
Luramyrveien 29, 4313, Sandnes, Norway
Tel.: (47) 51634310
Web Site: http://www.oceanor.com
Sales Range: $25-49.9 Million
Emp.: 5
Environmental Monitoring System Mfr
N.A.I.C.S.: 334513

Fugro Oceansismica S.p.A. (1)
Viale Charles Lenormant 268, 126, Rome,
Italy
Tel.: (39) 06 5219291
Web Site: http://www.fugro.it
Oil & Gas Exploration Services
N.A.I.C.S.: 213112

**Fugro Offshore Survey (Shenzhen)
Co. Ltd.** (1)
Unit 1009 10/F 1166 China Merchants
Tower Wanghai Road, Nanshan District,
Shenzhen, 518067, China
Tel.: (86) 75583458821
Oil & Gas Exploration Services
N.A.I.C.S.: 211120

**Fugro Pacifica Qinhuangdao Co.
Ltd.** (1)
3-1 Jinghe Road ETDZ, Qinhuangdao,
066004, China
Tel.: (86) 3358568130
Geotechnical & Survey Services
N.A.I.C.S.: 541360

Fugro Panama SA (1)
Ciudad del Saber CI Gustavo Lara Casa
141, Clayton, Panama, Panama
Tel.: (507) 317 1055
Web Site: http://www.fugroconsultants.com

Sales Range: $25-49.9 Million
Emp.: 14
Geophysical Surveying & Mapping Services
N.A.I.C.S.: 541360

Fugro Peru S.A. (1)
Calle Alvarez Calderon 185 Of 201 Edificio
Axxis, Lima, Peru
Tel.: (51) 14425353
Geotechnical & Survey Services
N.A.I.C.S.: 541360

Fugro Philippines Inc. (1)
Unit 303A The Taipan Place F Ortigas Jr
Road, San Antonio Ortigas Center, Pasig,
1605, Philippines
Tel.: (63) 288984690
Geotechnical & Survey Services
N.A.I.C.S.: 541360

Fugro RUE AS (1)
Stoltenberggaten 1, 5527, Haugesund, Nor-
way
Tel.: (47) 52 86 48 20
Web Site: http://www.fugrorue.com
Sales Range: $25-49.9 Million
Emp.: 3
Marine Offshore Engineering Services
N.A.I.C.S.: 541330
Paul Schiefloe (Gen Mgr)

Fugro Roadware, Inc. (1)
2505 Meadowvale Blvd, Mississauga, L5N
5S2, ON, Canada
Tel.: (905) 567-2870
Web Site: http://www.fugroroadware.com
Sales Range: $25-49.9 Million
Emp.: 100
Highway Management Software Develop-
ment Services
N.A.I.C.S.: 541511

Fugro Roames Pty Ltd (1)
Level 1 53 Brandl Street, Eight Mile Plains,
Brisbane, 4113, QLD, Australia
Tel.: (61) 738413433
Geotechnical & Survey Services
N.A.I.C.S.: 541360

Fugro S.A.E. (1)
Plot 76 & 78 The Industrial Zone, Zahraa
Al-Maadi, 11431, Cairo, Egypt
Tel.: (20) 223225450
Web Site: http://www.fugro-egypt.net
Sales Range: $25-49.9 Million
Emp.: 15
Offshore Geophysical Surveying Services
N.A.I.C.S.: 541360
John Evans (Mgr-Egypt)

Fugro SEA Ltd. (1)
7/F Guardian House 32 Oi Kwan Rd, Wan-
chai, China (Hong Kong)
Tel.: (852) 2577 9023
Web Site: http://www.fugro.com.hk
Emp.: 10
Geophysical Surveying & Mapping Services
N.A.I.C.S.: 541360

**Fugro Satellite Positioning Pte.
Ltd.** (1)
29 Loyang Crescent, Singapore, 509015,
Singapore
Tel.: (65) 68610878
Global Positioning System Support Services
N.A.I.C.S.: 541690

**Fugro Seacore (Australia) Pty
Ltd.** (1)
24 Geddes Street, Balcatta, 6021, WA, Aus-
tralia
Tel.: (61) 8 6477 4400
Web Site: http://www.seacore.com
Sales Range: $25-49.9 Million
Emp.: 4
Geophysical Surveying Services
N.A.I.C.S.: 541360

Fugro Seastar AS (1)
Karenslyst Allee 2, 0278, Oslo, Norway
Tel.: (47) 21501400
Web Site: http://www.seastar.co.uk
Navigation & Positioning Services
N.A.I.C.S.: 488330

Fugro Seastar Mauritius Ltd. (1)
IFS Court Twentyeight, Ebene, Mauritius
Tel.: (230) 467 1677
Geophysical Surveying & Mapping Services
N.A.I.C.S.: 541360

Fugro Sial Ltd. (1)
Farabi Sokak No 40/4, Kavaklidere, 6680,
Ankara, 6680, Turkiye
Tel.: (90) 3124273043
Geotechnical & Survey Services
N.A.I.C.S.: 541360

Fugro Singapore Land Pte Ltd (1)
29 Loyang Crescent, Singapore, 509015,
Singapore
Tel.: (65) 68610878
Web Site: https://www.loadtest.com
Sales Range: $50-74.9 Million
Emp.: 110
Deep Foundation Load Testing Services
N.A.I.C.S.: 238220

Fugro Singapore Marine Pte. Ltd (1)
35 Loyang Crescent, Singapore, 509012,
Singapore
Tel.: (65) 68610878
Web Site: http://www.fugro.com.sg
Sales Range: $75-99.9 Million
Emp.: 300
Geophysical Surveying & Mapping Services
N.A.I.C.S.: 541360

Fugro Singapore Pte Ltd. (1)
159 Sin Ming Rd No 06 07 Amtech Bldg,
Singapore, 575625, Singapore
Tel.: (65) 65528600
Web Site: http://www.fugro.com
Sales Range: $25-49.9 Million
Emp.: 50
Geotechnical, Surveys, Subsea & Geosci-
ence Services
N.A.I.C.S.: 541330

Fugro South America GmbH (1)
Bahnhofstrasse 29, 6300, Zug, Switzerland
Tel.: (41) 41 7280808
Geophysical Surveying & Mapping Services
N.A.I.C.S.: 541360

Fugro Spatial Solutions Pty Ltd. (1)
18 Prowse Street, West Perth, 6005, WA,
Australia
Tel.: (61) 8 9282 4100
Web Site: http://www.fugrospatial.com.au
Sales Range: $25-49.9 Million
Emp.: 60
Geospatial Mapping Services
N.A.I.C.S.: 541370

**Fugro Subsea Services Australia Pty
Ltd.** (1)
3-4 Martin place, Canning Vale, Canning
Vale, 6155, WA, Australia
Tel.: (61) 862538225
Web Site: http://www.fugro.com
Sales Range: $25-49.9 Million
Emp.: 14
Engineeering Services
N.A.I.C.S.: 541330

**Fugro Subsea Technologies Pte
Ltd.** (1)
35 Loyang Crescent, Singapore, 509012,
Singapore
Tel.: (65) 68610878
Web Site: http://www.fugro.com
Emp.: 20
Geophysical Surveying Services
N.A.I.C.S.: 541360

Fugro Survey (Brunei) Sdn Bhd. (1)
Lot 4237 X7 Simpang 394-15, Jalan Mau-
lana, Kuala Belait, KA2931, Brunei Darus-
salam
Tel.: (673) 3335340
Sales Range: $25-49.9 Million
Emp.: 1
Geophysical Surveying & Mapping Services
N.A.I.C.S.: 541360

Fugro Survey (Middle East) Ltd. (1)
PO Box 43088, Abu Dhabi, United Arab
Emirates
Tel.: (971) 25547810
Web Site: http://www.fugro-uae.com
Sales Range: $25-49.9 Million
Emp.: 100
Offshore Surveying & Positioning Services
N.A.I.C.S.: 541360

Fugro Survey AS (1)
Hoffsveien 1C, PO Box 490, Skoyen, Oslo,
213, Norway
Tel.: (47) 22 13 47 34
Web Site: http://www.fugro-survey.no

Fugro N.V.—(Continued)

Geophysical Offshore Surveying Services
N.A.I.C.S.: 541360

Fugro Survey Africa (Pty) Ltd. (1)
Woodbridge Business Park Koeberg Road,
Milnerton, 7441, Cape Town, South Africa
Tel.: (27) 21 527 8900
Web Site: http://www.fugro-africa.com
Geophysical Surveying & Positioning Services
N.A.I.C.S.: 541360

Fugro Survey Caribbean N.V. (1)
Schottegatweg Oost 62, Willemstad, Curacao
Tel.: (599) 9 736 5456
Web Site:
http://www.fugrosurveycaribbean.com
Sales Range: $25-49.9 Million
Emp.: 22
Geophysical Surveying & Mapping Services
N.A.I.C.S.: 541360

Fugro Survey International Ltd. (1)
7/F Guardian House 32 Oi Kwan Rd, Wanchai, China (Hong Kong)
Tel.: (852) 2577 9023
Web Site: http://www.fugro.com.hk
Sales Range: $25-49.9 Million
Emp.: 100
Geophysical Survey & Mapping Services
N.A.I.C.S.: 541360

Fugro Survey Ltd. (1)
Survey House Denmore Road, Bridge of
Don, Aberdeen, AB23 8JW, United Kingdom
Tel.: (44) 1224 257 500
Web Site: http://www.fugrosurvey.co.uk
Emp.: 150
Oil & Gas Offshore Services
N.A.I.C.S.: 211120

Fugro Survey Ltd. (1)
7/F Guardian House 32 Oi Kwan Rd, Wanchai, China (Hong Kong)
Tel.: (852) 2577 9023
Sales Range: $25-49.9 Million
Emp.: 13
Geophysical Surveying & Mapping Services
N.A.I.C.S.: 541360

Fugro Survey Mexico S.A. de C.V. (1)
Puerto Industrial Pesquero Laguna Azul
Cruzamiento Zofemat, Ciudad del Carmen,
24140, Mexico
Tel.: (52) 938 3811970
Web Site: http://www.fugro.com
Sales Range: $25-49.9 Million
Emp.: 45
Geophysical Surveying & Mapping Services
N.A.I.C.S.: 541360

Fugro Survey Pty Ltd. (1)
24 Geddes Street, Baicatta, Perth, 6021,
WA, Australia
Tel.: (61) 8 6477 4400
Web Site:
http://www.fugrosurveytechnical.com
Geophysical Surveying & Mapping Services
N.A.I.C.S.: 541360

Fugro Technical Services (Guangzhou) Ltd. (1)
No 6 Nongye Gongsi Road Hualong, Panyu, Guangzhou, 511434, Guangdong,
China
Tel.: (86) 2034828832
Web Site: http://www.fugro.cn
Construction Material Testing & Inspection
Services
N.A.I.C.S.: 926150

Fugro Technical Services (Macau) Ltd. (1)
Rua Wo Mok Lote P2, Taipa, China (Macau)
Tel.: (853) 851812
Web Site: http://www.fugro.com.hk
Geophysical Surveying & Mapping Services
N.A.I.C.S.: 541360

Fugro Technical Services Ltd. (1)
Fugro Development Centre 5 Lok Yi Street
17 MS Castle Peak Road, Tai Lam, Tuen
Mun, NT, China (Hong Kong)
Tel.: (852) 24508233

Space Research & Technology Services
N.A.I.C.S.: 927110

Fugro Trinidad Ltd. (1)
29 Alexandra Street, St Clair, Trinidad &
Tobago
Tel.: (868) 6283204
Surveying Services
N.A.I.C.S.: 541370

Fugro Weinhold Engineering GmbH (1)
Kofferer Strasse 40, 41812, Erkelenz,
41812, Germany
Tel.: (49) 2164940590
Web Site: http://www.vib-weinhold.com
Sales Range: $25-49.9 Million
Emp.: 3
Geo Spatial Services
N.A.I.C.S.: 927110
Wolfgang Weinhold (Co-Mng Dir)

Fugro-GEOS Ltd. (1)
Fugro House Hithercroft Road, Wallingford,
OX10 9RB, Oxfordshire, United Kingdom
Tel.: (44) 1491820500
Web Site: http://www.geos.com
Sales Range: $50-74.9 Million
Emp.: 105
Meteorological & Oceanographic Services
N.A.I.C.S.: 927110

Fugro-GEOS Pte Ltd. (1)
35 Loyang Crescent Level 1, Singapore,
509012, Singapore
Tel.: (65) 6885 4100
Sales Range: $25-49.9 Million
Emp.: 20
Meteorological & Oceanographic Services
N.A.I.C.S.: 927110
Kit Moss (Mng Dir)

Fugro-ImpROV Ltd. (1)
Kirkhill Commercial Park Dyce Avenue,
Dyce, Aberdeen, AB21 OLQ, United Kingdom
Tel.: (44) 1224709767
Web Site: http://www.improvltd.co.uk
Sales Range: $25-49.9 Million
Emp.: 60
Machine Tools Mfr
N.A.I.C.S.: 333517

Fugro-MAPS (UAE) (1)
Corniche Plaza 1, PO Box 5232, Sharjah,
5232, United Arab Emirates
Tel.: (971) 6 5725411
Web Site: http://www.fugromaps.com
Sales Range: $25-49.9 Million
Emp.: 61
Geophysical Surveying Services
N.A.I.C.S.: 541360

Fugro-MAPS GmbH (1)
Truderinger Str 13, 81677, Munich, Germany
Tel.: (49) 8924448840
Web Site: http://www.fugro-maps.com
Aerial Survey & Satelliete Mapping Services
N.A.I.C.S.: 541370

Fugro-MAPS S.a.r.l. (1)
Maamari Street Khoury Bldg, Clemenceau
District, Beirut, Lebanon
Tel.: (961) 1 367 470
Geophysical Surveying & Mapping Services
N.A.I.C.S.: 541360

Geofor Gabon SA (1)
Zone Industrielle d' Oloumi, B P 2826, Libreville, Gabon
Tel.: (241) 1765681
Geotechnical Drilling Oil & Gas Services
N.A.I.C.S.: 213112

Geotechnical Instruments (Hong Kong) Ltd. (1)
Units 8-10 10/F Worldwide Industrial Centre
43-47 Shan Mei Street, Fotan, New Territories, China (Hong Kong)
Tel.: (852) 2697 1126
Sales Range: $25-49.9 Million
Emp.: 6
Geophysical Surveying Services
N.A.I.C.S.: 541360

Hush Craft Ltd. (1)
Blackwater House Woodrolfe Road, Tollesbury, Maldon, CM9 8SE, United Kingdom
Tel.: (44) 1206625180
Web Site: https://www.hushcraft.com

Electric Motor Distr
N.A.I.C.S.: 423110

Labomosan S.A. (1)
Chemin du Fond des Coupes 6, Floreffe,
5150, Namur, Belgium
Tel.: (32) 81440666
Web Site:
http://www.labomosanessaisdesols.be
Engineering Laboratory Services
N.A.I.C.S.: 541380

MateriaLab Consultants Ltd. (1)
Fugro Development Centre 5 Lok Yi Street
17 MS Castle Peak Road, Tai Lam, Tuen
Mun, New Territories, China (Hong Kong)
Tel.: (852) 2450 8238
Web Site: http://www.materialab-consultant.com
Environmental Consulting Services
N.A.I.C.S.: 541620
Colin Yung (Asst Mgr)

P.T. Fugro Indonesia (1)
Jalan Asem Baris Raya No 1, Tebet Jakarta
Selatan, Jakarta, 12830, Indonesia
Tel.: (62) 21 831 5711
Web Site: http://www.fugro-singapore.com.sg
Sales Range: $25-49.9 Million
Emp.: 110
Geophysical Survey & Geotechnical Services
N.A.I.C.S.: 541360

TurbiGas Solar S.A. (1)
Tacuari 202 Piso 10, C 1071AAF, Buenos
Aires, Argentina
Tel.: (54) 11 5235 8200
Web Site: http://www.turbigas.com.ar
Sales Range: $25-49.9 Million
Emp.: 25
Mfr of Power Generation Machinery
N.A.I.C.S.: 335311

UAB Fugro Baltic (1)
Rasu Street 39, 11351, Vilnius, Lithuania
Tel.: (370) 5 2135115
Web Site: http://www.fugro.lt
Sales Range: $25-49.9 Million
Emp.: 1
Geophysical Surveying Services
N.A.I.C.S.: 541360

FUGUINIAO CO., LTD.

Room 1908 19/F West Tower, Shun
Tak Centre 168-200 Connaught
Road, Central, China (Hong Kong)
Tel.: (852) 3152 2366
Web Site: http://www.fuguiniao.com
Year Founded: 1991
Shoe & Men's Clothing Mfr & Distr
N.A.I.C.S.: 316210
Wo Ping Lam (Founder, Chm, Pres &
Exec Dir)

FUJAIRAH BUILDING INDUSTRIES COMPANY P.S.C.

Year Founded: 1978
Rev: $65,920,650
Assets: $111,464,848
Liabilities: $45,293,833
Net Worth: $66,171,015
Earnings: $4,085,397
Fiscal Year-end: 12/31/16
Building Materials Mfr
N.A.I.C.S.: 327120
Khalil Ebraheim Ebraheim Hassan
Shahdad Ahmed (Vice Chm)

Subsidiaries:

Fujairah Building Industries Company P.S.C. - Emirates Ceramic Factory (1)
PO Box 3040, Fujairah, United Arab Emirates
Tel.: (971) 9 222 3995
Web Site: http://www.emiratesceramics.com
Ceramic Products Mfr
N.A.I.C.S.: 327110

Fujairah Building Industries Company P.S.C. - Fujairah Marble & Tiles Factory (1)
Dibba region, PO Box 11419, Dibba, Fujai-

rah, United Arab Emirates
Tel.: (971) 9 244 4101
Sales Range: $75-99.9 Million
Emp.: 150
Marble & Tile Mfr
N.A.I.C.S.: 327991

Fujairah Building Industries Company P.S.C. - Fujairah Rockwool Factory (1)
PO Box 211, Fujairah, United Arab Emirates
Tel.: (971) 9 222 2297
Web Site: http://www.rockwoolfujairah.ae
Rockwool Insulation Product Mfr
N.A.I.C.S.: 327993

Fujairah National Quarry (1)
Siji Hotel Apartment - Fujairah, PO Box
383, Al Hail Industrial Area, Fujairah, 383,
United Arab Emirates
Tel.: (971) 9 224 1138
Web Site: http://www.nqfuj.com
Sales Range: $50-74.9 Million
Emp.: 12
Sand & Gravel Mining Services
N.A.I.C.S.: 212312
Abdalla Hussein Elyamany (Gen Mgr)

FUJAIRAH CEMENT INDUSTRIES COMPANY PSC

Emirates Islamic Bank Bldg Floor No
12 Room No 1203, Hamad Bin Abdulla Road, Fujairah, United Arab
Emirates
Tel.: (971) 92223111
Web Site:
https://www.fujairahcement.com
Year Founded: 1979
FCI—(ABU)
Rev: $102,000,714
Assets: $420,672,143
Liabilities: $233,493,689
Net Worth: $187,178,454
Earnings: ($39,170,846)
Emp.: 240
Fiscal Year-end: 12/31/22
Cement Mfr
N.A.I.C.S.: 327310
Mohammed Hamad Saif Al Sharqi
(Chm)

Subsidiaries:

Fujairah Cement Industries PJSC FZ (1)
PO Box 11477, Dibba, Fujairah, United
Arab Emirates
Tel.: (971) 92444011
Web Site: https://fujairahcement.com
Readymix Concrete Mfr
N.A.I.C.S.: 327320

FUJAIRAH TRADE CENTRE COMPANY

PO Box 761, Fujairah, United Arab
Emirates
Tel.: (971) 2222661
Web Site:
http://www.fujairahtradecentre.com
Sales Range: $1-9.9 Million
Leasing Business Services
N.A.I.C.S.: 561499

FUJI CHEMICAL INDUSTRIES CO., LTD

55 Yokohoonji Kamiichi-machi,
Nakaniikawa-gun, Toyama, 930-0355,
Japan
Tel.: (81) 76 472 2323　　JP
Web Site:
http://www.fujichemical.co.jp
Year Founded: 1946
Emp.: 407
Pharmaceuticals Product Mfr
N.A.I.C.S.: 325412
Hiroshi Nishida (Pres & CEO)

Subsidiaries:

AstaReal Holdings Co., Ltd. (1)
Sumitomo Fudosan Onarimon Tower 10th
Floor 1-1-1 Shiba Koen, Minato-ku, Tokyo,

105-0011, Japan **(100%)**
Tel.: (81) 3 5408 1129
Web Site: http://www.astareal.com
Holding Company; Pharmaceutical Products
Mfr & Distr
N.A.I.C.S.: 551111
Mitsutoshi Nishida *(Chm)*

Subsidiary (Non-US):

AstaReal (Australia) Pty Ltd **(2)**
PO Box 602, Bowral, 2576, NSW, Australia
Tel.: (61) 437 073 298
Health Supplements Distr
N.A.I.C.S.: 456191

AstaReal (India) Private Limited **(2)**
120 Ackruti Star Central Rd Opp Ackruti
Centre Point, MIDC Andheri East, Mumbai,
400093, India
Tel.: (91) 22 6236 9998
Pharmaceutical Products Distr
N.A.I.C.S.: 325412

AstaReal AB **(2)**
Forumvagen 14 Level 16, 131 53, Nacka,
Sweden
Tel.: (46) 8 570 139 50
Web Site: http://www.astareal.se
Pharmaceutical Products Mfr & Distr
N.A.I.C.S.: 325412
Annika Karlen *(CEO)*

Subsidiary (Domestic):

AstaReal Co., Ltd. **(2)**
Sumitomo Fudosan Onarimon Tower 10th
Floor 1-1-1 Shiba Koen, Minato-ku, Tokyo,
105-0011, Japan
Tel.: (81) 3 5408 1129
Web Site: http://www.astareal.com
Pharmaceutical Products Mfr & Distr
N.A.I.C.S.: 325412
Hiroshi Nishida *(Pres)*

Branch (Domestic):

AstaReal Co., Ltd. - Nagoya **(3)**
#12 e-bis MEIKEI Office 5-4-14 Meieki,
Nakamura-ku, Nagoya, 450-0002, Japan
Tel.: (81) 52 588 6721
Pharmaceutical Products Distr
N.A.I.C.S.: 456110

AstaReal Co., Ltd. - Osaka **(3)**
Kotera Plaza 9th Floor 2-5-23 Kitahama,
Chuo-ku, Osaka, 541-0041, Japan
Tel.: (81) 6 6202 8901
Pharmaceutical Products Distr
N.A.I.C.S.: 456110

AstaReal Co., Ltd. - Toyama **(3)**
55 Yokohoonji Kamiichi-machi Nakaniikawa-
gun, Toyama, 930-0355, Japan
Tel.: (81) 76 472 2323
Pharmaceutical Products Distr
N.A.I.C.S.: 456110

Subsidiary (Non-US):

AstaReal Pte. Ltd. **(2)**
138 Robinson Rd, #28-04 Oxley Tower, Sin-
gapore, 068906, Singapore
Tel.: (65) 6222 1778
Web Site: http://www.astareal.sg
Health Supplements Distr
N.A.I.C.S.: 456191

Subsidiary (US):

AstaReal, Inc. **(2)**
3 Terri Ln Unit 12, Burlington, NJ 08016
Tel.: (609) 614-6904
Web Site: http://astarealusa.com
Natural Dietary Supplements Distr
N.A.I.C.S.: 325412
Yasuko Kuroda *(Exec VP)*

Unit (Domestic):

AstaReal, Inc. - Washington **(3)**
7761 Randolph Rd NE, Moses Lake, WA
98837
Tel.: (509) 855-4370
Web Site: http://www.astarealusa.com
Pharmaceuticals Product Mfr
N.A.I.C.S.: 325412

Subsidiary (US):

Astavita, Inc. **(2)**

1750 112th Ave NE Ste D155, Bellevue,
WA 98004
Tel.: (425) 777-9881
Web Site: http://www.astavita.com
Natural Dietary Supplement Products Mfr &
Distr
N.A.I.C.S.: 325412

Fuji Chemical Industries Co., Ltd. -
Gohkakizawa **(1)**
1 Gohkakizawa Kamiichi-machi
Nakaniikawa-gun, Toyama, 930-0405, Ja-
pan
Tel.: (81) 76 472 2323
Pharmaceuticals Product Mfr
N.A.I.C.S.: 325412

Fuji Chemical Industries Co., Ltd. -
Osaka **(1)**
Kotera Plaza 9th Floor 2-5-23 Kitahama,
Chuo-ku, Osaka, 541-0041, Japan
Tel.: (81) 6 6202 8901
Pharmaceutical Products Distr
N.A.I.C.S.: 456110

Fuji Chemical Industries Co., Ltd. -
Tokyo **(1)**
Sumitomo Fudosan Onarimon Tower 10th
Floor 1-1-1 Shiba Koen, Minato-ku, Tokyo,
105-0011, Japan
Tel.: (81) 3 3437 2350
Pharmaceutical Products Mfr & Distr
N.A.I.C.S.: 325412

Fuji Chemical Industries USA,
Inc. **(1)**
3 Terri Ln Unit 12, Burlington, NJ
08016 **(100%)**
Tel.: (609) 386-3030
Web Site: http://www.fujichemicalusa.com
Pharmaceutical Products Mfr & Distr
N.A.I.C.S.: 325412
Yasuko Kuroda *(Pres)*

FUJI CO., LTD.
1-2-1 Miyanishi, Matsuyama, 790-
8567, Ehime, Japan
Tel.: (81) 899267111
Web Site: https://www.the-fuji.com
Year Founded: 1950
8278—(TKS)
Rev.: $5,679,245,980
Assets: $3,032,407,180
Liabilities: $1,500,279,450
Net Worth: $1,532,127,730
Earnings: $52,721,240
Emp.: 6,985
Fiscal Year-end: 02/29/24
Automobile Retail Store Operator
N.A.I.C.S.: 441330
Hiroshi Yamaguchi *(Pres & CEO)*

Subsidiaries:

Maxvalu Nishinihon Co., Ltd. **(1)**
5F Hiroshima Danbara Shopping Center
1-3-52 Danbara Minami, Minami-ku, Hiro-
shima, 732-0814, Japan
Tel.: (81) 825358500
Web Site: http://www.maxvalu.co.jp
Rev.: $4,979,218,300
Assets: $2,433,983,930
Liabilities: $1,522,916,920
Net Worth: $911,067,010
Earnings: ($48,848,590)
Fiscal Year-end: 02/29/2020
Supermarket Store Operator
N.A.I.C.S.: 445110

FUJI CORPORATION
19 Chausuyama Yamamachi, Chiryu,
472-8686, Aichi, Japan
Tel.: (81) 566812111 JP
Web Site: https://www.fuji.co.jp
Year Founded: 1959
6134—(NGO)
Rev.: $839,504,225
Assets: $1,657,990,946
Liabilities: $149,712,545
Net Worth: $1,508,278,402
Earnings: $68,906,489
Emp.: 2,911
Fiscal Year-end: 03/31/24

Surface Mount Equipment, Machine
Tools & LCD Assembly Equipment
Mfr
N.A.I.C.S.: 333519
Nobuyuki Soga *(Chm & CEO)*

Subsidiaries:

ALGAR S.p.A **(1)**
Via Gargano 44A, 20139, Milan, Italy
Tel.: (39) 025 749 5600
Web Site: https://www.algar.it
Sales Range: $50-74.9 Million
Emp.: 9
Printed Circuit Board Distr
N.A.I.C.S.: 423690

Adtek Fuji Co., Ltd. **(1)**
74-1 Shaguchi Nishihongo-cho, Okazaki,
444-0947, Aichi, Japan
Tel.: (81) 564314690
Web Site: https://adtek-fuji.co.jp
Emp.: 286
Automation Equipment Mfr
N.A.I.C.S.: 335314

Adtex Fuji Co., Ltd. **(1)**
74-1 Nishihongo- cho, Okazaki, 444-0947,
Aichi Prefecture, Japan
Tel.: (81) 564314690
Web Site: http://www.adtek-fuji.co.jp
Machine Tools Mfr
N.A.I.C.S.: 333517

American Tec Electronic India Pvt
Ltd. **(1)**
B-68 Sector 65, Noida, 201301, Uttar
Pradesh, India
Tel.: (91) 120 436 7122
Web Site: http://www.americantec.com
Sales Range: $25-49.9 Million
Emp.: 40
Electronic Components Mfr
N.A.I.C.S.: 334419
Stephen Wu *(Pres)*

Ascentex Industry Corp. **(1)**
7th Floor No 516 Section 1 Hu Road, Neihu
District, Taipei, 11493, Taiwan
Tel.: (886) 28 797 8788
Web Site: https://www.ascentex.com.tw
Sales Range: $25-49.9 Million
Emp.: 100
Automatic Vending Machine Mfr
N.A.I.C.S.: 333310

Subsidiary (Non-US):

Ascentek International Company
Limited **(2)**
Rml 26/F Zhaofeng World Trading Building
No 369 Jiangsu Road, No 369 Jiangsu
Road, Shanghai, 200050, China
Tel.: (86) 215 240 1458
Web Site: http://www.fuji.co.jp
Sales Range: $25-49.9 Million
Commercial & Service Industry Machinery
Mfr
N.A.I.C.S.: 333310

Astro Technologies Ltd. **(1)**
Astro House 7 Bessemer Way, Sawcliffe
Industrial Park, DN158XE, Scunthorpe,
United Kingdom
Tel.: (44) 1724295400
Electronic Parts & Equipment Whslr
N.A.I.C.S.: 423690

Brock Electronics Ltd. **(1)**
350 Harry Walker Pkwy N Unit 16, New-
market, L3Y 8L3, ON, Canada
Tel.: (905) 954-0505
Web Site: https://www.brockelectronics.com
Sales Range: $25-49.9 Million
Emp.: 7
Miscellaneous General Purpose Machinery
Mfr
N.A.I.C.S.: 333998
Paul Walsh *(Owner)*

EQUIPMENT SALES CO. **(1)**
8828 206th St SE Unit E, Snohomish, WA
98296
Tel.: (425) 415-1616
Web Site: http://www.fuji.co.jp
Electronic Equipment Distr
N.A.I.C.S.: 423690

Edeclinseysystem Co.,Ltd. **(1)**
331-9 Hamaike, Nishimiyuki-cho, Toyohashi,

441-8113, Aichi, Japan
Tel.: (81) 53 229 4131
Web Site: https://www.edeclinsey.jp
Sales Range: $25-49.9 Million
Emp.: 142
Electronic Components Mfr
N.A.I.C.S.: 334419
Kimihiko Yasuda *(Pres & CEO)*

FENWICK IBERICA S.A. **(1)**
Bailen 136 Ent2 a, 08037, Barcelona, Spain
Tel.: (34) 93 458 4001
Web Site: https://www.fenwick-iberica.es
Machine Tool Distr
N.A.I.C.S.: 423830

Fasford Technology Co., Ltd. **(1)**
610-5 Shimoimasuwa, Minami-Alps, 400-
0212, Yamanashi, Japan
Tel.: (81) 552846661
Web Site: https://www.fasford-tech.com
Emp.: 192
Semiconductor Fabrication Equipment Mfr
N.A.I.C.S.: 333242
Hideto Fujiwara *(Pres & CEO)*

First Technology China Ltd. **(1)**
Room 1913-15 19/F Paul Wah Corporate
Centre 51 Hung To Road, Kwun Tong, Kow-
loon, China (Hong Kong)
Tel.: (852) 3 420 8888
Web Site: https://www.1techchina.com
Scientific & Technical Consulting Services
N.A.I.C.S.: 541690

Subsidiary (Non-US):

First Technology (Beijing) Ltd. **(2)**
928-930 Xuan Wamen Wai Street Junefield
Plaza No 10, Xuanwu District, 100052, Bei-
jing, China
Tel.: (86) 10 6310 6696
Machine Tools Mfr
N.A.I.C.S.: 333517

First Technology Shanghai Ltd. **(2)**
Rm 3201 LT Square No 500 North
Chengdu Rd, Shanghai, 200003, China
Tel.: (86) 2151699850
Machine Tools Mfr
N.A.I.C.S.: 332216

Fuji America Corporation **(1)**
171 Corporate Woods Pkwy, Vernon Hills,
IL 60061
Tel.: (847) 913-0162
Web Site: http://www.fujiamerica.com
Sales Range: $25-49.9 Million
Emp.: 65
Miscellaneous General Purpose Machinery
Mfr
N.A.I.C.S.: 333998
Nick Kamura *(Pres)*

Fuji India Corporation Private
Limited **(1)**
Unit 414 4th Floor Emaar Capital Tower,
Virendra Gram Mehrauli Gurgaon Road Si-
kanderpur Ghosi, Gurgaon, 122022, India
Tel.: (91) 1244881050
Machine Tool Mfr & Distr
N.A.I.C.S.: 333517

Fuji Linear Corporation **(1)**
19 Chausuyama Yamamachi, Chiryu, 472-
8686, Aichi Prefecture, Japan
Tel.: (81) 566574000
Machine Tool Mfr & Distr
N.A.I.C.S.: 333517

Fuji Machine America
Corporation **(1)**
171 Corporate Woods Pkwy, Vernon Hills,
IL 60061
Tel.: (847) 821-7137
Web Site: https://www.fujimachine.com
Sales Range: $25-49.9 Million
Emp.: 25
Industrial Machinery Mfr
N.A.I.C.S.: 333248

Fuji Machine China Co.,Ltd. **(1)**
Pine City Hotel Room 1018 Dong'an Road
8, Shanghai, 200032, China
Tel.: (86) 216 403 1341
Web Site: https://www.fuji-mc.com.cn
Sales Range: $25-49.9 Million
Emp.: 5
Industrial Machinery Mfr
N.A.I.C.S.: 333248

Fuji Corporation—(Continued)

Fuji Machine Manufacturing (Europe) GmbH **(1)**
Peter-Sander-Str 43, Mainz-Kastel, 55252, Germany
Tel.: (49) 61342020
Web Site: http://www.fuji-euro.de
Sales Range: $25-49.9 Million
Emp.: 42
Miscellaneous General Purpose Machinery Mfr
N.A.I.C.S.: 333998
Niels Finzel *(Mgr-Svc)*

Fuji Machine Mfg. Co., Ltd. - Fujioka Plant **(1)**
480 Tojiri Hasama-cho, Toyota, 470-0452, Aichi, Japan
Tel.: (81) 565 76 2211
Web Site: http://www.fuji.co.jp
Machine Tools Mfr
N.A.I.C.S.: 333517

Fuji Machine Mfg. Co., Ltd. - Okazaki Plant **(1)**
1-3 Kitayoko Eta-cho, Okazaki, 444-2107, Aichi, Japan
Tel.: (81) 564 452000
Electronic Components Mfr
N.A.I.C.S.: 334419

Fuji do Brasil Maquinas Industriais Ltda. **(1)**
R dos Curupias 182, Jabaquara, Sao Paulo, 04344-050, Brazil
Tel.: (55) 1150151650
Web Site: https://www.fujibrasil.com.br
Sales Range: $25-49.9 Million
Emp.: 30
Surface Mounted Machinery Whslr
N.A.I.C.S.: 423830

KOBOT SYSTEMS PTY LTD. **(1)**
3 Mast Place Ocean Reef, Perth, 6027, WA, Australia
Tel.: (61) 89 307 8178
Web Site: http://www.kobot.com.au
Industrial Machine Tool Mfr
N.A.I.C.S.: 333517
Gerald Koh *(Gen Mgr)*

Kunshan Fuji Machine Mfg. Co., Ltd. **(1)**
No 2 Chenghu Road, Kunshan Economic and Technological Development Zone, Kunshan, Jiangsu, China
Tel.: (86) 51236870778
Web Site: http://www.ks-fuji.com
Machine Tool Mfr & Distr
N.A.I.C.S.: 333517

MECOMB (THAILAND) LTD. **(1)**
211 Soi Predee Phanomyong 11 Sukhumvit 71 Rd Prakanong-Nua, Wattana, Bangkok, Thailand
Tel.: (66) 271171019
Web Site: http://www.mecombthai.co.th
Emp.: 68
Electronic Components Mfr
N.A.I.C.S.: 334419

MS INTERNATIONAL CORP. **(1)**
Rm No 1205 Haechun Bld 831 Yucksam-dong, Kangnam-Ku, Seoul, 831, Korea (South)
Tel.: (82) 2 553 0901
Web Site: http://www.msinter.co.kr
Electronic Products Mfr & Distr
N.A.I.C.S.: 334419

PRODUCTION TECHNOLOGY **(1)**
6765 Westminster Blvd Ste C-422, Westminster, CA 92683-3769
Tel.: (909) 989-1987
Web Site: https://www.prod-tech.com
Printed Circuit Board Mfr & Distr
N.A.I.C.S.: 334418
Tom Szabo *(Mgr-Acctg & Sys)*

Perfecbore AG **(1)**
Mullerstrasse 2, Port, 2562, Bern, Switzerland
Tel.: (41) 323328444
Web Site: http://www.perfecbore.ch
Sales Range: $25-49.9 Million
Emp.: 10
Industrial Machinery Mfr
N.A.I.C.S.: 333248
Paerre Moser *(Mng Dir)*

Precitool-Fenwick NV **(1)**
Singel 5, 2550, Kontich, Belgium
Tel.: (32) 3 294 1600
Web Site: https://www.precitool-fenwick.be
Emp.: 5
Electronic Components Mfr
N.A.I.C.S.: 334419

Restronics Co., Inc **(1)**
11547 K Tel Dr, Minnetonka, MN 55343
Tel.: (952) 912-0004
Web Site: http://www.restronics.com
Sales Range: $25-49.9 Million
Emp.: 27
Printed Circuit Assembly Mfr
N.A.I.C.S.: 334418

Rich Sales, Inc. **(1)**
15547 N 77th St, Scottsdale, AZ 85260
Tel.: (480) 443-9255
Web Site: http://www.richsales.com
Sales Range: $25-49.9 Million
Emp.: 100
Electronic Components Mfr
N.A.I.C.S.: 334419
Andy Kella *(Pres & Principal)*

Scanditron Finland OY **(1)**
Kylvopolku 6, 00680, Helsinki, Finland
Tel.: (358) 20 752 8700
Web Site: https://www.scanditron.fi
Sales Range: $25-49.9 Million
Emp.: 15
Electronic Components Distr
N.A.I.C.S.: 423690

Smartech Electronics (Shenzhen) Co., Ltd **(1)**
Room 1105 South Block Li Jing Building, 48 Jin Tang Street Cai Wu Wei, Shenzhen, 518010, China
Tel.: (86) 75582481531
Professional Scientific & Technical Services
N.A.I.C.S.: 541990

Smartech Electronics Co., Ltd. **(1)**
Unit 1201 12/F Chevalier Commercial Centre 8 Wang Hoi Rd, Kowloon Bay, Kowloon, China (Hong Kong)
Tel.: (852) 82262265
Surface-mount Technology Equipment Mfr
N.A.I.C.S.: 334418

Smartech Enterprise Co., Ltd. **(1)**
Unit 1201 12th Floor Chevalier Comm Ctr, 8 Wang Hoi Road, Kowloon, China (Hong Kong)
Tel.: (852) 21171300
Professional Scientific & Technical Services
N.A.I.C.S.: 541990
Kenneth Koo *(Mng Dir)*

Smartech Equipment (Shenzhen) Co., Ltd. **(1)**
Rm 311 Building Zhuoyue, NO 1 Fuhhua Rd Futian Trade, 518048, Shenzhen, China
Tel.: (86) 75583484158
Professional Scientific & Technical Services
N.A.I.C.S.: 541990

FUJI CORPORATION LIMITED
1-4-23 Habu-cho, Kishiwada, 596-8588, Osaka-fu, Japan
Tel.: (81) 724378700   **JP**
Web Site: https://www.fuji-jutaku.co.jp
Year Founded: 1973
8860—(TKS)
Rev.: $795,764,680
Assets: $1,111,881,320
Liabilities: $774,744,880
Net Worth: $337,136,440
Earnings: $30,134,990
Emp.: 1,247
Fiscal Year-end: 03/31/24
Residential Development, Construction, Sales, Leasing & Property Management Services
N.A.I.C.S.: 236115
Mitsuo Imai *(Founder)*

Subsidiaries:

Fuji Amenity Service Co., Ltd. **(1)**
1-4-23 Habu-cho, Kishiwada, 596-8588, Osaka, Japan
Tel.: (81) 120737024
Web Site: https://www.fuji-amenity.com

Construction Contractor Services
N.A.I.C.S.: 236220

FUJI DIE CO., LTD.
2-17-10 Shimomaruko, Ota-ku, Tokyo, 146-0092, Japan
Tel.: (81) 337597181
Web Site: https://www.fujidie.co.jp
Year Founded: 1949
6167—(TKS)
Rev.: $110,241,580
Assets: $172,772,180
Liabilities: $36,295,510
Net Worth: $136,476,670
Earnings: $4,686,490
Emp.: 1,000
Fiscal Year-end: 03/31/24
Cemented Carbide Tools Mfr
N.A.I.C.S.: 333514
Morio Nishijima *(Chm)*

Subsidiaries:

FUJI SHAFT CO., LTD. **(1)**
110 Odakauchi, Nihonmatsu, 964-0974, Fukushima, Japan
Tel.: (81) 243232315
Web Site: https://www.fujishaft.co.jp
Emp.: 35
Steel Pipe Mfr & Distr
N.A.I.C.S.: 331210

FUJILLOY INDIA Private Limited **(1)**
3rd Floor Building No 9-A DLF Cyber City Phase-III, Gurgaon, 122002, Haryana, India
Tel.: (91) 1244545016
Cutting Tool Distr
N.A.I.C.S.: 423830

FUJILLOY MALAYSIA SDN. BHD. **(1)**
303-3-30 Krystal Point Jalan Sultan Azlan Shah, 11900, Bayan Lepas, 11900, Penang, Malaysia
Tel.: (60) 46468090
Cutting Tool Distr
N.A.I.C.S.: 423830
Tanchin Eng *(Mng Dir)*

Fuji Die Co., Ltd. - Hadano 1 & 2 Factory **(1)**
41-2 Hirasawa, Hadano, 257-0015, Kanagawa, Japan
Tel.: (81) 463820959
Web Site: https://www.fujidie.co.jp
Carbide Tool Mfr
N.A.I.C.S.: 333514

Fuji Die Co., Ltd. - Koriyama 2 Factory **(1)**
2-2-8 Machiikedai, Koriyama, 963-0215, Fukushima, Japan
Tel.: (81) 249632221
Carbide Tool Mfr
N.A.I.C.S.: 333514

Fuji Die Co., Ltd. - Moji Factory **(1)**
3-3-7 Kuzuha Moji-ku, Kitakyushu, Fukuoka, Japan
Tel.: (81) 933312136
Carbide Tool Mfr
N.A.I.C.S.: 333514

Fuji Die Co., Ltd. - Nagoya Factory **(1)**
2-106 Oneyama, Midori-ku, Nagoya, Aichi, Japan
Tel.: (81) 526225411
Carbide Tool Mfr
N.A.I.C.S.: 333514

Fuji Die Co., Ltd. - Osaka Factory **(1)**
2-18-5-101 Takezono Senriyama, Suita, Osaka, Japan
Tel.: (81) 648618092
Carbide Tool Mfr
N.A.I.C.S.: 333514

Fuji Die Trading (Shanghai) Co., **(1)**
Room 705 Block A Orient international Building No 85 Lou Shan Guan Rd, Changning District, Shanghai, 200336, China
Tel.: (86) 2162789105
Web Site: http://www.fujilloy.com.cn
Cutting Tool Distr

N.A.I.C.S.: 423830

Fujilloy Thailand Co., Ltd. **(1)**
Amata City Chonburi Industrial Estate 700/296 Moo 1, Tambol Bankao Amphur Panthong, Chon Buri, 20160, Thailand
Tel.: (66) 384653767
Web Site: https://www.fujilloy.co.th
Emp.: 88
Carbide Tool Mfr & Distr
N.A.I.C.S.: 333514

PT. FUJILLOY INDONESIA **(1)**
Jl Mitra Raya II Block F 9B Mitra Karawang Industrial Area, Karawang, 41361, West Java, Indonesia
Tel.: (62) 2678610241
Web Site: https://www.fujidie.co.jp
Die & Tool Mfr & Distr
N.A.I.C.S.: 333514
Toshikazu Tsubouchi *(Mng Dir)*

Shinwa Die Co., Ltd. **(1)**
749 Enzan-akao, Koshu, 404-0033, Yamanashi, Japan
Tel.: (81) 553334290
Carbide Tool Mfr
N.A.I.C.S.: 333514

FUJI ELECTRIC CO., LTD.
1-11-2 Osaki Gate City Osaki East Tower, Shinagawa-ku, Tokyo, 141-0032, Japan
Tel.: (81) 354357111   **JP**
Web Site:
  https://www.fujielectric.co.jp
Year Founded: 1923
6504—(NGO)
Rev.: $7,289,155,541
Assets: $8,398,900,853
Liabilities: $4,028,423,054
Net Worth: $4,370,477,798
Earnings: $542,252,904
Emp.: 28,049
Fiscal Year-end: 03/31/24
Power & Energy Systems, Industrial & Consumer Electronics, Information Processing, Water & Sewage Treatment Systems & Electronic Devices Mfr
N.A.I.C.S.: 449210
Michihiro Kitazawa *(Chm, Pres & Exec Officer)*

Subsidiaries:

Atai Fuji Electric Co., Ltd. **(1)**
No 32 Sec 2 Changxing Rd, Luzhu Dist, Taoyuan, 338020, Taiwan   **(100%)**
Tel.: (886) 3 321 3030
Web Site: https://www.ataifuji.com
Sales Range: $25-49.9 Million
Emp.: 60
Electronics Stores
N.A.I.C.S.: 449210

Chichibu Fuji Co., Ltd. **(1)**
755-1 Ogano Ogano-cho, Chichibu-gun, Chichibu, 368-0193, Saitama, Japan
Tel.: (81) 494751111
Web Site: https://www.ccf.co.jp
Emp.: 430
Control Equipment Mfr
N.A.I.C.S.: 335514

Dalian Fuji Bingshan Control Systems Co., Ltd. **(1)**
A7-104 Wisdom Park No 888 Xinan Rd, Shahekou District, Dalian, China
Tel.: (86) 41186536010
Electrical Equipment Distr
N.A.I.C.S.: 423690

Dalian Fuji Bingshan Vending Machine Co., Ltd. **(1)**
No 61 Huaihexi Road, Dalian Economy and Technological Development Zone, Dalian, Liaoning, China
Tel.: (86) 4006981666
Web Site: http://www.fujibingshan.com.cn
Vending Machine Mfr
N.A.I.C.S.: 333310

Dalian Fuji Electric Motor Co., Ltd. **(1)**
No 3-2 Northeast 3rd, Dalian Economic

Technical Development Zone, Dalian,
116600, China **(100%)**
Tel.: (86) 4118 763 6555
Web Site: http://www.fujielectric.com
N.A.I.C.S.: 449210

Fuji CAC Joint Stock Company (1)
No 18 Street No 22, An Khanh Ward Thu
Duc City, Ho Chi Minh City, Vietnam
Tel.: (84) 2837420959
Web Site: http://www.fujicac.com
Engineeering Services
N.A.I.C.S.: 541330

Fuji Electric (Asia) Co., Ltd. (1)
Rm 2015 24 The Metropolis Tower, 10 Me-
tropolis Drive Hung Hong, Kowloon, China
(Hong Kong) **(100%)**
Tel.: (852) 23118282
Web Site: http://www.fujielectric.co.jp
Sales Range: $25-49.9 Million
Emp.: 17
Marketing of Semiconductors, Power Dis-
tributors, Control Equipment & Inverters
N.A.I.C.S.: 423690
K. Ogawa *(Mng Dir)*

**Fuji Electric (Changshu) Co.,
Ltd.** (1)
No 18 Dongshan Road, Yushan High-tech
Industrial Park, Changshu, Jiangsu, China
Tel.: (86) 51252845642
Web Site: http://www.csfe.com.cn
Electromagnetic Contactor Mfr
N.A.I.C.S.: 335314

Fuji Electric (China) Co., Ltd. (1)
26th Floor Block B Global Harbor 1188
Kaixuan North Road, Putuo District, Shang-
hai, China
Tel.: (86) 2154961177
Web Site: http://www.fujielectric.com.cn
Electrical Equipment Distr
N.A.I.C.S.: 423690

**Fuji Electric (Hangzhou) Software
Co., Ltd.** (1)
18F Technology Building East Software
Park No 90 Wensan Rd, Xihu District,
Hangzhou, 310012, Zhejiang, China
Tel.: (86) 57188211661
Web Site: http://www.fujielectric.com.cn
Emp.: 119
Software Services
N.A.I.C.S.: 541511
Masanobu Ishibashi *(Chm)*

**Fuji Electric (Malaysia) Sdn.
Bhd.** (1)
Lot 4 and 5 Industrial Zone Phase 1, Kulim
Hi-Tech Park, 09090, Kulim, Kedah,
Malaysia **(100%)**
Tel.: (60) 4 403 1111
Web Site: https://www.fujielectric.com.my
Sales Range: $75-99.9 Million
Emp.: 1,500
Mfr of Magnetic Disks
N.A.I.C.S.: 334610

Fuji Electric (Shanghai) Co., Ltd. (1)
Ste E And F 12F E Bldg New Hua Lian
Mansion, 755 Huai Hai Rd, Shanghai,
200020, China **(100%)**
Tel.: (86) 2164662810
Sales Range: $50-74.9 Million
Emp.: 30
Marketing of Inverters, Switchgear & Trans-
formers
N.A.I.C.S.: 423690

Fuji Electric (Shenzhen) Co., Ltd. (1)
Tangwei High-tech Industrial Zone Fuhai
Street, Baoan District, Shenzhen, 518014,
Guangdong, China
Tel.: (86) 75527342910
Emp.: 860
Manufacture & Marketing of Photoconduc-
tive Drums
N.A.I.C.S.: 335999

Fuji Electric (Zhuhai) Co., Ltd. (1)
No 22 Hanqing Road, Pingsha Town Jinwan
District, Zhuhai, Guangdong, China
Tel.: (86) 7567267874
Web Site: http://www.fujielectric.com.cn
Industrial Electric Heating Device Mfr
N.A.I.C.S.: 333414

Fuji Electric Asia Pacific Pte. Ltd. (1)
151 Lorong Chuan 03-01/01A New Tech

Park Lobby A, Singapore, 556741, Singa-
pore
Tel.: (65) 65330014
Web Site: http://www.sg.fujielectric.com
Semiconductor Device Distr
N.A.I.C.S.: 423690

**Fuji Electric Consul Neowatt Private
Limited** (1)
119 120 120A Electrical and Electronics In-
dustrial Estate, Perungudi, Chennai, 600
096, Tamil Nadu, India
Tel.: (91) 4440004200
Web Site: http://www.india.fujielectric.com
UPS & Stabilizer Mfr
N.A.I.C.S.: 335000

Fuji Electric Corp of America (1)
50 Northfield Ave, Edison, NJ
08837 **(100%)**
Tel.: (732) 560-9410
Web Site: http://www.fujielectric.com
Sales Range: $25-49.9 Million
Emp.: 25
Provider of Business Supply Equipment
Services
N.A.I.C.S.: 334118
Phil Charatz *(Pres & CEO)*

Subsidiary (Non-US):

**Fuji Electric Brazil-Euipamentos de
Energia Ltda. (FEB)** (2)
625 Rua Conselheiro Saraiva, Sao Paulo,
Santana, Brazil **(100%)**
Tel.: (55) 11 2283 5991
Web Site: http://www.fujielectric.com
Emp.: 4
Sales of General Component Products:
Power Semiconductors, HMI, Control Equip-
ment, Electric Distribution, Photoconductors
& Instrumentation
N.A.I.C.S.: 334413
Giuseppe Privitera *(Mng Dir)*

**Fuji Electric Corporation of
America** (1)
50 Northfield Ave, Edison, NJ 08837
Tel.: (732) 560-9410
Web Site: https://americas.fujielectric.com
Sales Range: $10-24.9 Million
Emp.: 50
Marketing of Semiconductors & Power Dis-
tributors & Control Equipment & Ring Blow-
ers
N.A.I.C.S.: 423610
Yoshimi Meya *(Treas)*

Fuji Electric Dalian Co., Ltd. (1)
No 3 The Third Street of Northeast, Dalian
Economic and Technical Development
Zone, Dalian, 116600, China
Tel.: (86) 4118 762 2000
Web Site: http://www.fujielectric.co.jp
Mfr of Low-Voltage Circuit Breakers & Mo-
tors
N.A.I.C.S.: 335313

**Fuji Electric Device Technology
America, Inc.** (1)
50 Northfield Ave, Edison, NJ 08837
Tel.: (732) 560-9410
Web Site:
http://www.americas.fujielectric.com
Sales Range: $25-49.9 Million
Emp.: 45
Mfr & Marketing of Photoconductive Drums
for Copiers & Printers
N.A.I.C.S.: 333310
Phil Charatz *(CEO)*

Fuji Electric F-Tech Co., Ltd. (1)
160-1 Maesuna, Konosu, 369-0198, Sai-
tama, Japan
Tel.: (81) 485485571
Web Site: https://www.fujielectric.co.jp
Emp.: 198
Control Equipment Mfr
N.A.I.C.S.: 335314

**Fuji Electric FA Components & Sys-
tems Co., Ltd.** (1)
1-5-45 Minami, Chuo-ku, Konosu, 369-
0192, Saitama, Japan
Tel.: (81) 485481111
Web Site: https://www.fujielectric.com
Heavy Electric Machinery
N.A.I.C.S.: 335999
Masahiro Morimoto *(Pres)*

Subsidiary (Non-US):

Fuji Electric Europe GmbH (2)
Goethering 58, 63067, Offenbaoh, Germany
Tel.: (49) 69 669 0290
Web Site: https://www.fujielectric-
europe.com
Sales Range: $25-49.9 Million
Emp.: 108
Distr of Power & Control Equipment & Mar-
keting of Inverters
N.A.I.C.S.: 335999

Fuji Electric FA (Asia) Co., Ltd. (2)
Room 2015 20/F The Metropolis Tower 10
Metropolis Drive, Hunghom, Kowloon,
China (Hong Kong)
Tel.: (852) 2 311 8282
Web Site: http://www.fujielectric.com
Sales Range: $25-49.9 Million
Emp.: 20
Marketing of Inverters, Power Distributors,
Control Equipment & Semiconductors
N.A.I.C.S.: 335999

Fuji Electric FA Korea Co., Ltd. (2)
16th Fl Shinsong Bldg 25-4 Youido Dong,
Youngdungpo gu, Seoul, 150010, Korea
(South)
Tel.: (82) 27805011
Web Site: http://www.fujielectrickorea.co.kr
Sales Range: $25-49.9 Million
Emp.: 17
Materials Procurement & Marketing of Elec-
trical & Electronic Machinery & Components
N.A.I.C.S.: 335999
Insaut Kim *(Mng Dir)*

Fuji Electric FA Taiwan Co., Ltd. (2)
12F No 70 Cheng Teh North Road Sec 1,
Taipei, Taiwan
Tel.: (886) 25560716
Marketing of Power Distributors, Control
Equipment & Drive System Products in Tai-
wan
N.A.I.C.S.: 335999

Fuji Electric FA Korea Co., Ltd. (1)
16th floor Sinsong Building 25-4 Yeouido-
dong, Yeongdeungpo-gu, Seoul, 215151,
Korea (South) **(100%)**
Tel.: (82) 2 780 5011
Web Site: https://www.fujielectric.co.kr
Sales Range: $1-9.9 Million
Emp.: 25
Marketing of Semiconductors & Control
Equipment
N.A.I.C.S.: 423690
Hosoya Yuji *(CEO)*

Fuji Electric FA Service Co., Ltd. (1)
Minamitamagaki-cho 5520, Suzuka, 513-
8633, Mie, Japan
Tel.: (81) 593831859
Web Site: http://www.fujielectric.co.jp
Commercial & Industrial Machine Repair
Services
N.A.I.C.S.: 811310

**Fuji Electric Finance & Accounting
Support Co., Ltd.** (1)
Gate City Ohsaki East Tower 11-2 Osaki
1-chome, Shinagawa-ku, Tokyo, 141-0032,
Japan
Tel.: (81) 354357330
Financial Services
N.A.I.C.S.: 522390

Fuji Electric France S.A. (1)
46 rue Georges Besse-ZI du Brezet, 63039,
Clermont-Ferrand, Cedex 02,
France **(100%)**
Tel.: (33) 47 398 2698
Web Site: https://www.fujielectric.fr
Emp.: 140
N.A.I.C.S.: 449210

Fuji Electric Hong Kong Co., Ltd. (1)
Unit 1601-03 and 1605 16/F Tower 2 Grand
Century Place, 193 Prince Edward Road
West Mongkok, Kowloon, China (Hong
Kong)
Tel.: (852) 26648699
Web Site: https://www.hk.fujielectric.com
Semiconductor Device Distr
N.A.I.C.S.: 423690

Fuji Electric IT Center Co., Ltd. (1)
1-11-2 Osaki, Shinagawa-ku, Tokyo, 141-
0032, Japan

Tel.: (81) 354357300
Web Site: https://www.fujielectric.co.jp
Emp.: 290
Software Training Services
N.A.I.C.S.: 611420

**Fuji Electric IT Solutions Co.,
Ltd.** (1)
6-15-12 Sotokanda, Chiyoda-ku, Tokyo,
101-0021, Japan
Tel.: (81) 358175701
Web Site: https://www.fujielectric.co.jp
Emp.: 814
Computer & Communication Equipment
Distr
N.A.I.C.S.: 423430

Fuji Electric India Pvt. Ltd. (1)
Office No 1006 To 1009 1011 Centrum Plot
No C3, Opp Wagle Prabhag Samiti Office
MIDC Area Wagle Estate, Thane, 400 604,
Maharashtra, India
Tel.: (91) 2269024500
Web Site: https://www.india.fujielectric.com
Emp.: 130
Electric Drive Product Distr
N.A.I.C.S.: 423730

**Fuji Electric Industries Singapore Pri-
vate Ltd.** (1)
No 629 Aljunied Road 03-04 Cititech Indus-
trial Building, Singapore, 389838, Singapore
Tel.: (65) 6 742 7700
Web Site: http://www.fujielectric.com.sg
Sales Range: $25-49.9 Million
Emp.: 9
Marketing of Semiconductors & Inverters
N.A.I.C.S.: 423690

Fuji Electric Korea Co., Ltd. (1)
16F Shinsong Building 25-4 Yeouido-dong,
Yeongdeungpo-gu, Seoul, Korea (South)
Tel.: (82) 27805011
Web Site: https://www.fujielectric.co.kr
Thermal Power Services
N.A.I.C.S.: 541380

**Fuji Electric Manufacturing (Thailand)
Co., Ltd.** (1)
118/2 Moo 18 Klong Nueng, Klong Luang,
Khlong Luang, 12120, Pathumthani, Thai-
land
Tel.: (66) 21013000
Low Voltage Inverter Mfr
N.A.I.C.S.: 335999

Fuji Electric Meter Co., Ltd. (1)
2191 Horigane Karasugawa, Azumino, 399-
8211, Nagano, Japan
Tel.: (81) 263723262
Electric Meter Mfr & Distr
N.A.I.C.S.: 334515

**Fuji Electric Motor (Dalian) Co.,
Ltd.** (1)
No 3-2 Northeast 3rd, Dalian Economic and
Technical Development Zone, Dalian,
116600, China
Tel.: (86) 41187636555
Industrial Motor Mfr
N.A.I.C.S.: 335312

Fuji Electric Philippines, Inc. (1)
107 Enterprise Drive Special Export Pro-
cessing Zone II, Carmelray Industrial Park I
Canlubang, Calamba, 4131, Laguna,
Philippines **(100%)**
Tel.: (63) 28446183
Sales Range: $200-249.9 Million
Emp.: 800
Mfr of Power Semiconductors
N.A.I.C.S.: 334413

**Fuji Electric Power Semiconductor
Co., Ltd.** (1)
4-18-1 Chikuma, Matsumoto, 390-0821,
Nagano, Japan
Tel.: (81) 263277425
Web Site: https://www.fujielectric.co.jp
Emp.: 786
Semiconductor Devices Mfr
N.A.I.C.S.: 334413

**Fuji Electric Retail Sevice Co.,
Ltd.** (1)
4-5-4 Hatchobori, Chuo-ku, Tokyo, 104-
0032, Japan
Tel.: (81) 362801132
Web Site: http://www.fujielectric.co.jp
Vending Machine Repair Services

Fuji Electric Co., Ltd.—(Continued)

N.A.I.C.S.: 811310

Fuji Electric Sales Malaysia Sdn. Bhd. (1)
Unit 13A-15 Menara Q Sentral No 2A Jalan Stesen Sentral 2, Kuala Lumpur Sentral, 50470, Kuala Lumpur, Malaysia
Tel.: (60) 327809980
Web Site: http://www.my.fujielectric.com
Electrical Equipment Distr
N.A.I.C.S.: 423690

Fuji Electric Sales Philippines, Inc. (1)
Unit F 8th Floor Inoza Tower Lot 8 and 11 Block 32 40th Street, North Bonifacio BGC, Taguig, Philippines
Tel.: (63) 25418321
Web Site: http://www.ph.fujielectric.com
Electrical Equipment Distr
N.A.I.C.S.: 423690

Fuji Electric Taiwan Co., Ltd. (1)
10F No 168 Song Jiang Road, Sung Chiang Rd, Taipei, 10459, Taiwan (100%)
Tel.: (886) 22 511 1820
Web Site: http://www.fujielectric.co.jp
Sales Range: $25-49.9 Million
Emp.: 10
Semiconductor Devices, Power Distribution & Control Equipment, Sales of Control, Drive & Rotating Equipment
N.A.I.C.S.: 334413

Fuji Electric Technica Co., Ltd. (1)
5-7 Nihonbashi Odenmacho, Chuo-ku, Tokyo, 103-0011, Japan
Tel.: (81) 358478070
Electrical Equipment Distr
N.A.I.C.S.: 423610

Fuji Electric Tsugaru Semiconductor Co., Ltd. (1)
156 Nabekake, Urushikawa, Goshogawara, 037-0017, Aomori, Japan
Tel.: (81) 173355671
Web Site: https://www.fujielectric.co.jp
Semiconductor Device Mfr & Distr
N.A.I.C.S.: 334413

Fuji Electric Vietnam Co., Ltd. (1)
Room 401 4th FL CornerStone Buildding No 16 Phan Chu Trinh, Hoan Kiem, Hanoi, Vietnam
Tel.: (84) 2439351593
Web Site: http://www.vn.fujielectric.com
Electrical Equipment Distr
N.A.I.C.S.: 423690

Fuji FESTEC Co., Ltd. (1)
1 Fujimachi, Hino, 191-8502, Tokyo, Japan
Tel.: (81) 425856469
Web Site: http://www.fujielectric.co.jp
Electrical Equipment Repair Services
N.A.I.C.S.: 811210

Fuji Furmanite Co., Ltd. (1)
4-16-1 Miyauchi, Nakahara-ku, Kawasaki, 211-0051, Kanagawa, Japan
Tel.: (81) 449488833
Web Site: http://www.furmanite.co.jp
Plumbing Contract Services
N.A.I.C.S.: 238220

Fuji Gemco Private Limited (1)
14/3 Mathura Road, Faridabad, 121003, Haryana, India
Tel.: (91) 1292274831
Web Site: http://www.fujigemco.com
Drive Control System Mfr
N.A.I.C.S.: 335999

Fuji IT Co., Ltd. (1)
1 Fujicho, Hino, 191-8502, Tokyo, Japan
Tel.: (81) 428431920
Web Site: https://www.fujielectric.co.jp
Emp.: 483
IT Services
N.A.I.C.S.: 541511

Fuji N2telligence GmbH (1)
Alter Holzhafen 15, 23966, Wismar, Germany
Tel.: (49) 8417584500
Web Site: http://www.n2telligence.com
Fuel Cell Distr
N.A.I.C.S.: 423610

Fuji Office & Life Service, Co., Ltd. (1)

1-11-2 Osaki Gate City Ohsaki East Tower, Shinagawa-ku, Tokyo, 141-0032, Japan
Tel.: (81) 354357311
Web Site: https://www.fujielectric.co.jp
Emp.: 472
Insurance Services
N.A.I.C.S.: 524210

Fuji SEMEC Inc. (1)
230 J-A Bombardier Suite 1, Boucherville, J4B 8V6, QC, Canada
Tel.: (450) 641-4811
Web Site: http://www.fujisemec.com
Electromechanical System Product Mfr
N.A.I.C.S.: 335999

Fuji SMBE Electric Pte Ltd (1)
15 Senoko Avenue, Singapore, 758305, Singapore
Tel.: (65) 6756 0988
Web Site: http://www.smbelectric.com
Switchgear Mfr & Distr
N.A.I.C.S.: 335313
Lawrence Wee Hian Lee (CEO & Exec Dir)

Subsidiary (Non-US):

Bridex Australia Pty. Limited (2)
Unit 3 25 Narabang Way, Belrose, 2085, NSW, Australia
Tel.: (61) 299861711
Web Site: http://www.bridex.com.au
Sales Range: $25-49.9 Million
Emp.: 10
Switchgear Mfr & Distr
N.A.I.C.S.: 335313

Subsidiary (Domestic):

Bridex Singapore Pte Ltd. (2)
15 Senoko Ave, Singapore, 758305, Singapore
Tel.: (65) 67560833
Web Site: http://www.bridex.com.sg
Sales Range: $25-49.9 Million
Emp.: 50
Switchgear Mfr & Distr
N.A.I.C.S.: 335313
Winston Teo (Mgr-Logistic)

Subsidiary (Non-US):

Brighten Switchboard Builders (M) Sdn Bhd (2)
Plo 131 133 134 Jalan Cyber 5 Kawasan Perindustrian Senai 3, Senai, 81400, Johor, Malaysia
Tel.: (60) 7 598 3818
Sales Range: $50-74.9 Million
Electronic Switch Gear Mfr
N.A.I.C.S.: 335313
Javy Kam Choon Wah (Dir)

Subsidiary (Domestic):

Fuji SMBE Industries Pte Ltd (2)
15 Senoko Avenue, Singapore, 758305, Singapore
Tel.: (65) 6 756 0988
Web Site: http://www.smbelectric.com
Electronic Switch Gear Mfr
N.A.I.C.S.: 335313
Yoon Peng Tang (Mng Dir)

Fuji SMBE Systems Pte Ltd (2)
15 Senoko Avenue, Singapore, 758305, Singapore
Tel.: (65) 6 756 0988
Web Site: http://www.smbelectric.com
Electronic Switch Gear Mfr
N.A.I.C.S.: 335313

Fuji SMBE Technology Pte Ltd (2)
15 Senoko Avenue, Singapore, 758305, Singapore
Tel.: (65) 6 756 0988
Web Site: http://www.smbelectric.com
Electronic Switch Gear Mfr
N.A.I.C.S.: 335313
Kin Ming Ng (Mng Dir)

Subsidiary (Non-US):

SMB Brighten Switchboard Engineering Sdn. Bhd. (2)
23-1 Jalan 109E, Desa Business Park, Jalan Desa Taman Desa, 58100, Kuala Lumpur, Malaysia
Tel.: (60) 379842175
Web Site: http://www.smbunited.com

Sales Range: $25-49.9 Million
Emp.: 10
Switchgear Mfr & Distr
N.A.I.C.S.: 335313

SMB Harwal Electric Pty. Ltd. (2)
Unit D3 Lane Cove Business Park, 16 Mars Road, Lane Cove, 2066, NSW, Australia
Tel.: (61) 294207777
Web Site: http://www.smbharwal.com.au
Sales Range: $25-49.9 Million
Emp.: 30
Switchgear Mfr & Distr
N.A.I.C.S.: 335313

SMB Macquarie Electric Pty Ltd (2)
Unit 3 171-175 Newton Road, Wetherill Park, 2164, NSW, Australia (100%)
Tel.: (61) 2 9733 0600
Web Site: http://www.smbmacquarie.com.au
Low Voltage Electrical Switchboards Mfr
N.A.I.C.S.: 335313
Peter Silsby (Gen Mgr)

SMB Switchgear & Engineering Sdn Bhd (2)
134 Jalan Cyber 5, 81400, Johor, Malaysia
Tel.: (60) 75983818
Sales Range: $25-49.9 Million
Emp.: 250
Switchgear Mfr & Distr
N.A.I.C.S.: 335313
Javy Kam (Gen Mgr)

Fuji SMBE Pte. Ltd. (1)
15 Senoko Avenue, Singapore, 758305, Singapore
Tel.: (65) 67560988
Web Site: http://smbe.fujielectric.com
Switchgear & Switchboard Apparatus Mfr
N.A.I.C.S.: 335313
Albert Chow Peng Meng (CMO)

Fuji Tusco Co., Ltd. (1)
612-612/1 1888 Moo 4 Bangpoo Industrial Estate Soi 8 9A Pattana 1 Rd, T Praksa, Amphur Muang, 10280, Samutprakarn, Thailand
Tel.: (66) 23240100
Web Site: http://www.ftu.fujielectric.com
Emp.: 500
Transformer Mfr
N.A.I.C.S.: 335311

Fuji-Haya Electric Corp. of the Philippines (1)
Makati liaison 2nd Flr Matrinco Building 2178 Pasong Tamo St, Makati, 1201, Metro Manila, Philippines (100%)
Tel.: (63) 892 8886
Web Site: https://fujihayaelectric.com
Sales Range: $25-49.9 Million
Emp.: 65
Mfr of Switchboards
N.A.I.C.S.: 335313
Hikian Yu (Mng Dir)

Hakko Electronics Co., Ltd. (1)
238 Kamikashiwanocho, Hakusan, 924-0035, Ishikawa, Japan
Tel.: (81) 762748550
Web Site: https://www.hakko-elec.co.jp
Emp.: 161
Electronic Operation Board Mfr
N.A.I.C.S.: 334111

Hoei Denki Co., Ltd. (1)
2-6-60 Niitaka, Yodogawa-ku, Osaka, 532-0033, Japan
Tel.: (81) 663941111
Web Site: https://www.hoei-elec.co.jp
Emp.: 238
Electrical Apparatus Distr
N.A.I.C.S.: 423610

Hoei Electronics (S) Private Ltd. (1)
No1 Tampines North Drive 1 08-61 T-Space, Singapore, 528559, Singapore (60%)
Tel.: (65) 62853238
Web Site: http://www.hes.com.sg
Sales Range: $25-49.9 Million
Emp.: 25
Marketing of Semiconductors
N.A.I.C.S.: 423690

Hoei Hong Kong Co., Ltd. (1)
Unit 310-311 Mirror Tower 61 Mody Rd, Tsim Sha Tsui East, Kowloon, China (Hong Kong)

Tel.: (852) 23698186
Electrical Equipment Distr
N.A.I.C.S.: 423690

Hoei Plastics Co., Ltd. (1)
1-27 Fujicho, Yokkaichi, 510-0013, Mie, Japan
Tel.: (81) 593301572
Web Site: https://www.fujielectric.co.jp
Emp.: 100
Injection Molding Mfr
N.A.I.C.S.: 333511

Hokkaido Fuji Electric Co., Ltd. (1)
7-12-9 Odori Higashi, Chuo-ku, Sapporo, 060-0041, Hokkaido, Japan
Tel.: (81) 112215511
Web Site: https://www.hfd.co.jp
Emp.: 119
Electrical Apparatus Distr
N.A.I.C.S.: 423610

Hong Kong Fujidenki Co., Ltd. (1)
Unit 1601-03 1605 16/F Tower 2 Grand Century Place, 193 Prince Edward Road West Mongkok, Kowloon, NT, China (Hong Kong) (100%)
Tel.: (852) 2 664 8699
Web Site: https://www.hk.fujielectric.com
Sales Range: $25-49.9 Million
Emp.: 50
Photoconductive Drums for Copiers & Printers Mfr
N.A.I.C.S.: 334413

Korea FA Systems Co., Ltd. (1)
Suckcheon Bldg 3F 570 Samseong-ro, Gangnam-gu, Seoul, 06163, Korea (South)
Tel.: (82) 22 189 3700
Web Site: https://www.kfa.co.kr
Electronics Stores
N.A.I.C.S.: 449210

Mahajak International Electric Co., Ltd. (1)
Mahajak Bldg 4th Fl 46 Soi 3, Bangkok, 10110, Thailand (100%)
Tel.: (66) 22532350
Web Site: http://www.Mahajak.com
Sales Range: $50-74.9 Million
Emp.: 250
N.A.I.C.S.: 449210
Poantibul Canphanadsaytsoon (Mng Dir)

MetaWater Service Co., Ltd. (1)
1-chome JR Kanda Manseibashi Kanda Sudacho, Chiyoda-ku, Tokyo, 101-0041, Japan
Tel.: (81) 368537265
Web Site: http://www.metawaterservice.co.jp
Water Supply Maintenance & Repair Services
N.A.I.C.S.: 221310

Mie Fuji Co., Ltd. (1)
1-27 Fujicho, Yokkaichi, 510-8631, Mie, Japan
Tel.: (81) 593301616
Web Site: http://www.fujielectric.co.jp
Vending Machine Mfr
N.A.I.C.S.: 333310

P.T. Fuji Dharma Electric (1)
Jl Rawagelam I/10 Kawasan Industri, Pulogadung, Jakarta, 13930, Timur, Indonesia (100%)
Tel.: (62) 214600143
Web Site: https://www.fujidharma.co.id
Sales Range: $25-49.9 Million
Emp.: 300
Watt-Hour Meters Mfr
N.A.I.C.S.: 334514

PT. Fuji Metec Semarang (1)
Tanjung Emas Export Processing Zone, JL Coaster No 8 Block B 12A-16, Semarang, 50174, Central Java, Indonesia
Tel.: (62) 24 3520435
Web Site: http://www.fms.fujielectric.com
Consignment Mfr & Vending Machines Operations
N.A.I.C.S.: 445132

Reliable Turbine Services LLC (1)
858 Acid Mine Rd, Sullivan, MO 63080
Peripheral Equipment Repair & Maintenance Services
N.A.I.C.S.: 811210

Shanghai Electric Fuji Electric Power Technology (Wuxi) Co., Ltd. (1)

Lot No 28 2 Area 1 Xi Mei Road, New District, Wuxi, Jiangsu, China
Tel.: (86) 51088159229
Electric Drive Product Mfr
N.A.I.C.S.: 335999

Shanghai Fuji Electric Switchgear Co., Ltd. **(1)**
No 2 Huhang Road Nanqiao, Fengxian, Shanghai, 201400, China
Tel.: (86) 2157185740
Web Site: http://www.fujielectric.com.sg
Switchgear Mfr
N.A.I.C.S.: 335313

Shanghai Fuji Electric Transformer Co., Ltd. **(1)**
No 2 Huhang Rd, Nanqiao Fengxian, 2001400, Shanghai, China **(100%)**
Tel.: (86) 2157185747
Web Site: http://www.fujielectric.co.jp
Sales Range: $25-49.9 Million
Emp.: 100
Mfr of Cast-Resin Dry-Type Powers Transformers
N.A.I.C.S.: 335311

Shanghai General Fuji Refrigeration Equipment Co., Ltd. **(1)**
688 Xin Qu Rd, Qing Pu Industrial Park, Shanghai, China
Tel.: (86) 2169211088
Web Site: http://www.fujielectric.co.jp
Sales Range: $50-74.9 Million
Emp.: 160
Mfr of Refrigerated Showcases
N.A.I.C.S.: 333415

Shinshu Fuji Electric Co., Ltd. **(1)**
2535 Mitakedo, Ueda, Nagano, Japan
Tel.: (81) 268427111
Web Site: http://www.fujielectric.co.jp
Currency Handling Equipment Mfr
N.A.I.C.S.: 333310

Suzhou Lanlian-Fuji Instruments Co., Ltd. **(1)**
Songlin Economic & Technical, Development Zone, Wujiang, 215200, Jiangsu, China
Tel.: (86) 5123451594
Web Site: http://www.fujielectric.co.jp
N.A.I.C.S.: 449210

Wuxi Fuji Electric FA Co., Ltd. **(1)**
Lot No 28 Xi Mei Road, New District, Wuxi, 214028, Jiangsu, China
Tel.: (86) 51088152088
Low Voltage Inverter Mfr & Distr
N.A.I.C.S.: 335999

FUJI ELECTRIC INDUSTRY CO., LTD.
585 Higashihachiman-cho Oike-dori Tominokoji Nishi-iru, Nakagyo-ku, Kyoto, 604-0954, Japan
Tel.: (81) 752217978
Web Site: https://www.fujidk.co.jp
Year Founded: 1958
6654—(TKS)
Rev.: $36,026,879
Assets: $106,520,569
Liabilities: $6,944,916
Net Worth: $99,575,653
Earnings: $1,851,232
Emp.: 292
Fiscal Year-end: 01/31/22
Electric Equipment Mfr & Sales
N.A.I.C.S.: 334419
Yagi Satoshi *(Pres)*

Subsidiaries:

FUJI ELECTRIC INDUSTRY CO., LTD. - Kusatsu Factory **(1)**
3-4-1 Nomura, Kusatsu, 525-8521, Shiga, Japan
Tel.: (81) 775621215
Web Site: http://www.fujidk.co.jp
Sales Range: $50-74.9 Million
Electronic Switches & Devices Mfr
N.A.I.C.S.: 334419

FUJI ELECTRIC INDUSTRY CO., LTD. - Shin-Asahi Factory **(1)**
905-1 Aza-Nishigawara Shin-Asahi-cho, Ota, Takashima, 520-1512, Shiga, Japan

Tel.: (81) 740256338
Web Site: http://www.fujidk.co.jp
Electronic Switches & Devices Mfr
N.A.I.C.S.: 334419

FUJI FURUKAWA ENGINEERING & CONSTRUCTION CO., LTD.
Solid Square West Wing 580 Horikawa-cho, Saiwai-ku, Kawasaki, 212-0013, Kanagawa, Japan
Tel.: (81) 445484500
Web Site: https://www.ffec.co.jp
Year Founded: 1938
1775—(TKS)
Rev.: $685,119,890
Assets: $535,469,490
Liabilities: $256,712,570
Net Worth: $278,756,920
Earnings: $35,779,930
Emp.: 1,544
Fiscal Year-end: 03/31/24
Construction Engineering Services
N.A.I.C.S.: 541330
Takashi Kusaka *(Pres & CEO)*

Subsidiaries:

FFJMP Sdn. Bhd. **(1)**
E-10-12 Blok E Pusat Perdagangan Phileo Damansara 1 No 9 Jalan 16/11, Off Jalan Damansara, 46350, Petaling Jaya, Selangor, Malaysia
Tel.: (60) 37 612 5138
Web Site: https://www.jmpower.my
Electrical & Air Conditioning Construction Services
N.A.I.C.S.: 238220
Hideaki Yayoi *(Mng Dir)*

Fuji Furukawa E&C (Cambodia) Co. Ltd. **(1)**
TK Royal One Unit 2K No155 Confederation De La Russie Blvd Toul Kork, Boulevard Sangkat Tuk Thlar Khan Sensok, Phnom Penh, Cambodia
Tel.: (855) 23866369
Web Site: https://www.ffec-global.com
Construction Engineering Services
N.A.I.C.S.: 541330

Fuji Furukawa E&C (Malaysia) Sdn. Bhd. **(1)**
Tel.: (60) 392867422
Web Site: http://www.ffec.com.my
Engineering Services
N.A.I.C.S.: 541330

Fuji Furukawa E&C (Myanmar) Co., Ltd. **(1)**
Room No 12A Pansodan Business Tower No 123/133, Corner of Anawrahta Rd & Pansodan Rd Kyauktada Township, Yangon, Myanmar
Tel.: (95) 9420118547
Web Site: https://www.ffec-global.com
Construction Engineering Services
N.A.I.C.S.: 541330

Fuji Furukawa E&C (Vietnam) Co., Ltd. **(1)**
2nd Floor Sky City Tower 88 Lang Ha St, Lang Ha Ward Dong Da Dist, Hanoi, Vietnam
Tel.: (84) 2437555067
Web Site: https://www.ffec-global.com
Construction Engineering Services
N.A.I.C.S.: 541330

PT. Fuji Furukawa E&C Indonesia **(1)**
SUCACO Building 4th floor Jl Kebon Sirih No 71, Jakarta, 10340, Indonesia
Tel.: (62) 213100509
Web Site: https://www.ffec-global.com
Construction Engineering Services
N.A.I.C.S.: 541330

FUJI GLASS CO., LTD.
2-15-9 Bunka, Sumida-Ku, Tokyo, 131-0044, Japan
Tel.: (81) 33 617 5111
Web Site: http://www.silicox.co.jp
Year Founded: 1942

5212—(JAS)
Rev.: $25,129,280
Assets: $40,278,480
Liabilities: $11,606,320
Net Worth: $28,672,160
Earnings: $619,520
Fiscal Year-end: 03/31/22
Glass Container Mfr
N.A.I.C.S.: 327213
Shinichi Oguma *(Pres)*

FUJI KYUKO CO., LTD.
5-2-1 Shin-nishihara, Fujiyoshida, Yamanashi, Japan
Tel.: (81) 555227111
Web Site: https://www.fujikyu.co.jp
Year Founded: 1926
9010—(TKS)
Rev.: $335,133,610
Assets: $664,549,570
Liabilities: $450,709,460
Net Worth: $213,840,110
Earnings: $30,214,310
Emp.: 3,495
Fiscal Year-end: 03/31/24
Leisure Services
N.A.I.C.S.: 713110
Koichiro Horiuchi *(Pres)*

Subsidiaries:

PICA Co., Ltd. **(1)**
Nagatanaka 4-4-10, Higashiosaka, 577-0013, Osaka, Japan
Tel.: (81) 667476856
Web Site: https://www.pica-corp.jp
Steel Products Mfr
N.A.I.C.S.: 331210

FUJI LATEX CO., LTD.
3-19-1 Kanda Nishiki-cho, Chiyoda-ku, Tokyo, 101-0054, Japan
Tel.: (81) 332592543
Web Site: https://www.fujilatex.co.jp
Year Founded: 1949
5199—(TKS)
Rev.: $49,627,880
Assets: $74,864,860
Liabilities: $49,370,090
Net Worth: $25,494,770
Earnings: $1,910,290
Emp.: 272
Fiscal Year-end: 03/31/24
Rubber Products Mfr
N.A.I.C.S.: 326291
Kenji Ito *(Pres)*

Subsidiaries:

FUJI LATEX SHANGHAI CO., LTD. **(1)**
No 360 Changshou Road, Putuo District, Shanghai, 200060, China
Tel.: (86) 2132201596
Industrial Product Mfr & Distr
N.A.I.C.S.: 332322

FUJI MEDIA HOLDINGS, INC.
2-4-8 Daiba, Minato-ku, Tokyo, 137-8088, Japan
Tel.: (81) 335708000   JP
Web Site:
https://www.fujimediahd.co.jp
Year Founded: 1957
4676—(TKS)
Rev.: $3,744,188,230
Assets: $9,576,786,130
Liabilities: $3,828,545,050
Net Worth: $5,748,241,080
Earnings: $245,112,020
Emp.: 6,787
Fiscal Year-end: 03/31/24
Holding Company; Television, Production, Video, Music & Advertising
N.A.I.C.S.: 551112
Tomoyuki Minagawa *(Exec Mng Dir, Exec Mng Dir & Exec VP)*

Subsidiaries:

Basis Ltd. **(1)**
5-6-10 Tsukiji Hama Rikyu Parkside Place, Chuo-ku, Tokyo, 104-0045, Japan
Tel.: (81) 335474890
Web Site: https://www.basis-net.co.jp
Emp.: 126
Television Network Broadcasting Services
N.A.I.C.S.: 516120
Masayuki Ishii *(Dir)*

Dinos Cecile Co., Ltd. **(1)**
Nakano Sakagami Central Building 2-46-2 Honcho, Nakano-ku, Tokyo, 164-0012, Japan **(100%)**
Tel.: (81) 353531111
Web Site: http://www.dinos-cecile.co.jp
Sales Range: $5-14.9 Billion
Emp.: 1,189
Mail Order Distr
N.A.I.C.S.: 425120
Junichi Ishikawa *(Pres)*

Subsidiary (Domestic):

Dinex, Inc. **(2)**
2-46-2 Honcho Nakano Sakaue Ctr Bldg, Nakano-ku, Tokyo, 164-0012, Japan
Tel.: (81) 353531139
Mail Orders Distr
N.A.I.C.S.: 334512

FCG Research Institute, Inc. **(1)**
DiverCity Tokyo Office Tower 6F 1-1-20 Aomi, Koto-ku, Tokyo, 135-0064, Japan
Tel.: (81) 368918500
Web Site: http://www.fcg-r.co.jp
Sales Range: $25-49.9 Million
Emp.: 40
Information Research Development Services
N.A.I.C.S.: 541715
Masami Obitsu *(Pres & CEO)*

Fuji Art, Inc. **(1)**
17th floor DiverCity Tokyo Office Tower 1-1-20 Aomi, Koto-ku, Tokyo, 135-0064, Japan
Tel.: (81) 355201881
Web Site: https://www.fujiart.co.jp
Emp.: 162
Architectural Design Services
N.A.I.C.S.: 541310

Fuji Career Design Inc. **(1)**
10th floor X-PRESS Yurakucho 2-2-1 Yurakucho, Chiyoda-ku, Tokyo, 100-0006, Japan
Tel.: (81) 362814850
Web Site: https://www.fuji-cd.co.jp
Television Broadcasting Services
N.A.I.C.S.: 516120

Fuji Creative Corporation **(1)**
Diver City Tokyo Office Tower 18F 1-1-20 Aomi, Koto-ku, Tokyo, 135-0064, Japan
Tel.: (81) 368651188
Graphic Design Services
N.A.I.C.S.: 541430

Fuji Lighting and Technology, Inc. **(1)**
1-15-1 Kaigan, Minato-ku, Tokyo, Japan
Tel.: (81) 334321188
Web Site: http://www.flt-web.co.jp
Television Lighting Systems Mfr
N.A.I.C.S.: 335139

Fuji Media Technology, Inc. **(1)**
17F DiverCity Tokyo Office Tower 1-1-20 Aomi, Koto-ku, Tokyo, 135-0064, Japan
Tel.: (81) 355000900
Web Site: http://www.fuji-mt.co.jp
Emp.: 269
Television Broadcasting Services
N.A.I.C.S.: 516120

Fuji Satellite Broadcasting, Inc. **(1)**
22F Fuji Television Head Office Building Media Tower 2-4-8 Daiba, Minato-ku, Tokyo, 137-8088, Japan
Tel.: (81) 355001485
Web Site: https://www.bsfuji.tv
Emp.: 82
Television Broadcasting Services
N.A.I.C.S.: 516120

Fuji Television Bangkok Bureau **(1)**
Room no 1101 A 159/17 Serm-Mit Tower Sukhumvit 21 Rd, North Klongtoey Wat-

Fuji Media Holdings, Inc.—(Continued)

tana, Bangkok, 10110, Thailand **(100%)**
Tel.: (66) 22585023
Web Site: http://www.fujitv.com
Sales Range: $25-49.9 Million
Emp.: 10
Television Broadcasting
N.A.I.C.S.: 516120

Fuji Television Beijing Bureau **(1)**
6-2-41 Jianguomen Apt, Chaoyang Dist,
Beijing, 100600, China
Tel.: (86) 1065324840
Web Site: http://www.fujitv.co.jp
Television Broadcasting
N.A.I.C.S.: 516120

**Fuji Television Moscow Bureau/ FNN
Moscow Bureau** **(1)**
UL Bolshaya Dorogomilovskaya d 14 kv
10-11, 121059, Moscow, Russia **(100%)**
Tel.: (7) 4992437795
Web Site: http://www.fujitv.co.jp
Sales Range: $25-49.9 Million
Emp.: 12
Television Broadcasting
N.A.I.C.S.: 516120

Fuji Television Network, Inc. **(1)**
2-4-8 Daiba, Minato-ku, Tokyo, 137-8088,
Japan
Tel.: (81) 355008888
Web Site: https://www.fujitv.com
Emp.: 1,166
Television Broadcasting Services
N.A.I.C.S.: 516120
Masaki Miyauchi *(Chm)*

Fujimic, Inc. **(1)**
DiverCity Tokyo Office Tower 19F 1-1-20
Aomi, Koto-ku, Tokyo, 135-0064, Japan
Tel.: (81) 355201500
Web Site: https://www.fujimic.com
Emp.: 222
Data Processing Services
N.A.I.C.S.: 518210

Fujipacific Music Inc **(1)**
3-3-5 Kita Aoyama, Minato-ku, Tokyo, 107-
0061, Japan
Tel.: (81) 337968603
Web Site: http://www.fujipacific.co.jp
Sales Range: $25-49.9 Million
Emp.: 100
Music Publishing Services
N.A.I.C.S.: 512230
Toru Uehara *(Pres)*

Fujisankei Agency Co., Ltd. **(1)**
Shin-Tokyo Building 234 3-3-1 Marunouchi,
Chiyoda-ku, Tokyo, 100-0005, Japan
Tel.: (81) 332875505
Web Site: https://www.fs-agency.co.jp
Emp.: 10
Insurance Agency Services
N.A.I.C.S.: 524298

**Fujisankei Communications Interna-
tional, Inc.** **(1)**
150 E 52nd St 34th Fl, New York, NY
10022
Tel.: (212) 753-8100
Web Site: https://www.fujisankei.com
Sales Range: $25-49.9 Million
Emp.: 78
Television Network Broadcasting Services
N.A.I.C.S.: 516120
Makoto Wakamatsu *(Pres)*

Subsidiary (Domestic):

Fuji Entertainment America, Inc **(2)**
21241 S Western Ave Ste 200, Torrance,
CA 90501
Tel.: (310) 320-2700
Compact Disc Whslr
N.A.I.C.S.: 423990

Branch (Non-US):

**Fujisankei Communications Interna-
tional, Inc. - London Office** **(2)**
2nd Floor 1 Portland Place, London, W1B
1PN, United Kingdom
Tel.: (44) 2075803388
Web Site: http://www.fujisankeilondon.co.uk
Sales Range: $25-49.9 Million
Emp.: 14
Online Shopping Services

N.A.I.C.S.: 516120

Branch (Domestic):

**Fujisankei Communications Interna-
tional, Inc. - Los Angeles** **(2)**
10100 Santa Monica Blvd Ste 460, Los An-
geles, CA 90067-3101
Tel.: (310) 553-5828
Web Site: http://www.fujisankei.com
Sales Range: $25-49.9 Million
Emp.: 10
News Production Services
N.A.I.C.S.: 541618

Fujisankei Personnel Inc. **(1)**
1-7-1 Yurakucho Yurakucho Denki Bldg Mi-
namikan 18 F, Chiyoda-ku, Tokyo, 100-
0006, Japan
Tel.: (81) 332400888
Web Site: http://www.fs-jinzai.co.jp
Sales Range: $25-49.9 Million
Emp.: 40
Television Network Broadcasting Services
N.A.I.C.S.: 516120
Shoichiro Ishimaru *(Mng Dir)*

Fusosha Publishing Inc. **(1)**
10th floor Hamamatsucho Building 1-1-1
Shibaura, Minato-ku, Tokyo, 105-8070, Ja-
pan
Tel.: (81) 120887560
Web Site: https://www.fusosha.co.jp
Emp.: 167
Magazine Publishing Services
N.A.I.C.S.: 513120

Happo Television, Inc. **(1)**
17F DiverCity Tokyo Office Tower 1-1-20
Aomi, Koto-ku, Tokyo, 135-0064, Japan
Tel.: (81) 355000900
Web Site: http://www.happo-tv.co.jp
Sales Range: $50-74.9 Million
Emp.: 269
Television Network Broadcasting Services
N.A.I.C.S.: 516120

Kansai Telecasting Corporation **(1)**
2-1-7 Ogimachi, Kita-ku, Osaka, 530-8408,
Japan **(100%)**
Tel.: (81) 663148888
Web Site: https://www.ktv.jp
Sales Range: $200-249.9 Million
Emp.: 563
Television Network
N.A.I.C.S.: 516120
Sumio Fukui *(Pres)*

Kyodo Edit, Inc. **(1)**
16th floor DiverCity Tokyo Office Tower 1-20
Aomi, Koto-ku, Tokyo, 135-0064, Japan
Tel.: (81) 355005980
Web Site: https://www.kyodo-edit.co.jp
Emp.: 188
Television Network Broadcasting Services
N.A.I.C.S.: 516120

Kyodo Television,Ltd. **(1)**
11F /12F Hamarikyu Parkside Place 5-6-10
Tsukiji, Chuo-ku, Tokyo, 104-0045, Japan
Tel.: (81) 335474800
Web Site: https://www.kyodo-tv.co.jp
Emp.: 141
Television Network Broadcasting Services
N.A.I.C.S.: 516120

Nextep Tv Workshop Co., Ltd. **(1)**
16th floor Diver City Tokyo Office Tower
1-1-20 Aomi, Koto-ku, Tokyo, 135-0064,
Japan
Tel.: (81) 368528800
Web Site: https://www.nxtp.jp
Emp.: 127
Television Broadcasting Services
N.A.I.C.S.: 516120

Nippon Broadcasting Project Inc. **(1)**
3-6 Kioicho Kioicho Park Building 1 F,
Chiyoda-ku, Tokyo, 102-8569, Kioi-cho,
Japan
Tel.: (81) 332658261
Web Site: http://www.jolf-p.co.jp
Sales Range: $50-74.9 Million
Emp.: 137
Radio Broadcasting Services
N.A.I.C.S.: 516210

Pony Canyon Inc. **(1)**
1-5-17 Roppongi, Minato-ku, Tokyo, 106-
8487, Japan
Tel.: (81) 362309700

Web Site: https://www.ponycanyon.co.jp
Emp.: 450
Music & Game Publisher
N.A.I.C.S.: 512230
Shingo Inoue *(VP)*

Subsidiary (Domestic):

Pony Canyon Music Inc. **(2)**
2-5-10 Toranomon, Minato-ku, 105-0001,
Tokyo, Japan
Tel.: (81) 3 3507 5551
Web Site: http://www.pcmusic.jp
Music & Artists Services
N.A.I.C.S.: 711130

Pony Canyon Planning Inc. **(1)**
Izumi Garden ANNEX 1-5-17 Roppongi,
Minato-ku, Tokyo, 106-8487, Japan
Tel.: (81) 364530585
Web Site: https://www.pcpinc.jp
Movie & Entertainment Production Services
N.A.I.C.S.: 512110

Quaras Inc. **(1)**
ThinkPark Tower 7F Osaki 2-1-1,
Shinagawa-ku, Tokyo, 141-6007, Japan
Tel.: (81) 354875001
Web Site: https://quaras.co.jp
Sales Range: $300-349.9 Million
Emp.: 347
Business Communications Services
N.A.I.C.S.: 561499

**Sankei Building Asset Management
Co., Ltd.** **(1)**
Tel.: (81) 355421316
Web Site: http://www.sankei-am.co.jp
Investment Management Service
N.A.I.C.S.: 523940

**Sankei Building Well Care Co.,
Ltd.** **(1)**
Tel.: (81) 120114870
Web Site: http://www.sankeiwellcare.com
Nursing Care Services
N.A.I.C.S.: 623110

Sankei Kaikan Co., Ltd. **(1)**
Tel.: (81) 355773811
Web Site: https://www.sankeikaikan.co.jp
Emp.: 95
Catering Services
N.A.I.C.S.: 722310

Satellite Service Co., Ltd. **(1)**
Inside Fuji Television Head Office Building
2-4-8 Daiba, Minato-ku, Tokyo, 137-8088,
Japan
Tel.: (81) 355008236
Web Site: https://www.satellite-service.co.jp
Emp.: 10
Television Network Broadcasting Services
N.A.I.C.S.: 516120
Kenji Shimizu *(Auditor)*

Sendai Television Inc. **(1)**
5-8-33 Uesugi, Aoba-ku, Sendai, 980-0011,
Miyagi, Japan
Tel.: (81) 222671213
Web Site: https://www.ox-tv.co.jp
Emp.: 122
Television Broadcasting Services
N.A.I.C.S.: 516120
Koji Inaki *(CEO)*

Shizuoka Telecasting Co., Ltd **(1)**
18-65 Kurihara, Suruga-ku, Shizuoka, 422-
8525, Japan **(100%)**
Tel.: (81) 542616111
Web Site: http://www.sut-tv.com
Sales Range: $50-74.9 Million
Emp.: 170
Television Programming
N.A.I.C.S.: 516120

**The Sankei Bldg Techno Co.,
Ltd.** **(1)**
2F Kandabashi Park Building 1-19-1 Kanda
Nishikicho, Chiyoda-ku, Tokyo, 101-0054,
Japan
Tel.: (81) 355773001
Web Site: https://www.sankeibt.com
Emp.: 58
Architectural Design Services
N.A.I.C.S.: 541310
Masuo Takei *(Pres & CEO)*

The Sankei Building Co., Ltd. **(1)**
1-7-2 Otemachi, Chiyoda-ku, Tokyo, 100-
0004, Japan

Tel.: (81) 355421300
Web Site: https://www.sankeibldg.co.jp
Emp.: 221
Real Estate Agency Services
N.A.I.C.S.: 531210
Kazunobu Iijima *(Pres & CEO)*

**The Sankei Building Management
Co., Ltd.** **(1)**
12th floor Hibiya Central Building 1-2-9
Nishi-Shinbashi, Minato-ku, Tokyo, 105-
0003, Japan
Tel.: (81) 355118120
Web Site: https://www.sankei-building-
management.jp
Emp.: 217
Building Management Services
N.A.I.C.S.: 561790
Masayuki Okamoto *(Pres & CEO)*

**Tokai Television Broadcasting Co.,
Ltd.** **(1)**
1-14-27 Higashizakura, Higashi-ku, Nagoya,
461-8501, Aichi, Japan **(100%)**
Tel.: (81) 529512511
Web Site: https://www.tokai-tv.com
Emp.: 351
Television Broadcasting
N.A.I.C.S.: 516120

VASC Co., Ltd. **(1)**
NBF Commodio Shiodome 3F 2-14-1 Hi-
gashi Shimbashi, Minato-ku, Tokyo, 105-
0021, Japan
Tel.: (81) 366350288
Web Site: http://www.vasc.co.jp
Television Program Production Services
N.A.I.C.S.: 512199

Van Eight Productions, Inc. **(1)**
16F Divercity Tokyo Office Tower 1-20
Aomi, Koto-ku, Tokyo, 135-0064, Japan
Tel.: (81) 367388810
Web Site: https://www.van8.co.jp
Emp.: 160
Television Broadcasting Services
N.A.I.C.S.: 516120

FUJI OFFSET PLATES MANU-
FACTURING LTD
No 2 Jalan Rajah 06-26/28 Golden
Wall Flatted Factory, Singapore,
329134, Singapore
Tel.: (65) 62659111
Web Site: https://www.fopgroup.com
Year Founded: 1982
508—(CAT)
Rev.: $2,482,012
Assets: $25,811,558
Liabilities: $1,078,543
Net Worth: $24,733,015
Earnings: $707,415
Emp.: 83
Fiscal Year-end: 12/31/23
Aluminium Product Distr
N.A.I.C.S.: 331315
David Teo Kee Bock *(Founder &
Chm)*

Subsidiaries:

Fuji Roto Gravure Sdn. Bhd. **(1)**
Plo 158 Jalan Angkasa Mas 6 Kawasan
Perindustrian Tebrau II, 81100, Johor
Bahru, Johor, Malaysia
Tel.: (60) 73519111
Printing Machinery Equipment Mfr
N.A.I.C.S.: 333248
Nurul Nadiah Mohd Fauzi *(Officer-
Environmental, Health & Safety)*

FUJI OIL COMPANY, LTD.
Tennozu Parkside Building 5-8 Hi-
gashishinagawa 2-chome,
Shinakawa-ku, Tokyo, 140-0002, Ja-
pan
Tel.: (81) 354627761
Web Site: https://www.foc.co.jp
Year Founded: 2003
5017—(TKS)
Rev.: $4,783,855,300
Assets: $2,577,635,600
Liabilities: $2,006,862,100
Net Worth: $570,773,500

Earnings: $102,560,760
Emp.: 675
Fiscal Year-end: 03/31/24
Petroleum Products Import, Production & Sales
N.A.I.C.S.: 211120
Atsuo Watanabe *(Exec Officer)*

Subsidiaries:

Arabian Oil Company, Ltd.　**(1)**
8 1 Akashityo, Chuo Ku, Tokyo, 104-6591, Japan　**(100%)**
Tel.: (81) 335470226
Sales Range: $100-124.9 Million
Emp.: 140
Producer of Oil & Gas
N.A.I.C.S.: 211120

Subsidiary (Domestic):

AOC Egypt Petroleum Company, Ltd　**(2)**
10th Fl Tennozu Parkside Bldg 5-8 Higashi-ishinagawa 2 Chome, Shinagawa-ku, Tokyo, 140-0002, Japan
Tel.: (81) 354635010
Web Site: http://www.aochd.co.jp
Sales Range: $50-74.9 Million
Emp.: 70
Oil & Gas Exploration Services
N.A.I.C.S.: 213112

Blommer Chocolate Manufacturing (Shanghai) Company Ltd.　**(1)**
No 77 Maoye Road, Jinshan Industrial Zone, Shanghai, 201506, China
Tel.: (86) 2167225566
Confectionery Goods Mfr & Distr
N.A.I.C.S.: 311351

Petro Progress, Inc.　**(1)**
2-5-8 Higashi-Shinagawa Tennozu Parkside Building, Shinagawa-ku, Tokyo, 140-0002, Japan
Tel.: (81) 35 463 5006
Web Site: http://www.aochd.co.jp
Sales Range: $25-49.9 Million
Emp.: 6
Petroleum Products Transportation Services
N.A.I.C.S.: 486990

Subsidiary (Non-US):

Petro Progress Pte Ltd　**(2)**
5 Shenton Way 13-06 UIC Building, Singapore, 089763, Singapore
Tel.: (65) 62266468
Petroleum Products Sales
N.A.I.C.S.: 424720

Subsidiary (Domestic):

Aramo Shipping (Singapore) Pte Ltd　**(3)**
5 Shenton Way 13-07 UIC Building, Singapore, 89763, Singapore
Tel.: (65) 62261808
Sales Range: $25-49.9 Million
Emp.: 3
Marine Shipping Services
N.A.I.C.S.: 488390
Kensuke Kimura *(Mng Dir)*

FUJI OIL HOLDINGS INC.
Daibiru Honkan Building 3-6-32 Nakanoshima, Kita-ku, Osaka, 530-0005, Japan
Tel.: (81) 664590700
Web Site:
　https://www.fujioilholdings.com
Year Founded: 1950
2607—(TKS)
Rev.: $3,728,615,070
Assets: $3,108,160,810
Liabilities: $1,493,397,300
Net Worth: $1,614,763,510
Earnings: $43,123,640
Emp.: 141
Fiscal Year-end: 03/31/24
Holding Company; Food Ingredients Mfr
N.A.I.C.S.: 551112
Toshifumi Asada *(Exec Officer-HR, Legal & Gen Affairs)*

Subsidiaries:

Blommer Chocolate Company　**(1)**
600 W Kinzie St, Chicago, IL 60610
Tel.: (312) 226-7700
Web Site: https://www.blommer.com
Sales Range: $900-999.9 Million
Chocolate Mfr
N.A.I.C.S.: 311351
Peter Blommer *(Pres & CEO)*

Subsidiary (Domestic):

Blommer Chocolate Company - California Plant　**(2)**
1515 Pacific St, Union City, CA 94587
Chocolate Mfr
N.A.I.C.S.: 311351

Plant (Domestic):

Blommer Chocolate Company - Chicago Plant　**(2)**
600 W Kinzie St, Chicago, IL 60610
Web Site: https://www.blommer.com
Chocolate Mfr
N.A.I.C.S.: 311351
Owen Silva *(Mgr)*

Subsidiary (Domestic):

Blommer Chocolate Company - Pennsylvania Plant　**(2)**
1101 Blommer Dr, East Greenville, PA 18041
Emp.: 200
Chocolate Mfr
N.A.I.C.S.: 311351
Chris Milligan *(Mgr-Ops)*

Chiba Vegoil Tank Terminal Co., Ltd.　**(1)**
35-1 Shinminato, Mihama-ku, Chiba, 261-0002, Japan
Tel.: (81) 432388751
Edible Oil & Fats Whslr
N.A.I.C.S.: 424490

F&F Co., Ltd.　**(1)**
4-7-29 Oka Matsubara-shi, Osaka, 580 0014, Japan
Tel.: (81) 723368849
Sales Range: $25-49.9 Million
Emp.: 54
Chocolates & Bakery Ingredients Mfr
N.A.I.C.S.: 311351
Kazuyoshi Morikawa *(Pres)*

Freyabadi (Thailand) Co., Ltd.　**(1)**
300/121 Moo 1 T Tasit, Pluak Daeng, 21140, Rayong, Thailand
Tel.: (66) 389507524
Web Site: https://www.freyabadi.com
Emp.: 50
Industrial Chocolate Mfr
N.A.I.C.S.: 311351

Fuji Europe Africa B.V.　**(1)**
UN Studio 9th Floor Parnassusweg 819, 1082 LZ, Amsterdam, Netherlands
Tel.: (31) 203085021
Food Products Mfr
N.A.I.C.S.: 311999

Fuji Fresh Foods Co., Ltd.　**(1)**
62 Nakano, Tamba, Sasayama, 669-2213, Hyogo, Japan
Tel.: (81) 795942155
Web Site: http://www.fujifresh.com
Sales Range: $25-49.9 Million
Emp.: 96
Soy Protein & Tofu Mfr
N.A.I.C.S.: 311224

Fuji Global Chocolate (M) Sdn. Bhd.　**(1)**
Plot D32 Jalan DPB/6 Pelabuhan Tanjung Pelepas, 81550, Gelang Patah, Johor, Malaysia
Tel.: (60) 75044888
Web Site:
　https://www.fujiglobalchocolate.com
Industrial Chocolate Mfr
N.A.I.C.S.: 311351

Fuji Oil (China) Investment Co., Ltd.　**(1)**
Shanghai Mart Rm1808 No 2299 West Yanan Road, Shanghai, 200336, China
Tel.: (86) 2162363171
Food Products Mfr
N.A.I.C.S.: 311999

Fuji Oil (Singapore) Pte. Ltd.　**(1)**
45 Senoko Road, Singapore, 758114, Singapore
Tel.: (65) 67581801
Web Site: https://www.fujioil.com.sg
Sales Range: $25-49.9 Million
Emp.: 130
Edible Oil Mfr
N.A.I.C.S.: 111150

Fuji Oil (Thailand) Co., Ltd.　**(1)**
No 7/287 Moo6 Amata City Tambon Mab-Yangporn Amphur, Pluak Daeng, 21140, Rayong, Thailand
Tel.: (66) 38036240
Vegetable Oil & Fat Product Mfr
N.A.I.C.S.: 311225

Fuji Oil (Zhang Jia Gang) Co., Ltd.　**(1)**
North side of Zhangyang Highway, Economic Development Zone Yangshe Town, Zhangjiagang, 215600, Jiangsu, China
Tel.: (86) 51258678668
Web Site: http://www.fujioil.com.cn
Sales Range: $25-49.9 Million
Emp.: 250
Chocolate Confectioneries & Pastries Mfr
N.A.I.C.S.: 311352

Fuji Oil Asia Pte. Ltd.　**(1)**
6 Woodlands Square 09-04/05 Woods Square Tower 2, Singapore, 737737, Singapore
Tel.: (65) 68047799
Web Site: https://www.fujioil.asia
Vegetable Oil & Fat Product Mfr
N.A.I.C.S.: 311225

Fuji Oil Co., Ltd. - Chiba Plant　**(1)**
35-1 Shinminato, Mihama-ku, Chiba, 261-0002, Japan
Tel.: (81) 432043399
Web Site: http://www.fujioil.co.jp
Sales Range: $25-49.9 Million
Emp.: 30
Chocolates Confectioneries & Pastries Mfr
N.A.I.C.S.: 311340

Fuji Oil Co., Ltd. - Ishikawa Plant　**(1)**
30 Idaro-bu Nakanoto-machi, Kashima, 929-1721, Ishikawa, Japan
Tel.: (81) 767761518
Web Site: http://www.fujioil.co.jp
Chocolate Confectioneries & Pastries Mfr
N.A.I.C.S.: 311340

Fuji Oil Co., Ltd. - Kanto Plant　**(1)**
2600-8 Ago, Kasama, 319-0206, Ibaraki, Japan
Tel.: (81) 299458600
Web Site: http://www.fujioil.co.jp
Sales Range: $25-49.9 Million
Emp.: 50
Chocolate Confectioneries & Pastries Mfr
N.A.I.C.S.: 311340

Fuji Oil Co., Ltd. - Kobe Plant　**(1)**
2-18-24 Hamanaka-cho, Hyogo-ku, Kobe, 652-0875, Hyogo, Japan
Tel.: (81) 786523215
Web Site: http://www.fujioil.co.jp
Chocolates Confectioneries & Pastries Mfr
N.A.I.C.S.: 311340

Fuji Oil Co., Ltd. - Protein Foods Tsukuba Plant　**(1)**
27-3 Koshindaira, Bando, 306-0608, Ibaraki, Japan
Tel.: (81) 297474131
Web Site: http://www.fujioil.co.jp
Chocolates, Confectioneries & Pastries Mfr
N.A.I.C.S.: 311340

Fuji Oil Co., Ltd. - Rinku Plant　**(1)**
4-35 Rinku-minamihama, Sennan, 590-0535, Osaka, Japan
Tel.: (81) 724820631
Web Site: http://www.fujioil.co.jp
Food Ingredient Mfr
N.A.I.C.S.: 311999

Fuji Oil Co., Ltd. - Sakai Plant　**(1)**
3-37 Chikkoshinmachi Sakai-shi, Nishi-ku, Osaka, 592-8331, Japan
Tel.: (81) 722414811
Web Site: http://www.fujioil.co.jp
Chocolate Confectioneries & Pastries Mfr

N.A.I.C.S.: 311340

Fuji Oil Europe　**(1)**
Kuhlmannlaan 36, 9042, Gent, East Flanders, Belgium
Tel.: (32) 93430202
Web Site: https://www.fujioileurope.com
Sales Range: $25-49.9 Million
Emp.: 100
Oils & Fats Mfr
N.A.I.C.S.: 311225
Peter Claerhout *(Dir-Sls)*

Fuji Oil Ghana Ltd.　**(1)**
PO Box 836, Techiman-Bono East Region, Tema, Ghana
Tel.: (233) 352097900
Vegetable Oil & Fat Product Mfr
N.A.I.C.S.: 311225

Fuji Sunny Foods Co., Ltd.　**(1)**
3-12-12 Tokura, Toyonaka, 561-0845, Osaka, Japan
Tel.: (81) 668658720
Web Site: http://www.fujisunnyfoods.co.jp
Sales Range: $25-49.9 Million
Emp.: 41
Confectionery Materials Whslr
N.A.I.C.S.: 424450

Fuji Vegetable Oil Inc.　**(1)**
120 Brampton Rd, Savannah, GA 31408
Tel.: (912) 966-5900
Web Site: https://www.fujioilusa.com
Sales Range: $25-49.9 Million
Emp.: 5
Vegetable Oil Mfr
N.A.I.C.S.: 311225

Plant (Domestic):

Fuji Vegetable Oil Inc. - Plant　**(2)**
120 Brampton Rd, Savannah, GA 31408
Tel.: (912) 966-5900
Web Site: http://www.fujioilusa.com
Vegetable Oil Mfr
N.A.I.C.S.: 311225

Hannan Tank Terminal Co., Ltd.　**(1)**
1 Sumiyoshi-cho, Izumisano, 598-0061, Osaka, Japan
Tel.: (81) 724635394
Web Site: http://www.fujioil.co.jp
Edible Oil & Fat Products Whslr
N.A.I.C.S.: 424490

New Leyte Edible Oil Mfg. Corp.　**(1)**
Unit 1801 18th Fl The Peak Bldg 107 Leviste St, Salcedo Vlg, Makati, Philippines
Tel.: (63) 28482647
Sales Range: $25-49.9 Million
Emp.: 7
Edible Oils & Coconut Oil Mfr
N.A.I.C.S.: 311225

Omu Milk Products Co., Ltd.　**(1)**
1-38-1 Shinkatsudachi-machi, Omuta, 836-0895, Fukuoka, Japan
Tel.: (81) 944528282
Dairy Products Mfr
N.A.I.C.S.: 311514
Yoshikazu Iyoda *(Pres & CEO)*

P.T. Freyabadi Indotama　**(1)**
Jl Maligi III Lot J2A Kawasan Industri KIIC, Karawang, 41361, West Java, Indonesia
Tel.: (62) 2189109135
Chocolate Confectioneries & Pastries Mfr
N.A.I.C.S.: 311340

PT. Musim Mas-Fuji　**(1)**
Jl Raya Narogong Km 9 Bojong Menteng, Rawa Lumbu, Bekasi, 17117, Indonesia
Tel.: (62) 2182600912
Vegetable Oil & Fat Product Mfr
N.A.I.C.S.: 311225

Palmaju Edible Oil Sdn. Bhd.　**(1)**
Plo 223 Jalan Tembaga 4 Pasir Gudang Industrial Area, PO Box 59, 81700, Pasir Gudang, Johor, Malaysia
Tel.: (60) 72514630
Web Site: https://palmaju.com.my
Sales Range: $25-49.9 Million
Emp.: 168
Palm Oil Mfr
N.A.I.C.S.: 311224
Shoichi Harada *(Mng Dir)*

Shandong Longteng Fuji Foodstuffs Co., Ltd.　**(1)**

Fuji Oil Holdings Inc.—(Continued)

No 209 Heshan Dong Road, Laiyang, Yantai, 265200, Shangdong, China
Tel.: (86) 5357717155
Web Site: http://www.fujioil.co.jp
Sales Range: $100-124.9 Million
Emp.: 400
Protein Foods Mfr
N.A.I.C.S.: 311224

Shanghai Xuyang Food Co., Ltd. (1)
Room 602 Hesen Business Center No 1600
Yan'an West Road, Changning District,
Shanghai, 200052, China
Tel.: (86) 216 280 1170
Web Site: https://www.sh-xuyang.com
Soybean Based Food Product Mfr
N.A.I.C.S.: 311224

Soya Farm USA Inc. (1)
20675 S Western Ave Ste 210, Torrance,
CA 90501-1842
Tel.: (310) 781-9240
Web Site: http://www.soyafarmusa.com
Sales Range: $25-49.9 Million
Emp.: 3
Soybean Whslr
N.A.I.C.S.: 311224
Tatsumi Miyazaki (Pres)

Soyafarm Co., Ltd. (1)
Mita Hachiman Bldg 3-7-16 Mita, Minato-ku,
Tokyo, 108-0073, Japan
Tel.: (81) 354181920
Web Site: http://www.soyafarm.co.jp
Sales Range: $25-49.9 Million
Emp.: 30
Soy Milk & Related Products Mfr
N.A.I.C.S.: 311224

Tianjin Fuji Protein Co., Ltd. (1)
No 70 13th Avenue TEDA, Tianjin, 300457,
China
Tel.: (86) 2266230388
Soybean Based Food Product Mfr
N.A.I.C.S.: 311224

Unifuji Sdn. Bhd. (1)
Jendarata Estate, 36009, Teluk Intan,
Perak, Malaysia
Tel.: (60) 56418525
Vegetable Oil & Fat Product Mfr
N.A.I.C.S.: 311225
Kapil Punj (Mgr-Refinery)

Waltzfancy Co., Ltd. (1)
2-7-5 Miyawaki-cho, Nakagawa-ku, Nagoya,
454-0842, Aichi, Japan
Tel.: (81) 523692424
Confectionery Materials Sales & Services
N.A.I.C.S.: 424450

Woodlands Sunny Foods Pte.
Ltd. (1)
No 9 Senoko Crescent, Singapore, 758265,
Singapore
Tel.: (65) 67530088
Fermented Ingredient Food Product Mfr
N.A.I.C.S.: 311999

FUJI OOZX INC.

Kikugawa Industrial Park 1500-60
Misawa Kikugawa, Kikugawa, 439-0023, Shizuoka, Japan
Tel.: (81) 537355982
Web Site: https://www.oozx.co.jp
Year Founded: 1951
7299—(TKS)
Rev.: $154,555,020
Assets: $241,456,690
Liabilities: $42,257,730
Net Worth: $199,198,960
Earnings: $12,763,910
Emp.: 1,104
Fiscal Year-end: 03/31/24
Engine Valve Mfr & Whslr
N.A.I.C.S.: 336310
Satoshi Tsujimoto (Pres & Exec Officer)

Subsidiaries:

JATOS Inc. (1)
1-22-1 Engyo, Fujisawa, 252-0805,
Kanagawa-ken, Japan
Tel.: (81) 466870180
Industrial Valve Mfr

N.A.I.C.S.: 332911

Oozx Techno Inc. (1)
1500-50 Misawa, Kikugawa, 439-0023, Shizuoka, Japan
Tel.: (81) 53 736 4208
Transportation Machinery Equipment Mfr & Distr
N.A.I.C.S.: 336999

FUJI P.S CORPORATION

1-13-8 Yakuin Chuo-Ku, Fukuoka,
810-0022, Japan   JP
Web Site: http://www.fujips.co.jp
1848—(TKS)
Rev.: $188,821,260
Assets: $222,552,090
Liabilities: $153,761,820
Net Worth: $68,790,270
Earnings: $2,743,150
Emp.: 439
Fiscal Year-end: 03/31/24
Civil Engineering Services
N.A.I.C.S.: 541330
Tadahiko Tsutsumi (Pres)

FUJI PHARMA CO., LTD.

5-7 Sanban-cho, Chiyoda-ku, Tokyo,
102-0075, Japan
Tel.: (81) 335563344
Web Site: https://www.fujipharma.jp
Year Founded: 1965
4554—(TKS)
Rev.: $289,903,010
Assets: $605,003,880
Liabilities: $313,058,950
Net Worth: $291,944,930
Earnings: $24,354,150
Emp.: 1,658
Fiscal Year-end: 09/30/23
Pharmaceuticals Mfr
N.A.I.C.S.: 325412
Hirofumi Imai (Chm)

Subsidiaries:

OLIC (Thailand) Limited (1)
166 Moo 16 Bangpa-In Industrial Estate
Udomsorayuth Road, Bangkrason, Bangpa-in, 13160, Ayutthaya, Thailand
Tel.: (66) 35221031
Web Site: https://www.olic-thailand.com
Emp.: 800
Pharmaceutical Product Mfr & Distr
N.A.I.C.S.: 325412

FUJI SEAL INTERNATIONAL, INC.

4-1-9 Miyahara, Yodogawa-ku,
Osaka, 532-0003, Japan
Tel.: (81) 663501080
Web Site: https://www.fujiseal.com
Year Founded: 1958
7864—(TKS)
Rev.: $1,299,684,640
Assets: $1,273,641,240
Liabilities: $400,182,620
Net Worth: $873,458,620
Earnings: $67,930,970
Emp.: 48
Fiscal Year-end: 03/31/24
Packaging & Sealing Machines &
Equipment Mfr & Distr
N.A.I.C.S.: 339991
Akikazu Yada (CFO & Exec Officer)

Subsidiaries:

American Fuji Seal, Inc. (1)
1901 N Roselle Rd Ste 800, Schaumburg,
IL 60195-3176
Tel.: (847) 699-8200
Web Site: http://www.afseal.com
Converted Paper Product Mfr
N.A.I.C.S.: 322299

American Fuji Seal, Inc. (1)
Guillermo Gonzalez Camarena 1450 Piso 2
Col Cruz Manca, 01210, Mexico, Mexico
Tel.: (52) 5552618524
Adhesive Label & Spouted Pouched Mfr
N.A.I.C.S.: 326111

American Fuji Technical Services,
Inc (1)
900 Trey St, Jeffersonville, IN 47130
Tel.: (812) 258-5300
Sales Range: $25-49.9 Million
Emp.: 30
Packaging Machinery Mfr
N.A.I.C.S.: 333993

Fuji Astec, Inc. (1)
5-9-11 Shioe, Amagasaki, 661-0976, Hyogo,
Japan
Tel.: (81) 664283801
Web Site: http://www.fujiseal.co.jp
Sales Range: $400-449.9 Million
Emp.: 1,750
Construction Machinery Mfr
N.A.I.C.S.: 333120

Fuji Flex, Inc. (1)
1-9-1 Marunouchi, Chiyoda-ku, Tokyo, 100-0005, Japan
Tel.: (81) 352085913
Web Site: http://www.fujiseal.co.jp
Packaging Machinery Mfr
N.A.I.C.S.: 333993

Fuji Packaging Services, Inc (1)
419 miyahara yodogaeeaku, Osaka, 532-0003, Japan
Tel.: (81) 663502881
Web Site: http://www.fujibutsuryu.co.jp
Sales Range: $25-49.9 Million
Emp.: 20
Converted Paper Product Mfr
N.A.I.C.S.: 322299

Fuji Seal Engineering Co., Ltd. (1)
No 55/72 Moo 15, Bangsaothong, Samut
Prakan, 10570, Thailand
Tel.: (66) 213075667
Adhesive Label & Spouted Pouched Mfr
N.A.I.C.S.: 326111

Fuji Seal Europe B.V. (1)
Jacob Marisstraat 2, 5753 DB, Deurne,
Netherlands
Tel.: (31) 493352020
Web Site: http://www.fujiseal.com
Sales Range: $50-74.9 Million
Emp.: 130
Packaging Machinery Mfr
N.A.I.C.S.: 333993

Fuji Seal Europe Ltd. (1)
Scimitar Close - Gillingham Business Park,
Gillingham, ME8 0RJ, Kent, United Kingdom
Tel.: (44) 1634378656
Web Site: http://www.fujiseal.com
Sales Range: $50-74.9 Million
Emp.: 200
Gasket Packing & Sealing Device Mfr
N.A.I.C.S.: 339991

Fuji Seal Europe S.A.S. (1)
77 Route De Luxeuil, 70220, Fougerolles,
France
Tel.: (33) 384491044
Web Site: http://www.fujiseal.com
Chemical & Allied Products Merchant Whslr
N.A.I.C.S.: 424690

Fuji Seal France S.A.S. (1)
77 Route De Luxeuil, 70220, Fougerolles,
France
Tel.: (33) 384491044
Packaging Machinery Mfr
N.A.I.C.S.: 333993

Fuji Seal Iberia, S.L.U (1)
Gran Via de les Corts Catalanes 630,
08007, Barcelona, Spain
Tel.: (34) 932151571
Packaging Material Distr
N.A.I.C.S.: 423840

Fuji Seal India Pvt Ltd. (1)
12th Floor Office No H-10 EFS Parinee
Crescento G-Block, Bandra Kurla Complex
- BKC Bandra East, Mumbai, 400051, Maharashtra, India
Tel.: (91) 2248800675
Adhesive Label & Spouted Pouched Mfr
N.A.I.C.S.: 326111

Fuji Seal International, Inc - Nara
Factory (1)
622 Chishiro Tawaramoto-cho, Shiki-gun,
Nara, 636-0246, Japan

Tel.: (81) 744 32 5311
Web Site: http://www.fujiseal.co.jp
Label Application Machinery Mfr
N.A.I.C.S.: 333993

Fuji Seal Packaging (Thailand) Co.,
Ltd. (1)
475 Sri Ayutthaya Rd, Thanon Phayathai
Sub-district Ratchathewi District, Bangkok,
10400, Thailand
Tel.: (66) 22460828
Adhesive Label & Spouted Pouched Mfr
N.A.I.C.S.: 326111

Fuji Seal Packaging De Mexico, S.A.
De C.V (1)
Av Rio San Lorenzo No 670 Parque Industrial Castro Del Rio, 36810, Irapuato, Gto,
Mexico
Tel.: (52) 4626067980
Packaging Machinery Mfr
N.A.I.C.S.: 333993

Fuji Seal Personnel Services, S.A.
De C.V. (1)
Av Rio San Lorenzo No 670, Parque Industrial Castro Del Rio, 36810, Irapuato, Guanajuato, Mexico
Tel.: (52) 4626067980
Adhesive Label & Spouted Pouched Mfr
N.A.I.C.S.: 326111

Fuji Seal Poland Sp.zo.o (1)
ul Wschodnia 2, 99-300, Kutno, Poland
Tel.: (48) 243559300
Web Site: http://www.fujiseal.com
Sales Range: $100-124.9 Million
Emp.: 300
Packaging Machinery Mfr
N.A.I.C.S.: 333993

Fuji Seal Southeast Asia, Inc. (1)
4-1-9 Miyahara, Yodogawa-ku, Osaka, 532-0003, Japan
Tel.: (81) 663501065
Web Site: http://www.fujiseal.co.jp
Sales Range: $25-49.9 Million
Emp.: 10
Packaging Machinery Mfr
N.A.I.C.S.: 333993
Ryuji Konishi (Mgr)

Fuji Seal Vietnam Co., Ltd. (1)
No 5 VSIP II-A 15th Road, Vietnam - Singapore Industrial Park II-A VSIP II-A, Tan
Uyen, Binh Duong, Vietnam
Tel.: (84) 2742221035
Adhesive Label & Spouted Pouched Mfr
N.A.I.C.S.: 326111

Fuji Seal West, Inc. (1)
700-4 yamanaka-kabutoishi, Ube, 759-0132, Yamaguchi, Japan
Tel.: (81) 836625100
Adhesive Label & Spouted Pouched Mfr
N.A.I.C.S.: 326111

Fuji Seal, Inc. (1)
WATERRAS Tower 8F 2-101 Kanda Awaji-cho, Chiyoda-ku, Tokyo, 101-0063, Japan
Tel.: (81) 352085900
Web Site: http://www.fujiseal.co.jp
Sales Range: $50-74.9 Million
Emp.: 140
Commercial Printing
N.A.I.C.S.: 323111

Fuji Tack East, Inc. (1)
85 Chuo-kogyo-danchi, Sagae, 991-0061,
Yamagata, Japan
Tel.: (81) 237842121
Packaging & Labeling Machinery Mfr
N.A.I.C.S.: 333993

Fuji Tack, Inc. (1)
Waterras Tower 8F 2-101 Kanda Awaji-cho,
Chiyoda-ku, Tokyo, 101-0063, Japan
Tel.: (81) 352085911
Adhesive Label & Spouted Pouched Mfr
N.A.I.C.S.: 326111

PAGO AG (1)
Werdenstrasse 85, Postfach 145, St Gallen,
9472, Grabs, Switzerland
Tel.: (41) 817723511
Adhesive Label & Spouted Pouched Mfr
N.A.I.C.S.: 326111

PT. Fuji Seal Indonesia (1)
Menara Standard Chartered Lt 18 Zone F JI
Prof Dr Satrio No 164 RT. 003 / RW 004

Kel Karet Semanggi Kec Setiabudi, Jakarta, 12930, Selatan, Indonesia
Tel.: (62) 2125532713
Web Site: http://www.fujiseal.co.jp
Sales Range: $25-49.9 Million
Emp.: 5
Packaging Machinery Mfr
N.A.I.C.S.: 333993

PT.Fuji Seal Packaging
Indonesia (1)
Jl Rembang Industri IA No 2 Pier, Rembang, Pasuruan, 67152, Indonesia
Tel.: (62) 3435613991
Adhesive Label & Spouted Pouched Mfr
N.A.I.C.S.: 326111

Pago Etikettiersysteme GmbH (1)
Gutenbergstrasse 9, Aichtal-Aich, 72631, Esslingen, Germany
Tel.: (49) 712758010
Web Site: https://www.pago.com
Labeling Machine Mfr
N.A.I.C.S.: 333993

Pago S.r.l. (1)
Via Enzo Ferrari 33 Rivalta IT, Rodigo, Mantua, MN, Italy
Tel.: (39) 0376652011
Labeling Machine Mfr
N.A.I.C.S.: 333993

FUJI SEIKI CO., LTD.
Imon Kawaramachi No 2 Bldg 5F
4-8-4 Kawaramachi, Chuo-Ku,
Osaka, 541-0048, Japan
Tel.: (81) 671666820
Web Site: https://www.fujiseiki.com
Year Founded: 1955
6400—(TKS)
Rev.: $58,584,670
Assets: $60,272,090
Liabilities: $37,740,070
Net Worth: $22,532,020
Earnings: $1,644,880
Fiscal Year-end: 12/31/23
Precision Mold Mfr
N.A.I.C.S.: 333511
Takeshi Ii (Pres)

Subsidiaries:

Akimotoseikikogyo Co., Ltd. (1)
18-1 Okuma-cho, Tsuzuki-ku, Yokohama, 224-0042, Kanagawa, Japan
Tel.: (81) 454733225
Web Site: https://www.akimoto-sk.co.jp
Precision Press Mfr
N.A.I.C.S.: 332721

Changzhou Fuji Seiki Co., Ltd. (1)
No 81 Tianshan Road State High-tech Development Zone, Changzhou, 213022, China
Tel.: (86) 51988228880
Industrial Mold Mfr
N.A.I.C.S.: 333511

Fuji Seiki Co., Ltd. - Matsuyama
Factory (1)
41-14 Tanokubo, Toon, Ehime, Japan
Tel.: (81) 899644480
Industrial Mold Mfr
N.A.I.C.S.: 333511

PT. Fuji Seiki Indonesia (1)
Komp De Prima Terra Block A2 No 1 Tegalluar Bojongsoang, Bandung, West Java, Indonesia
Tel.: (62) 227533396
Precision Mold Mfr
N.A.I.C.S.: 333511

Shanghai Fuji Seiki Co., Ltd. (1)
No 26 Baosheng Road Songjiang Industrial Park, Shanghai, 201613, China
Tel.: (86) 2157746540
Industrial Mold Mfr
N.A.I.C.S.: 333511

Thai Fuji Seiki Co., Ltd. (1)
Amata Nakorn Industrial Estate 700/721
Moo 3 T Bankao A, Phan Thong, 20160,
Chonburi, Thailand
Tel.: (66) 38447580
Precision Mold Mfr & Distr
N.A.I.C.S.: 333511

FUJI TECHNO SOLUTIONS CO., INC.
3F Atsugi Azalea Bldg 4-10-8 Nakacho, Atsugi, 243-0018, Kanagawa, Japan
Tel.: (81) 462941061
Web Site: http://www.fjtsc.co.jp
2336—(TKS)
Rev.: $19,733,840
Assets: $7,216,790
Liabilities: $6,941,690
Net Worth: $275,100
Earnings: $165,060
Fiscal Year-end: 03/31/20
Enterprise Software Development Services
N.A.I.C.S.: 541511
Isao Takai (Chm & CEO)

FUJI YAKUHIN CO., LTD.
4-383 Sakuragicho, Omiya-ku, Saitama, 330-0854, Japan
Tel.: (81) 4 8644 3240 JP
Web Site: http://www.fujiyakuhin.co.jp
Year Founded: 1930
Pharmaceuticals Mfr & Distr
N.A.I.C.S.: 456110
Masayuki Takayanagi (Pres & CEO)

Subsidiaries:

OST Japan Group Inc. (1)
5-1-7 Atsubetuminami, Atsubetsu-ku, Sapporo, 004-0022, Hokkaido, Japan
Tel.: (81) 118965533
Web Site: http://www.ost-japan.com
Sales Range: $50-74.9 Million
Emp.: 300
Pharmacy & Residential Care Center Operator
N.A.I.C.S.: 456110
Makoto Murakami (Pres)

FUJIAN ACETRON NEW MATERIALS CO., LTD.
Minjiangkou Industrial Park Qinjiang Village Hangcheng Town, Changle, 350200, Fujian, China
Tel.: (86) 59128673333
Web Site: http://www.acetron.com.cn
Year Founded: 2002
300706—(CHIN)
Rev.: $134,924,060
Assets: $237,523,172
Liabilities: $127,730,273
Net Worth: $109,792,899
Earnings: $1,728,568
Fiscal Year-end: 12/31/23
Electronic Coating Material Mfr & Distr
N.A.I.C.S.: 334413
Chen Qinzhong (Chm & Gen Mgr)

FUJIAN ANJOY FOODS CO LTD
No 2508 Xinyang Road Haicang District, Xiamen, 361022, China
Tel.: (86) 5926884968
Web Site: http://www.anjoyfood.com
603345—(SHG)
Rev.: $1,710,445,899
Assets: $2,273,579,559
Liabilities: $602,958,765
Net Worth: $1,670,620,793
Earnings: $154,584,612
Emp.: 10,000
Fiscal Year-end: 12/31/22
Frozen Food Mfr & Distr
N.A.I.C.S.: 311824
Mingming Liu (Chm)

FUJIAN AONONG BIOLOGICAL TECHNOLOGY GROUP INCORPORATION LIMITED
Intersection of Xingting Road and Baolian Road, Jinfeng Economic Development Zone Xiangcheng District, Zhangzhou, 361008, Fujian, China
Tel.: (86) 5962586018
Web Site: http://www.aonong.com.cn
Year Founded: 2011
603363—(SHG)
Rev.: $3,034,470,746
Assets: $2,619,943,888
Liabilities: $2,138,093,517
Net Worth: $481,850,371
Earnings: ($145,879,293)
Emp.: 13,000
Fiscal Year-end: 12/31/22
Feed Product Mfr & Distr
N.A.I.C.S.: 311119
Wu Youlin (Chm, Pres & Gen Mgr)

FUJIAN APEX SOFTWARE CO., LTD.
Building 13 Area A Software Park No 89 Software Avenue Tangpan Road, Gulou District, Fuzhou, 350101, Fujian, China
Tel.: (86) 59188267679
Web Site:
   http://www.apexsoft.com.cn
Year Founded: 2000
603383—(SHG)
Rev.: $87,692,169
Assets: $249,950,189
Liabilities: $57,109,076
Net Worth: $192,841,113
Earnings: $23,311,890
Fiscal Year-end: 12/31/22
Software Development Services
N.A.I.C.S.: 513210

FUJIAN BOSS SOFTWARE CORP.
No 5 Gaoxin Avenue High-tech Zone, Fuzhou National Hi-tech Industrial Development Zone Shangjie Town, Fuzhou, 350000, Fujian, China
Tel.: (86) 59187664001
Web Site:
   https://www.bosssoft.com.cn
Year Founded: 2001
300525—(CHIN)
Rev.: $287,942,444
Assets: $605,008,963
Liabilities: $162,269,243
Net Worth: $442,739,721
Earnings: $46,009,638
Fiscal Year-end: 12/31/23
Software Development Services
N.A.I.C.S.: 513210
Chen Hang (Chm)

FUJIAN CEMENT INC.
Hongyang Xincheng Fuzhou Jianfu Building No 118 Yangqiao Road, Fuzhou, 350003, Fujian, China
Tel.: (86) 59187617751
Web Site: http://www.fjcement.com
Year Founded: 1993
600802—(SHG)
Rev.: $363,711,648
Assets: $588,761,307
Liabilities: $355,682,017
Net Worth: $233,079,290
Earnings: ($34,066,165)
Fiscal Year-end: 12/31/22
Cement Product Mfr & Whslr
N.A.I.C.S.: 327310
Wang Jinxing (Chm)

FUJIAN COSUNTER PHARMACEUTICAL CO., LTD.
Building 16 phase II innovation park No 7 middle wulongjiang Avenue, Fuzhou high tech Zone, Fuzhou, 350003, Fujian, China
Tel.: (86) 59138265199
Web Site: https://www.cosunter.com
Year Founded: 2001
300436—(CHIN)
Rev.: $54,162,108
Assets: $209,875,536
Liabilities: $75,706,488
Net Worth: $134,169,048
Earnings: ($17,886,960)
Emp.: 420
Fiscal Year-end: 12/31/22
Pharmaceuticals Mfr
N.A.I.C.S.: 325412
Guoping Li (Chm & Gen Mgr)

FUJIAN DONGBAI (GROUP) CO., LTD.
No 84 -185 excluding No 178-1 Bayiqi North Road, Gulou District, Fuzhou, 350001, Fujian, China
Tel.: (86) 59183815133
Web Site: http://www.dongbai.com
Year Founded: 1990
600693—(SHG)
Rev.: $234,662,861
Assets: $2,035,441,081
Liabilities: $1,455,991,861
Net Worth: $579,449,220
Earnings: $3,058,221
Fiscal Year-end: 12/31/22
Departmental Store Operator
N.A.I.C.S.: 455110
Wenyi Shi (Chm & Pres)

FUJIAN EXPRESSWAY DEVELOPMENT CO., LTD.
8th Floor Building 5 Linpu Plaza No 367 Linpu Road, Chengmen Town Cangshan District, Fuzhou, 350001, Fujian, China
Tel.: (86) 59187077366
Web Site: https://www.fjgs.com.cn
Year Founded: 1999
600033—(SHG)
Rev.: $375,100,011
Assets: $2,330,443,103
Liabilities: $480,533,223
Net Worth: $1,849,909,881
Earnings: $117,991,191
Emp.: 800
Fiscal Year-end: 12/31/22
Road Construction & Toll Operations
N.A.I.C.S.: 237310
Yang Fan (Sec)

FUJIAN FORECAM OPTICS CO., LTD.
No 158 Jiangbin East Avenue, Mawei District, Fuzhou, 350015, Fujian, China
Tel.: (86) 59163152888
Web Site: https://www.forecam.com
Year Founded: 2004
688010—(SHG)
Rev.: $109,648,132
Assets: $394,476,573
Liabilities: $142,160,630
Net Worth: $252,315,943
Earnings: $4,107,149
Fiscal Year-end: 12/31/22
Optical Instrument Mfr & Distr
N.A.I.C.S.: 333310
Wenbo He (Chm & Gen Mgr)

FUJIAN FOXIT SOFTWARE DEVELOPMENT JOINT STOCK CO., LTD.
Building 5 Zone G Software Park, Gulou, Fuzhou, 350003, Fujian, China
Tel.: (86) 59138509866
Web Site:
   https://www.foxitsoftware.cn
Year Founded: 2001
688095—(SHG)
Rev.: $81,414,647
Assets: $427,418,007
Liabilities: $53,708,616
Net Worth: $373,709,391
Earnings: ($244,844)
Fiscal Year-end: 12/31/22
Software Development Services

Fujian Foxit Software Development Joint Stock Co.,
Ltd.—(Continued)

N.A.I.C.S.: 541511
Yuqian Xiong *(Chm & Pres)*

FUJIAN FUNENG CO., LTD.

29th Floor Haixi Building No 75 Wusi
Road, Fuzhou, 350001, Fujian, China
Tel.: (86) 59186395317
Web Site: https://www.fjec.com.cn
Year Founded: 1994
600483—(SHG)
Rev.: $2,010,229,299
Assets: $6,813,139,156
Liabilities: $3,369,882,709
Net Worth: $3,443,256,746
Earnings: $364,082,472
Fiscal Year-end: 12/31/22
Textile Product Mfr & Distr
N.A.I.C.S.: 313110
Luo Rui *(Vice Chm & Gen Mgr)*

FUJIAN FURI ELECTRONICS CO., LTD.

12/13F Building 2 Zonshine Business
Center 153 Wuyi North Road, Fu-
zhou, 350005, Fujian, China
Tel.: (86) 59183317999
Web Site: https://www.furielec.com
Year Founded: 1999
600203—(SHG)
Rev.: $2,323,684,093
Assets: $1,259,188,365
Liabilities: $917,754,688
Net Worth: $341,433,678
Earnings: ($43,935,428)
Emp.: 5,773
Fiscal Year-end: 12/31/22
Electronic Component Mfr & Distr
N.A.I.C.S.: 334419
Hu Jintao *(Chm)*

Subsidiaries:

Fujian Fory Co., Ltd.   (1)
No 2 Wuyu Road, Gaishan Town Cangshan
District, Fuzhou, China
Tel.: (86) 59187277720
Web Site: http://www.fory.com.cn
Electronic Components Mfr
N.A.I.C.S.: 334419

Shenzhen Mary Photoelectricity Co.,
Ltd.   (1)
Tel.: (86) 75581791776
Web Site: http://www.mrled.cn
Electronic Components Mfr
N.A.I.C.S.: 334419

Shenzhen Runlite Technology Co.,
Ltd.   (1)
Building A15 No 4 Industrial Zone Tantou
Community Songgang Street, Bao'an Dis-
trict, Shenzhen, 518100, China
Tel.: (86) 7552 978 5901
Web Site: https://www.runlite.cn
Electronic Components Mfr
N.A.I.C.S.: 334419

FUJIAN FYNEX TEXTILE SCIENCE & TECHNOLOGY CO., LTD.

No 16 Yuanyuan East Road Andong,
Jinjiang, 362200, Fujian, China
Tel.: (86) 59585656506
Web Site: https://www.fynex.com.cn
600493—(SHG)
Rev.: $161,261,166
Assets: $288,905,882
Liabilities: $170,594,845
Net Worth: $118,311,036
Earnings: $3,660,607
Fiscal Year-end: 12/31/22
Textile Product Mfr & Distr
N.A.I.C.S.: 313110
Chengcheng Chen *(Chm)*

Subsidiaries:

Fujian Fynex Garment Co., Ltd.   (1)
Fengzhu Group, Meiling Industrial District,

Jinjiang, Fujian, China
Tel.: (86) 5958 560 1083
Web Site: https://www.fynex-garment.com
Emp.: 600
Import & Export Raw Material Services
N.A.I.C.S.: 522299

FUJIAN GREEN PINE CO., LTD.

Huiyao Industry Park, Jianyang,
354200, Fujian, China
Tel.: (86) 76022511366
Web Site: https://www.greenpine.cc
Year Founded: 1958
300132—(CHIN)
Rev.: $409,598,748
Assets: $448,521,840
Liabilities: $254,574,684
Net Worth: $193,947,156
Earnings: ($104,235,768)
Emp.: 250
Fiscal Year-end: 12/31/22
Petrochemical Products Mfr
N.A.I.C.S.: 325110
Fan Zhanhua *(Chm & Pres)*

Subsidiaries:

Nox Bellcow Cosmetics Co., Ltd.   (1)
No 50 Dongfu North Road, Nantou Town,
Zhongshan, China
Tel.: (86) 18967103880
Web Site: https://www.hknbc.com
Skin-Care Product Mfr & Distr
N.A.I.C.S.: 325620

FUJIAN HAIXIA ENVIRONMENTAL PROTECTION GROUP CO., LTD.

No 16 Yangli Road Gushan Town Ji-
nan District, Fuzhou, 350014, China
Web Site: http://www.fjhxhb.com
603817—(SHG)
Rev.: $146,671,331
Assets: $818,238,817
Liabilities: $426,330,202
Net Worth: $391,908,615
Earnings: $20,770,874
Fiscal Year-end: 12/31/22
Sewage Treatment Services
N.A.I.C.S.: 221320
Xu Ting *(Chm)*

FUJIAN HOLDINGS LIMITED

Units 3306-3308 33/F Shun Tak Cen-
tre West Tower 200 Connaught Road,
Central, China (Hong Kong)
Tel.: (852) 28109222   HK
Web Site:
   https://www.fujianholdings.com
Year Founded: 1958
0181—(HKG)
Rev.: $2,409,547
Assets: $52,840,707
Liabilities: $1,518,867
Net Worth: $51,321,841
Earnings: ($1,824,244)
Emp.: 110
Fiscal Year-end: 12/31/22
Hotel Business & Property Invest-
ment
N.A.I.C.S.: 561110
Alex Tao Ming Chan *(Sec)*

FUJIAN IDEAL JEWELLERY INDUSTRIAL CO., LTD.

2-3F North Building 1005 Dongxiao
Road, Luohu District, Shenzhen,
518020, Guangdong, China
Tel.: (86) 75525635988
Web Site: http://www.idr.com.cn
002740—(SSE)
Rev.: $51,455,196
Assets: $228,510,828
Liabilities: $309,160,800
Net Worth: ($80,649,972)
Earnings: ($99,479,016)
Emp.: 600

Fiscal Year-end: 12/31/22
Jewelry Stores
N.A.I.C.S.: 458310

FUJIAN JINSEN FORESTRY CO., LTD.

12-15F No 50 Sanhua South Road,
Shuinan Town Jiangle County, San-
ming, 353300, Fujian, China
Tel.: (86) 5982336158
Web Site:
   http://www.jinsenforestry.com
Year Founded: 1996
002670—(SSE)
Rev.: $24,440,832
Assets: $269,308,260
Liabilities: $162,077,760
Net Worth: $107,230,500
Earnings: $1,430,676
Emp.: 200
Fiscal Year-end: 12/31/22
Forestry Management
N.A.I.C.S.: 115310
Jinwen Zhang *(Vice Chm)*

FUJIAN KUNCAI MATERIAL TECHNOLOGY CO., LTD.

Yuanhong Investment Zone Cheng-
tou, Fuzhou, 350314, China
Tel.: (86) 59185588083
Web Site: https://www.fjkuncai.com
Year Founded: 1999
603826—(SHG)
Rev.: $115,021,858
Assets: $501,650,295
Liabilities: $249,253,707
Net Worth: $252,396,589
Earnings: $12,352,546
Fiscal Year-end: 12/31/22
Pearlescent Pigment Mfr & Distr
N.A.I.C.S.: 325130
Bing Kun Xie *(Chm, Pres & Gen Mgr)*

Subsidiaries:

Kuncai Americas LLC   (1)
130 E Wilson Bridge Rd Ste 210, Worthing-
ton, OH 43085
Tel.: (614) 547-7424
Synthetic & Pigment Mfr & Distr
N.A.I.C.S.: 325130

Kuncai Europe B.V.   (1)
Linie 506, 7325 DZ, Apeldoorn, Netherlands
Tel.: (31) 552100000
Synthetic & Pigment Mfr & Distr
N.A.I.C.S.: 325130

Kuncai International India Pvt.
Ltd.   (1)
No 04 Malbary Building Plot no TP-1,
Thane, 400604, India
Tel.: (91) 2225363981
Synthetic & Pigment Mfr & Distr
N.A.I.C.S.: 325130

FUJIAN LONGKING CO., LTD.

No 19 Gongye Middle Road, Xinluo
District, Longyan, 364000, Fujian,
China
Tel.: (86) 5972200539
Web Site:
   https://www.longking.com.cn
Year Founded: 1971
600388—(SHG)
Rev.: $1,667,972,386
Assets: $3,709,113,230
Liabilities: $2,645,343,469
Net Worth: $1,063,769,761
Earnings: $112,921,740
Emp.: 7,000
Fiscal Year-end: 12/31/22
Purification Equipment Mfr
N.A.I.C.S.: 333413
Lin Hongfu *(Chm)*

Subsidiaries:

Wuhan Longking EP Technologies
Co., Ltd   (1)
No 528 Dihou Street Baishazhou Inside City

Industrial Park, Wuhan, 430065, Hubeish-
eng, China
Tel.: (86) 13307154556
Purification Equipment Mfr
N.A.I.C.S.: 333413

FUJIAN LONGXI BEARING (GROUP) CORPORATION LIMITED

B1501-B1901 Building 1 Chengtou
Bihu City Square 1 Hubin Road, Lon-
gwen District, Zhangzhou, 363000,
Fujian, China
Tel.: (86) 5962072882
Web Site: https://www.ls.com.cn
Year Founded: 1997
600592—(SHG)
Rev.: $241,407,031
Assets: $501,144,729
Liabilities: $188,820,618
Net Worth: $312,324,110
Earnings: ($840,996)
Emp.: 120
Fiscal Year-end: 12/31/22
Mechanical Parts Mfr & Distr
N.A.I.C.S.: 333613
Chen Jinhui *(Chm)*

Subsidiaries:

Changsha Bode Metallurgic Material
Co., Ltd.   (1)
No 111 Pengjia Lane, Laodaohe Town Kaifu
District, Changsha, 410153, Hunan, China
Tel.: (86) 73185783138
Thrust Bearing Mfr & Distr
N.A.I.C.S.: 332991

Fujian Sanming Gear Case Co.,
Ltd.   (1)
No 1398 New City North Road, Sanming,
365000, Fujian, China
Tel.: (86) 5988254552
Motor Vehicle Parts Mfr
N.A.I.C.S.: 336350

Fujian Sanming Gearbox Co.,
Ltd.   (1)
No 13 Gaoyuan Industrial Zone, Chenda
Town Meilie District, Sanming, 365000, Fu-
jian, China
Tel.: (86) 5988254550
Web Site: https://www.smclx.cn
Engineering Machinery Mfr & Distr
N.A.I.C.S.: 333248

Zhangzhou Jinchi Automobile Parts
Co., Ltd.   (1)
Latian Industrial Development Zone,
Zhangzhou, 363005, Fujian, China
Tel.: (86) 5962683433
Motor Vehicle Parts Mfr
N.A.I.C.S.: 336350

FUJIAN MINDONG ELECTRIC POWER CO., LTD.

15F Building 9 Dongsheng Plaza No
2 Jinma North Road, Dongqiao Eco-
nomic Development Zone, Ningde,
352100, Fujian, China
Tel.: (86) 5932768811
Web Site: http://www.mdep.com.cn
Year Founded: 1998
000993—(SSE)
Rev.: $102,792,456
Assets: $622,520,964
Liabilities: $304,135,884
Net Worth: $318,385,080
Earnings: $25,827,984
Fiscal Year-end: 12/31/22
Electric Power Generation & Distribu-
tion Services
N.A.I.C.S.: 221111
Huang Jian'en *(Chm)*

FUJIAN MINFA ALUMINIUM CO., LTD.

South China Comprehensive Development Zone, Nan'an, 362300, Fujian, China
Tel.: (86) 59586286999

Web Site: https://www.minfa.com
Year Founded: 1993
002578—(SSE)
Rev.: $386,479,051
Assets: $329,932,626
Liabilities: $119,644,135
Net Worth: $210,288,491
Earnings: $6,911,968
Emp.: 630
Fiscal Year-end: 12/31/22
Aluminium Products Mfr
N.A.I.C.S.: 331318
Tianhuo Huang *(Chm)*

FUJIAN MINHANG ELECTRONICS CO., LTD.

Changsha High-tech and Technological Development Zone, Nanping, Fujian, China
Tel.: (86) 59 9860 9304   CN
Web Site:
    http://www.minhang.com.cn
Year Founded: 1970
Multilayer Ceramic Capacitors Mfr
N.A.I.C.S.: 335999
Brabeck Bright *(Mktg Mgr)*

FUJIAN NANPING SUN CABLE CO., LTD.

No 102 Gongye Road, Nanping, 353000, Fujian, China
Tel.: (86) 5998736341
Web Site: http://www.npcable.com
Year Founded: 1994
002300—(SSE)
Rev.: $1,839,694,896
Assets: $759,260,736
Liabilities: $454,676,976
Net Worth: $304,583,760
Earnings: $29,947,320
Fiscal Year-end: 12/31/22
Wire & Cable Mfr
N.A.I.C.S.: 335921
Yunxiao Li *(Chm & Pres)*

FUJIAN NEBULA ELECTRONICS CO., LTD.

No 7 Majiang Road, Fuzhou, 350015, Fujian, China
Tel.: (86) 59128051312   CN
Web Site: https://www.e-nebula.com
Year Founded: 2005
300648—(CHIN)
Rev.: $127,708,751
Assets: $345,422,413
Liabilities: $223,948,176
Net Worth: $121,474,237
Earnings: ($27,165,725)
Emp.: 2,641
Fiscal Year-end: 12/31/23
Electrical Equipment Mfr & Distr
N.A.I.C.S.: 334515
Li Youcai *(Chm)*

FUJIAN NEWCHOICE PIPE TECHNOLOGY CO., LTD.

Puan Industrial Zone, Quangang District, Quanzhou, 362800, Fujian, China
Tel.: (86) 5922117022
Web Site: https://www.nachuan.com
Year Founded: 2003
300198—(CHIN)
Rev.: $55,777,769
Assets: $399,024,261
Liabilities: $293,729,308
Net Worth: $105,294,953
Earnings: ($43,065,592)
Fiscal Year-end: 12/31/23
Drainage Pipe Mfr & Distr
N.A.I.C.S.: 326122
Chen Zhijiang *(Chm)*

FUJIAN QINGSHAN PAPER INDUSTRY CO., LTD.

Qingshan Paper Industry, Qingzhou Town Sha County, Sanming, 365056, Fujian, China
Tel.: (86) 5985656888
Web Site:
    https://www.qingshanpaper.com
Year Founded: 1958
600103—(SHG)
Rev.: $410,105,943
Assets: $817,665,325
Liabilities: $233,035,274
Net Worth: $584,630,051
Earnings: $29,166,345
Fiscal Year-end: 12/31/22
Paper Product Mfr & Whslr
N.A.I.C.S.: 322130
Jia Qinglin *(Sec)*

FUJIAN RAYNEN TECHNOLOGY CO., LTD.

No 26 Zone C Software Park No 89 Software Avenue Tongpan Road, Gulou District, Fuzhou, Fujian, China
Tel.: (86) 59188267288
Web Site: https://www.raynen.cn
Year Founded: 2007
603933—(SHG)
Rev.: $299,873,087
Assets: $295,951,308
Liabilities: $118,521,257
Net Worth: $177,430,051
Earnings: $7,534,805
Fiscal Year-end: 12/31/22
Integrated Circuit Product Mfr & Distr
N.A.I.C.S.: 334413
Weijian Yang *(Chm & Pres)*

Subsidiaries:

Quanzhou Raynen Automation Technology Co., Ltd.   **(1)**
No 12 Xiaxian Road Xiamei Community Beifeng Street, Fengze District, Quanzhou, 362000, Fujian, China
Tel.: (86) 59522868211
Semiconductor Mfr
N.A.I.C.S.: 334413

FUJIAN RONGJI SOFTWARE CO., LTD.

Block 15 Area A 89 Software Avenue, Gulou District, Fuzhou, 350003, Fujian, China
Tel.: (86) 59187860988
Web Site: https://www.rongji.com
Year Founded: 2007
002474—(SSE)
Rev.: $93,468,492
Assets: $382,627,908
Liabilities: $153,801,180
Net Worth: $228,826,728
Earnings: $1,868,724
Emp.: 400
Fiscal Year-end: 12/31/22
Software Publisher
N.A.I.C.S.: 513210
Feng Lu *(Chm & Pres)*

FUJIAN SANMU GROUP CO., LTD.

17F Sanmu Building No 93 Qunzhong East Road, Taijiang District, Fuzhou, 350005, Fujian, China
Tel.: (86) 59138170632
Web Site: http://www.san-mu.com
Year Founded: 1993
000632—(SSE)
Rev.: $1,959,152,832
Assets: $1,370,977,920
Liabilities: $1,097,715,996
Net Worth: $273,261,924
Earnings: $2,087,748
Fiscal Year-end: 12/31/22
Residential Building Development Services
N.A.I.C.S.: 531311
Lin Yu *(Chm & Pres)*

FUJIAN SBS ZIPPER SCIENCE

& TECHNOLOGY CO., LTD.

Wulou Goudong Industrial Zone, Shenhu, Jinjiang, 362246, Fujian, China
Tel.: (86) 59568866056
Web Site: https://www.sbs-zipper.com
Year Founded: 1992
002098—(SSE)
Rev.: $296,587,980
Assets: $259,007,112
Liabilities: $105,784,380
Net Worth: $153,222,732
Earnings: $11,456,640
Emp.: 3,100
Fiscal Year-end: 12/31/22
Zipper Product Mfr
N.A.I.C.S.: 339993
Zhang Guogen *(Chm)*

FUJIAN SEPTWOLVES INDUSTRY CO., LTD.

South Industrial Zone, Jinjing Town, Jinjiang, 362251, Fujian, China
Tel.: (86) 59585337739
Web Site: http://www.septwolves.com
Year Founded: 2001
002029—(SSE)
Rev.: $453,268,764
Assets: $1,551,455,100
Liabilities: $669,524,076
Net Worth: $881,931,024
Earnings: $21,151,260
Fiscal Year-end: 12/31/22
Apparel Product Mfr
N.A.I.C.S.: 315250
Shaoxiong Zhou *(Chm & Gen Mgr)*

FUJIAN SNOWMAN CO., LTD.

Dongjiang West Road Minjiangkou Industrial Zone, Changle, Fuzhou, 350200, Fujian, China
Tel.: (86) 59128926606
Web Site: https://www.snowkey.com
Year Founded: 2000
002639—(SSE)
Rev.: $276,030,612
Assets: $635,276,304
Liabilities: $285,434,604
Net Worth: $349,841,700
Earnings: ($28,463,292)
Fiscal Year-end: 12/31/22
Ice Making Machine Mfr
N.A.I.C.S.: 335220
Lin Rujie *(Chm & Gen Mgr)*

Subsidiaries:

Fujian Opcon Energy Technology Co., Ltd.   **(1)**
Dongshan Road, Minjiangkou Industrial District, Fuzhou, Fujian, China
Tel.: (86) 59128813280
Web Site: http://www.fj-opcon.com
Eletric Power Generation Services
N.A.I.C.S.: 221118

Hydrogen Energy Co., Ltd.   **(1)**
Dongjiang West Road, Minjiangkou Industrial Zone, Fuzhou, Fujian, China
Tel.: (86) 5912 892 1053
Ice Making Equipment Mfr & Distr
N.A.I.C.S.: 333415

PT. Snowman Mandiri Indonesia   **(1)**
Sedayu Square Blok M No 20 Jl Outer Ringroad Lkr Luar, Cengkareng Barat Kota Jakarta Barat, Jakarta, 11730, Indonesia
Tel.: (62) 212 255 4810
Web Site: https://www.snowkey.id
Ice Making Equipment Mfr & Distr
N.A.I.C.S.: 333415

Refcomp Italy S.r.l.   **(1)**
Tel.: (39) 0444726726
Web Site: http://www.refcomp.it
Refrigeration Compressor Mfr
N.A.I.C.S.: 333415

Sichuan Jiayun Oil Gas Equipment Co., Ltd.   **(1)**

4F-7F Building 2 Southwest Jiaotong University Research Institute, Section 4 Huafu Avenue Shuangliu District, Chengdu, Sichuan, China
Tel.: (86) 2885738777
Oil & Gas Mfr
N.A.I.C.S.: 333132

Snowman Middle East FZCO   **(1)**
PO Box 17723, Jebel Ali Free Zone, Dubai, United Arab Emirates
Tel.: (971) 42239835
Industrial Machinery Mfr
N.A.I.C.S.: 333242

Svenska Rotor Maskiner AB   **(1)**
Rotorslingan / Varmdovagen 120, Nacka, Sweden
Tel.: (46) 84664500
Web Site:
    http://www.svenskarotormaskiner.com
Compressor Mfr
N.A.I.C.S.: 333415
Marie Nilsson *(CFO)*

FUJIAN STAR-NET COMMUNICATION CO.,LTD

Xingwang Ruijie Technology Park No 33 Xingang Avenue High-tech Zone, Fuzhou, 350108, Fujian, China
Tel.: (86) 59128053888
Web Site: https://www.star-net.cn
Year Founded: 1996
002396—(SSE)
Rev.: $2,209,976,028
Assets: $2,028,232,440
Liabilities: $809,149,068
Net Worth: $1,219,083,372
Earnings: $80,878,824
Emp.: 8,000
Fiscal Year-end: 12/31/22
Network Communication System Equipment Production & Sales
N.A.I.C.S.: 334290
Yihao Huang *(Chm)*

Subsidiaries:

Akuvox (Xiamen) Networks Co., Ltd.   **(1)**
10/F No 56 Guanri Road Software Park II, Xiamen, China
Tel.: (86) 5922133061
Web Site: http://www.akuvox.com
Intercom Product Mfr
N.A.I.C.S.: 334290

Ruijie Networks Co., Ltd.   **(1)**
Building 19 No 618 Jinshan Road, Juyuanzhou Industrial Park Cangshan District, Fuzhou, Fujian, China
Tel.: (86) 280538886729
Web Site: https://www.ruijienetworks.com
Intercom Product Mfr
N.A.I.C.S.: 334290

FUJIAN START GROUP CO., LTD.

Standard Workshop C Community A Science & Technology Industrial Zone, Economic & Technological Development Zone, Fuzhou, 350101, Fujian, China
Tel.: (86) 59183708108
Web Site: http://www.start.com.cn
Year Founded: 1996
600734—(SHG)
Rev.: $36,829,012
Assets: $130,231,376
Liabilities: $80,380,039
Net Worth: $49,851,337
Earnings: ($13,700,386)
Fiscal Year-end: 12/31/22
Real Estate Services
N.A.I.C.S.: 531390
Lei Huanhua *(Chm)*

FUJIAN SUNNER DEVELOPMENT CO., LTD.

Office Building of Sunner Headquarters Shilipu, Guangze County, Nanping, 354100, Fujian, China

Fujian Sunner Development Co., Ltd.—(Continued)

Tel.: (86) 5997951242
Web Site: http://www.sunnercn.com
Year Founded: 1999
002299—(SSE)
Rev.: $2,361,119,436
Assets: $2,657,537,532
Liabilities: $1,261,548,756
Net Worth: $1,395,988,776
Earnings: $57,690,360
Fiscal Year-end: 12/31/22
Poultry Services
N.A.I.C.S.: 311615
Guangming Fu *(Chm & Gen Mgr)*

**FUJIAN SUPERTECH AD-
VANCED MATERIAL CO., LTD.**
No 5 Industrial Second Road, Lia-
ncheng Industrial Park, Shanghai,
366200, Fujian, China
Tel.: (86) 5926199915
Web Site: https://www.supertech-
vip.com
Year Founded: 2007
688398—(SHG)
Rev.: $89,534,231
Assets: $163,629,798
Liabilities: $31,750,955
Net Worth: $131,878,843
Earnings: $8,966,183
Fiscal Year-end: 12/31/22
Vacuum Insulation Material Mfr
N.A.I.C.S.: 334419
Kunming Wang *(Chm)*

FUJIAN TENDERING CO., LTD.
No 68 Hongshanyuan Road, Gulou
District, Fuzhou, 350002, Fujian,
China
Tel.: (86) 59183709309
Web Site: https://www.fjzbgf.com
Year Founded: 2016
301136—(CHIN)
Rev.: $96,649,704
Assets: $306,448,281
Liabilities: $92,309,549
Net Worth: $214,138,732
Earnings: $3,231,225
Fiscal Year-end: 12/31/23
Engineeering Services
N.A.I.C.S.: 541330
Qinyi Zhang *(Chm)*

**FUJIAN TIANMA SCIENCE &
TECHNOLOGY GROUP CO.,
LTD.**
Shangjing Town Industrial Zone,
Fuqing, 350308, Fujian, China
Tel.: (86) 59185628333
Web Site: https://www.jolma.cn
Year Founded: 2005
603668—(SHG)
Rev.: $983,857,268
Assets: $1,070,290,611
Liabilities: $729,450,404
Net Worth: $340,840,207
Earnings: $18,294,176
Fiscal Year-end: 12/31/22
Aquatic Compound Feed Mfr & Distr
N.A.I.C.S.: 311119
Zheng Kun *(Exec Dir)*

**FUJIAN TORCH ELECTRON
TECHNOLOGY CO., LTD.**
No 4 Zihua Road Jiangnan Park
High-tech Park, Quanzhou, 362000,
Fujian, China
Tel.: (86) 59522353689
Web Site: https://www.torch.cn
Year Founded: 1989
603678—(SHG)
Rev.: $499,643,600
Assets: $1,058,841,651
Liabilities: $291,501,962
Net Worth: $767,339,689
Earnings: $112,523,987

Fiscal Year-end: 12/31/22
Capacitor Mfr & Distr
N.A.I.C.S.: 334416
Cai Jinjun *(Chm & Gen Mgr)*

**FUJIAN WANCHEN BIOTECH-
NOLOGY GROUP CO., LTD.**
Taiwan Farmers Entrepreneurship
Park, Zhangzhou, 363204, Fujian,
China
Tel.: (86) 5966312889
Web Site: https://www.vanchen.com
Year Founded: 2011
300972—(SSE)
Rev.: $77,116,104
Assets: $166,969,296
Liabilities: $72,565,740
Net Worth: $94,403,556
Earnings: $6,706,908
Fiscal Year-end: 12/31/22
Mushroom Production Services
N.A.I.C.S.: 111411

**FUJIAN YANJING HUIQUAN
BREWERY CO., LTD.**
No 1999 Huiquan North Road, Lu-
ocheng Town Huian County, Quan-
zhou, 362100, Fujian, China
Tel.: (86) 59587396105
Web Site: http://www.hqbeer.com
Year Founded: 1997
600573—(SHG)
Rev.: $86,123,480
Assets: $197,881,782
Liabilities: $26,499,433
Net Worth: $171,382,349
Earnings: $5,594,701
Fiscal Year-end: 12/31/22
Beer Brewing & Distribution Services
N.A.I.C.S.: 312120
Zhenan Gao *(Chm & Gen Mgr)*

**FUJIAN YONGAN FORESTRY
(GROUP) CO., LTD.**
No 819 Yanjiang East Road, Yongan,
Sanming, 366000, Fujian, China
Tel.: (86) 5983614875
Web Site: http://www.yonglin.com
Year Founded: 1994
000663—(SSE)
Rev.: $106,230,852
Assets: $158,425,956
Liabilities: $26,574,912
Net Worth: $131,851,044
Earnings: $37,627,200
Fiscal Year-end: 12/31/22
Wood Products Mfr
N.A.I.C.S.: 321999
Lv Jincheng *(Chm)*

**FUJIAN YONGFU POWER EN-
GINEERING CO., LTD.**
No 3 Gaoxin Avenue Haixi Science
and Technology Park Shangjie Town,
Minhou County, Fuzhou, 350108, Fu-
jian, China
Tel.: (86) 59138269599
Web Site: http://www.fjyfdl.com
Year Founded: 1994
300712—(CHIN)
Rev.: $286,517,253
Assets: $608,371,785
Liabilities: $406,357,222
Net Worth: $202,014,563
Earnings: $7,652,268
Fiscal Year-end: 12/31/23
Power Engineering Technical Ser-
vices
N.A.I.C.S.: 541330

**FUJIAN YUANLI ACTIVE CAR-
BON CO., LTD**
Yuanli Building No 8 Zhuxi Road,
Yanping District, Nanping, 353004,
Fujian, China
Tel.: (86) 5998558381

Web Site:
https://www.yuanlicarbon.com
Year Founded: 1999
300174—(CHIN)
Rev.: $273,918,996
Assets: $513,802,224
Liabilities: $89,516,232
Net Worth: $424,285,992
Earnings: $31,512,780
Emp.: 142
Fiscal Year-end: 12/31/22
Activated Carbon Mfr
N.A.I.C.S.: 335991
Xu Wenxian *(Chm & Gen Mgr)*

**FUJIAN YUANXIANG NEW MA-
TERIALS CO., LTD.**
Suburban Industrial Park, Shaowu,
Nanping, 354000, Fujian, China
Tel.: (86) 5996301908
Web Site:
https://www.fjyuanxiang.com
Year Founded: 2006
301300—(CHIN)
Rev.: $51,523,992
Assets: $135,755,568
Liabilities: $19,625,112
Net Worth: $116,130,456
Earnings: $7,477,704
Fiscal Year-end: 12/31/22
Chemical Product Mfr & Distr
N.A.I.C.S.: 327120
Chenghui Wang *(Chm)*

**FUJIAN ZHANGZHOU DEVEL-
OPMENT CO., LTD.**
21F Zhangzhou Development Square
Shengli East Road, Zhangzhou,
363000, Fujian, China
Tel.: (86) 5962671029
Web Site: http://www.zzdc.com.cn
Year Founded: 1994
000753—(SSE)
Rev.: $400,493,808
Assets: $1,256,254,272
Liabilities: $853,953,516
Net Worth: $402,300,756
Earnings: $10,633,896
Fiscal Year-end: 12/31/22
Automobile Product Distr
N.A.I.C.S.: 423110
Lin Huijuan *(Sec)*

**FUJIAN ZHENYUN PLASTICS
INDUSTRY CO., LTD.**
Jingyang Industrial Zone, Fuqing, Fu-
jian, China
Tel.: (86) 591 38723876
Web Site:
http://www.zhenyunpipes.com
Year Founded: 1992
5KT—(CAT)
Sales Range: $50-74.9 Million
Emp.: 1,000
Plastic Pipe Product Mfr
N.A.I.C.S.: 326122
Chan Chin Huang *(Chm)*

FUJIBO HOLDINGS, INC.
1-18-12 Nihonbashi Ningyocho,
Chuo-ku, Tokyo, 103-0013, Japan
Tel.: (81) 336657777
Web Site: https://www.fujibo.co.jp
Year Founded: 1896
3104—(TKS)
Rev.: $238,673,880
Assets: $413,204,320
Liabilities: $122,542,790
Net Worth: $290,661,530
Earnings: $13,993,370
Emp.: 1,299
Fiscal Year-end: 03/31/24
Textile Products Mfr
N.A.I.C.S.: 313110
Mitsuo Nakano *(Chm, Pres & Exec
VP)*

Subsidiaries:

Fujichemi Co., Ltd.   (1)
159/14 Serm-Mit Tower Building No 903-
904 9th Floor, Soi Asoke Sukhumvit 21 Rd
North Klongtoey Wattana, Bangkok, 10110,
Thailand
Tel.: (66) 226086514
Web Site: https://www.fujichemithai.com
Chemical Products Mfr
N.A.I.C.S.: 325998

Yanai Chemical Industry Co.,
Ltd.   (1)
Tel.: (81) 336657784
Web Site: http://www.yanai.co.jp
Chemical Products Mfr
N.A.I.C.S.: 325998

FUJICCO CO., LTD.
6-13-4 Minatojima Nakamachi, Chuo-
Ku, Kobe, 650-8558, Hyogo, Japan
Tel.: (81) 783035911
Web Site: https://www.fujicco.co.jp
Year Founded: 1960
2908—(TKS)
Rev.: $368,276,150
Assets: $531,946,360
Liabilities: $75,704,330
Net Worth: $456,242,030
Earnings: $7,337,100
Emp.: 2,364
Fiscal Year-end: 03/31/24
Food Product Mfr & Whslr
N.A.I.C.S.: 311710
Masakazu Fukui *(Pres & CEO)*

FUJICOPIAN CO., LTD.
4-14 Mitejima 5-chome Nishi,
Yodogawa-ku, Osaka, 555-0012, Ja-
pan
Tel.: (81) 664717071
Web Site: https://www.fujicopian.com
Year Founded: 1950
7957—(TKS)
Rev.: $58,315,250
Assets: $114,602,760
Liabilities: $41,270,890
Net Worth: $73,331,870
Earnings: ($6,069,040)
Emp.: 272
Fiscal Year-end: 12/31/23
Office Goods Mfr & Whslr
N.A.I.C.S.: 339940
Kantaro Akashiro *(Pres)*

Subsidiaries:

FC VIETNAM CORPORATION   (1)
Long Binh Techno Park, Long Binh Ward,
Bien Hoa, Dong Nai, Vietnam
Tel.: (84) 613892145
Data Processing Equipment Distr
N.A.I.C.S.: 423430

Fuji Copian (H.K.) Ltd.   (1)
Unit 2202 22nd Floor Peninsula Tower No
538 Castle Peak Road, Cheung Sha Wan,
Kowloon, China (Hong Kong)
Tel.: (852) 21551488
Data Processing Equipment Distr
N.A.I.C.S.: 423430

Fujicopian Co., Ltd. - Okayama
Plant   (1)
12 banchi Taiheidai, Shoo-cho Katsuta-gun,
Okayama, Japan
Tel.: (81) 868385157
Data Processing Equipment Mfr
N.A.I.C.S.: 334513

**FUJIFILM HOLDINGS CORPO-
RATION**
7-3 Akasaka 9-chome, Minato-ku,
Tokyo, 107-0052, Japan
Tel.: (81) 362711111   **JP**
Web Site: https://holdings.fujifilm.com
Year Founded: 1934
FUJIY—(OTCIQ)
Rev.: $19,571,654,760
Assets: $31,618,670,600
Liabilities: $10,643,058,450

Net Worth: $20,975,612,150
Earnings: $1,609,594,490
Emp.: 72,254
Fiscal Year-end: 03/31/24
Holding Company
N.A.I.C.S.: 551112
Chisato Yoshizawa *(VP & Gen Mgr-Corp Comm, ESG & Global Audit Div)*

Subsidiaries:

ASSISTEC Co. Ltd.   **(1)**
1-1-1 Nishitsutsumihondorihigashi, Higashiosaka, Osaka, Japan
Tel.: (81) 664530541
Web Site: http://www.assistec.jp
Software Development Services
N.A.I.C.S.: 541511
Takayasu Ito *(CEO)*

BioCare Europe S.r.l.   **(1)**
Via Emilio Motta 10, 20144, Milan, Italy
Tel.: (39) 0644240341
Web Site: http://www.biocareeurope.com
Biotechnology Equipment Mfr
N.A.I.C.S.: 334516

Camera House Limited   **(1)**
4/108 Old Pittwater Road, Brookvale, Sydney, 2100, NSW, Australia
Tel.: (61) 2 8978 8700
Photographic Equipment Retailer
N.A.I.C.S.: 423410
Charlie David *(Mng Dir)*

Celltrust Animal Therapeutics Co., Ltd.   **(1)**
6F City Hearts Chojamachi Building 2-6-3 Chojamachi, Naka-ku, Yokohama, 231-0033, Kanagawa, Japan
Tel.: (81) 453348495
Web Site: http://www.celltrust.jp
Stem Cell Treatment Services
N.A.I.C.S.: 621340

DS Chemport (Australia) Pty LTD   **(1)**
41 Jesica Road, PO Box 29, Campbellfield, 3061, VIC, Australia
Tel.: (61) 3 9357 0933
Web Site: http://www.dschemport.com.au
Photographic Chemical Coating Mfr
N.A.I.C.S.: 325992

DS Chemport (Malaysia) SDN. BHD.   **(1)**
No 22 Jalan Jurunilai U1/20 Seksyen U1 Hicom Glenmarie Industrial Park, Shah Alam, 40150, Selangor Darul Ehsan, Malaysia
Tel.: (60) 3 5567 0452
Web Site: http://www.dscmal.com.my
Sales Range: $25-49.9 Million
Emp.: 14
Specialty Chemicals Mfr
N.A.I.C.S.: 325998
M. Balan *(Dir & Gen Mgr)*

FFGS Techno Service Co., Ltd.   **(1)**
1-4-11 Tatsumi St Bldg Tatsumibekkan, Koto-Ku, Tokyo, 135-0053, Japan
Tel.: (81) 335227074
Sales Range: $25-49.9 Million
Emp.: 19
Photographic Equipment Mfr
N.A.I.C.S.: 333310
Masanori Kato *(Mgr)*

FUJIFILM Business Expert Corporation   **(1)**
4-12-24 Nishi-Azabu Kowa Nishi-Azabu Building, Minato-ku, Tokyo, 106-0031, Japan
Tel.: (81) 354857760
Web Site: http://www.ffbx.co.jp
BPO Management Services
N.A.I.C.S.: 561990

FUJIFILM Business Supply Co., Ltd.   **(1)**
5F Shin-Nishi-Ginza Building 2-2-2 Ginza, Chuo-Ku, Tokyo, 104-0061, Japan
Tel.: (81) 3 3564 2224
Business Support Services
N.A.I.C.S.: 561499

FUJIFILM Colombia S.A.S   **(1)**
Carrera 15 N 88 - 64 Edificio Torre Zimma

Oficina 402, 110221, Bogota, Colombia
Tel.: (57) 15190806
N.A.I.C.S.: 456130

FUJIFILM Computer System Co., Ltd.   **(1)**
Odakyu Minamiaoyama Bldg, Minato-Ku, Tokyo, 107-0062, Japan
Tel.: (81) 354698300
Information Technology Consulting Services
N.A.I.C.S.: 541512

FUJIFILM Corporation   **(1)**
Midtown West 7-3 Akasaka 9-chome, Minato-ku, Tokyo, 107-0052, Japan   **(100%)**
Tel.: (81) 362713111
Web Site: https://www.fujifilm.com
Emp.: 39,010
Film & Digital Camera, Photographic Supplies, Film & Chemicals Mfr
N.A.I.C.S.: 333310
Kouichi Tamai *(Chm-FUJIFILM Bus Innovation)*

Subsidiary (Non-US):

FUJIFILM (China) Investment Co., Ltd.   **(2)**
28F One Lujiazui No 68 YinCheng Zhong Road Pudong New Area, Shanghai, 200120, China
Tel.: (86) 21 50106000
Web Site: http://www.fujifilm.com
Sales Range: $200-249.9 Million
Emp.: 700
Photographic Equipment Mfr & Distr
N.A.I.C.S.: 333310

FUJIFILM (Malaysia) Sdn. Bhd.   **(2)**
22 Jalan Jurunilai U1/20 Seksyen U1, Hicom-Glenmarie Industrial Park, 40150, Shah Alam, Selangor, Malaysia
Tel.: (60) 355698388
Web Site: http://www.fujifilm.com.my
Sales Range: $50-74.9 Million
Emp.: 170
Camera Film Distr
N.A.I.C.S.: 423410

FUJIFILM (NZ) Limited   **(2)**
2C William Pickering Drive, Rosedale, Auckland, 0632, New Zealand
Tel.: (64) 94140400
Web Site: http://www.fujifilm.co.nz
Sales Range: $25-49.9 Million
Emp.: 75
Film Processing
N.A.I.C.S.: 449210
Hayley Clarke *(Officer-Privacy)*

FUJIFILM (Singapore) Pte. Ltd.   **(2)**
10 New Industrial Road Fujifilm Building, Singapore, 536201, Singapore
Tel.: (65) 63839933
Web Site: http://www.fujifilm.com.sg
Sales Range: $50-74.9 Million
Emp.: 110
Photographic Supplies & Equipment Sales & Distr
N.A.I.C.S.: 423410

FUJIFILM (Thailand) Ltd.   **(2)**
8th Floor SP Building 388 Phahonyothin Road, Samsen Nai Subdistrict Phaya Thai District, Bangkok, 10400, Thailand
Tel.: (66) 2 270 6000
Web Site: http://www.fujifilm.co.th
Sales Range: $50-74.9 Million
Emp.: 232
Photographic Film Distr
N.A.I.C.S.: 424690

FUJIFILM ASIA PACIFIC PTE. LTD.   **(2)**
10 New Industrial Road Fujifilm Building, Singapore, 536201, Singapore
Tel.: (65) 6383 9933
Sales Range: $25-49.9 Million
Emp.: 150
Photographic & Binocular Lens Mfr
N.A.I.C.S.: 333310

FUJIFILM Australia Pty. Ltd.   **(2)**
114 Old Pittwater Rd, Brookvale, 2100, NSW, Australia
Tel.: (61) 294662600
Web Site: http://www.fujifilm.com.au
Sales Range: $50-74.9 Million
Emp.: 250
Photographic & Electronic Equipment

N.A.I.C.S.: 423410

FUJIFILM Canada Inc.   **(2)**
600 Suffolk Ct, Mississauga, L5R 4G4, ON, Canada
Tel.: (905) 890-6611
Web Site: http://www.fujifilm.ca
Sales Range: $50-74.9 Million
Emp.: 150
Photographic Supplies Distr
N.A.I.C.S.: 423410
Hideaki Tsuda *(Pres)*

Division (Domestic):

FUJIFILM Canda Inc.-Graphic Systems Division   **(3)**
600 Suffolk Court, Mississauga, L5R 4G4, ON, Canada
Tel.: (905) 890-6611
Web Site: http://www.fujifilm.ca
Sales Range: $25-49.9 Million
Graphic Arts & Imaging Technology Services
N.A.I.C.S.: 541430
Tony Karg *(Sr Dir-Bus Dev & Mktg)*

Subsidiary (Non-US):

FUJIFILM Diosynth Biotechnologies Denmark ApS   **(2)**
Biotek Alle 1, 3400, Hillerod, Denmark
Tel.: (45) 77416000
Web Site: https://fujifilmdiosynth.com
Biological Product Mfr
N.A.I.C.S.: 325414

FUJIFILM Diosynth Biotechnologies UK Limited   **(2)**
Belasis Avenue, Billingham, TS23 1LH, United Kingdom
Tel.: (44) 1642 363511
Sales Range: $100-124.9 Million
Emp.: 50
Biopharmaceutical Product Mfr
N.A.I.C.S.: 325412
Steve Bagshaw *(CEO)*

FUJIFILM Dis Ticaret A.S.   **(2)**
Mahmutbey Mahallesi Tasocagi Yolu Caddesi No 9, Bagcilar, Istanbul, 34218, Turkiye
Tel.: (90) 2127099200
Web Site: http://www.fujifilm.com.tr
Photographic Equipment Distr
N.A.I.C.S.: 423410

FUJIFILM Electronic Imaging Korea Co., Ltd.   **(2)**
3F Peco B/D 838 Seolleung-ro, Gangnam-ku, Seoul, 06014, Korea (South)
Tel.: (82) 2 30111800
Web Site: http://fujifilm.kr
Sales Range: $25-49.9 Million
Emp.: 15
Digital Camera Distr
N.A.I.C.S.: 423410

FUJIFILM Europe GmbH   **(2)**
Heesenstr 31, 40549, Dusseldorf, Germany
Tel.: (81) 21150890
Web Site: http://www.fujifilm.de
Sales Range: $125-149.9 Million
Emp.: 400
Cameras & Photographic Supplies Sales & Distr
N.A.I.C.S.: 423410

Subsidiary (Non-US):

FUJIFILM CZ, s.r.o.   **(3)**
U Nakladoveho Nadrazi 2, 130 00, Prague, 3, Czech Republic
Tel.: (420) 234703470
Web Site: http://www.fujifilm.cz
Sales Range: $25-49.9 Million
Emp.: 36
Photographic Products Distr
N.A.I.C.S.: 423410

FUJIFILM Denmark A/S   **(3)**
Stubbeled 2, PO Box 70, Trorod, 2950, Vedbaek, Denmark
Tel.: (45) 45 66 22 44
Sales Range: $25-49.9 Million
Emp.: 2
Photographic Equipment Mfr
N.A.I.C.S.: 333310

Subsidiary (Domestic):

FUJIFILM Electronic Imaging Europe GmbH   **(3)**

Fujistrasse 1, 47533, Kleve, Germany
Tel.: (49) 2821 7115 0
Web Site: http://www.fujifilm.eu
Emp.: 5
Digital Camera & Supplies Distr
N.A.I.C.S.: 423410

Subsidiary (Non-US):

FUJIFILM Espana, S.A.   **(3)**
Aragon 180, 08011, Barcelona, Spain
Tel.: (34) 934511515
Web Site: http://www.fujifilm.es
Sales Range: $50-74.9 Million
Emp.: 175
Cameras, Film & Photographic Supplies Distr
N.A.I.C.S.: 424690
Salbador Luna *(Mgr-Optical Div)*

FUJIFILM Europe B.V.   **(3)**
Oudenstaart 1, 5047 TK, Tilburg, Netherlands
Tel.: (31) 13 579 19 11
Web Site: http://www.fujifilm.com
Holding Company
N.A.I.C.S.: 551112

Subsidiary (Domestic):

FUJIFILM Manufacturing Europe B.V.   **(4)**
Oudenstaart 1, 5047 TK, Tilburg, Netherlands
Tel.: (31) 135791911
Web Site: http://www.fujitilburg.nl
Sales Range: $200-249.9 Million
Emp.: 850
Photosensitized Plates, Papers & Films Mfr & Distr
N.A.I.C.S.: 325992

Subsidiary (Non-US):

FUJIFILM Europe N.V.   **(3)**
Europark Noord 21-22, Saint-Niklaas, 9100, Belgium
Tel.: (32) 37600200
Web Site: http://www.fujifilm.eu
Sales Range: $75-99.9 Million
Emp.: 150
Camera, Film & Photographic Equipment & Supplies Mfr & Distr
N.A.I.C.S.: 423410
Alexis Van Oostende *(Gen Mgr)*

Subsidiary (Domestic):

FUJIFILM Electronic Materials (Europe) N.V.   **(4)**
Keetberglaan 1A Havennummer 1061, 2070, Zwijndrecht, Belgium
Tel.: (32) 3 250 0511
Web Site: http://www.fujifilm-ssen.com
Sales Range: $25-49.9 Million
Emp.: 140
Electronic Components Mfr
N.A.I.C.S.: 334419
Herman Driegh *(Mng Dir)*

FUJIFILM Hunt Chemicals Europe N.V.   **(4)**
Zwaluwbeekstraat 14, 9150, Kruibeke, Belgium
Tel.: (32) 37600200
Web Site: http://www.fujifilm.eu
Sales Range: $25-49.9 Million
Emp.: 100
Photographic Chemicals Mfr, Sales & Distr
N.A.I.C.S.: 325992
Shimichi Fujii *(Gen Mgr)*

Subsidiary (Non-US):

Fuji Hunt Iberica S.L.   **(5)**
Apdo Correnos 381, Vendrell, 43700, Tarragona, Spain
Tel.: (34) 97 716 87 00
Web Site: http://www.fujifilm.eu
Photochemical Distr
N.A.I.C.S.: 424690

Fuji Hunt Nordic AB   **(5)**
Bn Grand 6, PO Box 90185, 120 22, Stockholm, Sweden
Tel.: (46) 87740890
Web Site: http://www.fujifilm.com
Sales Range: $25-49.9 Million
Emp.: 5
Photographic Chemicals Sales & Distr

FUJIFILM Holdings Corporation—(Continued)
N.A.I.C.S.: 424690

Subsidiary (Domestic):

FUJIFILM Medical Systems Benelux N.V. **(4)**
Westpoort 62 Unit 2, 2070, Zwijndrecht, Belgium
Tel.: (32) 37600322
Web Site: http://www.fujimsb.be
Sales Range: $25-49.9 Million
Emp.: 30
X-Ray Film & Chemicals Sales & Distr
N.A.I.C.S.: 325992
Toyo Asai (Mng Dir)

Fuji Hunt Photographic Chemicals, N.V. **(4)**
Europark-Noord 21-22, 9100, Saint-Nicolas, Belgium
Tel.: (32) 3 760 0200
Sales Range: $50-74.9 Million
Emp.: 20
Photographic Chemicals Mfr
N.A.I.C.S.: 325998
Alexis van Oostende (Mng Dir & Dir-Fin)

Subsidiary (Non-US):

FUJIFILM France S.A.S. **(3)**
5 avenue des Chaumes, CS 40760, Montigny, 78066, Saint-Quentin-en-Yvelines, Cedex, France
Tel.: (33) 1 30 14 34 56
Web Site: http://www.fujifilm.fr
Sales Range: $25-49.9 Million
Emp.: 180
Photographic Equipment & Supplies Sales & Distr
N.A.I.C.S.: 333310

Subsidiary (Domestic):

FUJIFILM Medical Systems France S.A.S. **(4)**
Immeuble Objectif II 2 rue Louis Armand, Asnieres, 92600, France
Tel.: (33) 1 47 15 55 15
Medical Equipment Distr
N.A.I.C.S.: 423450

Subsidiary (Non-US):

FUJIFILM Hungary Ltd. **(3)**
Becsi ut 271, 1037, Budapest, Hungary
Tel.: (36) 1 577 9800
Photographic Equipment & Supplies Distr
N.A.I.C.S.: 423410

Subsidiary (Domestic):

FUJIFILM Imaging Germany GmbH & Co. KG **(3)**
Siemensring 1, 47877, Willich, Germany
Tel.: (49) 2154 89788 0
Sales Range: $75-99.9 Million
Emp.: 50
Photo Finishing & Photo Imaging Services
N.A.I.C.S.: 812921

Subsidiary (Non-US):

FUJIFILM Italia S.p.A. **(3)**
S S n 11 Padana Superiore 2/B, 20063, Cernusco sul Naviglio, Milan, Italy
Tel.: (39) 02929741
Web Site: http://www.fujifilm.it
Sales Range: $25-49.9 Million
Emp.: 100
Photographic Products Distr
N.A.I.C.S.: 423410

Subsidiary (Domestic):

FUJIFILM Recording Media Italia S.R.L **(4)**
Strada Statale N 11 Padana Superiore 2/B, 20063, Cernusco sul Naviglio, Milan, Italy
Tel.: (39) 02 92974 1
Web Site: http://www.fujifilm.it
Magnetic Recording Media Mfr
N.A.I.C.S.: 334610

Subsidiary (Non-US):

FUJIFILM Nordic AB **(3)**
Sveavagen 167, 104 35, Stockholm, Sweden
Tel.: (46) 8 506 141 00

Digital Camera Import & Distr
N.A.I.C.S.: 423410

FUJIFILM Polska Distribution Spolka zo.o **(3)**
Al Jerozolimskie 178, 02-486, Warsaw, Poland
Tel.: (48) 225176600
Web Site: http://www.fujifilm.pl
Photographic Products Distr
N.A.I.C.S.: 423410

Subsidiary (Domestic):

FUJIFILM Recording Media GmbH **(3)**
Fujistrasse 1, 47533, Kleve, Germany
Tel.: (49) 28215090
Web Site: http://www.fujifilm.eu
Sales Range: $25-49.9 Million
Emp.: 40
Audio & Video Tape & Computer Storage Systems Mfr & Distr
N.A.I.C.S.: 334610
Wolfgang May (Mng Dir)

Fujicolor Central Europe Photofinishing GmbH & Co. KG **(3)**
Siemens Ring 1, 47877, Willich, Germany
Tel.: (49) 896490870
Web Site: http://www.fujicolor.de
Sales Range: $10-24.9 Million
Emp.: 50
Film Processing & Finishing Services
N.A.I.C.S.: 812921

Branch (Non-US):

Fujicolor Benelux B.V. **(4)**
Franseweg 65, 4651 GE, Steenbergen, Netherlands
Tel.: (31) 167569911
Web Site: http://www.fujicolor.nl
Emp.: 150
Developing & Printing Services
N.A.I.C.S.: 323111
Gerardus Van Gendt (Mng Dir)

Fujicolor Sverige AB **(4)**
Hantverkargatan 25B, 11221, Stockholm, Sweden
Tel.: (46) 86806400
Web Site: http://www.fujicolor.se
Emp.: 5
Photographic Products & Services; Owned 75% by Fuji Photo Film (Europe) GmbH & 25% by Axel Johnson International AB
N.A.I.C.S.: 333310
Gorsten Seal (Gen Mgr)

Laboratoires Fujifilm SA **(4)**
16 Rue Etienne Jules Marey, 78390, Bois-d'Arcy, Cedex, France
Tel.: (33) 130143456
Web Site: http://www.fujifilmnet.com
Photographic Services
N.A.I.C.S.: 333310

Subsidiary (Domestic):

Fujinon (Europe) GmbH **(3)**
Halskestrasse 4, 47877, Willich, Germany
Tel.: (49) 021549240
Web Site: http://www.fujinon.de
Sales Range: $50-74.9 Million
Emp.: 140
TV Lenses & Medical Equipment Marketer & Distr
N.A.I.C.S.: 333310
Hidetoshi Kimura (Pres)

IP Labs GmbH **(3)**
Schwertberger Strasse 14-16, Bad Godesberg, 53177, Bonn, Germany
Tel.: (49) 228 18479 0
Web Site: http://www.iplabs.de
Sales Range: $25-49.9 Million
Emp.: 6
Photo Service Software Development Services
N.A.I.C.S.: 541511

Subsidiary (Non-US):

FUJIFILM FILMED Tibbi Cihazlar Pazarlama Ve Ticaret A.S. **(2)**
YeniSehir Mahallesi Baraj Yolu Caddesi Aral Sokak, Atasehir, Istanbul, Turkiye
Tel.: (90) 216 456 68 88
Web Site: http://www.filmed.com.tr

Endoscopic Equipment Distr
N.A.I.C.S.: 423450

FUJIFILM Hong Kong Limited **(2)**
Unit 1001-1007 10/F Metroplaza Tower 2 223 Hing Fong Road, Kwai Fong, NT, China (Hong Kong)
Tel.: (852) 2317 0307
Web Site: http://www.fujifilm.com
Optical Device & Diagnostic Imaging Equipment Distr
N.A.I.C.S.: 423460

FUJIFILM Hunt Chemicals Singapore Pte. Ltd. **(2)**
15 Tuas Avenue 7, Singapore, 639270, Singapore
Tel.: (65) 6862 2116
Web Site: http://www.fujifilm.com.sg
Sales Range: $25-49.9 Million
Emp.: 75
Photographic Chemicals Mfr & Distr
N.A.I.C.S.: 325992
Katsumi Nii (Gen Mgr)

FUJIFILM Imaging Colorants Limited **(2)**
Earls Road, Grangemouth, FK3 8XG, Stirlingshire, United Kingdom
Tel.: (44) 1324468468
Web Site: http://www.fujifilmusa.com
Sales Range: $25-49.9 Million
Emp.: 91
Printing Ink Mfr
N.A.I.C.S.: 325910
Ian Wilkinson (COO)

FUJIFILM Imaging Systems (Suzhou) Co., Ltd. **(2)**
138 Changjiang Road, New District, Suzhou, 215000, Jiangsu, China
Tel.: (86) 51268251188
Web Site: http://www.fujifilm.com.cn
Sales Range: $25-49.9 Million
Emp.: 55
Imaging Systems Mfr
N.A.I.C.S.: 333310

FUJIFILM Ireland Ltd. **(2)**
Unit 78A Lagan Road, Dublin Industrial Estate Glasnevin, Dublin, 11, Ireland
Tel.: (353) 18820200
Web Site: http://www.fujifilm.eu
Sales Range: $25-49.9 Million
Emp.: 24
Photographic Products Distr
N.A.I.C.S.: 423410

FUJIFILM Middle East FZE **(2)**
Jafza View 19 Level 23, Dubai, United Arab Emirates
Tel.: (971) 4 887 8722
Web Site: http://www.fujifilm.eu
Sales Range: $25-49.9 Million
Emp.: 22
Digital Camera & Medical Imaging Equipment Distr
N.A.I.C.S.: 423410

Subsidiary (US):

FUJIFILM North America Corporation **(2)**
200 Summit Lake Dr, Valhalla, NY 10595
Tel.: (914) 789-8100
Web Site: http://www.fujifilm.com
Digital & Analog Photographic Imaging Systems & Services
N.A.I.C.S.: 423410
Joan Rutherford (VP-Corp Comm)

Subsidiary (Domestic):

Cellular Dynamics International, Inc. **(3)**
525 Science Dr, Madison, WI 53711
Tel.: (608) 310-5100
Web Site: http://www.cellulardynamics.com
Sales Range: $10-24.9 Million
Human Cell Developer & Mfr
N.A.I.C.S.: 541715
Kazuyoshi Hirao (Chm & CEO)

FUJIFILM Dimatix, Inc. **(3)**
2250 Martin Ave, Santa Clara, CA 95050
Tel.: (408) 565-9150
Web Site: http://www.fujifilmusa.com
Inkjet Printer Mfr
N.A.I.C.S.: 333248
Martin Schoeppler (Pres & CEO)

FUJIFILM Diosynth Biotechnologies Inc. **(3)**
101 J Morris Commons Ln, Morrisville, NC 27560
Tel.: (919) 337-4477
Pharmaceuticals Product Mfr
N.A.I.C.S.: 325412

FUJIFILM Electronic Materials U.S.A. Inc. **(3)**
80 Circuit Dr, North Kingstown, RI 02852
Tel.: (401) 522-9499
Web Site: http://www.fujifilm-ffem.com
Sales Range: $25-49.9 Million
Emp.: 100
Mfr of Semiconductor Fabrication Products
N.A.I.C.S.: 334413

Subsidiary (Non-US):

FUJIFILM Electronic Materials (Europe) S.r.l. **(4)**
SS 11 Padana Superiore 2/B, Cernusco Sul Naviglio, 20063, Milan, Italy
Tel.: (39) 0298241060
Mfr of Semiconductor Fabrication Products
N.A.I.C.S.: 334413

Subsidiary (Domestic):

FUJIFILM Electronic Materials U.S.A., Inc. **(4)**
6550 S Mountain Rd, Mesa, AZ 85212
Tel.: (480) 987-7000
Web Site: http://www.fujifilm-ffem.com
Sales Range: $25-49.9 Million
Mfr of Semiconductor Fabrication Products
N.A.I.C.S.: 334413

FUJIFILM Planar Solutions, LLC **(4)**
6550 S Mountain Rd, Mesa, AZ 85212
Tel.: (480) 987-7226
Web Site: http://www.planarsolutions.com
Industrial Chemical Mfr & Distr
N.A.I.C.S.: 325998

FUJIFILM Ultra Pure Solutions Inc. **(4)**
11225 Commercial Pkwy, Castroville, CA 95012
Tel.: (831) 632-2120
Web Site: http://www.fujifilmusa.com
Sales Range: $1-9.9 Million
Emp.: 40
Chemical Products Mfr
N.A.I.C.S.: 325998
Bill Robb (VP-Mfg)

Subsidiary (Domestic):

FUJIFILM Hawaii, Inc. **(3)**
94 468 Akoki St, Waipahu, HI 96797
Tel.: (808) 677-3854
Web Site: http://www.fujifilmhawaii.com
Sales Range: $50-74.9 Million
Emp.: 90
Cameras, Film & Photographic Supplies Distr
N.A.I.C.S.: 423410
George Osuka (VP)

FUJIFILM Healthcare Americas Corporation **(3)**
81 Hartwell Ave Ste 300, Lexington, MA 02421
Tel.: (203) 324-2000
Web Site: https://healthcaresolutions-us.fujifilm.com
Diagnostic & Enterprise Imaging Solutions; Medical Digital Imaging Products & Film Distr
N.A.I.C.S.: 423450

Branch (Domestic):

FUJIFILM Medical Systems (California), Inc. **(4)**
2150 N 1st St Ste 550, San Jose, CA 95131
Tel.: (408) 501-2160
Web Site: http://www.fujimed.com
Sales Range: $25-49.9 Million
Emp.: 10
Photo Software Development & Research Services
N.A.I.C.S.: 449210

Division (Domestic):

FUJIFILM Medical Systems USA, Inc. - Endoscopy Div **(4)**

10 Highpoint Dr, Wayne, NJ 07470-7431
Tel.: (973) 633-5600
Web Site: http://www.fujifilmusa.com
Sales Range: $50-74.9 Million
Emp.: 85
Optics & Lenses Marketer
N.A.I.C.S.: 423460
Taisuke Fujita *(Gen Mgr-Endoscopy Div & Exec Dir)*

Subsidiary (Domestic):

FUJIFILM TeraMedica, Inc. **(4)**
10400 Innovation Dr Ste 200, Milwaukee, WI 53226
Tel.: (414) 008 7700
Web Site: https://www.teramedica.com
Sales Range: $1-9.9 Million
Emp.: 24
Medical Information Technology Solutions
N.A.I.C.S.: 541511
Gregory Strowig *(VP)*

Subsidiary (Domestic):

FUJIFILM Hunt Chemicals USA, Inc. **(3)**
40 Boroline Rd, Allendale, NJ 07401-1613
Tel.: (201) 995-2200
Web Site: http://www.fujihunt.com
Sales Range: $25-49.9 Million
Emp.: 70
Photographic Chemicals Mfr & Distr
N.A.I.C.S.: 325992

Division (Domestic):

FUJIFILM Hunt Chemicals Specialty Products Co. **(4)**
411 Manufacturers Rd, Dayton, TN 37321-5937
Tel.: (423) 775-2281
Web Site: http://www.fujihuntusa.com
Sales Range: $25-49.9 Million
Photographic Chemicals Mfr
N.A.I.C.S.: 325199
Mike Murray *(Gen Mgr)*

Subsidiary (Domestic):

FUJIFILM Hunt Photographic Chemicals Inc. **(3)**
40 Boroline Rd, Allendale, NJ 07401-0320
Tel.: (201) 995-2200
Web Site: http://www.fujihunt.com
Photochemical Mfr
N.A.I.C.S.: 325998

FUJIFILM Hunt Smart Surface, LLC **(3)**
40 Boroline Rd, Allendale, NJ 07401
Tel.: (201) 995-2200
Specialty Chemicals Mfr
N.A.I.C.S.: 325998

FUJIFILM Imaging Colorants Inc. **(3)**
233 Cherry Ln, New Castle, DE 19720
Tel.: (302) 472-1245
Web Site: http://www.fujifilm.eu
High Performance Colorant Mfr
N.A.I.C.S.: 325130

FUJIFILM Manufacturing USA, Inc. **(3)**
211 Puckett Ferry Rd, Greenwood, SC 29649-7915
Tel.: (864) 223-2888
Web Site: http://www.fujifilm.com
Sales Range: $500-549.9 Million
Emp.: 1,500
Cameras, Color Paper, Medical Imaging Products & Pre-Sensitized Plates Mfr
N.A.I.C.S.: 334610
Ron Confer *(Engr-Chemical)*

FUJIFILM Microdisks USA, Inc. **(3)**
45 Crosby Dr, Bedford, MA 01730-1401
Tel.: (781) 271-4400
Sales Range: $50-74.9 Million
Emp.: 102
Computed Information Storage Products Mfr & Packager
N.A.I.C.S.: 334118

FUJIFILM e-Systems, Inc. **(3)**
155 Bellwood Dr, Rochester, NY 14606-4226
Tel.: (585) 506-4800
Web Site: http://www.fujifilm.com

Sales Range: $75-99.9 Million
Emp.: 150
Photographic Equipment & Supplies
N.A.I.C.S.: 423410

Irvine Scientific Sales Company, Inc. **(3)**
1830 E Warner Ave, Santa Ana, CA 92705-5588 **(100%)**
Tel.: (949) 261-7800
Web Site: http://www.irvinesci.com
Industrial Cell Culture, Cytogenetic & Assisted Reproductive Technology Medical Products Designer, Mfr & Distr
N.A.I.C.S.: 325414

SonoSite, Inc. **(3)**
21919 30th Dr SE, Bothell, WA 98021-3904 **(100%)**
Tel.: (425) 951-1200
Web Site: http://www.sonosite.com
Emp.: 858
Hand-Carried Ultrasound & Other Medical Imaging Device Developer, Mfr & Distr
N.A.I.C.S.: 334510
Jun Higuchi *(Chm & CEO)*

Subsidiary (Domestic):

CardioDynamics International Corporation **(4)**
6175 Nancy Ridge Dr Ste 300, San Diego, CA 92121 **(100%)**
Tel.: (858) 535-0202
Sales Range: $10-24.9 Million
Emp.: 100
Cardiography Technologies Developer & Mfr
N.A.I.C.S.: 334510
Neil W. Treister *(Dir-Medical)*

Subsidiary (Non-US):

SonoSite Ltd. **(4)**
FUJIFILM SonoSite Ltd 5 New Street Square, London, SG4 0AP, Herts, United Kingdom **(100%)**
Tel.: (44) 1462 444800
Web Site: http://www.uk.sonosite.com
Sales Range: $25-49.9 Million
Emp.: 20
Miniaturized, High Performance Digital Ultrasound Imaging Devices
N.A.I.C.S.: 423450
Pasha Chauhan *(Mng Dir)*

Sonosite (Shanghai) Co. Ltd. **(4)**
27/F Shanghai One Lujiazui 68 Yin Cheng Road, Shanghai, 200120, China
Tel.: (86) 21 5239 6693
Sales Range: $100-124.9 Million
Emp.: 20
Miniaturized, High Performance Digital Ultrasound Imaging Devices
N.A.I.C.S.: 423450
Peng Cheng *(Gen Mgr)*

Subsidiary (Non-US):

FUJIFILM Sericol UK Limited **(2)**
Patricia Way Pysons Rd, Broadstairs, CT10 2LE, Kent, United Kingdom
Tel.: (44) 1843866668
Web Site: http://www.sericol.co.uk
Sales Range: $100-124.9 Million
Emp.: 300
Printing Inks & Screen Printing Supplies Mfr
N.A.I.C.S.: 325910

Subsidiary (Non-US):

FUJIFILM Sericol Brasil Produtos para Impressao Ltda **(3)**
Av New Jersey 1 030, Aruja, 07400-000, Brazil
Tel.: (55) 1146527831
Photographic Equipment Mfr
N.A.I.C.S.: 333310

Subsidiary (Domestic):

FUJIFILM Sericol Overseas Holdings Limited **(3)**
Patricia Way Pysons Road Industrial Estate, Broadstairs, CT10 2LE, Kent, United Kingdom
Tel.: (44) 1843 866668
Investment Management Service
N.A.I.C.S.: 523940

Subsidiary (Non-US):

FUJIFILM Sericol Polska Sp. z o.o. **(3)**
ul Muszkieterow 15a, 02-273, Warsaw, Poland
Tel.: (48) 228686322
Web Site: http://fujifilmsericol.com.pl
Sales Range: $25-49.9 Million
Emp.: 30
Printing Ink Distr
N.A.I.C.S.: 423840

Subsidiary (US):

FUJIFILM Sericol USA, Inc. **(3)**
1101 W Cambridge Cir Dr, Kansas City, KS 66103
Tel.: (913) 342-4060
Web Site: http://www.sericol.com
Sales Range: $50-74.9 Million
Emp.: 150
Printing Inks & Screen Printing Supplies Mfr
N.A.I.C.S.: 325910

Subsidiary (Non-US):

Fuji Film Sericol AG **(3)**
Baselstrasse 55, CH 6252, Dagmersellen, Switzerland
Tel.: (41) 627482030
Web Site: http://www.fujifilmsericol.com
Sales Range: $25-49.9 Million
Emp.: 6
Printing Inks & Screen Printing Supplies Mfr
N.A.I.C.S.: 325910

Fujifilm Sericol India Private Limited **(3)**
10/11 B U Bhandari Industrial Estate Sanaswadi, Shirur, Pune, 412 208, Maharashtra, India
Tel.: (91) 2137 392500
Web Site: http://www.fujifilmsericol.in
Sales Range: $50-74.9 Million
Emp.: 60
Printing Ink Mfr & Distr
N.A.I.C.S.: 325910
M. P. Raghav Rao *(Mng Dir)*

Fujifilm Sericol Nederland BV **(3)**
Aalsvoort 63, 7241 MA, Lochem, Netherlands
Tel.: (31) 573 408060
Web Site: http://www.fujifilm.eu
Sales Range: $25-49.9 Million
Emp.: 12
Printing Ink Mfr
N.A.I.C.S.: 325910
Jaap van Duren *(Gen Mgr)*

Sericol SAS **(3)**
50 Ave Des Freres Lumiere ZA, 78191, Trappes, Cedex, France
Tel.: (33) 00130693700
Web Site: http://www.fujifilmsericol.com
Sales Range: $25-49.9 Million
Emp.: 51
Printing Inks & Screen Printing Supplies Mfr
N.A.I.C.S.: 325910

Subsidiary (Non-US):

FUJIFILM South Africa (Pty) Ltd. **(2)**
Building 18 The Woodlands Office Park, 140 Western Service, Johannesburg, 2090, South Africa
Tel.: (27) 11 430 5400
Sales Range: $25-49.9 Million
Emp.: 46
Photographic Equipment Import & Distr
N.A.I.C.S.: 423410
Yuta Kawamura *(Mgr-Mktg-Electronic Imaging-Middle East & Africa)*

FUJIFILM Speciality Ink Systems Ltd. **(2)**
Pysons Road, Broadstairs, CT10 2LE, Kent, United Kingdom
Tel.: (44) 1843 866668
Web Site: http://www.fujifilm.eu
Digital Printing Ink Mfr
N.A.I.C.S.: 325910

FUJIFILM UK Ltd. **(2)**
Unit 10A St Martins Business Centre St Martins Way, Bedford, MK42 0LF, United Kingdom
Tel.: (44) 1234572000
Web Site: http://www.fujifilm.co.uk

Sales Range: $125-149.9 Million
Emp.: 400
Distr of Photographic Supplies & Equipment
N.A.I.C.S.: 423410

FUJIFILM UKRAINE LLC. **(2)**
11 Borysoglibska str, 04070, Kiev, Ukraine
Tel.: (380) 44 390 75 42
Web Site: http://www.fujifilm.eu
Digital Camera Distr
N.A.I.C.S.: 423410

FUJIFILM VIETNAM Co., Ltd. **(2)**
126 Nguyen Thi Minh Khai Str District 3, Ho Chi Minh City, Vietnam
Tel.: (84) 8 39306555
Sales Range: $25-49.9 Million
Emp.: 28
Digital Camera Import & Distr
N.A.I.C.S.: 423410

Subsidiary (Domestic):

FUJIFILM Wako Pure Chemical Corporation **(2)**
1-2 Doshomachi 3-chome, Chuo-ku, Osaka, 540-8605, Japan **(70.3%)**
Tel.: (81) 662033741
Web Site: http://ffwk.fujifilm.co.jp
Sales Range: $600-649.9 Million
Emp.: 2,179
Pharmaceuticals Products Mfr & Distr
N.A.I.C.S.: 325412
Masahiro Fukuoka *(Chm)*

Subsidiary (Non-US):

FUJIFILM do Brasil Ltda. **(2)**
Av Ibirapuera 2315 14 15 e 16 andares, Indianopolis, Sao Paulo, 04029-200, SP, Brazil
Tel.: (55) 1150914000
Web Site: http://www.fujifilm.com.br
Sales Range: $50-74.9 Million
Emp.: 200
Cameras & Photographic Supplies Distr
N.A.I.C.S.: 423410

Subsidiary (Domestic):

FUJIFILM Hunt do Brasil - Producao de Quimicos Ltda **(3)**
Av New Jersey 1031 - Centro Industrial, 07400 000, Sao Bernardo do Campo, Brazil
Tel.: (55) 11 4653 1840
Photographic Film Plate Mfr
N.A.I.C.S.: 325992

Subsidiary (Non-US):

Fujinon Australia Pty. Ltd. **(2)**
Unit 18 52 Holker St, Silverwater, 2128, NSW, Australia
Tel.: (61) 297482744
Web Site: http://www.fujinon.co.jp
Sales Range: $25-49.9 Million
Emp.: 11
TV Lens & Medical Equipment Sales
N.A.I.C.S.: 423450

PT. FUJIFILM INDONESIA **(2)**
Wisma Kelal 2nd Floor JL Jend Sudirman Kav 3, Jakarta, 10220, Indonesia
Tel.: (62) 21 5724069
Digital Camera Import & Distr
N.A.I.C.S.: 423410

Subsidiary (Domestic):

Yokogawa Medical Solutions Corporation **(2)**
4-30-16 Ogikubo Fujisawa Bldg 9kai, Suginami, Tokyo, 167-0051, Japan
Tel.: (81) 363836277
Emp.: 180
Software Development Services
N.A.I.C.S.: 541511

Subsidiary (Non-US):

ZAO FUJIFILM-RU **(2)**
Business Centre Magistral Plaza 4F 1st Magistralnyi tupik 5A, 123290, Moscow, 123290, Russia
Tel.: (7) 495 797 35 12
Emp.: 10
Photographic Equipment & Supplies Distr
N.A.I.C.S.: 423410
Kenichi Tanaka *(Mng Dir)*

FUJIFILM Holdings Corporation—(Continued)

FUJIFILM Diosynth Biotechnologies Holdings Denmark ApS (1)
Biotek Alle 1, 3400, Hillerod, Denmark
Tel.: (45) 77416000
N.A.I.C.S.: 325414

FUJIFILM Diosynth Biotechnologies Texas, LLC (1)
3939 Biomedical Way, College Station, TX 77845
Tel.: (979) 431-3500
Biopharmaceutical Product Mfr & Distr
N.A.I.C.S.: 325412

FUJIFILM Display Solutions Korea Co., Ltd. (1)
City Air Tower 2503 36 Teheran-Ro 87-Gil, Gangnam-gu, Seoul, Korea (South)
Tel.: (82) 220167230
N.A.I.C.S.: 423440

FUJIFILM Electronic Materials (Hong Kong) Co., Ltd. (1)
11F Capital Center 151 Gloucester Road, Wanchai, China (Hong Kong)
Tel.: (852) 23668303
Semiconductor Product Distr
N.A.I.C.S.: 423690
Masaru Tsunashima (Pres)

FUJIFILM Electronic Materials (Singapore) Pte. Ltd. (1)
91 Bencoolen Street 05-01 Sunshine Plaza, Singapore, 189652, Singapore
Tel.: (65) 68875380
Semiconductor Product Distr
N.A.I.C.S.: 423690
Masashi Enokido (Pres)

FUJIFILM Electronic Materials (Suzhou) Co., Ltd. (1)
No 206 Long Tan Road, Suzhou, 215021, China
Tel.: (86) 51288168898
CVD Chemical Mfr & Distr
N.A.I.C.S.: 325998
Henry Tso (Pres)

FUJIFILM Electronic Materials Co., Ltd. (1)
15th Arai-Bldg 19-20 Jingumae 6-chome, Shibuya-ku, Tokyo, 150-0001, Japan
Tel.: (81) 3 3406 6911
Specialty Chemicals Mfr
N.A.I.C.S.: 325998

FUJIFILM Electronic Materials Korea Co., Ltd. (1)
NC Tower 8F 509 Teheran-ro, Gangnam-gu, Seoul, 06169, Korea (South)
Tel.: (82) 25398033
Semiconductor Product Distr
N.A.I.C.S.: 423690
Masashi Enokido (Pres)

FUJIFILM Electronic Materials Manufacturing Korea Co., Ltd. (1)
79 2gongdan 3-ro, Seobuk-gu, Cheonan, 31075, Chungcheongnam, Korea (South)
Tel.: (82) 414127770
Semiconductor Product Mfr & Distr
N.A.I.C.S.: 334413
Masashi Enokido (Pres)

FUJIFILM Electronic Materials Taiwan Co., Ltd. (1)
30 Kuang-fu N Rd, Hsin-Chu Ind Park Hu-Kou Xiang, Hsin-chu, 30351, Taiwan
Tel.: (886) 3 597 7674
Web Site: http://www.fujifilm.com
Emp.: 8
Electronic Equipment Distr
N.A.I.C.S.: 423690

FUJIFILM Engineering Co., Ltd. (1)
210 Nakanuma, Minami, 250-0193, Kanagawa, Japan
Tel.: (81) 465736202
Web Site: http://fec.fujifilm.co.jp
Engineering Services
N.A.I.C.S.: 541330

FUJIFILM Europe Business Service sp.zo.o. (1)
Aleja Grunwaldzka 472C Olivia Star 10th Floor, 80-309, Gdansk, Poland
Tel.: (48) 587432900

Human Resource Consulting Services
N.A.I.C.S.: 541612

FUJIFILM Finechemicals Co., Ltd. (1)
2-3 Higashiyawata 5-chome, Hiratsuka, 254-0016, Kanagawa, Japan
Tel.: (81) 463 21 1560
Web Site: http://www.fffc.fujifilm.co.jp
Sales Range: $150-199.9 Million
Emp.: 421
Specialty Chemicals & Pharmaceutical Products Mfr
N.A.I.C.S.: 325998
Fumio Kawamoto (Pres & CEO)

Subsidiary (Non-US):

FUJIFILM Finechemicals (WUXI) Co., Ltd (2)
55 Xi Xing Lot Wu Xi New Technology Industry Development Area, Wuxi, 214028, Jiangsu, China
Tel.: (86) 510 8532 3030
Web Site: http://fffc.fujifilm.co.jp
Specialty Chemicals Mfr
N.A.I.C.S.: 325998

Plant (Domestic):

FUJIFILM Finechemicals Co., Ltd. - Hirono Factory (2)
1-34 Aza-Iwasawa Kamikitaba Hironomachi, Futaba-gun, Fukushima, 979-0401, Japan
Tel.: (81) 240 27 4171
Web Site: http://fffc.fujifilm.co.jp
Specialty Chemicals Mfr
N.A.I.C.S.: 325998

FUJIFILM Global Graphic Systems Co., Ltd. (1)
2-26-30 Nishi-Azabu FUJIFILM Nishi-Azabu Building, Minato-ku, Tokyo, 106-0031, Japan
Tel.: (81) 364190300
Web Site: http://www.fujifilm.com
Printing Material Distr
N.A.I.C.S.: 424110

FUJIFILM Graphic Systems Co., Ltd. (1)
Takebashi-Yasuda Bld 3-13 KandaNishiki-cho, Chiyoda-ku, Tokyo, 101-8452, Japan
Tel.: (81) 3 5259 2318
Graphic Design & Development Services
N.A.I.C.S.: 541430

FUJIFILM Healthcare Laboratory Co., Ltd. (1)
9-7-3 Akasaka Mid Town West, Minato-Ku, Tokyo, 107-0052, Japan
Tel.: (81) 362712161
Health Care Cosmetics Mfr & Distr
N.A.I.C.S.: 325620
Yutaka Yamaguchi (Gen Mgr)

FUJIFILM Holdings America Corporation (1)
200 Summit Lake Dr, Valhalla, NY 10595
Tel.: (914) 789-8100
Medical Equipment Mfr
N.A.I.C.S.: 339112

FUJIFILM Holdings Australasia Pty Ltd (1)
114 Old Pittwater Road, Brookvale, 2100, NSW, Australia
Tel.: (61) 2 9466 2600
Imaging Equipment Distr
N.A.I.C.S.: 423410

FUJIFILM Holdings NZ Limited (1)
2c William Pickering Drive, Rosedale, Auckland, 632, New Zealand
Tel.: (64) 94140400
Web Site: http://www.fujifilm.co.nz
Emp.: 6
Investment Management Service
N.A.I.C.S.: 523940
Steven Hodson (Gen Mgr)

FUJIFILM Imaging Products & Solutions GmbH & Co. KG. (1)
Siemensring 1, 47877, Willich, Germany
Tel.: (49) 2154897880
Web Site: http://www.fujifilm-fotoprodukte.de
Photographic Product Mfr
N.A.I.C.S.: 325992

FUJIFILM Imaging Protec Co., Ltd. (1)
1-67-1 Shibasaki, Chofu-shi, Tokyo, 182-8686, Japan
Tel.: (81) 424818101
Web Site: http://ffis.fujifilm.co.jp
Color Print Mfr
N.A.I.C.S.: 325992

FUJIFILM Imaging Systems Co., Ltd. (1)
Fujifilm Gotanda Building 3-6-30 Nishi Gotanda, Shinagawa-ku, Tokyo, 141-0031, Japan
Tel.: (81) 3 5745 2241
Web Site: http://www.ffis.fujifilm.co.jp
Emp.: 50
Photographic Equipment Mfr
N.A.I.C.S.: 333310
Koji Matsumoto (Pres)

FUJIFILM Imaging Systems GmbH & Co. KG (1)
Heesenstrasse 31, 40549, Dusseldorf, Germany
Tel.: (49) 21150890
On-Site Finishing Services
N.A.I.C.S.: 812921

FUJIFILM India Private Limited (1)
Unit No 801-807 8th Floor Tower C Sector 39, Unitech Cyber Park, Gurgaon, 122001, Haryana, India
Tel.: (91) 124 4325500
Web Site: http://www.fujifilm.in
Sales Range: $150-199.9 Million
Emp.: 10
Photographic & Imaging Equipment Distr
N.A.I.C.S.: 423410
Ramprasad S. M. (Head-Image Capturing)

FUJIFILM Irvine Scientific, Inc. (1)
1830 E Warner Ave, Santa Ana, CA 92705-5505
Tel.: (949) 261-7800
Web Site: https://www.irvinesci.com
Biopharmaceutical Product Mfr & Distr
N.A.I.C.S.: 325412

FUJIFILM Logistics Co., Ltd. (1)
Kanehiro Shin-Yokohama Building 7-17 Shin-Yokohama 3-chome, Kohoku-ku, Yokohama, 222-0033, Kanagawa, Japan
Tel.: (81) 454707600
Web Site: http://ffl.fujifilm.co.jp
Logistics Management Services
N.A.I.C.S.: 541614

FUJIFILM Logistics Solution (China) Limited (1)
6F Tower 7 Crystal Plaza No 6 Lane 100 Ping Jia Qiao Road, Pudong New Area, Shanghai, 200126, China
Tel.: (86) 2150106000
N.A.I.C.S.: 541614

FUJIFILM Media Crest Co., Ltd. (1)
2-10-8 Shimmeidai, Hamura, 205-0023, Tokyo, Japan
Tel.: (81) 425307600
Magnetic & Optical Recording Media Mfr
N.A.I.C.S.: 334610

FUJIFILM Media Manufacturing Co., Ltd. (1)
2-12-1 Ogicho, Odawara, 250-0001, Kanagawa, Japan
Tel.: (81) 465322028
Magnetic Tape Mfr
N.A.I.C.S.: 334610

FUJIFILM Medical Co., Ltd. (1)
Fujifilm Nishi-Azabu Building 2-26-30 Nishi-Azabu, Minato-ku, Tokyo, 106-0031, Japan
Tel.: (81) 364198000
Web Site: http://fms.fujifilm.co.jp
Medical Diagnostic Product Distr
N.A.I.C.S.: 423450

FUJIFILM Medical IT Solutions Co., Ltd. (1)
Kowa Nishiazabu Building 4-12-24 Nishi-azabu, Minato-ku, Tokyo, 106-0031, Japan
Tel.: (81) 364272360
N.A.I.C.S.: 541519
Takahiro Ishikawa (Pres)

FUJIFILM Medical Solutions Co., Ltd. (1)
Ogikubo 4-30-16 Fujisawa Building,

Suginami-ku, Tokyo, 167-0051, Japan
Tel.: (81) 363836277
Web Site: http://ffms.fujifilm.co.jp
Medical IT Product Mfr
N.A.I.C.S.: 339112

FUJIFILM Medical Systems Taiwan Co., Ltd. (1)
No 28 Sec 3 Nanjing E Rd, Zhongshan Dist, Taipei, 10491, Taiwan
Tel.: (886) 225018210
Photographic Film Mfr
N.A.I.C.S.: 325992

FUJIFILM Medical Technical Service (Shanghai) Co., Ltd (1)
Room 602 No 1000 Jinhai Road Pudong New Area, Shanghai, China
Tel.: (86) 2168876688
N.A.I.C.S.: 811210

FUJIFILM Myanmar Limited (1)
No 221 Sule Square Unit 10-13 Level-10 Sule Pagoda Road, Kyauktada Township, Yangon, Myanmar
Tel.: (95) 19255151
Medical & Graphic Product Whslr
N.A.I.C.S.: 423450

FUJIFILM Opt-Electronics (Tianjin) Co., Ltd. (1)
No 2 Hongyuan Road Xiqing Development Zone, Tianjin, 300385, China
Tel.: (86) 2283998610
Electronic Components Mfr
N.A.I.C.S.: 334419

FUJIFILM Optical Devices Europe GmbH (1)
Fujistr 1, 47533, Kleve, Germany
Tel.: (49) 28217115400
Optical Device Repair Services
N.A.I.C.S.: 811210

FUJIFILM Optics Co., Ltd. (1)
2720 Morigane, Hitachiomiya, 319-3102, Japan
Tel.: (81) 295 53 3131
Optical Lens Mfr
N.A.I.C.S.: 333310

FUJIFILM Optics Philippines Inc. (1)
107 Prosperity Avenue Carmelray Industrial Business Park, Special Economic Zone Canlubang, Calamba, 4028, Laguna, Philippines
Tel.: (63) 495083653
N.A.I.C.S.: 334610

FUJIFILM Opto Materials Co., Ltd. (1)
463-1 Ohata Yoshida-cho, Haibara, 463-1, Shizuoka, Japan
Tel.: (81) 548 34 2500
Optical Goods Mfr
N.A.I.C.S.: 333310

FUJIFILM Pharma Co., Ltd. (1)
2-26-30 Nishiazabu, Minato-ku, Tokyo, 106-0031, Japan
Tel.: (81) 364183800
Web Site: http://fri.fujifilm.co.jp
Emp.: 80
Pharmaceuticals Product Mfr
N.A.I.C.S.: 325412

FUJIFILM Philippines Inc. (1)
30th Floor Joy -Nostalg Center No 17 ADB Avenue Ortigas Center, Pasig, 1600, Philippines
Tel.: (63) 25502420
Photographic Film Mfr
N.A.I.C.S.: 325992

FUJIFILM Photo Manufacturing Co., Ltd. (1)
Nakanuma 210, Minami, 250-0193, Kanagawa, Japan
Tel.: (81) 465736768
Color Negative Film Mfr
N.A.I.C.S.: 325992

FUJIFILM Presentec Co., Ltd. (1)
Minato-Ku Nishiza 4-16-17 28 Moli Building, Minato-Ku, Tokyo, 106-0031, Japan
Tel.: (81) 357747630
Sales Range: $25-49.9 Million
Emp.: 100
Compact Disc Mfr
N.A.I.C.S.: 334610

Yoshihiro Matoba *(Mgr)*

FUJIFILM Printing Plate (China) Co., Ltd. **(1)**
No 202 Longtan Road, Suzhou Industrial Park, Suzhou, China
Tel.: (86) 5128168282
N.A.I.C.S.: 325910

FUJIFILM RI Pharma Co., Ltd. **(1)**
14-1 Kyobashi 2-Chome, Chuo-Ku, Tokyo, 104-0031, Japan
Tel.: (81) 3 5250 2600
Web Site: http://www.fri.fujifilm.co.jp
Sales Range: $150-199.9 Million
Emp.: 389
Pharmaceutical Products Mfr & Distr'
N.A.I.C.S.: 325412
Yoshiro Kumano *(Pres & CEO)*

FUJIFILM RUS LLC **(1)**
Business Centre Magistral Plaza 4F 1st Magistralnyi tupik 5A, 123290, Moscow, Russia
Tel.: (7) 4957973512
Web Site: http://www.fujifilm.com
Photographic Film Distr
N.A.I.C.S.: 423410

FUJIFILM Shizuoka Co., Ltd. **(1)**
200 Onakazato, Fujinomiya, 418-8666, Shizuoka, Japan
Tel.: (81) 544226479
X-ray Film Mfr
N.A.I.C.S.: 325992

FUJIFILM Software Co., Ltd. **(1)**
2-10-23 Shin-Yokohama Nomura Real Estate Shin-Yokohama Building, Kohoku-ku, Yokohama, 222-0033, Kanagawa, Japan **(100%)**
Tel.: (81) 454769300
Web Site: http://www.fujifilm.com
Software Development Services
N.A.I.C.S.: 541511

FUJIFILM SonoSite, Inc. **(1)**
21919 30th Dr SE, Bothell, WA 98021-3904
Tel.: (425) 951-1200
Web Site: https://www.sonosite.com
Ultrasound Mfr
N.A.I.C.S.: 334510
Richard Fabian *(CEO)*

FUJIFILM Systems Corporation **(1)**
3-6-1 Minato Mirai Minato Mirai Center Building, Nishi-ku, Yokohama, 220-0012, Kanagawa, Japan
Tel.: (81) 452118300
Software Development Services
N.A.I.C.S.: 541511

FUJIFILM Techno Products Co., Ltd. **(1)**
1250 Takematsu, Minami, 250-0111, Kanagawa, Japan
Tel.: (81) 465742121
Web Site: http://fftp.fujifilm.co.jp
Precision Parts Mfr
N.A.I.C.S.: 332721

FUJIFILM Techno Service Co., Ltd. **(1)**
95-1 Kawakita Naka character Wakayanagi character, Kurihara, 989-5501, Miyagi, Japan
Tel.: (81) 228302990
Web Site: http://www.ffts.fujifilm.co.jp
Sales Range: $25-49.9 Million
Emp.: 166
Digital Camera Maintenance Services
N.A.I.C.S.: 811210

FUJIFILM Toyama Chemical Co., Ltd. **(1)**
14-1 Kyobashi 2-Chome, Chuo-Ku, Tokyo, 104-0031, Japan
Tel.: (81) 352502600
Web Site: http://fftc.fujifilm.co.jp
Medical Equipment Mfr
N.A.I.C.S.: 339112
Mitsuhiro Sato *(Pres)*

FUJIFILM VET Systems Co., Ltd. **(1)**
8-31-6 Jindaiji Higashimachi, Chofu, 182-0012, Tokyo, Japan
Tel.: (81) 424437200
Veterinary Diagnostic Equipment Distr
N.A.I.C.S.: 423490

Fuji Hunt Asian Pacific Holding Pty Ltd **(1)**
41 Jesica Rd, Campbellfield, 3061, VIC, Australia
Tel.: (61) 3 93570933
Investment Management Service
N.A.I.C.S.: 523999

Fuji Xerox (Hong Kong) Limited **(1)**
11/F 12 Taikoo Wan Road, Taikoo Shing, China (Hong Kong)
Tel.: (852) 25132888
Web Site: http://www.fujixerox.hk
Emp.: 1,200
Document & Communication Services
N.A.I.C.S.: 517810

Fuji Xerox Asia Pacific Pte. Ltd. **(1)**
516 5th Floor Hledan Center Corner of Pyay Road and Hledan Road, Kamaryut Township, Yangon, Myanmar
Tel.: (95) 1230562325
Web Site: http://www.fujixerox.com.mm
Printing Material Distr
N.A.I.C.S.: 424110

Fuji Xerox Document Management Solutions Asia Limited **(1)**
8/F Safety Godown Industrial Building 56 Ka Yip Street, Chai Wan, Hong Kong, China (Hong Kong)
Tel.: (852) 2403 2288
Web Site: http://www.dms.fujixerox.com
Sales Range: $50-74.9 Million
Emp.: 120
Business Communications Printing & Publishing Services
N.A.I.C.S.: 561410

Fuji Xerox Far East Limited **(1)**
Units 3015-3018 Level 30 Tower I Millennium City 1 388 Kwun Tong Road, Kowloon, China (Hong Kong)
Tel.: (852) 29561838
Office Product Mfr
N.A.I.C.S.: 339940

Fuji Xerox InterField Co., Ltd. **(1)**
2-2-1 Toyosu Toyosu Bayside Cross Tower, Koto-ku, Tokyo, Japan
Tel.: (81) 366330391
Web Site: http://www.fxif.co.jp
Office Supply Mfr & Distr
N.A.I.C.S.: 339940

Fuji Xerox Korea Company Limited **(1)**
B-dong Baejaejeong-dong Building 19 Seosomun-ro 11-gil, Jeong-dong Jung-gu, Seoul, 04516, Korea (South)
Tel.: (82) 15448988
Web Site: http://www.fujixerox.co.kr
Management Consulting Services
N.A.I.C.S.: 541611

Fuji Xerox Manufacturing Co., Ltd. **(1)**
2274 Hongou, Ebina, 243-0497, Kanagawa, Japan
Tel.: (81) 462372611
Printing Material Distr
N.A.I.C.S.: 424110

Fuji Xerox Philippines Inc. **(1)**
25th Floor SM Aura Tower 26th Street Corner McKinley Parkway, Bonifacio Global City, Taguig, 1630, Philippines
Tel.: (63) 288785200
Web Site: http://www.fujixerox.com.ph
Emp.: 238
Document & Communication Services
N.A.I.C.S.: 517810
Hideaki Kato *(Pres)*

Fuji Xerox Service Creative Co., Ltd. **(1)**
28F Nakanosakaue Sun Bright Twin 2-46-1 Honcho, Nakano-ku, Tokyo, 164-8682, Japan
Tel.: (81) 353527575
Printing Material Distr
N.A.I.C.S.: 424110

Fuji Xerox Service Link Co., Ltd. **(1)**
10th Floor Nittamachi Building 5-34-6 Shiba, Minato-ku, Tokyo, 108-0014, Japan
Tel.: (81) 364353239
Web Site: http://www.fxsvl.co.jp
Printing Material Distr
N.A.I.C.S.: 424110

Fuji Xerox System Service Co., Ltd. **(1)**
5F Kowa Ichibashi Building 3-7-1, Kanda Nishikicho Chiyoda-ku, Tokyo, 101-0054, Japan
Tel.: (81) 332912600
Web Site: http://www.fxss.co.jp
Data Preparation Services
N.A.I.C.S.: 518210

Fuji Xerox Taiwan Corporation **(1)**
7F No 88 Dunhua N Road, Taipei, 10551, Taiwan
Tel.: (886) 227319099
Photographic Film Mfr
N.A.I.C.S.: 325992

Fujifilm Business Innovation Corporation **(1)**
9-7-3 Akasaka, Minato-ku, Tokyo, 107-0052, Japan **(100%)**
Tel.: (81) 362715111
Web Site: https://www.fujifilm.com
Sales Range: $5-14.9 Billion
Emp.: 39,483
Copiers, Duplicators & Other Office Equipment Mfr, Distr, Sales & Marketer
N.A.I.C.S.: 424120
Shigetaka Komori *(Chm)*

Subsidiary (US):

FX Global Inc. **(2)**
3174 Porter Dr, Palo Alto, CA 94304-1346
Tel.: (650) 842-4890
Web Site: http://www.fujixerox.com
Sales Range: $10-24.9 Million
Emp.: 47
Development & Research Services
N.A.I.C.S.: 541611

Subsidiary (Domestic):

Xerox International Partners **(3)**
3174 Porter Dr, Palo Alto, CA 94304
Tel.: (650) 953-2700
Photocopying Machinery Mfr
N.A.I.C.S.: 333310

Subsidiary (US):

FX Palo Alto Laboratory Inc. **(2)**
3174 Porter Dr, Palo Alto, CA 94304-1346
Tel.: (650) 842-4800
Web Site: http://www.fxpal.com
Sales Range: $10-24.9 Million
Emp.: 45
Software Research Services
N.A.I.C.S.: 541715
Tsutomu Abe *(Sr VP)*

Subsidiary (Non-US):

Fuji Xerox Asia Pacific Pte Ltd. **(2)**
80 Anson Road 01-01 Fuji Xerox Towers, 079907, Singapore, Singapore
Tel.: (65) 366711
Web Site: http://www.fxap.com.sg
Sales Range: $125-149.9 Million
Emp.: 400
Office Equipment Sales & Distr
N.A.I.C.S.: 423420

Subsidiary (Non-US):

Fuji Xerox (China) Limited **(3)**
5-7F Tower H Phoenix Place 5A Shuguang Xili, Chaoyang District, Beijing, 100028, China
Tel.: (86) 1058245000
Web Site: http://www.fujixerox.com.cn
Office Equipment Sales, Distr & Service
N.A.I.C.S.: 423420

Fuji Xerox Asia Pacific Pte Ltd. - IndoChina Operations **(3)**
12th Floor Vincom Center 72 Le Thanh Ton, Dist 1, Ho Chi Minh City, Vietnam
Tel.: (84) 2838290038
Web Site: http://www.fujixerox.com.vn
Sales Range: $25-49.9 Million
Emp.: 203
Office Equipment Sales, Distr & Service
N.A.I.C.S.: 423420

Fuji Xerox Asia Pacific Pte Ltd. - Malaysia **(3)**
Block C No 10 Jalan Bersatu 13/4, Axis Business Park, 46200, Petaling Jaya, Selangor, Malaysia

Tel.: (60) 378822888
Web Site: http://www.fujixerox.com.my
Sales Range: $125-149.9 Million
Emp.: 699
Office Equipment Sales, Distr & Service
N.A.I.C.S.: 423420

Fuji Xerox Australia Pty. Ltd. **(3)**
8 Khartoum Road, Macquarie Park, 2113, NSW, Australia
Tel.: (61) 298565000
Web Site: http://www.fujixerox.com.au
Emp.: 1,450
Office Equipment Sales & Service
N.A.I.C.S.: 423420
Takayuki Togo *(Mng Dir)*

Subsidiary (Domestic):

CSG Limited **(4)**
Level 1 357 Collins Street, Melbourne, 3000, VIC, Australia
Tel.: (61) 1800098445
Web Site: http://www.csg.com.au
Rev.: $176,158,154
Assets: $323,573,983
Liabilities: $259,255,363
Net Worth: $64,318,620
Earnings: ($117,174,183)
Emp.: 670
Fiscal Year-end: 06/30/2018
Holding Company; Information & Communication Technology Services & Consulting
N.A.I.C.S.: 551112
Ken Sugiyama *(Mng Dir)*

Subsidiary (Domestic):

Connected Services Group Pty. Ltd. **(5)**
Level 8 Jacana House 39 Woods Street, Darwin, 0800, NT, Australia **(100%)**
Tel.: (61) 889229000
Web Site: http://www.csg.com.au
Information & Communication Technology Services & Consulting
N.A.I.C.S.: 541990
Julie-Ann Kerin *(CEO & Mng Dir)*

Subsidiary (Domestic):

CSG Communications Pty. Ltd. **(6)**
252 Montague Rd, West End, 4101, QLD, Australia
Tel.: (61) 738401244
Web Site: http://www.csg.com.au
Emp.: 100
Communications Equipment Services
N.A.I.C.S.: 541990

CSG Print Services Pty. Ltd. **(6)**
Level 6 320 Adelaide Street, Brisbane, 4000, QLD, Australia **(100%)**
Tel.: (61) 7 3840 1244
Web Site: http://www.csg.com.au
Commercial Office Equipment & Telecommunications Network Services
N.A.I.C.S.: 541990
Declan Ramsay *(Gen Mgr)*

Subsidiary (Non-US):

Konica Minolta Business Solutions New Zealand Ltd. **(5)**
Khyber Pass And Nugent St, Graston, Auckland, 1001, New Zealand **(90%)**
Tel.: (64) 956356000
Web Site: http://www.konicaminolta.co.nz
Business Equipment Services
N.A.I.C.S.: 423420
Evan Johnson *(CEO)*

Subsidiary (Domestic):

Fuji Xerox Document Management Solutions Pty Ltd **(4)**
213-215 Robinsons Road, Ravenhall, 3023, VIC, Australia
Tel.: (61) 383581700
Web Site: http://www.dms.fujixerox.com
Business Communications Printing & Publishing Services
N.A.I.C.S.: 561410

Subsidiary (Non-US):

Fuji Xerox New Zealand Ltd. **(3)**
79 Carlton Gore Road, Newmarket, Auckland, 1023, New Zealand
Tel.: (64) 93564200
Web Site: http://www.fujixerox.co.nz

FUJIFILM Holdings Corporation—(Continued)

Sales Range: $125-149.9 Million
Emp.: 500
Office Equipment Sales & Service
N.A.I.C.S.: 423420

Subsidiary (Domestic):

Fuji Xerox Singapore Pte Ltd. **(3)**
80 Anson Road 01-01 Fuji Xerox Towers,
Singapore, 079907, Singapore
Tel.: (65) 67668888
Web Site: http://www.fujixerox.com.sg
Sales Range: $125-149.9 Million
Emp.: 828
Office Equipment Sales, Distr & Service
N.A.I.C.S.: 423420
Sharon Kong (Gen Mgr & Dir-Indus Solutions Grp)

Subsidiary (Non-US):

Thai Fuji Xerox Co., Ltd. **(3)**
23rd Floor Sathorn City Tower, 175 South
Sathorn Road, Tungmahamek Sathorn,
Bangkok, 10120, Thailand
Tel.: (66) 26796050
Office Equipment Sales, Distr & Service
N.A.I.C.S.: 423420
Hiroaki Abe (Pres)

Subsidiary (Domestic):

Fuji Xerox Learning Institute Inc. **(2)**
Roppongi T Cube 14F Roppongi 3-chome
Minato-ku, Tokyo, 106-0032, Japan
Tel.: (81) 355741511
Web Site: http://www.fxli.co.jp
Sales Range: $10-24.9 Million
Emp.: 200
Personnel Training Services
N.A.I.C.S.: 611430

Suzuka Fuji Xerox Co., Ltd. **(2)**
1900 Ifuna Cho, Suzuka, 519-0393, Mie,
Japan
Tel.: (81) 593718888
Web Site: http://www.suzukafx.co.jp
Sales Range: $150-199.9 Million
Emp.: 2,400
Digital Equipment, Copy Machines & Peripherals Developer & Mfr
N.A.I.C.S.: 335999

Japan Tissue Engineering Co.,
Ltd. **(1)**
6-209-1 Miyakitadori, Gamagori, 443-0022,
Aichi, Japan
Tel.: (81) 533662020
Web Site: https://www.jpte.co.jp
Sales Range: $10-24.9 Million
Emp.: 137
Medical Biotechnology Mfr
N.A.I.C.S.: 339112
Toshihiro Osuka (Sr Exec Officer)

Medwork GmbH **(1)**
Medworking 1, 91315, Hochstadt an der
Aisch, Germany
Tel.: (49) 9193500900
Web Site: https://www.medwork.com
Endoscopy Instrument Mfr
N.A.I.C.S.: 334510
Gerald Fischer (Mng Dir)

Toyama Chemical Co., Ltd. **(1)**
2 5 Nishishinjuku 3 Chome, Shinjuku ku,
Tokyo, 160 0023, Japan **(66%)**
Tel.: (81) 353813889
Web Site: http://www.toyamachemical.co.jp
Sales Range: $125-149.9 Million
Emp.: 800
Pharmaceutical Developer, Retailer & Mfr
N.A.I.C.S.: 325412
Masuji Sugata (Pres)

Joint Venture (Domestic):

Taisho Toyama Pharmaceutical Co.,
Ltd. **(2)**
3 25 1 Takada, Toshima ku, Tokyo, 171
0033, Japan
Tel.: (81) 339858100
Web Site: http://www.toyama-chemical.co.jp
Prescription Pharmaceuticals Distr; Owned
55% by Taisho Pharmaceutical Co., Ltd. &
45% by Toyama Chemical Co., Ltd.
N.A.I.C.S.: 325412

Upstream Print Solutions Australia
Pty Ltd **(1)**
154 Highbury Road, Burwood, 3125, VIC,
Australia
Tel.: (61) 388313500
Web Site: http://www.upstream.com.au
Document Management Services
N.A.I.C.S.: 561410
Scott Crosby (CEO)

FUJII SANGYO CORPORATION
41-3 Hiraide Kogyo Danchi Utsunomiya, Tochigi, 321-0905, Japan
Tel.: (81) 286626060
Web Site: https://www.fujii.co.jp
Year Founded: 1955
9906—(TKS)
Rev.: $601,899,990
Assets: $427,204,300
Liabilities: $184,419,000
Net Worth: $242,785,300
Earnings: $24,172,770
Emp.: 884
Fiscal Year-end: 03/31/24
Construction Machinery Maintenance
& Sales
N.A.I.C.S.: 423810
Shoichi Fujii (Pres)

Subsidiaries:

Fujii Tsushin Inc. **(1)**
2-11 Kikusuicho, Utsunomiya, 320-0844,
Tochigi, Japan
Tel.: (81) 28 636 2751
Electrical Equipment Whslr
N.A.I.C.S.: 423610

Kanto Sogo Shizai Co., Ltd. **(1)**
305-1 Kaminagaisomachi Maebashi,
Gunma, 379-2165, Japan
Tel.: (81) 27 261 1181
Electrical Equipment Whslr
N.A.I.C.S.: 423610

Komatsu Tochigi Inc. **(1)**
38-12 Hiraide Industrial Park, Utsunomiya,
321-0905, Tochigi, Japan
Tel.: (81) 286626093
Industrial Equipment Rental Services
N.A.I.C.S.: 532490

Towa Concrete Pumping Inc. **(1)**
43-87 Hiraide Kogyo Danchi, Utsunomiya,
321-0905, Tochigi, Japan
Tel.: (81) 28 663 2678
Concrete Pumping Construction Services
N.A.I.C.S.: 238110

FUJIKOH COMPANY., LIMITED
7-5 Komagata 2-chome, Taito-ku, Tokyo, 111-0043, Japan
Tel.: (81) 3 3841 5431
Web Site: http://www.fujikoh-net.co.jp
Year Founded: 1974
Rev.: $35,533,320
Assets: $54,840,180
Liabilities: $35,578,620
Net Worth: $19,261,560
Earnings: $1,449,600
Emp.: 109
Fiscal Year-end: 06/30/19
Waste Recycling Services
N.A.I.C.S.: 562212
Naoto Kobayashi (Pres & CEO)

FUJIKON INDUSTRIAL HOLD-INGS LTD
16/F Tower 1 138 Shatin Rural Committee Road Grand Central Plaza,
Sha Tin, China (Hong Kong)
Tel.: (852) 2 605 5008
Web Site: http://www.fujikon.com
0927—(HKG)
Rev.: $113,278,878
Assets: $117,654,137
Liabilities: $29,471,156
Net Worth: $88,182,981
Earnings: ($3,997,606)
Emp.: 2,398
Fiscal Year-end: 03/31/22

Electro Acoustic Products Mfr &
Sales
N.A.I.C.S.: 334310
Ben Siu Chung Yeung (Exec Dir)

Subsidiaries:

Fujikon Packing Material Company
Limited **(1)**
16/F Tower 1 Grand Central Plaza 138 Shatin Rural Committee Road, Sha Tin, NT,
China (Hong Kong)
Tel.: (852) 26886218
Web Site: http://www.fujikon-packing.com
Emp.: 900
Plastic Packaging Product Mfr & Distr
N.A.I.C.S.: 326199

FUJIKURA COMPOSITES INC.
TOC Ariake East Tower 10F 3-5-7
Ariake, Koto-ku, Tokyo, 135-0063,
Japan
Tel.: (81) 335278111
Web Site:
　　https://www.fujikuracomposites.jp
Year Founded: 1901
5121—(TKS)
Rev.: $249,758,850
Assets: $291,335,750
Liabilities: $50,077,360
Net Worth: $241,258,390
Earnings: $21,495,720
Emp.: 2,307
Fiscal Year-end: 03/31/24
Rubber Product Mfr & Whslr
N.A.I.C.S.: 326299
Kenji Morita (Pres)

Subsidiaries:

Anji Fujikura Rubber Co., Ltd. **(1)**
Zhuyi Road TangPu Industrial Zone Anji
Economic Development Area, Huzhou,
313300, Zhejiang, China
Tel.: (86) 5725115868
Industrial Rubber Part Mfr
N.A.I.C.S.: 326299

Fujikura Composite America, Inc. **(1)**
1819 Aston Ave Ste 101, Carlsbad, CA
92008
Tel.: (760) 597-7814
Web Site: https://www.fujikuragolf.com
Sporting Goods Mfr
N.A.I.C.S.: 339920
Dave Schnider (Pres & COO)

Fujikura Composite Haiphong,
Inc. **(1)**
Land Plot D3-6 Nomura Hai Phong IZ, An
Duong Dist, Haiphong, Vietnam
Tel.: (84) 2253618630
Industrial Rubber Part Mfr
N.A.I.C.S.: 326299

Fujikura Composite Korea, Ltd. **(1)**
B-602 Woolim-lionsvalley 371-28, Gasandong Geumcheon-gu, Seoul, 153-786, Korea (South)
Tel.: (82) 27139797
Industrial Rubber Part Mfr
N.A.I.C.S.: 326299

Fujikura Composites Europe B.V. **(1)**
Binderij 7R, 1185ZH, Amstelveen, Netherlands
Web Site: http://www.fujikuragraphics.com
Rubber Product Whslr
N.A.I.C.S.: 423840

Fujikura Graphics, Inc. **(1)**
700 Penhorn Ave Unit 2, Secaucus, NJ
07094
Tel.: (201) 420-5040
Web Site: http://www.fujikuragraphics.com
Emp.: 15
Printed Blanket Mfr
N.A.I.C.S.: 313230

Hangzhou Fujikura Rubber Ltd. **(1)**
No 120 BaHao Road, Qiantang New Area,
Hangzhou, 310018, Zhejiang, China
Tel.: (86) 57186912036
Web Site: http://www.hangzhoufujikura.com
Emp.: 360
Industrial Equipment Whsr
N.A.I.C.S.: 423830

R&R Fujikura Ltd. **(1)**
Web Site: http://www.fujikura-gcs.com
Rubber Products Mfr
N.A.I.C.S.: 326299

FUJIKURA KASEI CO., LTD.
6-15 Shibakoen 2-chome, Minato-ku,
Tokyo, 105-0011, Japan
Tel.: (81) 334361101
Web Site: https://www.fkkasei.co.jp
Year Founded: 1938
4620—(TKS)
Rev.: $347,765,320
Assets: $380,705,400
Liabilities: $105,945,080
Net Worth: $274,850,410
Earnings: $7,105,750
Emp.: 437
Fiscal Year-end: 03/31/24
Specialty Coating & Fine Chemical
Mfr
N.A.I.C.S.: 325998
Daisuke Kato (Pres)

Subsidiaries:

Fujichem Sonneborn Ltd. **(1)**
91-95 Peregrine Road, Hainault, Ilford, IG6
3XH, Essex, United Kingdom
Tel.: (44) 2085000251
Emp.: 130
Coating Material Mfr
N.A.I.C.S.: 325510
Edward Cox (Sec & Exec Dir)

Subsidiary (Domestic):

Fujichem Sonneborn Ltd. - Chesterfield Plant **(2)**
Holmewood Ind Estate Hardwick View
Road, Chesterfield, S42 5SA, Derbyshire,
United Kingdom
Tel.: (44) 1246851504
Coating Material Mfr
N.A.I.C.S.: 325510

Fujichemi Kinki Co., Ltd. **(1)**
1-3-21 Nichirei Temmabashi Building 1-3-21, Kita-Ku, Osaka, 530-0043, Japan
Tel.: (81) 663580291
Emp.: 50
Coating Material Mfr
N.A.I.C.S.: 313320

Fujichemi Tokyo Co., Ltd. **(1)**
5F 1-2-10 Nihonbashi Horidome-cho, Chuo-ku, Tokyo, 103-0012, Japan
Tel.: (81) 356515454
Web Site: https://www.fc-tokyo.co.jp
Coating Material Mfr
N.A.I.C.S.: 313320

Fujikura Kasei (Foshan) Coating Co.,
Ltd. **(1)**
No 6 Shunyuan Nan Rd Wusha section,
Daliang Shunde, Foshan, 528333, Guangdong, China
Tel.: (86) 75722803751
Specialty Coating & Fine Chemical Mfr
N.A.I.C.S.: 325998

Fujikura Kasei (Thailand) Co.,
Ltd. **(1)**
88-69 Asia Industrial Estate Suvarnabhumi
Moo 4, Khlongsuan, Bangkok, 10560, Samutprakarn, Thailand
Tel.: (66) 21829900
Emp.: 45
Specialty Coating & Fine Chemical Mfr
N.A.I.C.S.: 325998
Awut Nittayasomboon (Gen Mgr)

Fujikura Kasei Co., Ltd. - Sano Plant
1 **(1)**
Sakaecho 12-1, Sano, 327-0816, Tochigi,
Japan
Tel.: (81) 283231881
Coating Material Mfr
N.A.I.C.S.: 325510

Fujikura Kasei Co., Ltd. - Sano Plant
2 **(1)**
Sakaecho 14-2, Sano, 327-0816, Tochigi,
Japan
Tel.: (81) 283213590
Coating Material Mfr
N.A.I.C.S.: 325510

Fujikura Kasei Coating (Tianjin) Co., Ltd. **(1)**
No 200 MuNing Road TEDA, Tianjin, 300457, China
Tel.: (86) 2259815966
Specialty Coating & Fine Chemical Mfr
N.A.I.C.S.: 325998
Nikihito Nahshima *(Gen Mgr)*

Fujikura Kasei Coating India Private Ltd. **(1)**
Plot No 201-202 225-226 Sector-9 Phase-3 Imt-Bawal, Gurgaon, 123 501, Haryana, India
Tel.: (91) 128 427 0700
Web Site: https://www.fkkasei.co.jp
Specialty Coating & Fine Chemical Mfr
N.A.I.C.S.: 325998

Fujikura Kasei Malaysia Sdn. Bhd. **(1)**
No 2 Jalan Palam 34/18A, Taman Perindustrian Pak Chun, 40470, Shah Alam, Selangor, Malaysia
Tel.: (60) 35 167 3301
Chemical Products Mfr
N.A.I.C.S.: 325998

Fujikura Kasei Vietnam Co., Ltd. **(1)**
Plot 13 1 Road no 10 Cam Dien-Luong, Dien Industrial Park Luong Dien Commune Cam Giang District, Hai Duong, Vietnam
Tel.: (84) 220 355 5486
Chemicals Mfr
N.A.I.C.S.: 325199

PT. Fujikura Kasei Indonesia **(1)**
Kawasan Industri Jatake Jl Industri 3 Blok AC No 6B, Jatake, Tangerang, Banten, Indonesia
Tel.: (62) 215 931 7707
Chemical Products Mfr
N.A.I.C.S.: 325998

Shanghai Fujikura Kasei Coating Co., Ltd. **(1)**
No 177 Yingong Road, Fengxian District, Shanghai, 201417, China
Tel.: (86) 2137585100
Specialty Coating & Fine Chemical Mfr
N.A.I.C.S.: 325998

Tohkohjushi Co., Ltd. **(1)**
7th Floor NBF Higashi-ginza Square 13-14 Tsukiji 1-Chome, Chuo-Ku, Tokyo, 104-0045, Japan
Tel.: (81) 36 278 0561
Web Site: https://www.tohkoh-jushi.co.jp
Emp.: 37
Plastic Raw Material Distr
N.A.I.C.S.: 424610
Masao Ogawa *(CEO & Chm)*

FUJIKURA LTD.
1-5-1 Kiba, Koto-ku, Tokyo, 135-8512, Japan
Tel.: (81) 356061030   JP
Web Site: https://www.fujikura.co.jp
Year Founded: 1885
5803—(TKS)
Rev.—$5,286,413,600
Assets: $4,784,760,870
Liabilities: $2,361,653,850
Net Worth: $2,423,107,020
Earnings: $337,182,710
Emp.: 50,254
Fiscal Year-end: 03/31/24
Optical Transmission Systems, Network Systems, Electronics Materials, Power Systems, Coated Wires, Magnet Wires, Electronic Materials for Equipment & Metallic Materials Mfr
N.A.I.C.S.: 334419
Joseph E. Gallagher *(Corp Officer)*

Subsidiaries:

America Fujikura Ltd. **(1)**
170 Ridgeview Cir, Duncan, SC 29334 **(100%)**
Tel.: (864) 433-0333
Web Site: http://www.aflglobal.com
Sales Range: $400-449.9 Million
Emp.: 2,000
Fiber Optic Products
N.A.I.C.S.: 335921

Jody Gallagher *(Pres & CEO)*

Unit (Non-US):

AFL Telecommunications **(2)**
Radway Point 2 Radway Road, Hawksworth, Swindon, SN3 4ND, Wilts, United Kingdom
Tel.: (44) 1793647200
Web Site: http://www.aflglobal.com
Sales Range: $25-49.9 Million
Emp.: 60
Fiber Optic Cable
N.A.I.C.S.: 335921

Unit (Domestic):

AFL Telecommunications LLC **(2)**
170 Ridgeview Ctr Dr, Duncan, SC 29334
Tel.: (864) 433-0333
Web Site: http://www.aflglobal.com
Laser Welded Fiber Optic Tubes Mfr
N.A.I.C.S.: 335921

Subsidiary (Non-US):

AFL Telecommunications Europe Ltd. **(3)**
Newcombe Drive, Hawksworth, Swindon, SN2 1DZ, Wiltshire, United Kingdom
Tel.: (44) 1793 647 200
Web Site: http://www.aflglobal.com
Sales Range: $25-49.9 Million
Emp.: 60
Fiber Optic Cable Mfr
N.A.I.C.S.: 335921
Kurt Dallas *(Pres-Product Solutions)*

Subsidiary (Domestic):

ITC Service Group, Inc. **(3)**
7777 Greenback Ln Ste 201, Citrus Heights, CA 95610
Web Site: http://www.callitc.com
Drafting Services
N.A.I.C.S.: 541340
Tim Sauer *(Founder)*

Verrillon, Inc. **(3)**
15 Centennial Dr, North Grafton, MA 01536
Tel.: (508) 890-7100
Web Site: http://www.verrillon.com
Sales Range: $25-49.9 Million
Emp.: 30
Optical Fiber Mfr
N.A.I.C.S.: 335921
Abdel Soufiane *(Founder, Chm & CTO)*

Unit (Domestic):

Noise Fiber **(2)**
16 Eastgate Park Rd, Belmont, NH 03220
Tel.: (603) 528-7780
Web Site: http://www.aflglobal.com
Sales Range: $25-49.9 Million
Emp.: 70
Laser-Welded Fiber Optic Tubes
N.A.I.C.S.: 335921
Sean Adam *(Gen Mgr)*

Subsidiary (Domestic):

Optical & Telecommunication Solutions, Inc. **(2)**
16835 Addison Rd Ste 105, Addison, TX 75001
Tel.: (972) 931-0360
Web Site: http://www.optelsol.com
Rev.: $2,200,000
Emp.: 26
Fiscal Year-end: 12/31/2006
Telecommunications Resellers
N.A.I.C.S.: 517121
Sam Orendain *(Founder)*

Aomori Fujikura Kanaya Ltd. **(1)**
2-2-2 Kanaya, Rokunohe-cho Kamikita-gun, Aomori, 033-0073, Japan
Tel.: (81) 176511101
Electric Equipment Mfr
N.A.I.C.S.: 334419

DDK (Thailand) Ltd. **(1)**
55/25 Moo 13 Navanakorn Industrial Estate Paholyothin Road, Klong Nueng Klong Luang, Pathumthani, 12120, Thailand
Tel.: (66) 2529142831
Web Site: https://www.ddk.co.th
Electronic Connector Mfr & Distr
N.A.I.C.S.: 334417
Khun Phanlapa Tong-on *(Mgr-Sale Supply)*

DDK Ltd. **(1)**
1-5-1 Kiba, Koto-ku, Tokyo, 135-8512, Japan
Tel.: (81) 3 5606 1154
Web Site: http://www.ddknet.co.jp
Sales Range: $300-349.9 Million
Emp.: 550
Electric Connector Mfr & Distr
N.A.I.C.S.: 423610
Morio Suzuki *(VP)*

Subsidiary (Domestic):

Aomori DDK Ltd. **(2)**
1-6 Kanda 2-chome Oaza, Hirosaki, 036-8061, Aomori, Japan
Tel.: (81) 172 37 5511
Web Site: http://www.ddknet.co.jp
Electronic Components Mfr
N.A.I.C.S.: 334419

Subsidiary (Non-US):

DDK (Shanghai) Ltd. **(2)**
F No 888 Zhaoxian Road Jiading Industrial Zone, Shanghai, 201800, China
Tel.: (86) 2131296880
Web Site: http://www.fujikura.com
Electronic Connector Mfr & Distr
N.A.I.C.S.: 334417

DDK (Vietnam) LTD. **(2)**
20 VSIPII Dan Chu Street VSIP-II, Thu Dau Mot, 084, Binh Duong, Vietnam
Tel.: (84) 2743628207
Electronic Components Mfr
N.A.I.C.S.: 334419

Plant (Domestic):

DDK Ltd. - Moka Plant **(2)**
14 Matsuyama-cho, Moka, 321-4393, Tochigi, Japan
Tel.: (81) 285 82 4411
Web Site: http://www.ddknet.co.jp
Emp.: 481
Electronic Connector Mfr
N.A.I.C.S.: 334417
Nobuhiro Ogura *(Gen Mgr)*

FiberTech Co., Ltd. **(1)**
Sakura Research Center 409-1 Nishimikado, Sakura, 285-0074, Chiba, Japan
Tel.: (81) 434815381
Web Site: https://www.fibertech.jp
Medical Equipment Mfr & Distr
N.A.I.C.S.: 339112
Kazuyuki Nihonyanagi *(Pres)*

Fujikura (China) Co., Ltd. **(1)**
7th Floor Shanghai Hang Seng Bank Tower 1000 Lujiazui Ring Road, Pudong New Area, Shanghai, 200120, China
Tel.: (86) 21 6841 3636
Web Site: http://www.fujikura.com.cn
Sales Range: $25-49.9 Million
Emp.: 4
Electric Wire Mfr & Distr
N.A.I.C.S.: 332618

Fujikura (Malaysia) Sdn. Bhd. **(1)**
No 2 Jalan Delima 1 1 Subang Hi Tech Industrial Park, 40000, Shah Alam, Selangor, Malaysia **(100%)**
Tel.: (60) 356316366
Web Site: http://www.fujikura.com
Sales Range: $75-99.9 Million
Emp.: 125
Mfr & Sales of Magnet Wires
N.A.I.C.S.: 331222
Ken Yajima *(Mng Dir)*

Fujikura America Inc. **(1)**
2560 N 1st St Ste 100, San Jose, CA 95131 **(100%)**
Tel.: (408) 748-6991
Web Site: http://www.fujikura.com
Sales Range: $50-74.9 Million
Emp.: 7
Electrical Wiring Materials & Components
N.A.I.C.S.: 423610

Division (Domestic):

Fujikura America, Inc. - DDK Connector Division **(2)**
920 Stewart Dr Ste 150, Sunnyvale, CA 94085
Tel.: (408) 748-6991
Web Site: http://www.ddknet.co.jp
Power Connector Whslr

N.A.I.C.S.: 423690

Fujikura Asia (Malaysia) Sdn. Bhd. **(1)**
Ste W 403 Confplant 1, Jalan SS 16 4 Subang Jaya, 47500, Petaling Jaya, Selangor, Malaysia **(100%)**
Tel.: (60) 356364368
Web Site: http://www.fujikura.com
Sales Range: $25-49.9 Million
Emp.: 5
Sales of Electronic Components
N.A.I.C.S.: 449210
Ketsuya Komori *(Mng Dir)*

Fujikura Asia Limited **(1)**
438A Alexandra Road Block A Alexandra Technopark Lobby 1 08-03, Singapore, 119967, Singapore **(100%)**
Tel.: (65) 62788955
Web Site: https://www.fujikura.com.sg
Sales Range: $25-49.9 Million
Emp.: 50
Sales & Financing of Electronic Components
N.A.I.C.S.: 449210

Division (Domestic):

Fujikura Asia Ltd. - DDK Connector Division **(2)**
438A Alexandra Road Block A Alexandra Technopark 08-03, Singapore, 119967, Singapore
Tel.: (65) 62711151
Web Site: http://www.ddknet.co.jp
Sales Range: $25-49.9 Million
Emp.: 50
Electronic Connector Mfr
N.A.I.C.S.: 335931

Fujikura Automotive (Thailand) Ltd. **(1)**
111/2 Moo 7 Hemaraj Saraburi Industrial Land, Nongplamoh Nongkhae, Saraburi, 18140, Thailand
Tel.: (66) 36373481
Wire Harness Mfr & Distr
N.A.I.C.S.: 335931

Fujikura Automotive America LLC. **(1)**
27555 Executive Dr Ste 150, Farmington Hills, MI 48331
Tel.: (248) 957-0130
Web Site: http://www.fujikura.co.jp
Sales Range: $25-49.9 Million
Emp.: 35
Automotive Electronic Product Whslr
N.A.I.C.S.: 423690

Fujikura Automotive Asia Ltd. **(1)**
1-1-3 Hachimanpara, Yonezawa, 992-1128, Yamagata, Japan
Tel.: (81) 238289211
Web Site: http://www.fujikuradenso.co.jp
Automotive Electrical Equipment Mfr
N.A.I.C.S.: 336320

Fujikura Automotive Czech Republic, s.r.o. **(1)**
Na Vysluni 370, Bradlec, 293 06, Mlada Boleslav, Czech Republic
Tel.: (420) 326214301
Automotive Wire Harnesses Mfr & Distr
N.A.I.C.S.: 336320

Fujikura Automotive Europe GmbH **(1)**
Heinenkamp 22, 38444, Wolfsburg, Germany
Tel.: (49) 53085222235
Emp.: 8
Automotive Electronic Component Mfr
N.A.I.C.S.: 336320

Fujikura Automotive Europe S.A.U. **(1)**
Avda de Ranillas n 3 Edificio Dinamiza 3 A planta 1 oficina i, 50018, Zaragoza, Spain
Tel.: (34) 976729800
Web Site: https://www.fujikura-automotive.com
Automotive Electronic Parts Mfr & Distr
N.A.I.C.S.: 336320

Fujikura Automotive Guangzhou Co., Ltd. **(1)**
No 7 Yongxing Road, Xinzao Town Panyu, Guangzhou, 511436, Guangdong, China

Fujikura Ltd.—(Continued)

Tel.: (86) 2084728238
Electrical Equipment Mfr & Distr
N.A.I.C.S.: 335999

Fujikura Automotive MLD S.R.L. (1)
MD 2029 Muncesti Sauce 801 of 1 Mun,
Chisinau, Moldova
Tel.: (373) 22667252
Automotive Wire Harnesses Mfr & Distr
N.A.I.C.S.: 336320

**Fujikura Automotive Mexico Puebla,
S.A. de C.V.** (1)
Carretera a Canoa No 653 A, Col San
Miguel Canoa Puebla, 72900, Puebla,
Mexico
Tel.: (52) 2223096000
Automotive Wire Harnesses Mfr & Distr
N.A.I.C.S.: 336320

**Fujikura Automotive Mexico Quere-
taro, S.A. de C.V.** (1)
Rufino Tamayo No 3, Pueblo Nuevo El
Pueblito Corregidora, 76900, Queretaro,
Mexico
Tel.: (52) 4422113400
Automotive Wire Harnesses Mfr & Distr
N.A.I.C.S.: 336320

**Fujikura Automotive Mexico S. de
R.L. de C.V.** (1)
Lib Gral Manuel Perez Trevino S/N Parque
Industrial Amistad, Col Lomas del Norte,
26070, Piedras Negras, Coahuila, Mexico
Tel.: (52) 878 112 0050
Web Site: http://www.fujikura.co.jp
Automotive Wiring Products Mfr
N.A.I.C.S.: 336320

**Fujikura Automotive Mexico Sala-
manca, S.A. de C.V.** (1)
Carretera Salamanca - Celaya Km 86 100,
Rancho Valtierrilla, 36881, Guanajuato,
Mexico
Tel.: (52) 4646478900
Automotive Wire Harnesses Mfr & Distr
N.A.I.C.S.: 336320

**Fujikura Automotive Morocco Kenitra,
S.A.S.** (1)
Lots 216 21 218 et 219 Route Nationale 4,
Atlantic Free Zone Cummune Saflia,
Kenitra, Morocco
Tel.: (212) 530300530
Automotive Wire Harnesses Mfr & Distr
N.A.I.C.S.: 336320

**Fujikura Automotive Morocco Tangier,
S.A.S.** (1)
1 lot 7 local 3 4, 5 TFZ-Zone Franche,
Tangiers, 90000, Morocco
Tel.: (212) 539394143
Automotive Wire Harnesses Mfr & Distr
N.A.I.C.S.: 336320

**Fujikura Automotive Paraguay
S.A.** (1)
Ruta Internacional Nro 7 km 11 5 Zona
Franca Global Alto Parana, 7000, Ciudad
del Este, Paraguay
Tel.: (595) 61580280
Automotive Wire Harnesses Mfr & Distr
N.A.I.C.S.: 336320

**Fujikura Automotive Romania
S.R.L.** (1)
Streiului 18, 400599, Cluj-Napoca, Romania
Tel.: (40) 264207950
Automotive Electronic Product Mfr
N.A.I.C.S.: 336320

**Fujikura Automotive Ukraine Lviv,
LLC** (1)
European Street 1, Yavoriv District, Lviv,
81085, Ukraine
Tel.: (380) 322428401
Automotive Wire Harnesses Mfr & Distr
N.A.I.C.S.: 336320

Fujikura Automotive Vietnam Ltd. (1)
Road No 2, Hoa Cam Industrial Zone Cam
Le District, Da Nang, Vietnam
Tel.: (84) 2363675991
Electronics Product Mfr & Distr
N.A.I.C.S.: 334419

**Fujikura Automotive do Brazil
Ltda.** (1)

Rua Catequese 777-8 andar, Vila Guiomar,
Santo Andre, 09090-401, Sao Paulo, Brazil
Tel.: (55) 1149939969
Automotive Wire Harnesses Mfr & Distr
N.A.I.C.S.: 336320

**Fujikura Cabos Para Energia e Tele-
comunicacoes Ltda.** (1)
Via 2 Km 2, Bom Jardim do Cai Caixa
Postal 142, Montenegro, 95780-000, Rio
Grande do Sul, Brazil
Tel.: (55) 5133693105
Automotive Wire Harnesses Mfr & Distr
N.A.I.C.S.: 336320

Fujikura Components Ltd. (1)
4-2 Kashiwabara, Ishioka, 315-0002, Iba-
raki, Japan
Tel.: (81) 299235002
Web Site: http://www.fujikura-compo.co.jp
Spiral Grips Product Mfr
N.A.I.C.S.: 332618

Fujikura Dia Cable Ltd. (1)
5F Shin-Tokyo Blig 3-3-1, Marunouchi
Chiyoda-ku, Tokyo, 100-8306, Japan
Tel.: (81) 362506890
Electrical Equipment Mfr & Distr
N.A.I.C.S.: 335999

**Fujikura Electronics (Thailand)
Ltd.** (1)
1/80 Moo 5 Rojana Industrail Park Rojana
Road, Tambol Kanham Amphur U-Thai,
Phra Nakhon Si Ayutthaya, 13210,
Thailand **(100%)**
Web Site: http://www.fujikura-
electronics.co.th
Sales Range: $900-999.9 Million
Emp.: 11,000
Electronics & Electrical Products Mfr
N.A.I.C.S.: 334419

Subsidiary (Domestic):

**Fujikura Electronics (Thailand) Ltd. -
Ayutthaya Factory 1** (2)
1/80 Moo 5 Rojana Industrial Park Rojana
Road, Tambol Kanham Amphur U-Thai,
Ayutthaya, 13210, Thailand
Tel.: (66) 3571902128
Sales Range: $350-399.9 Million
Emp.: 200
Flexible Printed Circuit Mfr
N.A.I.C.S.: 334419
Foto Hideo (Gen Mgr)

Plant (Domestic):

**Fujikura Electronics (Thailand) Ltd. -
Lamphun Factory 1** (2)
68/1 Moo 4 Northern Region Industrial Es-
tate Super Highway Road, Tambol Bank-
lang Amphur Muang, Lamphun, 51000,
Thailand
Tel.: (66) 5 358 1002
Web Site: http://www.fujikura-
electronics.co.th
Electronic Components Mfr
N.A.I.C.S.: 334419

**Fujikura Electronics (Thailand) Ltd. -
Navanakorn Factory 2** (2)
101/53 Moo 20 Navanakorn Industrial Zone
Phaholyothin Road, Tambol Klongnueng,
Khlong Luang, 12120, Pathumthani, Thai-
land
Tel.: (66) 2 529 1804
Electronic Components Mfr
N.A.I.C.S.: 334419

**Fujikura Electronics (Thailand) Ltd. -
Navanakorn Factory 3** (2)
55/40 Moo 13 Navanakorn Industrial Zone
Phaholyothin Road, Tambol Klongnueng,
Khlong Luang, 12120, Pathumthani, Thai-
land
Tel.: (66) 2 529 2717
Sales Range: $75-99.9 Million
Emp.: 25
Printed Circuit Board Mfr
N.A.I.C.S.: 334412

**Fujikura Electronics (Thailand) Ltd. -
Prachinburi Factory 1** (2)
118/2 Moo 11 Suwannasorn Road, Tambol
Banpra, Amphur Muang, 25230, Prachin
Buri, Thailand
Tel.: (66) 3 721 3323
Flexible Printed Circuit Mfr

N.A.I.C.S.: 334418

**Fujikura Electronics Shanghai
Ltd.** (1)
Building 56A No 199 Ri Ying North Road,
Wai Gao Qiao Free Trade Zone, Shanghai,
China
Tel.: (86) 2150461771
Electronics Product Mfr & Distr
N.A.I.C.S.: 334419

Fujikura Electronics Vietnam Ltd. (1)
Lot No D-8 2 Long Binh Techno Park, Bien
Hoa, Vietnam
Tel.: (84) 2518890001
Electronics Product Mfr & Distr
N.A.I.C.S.: 334419

Fujikura Europe Ltd. (1)
C51 Barwell Business Park Leatherhead
Road, Chessington, KT9 2NY, Surrey,
United Kingdom
Tel.: (44) 208 240 2000
Web Site: https://www.fujikura.co.uk
Emp.: 44
Fiber Optic Cable Mfr
N.A.I.C.S.: 335921
Neil Bessant (Mgr-Fusion Splicer Div)

Division (Domestic):

**Fujikura Europe Ltd. - Fibre Optics
Division** (2)
C51 Barwell Business Park Leatherhead
Road, Chessington, KT9 2NY, Surrey,
United Kingdom
Tel.: (44) 20 8240 2000
Fiber Optic Cable Mfr
N.A.I.C.S.: 335921

Subsidiary (Domestic):

**Fujikura Europe Ltd. - Plant & Infra-
structure Cables Division** (2)
C51 Barwell Business Park Leatherhead
Road, Chessington, KT9 2NY, Surrey,
United Kingdom
Tel.: (44) 2082402000
Emp.: 40
Electronic Cable Mfr
N.A.I.C.S.: 335921
Roy Higgins (Deputy Mng Dir)

**Fujikura Europe Ltd. - DDK Connec-
tor Division** (1)
C51 Barwell Business Park Leatherhead
Road, Chessington, KT9 2NY, Surrey,
United Kingdom
Tel.: (44) 2082402000
Web Site: http://www.fujikura.co.uk
Emp.: 50
Fiber Optic Cable Mfr
N.A.I.C.S.: 335921

**Fujikura Europe Ltd. - Electronics
Division** (1)
C51 Barwell Business Park Leatherhead
Road, Chessington, v, Surrey, United King-
dom
Tel.: (44) 20 8240 2000
Web Site: http://www.fujikura.co.uk
Electronic Product Whslr
N.A.I.C.S.: 423690

**Fujikura Federal Cables Sdn
Bhd** (1)
5097 Kawasan Perindustrian Mak Mandin
Industrial Estate, 13400, Butterworth, Pen-
ang, Malaysia **(52%)**
Tel.: (60) 4 331 5577
Web Site: http://www.ffcpg.com.my
Sales Range: $25-49.9 Million
Emp.: 360
Mfr & Sales of Cables
N.A.I.C.S.: 332618

**Fujikura Fiber Optics Vietnam
Ltd.** (1)
9 VSIP St 6 Vietnam Singapore Industrial
Park, Binh Hoa Ward, Thuan An, Binh
Duong, Vietnam
Tel.: (84) 2743757848
Optical Fiber Product Mfr & Distr
N.A.I.C.S.: 335921

**Fujikura Fiber-Home Opto-Electronics
Material Technology Co., Ltd.** (1)
No 2 Fenghuang Middle Road, Fenghuang-
shan Industrial Park East Lake Development Zone, Wuhan, 430205, China

Tel.: (86) 2786699311
Optical Fiber Product Mfr & Distr
N.A.I.C.S.: 335921

**Fujikura Hengtong Aerial Cable Sys-
tem Ltd.** (1)
Qidu Township Industrial Zone, Wujiang,
215234, Jiangsu, China
Tel.: (86) 512 6381 7329
Sales Range: $100-124.9 Million
Emp.: 530
Wiring Device Mfr
N.A.I.C.S.: 335931

Fujikura High OPT Co., Ltd. (1)
1-5-1 Kiba, Koto-ku, Tokyo, 135-0042, Ja-
pan
Tel.: (81) 336494334
Web Site: https://fjk-hiopt.jp
Emp.: 110
Optical Fiber Cable Product Mfr & Distr
N.A.I.C.S.: 335921
Keisuke Okamura (Pres)

Fujikura Hong Kong Limited (1)
Rm 801 808 Mirror Tower 61 Mody Road
Tsimshatsui East, Kowloon, China (Hong
Kong) **(100%)**
Tel.: (852) 23664823
Web Site: http://www.fujikura.com.jp
Sales Range: $25-49.9 Million
Sales & Financing of Electronic Compo-
nents
N.A.I.C.S.: 449210

Division (Domestic):

**Fujikura Hong Kong Ltd. - DDK Con-
nector Division** (2)
Room 801 Mirror Tower 61 Mody Road,
Tsim Sha Tsui East, Kowloon, China (Hong
Kong)
Tel.: (852) 2369 7028
Power Connector Whslr
N.A.I.C.S.: 423690

Fujikura Korea Automotive Ltd. (1)
A-BD 2206 2211 Gwanggyo SK View Lake
25 Beopjo ro, Yeongtong gu, Suwon,
16514, Gyeonggi do, Korea (South)
Tel.: (82) 3180678861
Sales Range: $25-49.9 Million
Emp.: 21
Automotive Electrical Parts Mfr
N.A.I.C.S.: 336320

Fujikura Logistics Co., Ltd. (1)
1-5-1 Kiba, Koto-Ku, Tokyo, 135-0042, Ja-
pan
Tel.: (81) 356061386
Logistic Services
N.A.I.C.S.: 541614

Fujikura Ltd. (1)
Rm 1005 Fortune Building No 5 Tong San
Huan Telu, Chaoyangmen Beidajie, Beijing,
100004, China **(100%)**
Tel.: (86) 1065544520
Web Site: http://www.fujikura.com
Sales Range: $25-49.9 Million
Emp.: 3
Representative Office
N.A.I.C.S.: 335921
Yoichi Nagahama (Pres & CEO)

Fujikura Precision Ltd. (1)
748 Kajiya Kamoto-machi, Yamaga, 861-
0312, Kumamoto, Japan
Tel.: (81) 968466051
Electronic Connector Mfr & Distr
N.A.I.C.S.: 334417

**Fujikura Richard Manufacturing
Inc.** (1)
990 Lone Oak Rd Ste 110, Eagan, MN
55121-2226
Tel.: (651) 994-6810
Sales Range: $25-49.9 Million
Emp.: 8
Mfr of Electronic Cables & Wires, Printed
Circuit Boards & Optical Fiber Cables
N.A.I.C.S.: 332710
Mark McGruder (Mgr)

**Fujikura Shanghai Optical Compo-
nents Co., Ltd.** (1)
No 13 Lane80 Beiyang Rd, Songjiang Dis-
trict, Shanghai, China
Tel.: (86) 2157733331
Optical Fiber Product Mfr & Distr

N.A.I.C.S.: 335921

Fujikura Shanghai Trading Co., Ltd. (1)
16th Floor Shanghai Hang Seng Bank Tower 1000 Lujiazui Ring Road, Pudong New Area, Shanghai, 200120, China (100%)
Tel.: (86) 2168413636
Web Site: http://www.fujikura.com.cn
Sales Range: $50-74.9 Million
Emp.: 20
Representative Office
N.A.I.C.S.: 541840
Saita Akiie (Mng Dir)

Fujikura Shoji Co., Ltd. (1)
1-5-1 Kiba, Koto-ku, Tokyo, 135-0042, Japan
Tel.: (81) 356061461
Web Site: https://www.fshou.com
Emp.: 177
Optical Fiber Cable Product Mfr & Distr
N.A.I.C.S.: 335921

Fujikura Solutions Ltd. (1)
1565-6 Shirakusadai, Fukaya, 369-1106, Saitama, Japan
Tel.: (81) 485776886
Web Site: https://fujikura-solutions.co.jp
Emp.: 120
Optical Fiber Product Mfr & Distr
N.A.I.C.S.: 335921

Fujikura Technology Europe GmbH (1)
The Squaire 12 Am Flughafen, 60549, Frankfurt am Main, Germany
Tel.: (49) 69959325100
Customer Center Services
N.A.I.C.S.: 561421

Fujikura Zhuhai Co., Ltd. (1)
161 Shihua Xilu Jida, Zhuhai, 519015, Guangdong, China
Tel.: (86) 7563331111
Web Site: http://www.fujikura.co.jp
Wiring Harness Mfr
N.A.I.C.S.: 332618

IER Fujikura Inc. (1)
8271 Bavaria Rd, Macedonia, OH 44056
Tel.: (330) 425-7121
Web Site: http://ierfujikura.com
Sales Range: $25-49.9 Million
Emp.: 200
Molded Rubber Products Mfr
N.A.I.C.S.: 326299

Numazu Copper Refining & Rolling Co., Ltd. (1)
21-1 Kanayaizumicho, Shimada, 428-0014, Shizuoka, Japan
Tel.: (81) 547452181
Web Site: http://numazu-yodo.com
Copper Wires Mfr
N.A.I.C.S.: 331420

Optoenergy, Inc. (1)
1440 Mutsuzaki, Sakura, 285-8550, Chiba, Japan
Tel.: (81) 434840933
Electrical Equipment Mfr & Distr
N.A.I.C.S.: 335999

P.T. Jembo Cable Company (1)
Jl Pajajaran Kel Gandasari Kec, Jatiuwung, Tangerang, 15137, Indonesia (100%)
Web Site: http://jembo.co.id
Sales Range: $200-249.9 Million
Emp.: 640
Mfr & Sales of Cables
N.A.I.C.S.: 332618

PT Fujikura Indonesia (1)
Menara Standard Chartered 18th Floor Unit E Jl Prof DR Satrio No 164, Kecamatan Setia Budi, Jakarta Selatan, 12930, Indonesia
Tel.: (62) 2125983898
Optical Fiber Cable Product Mfr & Distr
N.A.I.C.S.: 335921

Precision Fiber Optics Ltd. (1)
1440 Mutuzaki Sakura, Chiba, 285-8550, Japan
Tel.: (81) 434842334
Electronic Connector Mfr & Distr
N.A.I.C.S.: 334417

Red Spot Paint & Varnish Co., Inc. (1)
1107 E Louisiana St, Evansville, IN 47703-0418
Tel.: (812) 428-9100
Web Site: https://www.redspot.com
Sales Range: $75-99.9 Million
Emp.: 390
Automotive & Industrial Coatings; Paints & Lacquers Mfr
N.A.I.C.S.: 325510
Akiro Takeda (Pres & CEO)

Subsidiary (Domestic):

Red Spot Westland Inc. (2)
550 S Edwin, Westland, MI 48186-3801
Tel.: (734) 729-7400
Web Site: http://www.redspot.com
Sales Range: $25-49.9 Million
Emp.: 20
Automotive & Industrial Coatings; Paints, Varnishes & Lacquers
N.A.I.C.S.: 325510

Shanghai Nanyang Fujikura Cable Co., Ltd. (1)
No 2188 Guanghua Road, Shanghai, 201111, China (100%)
Tel.: (86) 2164920958
Web Site: https://www.nfc.sh
Mfr & Sales of Cables
N.A.I.C.S.: 332618

Shinshiro Cable, Ltd. (1)
1-65 Kawada Hongudou, Shinshiro, 441-1347, Aichi, Japan
Tel.: (81) 536221094
Cable & Wire Mfr
N.A.I.C.S.: 335921

Suzuki Giken Co., Ltd. (1)
1440 Rokusaki, Sakura, 285-0812, Chiba, Japan
Tel.: (81) 434842185
Web Site: https://sg21.co.jp
Emp.: 100
Optical Fiber Cable Product Mfr & Distr
N.A.I.C.S.: 335921

The Stock Company Moskabel-Fujikura (1)
2-nd Kabelnaya Str 2 Bld 2, 111024, Moscow, Russia
Tel.: (7) 4951090988
Optical Fiber Cable Product Mfr & Distr
N.A.I.C.S.: 335921

Tohoku Fujikura Ltd. (1)
5-1-2 Goshono Yumoto, Akita, 010-1415, Japan
Tel.: (81) 188261111
Electrical Equipment Mfr & Distr
N.A.I.C.S.: 335999

US Conec Ltd. (1)
1138 25th St SE, Hickory, NC 28602
Tel.: (828) 323-8883
Web Site: https://www.usconec.com
Sales Range: $25-49.9 Million
Emp.: 43
Mfr of Electronic Cables & Wires, Printed Circuit Boards & Optical Fiber Cables
N.A.I.C.S.: 335921

United States Alumoweld Co. Inc. (1)
115 Usac Dr, Duncan, SC 29334 (100%)
Tel.: (864) 848-1901
Web Site: http://www.alumoweld.com
Sales Range: $25-49.9 Million
Emp.: 40
Fiber Optic Products
N.A.I.C.S.: 334220

Yonezawa Electric Wire Co., Ltd. (1)
1-1 Yazawamichi Takakura, Hiwadamachi, Koriyama, 963-0531, Fukushima, Japan
Tel.: (81) 249582220
Automotive Wire Harness Mfr
N.A.I.C.S.: 336390

FUJIKYU CORPORATION
210 Takayashiro 1-chome, Meito-ku, Nagoya, 465-8511, Aichi, Japan
Tel.: (81) 527741181
Web Site: https://www.fujikyu-corp.co.jp
Year Founded: 1961
9966—(TKS)
Sales Range: $150-199.9 Million

Apparel Product Store Operator
N.A.I.C.S.: 458110
Shigenori Goto (Pres)

FUJIMAK CORPORATION
1-7-23 Minamiazabu, Minato-ku, Tokyo, Japan
Tel.: (81) 342322200
Web Site: https://www.fujimak.biz
Year Founded: 1950
5965—(TKS)
Rev.: $272,688,490
Assets: $295,078,710
Liabilities: $139,850,250
Net Worth: $155,228,460
Earnings: $11,868,660
Emp.: 1,389
Fiscal Year-end: 12/31/23
Cooking Equipment Mfr
N.A.I.C.S.: 333310
Yosiharu Uehara (Corp Officer)

Subsidiaries:

FUJIMAK (THAILAND) COMPANY LIMITED (1)
No 66/2-3 33 Tower 1st Floor Sukhumvit 33 Deang-Udom Sukhumvit Road, Klongton Nuea Wattana, Bangkok, 10110, Thailand
Tel.: (66) 21182841
Kitchen Equipment Whslr
N.A.I.C.S.: 423440
Toshinori Kumagai (Pres)

FUJIMAK FOOD SERVICE EQUIPMENT SINGAPORE PTE., LTD. (1)
30 Hillview Terrace, Singapore, 669246, Singapore
Tel.: (65) 6762 0122
Kitchen Equipment Mfr & Whslr
N.A.I.C.S.: 332215
Yuji Kogure (Pres)

FUJIMAK GUAM CORPORATION (1)
Waterfield Hale 363R San Chez St Ste A-7, Harmon, GU 96913
Tel.: (671) 649-3263
Kitchen Equipment Whslr
N.A.I.C.S.: 423440
Toshinori Kumagai (Pres)

FUJIMAK HONG KONG COMPANY LIMITED (1)
Unit10 on 4th Floor Century Center No 44 And 46 Hung To Road, Kwun Tong, Kowloon, China (Hong Kong)
Tel.: (852) 23452177
Kitchen Equipment Whslr
N.A.I.C.S.: 423440
Toshinori Kumagai (Pres)

FUJIMAK SHANGHAI CORPORATION (1)
Room 105-205 Building 7 No 930-49 Zhenbei Road, Shanghai, 200060, China
Tel.: (86) 2162919060
Kitchen Equipment Whslr
N.A.I.C.S.: 423440
Toshinori Kumagai (Pres)

FUJIMAK TAIWAN CORPORATION (1)
3FL No 13 Lane 65 Sec 2 Zhong Shan N Rd Zhng Shan Chiu, Taipei, 104, Taiwan
Tel.: (886) 225815552
Kitchen Equipment Whslr
N.A.I.C.S.: 423440
Toshinori Kumagai (Pres)

FUXI SHANGHAI CORPORATION (1)
No 99 A Shang Xue Road Malu, Jiading District, Shanghai, China
Tel.: (86) 21 6916 9280
Kitchen Equipment Mfr
N.A.I.C.S.: 332215
Toshinori Kumagai (Pres)

Fujimak (Cambodia) Co., Ltd. (1)
No28 St 288 Sangkat Olympic, Khan Chamkarmon, Phnom Penh, Cambodia
Tel.: (855) 23982388
Kitchen Equipment Distr
N.A.I.C.S.: 423440

Fujimak Philippines Corporation (1)
23F Tower 6789 Ayala Avenue, Brgy Bel-air, Makati, 1209, Philippines
Tel.: (63) 285283114
Kitchen Equipment Distr
N.A.I.C.S.: 423440

FUJIMI INCORPORATED
1-1 Chiryo-2 Nishibiwajima-cho, Kiyosu, 452-8502, Aichi, Japan
Tel.: (81) 525038181
Web Site: http://www.fujimiinc.co.jp
Year Founded: 1953
5384—(NGO)
Rev.: $339,762,046
Assets: $548,390,993
Liabilities: $68,866,846
Net Worth: $479,524,147
Earnings: $42,940,193
Emp.: 1,110
Fiscal Year-end: 03/31/24
Synthetic Precision Abrasives Mfr
N.A.I.C.S.: 327910
Hirokazu Ito (Mng Dir)

Subsidiaries:

FUJIMI-MICRO TECHNOLOGY SDN. BHD (1)
Lot 13 Jalan Hi-Tech 3 Industrial Zone Phase 1, Kulim Hi-Tech Park, 09090, Kulim, Kedah Darul Aman, Malaysia
Tel.: (60) 44033700
Sales Range: $25-49.9 Million
Emp.: 70
Abrasive Product Mfr
N.A.I.C.S.: 327910
Toshiki Owaki (Mng Dir)

Fujimi Corporation (1)
11200 SW Leveton Dr, Tualatin, OR 97062
Tel.: (503) 682-7822
Web Site: https://www.fujimi.com
Sales Range: $50-74.9 Million
Emp.: 80
Abrasives & Polishing Products Mfr
N.A.I.C.S.: 327910

Fujimi Europe GmbH (1)
Schlossstrasse 5, 74653, Ingelfingen, Germany
Tel.: (49) 79409394990
Synthetic Precision Mfr
N.A.I.C.S.: 332721

Fujimi Shenzhen Technology Co., Ltd. (1)
12A-11 Shenzhen Free Trade Center 111 Taizi Road, Nanshan District, Shenzhen, 518067, China
Tel.: (86) 75522675151
Synthetic Precision Mfr
N.A.I.C.S.: 332721

FUJIMOTO FOODS INC.
928 Nakajima, Iwade, Wakayama, 649-6245, Japan
Tel.: (81) 736 63 6711
Web Site:
http://www.fujimotofoods.co.jp
Year Founded: 1973
Food Mfr
N.A.I.C.S.: 311991
Noriko Fujimoto (Rep Dir)

FUJIO FOOD GROUP INC.
FUJIO BLDG 2-16 Sugahara-cho, Kita-ku, Osaka, 530-0046, Japan
Tel.: (81) 663600301
Web Site: https://www.fujiofood.com
Year Founded: 1999
2752—(TKS)
Rev.: $210,970,040
Assets: $143,834,830
Liabilities: $133,681,950
Net Worth: $10,152,880
Earnings: ($5,005,540)
Emp.: 411
Fiscal Year-end: 12/31/23
Restaurant Management Services
N.A.I.C.S.: 722511
Masahiro Fujio (Pres)

Fujio Food Group Inc.—(Continued)

Subsidiaries:

FUJIO FOOD SYSTEM U.S.A. CO.,
LTD.   (1)
1345 S King St, Honolulu, HI 96814
Tel.: (808) 942-4848
Restaurant Operators
N.A.I.C.S.: 721110

FUJIPREAM CORPORATION
38-1 Shikisai Himeji, Hyogo, 671-
2216, Japan
Tel.: (81) 792666161
Web Site: https://www.fujipream.co.jp
Year Founded: 1982
4237—(TKS)
Rev.: $87,569,280
Assets: $121,861,960
Liabilities: $55,808,230
Net Worth: $66,053,730
Earnings: $3,794,140
Emp.: 241
Fiscal Year-end: 03/31/24
Optical Device Mfr
N.A.I.C.S.: 333310
Tomonaga Matsumoto *(Chm & Pres)*

Subsidiaries:

Fujipream Corporation - Himeji
Factory   (1)
116-1 Jihoji, Himeji, 671-2244, Hyogo, Ja-
pan
Tel.: (81) 792666815
Flat Panel Display Mfr & Distr
N.A.I.C.S.: 334118

Fujipream Corporation - PV
Factory   (1)
1-490-19 Koto Shingu-cho, Tatsuno, Hyogo,
Japan
Tel.: (81) 791598118
Flat Panel Displays Mfr
N.A.I.C.S.: 334118

FUJISASH CO., LTD.
4-32-1 Nishigotanda, Shinagawa-ku,
Tokyo, 141-0031, Japan
Tel.: (81) 445200034
Web Site: https://www.fujisash.co.jp
Year Founded: 1969
5940—(TKS)
Rev.: $669,328,600
Assets: $590,986,880
Liabilities: $452,487,550
Net Worth: $138,499,330
Earnings: $11,329,540
Emp.: 2,919
Fiscal Year-end: 03/31/24
Construction Material Mfr & Distr
N.A.I.C.S.: 332321
Tsutomu Yoshida *(Pres)*

FUJISHOJI CO., LTD.
1-1-4 Uchihon-machi, Chuo-ku,
Osaka, 540-0026, Japan
Tel.: (81) 669490323
Web Site:
  https://www.fujimarukun.co.jp
Year Founded: 1966
6257—(TKS)
Rev.: $286,586,080
Assets: $439,510,720
Liabilities: $84,971,040
Net Worth: $354,539,680
Earnings: ($17,259,440)
Emp.: 462
Fiscal Year-end: 03/31/22
Gaming Machinery Mfr
N.A.I.C.S.: 333998
Koji Inoue *(Pres)*

FUJISOFT INCORPORATED
1-1 Sakuragi-cho, Naka-ku, Yoko-
hama, 231-8008, Kanagawa, Japan
Tel.: (81) 456508811
Web Site: https://www.fsi.co.jp
Year Founded: 1970

9749—(TKS)
Rev.: $2,118,881,950
Assets: $1,826,355,640
Liabilities: $912,305,750
Net Worth: $914,049,890
Earnings: $84,009,410
Emp.: 19,056
Fiscal Year-end: 12/31/23
Software Development, Outsourcing
& Business Solutions Services
N.A.I.C.S.: 541512
Hiroshi Nozawa *(Chm)*

Subsidiaries:

4U Applications, Inc   (1)
Arca West 1-2-4 Kinshi, Sumida-ku, Tokyo,
130-0013, Japan
Tel.: (81) 366584011
Web Site: https://www.4uapplications.com
Software Development Services
N.A.I.C.S.: 541511

CCA Engineering Simulation Software
(Shanghai) Co., Ltd.
RM 908 No 777, Zhao Jia Bang Rd, Shang-
hai, 200032, China
Tel.: (86) 2164716037
Web Site: http://www.cca-es.com
Sales Range: $25-49.9 Million
Emp.: 20
Administrative Management & General
Management Consulting Services
N.A.I.C.S.: 541611

CYBERNET SYSTEMS TAIWAN Co.,
Ltd.   (1)
5th Floor No 178 Section 2 Gongdao 5th
Road, 5th Floor Nanshan Hsinchu Science
and Technology Building, Hsin-chu, Taiwan
Tel.: (886) 3 611 8668
Web Site: https://www.cybernet-ap.com.tw
Software Development Services
N.A.I.C.S.: 541511

Cyber Com Co., Ltd.   (1)
Asahi Seimei Sendai Ichibancho Building
2-7-17 Ichibancho, Aoba-ku, Sendai, 980-
0811, Miyagi, Japan
Tel.: (81) 22 213 1856
Web Site: https://www.cy-com.co.jp
Emp.: 1,169
Custom Computer Programming Services
N.A.I.C.S.: 541511

Cybernet MBSE Co., Ltd.   (1)
Arca Central 14F 1-2-1 Kinshi, Sumida-ku,
Tokyo, 130-0013, Japan
Tel.: (81) 7077993325
Web Site: https://www.cybernetmbse.co.jp
Engineeering Services
N.A.I.C.S.: 541330

Cybernet Systems Co., Ltd.   (1)
Fujisoft Bldg 3 Kanda-neribeicho, Chiyoda-
ku, Tokyo, 101-0022, Japan
Tel.: (81) 352973010
Web Site: http://www.cybernet.co.jp
Rev.: $142,941,120
Assets: $173,191,350
Liabilities: $67,441,020
Net Worth: $105,750,330
Earnings: $7,162,830
Emp.: 571
Fiscal Year-end: 12/31/2022
Computer Aided Engineering Services
N.A.I.C.S.: 541512
Hideyuki Tanaka *(Exec Officer)*

Subsidiary (Non-US):

CCA Engineering Simulation Software
(Shanghai) Co.,Ltd.   (2)
RM 908 No 777, Zhao Jia Bang Rd,
200032, Shanghai, China   **(100%)**
Tel.: (86) 2164716037
Web Site: http://www.cca-es.com
Sales Range: $25-49.9 Million
Emp.: 20
Software Reproducing
N.A.I.C.S.: 334610

Cybernet CAE Systems (Shanghai)
Co.,Ltd   (2)
Room 528 Qingsong City No 777 Jiajiabang
Road, Shanghai, 200032, China
Tel.: (86) 2164227122
Web Site: http://www.cybernet.sh.cn

Sales Range: $25-49.9 Million
Emp.: 40
Software Reproducing
N.A.I.C.S.: 334610

Noesis Solutions NV   (2)
Gaston Geenslaan 11 B4, 3001, Leuven,
Belgium
Tel.: (32) 1 631 7040
Web Site: https://www.noesissolutions.com
Sales Range: $25-49.9 Million
Emp.: 15
Computer Software Development Services
N.A.I.C.S.: 541511
Joost Van de Peer *(CTO)*

Cybernet Systems Malaysia Sdn
Bhd   (1)
SO-32-3A Menara 1 KL Eco City Jalan
Bangsar, 59200, Kuala Lumpur, Malaysia
Tel.: (60) 322011221
Web Site: https://www.cybernet.asia
Information Technology Services
N.A.I.C.S.: 541511

Fujisoft America Inc.   (1)
1710 S Amphlett Blvd Ste 215, San Mateo,
CA 94402
Tel.: (650) 235-9422
Web Site: https://www.fsi-america.com
Embedded Software Services
N.A.I.C.S.: 541511
Renhong Sun *(CEO)*

Fujisoft Kikaku Ltd.   (1)
2-13-18 Okamoto, Kamakura, 247-0072,
Kanagawa, Japan
Tel.: (81) 46 747 5944
Web Site: https://www.fsk-inc.co.jp
Sales Range: $25-49.9 Million
Emp.: 161
Custom Computer Programming Services
N.A.I.C.S.: 541511
Yoshito Takino *(Pres)*

Fujisoft SSS, Inc.   (1)
NTT West Japan Build, 1-3 Aioi-cho, Naga-
saki, 857-0044, Japan
Tel.: (81) 956259223
Web Site: http://www.fsisss.co.jp
Custom Computer Programming Services
N.A.I.C.S.: 541511

Fujisoft Service Bureau
Incorporated   (1)
2-19-7 Kotobashi, Sumida-ku, Tokyo, 130-
0022, Japan
Tel.: (81) 35 600 1731
Web Site: https://www.fsisb.co.jp
Emp.: 2,561
Custom Computer Programming Services
N.A.I.C.S.: 541511
Takashi Kaizuka *(Chm)*

Fujisoft Tissue Engineering Co.,
Ltd.   (1)
2-19-7 Kotobashi, Sumida-ku, Tokyo, 130-
0022, Japan
Tel.: (81) 33 635 6226
Web Site: https://www.fstec.co.jp
Medical Product Mfr & Distr
N.A.I.C.S.: 339112
Motohiro Harai *(Pres)*

Japan Internet News Co., Ltd.   (1)
9th Floor Kojimachi Garden Building, 2-3
Kojimachi Chiyoda-ku, Tokyo, 102-0083,
Japan
Tel.: (81) 352162030
Web Site: http://www.janjan.jp
Sales Range: $25-49.9 Million
Emp.: 35
Custom Computer Programming Services
N.A.I.C.S.: 541511

Maplesoft Europe GmbH   (1)
Auf Der Huls 198, Aachen, 52068,
Nordrhein-Westfalen, Germany
Tel.: (49) 24198091930
Sales Range: $25-49.9 Million
Emp.: 4
Analytical Software Development Services
N.A.I.C.S.: 541511

Mercury Staffing Co., Ltd.   (1)
9F Kawase Building 3 17 5 Sinjyuku,
Sinjyuku ku, Tokyo, 106-0022, Japan
Tel.: (81) 353662500
Web Site: http://www.msso.co.jp
Temporary Help Service

N.A.I.C.S.: 561320

Nihon Business Soft Co., Ltd.   (1)
27-1 Mikawauchi Shinmachi, Sasebo, 859-
3153, Nagasaki Prefecture, Japan
Tel.: (81) 956307200
Web Site: https://www.kknbs.co.jp
Emp.: 149
System Management Services
N.A.I.C.S.: 541511
Hidemi Ohara *(Mng Dir)*

OA Laboratory Co., Ltd.   (1)
2-15-41 Dai, Kamakura, 247-0061, Kana-
gawa Prefecture, Japan
Tel.: (81) 46 744 5566
Web Site: https://www.oalab.co.jp
Emp.: 162
Communication Equipment Mfr
N.A.I.C.S.: 334290
Yoshinori Ohara *(Mng Dir)*

OA Laboratory Co., Ltd. - Fujisawa
Plant   (1)
2021-10 Endo, Fujisawa, 252-0186, Kana-
gawa Prefecture, Japan
Tel.: (81) 466878711
Computer Peripheral Equipment Mfr
N.A.I.C.S.: 334118

SYSTEMS FORMULATIONS AND
INTEGRATIONS Incorporated   (1)
2-19-7 Kotobashi Fuji Soft Bldg, Sumida-
Ku, Tokyo, 130-0022, Japan
Tel.: (81) 356691811
Web Site: http://www.sfi-inc.co.jp
Packaging Services
N.A.I.C.S.: 561910

Serverware Corporation   (1)
1250 Pittsford Victor Rd, Pittsford, NY
14534
Tel.: (585) 785-6100
Web Site: http://www.serverw.com
Sales Range: $25-49.9 Million
Emp.: 25
IT Solutions
N.A.I.C.S.: 541512

Tosho Computer Systems Co.,
Ltd.   (1)
Mitsui Woody Building 3F 2-4-14 Toyo,
Koto-ku, Tokyo, 135-0016, Japan
Tel.: (81) 35 633 7600
Web Site: https://www.tcs.co.jp
Emp.: 345
Data Processing Hosting & Related Ser-
vices
N.A.I.C.S.: 518210

Ui2 Corporation   (1)
Nan-o Bldg Shintora 6F 2-20-1 Nishi-
Shinbashi, Minato-ku, Tokyo, 105-0003,
Japan
Tel.: (81) 368095871
Web Site: https://www.ui2.co.jp
Computer System Design Services
N.A.I.C.S.: 541512

VINX System Service (Thailand) Co.,
Ltd.   (1)
2 Jasmine Bldg 22nd Fl Soi Prasarnmitr
Sukhumvit 23 Sukhumvit Road, North
Klongtoey Wattana, Bangkok, 10110, Thai-
land
Tel.: (66) 26127390
Embedded Product Mfr & Distr
N.A.I.C.S.: 334419

VINX Vietnam Co., Ltd.   (1)
Waseco Building 10 Pho Quang St, Ward 2
Tan Binh Dist, Ho Chi Minh City, Vietnam
Tel.: (84) 2839970371
Web Site: https://www.vinx.com.vn
Information Technology Services
N.A.I.C.S.: 541519

Vincul[um] Japan Corporation   (1)
Toyobo Bldg, 2-2-8 Dojimahama Kita-ku,
530-0004, Osaka, Japan
Tel.: (81) 663488951
Web Site: http://www.vinculum-japan.co.jp
Software Reproducing
N.A.I.C.S.: 334610

Vinex Vietnam Co., Ltd.   (1)
10/106 Kim Ma Thuong, Cong Vi Ba Dinh,
Hanoi, Vietnam
Tel.: (84) 2432444485
Web Site: https://vinexvietnam.vn

Hand Tool Retailer
N.A.I.C.S.: 423710

WATERLOO MAPLE INC. (1)
615 Kumpf Dr, Waterloo, N2V 1K8, ON,
Canada
Tel.: (519) 747-2373
Sales Range: $25-49.9 Million
Emp.: 97
Analytical Software Development Services
N.A.I.C.S.: 541511

iDEA Consulting Inc. (1)
6th floor Akihabara Building 19 Kanda Mat-
sunagacho, Chiyoda-ku, Tokyo, 101-0023,
Japan
Tel.: (81) 35 289 3150
Web Site: https://www.ideacns.co.jp
Information Technology Consulting Services
N.A.I.C.S.: 541512

**FUJITA ENGINEERING CO.,
LTD.**
1174-5 Iizuka-cho, Takasaki, 370-
0069, Gunma, Japan
Tel.: (81) 273611111
Web Site: https://www.fujita-eng.co.jp
Year Founded: 1926
1770—(TKS)
Rev.: $213,324,530
Assets: $219,570,980
Liabilities: $102,058,400
Net Worth: $117,512,580
Earnings: $10,516,510
Emp.: 249
Fiscal Year-end: 03/31/24
Construction Services
N.A.I.C.S.: 236210
Fujita Minoru *(Pres & CEO)*

Subsidiaries:

Fujita Device Co., Ltd. (1)
298 Kamitakicho, Takasaki, Gunma Prefec-
ture, Japan
Tel.: (81) 273951211
Web Site: https://www.fujita-dev.co.jp
Electronic Components Mfr
N.A.I.C.S.: 334419

Fujita Solution Partners Co., Ltd. (1)
Komaigi-cho 361-1, Ota, 373-0818, Gunma
Prefecture, Japan
Tel.: (81) 276461288
Web Site: https://www.fujita-sp.co.jp
Emp.: 103
Industrial Equipment Distr
N.A.I.C.S.: 423830

FUJITA KANKO INC.
2-10-8 Sekiguchi, Bunkyo-ku, Tokyo,
112-8664, Japan
Tel.: (81) 359817700
Web Site: https://www.fujita-
kanko.com
Year Founded: 1955
9722—(TKS)
Rev.: $457,638,230
Assets: $662,886,640
Liabilities: $478,730,980
Net Worth: $184,155,660
Earnings: $57,528,260
Emp.: 1,342
Fiscal Year-end: 12/31/23
Hotel Operator
N.A.I.C.S.: 721110
Takeaki Yamada *(Dir-Admin, HR &
Plng Div)*

Subsidiaries:

Hotel Chinzanso Tokyo (1)
10-8 Sekiguchi 2-Chome, Bunkyo-ku, To-
kyo, 112-8667, Japan
Tel.: (81) 339432222
Web Site: http://www.hotel-chinzanso-
tokyo.com
Sales Range: $200-249.9 Million
Emp.: 400
Hotel Services
N.A.I.C.S.: 721110
Koichi Urashima *(Gen Mgr)*

PT. Fujita Kanko Indonesia (1)
Jl Maligi III Lot N-3A Kawasan Industri KIIC,

Karawang, 41361, West Java, Indonesia
Tel.: (62) 2189107777
Web Site: https://fujita.co.id
Machinery Equipment Mfr
N.A.I.C.S.: 333248
Yoshihisa Fujita *(Pres)*

Shimoda Aqua Service Inc. (1)
3-22-31 Shimoda, Shizuoka, 415-8502,
Japan
Tel.: (81) 55 822 3567
Hotel Services
N.A.I.C.S.: 721110

FUJITEC CO., LTD.
1-17-3 Shirokane, Minato-Ku, Tokyo,
108-8307, Japan
Tel.: (81) 749307111
Web Site: https://www.fujitec.com
Year Founded: 1948
FJC—(DEU)
Rev.: $1,488,413,130
Assets: $1,649,802,660
Liabilities: $616,476,600
Net Worth: $1,033,326,060
Earnings: $60,464,610
Emp.: 11,453
Fiscal Year-end: 03/31/23
Elevators, Escalators & Vertical
Transportation Equipment Mfr
N.A.I.C.S.: 333921
Takakazu Uchiyama *(Pres & CEO)*

Subsidiaries:

FSP Pte Ltd. (1)
204 Bedok S Ave 1, Singapore, 469333,
Singapore
Tel.: (65) 67671626
Transportation System Mfr
N.A.I.C.S.: 336999

FUJITEC ARGENTINA S.A. (1)
Av Belgrano 884, 1092 AAV, Buenos Aires,
Argentina
Tel.: (54) 1143426830
Web Site: http://www.fujitec.com.ar
Elevators Distr & Installation Services
N.A.I.C.S.: 423830

FUJITEC CANADA, INC. (1)
15 East Wilmot Street, Richmond Hill, L4B
1A3, ON, Canada
Tel.: (905) 731-8681
Web Site: http://www.fujiteccanada.com
Emp.: 27
Elevators & Escalators Mfr & Installation
Services
N.A.I.C.S.: 333921

FUJITEC EGYPT CO., LTD. (1)
Osmans Towers st Foq Motowaset Towers
5 25th Floor Flat 252, Cornishe El Nile
Maadi, Cairo, Egypt
Tel.: (20) 2 2528 5808
Web Site: http://www.fujitecegypt.com
Elevator Mfr
N.A.I.C.S.: 333921

FUJITEC INC. (1)
3F A & V Crystal Tower 105 Esteban Street,
Legaspi Village, Makati, 1229, Metro Ma-
nila, Philippines
Tel.: (63) 288933734
Web Site: http://www.fujitec.co.jp
Sales Range: $25-49.9 Million
Emp.: 20
Elevator Installation Services
N.A.I.C.S.: 238290
Ceazar Almario *(Mng Dir)*

FUJITEC INDIA PRIVATE LTD. (1)
Plot No-52 First Cross Road 8th Avenue
Mahindra World City, Kanchipuram Dist,
Chengalpattu, 603002, India
Tel.: (91) 4447418800
Web Site: http://www.fujitecindia.com
Emp.: 200
Elevators Mfr & Distr
N.A.I.C.S.: 333921
M. K. Panicker *(Mng Dir)*

FUJITEC KOREA CO., LTD. (1)
98B-3L Namdong Industrial Complex 151
Hogupo-Ro, Namdong-Gu, Incheon, 21691,
Korea (South)
Tel.: (82) 328177541
Web Site: http://www.fujiteckorea.co.kr

Sales Range: $50-74.9 Million
Emp.: 20
Elevator Mfr
N.A.I.C.S.: 333921
Seung-Soo Yoon *(CEO)*

**FUJITEC SAUDI ARABIA CO.,
LTD.** (1)
Jamjoom Center, PO Box 4376, Jeddah,
21491, Saudi Arabia
Tel.: (966) 2 667 0057
Escalator Installation & Maintenance Ser-
vices
N.A.I.C.S.: 238290

**FUJITEC SHANGHAI SOURCING
CENTER CO., LTD.** (1)
No 1000 Xin Fei Road Eastern New Area
Song Jiang Industrial Zone, Shanghai,
201612, China
Tel.: (86) 21 6760 1515
Transportation System Mfr
N.A.I.C.S.: 336999

**FUJITEC SHANGHAI TECHNOLO-
GIES CO., LTD.** (1)
No 1002 Xinfei Road, Songjiang, Shanghai,
201611, China
Tel.: (86) 21 6760 0566
Web Site: http://www.rdfujitec.com.cn
Transportation System Mfr
N.A.I.C.S.: 336999

FUJITEC UK LTD. (1)
Unit 43 The iO Centre Armstrong Road,
Woolwich, London, SE18 6RS, United King-
dom
Tel.: (44) 1322552450
Web Site: http://www.fujitec.uk.com
Sales Range: $25-49.9 Million
Emp.: 15
Escalators Sales & Installation Services
N.A.I.C.S.: 238290

FUJITEC VENEZUELA C.A. (1)
Calle 8 Con Calle6 Edieficio Luindos Plan-
tabaja, Urbanizacion La Urbina Municipio
Sucre, Caracas, 1070, Miranda, Venezuela
Tel.: (58) 212 241 0311
Web Site: http://www.fujitec.com.ve
Emp.: 60
Elevator Mfr
N.A.I.C.S.: 333922

FUJITEC VIETNAM CO., LTD. (1)
3rd Floor Tien Phuoc Bldg 542 Tran Hung
Dao St Ward 2, District 5, Ho Chi Minh City,
Vietnam
Tel.: (84) 839246556
Sales Range: $25-49.9 Million
Emp.: 1
Transportation System Services
N.A.I.C.S.: 488999
Toshikazu Nakata *(Gen Mgr)*

Fujitec (HK) Company Limited (1)
34/F Hong Kong Plaza 188 Connaught
Road West, Kowloon, China (Hong Kong)
Tel.: (852) 25478339
Web Site: http://www.fujitec-hk.com.hk
Sales Range: $25-49.9 Million
Emp.: 600
Building Equipment & Machinery Installation
Contractors
N.A.I.C.S.: 238220

Fujitec (Malaysia) Sdn Bhd (1)
Unit D-5-59 Block Dahlia 10 Boulevard Leb-
uhraya Sprint Pju 6A, Petaling Jaya, 47400,
Selangor Darul Ehsan, Malaysia
Tel.: (60) 377285351
Web Site: http://www.fujitecsg.com
Sales Range: $50-74.9 Million
Emp.: 75
Industrial Machinery & Equipment Whslr
N.A.I.C.S.: 423830

Fujitec (Thailand) Co., Ltd. (1)
No 1 1st Floor Sukhumvit Alley No 101/2,
Bang Na Nua Sub-District Bang Na District,
Bangkok, 10260, Thailand
Tel.: (66) 23961900
Industrial Machinery Mfr
N.A.I.C.S.: 333248

Fujitec America Inc (1)
7258 Innovation Way, Mason, OH 45040
Tel.: (513) 932-8000
Web Site: https://www.fujitecamerica.com
Sales Range: $25-49.9 Million
Emp.: 90
Elevator & Moving Stairway Mfr

N.A.I.C.S.: 333921
Gary Krupp *(Pres)*

Fujitec Elevator Co. Inc. (1)
1 Donna Dr, Wood Ridge, NJ 07075
Tel.: (201) 438-8400
Web Site: http://www.fujitecamerica.com
Rev.: $40,000,000
Emp.: 165
Elevator Manufacturing, Installation & Re-
pair
N.A.I.C.S.: 333921
K. C. Debra *(Dir-Mktg Comm)*

Fujitec Lanka (Private) Ltd. (1)
153 Union Place, Colombo, Sri Lanka
Tel.: (94) 2324365
Industrial Machinery Mfr
N.A.I.C.S.: 333248

Fujitec Myanmar Co., Ltd. (1)
418 4th Floor Yuzana Hotel No 130 Shwe
Gon Taing Road, Bahan Township, Yangon,
Myanmar
Tel.: (95) 18603493
Industrial Machinery Mfr
N.A.I.C.S.: 333248

Fujitec Pacific, Inc. (1)
128-C North Marine Corps Dr, Tamuning,
GU 96913
Tel.: (671) 646-4120
Industrial Machinery Mfr
N.A.I.C.S.: 333248

Fujitec Singapore Corporation
Limited (1)
204 Bedok South Avenue 1, Singapore,
469333, Singapore
Tel.: (65) 62416222
Web Site: https://www.fujitec.com.sg
Sales Range: $200-249.9 Million
Emp.: 700
Elevator & Moving Stairway Mfr
N.A.I.C.S.: 333921
Masashi Tsuchihata *(Mng Dir)*

Fujitec Taiwan Co. Ltd. (1)
13th Fl 37 Sec 3, Minchuan E Rd, Taipei,
Taiwan
Tel.: (886) 225167166
Sales Range: $25-49.9 Million
Emp.: 30
Elevator & Moving Stairway Mfr
N.A.I.C.S.: 333921

Fujitec Uruguay S.A. (1)
Av Italia y Biarritz Local 3 Edificio del Sol,
Punta del Este, Uruguay
Tel.: (598) 42493254
Web Site: http://www.fujitec.com.uy
Industrial Machinery Mfr
N.A.I.C.S.: 333248

Huasheng Fujitec Elevator Co.
Ltd. (1)
No 7 Chunming Road, Langfang Economic
and Technological Development Zone,
Langfang, 065001, Hebei, China
Tel.: (86) 3166086718
Web Site: http://www.fujitec.com.cn
Elevator & Moving Stairway Mfr
N.A.I.C.S.: 333921

PT. Fujitec Indonesia (1)
Perkantoran Puri Niaga III J1 Puri Kencana
Kembangan, 11610, Jakarta, Indonesia
Tel.: (62) 2158303406
Sales Range: $25-49.9 Million
Emp.: 40
Elevator & Moving Stairway Mfr
N.A.I.C.S.: 333921

Rich Mark Engineering Limited. (1)
Rm 3315 Hong Kong Plz 188 Connaught
Rd C, Sai Ying Pun, Hong Kong, China
(Hong Kong)
Tel.: (852) 29155198
Transportation System Mfr
N.A.I.C.S.: 336999

Shanghai Huasheng Fujitec Escalator
Co., Ltd. (1)
No 1002 Xinfei Road, Songjiang, Shanghai,
201611, China
Tel.: (86) 2151211001
Industrial Machinery Mfr
N.A.I.C.S.: 333248

**FUJITOMI SECURITIES CO.,
LTD.**

Fujitomi Securities Co., Ltd.—(Continued)

1-15-5 Kakigara-cho Nihombashi,
Chuo-Ku, Tokyo, 103-0014, Japan
Tel.: (81) 3 45895500
Web Site: http://www.fujitomi.co.jp
Year Founded: 1952
8740—(JAS)
Sales Range: $10-24.9 Million
Emp.: 134
Investment Services
N.A.I.C.S.: 523999
Ueda Tsutomu (*Auditor*)

FUJITRANS CORPORATION
7-41 Irifune 1-chome, Minato-ku, Na-
goya, 455-0032, Aichi, Japan
Tel.: (81) 52 653 3111   JP
Web Site: http://www.fujitrans.co.jp
Year Founded: 1952
Emp.: 1,265
Freight Transportation & Logistics
Services
N.A.I.C.S.: 488510
Tatsuo Keii (*Pres*)

Subsidiaries:

Fujitrans U.S.A., Inc.   (1)
1231 E 230th St, Carson, CA 90745
Tel.: (310) 830-5151
Freight Transportation & Logistics Services
N.A.I.C.S.: 488510

Joint Venture (Domestic):

Vascor, Ltd.   (2)
100 Farmers Bank Dr Ste 300, George-
town, KY 40324
Tel.: (502) 570-2020
Web Site: http://www.vascorlogistics.com
Logistic Services
N.A.I.C.S.: 541614
Jinny Daugherty (*CFO*)

FUJITSU COMPONENT LIM-
ITED
Shinagawa Seaside Park Tower 12-4
Higashi-shinagawa 4-chome,
Shinagawa-ku, Tokyo, 140-0002, Ja-
pan
Tel.: (81) 334501601
Web Site: http://www.fujitsu.com
Rev.: $438,849,600
Assets: $374,744,880
Liabilities: $348,229,200
Net Worth: $26,515,680
Earnings: $1,776,000
Emp.: 394
Fiscal Year-end: 03/31/18
Electronic Components Mfr
N.A.I.C.S.: 335313
Masahiro Kinoshita (*Pres*)

Subsidiaries:

Chikuma Tsushin Industry Co.,
Ltd.   (1)
1111-1 Seto, Saku, Nagano, Japan
Tel.: (81) 267641230
Relay Mfr
N.A.I.C.S.: 335314

Fujitsu Component (Malaysia) Sdn.
Bhd.   (1)
No 1 Lorong Satu Kawasan Perindustrian
Parit Raja Parit Raja, 86400, Batu Pahat,
Johor, Malaysia
Tel.: (60) 7 4542111
Electronic Components Mfr
N.A.I.C.S.: 333912
Onn Samad (*Mgr-Quality Control*)

Fujitsu Components (Changzhou)
Co., Ltd.   (1)
No 202 Taishan Road, Changzhou New
High-Tech Industrial Development Zone,
Changzhou, 213022, Jiangsu, China
Tel.: (86) 51985100380
Electronic Components Mfr
N.A.I.C.S.: 334419

Fujitsu Components Asia Pte.
Ltd.   (1)

102E Pasir Panjang Road 01-01 Citilink
Warehouse Complex, Singapore, 118529,
Singapore
Tel.: (65) 6375 8560
Electronic Components Distr
N.A.I.C.S.: 423690

Fujitsu Components Korea
Limited   (1)
Alpha Tower 403 645 Sampyeong-dong
Bundang-gu, Seongnam, 13524, Gyeonggi-
do, Korea (South)
Tel.: (82) 317087108
Electronic Components Distr
N.A.I.C.S.: 423690

Fujitsu Electronic Components
(Shanghai) Co., Ltd.   (1)
Unit 4306 InterContinental Center 100 Yu
Tong Road, Shanghai, 200070, China
Tel.: (86) 2132530998
Electronic Components Distr
N.A.I.C.S.: 423690

Miyazaki Fujitsu Components
Limited   (1)
1011 Higashibenbun Otsu Oaza, Nichinan,
Miyazaki, Japan
Tel.: (81) 987225211
Relay Mfr
N.A.I.C.S.: 335314

Qingdao Kowa Seiko Co., Ltd.   (1)
Chengqu Industrial Estate Chengyang Dis-
trict, Qingdao, 266109, Shandong, China
Tel.: (86) 53287963977
Electronic Components Mfr
N.A.I.C.S.: 334419

Shinano Fujitsu Limited   (1)
935 Nosakada Oaza, Iiyama, Nagano, Ja-
pan
Tel.: (81) 269621155
Electronic Components Mfr
N.A.I.C.S.: 333912

FUJITSU GENERAL (AUSTRA-
LIA) PTY. LIMITED
1 Telopea Place, Eastern Creek,
2766, NSW, Australia
Tel.: (61) 288222500
Web Site:
http://www.fujitsugeneral.com.au
Air Conditioner Distr
N.A.I.C.S.: 423620
Philip PerhamM (*Mng Dir*)

FUJITSU LIMITED
Shiodome City Center 1-5-2 Higashi-
Shimbashi, Minato-ku, Tokyo, 105-
7123, Japan
Tel.: (81) 362522220   JP
Web Site: https://www.fujitsu.com
Year Founded: 1935
067020—(NGO)
Rev.: $26,631,171,961
Assets: $24,920,727,435
Liabilities: $11,315,829,797
Net Worth: $13,604,897,638
Earnings: $1,890,811,869
Emp.: 124,000
Fiscal Year-end: 03/31/24
Electric Equipment Mfr
N.A.I.C.S.: 334111
Hidenori Furuta (*Sr Exec VP & Head-
Digital Svcs Bus*)

Subsidiaries:

Beijing Fujitsu System Engineering
Co., Ltd.   (1)
8F Tower A IFC No 8 Jianguomenwai Ave,
Chaoyang District, Beijing, 100022, China
Tel.: (86) 1059691000
Software Development Services
N.A.I.C.S.: 541511
Kitaro Shigeru (*Mgr*)

FDK Corporation   (1)
Shibaura Crystal Shinagawa 1-6-41 Konan,
Minato-ku, Tokyo, 108-8212, Japan
Tel.: (81) 357157400
Web Site: https://fdk.com
Rev.: $414,288,360
Assets: $340,785,160

Liabilities: $237,371,710
Net Worth: $103,413,450
Earnings: $793,200
Emp.: 2,418
Fiscal Year-end: 03/31/2024
Mfr & Sales of Electronics-Related Raw Ma-
terials, Components & Dry Batteries
N.A.I.C.S.: 334419
Ryo Nagano (*Pres & CEO*)

Subsidiary (Non-US):

Baotou FDK Co., Ltd.   (2)
No 21 Rare-earth Street, Rare-earth Hi-tech
Industrial Development Zone, Baotou,
014030, China   (94.4%)
Tel.: (86) 04725320163
Battery Materials & Rare Earth Alloy Mfr
N.A.I.C.S.: 335910

Subsidiary (US):

FDK America Inc.   (2)
250 E Caribbean Dr 200, Sunnyvale, CA
94089
Tel.: (408) 215-6500
Web Site: http://www.fdkamerica.com
Rev.: $85,493,206
Emp.: 12
Batteries & Optical Devices
N.A.I.C.S.: 423690
Kenji Fukuta (*Pres & CEO*)

Plant (Domestic):

FDK Corporation - Kosai Plant   (2)
2281 Washizu, Kosai, 431-0495, Shizuoka,
Japan
Tel.: (81) 53 576 2151
Web Site: http://www.fdk.com
Electronic Components Mfr
N.A.I.C.S.: 334413

FDK Corporation - Sanyo Plant   (2)
5 ku Hon-machi, Sanyoonoda-shi, Yamagu-
chi, 757-8585, Japan
Tel.: (81) 836 72 1311
Web Site: http://www.fdk.com
Piezoelectric Inverter Modules Mfr
N.A.I.C.S.: 334419

Subsidiary (Non-US):

FDK ELECTRONICS GMBH   (2)
Heerdter Lohweg 89, 40549, Dusseldorf,
Germany
Tel.: (49) 2115374640
Sales Range: $25-49.9 Million
Emp.: 17
Electronic Equipments Sales
N.A.I.C.S.: 423610

Subsidiary (Domestic):

FDK Ecotec Co., Ltd.   (2)
2281 Washizu, Kosai, 431-0431, Shizuoka,
Japan
Tel.: (81) 53 575 3001
Web Site: http://www.fdk.com
Sales Range: $25-49.9 Million
Emp.: 13
Scrap Metal Recycling Services
N.A.I.C.S.: 562920
Kenji Kawasaki (*Pres*)

Unit (Domestic):

FDK Ecotec Co., Ltd. - GIFU
WORKS   (2)
478 Ehigashi Tsuchikura Aza, Hirata-cho,
Kaizu, 503-0322, Gifu, Japan
Tel.: (81) 584664781
Web Site: http://www.fdk.com
Scrap Metal Recycling Services
N.A.I.C.S.: 423510
Kenji Kawasaki (*Pres*)

Subsidiary (Domestic):

FDK Energy Co., Ltd.   (2)
614 Washizu, Kosai, 431-0431, Shizuoka,
Japan
Tel.: (81) 535762111
Web Site: http://www.fdk.com
Sales Range: $50-74.9 Million
Emp.: 202
Batteries Mfr & Sales
N.A.I.C.S.: 335910
Nobuyuki Miyazaki (*Pres*)

FDK Engineering Co., Ltd.   (2)

281 Hirooka Hosoe-cho, Kita-ku, Ha-
mamatsu, 431-1302, Shizuoka, Japan
Tel.: (81) 535225280
Web Site: http://www.fdk.com
Emp.: 58
Electronic Components Making Machinery
Mfr
N.A.I.C.S.: 333242
Toshiaki Otsubo (*Pres*)

Subsidiary (Non-US):

FDK HONG KONG LTD.   (2)
Suite 1607-1608A 16/F Tower 3 China
Hong Kong City 33 Canton Road, Tsim Tsa
Tsui, Kowloon, China (Hong Kong)
Tel.: (852) 27999773
Sales Range: $25-49.9 Million
Emp.: 11
Electronic Product Whslr
N.A.I.C.S.: 423690

FDK KOREA LTD.   (2)
Room 614 Suseo Hyundai Venture-vill Bldg
10 Bamgogae-ro 1-gil, Gangnam-gu, Seoul,
06349, Korea (South)
Tel.: (82) 25828452
Emp.: 3
Electronic Component Sales
N.A.I.C.S.: 423690

FDK LANKA (PVT) LTD.   (2)
Ring Road 3 Phase 2, 11450, Katunayake,
Western Province, Sri Lanka
Tel.: (94) 112253492
Web Site: http://www.fdklanka.com
Sales Range: $400-449.9 Million
Emp.: 1,100
Electronic Components Mfr
N.A.I.C.S.: 334419
Kenji Yamada (*Pres*)

Subsidiary (Domestic):

FDK LIFETEC CORPORATION   (2)
2281 Washizu, Kosai, 431-0431, Shizuoka,
Japan
Tel.: (81) 535763121
Sales Range: $50-74.9 Million
Emp.: 8
Welfare Services
N.A.I.C.S.: 525120
Masahiro Adachi (*Pres*)

Subsidiary (Non-US):

FDK SINGAPORE PTE. LTD.   (2)
4 Leng Kee Road 04-08 SiS Bldg, Singa-
pore, 159088, Singapore
Tel.: (65) 64722328
Sales Range: $25-49.9 Million
Emp.: 8
Electronic Equipment Mfr & Sales
N.A.I.C.S.: 335910
Kawahara Kozo (*Mng Dir*)

FDK TAIWAN LTD.   (2)
8F-4 No 57 Sec 1 Chongqing S Rd,
Zhongzheng Dist, Taipei, 100, Taiwan
Tel.: (886) 223115161
Web Site: http://www.fdk.co.jp
Emp.: 5
Electronic Components Distr
N.A.I.C.S.: 423690

Subsidiary (Domestic):

FDK TWICELL Co., Ltd.   (2)
307-2 Koyagi-machi, Takasaki, 370-0071,
Gunma, Japan
Tel.: (81) 273617575
Web Site: http://www.fdk-twicell.com
Sales Range: $100-124.9 Million
Emp.: 462
Batteries Mfr
N.A.I.C.S.: 335910

FDK Tottori Co., Ltd.   (2)
28 Ota Iwami-cho, Iwami-gun, Tottori, 681-
0063, Japan
Tel.: (81) 857731771
Sales Range: $100-124.9 Million
Emp.: 331
Lithium Batteries Mfr
N.A.I.C.S.: 335910
Satoru Fukuoka (*Pres*)

Subsidiary (Non-US):

FUCHI ELECTRONICS CO.,
LTD.   (2)

No 355 Section 2 Nankan Road, Rutsu
Shan, Taoyuan, 338, Taiwan
Tel.: (886) 3 322 2124
Sales Range: $125-149.9 Million
Emp.: 358
Electronic Components Mfr & Whslr
N.A.I.C.S.: 335312

PT FDK INDONESIA (2)
Kawasan Industri MM 2100 Blok MM 1 Jati-
wangi, Cikarang Barat, 17520, Bekasi, West
Java, Indonesia
Tel.: (62) 21 8998 2111
Web Site: http://www.fdk.com
Sales Range: $200-249.9 Million
Emp.: 864
Batteries Mfr & Sales
N.A.I.C.S.: 335910
Hiroto Takahashi *(Pres)*

Xiamen FDK Corporation (2)
No 16 Malong Road Huoju Garden, Huoju
Hi-Tech District, Xiamen, 361006, Fujian,
China
Tel.: (86) 5926030576
Sales Range: $450-499.9 Million
Emp.: 401
Power Supplies Mfr & Whslr
N.A.I.C.S.: 335999

FUJITSU EMEA PLC (1)
22 Baker Street, London, W1U 3BW, United
Kingdom
Tel.: (44) 843 354 5555
Investment Financing Services
N.A.I.C.S.: 523999
Neil Walker *(Mgr-Channel Mktg-Document
Scanner)*

Fujitsu (China) Co., Ltd. (1)
Tel.: (86) 1059691000
Web Site: http://www.fujitsu.com
Information Technology Consulting Services
N.A.I.C.S.: 541512

Subsidiary (Domestic):

**Fujitsu (Xi'an) System Engineering
Co., Ltd.** (2)
Block A 1st Area Xi'an National Service
Outsourcing Base, No 11 Jinye 1 Lu Xi'an
High-tech Industries Development Zone
Y522, Xi'an, 710077, Shaanxi, China
Tel.: (86) 2987669766
Software Development Services
N.A.I.C.S.: 541511

**Fujitsu (China) Holdings Co.,
Ltd.** (1)
7F Building 1 Century metropolis No 1229
Century Avenue, Pudong New District,
Shanghai, 200122, China
Tel.: (86) 2158871000
Investment Management Service
N.A.I.C.S.: 523940

Fujitsu (Ireland) Limited (1)
Lakeshore Drive Airside Business Park,
Swords, Dublin, Ireland
Tel.: (353) 1 813 6000
Web Site: http://www.fujitsu.com
Sales Range: $150-199.9 Million
Emp.: 250
Information Technology Consulting Services
N.A.I.C.S.: 541512
Regina Moran *(CEO)*

Fujitsu (Singapore) Pte. Ltd. (1)
20 Science Park Road 02/01-03 TeleTech
Park, Singapore, 117674,
Singapore (100%)
Tel.: (65) 67734933
Web Site: http://www.fujitsu.com.sg
Sales Range: $100-124.9 Million
Emp.: 500
Mfr & Sales of Switching Equipment &
Computers
N.A.I.C.S.: 335313

Fujitsu A/S (1)
Lautrupbjerg 9, 2750, Ballerup, Denmark
Tel.: (45) 44894489
Web Site: http://www.fujitsu.com
Sales Range: $75-99.9 Million
Emp.: 350
Business Process Outsourcing Services
N.A.I.C.S.: 561499
Anton Therkildsen *(Mgr-Sls)*

Fujitsu America, Inc. (1)

1250 E Arques Ave, Sunnyvale, CA 94085-
3470
Tel.: (800) 831-3183
Web Site: http://www.fujitsu.com
Computers & Data Processing Systems,
Telecommunications Systems & Electronic
Components Mfr
N.A.I.C.S.: 334111
Robert D. Pryor *(Pres/CEO-North America)*

Branch (Domestic):

Fujitsu America, Inc. (2)
343 Thornall St, Edison, NJ
08837-2220 (100%)
Tel.: (732) 549-1100
Web Site: http://www.fujitsu.com
Emp.: 40
Technology Management & Process Out-
sourcing Consulting Services
N.A.I.C.S.: 541611
Duncan Tait *(CEO)*

Fujitsu America, Inc. (2)
10 Ray Ave, Burlington, MA 01803-4721
Tel.: (781) 272-5500
Sales Range: $25-49.9 Million
Emp.: 110
Business Technology Consulting Services
N.A.I.C.S.: 541690

Subsidiary (Domestic):

**Fujitsu Business Communication Sys-
tems, Inc.-Sales & Marketing** (2)
7776 S Pointe Pkwy W Ste 145, Phoenix,
AZ 85044-5424
Tel.: (480) 921-5800
N.A.I.C.S.: 334111

**Fujitsu Components America,
Inc.** (2)
250 E Caribbean Dr, Sunnyvale, CA 94089
Tel.: (408) 745-4900
Web Site: http://www.us.fujitsu.com
Sales Range: $25-49.9 Million
Emp.: 40
Electronic Components Distr
N.A.I.C.S.: 423690
Yas Hara *(Chm)*

**Fujitsu Computer Products of
America, Inc.** (2)
1250 E Arques Ave, Sunnyvale, CA
94085-5401 (100%)
Tel.: (408) 746-7000
Web Site: http://www.fcpa.fujitsu.com
Sales Range: $150-199.9 Million
Emp.: 350
Scanners, Magneto-Optical Drives, Ethernet
Switches, Biometric Devices, Degaussers
Mfr
N.A.I.C.S.: 423430
Scott Francis *(VP-Mktg)*

Division (Domestic):

**Fujitsu Computer Products of
America - Research &
Development** (3)
7245 Northwest Evergreen Pkwy, Hillsboro,
OR 97124
Tel.: (503) 681-7300
Web Site: http://www.fcpa.com
Sales Range: $25-49.9 Million
Emp.: 36
Research & Development
N.A.I.C.S.: 423430

Subsidiary (Domestic):

**Fujitsu Computer Systems
Corporation** (2)
1250 E Arques Ave, Sunnyvale, CA 94085-
3470
Tel.: (408) 746-6000
Sales Range: $125-149.9 Million
Emp.: 1,100
Computer Sales & Service
N.A.I.C.S.: 541519
Richard McCormack *(Sr VP-Mktg)*

Subsidiary (Domestic):

Fujitsu Software Corporation (3)
1250 E Arques Ave M/S 119, Sunnyvale,
CA 94085
Tel.: (408) 746-6182
Web Site: http://www.fujitsuusa.com
Software Development Services

N.A.I.C.S.: 541511
K. Randy *(Partner)*

Unit (Domestic):

Fujitsu Consulting (2)
301 Carlson Pkwy, Minnetonka, MN 55305-
5302
Tel.: (952) 258-6000
Web Site: http://www.us.fujitsu.com
Sales Range: $25-49.9 Million
Emp.: 4
Information Technology Services & Solu-
tions
N.A.I.C.S.: 541511

Fujitsu Consulting (2)
1450 E American Ln Ste 1700, Schaum-
burg, IL 60173-6087
Tel.: (847) 706-4000
Web Site: http://www.fujitsu.com
Sales Range: $50-74.9 Million
Emp.: 200
Technology Consulting, Computer Training
& Readiness Assessment Services
N.A.I.C.S.: 541512

Fujitsu Consulting (2)
11270 W Park Pl Ste 1000, Milwaukee, WI
53224-3643
Tel.: (414) 973-7000
Web Site: http://www.fujitsu.com
Sales Range: $50-74.9 Million
Emp.: 145
Technology Consulting Services
N.A.I.C.S.: 541512

Fujitsu Consulting (2)
24 Summit Park Dr Ste 100, Pittsburgh, PA
15275
Tel.: (412) 494-9800
Web Site: http://www.rapidigm.com
Sales Range: $25-49.9 Million
Emp.: 70
Business Technology Consulting Services
N.A.I.C.S.: 541690

Fujitsu Consulting (2)
8101 E Prentice Ave Ste 500, Greenwood
Village, CO 80111
Tel.: (303) 846-8000
Web Site: http://www.us.fujitsu.com
Sales Range: $25-49.9 Million
Emp.: 100
Business Technology Consulting Services
N.A.I.C.S.: 541690

Subsidiary (Domestic):

Fujitsu General America, Inc. (2)
353 Route 46 W, Fairfield, NJ
07004 (100%)
Tel.: (973) 575-0380
Web Site: http://www.fujitsugeneral.com
Sales Range: $25-49.9 Million
Emp.: 50
Air Conditioning Unit Mfr
N.A.I.C.S.: 333415
Erin Mezle *(Dir-Mktg)*

**Fujitsu Interconnect Technologies
Limited** (2)
250 E Caribbean Dr, Sunnyvale, CA 94089
Tel.: (408) 745-4966
Web Site: http://www.jp.fujitsu.com
Printed Circuit Board Mfr
N.A.I.C.S.: 334412
Yoichi Bando *(Pres)*

Fujitsu Limited (2)
733 3rd Ave, New York, NY 10017-3204
Tel.: (212) 599-9800
Web Site: http://www.fujitsu.com
Sales Range: $25-49.9 Million
Emp.: 3
Investor Relations Services
N.A.I.C.S.: 541512

**Fujitsu Management Services of
America, Inc.** (2)
1250 E Arques Ave, Sunnyvale, CA 94085-
5401
Tel.: (408) 746-6200
Web Site: http://www.fujitsu.com
Administrative & Financial Management
Consulting Services
N.A.I.C.S.: 541611
Hiroshi Haruki *(Pres & CEO)*

**Fujitsu Network Communications
Inc.** (2)

2801 Telecom Pkwy, Richardson, TX
75082-3515
Tel.: (972) 690-6000
Web Site: http://www.fujitsu.com
Sales Range: $50-74.9 Million
Emp.: 200
Mfr & Designer of Broadband Transmission
& Switching Products & Technologies
N.A.I.C.S.: 334210
Hans Roehrig *(Sr VP-Ops & Mfg)*

Plant (Domestic):

**Fujitsu Network Communications -
Richardson Plant** (3)
2001 Telecom Pkwy, Richardson, TX 75082
Tel.: (972) 690-6000
Web Site: http://www.fujitsu.com
Optical Transmission System Mfr
N.A.I.C.S.: 333613

Subsidiary (Domestic):

TrueNet Communications, Corp. (3)
7666 Blanding Blvd, Jacksonville, FL 32244
Web Site:
     http://www.truenetcommunications.com
Emp.: 350
Electrical Contractor
N.A.I.C.S.: 238210
Mark Lampke *(Chief Revenue Officer &
Exec VP)*

Subsidiary (Domestic):

Glovia International, Inc. (2)
2250 E Imperial Hwy, El Segundo, CA
90245-3457
Tel.: (310) 563-7000
Web Site: http://www.glovia.com
Sales Range: $25-49.9 Million
Emp.: 100
Provider of Computer Programming Ser-
vices
N.A.I.C.S.: 541511
Steven Pearlman *(Product Mgr & Partner-
Products)*

Fujitsu Asia Pte. Ltd. (1)
Nexus one north 1 Fusionopolis Link 04-01,
Singapore, 138542, Singapore
Tel.: (65) 65127555
Sales Range: $75-99.9 Million
Emp.: 40
Information Technology Consulting Services
N.A.I.C.S.: 541512

Fujitsu Australia Ltd. (1)
118 Talavera Road Macquarie Park, Syd-
ney, 2113, NSW, Australia (100%)
Tel.: (61) 291139200
Web Site: http://www.au.fujitsu.com
Sales Range: $300-349.9 Million
Emp.: 1,000
Mfr & Sales of Telecommunications Equip-
ment; Sales & Maintenance of Computers
N.A.I.C.S.: 532490

Subsidiary (Domestic):

Fujitsu Australia Pty. Ltd. (2)
118 Talavera Rd Macquarie Park, Sydney,
2113, NSW, Australia (100%)
Tel.: (61) 297764555
Sales Range: $50-74.9 Million
Emp.: 110
N.A.I.C.S.: 334111

**Fujitsu Broad Solution & Consulting
Inc.** (1)
TRADEPIA ODAIBA 2-3-1 Daiba Minato-ku,
Tokyo, 135-8300, Japan (100%)
Tel.: (81) 335704111
Web Site: http://www.fujitsu.com
Sales Range: $25-49.9 Million
Emp.: 1,844
Custom Software Development Services
N.A.I.C.S.: 541511
Yousuke Kondo *(Sr VP)*

Subsidiary (Non-US):

**Beijing Brain Cell Software Corpora-
tion Limited** (2)
11F Jiaoda Zhixing Building No 3 Shangyu-
ancun Haidian District, Beijing, 100044,
China (51%)
Tel.: (86) 1062579110
Computer Hardware Mfr & Distr

Fujitsu Limited—(Continued)
N.A.I.C.S.: 334118

Fujitsu Canada, Inc. (1)
6975 Credit View Rd Unit 1, Mississauga,
L5N 8E9, ON, Canada (100%)
Tel.: (905) 286-9666
Web Site: http://www.fujitsu.ca
Sales Range: $25-49.9 Million
Emp.: 60
Distr of Computers & Computer Related
Products
N.A.I.C.S.: 334111

Subsidiary (Domestic):

Fujitsu Canada Limited (2)
155 University Ave Suite 1600 Simcoe
Place, Toronto, M5H 3B7, ON,
Canada (100%)
Tel.: (416) 363-8661
Web Site: http://www.fujitsu.ca
Sales Range: $10-24.9 Million
Emp.: 100
Sales & Service of Data Processing Sys-
tems
N.A.I.C.S.: 541513
Olesya Chornenka (Mgr)

Subsidiary (Domestic):

Fujitsu Consulting (3)
1000 Sherbrooke St W Ste 1400, Montreal,
H3A 3R2, QC, Canada (100%)
Tel.: (514) 877-3301
Web Site: http://www.fujitsu.com
Emp.: 200
Information Management & Technology
N.A.I.C.S.: 541512
Andre Pouliot (Pres & CEO)

Fujitsu DMR Consulting (3)
1000 Sherbrooke W ste 1400, Montreal,
H3A 3R2, QC, Canada (100%)
Tel.: (514) 877-3300
Web Site: http://www.fujitsu.com
Software Services
N.A.I.C.S.: 541511
Andre Beauchemin (Mgr-Ops)

Groupe Conseil DMR, Inc. (3)
1000 Sherbrooke St W Ste 1400, Montreal,
H3A 3R2, QC, Canada (100%)
Tel.: (514) 877-3301
Web Site: http://www.fujitsu.com
Information Technology Consulting & Devel-
opment Firm
N.A.I.C.S.: 541512

Subsidiary (Domestic):

Macroscope Informatique, Inc. (4)
111 Duke St Ofc 4500, Montreal, H3C 2M1,
QC, Canada
Tel.: (514) 393-8822
Sales Range: $25-49.9 Million
Emp.: 200
Information Technology Consulting & Devel-
opment Services
N.A.I.C.S.: 541611

**Fujitsu Caribbean (Barbados)
Limited** (1)
Chelston Park Building 1 Collymore Rock,
Saint Michael, BB14018, Barbados
Tel.: (246) 4260242
Software Development Services
N.A.I.C.S.: 541511

**Fujitsu Caribbean (Trinidad)
Limited** (1)
6th Avenue Extension & Ibis Avenue, Bara-
taria, Trinidad & Tobago
Tel.: (868) 223 2826
Web Site: http://www.fujitsu.com
Emp.: 11
Software Development Services
N.A.I.C.S.: 541511
Jean-Paul Dookie (Gen Mgr)

**Fujitsu Components (Malaysia) Sdn.
Bhd.** (1)
No 1 Lorong Satu Kaw Perindustrian Parit
Raja, Parit Raja Johor Darul Takzim, 86400,
Johor Bahru, Malaysia (100%)
Tel.: (60) 74542111
Web Site: http://www.my.fujitsu.com
Sales Range: $400-449.9 Million
Emp.: 1,500
Mfr & Sales of Electronic Components

N.A.I.C.S.: 334118
Charles Lew (Pres)

Fujitsu Components Europe B.V. (1)
Diamantlaan 25, 2132 WV, Hoofddorp,
Netherlands
Tel.: (31) 235560910
Sales Range: $25-49.9 Million
Emp.: 35
Consumer Electronics Distr
N.A.I.C.S.: 423620

**Fujitsu Components Hong Kong Co.,
Limited** (1)
506 Intel Continental plaza No 94 Granville
Road, Tsim Tsa Tsui, Kowloon, China (Hong
Kong)
Tel.: (852) 2881 8495
Web Site: http://www.fujitsu.com
Electronic Components Mfr
N.A.I.C.S.: 334419

**Fujitsu Computer Products Of Viet-
nam, Inc.** (1)
No. 31 Street 3A Bien Hoa Industrial Zone
II, Dong Nai, Vietnam
Tel.: (84) 2513836562
Web Site: http://www.fujitsu.com
Electrical Supply
N.A.I.C.S.: 335999
Watanabe Shin Hisashi (Pres)

Fujitsu Conseil (Canada) Inc. (1)
1000 Sherbrooke Street West Suite 1400,
Montreal, H3A 3R2, QC, Canada
Tel.: (514) 877-3301
Sales Range: $75-99.9 Million
Emp.: 300
Information Technology Consulting Services
N.A.I.C.S.: 541512

Fujitsu Consulting S.A. (1)
River Plaza 29 Quai Aulagnier, 92665,
Asnieres, Cedex, France (100%)
Tel.: (33) 41979000
Sales Range: $50-74.9 Million
Emp.: 150
Hardware, Software, Networking & Busi-
ness Solutions
N.A.I.C.S.: 334111

**Fujitsu Denso International
Limited** (1)
9/F Lincoln House 979 King's Road Taikoo
Place, Island East, Hong Kong, China
(Hong Kong)
Tel.: (852) 2828 2850
Web Site: http://www.fujitsu.com
Electronic Components Mfr
N.A.I.C.S.: 334419

Fujitsu Deutschland GmbH (1)
(100%)
Web Site: http://www.fujitsu.com
Sales Range: $250-299.9 Million
Emp.: 60
Sale of Computers & Telecommunications
Equipment
N.A.I.C.S.: 449210
Peter Madsen (Gen Dir)

Fujitsu Do Brasil Ltda (1)
Rua Treze de Maio 1633 1 ao 7 andar, Sao
Paulo, 01327 905, SP, Brazil (100%)
Tel.: (55) 1132650880
Web Site: http://www.fujitsu.com.br
Sales Range: $50-74.9 Million
Emp.: 200
Sales of Computers
N.A.I.C.S.: 423690
Amelia Miura (Office Mgr)

**Fujitsu Enabling Software Technology
GmbH** (1)
Schwanthalerstr 75 A, Munich, 80336, Ger-
many
Tel.: (49) 89 360 908 502
Web Site: http://www.est.fujitsu.com
Emp.: 60
Software Development Services
N.A.I.C.S.: 541511
Yuji Takada (Mng Dir)

Fujitsu Europe Limited (1)
22 Baker Street, London, W1U 3BW, United
Kingdom
Tel.: (44) 870 242 7998
Web Site: http://www.fujitsu.com
Information Technology Development Ser-
vices

N.A.I.C.S.: 541511
Hiroaki Kashiwagi (CEO)

Fujitsu FIP Corporation (1)
Time 24 Building 2 45 Aomi, Koto-ku, To-
kyo, 135 8686, Japan
Tel.: (81) 355310200
Web Site: http://jp.fujitsu.com
Sales Range: $1-4.9 Billion
Emp.: 2,670
Information Technology & On-Line Informa-
tion Services
N.A.I.C.S.: 519290

Subsidiary (Domestic):

G-Search Ltd. (2)
Loop X Building 3 9 15 Kaigan, Minatu-ku,
Tokyo, 108 0022, Japan
Tel.: (81) 334521244
Web Site: http://www.g-search.jp
Sales Range: $50-74.9 Million
Emp.: 155
Online Information Services
N.A.I.C.S.: 519290

Fujitsu FSAS Inc. (1)
JR Kawasaki Tower 1-5 Omiyacho, Saiwai-
ku, Kawasaki, 212-0014, Kanagawa, Japan
Tel.: (81) 447543000
Emp.: 6,089
Business Process Outsourcing Services
N.A.I.C.S.: 561499

Fujitsu Finland Oy (1)
Valimotie 16, FI 00380, Helsinki,
Finland (100%)
Tel.: (358) 29 302 302
Web Site: http://www.fi.fujitsu.com
Emp.: 4,500
ICT Services & Hardware Distr
N.A.I.C.S.: 541519

Fujitsu Frontech Ltd. (1)
1776 Yanokuchi Inagi-shi, Tokyo, 206-8555,
Japan (87.73%)
Tel.: (81) 423775111
Rev.: $926,847,060
Assets: $667,676,700
Liabilities: $236,040,180
Net Worth: $431,636,520
Earnings: $14,160,780
Emp.: 3,829
Fiscal Year-end: 03/31/2019
Electronic Products Developer & Mfr
N.A.I.C.S.: 334111
Naoki Yoshida (CFO & Sr VP)

Subsidiary (Domestic):

**FUJITSU FRONTECH SYSTEMS
LIMITED** (2)
AQERU MAEBASHI 2-30-8 Omote-cho,
Maebashi, 371-0024, Gunma, Japan
Tel.: (81) 272256600
Sales Range: $75-99.9 Million
Emp.: 70
Software Development Services
N.A.I.C.S.: 541511
Shinichiro Noguchi (Pres)

Subsidiary (Non-US):

**Fujitsu Die-Tech Corporation Of The
Philippine** (2)
1113 East Science Avenue Special Export
Processing Zone, Laguna Technopark, Bi-
nan, 4024, Laguna, Philippines
Tel.: (63) 28430965
Web Site: http://www.fujitsu.com
Sales Range: $150-199.9 Million
Emp.: 527
Computer Peripheral Equipment Mfr
N.A.I.C.S.: 334118
Norikazu Tsuchida (Pres)

**Fujitsu Frontech (Shanghai)
Limited** (2)
2F B Block 501 Jingang Road, Pudong,
Shanghai, China
Tel.: (86) 21 5854 2228
Sales Range: $25-49.9 Million
Emp.: 55
Mechanical Components Mfr & Whslr
N.A.I.C.S.: 333310
Haruyuki Fujimoto (Chm-Japan)

Fujitsu Frontech Canada Inc. (2)
4700 de la Savane Ste 101, Montreal, H4P
1T7, QC, Canada

Tel.: (972) 479-6000
Software Development Services
N.A.I.C.S.: 541511

Plant (Domestic):

**Fujitsu Frontech Limited - Niigata
Plant** (2)
17-8 Yoshidahigashisakae-cho, Tsubame,
959-0294, Niigata-ken, Japan
Tel.: (81) 256933161
Web Site: http://www.frontech.fujitsu.com
Sales Range: $75-99.9 Million
Emp.: 500
Electric Equipment Mfr
N.A.I.C.S.: 333310

Subsidiary (US):

**Fujitsu Frontech North America
Inc.** (2)
27121 Towne Ctr Dr Ste 100, Foothill
Ranch, CA 92610-3436
Tel.: (949) 855-5500
Sales Range: $75-99.9 Million
Emp.: 256
Retail Checkout Machinery Mfr
N.A.I.C.S.: 333310
Howard Walter (Engr-Software)

Subsidiary (Domestic):

Fulcrum Biometrics, LLC (3)
1218 Arion Pkwy Ste 106, San Antonio, TX
78216-2813
Tel.: (210) 257-5615
Web Site: http://www.fulcrumbiometrics.com
Computer & Computer Peripheral Equip-
ment & Software Merchant Whslr
N.A.I.C.S.: 423430
Matt Osborne (VP-Engrg)

Subsidiary (Domestic):

LIFE CREATE LIMITED (2)
1776 Yanokuchi, Inagi-shi, Tokyo, 206-
8555, Japan (100%)
Tel.: (81) 423796661
Web Site: http://www.fujitsu.com
Emp.: 51
Employee Welfare Services
N.A.I.C.S.: 923130

**TOTALIZATOR ENGINEERING
LIMITED** (2)
6-20-14 East Square Omori Minami-oi,
Shinagawa-ku, Tokyo, Japan
Tel.: (81) 357625500
Web Site: http://www.tel-tota.com
Sales Range: $50-74.9 Million
Emp.: 127
Gaming Machine Operators
N.A.I.C.S.: 713290

Fujitsu General Ltd. (1)
3-3-17 Suenaga, Takatsu-ku, Kawasaki, 213
8502, Kanagawa, Japan
Tel.: (81) 448661111
Web Site: https://www.fujitsu-general.com
Rev.: $2,091,906,360
Assets: $1,821,940,740
Liabilities: $853,053,550
Net Worth: $968,887,190
Earnings: $20,272,870
Emp.: 1,734
Fiscal Year-end: 03/31/2024
Electronic Accessories Mfr
N.A.I.C.S.: 334111
Etsuro Saito (Pres)

Fujitsu Hong Kong Limited (1)
10/F Lincoln House Taikoo Place 979 King's
Road, Quarry Bay, China (Hong Kong)
Tel.: (852) 2827 5780
Web Site: http://www.fujitsu.com
Sales Range: $25-49.9 Million
Emp.: 200
Information Technology Consulting Services
N.A.I.C.S.: 541512

Fujitsu IT Products Ltd. (1)
1-1 To Kasashima, Kaho-ku, Ishikawa, 929-
1104, Japan
Tel.: (81) 762852331
Computer Peripheral Equipment Mfr
N.A.I.C.S.: 334118
Sadayuki Oyama (Pres)

Fujitsu Isotec Limited (1)
135 Higashinozaki Hobara-machi, Date,
960-0695, Fukushima, Japan

Tel.: (81) 24 574 2236
Web Site: http://www.jp.fujitsu.com
Printer Mfr & Distr
N.A.I.C.S.: 334118

Fujitsu Korea Ltd. (1)
Sunsong Tower Bldg 83 1 Susong Dong,
Jongno Gu, Seoul, 110 140, Korea
(South) (100%)
Tel.: (82) 237876000
Web Site: http://www.kr.fujitsu.com
Distr & Developer of Information Processing
Systems & Operating Systems
N.A.I.C.S.: 541512

Fujitsu Laboratories Ltd. (1)
4 1 1 Kamikodanaka, Nakahara-ku, Kawa-
saki, 211-8588, Japan (95.8%)
Tel.: (81) 447771111
Web Site: http://www.labs.fujitsu.com
Sales Range: $1-4.9 Billion
Emp.: 10,000
Computers, Data Processing Systems, Tele-
communications & Electronics Research &
Development
N.A.I.C.S.: 423430

Subsidiary (US):

**Fujitsu Laboratories of America,
Inc.** (2)
1240 E Arques Ave Mail Stop 345, Sunny-
vale, CA 94085 (100%)
Tel.: (408) 530-4500
Web Site: http://www.fla.fujitsu.com
Sales Range: $25-49.9 Million
Emp.: 90
Research & Development
N.A.I.C.S.: 541715
Dave Marvit *(VP-Strategy & Internet Svcs
Res)*

Subsidiary (Non-US):

**Fujitsu Laboratories of Europe
Ltd.** (2)
Hayes Park Central Hayes End Road,
Hayes, UB48FE, Middlesex, United King-
dom
Tel.: (44) 208 573 4444
Emp.: 45
Laboratory Testing Services
N.A.I.C.S.: 541380
Tsuneo Nakata *(Pres)*

**Fujitsu Limited - Aizu Wakamatsu
Plant** (1)
3 Kogyo Danchi Monden-machi, Aizuwaka-
matsu, 965-8502, Fukushima, Japan
Tel.: (81) 242286111
Web Site: http://www.fujitsu.com
Electronic Components Mfr
N.A.I.C.S.: 334419

Fujitsu Limited - Mie Plant (1)
1500 Mizono Tado-cho, Kuwana, 511-0192,
Mie, Japan
Tel.: (81) 594485511
Electronic Components Mfr
N.A.I.C.S.: 334419

Fujitsu Limited - Nasu Plant (1)
1388 Simoishigami, Otawara, 324-8555,
Tochigi, Japan
Tel.: (81) 287292111
Communication Equipment Mfr
N.A.I.C.S.: 334220

Fujitsu Limited - Numazu Plant (1)
140 Miyamoto, Numazu, 410-0396, Shi-
zuoka, Japan
Tel.: (81) 559232222
Web Site: http://www.fujitsu.com
Electronic Components Mfr
N.A.I.C.S.: 334419

Fujitsu Limited - Oyama Plant (1)
91 Oaza Nishikuroda, Oyama, 323-8511,
Tochigi, Japan
Tel.: (81) 285451326
Web Site: http://www.fujitsu.com
Electronic Components Mfr
N.A.I.C.S.: 334419

Fujitsu Limited - Suzaka Plant (1)
460 Oaza-Koyama, Suzaka, 382-8501, Na-
gano, Japan
Tel.: (81) 262512700
Communication Equipment Mfr
N.A.I.C.S.: 334220

Fujitsu Marketing Limited (1)
1-7-27 Koraku Korakukashima Bldg,
Bunkyo-Ku, Tokyo, 112-0004, Japan
Tel.: (81) 3 5804 8111
Web Site: http://www.fjm.fujitsu.com
Sales Range: $700-749.9 Million
Emp.: 3,951
Software Development Services
N.A.I.C.S.: 541511
Kenji Ikegai *(Pres)*

Subsidiary (Domestic):

Fujitsu Marketing Agent Ltd. (2)
2-15-3 Konan Shinagawa Intercity Tower,
Minato-ku, Tokyo, 108-6207, Japan
Tel.: (81) 3 6712 3430
Web Site: http://www.fujitsu.com
Sales Range: $10-24.9 Million
Emp.: 29
Human Resource Consulting Services
N.A.I.C.S.: 541612

**Fujitsu Marketing Office Services
Ltd.** (2)
3-banchi Kanda-neribeicho, Chiyoda-ku,
Tokyo, 101-0022, Japan
Tel.: (81) 3 5209 1890
Web Site: http://www.fjm.fujitsu.com
Computer Peripheral Equipment & Office
Supplies Distr
N.A.I.C.S.: 423430

Fujitsu Microdevices Ltd. (1)
Osaki West Building 8-8 Osaki, 2-Chome
Shinagawa Ku, Tokyo, 141-8583,
Japan (91.9%)
Tel.: (81) 334907396
Computer & Storage Devices Mfr
N.A.I.C.S.: 334111

Fujitsu Network Solutions Ltd. (1)
Computer Network Designing Services
N.A.I.C.S.: 541512

**Fujitsu Optical Components America,
Inc.** (1)
350 Cobalt Way MS Ste 350, Sunnyvale,
CA 94085
Tel.: (408) 746-6000
N.A.I.C.S.: 334513

Fujitsu PC Asia Pacific Ltd (1)
Unit 118 - 121 1/F Philips Electronics Build-
ing, No 5 Science Park East Avenue Hong
Kong Science Park, Sha Tin, New Territo-
ries, China (Hong Kong)
Tel.: (852) 31012898
Electronic Computer Mfr
N.A.I.C.S.: 334111

Subsidiary (Non-US):

**Fujian Fujitsu Communication Soft-
ware Co., Ltd.** (2)
22 Shui Tou Lu DouMen, Fuzhou, 350013,
Fujian, China
Tel.: (86) 591 87575150
Web Site: http://www.ffcs.cn
Information Technology Development Ser-
vices
N.A.I.C.S.: 541511

Fujitsu PC Asia Pacific Pte. Ltd. (2)
Siemens Center 60 Macpherson Road 06-
08A Block 1, Singapore, 348615, Singapore
Tel.: (65) 67760688
Computer Peripheral Equipment Distr
N.A.I.C.S.: 423430

Fujitsu PC Australia Pty Ltd (2)
Unit 3 83 Derby Street, Silverwater, 2128,
NSW, Australia
Tel.: (61) 2 8705 8700
Web Site: http://www.fujitsu.com
Computer Equipment Distr
N.A.I.C.S.: 423430

**Fujitsu South China Technology Ser-
vices Limited** (2)
No7 Nan 6 Lu Guicheng, Nanhai District,
Foshan, 528200, Guangdong, China
Tel.: (86) 75766868088
Information Technology Development Ser-
vices
N.A.I.C.S.: 541511

**Jiangsu Fujitsu Telecommunications
Technology Co., Ltd.** (2)
21st Block 158 Jin Feng RD, Suzhou,

215163, Jiangsu, China
Tel.: (86) 51268250097
Web Site: http://www.fujitsujtt.com
Transmission System Maintenance Services
N.A.I.C.S.: 811114
Xiao Li Yuan *(Gen Mgr)*

Fujitsu Peripherals Limited (1)
64 Okubochonishiwaki, Akashi, 674-0054,
Japan
Tel.: (81) 789348237
Sales Range: $50-74.9 Million
Emp.: 20
Computer Peripheral Equipment Mfr
N.A.I.C.S.: 334118
Toshio Okano *(CEO)*

Fujitsu Philippines, Inc. (1)
12th Floor NEX Tower 6786 Ayala Avenue,
Legaspi Village, Makati, 1223, Metro Ma-
nila, Philippines
Tel.: (63) 28418488
Sales Range: $150-199.9 Million
Emp.: 500
Communication Equipment Distr
N.A.I.C.S.: 423690

**Fujitsu Quality Laboratory (Suzhou)
Ltd.** (1)
2F West 5th Building Suzhou Science &
Technology Park 2 Keling Rd, Suzhou,
215163, Jiangsu, China
Tel.: (86) 51268320107
Web Site: http://www.fujitsu.com
Laboratory Testing Services
N.A.I.C.S.: 541380

**Fujitsu Research and Development
Center Co., Ltd.** (1)
Tel.: (86) 1059691000
Web Site: http://www.fujitsu.com
Research & Development for System LSIs,
Mobile & Telecommunications & Information
Processing
N.A.I.C.S.: 517810

Fujitsu Semiconductor Limited (1)
Kohoku-chome No 100 45 Shin-Yokohama
Central Building, Kanagawa-ku, Yokohama,
Kanagawa, Japan (100%)
Tel.: (81) 45 755 7000
Web Site: http://www.fujitsu.com
Semiconductor Mfr & Distr
N.A.I.C.S.: 334413
Haruki Okada *(Chm)*

Subsidiary (Non-US):

**Fujitsu Semiconductor (Shanghai)
Co., Ltd.** (2)
Rm 302-303 Building T2N EBA center
Hongqiao No 377 Songhong Road, Chang-
ning District, Shanghai, 200023, China
Tel.: (86) 2161463688
Web Site: https://www.kagafei.com
Emp.: 47
Semiconductor Devices Mfr
N.A.I.C.S.: 334413

Subsidiary (US):

**Fujitsu Semiconductor America,
Inc** (2)
1250 E Arques Ave M/S 333, Sunnyvale,
CA 94085-5401
Tel.: (408) 737-6000
Semiconductor Device Mfr & Distr
N.A.I.C.S.: 334413
Shinichi Machida *(Pres & CEO)*

Subsidiary (Non-US):

**Fujitsu Semiconductor Asia Pte.
Ltd.** (2)
Unit No 3 Level 8 Innovator International
Tech Park Whitefield Road, Bengaluru, 560
066, Karnataka, India
Tel.: (91) 8028419990
Sales Range: $25-49.9 Million
Emp.: 15
Semiconductor Devices Mfr
N.A.I.C.S.: 334413

**Fujitsu Semiconductor Embedded
Solutions Austria GmbH** (2)
Semmelweisstr 34, Linz, 4020, Austria
Tel.: (43) 7329 03050
Web Site: http://www.fujitsu.com
Sales Range: $25-49.9 Million
Emp.: 60
Semiconductor Devices Mfr

N.A.I.C.S.: 334413
Brendan McKearne *(Gen Mgr)*

**Fujitsu Semiconductor Europe
GmbH** (2)
Robert Bosch Strasse 25, 63225, Langen,
Germany (100%)
Tel.: (49) 6103690222
Web Site: https://kagafeieurope.com
Sales Range: $50-74.9 Million
Emp.: 230
Electronic Components
N.A.I.C.S.: 334419
Axel Tripkewitz *(Mng Dir)*

**Fujitsu Semiconductor Europe
GmbH** (2)
Building 3 Concorde Park Concorde Road,
Maidenhead, SL6 4FJ, Berkshire, United
Kingdom (100%)
Tel.: (44) 1628504600
Web Site: http://www.emea.fujitsu.com
Sales Range: $25-49.9 Million
Emp.: 80
Design & Development of ASIC's; Sales of
Electronic Devices
N.A.I.C.S.: 334413
Takeyuki Inoue *(VP)*

**Fujitsu Semiconductor Korea
Limited** (2)
902 416 Yeongdong-daero, Gangnam-Gu,
Seoul, 06176, Korea (South)
Tel.: (82) 234847100
Web Site: https://www.kagafei.com
Sales Range: $25-49.9 Million
Emp.: 17
Electronic Device Distr
N.A.I.C.S.: 423690
Kim Sung-Soo *(Gen Mgr)*

**Fujitsu Semiconductor Pacific Asia
Limited** (2)
10/F World Commerce Centre 11 Canton
Road, Tsimshatsui, Kowloon, China (Hong
Kong)
Tel.: (852) 2736 3232
Semiconductor Devices Mfr
N.A.I.C.S.: 334413

Fujitsu Services AB (1)
Ifafgordfgatan 35, PO Box 40, Kista, 16440,
Sweden (100%)
Tel.: (46) 87937000
Web Site: http://www.se.fujitsu.com
Sales Range: $50-74.9 Million
Emp.: 300
Sale of Computers & Telecommunications
Equipment
N.A.I.C.S.: 449210
Conway Kosi *(Mng Dir)*

Fujitsu Services Limited (1)
22 Baker Street, London, W1U 3BW, United
Kingdom (80%)
Tel.: (44) 2070097777
Web Site: http://www.fujitsu.com
Rev.: $2,260,260,000
Emp.: 150
Design, Development, Manufacture & Mar-
keting of Computer & Telecommunications
Systems & Networks; Related Products &
Services
N.A.I.C.S.: 334513

Subsidiary (Non-US):

AS Fujitsu Estonia (2)
Mustamae Tee 16, EE 10617, Tallinn, Esto-
nia
Tel.: (372) 627 2300
Web Site: http://www.fujitsu.com
Sales Range: $25-49.9 Million
Emp.: 17
Information Technology Consulting Services
N.A.I.C.S.: 541512
Harri Lehtimaki *(CEO)*

Fujitsu (Malaysia) Sdn. Bhd. (2)
Level 1and 2 No 3505 Jalan Teknokrat 5,
Cyberjaya, 63000, Selangor,
Malaysia (100%)
Tel.: (60) 383183700
Web Site: http://www.my.fujitsu.com
Distr of Computers & Related Products
N.A.I.C.S.: 449210
Michael Warren *(Country Pres)*

**Fujitsu Australia Software Technology
Pty., Ltd.** (2)

Fujitsu Limited—(Continued)

14 Rodborough Rd, French's Forest, 2086, NSW, Australia **(100%)**
Tel.: (61) 294529000
Web Site: http://www.fastware.com
Sales Range: $25-49.9 Million
Emp.: 50
Sales & Development of Software Products
N.A.I.C.S.: 449210
Bala Varadarajan *(Mng Dir)*

Fujitsu Consulting (Luxembourg) S.A. **(2)**
Parc d Activites Capellen 89 C rue Pafebruch, L 2350, Capellen, Luxembourg **(100%)**
Tel.: (352) 260991
Web Site: http://www.lu.fujitsu.com
Sales Range: $25-49.9 Million
Emp.: 80
Consulting Services
N.A.I.C.S.: 449210

Fujitsu Espana, S.A. **(2)**
Camino Cerro De Los Gamos 1 Building 2, Pozuelo De Alarcon, Madrid, 28224, Spain **(100%)**
Tel.: (34) 917849000
Web Site: http://www.es.fujitsu.com
Sales Range: $350-399.9 Million
Mfr, Developer & Distributor of Communications Systems
N.A.I.C.S.: 334290
Bernardo Diaz *(Dir-Mktg)*

Fujitsu New Zealand Ltd. **(2)**
141 Terrace Fujitsu Tower Level 12, PO Box 3547, Wellington, 6011, New Zealand **(100%)**
Tel.: (64) 44950700
Web Site: http://www.fujitsu.co.nz
Sales Range: $25-49.9 Million
Emp.: 30
Computer & Storage Devices Mfr
N.A.I.C.S.: 334111

Fujitsu Service A/S **(2)**
Sandakerveien 138, PO Box 4285, Nydalen, Oslo, 401, Norway **(95%)**
Tel.: (47) 22895500
Sales Range: $25-49.9 Million
Emp.: 60
Computer & Storage Devices Mfr
N.A.I.C.S.: 334111

Branch (Domestic):

Fujitsu Services **(2)**
Graston House Graston Way, Basingstoke, RG22 6HY, Hampshire, United Kingdom **(100%)**
Tel.: (44) 1256865100
Web Site: http://www.uk.fujitsu.com
Sales Range: $25-49.9 Million
Emp.: 30
Mfr of Computers, Computer Peripherals & Software
N.A.I.C.S.: 334111

Subsidiary (Non-US):

Fujitsu Services AB **(2)**
Ifafgordfgatan 35, PO Box 14, Kista, 164 93, Sweden **(100%)**
Tel.: (46) 87937000
Web Site: http://www.se.fujitsu.com
Sales Range: $150-199.9 Million
Computer & Storage Devices Mfr
N.A.I.C.S.: 334111
Conway Kosi *(Mng Dir)*

Fujitsu Services GmbH **(2)**
Mies-van-der-Rohe-Strasse 8 HighLight Towers, 80807, Munich, Germany
Tel.: (49) 211526101
Web Site: http://www.de.fujitsu.com
Emp.: 430
Information Technology Services
N.A.I.C.S.: 334111

Subsidiary (Domestic):

Fujitsu Services Holdings PLC **(2)**
22 Baker Street, London, W1U 3BW, United Kingdom
Tel.: (44) 8433545555
Investment Management Service
N.A.I.C.S.: 523999

Subsidiary (Non-US):

Fujitsu Services Limited **(2)**
Al Masaood Tower 15th Floor Hamdan Street, PO Box 7237, Abu Dhabi, 7237, United Arab Emirates
Tel.: (971) 2 6335200
Web Site: http://www.fujitsu.com
Emp.: 50
Information Technology Consulting Services
N.A.I.C.S.: 541512
Farid Alsabbach *(Mgr)*

Fujitsu Services Ltd **(2)**
Airside Business Park Swords, Dublin, Ireland **(100%)**
Tel.: (353) 1 813 6000
Web Site: http://www.fujitsu.com
Sales Range: $25-49.9 Million
Mfr, Designer & Operator of Information Technology Products & Services
N.A.I.C.S.: 541512
Regina Moran *(CEO)*

Branch (Domestic):

Fujitsu Services **(3)**
Lakeshore Drive Airside Retail Park, Swords, County Dublin, Ireland **(100%)**
Tel.: (353) 8136000
Web Site: http://www.ie.fujitsu.com
Sales Range: $25-49.9 Million
Emp.: 200
Sales of Computers
N.A.I.C.S.: 449210

Subsidiary (Non-US):

Fujitsu Services South Africa **(2)**
Technology Village 43 Homestead Road, Rivonia, 2128, South Africa
Tel.: (27) 11 233 5911
Web Site: http://www.fujitsu.com
Emp.: 100
Information Technology Consulting Services
N.A.I.C.S.: 541512
Quinton Scots *(Mng Dir)*

Fujitsu Services Sp. z.o.o. **(2)**
Tel.: (48) 422713001
Web Site: http://www.fujitsu.com
Information Technology Consulting Services
N.A.I.C.S.: 541512

Fujitsu Technology Solutions Lda **(2)**
Edificio Colombo Torre Oriente Av Colegio Militar N 37F - 3 Piso, Lisbon, Portugal **(100%)**
Tel.: (351) 217244444
Web Site: http://www.fujitsu.com
Sales Range: $25-49.9 Million
Emp.: 900
IT Infrastructure Solutions & Products
N.A.I.C.S.: 541519
Carlos Barros *(Mng Dir)*

Subsidiary (US):

GlobeRanger Corporation **(2)**
1130 E Arapaho Rd Ste 600, Richardson, TX 75081
Tel.: (972) 744-9977
Web Site: http://www.globeranger.com
Sales Range: $1-9.9 Million
Emp.: 43
RFID Software & Solutions Mfr
N.A.I.C.S.: 513210
George Brody *(Pres & CEO)*

Fujitsu South China Limited **(1)**
Room 2809 New World Center No 6009 Yitian Road, Futian District, Shenzhen, 518026, China
Tel.: (86) 755 2588 2589
Web Site: http://www.fujitsu.com
Information Technology Consulting Services
N.A.I.C.S.: 541512

Fujitsu Systems Business (Thailand) Ltd. **(1)**
22-23 flr Exchange Tower 388 Sukhumvit Road, Klongtoey, Bangkok, 10310, Thailand
Tel.: (66) 25126066
Information Technology Consulting Services
N.A.I.C.S.: 541512

Fujitsu Systems East Limited **(1)**
Shinagawa Season Terrace 1-2-70 Konan, Minato-ku, Tokyo, 108-0075, Japan **(100%)**
Tel.: (81) 3 6712 3700

Sales Range: $1-4.9 Billion
Emp.: 4,950
Software Publisher; System Integration & Consulting Services
N.A.I.C.S.: 541511
Susumu Ishikawa *(Pres)*

Fujitsu Systems West Limited **(1)**
Fujitsu Kansai Systems Laboratory 2-2-6 Shiromi, Chuo-ku, Osaka, 540-8514, Japan **(100%)**
Tel.: (81) 6 6920 4200
Sales Range: $800-899.9 Million
Emp.: 3,814
System Integration & Solution Services
N.A.I.C.S.: 541511
Kazuo Miyata *(Pres & Dir)*

Fujitsu Taiwan Limited **(1)**
19th floor No 39 Sec 1 Chung-Hwa Road, Taipei, 100, Taiwan
Tel.: (886) 23112255
Communication Equipment Sales & Maintenance Services
N.A.I.C.S.: 423690

Fujitsu Technology & Business of America, Inc. **(1)**
Tel.: (408) 746-6000
Information & Communication Technology Services
N.A.I.C.S.: 517810

Fujitsu Technology Solutions GmbH **(1)**
Mies-van-der-Rohe-Strasse 8, 80807, Munich, Germany **(100%)**
Web Site: http://www.fujitsu.com
Sales Range: $25-49.9 Million
Emp.: 50
Sales & Service of Computers
N.A.I.C.S.: 449210

Subsidiary (Non-US):

Fujitsu Technologies Solution International S.p.A. **(2)**
Via Delle Industrie n 11, Vimodrone, Milan, 20090, Italy **(100%)**
Tel.: (39) 022659321
Web Site: http://www.it.ts.fujitsu.com
Sales Range: $25-49.9 Million
Emp.: 10
Sales & Service of Computers
N.A.I.C.S.: 449210

Fujitsu Technology Solutions (Holding) B.V. **(2)**
Het Kwadrant 1, Maarssen, 3606 AZ, Netherlands
Tel.: (31) 34 659 8700
Web Site: http://www.fujitsu.com
Investment Management Service
N.A.I.C.S.: 523940
Kai Flore *(CEO)*

Subsidiary (Non-US):

Fujitsu India Pvt. Ltd. **(3)**
15th Floor Bldg No 9A Phase III DLF Cyber City, Gurgaon, 122002, Haryana, India
Tel.: (91) 124 470 5100
Web Site: http://www.fujitsu.com
Computer Peripheral Equipment Distr
N.A.I.C.S.: 423430
Santosh N. S. *(Head-Mktg & Alliance)*

Subsidiary (Domestic):

Fujitsu Consulting India Pvt Ltd. **(4)**
A-15 MIDC Technology Park Talawade, Pune, 412114, Maharashtra, India
Tel.: (91) 202769000
Sales Range: $700-749.9 Million
Emp.: 1,500
Software Consulting Services
N.A.I.C.S.: 541512

Subsidiary (Non-US):

Fujitsu Technology Solutions (Luxembourg) SA **(2)**
Parc d'Activites Capellen 89C rue Pafebruch, 8308, Capellen, Luxembourg
Tel.: (352) 260991
Web Site: http://www.fujitsu.com
Information Technology Consulting Services
N.A.I.C.S.: 541512
Frederic Salzmann *(Acct Mgr-Channel)*

Fujitsu Technology Solutions (PTY) Ltd. **(2)**

Technology Village 43 Homestead Road, Rivonia, 2128, South Africa
Tel.: (27) 11 233 5911
Information Technology Consulting Services
N.A.I.C.S.: 541512
M. Mudaliyar-Sheopershad *(Sec)*

Fujitsu Technology Solutions A.E. **(2)**
48 Egialias & Epidavrou Str, Marousi, Athens, Greece
Tel.: (30) 210 6863 500
Web Site: http://www.fujitsu.com
Information Technology Consulting Services
N.A.I.C.S.: 541512

Fujitsu Technology Solutions AB **(2)**
Alleva DG 1, 164 55, Kista, Sweden
Tel.: (46) 8 793 70 00
Information Technology Consulting Services
N.A.I.C.S.: 541512

Fujitsu Technology Solutions AG **(2)**
Althardstrasse 80, 8105, Regensdorf, Switzerland
Tel.: (41) 582588000
Sales Range: $25-49.9 Million
Emp.: 15
Information Technology Consulting Services
N.A.I.C.S.: 541512

Fujitsu Technology Solutions AS **(2)**
Ostensjoveien 32, Oslo, 0667, Norway
Tel.: (47) 23 24 80 00
Web Site: http://www.fujitsu.com
Sales Range: $25-49.9 Million
Information Technology Consulting Services
N.A.I.C.S.: 541512

Fujitsu Technology Solutions B.V. **(2)**
Het Kwadrant 1, 3606 AZ, Maarssen, Netherlands **(100%)**
Tel.: (31) 346 598111
Web Site: http://www.fujitsu.com
Sales Range: $150-199.9 Million
Emp.: 800
Notebook, Personal, Mainframe & Other Computer & Related Products Mfr
N.A.I.C.S.: 423430
Hussein Shehab *(Mgr-Fujitsu Tech Solutions-Egypt)*

Fujitsu Technology Solutions Bilisim Ltd. Sti. **(2)**
Yakacik Cd No 111, Kartal, 34870, Istanbul, Turkiye
Tel.: (90) 216 586 40 00
Web Site: http://www.fujitsu.com
Information Technology Consulting Services
N.A.I.C.S.: 541512

Fujitsu Technology Solutions FZ LLC **(2)**
Dubai Silicon Oasis Opp Academic City DSOA Head Quarter Building, PO Box 341045, Office 706 C-Wing, Dubai, United Arab Emirates
Tel.: (971) 45015704
Web Site: http://www.fujitsu.com
Information Technology Development Services
N.A.I.C.S.: 541511

Fujitsu Technology Solutions GesmbH **(2)**
Guglgasse 15, 1110, Vienna, Austria
Tel.: (43) 1716460
Information Technology Consulting Services
N.A.I.C.S.: 541512

Fujitsu Technology Solutions GesmbH **(2)**
Guglgasse 15, A 1110, Vienna, Austria **(100%)**
Tel.: (43) 1716460
Web Site: http://www.fujitsu.com
Sales Range: $25-49.9 Million
Emp.: 200
Electronics & Computer Mfr
N.A.I.C.S.: 334111
Marcin Olszewski *(Mng Dir)*

Fujitsu Technology Solutions GmbH **(2)**
Mustaqillik Ave 75, Tashkent, 150, Uzbekistan
Tel.: (998) 71 140 41 07
Web Site: http://www.fujitsu.com
Emp.: 3
Information Technology Consulting Services

N.A.I.C.S.: 541512

Fujitsu Technology Solutions International AG (2)
Althardstrasse 80, CH 8105, Regensdorf, Switzerland **(100%)**
Tel.: (41) 433886500
Web Site: http://www.ts.fujitsu.com
Sales Range: $25-49.9 Million
Emp.: 180
Sales & Service of Computers
N.A.I.C.S.: 449210

Fujitsu Technology Solutions International N.V. (2)
Mommaertslaan 16A, BE 1831, Diegem, Belgium **(100%)**
Tel.: (32) 271227711
Web Site: http://www.fujitsu.com
Sales Range: $25-49.9 Million
Emp.: 20
Sales & Service of Computers
N.A.I.C.S.: 449210

Fujitsu Technology Solutions International SA (2)
River Plaza 29 Quai Aulagnier, 92665, Asnieres, Cedex, France **(100%)**
Tel.: (33) 141979000
Web Site: http://www.fujitsu.com
Sales Range: $25-49.9 Million
Emp.: 180
Sales & Service of Computers
N.A.I.C.S.: 449210

Fujitsu Technology Solutions Ltd. (2)
Lakeshore Drive Airside Retail Park, Swords, Dublin, Ireland
Tel.: (353) 1 813 6000
Software Development Services
N.A.I.C.S.: 541511

Fujitsu Technology Solutions NV (2)
Square Marie Curie 12, 1070, Brussels, Belgium
Tel.: (32) 25366111
Web Site: http://www.fujitsu.com
Sales Range: $75-99.9 Million
Emp.: 30
Information Technology Consulting Services
N.A.I.C.S.: 541512

Fujitsu Technology Solutions OOO (2)
Zemlyanoy Val 9, Moscow, 105064, Russia
Tel.: (7) 495 730 62 20
Web Site: http://ru.fujitsu.com
Computer Hardware Mfr & Distr
N.A.I.C.S.: 334118

Fujitsu Technology Solutions S.A (2)
Lot N 2 Lotissement Mandarouna 300 Sidi Maarouf, Immeuble Business Center, 20000, Casablanca, Morocco
Tel.: (212) 522 58 17 17
Web Site: http://www.fujitsu.com
Sales Range: $25-49.9 Million
Emp.: 12
Information Technology Consulting Services
N.A.I.C.S.: 541512
Morillon Mireille *(Mgr-Marketing-Communications)*

Fujitsu Technology Solutions S.a.r.l. (2)
11 Chemin Doudou Mokhtar, Ben Aknoun, 16341, Algiers, Algeria
Tel.: (213) 21 91 58 25
Web Site: http://www.fujitsu.com
Information Technology Consulting Services
N.A.I.C.S.: 541512
Kamal Bouamrene *(Gen Mgr)*

Fujitsu Technology Solutions S.p.A. (2)
Via Delle Industrie n 11, 20090, Vimodrone, Milan, Italy
Tel.: (39) 022659321
Web Site: http://www.fujitsu.com
Information Technology Consulting Services
N.A.I.C.S.: 541512
Elena Bellini *(Mgr-Mktg & Comm)*

Fujitsu Technology Solutions SL (2)
Stree Camino Cerro de los Gamos 1 building 2, Bucolo De Alarcon, Madrid, 28224, Spain
Tel.: (34) 91 784 90 00
Web Site: http://www.fujitsu.com
Information Technology Consulting Services

N.A.I.C.S.: 541512

Fujitsu Technology Solutions Sp. z o.o. (2)
Tel.: (48) 225741000
Web Site: http://pl.cs.fujitsu.com
Computer Hardware Mfr & Distr
N.A.I.C.S.: 334118

Fujitsu Technology Solutions d.o.o. (2)
Pariske Komune 30, Novi Sad, 21000, Serbia
Tel.: (381) 21 445 256
Sales Range: $25-49.9 Million
Emp.: 2
Information Technology Consulting Services
N.A.I.C.S.: 541512
Harald Haubner *(Mng Dir)*

Fujitsu Technology Solutions s.r.o (2)
V Parku 2336/22 The Park, 148 00, Prague, Czech Republic
Tel.: (420) 233 034 007
Web Site: http://www.fujitsu.com
Sales Range: $25-49.9 Million
Information Technology Consulting Services
N.A.I.C.S.: 541512

Fujitsu Telecom Networks Limited (1)
1-17-3 Sakado, Takatsuku, Kawasaki, 213-8586, Japan
Tel.: (81) 4 4822 2121
Web Site: http://jp.fujitsu.com
Emp.: 1,300
Telecommunications Equipment Mfr
N.A.I.C.S.: 334290
Tomiko Kume *(Pres & CEO)*

Fujitsu Telecom Systems Philippines, Inc. (1)
8th Floor Dominion Building 833 Arnaiz Avenue Pasay Road, Legaspi Village, Makati, 1229, Philippines
Tel.: (63) 28930037
Emp.: 60
Computer Network Design & Installation Services
N.A.I.C.S.: 541512
Satoshi Tacoma *(Pres)*

Fujitsu Telecommunications Europe Limited (1)
Solihull Parkway Birmingham Business Park, Birmingham, B37 7YU, United Kingdom
Tel.: (44) 1217176000
Sales Range: $200-249.9 Million
Emp.: 700
Communication Equipment Mfr & Distr
N.A.I.C.S.: 334290
Nigel Kirby-Green *(Exec Dir-Public Sector)*

Fujitsu Telecommunications France SAS (1)
Les Boreales Batiment B 2 Avenue De Laponie, BP 204, 91941, Les Ulis, France
Tel.: (33) 160923040
Web Site: http://www.fujitsu.com
Sales Range: $25-49.9 Million
Emp.: 15
Telecommunications Equipment Mfr
N.A.I.C.S.: 334290
Catherine Rowe *(Pres)*

Fujitsu Telecomunicacoes Portugal, S.A. (1)
Rua Sebastiao e Silva n 67/69, Massama, Sintra, Portugal
Tel.: (351) 21 913 8600
Sales Range: $25-49.9 Million
Emp.: 100
Telecommunication Servicesb
N.A.I.C.S.: 517810

Fujitsu Transaction Solutions Canada Inc. (1)
155 University Ave Ste 1600, Toronto, M5H 3B7, ON, Canada
Tel.: (905) 286-9666
Hardware & Software Management Services
N.A.I.C.S.: 541512

Fujitsu Vietnam Limited (1)
Unit 01-03 17th Floor Keangnam Hanoi Landmark Tower, Lot E6 Cau Giay New Ur-

ban Area, Hanoi, Vietnam
Tel.: (84) 4 22203113
Web Site: http://www.fujitsu.com
Emp.: 90
Information Technology Consulting Services
N.A.I.C.S.: 541512
Sei Kudo *(Gen Mgr)*

GK Software SE (1)
Waldstrasse 7, 08261, Schoneck, Germany **(68.03%)**
Tel.: (49) 37464840
Web Site: https://www.gk-software.com
Rev.: $170,753,292
Assets: $179,849,989
Liabilities: $75,818,044
Net Worth: $104,031,945
Earnings: $12,258,796
Emp.: 1,168
Fiscal Year-end: 12/31/2022
Retail, Point of Sale & Transaction Processing Software Developer
N.A.I.C.S.: 513210
Rainer Glass *(Co-Founder, Chm-Mgmt Bd & CEO)*

Subsidiary (Domestic):

AWEK microdata GmbH (2)
Wendenstrasse 21a, 20097, Hamburg, Germany
Tel.: (49) 4035 985 4740
Web Site: https://www.awek-handel.de
Software Services
N.A.I.C.S.: 541511

Subsidiary (Non-US):

Eurosoftware s.r.o (2)
Radcicka 60/40, 301 00, Plzen, Czech Republic
Tel.: (420) 37 930 7311
Web Site: https://www.eurosoftware.cz
Computer Software Services
N.A.I.C.S.: 541511
Tomas Rauch *(Mgr-Test)*

GK Software Africa (Pty) Ltd. (2)
Woodlands Office Park Building 30 2nd Floor 20 Woodlands Dr, Woodmead, 2080, Sandton, South Africa
Tel.: (27) 115684600
Computer Software Services
N.A.I.C.S.: 541511

Subsidiary (US):

GK Software USA, Inc. (2)
9121 Anson Way Ste 150, Raleigh, NC 27615
Tel.: (984) 255-7995
Computer Software Services
N.A.I.C.S.: 541511

Subsidiary (Non-US):

OOO GK Software RUS (2)
Ul Marshala Rybalko Building 2, 123060, Moscow, Russia
Tel.: (7) 4956403994
Software Services
N.A.I.C.S.: 541511

Subsidiary (Domestic):

Prudsys AG (2)
Zwickauer Strasse 16, 09112, Chemnitz, Germany
Tel.: (49) 37 127 0930
Web Site: https://www.prudsys.de
Computer Software Services
N.A.I.C.S.: 541511
Jens Scholz *(CEO & Mng Dir)*

Subsidiary (Non-US):

StoreWeaver Gmbh (2)
Uberlandstrasse 105, 8600, Dubendorf, Switzerland
Tel.: (41) 37464840
Software Services
N.A.I.C.S.: 541511

TOV Eurosoftware-UA (2)
Lychakivska St 33A, 79000, Lviv, Ukraine
Tel.: (380) 322458588
Web Site: https://www.eurosoftware.com.ua
N.A.I.C.S.: 541511
Kosandyak Lyubov *(Mng Dir)*

Subsidiary (Domestic):

Valuephone Gmbh (2)
Friedrichstrasse 204, 10117, Berlin, Germany
Tel.: (49) 37464840
Software Services
N.A.I.C.S.: 541511

Subsidiary (Domestic):

NIFTY Corporation (1)
2-21-1 Kita-Shinjuku Shinjuku Front Tower, Shinjuku-ku, Tokyo, 169-8333, Japan
Tel.: (81) 359073803
Sales Range: $75-99.9 Million
Emp.: 495
Internet Hosting & Computer Communication Services
N.A.I.C.S.: 811210

Subsidiary (Domestic):

Gloczus, Inc. (2)
1-6-15 Hamamatsucho Minato-kun, Tokyo, 105-0013, Japan **(100%)**
Tel.: (81) 3 5733 3230
Web Site: http://www.gloczus.com
Emp.: 100
Digital Content Distribution Services
N.A.I.C.S.: 541511
Kenji Mitake *(Pres)*

Nice-business Solutions Finland Oy (1)
Valimotie 16, 00380, Helsinki, Finland
Tel.: (358) 29302302
Web Site: https://www.nico.fi
Sales Range: $75-99.9 Million
Emp.: 35
Software Services
N.A.I.C.S.: 541512
Jouko Seppa *(Mng Dir)*

Subsidiary (Domestic):

Nice-business Consulting Oy (2)
Valimotie 16, PO Box 458, 101, Helsinki, Finland
Tel.: (358) 45 78800
Web Site: http://www.nico.fi
Technology Consulting Services
N.A.I.C.S.: 541690
Antria Tarmo *(Mng Dir)*

Unit (Non-US):

Nice-business Solutions - Brighton (2)
Lees House 21 Dyke Road, Brighton, BN1 3FE, United Kingdom
Tel.: (44) 1273772306
Sales Range: $1-9.9 Million
Emp.: 30
Software Development & Testing Services
N.A.I.C.S.: 513210

Shimane Fujitsu Limited (1)
1180-6 Mitsukane Hikawacho, Hikawa-Gun, Shimane, 699-0504, Japan
Tel.: (81) 853722333
Personal Computer Mfr
N.A.I.C.S.: 334111

Shinko Electric Industries Co., Ltd. (1)
80 Oshimada-machi, Nagano, 381 2287, Japan **(50.02%)**
Tel.: (81) 262831000
Web Site: https://www.shinko.co.jp
Rev.: $2,053,186,860
Assets: $2,774,316,780
Liabilities: $974,546,400
Net Worth: $1,799,770,380
Earnings: $390,678,960
Emp.: 5,596
Fiscal Year-end: 03/31/2023
Mfr & Sales of Leadframe, Plastics Laminated Package, Glass-to-Metal Seals, Arrester & Precision Contact Parts; IC Assembly; Software Sales & Development
N.A.I.C.S.: 326199
Takahiro Kiyono *(Sr Corp Officer)*

Subsidiary (Non-US):

KOREA SHINKO MICROELECTRONICS CO., LTD. (2)
32 Sandan-1gil Seo-myeon, Suncheon, 57501, Jollanam-do, Korea (South)
Tel.: (82) 617538801
Web Site: https://www.koreashinko.co.kr

Fujitsu Limited—(Continued)

Emp.: 223
Metal Seal Mfr
N.A.I.C.S.: 332999

KOREA SHINKO TRADING CO., LTD. (2)
1223 Hyundai Venture Bldg 10 Bamgogae-ro 1-gil, Gangnam-gu, Seoul, 06349, Korea (South)
Tel.: (82) 25382851
Web Site: http://www.shinko.co.jp
Sales Range: $25-49.9 Million
Emp.: 5
Electronic Components Distr
N.A.I.C.S.: 423690
Toshihiko Ogiwara (Gen Mgr)

SHANGHAI SHINKO TRADING LTD. (2)
Room 2309 Shanghai Ruijin Building 205 Maoming South Road, Shanghai, 200020, China
Tel.: (86) 2164450898
Sales Range: $25-49.9 Million
Emp.: 6
Semiconductor Package Sales
N.A.I.C.S.: 423690

Subsidiary (US):

SHINKO ELECTRIC AMERICA, INC. (2)
2880 Zanker Rd Ste 204, San Jose, CA 95134
Tel.: (408) 232-0499
Web Site: http://www.shinko.com
Emp.: 20
Electronic Components Mfr
N.A.I.C.S.: 334419
Greg Bettencourt (Pres)

Subsidiary (Non-US):

SHINKO ELECTRIC INDUSTRIES (WUXI) CO., LTD. (2)
No 105 Xixian Road Mei Cun Industrial Park, Wuxi, 214112, Jiangsu, China
Tel.: (86) 51085343006
Web Site: https://www.shinko.co.jp
Emp.: 20
Electronic Components Mfr
N.A.I.C.S.: 334419
Komemula Masayoshi (Mgr)

SHINKO ELECTRONICS (MALAYSIA) SDN. BHD. (2)
Lot Pt 717A Jalan Serendah 26/17 Seksyen 26, 40400, Shah Alam, Selangor Darul Ehsan, Malaysia
Tel.: (60) 351913897
Electronic Components Mfr
N.A.I.C.S.: 334419
Murakami Yoshiyuki (Mng Dir)

SHINKO ELECTRONICS (SINGAPORE) PTE. LTD. (2)
09-67 Harbourfront Centre, Singapore, 099253, Singapore
Tel.: (65) 6225 3411
Sales Range: $25-49.9 Million
Emp.: 9
Computer Peripheral Equipment Mfr
N.A.I.C.S.: 334118
Toshihiko Ogiwara (Mng Dir)

Subsidiary (Domestic):

SHINKO PARTS CO., LTD. (2)
1553 Ko Naniai, Nagano, 381-3165, Japan
Tel.: (81) 262292710
Glass Veil Mfr
N.A.I.C.S.: 327215

SHINKO TECHNOSERVE CO., LTD. (2)
80 Oshimadamachi, Nagano, 381-2212, Japan
Tel.: (81) 262831000
Chemical Products Mfr
N.A.I.C.S.: 325998

Plant (Domestic):

Shinko Electric Industries Co., LTD. - Arai Plant
921-3 Himegawara, Myoko, 944-8588, Niigata, Japan
Tel.: (81) 255724154

Electronic Components Mfr
N.A.I.C.S.: 334419

Shinko Electric Industries Co., LTD. - Kyogase Plant (2)
1062-5 Kyogase Kogyodanchi, Agano, 959-2136, Niigata, Japan
Tel.: (81) 250615100
Electronic Components Mfr
N.A.I.C.S.: 334419

Shinko Electric Industries Co., LTD. - Takaoka Plant (2)
1216-9 Kusama, Nakano, 383-8581, Nagano, Japan
Tel.: (81) 269227111
Electronic Components Mfr
N.A.I.C.S.: 334419

Shinko Electric Industries Co., LTD. - Wakaho Plant (2)
1457-1 Wakaho Kawada, Nagano, 381-0103, Japan
Tel.: (81) 262824441
Web Site: http://www.shinko.co.jp
Sales Range: $150-199.9 Million
Emp.: 600
Electronic Components Mfr
N.A.I.C.S.: 334419

Subsidiary (Non-US):

TAIWAN SHINKO ELECTRONICS CO., LTD. (2)
14th Floor Area A1 Hung Kuo Building 167 Dunhua North Road, Songshan District, Taipei, 10549, Taiwan
Tel.: (886) 227195655
Electronic Components Mfr
N.A.I.C.S.: 334419

Transtron America, Inc. (1)
6500 Emerald Pkwy Ste 375, Dublin, OH 43016
Tel.: (614) 793-8263
Information & Communication Technology Services
N.A.I.C.S.: 517810

FUJIX LTD.
5 Miyamoto-cho Hirano, Kita-ku, Kyoto, 603-8322, Japan
Tel.: (81) 754638111
Web Site: http://www.fjx.co.jp
Year Founded: 1921
3600—(TKS)
Rev.: $38,371,050
Assets: $76,490,920
Liabilities: $10,443,800
Net Worth: $66,047,120
Earnings: $594,900
Emp.: 382
Fiscal Year-end: 03/31/24
Sewing & Embroidery Thread Mfr & Sales
N.A.I.C.S.: 313110
Ichiro Fujii (Pres)

Subsidiaries:

Changzhou Yingfu Textile Co., Ltd. (1)
68 Huashi Road, Daitou Town, Liyang, Jiangsu, China
Tel.: (86) 5198 736 8111
Emp.: 25
Sewing Thread Mfr
N.A.I.C.S.: 313110
Uehara Yasuhiro (Gen Mgr)

FUJIX (Shanghai) Thread Ltd. (1)
10157 North Qinggong Road, Qingpu District, Shanghai, China
Tel.: (86) 2159201110
Web Site: http://www.sh-fjx.com
Emp.: 151
Sewing & Embroidery Thread Mfr & Sales
N.A.I.C.S.: 313110

FUJIX International (Hong Kong) Ltd. (1)
Unit 5 19/F Kowloon Plaza, No 485 Castle Peak Road, Kowloon, China (Hong Kong)
Tel.: (852) 27851323
Sales Range: $50-74.9 Million
Emp.: 3

Sewing & Embroidery Thread International Trading Services
N.A.I.C.S.: 425120
Kenji Ohashi (Gen Mgr)

Sanghai FUJIX Trading Co., Ltd. (1)
2007 2F Sitong Bldg C 155 West Fute 1 Road Waigaoqiao, Free Trade Zone, Shanghai, China
Tel.: (86) 2158663902
Sales Range: $25-49.9 Million
Emp.: 4
Sewing & Embroidery Thread Trading Services
N.A.I.C.S.: 425120

Shanghai Fujix Trading Co., Ltd. (1)
1602 2 Changfang Building No 789 Tianshan Road, Shanghai, China
Tel.: (86) 216 236 3313
Emp.: 5
Sewing Thread & Embroidery Thread Distr
N.A.I.C.S.: 424310
Song Guo Rong (Gen Mgr)

Shanghai New Fujix Thread Ltd. (1)
10157 North Qinggong Road, Qingpu District, Shanghai, China
Tel.: (86) 2169573826
Web Site: http://www.fjx.co.jp
Sales Range: $25-49.9 Million
Emp.: 30
Sewing & Embroidery Thread Mfr & Sales
N.A.I.C.S.: 313110

FUJIYA CO., LTD.
2-15-6 Otsuka, Bunkyo-ku, Tokyo, 112-0012, Japan
Tel.: (81) 359788100
Web Site: https://www.fujiya-peko.co.jp
Year Founded: 1938
2211—(TKS)
Rev.: $748,236,060
Assets: $589,356,250
Liabilities: $159,418,650
Net Worth: $429,937,600
Earnings: $6,870,210
Emp.: 1,433
Fiscal Year-end: 12/31/23
Confectionery Store Operator
N.A.I.C.S.: 445292
Kensuke Yamada (Chm)

Subsidiaries:

Fujiya Food Service Co., Ltd. (1)
2-15-6 Otsuka, Bunkyo-ku, Tokyo, 112-0012, Japan
Tel.: (81) 369022000
Web Site: http://www.fujiya-fs.com
Emp.: 84
Food Products Distr
N.A.I.C.S.: 424490

Fujiya Kobe Co., Ltd. (1)
5-4-1 Takatsukadai, Nishi-ku, Kobe, 651-2271, Hyogo, Japan
Tel.: (81) 78 991 6700
Web Site: https://www.fujiyakobe.co.jp
Confectionery Product Mfr & Distr
N.A.I.C.S.: 311340

Fujiya Milk Product Co., Ltd. (1)
Numata 27 Orizawa Daito-cho, Ichinoseki, 029-0523, Iwate, Japan
Tel.: (81) 19 175 2215
Web Site: https://www.fujiya-m.jp
Emp.: 51
Dairy Products Mfr
N.A.I.C.S.: 311511

Fujiya Sanyo Ltd. (1)
28 Shimokawara, Date, 960-0401, Japan
Tel.: (81) 245833435
Emp.: 60
Food Beverage Mfr & Distr
N.A.I.C.S.: 311421
Takayuki Tsurumi (Pres)

Nihon Shokuzai Co., Ltd. (1)
1369-1 Kodamachokodama, Honjo, 367-0212, Japan
Tel.: (81) 495723660
Bakery Food Products Mfr
N.A.I.C.S.: 311812

Subsidiary (Domestic):

Fujiya System Center Co., Ltd. (2)
4th floor Nishikasai KYU Building 3-22-21 Nishikasai, Edogawa-ku, Tokyo, 134-0088, Japan
Tel.: (81) 35 675 5511
Web Site: http://www.fujiya-sc.co.jp
Emp.: 684
Administrative Management Services
N.A.I.C.S.: 561110

Sweet Garden Co., Ltd. (1)
5-4-1 Takatsukadai, Nishi-Ku, Kobe, 651-2271, Japan
Tel.: (81) 789916700
Web Site: http://www.sweetgarden.co.jp
Confectionery Product Mfr & Distr
N.A.I.C.S.: 311352

FUKOKU CO., LTD.
2F 3F 8F Asahi Life Urawa Building 1-1-1 Takasago, Urawa, 330-0063, Saitama, Japan
Tel.: (81) 486154400
Web Site: https://www.fukoku-rubber.co.jp
Year Founded: 1953
5185—(TKS)
Rev.: $587,278,670
Assets: $502,578,130
Liabilities: $224,892,030
Net Worth: $277,686,100
Earnings: $20,160,500
Emp.: 1,157
Fiscal Year-end: 03/31/24
Rubber Products Mfr
N.A.I.C.S.: 326291
Taro Kawamoto (Chm & Pres)

Subsidiaries:

Dongguan Fukoku Rubber & Plastics Industry Co., Ltd. (1)
11 Lianma Road, Daligshan Town, Dongguan, 523820, Guangdong, China
Tel.: (86) 76985656968
Web Site: https://dgfukoku.com
Electronic Components Mfr
N.A.I.C.S.: 334419

Fukoku (Shanghai) Trading Co., Ltd. (1)
Room1903 Gang TAI Building 700 Yan'AN East Road, Shanghai, 200001, China
Tel.: (86) 2153850699
Rubber Product Whslr
N.A.I.C.S.: 423840

Fukoku America, Inc. (1)
325 Hunter Industrial Park Rd, Laurens, SC 29360
Tel.: (864) 682-7212
Web Site: http://www.fukoku-rubber.co.jp
Emp.: 150
Rubber Product Whslr
N.A.I.C.S.: 423840
Masahiko Tsubota (Pres)

Fukoku Co., Ltd. - Aichi Plant (1)
5-1-1 Shinden-cho, Takahama, 444-1301, Aichi, Japan
Tel.: (81) 566526281
Industrial Valve Mfr
N.A.I.C.S.: 332911

Fukoku Co., Ltd. - Gunma Plant (1)
1508-2 Akabori, Ora District, Oura, 370-0614, Gunma, Japan
Tel.: (81) 276886301
Abrasive Product Mfr
N.A.I.C.S.: 327910

Fukoku Co., Ltd. - Gunma Plant 2 (1)
6 Showa Chiyoda-machi, Oura, 370-0723, Gunma, Japan
Tel.: (81) 276866121
Resin Mfr
N.A.I.C.S.: 325211

Fukoku Co., Ltd. - Nishio Plant (1)
77-2 Higashiwari Minaminakane-cho, Nishio, 445-0801, Aichi, Japan
Tel.: (81) 563536010
Rubber Products Mfr
N.A.I.C.S.: 326299

Fukoku Czech S.R.O. (1)
Tovarni 1162, 410 02, Lovosice, Czech Republic
Tel.: (420) 73 187 5681
Web Site: https://www.fukoku-rubber.cz
Automotive Plastic Parts Mfr
N.A.I.C.S.: 326199
Kiyoshi Kudo *(Mng Dir)*

Fukoku India Private Limited (1)
G - 4/1 Chankan Industrial Area Phase-III, Chakan Tal-Khed District, Pune, 410 501, India
Tel.: (91) 7558312966
Automobile Parts Mfr
N.A.I.C.S.: 336390
Prashant Joshi *(Mng Dir)*

Fukoku Korea Co., Ltd. (1)
4F 63 Dongsan-Ro, Danwon-Gu, Ansan, 15433, Gyeonggi-do, Korea (South)
Tel.: (82) 314949271
Web Site: https://www.fukokukorea.co.kr
Automobile Parts Mfr
N.A.I.C.S.: 336390
Kwon Soon-Mook *(Chm & CEO)*

Subsidiary (Domestic):

Fukoku Korea Co., Ltd. - Boryeong Plant (1)
1225-1 Gwanchang-ri Jugyo-myeon, Boryeong, 33448, Chungcheongnam-do, Korea (South)
Tel.: (82) 419369271
Automobile Parts Mfr
N.A.I.C.S.: 336390

Fukoku Vietnam Co., Ltd. (1)
Lot 1A 1B Noi Bai Industrial Zone, Quang Tien Commune Soc Son District, Hanoi, Vietnam
Tel.: (84) 435824532
Automobile Parts Mfr
N.A.I.C.S.: 336390

PT. Fukoku Tokai Rubber Indonesia (1)
Jl Industri Selatan 6A Blok GG 6A-F, Kawasan Industri Jababeka II Cikarang Pasir Sari Cikarang Selatan, Bekasi, 17532, Jawa Barat, Indonesia
Tel.: (62) 2189834083
Rubber Products Mfr
N.A.I.C.S.: 326299

Subsidiary (Domestic):

PT. Fukoku Tokai Rubber Indonesia - Factory 1 (2)
Jl Industri Selatan 2 Blok MM 18-19, Kawasan Industri Jababeka II Cikarang Pasir Sari Cikarang Selatan, Bekasi, 17532, Jawa Barat, Indonesia
Tel.: (62) 218934914
Rubber Products Mfr
N.A.I.C.S.: 326299

PT. Fukoku Tokai Rubber Indonesia - Factory 3 (2)
Jl Jababeka IX Blok E 18 C H Kawasan Industri Jababeka I, Cikarang, Bekasi, 17534, Jawa Barat, Indonesia
Tel.: (62) 2129566104
Rubber Products Mfr
N.A.I.C.S.: 326299

PT.Trim Rubber Co., Ltd. (1)
Kawasan Industri Jababeka Jl Jababeka IX Blok E 18 I, Cikarang Utara, Bekasi, 17534, Indonesia
Tel.: (62) 2189843010
Emp.: 47
Rubber Products Mfr
N.A.I.C.S.: 326299

Polymer Giken Co., Ltd. (1)
5-14-5 Nishi-Nakashima, Yodogawa-ku, Osaka, 532-0011, Japan
Tel.: (81) 6 7668 7111
Rubber Products Mfr
N.A.I.C.S.: 326299

Qingdao Fukoku Auto Fittings Co., Ltd. (1)
Tonghe Town, Pingdu-City, Qingdao, 266706, China
Tel.: (86) 53285335025
Rubber Products Mfr
N.A.I.C.S.: 326299

Shanghai Fukoku Rubber & Plastics Industry Co., Ltd. (1)
GATE 2 No 2866 Jiangshan Road, Nanhui County, Shanghai, 201309, China
Tel.: (86) 2158252100
Rubber Products Mfr
N.A.I.C.S.: 326299

Siam Fukoku Co., Ltd. (1)
157 Moo 16 Theparak Rd, Bang Sao Thong, 10570, Samut Prakan, Thailand
Tel.: (66) 27061018
Web Site: https://www.siamfukoku.co.th
Emp.: 74
Rubber Products Mfr
N.A.I.C.S.: 326299
Chalee Teamthaweesin *(Mgr-Factory)*

Subsidiary (Domestic):

Siam Fukoku Co., Ltd. - Korat Factory 1 (2)
678 Moo 1 Naklang, Sungnoen, Nakhon Ratchasima, 30380, Thailand
Tel.: (66) 44000140
Emp.: 513
Rubber Products Mfr
N.A.I.C.S.: 326299

Siam Fukoku Co., Ltd. - Korat Factory 2 (2)
999-6 Moo 1 Naklang, Sungnoen, Nakhon Ratchasima, 30380, Thailand
Tel.: (66) 44000870
Emp.: 699
Rubber Products Mfr
N.A.I.C.S.: 326299

Sueyoshi Kogyo Co., Ltd. (1)
10157 Oaza Komuro Ina-cho, Kitaadachi-gun, Saitama, 362-0806, Japan
Tel.: (81) 487213125
Emp.: 279
Construction Machinery Mfr
N.A.I.C.S.: 333120

Thai Fukoku Co., Ltd. (1)
Wellgrow Industrial Estate 104-1 Moo 5 Bangna Trad Km 36, Bang Samak, 24180, Chachoengsao, Thailand
Tel.: (66) 38570713
Web Site: https://www.thaifukoku.co.th
Emp.: 483
Rubber Products Mfr
N.A.I.C.S.: 326299

Thaifukoku Panaplus Foundry Co., Ltd. (1)
333 Moo 5 Bang Na Trad Rd Km 31, Bang Bo, Bangkok, 10560, Samut Prakan, Thailand
Tel.: (66) 23376262
Web Site: https://tfpf.co.th
Emp.: 175
Casting Mfr
N.A.I.C.S.: 331511

Tokyo Rubber MFG. Co., Ltd. (1)
48 Shobusawa, Fujisawa, 252-0823, Kanagawa, Japan
Tel.: (81) 466 48 2311
Web Site: http://www.tokyo-rub.com
Emp.: 140
Rubber Products Mfr
N.A.I.C.S.: 326299
Yoshiji Shibuya *(Pres)*

FUKOKU MUTUAL LIFE INSURANCE COMPANY
2-2 Uchisaiwaicho 2-chome, Chiyoda-ku, Tokyo, 100-0011, Japan
Tel.: (81) 335081101   JP
Web Site: http://www.fukoku-life.co.jp
Year Founded: 1923
Rev.: $7,218,410,040
Assets: $77,143,761,840
Liabilities: $71,588,831,220
Net Worth: $5,554,930,620
Earnings: $332,846,280
Emp.: 12,689
Fiscal Year-end: 03/31/19
Life Insurance Carrier
N.A.I.C.S.: 524113
Yoshiteru Yoneyama *(Pres & CEO)*

Subsidiaries:

Fukoku Life International (America) Inc. (1)

Times Sq Tower 7 Times Sq 35th Fl, New York, NY 10036
Tel.: (212) 221-7760
Sales Range: $50-74.9 Million
Emp.: 5
Fire Insurance Services
N.A.I.C.S.: 524113
Seiichi Nozaki *(Controller)*

Fukoku Life International (U.K.) Ltd. (1)
3rd Floor Baltic Exchange 38 Saint Mary Axe, London, EC3A 8EX, United Kingdom
Tel.: (44) 2072831331
Sales Range: $50-74.9 Million
Emp.: 6
Fire Insurance Services
N.A.I.C.S.: 524113
Eisho Noma *(Pres)*

Kyoei Kasai Shinrai Life Insurance Co. Ltd (1)
J. CITY BLD. 8-12, Takamatsu 5-Chome Nerima-Ku, Tokyo, 179-0075, Japan   **(80%)**
Tel.: (81) 120 700 651
Web Site: http://www.kyoeikasai.co.jp
Sales Range: $50-74.9 Million
Emp.: 62
Life Insurance
N.A.I.C.S.: 524113

FUKUDA CORPORATION
Shinagawa Prince Hotel Main Tower, Chuo-ku, Tokyo, 104-0044, Japan
Tel.: (81) 355656817
Web Site: https://www.fukudaco.co.jp
Year Founded: 1902
1899—(TKS)
Rev.: $1,150,302,870
Assets: $969,422,790
Liabilities: $399,861,820
Net Worth: $569,560,970
Earnings: $24,006,740
Emp.: 120
Fiscal Year-end: 12/31/23
Construction Engineering Services
N.A.I.C.S.: 237990
Masaki Araaki *(Pres & CEO)*

Subsidiaries:

AirCom Pneumatic GmbH (1)
Siemensstrasse 18, 40885, Ratingen, Germany
Tel.: (49) 2102733900
Web Site: https://www.aircom.net
Pressure Regulator & Volume Booster Mfr
N.A.I.C.S.: 334512

Colibri Spindles Ltd. (1)
Lavon Industrial Park, Lavon, 2011800, Israel
Tel.: (972) 49089102
Web Site: https://colibrispindles.com
Metal Machine Mfr & Distr
N.A.I.C.S.: 332999

Compo Tech PLUS, spol. s r.o. (1)
Nova 1316, 34201, Susice, Czech Republic
Tel.: (420) 376526839
Web Site: https://compotech.com
Composite Mfr & Distr
N.A.I.C.S.: 322219

JAKOB Antriebstechnik GmbH (1)
Daimler Ring 42, 63839, Kleinwallstadt, Germany
Tel.: (49) 602222080
Web Site: https://www.jakobantriebstechnik.de
Emp.: 45
Safety Coupling Mfr
N.A.I.C.S.: 333613

Lenord, Bauer & Co. GmbH (1)
Dohlenstrasse 32, 46145, Oberhausen, Germany
Tel.: (49) 20899630
Web Site: https://www.lenord.de
Emp.: 250
Drive Technology Services
N.A.I.C.S.: 518210

NILOS GmbH & Co. KG (1)
Reisholzstrasse 15, 40721, Hilden, Germany
Tel.: (49) 2103951200

Web Site: https://www.nilos.com
Emp.: 300
Conveyor Belt Equipment Mfr & Distr
N.A.I.C.S.: 326220

OTT-JAKOB Spanntechnik GmbH (1)
Industriestrasse 3-7, D-87663, Lengenwang, Germany
Tel.: (49) 836498210
Web Site: https://www.ott-jakob.de
Emp.: 253
Steep Taper & Rotary Union Mfr
N.A.I.C.S.: 333515

Schmid & Wezel GmbH (1)
Maybachstrasse 2, 75433, Maulbronn, Germany
Tel.: (49) 70431020
Web Site: https://www.biax-germany.com
Pneumatic Tool Mfr & Distr
N.A.I.C.S.: 326211

Sieb & Meyer AG (1)
Auf dem Schmaarkamp 21, 21339, Luneburg, Germany
Tel.: (49) 41312030
Web Site: https://www.sieb-meyer.com
Emp.: 260
Electronic Product Mfr & Distr
N.A.I.C.S.: 334413

SycoTec GmbH & Co. KG (1)
Wangener Strasse 78, 88299, Leutkirch, Germany
Tel.: (49) 7561860
Web Site: https://sycotec.eu
Emp.: 300
Motor Spindles Mfr & Distr
N.A.I.C.S.: 333248

Tokupi Co., Ltd. (1)
Ohtake 3-167, Yao, 581-0854, Osaka, Japan
Tel.: (81) 729412288
Web Site: https://www.tokupi.co.jp
Emp.: 21
Power Sprayer & Plunger Pump Mfr
N.A.I.C.S.: 333914

WEH GmbH (1)
Verbindungstechnikn Josef-Henle-Strasse 1, 89257, Illertissen, Germany
Tel.: (49) 730396090
Web Site: https://www.weh.com
Emp.: 200
Leak & Pressure Test Connector Mfr
N.A.I.C.S.: 334417

FUKUDA DENSHI CO., LTD.
2-35-8 Hongo, Bunkyo-ku, Tokyo, 113-8420, Japan
Tel.: (81) 356841455
Web Site: https://www.fukuda.co.jp
Year Founded: 1939
6960—(TKS)
Rev.: $1,278,708,640
Assets: $1,892,391,600
Liabilities: $441,775,840
Net Worth: $1,450,615,760
Earnings: $156,970,880
Emp.: 3,422
Fiscal Year-end: 03/31/22
Medical Electronics Equipment Developer, Mfr, Importer, Exporter & Sales
N.A.I.C.S.: 339112
Kotaro Fukuda *(Chm & CEO)*

Subsidiaries:

Beijing Fukuda Denshi Medical Instruments Co., Ltd. (1)
No 8 Hogda North Road, Beijing Economic-Technological Development Area, Beijing, 100176, China
Tel.: (86) 1067884155
Medical Device Mfr & Distr
N.A.I.C.S.: 339112

Fukuda Asia Pacific Pte. Ltd. (1)
1 Paya Lebar Link 04-01 Paya Lebar Quarter 1, Singapore, 408533, Singapore
Tel.: (65) 69558668
Medical Device Mfr & Distr
N.A.I.C.S.: 339112

Fukuda Denshi UK Ltd. (1)
Unit 6 Chambers Way Thorncliffe Park Es-

Fukuda Denshi Co., Ltd.—(Continued)

tate, Chapeltown, Sheffield, S35 2PH, Surrey, United Kingdom **(100%)**
Tel.: (44) 1483728065
Web Site: https://www.fukuda.co.uk
Emp.: 5
Surgical & Medical Instrument Mfr
N.A.I.C.S.: 339112

Fukuda Denshi USA, Inc. **(1)**
17725 NE 65th St Bldg C, Redmond, WA 98052
Tel.: (425) 558-1661
Web Site: https://www.fukuda.com
Sales Range: $25-49.9 Million
Emp.: 15
Medical Electronic Equipment Mfr & Sales
N.A.I.C.S.: 339112

FUKUI COMPUTER HOLDINGS INC.

1-2501 Takagi Chuo, Fukui, 910-8521, Japan
Tel.: (81) 776539200
Web Site: https://hd.fukuicompu.co.jp
Year Founded: 1979
9790—(TKS)
Rev.: $91,356,810
Assets: $196,733,430
Liabilities: $35,403,160
Net Worth: $161,330,270
Earnings: $25,230,370
Fiscal Year-end: 03/31/24
Holding Company
N.A.I.C.S.: 551112
Harukatsu Hayashi *(Pres)*

FUKUOKA CHUO BANK LTD.

2-12-1 Daimyo, Chuo-Ku, Fukuoka, 810-0041, Japan
Tel.: (81) 927514433
Web Site: https://www.fukuokachuo-bank.co.jp
8540—(FKA)
Sales Range: Less than $1 Million
Commercial Banking Services
N.A.I.C.S.: 522110
Jiro Furumura *(Pres)*

FUKUOKA FINANCIAL GROUP, INC.

1-8-3 Otemon, Chuo-ku, Fukuoka, 810-8693, Japan
Tel.: (81) 927232500
Web Site: https://www.fukuoka-fg.com
Year Founded: 2007
FKKFF—(OTCIQ)
Rev.: $2,675,351,230
Assets: $215,814,695,470
Liabilities: $209,060,954,410
Net Worth: $6,753,741,060
Earnings: $380,075
Emp.: 6,717
Fiscal Year-end: 03/31/24
Bank Holding Company
N.A.I.C.S.: 551111
Masayuki Aoyagi *(Exec Officer)*

Subsidiaries:

FFG Insurance Service Co., Ltd. **(1)**
2-2-26 Daimyo, Chuo-ku, Fukuoka, Japan
Tel.: (81) 927172235
Fire Insurance Services
N.A.I.C.S.: 524210

FFG Securities Co., Ltd. **(1)**
2-13-1 Tenjin, Chuo-ku, Fukuoka, Japan
Tel.: (81) 927713836
Financial Security Services
N.A.I.C.S.: 523999

R&D Business Factory Co., Ltd. **(1)**
2-13-1 Tenjin, Chuo-ku, Fukuoka, Japan
Tel.: (81) 927231810
Financial Security Services
N.A.I.C.S.: 523999

The Bank of Fukuoka, Ltd. **(1)**
183 Otemon, Chuo-ku, Fukuoka, 810-8727, Japan **(100%)**

Tel.: (81) 92 723 2622
Web Site: http://www.fukuokabank.co.jp
Sales Range: $1-4.9 Billion
Emp.: 487
Commercial Banking Services
N.A.I.C.S.: 522110

Subsidiary (Domestic):

FFG Business Consulting Co., Ltd. **(2)**
2-13-1 Tenjin, Chuo-ku, Fukuoka, 810-0001, Japan **(100%)**
Tel.: (81) 927232244
Web Site: http://www.ffgbc.com
Sales Range: $10-24.9 Million
Emp.: 30
Business Management Consulting Services
N.A.I.C.S.: 541611

FFG Card Co., Ltd. **(2)**
7-1 Meinohamaeki Minami 1-chome, Nishi-ku, Fukuoka, Japan **(100%)**
Tel.: (81) 928841785
Credit Card Processing Services
N.A.I.C.S.: 522320

Fukugin Business Operation Service Co., Ltd. **(2)**
1-7-7 Momochihama, Sawara-ku, Fukuoka, 814-0001, Japan **(100%)**
Tel.: (81) 928446001
Web Site: http://www.Fukuokabank.co.jp
Business Support Services
N.A.I.C.S.: 561439

Affiliate (Domestic):

Fukugin Guarantee Co., Ltd. **(2)**
1-7-1 Meinohamaeki Minami, Nishi-ku, Fukuoka, 819-0166, Japan **(45%)**
Tel.: (81) 928820431
Web Site: http://www.fukuoka-fg.com
Financial Support Services
N.A.I.C.S.: 522291

Subsidiary (Domestic):

Fukugin Real Estate Assessment Service Co., Ltd. **(2)**
1-4-13 Hakozaki, Higashi-ku, Fukuoka, 814-0001, Japan **(100%)**
Tel.: (81) 92 631 0301
Web Site: http://www.fukuoka-fg.com
Asset Management Services
N.A.I.C.S.: 523999

Affiliate (Domestic):

Fukuoka Computer Service Co., Ltd. **(2)**
6-6 Hakataekimae 2-chome, Hakata-ku, Fukuoka, 812-0011, Japan **(40%)**
Tel.: (81) 924736900
Web Site: http://www.fcs-web.co.jp
Business Management Software Development Services
N.A.I.C.S.: 541511

Subsidiary (Domestic):

Fukuoka Servicing Co., Ltd. **(2)**
2-13-1 Tenjin, Chuo-ku, Fukuoka, 810-8727, Japan **(100%)**
Tel.: (81) 927370881
Web Site: http://www.fukuoka-fg.com
Credit Management & Collection Services
N.A.I.C.S.: 561440

The Eighteenth Bank, Limited **(1)**
1-11 Doza-machi, Nagasaki, 850-8618, Japan
Tel.: (81) 958241818
Web Site: http://www.18bank.co.jp
Rev.: $423,416,160
Assets: $26,293,946,400
Liabilities: $24,824,155,440
Net Worth: $1,469,782,080
Earnings: $46,078,320
Emp.: 1,325
Fiscal Year-end: 03/31/2018
Banking Services
N.A.I.C.S.: 522110
Takujiro Mori *(Pres & CEO)*

Subsidiary (Domestic):

Juhachi Capital Co., Ltd. **(2)**
1-11 Dozamachi, Nagasaki, 850-0841, Japan
Tel.: (81) 958203818

Venture Capital Investment Services
N.A.I.C.S.: 523999

Nagasaki Hosho Service Co., Ltd. **(2)**
10-10 Dejimamachi, Nagasaki, 850-0862, Japan
Tel.: (81) 958243098
Investment Banking Services
N.A.I.C.S.: 523150

Nagasaki Research Institute Limited **(2)**
1-11 Dozamachi Juhachi-Affinity Bank, Nagasaki, 850-8618, Japan
Tel.: (81) 958288859
Web Site: http://www.nagasaki-keizai.co.jp
Sales Range: $25-49.9 Million
Emp.: 30
Economic Research & Development Services
N.A.I.C.S.: 541720

The Juhachi-Shinwa Bank, Ltd. **(1)**
10-12 Shimanosecho, Sasebo, Nagasaki, Japan
Tel.: (81) 956245111
Banking Services
N.A.I.C.S.: 522110

Subsidiary (Domestic):

Nagasaki Economic Research Institute Ltd **(2)**
1-11 Douzacho, Nagasaki, Japan
Tel.: (81) 958288859
Research & Development Services
N.A.I.C.S.: 541720

Nagasaki Guarantee Service Co., Ltd. **(2)**
10-10 Dejimamachi, Nagasaki, Japan
Tel.: (81) 958243098
Loan Guarantee Services
N.A.I.C.S.: 522291

The Eighteenth Card Co., Ltd. **(2)**
4-18 Douzacho, Nagasaki, Japan
Tel.: (81) 958262391
Credit Card Services
N.A.I.C.S.: 522210

The Eighteenth Lease Co., Ltd. **(2)**
4-18 Doza-cho, Nagasaki, 850-0841, Japan
Tel.: (81) 958221171
Web Site: http://www.18lease.co.jp
Leasing Services
N.A.I.C.S.: 532490

The Eighteenth Software Co., Ltd. **(2)**
6-5 Edomachi Edomachi Center Building, Nagasaki, 850-0861, Japan
Tel.: (81) 958240018
Web Site: http://www.18software.co.jp
Software Development Services
N.A.I.C.S.: 541511

The Kumamoto Bank, Ltd. **(1)**
6-29-20 Suizenji, Chuo-ku, Kumamoto, 862-8601, Japan
Tel.: (81) 96 385 1111
Web Site: https://www.kumamotobank.co.jp
Sales Range: $350-399.9 Million
Emp.: 879
Commercial Banking Services
N.A.I.C.S.: 522110

The Shinwa Bank, Ltd. **(1)**
10-12 Shimanose-cho, Sasebo, Nagasaki, 857-0806, Japan
Tel.: (81) 956245111
Web Site: http://www.shinwabank.co.jp
Sales Range: $700-749.9 Million
Emp.: 2,000
Commercial Banking Services
N.A.I.C.S.: 522110
Ryoji Takeyama *(Branch Mgr)*

Subsidiary (Domestic):

Nishi-Kyushu Credit Guarantee Co., Ltd. **(2)**
4-24 Shimanose-cho, Sasebo, 857-0806, Nagasaki, Japan **(100%)**
Tel.: (81) 956236326
Web Site: http://www.fukuoka-fg.com
Financial Support Services
N.A.I.C.S.: 522291

Shinwa Venture Capital Co., Ltd. **(2)**

10-11 Shimanose-cho, Sasebo, 850-0841, Nagasaki, Japan **(100%)**
Tel.: (81) 956246165
Web Site: http://www.shinwavc.co.jp
Securities Trading Services
N.A.I.C.S.: 523150

iBank marketing Co., Ltd. **(1)**
6-27 Nishinakasu, Chuo-ku, Fukuoka, 810-0002, Japan
Tel.: (81) 927917977
Web Site: https://www.ibank.co.jp
N.A.I.C.S.: 523150

FUKUOKA REIT CORPORATION

1-2-25 Sumiyoshi, Hakata, Fukuoka, 812-0018, Japan
Tel.: (81) 922723900
Web Site: https://www.fukuoka-reit.jp
Year Founded: 2004
89680—(TKS)
Sales Range: Less than $1 Million
Emp.: 41
Real Estate Related Services
N.A.I.C.S.: 531390
Etsuo Matsuyuki *(Exec Dir)*

FUKUSHIMA GALILEI CO. LTD.

2-6-18 Takeshima, Nishiyodogawa-ku, Osaka, 555-0011, Japan
Tel.: (81) 664772011
Web Site: https://www.galilei.co.jp
Year Founded: 1951
6420—(TKS)
Rev.: $765,537,150
Assets: $862,816,520
Liabilities: $249,236,660
Net Worth: $613,579,860
Earnings: $81,342,660
Emp.: 2,524
Fiscal Year-end: 03/31/24
Refrigerator Mfr & Distr
N.A.I.C.S.: 335220
Yutaka Fukushima *(Pres)*

Subsidiaries:

Beijing ER Shang-Fukushima Machinery Electric Co., Ltd **(1)**
No 8 No 1 RD West of Yanqi River Ynaqi Industrial Development Zone, Huairou District, Beijing, China
Tel.: (86) 10 6347 0639
Web Site: http://www.ershangfukushima.com
Refrigerator Mfr
N.A.I.C.S.: 335220

Fukushima Galilei (H.K.) Co., Ltd. **(1)**
Unit 903 9/F Westlands Centre 20 Westlands Road, Quarry Bay, China (Hong Kong)
Tel.: (852) 28855679
Commercial Freezer Refrigerator Mfr & Distr
N.A.I.C.S.: 335220

Fukushima Galilei (Shanghai) Co., Ltd. **(1)**
Room 8D No 831 Xinzha Road, Jingan District, Shanghai, 200041, China
Tel.: (86) 2162481512
Commercial Freezer Refrigerator Mfr & Distr
N.A.I.C.S.: 335220

Fukushima Galilei (Thailand)Co., Ltd. **(1)**
16 Asoke Court Gnd Fl Room 2G Sukhumvit 21 Asoke Rd, Klongtoey-Nua Wattana, Bangkok, 10110, Thailand
Tel.: (66) 22583690
Commercial Freezer Refrigerator Mfr & Distr
N.A.I.C.S.: 335220

Fukushima Galilei Malaysia Sdn. Bhd. **(1)**
Lot 6 01 6th Floor Wisma Central, PO Box 617, Jalan Ampang, 50450, Kuala Lumpur, Malaysia
Tel.: (60) 321811034

Commercial Freezer Refrigerator Mfr & Distr
N.A.I.C.S.: 335220

Fukushima Galilei Myanmar Co. Ltd. (1)
805 8F Sakura Tower 339 Bogyoke Aung San Rd, Kyauktada Township, Yangon, Myanmar
Tel.: (95) 9422389224
Commercial Freezer Refrigerator Mfr & Distr
N.A.I.C.S.: 335220

Fukushima Galilei Philippine Corporation (1)
26th Floor Twenty-Four Seven Mckinley Bldg 24th St Cor 7th Ave, Bonifacio Global City, Taguig, Metro Manila, Philippines
Tel.: (63) 28644141
Commercial Freezer Refrigerator Mfr & Distr
N.A.I.C.S.: 335220

Fukushima Galilei Singapore Pte. Ltd. (1)
1003 Bukit Merah Central 02-06, Singapore, 159836, Singapore
Tel.: (65) 62710460
Commercial Freezer Refrigerator Mfr & Distr
N.A.I.C.S.: 335220

Fukushima Galilei Taiwan Co., Ltd. (1)
Rm 5 12F No 112 Sec 2 Zhongshan N Rd, Zhongshan Dist, Taipei, 10449, Taiwan
Tel.: (886) 225219810
Commercial Freezer Refrigerator Mfr & Distr
N.A.I.C.S.: 335220

Fukushima Galilei Vietnam Co., Ltd. (1)
Floor 9 PVC Sai Gon 11Bis Nguyen Gia Thieu Ward 6, District 3, Ho Chi Minh City, Vietnam
Tel.: (84) 839333628
Commercial Freezer Refrigerator Mfr & Distr
N.A.I.C.S.: 335220

Fukushima Industries Corporation - Okayama Factory (1)
34-1 Taiheidai Shoo-cho, Katsuta-gun, Okayama, 709-4321, Japan
Tel.: (81) 868385555
Web Site: https://www.galilei.co.jp
Refrigerator Mfr
N.A.I.C.S.: 335220

Fukushima Industries Corporation - Shiga Factory (1)
26 Satsukigaoka Minakuchi-cho Koka, Shiga, 528-0062, Japan
Tel.: (81) 748637500
Refrigerator Mfr
N.A.I.C.S.: 335220

Fukushima International (Cambodia) Co., Ltd. (1)
Executive Room 2-E6 The iCON Professional Building 216, Norodom Boulevard Tonle Bassac Chamkarmorn, Phnom Penh, Cambodia
Tel.: (855) 77778610
Commercial Freezer Refrigerator Mfr & Distr
N.A.I.C.S.: 335220

Fukushima International Korea Corporation (1)
2F 202 200-8 Donggyo-dong, Mapo-gu, Seoul, 121-819, Korea (South)
Tel.: (82) 2 338 4731
Refrigerator Mfr
N.A.I.C.S.: 335220

Fukusima International (H.K.) Co., Limited (1)
Unit 1005 10/F Block B Sea View Estate 4-6 Watson Road, Hong Kong, China (Hong Kong)
Tel.: (852) 2885 5679
Refrigerator Mfr
N.A.I.C.S.: 335220
Takayasu Sinya (Gen Mgr)

Fukusima International (Shanghai) Co., Ltd (1)

Room 2204 Century Time and Space Mansion Wu Lu Mu Qi Road North, Jingan District, Shanghai, China
Tel.: (86) 2162481512
Refrigerator Mfr
N.A.I.C.S.: 335220

Fukusima International (Singapore) Pte., Ltd (1)
41 Toh Guan Road East 07-01 ADL Building, Singapore, 608605, Singapore
Tel.: (65) 62710460
Refrigerator Mfr
N.A.I.C.S.: 335220

Galilei (Thailand) Co., Ltd. (1)
60/105 Moo 3, Mabyangporn Sub-District Pluakdaeng District, Rayong, 21140, Thailand
Tel.: (66) 38020112
Commercial Freezer Refrigerator Mfr & Distr
N.A.I.C.S.: 335220

PT. Fukushima International Indonesia (1)
City Loft Sudirman 17th Floor Unit 1708 Jl KH Mas Mansyur No 121, Jakarta Pusat, 10220, Indonesia
Tel.: (62) 85780306345
Commercial Freezer Refrigerator Mfr & Distr
N.A.I.C.S.: 335220

Taiwan Fukusima International Co., Ltd (1)
Room8 11F No136 Minquan W RD, Datong District, Taipei, 103, Taiwan
Tel.: (886) 225530859
Refrigerator Mfr
N.A.I.C.S.: 335220

FUKUTOME MEAT PACKERS LTD.
2-6-75 Kusatsuminato, Nishi-ku, Hiroshima, 733-0832, Japan
Tel.: (81) 822786161
Web Site: https://www.fukutome.com
Year Founded: 1958
2291—(TKS)
Rev.: $166,525,730
Assets: $89,677,870
Liabilities: $74,018,780
Net Worth: $15,659,090
Earnings: $991,500
Emp.: 349
Fiscal Year-end: 03/31/24
Meat Product Mfr & Distr
N.A.I.C.S.: 333241
Fukuhara Haruhiko (Pres)

FUKUVI CHEMICAL INDUSTRY CO., LTD.
33-66 Sanjuhassha-cho, Fukui, 918-8585, Japan
Tel.: (81) 776388015
Web Site: https://fukuvi.co.jp
Year Founded: 1953
7871—(TKS)
Rev.: $262,648,350
Assets: $357,442,360
Liabilities: $111,801,540
Net Worth: $245,640,820
Earnings: $11,263,440
Emp.: 968
Fiscal Year-end: 03/31/24
Chemical Product Mfr & Whslr
N.A.I.C.S.: 325180

Subsidiaries:

Fukuvi (Thailand) Co., Ltd. (1)
141 Major Tower Building 10th Floor Unit No 6 Soi Sukhumvit 63 Ekamai, Sukhumvit Road Klongton-Nue Wattana, Bangkok, 10110, Thailand
Tel.: (66) 23923753
Web Site: http://www.fukuvi-th.com
Plastics Product Mfr
N.A.I.C.S.: 326199
Toshiyuki Kobayashi (Mng Dir)

Fukuvi Chemical Industry Co., Ltd. - Awara Factory (1)

10 Aza 34 Hasugaura, Awara, Japan
Tel.: (81) 776762029
Plastics Product Mfr
N.A.I.C.S.: 326199

Fukuvi Chemical Industry Co., Ltd. - Mikata Factory (1)
45 Aza-Sugawara Mikata 18 Wakasa-cho Sanpou, Mikatakaminaka-gun, Fukui, Japan
Tel.: (81) 770451260
Plastics Product Mfr
N.A.I.C.S.: 326199

Fukuvi Chemical Industry Co., Ltd. - Osaka Factory (1)
2-8-25 Nonaka-Minami, Yodogawa-ku, Osaka, 564-0053, Japan
Tel.: (81) 663021556
Plastics Product Mfr
N.A.I.C.S.: 326199

Fukuvi Chemical Industry Co., Ltd. - Sakai Factory (1)
1-1 Sadamune Sakai-cho, Sakai, 919-0506, Japan
Tel.: (81) 776668600
Plastics Product Mfr
N.A.I.C.S.: 326199

Fukuvi Housing Co., Ltd. (1)
738 Katayose-Aza-Shimoyachi Shiwa-Cho, Shiwa-Gun, Iwate, 028-3452, Japan
Tel.: (81) 196738252
Plastics Product Mfr
N.A.I.C.S.: 326199

Fukuvi USA, Inc. (1)
7631 Progress Ct, Huber Heights, OH 45424
Tel.: (937) 236-7288
Web Site: http://www.fukuvi-usa.com
Emp.: 65
Plastic Product Mfr & Distr
N.A.I.C.S.: 326199
Akinobu Masunaga (Pres & COO)

Fukuvi Vietnam Co., Ltd. (1)
Plot 510 Road 13 Amata Industrial Park, Long Binh Ward, Bien Hoa, Dong Nai, Vietnam
Emp.: 90
Plastic Product Mfr & Distr
N.A.I.C.S.: 326199

Refojoule Co., Ltd. (1)
33-66 Sanjuhassha-cho, Fukui, 918-8585, Japan
Tel.: (81) 35 742 6331
Ceiling System Distr
N.A.I.C.S.: 423390

FUKUYAMA CONSULTANTS COMPANY LIMITED
3-6-18 Hakata Station East, Hakata-ku, Fukuoka, 812-0013, Japan
Tel.: (81) 924710211
Web Site:
    http://www.fukuyamaconsul.co.jp
Year Founded: 1954
9608—(TKS)
Sales Range: $50-74.9 Million
Emp.: 31
Construction Services
N.A.I.C.S.: 541330

FULCRUM CAPITAL PARTNERS INC.
885 West Georgia Street Suite 1020, Vancouver, V6C 3E8, BC, Canada
Tel.: (604) 631-8088
Web Site:
    http://www.fulcrumcapital.ca
Rev.: $700,000,000
Emp.: 20
Privater Equity Firm
N.A.I.C.S.: 523999
Johan Lemmer (CFO)

Subsidiaries:

Athletica Sport Systems Inc. (1)
554 Parkside Drive, Waterloo, N2L 5Z4, ON, Canada
Tel.: (519) 747-1856
Web Site: http://www.athletica.com
Dasher Board Systems Installer & Mfr

N.A.I.C.S.: 236220
Andrew McRae (CEO)

Subsidiary (US):

Becker Arena Products Inc. (2)
720 Innovation Dr, Shakopee, MN 55379
Tel.: (952) 890-2690
Web Site: http://www.beckerarena.com
Commercial & Institutional Building Construction
N.A.I.C.S.: 236220
Laurie Preston (VP & Dir-HR & Contract Mgmt)

Nilex Inc. (1)
6810 8 Street NW, Edmonton, T6P 0C5, AB, Canada
Tel.: (780) 463-9535
Web Site: http://www.nilex.com
Sales Range: $25-49.9 Million
Emp.: 165
Geosynthetics & Erosion Control Products Mfr
N.A.I.C.S.: 326113
Ian Wilson (Pres & CEO)

FULCRUM IT PARTNERS
161 Bay St Suite 1310, Toronto, M5J 2S1, ON, Canada
Tel.: (808) 164-3628
Web Site: https://fulcrumitp.com
Year Founded: 2022
Holding Company
N.A.I.C.S.: 551112
Kelly Carter (Chief Strategy Officer)

Subsidiaries:

F3 Technology Partners LLC (1)
485 New Park Ave, West Hartford, CT 06110
Tel.: (860) 913-2500
Web Site: http://www.f3partners.com
Wired Telecommunications Carriers
N.A.I.C.S.: 517111

Stoneworks Technologies, Inc. (1)
2212 Gladwin Crescent Unit E9, Ottawa, K1B 5N1, ON, Canada
Tel.: (613) 736-6003
Web Site: http://www.stoneworkstech.com
Rev.: $12,189,078
Emp.: 17
Networking & Computer System Designs
N.A.I.C.S.: 541512
David Chow (Pres & CFO)

FULCRUM UTILITY SERVICES LIMITED
2 Europa View Sheffield Business Park, Sheffield, S9 1XH, United Kingdom
Tel.: (44) 3330146466   Ky
Web Site: http://www.fulcrum.co.uk
FCRM—(LSE)
Rev.: $62,776,715
Assets: $89,378,555
Liabilities: $63,660,877
Net Worth: $25,717,678
Earnings: ($31,218,852)
Emp.: 343
Fiscal Year-end: 03/31/23
Investment Management Service
N.A.I.C.S.: 523940
Terry Dugdale (CEO)

FULGENT SUN INTERNATIONAL (HOLDING) CO., LTD.
No 76 Sec 3 Yunke Road, Douliu, 64064, Taiwan
Tel.: (886) 55514619
Web Site:
    https://www.fulgentsun.com
9802—(TAI)
Rev.: $756,065,191
Assets: $715,338,524
Liabilities: $320,548,260
Net Worth: $394,790,264
Earnings: $106,167,339
Emp.: 37,644
Fiscal Year-end: 12/31/22
Sport Shoe Mfr

Fulgent Sun International (Holding) Co.,
Ltd.—(Continued)

N.A.I.C.S.: 316210
Judy Fang Chu Liao *(CEO & Gen Mgr)*

Subsidiaries:

Eversun Footwear Co., Ltd. **(1)**
Hamlet 2, An Noi Commune Binh Luc
Ditrict, Ha Nam, Vietnam
Tel.: (84) 2263967188
Outdoor Footwear Mfr & Distr
N.A.I.C.S.: 316210

Fujian Laya Outdoor Products Co.,
Ltd. **(1)**
Shuangyang Overseas Chinese Farm Yang-
shan Community, Luojiang District, Quan-
zhou, Fujian, China
Tel.: (86) 59522061931
Sport Shoe Mfr
N.A.I.C.S.: 316210
Liao Fang Chu *(Pres)*

Fujian Sunshine Footwear Co.,
Ltd. **(1)**
Shuangyang Subdistrict, Luojiang District,
Quanzhou, Fujian, China
Tel.: (86) 59522061931
Sport Shoe Mfr
N.A.I.C.S.: 316210

Fulgent Sun Footwear Co., Ltd. **(1)**
Pho Noi Xa Nghia Heip Huyen Tinh, Yen
My, Hung Yen, Vietnam
Tel.: (84) 3213972591
Sport Shoe Mfr
N.A.I.C.S.: 316210

Hubei Sunsmile Footwear Co.,
Ltd. **(1)**
Shenzhen Avenue No 1 Shenzhen Indus-
trial Park, Xiangyang, Hubei, China
Tel.: (86) 7102863991
Sport Shoe Mfr
N.A.I.C.S.: 316210

Laya Max Trading Co., Ltd. **(1)**
2F No 76 Section 3 Yunke Road, Yunlin
County, Douliu, Taiwan
Tel.: (886) 55514619
Sport Shoe Mfr
N.A.I.C.S.: 316210

Laya Outdoor Products Limited **(1)**
5F Dah Sing Life Building 99-105 Des
Voeux Road, Central, China (Hong Kong)
Tel.: (852) 55514619
Sport Shoe Mfr
N.A.I.C.S.: 316210

Lin Wen Chih Sunbow Enterprises
Co., Ltd. **(1)**
24 5km National Highway 2, Phnom Penh,
Kandal, Cambodia
Tel.: (855) 234799199
Sport Shoe Mfr
N.A.I.C.S.: 316210

NGOC Hung Footwear Co., Ltd. **(1)**
Luong Dien Industrial Zone, Tongxi Village
Luong Dien Township Cam Giang County,
Hai Duong, Vietnam
Tel.: (84) 3213789188
Sport Shoe Mfr
N.A.I.C.S.: 316210

Sunny Footwear Co., Ltd. **(1)**
Tengfei Economic Development Zone,
Datong Industrial Park Changting County,
Longyan, Fujian, China
Tel.: (86) 5976819399
Sport Shoe Mfr
N.A.I.C.S.: 316210

FULIN PLASTIC INDUSTRY (CAYMAN) HOLDING CO., LTD.

Km 9 Pham Van Dong St, Hai Thanh
Ward Duong Kinh Dist, Haiphong,
Vietnam
Tel.: (84) 2253860399
Year Founded: 2016
1341—(TAI)
Rev.: $82,280,287
Assets: $68,720,263
Liabilities: $26,094,345

Net Worth: $42,625,918
Earnings: $7,527,715
Emp.: 1,000
Fiscal Year-end: 12/31/23
Cut & Sew Apparel Contractors
N.A.I.C.S.: 315210
Yuan-Lin Wang *(Chm)*

FULING GLOBAL INC.

88 Jintang South Ave, East New Dis-
trict, Wenling, 317509, Zhejiang,
China
Tel.: (86) 576 86623058   **Ky**
Web Site:
http://www.fulingplastics.com
Rev.: $151,113,371
Assets: $134,327,068
Liabilities: $55,258,483
Net Worth: $79,068,585
Earnings: $15,015,220
Emp.: 1,723
Fiscal Year-end: 12/31/19
Disposable Plastic Food Service
Products Mfr
N.A.I.C.S.: 326199
Xinfu Hu *(CEO)*

Subsidiaries:

Direct Link USA LLC **(1)**
6690 Grant Way, Allentown, PA 18106
Tel.: (610) 366-8070
Web Site: http://www.directlinkusallc.com
Injection Product Distr
N.A.I.C.S.: 423450

FULL METAL MINERALS LTD.

Suite 1500 - 409 Granville Street,
Vancouver, V6C 1T2, BC, Canada
Tel.: (604) 484-7855   **BC**
Web Site:
http://www.fullmetalminerals.com
Year Founded: 2003
FMM—(TSXV)
Assets: $912,832
Liabilities: $282,815
Net Worth: $630,017
Earnings: ($1,131,308)
Fiscal Year-end: 05/31/21
Mineral Exploration Services
N.A.I.C.S.: 213114
Alastair Brownlow *(CFO)*

FULL MOON HOLDINGS LIM-ITED

Station Works Station Road,
Northampton, NN6 7PF, Northamp-
tonshire, United Kingdom
Tel.: (44) 1327 841600   **UK**
Web Site:
http://www.laiserperformance.com
Year Founded: 1985
Emp.: 50
Holding Company
N.A.I.C.S.: 551112
Gogol Kafi *(CEO)*

Subsidiaries:

LaserPerformance (Europe)
Limited **(1)**
Station Works Station Road, Long Buckby,
Northampton, NN6 7PF, Northamptonshire,
United Kingdom
Tel.: (44) 1327 841600
Web Site: http://www.laserperformance.com
Emp.: 20
Small Sailboats Mfr & Sales
N.A.I.C.S.: 336612
Farzad Rastegar *(Owner)*

Subsidiary (US):

Quarter Moon Inc. **(2)**
200 Highpoint Ave, Portsmouth, RI 02871
Tel.: (401) 683-0960
Sales Range: $10-24.9 Million
Small Sailboats Mfr & Sales
N.A.I.C.S.: 336612
Richard Gauvin *(Sec)*

FULL TRUCK ALLIANCE CO. LTD.

No 123 Kaifa Avenue, Economic and
Technical Development Zone, Gui-
yang, 550009, Guizhou, China
Tel.: (86) 85183842056   **Ky**
Web Site:
https://ir.fulltruckalliance.com
Year Founded: 2017
YMM—(NYSE)
Rev.: $1,031,661,597
Assets: $5,622,241,808
Liabilities: $465,617,140
Not Worth: $5,156,624,668
Earnings: $62,320,006
Emp.: 6,795
Fiscal Year-end: 12/31/22
Freight Transportation Software De-
velopment Services
N.A.I.C.S.: 541511
Simon Chong Cai *(CFO)*

FULL WANG INTERNATIONAL DEVELOPMENT CO., LTD.

4F-5 No 20 Dalong Rd, West Dist,
Taichung, 40310, Taiwan
Tel.: (886) 423273030
Web Site:
https://www.fwgroup.com.tw
Year Founded: 2008
6219—(TPE)
Rev.: $18,072,789
Assets: $303,087,640
Liabilities: $276,096,332
Net Worth: $26,991,308
Earnings: ($30,568,083)
Emp.: 84
Fiscal Year-end: 12/31/22
Building Construction Services
N.A.I.C.S.: 236220

FULLCAST HOLDINGS CO., LTD.

FORECAST Gotanda WEST 12F
8-9-5 Nishigotanda, Shinagawa-ku,
Tokyo, 141-0031, Japan
Tel.: (81) 345304848
Web Site:
https://www.fullcastholdings.co.jp
Year Founded: 1990
4848—(TKS)
Rev.: $489,025,660
Assets: $276,346,930
Liabilities: $86,441,280
Net Worth: $189,905,650
Earnings: $41,753,010
Emp.: 3,817
Fiscal Year-end: 12/31/23
Human Resources Solutions
N.A.I.C.S.: 541612
Kazuki Sakamaki *(Pres & CEO)*

Subsidiaries:

Deli Art Co., Ltd. **(1)**
Meitetsu Real Estate Takebashi Building 3F
3-15 Kanda Nishikicho, Chiyoda-ku, Tokyo,
101-0054, Japan
Tel.: (81) 355772841
Web Site: https://www.deliart.com
Emp.: 110
Sound System Operating Services
N.A.I.C.S.: 512240

Fullcast Advance Co., Ltd. **(1)**
8-9-5 Nishigotanda, Shinagawa-ku, Tokyo,
141-0031, Japan
Tel.: (81) 345501151
Web Site: https://www.fc-ad.co.jp
Security Guards & Patrol Services
N.A.I.C.S.: 561612

Fullcast Finance Co., Ltd. **(1)**
Forecast Gotanda WEST 12F 8-9-5 Nishig-
otanda, Tokyo, 141-0031, Japan
Tel.: (81) 45304848
Web Site: http://www.fullcast.co.jp
Nondepository Credit Intermediation
N.A.I.C.S.: 522290

Fullcast Technology Co., Ltd. **(1)**

Landmark Tower 21F 2-2-1 Minato-Mirai,
Nishi-ku, Yokohama, 220-8121, Kanagawa,
Japan
Tel.: (81) 452260108
Sales Range: $300-349.9 Million
Temporary Help Service
N.A.I.C.S.: 561320

Globeat Japan Inc. **(1)**
1-14-5 Kamiogi, Suginami-ku, Tokyo, 167-
0043, Japan
Tel.: (81) 353352510
Web Site: http://www.globeat.jp
Emp.: 139
Restaurant Management Services
N.A.I.C.S.: 722511

FULLER, SMITH & TURNER PLC

Pier House 86-93 Strand-on-the-
Green, London, W4 3NN, United
Kingdom
Tel.: (44) 2089962000   **UK**
Web Site: https://www.fullers.co.uk
Year Founded: 1845
FSTA—(LSE)
Rev.: $457,161,046
Assets: $919,923,619
Liabilities: $370,846,596
Net Worth: $549,077,023
Earnings: $11,584,978
Emp.: 5,047
Fiscal Year-end: 03/30/24
Brewery & Pub Operator
N.A.I.C.S.: 312120
Simon Emeny *(CEO)*

Subsidiaries:

Cotswold Inns & Hotels Limited **(1)**
Orchard House Crab Apple Way Vale Busi-
ness Park, Evesham, WR11 1G, United
Kingdom
Tel.: (44) 1386769100
Web Site: http://www.cotswold-inns-
hotels.co.uk
Hotel & Motel Services
N.A.I.C.S.: 721110

Griffin Catering Services Limited **(1)**
Griffin Brewery, Chiswick, London, W4 2QB,
United Kingdom
Tel.: (44) 2089962000
Web Site: http://www.fullers.co.uk
Sales Range: $75-99.9 Million
Emp.: 400
Managed house services
N.A.I.C.S.: 811411

FULLERTON TECHNOLOGY CO., LTD.

5F No 6-3 Baoqiang Rd, Xindian Dist,
Taipei, 23144, Taiwan
Tel.: (886) 289124300
Web Site: http://www.fullerton.com.tw
Year Founded: 1992
6136—(TAI)
Rev.: $16,554,759
Assets: $129,662,312
Liabilities: $3,390,497
Net Worth: $126,271,816
Earnings: $3,395,467
Emp.: 95
Fiscal Year-end: 12/31/23
Telecommunication Servicesb
N.A.I.C.S.: 517810

Subsidiaries:

Ilmagemore Co., Ltd. **(1)**
8F-3 No 95 Minquan Rd, Xindian Dist, New
Taipei City, 231, Taiwan
Tel.: (886) 222190000
Web Site: http://www.imagemore.com
Multimedia Designer & Publishing Services
N.A.I.C.S.: 541430

FULLSHARE HOLDINGS LIM-ITED

Unit 2805 Level 28 Admiralty Centre
Tower 1 18 Harcourt Road, Hong
Kong, China (Hong Kong)
Tel.: (852) 36188462   **Ky**

Web Site: http://www.fullshare.com
0607—(HKG)
Rev.: $3,049,259,288
Assets: $7,754,268,694
Liabilities: $5,210,185,874
Net Worth: $2,544,082,819
Earnings: $57,380,918
Emp.: 8,448
Fiscal Year-end: 12/31/22
Electrical Appliance Mfr & Whslr
N.A.I.C.S.: 335999
Ying Seto *(Sec)*

Subsidiaries:

China High Speed Transmission
Equipment Group Co., Ltd.   **(1)**
Room 1302 13th Floor COFCO Tower No
262 Gloucester Road, Causeway Bay,
China (Hong Kong)   **(100%)**
Tel.: (852) 28918361
Web Site: https://www.chste.com
Sales Range: $1-4.9 Billion
Emp.: 5,962
Transmission Equipment Design, Development & Mfr
N.A.I.C.S.: 333613
Edward Lui Wing Hong *(CFO & Sec)*

Subsidiary (Non-US):

Zhenjiang Tongzhou Propeller Co.,
Ltd.   **(2)**
No7 Si Ping Shan, Dingmao Economic Development Zone, Zhenjiang, Jiangsu,
China   **(76.33%)**
Tel.: (86) 51180962966
Web Site: https://en.zjtpp.com
Marine Propellers Mfr
N.A.I.C.S.: 331529
Zhangjin Long *(Mktg Mgr-Overseas)*

FULLSIX S.P.A.
Viale Jenner 53, 20159, Milan, Italy
Tel.: (39) 02899681
Web Site: https://www.beewize.it
FUL—(ITA)
Sales Range: $75-99.9 Million
Emp.: 595
E-Business & Marketing Services
N.A.I.C.S.: 541613
Marco Benatti *(Chm)*

Subsidiaries:

DMC SRL   **(1)**
Corso Vercelli 40, 20145, Milan,
Italy   **(100%)**
Tel.: (39) 02303241
Sales Range: $25-49.9 Million
Emp.: 170
Advertising Services
N.A.I.C.S.: 541890

OneTOne Research SRL   **(1)**
Corso Vercelli 40, 24145, Milan,
Italy   **(95.15%)**
Tel.: (39) 02303241
Direct Marketing Services
N.A.I.C.S.: 541860

**FULLSUN INTERNATIONAL
HOLDINGS GROUP CO., LIMITED**
Room 2118 21/F Leighton Centre, 77
Leighton Road Causeway Bay,
Causeway Bay, China (Hong Kong)
Tel.: (852) 82282318
Web Site: http://www.fullsun.com.hk
Men's & Women's Casual Wear Designer, Mfr, Distr & Retailer
N.A.I.C.S.: 458110
Kwok Hung Tang *(Exec Dir)*

Subsidiaries:

Radix Development Company
Limited   **(1)**
32nd Fl Billion Ctr, No 8 Cheung Yue St
Cheung Sha, Kowloon, China (Hong
Kong)   **(100%)**
Tel.: (852) 31021228
Holding Company
N.A.I.C.S.: 551112

Sky Fox Investment Limited   **(1)**
32nd Fl Billion Ctr, No 8 Cheung Yue St
Cheung Sha, Kowloon, China (Hong Kong)
Tel.: (852) 34036838
Holding Company
N.A.I.C.S.: 551112

Texcote Technology (International)
Limited   **(1)**
Ste 1A 21FL Tower 1 China Hong Kong
City, 33 Casnton Road, Tsim Sha Tsui,
Kowloon, China (Hong Kong)   **(46%)**
Tel.: (852) 21802618
Web Site: http://www.texcote.hk
Clothing & Furnishings Whslr
N.A.I.C.S.: 424350

Texnology Nano Textile (China)
Limited   **(1)**
32F Billion Plaza No 8 Cheung Yue St, Cheung Sha Wan, Kowloon, China (Hong
Kong)   **(90%)**
Tel.: (852) 757 2633 6988
Textile Product Mills
N.A.I.C.S.: 314999

U-Right (HK) Limited   **(1)**
32nd Fl Billion Ctr, No 8 Cheung Yue St
Cheung Sha, Kowloon, China (Hong
Kong)   **(100%)**
Tel.: (852) 34036828
Management Consulting Services
N.A.I.C.S.: 541618

U-Right Garments Limited   **(1)**
32nd Fl Billion Ctr, No 8 Cheung Yue St
Cheung Sha, Kowloon, China (Hong
Kong)   **(100%)**
Tel.: (852) 34036828
Family Clothing Stores
N.A.I.C.S.: 424350

FULLTECH CO., LTD.
Minami 1-jo Higashi 2-chome 8-2 SR
Building 3F, Chuo Ward, Sapporo,
060-0051, Japan
Tel.: (81) 112223572
Web Site:
    https://www.fulltech1963.com
Year Founded: 1963
6546—(TKS)
Rev.: $90,638,560
Assets: $85,058,730
Liabilities: $39,640,190
Net Worth: $45,418,540
Earnings: $1,694,510
Emp.: 701
Fiscal Year-end: 12/31/23
Automatic Door System Distr
N.A.I.C.S.: 423310
Shigeyuki Furuno *(Chm, Pres &
CEO)*

**FULLTECH FIBER GLASS
CORP.**
28F NO 216 Tunhwa South Road
SEC 2, Taipei, Taiwan
Tel.: (886) 227357658
Web Site: https://www.ffg.com.tw
Year Founded: 1999
1815—(TPE)
Rev.: $121,932,004
Assets: $514,021,145
Liabilities: $278,580,149
Net Worth: $235,440,996
Earnings: ($17,040,662)
Fiscal Year-end: 12/31/20
Blown Glass Product Mfr
N.A.I.C.S.: 327212
Yuan-Pin Chang *(Chm)*

**FULLWEALTH INTERNATIONAL GROUP HOLDINGS
LIMITED**
Shop 11-12 G/F Leung Choy Building
2 44 Ping Fai Path, Yuen Long, New
Territories, China (Hong Kong)
Tel.: (852) 24431029   Ky
Web Site: http://www.fullwealth.hk
Year Founded: 1997

1034—(HKG)
Rev.: $43,455,570
Assets: $39,499,245
Liabilities: $7,125,465
Net Worth: $32,373,780
Earnings: $9,160,748
Emp.: 249
Fiscal Year-end: 12/31/22
Building Construction & Civil Engineering Services
N.A.I.C.S.: 541330
Liu Xinyi *(CEO)*

FULONGMA GROUP CO., LTD.
19F & 27F Guanyinshan International
Business Center No 11, Xiamen, Fujian, China
Tel.: (86) 5928267302
Web Site:
    https://www.fulongmagroup.com
603686—(SHG)
Rev.: $713,177,778
Assets: $820,222,837
Liabilities: $328,229,703
Net Worth: $491,993,134
Earnings: $36,610,072
Fiscal Year-end: 12/31/22
Cleaning Equipment Mfr & Distr
N.A.I.C.S.: 333310

FULTON HOGAN LIMITED
Level 2 15 Sir William Pickering
Drive, PO Box 39185, Christchurch,
8545, Canterbury, New Zealand
Tel.: (64) 33571400
Web Site:
    http://www.fultonhogan.com
Sales Range: $700-749.9 Million
Emp.: 7,000
Civil Construction Services
N.A.I.C.S.: 237990
D. J. Faulkner *(Chm)*

Subsidiaries:

Fulton Hogan Limited - Allied Asphalt
Plant   **(1)**
54 Aerodrome Road, Mount Maunganui,
Tauranga, 3143, New Zealand
Tel.: (64) 7 575 9015
Construction Materials Mfr
N.A.I.C.S.: 327120

Fulton Hogan Limited - Bay of Plenty
Plant   **(1)**
Hewletts Rd Mount Maunganui, Tauranga,
3143, New Zealand
Tel.: (64) 7 575 0067
Web Site: http://www.fultonhogan.com
Emp.: 7
Construction Materials Mfr
N.A.I.C.S.: 327120
Aaron Gill *(Mgr)*

Fulton Hogan Limited - Burnham
Facility   **(1)**
Davis Rd Burnham Camp, Christchurch,
7600, New Zealand
Tel.: (64) 3 347 6572
Construction Materials Mfr
N.A.I.C.S.: 327120

Fulton Hogan Limited - Canterbury
Bagging Plant   **(1)**
333 Pound Road, Yaldhurst, Christchurch,
8441, New Zealand
Tel.: (64) 3 349 4179
Construction Materials Mfr
N.A.I.C.S.: 327120

Fulton Hogan Limited - Miners Road
Asphalt Plant   **(1)**
Miners Road, Yaldhurst, Christchurch, 8011,
New Zealand
Tel.: (64) 3 344 5614
Construction Materials Mfr
N.A.I.C.S.: 327120

Fulton Hogan Limited - Nelson Bitumen Plant   **(1)**
Carkeek Street Port Nelson Private Bag 1,
Nelson, 7042, New Zealand
Tel.: (64) 3 548 0550

Construction Materials Mfr
N.A.I.C.S.: 327120

Fulton Hogan Limited - Northland
Plant   **(1)**
21 Hewlett Street Port, Whangarei, 0110,
New Zealand
Tel.: (64) 9 470 0700
Web Site: http://www.fultonhogan.com
Emp.: 140
Construction Materials Mfr
N.A.I.C.S.: 327120
Keith Cocking *(Mgr)*

Fulton Hogan Limited - Papakura
Facility   **(1)**
86 Grove Rd, Papakura, Auckland, 2110,
New Zealand
Tel.: (64) 9 296 7195
Construction Materials Mfr
N.A.I.C.S.: 327120

Fulton Hogan Limited - Renwick
Plant   **(1)**
Pak Lims Road, Renwick, 7206, New Zealand
Tel.: (64) 3 572 8013
Construction Materials Mfr
N.A.I.C.S.: 327120

Fulton Hogan Limited - Southland
Plant   **(1)**
131 Bond Street, Invercargill, New Zealand
Tel.: (64) 3 218 7558
Construction Materials Mfr
N.A.I.C.S.: 327120

Fulton Hogan Limited - Warrnambool
Plant   **(1)**
Koroit Street, Warrnambool, 3280, VIC,
Australia
Tel.: (61) 3 5562 9038
Construction Materials Mfr
N.A.I.C.S.: 327120

Fulton Hogan Limited - Wellington
Plant   **(1)**
Hebden Crescent Belmont, Lower Hutt,
New Zealand
Tel.: (64) 4 565 0127
Construction Materials Mfr
N.A.I.C.S.: 327120

Pioneer Road Services Pty. Ltd.   **(1)**
Ste 1202 Level 12 Flinders Tower, World
Trade Centre, Melbourne, 3005, VIC, Australia
Tel.: (61) 39628080
Web Site: http://www.fultonhogan.com
Sales Range: $150-199.9 Million
Emp.: 1,000
Road Construction, Maintenance & Resurfacing Services; Joint Venture of Royal
Dutch Shell plc (50%) & Fulton Hogan Ltd.
(50%)
N.A.I.C.S.: 237310

FULTON INSURANCE AGENCIES LTD.
38 Young St, Truro, B2N 3W4, NS,
Canada
Tel.: (902) 895-3686
Web Site: http://fultonins.ca
Year Founded: 1936
Rev.: $20,000,000
Emp.: 10
Insurance Agency Services
N.A.I.C.S.: 524210
Adam Wyllie *(Pres)*

FULTRA SAPI DE CV
Miguel Aleman 1000 La Talaverna,
67110, Guadalupe, Nuevo Leon,
Mexico
Tel.: (52) 8183108460   MX
Web Site: https://fultra.mx
Year Founded: 2012
Truck Transportation Services
N.A.I.C.S.: 333924
Jorge Martinez *(CEO)*

Subsidiaries:

East Manufacturing Corp.   **(1)**
1871 SR 44, Randolph, OH 44265
Tel.: (330) 325-9921

Fultra SAPI de CV—(Continued)

Web Site: http://www.eastmfg.com
Sales Range: $25-49.9 Million
Emp.: 200
Mfr of Trailers
N.A.I.C.S.: 423120
Bill Wallace (Mgr-Sls-Northeast)

FULU HOLDINGS LIMITED

B2 Optics Valley Financial Port East
Lake High-tech Zone, Wuhan, Hubei,
China
Tel.: (86) 4000012806　　　**Ky**
Web Site: http://www.fulu.com
Year Founded: 2009
2101—(HKG)
Holding Company
N.A.I.C.S.: 551112
Wei Ren (CTO)

FULUHASHI EPO CORPORA-TION

A-PLACE Kanayama 6F 1-14-18 Ka-
nayama, Naka-ku, Nagoya, 460-
0022, Aichi, Japan
Tel.: (81) 52 324 9088
Web Site: http://www.fuluhashi.co.jp
Year Founded: 1947
Recycling & Environmental Services
N.A.I.C.S.: 423930
Naohiko Yamaguchi (Pres)

Subsidiaries:

FULUHASHI CORPORATION (VIET-
NAM) LTD.　　　　　　　　(1)
Lot G10 XN06 Dai An Industrial Zone ex-
pansion Lai Cach Ward, Cam Giang Dis-
trict, Hai Duong, Vietnam
Tel.: (84) 3203555177
Material Recycling Services
N.A.I.C.S.: 423940

Fuluhashi Corporation (Thailand)
Ltd　　　　　　　　　　　　(1)
Pinthong Industrial Estate 1 789/8 Moo 1
Nongkham, Si Racha, 20230, Chonburi,
Thailand
Tel.: (66) 382963657
Web Site: http://www.fuluhashi.co.th
Pallet Mfr & Distr
N.A.I.C.S.: 321920

Kawasaki Biomass Power Generation
Co., Ltd.　　　　　　　　　(1)
12-6 Ogimachi, Kawasaki, 2100867,
Japan　　　　　　　　　　(13%)
Tel.: (81) 897372142
Emp.: 50
Eletric Power Generation Services
N.A.I.C.S.: 221117

FULUM GROUP HOLDINGS LIMITED

15/F Luk Hop Industrial Building 8
Luk Hop Street San Po Kong, Kow-
loon, China (Hong Kong)
Tel.: (852) 3 667 7222　　　**Ky**
Web Site: http://www.fulumgroup.com
Year Founded: 1992
1443—(HKG)
Rev.: $187,030,545
Assets: $128,457,502
Liabilities: $112,762,313
Net Worth: $15,695,189
Earnings: ($6,341,818)
Emp.: 1,868
Fiscal Year-end: 03/31/22
Holding Company
N.A.I.C.S.: 551112
Wai Yeung (Co-Founder, Chm &
CEO)

Subsidiaries:

Central Dynamic International
Limited　　　　　　　　　(1)
901 9/F Heng Ngai Jewelry Center 4 Hok
Yuen Street East, Hung Hom, Kowloon,
China (Hong Kong)
Tel.: (852) 27226651

Web Site:
https://www.dynamicinternational.hk
Jewelry Product Distr
N.A.I.C.S.: 423940

Fulum Food (International)
Limited　　　　　　　　　(1)
15th Floor Liuhe Industrial Building 8 Liuhe
Street, San Po Kong, Kowloon, China
(Hong Kong)
Tel.: (852) 21520196
Web Site: http://www.flf.com.hk
Restaurant Operators
N.A.I.C.S.: 722511

FUMAKILLA LIMITED

11 Kanda Mikuracho, Chiyoda-ku,
Tokyo, 101-8606, Japan
Tel.: (81) 332525941
Web Site: https://www.fumakilla.co.jp
4998—(TKS)
Rev.: $447,311,920
Assets: $412,239,260
Liabilities: $243,010,040
Net Worth: $169,229,220
Earnings: $9,101,970
Emp.: 526
Fiscal Year-end: 03/31/24
Agricultural Chemical Mfr
N.A.I.C.S.: 325320
Kazuaki Ohshimo (Pres)

Subsidiaries:

Fumakilla America, S.A. DE C.V.　(1)
Insurgentes Sur No 1883 Ofiice 602, Dis-
trito Federal, Mexico, 01020, Mexico
Tel.: (52) 5555639866
Web Site: http://www.fumakilla.co.jp
Emp.: 10
Agricultural Chemical Mfr
N.A.I.C.S.: 325320
Tepsuo Takamura (Dir)

Fumakilla Malaysia Berhad　　(1)
Plot No 256 Tingkat Perusahaan 5 Ka-
wasan Perindustrian Peral 2, 13600, Perai,
Pulau Pinang, Malaysia
Tel.: (60) 43883777
Web Site:
http://www.texchemfamilycare.com
Household Insecticides Mfr
N.A.I.C.S.: 325320
Li-lian Foo (Mgr-Sls & Mktg)

Subsidiary (Non-US):

Technopia (Thailand) Ltd.　　(2)
323 Moo 6 Ratchasima-Chokchai Rd Nong
Rawiang Muang, 30000, Nakhon
Ratchasima, Thailand
Tel.: (66) 44212990
Web Site:
http://www.texchemfamilycare.com
Mosquito Coils & Insecticides Mfr
N.A.I.C.S.: 325320

P.T. Fumakilla Indonesia　　(1)
Jl Cilandak No 96, Jakarta, 12430, Indone-
sia
Tel.: (62) 217668341
Agricultural Chemical Mfr
N.A.I.C.S.: 325320

PT Technopia Jakarta　　　(1)
Jalan Terusan Interchange Anggadita, Klari,
41371, Karawang, Jawa Barat,
Indonesia　　　　　　　(70%)
Tel.: (62) 267432121
Mosquito Coils Mfr
N.A.I.C.S.: 325320

FUNAI ELECTRIC CO., LTD.

7-7-1 Nakagaito, Daito, Osaka, 574-
0013, Japan
Tel.: (81) 728704303
Web Site: http://www2.funai.co.jp
Year Founded: 1961
6839—(TKS)
Rev.: $810,857,250
Assets: $648,163,110
Liabilities: $178,759,980
Net Worth: $469,403,130
Earnings: ($21,934,640)
Emp.: 2,166

Fiscal Year-end: 03/31/20
Audio-Visual Equipment, Telecommu-
nications Products Mfr
N.A.I.C.S.: 334310
Yoshiaki Harada (Chm)

Subsidiaries:

Chugoku Funai Electric Co., Ltd.　(1)
387-2 Ashihara Kamo-cho, Fukuyama, 720-
2417, Hiroshima, Japan　　　(80%)
Tel.: (81) 849723110
Web Site: http://www2.funai.co.jp
Sales Range: $25-49.9 Million
Emp.: 40
Loudspeaker Mtr
N.A.I.C.S.: 334310

F.G.S. Co., Ltd.　　　　　(1)
1 16 22 Morinomiya Chuoo Chuoo Ku,
Osaka, 43836, Japan　　　　(100%)
Tel.: (81) 669665380
Web Site: http://www.funaiusa.com
Sales Range: $25-49.9 Million
Emp.: 5
N.A.I.C.S.: 334310
Yukio Fukuda (Pres)

FUNAI ELECTRIC EUROPE Sp.
z.o.o.　　　　　　　　　　(1)
17 stycznia 45b, 67-100, Warsaw, Poland
Tel.: (48) 683882605
Sales Range: $50-74.9 Million
Emp.: 7
Consumer Electronic Goods Mfr
N.A.I.C.S.: 334310
Yasuhito Ebine (Mng Dir)

Unit (Non-US):

FUNAI ELECTRIC EUROPE Sp.
z.o.o. - French Business Unit　(2)
Bat le Sysley - Paris Nord 2 23 Allee des
Impressionistes, BP 66169, Villepinte,
95978, Roissy-en-France, France
Tel.: (33) 1493896 70
Electronic Components Mfr
N.A.I.C.S.: 334419

FUNAI ELECTRIC EUROPE Sp.
z.o.o. - German Business Unit　(2)
Boschstr 23a, 22761, Hamburg, Germany
Tel.: (49) 40 386037 0
Sales Range: $25-49.9 Million
Emp.: 7
Electronic Components Mfr
N.A.I.C.S.: 334419
Yasuhito Ebine (Gen Mgr)

Unit (Domestic):

FUNAI ELECTRIC EUROPE Sp.
z.o.o. - Polish Business Unit　(2)
17 Stycznia 45 Zephirus Building Ground
Floor, 02-146, Warsaw, Poland
Tel.: (48) 2260721 92
Web Site: http://www.funaiworld.com
Sales Range: $25-49.9 Million
N.A.I.C.S.: 334419
Mariusz Zbiciak (Gen Mgr)

Division (Non-US):

Funai Deutschland　　　　(2)
Bosch Strasse 23a, 22761, Hamburg,
Germany　　　　　　　　(100%)
Tel.: (49) 403860370
Web Site: http://www.funai.de
Sales Range: $25-49.9 Million
Audio & Visual Equipment Mfr
N.A.I.C.S.: 334310

Funai (Thailand) Co., Ltd.　　(1)
835 Moo 15 Pakchong-Lumsompung Road,
Tambon Chantuek Amphur Pakchon, Nak-
hon Ratchasima, 30130, Thailand
Tel.: (66) 44310002
Web Site: http://www.funaiworld.com
Sales Range: $200-249.9 Million
Emp.: 580
Audio & Visual Equipment Mfr
N.A.I.C.S.: 334310

Funai Corporation, Inc.　　(1)
201 Route 17 N, Rutherford, NJ 07070
Tel.: (201) 288-2063
Web Site: http://www.funai-corp.com
Seller & Marketer of Consumer Electronics
N.A.I.C.S.: 423690

Subsidiary (Domestic):

Funai Service Corporation　　(2)
2425 Spiegel Dr, Groveport, OH 43125
Tel.: (614) 497-2689
Web Site: http://www.funaiservicecorp.com
Electronic Appliances Mfr & Distr
N.A.I.C.S.: 335220

P&F USA　　　　　　　　(2)
3015 Windward Plz Ste 100, Atlanta, GA
30005
Tel.: (678) 319-0439
Television Whslr
N.A.I.C.S.: 449210

Funai Electric (H.K.) Ltd.　　(1)
Unit 10 A 11th FlloorTower 2 Ever Gain
Plaza, 88 Container Port Road, Kwai
Chung, NT, China (Hong Kong)　(100%)
Tel.: (852) 26123300
Web Site: http://www.funaiworld.com
Emp.: 110
Audio & Visual Equipment Mfr
N.A.I.C.S.: 334310

Subsidiary (Domestic):

H.F.T. Industrial Ltd.　　　(2)
Unit 8-9 11F Tower2 Ever Gain Plaza 88
Container Port Road, Kwai Chung, China
(Hong Kong)
Tel.: (852) 26123300
Web Site: http://www.funai.jp.com
Audio & Video Equipment Mfr
N.A.I.C.S.: 334310

Funai Electric (Malasiya) Sdn.
Bhd.　　　　　　　　　　(1)
Plo 405 Jalan Perak Empat Pasir Gudang
Industrial Estate, PO Box 71, 81707, Pasir
Gudang, Johor Darul Takzim, Malaysia
Tel.: (60) 7 251 8381
Web Site: http://www.funaiworld.com
Sales Range: $200-249.9 Million
Emp.: 1,000
Audio & Video Equipment Mfr
N.A.I.C.S.: 334310

Funai Electric Advanced Applied
Technology Research Institute
Inc.　　　　　　　　　　　(1)
TCI 37A 2-1-6 Sengen, Tsukuba, 305 0047,
Ibaraki, Japan
Tel.: (81) 298866500
Web Site: http://www.funaiworld.com
Electronics & Audio & Video Equipment Re-
search & Development
N.A.I.C.S.: 334310

Subsidiary (Non-US):

Broadtec TV R&D Center Sdn.
Bhd.　　　　　　　　　　(2)
G-08 & G-10 Block B Permas Mall Jalan
Permas Utara, Bandar Baru Permas Jaya,
81750, Masai, Johor, Malaysia
Tel.: (60) 7 387 9704
Emp.: 82
Electric Component Research & Develop-
ment Services
N.A.I.C.S.: 541715
Zainuddin Adan (Gen Mgr)

Funai Electric Cebu, Inc.　　(1)
Block 2 Lot 2-5, Sinulog Drive MEPZ II Ba-
sak, Lapu-Lapu, 6015, Cebu, Philippines
Tel.: (63) 323491800
Electric Equipment Mfr
N.A.I.C.S.: 335999

Funai Electric Philippines Inc.　(1)
Phasa2-A BLK 1-LOT 3 4and5 Lima Tech-
nology Center, Lipa, 4217, Batangas, Phil-
ippines
Tel.: (63) 434556945
Electric Equipment Mfr
N.A.I.C.S.: 335999

Funai Electric R&D (Shenzhen) Co.,
Ltd.　　　　　　　　　　(1)
B303 Technology Building II 1057 Nanhai
Road, Nanshan District, Shenzhen, 518067,
China
Tel.: (86) 75586271026
Electric Equipment Mfr
N.A.I.C.S.: 335999

Funai General Service Co., Ltd.　(1)
1-16-22 Chuo Morinomiya, Chuo-ku, Osaka,

540-0003, Japan
Tel.: (81) 669665380
Electric Equipment Mfr
N.A.I.C.S.: 335999

Funai Lexington Technology
Corporation **(1)**
700 Setzer Way, Lexington, KY 40508-1187
Tel.: (859) 550-2070
Web Site: http://www.funailex.com
Thermal Inkjet Microfluidics Mfr
N.A.I.C.S.: 325910

Funai Service Co., Ltd. **(1)**
3rd floor Nagata SK Park Building 3-4-2-3
Nagatahigashi, Higasi-Osaka City, Osaka,
577-0012, Japan **(100%)**
Tel.: (81) 667463303
Web Site: http://www.funai-service.co.jp
Electronics Service & Repair
N.A.I.C.S.: 811210
Kenji Chiaya *(Pres & CEO)*

Funai Techo-Systems Co., Ltd. **(1)**
7 7 1 Nakagaito, Daito City, Osaka,
5740016, Japan **(100%)**
Tel.: (81) 667463303
Web Site: http://www.funaiservice.info
Audio & Video Equipment Manufacturing
N.A.I.C.S.: 334310

Funai Trading Corp. **(1)**
9765 Marconi Dr Ste 106A, San Diego, CA
92154
Tel.: (619) 423-4618
Electric Equipment Mfr
N.A.I.C.S.: 335999

FUNAI SOKEN HOLDINGS IN-CORPORATED
4-4-10 Kitahama, Chuo-ku, Osaka,
541-0041, Japan
Tel.: (81) 662320271
Web Site: https://hd.funaisoken.co.jp
Year Founded: 1970
9757—(TKS)
Rev.: $200,207,420
Assets: $224,263,790
Liabilities: $41,866,450
Net Worth: $182,397,340
Earnings: $36,875,090
Emp.: 1,535
Fiscal Year-end: 12/31/23
Holding Company
N.A.I.C.S.: 551112
Masaru Sumitomo *(Exec Officer)*

Subsidiaries:

Funai Consulting Shanghai, Inc. **(1)**
Room 18C Mega World Trade Building No
369 Jiangsu Road, Changning District,
Shanghai, 200050, China
Tel.: (86) 2152401398
Web Site: https://www.funaisoken.com.cn
Management Consulting Services
N.A.I.C.S.: 541611
Yoshizumi Nakano *(Pres)*

Funai Consulting, Inc. **(1)**
1-6 Marunouchi 6 Nippon Seimei
Marunouchi Building 21st Floor, Chiyoda-ku,
Tokyo, 100-0005, Japan
Tel.: (81) 36 212 2921
Web Site: http://www.funaisoken.co.jp
Business Management Consulting Services
N.A.I.C.S.: 541611
Kyohei Ideguchi *(Sr Mng Exec Officer)*

Funai Soken Corporate Relations,
Inc. **(1)**
6th floor Shinfushimimachi Bldg 4-4-10,
Fushimi-machi Chuo-ku, Osaka, 541-0044,
Japan
Tel.: (81) 661257116
Web Site: http://www.fcr.funaisoken.co.jp
Business Support Services
N.A.I.C.S.: 561499
Hitoshi Nagira *(Pres)*

Funai Soken Digital Inc. **(1)**
21st Floor Life Marunouchi Building
1-6-6, Marunouchi Chiyoda-ku, Tokyo, 100-0005, Japan
Tel.: (81) 120911610
Web Site: https://www.fsdg.co.jp
Emp.: 333

Digital Technology Services
N.A.I.C.S.: 518210

Funai Soken Logistics, Inc. **(1)**
1-6-6 Marunouchi Nihon Seimei Marunouchi
Building 22nd Floor, Chiyoda-ku, Tokyo,
Japan
Tel.: (81) 36 212 2936
Web Site: https://www.f-logi.com
Logistics Consulting Servies
N.A.I.C.S.: 541614
Shigehiro Kan *(Pres & CEO)*

HR Force, Inc. **(1)**
2-5-5 Hamamatsucho PMO Hamamatsucho
9th floor, Minato-ku, Tokyo, 105-0013, Ja-pan
Tel.: (81) 362122230
Web Site: https://www.hr-force.co.jp
Employment Recruiting Services
N.A.I.C.S.: 561311

Seichou Senryaku Inc. **(1)**
6-17-9 Hongo, Bunkyo-ku Hongo Tsuna
Building 7th floor, Tokyo, 113-0033, Japan
Tel.: (81) 358010172
Web Site: https://www.ss-kk.co.jp
Financial Services
N.A.I.C.S.: 541611

FUNCTION INTERNATIONAL PUBLIC COMPANY LIMITED
313 Charoen Phatthana Rd, Bang
Chan Khlong Sam Wa, Bangkok,
10510, Thailand
Tel.: (66) 25406263
Web Site:
　　https://www.functioninter.co.th
Year Founded: 1997
FTI—(THA)
Rev.: $22,731,237
Assets: $31,104,646
Liabilities: $10,198,610
Net Worth: $20,906,036
Earnings: $1,276,016
Emp.: 229
Fiscal Year-end: 12/31/23
Water Filter Mfr
N.A.I.C.S.: 334419
Naris Chaiyasoot *(Chm)*

FUND CREATION GROUP CO., LTD.
Hanzomon First Bldg 5F 1-4 Koji-machi, Chiyoda-ku, Tokyo, 102-0083,
Japan
Tel.: (81) 354135535
Web Site: http://www.fc-group.co.jp
3266—(TKS)
Rev.: $29,324,240
Assets: $40,200,300
Liabilities: $20,036,340
Net Worth: $20,163,960
Earnings: $1,297,470
Fiscal Year-end: 11/30/23
Real Estate Asset Management &
Investment Banking Services
N.A.I.C.S.: 523150
Katsuhiro Tajima *(Pres & CEO)*

Subsidiaries:

FC Investment Advisers Co., Ltd. **(1)**
2-10-3 Kojimachi Ri Nau Kojimachi 2F
Chiyoda-ku, Tokyo, 102-0083, Japan
Tel.: (81) 332634161
Investment Banking Services
N.A.I.C.S.: 523150

FUND ESTATES REIT
Tsarigradsko shose 159, 1784, Sofia,
1784, Bulgaria
Tel.: (359) 29625405
Web Site: http://www.fundestates.bg
FUES—(BUL)
Sales Range: Less than $1 Million
Real Estate Investment Services
N.A.I.C.S.: 531190

FUNDACION BANCARIA CAIXA D'ESTALVIS I PEN-

SIONS DE BARCELONA, LA CAIXA
Avinguda Diagonal 621-629, 08028,
Barcelona, Spain
Tel.: (34) 902223040 　　ES
Web Site:
　　http://www.fundacionbancaria.org
Year Founded: 1990
Banking Foundation
N.A.I.C.S.: 813910
Juan Jose Lopez Burniol *(Vice Chm)*

Subsidiaries:

Criteria Caixa, S.A. **(1)**
Avenida Diagonal 621-629, 08028, Barce-lona, Spain **(100%)**
Tel.: (34) 934092121
Web Site: http://www.criteriacaixa.com
Rev.: $3,527,775,561
Assets: $30,334,535,966
Liabilities: $8,819,313,726
Net Worth: $21,515,222,240
Earnings: $2,975,879,534
Fiscal Year-end: 12/31/2017
Investment Holding Company; Banking,
Real Estate & Equity Investments
N.A.I.C.S.: 551112
Isidro Faine Casas *(Chm)*

Holding (Domestic):

Saba Infraestructuras, S.A. **(2)**
Avenida Parc Logistic 22-26, 08040, Barce-lona, Spain **(99.5%)**
Tel.: (34) 93 557 5500
Web Site: http://www.saba.eu
Holding Company; Automobile Parking Fa-cilities Developer & Operator
N.A.I.C.S.: 551112
Salvador Alemany *(Pres)*

Subsidiary (Non-US):

Indigo Park Deutschland GmbH **(3)**
Friedrichstrasse 185-190, 10117, Berlin,
Germany
Tel.: (49) 30 20608680
Web Site: http://www.vincipark.de
Sales Range: $25-49.9 Million
Emp.: 10
Motor Vehicle Parking Management Solu-tions
N.A.I.C.S.: 812930
Adham Azzam *(Mng Dir)*

Indigo Park Services UK Ltd. **(3)**
Oak House Reeds Crescent, Watford,
WD24 4QP, Herts, United Kingdom
Tel.: (44) 1908 223 500
Web Site: http://www.vincipark.co.uk
Sales Range: $25-49.9 Million
Motor Vehicle Parking Management Solu-tions
N.A.I.C.S.: 812930
Gary Pickard *(Dir-Fin)*

Subsidiary (Domestic):

Karspace Management Ltd. **(4)**
Oak House Reeds Crescent, Watford,
WD24 4QP, Herts, United Kingdom
Tel.: (44) 1908 223500
Motor Vehicle Parking Management Solu-tions
N.A.I.C.S.: 812930

Meteor Parking Ltd. **(4)**
Meteor House, Crawley, RH10 9PF, United
Kingdom
Tel.: (44) 1293 551557
Web Site:
　　http://www.meteormeetandgreet.com
Automobile Parking Services
N.A.I.C.S.: 812930
Steve Waller *(Dir-Sls & Mktg)*

Subsidiary (Non-US):

Indigo Park Slovakia, s.r.o. **(3)**
Pri trati 25/A, 82106, Bratislava, Slovakia
Tel.: (421) 2 381 048 19
Web Site: http://www.vincipark.sk
Motor Vehicle Parking Management Solu-tions
N.A.I.C.S.: 812930
Mario Grega *(CEO)*

Subsidiary (Domestic):

Saba Aparcamientos, S.A. **(3)**
Avenida Parc Logistic 22-26, 08040, Barce-lona, Spain
Tel.: (34) 93 557 5500
Web Site: http://www.saba.es
Parking Garage Operator
N.A.I.C.S.: 812930
Jordi Diez *(Gen Dir)*

FUNDAMENTA REAL ESTATE AG
Poststrasse 4a, 6300, Zug, Switzer-land
Tel.: (41) 414442222
Web Site:
　　https://www.fundamentarealestate.ch
FREN—(SWX)
Sales Range: Less than $1 Million
Real Estate Agency Services
N.A.I.C.S.: 531210
Daniel Kuster *(CEO)*

FUNDELY CO., LTD.
3F NS3 Building 2-51-3 Akabane
Kita-ku, Tokyo, 115-0045, Japan
Tel.: (81) 3 5249 5080
Web Site: http://www.fundely.co.jp
3137—(TKS)
Sales Range: $10-24.9 Million
Emp.: 68
Healthy Meal Delivery Services &
Mail Order
N.A.I.C.S.: 492210
Kosuke Abe *(Founder & Pres)*

FUNDING CIRCLE HOLDINGS PLC
71 Queen Victoria Street, London,
EC4V 4AY, United Kingdom
Tel.: (44) 2074019111
Web Site:
　　https://corporate.fundingcircle.com
FCA—(DEU)
Rev.: $184,890,750
Assets: $462,528,000
Liabilities: $120,450,000
Net Worth: $342,078,000
Earnings: ($46,132,350)
Fiscal Year-end: 12/31/22
Other Financial Vehicles
N.A.I.C.S.: 525990
Samir Desai *(Founder & CEO)*

Subsidiaries:

Funding Circle Deutschland
GmbH **(1)**
Bergmannstrasse 72, 10961, Berlin, Ger-many
Tel.: (49) 303 119 8631
Web Site: https://www.fundingcircle.com
Loan Services
N.A.I.C.S.: 522390

Funding Circle Espana S.L. **(1)**
Calle Claudio Coello 124 Floor 7, 28006,
Madrid, Spain
Tel.: (34) 91 198 0962
Web Site: https://www.fundingcircle.com
Loan Services
N.A.I.C.S.: 522390

Funding Circle Nederland B.V. **(1)**
Strawinskylaan 3075 Atrium, 1077 ZX, Am-sterdam, Netherlands
Tel.: (31) 20 808 5560
Web Site: https://www.fundingcircle.com
Loan Services
N.A.I.C.S.: 522390

FUNDVISER CAPITAL (INDIA) LTD.
602 Floor 6th Plot 952/954 Orbit
Plaza CHS New Prabhadevi Road,
Nagusayajiwadi Prabhadevi, Mumbai,
400 025, Maharashtra, India
Tel.: (91) 2224320931
Web Site:
　　https://www.fundvisercapital.in

FUNDVISER CAPITAL (INDIA) LTD.

Fundviser Capital (India) Ltd.—(Continued)
Year Founded: 1985
530197—(BOM)
Rev.: $26,612
Assets: $783,578
Liabilities: $7,032
Net Worth: $776,546
Earnings: ($1,210)
Fiscal Year-end: 03/31/23
Dye Mfr & Distr
N.A.I.C.S.: 325130

FUNENG ORIENTAL EQUIP-MENT TECHNOLOGY CO., LTD.

Room 209 2nd Floor Building 1 Jing-chuang Community Project, Zumiao street Chancheng District, Foshan, 523039, Guangdong, China
Tel.: (86) 76922282669
Web Site: http://www.songde.com.cn
Year Founded: 1997
300173—(CHIN)
Rev.: $113,301,859
Assets: $551,755,173
Liabilities: $303,536,588
Net Worth: $248,218,585
Earnings: $1,775,704
Fiscal Year-end: 12/31/20
Packaging & Printing Machinery Mfr
N.A.I.C.S.: 333993
Yu Jing (Chm)

Subsidiaries:

Dongguan Chaoye Precision Equip-ment Co., Ltd. (1)
No 83 Shangxi Yixi 1st Road, Shangjia City Industrial Park, Dongguan, 523045, Guangdong, China
Tel.: (86) 76922285276
Web Site: http://en.supercom.com.cn
Emp.: 900
Power Battery Equipment Mfr
N.A.I.C.S.: 335999

FUNNY SOFTWARE LIMITED

407 Prabhat Kiran Building Rajendra Place, New Delhi, 110008, India
Tel.: (91) 11 42283003
Web Site:
http://www.funnysoftwarelimited.com
Rev.: $206,201
Assets: $4,214,955
Liabilities: $854,057
Net Worth: $3,360,898
Earnings: $9,445
Fiscal Year-end: 03/31/18
Software Publisher
N.A.I.C.S.: 513210
Ram Naresh (Exec Dir)

FUNPEP CO., LTD.

Nihonbashi Life Science Building 2
No 503 3-11-5 Nihonbashi-honcho, Chuo-ku, Tokyo, 103-0023, Japan
Tel.: (81) 53154200
Web Site: https://www.funpep.co.jp
Year Founded: 2013
4881—(TKS)
Assets: $17,661,190
Liabilities: $1,347,100
Net Worth: $16,314,090
Earnings: ($6,614,970)
Fiscal Year-end: 12/31/23
Pharmaceutical Product Mfr & Distr
N.A.I.C.S.: 325412
Toshimi Miyoshi (Pres & CEO)

FUNSHINE CULTURE GROUP CO., LTD.

Room 702 Building B Zhonghui Plaza
No 11 Dongzhimen South St, Dongcheng Dist, Beijing, 100010, China
Tel.: (86) 1059786058
Web Site: https://www.fssjart.com

Year Founded: 2002
300860—(CHIN)
Rev.: $95,324,252
Assets: $522,844,003
Liabilities: $55,296,471
Net Worth: $467,547,533
Earnings: $18,941,438
Fiscal Year-end: 12/31/23
Media Advertising Services
N.A.I.C.S.: 541840
Xiaolan Sha (Founder, Chm, Pres & Gen Mgr)

FUNTALK CHINA HOLDINGS LIMITED

21st Floor Block D The Place Tower
No 9 Guanghua Rd, Chaoyang District, Beijing, 100020, China
Tel.: (86) 1057091111
Web Site: http://www.funtalk.cn
Year Founded: 2003
Sales Range: $800-899.9 Million
Emp.: 9,800
Wireless Communications Devices, Accessories & Content Retailer & Distr
N.A.I.C.S.: 517112
Kuo Zhang (Chm)

FUQI INTERNATIONAL, INC.

5th Floor Block 1 Shi Hua Industrial Zone, Chu Zhu Road North, Shenzhen, 518019, Guangdong, China
Tel.: (86) 75525801888
Web Site: http://www.fuqi.com.cn
Year Founded: 2001
Sales Range: $300-349.9 Million
Emp.: 949
Precious Metal Jewelry Designer & Retailer
N.A.I.C.S.: 339910
Yu Kwai Chong (Chm)

Subsidiaries:

Shenzhen Fuqi Jewelry Co., Ltd. (1)
4-6/F 1 Block Shihua Industrial Area, Cuizhu North Road Luohu, Shenzhen, 518019, China
Tel.: (86) 75525801888
Web Site: http://www.fuqi.com.cn
Emp.: 1,200
Designer, Promotion & Sales of High Quality Precious Jewelry
N.A.I.C.S.: 339910
Yu Kwai Chong (Chm, Pres & CEO)

FUQIN FINTECH LIMITED

No 8 Guanghua Dongli Zhonghai Guangchang South Tower 7 th Floor, Chaoyang District, Beijing, 100020, China
Tel.: (86) 10 8018 0588
Web Site:
http://www.fuqinjinrong.com
Year Founded: 2017
Sales Range: $10-24.9 Million
Emp.: 1,980
Automobile Financing Services
N.A.I.C.S.: 522220
Huaishan Cao (Chm)

FURA GEMS INC.

65 Queen Street West Unit 800, Toronto, M5H 2M5, ON, Canada
Tel.: (416) 861-2269
Web Site: http://www.furagems.com
Year Founded: 2006
FURA—(TSXV)
Assets: $34,939,388
Liabilities: $22,169,833
Net Worth: $12,769,555
Earnings: ($21,478,373)
Fiscal Year-end: 12/31/19
Mineral Exploration Services
N.A.I.C.S.: 213115
Devidas Shetty (Pres & CEO)

Subsidiaries:

Fura Services DMCC (1)
26J Almas Tower Jumeirah Lakes Towers, PO Box 126515, Dubai, United Arab Emirates
Tel.: (971) 42408760
Gem Stone Distr
N.A.I.C.S.: 423940

FURAMA LTD.

405 Havelock Road, Singapore, 169633, Singapore
Tel.: (65) 67396470
Web Site: http://www.furama.com
Sales Range: $50-74.9 Million
Emp.: 546
Investment Services & Hotel Operations
N.A.I.C.S.: 523999
Kim Suan Ng (Chm)

FUREASU CO., LTD.

A-PLACE Gotanda 3F 2-27-3 Nishigotanda, Shinagawa-ku, Tokyo, 141-0031, Japan
Tel.: (81) 366329210
Web Site: https://www.fureasu.jp
7062—(TKS)
Rev.: $37,743,100
Assets: $40,915,900
Liabilities: $29,236,030
Net Worth: $11,679,870
Earnings: $383,380
Emp.: 834
Fiscal Year-end: 03/31/24
Chiropractic & Massaging Services
N.A.I.C.S.: 812199

FUREN GROUP PHARMACEU-TICAL CO., LTD.

9F Furen Building No 25 Huayuan Road, Zhengzhou, 450008, Henan, China
Tel.: (86) 37165359177
600781—(SHG)
Rev.: $231,730,125
Assets: $1,278,554,303
Liabilities: $1,161,380,827
Net Worth: $117,173,476
Earnings: ($490,126,451)
Fiscal Year-end: 12/31/21
Pharmaceutical Product Mfr & Distr
N.A.I.C.S.: 325412
Wenchen Zhu (Chm & Gen Mgr)

FURNESS BUILDING SOCIETY

51-55 Duke Street, Barrow-in-Furness, LA14 1RT, Cumbria, United Kingdom
Tel.: (44) 1229824560
Web Site: http://www.furnessbs.co.uk
Year Founded: 1865
Rev.: $33,706,808
Assets: $1,316,598,508
Liabilities: $1,222,866,325
Net Worth: $93,732,182
Earnings: $3,174,072
Emp.: 104
Fiscal Year-end: 12/31/19
Mortgage Lending & Other Financial Services
N.A.I.C.S.: 522310
Susan Jane Heron (Dir-Mktg & Sls)

FURNITURE VILLAGE LIMITED

258 Bath Road, Slough, SL1 4DX, Berkshire, United Kingdom
Tel.: (44) 1753 897720
Web Site:
http://www.furniturevillage.co.uk
Year Founded: 1989
Sales Range: $250-299.9 Million
Emp.: 758
Furniture Product Whslr
N.A.I.C.S.: 423210
Peter Harrison (CEO)

FURNIWEB HOLDINGS LIMITED

Lot 1883 Jalan KPB 9 Kg Bharu Balakong, 43300, Seri Kembangan, Selangor, Malaysia
Tel.: (60) 389612278
Web Site:
http://www.furniweb.com.my
Year Founded: 1987
8480—(HKG)
Rev.: $47,198,520
Assets: $43,508,054
Liabilities: $13,382,020
Net Worth: $30,120,034
Earnings: $2,711,363
Emp.: 631
Fiscal Year-end: 12/31/23
Apparel Product Mfr & Distr
N.A.I.C.S.: 313220
Eng Chuan Cheah (CEO)

Subsidiaries:

Furniweb (Vietnam) Shareholding Company (1)
No 18 Road 3A, Bien Hoa Industrial Zone II, Bien Hoa, Dong Nai, Vietnam
Tel.: (84) 2513832742
Web Site: https://www.fvsc.com.vn
Fabric Mill Product Mfr
N.A.I.C.S.: 313220

Measurement & Verification Pte. Ltd. (1)
8 Boon Lay Way 09-02 TradeHub 21, Singapore, 609964, Singapore
Tel.: (65) 66846640
Web Site: https://www.mnv.com.sg
Energy Management System Services
N.A.I.C.S.: 238220

West Bull Securities Limited (1)
Unit 2701-03 27/F Infinitus Plaza 199 Des Voeux Road, Sheung Wan, Central, China (Hong Kong)
Tel.: (852) 3 896 2968
Web Site: https://www.westbullsec.com.hk
Investment Advisory Services
N.A.I.C.S.: 523999

FURSYS, INC.

311 Ogeum-ro, Songpa-gu, Seoul, Korea (South)
Tel.: (82) 234006386
Web Site: https://www.fursys.com
Year Founded: 1983
016800—(KRS)
Rev.: $292,419,617
Assets: $417,865,081
Liabilities: $55,110,439
Net Worth: $362,754,642
Earnings: $4,507,480
Emp.: 219
Fiscal Year-end: 12/31/22
Office Furniture Mfr
N.A.I.C.S.: 337214
Sang Geun Park (VP & Exec Dir)

FURUBAYASHI SHIKO CO., LTD.

1-12 Ote-dori 3-chome, Chuo-ku, Osaka, 540-0021, Japan
Tel.: (81) 669418561
Web Site: https://www.furubayashi-shiko.co.jp
Year Founded: 1947
3944—(TKS)
Rev.: $126,988,990
Assets: $134,816,350
Liabilities: $67,815,850
Net Worth: $67,000,500
Earnings: $3,112,510
Emp.: 418
Fiscal Year-end: 12/31/23
Packaging Material Mfr & Distr
N.A.I.C.S.: 322219
Takahiro Furubayashi (Chm & Pres)

FURUKAWA CO., LTD.

6-4 Otemachi 2-chome, Chiyoda-ku, Tokyo, 100-8370, Japan
Tel.: (81) 366369501   JP
Web Site:
https://www.furukawakk.co.jp
Year Founded: 1875
5715—(TKS)
Rev.: $1,244,365,550
Assets: $1,717,793,580
Liabilities: $836,865,660
Net Worth: $880,927,920
Earnings: $106,401,170
Emp.: 2,855
Fiscal Year-end: 03/31/24
Holding Company; Industrial, Construction & Mining Machinery, Metals, Electronic Materials, Chemicals, Paint & Fuels
N.A.I.C.S.: 551112
Naohisa Miyakawa *(Pres)*

Subsidiaries:

Furukawa Castec Co., Ltd.   **(1)**
3-5 Shimomato Ashio-machi, Nikko, 321-1506, Tochigi, Japan
Tel.: (81) 28 893 3512
Web Site: https://www.furukawacastec.co.jp
Industrial Machinery Mfr
N.A.I.C.S.: 333248

Furukawa Chemicals Co., Ltd.   **(1)**
3-7-196 Ohno, Nishiyodogawa-ku, Osaka, 555-0043, Japan
Tel.: (81) 664721131
Emp.: 124
Chemicals Mfr
N.A.I.C.S.: 325199

Furukawa Co., Ltd. - Real Estate Division   **(1)**
6-4 Otemachi 2-chome, Chiyoda-ku, Tokyo, 100-8370, Japan
Tel.: (81) 366369509
Web Site: https://www.furukawakk.co.jp
Real Estate Manangement Services
N.A.I.C.S.: 531390

Furukawa Denshi Co., Ltd.   **(1)**
Kodate 20 KamiYoshima, Yoshima-machi, Iwaki, 970-1153, Fukushima, Japan
Tel.: (81) 246362016
Web Site: http://www.furukawa-denshi.co.jp
Sales Range: $50-74.9 Million
Emp.: 238
Arsenic Materials Mfr
N.A.I.C.S.: 325130

Plant (Domestic):

Furukawa Denshi Co., Ltd. - Optical Components Plant   **(2)**
11-10 Minamisakae-cho, Kasukabe, Saitama, Japan
Tel.: (81) 332123967
Web Site: http://www.furukawa-denshi.co.jp
Optical Component Mfr
N.A.I.C.S.: 333310

Subsidiary (Domestic):

Furukawa Denshi Co., Ltd. - Semiconductor Materials Plant   **(2)**
2982 Ashiomachi Tojimo, Nikko, 321-1521, Tochigi, Japan
Tel.: (81) 288932600
Semiconductor Material Mfr
N.A.I.C.S.: 334413

Furukawa Industrial Machinery Systems Co., Ltd.   **(1)**
Tokiwabashi Tower 6-4 2-Chome, Otemachi Chiyoda-ku, Tokyo, 100-8370, Japan
Tel.: (81) 366369512
Web Site: https://www.furukawa-sanki.co.jp
Sales Range: $100-124.9 Million
Emp.: 417
Industrial Machinery Mfr
N.A.I.C.S.: 333914

Subsidiary (Domestic):

Furukawa Industrial Machinery Systems Co., Ltd. - Oyama Unit   **(2)**
1-23-15 Wakagicho, Oyama, 323-8601, Tochigi, Japan
Tel.: (81) 285238650

Industrial Machinery Mfr
N.A.I.C.S.: 333914

Unit (Domestic):

Furukawa Industrial Machinery Systems Co., Ltd. - Tochigi Unit   **(2)**
2245 Omiyacho, Tochigi, 328-0011, Japan
Tel.: (81) 282273200
Web Site: http://www.furukawa-sanki.co.jp
Industrial Machinery Mfr
N.A.I.C.S.: 333914

Furukawa Machinery Asia Sdn. Bhd.   **(1)**
Unit 12-2 Level 12 2 Rio Tower Persiaran Rio Bandar Puteri, 47100, Puchong, Selangor Darul Ehsan, Malaysia
Tel.: (60) 386017601
Truck Machinery Mfr
N.A.I.C.S.: 333924

Furukawa Metals & Resources Co., Ltd.   **(1)**
6-4 Otemachi 2-chome, Chiyoda-ku, Tokyo, 100-8370, Japan
Tel.: (81) 366369527
Web Site: https://www.furukawakk.co.jp
Sales Range: $200-249.9 Million
Emp.: 12
Non-ferrous Metal Smelting Services
N.A.I.C.S.: 331410
Nakayama Noriyasu *(Asst Mgr)*

Furukawa Rock Drill Co., Ltd.   **(1)**
12th floor Tokiwabashi Tower 2-6-4 Otemachi, Chiyoda-ku, Tokyo, 100-8370, Japan
Tel.: (81) 366369521
Web Site:
https://www.furukawarockdrill.co.jp
Sales Range: $1-4.9 Billion
Emp.: 3,000
Construction & Mining Machinery Marketing & Distr
N.A.I.C.S.: 423810
Kiyohito Mitsumura *(Pres)*

Subsidiary (Non-US):

Furukawa Rock Drill (Shanghai) Co., Ltd.   **(2)**
125 Yingjin Street, Jinhui Town Feng Xian District, Shanghai, 201404, China
Tel.: (86) 2157486636
Web Site: http://www.frds.cn
Rock Crushers Mfr
N.A.I.C.S.: 333120

Plant (Domestic):

Furukawa Rock Drill Co., Ltd. - Takasaki Factory   **(2)**
35-1 Aza Nakahashi, Shimanomachi, Takasaki, 370-0015, Gunma, Japan
Tel.: (81) 273523511
Web Site: http://www.furukawarockdrill.co.jp
Construction & Mining Machinery Mfr
N.A.I.C.S.: 333120

Furukawa Rock Drill Co., Ltd. - Yoshii Factory   **(2)**
1058 Yoshii, Yoshii Town, Takasaki, 370-2132, Gunma, Japan
Tel.: (81) 273876111
Web Site: http://www.furukawarockdrill.co.jp
Sales Range: $100-124.9 Million
Emp.: 472
Construction & Mining Machinery Mfr
N.A.I.C.S.: 333120

Subsidiary (Non-US):

Furukawa Rock Drill Europe B.V.   **(2)**
Proostwetering 29, 3543 AB, Utrecht, Netherlands
Tel.: (31) 302412277
Web Site: https://www.frd.eu
Sales Range: $25-49.9 Million
Emp.: 20
Breakers & Crawler Drills Sales
N.A.I.C.S.: 423110

Furukawa Rock Drill Korea Co., Ltd.   **(2)**
70-7 Teoneokgol-ro 165beon-gil Paltan-Myeon, Hwaseong, 18531, Gyeonggi-Do, Korea (South)
Tel.: (82) 313528447
Web Site: http://www.furukawarockdrill.co.jp

Sales Range: $25-49.9 Million
Emp.: 2
Pneumatic Tools, Crawler & Jumbo Drills & Wheel Loader Mfr
N.A.I.C.S.: 333131

Division (US):

Furukawa Rock Drill USA Co., Ltd. - Breaker Division   **(2)**
805 Lake St, Kent, OH 44240
Tel.: (330) 673-5826
Web Site: https://frdusa.com
Demolition Tools Mfr
N.A.I.C.S.: 333991

Furukawa Rock Drill India Pvt. Ltd.   **(1)**
No 116 1st Floor 8th Cross Railway Parallel Road Kumara Park West, Bengaluru, 560 020, India
Tel.: (91) 8023460240
Industrial Machinery Mfr
N.A.I.C.S.: 333248
Sidhartha Sarkar *(Gen Sls Mgr)*

Furukawa Rock Drill Latin America S.A.   **(1)**
Edificio Plaza Real Av Centenario G40 Of 208, Costa del Este, Panama, Panama
Tel.: (507) 271 0917
Web Site: https://www.frd.la
Industrial Machinery Mfr
N.A.I.C.S.: 333248

Furukawa Rock Drill USA, Inc.   **(1)**
805 Lake St, Kent, OH 44240
Tel.: (330) 673-5826
Industrial Machinery Mfr
N.A.I.C.S.: 333248
Caroline Brichford *(VP & Controller)*

Furukawa Unic Corporation   **(1)**
2-6-4 Otemachi, Chiyoda-ku, Tokyo, 100-8370, Japan
Tel.: (81) 366369525
Web Site: http://uniccrane-global.com
Emp.: 419
Cranes Mfr & Distr
N.A.I.C.S.: 333923

Subsidiary (Non-US):

Furukawa Unic (Thailand) Co., Ltd.   **(2)**
1 MD Tower Building 14Fl Soi Bangna-Trad 25uza Bangna Nua, Bangna, Bangkok, 10260, Thailand
Tel.: (66) 2157486636
Web Site: http://www.furukawaunic.co.th
Sales Range: $25-49.9 Million
Emp.: 7
Marine Crane Mfr
N.A.I.C.S.: 333923

Unit (Domestic):

Furukawa Unic Corporation - Sakura Unit   **(2)**
2348 Ota Outer Field, Sakura, 285-8511, Chiba, Japan
Tel.: (81) 434855111
Web Site: http://www.furukawaunic.co.jp
Sales Range: $75-99.9 Million
Emp.: 419
Crane Mfr
N.A.I.C.S.: 333923

Furukawa Unyu Co., Ltd.   **(1)**
3-7-168 Ono, Nishiyodogawa-ku, Osaka, 555-0043, Japan
Tel.: (81) 664726171
Truck Machinery Mfr
N.A.I.C.S.: 333924
Norikazu Ito *(Pres)*

LLC Furukawa Unic Rus   **(1)**
Prospect Mira 105 bldg 1 office 437, vn ter g municipal district Ostankinsky, 129085, Moscow, Russia
Tel.: (7) 8002507111
Truck Machinery Mfr
N.A.I.C.S.: 333924

FURUNO ELECTRIC CO., LTD.
9-52 Ashihara-Cho, Nishinomiya, 662-8580, Hyogo, Japan
Tel.: (81) 798652111   JP
Web Site: https://www.furuno.co.jp
Year Founded: 1951

6814—(TKS)
Rev.: $814,286,500
Assets: $811,159,810
Liabilities: $375,578,570
Net Worth: $435,581,240
Earnings: $44,227,420
Emp.: 3,310
Fiscal Year-end: 02/29/24
Electric Equipment Mfr
N.A.I.C.S.: 334419
Yukio Furuno *(Pres)*

Subsidiaries:

Funotec (Dalian) Co., Ltd.   **(1)**
B6F No 1 Xueyuan Plaza, Dalian, China
Tel.: (86) 41184595168
Web Site: http://www.funotec.cn
Marine Products Distr
N.A.I.C.S.: 423860

Furuno (Cyprus) Ltd.   **(1)**
Kofteros Business Center Office 103 182 Agias Filaxeos, 3083, Limassol, Cyprus
Tel.: (357) 25734466
Web Site: https://www.furuno.com.cy
Marine Products Distr
N.A.I.C.S.: 423860

Furuno (UK) Ltd.   **(1)**
West Building Penner Road, Havant, PO9 1QY, Hampshire, United Kingdom
Tel.: (44) 2392441000
Web Site: https://www.furuno.co.uk
Sales Range: $25-49.9 Million
Transportation Equipment & Supplies Whslr
N.A.I.C.S.: 423860
John William *(Mng Dir)*

Furuno China Co., Limited   **(1)**
Unit C on 7th Floor KC100 No 100 Kwai Cheong Road NT, Kwai Chung, China (Hong Kong)
Tel.: (852) 21653700
Industrial Electronic Product Mfr & Retailer
N.A.I.C.S.: 334419

Furuno Circuitech Co., Ltd.   **(1)**
9-52 Ashihara-cho, Nishinomiya, 662-8580, Hyogo, Japan
Tel.: (81) 798631145
Web Site: http://www.furuno.co.jp
Engineeering Services
N.A.I.C.S.: 541330

Furuno Danmark A/S   **(1)**
Hammerholmen 44-48, 2650, Hvidovre, Denmark
Tel.: (45) 36774500
Web Site: https://www.furuno.dk
Sales Range: $25-49.9 Million
Emp.: 40
Electronic Parts & Equipment Whslr
N.A.I.C.S.: 423690
Freddie Hansen *(CEO)*

Furuno Deutschland GmbH   **(1)**
Siemensstrasse 31-33, 25462, Rellingen, Germany
Tel.: (49) 41018380
Web Site: https://www.furuno.de
Sales Range: $25-49.9 Million
Emp.: 35
Transportation Equipment & Supplies Whslr
N.A.I.C.S.: 423860
Claus B. Frederiksen *(Mng Dir)*

Furuno Dongguan Co., Ltd.   **(1)**
246 Bubugao RD, Jiangbei Wusha Changan, Dongguan, 523859, Guangdong, China
Tel.: (86) 76985075999
Industrial Electronic Product Mfr & Retailer
N.A.I.C.S.: 334419

Furuno Electric (Malaysia) Sdn. Bhd.   **(1)**
K03-03-13 Level 3 Tower 3 UOA Business Park No 1, Jalan Pengaturcara U1/51A Seksyen U1, 40150, Shah Alam, Selangor, Malaysia
Tel.: (60) 355693613
Web Site: https://www.furuno.my
Marine Products Distr
N.A.I.C.S.: 423860

Furuno Espana SA   **(1)**
Francisco Remiro 2 - Bloque B, 28028, Madrid, Spain

Furuno Electric Co., Ltd.—(Continued)

Tel.: (34) 917259088
Web Site: https://www.furuno.es
Sales Range: $25-49.9 Million
Emp.: 20
Industrial Machinery & Equipment Whslr
N.A.I.C.S.: 423830
Jose-Maria Olla-Curial *(Mng Dir)*

Furuno Europe BV (1)
Ridderhaven 19B, Ridderkerk, 2984 BT, Netherlands
Tel.: (31) 180416055
Web Site: http://www.furuno.co.jp
Sales Range: $25-49.9 Million
Emp.: 3
Management Consulting Services
N.A.I.C.S.: 541618
Takahiro Sakurai *(Mng Dir)*

Furuno Eurus LLC (1)
Voskresenskaya embankment 12 letter A office 3N, 191123, Saint Petersburg, Russia
Tel.: (7) 8126477025
Web Site: http://www.furuno.ru
Custom Computer Programming Services
N.A.I.C.S.: 541511

Furuno Finland OY (1)
Niittyrinne 7, 02270, Espoo, Finland
Tel.: (358) 94355670
Web Site: https://www.furuno.fi
Sales Range: $50-74.9 Million
Emp.: 60
Industrial Machinery & Equipment Whslr
N.A.I.C.S.: 423830
Arto Lindgren *(Mng Dir)*

Furuno France S.A.S. (1)
12 Avenue de la Grande Semaine Parc d'activite Vert Castel, 33700, Merignac, France
Tel.: (33) 825000150
Web Site: http://www.info.furuno.fr
Marine Product Mfr
N.A.I.C.S.: 333618

Furuno Hellas S.A. (1)
10 Thetidos str, 16675, Glyfada, Greece
Tel.: (30) 2104004426
Web Site: https://www.furuno.gr
Marine Equipment Mfr
N.A.I.C.S.: 334290

Furuno Hong Kong Co., Ltd. (1)
Room 301 3rd Floor Sun Hun Kai Centre 30 Harbor Road, Wanchai, China (Hong Kong)
Tel.: (852) 24980109
Marine, Ultrasonic & Electronic Technologies
N.A.I.C.S.: 334419

Furuno Kansai Hambai Co., Ltd. (1)
99-5 Ominato-cho, Ise City, Mie, 516-0001, Japan
Tel.: (81) 596350330
Electrical Apparatus & Equipment Wiring Supplies
N.A.I.C.S.: 423610

Furuno Kansai Hanbai Co., Ltd. (1)
Kobe KIMEC Center Building 4F 1-5-2 Minatojima-Minamimachi, Chuo-ku, Kobe, 650-0047, Hyogo, Japan
Tel.: (81) 783047008
Industrial Electronic Product Mfr & Retailer
N.A.I.C.S.: 334419

Furuno Korea Co., Ltd. (1)
1st-2nd F Cheong-hae Bldg Choryang-dong 16-14 Jungang-daero, 180 beon-gil Dong-gu, Busan, 48822, Korea (South)
Tel.: (82) 514408900
Industrial Electronic Product Mfr & Retailer
N.A.I.C.S.: 334419

Furuno Kyushu Hambai Co., Ltd. (1)
3-15 Asahimachi, Nagasaki, 852-8003, Japan
Tel.: (81) 958613261
Web Site: http://www.furuno.co.jp
Emp.: 90
Other Professional Equipment & Supplies Whslr
N.A.I.C.S.: 423490
Tomohiro Matsuguchi *(Asst Mgr-Branch)*

Furuno Life Best Co., Ltd. (1)
9-52 Ashihara-cho Nishinomiya City, 662-

8580, Hyogo, Japan
Tel.: (81) 798631040
Web Site: http://www.furuno.co.jp
Insurance Agencies & Brokerages
N.A.I.C.S.: 524210

Furuno Norge AS (1)
Sjomannsveien 19, 6008, Alesund, Norway
Tel.: (47) 70102950
Web Site: https://www.furuno.no
Emp.: 36
Sporting & Athletic Goods Mfr
N.A.I.C.S.: 339920
Trond Strommen *(CEO & Mng Dir)*

Furuno Panama, S.A. (1)
Zona Procesadora de CoroZal Edificio 354B, Panama, Panama
Tel.: (507) 3176556
Web Site: https://www.furuno.com.pa
Marine Products Distr
N.A.I.C.S.: 423860

Furuno Polska Sp. z o.o. (1)
ul Wolnosci 20, 81-327, Gdynia, Poland
Tel.: (48) 586690220
Web Site: https://www.furuno.pl
Transportation Equipment & Supplies Whslr
N.A.I.C.S.: 423860

Furuno Shanghai Co., Ltd. (1)
Unit 1201-1207 12F 647 Long Hua east road The Riverfront Huangpu, Shanghai, China
Tel.: (86) 2133933260
Web Site: http://www.furuno.com
Sales Range: $25-49.9 Million
Emp.: 30
Custom Computer Programming Services
N.A.I.C.S.: 541511
Yoshio Kitani *(Mng Dir)*

Furuno Singapore Pte Ltd (1)
17 Loyang Lane, Singapore, 508917, Singapore
Tel.: (65) 67458472
Web Site: https://www.furuno.sg
Marine Products Distr
N.A.I.C.S.: 423860
Nguyen Quang Tuyen *(Sls Mgr-Svc & Part)*

Furuno Softech (Dalian) Co ., Ltd. (1)
B-601 No1 Xueyuan Square, Shahekou District, Dalian, 116023, China
Tel.: (86) 41188120789
Web Site: http://www.furuno-dl.com
Custom Computer Programming Services
N.A.I.C.S.: 541511

Furuno Softech Co., Ltd. (1)
9-52 Awaramachi, Nishinomiya, 662-8580, Hyogo, Japan
Tel.: (81) 798631168 **(100%)**
Web Site: https://www.furunosoftech.co.jp
Emp.: 66
Custom Computer Programming Services
N.A.I.C.S.: 541511
Kiyotoshi Furuno *(Auditor)*

Furuno Sverige AB (1)
Gruvgatan 23, 421 30, Vastra Frolunda, Sweden
Tel.: (46) 317098940
Web Site: https://www.furuno.se
Emp.: 20
Industrial Machinery & Equipment Whslr
N.A.I.C.S.: 423830

Furuno Systems Co ,Ltd. (1)
JEI Ryogoku Building 3-25-5 Ryogoku, Sumida-ku, Tokyo, 130-0026, Japan
Tel.: (81) 356005111
Web Site: https://www.furunosystems.co.jp
Emp.: 140
Electrical Apparatus & Equipment Wiring Supplies
N.A.I.C.S.: 423610
Yukio Senou *(Pres)*

Furuno USA, Inc. (1)
4400 N W Pacific Rim Blvd, Camas, WA 98607-9408
Tel.: (360) 834-9300
Web Site: https://www.furunousa.com
Sales Range: $50-74.9 Million
Emp.: 100
Marine Electronics, Radar Systems, Fish Finders, Autopilots, Radios, Transceivers & Sonar & Sounder Systems Distribution & Repair

N.A.I.C.S.: 423860
Brad Reents *(Pres & CFO)*

Kyoritsu Radio Service Co., Ltd. (1)
3rd Floor Imagawa Bldg 2-6 Kanda Izumi-cho, Chiyoda-ku, Tokyo, 101-0024, Japan
Tel.: (81) 345312330
Web Site: https://www.kyoritsuradio.com
Satellite Communication Services
N.A.I.C.S.: 517410

Labotech International Co., Ltd. (1)
1-16 Fukazu-cho, Nishinomiya, 663-8203, Hyogo, Japan
Tel.: (81) 798631094
Web Site: https://www.labotech-intl.co.jp
Emp.: 33
Testing Laboratories
N.A.I.C.S.: 541380
Yuji Honda *(Pres & CEO)*

PT.Furuno Electric Indonesia (1)
Cowell Tower 8th floor Jl Great Monday No 135, Jakarta, 10410, Indonesia
Tel.: (62) 213511282
Web Site: https://www.furuno.id
Marine Products Distr
N.A.I.C.S.: 423860

FURUYA METAL CO., LTD.
MSB-21 Minami Otsuka Bldg 2-37-5 Minami Otsuka, Toshima-ku, Tokyo, 170-0005, Japan
Tel.: (81) 359773388
Web Site:
https://www.furuyametals.co.jp
Year Founded: 1951
7826—(TKS)
Rev.: $295,617,940
Assets: $701,124,620
Liabilities: $324,739,980
Net Worth: $376,384,640
Earnings: $46,090,200
Emp.: 406
Fiscal Year-end: 06/30/24
Industrial Metal Products Mfr
N.A.I.C.S.: 332322
Tsutomu Nishimura *(Operating Officer)*

Subsidiaries:

FURUYA METAL AMERICAS INC (1)
Waumbec Mill Ste 4012 250 Commercial St, Manchester, NH 03101
Tel.: (603) 518-7723
Web Site: https://www.furuya-ma.com
Metal Product Mfr & Distr
N.A.I.C.S.: 332999

Furuya Eco-Front Technology Co., Ltd. (1)
2-37-5 Minami Otsuka, Toshima-ku, Tokyo, 170-0005, Japan
Tel.: (81) 35 977 3388
Precious Metal Product Mfr & Distr
N.A.I.C.S.: 339910

Furuya Metal Co., Ltd. - Chitose Plant (1)
Izumisawa 1007-175, Hokkaido, Chitose, 066-0051, Japan
Tel.: (81) 123287330
Metal Product Mfr & Distr
N.A.I.C.S.: 332999

Furuya Metal Co., Ltd. - Tsuchiura Plant (1)
Higashitsukuba Niihari Kogyodanchi 57-4 Sawabe, Tsuchiura, 300-4104, Ibaraki, Japan
Tel.: (81) 298306777
Metal Products Mfr
N.A.I.C.S.: 332999

Furuya Metal Co., Ltd. - Tsukuba Plant (1)
Shimodate Daiichi Kogyodanchi 1915 Morisoejima, Chikusei, 308-0861, Ibaraki, Japan
Tel.: (81) 296253434
Metal Products Mfr
N.A.I.C.S.: 332999

Furuya Metal Korea Co., LTD. (1)
3rd Floor Dongam Bldg 13 Gangnam-daero

47-gil, Seocho-gu, Seoul, 06729, Korea (South)
Tel.: (82) 261210277
Metal Product Mfr & Distr
N.A.I.C.S.: 332999

FURY GOLD MINES LIMITED
401 Bay Street 16th Floor, Toronto, M5H 2Y4, ON, Canada
Tel.: (778) 729-0600 BC
Web Site:
https://www.furygoldmines.com
Year Founded: 2008
FURY—(NYSEAMFX)
Rev.: $31,364,734
Assets: $156,924,586
Liabilities: $4,541,918
Net Worth: $152,382,668
Earnings: $19,485,030
Emp.: 11
Fiscal Year-end: 12/31/22
Mineral Exploration Services
N.A.I.C.S.: 213114
Michael Timmins *(Pres & CEO)*

Subsidiaries:

Eastmain Resources Inc. (1)
34 King Street East Suite 600, Toronto, M5C 1X8, ON, Canada
Tel.: (416) 848-0105
Rev.: $52,352
Assets: $55,114,551
Liabilities: $3,557,227
Net Worth: $51,557,324
Earnings: ($12,697,441)
Emp.: 15
Fiscal Year-end: 10/31/2019
Gold Mining Services
N.A.I.C.S.: 212220

FURYU CORPORATION
COMS Bldg 2F 2-3 Uguisudani-cho, Shibuya-ku, Tokyo, 150-0032, Japan
Tel.: (81) 357281761
Web Site: https://www.furyu.jp
Year Founded: 2006
6238—(TKS)
Rev.: $282,696,480
Assets: $187,367,060
Liabilities: $42,859,240
Net Worth: $144,507,820
Earnings: $16,465,510
Emp.: 517
Fiscal Year-end: 03/31/24
Entertainment Related Services
N.A.I.C.S.: 713990
Yoshiro Tasaka *(Chm)*

FUSE 8 GROUP LTD
3370 Century Way Thorpe Park, Leeds, LS15 8ZB, United Kingdom
Tel.: (44) 1132604600
Web Site: http://www.fuse8.com
Year Founded: 2000
Sales Range: $10-24.9 Million
Emp.: 75
Digital Advertising Services
N.A.I.C.S.: 541810
Nigel Hunter *(CEO)*

Subsidiaries:

fuse8 Delete (1)
4 Golden Square, London, W1F 9HT, United Kingdom
Tel.: (44) 20 3214 0009
Web Site: http://www.deleteagency.com
Emp.: 15
Marketing Consulting Services
N.A.I.C.S.: 541613
Mark Walton *(CEO)*

fuse8 RUSSIA (1)
Akademik Korolev st, 454004, Chelyabinsk, Russia
Tel.: (7) 3512251874
Web Site: http://fuse8.ru
Marketing Consulting Services
N.A.I.C.S.: 541613

FUSE BATTERY METALS INC.

3028 Quadra Court, Coquitlam, V3B 5X6, BC, Canada
Tel.: (236) 521-0207
Web Site:
 https://fusebatterymetals.com
FUSE—(TSXV)
Rev.: $19
Assets: $4,316,779
Liabilities: $15,664
Net Worth: $4,301,115
Earnings: ($1,263,677)
Fiscal Year-end: 12/31/23
Mineral Exploration Services
N.A.I.C.S.: 213115
Robert Setter *(Pres & CEO)*

FUSEAU
Zac De L Hoirie Rue Charles Lacretelle, 49070, Beaucouze, Maine Et Loire, France
Tel.: (33) 241351090
Web Site: http://www.fuseau-sas.com
Rev.: $24,700,000
Emp.: 78
Groceries & Related Products
N.A.I.C.S.: 424490
Christophe Fuseau *(Pres)*

FUSEBILL INC.
Suite 203 232 Herzberg Road, Kanata, K2K 2A1, ON, Canada
Tel.: (613) 656-0002
Web Site: http://www.fusebill.com
Sales Range: $1-9.9 Million
Emp.: 16
Automated Invoicing, Billing & Collections
N.A.I.C.S.: 513210
Tyler Eyamie *(CEO)*

FUSEN PHARMACEUTICAL CO., LTD.
Jinhe Development Zone, Xichuan County, Nanyang, Henan, China
Tel.: (86) 37762002566   Ky
Web Site: https://www.fusenyy.com
Year Founded: 2003
1652—(HKG)
Rev.: $75,342,090
Assets: $206,874,560
Liabilities: $112,973,224
Net Worth: $93,901,337
Earnings: ($5,309,339)
Emp.: 1,159
Fiscal Year-end: 12/31/22
Pharmaceutical Product Mfr & Distr
N.A.I.C.S.: 325412
Changcheng Cao *(Founder)*

FUSHI COPPERWELD, INC.
TYG Center Tower B Suite 2601, Dong San Huan Bei Lu Bing 2, Beijing, 100027, China
Tel.: (86) 1084417742   NV
Web Site:
 http://www.fushiinternational.com
Sales Range: $250-299.9 Million
Emp.: 691
Steel & Copper Clad Wires Mfr
N.A.I.C.S.: 331420
Joseph J. Longever *(Co-CEO)*

Subsidiaries:

Copperweld Bimetallics, LLC   **(1)**
254 Cotton Mill Rd, Fayetteville, TN 37334-7249
Tel.: (931) 433-7177
Web Site: http://www.copperweld.com
Sales Range: $50-74.9 Million
Emp.: 130
Bimetallic Wire & Strand Products Mfr
N.A.I.C.S.: 332618
Roger Spurlock *(Gen Mgr)*

Subsidiary (Non-US):

Dalian Jinchuan Electric Cable Co. Ltd.   **(2)**

Beihai Industry Park, Maoyingzi Village Ganjingzi District, Dalian, 116031, Liaoning, China
Tel.: (86) 411 8711 2218
Electronic Cable Mfr
N.A.I.C.S.: 331420

Fushi Copperweld Europe   **(2)**
Unit B1 Heslop Halesfield 24, Telford, TF7 4NZ, Shropshire, United Kingdom   **(100%)**
Tel.: (44) 1952586771
Web Site: http://www.fushicopperweld.com
Sales Range: $25-49.9 Million
Emp.: 15
Silo Mfr
N.A.I.C.S.: 331420
Thomas Horton *(Mktg Dir)*

Copperweld Tubing Europe SPRL   **(1)**
Rue du Fourneau 43, B-4030, Liege, Belgium
Tel.: (32) 43499898
Bimetallic Wire Products Mfr & Distr
N.A.I.C.S.: 331420

Fushi International (Dalian) Bimetallic Cable Co., Ltd.   **(1)**
1 Shuang Qiang Rd, Jinzhou District, Dalian, 116100, Liaoning, China
Tel.: (86) 41187703333
Sales Range: $100-124.9 Million
Emp.: 500
Bimetallic Wire Products Mfr & Distr
N.A.I.C.S.: 335999

FUSHIKI KAIRIKU UNSO CO.,LTD.
5-1 Fushikiminatomachi, Takaoka, 933-0104, Toyama, Japan
Tel.: (81) 766451111
Web Site: https://www.fkk-toyama.co.jp
Year Founded: 1944
9361—(TKS)
Rev.: $80,455,700
Assets: $143,339,900
Liabilities: $67,493,220
Net Worth: $75,846,680
Earnings: $2,910,960
Fiscal Year-end: 06/30/24
Cargo Handling Services
N.A.I.C.S.: 488320
Yoshiyuki Daimon *(Pres)*

FUSHUN SPECIAL STEEL CO., LTD.
No 8 East Section of Anshan Road, Wanghua District, Fushun, 113001, Liaoning, China
Tel.: (86) 2456689161
Web Site: https://www.fs-ss.com
Year Founded: 1937
600399—(SHG)
Rev.: $1,097,197,106
Assets: $1,654,980,627
Liabilities: $804,946,629
Net Worth: $850,033,997
Earnings: $27,589,765
Emp.: 400
Fiscal Year-end: 12/31/22
Steel Products Mfr
N.A.I.C.S.: 331110
Sun Liguo *(Chm & Gen Mgr)*

FUSIC CO., LTD.
6F 3rd Myojo Building 4-1-7 Tenjin, Chuo-ku, Fukuoka, 810-0001, Japan
Tel.: (81) 927372616
Web Site: https://www.fusic.co.jp
Year Founded: 2003
5256—(TKS)
Information Technology Services
N.A.I.C.S.: 541512
Sadayoshi Notomi *(Pres)*

FUSION ANTIBODIES PLC
Springbank Industrial Estate 1 Springbank Rd, Dunmurry, Belfast, BT17 0QL, United Kingdom
Tel.: (44) 2890432800   UK

Web Site:
 https://www.fusionantibodies.com
Year Founded: 2001
FAB—(AIM)
Rev.: $6,293,760
Assets: $6,451,104
Liabilities: $1,625,888
Net Worth: $4,825,216
Earnings: ($1,573,440)
Fiscal Year-end: 03/31/22
Pharmaceutical Product Mfr & Distr
N.A.I.C.S.: 325412
Simon Douglas *(Chm)*

FUSION DATA CO., LTD.
515 2 5F Nonhyeon-ro, Gangnam-gu, Seoul, Korea (South)
Tel.: (82) 25477688
Web Site: http://www.fusiondata.co.kr
Year Founded: 2001
Rev.: $15,632,941
Assets: $20,429,884
Liabilities: $19,887,525
Net Worth: $542,359
Earnings: ($11,838,789)
Emp.: 118
Fiscal Year-end: 12/31/18
Software Development Services
N.A.I.C.S.: 541511
Ilhong Park *(CEO)*

FUSION DATA CO., LTD.
515 2-5F Nonhyeon-ro, Gangnam-gu, Seoul, Korea (South)
Tel.: (82) 2 547 7688
Web Site: http://www.fusiondata.co.kr
Year Founded: 2001
Cloud-based Services
N.A.I.C.S.: 518210
Jongmyeong Lee *(CEO)*

FUSION MEDIA LTD.
3076 Sir Francis Drake's Highway, Tortola, Virgin Islands (British)
Tel.: (908) 731-0750
Web Site: https://www.investing.com
Financial Markets Platform Services
N.A.I.C.S.: 523999
Shlomi Biger *(Chief Product Officer)*

Subsidiaries:

StreetInsider.com, Inc.   **(1)**
280 W Maple Ste 232, Birmingham, MI 48009
Tel.: (678) 459-8425
Web Site: http://www.streetinsider.com
Data Processing, Hosting & Related Services
N.A.I.C.S.: 518210
Lon Juricic *(Founder)*

FUSION MICRO FINANCE LIMITED
Plot No 86 Institutional Sector 32, Gurgaon, 122001, Haryana, India
Tel.: (91) 1246910500
Web Site:
 https://www.fusionmicrofinance.com
Year Founded: 1994
543652—(BOM)
Rev.: $163,984,139
Assets: $995,150,793
Liabilities: $812,520,482
Net Worth: $182,630,312
Earnings: $2,969,558
Emp.: 8,716
Fiscal Year-end: 03/31/22
Investment Management Service
N.A.I.C.S.: 523999

FUSION RETAIL BRANDS, PTY. LTD.
Level 1 850 Lorimer St, Port Melbourne, 3207, VIC, Australia
Tel.: (61) 39420 8444   AU
Web Site:
 http://www.fusionretailbrands.com

Year Founded: 1999
Sales Range: $350-399.9 Million
Emp.: 1,500
Footwear & Apparel Retailer & Wholesaler
N.A.I.C.S.: 458210
Nigel Pereira *(Gen Mgr)*

Subsidiaries:

Australian Footwear Pty Ltd   **(1)**
254-260 Burwood Rd, Hawthorn, 3122, VIC, Australia
Tel.: (61) 1800101285
Web Site: http://www.williamsshoes.com.au
Footwear Whslr
N.A.I.C.S.: 424340

Diana Ferrari (Australia) Pty Ltd   **(1)**
101 Cremorne Street, PO Box 218, 3121, Richmond, VIC, Australia   **(100%)**
Tel.: (61) 394208444
Footwear Whslr
N.A.I.C.S.: 424340

Mathers Shoes Pty Ltd.   **(1)**
109 Bunlvood Rd, Melbourne, 3122, QLD, Australia   **(100%)**
Tel.: (61) 738773333
Web Site: http://www.coloradogroup.com.au
Sales Range: $50-74.9 Million
Emp.: 200
Shoe Stores
N.A.I.C.S.: 458210

FUSIONEX INTERNATIONAL PLC
Level 33 25 Canada Square Canary Wharf, London, E14 5LB, United Kingdom
Tel.: (44) 207 038 8207   JE
Web Site: http://www.fusionex-international.com
Software Publisher
N.A.I.C.S.: 513210
Ivan Teh *(CEO & Mng Dir)*

Subsidiaries:

Fusionex Corp. Sdn. Bhd.   **(1)**
Level 12 Tower A Plaza 33 1 Jalan Kemajuan Section 13, 46200, Petaling Jaya, Selangor, Malaysia
Tel.: (60) 3 77115200
Software Development Services
N.A.I.C.S.: 541511

FUSIONTECH, INC.
No 26 Gaoneng Street, High Tech Zone, Dalian, 116025, Liaoning, China
Tel.: (86) 411 8479 9486   NV
Web Site:
 http://www.cleanfusiontech.com
Year Founded: 2007
Sales Range: $10-24.9 Million
Emp.: 100
Clean Technology Industrial Machinery Mfr
N.A.I.C.S.: 333248
Lixin Wang *(Chm & CEO)*

FUSO CHEMICAL CO., LTD.
Nissei Fushimi-machi Bldg Shinkan 3-10 Koraibashi 4-chome, Chuo-ku, Osaka, 541-0043, Japan
Tel.: (81) 662034771
Web Site: https://www.fusokk.co.jp
Year Founded: 1957
4368—(TKS)
Rev.: $389,791,700
Assets: $884,021,400
Liabilities: $255,906,150
Net Worth: $628,115,250
Earnings: $55,147,230
Fiscal Year-end: 03/31/24
Chemical & Coating Mfr
N.A.I.C.S.: 325998
Shozo Akazawa *(Founder)*

Fuso Chemical Co., Ltd.—(Continued)

Subsidiaries:

Fuso Chemical Co., Ltd - Juso
Factory (1)
10-30 Nonakakita 2 Chome, Yodogawa-ku,
Osaka, 532-0034, Japan
Tel.: (81) 663966231
Fruit Acids Mfr
N.A.I.C.S.: 325199

Fuso Chemical Co., Ltd - Kyoto Sec-
ond Factory (1)
8 Osadano-cho 2-chome, Fukuchiyama,
620 0853, Kyoto, Japan
Tel.: (81) 773205553
Web Site: http://www.fusokk.co.jp
Chemicals Mfr
N.A.I.C.S.: 325180
Ryota Akazawa (Pres)

Fuso Chemical Co., Ltd - Osaka
Factory (1)
27-10 Chikko-shinmachi 3-cho, Nishi-ku,
Sakai, 592-8331, Osaka, Japan
Tel.: (81) 722449091
Web Site: http://www.fusokk.co.jp
Fruit Acids Mfr
N.A.I.C.S.: 325199

Fuso Chemical Co., Ltd. - Kyoto First
Factory (1)
5 Osadano-cho 1-chome, Fukuchiyama,
620-0853, Kyoto, Japan
Tel.: (81) 773276925
Industrial Chemicals Mfr
N.A.I.C.S.: 325180

Fuso Corporation Co Ltd (1)
Honmachi Fuji Bldg 1-4-12 Utsubohon-
machi, Nishi-ku, Osaka, 550-0004, Japan
Tel.: (81) 663913421
Industrial Chemicals Mfr
N.A.I.C.S.: 325998

Fuso Teiyaku (Qingdao) Co., Ltd. (1)
No 200 Zhuzhou Road, Laoshan District,
Qingdao, China
Tel.: (86) 5328 870 5600
Web Site: https://www.teiyaku.com.cn
Medicated Mfr
N.A.I.C.S.: 339112
Kasai Mikiya (Gen Mgr)

PMP Fermentation Products, Inc. (1)
900 NE Adams St, Peoria, IL 61603-3904
Tel.: (309) 637-0400
Web Site: https://www.pmpinc.com
Sales Range: $50-74.9 Million
Mfr & Marketer of Industrial Chemicals
N.A.I.C.S.: 325199
Scot Whetsell (Mgr-Quality Control)

FUSO DENTSU CO., LTD.
Shiodome East Side Building 5-4-18
Tsukiji, Chuo-ku, Tokyo, 104-0045,
Japan
Tel.: (81) 335447211
Web Site:
https://www.fusodentsu.co.jp
Year Founded: 1948
7505—(TKS)
Sales Range: $350-399.9 Million
Emp.: 979
Communication Equipment Mainte-
nance Services
N.A.I.C.S.: 811210
Hideki Fujii (Chm)

FUSO PHARMACEUTICAL IN-
DUSTRIES, LTD.
1-7-10 Doshomachi, Chuo-ku, Osaka,
541-0045, Japan
Tel.: (81) 662316887
Web Site: https://www.fuso-
pharm.co.jp
Year Founded: 1937
4538—(TKS)
Sales Range: $400-449.9 Million
Emp.: 1,352
Pharmaceutical Product Mfr & Distr
N.A.I.C.S.: 325412
Mikio Toda (Pres)

FUSTELARKO BOREC BITOLA
AD
Industriska bb, Bitola, North Macedo-
nia
Tel.: (389) 47239200
Web Site:
https://www.fustelarko.com.mk
Year Founded: 1971
FUBT—(MAC)
Rev.: $3,902,603
Assets: $4,470,843
Liabilities: $779,036
Net Worth: $3,691,807
Earnings: $185,115
Emp.: 180
Fiscal Year-end: 12/31/19
Paper Board Product Mfr
N.A.I.C.S.: 322212

FUTABA CORPORATION
629 Oshiba, Mobara, 297-8588,
Chiba, Japan
Tel.: (81) 475241111 **JP**
Web Site: https://www.futaba.co.jp
Year Founded: 1948
6986—(TKS)
Rev.: $372,539,600
Assets: $689,178,430
Liabilities: $90,781,740
Net Worth: $598,396,690
Earnings: ($12,250,940)
Emp.: 2,997
Fiscal Year-end: 03/31/24
Radio Control Equipment, Mould &
Metal Die Parts & Vacuum Fluores-
cent Displays Mfr & Sales
N.A.I.C.S.: 334220
Motoaki Arima (Pres)

Subsidiaries:

FUTABA (Hong Kong) Corporation
Ltd. (1)
Unit No 5 19th Floor Millennium Trade Cen-
tre No 56 Kwai Cheong Road, Hong Kong,
China (Hong Kong)
Tel.: (852) 29635888
Electric Component Whslr
N.A.I.C.S.: 423690

FUTABA DENSHI Corp. (S) Pte.
Ltd. (1)
11 Tampines Concourse 03-07A, Singapore,
528729, Singapore
Tel.: (65) 62919882
Web Site: https://www.futaba.com.sg
Sales Range: $25-49.9 Million
Emp.: 13
Electronic Components Distr
N.A.I.C.S.: 423690

FUTABA International Trading
(Shanghai) Co., Ltd. (1)
Unit A 17F No 720 Pudong Avenue, Pudong
New District, Shanghai, 200120, China
Tel.: (86) 2150366399
Web Site: https://www.futabahk.com
Circuit Board Distr
N.A.I.C.S.: 423690

Futaba (Europe) GmbH (1)
Halskestrasse 9, 47877, Willich, Germany
Tel.: (49) 21549430
Vacuum Tube Mfr & Distr
N.A.I.C.S.: 334419

Futaba (Vietnam) Co., Ltd. (1)
Lot AN 35b-36b-37-46-47a-48a Road 12
Tan Thuan EPZ, Tan Thuan Dong Ward
District 7, Ho Chi Minh City, Vietnam
Tel.: (84) 28377005515
Vacuum Tube Mfr & Distr
N.A.I.C.S.: 334419

Futaba Business System Co.,
Ltd. (1)
629 Oshiba, Mobara, 297-0033, Chiba,
Japan
Tel.: (81) 475260192
Web Site: http://www.fbs.chiba.jp
Grocery Products Retailer
N.A.I.C.S.: 445110

Futaba Corporation - Akashi Machin-
ery & Tooling Factory (1)
20-4 Minamifutami Futami-cho, Akashi, 674-
0093, Hyogo, Japan
Tel.: (81) 78361871
Precision Die Sets Mfr
N.A.I.C.S.: 333514

Futaba Corporation - Chonan Ma-
chinery & Tooling Factory (1)
112 Kuramochi, Chosei-mura, Chosei, 297-
0123, Chiba, Japan
Tel.: (81) 475462611
Web Site: https://www.futaba.co.jp
Precision Die Sets Mfr
N.A.I.C.S.: 333514

Futaba Corporation - Chonan Ma-
chinery & Tooling Factory II (1)
472 Hoonji Chonan-machi, Chosei, 297-
0141, Chiba, Japan
Tel.: (81) 475463611
Web Site: http://en.futaba.co.jp
Molded Die Parts Mfr
N.A.I.C.S.: 333511

Futaba Corporation - Chosei Electron
Tube Factory (1)
1080 Yabutsuka, Chosei-mura, Chosei,
299-4395, Chiba, Japan
Tel.: (81) 475326051
Web Site: http://en.futaba.co.jp
Vacuum Fluorescent Displays Mfr
N.A.I.C.S.: 334513

Futaba Corporation - Chosei Elec-
tronic Systems Factory (1)
1080 Yabutsuka Chosei-mura, Chosei, 299-
4395, Chiba, Japan
Tel.: (81) 475326000
Sales Range: $100-124.9 Million
Emp.: 300
Radio Control Equipment Mfr
N.A.I.C.S.: 334220

Futaba Corporation - Chosei Machin-
ery & Tooling Factory (1)
1080 Yabutsuka Chosei-mura, Chosei, 299-
4395, Chiba, Japan
Tel.: (81) 475326036
Precision Die Sets Mfr
N.A.I.C.S.: 333514

Futaba Corporation - Chosei VFD
Module Factory (1)
1080 Yabutsuka, Chosei-mura, Chosei,
299-4395, Chiba, Japan
Tel.: (81) 475 32 6005
Web Site: http://en.futaba.co.jp
Vacuum Fluorescent Displays Mfr
N.A.I.C.S.: 334513

Futaba Corporation - Mobara Elec-
tron Tube Factory (1)
629 Oshiba, Mobara, 297-8588, Chiba,
Japan
Tel.: (81) 475241111
Web Site: http://www.futaba.co.jp
Vacuum Fluorescent Displays Mfr
N.A.I.C.S.: 334513

Futaba Corporation - Mutsuzawa Ma-
chinery & Tooling Factory (1)
2345 Kamiichiba Mutsuzawa-machi, Chosei,
299-4403, Chiba, Japan
Tel.: (81) 475441221
Web Site: http://www.futaba.co.jp
Sales Range: $25-49.9 Million
Emp.: 50
Precision Die Sets Mfr
N.A.I.C.S.: 333514

Futaba Corporation of America (1)
711 E State Pkwy, Schaumburg, IL
60173 (100%)
Tel.: (847) 884-1444
Web Site: http://www.futaba.com
Sales Range: $25-49.9 Million
Emp.: 20
Marketing of Vacuum Fluorescent Displays
& Digital Readout Equipment (PULSCALE)
N.A.I.C.S.: 334419
John Peroutka (Engr-CAD & Electronic De-
sign)

Futaba Corporation of America (1)
51111 Pontiac Trl, Wixom, MI 48393
Tel.: (734) 459-1177
Web Site: http://www.futaba.com
Sales Range: $50-74.9 Million
Emp.: 5

Mfr of Flat Panel Displays & Vacuum Fluo-
rescent Displays, VFD Modules & Radio
Control Systems
N.A.I.C.S.: 334519

Futaba Corporation of Huizhou (1)
4th Floor 1st Building No 2 Jin-da Road
Hui-ao Avenue, Huinan High-tech Industrial
Park, Huizhou, Guangdong, China
Tel.: (86) 7522627111
Vacuum Tube Mfr & Distr
N.A.I.C.S.: 334419

Futaba Corporation of the
Philippines (1)
120 North Science Avenue, Laguna Tech-
nopark Special Export Processing Zone,
Binan, 4024, Laguna, Philippines
Tel.: (63) 495411060
Web Site: http://www.futabaph.com
Vacuum Tube Mfr & Distr
N.A.I.C.S.: 334419

Futaba Electronics (Beijing) Co.,
Ltd. (1)
B337 3F Bldg6 No A15 Jinyuan Road, Dax-
ing District, Beijing, 102600, China
Tel.: (86) 1067051805
Vacuum Tube Mfr & Distr
N.A.I.C.S.: 334419

Futaba Electronics Components Ko-
rea Co., Ltd. (1)
A-1410 Woolim Lions Valley Gasan digital
1-ro 168 Gasan-dong, Geumcheon-gu,
Seoul, 153-802, Korea (South)
Tel.: (82) 220262518
Sales Range: $50-74.9 Million
Emp.: 9
Electric Component Whslr
N.A.I.C.S.: 423690

Futaba JTW (Thailand) Ltd. (1)
78 Moo 2 Bangna-Trad Road Tambon
Pimpa, Wellgrow Industrial Estate Bangpak-
png District, Chachoengsao, 24130, Thai-
land
Tel.: (66) 385222714
Web Site: http://www.fjthai.com
Emp.: 132
Mold & Die Component Mfr
N.A.I.C.S.: 333511
Yutaka Minagawa (Pres)

Futaba Mobile Display
Corporation (1)
1471-21 Hitana Nakago-cho, Kitaibaraki,
319-1556, Ibaraki, Japan
Tel.: (81) 293436788
Emp.: 70
Display Mfr
N.A.I.C.S.: 334419

Futaba Precision Co., Ltd. (1)
10-159-2 Kasshi-cho, Kamaishi, 026-0055,
Iwate Prefecture, Japan
Tel.: (81) 193230241
Vacuum Tube Mfr & Distr
N.A.I.C.S.: 334419

Futaba Precision Die & Mold Machin-
ery (China) Co., Ltd. (1)
1098 Fuchunjiang Road, Kunshan, 215300,
Jiangsu, China
Tel.: (86) 51257035900
Vacuum Tube Mfr & Distr
N.A.I.C.S.: 334419

Futaba Precision Mould (Shenzhen)
Corporation, Ltd. (1)
No 1 Futaba Road Nanwan Street, Dan-
zhutou Industrial Estate Longgang, Shen-
zhen, Guangdong, China
Tel.: (86) 75584736190
Vacuum Tube Mfr & Distr
N.A.I.C.S.: 334419

Futaba Tenneco U.K. Limited (1)
Liverpool Road Rosegrove, Burnley, BB12
6HJ, Lancashire, United Kingdom
Tel.: (44) 1282433171
Web Site: https://www.fmuk.ltd
Sales Range: $125-149.9 Million
Emp.: 300
Automobile Parts Mfr
N.A.I.C.S.: 336390
Kevin Schofield (Mng Dir)

Kabuku Inc. (1)
1F Watabishi Building 5-17-17, Shinjuku

Shinjuku-ku, Tokyo, 160-0022, Japan
Tel.: (81) 363802750
Web Site: http://www.kabuku.co.jp
Machine Tools Mfr
N.A.I.C.S.: 333517

Kishin Corporation (1)
111 Eunbong-ro, Namdong-gu, Incheon, Korea (South)
Tel.: (82) 328201501
Web Site: http://www.kishin.com
Rev.: $109,775,052
Assets: $201,511,066
Liabilities: $10,639,954
Net Worth: $190,871,111
Earnings: $3,327,077
Emp.: 429
Fiscal Year-end: 03/31/2023
Industrial Mold Mfr
N.A.I.C.S.: 333511

Kishin Megatec Co., Ltd. (1)
57 Jeyakdanji-ro Hyangnam-eup, Hwaseong, Gyeonggi-do, Korea (South)
Tel.: (82) 313559811
Vacuum Tube Mfr & Distr
N.A.I.C.S.: 334419

Kishin Vietnam Co., Ltd. (1)
Lot F4, Que Vo Industrial Zone Expanded Area Nam Son Commune, Bac Ninh, Vietnam
Tel.: (84) 22239030126
Vacuum Tube Mfr & Distr
N.A.I.C.S.: 334419

O.S. Engines Mfg. Co., Ltd. (1)
6-15 3-Chome Imagawa, Higashisumiyoshi-ku, Osaka, 546-0003, Japan (100%)
Tel.: (81) 66 702 0225
Web Site: https://www.os-engines.co.jp
Sales Range: $50-74.9 Million
Emp.: 80
Mfr & Sales of Engines & Locomotives for Models
N.A.I.C.S.: 333618
Seiichi Arata *(Pres)*

Satsuki Kizai Co., Ltd. (1)
598-1 Monoi, Yotsukaido, 284-0012, Chiba Prefecture, Japan
Tel.: (81) 434221447
Web Site: http://www.satsuki-kizai.co.jp
Press Equipment Mfr & Distr
N.A.I.C.S.: 333248
Takuya Hirose *(Pres & CEO)*

Sentoraru Denshi Seigyo Co., Ltd. (1)
3-2-1 Sakado Kanagawa Science Park R and D Business Park Building B, Building 9th Floor Room 913 Takatsu-ku, Kawasaki, 213-0012, Kanagawa, Japan
Tel.: (81) 447663802
Web Site: http://www.sdsg.co.jp
Communication Control Equipment Mfr & Distr
N.A.I.C.S.: 334290

Taiwan Futaba Electronics Corporation (1)
No 1 Xinkaifa Road, Nanzi District, Kaohsiung, 811-638, Taiwan
Tel.: (886) 73612321
Web Site: http://www.tw-futaba.com.tw
Electronic Components Mfr
N.A.I.C.S.: 334419

Wonjin Precision Co., Ltd. (1)
48 Namdongseo ro 53beon-gil, Namdong-gu, Incheon, 21696, Korea (South)
Tel.: (82) 328130941
Vacuum Tube Mfr & Distr
N.A.I.C.S.: 334419

FUTABA INDUSTRIAL CO., LTD.
1 Ochaya Hashime-cho, Okazaki, 444-8558, Aichi, Japan
Tel.: (81) 564312211
Web Site:
https://www.futabasangyo.com
Year Founded: 1945
7241—(TKS)
Rev.: $5,260,251,220
Assets: $2,212,895,800
Liabilities: $1,347,640,190
Net Worth: $865,255,610

Earnings: $84,812,910
Emp.: 10,690
Fiscal Year-end: 03/31/24
Automobile Parts Mfr & Whslr
N.A.I.C.S.: 336390
Mikio Iwatsuki *(Operating Officer)*

Subsidiaries:

Apics Co., Ltd. (1)
2-1 Sumi Minamiyama Kota-cho, Nukata, 444-0127, Aichi, Japan
Tel.: (81) 564561681
Emp.: 146
Automobile Parts Mfr
N.A.I.C.S.: 336390

Changsha Futaba Auto Parts Co., Ltd. (1)
No 18 South Section of East 11 Road, Changsha, 410000, Hunan, China
Tel.: (86) 73188702298
Emp.: 87
Automobile Parts Distr
N.A.I.C.S.: 423120

Chongqing Futaba Auto Parts Co., Ltd. (1)
NO 111 Yongjia Road, Bishan District, Chongqing, 402760, China
Tel.: (86) 2364305825
Automobile Parts Distr
N.A.I.C.S.: 423120

Dongguan Futaba Metal Products Co., Ltd. (1)
Dalingshan Science Industrial Park, Dong-guan, 523816, Guangdong, China
Tel.: (86) 76989202500
Emp.: 200
Automobile Parts Distr
N.A.I.C.S.: 423120

FIC America Corp. (1)
485 E Lies Rd, Carol Stream, IL 60188
Tel.: (630) 871-7609
Emp.: 700
Automobile Parts Distr
N.A.I.C.S.: 423120
Andrey Atanassov *(Gen Mgr)*

FIO Automotive Canada Corp. (1)
220 Dunn Road, PO Box 1105, Stratford, N4Z 0A7, ON, Canada
Tel.: (519) 275-6070
Automobile Parts Distr
N.A.I.C.S.: 423120

FMI Automotive Components Ltd. (1)
Plot No 1 Sub-Plot No 4 5 8 9 MSIL Supplier Park Phase-3A IMT Manesar, Gurgaon, 122 051, Haryana, India
Tel.: (91) 1244548405
Emp.: 300
Automobile Parts Distr
N.A.I.C.S.: 423120
Krishan Kumar *(Sec)*

Futaba (Tianjin) Co., Ltd. (1)
No 73 11th Street, Teda, China
Tel.: (86) 2258503473
Control & Management Support Services
N.A.I.C.S.: 561110

Futaba Changzhou Engineering & Marketing Co., Ltd. (1)
403 R&D HUB 1 Science & Education Town No 801 Middle Changwu Rd, Changzhou, 213161, Jiangsu, China
Tel.: (86) 51981085028
Emp.: 26
Automobile Parts Distr
N.A.I.C.S.: 423120

Futaba Czech, s.r.o. (1)
Bastinov 130, 580 01, Havlickuv Brod, Czech Republic
Tel.: (420) 569496400
Emp.: 1,000
Automobile Parts Mfr
N.A.I.C.S.: 336390
Uichi Maeda *(Pres)*

Futaba General Co., Ltd. (1)
1-13 Tatsumidai, Okazaki, 444-0873, Aichi, Japan
Tel.: (81) 564527421
Automobile Parts Mfr
N.A.I.C.S.: 336390

Futaba Hiraizumi Co., Ltd. (1)
65 Kamitokusawa Hiraizumi Hiraizumi-cho, Nishiiwai-gun, Iwate, 029-4102, Japan
Tel.: (81) 191341211
Web Site: https://www.futabahiraizumi.co.jp
Automobile Parts Mfr
N.A.I.C.S.: 336390

Futaba Indiana of America Corp. (1)
3320 S Keller Rd, Vincennes, IN 47591
Tel.: (812) 895-4700
Web Site: https://www.futabaindiana.com
Automobile Parts Mfr & Distr
N.A.I.C.S.: 336390
Noboru Shimizu *(Pres)*

Futaba Industrial Co., Ltd. - Chiryu Plant (1)
110 Donsuyama Aizuma-cho, Chiryu, 472-0021, Aichi, Japan
Tel.: (81) 566811851
Emp.: 220
Automobile Parts Mfr
N.A.I.C.S.: 336390

Futaba Industrial Co., Ltd. - Kota Plant (1)
1 Yanagisawa Nagamine, Kota-cho, Nukata, 444-0101, Aichi, Japan
Tel.: (81) 564560500
Emp.: 650
Automobile Parts Mfr
N.A.I.C.S.: 336390

Futaba Industrial Co., Ltd. - Midori Plant (1)
6-1 Midorigaoka, Toyota, 471-0838, Aichi, Japan
Tel.: (81) 565283411
Emp.: 400
Automobile Parts Mfr
N.A.I.C.S.: 336390

Futaba Industrial Co., Ltd. - Mutsumi Plant (1)
38 Mukaimaeda Zaike-cho, Okazaki, 444-0245, Aichi, Japan
Tel.: (81) 564432275
Emp.: 450
Automobile Parts Mfr
N.A.I.C.S.: 336390

Futaba Industrial Co., Ltd. - Tahara Plant (1)
1-5 Midorigahama, Tahara, 441-3401, Aichi, Japan
Tel.: (81) 531225111
Emp.: 270
Automobile Parts Mfr
N.A.I.C.S.: 336390

Futaba Industrial Co., Ltd. - Takahashi Plant (1)
24 Hifumi Takahashi-cho, Okazaki, 444-0231, Aichi, Japan
Tel.: (81) 564433800
Emp.: 410
Automobile Parts Mfr
N.A.I.C.S.: 336390

Futaba Industrial Gujarat Private Limited (1)
Plot No 10-11 Suppliers Park of Suzuki Motor Gujarat SMG, Block No-334 335 Village Hansalpur, Ahmedabad, Gujarat, India
Tel.: (91) 2715663137
Muffler Mfr
N.A.I.C.S.: 336390

Futaba Industrial Texas Corp. (1)
1 Lone Star Pass Bldg 34, San Antonio, TX 78264
Tel.: (210) 927-2288
Emp.: 180
Automobile Parts Distr
N.A.I.C.S.: 423120
Lance Biddle *(Mgr-Production)*

Futaba Industrial U.K. Ltd. (1)
Park Avenue Dove Valley, Foston, Derby, DE65 5BT, Derbyshire, United Kingdom
Tel.: (44) 1283585651
Web Site:
http://www.futabaindustrialuk.co.uk
Emp.: 480
Automobile Parts Mfr
N.A.I.C.S.: 336390
Paul Heard *(Mng Dir)*

Futaba Kyusyu Co., Ltd. (1)

5515 Kawabaru Okawa-cho, Imari-shi, Saga, 849-5257, Japan
Tel.: (81) 955292211
Automobile Parts Mfr
N.A.I.C.S.: 336390

Subsidiary (Domestic):

Futaba Kyusyu Co., Ltd. - Miyata Plant (2)
1 Kamiaruki, Miyawaka, 823-0015, Fukuoka, Japan
Tel.: (81) 949332255
Automobile Parts Mfr.
N.A.I.C.S.: 336390

Futaba Kyusyu Co., Ltd. - Nogata Plant (2)
1181-6 Nakaizumi, Nogata, 822-0011, Fukuoka, Japan
Tel.: (81) 949258500
Automobile Parts Mfr
N.A.I.C.S.: 336390

Futaba Manufacturing U.K. Ltd. (1)
Liverpool Road Rosegrove, Burnley, BB12 6HJ, Lancashire, United Kingdom
Tel.: (44) 1282433171
Web Site: http://www.fmuk.ltd
Emp.: 500
Automobile Body Parts Mfr
N.A.I.C.S.: 336211
Kevin Schofield *(Mng Dir)*

Futaba North America Engineering & Marketing Co. (1)
244 Knollwood Dr Ste 200, Bloomingdale, IL 60108
Tel.: (331) 456-6147
Emp.: 30
Automobile Parts Distr
N.A.I.C.S.: 423120

Futaba Sumi Corp. (1)
2-1 Sumi Minamiyama Kota-cho, Nukata, 444-0127, Aichi, Japan
Tel.: (81) 564561681
Automobile Body Parts Mfr
N.A.I.C.S.: 336211

Futaba Technology Ltd. (1)
RM3602 36F Tower 1 Enterprise Square 5 No 38 Wang Chiu Road, Kowloon Bay, Kowloon, China (Hong Kong)
Tel.: (852) 39620530
Emp.: 5
Office Equipment Distr
N.A.I.C.S.: 423420

Guangzhou Futaba Auto Parts Co., Ltd. (1)
No 22 Huangge Zhonglu Huangge Town, Nansha, Guangzhou, 511455, Guangdong, China
Tel.: (86) 2034973700
Emp.: 400
Automobile Parts Distr
N.A.I.C.S.: 423120

PT.Futaba Industrial Indonesia (1)
Kawasan Greenland International Industrial Center Blok AB No 7, Cikarang Pusat, Bekasi, 17530, Jawa Barat, Indonesia
Tel.: (62) 2150554689
Emp.: 70
Automobile Parts Distr
N.A.I.C.S.: 423120

Shenzhen Futaba Metal Products Co., Ltd. (1)
Unitl Yingxing Industrial Park Guan Lantown, Bacan District, Shenzhen, China
Tel.: (86) 75527990090
Emp.: 170
Automobile Parts Distr
N.A.I.C.S.: 423120

Tianjin Futaba Shye Chan Mechanical Co., Ltd. (1)
NO 73 11th Street of Teda, Tianjin, 300457, China
Tel.: (86) 2259887266
Emp.: 620
Automobile Parts Distr
N.A.I.C.S.: 423120

Tianjin Shuang Shye Mechanical Industrial Co., Ltd. (1)
Across Yingjian Branch Road From The Ground of Xiali Car Dongma, Xiqing, Tian-

Futaba Industrial Co., Ltd.—(Continued)
jin, 300380, China
Tel.: (86) 2258110000
Emp.: 520
Automobile Parts Distr
N.A.I.C.S.: 423120

FUTEBOL CLUBE DO PORTO

Dragon Stadium Via, 4350-415,
Porto, Portugal
Tel.: (351) 225070500
Web Site: http://www.fcporto.pt
FCP—(EUR)
Sales Range: $100-124.9 Million
Emp.: 243
Professional Football Club Operator
N.A.I.C.S.: 711211
Daniel Lorenz Rodrigues Pereira
(Sec)

Subsidiaries:

F.C. PortoMultimedia - Edicoes Multi-
media, S.A.   (1)
Avenida Fernao de Magalhaes 1862 14-S
1402, 4350-158, Porto, Portugal
Tel.: (351) 225 070 500
Commercial Production Services
N.A.I.C.S.: 512110

FUTONG GROUP CO., LTD.

8 Futong Road, Fuyang, 311400,
Zhejiang, China
Tel.: (86) 57163322660
Web Site:
    http://www.futonggroup.com.cn
Sales Range: $300-349.9 Million
Emp.: 2,000
Wire & Cable Mfr
N.A.I.C.S.: 332618

Subsidiaries:

Futong Group (Hong Kong) Co.,
Ltd.   (1)
18 Harbour Rd Unit 6707A 67/F Central
Plaza, Wanchai, China (Hong Kong)
Tel.: (852) 3118 6712
Fiber Optic Cable Mfr
N.A.I.C.S.: 335921
Xingfu He *(Pres)*

Futong Group Co., Ltd. - Chengdu
Plant   (1)
186 Tianyun Rd High tech Zone 8th Floor
Building E, High tech International Square,
Chengdu, 610041, Sichuan, China
Tel.: (86) 28 8282 8999
Fiber Optic Cable Mfr
N.A.I.C.S.: 335921

Futong Group Co., Ltd. - Shenzhen
Plant   (1)
10 Qiongyu Rd Science & Technology In-
dustrial Park, Nanshan District, Shenzhen,
518057, China
Tel.: (86) 755 2650 1333
Fiber Optic Cable Mfr
N.A.I.C.S.: 335921

Futong Group Co., Ltd. - Tianjin
Plant   (1)
West Building, Software Park High-tech
Zone 18 West Haiqin Rd, Huayuan Indus-
trial Zone, Tianjin, 300384, China
Tel.: (86) 22 5863 5000
Fiber Optic Cable Mfr
N.A.I.C.S.: 335921

SEI Optical Fiber and Cable (Shen-
zhen) Co., Ltd.   (1)
Shenzhen high-tech Song Ping North Road
2 Sumitomo Fiber Park, Nanshan, Shen-
zhen, 518057, China
Tel.: (86) 755 26990001
Web Site: http://www.sefc.cn
Fiber Optic Cable Mfr & Distr
N.A.I.C.S.: 335921

Transtech Optical Communication
Co., Ltd.   (1)
3 Dai Kwai Street Whole Building Tai Po
Industrial Estate, Hong Kong, New Territo-
ries, China (Hong Kong)
Tel.: (852) 2665 7799

Emp.: 70
Fiber Optic Cable Mfr
N.A.I.C.S.: 335921
Chan Winnie *(Mgr-Acctg)*

FUTONG TECHNOLOGY DE-VELOPMENT HOLDINGS LIM-ITED

Rooms 2406-2412 24th Floor Sun
Hung Kai Centre 30 Harbour Road,
Wanchai, China (Hong Kong)
Tel.: (852) 26222428   Ky
Web Site: http://www.futong.com.hk
0465—(HKG)
Rev.: $48,165,764
Assets: $69,984,907
Liabilities: $13,494,265
Net Worth: $56,490,642
Earnings: ($10,611,572)
Emp.: 329
Fiscal Year-end: 12/31/22
Software Products Distr
N.A.I.C.S.: 513210
Jian Chen *(Co-Founder & Chm)*

Subsidiaries:

Beijing Futong Dongfang Technology
Co., Ltd.   (1)
19F Block B Chaowaimen Bldg 26 Chaowai
Street Chaoyang, Beijing, 100020, China
Tel.: (86) 1085658181
Web Site: http://www.futong.com.cn
Computer Peripheral Equipment Distr
N.A.I.C.S.: 423430

FUTU HOLDINGS LIMITED

No 18 Bonham Strand W Sheung
Wan, 11/F Bangkok Bank Building,
Sheung Wan, China (Hong Kong)
Tel.: (852) 25233588   Ky
Web Site:
    https://www.futuholdings.com
Year Founded: 2014
FUTU—(NASDAQ)
Rev.: $982,057,202
Assets: $12,188,975,013
Liabilities: $9,498,222,758
Net Worth: $2,690,752,255
Earnings: $377,510,659
Emp.: 2,784
Fiscal Year-end: 12/31/22
Holding Company
N.A.I.C.S.: 551112
Leaf Hua Li *(Founder, Chm & CEO)*

Subsidiaries:

Futu Securities International (Hong
Kong) Limited   (1)
Room C1-2 13/F Unity Centre 95 Queen-
sway, Admiralty, Hong Kong, China (Hong
Kong)
Tel.: (852) 25233588
Web Site: https://www.futuhk.com
Stock Broking Services
N.A.I.C.S.: 523150

Moomoo Inc.   (1)
425 Middlefield Rd, Palo Alto, CA 94301
Web Site: http://www.moomoo.com
Stock Broking Services
N.A.I.C.S.: 523150

FUTURA CONSORCIO INMO-BILIARIO SA

Calle Begonias 415 7th floor, San
isidro, Peru
Tel.: (51) 2000222
Web Site:
    https://www.futuraconsorcioin.com
Year Founded: 1988
FUTURAC1—(LIM)
Rev.: $18,059,536
Assets: $353,278,817
Liabilities: $146,963,809
Net Worth: $206,315,008
Earnings: ($2,095,107)
Fiscal Year-end: 12/31/23
Real Estate Manangement Services
N.A.I.C.S.: 531390

Pedro Manuel Juan Brescia Moreyra
(Chm)

FUTURA MEDICAL PLC

Surrey Technology Centre 40 Occam
Road, Guildford, GU2 7YG, Surrey,
United Kingdom
Tel.: (44) 1483685670
Web Site:
    https://www.futuramedical.com
FUM—(AIM)
Assets: $8,170,490
Liabilities: $2,212,963
Net Worth: $5,957,527
Earnings: ($7,380,074)
Emp.: 12
Fiscal Year-end: 12/31/22
Sexual Healthcare & Pain Relief
Pharmaceutical Product Mfr
N.A.I.C.S.: 325412
James Barder *(CEO)*

Subsidiaries:

Futura Medical Developments
Limited   (1)
Surrey Technology Centre 40 Occam Road,
Guildford, GU2 7YG, Surrey, United King-
dom
Tel.: (44) 1483685670
Web Site: https://www.futuramedical.com
Pharmaceuticals Product Mfr
N.A.I.C.S.: 325412
James Barder *(CEO)*

FUTURA POLYESTERS LTD.

Paragon Condominium 3rd Floor,
Pandurang Budhkar Marg, Mumbai,
400 013, India
Tel.: (91) 22 24922999
Web Site:
    http://www.futurapolyesters.com
Sales Range: $125-149.9 Million
Polyester Resin Mfr
N.A.I.C.S.: 325211
S. B. Ghia *(Chm & Mng Dir)*

FUTURAQUA MINERAL WA-TER PRODUCTION AND AS-SET MANAGEMENT PUBLIC LIMITED COMPANY

7011 Alap Dozsa Gy Street, Alap,
8183, Pecs, Hungary
Tel.: (36) 9580014
Web Site: https://www.futuraqua.eu
FUTURAQUA—(BUD)
Rev.: $6,851
Assets: $1,189,677
Liabilities: $298,397
Net Worth: $891,280
Earnings: $155,316
Fiscal Year-end: 12/31/23
Mineral Water Production & Invest-
ment
N.A.I.C.S.: 221310
Zsolt Andras Hajnal *(Chm-Mgmt Bd)*

FUTURE ARAB INVESTMENT CO.

128 Sharif Naser Bin Jamil St Sport
City Cir, PO Box 20082, Al Shmei-
sani, Amman, 11118, Jordan
Tel.: (962) 65622100
Web Site: https://www.fainvest.com
Year Founded: 2006
FUTR—(AMM)
Rev.: $15,373,366
Assets: $39,918,216
Liabilities: $11,694,047
Net Worth: $28,224,170
Earnings: ($2,466,527)
Emp.: 3
Fiscal Year-end: 12/31/20
Investment Management Service
N.A.I.C.S.: 523999
Muhsen A. Quqa *(Chm)*

Subsidiaries:

Damia Agricultural Products Com-
pany Ltd.   (1)
Shumaysani Al-Sheikh Hussein Al-Jeser St,
PO Box 66, Building Num 11 GF, Amman,
16197, Jordan
Tel.: (962) 65692625
Web Site: https://www.daniaagri.com
Agricultural Product Mfr & Distr
N.A.I.C.S.: 333922

FUTURE BATTERY MINERALS LIMITED

Suite 10 38-40 Colin St, West Perth,
6005, WA, Australia
Tel.: (61) 863837817
Web Site:
    https://futurebatteryminerals.com.au
FBM—(ASX)
Rev.: $347,160
Assets: $21,689,436
Liabilities: $792,382
Net Worth: $20,897,054
Earnings: ($10,259,177)
Fiscal Year-end: 06/30/24
Gold Ore & Silver Ore Mining
N.A.I.C.S.: 212220

FUTURE BRIGHT HOLDINGS LIMITED

Room 1409 West Tower Shun Tak
Centre 200 Connaught Road, Cen-
tral, China (Hong Kong)
Tel.: (852) 25482115   BM
Web Site:
    http://www.innovo.etnet.hk
0703—(HKG)
Rev.: $36,344,640
Assets: $121,116,840
Liabilities: $83,440,208
Net Worth: $37,676,633
Earnings: ($16,301,768)
Emp.: 586
Fiscal Year-end: 12/31/22
Food & Beverage Mfr
N.A.I.C.S.: 311999

Subsidiaries:

FB Group Enterprises Management
Company Limited   (1)
Avenida da Amizade N1023 Edif Nam Fong
2 andar P-V, Nam Fong, Macau, China
(Macau)
Tel.: (853) 2 870 1166
Web Site:
    http://www.futurebrightgroup.com.mo
Sales Range: $200-249.9 Million
Emp.: 1,500
Restaurant Operating Services
N.A.I.C.S.: 722511

Nippon Gourmet Trading Company
Limited   (1)
Tel.: (853) 28725577
Food & Beverage Whslr
N.A.I.C.S.: 424420

FUTURE BRIGHT MINING HOLDINGS LIMITED

Unit 3006 30/F West Tower Shun Tak
Centre 168-200 Connaught, Road
Central Sheung Wan, Hong Kong,
China (Hong Kong)
Tel.: (852) 29892212
Web Site:
    http://www.futurebrightltd.com
2212—(HKG)
Rev.: $8,969,314
Assets: $10,401,674
Liabilities: $3,305,437
Net Worth: $7,096,237
Earnings: ($1,253,912)
Emp.: 39
Fiscal Year-end: 12/31/22
Marble Mining
N.A.I.C.S.: 212311
Ho Wai Wu *(Sec)*

FUTURE COMMUNICATIONS CO. GLOBAL K.S.C.C.

6th Floor Al-Awadi Tower 3 Ahmad Al Jaber Street Sharq, PO Box 1324, Safat, Kuwait, 13014, Kuwait
Tel.: (965) 22432555
Web Site: http://www.fccg.com.kw
Year Founded: 1998
Sales Range: $75-99.9 Million
Emp.: 530
Telecommunication Servicesb
N.A.I.C.S.: 517810

FUTURE CORPORATE RESOURCES LIMITED

Knowledge House Shyam Nagar Off Jogeshwari-Vikhroli Link Road, Jogeshwari East, Mumbai, 400 060, India
Tel.: (91) 22 3084 1300   In
Web Site: http://www.fcrl.in
Year Founded: 1996
Holding Company
N.A.I.C.S.: 551112
Kishore Biyani *(Founder & CEO)*

Subsidiaries:

Amar Chitra Katha Private Limited   (1)
Sumer Plaza 2nd Floor Marol Maroshi Road, Marol Andheri East, Mumbai, 400 059, India
Tel.: (91) 2240497431
Web Site: http://www.ack-media.com
Books Publishing Services
N.A.I.C.S.: 513130
Anuraag Agarwal *(CEO)*

Aussee Oats Milling (Private) Limited   (1)
Boi Epz, 11200, Mirigama, Sri Lanka
Tel.: (94) 112254411
Web Site: http://www.ausseeoats.com
Food Products Distr
N.A.I.C.S.: 445110
Harsha Suraweera *(Mgr-Pkg)*

Ezoneonline.in   (1)
8th Floor Tower C 247 Park LBS Marg Vikhroli West, Mumbai, 400083, India
Tel.: (91) 9223322999
Web Site: http://www.ezoneonline.in
Online Shopping Services
N.A.I.C.S.: 425120
Mandheer Singh *(CMO)*

Future Consumer Limited   (1)
Knowledge House Shyam Nagar Off Jogeshwari Vikhroli Link Road, Mumbai, 400 060, Maharashtra, India
Tel.: (91) 2266442200
Web Site: http://www.futureconsumer.in
Rev.: $48,639,158
Assets: $58,751,178
Liabilities: $80,854,325
Net Worth: ($22,103,147)
Earnings: ($40,169,426)
Emp.: 62
Fiscal Year-end: 03/31/2023
Food Product Retailer
N.A.I.C.S.: 445110
Kishore Biyani *(Vice Chm)*

Subsidiary (Domestic):

IBH Books and Magazines Distributors Limited   (2)
10 Bezzola Complex Opp Suman Nagar Sion Trombay Road, Chembur, Mumbai, 400071, India
Tel.: (91) 22 4049 7474
Web Site: http://www.ibhworld.com
Book Publishers
N.A.I.C.S.: 513130
Krishna Kiran *(Sr VP)*

Subsidiary (Domestic):

Ideas Box Entertainment Limited   (3)
701 Subha Palace Off Khar Station 4th Road Khar 7th Floor, Mumbai, 400052, India
Tel.: (91) 2265232335
Books Publishing Services
N.A.I.C.S.: 513130

Karadi Tales Company Private Limited   (3)
3A Dev Regency 11 First Main Road, Gandhinagar Adyar, Chennai, 600 020, India
Tel.: (91) 4424421775
Web Site: http://www.karaditales.com
Books Publishing Services
N.A.I.C.S.: 513130
Chidambaranath Krishnamani *(Area Mgr-Sls)*

Subsidiary (Domestic):

Nilgiris Mechanised Bakery Private Limited   (2)
28 Magrath Road, Bengaluru, 560025, Karnataka, India
Tel.: (91) 25572104
Food Products Distr
N.A.I.C.S.: 445110

Future Enterprises Limited   (1)
Knowledge House Shyam Nagar Off Jogeshwari-Vikhroli Link Road, Jogeshwari East, Mumbai, 400 060, India   **(41.9%)**
Tel.: (91) 2266442200
Web Site: http://www.felindia.in
Rev.: $217,127,820
Assets: $1,618,290,765
Liabilities: $1,218,936,810
Net Worth: $399,353,955
Earnings: ($166,553,205)
Emp.: 1,900
Fiscal Year-end: 03/31/2021
Holding Company
N.A.I.C.S.: 455219
Kishore Biyani *(Vice Chm)*

Subsidiary (Domestic):

Future Media (India) Limited   (2)
Future Retail Home Office Tower C 7th Floor 247, Park LBS Marg Vikhroli West, Mumbai, 400 083, India   **(93.1%)**
Tel.: (91) 2261190000
Web Site: http://www.futuremedia.in
Media Advertising Services
N.A.I.C.S.: 541840
Sandip Tarkas *(CEO)*

Future Supply Chain Solutions Ltd.   (2)
Bhagat House 5A Shyam Nagar Off Jogeshwari Vikhroli Link Road, Jogeshwari E, Mumbai, 400060, India   **(70.17%)**
Tel.: (91) 2229264500
Web Site: http://www.futuresupplychains.com
Logistics Consulting Servies
N.A.I.C.S.: 541614

Staples Future Office Products Limited   (2)
3rd Floor Orchid City Centre Mumbai Central E, Mumbai, 400 008, India   **(60%)**
Tel.: (91) 22 6000 3000
Web Site: http://www.staplesfuture.com
Food Products Distr
N.A.I.C.S.: 445110

Future Learning and Development Limited   (1)
2nd Floor Evershine Mall Main Link Road Opposite Mind Space Malad West, Mumbai, 400064, India
Tel.: (91) 2267424142
Food Products Distr
N.A.I.C.S.: 445110

Future Lifestyle Fashions Limited   (1)
Knowledge House Shyam Nagar Off Jogeshwari-Vikhroli Link Road, Jogeshwari East, Mumbai, 400 060, India
Tel.: (91) 22 6644 2200
Web Site: http://www.futurelifestyle.in
Rev.: $317,646,420
Assets: $849,945,915
Liabilities: $754,226,655
Net Worth: $95,719,260
Earnings: ($127,402,275)
Emp.: 6,663
Fiscal Year-end: 03/31/2021
Apparel Accessory Store Operator
N.A.I.C.S.: 458110
Kishore Biyani *(Mng Dir)*

Future Retail Limited   (1)
Knowledge House Shyam Nagar Off Jogeshwari-Vikhroli Link Road, Jogeshwari East, Mumbai, 400 060, India   **(38.39%)**

Tel.: (91) 2230841300
Web Site: http://www.futureretail.in
Rev.: $895,558,755
Assets: $2,596,947,990
Liabilities: $2,447,652,480
Net Worth: $149,295,510
Earnings: ($435,369,480)
Emp.: 21,839
Fiscal Year-end: 03/31/2021
Holding Company; Hypermarkets, Supermarkets & Home Center Retail Stores Operator
N.A.I.C.S.: 551112
Kishore Biyani *(Chm)*

Unit (Domestic):

Big Bazaar   (2)
Ahmedabad City Mall New Cotton Mills Compound Outside Raipur Gate, Opp Arya Sewa Samaj Hall Kankaria Road, Ahmedabad, 380022, Gujarat, India
Tel.: (91) 18002002255
Consumer Products Distr
N.A.I.C.S.: 423620
Kishore Biyani *(Mng Dir)*

Foodhall   (2)
Level 4 Gurgaon Central Mall Near Private Hospital Sector 25 M G Road, Gurgaon, 122001, India
Tel.: (91) 1244309970
Web Site: http://www.foodhallonline.com
Food Products Distr
N.A.I.C.S.: 445110

Futurebrands Ltd.   (1)
W4D-204/3 Keshav Kunj Sainik Farms, New Delhi, 110062, India
Tel.: (91) 1126548000
Web Site: http://www.futurebrands.co.in
Food Products Distr
N.A.I.C.S.: 445110
Santosh Desai *(CEO)*

Indus-League Clothing Limited   (1)
No 3 Puttapa Indl Estate White Field road Mahadevpura Post, Bengaluru, 560048, India
Tel.: (91) 8033423535
Web Site: http://www.indus-league.com
Food Products Distr
N.A.I.C.S.: 445110
Rachna Aggarwal *(CEO)*

FUTURE CORPORATION

1-2-2 Osaki, Shinagawa-ku, Tokyo, 141-0032, Japan
Tel.: (81) 357405721
Web Site: https://www.future.co.jp
Year Founded: 1989
4722—(TKS)
Rev.: $420,607,160
Assets: $468,244,870
Liabilities: $103,911,040
Net Worth: $364,333,830
Earnings: $65,376,890
Emp.: 2,948
Fiscal Year-end: 12/31/23
Information Technology Consulting Services
N.A.I.C.S.: 541512
Yasufumi Kanemaru *(Founder, Chm, Chm, Pres, Pres, CEO & CEO-Grp)*

Subsidiaries:

Ascendia Inc.   (1)
Osaki W City Bldg Osaki 2-9-3, Shinagawa-ku, Tokyo, 141-0031, Japan
Tel.: (81) 363616000
Web Site: http://www.ascendia.jp
Custom Software Design & Publishing Services
N.A.I.C.S.: 513210

Curiosity Inc.   (1)
2-13-16 Tomigaya, Shibuya-ku, Tokyo, 151-0063, Japan
Tel.: (81) 354520095
Web Site: https://curiosity.jp
Multidisciplinary Studio Services
N.A.I.C.S.: 541430

ELM Corporation   (1)
2-9-3 Uesutoshitibiru 5F, Shinagawa-ku, Tokyo, 141 0032, Osaki, Japan
Tel.: (81) 357196122

Web Site: http://www.elmcorp.jp
Sales Range: $25-49.9 Million
Emp.: 100
Business Software Publisher
N.A.I.C.S.: 513210
Kuniyasu Hiroi *(Mgr)*

Future Architect, Inc.   (1)
Art Osaki Central Tower 1-2-2, Shinagawa-ku, Tokyo, 141-0032, Japan
Tel.: (81) 357405721
Web Site: https://www.future.co.jp
Information Technology Services
N.A.I.C.S.: 541511

Future Financial Strategy Corp.   (1)
Art Vlg Osaki Cent Tower 1-2-2 Osaki, Shinagawa-ku, Tokyo, 141-0032, Japan
Tel.: (81) 357405722
Strategic Consulting & Financial Services
N.A.I.C.S.: 523940

Future Inspace, Inc.   (1)
Osaki West City Building 2-9-3 Osaki, Shinagawa-ku, Tokyo, 141-0032, Japan
Tel.: (81) 363616000
Web Site: https://www.inspace.co.jp
Emp.: 353
System Integration Services
N.A.I.C.S.: 541519

Innovation Laboratory, Inc.   (1)
705 Mouri Building 2-14-5, Kojima Taito-ku, Tokyo, Japan
Tel.: (81) 368691949
Web Site: http://www.ilab-inc.jp
Innovation Consulting Services
N.A.I.C.S.: 541690
Yukinobu Yokota *(Mng Dir)*

Micro CAD Co., Ltd.   (1)
14th Floor Art Village Osaki Central Tower 1-2-2 Osaki, Shinagawa-ku, Tokyo, 141-0032, Japan
Tel.: (81) 35 740 5060
Web Site: https://www.microcad.co.jp
System Integration Services
N.A.I.C.S.: 541519

Uoei Shoten Corporation   (1)
423-1 Ajigata, Minami, 950-1227, Niigata, Japan
Tel.: (81) 253733011
Web Site: http://www.uoei.co.jp
Supermarket Management Services
N.A.I.C.S.: 445110
Kenji Suzuki *(Pres & CEO)*

YDC Corporation   (1)
1-9 Fuchu-cho Keio Fuchu 1-chome Building, Fuchu, 183-8540, Tokyo, Japan   **(81%)**
Tel.: (81) 423526112
Web Site: http://www.ydc.co.jp
Emp.: 259
Electronic Components Mfr
N.A.I.C.S.: 334419
Kozo Iida *(VP)*

YOCABITO Co., Ltd.   (1)
6th floor Meiji Yasuda Life Gifu Kanamachi Building 4-30, Kanamachi, Gifu, 500-8842, Japan
Tel.: (81) 582144586
Web Site: https://corp.yocabito.co.jp
Emp.: 129
Health Food Mfr & Distr
N.A.I.C.S.: 311999

Zakura Inc.   (1)
2-9-3 Uesutoshitibiru 6F, Tokyo, 141-0032, Japan
Tel.: (81) 357405839
Web Site: http://www.zakura.jp
Sales Range: $25-49.9 Million
Emp.: 10
Internet Media Services
N.A.I.C.S.: 518210

dit Co., Ltd.   (1)
Osaki West City Building 2-9-3 Osaki, Shinagawa-ku, Tokyo, 141-0032, Japan
Tel.: (81) 356347651
Web Site: https://www.dit.co.jp
Emp.: 100
Information Security System Services
N.A.I.C.S.: 561621
Masaru Toda *(Pres)*

FUTURE DATA GROUP LIMITED

Future Data Group Limited—(Continued)

Suite 1507-08 15/F Two Chinachem Exchange Square 338 Kings Road, North Point, Hong Kong, China (Hong Kong)
Tel.: (852) 29070001 **Ky**
Web Site:
http://www.futuredatagroup.com
Year Founded: 1997
8229—(HKG)
Rev.: $78,749,228
Assets: $43,379,835
Liabilities: $26,379,623
Net Worth: $17,000,213
Earnings: ($506,048)
Emp.: 254
Fiscal Year-end: 12/31/22
Information Technology Support Services
N.A.I.C.S.: 541512
Seung Hyun Suh *(Co-Founder & Chm)*

Subsidiaries:

Maximus Consulting (Hong Kong) Ltd. **(1)**
Suite 1507-08 15/F Two Chinachem Exchange Square 338 King's Road, North Point, China (Hong Kong)
Tel.: (852) 28023953
Web Site: https://maximusholding.com
Cyber Security Consulting Services
N.A.I.C.S.: 561612

FUTURE ELECTRONICS INC.

237 Hymus Boulevard, Pointe-Claire, H9R 5C7, QC, Canada
Tel.: (514) 694-7710 **Ca**
Web Site:
http://www.futureelectronics.com
Year Founded: 1968
Sales Range: $1-4.9 Billion
Emp.: 1,300
Semi-Conductors & Passive, Interconnect & Electro-Mechanical Components Distr
N.A.I.C.S.: 423690
Pierre G. Guilbault *(CFO & Exec VP)*

Subsidiaries:

FAI Electronics **(1)**
237 Boul Hymus, Pointe-Claire, H9R 5C7, QC, Canada **(100%)**
Tel.: (514) 694-7710
Sales Range: $550-599.9 Million
Emp.: 1,200
Distr of Electronic Parts & Equipment
N.A.I.C.S.: 423690

Future Electronics (Shanghai) Co., Ltd **(1)**
26F Jin Long Building Cai Wu Wei Hong Bao Road, Luohu District, Shenzhen, 518001, China
Tel.: (86) 755 8304 0500
Electronic Components Distr
N.A.I.C.S.: 423690
Deo Fu *(Engr-Sls)*

Future Electronics A/S **(1)**
Skomagervej 13D, Vejle, 7100, Denmark
Tel.: (45) 764 08 764
Electronic Components Distr
N.A.I.C.S.: 423690

Future Electronics AB **(1)**
Tevlingveien 23, Oslo, NO-1081, Norway
Tel.: (47) 229 05800
Web Site: http://www.futureelectronics.com
Electronic Components Distr
N.A.I.C.S.: 423690

Future Electronics Austria GmbH **(1)**
Scheringgasse 2, Vienna, 1140, Austria
Tel.: (43) 1 577 33 00
Electronic Components Distr
N.A.I.C.S.: 423690
Michael Schlee *(Mgr-Technical Solution)*

Future Electronics Corp. **(1)**
8700 Indian Creek Pkwy Bldg 3, Overland Park, KS 66210-1442 **(100%)**

Tel.: (913) 498-1531
Web Site: http://www.future-active.com
Sales Range: $50-74.9 Million
Emp.: 9
Distr of Electronic Components
N.A.I.C.S.: 423690
Clem Noll *(Gen Mgr)*

Future Electronics Corp. **(1)**
255 Primera Blvd Ste 240, Lake Mary, FL 32746
Tel.: (407) 444-6302
Web Site: http://www.futureelectronics.com
Emp.: 15
Mfr of Electronic Products
N.A.I.C.S.: 420000
Sheldon Weiss *(Mgr-Sls)*

Future Electronics Corp. **(1)**
3000 Stonewood Dr Ste 320, Wexford, PA 15090 **(100%)**
Tel.: (724) 935-1113
Sales Range: $50-74.9 Million
Emp.: 7
Distribution of Electronic Component
N.A.I.C.S.: 423690

Future Electronics Corp. **(1)**
4700 Homewood Ct Ste 106, Raleigh, NC 27609 **(100%)**
Tel.: (919) 571-9942
Web Site: http://www.futureelectronics.com
Sales Range: $50-74.9 Million
Emp.: 10
Electronics Distribution
N.A.I.C.S.: 423690

Future Electronics Corp. **(1)**
3033 Express Dr N, Hauppauge, NY 11749-5309 **(100%)**
Tel.: (631) 234-4000
Web Site: http://www.futureelectronics.com
Sales Range: $25-49.9 Million
Emp.: 12
Distr of Electronic Components
N.A.I.C.S.: 423690

Future Electronics Corp. **(1)**
18000 W Sarah Ln Ste 170, Brookfield, WI 53045-5899
Tel.: (262) 879-0244
Web Site: http://www.futureelectronics.com
Sales Range: $50-74.9 Million
Emp.: 14
Electronics Distr
N.A.I.C.S.: 423610

Future Electronics Corp. **(1)**
5 Greentree Ctr 525 Rt 73 N Ste 217, Marlton, NJ 08053 **(100%)**
Tel.: (856) 985-2841
Web Site: http://www.futureelectronics.com
Sales Range: $25-49.9 Million
Emp.: 15
Provider of Electronics & Electrical Solutions
N.A.I.C.S.: 423690

Future Electronics Corp. **(1)**
4801 E Washington St Ste 265, Phoenix, AZ 85034-2021 **(100%)**
Tel.: (602) 629-3013
Web Site: http://www.futureelectronics.com
Sales Range: $25-49.9 Million
Emp.: 20
Electronics Distribution
N.A.I.C.S.: 423690

Future Electronics Corp. **(1)**
6550 SW Redwood Ln Ste 365, Portland, OR 97224
Tel.: (503) 603-0956
Web Site: http://www.futureelectronics.com
Sales Range: $50-74.9 Million
Emp.: 6
Electronic & Electromechanical Equipment Distr
N.A.I.C.S.: 423690
Jeff Hilden *(Gen Mgr)*

Future Electronics Corp. **(1)**
375 Woodcliff Dr Ste 11, Fairport, NY 14450-4276 **(100%)**
Tel.: (800) 444-1521
Web Site: http://www.futureelectronics.com
Sales Range: $25-49.9 Million
Emp.: 12
Sales of Electronic Components
N.A.I.C.S.: 423690
Anthony Lipari *(Gen Mgr)*

Future Electronics Corp. **(1)**
1640 Lead Hill Blvd Ste 200, Roseville, CA 95661-3895
Tel.: (916) 783-7877
Web Site: http://www.futureelectronics.com
Sales Range: $25-49.9 Million
Emp.: 15
Electronics Distr
N.A.I.C.S.: 423690
Jeff Yake *(Gen Mgr)*

Future Electronics Corp. **(1)**
6256 Greenwich Dr Ste 250, San Diego, CA 92122-5981
Tel.: (858) 625-2800
Sales Range: $25-49.9 Million
Emp.: 15
N.A.I.C.S.: 449210

Future Electronics Corp. **(1)**
690 N McCarthy Blvd Ste 220, Milpitas, CA 95035-1326
Tel.: (408) 434-1122
Web Site: http://www.futureelectronics.com
Sales Range: $50-74.9 Million
Emp.: 53
Sales of Electronic Products
N.A.I.C.S.: 423690
Todd Fiske *(VP)*

Future Electronics Corp. **(1)**
12125 Woodcrest Executive Dr Ste 200, Saint Louis, MO 63141
Tel.: (314) 317-8751
Sales Range: $25-49.9 Million
Emp.: 12
Electronic Goods Distr
N.A.I.C.S.: 423690

Future Electronics Corp. **(1)**
406 W South Jordan Pkwy Ste 580, South Jordan, UT 84095-3940 **(100%)**
Tel.: (801) 467-4448
Web Site: http://www.futureelectronics.com
Sales Range: $50-74.9 Million
Emp.: 7
Mfr of Electronic Components
N.A.I.C.S.: 423690

Future Electronics Corp. **(1)**
32 Discovery Ste 170, Irvine, CA 92618
Tel.: (949) 453-1515
Web Site: http://www.futureelectronics.com
Sales Range: $800-899.9 Million
Emp.: 12
Semiconductor Distr & Marketer
N.A.I.C.S.: 449210

Future Electronics Corp. **(1)**
22232 17th Ave SE Ste 301, Bothell, WA 98021
Tel.: (425) 489-3400
Web Site: http://www.futureelectronics.com
Rev.: $7,000,000
Emp.: 25
Electronics Distribution
N.A.I.C.S.: 423690
Andy Sidhu *(VP)*

Future Electronics Corp. **(1)**
301 Plainfield Rd Ste 275, Syracuse, NY 13212-4585 **(100%)**
Tel.: (315) 451-2371
Web Site: http://www.futureelectronics.com
Sales Range: $25-49.9 Million
Emp.: 12
Distributers of Electronics Company
N.A.I.C.S.: 423690

Future Electronics Corp., Australia **(1)**
Ste 503 Level 5, 425 Burwood Highway, Wantirna, 3152, VIC, Australia **(100%)**
Tel.: (61) 395586312
Web Site: http://www.future.com
Sales Range: $25-49.9 Million
Emp.: 5
N.A.I.C.S.: 449210

Future Electronics Corp., Australia **(1)**
Ste 6 752 Balckburn Rd, Clayton, Melbourne, 3168, VIC, Australia **(100%)**
Tel.: (61) 398997944
Web Site: http://www.future.com
N.A.I.C.S.: 449210

Future Electronics Corp., Belgium **(1)**
Ryvisspraat 118, Zwijnaarde, 9052, Belgium **(100%)**

Tel.: (32) 93405270
Web Site: http://www.futureelectronics.com
Emp.: 16
N.A.I.C.S.: 449210

Future Electronics Corp., Brazil **(1)**
Rua Luzitana 740/10 Andar Conjuntos 103/104 Centro, Campinas, 13015-121, Sao Paulo, Brazil **(100%)**
Tel.: (55) 1937374100
Web Site: http://www.futureelectronics.com
Sales Range: $25-49.9 Million
Emp.: 25
Distr & Marketing of Semiconductors & Passive Interconnect & Electro-Mechanical Components
N.A.I.C.S.: 334413
Edward Zamaro *(Gen Mgr)*

Future Electronics Corp., Bulgaria **(1)**
23 Andrej Saharov St, Sofia, 1784, Bulgaria
Tel.: (359) 29745952
Web Site: http://www.futureelectronics.com
N.A.I.C.S.: 449210

Future Electronics Corp., Canada **(1)**
6029 103rd St, Edmonton, T6H2H3, AB, Canada **(100%)**
Tel.: (780) 438-5888
Web Site: http://www.futureelectronics.com
Sales Range: $50-74.9 Million
Emp.: 1
Distribution of Electronic Semiconductor Components
N.A.I.C.S.: 423690

Future Electronics Corp., Canada **(1)**
900-2025 Willingdon Ave, Burnaby, V5C 0J3, BC, Canada **(100%)**
Tel.: (604) 294-1166
Web Site: http://www.futureelectronics.com
Sales Range: $25-49.9 Million
Emp.: 15
Retail Distribution of Electronic Equipment
N.A.I.C.S.: 423690

Future Electronics Corp., Denmark **(1)**
Skomagervej 13 D, Vejle, 7100, Denmark **(100%)**
Tel.: (45) 76408764
Web Site: http://www.futureelectronics.com
Sales Range: $25-49.9 Million
Emp.: 10
Electronics Distr
N.A.I.C.S.: 449210
Niels Bisgaard *(Gen Mgr)*

Future Electronics Corp., Erfurt **(1)**
Augsburger Strasse 10, Erfurt, 99091, Germany **(100%)**
Tel.: (49) 361420870
Web Site: http://www.futureelectronics.com
Sales Range: $25-49.9 Million
Emp.: 7
N.A.I.C.S.: 449210
Walter Mueller *(Branch Mgr)*

Future Electronics Corp., Finland **(1)**
Technopolis Aviapolis H-Building 3rd Floor Teknobulevardi 7, 1530, Vantaa, Finland **(100%)**
Tel.: (358) 95259950
Sales Range: $25-49.9 Million
Emp.: 10
N.A.I.C.S.: 449210
Paul Benford *(Branch Mgr)*

Future Electronics Corp., France **(1)**
Europarc Du Chene 4 Rue Edison Batiment A, Bron, 69673, Bron, France **(100%)**
Tel.: (33) 472158600
Web Site: http://www.futureelectronics.com
Sales Range: $25-49.9 Million
Emp.: 10
N.A.I.C.S.: 423690
Michael Loriot *(Gen Mgr)*

Future Electronics Corp., France **(1)**
6 Avenue Morane Saulnier, 78941, Velizy-Villacoublay, Cedex, France **(100%)**
Tel.: (33) 223456080
Sales Range: $10-24.9 Million
Emp.: 60
N.A.I.C.S.: 449210

Future Electronics Corp., France (1)
Le Magistere II 334 Rue des Vingt Toises,
38950, Saint-Martin-le-Vinoux,
France (100%)
Tel.: (33) 4 38 02 02 03
Sales Range: $25-49.9 Million
Emp.: 70
N.A.I.C.S.: 449210
Cyril Berquier (Gen Mgr)

Future Electronics Corp., France (1)
ZAC des Ramassiers 5 Boulevard, Jean
Auguste Ingres Batiment A 3rd Floor,
31770, Colomiers, France (100%)
Tel.: (03) 562747240
Distr & Marketing of Semiconductors & Pas-
sive Interconnect & Electro-Mechanical
Components
N.A.I.C.S.: 334413

**Future Electronics Corp.,
Germany** (1)
Oskar Messter Str 25, Ismaning, 85737,
Germany (100%)
Tel.: (49) 89957270
Web Site: http://www.futureelectronics.com
Sales Range: $25-49.9 Million
Emp.: 70
N.A.I.C.S.: 449210

**Future Electronics Corp.,
Hungary** (1)
Retkoz u 5 1st Floor, BudaWest Irodahaz,
1118, Budapest, Hungary (100%)
Tel.: (36) 12240510
Sales Range: $25-49.9 Million
Emp.: 10
N.A.I.C.S.: 449210
Zsolt Szabo (Office Mgr)

Future Electronics Corp., Ireland (1)
26 Merchants Square, Nangor Rd, Ennis,
Co Clare, Ireland (100%)
Tel.: (353) 656844130
Web Site: http://www.futureelectronics.com
Sales Range: $25-49.9 Million
Emp.: 8
N.A.I.C.S.: 449210

Future Electronics Corp., Israel (1)
Maskik 2 Builiding D Fl 6, PO Box 4024,
Herzliyya, 46140, Israel (100%)
Tel.: (972) 99701414
Sales Range: $25-49.9 Million
Emp.: 38
N.A.I.C.S.: 449210
Ilana Miller (Head-Fin)

Future Electronics Corp., Italy (1)
Galleria Ronzani 3 9, Casalecchio Di Reno,
Bologna, 40033, Italy (100%)
Tel.: (39) 0516136711
Sales Range: $25-49.9 Million
Emp.: 12
N.A.I.C.S.: 449210

Future Electronics Corp., Italy (1)
Via Longhin 11 Palazzo Galileo, Padua,
35129, Italy (100%)
Tel.: (39) 049 899 2012
Web Site: http://www.futureelectronics.com
Sales Range: $25-49.9 Million
Emp.: 10
Electronic Components Distribution
N.A.I.C.S.: 334419
Vittorio Pistorio (Reg Dir-Sls)

Future Electronics Corp., Mexico (1)
Chimalhuacan 3569 7 Piso, Ste 2 Ciudad
Del Sol, Zapopan, 45050, Jalisco,
Mexico (100%)
Tel.: (52) 3331220043
Web Site: http://www.globalcsamintra.net
Sales Range: $25-49.9 Million
Emp.: 11
N.A.I.C.S.: 449210
Mario Suarec (Gen Mgr)

Future Electronics Corp., Mexico (1)
Aquanaval 2206 Local 11, Col Roma, Mon-
terrey, 64700, Nuevo Leon,
Mexico (100%)
Tel.: (52) 8112342887
Sales Range: $25-49.9 Million
Emp.: 4
Electronics Distr
N.A.I.C.S.: 449210

**Future Electronics Corp., New
Zealand** (1)
Unit 5 Wordsworth St, PO Box 7500,
Sydenham, Christchurch, 8023, New
Zealand (100%)
Tel.: (64) 39823256
Web Site: http://www.futureelectronics.com
Sales Range: $25-49.9 Million
Emp.: 3
N.A.I.C.S.: 449210

Future Electronics Corp., Norway (1)
Tevlingveien 23, Oslo, 1081,
Norway (100%)
Tel.: (47) 229 05800
Web Site: http://www.futureelectronics.com
Sales Range: $25-49.9 Million
Emp.: 3
Electronic Product Distr
N.A.I.C.S.: 449210
Roger Hellstrom (Gen Mgr)

Future Electronics Corp., Norway (1)
Jordhus Industriomaade, Loekken Verk,
Trondheim, 7332, Norway (100%)
Tel.: (47) 72495990
Web Site: http://www.futureelectronics.com
Sales Range: $25-49.9 Million
Emp.: 1
N.A.I.C.S.: 449210

Future Electronics Corp., Poland (1)
Klopotowskiego 22 Str, 03-717, Warsaw,
Poland (100%)
Tel.: (48) 226189202
Web Site: http://www.euturelectronics.com
Sales Range: $10-24.9 Million
Emp.: 11
N.A.I.C.S.: 449210
Yer Derzycyszko (Dir-Mfg)

**Future Electronics Corp.,
Scotland** (1)
Mirren Ct 3, 123 Renfrew Rd, Paisley,
PA34EA, Renfrewshire, United
Kingdom (100%)
Tel.: (44) 418406500
Web Site: http://www.future.com
N.A.I.C.S.: 449210

Future Electronics Corp., Spain (1)
Centre D Empreses De Noves Tecnologies,
Parc Tecnologic Del Valles, Barcelona,
08290, Cerdanyola, Spain (100%)
Tel.: (34) 935824343
Web Site: http://www.futureelectronics.com
Electronic Equipment Mfr & Sales
N.A.I.C.S.: 449210
Rafael Ruiz (Mgr)

Future Electronics Corp., Spain (1)
Avenida Del Parenon 10, Campo de Las
Naciones, 28042, Madrid, Spain (100%)
Tel.: (34) 917214270
Sales Range: $25-49.9 Million
Emp.: 15
N.A.I.C.S.: 449210
Arriaga Anton (Branch Mgr)

**Future Electronics Corp.,
Sweden** (1)
Kabelgatan 9, Kungsbacka, 43437,
Sweden (100%)
Tel.: (46) 30030300
N.A.I.C.S.: 449210

**Future Electronics Corp.,
Sweden** (1)
Kista Science Tower, 164 51, Kista,
Sweden (100%)
Tel.: (46) 86248800
Web Site: http://www.futureelectronics.com
Sales Range: $25-49.9 Million
Emp.: 20
N.A.I.C.S.: 449210

**Future Electronics Corp.,
Sweden** (1)
Future Electronics AB Knarrarnasgatan 7,
Svedala, SE 16422, Kista,
Sweden (100%)
Tel.: (46) 40406990
Web Site: http://www.futureelectronics.com
Sales Range: $25-49.9 Million
Emp.: 30
N.A.I.C.S.: 449210

**Future Electronics Corp., The
Netherlands** (1)
Tinstraa 3, Breda, 4823,
Netherlands (100%)
Tel.: (31) 765444888

Web Site: http://www.futureelectronics.com
Sales Range: $25-49.9 Million
Emp.: 15
N.A.I.C.S.: 449210
Wilfred Poot (Branch Mgr)

Future Electronics Corp., Turkey (1)
Turkiye Irtibat Brosu, Sehit Mehmet, 34742,
Istanbul, Turkiye (100%)
Tel.: (90) 2164458700
Web Site: http://www.futureelectronics.com
Sales Range: $25-49.9 Million
Emp.: 7
N.A.I.C.S.: 449210

Future Electronics Deutschland (1)
Zum Pier 71, Dortmund, 44536, Lunen,
Germany (100%)
Tel.: (49) 2319750480
N.A.I.C.S.: 449210

**Future Electronics Deutschland
GmbH** (1)
Max Planck Strasse 3 2nd Floor, Aschheim,
85737, Germany (100%)
Tel.: (49) 89957270
Web Site: http://www.futureelectronics.com
Rev.: $45,030,000
Emp.: 60
Electronic Parts & Equipment
N.A.I.C.S.: 423690
Juergen Ruben (Gen Mgr)

Future Electronics Inc. (1)
41 Main St, Bolton, MA 01740-1107
Tel.: (978) 779-3000
Emp.: 8
Electronic Parts Sales
N.A.I.C.S.: 423690

**Future Electronics Inc. (Distribution)
Pte Ltd.** (1)
19 Loyang Way #01-08/09/10 CLC, Chungy
Logistic Ctr, Singapore, 508 724,
Singapore (100%)
Tel.: (65) 65945000
Web Site: http://www.futureelectronics.com
Electronic Parts & Equipment
N.A.I.C.S.: 423690

Branch (Non-US):

Future Electronics Corp., Japan (2)
Kawaramachi As Bldg No 5, 2 6 1 Kawara-
machi Chuo Ku, Osaka, 541-3048,
Japan (100%)
Tel.: (81) 662212201
Sales Range: $25-49.9 Million
Emp.: 4
N.A.I.C.S.: 449210

Future Electronics Corp., Korea (2)
5th Floor Yemizi Bldg Soonae-Dong 6-5
Boondang-Gu, Sungnam-Si, Seoul, 463-
020, Gyeonggi-Do, Korea (South) (100%)
Tel.: (82) 317868800
Sales Range: $25-49.9 Million
Emp.: 30
N.A.I.C.S.: 449210
J. Y. Wang (Country Mgr)

**Future Electronics Corp.,
Malaysia** (2)
51-7 A1 51 Jalan Sultan Ahmad Shah, Pen-
ang, 10050, Malaysia (100%)
Tel.: (60) 42277213
Web Site: http://www.futureelectronics.ca
Sales Range: $10-24.9 Million
Emp.: 15
N.A.I.C.S.: 449210

**Future Electronics Corp.,
Singapore** (2)
T8 And 9 No 66, GEM Plz Infantry Rd, Ben-
galuru, 560001, India (100%)
Tel.: (91) 8025593105
Web Site: http://www.futureelectronics.com
Sales Range: $25-49.9 Million
Emp.: 12
N.A.I.C.S.: 449210

Future Electronics Corp., Taiwan (2)
18F 2 295, Sec 2 Kuang Fu Rd, Hsin-chu,
300, Taiwan (100%)
Tel.: (886) 35744646
Web Site: http://www.futureelectronics.com
Sales Range: $25-49.9 Million
Emp.: 40
N.A.I.C.S.: 449210

Future Electronics Corp., Taiwan (2)

8F 172 Sec 4, Shih Lin Cheng Teh Rd, Tai-
pei, 111, Taiwan (100%)
Tel.: (886) 288615288
Sales Range: $25-49.9 Million
Emp.: 20
N.A.I.C.S.: 449210

**Future Electronics Corp.,
Thailand** (2)
947 Thosapol Land 3 Bldg Rm C2 18th Fl,
Bangna Trad Rd KM3 Bangna, Bangkok,
10260, Thailand
Tel.: (66) 23618400
Web Site: http://www.futureelectronics.com
Sales Range: $25-49.9 Million
Emp.: 9
N.A.I.C.S.: 449210

**Future Electronics Hong Kong
Limited** (2)
Unit 4607 19 Metroplaza Tower 1, 223 Hing
Fong Rd, Kwai Fong, China (Hong
Kong) (100%)
Tel.: (852) 24206238
Sales Range: $25-49.9 Million
Emp.: 15
N.A.I.C.S.: 449210

**Future Electronics Inc (Distribution)
Pte Ltd.** (2)
512 Ansal Tower 38 Nehru Pl, New Delhi,
110019, India (100%)
Tel.: (91) 01126461414
Web Site: http://www.futureelectronics.com
Sales Range: $10-24.9 Million
Emp.: 6
Global electronic components distributor.
N.A.I.C.S.: 449210

Future Electronics K.K. (2)
Yokohama Landmark Tower 24F 2 2 1 Mi-
natomirai Nishi Ku, Yokohama City Kana-
gawa Ken, Tokyo, 220 8124,
Japan (100%)
Tel.: (81) 452242155
Sales Range: $25-49.9 Million
Emp.: 90
Semiconductors & Electro Mechanical Com-
ponents
N.A.I.C.S.: 449210

**Future Electronics Service
Malaysia** (2)
Suite 801-1 Tower 1 Wisma Kelana Brem
Jalan SS7/15, Kelana Jaya, Petaling Jaya,
47301, Selangor, Malaysia (100%)
Tel.: (60) 3 7651 6888
Sales Range: $25-49.9 Million
Emp.: 4
N.A.I.C.S.: 449210
Kokbin Lee (Branch Mgr)

**Future Electronics Inc. (Warehouse)
Pte Ltd** (1)
19 Loyang Way Changi Logistics Centre
01-08, Singapore, 508724, Singapore
Tel.: (65) 6594 5000
Electronic Components Distr
N.A.I.C.S.: 423690

Future Electronics Kft (1)
Nagyszolos utca 11-15 BCW Irodahaz III
Emelet, Budapest, 1113, Hungary
Tel.: (36) 1 224 0510
Electronic Components Distr
N.A.I.C.S.: 423690
Kata Hujber (Acct Mgr)

Future Electronics Ltd. (1)
Future House, The Glanty, Egham, TW20
9AH, Surrey, United Kingdom (100%)
Tel.: (44) 1784275000
Web Site: http://www.futureelectronics.com
Rev.: $207,813,540
Emp.: 300
Electronic Part & Equipment Distr
N.A.I.C.S.: 423690

Branch (Domestic):

Future Electronics Ltd. (2)
Suite B2 Ground Floor Telegraphic House,
Waterfront 2000 Salford Quays, Man-
chester, M50 3XW, United
Kingdom (100%)
Tel.: (44) 1618760000
Web Site: http://www.futureelectronics.com
Sales Range: $25-49.9 Million
Emp.: 30

Future Electronics Inc.—(Continued)

Distr & Marketing of Semiconductors & Passive Interconnect & Electro-Mechanical Components
N.A.I.C.S.: 334413
Keith Thomas *(Reg Mgr-Sls)*

Future Electronics OU (1)
Ahtri 6, Tallinn, EE-10151, Estonia
Tel.: (372) 614 3201
Web Site: http://www.future.com
Emp.: 4
Electronic Components Distr
N.A.I.C.S.: 423690
Triin Muur *(Mgr-Sls)*

Future Electronics SAS (1)
ZAC des Ramassiers 5 Boulevard Jean Auguste Ingres, Batiment A 3rd Floor Colomiers, Toulouse, 31770, France
Tel.: (33) 562 74 7240
Electronic Components Distr
N.A.I.C.S.: 423690
Karim Hamami *(Engr-Sls-Field)*

Future Electronics Stuttgart (1)
Talstrasse 11, Korntal Munchingen, D 70825, Stuttgart, Germany (100%)
Tel.: (49) 711830830
Web Site: http://www.futureelectronics.com
Sales Range: $25-49.9 Million
Emp.: 12
N.A.I.C.S.: 449210

UAB Future Electronics (1)
Jurbarko 2-302, Kaunas, 47183, Lithuania
Tel.: (370) 37 408 482
Web Site: http://www.futureelectronics.com
Emp.: 25
Electronic Components Distr
N.A.I.C.S.: 423690
Arnoldas Bagdonas *(Mgr-Technical Solutions)*

FUTURE FARM TECHNOLOGIES INC.

Suite 501 543 Granville Street, Vancouver, V6C 1X8, BC, Canada
Tel.: (617) 834-9467 BC
Web Site:
http://www.futurefarmtech.com
Year Founded: 1984
FFT—(OTCIQ)
Sales Range: $1-9.9 Million
Investment Services
N.A.I.C.S.: 523999

FUTURE FILM GROUP PLC

10 Old Burlington Street, London, W1S 3AG, United Kingdom
Tel.: (44) 2070096767
Web Site:
http://www.futurefilmgroup.com
Year Founded: 2000
Motion Picture & Television Producer & Distr
N.A.I.C.S.: 512110
Stephen Margolis *(Head-Bus Affairs)*

Subsidiaries:

Future Films Limited (1)
115 Eastbourne Mews, London, W2 6LQ, United Kingdom
Tel.: (44) 20 7087 3570
Emp.: 15
Motion Picture Distribution Services
N.A.I.C.S.: 512120
Stephen Margolis *(CEO)*

Future Films USA LLC (1)
The Lot 1041 N Formosa Ave, West Hollywood, CA 90046
Tel.: (323) 850-2767
Motion Picture Distribution Services
N.A.I.C.S.: 512120

FUTURE FINTECH GROUP INC.

Room 2103 21st Floor SK Tower 6A Jianguomenwai Avenue, Chaoyang District, Beijing, 100022, China
Tel.: (86) 1085899303 FL
Web Site: http://www.ftft.top

FTFT—(NASDAQ)
Rev.: $23,881,006
Assets: $85,017,719
Liabilities: $19,332,078
Net Worth: $65,685,641
Earnings: ($13,627,545)
Emp.: 80
Fiscal Year-end: 12/31/22
Fruit Concentrate, Fruit Juice Beverages & Other Fruit Related Products Mfr & Sales
N.A.I.C.S.: 311411
Yongke Xue *(Pres)*

FUTURE FIRST TECHNOLOGIES LTD.

Level 11 410 Collins Street, Melbourne, 3000, VIC, Australia
Tel.: (61) 396822699
Web Site: http://futurefirsttech.io
ASV—(ASX)
Rev.: $2,730,398
Assets: $4,457,391
Liabilities: $1,369,442
Net Worth: $3,087,949
Earnings: ($36,914)
Emp.: 2,100
Fiscal Year-end: 06/30/24
IT Services
N.A.I.C.S.: 541519
Kurt Hansen *(Exec Gen Mgr-Security)*

FUTURE FORESTS FIJI LTD.

414 Victoria Parade, GPO Box 15850, Rear of Kadavu House, Suva, Fiji
Tel.: (679) 3310022 FJ
Web Site: http://www.fff.com.fj
Year Founded: 2005
Rev.: $364,299
Assets: $910,768
Liabilities: $854,810
Net Worth: $55,957
Earnings: $9,285
Fiscal Year-end: 06/30/17
Teak Plantation Services
N.A.I.C.S.: 111421

FUTURE GENERATION AUSTRALIA LIMITED

Level 26 Governor Phillip Tower 1 Farrer Place, Sydney, 2000, NSW, Australia
Tel.: (61) 292479202 AU
Web Site:
http://www.futuregeninvest.com.au
FGX—(ASX)
Rev.: $44,423,404
Assets: $372,692,596
Liabilities: $14,963,558
Net Worth: $357,729,038
Earnings: $31,219,944
Fiscal Year-end: 12/31/23
Investment Management Service
N.A.I.C.S.: 523940
Caroline Gurney *(CEO)*

FUTURE GENERATION GLOBAL LIMITED

Level 26 Governor Phillip Tower 1 Farrer Place, Sydney, 2000, NSW, Australia
Tel.: (61) 292479202 AU
Web Site:
http://www.futuregeninvest.com.au
Year Founded: 2015
FGG—(ASX)
Rev.: $58,001,499
Assets: $389,826,987
Liabilities: $17,682,038
Net Worth: $372,144,949
Earnings: $37,943,601
Fiscal Year-end: 12/31/23
Investment Management Service
N.A.I.C.S.: 523940

Louise Walsh *(CEO)*

FUTURE INNOVATION GROUP, INC.

2-5-60 Higashidaido, Higashiomichi, Oita, 870-0823, Japan
Tel.: (81) 975768730
Web Site: https://www.figinc.jp
Year Founded: 2018
4392—(TKS)
Rev.: $95,956,060
Assets: $161,900,150
Liabilities: $93,871,600
Net Worth: $68,028,550
Earnings: $1,488,900
Emp.: 774
Fiscal Year-end: 12/31/23
Information Communication Services
N.A.I.C.S.: 334290
Yuji Murai *(Pres & CEO)*

Subsidiaries:

Mobile Create Co., Ltd. (1)
2-5-60 Higashiomichi, Oita-shi, Oita, 870-0823, Japan
Tel.: (81) 975768181
Web Site: http://www.mcinc.jp
Wireless Communication Equipment Mfr
N.A.I.C.S.: 334220
Yuji Murai *(Pres)*

Subsidiary (US):

Mobile Create USA, Inc. (2)
Ste 658 2033 Gateway Pl, San Jose, CA 95110
Tel.: (408) 933-9588
Application Development Services
N.A.I.C.S.: 541511

Subsidiary (Domestic):

REALIZE Co., Ltd. (2)
2 5 5 Higashidai dori, Oita, 870-0823, Japan
Tel.: (81) 975441001
Web Site: https://www.realize-fig.jp
Emp.: 274
Semiconductor Machinery Mfr
N.A.I.C.S.: 333242
Akihiko Nakamura *(Pres)*

Plant (Domestic):

REALIZE Co., Ltd. - Kitsuki Plant (3)
2264 Noda Hino, Kitsuki, 873-0013, Oita, Japan
Tel.: (81) 978632278
Web Site: https://www.realize-fig.jp
Semiconductor Devices Mfr
N.A.I.C.S.: 334413

FUTURE INTERNATIONAL GROUP CORP.

Building G Lane 2577 Longhua Road, Xuhei District, Shanghai, China
Tel.: (86) 21 5087 2955 NV
Year Founded: 2013
Holding Company; Mobile Application Development Services
N.A.I.C.S.: 551112
Guobin Su *(Pres, CFO, Treas & Sec)*

FUTURE KID ENTERTAINMENT AND REAL ESTATE CO. K.S.C.C.

Free Trade Zone-Future Block D20, PO Box 4277, Kuwait, 13043, Kuwait
Tel.: (965) 22264747
Web Site:
https://www.futurekid.com.kw
Year Founded: 1986
FUTUREKID—(KUW)
Rev.: $23,116,848
Assets: $82,800,559
Liabilities: $38,958,842
Net Worth: $43,841,717
Earnings: $3,909,074
Emp.: 395
Fiscal Year-end: 12/31/22

Children's Entertainment & Play Centers
N.A.I.C.S.: 713990
Wael Ahmed Saud AlKhaled *(Chm)*

Subsidiaries:

Happy Land Entertainment (W.L.L.) (1)
Quba Road Al Hadiqa, Medina, 42383, Saudi Arabia
Tel.: (966) 148400006
Entertainment Services
N.A.I.C.S.: 532282

FUTURE MARKET NETWORKS LIMITED

Knowledge House Shyam Nagar Off Jogeshwari Vikhroli Link Road, Jogeshwari E, Mumbai, 400060, India
Tel.: (91) 2230841300
Web Site: https://www.fmn.co.in
533296—(NSE)
Rev.: $10,405,845
Assets: $88,012,115
Liabilities: $72,582,838
Net Worth: $15,429,278
Earnings: ($4,202,521)
Emp.: 55
Fiscal Year-end: 03/31/21
Investment Services
N.A.I.C.S.: 523999
Anil Cherian *(Officer-Compliance, Sec & Head-Legal)*

FUTURE MEDICINE CO., LTD

Rm 616 LH-Business Growth Center 54 changup-ro, Sujeong-gu, Seongnam, 13449, Gyeonggi-do, Korea (South)
Tel.: (82) 234293473
Web Site:
https://www.futuremedicine.co.kr
Year Founded: 2015
341170—(KRS)
Pharmaceutical Product Mfr & Distr
N.A.I.C.S.: 325412
Jeong Nak-Shin *(Co-CEO)*

FUTURE METALS NL

Level 3 1060 Hay Street, West Perth, 6005, WA, Australia
Tel.: (61) 894800414
Web Site: https://future-metals.com.au
Year Founded: 2007
FME—(AIM)
Rev.: $66,760
Assets: $13,018,200
Liabilities: $407,236
Net Worth: $12,610,964
Earnings: ($4,880,156)
Fiscal Year-end: 06/30/23
Support Activities for Oil & Gas Operations
N.A.I.C.S.: 213112
Gregory John Bandy *(Chm)*

FUTURE MOBILITY SOLUTIONS

2 Parkhead Place, Albany, Auckland, 0632, New Zealand
Tel.: (64) 94145542
Web Site:
https://www.futuremobiliesolution.net
Rev.: $208,997,743
Assets: $291,545,511
Liabilities: $222,089,304
Net Worth: $69,456,207
Earnings: $17,178,013
Emp.: 7
Fiscal Year-end: 03/31/18
Marine Craft Mfr
N.A.I.C.S.: 336411
Charles Mark Broadley *(CEO)*

Subsidiaries:

Sealegs (US) Corporation (1)
470 Atlantic Ave Fl 4, Boston, MA 02210-2241
Tel.: (617) 934-1876
Sales Range: $25-49.9 Million
Emp.: 4
Pleasure Boats Mfr & Distr
N.A.I.C.S.: 339999

Sealegs International Limited (1)
5 Unity Drive South, Albany, Auckland, 0632, New Zealand
Tel.: (64) 94145542
Web Site: http://www.sealegs.com
Sales Range: $25-49.9 Million
Emp.: 50
Amphibious Boats Mfr
N.A.I.C.S.: 336611
Ted Dixon (Mgr-Sls)

FUTURE MOBILITY SOLUTIONS LTD.
5 Unity Drive South, Albany, Auckland, 0632, New Zealand
Tel.: (64) 9 414 5542
Web Site:
http://www.futuremobilesolution.net
Year Founded: 1987
Amphibious Marine Craft Mfr
N.A.I.C.S.: 336612
Eric Series (Chm)

Subsidiaries:

Willard Marine, Inc. (1)
1412 Taylor Farm Rd, Virginia Beach, VA 23453-3453
Tel.: (757) 689-1095
Web Site: http://www.willardmarine.com
Boat Building
N.A.I.C.S.: 336612
Ulrich Gottschling (Pres & CEO)

FUTURE PIPE INDUSTRIES GROUP LTD.
Hamdan street, Abu Dhabi, 29205, United Arab Emirates
Tel.: (971) 2 627 0008
Web Site: http://www.futurepipe.com
Industrial Pipe Mfr
N.A.I.C.S.: 332996
Fouad Makhzoumi (Chm & CEO)

Subsidiaries:

Future Management Investments B.V. (1)
Piazza di Spagna 51, 00187, Rome, Italy
Tel.: (39) 0669921990
Industrial Pipe Distr
N.A.I.C.S.: 423720

Future Pipe Industries (Pvt) Ltd. (1)
Speedy Towers Suite 101 129/1 Main Korangi Road Phase 1 DHA, Karachi, Pakistan
Tel.: (92) 2135394771
Industrial Pipe Distr
N.A.I.C.S.: 423720

Future Pipe Industries L.L.C. (1)
PO Box 213PC, 124, Rusayl, Oman
Tel.: (968) 24449164
Industrial Pipe Distr
N.A.I.C.S.: 423720

Future Pipe Industries L.L.C. (1)
PO Box 8513, Al Khobar, 31492, Dammam, Saudi Arabia
Tel.: (966) 138123454
Industrial Pipe Distr
N.A.I.C.S.: 423720
Vikas Cheruvari (Mgr-Fin)

Future Pipe Industries Limited (1)
7th Floor Hansol Building 1621-3 Seocho-Dong, Seocho-Gu, Seoul, 137-879, Korea (South)
Tel.: (82) 25980743
Industrial Pipe Distr
N.A.I.C.S.: 423720

Future Pipe Industries Q.C.J.S.C (1)
PO Box 24678, Doha, Qatar
Tel.: (974) 44768111

Industrial Pipe Distr
N.A.I.C.S.: 423720

Future Pipe Industries S.A.E. (1)
Osman Ahmed Osman Street Osman Towers Deluxe Tower 2 Floor 31, Corniche El Maadi, Cairo, Egypt
Tel.: (20) 225285880
Industrial Pipe Distr
N.A.I.C.S.: 423720
Saad H. Elkhadem (Mng Dir)

Future Pipe Industries S.A.L. (1)
Mimosa Building Ain Mreisseh John F Kennedy Street, PO Box 13-5009, Beirut, Lebanon
Tel.: (961) 1369870
Industrial Pipe Distr
N.A.I.C.S.: 423720

Future Pipe Industries b.v. (1)
J C Kellerlaan 3, PO Box 255, 7770 AG, Hardenberg, Netherlands
Tel.: (31) 523280500
Industrial Pipe Distr
N.A.I.C.S.: 423720
Stephan Wipperfuerth (Area Mgr-Sls)

Future Pipe Industries, Inc. (1)
11905 Proctor Rd, Houston, TX 77038
Tel.: (281) 847-2987
Industrial Pipe Distr
N.A.I.C.S.: 423720
Joe Joseph (Sr Mgr-Production)

Future Pipe Limited (1)
11 Hobart Place, London, SW1W 0HP, United Kingdom
Tel.: (44) 2078388660
Industrial Pipe Distr
N.A.I.C.S.: 423720

Future Pipe Sarl (1)
42 Avenue Montaigne, 75008, Paris, France
Tel.: (33) 172762515
Industrial Pipe Distr
N.A.I.C.S.: 423720

PT Future Pipe Industries (1)
Setiabuti Building Atrium 4th Floor Suite 404, Jakarta, Indonesia
Tel.: (62) 215210038
Industrial Pipe Distr
N.A.I.C.S.: 423720
Helman Yahdi (Supvr-Site)

Specialty Plastics, Inc. (1)
15915 Perkins Rd, Baton Rouge, LA 70810-3630
Tel.: (225) 752-2705
Web Site: http://www.fiberbond.com
Sales Range: $25-49.9 Million
Emp.: 75
Composite Piping System Mfr
N.A.I.C.S.: 326122
Jeff Savoy (Controller)

FUTURE PLC
4 Callaghan Square, Cardiff, CF10 5BT, United Kingdom
Tel.: (44) 1225442244   UK
Web Site: https://www.futureplc.com
Year Founded: 1985
FUTR—(LSE)
Rev.: $934,517,880
Assets: $2,216,960,820
Liabilities: $1,016,036,280
Net Worth: $1,200,924,540
Earnings: $138,354,840
Fiscal Year-end: 09/30/22
Holding Company; Magazine & Website Publisher
N.A.I.C.S.: 551112
Zillah Byng-Thorne (CEO)

Subsidiaries:

Dennis Publishing Ltd. (1)
31-32 Alfred Place, London, WC1E 7DP, United Kingdom
Tel.: (44) 2038903890
Web Site: http://www.dennis.co.uk
Sales Range: $75-99.9 Million
Emp.: 350
Magazine Publisher & Website Operator
N.A.I.C.S.: 513120
Jack Griffin (Chm)

Subsidiary (US):

The Kiplinger Washington Editors, Inc. (2)
1100 13th St NW Ste 1000, Washington, DC 20005
Tel.: (202) 887-6400
Web Site: https://www.kiplinger.com
Publisher of Newsletters & Magazines
N.A.I.C.S.: 513120
Kevin McCormally (Chief Content Officer & Sr VP)

Subsidiary (Domestic):

Fairview Properties, Inc. (3)
1729 H St NW, Washington, DC 20006-3904
Tel.: (202) 887-6400
Web Site: http://www.kipplinger.com
Sales Range: $10-24.9 Million
Emp.: 3
Real Estate Services
N.A.I.C.S.: 531390

Kiplingers Personal Finance (3)
130 W 2nd St 7th Fl, New York, NY 10036   (100%)
Tel.: (212) 398-6320
Sales Range: $25-49.9 Million
Emp.: 11
Ad Representative Firm
N.A.I.C.S.: 522291

Subsidiary (Domestic):

The Week Ltd. (2)
121-141 Westbourne Terrace, London, W2 6jr, United Kingdom
Tel.: (44) 330 333 9494
Web Site: https://www.theweek.co.uk
Sales Range: $25-49.9 Million
Emp.: 14
Weekly Magazine Publisher
N.A.I.C.S.: 513120

Division (Domestic):

adnostic (2)
30 Cleveland Street, London, W1T 4JD, United Kingdom
Tel.: (44) 20 7907 6000
Web Site: http://www.adnostic.io
Digital Advertising Services
N.A.I.C.S.: 541850
Avril Donnelly (Grp Project Mgr)

Future France SA (1)
101 109 Rue Jean Jaures, Levallois, 92300, Perret, France   (100%)
Tel.: (33) 141273838
Web Site:
http://www.thefutureus.plc.uk
Sales Range: $50-74.9 Million
Emp.: 150
Magazine Publisher
N.A.I.C.S.: 513120

Future Publishing Ltd. (1)
Quay House The Ambury, Bath, BA1 1UA, United Kingdom   (100%)
Tel.: (44) 1225442244
Web Site: http://www.futurenet.com
Sales Range: $25-49.9 Million
Emp.: 400
Magazine Publisher
N.A.I.C.S.: 513120

Branch (Domestic):

Future Publishing Ltd. - London Office (2)
2 Balalcombe Street, London, NW1 6NW, United Kingdom
Tel.: (44) 2070424000
Web Site: http://www.futurenet.com
Magazine Publisher
N.A.I.C.S.: 513120

Future US, Inc. (1)
4000 Shoreline Ct Ste 400, San Francisco, CA 94080   (100%)
Tel.: (650) 872-1642
Web Site: http://www.futureus.com
Sales Range: $75-99.9 Million
Emp.: 150
Magazine Publisher
N.A.I.C.S.: 513120
Luke Edson (Chief Revenue Officer)

Subsidiary (Domestic):

NewBay Media, LLC (2)
28 E 28th St 12th Fl, New York, NY 10016
Tel.: (212) 378-0400
Media & Information Resources for Music & Consumer Electronics Industries; Magazine Publisher
N.A.I.C.S.: 513120

GoCo Group plc (1)
Imperial House, Imperial Way Newport, Gwent, NP10 8UH, United Kingdom
Tel.: (44) 1633 654 060
Web Site: http://www.gocogroup.com
Rev.: $199,887,840
Assets: $147,686,160
Liabilities: $156,080,400
Net Worth: ($8,394,240)
Earnings: $16,657,320
Emp.: 318
Fiscal Year-end: 12/31/2019
Financial Services
N.A.I.C.S.: 523999
Peter Wood (Chm)

Subsidiary (Domestic):

Gocompare.com Limited (2)
4 Callaghan Square, Wales, Cardiff, CF10 5BT, United Kingdom
Tel.: (44) 1633654019
Web Site: https://www.gocompare.com
Online Price Comparison Website
N.A.I.C.S.: 513140
Matthew Crummack (CEO)

Marie Claire US (1)
300 W 57th St, New York, NY 10019
Tel.: (212) 649-2000
Web Site: http://www.marieclaire.com
Sales Range: $50-74.9 Million
Emp.: 50
Fashion Magazine
N.A.I.C.S.: 513120
Anne Fulenwider (Editor-in-Chief)

Smartbrief, Inc. (1)
1100 13th St Ste 1000, Washington, DC 20005
Tel.: (202) 737-5500
Web Site: http://www.smartbrief.com
Periodical Publishers
N.A.I.C.S.: 513120

FUTURE VENTURE CAPITAL CO., LTD.
659 Tearamizu-cho Karasuma-dori Nishiki-koji Agaru, Nakagyo-ku, Kyoto, 604-8152, Japan
Tel.: (81) 752576656
Web Site: https://www.fvc.co.jp
Year Founded: 1998
8462—(TKS)
Rev.: $5,285,280
Assets: $30,414,560
Liabilities: $3,804,240
Net Worth: $26,610,320
Earnings: $1,384,240
Emp.: 38
Fiscal Year-end: 03/31/22
Investment Services
N.A.I.C.S.: 523999
Naoto Matsumoto (Pres & CEO)

FUTURE WORLD HOLDINGS LIMITED
Room 912 9/F New East Ocean Centre, 9 Science Museum Road, Kowloon, China (Hong Kong)
Tel.: (852) 23117728   Ky
Web Site: http://www.fw-fh.com
0572—(HKG)
Sales Range: $10-24.9 Million
Emp.: 15
Holding Company
N.A.I.C.S.: 551112
Yun Fat Siu (Chm)

FUTURECHEM CO LTD
3F B-dong PyeongHwa Building 59 Seongsuil-ro 8-gil, Seongdong-gu, Seoul, 04794, Korea (South)

FutureChem Co Ltd—(Continued)

Tel.: (82) 24973114
Web Site:
https://www.futurechem.co.kr
Year Founded: 1999
220100—(KRS)
Rev.: $9,643,970
Assets: $68,045,370
Liabilities: $14,138,123
Net Worth: $53,907,247
Earnings: ($10,706,835)
Emp.: 78
Fiscal Year-end: 12/31/22
Radiopharmaceutical Mfr & Distr
N.A.I.C.S.: 325412
Dae Yoon Chi (CEO)

FUTURECORE CO LTD
615 A6F 13 Sinwon-ro 250beon-gil,
Yeongtong-gu, Suwon, Gyeonggi-do,
Korea (South)
Tel.: (82) 3124039004
Web Site: https://futurecore.co.kr
Year Founded: 2004
151910—(KRS)
Rev.: $39,003,198
Assets: $74,927,128
Liabilities: $45,507,571
Net Worth: $29,419,557
Earnings: ($12,204,266)
Emp.: 89
Fiscal Year-end: 12/31/22
Optical Filter Mfr
N.A.I.C.S.: 333310
Kim Jong Hoon (Dir)

FUTUREGROWTH ASSET MANAGEMENT PTY. LTD.
3rd Floor Great Westerford Building
240 Main Road, Rondebosch, 7700,
Cape Town, South Africa
Tel.: (27) 21 659 5300
Web Site:
http://www.futuregrowth.co.za
Year Founded: 2000
Investment Management Service
N.A.I.C.S.: 523999
Amrish Narrandes (Head-Unlisted Equity Transactions)

Subsidiaries:

Thebe Tourism Group Pty
Limited   (1)
Office BBF1 Block B 1st Floor Sable
Square, Cnr Bosmansdam & Ratanga
Roads, Cape Town, South Africa
Tel.: (27) 21 551 0288
Web Site: http://www.thebetourism.co.za
Tourism Services
N.A.I.C.S.: 561520
Jerry Mabena (CEO)

Joint Venture (Domestic):

Thebe Reed Exhibitions Pty
Limited   (2)
Reed Place Bldg 1 Culross on Main Office
Park 134 Culross Road, Bryanston, 2191,
South Africa
Tel.: (27) 115498300
Convention & Trade Show Planning Services
N.A.I.C.S.: 561920
Carol Weaving (Mng Dir)

FUTURES CAPITAL AD
3rd Floor No 70B Ivan Ivanov Bulevard Inj, 1303, Sofia, 1303, Bulgaria
Tel.: (359) 24111444
Web Site: https://www.futures-capital.com
FCAD—(BUL)
Sales Range: Less than $1 Million
Investment Services
N.A.I.C.S.: 523999
Atanas Kanchev (Chm)

FUTURESTREAM NETWORKS CO., LTD.
7F 15 Yeocksam-ro 8-gil, Gangnam-gu, Seoul, Korea (South)
Tel.: (82) 7050209306
Year Founded: 2015
214270—(KRS)
Rev.: $158,094,085
Assets: $200,246,026
Liabilities: $87,197,808
Net Worth: $113,048,218
Earnings: ($8,198,679)
Emp.: 108
Fiscal Year-end: 12/31/22
Financial Investment Management
Services
N.A.I.C.S.: 523940

FUTURETEL S.A.
Av Rio Branco 311 - Sala 523/parte,
20040903, Rio de Janeiro, Brazil
Tel.: (55) 2121967200
Financial Investment Services
N.A.I.C.S.: 523999
Fernando Jose Do Amaral Friedheim
(CTO & Dir-IR)

FUTURISTIC OFFSHORE SERVICES & CHEMICAL LIMITED
Dina Building First Floor 53 M K
Road Marine Lines, Near Jankalyan
Bank Andheri - E, Mumbai, 400059,
Maharashtra, India
Tel.: (91) 2222001928
Year Founded: 1988
500154—(BOM)
Chemical Product Mfr & Distr
N.A.I.C.S.: 325199
Rishi R. Pilani (Chm)

FUTURISTIC SECURITIES LIMITED
202 Ashford Chambers Lady Jamshedji Road, Mahim West, Mumbai,
400 016, India
Tel.: (91) 2224476800
Web Site:
https://www.futuristicsecurities.com
Year Founded: 1971
523113—(BOM)
Rev.: $8,517
Assets: $174,632
Liabilities: $2,166
Net Worth: $172,467
Earnings: ($2,082)
Fiscal Year-end: 03/31/23
Security Brokerage Services
N.A.I.C.S.: 523150
Pradeep Jatwala (CFO)

FUTURISTIC SOLUTIONS LIMITED
M-50 IInd Floor M Block Market
Greater Kailash - I, New Delhi,
110048, India
Tel.: (91) 1141630436
Web Site: https://www.fsl.co.in
Year Founded: 1983
534063—(BOM)
Rev.: $453,606
Assets: $2,010,623
Liabilities: $216,881
Net Worth: $1,793,741
Earnings: $320,508
Emp.: 3
Fiscal Year-end: 03/31/23
Real Estate Development Services
N.A.I.C.S.: 531390
Mandeep Sandhu (Chm & Mng Dir)

FUTUROL INDUSTRIE
15 Grande Rue, 28170, Chartres,
France
Tel.: (33) 237387371
Web Site: http://www.futurol.com
Rev.: $20,300,000

Emp.: 41
Carpentry Work
N.A.I.C.S.: 238130
Gilles Jonquieres (Gen Mgr)

FUTURUM A.D.
Tosin Bunar br 268, Belgrade, Serbia
Tel.: (381) 11 21 58 741
Web Site: http://www.minel-elvo.co.rs
Year Founded: 1978
Sales Range: Less than $1 Million
Electric Equipment Mfr
N.A.I.C.S.: 336320

FUVA BRAIN LIMITED
4-1 Kioich New Otani Garden Court
22F, Chiyoda-ku, Tokyo, 102-0094,
Japan
Tel.: (81) 352103061
Web Site: https://fuva-brain.co.jp
Year Founded: 2001
3927—(TKS)
Rev.: $20,325,750
Assets: $28,766,720
Liabilities: $19,677,970
Net Worth: $9,088,750
Earnings: $178,470
Fiscal Year-end: 03/31/24
Information Security
N.A.I.C.S.: 561611
Keiichi Minemura (Pres)

FUXIN DARE AUTOMOTIVE PARTS CO., LTD.
No 55 E Road, Economic Development Zone, Fuxin, 123004, Liaoning,
China
Tel.: (86) 4183399321
Web Site:
https://www.fuxindareauto.com
Year Founded: 2004
300473—(CHIN)
Rev.: $605,575,251
Assets: $585,887,562
Liabilities: $364,271,031
Net Worth: $221,616,531
Earnings: $1,814,387
Fiscal Year-end: 12/31/23
Automobile Equipment Mfr
N.A.I.C.S.: 336110
Jialin Zhou (Vice Chm)

FUXIN SUMIRIN WOOD PRODUCTS CO., LTD.
No 71 Keji Street Fuxin High-Tech
Industrial Development Zone, Fuxin,
123000, Liaoning, China
Tel.: (86) 4182151588   JP
Sales Range: $150-199.9 Million
Emp.: 300
Plywood Mfr & Distr
N.A.I.C.S.: 321211
Akira Sekimoto (Pres)

FUXING CHINA GROUP LIMITED
Hangbian Industrial Area, Longhu
Town, Jinjiang, Fujian, China
Tel.: (86) 4008857688
Web Site: https://3fzipper.com
Year Founded: 1992
AWK—(SES)
Rev.: $105,994,742
Assets: $174,808,384
Liabilities: $85,672,539
Net Worth: $89,135,845
Earnings: ($5,560,723)
Emp.: 1,410
Fiscal Year-end: 12/31/19
Zipper Sliders & Chains Mfr
N.A.I.C.S.: 339993

FUXING GARMENTS CO., LTD.
1188 Donesheng Zhong Rd, Jiaxing,
314001, Zhejiang, China
Tel.: (86) 5732206132

Web Site: http://www.fuxingfz.com
Year Founded: 1988
Sales Range: $50-74.9 Million
Emp.: 500
Apparels Mfr
N.A.I.C.S.: 315990

FUYAO GLASS INDUSTRY GROUP CO., LTD.
Fuyao Industrial Zone II, Fuqing,
350301, Fujian, China
Tel.: (86) 59185383777   CN
Web Site:
https://www.fuyaogroup.com
Year Founded: 1987
600660—(SHG)
Rev.: $4,591,409,642
Assets: $7,842,332,604
Liabilities: $3,491,787,218
Net Worth: $4,350,545,387
Earnings: $779,316,571
Emp.: 32,721
Fiscal Year-end: 12/31/23
Holding Company; Automotive & Architectural Glass Products Mfr &
Whslr
N.A.I.C.S.: 551112
Xiangming Chen (CFO & Co-Sec)

Subsidiaries:

FYSAM Auto Decorative GmbH   (1)
Robert-Bosch-Strasse 13, Steinheim am
Albuch, 89555, Heidenheim, Germany
Tel.: (49) 733296600
Web Site: https://www.fysam-auto.com
Automotive Finished Product Mfr
N.A.I.C.S.: 336390

Fuyao Europe GmbH   (1)
Ohmstrasse 1, DE-74211, Leingarten, Germany
Tel.: (49) 71312708300
Automotive Glass Mfr
N.A.I.C.S.: 327215

Fuyao Glass America Inc.   (1)
800 Fuyao Ave, Moraine, OH 45439
Tel.: (937) 496-5777
Auto Glass Mfr & Distr
N.A.I.C.S.: 327215

Fuyao North America
Incorporated   (1)
301 Halton Rd Ste E, Greenville, SC 29607
Tel.: (864) 281-2760
Web Site: https://www.fygi.com
Holding Company; Regional Managing Office; Automotive & Architectural Glass Products Mfr & Whslr
N.A.I.C.S.: 327215

Subsidiary (Domestic):

Fuyao Automotive North America,
Inc.   (2)
909 N Sheldon Rd, Plymouth, MI 48170
Tel.: (734) 781-9777
Web Site: https://www.fuyoausa.com
Emp.: 100
Automotive Glass Warehousing & Distribution
N.A.I.C.S.: 423120

Fuyao Glass Illinois, Inc.   (2)
2768 E Elwin Rd, Mount Zion, IL 62549
Tel.: (217) 864-2392
Float Glass Products Mfr
N.A.I.C.S.: 327211
John Gaughier (CEO)

FUYO GENERAL LEASE CO., LTD.
Kojimachi Garden Tower 5-1-1 Kojimachi, Chiyoda-ku, Tokyo, 102-0083,
Japan
Tel.: (81) 352758800
Web Site: https://www.fgl.co.jp
Year Founded: 1969
8424—(TKS)
Rev.: $4,683,436,180
Assets: $22,410,041,640
Liabilities: $19,254,916,780
Net Worth: $3,155,124,860

Earnings: $312,117,590
Emp.: 3,803
Fiscal Year-end: 03/31/24
Commercial Banking Services
N.A.I.C.S.: 522110
Takashi Sato *(Chm)*

Subsidiaries:

Accretive Co., Ltd.   **(1)**
Kojimachi Garden Tower 5-1-1 Kojimachi, Chiyoda-ku, Tokyo, 102-0083, Japan   **(69.2%)**
Tel.: (81) 362614920
Web Site: http://www.accretive.jp
Sales Range: $25-49.9 Million
Emp.: 131
Financial Services
N.A.I.C.S.: 522320
Takeshi Sugahara *(Pres & CEO)*

Subsidiary (Domestic):

Medical Payment Corp.   **(2)**
1-28-44 Shinkawa, Chuo-ku, Tokyo, 104-0033, Japan   **(100%)**
Tel.: (81) 335528725
Web Site: http://www.medicalpayment.co.jp
Medical Payment Processing Services
N.A.I.C.S.: 522320
Kazuki Nakamura *(CEO)*

Aircraft Leasing & Management Limited   **(1)**
1st Floor Pegasus 2 Pegasus Place Gatwick Road, Crawley, RH10 9AY, West Sussex, United Kingdom
Tel.: (44) 1293872500
Web Site: https://www.alm-lease.co.uk
Emp.: 1,700
Airline Leasing Services
N.A.I.C.S.: 532411
Alan Robinson *(Mng Dir)*

Aqua Art Co., Ltd.   **(1)**
Hayashi Nakazu Building 6-9 Nihombashi Nakasu, Chuo-ku, Tokyo, 103-0008, Japan
Tel.: (81) 336661301
Sales Range: $25-49.9 Million
Emp.: 18
Glass Mfr
N.A.I.C.S.: 327212

FGL Aircraft Ireland Limited   **(1)**
AIB International Centre IFSC, Dublin, Ireland
Tel.: (353) 18291802
Aircraft Products Leasing Services
N.A.I.C.S.: 532411

FGL Group Business Service Co., Ltd.   **(1)**
Kojimachi Garden Tower 5-1-1, Kojimachi Chiyoda-ku, Tokyo, 102-0083, Japan
Tel.: (81) 352758495
N.A.I.C.S.: 541611

FGL Group Management Service Co., Ltd.   **(1)**
Kojimachi Garden Tower 5-1-1, Kojimachi Chiyoda-ku, Tokyo, 102-0083, Japan
Tel.: (81) 352758935
N.A.I.C.S.: 561110

Five Fox Management Co., Ltd.   **(1)**
Nicherei Building 3-3-23 Misaki-cho, Tokyo, 101-8380, Chiyoda-ku, Japan
Tel.: (81) 352758800
Real Estate Manangement Services
N.A.I.C.S.: 531390
Mitsuru Machida *(Pres)*

Fuyo Auto Lease Co., Ltd.   **(1)**
Sumitomo Fudosan Kojimachi Garden Tower 21F 5-1-1, Kojimachi, Chiyoda-ku, Tokyo, 102-0083, Japan
Tel.: (81) 352752920
Web Site: https://www.fuyoauto.co.jp
Sales Range: $125-149.9 Million
Emp.: 165
Auto Leasing Services
N.A.I.C.S.: 532112

Fuyo General Lease (Asia) Pte. Ltd.   **(1)**
80 Robinson Road 10-01A, Singapore, 068898, Singapore
Tel.: (65) 64206203
N.A.I.C.S.: 532490

Fuyo General Lease (HK) Limited   **(1)**
Room 910 and 912 9 / F Tower II Lippo Centre 89 Queensway, Admiralty, Central, China (Hong Kong)
Tel.: (852) 2528 9863
Web Site: http://www.fgl.co.jp
Equipment Leasing Services
N.A.I.C.S.: 532490

Fuyo General Lease (USA) Inc.   **(1)**
733 3rd Ave 20th Fl, New York, NY 10017
Tel.: (212) 867-1008
Web Site: http://www.fgl.co.jp
Equipment Leasing Services
N.A.I.C.S.: 532490

Fuyo Lease Sales Co., Ltd.   **(1)**
5-1-1 Sumitomo Real Estate Kojimachi Garden Tower, Kojimachi Chiyoda-ku, Tokyo, 102-0083, Japan   **(100%)**
Tel.: (81) 352137284
Web Site: http://flsfls.co.jp
Emp.: 85
Equipment Leasing Services
N.A.I.C.S.: 532490
Shinichi Arakawa *(Chm)*

Fuyo Network Service Co., Ltd.   **(1)**
5-1-1 Kojimachi Sumitomo Real Estate Kojimachi Garden Tower, Chiyoda-ku, Tokyo, 102-0083, Japan
Tel.: (81) 352759015
Web Site: https://www.f-net.co.jp
Customized Software Services
N.A.I.C.S.: 513210

Invoice Inc.   **(1)**
Sumitomo Real Estate Kojimachi Garden Tower 5-1-1, Tokyo, 102-0083, Japan
Tel.: (81) 120888448
Web Site: https://www.invoice.ne.jp
N.A.I.C.S.: 517810
Masami Kamo *(Pres)*

Japan Mortgage Co., Ltd.   **(1)**
8-1 Nihonbashikobunacho Hyurikku Kofunecho Bldg, Chuo-Ku, Tokyo, 103-0024, Japan
Tel.: (81) 332495560
Mortgage Brokerage Services
N.A.I.C.S.: 522310

NOC Outsourcing & Consulting Inc.   **(1)**
4F Toyosu Prime Square 5-6-36 Toyosu, Koto-ku, Tokyo, 135-0061, Japan
Tel.: (81) 369101750
Web Site: https://www.noc-net.co.jp
Outsourcing Consulting Services
N.A.I.C.S.: 541618

Pacific Rim Capital, Inc.   **(1)**
525 Technology Dr Ste 400, Irvine, CA 92618   **(51%)**
Tel.: (949) 389-0800
Web Site: https://www.pacificrimcapital.com
Sales Range: $25-49.9 Million
Emp.: 42
Leasing Services
N.A.I.C.S.: 525990
Marc Mills *(Pres)*

YF Leasing Co., Ltd.   **(1)**
1-19-18 Nakacho, Musashino, Tokyo, 180-0006, Japan
Tel.: (81) 422569352
Sales Range: $50-74.9 Million
Emp.: 9
Leasing Services
N.A.I.C.S.: 532490

FUZHOU ROCKCHIP ELECTRONICS CO., LTD.
No 18 Building No 89 Software Boulevard TongPan Rd, Fuzhou, 350003, Fujian, China
Tel.: (86) 59183991906
Web Site: https://www.rockchips.com
Year Founded: 2001
603893—(SHG)
Rev.: $284,966,384
Assets: $473,178,046
Liabilities: $63,160,246
Net Worth: $410,017,800
Earnings: $41,758,793

Fiscal Year-end: 12/31/22
Semiconductor Product Mfr & Distr
N.A.I.C.S.: 334413
Min Li *(Chm & Gen Mgr)*

FV PHARMA INTERNATIONAL CORP.
203 - 29 Gervais Drive, Toronto, M3C 1Y9, ON, Canada
Tel.: (905) 686-7079   NV
Web Site: http://www.fvpharma.com
Year Founded: 2012
Dental Care Product Distr
N.A.I.C.S.: 424210
Shaik M. Shami *(Pres, CEO, CFO & Treas)*

FV S.A.
Bernardo De Irigoyen 1053, B1604AFC, Florida, Buenos Aires, Argentina
Tel.: (54) 11 4730 5300
Web Site: http://www.fvsa.com
Sales Range: $250-299.9 Million
Emp.: 1,500
Mfr of Plumbing Fixtures
N.A.I.C.S.: 332913
Francisco Biegener *(Pres)*

Subsidiaries:

C.I.B.A. Compania Introductora de Buenos Aires S.A.   **(1)**
Chile 778, 1098, Buenos Aires, Argentina
Tel.: (54) 1143639200
Web Site: http://www.dosanclas.com.ar
Sales Range: $50-74.9 Million
Emp.: 155
Chemical Mfr & Distr
N.A.I.C.S.: 325199

FWU AG
Boschetsrieder Strasse 67, 81379, Munich, Germany
Tel.: (49) 89 748588 0   De
Web Site: http://www.forwardyou.com
Year Founded: 1983
Investment Services
N.A.I.C.S.: 523999
Manfred J. Dirrheimer *(Co-Founder & Chm-Exec Bd)*

Subsidiaries:

ATLANTICLUX Lebensversicherung S.A.   **(1)**
4a rue Albert Borschette, 1246, Luxembourg, Luxembourg   **(100%)**
Tel.: (352) 26494 200
Web Site: http://www.atlanticlux.info
Life Insurance Products & Services
N.A.I.C.S.: 524113
Michael Emmel *(Mng Dir)*

FWU Provisions-Factoring GmbH   **(1)**
Boschetsrieder Strasse 67, 81379, Munich, Germany   **(100%)**
Tel.: (49) 89 748588 0
Web Site: http://www.fwugroup.com
Factoring Services
N.A.I.C.S.: 522299
Angela S. Dirrheimer *(Mng Dir)*

Fortuna Lebens-Versicherungs AG Vaduz   **(1)**
Staedtle 35, LI 9490, Vaduz, Liechtenstein
Tel.: (423) 2361545
Web Site: http://www.fortuna.li
Life Insurance Products
N.A.I.C.S.: 524113

Skandia Austria Holding AG   **(1)**
Handelskai 92, Gate 2, 4th floor, 1200, Vienna, Austria
Tel.: (43) 153664299
Web Site: http://www.skandia.at
Life Insurance & Investment Products & Services
N.A.I.C.S.: 524113
Richard Zarycka *(Head-Customer & Sls)*

FWUSOW INDUSTRY CO., LTD.
No 45 Shatian Rd, Shalu District, Taichung, 433, Taiwan
Tel.: (886) 426362111
Web Site: https://www.fwusow.com.tw
Year Founded: 1920
1219—(TAI)
Rev.: $533,491,036
Assets: $333,087,335
Liabilities: $182,618,915
Net Worth: $150,468,420
Earnings: $10,817,554
Emp.: 605
Fiscal Year-end: 12/31/23
Pet Food, Edible Oil, Cereal & Soy Protein Products Mfr & Distr
N.A.I.C.S.: 311119
Yau-Kuen Hung *(Chm)*

Subsidiaries:

Fwusow Industry Co., Ltd. - Sha-Lu Factory   **(1)**
45 Shatian Road, Shalu Town, Taichung, 433, Taiwan
Tel.: (886) 426363439
Animal Feed Mfr
N.A.I.C.S.: 311119

Fwusow Industry Co., Ltd. - Taichung Harbor Factory   **(1)**
No 45 Shatian Road, Shalu Town, Taichung, 43354, Taiwan
Tel.: (886) 426362111
Sales Range: $200-249.9 Million
Emp.: 600
Cooking Oil & Breakfast Cereals Mfr
N.A.I.C.S.: 311224

FX HOTELS GROUP, INC.
Room 518 5th Floor FX Hotel No 68 North Fourth Ring Road West, Haidian District, Beijing, 100080, China
Tel.: (86) 1058986694
Web Site: https://www.fxhotels.com
2724—(TPE)
Rev.: $5,889,503
Assets: $25,503,121
Liabilities: $25,303,893
Net Worth: $199,228
Earnings: ($5,367,655)
Fiscal Year-end: 12/31/20
Hotel Operator
N.A.I.C.S.: 721110

FXPRO FINANCIAL SERVICES LTD
Karyatidon 1, Ypsonas, 4180, Cyprus
Tel.: (357) 25969222
Web Site: http://www.fxpro.com
Sales Range: $75-99.9 Million
Emp.: 170
Commodities Trading Services
N.A.I.C.S.: 523160
Jim Sutcliffe *(Chm)*

FY FINANCIAL (SHENZHEN) CO., LTD.
Room 1603 Cheung Kei Building No 128 Xinzhou 11th Street, Futian District, Shenzhen, Guangdong, China
Tel.: (86) 75582900700   CN
Web Site: https://www.fyleasing.com
Year Founded: 2012
8452—(HKG)
Rev.: $4,142,014
Assets: $71,832,799
Liabilities: $8,556,582
Net Worth: $63,276,217
Earnings: ($4,560,977)
Emp.: 48
Fiscal Year-end: 12/31/22
Financial Lending Services
N.A.I.C.S.: 522220
Peng Li *(Chm, Compliance Officer, Compliance Officer, Gen Mgr, Gen Mgr & Exec Dir)*

FYI Resources Limited—(Continued)

FYI RESOURCES LIMITED
Unit 8-9 88 Forrest Street, Cottesloe,
6011, WA, Australia
Tel.: (61) 893133920
Web Site:
  http://www.fyiresources.com.au
SDL—(BER)
Rev.: $7,601
Assets: $12,966,877
Liabilities: $173,352
Net Worth: $12,793,525
Earnings: ($3,177,647)
Fiscal Year-end: 06/30/22
Mineral Properties Development &
Exploration Services
N.A.I.C.S.: 212290
Phillip MacLeod (Sec)

FYLDE FRESH & FABULOUS LTD.
Stanley Villa Farm, Back Lane, Wee-
ton, Preston, PR4 3HN, United King-
dom
Tel.: (44) 01253836444
Web Site:
  https://www.fyldefreshfabulous.com
Year Founded: 2005
Fish, Chips & Food Services Mfg.
N.A.I.C.S.: 333241
David Linton (Owner)
Subsidiaries:
Troy Foods Ltd   (1)
Royds Farm Road, Leeds, LS12 6DX,
United Kingdom
Tel.: (44) 1133838400
Web Site: http://www.troyfoods.co.uk
Sales Range: $25-49.9 Million
Emp.: 270
Prepared Vegetables, Mayonnaise & Salad
Dressings Mfr
N.A.I.C.S.: 311411

FYNSKE BANK A/S
Centrumpladsen 19, 5700, Svend-
borg, Denmark
Tel.: (45) 62213322
Web Site: https://www.fynskebank.dk
FYNBK—(CSE)
Rev.: $69,059,918
Assets: $1,294,413,335
Liabilities: $1,097,781,829
Net Worth: $196,631,506
Earnings: $22,743,123
Emp.: 198
Fiscal Year-end: 12/31/23
Commercial Banking Services
N.A.I.C.S.: 522110
Petter Blondeau Rasmussen (CEO)